2025

LexisNexis®
Corporate Affiliations™

LexisNexis®

Content Operations:
Director-News & Business Content Operations & Metadata: Tammy Bair
Manager-Corporate Affiliations & Entity Management: Elizabeth A. Powers
Lead Content Analysts: Eric Eelman, Kevin Gaven

Production:
Senior Production Specialist: Joseph C. Stewart

Reed Elsevier Philippines-Corporate Affiliations Iloilo Team:
Operations Manager: Timothy J. Vilches
Operations Supervisor: Kristel Faye B. De la Cruz
Product Lead: Raquel G. Gajardo

2025

LexisNexis®
Corporate Affiliations™
U.S. Public Companies

Volume III
A-Z

LexisNexis®

QUESTIONS ABOUT THIS PUBLICATION?

For CONTENT questions concerning this publication, please call:

Content Operations Department at 800-340-3244
FAX 908-790-5405

For CUSTOMER SERVICE ASSISTANCE concerning shipments, billing or other matters, please call:
Customer Service at 800-340-3244, press 3

For SALES ASSISTANCE, please call:
The Sales Department at 800-340-3244, press 2

Library of Congress Catalog Card Number: 67-22770

U.S. Public Companies Volume 3, ISBN: 979-8-3417-0461-9

Corporate Affiliations 8-Volume Library, ISBN: 979-8-3417-0458-9

Corporate Affiliations

Content Operations
9443 Springboro Pike
Miamisburg, OH 45342

www.lexisnexis.com

ISBN 979-8-3417-0461-9

9 798341 704619

CONTENTS

CONTENTS

CORPORATE AFFILIATIONS

Corporate Affiliations is a logically organized business reference tool that covers major public and private businesses in the United States and throughout the world. The set consists of eight volumes:

Volume I   Master Index I
Volume II   Master Index II
Volume III   U.S. Public Companies
Volume IV   U.S. Private Companies I
Volume V   U.S. Private Companies II
Volume VI   International Public & Private Companies I
Volume VII   International Public & Private Companies II
Volume VIII International Public & Private Companies III

The principle of organization for the set is geographical (by parent company) and hierarchical (by company reportage). Subsidiaries of a parent company, no matter where they are located, will be found in the same volume as the ultimate parent.

Please note that guidelines on the organization of the entire set for this edition can be found in the *Master Index* Volume I.

Entry criteria for the set are flexible. Generally speaking, non-U.S. based companies must demonstrate revenue in excess of $10 million. U.S. based companies must demonstrate revenues in excess of $10 million, substantial assets, a work force in excess of 300 employees, or be traded on a major stock exchange.

THE *U.S. PUBLIC COMPANIES* VOLUME

Corporate Affiliations: U.S. Public Companies contains listings for companies with U.S. located head-quarters or holding companies. Subsidiaries for these parent companies are included, whether or not they are located in the United States. Also included are outside service firms attached to the parent companies. These are firms that perform specialized services such as accounting, legal, pension management, etc.

Content and Coverage in Corporate Affiliations-U.S. Public Companies

Listing statistics for this edition of U.S. Public are as follows:

Ultimate parent companies 7,645
U.S. located sub companies 53,609
Non-U.S. located sub companies 18,881
Total entry units listed....................................80,135

Outside service firms: 7,382

Companies are arranged alphabetically by the name of the parent company. Subsidiary companies follow the parent in order of reporting hierarchy. The bold number in parentheses shows the level of corporate reportage. Each listing can contain an extensive number of informational items. Please refer to the helpful 'How to Use' section for a guide to referencing methods and comprehensive listing samples.

The *U.S. Public Companies* volume also contains several useful features in the frontmatter including 'New Listings' for this edition, 'Mergers and Acquisitions' and 'Stock Market Abbreviations.'

COMPILATION

Corporate Affiliations is compiled and updated from information supplied by the companies themselves, business publications, internet research and annual reports.

RELATED SERVICES

For information on the corporateaffiliations.com web site, please call (800) 340-3244.

Mailing lists compiled from information contained in *Corporate Affiliations* may be ordered from:
R. Michael Patterson, Inside Sales Representative
DM2 Decision Maker
2000 Clearwater Drive, Oak Brook, IL
Tel: (630) 288-8348
E-mail: robert.patterson@dm2decisionmaker.com

Electronic database tapes of the directory in raw data format are available for licensing. For electronic database tapes or alliance opportunities, please contact:
LexisNexis, Corporate Affiliations
9443 Springboro Pike, Miamisburg, OH 45342
Tel: (800) 285-3947
E-mail: information@lexisnexis.com

Companies who wish to add or correct their listings can send information to:
LexisNexis, Corporate Affiliations Content Operations
9443 Springboro Pike
Miamisburg, OH 45342
Tel: (937) 865-6800

In addition to keeping the information in our directories as up to date as possible, we are constantly trying to improve their design, and add useful new features. Any comments or suggestions in this regard can be directed to the Managers of Operations at the above address.

HOW TO USE
U.S. PUBLIC COMPANIES

Corporate Affiliations, U.S. Public Companies contains a vast amount of useful information about firms whose ultimate parent companies are public and located in the United States.

This user guide is divided into three parts:

Part A, 'How to Locate a Company' gives referencing instructions and samples of indexes. It demonstrates many useful methods for getting the information you need from this volume and from the *Corporate Affiliations* set at large.

Part B, 'Sample Entries' shows the various data elements and listing style of companies in *Corporate Affiliations*.

Part C, 'Understanding Levels of Reportage' demonstrates how company reportage structures are simply and clearly presented throughout *Corporate Affiliations*.

PART A: HOW TO LOCATE A COMPANY

1. **If you know the name of the company, but do not know its nationality or ownership status:**

    Look in the 'Master Index of Company Names' located in volume I. This index will direct you to the correct volume of the set (i.e. Public, Private or International) and the correct page listing therein.

    > **KOMAG, INCORPORATED**; *U.S. Public*, pg. 1023
    > KOMAG MATERIAL TECHNOLOGY INC.—See
    >   Komag, Incorporated; *U.S. Public*, pg. 1023
    > KOMAGANE ELECTRONICS, INC.—See Kenwood
    >   Corporation; *Int'l*, pg. 638

2. **If you know the company is a privately held parent company:**

    You can turn directly to the company listings in volume III, all of which are alphabetized by the name of the parent company.

3. **If you cannot find the company's name in the master index:**

It may mean that the company has been acquired or changed its name. To confirm this, try looking in the 'Mergers and Acquisitions' section at the front of this volume.

Sample of Mergers and Acquisitions Section

Alloway Industries–acquired by Code, Hennessy & Simmons, Inc.
Alpha Wire Company–acquired by Belden Inc.
Ambassador Steel Co.–ceased operatins (no longer in business)

4. **To locate companies in a given line of business:**

Use the N.A.I.C.S. (North American Industrial Classification System) Master Index in volume II. This index interfiles data from all six volumes of *Corporate Affiliations*, arranging companies by particular products and services according to their primary N.A.I.C.S. code. The index is preceded by two helpful compendia: one sorts the codes alphabetically by the name of the product or service, the other numerically by the code itself.

Sample of Alpha Compendium of N.A.I.C.S. Codes

Description	N.A.I.C.S.
Administration of Conservation Programs	924120
Administration of Education Programs	923110

Sample of Numeric Compendium of N.A.I.C.S. Codes

Code	Description
111150	Corn Farming
111160	Rice Farming
111191	Oilseed and Grain Combination Farming

Both parent and sub companies are covered in this index; parent companies are printed in bold type, sub companies in regular typeface followed by the name of its ultimate parent. A sample of the N.A.I.C.S. Master Index is shown here:

337211 — WOOD OFFICE FURNITURE MANUFACTURING

PART B: BASIC COMPONENTS OF A PUBLIC COMPANY LISTING

Following is an example of a typical parent company listing with tags to some of its basic components.

STANDARD MEDICAL GROUP	**Company Name**
560 River Rd	**Company Address**
Richmond, VA 23219	
Tel: 804-223-3289 **DE**	**Telecommunications Data & State of Incorporation**
Fax: 804-555-8334	
Web Site: www.smg.com	**Electronic Address**
Year Founded: 1967	
SMG—(NYSE)	**Ticker Symbol & Stock Exchange Data**
Rev.: $32,000,000	**Financial Data**
Assets: $48,000,000	
Liabilities: $32,000,000	
Net Worth: $16,000,000	
Earnings: ($4,500,000)	
Emp: 620	**Number of Employees, Including Subsidiaries**
Fiscal Year End: 12/31/24	
Research Technology;	**Business Description**
Medical Products Mfr	
N.A.I.C.S.: 325411	**North American Industry Classification Code**
John R. Callahan (*Chm*)	**Key Personnel**
Cynthia I. Jenkins (*Pres & CEO*)	
William E. Kirkpatrick (*Exec VP*)	
Albert N. Hackett (*VP-Res & Dev*)	
Lawrence Woods (*VP-Sls*)	

Following each parent company listing are the entries for each of that company's divisions, subsidiaries, affiliates, joint ventures, units etc. Though companies vary widely in their usage of these terms, some of the more common company designations can be defined as follows:

Affiliate	A chartered business owned by the company at less than 50%.
Division	An internal unit of a company, not incorporated.
Joint Venture	A business in which two or more companies share responsibility and ownership.
Subsidiary	A chartered business owned by the company at 50% or more.

PART C: UNDERSTANDING LEVELS OF REPORTAGE

Each sub-unit of the company will have a number in parentheses to the right of the company name. This number represents the level of reportage for that particular company. Any company with a level (1) reports directly to the parent company. Level (2) companies report to the level (1) company immediately above them. Level (3) companies report to the level (2) company immediately above them, etc.

Subsidiaries:

Brock Corporation **(1)** ———— **Reports to the Parent Company**
6060 Wall St **(Standard Medical Group from**
Hartford, CT 06103 **from previous example)**
Tel: 203-251-6526 **(100%)** ———— **Percentage of Ownership**
Sales Range: $25-49.9 Million
Emp: 98
Pharmaceuticals Mfr
N.A.I.C.S.: 325199
J.M. McAleer *(Pres)*

Subsidiary:

Clark Technology **(2)** ———— **Reports Direct to Level 1 Company Above**
601 Pulaski St **(Brock Corporation)**
Jackson, MS 39215
Tel: 601-848-4626 **(100%)**
CT—(NYSE)
Sutures & Other Surgical Products Mfr
N.A.I.C.S.: 339113
Steven Colaccino *(Pres)*

Branch:

Clark Technology **(3)** ———— **Reports to Level 2 Company Above**
52 Main St **(Clark Technology)**
Wayne, NJ 07435
Tel: 201-662-7654
Sutures Mfr
N.A.I.C.S.: 339113

Non-U.S. Subsidiary:

Merieux Pharmaceuticals **(1)** ———— **Subsidiary Not Located in the U.S.**
1421 rue Gourbet, 75755 **Reports to the Parent Company**
Paris, Cedex 15, France **(Standard Medical Group)**
Tel: 42 73 10 08 **(100%)**
Rev.: $1,500,000
Emp: 118
Pharmaceuticals Mfr
N.A.I.C.S.: 325412
G. Bidaud *(Pres)*

ABBREVIATIONS

GENERAL TERMS

Acct	Account	Matl	Material
Acctg	Accounting	Matls	Materials
Accts	Accounts	Mdse	Merchandise
Acq	Acquisition(s)	Mdsg	Merchandising
Admin	Administration/Administrative	Mfg	Manufacturing
Adv	Advertising	Mfr	Manufacturer
Assoc	Associate	Mgmt	Management
Asst	Assistant	Mgr	Manager
Brdcst	Broadcast	Mktg	Marketing
Bus	Business	Mng	Managing
CEO	Chief Executive Officer	Natl	National
CFO	Chief Financial Officer	Ops	Operations
Chm	Chairman of the Board	Org	Organization
CIO	Chief Information Officer	Pkg	Packaging
CMO	Chief Marketing Officer	Plng	Planning
Comm	Communication(s)	Pres	President
Comml	Commercial	Prof	Professional
COO	Chief Operating Officer	Promo	Promotion
Coord	Coordinator	Promos	Promotions
Corp	Corporate/Corporation	Pub	Public
CTO	Chief Technology Officer	Pub Rel	Public Relations
Dept	Department	Publ	Publishing
Dev	Development	Publr	Publisher
Dir	Director	Pur	Purchasing
Distr	Distribution	R&D	Research & Development
Div	Division	Reg	Regional
DP	Data Processing	Rep	Representative
Engr	Engineer	Res	Research
Engrg	Engineering	Sec	Secretary
Environ	Environmental	Sls	Sales
Exec	Executive	Sr	Senior
Fin	Finance/Financial	Supvr	Supervisor
Gen	General	Svc	Service
Govt	Government	Svcs	Services
Grp	Group	Sys	Systems
HR	Human Resources	Tech	Technical/Technology
Indus	Industry/Industrial	Telecom	Telecommunication(s)
Info	Information	Treas	Treasurer
Intl	International	Trng	Training
IR	Investor Relations	Vice Chm	Vice Chairman
IT	Information Technology	VP	Vice President
Jr	Junior		

COMPANY DESIGNATIONS

The following designations indicate the forms of business enterprise in various countries; these forms usually represent the organization for large enterprises.

AB	Aktiebolag	Finland, Sweden
AG	Aktiengesellschaft	Austria, Germany, Switzerland, Liechtenstein
A/S	Aksjeselskap	Norway
	Aktieselskab	Denmark
B.V.	Besloten Vennootschap	Holland
C.V.	Commanditaire Vennootschap	Holland
Cie.	Compagnie France,	Luxembourg
Co.	Company	United States, France, South Africa, Luxembourg
Ets.	Etablissement(s)	France, Luxembourg
GmbH	Gesellschaft mit beschrankter	Haftung Austria, Germany, Switzerland
I/S	Interessantelskab	Denmark, Norway
KG	Kommanditgesellschaft	Austria, Germany, Switzerland
KK	Kabushiki Kaisha	Japan
K/S	Kommanditselskab	Denmark
Lda.	Limitada	Portugal
Ltd.	Limited	United Kingdom, United States, South Africa
Ltda.	Limitada	Brazil, Portugal
Ltee.	Limitee	Canada
Mij.	Maatschappij	Holland
N.V.	Naamloze Vennootschap	Belgium, Holland
OHG	Offene Handelsgesellschaft	Austria
Oy	Osakeyhtiot	Finland
PLC	Public Limited Company	United Kingdom
P.T.	Perusahaan Terbatas	Indonesia
Pte.	Private	Singapore
Pty.	Proprietary	Australia, South Africa
Pvt.	Private India,	Rhodesia
S.A.	Societe Anonyme	Belgium, France, Luxembourg, Switzerland
	Sociedad Anonima	Spain, Latin America
S.A.C.I.	Sociedad Anonima Comercial e Industrial	Latin America
S.A. de C.V.	Sociedad Anonima de Capital Variable	Mexico
S.A.E.	Sociedad Anonima Espanola	Spain
S.A.I.C.	Sociedad Anonima Industrial y Comercial	Latin America
S.A.R.L.	Sociedad Anonima de Responsabilidade Limitada	Brazil
	Sociedade a Responsabilitie Limitee	France, Luxembourg
S.A.S.	Societa in Accomandita Semplice	Italy
S.C.	Societe en Commandite	France
S.p.A.	Societa per Azioni	Italy
S.P.R.L.	Societe de Personnes a Responsabilitie Limitee	Belgium
S.R.L.	Societa a Responsabilita Limitata	Italy
Sdn. Bhd.	Sendirian Berhad	Malaysia
Ste.	Societe	France, Switzerland
Ste. Cve.	Societe Cooperative	Belgium
V.o.F.	Vennootschap onder firma	Holland

STOCK MARKET ABBREVIATIONS

ABU	Abu Dhabi Securities Exchange
AIM	AIM Market of the London Stock Exchange
AMM	Amman Stock Exchange
ARM	Armenian NASDAQ OMX Armenia
ASX	Australian Stock Exchange
ATH	Athens Stock Exchange
BAH	Bahrain Bourse
BAK	Baku Stock Exchange
BAN	Bangalore Stock Exchange
BANJ	Banja Luka Stock Exchange
BAR	Barcelona Stock Exchange
BARB	Barbados Stock Exchange
BEL	Belgrade Stock Exchange
BER	Borse Berlin-Bremen Stock Exchange
BERM	Bermuda Stock Exchange
BERN	Bern Stock Exchange
BESA	Bond Exchange of South Africa
BEY	Beirut Stock Exchange
BHU	Royal Securities Exchange of Bhutan
BIL	Bilbao Stock Exchange
BOA	BOAG Borsen (Merger of Hannover & Hamburg Exchanges)
BOL	Bolsa de Valores de Bolivia
BOM	Bombay (Mumbai) Stock Exchange
BOT	Botswana Stock Exchange
BRA	Bratislava Stock Exchange
BRAZ	Brazil Stock Exchange (BM&F& Bovespa)
BRVM	Bourse Regionale des Valeurs Mobilieres
BUC	Bucharest Stock Exchange
BUD	Budapest Stock Exchange
BUE	Buenos Aires Stock Exchange (Mercado de Valores Buenos Aires)
BUL	Bulgarian Stock Exchange
BVMAC	Securities Exchange of Central Africa
BVT	Bourse de Tunis
BX	Boston NASDAQ OMX BXSM
CAR	Caracas Stock Exchange
CAS	Casablanca Stock Exchange
CAT	Singapore Catalist
CAY	Cayman Islands Stock Exchange
CHA	Channel Islands Stock Exchange
CHI	Chicago Stock Exchange
CHIN	ChiNext (Chinese Exchange for Small & High-Tech Enterprises)
CHT	Chittagong Stock Exchange
CNSX	Canadian National Stock Exchange
COL	Colombo Stock Exchange
COLO	Colombia Bolsa de Valores
COR	Cordoba Stock Exchange
CSE	Copenhagen Stock Exchange
CYP	Cyprus Stock Exchange
DAR	Dar es Salaam Stock Exchange
DES	Delhi Stock Exchange
DEU	Deutsche Borse (Frankfurt Stock Exchange)
DFM	Dubai Financial Market
DHA	Dhaka Stock Exchange
DUS	Dusseldorf Stock Exchange
ECA	Eastern Caribbean Securities
EGX	Egyptian Exchange
EMI	Securities & Commodities Authority (d/b/a Emirates Securities Market)
EUR	Euronext
FKA	Fukuoka Stock Exchange
GEOR	Georgian Stock Exchange
GHA	Ghana Stock Exchange
GUA	Guayaquil Stock Exchange
HEL	Helsinki Stock Exchange
HKG	Hong Kong Stock Exchange
HNX	Hanoi Stock Exchange
HOSE	Ho Chi Minh Stock Exchange (Vietnam)
HYD	Hyderabad Stock Exchange
ICE	Iceland Stock Exchange
INDO	Indonesia Stock Exchange
IRAQ	Iraq Stock Exchange
ISDX	ICAP Securities & Derivatives Exchange Limited (formerly PLUS)
ISE	Irish Stock Exchange
ISL	Islamabad Stock Exchange
IST	Istanbul Stock Exchange
ISX	Inter-Connected Stock Exchange of India
ITA	Italian Stock Exchange
JAI	Jaipur Stock Exchange
JAM	Jamaica Stock Exchange
JAS	OSE JASDAQ
JSE	Johannesburg Stock Exchange
KAR	Karachi Stock Exchange
KAZ	Kazakhstan Stock Exchange
KHAR	Khartoum Stock Exchange
KLS	Bursa Malaysia (Formerly Kuala Lumpur Stock Exchange)
KOL	Kolkata Stock Exchange
KRS	Korea Exchange
KUW	Kuwait Stock Exchange
LAH	Lahore Stock Exchange
I IM	Lima Bolsa de Valores
LJU	Ljubljana Stock Exchange
LSE	London Stock Exchange
LUS	Lusaka Stock Exchange
LUX	Luxembourg Stock Exchange
MAC	Macedonian Stock Exchange
MAD	Madrid Stock Exchange
MAL	Malta Stock Exchange
MALA	Malawi Stock Exchange
MAU	Stock Exchange of Mauritius
MDS	Madras Stock Exchange
MEX	Bolsa Mexicana de Valores

MIC	MICEX Moscow Interbank Currency Exchange	PUN	Pune Stock Exchange (India)
MOLD	Moldova Stock Exchange	QE	Qatar Stock Exchange
MON	Montreal Stock Exchange	RIO	Rio de Janeiro, Bolsa de Valores
MONG	Mongolian Stock Exchange	RSE	Riga Stock Exchange
MUN	Munich Stock Exchange	RUS	Russian Trading System
MUS	Muscat Stock Exchange	SAP	Sapporo Stock Exchange
NAI	Nairobi Stock Exchange	SARE	Sarejevo Stock Exchange
NAM	Namibian Stock Exchange	SAU	Saudi Stock Exchange
NASDAQ	National Association of Securities Dealers, Inc.	SES	Singapore Stock Exchange
		SGO	Santiago Stock Exchange
NASDAQDBAI	NASDAQ Dubai	SHG	Shanghai Stock Exchange
NEP	Nepal Stock Exchange Ltd	SPSE	South Pacific Stock Exchange
NGO	Nagoya Stock Exchange	SSE	Shenzhen Stock Exchange
NIGE	Nigerian Stock Exchange	SSX	Swaziland Stock Exchange
NSE	National Stock Exchange of India	STU	Stuttgart Stock Exchange (Baden)
NSXA	National Stock Exchange of Australia	SWX	Swiss Stock Exchange
NYSA	New York Stock Exchange Arca Options Trading System	TAE	Tel-Aviv Stock Exchange
		TAI	Taiwan Stock Exchange
		TAL	Tallinn Stock Exchange
NYSE	New York Stock Exchange	TFE	Tokyo Financial Exchange (Futures)
NYSE AMERICAN	NYSE American	THA	Stock Exchange of Thailand
NZE	New Zealand Exchange Limited	THE	Tehran Stock Exchange
OMX	Stockholm/Nordic Stock Exchange	TKS	Tokyo Stock Exchange
OSE	Osaka Stock Exchange	TOSH	Tashkent Republican Stock Exchange
OSL	Oslo Stock Exchange	TRI	Trinidad & Tobago Stock Exchange
OTC	Over-the-Counter Pink Sheets	TSX	Toronto Stock Exchange
OTCB	Over-the-Counter Bulletin Board	TSXV	Toronto Stock Venture Exchange
OTCI	Over-the-Counter Exchange of India	UGAN	Uganda Securities Exchange
PAL	Palestine Securities Exchange	UKR	Ukranian Stock Exchange
PAN	Bolsa de Valores de Panama	VAL	Bolsa de Valencia
PET	Saint Petersburg Stock Exchange	VIE	Wiener Borse (Vienna Stock Exchange)
PHI	Philippine Stock Exchange	VLA	Vladivostok Stock Exchange
PHLX	Philadelphia - NASDAQ OMX PHLX	VSE	Vilnius Stock Exchange
POM	Port Moresby Stock Exchange Limited (Papua New Guinea)	WAR	Warsaw Stock Exchange
		ZAG	Zagreb Stock Exchange
PRA	Prague Stock Exchange	ZIM	Zimbabwe Stock Exchange

COUNTRY ABBREVIATIONS

AF	Afghanistan	DK	Denmark	KG	Kyrgyzstan	KN	Saint Kitts & Nevis
AI	Albania	DJ	Djibouti	La	Laos	LC	Saint Lucia
DG	Algeria	DM	Dominica	LV	Latvia	VC	Saint Vincent & Grenadines
AD	Andorra	DO	Dominican Republic	LB	Lebanon	WS	Samoa
AO	Angola			LS	Lesotho	SA	Saudi Arabia
AI	Anguilla	EC	Ecuador	LR	Liberia	SN	Senegal
AG	Antigua & Barbuda	EG	Egypt	LY	Libya	YU	Serbia & Montenegro
Ar	Argentina	SV	El Salvador	LI	Liechtenstein	Sc	Seychelles
AM	Armenia	GQ	Equatorial Guinea	LT	Lithuania	SL	Sierra Leone
AW	Aruba	ER	Eritrea	LU	Luxembourg	SG	Singapore
AU	Australia	EE	Estonia	Mo	Macau	Sk	Slovakia
AT	Austria	ET	Ethiopia	MK	Macedonia	SI	Slovenia
Az	Azerbaijan	FO	Faroe Islands	MG	Madagascar	SB	Solomon Islands
BS	Bahamas	FJ	Fiji	MW	Malawi	SO	Somalia
BH	Bahrain	FI	Finland	MY	Malaysia	ZA	South Africa
BD	Bangladesh	FR	France	MV	Maldives	ES	Spain
BB	Barbados	GFA	French Guiana	ML	Mali	LK	Sri Lanka
BY	Belarus	PF	French Polynesia	Mt	Malta	Sd	Sudan
BE	Belgium	Ga	Gabon	MQ	Martinique	SR	Suriname
BZ	Belize	GM	Gambia	MR	Mauritania	SZ	Swaziland
BJ	Benin	GE	Georgia	MU	Mauritius	SE	Sweden
BM	Bermuda	De	Germany	MX	Mexico	CH	Switzerland
BT	Bhutan	GH	Ghana	Md	Moldova	SY	Syria
BO	Bolivia	GI	Gibraltar	MC	Monaco	TW	Taiwan
BA	Bosnia & Herzegovina	GR	Greece	Mn	Mongolia	TJ	Tajikistan
		GL	Greenland	Ms	Montserrat	TZ	Tanzania
BW	Botswana	GD	Grenada	Ma	Morocco	TH	Thailand
BR	Brazil	GP	Guadeloupe	MZ	Mozambique	TG	Togo
BN	Brunei Darussalam	GT	Guatemala	MM	Myanmar	TO	Tonga
BG	Bulgaria	Gu	Guiana	NA	Namibia	TT	Trinidad & Tobago
BF	Burkina Faso	GN	Guinea	NP	Nepal	Tn	Tunisia
BI	Burundi	GW	Guinea-Bissau	NL	Netherlands	TR	Turkey
KH	Cambodia	GY	Guyana	AN	Netherlands Antilles	TM	Turkmenistan
CM	Cameroon	HT	Haiti			TC	Turks & Caicos Islands
Ca	Canada	HN	Honduras	Nc	New Caledonia		
CV	Cape Verde	HK	Hong Kong	NZ	New Zealand		
Ky	Cayman Islands	HU	Hungary	NI	Nicaragua	TV	Tuvalu
CF	Central African Republic	IS	Iceland	Ne	Niger	UG	Uganda
TD	Chad	In	India	NG	Nigeria	UA	Ukraine
CL	Chile	Id	Indonesia	NO	Norway	AE	United Arab Emirates
CN	China	IR	Iran	OM	Oman		
Co	Colombia	IQ	Iraq	PK	Pakistan	UK	United Kingdom
KM	Comoros	IE	Ireland	Pa	Panama	UY	Uruguay
CD	Congo, Democratic Republic of	Il	Israel	PG	Papua New Guinea	UZ	Uzbekistan
		IT	Italy	PY	Paraguay	VU	Vanuatu
CG	Congo, Republic of	JM	Jamaica	PE	Peru	VE	Venezuela
CK	Cook Islands	JP	Japan	PH	Philippines	VN	Vietnam
CR	Costa Rica	JO	Jordan	PL	Poland	VG	Virgin Islands (British)
CI	Cote d'Ivoire	KZ	Kazakhstan	PT	Portugal		
HR	Croatia	KE	Kenya	QA	Qatar	YE	Yemen
CU	Cuba	KI	Kiribati	RE	Reunion	ZM	Zambia
CY	Cyprus	KN	Korea (North)	RO	Romania	ZW	Zimbabwe
CZ	Czech Republic	Ks	Korea (South)	RU	Russia		
		KW	Kuwait	RW	Rwanda		

NEW LISTINGS 2025
Appearing for the first time in this publication

1

1812 BREWING COMPANY, INC.; WATER-TOWN, NY

2

2SEVENTY BIO, INC.; CAMBRIDGE, MA

9

99 ACQUISITION GROUP INC.; GAITH-ERSBURG, MD

A

ABPRO HOLDINGS, INC.; WOBURN, MA

ACHARI VENTURES HOLDINGS CORP. I; CLARK, NJ

ACRI CAPITAL ACQUISITION CORPORA-TION; AUSTIN, TX

ADLAI NORTYE LTD.; NORTH BRUNS-WICK, NJ

AFFINITY BANCSHARES, INC.; COVING-TON, GA

AGRICULTURE & NATURAL SOLUTIONS ACQUISITION CORPORATION; NEW YORK, NY

AIMEI HEALTH TECHNOLOGY CO., LTD.; NEW YORK, NY

ALTO NEUROSCIENCE, INC.; LOS AL-TOS, CA

APOLLO GLOBAL MANAGEMENT, INC.; NEW YORK, NY

APPRECIATE HOLDINGS, INC.; MINNE-TONKA, MN

ARISZ ACQUISITION CORP.; NEW YORK, NY

ARRIVENT BIOPHARMA, INC.; NEW-TOWN SQUARE, PA

ASHLAND INC.; WILMINGTON, DE

AUTONOMIX MEDICAL, INC.; THE WOODLANDS, TX

B

BBX CAPITAL, INC.; FORT LAUDER-DALE, FL

BETTER FOR YOU WELLNESS, INC.; CO-LUMBUS, OH

BIOHAVEN LTD.; NEW HAVEN, CT

BLACK HAWK ACQUISITION CORPORA-TION; DANVILLE, CA

BLACKWELL 3D CONSTRUCTION CORP; CARSON CITY, NV

BOWEN ACQUISITION CORP.; NEW YORK, NY

C

CALUMET, INC.; INDIANAPOLIS, IN

CANNABIS BIOSCIENCE INTERNA-TIONAL HOLDINGS, INC.; HOUSTON, TX

CANNABIST CO HOLDINGS INC.; NEW YORK, NY

CAPITAL BANCORP, INC.; ROCKVILLE, MD

CARGO THERAPEUTICS, INC.; SAN CARLOS, CA

CARMELL CORPORATION; PITTS-BURGH, PA

CBB BANCORP, INC.; LOS ANGELES, CA

CENTRAL PLAINS BANCSHARES, INC.; GRAND ISLAND, NE

CG ONCOLOGY, INC.; IRVINE, CA

CHROMOCELL THERAPEUTICS CORPO-RATION; FREEHOLD, NJ

COPPER PROPERTY CTL PASS THROUGH TRUST; PLANO, TX

CSLM ACQUISITION CORP.; FORT LAU-DERDALE, FL

D

DETROIT LEGAL NEWS COMPANY; DE-TROIT, MI

DMY SQUARED TECHNOLOGY GROUP, INC.; LAS VEGAS, NV

DOGWOOD STATE BANK; RALEIGH, NC

DRAGONFLY ENERGY HOLDINGS CORP.; RENO, NV

DYNATRACE, INC.; WALTHAM, MA

E

EALIXIR, INC.; MIAMI, FL

ELITE HEALTH SYSTEMS INC.; ON-TARIO, CA

EMBECTA CORP.; FRANKLIN LAKES, NJ

F

FALCON'S BEYOND GLOBAL, INC.; OR-LANDO, FL

FIBROBIOLOGICS, INC.; HOUSTON, TX

FIRST CAPITAL BANCSHARES INC; CHARLESTON, SC

FIRST SEACOAST BANCORP, INC.; DO-VER, DE

FLY-E GROUP, INC.; FLUSHING, NY

FOUR LEAF ACQUISITION CORPORA-TION; LOS ALTOS, CA

G

GAMER PAKISTAN INC.; HENDERSON, NV

GE VERNOVA INC.; CAMBRIDGE, MA

GENERATIONS BANCORP NY, INC.; SEN-ECA FALLS, NY

GETAROUND, INC.; SAN FRANCISCO, CA

GOLDEN STAR ACQUISITION CORP.; NEW YORK, NY

GRIID INFRASTRUCTURE INC.; CINCIN-NATI, OH

H

HEALTHPEAK PROPERTIES, INC.; DEN-VER, CO

HIGHPEAK ENERGY, INC.; FORT WORTH, TX

HOLDCO NUVO GROUP D.G LTD.; PRINCETON, NJ

HOLLEY INC.; BOWLING GREEN, KY

HUT 8 CORP.; MIAMI, FL

I

INNO HOLDINGS, INC.; BROOKSHIRE, TX

IONQ, INC.; COLLEGE PARK, MD

ISRAEL ACQUISITIONS CORP.; BEE CAVE, TX

J

JUSHI HOLDINGS INC.; BOCA RATON, FL

K

KALERA PUBLIC LIMITED COMPANY; ORLANDO, FL

KEEN VISION ACQUISITION CORPORA-TION; SUMMIT, NJ

KENVUE INC.; SKILLMAN, NJ

KIMCO REALTY CORPORATION; JER-ICHO, NY

KINDLY MD, INC.; SALT LAKE CITY, UT

KYVERNA THERAPEUTICS, INC.; EM-ERYVILLE, CA

L

LANZATECH GLOBAL, INC.; SKOKIE, IL

LEEP INC; TWIN FALLS, ID

LEGACY EDUCATION INC.; LANCASTER, PA

LEXEO THERAPEUTICS, INC.; NEW YORK, NY

LIVEWIRE ERGOGENICS, INC.; ANA-HEIM, CA

LUCID GROUP, INC.; NEWARK, CA

M

M3-BRIGADE ACQUISITION V CORP.; NEW YORK, NY

MACH NATURAL RESOURCES LP; OKLAHOMA CITY, OK

MACHTEN, INC.; TRAVERSE CITY, MI

MARINE BANCORP OF FLORIDA, INC.; VERO BEACH, FL

MASSIMO GROUP; GARLAND, TX

MASTERBRAND, INC.; JASPER, IN

MIAMI BREEZE CAR CARE, INC.; MIAMI, FL

MILLENNIUM SUSTAINABLE VENTURES CORP.; OLD BETHPAGE, NY

MONTANA TECHNOLOGIES CORPORA-TION; RONAN, MT

MSC INCOME FUND, INC.; HOUSTON, TX

N

NATURE'S MIRACLE HOLDING INC.; ON-TARIO, CA

NAUTILUS BIOTECHNOLOGY, INC.; SE-ATTLE, WA

NB BANCORP, INC.; NEEDHAM, MA

NCR ATLEOS CORPORATION; ATLANTA, GA

NET LEASE OFFICE PROPERTIES; NEW YORK, NY

NEXSCIENT, INC.; LOS ANGELES, CA

NORTHANN CORP.; ELK GROVE, CA

NUGL, INC.; CHINO, CA

O

O'REILLY AUTOMOTIVE, INC.; SPRING-FIELD, MO

OMNIAB, INC.; EMERYVILLE, CA

ON4 COMMUNICATIONS INC.; NEW YORK, NY

OVINTIV INC.; DENVER, CO

P

PAGAYA TECHNOLOGIES LTD.; NEW YORK, NY

PERMEX PETROLEUM CORPORATION; DALLAS, TX

PONO CAPITAL TWO, INC.; HONOLULU, HI

PROFICIENT AUTO LOGISTICS, INC.; JACKSONVILLE, FL

PYXUS INTERNATIONAL, INC.; MORRIS-VILLE, NC

Q

QUANTUM COMPUTING INC.; HOBOKEN, NJ

QUETTA ACQUISITION CORPORATION; NEW YORK, NY

QUIDELORTHO CORPORATION; SAN DI-EGO, CA

R

RBAZ BANCORP, INC.; PHOENIX, AZ

REALPHA TECH CORP.; DUBLIN, OH

REGIONAL HEALTH PROPERTIES, INC.; ATLANTA, GA

RLI CORP.; PEORIA, IL

ROCKY MOUNTAIN CHOCOLATE FAC-TORY, INC.; DURANGO, CO

ROOT, INC.; COLUMBUS, OH

ROTH CH ACQUISITION CO.; MIAMI BEACH, FL

S

SHARKNINJA, INC.; NEEDHAM, MA

SHARPLINK GAMING, INC.; MINNEAPO-LIS, MN

SHF HOLDINGS, INC.; GOLDEN, CO

SHIFT4 PAYMENTS, INC.; CENTER VAL-LEY, PA

SHIMMICK CORPORATION; IRVINE, CA

SIGNING DAY SPORTS, INC.; SCOTTS-DALE, AZ

SINCLAIR, INC.; HUNT VALLEY, MD

SMITH DOUGLAS HOMES CORP.; WOODSTOCK, GA

SOLVENTUM CORPORATION; MAPLE-WOOD, MN

SOUTH DAKOTA SOYBEAN PROCES-SORS LLC; VOLGA, SD

SPECTAIRE HOLDINGS INC.; WATER-TOWN, MA

SPECTRAL AI, INC.; DALLAS, TX

STAGWELL, INC.; NEW YORK, NY

STRYVE FOODS, INC.; PLANO, TX

SURF AIR MOBILITY INC.; HAWTHORNE, CA

T

TELOMIR PHARMACEUTICALS, INC.; BALTIMORE, MD

TROPICAL BATTERY COMPANY LIM-ITED; JAMAICA, NY

U

UBUYHOLDINGS, INC.; WHITE PLAINS, NY

UNUSUAL MACHINES, INC.; ORLANDO, FL

V

VALVOLINE INC.; LEXINGTON, KY

VECTOR 21 HOLDINGS, INC.; LAKE-WOOD, CO

VERALTO CORPORATION; WALTHAM, MA

VICI PROPERTIES L.P.; NEW YORK, NY

VIEW, INC.; MILPITAS, CA

VITESSE ENERGY, INC.; CENTENNIAL, CO

VOCODIA HOLDINGS CORP.; BOCA RA-TON, FL

VOLATO GROUP, INC.; CHAMBLEE, GA

W

WEST COAST COMMUNITY BANCORP; SANTA CRUZ, CA

WILLIAM PENN BANCORPORATION;
BRISTOL, PA

Z

ZIMVIE INC.; PALM BEACH GARDENS,
FL

ZYMEWORKS INC.; BELLEVUE, WA

WILLIAM PENN BANCORPORATION,

Mergers and Acquisitions
January 2024—December 2024
(Parent Companies Only)

A

AB&T FINANCIAL CORPORATION—acquired & absorbed by Commercial Bancgroup, Inc.

AIB Acquisition Corporation—acquired by PSI Group Holdings Ltd.

Akili Inc.—acquired by UnitedHealth Group Incorporated

Alimera Sciences, Inc.—acquired by ANI Pharmaceuticals, Inc.

Alpine Immune Sciences, Inc.—acquired by Vertex Pharmaceuticals Incorporated

Alteryx, Inc.—acquired by Clearlake Capital Group, L.P. and Insight Venture Management, LLC

Ambrx Biopharma Inc.—acquired by Johnson & Johnson

American Equity Investment Life Holding Company—acquired by Brookfield Reinsurance Ltd.

American National Bankshares Inc.—acquired by Atlantic Union Bankshares Corporation

Asensus Surgical, Inc.—acquired by Karl Storz GmbH & Co.

Athersys, Inc.—acquired by Healios K.K.

Atrion Corporation—acquired by Nordson Corporation

Augmedix, Inc.—acquired by HCA Healthcare, Inc.

B

Bite Acquisition Corp.—merged with Above Food Corp., to form Above Food Ingredients Inc.

Bluegreen Vacations Holding Corporation—acquired by Hilton Grand Vacations Inc.

BowFlex Inc.—acquired by Johnson Health Tech. Co., Ltd.

C

California BanCorp—merged with Southern California Bancorp, to form California BanCorp

Callon Petroleum Company—acquired by APA Corporation

CapStar Financial Holdings, Inc.—acquired by Old National Bancorp

Carrols Restaurant Group, Inc.—acquired by Restaurant Brands International Inc.

CBOA Financial, Inc.—acquired by Bancorp 34, Inc.

Cerevel Therapeutics Holdings, Inc.—acquired by AbbVie Inc.

Chico's FAS, Inc.—acquired by Sycamore Partners Management, LP

Chuy's Holdings, Inc.—acquired by Darden Restaurants, Inc.

Coastal Bank & Trust—acquired & absorbed by PB Financial Corporation

Codorus Valley Bancorp, Inc.—acquired by Orrstown Financial Services, Inc.

Community Financial Group, Inc.—acquired by Glacier Bancorp, Inc.

COMMUNITY WEST BANCSHARES—merged with Central Valley Community Bancorp, to form Community West Bancshares

Cornerstone Financial Corporation—acquired by Princeton Bancorp, Inc.

CymaBay Therapeutics, Inc.—acquired by Gilead Sciences, Inc.

D

Daseke, Inc.—acquired by TFI International Inc.

Deciphera Pharmaceuticals, Inc.—acquired by Ono Pharmaceutical Co., Ltd.

DecisionPoint Systems, Inc.—acquired by The Graham Group, Inc.

DermTech, Inc.—merged with DERM-JES Holdings, LLC, to form DermTech, LLC

E

Eagle Financial Bancorp, Inc.—acquired by LCNB Corp.

Ebix Inc.—acquired by Eraaya Lifespaces Limited and Vikas Lifecare Ltd. [et al]

Encore Wire Corporation—acquired by Prysmian S.p.A.

EngageSmart, Inc.—acquired by Vista Equity Partners, LLC

Envestnet, Inc.—acquired by Bain Capital, LP [et al]

Equitrans Midstream Corporation—acquired by EQT Corporation

Everbridge, Inc.—acquired by Thoma Bravo, L.P.

F

FaZe Holdings Inc.—acquired by GameSquare Holdings, Inc.

FG Group Holdings Inc.—merged with Kingsway Financial Services Inc., to form Fundamental Global Inc.

FNCB Bancorp, Inc.—acquired by Peoples Financial Services Corp.

Forza X1, Inc.—acquired by Twin Vee PowerCats Co.

Silk Road Medical, Inc.—acquired by Boston Scientific Corporation

Silverbow Resources, Inc.—acquired by KKR & Co. Inc.

Sizzle Acquisition Corp.—acquired by European Lithium Limited

Societal CDMO, Inc.—acquired by NovaQuest Capital Management, LLC

SomaLogic, Inc.—acquired by Standard BioTools Inc.

Southwestern Energy Company—merged with Chesapeake Energy Corporation, to form Expand Energy Corporation

Sovos Brands, Inc.—acquired by Campbell Soup Company

SP Plus Corporation—acquired by Eldridge Industries LLC

Splunk Inc.—acquired by Cisco Systems, Inc.

Squarespace Inc.—acquired by Permira Advisers LLP

Stericycle, Inc.—acquired by Waste Management Inc.

Strategic Asset Leasing, Inc.—acquired by Redwoods Acquisition Corp.

Superior Drilling Products, Inc.—acquired by Drilling Tools International Corp

T

Tellurian Inc.—acquired by Woodside Energy Group Ltd

Terran Orbital Corporation—acquired by Lockheed Martin Corporation

The L.S. Starrett Company—acquired by Middleground Management, LP

Theseus Pharmaceuticals, Inc.—acquired by Concentra Biosciences, LLC

Timberline Resources Corporation—acquired by McEwen Mining Inc.

Transphorm, Inc.—acquired by Renesas Electronics Corporation

Trilogy International Partners Inc.—acquired by SG Enterprises II, LLC

U

U.S. Silica Holdings, Inc.—acquired by Apollo Global Management, Inc.

UGE International Ltd.—acquired by Nova Infrastructure Management, LLC

V

Vapotherm, Inc.—acquired by Perceptive Advisors, LLC

Vector Group Ltd.—acquired by Japan Tobacco Inc.

Verde Bio Holdings, Inc.—merged with SensaSure

Technologies, Inc., to form Formation Minerals, Inc.

VisioUazia, Inc.—acquired by KKR & Co. Inc., and Accel Partners L.P.

W

Wayne Savings Bancshares, Inc.—acquired by Main Street Financial Services Corp.

X

XS Financial, Inc.—acquired by Mavik Capital Management, LP and Axar Capital Management LP

Z

ZeroFox Holdings, Inc.—acquired by Whanau Interests LLC

U.S. PUBLIC COMPANIES

1-800-FLOWERS.COM, INC.
2 Jericho Plz Ste 200, Jericho, NY 11753
Tel.: (516) 237-6000   DE
Web Site:
https://www.1800flowers.com
Year Founded: 1976
FLWS—(NASDAQ)
Rev.: $1,831,421,000
Assets: $1,032,648,000
Liabilities: $566,306,000
Net Worth: $466,342,000
Earnings: ($6,105,000)
Emp.: 4,000
Fiscal Year-end: 06/30/24
Flowers & Gifts Mail-Order & Internet Retailer
N.A.I.C.S.: 459310
Steve Roberts (Sr VP-Business Development)
Jason John (CMO)
Joseph Rowland (Grp Pres)
Abhay Patel (Pres-Brand)
James M. Langrock (CFO & Chief Admin Officer)
Maureen Paradine (Sr VP-HR)

Subsidiaries:

1-800-FLOWERS Retail, Inc.   (1)
7117 Blanco Rd, San Antonio, TX 78216
Tel.: (210) 524-1006
Web Site:
http://www.1800flowerssanantonio.com
Emp.: 15
Florist & Gift Retailer
N.A.I.C.S.: 459310

1-800-FLOWERS Team Services, Inc.   (1)
1 Old Country Rd Ste 500, Carle Place, NY 11514
Tel.: (516) 237-6000
Florist & Gift Retailer
N.A.I.C.S.: 459310

1-800-FLOWERS.COM Franchise Co., Inc.   (1)
1 Old Country Rd Ste 500, Carle Place, NY 11514
Web Site: https://franchise.1800flowers.com
Florist & Gift Retailer
N.A.I.C.S.: 459310

Bear Creek Orchards, Inc.   (1)
2500 S Pacific Hwy, Medford, OR 97504
Tel.: (541) 864-2362
Food Products Distr
N.A.I.C.S.: 424490

Celebrations.com, LLC   (1)
220 5th Ave Ste 17-03, New York, NY 10001
Tel.: (516) 237-6087
Software Development Services
N.A.I.C.S.: 541511

Cheryl & Co.   (1)
646 McCorkle Blvd, Westerville, OH 43082
Tel.: (614) 901-0046
Web Site: https://www.cheryls.com
Rev.: $24,106,368

Emp.: 200
Cookies, Desserts & Gift Baskets Retailer & Catalog Sales
N.A.I.C.S.: 311821

Conroy's Inc.   (1)
3377 W Shaw Ave, Fresno, CA 93711
Tel.: (559) 490-4242
Web Site:
https://www.conroysflowersfresno.com
Sales Range: Less than $1 Million
Emp.: 25
Flower Retailer
N.A.I.C.S.: 424930

Harry & David Holdings, Inc.   (1)
Tel.: (541) 864-2500
Web Site: https://www.harryanddavid.com
Holding Company; Gift Baskets, Specialty Foods, Flowers & Other Novelties Direct Marketer
N.A.I.C.S.: 551112

Subsidiary (Domestic):

Harry & David Operations, Inc.   (2)
2500 S Pacific Hwy, Medford, OR 97501
Tel.: (541) 864-2362
Gift Baskets, Specialty Foods, Flowers & Other Novelties Direct Marketer
N.A.I.C.S.: 551112
Craig Johnson (Pres & CEO)

Harry & David, LLC   (1)
2500 S Pacific Hwy, Medford, OR 97501-2675
Web Site: https://www.harryanddavid.com
Gourmet Food Product Distr
N.A.I.C.S.: 445298

MyFlorist.net, LLC   (1)
1984 Chain Bridge Rd Ste 204, McLean, VA 22102
Tel.: (703) 442-8203
Web Site: https://www.myflorist.com
Fresh Flower Distr
N.A.I.C.S.: 459310

PersonalizationMall.Com, LLC   (1)
51 Shore Dr, Burr Ridge, IL 60527-5880   (100%)
Tel.: (630) 910-6000
Web Site:
https://www.personalizationmall.com
Emp.: 100
Online Shopping
N.A.I.C.S.: 423940
Andrew Deren (COO & CTO)

The Popcorn Factory, Inc.   (1)
2457 W N Ave, Melrose Park, IL 60160
Tel.: (847) 362-0028
Web Site: http://www.thepopcornfactory.com
Sales Range: $50-74.9 Million
Emp.: 100
Popcorn Mfr & Distr
N.A.I.C.S.: 311919
James F. McCann (Chm & CEO)

The Winetasting Network   (1)
578 Gateway Dr, Napa, CA 94558
Tel.: (800) 435-2225
Web Site: http://www.winetasting.com
Wines Mfr & Distr
N.A.I.C.S.: 312130

Vital Choice Seafood LLC   (1)

2500 S Pacific Hwy, Medford, OR 97501
Web Site: https://www.vitalchoice.com
Seafood & Organic Food Retailer
N.A.I.C.S.: 311710

WTN Services LLC   (1)
2545 Napa Valley Corporate Dr, Napa, CA 94558
Tel.: (707) 265-2934
Sales Range: $150-199.9 Million
Wine Distribution Services
N.A.I.C.S.: 424810

1.12 ACQUISITION CORP.
41 Madison Ave Ste 2020, New York, NY 10010
Tel.: (646) 450-9187   Ky
Year Founded: 2020
OPOTU—(NASDAQ)
Investment Services
N.A.I.C.S.: 523999
Tanmay Kumar (CFO)
Frank R. Martire Jr. (Founder & Chm)
Frank Martire III (Pres)

10X CAPITAL VENTURE ACQUISITION CORP. II
(Name Changed to African Agriculture Holdings Inc.)

10X CAPITAL VENTURE ACQUISITION CORP.
1 World Trade Center 85th Fl, New York, NY 10007
Tel.: (212) 257-0069   DE
Year Founded: 2020
VCVCU—(NASDAQ)
Investment Services
N.A.I.C.S.: 523999
David Weisburd (Gen Partner-10X Capital Holdings LLC, COO & Co-Head-Venture Capital-10X Capital Holdings LLC)
Oliver Wriedt (Pres & Head-Capital Markets)
Russell Read (Chief Investment Officer-Alternative Investment)
Hans Thomas (Founder, Chm & CEO)
Guhan Kandasamy (CFO)
John Petersen (Mng Partner)

10X CAPITAL VENTURE ACQUISITION CORP. III
1 Word Trade Ctr 85th Fl, New York, NY 10007
Tel.: (212) 220-7218   Ky
Web Site: https://www.10xcapital.com
Year Founded: 2004
VCXA—(NYSE)
Rev.: $4,161,515
Assets: $308,854,832
Liabilities: $325,448,311
Net Worth: ($16,593,479)
Earnings: $698,292

Emp.: 4
Fiscal Year-end: 12/31/22
Investment Holding Company
N.A.I.C.S.: 551112
David Weisburd (Founder, CEO, COO & Head-Venture Capital)
Max Staedtler (Partner)
Curtis Pierce (Sr VP)
Russell Read (Chief Investment Officer)
Yael Steiner (Assoc Gen Counsel)
Nolan Berkenfeld (VP)
Patrik Hansson (Dir-Business Development)
Guhan Kandasamy (Partner & Chief Data Officer)
Alex Monje (Partner & Chief Legal Officer)
Osman H. Ahmed (Pres, Mng Dir & Head-Private Equity)

10X GENOMICS, INC.
6230 Stoneridge Mall Rd, Pleasanton, CA 94588
Tel.: (925) 401-7300   DE
Web Site:
https://www.10xgenomics.com
Year Founded: 2012
TXG—(NASDAQ)
Rev.: $618,727,000
Assets: $965,143,000
Liabilities: $224,100,000
Net Worth: $741,043,000
Earnings: ($255,099,000)
Emp.: 1,259
Fiscal Year-end: 12/31/23
Biotechnology Research & Development Services
N.A.I.C.S.: 541714
Brad Crutchfield (Chief Comml Officer)
Eric Whitaker (Gen Counsel)
Michael Schnall-Levin (Sr VP-R&D)
Alexander Wong (Sr VP-Product, Software & Infrastructure)
Jean Philibert (Chief People Officer)
Paul Wyatt (VP-Ops)
Jonathan Schimmel (VP-Global Support & Sls Ops)
Ruth De Backer (Chief Bus Officer)
Edwin Hauw (VP-Mktg)
Adam S. Taich (CFO, Principal Acctg Officer & Treas)
Serge Saxonov (Co-Founder & CEO)
Benjamin J. Hindson (Co-Founder, Pres & Chief Scientific Officer)

12 RETECH CORPORATION
515 E Grant St Ste 150, Phoenix, AZ 85004
Tel.: (530) 539-4329   NV
Web Site: http://www.12retech.com
Year Founded: 2014
RETC—(OTCIQ)
Rev.: $660,206

12 ReTech Corporation—(Continued)

Assets: $863,895
Liabilities: $17,930,694
Net Worth: ($17,066,799)
Earnings: ($5,260,898)
Fiscal Year-end: 12/31/21
Software Development Services
N.A.I.C.S.: 541511
Angelo Ponzetta (Founder, Chm, Pres, CEO & Sec)
Daniele Monteverde (CFO)

1399 INTERNET TECHNOLOGY APPLICATION GROUP, INC.

401 Ryland St Ste 200a, Reno, NV 89502
Tel.: (425) 291-8274　　　　NV
Year Founded: 2020
YSGG—(OTCIQ)
Information Technology Services
N.A.I.C.S.: 541512
Kaiwen Luo (Sec)
Premashanth Kumalarsan (Co-Pres, Co-CEO & Exec Dir)
Luo Hua (Co-Pres, Co-CEO & Treas)

141 CAPITAL, INC.

Ste 333 29 S LaSalle St, Chicago, IL 60603
Tel.: (312) 265-3767
ONCP—(OTCIQ)
Trading Services
N.A.I.C.S.: 523160
Howard Salamon (Chm & CEO)

180 DEGREE CAPITAL CORP.

7 N Willow St Ste 4B, Montclair, NJ 07042
Tel.: (973) 746-4500　　　NY
Web Site:
　https://www.180degreecapital.com
TURN—(NASDAQ)
Rev.: $3,466,681
Assets: $99,253,342
Liabilities: $2,935,548
Net Worth: $96,317,794
Earnings: ($510,224)
Emp.: 7
Fiscal Year-end: 12/31/20
Nanotechnology & Microsystems
Venture Capital Firm
N.A.I.C.S.: 523999
Daniel B. Wolfe (Pres, CFO, Chief Compliance Officer & Portfolio Mgr)
Alicia M. Gift (Treas & Sec)
Kevin M. Rendino (Chm, CEO & Portfolio Mgr)

Subsidiaries:

Orig3n Inc.　　　　　　　　(1)
27 Drydock Ave 3rd Fl, Boston, MA 02210
Tel.: (800) 913-6351
Web Site: http://www.orig3n.com
Biological Science & Emerging Technology Services
N.A.I.C.S.: 541714
Kate Blanchard (COO)
Marcie Glicksman (Chief Scientific Officer)
Robin Smith (CEO)

180 LIFE SCIENCES CORP.

3000 El Camino Real Bldg 4 Ste 200, Palo Alto, CA 94306
Tel.: (650) 507-0669　　　DE
Web Site: https://180lifesciences.com
Year Founded: 2016
ATNF—(NASDAQ)
Assets: $19,650,248
Liabilities: $8,306,330
Net Worth: $11,343,918
Earnings: ($38,726,259)
Emp.: 5
Fiscal Year-end: 12/31/22
Investment Services
N.A.I.C.S.: 523999

Joseph A. Williamson (COO)
George R. Hornig (Chm)
Blair Jordan (Interim CEO)
Marc Feldman (Co-Founder)
Jagdeep Nanchahal (Co-Founder & Chm)
Omar Jimenez (CFO, Principal Acctg Officer & Sec)

1812 BREWING COMPANY, INC.

PO BOX 6192, 981 WATERMAN DRIVE, WATERTOWN, NY 13601
Tel.: (315) 788-1812　　　FL
KEGS—(OTC)
N.A.I.C.S.:

1847 HOLDINGS LLC

590 Madison Ave 21st Fl, New York, NY 10022
Tel.: (212) 417-9800　　　DE
Web Site:
　https://www.1847holdings.com
Year Founded: 2013
EFSH—(NYSEAMEX)
Rev.: $48,929,124
Assets: $45,484,699
Liabilities: $42,594,865
Net Worth: $2,889,834
Earnings: ($10,159,600)
Emp.: 219
Fiscal Year-end: 12/31/22
Investment Holding Company
N.A.I.C.S.: 551112
Glyn C. Milburn (VP-Ops)
Robert D. Patterson (Operating Partner)
Vernice L. Howard (CFO)
Ellery W. Roberts (Chm, Pres & CEO)
Eric VanDam (COO)

Subsidiaries:

Asiens Appliance, Inc.　　　(1)
1801 Piner Rd, Santa Rosa, CA 95403
Tel.: (707) 546-3749
Web Site: https://www.asiensappliance.com
Sales Range: $1-9.9 Million
Emp.: 27
Household Appliance Stores
N.A.I.C.S.: 449210

ICU Eyewear, Inc.　　　　　(1)
1900 Shelton Dr, Hollister, CA 95023
Tel.: (800) 393-9273
Web Site: https://www.icueyewear.com
Eyewear Products Designer
N.A.I.C.S.: 423460

Kyle's Custom Wood Shop, Inc.　(1)
10849 W Emerald St, Boise, ID 83713
Tel.: (208) 375-7776
Web Site: https://www.kylescabinets.com
Cabinet Product Mfr
N.A.I.C.S.: 337110

Neese, Inc.　　　　　　　　(1)
303 Division St, Grand Junction, IA 50107
Tel.: (515) 738-2744
Web Site: https://www.neeseinc.com
Sales Range: $1-9.9 Million
Farm Machinery & Equipment Sales, Service & Rental
N.A.I.C.S.: 423820

Wolo Manufacturing Corp.　(1)
1 Saxwood St Ste 1, Deer Park, NY 11729
Tel.: (631) 242-0333
Web Site: http://www.wolo-mfg.com
Hardware, Nec
N.A.I.C.S.: 332510

1867 WESTERN FINANCIAL CORPORATION

301 E Miner Ave, Stockton, CA 95202
Tel.: (209) 929-1600　　　CA
Web Site:
　http://www.bankofstockton.com
Year Founded: 1988

WFCL—(OTCIQ)
Rev.: $149,001,000
Assets: $3,381,084,000
Liabilities: $2,748,813,000
Net Worth: $632,271,000
Earnings: $130,482,000
Fiscal Year-end: 12/31/19
Bank Holding Company
N.A.I.C.S.: 551111
Douglass M. Eberhardt (Chm & CEO)
John F. Dentoni (CFO)
Sarah Thompson (VP & Controller)

Subsidiaries:

Bank of Stockton　　　　　(1)
301 E Miner Ave, Stockton, CA 95202
Tel.: (209) 929-1600
Web Site: http://www.bankofstockton.com
Sales Range: $1-4.9 Billion
Emp.: 180
State Commercial Banks
N.A.I.C.S.: 522110
Mary Elizabeth Eberhardt-Sandstrom (VP-Comml Loans)
Kristin Reza (Asst VP-Community Branch Mgr)

1895 BANCORP OF WISCONSIN, INC.

7001 W Edgerton Ave, Greenfield, WI 53220
Tel.: (414) 421-8200
Web Site:
　https://www.pyramaxbank.com
Year Founded: 2019
BCOW—(NASDAQ)
Rev.: $18,175,000
Assets: $543,016,000
Liabilities: $467,654,000
Net Worth: $75,362,000
Earnings: ($148,000)
Emp.: 191
Fiscal Year-end: 12/31/22
Bank Holding Company
N.A.I.C.S.: 551111
Monica Baker (COO & Exec VP)
Thomas K. Peterson (Sr VP)
David R. Ball (Pres & CEO)
Steven T. Klitzing (CFO & Exec VP)
Daniel K. Kempel (Chief Credit Officer & Sr VP)

Subsidiaries:

PyraMax Bank　　　　　　　(1)
7001 W Edgerton Ave, Greenfield, WI 53220
Tel.: (414) 421-8200
Web Site: https://www.pyramaxbank.com
Sales Range: $1-9.9 Million
Emp.: 123
Commercial Banking Services
N.A.I.C.S.: 522110
Richard B. Hurd (Exec VP-Strategic Plng)
Monica Baker (COO & Exec VP)
Thomas K. Peterson (Sr VP)
David R. Ball (Pres & CEO)
Steven T. Klitzing (CFO & Exec VP)
Daniel K. Kempel (Chief Creative Officer & Sr VP)
Charles Mauer (Chief Credit Officer)

1LIFE HEALTHCARE, INC.

(Acquired by Amazon.com, Inc.)

1ST CONSTITUTION BANCORP (Acquired by Lakeland Bancorp, Inc.)

1PM INDUSTRIES, INC.

1930 Village Center Cir 3 6189, Las Vegas, NV 89134
Tel.: (424) 253-9991　　　CO
Web Site:
　http://www.1pmindustries.com
OPMZ—(OTCIQ)
Sales Range: $10-24.9 Million

Health & Wellness Products Direct Marketing & Infomercials
N.A.I.C.S.: 424210
Joseph Wade (Chm, Pres, CEO, CFO & Principal Acctg Officer)
Matt Billington (COO)

1ST COLONIAL COMMUNITY BANK

1040 Haddon Ave, Collingswood, NJ 08108
Tel.: (856) 858-1100　　　PA
Web Site:
　https://www.1stcolonial.com
FCOB—(OTCIQ)
Rev.: $28,869,000
Assets: $825,644,000
Liabilities: $757,721,000
Net Worth: $67,923,000
Earnings: $7,431,000
Emp.: 101
Fiscal Year-end: 12/31/23
Commercial Banking Services
N.A.I.C.S.: 522110
Linda M. Rohrer (Chm)
Robert B. White (Pres & CEO)
Frank J. Monaghan (COO & Exec VP)
Mary Kay Shea (CFO & Exec VP)
Michele M. Kraemer (Sr VP & Dir-HR)

1ST NRG CORP.

1531 Stout St 607, Denver, CO 80202
Tel.: (816) 256-8561　　　DE
Web Site: http://www.1stnrg-corp.com
FNRC—(OTCIQ)
Sales Range: Less than $1 Million
Oil & Gas Exploration Services
N.A.I.C.S.: 211120
Kevin Norris (CEO)
Joseph J. Schmidt (CFO & Sec)

1ST SOURCE CORPORATION

100 N Michigan St Ste 800, South Bend, IN 46601
Tel.: (574) 235-2000　　　IN
Web Site: https://www.1stsource.com
Year Founded: 1863
SRCE—(NASDAQ)
Rev.: $385,078,000
Assets: $8,339,416,000
Liabilities: $7,415,650,000
Net Worth: $923,766,000
Earnings: $120,532,000
Emp.: 1,150
Fiscal Year-end: 12/31/22
Offices of Bank Holding Companies
N.A.I.C.S.: 551111
Christopher J. Murphy III (Chm & CEO)
Christopher J. Murphy III (Chm & CEO)
John B. Griffith (Chief Admin Officer, Gen Counsel & Sec)
Andrea Gayle Short (Pres)
Brett A. Bauer (CFO, Principal Acctg Officer, Treas & Sr VP)

Subsidiaries:

1st Source Bank　　　　　　(1)
100 N Michigan St Ste 800, South Bend, IN 46601-1630　　　(100%)
Tel.: (574) 235-2000
Web Site: https://www.1stsource.com
Sales Range: $125-149.9 Million
Emp.: 1,100
Commercial Banking Services
N.A.I.C.S.: 522110
Christopher J. Murphy III (Chm, Pres & CEO)
John B. Griffith (Chief Admin Officer, Gen Counsel, Sec & Exec VP)
Andrea Gayle Short (Pres & CEO)
Christopher L. Craft (Pres/COO-Specialty Fin Grp)

Subsidiary (Domestic):

1st Source Capital Corporation (2)
100 N Michigan St, South Bend, IN
46601-1630 (100%)
Tel.: (574) 235-2180
Web Site: https://www.1stsource.com
Sales Range: $1-9.9 Million
Emp.: 1
Small Business Investment Company
N.A.I.C.S.: 522110

1st Source Insurance, Inc. (2)
6909 Grape Rd, Mishawaka, IN
46545 (100%)
Tel.: (574) 271-5200
Web Site:
https://www.1stsourceinsurance.com
Sales Range: $1-9.9 Million
Emp.: 25
General Insurance Agency
N.A.I.C.S.: 524210

**1st Source Corporation Investment
Advisors, Inc.** (1)
100 N Michigan St, South Bend, IN 46601
Tel.: (574) 235-2756
Investment Advisory Services
N.A.I.C.S.: 523940
Paul Gifford (Chief Investment Officer)

1st Source Leasing, Inc. (1)
100 N Michigan St, South Bend, IN
46601-1630 (100%)
Tel.: (574) 235-2475
Web Site: http://www.1stsource.com
Sales Range: $100-124.9 Million
Emp.: 300
Leases Tangible Property & Equipment
N.A.I.C.S.: 522220

1ST SUMMIT BANCORP JOHNSTOWN, INC.

125 Donald Ln, Johnstown, PA 15904
Tel.: (814) 262-4010
Web Site:
https://www.1stsummit.bank
Year Founded: 1924
FSMK—(OTCIQ)
Rev.: $46,424,000
Assets: $1,257,438,000
Liabilities: $1,132,142,000
Net Worth: $125,296,000
Earnings: $8,230,000
Emp.: 228
Fiscal Year-end: 12/31/20
Bank Holding Company
N.A.I.C.S.: 551111
Elmer C. Laslo (Pres & CEO)
Carol A. Myers (Treas & Exec VP)
Joseph R. Kondisko (Chm)
Jeffry D. Cramer (Exec VP)
Timothy W. Smith (Sec & Sr VP)
Donald F. Yeager (Sr VP)
Michael Seigh (Sr VP & Asst Treas)
Polly A. Previte (Sr VP)
J. Eric Renner (Exec VP)

Subsidiaries:

1st Summit Bank (1)
125 Donald Ln, Johnstown, PA 15904
Tel.: (814) 262-4000
Web Site: http://www.1stsummit.com
Emp.: 100
Banking Services
N.A.I.C.S.: 522110
Elmer C. Laslo (Pres & CEO)
Carol A. Myers (CFO, Treas & Exec VP)
Jeffry D. Cramer (Chief Lending Officer,
Exec VP & Sec)
Timothy W. Smith (Sr VP & Sec)
Donald F. Yeager (Sr VP & Head-Retail
Banking Grp)
Michael Seigh (Sr VP-Fin)
Polly A. Previte (Officer-Ops & Sr VP)
Robert J. Salerno (Sr VP-Bus Dev)
J. Eric Renner (COO & Exec VP)

1STDIBS.COM, INC.

51 Astor Pl 3rd Fl, New York, NY
10003
Tel.: (212) 627-3927 DE
Web Site: https://www.1stdibs.com

Year Founded: 2020
DIBS—(NASDAQ)
Rev.: $96,849,000
Assets: $195,796,000
Liabilities: $47,774,000
Net Worth: $148,022,000
Earnings: ($22,538,000)
Emp.: 310
Fiscal Year-end: 12/31/22
Online Shopping Services
N.A.I.C.S.: 459999
Thomas J. Etergino (CFO)
David S. Rosenblatt (Chm & CEO)
Alison Lipman (Chief People Officer)
Nancy Hood (CMO)
Sarah Liebel (Chief Revenue Officer)
Xiaodi Zhang (Chief Product Officer)
Melanie Goins (Gen Counsel)
Anthony Barzilay Freund (Dir-
Editorial)

20/20 GLOBAL, INC. (See Under Ehave, Inc.)

22ND CENTURY GROUP, INC.

321 Farmington Rd, Mocksville, NC
14204
Tel.: (336) 940-3769 NV
Web Site:
https://www.xxiicentury.com
Year Founded: 1998
XXII—(NASDAQ)
Rev.: $62,111,000
Assets: $114,651,000
Liabilities: $18,676,000
Net Worth: $95,975,000
Earnings: ($59,801,000)
Emp.: 198
Fiscal Year-end: 12/31/22
Plant Biotechnology Research
N.A.I.C.S.: 541714
Lawrence D. Firestone (Chm & CEO)
John D. Pritchard (VP-Regulatory
Science)
John J. Miller (Pres-Tobacco Ops
Bus)
Calvin Treat (Chief Scientific Officer)
Sebastian Ravitz (VP)
R. Hugh Kinsman (CFO)
Juan Sanchez Tamburrino (VP-R&D)
Robert Manfredonia (Exec VP-Sales
& Marketing)
Scott Marion (VP-Operations)
Dan Otto (CFO)
Jonathan Staffeldt (Gen Counsel)
Robert Manfredonia (Exec VP-Sls &
Mktg)

Subsidiaries:

22nd Century Limited, LLC (1)
9530 Main St, Clarence, NY 14031
Tel.: (716) 270-1523
Emp.: 4
Commercial Physical Research Services
N.A.I.C.S.: 541715

23ANDME, INC. (Merged with VG Acquisition Corp. to form 23andMe Holding Co.)

23ANDME HOLDING CO.

349 Oyster Point Blvd, San Fran-
cisco, CA 94080
Tel.: (650) 938-6300 DE
Year Founded: 2006
ME—(NASDAQ)
Rev.: $299,489,000
Assets: $942,598,000
Liabilities: $228,659,000
Net Worth: $713,939,000
Earnings: ($311,656,000)
Emp.: 816
Fiscal Year-end: 03/31/23
Consumer Genetic & Research De-
velopment Services

N.A.I.C.S.: 541714
Evan Lovell (CFO)
Anne Wojcicki (CEO & Dir)
Joseph Selsavage (CFO, Principal
Acctg Officer, Gen Counsel & Sec)
Richard Scheller (Dir)

Subsidiaries:

23andMe, Inc. (1)
223 N Mathilda Ave, Sunnyvale, CA 94086
Emp.: 100
Consumer Genetic & Research Develop-
ment Services
N.A.I.C.S.: 541714

26 CAPITAL ACQUISITION CORP.

701 Brickell Ave Ste 1550, Miami, FL
33131
Tel.: (305) 709-6664 DE
Year Founded: 2020
ADER—(NASDAQ)
Rev.: $11,964,216
Assets: $35,511,910
Liabilities: $56,203,239
Net Worth: ($20,691,329)
Earnings: $7,258,882
Emp.: 2
Fiscal Year-end: 12/31/22
Investment Services
N.A.I.C.S.: 523999
Jason Ader (Chm & CEO)
John Lewis (CFO)

2SEVENTY BIO, INC.

60 Binney St, Cambridge, MA 02142
Tel.: (617) 675-7270 DE
Web Site:
https://www.2seventybio.com
Year Founded: 2021
TSVT—(NASDAQ)
Rev.: $91,496,000
Assets: $656,665,000
Liabilities: $346,199,000
Net Worth: $310,466,000
Earnings: ($254,153,000)
Emp.: 425
Fiscal Year-end: 12/31/22
Immuno-oncology Cell Therapy Ser-
vices
N.A.I.C.S.: 541714
Susan Abu-Absi (CTO)
William Baird (COO)
Teresa Jurgensen (Gen Counsel & Sr
VP)
Nick Leschly (Chm, Pres & CEO)
Vicki Eatwell (CFO)
Jessica Snow (Sr VP-Quality & Head-
Operations)
Anna Truppel-Hartmann (Chief Medi-
cal Officer)
Daniel S. Lynch (Co-Chm)
William Baird (COO)
William D. Baird III (Pres & CEO)

2U, INC.

7900 Harkins Rd, Lanham, MD
20706
Tel.: (301) 892-4350 DE
Web Site: https://www.2u.com
Year Founded: 2008
TWOU—(NASDAQ)
Rev.: $945,953,000
Assets: $1,459,683,000
Liabilities: $1,240,638,000
Net Worth: $219,045,000
Earnings: ($317,607,000)
Emp.: 2,961
Fiscal Year-end: 12/31/23
Education Software
N.A.I.C.S.: 513210
Christopher J. Paucek (Founder)
Brad Adams (Chief University Ops
Officer)
Stephen A. Virostek (Sr VP-IR)
Andrew Hermalyn (Pres-Degree Pro-
gram Segment)

Matthew J. Norden (CFO & Chief Le-
gal Officer)
Katie Race Brin (Chief Privacy Offi-
cer)
Paul S. Lalljie (CEO)
Todd Glassman (Gen Counsel)
Michael Kurbjeweit (CMO)
Andy Morgan (Exec VP)
David Sutphen (Chief Strategy & En-
gagement Officer)
David Sutphen (Chief Strategy & En-
gagement Officer)

Subsidiaries:

CritiqueIt, Inc. (1)
235 E Broadway Ste 506, Long Beach, CA
90802
Web Site: http://www.critiqueit.com
Software Development Services
N.A.I.C.S.: 541511

**Get Educated International Propri-
etary Limited** (1)
Fairland House 4th Floor, Cape Town,
7925, South Africa
Tel.: (27) 214477565
Educational Support Services
N.A.I.C.S.: 611710

GetSmarter Online Limited (1)
74 Rivington Street, London, EC2A 3AY,
United Kingdom
Tel.: (44) 2038236998
Web Site: http://www.getsmarter.com
Educational Support Services
N.A.I.C.S.: 611710

edX, Inc. (1)
1 Broadway 14th Fl, Cambridge, MA 02142
Tel.: (617) 324-4049
Web Site: https://www.axim.org
Sales Range: $25-49.9 Million
Emp.: 150
Educational Support Services
N.A.I.C.S.: 611710
Kathy Pugh (VP-Education Svcs)
Tena Herlihy (Gen Counsel & VP)
Johannes Heinlein (VP-Strategic Partner-
ships)
Beth Porter (VP-Product)
Lee Rubenstein (VP-Bus Dev)
Adam Medros (Pres & COO)

30DC, INC.

80 Broad St 5th Fl, New York, NY
10004
Tel.: (212) 962-4400
Web Site: http://www.30dcinc.com
Year Founded: 2005
TDCH—(OTCIQ)
Software Publishing Services
N.A.I.C.S.: 513210
Edward Dale (CEO)

374WATER, INC.

701 W Main St Ste 410, Durham, NC
27701
Tel.: (919) 888-8194 DE
Web Site: https://www.374water.com
Year Founded: 1991
SCWO—(NASDAQ)
Rev.: $3,015,521
Assets: $9,916,831
Liabilities: $1,663,219
Net Worth: $8,253,612
Earnings: ($4,689,967)
Emp.: 23
Fiscal Year-end: 12/31/22
Waste & Wastewater Treatment &
Management
N.A.I.C.S.: 924110
Christian M. Gannon (Pres & CEO)
Yaacov Nagar (CEO)
Marc Deshusses (Co-Founder)
Sudhakar Viswanathan (VP-Sales)
Adrienne Anderson (CFO)
Brad Meyers (COO)
Deborah Cooper (Chief Acctg Officer)
Howard Teicher (Head-Government)

374Water, Inc.—(Continued)

Steve McKnight (*Head-Corporate Development*)
Peter Mandel (*Gen Counsel*)
Rene Estes (*Chm*)

3D PIONEER SYSTEMS, INC.
3651 Lindell Rd Ste D643, Las Vegas, NV 89103
Tel.: (702) 318-7523   NV
DPSM—(OTCIQ)
Software Development Services
N.A.I.C.S.: 541511
Barbara M. Bauman (*Pres, Treas & Sec*)

3D SYSTEMS CORPORATION
333 3 D Systems Cir, Rock Hill, SC 29730
Tel.: (803) 326-3907   DE
Web Site:
    https://www.3dsystems.com
Year Founded: 1986
DDD—(NYSE)
Rev.: $488,069,000
Assets: $990,660,000
Liabilities: $563,907,000
Net Worth: $426,753,000
Earnings: ($362,953,000)
Emp.: 1,925
Fiscal Year-end: 12/31/23
Solid Imaging Systems Designed to Rapidly Produce 3-D Objects Mfr, Developer & Marketer
N.A.I.C.S.: 513210
Charles W. Hull (*Founder, CTO & Exec VP*)
Jeffrey Alan Graves (*Pres & CEO*)
Reji Puthenveetil (*Chief Comml Officer & Exec VP-Additive Solutions*)
Joseph Zuiker (*Exec VP-Engrg & Ops*)
Brent Stucker (*CTO-Additive Mfg*)
Phyllis Nordstrom (*Chief People Officer*)

Subsidiaries:

3D European Holdings Ltd.   (1)
2nd Floor West South Wing The Mayland Bldg 200 Maylands Ave, Hemel Hempstead Industrial Estate, Hemel Hempstead, HP2 7TG, Herts, United Kingdom
Tel.: (44) 1442282600
Industrial Machinery & Equipment Whslr
N.A.I.C.S.: 420000

3D Systems - Burlington   (1)
19 Connector Rd, Andover, MA 01810
Tel.: (781) 852-5005
Web Site: http://www.3dsystems.com
Sales Range: $10-24.9 Million
Emp.: 130
3-D CAD Printer Mfr
N.A.I.C.S.: 333248

3D Systems Asia-Pacific Pty Ltd   (1)
5 Lynch Street, Hawthorn, 3122, VIC, Australia
Tel.: (61) 398194422
Computer Peripheral Component Distr
N.A.I.C.S.: 423430

3D Systems Europe Ltd.   (1)
200 Maylands Avenue, Hemel Hempstead, HP2 7TG, Herts, United Kingdom
Tel.: (44) 1442282600
Sales Range: $25-49.9 Million
Emp.: 25
Computer Peripheral Component Distr
N.A.I.C.S.: 423430

3D Systems France SARL   (1)
ZA Les Petites Forges Zone d Activites Professionnelle, 72380, Joue-l'Abbe, France
Tel.: (33) 890109376
Web Site: http://www.3dsystems.com
Sales Range: $150-199.9 Million
Emp.: 35
Computer Peripheral Component Distr
N.A.I.C.S.: 423430

3D Systems GmbH   (1)
Waldeckerstrasse 13, 64546, Morfelden-Walldorf, Germany   (100%)
Tel.: (49) 6151357357
Sales Range: $25-49.9 Million
Emp.: 46
Computer Peripheral Component Distr
N.A.I.C.S.: 423430

3D Systems Industria E Comercio LTDA   (1)
Av Riachuelo 92, 09912-190, Diadema, SP, Brazil
Tel.: (55) 1133185100
Computer Peripheral Component Distr
N.A.I.C.S.: 423430

3D Systems Italia S.r.l.   (1)
Via R Incerti 25, 10064, Pinerolo, TO, Italy
Tel.: (39) 0396890400
Sales Range: $50-74.9 Million
Emp.: 8
Computer Peripheral Component Distr
N.A.I.C.S.: 423430

3D Systems Japan K.K.   (1)
Ebisu Garden Place Tower 27F, 4-20-3 Ebisu Shibuya-ku, Tokyo, 050-6027, Japan
Tel.: (81) 357982500
Web Site: http://www.3dsystems.co.jp
Sales Range: $25-49.9 Million
Emp.: 20
Computer Peripheral Component Distr
N.A.I.C.S.: 423430

3D Systems S.A.   (1)
Route De l Ancienne Papeterie 185, 1723, Marly, 1723, Switzerland
Tel.: (41) 264399590
Sales Range: $25-49.9 Million
Emp.: 20
Computer Peripheral Component Distr
N.A.I.C.S.: 423430

3D Systems Software srl   (1)
Via C Collodi 1 Caldera di Reno, Bologna, 40012, Italy
Tel.: (39) 0514145611
Printing Machinery Distr
N.A.I.C.S.: 423430

3D Systems, Inc.   (1)
333 3D Systems Cir, Rock Hill, SC 29730-7811
Tel.: (803) 326-3900
Web Site: http://www.3dsystems.com
3D Printer Mfr
N.A.I.C.S.: 423840

Alibre, Inc.   (1)
1750 N Collins Blvd Ste 212, Richardson, TX 75080
Web Site: https://www.alibre.com
Sales Range: $10-24.9 Million
Emp.: 35
Software Publisher
N.A.I.C.S.: 513210
Jonathan Pace (*COO*)

Bits From Bytes, Ltd.   (1)
Unit 17 Hither Green Industrial Estate, Clevedon, BS21 6XU, United Kingdom
Tel.: (44) 1275873792
Web Site: http://www.bitsfrombytes.com
Industrial Machinery & Equipment Whslr
N.A.I.C.S.: 423830

Freedom of Creation B.V.   (1)
Cruquiuskade 85-87, Amsterdam, 1018 AM, Netherlands
Tel.: (31) 20 675 84 15
Web Site: http://www.freedomofcreation.com
Graphic Design Services
N.A.I.C.S.: 541430

Gentle Giant Studios, Inc.   (1)
7511 N San Fernando Rd, Burbank, CA 91505
Tel.: (818) 504-3555
Web Site: http://www.gentlegiantstudios.com
Sales Range: $1-9.9 Million
Emp.: 56
Computer Designing Services
N.A.I.C.S.: 541511

Geomagic (Shanghai) Software Co., Ltd.   (1)
Room 416 Xinyin Building No 888 Yi Shan Road, Shanghai, 200233, China
Tel.: (86) 2164320776
Computer Software Designing Services
N.A.I.C.S.: 423430

Geomagic GmbH   (1)
Maximilianallee 4, 04129, Leipzig, Germany
Tel.: (49) 341656757
Web Site: https://www.geomagic.de
Emp.: 90
Software Development Services
N.A.I.C.S.: 541511

Geomagic, Inc.   (1)
430 Davis Dr Ste 300, Morrisville, NC 27560
Tel.: (919) 474-0122
Web Site: http://www.geomagic.com
Sales Range: $25-49.9 Million
Emp.: 120
Software Designing Services
N.A.I.C.S.: 541511

Subsidiary (Non-US):

3D Systems Korea, Inc.   (2)
Yuksam-Dong Kangnam-Gu, 601-20, Seoul, Korea (South)
Tel.: (82) 262629900
Web Site: https://ko.3dsystems.com
Emp.: 50
Engineering Software Publisher
N.A.I.C.S.: 513210

LayerWise NV   (1)
Grauwmeer 14, 3001, Leuven, Belgium
Tel.: (32) 16298420
Web Site: http://www.layerwise.com
Medical Instrument Mfr
N.A.I.C.S.: 334510

Medical Modeling Inc.   (1)
17301 W Colfax Ave Ste 300, Golden, CO 80401
Tel.: (303) 273-5344
Surgical Treatment Services
N.A.I.C.S.: 541940

Microsystem srl   (1)
Via Carlo Collodi 1, 40012, Calderara di Reno, Italy
Tel.: (39) 0514145611
Web Site: http://www.microsystem.it
Software Development Services
N.A.I.C.S.: 541511

NextDent B.V.   (1)
Centurionbaan 190, 3769 AV, Soesterberg, Netherlands
Tel.: (31) 886160440
Web Site: https://www.nextdent.com
Biocompatible Dental Material Mfr
N.A.I.C.S.: 339114

Phenix Systems SA   (1)
Parc Europeen d Entreprises Rue Richard Wagner, 63200, Riom, France
Tel.: (33) 473153838
Web Site: http://www.phenix-systems.com
Sales Range: $25-49.9 Million
Emp.: 67
Industrial Machinery Mfr
N.A.I.C.S.: 333248

Subsidiary (US):

AMT, Inc.   (2)
1201 Oakton Ste 1, Elk Grove Village, IL 60007-2018
Tel.: (847) 258-4475
Web Site: http://www.amtincorp.com
All Other Product Mfr
N.A.I.C.S.: 339999

Provel, S.r.l.   (1)
Via Roberto Incerti 25, Area Industriale Porporata, 10064, Pinerolo, Italy
Tel.: (39) 0121376966
Web Site: http://www.provel.it
Sales Range: $25-49.9 Million
Emp.: 30
Industrial Machinery & Equipment Whslr
N.A.I.C.S.: 423830

Robtec Uruguay   (1)
Daniel Munoz 1960, Democracia, Montevideo, Uruguay
Tel.: (598) 24025290
Electronic Components Distr
N.A.I.C.S.: 423690

VIDAR Systems Corporation   (1)
365 Herndon Pkwy, Herndon, VA 20170
Tel.: (703) 471-7070
Web Site: https://www.vidar.com
Medical Imaging Mfr

N.A.I.C.S.: 334510

Vertex-Dental B.V.   (1)
Centurionbaan 190, 3769 AV, Soesterberg, Netherlands
Web Site: https://www.vertex-dental.com
Emp.: 32
Biocompatible Dental Material Mfr
N.A.I.C.S.: 339114
Rik Jacobs (*Comml Dir*)
Connie Peterse-van der Koppel (*VP, Gen Mgr-R&D & Dir-Ops*)
Otto Beckeringh van Loenen (*COO*)
Jan Willem Carelse (*Sr Mgr-Sls-Area*)
Stef Vanneste (*CEO*)
Adele Zandbergen (*Area Mgr-Sls*)
Loes Vloet-Emonts (*Mgr-Quality Assurance & Regulatory Affairs*)
Stephanie de Souza (*Officer-Regulatory*)
Menno Pot (*Officer-Application & Tech*)

Viztu Technologies, Inc.   (1)
701 Concord Ave, Cambridge, MA 02138
Tel.: (617) 858-0849
Software Development Services
N.A.I.C.S.: 541511

Wuxi Easyway Model Design & Manufacture Co. Ltd.   (1)
Third building Wuxi National Industrial design Park Originality Park, No 100 Diquiroad, Wuxi, 214072, Jiangsu, China
Tel.: (86) 51066072366
Web Site: http://www.en.easyway-model.com
Computer Equipment Mfr
N.A.I.C.S.: 334118

3DSHOPPING.COM INC.
30 N Gould St Ste 5835, Sheridan, WY 82801
Tel.: (307) 278-1360   CA
THDS—(OTCIQ)
Web Based Marketing Services
N.A.I.C.S.: 541613
Benjamin Robert Berry (*Pres, CEO, CFO & Sec*)

3DX INDUSTRIES, INC.
6920 Salashan Pkwy Ste D-101, Ferndale, WA 98248
Tel.: (360) 366-8858   NV
Web Site:
    https://www.3dxindustries.com
Year Founded: 2008
DDDX—(OTCIQ)
Investment Services
N.A.I.C.S.: 523999
Earl W. Abbott (*VP-Exploration*)
Roger Janssen (*Pres, CEO & CFO*)

3M COMPANY
3M Ctr, Saint Paul, MN 55144-1000
Tel.: (651) 733-1110   DE
Web Site: https://www.3m.com
Year Founded: 1902
MMM—(NYSE)
Rev.: $32,681,000,000
Assets: $50,580,000,000
Liabilities: $45,712,000,000
Net Worth: $4,868,000,000
Earnings: ($6,995,000,000)
Emp.: 85,000
Fiscal Year-end: 12/31/23
Miscellaneous Product Mfr
N.A.I.C.S.: 325520
Michael F. Roman (*Exec Chm*)
William M. Brown (*CEO*)
John P. Banovetz (*CTO & Exec VP*)
Denise R. Rutherford (*Chief Corp Affairs Officer & Chief Corp Affairs Officer*)
Michael A. Duran (*Chief Ethics & Compliance Officer & Sr VP*)
Bruce Jermeland (*Sr VP-IR*)
Tony Riter (*Dir-Investor Relations*)
Zoe Dickson (*Cheif HR Officer & Exec VP*)
C. Michael Geise (*Asst Sec*)
Rodolfo Espinosa (*Asst Treas*)

Karina Chavez (Grp Pres-Consumer Bus)
Mark Murphy (CIO, Chief Digital Officer & Exec VP)
Kevin H. Rhodes (Chief Legal Affairs Officer & Exec VP)
Asraf Bhugaloo (Sr VP)
Ashish Khandpur (Grp Pres-Transportation & Electronics business group)
Chris Goralski (Grp Pres-Safety & Industrial Bus)
Anurag Maheshwari (CFO & Exec VP)
Theresa E. Reinseth (Chief Acctg Officer, Sr VP & Controller)
Bryan C. Hanson (CEO-Healthcare Bus Grp)

Subsidiaries:

3M (East) AG   (1)
Industriestrasse 21, 6343, Rotkreuz, Switzerland   (100%)
Tel.: (41) 417993100
Web Site: http://solutions.3m.com
Sales Range: $25-49.9 Million
Emp.: 30
Management Investment Activities; Major Markets Include Automotive, Consumer Products, Electronics/Electrical, Health Care, Telecommunications & Transportation Safety
N.A.I.C.S.: 525910

3M (Schweitz) GmbH   (1)
Eggstrasse 93, 8803, Ruschlikon, Switzerland
Tel.: (41) 447249090
Web Site:
   http://www.solutions.3mschweiz.ch
Industrial Safety Equipment Mfr
N.A.I.C.S.: 339113

3M (Suisse) SA   (1)
Eggstrasse 93, 8803, Ruschlikon, Switzerland   (100%)
Tel.: (41) 447249090
Web Site: http://www.solutions.3msuisse.ch
Sales Range: $100-124.9 Million
Emp.: 200
Distr of Tape & Adhesive Products, Electrical Connectors & Devices & Consumer Products
N.A.I.C.S.: 424690
Felix Thun-Hohenstein (Mng Dir)

3M A/S   (1)
Fabriksparken 15, PO Box 1393, Glostrup, 2600, Denmark   (100%)
Tel.: (45) 043480100
Web Site: http://www.mmm.com
Sales Range: $100-124.9 Million
Emp.: 145
Distr Chemicals, Imaging Technology & Electronic Supplies
N.A.I.C.S.: 424690

3M Abrasive Systems Division   (1)
2501 Hudson Road, Saint Paul, MN 55144
Tel.: (651) 737-6501
Web Site: http://www.3m.com
Sales Range: $150-199.9 Million
Coated Abrasive Mfr
N.A.I.C.S.: 327910

Branch (Domestic):

3M Abrasive Systems   (2)
140 Algonquin Pkwy, Whippany, NJ 07981
Tel.: (973) 884-2500
Sales Range: $25-49.9 Million
Emp.: 50
Industrial Diamond Tools, Wheels & Mining Bits
N.A.I.C.S.: 327910

3M Australia Pty. Ltd.   (1)
Building A 1 Rivett Road, North Ryde, 2113, NSW, Australia   (100%)
Tel.: (61) 136136
Web Site: https://www.3m.com.au
Sales Range: $450-499.9 Million
Emp.: 650
Mfr of Tape & Paper Products; Video & Audio Recording Tape
N.A.I.C.S.: 322220

Paul Madden (Mng Dir)

Subsidiary (Domestic):

TECRA International Pty. Ltd.   (2)
13 Rodborough Rd, French's Forest, 2086, NSW, Australia
Tel.: (61) 289773000
Web Site: http://www.tecra.net
Sales Range: $10-24.9 Million
Emp.: 30
Microbiology Product Testing Kits & Assays Mfr
N.A.I.C.S.: 334516

3M Automotive Aftermarket Division   (1)
3M Center Bldg 0223-06-N-01, Saint Paul, MN 55144-1000
Tel.: (651) 733-1110
Web Site: http://www.3m.com
Sales Range: $75-99.9 Million
Automotive Paint & Vehicle Body Maintenance Products
N.A.I.C.S.: 811121

Subsidiary (Domestic):

Meguiar's, Inc.   (2)
213 Technology Dr, Irvine, CA 92618
Tel.: (949) 752-8000
Web Site: http://www.meguiars.com
Sales Range: $25-49.9 Million
Car Care Products Mfr & Whslr
N.A.I.C.S.: 325998

3M Belgium N.V./S.A.   (1)
Hermeslaan 7, Machelen, 1831, Diegem, Belgium   (100%)
Tel.: (32) 27225111
Web Site: http://www.3mbelgie.be
Sales Range: $75-99.9 Million
Mfr & Distr of Chemicals
N.A.I.C.S.: 325998

3M Bricolage and Batiment   (1)
Parc Industriel Ouest-65 Rue De Chambourg, PO Box 2011, Veyziat, 01117, Oyonnax, Cedex, France
Tel.: (33) 474120510
Web Site: http://www.dinac.fr
Floor Adhesive Mfr
N.A.I.C.S.: 325520
Frederic Chevallier (Dir Gen)

3M Canada Company   (1)
300 Tartan Drive, PO Box 5840, London, N5V 4M9, ON, Canada   (100%)
Web Site: https://www.3mcanada.ca
Sales Range: $1-4.9 Billion
Emp.: 1,900
Distr Adhesive Products, Abrasives & Imaging Equipment
N.A.I.C.S.: 424690
Penny Wise (Mng Dir)
Carrie Ramsay (Mgr-USAC HCBG Fin)
Tiffany Koch (Gen Counsel)
Erin Meagher (Dir-USAC Customer Ops)
Brenda Walsh (Controller)

Plant (Domestic):

3M Canada Company   (2)
300 Tartan Drive, London, N5V 4M9, ON, Canada   (100%)
Tel.: (613) 345-0111
Web Site: http://www.3mcanada.ca
Sales Range: $25-49.9 Million
Industrial Respiratory Protection Filters & Military & Civil Defense NBC Gas Mask Filters & Air Filters
N.A.I.C.S.: 928110

Subsidiary (Domestic):

MTI Polyfab Inc.   (2)
7381 Pacific Cir, Mississauga, L5T 2A4, ON, Canada
Tel.: (905) 564-9700
Sales Range: $25-49.9 Million
Emp.: 200
Aerospace & Fabricated Products Mfr
N.A.I.C.S.: 334511

3M Chile S.A.   (1)
Santa Isabel 1001 Providencia, Post Office 3068, Santiago, 7501412, Chile   (100%)
Tel.: (56) 224103000
Web Site: https://www.3mchile.cl
Sales Range: $50-74.9 Million
Emp.: 200

Tape & Adhesive Products, Electronic Products, Surgical & Medical Supplies & Consumer Products Distr
N.A.I.C.S.: 424690

3M China Limited   (1)
38th Floor No 8 Xingyi Road, Changning District, Shanghai, 200336, China (100%)
Tel.: (86) 2162753535
Web Site: https://www.3m.com.cn
Sales Range: $25-49.9 Million
Mfr & Distr of Tape & Adhesive Products, Electronic Connectors, Surgical & Medical Supplies & Consumer Products
N.A.I.C.S.: 325520

3M Colombia S.A.   (1)
Calle 26 75-93, Cundinamarca, Bogota, Y12693, Colombia   (100%)
Tel.: (57) 14161666
Web Site: http://www.3m.com
Sales Range: $150-199.9 Million
Distr of Industrial Supplies & Equipment, Imaging & Computer Equipment, Chemicals & Pharmaceuticals & Surgical & Medical Equipment
N.A.I.C.S.: 423690

3M Company - Conover Plant   (1)
500 Thornburg Dr SE, Conover, NC 28613
Tel.: (828) 465-3053
Emp.: 125
Packaging Materials Mfr
N.A.I.C.S.: 322230

3M Company - Montrose   (1)
16 Ponderosa Ct, Montrose, CO 81401
Tel.: (970) 249-6200
Web Site: http://www.3m.com
Sales Range: $1-9.9 Million
Emp.: 20
Machine Tools Mfr
N.A.I.C.S.: 333517

3M Company - Royersford   (1)
546 Enterprise Dr, Royersford, PA 19468
Tel.: (610) 495-2850
Web Site: http://www.3m.com
Emp.: 95
Abrasive Grinding Wheels Mfr
N.A.I.C.S.: 327910

3M Company - Santa Cruz   (1)
3601 Caldwell Dr Ste A, Soquel, CA 95073
Tel.: (831) 459-7488
Sales Range: $10-24.9 Million
Emp.: 12
Electronic Monitoring Equipment Mfr
N.A.I.C.S.: 334515

3M Costa Rica, S.A.   (1)
1Km al este del cruce de pasaje de la Valencia, PO Box 1000, Santa Rosa de Santo Domingo, 1000, San Jose, Heredia, Costa Rica   (100%)
Tel.: (506) 2771000
Web Site: http://www.3m.com
Sales Range: $50-74.9 Million
Emp.: 100
Distr of Tape & Adhesive Products; Electronic Connectors & Devices; Surgical & Medical Supplies; Consumer Products
N.A.I.C.S.: 425120

3M Czech Republic   (1)
V Parku 2343/24, 148 00, Prague, Czech Republic   (100%)
Tel.: (420) 848100303
Web Site: https://www.3mcesko.cz
Sales Range: $50-74.9 Million
Emp.: 100
Coated Fabrics
N.A.I.C.S.: 313320

3M Deutschland GmbH   (1)
Carl-Schurz-Str 1, 41453, Neuss, Germany   (100%)
Tel.: (49) 2131140
Web Site: https://www.3mdeutschland.de
Emp.: 6,236
Miscellaneous Product Mfr
N.A.I.C.S.: 339999
Gunter Gressler (Chm-Supervisory Bd)

Division (Domestic):

3M Deutschland GmbH - Separation and Purification Sciences Division   (2)
Ohder Strasse 28, 42289, Wuppertal, Germany

Tel.: (49) 20260990
Web Site: http://www.membrana.de
Microporous Membrane & Module Mfr
N.A.I.C.S.: 339999
Joerg Dederichs (Mng Dir)

Subsidiary (Domestic):

3M Real Estate GmbH & Co. KG   (2)
Carl-Schurz-Str 1, 41453, Neuss, Germany
Tel.: (49) 2131140
Holding Company
N.A.I.C.S.: 551112

Dyneon GmbH   (2)
Gebaude 172 Industrieparkstrasse 1, 84508, Burgkirchen an der Alz, Germany
Tel.: (49) 867974709
Plastic Product Mfr & Whslr
N.A.I.C.S.: 325211

3M Dominicana S.A.   (1)
Avenida Luperon, Distrito Nacional, Santo Domingo, 1032, Dominican Republic
Tel.: (809) 5306560
Web Site: http://www.3m.com
Sales Range: $75-99.9 Million
Emp.: 92
Distr of Tape & Adhesive Products, Electronic Connectors & Products, Surgical & Medical Supplies & Consumer Products
N.A.I.C.S.: 424690

3M ECC Europa B.V.   (1)
Amsterdamsweg 61, NL 3012 RR, Amersfoort, Netherlands
Tel.: (31) 334221100
Web Site: http://www.3m.com
Sales Range: $25-49.9 Million
Emp.: 50
Heatshrink Tubing Mfr
N.A.I.C.S.: 331491

3M EMEA, GmbH   (1)
Kuhlhausstrasse 2, 4900, Langenthal, Switzerland
Tel.: (41) 629233223
Plastic Material Whslr
N.A.I.C.S.: 424610
Andrew Dobson (Mgr-Sourcing)

3M Ecuador C.A.   (1)
Via Duran Tambo Km 1 5, Guayaquil, Ecuador   (100%)
Tel.: (593) 43721800
Web Site: http://www.3m.com
Sales Range: $50-74.9 Million
Emp.: 60
Distr of Tape & Adhesive Products, Electronic Connectors, Surgical & Medical Supplies & Consumer Products
N.A.I.C.S.: 424690

3M Egypt Ltd.   (1)
Kattamya Heights Compound Business center office N O S16 2nd Floor, 5th Settlement New Cairo, Cairo, Egypt
Tel.: (20) 220200612
Web Site: http://www.3megypt.com.eg
Science-based Company; Home Care, Abrasive, Chemical & Medical Products Mfr & Distr
N.A.I.C.S.: 325998

3M Espana S.A.   (1)
C/ Juan Ignacio Luca de Tena 19-25, 28027, Madrid, Spain   (100%)
Tel.: (34) 91 722 4059
Web Site: https://www.3m.com.es
Sales Range: $300-349.9 Million
Emp.: 690
Mfr of Tape & Adhesive Products; Distributor of Chemicals
N.A.I.C.S.: 325520

3M Fall Protection Business   (1)
3833 Sala Way, Red Wing, MN 55066
Tel.: (651) 388-8282
Web Site: http://3M.com
Emp.: 1,500
Construction & Industrial Safety Equipment Designer, Mfr & Distr
N.A.I.C.S.: 339999

Subsidiary (Domestic):

D B Industries, LLC   (2)
3833 Sala Way, Red Wing, MN 55066
Tel.: (651) 388-8282
Web Site: http://www.3m.com

3M Company—(Continued)

Protection & Rescue Equipment Designer
Mfr
N.A.I.C.S.: 339999

**3M Financial Management
Company** (1)
2501 Hudson Rd, Maplewood, MN 55144
Tel.: (651) 733-1110
Financial Management Services
N.A.I.C.S.: 541611

3M France S.A.S. (1)
1 Parvis de l'Innovation, 95006, Pontoise,
Cedex, France
Tel.: (33) 96 932 1478
Web Site: https://www.3mfrance.fr
Emp.: 2,400
Tape, Electronic & Adhesive Products Distr
N.A.I.C.S.: 325520
Wilns Coenreed (Mng Dir)

Subsidiary (Domestic):

FAAB Fabricauto (2)
400 Rue de la Craz, CS 37132, Viriat,
01007, Bourg-en-Bresse, Cedex, France
Tel.: (33) 474223435
Web Site: http://www.faabfabricauto.com
Emp.: 150
License Plate Mfr
N.A.I.C.S.: 339999

GPI (SAS) (2)
23 Rue du Souvenir, Lons, 64140, France
Tel.: (33) 559720900
Building Material Mfr & Whslr
N.A.I.C.S.: 326199

Laboratoires 3M Sante SAS (2)
Boulevard de l'Oise, 95006, Cergy-
Pontoise, France
Tel.: (33) 130318282
Web Site: http://www.3mdirect.fr
Emp.: 800
Healthcare Services
N.A.I.C.S.: 424210

SAS Fabricauto (2)
558 rue des Essards Zone Industrielle sud,
BP 222, 71009, Macon, France
Tel.: (33) 385328383
Web Site: http://www.fabricauto.com
Plastic & Aluminium Plate Mfr
N.A.I.C.S.: 326199

3M Guatemala, S.A. (1)
Calzada Roosevelt 12-33 Zona 3 de Mixco,
PO Box 2103, Guatemala,
Guatemala (100%)
Tel.: (502) 23793636
Web Site: https://www.3m.com.gt
Sales Range: $75-99.9 Million
Emp.: 100
Distr of Tape & Adhesive Products, Electri-
cal Connectors & Devices, Surgical & Medi-
cal Supplies & Consumer Products
N.A.I.C.S.: 424690

3M Gulf Ltd. (1)
Dubai Internet City Building 11, PO Box
20191, Dubai, United Arab Emirates
Tel.: (971) 43670777
Web Site: https://www.3mae.ae
Healthcare Services
N.A.I.C.S.: 621610

3M Healthcare Germany GmbH (1)
Carl-Schurz-Strasse 1, 41453, Neuss, Ger-
many
Tel.: (49) 2131140
Electrical Component Mfr & Distr
N.A.I.C.S.: 335999

3M Hong Kong Limited (1)
38/F Manhattan Place 23 Wang Tai Road,
Kowloon Bay, Kowloon, China (Hong
Kong) (100%)
Tel.: (852) 28066111
Web Site: https://www.3m.com.hk
Sales Range: $75-99.9 Million
Emp.: 100
Distr of Tape & Adhesive Products; Electri-
cal Connectors & Devices, Surgical & Medi-
cal Supplies & Consumer Products
N.A.I.C.S.: 424690

3M Hungaria Kft. (1)
Neumann J u 1/E, 1117, Budapest,
Hungary (100%)

Tel.: (36) 12707777
Web Site: http://www.3mmagyarorszag.hu
Sales Range: $50-74.9 Million
Emp.: 80
Home Care, Abrasive, Chemical, Telecom-
munications & Medical Products Mfr & Distr
N.A.I.C.S.: 339999
Redsooslv Kiskiav (Mng Dir)

3M India Ltd. (1)
48-51 Phase 1 Electronics City Hosur
Road, Bengaluru, 560100, Karnataka,
India (100%)
Tel.: (91) 8045543000
Web Site: https://www.3mindia.in
Rev.: $44,327,100
Emp.: 400
Distribution of Industrial Supplies & Con-
sumer Items
N.A.I.C.S.: 424690
G. Thulin (Chm, Pres & CEO)

**3M Industrial Adhesives & Tapes
Division** (1)
3M Center, Saint Paul, MN 55144-1000
Tel.: (651) 737-6501
Web Site: http://www.3m.com
Sales Range: $75-99.9 Million
Emp.: 3,000
Designs, Manufactures & Markets Bonding
Tapes, Masking Tapes, Adhesives, Paper &
Printing & Packaging Tapes & Equipment
N.A.I.C.S.: 325520

Subsidiary (Domestic):

Venture Tape Corp. (2)
30 Commerce Rd, Rockland, MA 02370-
1053
Tel.: (781) 331-5900
Coated & Laminated Paper Mfr
N.A.I.C.S.: 322220
Brett Webster (Product Mgr)

3M Innovation Singapore Pte Ltd (1)
Tuas Plant 2 Tuas Link 4, Singapore,
637321, Singapore
Tel.: (65) 65916100
Web Site: http://www.3m.com.sg
Electronic Components Mfr
N.A.I.C.S.: 334419

**3M Innovation Singapore Pte
Ltd.** (1)
Tuas Plant 2 Tuas Link 4, Singapore,
637321, Singapore
Tel.: (65) 65916100
Healtcare Services
N.A.I.C.S.: 621610

**3M Innovative Properties
Company** (1)
Building 220-9E-01 3M Ctr, Saint Paul, MN
55144
Tel.: (651) 733-1500
Web Site: http://www.3m.com
Law firm
N.A.I.C.S.: 541110

3M Interamerica, Inc. (1)
PO Box 681, Antiguo Cuzcatlan La Liber-
tad, San Salvador, El Salvador (100%)
Tel.: (503) 242444
Web Site: http://www.3m.com
Sales Range: $50-74.9 Million
Emp.: 65
Distr of Tape & Adhesive Products; Electri-
cal Connectors & Devices, Surgical & Medi-
cal Supplies & Consumer Products
N.A.I.C.S.: 424690

3M Interamerica, Inc. (1)
20-24 Barbados Ave, 14 1/2 Retirement
Road, Kingston, 5, Jamaica
Tel.: (876) 9201787
Web Site: http://www.3m.com
Tape & Adhesive Products, Surgical &
Medical Supplies, Electronic Connectors &
Devices & Consumer Products Mfr
N.A.I.C.S.: 424690

**3M Interamerica, Inc. (Trinidad & To-
bago Div.)** (1)
Invaders Bay Tower Office Level 2, Invad-
ers Bay off Audrey Jeffers Highway, Port of
Spain, Trinidad & Tobago (100%)
Tel.: (868) 8682245000
Web Site: http://www.3m.com
Sales Range: $150-199.9 Million
Emp.: 40

Distr of Tape & Adhesives; Electronic Connectors & Devices; Surgical & Medical Supplies; Consumer Products
N.A.I.C.S.: 424690

3M Ireland Ltd. (1)
The Iveagh Building The Park, Carrick-
mines, Dublin, D18 X015, Ireland (100%)
Tel.: (353) 12803555
Web Site: http://www.3mireland.ie
Sales Range: $25-49.9 Million
Emp.: 50
Medical & Surgical Devices & Equipment
Distr
N.A.I.C.S.: 423450

3M Italia S.p.A. (1)
Via Norberto Bobbio 21, 20096, Pioltello,
MI, Italy (100%)
Tel.: (39) 0270351
Web Site: http://www.3m.com
Sales Range: $400-449.9 Million
Emp.: 1,000
Mfr & Distr of Photocopiers & Supplies
N.A.I.C.S.: 333310

3M Italia srl (1)
Via Norberto Bobbio 21, 20096, Pioltello,
Milan, Italy
Tel.: (39) 0270351
Web Site: https://www.3mitalia.it
Healthcare Services
N.A.I.C.S.: 621610

3M Japan Holdings Company (1)
6 7 29 Kitashinagawa, Shinagawa-Ku, To-
kyo, 141-8684, Japan
Tel.: (81) 337098111
Holding Company
N.A.I.C.S.: 551112

3M Japan Products Limited (1)
6729 Kitashinagawa, Shinagawa-ku, Tokyo,
141-8684, Japan
Tel.: (81) 364093800
Web Site: http://www.mmm.co.jp
Industrial & Electronic Products Mfr
N.A.I.C.S.: 423830

3M Kenya Ltd. (1)
3rd Floor Victoria Towers, PO Box 48567,
00100, Nairobi, Kenya (100%)
Tel.: (254) 202730626
Web Site: http://www.3m.co.ke
Sales Range: $50-74.9 Million
Emp.: 20
Distr of Tape & Adhesives, Electronic Con-
nectors & Devices, Surgical & Medical Sup-
plies & Consumer Products
N.A.I.C.S.: 424690

3M Korea Ltd. (1)
19th floor 82 Uisadang-daero,
Yeongdeungpo-gu, Seoul, 150-705, Korea
(South) (100%)
Tel.: (82) 800334114
Web Site: https://www.3m.co.kr
Sales Range: $125-149.9 Million
Emp.: 1,400
Distr of Tape & Adhesives, Electronic Con-
nectors & Devices, Surgical & Medical Sup-
plies & Consumer Products
N.A.I.C.S.: 424690

**3M Manufacturera Venezuela
S.A.** (1)
Av Tamanaco Centro Emprasarial El Rosal,
Piso 6 El Rosal, Caracas, 1060,
Venezuela (100%)
Tel.: (58) 2129578111
Web Site: http://wwwsolutions.3m.com.ve
Sales Range: $75-99.9 Million
Emp.: 90
Distr of Tape & Adhesive Products, Elec-
tronic Supplies & Devices, Surgical & Medi-
cal Supplies & Consumer Products
N.A.I.C.S.: 424690
Daniel Blanco (Pres)

3M Mexico S.A. de C.V. (1)
Av Santa Fe No 190 Colonia Santa Fe, Del-
egacion Alvaro Obregon, 01210, Mexico,
DF, Mexico (100%)
Tel.: (52) 8001203636
Web Site: https://www.3m.com.mx
Sales Range: $1-4.9 Billion
Emp.: 1,000
Distr of Tape & Adhesive Products, Electri-
cal Connectors & Devices, Surgical & Medi-
cal Supplies & Consumer Products

N.A.I.C.S.: 325520

3M Nederland B.V. (1)
Industrieweg 24, 2382 KW, Zoeterwoude,
Netherlands (100%)
Tel.: (31) 715450377
Web Site: http://www.3m.nl
Sales Range: $300-349.9 Million
Emp.: 350
Distr of Tape & Adhesive Products, Electri-
cal Connectors & Devices, Surgical & Medi-
cal Supplies & Consumer Products
N.A.I.C.S.: 424690

3M New Zealand Ltd. (1)
94 Apollo Drive, PO Box 246, Rosedale
North Shore, Auckland, 0632, New
Zealand (100%)
Tel.: (64) 94774040
Web Site: http://www.3m.com
Sales Range: $125-149.9 Million
Emp.: 100
Distr of Tape & Adhesive Products, Electri-
cal Connectors & Devices, Surgical & Medi-
cal Supplies, Pharmaceuticals & Consumer
Products
N.A.I.C.S.: 424690
Makoto Itoh (Mng Dir)

3M Norge A/S (1)
Taerudgata 16, 2004, Lillestrom, Norway
Tel.: (47) 63847500
Web Site: http://www.3mnorge.no
Tape & Adhesive Products, Electronic Con-
nectors & Devices, Surgical & Medical Sup-
plies & Consumer Products Distr
N.A.I.C.S.: 424690

3M Oesterreich Ges mbH (1)
Kranichberggasse 4, PO Box 611, 1120,
Vienna, Austria
Tel.: (43) 1866860
Web Site: http://www.3m.com
Sales Range: $100-124.9 Million
Emp.: 140
Distr of Tape & Adhesive Products, Electri-
cal Connectors, Surgical & Medical Sup-
plies & Consumer Products
N.A.I.C.S.: 424690

3M Pakistan (PVT) Ltd. (1)
Islamic Chamber of Commerce Building ST-
2/A Block-9 KDA Scheme 5, Clifton, Kara-
chi, 75600, Pakistan (100%)
Tel.: (92) 21111225536
Web Site: http://www.3m.com.pk
Sales Range: $1-9.9 Million
Emp.: 150
Coated Fabrics
N.A.I.C.S.: 313320
Adnan Khan (Mng Dir)

3M Panama S.A. (1)
Via Ricardo J Alfaro, Panama,
Panama (100%)
Tel.: (507) 3028100
Web Site: http://www.3m.com
Sales Range: $75-99.9 Million
Emp.: 80
Distr of Tape & Adhesive Products, Elec-
tronic Connectors & Devices, Surgical &
Medical Supplies & Consumer Products
N.A.I.C.S.: 424690

3M Peru S.A. (1)
Av Canaval Moreyra 641, San Isidro, Lima,
Peru (100%)
Tel.: (51) 2242728
Web Site: http://www.3m.com.pe
Sales Range: $75-99.9 Million
Emp.: 79
Importer & Distr of 3M Products in Peru
N.A.I.C.S.: 424690

3M Philippines (1)
10th and 11th Floors The Finance Center
26th Street corner 9th Avenue, Bonifacio,
Taguig, Philippines
Tel.: (63) 22711680
Web Site: http://www.3mphilippines.com.ph
Tape & Adhesive Products, Electrical Con-
nectors & Devices, Surgical & Medical Sup-
plies & Consumer Products Distr
N.A.I.C.S.: 424690

3M Poland Sp. z.o.o. (1)
Al Katowicka 117, 05-830, Nadarzyn,
Poland (100%)
Tel.: (48) 227396000
Web Site: https://www.3mpolska.pl

Sales Range: $10-24.9 Million
Emp.: 800
Coated Fabrics & Other Products
N.A.I.C.S.: 313320

3M Portugal, Lda (1)
Edificio Office Oriente Rua do Mar da China
N 3 - 3 Piso A, 1990-138, Lisbon,
Portugal (100%)
Tel.: (351) 213134606
Web Site: https://www.3m.com.pt
Sales Range: $10-24.9 Million
Emp.: 80
Distribution of Document Management Systems, Graphics Products & Imaging Technology
N.A.I.C.S.: 424120

3M Precision Grinding GmbH (1)
St Magdalener Strasse 85, 9500, Villach,
Austria
Tel.: (43) 4242418110
Adhesive Whlsr
N.A.I.C.S.: 424690

3M Puerto Rico, Inc. (1)
B7 Tabonuco St 16th Fl Ste 1601, Guaynabo, PR 00968-3028
Tel.: (787) 620-3000
Web Site: http://www.3m.com.pr
Sales Range: $75-99.9 Million
Emp.: 82
Sales & Distribution of Pharmaceutical &
Industrial Products
N.A.I.C.S.: 424690
Belmiro Montaldi *(Mng Dir)*

3M Purification Inc. (1)
400 Research Pkwy, Meriden, CT 06450-
7172
Tel.: (203) 237-5541
Web Site: http://solutions.3m.com
Sales Range: $350-399.9 Million
Emp.: 2,200
Filtration Products Mfr
N.A.I.C.S.: 322299

Subsidiary (Non-US):

3M Purification Pty. Limited (2)
140 Sunnyholt Rd, Blacktown, 2148, NSW,
Australia
Tel.: (61) 1300367362
Web Site: http://www.3mpurification.com.au
Sales Range: $50-74.9 Million
Emp.: 100
Filtration Products Mfr
N.A.I.C.S.: 333998

Subsidiary (Domestic):

CUNO Engineered Products, Inc, (2)
3130 Lexington Ave S, Saint Paul, MN
55121 (100%)
Tel.: (651) 554-3140
Sales Range: $25-49.9 Million
Emp.: 215
Water Filtration Equipment Mfr
N.A.I.C.S.: 322299

Subsidiary (Non-US);

CUNO Latina Ltda. (2)
Rua Amf Do Brasil 251, Distrito Industrial,
Mairinque, 18120-000, SP, Brazil
Tel.: (55) 1147188555
Web Site: http://www.cunolatina.com.br
Rev.: $1,200,000
Emp.: 150
Filtration Products Mfr
N.A.I.C.S.: 333998

3M Romania S.R.L. (1)
Bucharest Business Park Str Menuetului nr
12 corp D etaj 3 sector 1, 013713, Bucharest, Romania
Tel.: (40) 212028000
Web Site: https://www.3m.com.ro
Healtcare Services
N.A.I.C.S.: 621610

3M Russia (1)
Krylatskaya St 17 Bldg 3 Krylatskaya Hills
Business Park, Block D, 121614, Moscow,
Russia
Tel.: (7) 4957847474
Web Site: http://solutions.3mrussia.ru
Sales Range: $150-199.9 Million
Emp.: 500
Distr of Tape & Adhesive Products, Electrical Connectors & Devices, Surgical & Medical Supplies & Consumer Products

N.A.I.C.S.: 424690

3M Sanayi ve Ticaret AS (1)
Topcu Yuzbasi Sinan Eroglu Cad Akel Is
Merkezi No 6, A Blok Kavacik Beykoz,
34805, Istanbul, Turkiye
Tel.: (90) 2165380777
Web Site: http://www.3m.com.tr
Sales Range: $75-99.9 Million
Emp.: 180
Distr of Tape & Adhesive Products, Surgical
& Medical Supplies, Electronic Products &
Consumer Products
N.A.I.C.S.: 424690

3M Singapore Pte. Ltd. (1)
100 Woodlands Avenue 7, Singapore,
738205, Singapore (100%)
Tel.: (65) 65771266
Web Site: http://www.3m.com.sg
Sales Range: $150-199.9 Million
Distr of Tape & Adhesive Products, Electronic Connectors & Devices, Surgical &
Medical Supplies, Pharmaceuticals & Consumer Products
N.A.I.C.S.: 424690
Arthur Fong *(Mng Dir)*

3M South Africa (Pty.) Ltd. (1)
146a Kelvin Drive, Western Service Rd,
Woodmead, 2196, South Africa (100%)
Tel.: (27) 118062000
Web Site: http://www.3m.co.za
Sales Range: $100-124.9 Million
Emp.: 186
Distr of Tape & Adhesive Products, Electrical Connectors & Devices, Surgical & Medical Supplies & Consumer Products
N.A.I.C.S.: 424690

3M Svenska AB (1)
Herrjarva torg 4, 170 67, Solna,
Sweden (100%)
Tel.: (46) 8922100
Web Site: https://www.3msverige.se
Sales Range: $75-99.9 Million
Emp.: 200
Mfr & Distr of Pharmaceuticals
N.A.I.C.S.: 325412
Eric Aumam *(Mng Dir)*

3M Taiwan Limited (1)
11568 3rd Floor No 198 Jingmao 2nd Road,
Nangang District, Taipei, 11568,
Taiwan (100%)
Tel.: (886) 227859338
Web Site: http://www.3m.com.tw
Sales Range: $150-199.9 Million
Distr of Tape & Adhesive Products, Electronic Connectors & Devices, Surgical &
Medical Supplies & Consumer Products
N.A.I.C.S.: 424690

Subsidiary (Domestic):

Alpha Beta Global Tapes & Adhesives Co., Ltd. (2)
6F No 216 Wen Lin North Road, Taipei,
Taiwan
Tel.: (886) 228277996
Web Site: http://www.alphabetagta.com
Adhesive Tape Mfr
N.A.I.C.S.: 322220

3M Technologies Private Limited (1)
10 Ang Mo Kio Street 65 Techpoint 01-01,
Singapore, 569059, Singapore
Tel.: (65) 64508888
Healtcare Services
N.A.I.C.S.: 621610

3M Thailand Limited (1)
88 The Park Building 14th Floor Ratchadaphisek Road, Khlong Toei Subdistrict Khlong Toei District, Bangkok, 10110,
Thailand (100%)
Tel.: (66) 26663666
Web Site: https://www.3m.co.th
Sales Range: $200-249.9 Million
Emp.: 500
Distr of Tape & Adhesive Products, Electronic Connectors & Devices, Surgical &
Medical Supplies & Consumer Products
N.A.I.C.S.: 425120

3M Touch Systems, Inc. (1)
501 Griffin Brook Park Dr, Methuen, MA
01844-1873
Tel.: (978) 659-9000
Web Site: http://www.3mtouch

Sales Range: $350-399.9 Million
Emp.: 300
Touch Screen Products Mfr
N.A.I.C.S.: 334118

Plant (Domestic):

3M Touch Systems, Inc. (2)
1640 Western Ave, Cumberland, WI 54829
Tel.: (715) 822-8501
Web Site: http://www.solutions.3m.com
Sales Range: $75-99.9 Million
Emp.: 220
Mfr & Distr of Hand & Floor Pads, Microfinishing Film, Superabrasive Products, Lapping Film & Diamond Lapping Film Products
& Services
N.A.I.C.S.: 327910

3M United Kingdom, PLC (1)
3M Centre Cain Road, Bracknell, RG12
8HT, United Kingdom (100%)
Tel.: (44) 8705360036
Web Site: http://www.3m.co.uk
Sales Range: $1-4.9 Billion
Distr of Tape & Adhesive Products., Electronic Connectors & Devices, Surgical &
Medical Supplies, Pharmaceuticals & Consumer Products
N.A.I.C.S.: 424690

Subsidiary (Domestic):

3M UK Holdings Limited (2)
Hudson Road Distribution Centre, Bedford,
MK41 0HR, United Kingdom
Tel.: (44) 1234268868
Web Site: http://www.3m.com
Stationery Product Whlsr
N.A.I.C.S.: 424120

Subsidiary (Domestic):

3M Northallerton (3)
Standard Way, Northallerton, DL6 2XA,
United Kingdom
Tel.: (44) 1609780170
Web Site: http://www.3m.co.uk
Sales Range: $50-74.9 Million
Emp.: 154
Protective Coatings Mfr
N.A.I.C.S.: 325510

**3M Security Printing and Systems
Ltd.** (3)
Gorse Street Chadderton, Oldham, OL9
9QH, United Kingdom
Tel.: (44) 1616832460
Printing Services
N.A.I.C.S.: 561990

3M Uruguay SA (1)
Cr Luis Lecueder 3536 Local SS2001 World
Trade Center, Montevideo, 11300, Uruguay
Tel.: (598) 26283636
Web Site: http://www.3m.com.uy
Tape & Adhesive Products., Electronic Connectors & Devices, Pharmaceuticals, Surgical & Medical Supplies & Consumer Products Distr
N.A.I.C.S.: 424690

Acelity Holdings, Inc. (1)
12930 W Interstate 10, San Antonio, TX
78249
Tel.: (210) 524-9000
Web Site: http://www.acelity.com
Sales Range: $1-4.9 Billion
Emp.: 5,600
Holding Company; Medical Products
N.A.I.C.S.: 551112

Subsidiary (Domestic):

Kinetic Concepts, Inc. (2)
8023 Vantage Dr, San Antonio, TX 78230-
4769
Tel.: (210) 524-9000
Web Site: http://www.kci1.com
Sales Range: $1-4.9 Billion
Wound Treatment Solution, Clinical Beds &
Medical Devices Designer, Mfr & Marketer
N.A.I.C.S.: 339112

Subsidiary (Non-US):

KCI Australia Pty. Ltd. (3)
15 Orion Road Level 7 West, Lane Cove,
2066, NSW, Australia
Tel.: (61) 294224322
Web Site: http://www.kci-medical.com

Sales Range: $100-124.9 Million
Patient Bedding & Medical Device Developer & Mfr
N.A.I.C.S.: 339112
Jim Stack *(Mng Dir)*

KCI Austria GmbH (3)
Lembockgasse 49, Stiege A, 1230, Vienna,
Austria
Tel.: (43) 1 86 330
Web Site: http://www.kci-medical.at
Sales Range: $100-124.9 Million
Clinical Bedding & Patient Therapy System
Developer & Mfr
N.A.I.C.S.: 339112

KCI Clinic Spain S.L. (3)
Centro Empresarial Arco Edificio 4 Modulo
A C/ Virgilio, No 2 Ciudad de la Imagen
Pozue, 28223, Madrid, Spain
Tel.: (34) 902100835
Web Site: http://www.kci-medical.com
Sales Range: $100-124.9 Million
Emp.: 15
Clinical Bedding & Medical Device Developer, Mfr & Whlsr
N.A.I.C.S.: 339112

KCI KK (3)
Kioicho Building 5F 3-12 Kioicho, Chiyoda
Ku, Tokyo, 102-0094, Japan
Tel.: (81) 332303854
Sales Range: $100-124.9 Million
Emp.: 50
Clinical Bedding & Medical Device Developer, Mfr & Whlsr
N.A.I.C.S.: 339112

KCI Medical AB (3)
Automatakveg 1, 2570, Ballerup, Denmark
Tel.: (45) 3990 0180
Web Site: http://www.kci-medical.com
Sales Range: $1-9.9 Million
Emp.: 10
Clinical Bedding & Medical Device Developer, Mfr & Whlsr
N.A.I.C.S.: 339112

KCI Medical ApS (3)
Telegrafvej 4 3 Flr, 2750, Ballerup, Denmark
Tel.: (45) 39900180
Web Site: http://www.kci-medical.com
Sales Range: $10-24.9 Million
Emp.: 50
Clinical Bedding & Medical Device Developer, Mfr & Whlsr
N.A.I.C.S.: 339112

KCI Medical Asia Pte. Ltd. (3)
10 Ang Mo Kio Street 65 01-01 Techpoint,
Singapore, 569059, Singapore
Tel.: (65) 18007429929
Web Site: http://www.kcimedical.com
Sales Range: $100-124.9 Million
Emp.: 20
Clinical Bedding & Medical Device Developer, Mfr & Whlsr
N.A.I.C.S.: 339112

KCI Medical B.V. (3)
Duikboot 1, 3991 CK, Houten, Netherlands
Tel.: (31) 306355885
Web Site: http://www.kci-medical.com
Sales Range: $100-124.9 Million
Emp.: 65
Clinical Bedding & Medical Device Developer, Mfr & Whlsr
N.A.I.C.S.: 339112

KCI Medical Canada, Inc. (3)
75 Courtneypark Drive W Unit 4, Mississauga, L5W 0E3, ON, Canada
Tel.: (216) 275-3535
Sales Range: $100-124.9 Million
Emp.: 25
Clinical Bedding & Medical Device Developer, Mfr & Whlsr
N.A.I.C.S.: 339112
Chris Letford *(Gen Mgr)*

KCI Medical GmbH (3)
Ifangstrasse 91, 8153, Rumlang, Switzerland
Tel.: (41) 848848900
Web Site: http://www.kci-medical.com
Sales Range: $100-124.9 Million
Clinical Bedding & Medical Device Developer, Mfr & Whlsr
N.A.I.C.S.: 339112

3M Company—(Continued)

KCI Medical Ltd. (3)
2050 Orchard Avenue, Citywest Business
Campus, Dublin, 24, Ireland
Tel.: (353) 14659510
Web Site: http://www.kci-medical.com
Sales Range: $100-124.9 Million
Emp.: 15
Clinical Bedding & Medical Device Devel-
oper, Mfr & Whslr
N.A.I.C.S.: 339112

KCI Medical S.R.L. (3)
Viale Ferdinando di Savoia no 2, 20124,
Milan, Italy
Tel.: (39) 01344921178
Web Site: http://www.kci-medical.it
Sales Range: $25-49.9 Million
Emp.: 150
Clinical Bedding & Medical Device Devel-
oper, Mfr & Whslr
N.A.I.C.S.: 339112

KCI Medical South Africa Pty.
Ltd. (3)
Thornhill Office Park Unit 24, 94 Bekker
Road, Midrand, 1685, South Africa
Tel.: (27) 113150445
Sales Range: $10-24.9 Million
Emp.: 40
Clinical Bedding & Medical Device Devel-
oper, Mfr & Whslr
N.A.I.C.S.: 339112
Charl Louw *(Gen Mgr)*

KCI Medizinproduckte GmbH (3)
Hagenauer Strasse 47, Wiesbaden, 65203,
Germany
Tel.: (49) 611335440
Web Site: http://www.kci-medical.com
Emp.: 60
Clinical Bedding & Medical Device Devel-
oper, Mfr & Whslr
N.A.I.C.S.: 339112

Laboratoire KCI Medical (3)
Parc Technopolis 17 Ave du Parc, Chilly-
Mazarin, 91380, Paris, France
Tel.: (33) 169747171
Web Site: http://www.kci-medical.com
Sales Range: $25-49.9 Million
Emp.: 100
Clinical Bedding & Medical Device Devel-
oper, Mfr & Whslr
N.A.I.C.S.: 339112

Aearo Technologies LLC (1)
7911 Zionsville Rd, Indianapolis, IN 46268-
1675
Tel.: (612) 284-1232
Web Site: http://www.earglobal.com
Sales Range: $500-549.9 Million
Emp.: 1,700
Hearing, Eye & Respiratory Protection &
Energy Absorbing Products Mfr
N.A.I.C.S.: 339115

Arizant, Inc. (1)
10393 W 70th St, Eden Prairie, MN 55344
Tel.: (952) 947-1200
Web Site: http://www.arizant.com
Sales Range: $150-199.9 Million
Emp.: 375
Medicinal Product Mfr
N.A.I.C.S.: 339113
John Rock *(Sr Dir-Legal Affairs)*

Subsidiary (Non-US):

Arizant Deutschland GmbH (2)
Technologiepark 24, 22946, Schleswig,
Germany
Tel.: (49) 415499340
Web Site: http://www.arizant.com
Sales Range: $10-24.9 Million
Emp.: 5
Medicinal Product Mfr
N.A.I.C.S.: 339113

Arizant France SAS (2)
ZI Athelia IV Avenue du Mistral, 13705, La
Ciotat, Cedex, France
Tel.: (33) 442981400
Web Site: http://www.arizant.com
Sales Range: $10-24.9 Million
Emp.: 10
Medicinal Product Mfr
N.A.I.C.S.: 339113

Marianne Lagier *(Gen Mgr)*

Subsidiary (Domestic):

Arizant Holdings Inc. (2)
10393 W 70th St, Eden Prairie, MN 55344-
3446
Tel.: (952) 947-1200
Sales Range: $25-49.9 Million
Emp.: 20
Offices of Other Holding Companies
N.A.I.C.S.: 551112

Arizant International Corporation (2)
10393 W 70th St, Eden Prairie, MN 55344
Tel.: (952) 947-1200
Medicinal Product Mfr
N.A.I.C.S.: 339113

Subsidiary (Non-US):

Arizant Osterreich GmbH (2)
Mariahilfer Strasse 123/3, 1060, Vienna,
Austria
Tel.: (43) 1 599 99 6
Medicinal Product Mfr
N.A.I.C.S.: 339113

Arizant UK Limited (2)
Calder Island Way, Wakefield, Wf2 7AW,
United Kingdom
Tel.: (44) 1924200550
Web Site: http://www.arizant.co.uk
Sales Range: $10-24.9 Million
Emp.: 15
Medicinal Product Mfr
N.A.I.C.S.: 339113

Capital Safety Group EMEA (1)
Le Broc Center-BP 15 Z I 1ere Avenue Car-
ros le Broc BP 15, 06511, Carros, France
Tel.: (33) 497100010
Web Site: http://www.capitalsafety.com
Industrial Safety Equipment Whlsr
N.A.I.C.S.: 423450

Capital Safety ROW Ltd (1)
5 Merse Road Moons Moat North Industrial
Estate, Redditch, B98 9HL, Worcestershire,
United Kingdom
Tel.: (44) 1915794433
Electronic Safety Equipment Mfr & Distr
N.A.I.C.S.: 334513

Ceradyne, Inc. (1)
3169 Red Hill Ave, Costa Mesa, CA
92626 (100%)
Tel.: (714) 549-0421
Web Site: http://www.ceradyne.com
Sales Range: $550-599.9 Million
Emp.: 2,112
Industrial Supply Merchant Whslr
N.A.I.C.S.: 423840

Subsidiary (Domestic):

Boron Products, LLC (2)
3250 South 614 Rd, Quapaw, OK 74363
Tel.: (918) 673-2201
Web Site: http://www.ceradyneboron.com
Emp.: 120
Processor of Boron
N.A.I.C.S.: 334413
Ramin Zarrabi *(Mgr-Site)*

Ceradyne ESK, LLC (2)
1201 N Industrial Dr, Saline, MI 48176
Tel.: (734) 944-8232
Sales Range: $150-199.9 Million
Advanced Technical Ceramics Mfr for In-
dustrial, Electronics, Defense & Medical
Applications
N.A.I.C.S.: 327999

Unit (Domestic):

Ceradyne Thermo Materials (2)
780 Park North Blvd Ste 122, Clarkston, GA
30021
Tel.: (404) 292-4242
Web Site: http://www.ceradyne-thermo.com
Sales Range: $25-49.9 Million
Emp.: 73
Fused Silica Ceramic Products Mfr
N.A.I.C.S.: 327120
Earl Conabee *(VP-Mktg)*

Subsidiary (Domestic):

Minco, Inc. (2)
510 Midway Cir, Midway, TN 37809
Tel.: (423) 422-6051

Web Site: http://www.mincoitc.com
Sales Range: $10-24.9 Million
Emp.: 259
Fused Silica Products Mfr
N.A.I.C.S.: 327120

Subsidiary (Non-US):

Ceradyne (Tianjin) Technical Ceram-
ics Co., Ltd. (3)
No 4737 Dongjiang Road Tianjin Tanggu
Marine Hi-Tech Development Area, Tianjin,
300451, China
Tel.: (86) 2225210701
Web Site: http://www.ceradyne.com
Advanced Technical Ceramics Mfr for In-
dustrial, Electronics, Defense & Medical
Applications
N.A.I.C.S.: 327999

Subsidiary (Domestic):

SemEquip, Inc. (2)
34 Sullivan Rd, North Billerica, MA 01862-
2000
Tel.: (978) 262-0911
Web Site: http://www.semequip.com
Developer of Cluster Ion Implantation Sub-
Systems & Advanced Ion Source Materials
for Manufacture of Logic & Memory Chips
N.A.I.C.S.: 334413

Unit (Domestic):

Semicon Associates (2)
695 Laco Dr, Lexington, KY 40510 (100%)
Tel.: (859) 255-3664
Web Site:
   http://www.semiconassociates.com
Sales Range: $25-49.9 Million
Emp.: 80
Advanced Technical Ceramics Mfr
N.A.I.C.S.: 327999

CodeRyte, Inc. (1)
7500 Old Georgetown Rd Ste 800,
Bethesda, MD 20814
Tel.: (301) 951-5300
Web Site: http://www.coderyte.com
Sales Range: $10-24.9 Million
Emp.: 130
Medical Coding & Clinical Data Extraction
Solutions
N.A.I.C.S.: 513210

Dyneon GmbH (1)
3M Advanced Materials Division Carl
Schurz Strasse 1, 41453, Neuss, Germany
Tel.: (49) 2131142265
Healthcare Services
N.A.I.C.S.: 621610

EMFI SAS (1)
3 rue Ettore Bugatti, 67500, Haguenau,
France
Tel.: (33) 388906000
Web Site: https://www.emfi.com
Healthcare Services
N.A.I.C.S.: 621610

GTA-NHT, Inc. (1)
30 Commerce Rd, Rockland, MA 02370-
1053
Tel.: (781) 331-5900
Web Site: http://www.venturetape.com
Adhesive Tape Mfr
N.A.I.C.S.: 322220

KCI Europe Holding B.V. (1)
Papendorpseweg 95, 3528 BJ, Utrecht,
Netherlands
Tel.: (31) 1344921178
Medical Device Mfr
N.A.I.C.S.: 339112

KCI USA, Inc. (1)
12930 W Interstate 10, San Antonio, TX
78249-2248
Medical Device Mfr
N.A.I.C.S.: 339112

PT. 3M Indonesia (1)
Perkantoran Hijau Arkadia Tower F 8th
Floor JL TB Simatupang Kav 88, Jakarta,
12520, Selatan, Indonesia
Tel.: (62) 2129974000
Web Site: http://www.3m.com
Sales Range: $150-199.9 Million
Emp.: 300

Distr of Tape & Adhesive Products, Electri-
cal Connectors & Products, Surgical &
Medical Supplies & Consumer Products
N.A.I.C.S.: 424690

Scott Technologies, Inc. (1)
4320 Goldmine Rd, Monroe, NC 28110
Tel.: (704) 291-8300
Web Site: http://scottu.3m.com
Respiratory Equipment Mfr
N.A.I.C.S.: 334519

Subsidiary (Non-US):

Scott Health & Safety Limited (2)
3m Centre Cain Road, Bracknell, RG12
8HT, Berks, United Kingdom
Tel.: (44) 1695711711
Web Site: http://www.3mscott.com
Safety Products Mfr
N.A.I.C.S.: 339113

Simtronics AS (2)
Kabelgaten 8, PO Box 314, Okern Naeing-
spark, NO-0511, Oslo, Norway
Tel.: (47) 22645055
Combustible & Toxic Gas Detection, Flame
Detection & Other Industrial Safety Systems
& Controls Mfr & Whslr
N.A.I.C.S.: 334513

Subsidiary (Non-US):

Simtronics SAS (3)
Z I des Paluds 792 Av de la Fleuride, BP
11061, 13781, Aubagne, Cedex, France
Tel.: (33) 321608080
Combustible & Toxic Gas Detection, Flame
Detection & Other Industrial Safety Systems
& Controls Mfr & Whslr
N.A.I.C.S.: 334513

Sumitomo 3M Limited (1)
2 33 1 Tamagawa Dai, Setagaya-ku, Tokyo,
158 8583, Japan (75%)
Tel.: (81) 337098111
Web Site: http://www.3m.com
Sales Range: $75-99.9 Million
Emp.: 100
Distribution of Tape & Adhesive Products;
Electrical Connectors & Products; Surgical
& Medical Supplies & Consumer Products
N.A.I.C.S.: 424690

Suomen 3M Oy (1)
Keilaniementie 1, PO Box 90, 02150, Es-
poo, Finland (100%)
Tel.: (358) 952521
Web Site: http://www.3m.com
Sales Range: $25-49.9 Million
Emp.: 150
Retail Distr of Computer Equipment & Soft-
ware
N.A.I.C.S.: 449210

Winterthur Technologie AG (1)
Innere Gueterstrasse 4, Zug, 6300, Switzer-
land
Tel.: (41) 522344141
Web Site:
   http://www.winterthurtechnology.com
Sales Range: $200-249.9 Million
Emp.: 1,369
Industrial Grinding Wheels Mfr
N.A.I.C.S.: 333248

Subsidiary (Non-US):

3M a/s (2)
Hannemanns Alle 53, 2300, Copenhagen,
Denmark
Tel.: (45) 43480100
Web Site: http://www.3m.dk
Sales Range: $25-49.9 Million
Emp.: 130
Industrial Abrasive & Machine Tools Distr
N.A.I.C.S.: 423830

Rappold Winterthur Technologie
GmbH (2)
St Magdalener Strasse 85, Villach, 9500,
Austria
Tel.: (43) 4242811700
Sales Range: $75-99.9 Million
Emp.: 360
Grinding Equipment Distr
N.A.I.C.S.: 333517

SlipNaxos AB (2)
Folkparksvagen 31, SE 593 83, Vastervik,
Sweden

Tel.: (46) 49084300
Web Site: http://www.slipnaxos.se
Sales Range: $25-49.9 Million
Emp.: 175
Grinding Wheel Mfr
N.A.I.C.S.: 333248

Stankowendt Russia (2)
ul Skladochnaya d 1 str 22, 127018, Moscow, Russia
Tel.: (7) 4956894507
Web Site:
    http://www.winterthurtechnology.ru
Sales Range: $25-49.9 Million
Emp.: 50
Grinding Machine Mfr
N.A.I.C.S.: 333517
Alexander Emeliyanov (Gen Dir)

Subsidiary (Domestic):

Winterthur Schleiftechnik AG (2)
Oberer Deutweg 4, PO Box 56, 8411, Winterthur, Switzerland
Tel.: (41) 522344141
Machine Tools Mfr
N.A.I.C.S.: 333517

Subsidiary (Non-US):

Winterthur Technology (France) S.a.r.l. (2)
565 rue de Sans Souci, 69760, Limonest, Rhone, France
Tel.: (33) 472522540
Web Site:
    http://www.winterthurtechnology.com
Sales Range: $25-49.9 Million
Emp.: 6
Grinding Products Mfr & Distr
N.A.I.C.S.: 327910

Winterthur Technology Korea Ltd. (2)
706 Venture Valley 958 Gosaek-Dong, Gwonseon-gu, Suwon, 441 813, Gyeonggi, Korea (South)
Tel.: (82) 312981777
Web Site:
    http://www.winterthurtechnology.com
Grinding Equipment Mfr & Distr
N.A.I.C.S.: 327910

Winterthur Technology Taicang Co. Ltd. (2)
No 8 Loujiang Road North, Taicang Economy Dev Zone, Taicang, 215400, Jiangsu, China
Tel.: (86) 51281616802
Web Site:
    http://www.winterthurtechnology.com
Sales Range: $25-49.9 Million
Emp.: 40
Grinding Accessories Mfr
N.A.I.C.S.: 333310

Winterthur Technology UK Ltd. (2)
Unit 1 M1 Distribution Centre, Parkwood Industrial Estate, Sheffield, S91 EW, South Yorkshire, United Kingdom
Tel.: (44) 1142754211
Web Site:
    http://www.winterthurtechnology.com
Grinding Wheel Mfr
N.A.I.C.S.: 333248

420 PROPERTY MANAGEMENT LLC
137 Cresta Rd, Colorado Springs, CO 80906
Web Site: http://www.420prop.com
FTPM—(OTCIQ)
Property Management Services
N.A.I.C.S.: 531312
Jamie Payton (Pres)

4CABLE TV INTERNATIONAL, INC.
1248 1256 Hwy 501 Business, Conway, SC 29526
Tel.: (843) 347-4933   NV
Web Site: https://www.4cable.tv
Year Founded: 2007
CATV—(OTCIQ)
Sales Range: $1-9.9 Million
Emp.: 14

Radio & Television Broadcasting & Wireless Communications Equipment Manufacturing
N.A.I.C.S.: 334220
Susan Richey (Sec)
Andrew F. Staniak (CTO & VP)
John Homsey (VP-Sls & Mktg)
Paul A. Passey (VP-Ops)
Michael Feldenkrais (Pres & CEO)

4D MOLECULAR THERAPEUTICS, INC.
5858 Horton St Ste 455, Emeryville, CA 94608
Tel.: (510) 505-2680   DE
Web Site:
    https://www.4dmoleculartherapeu
    tics.com
Year Founded: 2013
FDMT—(NASDAQ)
Rev.: $3,129,000
Assets: $261,846,000
Liabilities: $30,509,000
Net Worth: $231,337,000
Earnings: ($107,494,000)
Emp.: 140
Fiscal Year-end: 12/31/22
Research & Development in Biotechnology (except Nanobiotechnology)
N.A.I.C.S.: 541714
John F. Milligan (Exec Chm)
Uneek Mehra (Chief Fin & Bus Officer, Principal Acctg Officer & Asst Sec)
David Kirn (Co-Founder, Pres & CEO)
David Schaffer (Co-Founder)
John F. Milligan (Chm)
Julian Pei (Head-IR & Corp Comm)
Scott Bizily (Chief Legal Officer)
Robert Y. Kim (Chief Medical Officer)
An Song (Chief Dev Officer)

4FRONT VENTURES CORP.
7010 E Chauncey Ln Ste 235, Phoenix, AZ 85054
Tel.: (602) 633-3067
Web Site:
    https://www.4frontventures.com
Year Founded: 2011
FFNT—(CNSX)
Rev.: $118,577,000
Assets: $344,732,000
Liabilities: $316,381,000
Net Worth: $28,351,000
Earnings: ($46,898,000)
Emp.: 641
Fiscal Year-end: 12/31/22
Cannabis Product Mfr & Distr
N.A.I.C.S.: 325412
Peter Kampian (CFO)
Joshua N. Rosen (Co-Founder)
Andrew Thut (CEO)
Joshua N. Rosen (Co-Founder)
Christopher Wimmer (Gen Counsel)
Ray Landgraf (Pres-Ops-California)
Brandon Mills (Exec VP)
Kris Krane (Co-Founder, Chm & Pres)

Subsidiaries:

Healthy Pharms, Inc. (1)
98 Winthrop St, Cambridge, MA 02138
Cannabis Treatment Services
N.A.I.C.S.: 621420

Om of Medicine LLC (1)
111 S Main St, Ann Arbor, MI 48104
Tel.: (734) 369-8255
Web Site: http://www.omofmedicine.org
Cannabis Distr
N.A.I.C.S.: 459999
Mark Passerini (Founder & Chm)
Michael Caruso (VP-Ops)

Pure Ratios Inc. (1)
2077 Kurtz St, San Diego, CA 92110
Tel.: (619) 955-1339

Web Site: http://www.pureratioscbd.com
Natural Medicine Distr
N.A.I.C.S.: 424210
Chad Conner (Founder)

5:01 ACQUISITION CORP.
501 Second St Ste 350, San Francisco, CA 94107
Tel.: (415) 993-8570   DE
Year Founded: 2020
FVAM—(NASDAQ)
Assets: $83,016,808,000
Liabilities: $85,683,206,000
Net Worth: ($2,666,398,000)
Earnings: ($1,036,231,000)
Emp.: 5
Fiscal Year-end: 12/31/21
Investment Services
N.A.I.C.S.: 523999
Andrew J. Schwab (Co-CEO)
Galya D. Blachman (Gen Counsel & Sec)
Rebecca L. Lucia (CFO & Treas)
Jason R. Ruth (Chief Bus Officer)
Kush M. Parmar (Co-CEO)

5E ADVANCED MATERIALS, INC.
9329 Mariposa Rd Ste 210, Hesperia, CA 92344
Tel.: (442) 221-0225   AU
Web Site:
    https://www.5eadvancedmateri
    als.com
Year Founded: 2016
FEAM—(NASDAQ)
Rev.: $252,000
Assets: $89,504,000
Liabilities: $78,798,000
Net Worth: $10,706,000
Earnings: ($62,013,000)
Emp.: 57
Fiscal Year-end: 06/30/24
Mineral Exploration Services
N.A.I.C.S.: 213114
David Jay Salisbury (Chm)
Aaron Bertolatti (Sec)

5G EDGE ACQUISITION CORP.
30 E 85th St Ste 3A, New York, NY 10028
Tel.: (212) 960-8674   DE
Year Founded: 2021
ARKE—(NASDAQ)
Investment Services
N.A.I.C.S.: 523999
Douglas Maine (Chm & CFO)
Allen Salmasi (CEO & Sec)

60 DEGREES PHARMACEUTICALS, INC.
1025 Connecticut Ave NW Ste 1000, Washington, DC 20036
Tel.: (202) 327-5422   DE
Web Site:
    https://60degreespharma.com
Year Founded: 2022
SXPT—(NASDAQ)
Rev.: $253,573
Assets: $7,783,771
Liabilities: $2,985,675
Net Worth: $4,798,096
Earnings: ($3,924,563)
Emp.: 3
Fiscal Year-end: 12/31/23
Pharmaceutical Product Mfr & Distr
N.A.I.C.S.: 325412

6D GLOBAL TECHNOLOGIES, INC.
17 State St Ste 2550, New York, NY 10004
Tel.: (646) 681-2345   NV
Web Site: http://www.6dglobal.com
SIXD—(OTCIQ)
Sales Range: $10-24.9 Million

Emp.: 104
Holding Company; Digital Business Solutions
N.A.I.C.S.: 551112
Tejune Kang (Chm & CEO)
Hilary Smith (Dir-Mktg)
Tandy Harris (VP-Global HR)
Mike Telatovich (VP-Global Delivery)
Raymond Robinson (Sr VP-Global Sls)
Bradley N. Timchuk (Pres & COO)

7 ACQUISITION CORPORATION
750 E Main St Ste 600, Stamford, CT 06902
Tel.: (617) 663-5988   Ky
Web Site:
    https://www.7acquisitioncorp.com
Year Founded: 2021
SVNA—(NASDAQ)
Rev.: $15,521,415
Assets: $238,858,934
Liabilities: $249,126,691
Net Worth: ($10,267,757)
Earnings: $13,861,651
Fiscal Year-end: 12/31/22
Investment Services
N.A.I.C.S.: 523999
Craig Cogut (Chm)
Joel Haney (CFO)
Brian Friedman (Gen Counsel)

727 COMMUNICATIONS, INC.
818 SW 3rd Ste 141, Portland, OR 97204
Tel.: (503) 210-5378   FL
SVNJ—(OTCIQ)
Wireless Telecommunication Services
N.A.I.C.S.: 517112
Tyroe Chhim (Pres & CEO)

7GC & CO. HOLDINGS INC.
388 Market St Ste 1300, San Francisco, CA 94111
Tel.: (628) 400-9284   DE
Web Site: http://www.7gc.holdings
Year Founded: 2020
VII—(NASDAQ)
Assets: $53,150,023
Liabilities: $66,630,715
Net Worth: ($13,480,692)
Earnings: $9,438,181
Emp.: 2
Fiscal Year-end: 12/31/22
Investment Services
N.A.I.C.S.: 523999
Jack Leeney (Pres, CEO, Partner-7GC & Co Sarl & Chm)
Christopher Walsh (CFO, COO & Sec)

808 RENEWABLE ENERGY CORP.
850 Tidewater Shores Loop Ste 402, Bradenton, FL 34208
Tel.: (631) 397-1111   NV
Year Founded: 2009
RNWR—(OTCIQ)
Rev.: $424,462
Assets: $1,999,941
Liabilities: $2,699,034
Net Worth: ($699,093)
Earnings: ($404,926)
Emp.: 10
Fiscal Year-end: 12/31/22
Renewable Energy Services
N.A.I.C.S.: 221114
David Chen (Pres)
Peter Yaugh Chen (CEO)

Subsidiaries:

SilverLight Aviation, LLC (1)
39514 Aviation Ave, Zephyrhills, FL 33542
Tel.: (813) 786-8290
Web Site:
    https://www.silverlightaviation.com

808 Renewable Energy Corp.—(Continued)

Sports Aircraft Mfr
N.A.I.C.S.: 336411

890 5TH AVENUE PARTNERS, INC. (Name Changed to BuzzFeed, Inc.)

89BIO, INC.
142 Sansome St 2nd Fl, San Francisco, CA 94104
Tel.: (415) 432-9270 DE
Web Site: https://www.89bio.com
Year Founded: 2019
ETNB—(NASDAQ)
Rev.: $2,164,000
Assets: $196,824,000
Liabilities: $44,992,000
Net Worth: $151,832,000
Earnings: ($102,026,000)
Emp.: 45
Fiscal Year-end: 12/31/22
Biotechnology Research & Development Services
N.A.I.C.S.: 541714
Rohan Palekar (CEO)
Ryan Martins (CFO)
Hank Mansbach (Chief Medical Officer)
Quoc Le-Nguyen (Chief Technical Ops Officer & Head-Quality)
Melissa Abel (VP-Comml Strategy & Comm)
Michael Baldwin (VP-Quality Assurance)
Will Charlton (VP-Clinical Dev)
Shiva Natarajan (Principal Acctg Officer & VP-Fin)
Moti Rosenstock (VP-Preclinical Dev)
Paul Shin (VP-R&D Ops)
Ram Waisbourd (Chief Bus Officer)
Francis W. Sarena (COO)

8X8, INC.
675 Creekside Way, Campbell, CA 95008
Tel.: (408) 727-1885 DE
Web Site: https://www.8x8.com
Year Founded: 1987
EGHT—(NASDAQ)
Rev.: $638,130,000
Assets: $910,268,000
Liabilities: $727,902,000
Net Worth: $182,366,000
Earnings: ($175,383,000)
Emp.: 2,216
Fiscal Year-end: 03/31/22
Digital Telecommunications Products; VoIP Business Phone Services
N.A.I.C.S.: 334290
Scott Sampson (Sr VP-Midmarket & Enterprise)
Matthew Zinn (Chief Privacy Officer, Gen Counsel, Sec & Sr VP)
Olivier Gerhardt (Gen Mgr-CPaaS)
Amritesh Chaudhuri (CMO & Exec VP)
Tim Young (VP-Revenue Ops-Global)
Kevin Kraus (CFO)
Bruno Bertini (CMO)
Jaswinder Pal Singh (Chm)
Samuel C. Wilson (CEO)
Suzy Seandel (Chief Acctg Officer & Sr VP)
Walt Weisner (Chief Customer Officer)
Mehdi Salour (Sr VP-Global Network & Dev Ops)
Laurence Denny (Chief Legal Officer)
Rob Pilgrim (Sr VP)
Jamie Snaddon (Mng Dir-EMEA & VP)
Dan Timpson (Sr VP-Engineering)
Hunter Middleton (Chief Product Officer)
Jeanette Winters (Chief HR Officer)
Lisa Martin (Chief Revenue Officer)

Subsidiaries:
8x8 International Pty Ltd. (1)
Level 13 2 Park Street, Sydney, 2000, NSW, Australia
Tel.: (61) 1800854171
Information Technology Services
N.A.I.C.S.: 513210
Pablo Munoz (Mktg Mgr)

8x8 International SRL (1)
Bulevardul 21 Decembrie 1989 77, 400124, Cluj-Napoca, Romania
Tel.: (40) 364630189
Information Technology Services
N.A.I.C.S.: 513210

8x8 UK Limited (1)
3rd Floor The Relay Building 114 Whitechapel High St Aldgate East, London, E1 7PT, United Kingdom
Tel.: (44) 2070966000
Information Technology Services
N.A.I.C.S.: 513210
Charone Connell (Mktg Mgr-EMEA)

Contactual, Inc. (1)
959 Skyway Ste 350, San Carlos, CA 94070
Tel.: (650) 292-8603
Sales Range: $25-49.9 Million
Emp.: 50
Software Publisher
N.A.I.C.S.: 513210

Fuze, Inc. (1)
2 Copley Pl 7th Fl, Boston, MA 02116
Tel.: (702) 266-9583
Web Site: http://www.fuze.com
Computer Software Solutions
N.A.I.C.S.: 423430
Brian Day (CEO)
Elisa Gilmartin (Chief People Officer)
Rob Scudiere (CTO)
John Milton (Gen Counsel)

Voicenet Solutions Limited (1)
Oxford House Bell Business Park, Aylesbury, HP19 8JR, Buckinghamshire, United Kingdom
Tel.: (44) 2070966000
Telecommunication Servicesb
N.A.I.C.S.: 517810

Zerigo, Inc. (1)
2125 O'Neil, San Jose, CA 95131
Tel.: (720) 210-5439
Web Site: http://www.zerigo.com
Sales Range: $50-74.9 Million
Emp.: 300
Telecommunication Servicesb
N.A.I.C.S.: 517810
Zik Verma (CEO)

9 METERS BIOPHARMA, INC.
2722 N Green Valley Pkwy, Henderson, NV 89014
Tel.: (702) 530-7696 DE
Web Site: https://www.9meters.com
Year Founded: 2010
NMTR—(NASDAQ)
Rev.: $501,228
Assets: $33,147,844
Liabilities: $30,747,301
Net Worth: $2,400,543
Earnings: ($43,766,415)
Emp.: 10
Fiscal Year-end: 12/31/22
Biotechnology Research & Development Services
N.A.I.C.S.: 541714
Mark A. Sirgo (Chm)
Patrick H. Griffin (Chief Medical Officer)
Al Medwar (Sr VP-IR & Corp Comm)
Sireesh Appajosyula (Sr VP-Corp Dev & Ops)
Sara Liu (Chief Comml Officer)

908 DEVICES INC.
645 Summer St, Boston, MA 02210
Tel.: (857) 254-1500 DE
Web Site:
https://www.908devices.com
Year Founded: 2012

MASS—(NASDAQ)
Rev.: $50,229,000
Assets: $202,981,000
Liabilities: $37,490,000
Net Worth: $165,491,000
Earnings: ($36,399,000)
Emp.: 230
Fiscal Year-end: 12/31/23
Medical Device Mfr
N.A.I.C.S.: 339112
Kevin J. Knopp (Co-Founder & CEO)
John Kenneweg (VP-Govt)
Andrew Bartfay (Co-Founder & Dir-Hardware Dev)
Kevin McCallion (VP-Production & New Product Introduction)
Michael Jobin (Co-Founder & Dir-Product Dev)
Scott Miller (Co-Founder & Dir-Mass Spectrometer Engrg)
E. Kevin Hrusovsky (Chm)
Steve Davenport (VP-Comml Bus & Sls)
Don Osmer (VP)
Joseph H. Griffith IV (CFO)

99 ACQUISITION GROUP INC.
14 Noblewood Ct, Gaithersburg, MD 20878
Tel.: (703) 371-4260 DE
Web Site:
https://www.99acquisitiongroup.com
Year Founded: 2022
NNAG—(NASDAQ)
Rev.: $1,475,275
Assets: $77,758,038
Liabilities: $80,255,594
Net Worth: ($2,497,556)
Earnings: $756,057
Fiscal Year-end: 12/31/23
Investment Management Service
N.A.I.C.S.: 523999

A&D MAINTENANCE LEASING & REPAIRS, INC. (Acquired by Custom Truck One Source, Inc.)

A-MARK PRECIOUS METALS, INC.
2121 Rosecrans Ave Ste 6300, El Segundo, CA 90245
Tel.: (310) 587 1477 DE
Web Site: https://www.amark.com
Year Founded: 1965
AMRK—(NASDAQ)
Rev.: $9,699,039,000
Assets: $1,827,820,000
Liabilities: $1,165,964,000
Net Worth: $661,856,000
Earnings: $69,033,000
Emp.: 489
Fiscal Year-end: 06/30/24
Coins & Precious Metals Distr
N.A.I.C.S.: 423940
David W. G. Madge (CMO)
Michael R. Wittmeyer (Exec VP-Direct Sls Segment)
Gregory N. Roberts (CEO)
Thor G. Gjerdrum (Pres)
Carol Meltzer (Gen Counsel, Sec & Exec VP)
Brian Aquilino (COO)
Kathleen Simpson-Taylor (CFO)
Armik Zakian (CIO)
Steven Reiner (Pres-CFC)
Jamie Meadows (Pres-AMST)
Jeffrey D. Benjamin (Chm)

Subsidiaries:
AM Services, Inc. (1)
3460 E Ellsworth Rd, Ann Arbor, MI 48108
Tel.: (734) 973-0930
Web Site: http://www.amservicesinc.com
Lawn Maintenance Services

N.A.I.C.S.: 811411

Buy Gold and Silver Corp. (1)
6125 Luther Ln Ste 474, Dallas, TX 75225-6202
Web Site: https://www.bgasc.com
Gold & Silver Distr
N.A.I.C.S.: 423940

Collateral Finance Corporation (1)
2121 Rosecrans Ave Ste 6301, El Segundo, CA 90245
Tel.: (310) 587-1410
Web Site: https://www.cfcgoldloans.com
Metal Product Whslr
N.A.I.C.S.: 423510

Cybermetals, Corp. (1)
11700 Preston Rd Ste 660517, Dallas, TX 75230
Web Site: https://www.cybermetals.com
Metal Product Investing Services
N.A.I.C.S.: 523999

Gold Price Group, Inc. (1)
10440 N Central Expy Ste 800, Dallas, TX 75231
Tel.: (214) 265-6567
Web Site: https://dev-d9.goldprice.org
Commodity Contracts Dealing Services
N.A.I.C.S.: 523160

Goldline Inc. (1)
11835 W Olympic Blvd Ste 500, Los Angeles, CA 90064
Web Site: https://www.goldline.com
Precious Metals & Collectable Coins
N.A.I.C.S.: 423940

JM Bullion, Inc. (1)
11700 Preston Rd Ste 660153, Dallas, TX 75230
Tel.: (800) 276-6508
Web Site: http://www.jmbullion.com
Sales Range: $650-699.9 Million
Online Gold & Silver Distr
N.A.I.C.S.: 455110
Michael R. Wittmeyer (Co-Founder)
Thomas Fougerousse (VP-Ops)
Bert Byerley (CFO & Exec VP)
Al Lee (Dir-Web Technologies)

Provident Metals Corp. (1)
6125 Luther Ln Ste 465, Dallas, TX 75225
Web Site: https://www.providentmetals.com
Precious Metal Product Distr
N.A.I.C.S.: 423940

Transcontinental Depository Services, LLC (1)
2121 Rosecrans Ave Ste 6300, El Segundo, CA 90245
Tel.: (310) 587-1408
Web Site: https://www.tdsvaults.com
Precious Metals Storage Services
N.A.I.C.S.: 493190
David W. G. Madge (Founder & Pres)

A. M. CASTLE & CO.
1420 Kensington Rd Ste 220, Oak Brook, IL 60523
Tel.: (847) 455-7111 MD
Web Site:
http://www.castlemetals.com
Year Founded: 1890
CTAM—(OTCQB)
Rev.: $368,253,000
Assets: $289,597,000
Liabilities: $306,777,000
Net Worth: ($17,180,000)
Earnings: ($40,660,000)
Emp.: 681
Fiscal Year-end: 12/31/20
Specialty Metal & Plastic Products Distr
N.A.I.C.S.: 423510
Patrick R. Anderson (Exec VP-Fin & Admin)
Marec Elden Edgar (Pres & CEO)
Michael J. Sheehan (Chm)
Edward M. Quinn (Chief Acctg Officer, VP & Controller)
Mark D. Zundel (Exec VP-Aerospace & Supply-Global)
Jeremy T. Steele (Gen Counsel, Sec & Sr VP)

Joseph Bonnema (Sr VP-Strategic Accounts)
Damien Mancini (Sr VP-Intl & Aerospace)
Lily Framarin (VP-HR)
Thomas Gries (VP-Fin & Global Branch Ops)
Peter Hreska (VP-Corp Fin & Asst Treas)

Subsidiaries:

A. M. Castle & Co. (Canada) Inc. (1)
835 Selkirk Ave, Pointe-Claire, H9R 3S2, QC, Canada   **(100%)**
Tel.: (514) 694-9575
Web Site: http://www.castle.com
Sales Range: $25-49.9 Million
Emp.: 15
Metals Distributor
N.A.I.C.S.: 423510

A.M. Castle & Co. (Canada) Inc. (1)
2150 Argentia Rd, Mississauga, L5N 2K7, ON, Canada
Tel.: (905) 858-3888
Web Site: http://www.castlemandle.com
Emp.: 30
Metal Ore Mining Services
N.A.I.C.S.: 213114
Tim Hardman (Mng Dir)

A.M. Castle Metal Materials (Shanghai) Co., Ltd. (1)
258 North Riying Road, Waigaoqiao Free Trade Zone, Shanghai, 200131, China
Tel.: (86) 2150463699
Web Site: http://www.castlemetals.com
Emp.: 30
Seal Products Distr
N.A.I.C.S.: 423510

A.M. Castle Metals UK Limited (1)
Units 10/11 Walker Industrial Park, Guide, Blackburn, BB1 2QE, United Kingdom
Tel.: (44) 1254586700
Web Site:
    http://www.castlemetalseurope.com
Metal Ore Mining Services
N.A.I.C.S.: 213114

Castle Metals Aerospace (1)
14400 S Figeroua St, Gardena, CA 90248
Tel.: (323) 321-1700
Web Site: http://www.castlemetals.com
Sales Range: $250-299.9 Million
Emp.: 450
Distr of High-Performance Metals to Aerospace & Defense Industries
N.A.I.C.S.: 331318

Plant (Domestic):

Castle Metal-Phoenix (2)
2302 E Magnolia St, Phoenix, AZ 85034
Tel.: (602) 275-7861
Web Site: http://www.amcastle.com
Rev.: $5,700,000
Emp.: 2
Metal Service Centers & Other Metal Merchant Whslr
N.A.I.C.S.: 423510

Castle Metals - Cleveland (2)
26800 Miles Rd, Bedford Heights, OH 44146-1405
Tel.: (216) 292-7600
Web Site: http://www.amcastle.com
Metal Distribution
N.A.I.C.S.: 423510

Castle Metals - Los Angeles (2)
14001 Orange Ave, Paramount, CA 90723-2017   **(100%)**
Tel.: (562) 630-1400
Web Site: http://www.amcastle.com
Metal Distribution
N.A.I.C.S.: 423510

Subsidiary (Domestic):

Oliver Steel Plate Co. (2)
7851 Bavaria St, Twinsburg, OH 44087-2263
Tel.: (330) 425-7000
Web Site: http://www.oliversteel.com
Emp.: 185
Carbon & Alloy Steel Plate Processor & Distr

N.A.I.C.S.: 423510
Blain A. Tiffany (Pres)

Paramont Machine Company, Inc. (2)
963 Commercial Ave SE, New Philadelphia, OH 44663
Tel.: (330) 339-3489
Web Site:
    http://www.paramontmachineco.com
Sales Range: $1-9.9 Million
Emp.: 35
Plastic Material Engineering
N.A.I.C.S.: 326199

Castle Metals France (1)
Du Pre Cadeau Zone Internationale de Fret, 44550, Montoir-de-Bretagne, France
Tel.: (33) 240458354
Metal Product Whslr
N.A.I.C.S.: 423510

Castle Metals France (1)
Du Pre Cadeau Zone Internationale de Fret, 44550, Montoir-de-Bretagne, France
Tel.: (33) 240458354
Web Site: http://www.castlemetals.com
Emp.: 45
Metal Ore Mining Services
N.A.I.C.S.: 213114

Castle Metals UK Limited (1)
Unit 10 and 11 Walker Industrial Park, Guide, Blackburn, BB1 2QE, United Kingdom
Tel.: (44) 1254367410
Web Site: http://www.castlemetalsuk.com
Sales Range: $25-49.9 Million
Emp.: 50
Metal Product Whslr
N.A.I.C.S.: 423510

Castle Metals de Mexicali, S.A. de C.V. (1)
Avenida Ruelia 1999 Colonia Desarrollo, Urbano Parque Industrial Palaco, Mexicali, 21385, Mexico
Tel.: (52) 6865634981
Metal Ore Mining Services
N.A.I.C.S.: 213114
Guillermo Rivera (Plant Mgr)

E.Harding & Sons Limited (1)
Units 10 & 11 Walker Industrial Estate, Guide, Blackburn, BB1 2QE, United Kingdom
Tel.: (44) 1254581276
Metal Ore Mining Services
N.A.I.C.S.: 213114

LOKS Plasma Services Limited (1)
Unit 10 11, Blackburn, BB1 2QE, Lancs, United Kingdom
Tel.: (44) 1254689111
Emp.: 32
Metal Service Center Operator
N.A.I.C.S.: 423510

Transtar Metals Limited (1)
1 Meredews, Letchworth, SG61WH, Hertfordshire, United Kingdom
Tel.: (44) 1462687650
Sales Range: $10-24.9 Million
Emp.: 2
Aircraft Product Mfr
N.A.I.C.S.: 336411
Pierre Sheppard (Gen Mgr)

A. O. SMITH CORPORATION

11270 W Park Pl Ste 170, Milwaukee, WI 53224-9508
Tel.: (414) 359-4000   DE
Web Site: https://www.aosmith.com
Year Founded: 1874
AOS—(NYSE)
Rev.: $3,852,800,000
Assets: $3,213,900,000
Liabilities: $1,369,500,000
Net Worth: $1,844,400,000
Earnings: $556,600,000
Emp.: 12,000
Fiscal Year-end: 12/31/23
Residential & Commercial Water Heating Equipment & Protective Coatings Mfr
N.A.I.C.S.: 332410

Stephen M. Shafer (Pres & COO)
Kevin J. Wheeler (Chm & CEO)
Charles T. Lauber (CFO & Exec VP)
Robert J. Heideman (CTO & Sr VP)
James F. Stern (Gen Counsel, Sec & Exec VP)
Paul R. Dana (Sr VP-Operations-Global)
D. Samuel Karge (Pres-Water Treatment-North America & Sr VP)
S. Melissa Scheppele (CIO & Sr VP)
Holly Haseley (Dir-Corporate Communications)

Subsidiaries:

A. O. Smith (China) Environmental Products Co., Ltd. (1)
No 9 Zhongxing west Rd, Lishui Economic Development Zone, Nanjing, 211200, China
Tel.: (86) 2556231999
Commercial Water Heater & Boiler Mfr
N.A.I.C.S.: 333414

A. O. Smith Enterprises Ltd. (1)
599 Hill Street West, Fergus, N1M 2X1, ON, Canada
Tel.: (519) 271-5800
Web Site: http://www.hotwatercanada.ca
Sales Range: $25-49.9 Million
Mfr of Commercial Water Heaters & Hydronic Heating Equipment
N.A.I.C.S.: 333310

A. O. Smith India Water Products Private Limited (1)
Plot No 300 Phase - 2 KIADB Industrial Area, Harohalli, Kanakapura, 562 112, Karnataka, India
Tel.: (91) 8028011200
Web Site: https://www.aosmithindia.com
Water Treatment Equipment Distr
N.A.I.C.S.: 423620

A. O. Smith Vietnam Company Limited (1)
12th Floor Harec Building No 4A Lang Ha, Thanh Cong Ward Ba Dinh District, Hanoi, Vietnam
Tel.: (84) 8001228
Web Site: https://www.aosmith.com.vn
Water Treatment Equipment Mfr & Distr
N.A.I.C.S.: 335220

A. O. Smith Water Products (1)
500 Tennessee Waltz Pkwy, Ashland City, TN 37015
Web Site: http://www.hotwater.com
Water Heaters & Pump Tanks Mfr
N.A.I.C.S.: 333996
John Brenzie (Treas & VP-Fin)

Division (Domestic):

APCOM Inc. (2)
125 SE Pkwy, Franklin, TN 37064-3925
Tel.: (615) 794-5574
Web Site: https://www.apcom.com
Rev.: $10,700,000
Emp.: 325
Water Heater Components Mfr
N.A.I.C.S.: 334512
Fred Fann (Mgr-Sls & Mktg)
Matt Witherspoon (Mgr-Quality)
Darrell Schuh (VP & Gen Mgr)
Bill Jacobs (Dir-Ops)
Paul Brown (Controller-Plant)
Amy Williams (Mgr-HR)

Division (Domestic):

A.O. Smith - Protective Coatings Division (3)
8160 Holton Dr, Florence, KY 41042
Tel.: (859) 727-3500
Web Site: https://www.aospcd.com
Protective Metal Coatings Mfr
N.A.I.C.S.: 332812

Plant (Domestic):

APCOM Inc. - Cookeville Plant (3)
1010 Volunteer Dr, Cookeville, TN 38501
Tel.: (931) 526-2137
Web Site: http://www.apcom-inc.com
Sales Range: $10-24.9 Million
Emp.: 100
Water Heater Components Mfr

N.A.I.C.S.: 335220
Mike Galloway (Mgr-HR & EHS)

A. O. Water Products Company (1)
500 Tennessee Waltz Pkwy, Ashland City, TN 37015
Tel.: (615) 792-4371
Web Site: http://www.hotwater.com
Emp.: 800
Holding Company; Water Heaters & Related Products Mfr
N.A.I.C.S.: 551112

Subsidiary (Non-US):

A. O. Smith Water FZE (2)
Jebel Ali Free Zone, PO Box 261886, Jafza, Dubai, 261886, United Arab Emirates
Tel.: (971) 48812666
Household Appliances Mfr
N.A.I.C.S.: 335210

Plant (Domestic):

A. O. Smith Water Products Co. - Charlotte Plant (2)
4302 Raleigh St, Charlotte, NC 28213-6904
Tel.: (704) 597-8910
Web Site: http://www.hotwater.com
Sales Range: $50-74.9 Million
Emp.: 80
Mfr of Steel Tanks
N.A.I.C.S.: 332420

Subsidiary (Non-US):

A.O. Smith Water Products Company B.V. (2)
De Run 5305, 5503 LW, Veldhoven, Netherlands
Tel.: (31) 40 294 2500
Web Site: https://aosmithinternational.com
Sales Range: $10-24.9 Million
Emp.: 70
Assembles & Markets Residential & Commercial Water Heaters
N.A.I.C.S.: 333310
Can Hamscoort (Mng Dir)

Subsidiary (Domestic):

American Water Heater Company (2)
500 Princeton Rd, Johnson City, TN 37601-2030
Tel.: (423) 283-8000
Web Site:
    https://www.americanwaterheater.com
Sales Range: $300-349.9 Million
Emp.: 1,200
Flammable Vapour-Resistant Water Heater Mfr
N.A.I.C.S.: 333414

Unit (Non-US):

GSW Water Heaters (2)
599 Hill Street West, Fergus, N1M 2X1, ON, Canada
Tel.: (519) 843-1616
Web Site: http://www.gsw-wh.com
Sales Range: $50-74.9 Million
Emp.: 180
Water Heating Systems Mfr
N.A.I.C.S.: 333415

Aquasana, Inc. (1)
1609 Shoal Creek Blvd Ste 200, Austin, TX 78701
Tel.: (817) 536-5250
Web Site: https://www.aquasana.com
Home Water Filtration Systems Mfr & Sales
N.A.I.C.S.: 312112

Atlantic Filter Corp. (1)
3112 45th St, West Palm Beach, FL 33407
Tel.: (561) 683-0100
Web Site: http://www.atlanticfilter.com
Motor Vehicle Supplies & New Parts Merchant Whslr
N.A.I.C.S.: 423120
Bill Hartman (Mgr-Retail)
James W. Wakem II (Pres & CEO)

Clean Water Testing (1)
1990 Prospect Ct, Appleton, WI 54914
Tel.: (920) 733-7590
Web Site:
    https://www.cleanwatertesting.com
Water Testing Laboratory Operator
N.A.I.C.S.: 541380

A. O. Smith Corporation—(Continued)

Giant Factories Inc. (1)
40 Avenue Lesage, East Montreal, H1B
5H3, QC, Canada
Tel.: (514) 645-8893
Web Site: https://giantinc.com
Emp.: 300
Water Heater Equipment Mfr
N.A.I.C.S.: 333414

Lochinvar, LLC (1)
300 Maddox Simpson Pkwy, Lebanon, TN
37090
Tel.: (615) 889-8900
Web Site: https://www.lochinvar.com
Sales Range: $200-249.9 Million
Emp.: 350
Power Boiler & Heat Exchanger Mfr
N.A.I.C.S.: 332410
Stephen O'Brien (COO)
Eddie Goodwin (Pres & Gen Mgr)

Subsidiary (Non-US):

Lochinvar Limited (2)
7 Lombard Way The MXL Centre, Banbury,
ON16 4TJ, Oxon, United Kingdom
Tel.: (44) 1295269981
Web Site: http://www.lochinvar.ltd.uk
Sales Range: $25-49.9 Million
Water Heater Mfr
N.A.I.C.S.: 335220
Liam Elmore (Dir-Sls)

Mineral-Right Inc (1)
10 W Quail Rd, Phillipsburg, KS 67661
Tel.: (785) 543-6571
Web Site: https://www.mineral-right.com
Zeolite Crystal Mfr
N.A.I.C.S.: 325998

Smith Investment Company (1)
11270 W Park Pl, Milwaukee, WI 53224
Tel.: (414) 359-4030
Web Site: http://www.aosmith.com
Sales Range: $75-99.9 Million
Emp.: 500
Holding Company; Printing & Warehousing
Services
N.A.I.C.S.: 551112

Water-Right, Inc. (1)
1900 Prospect Ct, Appleton, WI 54914
Tel.: (920) 739-9401
Web Site: http://www.water-right.com
Sales Range: $50-74.9 Million
Emp.: 90
Water Treatment System Mfr
N.A.I.C.S.: 221310
Glenn H. Gruett (Founder)
Chris Schwersenska (Mgr-Pur)
Guy Gruett (VP)
Luke Java (Dir-Sls & Mktg)
Erik Koglin (Natl Mgr-Channel)
Mike Manley (Mgr-Retail Field)
Luis Santiago (Mgr-Dealer Field)
Melanie Jayjack (Mktg Mgr)
Vicki Andersen (Assoc Mgr-Brand)
Christine Van Sickle (Assoc Mgr-Brand)
Derick Wasinger (Mgr-Customer Svc)
Mike Hanten (Dir-Lab)
Kirk Guthrie (Mgr-Technical Svcs)
Gary Bauer (Mgr-Customer Care)
Angie Lom (Controller)
Tom Tegen (Production Mgr)

Subsidiary (Domestic):

WaterCare Corporation (2)
1900 Prospect Ct, Appleton, WI 54914
Tel.: (920) 739-9401
Web Site: http://www.watercare.com
Sales Range: $10-24.9 Million
Emp.: 15
Water Filters, Softeners & Other Water Puri-
fication Equipment Mfr
N.A.I.C.S.: 333310
Glenn Gruett (Founder & CEO)
Luke Java (Dir-Sls & Mktg)
Kurt Gruett (Pres)
Guy Gruett (VP)

Waterboss Europe, SRL (1)
4 Quai Joseph Gillet, Lyon, 69004, France
Tel.: (33) 478583264
Water Treatment Equipment Distr
N.A.I.C.S.: 423720

A.D. MAKEPEACE COMPANY

158 Tihonet Rd, Wareham, MA 02571
Tel.: (508) 295-1000   MA
Web Site:
  https://www.admakepeace.com
MAKE—(OTCIQ)
Other Activities Related to Real Es-
tate
N.A.I.C.S.: 531390
Robert Karam (Chm)
James F. Kane (Pres & CEO)
Linda M. Burke (VP-Mktg & Comml)
Renee Gonsalves (VP-Admin Ops)
Christopher Ierardi (Gen Mgr-Custom
Soils)

Subsidiaries:

A.H. BELO CORPORATION
(Name Changed to Dallas-
News Corporation)

A.K.A. BRANDS HOLDING CORP.

100 Montgomery St Ste 2270, San
Francisco, CA 94104
Tel.: (415) 295-6085   DE
Web Site: https://www.aka-
  brands.com
Year Founded: 2021
AKA—(NYSE)
Rev.: $611,738,000
Assets: $509,638,000
Liabilities: $262,561,000
Net Worth: $247,077,000
Earnings: ($176,697,000)
Emp.: 1,000
Fiscal Year-end: 12/31/22
Holding Company
N.A.I.C.S.: 551112
Jill Ramsey (Pres)
Ciaran Long (Interim CEO & CFO)
John Gonneville (VP-Strategy &
M&A)
Michael Trembley (CIO & Sr VP-Ops)
Emily Goldberg (Head-Corporate
Communications)
Kenneth White (Head-People)

A.L. JOHNSON COMPANY

4671 Calle Carga, Camarillo, CA
93012
Tel.: (805) 389-4631   CA
Web Site: http://www.aljcast.com
Year Founded: 1954
GCIN—(OTCIQ)
Precision Aluminum Mfr
N.A.I.C.S.: 331529
Richard A. Carlson (Pres & COO)

A.R.T. DIGITAL HOLDINGS CORP.

12600 Hill Country Blvd Ste R-275,
Bee Cave, TX 78738
Tel.: (612) 889-2418   NV
Web Site:
  https://www.artdigitalcorp.com
Year Founded: 2007
CGAC—(OTCIQ)
Sales Range: Less than $1 Million
Investment Services
N.A.I.C.S.: 523940
Logan William Rice (Pres)
George J. Powell III (CEO, Interim
CFO & Sec)

A10 NETWORKS, INC.

2300 Orchard Pkwy, San Jose, CA
95131
Tel.: (408) 325-8668   CA
Web Site:
  https://www.a10networks.com
Year Founded: 2004
ATEN—(NYSE)
Rev.: $280,338,000
Assets: $369,105,000
Liabilities: $188,093,000
Net Worth: $181,012,000

Earnings: $46,908,000
Emp.: 575
Fiscal Year-end: 12/31/22
Network Security Technology Devel-
oper
N.A.I.C.S.: 561621
Karen Thomas (Exec VP-Worldwide
Sls & Mktg)
Dhrupad Trivedi (Chm, Pres & CEO)
Mikko Disini (VP-Product Line Mgmt)
Scott Weber (Gen Counsel)
Eric Kwok (VP-Support & Svcs-
Worldwide)
Andrew Kim (VP-HR-Worldwide)
Aris Wong (VP-Engrg-Worldwide)
Bret Sloan (Head-Global Ops)
Sean Pike (Head-Information Secu-
rity)

Subsidiaries:

A10 Networks Inc. (1)
Suite 800 8F Beijing Sunflower Tower No
37 Maizidian Street, Chaoyang District, Bei-
jing, 100125, China
Tel.: (86) 13301103258
Software Application Development Services
N.A.I.C.S.: 541511

**A10 Networks Malaysia Sdn.
Bhd.** (1)
Level 8 MCT Tower Sky Park One CityJalan
USJ 25/1, 47650, Subang Jaya, Selangor,
Malaysia
Tel.: (60) 380228242
Wireless Network Installation Services
N.A.I.C.S.: 517112

A10 Networks, Inc. (1)
6F No 66 San-Chung Rd, Nangang Dist,
New Taipei City, 115, Taiwan
Tel.: (886) 227852729
Software Application Development Services
N.A.I.C.S.: 541511

AADI BIOSCIENCE, INC.

17383 Sunset Blvd Ste A250, Pacific
Palisades, CA 90272
Tel.: (424) 473-8055   DE
Web Site: https://aadibio.com
Year Founded: 2007
AADI—(NASDAQ)
Rev.: $15,216,000
Assets: $184,237,000
Liabilities: $25,859,000
Net Worth: $158,378,000
Earnings: ($60,513,000)
Emp.: 79
Fiscal Year-end: 12/31/22
Biopharmaceutical Product Research
& Development Services
N.A.I.C.S.: 541714
Scott M. Giacobello (CFO)
Stephen M. Rodin (Gen Counsel & Sr
VP)
Dave Lennon (Pres & CEO)
Jill Gardi (VP-Commercial)
Andrew Kwon (VP-BD & Corporate
Strategy)
Bryan Ball (Chief Technical Ops Offi-
cer)
Caley Castelein (Co-Chm)
Neil P. Desai (Founder)

AAON, INC.

2425 S Yukon Ave, Tulsa, OK 74107
Tel.: (918) 583-2266   NV
Web Site: https://www.aaon.com
AAON—(NASDAQ)
Rev.: $888,788,000
Assets: $813,903,000
Liabilities: $253,189,000
Net Worth: $560,714,000
Earnings: $100,376,000
Emp.: 3,666
Fiscal Year-end: 12/31/22
Mfr & Marketer of Rooftop Air Condi-
tioning, Heating & Heat Recovery
Systems
N.A.I.C.S.: 333415

Matthew Tobolski (Pres & COO)
Gary D. Fields (CEO)
Dave Benson (VP)
Norman H. Asbjornson (Founder)
Caron A. Lawhorn (Vice Chm)
Luke A. Bomer (Sec)
Stephen Wakefield (VP)
Christopher D. Eason (Chief Acctg
Officer)
Robert P. Teis (VP-Bus Tech)
Doug Wichman (Pres-Coil Products &
VP)

Subsidiaries:

BasX, LLC (1)
3500 SW 21st Pl, Redmond, OR 97756
Tel.: (541) 647-6650
Web Site: https://www.basxsolutions.com
Precision Engineering Product Mfr
N.A.I.C.S.: 333415
Matthew Tobolski (Co-Founder & Pres)
Gary D. Fields (CEO)
Dave Benson (Co-Founder, Chm, Pres &
CEO)
Matthew Tobolski (Co-Founder & Pres)
Larry Hopkins (Dir-R&D)
Jim Tarala (Dir-Green Solutions)

Wattmaster Controls, Inc. (1)
8500 NW River Pk Dr 108A, Parkville, MO
64152
Tel.: (816) 505-1100
Web Site: http://www.wattmaster.com
Automatic Environmental Control Mfr for
Residential, Commercial & Appliance Use
N.A.I.C.S.: 334512
Lena Hogan (Mgr-HR)
Michael Hobbs (Pres)

AAR CORP.

1100 N Wood Dale Rd, Wood Dale,
IL 60191
Tel.: (630) 227-2000   DE
Web Site: https://www.aarcorp.com
Year Founded: 1951
AIR—(NYSE)
Rev.: $2,318,900,000
Assets: $2,770,000,000
Liabilities: $1,580,200,000
Net Worth: $1,189,800,000
Earnings: $46,300,000
Emp.: 5,700
Fiscal Year-end: 05/31/24
Aviation & Aerospace Services
N.A.I.C.S.: 336412
John McClain Holmes (Chm, Pres &
CEO)
Dylan Wolin (Treas & VP-Strategic-
Corporate Development)
Sarah L. Flanagan (VP-Financial
Ops)
Christopher A. Jessup (Chief Comml
Officer & VP)
Eric S. Pachapa (Chief Acctg Officer
& VP)
Sean M. Gillen (CFO & VP)
Nicholas P. Gross (VP-Integrated So-
lutions)
Brian E. Sartain (VP-Repair-
Engineering)
Jessica A. Garascia (Gen Counsel,
Sec & VP)
Nicole Colon (VP Human Resources)
Rahul Ghai (Chief Digital Officer)
Art R. Smith (Chief Quality Officer &
VP)
Eric J. Young (VP-OEM Solutions)
John B. Cooper (VP-Defense & Govt-
Global)
Gerianne Tatone (Dir-Exec Office)
Lori Knudson (Chief Ethics & Compli-
ance Officer & VP)
Andrew Schmidt (Sr VP-Digital Svcs
& Trax)

Subsidiaries:

AAR Aircraft & Engine Sales &
Leasing (1)

1100 N Wood Dale Rd, Wood Dale, IL 60191
Tel.: (630) 227-2347
Aircraft Engine Sales & Leasing Services
N.A.I.C.S.: 336412

AAR Aircraft Services, Inc. (1)
6611 S Meridian Will Rogers World Airport, Oklahoma City, OK 73159
Tel.: (630) 227-2000
Holding Company; Aircraft Repair Services
N.A.I.C.S.: 551112

Unit (Domestic):

AAR Aircraft Services - Miami (2)
5300 NW 36th St Bldg 850, Miami, FL 33122
Tel.: (305) 871-2104
Sales Range: $250-299.9 Million
Emp.: 530
Airport Services
N.A.I.C.S.: 488190
Bob Scoble (VP-Quality & Safety)

AAR Aircraft Services - Oklahoma (2)
6611 S Meridian Ave, Oklahoma City, OK 73159-1118
Tel.: (405) 218-3000
Web Site: http://www.aacorp.com
Sales Range: $250-299.9 Million
Emp.: 500
Airplane Repair & Sales
N.A.I.C.S.: 488190

AAR Aircraft Turbine Center (1)
1100 N Wood Dale Rd, Wood Dale, IL 60191-1060 (100%)
Tel.: (630) 227-2000
Web Site: http://www.aarcorp.com
Sales Range: $125-149.9 Million
Emp.: 300
Aircraft Engine Parts Distr
N.A.I.C.S.: 423860
John McClain Holmes (Pres & CEO)
John M. Holmes (Pres & CEO)

AAR Airlift Group, Inc. (1)
2301 Commerce Park Dr NE, Palm Bay, FL 32905
Tel.: (321) 837-2345
Web Site: http://www.aarcorp.com
Aviation Logistical Support Services
N.A.I.C.S.: 488119

AAR Allen Asset Management (1)
1100 N Wood Dale Rd, Wood Dale, IL 60191-1060
Tel.: (630) 227-5500
Web Site: http://www.aarcorp.com
Sales Range: $50-74.9 Million
Emp.: 300
Aircraft Equipment Inventory Management Services
N.A.I.C.S.: 561499

AAR Corp. - Aviation Supply Chain (1)
1100 N Wood Dale Rd, Wood Dale, IL 60191
Tel.: (630) 227-2000
Web Site: http://www.aarcorp.com
Sales Range: $150-199.9 Million
Emp.: 400
Commercial & Defense Aircraft Supply Mfr
N.A.I.C.S.: 336412

Unit (Non-US):

AAR Aircraft Component Services-Amsterdam (2)
705 Kruisweg, PO Box 52, Hoofddorp, 2132 ND, Netherlands (100%)
Tel.: (31) 206552222
Sales Range: $25-49.9 Million
Emp.: 110
Major Overhaul & Maintenance Facility for Commercial & Military Aircraft Operations
N.A.I.C.S.: 334511
Mat Van Vugt (Gen Mgr)

AAR Aircraft Component Services-London (2)
World Business Center 1 New Road, Heathrow Airport, Hounslow, TW6 2BP, Mddx, United Kingdom (100%)
Tel.: (44) 2089906700
Web Site: http://www.aarcorp.com

Sales Range: $350-399.9 Million
Emp.: 18
Aviation Services
N.A.I.C.S.: 488119

Unit (Domestic):

AAR Aircraft Component Services-New York (2)
747 Zeckendorf Blvd, Garden City, NY 11530-2110 (100%)
Tel.: (516) 222-9000
Web Site: http://www.aarcorp.com
Sales Range: $50-74.9 Million
Emp.: 200
Overhaul of Aircraft Systems & Components
N.A.I.C.S.: 334419

Subsidiary (Non-US):

Airinmar Holdings Limited (2)
1 Ivanhoe Road Hogwood Industrial Estate, Finchampstead, Wokingham, RG40 4QQ, Berks, United Kingdom
Tel.: (44) 118 932 8880
Web Site: http://www.airinmar.com
Sales Range: $50-74.9 Million
Holding Company; Aircraft Component Repair Management Services
N.A.I.C.S.: 551112
Peter O'Dea (Head-Global Sls & Bus Dev)

Subsidiary (Domestic):

Airinmar Ltd. (3)
1 Ivanhoe Road, Finchampstead, RG40 4QQ, Berkshire, United Kingdom
Tel.: (44) 118 932 8880
Web Site: http://www.airinmar.com
Aircraft Component Repair Management Services
N.A.I.C.S.: 551112
Matthew Davies (Gen Mgr)
Jon Clucas (Sr Dir-Technical Svcs)
Byron Mawdsley (VP-Fin)
Peter O'Dea (Head-Sls & Bus Dev-Global)
Debbie Goodman (Partner-HR)
Richard Wood (Sr Dir-Customer Accounts)

AAR Defense Systems & Logistics (1)
1100 N Wood Dale Rd, Wood Dale, IL 60191-1060
Tel.: (630) 227-2353
Web Site: http://www.aarcorp.com
Sales Range: $150-199.9 Million
Sales, Marketing, Preparation & Contract Administration for Military & Government Business
N.A.I.C.S.: 423860

AAR International (France) S.A.R.L. (1)
41 Boulevard Edouard Vaillan, 92100, Boulogne, France (99%)
Tel.: (33) 146042211
Web Site: http://www.aarcop.com
Sales Range: $10-24.9 Million
Emp.: 4
Aviation Instruments & Equipment Mfr
N.A.I.C.S.: 336412
Pascal Parant (VP-Sls & Mktg)

AAR Landing Gear LLC (1)
9371 NW 100th St, Miami, FL 33178
Tel.: (305) 887-4027
Web Site: http://www.aarcorp.com
Sales Range: $125-149.9 Million
Emp.: 300
FAA Certified Facility Specializing in Exchange & Overhaul of Landing Gear
N.A.I.C.S.: 423860

Division (Domestic):

Mars Aircraft Services Co. of New Jersey (2)
333 Industrial, Teterboro, NJ 07608 (100%)
Tel.: (201) 288-0222
Web Site: http://www.aarcorp.com
Sales Range: $1-9.9 Million
Emp.: 3
Installation & Repair of Radios for Aircrafts
N.A.I.C.S.: 811210

AAR Supply Chain, Inc. (1)
1100 N Wood Dale Rd, Wood Dale, IL 60191
Tel.: (630) 227-2000

Web Site: http://www.aarcorp.com
Aeronautical Equipment Merchant Whslr
N.A.I.C.S.: 423860

Trax USA, Corp. (1)
2601 S Douglas Rd, Miami, FL 33145
Tel.: (305) 662-7400
Emp.: 110
Computer System Design Services
N.A.I.C.S.: 541512
Jose Almeida (Pres & CEO)
Juan Isaza (Acct Mgr)
Christian Olivera (Mgr-DM)
Ramona Vendryes (Mgr-QA)
Lester De La Paz (Mgr-Quality Assurance)
Miguel Sosa (Mgr-Software Dev)

AARON'S COMPANY, INC.
400 Galleria Pkwy SE Ste 300, Atlanta, GA 30339-3182
Tel.: (678) 402-3000   GA
Web Site: https://investor.aarons.com
Year Founded: 1955
AAN—(NYSE)
Rev.: $3,947,656,000
Assets: $3,297,800,000
Liabilities: $1,560,541,000
Net Worth: $1,737,259,000
Earnings: $31,472,000
Emp.: 12,100
Fiscal Year-end: 12/31/19
Furniture, Consumer Electronics & Home Appliances Rental & Rent-to-Own Services
N.A.I.C.S.: 532310
John T. Trainor (CIO & Sr VP-Omni-Channel)
Kirby M. Salgado (VP-Mdsg)
Gregory G. Bellof (Sr VP-Mid-Atlantic Ops)
David T. Bier (VP-Northeast Ops)
Ryan E. Malone (VP-Bus Transformation)
Jason M. McFarland (Sr VP-Midwest Ops)
Curtis L. Doman (Co-Founder)
Garet Hayes (Dir-PR)
David Korn (Chief Compliance Officer & VP)
Douglas A. Lindsay (CEO)
Ted M. Scartz (VP & Deputy Gen Counsel)
Cory Voglesonger (VP-Tech Strategy & Innovation)
Jill S. Young (VP-Internal Audit)
Kelly Wall (Sr VP-Fin & Treasury)
Larry F. Maher (VP-Strategy)
Russell S. Falkenstein (VP-Fin Plng & Strategic Analytics)
Almir Hadzialjevic (VP-Enterprise Risk & Security)
John H. Karr (VP-Compensation & Benefits)
Michael T. King (VP)
Blake W. Wakefield (Chief Revenue - Officer-Progressive Leasing & Pres-)
Michael P. Dickerson (VP-Corp Comm & IR)
Barbara Bernard (VP-Western Ops)
Rob O'Connell (Sr VP-HR)
Bill Gentner (CMO)
Brian Bohanon (VP-IT Engrg)
Stephanie Davis Neill (VP-Store Support)
Kim Anderson (VP-Progressive Ops)

Subsidiaries:

Aaron's Sales & Lease Ownership (1)
309 E Paces Ferry Rd NE, Atlanta, GA 30305 (100%)
Tel.: (404) 231-0011
Web Site: http://www.aarons.com
Sales Range: $100-124.9 Million
Emp.: 200
Residential Furniture, Electronics & Appliances Rental & Sales
N.A.I.C.S.: 532210

DAMI LLC (1)

2160 Esten Rd, Quakertown, PA 18951
Tel.: (484) 942-8713
Web Site: http://www.woodbydami.com
Architectural Woodwork & Millwork Mfr
N.A.I.C.S.: 337212

Progressive Finance Holdings, LLC (1)
11629 South 700 E, Draper, UT 84020
Tel.: (801) 316-6777
Holding Company
N.A.I.C.S.: 551112

SEI/Aaron's, Inc. (1)
3108 Piedmont Rd Ste 160, Atlanta, GA 30305
Tel.: (404) 495-9707
Web Site: http://www.seiaarons.com
Sales Range: $1-9.9 Million
Emp.: 12
Furniture Retailer
N.A.I.C.S.: 449110
Charles Smithgall (Founder)

Vive Financial, LLC (1)
PO Box 268808, Oklahoma City, OK 73126-8808
Web Site: https://vivecard.com
Financial Services
N.A.I.C.S.: 541611

Woodhaven Furniture Industries (1)
PO Box 460, Coolidge, GA 31738 (100%)
Tel.: (229) 346-3531
Sales Range: $75-99.9 Million
Emp.: 400
Residential & Office Furniture Mfr
N.A.I.C.S.: 337121
Mike Jarnagin (Pres)

AB INTERNATIONAL GROUP CORP.
144 Main St, Mount Kisco, NY 10549
Tel.: (914) 202-3108   NV
Web Site: https://www.abqqs.com
Year Founded: 2013
ABQQ—(OTCIQ)
Rev.: $3,300,467
Assets: $2,349,170
Liabilities: $889,268
Net Worth: $1,459,902
Earnings: $542,331
Emp.: 11
Fiscal Year-end: 08/31/24
Used Car Sales
N.A.I.C.S.: 441120
Chiyuan Deng (Pres, CEO & CFO)
Dennis Chung (CTO)
Enhai Liang (VP)
Jeff Deng (Treas & Sec)
Mingpeng Ou (VP)

Subsidiaries:

AB Cinemas NY, Inc. (1)
144 Main St, Mount Kisco, NY 10549
Tel.: (914) 864-0313
Web Site: https://www.abcinemasny.com
Movie Theatre Operator
N.A.I.C.S.: 512131

ABACUS LIFE, INC.
2101 Park Ctr Dr Ste 250, Orlando, FL 32835
Tel.: (561) 826-3620   DE
Web Site: https://abacuslife.com
Year Founded: 2020
ABL—(NASDAQ)
Rev.: $11,131,208
Assets: $99,374,190
Liabilities: $117,764,046
Net Worth: ($18,389,856)
Earnings: ($643,564)
Emp.: 6
Fiscal Year-end: 12/31/22
Direct Life Insurance Carriers
N.A.I.C.S.: 524113
Seth Miller (Chief Revenue Officer)
Adam S. Gusky (Bd of Dirs, Executives)
Jay Jackson (Pres & CEO)
Sean McNealy (Mng Partner)
Matthew Ganovsky (Mng Partner)

Abacus Life, Inc.—(Continued)

Scott Kirby *(Mng Partner)*
Bill McCauley *(CFO)*
Dani Theobald *(Gen Counsel)*

ABBOTT LABORATORIES
100 Abbott Park Rd, Abbott Park, IL
60064-6400
Tel.: (224) 667-6100   IL
Web Site: https://www.abbott.com
Year Founded: 1888
ABT—(NYSE)
Rev.: $40,109,000,000
Assets: $73,214,000,000
Liabilities: $34,387,000,000
Net Worth: $38,827,000,000
Earnings: $5,723,000,000
Emp.: 114,000
Fiscal Year-end: 12/31/23
Pharmaceuticals, Hospital Equipment
& Solutions, Nutritional Products, In-
dustrial Chemicals, Diagnostic Prod-
ucts, Pediatric Products, Hygienic
Products & Medical Electronics
Equipment Mfr
N.A.I.C.S.: 325412
Robert B. Ford *(Chm & CEO)*
John F. Ginascol *(Exec VP-Core Di-
agnostics)*
Hubert L. Allen *(Gen Counsel, Sec &
Exec VP)*
John A. McCoy Jr. *(VP & Controller)*
Jared L. Watkin *(Sr VP-Dibetes Care)*
Sammy G. Karam *(Sr VP-Emerging
Markets Established Pharmaceuti-
cals)*
Alejandro D. Wellisch *(Sr VP-
Established Pharmaceuticals-Latin
America)*
Lisa D. Earnhardt *(Exec VP-Medical
Devices)*
Mary K. Moreland *(Exec VP-HR)*
Andrea F. Wainer *(Exec VP-Rapid &
Molecular Diagnostics)*
J. Scott House *(Sr VP-Quality Assur-
ance, Regulatory, and Engrg Svcs)*
Randel Woodgrift *(Sr VP-Cardiac
Rhythm Mgmt)*
Philip P. Boudreau *(CFO & Sr VP-
Fin)*
Gregory A. Ahlberg *(Sr VP-Core
Laboratory Diagnostics-Comml Ops)*
Christopher J. Calamari *(Sr VP)*
Fernando Mateus *(Sr VP)*
Louis H. Morrone *(Sr VP)*
Julie Tyler *(Sr VP)*
Michael Dale *(Sr VP-Structural Heart)*

Subsidiaries:

Abbott (Shanghai) Diagnostics Sales
Co., Ltd.   **(1)**
Suite 4306 Wheelock Square No 1717
West Nanjing Road, Shanghai, 20040,
China
Tel.: (86) 2151315388
Medical Device Mfr
N.A.I.C.S.: 339112

Abbott AG   **(1)**
Neuhofstrasse 23, 6341, Baar, Switzerland
Tel.: (41) 417684444
Medical Device Mfr
N.A.I.C.S.: 339112

Abbott AG   **(1)**
Neuhofstrasse 23, 6341, Baar, Switzerland
Tel.: (41) 417684333
Web Site: http://www.abbott.ch
Pharmaceuticals Product Mfr
N.A.I.C.S.: 325412

Abbott Australasia Pty. Ltd.   **(1)**
299 Lane Cove Road, Macquarie Park,
2113, NSW, Australia   **(100%)**
Tel.: (61) 293849700
Web Site: http://www.abbott.com
Sales Range: $125-149.9 Million
Emp.: 200
Pharmaceuticals, Adult & Pediatric Nutri-
tional Products & Hospital Devices Distr

N.A.I.C.S.: 424210

Abbott Automation Solutions
GmbH   **(1)**
Sachsenkamp 5, 20097, Hamburg, Ger-
many
Tel.: (49) 408090510
Medical Device Mfr
N.A.I.C.S.: 339112

Abbott B.V.   **(1)**
Wegalaan 9, 2132 JD, Hoofddorp, Nether-
lands
Tel.: (31) 888222688
Web Site: http://www.nl.abbott
Sales Range: $50-74.9 Million
Nutritionals & Pharmaceuticals Mfr
N.A.I.C.S.: 325412

Subsidiary (Domestic):

Abbott Biologicals BV   **(2)**
Veerweg 12, Olst, 8121 AA, Deventer,
Netherlands
Tel.: (31) 570568211
Pharmaceuticals Product Mfr
N.A.I.C.S.: 325412

Abbott Finance B.V.   **(2)**
Meeuwenlaan 4, 8011 BZ, Zwolle, Nether-
lands
Tel.: (31) 384256500
Web Site: http://www.abbott.com
Sales Range: $25-49.9 Million
Emp.: 50
Financial Management Services
N.A.I.C.S.: 541611

Abbott Healthcare B.V.   **(2)**
C J Van Houtenlaan 36, 1381 CP, Weesp,
Netherlands
Tel.: (31) 29 447 7000
Web Site: https://www.nl.abbott
Pharmaceutical Products Distr
N.A.I.C.S.: 424210

Abbott Logistics B.V.   **(2)**
Meeuwenlaan 4, 8011 BZ, Zwolle, Nether-
lands
Tel.: (31) 384256500
Web Site: http://www.abbottnederland.nl
Sales Range: $75-99.9 Million
Logistics & Distribution Services
N.A.I.C.S.: 541611

Abbott Nederland C.V.   **(2)**
Meeuwenlaan 4, PO Box 365, 8011 BZ,
Zwolle, Netherlands
Tel.: (31) 384256500
Women Healthcare Services
N.A.I.C.S.: 621610

Abbott Capital India Limited   **(1)**
Abbott House Vanwall Business Park Van-
wall Road, Maidenhead, SL6 4XE, United
Kingdom
Tel.: (44) 1628773355
Pharmaceutical Product Mfr & Distr
N.A.I.C.S.: 325412

Abbott Diabetes Care Limited   **(1)**
Abbott House Vanwall Business Park Van-
wall Road, Maidenhead, SL6 4UD, Berk-
shire, United Kingdom
Tel.: (44) 800 170 1177
Web Site: https://www.diabetescare.abbott
Women Healthcare Services
N.A.I.C.S.: 621610

Abbott Diagnosticos Rapidos
S.A.   **(1)**
Rua dos Pinheiros 498 - 7 andar - Pin-
heiros, Sao Paulo, 05422-000, Brazil
Tel.: (55) 1121315100
Medical Device Mfr
N.A.I.C.S.: 339112

Abbott Diagnostics   **(1)**
675 N Field Dr, Lake Forest, IL 60045
Tel.: (224) 667-6100
Web Site: http://www.abbottdiagnostics.com
Sales Range: $25-49.9 Million
Emp.: 150
Medical Diagnostic Product Mfr
N.A.I.C.S.: 339112

Subsidiary (Non-US):

Abbott AG-Diagnostics   **(2)**
Neuhofstrasse 23, 6341, Baar, Switzerland
Tel.: (41) 417684444

Web Site: http://www.abbott.com
Sales Range: $25-49.9 Million
Emp.: 30
Nutritionals & Pharmaceuticals Mfr
N.A.I.C.S.: 325412
Dominik Hochley *(CEO)*

Abbott Cientifica, S.A.   **(2)**
Costa Brava 13, 28034, Madrid, Spain
Tel.: (34) 913373400
Web Site: http://www.abbott.es
Sales Range: $25-49.9 Million
Emp.: 90
Diagnostic Products
N.A.I.C.S.: 339112

Subsidiary (Domestic):

Abbott Diabetes Care, Inc.   **(2)**
1360 S Loop Rd, Alameda, CA 94502-7000
Tel.: (510) 749-5400
Medical Device Mfr
N.A.I.C.S.: 325413

Subsidiary (Non-US):

Abbott Diabetes Care   **(3)**
Range Road, Witney, OX29 0YL, Oxford-
shire, United Kingdom
Tel.: (44) 8001701177
Web Site: http://www.diabetesnow.co.uk
Sales Range: $200-249.9 Million
Emp.: 800
Pharmaceuticals & Medical Equipment Mfr
N.A.I.C.S.: 325412
Namvar Kiaie *(Sr Dir-R&D)*

Abbott Diabetes Care B.V.   **(3)**
Wegalaan 9, 2132 JD, Hoofddorp, Nether-
lands
Tel.: (31) 8000228828
Web Site: http://www.diabetescare.com
Sales Range: $10-24.9 Million
Emp.: 45
Pharmaceuticals & Medical Equipment Mfr
N.A.I.C.S.: 325412

Branch (Domestic):

Abbott Diagnostics   **(2)**
1921 Hurd Dr, Irving, TX 75038
Tel.: (972) 518-6000
Web Site:
http://www.abbottdiagnostics.co.uk
Diagnostic Equipment Medical
N.A.I.C.S.: 423450

Subsidiary (Non-US):

Abbott Diagnostics GmbH   **(2)**
Max-Planck-Ring 2, 65205, Wiesbaden,
Germany
Tel.: (49) 6122580
Web Site: http://www.abbott.de
Diagnostic Medical Equipment Mfr
N.A.I.C.S.: 339112

Division (Domestic):

Abbott Hematology- Diagnostics
Division   **(2)**
5440 Patrick Henry Dr, Santa Clara, CA
95054   **(100%)**
Tel.: (408) 982-4850
Web Site: http://www.abbott.com
Sales Range: $75-99.9 Million
Medical Equipments & Instruments
N.A.I.C.S.: 339112

Subsidiary (Domestic):

Abbott Molecular Inc.   **(2)**
1300 E Touhy Ave, Des Plaines, IL
60018   **(100%)**
Tel.: (224) 361-7800
Web Site: https://www.molecular.abbott
Emp.: 1,000
DNA-Based Clinical Products Developer &
Marketer
N.A.I.C.S.: 325412

Abbott Point of Care, Inc.   **(2)**
400 College Rd E, Princeton, NJ 08540
Tel.: (609) 454-9000
Web Site: http://www.pointofcare.abbott
Emp.: 300
Hand-Held Blood Test Products Mfr
N.A.I.C.S.: 339112

Subsidiary (Non-US):

Abbott Point of Care Canada
Ltd.   **(3)**

185 Corkstown Road, Nepean, K2H 8V4,
ON, Canada
Tel.: (613) 688-5949
Web Site: http://www.abbottpointofcare.ca
Sales Range: $200-249.9 Million
Medical Diagnostic Product Mfr
N.A.I.C.S.: 339112

Abbott Point of Care
International   **(3)**
Concorde House Trinity Pk, Solihull, B37
7UQ, Birmingham, United Kingdom
Tel.: (44) 1216355080
Web Site: http://www.abbottpointofcare.com
Sales Range: $10-24.9 Million
Emp.: 10
Handheld Blood Analyzer Mfr
N.A.I.C.S.: 334510

Subsidiary (Non-US):

Abbott Vascular Devices (2)
Limited   **(2)**
Abbott House Vanwall Business Park Van-
wall Road, Maidenhead, SL6 4XE, United
Kingdom
Tel.: (44) 1628773355
Web Site: http://www.abbottvascular.co.uk
Sales Range: $100-124.9 Million
Medical Equipment
N.A.I.C.S.: 339112

Abbott Vascular Devices Holland
B.V.   **(2)**
Bamfordweg 1, 6235 NS, Ulestraten, Neth-
erlands
Tel.: (31) 433586750
Web Site: http://www.abbottvascular.com
Sales Range: $25-49.9 Million
Emp.: 100
Cardio-Vascular Surgical Supplies & Instru-
ments Mfr & Developer
N.A.I.C.S.: 339112

Abbott Vascular Devices Ireland
Limited   **(2)**
Cashel Rd, Clonmel, Tipperary, Ireland
Tel.: (353) 526173000
Web Site: http://www.abbott.in
Medical Device Mfr
N.A.I.C.S.: 339112

Abbott Vascular Devices Limited   **(2)**
Abbott House Vanwall Business Park, Van-
wall Road, Maidenhead, SL6 4XE, Berks,
United Kingdom
Tel.: (44) 1628773355
Web Site: http://www.abbottvascular.co.uk
Sales Range: $100-124.9 Million
Emp.: 200
Medical Equipment
N.A.I.C.S.: 339112

Abbott Vascular International
BVBA   **(2)**
Park Lane Culliganlaan 2B, 1831, Diegem,
Belgium
Tel.: (32) 27141411
Vascular Devices Mfr
N.A.I.C.S.: 339112

Abbott Diagnostics Korea, Inc.   **(1)**
65 Borahagal-ro, Giheung-gu, Yongin, 446-
930, Gyeonggi-do, Korea (South)
Tel.: (82) 318992800
Web Site: https://globalpointofcare.abbott
Diagnostic Lab Healthcare Services
N.A.I.C.S.: 621511

Abbott Diagnostics Medical Co.,
Ltd.   **(1)**
7F Shinjuku NS Building 2-4-1, Nishi-
Shinjuku Shinjuku-ku, Tokyo, 163-0807,
Japan
Tel.: (81) 353267300
Medical Device Mfr
N.A.I.C.S.: 339112

Abbott Diagnostics Scarborough,
Inc.   **(1)**
10 Southgate Rd, Scarborough, ME 04074
Tel.: (207) 730-5750
Medical Device Mfr
N.A.I.C.S.: 339112

Abbott Diagnostics Technologies
AS   **(1)**
Kjelsasveien 161, PO Box 6863, Rode-
lokka, 0504, Oslo, Norway
Tel.: (47) 24056000

Diagnostic Lab Healthcare Services
N.A.I.C.S.: 621511
Ulf Naess *(Production Mgr)*

Abbott France S.A. **(1)**
40/48 rue d'Arcueil Miami Building, 94593,
Rungis, Cedex, France **(100%)**
Tel.: (33) 145602500
Web Site: https://www.fr.abbott
Sales Range: $150-199.9 Million
Diagnostic Products Mfr
N.A.I.C.S.: 325413

Abbott Gesellschaft m.b.H. **(1)**
Perfektastr 84A, 1230, Vienna,
Austria **(100%)**
Tel.: (43) 1891220
Web Site: https://www.at.abbott
Sales Range: $75-99.9 Million
Pharmaceuticals, Diabetes Care Products &
Diagnostic Equipment
N.A.I.C.S.: 325412

Abbott GmbH & Co. KG **(1)**
Max-Planck-Ring 2, PO Box 1303, 65205,
Wiesbaden, Germany
Tel.: (49) 6122580
Web Site: http://www.de.abbott
Sales Range: $1-4.9 Billion
Emp.: 1,500
Nutritionals, Pharmaceuticals & Hospital
Products Whslr & Distr
N.A.I.C.S.: 325412

Subsidiary (Domestic):

**Abbott Biotechnology Deutschland
GmbH** **(2)**
Max-Planck-Ring 2, Wiesbaden, 65 205,
Germany
Tel.: (49) 6122580000
Web Site: http://www.abbott.de
Women Healthcare Services
N.A.I.C.S.: 621610

Abbott Deutschland GmbH **(2)**
Max-Planck-Ring 2, 65205, Wiesbaden,
Germany
Tel.: (49) 6122580
Web Site: http://www.abbott.com
Women Healthcare Services
N.A.I.C.S.: 621610

Division (Domestic):

**Abbott GmbH & Co. KG - Pharma-
ceutical Division** **(2)**
Max Planck Ring 2, Wiesbaden, 65205,
Germany **(100%)**
Tel.: (49) 6122580
Web Site: http://www.abbott.de
Pharmaceuticals & Pharmaceutical Chemi-
cals Mfr
N.A.I.C.S.: 325412

Subsidiary (Domestic):

Abbott Holding GmbH **(2)**
Max Planck Ring 2, 65205, Wiesbaden,
Germany **(100%)**
Tel.: (49) 6122580
Holding Company
N.A.I.C.S.: 551112
Karen Peterson *(Mng Dir)*

Abbott Management GmbH **(2)**
Max Planck Ring 2, 65205, Wiesbaden,
Germany **(100%)**
Tel.: (49) 6122580
Web Site: http://www.abbott.de
Sales Range: $150-199.9 Million
Emp.: 1,000
Management Services
N.A.I.C.S.: 561110

**Abbott Healthcare Connections
Limited** **(1)**
Unit 8 Prospect Business Park Langston
Road, Loughton, IG10 3TR, Essex, United
Kingdom
Tel.: (44) 8456773002
Medical Device Mfr
N.A.I.C.S.: 339112

**Abbott Healthcare Costa Rica,
S.A.** **(1)**
Edificio Torre La Sabana 3er Piso, San
Jose, Costa Rica
Tel.: (506) 22909200
Medical Device Mfr

N.A.I.C.S.: 339112

**Abbott Healthcare Vietnam Company
Limited** **(1)**
Me Linh Point Tower Tang 9 So 2 Ngo Duc
Ke, Quan 1, Ho Chi Minh City, Vietnam
Tel.: (84) 2838256551
Web Site: https://www.vn.abbott
Emp.: 2,200
Nutritional Product Mfr & Distr
N.A.I.C.S.: 325412

Abbott Holdings B.V. **(1)**
Meeuwenlaan 4, Zwolle, 8011 BZ, Overijs-
sel, Netherlands
Tel.: (31) 384256500
Web Site: http://www.abbott.com
Emp.: 70
Holding Company
N.A.I.C.S.: 551112

Abbott India Limited **(1)**
3 Corporate Park Sion Trombay Road,
Mumbai, 400 071, India **(65.14%)**
Tel.: (91) 22 6797 8888
Web Site: http://www.abbott.co.in
Sales Range: $100-124.9 Million
Emp.: 1,100
Nutritionals, Pharmaceuticals & Medical Di-
agnostic Products Mfr
N.A.I.C.S.: 325412
Munir Shaikh *(Chm)*
Kunal Chowdhury *(Comml Dir-)*
Jejoe Karankumar *(Dir-Medical Affairs)*
Namita Shah *(Assoc Dir-)*
Swati Dalal *(Mng Dir)*

**Abbott Informatics Asia Pacific
Limited** **(1)**
701 7/F Bio-Informatics Center No 2 Sci-
ence Park West Avenue NT, Hong Kong
Science Park, Sha Tin, China (Hong Kong)
Tel.: (852) 27930699
Web Site: http://www.abbottinformatics.com
Laboratory Information Management Ser-
vices
N.A.I.C.S.: 519290

**Abbott Informatics Australia Pty
Limited** **(1)**
Level 11 350 Collins Street, Melbourne,
3000, VIC, Australia
Tel.: (61) 396700678
Laboratory Information Management Ser-
vices
N.A.I.C.S.: 519290
Gary Lazaro *(Project Mgr)*

Abbott Informatics Corporation **(1)**
4000 Hollywood Blvd Ste 333 S, Hollywood,
FL 33021-6755
Tel.: (954) 964-8663
Emp.: 400
Laboratory Information Management Ser-
vices
N.A.I.C.S.: 519290

**Abbott Informatics Europe
Limited** **(1)**
2nd Floor Crossgate House Cross Street,
Sale, M33 7FT, Cheshire, United Kingdom
Tel.: (44) 1617110340
Pharmaceutical Product Mfr & Distr
N.A.I.C.S.: 325412

Abbott Informatics France **(1)**
11 Rue Jacques Cartier ZA De Villaroy,
78280, Guyancourt, France
Tel.: (33) 161370200
Web Site: http://www.starlims.com
Pharmaceutical Preparation Mfr
N.A.I.C.S.: 325412

**Abbott Informatics Germany
GmbH** **(1)**
Alfred-Herrhausen-Str 45, 58455, Witten,
Germany
Tel.: (49) 2302915245
Web Site: http://www.starlims.de
Laboratory Information Management Ser-
vices
N.A.I.C.S.: 519290

**Abbott Informatics Netherlands
B.V.** **(1)**
Rogier van der Weydestraat 8-F, 1817 MJ,
Alkmaar, Netherlands
Tel.: (31) 725118100
Web Site: http://www.abbott.com
Emp.: 15

Laboratory Information Management Services
N.A.I.C.S.: 519290

**Abbott Informatics Singapore Pte.
Limited** **(1)**
DUO Tower 3 Fraser Street 23-28, Singa-
pore, 189352, Singapore
Tel.: (65) 69148000
Laboratory Information Management Ser-
vices
N.A.I.C.S.: 519290
Johanna Dela Cruz *(Sr Engr-Technical Sup-
port)*

Abbott Informatics Spain, S.A. **(1)**
Avd de Burgos 91, 28050, Madrid, Spain
Tel.: (34) 916636764
Pharmaceutical Products Distr
N.A.I.C.S.: 424210

**Abbott Informatics Technologies
LTD** **(1)**
Science Park Bldg 4, PO Box 58099, Tel
Aviv, 61580, Israel
Tel.: (972) 37691413
Laboratory Information Management Ser-
vices
N.A.I.C.S.: 519290
Gonen Globerman *(Controller-Intl)*

Abbott International LLC **(1)**
100 Abbott Park Rd, Abbott Park, IL 60064-
6057
Tel.: (224) 667-6100
Sales Range: $1-4.9 Billion
Emp.: 13,000
Pharmaceutical, Hospital, Consumer & Nu-
tritional Products
N.A.I.C.S.: 325412

Abbott Ireland **(1)**
Block G Cherrywood Business Park, Lough-
linstown, Dublin, D18 T3Y1, Ireland
Tel.: (353) 17781000
Web Site: http://www.ie.abbott
Emp.: 5,000
Pharmaceutical Preparation Mfr
N.A.I.C.S.: 325412

Abbott Ireland Limited **(1)**
Block B Liffey Valley Office Campus, Quar-
ryvale, Dublin, D22 X0Y3, Ireland
Tel.: (353) 14691500
Web Site: http://www.ie.abbott
Sales Range: $75-99.9 Million
Nutritionals, Pharmaceuticals & Hospital
Products Distr
N.A.I.C.S.: 424210

Abbott Japan Co., Ltd. **(1)**
3-5-27 Mita, Minato-ku, Tokyo, 108-6305,
Japan
Tel.: (81) 34 555 1000
Web Site: https://www.abbott.co.jp
Emp.: 2,300
Pharmaceuticals Mfr
N.A.I.C.S.: 325412

Abbott Korea Limited **(1)**
421 Yeongdong-daero 3rd 5th 7th floor
Samtan Building, Gangnam-gu, Seoul,
06182, Korea (South)
Tel.: (82) 23 429 3500
Web Site: https://www.kr.abbott
Sales Range: $100-124.9 Million
Nutritionals & Pharmaceuticals Mfr
N.A.I.C.S.: 325412

Abbott Laboratories (Hellas) S.A. **(1)**
Agiou Dimitriou 63, Alimos, 174 56, Athens,
Greece
Tel.: (30) 2109985222
Web Site: http://www.abbott.gr
Sales Range: $150-199.9 Million
Nutritionals, Pharmaceuticals, Diagnostics &
Diabetes Care Products Mfr
N.A.I.C.S.: 325412

**Abbott Laboratories (Malaysia) Sdn.
Bhd.** **(1)**
27-02 Level 27 Imazium No 8 Jalan SS
21/37, Damansara Uptown, 47400, Petaling
Jaya, Selangor, Malaysia
Tel.: (60) 37 988 7000
Web Site: https://www.my.abbott
Emp.: 250
Pediatric/Medical Nutrition & Pharmaceuti-
cal Products
N.A.I.C.S.: 325412

Abbott Laboratories (N.Z.) Ltd. **(1)**
Ground Floor Bldg D 4 Pacific Rise, Mount
Wellington, Auckland, 1060, New
Zealand **(100%)**
Tel.: (64) 800106100
Diagnostics, Molecular, Diabetes Care,
Pharmaceuticals & Nutritional Products Mfr
N.A.I.C.S.: 325412

**Abbott Laboratories (Pakistan)
Limited** **(1)**
Opposite Radio Pakistan Transmission
Hyderabad Road, PO Box 7229, Landhi,
Karachi, 75120, Pakistan **(83.42%)**
Tel.: (92) 21111222688
Web Site: https://www.pk.abbott
Sales Range: $150-199.9 Million
Nutritionals & Pharmaceuticals Mfr
N.A.I.C.S.: 325412

Abbott Laboratories (Philippines) **(1)**
8th Floor Venice Corporate Center No 8
Turin Street, Mckinley Town Center Fort
Bonifacio, Taguig, 1634, Metro Manila, Phil-
ippines
Tel.: (63) 287028622
Web Site: https://www.ph.abbott
Nutritionals, Pharmaceuticals & Medical Di-
agnostic Products Mfr
N.A.I.C.S.: 325412

**Abbott Laboratories (Puerto Rico)
Incorporated** **(1)**
9615 Los Romero Ave Ste 700, San Juan,
PR 00926-7038
Tel.: (787) 750-5454
Pharmaceutical Preparation Mfr
N.A.I.C.S.: 325412

**Abbott Laboratories (Singapore) Pri-
vate Limited** **(1)**
3 Fraser Street 23-28 DUO Tower, Singa-
pore, 189352, Singapore
Tel.: (65) 6 914 8000
Web Site: https://www.abbott.com.sg
Emp.: 900
Nutritionals & Pharmaceuticals Product Mfr
N.A.I.C.S.: 325412

Abbott Laboratories A/S **(1)**
Emdrupvej 28 C, 2100, Copenhagen, Den-
mark
Tel.: (45) 3 977 0000
Web Site: http://www.abbott.com
Sales Range: $25-49.9 Million
Nutritionals, Pharmaceuticals & Medical
Equipment Mfr
N.A.I.C.S.: 325412

**Abbott Laboratories Argentina,
S.A.** **(1)**
Cazadores De Coquimbo 2860, Correo
Central, B1605AZE, Munro, Argentina
Tel.: (54) 1160903100
Web Site: https://www.medicine.abbott
Sales Range: $200-249.9 Million
Emp.: 600
Mfr of Pharmaceuticals & Medical Prepara-
tions
N.A.I.C.S.: 325412

Abbott Laboratories B.V. **(1)**
Rieteweg 21, 8041 AJ, Zwolle, Netherlands
Tel.: (31) 384279500
Pharmaceuticals Product Mfr
N.A.I.C.S.: 325412

Abbott Laboratories Baltics **(1)**
Mukusalas 11, Riga, LV-1004, Latvia
Tel.: (371) 67605580
Web Site: http://www.abbott.com
Emp.: 5
Pharmaceutical Services
N.A.I.C.S.: 325412

Abbott Laboratories Finance B.V. **(1)**
Meeuwenlaan 4, 8011 BZ, Zwolle, Nether-
lands
Tel.: (31) 384256500
Pharmaceutical Products Distr
N.A.I.C.S.: 424210

Abbott Laboratories GmbH **(1)**
Freundallee 9A, 30173, Hannover, Ger-
many
Tel.: (49) 51167500
Pharmaceuticals Product Mfr
N.A.I.C.S.: 325412

**Abbott Laboratories International
Co.** **(1)**

Abbott Laboratories—(Continued)

1015 Distributors Row, New Orleans, LA
70123
Tel.: (504) 731-2613
Web Site: http://www.abbott.com
Sales Range: $10-24.9 Million
Emp.: 40
Nutrients Distr
N.A.I.C.S.: 621610

Abbott Laboratories Limited (1)
Abbott House Vanwall Business Park Van-
wall Road, Maidenhead, SL6 4XE, Berk-
shire, United Kingdom
Tel.: (44) 1628773355
Web Site: http://www.abbott.co.uk
Sales Range: $200-249.9 Million
Nutritionals, Pharmaceuticals & Medical
Equipment Mfr
N.A.I.C.S.: 325412

Subsidiary (Domestic):

Abbott (UK) Finance Limited (2)
Abbott Laboratories Vanwall Business Park
Vanwall Rd, Maidenhead, SL6 4XE, Berks,
United Kingdom
Tel.: (44) 1628773355
Sales Range: $650-699.9 Million
Financial Services
N.A.I.C.S.: 523940

Abbott (UK) Holdings Limited (2)
Abbott House Vanwall Business Park
wall Road, Maidenhead, SL6 4XE, Berks,
United Kingdom
Tel.: (44) 1628773355
Sales Range: $250-299.9 Million
Holding Company
N.A.I.C.S.: 551112

Abbott Equity Holdings Ltd. (2)
Vanwall Business Park Vanwall Road, Maid-
enhead, SL6 4XE, Berkshire, United King-
dom
Tel.: (44) 1628773355
Web Site: http://www.abbott.co.uk
Sales Range: $150-199.9 Million
Emp.: 350
Holding Company
N.A.I.C.S.: 551112

Abbott Healthcare Products Ltd. (2)
Habbot House Dunwall Business Park,
Maidenhead, S06 4XE, Hampshire, United
Kingdom
Tel.: (44) 2380467000
Women Healthcare Services
N.A.I.C.S.: 621610

Abbott Investments Limited (2)
Abbott House Vanwall Business Park Van-
wall Road, Maidenhead, SL6 4XE, Berk-
shire, United Kingdom
Tel.: (44) 1628561090
Sales Range: $650-699.9 Million
Investment Services
N.A.I.C.S.: 523940

Division (Domestic):

**Abbott Laboratories Limited - Diag-
nostic Division** (2)
Abbott House Vanwall Business Park, Van-
wall Road, Maidenhead, SL6 4XE, United
Kingdom (100%)
Tel.: (44) 1628773355
Web Site: http://www.abbott.co.uk
Sales Range: $50-74.9 Million
Emp.: 350
Medical Diagnostic Equipment Mfr
N.A.I.C.S.: 339112

Subsidiary (Domestic):

**Abbott Laboratories Trustee Com-
pany Limited** (2)
Abbott House Vanwall Business Park Van-
wall Road, Maidenhead, SL6 4XE, Berks,
United Kingdom
Tel.: (44) 1628773355
Sales Range: $250-299.9 Million
Holding Company
N.A.I.C.S.: 551112

Abbott Laboratories Limited (1)
20/F AIA Tower 183 Electric Road, North
Point, China (Hong Kong)
Tel.: (852) 25668711
Web Site: http://www.hk.abbott

Sales Range: $50-74.9 Million
Molecular & Medical Diagnostic Products
Mfr
N.A.I.C.S.: 621511

Abbott Laboratories Limited (1)
No 1 Q House Lumpini 33rd Floor South
Sathorn Road, Thungmahamek Sathorn,
Bangkok, 10120, Thailand
Tel.: (66) 26575555
Medical Device Mfr
N.A.I.C.S.: 339112

Abbott Laboratories Pacific Ltd. (1)
100 Abbott Pk Rd, Abbott Park, IL 60064-
3502
Tel.: (847) 937-6100
Pharmaceutical Preparations
N.A.I.C.S.: 325412

**Abbott Laboratories Poland Sp
z.o.o.** (1)
Ul Postepu 21B, 02-676, Warsaw, Poland
Tel.: (48) 22 319 1200
Web Site: https://www.pl.abbott
Emp.: 170
Pharmaceuticals Product Mfr
N.A.I.C.S.: 325412

**Abbott Laboratories Slovakia
s.r.o.** (1)
Karadzicova 8, mestská cast Ruzinov, 821
08, Bratislava, Slovakia
Tel.: (421) 244454188
Web Site: https://www.sk.abbott
Sales Range: $150-199.9 Million
Emp.: 130
Nutritionals & Pharmaceuticals Mfr
N.A.I.C.S.: 325412
Patrecea Trencanova (Office Mgr-Abbie)

**Abbott Laboratories South Africa
(Proprietary) Limited** (1)
Abbott Place 219 Golf Club Terrace, Con-
stantia Kloof, Johannesburg, 1709, South
Africa (100%)
Tel.: (27) 118582000
Web Site: https://www.za.abbott
Nutritionals, Pharmaceuticals & Diagnostic
Products Mfr
N.A.I.C.S.: 325412

Abbott Laboratories Taiwan (1)
6th Floor No 51 & No 49 Min Sheng East
Road Section 3, Taipei, 104,
Taiwan (100%)
Tel.: (886) 225050828
Web Site: http://www.abbott.com.tw
Sales Range: $100-124.9 Million
Emp.: 300
Nutritionals & Pharmaceuticals Mfr
N.A.I.C.S.: 325412

**Abbott Laboratories Trading (Shang-
hai) Co., Ltd.** (1)
23 26 27 28 31 32 33 36 37 39 Floor of
Xianles Plaza, 388 Nanjing West Road,
Shanghai, 200003, China
Tel.: (86) 212 320 4388
Web Site: https://www.abbott.com.cn
Women Healthcare Services
N.A.I.C.S.: 621610

**Abbott Laboratories Uruguay
S.A.** (1)
Av Gral Rivera 6329/201, 11500, Montevi-
deo, Uruguay
Tel.: (598) 2600 9966
Web Site: http://latam.abbott
Diabetes Care Product Mfr
N.A.I.C.S.: 325412

Abbott Laboratories d.o.o. (1)
Koranska 2, Zagreb, 10000, Croatia
Tel.: (385) 12350560
Pharmaceuticals Product Mfr
N.A.I.C.S.: 325412

Abbott Laboratories d.o.o. HRK (1)
Koranska 2, 10000, Zagreb, Croatia
Tel.: (385) 800333344
Diabetes Care Services
N.A.I.C.S.: 624190

**Abbott Laboratories de Chile
Limitada** (1)
Avenida El Salto 5380 Huechuraba Casilla,
169-D, Santiago, Chile
Tel.: (56) 27506000

Sales Range: $25-49.9 Million
Emp.: 106
Nutritionals, Diabetes Care, Diagnostics &
Pharmaceuticals Mfr
N.A.I.C.S.: 325412

**Abbott Laboratories de Colombia,
S.A.** (1)
Calle 100 9A-45 Piso 14, Bogota, DC, Co-
lombia
Tel.: (57) 16285600
Web Site: http://www.abbott.com
Sales Range: $200-249.9 Million
Nutritionals, Pharmaceuticals & Diagnostics
Mfr
N.A.I.C.S.: 325412

**Abbott Laboratories de Mexico S.A.
de C.V.** (1)
Calzada De Tlalpan 3092 Colonia Ex Haci-
enda Coapa, Mexico, 04980, Distrito Fed-
eral, Mexico (100%)
Tel.: (52) 5558097500
Sales Range: $800-899.9 Million
Emp.: 1,000
Nutritionals, Pharmaceuticals & Medical
Product Distr
N.A.I.C.S.: 424210
Julio Hernandez (Dir-Ops)
Martin Ocana (Mgr-Sls)

**Abbott Laboratories druzba za far-
macijo in diagnostiko d.o.o.** (1)
Dolenjska Cesta 242C, 1000, Ljubljana,
Slovenia
Tel.: (386) 1 236 3160
Web Site: http://www.abbott-laboratories.si
Emp.: 10
Pharmaceuticals Product Mfr
N.A.I.C.S.: 325412

Abbott Laboratories s.r.o. (1)
Evropska 2591/33d, 160 00, Prague, Czech
Republic (100%)
Tel.: (420) 267292111
Web Site: https://www.cz.abbott
Sales Range: $25-49.9 Million
Nutritionals, Pharmaceuticals & Diagnostic
Equipment Mfr
N.A.I.C.S.: 325412

Abbott Laboratories, C.A. (1)
Calle Los Laboratorios Centro Gerencial
Los Cortijos, Urb Los Cortijos de Lourdes,
Caracas, 1071, Venezuela (100%)
Tel.: (58) 2127007000
Web Site: http://www.corelaboratory.abbott
Nutritionals & Pharmaceuticals Distr
N.A.I.C.S.: 325412

Abbott Laboratories, Limitada (1)
Estrada De Alfragide 67 Alfrapark, Edificio
D, 2610-008, Amadora, Portugal
Tel.: (351) 214727200
Web Site: http://www.abbott.com
Sales Range: $50-74.9 Million
Emp.: 200
Diagnostic Products Mfr
N.A.I.C.S.: 325413

Abbott Laboratories, Limited (1)
8625 Trans-Canada Highway, Saint Lau-
rent, H4S 1Z6, QC, Canada (100%)
Tel.: (514) 832-7000
Web Site: http://www.ca.abbott
Sales Range: $100-124.9 Million
Emp.: 1,500
Nutritionals & Pharmaceuticals Mfr
N.A.I.C.S.: 325412

Abbott Laboratories,S.A. (1)
Apartado de Correos 967 Avenida de Bur-
gos n 91, 28050, Madrid, Spain (100%)
Tel.: (34) 901200102
Web Site: https://www.es.abbott
Sales Range: $200-249.9 Million
Nutritionals & Pharmaceuticals Mfr
N.A.I.C.S.: 325412

Abbott Laboratorios S.A. (1)
Av Republica de Panama 3591 Floor 7,
01014, Lima, Peru
Tel.: (51) 12193300
Web Site: http://www.abbott.com
Sales Range: $25-49.9 Million
Diagnostics Equipment Mfr
N.A.I.C.S.: 325412

**Abbott Laboratorios del Ecuador Cia.
Ltda.** (1)

Av Republica de El Salvador N34-493 y Av,
Edif Torre Gibraltar Piso 10, Quito, Ecuador
Tel.: (593) 23992500
Web Site: http://www.abbott.com
Sales Range: $25-49.9 Million
Nutritionals & Pharmaceuticals Product Mfr
N.A.I.C.S.: 325412

**Abbott Laboratorios do Brasil
Ltda** (1)
Rua Michigan 735, PO Box 21 111, Sao
Paulo, 04566-905, SP, Brazil (100%)
Tel.: (55) 8007031050
Web Site: https://www.abbottbrasil.com.br
Emp.: 2,600
Nutritionals & Pharmaceuticals Mfr
N.A.I.C.S.: 325412

Abbott Laboratorios, Limitada (1)
Estrada de Alfragide 67 Alfrapark - Edificio
D, 2610-008, Amadora, Portugal
Tel.: (351) 214727200
Web Site: https://www.pt.abbott
Sales Range: $100-124.9 Million
Nutritionals, Pharmaceuticals & Medical
Equipment Mfr
N.A.I.C.S.: 325412

Abbott Laboratorios, S.A. (1)
5 Ave 5-55 Zona 14 Edif Europlaza Torre I
Nivel 10, 01014, Guatemala, Guatemala
Tel.: (502) 24209797
Diagnostic Lab Healthcare Services
N.A.I.C.S.: 621511

**Abbott Laboratuarlari Ithalat Ihracat
Ve Tecaret Limited Sirketi** (1)
Saray Mah Dr Adnan Buyukdeniz Cad No 2
Akkom Office Park Kelif Plaza 3, Block
Floor 12-20 Umraniye, 34768, Istanbul,
Turkiye (100%)
Tel.: (90) 2166360600
Web Site: http://www.tr.abbott
Sales Range: $200-249.9 Million
Pharmaceuticals, Nutritional & Diagnostics
Product Mfr
N.A.I.C.S.: 325412

**Abbott Laboratuarlari Ithalat Ihracat
Ve Ticaret Limited Sirketi** (1)
Saray Mah Dr Adnan Buyukdeniz Cad No2
Akkom Ofis Park Kelif Plaza 3, Blok Kat
12-20 Umraniye, Istanbul, 34768, Turkiye
Tel.: (90) 2166360600
Web Site: https://www.tr.abbott
Pharmaceuticals Product Mfr
N.A.I.C.S.: 325412

**Abbott Manufacturing Singapore Pri-
vate Limited** (1)
26 Tuas South Ave 10, Singapore, 637437,
Singapore
Tel.: (65) 65008500
Nutritional Powder Mfr
N.A.I.C.S.: 311999

**Abbott Medical (Malaysia) Sdn.
Bhd.** (1)
27-02 Level 27 Imazium No 8 Jalan SS
21/37, Damansara Uptown, 47400, Petaling
Jaya, Selangor Darul Ehsan, Malaysia
Tel.: (60) 379887000
Medical Device Mfr
N.A.I.C.S.: 339112

**Abbott Medical (Portugal) Distribuicao
de Produtos Medicos Lda** (1)
Rua Carlos Alberto Da Mota Pinto 17 7 B,
Edificio Amoreiras Square, 1070-313, Lis-
bon, Portugal
Tel.: (351) 213815510
Pharmaceutical Products Distr
N.A.I.C.S.: 424210

Abbott Medical (Schweiz) AG (1)
Neuhofstrasse 23, 6341, Baar, Switzerland
Tel.: (41) 7684949
Web Site: http://www.ch.abbott
Pharmaceutical Products Distr
N.A.I.C.S.: 424210

Abbott Medical Australia Pty. Ltd. (1)
299 Lane Cove Road, Macquarie Park,
2113, NSW, Australia
Tel.: (61) 298571111
Web Site: http://www.aus.abbott
Pharmaceuticals Product Mfr
N.A.I.C.S.: 325412

**Abbott Medical Austria
Ges.m.b.H.** (1)

Perfektastrasse 84A, 1230, Vienna, Austria
Tel.: (43) 1891220
Medical Device Mfr
N.A.I.C.S.: 339112

Abbott Medical Canada Co.   **(1)**
6975 Creditview Road - Unit 1, Mississauga, L5N 8E9, ON, Canada
Tel.: (905) 286-4098
Diabetes Care Services
N.A.I.C.S.: 624190

Abbott Medical Danmark AS   **(1)**
Produktionsvej 14, 2600, Glostrup, Denmark
Tel.: (45) 44947541
Pharmaceutical Products Distr
N.A.I.C.S.: 424210

Abbott Medical Devices Trading (Shanghai) Co., Ltd.   **(1)**
12th Floor Guojin Phase II No 8 Century Avenue, Pudong New District, Shanghai, 200120, China
Tel.: (86) 2120335000
Medical Equipment Mfr
N.A.I.C.S.: 334510

Abbott Medical Espana, S.A.   **(1)**
Avenida de Burgos n 91, 28050, Madrid, Spain
Tel.: (34) 917278910
Medical Device Mfr
N.A.I.C.S.: 339112

Abbott Medical Estonia OU   **(1)**
Liivalaia 13/15, Tallinn, 10118, Estonia
Tel.: (372) 6363052
Pharmaceutical Products Distr
N.A.I.C.S.: 424210

Abbott Medical France SAS   **(1)**
40/48 rue d'Arcueil Immeuble Miami, 94593, Rungis, Cedex, France
Tel.: (33) 145602500
Medical Device Mfr
N.A.I.C.S.: 339112

Abbott Medical GmbH   **(1)**
Helfmann Park 7, 65760, Eschborn, Germany
Tel.: (49) 619677110
Pharmaceutical Products Distr
N.A.I.C.S.: 424210

Abbott Medical Italia S.p.A.   **(1)**
Edison Center - Edificio C Viale Thomas A Edison 110, 20099, Sesto San Giovanni, MI, Italy
Tel.: (39) 02359611
Medical Device Mfr
N.A.I.C.S.: 339112

Abbott Medical Laboratories LTD   **(1)**
Atidim Science Park Building 4, PO Box 58099, Tel Aviv, 6158002, Israel
Tel.: (972) 3 769 1000
Web Site: https://www.il.abbott
Pharmaceuticals Product Mfr
N.A.I.C.S.: 325412

Abbott Medical Nederland B.V.   **(1)**
Standaardruiter 13, 3905 PT, Veenendaal, Netherlands
Tel.: (31) 318583250
Nutritional Product Mfr & Distr
N.A.I.C.S.: 325412

Abbott Medical Sweden AB   **(1)**
Isafjordsgatan 15, 164 40, Kista, Sweden
Tel.: (46) 84744000
Pharmaceutical Products Distr
N.A.I.C.S.: 424210

Abbott Medical spolka z ograniczona odpowiedzialnoscia   **(1)**
Ul Postepu 21B, 02-676, Warsaw, Poland
Tel.: (48) 223191200
Medical Device Mfr
N.A.I.C.S.: 339112

Abbott Norge AS   **(1)**
PO Box 1, 1330, Fornebu, Norway
Tel.: (47) 8 155 9920
Web Site: http://www.abbott.no
Sales Range: $25-49.9 Million
Nutritionals, Pharmaceuticals & Medical Equipment Mfr
N.A.I.C.S.: 325412

Abbott Nutrition   **(1)**

208 SO Lasalle St Ste 814, Chicago, IL 60045   **(100%)**
Tel.: (614) 624-7677
Web Site: http://www.abbottnutrition.com
Develops & Markets Infant Formulas, Medical Nutritionals, Nutrition & Energy Bars & Related Products
N.A.I.C.S.: 311999
Roger M. Bird (Sr VP-US Nutrition)

Subsidiary (Non-US):

Abbott AG-Nutritionals   **(2)**
Neuhofstrasse 23, 6341, Baar, Switzerland
Tel.: (41) 417684333
Web Site: http://www.abbott.ch
Sales Range: $25-49.9 Million
Emp.: 250
Pharmaceuticals & Medical Equipment Mfr
N.A.I.C.S.: 325412

Subsidiary (Domestic):

Abbott Nutrition   **(2)**
1250 W Maricopa Hwy, Casa Grande, AZ 85193-5504
Tel.: (520) 421-6600
Web Site: http://www.abbottnutrition.com
Sales Range: $150-199.9 Million
Emp.: 325
Pharmaceuticals
N.A.I.C.S.: 325412

Abbott Nutrition   **(2)**
1518 Main St, Altavista, VA 24517   **(100%)**
Tel.: (434) 369-3100
Web Site: http://www.abbottnutrition.com
Sales Range: $400-449.9 Million
Emp.: 800
Baby Formulas
N.A.I.C.S.: 311514

Abbott Nutrition Limited   **(1)**
Fort Gary Finisklin Business Park, Sligo, Ireland
Tel.: (353) 719195900
Medical Device Mfr
N.A.I.C.S.: 339112

Abbott Oy   **(1)**
Linnoitustie 4, 02600, Espoo, Finland
Tel.: (358) 409022425
Web Site: http://www.abbott.fi
Nutritionals, Pharmaceuticals & Medical Equipment Mfr
N.A.I.C.S.: 325412

Abbott Pharmaceutical Corporation   **(1)**
100 Abbott Park Rd, Abbott Park, IL 60064-3500
Tel.: (224) 667-6100
Web Site: http://www.rxabbott.com
Adult & Pediatric Pharmaceuticals, Vitamins & Hematinics Mfr
N.A.I.C.S.: 325412

Subsidiary (Non-US):

Abbott Arzneimittel GmbH   **(2)**
Freundallee 9A, 30173, Hannover, Germany   **(100%)**
Tel.: (49) 51167500
Web Site: http://www.abbott.com
Sales Range: $300-349.9 Million
Emp.: 700
Mfr of Chemicals, Plastics, Pharmaceuticals & Biochemicals
N.A.I.C.S.: 325412

Abbott Healthcare Private Limited   **(2)**
1 Nirlon Complex Off Western Express Highway, Goregaon East, Mumbai, 400 063, India
Tel.: (91) 2267367000
Web Site: http://www.abbottep.in
Women Healthcare Services
N.A.I.C.S.: 621610

Abbott Healthcare Products B.V.   **(2)**
C J Van Houtenlaan 36, 1381 CP, Weesp, Netherlands
Tel.: (31) 294477000
Web Site: http://www.abbottgrowth.nl
Sales Range: $300-349.9 Million
Pharmaceutical Sales
N.A.I.C.S.: 325412

Subsidiary (Domestic):

Abbott Laboratories Pharmaceuticals (PR) Ltd.   **(2)**

Rd 2 Cruce Davila km 58 0, Barceloneta, PR 00617
Tel.: (787) 846-3500
Web Site: http://www.abbott.com
Sales Range: $1-4.9 Billion
Emp.: 2,300
Pharmaceutical Preparations
N.A.I.C.S.: 325412

Subsidiary (Non-US):

Abbott Products AG   **(2)**
Untermattweg 8, 3027, Bern, Switzerland
Tel.: (41) 319969600
Web Site: http://www.abbottgrowth.ch
Sales Range: $25-49.9 Million
Emp.: 35
Pharmaceuticals Mfr
N.A.I.C.S.: 325412

Abbott-Established Products Division   **(2)**
60 Columbia Way Ste 207, Markham, L3R 0C9, ON, Canada
Tel.: (905) 944-2480
Web Site: http://www.abbott.ca
Sales Range: $25-49.9 Million
Emp.: 40
Pharmaceuticals Mfr
N.A.I.C.S.: 325412

Shanghai Abbott Pharmaceutical Co., Ltd.   **(2)**
16F/17F Chonghing Finance Centre, No 288 West Nanjing Road, Shanghai, 200003, China
Tel.: (86) 2123204388
Web Site: http://www.abbott.com.cn
Pharmaceuticals Mfr
N.A.I.C.S.: 325412

Abbott Products Operations AG   **(1)**
Hegenheimermattweg 127, 4123, Allschwil, Switzerland
Tel.: (41) 614870200
Pharmaceuticals Product Mfr
N.A.I.C.S.: 325412

Abbott Products Romania S.R.L.   **(1)**
Floreasca Business Park Calea Floreasca 169A Corp B Parter Sect 1, Bucharest, 014459, Romania
Tel.: (40) 215293000
Pharmaceuticals Product Mfr
N.A.I.C.S.: 325412

Abbott Produtos Oticos Ltda.   **(1)**
Avenida General Charles Gaulle 100 Prq Sao Domingos, Parque Sao Domingos, Sao Paulo, 51240-000, Brazil
Tel.: (55) 30935020
Pharmaceutical Products Distr
N.A.I.C.S.: 424210

Abbott Rapid DX International Limited   **(1)**
Parkmore East Business Park, Ballybrit, Galway, H91 VK7E, Ireland
Tel.: (353) 91429900
Diagnostic Lab Healthcare Services
N.A.I.C.S.: 621511
Lisa Fahy (Mgr-Contract-EMEA)

Abbott Rapid Diagnostics   **(1)**
Da Vincilaan 11, Box F1, 1935, Zaventem, Belgium
Tel.: (32) 393333000
Diagnostic Lab Healthcare Services
N.A.I.C.S.: 621511

Abbott Rapid Diagnostics (Pty) Ltd.   **(1)**
20 Woodlands Drive, Woodlands Office Park Building 28, Woodmead, 2191, South Africa
Tel.: (27) 113921412
Medical Device Mfr
N.A.I.C.S.: 339112

Abbott Rapid Diagnostics AB   **(1)**
Tryffelslingan 12, Box 1215, 181 24, Lidingo, Sweden
Tel.: (46) 854481200
Diagnostic Lab Healthcare Services
N.A.I.C.S.: 621511

Abbott Rapid Diagnostics AS   **(1)**
Kjelsasveien 161, 0884, Oslo, Norway
Tel.: (47) 24056600
Diagnostic Lab Healthcare Services

N.A.I.C.S.: 621511
Anette Kilander (Program Mgr)

Abbott Rapid Diagnostics Argentina S.A.   **(1)**
14 de Julio 618, C1427CJN, Buenos Aires, Argentina
Tel.: (54) 1145544007
Medical Device Mfr
N.A.I.C.S.: 339112

Abbott Rapid Diagnostics Austria GmbH   **(1)**
Johann-Konrad-Vogel-Strasse 7-9, 4020, Linz, Austria
Tel.: (43) 800298042
Diagnostic Lab Healthcare Services
N.A.I.C.S.: 621511

Abbott Rapid Diagnostics Germany GmbH   **(1)**
On Aquarius 28, 50829, Cologne, Germany
Tel.: (49) 221271430
Blood Analysis Services
N.A.I.C.S.: 621511

Abbott Rapid Diagnostics Health Corp.   **(1)**
Rm B 11F No 16 Sec 4 Nanjing E Rd, Songshan Dist, Taipei, 10553, Taiwan
Tel.: (886) 225706669
Medical Device Mfr
N.A.I.C.S.: 339112

Abbott Rapid Diagnostics Healthcare, S.L.   **(1)**
Plaza Europa 9-11 6 Planta, Hospitalet de Llobregat, 08908, Barcelona, Spain
Tel.: (34) 936008000
Medical Device Mfr
N.A.I.C.S.: 339112

Abbott Rapid Diagnostics Jena GmbH   **(1)**
Orlaweg 1, 7743, Jena, Germany
Tel.: (49) 364131110
Novel Diagnostic Product Mfr
N.A.I.C.S.: 325413

Abbott Rapid Diagnostics LDA   **(1)**
Praceta da Rasa 43 Mafamude, 4400-348, Vila Nova de Gaia, Portugal
Tel.: (351) 227127418
Diagnostic Lab Healthcare Services
N.A.I.C.S.: 621511

Abbott Rapid Diagnostics Medical   **(1)**
Da Vincilaan 11, Box F1, 1935, Zaventem, Belgium
Tel.: (32) 93333000
Medical Device Mfr
N.A.I.C.S.: 339112

Abbott Rapid Diagnostics Oy Ab   **(1)**
Rajatorpantie 41 C, 01640, Vantaa, Finland
Tel.: (358) 985202400
Diagnostic Lab Healthcare Services
N.A.I.C.S.: 621511

Abbott Rapid Diagnostics Pty. Ltd.   **(1)**
12 Mowbray Tce, ANZPI Regional Head Office, Brisbane, 4169, QLD, Australia
Tel.: (61) 733637100
Health Care Srvices
N.A.I.C.S.: 621999

Abbott Rapid Diagnostics S.A.S   **(1)**
Parc Burospace Batiment 6 Route de Gisy, 91570, Bievres, France
Tel.: (33) 139468318
Diagnostic Lab Healthcare Services
N.A.I.C.S.: 621511

Abbott Rapid Diagnostics S.r.l.   **(1)**
Via Drizzagno 11, 30037, Scorze, VE, Italy
Tel.: (39) 0415841546
Web Site:
  https://www.globalpointofcare.abbott
Diagnostic Lab Healthcare Services
N.A.I.C.S.: 621511
Francesca Navoni (Sls Mgr)

Abbott Rapid Diagnostics Schweiz GmbH   **(1)**
Neuhofstrasse 23, 6341, Baar, Switzerland
Tel.: (41) 7684777
Web Site: https://www.ch.abbott
Pharmaceuticals Product Mfr

Abbott Laboratories—(Continued)
N.A.I.C.S.: 325412

Abbott Rapid Diagnostics ULC (1)
1-57 Iber Road, Ottawa, K2S 1E7, ON,
Canada
Tel.: (613) 271-1144
Diagnostic Lab Healthcare Services
N.A.I.C.S.: 621511

Abbott S.A. (1)
Avenue Einstein 14, 1300, Wavre, Belgium
Tel.: (32) 10475311
Pharmaceuticals Product Mfr
N.A.I.C.S.: 325412

Abbott S.r.l. (1)
Viale Giorgio Ribotta 9, 00141, Rome, Italy
Tel.: (39) 0652 9911
Web Site: https://www.it.abbott
Sales Range: $1-4.9 Billion
Nutritionals & Pharmaceuticals
N.A.I.C.S.: 325412

Abbott SA/NV (1)
Avenue Einstein 14, 1300, Wavre, Belgium
Tel.: (32) 10475311
Web Site: http://www.abbott.be
Emp.: 8
Pharmaceutical, Diagnostic & Specialty
Medical Products Mfr
N.A.I.C.S.: 339112

Division (Domestic):

**Abbott SA/NV - Diagnostics
Division** (2)
Avenue Einstein 14, 1300, Wavre, Belgium
Tel.: (32) 10475342
Web Site: http://www.abbott.com
Sales Range: $75-99.9 Million
Emp.: 200
Nutritionals, Pharmaceuticals & Medical
Equipment Mfr
N.A.I.C.S.: 325412

**Abbott Saudi Arabia Trading
Company** (1)
PO Box 16082, Riyadh, 11464, Saudi Ara-
bia
Tel.: (966) 112848100
Web Site: https://www.arabia.abbott
Emp.: 1,000
Medical Device Mfr
N.A.I.C.S.: 339112

Abbott Saudi Arabia for Trading (1)
PO Box 16082, Riyadh, 11464, Saudi Ara-
bia
Tel.: (966) 112848100
Web Site: https://www.arabia.abbott
Health Care Srvices
N.A.I.C.S.: 621999

Abbott Scandinavia A.B. (1)
Hemvarnsgatan 9, Box 1498, 171 29,
Solna, Sweden (100%)
Tel.: (46) 201901111
Web Site: https://www.freestyle.abbott
Sales Range: $100-124.9 Million
Nutritionals, Pharmaceuticals & Diagnostic
Equipment Mfr
N.A.I.C.S.: 325412

Abbott Toxicology Limited (1)
21 Blacklands Way, Abingdon Business
Park, Abingdon, OX14 1DY, Oxfordshire,
United Kingdom
Tel.: (44) 1235861483
Medical Device Mfr
N.A.I.C.S.: 339112

**Abbott Truecare Pharma Private
Limited** (1)
D Mart Bldg Goregaon Mulund Link Road,
Mulund W, Mumbai, 400 080, India
Tel.: (91) 2230781000
Web Site: http://www.truecare.in
Pharmaceuticals Product Mfr
N.A.I.C.S.: 325412

**Abbott Vascular Deutschland
GmbH** (1)
Schanzenfeldstrasse 2, 35578, Wetzlar,
Germany
Tel.: (49) 6441870750
Medical Device Mfr
N.A.I.C.S.: 339112

**Abbott Vascular Deutschland
GmbH** (1)

Schanzenfeldstrasse 2, 35578, Wetzlar,
Germany
Tel.: (49) 6441870750
Pharmaceuticals Product Mfr
N.A.I.C.S.: 325412

Abbott Vascular Inc. (1)
3200 Lakeside Dr, Santa Clara, CA 95054-
2807
Tel.: (408) 845-3000
Web Site: http://www.cardiovascular.abbott
Medical Device Mfr
N.A.I.C.S.: 334510
Charles Brynelsen (CEO)

**Abbott Vascular Instruments
Deutschland GmbH** (1)
Rudolf-Diesel-Strasse 29, Zollernalbkreis,
Rangendingen, 72414, Germany
Tel.: (49) 747199730
Medical Device Mfr
N.A.I.C.S.: 334510

Abbott Vascular Japan Co., Ltd (1)
Sumitomo Fudosan Mita Twin Bldg 4F
3-5-27 Mita, Minato-ku, Tokyo, 108-6304,
Japan
Tel.: (81) 345600700
Medical Device Mfr
N.A.I.C.S.: 339112

Abbott Vascular Japan Co., Ltd. (1)
Sumitomo Fudosan Mita Twin Bldg 4F 3-5-
27, Mita Minato-ku, Tokyo, 108-6304, Japan
Tel.: (81) 345600700
Web Site: https://www.abbottvascular.jp
Medical Device Mfr
N.A.I.C.S.: 334510

Abbott Vascular Netherlands B.V. (1)
Argonstraat 1, 6422 PH, Heerlen, Nether-
lands
Tel.: (31) 455435700
Medical Device Mfr
N.A.I.C.S.: 339112

Alere Colombia S.A. (1)
Calle 110 9-25 of 501, Bogota, Colombia
Tel.: (57) 14824033
Medical Device Mfr
N.A.I.C.S.: 339112

**Alere Healthcare Connections
Limited** (1)
Unit 8 Prospect Business Park Langston
Road, Loughton, IG10 3TR, Essex, United
Kingdom
Tel.: (44) 8456773002
Web Site: http://www.alerehealthcareconnec
tions.com
Drug Screening Services
N.A.I.C.S.: 621999

Alere Inc. (1)
51 Sawyer Rd Ste 200, Waltham, MA
02453
Tel.: (781) 647-3900
Web Site: http://www.alere.com
Rev.: $2,376,335,000
Assets: $5,648,279,000
Liabilities: $3,816,672,000
Net Worth: $1,831,607,000
Earnings: ($137,619,000)
Emp.: 9,700
Fiscal Year-end: 12/31/2016
Consumer & Professional Medical Diagnos-
tic Products, Vitamins & Nutritional Supple-
ments Developer & Mfr
N.A.I.C.S.: 325413

Subsidiary (Non-US):

**ABON Biopharm (Hangzhou) Co.,
Ltd.** (2)
198 12th Street No 12 East Hangzhou Eco-
nomic & Technological Development Area,
Hangzhou, 310018, Zhejiang,
China (100%)
Tel.: (86) 57181638000
Web Site:
https://www.globalpointofcare.abbott
Pharmaceuticals Product Mfr
N.A.I.C.S.: 325412

Subsidiary (Domestic):

ATS Laboratories Inc. (2)
28301 Industrial Blvd, Hayward, CA 94545
Tel.: (760) 344-2532
Pharmaceuticals Product Mfr
N.A.I.C.S.: 325412

Subsidiary (Non-US):

**Abbott Healthcare Connections
Limited** (2)
Unit 8 Prospect Business Park Langston
Road, Loughton, IG10 3TR, Essex, United
Kingdom
Tel.: (44) 8456773002
Web Site: https://www.toxicology.abbott
Health Care Consulting Services
N.A.I.C.S.: 621498

Abbott Rapid Diagnostics BV (2)
Dr Hub van Doorneweg 175, 5026 RD, Til-
burg, Netherlands (51%)
Tel.: (31) 134672700
Web Site:
https://www.globalpointofcare.abbott
Health Care Srvices
N.A.I.C.S.: 621498

Subsidiary (Domestic):

**Abbott Rapid Diagnostics Informatics,
Inc.** (2)
2000 Holiday Dr Ste 500, Charlottesville,
VA 22901 (100%)
Tel.: (434) 971-7953
Web Site: http://www.rals.com
Data Management System
N.A.I.C.S.: 518210

Subsidiary (Non-US):

Abbott Rapid Diagnostics Limited (2)
Bio-Stat House Pepper Grove, Hazel
Grove, Stockport, SK7 5BW, United King-
dom
Tel.: (44) 1614835884
Web Site:
https://www.globalpointofcare.abbott
Diagnostic Testing Product Mfr & Sales
N.A.I.C.S.: 339112

Subsidiary (Domestic):

**Abbott Rapid Dx North America,
LLC** (2)
30 S Keller Rd Ste 100, Orlando, FL 32810
Tel.: (321) 441-7200
Web Site:
https://www.globalpointofcare.abbott
Pharmaceuticals Product Mfr
N.A.I.C.S.: 325412

Subsidiary (Non-US):

Abbott Toxicology Limited (2)
21 Blacklands Way, Abingdon Business
Park, Abingdon, OX14 1DY, Oxon, United
Kingdom (100%)
Tel.: (44) 1235861483
Web Site: https://www.toxicology.abbott
Drug & Alcohol Testing Laboratories Opera-
tor & Testing Equipment Mfr
N.A.I.C.S.: 541380

Branch (Domestic):

Abbott Toxicology Limited (3)
Unit 8 Prospect Business Park Langston
Road, Loughton, IG10 3TR, Essex, United
Kingdom
Tel.: (44) 2077128000
Web Site: https://www.toxicology.abbott
Drug & Alcohol Testing Laboratory
N.A.I.C.S.: 541380

Subsidiary (Non-US):

Quantum Diagnosticos Ltda (3)
Al Lucas N Garcez 859 Vila Thais, Atibaia,
Sao Paulo, Brazil
Tel.: (55) 1144148888
Web Site:
https://www.quantumdiagnostico.com.br
Medical Device Mfr
N.A.I.C.S.: 339112

Subsidiary (Non-US):

Alere AB (2)
Knarrarnasgatan 7, PO Box 1147, 164 22,
Kista, Sweden
Tel.: (46) 812099320
Emp.: 20
Medical Device Distr
N.A.I.C.S.: 339112
Andreas Juhlin (Mng Dir)

Alere GmbH (2)

Am Wassermann 28, 50829, Cologne,
Germany (100%)
Tel.: (49) 221271430
Web Site:
https://www.globalpointofcare.abbott
Women's-Health Diagnostic Tests Distr
N.A.I.C.S.: 541380

Alere GmbH (2)
Johann-Konrad-Vogel-Strasse 7-9, 4020,
Linz, Austria
Tel.: (43) 800298042
Web Site: http://www.alere.at
Emp.: 1
Pharmaceuticals Product Mfr
N.A.I.C.S.: 325412

Alere Health B.V. (2)
Dr Hub van Doorneweg 175, 5026 RD, Til-
burg, Netherlands (100%)
Tel.: (31) 134672700
Diagnostic Products Mfr
N.A.I.C.S.: 325412

Alere Health BVBA (2)
Da Vincilaan 11, box F1, Sint-Denijs-
Westrem, 1935, Zaventem,
Belgium (100%)
Tel.: (32) 93333000
Pharmaceuticals Product Mfr
N.A.I.C.S.: 325412

Alere Healthcare (Pty) Limited (2)
20 Woodlands Drive Building 28, Wood-
lands Office Park, Woodmead, 2191, South
Africa
Tel.: (27) 114504411
Web Site: http://www.alerehealthcare.co.za
Sales Range: $25-49.9 Million
Emp.: 15
Diagnostics Products Distr
N.A.I.C.S.: 325412

Alere Healthcare Inc. (2)
166 Jeongjail-ro, Bundang-gu, Seongnam,
463-867, Gyeonggi-do, Korea (South)
Tel.: (82) 3180146700
Pharmaceuticals Product Mfr
N.A.I.C.S.: 325412

Subsidiary (Domestic):

Alere Home Monitoring Inc (2)
6465 National Dr, Livermore, CA 94550
Tel.: (925) 606-6964
Web Site:
http://www.globalpointofcare.abbott
Pharmaceuticals Product Mfr
N.A.I.C.S.: 325412

Subsidiary (Non-US):

Alere Medical Co., Ltd. (2)
7F Shinjuku Ns Building 2-4-1 Nishi-
Shinjuku, Shinjuku-ku, Tokyo, 163-0807,
Japan
Tel.: (81) 353267300
Pharmaceuticals Product Mfr
N.A.I.C.S.: 325412

Alere Medical Private Limited (2)
No 404 4th Floor BPTP Park Centra NH-8
Opposite 32nd Milestone, Gurgaon,
122001, Haryana, India
Tel.: (91) 1244569000
Pharmaceuticals Product Mfr
N.A.I.C.S.: 325412

Alere Philippines, Inc. (2)
Bonifacio One Technology Tower 21st Floor
Corner 31st Street Rizal Dr, Bonifacio
Global City, Taguig, 1634, Philippines
Tel.: (63) 26214000
Web Site:
https://www.globalpointofcare.abbott
Health Care Srvices
N.A.I.C.S.: 621498

Alere S.A. (2)
Rua dos Pinheiros 498-7 andar, Pinheiros,
05422-000, Sao Paulo, Brazil
Tel.: (55) 1121315100
Pharmaceuticals Product Mfr
N.A.I.C.S.: 325412

Alere S.r.l. (2)
Via B Eustachi 36, 20129, Milan, Italy
Tel.: (39) 022774131
Pharmaceuticals Product Mfr
N.A.I.C.S.: 325412

Alere SAS (2)
21 Rue Albert Calmette Batiment B4,
78350, Jouy-en-Josas, France
Tel.: (33) 139468318
Web Site: http://www.alere.fr
Sales Range: $25-49.9 Million
Emp.: 45
Pharmaceuticals Product Mfr
N.A.I.C.S.: 325412

Subsidiary (Domestic):

Alere San Diego, Inc. (2)
9975 Summers Ridge Rd, San Diego, CA
92121-2997
Tel.: (858) 805-2000
Web Site:
    http://www.globalpointofcare.abbott
Blood Coagulation Monitoring Device Devel-
oper & Mfr
N.A.I.C.S.: 339112

Subsidiary (Non-US):

Alere Spain, S.L. (2)
Plaza Europa 9-11 6 Planta, Hospitalet de
Llobregat, 08908, Barcelona, Spain
Tel.: (34) 936008000
Pharmaceuticals Product Mfr
N.A.I.C.S.: 325412
Arturo Auaps (Mgr)

Alere Technologies GmbH (2)
Lobstedter Str 103-105, 7749, Jena, Ger-
many
Tel.: (49) 364131110
Web Site: http://www.alere-
technologies.com
Medical Diagnostic Product Mfr
N.A.I.C.S.: 325412

Subsidiary (Domestic):

Alere Toxicology Services, Inc. (2)
1121 Newton St, Gretna, LA 70053
Tel.: (504) 361-8989
Web Site: https://www.toxicology.abbott
Drug & Alcohol Testing Laboratory
N.A.I.C.S.: 541380

Alere Toxicology, Inc. (2)
100 Abbott Park Rd, Abbott Park, IL 60064
Tel.: (224) 667-6100
Pharmaceuticals Product Mfr
N.A.I.C.S.: 325412

Subsidiary (Non-US):

Arriva Medical Philippines, Inc. (2)
21-23/F Bonifacio One Technology Tower,
Rizal Drive corner 31st Street, Taguig,
1634, Philippines   (100%)
Tel.: (63) 26214000
Health Care Srvices
N.A.I.C.S.: 621498

Axis-Shield Limited (2)
Luna Place The Technology Park, Dundee,
DD2 1XA, United Kingdom
Tel.: (44) 1382422000
Web Site: http://www.axis-shield.com
Sales Range: $150-199.9 Million
Emp.: 120
Holding Company; In Vitro Diagnostic Test-
ing Services
N.A.I.C.S.: 551112

Subsidiary (Non-US):

Alere Technologies AS (3)
Kjelsasveien 161, 0884, Oslo, Norway
Tel.: (47) 24056000
Medical Device Mfr
N.A.I.C.S.: 339112

Axis-Shield AS (3)
Kjelsasveien 161, 0884, Oslo,
Norway   (100%)
Tel.: (47) 24056000
Diagnostic Testing Product Mfr
N.A.I.C.S.: 339112

Subsidiary (Domestic):

Axis-Shield Diagnostics Limited (3)
Luna Place the Technology Park, Dundee,
DD2 1XA, United Kingdom   (100%)
Tel.: (44) 1382422000
Web Site: http://www.axis-shield.com
Surgical & Medical Instrument Mfr
N.A.I.C.S.: 339112

Subsidiary (Non-US):

Biolinker S.A. (2)
14 de Julio 618, Buenos Aires, C1427CJN,
Argentina
Tel.: (54) 1145544007
Web Site: http://www.biolinker.com.ar
Medical Laboratory Instruments Distr
N.A.I.C.S.: 334516

Bionote, Inc. (2)
22 Samsung 1-ro 4-gil, Gyeonggi-do,
Hwaseong, 445-170, Korea (South)
Tel.: (82) 312110516
Web Site: https://www.bionote.co.kr
Pharmaceuticals Product Mfr
N.A.I.C.S.: 325412

Biozyme Holdings Limited (2)
Gilchrist Thomas Industrial Estate, Ponty-
pool, NP4 9RL, United Kingdom
Tel.: (44) 1495790678
Pharmaceuticals Product Mfr
N.A.I.C.S.: 325412

Subsidiary (Domestic):

First Check Diagnostics, LLC (2)
100 Abbott Park Rd, Abbott Park, IL 60064
Tel.: (224) 667-6100
Diagnostic Device Mfr & Distr
N.A.I.C.S.: 334510

**Global Analytical Development
LLC** (2)
5990 142nd Ave N, Clearwater, FL 33760
Tel.: (727) 530-9996
Web Site: http://www.gadevelop.com
Pharmaceuticals Product Mfr
N.A.I.C.S.: 325412
Mary Hubbard (Dir-Ops)

Subsidiary (Non-US):

IG Innovations Limited (2)
Gernos Maesllyn, Llandysul, SA44 5LP,
United Kingdom
Tel.: (44) 1239858972
Medical Diagnostic Product Mfr
N.A.I.C.S.: 325412

Mologic Limited (2)
Bedford Technology Park Thurleigh, Sharn-
brook, Bedford, MK44 2YA, United Kingdom
Tel.: (44) 1234780020
Web Site: https://www.globalaccessdx.com
Sales Range: $25-49.9 Million
Emp.: 35
Medical Research & Development Services
N.A.I.C.S.: 325412

Orgenics Ltd. (2)
North Industrial Zone, Yavne, 70650, Israel
Tel.: (972) 89429201
Pharmaceuticals Product Mfr
N.A.I.C.S.: 325412

PT Alere Health (2)
K-Link Tower 18th Floor Zone DEF Jl Gatot
Subroto Kav 59A, Jakarta Selatan, 12950,
Jakarta, Indonesia
Tel.: (62) 2129026929
Medical Device Mfr
N.A.I.C.S.: 339112

Subsidiary (Domestic):

**Pembrooke Occupational Health,
Inc.** (2)
9201 Arboretum Pkwy Ste 200, Richmond,
VA 23236
Tel.: (804) 346-1010
Health Care Consulting Services
N.A.I.C.S.: 621498

**Redwood Toxicology Laboratory,
Inc.** (2)
3650 Westwind Blvd, Santa Rosa, CA
95403
Tel.: (707) 577-7959
Web Site:
    https://www.redwoodtoxicology.com
Pharmaceuticals Product Mfr
N.A.I.C.S.: 325412

Standing Stone LLC (2)
30 S Keller Rd Ste 100B, Orlando, FL
32810
Pharmaceuticals Product Mfr
N.A.I.C.S.: 325412

Subsidiary (Non-US):

TwistDX Limited (2)
Abbott House Vanwall Business Park Van-
wall Road, Maidenhead, SL6 4XE, United
Kingdom
Tel.: (44) 8774506901
Web Site: https://www.twistdx.co.uk
Pharmaceuticals Product Mfr
N.A.I.C.S.: 325412

Subsidiary (Domestic):

US Diagnostics, Inc. (2)
2 Parade St, Huntsville, AL 35806
Tel.: (256) 534-4881
Web Site: http://www.usdiagnostics.com
Sales Range: $1-9.9 Million
Emp.: 23
Drug Screening Test Equipment Distr
N.A.I.C.S.: 423450

Subsidiary (Non-US):

eScreen Canada ULC (2)
4760 72 Ave SE, Calgary, T2C 3Z2, AB,
Canada
Tel.: (800) 818-8335
Web Site: http://www.escreen.com
Health Care Srvices
N.A.I.C.S.: 621498

Subsidiary (Domestic):

eScreen, Inc. (2)
8140 Ward Pkwy Ste 300, Kansas City, MO
64114
Web Site: http://www.escreen.com
Medical Laboratories
N.A.I.C.S.: 621511

Andland Overseas S.A. (1)
Calle 50 Edificio Torre Global Bank,
Panama, Panama
Tel.: (507) 8306453
Pharmaceutical Products Distr
N.A.I.C.S.: 424210

Aquagestion Capacitacion S.A. (1)
Av Pacheco Altamirano 2779, Puerto Montt,
Chile
Tel.: (56) 652367337
Pharmaceuticals Product Mfr
N.A.I.C.S.: 325412

Aquagestion S.A. (1)
Panamericana Sur 581, Puerto Montt, Chile
Tel.: (56) 652206300
Web Site: http://www.aquagestion.cl
Pharmaceuticals Product Mfr
N.A.I.C.S.: 325412

Atlas Farmaceutica S.A. (1)
Cazadores de Coquimbo 2860 Piso 3ro,
Munro, B1605EAB, Buenos Aires, Argentina
Tel.: (54) 116 090 3100
Web Site:
    https://www.atlasfarmaceutica.com.ar
Pharmaceuticals Product Mfr
N.A.I.C.S.: 325412

Banco de Vida S.A. (1)
Av Pedro de Valdivia 295, Providencia,
Chile
Tel.: (56) 223505200
Web Site: http://www.bancodevida.cl
Pharmaceuticals Product Mfr
N.A.I.C.S.: 325412

Bigfoot Biomedical, Inc. (1)
1820 McCarthy Blvd, Milpitas, CA 95035
Tel.: (408) 716-5600
Web Site:
    https://www.bigfootbiomedical.com
Medical Device Mfr & Distr
N.A.I.C.S.: 339112

Bioalgae S.A. (1)
Serrano 551 of 11 Viii, Concepcion, Chile
Tel.: (56) 412207119
Pharmaceutical Products Distr
N.A.I.C.S.: 424210

Brandex Europe C.V. (1)
Ditlaar 7, 1066EE, Amsterdam, Noord-
Holland, Netherlands
Tel.: (31) 207025005
Financial Trust Management Services
N.A.I.C.S.: 541611

**California Property Holdings III
LLC** (1)

4885 Calle Alto, Camarillo, CA 93012
Tel.: (805) 437-8610
Emp.: 3
Building Construction Services
N.A.I.C.S.: 531312

Cardiovascular Systems, Inc. (1)
1225 Old Hwy 8 NW, Saint Paul, MN
55112-6416
Tel.: (651) 259-1600
Web Site: http://www.csi360.com
Rev.: $236,222,000
Assets: $322,677,000
Liabilities: $73,197,000
Net Worth: $249,480,000
Earnings: ($36,933,000)
Emp.: 725
Fiscal Year-end: 06/30/2022
Biopharmaceutical Developer
N.A.I.C.S.: 325412
Rhonda J. Robb (COO)
Jeffrey S. Points (CFO)
Alexander Rosenstein (Gen Counsel & Sec)
Sandra M. Sedo (Chief Compliance Officer)
David S. Whitescarver (VP-Corp Dev & In-
tellectual Property)
John E. Nielsen (VP-IR & Corp Comm)
Stephen J. Rempe (Chief HR Officer)
Robert T. Beverly (VP & Gen Mgr-Coronary
Sls)

Continuum Services LLC (1)
6020 NW 4th Pl Ste A, Gainesville, FL
32607
Web Site: https://continuuminc.com
Medical Equipment Mfr
N.A.I.C.S.: 334510

Distribuciones Uquifa S.A.S. (1)
Carrera 1 46 84, Cali, Valle, Colombia
Tel.: (57) 26877700
Pharmaceutical Products Distr
N.A.I.C.S.: 424210

Evalve, Inc. (1)
4045 Campbell Ave, Menlo Park, CA 94025
Tel.: (650) 833-1600
Medical Device Mfr
N.A.I.C.S.: 334510

Fadapharma del Ecuador S.A. (1)
Av Diego De Almagro N30-134 Y Av Repu-
blica, La Carolina, Quito, Pichincha, Ecua-
dor
Tel.: (593) 22220550
Pharmaceutical Products Distr
N.A.I.C.S.: 424210

Farmaceutica Mont Blanc, S.L. (1)
C/ Hermosilla 6 - 50 Izquierda, Madrid,
Spain
Tel.: (34) 915781384
Pharmaceutical Products Distr
N.A.I.C.S.: 424210

**Farmacologia Em Aquicultura Veteri-
naria Ltda.** (1)
Rua Bruno Veloso 603 - Sala 803 - Boa
Viagem, 51021-280, Recife, Brazil
Tel.: (55) 8130943038
Pharmaceutical Products Distr
N.A.I.C.S.: 424210

**Farmacologia en Aquacultura Veteri-
naria FAV Ecuador S.A.** (1)
Av De Los Shyris 2680 Y Av Gaspar De
Villarroel, La Concepcion, Quito, Pichincha,
Ecuador
Tel.: (593) 22250223
Pharmaceutical Product & Medical Device
Mfr
N.A.I.C.S.: 325412

**Farmacologia en Aquacultura Veteri-
naria FAV S.A.** (1)
Pedro de Valdivia 295, Providencia, San-
tiago, Chile
Tel.: (56) 2 879 5176
Web Site: https://www.fav.cl
Pharmaceutical Product Mfr & Distr
N.A.I.C.S.: 325412

Farmindustria S.A. (1)
Avda Cesar Vallejo 565 Lince, Lima, 14,
Peru
Tel.: (51) 12212100
Web Site: http://www.farmindustria.com.pe
Pharmaceutical Products Distr
N.A.I.C.S.: 424210

Fournier Pharma GmbH (1)

Abbott Laboratories—(Continued)

Justus-Von-Liebig-Str 16, Sulzbach, 66280, Saarland, Germany
Tel.: (49) 68975790
Pharmaceuticals Product Mfr
N.A.I.C.S.: 325412

Gene-Trak, Inc. **(1)**
121 W Swannanoa Ave, Liberty, NC 27298
Tel.: (336) 622-5266
Women Healthcare Services
N.A.I.C.S.: 621610

Glomed Pharmaceutical Company Limited **(1)**
No 35 Tu Do Boulevard Vietnam Singapore Industrial Park Vsip, An Phu Ward, Thuan An, Binh Duong, Vietnam
Tel.: (84) 2743768824
Pharmaceutical Products Distr
N.A.I.C.S.: 424210

Gynopharm S.A. **(1)**
Carrera 49 C 80 125 of 512, Barranquilla, Colombia
Tel.: (57) 53738280
Pharmaceutical Products Distr
N.A.I.C.S.: 424210

Gynopharm de Venezuela, C.A. **(1)**
Final Cl Vargas Edif Centro Berimer Torre Este Piso 2, Boleita, Caracas, Venezuela
Tel.: (58) 2122036711
Pharmaceutical Products Distr
N.A.I.C.S.: 424210

IDEV Technologies B.V. **(1)**
Kapershof 46, Gelderland, 6641 JS, Beuningen, Netherlands
Tel.: (31) 653152702
Pharmaceutical Products Distr
N.A.I.C.S.: 424210

Ibis Biosciences LLC **(1)**
7330 Smoke Ranch Rd, Las Vegas, NV 89128
Tel.: (702) 901-5407
Web Site: https://www.ibisscientific.com
Laboratory Product Distr
N.A.I.C.S.: 423490

Idev Technologies, Inc. **(1)**
253 Medical Center Blvd, Webster, TX 77598
Tel.: (281) 525-2000
Web Site: http://www.idevtechnologies.com
Sales Range: $25-49.9 Million
Emp.: 25
Medical Equipment & Supplies Mfr
N.A.I.C.S.: 423450

Kalila Medical, Inc. **(1)**
745 Camden Ave Ste A, Campbell, CA 95008
Tel.: (408) 903-4094
Web Site: http://www.kalilamedical.com
Pharmaceutical Preparation Mfr
N.A.I.C.S.: 325412

LaFrancol Internacional S.A.S. **(1)**
Zona Franca Del Pacifico Supermanz Airport, Palmira, Valle, Colombia
Tel.: (57) 22801010
Pharmaceuticals Product Mfr
N.A.I.C.S.: 325412

Laboratorio Franco Colombiano Lafrancol S.A.S. **(1)**
Street 108 No 51 - 45, Bogota, Colombia
Tel.: (57) 17422525
Web Site: http://www.lafrancol.com
Pharmaceuticals Product Mfr
N.A.I.C.S.: 325412

Laboratorio Synthesis S.A.S. **(1)**
Carrera 44 20 C 73, Bogota, Colombia
Tel.: (57) 13692222
Web Site: http://www.synthesis.com.co
Medical Laboratory Services
N.A.I.C.S.: 621511

Laboratorios Recalcine S.A. **(1)**
Av Carrascal 5650, Santiago, Chile
Tel.: (56) 223505200
Web Site: http://www.recalcine.cl
Pharmaceuticals Product Mfr
N.A.I.C.S.: 325412

Limited Liability Company "Abbott Ukraine" **(1)**

Moskovska St 32/2 7th floor, 01010, Kiev, Ukraine
Tel.: (380) 444986080
Medical Device Mfr
N.A.I.C.S.: 339112

Midwest Properties LLC **(1)**
7202 N 40th St, Omaha, NE 68112
Tel.: (402) 660-2693
Real Estate Management Services
N.A.I.C.S.: 531390

Murex Biotech South Africa **(1)**
186 Kyalami Blvd Kyalami Business Pk, Midrand, 1684, Gauteng, South Africa
Tel.: (27) 117993200
Medical Instrument Mfr & Distr
N.A.I.C.S.: 339112

Murex Diagnosticos S.A. **(1)**
C/ Costa Brava 13, 28034, Madrid, Spain
Tel.: (34) 913373400
Health Care Products Mfr
N.A.I.C.S.: 325412

Novamedi S.A. **(1)**
Avenida 12 De Octubre 4444/60, Quilmes Oeste, 1879, Buenos Aires, Argentina
Tel.: (54) 1142501013
Financial Security Brokerage Services
N.A.I.C.S.: 523150

Novasalud S.A. **(1)**
Malaga 89 oficina 22, 7550144, Las Condes, Metropolitana, Chile
Tel.: (56) 976520613
Web Site: https://www.novasaludsa.cl
Medical Device Mfr
N.A.I.C.S.: 339112

Omnilab S.r.l **(1)**
Piazza della Trivulziana 4/A, 20126, Milan, Italy
Tel.: (39) 022688901
Web Site: http://www.omnilab.it
Pharmaceutical Preparation Mfr
N.A.I.C.S.: 325412

P.T. Solvay Pharma Indonesia **(1)**
Wisma Pondok Indah 2 Ste 1000 r Sultan Iskandar, Muda Kav.V - T, Jakarta, 12310, Pondok Indah, Indonesia **(100%)**
Tel.: (62) 2127587888
Web Site: http://www.abbott.com
Sales Range: $200-249.9 Million
Emp.: 300
Nutritionals, Pharmaceuticals & Diagnostic Medical Products Mfr
N.A.I.C.S.: 325412

PSC "VEROPHARM" **(1)**
2nd Yuzhnoportovy proezd house 18 building 9 floor 2, 115088, Moscow, Russia
Tel.: (7) 4957925330
Web Site: http://www.veropharm.ru
Emp.: 250
Pharmaceutical Product Mfr & Distr
N.A.I.C.S.: 325412

PT. Abbott Indonesia **(1)**
Jalan Raya Jakarta Bogor KM 37, Cimanggis, Depok, 16415, Indonesia
Tel.: (62) 218751735
Web Site: https://www.id.abbott
Medical Device Mfr
N.A.I.C.S.: 339112

PT. Abbott Indonesia **(1)**
Wisma Pondok Indah 2 Suite 1000 Jalan Sultan Iskandar Muda Kav V - TA, Pondok Indah, Jakarta, 12310, Indonesia
Tel.: (62) 2127587888
Web Site: http://www.id.abbott
Pharmaceuticals Product Mfr
N.A.I.C.S.: 325412

PT. Abbott Products Indonesia **(1)**
Wisma Pondok Indah 2 Suite 1000 Jalan Sultan Iskandar Muda Kav V - TA, Pondok Indah, Jakarta, 12310, Indonesia
Tel.: (62) 2127587888
Medical Device Mfr
N.A.I.C.S.: 339112

Patients Pending Ltd. **(1)**
20-22 Wenlock Road, London, N1 7GU, United Kingdom
Tel.: (44) 2071932757
Web Site: https://timesulin.com
Insulin Pen Mfr & Distr
N.A.I.C.S.: 339112

Pharma International S.A. **(1)**
Lopez Moreira Casi Aviadores Del Chaco Edificio Royal Tower 3er Piso, Asuncion, Paraguay
Tel.: (595) 21622740
Web Site: http://www.pharma.com.py
Pharmaceutical Products Distr
N.A.I.C.S.: 424210

STARLIMS France S.A.S. **(1)**
11 Rue Jacques Cartier ZA de Villaroy, 78280, Guyancourt, France
Tel.: (33) 161370200
Web Site: http://www.starlims.com
Emp.: 20
Software Development Services
N.A.I.C.S.: 541511

STARLIMS Iberica, S.A. **(1)**
Avd de la Industria 37 Despacho B6, 28760, Tres Cantos, Madrid, Spain
Tel.: (34) 916636764
Software Development Services
N.A.I.C.S.: 541511

STARLIMS Netherlands B.V. **(1)**
Rogier van der Weydestraat 8F, 1817 MJ, Alkmaar, Netherlands
Tel.: (31) 725118100
Web Site: http://www.abbottinformatics.com
Software Development Services
N.A.I.C.S.: 541511

STARLIMS Technologies Ltd. **(1)**
32b Habarzel Street, 69710, Tel Aviv, Israel
Tel.: (972) 37694000
Web Site: http://www.starlims.com
Sales Range: $50-74.9 Million
Emp.: 162
Laboratory Information Management Systems Development Services
N.A.I.C.S.: 541512

Subsidiary (Non-US):

Abbott Informatics Europe Limited **(2)**
2nd Floor Crossgate House Cross Street, Sale, M33 7FT, Cheshire, United Kingdom
Tel.: (44) 1617110340
Women Healthcare Services
N.A.I.C.S.: 621610

Axel Semrau GmbH & Co. KG **(2)**
Stefansbecke 42, 45549, Sprockhovel, Germany
Tel.: (49) 233912090
Web Site: https://www.axelsemrau.de
Laboratory Information Management Systems Development Services
N.A.I.C.S.: 541512
Andreas Bruchmann (Head-Bus Unit Chromatography)
Frank Gasse (Head-Bus Unit Natural Gas Analysis & Odorization Control)
Govert Schroder (Mgr-Bus Dev)
Marco Nestola (Head-R&D)
Tobias Uber (Head-Application Team)
Patrick Kursawe (Head-Software Dev)

Beijing SunwayWorld Science and Technology Co., Ltd. **(2)**
Bldg 12 Yard 6 Haiying Road, Fengtai District, Beijing, 100070, China
Tel.: (86) 1052250988
Web Site: http://www.sunwayworld.com
Professional Software & Application Services; Testing Management Platform, Master Data Management Platform & E-Commerce Platform
N.A.I.C.S.: 541512

OTC Laboratory Systems Corporation **(2)**
16-7 Komazawa 1 chome, Setagaya-ku, Tokyo, 154-0012, Japan
Tel.: (81) 3 3419 9403
Web Site: http://www.starlims.com
Laboratory Information Management Systems Development Services
N.A.I.C.S.: 334516

Corporacion Tecnologa Global 21, C.A. **(2)**
Av Romulo Gallegos Torre Poliprima Piso 1 Ofic 1-A Urb Santa Eduvigis, Piso 1 Urb Santa Eduvigis, Caracas, 1071, Venezuela
Tel.: (58) 2122850320
Web Site: http://www.ctg21.com
Emp.: 30

Laboratory Information Management Systems Development Services
N.A.I.C.S.: 541512

INNOVATEK Innovation Technolgies LTDA **(2)**
Carrera 21 No 41-26, 111311, Bogota, Colombia
Tel.: (57) 13380711
Web Site: http://www.innovatek.com.co
Laboratory Information Management Systems Development Services
N.A.I.C.S.: 541512

STARLIMS Asia Pacific Limited **(2)**
Units 807-808 8/F Building 12W Phase 3 No12 Science Park West Avenue, Hong Kong Science Park Pak Shek Kok, Hong Kong, China (Hong Kong)
Tel.: (852) 27930699
Web Site: http://www.starlims.com
Sales Range: $25-49.9 Million
Emp.: 35
Laboratory Information Management Systems Development Services
N.A.I.C.S.: 541512

Subsidiary (US):

STARLIMS Corporation **(2)**
4000 Hollywood Blvd Ste 333 S, Hollywood, FL 33021-6755
Tel.: (954) 964-8663
Web Site: https://www.starlims.com
Sales Range: $25-49.9 Million
Emp.: 60
Laboratory Information Management Systems Development Services
N.A.I.C.S.: 541512

Subsidiary (Non-US):

STARLIMS Germany GmbH **(2)**
Alfred-Herrhausen-Str 45, 58455, Witten, Germany
Tel.: (49) 2302915244
Web Site: http://www.starlims.com
Laboratory Information Management Systems Development Services
N.A.I.C.S.: 541512

Subsidiary (Domestic):

STARLIMS Israel Ltd. **(2)**
Regus Ramat Hahayal Hanehoshet 3 CU Complex Building B Floor 7, Tel Aviv, 6971068, Israel
Tel.: (972) 33751195
Sales Range: $25-49.9 Million
Emp.: 5
Laboratory Information Management Systems Development Services
N.A.I.C.S.: 541512

Subsidiary (Non-US):

STARLIMS Thailand Co., LTD. **(2)**
634/4 Soi Ramkhamhaeng 39, Pracha-Utit Rd, Bangkok, 10310, Wangthonglang, Thailand
Tel.: (66) 2 725 0888
Laboratory Information Management Systems Development Services
N.A.I.C.S.: 541512

Subsidiary (US):

TTC Analytical Service Corp. **(2)**
N-19 Ave Jose Villares Urb Jose Delgado, Caguas, PR 00725
Tel.: (787) 286-1090
Web Site: https://www.ttcanalytical.com
Emp.: 8
Maintenance, Repairs & Calibration Services
N.A.I.C.S.: 541512

Subsidiary (Non-US):

Tecno Diagnostica **(2)**
50 metros sur cruce Colima intersection, Carretera a Tibaa, San Jose, Costa Rica
Tel.: (506) 22408595
Web Site: http://www.tecnodiagnostica.com
Emp.: 40
Laboratory Information Management Systems Development Services
N.A.I.C.S.: 541512

St. Jude Medical, LLC **(1)**
5050 Nathan Ln N, Plymouth, MN 55442

Tel.: (651) 756-5400
Web Site: http://www.cardiovascular.abbott
Cardiovascular Medical Devices Mfr, Distr &
Marketer
N.A.I.C.S.: 339112
Randel Woodgrift (Sr VP-Cardiac Rhythm
Mgmt)

Subsidiary (Non-US):

St. Jude Medical Brasil, Ltda. (2)
Rua Itapeva 538 5 ao 8 andares, Sao
Paulo, 01332-000, Brazil
Tel.: (55) 1150805400
Medical Device Mfr
N.A.I.C.S.: 339112

Starlims (SEA) PTE. LTD. (1)
1 Maritime Square 11-10, Harbourfront Cen-
tre, Singapore, 099253, Singapore
Tel.: (65) 62773209
Software Development Services
N.A.I.C.S.: 541511

Tendyne Holdings, Inc. (1)
2825 Fairview Ave N, Roseville, MN 55113
Tel.: (651) 289-5500
Web Site: http://www.tendyne.com
Holding Company
N.A.I.C.S.: 551112

Tendyne Medical, Inc. (1)
300 E Lombard St Ste 840, Baltimore, MD
21202-3231
Tel.: (443) 552-3308
Pharmaceutical Preparation Mfr
N.A.I.C.S.: 325412

Topera, Inc. (1)
1530 O'Brien Dr Ste A, Menlo Park, CA
94025
Tel.: (650) 681-1740
Web Site: http://www.toperamedical.com
Electrophysiological Mapping Systems Mfr
N.A.I.C.S.: 334510

UAB Abbott Medical Lithuania (1)
Zalgirio str 92 entrance No 2, Vilnius,
09303, Lithuania
Tel.: (370) 52051288
Pharmaceutical Products Distr
N.A.I.C.S.: 424210

Vida Cell S.A. (1)
Av Juan XXIII 6323, Vitacura, Chile
Tel.: (56) 22 945 5400
Web Site: https://www.vidacel.cl
Pharmaceuticals Product Mfr
N.A.I.C.S.: 325412
Fernanda Ross (COO)

Walk Vascular, LLC (1)
17171 Daimler St, Irvine, CA 92614
Web Site: https://www.jeti.tv
Medical Device Mfr
N.A.I.C.S.: 339112
David Look (Pres & CEO)
Brad Culbert (VP-Engineering)
Alan Schuster (VP-Sales)

Western Pharmaceuticals S.A. (1)
Av De Los Shyris 2680 Y Gaspar De Villar-
roel Edf Cobadelsa Piso 2 - No, Quito, Ec-
uador
Tel.: (593) 22250222
Pharmaceutical Products Distr
N.A.I.C.S.: 424210

X Technologies Inc. (1)
100 Sandau Ste 300, San Antonio, TX
78216
Tel.: (210) 822-8712
Web Site: https://www.x-technologies.com
Medical Device Mfr
N.A.I.C.S.: 339112

ABBVIE INC.
Tel.: (847) 932-7900   DE
Web Site: https://www.abbvie.com
Year Founded: 2013
ABBV—(NYSE)
Rev.: $54,318,000,000
Assets: $134,711,000,000
Liabilities: $124,314,000,000
Net Worth: $10,397,000,000
Earnings: $4,863,000,000
Emp.: 50,000
Fiscal Year-end: 12/31/23

Biopharmaceutical Research & De-
velopment Services
N.A.I.C.S.: 325412
Azita Saleki-Gerhardt (Chief Ops Offi-
cer & Exec VP)
Scott T. Reents (CFO & Exec VP)
Richard A. Gonzalez (Founder, Chm
& Exec Chm)
Timothy J. Richmond (Chief HR Offi-
cer & Exec VP)
Robert A. Michael (CEO)
Kevin K. Buckbee (Sr VP & Control-
ler)
Tracie Haas (Sr VP-Corp Affairs)
Greg Miley (Sr VP-Gove Affairs)
Perry C. Siatis (Gen Counsel, Sec &
Exec VP)
Roopal Thakkar (Chief Scientific Offi-
cer & Exec VP-Research & Develop-
ment)
Carrie Strom (Pres-AbbVie & Sr VP-
Global Allergan Aesthetics)
Wulff-Erik von Borcke (Pres-AbbVie &
Sr VP-Oncology)
Assil Omar (Chief Equity Officer & Sr
VP)
Jag Dosanjh (Pres-AbbVie & Sr VP-
Neuroscience & Eye Care)
Nicole Mowad-Nassar (Pres-AbbVie
& Sr VP-Specialty, U. ., S. ., and
Therapeutics Ops)
Sanjay Narayan (Chief Compliance
Officer, Chief Ethics Officer & Sr VP)
Elizabeth Shea (Sr VP-Investor Rela-
tions)
Latif Akintade (Sr VP-Medical Affairs
& Health Economics Outcomes Res)
Alberto Colzi (Pres-AbbVie & Sr VP-
Intl Therapeutics)

Subsidiaries:

AbbVie AB (1)
Hemvarnsgatan 9, Box 1523, 171 29,
Solna, Sweden
Tel.: (46) 86 844 4600
Web Site: https://www.abbvie.se
Emp.: 150
Pharmaceutical Preparation Mfr
N.A.I.C.S.: 325412

AbbVie AG (1)
Alte Steinhauserstrasse 14, 6330, Cham,
Switzerland
Tel.: (41) 41 399 1500
Web Site: https://www.abbvie.ch
Emp.: 250
Pharmaceutical Preparation Mfr
N.A.I.C.S.: 325412

AbbVie AS (1)
Martin Linges Vei 25, 1364, Fornebu, Nor-
way
Tel.: (47) 67818000
Web Site: http://www.abbvie.no
Pharmaceuticals Product Mfr
N.A.I.C.S.: 325412

AbbVie B.V. (1)
Wegalaan 9, 2132 JD, Hoofddorp, Nether-
lands
Tel.: (31) 88 322 2843
Web Site: https://www.abbvie.nl
Pharmaceutical Preparation Mfr
N.A.I.C.S.: 325412

**AbbVie Biofarmacevtska druzba
d.o.o.** (1)
Dolenjska Cesta 242C, 1000, Ljubljana,
Slovenia
Tel.: (386) 13208070
Web Site: https://www.abbvie.com
Pharmaceutical Products Distr
N.A.I.C.S.: 424210

AbbVie Biopharmaceuticals Ltd. (1)
AbbVie Israel Haharash St D 4 Neve
Ne'eman Building, Hod Hasharon, 4524075,
Israel
Tel.: (972) 9 790 9600
Web Site: https://www.abbvie.co.il
Emp.: 180
Drug Product Distr
N.A.I.C.S.: 424210

AbbVie Bioresearch Center Inc. (1)
100 Research Dr, Worcester, MA 01605-
4312
Tel.: (508) 849-2500
Sales Range: $50-74.9 Million
Emp.: 700
Commercial Physical Research Services
N.A.I.C.S.: 541715

AbbVie Biotech Ventures Inc. (1)
100 Abbott Park Rd Abbott Park, North Chi-
cago, IL 60064-3500
Tel.: (847) 937-6100
Web Site:
    https://www.abbviebiotechventures.com
Venture Capital Management Services
N.A.I.C.S.: 523910

AbbVie Biotherapeutics Inc. (1)
1500 Seaport Blvd, Redwood City, CA
94063
Tel.: (650) 454-1000
Emp.: 189
Drug Product Mfr
N.A.I.C.S.: 325411

AbbVie Corporation (1)
8401 Trans-Canada Highway, Saint-
Laurent, Montreal, H4S 1Z1, QC, Canada
Tel.: (514) 906-9700
Web Site: https://www.abbvie.ca
Emp.: 500
Pharmaceutical Preparation Mfr
N.A.I.C.S.: 325412

**AbbVie Deutschland GmbH & Co.
KG** (1)
Mainzer Strasse 81, 65189, Wiesbaden,
Germany
Tel.: (49) 6 111 7200
Web Site: https://www.abbvie.de
Pharmaceutical Preparation Mfr
N.A.I.C.S.: 325412
Christian Maurer (Mng Dir-Operations)
Martin Gastens (VP-Biologics Drug Product
Dev)
Lennaert Rijken (VP- & Commercial)

Subsidiary (Domestic):

AbbVie Biotechnology GmbH (2)
Max-Planck-Ring 2, Wiesbaden, 65205,
Hessen, Germany
Tel.: (49) 6122580
Management Consulting Services
N.A.I.C.S.: 541618

**AbbVie Real Estate Management
GmbH** (2)
Knollstr 50, 67061, Ludwigshafen, Germany
Tel.: (49) 6215890
Real Estate Asset Management Services
N.A.I.C.S.: 531390

AbbVie Endocrinology Inc. (1)
5204 Jackson Rd Ste C, Ann Arbor, MI
48103
Tel.: (734) 821-8000
Web Site:
    https://pharmacysolutionsonline.com
Pharmaceuticals Product Mfr
N.A.I.C.S.: 325412

AbbVie Farmaceutica, S.L.U. (1)
Avenida de Burgos 91, 28050, Madrid,
Spain
Tel.: (34) 913840910
Web Site: http://www.abbvie.es
Pharmaceutical Preparation Mfr
N.A.I.C.S.: 325412

**AbbVie Farmaceuticos, S.A. de
C.V.** (1)
Boulevard Adolfo Ruiz Cortines No 3720
Torre 3 - Oficina 10-001, Colonia Jardines
del Pedregal Alcaldia Alvaro Obregon,
01900, Mexico, Mexico
Tel.: (52) 559 183 4600
Web Site: https://www.abbvie.com.mx
Pharmaceutical Preparation Mfr
N.A.I.C.S.: 325412

AbbVie GK (1)
3-1-21 Shibaura, Minato-ku, Tokyo, 108-
0023, Japan
Tel.: (81) 345771111
Web Site: https://www.abbvie.co.jp
Emp.: 1,577
Pharmaceutical Preparation Mfr
N.A.I.C.S.: 325412

Kyoko Deguchi (Gen Mgr)

AbbVie GmbH (1)
Lembockgasse 61 / 3rd Floor, 1230, Vi-
enna, Austria
Tel.: (43) 1205890
Web Site: https://www.abbvie.at
Pharmaceutical Preparation Mfr
N.A.I.C.S.: 325412

**AbbVie Healthcare India Private
Limited** (1)
No 3 Kasturba Road Level 6 & 7 Prestige
Obelisk, Bengaluru, 560 001, Karnataka,
India
Tel.: (91) 8040707070
Web Site: https://www.abbvie.in
Pharmaceuticals Product Mfr
N.A.I.C.S.: 325412

AbbVie Investment Kft. (1)
7 Lechner OdOn fasor, 1095, Budapest,
Hungary
Tel.: (36) 14558600
Investment Management Service
N.A.I.C.S.: 523940

AbbVie Ireland Limited (1)
14 Riverwalk Citywest Business Campus,
Dublin, D24 XN32, Ireland
Tel.: (353) 14287900
Web Site: http://www.abbvie.ie
Pharmaceutical Preparation Mfr
N.A.I.C.S.: 325412

AbbVie Ireland NL B.V. (1)
14 Riverwalk Citywest Business Campus,
Dublin, D24 XN32, Ireland
Tel.: (353) 14287900
Web Site: http://www.abbvie.ie
Pharmaceutical Preparation Mfr
N.A.I.C.S.: 325412

AbbVie Kft. (1)
Lechner Odon fasor 7 7 Emelet Millenium
Tower II, 1095, Budapest, Hungary
Tel.: (36) 614558600
Web Site: https://www.abbvie.hu
Pharmaceutical Preparation Mfr
N.A.I.C.S.: 325412

AbbVie Limited (1)
14 Riverwalk Citywest Business Campus,
Dublin, D24 XN32, Ireland
Tel.: (353) 14287900
Web Site: https://www.abbvie.ie
Pharmaceuticals Product Mfr
N.A.I.C.S.: 325412

AbbVie Limited (1)
Unit 2405-08 24/F AIA Tower 183 Electric
Road, North Point, China (Hong Kong)
Tel.: (852) 34678888
Web Site: https://www.abbvie.com.hk
Emp.: 46
Pharmaceuticals Product Mfr
N.A.I.C.S.: 325412

AbbVie Limited (1)
L6 156-158 Victoria Street, Wellington, New
Zealand
Tel.: (64) 800900030
Web Site: http://www.abbvie.co.nz
Pharmaceuticals Product Mfr
N.A.I.C.S.: 325412

AbbVie Ltd (1)
1 Q House Lumpini Building 12th Floor
South Sathorn Road, Thungmahamek
Sathorn, Bangkok, 10120, Thailand
Tel.: (66) 26970700
Web Site: http://www.abbvie.co.th
Pharmaceuticals Product Mfr
N.A.I.C.S.: 325412

AbbVie Ltd (1)
6th Floor SamTan Bldg 421 YoungDong-
Daero, Kangnam-Ku, Seoul, 061-82, Korea
(South)
Tel.: (82) 23 429 9300
Web Site: https://www.abbvie.co.kr
Pharmaceuticals Product Mfr
N.A.I.C.S.: 325412

AbbVie Ltd. (1)
AbbVie House, Vanwall Business Park Van-
wall Road, Maidenhead, SL6 4UB, Berk-
shire, United Kingdom
Tel.: (44) 1628561090
Web Site: https://www.abbvie.co.uk
Pharmaceuticals Product Mfr

AbbVie Inc.—(Continued)
N.A.I.C.S.: 325412

AbbVie Oy (1)
Pasila asema-aukio 1 Main entrance
D-stairs 13th floor, 00520, Helsinki, Finland
Tel.: (358) 10 241 1200
Web Site: https://www.abbvie.fi
Emp.: 85
Pharmaceutical Preparation Mfr
N.A.I.C.S.: 325412
Bernd Krones (Mng Dir)

AbbVie Polska Sp. z o.o. (1)
ul Postepu 21 B, 02-676, Warsaw, Poland
Tel.: (48) 22 372 7800
Web Site: https://www.abbvie.pl
Emp.: 230
Pharmaceutical Preparation Mfr
N.A.I.C.S.: 325412

AbbVie Productos Farmaceuticos Limitada (1)
Av Apoquindo 5550 piso 7 Torre Apoquindo,
Las Condes, Santiago, Chile
Tel.: (56) 232133900
Web Site: https://www.abbvie.cl
Pharmaceuticals Product Mfr
N.A.I.C.S.: 325412

AbbVie Promocao, L.da (1)
Estrada De Alfragide 67 Alfrapark Edificio
D, 2610-008, Amadora, Portugal
Tel.: (351) 21 190 8400
Web Site: https://www.abbvie.pt
Emp.: 200
Drug Product Distr
N.A.I.C.S.: 424210

AbbVie Pte. Ltd. (1)
9 North Buona Vista Drive 19-01 The Metropolis Tower One, Singapore, 138588,
Singapore
Tel.: (65) 6 715 8100
Web Site: https://www.abbvie.com.sg
Emp.: 400
Pharmaceutical Preparation Mfr
N.A.I.C.S.: 325412

AbbVie Pty Ltd (1)
Gateway 241 Level 7 241 O Riordan Street,
Mascot, 2020, NSW, Australia
Tel.: (61) 290358600
Web Site: https://www.abbvie.com.au
Pharmaceuticals Product Mfr
N.A.I.C.S.: 325412

AbbVie S.A. (1)
Avda Italia 7519 Piso 4 oficina 401, Montevideo, 11500, Uruguay
Tel.: (598) 26009495
Web Site: http://www.abbvie.com.uy
Pharmaceuticals Product Mfr
N.A.I.C.S.: 325412

AbbVie S.A. (1)
Ing Butty 240 - Piso 13 - Edificio Laminar
Plaza, C1001AFB, Buenos Aires, Argentina
Tel.: (54) 1152827200
Web Site: https://www.abbvie.com.ar
Pharmaceutical Preparation Mfr
N.A.I.C.S.: 325412

AbbVie S.A.S. (1)
Carrera 11 94 A - 34 Piso 4, Bogota,
110221, Colombia
Tel.: (57) 16385000
Capsule & Ointment Mfr
N.A.I.C.S.: 325412

AbbVie SA (1)
avenue Einstein 14, 1300, Wavre, Belgium
Tel.: (32) 10477811
Web Site: http://www.abbvie.be
Pharmaceutical Preparation Mfr
N.A.I.C.S.: 325412

AbbVie Sarl (1)
Immeuble Carthage Bloc A RDC lot 155 les
jardins du Lac, Les Berges du Lac II, 1053,
Tunis, Tunisia
Tel.: (216) 71191154
Pharmaceuticals Product Mfr
N.A.I.C.S.: 325412

AbbVie Sdn. Bhd. (1)
Level 9 Menara Lien Ho No 8 Persiaran
Tropicana, 47410, Petaling Jaya, Selangor,
Malaysia
Tel.: (60) 7 883 6888

Web Site: https://www.abbvie.com.my
Pharmaceutical Preparation Mfr
N.A.I.C.S.: 325412

AbbVie Sp. z o.o. (1)
ul Postepu 21 B, 02-676, Warsaw, Poland
Tel.: (48) 223727800
Web Site: https://www.abbvie.pl
Emp.: 230
Pharmaceuticals Product Mfr
N.A.I.C.S.: 325412

AbbVie Spain, S.L. (1)
Avenida de Burgos 91, 28050, Madrid,
Spain
Tel.: (34) 913840910
Web Site: https://www.abbvie.es
Pharmaceuticals Product Mfr
N.A.I.C.S.: 325412

AbbVie Tibbi Ilaclar Sanayi ve Ticaret Limited Sirketi (1)
Barbaros Mah Begonya Sk Nidakule Atasehir Bati Blok No 1 ic Kapi No 33, Kelif Plaza
3 Blok Kat 1-16-17 Umraniye, 34746, Istanbul, Türkiye
Tel.: (90) 216 633 2300
Web Site: https://www.abbvie.com.tr
Pharmaceutical Preparation Mfr
N.A.I.C.S.: 325412

AbbVie Tibbi Liaclar Sanayi ve Ticaret Limited Sirketi (1)
Barbaros Mah Begonia St Nidakule Atasehir
Bati Blok No1 Ic Kapi No 33, Atasehir,
34746, Istanbul, Türkiye
Tel.: (90) 2166332300
Web Site: https://www.abbvie.com.tr
Pharmaceuticals Product Mfr
N.A.I.C.S.: 325412

AbbVie d.o.o. (1)
Kolodvorska 12/3, 71000, Sarajevo, Bosnia
& Herzegovina
Tel.: (387) 33725910
Web Site: https://www.abbvie.com
Pharmaceuticals Product Mfr
N.A.I.C.S.: 325412

AbbVie s.r.o. (1)
Metronom Business Center Bucharova
2817/13 Nove Butovice, 158 00, Prague, 5,
Czech Republic
Tel.: (420) 233098111
Web Site: https://www.abbvie.cz
Pharmaceutical Preparation Mfr
N.A.I.C.S.: 325412

AbbVie s.r.o. (1)
City Business Center II Karadzicova 10,
821 08, Bratislava, Slovakia
Tel.: (421) 250500777
Web Site: https://www.abbvie.sk
Emp.: 48,000
Pharmaceuticals Product Mfr
N.A.I.C.S.: 325412

AbbVie, L.da (1)
Estrada de Alfragide 67 Alfrapark Edificio D,
2610-008, Amadora, Portugal
Tel.: (351) 211908400
Web Site: https://www.abbvie.pt
Pharmaceuticals Product Mfr
N.A.I.C.S.: 325412

AbbVie, S.R.L. (1)
S R 148 Pontina Km 52 snc, Campoverde
di Aprilia, LT, Italy
Tel.: (39) 06928921
Web Site: https://www.abbvie.it
Pharmaceutical Product Mfr
N.A.I.C.S.: 325412

Allergan GmbH (1)
Stichlingstrasse 1, 60327, Frankfurt am
Main, Germany
Tel.: (49) 699203810
Web Site: http://www.allergan.de
Pharmaceuticals Product Mfr
N.A.I.C.S.: 325412

Allergan plc (1)
Clonshaugh Business and Technology Park,
Coolock, Coolock, Dublin, D17 E400, Ireland
Tel.: (353) 14357700
Web Site: http://www.allergan.com
Holding Company; Pharmaceutical & Biopharmaceutical Developer, Mfr & Distr
N.A.I.C.S.: 551112

Matthew M. Walsh (CFO & Exec VP)
Brenton L. Saunders (Chm, Pres & CEO)

Subsidiary (Non-US):

Allergan CZ, s.r.o. (2)
Nadrazni 344/23 Regus - Prague Andel
Business Centre, 15000, Prague, Czech
Republic
Tel.: (420) 234234719
Pharmaceutical Products Distr
N.A.I.C.S.: 424210

Allergan Development Ventures I UK (2)
1st Floor Marlow International The Parkway,
Marlow, SL7 1YL, Buckinghamshire, United
Kingdom
Tel.: (44) 1628494444
Pharmaceutical Products Distr
N.A.I.C.S.: 424210

Allergan Hungary Kft. (2)
Vaci Ut 22-24 Westend Business Center,
Budapest, 1132, Hungary
Tel.: (36) 18089439
Pharmaceutical Products Distr
N.A.I.C.S.: 424210
Klara Merei (Mgr-Territory)

Allergan Middle East Limited (2)
Index Tower Level 8 Unit 802 Dubai International Financial Centre, PO Box 50964,
Dubai, United Arab Emirates
Tel.: (971) 44501162
Pharmaceutical Products Distr
N.A.I.C.S.: 424210

Allergan Productos Farmaceuticos Ltda. (2)
Av Dr Cardoso De Melo 1955 13 Andar Edifcio Brasilio Machado, 04548-005, Sao
Paulo, SP, Brazil
Tel.: (55) 1130480500
Pharmaceutical Products Distr
N.A.I.C.S.: 424210

Allergan SK S.r.o. (2)
Karadzicova 8/A, 82108, Bratislava, Slovakia
Tel.: (421) 259396101
Pharmaceutical Products Distr
N.A.I.C.S.: 424210
Branislav Kucharovic (Sr Mgr-Sls & Mktg)

Allergan SRL (2)
15 Charles De Gaulle Square Charles De
Gaulle Plaza Building, 3rd Floor Office 306-307 315 And 333 1st District, Bucharest,
011857, Romania
Tel.: (40) 318604724
Pharmaceutical Products Distr
N.A.I.C.S.: 424210

Allergan Saudi Arabia LLC (2)
Al Ma Amoun Building 2nd Floor Ali Bin Abi
Taleb St Al-sharafeya Dist, PO Box 21435,
Jeddah, 19435, Saudi Arabia
Tel.: (966) 126148062
Pharmaceutical Products Distr
N.A.I.C.S.: 424210

Allergan Scientific Office (2)
53 El Sheikm Mohd El Nadi Street Nasr
City 6th Zone, Cairo, Egypt
Tel.: (20) 26701644
Pharmaceutical Products Distr
N.A.I.C.S.: 424210

Allergan Singapore Pte. Ltd. (2)
21st Floor Saigon Trade Center 37 Ton Duc
Thang District 1, Ho Chi Minh City, Vietnam
Tel.: (84) 839115522
Pharmaceutical Products Distr
N.A.I.C.S.: 424210
Huynh Thi Hoai Thanh (Chief Rep Officer)

Allergan Singapore Pte. Ltd. (2)
Eighty Eight Kasablanka Office Tower 10th
Floor Unit D, Jl Casablanca Raya Kav 88,
South Jakarta, 12870, Indonesia
Tel.: (62) 2129612648
Pharmaceutical Products Distr
N.A.I.C.S.: 424210

Allergan Sp. Z o.o. (2)
Ul Marynarska 15, 02-674, Warsaw, Poland
Tel.: (48) 222563700
Pharmaceutical Products Distr
N.A.I.C.S.: 424210

Allergan Ukraine, LLC (2)
Sportivnaya Sq 1, Kiev, Ukraine
Tel.: (380) 503393536
Pharmaceutical Products Distr
N.A.I.C.S.: 424210

Allergan d.o.o. Beograd (2)
Maglajska 24, 11040, Novi Beograd, Serbia
Tel.: (381) 114084509
Pharmaceutical Products Distr
N.A.I.C.S.: 424210
Djordje Tanackovic (Country Mgr)

Subsidiary (US):

Allergan, Inc. (2)
2525 Dupont Dr, Irvine, CA 92612
Tel.: (714) 246-4500
Web Site: http://www.allergan.com
Holding Company
N.A.I.C.S.: 551112
A. Robert D. Bailey (Chief Legal Officer,
Sec & Exec VP)
C. David Nicholsan (Chief R&D Officer &
Exec VP)
Neal S. Walker (Founder)

Subsidiary (Non-US):

Allergan AG (3)
Puls 5 Hardturmstrasse 11, 8005, Zurich,
Switzerland (100%)
Tel.: (41) 442042300
Web Site: http://www.allergan.ch
Sales Range: $10-24.9 Million
Emp.: 30
Retailer of Pharmaceutical Products
N.A.I.C.S.: 325412

Allergan AS (3)
Nordenflychtsvagen 74, 112 52, Stockholm,
Sweden (100%)
Tel.: (46) 859410000
Web Site: http://www.allergan.com
Sales Range: $10-24.9 Million
Emp.: 15
Retailer of Pharmaceutical Products
N.A.I.C.S.: 325412

Allergan ApS (3)
Naverland 22, 2600, Glostrup, Broendby,
Denmark
Tel.: (45) 21689226
Pharmaceutical Preparation Mfr
N.A.I.C.S.: 424210

Allergan Australia (Pty.) Ltd. (3)
Level 4 810 Pacific Highway, PO Box 1004,
Gordon, 2073, NSW, Australia (100%)
Tel.: (61) 294980100
Web Site: http://www.allergan.com.au
Sales Range: $25-49.9 Million
Emp.: 100
Mfr of Eye Care Products
N.A.I.C.S.: 339113

Allergan B.V. (3)
Fellenoord 130, 5611 ZB, Eindhoven,
Netherlands (100%)
Tel.: (31) 402668758
Web Site: http://www.allergan.nl
Sales Range: $10-24.9 Million
Emp.: 20
Retailer of Pharmaceutical Products
N.A.I.C.S.: 325412

Allergan Botox Limited (3)
Castlebar Road, Westport, Co Mayo,
Ireland (100%)
Tel.: (353) 9825222
Web Site: http://www.allergan.com
Sales Range: $150-199.9 Million
Chemicals Mfr
N.A.I.C.S.: 325199

Allergan C.I.S. SARL (3)
21 bld 2 floor 4 Stanislavskogo Street,
109004, Moscow, Russia
Tel.: (7) 4959740353
Web Site: https://www.allergan.com
Emp.: 100
Pharmaceutical Preparation Mfr
N.A.I.C.S.: 325412

Allergan Colombia S.A. (3)
Calle 113 No 7-21 Torre A - Oficina 713 -
Teleport Business, Bogota,
Colombia (100%)
Tel.: (57) 1 653 8383

Web Site: http://www.allergan.com
Sales Range: $150-199.9 Million
Emp.: 48
Retailer of Pharmaceutical Products
N.A.I.C.S.: 325412

Allergan France S.A.S. (3)
12 Place de la Defense, 92400, Courbevoie, France **(100%)**
Tel.: (33) 149078300
Web Site: http://www.allergan.fr
Sales Range: $25-49.9 Million
Emp.: 50
Mfr of Eye & Skin Care Products
N.A.I.C.S.: 339113

Subsidiary (Domestic):

Allergan Industrie S.A.S. (4)
Route De Promery Zone Artisanale De Pre-Mairy, 74370, Pringy, France
Tel.: (33) 450272703
Sales Range: $50-74.9 Million
Emp.: 200
Pharmaceutical Preparation Mfr
N.A.I.C.S.: 325412

S.C.I. Val Promery (4)
Rouge De Promiry, 74370, Pringy, France
Tel.: (33) 450272703
Emp.: 10
Pharmaceutical Preparation Mfr
N.A.I.C.S.: 325412

Subsidiary (Non-US):

Allergan Hong Kong Limited (3)
Suites 1309-10 & Pt 8 CityPlaza Four 12 Taikoo Wan Road Island East, 7/F City Plaza Three, Taikoo Shing, China (Hong Kong)
Tel.: (852) 26102525
Pharmaceutical Preparation Mfr
N.A.I.C.S.: 325412

Allergan Inc. (3)
85 Enterprise Blvd Suite 500, Markham, L6G 0B5, ON, Canada **(100%)**
Tel.: (905) 940-1660
Web Site: http://www.allergan.ca
Pharmaceutical Product Whslr
N.A.I.C.S.: 424210
Tracey Ramsay (VP & Country Mgr)
Fiona McCloskey (Head-Bus Unit & Exec Dir-Eyecare)
Arima Ventin (Exec Dir-Market Access, Pricing & Govt Rels)
Foo-Lim Yeh (Dir-Regulatory Affairs)
Leonard Bernstein (Assoc Dir-Legal & Compliance Counsel)

Subsidiary (Domestic):

Allergan Pharma Co. (4)
6733 Mississauga Road Suite 400, Mississauga, L5N 6J5, ON, Canada
Tel.: (905) 829-2979
Specialty Pharmaceutical Product Mfr & Distr
N.A.I.C.S.: 325412
Rob Tessarolo (Gen Mgr)

Subsidiary (Non-US):

Allergan India Limited (3)
No 3 Kasturba Road Level 6 & 7 Prestige Obelisk, Bengaluru, 560001, Karnataka, India **(100%)**
Tel.: (91) 8040707070
Web Site: http://www.allergan.co.in
Sales Range: $150-199.9 Million
Emp.: 500
Distr of Eyecare Pharmaceutical, Surgical & Optical Products; Specialty Pharmaceutical Researcher
N.A.I.C.S.: 327215
R. Raghukumar (Mng Dir)

Allergan K.K. (3)
Yebisu Garden Place Tower 35F 4-20-3 Ebisu, Shibuya-ku, Tokyo, 150-6035, Japan
Tel.: (81) 364095001
Web Site: https://www.allergan.co.jp
Sales Range: $150-199.9 Million
Ophthalmic Goods Sales
N.A.I.C.S.: 423460

Allergan Korea Ltd. (3)
GT Tower 14F 1317-23, Seocho-dong Seocho-gu, Seoul, 137-856, Korea (South) **(100%)**

Tel.: (82) 230194500
Web Site: http://www.allergan.co.kr
Sales Range: $10-24.9 Million
Emp.: 50
Retailer of Pharmaceutical Products
N.A.I.C.S.: 325412

Allergan Laboratorios Ltda. (3)
Apoquindo 3472 Esquina Enrique Foster Norte 21- Oficina 802, Las Condes, Chile **(100%)**
Tel.: (56) 227291800
Web Site: http://www.allergan.cl
Sales Range: $150-199.9 Million
Retailer of Pharmaceutical Products
N.A.I.C.S.: 325412

Allergan Limited (3)
Marlow International The Parkway, Marlow, SL7 1YL, Buckinghamshire, United Kingdom **(100%)**
Tel.: (44) 1628494444
Sales Range: $25-49.9 Million
Emp.: 550
Mfr of Eye & Skin Care Products
N.A.I.C.S.: 339113

Subsidiary (Domestic):

Allergan Biologics Limited (4)
10-12 Estuary Banks Estuary Commerce Park, Speke Road, Liverpool, L24 8RB, United Kingdom
Tel.: (44) 1517281750
Emp.: 80
Biopharmaceutical Research & Development Services
N.A.I.C.S.: 325412
Crawford Brown (CEO & Head-Biologics R&D-Global)
Johanne Tabern (Comm Mgr)
Helen Hughes (Dir-HR)

Allergan Holdings Limited (4)
1st Floor Marlow International the Parkway, Marlow, SL7 1YL, Buckinghamshire, United Kingdom
Tel.: (44) 1628494444
Pharmaceutical Preparation Mfr
N.A.I.C.S.: 325412

Subsidiary (Non-US):

Allergan N.V. (3)
Cerhulesesceenweh 1560, 3439 MN, Hoeilaart, Netherlands **(100%)**
Tel.: (31) 307503750
Web Site: http://www.allergan.nl
Sales Range: $10-24.9 Million
Emp.: 50
Retailer of Pharmaceutical Products
N.A.I.C.S.: 325412

Allergan New Zealand Limited (3)
Cnr Manu Tapu Drive & Joseph Hammond Place, Auckland International Airport, Mangere, New Zealand **(100%)**
Tel.: (64) 800659912
Web Site: http://www.allergan.com
Sales Range: $10-24.9 Million
Emp.: 6
Retailer of Pharmaceutical Products
N.A.I.C.S.: 325412

Allergan Norden AB (3)
Nordenflychtsvagen 74, 112 52, Stockholm, Sweden **(100%)**
Tel.: (46) 859410000
Web Site: http://www.allergan.se
Sales Range: $10-24.9 Million
Emp.: 35
Retailer of Pharmaceutical Products
N.A.I.C.S.: 325412

Allergan Pharmaceuticals (Ireland) Ltd., Inc. (3)
Castlebar Road, Westport, Co Mayo, Ireland **(100%)**
Tel.: (353) 9825222
Web Site: http://www.allergan.ie
Sales Range: $150-199.9 Million
Emp.: 700
Mfr of Eye Care Products
N.A.I.C.S.: 339113
Patrick Donnell (Sr VP-Global Mfg)

Allergan Pharmaceuticals (Proprietary) Limited (3)
2nd Floor Allandale Building Magwa Crescent Waterfall City, Jukskei View, Midrand,

2090, South Africa
Tel.: (27) 115456600
Web Site: https://www.allergan.co.za
Emp.: 22
Real Estate Services
N.A.I.C.S.: 531210

Allergan Pharmaceuticals Ireland (Eurocentre) (3)
Block J The Earlsfort Centre Lower Leeson St Longphort House, Dublin, Ireland **(100%)**
Tel.: (353) 16445200
Web Site: http://www.allergan.com
Sales Range: $150-199.9 Million
Emp.: 81
Distr of Pharmaceutical Products
N.A.I.C.S.: 325412

Allergan Produtos Farmaceuticos, Ltda. (3)
Av Guarulhos 3272, Guarulhos, 07030-000, Sao Paulo, Brazil **(100%)**
Tel.: (55) 1124232000
Web Site: http://www.allergan.com.br
Sales Range: $75-99.9 Million
Emp.: 300
Mfr of Eye & Skin Care Products
N.A.I.C.S.: 339113

Allergan S.A. de C.V. (3)
Av Santa Fe 505 piso 11 Col Cruz Manca Santa Fe Del, Cuajimalpa, 05349, Mexico, DF, Mexico **(100%)**
Tel.: (52) 5559998500
Web Site: http://www.allergan.com.mx
Sales Range: $10-24.9 Million
Emp.: 40
Sales of Eye & Skin Care Products
N.A.I.C.S.: 423460

Allergan S.A.U. (3)
Plaza de la Encina 10-11 Edificio La Encina-Nucleo 4-3 Planta, Tres Cantos, 28760, Madrid, Spain **(100%)**
Tel.: (34) 918076130
Web Site: http://www.allergan.es
Sales Range: $25-49.9 Million
Emp.: 150
Mfr of Eye & Skin Care Products
N.A.I.C.S.: 339113

Allergan S.p.A. (3)
Via Salvatore Quasimodo 134/138, 00144, Rome, Italy **(100%)**
Tel.: (39) 06509561
Web Site: http://www.allergan.it
Sales Range: $50-74.9 Million
Emp.: 80
Mfr of Eye Care Products
N.A.I.C.S.: 339113

Allergan Singapore Pte. Ltd. (3)
279 Jalan Ahmad Ibrahim 03-01, Singapore, 639938, Singapore **(100%)**
Tel.: (65) 147585
Web Site: https://www.allergan.com
Sales Range: $10-24.9 Million
Emp.: 9
Retailer of Pharmaceutical Products
N.A.I.C.S.: 325412

Subsidiary (Domestic):

Allergan USA, Inc. (3)
5 Giralda Farms, Madison, NJ 07940
Tel.: (862) 261-7000
Web Site: http://www.allergan.com
Regional Managing Office; Office Administrative Services
N.A.I.C.S.: 561110

Subsidiary (Non-US):

Allergan-Loa S.A. (3)
Av Del Libertador 498 Piso 29 - Sector Norte, C1001ABR, Buenos Aires, Argentina **(100%)**
Tel.: (54) 1163226464
Web Site: http://www.allergan.com.ar
Sales Range: $150-199.9 Million
Retailer of Pharmaceutical Products
N.A.I.C.S.: 325412

Forest Laboratories Ireland Limited (3)
Clonshaugh Business & Technology Park, Dublin, 17, Ireland **(100%)**
Tel.: (353) 14357700
Pharmaceuticals Mfr

N.A.I.C.S.: 325412

Subsidiary (Domestic):

Forest Tosara Ltd. (4)
146 Baldoyle Industrial Estate Grange Road, Baldoyle, Dublin, 13, Ireland
Tel.: (353) 18321199
Web Site: http://www.allergan.com
Pharmaceuticals Mfr
N.A.I.C.S.: 325412

Subsidiary (Domestic):

Keller Medical, Inc. (3)
1239 SE Indian St Ste 112, Stuart, FL 34997
Tel.: (772) 219-9993
Web Site: https://www.kellerfunnel.com
Pharmaceuticals Product Mfr
N.A.I.C.S.: 325412
Howard Preissman (Founder & CEO)

Subsidiary (Non-US):

Pharm-Allergan GmbH (3)
Westhafenplatz 6-8, 60327, Frankfurt am Main, Germany **(100%)**
Tel.: (49) 699203810
Web Site: http://www.allergan.com.de
Sales Range: $75-99.9 Million
Emp.: 300
Mfr of Pharmaceutical Products
N.A.I.C.S.: 325412

Subsidiary (Domestic):

Repros Therapeutics Inc. (3)
5 Giralda Farms, Madison, NJ 07940
Tel.: (862) 261-7000
Web Site: https://www.allergan.com
Pharmaceuticals Product Mfr
N.A.I.C.S.: 325412
Patrick P. Fourteau (Chm)

RetroSense Therapeutics, LLC (3)
330 E Liberty St LL, Ann Arbor, MI 48104
Tel.: (734) 369-9333
Web Site: http://www.retro-sense.com
Eye Care Biopharmaceutical Developer
N.A.I.C.S.: 325412
Sean Ainsworth (Founder, Chm & CEO)

Soliton, Inc. (3)
5304 Ashbrook Dr, Houston, TX 77081-4102
Tel.: (832) 661-3453
Web Site: http://www.soliton.com
Rev.: $153,000
Assets: $33,801,000
Liabilities: $2,820,000
Net Worth: $30,981,000
Earnings: ($14,541,000)
Emp.: 13
Fiscal Year-end: 12/31/2020
Medical Technology Research & Development Services
N.A.I.C.S.: 541715
Walter V. Klemp (Co-Founder & Chm)
Christopher Capelli (Co-Founder, Vice Chm & Chief Scientific Officer)
Lori Bisson (CFO)
Joe Tanner (COO)
Mary Stoll (Sr Dir-Clinical Dev)
Robert Mills (VP-Supply Chain)
Sean J. Shapiro (VP-Sls)

Tobira Therapeutics, Inc. (3)
701 Gateway Blvd Ste 300, South San Francisco, CA 94080
Tel.: (650) 741-6625
Web Site: https://ir.tobiratx.com
Pharmaceutical Product Whslr
N.A.I.C.S.: 424210

Subsidiary (Non-US):

Uteron Pharma SPRL (3)
Liege Airport Business Park Liege Airport-Cargo Nord, Rue Saint Exupery 17, Grace-Hollogne, 4460, Belgium
Tel.: (32) 42209630
Pharmaceuticals Product Mfr
N.A.I.C.S.: 424210

Subsidiary (Domestic):

Vicuron Pharmaceuticals, Inc (3)
455 S Gulph Rd Ste 305, King of Prussia, PA 19406
Tel.: (610) 205-2300

AbbVie Inc.—(Continued)
Emp.: 216
Pharmaceutical Products Distr
N.A.I.C.S.: 325412

Warner Chilcott Corporation (3)
100 Enterprise Dr, Rockaway, NJ 07866
Tel.: (973) 442-3200
Web Site: http://www.wcrx.com
Sales Range: $200-249.9 Million
Emp.: 582
Women's Healthcare & Dermatology Pharmaceuticals Mfr
N.A.I.C.S.: 325412
Izumi Hara (Gen Counsel, Sec & Sr VP)

Subsidiary (Non-US):

WC Pharmaceuticals I Limited (4)
Icom House Suite 3 Second Floor 1/5 Irish Town, Gibraltar, Gibraltar
Tel.: (350) 20050418
Pharmaceuticals Product Mfr
N.A.I.C.S.: 325412

Subsidiary (US):

Warner Chilcott Company, LLC (5)
Union St Rd 195 Km 1 1, Fajardo, PR 00738
Tel.: (787) 863-1850
Pharmaceuticals Product Mfr
N.A.I.C.S.: 325412
Frank Rodriguez (Mgr)
Vance Russell (Gen Mgr)

Subsidiary (Non-US):

Warner Chilcott (Ireland) Limited (4)
Building B Xerox Technology Park, Dundalk, Louth, Ireland
Tel.: (353) 429395900
Web Site: http://www.wcrx.com
Pharmaceuticals Product Mfr
N.A.I.C.S.: 325412

Subsidiary (Domestic):

Warner Chilcott (US), LLC (4)
2525 Dupont Dr, Irvine, CA 92612
Tel.: (973) 442-3200
Pharmaceutical Preparation Mfr
N.A.I.C.S.: 325412
Roger M. Boissonneault (CEO)

Subsidiary (Non-US):

Warner Chilcott Nederland B.V (4)
Keizerstraat 13, 4811 HL, Breda, Netherlands
Tel.: (31) 767630539
Pharmaceutical Product Whslr
N.A.I.C.S.: 424210

Subsidiary (Non-US):

Warner Chilcott Italy S.r.l. (5)
Viale Giorgio Ribotta 11, 00144, Rome, Italy
Tel.: (39) 0687504060
Pharmaceuticals Product Mfr
N.A.I.C.S.: 325412

Warner Chilcott Pharmaceuticals B.V.B.A. (5)
Pegasuslaan 5, 1831, Diegem, Vlaams Brabant, Belgium
Tel.: (32) 27092069
Pharmaceuticals Product Mfr
N.A.I.C.S.: 325412

Warner Chilcott Pharmaceuticals S.a.r.l. (5)
Rue De La Corraterie 14, 1204, Geneva, Switzerland
Tel.: (41) 227096111
Pharmaceutical Product Whslr
N.A.I.C.S.: 424210

Subsidiary (Domestic):

Warner Chilcott Puerto Rico LLC (4)
RR 2, Manati, PR 00674-9801
Tel.: (787) 854-1520
Sales Range: $25-49.9 Million
Emp.: 126
Pharmaceuticals Mfr
N.A.I.C.S.: 325412
Dave Cabarrery (Plant Mgr)

Subsidiary (Non-US):

Warner Chilcott UK Ltd. (4)
Old Belfast Road, Millbrook, Larne, BT40 2SH, Co Antrim, United Kingdom
Tel.: (44) 2828267222
Web Site: http://www.wcx.com
Developer & Mfr of Pharmaceuticals for Dermatology & Women's Health
N.A.I.C.S.: 325412
Clarie Gilligan (VP-Ops)

Subsidiary (Non-US):

Warner Chilcott Deutschland GmbH (5)
Dr-Otto-Rohm-Strasse 2-4, 64331, Weiterstadt, Germany
Tel.: (49) 61518770
Web Site: http://www.wcrx.com
Pharmaceuticals Product Mfr
N.A.I.C.S.: 325412

Subsidiary (Domestic):

ZELTIQ Aesthetics, Inc. (3)
4410 Rosewood Dr, Pleasanton, CA 94588
Tel.: (925) 474-2500
Web Site: https://www.coolsculpting.com
Sales Range: $200-249.9 Million
Medicinal Product Mfr
N.A.I.C.S.: 339112

Subsidiary (Non-US):

ZELTIQ Limited (4)
Unit 4 the Io Centre Salbrook Road, Redhill, RH1 5GJ, Surrey, United Kingdom
Tel.: (44) 1293312070
Web Site: http://www.coolsculpting.com
Medical Instrument Mfr
N.A.I.C.S.: 339112

Subsidiary (Non-US):

LifeCell EMEA Limited (2)
Ellebjergvej 52, 2450, Copenhagen, Denmark
Tel.: (45) 33389800
Emp.: 67
Pharmaceutical Products Distr
N.A.I.C.S.: 424210

LifeCell EMEA Limited (2)
Leutschenbachstrasse 45, 8050, Zurich, Switzerland
Tel.: (41) 434885100
Pharmaceutical Products Distr
N.A.I.C.S.: 424210

Pharm-Allergan GmbH (2)
Twin Tower 12 A Wienerbergstrasse 11, 1100, Vienna, Austria
Tel.: (43) 1994606355
Web Site: http://www.allergan.at
Pharmaceutical Products Distr
N.A.I.C.S.: 424210

Cerevel Therapeutics Holdings, Inc. (1)
222 Jacobs St Ste 200, Cambridge, MA 02141
Web Site: https://www.cerevel.com
Rev.: $9,619,000
Assets: $1,017,822,000
Liabilities: $496,584,000
Net Worth: $521,238,000
Earnings: ($351,511,000)
Emp.: 298
Fiscal Year-end: 12/31/2022
Offices of Other Holding Companies
N.A.I.C.S.: 551112
N. Anthony Coles (Chm & CEO)

Subsidiary (Domestic):

Cerevel Therapeutics, Inc. (2)
222 Jacobs St Ste 200, Cambridge, MA 02141
Tel.: (844) 304-2048
Web Site: https://www.cerevel.com
Holding Company; Biopharmaceutical Developer & Mfr
N.A.I.C.S.: 551112

Subsidiary (Domestic):

Cerevel Therapeutics, LLC (3)
222 Jacobs St Ste 200, Cambridge, MA 02141
Tel.: (844) 304-2048

Web Site: https://www.cerevel.com
Biopharmaceutical Developer & Mfr
N.A.I.C.S.: 325412

DJS Antibodies Ltd. (1)
Stansfeld Park Quarry Rd, Headington, Oxford, OX3 8SB, United Kingdom
Tel.: (44) 1865546471
Web Site: https://www.djsantibodies.com
Antibody Therapeutic Services
N.A.I.C.S.: 541714

Fundacion AbbVie (1)
Avenida de Burgos 91, 28050, Madrid, Spain
Tel.: (34) 913206515
Web Site: https://www.fundacionabbott.es
Pharmaceutical Preparation Mfr
N.A.I.C.S.: 325412

ImmunoGen, Inc. (1)
830 Winter St, Waltham, MA 02451
Tel.: (781) 895-0600
Web Site: https://www.immunogen.com
Rev.: $108,782,000
Assets: $348,936,000
Liabilities: $193,110,000
Net Worth: $155,826,000
Earnings: ($222,929,000)
Emp.: 277
Fiscal Year-end: 12/31/2022
Cancer Therapeutics Developer
N.A.I.C.S.: 325412
Theresa G. Wingrove (Sr VP-Regulatory Affairs & Quality)
Mark J. Enyedy (Pres & CEO)
Daniel S. Char (Chief Legal Officer & Sr VP)
Audrey Bergan (Chief HR Officer & Sr VP)
Renee Lentini (Chief Acctg Officer & VP-Fin)
Stacy Coen (Chief Bus Officer & Sr VP)
Lauren White (CFO & Sr VP)
Isabel Kalofonos (Chief Comml Officer & Sr VP)
Robert Herbst (VP)
Massimo Radaelli (Sr VP)
Mike Vasconcelles (Exec VP)
Jennifer L. Herron (Chief Comml Officer & Exec VP)
Anna Berkenblit (Chief Medical Officer & Sr VP)

Subsidiary (Non-US):

ImmunoGen Europe Limited (2)
2nd Floor 168 Shoreditch High Street, London, E1 6RA, United Kingdom
Tel.: (44) 2073821820
Biotechnology Research & Development Services
N.A.I.C.S.: 541714

Subsidiary (Domestic):

ImmunoGen Securities Corp. (2)
830 Winter St Ste 6, Waltham, MA 02451
Tel.: (617) 995-2500
Emp.: 24
Biotechnology Research & Development Services
N.A.I.C.S.: 541714

Jnana Therapeutics Inc (1)
1 Design Ctr Place Suite 19-400, Boston, MA 02210
Tel.: (857) 349-9200
Web Site: https://www.jnanatx.com
Biotechnology Company
N.A.I.C.S.: 541714

Landos Biopharma, Inc. (1)
1800 Kraft Dr Ste 216, Blacksburg, VA 24060
Tel.: (540) 218-2232
Web Site: http://www.landosbiopharma.com
Rev.: $1,285,000
Assets: $45,253,000
Liabilities: $6,122,000
Net Worth: $39,131,000
Earnings: ($39,276,000)
Emp.: 22
Fiscal Year-end: 12/31/2022
Biotechnology Research & Development Services
N.A.I.C.S.: 541714
Jyoti Chauhan (Exec VP-Ops & Regulatory Affairs)
Andrew Leber (Exec Dir-Scientific)
Jennifer Collette (VP-Fin & Contr)
Simon Lichtiger (Dir-Medical)

Pharmacyclics LLC (1)
995 E Arques Ave, Sunnyvale, CA 94085-4521
Tel.: (408) 215-3000
Web Site: https://www.pharmacyclics.com
Cancer Treatment Drug Developer
N.A.I.C.S.: 325412

Subsidiary (Non-US):

Pharmacyclics (Shanghai) Management Consulting Service Limited (2)
Room 2515 One Prime No 1361 North Sichuan Road, Shanghai, China
Tel.: (86) 2167256488
Management Consulting Services
N.A.I.C.S.: 541618

ABCO ENERGY, INC.
2505 N Alvernon Way, Tucson, AZ 85712
Tel.: (520) 777-0511 NV
Web Site: https://www.abcosolar.com
ABCE—(OTCIQ)
Rev.: $1,372,410
Assets: $745,839
Liabilities: $2,249,620
Net Worth: ($1,503,781)
Earnings: ($668,375)
Emp.: 12
Fiscal Year-end: 12/31/21
Other Electronic Parts & Equipment Merchant Wholesalers
N.A.I.C.S.: 423690
David Shorey (Founder, Pres, CEO & CFO)

ABEONA THERAPEUTICS INC.
1330 Avenue of the Americas 33rd Fl, New York, NY 10019
Tel.: (646) 813-4701 DE
Web Site: https://www.abeonatherapeutics.com
Year Founded: 1974
ABEO—(NASDAQ)
Rev.: $1,414,000
Assets: $64,214,000
Liabilities: $37,453,000
Net Worth: $26,761,000
Earnings: ($43,478,000)
Emp.: 57
Fiscal Year-end: 12/31/22
Pharmaceuticals Developer & Mfr
N.A.I.C.S.: 325412
Juan Ruiz (Head-European Medical Affairs)
Joseph Walter Vazzano (CFO)
Kristina Maximenko (VP-HR)
Jodie Gillon (Chief Patient Officer)
Scott Nogi (VP-Bus Ops & Head-Cleveland facility)
Brendan O'Malley (Gen Counsel & Sr VP)
Vishwas Seshadri (Pres, CEO & Principal Operating Officer)
Greg Gin (VP-IR & Corp Comm)
Brian Kevany (CTO, VP & Head-Res)
Linas Padegimas (Sr Dir-Product Dev)
Jon Voss (VP & Head-Quality)
Carl Denny (VP-Regulatory Affairs)
Kate Imhoff (Sr Dir-Regulatory Affairs)
Michael Amoroso (Chm)

ABERCROMBIE & FITCH CO.
6301 Fitch Path, New Albany, OH 43054
Tel.: (614) 283-6500 DE
Web Site: https://www.abercrombie.com
Year Founded: 1892
ANF—(NYSE)
Rev.: $3,697,751,000
Assets: $2,713,100,000
Liabilities: $2,006,531,000
Net Worth: $706,569,000
Earnings: $2,816,000
Emp.: 7,200

Fiscal Year-end: 01/28/23
Retail & Mail Order Casual Apparel
N.A.I.C.S.: 458110
Scott D. Lipesky *(CFO, COO & Exec VP)*
Gregory J. Henchel *(Gen Counsel, Sec & Sr VP)*
Samir Desai *(Chief Digital & Tech Officer)*
Fran Horowitz *(CEO)*
Jay Rust *(Exec VP-Human Resources)*
Nigel Travis *(Chm)*

Subsidiaries:

Abercrombie & Fitch Europe SA **(1)**
Via Moree, 6850, Mendrisio, Switzerland
Tel.: (41) 916400101
Sales Range: $1-4.9 Billion
Men's, Women's & Children's Clothing Retailer
N.A.I.C.S.: 424350

Subsidiary (Non-US):

AFH Australia Pty. Ltd. **(2)**
L 20 821 Pacific Hwy, Chatswood, 2067, NSW, Australia
Tel.: (61) 393696200
Web Site: https://www.afhpl.com.au
Apparel & Accessory Store Operator
N.A.I.C.S.: 458110

AFH Stores UK Limited **(2)**
3 Savile Row, London, W1S 3PB, United Kingdom
Tel.: (44) 2072979400
Apparel & Accessory Store Operator
N.A.I.C.S.: 458110

Abercrombie & Fitch Holding Corp. **(1)**
6301 Fitch Path, New Albany, OH 43054-9269
Tel.: (614) 283-6751
Web Site: https://www.abercrombie.com
Men's Clothing Stores
N.A.I.C.S.: 458110

Abercrombie & Fitch Trading Co. **(1)**
6301 Fitch Path, New Albany, OH 43054-9269
Tel.: (614) 283-6500
Web Site: http://www.abercrombie.com
Sales Range: $150-199.9 Million
Emp.: 300
Men's, Women's & Children's Clothing Whslr
N.A.I.C.S.: 424350

Gilly Hicks LLC **(1)**
1520 Fox Valley Center Dr, Aurora, IL 60504-4140
Tel.: (630) 898-3582
Men's Clothing Stores
N.A.I.C.S.: 458110

Hollister Co. **(1)**
24201 Valencia Blvd Ste 1234, Valencia, CA 91355
Tel.: (661) 753-9491
Web Site: https://www.hollisterco.com
Sales Range: $1-9.9 Million
Emp.: 85
Family Clothing Retailer
N.A.I.C.S.: 458110

Hollister Fashion L.L.C **(1)**
Financial Centre Road, Downtown Dubai, Dubai, United Arab Emirates
Tel.: (971) 43572699
Unisex Clothing Retailer
N.A.I.C.S.: 458110

ABERDEEN GLOBAL INCOME FUND, INC.
1900 Market St Ste 200, Philadelphia, PA 19103
Tel.: (215) 405-5700   MD
FCO—(NYSEAMEX)
Rev.: $5,482,154
Assets: $99,255,889
Liabilities: $30,920,447
Net Worth: $68,335,442
Earnings: $3,096,467

Fiscal Year-end: 10/31/19
Investment Management Service
N.A.I.C.S.: 525990

ABLE BRANDS CO.
30 Hudson Yards, New York, NY 10001
Tel.: (212) 801-1178   Ky
Year Founded: 2021
ABCOU—(NASDAQ)
Investment Services
N.A.I.C.S.: 523999
Lisa J. Blau *(Chm)*
Amanda Eilian *(CEO)*
Alison Ryu *(CFO)*

ABM INDUSTRIES, INC.
1 Liberty Plz 7th Fl, New York, NY 10006
Tel.: (212) 297-0200   DE
Web Site: https://www.abm.com
Year Founded: 1909
ABM—(NYSE)
Rev.: $8,359,400,000
Assets: $5,097,200,000
Liabilities: $3,315,300,000
Net Worth: $1,781,900,000
Earnings: $81,400,000
Emp.: 117,000
Fiscal Year-end: 10/31/24
Building Maintenance Services; Facility Services Contractor
N.A.I.C.S.: 561720
Andrea R. Newborn *(Gen Counsel, Sec & Exec VP)*
Rene Jacobsen *(COO & Exec VP)*
Sean M. Mahoney *(Pres-Sls & Mktg & Exec VP)*
Cary Bainbridge *(CMO)*
Earl R. Ellis *(CFO & Exec VP)*
Valerie Burd *(Pres-Education)*
Mark Hawkinson *(Pres-Technical Solutions)*
Nadeen Ayala *(Chief Comm Officer)*
Melanie Kirkwood Ruiz *(CIO)*
Sean Bromfield *(Pres & Pres-Aviation)*
Ed Marcil *(Pres & Pres-Manufacturing & Distribution)*
Marty Mantagne *(Pres-Engineering)*
Scott Camp *(Pres-Education)*
Dean Chin *(Chief Acctg Officer, Treas, Sr VP & Controller)*
Raul J. Valentin *(Chief HR Officer & Exec VP)*
Scott B. Salmirs *(Pres & CEO)*

Subsidiaries:

ABM Facility Solutions Group, LLC **(1)**
152 Technology, Irvine, CA 92618
Tel.: (949) 330-1555
Web Site: http://www.abm.com
Sales Range: $250-299.9 Million
Emp.: 4,200
Facilities Management & Building Systems Services
N.A.I.C.S.: 561210

Corporate Headquarters (Domestic):

ABM Facility Solutions Group, LLC **(2)**
1201 Louisiana St Ste 2700, Houston, TX 77002   **(100%)**
Tel.: (832) 214-5566
Web Site: http://www.abm.com
Executive Office
N.A.I.C.S.: 921110

Subsidiary (Domestic):

ABM Building Services, LLC **(3)**
6480 Cameron St Ste 303, Las Vegas, NV 89118
Tel.: (702) 260-7012
Sales Range: $25-49.9 Million
Emp.: 40
Heating, Ventilation & Air-Conditioning Contractor Services

N.A.I.C.S.: 238220
Greg Spears *(Gen Mgr)*

ABM Building Solutions, LLC **(3)**
4251 NW 1st Ave, Boca Raton, FL 33431
Tel.: (561) 395-5773
Web Site: http://www.abm.com
Sales Range: $1-9.9 Million
Emp.: 15
Heating, Ventilation & Air Conditioning
Unionized Contractor Services
N.A.I.C.S.: 238220

ABM Electrical & Lighting Solutions, Inc. **(3)**
152 Technology Dr, Irvine, CA 92618
Tel.: (949) 888-2340
Facility Services
N.A.I.C.S.: 561720

Subsidiary (Domestic):

ABM Electrical & Lighting Services, LLC **(4)**
321 W 44th St 6th Fl, New York, NY 10036
Tel.: (917) 975-8880
Web Site: http://www.abm.com
Emp.: 10
Building Maintenance & Facility Services
N.A.I.C.S.: 561790

Subsidiary (Domestic):

ABM Electrical Power Solutions, LLC **(3)**
4390 Parliament Pl, Lanham, MD 20706
Tel.: (301) 967-3500
Web Site: http://www.abm.com
Emp.: 30
Electrical Testing Services
N.A.I.C.S.: 334515

Subsidiary (Domestic):

ABM Electrical Power Services, LLC **(4)**
6541 Meridien Dr Ste 113, Raleigh, NC 27616-1859
Tel.: (919) 877-1008
Web Site: http://www.abm.com
Sales Range: $25-49.9 Million
Emp.: 12
Electrical Power Services

Subsidiary (Domestic):

ABM Facility Services **(3)**
5300 S Eastern Ave Ste 100, Los Angeles, CA 90040-2943
Tel.: (323) 234-2001
Web Site:
    http://www.abmfacilityservices.com
Sales Range: $500-549.9 Million
Emp.: 100
Janitorial Services
N.A.I.C.S.: 561720

ABM Facility Services, Inc. **(3)**
180 N LaSalle Ste 1700, Chicago, IL 60601
Tel.: (312) 541-0050
Web Site: http://www.abm.com
Sales Range: $100-124.9 Million
Emp.: 100
Engineeering Services
N.A.I.C.S.: 561720

ABM Franchising Group, LLC **(3)**
501 Technology Dr, Canonsburg, PA 15317
Tel.: (724) 873-2999
Web Site: http://www.lincservice.com
Sales Range: $50-74.9 Million
Emp.: 30
Heating, Ventilation & Air Conditioning Services Franchisor
N.A.I.C.S.: 533110
Scott J. Giacobbe *(Pres)*

Subsidiary (Domestic):

Airite Heating, Air Conditioning & Sheet Metal, Inc. **(4)**
10779 Fremont Ave, Ontario, CA 91762
Tel.: (909) 628-6035
Web Site: http://www.airite.com
Emp.: 20
Heating, Ventilation & Air-Conditioning Contractor Services
N.A.I.C.S.: 238220

John Reynolds *(Supvr-Field)*
Richard Mace Sr. *(Owner)*
Richard Mace Jr. *(Gen Mgr)*

GreenHomes America, LLC **(4)**
801 Hiawatha E Ste1, Syracuse, NY 13208
Tel.: (315) 474-6549
Web Site:
    http://www.greenhomesamerica.com
Energy Conservation Products & Services
N.A.I.C.S.: 561720

ABM Healthcare Support Services, Inc. **(1)**
22100 Greater Mack Ave Ste 101, Saint Clair Shores, MI 48080
Tel.: (586) 771-3040
Web Site: http://www.abm.com
Emp.: 30
Support Services for Healthcare Industry
N.A.I.C.S.: 561210

ABM Onsite Services, Inc. **(1)**
705 Illinois Ave Ste 10B, Joplin, MO 64801
Tel.: (417) 781-1444
Janitorial Services
N.A.I.C.S.: 561720

Subsidiary (Domestic):

ABM Janitorial Services, Inc. **(2)**
2131 Gulf Central Dr, Houston, TX 77023-4513   **(100%)**
Tel.: (713) 928-5344
Sales Range: $25-49.9 Million
Emp.: 150
Janitorial Services
N.A.I.C.S.: 561720
Mike Morris *(VP)*

Branch (Domestic):

ABM Janitorial Services - Hawaiian Region **(3)**
500 Alla Mana Blvd Ste6230, Honolulu, HI 96813
Tel.: (808) 545-7733
Web Site: http://www.abm.com
Sales Range: $100-124.9 Million
Facility Services
N.A.I.C.S.: 561720

ABM Janitorial Services - Mid-Atlantic Region **(3)**
103 Clermont Ave Ste-201, Alexandria, VA 22304-4837
Tel.: (703) 461-7501
Web Site: http://www.abm.com
Janitorial Services
N.A.I.C.S.: 561720

ABM Janitorial Services - Midwest Region **(3)**
180 N Lasalle St Ste 1700, Chicago, IL 60601
Tel.: (312) 541-0050
Web Site: http://www.abm.com
Janitorial Services
N.A.I.C.S.: 561720

ABM Janitorial Services - National Accounts **(3)**
650 Warrenville Rd Ste 550, Lisle, IL 60532
Tel.: (630) 663-1076
Web Site: http://www.ampcoexpress.com
Sales Range: $10-24.9 Million
Emp.: 15
Janitorial Services
N.A.I.C.S.: 561720

ABM Janitorial Services - North Central Region **(3)**
965 Decatur Ave N, Golden Valley, MN 55427
Tel.: (612) 378-0646
Web Site: http://www.abm.com
Sales Range: $10-24.9 Million
Janitorial Services
N.A.I.C.S.: 561720

ABM Janitorial Services - Northern California Region **(3)**
420 Taylor St 2nd Fl, San Francisco, CA 94102
Tel.: (415) 351-4500
Web Site: http://www.ampcoexpress.com
Sales Range: $100-124.9 Million
Janitorial Services
N.A.I.C.S.: 561720

ABM Industries, Inc.—(Continued)

ABM Janitorial Services - Northwest Mountain Region **(3)**
16 E Columbia Dr, Kennewick, WA 99336
Tel.: (509) 582-9776
Web Site: http://www.ampcoexpress.com
Sales Range: $10-24.9 Million
Emp.: 30
Janitorial Services
N.A.I.C.S.: 561720

ABM Janitorial Services - Northwest Pacific Region **(3)**
2001 22nd Ave S, Seattle, WA 98144
Tel.: (206) 329-8545
Web Site: http://www.abm.com
Sales Range: $100-124.9 Million
Janitorial Services
N.A.I.C.S.: 561720

ABM Janitorial Services - South Central Region **(3)**
1 Greenway Plz Ste 500, Houston, TX 77046
Tel.: (713) 928-5344
Web Site: http://www.ampcoexpress.com
Sales Range: $100-124.9 Million
Janitorial Services
N.A.I.C.S.: 561720

ABM Janitorial Services - Southeast Region **(3)**
3305 Breckinridge Blvd Ste 134, Duluth, GA 30096
Tel.: (678) 380-8588
Web Site: http://www.ampcoexpress.com
Sales Range: $10-24.9 Million
Emp.: 40
Janitorial Services
N.A.I.C.S.: 561720
John Amidei (VP-Southeast)

ABM Janitorial Services - West Central & West Pacific Region **(3)**
5300 S Eastern Ave St 100, Commerce, CA 90040
Tel.: (323) 234-2001
Web Site: http://www.abm.com
Janitorial Services
N.A.I.C.S.: 561720

Subsidiary (Non-US):

ABM Janitorial Services Company, Ltd. **(3)**
1075 Clark Dr-107 W 6 Avenue, Vancouver, V5Y 1K6, BC, Canada **(100%)**
Tel.: (604) 255-9595
Web Site: http://www.abmcanada.com
Sales Range: $50-74.9 Million
Janitorial Services
N.A.I.C.S.: 561720

Subsidiary (Domestic):

ABM Parking Services, Inc. **(2)**
808 S Olive St, Los Angeles, CA 90014-3006 **(100%)**
Tel.: (213) 624-6065
Web Site: http://www.abm.com
Sales Range: $10-24.9 Million
Emp.: 85
Parking Services
N.A.I.C.S.: 812930

Branch (Domestic):

ABM Parking Services, Inc. **(3)**
3049 Ualena St Ste 801, Honolulu, HI 96801 **(100%)**
Tel.: (808) 522-1280
Sales Range: $1-9.9 Million
Emp.: 10
Parking Services
N.A.I.C.S.: 812930

Ampco System Parking **(3)**
153 E Main St Ste 230, Columbus, OH 43215-5268 **(100%)**
Tel.: (614) 621-1208
Web Site: http://www.abm.com
Parking Services
N.A.I.C.S.: 561720

Ampco System Parking **(3)**
10521 Gulfdale St, San Antonio, TX 78216 **(100%)**
Tel.: (210) 226-5328

Sales Range: $1-9.9 Million
Emp.: 20
Parking Services
N.A.I.C.S.: 812930
Julio De Leon (Gen Mgr)

Ampco System Parking **(3)**
9800 E Geddes Ave Unit A150, Englewood, CO 80112 **(100%)**
Tel.: (303) 573-8121
Web Site: http://www.abm.com
Sales Range: $1-9.9 Million
Emp.: 15
Parking Services
N.A.I.C.S.: 812930

Ampco System Parking **(3)**
2600 N Central Ave Ste 750, Phoenix, AZ 85004-3091
Tel.: (602) 265-3505
Web Site: http://www.covan.com
Parking Services
N.A.I.C.S.: 812930

Ampco System Parking **(3)**
165 Technology Dr Ste 100, Irvine, CA 92618-2440
Tel.: (949) 252-0678
Web Site: http://www.abm.com
Sales Range: $1-9.9 Million
Emp.: 7
Parking Services
N.A.I.C.S.: 812930

Ampco System Parking **(3)**
40 E Gallivan Ave Ste 100, Salt Lake City, UT 84111
Tel.: (801) 364-7275
Sales Range: $1-9.9 Million
Emp.: 300
Parking Services
N.A.I.C.S.: 812930

Subsidiary (Domestic):

Diversco Inc. **(2)**
105 Diversco Dr, Spartanburg, SC 29307-5408
Tel.: (864) 579-3420
Web Site: http://www.diversco.com
Building Maintenance Services
N.A.I.C.S.: 551112

Air Serv Corporation **(1)**
3399 Peachtree Rd NE Ste 1800, Atlanta, GA 30326
Tel.: (404) 926-4200
Web Site: http://www.airservcorp.com
Sales Range: $300-349.9 Million
Emp.: 10,000
Aviation Support Services
N.A.I.C.S.: 488119

Subsidiary (Non-US):

ABM Group UK Limited **(2)**
George House 75-83 Borough High Street, London, SE1 1NH, United Kingdom
Tel.: (44) 2070896600
Web Site: https://www.abm.co.uk
Building Maintenance & Facility Services
N.A.I.C.S.: 561790
David Ford (CEO)
David Donovan (Dir-Ops)
Mike Smith (Head-Fin)
Sandra Parr (Dir-Bus Dev)
John Mcpherson (Dir-Scotland)
Lee Fitzgerald (Head-Retail)

Omni Serv Limited **(2)**
World Business Centre 2 Newall Road London Heathrow Airport, Hounslow, TW6 2SF, Middlesex, United Kingdom
Tel.: (44) 2036175149
Web Site: http://www.omniserv.eu
Building Maintenance & Facility Services
N.A.I.C.S.: 561790

Crown Building Maintenance Co. **(1)**
868 Folsom St, San Francisco, CA 94107-1123
Tel.: (415) 981-8070
Web Site: https://www.ableserve.com
Janitorial Services
N.A.I.C.S.: 561720
Paul Boschetto (CEO)
Mark Kelly (Pres)

GCA Services Group, Inc. **(1)**
1350 Euclid Ave, Cleveland, OH 44115
Tel.: (216) 535-4900

Facility Support Services
N.A.I.C.S.: 561210

Mechanical Solutions, Inc. **(1)**
3235 Halifax St, Dallas, TX 75247
Tel.: (972) 893-3400
Site Preparation Contractor
N.A.I.C.S.: 238910

OFJ Airlinks Limited **(1)**
Unit 2 Runway Park Church Road Lowfield Heath, Crawley, RH11 0PQ, United Kingdom
Tel.: (44) 1293554920
Web Site: http://www.ofjairlinks.com
Airport Transportation Services
N.A.I.C.S.: 485999

Quality Uptime Services, LLC **(1)**
9 Parklawn Dr, Bethel, CT 06801
Tel.: (203) 740-7877
Web Site: http://www.qualityuptime.com
UPS Battery Maintenance Services
N.A.I.C.S.: 237130
John Raio (CEO)
Benedict Caiola (CFO)
James Uhalt (Chief Revenue Officer)
Kody Pike (VP-Bus Ops)

Subsidiary (Domestic):

Sonoma Technical Service, Inc. **(2)**
140 Ethel Rd W Ste D, Piscataway, NJ 08854
Tel.: (732) 566-4700
Web Site: https://www.sonomats.com
Rev.: $2,691,000
Emp.: 13
Engineering Services
N.A.I.C.S.: 541330
Dennis Morris (Pres)

ABPRO HOLDINGS, INC.
68 Cummings Park Dr, Woburn, MA 01801 **DE**
Year Founded: 2021
ABP—(NASDAQ)
Holding Company
N.A.I.C.S.: 551112

Subsidiaries:

Abpro Corporation **(1)**
68 Cummings Park Dr, Woburn, MA 01801
Tel.: (617) 225-0808
Web Site: http://www.abpro.com
Sales Range: $1-9.9 Million
Emp.: 42
Biotechnology Research & Development Services
N.A.I.C.S.: 541714
Ian Chan (Co-Founder, Chm, Pres & CEO)
Adam Mostafa (CFO)
Gavin MacBeath (Chief Scientific Officer)
Yangde Chen (VP-Antibody Discovery)
John Xu (Sr VP-Strategic Alliances)
Antoine Awad (Sr VP-Mfg & Ops)
Eugene Chan (Co-Founder & Vice Chm)

ABRAXAS PETROLEUM CORPORATION
19100 Ridgewood Pkwy Ste 1200, San Antonio, TX 78259
Tel.: (210) 490-4788 **NV**
Web Site:
https://www.abraxaspetroleum.com
Year Founded: 1977
AXAS—(OTCIQ)
Rev.: $49,737,000
Assets: $70,547,000
Liabilities: $9,410,000
Net Worth: $61,137,000
Earnings: $37,328,000
Emp.: 18
Fiscal Year-end: 12/31/22
Oil & Natural Gas Exploration & Production
N.A.I.C.S.: 211120
Robert L. G. Watson (Chm, Pres & CEO)
Stephen T. Wendel (Sec & VP-Mktg & Contracts)
Tod A. Clarke (VP-Land)

ABRDN GLOBAL DYNAMIC

DIVIDEND FUND
1900 Market St Ste 200, Philadelphia, PA 19103
Tel.: (215) 405-5700 **DE**
AGD—(NYSE)
Rev.: $11,157,939
Assets: $140,266,458
Liabilities: $490,695
Net Worth: $139,775,763
Earnings: $9,523,348
Fiscal Year-end: 10/31/19
Investment Management Service
N.A.I.C.S.: 525990

ABRDN GLOBAL PREMIER PROPERTIES FUND
1900 Market St Ste 200, Philadelphia, PA 19103
Tel.: (215) 405-5700 **PA**
AWP—(NYSE)
Rev.: $21,525,459
Assets: $663,899,181
Liabilities: $41,971,821
Net Worth: $621,927,360
Earnings: $13,786,213
Fiscal Year-end: 10/31/19
Investment Management Service
N.A.I.C.S.: 525990

ABRDN GOLD ETF TRUST
1900 Market St Ste 200, Philadelphia, PA 19103 **NY**
Web Site: https://www.abrdn.com
SGOL—(NYSA)
Assets: $2,443,129,000
Liabilities: $346,000
Net Worth: $2,442,783,000
Earnings: ($4,233,000)
Fiscal Year-end: 12/31/22
Investment Trust Services
N.A.I.C.S.: 523991

ABRDN HEALTHCARE OPPORTUNITIES FUND
1900 Market St Ste 200, Philadelphia, PA 19103
Tel.: (617) 772-8500
Web Site: http://www.teklacap.com
Year Founded: 2014
THQ—(NYSE)
Rev.: $22,422,231
Assets: $1,010,097,261
Liabilities: $230,411,144
Net Worth: $779,686,117
Earnings: $3,086,033
Fiscal Year-end: 09/30/19
Investment Management Service
N.A.I.C.S.: 525990
Daniel R. Omstead (Pres & CEO)

ABRDN INCOME CREDIT STRATEGIES FUND
1900 Market St Ste 200, New Philadelphia, PA 19103
Tel.: (215) 405-5700
Web Site:
http://www.avenuecapital.com
ACP—(NYSE)
Sales Range: $25-49.9 Million
Investment Services
N.A.I.C.S.: 523999

ABRDN JAPAN EQUITY FUND INC.
1900 Market St Ste 200, Philadelphia, PA 19103
Tel.: (215) 405-5700 **MD**
Web Site: https://www.abrdnjeq.com
JEQ—(NYSE)
Closed-End Investment Fund
N.A.I.C.S.: 525990

ABRDN LIFE SCIENCES INVESTORS
100 Federal St 19th Fl, Boston, MA 02110

Tel.: (617) 772-8500   MA
Web Site: http://www.teklacap.com
HQL—(NYSE)
Rev.: $2,440,586
Assets: $386,981,946
Liabilities: $3,330,580
Net Worth: $383,651,366
Earnings: ($2,879,038)
Fiscal Year-end: 09/30/19
Diversified Closed-End Healthcare
Fund
N.A.I.C.S.: 523940
Daniel R. Omstead (Pres & CEO)

**ABRDN NATIONAL MUNICIPAL
INCOME FUND**
1900 Market St Ste 200, Philadel-
phia, PA 19103-7057
Tel.: (215) 405-5700   MA
Web Site:
   http://www.delawarefunds.com
VFL—(NYSEAMEX)
Rev.: $3,983,395
Assets: $93,401,923
Liabilities: $31,317,262
Net Worth: $62,084,661
Earnings: $2,465,717
Fiscal Year-end: 03/31/19
Investment Management Service
N.A.I.C.S.: 523940
Denise A. Franchetti (Mgr-Fund)
Shawn K. Lytle (Pres & CEO)
Thomas L. Bennett (Chm)

ABRDN SILVER ETF TRUST
1900 Market St Ste 200, Philadel-
phia, PA 19103   NY
Web Site: https://www.abrdn.com
SIVR—(NYSA)
Assets: $1,119,097,000
Liabilities: $280,000
Net Worth: $1,118,817,000
Earnings: ($3,061,000)
Fiscal Year-end: 12/31/22
Silver Related Investment Services
N.A.I.C.S.: 525910

**ABRDN TOTAL DYNAMIC DIVI-
DEND FUND**
1900 Market St Ste 200, Philadel-
phia, PA 19103
Tel.: (215) 405-5700   DE
AOD—(NYSE)
Rev.: $80,067,435
Assets: $1,009,370,863
Liabilities: $1,521,076
Net Worth: $1,007,849,787
Earnings: $68,105,125
Fiscal Year-end: 10/31/19
Investment Management Service
N.A.I.C.S.: 525990

**ABRDN WORLD HEALTHCARE
FUND**
1900 Market St Ste 200, Philadel-
phia, PA 19103
Tel.: (617) 772-8515   MA
THW—(NYSE)
Investment Services
N.A.I.C.S.: 523999
Laura Woodward (CFO & Treas)

ABSCI CORP.
18105 SE Mill Plain Blvd, Vancouver,
WA 98683
Tel.: (360) 949-1041   DE
Web Site: https://www.absci.com
Year Founded: 2011
ABSI—(NASDAQ)
Rev.: $5,747,000
Assets: $321,008,000
Liabilities: $46,594,000
Net Worth: $274,414,000
Earnings: ($104,904,000)
Emp.: 193
Fiscal Year-end: 12/31/22

Research & Development in Biotech-
nology (except Nanobiotechnology)
N.A.I.C.S.: 541714
Andreas E. Busch (Chief Innovation
Officer)
Denise Dettore (Chief People Officer)
Jack Gold (CMO)
Sean McClain (Founder & CEO)
Zachariah Jonasson (CFO, Chief Bus
Officer & Treas)

ABSECON BANCORP
106 New Jersey Ave, Absecon, NJ
08201
Tel.: (609) 641-6300
Web Site:
   https://www.fnbabsecon.com
ASCN—(OTCIQ)
Sales Range: Less than $1 Million
Bank Holding Company
N.A.I.C.S.: 551111
Christian Eric Gaupp (Pres & CEO)
Brenda Conover (Asst VP & Mgr-
Northfield)
Diann Goos (Asst VP & Mgr-Ops)
Helen D. Greis (Officer-Security &
VP)
John A. Montgomery (CFO & Exec
VP)
Kathy DeMari (Asst VP)
Priscilla Platt (Mgr)
Steve Hoffman (Chief Loan Officer &
Sr VP)
Theresa Abouras (Mgr)
Thomas Campbell (Sr Officer-Lending
& VP)
Harry Elwell III (Chm)

Subsidiaries:

First National Bank of Absecon   (1)
106 New Jersey Ave, Absecon, NJ 08201
Tel.: (609) 641-6300
Web Site: http://www.fnbabsecon.com
Sales Range: $1-9.9 Million
Emp.: 40
Commericial Banking
N.A.I.C.S.: 522110
Christian Eric Gaupp (Pres & CEO)

**ABSOLUTE HEALTH & FIT-
NESS, INC.**
50 W Liberty St Ste 880, Reno, NV
89501
Tel.: (631) 707-3139   NV
Web Site:
   https://www.absolutehf.com
AHFI—(OTCIQ)
Fitness Center Operator
N.A.I.C.S.: 713940
Darlene Calabrese (Owner)

ABVC BIOPHARMA, INC.
44370 Old Warm Springs Blvd, Fre-
mont, CA 94538
Tel.: (845) 291-1291   NV
Web Site:
   https://www.abvcpharma.com
Year Founded: 2002
ABVC—(NASDAQ)
Rev.: $969,783
Assets: $9,855,475
Liabilities: $6,619,336
Net Worth: $3,236,139
Earnings: ($16,423,239)
Emp.: 19
Fiscal Year-end: 12/31/22
Pharmaceuticals Product Mfr
N.A.I.C.S.: 325412
Tsung-Shann Jiang (Chief Scientific
Officer)
Uttam Yashwant Patil (CEO)
Leeds Chow (CFO, Principal Acctg
Officer & Controller)

**ACACIA DIVERSIFIED HOLD-
INGS, INC.**

13575 58th St N Ste 138, Clearwater,
FL 33760
Tel.: (727) 678-4420   TX
Web Site:
   http://www.acaciadiversifiedhol
   dings.com
ACCA—(OTCIQ)
Rev.: $519,221
Assets: $654,237
Liabilities: $2,167,975
Net Worth: ($1,513,738)
Earnings: ($1,588,928)
Emp.: 5
Fiscal Year-end: 12/31/19
Holding Company
N.A.I.C.S.: 551112
Danny R. Gibbs (Founder)
Kim Edwards (COO & VP)
Larnell C. Simpson Jr. (VP)
Timothy L. Matthews Jr. (Pres)

**ACACIA RESEARCH CORPO-
RATION**
767 3rd Ave 6th Fl, New York, NY
10017
Tel.: (332) 236-8484   DE
Web Site:
   https://www.acaciaresearch.com
ACTG—(NASDAQ)
Year Founded: 1999
Rev.: $59,223,000
Assets: $482,928,000
Liabilities: $213,606,000
Net Worth: $269,322,000
Earnings: ($125,065,000)
Emp.: 263
Fiscal Year-end: 12/31/22
Engineering, Production & Research
Services
N.A.I.C.S.: 334419
Kirsten Hoover (Interim CFO & Princi-
pal Acctg Officer)
Jason W. Soncini (Gen Counsel)
Li Yu (Controller)
Martin D. McNulty Jr. (Interim CEO)
Martin D. McNulty Jr. (CEO)
Robert Rasamny (Chief Admin Offi-
cer)
Gavin Molinelli (Chm)

Subsidiaries:

Acacia Research Group, LLC   (1)
4 Park Plz Ste 550, Irvine, CA 92614
Tel.: (949) 480-8300
Web Site: http://acaciaresearch.com
Commercial Physical Research Services
N.A.I.C.S.: 541715
Marvin E. Key (CEO)

Printronix, Inc.   (1)
7700 Irvine Ctr Dr Ste 700, Irvine, CA
92618
Tel.: (714) 368-2300
Web Site: http://www.printronix.com
Sales Range: $125-149.9 Million
Line Matrix Printers, Page Printers & Con-
tinuous Form Laser Printers & Thermal
Transfer Printers Mfr
N.A.I.C.S.: 334118
Albert Ching (VP-Sls & Mktg-Asia Pacific)
William D. Mathewes (CTO & VP-
Worldwide Engrg)
Francine Meza (VP-HR)
Rosemarie Zito (VP-Sls & Mktg-EMEA)
Werner Heid (CEO)
Ron Gillies (VP-Sls & Mktg-Americas)
Marlon Woolforde (Pres)
Arthur Verweij (Dir-Brand & Customer Dev-
Global)

**ACADEMY SPORTS AND OUT-
DOORS, INC.**
1800 N Mason Rd, Katy, TX 77449
Tel.: (281) 646-5200   DE
Web Site: https://www.academy.com
Year Founded: 2020
ASO—(NASDAQ)
Holding Company; Sporting Goods &
Outdoor Recreation Retailer

N.A.I.C.S.: 551112
Samuel J. Johnson (Pres)
Earl Carlton Ford IV (CFO & Exec
VP)
Matthew M. McCabe (Exec VP-
Officer)
William S. Ennis (Chief Admin Officer
& Exec VP)
Chad Fox (Exec VP-Officer)
Steven P. Lawrence (CEO)

Subsidiaries:

Academy, Ltd.   (1)
1800 N Mason Rd, Katy, TX 77449
Tel.: (281) 646-5200
Web Site: http://www.academy.com
Sales Range: $1-4.9 Billion
Emp.: 16,000
Sporting Goods, Sports Apparel & Athletic
Footwear Retailer
N.A.I.C.S.: 459110
Kenneth C. Hicks (Chm, Pres & CEO)
Michelle J. Gloeckler (Executives)

**ACADIA HEALTHCARE COM-
PANY, INC.**
6100 Tower Cir Ste 1000, Franklin,
TN 37067
Tel.: (615) 861-6000   DE
Web Site:
   https://www.acadiahealthcare.com
Year Founded: 2005
ACHC—(NASDAQ)
Rev.: $2,928,738,000
Assets: $5,358,841,000
Liabilities: $2,576,867,000
Net Worth: $2,781,974,000
Earnings: ($21,667,000)
Emp.: 17,000
Fiscal Year-end: 12/31/23
Holding Company; Behavioral Health-
care Facilities Operator
N.A.I.C.S.: 551112
Reeve Byron Waud (Founder)
Christopher H. Hunter (CEO)
Brian Farley (Gen Counsel, Sec &
Exec VP)
Isa Diaz (Sr VP-Strategic Affairs)
Michael Genovese (Chief Medical
Officer)
Anne Kelly (Chief Quality & Compli-
ance Officer)
David M. Keys (Chief Dev Officer)
J. L. Osei Mevs (VP-Govt Rels)
Gretchen Hommrich (VP-IR)
Laura Groschen (CIO)
Judith Scimone (Chief HR Officer)
Tim Sides (Sr VP-Ops Fin)
Bill Priest (Chief Compliance Officer)
Mark Palmenter (CMO)
Brett Bearfield (Sr VP)
Andrew Lynch (Chief Strategy Officer)
Heather Dixon (CFO)

Subsidiaries:

ATS of Delaware, Inc.   (1)
2999 Philadelphia Pike, Claymont, DE
19703
Tel.: (302) 792-0700
Web Site: http://www.claymontctc.com
Health Care Srvices
N.A.I.C.S.: 622110

Acadia - YFCS Holdings, Inc.   (1)
6100 Twr Cir Ste 1000, Franklin, TN 37067
Tel.: (615) 861-6000
Web Site:
   https://www.acadiahealthcare.com
Investment Management Service
N.A.I.C.S.: 551112

Acadia Montana, Inc.   (1)
55 Basin Creek Rd, Butte, MT 59701
Web Site: http://www.acadiamontana.com
Inpatient Behavioral Healthcare Services
N.A.I.C.S.: 622210

Acadiana Addiction Center, LLC   (1)
156 Choctaw Rd, Sunset, LA 70584
Tel.: (337) 233-1111

Acadia Healthcare Company, Inc.—(Continued)

Web Site:
https://www.acadianatreatmentcenter.com
Sales Range: $10-24.9 Million
Emp.: 50
Health Care Srvices
N.A.I.C.S.: 622210
Amy Apperson (CEO)
Melissa Meche (CFO)

Advanced Treatment Systems,
Inc.   (1)
1825 E Lincoln Hwy, Coatesville, PA 19320
Tel.: (610) 364-5585
Web Site:
https://www.acadiahealthcare.com
Health Care Srvices
N.A.I.C.S.: 622210
Tracie Purnell (Dir-Clinic)

Affinity Hospitals Holding Limited (1)
38-40 Mansionhouse Road, Glasgow, G41
3DW, United Kingdom
Tel.: (44) 1315104839
Web Site: http://www.affinityhospital-ltd.com
Health Care Srvices
N.A.I.C.S.: 622110

Aspen Education Group, Inc.   (1)
17777 Ctr Ct Dr Ste 300, Cerritos, CA
90703
Tel.: (562) 467-5500
Web Site:
http://www.aspeneducation.crchealth.com
Health Care Srvices
N.A.I.C.S.: 622110
Susan Cambria (Pres)

Aspen Youth, Inc.   (1)
17777 Center Court Dr N ste 300, Cerritos,
CA 90703
Tel.: (562) 567-5507
Emp.: 31
Health Care Srvices
N.A.I.C.S.: 622110

Aspire Scotland Limited.   (1)
Radio City Building 1A Bridgend Kilbirnie,
Bridgend, KA25 7DF, North Ayrshire, United
Kingdom
Tel.: (44) 1505685714
Web Site: https://www.aspirescotland.co.uk
Health Care Srvices
N.A.I.C.S.: 622110

Azure Acres Treatment Center,
LLC   (1)
2264 Green Hill Rd, Sebastopol, CA 95472
Tel.: (707) 284-0361
Web Site: https://www.azureacres.com
Health Care Srvices
N.A.I.C.S.: 622110
Lynette Grelet (Dir-HR)

BGI of Brandywine, Inc.   (1)
1375 Newark Rd, Kennett Square, PA
19348
Tel.: (610) 268-3589
Web Site:
https://www.bowlinggreenbrandywine.com
Emp.: 60
Health Care Srvices
N.A.I.C.S.: 622110

Baton Rouge Treatment Center,
Inc.   (1)
11445 Reiger Rd, Baton Rouge, LA 70809
Tel.: (877) 959-4906
Web Site: http://www.batonrougectc.com
Health Care Srvices
N.A.I.C.S.: 622110

Bayside Marin, Inc.   (1)
718 4th St, San Rafael, CA 94901
Tel.: (415) 721-2000
Web Site: https://www.baysidemarin.com
Health Care Srvices
N.A.I.C.S.: 622110
Cathy Kohs (Mgr-Continuing Care Case)
James Winder (Program Dir)
Candice Lipson (Chief Nursing Officer)

Beckley Treatment Center, LLC   (1)
175 Philpot Ln, Beaver, WV 25813
Tel.: (304) 254-9262
Web Site: https://www.ctcprograms.com
Health Care Srvices
N.A.I.C.S.: 622110
Sarah Carkin (Dir-Clinic)

Belmont Behavioral Hospital,
LLC   (1)
4200 Monument Rd, Philadelphia, PA
19131
Tel.: (215) 515-7641
Web Site:
https://www.belmontbehavioral.com
Health Care Srvices
N.A.I.C.S.: 622110
Laura Longstreet (CEO)
Jacqueline Basile (COO)
Fayez El-Gabalawi (Chief Medical Officer)
Adria Filmore (Chief Clinical Officer)
Jennifer Fitzgerald (CFO)
Eve Barnett (Chief Compliance Officer)
Dawn Bausman (Chief Nursing Officer)

Blue Ridge Mountain Recovery Cen-
ter, LLC   (1)
255 Depot St Ste 200, Ball Ground, GA
30107
Tel.: (678) 515-9867
Web Site:
https://www.blueridgemountainreco
very.com
Health Care Srvices
N.A.I.C.S.: 622110
Todd Stumbo (CEO)
Amy Dillon (CFO)
Heather Powell (Mgr-HR)
Michelle Robas (Mgr-Nurse)
Christopher Anderson (Dir-Medical)
Kent Stump (Dir-Utilization Review)
Marcos Sanchez (Dir-Admissions)

Bowling Green Inn of Pensacola,
Inc.   (1)
7940 N Federal Hwy, Boca Raton, FL
33487-1679
Tel.: (561) 995-7388
Web Site:
https://www.wellnessresourcecenter.com
Health Care Srvices
N.A.I.C.S.: 622110
Jennifer Camposano-Wallace (CEO)
Andrew James (Dir-Admissions)
John Binns (Mgr-HR & Risk)
Sharon Burns-Carter (Founder)
Jaqueline Pevny (Dir-Medical)
Andrew Vereecke (CFO)

Bowling Green Inn of South Dakota,
Inc.   (1)
1010 E 2nd St, Canton, SD 57013
Tel.: (605) 987-5659
Web Site:
https://www.keystonetreatment.com
Drug Addiction Rehabilitation Services
N.A.I.C.S.: 622110
Josh Merkley (CFO)
Erik Miller (Dir-Bus Dev)
Marsha Eliason (Dir-HR)
Nick Welter (CFO)

CRC Health Group, Inc.   (1)
20400 Stevens Creek Blvd 6th Fl, Cuper-
tino, CA 95014
Web Site: http://www.crchealth.com
Health Care & Treatment Services
N.A.I.C.S.: 551112

CRC Health Treatment Clinics,
LLC   (1)
6639 Southpoint Pkwy Ste 108, Jackson-
ville, FL 32216
Web Site:
https://www.acadiahealthcare.com
Health Care Srvices
N.A.I.C.S.: 622110

CRC Health, LLC   (1)
20100 Stevens Creek Fl 6, Cupertino,
CA 95014
Web Site: http://www.crchealth.com
Health Care Srvices
N.A.I.C.S.: 622110

CRC Wisconsin RD, LLC   (1)
615 Old Mill Rd, Hudson, WI 54016
Tel.: (715) 386-6125
Web Site:
https://www.burkwoodtreatmentcenter.com
Health Care Srvices
N.A.I.C.S.: 622110
Danielle Schwartz (Dir-HR)
Kelly Maas (Dir-Clinical)
Jamie Hawley (Dir-Bus Dev)
Rachael Flohrs (CEO)

California Treatment Services   (1)

2101 E 1st St, Santa Ana, CA 92705
Tel.: (714) 581-9181
Web Site: https://www.ctcprograms.com
Health Care Srvices
N.A.I.C.S.: 622110

Cartersville Center, Inc.   (1)
218 Stonewall St, Cartersville, GA 30120
Tel.: (770) 386-1907
Web Site: https://www.ctcprograms.com
Health Care Srvices
N.A.I.C.S.: 622110

Cascade Behavioral Hospital,
LLC   (1)
12844 Military Rd S, Tukwila, WA 98168
Tel.: (206) 244-0180
Web Site: https://www.cascadebh.com
Health Care Srvices
N.A.I.C.S.: 622110

Centerpointe Community Based Ser-
vices, LLC   (1)
6919 E 10th St Bldg C, Indianapolis, IN
46219
Tel.: (317) 787-4024
Web Site: http://www.centerpointecbs.com
Health Care Srvices
N.A.I.C.S.: 622110
Stanley Frank (CEO)

Charleston Treatment Center,
LLC   (1)
2157 Greenbrier St, Charleston, WV 25311
Tel.: (844) 243-9078
Web Site: http://www.westvirginiactc.com
Health Care Srvices
N.A.I.C.S.: 622110

Children's Behavioral Solutions,
LLC   (1)
47 Oliver Ct, Signal Mountain, TN 37377
Tel.: (423) 280-4472
Web Site: http://www.acadiahealthcare.com
Inpatient Behavioral Healthcare Service
Provider
N.A.I.C.S.: 622210

Clarksburg Treatment Center,
LLC   (1)
706 Oakmound Rd, Clarksburg, WV 26301
Tel.: (304) 622-7511
Web Site: http://www.westvirginiactc.com
Health Care Srvices
N.A.I.C.S.: 622110

Clarksville Treatment Center,
LLC   (1)
495 Dunlop Ln Ste 106, Clarksville, TN
37040
Web Site:
https://www.acadiahealthcare.com
Health Care Srvices
N.A.I.C.S.: 621999

Conquest Care Homes (Soham)
Limited   (1)
Dereham Road, Norfolk, Thetford, IP25
6HA, United Kingdom
Tel.: (44) 1953884597
Health Care Srvices
N.A.I.C.S.: 622110

Conway Behavioral Health, LLC   (1)
2255 Sturgis Rd, Conway, AR 72034
Tel.: (501) 404-4201
Web Site: https://www.conwaybh.com
Health Care Srvices
N.A.I.C.S.: 622110
Thomas Stinnett (Dir-Medical)
Beau Lynch (CEO)
Jessica Satterfield (CFO)
Cynthia Ellis (Chief Nursing Officer)

Crossroads Regional Hospital,
LLC   (1)
44 Versailles Blvd, Alexandria, LA 71303
Tel.: (318) 562-4988
Web Site: https://www.longleafhospital.com
Health Care Srvices
N.A.I.C.S.: 622110
Cynthia Donnelly (Dir-HR)
Robert McGinnis (Dir-Plant Ops & IT)
Gaston Coco (Dir-Bus Dev)
Ashley Knippers (CFO)

DMC-Memphis, Inc.   (1)
3000 Getwell Rd, Memphis, TN 38118
Tel.: (901) 369-8100

Web Site:
https://www.deltaspecialhospital.com
Health Care Srvices
N.A.I.C.S.: 622110

Detroit Behavioral Institute, Inc.   (1)
1333 Brewery Park Blvd Ste 140, Detroit,
MI 48207   (100%)
Tel.: (313) 831-3500
Web Site: http://www.dbinstitute.com
Sales Range: $50-74.9 Million
Health Care Srvices
N.A.I.C.S.: 622110

Discovery House TV, Inc.   (1)
5983 S Redwood Rd, Taylorsville, UT
84123
Tel.: (801) 293-9999
Web Site: https://www.ctcprograms.com
Health Care Srvices
N.A.I.C.S.: 622110

Discovery House WC, Inc.   (1)
12 Beech St, Calais, ME 04619
Tel.: (207) 454-1300
Web Site: https://www.ctcprograms.com
Health Care Srvices
N.A.I.C.S.: 622110

Discovery House-LT, Inc.   (1)
523 W Heritage Park Blvd Ste 4, Layton,
UT 84041
Tel.: (801) 525-9998
Web Site: https://www.ctcprograms.com
Health Care Srvices
N.A.I.C.S.: 622110

Discovery House-UC, Inc.   (1)
714 S State St, Orem, UT 84058
Tel.: (801) 426-6565
Web Site: https://www.ctcprograms.com
Health Care Srvices
N.A.I.C.S.: 622110

Duffys Napa Valley Rehab, LLC   (1)
3076 Myrtledale Rd, Calistoga, CA 94515
Tel.: (707) 998-5385
Web Site: https://www.duffysrehab.com
Health Care Srvices
N.A.I.C.S.: 622110
Hide Miyamoto (CFO)
Jeremy Campbell (CEO)
Noelia Ruiz-Angel (Mktg Dir)
Gene Duffy (Founder)
Maren Vick (Dir-Human Svcs)
Joe Soares (Coord-Outreach)
Carter Q. Serrett (Dir-Clinical Svcs)
Margaret Bourne (Dir-Medical)

East Indiana Treatment Center,
LLC   (1)
816 Rudolph Way, Lawrenceburg, IN 47025
Web Site:
https://www.acadiahealthcare.com
Health Care Srvices
N.A.I.C.S.: 622110

Erlanger Behavioral Health, LLC   (1)
804 N Holtzclaw Ave, Chattanooga, TN
37404
Tel.: (423) 498-4650
Web Site: https://www.erlangerbh.com
Healtcare Services
N.A.I.C.S.: 622210
Matthew Whitley (COO)
Jennie Mahaffey (Chief Medical Officer)
Lori Grider (Chief Nursing Officer)

Evansville Treatment Center,
LLC   (1)
1510 W Franklin St, Evansville, IN 47710
Web Site: https://www.ctcprograms.com
Health Care Srvices
N.A.I.C.S.: 622110

Four Circles Recovery Center,
LLC   (1)
156 Clear Crossing Ln, Horse Shoe, NC
28742
Tel.: (828) 891-2221
Web Site:
http://www.fourcirclesrecovery.com
Rehabilitation Services
N.A.I.C.S.: 622310
Shane Applegate (CEO)

Galax Treatment Center, Inc.   (1)
112 Painter St, Galax, VA 24333
Web Site:
https://www.acadiahealthcare.com

Medical Hospital Services
N.A.I.C.S.: 622210
Kathy Kirkland (CFO)

Generations Behavioral Health, LLC (1)
196 Colonial Dr, Youngstown, OH 44505
Tel.: (234) 232-7500
Web Site:
https://www.generationsbehavioral
health.com
Health Care Srvices
N.A.I.C.S.: 621999
Sean Haywood (Dir-Market & HR)

Gifford Street Wellness Center, LLC (1)
34 Gifford St, New Bedford, MA 02744
Web Site: http://www.semassctc.com
Health Care Srvices
N.A.I.C.S.: 622110

Greenbrier Realty, L.L.C. (1)
2345 Hwy 41 S, Greenbrier, TN 37073
Tel.: (615) 643-4587
Emp.: 7
Health Care Srvices
N.A.I.C.S.: 622110

Greenleaf Center, LLC (1)
2209 Pineview Dr, Valdosta, GA 31602
Tel.: (562) 945-5108
Web Site:
https://www.greenleafhospital.com
Health Care Srvices
N.A.I.C.S.: 622110
Eugene Sun (Chief Medical Officer)
Michelle Neville (CEO)
Denida Cox (Chief Nursing Officer)

HMIH Cedar Crest, LLC (1)
3500 S IH-35, Belton, TX 76513
Tel.: (254) 939-2100
Web Site:
https://www.cedarcresthospital.com
Health Care Srvices
N.A.I.C.S.: 622110
Brady Serafin (CEO)
Melissa West (CFO)
Monica Gauna (COO)
Appolonia Okereke (Chief Nursing Officer)

Subsidiary (Domestic):

Cedar Crest Clinic (2)
3106 S W S Young Dr Ste 201, Killeen, TX 76542
Tel.: (254) 519-4162
Web Site:
http://www.cedarcresthospital.com
Emp.: 8
Health Care Srvices
N.A.I.C.S.: 622110

Habit Holdings, Inc. (1)
500 N Gulph Rd Ste 500, King of Prussia, PA 19406
Tel.: (610) 567-2398
Emp.: 20
Holding Company Services
N.A.I.C.S.: 551114

Huntington Treatment Center, LLC (1)
135 4th Ave, Huntington, WV 25701
Tel.: (304) 932-0106
Web Site: http://www.westvirginiactc.com
Health Care Srvices
N.A.I.C.S.: 622110

Indianapolis Treatment Center, LLC (1)
2626 E 46th St Ste J, Indianapolis, IN 46205
Web Site:
https://www.acadiahealthcare.com
Health Care Srvices
N.A.I.C.S.: 622110
Brandon J. Golder (Exec Dir)

Kids Behavioral Health of Montana, Inc. (1)
55 Basin Creek Rd, Butte, MT 59701
Tel.: (406) 496-6300
Emp.: 630
Health Care Srvices
N.A.I.C.S.: 622110

Lakeland Behavioral Health System (1)

440 S Market Ave, Springfield, MO 65806
Web Site:
https://www.lakelandbehavioralhealth.com
Health Care Srvices
N.A.I.C.S.: 622110
Nate Duncan (CEO)
Richard Aiken (Dir-Medical)
Mark David (Dir-Rehabilitation Svcs)
Dave England (Dir-HR)
John Kellerman (Dir-Nursing)
Rebecca Granden (Dir-Performance Improvement & Risk Mgmt)
Max Loya (Dir-Residential Ops)

Lewistown Comprehensive Treatment Center, LLC (1)
129 S Main St Ste T, Lewistown, PA 17044
Medical Counseling Services
N.A.I.C.S.: 621330

Life Works Community Limited (1)
The Grange High Street, Old Woking, GU22 8LB, Surrey, United Kingdom
Tel.: (44) 1483378227
Web Site:
https://www.lifeworkscommunity.com
Health Care Srvices
N.A.I.C.S.: 622110

MMO Behavioral Health Systems LLC (1)
728 N Blvd, Baton Rouge, LA 70802
Tel.: (225) 293-6774
Web Site: http://www.mmoinc.com
Health Care Srvices
N.A.I.C.S.: 622210
Chris Nichols (Founder)

Mark College Limited (1)
Highbridge, Somerset, TA9 4NP, United Kingdom
Tel.: (44) 1278641632
Emp.: 60
Health Care Srvices
N.A.I.C.S.: 622110

McCallum Group, LLC (1)
231 W Lockwood Ave Ste 202, Saint Louis, MO 63119
Tel.: (314) 968-1900
Web Site: https://www.mccallumplace.com
Health Care Srvices
N.A.I.C.S.: 622110
Kimberli McCallum (Founder)
Alexis Hughes (Mgr-Nutrition)
Michelle Petrosky (CEO)
Corey Hastings (CFO)

Millcreek Management Corporation (1)
830 Crescent Ctr Dr 6 Ste 610, Franklin, TN 37067
Tel.: (843) 206-0730
Inpatient Behavioral Healthcare Service Provider
N.A.I.C.S.: 622210

Mount Bachelor Educational Center, Inc. (1)
967 NE 2nd St, Prineville, OR 97754
Tel.: (541) 462-3404
Health Care Educational Services
N.A.I.C.S.: 611310

Muncie Treatment Center, LLC (1)
3640 N Briarwood Ln Ste 1, Muncie, IN 47304
Web Site: http://www.indianactc.com
Health Care Srvices
N.A.I.C.S.: 621999

National Specialty Clinics, LLC (1)
618 Church St Ste 510, Nashville, TN 37219
Tel.: (615) 312-7017
Health Care Srvices
N.A.I.C.S.: 622110

New Directions (St. Leonards on Sea) Limited (1)
Priory Group 5th Floor 80 Hammersmith Road, London, W14 8UD, United Kingdom
Tel.: (44) 1424720320
Health Care Srvices
N.A.I.C.S.: 622110

New Leaf Academy, Inc. (1)
PO Box 6454, Bend, OR 97708
Tel.: (541) 318-1676
Web Site: http://www.newleafacademy.com

Drug Addiction Rehabilitation Services
N.A.I.C.S.: 622220
Craig A. Christiansen (Co-Founder & Co-Owner)
Christy Christiansen (Co-Founder, Co-Owner & Mgr-Bus)
Deveney Marshall (Exec Dir)
Jennifer Parker (Dir-Admissions & Mktg)
Joshua Goldstein (Dir-Academic)
Stacie Fox (Dir-Ops)
Cathryn Perkins (Coord-Aftercare Program)
Susan Wallace (Mgr-House)
Jess Joseph (Coord-Wellness)
Naomi Healy (Program Dir)
Erin Christiansen (Dir-Interim Clinical)

Next Generation Behavioral Health, LLC (1)
2256 1/2 E Main St Ste C, Bexley, OH 43209
Tel.: (800) 570-1509
Web Site: http://www.behaveforward.com
Health Care Srvices
N.A.I.C.S.: 622110

Ochsner-Acadia, LLC (1)
500 Rue de Sante, La Place, LA 70068
Web Site: https://www.riverplacebh.com
Health Care Srvices
N.A.I.C.S.: 622110

Ohio Hospital for Psychiatry, LLC (1)
880 Greenlawn Ave, Columbus, OH 43223
Tel.: (614) 532-4307
Web Site:
https://www.ohiohospitalforpsychiatry.com
Health Care Srvices
N.A.I.C.S.: 622110
Chris Bockelman (CFO)
Karen Core (Dir-Bus Dev)
Monica Jones (Dir-HM)
Natasha Schafer (CEO)

Options Treatment Center Acquisition Corporation (1)
5602 Caito Dr, Indianapolis, IN 46226
Tel.: (317) 544-4340
Web Site:
https://www.optionsbehavioralhealth
system.com
Sales Range: $25-49.9 Million
Emp.: 200
Health Care Srvices
N.A.I.C.S.: 622110
Ryan Cassedy (CEO)
Chris Stewart (CFO)

PHC Meadowwood, LLC (1)
575 S Dupont Hwy, New Castle, DE 19720
Tel.: (302) 328-3330
Web Site:
https://www.meadowwoodhospital.com
Health Care Srvices
N.A.I.C.S.: 622110
Jennifer Shalk (CEO)

PHC of Michigan, Inc. (1)
35031 23 Mile Rd, New Baltimore, MI 48047 (100%)
Web Site: https://www.harboroaks.com
Sales Range: $50-74.9 Million
Health Care Srvices
N.A.I.C.S.: 622110

PHC of Nevada, Inc. (1)
1701 W Charleston Ste 300, Las Vegas, NV 89102
Tel.: (702) 251-8000
Web Site: https://www.harmonyhc.com
Sales Range: $50-74.9 Million
Emp.: 40
Health Care Srvices
N.A.I.C.S.: 622110
Allen Flagg (CEO)
Adekunle Ajayi (Dir-Medical)
John Duerr (Dir-Horizon Ridge Clinical-Outpatient Clinic)
Paul Kane (Dir-Clinical-West Charleston)
Chava Peebles (Mgr-Bus Office)
Hoda Hassanieh (Mgr-Care)
Meg Blair (VP)

Subsidiary (Domestic):

Seven Hills Hospital, Inc. (2)
3021 W Horizon Rdg Pkwy, Henderson, NV 89052 (100%)
Web Site: https://www.sevenhillsbi.com
Sales Range: $50-74.9 Million
Health Care Srvices
N.A.I.C.S.: 622110

Mustafa Rawaf (Dir-Medical)

PHC of Utah, Inc. (1)
7309 S 180 W, Midvale, UT 84047 (100%)
Tel.: (801) 569-2153
Web Site:
https://www.highlandridgehospital.com
Sales Range: $50-74.9 Million
Health Care Srvices
N.A.I.C.S.: 622110

PHC of Virginia, Inc. (1)
125 Knotbreak Rd, Salem, VA 24153
Tel.: (540) 389-4761
Web Site: https://www.mtregis.com
Health Care Srvices
N.A.I.C.S.: 622110
Mukesh P. Patel (Dir-Medical)
Ashley Neighbors (Dir-Nursing)
Michael T. Bolton (CFO)

Parkersburg Treatment Center, LLC (1)
184 Holiday Hills Dr, Parkersburg, WV 26104
Tel.: (304) 420-2400
Web Site: https://www.ctcprograms.com
Health Care Srvices
N.A.I.C.S.: 622110

Partnerships in Care Limited (1)
2 Imperial Place Maxwell Road, Borehamwood, WD6 1JN, Hertfordshire, United Kingdom
Tel.: (44) 2083271800
Web Site:
http://www.partnershipsincare.co.uk
Health Care Srvices
N.A.I.C.S.: 622110
Sarah Livingston (Gen Counsel & Sec)

Passages to Recovery, LLC (1)
30 S Main St, Loa, UT 84747
Tel.: (435) 836-1199
Drug Addiction Rehabilitation Services
N.A.I.C.S.: 622210

Philadelphia Crisis Response Center, LLC (1)
3300 Henry Ave, Philadelphia, PA 19129
Tel.: (215) 878-2600
Health Care Srvices
N.A.I.C.S.: 622110

Pinewood Healthcare Realty, L.P. (1)
699 Heritage Oaks Rd, Texarkana, TX 75503
Tel.: (903) 277-9295
Inpatient Behavioral Healthcare Service Provider
N.A.I.C.S.: 622210

Progress Adult Services Limited (1)
Dixons Farm Wigan Road Bamber Bridge, Preston, PR5 6AS, Lancashire, United Kingdom
Tel.: (44) 1772626916
Health Care Srvices
N.A.I.C.S.: 622110

Quality Addiction Management Inc. (1)
2422 N Grandview Blvd, Waukesha, WI 53188
Tel.: (262) 549-6600
Web Site:
http://www.methadonetreatment.com
Health Care Srvices
N.A.I.C.S.: 622110

Quantum Care (UK) Limited (1)
Quantum Care 4 Silver Court Watchmead, Welwyn Garden City, AL7 1TS, Hertfordshire, United Kingdom
Tel.: (44) 1707393293
Web Site: https://www.quantumcare.co.uk
Healtcare Services
N.A.I.C.S.: 621610

Red River Holding Company, LLC (1)
2047 Vista Pkwy, West Palm Beach, FL 33411
Tel.: (561) 296-9842
Health Care Srvices
N.A.I.C.S.: 622110

Red River Hospital, LLC (1)
1505 8th St, Wichita Falls, TX 76301
Tel.: (940) 322-3171
Web Site: https://www.redriverhospital.com

Acadia Healthcare Company, Inc.—(Continued)

Health Care Srvices
N.A.I.C.S.: 622110
Michele Middlesworth (Dir-Utilization Review & Intake)
Kristi McCasland (CFO)
Alex Wanee (CEO)

Rehabilitation Centers, Inc. (1)
900 1st Ave NE, Magee, MS 39111
Tel.: (601) 849-4221
Web Site:
https://www.millcreekofmagee.com
Health Care Srvices
N.A.I.C.S.: 622110

Subsidiary (Domestic):

Habilitation Center, Inc. (2)
PO Box 727, Fordyce, AR 71742
Tel.: (870) 352-8203
Web Site:
http://www.millcreekofarkansas.com
Inpatient Behavioral Healthcare Service Provider
N.A.I.C.S.: 622210

Resolute Acquisition Corporation (1)
1404 S State Ave, Indianapolis, IN 46203
Tel.: (317) 630-5215
Web Site:
https://www.resourcetreatmentcenter.com
Sales Range: $25-49.9 Million
Emp.: 100
Health Care Srvices
N.A.I.C.S.: 622110

Richmond Treatment Center, LLC (1)
4265 S A St, Richmond, IN 47374
Web Site:
https://www.acadiahealthcare.com
Health Care Srvices
N.A.I.C.S.: 622110
Luke Mohr (Exec Dir)

RiverWoods Behavioral Health, LLC (1)
223 Medical Center Dr, Riverdale, GA 30274
Tel.: (770) 766-3367
Web Site:
https://www.riverwoodsbehavioral.com
Emp.: 100
Health Care Srvices
N.A.I.C.S.: 622110
Shani Studstill (Dir-Outpatient)

Riverview Behavioral Health, LLC (1)
701 Arkansas Blvd, Texarkana, AR 71854
Tel.: (870) 772-5028
Web Site:
https://www.riverviewbehavioralhealth.com
Health Care Srvices
N.A.I.C.S.: 622110
Colleen Vicari (CEO)
Kelcey Caletka (CFO)

Rolling Hills Hospitals, Inc. (1)
1000 Rolling Hills Ln, Ada, OK 74820
Web Site:
https://www.rollinghillshospital.com
Psychiatric Healthcare Service Provider
N.A.I.C.S.: 621420
Robert Morton (Dir-Medical)
David Butler (Dir-Admissions)
Shana Booth (Dir-Health Information Mgmt)
Sherri Chandler (CEO)
Chris Mann (CFO)
Curtis Classen (Dir-Bus Dev)
Janet Strayhorn (Chief Nursing Officer)

Rossendale School Limited (1)
Higher Moss Bamford Road, Bury, BL0 0RT, Lancashire, United Kingdom
Tel.: (44) 1706822779
Health Care Srvices
N.A.I.C.S.: 622110

SUWS of the Carolinas, Inc. (1)
363 Graphite Rd, Old Fort, NC 28762
Web Site: https://www.suwscarolinas.com
Health Care Srvices
N.A.I.C.S.: 622110
Daniel Fishburn (CEO)
Camille Edmonds (Dir-Ops)
Josh Gunalda (Dir-Admissions)
Kelly Dunbar (Dir-Bus Dev)

Bryan Delaney (Dir-Program)
Erica Thiessen-House (Dir-Clinical)
Drew Schnyder (Dir-Medical)
Kevin Waller (Mgr-Family Program)
John Uberto (Mgr-Bus Dev Account)

San Diego Health Alliance (1)
234 N Magnolia Ave, El Cajon, CA 92020
Tel.: (619) 579-8373
Web Site: https://www.ctcprograms.com
Health Care Srvices
N.A.I.C.S.: 622110
Julie Brunetto (Supvr-Clinical)

San Diego Treatment Services (1)
1161 3rd Ave, Chula Vista, CA 91911-3136
Tel.: (619) 498-8260
Drug Addiction Rehabilitation Services
N.A.I.C.S.: 622210

San Juan Capestrano Hospital, Inc. (1)
State Rd 877 Km 1 6 Camino Las Lomas
Rio Piedras, San Juan, PR 00926
Tel.: (787) 826-2900
Web Site: https://en.sanjuancapestrano.com
Health Care Srvices
N.A.I.C.S.: 622110
Marta Rivera Plaza (CEO)
Martha Gay (Dir-HR)
Luis Gonzalez (CFO)

Serenity Knolls (1)
145 Tamal Rd, Forest Knolls, CA 94933
Web Site: https://www.serenityknolls.com
Emp.: 35
Health Care Srvices
N.A.I.C.S.: 622110
Catherine McQuilkin (Co-CEO)
Heather McCrea (Co-CEO)
Kris Bazavilvazo (Grp CFO)

Shaker Clinic, LLC (1)
20600 Chagrin Blvd Ste 620, Shaker Heights, OH 44122
Web Site: http://www.shakerclinic.com
Sales Range: $25-49.9 Million
Emp.: 60
Health Care Srvices
N.A.I.C.S.: 622110

Sierra Tucson Inc. (1)
39580 S Lago del Oro Pkwy, Tucson, AZ 85739
Tel.: (520) 818-5811
Web Site: https://www.sierratucson.com
Health Care Srvices
N.A.I.C.S.: 622110
Valerie M. Kading (CEO)
Blake Master (Chief Admissions & Relationship Officer)
Amy C. Fritton Grudinschi (CFO-Grp)
Sue Menzie (Chief Risk Officer & Chief Quality Officer)
Donnie Sansom (Assoc Dir-Medical)
Bennet E. Davis (Dir-Pain Recovery Program)
Jasleen Chhatwal (Chief Medical Officer & Dir-Mood Program)
Maureen Schwehr (Dir-Integrative Svcs)
Scott Frazier (Mgr-Program)
David Cato (Dir-HR)
Caitlin Railson (Coord-Admissions)
Dasa Schmidt (Coord-Admissions)
Rachel Bennet (Coord-Admissions)
Rachelle Baldenegro (Coord-Admissions)
Samantha Wommack (Coord-Admissions)
Dane Binder (COO)
Angela Kistler (Chief Nursing Officer)
Michele Jewell (Dir-Admissions)
Carla Carpentier (Dir-HR)
Robert Santiago (Mktg Dir)
Kelly Palmiero (Dir-Resident Experience)
Larisa Biznichuk (Dir-Secondary Eating Recovery Svcs)
Antoinette Giedzinska (Dir-Applied Neuroscience & Outcomes)
James Seymour (Dir-Chrysalis Program)
Bill Reynolds (Dir-Military & First Responder Trauma Recovery Program)
Elaine Hixson (Assoc Dir-Clinical)
Steven Goldsmith (Coord-Admissions)
Claudio Hayes (Coord-Admissions)
Mercedes Lawlor (Coord-Admissions)
Clayton Stephens (Coord-Admissions)
Juan Carlos (Dir-Licensed Professionals Program)
Sean Kewin (Program Mgr)
Ryan Drzewiecki (Chief Clinical Officer)

Skyway House, LLC (1)
392 Connors Ct Ste C, Chico, CA 95926
Tel.: (530) 898-8326
Web Site:
https://www.skywayhouserecovery.com
Fiscal Year-end: 06/30/2014
Health Care Srvices
N.A.I.C.S.: 622110

Sober Living by the Sea, Inc. (1)
2800 Lafayette Ave, Newport Beach, CA 92663
Web Site: https://www.sierrabythesea.com
Emp.: 50
Health Care Srvices
N.A.I.C.S.: 622110

Sonora Behavioral Health Hospital, LLC (1)
6050 N Corona Rd, Tucson, AZ 85704
Tel.: (520) 469-8700
Web Site:
https://www.sonorabehavioral.com
Health Care Srvices
N.A.I.C.S.: 622110
Aaron Wilson (Chief Medical Officer)
Greer Foister (CEO)
Nicole Padilla (Dir-Admissions)
Anthony Ventola (Chief Nursing Officer)
Alex Albrecht (COO)
Joseph Ponessi (CFO)

Southern Indiana Treatment Center, LLC (1)
7509 Charlestown Pike, Charlestown, IN 47111
Tel.: (855) 831-7456
Health Care Srvices
N.A.I.C.S.: 622110

Southstone Behavioral Healthcare Center, LLC (1)
3046 Carlbrook Rd, South Boston, VA 24592
Tel.: (434) 248-3516
Web Site: http://www.southstonebhc.com
Health Care Srvices
N.A.I.C.S.: 622110

Southwestern Children's Health Services, Inc. (1)
2190 N Grace Blvd, Chandler, AZ 85225
Tel.: (480) 917-9301
Web Site: https://www.obhhospital.com
Health Care Srvices
N.A.I.C.S.: 622110
James Gallager (CEO)

Southwood Psychiatric Hospital, Inc. (1)
2575 Boyce Plz Rd, Pittsburgh, PA 15241
Tel.: (412) 257-2290
Web Site:
https://www.southwoodhospital.com
Health Care Srvices
N.A.I.C.S.: 622110

Starlite Recovery Center, LLC (1)
230 Mesa Verde Dr, Center Point, TX 78010
Web Site: https://www.starliterecovery.com
Health Care Srvices
N.A.I.C.S.: 622110
Randy Morton (CFO)
Sharon VanOverborg (Office Dir-Bus)
Laurie Stevens-Beck (Dir-Clinical Svcs)
Clarence Stewart (Mgr-Activity Therapy)
Paul Johns (Dir-Plant Ops)
Bryan M. Davis (Dir-Medical)
Stephanie Evan (CEO)

Stone Mountain School, Inc. (1)
126 Camp Elliott Rd, Black Mountain, NC 28711
Tel.: (855) 912-6384
Disabled People Educational Support Services
N.A.I.C.S.: 623210

Strathmore College Limited (1)
Unit 7 Imex Centre Technology Park, Stoke-on-Trent, ST4 8LJ, Staffordshire, United Kingdom
Tel.: (44) 1782647380
Emp.: 60
Health Care Srvices
N.A.I.C.S.: 622110

Structure House, LLC (1)
3017 Pickett Rd, Durham, NC 27705-6001,

Web Site: https://www.structurehouse.com
Weight Loss Center Operators
N.A.I.C.S.: 812191
Katie Rickel (CEO)
Pamela Bass (Mgr-HR & Risk)
Medardo Gomez (Dir-Facilities)
Katie Krasinski (Dir-Fitness)
Benjamin White (Dir-Nutrition)

Success Acquisition Corporation (1)
1500 Fashion Island Blvd, San Mateo, CA 94404
Tel.: (650) 645-2360
Health Care Srvices
N.A.I.C.S.: 622110

Swift River Academy, L.L.C. (1)
151 S St, Cummington, MA 01026
Tel.: (844) 906-0978
Web Site: https://www.swiftriver.com
Health Care Srvices
N.A.I.C.S.: 622110

TK Behavioral, LLC (1)
40 Timberline Dr, Lemont, IL 60439
Tel.: (630) 844-3351
Web Site: https://www.timberlineknolls.com
Health Care Srvices
N.A.I.C.S.: 622110
Sarah Sadkowski (COO)
Maria Meintanis (Dir-Continuing Care)
Camille Williams (Coord-Eating Disorder Program)
Joann Wright (Dir-Clinical Svcs)
Ozlem Dubauskas (Dir-Interim-Medical)
Soraya Soto (Dir-Admin)

Ten Broeck Tampa, LLC (1)
29910 SR-56, Wesley Chapel, FL 33543
Tel.: (813) 333-0000
Web Site: https://www.northtampabehavioral health.com
Health Care Srvices
N.A.I.C.S.: 622110

Ten Lakes Center, LLC (1)
819 N First St 3rd Fl, Dennison, OH 44621
Tel.: (740) 809-3165
Web Site: http://www.tenlakescenter.com
Sales Range: $1-9.9 Million
Emp.: 20
Health Care Srvices
N.A.I.C.S.: 622110
Deb Garner (CEO)

Texarkana Behavioral Associates, L.C. (1)
4253 N Crossover Rd, Fayetteville, AR 72703
Tel.: (479) 521-5731
Web Site: https://www.vantagepointnwa.com
Health Care Srvices
N.A.I.C.S.: 622110
Ben Winbery (CFO)
Rose Woods (Dir-Performance Improvement)
Kathy Vickers (Dir-HR)
Brandon Albright (Dir-Plant Ops)
Trish Marshall (Dir-Education)
Stephen Dollins (Dir-Medical)
Renee Bates (Dir-Clinical Svcs)
Megan Wedgworth (CEO)

The Camp Recovery Center, LLC (1)
3192 Glen Canyon Rd, Scotts Valley, CA 95066
Web Site: https://www.camprecovery.com
Alcohol Addiction Treatment Services
N.A.I.C.S.: 621420

The Camp Recovery Centers, L.P. (1)
3192 Glen Canyon Rd, Scotts Valley, CA 95066
Web Site: https://www.camprecovery.com
Health Care Srvices
N.A.I.C.S.: 622110
Sue Berlet (Dir-Adult Unit Program)
T. Y. Newcomb (Mgr-Ops)
Shannon Campbell (Dir-Health Svcs)
Leo Saavedra (CFO)
Bradley Lodge (Mgr-Admissions)
Lester Dizon (Mgr-Utilization Review)
Kellee Rimici (Office Mgr-Bus)
Eric Forestal (CEO)

The Manor Clinic Limited (1)
Mansbridge Road, Southampton, SO18 3HW, Hampshire, United Kingdom

Tel.: (44) 2380464721
Web Site: http://www.themanorclinic.com
Health Care Srvices
N.A.I.C.S.: 622110
Sarina Wheatman (Mgr-Addiction Treatment Programme)
Jacqui Newbold (Mgr-Addictions & Aftercare)
Jane Willet (Dir-Clinic)

The Pavilion at HealthPark, LLC (1)
9241 Park Royal Dr, Fort Myers, FL 33908
Web Site: https://www.parkroyalhospital.com
Emp.: 200
Health Care Srvices
N.A.I.C.S.: 622110
Asaf Aleem (Chief Medical Officer)
Amber Hentz (Dir-Admissions)
Lauren Aigner (Dir-Bus Office)
Sherilene De Leon (CFO)

The Priory Group Limited (1)
Floor 5 80 Hammersmith Road, London,
W14 8UD, United Kingdom
Tel.: (44) 2076050910
Web Site: https://www.priorygroup.com
Emp.: 10,000
Health Care Srvices
N.A.I.C.S.: 622110
Dave Hall (Gen Counsel & Sec)
Jim Lee (Dir-Fin & Tax)
Jane Stone (COO-Healthcare-Interim)
Louise Griffiths (Dir-Bus Dev-Interim)
Ryan Jervis (CFO)

**The Refuge, A Healing Place,
LLC** (1)
14835 SE 85th St, Ocklawaha, FL 32179
Tel.: (352) 288-0133
Web Site: https://www.therefuge-ahealingplace.com
Health Care Srvices
N.A.I.C.S.: 622110
Jeanine Ballantine (CFO)
Peter Pennington (CEO)

The Refuge-The Nest, LLC (1)
12850 E Hwy 25 Marion, Ocklawaha, FL
32179-5100
Tel.: (352) 288-1403
Health Care Srvices
N.A.I.C.S.: 622110

**Transcultural Health Development,
Inc.** (1)
117 E Harry Bridges Blvd, Wilmington, CA
90744
Tel.: (310) 549-8383
Health Care Srvices
N.A.I.C.S.: 622110

Treatment Associates, Inc. (1)
7225 E Southgate Dr Ste D, Sacramento,
CA 95823
Tel.: (916) 394-1000
Web Site: http://www.sacramentoctc.com
Health Care Srvices
N.A.I.C.S.: 622110

TrustPoint Hospital, LLC (1)
1009 N Thompson Ln, Murfreesboro, TN
37129
Web Site: https://www.trustpointhospital.com
Health Care Srvices
N.A.I.C.S.: 622110

**Valley Behavioral Health System,
LLC** (1)
10301 Mayo Dr, Barling, AR 72923
Tel.: (479) 494-5700
Web Site: https://www.valleybehavioral.com
Sales Range: $25-49.9 Million
Emp.: 200
Health Care Srvices
N.A.I.C.S.: 622110
Andrea Wilson (CEO)
Brian Hatfield (CFO)
Tammy Rodgers (Chief Nursing Officer)

Vermilion Hospital, LLC (1)
2520 N University Ave, Lafayette, LA 70507
Tel.: (337) 234-5614
Web Site: https://www.acadiavermilion.com
Sales Range: $25-49.9 Million
Emp.: 250
Health Care Srvices
N.A.I.C.S.: 622110
Amy Apperson (CEO)
Natalie Lemelle (CFO)

Village Behavioral Health, LLC (1)
2431 Jones Bend Rd, Louisville, TN 37777
Tel.: (865) 970-3255
Web Site: https://www.villagebh.com
Health Care Srvices
N.A.I.C.S.: 622110
Chris Shields (CEO)
Jeanne Overbay (CFO)
Jim Chamberlain (Chief Compliance Officer)

Virginia Treatment Center, Inc. (1)
3208 Herschberger Rd, Roanoke, VA 24017
Tel.: (540) 366-5248
Drug Addiction Rehabilitation Services
N.A.I.C.S.: 622210

Vista Behavioral Health, LLC (1)
136 Simsbury Rd, Avon, CT 06001
Tel.: (860) 269-3101
Web Site: https://www.consultantpsych.com
Inpatient Behavioral Healthcare Service
Provider
N.A.I.C.S.: 622210

Vita Nova, LLC (1)
321 E Main St Ste B, Charlottesville, VA
22902-3201
Tel.: (434) 977-0162
Emp.: 8
Health Care Srvices
N.A.I.C.S.: 622110

Volunteer Treatment Center, Inc. (1)
6100 Tower Cir Ste 1000, Franklin, TN
37067-1509
Web Site: http://www.chattanoogactc.com
Health Care Srvices
N.A.I.C.S.: 622110

WCHS, Inc. (1)
1095 Nickerson St, Waynoka, OK 73860
Tel.: (580) 824-0674
Web Site: https://www.nwtreatment.org
Health Care Srvices
N.A.I.C.S.: 622110

WP Acquisition Sub, LLC (1)
76 Summer St, Haverhill, MA 01830
Web Site: https://www.haverhillpavilion.com
Healtcare Services
N.A.I.C.S.: 622210

**Webster Wellness Professionals,
LLC** (1)
231 W Lockwood Ave Ste 202, Saint Louis,
MO 63119
Tel.: (314) 737-4070
Web Site: http://www.websterwellnessprofessionals.com
Health Care Srvices
N.A.I.C.S.: 622110

Wellplace, Inc. (1)
4326 Northern Pike Ste 202, Monroeville,
PA 15146
Tel.: (412) 373-7173
Web Site: http://www.wellplace.com
Health Care Srvices
N.A.I.C.S.: 622110

Wheeling Treatment Center, LLC (1)
40 Orrs Ln, Triadelphia, WV 26059
Tel.: (304) 547-9197
Health Care Srvices
N.A.I.C.S.: 622110
Charles Clark (Dir-Clinical)

White Deer Run, Inc. (1)
360 White Deer Run Rd, Allenwood, PA
17810
Tel.: (570) 538-2567
Web Site: https://www.whitedeerrun.com
Health Care Srvices
N.A.I.C.S.: 622110
Thomas J. Callahan (Reg VP & Exec Dir)
Denise M. Lopez (Sr Dir-Mktg & Bus Dev)
June Steiner (Reg Dir-Outpatient Programs)
Shadi Duchesne (Dir-Medical)
Mari Rangel (Dir-Admissions)
Kieran Pelletier (Dir-Medical Svcs)
Julie McElwee (Dir-HR)
Donna Bookhammer (Dir-Clinical)

Wichita Treatment Center Inc. (1)
939 N Main St, Wichita, KS 67203
Tel.: (844) 920-2082
Web Site: http://www.ctcwichita.com
Health Care Srvices
N.A.I.C.S.: 622110

**Williamson Treatment Center,
LLC** (1)

1609 W 3rd Ave, Williamson, WV 25661
Health Care Srvices
N.A.I.C.S.: 622110

**Youth & Family Centered Services of
New Mexico, Inc.** (1)
5310 Sequoia Rd NW, Albuquerque, NM
87120
Tel.: (505) 836-7330
Web Site: http://www.deserthills-nm.com
Health Care Srvices
N.A.I.C.S.: 622110

Youth Care of Utah, Inc. (1)
12595 S Minuteman Dr, Draper, UT 84020
Tel.: (801) 523-5077
Web Site: https://www.youthcare.com
Emp.: 135
Health Care Srvices
N.A.I.C.S.: 622110
Trina Quinney-Packard (Exec Dir)
Jodi Winter (Dir-HR)
Tanya May (Dir-Admissions)
Stacey Astin (Dir-Compliance & Ops)
Mindy Exon (Dir-Program)
Richard Mickelsen (Dir-Medical)

ACADIA PHARMACEUTICALS INC.

12830 El Camino Real Ste 400, San
Diego, CA 92130
Tel.: (858) 558-2871   DE
Web Site: https://www.acadia.com
Year Founded: 1993
ACAD—(NASDAQ)
Rev.: $517,235,000
Assets: $587,812,000
Liabilities: $187,399,000
Net Worth: $400,413,000
Earnings: ($215,975,000)
Emp.: 511
Fiscal Year-end: 12/31/22
Pharmaceutical Preparations Services
N.A.I.C.S.: 325412
Austin D. Kim (Gen Counsel, Sec & Exec VP)
Ponni Subbiah (Chief Medical Officer, Sr VP & Head-Medical Affairs-Global)
Amanda Morgan (Chief Revenue & Customer Officer & Sr VP)
James K. Kihara (Principal Acctg Officer, VP & Controller)
Mark Schneyer (CFO & Exec VP)
Kevin R. Oliver (Chief Bus Officer & Sr VP)
Doug Williamson (Exec VP)
Rob Ackles (Chief People Officer)
Julie Fisher (Sr VP)
Parag Meswani (Sr VP)
Sanjeev Pathak (Sr VP)
Benir Ruano (Sr VP)
Holly Valdiviez (Sr VP)
Stephen R. Biggar (Chm)

Subsidiaries:

Nordsviten AB (1)
Per albin hanssons vag 35, 214 32, Malmo,
Sweden
Tel.: (46) 406013400
Sales Range: $10-24.9 Million
Emp.: 5
Biopharmaceutical Researcher & Developer
N.A.I.C.S.: 325412

ACADIA REALTY TRUST

411 Theodore Fremd Ave Ste 300,
Rye, NY 10580
Tel.: (914) 288-8100   MD
Web Site:
https://www.acadiarealty.com
Year Founded: 1993
AKR—(NYSE)
Rev.: $338,692,000
Assets: $4,291,154,000
Liabilities: $2,207,937,000
Net Worth: $2,083,217,000
Earnings: $19,873,000
Emp.: 117
Fiscal Year-end: 12/31/23

Real Estate Investment Trust
N.A.I.C.S.: 525990
Joseph M. Napolitano (Chief Admin Officer & Sr VP)
Karen Yamrus (Asst VP)
Richard M. Hartmann (Chief Acctg Officer & Sr VP)
Mark O'Connor (Sr VP-Property Mgmt)
Douglas R. Miller (VP-Lease Admin)
Robert Pappa (VP & Controller)
John Gottfried (CFO & Exec VP)
Maria Caronna (VP-Cash Mgmt)
David Rodriguez (VP-IT)
Jeremy Hill (VP-Property Mgmt)
Alexander J. Levine (Sr VP-Leasing & Dev)
Elizabeth King (VP-Treasury)
Douglas Austin (VP-Tenant Coordination)
Tulani Thaw (VP & Asst Gen Counsel)
German Rodriguez (VP-Construction)
Tracey Mitnick (VP-Leasing)
Antonella Pomara (Gen Counsel)
Ryan Segal (VP)
Lesley Valente (VP)
Kenneth F. Bernstein (Co-Founder, Pres & CEO)

Subsidiaries:

Cortlandt Town Center LLC (1)
51 Madison Ave, New York, NY 10708
Tel.: (914) 526-4995
Real Estate Investment Services
N.A.I.C.S.: 531120

Shops at Grand Avenue LLC (1)
275 W Wisconsin Ave, Milwaukee, WI
53203
Tel.: (414) 224-0655
Web Site:
http://www.grandavenueshops.com
Shopping Mall Operator
N.A.I.C.S.: 531120

ACCEL ENTERTAINMENT, INC.

140 Tw Dr, Burr Ridge, IL 60527
Tel.: (630) 972-2235   DE
Web Site:
https://www.accelentertainment.com
Year Founded: 2017
ACEL—(NYSE)
Rev.: $969,797,000
Assets: $862,769,000
Liabilities: $684,179,000
Net Worth: $178,590,000
Earnings: $74,102,000
Emp.: 1,300
Fiscal Year-end: 12/31/22
Holding Company
N.A.I.C.S.: 551112
Derek Harmer (Chief Compliance Officer, Gen Counsel & Sec)
Mark Phelan (Chief Revenue Officer)
Michael Pappas (Exec VP-Bus Dev & Govt Affairs)
Mathew Ellis (CFO)
Karl Peterson (Sr Partner)
Christie Kozlik (Chief Acctg Officer)
Gordon Rubenstein (Vice Chm & Dir)
Andrew H. Rubenstein (Founder, Pres & CEO)
David W. Ruttenberg (Dir)
Eden Godsoe (Dir)
Kenneth B. Rotman (Dir)
Dee Robinson (Dir)
Karen Raviv (Chief People Officer)

Subsidiaries:

Accel Entertainment, LLC (1)
140 Tower Dr, Burr Ridge, IL 60527
Tel.: (630) 972-2235
Slot Machines & Electronic Terminal Support Services
N.A.I.C.S.: 541990
Derek Harmer (Chief Compliance Officer, Gen Counsel & Sec)

Accel Entertainment, Inc.—(Continued)

Mark Phelan (Chief Revenue Officer)
Michael Pappas (Exec VP-Bus Dev & Govt Affairs)
Mathew Ellis (CFO)
Karl Peterson (Chm)
Christie Kozlik (Chief Acctg Officer)
Gordon Rubenstein (Vice Chm)
Andrew H. Rubenstein (Founder, Pres & CEO)

Subsidiary (Domestic):

Century Gaming, Inc.   (2)
1327 Weil St, Billings, MT 59101
Tel.: (406) 896-9900
Administrative Management & General Management Consulting Service
N.A.I.C.S.: 541611
Steven Arntzen (CEO)
Heidi Schmalz (CFO)

Tom's Amusement Company, Inc.   (1)
135 McKinney Rd, Blue Ridge, GA 30513
Tel.: (706) 632-5050
Web Site: http://www.tomsamusement.com
Sales Range: $1-9.9 Million
Emp.: 33
Amusement & Recreation Services
N.A.I.C.S.: 713990
Emily Dunn (CEO & Sec)

ACCELERA INNOVATIONS, INC.

20511 Abbey Dr, Frankfort, IL 60423   DE
Web Site:
    https://www.accelerainnovation.com
Year Founded: 2008
ACNV—(OTCIQ)
Sales Range: Less than $1 Million
Emp.: 3
Healthcare Software
N.A.I.C.S.: 513210
John F. Wallin (Pres, CEO, Interim CFO & CMO)
Geoff Thompson (Chm)

ACCELERATE ACQUISITION CORP.

51 John F Kennedy Pkwy, Short Hills, NJ 07078
Tel.: (973) 314-3060   DE
Web Site: http://www.xlr8ac.com
Year Founded: 2020
AAQC—(NYSE)
Rev.: $3,776,744
Assets: $401,638,598
Liabilities: $431,506,799
Net Worth: ($29,868,201)
Earnings: $2,597,482
Fiscal Year-end: 12/31/21
Investment Services
N.A.I.C.S.: 523999
Robert Nardelli (Chm & CEO)
Michael Simoff (CFO, COO & Treas)
Jeffrey Kaplan (Sec & Head-Bus Dev)

ACCELERATE DIAGNOSTICS, INC.

3950 S Country Club Rd Ste 470 4th Fl, Tucson, AZ 85714
Tel.: (520) 365-3100   DE
Web Site:
    https://www.acceleratediagnos
    tics.com
Year Founded: 1987
AXDX—(NASDAQ)
Rev.: $12,752,000
Assets: $65,015,000
Liabilities: $87,279,000
Net Worth: ($22,264,000)
Earnings: ($62,493,000)
Emp.: 179
Fiscal Year-end: 12/31/22
Medical Device Mfr
N.A.I.C.S.: 339112

Constance Bridges (Sr VP & Head-Quality & Regulatory)
Jack Phillips (Pres & CEO)
Gretchen Strohminger (Sr VP & Head-HR & Culture)
Cherif Bousselham (Sr VP & Head-Sls-EMEA)
Laura Costa (Sr VP & Head-Customer Support-Global)
John Meduri (Chief Strategy Officer & Chief Startegy Officer)
Lawrence Mertz (CTO)
Chris Thode (Sr VP-US Comml)
Rita Boukamel (Sr VP & Head-EMEA)
Maya Gowri (Sr VP & Head-Operations)

ACCELERATED TECHNOLOGIES HOLDING CORP.

260 Madison Ave, New York, NY 10016
Tel.: (212) 508-7475   DE
Year Founded: 2000
ATHC—(OTCIQ)
Business Solution & Technology Services
N.A.I.C.S.: 561499
Igor Kogan (CIO)

ACCESS BIO, INC.

65 Clyde Rd Ste A, Somerset, NJ 08873
Tel.: (732) 873-4040
Web Site: https://www.accessbio.net
Year Founded: 2001
950130—(KRS)
Rev.: $800,234,602
Assets: $698,713,619
Liabilities: $204,672,950
Net Worth: $494,040,669
Earnings: $270,711,363
Emp.: 101
Fiscal Year-end: 12/31/22
In-Vitro Diagnostic Test Mfr
N.A.I.C.S.: 339112
Young H. Choi (CEO)
Jason Kum (Assoc Dir-Fin)
Jin S. Jung (Asst Mgr-Production Lab)
Minho Choi (Exec Dir)

ACCESS WORLDWIDE COMMUNICATIONS, INC.

6402 Arlington Blvd 4th Fl, Falls Church, VA 22042
Tel.: (571) 384-7400   DE
Web Site: http://www.accessww.com
Year Founded: 1983
AWWC—(OTCIQ)
Sales Range: Less than $1 Million
Emp.: 1,000
Business Outsourcing Services Including Telecommunication & IT Services
N.A.I.C.S.: 561499
Richard Lyew (CFO & Exec VP)
Shawkat Raslan (Chm, Pres & CEO)
Bob Bryan (COO & VP-Sls)

Subsidiaries:

Access Worldwide Communications, Inc. - Augusta   (1)
45 Commerce Dr 8, Augusta, ME 04330
Tel.: (207) 703-1010
Web Site: http://www.accessww.com
Sales Range: $25-49.9 Million
Emp.: 100
Marketing Services
N.A.I.C.S.: 541613
Bob Bryan (SVP-Bus Dev)

ACCO BRANDS CORPORATION

4 Corporate Dr, Lake Zurich, IL 60047

Tel.: (847) 541-9500   DE
Web Site:
    https://www.accobrands.com
Year Founded: 1922
ACCO—(NYSE)
Rev.: $1,832,800,000
Assets: $2,644,800,000
Liabilities: $1,857,800,000
Net Worth: $787,000,000
Earnings: $21,800,000
Emp.: 5,600
Fiscal Year-end: 12/31/23
Office Supplies, Binders, Fasteners, Staplers, Staples, Punches, Clips, Time Management Products, Presentation Aids, Computer-Related Supplies Mfr
N.A.I.C.S.: 323111
Cezary L. Monko (Pres-Intl & Exec VP)
Cezary L. Monko (Pres-Europe, Middle East, and Africa & Exec VP)
Mark C. Anderson (Sr VP-Corp Dev)
Thomas W. Tedford (Pres & CEO)
Pamela R. Schneider (Gen Counsel, Sec & Sr VP)
Patrick H. Buchenroth (Pres-Americas & Exec VP)
Patrick H. Buchenroth (Pres-ACCO Brands Intl & Exec VP)
Jagannath Bobji (Treas & Sr VP-Global Plng & Fin Analysis)
Roxanne M. Bernstein (Pres-North America & Exec VP)
Paul Daniel (CIO)
Greg McCormack (Sr-VP)
James M. Dudek Jr. (Chief Acctg Officer, Sr VP & Controller)
Deborah A. O'Connor (CFO & Exec VP)

Subsidiaries:

ACCO Asia Limited   (1)
Unit 2604 26th Floor BEA Tower Millennium City 5 418 Kwun Tong Road, Kwun Tong, Kowloon, China (Hong Kong)
Tel.: (852) 34653200
Stationery & Office Product Distr
N.A.I.C.S.: 424120

ACCO Australia Pty. Ltd.   (1)
2 Coronation Ave, Kings Park, Sydney, 2148, NSW, Australia
Tel.: (61) 296740900
Web Site: http://www.accobrands.com
Sales Range: $25-49.9 Million
Emp.: 50
Office Products Distr
N.A.I.C.S.: 459410

Joint Venture (Domestic):

Pelikan-Artline Pty., Ltd.   (2)
2 Coronation Ave, Kings Park, 2148, NSW, Australia
Tel.: (61) 296740900
Web Site: http://www.pelikanartline.com.au
Office Supplies Distr; Owned 50% by Pelikan International Corp Berhad & 50% by ACCO Brands Corporation
N.A.I.C.S.: 459410

ACCO Brands Australia Holding Pty Ltd.   (1)
2 Coronation Ave, Kings Park, 2148, NSW, Australia
Tel.: (61) 29 674 0900
Web Site: https://www.accobrands.com.au
Emp.: 50
Stationery & Office Supplies Whslr
N.A.I.C.S.: 424120

ACCO Brands Canada Inc.   (1)
7381 Bramalea Road, Mississauga, L5S 1C4, ON, Canada
Tel.: (905) 364-2600
Web Site:
    https://www.accobrandscanada.com
Sales Range: $50-74.9 Million
Emp.: 200
Binders, Fasteners & Filing Systems Mfr
N.A.I.C.S.: 323111

ACCO Brands Italia S.r.l.   (1)

Strada Della Merla 49d, PO Box 262, Settimo Torinese, 10036, Italy
Tel.: (39) 0118961111
Industrial & Personal Services
N.A.I.C.S.: 424130
Luciano Jelmetti (Gen Mgr)

ACCO Brands Japan K.K.   (1)
14F Harmony Tower Building 1-32-2 Honcho, Nakano-Ku, Tokyo, 164-8721, Japan
Tel.: (81) 353511921
Web Site: https://accobrands.co.jp
Emp.: 65
Office Equipment Distr
N.A.I.C.S.: 423420

ACCO Brands New Zealand Limited   (1)
29 Pukekiwiriki Pl Highbrook Business Park, East Tamaki, Auckland, 2013, New Zealand
Tel.: (64) 96332288
Web Site: http://www.accobrands.co.nz
Writing Instrument Mfr & Distr
N.A.I.C.S.: 339940

ACCO Brands Portuguesa Lda   (1)
Zona Industial Paco, Arcos de Valdevez, 4970-249, Paco d'Arcos, Portugal
Tel.: (351) 258480000
Stationery & Office Supply Merchant Whslr
N.A.I.C.S.: 424120

ACCO Europe Limited   (1)
Oxford House Oxford Road, Aylesbury, HP21 8SZ, Bucks, United Kingdom
Tel.: (44) 01296397444
Holding Company
N.A.I.C.S.: 551112

Subsidiary (Domestic):

ACCO UK Limited   (2)
Millennium House 65 Walton Street, Aylesbury, HP21 7QG, Buckinghamshire, United Kingdom
Tel.: (44) 8456031730
Business Machines & Stationery Mfr
N.A.I.C.S.: 322230

Subsidiary (Non-US):

Esselte AB   (2)
Sundbybergsvaegen 1, 171 73, Solna, Sweden
Tel.: (46) 87051500
Web Site: http://www.esselte.com
Holding Company; Office Supplies Mfr & Distr
N.A.I.C.S.: 551112

Subsidiary (Non-US):

Esselte A/S   (3)
Smedeholm 10, 2730, Herlev, Denmark
Tel.: (45) 38167800
Web Site: http://www.esselte.com
Office Product & Supplies Store
N.A.I.C.S.: 459410

Subsidiary (Domestic):

Esselte Danmark ApS   (4)
Smedeholm 10, 2730, Herlev, Denmark
Tel.: (45) 38167800
Web Site: https://www.esselte.com
Office Supplies Distr
N.A.I.C.S.: 424120

Subsidiary (Non-US):

Esselte AS   (3)
Ulvenveien 82E, 0581, Oslo, Norway
Tel.: (47) 21611100
Web Site: https://www.esselte.com
Office Product & Supplies Store
N.A.I.C.S.: 459410

Esselte B.V.   (3)
Vijzelmolenlaan 6, 3447 GX, Woerden, Netherlands
Tel.: (31) 348415084
Web Site: https://www.esselte.com
Office Product & Supplies Store
N.A.I.C.S.: 459410

Esselte Business BVBA   (3)
Industriepark Noord 29, 9100, Saint-Niklaas, Belgium
Tel.: (32) 3 760 3311
Web Site: https://www.esselte.com

Office Product & Supplies Store
N.A.I.C.S.: 459410

Esselte Kft (3)
Lomb u 37-39 A ep, 1139, Budapest, Hungary
Tel.: (36) 14246600
Web Site: http://www.esselte.hu
Office Product & Supplies Store
N.A.I.C.S.: 459410

Esselte Leitz Buro Malzemeleri Sanayi Ve Ticaret A.S. (3)
Maslak Mahallesi Sumer Sokak Ayazaga Trade Center No 3 Kat 2, Maslak, 34398, Turkiye
Tel.: (90) 2122862630
Web Site: http://www.esselte.com
Stationery & Office Supply Mfr
N.A.I.C.S.: 322230

Esselte Limited (3)
Waterside House Cowley Business Park, Uxbridge, UB8 2HP, United Kingdom
Tel.: (44) 1895878700
Office Supplies & Organizational Solutions Mfr & Distr
N.A.I.C.S.: 459410

Subsidiary (Domestic):

Esselte UK Ltd. (4)
Waterside House Cowley Business Park, Cowley, Uxbridge, UB8 2HP, United Kingdom
Tel.: (44) 1895878700
Office Supplies & Organizational Solutions Mfr & Distr
N.A.I.C.S.: 339940

Subsidiary (Non-US):

Esselte OOO (3)
3rd street of Yamskogo pole 18, 125040, Moscow, Russia
Tel.: (7) 4959332763
Web Site: http://www.esselte.com
Office Supplies
N.A.I.C.S.: 459410

Esselte Office Products GmbH (3)
Ared Strasse 22, 2544, Leobersdorf, Austria
Tel.: (43) 225664000
Stationery Product Mfr
N.A.I.C.S.: 322230

Esselte Office Products Oy (3)
Klovinpellontie 1-3, 02180, Espoo, Finland (100%)
Tel.: (358) 975104200
Web Site: https://www.esselte.com
Office Supplies Distr
N.A.I.C.S.: 459410

Esselte Polska Sp.z.o.o. (3)
ul Przemyslowa 11A, 26-900, Kozienice, Poland (100%)
Tel.: (48) 22 874 3050
Web Site: https://www.esselte.com
Office Supplies Distr
N.A.I.C.S.: 459410

Esselte S.A. (3)
Via Augusta 20-26, Barcelona, 08006, Spain
Tel.: (34) 932384400
Web Site: http://www.esselte.com
School & Office Supplies Mfr & Distr
N.A.I.C.S.: 459410

Representative Office (Non-US):

Esselte S.A. - Portugal Office (4)
Estrada de Paco Arcos 9, 2770-218, Paco d'Arcos, Portugal
Tel.: (351) 214461670
Office Supplies Distr
N.A.I.C.S.: 459410

Subsidiary (Non-US):

Esselte S.p.a (3)
Via Milano 35, 20064, Gorgonzola, MI, Italy
Tel.: (39) 0295 0991
Web Site: https://www.esselte.com
Office Products Distr
N.A.I.C.S.: 424120

Esselte Sales S.R.L (3)
Strada Gheorghe Titeica Nr 121 C Etaj Mezanin Sector 2, Bucharest, 020295, Romania

Tel.: (40) 212 424 070
Web Site: http://www.esselte.ro
Office Supplies Mfr
N.A.I.C.S.: 322230

Subsidiary (Domestic):

Esselte Sverige AB (3)
Rasundavagen 6, SE-169 67, Solna, Sweden (100%)
Tel.: (46) 87051510
Web Site: https://www.esselte.com
Office Product & Supplies Store
N.A.I.C.S.: 459410

Subsidiary (Domestic):

Isaberg Rapid AB (4)
Metallgatan 5, 335 71, Hestra, Sweden
Tel.: (46) 370339500
Web Site: https://www.rapid.com
Hand Tool Product Mfr
N.A.I.C.S.: 333991

Subsidiary (Non-US):

LEITZ ACCO Brands GmbH & Co. KG (3)
Siemensstrasse 64, Postfach 30 07 20, 70469, Stuttgart, Germany
Tel.: (49) 71181030
Web Site: https://www.leitz.com
Stationery & Office Supply Merchant Whslr
N.A.I.C.S.: 424120
Katrin Schuh (Mng Dir)
Ard-Jen Spijkervet (Mng Dir)
Christopher Neil Hopkinson (Mng Dir)

Tarifold S.A. (3)
1 rue de l'Industrie, 67118, Geispolsheim, France
Tel.: (33) 388660312
Web Site: https://www.tarifold.com
Office Supplies Distr
N.A.I.C.S.: 459410
Annabelle Schaeffer (Mgr-Customer Svc-South Reg)
Jes Larsen (Sls Mgr-Industrial Products)
Kim Berg (CEO-T3L Grp)
Peter Elleman (Mgr-Export-South East Asia)
Laura Rebstock (Officer-Communications)

Subsidiary (US):

Xyron Inc. (3)
8777 E Hartford Dr #130, Scottsdale, AZ 85255
Tel.: (480) 443-9419
Web Site: http://www.xyron.com
Printing Trades Machinery
N.A.I.C.S.: 332813

ACCO International Holdings, Inc. (1)
300 Tower Pkwy, Lincolnshire, IL 60069
Tel.: (847) 484-4800
Web Site: http://www.gbcconnect.com
Office Product Mfr
N.A.I.C.S.: 323111

Day-Timers, Inc. (1)
1 Willow Ln, East Texas, PA 18046
Tel.: (610) 398-1151
Web Site: http://www.daytimer.com
Sales Range: $75-99.9 Million
Emp.: 500
Time Management & Organizational Solutions
N.A.I.C.S.: 323111

Esselte SRO (1)
V Luzich 818, Libus, 142 00, Prague, Czech Republic
Tel.: (420) 261912720
Web Site: https://www.esselte.com
Office Product Mfr
N.A.I.C.S.: 339940

General Binding LLC (1)
4 Corporate Dr, Lake Zurich, IL 60047
Tel.: (847) 541-9500
Web Site: http://www.gbc.com
Office Products Distr
N.A.I.C.S.: 424120
Thomas W. Tedford (Pres)

Kensington Technology Group (1)
333 Twin Dolphin Dr, Redwood City, CA 94065
Tel.: (650) 572-2700
Web Site: http://www.kensington.com

Sales Range: $100-124.9 Million
Emp.: 100
Computer Accessories Mfr & Designer
N.A.I.C.S.: 334118

Tilibra Produtos de Papelaria Ltda (1)
Rua Aymores 6-9 Vila Antartica, Bauru, 17013-900, Sao Paulo, Brazil
Tel.: (55) 1432354003
Web Site: https://www.tilibra.com.br
Paper Product Distr
N.A.I.C.S.: 424130

ACCOLADE, INC.
1201 3rd Ave Ste 1700, Seattle, WA 98101
Tel.: (206) 926-8100
Web Site: https://www.accolade.com
Year Founded: 2007
ACCD—(NASDAQ)
Rev.: $363,142,000
Assets: $903,069,000
Liabilities: $429,283,000
Net Worth: $473,786,000
Earnings: ($459,650,000)
Emp.: 2,370
Fiscal Year-end: 02/28/23
Direct Health & Medical Insurance Carriers
N.A.I.C.S.: 524114
Tom Spann (Founder & COO)
Rajeev Singh (CEO & Chm)
Rob Cavanaugh (Pres-Field Ops)
Steve Barnes (CFO)

Subsidiaries:

PlushCare, Inc. (1)
101 Mission St Ste 800, San Francisco, CA 94105
Tel.: (415) 231-5333
Web Site: https://www.plushcare.com
Hospital & Health Care Services
N.A.I.C.S.: 622110

ACCREDITED SOLUTIONS, INC.
201 W Main St Ste 300 PMB 310, Durham, NC 27701
Tel.: (704) 790-9799   NV
Web Site: https://www.accredit-solutions.com
Year Founded: 2007
ASII—(OTCIQ)
Rev.: $688,875
Assets: $229,505
Liabilities: $5,302,542
Net Worth: ($5,073,037)
Earnings: ($1,488,595)
Emp.: 2
Fiscal Year-end: 12/31/23
Gold Exploration Services
N.A.I.C.S.: 212220

ACCRETION ACQUISITION CORP.
240 Saint Paul Ste 502, Denver, CO 80206
Tel.: (720) 328-5070   DE
Web Site:
https://www.accretionacquisition.com
Year Founded: 2021
ENER—(NASDAQ)
Rev.: $3,064,160
Assets: $212,437,412
Liabilities: $220,676,861
Net Worth: ($8,239,449)
Earnings: $1,043,369
Emp.: 6
Fiscal Year-end: 12/31/22
Investment Services
N.A.I.C.S.: 523999
Brad Morse (CEO)
M. Grant Farn (CFO)
Daniel Silverman (COO)
Ryan Sullivan (Sec & Sr VP)
Doug Sandridge (VP)
Conor Hess (VP)

ACCURAY INCORPORATED
1240 Deming Way, Madison, WI 53717
Tel.: (608) 824-2800   DE
Web Site: https://www.accuray.com
Year Founded: 1990
ARAY—(NASDAQ)
Rev.: $446,551,000
Assets: $468,627,000
Liabilities: $423,543,000
Net Worth: $45,084,000
Earnings: ($15,545,000)
Emp.: 987
Fiscal Year-end: 06/30/24
Robotic Radiosurgery & Radiation Oncology Equipment Mfr
N.A.I.C.S.: 339112
Patrick Spine (Chief Admin Officer & Sr VP)
Scott Chapman (Sr VP-Svc-Global)
Jean-Philippe Pignol (Chief Medical & Tech Officer & Sr VP)
Ali Pervaiz (CFO, Interim Principal Acctg Officer & Sr VP)
Joseph E. Whitters (Chm)
Suzanne Winter (Pres & CEO)
Sandeep Chalke (Chief Comml Officer & Sr VP)
Jesse Chew (Chief Legal Officer, Gen Counsel, Sec & Sr VP)
Michael Hoge (Sr VP-Ops-Global)
Jim Dennison (Chief Dev Officer, Chief Quality Officer & Sr VP-Global)
Seth Blacksburg (Chief Medical Officer & Sr VP)
Melaine Rivers (Chief HR Officer & Sr VP)
Mu Young Lee (Sr VP-Res & Product Development)

Subsidiaries:

Accuray Europe SAS (1)
Tour Monge 3e etage 22 place des Vosges, 92400, Courbevoie, France
Tel.: (33) 155232020
Medical Device Mfr
N.A.I.C.S.: 339112

Accuray Japan K.K. (1)
7th floor Shin-Otemachi Building 2-2-1 Otemachi, Chiyoda-ku, Tokyo, 100-0004, Japan
Tel.: (81) 362651526
Web Site: https://www.accuray.co.jp
Emp.: 101
Medical & Surgical Appliance Mfr
N.A.I.C.S.: 339112

TomoTherapy Incorporated (1)
1240 Deming Way, Madison, WI 53717-2911
Tel.: (608) 824-2800
Web Site: http://www.tomotherapy.com
Sales Range: $150-199.9 Million
Emp.: 636
Radiation Therapy Systems Developer, Mfr & Sales
N.A.I.C.S.: 334517

Subsidiary (Non-US):

TomoTherapy Belgium BVBA (2)
Pegasuslaan 5, 1831, Diegem, Belgium
Tel.: (32) 24004400
Web Site: http://www.accuray.com
Sales Range: $25-49.9 Million
Emp.: 150
Mfr of Radiation Therapy Systems
N.A.I.C.S.: 334510

ACELYRIN, INC.
4149 Liberty Canyon Rd, Agoura Hills, CA 91301
Tel.: (805) 730-0360   DE
Web Site: https://www.acelyrin.com
Year Founded: 2020

Acelyrin, Inc.—(Continued)
SLRN—(NASDAQ)
Rev.: $4,052,000
Assets: $319,923,000
Liabilities: $422,785,000
Net Worth: ($102,862,000)
Earnings: ($64,772,000)
Emp.: 51
Fiscal Year-end: 12/31/22
Research & Development in Biotech-
nology (except Nanobiotechnology)
N.A.I.C.S.: 541714
Shao-Lee Lin (Founder)
Gil M. Labrucherie (CFO & Principal
Acctg Officer)
Mina Kim (CEO)
Patricia A. Turney (Chief Technical
Ops Officer)
Shao-Lee Lin (Founder)
Tyler Marciniak (VP-IR, Comm, and
Corp Ops)
Robert F. Carey (Co-Founder)

ACERAGEN, INC.
505 Eagleview Blvd Ste 212, Exton,
PA 19341
Tel.: (484) 348-1600 DE
Web Site: https://www.aceragen.com
Year Founded: 1989
ACGN—(NASDAQ)
Rev.: $4,862,000
Assets: $101,107,000
Liabilities: $89,281,000
Net Worth: $11,826,000
Earnings: ($23,360,000)
Emp.: 26
Fiscal Year-end: 12/31/22
Pharmaceuticals Mfr
N.A.I.C.S.: 325414

**ACHARI VENTURES HOLD-
INGS CORP. I**
60 Walnut Ave Ste 400, Clark, NJ
07066
Tel.: (416) 992-4539 DE
Web Site: https://acharispac.com
Year Founded: 2021
AVHI—(NASDAQ)
Investment Holding Company
N.A.I.C.S.: 551112
Vikas Desai (Chm & CEO)
Merrick Friedman (Chief Investment
Officer & Dir)
Mitchell Hara (CFO & COO)

ACI WORLDWIDE, INC.
2811 Ponce de Leon Blvd PH 1,
Coral Gables, FL 33134
Tel.: (305) 894-2200 DE
Web Site:
https://www.aciworldwide.com
ACIW—(NASDAQ)
Rev.: $1,421,901,000
Assets: $3,209,895,000
Liabilities: $2,016,708,000
Net Worth: $1,193,187,000
Earnings: $142,177,000
Emp.: 3,349
Fiscal Year-end: 12/31/22
Offices of Other Holding Companies
N.A.I.O.O.: 551112
Craig A. Maki (Chief Dev Officer)
Abe Kuruvilla (CTO)
Alessandro da Silva (Chief Revenue
Officer)
Debbie Guerra (Chief Product Officer)
Katrin Boettger (Dir-Comm & Corp
Affairs-Europe, Middle East & Africa)
Jaime Danielson (Head-Comm &
Corp Responsibility)
Thomas W. Warsop III (Pres & CEO)

Subsidiaries:

ACI (Singapore) Pte. Ltd. (1)
DUO Tower 3 Fraser Street 20th Floor Units
20-21, Singapore, 189352, Singapore

Tel.: (65) 63344843
Web Site: http://www.acisin.com
Financial Market Association Services
N.A.I.C.S.: 523999
R. Ravichandran (Mng Dir)

ACI Australia Pty. Ltd (1)
Level 2 Suite 208/83 York St, Sydney,
2000, NSW, Australia
Tel.: (61) 422139643
Web Site: https://www.aciaustralia.com.au
Emp.: 320
Software Development Services
N.A.I.C.S.: 541511
Chris Howlett (COO & Gen Mgr)

ACI Global Limited (1)
Palm Court Centre Cnr Short & William
Streets, Port Macquarie, 2444, NSW, Aus-
tralia
Tel.: (61) 280034997
Web Site: https://www.aciglobal.com.au
Software Development Services
N.A.I.C.S.: 541511
Ian Erskine (CEO & Mng Dir)
Jon Bergsson (Mgr-Pharmaceutical Industry
& GMP Trng-Intl)
Ribhu Nath Lavania (Mgr-Cultural Affairs &
Specializing-Project Mgmt Trng)
Ivan Pearson (Mgr-Specializing-Aviation
Trng-Intl)

ACI Global Limited (1)
Red House Cemetery Pales 1st Floor,
Brookwood, London, GU24 0BL, Surrey,
United Kingdom
Tel.: (44) 1483728700
Software & Solution Services
N.A.I.C.S.: 541511

ACI Worldwide (Asia) Pte. Ltd. (1)
DUO Tower 3 Fraser Street 20th Floor Units
20-21, Singapore, 189352, Singapore
Tel.: (65) 63344843
Sales Range: $25-49.9 Million
Developer, Designer & Marketer of Elec-
tronic Funds Transfer Applications Software
N.A.I.C.S.: 513210

ACI Worldwide (EMEA) Limited (1)
Woking One 6 Albion House High Street,
Woking, GU21 6BG, Surrey, United King-
dom
Tel.: (44) 1923816393
Sales Range: $50-74.9 Million
Emp.: 200
Developer, Designer & Marketer of Elec-
tronic Funds Transfer Applications Software
N.A.I.C.S.: 513210

Subsidiary (Non-US):

ACI Worldwide (Hellas) EPE (2)
Athens Tower B Building 2nd Floor Meso-
geion 2-4, 11527, Athens, Greece
Tel.: (30) 2107475461
Sales Range: $25-49.9 Million
Emp.: 10
Electronic Financial Payment Processing
Services
N.A.I.C.S.: 522320

Subsidiary (Domestic):

ACI Worldwide (UK Development)
Limited (2)
55-57 Clarendon Road, Watford, WD17
1FQ, Hertfordshire, United Kingdom
Tel.: (44) 1923816393
Web Site: http://www.aciworldwide.com
Sales Range: $50-74.9 Million
Emp.: 250
Applications Software Programming Ser-
vices
N.A.I.C.S.: 513210

Subsidiary (Non-US):

ACI Worldwide (eps) AG (2)
Otto-Volger-Strasse 9A, 65843, Sulzbach,
Germany
Tel.: (49) 6196770970
Web Site: http://www.aciworldwide.com
Sales Range: $25-49.9 Million
Emp.: 30
Developer & Marketer of Electronic Funds
Transfer Applications Software
N.A.I.C.S.: 423430
Sylvie Boucheron-Saunier (VP)

ACI Worldwide B.V. (2)

Tielweg 3, 2803 PK, Gouda, Netherlands
Tel.: (31) 182711600
Web Site: http://www.aciworldwide.com
Sales Range: $25-49.9 Million
Developer, Designer & Marketer of Elec-
tronic Funds Transfer Applications Software
N.A.I.C.S.: 423430

ACI Worldwide Eastern Europe De-
velopment S.R.L. (2)
Piata Consiliul Europei No 2 Building U2
2-3rd Floor, 300627, Timisoara, Romania
Tel.: (40) 356434844
Web Site: http://www.aciworldwide.com
Sales Range: $100-124.9 Million
Emp.: 200
Marketer of Electronic Funds Transfer Appli-
cations Software
N.A.I.C.S.: 423430
Shelley Ahlers (Sr VP-Product Dev)

ACI Worldwide France S.A.R.L. (2)
3 Square Desaix 4th 5th Floor, 75015,
Paris, France
Tel.: (33) 170706555
Web Site: http://www.aciworldwide.com
Emp.: 20
Marketer of Electronic Funds Transfer Appli-
cations Software
N.A.I.C.S.: 423430
Sylvie Boucheron-Saunier (Gen Mgr)

ACI Worldwide Italia S.r.l. (2)
Via Alessandro Scarlatti 88, 80127, Naples,
Italy
Tel.: (39) 0812209711
Web Site: http://www.aciworldwide.com
Sales Range: $25-49.9 Million
Emp.: 23
Electronic Funds Transfer Applications Soft-
ware Sales
N.A.I.C.S.: 423430

Applied Communications Ireland
Limited (2)
Kilmurry Business Centre National Technol-
ogy Park, Castletroy, Limerick, V94 RX49,
Ireland
Tel.: (353) 61261000
Marketer of Electronic Funds Transfer Appli-
cations Software
N.A.I.C.S.: 423430

ACI Worldwide (Germany)
GmbH (1)
Grillparzerstrasse 18, 81675, Munich, Ger-
many
Tel.: (49) 89452300
Software Development Services
N.A.I.C.S.: 541511

ACI Worldwide (Japan) K.K. (1)
PMO Uchikanda 8th floor 1-14-10 Uchi-
kanda, Chiyoda-ku, Tokyo, 101-0047, Japan
Tel.: (81) 351591530
Application Software Developing Services
N.A.I.C.S.: 513210

ACI Worldwide (Pacific) Pty. Ltd. (1)
Governor Phillip Tower Level 36 1 Farrer
Place, Sydney, 2000, NSW, Australia
Tel.: (61) 295120200
Sales Range: $50-74.9 Million
Developer, Designer & Marketer of Elec-
tronic Funds Transfer Applications Software
N.A.I.C.S.: 423430

ACI Worldwide (Thailand)
Limited (1)
No 399 Interchange 21 Suite No 2310 23rd
floor Sukhumvit Road, Klongtoey Nua Wat-
tana, Bangkok, 10110, Thailand
Tel.: (66) 21268000
Application Software Developing Services
N.A.I.C.S.: 513210

ACI Worldwide Brasil Ltda. (1)
Avenida Engenheiro Luiz Carlos Berrini 105
- 5th Andar - Conjunto 52, Sao Paulo,
04571-010, Brazil
Tel.: (55) 1133650765
Web Site: http://www.aciworldwide.com
Sales Range: $25-49.9 Million
Emp.: 34
Marketer of Electronic Funds Transfer Appli-
cations Software
N.A.I.C.S.: 423430

ACI Worldwide Canada, Inc. (1)
200 Wellington Street West Suite 700, To-

ronto, M5V 3C7, ON, Canada
Tel.: (416) 813-3000
Web Site: http://www.aciworldwide.com
Sales Range: $75-99.9 Million
Emp.: 51
Marketer of Electronic Funds Transfer Appli-
cations Software
N.A.I.C.S.: 423430

ACI Worldwide Colombia S.A.S. (1)
Titan Plaza Commercial and Business Cen-
ter Av Carrera 72 No 80-94, Ofc 502, Bo-
gota, Colombia
Tel.: (57) 8009547516
Emp.: 93
Custom Computer Programming Services
N.A.I.C.S.: 541511

ACI Worldwide Corp. (1)
6060 Coventry Dr, Elkhorn, NE 68022-6482
Tel.: (402) 390-7600
Sales Range: $200-249.9 Million
Emp.: 1,111
Electronic Payment & Funds Transfer Appli-
cation Software Developer, Marketer & Sup-
port Services
N.A.I.C.S.: 513210

Branch (Domestic):

ACI Worldwide Corp. - Austin
Office (2)
12401 Research Blvd, Austin, TX 78759
Tel.: (512) 336-3000
Enterprise eSolutions for Community & Re-
gional Financial Institutions
N.A.I.C.S.: 513210

ACI Worldwide Corp. - Chantilly
Office (2)
15049 Conference Ctr Dr Ste 400, Chan-
tilly, VA 20151
Tel.: (703) 653-3100
Web Site: https://www.aciworldwide.com
Web-Based Financial Services
N.A.I.C.S.: 522320

ACI Worldwide Corp. - Columbus
Office (2)
7720 Rivers Edge Dr, Columbus, OH 43235
Tel.: (614) 310-6714
Web Site: http://www.aciworldwide.com
Sales Range: $10-24.9 Million
Emp.: 35
Internet Payment Services
N.A.I.C.S.: 522320

ACI Worldwide Corp. - Princeton
Office (2)
650 College Rd E Second Floor, Princeton,
NJ 08540-6624
Tel.: (609) 606-3000
Web Site: http://www.aciworldwido.com
Sales Range: $25-49.9 Million
Emp.: 135
Electronic Bill Payment Services
N.A.I.C.S.: 522320

ACI Worldwide Corp. - West Hills
Office (2)
8501 Fallbrook Ave Ste 200, West Hills, CA
91304
Tel.: (818) 992-3299
Branch Automation, Teller, Call Center &
CRM Solutions for Financial Institutions
N.A.I.C.S.: 513210

ACI Worldwide Korea Yuhan
Hoesa (1)
Seoul Finance Center 21F 136 Sejong-
daero, Jung-gu, Seoul, 04520, Korea
(Suull)
Tel.: (82) 27384107
Sales Range: $10-24.9 Million
Emp.: 2
Application Software Developing Services
N.A.I.C.S.: 513210

ACI Worldwide Mexico S.A. de
C.V. (1)
Insurgentes Sur 1605 Torre Mural Piso 14
Modulo 1, San Jose Insurgentes, Mexico,
03900, DF, Mexico
Tel.: (52) 5585038000
Web Site: http://www.aciworldwide.com
Sales Range: $50-74.9 Million
Emp.: 20
Marketer of Electronic Funds Transfer Appli-
cations Software

N.A.I.C.S.: 423430

ACI Worldwide Solutions Pvt. Ltd. (1)
9 Salarpuria Cambridge Mall Cambridge Road, Bengaluru, 560008, Karnataka, India
Tel.: (91) 8066165340
Sales Range: $25-49.9 Million
Marketer of Electronic Funds Transfer Applications Software
N.A.I.C.S.: 423430

ACI Worldwide de Argentina S.A. (1)
Maipu 1210 Piso 8, C1006ACT, Buenos Aires, Argentina
Tel.: (54) 1137241000
Sales Range: $25-49.9 Million
Emp.: 20
Applications Software Programming Services
N.A.I.C.S.: 541511

S-1 Corporation (1)
25 Sejong-daero 7-gil, Jung-gu, Seoul, Korea (South)
Tel.: (82) 221317581
Web Site: https://www.s1.co.kr
Rev.: $1,892,925,532
Assets: $1,592,030,143
Liabilities: $423,897,378
Net Worth: $1,168,132,764
Earnings: $115,841,443
Emp.: 6,822
Fiscal Year-end: 12/31/2022
Video Surveillance Product Mfr
N.A.I.C.S.: 238210
Moriya Kiyoshi (VP)
Joon-sung Park (Exec Dir & Exec Dir)
Young-gi Kwon (Exec Dir)
Namgoong Beom (Chm, Pres, CEO & Exec Dir)
Hanaoka Takuro (VP & Exec Dir)

SpeedPay, Inc. (1)
12500 E Belford Ave, Englewood, CO 80112
Tel.: (720) 332-4767
Web Site: http://www.speedpay.com
Electronic Payment Services
N.A.I.C.S.: 525990

Transend Corporation (1)
225 Emerson St, Palo Alto, CA 94301-1026
Tel.: (650) 324-5370
Web Site: http://www.transend.com
E-Mail Migration & Coexistence Software Mfr
N.A.I.C.S.: 541511

ACLARION, INC.
8181 Arista Pl Ste 100, Broomfield, CO 80021
Tel.: (650) 241-1741   DE
Web Site: https://aclarion.com
Year Founded: 2015
ACON—(NASDAQ)
Rev.: $60,444
Assets: $3,205,961
Liabilities: $1,418,210
Net Worth: $1,787,751
Earnings: ($7,605,542)
Emp.: 7
Fiscal Year-end: 12/31/22
Healthcare Software Development Services
N.A.I.C.S.: 541511
Jeff Thramann (Chm & Exec Dir)
Brent Ness (Pres, CEO, Treas & Sec)
John Lorbiecki (CFO)
Ryan Bond (Chief Strategy Officer)

ACLARIS THERAPEUTICS, INC.
701 Lee Rd Ste 103, Wayne, PA 19087
Tel.: (484) 324-7933   DE
Web Site: https://www.aclaristx.com
Year Founded: 2012
ACRS—(NASDAQ)
Rev.: $29,752,000
Assets: $254,596,000
Liabilities: $56,975,000
Net Worth: $197,621,000
Earnings: ($86,908,000)

Emp.: 100
Fiscal Year-end: 12/31/22
Pharmaceuticals Mfr
N.A.I.C.S.: 325412
Neal S. Walker (Co-Founder, Chm, Pres & Interim CEO)
Kamil Ali-Jackson (Co-Founder)
Frank Ruffo (Co-Founder)
Joseph Monahan (Chief Scientific Officer)
Kevin Balthaser (CFO)

Subsidiaries:

Confluence Discovery Technologies, Inc. (1)
4340 Duncan Ave Ste 400, Saint Louis, MO 63110
Tel.: (314) 932-4032
Web Site: https://www.confluencediscovery.com
Pharmaceuticals Product Mfr
N.A.I.C.S.: 325412
Joseph Monahan (Exec VP/Head-R&D)
Jon Jacobsen (Sr VP/VP-Chemistry & Head-Louis Site, St, and .)

ACM RESEARCH, INC.
42307 Osgood Rd Unit I, Fremont, CA 94539
Tel.: (510) 445-3700
Web Site: https://www.acmr.com
Year Founded: 1998
ACMR—(NASDAQ)
Rev.: $388,832,000
Assets: $1,235,500,000
Liabilities: $423,329,000
Net Worth: $812,171,000
Earnings: $39,263,000
Emp.: 1,209
Fiscal Year-end: 12/31/22
Semiconductor Machinery Manufacturing
N.A.I.C.S.: 333242
Lisa Feng (Chief Acctg Officer-ACM Research Shanghai Inc)
David H. Wang (Founder, Founder, Pres, Pres, CEO & CEO)
Jian Wang (VP-R&D-ACM Research Shanghai, Inc)
Sotheara Cheav (VP-Mfg-ACM Research Shanghai Inc)
Mark A. McKechnie (CFO, Treas & Exec VP)
Jim Straus (VP-Sls-North America)

Subsidiaries:

ACM Research (Shanghai), Inc. (1)
Building 4 No 1690 Cailun Rd Zhangjiang High-tech Park, Shanghai, 201203, China
Tel.: (86) 2150808868
Semiconductor & Electronic Component Distr
N.A.I.C.S.: 423690
Lisa Feng (CFO)

ACMAT CORPORATION
30 S Rd, Farmington, CT 06032
Tel.: (860) 946-4800   CT
Web Site: https://www.acmatcorp.com
Year Founded: 1950
ACMT—(OTCIQ)
Rev.: $3,022,179
Assets: $57,741,687
Liabilities: $26,437,119
Net Worth: $31,304,568
Earnings: $696,017
Emp.: 6
Fiscal Year-end: 12/31/20
Holding Company; Surety Bonds, Specialty Trade & Construction Contracting Services
N.A.I.C.S.: 551112
Henry W. Nozko III (Sec & Exec VP)
Gary M. Case (Gen Counsel & VP)
Brian P. Marshall (VP-Fin)

Subsidiaries:

ACMAT Companies, Inc. (1)

233 Main St, New Britain, CT 06050-2350   (100%)
Tel.: (860) 229-9000
Sales Range: $10-24.9 Million
Emp.: 16
Insurance Related Services
N.A.I.C.S.: 524126
Henry W. Nozko Jr. (Chm, Pres & CEO)

ACMAT of Texas, Inc. (1)
233 Main St, New Britain, CT 06050   (100%)
Tel.: (860) 229-9000
Sales Range: $25-49.9 Million
Emp.: 20
Holding Company
N.A.I.C.S.: 524126

ACSTAR Holdings, Inc. (1)
233 Main St, New Britain, CT 06050-2350   (100%)
Tel.: (860) 229-9000
Sales Range: $25-49.9 Million
Emp.: 50
Holding Company
N.A.I.C.S.: 551112

Subsidiary (Domestic):

ACSTAR Insurance Company (2)
233 Main St, New Britain, CT 06051-4204   (100%)
Tel.: (860) 224-2000
Web Site: http://www.acstarins.com
Sales Range: $10-24.9 Million
Emp.: 8
Insurance
N.A.I.C.S.: 524126
Henry W. Nozko Jr. (Chm, Pres & CEO)

United Coastal Insurance Company (1)
233 Main St, New Britain, CT 06051-4204   (66%)
Tel.: (860) 223-5000
Environmental, Pollution, Lead & Asbestos Abatement Liability Insurance for Contractors
N.A.I.C.S.: 524126

ACME UNITED CORPORATION
1 Waterview Dr, Shelton, CT 06484
Tel.: (203) 254-6060   CT
Web Site: https://www.acmeunited.com
Year Founded: 1867
ACU—(NYSEAMEX)
Rev.: $191,500,947
Assets: $149,241,316
Liabilities: $51,342,632
Net Worth: $97,898,684
Earnings: $17,793,160
Emp.: 645
Fiscal Year-end: 12/31/23
Cutting, Measuring & Safety Products Mfr & Distr
N.A.I.C.S.: 339113
Walter C. Johnsen (Chm & CEO)
Brian S. Olschan (Pres & COO)
Paul G. Driscoll (CFO, Treas, Sec & VP)

Subsidiaries:

Acme United (Asia Pacific) Ltd. (1)
Tel.: (852) 31677878
Emp.: 9
Cutting, Measuring & Safety Products Distr
N.A.I.C.S.: 423710
Y. B. Pek (Sr VP & Gen Mgr)

Acme United Europe GmbH (1)
Junkerstr 13-15, 42699, Solingen, Germany   (100%)
Tel.: (49) 212232450
Web Site: https://www.acmeunited.de
Sales Range: $25-49.9 Million
Emp.: 20
Cold-Formed Scissors & Disposable Scissors Mfr & Marketer
N.A.I.C.S.: 332215
Georg Bettin (Mng Dir)
Walter C. Johnson (Mng Dir)

Acme United Limited (1)
210 Broadway Avenue Suite 204, Orangeville, L9W 5G4, ON, Canada   (100%)

Web Site: https://www.acmeunited.ca
Sales Range: $25-49.9 Million
Emp.: 19
Mfr & Whslr of Rulers, Yardsticks, Scissors & Shears
N.A.I.C.S.: 332216

First Aid Only Inc. (1)
11101 NE 37th Cir, Vancouver, WA 98682
Tel.: (360) 254-9291
Web Site: http://www.firstaidonly.com
Sales Range: $10-24.9 Million
Emp.: 100
First Aid Kits Mfr & Distr
N.A.I.C.S.: 339113

Med-Nap LLC (1)
301 Marianne St, Brooksville, FL 34601-3412
Tel.: (352) 796-6020
Web Site: https://www.mednap.us
Toilet Preparation Mfr
N.A.I.C.S.: 325620
Pierre Sanfacon (Founder & Pres)

Pac-Kit Safety Equipment (1)
57 Chestnut St, South Norwalk, CT 06854
Tel.: (203) 857-5361
Web Site: http://www.pac-kit.com
Sales Range: $1-9.9 Million
Emp.: 39
First Aid Kit Mfr
N.A.I.C.S.: 339113

ACNB CORPORATION
16 Lincoln Sq, Gettysburg, PA 17325
Tel.: (717) 334-3161   PA
Web Site: https://www.acnb.com
Year Founded: 1983
ACNB—(NASDAQ)
Rev.: $87,049,000
Assets: $2,525,507,000
Liabilities: $2,280,465,000
Net Worth: $245,042,000
Earnings: $35,752,000
Emp.: 397
Fiscal Year-end: 12/31/22
Bank Holding Company
N.A.I.C.S.: 551111
James P. Helt (Pres & CEO)
Jason H. Weber (CFO, Treas & Exec VP)
Todd L. Herring (Vice Chm)
Kevin J. Hayes (Chief Governance Officer)

Subsidiaries:

ACNB Bank (1)
100 V-Twin Dr, Gettysburg, PA 17325
Tel.: (717) 334-3161
Web Site: https://www.acnb.com
Rev.: $37,897,000
Emp.: 225
Banking Services
N.A.I.C.S.: 522110
Alan J. Stock (Chm)
James P. Helt (Pres & CEO)
Jason H. Weber (CFO, Treas & Exec VP)
Lynda L. Glass (Chief Risk & Governance Officer, Sec & Exec VP)
Todd L. Herring (Vice Chm)
Laurie A. Laub (Chief Credit & Ops Officer & Exec VP)
Sarah E. Brechbuehl (VP)
Tim Owings (VP)
Linda Roth (VP)
Patrick Sease (VP)

ACNB Insurance Services Inc. (1)
2526 W Liberty Rd, Westminster, MD 21157
Tel.: (410) 875-5617
Web Site: https://www.acnbinsurance.com
Insurance Services
N.A.I.C.S.: 524210
Thomas A. Ritter (Chm)
Frank Elsner III (Vice Chm)
James P. Helt (Chm)
Jason H. Weber (Treas & VP)
James P. Helt (Chm)

Subsidiary (Domestic):

Hockley & O'Donnell Insurance Agency, LLC (2)
132 Buford Ave, Gettysburg, PA 17325
Tel.: (717) 334-6741

ACNB Corporation—(Continued)

Web Site:
  http://www.hockleyandodonnell.com
Insurance Agencies & Brokerages
N.A.I.C.S.: 524210
Susan Bailey (Controller)

Frederick County Bancorp, Inc. (1)
9 N Market St, Frederick, MD 21701
Tel.: (301) 620-1400
Web Site: http://www.fcbmd.com
Rev.: $16,595,000
Assets: $405,796,000
Liabilities: $373,175,000
Net Worth: $32,621,000
Earnings: $2,050,000
Emp.: 75
Fiscal Year-end: 12/31/2017
Bank Holding Company
N.A.I.C.S.: 551111
William R. Talley (Pres & CEO)

ACORDA THERAPEUTICS, INC.
2 Blue Hill Plz 3rd Fl, Pearl River, NY
10965
Tel.: (914) 347-4300   DE
Web Site: https://www.acorda.com
Year Founded: 1995
ACOR—(NASDAQ)
Rev.: $118,566,000
Assets: $395,595,000
Liabilities: $301,973,000
Net Worth: $93,622,000
Earnings: ($65,916,000)
Emp.: 111
Fiscal Year-end: 12/31/22
Pharmaceutical Products Developer
for Restoration of Neurological Func-
tion to People With Spinal Cord Injury
(SCI), Multiple Sclerosis (MS) & Re-
lated Nervous System Conditions
N.A.I.C.S.: 325414
Ron Cohen (Founder, Pres & CEO)
Denise Duca (Exec VP-HR)
John P. Kelley (Chm)
Kerry Clem (Chief Comml Officer)
Neil S. Belloff (Gen Counsel)
Michael Gesser (CFO)

ACORN ENERGY, INC.
1000 N W St Ste 1200, Wilmington,
DE 19801
Tel.: (410) 654-3315   DE
Web Site:
  https://www.acornenergy.com
Year Founded: 1986
ACFN—(OTCQB)
Rev.: $7,000,000
Assets: $5,984,000
Liabilities: $6,995,000
Net Worth: ($1,011,000)
Earnings: ($633,000)
Emp.: 26
Fiscal Year-end: 12/31/22
Holding Company: Energy Production
N.A.I.C.S.: 551112
Jan H. Loeb (Pres & CEO)
Tracy Simmons Clifford (CFO &
COO)

Subsidiaries:

Paketeria GmbH   (1)
KundenServiceCenter Hahnemannsplatz
21, 01662, Meissen, Germany   (32%)
Tel.: (49) 3521 467 500
Web Site: http://www.vr-meissen.de
Sales Range: $75-99.9 Million
Logistics & Supply Chain Operations
N.A.I.C.S.: 541614

US Sensor Systems Inc.   (1)
9601 Variel Ave, Chatsworth, CA 91311
Tel.: (818) 435-4020
Web Site: http://www.ussensorsystems.com
Fiber Optic Sensing Systems Mfr
N.A.I.C.S.: 334413

dsIT Solutions Ltd.   (1)
2 Rechavam Zeevi St, Giv'at Shemu'el,
5401852, Israel   (58%)

Tel.: (972) 35318333
Web Site: https://www.dsit.co.il
Sales Range: $50-74.9 Million
Emp.: 70
Computer Software Consulting & Develop-
ment Services; Port Security, Oncology
Treatment & Billing Services Equipment De-
veloper & Mfr
N.A.I.C.S.: 541519
Ran Avgar (VP-Ops)
Yitshak Peery (Head-Naval Sys)
Gadi Leibovich (Pres & CEO)
Hanan Marom (VP-Bus Dev, Mktg & Sls)
Eyal Oz (CFO)
Shalhevet Moor-Gilboa (Compliance Officer,
Gen Counsel & VP)
Ayala Geron (Mgr-Integrated Quality)

ACREAGE HOLDINGS, INC.
366 Madison Ave 14th Fl, New York,
NY 10017
Tel.: (646) 600-9181   Ca
Web Site:
  https://www.acreageholdings.com
Year Founded: 2014
ACRHF—(OTCQX)
Rev.: $237,138,000
Assets: $360,573,000
Liabilities: $320,394,000
Net Worth: $40,179,000
Earnings: ($139,876,000)
Emp.: 1,016
Fiscal Year-end: 12/31/22
Holding Company
N.A.I.C.S.: 551112
Kevin P. Murphy (Founder)
Philip Himmelstein (Interim CFO)
Dennis Curran (Chm, CEO & COO)
Corey Sheahan (Gen Counsel, Sec &
Exec VP)
Rebecca Kirk (COO)
Sharon Ali (Exec VP-Mid-Atlantic
Reg)
Lisa Collie (VP-Human Resources)
Bryan Murray (Exec VP-Government
Relations & Communications)
Kate Ols (Exec VP-OH Ops)

Subsidiaries:

22nd & Burn Inc.   (1)
2231 W Burnside St, Portland, OR 97210
Tel.: (971) 279-5570
Cannabis Retailer
N.A.I.C.S.: 459999

D&B Wellness, LLC   (1)
4 Garella Rd, Bethel, CT 06801
Tel.: (203) 909-6869
Web Site: http://ccc-ct.com
Nursing Care Services
N.A.I.C.S.: 623110

Health Circle, Inc.   (1)
21 Commerce Rd, Rockland, MA 02370
Tel.: (781) 384-2001
Web Site: https://www.healthcirclema.com
Cannabis Distr
N.A.I.C.S.: 459999

Prime Wellness of Connecticut,
LLC   (1)
75 John Fitch Blvd, South Windsor, CT
06074
Tel.: (860) 331-8918
Web Site:
  https://www.primewellnessofct.com
Alternative Medicine Distr
N.A.I.C.S.: 424210
Sara Harris (Mgr-Dispensary)

Prime Wellness of Pennsylvania,
LLC   (1)
S Heidelberg Industrial Park 2 Corporate
Blvd, Sinking Spring, PA 19608
Tel.: (484) 516-2398
Web Site: https://www.primewellnesspa.com
Alternative Medicine Distr
N.A.I.C.S.: 424210

Thames Valley Apothecary, LLC (1)
887 Norwich-New London Tpke, Uncasville,
CT 06382
Tel.: (860) 848-0865
Web Site: http://www.thamesvalleyrelief.com

Alternative Medicine Distr
N.A.I.C.S.: 424210
Laurie Zrenda (Mgr-Dispensary)

The Botantist, Inc.   (1)
10520 Spring Hill Dr, Spring Hill, FL 34608
Tel.: (352) 355-4322
Tobacco Mfr
N.A.I.C.S.: 312230

The Firestation 23 Inc.   (1)
1917 SE 7th Ave, Portland, OR 97214
Tel.: (503) 719-4338
Cannabis Retailer
N.A.I.C.S.: 459999

Universal Hemp, LLC   (1)
1188 Bishop St PH2, Honolulu, HI 96813
Tel.: (808) 465-3657
Web Site: http://www.universalhemp.co
Cannabidiol Ingredient Distr
N.A.I.C.S.: 424490
Chad K. Kahunahana (Founder & CEO)
Scott Farley (Pres & COO)
Neshama Abraham (Comm Mgr)

ACRES COMMERCIAL RE-
ALTY CORP.
390 RXR Plz, Uniondale, NY 11556
Tel.: (516) 862-2385   MD
Web Site: https://www.acresreit.com
ACR—(NYSE)
Rev.: $75,170,000
Assets: $2,376,652,000
Liabilities: $1,935,338,000
Net Worth: $441,314,000
Earnings: $10,426,000
Emp.: 83
Fiscal Year-end: 12/31/22
Other Financial Vehicles
N.A.I.C.S.: 525990
Eldron C. Blackwell (CFO, Treas & Sr
VP)
Jaclyn Jesberger (Chief Legal Officer
& Sec)
Mark S. Fogel (Pres & CEO)

ACRI CAPITAL ACQUISITION
CORPORATION
13284 Pond Springs Rd Ste 405,
Austin, TX 78729
Tel.: (512) 666-1277   DE
Year Founded: 2022
ACAC—(NASDAQ)
Rev.: $2,118,942
Assets: $36,732,926
Liabilities: $41,370,720
Net Worth: ($1,637,704)
Earnings: $886,366
Fiscal Year-end: 12/31/23
Investment Management Service
N.A.I.C.S.: 523999
Yi Hua V (CEO, CFO & Chm)

ACROPOLIS INFRASTRUC-
TURE ACQUISITION CORP.
9 W 57th St 43rd Fl, New York, NY
10019
Tel.: (212) 515-3200   DE
Year Founded: 2020
ACRO—(NYSE)
Rev.: $3,921,380
Assets: $348,536,442
Liabilities: $16,227,766
Net Worth: $332,308,677
Earnings: $205,069
Emp.: 2
Fiscal Year-end: 12/31/22
Investment Services
N.A.I.C.S.: 523999
Sanjay Hiralal Patel (CEO)
James Crossen (CFO & Chief Acctg
Officer)
Dylan Foo (Chm)

ACTAVIA LIFE SCIENCES, INC.
5 Penn Plz 19th Fl, New York, NY
10001
Tel.: (646) 396-4087   NV

Web Site: https://www.rasna.com
Year Founded: 2012
RASP—(OTCIQ)
Assets: $95,657
Liabilities: $2,051,566
Net Worth: ($1,955,909)
Earnings: ($4,442,535)
Emp.: 1
Fiscal Year-end: 09/30/23
Investment Services
N.A.I.C.S.: 523999
Willy J. Simon (Chm)
Keeren Shah (Fin Dir)

ACTELIS NETWORKS, INC.
4039 Clipper Ct, Fremont, CA 94538-
6540
Tel.: (510) 545-1045
Web Site: https://www.actelis.com
Year Founded: 1998
ASNS—(NASDAQ)
Rev.: $8,831,000
Assets: $14,819,000
Liabilities: $11,554,000
Net Worth: $3,265,000
Earnings: ($10,982,000)
Emp.: 44
Fiscal Year-end: 12/31/22
Telephone Apparatus Mfr
N.A.I.C.S.: 334210
Tuvia Barlev (Founder, Chm & CEO)
Yoav Efron (Deputy CEO)
Ze'Ev Rom (CFO)
Hemi Kabir (VP-Ops)
Oded Sinai (VP-R&D)
Michal Solomon Solomon (VP-
Product Mktg)
Joe Kenyon (VP-Customer Svc &
Support-Global)
Hans-Erhard Reiter (Exec VP-
Strategic Bus Dev)
Yaron Altit (Exec VP-Intl-Sls)
Bruce Hammergren (Exec VP-Sls-
Americas)
Bret Harrison (Sr VP-Svcs & Sls-
Americas)
Sean Renn (VP-Mktg & Comm-
Global)

ACTINIUM PHARMACEUTI-
CALS, INC.
100 Park Ave 23rd Fl, New York, NY
10017
Tel.: (646) 677-3870   NV
Web Site:
  https://www.actiniumpharma.com
ATNM—(NYSEAMEX)
Rev.: $1,030,000
Assets: $114,192,000
Liabilities: $47,711,000
Net Worth: $66,481,000
Earnings: ($33,017,000)
Emp.: 49
Fiscal Year-end: 12/31/22
Pharmaceuticals Mfr
N.A.I.C.S.: 325412
Lynn M. Bodarky (Chief Bus Officer)
Sandesh C. Seth (Chm & CEO)
Steve O'Loughlin (CFO)
Avinash Desai (Chief Medical Officer)
Jenny Hsieh (Chief Strategy Officer)
Sunitha Lakshminarayanan (Sr VP &
Head-CMC & Product Dev)
Stephen Dressel (VP-Strategic Fin &
Analysis)
Micah Riskin (Dir-Product Steward,
Mfg Sciences & Tech)

ACUITY BRANDS, INC.
1170 Peachtree St NE Ste 1200, Atlanta, GA 30309
Tel.: (404) 853-1400   DE
Web Site:
  https://www.acuitybrands.com
Year Founded: 2001

AYI—(NYSE)
Rev.: $3,841,000,000
Assets: $3,814,600,000
Liabilities: $1,435,800,000
Net Worth: $2,378,800,000
Earnings: $422,600,000
Emp.: 13,200
Fiscal Year-end: 08/31/24
Specialty Cleaning, Sanitation Preparations & Commercial & Industrial Lighting Fixtures Mfr
N.A.I.C.S.: 335131
Karen J. Holcom (CFO & Sr VP)
Neil M. Ashe (Chm, Pres & CEO)
Dianne S. Mills (Chief HR Officer & Sr VP)
Trevor S. Palmer (Pres-Lighting & Lighting Controls Bus)
Tyler H. Moon (COO & Sr VP)
Candace Steele Flippin (Chief Comm Officer & Sr VP)
Vijay Raghavendra (CTO)
Peter Han (Pres-Intelligent Spaces Grp)
Charlotte McLaughlin (VP-IR)
Sach Sankpal (Sr VP)
Philippe Brzuszczak (Sr VP)

Subsidiaries:

Acuity Brands Lighting, Inc.   (1)
1 Lithonia Way, Conyers, GA 30012
Tel.: (770) 922-9000
Sales Range: $150-199.9 Million
Emp.: 500
Lighting Systems & Fixtures Mfr
N.A.I.C.S.: 335132

Subsidiary (Non-US):

Acuity Brands Lighting Canada, Inc.   (2)
35B Minthorn Blvd, Thornhill, L3T 7N5, ON, Canada   (100%)
Tel.: (905) 886-8967
Web Site:
http://www.acuitybrandstoronto.com
Lighting Product Mfr
N.A.I.C.S.: 335132

Subsidiary (Domestic):

Distech Controls Inc.   (3)
4205 Place de Java, Brossard, J4Y 0C4, QC, Canada
Tel.: (450) 444-9898
Web Site: https://www.distech-controls.com
Emp.: 140
Building Automation System Mfr
N.A.I.C.S.: 236210
Elisabeth Gagnon (VP-Ops)
Scott Hamilton (VP-Sls)
Mathieu Houle (VP-Customer Experience)
Christina Carvalho (VP)
Guylaine Ruel (VP)
Olivier Fillot (VP)

Subsidiary (US):

Distech Controls Energy Services Inc.   (4)
320 Decker Dr, Irving, TX 75062
Tel.: (450) 444-9898
Electronic Equipment Distr
N.A.I.C.S.: 423690
Scott Hamilton (VP-Sls)

Subsidiary (Non-US):

Distech Controls Polen Sp. z o.o.   (4)
ul Parkowa 25, 51-616, Wroclaw, Poland
Tel.: (48) 713456423
Web Site: https://www.distech.pl
Building Automation Systems Distr
N.A.I.C.S.: 238290

Distech Controls Portugal Domebus   (4)
R das Olhalvas Ed Europa Lt6 Lj11, 2410-196, Leiria, Portugal
Tel.: (351) 244828967
Emp.: 4
Electronic Equipment Distr
N.A.I.C.S.: 423690

Distech Controls Pte Ltd   (4)
66 Tannery Lane 04-10 Sindo Building, Singapore, 347805, Singapore
Tel.: (65) 68411788
Emp.: 20
Electronic Equipment Distr
N.A.I.C.S.: 423690

Distech Controls SAS   (4)
ZAC de Sacuny 558 avenue Marcel Merieux, 69530, Brindas, France
Tel.: (33) 478450123
Web Site: https://www.distech-controls.com
Electronic Equipment Distr
N.A.I.C.S.: 423690

Subsidiary (Non-US):

Acuity Brands Lighting Mexico, S. de R.L. de C.V.   (2)
La Silla No 7711, Guadalupe, 67193, Nuevo Leon, Mexico
Tel.: (52) 8183180460
Electric Lighting Fixture Mfr
N.A.I.C.S.: 335131

Subsidiary (Domestic):

Holophane, S.A. de C.V.   (3)
Km 31 Carrtera, Cuautitlan, 54900, Tultitlan, Mexico   (100%)
Tel.: (52) 5558990100
Web Site: http://www.holophane.com.mx
Sales Range: $25-49.9 Million
Emp.: 200
Commercial Lighting Systems & Fixtures; Polyoletin Manufacturing; Paper & Corrugated Containers Mfr
N.A.I.C.S.: 335132

Subsidiary (Non-US):

Holophane Europe Ltd.   (2)
Bond Avenue, Bletchley, Milton Keynes, MK1 1JG, Buckinghamshire, United Kingdom   (100%)
Tel.: (44) 1908649292
Web Site: https://www.holophane.co.uk
Sales Range: $75-99.9 Million
Emp.: 250
Holding Company; Regional Managing Office; Industrial & Infrastructure Lighting Products Mfr & Whslr
N.A.I.C.S.: 551112

Subsidiary (Domestic):

Holophane Lighting Ltd.   (3)
Bond Avenue, Milton Keynes, MK1 1JG, Buckinghamshire, United Kingdom
Tel.: (44) 1908649292
Emp.: 25
Industrial & Infrastructure Lighting Products Mfr & Whslr
N.A.I.C.S.: 335132

Subsidiary (Domestic):

Juno Lighting, LLC   (2)
1300 S Wolf Rd, Des Plaines, IL 60018
Tel.: (847) 827-9880
Web Site: http://juno.acuitybrands.com
Recessed & Track Lighting Fixtures Mfr
N.A.I.C.S.: 335131

Lithonia Lighting   (2)
1400 Lester Rd, Conyers, GA 30012
Tel.: (770) 922-9000
Web Site: http://www.lithonia.com
Sales Range: $900-999.9 Million
Emp.: 100
Flourescent & High Intensity Lighting Fixtures Mfr
N.A.I.C.S.: 335139

Mark Lighting Fixture Co., Inc.   (2)
3 Kilmer Rd, Edison, NJ 08817-2412
Tel.: (732) 985-2600
Web Site: http://www.marklighting.com
Sales Range: $25-49.9 Million
Emp.: 96
Commercial Lighting Fixtures Mfr
N.A.I.C.S.: 335132

Peerless Lighting Corp.   (2)
2246 5th St, Berkeley, CA 94710-2217
Tel.: (510) 845-2760
Web Site: http://www.peerless-lighting.com
Sales Range: $25-49.9 Million
Emp.: 100
Lighting Equipment Mfr

N.A.I.C.S.: 335132

IOTA Engineering, L.L.C.   (1)
1361 E Wieding Rd, Tucson, AZ 85706
Tel.: (520) 294-3292
Web Site: http://www.iotaengineering.com
Lighting Equipment Mfr
N.A.I.C.S.: 335139
John Kehm (Mgr-Technical Support)
Cybil Bailey (Dir-Customer Care)

KE2 Therm Solutions, Inc.   (1)
12 Chamber Dr, Washington, MO 63090
Tel.: (636) 266-0140
Web Site: https://ke2therm.com
Electronic Refrigerator Mfr
N.A.I.C.S.: 333415

eldoLED B.V.   (1)
Science Park Eindhoven 5125, 5692 ED, Son, Netherlands
Tel.: (31) 407820400
Web Site: http://www.eldoled.com
Electric Equipment Mfr
N.A.I.C.S.: 334515

ACUMEN PHARMACEUTICAL, INC.
427 Park St, Charlottesville, VA 22902
Tel.: (434) 297-1000
Web Site:
https://www.acumenpharm.com
Year Founded: 1996
ABOS—(NASDAQ)
Rev.: $10,791,000
Assets: $310,125,000
Liabilities: $43,152,000
Net Worth: $266,973,000
Earnings: ($52,371,000)
Emp.: 51
Fiscal Year-end: 12/31/23
Immunotherapy Services
N.A.I.C.S.: 541714
James Doherty (Pres & Chief Dev Officer)
Daniel O'Connell (CEO)

ACURX PHARMACEUTICALS, INC.
259 Liberty Ave, Staten Island, NY 10305
Tel.: (917) 533-1469   DE
Web Site:
https://www.acurxpharma.com
Year Founded: 2017
ACXP—(NASDAQ)
Assets: $9,376,706
Liabilities: $2,061,685
Net Worth: $7,315,021
Earnings: ($12,092,776)
Emp.: 4
Fiscal Year-end: 12/31/22
Research & Development in Biotechnology (except Nanobiotechnology)
N.A.I.C.S.: 541714
David P. Luci (Pres & CEO)
Robert J. DeLuccia (Chm)
Robert G. Shawah (CFO)
Michael Silverman (Dir-Medical)
Les Johnson (Dir-Mfg)
Xiang Yu (Dir-Pre-Clinical Dev)

ACUTUS MEDICAL, INC.
2210 Faraday Ave Ste 100, Carlsbad, CA 92008
Tel.: (442) 232-6080   DE
Web Site:
https://www.acutusmedical.com
Year Founded: 2011
AFIB—(NASDAQ)
Rev.: $16,363,000
Assets: $133,440,000
Liabilities: $58,421,000
Net Worth: $75,019,000
Earnings: ($39,616,000)
Emp.: 225
Fiscal Year-end: 12/31/22
Medical Device Mfr & Distr
N.A.I.C.S.: 334510

Tom Sohn (Gen Counsel, Sec & Sr VP)
R. Scott Huennekens (Chm)
Takeo Mukai (CEO, CFO & Sr VP)
Diane Flynn (VP-Business Development)
Shaden Marzouk (Chm)

Subsidiaries:

Acutus Medical, N.V.   (1)
Ikaroslaan 25, 1930, Zaventem, Belgium
Tel.: (32) 26697500
Medical Device Mfr
N.A.I.C.S.: 339112

ACV AUCTIONS INC.
640 Ellicott St Ste 321, Buffalo, NY 14203
Tel.: (512) 632-1200   DE
Web Site: https://www.acvauto.com
Year Founded: 2014
ACVA—(NASDAQ)
Rev.: $481,234,000
Assets: $922,924,000
Liabilities: $466,396,000
Net Worth: $456,528,000
Earnings: ($75,261,000)
Emp.: 2,170
Fiscal Year-end: 12/31/23
Online Auction Services
N.A.I.C.S.: 459420
George G. Chamoun (CEO)
George Chamoun (CEO)
Craig Anderson (Chief Legal Officer & Chief Corp Dev & Strategy Officer)
Vikas Mehta (COO)
Michael Waterman (Chief Sls Officer)
William Zerella (CFO)
Kate Clegg (CMO)
Joseph Neiman (Founder & Chief Customer Success Officer)
Dan Magnuszewski (CTO)
Sallie Reid (VP-People & Culture)

Subsidiaries:

MAX Digital, LLC   (1)
833 W Jackson Blvd Ste 200, Chicago, IL 60607
Web Site: https://maxdigital.com
Sales Range: $1-9.9 Million
Emp.: 32
Software Development Services
N.A.I.C.S.: 541512
Steve Fitzgerald (Pres)
Brad Kruse (Sr VP-Sales-Marketing)
Rob Levin (CFO)
Patrick McMullen (Sr VP-Customer Success)
Denis Dwyer (Sr VP-Operations)
Robert Granados (CEO)
John Aiello (Chm)
Ryan Walker (VP-Engineering)
Pat Ryan Jr. (Founder)

ADAMAS ONE CORP.
17767 N Perimeter Dr Ste B115, Scottsdale, AZ 85255
Tel.: (480) 356-8798   NV
Web Site:
https://www.adamasone.com
Year Founded: 2018
JEWL—(NASDAQ)
Rev.: $1,007,705
Assets: $12,894,511
Liabilities: $9,771,020
Net Worth: $3,123,491
Earnings: ($22,543,940)
Emp.: 12
Fiscal Year-end: 09/30/23
Diamond Product Mfr
N.A.I.C.S.: 339910
John G. Grdina (Pres, CEO & Chm)
Steven R. Staehr (CFO)
Gerald A. McGuire (COO)

Subsidiaries:

Scio Diamond Technology Corp.   (1)

Adamas One Corp.—(Continued)

411 University Ridge Ste 110, Greenville,
SC 29601
Tel.: (864) 751-4880
Web Site: http://www.sciodiamond.com
Sales Range: Less than $1 Million
Cultured Diamond Producer
N.A.I.C.S.: 339910

ADAMS DIVERSIFIED EQUITY FUND, INC.

500 E Pratt St Ste 1300, Baltimore,
MD 21202
Tel.: (410) 752-5900   **MD**
Web Site:
    http://www.adamsfunds.com
Year Founded: 1854
ADX—(NYSE)
Financial Investment & Management
Services
N.A.I.C.S.: 523999
James P. Haynie (CEO)
Michael E. Rega (VP-Res)
D. Cotton Swindell (Exec VP)
Steven R. Crain (VP-Res)
Janis F. Kerns (Chief Compliance Officer, Gen Counsel, Sec & VP)
Gregory W. Buckley (Exec VP & VP-Res)
Xuying Chang (VP-Res)

ADAMS NATURAL RESOURCES FUND, INC.

500 E Pratt St Ste 1300, Baltimore,
MD 21202
Tel.: (410) 752-5900   **NY**
Web Site:
    http://www.adamsfunds.com
Year Founded: 1929
PEO—(NYSE)
Sales Range: $10-24.9 Million
Emp.: 20
Closed-End Investment Company
Emphasizing Natural Resource
Stocks
N.A.I.C.S.: 525990
Brian S. Hook (CFO, Treas & VP)
James P. Haynie (Pres & CEO)
Michael E. Rega (VP-Res)
Christine M. Sloan (Asst Treas)
Gregory W. Buckley (VP-Res)
Michael A. Kijesky (VP-Res)
Janis F. Kerns (Chief Compliance Officer, Gen Counsel, Sec & VP)
Jeffrey R. Schollaert (VP-Res)

ADAMS RESOURCES & ENERGY, INC.

17 S Briar Hollow Ln Ste 300, Houston, TX 77027
Tel.: (713) 881-3600   **DE**
Web Site:
    https://www.adamsresources.com
Year Founded: 1973
AE—(NYSEAMEX)
Rev.: $3,366,917,000
Assets: $384,159,000
Liabilities: $290,982,000
Net Worth: $93,177,000
Earnings: $3,487,000
Emp.: 882
Fiscal Year-end: 12/31/22
Holding Company; Crude Oil, Natural
Gas & Petrochemical Products Marketer & Distr
N.A.I.C.S.: 551112
Kevin J. Roycraft (Pres & CEO)
Tracy E. Ohmart (CFO, Treas & Exec VP)
Wade Harrison (Pres-Svc Transport)
Mike Leggio (COO)

Subsidiaries:

Ada Resources, Inc.   (1)
6603 Kirbyville St, Houston, TX
77033   (100%)

Tel.: (713) 881-3600
Sales Range: $50-74.9 Million
Emp.: 35
Petroleum Products Marketer & Distr
N.A.I.C.S.: 424710

Firebird Bulk Carriers, Inc.   (1)
2015 N Houston Ave, Humble, TX 77338
Tel.: (281) 548-2700
Web Site: http://firebird-tx.com
Rev.: $1,100,000
Emp.: 10
General Freight Trucking, Long-Distance,
Truckload
N.A.I.C.S.: 484121
Scott Bosard (Pres)
Joy Weatherspoon (Office Mgr)
Lisa Johnson (Office Mgr)

GulfMark Energy, Inc.   (1)
17 S Briar Hollow Ln Ste 100, Houston,
TX
77027   (100%)
Tel.: (713) 881-3603
Web Site: https://www.gulfmarkenergy.com
Emp.: 307
Marketing & Transportation of Crude Oil to
Refineries & Other Customers
N.A.I.C.S.: 486110
Kevin J. Roycraft (CEO)
David Miller (Mgr-Crude Oil Acquisitions)
Shelly Smith (Dir-Crude Oil Supply & Logistics)
Tim Rudolph (Mktg Mgr-Reg)
Michael Horwith (Dir-Rockies/Permian
Crude Oil Supply & Logistics)
Lanny Opheim (Mgr-Permian Basin Supply
& Logistics)

Phoenix Oil, Inc.   (1)
2015 N Houston Ave, Humble, TX 77338
Tel.: (281) 446-5029
Web Site: http://www.phoenixoil-tx.com
Sales Range: $1-9.9 Million
Emp.: 12
Petroleum & Petroleum Products Merchant
Whslr (except Bulk Stations & Terminals)
N.A.I.C.S.: 424720

Service Transport Company   (1)
7979 Almeda Genoa Rd, Houston, TX
77075   (100%)
Tel.: (713) 209-2500
Web Site: https://www.svtn.com
Sales Range: $50-74.9 Million
Emp.: 200
Chemical Tank Transportation Services
N.A.I.C.S.: 484230

ADAPTHEALTH CORP.

220 W Germantown Pike Ste 250,
Plymouth Meeting, PA 19462
Tel· (610) 424-4515   **DE**
Web Site:
    https://www.adapthealth.com
Year Founded: 2017
AHCO—(NASDAQ)
Rev.: $2,970,595,000
Assets: $5,219,587,000
Liabilities: $3,061,829,000
Net Worth: $2,157,758,000
Earnings: $69,316,000
Emp.: 10,900
Fiscal Year-end: 12/31/22
Investment Services
N.A.I.C.S.: 523999
Shaw Rietkerk (COO-AdaptHealth
Holding)
Christine Archbold (Chief Acctg Officer)
Jason Clemens (CFO)
Anton Hie (VP-IR)
Albert Prast (CTO)
Wendy Russalesi (Chief Compliance
Officer)
Joel Mills (Chief People Officer)
Leila Vargas (Exec VP)
Shaw Rietkerk (Chief Bus Officer)
Suzanne Foster (CEO)

Subsidiaries:

ABC Medical, LLC   (1)
6185 Rivers Ave Ste B, North Charleston,
SC 29406-4999
Tel.: (843) 767-0580

Medical Equipment Mfr & Distr
N.A.I.C.S.: 325412

Activstyle, Inc   (1)
3100 Pacific St, Minneapolis, MN 55411
Tel.: (612) 520-9333
Web Site: http://www.activstyle.com
Sales Range: $25-49.9 Million
Emp.: 25
Medical, Dental & Hospital Equipment &
Supplies Merchant Whslr
N.A.I.C.S.: 423450
Gayle Devi (CEO)

Subsidiary (Domestic):

Home Wellness, Inc.   (2)
700 Route 130 N Ste 208, Cinnaminson, NJ
08077-3366
Tel.: (856) 864-1549
Web Site: http://www.homewellness.net
Sales Range: $10-24.9 Million
Emp.: 20
Hospital Equipment Distr
N.A.I.C.S.: 339113
Evelyn Williams (Mgr-Sls)

AdaptHealth Patient Care Solutions,
Inc.   (1)
Airside Business Park 600 Lindbergh Dr,
Moon Township, PA 15108
Web Site: https://www.pcs.adapthealth.com
Healtcare Services
N.A.I.C.S.: 621999
Rodney Carson (Pres)

Advanced Home Care Inc.   (1)
4001 Piedmont Pkwy, High Point, NC
27265
Tel.: (336) 878-8822
Web Site: http://www.advhomecare.org
Women Healthcare Services
N.A.I.C.S.: 621610
Joel Mills (CEO)

AeroCare Holdings, Inc.   (1)
3325 Bartlett Blvd, Orlando, FL 32811
Tel.: (407) 206-0040
Web Site: http://www.aerocareusa.com
Emp.: 50
Home Health Equipment Rental Services
N.A.I.C.S.: 532283
Steve Griggs (Founder & CEO)

Aerocare Home Medical Equipment,
Inc.   (1)
209 M and M Ranch Rd Ste 110, Granbury,
TX 76049
Tel.: (817) 578-8970
Medical Equipment Distr
N.A.I.C.S.: 423450

Airway Oxygen, Inc.   (1)
2955 Clydon Ave SW, Wyoming, MI 49519-
2485
Tel.: (616) 247-3900
Web Site: http://www.airwayoxygeninc.com
Emp.: 250
Medical Equipment Distr
N.A.I.C.S.: 423450
Gary Esman (Mgr)

Ameri-Quipt of North Carolina,
Inc.   (1)
Tel.: (828) 692-5577
Rev.: $1,600,000
Emp.: 9
Medical Equipment Mfr & Distr
N.A.I.C.S.: 423450
Sharlyn Page (Pres)

American Home Medical, Inc.   (1)
3325 S University Dr Ste 106, Davie, FL
33328-2005
Tel.: (954) 423-8770
Medical Equipment Mfr & Distr
N.A.I.C.S.: 325412

Atlantic Medical, Inc.   (1)
127 N Mecklenburg Ave, South Hill, VA
23970-2045
Tel.: (434) 447-4694
Medical Equipment Mfr & Distr
N.A.I.C.S.: 325412

Beacon Respiratory Services,
Inc.   (1)
1023B W Dekalb St, Camden, SC 29020-
4162
Tel.: (803) 572-4391
Medical Equipment Distr

N.A.I.C.S.: 423450

BestMED Respiratory, Inc.   (1)
104 W 5th St, Carroll, IA 51401
Tel.: (712) 775-1111
Medical Equipment Distr
N.A.I.C.S.: 423450

Bluegrass Oxygen, Inc.   (1)
1032 Majaun Rd, Lexington, KY 40511-
1151
Tel.: (859) 277-2583
Web Site: http://www.bluegrassoxygen.com
Medical Equipment Distr
N.A.I.C.S.: 532283
Michael Marnhout (Pres & CEO)

Breathe Grace Medical Supply,
LLC   (1)
221 S 3rd St, Oakland, MD 21550
Tel.: (240) 657-0030
Medical Equipment Distr
N.A.I.C.S.: 423450

Buffalo Wheelchair, Inc.   (1)
1900 Ridge Rd Ste 103, West Seneca, NY
14224-3332
Tel.: (716) 206-0208
Web Site: http://www.buffalowheelchair.com
Rev.: $5,025,000
Emp.: 25
Medical Equipment Distr
N.A.I.C.S.: 459999
Devon Wyman Zglinicki (Coord-QA Control)

Clay Home Medical, Inc.   (1)
175 Commerce Park Rd, Franklin, VA
23851
Tel.: (434) 348-0888
Rev.: $4,000,000
Emp.: 43
CPAP Equipment Distr
N.A.I.C.S.: 621610
Sam Clay (Founder)

Clearview Medical Incorporated   (1)
2503 Gravel Dr, Fort Worth, TX 76118-6904
Tel.: (817) 924-2121
Medical Equipment Distr
N.A.I.C.S.: 423450

Diabetes Management & Supplies
LLC   (1)
10 Commerce Ct, New Orleans, LA 70123-
3236
Tel.: (504) 734-7165
Web Site: https://www.diabetesms.com
Medical Device Distr
N.A.I.C.S.: 423450

Diabetes Medical Supply Center of
the Midlands   (1)
2910 S 84th St, Omaha, NE 68124
Tel·(402) 399-8444
Web Site: http://www.diabetes-supply.com
Medical Device Distr
N.A.I.C.S.: 423450

Ellis Home Oxygen & Medical Equipment, Inc.   (1)
925 N Main St, Marion, VA 24354
Tel.: (276) 783-6868
Medical Equipment Distr
N.A.I.C.S.: 423450

First Choice Home Medical Equipment, LLC   (1)
77 Commerce Way, Bethlehem, PA 18017
Web Site: http://fchoicehme.hmebillpay.com
Medical Equipment Distr
N.A.I.C.S.: 423450

GMF Medical Supply, Inc   (1)
Tel.: (276) 300-0505
Web Site: http://www.gmemedical.com
Medical Equipment Distr
N.A.I.C.S.: 621512
Gary Morris (Pres)

Georgia Home Medical, Inc.   (1)
416 Pine Ave, Albany, GA 31701
Tel.: (229) 883-5600
Rev.: $1,100,000
Emp.: 24
CPAP Equipment Distr
N.A.I.C.S.: 561320
Gerri Alexander (Pres)

Grace Healthcare Medical, Inc.   (1)
2609 Catalpa Ave Ste B, Pascagoula, MS
39567

Tel.: (228) 863-3331
Medical Equipment Distr
N.A.I.C.S.: 423450

Halprin, Incorporated (1)
220 W Germantown Pike Ste 250, Plymouth Meeting, PA 19462
Tel.: (585) 396-9993
Sales Range: $1-9.9 Million
Emp.: 14
Medical Equipment Distr
N.A.I.C.S.: 423450
James Karls (Principal)

Health Products Plus, Inc. (1)
Tel.: (706) 622-6898
Medical Equipment Distr
N.A.I.C.S.: 423450

Healthline Medical Equipment, Inc. (1)
4709 Lydia Dr, Wichita Falls, TX 76308-4537
Tel.: (940) 691-6100
Web Site: http://www.healthlinedme.com
Commercial & Industrial Machinery & Equipment Rental & Leasing
N.A.I.C.S.: 532490

Home Medical Express, Inc. (1)
Tel.: (630) 530-9777
Web Site:
    http://www.homemedicalexpress.net
Medical Equipment Distr
N.A.I.C.S.: 423450

Kentucky Medical Supply, Inc. (1)
102 Castle Ridge Dr, Edmonton, KY 42129-8176
Medical Equipment Distr
N.A.I.C.S.: 423450

Legacy Medical, LLC (1)
Tel.: (937) 335-9199
Web Site: https://www.legacymedllc.com
Spa Services
N.A.I.C.S.: 812199

Lehigh Valley Respiratory Care - Lancaster, Inc. (1)
1176 Enterprise Ct, East Petersburg, PA 17520-1647
Tel.: (717) 569-4667
Rev.: $5,600,000
Emp.: 31
Medical Equipment Distr
N.A.I.C.S.: 532283
John Weber (CFO)
Richard L. Harnish (Pres)

LifeHME, Inc. (1)
454 Berryhill Rd Ste A, Columbia, SC 29210
Tel.: (803) 254-8775
Web Site: https://www.lifehme.com
Emp.: 100
Medical Equipment Distr
N.A.I.C.S.: 423450

Loftis Home Medical, LLC (1)
Tel.: (828) 624-0174
Medical Equipment Distr
N.A.I.C.S.: 423450

Madison County Medical Equipment, Inc. (1)
Tel.: (641) 322-5453
Rev.: $1,900,000
Emp.: 10
Medical Equipment Distr
N.A.I.C.S.: 423450
Bill Brookhart (Pres)

Major Medical Supply of Colorado Springs, LLC (1)
5620 N Union Blvd, Colorado Springs, CO 80918-1940
Tel.: (719) 475-1236
Medical Equipment Distr
N.A.I.C.S.: 423450

Major Medical Supply of Denver, LLC (1)
7000 Broadway Ste 412, Denver, CO 80221-2910
Tel.: (303) 654-0720
Medical Equipment Distr
N.A.I.C.S.: 423450

Major Medical Supply of Fort Collins, LLC (1)

1420 Riverside Ave Ste 108, Fort Collins, CO 80524-4380
Tel.: (970) 484-6616
Medical Equipment Distr
N.A.I.C.S.: 423450

Med Way Medical, Inc. (1)
Tel.: (806) 797-8888
Web Site: https://www.medwaymedical.net
Medical Equipment Distr
N.A.I.C.S.: 423450

Medbridge Home Medical LLC (1)
430 Woodruff Rd Ste 500, Greenville, SC 29607
Tel.: (864) 609-9423
Web Site:
    http://www.medbridgehomemedical.com
Emp.: 30
Medical Equipment Distr
N.A.I.C.S.: 423450

Medway Medical Equipment, LLC (1)
3302 W Loop 306, San Angelo, TX 76904-5990
Tel.: (325) 223-0231
Medical Equipment Distr
N.A.I.C.S.: 423450

New England Home Medical Equipment LLC (1)
Tel.: (978) 221-2323
Web Site: https://www.nehme.care
Medical Equipment Distr
N.A.I.C.S.: 423450

Olympia Respiratory Services LLC (1)
1404 Harrison Ave NW, Olympia, WA 98502-8661
Tel.: (360) 236-0311
Medical Equipment Distr
N.A.I.C.S.: 423450
Brent McDonald (Owner)

Oxygen One, Inc. (1)
1900 Pewaukee Rd Ste F, Waukesha, WI 53188-2447
Tel.: (262) 521-2202
Web Site: https://www.oxygenone.com
Medical Equipment Distr
N.A.I.C.S.: 423450
Rick Adamich (Pres)
Ashley Bergner (VP-Operations)
Amy Bettinger (Mgr)
Lori Corey (Sr VP)
Macy Zamitalo (Mgr-Business Development)

Palmetto Oxygen, LLC (1)
1445 Shop Rd Ste A, Columbia, SC 29201-4817
Tel.: (803) 926-0252
Rev.: $3,588,000
Emp.: 6
Medical Equipment Distr
N.A.I.C.S.: 423450
Ken Magee (Owner)

Parrish Home Medical Inc (1)
516 Epting Ave, Greenwood, SC 29646-4091
Tel.: (864) 223-4663
Web Site:
    http://www.parrishhomemedical.com
CPAP Equipment Distr
N.A.I.C.S.: 423450
Nancy Voiselle (Owner)

Pharmacy, Inc. (1)
Tel.: (270) 762-0602
Web Site: http://www.pharmacy.org
Rev.: $1,100,000
Emp.: 8
CPAP Equipment Distr
N.A.I.C.S.: 423450
Thomas Fry (Pres)

Pinnacle Medical Solutions LLC (1)
6856 Cobblestone Blvd, Southaven, MS 38672
Tel.: (662) 536-1025
Web Site:
    https://www.pinnaclemedicalsolutions.com
Medical Equipment Distr
N.A.I.C.S.: 423450
Keenan Ryan (Gen Mgr)
Kent Stoneking (Dir-Pharmacy & Wellness)
Kevin Wood (Sr Mgr-Sls)

Prattville Medical Equipment, Inc. (1)
466 E Main St, Prattville, AL 36067
Tel.: (334) 358-7500
Medical Equipment Distr
N.A.I.C.S.: 423450

Promise Home, Inc. (1)
1731 Grandstand Dr, San Antonio, TX 78238
Tel.: (210) 804-0565
Medical Equipment Distr
N.A.I.C.S.: 423450

Reliable Medical Equipment LLC (1)
217 Cember Way Ste B, Summerville, SC 29483-5414
Tel.: (843) 881-4928
CPAP Equipment Distr
N.A.I.C.S.: 423450
Alan Richey (Owner)

Reliable Medical of Conway, LLC (1)
2381 Hwy 544 Unit 1 and 2, Conway, SC 29526
Tel.: (843) 234-1249
Medical Equipment Distr
N.A.I.C.S.: 423450

Respiratory Home Care of Bristol, LLC (1)
Tel.: (865) 240-2386
Medical Equipment Distr
N.A.I.C.S.: 423450

Respiratory Services of Western New York, Inc. (1)
80 French Rd, Cheektowaga, NY 14227
Tel.: (716) 683-6699
Web Site:
    https://www.respiratoryservices.com
Sales Range: $1-9.9 Million
Medical Equipment Distr
N.A.I.C.S.: 423450

Skoro Enterprises LLC (1)
203 S Ector Dr Ste A, Euless, TX 76040
Web Site: http://www.xmed4u.com
Medical Equipment Distr
N.A.I.C.S.: 423450

Solara Medical Supplies, LLC (1)
2084 Otay Lakes Rd 102, Chula Vista, CA 91913
Web Site:
    https://www.solaramedicalsupplies.com
Surgical Appliance & Supplies Mfr
N.A.I.C.S.: 339113

Subsidiary (Non-US):

J.M.R. Medical, Inc. (2)
Tel.: (803) 791-9013
Surgical Appliance & Supplies Mfr
N.A.I.C.S.: 339113

Subsidiary (Domestic):

Pal-Med, LLC (2)
454 Berryhill Rd Ste B, Columbia, SC 29210-6447
Tel.: (803) 791-9013
Medical Equipment Distr
N.A.I.C.S.: 423450

Southern Home Respiratory & Equipment, Inc. (1)
Tel.: (276) 546-2050
Medical Equipment Distr
N.A.I.C.S.: 423450

Spiro Health Services, LLC (1)
28 Jan Sebastian Dr, Sandwich, MA 02563
Web Site:
    http://www.spirohealthservices.com
Home Medical & Supplies Distr
N.A.I.C.S.: 423450
Gary Sheehan (CEO)
Mike Sheehan (COO)

Subsidiary (Domestic):

Cape Medical Supply, Inc. (2)
28 Jan Sebastian Dr Unit 2, Sandwich, MA 02563
Tel.: (508) 888-3113
Web Site: http://www.capemedical.net
Rev.: $5,100,000
Emp.: 40
Women Healthcare Services
N.A.I.C.S.: 621610

Ellen Burke (Exec VP-Revenue Cycle Mgmt)

Subsidiary (Domestic):

America's Health Care At Home, Inc. (3)
1510 Caton Ctr Dr Ste R, Halethorpe, MD 21227-1526
Tel.: (410) 737-9200
Web Site: http://www.ahcah.com
Other Health & Personal Care Stores
N.A.I.C.S.: 456199
Mark Kassir (CEO)

Health Complex Medical, Inc. (3)
84 Progress Ln, Waterbury, CT 06705
Tel.: (203) 753-7778
Web Site: http://www.healthcomplex.biz
All Other Miscellaneous Ambulatory Health Care Services
N.A.I.C.S.: 621999
Debbie Lupo (Acct Mgr)

TMS VT, LLC (1)
1225 Airport Pkwy Ste A, South Burlington, VT 05403
Tel.: (802) 864-0908
Web Site: https://www.tmsvt.com
Medical Equipment Distr
N.A.I.C.S.: 423450

Twin Rivers Respiratory Care, Inc. (1)
521 S 7th St, Arkadelphia, AR 71923
Tel.: (870) 230-1518
Medical Equipment Distr
N.A.I.C.S.: 423450

WeCare Medical, LLC (1)
2200 Winchester Ave, Ashland, KY 41101
Tel.: (606) 325-9222
Web Site: https://wecaremedical.com
Emp.: 250
Medical Equipment Distr
N.A.I.C.S.: 423450

ADAPTIVE AD SYSTEMS, INC.
4400 NE 77th Ave Ste 275, Vancouver, WA 98662
Tel.: (310) 321-4958   NV
Web Site:
    https://www.adaptivemedia.com
AATV—(OTCIQ)
Television Advertising Services
N.A.I.C.S.: 541890
Michael J. Heil (Pres, CEO & Sec)

Subsidiaries:

Adaptive Media, Inc. (1)
47 Discovery Ste 220, Irvine, CA 92618
Tel.: (949) 525-4634
Web Site: http://www.adaptivem.com
Video Syndication Services
N.A.I.C.S.: 512191
John Strong (Chm & CEO)
Omar Akram (Pres)
Sal Aziz (Founder & Exec VP)

ADAPTIVE BIOTECHNOLOGIES CORPORATION
1165 Eastlake Ave E, Seattle, WA 98109
Tel.: (206) 659-0067   WA
Web Site:
    https://www.adaptivebiotech.com
Year Founded: 2009
ADPT—(NASDAQ)
Rev.: $185,308,000
Assets: $856,617,000
Liabilities: $392,519,000
Net Worth: $464,098,000
Earnings: ($200,191,000)
Emp.: 790
Fiscal Year-end: 12/31/22
Biotechnology Research & Development Services
N.A.I.C.S.: 541714
Harlan Robins (Co-Founder & Chief Scientific Officer)
Julie Rubinstein (Pres)
Francis Lo (Chief People Officer)
Stacy Taylor (Gen Counsel & Sr VP)

Adaptive Biotechnologies Corporation—(Continued)

Karina Calzadilla *(VP-IR)*
Susan Bobulsky *(Sr VP-Diagnostics-clonoSEQ)*
Kyle Piskel *(CFO & Principal Acctg Officer)*
Yi Zhou *(Chief Technical Officer)*
Chad Robins *(Co-Founder, Chm & CEO)*

ADDMASTER CORPORATION
225 E Huntington Dr, Monrovia, CA 91016
Tel.: (626) 358-2395   CA
Web Site: http://www.addmaster.com
Year Founded: 1962
ADDC—(OTCIQ)
Inkjet Printing Machinery Mfr
N.A.I.C.S.: 333248
John A. Clary *(Pres & CEO)*

ADDUS HOMECARE CORPORATION
6303 Cowboys Way Ste 600, Frisco, TX 75034
Tel.: (469) 535-8200   DE
Web Site: https://www.addus.com
Year Founded: 2006
ADUS—(NASDAQ)
Rev.: $951,120,000
Assets: $937,994,000
Liabilities: $304,454,000
Net Worth: $633,540,000
Earnings: $46,025,000
Emp.: 6,284
Fiscal Year-end: 12/31/22
Women Healthcare Services
N.A.I.C.S.: 621610
R. Dirk Allison *(Chm & CEO)*
Michael Wattenbarger *(CIO & Exec VP)*
Brad Bickham *(Pres & COO)*
Cliff Blessing *(Chief Dev Officer)*
Robby Stevenson *(Chief HR Officer)*
Zach Simpson *(Chief Acctg Officer)*

Subsidiaries:

A Plus Health Care, Inc.   **(1)**
1310 S Main St, Kalispell, MT 59901
Tel.: (406) 755-4968
Web Site: https://www.aplushc.com
Emp.: 650
Women Healthcare Services
N.A.I.C.S.: 621610

Addus HealthCare, Inc.   **(1)**
2300 Warrenville Rd, Downers Grove, IL 60515
Tel.: (630) 296-3400
Women Healthcare Services
N.A.I.C.S.: 621610

Subsidiary (Domestic):

Addus HealthCare (Delaware), Inc.   **(2)**
1675 S State St, Dover, DE 19901
Tel.: (302) 322-7087
Women Healthcare Services
N.A.I.C.S.: 621610
Randy Nelson *(Dir-Agency)*

Addus HealthCare (Idaho), Inc.   **(2)**
100 W Overland Rd Ste 103, Meridian, ID 83642
Tel.: (208) 342-1222
Women Healthcare Services
N.A.I.C.S.: 621610

Addus HealthCare (Nevada), Inc.   **(2)**
2500 W Sahara Ave, Las Vegas, NV 89102
Tel.: (702) 598-2048
Women Healthcare Services
N.A.I.C.S.: 621610

Addus HealthCare (South Carolina), Inc.   **(2)**
1612 Marion St Ste 103, Columbia, SC 29201
Tel.: (803) 758-4000
Women Healthcare Services
N.A.I.C.S.: 621610

Ambercare Corporation   **(2)**
2129 Osuna Rd NE, Albuquerque, NM 87113
Tel.: (505) 792-8230
Web Site: http://ambercare.com
Women Healthcare Services
N.A.I.C.S.: 621610
Suzette Pierce *(Mgr-Payroll)*

South Shore Home Health Services, Inc.   **(2)**
1225 Montauk Hwy 2, Oakdale, NY 11769
Tel.: (631) 567-6555
Web Site:
   http://www.southshorehomehealth.com
Sales Range: $50-74.9 Million
Women Healthcare Services
N.A.I.C.S.: 621610

Apple Home Health Care Ltd   **(1)**
3170 N Sheridan Rd, Chicago, IL 60657
Tel.: (773) 871-8700
Web Site:
   http://www.applehomehealthcare.com
Rev.: $3,000,000
Emp.: 100
Women Healthcare Services
N.A.I.C.S.: 621610
Steven Frank *(Pres)*

Benefits Assurance Co., Inc.   **(1)**
4581 Weston Rd Ste 112, Weston, FL 33326
Tel.: (954) 296-7800
Women Healthcare Services
N.A.I.C.S.: 621610

Cura Partners, LLC   **(1)**
1241 Volunteer Pkwy Ste 420, Bristol, TN 37620
Tel.: (423) 764-5000
Web Site: http://www.addus.com
Women Healthcare Services
N.A.I.C.S.: 621610

House Calls of New Mexico, LLC   **(1)**
2129 Osuna Rd NE, Albuquerque, NM 87113-1002
Tel.: (505) 898-2468
Healtcare Services
N.A.I.C.S.: 621999

JourneyCare, Inc.   **(1)**
405 Lake Zurich Rd, Barrington, IL 60010
Tel.: (847) 381-5599
Web Site: http://www.journeycare.org
Sales Range: $25-49.9 Million
Emp.: 295
Community Health Care Services
N.A.I.C.S.: 621498
Daniel Barron *(VP-IT)*

Miracle City Hospice, LLC   **(1)**
9150 S Hills Blvd Ste 100, Broadview Heights, OH 44147
Tel.: (440) 397-4111
Web Site:
   https://www.miraclecityhospice.com
Home Care Services
N.A.I.C.S.: 621610

Options Services, Inc.   **(1)**
1200 W 21st St A, Clovis, NM 88101
Tel.: (505) 762-2023
Web Site: http://www.optionsservices.net
Sales Range: $1-9.9 Million
Emp.: 120
Women Healthcare Services
N.A.I.C.S.: 621610

Priority Home Health Care, Inc.   **(1)**
181 Jefferson Pk Rd Ste 105, Middlebury, OH 44130
Tel.: (216) 251-4300
Web Site: http://www.adddushomecare.com
Emp.: 300
Women Healthcare Services
N.A.I.C.S.: 621610

Professional Reliable Nursing Service Inc.   **(1)**
817 Coffee Rd Ste B, Modesto, CA 95355
Tel.: (209) 578-3231
Women Healthcare Services
N.A.I.C.S.: 621610

Queen City Hospice, LLC   **(1)**
4605 Duke Dr Ste 220, Mason, OH 45040
Tel.: (513) 510-4406
Web Site:
   https://www.queencityhospice.com

Home Care Services
N.A.I.C.S.: 621610

Serenity Palliative Care & Hospice, LLC   **(1)**
2999 N 44th St Ste 225, Phoenix, AZ 85018
Tel.: (602) 216-2273
Web Site: http://www.serenityhospiceaz.com
Women Healthcare Services
N.A.I.C.S.: 621610
Shawn McAffee *(CEO)*

VIP Health Care Services, Inc.   **(1)**
116 12 Myrtle Ave, Richmond Hill, NY 11418
Tel.: (718) 847-9800
Web Site: http://www.viphealth.com
Women Healthcare Services
N.A.I.C.S.: 621610

ADDVANTAGE TECHNOLO-GIES GROUP, INC.
1430 Bradley Ln Ste 196, Carrollton, TX 75007
Tel.: (918) 251-9121   OK
Web Site:
   https://www.addvantagetechnolo
   gies.com
Year Founded: 1985
AEY—(NASDAQ)
Rev.: $97,028,000
Assets: $27,218,000
Liabilities: $15,171,000
Net Worth: $12,047,000
Earnings: $471,000
Emp.: 145
Fiscal Year-end: 12/31/22
New & Used Cable TV Equipment Sales
N.A.I.C.S.: 423440
James C. McGill *(Chm)*
Michael A. Rutledge *(CFO)*

Subsidiaries:

Adams Global Communications, LLC   **(1)**
9635 Widmer Rd, Lenexa, KS 66215
Tel.: (913) 888-5100
Web Site: http://www.adamsglobal.com
Telecommunication Equipment Distr
N.A.I.C.S.: 423690

Fulton Technologies, Inc.   **(1)**
1430 Bradley Ln Ste 196, Carrollton, TX 75007
Tel.: (469) 581-8532
Web Site: https://www.fultontechinc.com
Wireless Telecommunication Services
N.A.I.C.S.: 517112

Nave Communications Company   **(1)**
1430 Bradley Ln Ste 196, Carrollton, TX 75007
Tel.: (301) 725-6283
Web Site: https://www.ncctel.com
Sales Range: $1-9.9 Million
Emp.: 35
Telecommunication Equipment Whslr
N.A.I.C.S.: 423690
Michael Burch *(VP-Network Solutions)*
Reggie Jaramillo *(Pres)*

Tulsat Corp.   **(1)**
1221 E Houston St, Broken Arrow, OK 74012-4405
Tel.: (918) 251-2887
Web Site: https://www.tulsat.com
Sales Range: $50-74.9 Million
Emp.: 100
Business Services
N.A.I.C.S.: 423610
David E. Chymiak *(Pres-Sls)*
Mark Schumacher *(Dir-Sls)*
Tony Cameron *(Dir-Sls-Latin America)*

Tulsat-Nebraska   **(1)**
701 3rd St, Deshler, NE 68340
Tel.: (402) 365-7520
Sales Range: $10-24.9 Million
Emp.: 4
Sales of Cable Equipment
N.A.I.C.S.: 516210
John Noojin *(Mgr-Sls)*
John Denner *(Mgr-Tech & Sls)*

ADEIA INC.
3025 Orchard Pkwy, San Jose, CA 95134
Tel.: (408) 473-2500   DE
Web Site: https://www.adeia.com
Year Founded: 2020
ADEA—(NASDAQ)
Rev.: $438,933,000
Assets: $1,210,526,000
Liabilities: $909,114,000
Net Worth: $301,412,000
Earnings: ($295,880,000)
Emp.: 120
Fiscal Year-end: 12/31/22
Offices of Other Holding Companies
N.A.I.C.S.: 551112
Paul E. Davis *(CEO)*
Jarl Berntzen *(Chief Corp Dev Officer)*
Keith Jones *(CFO)*
Daniel Moloney *(Chm)*
Kevin Tanji *(Chief Legal Officer)*
Serhad Doken *(CTO)*
Mark Kokes *(Co-Chief Licensing Officer & Gen Mgr-Media)*
Dana Escobar *(Co-Chief Licensing Officer & Gen Mgr-Semiconductor)*
Christina Sawyer *(Chief People Officer)*
Joseph Guiliano *(Chief IP Officer)*

Subsidiaries:

Xperi Corporation   **(1)**
2190 Gold St, San Jose, CA 95002
Tel.: (408) 519-9100
Web Site: https://www.xperi.com
Rev.: $280,067,000
Assets: $1,047,945,000
Liabilities: $502,845,000
Net Worth: $545,100,000
Earnings: ($62,530,000)
Emp.: 700
Fiscal Year-end: 12/31/2019
Holding Company; Semiconductor Engineering & Digital Imaging Technologies Mfr
N.A.I.C.S.: 551112
Craig Mitchell *(Pres-Invensas)*
Richard S. Hill *(Chm)*
Geir R. Skaaden *(Chief Product & Svcs Officer)*

Subsidiary (Non-US):

All In Media Pty. Ltd.   **(2)**
National Innovation Centre Australian Technology Park, 4 Cornwallis Street Eveleigh, Sydney, 2015, NSW, Australia
Tel.: (61) 292094182
Web Site: http://www.thisisaim.com
Advertising & Media Services
N.A.I.C.S.: 541810

DigitalOptics Corporation Israel Limited   **(2)**
Tel Aviv Development Center, 6 Habarzel St, Tel Aviv, 69710, Israel   **(100%)**
Tel.: (972) 73 648 4007
Web Site: http://www.doc.com
Miniaturization Technology for the Electronics Industry
N.A.I.C.S.: 334418

DigitalOptics Corporation Japan GK   **(2)**
Shinagawa East One Tower 4F 2-16-1 Konan, Minato-ku, Tokyo, 108-0075, Japan
Tel.: (81) 45 338 1705
Web Site: http://www.doc.com
Digital Imaging Products Mfr & Distr
N.A.I.C.S.: 333310

DigitalOptics Corporation Korea Limited   **(2)**
1101 11F Parkview Tower 6 Jeongja-dong, Bundang-gu, Seongnam, 463-863, Gyeonggi-do, Korea (South)   **(100%)**
Tel.: (82) 2 578 4271
Web Site: http://www.doc.com
Miniaturization Technology for the Electronics Industry
N.A.I.C.S.: 334418

DigitalOptics Corporation Taiwan Limited   **(2)**

3F 257 Sec 1 Guangming 6th Av East Chu-pei, Hinschu, Taipei, 302, Taiwan **(100%)**
Tel.: (886) 35507549
Web Site: http://www.doc.com
Miniaturization Technology for the Electron-ics Industry
N.A.I.C.S.: 334418

Subsidiary (Domestic):

FotoNation Corporation **(2)**
3025 Orchard Pkwy, San Jose, CA 95134
Tel.: (408) 321-6000
Web Site: http://www.fotonation.com
Image Processing Services
N.A.I.C.S.: 518210
Sumat Mehra *(Sr VP & Gen Mgr)*

Invensas Corporation **(2)**
3025 Orchard Pkwy, San Jose, CA 95134
Tel.: (408) 324-5100
Web Site: http://www.invensas.com
Emp.: 150
Electronic Components Mfr
N.A.I.C.S.: 334413

Branch (Non-US):

Tessera, Inc. - Yokohama Facility **(2)**
Yokohama Business Park Technical Center
134 Goudo-cho, Hodogaya-ku, Yokohama, 240-0005, Kanagawa, Japan
Tel.: (81) 453381705
Web Site: http://www.tessera.com
Semiconductor Engineering
N.A.I.C.S.: 334413

Subsidiary (Domestic):

TiVo Corporation **(2)**
2160 Gold St, San Jose, CA 95002
Tel.: (408) 519-9100
Web Site: http://www.tivo.com
Rev.: $668,129,000
Assets: $2,382,572,000
Liabilities: $1,308,889,000
Net Worth: $1,073,683,000
Earnings: ($410,067,000)
Emp.: 1,450
Fiscal Year-end: 12/31/2019
Holding Company; Entertainment Streaming & Recording Products Developer, Mfr, Whslr & Services
N.A.I.C.S.: 551112
John Kirchner *(Pres & CEO)*
Robert Anderson *(CFO & Exec VP)*
John Allen *(Sr VP & Controller)*
Paul Davis *(Gen Counsel, Sec & Sr VP)*

Subsidiary (Domestic):

Rovi Corporation **(3)**
2160 Gold St, San Jose, CA 95002
Tel.: (408) 519-9100
Sales Range: $500-549.9 Million
Digital Programming Directory, Video Re-cording, Anti-Piracy & Entertainment Soft-ware Developer & Mfr
N.A.I.C.S.: 513210
Wesley Gutierrez *(Chief Acctg Officer & Treas)*
Michael Hawkey *(Sr VP & Gen Mgr-User Experience)*
Pamela A. Sergeeff *(Gen Counsel, Sec & Exec VP)*
Peter C. Halt *(CFO)*
Matt Milne *(Chief Revenue Officer)*
Ted Schremp *(CMO)*

Subsidiary (Non-US):

Macrovision Korea Co., Ltd. **(4)**
Suite 417 Korea City Air Terminal Building
159 6 Samsung dong, Seoul, 135-728, Kangnam ku, Korea (South)
Tel.: (82) 262415700
Web Site: http://www.macrovision.com
Sales Range: $10-24.9 Million
Emp.: 2
Digital Programming Directory, Video Re-cording, Anti-Piracy & Entertainment Soft-ware Developer & Mfr
N.A.I.C.S.: 513210

Subsidiary (Domestic):

Macrovision Solutions Networks **(4)**
7140 S Lewis Ave, Tulsa, OK 74136-5401
Tel.: (918) 488-4000
Web Site: http://www.gemstartvguide.com

Sales Range: $50-74.9 Million
Emp.: 170
Digital Television Programming Directory Publisher
N.A.I.C.S.: 516120

Subsidiary (Non-US):

Rovi Europe Limited **(4)**
1st Floor York House Sheet Street, Wind-sor, SL4 1DD, Berkshire, United Kingdom
Tel.: (44) 1628677300
Web Site: http://www.dvdit.com
Entertainment Software Publisher
N.A.I.C.S.: 513210

Rovi KK **(4)**
1-8 Marunouchi 2F Trust Tower Main Build-ing Marunouchi, Chiyoda-ku, Tokyo, 100-0005, Japan
Tel.: (81) 345771500
Web Site: http://business.tivo.com
Entertainment Software Publisher
N.A.I.C.S.: 513210

Rovi Netherlands BV **(4)**
Herikerbergweg 238, 1101 CM, Amsterdam, Netherlands
Tel.: (31) 205755600
Television Broadcasting Services
N.A.I.C.S.: 516120

Subsidiary (Domestic):

Sonic Solutions LLC **(4)**
9951 W 190th S Unit B, Mokena, IL 60448
Tel.: (708) 478-8777
Web Site: https://www.sonicsolutionsusa.com
Sales Range: $100-124.9 Million
Emp.: 490
Digital Media Management Software Devel-oper & Publisher
N.A.I.C.S.: 513210

Subsidiary (Non-US):

TiVo KK **(3)**
12F Marunouchi Trust Tower North 1-8-1 Marunouchi, Chiyoda-ku, Tokyo, 100-0005, Japan
Tel.: (81) 345771500
Information Technology Services
N.A.I.C.S.: 541511

TiVo Korea Co. Ltd. **(3)**
30F ASEM Tower 517 Yeongdong-Daero, Gangham-gu, Seoul, 06164, Korea (South)
Tel.: (82) 269485700
Information Technology Services
N.A.I.C.S.: 541511

TiVo Poland Sp. z o. o. **(3)**
8th Floor Equator IV Building Al Jerozolim-skie 100, 00-807, Warsaw, Poland
Tel.: (48) 222072941
Information Technology Services
N.A.I.C.S.: 541511
Dariusz Przybylski *(Dir-Project Mgmt)*

TiVo Singapore Pte. Ltd. **(3)**
514 Chai Chee Lane 05-15, Singapore, 469029, Singapore
Tel.: (65) 62883858
Web Site: http://www.tivo-tech.com
Information Technology Services
N.A.I.C.S.: 541511
Winston Lim *(Dir-Sls)*

TiVo Tech Private Limited **(3)**
Embassy Tech Village 7B Primrose 10th Floor Devarabisanahalli, Outer Ring Road, Bengaluru, 560103, India
Tel.: (91) 8046612200
Information Technology Services
N.A.I.C.S.: 541511

Subsidiary (Domestic):

Ziptronix, Inc. **(2)**
800 Perimeter Park Dr, Morrisville, NC 27560
Tel.: (919) 459-2400
Web Site: http://www.ziptronix.com
Rev.: $1,800,000
Emp.: 16
Semiconductor & Related Device Mfr
N.A.I.C.S.: 334413

ADHERA THERAPEUTICS, INC.

8000 Innovation Pkwy, Baton Rouge, LA 70820
Tel.: (919) 518-3748   DE
Web Site: http://adherathera.com
Year Founded: 1983
ATRX—(OTCQB)
Assets: $79,000
Liabilities: $22,265,000
Net Worth: ($22,186,000)
Earnings: ($2,114,000)
Emp.: 2
Fiscal Year-end: 12/31/22
Pharmaceuticals Mfr
N.A.I.C.S.: 325412
Andrew Kucharchuk *(Vice Chm)*

ADIA NUTRITION, INC.

4421 Gabriella Ln, Winter Park, FL 32792
Tel.: (321) 788-0850   NV
Web Site: https://www.adianutrition.com
Year Founded: 1999
ADIA—(OTCIQ)
Sales Range: Less than $1 Million
Emp.: 38
Nutritional Products
N.A.I.C.S.: 325411
Larry Powalisz *(CEO)*
Rebecca Miller *(CFO)*

ADIAL PHARMACEUTICALS, INC.

4870 Sadler Rd Ste 300, Glen Allen, VA 23060
Tel.: (804) 487-8196   DE
Web Site: https://www.adial.com
Year Founded: 2010
ADIL—(NASDAQ)
Rev.: $585,209
Assets: $5,732,804
Liabilities: $2,456,310
Net Worth: $3,276,494
Earnings: ($12,731,416)
Emp.: 16
Fiscal Year-end: 12/31/22
Research & Development in Biotech-nology (except Nanobiotechnology)
N.A.I.C.S.: 541714
Cary J. Claiborne *(Pres & CEO)*
Joseph M. Truluck *(CFO)*
Tony Goodman *(COO)*
Bankole A. Johnson *(Founder)*
Alex Lugovoy *(Chief Bus Officer)*
Schuyler Vinzant *(VP-Dev)*
Mark H. Peikin *(Chief Strategy Offi-cer)*
Cary J. Claiborne *(COO)*
Kevin Schuyler *(Chm)*

ADICET BIO, INC.

131 Dartmouth St 3rd Fl, Boston, MA 02116
Tel.: (650) 503-9095   DE
Web Site: https://www.adicetbio.com
Year Founded: 2016
ACET—(NASDAQ)
Rev.: $24,990,000
Assets: $330,690,000
Liabilities: $38,352,000
Net Worth: $292,338,000
Earnings: ($69,790,000)
Emp.: 132
Fiscal Year-end: 12/31/22
Biotechnology Research & Develop-ment Services
N.A.I.C.S.: 541714
Francesco Galimi *(Chief Medical Offi-cer)*
Nick Harvey *(CFO)*
Don Healey *(CTO)*
Nancy Boman *(Chief Regulatory Offi-cer)*
Amy Locke *(Head)*
Chen Schor *(Co-Founder, Pres & CEO)*
Aya Jakobovits *(Co-Founder)*
Donald J. Santel *(Interim CEO)*

ADITXT, INC.

2569 Wyandotte St Ste 101, Moun-tain View, CA 94043
Tel.: (650) 870-1200   DE
Web Site: https://www.aditxt.com
Year Founded: 2017
ADTX—(NASDAQ)
Rev.: $933,715
Assets: $10,735,249
Liabilities: $5,528,942
Net Worth: $5,206,307
Earnings: ($27,612,199)
Emp.: 61
Fiscal Year-end: 12/31/22
Biotechnology Research & Develop-ment Services
N.A.I.C.S.: 541714
Amro A. Albanna *(Founder, Chm, Pres & CEO)*
Shahrokh Shabahang *(Chief Innova-tion Officer)*
Corinne Pankovcin *(CFO)*
Rowena Albanna *(COO)*
Sunny Uberoi *(Chief Comm Officer)*
Thomas J. Farley *(Principal Acctg Officer & Controller)*
Maureen Connolly *(Chief Content & Engagement Officer)*

Subsidiaries:

Pearsanta, Inc. **(1)**
737 N 5th St Ste 200, Richmond, VA 23219
Web Site: https://www.pearsanta.com
Health & Medical Care Services
N.A.I.C.S.: 524114

ADLAI NORTYE LTD.

685 US Hwy 1, North Brunswick, NJ 08902
Tel.: (848) 230-7430   Ky
Web Site: https://www.adlainortye.com
Year Founded: 2018
ANL—(NASDAQ)
Holding Company; Biopharmaceutical Developer
N.A.I.C.S.: 551112
Lars Erik Birgerson *(Chief Medical Officer)*
Yang Lu *(Chm & CEO)*
Wei Zhang *(CFO & CFO-China)*
Kaiyang Tang *(Pres)*
Archie Tse *(Head-Research & Development-China)*
Nanhai He *(VP-Drug Discovery)*
Zhiyong Yu *(VP-Operations-China)*
Xiaofeng Ye *(VP-Bus Dev Commer-cialization Strategy)*
Victoria Elizabeth Demby *(Sr VP & Head-Global Regulatory Affairs)*

Subsidiaries:

Adlai Nortye Biopharma Co., Ltd. **(1)**
Bldg 6 1008 Xiangwang Street, Hangzhou, Zhejiang, China
Tel.: (86) 57128918385
Biopharmaceutical Developer
N.A.I.C.S.: 541714

Adlai Nortye USA INC **(1)**
685 US Hwy 1 2nd Fl, North Brunswick, NJ 08902
Tel.: (848) 230-7430
Biopharmaceutical Developer
N.A.I.C.S.: 541714
Lars Erik Birgerson *(Pres & CEO)*

ADM ENDEAVORS, INC.

5941 Posey Ln, Haltom City, TX 76117
Tel.: (209) 274-9143   NV
Web Site: https://www.admendeavors.com
ADMQ—(OTCQB)
Rev.: $5,624,500
Assets: $4,400,255
Liabilities: $1,961,645
Net Worth: $2,438,610

ADM Endeavors, Inc.—(Continued)
Earnings: $149,752
Fiscal Year-end: 12/31/22
Printing Products Mfr
N.A.I.C.S.: 323111
Marc Johnson *(Chm, CEO & CFO)*
Sarah Nelson *(COO)*
Subha Puthalath *(VP-Mktg)*
David Kirk *(VP-Sls)*

Subsidiaries:

Just Right Products, Inc.   **(1)**
5941 Posey Ln, Haltom City, TX 76117
Tel.: (817) 840-6277
Web Site: https://www.justrightproducts.com
Merchandise Product Distr
N.A.I.C.S.: 455219

ADM TRONICS UNLIMITED, INC.
224s Pegasus Ave, Northvale, NJ 07647
Tel.: (201) 767-6040   **DE**
Web Site:
   https://www.admtronics.com
Year Founded: 1969
ADMT—(OTCQB)
Rev.: $2,965,406
Assets: $2,138,728
Liabilities: $1,446,337
Net Worth: $692,391
Earnings: ($877,222)
Fiscal Year-end: 03/31/24
Chemical Products, Resins & Medical
Electronic Devices Mfr & Sales
N.A.I.C.S.: 325211
Andre A. DiMino *(Pres, CEO & CFO)*

ADMA BIOLOGICS, INC.
465 Rte 17 S, Ramsey, NJ 07446
Tel.: (201) 478-5552   **DE**
Web Site:
   https://www.admabiologics.com
ADMA—(NASDAQ)
Rev.: $154,079,692
Assets: $348,461,881
Liabilities: $196,487,666
Net Worth: $151,974,215
Earnings: ($65,903,950)
Emp.: 617
Fiscal Year-end: 12/31/22
Plasma-Derived, Human Immune
Globulins Developer
N.A.I.C.S.: 541715
Adam S. Grossman *(Co-Founder, Pres, CEO & Interim CFO)*
Jerrold B. Grossman *(Co-Founder, Vice Chm & Vice Chm)*
Daniel Garcia *(VP-IgG Product Mgmt)*
Kaitlin Kestenberg *(COO & Sr VP-Compliance)*
Drew Pantello *(VP-Mktg & Corp Dev)*
Ricardo Carneiro *(Sr Dir-Market Access & Reimbursement)*
Marc Gelberg *(Controller & Sr Dir)*
James Maloney *(Sr Dir-Regulatory Affairs)*
Frank Sananes *(Sr Dir-Mfg & Validation)*
Neal C. Fitzpatrick *(VP-Sls)*
Jeffrey Janek *(VP-Production Ops)*
Vernon Atkinson *(Sr Dir-Ops-BioCenters)*
Michael Goldstein *(Gen Counsel & Sr Dir)*
Marcin Szutkowski *(Sr Dir-Quality Assurance)*
Doug Chambers *(VP)*
Shane Stremming *(VP)*
Cindy Petersen *(Exec Dir)*

Subsidiaries:

ADMA Bio Centers Georgia Inc.   **(1)**
166 Ernest W Barrett Pkwy NW, Marietta, GA 30066
Tel.: (770) 779-9222

Web Site: https://www.admabiocenters.com
Research & Development Biotechnology
Services
N.A.I.C.S.: 541714

ADOBE INC.
345 Park Ave, San Jose, CA 95110-2704
Tel.: (408) 536-2800   **DE**
Web Site: https://www.adobe.com
Year Founded: 1982
ADBE—(NASDAQ)
Rev.: $19,409,000,000
Assets: $29,779,000,000
Liabilities: $13,261,000,000
Net Worth: $16,518,000,000
Earnings: $5,428,000,000
Emp.: 29,945
Fiscal Year-end: 12/01/23
Software Solutions for Network Publishing Including Web, Print, ePaper, Video, Wireless & Broadband Applications
N.A.I.C.S.: 513210
Ann Lewnes *(CMO & Exec VP-Corp Strategy & Dev)*
David Wadhwani *(Pres-Digital Media Bus)*
Daniel J. Durn *(CFO & Exec VP-Fin, Ops, and Tech Svcs)*
Gloria Chen *(Chief People Officer & Exec VP-Employee Experience)*
Jonathan Vaas *(VP-IR)*
Guido Quaroni *(Sr Dir-Engineering-3D,Immersive)*
Daniel J. Durn *(CFO & Exec VP)*
Anil Chakravarthy *(Pres-Digital Experience Bus)*
Heather Hopkins Freeland *(Chief Brand Officer)*
Scott Belsky *(Chief Product Officer)*
Ashley Still *(Sr VP & Gen Mgr-Digital Media)*
Shantanu Narayen *(Chm & CEO)*

Subsidiaries:

Adobe Systems Benelux BV   **(1)**
Europlaza Hoogoorddreef 54a, 1101 BE, Amsterdam, Netherlands   **(100%)**
Tel.: (31) 206511200
Web Site: http://www.adobe.com
Sales Range: $1-9.9 Million
Emp.: 54
Sales & Marketer of Computer Software
N.A.I.C.S.: 449210

Adobe Systems Canada   **(1)**
343 Preston Street, Ottawa, K1S 1N4, ON, Canada   **(100%)**
Tel.: (613) 940-3676
Sales Range: $100-124.9 Million
Emp.: 280
Developer of Electronic Forms & Enterprise
Workflow Solutions
N.A.I.C.S.: 541511

Adobe Systems Co., Ltd.   **(1)**
Gate City Osaki East Tower 1-11-2 Osaki, Shinagawa-ku, Tokyo, 141-0032, Japan   **(80%)**
Tel.: (81) 357402400
Web Site: http://www.adobesystems.co.jp
Sales Range: $25-49.9 Million
Emp.: 190
Software Development, Sales & Marketing
N.A.I.C.S.: 449210
James McCready *(Pres-Japan & Asia Pacific)*

Adobe Systems Europe Limited. **(1)**
Market House, Maidenhead, SL6 8AG, United Kingdom
Tel.: (44) 1628590000
Web Site: http://www.adobe.com
Digital Marketing Services
N.A.I.C.S.: 541613

Adobe Systems France   **(1)**
                                   (100%)
Tel.: (33) 170981400
Web Site: http://www.adobe.fr
Sales Range: $25-49.9 Million
Retailer of Software
N.A.I.C.S.: 449210

Pierre Casanova *(Gen Dir)*

Adobe Systems GmbH   **(1)**
Georg-Brauchle-Ring 58, 80992, Munich, Germany   **(100%)**
Tel.: (49) 89317050
Web Site: http://www.adobe.de
Sales Range: $10-24.9 Million
Sales & Marketing of Software
N.A.I.C.S.: 449210

Adobe Systems Hong Kong
Limited   **(1)**
Suite 4102 41/F Lee Garden One 33 Hysan Avenue, Causeway Bay, China (Hong Kong)
Tel.: (852) 2 916 2100
Web Site: http://www.adobe.com
Software Publisher
N.A.I.C.S.: 513210

Adobe Systems Iberica SL   **(1)**
Carrer Llacuna 56-70 1 a Planta, 08005, Barcelona, Spain
Tel.: (34) 93 326 8464
Web Site: https://www.adobe.com
Custom Computer Programming Services
N.A.I.C.S.: 541511

Adobe Systems Inc. - San
Francisco   **(1)**
601 Townsend St, San Francisco, CA 94103
Tel.: (415) 832-2000
Web Site: http://www.adobe.com
Emp.: 1,400
Software Producer
N.A.I.C.S.: 334610
Cynthia Stoddard *(CIO & Sr VP)*

Adobe Systems Incorporated -
Seattle   **(1)**
801 N 34th St, Seattle, WA 98103
Tel.: (206) 675-7000
Web Site: http://www.adobe.com
Desktop Publishing Software Mfr
N.A.I.C.S.: 541511

Adobe Systems Italia SRL   **(1)**
Via Roberto Bracco 6 Terzo Piano, 20159, Milan, Italy
Tel.: (39) 03965501
Web Site: http://www.adobe.com
Software Publishing Services
N.A.I.C.S.: 513210

Adobe Systems Nordic AB   **(1)**
Kista Entre Knarrarnasgatan 7, PO Box 47, 164 93, Kista, Sweden
Tel.: (46) 87523300
Web Site: http://www.adobe.com
Sales Range: $10-24.9 Million
Software Whslr
N.A.I.C.S.: 440210

Adobe Systems Pte. Ltd.   **(1)**
8 Temasek Boulevard, Singapore, 038988, Singapore
Tel.: (65) 65115500
Web Site: http://www.adobe.com
Digital Marketing & Media Solutions
N.A.I.C.S.: 541618

Adobe Systems Pty. Ltd.   **(1)**
Tower 2 Level 27 201 Sussex St, Sydney, 2000, NSW, Australia
Tel.: (61) 297784100
Web Site: http://www.adobe.com
Software Publisher
N.A.I.C.S.: 513210

Adobe Systems Romania SRL   **(1)**
Anchor Plaza 10th Floor 26 Z Timisoara Blvd, 061331, Bucharest, Romania
Tel.: (40) 314133500
Web Site: http://www.adobe.com
Software Publisher
N.A.I.C.S.: 513210

Adobe Systems Software Ireland
Limited   **(1)**
6 Riverwalk Naas Road 24, Dublin, Ireland
Tel.: (353) 1 242 6700
Software Publisher
N.A.I.C.S.: 513210

Adobe Systems UK   **(1)**
Waterview House 3 Roundwood Ave, Stockley Park, Uxbridge, UB11 1AY, United Kingdom
Tel.: (44) 2086061100

Web Site: http://www.adobe.co.uk
Sales Range: $25-49.9 Million
Emp.: 110
Computer Software Whslr
N.A.I.C.S.: 449210

Adobe Ventures   **(1)**
345 Park Ave, San Jose, CA 95110-2704
Tel.: (408) 536-6000
Web Site: http://www.adobe.com
Investment Holding Company
N.A.I.C.S.: 551112

Auditude, Inc.   **(1)**
209 Hamilton Ave Ste 200, Palo Alto, CA 94301
Tel.: (650) 326-1160
Web Site: http://www.auditude.com
Video Advertising Software Developer
N.A.I.C.S.: 513210

Efficient Frontier Technology India
Private Limited   **(1)**
Sreyas Building/Chamiers Towers 23-24 Chamiers Road, 23-24 Chamiers Road Teynampet, Chennai, 600018, Tamil Nadu, India
Tel.: (91) 4443009125
Marketing Consulting Services
N.A.I.C.S.: 541613

Fotolia LLC   **(1)**
345 Park Ave, San Jose, CA 95110-2704
Tel.: (718) 577-1321
Web Site: http://www.fotolia.com
Emp.: 5
Online Photography Retail Services
N.A.I.C.S.: 541922

Frame.io, Inc.   **(1)**
22 Cortlandt St Fl 31, New York, NY 10007
Web Site: https://www.frame.io
Software Development Services
N.A.I.C.S.: 541511

Marketo, Inc.   **(1)**
901 Mariners Island Blvd Ste 500, San Mateo, CA 94404
Tel.: (650) 376-2300
Web Site: http://www.marketo.com
Business Management & Marketing Software
N.A.I.C.S.: 513210

Subsidiary (Domestic):

Bizible Inc.   **(2)**
542 1st Ave S 200, Seattle, WA 98104
Tel.: (888) 307-6614
Web Site: http://www.bizible.com
Marketing Software Development Services
N.A.I.C.S.: 513210
Aaron Bird *(Co-Founder)*
Andy Turman *(Co-Founder)*
Peter B. Thompson *(Co-Founder)*

Subsidiary (Non-US):

Marketo Australia Pty Ltd.   **(2)**
Tower 2 Level 27 201 Sussex St, Sydney, 2000, NSW, Australia
Tel.: (61) 283107646
Web Site: http://www.marketo.com
CRM Software Marketing Solutions
N.A.I.C.S.: 513210

Marketo EMEA Ltd.   **(2)**
Level 2 Red Oak North South County Business Park, Leopardstown, Dublin, 18, Ireland
Tel.: (353) 15119556
Web Site: http://www.marketo.com
Business Management & Marketing Software
N.A.I.C.S.: 513210

Mixamo, Inc.   **(1)**
2415 3rd St Ste 239, San Francisco, CA 94107
Tel.: (415) 255-7455
Web Site: http://www.mixamo.com
Computer Graphic & Animation Services
N.A.I.C.S.: 541511

Neolane S.A.   **(1)**
18 rue Roger-Simon Barboux, 94110, Arcueil, France
Tel.: (33) 141983535
Web Site: http://www.adobe.com
Sales Range: $50-74.9 Million
Emp.: 300
Marketing Software

N.A.I.C.S.: 513210

Subsidiary (Non-US):

Neolane Nordic **(2)**
Hyldegaardsvej 56, DK-2920, Charlottenlund, Denmark
Tel.: (45) 39652130
Marketing Software
N.A.I.C.S.: 513210
Benoit Gourdon (*Exec VP-Ops-Europe*)

Subsidiary (US):

Neolane, Inc. **(2)**
275 Washington St 3rd Fl, Newton, MA 02458
Tel.: (617) 467-6760
Web Site: http://www.adobe.com
Sales Range: $25-49.9 Million
Emp.: 40
Marketing Software
N.A.I.C.S.: 513210

TubeMogul, Inc. **(1)**
1250 53rd St Ste 2, Emeryville, CA 94608
Tel.: (510) 653-0126
Emp.: 577
Digital Branding Software Services
N.A.I.C.S.: 513210
Brett Wilson (*Founder & CEO*)
Jason Lopatecki (*Chief Strategy Officer & Chief Innovation Officer*)
Chip Scovic (*Chief Revenue Officer*)
Sam Smith (*Mng Dir-Australia*)
Pavel Klymenko (*Mng Dir-Ukraine & Project Mgr*)
Nick Reid (*Mng Dir-UK*)
Todd Gordon (*Gen Mgr-Programmatic TV*)
Vasanthi Holtcamp (*VP-Engrg*)
Dana Toering (*Mng Dir-Canada*)

Workfront, Inc. **(1)**
3301 N Thanksgiving Way Ste 500, Lehi, UT 84043
Tel.: (801) 373-3266
Web Site: https://www.workfront.com
Project & Portfolio Management Software Publisher
N.A.I.C.S.: 513210
Scott Johnson (*Founder & Chm*)
Alex Shootman (*Pres & CEO*)
Sue Fellows (*Chief Customer Officer*)
Brent Nixon (*Sr VP-Global Alliances*)
Laura Butler (*Sr VP-People & Culture*)
Paige Erickson (*Mng Dir-Europe, the Middle East & Africa*)
Jon Pexton (*CFO*)
David Burggraaf (*CTO*)
Carl Cross (*Exec VP-Sls*)
Steve Holsten (*Gen Counsel & Sec*)
Scott Lee (*VP-Product Mgmt*)

X.commerce, Inc. **(1)**
54 N Central Ave Ste 200, Campbell, CA 95008
Web Site: http://www.magento.com
Electronic Shopping
N.A.I.C.S.: 425120
Kris Taylor (*Head-Customer Succcess*)

ADTALEM GLOBAL EDUCATION INC.
500 W Monroe St Ste 13, Chicago, IL 60661
Tel.: (312) 651-1400   DE
Web Site: https://www.adtalem.com
Year Founded: 1987
ATGE—(NYSE)
Rev.: $1,584,652,000
Assets: $2,741,417,000
Liabilities: $1,372,282,000
Net Worth: $1,369,135,000
Earnings: $136,777,000
Emp.: 4,624
Fiscal Year-end: 06/30/24
Undergraduate & Graduate Educational Programs
N.A.I.C.S.: 611310
Donna N. Jennings (*Chief HR Officer & Sr VP*)
Christopher C. Nash (*CIO & Sr VP*)
Michael W. Malafronte (*Chm*)
Katherine Boden Holland (*Pres-Medical & Healthcare Education Grp*)
Stephen W. Beard (*Pres & CEO*)

James Bartholomew (*Sr VP-Integration & Transformation*)
Karen Cox (*Pres-Chamberlain University*)
Robert J. Phelan (*CFO & Sr VP*)
Douglas G. Beck (*Gen Counsel, Sec & Sr VP*)
Maurice Herrera (*CMO*)
Larry Bachman (*Interim Gen Counsel*)
Manjunath Gangadharan (*Chief Acctg Officer & VP*)
Blake Simpson (*Chief Comm Officer & Sr VP-Sustainability*)

Subsidiaries:

Becker Conviser Professional Review **(1)**
3005 Highland Pkwy, Downers Grove, IL 60515 **(100%)**
Tel.: (630) 472-2239
Web Site: http://www.beckercpa.com
Sales Range: $50-74.9 Million
CPA Review Programs
N.A.I.C.S.: 611691

Carrington College, Inc. **(1)**
1001 W Southern Ave Ste 130, Mesa, AZ 85210
Tel.: (480) 586-2787
Web Site: http://www.carrington.edu
Career Oriented Educational Services
N.A.I.C.S.: 611519
Donna M. Loraine (*Pres*)

Chamberlain University LLC **(1)**
500 W Monroe St Ste 1300, Chicago, IL 60661
Web Site: https://www.chamberlain.edu
Education Services
N.A.I.C.S.: 611710
Karen Cox (*Pres*)
Patrick Rombalski (*VP-Ops*)
Ray Francis (*VP-Fin*)
Scott Murphy (*VP-Enrollment Mgmt*)
Joanne Disch (*Chm*)
Katie Gilles (*VP*)
Nancy Johnson (*VP*)

DeVry Canada, LLC **(1)**
Unit 1950 520 5th Ave SW, Calgary, T2P 3R7, AB, Canada
Tel.: (403) 235-3450
Web Site: http://www.cal.devry.edu
Sales Range: $25-49.9 Million
Emp.: 6
Career-Oriented Educational Services
N.A.I.C.S.: 611710

DeVry Educacional do Brasil S/A **(1)**
Av Santos Dumont, 7800, Fortaleza, Brazil
Tel.: (55) 8530524814
Web Site: http://www.devrybrasil.edu.br
Educational Support Services
N.A.I.C.S.: 611710

DeVry/Becker Educational Development Corp. **(1)**
205 W Wacker Rd, Chicago, IL 60606
Tel.: (800) 868-3900
Career Oriented Educational Services
N.A.I.C.S.: 611519

DeVry/New York, Inc. **(1)**
180 Madison Ave Ste 900, New York, NY 10016
Tel.: (212) 312-4301
Web Site: http://www.ny.devry.edu
Educational Support Services
N.A.I.C.S.: 611310
Anthony A. Stanziani (*Pres*)

Devry University **(1)**
3005 Highland Pkwy, Downers Grove, IL 60515-5683
Tel.: (602) 216-7700
Web Site: http://www.devry.edu
Colleges & Universities
N.A.I.C.S.: 611310
Thomas L. Monahan III (*Vice Chm*)
Thomas L. Monahan III (*Pres & CEO*)
John Lorenz (*CFO*)
Michael A. Peel (*Chm*)
Remberto Del Real (*CMO*)
Scarlett Howery (*VP-Campus & University Partnerships*)

Shantanu Bose (*Chief Academic Officer & Provost*)
Chris Campbell (*VP-IT*)
David Barnett (*Chief HR & University Rels Officer*)
Elise Awwad (*COO*)
Robert Wrubel (*Chief Innovation & Partnerships Officer*)
F. Willis Caruso Jr. (*Gen Counsel, Sec & VP-Regulatory Affairs*)

Division (Domestic):

Keller Graduate School of Management **(2)**
18624 W Creek Dr, Tinley Park, IL 60477 **(100%)**
Tel.: (708) 342-3750
Web Site: http://www.keller.edu
Sales Range: $75-99.9 Million
Emp.: 9
Graduate School
N.A.I.C.S.: 611310

Dominica Services, Inc. **(1)**
814 Commerce Dr Ste 100, Oak Brook, IL 60523-8822
Tel.: (630) 571-7700
Educational Support Services
N.A.I.C.S.: 541990

OCL Financial Services LLC **(1)**
11350 McCormick Rd Executive Plz 2 Ste 1000, Hunt Valley, MD 21031
Tel.: (877) 878-3600
Web Site: http://www.trainingpro.com
Web-Based & In-House Educational Programs & Services
N.A.I.C.S.: 611710
Josh Braunstein (*Pres*)
Todd Premo (*Chief Product Officer*)
Ann Reist (*VP-Mktg*)
Mike O'Brien (*Sr VP-Sls*)
Kyle Bennett (*Sr VP-TTS*)
Andrew Stein (*VP-Fin & Ops*)

ADTEGRITY.COM INTERNATIONAL, INC.
38 Commerce Ave SW Ste 200, Grand Rapids, MI 49503
Tel.: (616) 285-5429   DE
ADTY—(OTCIQ)
Advertising Agency Services
N.A.I.C.S.: 541810
Scott Brew (*Pres & CEO*)

ADTHEORENT HOLDING COMPANY, INC.
330 Hudson St 13th Fl, New York, NY 10013
Tel.: (312) 258-8300   DE
Web Site:
    https://www.adtheorent.com
Year Founded: 2020
ADTH—(NASDAQ)
Rev.: $166,082,000
Assets: $190,604,000
Liabilities: $35,179,000
Net Worth: $155,425,000
Earnings: $29,338,000
Emp.: 297
Fiscal Year-end: 12/31/22
Miscellaneous Financial Investment Activities
N.A.I.C.S.: 523999
Theodore L. Koenig (*Chm, Co-Pres & CEO*)
Mark A. Solovy (*Co-Pres*)
Scott A. Marienau (*CFO*)

Subsidiaries:

AdTheorent, Inc. **(1)**
155 Avenue of the Americas Fl 2, New York, NY 10013
Tel.: (646) 676-4767
Web Site: http://www.adtheorent.com
Digital Advertising Services
N.A.I.C.S.: 541850
James Lawson (*Chief Legal Officer & Mng Partner*)
Amy Raucher (*VP*)
Andrew Anderson (*CTO*)
Bryan Leach (*VP*)

Calynn Krieger (*Sr VP*)
Chuck Jordan (*CFO*)
Dan Grubert (*VP*)
Dan Jenkins (*Sr VP*)
Emily Marcil (*VP*)
Indir Avdagic (*Chief Information Security Officer*)
Jason Han (*Sr VP*)
Katie Brauer Trapanese (*VP*)
Kurt Roocke (*Sr VP*)
Melanie Berger (*VP*)
Nick Cheetany (*Sr VP*)
Paul Dolan (*Mng Dir*)
Rachel Quigley (*VP*)
Rick Dalton (*Sr VP*)
Robert Lawrence (*VP*)
Tanya Sabharwal (*VP*)

ADTRAN HOLDINGS, INC.
901 Explorer Blvd, Huntsville, AL 35806
Tel.: (256) 963-8000   DE
Web Site: https://www.adtran.com
Year Founded: 2021
ADTN—(NASDAQ)
Offices of Other Holding Companies
N.A.I.C.S.: 551112
Thomas R. Stanton (*Chm & CEO*)
Uli Dopfer (*CFO*)

Subsidiaries:

ADTRAN, Inc. **(1)**
901 Explorer Blvd, Huntsville, AL 35806-2807
Tel.: (256) 963-8000
Web Site: http://www.adtran.com
Rev.: $563,004,000
Assets: $569,017,000
Liabilities: $211,915,000
Net Worth: $357,102,000
Earnings: ($8,635,000)
Emp.: 1,335
Fiscal Year-end: 12/31/2021
Digital Telephone Transmission Equipment Mfr
N.A.I.C.S.: 334210
Thomas R. Stanton (*Chm & CEO*)
Ronald D. Centis (*Sr VP-Ops Global*)
Brian L. Protiva (*Vice Chm*)
Ronan Kelly (*CTO-EMEA & APAC*)
Raymond Harris (*CIO*)
Marc Kimpe (*Sr VP-R&D*)
Robert Conger (*Sr VP-Tech & Strategy*)
James D. Wilson Jr. (*Chief Revenue Officer*)

Subsidiary (Non-US):

ADTRAN Europe Limited **(2)**
1420 Arlington Business Park Theale, Reading, RG7 4SA, Berkshire, United Kingdom
Tel.: (44) 1189317080
Communication Equipment Mfr
N.A.I.C.S.: 334210

ADTRAN Networks Canada, Inc. **(2)**
308 Legget Drive, Kanata, K2K 1Y6, ON, Canada
Tel.: (613) 599-9698
Web Site: http://www.adtran.com
Networking & Communication Equipment Provider
N.A.I.C.S.: 541512

ADTRAN Networks Hong Kong Limited **(2)**
Suite 1207-08 Prosperity Millennia Plaza 663 King's Road, North Point, Hong Kong, China (Hong Kong)
Tel.: (852) 28569090
Sales Range: $1-9.9 Million
Emp.: 9
Computer Networking Services
N.A.I.C.S.: 541519

ADTRAN Networks India Private Limited **(2)**
3rd Floor NCC Building Survey No: 64 Durgam Cheru, Hyderabad, 500081, India
Tel.: (91) 4030114800
Telecommunication Networking Equipment Distr
N.A.I.C.S.: 532490
Bhadru Bhanothu (*Mgr-Sys Design Verification Testing*)

ADTRAN Holdings, Inc.—(Continued)

ADTRAN Networks, PTY. Ltd. (2)
L 5 330 Collins St, Melbourne, 3000, VIC,
Australia
Tel.: (61) 396580500
Web Site: http://www.adtran.com
Computer Networking Services
N.A.I.C.S.: 541519

Subsidiary (Domestic):

SmartRG, Inc. (2)
501 SE Columbia Shores Blvd Ste 500,
Vancouver, WA 98661
Tel.: (360) 859-1780
Web Site: http://www.smartrg.com
Internet Service Provider
N.A.I.C.S.: 517111

Adtran Networks SE (1)
Campus Martinsried Fraunhoferstrasse 9a,
Martinsried, 82152, Munich, Germany
Tel.: (49) 898906650
Web Site: https://www.adva.com
Rev.: $677,411,903
Assets: $726,147,763
Liabilities: $308,895,942
Net Worth: $417,251,821
Earnings: ($16,017,154)
Emp.: 2,069
Fiscal Year-end: 12/31/2023
Optical Ethernet Solutions
N.A.I.C.S.: 335921
Johanna Hey (Chm-Supervisory Bd)
Brian L. Protiva (Co-Founder)
Christoph Glingener (CEO & CTO)
Ulrich Dopfer (CFO & Member-Mgmt Bd)
Scott St. John (Chief Mktg & Sls Officer &
Member-Mgmt Bd)

Subsidiary (Non-US):

**ADVA Optical Networking (India) Pri-
vate Ltd.** (2)
Unit 4A Ground Floor Building 10 Tower C
DLF Cyber City, Gurgaon, 122002, Hary-
ana, India
Tel.: (91) 1244987150
Telecommunication Equipment Distr
N.A.I.C.S.: 423690
Devender Gayr (Mgr-Acctg)

**ADVA Optical Networking (Shenzhen)
Ltd** (2)
18/F Maoye Times Square Haide 2nd Road,
Nanshan District, Shenzhen, 518054, China
Tel.: (86) 7558 621 7400
Web Site: https://www.adva.com
Communication Systems Mfr
N.A.I.C.S.: 334210

ADVA Optical Networking AB (2)
Finlandsgatan 12, 164 74, Kista, Sweden
Tel.: (46) 859463300
Telecommunication Equipment Distr
N.A.I.C.S.: 423690

ADVA Optical Networking AS (2)
Fyrstikkalleen 3 A, PO Box 6379, Etterstad,
0604, Oslo, Norway
Tel.: (47) 21609950
Web Site: http://www.advaoptical.com
Sales Range: $25-49.9 Million
Emp.: 29
Communication Devices Mfr
N.A.I.C.S.: 334210

ADVA Optical Networking Corp. (2)
Ibasen Bldg 7F Nihonbashi-kobunacho 4-1,
Chuo-ku, Tokyo, 103-0024, Japan
Tel.: (81) 36 667 5830
Web Site: http://www.advaoptical.com
Sales Range: $25-49.9 Million
Emp.: 6
Optical Networking Equipments Mfr
N.A.I.C.S.: 334210

**ADVA Optical Networking Hong
Kong, Ltd.** (2)
1063 Kings Rd Rm 1106, 663 King Rd,
Hong Kong, China (Hong Kong)
Tel.: (852) 28569090
Sales Range: $25-49.9 Million
Emp.: 5
Optical Networking Equipments Mfr
N.A.I.C.S.: 334210
Thomas Yeo (Mng Dir)

**ADVA Optical Networking Israel
Ltd** (2)
Millennium House Floor 12 2 Hatidhar
Street, PO Box 2552, Ra'anana, 4366105,
Israel
Tel.: (972) 9 7750 101
Web Site: http://www.adva.com
Optical Transport, Ethernet Access, Network
Management & Network Services
N.A.I.C.S.: 334118

ADVA Optical Networking Ltd. (2)
Advantage House Tribune Way Clifton
Moor, York, YO30 4RY, United Kingdom
Tel.: (44) 1904692700
Telecommunication Equipment Distr
N.A.I.C.S.: 423690
Natalie Scott (Project Mgr)

Subsidiary (US):

**ADVA Optical Networking North
America, Inc.** (2)
511 Davis Dr Ste 400, Morrisville, NC
27560
Tel.: (919) 337-4100
Web Site: http://www.advaoptical.com
Telecommunication Network Design, Mfr &
Distr
N.A.I.C.S.: 517810

**ADVA Optical Networking North
America, Inc.** (2)
2301 N Greenville Ave Ste 300, Richard-
son, TX 75082
Tel.: (972) 759-1200
Web Site: http://www.advaoptical.com
Telecommunications Equipment Design, Mfr
& Distr
N.A.I.C.S.: 517810

**ADVA Optical Networking North
America, Inc.** (2)
5755 Peachtree Industrial Blvd, Norcross,
GA 30092
Tel.: (678) 728-8600
Telecommunication Network Design, Mfr &
Distr
N.A.I.C.S.: 517810

**ADVA Optical Networking North
America, Inc. - Chatsworth** (2)
20520 Nordhoff St, Chatsworth, CA 91311
Tel.: (978) 674-6800
Web Site: https://www.adva.com
Laser Components & Equipment & Com-
puter Networking Products Mfr & Whslr
N.A.I.C.S.: 334413

Subsidiary (Non-US):

Appointech, Inc. (3)
6F-2 No 192 Tung-Kuan Rd, Hsinchu, Tai-
wan
Tel.: (886) 3 573 8478
Web Site: https://www.appointech.com
Fiber Optic Module Mfr
N.A.I.C.S.: 335921

Subsidiary (Domestic):

**MRV Communications Americas,
Inc.** (3)
300 Apollo Dr, Chelmsford, MA 01824
Tel.: (978) 674-6800
Web Site: http://www.advaoptical.com
Telecommunication Servicesb
N.A.I.C.S.: 517121

Branch (Domestic):

**MRV Communications, Inc. -
Littleton** (3)
295 Foster St, Littleton, MA 01460
Tel.: (978) 952-4700
Communications & Computer Networking
Products & Systems Whslr
N.A.I.C.S.: 423430

Subsidiary (Non-US):

**ADVA Optical Networking Pty
Ltd.** (2)
Level 31 120 Collins St, Melbourne, 3000,
VIC, Australia
Tel.: (61) 392255149
Telecommunication Equipment Distr
N.A.I.C.S.: 423690

ADVA Optical Networking SE (2)
Millenium Tower 24th Floor Handelskai 94-
96, 1200, Vienna, Austria
Tel.: (43) 1270333010
Telecommunication Equipment Distr
N.A.I.C.S.: 423690
Stefan Jakl (Acct Mgr-DACH)

ADVA Optical Networking SE (2)
Parco di Villa Grazioli Via Umberto Pavoni
34-7, Grottaferrata, Rome, Italy
Tel.: (39) 0686761027
Telecommunication Equipment Distr
N.A.I.C.S.: 423690

ADVA Optical Networking SE (2)
Technoparkstr 1, 8005, Zurich, Switzerland
Tel.: (41) 795915463
Telecommunication Equipment Distr
N.A.I.C.S.: 423690

ADVA Optical Networking SE (2)
Branch Office South Africa Unit No 19 Cam-
bridge Office Park 5, Bauhinia Street High-
veld Techno Park, Centurion, 0167, South
Africa
Tel.: (27) 126652055
Telecommunication Equipment Distr
N.A.I.C.S.: 423690

ADVA Optical Networking SE (2)
Executive Office 3 Dubai Internet City Build-
ing 12, Dubai, United Arab Emirates
Tel.: (971) 558258314
Telecommunication Equipment Distr
N.A.I.C.S.: 423690

ADVA Optical Networking SE (2)
Le Montreal 19 Bis Avenue du Quebec,
91140, Villebon-sur-Yvette, France
Tel.: (33) 160135953
Telecommunication Equipment Distr
N.A.I.C.S.: 423690
Valentin Grempka (Engr-Technical Svcs)

**ADVA Optical Networking Servicos
Brazil Ltda.** (2)
Av Paulista 37 - 4 andar - Suite 35, São
Paulo, 01311-902, Brazil
Tel.: (55) 1122462880
Telecommunication Equipment Distr
N.A.I.C.S.: 423690

**ADVA Optical Networking Singapore
Pte. Ltd.** (2)
25 International Business Park 05-106 Ger-
man Centre, Singapore, 609916, Singapore
Tel.: (65) 65925384
Telecommunication Equipment Distr
N.A.I.C.S.: 423690
Weicong Zhou (Dir-Bus Dev)

**ADVA Optical Networking Sp.
z.o.o.** (2)
Ul uzycka 8 C Business Park, Tensor Build-
ing Y, 81-537, Gdynia, Poland
Tel.: (48) 58 771 6100
Web Site: http://www.advaoptical.com
Sales Range: $50-74.9 Million
Emp.: 182
Optical Networking Equipments Mfr
N.A.I.C.S.: 334210

**ADVA Optical Networking Trading
(Shenzhen) Ltd.** (2)
Room 108 Dasheng Building No 1-3
Taohua Road, Futian Free Trade Zone Fu-
tian District, Shenzhen, 518058, China
Tel.: (86) 75586217400
Telecommunication Equipment Distr
N.A.I.C.S.: 423690
Jun Liu (Sr Mgr-Supply Chain Mgmt)

Oscilloquartz Finland Oy (2)
Tekniikantie 14, 02150, Espoo, Finland
Tel.: (358) 405433379
Telecommunication Equipment Distr
N.A.I.C.S.: 423690

Oscilloquartz S.A. (2)
Avenue des Paquiers 1, 2072, Saint-Blaise,
Switzerland (100%)
Tel.: (41) 32 722 5555
Web Site: https://www.oscilloquartz.com
Sales Range: $25-49.9 Million
Emp.: 50
Quartz Crystal Oscillators Developer & Mfr
N.A.I.C.S.: 334519

ADVANCE AUTO PARTS, INC.
4200 Six Forks Rd, Raleigh, NC
27609

Tel.: (540) 362-4911　　　　　DE
Web Site:
https://www.advanceautoparts.com
Year Founded: 1932
AAP—(NYSE)
Rev.: $11,287,607,000
Assets: $12,276,326,000
Liabilities: $9,756,598,000
Net Worth: $2,519,728,000
Earnings: $29,735,000
Emp.: 40,000
Fiscal Year-end: 12/30/23
Automobile Parts Mfr
N.A.I.C.S.: 441330
Shane M. O'Kelly (Pres & CEO)
Elizabeth E. Dreyer (Chief Acctg Offi-
cer, Sr VP & Controller)
Tammy Moss Finley (Gen Counsel,
Sec & Exec VP)
Robert B. Cushing (Exec VP-
Professional)
Sri Donthi (CTO & Exec VP)
Elisabeth Eisleben (Sr VP-Comm)
Dena LaMar (Chief Inclusion, Equity
& Diversity Officer & VP)
Ryan P. Grimsland (CFO & Exec VP)
Stephen J. Szilagyi (Exec VP-Supply
Chain)
Shane O'Kelly (Pres & CEO)
Anthony A. Iskander (Treas & Sr VP-
Fin)
Stephen J. Szilagyi (Exec VP-Supply
Chain)

Subsidiaries:

Advance Auto Parts (1)
3504 McFarland Blvd E, Tuscaloosa, AL
35405
Tel.: (205) 553-5582
Web Site: http://www.advanceautoparts.com
Sales Range: $10-24.9 Million
Emp.: 13
Auto & Home Supply Stores
N.A.I.C.S.: 423120
Kevin Quinn (Treas & VP)

**Advance e-Service Solutions,
Inc.** (1)
100 Shockoe Slip Fl 2, Richmond, VA
23219-4100
Tel.: (540) 362-4911
Emp.: 21
Automobile Parts Distr
N.A.I.C.S.: 423120

Autopart International Inc. (1)
192 Mansfield Ave, Norton, MA 02766
Tel.: (781) 784-1111
Web Site: https://www.autopartintl.com
Sales Range: $75-99.9 Million
Emp.: 3,100
Automotive Supplies & Parts
N.A.I.C.S.: 441330
Stephen Patkin (Founder & Chm)

Driverside, Inc. (1)
110 Sutter St Ste 300, San Francisco, CA
94104
Tel.: (415) 217-8800
Web Site: http://www.driverside.com
Car Distr
N.A.I.C.S.: 441110

General Parts International, Inc. (1)
2635 Millbrook Rd, Raleigh, NC 27604
Tel.: (919) 876-8643
Web Site: http://www.carquest.com
Automotive Parts Distribution Services
N.A.I.C.S.: 423120

Subsidiary (Domestic):

American Weldering & Gas, Inc. (2)
320 N 11th St, Billings, MT 59101
Tel.: (406) 256-3330
Web Site: http://www.amwelding.com
Sales Range: $10-24.9 Million
Emp.: 12
Industrial Machinery & Equipment Mfr
N.A.I.C.S.: 423830
Paul Scott (Sr VP-South Div)
Jason Krieger (Pres & CEO)
Sean Bennett (CFO & VP)
George Golliday (CEO)

Kevin Adkins *(Sr VP)*
Mike Maxey *(Sr VP)*

Subsidiary (Non-US):

CARQUEST Canada, Ltd. (2)
35 Worcester Rd, Toronto, M9W 1K9, ON, Canada
Tel.: (416) 675-2100
Web Site: http://www.carquest.com
Sales Range: $25-49.9 Million
Emp.: 200
Car Parts Distr
N.A.I.C.S.: 441330

Subsidiary (Domestic):

CARQUEST Corporation (2)
3907 New Bern Ave, Raleigh, NC 27610
Tel.: (919) 255-1753
Sales Range: $50-74.9 Million
Emp.: 750
Automotive Supplies & Parts Mfr
N.A.I.C.S.: 423120
John Gardner *(Sr VP-Fin)*

Subsidiary (Domestic):

Automotive Warehouse, Inc. (3)
2736 Waiwai Loop, Honolulu, HI 96819-1940
Tel.: (808) 664-1523
Web Site: http://www.carquesthawaii.com
Sales Range: $25-49.9 Million
Emp.: 30
Automotive Parts & Accessories Mfr
N.A.I.C.S.: 423120

Unit (Domestic):

CARQUEST (3)
1962 S Alamo St, San Antonio, TX 78204
Tel.: (210) 226-0101
Sales Range: $25-49.9 Million
Emp.: 60
Distr Automotive Parts
N.A.I.C.S.: 423120

CARQUEST (3)
955 Fee Dr, Sacramento, CA 95815
Tel.: (916) 568-2224
Web Site: http://www.carquest.com
Sales Range: $25-49.9 Million
Emp.: 10
Provider of Motor Vehicle Supply Services
N.A.I.C.S.: 423120

CARQUEST (3)
W62 N226 Washington Ave, Cedarburg, WI 53012
Tel.: (262) 377-0200
Web Site: http://www.carquest.com
Sales Range: $25-49.9 Million
Emp.: 12
Distribute Automotive Supplies & Parts
N.A.I.C.S.: 423120

CARQUEST (3)
2305 2307 11 Ave S, Great Falls, MT 59405
Tel.: (406) 452-8555
Web Site: http://www.carquest.com
Sales Range: $10-24.9 Million
Emp.: 9
Automotive Supplies & Parts Distr
N.A.I.C.S.: 423120

CARQUEST Albuquerque (3)
10026 Ctr Ave SE, Albuquerque, NM 87123
Tel.: (505) 299-9499
Sales Range: $25-49.9 Million
Emp.: 50
Car Parts Distr
N.A.I.C.S.: 441330
James McDuffie *(Media Buyer)*

CARQUEST Auto Parts (3)
2635 Belknap Ave, Billings, MT 59101-4539
Tel.: (406) 259-3376
Web Site: http://www.carquest.com
Sales Range: $10-24.9 Million
Emp.: 27
Automotive Supplies & Parts
N.A.I.C.S.: 423120

**CARQUEST Auto Parts Inc -
California** (3)
1350 E Thompson Blvd, Ventura, CA 93001
Tel.: (805) 643-2247
Web Site: http://www.carquest.ca

Sales Range: $25-49.9 Million
Emp.: 20
Auto Parts Warehouse
N.A.I.C.S.: 441330

**CARQUEST Auto Parts of
Anderson** (3)
1705 E Greenville St, Anderson, SC 29621
Tel.: (864) 305-4295
Web Site: http://www.carquest.com
Sales Range: Less than $1 Million
Emp.: 10
Automotive Supplies & Parts
N.A.I.C.S.: 423120

CARQUEST Auto Parts of Caro (3)
1042 E Caro Rd, Caro, MI 48723
Tel.: (989) 672-6330
Web Site: http://www.carquest.com
Sales Range: Less than $1 Million
Emp.: 6
Automotive Parts
N.A.I.C.S.: 441330

**CARQUEST Auto Parts of Grand
Forks** (3)
2521 S Washington St, Grand Forks, ND 58201
Tel.: (701) 775-4618
Web Site: http://www.carquest.com
Sales Range: $1-9.9 Million
Emp.: 6
Automotive Supplies & Parts
N.A.I.C.S.: 423120

**CARQUEST Auto Parts of
Hattiesburg** (3)
6112 U S Hwy 49, Hattiesburg, MS 39401
Tel.: (601) 545-8181
Web Site: http://www.carquest.com
Sales Range: $1-9.9 Million
Emp.: 6
Automotive Parts
N.A.I.C.S.: 441330

**CARQUEST Auto Parts of
McMinnville** (3)
1614 Smithville Hwy, McMinnville, TN 37110
Tel.: (931) 473-4424
Web Site: http://www.carquest.com
Sales Range: Less than $1 Million
Emp.: 4
Automotive Parts
N.A.I.C.S.: 441330

**CARQUEST Distribution Center -
Alabama** (3)
3065 Selma Hwy, Montgomery, AL 36108
Tel.: (334) 284-2516
Web Site: http://www.carquest.com
Sales Range: $25-49.9 Million
Emp.: 120
Distr of Automotive Parts & Accessories
N.A.I.C.S.: 423120

**CARQUEST Distribution Center -
California** (3)
600 Sequoia Pacific Blvd, Sacramento, CA 95814-0230
Tel.: (916) 446-4666
Sales Range: $25-49.9 Million
Emp.: 150
Sales Of Auto Parts
N.A.I.C.S.: 621310

**CARQUEST Distribution Center -
California** (3)
34928 McMurtrey Ave, Bakersfield, CA 93308
Tel.: (919) 573-3892
Web Site: http://www.carquest.com
Sales Range: $25-49.9 Million
Emp.: 100
Distr of Automotive Parts & Accessories
N.A.I.C.S.: 423120

**CARQUEST Distribution Center -
Maine** (3)
153 Perry Rd, Bangor, ME 04401
Tel.: (207) 941-0030
Web Site: http://www.carquest.com
Sales Range: $25-49.9 Million
Emp.: 40
Auto Parts Distr
N.A.I.C.S.: 457120

**CARQUEST Distribution Center -
Michigan**

902 Columbus Ave, Bay City, MI 48708
Tel.: (989) 892-2832
Web Site: http://www.carquest.com
Sales Range: $25-49.9 Million
Emp.: 100
Distr of Automotive Parts & Accessories
N.A.I.C.S.: 423120

**CARQUEST Distribution Center -
Michigan** (3)
4722 N Grand River Ave, Lansing, MI 48906-2536
Tel.: (517) 321-2051
Web Site: http://www.thermosets.com
Sales Range: $25-49.9 Million
Emp.: 12
Distr of Automotive Parts & Accessories
N.A.I.C.S.: 423120

**CARQUEST Distribution Center -
Minnesota** (3)
21560 Granada Ave, Lakeville, MN 55044
Tel.: (952) 469-5584
Rev.: $840,000
Emp.: 200
Selling Autoparts
N.A.I.C.S.: 423120
David Harman *(Gen Mgr)*

**CARQUEST Distribution Center -
Missouri** (3)
800 N 17th St, Saint Louis, MO 63106
Tel.: (314) 345-4800
Sales Range: $25-49.9 Million
Emp.: 75
Distr of Automotive Parts & Accessories
N.A.I.C.S.: 423120

**CARQUEST Distribution Center -
Montana** (3)
2635 Belknap Ave, Billings, MT 59101
Tel.: (406) 259-3376
Web Site: http://www.carquest.com
Sales Range: $25-49.9 Million
Emp.: 150
Distr of Automotive Parts & Accessories
N.A.I.C.S.: 423120

**CARQUEST Distribution Center -
New Mexico** (3)
4001 Hawkins St NE, Albuquerque, NM 87109
Tel.: (505) 343-1234
Web Site: http://www.windwardhomes.com
Sales Range: $25-49.9 Million
Emp.: 40
Distr of Automotive Parts & Accessories
N.A.I.C.S.: 441330

**CARQUEST Distribution Center -
North Carolina** (3)
150 Old Shoals Rd Buncombe, Arden, NC 28704-5501
Tel.: (828) 651-2000
Web Site: http://www.carquest.com
Sales Range: $25-49.9 Million
Emp.: 60
Distr of Automotive Parts & Accessories
N.A.I.C.S.: 423120

**CARQUEST Distribution Center -
North Carolina** (3)
3517 Capital Blvd, Raleigh, NC 27604
Tel.: (919) 872-2981
Web Site: http://www.carquest.com
Sales Range: $50-74.9 Million
Distr of Automotive Parts & Accessories
N.A.I.C.S.: 423120

**CARQUEST Distribution Center -
Tennessee** (3)
417 Brick Church Pk Dr, Nashville, TN 37207
Tel.: (615) 227-9595
Sales Range: $25-49.9 Million
Emp.: 50
Distr of Automotive Parts & Accessories
N.A.I.C.S.: 423120

**CARQUEST Distribution Center -
Texas** (3)
328 W Peden Alley, San Antonio, TX 78204
Tel.: (210) 200-8056
Web Site: http://www.carquest.com
Sales Range: $25-49.9 Million
Emp.: 60
Automotive Parts & Accessories Distr
N.A.I.C.S.: 423120

**CARQUEST Distribution Center -
Texas** (3)

1991 Lakepointe Dr, Lewisville, TX 75057
Tel.: (972) 459-9144
Web Site: http://www.carquest.com
Sales Range: $25-49.9 Million
Emp.: 33
Distr of Automotive Parts & Accessories
N.A.I.C.S.: 423120

**CARQUEST Distribution Center -
Washington** (3)
7812 S 186th Pl, Kent, WA 98032
Tel.: (425) 251-0560
Web Site: http://www.carquest.com
Sales Range: $25-49.9 Million
Emp.: 70
Auto Parts Distr
N.A.I.C.S.: 423120

**CARQUEST Distribution Center -
Wisconsin** (3)
1906 N Peach Ave, Marshfield, WI 54449
Tel.: (715) 384-2127
Web Site: http://www.carquest.com
Sales Range: $25-49.9 Million
Emp.: 100
Whslr of Auto Parts
N.A.I.C.S.: 423120

**CARQUEST Distribution Center- New
York** (3)
4091 Jeffrey Blvd, Blasdell, NY 14219-2338
Tel.: (716) 821-9694
Web Site: http://www.carquest.com
Rev.: $22,000,000
Emp.: 81
Distribution & Whole Sale of Car Parts
N.A.I.C.S.: 423120

Subsidiary (Domestic):

CARQUEST Inc. (3)
189 E S Blvd, Crawfordsville, IN 47933
Tel.: (765) 362-5201
Web Site: http://www.carquest.com
Sales Range: Less than $1 Million
Emp.: 12
Automotive Accessories Mfr
N.A.I.C.S.: 441330

Unit (Domestic):

CARQUEST Winchester (3)
3633 Valley Pike, Winchester, VA 22602
Tel.: (540) 868-2207
Web Site: http://www.carquest.com
Sales Range: $25-49.9 Million
Emp.: 80
Auto Parts Distr
N.A.I.C.S.: 441330

CARQUEST of Butte (3)
3639 Harrison Ave, Butte, MT 59701
Tel.: (406) 723-4357
Web Site: http://www.carquest.com
Sales Range: Less than $1 Million
Emp.: 9
Motor Vehicle Supplies & New Parts
N.A.I.C.S.: 424410

CARQUEST-Memphis (3)
7337 Airways Blvd Ste 7339, Southaven, MS 38671-5803
Tel.: (662) 349-2562
Web Site: http://www.carquest.com
Sales Range: $25-49.9 Million
Emp.: 100
Automotive Supplies & Parts
N.A.I.C.S.: 423120

Subsidiary (Domestic):

General Parts, Inc. (2)
800 N 17th St, Saint Louis, MO 63106-3730
Tel.: (314) 345-4900
Sales Range: $25-49.9 Million
Emp.: 110
Motor Vehicle Supplies & New Parts Mfr
N.A.I.C.S.: 423120

Industrial Gas Distributors (2)
1346 Monad Rd, Billings, MT 59101-3327
Tel.: (406) 256-3344
Sales Range: $10-24.9 Million
Emp.: 15
Compressed Gas
N.A.I.C.S.: 424690
George Golliday *(Pres)*

Steinway Auto Parts Inc. (1)
180 Frnt St, Hempstead, NY 11550
Tel.: (718) 274-0306

Advance Auto Parts, Inc.—(Continued)

Sales Range: $25-49.9 Million
Emp.: 35
Automotive Supplies & Parts Mfr
N.A.I.C.S.: 423120

Western Auto of St. Thomas,
Inc.   (1)
300 S Grand Ave, Los Angeles, CA 90071
Tel.: (213) 229-5069
Automobile Parts Distr
N.A.I.C.S.: 423120

Worldpac, Canada, Inc.   (1)
6956 Columbus Road, Mississauga, L5T
2G1, ON, Canada
Web Site: https://www.worldpac.ca
Automobile Parts Distr
N.A.I.C.S.: 423120
Jason Yurchak (Sr VP)
Pam Neely (Sls Mgr-Ontario,Maritimes)
Anthony Calcara (Sls Dir)
Shaun Casey (Sls Dir)
Joe Mercanti (Nat'l Sls Mgr-Nat'l,Corp)
Alex Smith (Nat'l Sls Mgr-Corp)

Worldwide Auto Parts, Inc.   (1)
4144 El Cajon Blvd, San Diego, CA 92105
Tel.: (619) 283-2381
Automobile Parts Distr
N.A.I.C.S.: 423120

ADVANCED BIOENERGY, LLC

8000 Norman Ctr Dr Ste 610, Bloom-
ington, MN 55437
Tel.: (763) 226-2701   DE
Web Site:
    http://www.advancedbioenergy.com
Year Founded: 2005
ABENU—(OTCQB)
Rev.: $127,991,000
Assets: $50,700,000
Liabilities: $36,854,000
Net Worth: $13,846,000
Earnings: ($14,577,000)
Emp.: 55
Fiscal Year-end: 09/30/19
Ethynol Products Mfr
N.A.I.C.S.: 325193

ADVANCED BIOMEDICAL
TECHNOLOGIES, INC.

2600 Woods Trail S, Burnsville, MN
55306
Tel.: (651) 681-0198   NV
Web Site: https://www.abtlafleur.com
ABMT—(OTCIQ)
Rev.: $123,587
Assets: $469,226
Liabilities: $7,871,024
Net Worth: ($7,401,798)
Earnings: ($672,000)
Emp.: 17
Fiscal Year-end: 10/31/20
Self-Reinforced & Re-Absorbable Bio-
degradable Internal Fixation Devices
Developer & Mfr
N.A.I.C.S.: 325520
Kai Gui (CFO, COO & Sec)
Puyi Sheng (Chief Medical Officer)

ADVANCED CONTAINER
TECHNOLOGIES, INC.

1620 Commerce St, Corona, CA
92880
Tel.: (951) 547-0788   FL
Web Site:
    https://www.medtainerinc.com
ACTX—(OTCIQ)
Rev.: $5,349,012
Assets: $4,024,793
Liabilities: $2,098,651
Net Worth: $1,926,142
Earnings: ($845,056)
Emp.: 6
Fiscal Year-end: 12/31/21
All Other Plastics Product Manufac-
turing
N.A.I.C.S.: 326199

Douglas P. Heldoorn (Founder, Chm,
Pres, CEO & COO)
Jeffory A. Carlson (CFO, Principal
Acctg Officer & Treas)
Daniel Salinas (Pres-Advanced)

Subsidiaries:

D&C Distributors, LLC   (1)
1620 Commerce St, Corona, CA 92880
Tel.: (951) 284-7550
Web Site: http://www.dcdistributor.com
Piastic Storage Container Distr
N.A.I.C.S.: 423840
Douglas Heldoorn (COO)

ADVANCED DEPOSITION
TECHNOLOGIES, INC.

9160 S 300 W Ste 101, Salt Lake
City, UT 84070
Tel.: (801) 706-9429   DE
ADTC—(OTCIQ)
Oil & Gas Exploration Services
N.A.I.C.S.: 213112
Tsunenobu Arai (CEO)

ADVANCED DRAINAGE SYS-
TEMS, INC.

4640 Trueman Blvd, Hilliard, OH
43026
Tel.: (614) 658-0050   DE
Web Site: https://www.adspipe.com
Year Founded: 1966
WMS—(NYSE)
Rev.: $2,874,473,000
Assets: $3,268,913,000
Liabilities: $1,988,214,000
Net Worth: $1,280,699,000
Earnings: $509,915,000
Emp.: 5,705
Fiscal Year-end: 03/31/24
Polyethylene Drainage Products Mfr
& Whslr
N.A.I.C.S.: 326122
Kevin Lee (Treas)
Robert M. Klein (Exec VP-Sls)
Robert M. Eversole (Chm)
Scott A. Cottrill (CFO, Sec & Exec
VP)
Tim A. Makowski (Chief Acctg Officer,
VP & Controller)
D. Scott Barbour (Pres & CEO)
Darin Harvey (Exec VP-Supply
Chain)
Kevin Talley (Chief Admin Officer &
Exec VP)
Thomas Waun (Sr VP-Int'l)
Michael Higgins (VP-Strategy & IR)
Craig Taylor (Exec VP)

Subsidiaries:

ADS Canada Inc   (1)
250A Boul Industriel, Saint-Germain-de-
Grantham, Saint-Germain, J0C 1K0, QC,
Canada
Tel.: (819) 395-4244
Web Site: https://www.ads-pipecanada.ca
Emp.: 75
Plastic Tank Mfr
N.A.I.C.S.: 326122

ADS Europe B.V.   (1)
Marco Polostraat 2-14, 3165 AL , Rotter-
dam, Netherlands
Tel.: (31) 102996410
Plastic Drainage Pipe Distr
N.A.I.C.S.: 424610

ADS Mexicana, S.A de C.V.   (1)
Carretera Villa de Garcia Kilometro 0 8, In-
dustrial Zone of the President, 66370,
Santa Catarina, Nuevo Leon, Mexico
Tel.: (52) 8186254500
Web Site: https://www.adsmexicana.com
Plastic Tank Mfr
N.A.I.C.S.: 326122

ADS Structures, Inc.   (1)
433 Olive St, Findlay, OH 45840
Tel.: (614) 658-0242
Business Support Services

N.A.I.C.S.: 561990

BaySaver Technologies, LLC   (1)
1030 Deer Hollow Dr, Mount Airy, MD
21771   (65%)
Tel.: (301) 829-6470
Web Site: http://www.baysaver.com
Waste Treatment Services
N.A.I.C.S.: 221310

Cultec, Inc.   (1)
878 Federal Rd, Brookfield, CT 06804
Tel.: (203) 775-4416
Web Site: http://www.cultec.com
Sales Range: $1-9.9 Million
Emp.: 15
Plastics Product Mfr
N.A.I.C.S.: 326199
Gina Carolan (COO & Mktg Dir)
Christina DiTullio (CFO)
John DiTullio (VP-Sls)
Fred Dotson (Pres)
Robert J. Ditullio Sr. (Founder & CEO)
Robert J. Ditullio Jr. (Chief Bus Dev Officer)

Green Line Polymers, Inc.   (1)
140 Vineland Ave, Bakersfield, CA 31015
Tel.: (661) 336-1520
Web Site:
    http://www.greenlinepolymers.com
Recycling Center Operator
N.A.I.C.S.: 562212

Ideal Pipe   (1)
1100 Ideal Drive, PO Box 100, Thorndale,
N0M 2P0, ON, Canada
Tel.: (519) 473-2669
Web Site: http://www.idealpipe.ca
Plastic Pipe & Pipe Fitting Mfr
N.A.I.C.S.: 326122

Infiltrator Water Technologies,
LLC   (1)
4 Business Park Rd, Old Saybrook, CT
06475
Tel.: (860) 577-7000
Web Site: https://www.infiltratorwater.com
Waste Water Treatment Services
N.A.I.C.S.: 221320
Craig Taylor (VP-Fin)
Bryan A. Coppes (VP-Engrg & R&D)
Carl Thompson (VP-Sls & Mktg)
Ronald Brochu (VP-Mfg)
Roy E. MooreJr. (Exec VP)

Subsidiary (Domestic):

Delta Treatment Systems, LLC   (2)
9125 Comar Dr, Walker, LA 70785
Tel.: (225) 665-6162
Waste Water Treatment Services
N.A.I.C.S.: 221320
Scott Miller (Mgr)

Jet Polymer Recycling, Inc.   (1)
4811 Gault Ave N, Fort Payne, AL 35967-
8169
Tel.: (256) 638-7144
Web Site: https://www.jetpolymer.com
Waste Management Services
N.A.I.C.S.: 562998
Trulie Roberts (Mgr-Sls & Mktg)

Presby Environmental, Inc.   (1)
143 Airport Rd, Whitefield, NH 03598
Waste Water Treatment Services
N.A.I.C.S.: 221320

Sewer Tap, Inc.   (1)
3707 24th Ave, Forest Grove, OR 97116
Tel.: (503) 357-2110
Web Site: http://www.insertatee.com
Plumbing Equipment Whslr
N.A.I.C.S.: 444180

Spartan Concrete, Inc.   (1)
105 Central Way Ste 203, Kirkland, WA
98033
Tel.: (425) 739-4449
Web Site:
    https://www.spartanconcreteinc.com
Industrial Building Contract Services
N.A.I.C.S.: 238110

StormTech LLC   (1)
520 Cromwell Ave, Rocky Hill, CT 06067
Tel.: (860) 529-8188
Web Site: http://www.stormtech.com
Water Treatment Chemical Product Distr
N.A.I.C.S.: 424690

Tigre-ADS Colombia Limitada   (1)
Av Troncal de Occidente N 18-76 Bodega 1
Manzana E, Suba, Bogota, Colombia
Tel.: (57) 3123645189
Plastic Pipe & Pipe Fitting Mfr
N.A.I.C.S.: 326122

Tigre-ADS Peru S.A.C.   (1)
Av Carlos Roberto Hansen S N Industrial
Allotment the Lucumo, Lotizacion Industrial
El Lucumo Lurin, Lima, Peru
Tel.: (51) 14106730
Web Site: http://www.tigre.pe
Plastic Pipe & Pipe Fitting Mfr
N.A.I.C.S.: 326122

Tubos Tigre-ADS do Brasil
Limitada   (1)
Av Pennwalt 270 - Distrito Industrial, Rio
Claro, 13505-650, Sao Paulo, Brazil
Tel.: (55) 8006021350
Web Site: https://www.adstigre.com
Plastic Pipe & Pipe Fitting Mfr
N.A.I.C.S.: 326122
Eduardo Reis (Product Mgr-Application)

Tubos y Plasticos ADS Chile
Limitada   (1)
Panamericana Norte 20500, Lampa, 832,
Chile
Tel.: (56) 24130000
Plastic Pipe & Pipe Fitting Mfr
N.A.I.C.S.: 326122

ADVANCED EMISSIONS SO-
LUTIONS, INC.

8051 E Maplewood Ave Ste 210,
Greenwood Village, CO 80111
Tel.: (720) 598-3500   DE
Web Site:
    https://www.advancedemissionsso
lutions.com
ADES—(NASDAQ)
Rev.: $102,987,000
Assets: $181,164,000
Liabilities: $41,185,000
Net Worth: $139,979,000
Earnings: ($8,917,000)
Emp.: 147
Fiscal Year-end: 12/31/22
Holding Company; Clean Coal Tech-
nologies & Associated Specialty
Chemicals Mfr
N.A.I.C.S.: 551112
Robert E. Rasmus (Pres & CEO)
Joe Wong (CTO)
Lorraine Lang (VP-HR)
Dennis Sewell (VP-Mfg)
Oscar Velasquez (VP-Sls)
Clay Smith (Gen Counsel)
Coy K. Lane (Dir)
Jeremy Deke Williamson (COO)

Subsidiaries:

ADA Carbon Solutions, LLC   (1)
1460 W Canal Ct Ste 100, Littleton, CO
80120-5632
Tel.: (303) 962-1977
Web Site: http://www.ada-cs.com
Powdered Activated Carbon Products Mfr
N.A.I.C.S.: 325998

ADA-ES, Inc.   (1)
8051 E Maplewood Ave Ste 210, Green-
wood Village, CO 80111
Tel.: (720) 598-3500
Web Site: http://www.adaes.com
Emp.: 57
Fiscal Year-end: 12/31/2012
Specialty Chemicals Mfr
N.A.I.C.S.: 325199

ADVANCED ENERGY INDUS-
TRIES, INC.

1595 Wynkoop St Ste 800, Denver,
CO 80202
Tel.: (970) 221-0108   DE
Web Site:
    https://www.advancedenergy.com
Year Founded: 1981
AEIS—(NASDAQ)
Rev.: $1,845,422,000
Assets: $1,992,168,000

Liabilities: $925,901,000
Net Worth: $1,066,267,000
Earnings: $199,660,000
Emp.: 12,000
Fiscal Year-end: 12/31/22
Mfr of Electronic Power Supplies &
Controls
N.A.I.C.S.: 334419
Stephen D. Kelley *(Pres & CEO)*
Juergen Braun *(Sr VP-Plasma Power
Products)*
Shrinidhi Chandrasekharan *(VP-
Medical Power Products)*
Maria Cortez *(Sr VP)*
Peter Gillespie *(Sr VP-Corporate
Marketing & Strategy)*
Paul R. Oldham *(CFO & Exec VP)*
Rory O'Byrne *(Chief People Officer &
Sr VP)*
Elizabeth K. Vonne *(Gen Counsel,
Sec & Exec VP)*
John Donaghey *(Exec VP & Head-
Global Sls)*
Emdrem Tan *(Exec VP-Sys Power &
Sr VP)*
Grant H. Beard *(Chm)*
Eduardo Bernal *(COO & Exec VP)*
Cathy Mackinnon *(Sr VP-Corporate
Development)*

Subsidiaries:

AE Korea, Ltd.   (1)
No 701 Sicox Tower 484 Dunchon Daero,
Jungwon Gu, Seongnam, 013-229,
Gyeonggi-Do, Korea (South)
Tel.: (82) 317779191
Electric Equipment Mfr
N.A.I.C.S.: 334419

AE Precision Power Products Pvt.
Ltd.   (1)
Khannas House Ground Floor Plot No 39
and 40 Nehru Nagar Road, Pimpri, Pune,
411018, Maharashtra, India
Tel.: (91) 2066789500
Electric Equipment Mfr
N.A.I.C.S.: 334419

AEI Power GmbH   (1)
Uracher Str 91, 72555, Metzingen, Ger-
many
Tel.: (49) 71239690
Photovoltaic Inverter Mfr
N.A.I.C.S.: 334413

AEI Power India Pvt. Ltd.   (1)
Khanna's House Ground Floor Plot No 39
and 40 Nehru Nagar Road, Pimpri, Pune,
411018, Maharashtra, India
Tel.: (91) 2066789500
Semiconductor Devices Mfr
N.A.I.C.S.: 334413

AES Global Holdings PTE Ltd.   (1)
18 Tai Seng 05-07, Singapore, 539775,
Singapore
Tel.: (65) 65616482
Power Supply Equipment Distr
N.A.I.C.S.: 423840

Advanced Energy Industries   (1)
Room 1506 Building 1 No 2290 Zu Chong
Zhi Road, Pudong, Shanghai, 201210,
China
Tel.: (86) 2158997915
Power Supply Equipment Distr
N.A.I.C.S.: 423840

Advanced Energy Industries
GmbH   (1)
Uracher Str 91, 72555, Metzingen,
Germany   (100%)
Tel.: (49) 71239690
Web Site: https://www.advancedenergy.com
Complex Power Conversion & Control Sys-
tems
N.A.I.C.S.: 334519

Advanced Energy Industries Sdn.
Bhd.   (1)
Lot 10 Bandar Darulaman, 06000, Jitra, Ke-
dah, Malaysia
Tel.: (60) 49199355
Web Site: http://www.advance-
energy.com.my

Seal Weld Valve Care Product Mfr
N.A.I.C.S.: 332911

Advanced Energy Industries UK
Ltd.   (1)
Unit 5 Minton Place Market Court, Victoria
Road, Bicester, OX6 7QB, Oxfordshire,
United Kingdom   (100%)
Tel.: (44) 1869320022
Web Site: https://www.advanced-
energy.com
Sales Range: $1-9.9 Million
Emp.: 3
Complex Power Conversion & Control Sys-
tems
N.A.I.C.S.: 334519

Advanced Energy Industries, Inc.   (1)
888 E Tasman Dr Ste 100, Milpitas, CA
95035
Tel.: (408) 281-7772
Web Site: http://www.advancedenergy.com
Sales Range: $1-4.9 Billion
N.A.I.C.S.: 334220

Advanced Energy Industries, Inc.,
Shanghai   (1)
Room 1506 Building 1 No 2290 Zu Chong
Zhi Road, Pudong, Shanghai, 201210,
China
Tel.: (86) 2158997915
Sales Range: $125-149.9 Million
Emp.: 600
Complex Power Conversion & Control Sys-
tems
N.A.I.C.S.: 334519

Advanced Energy Japan K.K.   (1)
1F Iwasaki Nishikicho Bldg 1-6-6, Nishi-
kicho, Tachikawa, 190-0022, Japan
Tel.: (81) 42 512 8440
Web Site: http://www.advanced-energy.com
Sales Range: $100-124.9 Million
Complex Power Conversion & Control Sys-
tems
N.A.I.C.S.: 334519

Advanced Energy Renewables,
Inc.   (1)
20720 Brinson Blvd, Bend, OR 97701
Tel.: (541) 312-3832
Electronic Power Supplies & Control Sys-
tems Mfr
N.A.I.C.S.: 334413
Taylor Paul *(Engr-Power Electronics-III)*

Advanced Energy Singapore, Pte.
Ltd.   (1)
No 03-02 APP Enterprise Building 11 Toh
Guan Road East, Singapore, 608603, Sin-
gapore
Tel.: (65) 616482
Sales Range: $10-24.9 Million
Emp.: 2
Electronic Power Supplies & Control Sys-
tems Mfr
N.A.I.C.S.: 334418
Michael Smith *(Gen Mgr)*

Advanced Energy Taiwan, Ltd.   (1)
10F No 110 Chung Shan Rd Sec 3, Chun-
gho District, New Taipei City, 23544, Taiwan
Tel.: (886) 282215599
Web Site:
    https://www.advancedenergy.com.tw
Sales Range: $10-24.9 Million
Complex Power Conversion & Control Sys-
tems
N.A.I.C.S.: 334519

Advanced Energy Xi'an Co. Ltd.   (1)
Unit 3 Bonded Warehouse Southern Area
Xi'an Hi-tech CBZ North of Road, G3 Xi'an
Hi-tech Zone, Xi'an, 710075, China
Tel.: (86) 2158997915
Power Supply Equipment Distr
N.A.I.C.S.: 423840

Aera Korea Ltd.   (1)
145 Yatap-dong Pundang-ku, Songnam,
Gyeonggi-Do, Korea (South)
Tel.: (82) 31 706 0494
Sales Range: $100-124.9 Million
Complex Power Conversion & Control Sys-
tems
N.A.I.C.S.: 334519

Artesyn Embedded Power   (1)
2900 S Diablo Way Ste B100, Tempe, AZ
85282

Tel.: (888) 412-7832
Web Site: http://www.artesyn.com
Customized Power Conversion Products
Mfr
N.A.I.C.S.: 334419

Subsidiary (Non-US):

Artesyn Holding GmbH   (2)
Helmut-Qualtinger-Gasse 2 1 4th Fl, 1030,
Vienna, Austria
Tel.: (43) 180150
Web Site: http://www.artesyn.com
Holding Company
N.A.I.C.S.: 551112

Astec Custom Power (Singapore) Pte
Ltd.   (2)
7500A Beach Road Unit 11-324, Singapore,
199591, Singapore
Tel.: (65) 63366991
Web Site: https://www.powerconversion.com
Sales Range: $100-124.9 Million
Emp.: 6
Power Supplies Sales
N.A.I.C.S.: 335311

Astec Europe Limited   (2)
4 Harbour Buildings Waterry Hill, Dudley
Road Barberry House Ground Floor Brierley
Hill, Birmingham, DY5 1LN, W Mids, United
Kingdom
Tel.: (44) 1384842211
AC/DC Power Supplies
N.A.I.C.S.: 335311

Astec Power Philippines, Inc.   (2)
Main Rd Corner Rd J, Cavite Economic Zn
Authority, Cavite, 4106, Philippines
Tel.: (63) 469712000
Sales Range: $550-599.9 Million
Emp.: 5,000
Power Supplies Mfr
N.A.I.C.S.: 335311

Excelsys Technologies Ltd.   (1)
27 Eastgate Business Park, Little Island,
Cork, Ireland
Tel.: (353) 214354716
Web Site: http://www.excelsys.com
Power Supply Equipment Mfr & Distr
N.A.I.C.S.: 335999

HiTek Power Ltd. U.K.   (1)
Hawthorn Road, Littlehampton, BN17 7LT,
West Sussex, United Kingdom
Tel.: (44) 1903712400
Web Site: http://www.lhvpower.com
Power Supply Equipment Mfr
N.A.I.C.S.: 335999

LumaSense Equipment India Pvt. Ltd.
Co.   (1)
514 A Wing Sagar Tech Plaza Sakinaka
Junction Andheri Kurla Road, Andheri East,
Mumbai, 400072, India
Tel.: (91) 2267419203
Temperature Control Sensor Distr
N.A.I.C.S.: 423610

LumaSense Technologies A/S   (1)
Energivej 30, 2750, Ballerup, Denmark
Tel.: (45) 44200100
Oil & Gas Field Machinery & Equipment
Distr
N.A.I.C.S.: 423330

LumaSense Technologies, Inc.   (1)
3301 Leonard Ct, Santa Clara, CA 95054-
2054
Tel.: (408) 727-1600
Web Site: http://www.lumasenseinc.com
Sales Range: $50-74.9 Million
Industrial, Medical & Energy Market Sensor
Instrumentation Mfr
N.A.I.C.S.: 334513

Subsidiary (Domestic):

Andros Incorporated   (2)
3301 Leonard Ct, Santa Clara, CA 95054
Tel.: (408) 727-1600
Web Site: http://www.lumasenseinc.com
Sales Range: $25-49.9 Million
Mfr, Designer & Sales of Environmental &
Medical Monitoring Equipment
N.A.I.C.S.: 334516
Steve Abely *(Pres)*

Subsidiary (Non-US):

LumaSense Technologies Europe
GmbH   (2)

Kleyerstrasse 90, 60326, Frankfurt am
Main, Germany
Tel.: (49) 69 97373 0
Web Site: http://www.lumasenseinc.com
Holding Company; Regional Managing Of-
fice
N.A.I.C.S.: 551112

Subsidiary (Non-US):

LumaSense Technologies Benelux
B.V.   (3)
Pavana 2, Sint Willebrord, 4711 VG, Neth-
erlands
Tel.: (31) 165381800
Measuring Instruments Mfr
N.A.I.C.S.: 334413

Subsidiary (Domestic):

LumaSense Technologies GmbH   (3)
Kelsterbacher Strasse 14, 65479, Raun-
heim, Germany
Tel.: (49) 61427892800
Sales Range: $10-24.9 Million
Engineeering Services
N.A.I.C.S.: 541330

Subsidiary (Domestic):

LumaSense Sensor GmbH   (4)
Lubecker Str 53-63, 39124, Magdeburg,
Germany
Tel.: (49) 3915441830
Engineeering Services
N.A.I.C.S.: 541330

Subsidiary (Non-US):

LumaSense Technologies
Limited   (3)
Summit house London Road, Bracknell,
RG12 2AQ, Berks, United Kingdom
Tel.: (44) 1344 707 323
Web Site: http://www.lumasenseinc.com
Sales Range: $10-24.9 Million
Emp.: 5
Provider of Engineering Services
N.A.I.C.S.: 541330

LumaSense Technologies Sarl   (3)
6 rue de l Expansion, 67150, Erstein,
France
Tel.: (33) 388989801
Sales Range: $10-24.9 Million
Emp.: 4
Measuring Instruments Mfr
N.A.I.C.S.: 334513

Subsidiary (Non-US):

LumaSense Technologies GmbH
Merkezi   (2)
Dogu Mahallesi Dere Sok No 31/2, 34890,
Istanbul, Turkiye
Tel.: (90) 2163901300
Thermal Comfort Instrument Mfr
N.A.I.C.S.: 541380

LumaSense, Vendas Brasil   (2)
Rua Sampainho 441 / 74, Campinas,
13025-300, Sao Paulo, Brazil
Tel.: (55) 1933676533
Petrochemical Sensor Mfr
N.A.I.C.S.: 325110

SL Power Electronics
Corporation   (1)
6050 King Dr, Ventura, CA 93003
Tel.: (805) 486-4565
Web Site: http://www.slpower.com
Emp.: 1,000
Electronic Protection & Power Conversion
Equipment Mfr & Distr
N.A.I.C.S.: 335999
Karim Alhusseini *(Pres)*

Sekidenko, Inc.   (1)
2501 SE Columbia Way Ste 200, Vancou-
ver, WA 98661   (100%)
Tel.: (360) 694-7871
Sales Range: $50-74.9 Million
Emp.: 23
Antenna & Electronic Mfr
N.A.I.C.S.: 334220

TEGAM, Inc.   (1)
Ten Tegam Way, Geneva, OH 44041
Tel.: (440) 466-6100
Web Site: http://www.tegam.com
Rev.: $6,666,666

Advanced Energy Industries, Inc.—(Continued)

Emp.: 54
Instrument Manufacturing for Measuring & Testing Electricity & Electrical Signals
N.A.I.C.S.: 334515
A. Brush (Co-CEO)

Trek Japan K.K. (1)
Kudankita325 Building 7F 3-2-5 Kudankita, Chiyoda-ku, Tokyo, 102-0073, Japan
Tel.: (81) 362614680
Oil & Gas Field Machinery & Equipment Distr
N.A.I.C.S.: 423330

Trek, Inc. (1)
190 Walnut St, Lockport, NY 14094
Tel.: (716) 438-7555
Web Site: https://www.trekinc.com
Oil & Gas Industry Equipment Mfr
N.A.I.C.S.: 333132

UltraVolt, Inc. (1)
1800 Ocean Ave, Ronkonkoma, NY 11779
Tel.: (631) 471-4444
Web Site: https://www.ultravolt.com
Emp.: 70
High Voltage Power Converters Mfr
N.A.I.C.S.: 335999

Versatile Power, Inc. (1)
743 Camden Ave, Campbell, CA 95008
Tel.: (408) 341-4600
Web Site: http://www.versatilepower.com
Electrical & Electronic Mfr
N.A.I.C.S.: 335999
Dave Hoffman (Co-Founder & VP-Engrg)

ADVANCED MERGER PARTNERS, INC.
555 W 57th St Ste 1326, New York, NY 10019
Tel.: (212) 951-1223   DE
Web Site:
   http://www.advancedmerger.com
Year Founded: 2020
AMPI—(NYSE)
Rev.: $3,987,282
Assets: $289,456,439
Liabilities: $305,611,156
Net Worth: ($16,154,717)
Earnings: $2,349,573
Emp.: 3
Fiscal Year-end: 12/31/21
Investment Services
N.A.I.C.S.: 523999
John Mavredakis (Chm)
Roy J. Katzovicz (Founder & CEO)
Gregory S. Lyss (COO)
Mark Goldman (Chief Investment Officer)

ADVANCED MICRO DEVICES, INC.
2485 Augustine Dr, Santa Clara, CA 95054
Tel.: (408) 749-3124   DE
Year Founded: 1969
AMD—(NASDAQ)
Rev.: $22,680,000,000
Assets: $67,885,000,000
Liabilities: $11,993,000,000
Net Worth: $55,892,000,000
Earnings: $854,000,000
Emp.: 26,000
Fiscal Year-end: 12/30/23
Complex Integrated Circuits Mfr; Microprocessors & Related Peripherals, Memories, Programmable Logic Devices; Circuits for Telecommunications, Office Automation & Networking Applications
N.A.I.C.S.: 334413
Darren Grasby (Chief Sls Officer, Pres-EMEA & Exec VP)
Robert Gama (Chief HR Officer & Sr VP)
Phil Guido (Chief Comml Officer & Exec VP)
Jean Hu (CFO, Treas & Exec VP)
Lisa T. Su (Chm, Pres & CEO)

Hasmukh Ranjan (Board of Directors, CIO- & Sr VP-)
Mark Papermaster (CTO & Exec VP)
Mathew Hein (Chief Strategy Officer & Sr VP-Corp Dev)
Forrest E. Norrod (Exec VP, Sr VP & Gen Mgr-Datacenter & Embedded Solutions Bus Grp)
David Wang (Sr VP-Engrg & Engrg-Radeon Technologies Grp)
Keivan Keshvari (Sr VP-Global Ops)
Dan McNamara (Sr VP & Gen Mgr-Server Bus Unit)
Jane Roney (Sr VP-Bus Ops)
Martin Ashton (Sr VP-Hardware IP & Architecture)
Mark Fuselier (Sr VP-Tech & Product Engrg)
Brian Amick (Sr VP-Central Engrg)
Vamsi Boppana (Sr VP-Artificial Intelligence)
Ava Hahn (Gen Counsel, Sec & Sr VP)
Jack Huynh (Sr VP & Gen Mgr-Computing & Graphics Group)
Salil Raje (Sr VP & Gen Mgr-Adaptive & Embedded Computing Group)
Keith Strier (Sr VP-Global AI Markets)
Andrej Zdravkovic (Chief Software Officer & Sr VP-GPU Tech & Engrg Software)

Subsidiaries:

AMD Advanced Micro Devices (ROU) S.R.L. (1)
39A St Andrew Street Building B1/B2 3rd floor, 700028, Iasi, Romania
Tel.: (40) 799333778
Computer Peripheral Equipment Mfr
N.A.I.C.S.: 334118

AMD Advanced Micro Devices Israel Ltd. (1)
Gibor Sport Bldg 28th floor 7 Menachem Begin Rd, Ramat Gan, 52681, Israel
Tel.: (972) 37235353
Semiconductor Devices Mfr
N.A.I.C.S.: 334413

AMD Advanced Research LLC (1)
2485 Augustine Dr, Santa Clara, CA 95054
Tel.: (408) 749-4000
Semiconductor Devices Mfr
N.A.I.C.S.: 334413

AMD Far East, Ltd. (1)
Unit 1619-1629 Level 16 Tower II Grand Century Plac, 193 Prince Edward Road West Mongkok Kowloon, Hong Kong, China (Hong Kong) (100%)
Tel.: (852) 22365700
Web Site: http://www.amd.com
Sales Range: $10-24.9 Million
Emp.: 30
Complex Semiconductors Mfr
N.A.I.C.S.: 334413

AMD India Private Limited (1)
102-103 Export Promotion Industrial Park, Whitefield, Bengaluru, 560066, Karnataka, India
Tel.: (91) 803 323 0000
Web Site: http://www.amd.com
Sales Range: $50-74.9 Million
Emp.: 300
Microprocessor Mfr
N.A.I.C.S.: 334413

AMD International Sales & Service, Ltd. (1)
2485 Augustine Dr, Santa Clara, CA 95054
Tel.: (408) 749-4000
Computer Peripheral Equipment Distr
N.A.I.C.S.: 423430

Subsidiary (Non-US):

AMD South America LTDA (2)
230 George Ohm Street, Offices 221 and 222, Sao Paulo, 04576-020, SP, Brazil
Tel.: (55) 1134782150
Web Site: http://www.amd.com.br

Emp.: 25
Microprocessor & Graphics Card Distr
N.A.I.C.S.: 423430

AMD Japan Ltd. (1)
Marunouchi Trust Tower Main Bldg 10F 1-8-3 Marunouchi, Chiyoda-ku, Tokyo, 100-0005, Japan (100%)
Tel.: (81) 364791550
Web Site: http://www.amd.com
Sales Range: $100-124.9 Million
Micro Devices Sales
N.A.I.C.S.: 423690

AMD Research & Development Center India Private Limited (1)
Plot No 2/A Trendset Towers Road No 2, Banjara Hills, Hyderabad, 500 034, Andhra Pradesh, India
Tel.: (91) 40 30615000
Sales Range: $125-149.9 Million
Emp.: 600
Research & Development Services
N.A.I.C.S.: 541715

AMD Technologies (China) Co. Ltd. (1)
88 Su Tong Road, Suzhou Industrial Park, Suzhou, 215021, China
Tel.: (86) 5222365700
Microprocessor & Graphics Card Mfr
N.A.I.C.S.: 334413

AMD Technology Development (Beijing) Co. (1)
19/F North Building Tower C No 2 Science Institute South Rd, Zhong Guan Cun Haidian Dist, Beijing, 100190, China
Tel.: (86) 1082861888
Web Site: http://www.amd.com
Emp.: 300
Microprocessor & Graphics Card Mfr
N.A.I.C.S.: 334413

ATI Technologies (L) Inc. (1)
Lot E 10th Floor Labuan Financial Park Jln Merdeka, Labuan, 87000, Malaysia
Tel.: (60) 87 42 8818
Sales Range: $25-49.9 Million
Emp.: 54
Research & Development Services
N.A.I.C.S.: 541715
Kelly Liang (Mgr)

ATI Technologies ULC (1)
1 Commerce Valley Dr East, Markham, L3T 7X6, ON, Canada
Tel.: (905) 882-2600
Computer Peripheral Equipment Mfr
N.A.I.C.S.: 334118

Advanced Micro Devices (China) Co. Ltd. (1)
Building I Candor Plaza No 669 Huanke Road, Pudong District, Shanghai, 201210, China
Tel.: (86) 2161601838
Computer Peripheral Equipment Mfr
N.A.I.C.S.: 334118

Advanced Micro Devices (Shanghai) Co. Ltd. (1)
88 Sutong Rd, Suzhou Industrial Park, Suzhou, 215021, China
Tel.: (86) 22365700
Computer Peripheral Equipment Mfr
N.A.I.C.S.: 334118

Advanced Micro Devices (Singapore) Pte. Ltd. (1)
508 Chai Chee Lane 06-01, Singapore, 469032, Singapore
Tel.: (65) 67969888
Web Site: http://www.amd.com
Sales Range: $100-124.9 Million
Emp.: 400
Microcomputer Mfr
N.A.I.C.S.: 334419

Advanced Micro Devices (U.K.) Limited (1)
Regus - Midsummer Court 314 Midsummer Boulevard, Harvest Cresent, Milton Keynes, MK9 2UB, United Kingdom (100%)
Tel.: (44) 1908440066
Web Site: http://www.amd.com
Sales Range: $10-24.9 Million
Emp.: 75
Research & Development & Design of Micro Devices

N.A.I.C.S.: 334413

Advanced Micro Devices Export Sdn. Bhd. (1)
Phase III Free Industrial Zone, Bayan Lepas, 11900, Pulau Pinang, Malaysia
Tel.: (60) 4 252 2000
Web Site: http://www.amd.com
Sales Range: $150-199.9 Million
Emp.: 700
Microprocessors Assembling & Testing Services
N.A.I.C.S.: 541380
Neoh Soonee (Mng Dir)

Advanced Micro Devices Global Services (M) Sdn. Bhd. (1)
Block 3750 Persiaran APEC Cyber 8, 63500, Cyberjaya, Selangor Darul Ehsan, Malaysia
Tel.: (60) 383163888
Computer Peripheral Equipment Mfr
N.A.I.C.S.: 334118

Advanced Micro Devices GmbH (1)
Einsteinring 24, Dornach, 85609, Munich, Germany (100%)
Tel.: (49) 8945053100
Web Site: http://www.amd.com
Sales Range: $25-49.9 Million
Emp.: 60
Sales of Microcircuits & Devices
N.A.I.C.S.: 449210
Darren Grasby (Mng Dir)

Advanced Micro Devices Inc. (1)
1 Commerce Valley Dr E, Markham, L3T 7X6, ON, Canada
Tel.: (905) 882-2600
Web Site: http://www.amd.com
Rev.: $22,680,000,000
Assets: $67,885,000,000
Liabilities: $11,993,000,000
Net Worth: $55,892,000,000
Earnings: $854,000,000
Emp.: 26,000
Fiscal Year-end: 12/31/2023
Designer, Mfr & Marketer of Multimedia Solutions & Graphics Components for Personal Computers
N.A.I.C.S.: 334118

Advanced Micro Devices SpA (1)
Via Polidoro da Caravaggio 6, 20156, Milan, Italy (100%)
Tel.: (39) 023008161
Web Site: http://www.amd.com
Sales Range: $25-49.9 Million
Emp.: 40
Integrated Circuits, Microprocessors & Chips Whslr
N.A.I.C.S.: 423430

Advanced Micro Devices, Inc. (1)
2485 Augustine Dr, Santa Clara, CA 95054
Tel.: (408) 749-4000
Web Site: http://www.amd.com
Sales Range: $100-124.9 Million
Emp.: 400
N.A.I.C.S.: 449210

Advanced Micro Devices, Inc. (1)
90 Central St Fl 1 2 3, Boxborough, MA 01719-1200
Tel.: (978) 795-2500
Web Site: http://www.amd.com
Software Architectural Designs
N.A.I.C.S.: 513210

Advanced Micro Devices, S.A. (1)
13 rue Camille Desmoulins, 92130, Issy-les-Moulineaux, France (100%)
Tel.: (33) 158042361
Web Site: http://www.amd.com
Sales Range: $10-24.9 Million
Emp.: 30
Sales of Microcircuit Devices
N.A.I.C.S.: 423690

Xilinx, Inc. (1)
2100 Logic Dr, San Jose, CA 95124
Tel.: (408) 559-7778
Web Site: http://www.xilinx.com
Rev.: $3,147,599,000
Assets: $5,519,201,000
Liabilities: $2,632,240,000

Net Worth: $2,886,961,000
Earnings: $646,508,000
Emp.: 4,890
Fiscal Year-end: 04/03/2021
Custom Software Design; User-Programmable Logic Integrated Circuits Mfr
N.A.I.C.S.: 334413
Ivo Bolsens (CTO & Sr VP)
Vincent L. Tong (Exec VP-Ops & Quality-Global)
Catia Hagopian (Chief Compliance Officer, Gen Counsel, Sec & Sr VP)
William Christopher Madden (Exec VP & Gen Mgr-Wired & Wireless Grp)
Salil Raje (Exec VP & Gen Mgr-Data Center Grp)
Mark David Wadlington (Sr VP-Core Markets Grp)
Vamsi Boppana (Sr VP-Central Products Grp)
Mini Khroad (Chief People Officer & Sr VP)
Andee Nieto (VP)

Subsidiary (Domestic):

Solarflare Communications, Inc. (2)
7505 Irvine Center Dr Ste 100, Irvine, CA 92618
Tel.: (949) 581-6830
Web Site: http://www.solarflare.com
Electronic Computer Components Mfr
N.A.I.C.S.: 334413

Subsidiary (Non-US):

Xilinx AB (2)
Knarrarnasgatan 15, 164 40, Kista, Sweden
Tel.: (46) 859461660
Web Site: http://www.xilinx.com
Software Development Services
N.A.I.C.S.: 541511

Xilinx Asia Pacific Pte. Ltd. (2)
5 Changi Business Park Vista, Singapore, 486040, Singapore
Tel.: (65) 64073000
Web Site: http://www.xilinx.com
Sales Range: $650-699.9 Million
Emp.: 350
Programmable Logic Semiconductors Distr
N.A.I.C.S.: 423430

Xilinx Benelux B.V.B.A. (2)
Villalaan 16, 9320, Aalst, Belgium
Tel.: (32) 53848310
Web Site: http://www.xilinx.com
Semiconductor Devices Mfr
N.A.I.C.S.: 334413

Xilinx Development Corporation (2)
Darwin House Edinburgh Technopole Bush Estate, Edinburgh, EH26 0PY, United Kingdom (100%)
Tel.: (44) 1313125050
Sales Range: $10-24.9 Million
Emp.: 34
Custom Software Design; Manufacturer of User-Programmable Logic Integrated Circuits
N.A.I.C.S.: 334413

Xilinx Estonia O.U. (2)
Parnu mnt 158/1 Floor 8, 11317, Tallinn, Estonia
Tel.: (372) 6844300
Electronic Equipment Distr
N.A.I.C.S.: 423690

Xilinx GmbH (2)
Willy-Brandt-Allee 4, 81829, Munich, Germany
Tel.: (49) 89930880
Web Site: http://www.xilinx.com
Sales Range: $10-24.9 Million
Emp.: 13
Custom Software Design; Manufacturer of User-Programmable Logic Integrated Circuits
N.A.I.C.S.: 334413

Xilinx Hong Kong Limited (2)
Unit 101 Wireless Centre No 3 Science Park East Avenue, Hong Kong Science Park, Sha Tin, New Territories, China (Hong Kong)
Tel.: (852) 24245200
Web Site: http://www.xilinx.com
Sales Range: $10-24.9 Million
Emp.: 15

Custom Software Design; Manufacturer of User-Programmable Logic Integrated Circuits
N.A.I.C.S.: 334413

Xilinx India Technology Services Pvt. Ltd. (2)
10th to 16th Floors Unit 2A & 2B Parcel Four, Salarpuria Sattva Knowledge City, Hyderabad, 500 081, Telangana, India
Tel.: (91) 4067214000
Web Site: http://www.xilinx.com
Sales Range: $50-74.9 Million
Emp.: 200
Custom Software Designer; User-Programmable Logic Integrated Circuits Mfr
N.A.I.C.S.: 334413

Subsidiary (Domestic):

Xilinx International, Inc. (2)
3100 Logic Dr, Longmont, CO 80503
Tel.: (720) 652-3600
Sales Range: $50-74.9 Million
Emp.: 250
Integrated Circuits Mfr
N.A.I.C.S.: 541511

Subsidiary (Non-US):

Xilinx Ireland (2)
Bianconi Avenue, Citywest Business Campus, Saggart, Co Dublin, Ireland (100%)
Tel.: (353) 14640311
Web Site: http://www.xilinx.com
Sales Range: $100-124.9 Million
Emp.: 350
Custom Software Design; Manufacturer of User-Programmable Logic Integrated Circuits
N.A.I.C.S.: 334413

Xilinx Ireland Unlimited Company (2)
Logic Drive Bianconi Avenue Citywest, Saggart, Dublin, D24 T683, Ireland
Tel.: (353) 4032111
Computer Hardware Product Distr
N.A.I.C.S.: 423430

Xilinx Israel Limited (2)
26 Harokmim St Asrieli Center Building B Floor 9, 5885849, Holon, Israel
Tel.: (972) 39003030
Web Site: http://www.xilinx.com
Integrated Circuits Mfr
N.A.I.C.S.: 541511

Xilinx K.K. (2)
Art Village Osaki Central Tower 4F 1-2-2, Osaki Shinagawa-ku, Tokyo, 141-0032, Japan
Tel.: (81) 367447777
Web Site: http://www.xilinx.com
Sales Range: $25-49.9 Million
Emp.: 75
Custom Software Design; Manufacturer of User-Programmable Logic Integrated Circuits
N.A.I.C.S.: 334413
Sam Rogan (Pres)

Xilinx Ltd. (2)
Darwin House Edinburgh Technopole Bush Estate, Edinburgh, EH26 0PY, Surrey, United Kingdom
Tel.: (44) 1313125050
Web Site: http://www.xilinx.com
Sales Range: $10-24.9 Million
Emp.: 30
Custom Software Design; Manufacturer of User-Programmable Logic Integrated Circuits
N.A.I.C.S.: 334413

Xilinx SARL (2)
Bat B 2 Rue Rene Caudron, Voisins Le Bretonneux, 78960, Voisins-le-Bretonneux, France
Tel.: (33) 161371919
Semiconductor & Related Device Distr
N.A.I.C.S.: 423690

Branch (Domestic):

Xilinx, Inc.- Albuquerque (2)
5051 Journal Center Blvd NE Ste 310, Albuquerque, NM 87109-4351 (100%)
Tel.: (505) 798-6860
Web Site: http://www.xilinx.com

Sales Range: $25-49.9 Million
Emp.: 80
Programmable Logic Solutions
N.A.I.C.S.: 334413

Xilinx, Inc.- Longmont (2)
3100 Logic Dr, Longmont, CO 80503
Tel.: (720) 652-3600
Web Site: http://www.xilinx.com
Sales Range: $100-124.9 Million
Mfr of User-Programmable Logic Integrated Circuits
N.A.I.C.S.: 334413

ADVANCED OXYGEN TECH-NOLOGIES, INC.
653 VT Route 12A, Randolph, VT 05060
Tel.: (212) 727-7085   DE
Web Site: https://www.aoxy-ca.com
Year Founded: 1981
AOXY—(OTCIQ)
Rev.: $39,406
Assets: $697,707
Liabilities: $346,928
Net Worth: $350,779
Earnings: $2,271
Emp.: 2
Fiscal Year-end: 06/30/23
Commercial Real Estate Development Services
N.A.I.C.S.: 531390
Robert E. Wolfe (Chm, CEO & CFO)

ADVANCED POWERLINE TECHNOLOGIES, INC.
370 Amapola Ave Ste 200-A, Torrance, CA 90501
Tel.: (310) 895-1839   NV
Year Founded: 1982
APWL—(OTCIQ)
Communication Equipment Mfr
N.A.I.C.S.: 334290
Nathanil Martin (COO)
Frank Lkechukwu Igwealor (Pres & CEO)

ADVANCED PROTEOME THERAPEUTICS CORPORATION
Ste 113 650 Albany St, Boston, MA 02118
Tel.: (617) 638-0340   BC
Web Site:
  http://www.advancedproteome.com
Year Founded: 2005
APTCF—(TSXV)
Sales Range: Less than $1 Million
Emp.: 5
Protein Therapy Pharmaceutical Developer & Mfr
N.A.I.C.S.: 325412
Alexander Krantz (Founder & Sec)
Kenneth Clifford Phillippe (CFO)
Allen Krantz (COO & Chief Scientific Officer)

ADVANCED VOICE RECOGNITION SYSTEMS, INC.
7659 E Wood Dr, Scottsdale, AZ 85260
Tel.: (480) 704-4183   NV
Web Site: https://www.avrsys.com
AVOI—(OTCIQ)
Rev.: $43,426
Assets: $1,409
Liabilities: $350,196
Net Worth: ($348,787)
Earnings: ($310,877)
Emp.: 3
Fiscal Year-end: 12/31/23
Speech Recognition Technology Interface & Application Solutions
N.A.I.C.S.: 513210
Walter Geldenhuys (Pres, CEO & CFO)
Diana Jakowchuk (Chief Acctg Officer, Treas & Sec)

ADVANSIX INC.
300 Kimball Dr Ste 101, Parsippany, NJ 07054
Tel.: (973) 526-1800   DE
Web Site: https://www.advansix.com
Year Founded: 2016
ASIX—(NYSE)
Rev.: $1,945,640,000
Assets: $1,495,331,000
Liabilities: $757,151,000
Net Worth: $738,180,000
Earnings: $171,886,000
Emp.: 586
Fiscal Year-end: 12/31/22
Chemicals Mfr
N.A.I.C.S.: 325211
Christopher Gramm (VP & Controller)
Michael L. Marberry (Chm)
Erin N. Kane (Pres & CEO)
Willem Blindenbach (Sr VP-Integrated Supply Chain)
Achilles B. Kintiroglou (Gen Counsel, Sec & Sr VP)
Kelly Slieter (Chief HR Officer & Sr VP)
Jacqueline Grunwald (CIO & VP)
Mike Hamilton (VP & Bus Dir-Plant Nutrients)
Kori Anderson (VP & Gen Mgr-Nylon Solutions)
Andy Girvin (Plant Mgr-Hopewell)
Sidd Manjeshwar (CFO & Sr VP)

ADVANT-E CORPORATION
2434 Esquire Dr, Beavercreek, OH 45431
Tel.: (937) 429-4288   DE
Web Site: http://www.advant-e.com
Year Founded: 1994
ADVC—(OTCIQ)
Sales Range: $1-9.9 Million
Emp.: 67
Software Publisher
N.A.I.C.S.: 513210
Jason K. Wadzinski (Pres & CEO)
James E. Lesch (Chief Acctg Officer)
Jason A. Boone (Controller)

ADVANTAGE SOLUTIONS INC.
8001 Forsyth Blvd Ste 1025, Clayton, MO 63105
Tel.: (949) 797-2900   DE
Web Site:
  https://www.advantagesolutions.net
ADV—(NASDAQ)
Rev.: $4,049,742,000
Assets: $4,262,371,000
Liabilities: $3,036,647,000
Net Worth: $1,225,724,000
Earnings: ($1,380,502,000)
Emp.: 22,000
Fiscal Year-end: 12/31/22
Business Solutions Provider
N.A.I.C.S.: 561499
Francesco Tinto (Chief Digital Officer)
Jack A. Pestello (COO)
Francesco Tinto (Chief Digital Officer)
Christopher Growe (CFO)
Brian McRoskey (Chief Growth Officer)
David A. Peacock (CEO)

ADVENT CONVERTIBLE & INCOME FUND
227 W Monroe St, Chicago, IL 60606
Tel.: (312) 827-0100   DE
AVK—(NYSE)
Fund Management Services
N.A.I.C.S.: 523940

ADVENT TECHNOLOGIES HOLDINGS, INC.
Tel.: (925) 455-9400   DE
Web Site: https://www.advent.energy
Year Founded: 2018

Advent Technologies Holdings, Inc.—(Continued)

ADN—(NASDAQ)
Rev.: $4,859,000
Assets: $34,737,000
Liabilities: $21,289,000
Net Worth: $13,448,000
Earnings: ($71,397,000)
Emp.: 100
Fiscal Year-end: 12/31/23
Fuel Cell Systems Mfr & Developer
N.A.I.C.S.: 334413
Vasilis Gregoriou *(Chm & CEO)*
Emory De Castro *(CTO)*
James F. Coffey *(COO & Gen Counsel)*
Christos Kaskavelis *(CMO)*
Ian Kaye *(Sr VP-Product Dev)*
Panoraia Gourdoupi *(Sr VP-Corp Bus Dev)*

ADVERUM BIOTECHNOLOGIES, INC.
100 Cardinal Way, Redwood City, CA 94063
Tel.: (650) 656-9323   DE
Web Site: https://www.adverum.com
Year Founded: 2006
ADVM—(NASDAQ)
Rev.: $3,600,000
Assets: $173,010,000
Liabilities: $89,541,000
Net Worth: $83,469,000
Earnings: ($117,165,000)
Emp.: 121
Fiscal Year-end: 12/31/23
Biopharmaceutical Mfr
N.A.I.C.S.: 325412
Laurent Fischer *(Pres, CEO & Interim Chief Medical Officer)*
John Rakow *(Gen Counsel)*
Mehdi Gasmi *(Officer)*
R. Andrew Ramelmeier *(CTO)*
Kishor Peter Soparkar *(COO)*
Thomas Kochy *(VP-Comml & Program Strategy)*
Brigit Riley *(Chief Scientific Officer)*
Linda Rubinstein *(CFO & Principal Acctg Officer)*
Star Seyedkazemi *(Chief Dev Officer)*
Anand Reddi *(VP & Head-Corp Strategy, External Affairs, and Engagement)*
Rabia Gurses Ozden *(Chief Medical Officer)*
Patrick Machado *(Chm)*

ADYNXX, INC.
100 Pine St, San Francisco, CA 94111
Tel.: (415) 512-7740   DE
Web Site: https://www.adynxxinc.com
Year Founded: 1997
ADYX—(OTCEM)
Sales Range: $1-9.9 Million
Emp.: 6
Biomedical Wound Care Products Developer, Mfr & Whslr
N.A.I.C.S.: 339112
Dennis G. Podlesak *(Chm)*
Julien Mamet *(Founder & Chief Scientific Officer)*

Subsidiaries:

Celleration, Inc.   **(1)**
6321 Bury Dr Ste 15, Eden Prairie, MN 55346-1739
Tel.: (952) 224-8700
Web Site: http://www.misttherapy.com
Sales Range: $1-9.9 Million
Emp.: 75
Ultrasound Medical Healing Technologies Developer, Mfr & Whslr
N.A.I.C.S.: 334510

Choice Therapeutics, Inc.   **(1)**
190 Industrial Rd, Wrentham, MA 02093
Tel.: (508) 720-9803

Health Care Srvices
N.A.I.C.S.: 621610

AECOM
13355 Noel Rd 400, Dallas, TX 75240
Tel.: (972) 788-1000   DE
Web Site: https://aecom.com
Year Founded: 1990
ACM—(NYSE)
Rev.: $14,378,461,000
Assets: $11,233,398,000
Liabilities: $8,849,687,000
Net Worth: $2,383,711,000
Earnings: $100,141,000
Emp.: 52,000
Fiscal Year-end: 09/30/23
Engineeering Services
N.A.I.C.S.: 541330
David Y. Gan *(Chief Legal Officer)*
W. Troy Rudd *(CEO)*
Michael Della Rocca *(CEO-Americas)*
Douglas W. Stotlar *(Chm)*
Lara Poloni *(Pres)*
Karl Jensen *(Exec VP-Natl Governments Bus)*
Michael Della Rocca *(CEO-Americas)*
Shirley Adams *(Chief HR Officer)*
Jay Badame *(Pres-Construction Mgmt)*
Troy Battley *(Chief Strategy Officer)*
Sarah Urbanowicz *(CIO)*
Brian Schoenemann *(Sr Project Mgr-San Antonio)*
Brendan Ranson-Walsh *(Sr VP-Global Comm)*
Todd Battley *(Chief Strategy Officer)*
Gaurav Kapoor *(CFO & Chief Operations Officer)*

Subsidiaries:

AECOM   **(1)**
Mustafa Kemal Mah Tepe Prime B Blok Suite No 51, Dumlupinar Bulvari No 266 Cankaya, 06800, Ankara, Turkiye
Tel.: (90) 3124429863
Web Site: http://www.aecom.com
Sales Range: $75-99.9 Million
Emp.: 225
Environmental Services
N.A.I.C.S.: 541620

AECOM   **(1)**
8F Grand Central Plaza Tower 2, 138 Shatin Rural Committee Rd, Sha Tin, China (Hong Kong)
Tel.: (852) 2605 6262
Web Site: http://www.aecom.com
Sales Range: $1-9.9 Million
Emp.: 4
Environmental Services
N.A.I.C.S.: 541620

AECOM   **(1)**
Suite 2A Level 2 Tower Block Menara KLK, No 1 Jalan PJU 7 6 Mutiara, Petaling Jaya, 47810, Malaysia
Tel.: (60) 378637800
Sales Range: $1-9.9 Million
Emp.: 50
Environmental Services
N.A.I.C.S.: 541620
Dickson Lo *(CEO-Asia)*

AECOM   **(1)**
23rd Floor Fort Legend Towers 3rd Ave Cr 31st Street, Bonifacio Global City Fort, Manila, Philippines
Tel.: (63) 24783266
Web Site: http://www.aecom.com
Sales Range: $10-24.9 Million
Emp.: 170
Environmental Services
N.A.I.C.S.: 541620

AECOM Brasil Ltda.   **(1)**
Rua Tenente Negrao 140, Conj. 21 E 22, Sao Paulo, 04530-030, Brazil
Tel.: (55) 11 3627 2077
Web Site: http://www.aecom.com
Sales Range: $10-24.9 Million
Emp.: 42
Environmental Services

N.A.I.C.S.: 541620

AECOM Canada   **(1)**
105 Commerce Vly Dr W 7th Fl, Markham, L3T 7W3, ON, Canada
Tel.: (905) 886-7022
Web Site: http://www.aecom.com
Sales Range: $50-74.9 Million
Emp.: 250
Engineeering Services
N.A.I.C.S.: 541330

Branch (Domestic):

AECOM Canada   **(2)**
4700 boulevard Wilfrid Hamel, Quebec, G1P 2J9, QC, Canada
Tel.: (418) 871-2444
Web Site: http://www.aecom.com
Sales Range: $50-74.9 Million
Emp.: 90
Engineering Consulting Services
N.A.I.C.S.: 541330

AECOM USA, Inc.   **(1)**
300 S Grand Ste 900, Los Angeles, CA 90071   **(100%)**
Tel.: (213) 593-8100
Web Site: http://www.aecom.com
Sales Range: $50-74.9 Million
Emp.: 200
Engineering & Construction Services
N.A.I.C.S.: 541330

Branch (Domestic):

AECOM   **(2)**
800 LaSalle Ave, Minneapolis, MN 55402-2014
Tel.: (612) 376-2000
Web Site: http://www.aecom.com
Sales Range: $50-74.9 Million
Emp.: 150
Construction & Design Services
N.A.I.C.S.: 541420
Kate Zwicky *(Assoc VP-Mechanical Engrg & Reg Mgr)*

AECOM   **(2)**
999 Town & Country Rd, Orange, CA 92868-4713   **(100%)**
Tel.: (714) 567-2400
Web Site: http://www.aecom.com
Sales Range: $75-99.9 Million
Architectural & Engineering Services
N.A.I.C.S.: 541310

AECOM   **(2)**
3950 Sparks Dr SE, Grand Rapids, MI 49546-2009
Tel.: (616) 942-9600
Web Site: http://www.aecom.com
Sales Range: $25-49.9 Million
Emp.: 179
Engineering & Scientific Consulting Services
N.A.I.C.S.: 541690

AECOM   **(2)**
2 Technology Park Dr, Westford, MA 01886-3140
Tel.: (978) 589-3000
Web Site: http://www.aecom.com
Sales Range: $75-99.9 Million
Environmental Services
N.A.I.C.S.: 541690

AECOM   **(2)**
106 Newberry St SW, Aiken, SC 29801-3852
Tel.: (803) 502-5730
Web Site: http://www.aecom.com
Emp.: 35
Architectural & Engineering Services
N.A.I.C.S.: 541330

AECOM   **(2)**
701 Edgewater Dr, Wakefield, MA 01880-3208
Tel.: (781) 246-5200
Web Site: http://www.aecom.com
Sales Range: $75-99.9 Million
Environmental Engineering Services
N.A.I.C.S.: 541330

AECOM   **(2)**
1601 Prospect Pkwy, Fort Collins, CO 80525-9769
Tel.: (970) 493-8878
Web Site: http://www.aecom.com

Sales Range: $25-49.9 Million
Emp.: 80
Environmental Services
N.A.I.C.S.: 541620

AECOM   **(2)**
9 Jonathan Bourne Dr, Pocasset, MA 02559
Tel.: (508) 888-3900
Web Site: http://www.aecom.com
Sales Range: $1-9.9 Million
Emp.: 20
Environmental Services
N.A.I.C.S.: 541620
Robert C. Weber *(COO-Bus Lines)*

AECOM   **(2)**
30 Knightsbridge Rd Ste 520, Piscataway, NJ 08854-3963
Tel.: (732) 564-3200
Web Site: http://www.aecom.com
Sales Range: $10-24.9 Million
Emp.: 100
Environmental Services
N.A.I.C.S.: 541620

AECOM   **(2)**
W239 North 2890 Pewauka Rd Unit D, Pewaukee, WI 53072
Tel.: (262) 523-2040
Web Site: http://www.ensr.com
Sales Range: $10-24.9 Million
Emp.: 75
Environmental Services
N.A.I.C.S.: 541330

AECOM   **(2)**
10 Patewood Dr Ste 500 Bldg 6, Greenville, SC 29615-3517
Tel.: (864) 234-3000
Web Site: http://www.aecom.com
Sales Range: $50-74.9 Million
Emp.: 100
Engineering, Environmental, Remediation & Waste Management Services
N.A.I.C.S.: 541330

AECOM   **(2)**
5757 Woodway Dr Ste 101 W 5444 Westheimer Ste 200, Houston, TX 77056
Tel.: (713) 780-4100
Web Site: http://www.aecom.com
Sales Range: $75-99.9 Million
Consulting & Construction Services
N.A.I.C.S.: 541330

AECOM   **(2)**
303 E Wacker Dr Ste 1300, Chicago, IL 60601   **(100%)**
Tel.: (312) 373-7700
Web Site: http://www.aecom.com
Sales Range: $100-124.9 Million
Architectural Services
N.A.I.C.S.: 541310

AECOM   **(2)**
300 Lakeside Dr Ste 400, Oakland, CA 94612-1924
Tel.: (510) 893-3600
Web Site: http://www.aecom.com
Design, Construction & Engineering Services
N.A.I.C.S.: 541330
Louis Armstrong *(Exec VP & Gen Mgr-Pacific)*

Subsidiary (Domestic):

AECOM C&E, Inc.   **(2)**
250 Apollo Dr, Chelmsford, MA 01824
Tel.: (978) 905-2100
Web Site: http://www.aecom.com
Emp.: 450
Environmental Consulting Services
N.A.I.C.S.: 541620

Unit (Domestic):

AECOM Environment   **(2)**
2020 L St, Sacramento, CA 95827-2524
Tel.: (916) 362-7100
Web Site: http://www.aecom.com
Sales Range: $10-24.9 Million
Emp.: 24
Environmental Services
N.A.I.C.S.: 541690

AECOM Environment   **(2)**
27755 Diehl Rd Ste 100, Warrenville, IL 60555-3926   **(100%)**
Tel.: (630) 836-1700

Web Site: http://www.ensr.aecom.com
Sales Range: $10-24.9 Million
Emp.: 65
Environmental Services
N.A.I.C.S.: 541330

AECOM Environment   **(2)**
625 West Rdg Pike, Conshohocken, PA
19428   **(100%)**
Tel.: (215) 315-4150
Web Site: http://www.ensr.aecom.com
Sales Range: $10-24.9 Million
Emp.: 400
Environmental Services
N.A.I.C.S.: 541690
Al Hannum *(CEO-Consulting Bus)*

Subsidiary (Domestic):

**AECOM Government Services,
Inc.**   **(2)**
4840 Cox Rd, Glen Allen, VA 23060
Tel.: (804) 515-8300
Web Site: http://www.aecom.com
Facilities Support Services
N.A.I.C.S.: 561210

Branch (Domestic):

AECOM-Latham   **(2)**
40 British American Blvd, Latham, NY
12110-1421
Tel.: (518) 951-2200
Web Site: http://www.aecom.com
Sales Range: $10-24.9 Million
Emp.: 80
Engineering Services
N.A.I.C.S.: 541330

Subsidiary (Domestic):

Davis Langdon LLP   **(2)**
300 California St Ste 600, San Francisco,
CA 94104
Tel.: (415) 981-1004
Web Site: http://www.davislangdon.com
Architectural Services
N.A.I.C.S.: 541310

URS Corporation   **(2)**
600 Montgomery St 26th Fl, San Francisco,
CA 94111-2728
Tel.: (415) 774-2700
Sales Range: $5-14.9 Billion
Emp.: 50,000
Urban & Environmental Analysis, Planning
& Design Services
N.A.I.C.S.: 541330
Joseph Masters *(Gen Counsel, Sec & VP)*

Subsidiary (Domestic):

Cleveland Wrecking Company   **(3)**
628 E Edna Pl, Covina, CA 91723-1312
Tel.: (626) 967-9799
Web Site:
   http://www.clevelandwrecking.com
Sales Range: $100-124.9 Million
Emp.: 500
Wrecking & Demolition Services
N.A.I.C.S.: 238910

D&M Consulting Engineers, Inc.   **(3)**
3121 Diablo Ave, Hayward, CA 94545
Tel.: (831) 372-3716
Sales Range: $75-99.9 Million
Engineering Consulting Services
N.A.I.C.S.: 541330

EC Driver & Associates, Inc.   **(3)**
500 N Westshore Blvd Ste 500, Tampa, FL
33609-1913
Tel.: (813) 282-9886
Web Site: http://www.ecdriver.com
Sales Range: $10-24.9 Million
Emp.: 28
Engineering Services
N.A.I.C.S.: 541330
James Phillips *(VP)*

Flint Energy Services Inc.   **(3)**
7633 E 63rd Pl Ste 500 PO Box 3044,
Tulsa, OK 74133-1218
Tel.: (918) 294-3030
Sales Range: $25-49.9 Million
Emp.: 75
Natural Gas Distribution
N.A.I.C.S.: 221210
Bryce Satter *(Pres)*

Subsidiary (Domestic):

J.W. Williams, Inc.   **(4)**
2180 Renauna Ave, Casper, WY 82601
Tel.: (307) 237-8345
Gas Field Machinery & Equipment
N.A.I.C.S.: 333132
Kelly McGowan *(Reg Mgr)*

Subsidiary (Domestic):

URS Caribe, LLP   **(3)**
954 Ponce de Leon Miramar Plaza Ste 304,
San Juan, PR 00907
Tel.: (787) 723-3332
Sales Range: $25-49.9 Million
Emp.: 50
Construction & Engineering Services
N.A.I.C.S.: 541330
Rene Purzell *(VP)*

Subsidiary (Non-US):

URS Consulting (Shanghai) Ltd.   **(3)**
Kerry Parkside Office Tower 31st Fl 1155
Fang Dian Road, Shanghai, 201204, Pu-
dong, China
Tel.: (86) 21 2089 2888
Web Site: http://www.urs.com
Sales Range: $10-24.9 Million
Emp.: 50
Engineering, Construction & Technical Ser-
vices
N.A.I.C.S.: 541330

Branch (Non-US):

URS Corp. - Riyadh   **(3)**
614 Olaya Akharia II, PO Box 2384, 11451,
Riyadh, Saudi Arabia
Tel.: (966) 14191660
Engineering Consulting Services
N.A.I.C.S.: 541330

Subsidiary (Domestic):

URS Corporation   **(3)**
7125 W Jefferson Ave Ste 400, Lakewood,
CO 80235
Tel.: (303) 969-0223
Sales Range: $25-49.9 Million
Emp.: 150
Project Management, Construction Ser-
vices, Engineering & Design for Oil & Gas
Pipelines, Compression, Storage & Pro-
cessing Facilities
N.A.I.C.S.: 541330

Subsidiary (Non-US):

URS Corporation Bolivia SA   **(3)**
Lanza 940, Cochabamba, Bolivia
Tel.: (591) 44488400
Web Site: http://www.urscorp.com
Sales Range: $75-99.9 Million
Emp.: 7
Engineering Services
N.A.I.C.S.: 541330

URS Corporation S.A.   **(3)**
Suipacha 280 6th Floor, C1008 AAF, Bue-
nos Aires, Argentina
Tel.: (54) 1143272054
Sales Range: $75-99.9 Million
Emp.: 17
Engineering Consulting Services
N.A.I.C.S.: 541330

**URS Corporation de Mexico S de RL
de CV**   **(3)**
Av Ejercito Nacional No 418 Oficina 719,
Colonia Chapultepec Morales, Mexico,
11570, Mexico
Tel.: (52) 555 203 2949
Web Site: http://www.urscorp.com
Sales Range: $10-24.9 Million
Emp.: 15
Engineering Services
N.A.I.C.S.: 541330
Pedro Zuloaga *(Pres-Div)*

Branch (Non-US):

**URS Holdings, Inc. - Panamanian
Branch**   **(3)**
Edificio Torre Genrali Piso 27 Oficina 2,
Obarrio, Panama, Panama
Tel.: (507) 2650601
Web Site: http://www.urscorp.com

Sales Range: $25-49.9 Million
Emp.: 28
Holding Company
N.A.I.C.S.: 551112

Subsidiary (Non-US):

URS New Zealand Ltd.   **(3)**
13 15 College Hill, PO Box 821, Auckland,
1140, New Zealand   **(100%)**
Tel.: (64) 93551300
Sales Range: $50-74.9 Million
Emp.: 250
Professional Services in Urban & Environ-
mental Analysis, Planning & Design, Engi-
neering, Architectural, Environmental & Eco-
nomic Analysis
N.A.I.C.S.: 541330
Mark Drury *(CEO)*

Subsidiary (Domestic):

**URS Safety Management
Solutions**   **(3)**
2131 S Centennial Ave SE, Aiken, SC
29803
Tel.: (803) 502-9767
Web Site: http://www.urscorp.com
Sales Range: $100-124.9 Million
Emp.: 350
Safety, Security & Environmental Manage-
ment Services
N.A.I.C.S.: 541618

AECOM Venezuela   **(1)**
Av Solano con calle Los Mangos Torre Los
Mangos 4 Oficinas 4C Y 4D, Caracas, Ven-
ezuela
Tel.: (58) 2127626339
Web Site: http://www.aecom.com
Sales Range: $1-9.9 Million
Emp.: 8
Environmental Services
N.A.I.C.S.: 541620

Hunt Construction Group, Inc.   **(1)**
6720 N Scottsdale Rd, Scottsdale, AZ
85253
Tel.: (480) 368-4700
Web Site:
   http://www.huntconstructiongroup.com
Sales Range: $1-4.9 Billion
Emp.: 700
Building Construction Services
N.A.I.C.S.: 236220

Division (Domestic):

**Hunt Construction Group, Inc. - East
Division**   **(2)**
2450 S Tibbs Ave, Indianapolis, IN 46241
Tel.: (317) 227-7800
Web Site:
   http://www.huntconstructiongroup.com
Emp.: 200
Contracting & Construction Services
N.A.I.C.S.: 236220

Branch (Domestic):

**Hunt Construction Group, Inc. -
Orlando**   **(3)**
7680 Universal Blvd Ste 250, Orlando, FL
32819-7967
Tel.: (407) 352-8182
Web Site:
   http://www.huntconstructiongroup.com
Sales Range: $25-49.9 Million
Emp.: 15
Construction Managers & General Contrac-
tors
N.A.I.C.S.: 236220

Subsidiary (Domestic):

The Hunt Paving Company, Inc.   **(3)**
2450 S Pidzs Ave, Indianapolis, IN 46206-
0128
Tel.: (317) 241-8313
Sales Range: $25-49.9 Million
Emp.: 30
Concrete Paving Contractor & Road Con-
struction
N.A.I.C.S.: 236220

Division (Domestic):

**Hunt Construction Group, Inc. - South
Division**   **(2)**

4099 Mcewen Rd Ste 400, Dallas, TX
75244
Tel.: (972) 788-1000
Web Site:
   http://www.huntconstructiongroup.com
General Building Contractor & Construction
Manager
N.A.I.C.S.: 236115

**Hunt Construction Group, Inc. - West
Division**   **(2)**
426 N 44th St Ste 410, Phoenix, AZ 85008-
7696
Tel.: (602) 225-9500
Web Site:
   http://www.huntconstructiongroup.com
General Building Contractor; Construction
Manager
N.A.I.C.S.: 236220

Branch (Domestic):

**Hunt Construction Group, Inc. - San
Francisco**   **(3)**
100 Pine St Ste 725, San Francisco, CA
94111-5103
Tel.: (415) 391-3930
Web Site:
   http://www.huntconstructiongroup.com
Sales Range: $25-49.9 Million
Emp.: 10
Construction Managers & General Contrac-
tors
N.A.I.C.S.: 541618

LLW Repository Limited   **(1)**
Pelham House, Pelham Drive Calderbridge,
Seascale, CA20 1DB, Cumbria, United
Kingdom
Tel.: (44) 1946770200
Web Site: http://www.llwrsite.com
Nuclear Waste Management Services
N.A.I.C.S.: 237990
Cath Giel *(Head-Pub Affairs)*

**Proyectos Especiales Pacifico
S.A.**   **(1)**
Av Republica de Panama 3635 4th Fl, San
Isidro, Lima, Peru
Tel.: (51) 16114100
Web Site: http://www.pepsa.com.pe
Sales Range: $10-24.9 Million
Emp.: 80
Engineering Services
N.A.I.C.S.: 541330

Sellafield Limited   **(1)**
Sellafield, Seascale, CA20 1PG, Cumbria,
United Kingdom
Tel.: (44) 1946728333
Web Site: http://www.sellafieldsites.com
Nuclear Waste Management Services
N.A.I.C.S.: 237990
Martin Chown *(CEO)*

**Shimmick Construction Company,
Inc.**   **(1)**
8201 Edgewater Dr Ste 202, Oakland, CA
94621-2216
Tel.: (510) 777-5000
Web Site: http://www.shimmick.com
Civil Engineering Contractors & Construc-
tion Services
N.A.I.C.S.: 237990
Paul Cocotis *(Pres)*
Paul Camaur *(COO)*
Scott Fairgrieve *(VP-Fin & Acctg)*
Andrew Sloane *(Exec VP-Integrated Deliv-
eries & Mega Projects)*
Matt Kuzmick *(Exec VP-Southwest Area)*
Greg Dukellis *(Gen Counsel & VP)*

Spectral-AECOM   **(1)**
A 197 Sector 63, Noida, 201301, India
Tel.: (91) 120 4049000
Web Site: http://www.aecom.com
Sales Range: $100-124.9 Million
Emp.: 500
Building & Environmental Consultancy Ser-
vices
N.A.I.C.S.: 541620

**Tishman Construction
Corporation**   **(1)**
100 Park Ave, New York, NY 10017-0256
Tel.: (212) 973-2999
Web Site:
   http://www.tishmanconstruction.com
Sales Range: $1-4.9 Billion
Emp.: 1,000

AECOM—(Continued)

Real Estate Owner, Operator, Developer & Advisor
N.A.I.C.S.: 531390

Subsidiary (Domestic):

Tishman Hotel Corporation (2)
100 Park Ave 18th Fl, New York, NY 10017
Tel.: (212) 708-6882
Web Site: http://www.tishmanhotels.com
Sales Range: $10-24.9 Million
Emp.: 60
Owner & Manager of Hotels
N.A.I.C.S.: 721110
Daniel R. Tishman (Vice Chm)

Holding (Domestic):

Walt Disney World Swan & Dolphin Resorts (3)
1500 Epcot Resorts Blvd, Lake Buena Vista, FL 32830
Tel.: (407) 934-4000
Web Site: http://www.swandolphin.com
Emp.: 2,000
Resort Hotel
N.A.I.C.S.: 721110
Luciano Sperduto (Dir-Food & Beverage)
Sean Verney (Gen Mgr-Area)

Subsidiary (Domestic):

Tishman Realty Corporation (2)
100 Park Ave 5th Fl, New York, NY 10017
Tel.: (212) 708-6882
Web Site: http://www.tishmanhotels.com
Real Estate Owner & Developer
N.A.I.C.S.: 531390
Daniel R. Tishman (Vice Chm)
David Rothenberg (Pres)

URS Worldwide Holdings UK Limited (1)
3rd Floor 401 Faraday Street, Birchwood Park, Warrington, WA3 6GA, Cheshire, United Kingdom
Tel.: (44) 1925858740
Holding Company
N.A.I.C.S.: 551112

AEHR TEST SYSTEMS
400 Kato Ter, Fremont, CA 94539
Tel.: (510) 623-9400 CA
Web Site: https://www.aehr.com
Year Founded: 1977
AEHR—(NASDAQ)
Rev.: $66,218,000
Assets: $127,912,000
Liabilities: $16,319,000
Net Worth: $111,593,000
Earnings: $33,156,000
Emp.: 115
Fiscal Year-end: 05/31/24
Computer Logic & Memory Test Systems Designer & Mfr
N.A.I.C.S.: 333242
Rhea J. Posedel (Chm)
Chris P. Siu (CFO, Sec & Exec VP-Fin)
Gayn Erickson (Pres & CEO)
Don Richmond (VP-Engineering)
Vernon Rogers (Exec VP-Sales-Marketing)
Adil Engineer (COO)
Avi Ray-Chaudhuri (Exec VP-Research & Development)
Nick Sporck (VP-Contactor Bus)

Subsidiaries:

Aehr Test Systems GmbH (1)
Industriestrasse 9, 86919, Utting, Germany
Tel.: (49) 88062021
Web Site: http://www.aehr.com
Sales Range: $1-9.9 Million
Emp.: 4
Semiconductor Test Equipment
N.A.I.C.S.: 334413
Detles Claren (Mng Dir)

Aehr Test Systems Japan K.K. (1)
Hashikan Bldg 1-14 Azuma-Cho, Hachioji, Tokyo, 192-0082, Japan
Tel.: (81) 426423530

Sales Range: $25-49.9 Million
Semiconductor Test Equipment Mfr
N.A.I.C.S.: 334413

AELUMA, INC.
27 Castilian Dr, Goleta, CA 93117
Tel.: (805) 351-2707 DE
Web Site: https://www.aeluma.com
Year Founded: 2020
ALMU—(OTCQB)
Rev.: $918,554
Assets: $3,844,047
Liabilities: $1,567,886
Net Worth: $2,276,161
Earnings: $4,562,295
Emp.: 11
Fiscal Year-end: 06/30/24
Miscellaneous Financial Investment Activities
N.A.I.C.S.: 523999
Jonathan Klamkin (Pres & CEO)
Lee McCarthy (COO)
Matthew Dummer (Dir-Tech)

AEMETIS, INC.
20400 Stevens Creek Blvd Ste 700, Cupertino, CA 95014
Tel.: (408) 213-0940 NV
Web Site: https://www.aemetis.com
AMTX—(NASDAQ)
Rev.: $256,513,000
Assets: $207,114,000
Liabilities: $408,968,000
Net Worth: ($201,854,000)
Earnings: ($107,758,000)
Emp.: 167
Fiscal Year-end: 12/31/22
Renewable Chemicals & Fuels Producer
N.A.I.C.S.: 457210
Eric A. McAfee (Co-Founder, Chm & CEO)
Todd Waltz (CFO & Exec VP)
Andy Foster (Exec VP-North America)

Subsidiaries:

AE Advanced Fuels, Inc. (1)
4209 Jessup Rd, Ceres, CA 95307
Tel.: (209) 632-4511
Petroleum Product Distr
N.A.I.C.S.: 424720

Aemetis Advanced Fuels Keyes, Inc. (1)
4209 Jessup Rd, Ceres, CA 95307-9604
Tel.: (408) 418-2415
Methanol Mfr
N.A.I.C.S.: 325193

Biofuels Marketing, Inc. (1)
79 Degas Park Dr, Spring, TX 77382
Tel.: (281) 296-7078
Marketing Consulting Services
N.A.I.C.S.: 541613

Universal Biofuels Private Limited (1)
Diamond House Flat No 203 Door No 6-3-663/E, Punjagutta, Hyderabad, 500 082, India
Tel.: (91) 4040058029
Web Site: https://universalbiofuelsltd.com
Petroleum Product Distr
N.A.I.C.S.: 424720
Y. S. Rao (Mgr-HR-Factory & Corp Office)

AEOLUS PHARMACEUTI-CALS, INC.
26361 Crown Valley Pkwy Ste 150, Mission Viejo, CA 92691
Tel.: (949) 481-9825 DE
Web Site: http://www.aolsrx.com
AOLS—(OTCIQ)
Sales Range: $1-9.9 Million
Emp.: 3
Pharmaceuticals Mfr
N.A.I.C.S.: 325412

David Charles Cavalier (Chm, CFO & COO-Investor Relations)
John L. McManus (Pres & CEO)

AEON BIOPHARMA, INC.
5 Park Plz Ste 1750, Irvine, CA 92614
Tel.: (949) 354-6499 DE
Web Site: https://aeonbiopharma.com
Year Founded: 2020
AEON—(NYSEAMEX)
Rev.: $14,189,108
Assets: $279,493,625
Liabilities: $288,930,578
Net Worth: ($9,436,953)
Earnings: $9,980,174
Emp.: 3
Fiscal Year-end: 12/31/22
Holding Company; Biopharmaceutical Developer
N.A.I.C.S.: 551112
Marc Forth (Pres, CEO & Principal Fin Officer)
Oleg Grodnensky (CFO, COO & Sec)

Subsidiaries:

AEON Biopharma Sub, Inc. (1)
4040 MacArthur Blvd Ste 260, Newport Beach, CA 92660
Tel.: (949) 354-6499
Web Site: http://www.aeonbiopharma.com
Rev.: $2,518,000
Assets: $21,214,000
Liabilities: $224,448,000
Net Worth: ($203,234,000)
Earnings: ($32,913,000)
Emp.: 6
Fiscal Year-end: 12/31/2020
Biopharmaceutical Developer
N.A.I.C.S.: 325412
Marc Forth (Pres & CEO)
Del Stagg (VP-Technical Ops & Regulatory)
Jost Fischer (Chm)

AEQUI ACQUISITION CORP.
500 W Putnam Ave Ste 400, Greenwich, CT 06830
Tel.: (917) 297-4075 DE
Year Founded: 2020
ARBG—(NASDAQ)
Rev.: $8,591,096
Assets: $36,667,491
Liabilities: $45,564,425
Net Worth: ($8,896,934)
Earnings: $6,860,102
Emp.: 2
Fiscal Year-end: 12/31/22
Investment Services
N.A.I.C.S.: 523999
Susan Hassan (COO)
Hope Schefler Taitz (Chm, CEO & Interim CFO)

AERIES TECHNOLOGY, INC.
Office 5000 CentreGreen Way, Ste 500 Cary,, Raleigh, NC 27513
Tel.: (919) 228-6404 Ky
Web Site: https://aeriestechnology.com
Year Founded: 2021
AERT—(NASDAQ)
Assets: $235,076,020
Liabilities: $239,583,662
Net Worth: ($4,506,842)
Earnings: $9,759,713
Emp.: 1
Fiscal Year-end: 12/31/22
IT Services
N.A.I.C.S.: 513210
Daniel S. Webb (Chief Investment Officer)

AERKOMM INC.
44043 Fremont Blvd, Fremont, CA 94538
Tel.: NV
Web Site: https://www.aerkomm.com
Year Founded: 2013

AKOM—(EUR)
Rev.: $740,315
Assets: $70,640,512
Liabilities: $45,572,742
Net Worth: $25,067,770
Earnings: ($11,878,723)
Emp.: 26
Fiscal Year-end: 12/31/22
Holding Company
N.A.I.C.S.: 551112
Georges Caldironi (COO)
Jeffrey Wun (Pres & CTO)
Jan-Yung Lin (Sec)

Subsidiaries:

AirCom Pacific Inc. (1)
44043 Fremont Blvd, Fremont, CA 94538 (100%)
Tel.: (408) 502-6891
Web Site: http://www.aircom4u.com
In-Flight Entertainment & Connectivity Solutions
N.A.I.C.S.: 517810

AEROVATE THERAPEUTICS, INC.
930 Winter St Ste M 500, Waltham, MA 02451
Tel.: (617) 443-2400 DE
Web Site: https://www.aerovatetx.com
Year Founded: 2018
AVTE—(NASDAQ)
Rev.: $1,751,000
Assets: $135,301,000
Liabilities: $8,558,000
Net Worth: $126,743,000
Earnings: ($51,511,000)
Emp.: 43
Fiscal Year-end: 12/31/22
Research & Development in Biotechnology (except Nanobiotechnology)
N.A.I.C.S.: 541714
Timothy P. Noyes (CEO)
Benjamin T. Dake (Pres, COO & Sec)
Hunter Gillies (Chief Medical Officer)
Ralph Niven (Chief Dev Officer)
George A. Eldridge (CFO & Treas)
Timothy P. Noyes (CEO)

AEROVIRONMENT, INC.
241 18th St S Ste 650, Arlington, VA 22202
Tel.: (805) 520-8350 DE
Web Site: https://www.avinc.com
Year Founded: 1971
AVAV—(NASDAQ)
Rev.: $716,720,000
Assets: $1,015,860,000
Liabilities: $193,115,000
Net Worth: $822,745,000
Earnings: $59,666,000
Emp.: 1,403
Fiscal Year-end: 04/30/24
Small Unmanned Aircraft Systems Designer, Developer & Producer
N.A.I.C.S.: 336411
Wahid Nawabi (Chm, Pres & CEO)
Melissa Brown (Gen Counsel, Sec & VP)
Scott Newbern (CTO & VP)
Brian Charles Shackley (VP & Controller)
Kevin P. McDonnell (CFO & Sr VP)
Trace Stevenson (VP & Gen Mgr-Product Line-SUAS)
Gorik Hossepian (VP & Gen Mgr-Product Line-MUAS)
Colin Walker (VP-Fulfillment)
Brett Hush (VP & Gen Mgr-Product Line-Tactical Missile Systems)
Brian Young (VP & Gen Mgr-Product Line-Unmanned Ground Vehicles)
Jonah Teeter-Balin (Sr Dir-Corp Dev & IR)
Paul Hutton (VP-Govt Rels)

Subsidiaries:

Altoy Savunma Sanayi ve Havacilik
Anonim Sirketi   **(1)**
Kizilirmak Mah 1446 Cad Alternatif Plaza
No 12/18 Cukurambar, Cankaya, 06530,
Ankara, Turkiye
Tel.: (90) 3122843012
Web Site: https://www.altoy.com.tr
Camera Mfr & Distr
N.A.I.C.S.: 334610

Arcturus UAV, Inc.   **(1)**
1035 N McDowell Blvd, Petaluma, CA
94954
Tel.: (707) 206-9372
Web Site: http://www.arcturus-uav.com
Aircraft Systems Design & Mfr
N.A.I.C.S.: 336412
Dmilo Hallerberg *(Pres & CEO)*

Pulse Aerospace, LLC   **(1)**
450 N Iowa St Ste A1, Lawrence, KS 66044
Tel.: (785) 289-8402
Web Site: http://www.pulseaero.com
Aircraft Mfr
N.A.I.C.S.: 336411
Aaron Lessig *(CEO)*

AERSALE CORP

255 Alhambra Cir Ste 435, Coral
Gables, FL 33134
Tel.: (305) 764-3200   DE
Web Site: https://www.aersale.com
Year Founded: 2018
ASLE—(NASDAQ)
Rev.: $408,544,000
Assets: $531,579,000
Liabilities: $86,599,000
Net Worth: $444,980,000
Earnings: $43,861,000
Emp.: 606
Fiscal Year-end: 12/31/22
Motorcycle, ATV & All Other Motor
Vehicle Dealers
N.A.I.C.S.: 441227
Gary Jones *(COO & Pres-Airframe &
Materials)*
Charles P. McDonald *(Chief Technical
Officer & Pres-Heavy MRO Svcs)*
Martin Garmendia *(CFO, Treas &
Sec)*
Guillermo Garces *(VP-IT)*
Nicolas Finazzo *(Chm & CEO)*
Robert Nichols *(Vice Chm)*
Nicolas Finazzo *(Co-Founder, Chm &
CEO)*
Robert B. Nichols *(Co-Founder)*

AETHERIUM ACQUISITION CORP.

79B Pemberwick Rd, Greenwich, CT
06831
Tel.: (650) 450-6836   DE
Web Site:
  https://www.aetheriumcorp.com
Year Founded: 2021
GMFI—(NASDAQ)
Rev.: $1,189,699
Assets: $117,915,033
Liabilities: $122,906,937
Net Worth: ($4,991,904)
Earnings: ($623,874)
Emp.: 2
Fiscal Year-end: 12/31/22
Investment Services
N.A.I.C.S.: 523999
Jonathan Chan *(Chm, Co-CEO, COO
& Dir)*
Alex Lee *(CFO)*
Eddie Lim *(Chief Sls Officer)*

AETHLON MEDICAL, INC.

11555 Sorrento Valley Rd Ste 203,
San Diego, CA 92121
Tel.: (619) 941-0360   NV
Web Site:
  https://www.aethlonmedical.com
Year Founded: 1984

AEMD—(NASDAQ)
Rev.: $428,394
Assets: $8,245,982
Liabilities: $2,479,650
Net Worth: $5,766,332
Earnings: ($12,208,174)
Emp.: 14
Fiscal Year-end: 03/31/24
Medical Device Mfr
N.A.I.C.S.: 339112
Guy F. Cipriani *(COO & Sr VP)*
James B. Frakes *(Interim CEO, CFO
& Principal Acctg Officer)*
Edward G. Broenniman *(Chm)*
Guy F. Cipriani *(Chief Bus Officer &
Sr VP)*
Steven LaRosa *(Chief Medical Offi-
cer)*

Subsidiaries:

Exosome Sciences, Inc.   **(1)**
9635 Granite Ridge Dr Ste 100, San Diego,
CA 92123   **(80%)**
Tel.: (858) 459-7800
Web Site: http://www.exosomesciences.com
Biotechnology Research & Development
N.A.I.C.S.: 541714
Timothy C. Rodell *(CEO-Interim)*
James B. Frakes *(CFO-Interim)*

AEVA TECHNOLOGIES, INC.

555 Ellis St, Mountain View, CA
94043
Tel.: (650) 481-7070   DE
Web Site: https://www.aeva.com
Year Founded: 2019
AEVA—(NYSE)
Rev.: $4,192,000
Assets: $356,632,000
Liabilities: $26,706,000
Net Worth: $329,926,000
Earnings: ($147,305,000)
Emp.: 306
Fiscal Year-end: 12/31/22
Other Motor Vehicle Parts Manufac-
turing
N.A.I.C.S.: 336390
Soroush Salehian Dardashti *(CEO)*
Mina Rezk *(Chm, Pres & CTO)*
Saurab Sinha *(CFO)*
Saurabh Sinha *(CFO)*

Subsidiaries:

Aeva, Inc.   **(1)**
555 Bryant St #940, Palo Alto, CA 94301
Tel.: (650) 481-7070
Web Site: http://www.aeva.ai
Perception Technology & Applications (for
Automated Driving)
N.A.I.C.S.: 336390
Soroush Salehian *(Co-Founder)*
Mina Rezk *(Co-Founder)*

AEYE, INC.

1 Park Pl Ste 200, Dublin, CA 94568
Tel.: (925) 400-4366   DE
Web Site: https://www.aeye.ai
Year Founded: 2013
LIDR—(NASDAQ)
Rev.: $1,464,000
Assets: $54,317,000
Liabilities: $25,294,000
Net Worth: $29,023,000
Earnings: ($87,126,000)
Emp.: 60
Fiscal Year-end: 12/31/23
Software Development Services
N.A.I.C.S.: 541511
Matthew Fisch *(Chm & CEO)*

AF ACQUISITION CORP.

139 N County Rd Fl 2 Ste 35, Palm
Beach, FL 33480
Tel.: (561) 838-9494   DE
Web Site: http://www.afacq.com
Year Founded: 2021
AFAQ—(NASDAQ)
Investment Services

N.A.I.C.S.: 523999
Andrew Scharf *(Chm & Pres)*
Jordan Gaspar *(CEO)*
Christopher Bradley *(CFO & Sec)*

AFC GAMMA, INC.

525 Okeechobee Blvd Ste 1650,
West Palm Beach, FL 33401
Tel.: (561) 510-2390   MD
Web Site:
  https://investors.afcgamma.com
Year Founded: 2020
AFCG—(NASDAQ)
Rev.: $74,684,642
Assets: $519,176,899
Liabilities: $180,117,530
Net Worth: $339,059,369
Earnings: $35,932,397
Fiscal Year-end: 12/31/22
Offices of Real Estate Agents & Bro-
kers
N.A.I.C.S.: 531210
Leonard Mark Tannenbaum *(Founder,
Exec Chm & Chief Investment Offi-
cer)*
Leonard M. Tannenbaum *(Chm, CEO
& Partner)*
Robyn Tannenbaum *(Pres)*
Jeffrey Boccuzzi *(VP)*
Christopher Gioia *(VP-Origination &
IR)*
Edwin Gomez *(Dir-Portfolio Mgmt)*
Brandon Hetzel *(CFO & Treas)*
Gabe Katz *(Dir-Legal)*
Jacob Levin *(Dir-Real Estate Under-
writing)*
Daniel Neville *(CEO)*

AFFILIATED BANK, N.A

500 Harwood Rd, Bedford, TX 76021
Tel.: (817) 285-6195
Web Site:
  http://www.affiliatedbank.com
Year Founded: 1959
BAFI—(OTCIQ)
Commercial Banking Services
N.A.I.C.S.: 522110
Jeffrey R. Schmid *(Pres & CEO)*

AFFILIATED MANAGERS GROUP, INC.

777 S Flagler Dr, West Palm Beach,
FL 33401   DE
Web Site: https://www.amg.com
Year Founded: 1993
AMG—(NYSE)
Rev.: $2,057,800,000
Assets: $9,059,600,000
Liabilities: $4,489,500,000
Net Worth: $4,570,100,000
Earnings: $906,100,000
Emp.: 4,000
Fiscal Year-end: 12/31/23
Holding Company; Asset Manage-
ment & Investment Services
N.A.I.C.S.: 523940
Aaron M. Galis *(Chief Acctg Officer &
Sr VP)*
Jay C. Horgen *(Pres & CEO)*
Alexandra K. Lynn *(Chief Admin Offi-
cer)*
Laura Thompson *(Sr VP-Fin)*
Stephen Pruell *(CIO & Sr VP)*
Thomas M. Wojcik *(COO)*
Dava E. Ritchea *(CFO)*
Jeffrey W. Parker *(Mng Dir)*
Cheerag B. Patel *(Mng Dir)*
Benjamin Scott *(Mng Dir)*
Louis T. Somma *(Mng Dir)*
Adam R. Swanson *(Mng Dir)*
Dana C. Troxell *(Mng Dir)*

Subsidiaries:

AMG Canada Corp.   **(1)**
1 Adelaide Street East Suite 2600, Toronto,
M5C 2V9, ON, Canada

Tel.: (416) 920-1944
Web Site: http://www.amg.com
Emp.: 2
Investment Management Service
N.A.I.C.S.: 523940

AMG Funds LLC   **(1)**
1 Stamford Plz 263 Tresser Blvd Ste 949,
Stamford, CT 06830
Tel.: (617) 747-3300
Web Site: http://amgfunds.com
Investment Advisory Services
N.A.I.C.S.: 523940
John Bishop *(Dir & Reg Mgr-Souther Reg)*
Paul Ledenko *(Mng Dir & Head-Sls)*

Abacus Capital Group LLC   **(1)**
100 Park Ave Ste 3500, New York, NY
10017
Tel.: (212) 203-4960
Web Site:
  https://www.abacuscapitalgroup.com
Real Estate Investment Services
N.A.I.C.S.: 531312
Benjamin Friedman *(Pres & CEO)*
Kyle Ellis *(VP)*
Mike Aidekman *(CFO)*
Autumn Sorrow Stout *(Mng Dir)*
Jim LePorte *(Dir)*
Jeff Remillard *(CIO)*
Mike Sarno *(Mng Dir)*

Abax Investments Proprietary
Limited   **(1)**
2nd Floor Colinton House the Oval 1 Oak-
dale Road Newlands, Cape Town, 7700,
South Africa
Tel.: (27) 216708960
Web Site: http://www.abax.co.za
Fund Management Services
N.A.I.C.S.: 523940
Cynthia Mjoni *(Office Mgr)*
Anthony Sedgwick *(Co-Founder)*
Marius van Rooyen *(Co-Founder)*

Affiliated Managers Group (Switzer-
land) AG   **(1)**
Bahnhofstrasse 100, 8001, Zurich, Switzer-
land
Tel.: (41) 438886363
Asset Management Services
N.A.I.C.S.: 523940

Affiliated Managers Group
Limited   **(1)**
35 Park Lane, London, W1K 1RB, United
Kingdom
Tel.: (44) 207 290 6800
Web Site: https://www.amg.com
Investment Management Service
N.A.I.C.S.: 523999

Ara Partners Group, LLC   **(1)**
The Ion 4201 Main St Ste 370, Houston, TX
77002
Tel.: (713) 337-9150
Web Site: https://www.arapartners.com
Investment Management Service
N.A.I.C.S.: 523940

Arrow Acquisition LLC   **(1)**
6805 Veterans Memorial Blvd, New Or-
leans, LA 70112
Tel.: (504) 457-6399
Investment Management Service
N.A.I.C.S.: 523940

Artemis Investment Management
LLP   **(1)**
Cassini House 57 St James's Street, Lon-
don, SW1A 1LD, United Kingdom
Tel.: (44) 207 399 6000
Web Site: https://www.artemisfunds.com
Investment Management Service
N.A.I.C.S.: 523940

Baker Street Advisors, LLC   **(1)**
575 Market St Ste 600, San Francisco, CA
94105
Tel.: (415) 344-6180
Web Site:
  https://www.bakerstreetadvisors.com
Sales Range: $1-9.9 Million
Investment Advice
N.A.I.C.S.: 523940
Jeff Colin *(Partner)*
Jennifer Bonvechio *(Sr VP)*
Catherine Less *(Dir-Special Projects)*
Gene Schwartz *(VP-Reporting)*
John Siu *(VP)*

Affiliated Managers Group, Inc.—(Continued)

Patrick Burke (Dir-Client Svc)
Rhonda Thomas (Sr VP)
Shelby Rogers (Sr VP-Ops)
Stephanie Moon (VP)
Wendy Umphrey (Partner)
Chris Wilkens (Partner)
Heather Pelant (Partner)
Jim Milligan (Partner)
Madeline Rogers (Sr VP)
Michael van den Akker (Partner)
Alison Elliott (VP)
Jeff Bardini (Mng Dir)
May Ly (VP)
Rob McFadden (VP)
Annie Endozo Roth (VP)
Alex Gannon (VP)
Tara Sahdev (VP)
Nancy Romney (Mgr)
Natalie Weidemier (Mgr)
Susan Caston (VP-Tax)
Jordan Kienzle (Sr VP)
Christopher Gordon (VP)
Golzar Rassouli (Mgr)
Luis Ayala (VP)
Jenny Woodworth (Mgr-Tax & Ops)
Emilee Copeland (VP)
Alexandra Kearney Maher (Mgr)
Brian Kretz (VP)
Adam T. Elegant (Mng Dir)
Austin Rainville (Mgr-Client Svc)
Michael Tideman (Mgr-Client Svc)
Kenny Liao (Ops Mgr)
Jessica Richardson (Ops Mgr)
Alexey Veksler (Mgr-Reporting)

Baring Private Equity Asia K.K. (1)
37/F Roppongi Hills Mori Tower 6-10-1 Roppongi, Minato-ku, Tokyo, 106-6137, Japan
Tel.: (81) 345907200
Portfolio Management Services
N.A.I.C.S.: 523940

Baring Private Equity Asia Pte Limited (1)
50 Collyer Quay 11-03/04 OUE Bayfront, Singapore, 049321, Singapore
Tel.: (65) 62326300
Portfolio Management Services
N.A.I.C.S.: 523940

Beutel, Goodman & Company Ltd. (1)
20 Eglinton Avenue West Suite 2000, PO Box 2005, Toronto, M4R 1K8, ON, Canada
Tel.: (416) 485-1010
Web Site: http://www.beutelgoodman.com
Sales Range: $50-74.9 Million
Investment Advisory & Fund Management Services
N.A.I.C.S.: 523940
Steven Smith (Sr VP-)
Jeffrey Young (Mng Dir-Private Client Grp)
Stephen J. Arpin (Mng Dir-Canadian Equities)
James W. Black (VP-Canadian Equities & Dir-Equities Res)
William Otton (VP-Canadian Equities)
Eva Grant (VP-Responsible Investing & Portfolio Analytics)
Derek Brown (Sr VP & Co Head-Fixed Income)
John Fuca (Asst VP-Fixed Income)
Tim Hylton (Sr VP-Bus Dev & Client Svc)
Craig Auwaerter (VP-Bus Dev & Client Svc)
Nancy Chew (VP-Bus Dev & Client Svc)
Dominic Plante (VP-Bus Dev & Client Svc)
Paul Hamilton (VP-Managed Assets)
Jillian Sumner (Dir-Managed Assets-Eastern)
Luis Chu (Reg Dir-Managed Assets)
Jackie Corneil (VP-Admin & Fin)
Bob Livingston (VP-Private Client)
Darren Bahadur (VP-Private Client)
Michal L. Pomotov (Chief Compliance Officer & Gen Counsel)
Colinda Ravlic (Dir-)
Shadi Shakra (CTO)
Simon Phillips (VP)
Glenn Fortin (VP-International-US)
Colin Ramkissoon (VP-International-US)
Rui Cardoso (Mng Dir-Equities-Intl)
Stanley Wu (VP-International-US)
K. C. Parker (VP-International-US)
Charlotte Daughney (VP-Equity Trading)
Vim Thasan (VP-Equities)
Kathy Tausz (VP-Fixed Income)
Mary Crowe (VP)

Chris Mudie (Asst VP-Fixed Income)
Ivo Mandadjiev (VP)
Nancy Turner (VP-Communications)
Tiana Kauder (Supvr-)
Mickey Anand (Mgr-Managed Assets)
Michelle Corrado (VP-Human Resources)

BlueMountain Capital Management, LLC (1)
280 Park Ave 12th Fl, New York, NY 10017
Tel.: (212) 905-3900
Web Site:
http://www.bluemountaincapital.com
Sales Range: $1-4.9 Billion
Investment Management Service
N.A.I.C.S.: 523940
Andrew Todd Feldstein (Co-Founder)
Lee Kempler (COO & Head-Distr)
Brandon Cahill (Co-Head-CLO Bus)
Brad Schwartz (Head-Asset-Based Investing)
David Buzen (Co-CEO & Co-Chief Investment Officer)
Evan Boulukos (Head-Municipal Bonds & Portfolio Mgr)
Robert de Veer (Chief Risk Officer)
Dawn Jasiak (Gen Counsel)
Matthew Lindsay (Head-Ops & Investment Acctg)
Steve McMillan (Head-Fund Mgmt & IR)
Dave Ray (Chief Compliance Officer & Deputy Gen Counsel)

Joint Venture (Domestic):

Koosharem, LLC (2)
3820 State St, Santa Barbara, CA 93105
Tel.: (805) 882-2200
Web Site: http://www.selectstaffing.com
Sales Range: $1-4.9 Billion
Emp.: 1,250
Holding Company; Temporary Personnel Services
N.A.I.C.S.: 551112
Paul J. Sorensen (Pres)
Laurie C. Maxwell (VP-Ops)
Richard K. Hulme (Chief Admin Officer)
Melissa J. Porter (Chief Sls Officer)
Mark R. McComb (COO)
Gunnar Gooding (Sr VP)
Irwin Much (Pres-Franchise Div)
Fred R. Herbert (Pres-RemX Specialty Staffing)
Thomas A. Bickes (CEO)
Shawn W. Poole (CFO & Exec VP)

Holding (Domestic):

Remedy Intelligent Staffing, Inc. (3)
3820 State St, Santa Barbara, CA 93105
Tel.: (805) 882-2200
Web Site: http://www.remedystaff.com
Emp.: 100
Staffing & People Placement
N.A.I.C.S.: 561311
Melissa J. Porter (Chief Sls Officer)

Select Staffing (3)
Park Central Bldg 410 Ware Blvd Ste 205, Tampa, FL 33619
Tel.: (813) 830-7700
Web Site: http://www.selectremedy.com
Sales Range: $125-149.9 Million
Emp.: 100
Staffing Services
N.A.I.C.S.: 561320
Shawn Levisky (Gen Mgr & Dir-IT)
Lori Weathers (Dir-Sls & Mktg)

SelectRemedy (3)
3820 State St, Santa Barbara, CA 93105-3112
Tel.: (805) 882-2200
Web Site: http://www.selectremedy.com
Temporary Employment Services
N.A.I.C.S.: 561320
Laurie Maxwell (COO)
Melissa J. Porter (Chief Sls Officer)

BlueMountain Capital Partners (London) LLP (1)
6 Bevis Marks 12th Floor, London, EC3A 7BA, United Kingdom
Tel.: (44) 2076470700
Asset Management Services
N.A.I.C.S.: 523940

Capeview Capital LLP (1)
2 London Bridge, London, SE1 9RA, United Kingdom

Tel.: (44) 207 563 9402
Web Site: https://www.capeviewcapital.com
Asset Management Services
N.A.I.C.S.: 523940

Capula Investment Japan Limited (1)
22nd Floor Tokyo Toranomon Square 1-3-1 Toranomon, Minato-ku, Tokyo, 105-0001, Japan
Tel.: (81) 345304800
Investment Management Service
N.A.I.C.S.: 523940

Capula Investment Management Asia Limited (1)
3602-04 Edinburgh Tower The Landmark 15 Queen's Road, Central, China (Hong Kong)
Tel.: (852) 26162900
Investment Management Service
N.A.I.C.S.: 523940

Capula Investment Management LLP (1)
7 Clarges Street, London, W1J 8AE, United Kingdom
Tel.: (44) 207 071 0900
Web Site: https://www.capulaglobal.com
Investment Management Service
N.A.I.C.S.: 523940
Yan Huo (Mng Partner)
Masao Asai (Co-Partner)

Capula Investment US LP (1)
60 Arch St 3rd Fl, Greenwich, CT 06830
Tel.: (203) 542-2400
Investment Management Service
N.A.I.C.S.: 523940

Chicago Equity Partners, LLC (1)
180 N LaSalle St Ste 3800, Chicago, IL 60601
Tel.: (312) 629-8200
Web Site:
http://www.chicagoequitypartners.com
Sales Range: $1-4.9 Billion
Emp.: 50
Portfolio Management & Investment Advisory Services
N.A.I.C.S.: 523940
Robert H. Kramer (Founder, Partner & Co-Chief Investment Officer-Equities)
Patrick C. Lynch (Founder & Pres)
Feng Zhao (Sr Portfolio Mgr-Fixed Income)
Patricia Halper (Partner & Co-Chief Investment Officer)
Venkat Eleswarapu (Mng Dir)
Anjanette Wroblewski (Dir-Ops)
Kelsey L. Renfro (Dir-Product Mgmt)
Curt A. Mitchell (Partner & Chief Investment Officer-Fixed Income)
George Gao (Partner & Mng Dir)
Keith E. Gustafson (Partner & Mng Dir)
Michael J. Lawrence (Partner & Mng Dir)
Patrick J. Morris (Partner & Mng Dir)
Christopher C. Ashbee (Portfolio Mgr-Fixed Income)
James A. DeZellar (Partner & Mng Dir)
Martin J. Dorow (Mng Dir)
Michelle D. Maguire (Mng Dir)
Scott Brown (Dir-IT)
Anne Kellman (Controller)
Robert Nanney (Chief Compliance Officer)

Deans Knight Capital Management Ltd. (1)
999 West Hastings Street Suite 1500, Vancouver, V6C 2W2, BC, Canada
Tel.: (604) 669-0212
Web Site: http://www.deansknight.com
Investment Management Service
N.A.I.C.S.: 523940
Wayne Deans (Co-Founder & Portfolio Mgr)
Dillon Cameron (Portfolio Mgr)
Steve Conway (CEO)
Philip Hampson (Chm)

EIG Global Energy (Asia) Ltd. (1)
36/F Two International Finance Centre 8 Finance Street, Central, China (Hong Kong)
Tel.: (852) 37134333
Web Site: http://www.eigpartners.com
Investment Management Service
N.A.I.C.S.: 523940
Jen Phua (VP)
Hyunju Choi (Office Mgr)
Natalie Liu (Asst VP)
Harris So (Asst VP)
Natalie Liu (Asst VP)
Harris So (Asst VP)

EIG Global Energy (Australia) Pty. Ltd. (1)
Suite 2001 Level 20 Gateway 1 Macquarie Place, Sydney, 2000, NSW, Australia
Tel.: (61) 293382100
Investment Management Service
N.A.I.C.S.: 523940

EIG Global Energy (Brasil) Representacoes Ltda. (1)
Rua Anibal de Mendonca 27 - 3 Andar Ipanema, Rio de Janeiro, 22410-050, Brazil
Tel.: (55) 2135580801
Investment Management Service
N.A.I.C.S.: 523940
Shana Zoellner (Office Mgr)
Joao Mariz (Sr VP)
Alan Parker (VP)
Flavio Valle (Mng Dir)

EIG Global Energy (Europe) Ltd. (1)
20 St James's Street 7th Floor, London, SW1A 1ES, United Kingdom
Tel.: (44) 2073990910
Web Site: http://www.eigpartners.com
Investment Management Service
N.A.I.C.S.: 523940
Emiliano Vovard (VP)
Jean-Daniel Borgeaud (Mng Dir & Head-Power & Renewables)
Simon Hayden (Mng Dir)
Tatiana Levin (Ops Mgr)
Jerome Briens (Asst VP)
Joao Mariz (VP)
Jonathan Mottura (Sr VP)
Etienne Renault (VP)
Jerome Briens (Asst VP)
Joao Mariz (VP)
Jonathan Mottura (Sr VP)
Etienne Renault (VP)
Nicole Taylor (VP)
Tom Wheeler (VP)
Venter De la Rey (CEO)

EIG Global Energy Korea, Ltd. (1)
10 Gukjegeumyung-ro, Yeongdeungpo-gu, Seoul, 07326, Korea (South)
Tel.: (82) 261379595
Web Site: http://www.eigpartners.com
Investment Management Service
N.A.I.C.S.: 523940
Barton Lee (Mng Dir)

First Quadrant, L.P. (1)
800 E Colorado Blvd Ste 900, Pasadena, CA 91101
Tel.: (626) 795-8220
Web Site: http://www.firstquadrant.com
Rev.: $17,300,000,000
Emp.: 67
Investment Management Service
N.A.I.C.S.: 523940
Max Darnell (Partner & Chm)
Dori Levanoni (Partner-Investments)
Edgar Peters (Mng Partner)
Jeppe Ladekarl (Partner & Chief Investment Officer)
Jia Ye (Partner & Co-Chief Investment Officer)
Joel Brouwer (Partner & CFO)
Earl Kleckner (Mng Dir & Head-Sls)
Lisa Limin (Assoc Dir-Relationship Mgmt)
Andy Pellegrino (Dir-Mktg & Consultant Rels)
Brian Rowe (Dir-Mktg & Client Rels)
Susan Stannard (Dir-Relationship Mgmt)
Ray Johnson (Mng Dir & Gen Mgr)

Forbion Group Holding B.V. (1)
Gooimeer 2-35, 1411 DC, Naarden, Netherlands
Tel.: (31) 356993000
Web Site: https://forbion.com
Emp.: 46
Finance Investment Services
N.A.I.C.S.: 523999

Foyston Gordon & Payne Inc. (1)
1 Adelaide Street East Suite 2600, Toronto, M5C 2V9, ON, Canada
Tel.: (416) 362-4725
Web Site: http://www.foyston.com
Emp.: 50
Portfolio Management Services
N.A.I.C.S.: 523940
Kimberley Woolverton (Exec VP & Head-Distr)
Cameron Greenwood (VP & Portfolio Mgr-Fixed Income)

Mohammed Ahmad *(VP & Portfolio Mgr-Emerging Markets Equities)*
Tom Duncanson *(VP & Portfolio Mgr-Equities)*
Brandon Tu *(VP & Portfolio Mgr-Equities)*
Graeme Lang *(Head-Equity Trader)*
Charles McCracken *(Mgr-IT)*
Phil Chen *(VP & Portfolio Mgr-Client)*
Robert Laughton *(VP-Client Relationship & Mgr-Bus Dev)*
Gabriel Lopezpineda *(VP-Client Relationship & Mgr-Bus Dev)*
George Haim *(VP-Mktg & Comm)*
Laura Sebesta *(Principal)*
Albert Cama *(Principal)*
Robert Head *(Sr VP)*
Mark Klinkow *(VP)*
Patrick Osler *(VP)*
Susan Eapen *(Chief Compliance Officer)*
Zubaida Mirza *(VP)*
Andrew Aucoin *(VP)*

Foyston, Gordon & Payne Inc. (1)
1 Adelaide Street East Suite 2600, Toronto, M5C 2V9, ON, Canada
Tel.: (416) 362-4725
Web Site: http://www.foyston.com
Emp.: 50
Investment Management & Advisory Services
N.A.I.C.S.: 523940
John C. Berry *(Sr VP & Portfolio Mgr)*
Bryan W. Pilsworth *(Pres, CEO & Portfolio Mgr)*
Robert J. Head *(Sr VP & Co-Head)*
Mohammed Ahmad *(VP & Portfolio Mgr-Emerging Markets Equities)*
Ryan Domsy *(Exec VP & Co-Head)*
Cameron C. Greenwood *(VP & Portfolio Mgr-Fixed Income)*
Patrick C. Osler *(VP & Head-Wealth Mgmt)*
Mark G. Klinkow *(VP & Portfolio Mgr-Client)*
Donald Foyston *(Partner)*
Kimberley Woolverton *(Exec VP & Head-Distr)*
Stephen Mitchell *(Sr VP & Portfolio Mgr-Global Equities)*
Tom Duncanson *(VP & Portfolio Mgr-Canadian Equities)*
Brandon Tu *(VP & Portfolio Mgr-Canadian Equities)*
William Cunningham *(VP-Ops & Fin)*
Charles McCracken *(Mgr-IT)*
Gabriel Lopezpineda *(VP & Mgr-Bus Dev & Client Relationship)*
George Haim *(VP-Comm & Mktg)*
Marina Mascarenhas *(Mgr-Client Svcs)*
Graeme Lang *(Head-Canadian Equity Trader)*
Phil Chen *(VP & Portfolio Mgr-Client)*
Bren Tan *(Mgr-Client Svc)*
Tina Chiu *(Mgr-Investment Ops)*
Konstantine Zhadan *(Mgr-Portfolio Analytics & Risk Mgmt)*
Peter Gordon *(Partner)*
Malcolm Payne *(Partner)*
Susan Eapen *(Chief Compliance Officer)*
Ray Szutu *(Portfolio Mgr)*
Zubaida Mirza *(VP-)*

Friess Associates, LLC (1)
3711 Kennett Pike Ste 205, Greenville, DE 19807-2156
Tel.: (302) 656-3017
Web Site: https://www.friess.com
Sales Range: $250-299.9 Million
Emp.: 35
Open-End Fund & Portfolio Management Services
N.A.I.C.S.: 525910
Dave Marky *(Mng Partner, COO & Chief Compliance Officer)*

Subsidiary (Domestic):

Friess Associates of Delaware, LLC (2)
3711 Kennett Pike Ste 205, Greenville, DE 19807-2156
Tel.: (302) 656-3017
Web Site: http://www.friess.com
Sales Range: $250-299.9 Million
Emp.: 32
Open-End Fund & Portfolio Management Services
N.A.I.C.S.: 525910
Dave Marky *(Mng Partner, COO & Chief Compliance Officer)*
Joe Fields *(Mng Partner-Client Svcs)*

Scott Gates *(Mng Partner & Chief Investment Officer)*
Genevieve Cozzens *(Mgr-Res)*
Jeanie Firestone *(Mgr-Res)*
Amy Mottola *(Mgr-Res)*
Gretchen Sailer *(Mgr-Res)*
Chris Aregood *(Dir-Comm)*

Frontier Capital Management Company, LLC (1)
99 Summer St 20th Fl, Boston, MA 02110
Tel.: (617) 261-0777
Web Site: https://www.frontiercap.com
Sales Range: $1-4.9 Billion
Investment Management Service
N.A.I.C.S.: 523940
Michael A. Cavarretta *(Chm & Portfolio Mgr)*
William A. Teichner *(Mng Partner & Portfolio Mgr-Frontier Small Cap Value Strategy)*
Andrew B. Bennett *(VP & Portfolio Mgr-Frontier Capital Appreciation Strategy)*
Rushan Jiang *(VP & Portfolio Mgr-Small Cap Value Strategy)*
Christopher J. Scarpa *(VP & Portfolio Mgr)*
Sarah J. Jankowski *(COO)*
Leigh Anne Yoo *(Dir-Sls & Mktg)*
Amy L. Janezic *(VP-Marketing-Client Service)*
Carolyn C. Shea *(VP)*
Ravi Dabas *(VP & Portfolio Mgr-Mid Cap Growth Strategy)*
Kristina Catinazzo *(Asst VP-Mktg & Client Svcs)*
Jillian P. Berggren *(Controller)*
W. Ryan Eaton *(Ops Mgr)*
G. Michael Novak Jr. *(Sr VP)*
Robert E. Phay Jr. *(Chief Compliance Officer & Gen Counsel)*

GW&K Investment Management, LLC (1)
222 Berkeley St 15th Fl, Boston, MA 02116
Tel.: (617) 236-8900
Web Site: https://www.gwkinvest.com
Emp.: 184
Investment & Asset Management Services
N.A.I.C.S.: 523940
Harold G. Kotler *(CEO & Chief Investment Officer)*
Nancy G. Angell *(Partner & Dir-Fixed Income)*
John B. Fox *(Partner & Dir-Fixed Income)*
Robert L. Gray *(Partner & Head)*
Mary F. Kane *(Partner & Portfolio Mgr)*
James M. McCarthy *(Partner & Dir-Client Svc)*
Brian T. Moreland *(Partner & Portfolio Mgr)*
Jeffrey O. Whitney *(Partner & Portfolio Mgr-Equity)*
Daniel L. Miller *(Partner & Dir-Equities)*
Michael J. Clare *(Partner & Dir-Institutional)*
Sheila R. May *(Principal & Dir-Municipal Bond Res)*
Lewis Collins *(Partner & Gen Counsel)*
Benjamin Klaas *(Principal)*
Cristina G. DeCotis *(VP)*
Jeffrey R. Simmons *(VP-Institutional Bus Dev)*
John Ferguson *(VP & Sls Dir-Northeast Reg)*
Vincent E. Zupo *(Sls Dir)*
David E. Borah *(VP)*
David J. Rouse *(Chief Compliance Officer)*
Kyle A. Bush *(VP)*
Matthew J. Clemmer *(VP)*
Taylor Cope *(VP)*
Jeffrey T. Devine *(VP)*
Vasu Kasibhotla *(VP)*
Patrick J. Keogh *(VP)*
Nate McNamee *(VP)*
Bradley S. Wilds *(VP)*
David J. Rouse *(Chief Compliance Officer)*
Kyle A. Bush *(VP)*
Matthew J. Clemmer *(VP)*
Taylor Cope *(VP)*
Jeffrey T. Devine *(VP)*
Vasu Kasibhotla *(VP)*
Patrick J. Keogh *(VP)*
Nate McNamee *(VP)*
Bradley S. Wilds *(VP)*
David J. Rouse *(Chief Compliance Officer)*
Kyle A. Bush *(VP)*
Matthew J. Clemmer *(VP)*
Taylor Cope *(VP)*
Jeffrey T. Devine *(VP)*
Vasu Kasibhotla *(VP)*
Patrick J. Keogh *(VP)*
Nate McNamee *(VP)*
Bradley S. Wilds *(VP)*

T. Williams Roberts III *(Partner)*
Reid T. Galas *(Partner)*
Charles J. Kace III *(VP)*
Maya Mirson-Tohme *(VP)*
Siva Natarajan *(VP)*
Sunil Parthasarathy *(VP)*
Robert P. Shea *(VP)*
Yongtao Shi *(VP)*
Kara M. South *(Principal)*
Leigh S. Williamson *(Principal)*
Kristin Chisholm *(VP)*
Alec DeWitt *(VP)*
Terrence W. Walsh *(Principal)*
Kevin G. Furey *(Principal)*
Melissa F. Jacoby *(VP)*
Scott R. Peterson *(VP)*
John-Ryan Quick *(VP)*

Garda Capital Partners LP (1)
90 S 7th St Ste 4900, Minneapolis, MN 55402
Tel.: (612) 330-4900
Web Site: http://www.gardacp.com
Investment Management Service
N.A.I.C.S.: 523940
Tim Magnusson *(Chief Investment Officer)*
Ted Farrell *(Chief Risk Officer)*
Peter McGarry *(Portfolio Mgr)*
Gary Cameron *(Portfolio Mgr)*
Jeff Drobny *(CEO)*
Jacob Jorgensen *(Portfolio Mgr)*
Michael Grover *(Head-Investor Relations)*
Kris Kittiko *(CFO)*
Ashwin Kumar *(CTO)*
Patrick Shane *(Gen Counsel)*

Genesis Investment Management, LLP (1)
16 St James's Street, London, SW1A 1ER, United Kingdom
Tel.: (44) 2072017200
Web Site: https://www.giml.co.uk
Sales Range: $1-4.9 Billion
Investment Management & Advisory Services
N.A.I.C.S.: 523940
Marguerite Mills *(Assoc Partner & Head)*
Catherine Vlasto *(Mng Partner & Portfolio Mgr)*
Karen Roydon *(Partner & Portfolio Mgr)*
Arindam Bhattacharjee *(Mng Partner & Portfolio Mgr)*
Chris Ellyatt *(Partner & Mng Dir)*
Jens Moller-Butcher *(Assoc Partner-Ops & COO)*
Mario Solari *(Partner & Portfolio Mgr)*
Sebastian Peters *(Partner & Portfolio Mgr)*
Richard Mather *(Partner & Portfolio Mgr)*
Xing Hu *(Partner & Portfolio Mgr)*
Mireli Antun *(Sr Mgr)*
Nick Archer *(Mgr)*
Martina Jersakova *(Sr Mgr)*
Aranzazu Sardina *(Sr Mgr)*
Mireli Antun *(Sr Mgr)*
Nick Archer *(Mgr)*
Martina Jersakova *(Sr Mgr)*
Aranzazu Sardina *(Sr Mgr)*

Ivory Capital Group, LLC (1)
900 3rd Ave Ste 1102, New York, NY 10022
Tel.: (212) 317-6600
Web Site: http://www.ivorycapital.co
Emp.: 10
Asset Management Services
N.A.I.C.S.: 523940

Jackson Square Partners, LLC (1)
1 Letterman Dr Bldg A Ste A3-200, San Francisco, CA 94129
Tel.: (415) 635-0220
Web Site: https://www.jspartners.com
Emp.: 24
Portfolio Management Services
N.A.I.C.S.: 523940
Van Tran *(CFO)*
Deborah Sabo *(Partner)*
Jeffrey Van Harte *(Chief Investment Officer)*
Sean Kreiger *(Chief Compliance Officer)*

MyCIO Wealth Partners, LLC (1)
2929 Walnut St Ste 1200, Philadelphia, PA 19104
Tel.: (215) 295-2280
Web Site: http://www.myciowp.com
Emp.: 30
Financial Investment & Advisory Services
N.A.I.C.S.: 523940
David E. Lees *(Co-Founder & Sr Partner)*
James Biles *(Co-Founder & Partner)*

Paul J. Bracaglia *(Partner)*
Phil J. Bonelli *(Partner)*
Bruce J. Fenster *(Partner)*
Michael D. Finelli *(Partner)*
James L. Henry *(Partner)*
Justin Pagliei *(Partner)*
Robert Shaw *(Partner)*
Jonathan P. Michewicz *(Partner)*
Christopher D. Morello *(Partner)*
Stephen J. Rennard *(Partner)*
William J. Stanley Jr. *(Partner)*

Pantheon (US) LLC (1)
One International Blvd Ste 624, Mahwah, NJ 07495
Tel.: (201) 529-6842
Investment Management Service
N.A.I.C.S.: 523940
Chris Meads *(Chief Investment Officer)*

Pantheon Capital (Asia) Limited (1)
Suite 1606 16 floor Two Exchange Square 8 Connaught Road, Central, China (Hong Kong)
Tel.: (852) 2810 8063
Web Site: http://www.pantheon.com
Emp.: 10
Financial Investment Services
N.A.I.C.S.: 523940

Pantheon Holdings Limited (1)
31 St James Square Norfolk House, London, SW1Y 4JR, United Kingdom
Tel.: (44) 2074846200
Web Site: http://www.pantheon.com
Financial Investment Services
N.A.I.C.S.: 523940

Pantheon Korea Inc. (1)
44th floor Three IFC 10 Gukjegeumyung-ro, Youngdeungpo-gu, Seoul, 07326, Korea (South)
Tel.: (82) 260220573
Investment Advisory Services
N.A.I.C.S.: 523940

Pantheon Securities LLC (1)
1095 Ave Of The Americas 6th Ave 24th Fl, New York, NY 10036
Tel.: (212) 205-2000
Asset Management Services
N.A.I.C.S.: 523940

Pantheon Ventures (HK) LLP (1)
Unit 1506-07 15/F Two Chinachem 26 Des Voeux Road Central, Central, China (Hong Kong)
Tel.: (852) 37189600
Web Site: http://www.pantheon.com
Emp.: 25
Investment Management Service
N.A.I.C.S.: 523940

Pantheon Ventures (UK) LLP (1)
10 Finsbury Square 4th Floor, London, EC2A 1AF, United Kingdom
Tel.: (44) 203 356 1800
Web Site: https://www.pantheon.com
Emp.: 250
Investment Management Service
N.A.I.C.S.: 523940
Robin Bailey *(Partner)*
Paul Ward *(Mng Partner)*

River Road Asset Management LLC (1)
Meidinger Tower 462 S 4th St Ste 2000, Louisville, KY 40202
Tel.: (502) 371-4100
Web Site: https://www.riverroadam.com
Emp.: 25
Investment Advice & Wealth Management Services
N.A.I.C.S.: 523940
Robert W. Wainwright *(Chief Bus Dev Officer)*
Daniel R. Johnson *(VP & Portfolio Mgr)*
Matt W. Moran *(VP & Portfolio Mgr)*
Benjamin T. Brady *(VP-Bus Dev)*
Thomas D. Mueller *(COO & Chief Compliance Officer)*
J. Alex Brown *(Co-Chief Investment Officer-)*
Todd D. Mayberry *(Assoc Portfolio Mgr)*
Emma M. Travis *(Coord-Compliance)*
Shawn R. Schmidt *(Fin Mgr)*
Henry W. Sanders III *(Exec VP)*
Wenjun Yang *(VP)*

SouthernSun Asset Management, LLC (1)

Affiliated Managers Group, Inc.—(Continued)

240 Madison Ave Ste 800, Memphis, TN
38103
Tel.: (901) 341-2700
Web Site: https://southernsunam.com
Financial Investment Services
N.A.I.C.S.: 523940
Michael S. Cross (Principal & Portfolio Mgr)
S. Elliot Cunningham (Principal)
James P. Dorman (Principal & Portfolio
Mgr)
Andrew E. Willson (Principal)
Michael McNamara (Principal)
John M. Roach (Chief Admin Officer & Prin-
cipal)
Ashley McNeely (CFO)
Angela Wimmer (VP)
Michael Cook (Founder)
Phillip Cook (Co-Chief Investment Officer)
Tread Thompson (Principal)
William Halliday (COO)
Brad Clayton (Officer)

Systematic Financial Management,
L.P.   (1)
300 Frank W Burr Blvd Glenpointe E 7th Fl,
Teaneck, NJ 07666-6798
Tel.: (201) 928-1982
Web Site: https://www.sfmlp.com
Sales Range: $75-99.9 Million
Investment Advisory & Management Ser-
vices
N.A.I.C.S.: 523940
Roger H. Chang (Head)
James V. Wallerius (Sr VP-Mktg & Client
Svc)
Eoin E. Middaugh (Portfolio Mgr)
Ryan Wick (Asst Portfolio Mgr)
Rick Plummer (Asst Portfolio Mgr)
Steven C. Shaw (Sr VP-Mktg & Client Svc)
Karen Kohler (COO)
Ken Burgess (Chief Investment Officer)
Michael Saroyan (Mng Dir)
Michele Egeberg (Mng Dir)
William Skayhan (Mng Dir)
Thomas Poutre (Mng Dir)
Scott Tyndale (Mng Dir)

Systematica Investments Limited   (1)
29 Esplanade, Saint Helier, JE2 3QA, Jer-
sey
Tel.: (44) 153 484 1090
Web Site: http://www.systematica.com
Asset Management Services
N.A.I.C.S.: 523940
Leda Braga (Founder & CEO)
Paul Rouse (CFO & COO)
David Kitson (Chief Investment Officer &
Acting Head-)
Jean-Pierre Selvatico (Head-Trading-
Counterparty Mgmt)
Ben Dixon (Chief Compliance Officer & Gen
Counsel)

Systematica Investments US
LLC   (1)
650 5th Ave, New York, NY 10019
Tel.: (646) 927-5300
Web Site: http://www.systematica.com
Asset Management Services
N.A.I.C.S.: 523940

The Renaissance Group LLC   (1)
50 E Rivercenter Blvd Ste 1200, Covington,
KY 41011
Tel.: (513) 723-4500
Web Site: http://www.reninv.com
Sales Range: $650-699.9 Million
Emp.: 22
Investment Management Service
N.A.I.C.S.: 523940

TimesSquare Capital Management,
LLC   (1)
Times Sq Tower 7 Times Sq 42nd FL, New
York, NY 10036-6524
Tel.: (917) 342-7800
Web Site: https://www.tscmllc.com
Emp.: 30
Equity Investment Management Firm
N.A.I.C.S.: 523999
Stephen Green (Sr Partner, Mng Dir &
Head-Bus Dev-Global)
David M. Cielusniak (COO)

Trilogy Global Advisors International
LLP   (1)
23 Austin Friars, London, EC2N 2QP,
United Kingdom

Tel.: (44) 2037909640
Web Site: http://www.trilogyadvisors.com
Emp.: 2
Investment Management Service
N.A.I.C.S.: 523940

Trilogy Global Advisors, LP   (1)
1140 Ave of the Americas 18th Fl, New
York, NY 10036
Tel.: (212) 703-3100
Investment Management Service
N.A.I.C.S.: 523940

Tweedy, Browne Company LLC   (1)
1 Station Pl, Stamford, CT 06902
Tel.: (203) 703-0600
Web Site: https://www.tweedy.com
Rev.: $7,000,000,000
Emp.: 50
Investment & Asset Management Services
N.A.I.C.S.: 523940
Thomas H. Shrager (Mng Dir)
John D. Spears (Mng Dir)
Roger R. de Bree (Mng Dir)
Frank H. Hawrylak (Mng Dir)
Jay Hill (Mng Dir)
Andrew Ewert (Mng Dir)
Robert Q. Wyckoff Jr. (Mng Dir)

Veritable, LP   (1)
6022 W Chester Pike, Newtown Square, PA
19073
Tel.: (610) 640-9551
Emp.: 83
Investment Advisory Services
N.A.I.C.S.: 523940
Darren Bramen (Partner)
Michael A. Stolper (Founder)
Michael Stolper (Partner)
Fred Bacani (Partner)
Brian Badgley (Partner)
Jeffrey Beachell (Partner)
David Belej (Partner)
Emily Bless (Partner)
Regina DiFelice (Partner)
Patrick Dougherty (Partner)
Meghan Freehoff (Partner)
Jeannette Grabe (Partner)
Andrew John (Partner)
Vanessa Kyranakis (Partner)
Robert Lazaroff (Partner)
Thomas Mahoney (Partner)
Douglas McCall (Partner)
Jeff Morrison (Partner)
Sonia Peterson (Partner)
Brett Rubinson (Partner)
Jonathan Scott (Partner)
John Scuteri (Partner)
Robert Stetson (Partner)
Eric Shulenberger (Partner)

Veritas Asset Management LLP   (1)
1 Smart's Place, London, WC2B 5LW,
United Kingdom
Tel.: (44) 2037589900
Web Site: https://www.vamllp.com
Investment Advisory Services
N.A.I.C.S.: 523940
Antony Burgess (Head-Client & Investment
Specialists)
Guy Davidson (Specialist-Investment)
James Trietline (Head-Client Svc)
Sandeep Bandesha (Gen Counsel)
Alison Moitysee (Compliance Officer)
Nicola Smith (CFO)
Nurul Islam (Head-Investment Ops)
Matt Smith (Head-Risk & Performance)
Ian Clark (Mgr-Fund)
Andy Headley (Head-Global & Mgr-Fund)
Mike Moore (Mgr-Fund)
Adam Matson (Head-Tech)

WP Group, LLC   (1)
383 Alder St, Arroyo Grande, CA 93420
Tel.: (805) 270-5381
Web Site: http://www.wpgroupllc.com
Emp.: 10
Asset Management Services
N.A.I.C.S.: 523940

Wealth Partners Capital Group,
LLC   (1)
230 Royal Palm Way Ste 201, Palm Beach,
FL 33480
Tel.: (561) 567-8160
Web Site: http://www.wealthpcg.com
Investment Advisory Services
N.A.I.C.S.: 523940
John W. Copeland (Mng Partner)
Allison B. Sempier (Partner)

Paul S. Lawler (Gen Counsel)
Daniel W. Stanton (Principal)
Nicholas M. Trepp (Principal)
Rich P. Gill (Partner)
Colin L. Mckee (Assoc Gen Counsel)
Mac J. Selverian (Principal)
Rich P. Gill (Partner)
Colin L. Mckee (Assoc Gen Counsel)
Mac J. Selverian (Principal)

Joint Venture (Domestic):

Waverly Advisors, LLC   (2)
600 University Park Pl Ste 501, Birming-
ham, AL 35209
Tel.: (205) 871-3334
Web Site: https://waverly-advisors.com
Emp.: 100
Investment Adviser; Investment Manage-
ment & Wealth Planning
N.A.I.C.S.: 523940
Joshua L. Reidinger (CEO & Partner)

Subsidiary (Domestic):

Omni Wealth Advisors, LLC.   (3)
110 S Hoover Blvd, Tampa, FL 33609
Tel.: (813) 281-0028
Web Site: http://www.omniadvisors.com
Rev.: $2,905,000
Emp.: 7
Portfolio Management
N.A.I.C.S.: 523940
Brian Hershberger (Pres)

Rainsberger Wealth Advisors,
Inc.   (3)
980 Pico Pt, Colorado Springs, CO 80905
Tel.: (719) 328-1944
Web Site: http://www.rwapartners.com
Miscellaneous Financial Investment Activi-
ties
N.A.I.C.S.: 523999
Ellis Rainsberger (Pres)

Welch & Forbes LLC   (1)
Old City Hall 45 School St -5th Fl, Boston,
MA 02108-3207
Tel.: (617) 523-1635
Web Site: https://www.welchforbes.com
Sales Range: $1-4.9 Billion
Investment Management & Fiduciary Ser-
vices
N.A.I.C.S.: 523940
Kurt H. Walter (CFO)
Todd R. Jundi (Chief Compliance Officer)
Wayne R. Kurpiel (Mgr-Tax Dept)
Daniel R. Gorman (Portfolio Mgr)
Naomi T. Dalessandro (Portfolio Mgr)
Peter P. Brown (Portfolio Mgr)
Charles P. Curtis (Portfolio Mgr)
Benjamin L. B. Garfield (Portfolio Mgr)
Seth Gelsthorpe (Portfolio Mgr)
Theodore E. Ober (Portfolio Mgr)
Drew M. Schneller (Portfolio Mgr)
Adrienne G. Silbermann (Dir)
Justin T. Wolstenholme (Portfolio Mgr)
Lori A. Haller (Mgr)
Peter P. Brown (Portfolio Mgr)
Charles P. Curtis (Portfolio Mgr)
Benjamin L. B. Garfield (Portfolio Mgr)
Seth Gelsthorpe (Portfolio Mgr)
Theodore E. Ober (Portfolio Mgr)
Drew M. Schneller (Portfolio Mgr)
Adrienne G. Silbermann (Dir)
Benjamin J. Williams (Portfolio Mgr)
Justin T. Wolstenholme (Portfolio Mgr)
Lori A. Haller (Mgr)
Peter P. Brown (Portfolio Mgr)
Charles P. Curtis (Portfolio Mgr)
Benjamin L. B. Garfield (Portfolio Mgr)
Seth Gelsthorpe (Portfolio Mgr)
Theodore E. Ober (Portfolio Mgr)
Drew M. Schneller (Portfolio Mgr)
Adrienne G. Silbermann (Dir)
Benjamin J. Williams (Portfolio Mgr)
Justin T. Wolstenholme (Portfolio Mgr)
Lori A. Haller (Mgr)
Benjamin J. Williams Jr. (Portfolio Mgr)

Winton Capital Asia Limited   (1)
Room 2707 27/F The Center 99 Queen's
Road Central, Central, China (Hong Kong)
Tel.: (852) 39158500
Asset Management Services
N.A.I.C.S.: 523940

Winton Capital US LLC   (1)
6th Fl 510 Madison Ave, New York, NY
10010

Tel.: (212) 702-3100
Asset Management Services
N.A.I.C.S.: 523940

Winton Group Limited   (1)
Grove House 27 Hammersmith Grove, Lon-
don, W6 0NE, United Kingdom
Tel.: (44) 208 576 5800
Web Site: https://www.winton.com
Investment Management Service
N.A.I.C.S.: 523940
David Harding (CEO & Founder)
Simon Judes (Co-Chief Investment Officer)
Carsten Schmitz (Co-Chief Investment Offi-
cer)
Nick Saunders (COO)
Brigid Rentoul (Gen Counsel)
James Gilbert (Head)
Omar Iqbal (Head-Human Capital)

Yacktman Asset Management LP   (1)
6300 Bridgepoint Pkwy Bldg One Ste 500,
Austin, TX 78730
Tel.: (512) 767-6711
Web Site: https://yacktman.com
Investment Advisory Services
N.A.I.C.S.: 523940
Donald Yacktman (Partner & Portfolio Mgr)
Stephen Yacktman (Partner, Chief Invest-
ment Officer & Portfolio Mgr)
Jason Subotky (Partner & Portfolio Mgr)
Russell Wilkins (Partner & Portfolio Mgr)
Adam Sues (Partner & Portfolio Mgr)

AFFINITY BANCSHARES, INC.
3175 Hwy 278, Covington, GA 30014
Tel.: (770) 786-7088   **MD**
Web Site:
   https://affinitybankshares.q4ir.com
Year Founded: 2021
AFBI—(NASDAQ)
Rev.: $34,536,000
Assets: $791,283,000
Liabilities: $674,180,000
Net Worth: $117,103,000
Earnings: $7,134,000
Emp.: 89
Fiscal Year-end: 12/31/22
Bank Holding Company
N.A.I.C.S.: 551111
Edward J. Cooney (CEO)
Brandi Pajot (CFO & Sr VP)
Clark N. Nelson (Chief Comml Officer
& Exec VP)
Elizabeth M. Galazka (Exec VP-
Lending)
Robert A. Vickers (COO & Sr VP)

Subsidiaries:

Affinity Bank, National
Association   (1)
8258 Hwy 278 NE, Covington, GA 30014
Tel.: (770) 786-7088
Web Site: https://myaffinitybank.com
Rev.: $1,806,000
Emp.: 6
Commercial Banking Services
N.A.I.C.S.: 522180
Gregory J. Proffitt (COO & Exec VP)
Nancy Mask (VP-Comml Loans)
Tabitha Henderson (Asst VP-Mortgage
Lending)
Johnny S. Smith (Pres & CEO)
Reed Beard (VP)
Greta Heard (VP & Branch Mgr-Sls)
David Dyer (VP)
Ionya Burnett (VP & Dir-Mortgage Svcs)
Dee Cook (VP)
Jimmy Tanner (VP-Bus Dev & Retail Sls)

Community First Bancshares,
Inc.   (1)
3175 Hwy 278, Covington, GA 30014
Tel.: (770) 786-7088
Web Site: http://www.snl.com
Rev.: $16,642,000
Assets: $319,294,000
Liabilities: $242,127,000
Net Worth: $77,167,000
Earnings: $355,000
Emp.: 80
Fiscal Year-end: 12/31/2019
Bank Holding Company
N.A.I.C.S.: 551111

Johnny S. Smith *(Pres)*
Tessa M. Nolan *(CFO & Sr VP)*
Gregory J. Proffitt *(COO & Exec VP)*
Kenneth D. Lumpkin *(CMO, Chief Lending Officer & Exec VP)*

AFFINITY BEVERAGE GROUP, INC.

810 7th St NE 01-244, Washington, DC 20002　　　　　　　　NV
ABVG—(OTCIQ)
Beverage Services
N.A.I.C.S.: 312120

AFFIRM HOLDINGS, INC.

650 California St, San Francisco, CA 94108
Tel.: (415) 960-1518　　　　DE
Web Site: https://www.affirm.com
Year Founded: 2019
AFRM—(NASDAQ)
Rev.: $2,322,999,000
Assets: $9,519,619,000
Liabilities: $6,787,630,000
Net Worth: $2,731,989,000
Earnings: ($517,757,000)
Emp.: 2,006
Fiscal Year-end: 06/30/24
Holding Company
N.A.I.C.S.: 551112
Alastair Rampell *(Co-Founder)*
Max Roth Levchin *(Founder, Chm & CEO)*
Michael Linford *(CFO)*
Siphelele Jiyane *(VP & Controller)*
Libor Michalek *(Pres)*
Katherine Adkins *(Chief Legal Officer)*

Subsidiaries:

Paybright Inc.　　　　　　　　(1)
161 Bay Street Suite 4530, Toronto, M5J 2S1, ON, Canada
Web Site: https://app.paybright.com
Financial Services
N.A.I.C.S.: 522291
Madge Rumman *(Sr Product Dir)*

AFFLUENCE CORP.

1942 Broadway St Ste 314C, Boulder, CO 80302
Tel.: (702) 295-6409　　　　CO
Web Site: https://affucorp.com
Year Founded: 2008
AFFU—(OTCIQ)
Telecommunication Servicesb
N.A.I.C.S.: 517810
Yossi Hazan *(CFO)*
Robert Pollan *(Chm)*
Patrick C. Shutt *(Vice Chm & CEO)*
Mary Stanhope *(Pres & COO)*
James E. Honan Jr. *(CEO)*

AFFYMAX, INC.

19200 Stevens Creek Blvd Ste 240, Cupertino, CA 95014
Tel.: (650) 812-8700　　　　DE
Web Site: http://www.affymax.com
Year Founded: 2001
AFFY—(OTCIQ)
Sales Range: Less than $1 Million
Emp.: 4
Biopharmaceutical Mfr
N.A.I.C.S.: 325412
Mark Thompson *(CFO)*

AFLAC INCORPORATED

1932 Wynnton Rd, Columbus, GA 31999
Tel.: (706) 323-3431　　　　GA
Web Site: https://www.aflac.com
Year Founded: 1955
AFL—(NYSE)
Rev.: $18,701,000,000
Assets: $126,724,000,000
Liabilities: $104,739,000,000
Net Worth: $21,985,000,000
Earnings: $4,659,000,000

Emp.: 12,785
Fiscal Year-end: 12/31/23
Holding Company; Supplemental Life & Health Insurance
N.A.I.C.S.: 524113
Daniel Paul Amos *(Chm, Pres & CEO)*
Masatoshi Koide *(Pres-Aflac Japan)*
Frederick J. Crawford *(Pres & COO)*
Max K. Broden *(CFO & Exec VP)*
Virgil R. Miller *(Pres- Individual Benefits Div & Exec VP)*
Albert A. Riggieri *(Chief Actuary, Chief Risk Officer-Global & Sr VP)*
Audrey Boone Tillman *(Gen Counsel & Exec VP)*

Subsidiaries:

Aflac International, Incorporated　(1)
1932 Wynnton Rd, Columbus, GA 31999-0001　　　　　　　(100%)
Tel.: (706) 323-3431
Web Site: https://www.aflac.com
Sales Range: $10-24.9 Million
Emp.: 4,000
Insurance Services
N.A.I.C.S.: 524210

Subsidiary (Non-US):

Aflac Heartful Services Company Limited　　　　　　　　　(2)
2-48-26 Kojima-cho South Gate Building, Chofu, Tokyo, 182-8001, Japan　(70%)
Tel.: (81) 4 2441 3180
Web Site: http://www.aflac-hs.co.jp
Emp.: 153
Fire Insurance Services
N.A.I.C.S.: 524113
Mikaru Manabe *(Pres & CEO)*

Aflac Insurance Service Company, Ltd.　　　　　　　　　(2)
1-24-1 Nishishinjuku, Shinjuku-Ku, Tokyo, 160-0023, Japan　　　(100%)
Tel.: (81) 353203777
Web Site: http://www.aflac.co.jp
Supplemental & Life Insurance Services
N.A.I.C.S.: 524128

Aflac Japan　　　　　　　　　(2)
2-1-1 Shinjuku Mitsui Building 19F, Nishi-Shinjuku Shinjuku-ku, Tokyo, 163-0456, Japan　　　　　　　　　(78%)
Tel.: (81) 63115095
Web Site: http://www.aflac.co.jp
Sales Range: $10-24.9 Million
Emp.: 30
Supplemental Insurance Products
N.A.I.C.S.: 524128
Masatoshi Koide *(Pres & CEO)*
Koji Ariyoshi *(Sr Mng Exec Officer)*
Andrew J. Conrad *(Mng Exec Officer)*
Kazuhiro Yamazaki *(Auditor)*
J. Todd Daniels *(Sr Mng Exec Officer)*
Charles D. Lake II *(Chm)*

Aflac Payment Service Company, Ltd.　　　　　　　　　(2)
Chofumaruzen Bldg 3rd Fl 4-6-1 Fuda, Chofu, Tokyo, 182-0024, Japan　(100%)
Tel.: (81) 424885120
Supplemental Insurance Provider
N.A.I.C.S.: 524128
Susan R. Blanck *(First Sr VP)*

Aflac Pet Small-amount-and-Short-term Insurance Co., Ltd.　　　(1)
2-1-1 Nishi-Shinjuku, Shinjuku-ku, Tokyo, 163-0416, Japan
Tel.: (81) 359312776
Web Site: https://www.aflacpet.co.jp
Short Term Insurance Services
N.A.I.C.S.: 524210

American Family Life Assurance Company of Columbus　　　(1)
1932 Wynnton Rd, Columbus, GA 31999-0001　　　　　　　(100%)
Tel.: (706) 323-3431
Web Site: https://www.aflac.com
Sales Range: $700-749.9 Million
Life, Health & Accident Insurance
N.A.I.C.S.: 524114
Daniel Paul Amos *(Chm & CEO)*

Subsidiary (Domestic):

American Family Life Assurance Company of New York　　　(2)
22 Corporate Woods Blvd, Albany, NY 12211　　　　　　　(100%)
Tel.: (518) 438-0764
Web Site: https://www.aflacny.com
Sales Range: $50-74.9 Million
Emp.: 115
Fire Insurance Services
N.A.I.C.S.: 524113

Apollo AF Loan Trust　　　　　(2)
1 Manhattanville Rd Ste 201, Purchase, NY 10577
Tel.: (212) 822-0456
Portfolio Management Services
N.A.I.C.S.: 523940

Communicorp, Inc.　　　　　　(1)
1001 Lockwood Ave, Columbus, GA 31999　　　　　　　　(100%)
Tel.: (706) 324-1182
Web Site: http://communicorp.com
Sales Range: $75-99.9 Million
Marketing Solution Services
N.A.I.C.S.: 541910
Eric B. Seldon *(Pres & CEO)*
Mike Thomas *(VP)*
Tony Mixon *(Dir-Shared Svcs)*
John Shutter *(Sr Mgr-Sls & Mktg Svcs)*
Gary Robinette *(Dir-Tech)*

Continental American Insurance Company　　　　　　　　(1)
2801 Devine St, Columbia, SC 29205
Tel.: (803) 256-6265
Web Site: https://www.caicworksite.com
Group & Employee Insurance
N.A.I.C.S.: 524210

Empoweredbenefits, LLC　　　(1)
525 N Tryon St Ste 900, Charlotte, NC 28202-0217
Tel.: (704) 369-0200
Web Site: http://empowered.net
Management Consulting Services
N.A.I.C.S.: 541618

Hatch Insight KK　　　　　　　(1)
WeWork the ARGYLE aoyama 6F 2-14-4 Kitaaoyama, Minato-ku, Tokyo, 107-0061, Japan
Tel.: (81) 367581655
Web Site: http://www.hatch-insight.co.jp
Data Collection & Management Services
N.A.I.C.S.: 518210

Medical Note, Inc.　　　　　　(1)
9F Ivy East Building 3-11-11 Shibuya, Shibuya-ku, Tokyo, 150-0002, Japan
Tel.: (81) 364190822
Web Site: https://www.medicalnote.co.jp
Emp.: 100
Medical Care Services
N.A.I.C.S.: 621610

Varagon Capital Partners, L.P.　(1)
299 Park Ave 3rd Fl, New York, NY 10171
Tel.: (212) 235-2600
Web Site: https://www.varagon.com
Emp.: 80
Investment Management Service
N.A.I.C.S.: 523940
Walter Owens *(CEO & Partner)*
Robby Bourgeois *(Partner, CFO & Chief Compliance Officer)*
Kevin Marchetti *(Partner & Chief Risk Officer)*
Zeshan Ashfaque *(Co-Mng Dir)*
Michael Blumberg *(Co-Mng Dir)*

Wellthie, Inc.　　　　　　　　(1)
110 Wall St, New York, NY 10005
Web Site: http://www.wellthie.com
Dental Insurance Services
N.A.I.C.S.: 524114
Sally Poblete *(Founder & CEO)*
Orlando Keise *(CTO & Chief Product Officer)*
Angela Sluss *(COO)*
Jeff Martin *(CFO)*

AFRICAN AGRICULTURE HOLDINGS INC.

445 Park Ave 9th Fl, New York, NY 10022
Tel.: (212) 745-1164　　　　NY

AAGR—(NASDAQ)
Holding Company
Michael Rhodes *(CEO & Sec)*
Kiran Peethambaran Shylaja *(Chief Technical Officer)*
Edward Meiring *(COO)*

Subsidiaries:

African Agriculture, Inc.　　　(1)
445 Park Ave 9th Fl, New York, NY 10022
Tel.: (212) 307-3154
Assets: $21,548,911
Liabilities: $36,064,675
Net Worth: ($14,515,764)
Earnings: ($4,293,335)
Emp.: 75
Fiscal Year-end: 12/31/2021
Food Products Mfr
N.A.I.C.S.: 311999

AFRICAN GOLD ACQUISITION CORPORATION

322 W 52nd St Ste 2322, New York, NY 10019-9998
Tel.: (860) 214-3714　　　　Ky
Year Founded: 2020
AGAC—(NYSE)
Rev.: $9,921,641
Assets: $415,030,603
Liabilities: $449,672,190
Net Worth: ($34,641,587)
Earnings: $8,472,897
Emp.: 3
Fiscal Year-end: 12/31/21
Investment Services
N.A.I.C.S.: 523999
Brian A. Hinchcliffe *(Vice Chm)*
Robert Hersov *(Chm)*
Christopher Chadwick *(CEO)*

AFTERMASTER, INC.

6671 Sunset Blvd Ste 1520, Hollywood, CA 90028
Tel.: (310) 657-4886　　　　DE
Web Site: http://www.aftermaster.com
Year Founded: 1988
AFTM—(OTCEM)
Rev.: $976,322
Assets: $1,093,447
Liabilities: $13,899,817
Net Worth: ($12,806,370)
Earnings: ($9,302,739)
Emp.: 9
Fiscal Year-end: 06/30/19
Audio & Video Recording Studio Operator
N.A.I.C.S.: 512240
Mirella Chavez *(CFO, Treas & Sec)*
Lawrence G. Ryckman *(Chm, Pres & CEO)*
Mark Depew *(Sr VP-Fin)*
Aaron Ryckman *(Sr VP-Bus Dev)*

AFTERNEXT HEALTHTECH ACQUISITION CORP.

301 Commerce St Ste 3300, Fort Worth, TX 76102
Tel.: (817) 871-4000　　　　Ky
Web Site:
　https://www.afternexthealthtech.com
Year Founded: 2021
AFTR—(NYSE)
Rev.: $3,635,404
Assets: $254,624,832
Liabilities: $265,580,364
Net Worth: ($10,955,532)
Earnings: $10,227,267
Emp.: 4
Fiscal Year-end: 12/31/22
Investment Services
N.A.I.C.S.: 523999
R. Halsey Wise *(Chm & CEO)*
Martin Davidson *(CFO)*
Anthony Colaluca Jr. *(Pres)*
Art Heidrich *(Sec)*
Cam Mullen *(VP)*

AfterNext HealthTech Acquisition Corp.—(Continued)

AGCO CORPORATION

4205 River Green Pkwy, Duluth, GA 30096-2568
Tel.: (770) 813-9200   DE
Web Site: https://www.agcocorp.com
Year Founded: 1990
AGCO—(NYSE)
Rev.: $14,412,400,000
Assets: $11,421,200,000
Liabilities: $6,764,400,000
Net Worth: $4,656,800,000
Earnings: $1,171,400,000
Emp.: 27,900
Fiscal Year-end: 12/31/23
Agriculture Equipment Mfr
N.A.I.C.S.: 333111
Eric P. Hansotia (Chm, Pres & CEO)
Damon J. Audia (CFO & Sr VP)
Indira Agarwal (Chief Acctg Officer & VP)
Ivory Harris (Chief HR Officer & Sr VP)
Kelvin Bennett (Sr VP-Engrg)
Stephen Caspari (Sr VP & Gen Mgr-Grain & Protein)
Seth H. Crawford (Sr VP & Gen Mgr-Precision Ag & Digital)
Damon J. Audia (CFO & Sr VP)
Tim Millwood (Sr VP & Chief Supply Chain Officer)
Viren Shah (Chief Digital & Info Officer & Sr VP)
Rachel Potts (Chief Comm Officer & VP)

Subsidiaries:

AGCO (China) Investment Co., Ltd. **(1)**
Room 810 Tower A Yingke Center No 2A Gongti North Road, Chaoyang District, Beijing, 100027, China
Tel.: (86) 105 706 2999
Web Site: https://www.agcocorp.cn
Agricultural Machinery & Equipment Distr
N.A.I.C.S.: 423820

AGCO A/S **(1)**
Stationsparken 37, 2600, Glostrup, Denmark
Tel.: (45) 3 639 4959
Web Site: https://www.agco.dk
Sales Range: $25-49.9 Million
Emp.: 15
Farm Machinery & Equipment Distr
N.A.I.C.S.: 423820

AGCO AB **(1)**
Sylveniusgatan 2, PO Box 18, 754 50, Uppsala, Sweden **(100%)**
Tel.: (46) 1 866 0000
Web Site: http://www.agco.se
Agricultural Machinery Product Distr
N.A.I.C.S.: 333111

AGCO Argentina S.A. **(1)**
Ruta 24 Km 18, General Rodriguez, 1748, Buenos Aires, Argentina
Tel.: (54) 2374858100
Sales Range: $250-299.9 Million
Emp.: 800
Financial Services; Farm Machinery & Equipment Mfr
N.A.I.C.S.: 333111

AGCO Australia Ltd. **(1)**
615 Somerville Road, Sunshine West, Melbourne, 3020, VIC, Australia **(100%)**
Tel.: (61) 39 313 0313
Web Site: http://www.agcocorp.com
Sales Range: $50-74.9 Million
Emp.: 100
Agriculture Product Distr
N.A.I.C.S.: 424690
Warwick McCormick (Mng Dir)

AGCO Austria GmbH **(1)**
Grautschenhof 24, 8684, Spital am Semmering, Austria
Tel.: (43) 385334810
Farm Machinery & Equipment Mfr
N.A.I.C.S.: 333111
Siegfried Aigner (Mgr-Mktg)

AGCO Canada Ltd. **(1)**
515 Dewdney Ave, Regina, S4P 3Y3, SK, Canada
Tel.: (306) 352-1692
Web Site: http://www.agco.com
Sales Range: $10-24.9 Million
Emp.: 60
Farm Machinery & Equipment Distr
N.A.I.C.S.: 423820
Martin H. Richenhagen (Chm, Pres & CEO)

AGCO Corporation-Jackson Operations **(1)**
202 Industrial Pk, Jackson, MN 56143
Tel.: (507) 847-2690
Sales Range: $250-299.9 Million
Emp.: 1,000
Mfr of Powered Orchard & Row Crop Sprayers
N.A.I.C.S.: 332323

AGCO Danmark A/S **(1)**
Stationsparken 37, 2600, Glostrup, Denmark **(100%)**
Tel.: (45) 3 639 4959
Web Site: https://www.agco.dk
Sales Range: $25-49.9 Million
Emp.: 40
Agriculture Product Distr
N.A.I.C.S.: 424690

AGCO Deutschland GmbH **(1)**
Johann-Georg-Fendt-Strasse 4, 87616, Marktoberdorf, Germany
Tel.: (49) 8342770
Web Site: http://www.fendt.com
Sales Range: $600-649.9 Million
Emp.: 3,000
Farm & Garden Machinery Mfr
N.A.I.C.S.: 333111

AGCO Feucht GmbH **(1)**
Fellastrasse 1-3, 90537, Feucht, Germany
Tel.: (49) 9128730
Web Site: https://fella.eu
Agricultural Machinery & Equipment Distr
N.A.I.C.S.: 423820

AGCO Feucht GmbH **(1)**
Fellastrasse 1-3 Feucht, Nuremberg, 90537, Germany
Tel.: (49) 9128730
Agricultural Equipment Distr
N.A.I.C.S.: 423820
Jochen Gnann (Dir-Supply Chain)

AGCO Finance LLC **(1)**
8001 Birchwood Crt, Johnston, IA 50131-0020
Web Site: http://www.agcofinance.com
Credit Services
N.A.I.C.S.: 522390

AGCO Funding Corporation **(1)**
4205 River Green Pkwy, Duluth, GA 30096-2563
Tel.: (770) 813-9200
Web Site: http://www.agcocorp.com
Business Support Services
N.A.I.C.S.: 561499
Martin H. Richenhagen (Chm, Pres & CEO)

AGCO GSI Asia Sdn Bhd **(1)**
Plot 218 Jalan Perindustrian Bukit Minyak 6, Kawasan Perindustrian Bukit Minyak Simpang Ampat, 14100, Penang, Malaysia
Tel.: (60) 45057598
Web Site: http://www.gsiasia.net
Grain Storage Services
N.A.I.C.S.: 493130

AGCO Holding BV **(1)**
Horsterweg 66A, 5971 NG, Grubbenvorst, Netherlands
Tel.: (31) 773278400
Web Site: http://www.challenger-ag.com
Sales Range: $75-99.9 Million
Emp.: 90
Holding Company
N.A.I.C.S.: 551112

Subsidiary (Non-US):

AGCO GmbH **(2)**
Johann-Georg-Fendt-Strasse 4, 87616, Marktoberdorf, Germany
Tel.: (49) 8342770
Web Site: http://www.fendt.com
Farm Machinery & Equipment Sales & Distr
N.A.I.C.S.: 423820

AGCO Holdings (Singapore) Pte. Ltd **(1)**
101 Thomson Road 31-05 United Square, Singapore, 307591, Singapore
Tel.: (65) 62558311
Holding Company
N.A.I.C.S.: 551112
Alex Baker (Reg Mgr)

AGCO Iberia SA **(1)**
Via de las Dos Castillas 33 ATTICA 7 Pozuelo de Alarcon, 28224, Madrid, Barcelona, Spain **(100%)**
Tel.: (34) 913529622
Agriculture Product Distr
N.A.I.C.S.: 424690

AGCO International Ltd. **(1)**
Victor-von-Bruns-Strasse 17, 8212, Neuhausen am Rheinfall, Switzerland **(100%)**
Tel.: (41) 527252200
Web Site: http://www.agcocorp.com
Emp.: 160
Agricultural Supplies Mfr & Distr
N.A.I.C.S.: 325320

AGCO Ltd. **(1)**
Abbey Park Stoneleigh Stareton, Kenilworth, CV8 2TQ, Warwickshire, United Kingdom
Tel.: (44) 247 669 4400
Web Site: http://www.agco.com
Sales Range: $250-299.9 Million
Emp.: 400
Farm Machinery & Equipment Sales & Distr
N.A.I.C.S.: 423820

AGCO Machinery Ltd **(1)**
Rochdelskaya street 15 Building 1, 123022, Moscow, Russia
Tel.: (7) 4957300805
Agriculture Machinery & Equipment Mfr
N.A.I.C.S.: 333111
Christine Klemmer (Gen Mgr)

AGCO Mexico S de RL de CV **(1)**
Carretera libre a Celaya Km 8 900, Fracc Industrial Balvanera Corregidora, 76908, Queretaro, Mexico
Tel.: (52) 442 229 5800
Web Site: https://www.agcocorp.mx
Agricultural Equipments Mfr & Distr
N.A.I.C.S.: 333924

AGCO Power Oy **(1)**
Linnavuorentie 8-10, 37240, Linnavuori, Finland
Tel.: (358) 207863600
Web Site: http://www.agcopower.com
Agricultural Machinery & Equipment Distr
N.A.I.C.S.: 423820

AGCO Suomi Oy **(1)**
Valmetinkatu 2, 44200, Suolahti, Finland
Tel.: (358) 2045501
Web Site: http://www.agcosuomi.fi
Farm Machinery & Equipment Mfr
N.A.I.C.S.: 333111
Matti Kallio (Dir-Sls)

Ag-Chem Europe Fertilizer Equipment BV **(1)**
Horsterweg 66A, Grubbenvorst, 5971 NG, Netherlands
Tel.: (31) 773278400
Web Site: http://www.challenger-ag.com
Emp.: 100
Farm & Garden Machinery Whslr
N.A.I.C.S.: 423820

AgRevolution, LLC **(1)**
1776 S Green St, Henderson, KY 42420
Tel.: (270) 854-1750
Web Site: http://www.agrev.com
Farm Machinery & Equipment Mfr
N.A.I.C.S.: 333111

AgTech, LLC **(1)**
1717 2nd Ave, Greeley, CO 80631
Tel.: (970) 360-4567
Web Site: https://redlund.com
Agricultural Machinery Mfr & Distr
N.A.I.C.S.: 333111

Subsidiary (Domestic):

Sorum Tractor Co., Inc. **(2)**
7727 W US Highway 160, Alamosa, CO 81101
Tel.: (719) 589-2822
Web Site: http://www.sorumtractor.com

Sales Range: $1-9.9 Million
Emp.: 12
Farm & Garden Machinery Mfr
N.A.I.C.S.: 423820
Greg Curtis (Gen Mgr)

Agri-Service, LLC **(1)**
300 Agri-Service Way, Kimberly, ID 83341
Tel.: (208) 734-7772
Web Site: https://agri-service.com
Farm & Agricultural Equipment Mfr
N.A.I.C.S.: 333111
Kevin Vivian (Pres)

Subsidiary (Domestic):

Blue Mountain Agri Support, Inc. **(2)**
620 Thain Rd, Lewiston, ID 83501
Tel.: (208)-746-6447
Web Site: http://www.bluemountainag.com
Sales Range: $1-9.9 Million
Emp.: 12
Outdoor Power Equipment Stores
N.A.I.C.S.: 444230
Dan Borders (VP)
David Hoekema (Mgr-Svc & Founder)

C-Lines France SAS **(1)**
1 Avenue Jean Zay, 45000, Orleans, 45000, France
Tel.: (33) 238224350
Agricultural Equipment Distr
N.A.I.C.S.: 423820

Cimbria Heid Italia SRL **(1)**
Via Colombarotto 2, 40026, Imola, Italy
Tel.: (39) 0542643302
Agricultural Equipment Distr
N.A.I.C.S.: 423820
Ugo Balestrieri (Mng Dir)

Eikmaskin AS **(1)**
Jogstadveien 25, Postboks 123, 2021, Skedsmokorset, Norway
Tel.: (47) 6 483 7300
Web Site: https://www.eikmaskin.no
Emp.: 30
Farm Machinery & Equipment Sales & Distr
N.A.I.C.S.: 423820

Farmer Automatic GmbH & Co. KG **(1)**
Konigstr 51, 48366, Laer, Germany
Tel.: (49) 25549110
Web Site: http://www.farmerautomatic-inc.com
Agricultural Equipment Distr
N.A.I.C.S.: 423820
Dieter Zenker (Member-Exec Bd)
Michael Gschwender (Member-Exec Bd)

GSI Brasil Industria e Comercio de Equipamentos Agropecuarios Ltd **(1)**
Rodovia ERS 324 Km 80, Marau, 99150-000, Rio Grande do Sul, Brazil
Tel.: (55) 5433427500
Web Site: https://www.gsibrasil.ind.br
Emp.: 500
Industrial Machinery Mfr
N.A.I.C.S.: 333111
Perro Abbonde (Dir Gen)

GSI Cumberland De Mexico, S. De RL De CV **(1)**
Acceso B No 103 - B, Parque Industrial Jurica, 76120, Santiago de Queretaro, Queretaro, Mexico
Tel.: (52) 442 218 9981
Web Site: http://www.gsigroupmexico.com
Farm Machinery & Equipment Distr
N.A.I.C.S.: 423820

GSI Electronique Inc **(1)**
5200 Armand-Frappier, Saint-Hubert, J3Z 1G5, QC, Canada
Tel.: (450) 926-3164
Web Site: http://www.gsi-electronics.com
Electric Equipment Mfr
N.A.I.C.S.: 334513

GSI Group, LLC **(1)**
1004 E Illinois St, Assumption, IL 62510
Tel.: (217) 226-2467
Web Site: http://www.grainsystems.com
Sales Range: $25-49.9 Million
Emp.: 1,916
Farm Supplies Whslr
N.A.I.C.S.: 424910

Subsidiary (Domestic):

Intersystems International, LLC **(2)**

9575 N 109th Ave, Omaha, NE 68142
Tel.: (402) 330-1500
Sales Range: $25-49.9 Million
Emp.: 185
Material Handling Equipment Mfr
N.A.I.C.S.: 333922
Randy Stauffer (VP-Sls & Mktg)

Johnson System, Inc. **(2)**
18999 US Highway 27 N, Marshall, MI
49068
Tel.: (555) 555-5555
Web Site: http://www.johnsonsysteminc.com
Sales Range: $1-9.9 Million
Emp.: 70
Catwalks, Towers & Support Structures Mfr
N.A.I.C.S.: 339999

Industrial Agricola Fortaleza Importa-
cao E Exportacao Ltda **(1)**
Rua James Joule 92 - Conj 161, Brooklin,
Sao Paulo, 04576-080, Brazil
Tel.: (55) 1147952000
Sales Range: $150-199.9 Million
Emp.: 400
Agriculture Product Distr
N.A.I.C.S.: 424690
Martin Richenhagen (CEO)

Laverda AGCO SPA **(1)**
Via F Laverda 15/17, 36042, Breganze, VI,
Italy
Tel.: (39) 0445385311
Web Site: http://www.laverdaworld.com
Industrial Machinery Mfr & Distr
N.A.I.C.S.: 333998

Laverda S.p.A **(1)**
Via F Laverda 15/17, 36042, Breganze,
Italy **(50%)**
Tel.: (39) 04453853111
Web Site: http://www.laverdaworld.com
Sales Range: $75-99.9 Million
Emp.: 450
Agriculture Product Distr
N.A.I.C.S.: 333111

Lely Australia Pty Ltd **(1)**
48 MacKay Street, Coorparoo, 3561, QLD,
Australia
Tel.: (61) 3548440001
Web Site: http://www.lely.com
Emp.: 20
Agricultural Equipment Distr
N.A.I.C.S.: 423820

Massey Ferguson Corp. **(1)**
4205 River Green Pkwy, Duluth, GA 30096
Tel.: (770) 813-9200
Web Site: http://www.masseyferguson.com
Sales Range: $100-124.9 Million
Farm Equipment Mfr, Sales & Distr
N.A.I.C.S.: 333111

Subsidiary (Non-US):

Massey Ferguson Tarim Makineleri
Ltd **(2)**
Perdemsac Plaza Bayar Cad No 17 Ka
11/116, 34742, Istanbul, Turkiye
Tel.: (90) 2163622100
Web Site:
   http://www.masseyferguson.com.tr
Farm Equipment Mfr, Sales & Distr
N.A.I.C.S.: 333111

Massey Ferguson Works Pension
Trust Ltd. **(1)**
Abbey Park, PO Box 62, Kenilworth, CV8
2TQ, Stoneleigh, United Kingdom
Tel.: (44) 2476694400
Fund Services
N.A.I.C.S.: 525110
Debbie Coltman (Mgr-Pension)

Precision Planting, LLC **(1)**
23207 Townline Rd, Tremont, IL 61568
Tel.: (309) 925-5050
Web Site: https://www.precisionplanting.com
Farming Equipment Developer, Mfr & Whslr
N.A.I.C.S.: 333111

Sparex Limited ApS **(1)**
Messevej 1, 9600, Aars, Denmark
Tel.: (45) 64722287
Web Site: https://dk.sparex.com
Agricultural Machinery & Equipment Distr
N.A.I.C.S.: 423820
Michael Pavar (Mgr-Customer Svc)

Sparex Ltd. **(1)**

Exeter Airport, Exeter, EX5 2LJ, Devon,
United Kingdom
Tel.: (44) 139 244 9168
Web Site: https://www.gb.sparex.com
Sales Range: $150-199.9 Million
Emp.: 400
Motor Vehicle Parts Distr
N.A.I.C.S.: 423110

Subsidiary (Non-US):

Sparex (Tractor Accessories)
Limited **(2)**
Grannagh, Waterford, X91 HRR3, Ireland
Tel.: (353) 51855592
Vehicle Components Mfr
N.A.I.C.S.: 336390

Sparex Agrirepuestos SL **(2)**
Bulevar De Salburua 8 10 B, 01002, Vitoria-
Gasteiz, Alava, Spain
Tel.: (34) 94 513 3524
Web Site: https://es.sparex.com
Agriculture Machinery & Equipment Mfr
N.A.I.C.S.: 333111

Sparex ApS **(2)**
Messevej 1, 9600, Aars, Denmark
Tel.: (45) 64722287
Web Site: http://dk.sparex.com
Sales Range: $10-24.9 Million
Emp.: 5
Farm & Garden Machinery Mfr
N.A.I.C.S.: 333111

Sparex Handels-und Vertriebs
GmbH **(2)**
Hansestrasse 22, 27419, Sittensen, Ger-
many
Tel.: (49) 42 829 3100
Web Site: https://de.sparex.com
Farm Machinery & Equipment Mfr
N.A.I.C.S.: 333111

Subsidiary (US):

Sparex Inc. **(2)**
190 Lena Dr, Aurora, OH 44202
Tel.: (330) 562-8150
Web Site: https://www.us.sparex.com
Tractor Parts & Equipment Whslr
N.A.I.C.S.: 423820
Robert Meiszner (Mng Dir)

Subsidiary (Non-US):

Sparex Limited Vestiging Holland
BV **(2)**
Luzernestraat 19 N, Nieuw-Vennep, 2153
GM, Zwaanshoek, Netherlands
Tel.: (31) 23 584 1020
Web Site: https://nl.sparex.com
Farm & Garden Machinery Equipment Mfr
N.A.I.C.S.: 333111

Sparex Polska Sp. Z.o.o. **(2)**
Ul Wagrowska 2, 61-369, Poznan, Poland
Tel.: (48) 61 816 1937
Web Site: https://pl.sparex.com
Emp.: 10
Agricultural Machinery Mfr & Distr
N.A.I.C.S.: 333111

Sparex Portugal Importacao e Com-
ercio de Pecas Lda **(2)**
Lugar da Espera, Runa, 2565-716, Torres
Vedras, Portugal
Tel.: (351) 26 131 1107
Web Site: https://pt.sparex.com
Farm Machinery & Equipment Mfr
N.A.I.C.S.: 333111

Sparex S.A.R.L. **(2)**
Z A E de Ty Douar, 29450, Commana,
France
Tel.: (33) 29 878 9234
Web Site: https://fr.sparex.com
Emp.: 30
Agricultural Machinery & Equipment Mfr
N.A.I.C.S.: 333111

Sparex Maschinensubehor Han-
delsgesellschaft m.b.H **(1)**
Gewerbezone 11 Hunnenbrunn, 9300,
Sankt Veit an der Glan, Austria
Tel.: (43) 42126400
Agricultural Machinery & Equipment Mfr
N.A.I.C.S.: 333922

Sparex New Zealand Ltd **(1)**

142 Neilson Street, Onehunga, Auckland,
New Zealand
Tel.: (64) 9 634 4121
Web Site: https://nz.sparex.com
Agricultural Machinery & Equipment Distr
N.A.I.C.S.: 423820

Spenco Engineering Company
Ltd **(1)**
Station Road, Clyst Honiton, Exeter, EX5
2DX, Devon, United Kingdom
Tel.: (44) 139 236 9795
Web Site: https://www.spenco.co.uk
Emp.: 40
Industrial Machinery Mfr & Distr
N.A.I.C.S.: 333998

Sunflower Manufacturing Inc. **(1)**
3154 Hallie Trl, Beloit, KS 67420-0566
Tel.: (785) 738-2261
Web Site: http://www.sunflowermfg.com
Sales Range: $100-124.9 Million
Emp.: 290
Tillage Tools
N.A.I.C.S.: 333111

Tecno Poultry Equipment S.P.A. **(1)**
via Salvo d'Acquisto 11 Ronchi di Vil-
lafranca Padovana, Campo San Martino,
35010, Padua, 35010, Italy
Tel.: (39) 0499699666
Web Site:
   https://www.poultryequipment.com
Agricultural Equipment Distr
N.A.I.C.S.: 423820
Luigino Pellizzer (Mgr-Area)

The GSI Asia Group Sdn. Bhd **(1)**
Plot 16 Lorong Perusahaan Maju 6 Phase 4
Prai Industrial Estate Prai, Seberang Perai
Tengah, 13600, Penang, Malaysia
Tel.: (60) 45083319
Grain Storage Services
N.A.I.C.S.: 493130
Muhammad Abdul Wadud (Gen Mgr)

The GSI Group (Shanghai) Co.
Ltd **(1)**
No 518 Xinzhuan Road, Songjiang District,
Shanghai, 201612, China
Tel.: (86) 216 615 9777
Web Site: http://www.gsiasia.net
Farming Equipments Mfr
N.A.I.C.S.: 333922

Valtra Voukraus OY **(1)**
Valmetinkatu 2, 44200, Suolahti, Finland
Tel.: (358) 2045501
Web Site: http://www.valtra.fi
Sales Range: $200-249.9 Million
Emp.: 800
Machinery Rental Services
N.A.I.C.S.: 532412

Valtra, Inc. **(1)**
Valmetinkatu 2, 44200, Suolahti,
Finland **(100%)**
Tel.: (358) 2045501
Web Site: http://www.valtra.com
Sales Range: $200-249.9 Million
Emp.: 700
Mfr of Tractors
N.A.I.C.S.: 333924
Jari Rraueja (Mng Dir)

Subsidiary (Domestic):

AGCO Power Oy **(2)**
Linnavuorentie 8-10, 37240, Linnavuori,
Finland
Tel.: (358) 20 786 3600
Web Site: https://www.agcopower.com
Diesel Engine Mfr
N.A.I.C.S.: 336310
Jarmo Tuorila (Dir-Sls & Mktg)
Alexander Duray (Acct Mgr)
Jarmo Oksanen (Mgr-Sls, Power & Genera-
tion Svc)

Subsidiary (Non-US):

AGCO SPZOO **(2)**
ul Poznanska 5, Pączkowo, 62-021,
Poznan, Poland
Tel.: (48) 61 662 9050
Web Site: http://traktory.info.pl
Agriculture Product Distr
N.A.I.C.S.: 424690

Valtra GmbH **(2)**
Grautschenhof 24, A 8684, Spital am Sem-

mering, Austria **(100%)**
Tel.: (43) 38533480
Web Site: http://www.valtra.at
Sales Range: $1-9.9 Million
Emp.: 7
Mfr of Tractors
N.A.I.C.S.: 333924

Valtra International B.V. **(2)**
Horsterweg 66A, 5971 NG, Grubbenvorst,
Netherlands
Tel.: (31) 773278400
Web Site: http://www.valtra.com
Agricultural Machinery Mfr
N.A.I.C.S.: 333111

Subsidiary (Non-US):

Valtra do Brasil S.A. **(3)**
Rua Capitao Francisco De Almeida 695,
Mogi Das Cruzes, Sao Paulo, SP, Brazil
Tel.: (55) 1147952000
Web Site: http://www.valtra.com.br
Mfr of Tractors
N.A.I.C.S.: 333924

Subsidiary (Non-US):

Valtra Tractores S.A. **(2)**
Hnos Garcia Noblejas 39 - 5, Atica 7 Edifi-
cio 6, 28037, Madrid, Spain **(100%)**
Tel.: (34) 913770848
Web Site: http://www.valtra.es
Sales Range: $25-49.9 Million
Emp.: 40
Mfr of Tractors
N.A.I.C.S.: 333924

Valtra Tractores S.A. **(2)**
Valentin Gomez 577, Haedo, Buenos Aires,
Argentina
Tel.: (54) 1144897100
Web Site: http://www.valtra.com.ar
Sales Range: $10-24.9 Million
Emp.: 120
Mfr of Tractors
N.A.I.C.S.: 333924

Valtra Tractors (UK) Ltd. **(2)**
Abbey Park Stoneleigh, Stareton, Kenil-
worth, CV8 2TQ, Warwickshire, United
Kingdom **(100%)**
Tel.: (44) 2476694400
Web Site: http://www.agco.com
Sales Range: $25-49.9 Million
Emp.: 30
Mfr of Tractors
N.A.I.C.S.: 333924

Joint Venture (Non-US):

Valtra Traktor AB **(2)**
Hjalmarvagen 85, PO Box 6016, S 702 20,
Orebro, Sweden
Tel.: (46) 34685000
Web Site: http://www.valtra.se
Sales Range: $75-99.9 Million
Emp.: 50
Tractor Mfr
N.A.I.C.S.: 333924

Subsidiary (Non-US):

Valtra Vertriebs GmbH **(2)**
Johann Georg Fendt Str 14, 87616, Markto-
berdorf, Germany **(100%)**
Tel.: (49) 8342778100
Web Site: http://www.valtra.de
Sales Range: $10-24.9 Million
Emp.: 23
Mfr of Tractors
N.A.I.C.S.: 333924

Valtractor SA **(2)**
Parque Industrial Vale Do Alecrim Rua Do
Ferro 150, Palmela, Pinhal Novo, 2950-007,
Portugal
Tel.: (351) 212388680
Web Site: http://www.valtra.pt
Sales Range: $10-24.9 Million
Emp.: 7
Mfr of Tractors
N.A.I.C.S.: 333924

Valtractor Comercio de Tractores e
Maquinas Agricolas SA **(1)**
Parque Industrial Vale do Alecrim Rua do
Ferro 150, Pinhal Novo, Palmela, 2950-007,
Portugal
Tel.: (351) 212388680
Farm Machinery & Equipment Mfr & Distr

AGCO Corporation—(Continued)

N.A.I.C.S.: 333111

Western District Agricentre Pty. Ltd.   (1)
94 Caramut Road, PO Box 301, Warrnambool, 3280, VIC, Australia
Tel.: (61) 355621744
Web Site:
http://www.westerndistrictagricentre.com
Farm Machinery & Equipment Whslr
N.A.I.C.S.: 423820

AGEAGLE AERIAL SYSTEMS INC.

8201 E 34th St N Ste 1307, Wichita, KS 67226
Tel.: (620) 325-6363   NV
Web Site: https://www.ageagle.com
Year Founded: 1999
UAVS—(NYSEAMEX)
Rev.: $19,094,425
Assets: $54,184,874
Liabilities: $10,960,399
Net Worth: $43,224,475
Earnings: ($58,253,723)
Emp.: 92
Fiscal Year-end: 12/31/22
Holding Company; Aerial Vehicle Mfr
N.A.I.C.S.: 551112
Mark DiSiena (CFO & Principal Acctg Officer)
William Irby (Pres & CEO)

Subsidiaries:

Eagle Aerial Systems, Inc.   (1)
117 S 4th St, Neodesha, KS 66757
Tel.: (620) 325-6363
Web Site: http://www.ageagle.com
Rev.: $116,035
Assets: $311,263
Liabilities: $1,967,419
Net Worth: ($1,656,156)
Earnings: ($797,215)
Emp.: 9
Fiscal Year-end: 12/31/2017
Aerial Vehicle Mfr
N.A.I.C.S.: 336411

senseFly SA   (1)
Route de Geneve 38, 1033, Cheseaux-sur-Lausanne, Switzerland
Tel.: (41) 215520440
Web Site: http://www.sensefly.com
Drone Mfr
N.A.I.C.S.: 336411
Brock Ryder (Head-Sls)
Michael O'Sullivan (Mng Dir)
Damien Gentilhomme (Head-Admin)
Raphael Zaugg (Head-R&D)

AGENT INFORMATION SOFTWARE, INC.

15218 Summit Ave Ste 300 240, Fontana, CA 92336
Tel.: (909) 595-7004
Web Site:
https://www.agentinformationsoft
ware.com
AIFS—(OTCIQ)
Rev.: $5,355,510
Assets: $6,047,621
Liabilities: $2,242,819
Net Worth: $3,804,802
Earnings: $408,667
Fiscal Year-end: 12/31/20
Software Development Services
N.A.I.C.S.: 541714
Paul R. Cope (Pres)

AGENTIX CORP.

32932 Pacific Coast Hwy Ste 14-254, Dana Point, CA 92629
Tel.: (321) 299-2014   NV
Web Site:
https://www.agentixcorp.com
Year Founded: 2013
AGTX—(OTCIQ)
Assets: $106,372
Liabilities: $2,666,594

Net Worth: ($2,560,222)
Earnings: ($585,154)
Emp.: 2
Fiscal Year-end: 03/31/24
Oil & Gas Field Machinery & Equipment Manufacturing
N.A.I.C.S.: 333132
Rudy Mazzocchi (Chm, Pres & CEO)
Salman Hoda (Treas & Sec)
Martin Schroeder (Chief Scientific Officer)

AGENUS INC.

3 Forbes Rd, Lexington, MA 02421-7305
Tel.: (781) 674-4400   DE
Web Site:
https://www.agenusbio.com
Year Founded: 1994
AGEN—(NASDAQ)
Rev.: $98,024,000
Assets: $413,556,000
Liabilities: $468,458,000
Net Worth: ($54,902,000)
Earnings: ($220,286,000)
Emp.: 533
Fiscal Year-end: 12/31/22
Cancer Treatment Biotechnology Mfr, Researcher & Developer
N.A.I.C.S.: 325412
Stephanie Fagan (Chief Comm Officer)
Christine M. Klaskin (CFO, Chief Acctg Officer & VP-Fin)
Robin G. Taylor (Chief Comml Officer)
Alfred Dadson (Chief Mfg Officer)
Homa Yeganegi (Chief Product Strategy & Global Medical Affairs Officer)
Steven O'Day (Chief Medical Officer)
Robin Abrams (Chief Legal Officer)
Tracy Mazza Clemente (Chief People Officer)
Eric Humes (Chief Quality Officer)
Craig Winter (CIO)
Garo H. Armen (Founder, Chm & CEO)

Subsidiaries:

AgenTus Therapeutics, Inc.   (1)
149 5th Ave Ste 500, New York, NY 10010
Tel.: (212) 994-8250
Web Site: https://minktherapeutics.com
Pharmaceuticals Product Mfr
N.A.I.C.S.: 325412
Garo Armen (Chm)
Walter Flamenbaum (CEO)
Peter Suenaert (Head-Clinical Dev-Global)
Mark Exley (Head-Cellular Immunology)
Mark van Dijk (CTO)

Agenus Switzerland Inc.   (1)
Hochbergerstrasse 60C, 4057, Basel, Switzerland
Tel.: (41) 616332260
Web Site: http://www.agenusbio.com
Life Science, Physical, Engineering Research & Development Services
N.A.I.C.S.: 541715

AGILE GROWTH CORP.

Riverside Ctr 275 Grove St Ste 2-400, Newton, MA 02466
Tel.: (617) 663-5997   Ky
Web Site:
http://www.agilegrowthcorp.com
Year Founded: 2021
AGGRU—(NASDAQ)
Investment Services
N.A.I.C.S.: 523999
Jay Bhatt (CEO & CFO)
Tony Aquilina (Chief Sourcing Officer)
Sally Baraka (Chief Admin Officer)
Tony Grout (CTO)
John Newton (Chief Strategy Officer)

AGILE THERAPEUTICS, INC.

500 College Rd E Ste 310, Princeton, NJ 08540
Tel.: (609) 683-1880   DE
Web Site:
https://www.agiletherapeutics.com
Year Founded: 1997
AGRX—(OTCQB)
Rev.: $10,884,000
Assets: $14,242,000
Liabilities: $19,787,000
Net Worth: ($5,545,000)
Earnings: ($25,412,000)
Emp.: 22
Fiscal Year-end: 12/31/22
Pharmaceuticals Mfr
N.A.I.C.S.: 325412
Alfred F. Altomari (Chm & CEO)
Scott M. Colante (CFO, Treas & Sr VP)
Geoffrey P. Gilmore (Chief Admin Officer)
John W. Hubbard (Chm)
Amy Welsh (Chief Comml Officer)
Paul Korner (Chief Medical Officer)
Kimberly Whelan (VP-Policy, Advocacy, and Market Access)
Robert G. Conway (Chief Corp Plng & Supply Chain Officer)
Matt Riley (Head-IR & Corp Comm)

AGILENT TECHNOLOGIES, INC.

5301 Stevens Creek Blvd, Santa Clara, CA 95051
Tel.: (408) 345-8886   DE
Web Site: https://www.agilent.com
Year Founded: 1999
A—(NYSE)
Rev.: $6,510,000,000
Assets: $11,846,000,000
Liabilities: $5,948,000,000
Net Worth: $5,898,000,000
Earnings: $1,289,000,000
Emp.: 17,900
Fiscal Year-end: 10/31/24
Life Sciences, Diagnostics & Chemical Analysis Services
N.A.I.C.S.: 541380
Rodney Gonsalves (Chief Acctg Officer, VP & Controller)
Henrik Ancher-Jensen (Pres-Order Fulfillment & Supply Chain & Sr VP)
Robert W. McMahon (CFO & Sr VP)
Diana Chiu (VP, Asst Sec & Asst Gen Counsel)
Jenipher E. Dalton (Sr VP-Enterprise Regulatory Affairs & Quality Assurance)
Katharine Knobil (Chief Medical Officer)
Philip Binns (Pres-Life Sciences & Applied Markets Grp)
Padraig McDonnell (Pres, CEO, COO & Pres-CrossLab Grp)
Angelica Riemann (Pres-Agilent CrossLab Grp & Sr VP)
Fred Schwarz (Chief Corp Dev Officer & Sr VP)
Chris Swenson (VP)
Tom Callihan (Chief Enterprise Transformation Officer & Sr VP-Agilent)
Guillermo Gualino (Treas & VP)
Jonah Kirkwood (Chief Comml Officer-Comml Organization & Sr VP-Agilent)
John Kohl (CIO & Sr VP-Agilent)
Simon May (Pres-Diagnostics & Genomics Grp & Sr VP-Agilent)
Bret DiMarco (Chief Legal Officer, Sec & Sr VP-Agilent)
Kari Fosser (Sr VP-Agilent)

Subsidiaries:

AT Singapore (Global) Pte. Ltd.   (1)
Agilent Technologies Building 1 Yishun Avenue 7, Singapore, 768923, Singapore

Tel.: (65) 62158045
Medical Equipment & Device Mfr
N.A.I.C.S.: 339112

Acea Biosciences Inc.   (1)
6779 Mesa Ridge Rd, San Diego, CA 92121
Tel.: (858) 724-0928
Web Site: http://www.aceabio.com
Cell-based Assays, Cardiotoxicity Research, Stem Cell Research & Immunotherapy
N.A.I.C.S.: 541714
Xiao Xu (CEO)

Agilent Technologies (Malaysia) Sdn. Bhd.   (1)
Bayan Lepas Free Industrial Zone Phase 3 Pulau Pinang, 11900, Penang, Malaysia   (100%)
Tel.: (60) 46430611
Web Site: http://www.jobs.agilent.com
Sales Range: $700-749.9 Million
Emp.: 6,003
Communications Components, Electronic & Optical Test Measuring & Monitoring Instruments Designer, Developer, Mfr & Provider
N.A.I.C.S.: 334519

Agilent Technologies Australia Pty Ltd   (1)
347 Burwood Hwy, Forest Hill, 3131, Victoria, Australia   (100%)
Tel.: (61) 392102890
Web Site: http://www.agilent.com.au
Sales Range: $50-74.9 Million
Emp.: 100
Designs, Develops, Manufactures & Provides Communications Components, Electronic & Optical Test Measuring & Monitoring Instruments
N.A.I.C.S.: 334519

Agilent Technologies Brasil Ltda.   (1)
Alameda Araguaia 1142, Alphaville Barueri, Sao Paulo, 06455 940, CEP, Brazil   (100%)
Tel.: (55) 1141973500
Web Site: http://www.home.agilent.com
Sales Range: $25-49.9 Million
Emp.: 150
Designs, Develops, Manufactures & Provides Communications Components, Electronic & Optical Test Measuring & Monitoring Instruments
N.A.I.C.S.: 334519

Agilent Technologies Canada Inc.   (1)
6705 Millcreek Dr Unit 5, Mississauga, L5N 5M4, ON, Canada
Web Site: http://www.agilent.com
Designs, Develops, Manufactures & Provides Communications Components, Electronic & Optical Test Measuring & Monitoring Instruments
N.A.I.C.S.: 334519

Agilent Technologies Europe B.V.   (1)
Groenelaan 5, Amstelveen, 1186 AA, Netherlands
Tel.: (31) 205472000
Measuring Instruments Mfr
N.A.I.C.S.: 334515

Subsidiary (Non-US):

Agilent Technologies Belgium S.A./N.V.   (2)
Kleetlaan 5 Box 9, Diegem, 1831, Belgium   (100%)
Tel.: (32) 24049000
Web Site: http://www.agilent.com
Sales Range: $10-24.9 Million
Emp.: 40
Designs, Develops, Manufactures & Provides Communications Components, Electronic & Optical Test Measuring & Monitoring Instruments
N.A.I.C.S.: 334519
Alain Cervervaecke (Mng Dir)

Agilent Technologies Deutschland Holding GmbH   (2)
Herrenberger Str 130, Boblingen, 71034, Germany
Tel.: (49) 70314640
Web Site:
http://www.agilenttechnologies.com
Sales Range: $150-199.9 Million
Emp.: 600

Designs, Develops, Manufactures & Provides Communications Components, Electronic & Optical Test Measuring & Monitoring Instruments
N.A.I.C.S.: 334519

Subsidiary (Domestic):

Agilent Technologies Deutschland Alpha GmbH (3)
Herrenberger St 130, 71034, Boblingen, Germany
Tel.: (49) 70314640
Web Site: http://www.agilent.com
Measuring Instruments Mfr
N.A.I.C.S.: 334515

Agilent Technologies Deutschland GmbH (3)
Herrenberger Strasse 130, 71034, Boblingen, Germany
Tel.: (49) 70314640
Web Site: http://www.home.agilent.com
Sales Range: $125-149.9 Million
Emp.: 600
Designs, Develops, Manufactures & Provides Communications Components, Electronic & Optical Test Measuring & Monitoring Instruments
N.A.I.C.S.: 334519

Subsidiary (Non-US):

Agilent Technologies France SAS (2)
Tare Technopolis Zade Courtaboeus 3 Ave Gu Canada, 91745, Les Ulis, Cedex, France (100%)
Tel.: (33) 164535000
Web Site: http://www.agilent.fr
Sales Range: $25-49.9 Million
Emp.: 120
Designs, Develops, Manufactures & Provides Communications Components, Electronic & Optical Test Measuring & Monitoring Instruments
N.A.I.C.S.: 334519
Banoit Naal (Gen Dir)

Agilent Technologies International SARL (2)
39 Rue De Veyrot, 1217, Meyrin, Switzerland (100%)
Tel.: (41) 227806111
Sales Range: $10-24.9 Million
Emp.: 40
Designs, Develops, Manufactures & Provides Communications Components, Electronic & Optical Test Measuring & Monitoring Instruments
N.A.I.C.S.: 334519

Agilent Technologies Ireland Ltd. (2)
Unit 3 Euro House Euro Business Park, Little Island, Cork, Ireland (100%)
Tel.: (353) 0 1 605 8324
Web Site: http://www.agilent.com
Designs, Develops, Manufactures & Provides Communications Components, Electronic & Optical Test Measuring & Monitoring Instruments
N.A.I.C.S.: 334519

Subsidiary (Domestic):

Agilent Technologies Ireland Finance Limited (3)
Unit C Euro House Euro Business Park, Little Island, Cork, Ireland (100%)
Tel.: (353) 16058320
Web Site: http://www.agilent.co.uk
Sales Range: $10-24.9 Million
Emp.: 17
Designs, Develops, Manufactures & Provides Communications Components, Electronic & Optical Test Measuring & Monitoring Instruments
N.A.I.C.S.: 334519

Subsidiary (Non-US):

Agilent Technologies Italia S.p.A.. (2)
Centro Direzionale di Villa Fiorita Via Piero Gobetti 2/C, Cernusco Sul Naviglio, 20063, Milan, Italy
Tel.: (39) 02926081
Web Site: http://www.home.agilent.com

Sales Range: $100-124.9 Million
Emp.: 60
Designs, Develops, Manufactures & Supplies Communications Components, Electronic & Optical Test Measuring & Monitoring Instruments
N.A.I.C.S.: 334519

Agilent Technologies Sweden Holding AB (2)
Kronborgsgrand 23, PO Box 52, 164 94, Kista, Sweden (100%)
Tel.: (46) 850648600
Sales Range: $10-24.9 Million
Emp.: 55
Designs, Develops, Manufactures & Provides Communications Components, Electronic & Optical Test Measuring & Monitoring Instruments
N.A.I.C.S.: 334519

Dako Denmark A/S (2)
Produktionsvej 42, 2600, Glostrup, Denmark
Tel.: (45) 44859500
Web Site: http://www.dako.com
Sales Range: $250-299.9 Million
Emp.: 500
Reagents & Systems for Cancer Diagnosis & Cell Analysis
N.A.I.C.S.: 325413
Egil Molsted Madsen (CFO)

Subsidiary (Non-US):

Dako Belgium N.V. (3)
Interleuvenlaan 12B, Heverlee, Belgium (100%)
Tel.: (32) 16387220
Web Site: http://www.dako.be
Sales Range: $25-49.9 Million
Emp.: 10
In-Vitro Diagnostic Substance Manufacturing
N.A.I.C.S.: 325413

Dako Deutschland GmbH (3)
Weidestrasse 134, 22769, Hamburg, Germany (100%)
Tel.: (49) 406969470
Web Site: http://www.dakogmbh.de
Drugs & Druggists Sundries Whslr
N.A.I.C.S.: 424210

Dako Diagnosticos S.A. (3)
C- Federico Mompou 5, 5 Bajos A 1a, 08960, Barcelona, Spain (100%)
Tel.: (34) 934990506
Web Site: http://www.dako.es
Sales Range: $25-49.9 Million
Emp.: 34
Medical Dental & Hospital Equipment & Supplies Merchant Whsrl
N.A.I.C.S.: 423450
Mateo Ijlesias (Mng Dir)

Dako France S.A.S. (3)
Rue des Charmes, 78196, Trappes, France
Tel.: (33) 130500050
Web Site: http://www.dako.fr
Sales Range: $25-49.9 Million
Emp.: 24
Drugs & Druggists Sundries Whslr
N.A.I.C.S.: 424210

Dako Italia S.p.A. (3)
Via Piero Portaluppi 11-2, Milan, 20138, Italy (100%)
Tel.: (39) 02580781
Web Site: http://www.dako.com
Sales Range: $25-49.9 Million
Emp.: 20
In-Vitro Diagnostic Substance Mfr
N.A.I.C.S.: 325413

Dako Japan Inc. (3)
Sumitomo fudosan Iidabashi Building, 2-5-1 Koraku Bunkyo-ku, 112-0004, Tokyo, Japan (100%)
Tel.: (81) 358027211
Web Site: http://www.dako.jp
Drugs & Druggists Sundries Whslr
N.A.I.C.S.: 424210

Dako Netherlands B.V. (3)
p/a Interleuvenlaan 12B, B-3001, Heverlee, Belgium (100%)
Tel.: (32) 204211100
Web Site: http://www.dakobv.nl
Sales Range: $10-24.9 Million
Emp.: 2
Medical Laboratories

N.A.I.C.S.: 621511

Subsidiary (US):

Dako North America, Inc. (3)
6392 Via Real, Carpinteria, CA 93013
Tel.: (805) 566-6655
Emp.: 300
Reagents & Systems for Cancer Diagnosis & Cell Analysis
N.A.I.C.S.: 327910
Rosanne Welcher (Sr Dir-Regulatory, Quality & Clinical Affairs)
Dave Stanforth (Head-R&D-Companion Diagnostics)
Trevor Page (Dir-Corp Bus Dev)

Subsidiary (Non-US):

Dako Schweiz GmbH (3)
Grabenstrasse 27, 6341, Baar, Switzerland (100%)
Tel.: (41) 417601166
Web Site: http://www.dako.ch
Medicinal & Botanical Mfr
N.A.I.C.S.: 325411
Matthias Mund (Mng Dir)

Dako Sweden AB (3)
Kronborgsgrand 23 Kista, Stockholm, S-164 94, Sweden (100%)
Tel.: (46) 855620600
Web Site: http://www.agilent.com
Sales Range: $25-49.9 Million
Emp.: 10
Cancer Diagnostics Mfr & Sales
N.A.I.C.S.: 325413

Dako UK Ltd (3)
Cambridge House St Thomas Pl Ely, CB7 4EX, Cambridge, United Kingdom - England (100%)
Tel.: (44) 1353669911
Web Site: http://www.dako.co.uk
Sales Range: $25-49.9 Million
Emp.: 10
Drugs & Druggists Sundries Whslr
N.A.I.C.S.: 424210

Agilent Technologies Japan, Ltd. (1)
9 1 Takakura cho, Hachioji, Tokyo, Japan (100%)
Tel.: (81) 426603111
Web Site: http://www.agilent.co.jp
Sales Range: $100-124.9 Million
Designs, Develops, Manufactures & Provides Communications Components, Electronic & Optical Test Measuring & Monitoring Instruments
N.A.I.C.S.: 334519

Agilent Technologies Mexico, S.de R.L. de C.V. (1)
Av Insurgentes Sur 1602 Oficina 801, Mexico, 03940, Mexico (100%)
Tel.: (52) 5512532000
Web Site: http://www.agilent.com
Communications Components, Electronic & Optical Test Measuring & Monitoring Instruments Designer, Developer & Mfr
N.A.I.C.S.: 334519

Agilent Technologies Singapore Pte. Ltd. (1)
1 Yishun Ave 7, Singapore, 768923, Singapore (100%)
Tel.: (65) 63771688
Web Site: http://www.home.agilent.com
Sales Range: $150-199.9 Million
Emp.: 800
Designs, Develops, Manufactures & Provides Communications Components, Electronic & Optical Test Measuring & Monitoring Instruments
N.A.I.C.S.: 334519
Gooi Soon Chai (Mng Dir)

Subsidiary (Domestic):

Agilent Technologies Singapore Vision Operation Pte Ltd. (2)
1 Yishun Ave 7, Singapore, 768923, Singapore (100%)
Tel.: (65) 63771688
Web Site: http://www.home.agilent.com
Sales Range: $150-199.9 Million
Emp.: 800
Designs, Develops, Manufactures & Provides Communications Components, Electronic & Optical Test Measuring & Monitoring Instruments

N.A.I.C.S.: 334519

Agilent Technologies Taiwan Ltd. (1)
7F No 2 Sec 1 Fushing S Rd, Taipei, 104, Taiwan (100%)
Tel.: (886) 2 8171 5681
Web Site: http://www.chem.agilent.com
Sales Range: $50-74.9 Million
Emp.: 200
Designs, Develops, Manufactures & Provides Communications Components, Electronic & Optical Test Measuring & Monitoring Instruments
N.A.I.C.S.: 334519

Agilent Technologies World Trade, Inc. (1)
5301 Stevens Creek Blvd, Santa Clara, CA 95051
Tel.: (408) 345-8886
Web Site: http://www.home.agilent.com
Sales Range: $100-124.9 Million
Designs, Develops, Manufactures & Supplies Communications Components, Electronic & Optical Test Measuring & Monitoring Instruments
N.A.I.C.S.: 334515

Agilent Technologies, Inc. - Vacuum Products (1)
121 Hartwell Ave, Lexington, MA 02421-3125
Tel.: (781) 861-7200
Web Site: http://www.chem.agilent.com
Sales Range: $75-99.9 Million
Emp.: 200
Leak Detectors, Gauges, Vacuum Pumps, Accessories & Systems Mfr
N.A.I.C.S.: 333310

BioTek Instruments, Inc. (1)
100 Tigan St, Winooski, VT 05404
Tel.: (802) 655-4740
Web Site: http://www.biotek.com
Design, Manufacture & Sale of Microplate Instrumentation & Software for Life Science Research
N.A.I.C.S.: 334516
Norman Alpert (Founder)

Subsidiary (Non-US):

BioTek Instruments (I) Pvt. Ltd. (2)
223 Linkway Estate, New Link Road Malad West, Mumbai, 400 064, India
Tel.: (91) 22 28789966
Web Site: http://www.biotek.in
Microplate Instrumentation Sales & Service
N.A.I.C.S.: 334516
Vipul Chatbar (CEO)
Ajay Mody (Product Mgr)

BioTek Instruments (Switzerland) GmbH (2)
Zentrum Fanghofli 8, CH 6014, Lucerne, Switzerland
Tel.: (41) 41 250 40 60
Web Site: http://www.biotek.ch
Emp.: 5
Microplate Instrumentation Sales & Service
N.A.I.C.S.: 334118
Jurg Wetterwald (Mng Dir)
Priska Kramer (Mgr-After Sls & Svc)
Yasmina Dib (Mgr-Area)

BioTek Instruments GmbH (2)
Kocherwaldstrasse 34, 74177, Bad Friedrichshall, Germany
Tel.: (49) 71369680
Web Site: http://www.biotek.de
Sales Range: $10-24.9 Million
Emp.: 20
Microplate Instrumentation Sales
N.A.I.C.S.: 423450
Frank Siefert (Mng Dir)

BioTek Instruments Limited (2)
6 Bull Street, Potton, SG19 2NR, Beds, United Kingdom
Tel.: (44) 1767 262000
Web Site: http://www.biotek.com
Microplate Instrumentation Sales & Service
N.A.I.C.S.: 423430

BioTek Instruments SAS (2)
50 Avenue d'Alsace, 68025, Colmar, Cedex, France
Tel.: (33) 3 89206329
Web Site: http://www.biotek.fr
Emp.: 3

Agilent Technologies, Inc.—(Continued)

Life Science Instrument Distr
N.A.I.C.S.: 423490

BioTek Instruments South Korea Ltd. (2)
3F Gyungnam Building 830-48 Yeoksam-dong, Gangnam-gu, Seoul, 135-936, Korea (South)
Tel.: (82) 2 562 4740
Web Site:
    http://www.biotekinstruments.co.kr
Emp.: 8
Microplate Instrumentation Sales & Service
N.A.I.C.S.: 334118
Yunki Kyung (Gen Mgr)

BioTek Instruments Taiwan, Inc. (2)
5F-4 No 15 Lane 360 Sec 1 Neihu Road, Neihu District, Taipei, 114, Taiwan
Tel.: (886) 2 2627 7725
Web Site: http://www.biotek.com
Emp.: 7
Microplate Instrumentation Sales & Service
N.A.I.C.S.: 423430
Sander Chi (Mgr-Sls)
Jean Kuo (Mgr-Sls)
Bryant Chiu (Engr-Technical Svc)

BioVectra Inc. (1)
11 Aviation Avenue, Charlottetown, C1E 0A1, PE, Canada
Tel.: (902) 566-9116
Web Site: http://www.biovectra.com
Biotechnology Chemical Mfr
N.A.I.C.S.: 541714
Oliver Technow (Pres)
Heather Delage (VP-Bus Dev)
Mark Wellman (VP-Mfg)
Scott Doncaster (VP-Mfg, Technologies & Engrg)
Marc Sauer (Gen Counsel)
Valana Deighan (Gen Counsel)
Amanda Sauer (Mgr-Client Svcs & Project Mgmt)
Stephanie Veenhuis (Project Mgr)
George Rowat (VP-Fin & Admin)
Peter Phillips (VP-Quality Assurance & Regulatory Affairs)
David Young (Mgr-Sls)
Alex Hendry (Project Mgr)
Evan Owen (Project Mgr)
Jessica Fritz (Project Mgr)
Andrea McCormick (Project Mgr)
Krista Affleck (Dir-Analytical Dev)
Atul Pathak (Dir-Drug Dev)
John Riley (Dir-Process Dev & Technical Support Chemistry)
Gailene Tobin (Program Mgr-R&D)
Lester Wood (Exec Dir-HR)
Matt Frizzle (Dir-Bus Dev-CMO Svcs)
Suneel Singh (Mgr-Bus Dev)
Fahim Naeem (Mgr-Bus Dev)

Lasergen, Inc. (1)
8052 El Rio St, Houston, TX 77054 (100%)
Tel.: (713) 747-3380
Research & Development in Biotechnology
N.A.I.C.S.: 541714

Precision Electronique (1)
6 Sousse Bardo Street, Tunis, Tunisia
Tel.: (216) 71500404
Web Site:
    http://www.precisionelectronique.com
Computer Mfr
N.A.I.C.S.: 334118

Scientific & Medical Supplies Co. (SMS) (1)
9 Sha'ban Street Jabal Amman Bldg 5, PO Box 1387, Amman, 11118, Jordan (100%)
Tel.: (962) 6 460 3666
Web Site: http://www.sms.com.jo
Sales Range: $1-9.9 Million
Emp.: 80
Scientific & Medical Supplies
N.A.I.C.S.: 339113

Stratagene Corp. (1)
11011 N Torrey Pines Rd, La Jolla, CA 92037
Tel.: (858) 535-5400
Web Site: http://www.stratagene.com
Sales Range: $200-249.9 Million
Emp.: 400
Biological Product Mfr
N.A.I.C.S.: 325414

Yokogawa Analytical Systems, Inc. (1)
9 1 Takakura cho, Hachioji, Tokyo, 192 8510, Japan (51%)
Tel.: (81) 426603111
Web Site: http://www.agilent.com
Sales Range: $75-99.9 Million
Emp.: 300
Designs, Develops, Manufactures & Provides Communications Components, Electronic & Optical Test Measuring & Monitoring Instruments
N.A.I.C.S.: 334519

Young-In Scientific Co., Ltd. (1)
577-7 Shinsa-dong Gangnam-Gu, Shin Sa Dong, Seoul, 135-891, Korea (South)
Tel.: (82) 25197300
Web Site: http://www.youngin.com
Sales Range: $75-99.9 Million
Emp.: 200
N.A.I.C.S.: 334118

iLab Solutions, LLC (1)
10th Post Office Sq Fl 8, Boston, MA 02109 (100%)
Tel.: (617) 297-2805
Web Site: http://www.ilabsolutions.com
Sales Range: $1-9.9 Million
Emp.: 70
Application Software Development Services
N.A.I.C.S.: 541511

AGILON HEALTH, INC.
6210 E Hwy 290 Ste 450, Austin, TX 78723
Tel.: (562) 256-3800 DE
Web Site:
    https://www.agilonhealth.com
Year Founded: 2017
AGL—(NYSE)
Rev.: $4,316,363,000
Assets: $1,740,866,000
Liabilities: $1,079,845,000
Net Worth: $661,021,000
Earnings: ($262,596,000)
Emp.: 1,117
Fiscal Year-end: 12/31/23
Health Care Srvices
N.A.I.C.S.: 621610
Jeffrey A. Schwaneke (CFO & Exec VP)
Ravi Sachdev (Vice Chm)
Steven J. Sell (Pres & CEO)
Theodore Halkias (Chief Bus Officer)
Veeral Desai (Chief Strategy & Dev Officer)
Ben Shaker (Chief Markets Officer)
Cirioh Venkatachaliah (CTO)
Mat Varghese (Chief People Officer)
Matthew Gillmor (VP-IR)
Claire Mulhearn (VP-Comm)
Megan Strothman (Dir-Comm & Pub Affairs)
Timothy Gertsch (Chief Acctg Officer)
Ronald A. Williams (Founder & Chm)

AGILYSYS, INC.
3655 Brookside Pkwy Ste 300, Alpharetta, GA 30022
Tel.: (770) 810-7800 OH
Web Site: https://www.agilysys.com
Year Founded: 1963
AGYS—(NASDAQ)
Rev.: $237,404,000
Assets: $350,430,000
Liabilities: $113,953,000
Net Worth: $236,477,000
Earnings: $86,195,000
Emp.: 1,900
Fiscal Year-end: 03/31/24
Information Technology Services
N.A.I.C.S.: 541519
Chris J. Robertson (Treas & Controller)
Sridhar Laveti (VP-Established Products & Customer Support)
Prakash Bhat (Mng Dir-India Development Center & VP)
Jeba Kingsley (VP-Professional Svcs)

Dave Wood (CFO)
Ramesh Srinivasan (Pres & CEO)
Kyle C. Badger (Gen Counsel, Sec & Sr VP)
Theresa Putnal (VP-HR)
Joe Youssef (Chief Comml Officer & Sr VP-Sales-Americas,EMEA)
Terrie O'hanlon (CMO & Sr VP)
Sethuram Shivashankar (CIO, CTO & Sr VP)
Tony Marshall (Mng Dir & VP)
Rohith Kori (Sr VP-Corp & Product Strategy)
Frank Pitsikalis (Sr VP-Product Strategy)

Subsidiaries:

Agilysys HK Limited (1)
Ste 2705 27/F 148 Electric Rd, North Point, Hong Kong, China (Hong Kong)
Tel.: (852) 25261750
Web Site: http://www.agilysys.com
Sales Range: $25-49.9 Million
Emp.: 15
Applications Software Programming Services
N.A.I.C.S.: 541511
Raymond Chin (Pres & CEO)

Agilysys Singapore Pte. Ltd. (1)
12 Kallang Avenue 04-20 Aperia Annex, Singapore, 339511, Singapore
Tel.: (65) 66320670
Web Site: http://www.agilysys.com
Sales Range: $25-49.9 Million
Emp.: 28
Applications Software Programming Services
N.A.I.C.S.: 541511

Agilysys Technologies India Private Limited (1)
3rd Floor Cambridge Tower Ramanujan IT City Taramani, Chennai, Tamil Nadu, India
Tel.: (91) 4466239200
Software Development Services
N.A.I.C.S.: 541511

Agilysys UK Ltd. (1)
1st Floor York House 41 Sheet Street, Windsor, SL4 1DD, United Kingdom
Tel.: (44) 1753972265
Software Development Services
N.A.I.C.S.: 541511

AGILYX ASA
7370 NW Durham Rd, Portland, OR 97224
Tel.: (503) 213-1860
Web Site: https://www.agilyx.com
Year Founded: 2004
AGXXF—(OTCQX)
Rev.: $16,457,319
Assets: $24,590,661
Liabilities: $17,531,053
Net Worth: $7,059,608
Earnings: ($23,485,765)
Emp.: 117
Fiscal Year-end: 12/31/22
Biotechnology Research & Development Services
N.A.I.C.S.: 541714
Jan Secher (Chm)
Tim Stedman (CEO)

AGIOS PHARMACEUTICALS INC.
88 Sidney St, Cambridge, MA 02139-4169
Tel.: (617) 649-8600 DE
Web Site: https://www.agios.com
Year Founded: 2007
AGIO—(NASDAQ)
Rev.: $14,240,000
Assets: $1,238,718,000
Liabilities: $137,904,000
Net Worth: $1,100,814,000
Earnings: ($231,801,000)
Emp.: 389
Fiscal Year-end: 12/31/22

Pharmaceutical Preparation Manufacturing
N.A.I.C.S.: 325412
Cecilia Jones (CFO)
Jessi Rennekamp (Dir-Corp Comm)
Sarah Gheuens (Chief Medical Officer)
T.J. Washburn (Principal Acctg Officer)
Brian Goff (CEO)
Tsveta Milanova (Chief Comml Officer)
Chris Taylor (VP-IR & Corp Comm)
Jim Burns (Chief Legal Officer)
Ellen Lopresti (Chief People Officer)
Charlie Newman (Chief Bus Officer)
Brian Goff (CEO)

AGNC INVESTMENT CORP.
7373 Wisconsin Ave 22nd Fl, Bethesda, MD 20814
Tel.: (301) 968-9315 DE
Web Site: https://www.agnc.com
Year Founded: 2008
AGNC—(NASDAQ)
Rev.: $2,041,000,000
Assets: $71,596,000,000
Liabilities: $63,339,000,000
Net Worth: $8,257,000,000
Earnings: $32,000,000
Emp.: 53
Fiscal Year-end: 12/31/23
Investment Services; Residential Mortgage Lending Services
N.A.I.C.S.: 523150
Gary D. Kain (Exec Chm)
Christopher J. Kuehl (Chief Investment Officer & Exec VP)
Prue B. Larocca (Vice Chm)
Bernice E. Bell (CFO & Sr VP)
Aaron J. Pas (Sr VP)
Scott Bost (VP & Controller)
Chris McCormack (VP-Portfolio Mgmt)
Katie R. Wisecarver (VP-IR)
Amie Wright (Sr VP-Internal Audit)
Jie You (VP-Tax)
Chris Erhorn (CTO & Sr VP)
Joseph Anastasio (VP)
Matthew J. Felts (VP)
Donald W. Holley (Sr VP)
Cynthia Warnick (VP)
Peter J. Federico (Pres & CEO)

AGORA, INC.
2804 Mission College Blvd Ste 110, Santa Clara, CA 95054
Tel.: (408) 879-5885 Ky
Web Site: https://www.agora.io
Year Founded: 2013
API—(NASDAQ)
Rev.: $160,670,000
Assets: $800,715,000
Liabilities: $72,455,000
Net Worth: $728,260,000
Earnings: ($120,380,000)
Emp.: 1,001
Fiscal Year-end: 12/31/22
Holding Company
N.A.I.C.S.: 551112
Bin Zhao (Founder, Chm & CEO)
Regev Yativ (Chief Revenue Officer & COO-Agora Lab)
Jingbo Wang (CFO)
Ke Wei (Chief Strategy Officer)

AGREE REALTY CORPORATION
70 E Long Lake Rd, Bloomfield Hills, MI 48304
Tel.: (248) 737-4190 DE
Web Site:
    https://www.agreerealty.com

ADC—(NYSE)
Rev.: $537,495,000
Assets: $7,774,836,000
Liabilities: $2,574,683,000
Net Worth: $5,200,153,000
Earnings: $162,522,000
Emp.: 72
Fiscal Year-end: 12/31/23
Real Estate Investment Trust
N.A.I.C.S.: 525990
Richard A. Agree (Exec Chm)
Joel N. Agree (Pres & CEO)
Leah Marsaglia (VP & Controller)
Danielle M. Spehar (Gen Counsel)
Marc Brandt (VP-Asset Mgmt)
Cheryl Hamilton (Controller)
Ryan Cockerill (Sr VP-Acquisitions
Strategy-Eastern Lead)
Phil Carbone (Sr VP-Transactions)
Jeff Konkle (VP-Construction)
Craig Erlich (Chief Growth Officer)
Josh Bratton (Dir-Dev)
Bill Vitale (Dir-Acquisitions-Western
Reg)
Nicole Witteveen (COO)
Chris Bird (Dir-Lease Admin)
Riley Kennedy (Dir-Acquisitions-
Western Reg)
Terra Stenerson (Dir-Due Diligence)
Alisa Morche (Dir-Asset Mgmt Admin)
Brian Pearson (Dir-Transactions)
Emily Schey (Sr Dir-Transactions)
David D. Darling (VP-Real Estate)
Stephen Breslin (Deputy Chief Acctg
Officer)
Larry Kafuman (CIO)

AGRI-DYNAMICS, INC.
107-23 70th Rd Ste 193, Forest Hills,
NY 11375
Tel.: (515) 329-0208   IA
Web Site: https://www.agri-
dynamicsinc.com
Year Founded: 1961
AGDY—(OTCIQ)
Support Activities for Metal Mining
N.A.I.C.S.: 213114
Joseph Amram (Pres & CEO)

AGRI-FINTECH HOLDINGS, INC.
28 West Grand Ave Ste 3, Montvale,
NJ 7645
Tel.: (201) 225-0190   NV
Web Site:
https://www.tingogroup.com
Year Founded: 2015
TMNA—(OTCEM)
Rev.: $5,095
Assets: $776,102
Liabilities: $1,181,480
Net Worth: ($405,378)
Earnings: ($1,034,700)
Emp.: 11
Fiscal Year-end: 12/31/20
Holding Company
N.A.I.C.S.: 551112
Anthony R. Moore (Chm & CEO)
Wai Hok Fung (Pres)
Zoliwe Macanda-Simbodyal (CFO,
Treas & Sec)

AGRICULTURE & NATURAL SOLUTIONS ACQUISITION CORPORATION
712 5th Ave 36th Fl, New York, NY
10019
Tel.: (212) 993-0076   Ky
Web Site: https://www.ansc.co
Year Founded: 2021
ANSC—(NASDAQ)
Rev.: $2,456,838
Assets: $348,222,058
Liabilities: $360,354,908
Net Worth: ($12,132,850)
Earnings: $1,305,390

Fiscal Year-end: 12/31/23
Investment Management Service
N.A.I.C.S.: 523999

AGRIFY CORPORATION
2468 Industrial Row Dr, Troy, MI
48084
Tel.: (617) 896-5243   NV
Web Site: https://www.agrify.com
Year Founded: 2016
AGFY—(NASDAQ)
Rev.: $58,259,000
Assets: $69,687,000
Liabilities: $78,728,000
Net Worth: ($9,041,000)
Earnings: ($188,173,000)
Emp.: 72
Fiscal Year-end: 12/31/22
Farm Machinery & Equipment Manu-
facturing
N.A.I.C.S.: 333111
Timothy Hayden (Interim CFO & Prin-
cipal Acctg Officer)
Raymond Nobu Chang (Chm, Pres &
CEO)
Robert Harrison (Sr VP-
Commercialization)
Thomas Massie (Pres)
David Kessler (Chief Science Officer,
Exec VP & Gen Mgr-Cultivation)
Chris Benyo (Chief Revenue Officer)
Brian Towns (Exec VP & Gen Mgr-
Extraction)
Sheryl Elliott (Sr VP-HR)

AGRISTAR, INC.
711 Liberty St, Norfolk, VA 23224
Tel.: (757) 543-5880   DE
AGRS—(OTCIQ)
Plastic Material Distr
N.A.I.C.S.: 424610
Terry A. Branson (Chm, Pres, CEO &
CFO)

AGRO CAPITAL MANAGE-MENT CORP.
318 Ave I Ste 852, Redondo Beach,
CA 90277
Tel.: (702) 690-9614   NV
Web Site: https://acmbinc.com
Year Founded: 2013
ACMB—(OTCIQ)
Emp.: 1
Investment Services
N.A.I.C.S.: 523999
Scott Benson (CEO)
Ted Hicks (COO)

AGTECH GLOBAL INTERNA-TIONAL, INC.
2361 Campus Dr Str 140, Irvine, CA
92612
Tel.: (949) 228-0049
Web Site:
http://www.agtechglobal.net
AGGL—(OTCIQ)
Agriculture Product Distr
N.A.I.C.S.: 424910
George T. Roth (Pres)

AI TECHNOLOGY GROUP, INC.
50W Liberty Ste880, Reno, NV 89501
Tel.: (646) 768-8417   NV
Web Site: http://www.energenx.com
AIPG—(OTCIQ)
Electro Magnetic Motor & Generator
Mfr
N.A.I.C.S.: 335312
Wan Jia Lin (CEO)
Yuan Mei Lin (CFO)
David E. Lazar (CEO)

AIADVERTISING, INC.
1114 S St Marys Ste 120, San Antonio, TX 78210
Tel.: (973) 818-2879   NV

Web Site:
https://www.aiadvertising.com
Year Founded: 1983
AIAD—(OTCEM)
Rev.: $8,170,957
Assets: $936,794
Liabilities: $2,295,046
Net Worth: ($1,358,252)
Earnings: ($6,265,359)
Emp.: 27
Fiscal Year-end: 12/31/23
Digital Marketing & Data Analytics
N.A.I.C.S.: 518210
Andrew Van Noy (Chm)
John C. Small (CFO)
Jerry Hug (Exec Chm & CEO)
Kevin Myers (CMO, Chief Product
Officer & Chief Product & Mktg Offi-
cer)
Thane Tennison (Sr VP-Media Strat-
egy)

Subsidiaries:

WebTegrity, LLC   (1)
321 6th St, San Antonio, TX 78215
Tel.: (210) 920-9204
Web Site: https://www.webtegrity.com
Digital Marketing & Advertising Services;
Search Engine Optimization, User Experi-
ence Design & Content Management
N.A.I.C.S.: 541810

AIKIDO PHARMA INC.
1 Rockefeller Plz 11th Fl, New York,
NY 10020
Tel.: (212) 745-1374   DE
Web Site:
https://www.aikidopharma.com
Year Founded: 1967
DOMH—(NASDAQ)
Rev.: $2,039,000
Assets: $57,558,000
Liabilities: $4,635,000
Net Worth: $52,923,000
Earnings: ($22,882,000)
Emp.: 26
Fiscal Year-end: 12/31/23
Intellectual Property Assets Invest-
ment Services
N.A.I.C.S.: 523999
Anthony C. Hayes (Chm, CEO, CFO
& Chief Acctg Officer)
Kyle M. Wool (Pres & CEO-Dominari
Financial Inc.)
Christopher Devall (COO)
George Way (CFO)
Matthew B. McCullough (Gen Coun-
sel)

Subsidiaries:

Dominari Financial Inc.   (1)
725 5th Ave, New York, NY 10022
Tel.: (212) 393-4560
Web Site: https://www.dominarifinancial.com
Investment Financing Services
N.A.I.C.S.: 523999

Dominari Securities LLC   (1)
725 5th Ave 23rd Fl, New York, NY 10022
Tel.: (212) 393-4500
Web Site:
https://www.dominarisecurities.com
Investment Financing Services
N.A.I.C.S.: 523999

Gerald Eve Financial Services
Limited   (1)
One Fitzroy 6 Mortimer Street, London,
W1T 3JJ, United Kingdom
Tel.: (44) 2074933338
Web Site: https://www.geraldeve.com
Emp.: 600
Financial Insurance Services
N.A.I.C.S.: 524210

AILERON THERAPEUTICS, INC.
490 Arsenal Way, Watertown, MA
02472
Tel.: (617) 995-0900   DE

Web Site: https://www.aileronrx.com
Year Founded: 2001
ALRN—(NASDAQ)
Rev.: $318,000
Assets: $22,007,000
Liabilities: $3,384,000
Net Worth: $18,623,000
Earnings: ($27,329,000)
Emp.: 6
Fiscal Year-end: 12/31/22
Biopharmaceutical Product Research
& Development Services
N.A.I.C.S.: 541715
D. Allen Annis (Sr VP-Res)
Timothy M. Cunningham (Interim
CFO)
Josef H. von Rickenbach (Chm)
Brian Windsor (Pres & CEO)
Andres Brainsky (VP)
Christopher Zergebel (VP)
Huw M. Nash (Co-Founder)

AIM EXPLORATION INC.
170 S Green Valley Pkwy Ste 300,
Henderson, NV 89012   NV
Web Site: https://aimexploration.com
Year Founded: 2010
AEXE—(OTCIQ)
Emp.: 3
Mineral Exploration Services
N.A.I.C.S.: 212290
James Robert Todhunter (Pres &
CEO)
Dhanesh Ranjan (Dir-Mktg-DMCC)

AIM IMMUNOTECH INC.
2117 SW Hwy 484, Ocala, FL 34473
Tel.: (352) 448-7797   DE
Web Site:
https://www.aimimmuno.com
AIM—(NYSEAMEX)
Rev.: $141,000
Assets: $40,488,000
Liabilities: $2,020,000
Net Worth: $38,468,000
Earnings: $19,445,000)
Emp.: 22
Fiscal Year-end: 12/31/22
Biological Product (except Diagnostic)
Manufacturing
N.A.I.C.S.: 325414
David R. Strayer (Chief Scientific Offi-
cer & Dir-Medical)
William M. Mitchell (Chm)
Thomas Kenwood Equels (Vice Chm,
Pres & CEO)
Robert Dickey IV (CFO)
Peter W. Rodino III (COO, Gen
Counsel, Sec & Exec Dir-Govt Rels)

Subsidiaries:

Hemispherx Biopharma Europe   (1)
97 rue Jean Jaures, 92300, Levallois-
Perret, France
Tel.: (33) 147312032
Web Site: http://www.hemispherx.net
Sales Range: $150-199.9 Million
Pharmaceutical Services
N.A.I.C.S.: 325412

AIMEI HEALTH TECHNOLOGY CO., LTD.
10 E 53rd St Ste 3001, New York, NY
10022
Tel.: (346) 780-3520   NY
Year Founded: 2023
AFJK—(NASDAQ)
Emp.: 2
Asset Management Services
N.A.I.C.S.: 523999
Lin Bao (Dir)
Julianne Huh (Dir)
Robin Karlsen (Dir)
Heung Ming Wong (CFO & Dir)

AIMRITE HOLDINGS CORP.

Aimrite Holdings Corp.—(Continued)

9350 Wilshire Bl Ste 203, Beverly
Hills, CA 90212
Tel.: (310) 487-0080   **NV**
Year Founded: 1988
AIMH—(OTCIQ)
Consulting Services
N.A.I.C.S.: 541618
Adam Sexton *(Pres, CEO & Treas)*
Russell Lee White *(Pres & Chief Acctg Officer)*

AINOS, INC.
8880 Rio San Diego Dr Ste 800, San
Diego, CA 92108
Tel.: (858) 869-2986   **TX**
Web Site: https://www.ainos.com
Year Founded: 1984
AIMD—(NASDAQ)
Rev.: $3,519,627
Assets: $37,109,014
Liabilities: $2,481,008
Net Worth: $34,628,006
Earnings: ($14,006,690)
Emp.: 43
Fiscal Year-end: 12/31/22
Biopharmaceutical Researcher, Developer & Mfr
N.A.I.C.S.: 325412
Stephen T. Chen *(Chm, Pres, CEO & COO)*
Christopher Hsin-Liang Lee *(CFO)*

AIR INDUSTRIES GROUP
1460 5th Ave, Bay Shore, NY 11706
Tel.: (631) 968-5000   **DE**
Web Site:
   https://www.airindustriesgroup.com
AIRI—(NYSEAMEX)
Rev.: $58,939,000
Assets: $53,425,000
Liabilities: $36,036,000
Net Worth: $17,389,000
Earnings: $1,627,000
Emp.: 197
Fiscal Year-end: 12/31/21
Holding Company; Aircraft Structural
Parts Mfr
N.A.I.C.S.: 551112
Peter D. Rettaliata *(Chm)*
Michael N. Taglich *(Executives, Bd of Dirs)*
Scott A. Glassman *(CFO, Chief Acctg Officer & Sec)*
Luciano Melluzzo *(Pres & CEO)*

Subsidiaries:

Air Industries Machining
Corporation   **(1)**
1460 5th Ave, Bay Shore, NY 11706
Tel.: (631) 328-7000
Web Site: http://www.airindmc.com
Sales Range: $10-24.9 Million
Emp.: 120
Aircraft Parts & Equipment Mfr
N.A.I.C.S.: 336413

Nassau Tool Works, Inc.   **(1)**
1479 N Clinton Ave, Bay Shore, NY 11706
Tel.: (631) 328-7000
Aircraft Parts & Auxiliary Equipment Mfr
N.A.I.C.S.: 336413

Sterling Engineering Corporation   **(1)**
236 New Hartford Rd, Barkhamsted, CT 06063
Tel.: (860) 379-3366
Web Site: http://www.airindustriesgroup.com
Jet Engine Components Mfr
N.A.I.C.S.: 336412

AIR LEASE CORPORATION
2000 Avenue of the Stars Ste 1000N,
Los Angeles, CA 90067
Tel.: (310) 553-0555   **DE**
Web Site:
   https://www.airleasecorp.com
Year Founded: 2010

AL—(NYSE)
Rev.: $2,684,977,000
Assets: $30,452,252,000
Liabilities: $23,292,214,000
Net Worth: $7,160,038,000
Earnings: $572,922,000
Emp.: 163
Fiscal Year-end: 12/31/23
Aircraft Leasing Services
N.A.I.C.S.: 532411
Steven F. Udvar-Hazy *(Founder)*
Gregory B. Willis *(CFO & Exec VP)*
Sabrina Lemmens *(Sr VP & Controller)*
Eric Hoogenkamp *(Sr VP-Technical Asset Mgmt)*
Kishore Korde *(Exec VP-Mktg)*
Carol H. Forsyte *(Chief Compliance Officer, Gen Counsel, Sec & Exec VP)*
Sara Evans *(Sr VP-Comml Contracts & Insurance)*
John Rojas *(VP-IT)*
Laura Woeste *(Sr Mgr-Media & IR)*
David Beker *(Sr VP-Mktg & Head-Aircraft Sls & Trading)*

AIR PRODUCTS & CHEMICALS, INC.
1940 Air Products Blvd, Allentown,
PA 18106-5500
Tel.: (610) 481-4911   **DE**
Web Site:
   https://www.airproducts.com
Year Founded: 1940
APD—(NYSE)
Rev.: $12,600,000,000
Assets: $32,002,500,000
Liabilities: $16,342,200,000
Net Worth: $15,660,300,000
Earnings: $2,338,600,000
Emp.: 23,000
Fiscal Year-end: 09/30/23
Chemical Products Mfr
N.A.I.C.S.: 424690
Sean D. Major *(Gen Counsel, Sec & Exec VP)*
William J. Pellicciotti Jr. *(Chief Acctg Officer, VP & Controller)*
Simon R. Moore *(VP-IR, Corp Rels & Sustainability)*
Ivo Bols *(Pres-Europe & Africa)*
Victoria Brifo *(Chief HR Officer & Sr VP)*
Christopher Alsop *(Dir-Air Separation Unit Product Line)*
Raymond R. Bailey *(VP-Environment, Health, Safety & Quality)*
Patrick J. Garay *(VP-Strategic Projects)*
Dorothy L. Jarosik *(VP-Shared Bus Svcs)*
Joerg Linsenmaier *(VP-Project Mgmt, Mfg & Construction)*
Melissa Schaeffer *(CFO & Sr VP)*
Aimee White *(Dir-Standard Plants Product Line)*
Frank M. Maupay *(Dir-Equipment Sls & Plant Support)*
Francesco Maione *(Pres-Americas)*
Joff Fan *(VP & Gen Mgr-Northern & Western China)*
Tammy Han *(VP-Asia Strategic Initiatives & Dev)*
Frank Yu *(VP-Central & Eastern China)*
Kurt Lefevere *(VP-Northern Continent)*
Vaclav Harant *(VP-Central Europe, Russia & CIS)*
Katie McDonald *(VP-Corp Comm)*
Christopher Rodriguez *(VP-Talent, Culture & Engagement)*
Robert Tikovsky *(VP-Process Gases Product Line)*
Mun Shieh *(Dir-IR)*

Mary Haas *(Gen Mgr-Gardner Cryogenics & Rotoflow)*
Walter L. Nelson *(VP-Global Helium & Rare Gases)*
Erin Sorensen *(Gen Mgr-Air Products Membrane Solutions)*
Brian Galovich *(CIO & Sr VP)*
Rehan Ashraf *(VP)*
Roger Dewing *(Exec Dir-Tech)*
Eric Guter *(VP-Hydrogen for Mobility Solutions)*
Seifollah Ghasemi *(Chm, Pres, CEO & Member-Mgmt Bd)*
Sean D. Major *(Gen Counsel, Sec & Exec VP)*

Subsidiaries:

ACP Belgium NV   **(1)**
Dellestraat 55, Heusden-Zolder, 3550, Heusden, Belgium
Tel.: (32) 13530303
Chemicals Mfr
N.A.I.C.S.: 325199

Abdulla Hashim Gases & Equipment
Co. Limited   **(1)**
7413 Al-Madinah Al-Munawarah Rd, Al
Bawadi, Jeddah, 23443, Saudi Arabia
Tel.: (966) 122638222
Web Site: https://www.ahg.com.sa
Industrial Gas Mfr & Distr
N.A.I.C.S.: 325120

Air Products & Chemicals, Inc.   **(1)**
11444 Lackland Rd, Saint Louis, MO
63146-3523
Tel.: (314) 995-3300
Web Site: http://www.airproducts.com
Rev.: $12,600,000,000
Assets: $32,002,500,000
Liabilities: $16,342,200,000
Net Worth: $15,660,300,000
Earnings: $2,331,200,000
Emp.: 23,000
Fiscal Year-end: 09/30/2023
Gas Separation Systems
N.A.I.C.S.: 333998

Air Products (BR) Limited   **(1)**
Hersham Place Technology Park Molesey
Rd, Walton-on-Thames, KT12 4RZ, Surrey,
United Kingdom
Tel.: (44) 1932249200
Web Site: http://www.airproducts.com
Emp.: 500
Inorganic Basic Chemical Product Mfr
N.A.I.C.S.: 325180

Air Products (Chemicals) Public Limited Company   **(1)**
Clayton Lane, Manchester, M11 4SH,
United Kingdom
Tel.: (44) 1612304230
Emp.: 30
Inorganic Chemical Product Mfr
N.A.I.C.S.: 325180
Howard Lynn *(Plant Mgr)*

Air Products (Middle East) FZE   **(1)**
Jebel Ali Free Zone, PO Box 16912, Dubai,
United Arab Emirates   **(100%)**
Tel.: (971) 48835578
Web Site: http://www.airproducts.ae
Sales Range: $10-24.9 Million
Emp.: 30
Industrial Gas Mfr
N.A.I.C.S.: 325120

Air Products A/S   **(1)**
Vige Havnevej 78, 4633, Kristiansand,
Norway   **(100%)**
Tel.: (47) 38039900
Web Site: http://www.airproducts.no
Sales Range: $25-49.9 Million
Emp.: 40
Mfr of Inert Gas Combustion Systems, Nitrogen Systems & Hydrocarbon Separation
& Purification Systems for Maritime & Offshore Businesses
N.A.I.C.S.: 325120
Rune Damsgaard *(Bus Dir)*

Air Products Asia, Inc.   **(1)**
2503-5 25/F 148 Electric Road, North Point,
China (Hong Kong)   **(100%)**
Tel.: (852) 25271922
Web Site: http://www.airproducts.com.hk

Sales Range: $10-24.9 Million
Emp.: 20
Industrial Gas Mfr
N.A.I.C.S.: 325120

Air Products Brasil Ltda.   **(1)**
Av Francisco Matarazzo 1400, Agua
Branca, Sao Paulo, 05000-903, SP,
Brazil   **(100%)**
Tel.: (55) 1138561700
Web Site: http://www.airproducts.com.br
Emp.: 300
Industrial Gas Mfr & Distr
N.A.I.C.S.: 325120

Air Products Canada Ltd.   **(1)**
989 Derry Rd E Ste 102, Mississauga, L5T
2J8, ON, Canada   **(100%)**
Tel.: (905) 364-3064
Web Site: http://www.airproducts.com
Sales Range: $10-24.9 Million
Emp.: 15
Mfr of Industrial Gases
N.A.I.C.S.: 325120

Plant (Domestic):

Air Products Canada Ltd.   **(2)**
2233 Argentia Rd Suite 203, Mississauga,
L5N 2X7, ON, Canada   **(100%)**
Tel.: (905) 816-6670
Web Site: http://www.airproducts.com
Sales Range: $10-24.9 Million
Emp.: 10
Industrial, Medical & Specialty Gases, Intermediate Chemicals & Performance Processing Equipment
N.A.I.C.S.: 325998

Air Products Canada Ltd.   **(2)**
Regional Rd 3 Lk Erie Industrial Pk, Nanticoke, N0A 1L0, ON, Canada   **(100%)**
Tel.: (519) 587-2401
Web Site: http://www.airproducts.com
Sales Range: $10-24.9 Million
Emp.: 45
Industrial, Medical & Specialty Gases, Intermediate Chemicals & Performance Processing Equipment
N.A.I.C.S.: 325998

Air Products Canada Ltd.   **(2)**
2233 Argentia Rd Ste 203, Mississauga,
L5N 2X7, ON, Canada   **(100%)**
Tel.: (905) 816-6670
Web Site: http://www.airproducts.ca
Sales Range: $10-24.9 Million
Emp.: 20
Industrial, Medical & Specialty Gases, Intermediate Chemicals & Performance Processing Equipment
N.A.I.C.S.: 325998

Air Products Canada Ltd.   **(2)**
20 Indians Rd S, PO Box 1059, Sarnia,
N7T 3W8, ON, Canada   **(100%)**
Tel.: (519) 332-1500
Web Site: http://www.airproducts.com
Sales Range: $10-24.9 Million
Industrial, Medical & Specialty Gases, Intermediate Chemicals & Performance Processing Equipment
N.A.I.C.S.: 325998

Air Products Chile S. A.   **(1)**
Las Americas 585 Cerrillos Santiago Casilla
13850 Correo 21, Santiago, 9230117, Codigo, Chile
Tel.: (56) 225303000
Industrial Gas Mfr & Distr
N.A.I.C.S.: 325120
Hernan Briones Goich *(Pres)*
Pedro Riveros *(Gen Mgr)*

Air Products China Inc.   **(1)**
Air China Plaza No 36 Xiaoyun Road, Chaoyang District, Beijing, 100027, China
Tel.: (86) 10 641 06156
Web Site: http://www.airproducts.com
Sales Range: $1-4.9 Billion
Emp.: 3
Industrial, Medical & Specialty Gases, Intermediate Chemicals & Performance Processing Equipment
N.A.I.C.S.: 325998

Subsidiary (Domestic):

Beijing AP BAIF Gas Industry Co.,
Ltd.   **(2)**

Wen Quan Haidian District 16, 100095, Beijing, China
Tel.: (86) 1062459280
Web Site: http://www.bapb.com.cn
Industrial Gas Mfr
N.A.I.C.S.: 325120

Air Products GB Limited   **(1)**
Hersham Place Technology Park Molesey Road, Walton-on-Thames, KT12 4RZ, Surrey, United Kingdom
Tel.: (44) 1932249200
Emp.: 400
Industrial Gas Mfr
N.A.I.C.S.: 325120
Huib Schreurs *(Mng Dir)*

Air Products Gas O.O.O.   **(1)**
Budennovsky prospect 60 business center ature Gedon office 301, 344000, Rostov-na-Donu, Russia
Tel.: (7) 8633034545
Industrial Gas & Chemical Distr
N.A.I.C.S.: 424690
Robert Mills *(Mng Dir)*

Air Products Gaz Sanayi vi Ticaret Limited   **(1)**
Level 2 Iz Giz Plaza No 9 Eski Buyukdere Caddesi, Maslak Sisli, 34398, Istanbul, Turkiye
Tel.: (90) 2122906088
Industrial Gas & Chemical Distr
N.A.I.C.S.: 424690
Hamid Sabzikari *(Mng Dir)*

Air Products GmbH   **(1)**
Huttenstrasse 50, 45527, Hattingen, Germany   **(100%)**
Tel.: (49) 23246890
Web Site: http://www.airproducts.de
Sales Range: $100-124.9 Million
Emp.: 100
Industrial Gases Mfr, Distr & Whslr
N.A.I.C.S.: 325120
Markus Robertz *(Mng Dir)*
Jorg Homberg *(Mng Dir)*
Kurt Andre E. Lefevere *(Mng Dir)*
Stephan Konig *(Mng Dir)*
Marc Jamie Sambrook *(Mng Dir)*

Plant (Domestic):

Air Products GmbH   **(2)**
Huttenstrasse 50, 45527, Hattingen, Germany   **(100%)**
Tel.: (49) 23246890
Web Site: http://www.airproducts.de
Sales Range: $10-24.9 Million
Emp.: 10
Industrial Gas Mfr
N.A.I.C.S.: 325120

Air Products Helium, Inc.   **(1)**
15139 County Rd 9, Gruver, TX 79040-6001
Tel.: (806) 339-5885
Inorganic Chemical Product Mfr
N.A.I.C.S.: 325180

Air Products Holdings B.V.   **(1)**
Kanaalweg 15, Utrecht, 3526 KL, Netherlands
Tel.: (31) 302857100
Inorganic Chemical Product Mfr
N.A.I.C.S.: 325180

Air Products Iberica, S.L.   **(1)**
Av de la Fama 1-5, Cornella, 08940, Spain
Tel.: (34) 932902600
Gas Products Distr
N.A.I.C.S.: 221210

Air Products International Corporation   **(1)**
7201 Hamilton Blvd, Allentown, PA 18195-9642
Tel.: (610) 481-4911
Gas Products Mfr & Distr
N.A.I.C.S.: 221210
John Repasky *(Mgr-Dev)*

Air Products Investments B.V.   **(1)**
Kanaalweg 15, Utrecht, 3526 KL, Netherlands
Tel.: (31) 302857100
Inorganic Chemical Product Mfr
N.A.I.C.S.: 325180

Air Products Investments Espana, S.L.   **(1)**

Calle Arago 300, Barcelona, 8009, Spain
Tel.: (34) 932902600
Atmospheric & Specialty Gas Distr
N.A.I.C.S.: 221210

Air Products Ireland Limited   **(1)**
Unit 950 Western Industrial Estate Killeen Rd, Dublin, Ireland
Tel.: (353) 14659650
Web Site: http://www.airproducts.ie
Industrial Gas & Chemical Distr
N.A.I.C.S.: 424690

Air Products Italia   **(1)**
Via Indipendenza 11, 27100, Pavia, Italy
Tel.: (39) 0382305611
Web Site: http://www.airproducts.it
Sales Range: $150-199.9 Million
Emp.: 21
Industrial Gas Mfr
N.A.I.C.S.: 325120

Air Products Japan K.K.   **(1)**
Kamiyacho Prime Place 9F 4-1-17 Toranomon, Minato-Ku, Tokyo, 105-0001, Japan
Tel.: (81) 354056300
Web Site: http://www.airproducts.co.jp
Industrial Gas & Chemical Products Distr
N.A.I.C.S.: 221210

Air Products Korea, Inc.   **(1)**
7th Floor Gateway Tower Bldg 12 Dongja-Dong, Yongsan-Gu, Seoul, 140-709, Korea (South)
Tel.: (82) 221708000
Web Site: http://www.apkchem.co.kr
Sales Range: $25-49.9 Million
Emp.: 100
Industrial Gas Mfr
N.A.I.C.S.: 325120

Air Products Malaysia Sdn Bhd   **(1)**
Level 6 Horizon Tower 2A Avenue 5 Bangsar South 8 Jalan Kerinchi, 59200, Kuala Lumpur, Malaysia
Tel.: (60) 327428118
Web Site: http://www.airproducts.com.my
Emp.: 30
Industrial Gas & Chemical Distr
N.A.I.C.S.: 424690

Air Products Management S.A.   **(1)**
Chaussee De Wavre 1789, Brussels, 1160, Belgium
Tel.: (32) 26749411
Web Site: http://www.airproducts.com
Sales Range: $25-49.9 Million
Emp.: 7
Gas Products Mfr & Distr
N.A.I.C.S.: 221210

Air Products Manufacturing Corporation   **(1)**
6601 S Ridge Rd, Haysville, KS 67060
Tel.: (316) 522-8181
Industrial Gas Mfr
N.A.I.C.S.: 325120

Air Products N.V.   **(1)**
J F Willemsstraat 100, 1800, Vilvoorde, Belgium   **(100%)**
Tel.: (32) 22552895
Web Site: http://www.airproducts.be
Sales Range: $50-74.9 Million
Emp.: 40
Industrial, Medical & Specialty Gases, Intermediate Chemicals & Performance Processing Equipment
N.A.I.C.S.: 325998

Plant (Domestic):

Air Products N.V.   **(2)**
Helium Europe Houtemsesteenweg 20, Vilvoorde, 1800, Belgium   **(100%)**
Tel.: (32) 22559111
Sales Range: $10-24.9 Million
Emp.: 30
Producer & Distributor of Industrial, Medical & Specialty Gases, Intermediate Chemicals & Performance Processing Equipment
N.A.I.C.S.: 325998
Aannamea Lemmens *(Sec)*

Air Products S.A.   **(2)**
Airport Plaza - Kyoto Building Leonardo Da Vincilaan 19C-Bus4, 1831, Diegem, Belgium   **(100%)**
Tel.: (32) 22552895
Web Site: http://www.airproducts.be

Sales Range: $50-74.9 Million
Industrial Gas Mfr
N.A.I.C.S.: 424690

Air Products Nederland B.V.   **(1)**
Schalkwijkpolderweg 2, 1165 AC, Halfweg, Netherlands   **(100%)**
Tel.: (31) 204353535
Web Site: http://www.airproducts.nl
Sales Range: $25-49.9 Million
Emp.: 60
Industrial Gases Mfr, Distr & Whslr
N.A.I.C.S.: 325120

Plant (Domestic):

Air Products Nederland B.V.   **(2)**
Hoofdkantoor Gassen Schalkwijkpolderweg 2, 1165 AC, Halfweg, Netherlands   **(100%)**
Tel.: (31) 204353535
Web Site: https://www.airproducts.nl
Sales Range: $25-49.9 Million
Emp.: 100
Industrial Gas Mfr
N.A.I.C.S.: 325120

Air Products Nederland B.V.   **(2)**
Willemskerkeweg 3, PO Box 108, 4542, Hoek van Holland, Netherlands   **(100%)**
Tel.: (31) 115695155
Sales Range: $10-24.9 Million
Emp.: 15
Industrial Gas Mfr
N.A.I.C.S.: 325120

Air Products Nederland B.V.   **(2)**
Schalkwijkpolderweg 2, 1165, Halfweg, AC, Netherlands
Tel.: (31) 204353535
Web Site: http://www.airproducts.nl
Industrial Gas Mfr
N.A.I.C.S.: 325120

Division (Domestic):

Air Products Nederland B.V.-Chemicals Div   **(2)**
Kanaalweg 15, PO Box 59031, Utrecht, 300 PA, Netherlands   **(100%)**
Tel.: (31) 302857100
Sales Range: $10-24.9 Million
Emp.: 35
Chemicals Mfr
N.A.I.C.S.: 325998

Air Products O.O.O.   **(1)**
1st Tverskaya-Yamskaya street 23 building 1 business center ature, Parus 1 Entrance 5th Floor, 125047, Moscow, Russia
Tel.: (7) 4957770307
Web Site: http://www.airproducts.ru
Gas Products Mfr & Distr
N.A.I.C.S.: 221210

Air Products PLC   **(1)**
Hersham Place Technology Park Molesey Road, Walton-on-Thames, KT12 4RZ, Surrey, United Kingdom
Tel.: (44) 1932249200
Web Site: http://www.airproducts.co.uk
Sales Range: $350-399.9 Million
Emp.: 805
Chemicals & Allied Products Mfr
N.A.I.C.S.: 325998

Plant (Domestic):

Air Products PLC   **(2)**
Hersham Place Technology Park Molesey Road, Walton-on-Thames, KT12 4RZ, Surrey, United Kingdom   **(100%)**
Tel.: (44) 1932249200
Web Site: http://www.airproducts.co.uk
Sales Range: $50-74.9 Million
Emp.: 500
Industrial Gas Mfr
N.A.I.C.S.: 325120

Air Products PLC   **(2)**
Westhill Industrial Est, Aberdeen, AB32 6TQ, Scotland, United Kingdom   **(100%)**
Tel.: (44) 224746210
Sales Range: $10-24.9 Million
Emp.: 20
Industrial Gas Mfr
N.A.I.C.S.: 325120

Air Products Performance Manufacturing, Inc.   **(1)**
337 Vincent St, Milton, WI 53563-1146
Tel.: (608) 868-6811

Emp.: 50
Gas Products Mfr & Distr
N.A.I.C.S.: 221210

Air Products Performance Materials GmbH   **(1)**
Paul-Baumann-Strasse 1, 45772, Marl, Germany
Tel.: (49) 23654919000
Chemical Products Distr
N.A.I.C.S.: 424690

Air Products Peru S.A.   **(1)**
Avenida El Pacifico Independencia, 401-423, Lima, Peru
Tel.: (51) 80170670
Web Site: http://www.airproducts.com.pe
Industrial Gas Mfr
N.A.I.C.S.: 325120

Air Products S.A.   **(1)**
78 Rue Championnet, 75018, Paris, Cedex 18, France
Tel.: (33) 144925100
Web Site: http://www.airproducts.fr
Sales Range: $150-199.9 Million
Emp.: 100
Industrial Gas Mfr
N.A.I.C.S.: 325120

Air Products SAS   **(1)**
45 Avenue Victor Hugo Batiment 270 Parc des Portes de, PO Box 20023, Aubervilliers, 93300, Paris, France
Tel.: (33) 800480030
Web Site: http://www.airproducts.fr
Chemical Products Distr
N.A.I.C.S.: 424690

Air Products STB   **(1)**
Lot HS D 3831 PT 1627 Daerah Kuantan, 26080, Pahang, Malaysia
Tel.: (60) 95833357
Web Site: http://www.airproducts.com.my
Sales Range: $10-24.9 Million
Emp.: 14
Industrial Gas Mfr
N.A.I.C.S.: 325120

Air Products STB   **(1)**
Kawasan Perusahaan Pasir Gudang Jalan Perak Satu 1, Pasir Gudang, 81700, Johor, Malaysia   **(100%)**
Tel.: (60) 72514719
Web Site: http://www.airproducts.com
Sales Range: $10-24.9 Million
Emp.: 6
Industrial Gas Mfr
N.A.I.C.S.: 325120

Air Products San Fu Co., Ltd.   **(1)**
5 Floor No 21 Section 2 Zhongshan North Road, Chung Shan North Road, Taipei, Taiwan
Tel.: (886) 225214161
Web Site: http://www.airproducts.com.tw
Chemical Products Mfr
N.A.I.C.S.: 325998

Air Products San Fu Gas Co., Ltd.   **(1)**
5th Fl Shankong Bldg 21 Sec 2, Chung Shan N Rd, Taipei, 10419, Taiwan
Tel.: (886) 225214161
Industrial Gas Mfr
N.A.I.C.S.: 325120

Air Products Schluchtern GmbH   **(1)**
Breitwiesenstr 1, Schluctern, 36381, Hessen, Germany
Tel.: (49) 6661967600
Industrial Gas Whslr
N.A.I.C.S.: 424690

Air Products Services Europe, S.A.   **(1)**
Avenidadelafama No 1, Barcelona, 08940, Spain
Tel.: (34) 932902600
Web Site: http://www.carburos.com
Emp.: 500
Natural Gas Distribution Services
N.A.I.C.S.: 221210

Air Products Singapore Industrial Gases Pte. Ltd.   **(1)**
2 International Business Park 03-20 The Strategy, Singapore, 609930, Singapore
Tel.: (65) 64942240
Web Site: http://www.airproducts.com.sg

Air Products & Chemicals, Inc.—(Continued)

Industrial Gas Mfr
N.A.I.C.S.: 325120

Air Products Singapore Pte Ltd. (1)
2 Science Park Drive 05-01/12 Ascent, Singapore, 118222, Singapore (100%)
Tel.: (65) 64942240
Web Site: http://www.airproducts.com.sg
Rev.: $5,646,500
Emp.: 150
Industrial Gas Mfr
N.A.I.C.S.: 325120

Air Products Slovakia s.r.o. (1)
Mlynske nivy 74, 821 05, Bratislava, Slovakia
Tel.: (421) 800100700
Web Site: http://www.airproducts.sk
Industrial Gas & Chemical Distr
N.A.I.C.S.: 424690

Air Products South Africa (Pty) Ltd. (1)
Silver Stream Business Park Building 3 1st Floor 10 Muswell Drive, Bryanston, 2191, South Africa (50%)
Tel.: (27) 11 570 5000
Web Site: https://www.airproducts.co.za
Sales Range: $50-74.9 Million
Emp.: 350
Industrial Gas Mfr
N.A.I.C.S.: 325120
Robert Richardson (Mng Dir)

Air Products Sp. z.o.o. (1)
ul Komitetu Obrony Robotnikow 48, 02-146, Warsaw, Poland
Tel.: (48) 326730730
Gas Products Mfr
N.A.I.C.S.: 333912

Air Products Taiwan Co., Ltd. (1)
25 Lane 62 Chung Ho Street, Chu Pei, Hsin-chu, 302, Taiwan
Tel.: (886) 35538731
Web Site: http://www.airproduct.com
Sales Range: $10-24.9 Million
Emp.: 20
Industrial Gas Mfr
N.A.I.C.S.: 325120

Air Products and Chemicals (China) Investment Co. Ltd. (1)
1-2F Building 88 887 Zu Chong Zhi Road, Zhangjiang Hi-Tech Park, Shanghai, 201203, China
Tel.: (86) 2138962000
Web Site: http://www.airproducts.com.cn
Inorganic Chemical Product Mfr
N.A.I.C.S.: 325180

Air Products and Chemicals (Nanjing) Co., Ltd. (1)
Room 201 and 203 No 158 Fangshui Road, Liuhe District, Nanjing, 210047, Jiangsu, China
Tel.: (86) 2558368458
Emp.: 20
Industrial Gas Mfr
N.A.I.C.S.: 325120
Clay Wang (Plant Mgr)

Air Products and Chemicals (Shanghai) Co. Ltd. (1)
Floor 1 Building 87 East Wing Floor 1 and 2 and 4 Building 88 Lane 887, Zu Chong Zhi Road Zhangjiang Hi-tech Park, Shanghai, 201203, China
Tel.: (86) 2138962000
Inorganic Chemical Product Mfr
N.A.I.C.S.: 325180

Air Products and Chemicals (Shanghai) Gases Co., Ltd. (1)
Floor 1 Building 87 East Wing Floor 1 - 2 - 4 Building 88 Lane 887, Zu Chong Zhi Road Zhangjiang Hi-tech Park, Shanghai, 201203, China
Tel.: (86) 2138962000
Web Site: http://www.airproducts.com
Inorganic Chemical Product Mfr
N.A.I.C.S.: 325180

Air Products spol s.r.o. (1)
Ustecka 30, 405 02, Decin, Czech Republic
Tel.: (420) 800100700
Web Site: http://www.airproducts.cz
Chemical Products Distr

N.A.I.C.S.: 424690

Air Products-Specialty Gases Facility (1)
Zone Indus de Keumiee rue de la Spinette, Sombreffe, 5140, Belgium (100%)
Tel.: (32) 71822111
Web Site: http://www.apci.com
Sales Range: $25-49.9 Million
Emp.: 70
Industrial, Medical & Specialty Gases, Intermediate Chemicals & Performance Processing Equipment
N.A.I.C.S.: 325998

American Shoe S.A. (1)
Carlos Fernandez Concha 255, San Joaquin, Santiago, Chile
Tel.: (56) 224229500
Web Site: http://www.americanshoe.cl
Emp.: 18
Footwear Mfr
N.A.I.C.S.: 316210

Bangkok Cogeneration Company Limited (1)
3 Rajanakarn Building South Sathorn Road, Yannawa Subdistrict Sathorn District, Bangkok, 10120, Thailand
Tel.: (66) 26856700
Web Site: https://bkkcogen.com
Eletric Power Generation Services
N.A.I.C.S.: 221118

Bangkok Industrial Gas Co., Ltd. (1)
183 Rajanakarn Building 11th Floor South Sathrorn Road, Yannawa, Bangkok, 10120, Thailand
Tel.: (66) 26856789
Web Site: http://www.bigth.com
Sales Range: $25-49.9 Million
Emp.: 70
Industrial Gas Mfr
N.A.I.C.S.: 325120
Piyabut Charuphen (Mng Dir)
Chokchai Aksaranan (Chm)
Suchat Phasuvanitkun (Deputy Mng Dir)
Chana Tantivasinchai (Dir-Project Engrg Mgmt)
Anupong Kruesuwanvas (Sr Dir-Bus)
Mechai Amornruttanabongkot (Comml Dir-Merchant Bus)
Yodchai Chaitup (Dir-Operational Excellence)
Rithidej Wadlom (Dir-Technical Solutions & Analytics)
Orla Charoenlarp (Dir-Fin & Corp Affairs)
Nattakorn Chirapornpanich (Dir-Human Capital)

Carbolim B.V. (1)
Oude Postbaan 20, 6167 RG, Geleen, Netherlands
Tel.: (31) 464268060
Web Site: https://www.carbolim.nl
Gas Services
N.A.I.C.S.: 213112

Centro Tecnico Indura Limitada (1)
Avenida Pedro Aguirre Cerda 7060, Cerrillos, Santiago, Chile
Tel.: (56) 6006003030
Web Site: http://www.ceti.cl
Industrial Gas & Chemical Distr
N.A.I.C.S.: 424690

Contse, S.A.U. (1)
Avenida Camino de lo Cortao 28, San Sebastian de los Reyes, 28703, Madrid, Spain
Tel.: (34) 902444344
Web Site: https://www.contse.com
Industrial Gas Mfr
N.A.I.C.S.: 325120

Cryoservice Limited (1)
Warndon Business Park Prescott Drive, Worcester, WR4 9RH, United Kingdom
Tel.: (44) 1905758200
Web Site: http://www.cryoservice.co.uk
Gas Products Mfr & Distr
N.A.I.C.S.: 221210

Dixons of Westerhope (1)
Newbiggin Lane Westerhope, Newcastle upon Tyne, NE5 1LX, United Kingdom
Tel.: (44) 1912714888
Web Site: http://www.dixonsgas.co.uk
Chemical & Allied Product Distr
N.A.I.C.S.: 424690

Envases de Acero, S.A. de C.V. (1)

Av Primero de Mayo No 151 Colonia San Luis Tlatilco, Naucalpan de Juarez, 53630, Naucalpan, Mexico
Tel.: (52) 5553000488
Web Site: http://www.edasainfra.com
Cryogenic Vessels for Transportation & Storage of Liquid Gases Mfr
N.A.I.C.S.: 332420

Garmendia Macus S.A. (1)
Carlos Fernandez Concha 255, San Joaquin, 8940575, Santiago, Chile
Tel.: (56) 224229500
Web Site: http://www.garmendia.cl
Safety Equipment Mfr
N.A.I.C.S.: 332911

Gas Direct Limited (1)
White House Farm Valley Lane, Long Bennington, Newark, NG23 5EE, Nottinghamshire, United Kingdom
Tel.: (44) 1400282626
Web Site: http://www.gas-direct.co.uk
Oil & Gas Related Services
N.A.I.C.S.: 213112

Gases Industriales de Columbia S.A. (1)
CR 43A N 3 Sur - 130 Torre 1 Piso 18, Distrito de Negocios Milla de Oro, Medellin, Colombia
Tel.: (57) 45400280
Web Site: http://www.cryogas.com.co
Industrial Gas Mfr
N.A.I.C.S.: 325120

Gasin - Gases Industriais, S.A.R.L. (1)
Rua Progresso 53, Perafita, 4455-533, Portugal
Tel.: (351) 229998300
Web Site: http://www.gasin.com
Emp.: 60
Gas Products Mfr & Distr
N.A.I.C.S.: 333132

Gasin II Unipessoal LDA (1)
Rua do Progresso 53 Perafita Apartado 3051, 4451-801, Leca da Palmeira, Portugal
Tel.: (351) 229998300
Web Site: http://www.gasin.com.pt
Industrial Gas Mfr
N.A.I.C.S.: 325120

Gasproject S.A. (1)
Carrera 64 N 39-16, Medellin, Colombia
Tel.: (57) 42357708
Web Site: http://www.gasproject.com.co
Industrial Gas Equipment Mfr
N.A.I.C.S.: 333132
Ivan Dario Aguirre Maya (Gen Mgr)
Velasquez Roldan (Mgr-Technical-Comml)

INOX Air Products Pvt. Ltd. (1)
7th Floor Ceejay House Dr A B Road, Worli, Mumbai, 400 018, India
Tel.: (91) 2240323195
Web Site: https://www.airproducts.in
Industrial Gas Mfr & Distr
N.A.I.C.S.: 325120

Inacui S.A. (1)
Fundo Los Tilcos San Javier s/n Rio Chico, Puerto Montt, Chile
Tel.: (56) 65316181
Industrial Engineering Services
N.A.I.C.S.: 541330

Indura Argentina S.A. (1)
Rivadavia 50, Centro Industrial Garin Escobar, Buenos Aires, Argentina
Tel.: (54) 8108106003
Web Site: http://www.indura.com.ar
Industrial Gas Mfr & Distr
N.A.I.C.S.: 325120

Indura Ecuador S.A. (1)
Km 14 5 Via a Daule y Av El Cenaculo S/N, Guayaquil, Ecuador
Tel.: (593) 42597610
Web Site: http://www.indura.com.ec
Industrial Gas & Chemical Distr
N.A.I.C.S.: 424690
Francisco Oliva Lopez (Mgr-Procurement-South America)

Indura Peru S.A. (1)
Av El Pacifico 401 - 423 Independencia, Lima, Peru
Tel.: (51) 170842000

Web Site: http://www.indura.com.pe
Emp.: 140
Industrial Gas & Chemical Distr
N.A.I.C.S.: 424690

Indura S.A. (1)
Las Americas 585, Cerrillos, Santiago, 13850-E 21, Chile
Tel.: (56) 22 530 3000
Web Site: http://www.indura.cl
Industrial Gas Mfr
N.A.I.C.S.: 325120
Robert W. Keller (Mgr-Ops-South America)

Indura Uruguay S.A. (1)
Galicia 1049, 11100, Montevideo, Uruguay
Tel.: (598) 29022902
Industrial Gas & Chemical Distr
N.A.I.C.S.: 424690

Infra Del Sur, S.A. de C.V. (1)
Calle 60 No 337 x 35 Merida, Merida, Yucatan, Mexico
Tel.: (52) 559254944
Web Site: http://www.airproducts.com
Industrial Gas Mfr
N.A.I.C.S.: 325120

Infra, S.A. de C.V. (1)
Via Gustavo Paz No 56 Col San Pedro Barrientos, CEP 54110, Tlalnepantla, Mexico
Tel.: (52) 55 5321 5123
Sales Range: $150-199.9 Million
Industrial Gas Mfr
N.A.I.C.S.: 325120

Subsidiary (Domestic):

CryoInfra S.A. de C.V. (2)
Felix Guzman No 16 Colonia El Parque, Naucalpan, 53390, Mexico
Tel.: (52) 5553293300
Web Site: http://www.cryoinfra.com
Sales Range: $50-74.9 Million
Emp.: 200
Industrial Gas Mfr
N.A.I.C.S.: 325120

Jazan Gas Projects Company (1)
1F Jazadco Building, PO Box 2576, Jazan, 45142, Saudi Arabia
Tel.: (966) 173227076
Web Site: http://www.jazangas.com
Industrial Gas Mfr
N.A.I.C.S.: 325120

Kulim Industrial Gases Sdn. Bhd. (1)
Lot 31 Jalan Hi-tech 4 Kulim Hi-tech Park, Kulim, 9000, Malaysia
Tel.: (60) 44032288
Web Site: http://www.airproducts.com
Emp.: 14
Industrial Gas Mfr
N.A.I.C.S.: 325120

Lida SAS (1)
95 Avenue Des Arrivaux, Saint-Quentin-Fallavier, 38070, France
Tel.: (33) 474948540
Industrial Gas Equipment Whslr
N.A.I.C.S.: 423830

Lidergas S.A. E.S.P. (1)
Cr49 52 S-30, Sabaneta, Antioquia, Colombia
Tel.: (57) 43773027
Industrial Gas Mfr
N.A.I.C.S.: 325120

M y H Comercial e Industrial Limitada (1)
Avenida Presidente Eduardo Frei Montalva 4800, Renca, Santiago, Chile
Tel.: (56) 6006002040
Web Site: http://www.myh.cl
Industrial Machinery Mfr
N.A.I.C.S.: 333310

M&M Gases Limited (1)
Unit 15 Sundorne Trade Park Henley Way, Shrewsbury, SY1 4YQ, United Kingdom
Tel.: (44) 174 344 9911
Web Site: https://www.mandmgases.com
Industrial Gas Mfr & Distr
N.A.I.C.S.: 325120

Oxygen & Argon Works, Ltd. (1)
Tel.: (972) 46174500
Web Site: http://www.oxar.co.il
Industrial & Medical Gas Mfr
N.A.I.C.S.: 325120

PT Air Products Indonesia **(1)**
Cikarang Industrial Estate Blok F1-3 Cikarang, Bekasi, 17530, West Java, Indonesia **(100%)**
Tel.: (62) 2128638600
Web Site: http://www.airproducts.co.id
Sales Range: $10-24.9 Million
Emp.: 40
Industrial Gas Mfr
N.A.I.C.S.: 325120

PT United Air Products Indonesia **(1)**
Jl Raya Merak Km 116 Desa Rawa Arum, Merak, Cilegon, 42436, West Java, Indonesia
Tel.: (62) 254571291
Web Site: http://www.airproducts.co.id
Sales Range: $150-199.9 Million
Emp.: 24
Industrial Gas Mfr
N.A.I.C.S.: 325120

Permea China, Ltd. **(1)**
60 Jinsha Rd Yantai ETDZ, Shandong, China
Tel.: (86) 5352165333
Web Site: http://www.permea.com.cn
Sales Range: $10-24.9 Million
Emp.: 23
Industrial Gas Mfr
N.A.I.C.S.: 325120

Permea Inc. **(1)**
11444 Lackland Rd, Saint Louis, MO 63146-3523
Tel.: (314) 995-3491
Industrial Gas Mfr
N.A.I.C.S.: 325120

Prodair et Cie S.C.S. **(1)**
72 Bis Quai Jacoutôt, 67000, Strasbourg, France
Tel.: (33) 388614920
Web Site: http://www.airproducts.com
Emp.: 20
Gas Products Mfr & Distr
N.A.I.C.S.: 221210

Roboprojekt Sp. z.o.o **(1)**
ul Pory 59, Warsaw, 02-757, Poland
Tel.: (48) 326728916
Web Site: http://www.roboprojekt.pl
Emp.: 96
Industrial Gas & Chemical Distr
N.A.I.C.S.: 424690

S.E. Carburos Metalicos S.A. **(1)**
Adinida Dela Fama No. 1, Cornella, Barcelona, 08940, Spain **(100%)**
Tel.: (34) 932902600
Web Site: http://www.carburos.com
Sales Range: $200-249.9 Million
Emp.: 500
Mfr of Industrial Gases
N.A.I.C.S.: 325120
Arvin Sweckete (Mng Dir)

STP & DIN Chemicals Sp. z o.o. **(1)**
ul Mostowa 5, 43-300, Bielsko-Biala, Poland
Tel.: (48) 324482861
Web Site: http://www.dinchemicals.com
Chemical & Allied Product Distr
N.A.I.C.S.: 424690

San-Apro Ltd **(1)**
No 10 Chuo Bldg, 1-5-6 Nihonbashi Honcho Chuo, Tokyo, 103-0023, Japan
Tel.: (81) 332412491
Web Site: http://www.san-apro.co.jp
Chemical Products Mfr
N.A.I.C.S.: 325998
Satoshi Sugawara (Pres)

Sociedad Espanola de Carburos Metalicos S.A. **(1)**
Av de la Fama 1, Cornella de Llobregat, 08940, Barcelona, Spain
Tel.: (34) 932902600
Web Site: http://www.carburos.com
Industrial Gas & Chemical Distr
N.A.I.C.S.: 424690

Tanasio Industrial Gases Cyf **(1)**
The Old Coal Yard, Glandon Industrial Estate Pwllheli, Gwynedd, LL53 5YT, United Kingdom
Tel.: (44) 175 861 3717
Web Site: https://www.tanasioindustrialgases.com

Industrial & Medical Gas Distr
N.A.I.C.S.: 423830

Tyczka Industrie-Gase GmbH **(1)**
Hauptverwaltung Landzungenstrasse 17, 68159, Mannheim, Germany
Tel.: (49) 621180090
Web Site: http://www.tig.de
Emp.: 130
Industrial Gas Mfr & Whslr
N.A.I.C.S.: 325120

Vitalox Industrial S.L.U. **(1)**
C/ Sierra de Cazorla 2A Area Empresarial Andalucia, 28320, Pinto, Madrid, Spain
Tel.: (34) 916903297
Web Site: http://www.vitalox.es
Industrial Gas Mfr
N.A.I.C.S.: 325120

AIR T, INC.
11020 David Taylor Dr Ste 305, Charlotte, NC 28262
Tel.: (980) 595-2840   DE
Web Site: https://www.airt.net
Year Founded: 1980
AIRT—(NASDAQ)
Rev.: $286,834,000
Assets: $177,167,000
Liabilities: $171,347,000
Net Worth: $5,820,000
Earnings: ($6,819,000)
Emp.: 624
Fiscal Year-end: 03/31/24
Holding Company; Overnight Air Freight Delivery & Aviation Ground Equipment Mfr & Sales
N.A.I.C.S.: 551112
Nicholas John Swenson (Chm)
Mitch Pothen (VP-Technology)
Mark R. Jundt (Gen Counsel & Sec)

Subsidiaries:

Air'Zona Aircraft Services, Inc. **(1)**
7100 Flightline Dr Kingman Airport, Kingman, AZ 86402-3491
Tel.: (928) 757-7744
Web Site: https://www.airzonaaircraft.com
Aircraft Maintenance Services
N.A.I.C.S.: 488190

AirCo Services, LLC **(1)**
1851 S Eisenhower Ct, Wichita, KS 67209
Tel.: (316) 945-9820
Air Cargo Transportation Services
N.A.I.C.S.: 481112

Ambry Hills Technologies, LLC **(1)**
134 Adams St S, Cambridge, MN 55008
Tel.: (612) 367-8472
Web Site: https://www.ambryhill.com
Courier & Express Delivery Services
N.A.I.C.S.: 492110
Paul Stewart (Pres & CEO)
Malkesh Mangukiya (Dir-Software Tech)
Eric Schech (Product Mgr-Brand)
Cole Davisson (VP-Software Innovation)
Richard Frisk (VP-Sls)
Jason Harders (Mgr-Customers Rels)
Jeanie Webb (Mgr-Customer Success)
Neil Prodger (Dir-Tech Sls-European)

BCCM Advisors, LLC **(1)**
5000 W 36th St Ste 200, Minneapolis, MN 55416
Tel.: (612) 200-1740
Web Site: https://bccmadvisors.com
Investment Management Service
N.A.I.C.S.: 523940
Nicholas John Swenson (Pres)
Gary S. Kohler (Founder, Chief Investment Officer & Portfolio Mgr)

CSA Air Inc. **(1)**
260 River Hills Rd, Kingsford, MI 49802 **(100%)**
Tel.: (906) 774-3101
Web Site: http://www.airt.net
Sales Range: $400-449.9 Million
Emp.: 50
Air Courier Services
N.A.I.C.S.: 492110

Contrail Aviation Support, LLC **(1)**
435 Investment Ct, Verona, WI 53593
Tel.: (608) 848-8100

Web Site: http://www.contrail.com
Engine, Component Distr
N.A.I.C.S.: 423860
Joseph Kuhn (CEO)
Miriam Cohen-Kuhn (CFO)
Jeff Preininger (VP-Global Component Sls)
Mark Shaw (Sr VP-Airline Mktg)
Jackie Servi (Office Mgr)
Tyler DeNure (Controller)
Gerard Browne (Sr VP-Mktg & Origination)

Global Ground Support LLC **(1)**
540 Old 56 Hwy, Olathe, KS 66061-4640
Tel.: (913) 780-0300
Web Site: http://globalgroundsupport.com
Sales Range: $25-49.9 Million
Emp.: 50
Mfr of Aircraft Parts & Equipment
N.A.I.C.S.: 336413

Jet Yard Solutions, LLC **(1)**
25233 E Pinal Airpark Rd Ste 101, Marana, AZ 85653
Tel.: (952) 224-2426
Web Site: https://www.jetyard.com
Aircraft Storage & Parking Services
N.A.I.C.S.: 488119
Patrick J. Connell (Gen Mgr)
David W. Bixler (Pres)

Jet Yard, LLC **(1)**
25233 E Pinal Airpark Rd Ste 101, Marana, AZ 85653
Tel.: (952) 224-2424
Web Site: http://www.jetyard.com
Aircraft Repair Services
N.A.I.C.S.: 488190
Patrick J. Connell (Gen Mgr)
David W. Bixler (Pres)

Mountain Air Cargo Inc. **(1)**
5930 Balsom Ridge Rd, Denver, NC 28037
Tel.: (828) 464-8741
Web Site: https://www.mtaircargo.com
Sales Range: $400-449.9 Million
Emp.: 60
Air Cargo
N.A.I.C.S.: 492110

AIR TRANSPORT SERVICES GROUP, INC.
145 Hunter Dr, Wilmington, OH 45177
Tel.: (937) 382-5591   DE
Web Site: https://www.atsginc.com
Year Founded: 1980
ATSG—(NASDAQ)
Rev.: $2,045,469,000
Assets: $3,589,893,000
Liabilities: $2,177,387,000
Net Worth: $1,412,506,000
Earnings: $198,581,000
Emp.: 5,320
Fiscal Year-end: 12/31/22
Air Cargo Transportation, Aircraft Leasing, Aircraft Maintenance Services & Airport Ground Services
N.A.I.C.S.: 481112
Joseph C. Hete (Exec Chm)
Quint O. Turner (CFO)
Jeffrey A. Dominick (Pres)
Michael L. Berger (CEO)
Matt Fedders (VP & Controller)
Debbie Loveless (VP-Human Capital)
Russ Smethwick (VP-Corp Dev)
Trisha Frank (VP-Govt Programs)
Paul Chase (Chief Comml Officer)
Paul Harding (VP)
Joe Payne (Chief Legal Officer & Sec)
Edward J. Koharik III (COO)

Subsidiaries:

ABX Air, Inc. **(1)**
145 Hunter Dr, Wilmington, OH 45177
Tel.: (937) 382-5591
Web Site: https://www.abxair.com
Sales Range: $1-4.9 Billion
Air Cargo Transportation & Aircraft Maintenance Services
N.A.I.C.S.: 481112
Phil Flowers (VP-Aircraft Maintenance)
David Soaper (Pres)
John Maloney (VP-Flight Ops)

Air Transport International Limited Liability Company **(1)**
145 Hunter Dr, Wilmington, OH 45177
Tel.: (937) 382-5591
Web Site: http://www.airtransport.cc
Oil Transportation Services
N.A.I.C.S.: 481111
Jim O'Grady (Pres)
John Vestal (VP-Flight Ops)
Michael P. Holt (VP-Sls & Mktg)
Brian Dufour (VP-Technical Ops)
Michael Sammon (Dir-Technical Svcs)

Air Transport International, Inc. **(1)**
145 Hunter Dr Mailstop 2061T, Wilmington, OH 45177
Tel.: (937) 382-5591
Web Site: https://www.airtransport.cc
Air Transport Services
N.A.I.C.S.: 481211

Air Transport International, LLC **(1)**
2800 Cantrell Rd, Little Rock, AR 72202
Tel.: (501) 615-3500
Web Site: http://www.airtransport.cc
Sales Range: $200-249.9 Million
Emp.: 570
Passenger & Cargo Charter Airline Services
N.A.I.C.S.: 481212

Airborne Maintenance and Engineering Services, Inc. **(1)**
145 Hunter Dr, Wilmington, OH 45177
Tel.: (937) 366-2994
Web Site: https://www.airbornemx.com
Aircraft Maintenance, Repair & Overhaul Services
N.A.I.C.S.: 488190
Mark Snook (Pres)
Sam Jackson (Gen Mgr-Wilmington)
Mike Livingston (Gen Mgr-Tampa)
Christopher Brown (VP-Technical Ops-Wilmington)
Ernie Kiss (VP-Quality & Safety-Tampa)
Pete Morelli (VP-Operations-Tampa)

Subsidiary (Domestic):

PEMCO World Air Services Inc. **(2)**
Tampa International Airport 4102 N Westshore Blvd, Tampa, FL 33614
Tel.: (813) 322-9600
Emp.: 1,000
Aircraft Maintenance & Repair Services
N.A.I.C.S.: 488190

Capital Cargo International Airlines, Inc. **(1)**
7100 TPC Dr Ste 200, Orlando, FL 32822
Tel.: (407) 855-2004
Sales Range: $25-49.9 Million
Emp.: 191
Air Cargo Services
N.A.I.C.S.: 481212

Cargo Aircraft Management, Inc. **(1)**
145 Hunter Dr, Wilmington, OH 45177
Tel.: (937) 366-2216
Web Site: https://www.cargoleasing.com
Passenger To Cargo Aircraft Conversion Management Services
N.A.I.C.S.: 481212
Todd France (Pres)

LGSTX Services, Inc. **(1)**
145 Hunter Dr, Wilmington, OH 45177
Tel.: (937) 366-2337
Web Site: https://www.lgstx.com
Aviation Support & Facility Services
N.A.I.C.S.: 488190
Todd Reed (Dir-Equipment & Support Svcs)
Jim Pradetto (Pres)
Chris Copsey (VP-Ops)
Jeremy Heard (Dir-Facilities Maintenance)
Jason Shoemaker (Dir-Postal Ops)

Subsidiary (Domestic):

LGSTX Distribution Services, Inc. **(2)**
145 Hunter Dr, Wilmington, OH 45177-9390
Tel.: (937) 366-2449
Web Site: http://www.lgstx.com
Sales Range: $100-124.9 Million
Freight Transportation Arrangement
N.A.I.C.S.: 488510

TriFactor LLC **(2)**
2401 Drane Field Rd, Lakeland, FL 33811
Tel.: (863) 646-9671

Air Transport Services Group, Inc.—(Continued)

Web Site: http://www.trifactor.com
Materials Handling Machinery
N.A.I.C.S.: 423830

Omni Air International, LLC (1)
3303 N Sheridan Road Hangar 19, Tulsa, OK 74115
Tel.: (918) 836-5393
Web Site: https://www.oai.aero
Travel Arrangement & Reservation Services
N.A.I.C.S.: 561599
Dan Orcutt *(Pres)*
Robert Jared *(VP-Bus Plng & Strategy)*
Sean Ralson *(Dir-Comml Sls)*
Alana Brazel *(Dir-Govt Programs)*
Shonda Fisher *(VP-Acctg & Fin)*
Daniel Boehler *(Mgr-Govt Programs)*
Cathie Miller *(Mgr-Customer Support)*
David Ray *(COO)*
James Savastano *(VP-, &, Engineering, Maintenance, and Material)*

AIRBNB, INC.
888 Brannan St, San Francisco, CA 94103
Tel.: (415) 510-4027
Web Site: https://www.airbnb.com
Year Founded: 2008
ABNB—(NASDAQ)
Rev.: $9,917,000,000
Assets: $20,645,000,000
Liabilities: $12,480,000,000
Net Worth: $8,165,000,000
Earnings: $4,792,000,000
Emp.: 6,907
Fiscal Year-end: 12/31/23
Online Travel Arrangement Services
N.A.I.C.S.: 561599
David E. Stephenson *(Chief Bus Officer & Head-Employee Experience)*
Tara Bunch *(Head-Ops-Global)*
Hiroki Asai *(Head-Global Mktg)*
Rich Baer *(Chief Legal Officer)*
Ari Balogh *(CTO)*
Jay Carney *(Head)*
Brian Chesky *(Co-Founder, Chm & CEO)*
Joseph Gebbia *(Co-Founder)*
Nathan Blecharczyk *(Co-Founder, Chief Strategy Officer & Chm-China)*
David E. Stephenson *(Chief Bus Officer & Head-Employee Experience)*
Elinor Mertz *(CFO)*

AIRBORNE SECURITY & PRO-TECTION SERVICES, INC.
633 NE 167th St Ste 1001 N, Miami, FL 33162
Tel.: (305) 770-0033   FL
Year Founded: 1996
ABPR—(OTCIQ)
Residential & Commercial Property Development Services
N.A.I.C.S.: 531210
Jerry Deutsch *(CEO)*
Mathilda Deutsche *(Pres)*
Judith Zand *(Sec)*

AIRGAIN, INC.
3611 Valley Centre Dr Ste 150, San Diego, CA 92130
Tel.: (760) 579-0200   DE
Web Site: https://www.airgain.com
Year Founded: 1995
AIRG—(NASDAQ)
Rev.: $75,895,000
Assets: $54,400,000
Liabilities: $14,575,000
Net Worth: $39,825,000
Earnings: ($8,659,000)
Emp.: 141
Fiscal Year-end: 12/31/22
Communication Antenna System Provider
N.A.I.C.S.: 423690

Michael Elbaz *(CFO & Sec)*
Evan Jones *(VP-Engrg & Engrg)*
Victor Blair *(Sr VP-Global Ops & VP)*
Jacob Suen *(Pres & CEO)*

Subsidiaries:

Antenna Plus, LLC (1)
8350 E Evans Rd Ste D-2, Scottsdale, AZ 85260
Tel.: (480) 657-7354
Web Site: http://www.airgain.com
Wired Telecommunications Carriers
N.A.I.C.S.: 517111

NimbeLink Corp. (1)
3650 Fernbrook Ln N Ste 110, Plymouth, MN 55447
Tel.: (612) 285-3433
Web Site: http://www.nimbelink.com
Sales Range: $10-24.9 Million
Emp.: 18
Telecommunication Servicesb
N.A.I.C.S.: 517810
Scott Schwalbe *(Co-Founder & CEO)*
Kurt Larson *(Co-Founder & CTO)*
John Young *(CIO)*
Mike Tackaberry *(VP-Sls)*

AIRSCULPT TECHNOLOGIES, INC.
1111 Lincoln Rd Ste 800, Miami Beach, FL 33139
Tel.: (305) 391-2173   DE
Web Site: https://airsculpt.com
Year Founded: 2021
AIRS—(NASDAQ)
Rev.: $168,794,000
Assets: $200,759,000
Liabilities: $129,993,000
Net Worth: $70,766,000
Earnings: ($14,679,000)
Emp.: 291
Fiscal Year-end: 12/31/22
Personal Care Services
N.A.I.C.S.: 812199
Aaron Rollins *(Founder, Chm & CEO)*
Dennis Dean *(CFO)*
Ronald P. Zelhof *(Pres & COO)*
Peter Quinones *(CMO)*
Danna Hopkins *(Chief Experience Officer & Exec VP)*

AIRSHIP AI HOLDINGS, INC.
8210 154th Ave NE, Redmond, WA 98052
Tel.: (877) 462-4250   DE
Web Site: https://airship.ai
Year Founded: 2021
AISP—(NASDAQ)
Rev.: $12,299,584
Assets: $6,982,575
Liabilities: $23,575,140
Net Worth: $16,592,565
Earnings: $16,368,432
Emp.: 47
Fiscal Year-end: 12/31/23
Computer Related Services
N.A.I.C.S.: 541511
Vadim Komissarov *(Founder)*
Victor Huang *(Chm & CEO)*
Yanda Ma *(CTO)*
Paul Allen *(Pres)*
Derek Xu *(COO, Treas & Sec)*
Mark E. Scott *(CFO)*

AIRSPAN NETWORKS HOLD-INGS INC.
777 Yamato Rd Ste 310, Boca Raton, FL 33431
Tel.: (561) 893-8670   DE
Web Site: https://www.airspan.com
Year Founded: 2020
MIMOQ—(OTCEM)
Rev.: $77,568,000
Assets: $47,272,000
Liabilities: $198,241,000
Net Worth: ($150,969,000)
Earnings: ($78,885,000)

Emp.: 428
Fiscal Year-end: 12/31/23
Miscellaneous Financial Investment Activities
N.A.I.C.S.: 523999
Glenn Laxdal *(Pres)*
Eric D. Stonestrom *(CEO)*
David Brant *(CFO, Sec, Treas & Sr VP)*
Uzi Shalev *(CTO)*

Subsidiaries:

Airspan Networks Inc. (1)
777 Yamato Rd Ste 310, Boca Raton, FL 33431
Tel.: (561) 893-8670
Web Site: https://www.airspan.com
Wireless Communications Systems Sales & Solutions
N.A.I.C.S.: 517112
Eric D. Stonestrom *(Pres & CEO)*
Uzi Shalev *(COO)*
David Brant *(CFO & Sr VP)*

Subsidiary (Non-US):

Airspan Communications (Shanghai) Co. Ltd. (2)
Room 2001 New Shanghai Bund International Tower, Shanghai, 200080, China
Tel.: (86) 2163648733
Sales Range: $100-124.9 Million
Wireless Communications Equipment Mfr & Whslr
N.A.I.C.S.: 334220

Airspan Communications Ltd. (2)
Capital Point 33 Bath Road, Slough, SL1 3UF, Berkshire, United Kingdom
Tel.: (44) 1895467100
Sales Range: $10-24.9 Million
Emp.: 70
Wireless Communication Equipment Mfr
N.A.I.C.S.: 334220
Eric D. Stonestrom *(Pres)*

Subsidiary (Non-US):

Airspan Networks (Israel) Ltd (3)
Bareket 2 Building Negev Street, PO Box 199, Airport City, 70100, Israel
Tel.: (972) 39777444
Wireless Communications Equipment Mfr & Whslr
N.A.I.C.S.: 334220
Uzi Shalev *(COO)*

Airspan Networks Pty Ltd (3)
Level 5 815 Pacific Highway, Chatswood, 2067, NSW, Australia
Tel.: (61) 282588300
Web Site: http://www.airspan.com.au
Sales Range: $10-24.9 Million
Emp.: 3
Wireless Communications Equipment Mfr & Sales
N.A.I.C.S.: 334220
Marcus Deratz *(Dir-Sls)*

Subsidiary (Non-US):

Airspan Japan KK (Kabushiki Kaisha) (2)
DLX Building 4F 1-13-1 Nishi-Shinbashi, Minato-ku, Tokyo, 105-0003, Japan
Tel.: (81) 362571875
LTE Small Cells & Small Cell Backhaul Technologies
N.A.I.C.S.: 334220

P.T. Airspan Networks Indonesia (2)
The Plaza Office Tower 40th Floor JI M H Thamrin Kav 28-30, RT 009/RW 005 Gondangdia-Menteng, Jakarta Pusat, 10350, Indonesia
Tel.: (62) 2129923599
Web Site: https://www.airspan.com
Sales Range: $10-24.9 Million
Emp.: 10
Wireless Communications Equipment Mfr & Whslr
N.A.I.C.S.: 334220
Sresina Naibaho *(Office Mgr)*

AJIA INNOGROUP HOLDINGS, LTD.

187 E Warm Springs Rd Ste B307, Las Vegas, NV 89119
Tel.: (702) 362-2677   NV
Web Site:
  https://www.ajiainnogroup.com
Year Founded: 2014
AJIA—(OTCIQ)
Rev.: $98,394
Assets: $107,185
Liabilities: $335,747
Net Worth: ($228,562)
Earnings: ($184,262)
Emp.: 1
Fiscal Year-end: 06/30/21
Offices of Other Holding Companies
N.A.I.C.S.: 551112
Elaine Yin Ling Wan *(Treas & Sec)*
Samuel Wai Hing Lai *(CFO)*
Terence Kwai Lam Wong *(Pres & CEO)*

AKAMAI TECHNOLOGIES, INC.
145 Broadway, Cambridge, MA 02142
Tel.: (617) 444-3000   DE
Web Site: https://www.akamai.com
Year Founded: 1995
AKAM—(NASDAQ)
Rev.: $3,811,920,000
Assets: $9,900,037,000
Liabilities: $5,302,882,000
Net Worth: $4,597,155,000
Earnings: $547,629,000
Emp.: 10,250
Fiscal Year-end: 12/31/23
Logistic Services
N.A.I.C.S.: 541614
Robert Blumofe *(CTO & Exec VP)*
Edward McGowan *(CFO & Exec VP)*
Adam Karon *(COO)*
Aaron Ahola *(Gen Counsel, Sec & Exec VP)*
Melanie Francis *(VP)*
Anthony Williams *(Chief HR Officer & Exec VP)*
Kim Salem-Jackson *(CMO & Exec VP)*
F. Thomson Leighton *(Founder & CEO)*

Subsidiaries:

AKAMAI TECHNOLOGIES ISRAEL LIMITED (1)
8 Totseret HaArets St, PO Box 12416, Tel Aviv, 6744130, Israel
Tel.: (972) 514082999
Wireless Telecommunication Services
N.A.I.C.S.: 517810

Akamai Japan K.K. (1)
6th floor of Kyobashi Trust Tower 2-1-3, Kyobashi Chuo ku, Tokyo, 104-0031, Japan   (100%)
Tel.: (81) 345896640
Web Site: http://www.akamai.com
Sales Range: $900-999.9 Million
Software Development Services
N.A.I.C.S.: 513210

Akamai Technologies GmbH (1)
Parkring 22, Garching bei, 85748, Munich, Germany
Tel.: (49) 89940060
Web Site: http://www.akamai.com
Sales Range: $900-999.9 Million
Global Internet Network Platform Services
N.A.I.C.S.: 518210

Akamai Technologies Hong Kong Limited (1)
Unit 3908-11 Tower Two Times Square 1 Matheson Street, Causeway Bay, Hong Kong, China (Hong Kong)
Tel.: (852) 22718518
Software Development Services
N.A.I.C.S.: 513210

Akamai Technologies India Private Ltd. (1)

Embassy Golf Links Business Park Ground Floor Augusta Building, Off Intermediate Ring Road, Bengaluru, 560 071, India
Tel.: (91) 804 600 1000
Web Site: http://www.akamai.com
Sales Range: $150-199.9 Million
Emp.: 500
Global Internet Network Platform Services
N.A.I.C.S.: 518210

Akamai Technologies International AG (1)
Grafenauweg 8, 6300, Zug, Switzerland
Tel.: (41) 432109140
Web Site: https://www.akamai.com
Cloud Optimisation Services
N.A.I.C.S.: 541511

Akamai Technologies Ltd. (1)
Charta House 30/38 Church St, Staines-upon-Thames, TW18 4EP, Middlesex, United Kingdom
Tel.: (44) 1784895003
Web Site: http://www.akamai.com
Sales Range: $900-999.9 Million
Global Internet Network Platform Services
N.A.I.C.S.: 518210

Akamai Technologies Netherlands B.V. (1)
Grote Bickersstraat 74-78, 1013 KS, Amsterdam, Netherlands
Tel.: (31) 207995440
Information Technology Services
N.A.I.C.S.: 541512

Akamai Technologies Poland Sp. z o.o. (1)
Centrum Biurowe Vinci ul Opolska 100, 31 323, Krakow, Poland
Tel.: (48) 12 384 7740
Web Site: http://www.akamai.com
Emp.: 400
Content Delivery Products & Services
N.A.I.C.S.: 541512

Akamai Technologies S.R.I. (1)
Via Paleocapa 7, 20123, Milan, Italy
Tel.: (39) 0200621440
Cloud Security Services
N.A.I.C.S.: 541511

Akamai Technologies SARL (1)
40/44 Rue Washington, 75008, Paris, France
Tel.: (33) 15 669 6200
Web Site: https://www.akamai.com
Global Internet Network Platform Services
N.A.I.C.S.: 518210

Asavie Technologies Limited (1)
100 Mount Street Lower, Dublin, D02 TY46, Ireland
Tel.: (353) 16763585
Web Site: http://www.asavie.com
Mobile Network Services
N.A.I.C.S.: 517810
Ralph Shaw (CEO)
Tom Maher (Founder & CTO)
Chris Meehan (CFO)
Hugh Carroll (VP-Mktg)
Lars Jerkland (VP-Ecosystem)

Asavie UK Limited (1)
960 Capability Green, Luton, LU1 3PE, United Kingdom
Tel.: (44) 1582635013
Mobile Network Services
N.A.I.C.S.: 517810

Janrain, Inc. (1)
1233 NW 12th Ave Ste 150, Portland, OR 97209
Web Site: http://www.janrain.com
Sales Range: $1-9.9 Million
Emp.: 97
Software Developer
N.A.I.C.S.: 513210
Larry Drebes (Founder)
Lewis Barr (Gen Counsel & VP-Policy)
Jamie Beckland (VP-Product)
Jim Lodestro (Sr VP-Sls-Worldwide)
Mayur Upadhyaya (Sr Dir-Advanced Initiatives)
Darryl Nicholson (VP-Engrg)
Martin Day (CFO)
Marlene Bauer (VP-Global Svcs)
Alan Elliot (VP-Sls & Alliances-Worldwide)
Carol Ward (VP-HR)

Subsidiary (Non-US):

Janrain UK Limited (2)
8 Devonshire Square, Richmond, London, EC2M 4PL, United Kingdom
Tel.: (44) 1784225531
Web Site: http://www.janrain.com
Emp.: 35
Software Development Services
N.A.I.C.S.: 513210

Linode, LLC (1)
329 E Jimmie Leeds Rd Ste A, Galloway Township, NJ 08205
Tel.: (609) 380-7100
Web Site: http://www.linode.com
Sales Range: $10-24.9 Million.
Emp.: 100
Virtual Server Cloud Hosting Solutions
N.A.I.C.S.: 517810
Christopher S. Aker (Founder & CEO)
Will Charnock (CTO)

Prolexic Technologies Inc. (1)
200 E Las Olas Blvd Ste 105, Fort Lauderdale, FL 33020
Tel.: (954) 620-6005
Web Site: http://www.prolexic.com
Sales Range: $10-24.9 Million
Emp.: 75
Internet Security Services
N.A.I.C.S.: 541519

AKEBIA THERAPEUTICS, INC.
245 1st St Ste 1400, Cambridge, MA 02142
Tel.: (617) 871-2098   DE
Web Site: https://www.akebia.com
Year Founded: 2007
AKBA—(NASDAQ)
Rev.: $292,602,000
Assets: $351,830,000
Liabilities: $342,488,000
Net Worth: $9,342,000
Earnings: ($92,562,000)
Emp.: 204
Fiscal Year-end: 12/31/22
Pharmaceuticals Mfr
N.A.I.C.S.: 325412
John P. Butler (Pres, CEO & Interim Principal Fin Officer)
Karen L. Tubridy (Chief Dev Officer & Sr VP-Program Ops-Global)
Steven K. Burke (Chief Medical Officer & Sr VP-R&D)
Meredith Bowman (Sr VP)
Kimberly Garko (Sr VP)
Carolyn Rucci (Gen Counsel)
Bennett Smith (Sr VP)
Tracey Vetterick (VP)
Erik Ostrowski (CFO, Chief Bus Officer, Treas & Sr VP)

Subsidiaries:

Keryx Biopharmaceuticals, Inc. (1)
1 Marina Park Dr 12th Fl, Boston, MA 02210
Tel.: (617) 466-3500
Web Site: http://www.keryx.com
Rev.: $60,641,000
Assets: $158,872,000
Liabilities: $172,967,000
Net Worth: ($14,095,000)
Earnings: ($163,440,000)
Emp.: 210
Fiscal Year-end: 12/31/2017
Pharmaceutical Products Acquisition, Development & Commercialization
N.A.I.C.S.: 325412

Subsidiary (Domestic):

ACCESS Oncology Inc. (2)
750 Lexington Ave 26th Fl, New York, NY 10022   (100%)
Tel.: (212) 531-5960
Sales Range: $10-24.9 Million
Emp.: 20
Acquire, Develop & Market Therapeutics for Cancer & Related Conditions
N.A.I.C.S.: 541715

AOI Pharmaceuticals, Inc. (2)
750 Lexington Ave Ste 20, New York, NY 10022-9819

Tel.: (212) 531-5965
Emp.: 20
Pharmaceutical Preparation Mfr
N.A.I.C.S.: 325412
Ron Bentsur (CEO)

AKERO THERAPEUTICS, INC.
601 Gateway Blvd Ste 350, South San Francisco, CA 94080
Tel.: (650) 487-6488   DE
Web Site: https://www.akerotx.com
Year Founded: 2017
AKRO—(NASDAQ)
Rev.: $3,862,000
Assets: $356,570,000
Liabilities: $30,008,000
Net Worth: $326,562,000
Earnings: ($112,033,000)
Emp.: 38
Fiscal Year-end: 12/31/22
Biotechnology Research & Development Services
N.A.I.C.S.: 541714
Andrew Cheng (Pres & CEO)
Jonathan Young (Co-Founder & COO)
Timothy Rolph (Co-Founder & Chief Scientific Officer)
Kitty Yale (Chief Dev Officer)
Arin Bose (VP-Drug Substance Process Dev)
Steve Cockrill (VP-Analytical Dev & Quality Control)
Reshma Shringarpure (VP-Clinical Res & Medical Affairs)
William R. White (CFO, Exec VP & Head-Corp Dev)

AKOUSTIS TECHNOLOGIES, INC.
9805 A Ncross Ctr Ct, Huntersville, NC 28078
Tel.: (704) 997-5735   NV
Web Site: https://www.akoustis.com
Year Founded: 2014
AKTS—(NASDAQ)
Rev.: $27,121,000
Assets: $148,917,000
Liabilities: $62,678,000
Net Worth: $86,239,000
Earnings: ($63,557,000)
Emp.: 222
Fiscal Year-end: 06/30/23
Investment Services
N.A.I.C.S.: 523999
Arthur E. Geiss (Co-Chm)
Jerry D. Neal (Co-Chm)
Thomas Sepenzis (VP-Corp Dev & IR)
Kenneth E. Boller (Interim CFO)
Mary Winters (VP-Wafer Fab)
Drew Wright (Sec & Gen Counsel)
Joel Morgan (VP-Quality)
Colin Hunt (VP-Sls & Bus Dev)
Jeffrey B. Shealy (Founder)

Subsidiaries:

Akoustis, Inc. (1)
9805-A Northcross Ctr Ct, Huntersville, NC 28078
Tel.: (704) 997-5735
Financial Investment Services
N.A.I.C.S.: 523999

Grinding & Dicing Services, Inc. (1)
925 Berryessa Rd, San Jose, CA 95133
Tel.: (408) 451-2000
Web Site: https://www.stealthdicing.com
Semiconductor & Related Device Mfr
N.A.I.C.S.: 334413
Joe Collins (Mgr)
Beatrice Duarte (Mgr-QA)

RFM Integrated Device Inc. (1)
Ste 1155 4100 Midway Rd, Carrollton, TX 75007
Tel.: (972) 256-8478
Web Site: https://www.rfmi.co
Telephone Communication Carrier Services
N.A.I.C.S.: 334220

AKOYA BIOSCIENCES, INC.
100 Campus Dr 6th Fl, Marlborough, MA 01752   DE
Web Site: https://www.akoyabio.com
Year Founded: 2015
AKYA—(NASDAQ)
Rev.: $74,859,000
Assets: $176,031,000
Liabilities: $117,450,000
Net Worth: $58,581,000
Earnings: ($70,641,000)
Emp.: 369
Fiscal Year-end: 12/31/22
Biotechnology Research & Development Services
N.A.I.C.S.: 541714
Garry Nolan (Co-Founder)
Johnny Ek (CFO & Principal Acctg Officer)
Niro Ramachandran (Chief Bus Officer)
Jennifer Kamocsay (Chief Legal Officer)
Pascal Bamford (Sr VP-Research & Development & Laboratory Ops)
Peter Miller (VP-R&D)
Sarilyn Johnson-Carter (VP-Global Comml Ops)
Cliff Hoyt (Co-Founder & VP-Translational & Scientific Affairs)
Brian McKelligon (Pres & CEO)

AKUMIN, INC.
8300 W Sunrise Blvd, Plantation, FL 33322
Web Site: https://akumin.com
AKU—(NASDAQ)
Rev.: $749,631,000
Assets: $1,765,115,000
Liabilities: $1,654,161,000
Net Worth: $110,954,000
Earnings: ($151,587,000)
Emp.: 3,631
Fiscal Year-end: 12/31/22
Health Care Srvices
N.A.I.C.S.: 621999
Riadh Zine-El-Abidine (Chm & CEO)
Rohit Navani (Chief Corp Affairs Officer)
Christopher Fitzgerald (Chief Revenue Officer)
Laura Kassa (Sr VP)
Darren Speed (Chief Compliance Officer)
Jason Richardson (VP-Mktg)
Michael Luckey (VP-Bus Dev)
Michael Meredith (VP-Equipment Mgmt)
Lori Marker (VP-HR)
Adam Fabian (Controller)
David Kretschmer (CFO)
Krishna Kumar (Pres & COO)

Subsidiaries:

Advanced Diagnostic Group, LLC (1)
4511 N Himes Ave Ste 260, Tampa, FL 33614
Web Site: https://advanceddiagnosticgroup.com
Diagnostic Radiology Services
N.A.I.C.S.: 621512

Alliance HealthCare Services, Inc. (1)   (51.5%)
18201 Von Karman Ave Ste 600, Irvine, CA 92612
Tel.: (949) 242-5300
Web Site: https://www.alliancehealthcareservices-us.com
Sales Range: $500-549.9 Million
Diagnostic Imaging Services
N.A.I.C.S.: 621512
Rhonda A. Longmore-Grund (CEO)
Richard A. Jones (Pres-Radiology Div)
Richard W. Johns (COO & Chief Legal Officer)
Larry C. Buckelew (Vice Chm)

Akumin, Inc.—(Continued)

Laurie Miller *(Exec VP-HR & Mktg Comm)*
Qisen Huang *(Chm)*
Holly Huso *(Sr VP-Sls Strategy)*
Steven M. Siwek *(Pres-Interventional)*
Trish Elliott *(Sr VP & Gen Mgr-TRX Talent)*
Tracy Wiese *(Chief Strategy & Mktg Officer)*
Prudence Kuai *(CIO)*
Gregory E. Spurlock *(Pres-Oncology Div)*

Subsidiary (Domestic):

Alliance Oncology, LLC (2)
1801 W End Ave Ste 700, Nashville, TN
37203
Tel.: (615) 263-7888
Web Site:
http://www.alliancehealthcareservices-
us.com
Radiation Therapy Services
N.A.I.C.S.: 541380

CAMC Cancer Centers, LLC (1)
3415 MacCorkle Ave SE, Charleston, WV
25304
Tel.: (304) 388-8380
Medical Center Services
N.A.I.C.S.: 622110

Columbus CyberKnife, LLC (1)
495 Cooper Rd Ste 125, Westerville, OH
43081
Tel.: (380) 898-8300
Radiation Therapy Services
N.A.I.C.S.: 621111
Douglas W. Widman *(Dir-Medical)*

CyberKnife Center of Philadelphia,
LLC (1)
2010 W Chester Pike Ste 115, Havertown,
PA 19083
Tel.: (610) 446-6850
Web Site: https://phillycyberknife.com
Radiation Therapy Services
N.A.I.C.S.: 621111
John Lamond *(Dir-Medical)*

Greater Springfield MRI, LP (1)
271 Carew St, Springfield, MA 01104
Tel.: (413) 739-0290
Web Site: https://greaterspringfieldmri.com
Scan Center Services
N.A.I.C.S.: 621512

Illinois CyberKnife, LLC (1)
1700 Luther Ln Ste 1110, Park Ridge, IL
60068
Tel.: (847) 723-0100
Web Site: https://illinoisck.com
Radiation Therapy Services
N.A.I.C.S.: 621111
Arica Hirsch *(Dir-Medical)*

MetroWest Imaging Center, LLC (1)
761 Worcester Rd Rt 9 W, Framingham,
MA 01701
Tel.: (508) 872-7674
Web Site: https://metrowestmri.com
Diagnostic Imaging Services
N.A.I.C.S.: 621512
David Marchione *(Mgr)*
Anatoly Sukharsky *(Mng Dir)*

Montvale PET/CT, LLC (1)
41 Montvale Ave, Stoneham, MA 02180
Medical Center Services
N.A.I.C.S.: 622110

Mt. Baker PETCT, LLC (1)
4029 NW Ave Ste 202, Bellingham, WA
98226
Tel.: (425) 361-0045
Web Site: https://mtbakerimaging.com
Diagnostic Radiology Services
N.A.I.C.S.: 621512
Jason Perry *(Exec Dir & CFO)*
Devlin Sturdevant *(COO)*
Elaine Haser *(Dir-Human Resources)*
Aaron Bathum *(CIO)*
Belinda Botzong *(Mgr)*

Oklahoma CyberKnife, LLC (1)
6802 S Olympia Ave Ste G100, Tulsa, OK
74132
Tel.: (918) 949-6676
Web Site: https://oklahomack.com
Cancer Care Center Services
N.A.I.C.S.: 622310

Diane Heaton *(Dir-Medical)*
Allie Gibson *(Mgr)*

Pacific Cancer Institute, LLC (1)
227 Mahalani St, Wailuku, HI 96793-2526
Tel.: (808) 249-1600
Web Site: https://pacificcancerinstitute.com
Cancer Institute Services
N.A.I.C.S.: 622310
Benjamin Falit *(Dir-Medical)*

Preferred Imaging of Amarillo,
LLC (1)
14 Medical Dr, Amarillo, TX 79106
Tel.: (806) 355-5136
Medical Center Services
N.A.I.C.S.: 622110

Preferred Imaging of Austin, LLC (1)
711 W 38th St Ste B-1, Austin, TX 78705
Tel.: (512) 420-0000
Medical Center Services
N.A.I.C.S.: 622110

Preferred Imaging of Corinth,
LLC (1)
4851 S Interstate 35E Ste C-105, Corinth,
TX 76210
Tel.: (940) 536-0513
Medical Center Services
N.A.I.C.S.: 622110

Preferred Imaging of Denton,
LLC (1)
1614 Scripture St Ste 2, Denton, TX 76201
Tel.: (940) 387-6159
Medical Center Services
N.A.I.C.S.: 622110

Preferred Imaging of Fort Worth,
LLC (1)
851 Grainger St Ste 101, Fort Worth, TX
76104
Tel.: (817) 659-2870
Medical Center Services
N.A.I.C.S.: 622110

Preferred Imaging of Frisco, LLC (1)
4525 Ohio Dr Ste 200, Frisco, TX 75035
Tel.: (469) 300-2025
Medical Center Services
N.A.I.C.S.: 622110

Preferred Imaging of
Grapevine/Colleyville, LLC (1)
1600 W Northwest Hwy Ste 1000, Grape-
vine, TX 76051
Tel.: (817) 416-7545
Medical Center Services
N.A.I.C.S.: 622110

Preferred Imaging of Irving, LLC (1)
660 W Lyndon B Johnson Fwy, Irving, TX
75063
Tel.: (972) 833-6120
Medical Center Services
N.A.I.C.S.: 622110

Preferred Imaging of McKinney,
LLC (1)
1717 W University Dr Ste 405, McKinney,
TX 75069
Tel.: (214) 544-1118
Medical Center Services
N.A.I.C.S.: 622110

Preferred Imaging of Mesquite,
LLC (1)
2540 N Galloway Ave Ste 202, Mesquite,
TX 75150
Tel.: (972) 681-6340
Medical Center Services
N.A.I.C.S.: 622110

Preferred Imaging on Plano Parkway,
LLC (1)
5072 W Plano Pkwy Ste 170, Plano, TX
75093
Tel.: (972) 248-1924
Medical Center Services
N.A.I.C.S.: 622110

Reno CyberKnife, LLC (1)
645 N Arlington Ave Ste 120, Reno, NV
89503
Tel.: (775) 770-7407
Web Site: https://www.renocyberknife.com
Cancer Care Center Services
N.A.I.C.S.: 622310

Jamie Shuff *(Dir-Medical)*
Jonathan Tay *(Dir-Medical)*
James Tatum *(Mgr-Compliance)*

San Francisco CyberKnife, LLC (1)
900 Hyde St, San Francisco, CA 94109
Tel.: (415) 674-8200
Web Site: https://cksanfrancisco.com
Radiation Therapy Services
N.A.I.C.S.: 621111
Alexander Geng *(Dir-Medical)*

St. Louis CyberKnife, LLC (1)
1011 Bowles Ave Ste G-50, Fenton, MO
63026
Tel.: (636) 496-4661
Web Site: https://stlouiscyberknife.com
Cancer Care Center Services
N.A.I.C.S.: 622310
Mae Dutton *(Coord)*
John Bedwinek *(Dir-Medical-Radiation On-*
cologist)

Tri City Petct llc (1)
902 Sycamore Ave Ste 120, Vista, CA
92081-7879
Tel.: (760) 599-9940
Web Site: http://www.tricitypetct.com
Diagnostic Imaging Services
N.A.I.C.S.: 621512
Steve Palmeri *(Mgr)*

USR Holdings, LLC (1)
2000 SE Port Saint Lucie Blvd Ste C, Port
Saint Lucie, FL 34952
Tel.: (772) 207-7604
Web Site: https://usrholdings.com
Addiction Recovery Services
N.A.I.C.S.: 623220

Western Massachusetts PET/CT Im-
aging Center LLC (1)
271 Carew St, Springfield, MA 01104
Tel.: (413) 748-9331
Web Site: https://westernmasspetct.com
Diagnostic Imaging Services
N.A.I.C.S.: 621512

Woodland Diagnostic Imaging,
LLC (1)
632 W Gibson Rd, Woodland, CA 95695
Tel.: (530) 668-2632
Web Site: https://dignityhealth.org
Diagnostic Imaging Services
N.A.I.C.S.: 621512

ALADDIN SEPARATION TECH-
NOLOGIES, INC.
400 Trade Ctr Ste 5900, Woburn, MA
01801
Tel.: (516) 771-0636
Web Site:
https://www.aladdinseparation.com
ASPT—(OTCIQ)
Analytical Laboratory Instrument Mfr
N.A.I.C.S.: 334516

ALAMO GROUP INC.
1627 E Walnut, Seguin, TX 78155
Tel.: (830) 379-1480   DE
Web Site: https://www.alamo-
group.com
Year Founded: 1987
ALG—(NYSE)
Rev.: $1,513,616,000
Assets: $1,308,508,000
Liabilities: $523,148,000
Net Worth: $785,360,000
Earnings: $101,928,000
Emp.: 4,200
Fiscal Year-end: 12/31/22
Holding Company; Agricultural & In-
frastructure Maintenance Equipment
Designer, Mfr & Whslr
N.A.I.C.S.: 551112
Dan E. Malone *(Chief Sustainability*
Officer & Exec VP)
Jeffery A. Leonard *(Pres & CEO)*
Janet S. Pollock *(VP-HR)*
Lori L. Sullivan *(VP-Internal Audit)*

Subsidiaries:

Alamo Group (Europe) Limited (1)
Station Road, Salford Priors, Evesham,

WR11 8SW, Worcestershire, United King-
dom
Tel.: (44) 1789774300
Web Site: https://www.alamoeur.com
Sales Range: $25-49.9 Million
Farm Machinery & Equipment Mfr & Distr
N.A.I.C.S.: 333111

Subsidiary (Domestic):

Alamo Manufacturing Services (UK)
Limited (2)
Station Road Salford Priors, Evesham,
WR11 8SW, Worcestershire, United King-
dom
Tel.: (44) 1789773383
Web Site: https://www.bomford-turner.com
General Purpose Machinery Mfr
N.A.I.C.S.: 333111

Subsidiary (Domestic):

Bomford Turner Limited (3)
Statin Road Salford Priors, Evesham, WR11
8SW, Worcestershire, United Kingdom
Tel.: (44) 1789773383
Web Site: https://bomford-turner.com
Sales Range: $50-74.9 Million
Emp.: 200
Agricultural Machinery Mfr
N.A.I.C.S.: 333111
Debbie Winters *(Mgr-Sls Admin)*
Craig Whiting *(Mgr-Export Sls)*

Bomford Turner Limited (3)
Station Road Salford Priors, Evesham,
WR11 8SW, Worcestershire, United King-
dom
Tel.: (44) 178 977 3383
Web Site: https://www.bomford-turner.com
Farm Machinery & Equipment Mfr
N.A.I.C.S.: 333111

Subsidiary (Domestic):

Kellands Agricultural Ltd. (2)
Brimpsfield Road, Birdlip, GL4 8JH, Glouc-
estershire, United Kingdom
Tel.: (44) 1452863900
Web Site: https://www.kellands.co.uk
Farm Machinery & Equipment Distr
N.A.I.C.S.: 423820

McConnel Ltd. (2)
Temeside Works, Ludlow, SY8 1JL, Shrop-
shire, United Kingdom
Tel.: (44) 1584873131
Web Site: https://www.mcconnel.com
Sales Range: $25-49.9 Million
Machinery Equipment Mfr
N.A.I.C.S.: 333111
Jonathan Webb *(Mgr-Sls)*
Simon Vickers *(Mgr-Parts)*
Edward Hall *(Mgr-Export Sls)*
Ian Morgan *(Sls Mgr-South West)*
Paul Jinks *(Sls Mgr-South East & East)*
Paul Lloyd *(Sls Mgr-Wales & Central)*
Ian Lax *(Sls Mgr-Scotland & North)*

Subsidiary (Non-US):

Rousseau SAS (2)
40 Avenue Auguste Wissel, CS 10132,
69583, Neuville-sur-Saone, Cedex, France
Tel.: (33) 47 898 6929
Web Site: https://www.rousseau-web.com
Emp.: 130
Farm Machinery & Equipment Mfr
N.A.I.C.S.: 333111

SMA Faucheux SAS (2)
40 Avenue Auguste Wissel, 69250,
Neuville-sur-Saone, France
Tel.: (33) 426553650
Web Site: http://www.smafaucheux.com
Emp.: 50
Farm Machinery & Equipment Mfr
N.A.I.C.S.: 333111

Subsidiary (Domestic):

Spearhead Machinery Ltd. (2)
Station Road, Salford Priors, Evesham,
WR11 8SW, Worcestershire, United King-
dom
Tel.: (44) 1789491860
Web Site:
https://www.spearheadmachinery.com
Emp.: 14
Farm Machinery & Equipment Mfr
N.A.I.C.S.: 333111

Alamo Group (IA) Inc. (1)
1301 N 14th St, Indianola, IA
50125-1509 (100%)
Tel.: (515) 961-7481
Web Site: http://www.herschelparts.com
Sales Range: $50-74.9 Million
Emp.: 100
Mfr & Distributor of Agricultural Replacement Parts & Equipment
N.A.I.C.S.: 423820

Alamo Group (IL) Inc. (1)
1020 S Sangamon Ave, Gibson City, IL
60936
Tel.: (217) 784-4261
Web Site: http://www.mw-gear.com
Sales Range: $50-74.9 Million
Emp.: 150
Farm Equipment Retailer
N.A.I.C.S.: 333111

Alamo Group (TX), Inc. (1)
1502 E Walnut St, Seguin, TX 78155-5202
Tel.: (800) 882-5762
Web Site: http://www.alamo-industrial.com
Rotary Cutters, Rear Mounted Blades, Tillage & Field Cultivators Mfr
N.A.I.C.S.: 423820
Ian Burden (Pres)
Doug Baker (Dir-Sls)
Brian Billeaudeaux (Div Controller)
Amanda Barbaro (Mktg Mgr)
Chuck Pavliska (Product Mgr)
Marisa Gras (Asst Product Mgr)
Anna Guttierez (Supvr)

Alamo Group The Netherlands B.V. (1)
Industrieweg 18, 4283 GZ, Giessen, Netherlands
Tel.: (31) 183447280
Web Site: https://alamo-groupnl.com
Farm Machinery Maintenance & Repair Services
N.A.I.C.S.: 811310

Alamo Group The Netherlands Middelburg B.V. (1)
Herculesweg 6, 4338 PL, Middelburg, Netherlands
Tel.: (31) 118679500
Web Site: https://herder.nl
Farm Machinery Maintenance & Repair Services
N.A.I.C.S.: 811310

Bush Hog, Inc. (1)
2501 Griffin Ave, Selma, AL 36701
Tel.: (334) 874-2700
Web Site: https://www.bushhog.com
Sales Range: $100-124.9 Million
Landscape & Farm Equipment Mfr
N.A.I.C.S.: 333111

Dutch Power Company B.V. (1)
Distributiestraat 55A, 4283 JN, Giessen, Netherlands
Tel.: (31) 183447280
Web Site:
    http://www.dutchpowercompany.com
Vegetation Management Machine Mfr
N.A.I.C.S.: 333111
Michel de Vries (Dir-Fin)

Subsidiary (Domestic):

Conver B.V. (2)
Industrieweg 18, 4283 GZ, Giessen, Netherlands
Tel.: (31) 183447272
Web Site: http://www.conver.com
Mowing Boat Mfr
N.A.I.C.S.: 336612

Subsidiary (Non-US):

DPC Maschinen Vertrieb GmbH (2)
Alt-Heerdt 104, Dusseldorf, 40549, Germany
Tel.: (49) 21193670235
Mowing Boat Mfr
N.A.I.C.S.: 336612

Subsidiary (Domestic):

Herder B.V. (2)
Herculesweg 6, 4338 PL, Middelburg, Netherlands
Tel.: (31) 118679500
Web Site: http://www.herder.nl

Industrial Machinery Mfr
N.A.I.C.S.: 333248

Roberine B.V. (2)
Goolkatenweg 65, 7521 BE, Enschede, Netherlands
Tel.: (31) 534838383
Web Site: https://www.roberine.com
Industrial Machinery Mfr
N.A.I.C.S.: 333248

Everest Equipment Co. (1)
1077 Westmount Street, Ayer's Cliff, J0B
1C0, QC, Canada
Tel.: (819) 838-4257
Web Site:
    https://www.everestequipment.com
Emp.: 100
Construction Engineering Services
N.A.I.C.S.: 541330

Gradall Industries, Inc. (1)
406 Mill Ave SW, New Philadelphia, OH
44663
Tel.: (330) 339-2212
Web Site: https://www.gradall.com
Sales Range: $100-124.9 Million
Construction Machinery Whslr
N.A.I.C.S.: 423810

Herder Implementos e Maquinas Agricolas Ltda. (1)
Av Dolores Martins Rubinho n 925 Distrito
Industrial II, Sao Joao de Boa Vista, Sao
Paulo, Brazil
Tel.: (55) 193 636 2100
Web Site: https://www.herderdobrasil.com.br
Farm Machinery Distr
N.A.I.C.S.: 423820

Morbark LLC (1)
8507 S Winn Rd, Winn, MI 48896
Tel.: (989) 866-2381
Web Site: https://www.morbark.com
Emp.: 450
Machine Product Mfr
N.A.I.C.S.: 332710

Subsidiary (Non-US):

Denis Cimaf Inc. (2)
211 rue Notre-Dame, Roxton Falls, Quebec,
J0H 1E0, QC, Canada
Tel.: (450) 548-7007
Web Site: http://deniscimaf.com
Industrial Machinery Mfr
N.A.I.C.S.: 333248

Subsidiary (Domestic):

Rayco Manufacturing, Inc. (2)
5520 Bridgewood Dr, Sterling Heights, MI
48310
Tel.: (586) 795-3260
Web Site: http://www.raycofixture.com
Hand & Edge Tool Mfr
N.A.I.C.S.: 332216
Douglas Cole (Pres)

Old Dominion Brush Company, Inc. (1)
5118 Glen Alden Dr, Richmond, VA 23231
Web Site: https://www.odbco.com
Brushes, Household Or Industrial Mfr
N.A.I.C.S.: 339994

R.P.M. Tech Inc. (1)
2220 Michelin Street, Laval, H7L 5C3, QC,
Canada
Tel.: (450) 687-3280
Web Site: http://www.grouperpmtech.com
Farm & Garden Machinery Equipment Distr
N.A.I.C.S.: 423820

RhinoAg, Inc. (1)
1020 S Sangamon Ave, Gibson City, IL
60936
Tel.: (217) 784-4261
Web Site: https://www.rhinoag.com
Farm Machinery Equipment Mfr & Distr
N.A.I.C.S.: 333111

Royal Truck & Equipment, LLC (1)
1100 Pottstville Pike, Shoemakersville, PA
19555
Web Site:
    https://royaltruckandequipment.com
Truck & Equipment Mfr
N.A.I.C.S.: 333924

Santa Izabel Agro Industria Ltda. (1)

Av Dolores M Rubinho 925, Distrito Industrial I Sao Joao da Boa Vista, Sao Paulo, Brazil
Tel.: (55) 1936362100
Web Site: https://www.santaizabel.ind.br
Farm Machinery Equipment Mfr & Distr
N.A.I.C.S.: 333111

Schwarze Industries Australia PTY Ltd. (1)
31 Antimony Street, Carole Park, 4300,
QLD, Australia
Tel.: (61) 732719777
Web Site: https://www.schwarze.com
Emp.: 10
Equipment Mfr
N.A.I.C.S.: 333111

Subsidiary (Domestic):

Fieldquip PTY Ltd. (2)
199 Bridge St, Oakey, 4401, QLD, Australia
Tel.: (61) 746911500
Web Site: https://fieldquip.com.au
Agricultural Machinery & Equipment Mfr
N.A.I.C.S.: 333922

Superior Equipment PTY Ltd. (2)
19 Quindus St, Wacol, 4076, QLD, Australia
Tel.: (61) 732713177
Web Site:
    http://www.superiorequipment.com.au
Industrial Equipment Mfr
N.A.I.C.S.: 334513

Super Products LLC (1)
130 W Boxhorn Dr, Mukwonago, WI 53149
Tel.: (262) 784-7100
Web Site: https://www.superproducts.com
Emp.: 180
Vacuum Equipment Mfr
N.A.I.C.S.: 333912

Tenco Inc. (1)
1318 rue Principale, St-Valerien-de-Milton,
J0H 2B0, QC, Canada
Tel.: (450) 388-1328
Web Site: https://www.tenco.ca
Sales Range: $25-49.9 Million
Snow & Ice Removal Equipment Mfr
N.A.I.C.S.: 333998
Daniel Beaudoin (Pres)

Subsidiary (US):

Tenco (USA), Inc. (2)
5700 S Lima Rd, Lakeville, NY 14480
Tel.: (585) 346-3040
Web Site: http://www.tenco.ca
Sales Range: $1-9.9 Million
Emp.: 20
Snow & Ice Removal Equipment Mfr
N.A.I.C.S.: 333998

Tenco Industries, Inc. (2)
29 Pitman Rd Ste 2, Barre, VT 05641
Tel.: (802) 476-3161
Web Site: http://www.tenconewengland.com
Snow & Ice Removal Equipment Mfr
N.A.I.C.S.: 333998

Tenco Industries, Inc. (1)
710 Gateway Dr, Ottumwa, IA 52501-2204
Tel.: (641) 682-8114
Web Site: http://www.tenco.org
Sales Range: $1-9.9 Million
Emp.: 120
Vocational Rehabilitation Services
N.A.I.C.S.: 624310
Deb Pumphre (Chm)
Marc Roe (Interim CEO & CFO)

Wausau Equipment Company, Inc. (1)
1905 S Moorland Rd, New Berlin, WI
53151-2321
Tel.: (262) 784-6066
Web Site:
    https://www.wausauequipment.com
General Purpose Machinery Mfr
N.A.I.C.S.: 333998

ALANCO TECHNOLOGIES, INC.
7950 E Acoma Dr Ste 111, Scottsdale, AZ 85260
Tel.: (480) 607-1010   AZ
Web Site: http://www.alanco.com
Year Founded: 1969

ALAN—(OTCIQ)
Sales Range: Less than $1 Million
Emp.: 3
RFID Tracking & Asset Management Solutions
N.A.I.C.S.: 334112
John A. Carlson (Pres & CEO)

ALASKA AIR GROUP, INC.
19300 Intl Blvd, Seattle, WA 98188
Tel.: (206) 433-3200   DE
Web Site: https://www.alaskaair.com
Year Founded: 1985
ALK—(NYSE)
Rev: $10,426,000,000
Assets: $14,613,000,000
Liabilities: $10,500,000,000
Net Worth: $4,113,000,000
Earnings: $235,000,000
Emp.: 26,043
Fiscal Year-end: 12/31/23
Holding Company; Air Transportation Services
N.A.I.C.S.: 551112
Constance von Muehlen (COO & Exec VP)
Andrea L. Schneider (Sr VP-People-Alaska Airlines Inc)
Andrea L. Schneider (Sr VP-People-Alaska Airlines Inc)
Benito Minicucci (Pres & CEO)
Shane R. Tackett (CFO & Exec VP-Fin)
Emily Halverson (Principal Acctg Officer, VP-Fin & Controller)
Wayne Newton (VP-Airport Ops & Customer Svc-Alaska Airlines Inc)
Kyle B. Levine (Gen Counsel, Sec & Sr VP-Legal)

Subsidiaries:

Alaska Airlines, Inc. (1)
PO Box 68900, Seattle, WA
98168-0900 (100%)
Tel.: (206) 433-3200
Web Site: https://www.alaskaair.com
Sales Range: $1-4.9 Billion
Air Transportation, Tours & Cargo
N.A.I.C.S.: 481111
Bradley D. Tilden (Chm)
Constance von Muehlen (COO & Exec VP)
Andrea L. Schneider (Sr VP-People)
Andrea L. Schneider (Sr VP-People)
Benito Minicucci (Pres & CEO)
Charu Jain (Sr VP-Mdsg & Innovation)
Sangita Woerner (Sr VP-Mktg)
Wayne Newton (VP-Airport Ops & Customer Svc)
Andrew R. Harrison (Chief Comml Officer)
John Ladner (VP-Flight Ops)
Kyle Levine (Gen Counsel & Sr VP-Legal)
Chris Berry (VP-Fin & Controller)
Diana Birkett Rakow (VP-External Rels)
Jenny Wetzel (VP-Labor Rels)
Shane Jones (VP-Airport Real Estate & Dev)
Nathaniel Pieper (Treas & Sr VP-Fleet, Fin & Alliances)
Travis Gelbrich (VP-Inflight)
Brett Catlin (VP-Network & Alliances)
Brooke Vatheuer (VP-Strategic Performance)
Toni Freeberg (Mng Dir-Sls)
Donald Wright (VP-Maintenance & Engrg)

Hawaiian Holdings, Inc. (1)
3375 Koapaka St Ste G-350, Honolulu, HI
96820
Tel.: (808) 835-3700
Web Site: https://www.hawaiianairlines.com
Rev: $2,641,267,000
Assets: $4,139,623,000
Liabilities: $3,806,358,000
Net Worth: $333,265,000
Earnings: ($240,081,000)
Emp.: 7,108
Fiscal Year-end: 12/31/2022
Holding Company; Air Transportation Services
N.A.I.C.S.: 551112
Peter R. Ingram (Pres & CEO)
Shannon Lei Okinaka (CFO, Treas & Exec VP)

Alaska Air Group, Inc.—(Continued)

Subsidiary (Domestic):

Hawaiian Airlines, Inc. **(2)**
3375 Koapaka St Ste G-350, Honolulu, HI 96819 **(100%)**
Tel.: (808) 835-3700
Web Site: https://www.hawaiianairlines.com
Sales Range: $1-4.9 Billion
Emp.: 7,000
Commercial Passenger Airline
N.A.I.C.S.: 481111
Peter R. Ingram *(Pres & CEO)*
Shannon Lei Okinaka *(Sr Dir-Sarbanes-Oxley compliance & Special Projects)*
Jonathan D. Snook *(Exec VP)*
Avi A. Mannis *(Sr VP-Mktg)*
Robin Kobayashi *(Sr VP-HR)*
Takaya Shishido *(Dir-Japan)*
Jim Landers *(Sr VP-Technical Ops)*
Beau Tatsumura *(VP-Maintenance & Engrg)*
Sayle Hirashima *(VP & Controller)*
Soojin Yu *(Dir-South Korea)*
Aaron Alter *(Chief Legal Officer, Sec & Exec VP)*
Jay Schaefer *(Treas & VP)*
Robin Sparling *(VP-In-Flight Svcs)*
Robert Sorensen *(VP-Mktg & ECommerce)*
Andrew Stanbury *(Dir-Australia & New Zealand)*
Justin Doane *(VP-Labor Rels)*
David LeNoir *(VP-Fin Plng & Analysis)*
Russell Williss *(Dir-New Zealand)*
Robert Johnson *(VP-Flight Ops)*
Jon D. Snook *(COO)*
Tom Zheng *(VP)*

Horizon Air Industries **(1)**
19521 International Blvd, Seattle, WA 98188 **(100%)**
Tel.: (206) 241-6757
Web Site: http://www.horizonair.com
Rev.: $300,000,000
Emp.: 120
Airline
N.A.I.C.S.: 481111
Bradley D. Tilden *(Executives)*
Gary L. Beck *(CEO)*
Matt Prainito *(VP-Station & Inflight Ops)*
Nathaniel Pieper *(Treas)*
Joe Sprague *(Pres)*
Allie Wittenberger *(Asst Sec)*
Jeanne Gammon *(Asst Sec)*
Carlos Zendejas *(VP-Flight Ops)*

McGee Air Services, Inc. **(1)**
901 Powell Ave SW Ste 200, Renton, WA 98057
Tel.: (206) 788-8000
Web Site:
  https://www.mcgeeairservices.com
Airline Services
N.A.I.C.S.: 488190
Rachel Steitz *(Mng Dir-Ops-Seattle)*
Ben Reed *(Mng Dir-Safety & Compliance)*
Marie Underwood *(CFO & Mng Dir-Fin)*
Cheri Ruger *(Mng Dir-HR)*
Constance von Muehlen *(Chm)*
Michael Francis *(Mng Dir-Ops)*

ALASKA POWER & TELE-PHONE COMPANY
136 Misty Marie Ln, Ketchikan, AK 99901
Tel.: (360) 385-1733   **AK**
Web Site: https://www.aptalaska.com
Year Founded: 1957
APTL—(OTCIQ)
Rev.: $55,406,502
Assets: $124,914,190
Liabilities: $69,336,644
Net Worth: $55,577,546
Earnings: $8,739,884
Emp.: 132
Fiscal Year-end: 12/31/20
Holding Company;Electric Power & Telecommunications Products & Services
N.A.I.C.S.: 551112
Chad A. Haggar *(CFO, Treas & VP)*
Michael Garrett *(Pres & CEO)*
Tom Ervin *(COO-Power & Telecom Ops & Exec VP)*
Mike Barry *(Chm)*
Robert B. Engel *(Vice Chm)*

Subsidiaries:

Alaska Power & Telephone **(1)**
20 Front St, Wrangell, AK 99929
Tel.: (907) 874-3000
Web Site: http://www.aptalaska.com
Sales Range: $10-24.9 Million
Emp.: 5
Local & Long Distance Telephone Communications
N.A.I.C.S.: 517121
Arne Sather *(VP-HR)*

ALAUNOS THERAPEUTICS, INC.
2617 Bissonnet St Ste 225, Houston, TX 77005
Tel.: (346) 355-4099   **DE**
Web Site: https://www.alaunos.com
TCRT—(NASDAQ)
Rev.: $2,922,000
Assets: $64,937,000
Liabilities: $26,382,000
Net Worth: $38,555,000
Earnings: ($37,730,000)
Emp.: 34
Fiscal Year-end: 12/31/22
Biopharmaceutical Products Developer
N.A.I.C.S.: 325412
James Z. Huang *(Chm)*
Timothy Cunningham *(CFO-Interim)*
Abhishek Srivastava *(VP-Technical Ops)*

ALBANY INTERNATIONAL CORP.
216 Airport Dr, Rochester, NH 03867
Tel.: (603) 330-5850   **DE**
Web Site: https://www.albint.com
Year Founded: 1895
AIN—(NYSE)
Rev.: $1,034,887,000
Assets: $1,642,255,000
Liabilities: $774,712,000
Net Worth: $867,543,000
Earnings: $95,762,000
Emp.: 4,100
Fiscal Year-end: 12/31/22
Paper-Machine Clothing & Industrial Products Mfr
N.A.I.C.S.: 313210
Joseph M. Gaug *(Gen Counsel, Sec & VP)*
Robert A. Hansen *(CTO & Sr VP)*
Gunnar Kleveland *(Pres & CEO)*
Alice McCarvill *(Chief HR Officer & Exec VP-HR)*
John J. Tedone *(Chief Acctg Officer, VP & Controller)*
Robert D. Starr *(CFO & Treas)*

Subsidiaries:

Albany Engineered Composites, Inc. **(1)**
1281 N Main St, Boerne, TX 78006-3014
Tel.: (830) 249-4400
Broadwoven Fabric Mills
N.A.I.C.S.: 313210

Branch (Domestic):

Albany Engineered Composites - Salt Lake City **(2)**
506 Billy Mitchell Rd, Salt Lake City, UT 84116
Tel.: (801) 537-1800
Sales Range: $75-99.9 Million
Emp.: 200
Fiber Reinforced Composite Aerostructures Designer, Mfr & Whslr
N.A.I.C.S.: 336413
Grant Hall *(Dir-Strategy & Bus Dev)*

Albany International AB **(1)**
Kristinebergsvagen 14, Box 510, S-301 80, Halmstad, Sweden **(100%)**
Tel.: (46) 35147000
Sales Range: $150-199.9 Million
Mfr of Paper Machine Clothing
N.A.I.C.S.: 333243

Albany International Canada Corp. **(1)**
300 Westmount Street, Cowansville, J2K 1S9, QC, Canada **(100%)**
Tel.: (450) 263-2880
Web Site: http://www.aiportal.albint.com
Sales Range: $100-124.9 Million
Emp.: 200
Mfr of Fabrics for Paper Making Machinery
N.A.I.C.S.: 332999

Albany International Canada Corp. **(1)**
2947 Rideau Ferry Road, PO Box 100, Perth, K7H 3E3, ON, Canada **(100%)**
Tel.: (613) 267-6600
Sales Range: $25-49.9 Million
Mfr of Process Control Equipment For Forming Fabric
N.A.I.C.S.: 334519

Albany International Engineered Fabrics **(1)**
3601 Electric City Blvd, Kaukauna, WI 54130
Tel.: (920) 521-4600
Sales Range: $50-74.9 Million
Emp.: 165
Fabrics
N.A.I.C.S.: 313210

Albany International Forming Fabrics **(1)**
435 6th St, Menasha, WI 54952 **(100%)**
Tel.: (920) 725-2600
Sales Range: $75-99.9 Million
Emp.: 150
Paper Machine Fabrics Mfr
N.A.I.C.S.: 332618
Joseph G. Morone *(Pres & CEO)*

Albany International France S.A.S. **(1)**
Z I Pavillon - Axial 1 rue Jacquard, PO Box 38, Saint Junien, 87202, Saint-Auvent, Cedex, France **(100%)**
Tel.: (33) 555719200
Web Site: http://www.albint.com
Sales Range: $50-74.9 Million
Mfr of Fabrics for Paper Machine Clothing
N.A.I.C.S.: 332999

Albany International Japan Kabushiki Kaisha **(1)**
Sapporo Electronics Center 307 1-1-10 Shimonopporo Techno-Park, Atsubetsu-ku, Sapporo, 004-0015, Hokkaido, Japan **(1)**
Tel.: (81) 118984111
Apparel Distr
N.A.I.C.S.: 458110

Albany International Ltd. **(1)**
Pilsworth Road, Bury, BL9 8RS, Lancashire, United Kingdom **(100%)**
Tel.: (44) 1617677531
Sales Range: $50-74.9 Million
Emp.: 68
Mfr of Process Belts for Paper Making Machinery
N.A.I.C.S.: 332999
Darren Johnson *(Mgr-HR)*

Albany International Oy **(1)**
Ruosilantie 10, Helsinki, 00390, Finland **(100%)**
Tel.: (358) 9547871
Sales Range: $1-9.9 Million
Emp.: 200
Paper Machine Clothing & Drying Machine Mfr
N.A.I.C.S.: 332999

Albany International Pty. Ltd. **(1)**
23 Faunce Street, PO Box 510, Ettalong Beach, Gosford, 2250, NSW, Australia **(100%)**
Tel.: (61) 243280200
Web Site: https://www.albint.com
Sales Range: $25-49.9 Million
Industrial Machinery & Equipment Distr
N.A.I.C.S.: 423830

Albany International Techniweave, Inc. **(1)**
112 Airport Dr, Rochester, NH 03867 **(100%)**
Tel.: (603) 330-5800
Web Site: http://www.albint.com
Sales Range: $75-99.9 Million
Emp.: 200
Mfr of Composite Fabrics

N.A.I.C.S.: 313210

Albany International Tecidos Tecnicos Ltda. **(1)**
Rua Colorado 350, PO Box 141, Indaial, 89130-000, Santa Catarina, Brazil **(100%)**
Tel.: (55) 4733337500
Web Site: https://www.albint.com
Sales Range: $125-149.9 Million
Synthetic Monofilament Forming, Press & Drying Fabrics for Paper Making Machinery & Industrial Products
N.A.I.C.S.: 332999

Albany International de Mexico S.A. de C.V. **(1)**
Km 18 5 Carretera Tlalnepantla-Cuautitlan Col, El Partidor, 54800, Cuautitlan, Mexico **(100%)**
Tel.: (52) 5558991600
Sales Range: $75-99.9 Million
Emp.: 200
Mfr of Press, Forming & Dryer Fabrics for Paper Making Machinery
N.A.I.C.S.: 332999

Albany International/Engineered Fabrics **(1)**
1373 Broadway, Menands, NY 12204-2628
Tel.: (615) 325-6767
Sales Range: $50-74.9 Million
Emp.: 150
Engineered Fabrics
N.A.I.C.S.: 322120

CirComp GmbH **(1)**
Marie-Curie-Strasse 11, 67661, Kaiserslautern, Germany
Tel.: (49) 63 017 1520
Web Site: https://www.circomp.de
Aerospace Parts Mfr
N.A.I.C.S.: 336413
Hans-Peter Fuchs *(Production Mgr)*

ProfileComp GmbH **(1)**
Marie-Curie-Strasse 11, 67661, Kaiserslautern, Germany
Tel.: (49) 63017152250
Web Site: http://www.profilecomp.de
Aerospace Parts Mfr
N.A.I.C.S.: 336413

Wurttembergische Filztuchfabrik D. Geschmay GmbH **(1)**
Im Pfingstwasen, 73035, Goppingen, Germany **(100%)**
Tel.: (49) 71616040
Sales Range: $75-99.9 Million
Emp.: 100
Press Fabric & Drying Paper Machine Clothing Mfr
N.A.I.C.S.: 332999

ALBEMARLE CORPORATION
4250 Congress St Ste 900, Charlotte, NC 28209
Tel.: (980) 299-5700   **NC**
Web Site: https://www.albemarle.com
Year Founded: 1993
ALB—(NYSE)
Rev.: $9,617,203,000
Assets: $18,270,652,000
Liabilities: $8,605,553,000
Net Worth: $9,665,099,000
Earnings: $1,573,476,000
Emp.: 9,000
Fiscal Year-end: 12/31/23
Specialty Chemicals & Services Developer, Mfr & Whslr
N.A.I.C.S.: 325998
Neal Sheorey *(CFO & Exec VP)*
Melissa H. Anderson *(Chief HR Officer, Chief HR Officer, Sr VP & Sr VP)*
Meredith Bandy *(VP-IR & Sustainability)*
Melissa H. Anderson *(Chief HR Officer & Sr VP)*
Netha N. Johnson Jr. *(Pres)*
Sean O'Hollaren *(Chief External Affairs Officer)*

Cynthia Lima *(Chief External Affairs & Comm Officer & Sr VP)*
Kristin M. Coleman *(Gen Counsel, Sec & Exec VP)*
John C. Barichivich III *(Chief Acctg Officer, VP & Controller)*
J. Kent Masters Jr. *(Chm & CEO)*

Subsidiaries:

Albemarle Amendments, LLC (1)
1664 E Highland Rd Unit 3, Twinsburg, OH 44087
Tel.: (330) 425-2354
Chemical Element Mfr & Distr
N.A.I.C.S.: 325611

Albemarle Chemicals (Shanghai) Company Limited (1)
Room 3202 Pingan Riverfront Financial Center 757 Mengzi Road, Huangpu District, Shanghai, 200023, China
Tel.: (86) 2161038666
Pharmaceutical Preparation Mfr
N.A.I.C.S.: 325412

Albemarle Chemicals South Africa (PTY) Ltd. (1)
15 Clyde Ave, Musgrave, 4001, Durban, KwaZulu-Natal, South Africa
Tel.: (27) 31 202 0960
Web Site: http://www.albemarle.com
Emp.: 1
Industrial Organic Chemicals Mfr
N.A.I.C.S.: 325199

Albemarle Chemicals U.K. Limited (1)
Avonmouth Works, Bristol, BS11 0YT, United Kingdom
Tel.: (44) 1179823611
Sales Range: $50-74.9 Million
Emp.: 200
Industrial Organic Chemicals Mfr
N.A.I.C.S.: 325199

Albemarle Corp. - Pennsylvania (1)
2858 Back Vail Rd, Tyrone, PA 16686   **(100%)**
Tel.: (814) 684-4310
Web Site: http://www.albemarle.com
Sales Range: $75-99.9 Million
Emp.: 200
Mfr of Specialty Chemical Intermediates, Fine Chemicals & Custom Manufacturing of Chemicals
N.A.I.C.S.: 325199

Albemarle Deutschland GmbH (1)
Industriepark Hochst Building G879, 65926, Frankfurt am Main, Germany
Tel.: (49) 69401260
Web Site: https://www.albemarle.de
Emp.: 550
Pharmaceutical Preparation Mfr
N.A.I.C.S.: 325412

Albemarle Europe Sprl (1)
Rue du Bosquet 9, 1348, Louvain-la-Neuve, Belgium
Tel.: (32) 10481711
Pharmaceutical Preparation Mfr
N.A.I.C.S.: 325412

Albemarle Germany GmbH (1)
Industriepark Hochst Gebaude G 879, 65926, Frankfurt am Main, Germany
Tel.: (49) 69401260
Chemical Products Mfr
N.A.I.C.S.: 325998

Albemarle Hungary Ltd. (1)
Vaci ut 76, 1133, Budapest, Hungary
Tel.: (36) 18839600
Cleaning Product Mfr
N.A.I.C.S.: 325612

Albemarle Japan Corporation (1)
7-1-1 Akasaka Aoyama Yasuda Building 11F, Minato-Ku, Tokyo, 107-0052, Japan
Tel.: (81) 36 438 5201
Web Site: https://www.albemarle.jp
Emp.: 2
Pharmaceutical Preparation Mfr
N.A.I.C.S.: 325412

Albemarle Korea Corporation (1)
Samseong-dong Trade Center Room 602 511, Yeongdong-daero Gangnam-gu, Seoul, 06164, Korea (South)

Tel.: (82) 2 555 3005
Web Site: https://www.albemarle.com
Pharmaceutical Preparation Mfr
N.A.I.C.S.: 325412

Albemarle Limitada (1)
Avenida Hector Gomez Cobo 975 lote 4, Antofagasta, Chile
Tel.: (56) 552351000
Web Site: https://www.albemarlelitio.cl
Emp.: 1,000
Chemical Products Mfr
N.A.I.C.S.: 325998

Albemarle Lithium Pty. Ltd. (1)
Level 1 197 St George's Terrace, PO Box 7423, Perth, 6850, WA, Australia
Tel.: (61) 1300925400
Chemical Products Mfr
N.A.I.C.S.: 325998

Albemarle Management (Shanghai) Co., Ltd. (1)
Room 3202 Gopher Center No 757 Mengzi Road, Huangpu District, Shanghai, 200023, China
Tel.: (86) 2161038666
Transportation Energy & Electronic Material Mfr
N.A.I.C.S.: 336999

Albemarle Middle East Corporation FZE (1)
6W Block-A Office-201 2nd Floor, PO Box 293774, Dubai Airport Free Zone, Dubai, United Arab Emirates
Tel.: (971) 47017770
Cleaning Product Mfr
N.A.I.C.S.: 325612
Rohit Irabatti *(Mgr-Bus Dev-Middle East & India)*

Albemarle Singapore PTE LTD (1)
30 Cecil Street 28-05/08 Prudential Tower, Singapore, 049712, Singapore
Tel.: (65) 6 424 8400
Web Site: https://www.albemarle.com
Emp.: 50
Pharmaceutical Preparation Mfr
N.A.I.C.S.: 325412

Albemarle Sorbent Technologies (1)
1664 E Highland Rd Unit Ste 3, Twinsburg, OH 44087
Tel.: (330) 425-2354
Web Site: http://www.albemarle.com
Sales Range: $25-49.9 Million
Emp.: 7
Specialty Chemicals Mfr
N.A.I.C.S.: 325110

Albemarle U.S., Inc. (1)
348 Holiday Inn Dr, Kings Mountain, NC 28086
Tel.: (704) 739-2501
Chemical Products Mfr
N.A.I.C.S.: 325998

Chongqing Chemetall Chemicals Co., Ltd. (1)
No 43 Baihe Road, Nanping, 400060, Chongqing, China
Tel.: (86) 2362751313
Web Site: http://www.chemetall.com.cn
Emp.: 80
Chemical Distr
N.A.I.C.S.: 424690

Jiangxi Albemarle Lithium Co., Ltd. (1)
Industrial Park of Fenyi County, Xinyu, 336600, Jiangxi, China
Tel.: (86) 7905890866
Chemical Products Mfr
N.A.I.C.S.: 325998

Jordan Bromine Company Limited (1)
PO Box 941967, Amman, 11194, Jordan
Tel.: (962) 32308050
Web Site: https://www.jordanbromine.com
Emp.: 350
Chemical Distr
N.A.I.C.S.: 424690

Ketjen Catalysts (Shanghai) Company Limited (1)
Room 3202 No 757 Mengzi Road Pingan Riverfront Financial Center, Huangpu District, Shanghai, 200023, China

Tel.: (86) 2161038666
Chemical Element Mfr & Distr
N.A.I.C.S.: 325611

Ketjen Corporation (1)
13100 Space Ctr Blvd Ste 400, Houston, TX 77059
Tel.: (281) 480-4747
Web Site: https://www.ketjen.com
Chemical Element Mfr & Distr
N.A.I.C.S.: 325611

Ketjen Hungary Limited Liability Company (1)
23-27 Vaci ut, 1134, Budapest, Hungary
Tel.: (36) 18839600
Chemical Element Mfr & Distr
N.A.I.C.S.: 325611

Ketjen India Private Limited (1)
103 Windfall Sahar Plaza Complex JB Nagar, Andheri East, Mumbai, 400059, India
Tel.: (91) 2261386138
Chemical Element Mfr & Distr
N.A.I.C.S.: 325611

Ketjen Japan GK (1)
Aoyama Yasuda Bldg 1-1 Akasaka 7-Chome, Minato-ku, Tokyo, 107-0052, Japan
Tel.: (81) 364385201
Chemical Element Mfr & Distr
N.A.I.C.S.: 325611

Ketjen Korea Limited (1)
1301 511 Yeongdong-Daero, Gangam-gu, Seoul, 06164, Korea (South)
Tel.: (82) 25553005
Chemical Element Mfr & Distr
N.A.I.C.S.: 325611

Ketjen Malaysia Sdn Bhd. (1)
Suite 8 01 Level 8 Menara Binjai No 2 Jalan Binjai, 50450, Kuala Lumpur, Malaysia
Tel.: (60) 323867700
Chemical Element Mfr & Distr
N.A.I.C.S.: 325611

Ketjen Netherlands B.V. (1)
Nieuwendammerkade 1-3, 1022 AB, Amsterdam, Netherlands
Tel.: (31) 206347000
Chemical Element Mfr & Distr
N.A.I.C.S.: 325611

Ketjen Singapore Private Limited (1)
30 Cecil Street 28-05/08 Prudential Tower, Singapore, 049712, Singapore
Tel.: (65) 64248400
Chemical Element Mfr & Distr
N.A.I.C.S.: 325611

Ketjen Vietnam Limited Liability Co., Ltd. (1)
Unit 1636 Level 16 Daeha Business Center 360 Kim Ma Street, Khanh Ward Ba Dinh District, Hanoi, Vietnam
Tel.: (84) 2432673443
Chemical Element Mfr & Distr
N.A.I.C.S.: 325611

Martinswerk GmbH (1)
Kolner Strasse 110, 50127, Bergheim, Germany   **(100%)**
Tel.: (49) 22719020
Web Site: http://www.martinswerk.de
Sales Range: $150-199.9 Million
Emp.: 530
Inorganic Chemicals & Special Pigments Mfr & Marketer
N.A.I.C.S.: 325998
Klaus Kramer *(Bus Mgr-Global)*
Timo Kremer *(Mgr-Technology)*
Jochen Bust *(Mgr-Supply Chain)*
Philipp Kohn *(Mng Dir & VP)*
Markus Klugge *(Bus Mgr-Global)*
Judy Lim *(Bus Mgr-Global)*
Ivo Jurjevic *(Mgr-Engineering-FRA)*
Dirk Ballas *(Head)*
Philipp Kohn *(Mng Dir & VP)*
Markus Klugge *(Bus Mgr-Global)*
Judy Lim *(Bus Mgr-Global)*
Ivo Jurjevic *(Mgr-Engineering-FRA)*
Dirk Ballas *(Head)*
Philipp Kohn *(Mng Dir & VP)*
Markus Klugge *(Bus Mgr-Global)*
Judy Lim *(Bus Mgr-Global)*
Ivo Jurjevic *(Mgr-Engineering-FRA)*
Dirk Ballas *(Head)*

Nippon Aluminum Alkyls, Ltd. (1)
16F Fukoku Seimei Bldg 2-2 Uchisaiwai-cho 2-chome, Chiyoda-ku, Tokyo, 100-0011, Japan
Tel.: (81) 335040811
Web Site: https://www.naa.co.jp
Sales Range: $25-49.9 Million
Emp.: 50
Organic Compounds such as Alkylaluminum & Their Derivatives Mfr & Sales; Owned 50% by Mitsui Chemicals, Inc. & Albemarle Corporation
N.A.I.C.S.: 325199
Masanobu Itaya *(Pres)*

Nippon Ketjen Co., Ltd. (1)
1-2-1 Shibaura 20F Seavans N Building, Minato-ku, Tokyo, 105-6791, Japan   **(50%)**
Tel.: (81) 354425061
Web Site: http://www.nippon-ketjen.co.jp
Sales Range: $50-74.9 Million
Emp.: 159
Development, Production & Sales of Hydro-processing Catalysts
N.A.I.C.S.: 325998
Hiromasa Ooba *(Pres)*

Rockwood Lithium India Pvt. Ltd. (1)
103 Windfall Sahar Plaza J B Nagar, Andheri, Mumbai, 400 059, India
Tel.: (91) 2261386138
Chemical Distr
N.A.I.C.S.: 424690

Rockwood Lithium Korea LLC (1)
602 Trade Tower World Trade Center, Samsung-dong Gangnam District, Seoul, 135-729, Korea (South)
Tel.: (82) 263252111
Chemical Distr
N.A.I.C.S.: 424690

Rockwood Lithium Shanghai Co., Ltd. (1)
Building 6 A-Sun Science & Technology Park Lane 399 Shengxia Road, Pudong, Shanghai, 201210, China
Tel.: (86) 2161038666
Chemical Distr
N.A.I.C.S.: 424690
Fei Li *(Sr Mgr-Sls)*

Rockwood Lithium Taiwan Co., Ltd. (1)
2 Hsien-Kong N 1st Road Hsien Si, Chang-Bin Industrial Park, Taipei, Chang Hua, Taiwan
Tel.: (886) 223699001
Chemical Distr
N.A.I.C.S.: 424690

Sales De Magnesio Ltda (1)
Sec La Negra Lotes 1 Y 2 Antofagasta, El Trovador 4285, Santiago, Chile
Tel.: (56) 24252428
Chemical & Allied Products Whslr
N.A.I.C.S.: 424690

Shandong Sinobrom Albemarle Bromine Chemicals Company Limited (1)
504 505 506 508 Room Yinhai Hengji Bldg 338 Dongfeng East Street, Weifang, 261041, Shandong, China
Tel.: (86) 5368199882
Web Site: https://www.sinobrom.cn
Chemical Products Mfr
N.A.I.C.S.: 325180

Sichuan Guorun New Material Co., Ltd. (1)
Pengshan Economic Development Zone, Meishan, 620866, Sichuan, China
Tel.: (86) 2837668532
Chemical Products Mfr
N.A.I.C.S.: 325998
Julia Fu *(Sls Mgr)*

Talison Lithium Pty. Ltd. (1)
Level 15 216 St Georges Terrace, Perth, 6000, WA, Australia
Tel.: (61) 892635555
Web Site: https://www.talisonlithium.com
Sales Range: $125-149.9 Million
Emp.: 140
Lithium Mining Services
N.A.I.C.S.: 212290
Lorry Mignacca *(CEO & Mng Dir)*

Albemarle Corporation—(Continued)

hebro chemie Zweigniederlassung der Rockwood Specialties Group GmbH (1)
Rostocker Strasse 40, 41199, Monchengladbach, Germany
Tel.: (49) 216660090
Web Site: https://www.hebro-chemie.de
Chemical Products Mfr
N.A.I.C.S.: 325998

ALBIREO PHARMA, INC.
10 Post Office Sq Ste 1000 S, Boston, MA 02109
Tel.: (857) 254-5555 DE
Web Site:
http://www.albireopharma.com
ALBO—(NASDAQ)
Rev.: $40,579,000
Assets: $302,051,000
Liabilities: $126,443,000
Net Worth: $175,608,000
Earnings: ($34,030,000)
Emp.: 130
Fiscal Year-end: 12/31/21
Pharmaceutical Researcher, Developer & Marketer
N.A.I.C.S.: 325412
Jan P. Mattsson (Chief Scientific Officer, Chief Scientific Officer & Mng Dir-Sweden & Interim Head-R&D)
Martha J. Carter (Chief Regulatory Officer)
David Chiswell (Chm)
Jason Duncan (Chief Legal Officer & Gen Counsel)
Michelle Graham (Chief HR Officer)
Pamela Stephenson (Chief Comml Officer)
Joan Connolly (CTO)

Subsidiaries:

Albireo AB (1)
Arvid Wallgrens Backe 20, 413 46, Gothenburg, Sweden
Tel.: (46) 317411480
Pharmaceutical Product Whslr
N.A.I.C.S.: 424210

ALCOA CORPORATION
201 Isabella St Ste 500, Pittsburgh, PA 15212-5858
Tel.: (412) 315-2900 DE
Web Site: https://www.alcoa.com
Year Founded: 2016
AA—(NYSE)
Rev.: $10,551,000,000
Assets: $14,155,000,000
Liabilities: $8,310,000,000
Net Worth: $5,845,000,000
Earnings: ($651,000,000)
Emp.: 13,600
Fiscal Year-end: 12/31/23
Holding Company; Bauxite Mining & Aluminum Refining
N.A.I.C.S.: 551112
William F. Oplinger (Pres & CEO)
Jeffrey D. Heeter (Corp Counsel & Exec VP)
Molly S. Beerman (CFO & Exec VP)
Catherine Garfinkel (Chief Ethics & Compliance Officer & Sr VP)
Renato Bacchi (Chief Comml Officer & Exec VP)
Heather Hudak (Sr VP-Tax)
Marissa P. Earnest (Sec & Sr VP)
Sonya Elam Harden (Chief External Affairs Officer & Exec VP)
Tammi A. Jones (Chief HR Officer & Exec VP)
Louis Langlois (Treas)

Subsidiaries:

Alcoa Aluminio S.A. (1)
Avenida das Nacoes Unidas 14 261 Ala B 17 Andar Conj A, CEP04533-085, Sao Paulo, SP, Brazil

Tel.: (55) 1132963026
Web Site: http://www.alcoa.com
Alumina & Aluminum Powder Mining, Refining & Smelting
N.A.I.C.S.: 331313

Alcoa Australian Holdings Pty. Ltd. (1)
corner Davy and Marmion Streets, Booragoon, 6154, WA, Australia
Tel.: (61) 893165111
Holding Company
N.A.I.C.S.: 551112
Michael A. Parker (Chm & Mng Dir)

Subsidiary (Domestic):

Alcoa of Australia Limited (2)
181 - 205 Davy Road, Booragoon, 6154, WA, Australia (60%)
Tel.: (61) 893165111
Web Site: https://www.alcoa.com
Bauxite Mining & Alumina Refining, Aluminum Smelting & Recycling Services
N.A.I.C.S.: 331313

Alcoa Canada Ltd. (1)
1 Place Ville Marie bur 2310, Montreal, H3B 3M5, QC, Canada
Tel.: (514) 904-5030
Web Site: http://www.alcoa.com
Sales Range: $1-4.9 Billion
Emp.: 3,960
Aluminium Products Mfr
N.A.I.C.S.: 331313

Subsidiary (Domestic):

Alcoa Ltd. (2)
100 Rte Maritime, PO Box 1530, Baie Comeau, G4Z 2L6, QC, Canada (100%)
Tel.: (418) 296-3311
Sales Range: $750-799.9 Million
Emp.: 800
Primary Aluminum Mfr
N.A.I.C.S.: 331313

Alcoa Inespal, S.A. (1)
Poligono Industrial de Grela, La Coruna, 15008, Spain
Tel.: (34) 985128900
Electronics Appliances Rental Service
N.A.I.C.S.: 532210

Subsidiary (Domestic):

Alumina Espanola, S.A. (2)
Calle Pedro Teixeira 8 Edificio Iberia Mart Planta 3, 28020, Madrid, Spain
Tel.: (34) 914068200
Sales Range: $250-299.9 Million
Emp.: 600
Aluminum Producer
N.A.I.C.S.: 331318
Jose Ramon Camimo (Pres)

Alcoa Intalco Works (1)
4050 Mountain View Rd, Ferndale, WA 98248-0937 (100%)
Tel.: (360) 384-7061
Sales Range: $300-349.9 Million
Emp.: 660
Aluminum Producer
N.A.I.C.S.: 331313
John Thuestad (Pres)

Alcoa Remediation Management, Inc. (1)
201 Isabella St, Pittsburgh, PA 15212-5858
Tel.: (412) 553-4545
Sales Range: $100-124.9 Million
Remediation Services
N.A.I.C.S.: 561499
Ed Votas (Fin Analyst)

Alcoa World Alumina LLC (1)
201 Isabella St Ste 500, Pittsburgh, PA 15212-5858 (60%)
Tel.: (412) 315-2900
Aluminium Products Mfr
N.A.I.C.S.: 331313
Michael A. Parker (Pres)

Affiliate (Non-US):

Compagnie des Bauxites de Guinee SA (2)
9th Floor Zein building, BP 523, Quartier Almamya Commune de Kaloum, Conakry, Guinea (22.95%)
Tel.: (224) 623233898

Web Site: https://www.cbg-guinee.com
Bauxite Mining
N.A.I.C.S.: 212290

Subsidiary (Non-US):

Suriname Aluminum Company, L.L.C. (2)
13 Van't Hogerhuysstraat, PO Box 1810, Paramaribo, Suriname (60%)
Tel.: (597) 323281
Aluminum Mining Services
N.A.I.C.S.: 212290

Alumina Limited (1)
Level 12 IBM Centre 60 City Road, Southbank, 3006, VIC, Australia
Tel.: (61) 3 8699 2600
Web Site: http://www.aluminalimited.com
Sales Range: $1-9.9 Million
Investment Services; Bauxite & Aluminum Mining & Smelting Operations
N.A.I.C.S.: 523999
Stephen Foster (Gen Counsel & Sec)
Michael Peter Ferraro (Mng Dir)
Galina Kraeva (Gen Mgr-Fin)
Grant A. Dempsey (CFO)

Aluminerie de Becancour Inc. (1)
5555 Pierre Thibault, PO Box 30, Becancour, G9H 2T7, QC, Canada
Tel.: (819) 294-6101
Web Site: http://www.alcoa.com
Aluminum Smelting Services; Owned 74.95% by Alcoa, Inc. & 24.05% by Rio Tinto Alcan Inc.
N.A.I.C.S.: 331313

Norsk Alcoa AS (1)
Havnegt 40, PO Box 566, Mosjoen, 8663, Norland, Norway
Tel.: (47) 75179100
Sales Range: $150-199.9 Million
Emp.: 400
Aluminium Processing
N.A.I.C.S.: 331523
Eivind Mikalfsen (Gen Mgr)

Subsidiary (Domestic):

Alcoa Norway ANS (2)
Drammensveien 147A, 0277, Oslo, Norway
Tel.: (47) 75 17 91 00
Aluminium Products Mfr
N.A.I.C.S.: 331524

Division (Domestic):

Alcoa Lista-Norway (3)
Vollmonaveien 40, 4550, Farsund, 4500, Norway
Tel.: (47) 38399100
Web Site: http://www.alcoa.no
Aluminium Products Mfr
N.A.I.C.S.: 331524

Alcoa Mosjoen (3)
Havnegata 40, 8663, Mosjoen, 8663, Norway
Tel.: (47) 75179100
Mfr of Aluminium
N.A.I.C.S.: 331524

ALDEYRA THERAPEUTICS, INC.
131 Hartwell Ave Ste 320, Lexington, MA 02421
Tel.: (781) 761-4904 DE
Web Site: https://www.aldeyra.com
Year Founded: 2004
ALDX—(NASDAQ)
Rev.: $2,049,449
Assets: $181,291,657
Liabilities: $30,283,628
Net Worth: $151,008,029
Earnings: ($62,024,636)
Emp.: 15
Fiscal Year-end: 12/31/22
Pharmaceuticals Mfr
N.A.I.C.S.: 325412
Todd C. Brady (Pres & CEO)
Stephen G. Machatha (Chief Dev Officer)
Caitlin Pazzano (VP-Quality Assurance)
Michael Alfieri (CFO & Principal Acctg Officer)

Subsidiaries:

Helio Vision Germany GmbH (1)
Keniastrasse 12, 47269, Duisburg, Germany
Tel.: (49) 2035094960
Web Site: https://www.helion-vision.com
Camera Mfr & Distr
N.A.I.C.S.: 333310

ALECTOR, INC.
131 Oyster Point Blvd Ste 600, South San Francisco, CA 94080
Tel.: (415) 231-5660 DE
Web Site: https://www.alector.com
Year Founded: 2013
ALEC—(NASDAQ)
Rev.: $133,617,000
Assets: $787,648,000
Liabilities: $573,206,000
Net Worth: $214,442,000
Earnings: ($133,310,000)
Emp.: 273
Fiscal Year-end: 12/31/22
Biotechnology Research & Development Services
N.A.I.C.S.: 541714
Marc Grasso (CFO)
Calvin Yu (VP-Fin)
Clare Hunt (Head-People)
David Oh (VP-Corp Law)
Daniel Maslyar (VP-Clinical Dev-Oncology)
Virginia DeJesus-Rueff (VP-Portfolio & Program Mgmt)
Charles Wolfus (VP-Tech & Digital Health)
Gary Romano (Chief Medical Officer)
Kristina Vlaovic (VP-Regulatory)
Tina Schwabe (Head-Immuno-Neurology)
Hua Long (Sr Dir-Pre-Clinical Res)
Spencer Liang (Head-Immuno-Oncology)
Herve Rhinn (Head-Target Discovery & Genomics)
Erica Jefferson (VP-Comm & Pub Affairs)
Brian Sander (Gen Counsel)
Arnon Rosenthal (CEO)
Saraswati Kenkare-Mitra (Pres & Head-R&D)

ALERUS FINANCIAL CORPORATION
401 DeMers Ave, Grand Forks, ND 58201
Tel.: (701) 795-3200 DE
Web Site: https://www.alerus.com
Year Founded: 1879
ALRS—(NASDAQ)
Rev.: $226,800,000
Assets: $3,779,637,000
Liabilities: $3,422,765,000
Net Worth: $356,872,000
Earnings: $40,005,000
Emp.: 773
Fiscal Year-end: 12/31/22
Bank Holding Company
N.A.I.C.S.: 551111
Daniel E. Coughlin (Exec Chm)
Katie A. Lorenson (Pres & CEO)
Karin M. Taylor (Chief Risk Officer & Exec VP)
Missy S. Keney (Chief Engagement Officer & Exec VP)
Alan A. Villalon (CFO & Exec VP)
Jim Collins (Chief Banking & Revenue Officer & Exec VP)
Kari Koob (Principal Acctg Officer & Dir-Acctg)
Kris Bevill (Mgr-PR)

Subsidiaries:

Alerus Financial, National Association (1)
401 Demers Ave, Grand Forks, ND 58201

Tel.: (701) 795-3200
Web Site: http://www.alerus.com
Federal Savings Bank
N.A.I.C.S.: 522180
Randy Louis Newman *(Chm, Pres & CEO)*

Subsidiary (Domestic):

Home Federal Savings Bank (2)
1201 S Broadway, Rochester, MN 55904
Tel.: (507) 536-2416
Web Site: https://www.justcallhome.com
Sales Range: $25-49.9 Million
Federal Savings Bank
N.A.I.C.S.: 522180
Jon J. Eberle *(CFO, Treas & Exec VP)*
Bradley C. Krehbiel *(Pres & CEO)*
Joe Langel *(Dir-Bus Banking & Sr VP)*
Jason Williamson *(Dir-Compliance & VP)*

Division (Domestic):

Home Federal Private Banking (3)
1016 Civic Ctr Dr NW Ste 101, Rochester, MN 55901
Tel.: (507) 535-1309
Web Site: http://www.justcallhome.com
Private Banking & Wealth Management Services
N.A.I.C.S.: 523150

HMN Financial, Inc. (1)
1110 Centre Pointe Curve Ste 101, Mendota Heights, MN 55120
Tel.: (507) 535-1309
Web Site: https://www.hmnf.com
Rev.: $43,142,000
Assets: $1,096,202,000
Liabilities: $998,866,000
Net Worth: $97,336,000
Earnings: $8,045,000
Emp.: 164
Fiscal Year-end: 12/31/2022
Bank Holding Company
N.A.I.C.S.: 551111
Jon J. Eberle *(CFO, Treas & Sr VP)*

ALEXANDER & BALDWIN, INC.

822 Bishop St, Honolulu, HI 96813
Tel.: (808) 525-6611   HI
Web Site:
    https://www.alexanderbaldwin.com
Year Founded: 1870
ALEX—(NYSE)
Rev.: $230,500,000
Assets: $1,787,300,000
Liabilities: $751,600,000
Net Worth: $1,035,700,000
Earnings: ($50,600,000)
Emp.: 144
Fiscal Year-end: 12/31/22
Offices of Other Holding Companies
N.A.I.C.S.: 551112
Meredith J. Ching *(Exec VP-External Affairs)*
Clayton K. Y. Chun *(CFO, Treas & Exec VP)*
Jerrod Schreck *(Exec VP)*
Jordan Brant *(Sr VP-Leasing-Real Estate)*
Kit Millan *(Sr VP-Asset Mgmt-Real Estate)*
Francisco Gutierrez *(Sr VP-Dev-Real Estate)*
Derek Kanehira *(Sr VP-HR)*
Anthony J. Tommasino *(Principal Acctg Officer, VP & Controller)*
Derek T. Kanehira *(Sr VP)*
Lance K. Parker *(Pres & CEO)*

Subsidiaries:

A&B II, LLC (1)
822 Bishop St, Honolulu, HI 96813
Tel.: (808) 525-6611
Nonresidential Property Managers
N.A.I.C.S.: 531312

Subsidiary (Domestic):

G P Maintenance Solutions, Inc. (2)
660 Mapunapuna St, Honolulu, HI 96819
Tel.: (808) 682-6081

Web Site:
    https://www.gpmaintenancesolutions.com
Industrial Safety Product Provider
N.A.I.C.S.: 423450

GP/RM Prestress, LLC (2)
91-063 Malakole St, Kapolei, HI 96707
Tel.: (808) 682-6000
Web Site: https://www.gprmp.com
Emp.: 100
Concrete Products Mfr
N.A.I.C.S.: 327390
Les Kempers *(VP)*
Andy Boyd *(Pres)*

Maui Paving, LLC (2)
Ameron Quarry Camp 10, Puunene, HI 96784
Tel.: (808) 877-2755
Web Site: http://www.gracepacific.com
Highway/Street Construction
N.A.I.C.S.: 237310
Gorden Yee *(Pres)*

Oahu Paving Company, Inc (2)
110 Puuhale Rd, Honolulu, HI 96819
Tel.: (808) 845-3991
Real Estate Services
N.A.I.C.S.: 531390

A&B Inc. (1)
822 Bishop St, Honolulu, HI 96813
Tel.: (808) 525-6611
Web Site: http://www.abprop.com
Real Estate Property Services
N.A.I.C.S.: 531190

A&B Properties, Inc. (1)
822 Bishop St, Honolulu, HI 96813 **(100%)**
Tel.: (808) 525-6676
Web Site: http://www.abprop.com
Real Estate Acquisition, Development & Property Management Services
N.A.I.C.S.: 531390

Subsidiary (Domestic):

A&B Waianae LLC (2)
86-120 Farrington Hwy Ste 210, Waianae, HI 96792
Tel.: (808) 696-2503
Real Estate Developers
N.A.I.C.S.: 522292

ABP Kakaako Commerce 1 LLC (2)
875 Waimanu St Ste 611, Honolulu, HI 96813
Tel.: (808) 591-2746
Real Estate Services
N.A.I.C.S.: 531390

Crossroads Plaza Development Partners, LLC (2)
28060 Hasley Canyon Rd, Castaic, CA 91384
Tel.: (661) 295-0771
Commercial Real Estate Developer
N.A.I.C.S.: 522292

ABL Exchange LLC (1)
200 W State St Ste 205, Belle Plaine, MN 56011
Tel.: (952) 873-6210
Web Site:
    http://www.ablexchangebarternetwork.com
Real Estate Developers
N.A.I.C.S.: 522292

Alexander & Baldwin Sugar Museum (1)
3957 Hansen Rd, Puunene, HI 96784
Tel.: (808) 871-8058
Web Site: https://www.sugarmuseum.com
Sales Range: $25-49.9 Million
Sugar Cane Mfr
N.A.I.C.S.: 111930
Douglas A. Sheehan *(Pres)*
Alyson Nakamura *(Sec)*
Ken S. Ota *(VP)*
Will Cambra *(Treas & Controller)*

East Maui Irrigation Co., Ltd. (1)
497 Baldwin Ave, Paia, HI 96779 **(100%)**
Tel.: (808) 579-9516
Sales Range: $10-24.9 Million
Emp.: 15
Real Estate Services
N.A.I.C.S.: 531390
G.W.C. Hew *(Gen Mgr)*

Kahului Trucking & Storage, Inc. (1)

140 Hobron Ave Maui, Kahului, HI 96732   **(100%)**
Tel.: (808) 877-5001
Web Site: http://www.kahuluitrucking.com
Sales Range: $50-74.9 Million
Freight & Storage Services
N.A.I.C.S.: 484110

Kukui'ula Development Company, Inc. (1)
2700 Ke Alaula St Ste B, Koloa, HI 96756-8588   **(100%)**
Tel.: (808) 742-6304
Web Site: http://www.kukuiula.com
Sales Range: $300-349.9 Million
Emp.: 100
Property Management Services
N.A.I.C.S.: 531210

Kukui'ula Village LLC (1)
2700 Ke Alaula St, Koloa, HI 96756
Tel.: (808) 742-0234
Web Site: https://www.kukuiula.com
Real Estate Developers
N.A.I.C.S.: 522292

McBryde Resources, Inc. (1)
822 Bishop St, Honolulu, HI 96813 **(100%)**
Tel.: (808) 525-6611
Web Site: http://www.alexanderbaldwin.com
Sales Range: $100-124.9 Million
Infrastructure & Agricultural Support Services To Lands Owned by Alexander & Baldwin
N.A.I.C.S.: 115116

Subsidiary (Domestic):

Kauai Coffee Company, Inc. (2)
870 Halewili Rd, Kalaheo, HI 96741   **(100%)**
Tel.: (808) 335-5102
Web Site: https://www.kauaicoffee.com
Sales Range: $25-49.9 Million
Emp.: 80
Coffee Producer & Distr
N.A.I.C.S.: 311920

ALEXANDER'S, INC.

210 Rte 4 E, Paramus, NJ 07652
Tel.: (201) 587-8541   DE
Web Site: https://www.alx-inc.com
Year Founded: 1955
ALX—(NYSE)
Rev.: $224,962,000
Assets: $1,403,680,000
Liabilities: $1,166,023,000
Net Worth: $237,657,000
Earnings: $102,413,000
Emp.: 92
Fiscal Year-end: 12/31/23
Real Estate Investment Trust
N.A.I.C.S.: 525990
Gary Hansen *(CFO)*
Steven Roth *(Chm & CEO)*

ALEXANDRIA ADVANTAGE WARRANTY COMPANY

317 Rosecrans Ave Ste 200, Manhattan Beach, CA 90266
Tel.: (310) 953-9680
Web Site:
    http://www.alexandriaadvantage
    warranty.com
AAWC—(OTCIQ)
New & Used Car Warranty Services
N.A.I.C.S.: 525990
Jay Pignatello *(CEO)*

ALEXANDRIA REAL ESTATE EQUITIES, INC.

26 N Euclid Ave, Pasadena, CA 91101
Tel.: (626) 578-0777   MD
Web Site: https://www.are.com
Year Founded: 1994
ARE—(NYSE)
Rev.: $2,885,699,000
Assets: $36,771,420,000
Liabilities: $14,148,409,000
Net Worth: $22,622,993,000
Earnings: $92,444,000
Emp.: 568

Fiscal Year-end: 12/31/23
Real Estate Investment Trust
N.A.I.C.S.: 525990
Peter M. Moglia *(CEO & Chief Investment Officer)*
Daniel J. Ryan *(Co-Pres & Reg Dir-Market-San Diego)*
Marc E. Binda *(CFO & Treas)*
Andres R. Gavinet *(Chief Acctg Officer)*
Joseph Hakman *(Co-COO & Chief Strategic Transactions Officer)*
Jackie B. Clem *(Gen Counsel & Sec)*
Hunter L. Kass *(Co-Pres & Reg Dir-Market-Greater Boston)*
Vincent R. Ciruzzi *(Chief Dev Officer)*
Joel S. Marcus *(Co-Founder, Chm & Exec Chm)*

Subsidiaries:

ARE - QRS Corp. (1)
401 Professional Dr, Gaithersburg, MD 20879
Tel.: (301) 740-2577
Real Estate Investment Management Services
N.A.I.C.S.: 523940

ARE - Tech Square, LLC (1)
400 Technology Sq, Cambridge, MA 02139-3557
Tel.: (617) 661-6962
Web Site: http://www.tech-square.com
Sales Range: $25-49.9 Million
Emp.: 14
Real Estate Investment Management Services
N.A.I.C.S.: 523940
Tom Andrews *(Gen Mgr)*

ALFI, INC.

429 Lenox Ave Ste 547, Miami Beach, FL 33139
Tel.: (305) 395-4520   DE
Web Site: https://www.getalfi.com
Year Founded: 2018
ALF—(NASDAQ)
Rev.: $26,465
Assets: $11,373,005
Liabilities: $2,362,757
Net Worth: $9,010,248
Earnings: ($18,944,442)
Emp.: 33
Fiscal Year-end: 12/31/21
Software Development Services
N.A.I.C.S.: 541511

ALIGHT, INC.

4 Overlook Point, Lincolnshire, IL 60069
Tel.: (224) 737-7000   DE
Web Site: https://www.alight.com
ALIT—(NYSE)
Rev.: $3,132,000,000
Assets: $11,235,000,000
Liabilities: $6,146,000,000
Net Worth: $5,089,000,000
Earnings: ($62,000,000)
Emp.: 18,000
Fiscal Year-end: 12/31/22
Cloud-based Digital Human Capital & Business Solutions
N.A.I.C.S.: 518210
Gregory R. Goff *(Pres, CTO & Chief Delivery Officer)*
Christopher A. Michalak *(CEO)*
MacKenzie Lucas *(VP-Comm)*
David D. Guilmette *(Vice Chm & CEO)*

Subsidiaries:

Alight Health Market Insurance Solutions Inc. (1)
199 Fremont St Ste 1500, San Francisco, CA 94105
Tel.: (847) 442-1876
Web Site: https://retiree.alight.com
Health Insurance Services
N.A.I.C.S.: 524298

Alight, Inc.—(Continued)

Alight Solutions LLC **(1)**
4 Overlook Pt, Lincolnshire, IL 60069
Tel.: (847) 295-5000
Web Site: https://www.alight.com
Sales Range: $1-4.9 Billion
Emp.: 23,000
Financial & Human Resource Consulting
Services
N.A.I.C.S.: 541611
Stephan D. Scholl (CEO)

Subsidiary (Domestic):

Alight Financial Solutions, LLC **(2)**
100 Half Day Rd, Lincolnshire, IL 60069
Tel.: (847) 295-5000
Sales Range: $1-4.9 Billion
Emp.: 9,000
Financial Services
N.A.I.C.S.: 523150

Subsidiary (Non-US):

Aon Hewitt (Cyprus) Limited **(2)**
13 Atho Street, CY-1087, Nicosia, Cyprus
Tel.: (357) 22458011
Web Site: https://www.aonsolutions.com.cy
Management Consulting Services
N.A.I.C.S.: 541618

Aon Hewitt (PNG) Ltd. **(2)**
Level 4 Aon Haus MacGregor Street, Port
Moresby, Papua New Guinea
Tel.: (675) 3224544
Web Site: http://www.aon.com
Insurance Management Services
N.A.I.C.S.: 524298

Aon Hewitt (Switzerland) S.A. **(2)**
Avenue Edouard-Dubois 20, 2000, Neucha-
tel, Switzerland
Tel.: (41) 582661011
Web Site: http://www.cacp.ch
Insurance Management Services
N.A.I.C.S.: 524298

Aon Hewitt (Thailand) Ltd. **(2)**
12B Fl Unit A1 Siam Tower 989 Rama I Rd
Patumwan, Silom Bangrak, Bangkok,
10330, Thailand **(100%)**
Tel.: (66) 23054700
Sales Range: $25-49.9 Million
Emp.: 22
Human Resources Outsourcing & Consult-
ing Services
N.A.I.C.S.: 541612

Aon Hewitt - Toronto **(2)**
2 Sheppard Ave E, Toronto, M2N 7A4, ON,
Canada **(100%)**
Tel.: (416) 225-5001
Sales Range: $100-124.9 Million
Emp.: 300
Human Resources Outsourcing & Consult-
ing Services
N.A.I.C.S.: 541612
Brenda Prysko (Partner-Calgary)

Aon Hewitt Belgium **(2)**
Telecomlaan 5-7, The Lighthouse, 1831,
Diegem, Belgium **(100%)**
Tel.: (32) 27309511
Sales Range: $25-49.9 Million
Emp.: 25
Human Resources Outsourcing & Consult-
ing Services
N.A.I.C.S.: 541612

Aon Hewitt Espana S.A.U. **(2)**
Rosario Pino 14-16, Madrid, 28020, Spain
Tel.: (34) 902114611
Web Site: http://www.aon.com
Insurance Brokerage Service Provider
N.A.I.C.S.: 524291

Aon Hewitt GmbH **(2)**
St-Martin-Strasse 58-68, 81541, Munich,
Germany
Tel.: (49) 89523050
Web Site: http://www.aonhewitt.com
Sales Range: $25-49.9 Million
Emp.: 250
Human Capital & Financial Management
Consultants
N.A.I.C.S.: 541611

Aon Hewitt GmbH **(2)**
Dantestr 4-6, 65189, Wiesbaden,
Germany **(100%)**

Tel.: (49) 611928830
Sales Range: $25-49.9 Million
Emp.: 70
Provider of Human Resources Outsourcing
& Consulting Services
N.A.I.C.S.: 541612

Aon Hewitt GmbH **(2)**
Dantestrasse 4-6, 65189, Wiesbaden, Ger-
many
Tel.: (49) 611172086700
Web Site: http://www.aonhewitt.com
Sales Range: $25-49.9 Million
Emp.: 7
Risk Managemeng Srvices
N.A.I.C.S.: 524210

Aon Hewitt HR One Corporation **(2)**
Shiba Park Bldg B-12F 2-4-1 Shibakoen,
Minato-ku, Tokyo, Japan
Tel.: (81) 354014318
Human Resource Consulting Services
N.A.I.C.S.: 541612

Aon Hewitt Korea **(2)**
29F Center 1 East Tower 26 Eulji-Ro 5-Gil,
Jung-gu, Seoul, 04539, Korea
(South) **(100%)**
Tel.: (82) 222602600
Sales Range: $10-24.9 Million
Emp.: 50
Human Resources Outsourcing & Consult-
ing Services
N.A.I.C.S.: 541612
Stewart Fotheringham (CEO-Asia Pacific,
Middle East, and Africa)

Aon Hewitt Limited **(2)**
8 Devonshire Square, London, EC2M 4PL,
United Kingdom
Tel.: (44) 8002795588
Web Site: http://www.nbsc.co.uk
Management Consulting Services on Ex-
ecutive Pay & Share Plans
N.A.I.C.S.: 541618

Aon Hewitt Malaysia Sdn. Bhd **(2)**
Level 10 Tower 3 Avenue 7 the Horizon
Bangsar South No 8, Jalan Kerinchi, 59200,
Kuala Lumpur, Malaysia
Tel.: (60) 327736800
Web Site: http://www.apac.aonhewitt.com
Emp.: 100
Insurance Management Services
N.A.I.C.S.: 524298

Aon Hewitt Risk & Consulting Srl **(2)**
Via Andrea Ponti 8/10, Milan, 20143, Italy
Tel.: (39) 02454341
Insurance Brokerage Services
N.A.I.C.S.: 524210

Aon Hewitt S.A. **(2)**
Emma do la Barra 353, 4to pioo, Buonoo
Aires, C1428ADB, Argentina **(100%)**
Tel.: (54) 1155564900
Emp.: 500
Human Resources Outsourcing & Consult-
ing Services
N.A.I.C.S.: 541612

Aon Hewitt Singapore Pte. Ltd. **(2)**
89 Science Park Dr 03-01/02 the Ruther-
ford, Singapore, 118261,
Singapore **(100%)**
Tel.: (65) 68727668
Sales Range: $25-49.9 Million
Emp.: 50
Human Resources Outsourcing & Consult-
ing Services
N.A.I.C.S.: 541612

Aon Howitt Sp. z o.o. **(2)**
Al Jerozolimskie 96, 00-807, Warsaw, Po-
land
Tel.: (48) 226965220
Web Site: http://www.aon.com
Human Resource Consulting Services
N.A.I.C.S.: 541612

**Aon Hewitt Wealth Management Pte.
Ltd.** **(2)**
2 Shenton Way 26-01 SGX Centre 1, Sin-
gapore, 068804, Singapore
Tel.: (65) 62218222
Web Site:
  http://wealthmanagement.aon.com
Financial Services
N.A.I.C.S.: 551112
Shikha Gaur (Exec Dir)

Aon Hong Kong Limited **(2)**
28/F Tower 1 Times Square, Causeway
Bay, 999077, China (Hong Kong)
Tel.: (852) 28616666
Human Resources Outsourcing & Consult-
ing Services
N.A.I.C.S.: 541612

Aon Poland Sp. z.o.o. **(2)**
ul Prosta 67, 00-838, Warsaw,
Poland **(100%)**
Tel.: (48) 223788650
Web Site: https://www.aon.com
Sales Range: $10-24.9 Million
Emp.: 1,700
Human Resources Outsourcing & Consult-
ing Services
N.A.I.C.S.: 541612

Aon Solutions Ireland Limited **(2)**
Block D Iveagh Court Harcourt Road, Dub-
lin, D02 VH94, Ireland
Tel.: (353) 12666000
Web Site: http://www.aon.com
Insurance Brokerage Service Provider
N.A.I.C.S.: 524210
Rachael Ingle (Mng Dir-Retirement & In-
vestment)

Aon Solutions Japan Ltd **(2)**
Capitol Tower 11th Floor 2-10-3, Nagatacho
Chiyoda-ku, Tokyo, 100-0014, Japan
Tel.: (81) 345894300
Insurance Brokerage Service Provider
N.A.I.C.S.: 524210
Steven Kusumi (Pres & Dir-Rep)

**Aon Solutions Middle East
Limited** **(2)**
DIFC Al Fattan Currency House Tower 2
Level 5, PO Box 10764, Dubai, United Arab
Emirates
Tel.: (971) 43896300
Human Resource Consulting Services
N.A.I.C.S.: 541612
Amanda Edmunds (Head-Mktg & Comm)

Aon Solutions Sweden AB **(2)**
Valhallavagen 117 H, PO Box 27093, 102
51, Stockholm, Sweden
Tel.: (46) 86974000
Emp.: 210
Insurance Management Services
N.A.I.C.S.: 524298
Jacob Schlawitz (Dir Gen)

Hewitt Associates (Chile) Ltda. **(2)**
Av Providencia 655 Piso 3, Santiago,
6640305, Chile **(100%)**
Tel.: (56) 223600900
Sales Range: $10-24.9 Million
Emp.: 15
Provider of Human Resources Outsourcing
& Consulting Services
N.A.I.C.S.: 541612

Hewitt Associates GmbH **(2)**
Landstrasser Hauptstrasse 1/10, Vienna,
1030, Austria **(100%)**
Tel.: (43) 0017129981
Web Site: http://www.hewitt.at
Sales Range: $10-24.9 Million
Emp.: 15
Provider of Human Resources Outsourcing
& Consulting Services
N.A.I.C.S.: 541612

**Hewitt Associates Kabushiki
Gaisya** **(2)**
Mitakokusai Bldg 24 fl 1-4-28 Mitaminatoku,
Tokyo, 108-0073, Minato Ku,
Japan **(100%)**
Tel.: (81) 345802360
Sales Range: $10-24.9 Million
Emp.: 20
Human Resources Outsourcing & Consult-
ing Services
N.A.I.C.S.: 541612

**Hewitt Associates Korea Yuhan
Hoesa** **(2)**
Gwanghwamun Building 211 Sejongno
Jongno-ku, Seoul, 110-730, Korea (South)
Tel.: (82) 23993600
Risk Managemeng Srvices
N.A.I.C.S.: 524210

Hewitt Associates S.A. **(2)**
Ed Gorbea 2 Plt 5, Paseo Castellana 149,
28046, Madrid, Spain **(100%)**

Tel.: (34) 914059350
Sales Range: $10-24.9 Million
Emp.: 50
Provider of Human Resources Outsourcing
& Consulting Services
N.A.I.C.S.: 541612

Hewitt Associates SARL **(2)**
7 Ave Georges Pompidou, Levallois-Perret,
92300, France **(90%)**
Tel.: (33) 147480228
Web Site: http://www.hewittassociates.com
Sales Range: $25-49.9 Million
Emp.: 90
Human Resources Outsourcing & Consult-
ing Services
N.A.I.C.S.: 541612

Hewitt Associates Sdn Bhd **(2)**
Ste 201 Wisma E & C No 2 Lorong Dungun
Kiri, Kuala Lumpur, 50490,
Malaysia **(100%)**
Tel.: (60) 320944088
Sales Range: $10-24.9 Million
Emp.: 30
Provider of Human Resources Outsourcing
& Consulting Services
N.A.I.C.S.: 541612

Hewitt Associates Srl **(2)**
V Alessandro Volta 16, 20093, Cologno
Monzese, Italy **(100%)**
Tel.: (39) 0227305881
Sales Range: $100-124.9 Million
Provider of Human Resources Outsourcing
& Consulting Services
N.A.I.C.S.: 541612

Subsidiary (Domestic):

Modern Survey, Inc. **(2)**
1209 Tyler St NE Ste 170, Minneapolis, MN
55413
Tel.: (612) 399-3837
Web Site: http://www.modernsurvey.com
Surveying & Management Consulting Ser-
vices
N.A.I.C.S.: 541370

Subsidiary (Non-US):

**Northgate Information Solutions
Limited** **(2)**
Peoplebuilding 2 Peoplebuilding Estate,
Marylands Avenue, Hemel Hempstead, HB2
4NW, Herts, United Kingdom
Tel.: (44) 1442204500
Holding Company; Human Resources Soft-
ware & Services
N.A.I.C.S.: 551112

Subsidiary (Domestic):

**Northgate Information Solutions Hold-
ings Limited** **(3)**
Peoplebuilding 2 Peoplebuilding Estate,
Maylands Avenue, Hemel Hempstead, HP2
4NW, Herts, United Kingdom
Tel.: (44) 1442708100
Web Site: http://www.ngahr.com
Public Safety, Local Government, Education
& Human Resource Outsourcing & Software
Services
N.A.I.C.S.: 551112

Subsidiary (Non-US):

NGA HR SP. Z O.O. **(4)**
Ul Ks Sciegiennego 3, 40-114, Katowice,
Poland
Tel.: (48) 327367100
Web Site: http://www.northgatearinso.com
Sales Range: $25-49.9 Million
Emp.: 200
Human Resources Software & Services
N.A.I.C.S.: 541612
Agnieszka Hetnannczyk (Mng Dir)

**NGA Human Resources Sweden
AB** **(4)**
Gustavslundsvagen 135, Bromma, 167 51,
Sweden
Tel.: (46) 852253300
Web Site: http://www.ngahr.se
Sales Range: $25-49.9 Million
Emp.: 13
Administration of Human Resources Soft-
ware & Services
N.A.I.C.S.: 923130

Alita Lettink *(VP-Enterprise Strategy & Portfolio)*

NorthgateArinso Argentina SA (4)
Tronador 4890, C1430DNN, Buenos Aires, Argentina
Tel.: (54) 1148763300
Web Site: http://www.ngahr.com
Human Resources Business Process Services
N.A.I.C.S.: 923130

NorthgateArinso Australia Pty Ltd (4)
Level 1 616 St Kilda Rd, Melbourne, 3004, VIC, Australia
Tel.: (61) 395294533
Web Site: http://www.arinso.com
Sales Range: $25-49.9 Million
Emp.: 20
Human Resources Software & Services
N.A.I.C.S.: 923130

NorthgateArinso Austria GmbH (4)
Mariahilferstrasse 123 3, 1060, Vienna, Austria
Tel.: (43) 1599990
Web Site: http://de.ngrhr.com
Sales Range: $25-49.9 Million
Emp.: 40
Human Resources Software & Services
N.A.I.C.S.: 541612

NorthgateArinso Belgium BV (4)
Boulevard De L humanite 116, PO Box 2, Humaniteitslaan 116, Brussels, 1070, Belgium
Tel.: (32) 25580670
Web Site: http://www.northgatearinso.com
Sales Range: $250-299.9 Million
Emp.: 2,562
Human Resources Software & Services
N.A.I.C.S.: 923130
Olivier Poot *(Mng Dir)*
Olivia Booth *(Mng Dir)*

NorthgateArinso Belgium People Services SA (4)
Lenniksebaan 451, 1070, Brussels, Belgium
Tel.: (32) 25580670
Web Site: http://www.ngahr.com
Sales Range: $50-74.9 Million
Emp.: 130
Human Resources Software & Services
N.A.I.C.S.: 923130
Luca Faracino *(Mng Dir-Spain)*

NorthgateArinso Brazil Informatica Ltda. (4)
Alameda Madeira 53 5th Floor Bl 52 Alphaville, Barueri, 06454-010, Brazil
Tel.: (55) 1130288910
Web Site: http://www.ngahr.com
Sales Range: $25-49.9 Million
Emp.: 100
Human Resources Software & Services
N.A.I.C.S.: 513210

NorthgateArinso Canada Inc. (4)
121 King Street W Ste 2220, PO Box 102, Toronto, M5H 3T9, ON, Canada
Tel.: (416) 622-9559
Web Site: http://www.ngahr.com
Sales Range: $25-49.9 Million
Emp.: 100
Human Resources Software & Services
N.A.I.C.S.: 923130

NorthgateArinso Deutschland AG (4)
Waldeckerstrasse 9, 64546, Morfelden, Germany
Tel.: (49) 6105703670
Web Site: http://www.ngahr.com
Sales Range: $200-249.9 Million
Emp.: 100
Human Resources Software & Services
N.A.I.C.S.: 923130

NorthgateArinso Finland Oy (4)
Italahdenkatu 22 A, 00210, Helsinki, Finland
Tel.: (358) 92510450
Web Site: http://www.northgatearinso.com
Sales Range: $25-49.9 Million
Emp.: 32
Human Resources Software & Services
N.A.I.C.S.: 923130

NorthgateArinso France S.A.S. (4)
2 Rue de lEgalite, 92748, Nanterre, France
Tel.: (33) 149003131
Web Site: http://fr.ngahr.com

Human Resources Software & Services
N.A.I.C.S.: 923130

NorthgateArinso Italia S.r.l. (4)
Via G Murat 23, 20159, Milan, Italy
Tel.: (39) 02694321
Web Site: http://www.northgatearinso.com
Sales Range: $25-49.9 Million
Emp.: 114
Human Resources Software & Services
N.A.I.C.S.: 923130
Sabino Pisano *(Dir-Sls)*

NorthgateArinso Luxembourg SA (4)
32-36 Boulevard d Avranches, 1160, Luxembourg, Luxembourg
Tel.: (352) 2649791118
Web Site: http://www.ngahr.com
Sales Range: $25-49.9 Million
Emp.: 23
Human Resources Software & Services
N.A.I.C.S.: 923130

NorthgateArinso Madrid SA (4)
Edificio America II C- Procion 7 C, Portal 3 Planta 1, 28023, Madrid, Spain
Tel.: (34) 916402890
Web Site: http://www.northgatearinso.com
Sales Range: $25-49.9 Million
Emp.: 100
Human Resources Software & Services
N.A.I.C.S.: 923130
Victor D'Angelo *(Mng Dir)*

NorthgateArinso Malaysia Sdn Bhd (4)
Level 15 The Gardens North Tower, Midth Rally City, Kuala Lumpur, 59200, Malaysia
Tel.: (60) 322991600
Web Site: http://www.northgatearinso.com
Sales Range: $25-49.9 Million
Emp.: 75
Human Resources Software & Services
N.A.I.C.S.: 923130
Ya'acob Aiyub Razali *(Mng Dir)*

NorthgateArinso Milano S.r.l. (4)
Via G Murat 23, Milan, 20159, Italy
Tel.: (39) 02694321
Web Site: http://www.northgatearinso.com
Sales Range: $25-49.9 Million
Emp.: 100
Human Resources Software & Services
N.A.I.C.S.: 923130
Sabino Pisano *(Dir-Sls)*
Luca Saracino *(Mng Dir)*

NorthgateArinso Philippines Inc. (4)
4/F Bldg 1 Eton Cyberpod Corinthian Ortigas Avenue, Corner EDSA, Quezon City, 1110, Philippines
Tel.: (63) 26261200
Web Site: http://www.northgatearinso.com
Sales Range: $50-74.9 Million
Emp.: 200
Human Resources Software & Services
N.A.I.C.S.: 923130
Jan Mees *(Mng Dir-Global Delivery Center)*

NorthgateArinso Singapore Pte Ltd (4)
20 McCallum Street 16-02 Tokio Marine Centre, Singapore, 069046, Singapore
Tel.: (65) 594500
Web Site: http://www.northgatearinso.com
Sales Range: $25-49.9 Million
Emp.: 60
Human Resources Software & Services
N.A.I.C.S.: 923130

NorthgateArinso Switzerland Ltd. (4)
Avenue Viollier 13, Nyon, 1260, Switzerland
Tel.: (41) 588009500
Web Site: http://www.northgatearinso.com
Sales Range: $25-49.9 Million
Emp.: 30
Human Resources Software & Services
N.A.I.C.S.: 541612

NorthgateArinso Thailand (Co.) Ltd (4)
990 Abulrahim Building 12 Floor Rama IV Road Silom Bangrak, Bangkok, 10500, Thailand
Tel.: (66) 22664100
Web Site: http://www.nvasr.com
Sales Range: $25-49.9 Million
Emp.: 16
Human Resources Software & Services
N.A.I.C.S.: 923130

Subsidiary (US):

PROIV Technology Inc (4)
65 Enterprise, Aliso Viejo, CA 92656
Tel.: (949) 330-7850
Web Site: http://www.proivinc.com
Sales Range: $450-499.9 Million
Emp.: 3,025
Rapid Application Development
N.A.I.C.S.: 541511
Nick Pellicano Jr. *(Acct Dir-Mgmt & Mktg)*

Reed Group Management LLC (1)
10355 Westmoor Dr, Westminster, CO 80021
Tel.: (303) 464-2443
General Management Consulting Services
N.A.I.C.S.: 541611

ALIGN TECHNOLOGY, INC.
410 N Scottsdale Rd Ste 1300, Tempe, AZ 85288
Tel.: (602) 742-2000   DE
Web Site: https://www.aligntech.com
Year Founded: 1997
ALGN—(NASDAQ)
Rev.: $3,862,260,000
Assets: $6,083,877,000
Liabilities: $2,453,388,000
Net Worth: $3,630,489,000
Earnings: $445,053,000
Emp.: 21,610
Fiscal Year-end: 12/31/23
Medical Equipment Mfr & Distr
N.A.I.C.S.: 339112
Emory M. Wright *(Exec VP-Direct Fabrication Platform Ops & Dir-Fabrication Mfg Platform)*
Joseph M. Hogan *(Pres & CEO)*
V.M. Raj Pudipeddi *(Chief Product & Mktg Officer, Exec VP & Mng Dir-Asia Pacific)*
David Carr *(Exec VP & Mng Dir-Asia Pacific)*
Sreelakshmi Kolli *(Chief Product Officer, Chief Digital Officer & Exec VP)*
Jennifer Olson *(Chief Customer Officer & Exec VP)*
Julie Coletti *(Chief Legal Officer, Chief Regulatory Officer, Exec VP & Sr VP)*
Mitra Derakhshan *(Chief Clinical Officer & Exec VP)*
C. Raymond Larkin Jr. *(Chm)*

Subsidiaries:

Align Technology Switzerland GmbH (1)
Suurstoffi 22, 6343, Rotkreuz, Switzerland
Tel.: (41) 415610400
Medical Device Mfr
N.A.I.C.S.: 339112

Align Technology, B.V. (1)
Arlandeaweg 161, 1043 HS, Amsterdam, Netherlands
Tel.: (31) 205863600
Web Site: http://www.invisalign.com
Sales Range: $10-24.9 Million
Emp.: 70
Orthodontic Products
N.A.I.C.S.: 339114

Invisalign Australia Pty Ltd (1)
Level 6 154 Pacific Highway, Saint Leonards, 2065, NSW, Australia
Tel.: (61) 289201011
Web Site: http://www.invisalign.com.au
Health Care Srvices
N.A.I.C.S.: 621610
Karen McGoldrick *(Mng Dir)*

ALIGNMENT HEALTHCARE, INC.
1100 W Town and Country Rd Ste 1600, Orange, CA 92868   DE
Web Site:
   https://www.alignmenthealth.com
Year Founded: 2013
ALHC—(NASDAQ)
Rev.: $1,434,159,000

Assets: $633,863,000
Liabilities: $394,561,000
Net Worth: $239,302,000
Earnings: ($149,547,000)
Emp.: 1,037
Fiscal Year-end: 12/31/22
Software Development Services
N.A.I.C.S.: 541511
Christopher J. Joyce *(Chief Legal & Admin Officer)*
John Kao *(Founder & CEO)*
Dawn Maroney *(Pres-Markets)*
Thomas Freeman *(CFO)*
Donald Furman *(Chief Clinical Officer)*
Joseph Konowiecki *(Chm)*
Melinda Kimbro *(Chief People Officer)*
Hakan Kardes *(CTO)*
Rob Scavo *(CIO)*
Amanda Root *(VP)*
Ken Hyong Kim *(Chief Medical Officer)*

ALIGOS THERAPEUTICS, INC.
1 Corporate Dr 2nd Fl, South San Francisco, CA 94080   DE
Web Site: https://www.aligos.com
Year Founded: 2018
ALGS—(NASDAQ)
Rev.: $13,907,000
Assets: $146,693,000
Liabilities: $42,793,000
Net Worth: $103,900,000
Earnings: ($96,046,000)
Emp.: 83
Fiscal Year-end: 12/31/22
Biotechnology Research & Development Services
N.A.I.C.S.: 541714
Leonid Beigelman *(Co-Founder)*
Lawrence M. Blatt *(Co-Founder, Co-Chm & CEO)*
Leonid Beigelman *(Co-Founder & Pres)*
Lesley Ann Calhoun *(CFO & Exec VP)*
Lucinda Y. Quan *(Chief Bus Officer, Gen Counsel & Exec VP)*
Julian Symons *(Chief Scientific Officer & Exec VP)*
John Fry *(Exec VP-Clinical Dev)*
Sushmita M. Chanda *(Exec VP-Translational Safety Sciences)*
David B. Smith *(Exec VP & Head-Chemical Ops)*
Pierre J. M. B. Raboisson *(Exec VP & Head-Small Molecule Medicinal Chemistry)*
Jack B. Nielsen *(Co/Co-Chm)*

ALJ REGIONAL HOLDINGS, INC.
244 Madison Ave PMB Ste 358, New York, NY 10016
Tel.: (212) 883-0083   DE
Web Site:
   http://www.aljregionalholdings.com
Year Founded: 1999
ALJJ—(NASDAQ)
Rev.: $440,853,000
Assets: $214,653,000
Liabilities: $202,077,000
Net Worth: $12,576,000
Earnings: ($4,643,000)
Emp.: 5
Fiscal Year-end: 09/30/21
Holding Company; Multi-Channel Contact Center Solutions
N.A.I.C.S.: 551112
Jess Marshall Ravich *(Chm & CEO)*
John Scheel *(Vice Chm)*
Brian C. Keck *(CFO-Phoenix)*
Bradd Robison *(COO-Carpets)*
Kevin P. Hayden *(COO-Phoenix)*

ALJ Regional Holdings, Inc.—(Continued)

Alden Eldredge *(Gen Counsel/Sr VP-Faneuil)*
Steven M. Chesin *(CEO-Carpets)*
Jeff Wiens *(CFO-Carpets)*

Subsidiaries:

Floors-N-More, LLC   (1)
4580 W Teco Ave, Las Vegas, NV 89118
Tel.: (702) 458-9999
Web Site: http://www.carpetsnmore.com
Wood Preservation Product Mfr
N.A.I.C.S.: 321114

Ranew's Truck & Equipment Co. LLC   (1)
1308 Hwy 41 N, Milner, GA 30257-3734
Tel.: (770) 229-5090
Web Site: http://www.ranews.com
Motor Vehicle Supplies & New Parts Merchant Whslr
N.A.I.C.S.: 423120
Lester Ranew *(Owner)*

ALKAME HOLDINGS, INC.
3651 Lindell Rd Ste D 356, Las Vegas, NV 89103
Tel.: (702) 273-9714   NV
Web Site:
   https://www.alkameholdingsinc.com
Year Founded: 2010
ALKM—(OTCEM)
Emp.: 25
Bottled Water Distr & Sales
N.A.I.C.S.: 312112
Robert Eakle *(Pres & CEO)*

Subsidiaries:

Alkame Water Inc.   (1)
3651 Lindell Rd Ste D #356, Las Vegas, NV 89103
Tel.: (702) 273-9714
Web Site: http://www.akkamewater.com
Bottled Water Producer & Sales
N.A.I.C.S.: 312112
Robert Eakle *(CEO)*

ALKAMI TECHNOLOGY, INC.
5601 Granite Pkwy Ste 120, Plano, TX 75024
Tel.: (972) 200-1937   DE
Web Site: https://www.alkami.com
Year Founded: 2009
ALKT—(NASDAQ)
Rev.: $204,270,000
Assets: $488,885,000
Liabilities: $154,839,000
Net Worth: $334,046,000
Earnings: ($58,600,000)
Emp.: 851
Fiscal Year-end: 12/31/22
Information Technology Management Services
N.A.I.C.S.: 541512
Alex P. Shootman *(Pres & CEO)*
Gary Nelson *(Co-Founder)*
Stephen Bohanon *(Co-Founder, Chief Strategy Officer & Chief Strategy & Sls Officer)*
Allison Cerra *(CMO)*
Carl Cross *(Chief Revenue Officer)*
Julie Hoagland *(Chief HR Officer)*
Gagan Kanjlia *(Chief Product Officer)*
Doug Linebarger *(Chief Legal Officer)*
Wayne McCulloch *(Chief Customer Officer)*
Deep Varma *(CTO)*
Bryan Hill *(CFO)*

ALKANE, INC.
2205 York Rd Ste 14, Lutherville, MD 21093
Tel.: (410) 666-7837   FL
Year Founded: 1988
ALKN—(OTCIQ)
Industrial Organic Chemicals Mfr
N.A.I.C.S.: 325199

Mathew Zuckerman *(Pres & CEO)*
Louis Petrucci *(VP)*

ALKURI GLOBAL ACQUISITION CORP.
4235 Hillsboro Pike Ste 300, Nashville, TN 37215
Tel.: (615) 632-0303   DE
Year Founded: 2020
KURI—(NASDAQ)
Emp.: 2
Investment Services
N.A.I.C.S.: 523999
Sultan Almaadeed *(Chm)*
Richard Williams *(CEO)*
Steve Krenzer *(CFO)*

ALL FOR ONE MEDIA CORP.
236 Sarles St, Mount Kisco, NY 10549
Tel.: (914) 574-6174   UT
Web Site: http://www.allforone.media
Year Founded: 2004
AFOM—(OTCIQ)
Rev.: $9,493
Assets: $122,622
Liabilities: $18,614,047
Net Worth: ($18,491,425)
Earnings: ($3,110,176)
Emp.: 1
Fiscal Year-end: 09/30/21
Entertainment Services
N.A.I.C.S.: 512131
Brian J. Lukow *(Pres, CEO & CFO)*
Aimee Ventura O'Brien *(Bd of Dirs & Sec)*

ALL THINGS MOBILE ANALYTIC, INC.
209 W 29TH ST Ste 6241, New York, NY 10001
Tel.: (212) 971-6700   NV
Web Site:
   https://allthingsmobileanalytic.com
Year Founded: 2008
ATMH—(OTCIQ)
Assets: $12,000
Liabilities: $994,000
Net Worth: ($982,000)
Earnings: ($163,000)
Fiscal Year-end: 01/31/20
Other Metal Ore Mining
N.A.I.C.S.: 212290
Massimo Meneghello *(Pres & CEO)*
Massimo Travagli *(CFO, Treas & Sec)*

Subsidiaries:

Inmed Group, Inc.   (1)
60 Commerce St #700, Montgomery, AL 36104
Tel.: (334) 386-0343
Administrative Management & General Management Consulting Service
N.A.I.C.S.: 541611

ALLAKOS, INC.
825 Industrial Rd Ste 500, San Carlos, CA 94070
Tel.: (650) 597-5002   DE
Web Site: https://www.allakos.com
Year Founded: 2012
ALLK—(NASDAQ)
Rev.: $3,673,000
Assets: $386,420,000
Liabilities: $75,987,000
Net Worth: $310,433,000
Earnings: ($319,952,000)
Emp.: 123
Fiscal Year-end: 12/31/22
Research & Development in Biotechnology (except Nanobiotechnology)
N.A.I.C.S.: 541714
Robert Alexander *(CEO)*
Adam Tomasi *(Pres)*

Baird Radford *(CFO & Principal Acctg Officer)*
Craig Paterson *(Chief Medical Officer)*
Alex Schwartz *(VP-Strategic Fin & IR)*
Mary Cromwell *(Sr VP)*
Brad Youngblood *(Head)*

ALLARITY THERAPEUTICS, INC.
24 School St 2nd Fl, Boston, MA 02108
Tel.: (401) 426-4664   DE
Web Site: https://www.allarity.com
Year Founded: 2004
ALLR—(NASDAQ)
Rev.: $30,000
Assets: $14,544,000
Liabilities: $14,657,000
Net Worth: ($113,000)
Earnings: ($21,051,000)
Emp.: 9
Fiscal Year-end: 12/31/22
Research & Development in Biotechnology (except Nanobiotechnology)
N.A.I.C.S.: 541714
Jerry McLaughlin *(Chm)*

ALLBIRDS, INC.
730 Montgomery St, San Francisco, CA 94111
Tel.: (628) 225-4848   DE
Web Site: https://www.allbirds.com
Year Founded: 2015
BIRD—(NASDAQ)
Rev.: $297,766,000
Assets: $462,364,000
Liabilities: $145,595,000
Net Worth: $316,769,000
Earnings: ($101,354,000)
Emp.: 760
Fiscal Year-end: 12/31/22
Footwear & Apparel Distr
N.A.I.C.S.: 424340
Joseph Zwillinger *(Co-Founder & Co-CEO)*
Timothy Brown *(Co-Founder & Chief Innovation Officer)*
Joe Vernachio *(COO)*
Annie Mitchell *(CFO)*
Joseph Zwillinger *(Co-Founder)*
Joe Vernachio *(Pres, CEO & Sec)*

ALLEGIANT TRAVEL COMPANY
Tel.: (702) 851-7300   NV
Web Site: https://www.allegiant.com
ALGT—(NASDAQ)
Rev.: $2,301,829,000
Assets: $4,511,297,000
Liabilities: $3,290,599,000
Net Worth: $1,220,698,000
Earnings: $2,493,000
Emp.: 5,315
Fiscal Year-end: 12/31/22
Travel Agency
N.A.I.C.S.: 481111
Andrew C. Levy *(Co-Founder)*
Rob Goldberg *(Sec & Sr VP)*
John T. Redmond *(CEO)*
Robert J. Neal *(CFO & Sr VP)*
Keny Wilper *(Interim COO & Sr VP)*
Rebecca Henry *(Chief HR Officer & Sr VP)*
Michael Broderick *(Exec VP & Sr VP-Fin Plng & Bus Transformation)*
Gregory Clark Anderson *(Bd of Dirs, Pres & CEO)*

Subsidiaries:

Allegiant Nonstop Michigan, LLC   (1)
28300 Dequindre Rd, Warren, MI 48092
Tel.: (586) 510-1666
Travel Services
N.A.I.C.S.: 561510

Patrick Baum *(Asst Gen Mgr)*

Allegiant Systems, Inc.   (1)
1201 N Town Ctr Dr Ste 110, Las Vegas, NV 89144
Tel.: (702) 851-7300
Emp.: 12
Software Development Services
N.A.I.C.S.: 541511
Brian Sorel *(Project Mgr-Sys Integration)*

ALLEGRO MICROSYSTEMS, INC.
955 Perimeter Rd, Manchester, NH 03103
Tel.: (603) 626-2300   DE
Web Site:
   https://www.allegromicro.com
Year Founded: 2013
ALGM—(NASDAQ)
Rev.: $1,049,367,000
Assets: $1,530,603,000
Liabilities: $398,887,000
Net Worth: $1,131,716,000
Earnings: $152,888,000
Emp.: 4,593
Fiscal Year-end: 03/29/24
Holding Company
N.A.I.C.S.: 551112
Vineet Nargolwala *(Pres & CEO)*
Katherine Blye *(Sr Dir-IR & Marcom)*
Yoshihiro Suzuki *(Chm)*
Sharon Briansky *(Gen Counsel, Sec & Sr VP)*
Derek P. D'Antilio *(CFO, Treas & Sr VP)*
Vineet Nargolwala *(Pres & CEO)*
Michael C. Doogue *(CTO & Sr VP)*
Suman Narayan *(Sr VP-Products)*

Subsidiaries:

Allegro (Shanghai) Micro Electronics Commercial & Trading Co., Ltd.   (1)
Room 601 First Building Guangqi Cultural Plaza No 2899 JIA Xietu Road, Xuhui District, Shanghai, 200030, China
Tel.: (86) 2154500188
Sensor Mfr
N.A.I.C.S.: 334413

Allegro MicroSystems Argentina, S.A.   (1)
Tel.: (54) 1145410444
Sensor Mfr
N.A.I.C.S.: 334413

Allegro MicroSystems France SAS   (1)
60 Rue Cassiopee Parc Altais, 74650, Chavanod, France
Tel.: (33) 450512359
Sensor Mfr
N.A.I.C.S.: 334413

Allegro MicroSystems Germany GmbH   (1)
Vangerowstr 18/1, 69115, Heidelberg, Germany
Tel.: (49) 622187235
Sensor Mfr
N.A.I.C.S.: 334413

Allegro MicroSystems Marketing India Private Limited   (1)
5th Floor 97-Varsha Plot No 96-97 Anand Park Above AU Finance Bank, Aundh, Pune, 411 007, Maharashtra, India
Tel.: (91) 2066878400
Power Integrated Circuit Mfr
N.A.I.C.S.: 334413

Allegro MicroSystems Philippines Realty Inc.   (1)
4756 Sampaguita St, Marimar Village Barangay Sun Valley, Paranaque, 1700, Philippines
Tel.: (63) 28235000
Web Site: https://www.allegromicro.com
Semiconductor Mfr
N.A.I.C.S.: 333242

Crocus Technology International Inc.   (1)

870 N McCarthy Blvd Ste 220, Milpitas, CA 95035
Tel.: (408) 732-0000
Web Site: http://www.crocus-technology.com
Semiconductor & Related Device Mfr
N.A.I.C.S.: 334413
Wayne Godwin *(VP)*

ALLENA PHARMACEUTICALS, INC.

1 Newton Executive Park Ste 202, Newton, MA 02462
Tel.: (617) 467-4577   DE
Web Site:
  http://www.allenapharma.com
Year Founded: 2011
ALNAQ—(NASDAQ)
Assets: $34,757,000
Liabilities: $15,889,000
Net Worth: $18,868,000
Earnings: ($48,663,000)
Emp.: 22
Fiscal Year-end: 12/31/21
Chemicals Mfr
N.A.I.C.S.: 325412
Louis Brenner *(Pres & CEO)*
Hugh Wight *(Sr VP-Technical Ops)*
Alexey L. Margolin *(Chm)*
Geoffrey A. Swire *(Acting COO & Sr VP-Corp Dev)*
Stephen Yu *(Sr VP-Corp Quality)*
David J. Clark *(Chief Medical Officer)*
Allcja Januszewicz *(VP-People & Culture)*
Richard D. Katz *(CFO & Principal Acctg Officer)*

ALLETE, INC.

30 W Superior St, Duluth, MN 55802
Tel.: (218) 279-5000   MN
Web Site: https://www.allete.com
Year Founded: 1906
ALE—(NYSE)
Rev.: $1,570,700,000
Assets: $6,845,600,000
Liabilities: $3,497,300,000
Net Worth: $3,348,300,000
Earnings: $189,300,000
Emp.: 1,467
Fiscal Year-end: 12/31/22
Holding Company; Electric, Natural Gas & Water Supply Utilities Operator; Energy Infrastructure & Related Services
N.A.I.C.S.: 551112
Nicole R. Johnson *(Chief Admin Officer & VP)*
Steven W. Morris *(CFO, Chief Acctg Officer & Sr VP)*
Patrick L. Cutshall *(Treas & VP)*
Bethany M. Owen *(Chm, Pres & CEO)*
Josh Skelton *(COO)*

Subsidiaries:

ACE Solar LLC   (1)
117 W Madison St, Pulaski, TN 38478-7097
Tel.: (256) 319-3420
Web Site: https://www.acellcsolar.com
Renewable Energy Services
N.A.I.C.S.: 213112
Chuck Boggs *(Pres & CEO)*

ALLETE Clean Energy, Inc.   (1)
30 W Superior St, Duluth, MN 55802   (100%)
Tel.: (218) 355-3232
Web Site: https://alletecleanenergy.com
Clean & Renewable Energy Projects
N.A.I.C.S.: 221115
Nicole R. Johnson *(Pres)*
Jim Klempir *(Corp Counsel)*

ALLETE Enterprises, Inc.   (1)
30 W Superior St, Duluth, MN 55802
Tel.: (218) 722-2625
Electric Power Distr
N.A.I.C.S.: 221122

Subsidiary (Domestic):

BNI Energy, Inc.   (2)
1637 Burnt Boat Dr, Bismarck, ND 58502-0897
Tel.: (701) 355-5500
Web Site: https://www.bnienergy.com
Eletric Power Generation Services
N.A.I.C.S.: 221112
Wade W. Boeshans *(Pres & Gen Mgr)*

Subsidiary (Domestic):

BNI Coal, Ltd.   (3)
1637 Burnt Boat Dr, Bismarck, ND 58502-0897   (100%)
Tel.: (701) 355-5500
Web Site: http://www.bnicoal.com
Surface Mining & Lignite Coal Distr
N.A.I.C.S.: 423830
Wade Boeshans *(Pres & Gen Mgr)*
Mike Heger *(Gen Mgr)*
Ryan Wrolstad *(Mgr-Finance-Accounting)*
Jon Rudnick *(Production Mgr)*
Jodey Houn *(Mgr-Engineering)*
Mike Heger *(Gen Mgr)*
Ryan Wrolstad *(Mgr-Finance-Accounting)*
Jon Rudnick *(Production Mgr)*
Jodey Houn *(Mgr-Engineering)*

Caddo Holding Company, LLC   (1)
130 E John W Carpenter Fwy St 230, Irving, TX 75062
Tel.: (214) 366-2020
Web Site: https://www.caddoholdings.com
Real Estate Agency Services
N.A.I.C.S.: 531210
Dustin Schilling *(Mng Partner)*
Tim Slaughter *(Mng Partner)*
Justin Engler *(Mng Partner)*

Minnesota Power   (1)
30 W Superior St, Duluth, MN 55802-2093   (100%)
Tel.: (218) 722-2641
Web Site: https://www.mnpower.com
Sales Range: $1-9.9 Million
Emp.: 1,200
Generator, Transmitter & Distributor of Electricity
N.A.I.C.S.: 531190
Amy Rutledge *(Mgr-Corp Comm)*

New Energy Equity LLC   (1)
705 Melvin Ave Ste 100, Annapolis, MD 21401-1534
Tel.: (443) 267-5012
Web Site: http://www.newenergyequity.com
Emp.: 100
Electric Power Generation
N.A.I.C.S.: 221114
Jamil White *(Controller)*
Matthew Hankey *(Pres & CEO)*

Palm Coast Holdings, Inc.   (1)
145 City Pl Ste 300, Palm Coast, FL 32164
Tel.: (386) 446-6226
Web Site: https://www.douglaspd.com
Emp.: 10
Real Estate Manangement Services
N.A.I.C.S.: 531210

Superior Water, Light & Power Company   (1)
2915 Hill Ave, Superior, WI 54880-0519   (100%)
Tel.: (715) 394-2200
Web Site: https://www.swlp.com
Sales Range: $25-49.9 Million
Electric, Natural Gas & Water Utility
N.A.I.C.S.: 221118

ALLIANCE CREATIVE GROUP, INC.

7366 N Lincoln Ave Ste 105, Lincolnwood, IL 60712
Tel.: (847) 885-1800   NV
Web Site:
  https://www.alliancecreative group.com
Year Founded: 2000
ACGX—(OTCIQ)
Rev.: $9,344,030
Assets: $3,718,340
Liabilities: $2,442,128
Net Worth: $1,276,212
Earnings: $205,267

Emp.: 11
Fiscal Year-end: 12/31/20
Graphic Design Services
N.A.I.C.S.: 541430
Paul Sorkin *(COO & Gen Counsel)*
Steven Louis *(Chm & CEO)*
Greg Kardasz *(VP-Sls-Printing)*
Kevin Piemonte *(VP-Sls-Pkg)*
Stephen Taucher *(Mgr-Production)*
Beth Messinger *(Controller)*
Donna Hamilton *(Controller & Dir-Ops)*
Donna Hamilton *(Controller & Dir-Ops)*

ALLIANCE ENTERTAINMENT HOLDING CORPORATION

8201 Peters Rd Ste 1000, Plantation, FL 33324
Tel.: (954) 255-4000   DE
Web Site: https://www.aent.com
Year Founded: 2020
AENT—(NASDAQ)
Rev.: $1,100,483,000
Assets: $340,812,000
Liabilities: $253,183,000
Net Worth: $87,629,000
Earnings: $4,581,000
Emp.: 657
Fiscal Year-end: 06/30/24
Investment Services
N.A.I.C.S.: 523999
Bruce Ogilvie *(Exec Chm)*
Jeff Walker *(CEO)*
Thomas Finke *(Chm)*
Warwick Goldby *(COO)*
Robert Black *(Chief Compliance Officer)*
Amanda Gnecco *(Chief Acctg Officer)*

Subsidiaries:

Alliance Entertainment, LLC   (1)
8201 Peters Rd Ste 1000, Plantation, FL 33324
Tel.: (954) 255-4000
Web Site: https://www.aent.com
Music, Video, Book & Entertainment Retail Services
N.A.I.C.S.: 512120

ALLIANCE MEDIA HOLDINGS, INC.

123 Grove St Ste 109, Cedarhurst, NY 11516
Tel.: (212) 894-4750   DE
Web Site: https://www.alliance.games
Year Founded: 1989
ADTR—(OTCIQ)
Software Development Services
N.A.I.C.S.: 541511
Jay Gelman *(Chm & CEO)*

ALLIANCE RECOVERY CORP.

1000 NW St Ste 1200, Wilmington, DE 19801
Tel.: (519) 671-0417   DE
Year Founded: 2001
ARVY—(OTCIQ)
Trading Consulting Services
N.A.I.C.S.: 523160
Zonghan Wu *(Sec)*

ALLIANCEBERNSTEIN GLOBAL HIGH INCOME FUND, INC.

1345 Ave of the Americas, New York, NY 10105
Tel.: (212) 969-1000   MD
AWF—(NYSE)
Investment Management Service
N.A.I.C.S.: 525990
Onur Erzan *(Pres & CEO)*
Christian DiClementi *(VP)*
Gershon M. Distenfeld *(VP)*
Fahd Malik *(VP)*
Matthew S. Sheridan *(VP)*

William Smith *(VP)*
Nancy E. Hay *(Sec)*
Michael B. Reyes *(Sr VP)*
Phyllis J. Clarke *(Controller)*
Jennifer Friedland *(Chief Compliance Officer)*
Stephen M. Woetzel *(CFO & Treas)*

ALLIANCEBERNSTEIN NATIONAL MUNICIPAL INCOME FUND, INC.

1345 Avenue of the Americas, New York, NY 10105
Tel.: (212) 969-2124
Year Founded: 2002
AFB—(NYSE)
Investment Management Service
N.A.I.C.S.: 525990
Onur Erzan *(Pres & CEO)*
Matthew Norton *(Chief Investment Officer-Municipal Bonds)*

ALLIANT ENERGY CORPORATION

4902 N Biltmore Ln, Madison, WI 53718
Tel.: (608) 458-3311   WI
Web Site:
  https://www.alliantenergy.com
Year Founded: 1981
LNT—(NASDAQ)
Rev.: $4,027,000,000
Assets: $21,237,000,000
Liabilities: $14,460,000,000
Net Worth: $6,777,000,000
Earnings: $703,000,000
Emp.: 3,281
Fiscal Year-end: 12/31/23
Public Utility Holding Company; Regulated Electricity & Natural Gas Services
N.A.I.C.S.: 551112
John O. Larsen *(Exec Chm)*
Lisa M. Barton *(Pres & CEO)*
Robert J. Durian *(CFO & Exec VP)*
Terry L. Kouba *(Pres-Iowa Energy Company & Sr VP-Ops)*
David de Leon *(Pres-Wisconsin Energy Company & Sr VP-Ops)*
J.P. Brummond *(VP-Bus Plng)*
Diane Cooke *(VP-HR)*
Susan Trapp Gille *(Mgr-IR)*
J. P. Brummond *(VP)*
Mayuri Farlinger *(VP)*
James H. Gallegos *(Gen Counsel, Sec & Exec VP)*

Subsidiaries:

Wisconsin Power and Light Company   (1)
4902 N Biltmore Ln, Madison, WI 53718-2148
Tel.: (608) 458-3956
Web Site: https://investors.alliantenergy.com
Rev.: $1,856,000,000
Assets: $8,987,000,000
Liabilities: $5,496,000,000
Net Worth: $3,491,000,000
Earnings: $315,000,000
Emp.: 1,001
Fiscal Year-end: 12/31/2022
Electric Power Distr
N.A.I.C.S.: 221112
John O. Larsen *(Chm)*
Lisa M. Barton *(CEO & CFO)*
Robert J. Durian *(CFO & Exec VP)*

Joint Venture (Domestic):

Wisconsin River Power Company   (2)
PO Box 325, Necedah, WI 54646
Tel.: (608) 565-7961
Web Site:
  http://www.wisconsinriverpower.com
Emp.: 10
Electronic Services
N.A.I.C.S.: 221118

Alliant Energy Corporation—(Continued)

ALLIED ENERGY CORP.
Tel.: (972) 632-2393   NV
Web Site:
   http://www.alliedengycorp.com
AGYP—(OTCIQ)
Assets: $238,000
Liabilities: $2,126,000
Net Worth: ($1,888,000)
Earnings: ($381,000)
Emp.: 2
Fiscal Year-end: 12/31/20
Organic Fertilizer Marketer & Distr
N.A.I.C.S.: 424690
George Monteith (CEO)

ALLIED ENERGY, INC.
2105 Camino Vida Roble, Carlsbad, CA 92011
Tel.: (760) 746-1248   FL
Web Site: https://www.alliedenergy-us.com
AGGI—(OTCIQ)
Solar Energy Generate Services
N.A.I.C.S.: 221114
Simon Allan (Founder)

ALLIED GAMING & ENTERTAINMENT, INC.
745 5th Ave Ste 500, New York, NY 10151
Tel.: (646) 768-4240   DE
Web Site:
   https://www.alliedesports.gg
Year Founded: 2017
AGAE—(NASDAQ)
Rev: $6,352,470
Assets: $97,729,675
Liabilities: $9,825,607
Net Worth: $87,904,068
Earnings: ($10,823,885)
Emp.: 78
Fiscal Year-end: 12/31/22
Investment Services
N.A.I.C.S.: 523999
Lyle A. Berman (Co-Chm, Pres & VP-Acq & Merger)
Yinghua Chen (CEO)
Yangyang Li (Chm & Pres)
Roy Anderson (CFO & Sec)

Subsidiaries:

WPT Enterprise Inc.   (1)
1920 Main St Ste 1150, Irvine, CA 92614
Tel.: (949) 225-2600
Web Site: http://www.worldpokertour.com
Brand Licensing Services & Televised Gaming & Entertainment
N.A.I.C.S.: 533110
Adam Pliska (Pres & CEO)
Angelica Hael (VP-Global Tour Mgmt)
Deborah Frazzetta (VP-Fin)
John McMahon (VP-Studios)
Jeremy Clemons (VP-Online Svcs)

ALLIED MINDS PLC
374 Congress St Ste 308, Boston, MA 02210
Tel.: (617) 419-1800   UK
Web Site:
   https://www.alliedminds.com
ALM (LSE)
Sales Range: $25-49.9 Million
Emp.: 117
Investment Holding Company; Science & Technology Development Services
N.A.I.C.S.: 551112
Mark Pritchard (Founder)

ALLIED RESOURCES INC.
1403 E 900 S, Salt Lake City, UT 84105
Tel.: (801) 232-7395   NV
Web Site:
   http://www.alliedresourcesinc.com
Year Founded: 1979

ALOD—(OTCIQ)
Oil & Gas Production
N.A.I.C.S.: 213112
Paul Crow (Pres)

ALLIED SECURITY INNOVATIONS, INC.
224 Datura St, West Palm Beach, FL 33401
Tel.: (561) 570-4301   DE
Web Site: https://adsvcorporate.com
Year Founded: 1986
ADSV—(OTCIQ)
Sales Range: Less than $1 Million
Indicative & Barrier Security Seals, Security Tapes & Related Packaging Security Systems & Protective Security Products Mfr & Distr
N.A.I.C.S.: 322220
Caren D. Currier (CEO)

ALLIENT INC.
495 Commerce Dr, Buffalo, NY 14228
Tel.: (716) 242-7535   CO
Web Site: https://allient.com
Year Founded: 1962
ALNT—(NASDAQ)
Rev: $502,988,000
Assets: $588,347,000
Liabilities: $372,882,000
Net Worth: $215,465,000
Earnings: $17,389,000
Emp.: 2,254
Fiscal Year-end: 12/31/22
Motion Application Solutions & Services
N.A.I.C.S.: 334519
Richard S. Warzala (Chm, Pres & CEO)
William Jesse (VP-Sls-North America)
Ashish Bendre (Co-Pres & VP)
Helmut Pirthauer (Co-Pres & VP)
Geoff Rondeau (VP-Operational Excellence)
Ken May (CTO & VP)
Steve Warzala (Dir-Strategic Bus Dev)
James A. Michaud (CFO & Sr VP)
Rob Mastromattei (Chief Comml Officer)

Subsidiaries:

ALIO Industries, LLC   (1)
5335 Xenon St, Arvada, CO 80002
Tel.: (303) 339-7500
Web Site: https://www.alioindustries.com
Instrument Mfr
N.A.I.C.S.: 334515
Nathan Brown (VP-Engrg)
Bill Hennessey (Pres)

Airex, LLC   (1)
15 Lilac Ln, Somersworth, NH 03878
Tel.: (603) 841-2040
Web Site: http://www.airex.com
Sales Range: $1-9.9 Million
Emp.: 25
Mfg Transformers
N.A.I.C.S.: 335311
James Sedgewick (Pres)
Lindsay Badger (Mng Partner)

Allied Motion Canada Inc.   (1)
A12-550 Parkside Drive, Waterloo, N2L 5V4, ON, Canada
Tel.: (519) 886-2000
Web Site: http://www.alliedmotion.com
Motion Control Component Mfr
N.A.I.C.S.: 333618

Allied Motion Dordrecht B.V.   (1)
Opaal 600, 3316 LE, Dordrecht, Netherlands
Tel.: (31) 786219940
Web Site: https://www.alliedmotion.nl
Emp.: 120
Motor Product Whslr
N.A.I.C.S.: 423610

Allied Motion Portugal   (1)

Rua da Longa 300, Modivas, 4485-595, Vila do Conde, Portugal
Tel.: (351) 229288000
Motor Product Whslr
N.A.I.C.S.: 423610

Allied Motion Stockholm   (1)
Ekbacksvagen 26, 168 69, Bromma, Sweden
Tel.: (46) 854611100
Motor Product Whslr
N.A.I.C.S.: 423610

Dynamic Controls, Ltd.   (1)
39 Princess Street, Riccarton, Christchurch, 8041, New Zealand
Tel.: (64) 3 962 2519
Web Site: https://www.dynamiccontrols.com
Sales Range: $25-49.9 Million
Emp.: 150
Mfr, Distr & Servicing of Electronic Control Systems for Wheelchairs & Scooters
N.A.I.C.S.: 334519

Globe Motors de Mexico, S.A. de C.V.   (1)
Calle Abraham Zepeda No 7 Col Bellavista, 62140, Cuernavaca, Morelos, Mexico
Tel.: (52) 7776029179
Web Site:
   https://www.globalmotorsmexico.com
Industrial Motor Mfr
N.A.I.C.S.: 333618

Globe Motors, Inc.   (1)
2275 Stanley Ave, Dayton, OH 45404-1249
Tel.: (937) 228-3171
Web Site: http://www.globemotors.com
Sales Range: $100-124.9 Million
Emp.: 75
Industrial Motors Mfr
N.A.I.C.S.: 333618
Lee Henderson (Pres)

Unit (Domestic):

Globe Motors   (2)
3887 Napier Field Rd, Dothan, AL 36303   (100%)
Tel.: (334) 983-3542
Web Site: http://www.globemotors.com
Sales Range: $50-74.9 Million
Emp.: 200
Aircraft Engines & Engine Parts Mfr
N.A.I.C.S.: 335312

Subsidiary (Non-US):

Globe Motors Portugal Lda.   (2)
R da Longa 300, 4485-595, Vila do Conde, Portugal
Tel.: (351) 229288000
Emp.: 240
Electric Motor Mfr
N.A.I.C.S.: 335312

Hathaway Systems Corporation   (1)
23 Inverness Way E Ste 150, Englewood, CO 80112   (100%)
Tel.: (516) 352-0022
Real Estate Mgr
Sales Range: $10-24.9 Million
Emp.: 22
Sales & Service of Fault Recorders, Fault Locators, GPS Clocks & Circuit Breaker Measurement & Test Equipment
N.A.I.C.S.: 334515

Heidrive GmbH   (1)
Starenstrasse 23, D-93309, Kelheim, Germany
Tel.: (49) 94417070
Web Site: http://www.heidrive.com
Emp.: 300
Electronic Control Equipment Mfr
N.A.I.C.S.: 334513
Helmut Pirthauer (Mng Dir)
Hendrik Nugteren (Mng Dir)
Thomas Emmerle (Head-Svc)
Franz Treitinger (Mgr-Pur)
Knut Martinetz (Mgr-Key Acct & Project)
Armin Bernklau (Officer-Data Protection)

Heidrive s.r.o.   (1)
Stary Klicov 142 Mrakov okr Domazlice, 345 01, Plzen, Czech Republic
Tel.: (420) 379738112
Web Site: https://www.heidrive.cz
Emp.: 80
Motor Product Whslr
N.A.I.C.S.: 423610

Motor Products Corporation   (1)
201 S Delaney Rd, Owosso, MI 48867
Tel.: (989) 725-5151
Web Site: http://www.motorproducts.net
Sales Range: $25-49.9 Million
Emp.: 140
Mfr of Electric Motors
N.A.I.C.S.: 335312

Pasotec GmbH   (1)
Starenstrasse 50, D-93309, Kelheim, Germany
Tel.: (49) 9441174990
Web Site: https://www.pasotec.de
Motor Product Whslr
N.A.I.C.S.: 423610
Helmut Pirthauer (Mng Dir)
Christian Buchholz (Project Mgr)

SNC Manufacturing Company, Inc.   (1)
101 W Waukau Ave, Oshkosh, WI 54902-7209
Tel.: (920) 231-7370
Web Site: http://www.sncmfg.com
Sales Range: $10-24.9 Million
Emp.: 100
Power Distribution & Specialty Transformers
N.A.I.C.S.: 335311
Ben Bloom (VP-ICT/Utility Div)
Jim Koepke (VP & Gen Mgr-Tech Unit)
Joline Gibeault (Mgr-Acctg)
Phillip Vette-Moseley (VP-Fin)
Kevin Harvot (Mgr-Pur)
Rick Winter (VP-Sls-Global)

Spectrum Control, Inc.   (1)
1705 132nd Ave NE, Bellevue, WA 98005
Tel.: (425) 746-9481
Web Site: http://www.spectrumcontrol.com
Electromagnetic Interference & Radio Frequency Interference Suppression & Elimination Products Mfr
N.A.I.C.S.: 334419
Bruce Wanda (Founder & Pres)

Subsidiary (Non-US):

Spectrum Control GmbH   (2)
Hansastrasse 6, Schwabach, 91126, Germany
Tel.: (49) 91227950
EMC Products Whslr
N.A.I.C.S.: 334220

Subsidiary (Domestic):

Spectrum Control Technology Inc.   (2)
8061 Avania Rd, Fairview, PA 16415
Tel.: (814) 474-1571
Ceramic Capacitor Chips Mfr
N.A.I.C.S.: 334416

Subsidiary (Non-US):

Spectrum Control de Mexico, S.a. De C.v.   (2)
Av 20 de Noviembre 112, Guadalupe, 54800, Cuautitlan, Mex, Mexico
Tel.: (52) 63863350
Electromagnetic Interference & Radio Frequency Interference Suppression & Elimination Products Mfr
N.A.I.C.S.: 334416

Unit (Domestic):

Spectrum Power Management Systems   (2)
1900 W College Ave, State College, PA 16801
Tel.: (814) 272-2700
Power Strips, Power Distribution & Circuit Protection Systems Mfr
N.A.I.C.S.: 335311
James Kozel (Mgr-Product Line)
Leonardo Marsala (Dir-Bus Dev & Sls)

Stature Electric, Inc.   (1)
22543 Fisher Rd, Watertown, NY 13601
Tel.: (315) 782-5910
Web Site: http://www.statureelectric.com
Sales Range: $25-49.9 Million
Emp.: 100
Electric Motor Mfr
N.A.I.C.S.: 333618

TCI, LLC   (1)

W132 N10611 Grant Dr, Germantown, WI 53022
Tel.: (414) 357-4540
Web Site: https://www.transcoil.com
Emp.: 200
Electronic Coil Mfr
N.A.I.C.S.: 334416

ThinGap, Inc.   (1)
2064 Eastman Ave Ste 110, Ventura, CA 93003
Tel.: (805) 477-9741
Web Site: http://www.thingap.com
Sales Range: $1-9.9 Million
Emp.: 14
Motor & Generator Mfr
N.A.I.C.S.: 335312

ALLIN CORPORATION

381 Mansfield Ave, Pittsburgh, PA 15220
Tel.: (412) 928-8800   DE
Web Site: http://www.allin.com
Year Founded: 1996
ALLN—(OTCIQ)
Sales Range: Less than $1 Million
Emp.: 79
Software Technology Designer & Marketer
N.A.I.C.S.: 541512

Subsidiaries:

Allin Interactive Corporation   (1)
3223 NW 10th Ter Ste 605, Fort Lauderdale, FL 33309-5940   (100%)
Tel.: (954) 630-1020
Web Site: http://www.allin.com
Networking
N.A.I.C.S.: 541512

Subsidiary (Domestic):

Allin Digital Imaging   (2)
400 Greentree Commons 381 Mansfield Ave, Pittsburgh, PA 15220-2751
Tel.: (412) 928-8800
IT Consulting Firm
N.A.I.C.S.: 561499

ALLISON TRANSMISSION HOLDINGS, INC.

1 Allison Way, Indianapolis, IN 46222
Tel.: (317) 242-5000   DE
Web Site:
    https://www.allisontransmission.com
Year Founded: 1915
ALSN—(NYSE)
Rev.: $3,035,000,000
Assets: $5,025,000,000
Liabilities: $3,792,000,000
Net Worth: $1,233,000,000
Earnings: $673,000,000
Emp.: 3,700
Fiscal Year-end: 12/31/23
Holding Company; Heavy Duty Automatic & Power Shift Transmission Systems Designer & Mfr
N.A.I.C.S.: 551112
David S. Graziosi (Chm, Pres & CEO)
Eric C. Scroggins (Gen Counsel, Sec & VP)
Teresa J. van Niekerk (VP-Supplier Quality & Global Purchasing)
G. Frederick Bohley III (CFO, COO, Treas & Sr VP)
John M. Coll (Sr VP-Sls, Svc, and Mktg-Global)
Dana J. H. Pittard (VP-Defense Programs)
Conrad Rockey (VP-Comml Powertrain Engrg)
Heidi K. Schutte (VP-Sls-EMEA, APAC, South America & Mexico)
Teresa J. van Niekerk (VP-Supplier Quality & Pur-Global)
Lorraine Parker-Clegg (Chief People Officer & VP-HR)
Claire Gregory (Dir-External Comm-Global)
Rafael Basso (VP-Ops)

Subsidiaries:

Allison Transmission, Inc.   (1)
1 Allison Way, Indianapolis, IN 46222-3271
Tel.: (317) 242-5000
Web Site:
    https://www.allisontransmission.com
Heavy Duty Automatic & Power Shift Transmission Systems Designer & Mfr
N.A.I.C.S.: 336350
David S. Graziosi (Pres, CFO & Asst Sec)
Eric C. Scroggins (Gen Counsel, Sec & VP)
Teresa J. van Niekerk (VP-Global Pur & Supplier Quality)
Dana J. H. Pittard (VP-Defense Programs)
Heidi K. Schutte (VP-Sls-EMEA, APAC & South America)
G. Frederick Bohley (CFO)
John M. Coll (Sr VP)
Rafael Basso (VP)
Ryan Milburn (VP)
Lorranie Parker-Clegg (Chief HR Officer)
Conard Rockey (VP)

Subsidiary (Non-US):

Allison Transmission Japan Co., Ltd.   (2)
Shinagawa East One Tower 3F 2-16-1 Konan, Minato-ku, Tokyo, 108-0075, Japan
Tel.: (81) 367181660
Web Site:
    http://www.allisontransmission.com
Heavy-Duty Automatic Transmissions Sales & Distr
N.A.I.C.S.: 336350

Walker Die Casting, Inc.   (1)
1125 Higgs Rd, Lewisburg, TN 37091
Tel.: (931) 359-6206
Web Site: http://www.walkerdiecasting.com
Sales Range: $150-199.9 Million
Emp.: 500
Aluminum Die-Castings Mfr
N.A.I.C.S.: 331523
Robert H. Walker (Chm)

ALLOGENE THERAPEUTICS, INC.

210 E Grand Ave, South San Francisco, CA 94080
Tel.: (650) 457-2700   DE
Web Site: https://www.allogene.com
Year Founded: 2017
ALLO—(NASDAQ)
Rev.: $243,000
Assets: $817,079,000
Liabilities: $151,209,000
Net Worth: $665,870,000
Earnings: ($332,632,000)
Emp.: 361
Fiscal Year-end: 12/31/22
Biotechnology Research & Development Services
N.A.I.C.S.: 541714
Geoffrey M. Parker (CFO, Principal Acctg Officer & Exec VP)
Christine Cassiano (Chief Corp Affairs Officer & Chief Brand Strategy Officer)
Earl Douglas (Gen Counsel)
Susie Lundeen (Chief People Officer)
Zachary J. Roberts (Chief Medical Officer & Exec VP-Research & Development)
Arie S. Belldegrun (Co-Founder & Exec Chm)
David Chang (Co-Founder, Pres & CEO)
Joshua A. Kazam (Co-Founder)
Timothy L. Moore (Chief Technical Officer & Exec VP)

ALLOVIR, INC.

1100 Winter St, Waltham, MA 02451
Tel.: (617) 433-2605   DE
Web Site: https://www.allovir.com
Year Founded: 2013
ALVR—(NASDAQ)
Rev.: $2,227,000
Assets: $277,079,000
Liabilities: $52,560,000

Net Worth: $224,519,000
Earnings: ($168,710,000)
Emp.: 106
Fiscal Year-end: 12/31/22
Biotechnology Research & Development Services
N.A.I.C.S.: 541714
Ann Leen (Chief Scientific Officer)
Edward Miller (Gen Counsel)
Ercem Atillasoy (Chief Regulatory & Safety Officer)
Medha Chadha (Sr VP-Strategic Planning-Investor Relations)
Dana Alexander (Sr VP-Technical Ops)
Sonia Choi (Sr VP-IR)
Vikas Sinha (Pres & CFO)
Malcolm Brenner (Co-Founder)
Diana M. Brainard (CEO)
Juan F. Vera (Co-Founder)
David L. Hallal (Exec Chm & CEO)

ALLSPRING GLOBAL DIVIDEND OPPORTUNITY FUND

1415 Vantage Pk Dr 3Rd Fl, Charlotte, NC 28203
Tel.: (857) 776-4824   DE
EOD—(NYSE)
Rev.: $12,469,285
Assets: $308,985,790
Liabilities: $50,995,752
Net Worth: $257,990,038
Earnings: $7,616,074
Fiscal Year-end: 10/31/19
Investment Management Service
N.A.I.C.S.: 525990
Timothy J. Penny (Chm)

ALLSPRING INCOME OPPORTUNITIES FUND

1415 Vantage Pk Dr 3Rd Fl, Charlotte, NC 28203
Tel.: (857) 776-4824   DE
EAD—(NYSEAMEX)
Rev.: $50,555,604
Assets: $802,485,931
Liabilities: $236,150,768
Net Worth: $566,335,163
Earnings: $37,947,790
Fiscal Year-end: 04/30/19
Investment Management Service
N.A.I.C.S.: 525990

ALLSPRING UTILITIES & HIGH INCOME FUND

1415 Vantage Pk Dr 3Rd Fl, Charlotte, NC 28203
Tel.: (857) 776-4824   DE
ERH—(NYSEAMEX)
Rev.: $9,521,715
Assets: $149,469,446
Liabilities: $29,649,791
Net Worth: $119,819,655
Earnings: $7,638,970
Fiscal Year-end: 08/31/19
Investment Management Service
N.A.I.C.S.: 525990
Timothy J. Penny (Chm)

ALLURION TECHNOLOGIES, INC.

11 Huron Dr, Natick, MA 01760
Tel.: (508) 647-4000   DE
Web Site: https://www.allurion.com
Year Founded: 2023
ALUR—(NYSE)
Holding Company; Medical Apparatus Designer & Mfr
N.A.I.C.S.: 551112
Shantanu Gaur (CEO)
Chris Geberth (CFO)
Ram Chuttani (Chief Medical Officer)
Brendan Gibbons (Chief Legal Officer)
Ojas Buch (COO)

ALLY FINANCIAL INC.

Ally Detroit Ctr 500 Woodward Ave Fl 10, Detroit, MI 48226   DE
Web Site: https://www.ally.com
Year Founded: 1919
ALLY—(NYSE)
Rev.: $13,958,000,000
Assets: $194,200,000,000
Liabilities: $180,636,000,000
Net Worth: $13,564,000,000
Earnings: $910,000,000
Emp.: 11,100
Fiscal Year-end: 12/31/23
Holding Company; Consumer & Commercial Lending, Automotive Sales Financing, Insurance & Mortgage Services
N.A.I.C.S.: 551112
Douglas R. Timmerman (Pres-Dealer Fin Svcs)
Michael G. Rhodes (CEO)
Isvara W. A. Wilson (Acting Gen Counsel)
Dinesh Chopra (Chief Strategy & Corp Dev Officer)
Bradley J. Brown (Treas)
Kathleen L. Patterson (Chief HR Officer)
Jason E. Schugel (Chief Risk Officer)
Dan Soto (Chief Compliance Officer)
Sathish Muthukrishnan (Chief Info & Data Officer)
Russell E. Hutchinson (CFO)
William Hall Jr. (Pres-Corp Fin)
David J. Debrunner (Chief Acctg Officer, VP & Controller)
David J. DeBrunner (Chief Acctg Officer, VP & Controller)

Subsidiaries:

Ally Bank   (1)
6985 Union Park Ctr Ste 435, Midvale, UT 84047
Tel.: (757) 247-2559
Web Site: http://www.ally.com
Commercial Banking
N.A.I.C.S.: 522110
Michael G. Rhodes (CEO)

Ally Commercial Finance LLC   (1)
300 Park Ave, New York, NY 10022
Tel.: (212) 884-7000
Web Site: http://www.allycf.com
Commercial Lending Services
N.A.I.C.S.: 522299

Ally Servicing, LLC   (1)
40600 Ann Arbor Rd E Ste 201, Plymouth, MI 48170
Tel.: (248) 948-7702
Emp.: 3,455
Accounting Services
N.A.I.C.S.: 541219

ALNYLAM PHARMACEUTICALS, INC.

675 W Kendall St Henri A Termeer Sq, Cambridge, MA 02142
Tel.: (617) 551-8200   DE
Web Site: https://www.alnylam.com
ALNY—(NASDAQ)
Rev.: $1,828,292,000
Assets: $3,829,880,000
Liabilities: $4,050,524,000
Net Worth: ($220,644,000)
Earnings: ($440,242,000)
Emp.: 2,100
Fiscal Year-end: 12/31/23
RNAi Therapeutics in the Treatment of Liver Cancers
N.A.I.C.S.: 325412
John K. Clarke (Founder)
Yvonne L. Greenstreet (CEO)
Akshay K. Vaishnaw (Chief Innovation Officer)
Kelley Boucher (Chief HR Officer & Member-Mgmt Bd)
Jeffrey V. Poulton (CFO & Exec VP)

Alnylam Pharmaceuticals, Inc.—(Continued)

Christine Lindenboom *(Sr VP-IR & Corp Comm)*
Al Boyle *(Chief Technical Ops & Quality Officer & Member-Mgmt Bd)*
Tolga Tanguler *(Chief Comml Officer & Member-Mgmt Bd)*
Phillip A. Sharp *(Founder)*

Subsidiaries:

Alnylam Austria GmbH (1)
Karntner Ring 5-7, 1010, Vienna, Austria
Tel.: (43) 720778071
Pharmaceutical Products Distr
N.A.I.C.S.: 424210

Alnylam Brasil Farmaceutica Ltda. (1)
Av Pres Juscelino Kubitscheck 2041 5 Andar Bloco B - Vila Olimpia, Sao Paulo, 04543-011, Brazil
Tel.: (55) 1142107911
Web Site: https://www.alnylam.com.br
Pharmaceutical Products Distr
N.A.I.C.S.: 424210

Alnylam Germany GmbH (1)
Maximilianstrasse 35a, 80539, Munich, Germany
Tel.: (49) 892 019 0100
Web Site: https://www.alnylam.de
Pharmaceutical Products Distr
N.A.I.C.S.: 424210

Alnylam Pharmaceuticals Spain SL (1)
Cuzco IV - Paseo de la Castellana 141, 28046, Madrid, Spain
Tel.: (34) 910603753
Web Site: https://www.alnylam.com
Pharmaceuticals Product Mfr
N.A.I.C.S.: 325412
Elena Perez Castro *(Acct Mgr)*

Alnylam UK Limited (1)
Braywick Gate Braywick Road, Maidenhead, SL6 1DA, Berkshire, United Kingdom
Tel.: (44) 1255444400
Web Site: https://www.alnylam.com
Pharmaceuticals Product Mfr
N.A.I.C.S.: 325412

ALPHA CAPITAL ACQUISITION COMPANY
1230 Avenue of the Americas 16 Fl, New York, NY 10020
Tel.: (732) 838-4533   **Ky**
Year Founded: 2020
ASPCU—(NASDAQ)
Rev.: $197,361
Assets: $230,762,507
Liabilities: $254,531,853
Net Worth: ($23,769,346)
Earnings: ($2,103,788)
Emp.: 4
Fiscal Year-end: 12/31/21
Investment Services
N.A.I.C.S.: 523999
Alec Oxenford *(Chm & CEO)*
Rafael Steinhauser *(Pres)*
Rahim Lakhani *(CFO)*
Alfredo Capote *(Chief Strategy Officer)*

ALPHA METALLURGICAL RESOURCES, INC.
340 Martin Luther King Jr Blvd, Bristol, TN 37620
Tel.: (423) 573-0300   **DE**
Web Site:
https://www.alphametresources.com
Year Founded: 2016
AMR—(NYSE)
Rev.: $3,471,417,000
Assets: $2,406,057,000
Liabilities: $832,129,000
Net Worth: $1,573,928,000
Earnings: $721,956,000
Emp.: 4,160
Fiscal Year-end: 12/31/23

Coal Mining Services
N.A.I.C.S.: 213113
Daniel E. Horn *(Chief Comml Officer & Exec VP)*
Jason Whitehead *(COO & Exec VP)*
Mark M. Manno *(Gen Counsel, Sec & Exec VP)*
J. Todd Munsey *(CFO)*
Charles Andrew Eidson *(CEO)*

Subsidiaries:

Contura Coal Sales, LLC (1)
340 Martin Luther King Jr Blvd, Bristol, TN 37620
Tel.: (423) 573-0300
Coal Distr
N.A.I.C.S.: 457210

Cumberland Contura, LLC (1)
158 Portal Rd, Waynesburg, PA 15370
Tel.: (724) 627-7500
Coal Distr
N.A.I.C.S.: 457210

Dickenson-Russell Contura, LLC (1)
2079 Herndon Rd, McClure, VA 24269
Tel.: (276) 835-3180
Coal Distr
N.A.I.C.S.: 457210

Nicholas Contura, LLC (1)
Ste 3 Jerrys Fork Rd, Drennen, WV 26667
Tel.: (304) 872-5065
Coal Distr
N.A.I.C.S.: 457210
Robert Gordon *(Gen Mgr)*

Paramont Contura, LLC (1)
5703 Crutchfield Dr, Norton, VA 26667
Tel.: (276) 679-7020
Coal Distr
N.A.I.C.S.: 457210

Power Mountain Contura, LLC (1)
Ste 4 Jerrys Fork Rd, Drennen, WV 26667
Tel.: (304) 872-5065
Coal Distr
N.A.I.C.S.: 457210

ALPHA NETWORK ALLIANCE VENTURES INC.
11801 Pierce St 2nd Fl, Riverside, CA 92505
Tel.: (951) 530-1862   **DE**
Web Site:
http://www.kababayanko.com
Year Founded: 2010
ANAV—(OTCIQ)
Rev.: $141,867
Assets: $72,989
Liabilities: $4,296,043
Net Worth: ($4,223,054)
Earnings: ($645,554)
Emp.: 5
Fiscal Year-end: 12/31/20
Social Networking Website
N.A.I.C.S.: 516210
Eleazar Rivera *(Pres, CEO, Treas & Co-Sec)*
Ronie Tan *(Chm & Co-Sec)*

ALPHA STAR ACQUISITION CORPORATION
80 Broad St 5th Fl, New York, NY 10004
Tel.: (212) 837-7977   **Ky**
Year Founded: 2021
ALSA—(NASDAQ)
Rev.: $5,359,385
Assets: $101,603,162
Liabilities: $110,669,684
Net Worth: ($9,066,522)
Earnings: $4,924,098
Fiscal Year-end: 12/31/23
Investment Services
N.A.I.C.S.: 523999
Zhe Zhang *(Chm, CEO & Dir)*
Guojian Chen *(CFO)*
Patrick Swint *(Dir)*

ALPHA TEKNOVA, INC.

2451 Bert Dr, Hollister, CA 95023
Tel.: (831) 637-1100   **CA**
Web Site: https://www.teknova.com
Year Founded: 1995
TKNO—(NASDAQ)
Sales Range: $10-24.9 Million
Research & Development in the Physical, Engineering & Life Sciences
N.A.I.C.S.: 541715
Stephen Gunstream *(Pres & CEO)*
Neal Goodwin *(Chief Scientific Officer)*
Lisa McCann *(Chief People Officer)*
Damon Terrill *(Chief Compliance Officer & Gen Counsel)*
Matthew Lowell *(CFO)*
Ken Gelhaus *(Chief Comml Officer)*
Jennifer Henry *(Sr VP-Mktg)*

ALPHA-EN CORPORATION
28 Wells Ave 2nd Fl, Yonkers, NY 10701
Tel.: (914) 418-2000   **DE**
Web Site: https://www.alpha-encorp.com
Year Founded: 1997
ALPE—(OTCIQ)
Sales Range: Less than $1 Million
Emp.: 8
Metallic Lithium Battery Mfr
N.A.I.C.S.: 335910
Thomas A. Suppanz *(CFO)*
Kyra Paris *(Dir-Military Affairs)*
Lawrence Swonger *(CTO)*
Roald Hoffmann *(Chm)*

ALPHABET INC.
1600 Amphitheatre Pkwy, Mountain View, CA 94043
Tel.: (650) 253-0000   **DE**
Web Site: http://www.abc.xyz
Year Founded: 2015
GOOGL—(NASDAQ)
Rev.: $307,394,000,000
Assets: $402,392,000,000
Liabilities: $119,013,000,000
Net Worth: $283,379,000,000
Earnings: $73,795,000,000
Emp.: 182,502
Fiscal Year-end: 12/31/23
Holding Company
N.A.I.C.S.: 551112
James Manyika *(Sr VP)*
Torrence N. Boone *(VP-Client Partnerships-Global)*
Torrence N. Boone *(VP-Client Partnerships-Global)*
Anat Ashkenazi *(CFO & Sr VP)*
Ruth M. Porat *(Pres & Chief Investment Officer)*
Sundar Pichai *(CEO)*
Larry Page *(Executives)*
Sergey Brin *(Executives, Bd of Dirs)*
Lawrence Edward Page *(Executives, Bd of Dirs)*
John L. Hennessy *(Chm)*
John L. Hennessy *(Chm)*
Amie Thuener O'Toole *(Chief Acctg Officer & VP)*
Yolande G. Piazza *(VP-Fin Svcs-Google Cloud Div)*

Subsidiaries:

Calico LLC (1)
1170 Veterans Blvd, South San Francisco, CA 94080
Tel.: (650) 754-6200
Web Site: http://www.calicolabs.com
Biological Research & Development
N.A.I.C.S.: 541714
Arthur D. Levinson *(Founder & CEO)*
David Botstein *(Chief Scientific Officer)*
Cynthia Kenyon *(VP-Aging Res)*
Jonathan W. Lewis *(Chief Bus Officer)*
Daniel Gottschling *(Head-Res)*
Ganesh Kolumam *(Head-Physiology)*
Andrew York *(Head-Microscopy)*
Bryson Bennett *(Head-Mass Spectrometry)*

Margaret Roy *(Head-Genomic Sequencing)*
Aarif Khakoo *(Head-Drug Dev)*
Amoolya Singh *(Head-Computing)*
Dan Eaton *(Head-Biochemistry)*
Aide Castro *(Dir-Clinical Ops)*
Rachel Lane *(Dir-Bus Dev)*
Barbara Leyman *(Dir-Bus Dev)*
Amos Baruch *(Dir-Biomarker Dev & Translational Medicine)*
Lindsay Keever *(Dir-Alliance & Contracts Mgmt)*
Denise Smith-Hams *(Head-HR)*
John Whiting *(CFO)*

CapitalG Management Company LLC (1)
1600 Ampitheatre Pkwy, Mountain View, CA 94023
Tel.: (650) 253-0000
Web Site: http://www.capitalg.com
Equity Investment Firm
N.A.I.C.S.: 523999
David Lawee *(Founder & Partner)*
Laela Sturdy *(Partner)*
Gene Frantz *(Partner)*
Jeremiah Gordon *(Chief Compliance Officer & Gen Counsel)*
Kristin Drew *(CFO)*
Alex Nichols *(VP-Investment)*
Chengpeng Mou *(VP-Investment)*
James Luo *(VP-Investment)*
Mo Jomaa *(VP-Investment)*
Victor Chen *(VP-Investment)*
Kathryn Karaczoff *(VP-Growth)*
Luke Erickson *(VP-Growth)*
Terese Hougaard *(Partner-Growth)*
Johan Duramy *(Partner-Data Platform)*
Allison Caragan *(Partner-Admin Bus)*
Alli McKulla *(Partner-Admin Bus)*
Derek Zanutto *(Partner)*
Jesse Wedler *(Partner)*
Sumiran Das *(Partner)*
Shannon Beal *(Mgr-Program)*
Lana Devlikamova *(Mgr-Legal Ops)*
David Meyer *(Mgr-Fin)*
Janelle Mekaru *(Mgr-Fin)*
Manny Ojobaro *(Mgr-Fin)*
Wendy Alexander *(Chief People Officer)*
Alex Kingsley *(Assoc Gen Counsel)*
Jackson Georges Jr. *(VP-Growth)*

GV Management Company, LLC (1)
1600 Amphitheatre Pkwy, Mountain View, CA 94043
Tel.: (650) 335-5278
Web Site: http://www.gv.com
Venture Capital Investment Firm
N.A.I.C.S.: 523999
Krishna Yeshwant *(Mng Partner)*
David Krane *(CEO & Mng Partner)*
Blake Byers *(Gen Partner)*
Daphne Chang *(Gen Counsel)*
Graham Spencer *(Mng Partner-Engrg)*
Kate Aronowitz *(Partner-Lead Ops)*
Robin Teng *(Controller)*
Celeste Schnackenberg *(Partner-Bus)*
Shane Peltzman *(Partner-Bus)*
Gina Novak *(Controller)*
Victoria Miller *(Partner-Bus)*
Danielle Lewis *(Partner-Bus)*
Anne Kelly *(Partner-Bus)*
Christina Kelleher *(Partner-Bus)*
Laura Gifford *(Partner-Bus)*
Nicole Doherty *(Partner-Bus)*
Marissa Benson *(Partner-Bus)*
Cissy Hu *(Coord-Portfolio Ops)*
Graham Hancock *(Partner-Mktg)*
Mandy Kakavas *(Partner-Comm)*
Jodi Olson *(Partner-Comm & Mktg)*
Daniel Yehuda *(Partner-Engrg)*
Jeremy Whelchel *(Partner-Engrg)*
Brian Bendett *(Partner)*
Brendan Bulik-Sullivan *(Partner)*
Terri Burns *(Partner)*
Tyson Clark *(Gen Partner)*
Frederique Dame *(Partner)*
Karim Faris *(Gen Partner)*
Tom Hulme *(Partner)*
Laura Melahn *(Partner)*
Dave Munichiello *(Gen Partner)*
Erik Nordlander *(Partner)*
David Schenkein *(Gen Partner)*
M. G. Siegler *(Gen Partner)*
Jessica Verrilli *(Gen Partner)*
Andy Wheeler *(Gen Partner)*
Vanessa Cho *(Partner-Design)*
Candice Morgan *(Partner-Equity, Diversity & Inclusion)*
Reuben Antman *(Partner-Engrg)*

Choongsoon Bae *(Partner-Engrg)*
Kristina Chodorow *(Partner-Engrg)*
Greg Dooley *(Partner-Engrg)*
Barkha Gvalani *(Partner-Engrg)*
Fei Li *(Partner-Engrg)*
Jon Stritar *(Partner-Engrg)*
Jessica Ashford *(Controller)*
Krishna Yeshwant *(Gen Partner)*

Google LLC   **(1)**
1600 Amphitheatre Pkwy, Mountain View,
CA 94043
Tel.: (650) 253-0000
Web Site: https://about.google
Online Information Services
N.A.I.C.S.: 513210
John Hernandez *(Head-Health Impact)*
Lori Mitchell-Keller *(VP-Industry Solutions-Cloud)*
Susan D. Wojcicki *(CEO-YouTube)*
Lori Mitchell-Keller *(VP-Industry Solutions-Cloud)*
Jim F. Anderson *(Mng Dir-Cloud)*
James Manyika *(Sr VP-Tech & Society)*

Subsidiary (Domestic):

Actifio, Inc.   **(2)**
333 Wyman St, Waltham, MA 02451
Tel.: (781) 790-7676
Web Site: http://www.actifio.com
Data Processing Services
N.A.I.C.S.: 513199
David Chang *(Co-Founder & Sr VP-Solutions Dev)*
Ash Ashutosh *(Co-Founder & CEO)*
Brian Reagan *(CMO)*
Paul Forte *(Chief Revenue Officer)*
Brylan Achilles *(CTO-Global Field)*
Ashok Ramu *(CTO)*
John A. Meyers *(Chief Information Security Officer)*
Ranajit Nevatia *(Sr VP & Gen Mgr-Actifio Go Sls & Cloud Bus Dev)*
Micah Waldman *(VP-Product Mgmt)*
Tom Gelson *(Sr VP & Gen Mgr-Accounts & Alliances)*
Patrick O'Donnell *(Sr VP & Gen Mgr-OEM Sls & Bus Dev)*

Admeld Inc.   **(2)**
76 Ninth Ave 4th Fl, New York, NY 10011
Tel.: (212) 244-1144
Web Site: http://www.admeld.com
Sales Range: $25-49.9 Million
Emp.: 40
Online Advertising Technology Services
N.A.I.C.S.: 541519

Anvato, Inc.   **(2)**
1600 Amphitheatre Pkwy, Mountain View,
CA 94043   **(100%)**
Web Site: http://www.anvato.com
Emp.: 50
Develops Content Protection & Contextual
Advertising Technology Solutions
N.A.I.C.S.: 513210

Apigee Corporation   **(2)**
10 S Almaden Blvd 16th Fl, San Jose, CA
95113
Tel.: (408) 343-7300
Web Site: http://www.apigee.com
Rev.: $92,027,000
Assets: $118,837,000
Liabilities: $69,387,000
Net Worth: $49,450,000
Earnings: ($41,512,000)
Emp.: 374
Fiscal Year-end: 07/31/2016
Software Publisher
N.A.I.C.S.: 513210

Fitbit, Inc.   **(2)**
199 Fremont St 14th Fl, San Francisco, CA
94105
Tel.: (415) 513-1000
Web Site: https://www.fitbit.com
Rev.: $1,434,788,000
Assets: $1,368,086,000
Liabilities: $880,823,000
Net Worth: $487,263,000
Earnings: ($320,711,000)
Emp.: 1,684
Fiscal Year-end: 12/31/2019
Fitness Tracking Device Mfr
N.A.I.C.S.: 339920
James Park *(Co-Founder)*

Google Fiber Inc.   **(2)**

1600 Amphitheatre Pkwy, Mountain View,
CA 94043
Web Site: http://www.fiber.google.com
Internet Telecommunication Services
N.A.I.C.S.: 517111
Gregory J. McCray *(Pres)*
Dinesh C. Jain *(CEO)*
Melani Griffith *(Chief Growth Officer)*
John H. Keib *(Chief Tech & Product Officer)*

Google International LLC   **(2)**
2400 Bayshore Pkwy, Mountain View, CA
94043
Tel.: (650) 623-4000
Holding Company
N.A.I.C.S.: 551112

Subsidiary (Non-US):

Google Australia Pty. Ltd.   **(3)**
48 Pirrama Road, Sydney, 2009, NSW,
Australia   **(100%)**
Tel.: (61) 293744000
Web Site: http://www.google.com.au
Internet Data Processing, Hosting & Related Services
N.A.I.C.S.: 518210
Jason Pellegrino *(Mng Dir-Australia & New Zealand)*

Branch (Non-US):

Google India Pvt Ltd   **(3)**
Unitech Signature Tower II Tower B Sector
15, Part II Village Silokhera, Gurgaon, 122
001, India
Tel.: (91) 12 44512900
Web Site: http://www.google.co.in
Internet Data Processing, Hosting & Related Services
N.A.I.C.S.: 518210
Rick Harshman *(Mng Dir-Google Cloud-Asia Pacific)*
Anil Bhansali *(VP-Engrg-Cloud Div)*
Karan Bajwa *(Mng Dir-Cloud)*

Group (Non-US):

Google Ireland Holdings   **(3)**
Gordon House Barrow St, Dublin, 4, Ireland
Tel.: (353) 14361000
Web Site: http://www.google.ie
Holding Company
N.A.I.C.S.: 551112

Subsidiary (Non-US):

Google France Sarl   **(4)**
8 Rue de Londres, 75009, Paris,
France   **(100%)**
Tel.: (33) 142685300
Web Site: http://www.google.fr
Internet Data Processing, Hosting & Related Services
N.A.I.C.S.: 518210
Mats Carduner *(CEO)*

Google Germany GmbH   **(4)**
ABC-Strasse 19, 20354, Hamburg, Germany
Tel.: (49) 40808179000
Web Site: http://www.google.de
Sales Range: $75-99.9 Million
Internet Data Processing, Hosting & Related Services
N.A.I.C.S.: 518210

Subsidiary (Domestic):

Nik Software GmbH   **(5)**
Hammerbrookstrasse 93, Hamburg,
D-20097, Germany
Tel.: (49) 4025404870
Web Site: http://www.niksoftware.com
Photo Editing Software Developer & Publisher
N.A.I.C.S.: 513210

Subsidiary (US):

Nik Software, Inc.   **(6)**
7588 Metropolitan Dr, San Diego, CA 92108
Tel.: (619) 725-3150
Web Site: http://www.niksoftware.com
Photo Editing Software Developer & Publisher
N.A.I.C.S.: 513210

Subsidiary (Domestic):

Google Ireland Limited   **(4)**

Gordon House Barrow St, Dublin, 4, Ireland
Tel.: (353) 14361000
Web Site: http://www.google.com
Internet Data Processing, Hosting & Related Services
N.A.I.C.S.: 518210

Subsidiary (Non-US):

Google Italy s.r.l.   **(4)**
Corso Europa 2, 20122, Milan,
Italy   **(100%)**
Tel.: (39) 02 36618 300
Web Site: http://www.google.it
Sales Range: $75-99.9 Million
Internet Data Processing, Hosting & Related Services
N.A.I.C.S.: 518210

Google Netherlands B.V.   **(4)**
Claude Debussylaan 34, 1082 MD, Amsterdam, Netherlands
Tel.: (31) 205045100
Web Site: https://www.google.nl
Internet Data Processing, Hosting & Related Services
N.A.I.C.S.: 518210

Google Spain, S.L.   **(4)**
Plaza Pablo Ruiz Picasso Torre Picasso 1,
Madrid, 28020, Spain   **(100%)**
Tel.: (34) 917486645
Web Site: http://www.google.es
Sales Range: $75-99.9 Million
Internet Data Processing, Hosting & Related Services
N.A.I.C.S.: 518210
Fuencisla Clemares *(Mng Dir-Spain & Portugal)*

Google UK Limited   **(4)**
Belgrave House 76 Buckingham Palace
Road, London, SW1W 9TQ, United
Kingdom   **(100%)**
Tel.: (44) 2070313000
Web Site: http://www.google.co.uk
Sales Range: $75-99.9 Million
Internet Data Processing, Hosting & Related Services
N.A.I.C.S.: 518210

Subsidiary (Non-US):

Google Japan Inc.   **(3)**
6F Cerulean Tower 26-1 Sakuragaoka-cho,
Shibuya-ku, Tokyo, 150-8512, Japan
Tel.: (81) 364155200
Web Site: http://www.google.co.jp
Internet Data Processing, Hosting & Related Services
N.A.I.C.S.: 518210

Branch (Non-US):

Google-Canada   **(3)**
111 Richmond Street West, Toronto, M5H
2G4, ON, Canada   **(100%)**
Tel.: (416) 915-8200
Web Site: http://www.google.ca
Internet Data Processing, Hosting & Related Services
N.A.I.C.S.: 518210
Laura Pearce *(Head-Mktg)*

Google-Greater China   **(3)**
Tsinghua Science Park Building 6 1 Zhongguancun East Road, Haidian District, Beijing, 100084, China
Tel.: (86) 1062503000
Web Site: http://www.google.cn
Internet Data Processing, Hosting & Related Services
N.A.I.C.S.: 518210

Subsidiary (Non-US):

Waze Ltd.   **(3)**
2 Hasadna Street, Ra'anana, 43561, Israel
Tel.: (972) 9 748 6437
Web Site: http://www.waze.com
Mobile Navigation Application Developer
N.A.I.C.S.: 513210
Amir Shinar *(Founder)*
Di-Ann Eisnor *(Founder-U.S. office)*
Neha Parikh *(CEO)*

Branch (Domestic):

Google-Atlanta   **(2)**
10 10th St NE, Atlanta, GA 30309
Tel.: (404) 487-9000

Web Site: http://www.google.com
Internet Data Processing, Hosting & Related Services
N.A.I.C.S.: 518210
Jason Mills *(Exec Dir & Head-Customer Engrg Cloud Industries)*

Google-Boston   **(2)**
5 Cambridge Ctr, Cambridge, MA 02142
Tel.: (617) 575-1300
Web Site: http://www.google.com
Sales Range: $75-99.9 Million
Emp.: 900
Internet Data Processing, Hosting & Related Services
N.A.I.C.S.: 518210

Google-Chicago   **(2)**
20 W Kinzie St Ste 900, Chicago, IL 60654
Tel.: (312) 840-4100
Web Site: http://www.google.com
Sales Range: $150-199.9 Million
Emp.: 400
Internet Data Processing, Hosting & Related Services
N.A.I.C.S.: 518210

Google-Detroit   **(2)**
114 Willits St, Birmingham, MI 48009
Tel.: (248) 593-4000
Web Site: http://www.google.com
Sales Range: $25-49.9 Million
Emp.: 100
Internet Data Processing, Hosting & Related Services
N.A.I.C.S.: 518210

Google-New York   **(2)**
111 8th Ave, New York, NY 10011
Tel.: (212) 565-0000
Web Site: http://www.google.com
Sales Range: $25-49.9 Million
Emp.: 100
Internet Data Processing, Hosting & Related Services
N.A.I.C.S.: 518210

Google-Seattle   **(2)**
601 N 34th St, Seattle, WA 98103
Tel.: (206) 876-1800
Web Site: http://www.google.com
Sales Range: $75-99.9 Million
Internet Data Processing, Hosting & Related Services
N.A.I.C.S.: 518210

Subsidiary (Domestic):

ITA Software, Inc.   **(2)**
141 Portland St, Cambridge, MA 02139
Tel.: (617) 714-2100
Web Site: http://www.itasoftware.com
Sales Range: $100-124.9 Million
Emp.: 500
Flight Information Software Developer
N.A.I.C.S.: 513210

Looker Data Sciences Inc.   **(2)**
101 Church St, Santa Cruz, CA 95060
Tel.: (831) 244-0340
Web Site: http://www.looker.com
Business Intelligence Software Developer
N.A.I.C.S.: 513210
Lloyd Tabb *(Co-Founder)*
Frank Bien *(Co-Founder)*

Lumedyne Technologies Incorporated   **(2)**
9275 Sky Park Ct Ste 100, San Diego, CA
92123-5310
Tel.: (619) 602-5414
Web Site:
http://www.lumedynetechnologies.com
Micro-Electromechanical Systems Sensors
Mfr
N.A.I.C.S.: 334413
Brad Chisum *(Co-Founder & CEO)*
Richard Waters *(Co-Founder & CTO)*

Mandiant, Inc.   **(2)**
601 McCarthy Blvd, Milpitas, CA 95035
Tel.: (408) 321-6300
Web Site: https://www.mandiant.com
Rev.: $940,584,000
Assets: $3,245,882,000
Liabilities: $2,512,978,000
Net Worth: $732,904,000
Earnings: ($207,303,000)
Emp.: 3,400
Fiscal Year-end: 12/31/2020

Alphabet Inc.—(Continued)

Computer Security Software & Solutions
N.A.I.C.S.: 513210
John P. Watters *(Pres & COO)*
Alexa King *(Gen Counsel, Sec & Exec VP-Corp & Legal Affairs)*
Jurgen Kutscher *(Exec VP-Svc Delivery)*
Bryan Palma *(Exec VP-FireEye Products)*
Marshall Heilman *(Exec VP-Managed Defense & Advanced Practices)*
Chris Key *(Exec VP-Products & Mandiant Solutions)*

Subsidiary (Non-US):

Clean Communication Limited   (3)
Ellenborough House Dublin Road, Kildare, Naas, Ireland
Tel.: (353) 45897766
Cyber Security Solution Services
N.A.I.C.S.: 541511

Subsidiary (Domestic):

Cloudvisory LLC   (3)
6238 Prestonshire Ln, Dallas, TX 75225
Tel.: (214) 912-3203
Cloud Security Services
N.A.I.C.S.: 541511

Subsidiary (Non-US):

Mandiant Australia Pty Ltd   (3)
Level 6 100 Pacific Highway, North Sydney, 2060, NSW, Australia
Tel.: (61) 280743444
Cyber Security Solutions
N.A.I.C.S.: 513210

Subsidiary (Domestic):

Mandiant Corporation   (3)
2318 Mill Rd Ste 500, Alexandria, VA 22314
Tel.: (703) 935-1700
Web Site: http://www.mandiant.com
Sales Range: $25-49.9 Million
Emp.: 150
Security Software
N.A.I.C.S.: 513210
David G. DeWalt *(Chm)*
John P. Watters *(Pres & CQO)*
Vikram Ramesh *(CMO)*

Subsidiary (Non-US):

Mandiant Cybersecurity Private Limited   (3)
Salarpuria Infinity 2nd Floor Front Wing 5 Bannerghatta Road, Bengaluru, 560029, India
Tel.: (91) 8000503434
Security System Services
N.A.I.C.S.: 513210

Mandiant Deutschland GmbH   (3)
Tel.: (49) 8001801787
Cyber Security Solutions
N.A.I.C.S.: 513210

Mandiant Ireland Limited   (3)
2 Park Place City Gate Park, Mahon, Cork, Ireland
Tel.: (353) 818021042
Cyber Security Solutions
N.A.I.C.S.: 513210

Mandiant K.K.   (3)
3-22 Kandanishikicho Terasusukuea 8F, Chiyuda-ku, Tokyo, 101-0054, Japan
Tel.: (81) 120914657
Cyber Security Solutions
N.A.I.C.S.: 513210

Mandiant Korea Limited   (3)
518 Teheran-ro, Gangnam-gu, Seoul, 06180, Korea (South)
Tel.: (82) 269594017
Cyber Security Solutions
N.A.I.C.S.: 513210

Mandiant Singapore Private Limited   (3)
8 Marina Boulevard #05-02 Marina Bay Financial Centre, Singapore, 018981, Singapore
Tel.: (65) 31585588
Cyber Security Solutions
N.A.I.C.S.: 513210

Mandiant UK Ltd.   (3)
18th Floor Angel Court Bank, London,

EC2R 7HJ, Berkshire, United Kingdom
Tel.: (44) 2081383274
Cyber Security Solutions
N.A.I.C.S.: 513210

Subsidiary (Domestic):

Verodin, LLC   (3)
8200 Greensboro Dr Ste 1400, McLean, VA 22102
Tel.: (571) 418-8684
Web Site: http://www.verodin.com
Emp.: 120
Cyber Security Services
N.A.I.C.S.: 561621
Christopher May *(Co-Founder & CEO)*
Ben Cianciaruso *(Co-Founder & COO)*
Tracey Moon *(CMO)*
Colby Derodeff *(CTO)*
Lyndon Brown *(VP-Bus Dev)*

Subsidiary (Domestic):

Nest Labs, Inc.   (2)
3400 Hillview Ave, Palo Alto, CA 94304
Tel.: (650) 397-4333
Web Site: http://www.nest.com
Thermostats, Safety & Security Products Developer & Mfr
N.A.I.C.S.: 334290
Matt Rogers *(Founder & Chief Product Officer)*

Subsidiary (Domestic):

Quickoffice, Inc.   (2)
4965 Preston Park Blvd Ste 500, Plano, TX 75093
Tel.: (972) 931-8181
Web Site: http://www.quickoffice.com
Sales Range: $25-49.9 Million
Emp.: 50
Mobile Office Software Developer
N.A.I.C.S.: 513210
Alan B. Masarek *(Co-Founder)*

Slide, Inc.   (2)
301 Brannan St Fl 4, San Francisco, CA 94107-3816
Tel.: (415) 618-0506
Sales Range: $25-49.9 Million
Emp.: 120
Publisher of Social Entertainment Applications
N.A.I.C.S.: 513210

Teracent Corporation   (2)
400 S El Camino Real Ste 575, San Mateo, CA 94402
Tel.: (650) 525-9900
Customized Display Advertising Technology Developer
N.A.I.C.S.: 513210

Webpass, Inc.   (2)
267 8th St, San Francisco, CA 94103   (100%)
Tel.: (415) 233-4100
Web Site: http://www.webpass.net
Sales Range: $10-24.9 Million
Emp.: 90
Internet Services
N.A.I.C.S.: 517121
Charles Barr *(Founder)*

Widevine Technologies, Inc.   (2)
425 Urban Plaza Ste 223, Kirkland, WA 98033
Tel.: (206) 254-3000
Web Site: http://www.widevine.com
Sales Range: $25-49.9 Million
Emp.: 50
Software Developer
N.A.I.C.S.: 513210

Wildfire Interactive, Inc.   (2)
323 Fairchild Dr Building 2, Mountain View, CA 94043
Web Site: http://www.wildfireapp.com
Sales Range: $25-49.9 Million
Emp.: 25
Social Media Marketing & Advertising Management Services
N.A.I.C.S.: 541890
Victoria Ransom *(Co-Founder & CEO)*

YouTube, LLC   (2)
901 Cherry Ave Second Fl, San Bruno, CA 94066
Tel.: (650) 253-0000
Web Site: http://www.youtube.com
Sales Range: $1-9.9 Million
Emp.: 67

Consumer-Oriented Online Video Broadcasting Services
N.A.I.C.S.: 518210
Neal Mohan *(CEO)*
Tara Walpert Levy *(VP-Americas)*
Susan D. Wojcicki *(CEO)*
Mary Ellen Coe *(Chief Bus Officer)*
Cecile Frot-Coutaz *(Head-Europe, Middle East & Africa)*
Iain Bundred *(Head-Pub Policy-UK & Ireland)*
Garth Graham *(Head-Health Care & Pub Health Partnerships-Global)*
Mary Ellen Coe *(Chief Bus Officer)*

Subsidiary (Domestic):

BandPage, Inc.   (3)
334 Brannan St, San Francisco, CA 94107
Tel.: (415) 800-8614
Web Site: http://www.bandpage.com
Emp.: 20
Internet Publishing & Broadcasting Services
N.A.I.C.S.: 516210
J. Sider *(Founder & CEO)*

Subsidiary (Domestic):

eBook Technologies, Inc.   (2)
7745 Herschel Ave, La Jolla, CA 92037
Tel.: (858) 454-0565
Sales Range: $10-24.9 Million
Emp.: 12
Electronic Book Software Developer
N.A.I.C.S.: 513210

Verily Life Sciences LLC   (1)
269 E Grand Ave, South San Francisco, CA 94080
Tel.: (650) 214-2704
Web Site: http://www.verily.com
Emp.: 4
Life Sciences Research & Development
N.A.I.C.S.: 541715
Stephen E. Gillett *(CEO & CEO)*
Andrew Conrad *(Founder & Exec Chm)*
Brian Otis *(CTO)*
Sheela Krothapalli *(Head-People Ops)*
Linus Upson *(Head-Engrg)*
Carolyn Wang *(Head-Comm)*
Utpal Koppikar *(CFO)*
Jessica L. Mega *(Co-Founder)*
Scott Burke *(Head-Software)*
Jordi Parramon *(Head-Hardware & Medical Devices)*
Rob M. Califf *(Head-Clinical Policy & Strategy)*
Andrew Harrison *(Head-Bus & Corp Dev)*
Kerrie Peraino *(Chief People Officer)*
Preston Simons *(CIO)*
Stephen Gillett *(CEO & CEO)*
Stephen Gillett *(CEO)*

Waymo LLC   (1)
1600 Amphitheater Pkwy, Mountain View, CA 94043
Tel.: (650) 669-7376
Web Site: http://www.waymo.com
Autonomous Driving Services
N.A.I.C.S.: 488490
Tekedra N. Mawakana *(Co-CEO)*
Dmitri Dolgov *(Co-CEO)*
Becky Bucich *(Chief People Officer)*
Dan Chu *(Chief Product Officer)*
Mauricio Pena *(Chief Safety Officer)*
Kevin Vosen *(Chief Legal Officer)*

ALPHATEC HOLDINGS, INC.
1950 Camino Vida Roble, Carlsbad, CA 92008
Tel.: (760) 431-9286   DE
Web Site: https://www.atecspine.com
Year Founded: 2005
ATEC—(NASDAQ)
Rev.: $350,867,000
Assets: $513,376,000
Liabilities: $550,089,000
Net Worth: ($36,713,000)
Earnings: ($152,149,000)
Emp.: 705
Fiscal Year-end: 12/31/22
Holding Company; Spine Disorder Treatment Products Developer, Mfr & Distr
N.A.I.C.S.: 551112
Scott Lish *(COO)*
Patrick S. Miles *(Chm & CEO)*

Kelli Howell *(Exec VP-Clinical Strategies)*
Craig Hunsaker *(Gen Counsel & Exec VP-People & Culture)*
Todd Koning *(CFO)*
Dave Sponsel *(Exec VP-Sls)*
Eric Dasso *(Exec VP)*
Ali Shorooghi *(Sr VP)*

Subsidiaries:

Alphatec Spine, Inc.   (1)
5818 El Camino Real, Carlsbad, CA 92008-8816
Tel.: (760) 431-9286
Web Site: http://www.alphatecspine.com
Spine Disorder Treatment Products Developer, Mfr & Distr
N.A.I.C.S.: 339112
Scott Lish *(Sr VP-R&D)*
Craig Hunsaker *(Chief Legal Officer, Gen Counsel, Sec & Exec VP-People & Culture)*
Dave Sponsel *(Exec VP-Sls)*
Kelli Howell *(Sr VP)*
Patrick S. Miles *(CEO)*
Scott Lish *(Sr VP)*
Todd Koning *(CFO)*

Subsidiary (Non-US):

Milverton Ltd.   (2)
Room 910 9/F Austin Tower 22-26 Austin Avenue, Tsim Tsa Tsui, China (Hong Kong)
Tel.: (852) 23678123
Web Site: http://www.milvertonltd.com
Surgical Implant & Medical Supplies Distr
N.A.I.C.S.: 423450

EOS Imaging S.A.   (1)
10 rue Mercoeur, 75011, Paris, France
Tel.: (33) 155256060
Web Site: https://www.eos-imaging.com
Medical Imaging Products
N.A.I.C.S.: 339112
Marie Meynadier *(Founder)*
Eric Maulave *(COO & Gen Mgr)*
Valerie Worrall *(CFO)*

Subsidiary (Non-US):

EOS Imaging Canada   (2)
3630 Montee Saint Hubert, Saint-Hubert, J3Y 4J7, QC, Canada
Tel.: (514) 875-0300
Medical Imaging Products
N.A.I.C.S.: 339112

EOS Imaging GmbH   (2)
Dieselstrasse 12, 64347, Griesheim, Germany
Tel.: (49) 6155 89811 10
Medical Imaging Products
N.A.I.C.S.: 339112

Subsidiary (US):

EOS Imaging Inc.   (2)
1950 Camino Vida Roble, Carlsbad, CA 92008
Tel.: (678) 564-5400
Web Site: http://www.eos-imaging.com
Medical Imaging Products
N.A.I.C.S.: 339112

Subsidiary (Non-US):

EOS image, Inc.   (2)
6525 Boulevard Saint Laurent Suite 200, Montreal, H2S 3S2, QC, Canada
Tel.: (514) 875-0030
Web Site: https://www.eos-imaging.com
Medical Instrument Mfr
N.A.I.C.S.: 339112

SafeOp Surgical, Inc.   (1)
11350 McCormick Rd EP III Ste 1003, Hunt Valley, MD 21031
Web Site: http://www.safeop.net
Surgical Appliance Mfr
N.A.I.C.S.: 339113
Robert Snow *(CMO)*

ALPHATIME ACQUISITION CORP.
500 5th Ave Ste 938, New York, NY 10110
Tel.: (347) 627-0058   Ky
Year Founded: 2021

Assets: $592,570
Liabilities: $577,372
Net Worth: $15,198
Earnings: ($784)
Emp.: 2
Fiscal Year-end: 12/31/22
Investment Management Service
N.A.I.C.S.: 523999
Dajiang Guo (CEO)
Jichuan Yang (CFO)
Xinfeng Feng (Chm)

ALPHAVEST ACQUISITION CORP.
420 Lexington Ave Ste 2446, New York, NY 10170
Tel.: (203) 998-5540   Ky
Web Site:
https://www.alphavestacquisi tion.com
Year Founded: 2022
ATMV—(NASDAQ)
Rev.: $38,228
Assets: $71,192,414
Liabilities: $70,637,871
Net Worth: $554,543
Earnings: ($42,578)
Fiscal Year-end: 12/31/22
Investment Management Service
N.A.I.C.S.: 523999
Pengfei Zheng (Chm)
Yong Yan (CEO)
Song Jing (CFO)

ALPINE 4 HOLDINGS, INC.
2525 E Arizona Biltmore Cir Ste C 237, Phoenix, AZ 85016
Tel.: (480) 702-2431   DE
Web Site: https://www.alpine4.com
Year Founded: 2014
ALPP—(NASDAQ)
Rev.: $33,454,349
Assets: $40,734,183
Liabilities: $49,522,475
Net Worth: ($8,788,292)
Earnings: ($8,049,873)
Emp.: 273
Fiscal Year-end: 12/31/20
Holding Company
N.A.I.C.S.: 551112
Christopher J. Meinerz (CFO)
Kent B. Wilson (Pres, CEO & Sec)
Jeffrey Hail (COO)
Shannon Rigney (VP-Social Media & PR)
Ian Kantrowitz (VP-IR)
Tim Garcia (VP-Corp Sls)
Gerry Garcia (Chm)
SaVonnah Osmanski (Sr VP & Controller)

Subsidiaries:

Alternative Laboratories, LLC   (1)
4740 S Cleveland Ave, Fort Myers, FL 33907
Tel.: (239) 692-9160
Web Site: https://alternativelabs.com
Nutritional Product Mfr
N.A.I.C.S.: 325411

Deluxe Sheet Metal, Inc.   (1)
6661 Lonewolf Dr Ste 100, South Bend, IN 46628
Tel.: (574) 233-5183
Web Site: http://www.deluxesheetmetal.com
Sales Range: $1-9.9 Million
Emp.: 70
Plumbing, Heating & Air-Conditioning Contractors
N.A.I.C.S.: 238220
Kevin Smith (Owner & Pres)
Tom Stull (Project Mgr)
John Walczewski (Project Mgr)
John A. Hudkins (Project Mgr)
John R. Drews (Project Mgr)
Phil La Bounty (Project Mgr)

Identified Technologies, Corp   (1)

6401 Penn Ave Ste 211, East Pittsburgh, PA 15206
Tel.: (412) 307-5174
Web Site: https://www.identifiedtech.com
Geophysical Surveying & Mapping Services
N.A.I.C.S.: 541360

ALPINE ACQUISITION CORP.
10141 N Canyon View Ln, Fountain Hills, AZ 85268
Tel.: (703) 899-1028   DE
Year Founded: 2021
REVE—(NASDAQ)
Investment Services
N.A.I.C.S.: 523999
Elan J. Blutinger (Founder & Chm)
Kim Schaefer (CEO)
Alex Lombardo (CFO)

ALPINE AUTO BROKERS INC.
749 S State St, Salt Lake City, UT 84111
Tel.: (646) 768-8417   NY
Year Founded: 2011
ALTB—(OTCIQ)
Liabilities: $44,444
Net Worth: ($44,444)
Earnings: ($29,740)
Fiscal Year-end: 12/31/22
Automotive Retailer
N.A.I.C.S.: 423110
Zonghan Wu (Chm, CFO, Treas & Sec)
Yufeng Zhang (Pres, CEO & Dir)

ALPINE BANKS OF COLORADO
Tel.: (970) 945-2424   CO
Web Site:
https://www.alpinebank.com
Year Founded: 1980
ALPIB—(OTCQX)
Sales Range: $50-74.9 Million
Emp.: 852
Bank Holding Company
N.A.I.C.S.: 551111
L. Kristine Gardner (Exec VP)
Amanda Miller (Asst VP)
Dan McCaslin (VP)

Subsidiaries:

Alpine Bank   (1)
2200 Grand Ave, Glenwood Springs, CO 81602
Tel.: (970) 945-2424
Web Site: http://www.alpinebank.com
Sales Range: $10-24.9 Million
Emp.: 42
Commercial Banking Services
N.A.I.C.S.: 522110
Seth Ashton (Officer-Wealth Mgmt)
Gena Cooper (VP)
Adam Dentlinger (Sr VP)
Andrew A. Karow (Pres-Grand Junction)
Dan McCaslin (VP)
Amanda Miller (Officer-Wealth Mgmt)
Julia A. Prejs (Officer-Wealth Mgmt)

ALPINE INCOME PROPERTY TRUST, INC.
369 N New York Ave Ste 201, Winter Park, FL 32789
Tel.: (386) 274-2202
Web Site: https://www.alpinereit.com
Year Founded: 2019
PINE—(NYSE)
Rev.: $45,644,000
Assets: $564,560,000
Liabilities: $288,947,000
Net Worth: $275,613,000
Earnings: $2,917,000
Fiscal Year-end: 12/31/23
Real Estate Investment Services
N.A.I.C.S.: 531210
Philip R. Mays (CFO, Treas & Sr VP)
Lisa M. Vorakoun (Interim CFO, Chief Acctg Officer, Treas & Sr VP)

Steven R. Greathouse (Chief Investment Officer & Sr VP-Investments)
Daniel E. Smith (Gen Counsel, Gen Counsel & Gen Counsel)
Andrew C. Richardson (Chm)
Lisa M. Vorakoun (Interim CFO, Chief Acctg Officer, Treas & Sr VP)
Helal Ismail (VP-Investments)
John P. Albright (Pres & CEO)

ALPINE SUMMIT ENERGY PARTNERS, INC.
3322 W End Ave Ste 450, Nashville, TN 37203
Tel.: (346) 264-2900   BC
Web Site:
https://www.alpinesummitener gy.com
ALPSQ—(OTCIQ)
Rev.: $185,625,462
Assets: $344,081,483
Liabilities: $252,578,589
Net Worth: $91,502,894
Earnings: $7,428,135
Fiscal Year-end: 12/31/22
Oil & Gas Exploration
N.A.I.C.S.: 211120
Darren Moulds (CFO)
Craig Perry (Chm, CEO & Dir)
Porter Collins (Dir)
Stephen Schaefer (Dir)
James Russo (Dir)

ALR TECHNOLOGIES INC.
7400 Beaufont Spgs Dr Ste 300, Richmond, VA 23225
Tel.: (804) 554-3500   NV
Web Site: http://www.alrt.com
Year Founded: 1987
ALRT—(OTCIQ)
Rev.: $7,468
Assets: $193,217
Liabilities: $24,505,360
Net Worth: ($24,312,143)
Earnings: ($8,443,315)
Emp.: 6
Fiscal Year-end: 12/31/21
Healthcare Monitoring System Services
N.A.I.C.S.: 621999
Sidney S. Chan (Chm, CEO, CFO & Chief Acctg Officer)
Kent Stoneking (Dir-Clinical Program Dev)

ALSERES PHARMACEUTICALS, INC.
275 Grove St Ste 2-400, Auburndale, MA 02466
Tel.: (617) 419-3289   DE
Web Site: https://www.alseres.com
Year Founded: 1992
ALSE—(OTCIQ)
Sales Range: Less than $1 Million
Emp.: 3
Biotech Pharmaceutical Research & Development Services
N.A.I.C.S.: 325412
Kenneth L. Rice Jr. (CFO & Exec VP-Fin & Admin)

ALT5 SIGMA CORPORATION
325 E Warm Springs Rd Ste 102, Las Vegas, NV 89119
Tel.: (702) 997-5968   MN
Web Site: https://alt5sigma.com
Year Founded: 1983
ALT5—(NASDAQ)
Rev.: $40,022,000
Assets: $15,165,000
Liabilities: $23,841,000
Net Worth: ($8,676,000)
Earnings: ($16,887,000)
Emp.: 161
Fiscal Year-end: 01/01/22
Materials Recovery Facilities

N.A.I.C.S.: 562920
Virland A. Johnson (CFO)
Tony Giordano (Chief Scientific Officer)
Amol Soin (Chief Medical Officer)
Tony Isaac (Chm & Pres)
Peter Tassiopoulos (CEO)

Subsidiaries:

ARCA California   (1)
1920 S Acacia Ave, Compton, CA 90220-4945   (100%)
Tel.: (310) 223-2800
Web Site: http://www.arcarecyclinginc.com
Sales Range: $25-49.9 Million
Emp.: 50
Appliance Recycling Center
N.A.I.C.S.: 562920

ARCA Canada Inc.   (1)
100 Wright Avenue Unit 10, Dartmouth, B3B 1L2, NS, Canada
Web Site: https://www.arcacanada.ca
Sales Range: $25-49.9 Million
Emp.: 10
Household Appliances Recycling
N.A.I.C.S.: 562920

ARCA Minnesota   (1)
7400 Excelsior Blvd, Saint Louis Park, MN 55426   (100%)
Tel.: (952) 930-9000
Web Site: http://www.appliancesmart.com
Sales Range: $25-49.9 Million
Emp.: 100
Appliance Recycling Center & Appliance Retail Store
N.A.I.C.S.: 562920

Alt 5 Sigma Inc.   (1)
420 Lexington Ave Ste 2320, New York, NY 10170
Tel.: (800) 204-6203
Web Site: http://www.alt5sigma.com
Software Solutions
N.A.I.C.S.: 513210
Andre Beauchesne (Chm & CEO)
Paul Goodman (Chief Legal Officer & Sec)

Subsidiary (Domestic):

Wynston Hill Capital LLC   (2)
488 Madison Ave 24th Fl, New York, NY 10022
Tel.: (212) 521-1900
Secondary Market Financing
N.A.I.C.S.: 522299

Customer Connexx, LLC   (1)
325 E Warm Springs Rd Ste 102, Las Vegas, NV 89119
Tel.: (702) 522-7821
Web Site:
https://www.customerconnexx.com
Customer Management Services
N.A.I.C.S.: 541613

GeoTraq Inc.   (1)
1771 E Flamingo Rd Ste 208-A, Las Vegas, NV 89119
Tel.: (702) 757-4080
Web Site: http://geotraq.com
Cellular Transceiver Module Mfr
N.A.I.C.S.: 334220

ALTA EQUIPMENT GROUP INC.
13211 Merriman Rd, Livonia, MI 48150
Tel.: (248) 449-6700   DE
Web Site: https://altg.com
Year Founded: 2018
ALTG—(NYSE)
Rev.: $1,571,800,000
Assets: $1,290,600,000
Liabilities: $1,150,800,000
Net Worth: $139,800,000
Earnings: $9,300,000
Emp.: 2,800
Fiscal Year-end: 12/31/22
Investment Services
N.A.I.C.S.: 523999
Anthony J. Colucci (CFO)
Bob Kohler (Pres-Industrial Grp)
Craig Brubaker (COO)

Alta Equipment Group Inc.—(Continued)

Jeremy Cionca (VP-Information Svcs)
Paul Ivankovics (VP-HR)
Ryan Greenawalt (Chm & CEO)

Subsidiaries:

Alta Equipment Holdings, Inc.   (1)
28775 Beck Rd, Wixom, MI 48393-3416
Tel.: (248) 449-6700
Web Site: http://www.altaequipment.com
Sales Range: $50-74.9 Million
Emp.: 200
Material Handling Equipment Dealer
N.A.I.C.S.: 423830
Ryan Greenawalt (CEO)

Division (Domestic):

Alta Lift Truck Services, Inc.
4716 Talon Ct SE, Grand Rapids, MI 49512
Tel.: (616) 452-2177
Web Site: http://www.altlift.com
Sales Range: $25-49.9 Million
Emp.: 40
Materials Handling Machinery & Equipment
Services
N.A.I.C.S.: 423830

Subsidiary (Domestic):

FlaglerCe Holdings, LLC   (2)
8418 Palm River Rd, Tampa, FL 33619
Tel.: (407) 659-8700
Web Site: http://www.flaglerce.com
Construction Equipment Distr
N.A.I.C.S.: 423830

Liftech Equipment Companies,
Inc.   (2)
6847 Ellicott Dr 2, East Syracuse, NY
13057-1045
Tel.: (315) 463-7333
Web Site: https://materialhandling.altg.com
Sales Range: $125-149.9 Million
Emp.: 160
Industrial Machinery & Equipment Distr
N.A.I.C.S.: 423830
Mike Vaughan (CFO)
Corky McCombie (Mgr-Fleet, Trng & Track-
mobile)

Baron Industries, Inc.   (1)
60 Jonspin Rd, Wilmington, MA 01887
Tel.: (781) 270-4070
Web Site: http://baronind.com
Rev.: $6,200,000
Emp.: 29
Material Handling Equipment Dealer
N.A.I.C.S.: 423830
Alan S. Esbitt (Pres)
Jan Sheehan (Office Mgr)

Burris Equipment Co   (1)
27939 W Concrete Dr, Ingleside, IL 60041
Tel.: (815) 363-4100
Web Site: http://www.burrisequipment.com
Rev.: $5,328,000
Emp.: 8
Construction & Mining, except Oil Well, Ma-
chinery & Equipment Merchant Whslr
N.A.I.C.S.: 423810
Barry Heinrichs (Pres)
David Zenner (VP & Mgr-Rental)
Jeff Glasel (Mgr-Parts)
John Glasel (Mgr-Svc)
Nathan Ryan (Mgr-Svc)
Pete Mirkes (Mgr-Rental)

Northland Industrial Truck Co.
Inc.   (1)
6 Jonspin Rd, Wilmington, MA 01887-4408
Tel.: (978) 658-5900
Web Site: http://www.nitco-lift.com
Sales Range: $25-49.9 Million
Emp.: 500
Industrial Machinery & Equipment
N.A.I.C.S.: 423830
Stephen Q. O'Leary (Owner)
Richard Papalia (VP)
Brian Haaf (Controller)

Peaklogix, Inc.   (1)
14409 Justice Rd, Midlothian, VA 23113-
6875
Tel.: (804) 794-5700
Web Site: https://www.peaklogix.com
Business to Business Electronic Markets
N.A.I.C.S.: 425120

Nancy Green (Mgr-Acct)
Ron Turkaly (Dir-Engrg)
David Armentrout (Dir-Bus Dev)
John Garrett (Mgr-Svc)
Karen Lynch (Dir-Client Svcs)
Sandy Giberson (VP)

ALTABA INC.
140 E 45th St 15A, New York, NY
10017
Tel.: (646) 679-2000   DE
Web Site: http://www.altaba.com
Year Founded: 1994
AABA—(NASDAQ)
Sales Range: $5-14.9 Billion
Closed-End Investment Fund
N.A.I.C.S.: 525990
Thomas J. McInerney (Chm)
DeAnn Fairfield Work (Chief Compli-
ance Officer)
Arthur Chong (Gen Counsel & Sec)
Alexi A. Wellman (CEO)

ALTAIR CORPORATION
350 Barclay Blvd, Lincolnshire, IL
60069-3606
Tel.: (847) 634-9540   DE
Year Founded: 1957
ATCD—(OTCIQ)
Holding Company; Industrial Elec-
tronic Equipment & Control Systems
Mfr
N.A.I.C.S.: 551112
Garry Brainin (Pres & CEO)
Tom Morthorst (CFO)

Subsidiaries:

Hurletron Inc.   (1)
1820 Temple Dr, Libertyville, IL
60048   (100%)
Tel.: (847) 680-7022
Web Site: http://www.hurletron.com
Sales Range: $10-24.9 Million
Emp.: 11
Electronic Automation Controls & Auxiliary
Equipment for Hi Speed Printing Presses
for Publishing & Packaging Indus.
N.A.I.C.S.: 335314
Steve J. Siler (Gen Mgr)

Vacudyne Inc.   (1)
375 E Joe Orr Rd, Chicago Heights, IL
60411-1237   (100%)
Tel.: (708) 757-5200
Web Site: http://www.vacudyne.com
Rev.: $6,000,000
Emp.: 20
Vacuum Conditioning Equipment; Steam &
Gas Sterilizers, Fumigators & Tobacco Con-
ditioners Mfr
N.A.I.C.S.: 333248

Subsidiary (Domestic):

Sterilization Services of Georgia   (2)
6005 Boat Rock Blvd SW, Atlanta, GA
30336-2703   (100%)
Tel.: (404) 344-8423
Web Site: http://www.vacudyne.com
Sales Range: $1-9.9 Million
Emp.: 7
Mfr of Process Control Equipment; Auto-
mated Control Systems; Animal Feed &
Feed Supplements
N.A.I.C.S.: 621999
Garry Brainin (Pres)

Sterilization Services of
Tennessee   (2)
2396 Florida St, Memphis, TN
38109-2529   (100%)
Tel.: (901) 947-2217
Web Site: http://www.sterilization-
services.com
Sales Range: $1-9.9 Million
Emp.: 7
Mfr of Process Control Equipment, Auto-
mated Control Systems, Animal Feed &
Feed Supplements
N.A.I.C.S.: 561990
Jodie Jefferson (Plant Mgr)

Sterilization Services of Virginia   (2)

5674 Eastport Blvd, Richmond, VA 23231-
4442
Tel.: (804) 236-1652
Web Site: http://www.sterilization-
services.com
Sales Range: $10-24.9 Million
Emp.: 7
Mfr of Process Control Equipment; Auto-
mated Control Systems; Animal Feed &
Feed Supplements
N.A.I.C.S.: 561499

ALTAIR ENGINEERING, INC.
1820 E Big Beaver Rd, Troy, MI
48083
Tel.: (248) 614-2400   DE
Web Site: https://www.altair.com
Year Founded: 1985
ALTR—(NASDAQ)
Rev.: $612,701,000
Assets: $1,363,493,000
Liabilities: $652,162,000
Net Worth: $711,331,000
Earnings: ($8,926,000)
Emp.: 3,200
Fiscal Year-end: 12/31/23
Product Design Consulting & Tech-
nology Services; Software Developer
N.A.I.C.S.: 513210
James R. Scapa (Co-Founder, Chm
& CEO)
Nelson Dias (Chief Revenue Officer)
Jeff Marraccini (Chief Information Se-
curity Officer)
Stephanie Buckner (COO)
Amy Messano (CMO)
Raoul Maitra (Chief Legal Officer)
Gilma Saravia (Chief People Officer)
Brian Gayle (Chief Acctg Officer)
Ravi Kunju (Chief Strategy Officer &
Chief Product Officer)

Subsidiaries:

AD Solutions S.R.L.   (1)
Via Leonardo Da Vinci 4, 30020, Torre di
Mosto, VE, Italy
Tel.: (39) 0421303006
Web Site: https://www.ad-solutions.it
Aluminium Product Mfr & Distr
N.A.I.C.S.: 331313

Altair Engineering (Pty.) Ltd.   (1)
32 Techno Avenue Technopark, Stellenbo-
sch, 7600, Western Cape, South Africa
Tel.: (27) 211409234
Engineering Consultancy Services
N.A.I.C.S.: 541330

Altair Engineering (Singapore) Ptd.
Ltd.   (1)
8 Boon Lay Way 05-109 Tradehub 21, Sin-
gapore, 609966, Singapore
Tel.: (65) 64650877
Web Site: https://altairengg.com
Technical Consulting Services
N.A.I.C.S.: 541690

Altair Engineering AB   (1)
Bror Nilssons Gata 4, 417 55, Gothenburg,
Sweden
Tel.: (46) 464602800
Engineering Consultancy Services
N.A.I.C.S.: 541330

Altair Engineering Canada, Ltd.   (1)
550 Beaumont Ave Suite 502, Monreal,
Montreal, H3N 1V1, QC, Canada
Tel.: (416) 447-6463
Engineering Consultancy Services
N.A.I.C.S.: 541330

Altair Engineering France S.A.S.   (1)
5/10 Rue de la Renaissance Centre d Af-
faires Bat C, 92 184, Antony, CEDEX,
France
Tel.: (33) 141330990
Web Site: https://altairengineering.fr
Engineering Consultancy Services
N.A.I.C.S.: 541330

Altair Engineering France, Sarl   (1)
5/10 rue de la Renaissance Centre d Affaires Bat C, 92184, Antony, Cedex, France
Tel.: (33) 141330990
Web Site: https://altairengineering.fr

Software Publishing Services
N.A.I.C.S.: 513210

Altair Engineering GmbH   (1)
Reininghausstrasse 13 A, 8020, Graz, Aus-
tria
Tel.: (43) 316908811
Web Site: http://www.altair.de
Software Publishing Services
N.A.I.C.S.: 513210

Altair Engineering India Pvt. Ltd.   (1)
SVK Towers 6th Floor Plot No A-24/25, Tiru
Vi-Ka Industrial Estate Guindy, Chennai,
600032, India
Tel.: (91) 4449014050
Software Publishing Services
N.A.I.C.S.: 513210

Altair Engineering Israel Ltd.   (1)
Ha-Tsmikha St 1 High-Tech Park North,
Yokneam, 2066733, Israel
Tel.: (972) 765670590
Electronic Equipment Mfr & Distr
N.A.I.C.S.: 335311

Altair Engineering Sdn. Bhd.   (1)
41-13 Level 41 Q Sentral Jalan Stesen
Sentral 2, Kuala Lumpur Sentral, 50470,
Kuala Lumpur, Malaysia
Tel.: (60) 327427890
Engineering Consultancy Services
N.A.I.C.S.: 541330

Altair Software and Services S.L.   (1)
Avnida Diagonal 682 Piso 9, 08034, Barce-
lona, Spain
Tel.: (34) 936338145
Engineering Consultancy Services
N.A.I.C.S.: 541330

Datawatch Corporation   (1)
4 Crosby Dr, Bedford, MA 01730
Tel.: (978) 441-2200
Web Site: http://www.datawatch.com
Sales Range: $25-49.9 Million
Report Mining Software Mfr
N.A.I.C.S.: 513210

Subsidiary (Non-US):

Datawatch AB   (2)
World Trade Center, Klarabergsviadukten
70, 111 87, Stockholm, Sweden
Tel.: (46) 853480480
Web Site: http://www.panopticon.com
Data Visualization Software Developer
N.A.I.C.S.: 513210

Datawatch International Limited   (2)
Siena Court Broadway, Maidenhead, SL6
1NJ, Berks, United Kingdom
Tel.: (44) 8453623270
Product Design Consulting & Technology
Services, Software Developer
N.A.I.C.S.: 334610

Subsidiary (Non-US):

Datawatch Analytics (Singapore) Pte
Ltd.   (3)
18 Boon Lay Way 05-109, Tradehub 21,
Singapore, 609966, Singapore   (100%)
Tel.: (65) 64650877
Emp.: 10
Software Whslr
N.A.I.C.S.: 423430
Karl Mouantri (Mng Dir)

Runtime Design Automation   (1)
2560 Mission College Blvd Ste 130, Santa
Clara, CA 95054
Tel.: (408) 492-0940
Engineering Services
N.A.I.C.S.: 541330

Univa Corporation   (1)
2300 N Barrington Rd Ste 400, Hoffman
Estates, IL 60169
Tel.: (647) 478-5901
Web Site: http://www.univa.com
Software Publisher
N.A.I.C.S.: 513210
Fritz Ferstl (CTO)

ALTAIR INTERNATIONAL
CORP.
322 N Shore Dr Bldg 1B Ste 200,
Pittsburgh, PA 15212
Tel.: (412) 770-3140   NV

Web Site:
https://www.altairinternational
corp.com
Year Founded: 2012
ATAO—(OTCQB)
Assets: $10,798
Liabilities: $193,428
Net Worth: ($182,630)
Earnings: ($398,885)
Fiscal Year-end: 03/31/24
Sports Related Products Mfr & Distr
N.A.I.C.S.: 339920
Leonard Lovallo (Pres & CEO)

ALTC ACQUISITION CORP.
640 5th Ave 12th Fl, New York, NY
10019
Tel.: (212) 380-7500   DE
Year Founded: 2021
ALCC—(NYSE)
Rev.: $7,209,610
Assets: $510,138,267
Liabilities: $523,941,015
Net Worth: ($13,802,748)
Earnings: $3,925,770
Emp.: 2
Fiscal Year-end: 12/31/22
Investment Services
N.A.I.C.S.: 523999
Michael Klei (Chm, Pres & CEO)
Jay Taragin (CFO)
Sam Altman (Exec Officer)

ALTENERGY ACQUISITION CORP.
600 Lexington Ave 9th Fl, New York,
NY 10022
Tel.: (203) 299-1400   DE
Web Site:
https://www.altenergyacquisi
tion.com
Year Founded: 2021
AEAE—(NASDAQ)
Rev.: $15,967,559
Assets: $237,965,034
Liabilities: $246,507,824
Net Worth: ($8,542,790)
Earnings: $13,805,233
Emp.: 3
Fiscal Year-end: 12/31/22
Investment Services
N.A.I.C.S.: 523999
Russell M. Stidolph (Chm & CEO)
Jonathan Darnell (CFO)

ALTERNUS CLEAN ENERGY INC.
360 Kingsley Park Dr Ste 250, Fort
Mill, SC 29715   DE
Web Site: https://alternusce.com
Year Founded: 2017
ALCE—(NASDAQ)
Rev.: $3,286,031
Assets: $236,522,122
Liabilities: $243,445,889
Net Worth: ($6,923,767)
Earnings: $59,955
Emp.: 2
Fiscal Year-end: 12/31/22
Power Generation Services
N.A.I.C.S.: 221114
Taliesin Durant (Chief Legal Officer)
Gita Shah (Chief Sustainability Officer)
Vincent Browne (Chm & CEO)
David Farrell (Chief Comml Officer)
Gary Swan (Chief Technical Officer)
Larry Farrell (CIO)

Subsidiaries:

Alternus Energy Group Plc   (1)
Ste 9/10 Plz 212, Blanchardstown Corporate Park 2, Dublin, D15 R504, Ireland
Tel.: (353) 003531907344
Power Generation Services
N.A.I.C.S.: 221118

ALTERNUS ENERGY, INC.
1 World Trade Ctr Ste 8500, New
York, NY 10007
Tel.: (212) 220-7434
Web Site:
http://www.alternusenergy.com
ALTN—(OTCIQ)
Rev.: $2,585,568
Assets: $45,613,562
Liabilities: $41,735,401
Net Worth: $3,878,161
Earnings: ($3,028,918)
Emp.; 6
Fiscal Year-end: 12/31/19
Electric Power Distribution Services
N.A.I.C.S.: 221114
Taliesin Durant (Gen Counsel & Sec)
Gita Shah (Mgr-Strategic Plng)
Vincent Browne (Chm, Pres & CEO)
Joseph E. Duey (CFO & Treas)
Taliesin Durant (Gen Counsel & Sec)
Stefano Stavrogiannis (Mgr-Italian Ops)
David Farrell (Chief Comml Officer)

ALTEX INDUSTRIES, INC.
700 Colorado Blvd Ste 273, Denver,
CO 80206-4084
Tel.: (303) 265-9312   DE
Year Founded: 1985
ALTX—(OTCIQ)
Rev.: $23,000
Assets: $2,726,000
Liabilities: $1,180,000
Net Worth: $1,546,000
Earnings: $437,000
Emp.: 1
Fiscal Year-end: 09/30/24
Holding Company; Oil & Gas Exploration & Production; Oil Development & Oil Field Services; Minerals Exploration & Mining
N.A.I.C.S.: 551112
Steven H. Cardin (Chm, CEO, CFO & Principal Acctg Officer)

ALTI GLOBAL, INC.
520 Madison Ave 26th Fl, New York,
NY 10022
Tel.: (212) 396-5900   DE
Web Site: https://alti-global.com
ALTI—(NASDAQ)
Rev.: $17,637,665
Assets: $350,069,379
Liabilities: $376,892,547
Net Worth: ($26,823,168)
Earnings: $8,779,014
Emp.: 151
Fiscal Year-end: 12/31/22
Offices of Other Holding Companies
N.A.I.C.S.: 551112
Michael Glenn Tiedemann (CEO)
Timothy F. Keaney (Chm)
Nancy Ann Curtin (Chief Investment Officer-Global)
Reid Parmelee (Interim CFO)
Beth Michelson (Sr Mng Dir)
Kevin Moran (Pres & COO)
Nancy Curtin (Chief Investment Officer)
Jed Emerson (Chief Impact Officer)
Colleen Graham (Corp Counsel-Global)
Laurie Jelenek (Chief Administration Officer-Asset Mgmt)
Spiros Maliagros (Head-Alternatives)
Craig Smith (Chm-Global Wealth Mgmt)
Ali Trauttmansdorff (Chief HR Officer)
Claire Verdirame (CMO)
Rob Weeber (Head-Intl Client Advisory)

Subsidiaries:

Tiedemann Wealth Management,
LLC   (1)

520 Madison Ave 26th Fl, New York, NY
10022
Tel.: (212) 396-5900
Web Site:
http://www.tiedemannadvisors.com
Investment, Wealth Management & Advisory Services
N.A.I.C.S.: 523940
Michael Glenn Tiedemann (CEO)
Craig Smith (Pres)
Stephen Aucamp (Mng Dir)
Kristen Bauer (Mng Dir)
James Bertles (Mng Dir)
Julie Dunnington (CMO)
Maura Fleming (Sr VP)
Jill Shipley (Head-Family Governance & Education)
Jed Emerson (Mng Dir-Impact Investing)

Subsidiary (Domestic):

Envoi, LLC   (2)
4350 Baker Rd, Minnetonka, MN 55343
Tel.: (952) 358-6260
Web Site: http://www.envoillc.com
Financial Investment Activities
N.A.I.C.S.: 523999
Elizabeth Gustafson (VP)
Ryan Steensland (Principal)

The Threshold Group, LLC   (2)
3025 Harborview Dr, Gig Harbor, WA 98335
Tel.: (253) 851-4300
Administrative Management & General Management Consulting Services
N.A.I.C.S.: 541611

ALTICE USA, INC.
1 Court Sq, Long Island City, NY
11101
Tel.: (516) 803-2300   DE
Web Site: https://www.alticeusa.com
Year Founded: 1973
ATUS—(NYSE)
Rev.: $9,237,064,000
Assets: $31,923,616,000
Liabilities: $32,358,034,000
Net Worth: ($434,418,000)
Earnings: $53,198,000
Emp.: 10,600
Fiscal Year-end: 12/31/23
Holding Company; Cable Television & Media Products & Services
N.A.I.C.S.: 551112
Maria Bruzzese (Chief Acctg Officer)
Marc Sirota (CFO)
Colleen Schmidt (Exec VP-HR)
Michael E. Olsen (Chief Corp Responsibility Officer & Corp Counsel)
Philippe Le May (CTO)
Alexandre Fonseca (Chm)
Patrick Drahi (Founder)
Yossi Benchetrit (Chief Procurement & Programming Officer)
Matthew Grover (Exec VP-Business Services & Dir-Sls Plng)
Dennis Mathew (CEO)
Kai W. Kasigurán (Principal Acctg Officer, VP & Controller)
Leroy Williams (Chief Growth Officer)
David Williams (Chief Revenue Officer)
Shuvankar Roy (Chief Customer Experience Officer)
Dennis Mathew (Chm & CEO)

Subsidiaries:

Audience Partners, LLC   (1)
414 Commerce Dr Ste 100, Fort Washington, PA 19034
Tel.: (484) 928-1010
Web Site: http://www.audiencepartners.com
Business Support Services
N.A.I.C.S.: 561499

Cable Systems, Inc.   (1)
178 Turk Hill Park, Fairport, NY 14450
Tel.: (315) 986-4823
Web Site: https://cablesysinc.com
Emp.: 1,989
Telecommunication Servicesb
N.A.I.C.S.: 517810
David S. Lanni (Pres)

Cablevision Lightpath, LLC   (1)
1111 Stewart Ave, Bethpage, NY 11714
Web Site: https://www.lightpathfiber.com
Network Upgrade Services
N.A.I.C.S.: 541512

Cablevision Systems Corporation   (1)
1111 Stewart Ave, Bethpage, NY
11714   (70%)
Tel.: (516) 803-2300
Web Site: http://www.alticeusa.com
Holding Company; Cable Television Transmission Services
N.A.I.C.S.: 551112

Subsidiary (Domestic):

CSC Holdings, LLC   (2)
1111 Stewart Ave, Bethpage, NY
11714   (100%)
Tel.: (516) 803-2300
Web Site: http://www.alticeusa.com
Holding Company; Cable Television Programming & Transmission Services
N.A.I.C.S.: 551112

Subsidiary (Domestic):

CSC Transport Inc.   (3)
8000 Republic Airport Hangar 5,
Farmingdale, NY 11735
Tel.: (516) 694-3023
Business Aviation Services
N.A.I.C.S.: 488190

Cablevision Systems Westchester Corporation   (3)
6 Executive Plz, Yonkers, NY 10701-6802
Tel.: (914) 378-8960
Internet Access & Digital Cable Tv Services
N.A.I.C.S.: 516210

Cablevision of Monmouth, Inc.   (3)
1501 18th Ave, Belmar, NJ 07719-3721
Tel.: (732) 681-8222
Cable & Other Pay Television Services
N.A.I.C.S.: 516210

Joint Venture (Domestic):

Canoe Ventures LLC   (3)
200 Union Blvd Ste 590, Lakewood, CO
80228
Tel.: (212) 364-3600
Web Site: https://www.canoeventures.com
Television Advertising Services
N.A.I.C.S.: 541890
Tom Huber (COO)
Joel Hassell (CEO)
Chris Pizzurro (Sr VP-Sls & Mktg-Global)
Ed Knudson (Chief Revenue Officer)
Sid Gregory (CTO)
David Porter (Sr VP & Gen Mgr-Addressable)

Subsidiary (Domestic):

Newsday LLC   (3)
6 Corporate Center Dr, Melville, NY
11747-4250   (97%)
Tel.: (631) 843-4725
Web Site: http://www.newsday.com
Holding Company; Newspaper & Online Media Publisher
N.A.I.C.S.: 551112
Debby Krenek (Publr)
Pat Dolan (Owner & Pres)
Robert Levin (Asst Mng Dir)
Rochell Sleets (Mng Editor)

Unit (Domestic):

AM New York   (4)
240 W 35th St 9th Fl, New York, NY 10001
Tel.: (646) 293-9499
Web Site: http://www.amny.com
Daily Newspaper Publisher
N.A.I.C.S.: 513110
Meghan Giannotta (Editor)
Michael Israel (Mgr-Sales)

Subsidiary (Domestic):

News 12 New Jersey, Inc.   (4)
450 Raritan Center Pkwy, Edison, NJ
08837
Tel.: (732) 346-3333
Web Site: http://newjersey.news12.com
Cable TV Services
N.A.I.C.S.: 516210

Altice USA, Inc.—(Continued)

Cequel Communications Holdings I, LLC (1)
1111 Stewart Ave, Bethpage, NY 11714
Tel.: (516) 803-2300
Web Site: https://www.optimum.com
Holding Company; Cable Television Distr
N.A.I.C.S.: 551112

Subsidiary (Domestic):

Cequel Communications, LLC (2)
201 Quality Cir, College Station, TX
77845 (100%)
Tel.: (888) 822-5151
Web Site: https://www.optimum.com
Digital Cable TV, High-Speed Internet &
Home Security Services
N.A.I.C.S.: 517111

Cheddar Inc. (1)
130 E 75th St Apt 8B, New York, NY 10004
Tel.: (917) 267-2494
Web Site: http://www.cheddar.com
Post-Cable Network Company
N.A.I.C.S.: 518210
Devin Emery (VP)

Subsidiary (Domestic):

RateMyProfessors.com, LLC (2)
1515 Broadway, New York, NY 10036
Tel.: (212) 654-7763
Web Site: http://www.ratemyprofessors.com
Online Educational Support Services
N.A.I.C.S.: 611710
Will De Santis (Pres)

Classic Communications, Inc. (1)
38 Mechanic St Ste 101, Foxboro, MA
02035
Tel.: (508) 698-6810
Web Site: https://www.classic-communications.com
Event Management Services
N.A.I.C.S.: 711310
Marty Bauman (Owner & Pres)
Meg Rivett (Dir-Ops)
Abby Tavilla (Dir-Client Svcs)

Service Electric Cable T.V. of New Jersey, Inc. (1)
320 Sparta Ave, Sparta, NJ 07871
Tel.: (570) 773-2585
Web Site: http://www.secable.com
Cable Television Services
N.A.I.C.S.: 516210

ALTIGEN COMMUNICATIONS, INC.
670 N McCarthy Blvd Ste 200, Milpitas, CA 95035
Tel.: (408) 597-9000 DE
Web Site: https://www.altigen.com
Year Founded: 1994
ATGN—(OTCQB)
Rev.: $13,681,000
Assets: $13,921,000
Liabilities: $2,583,000
Net Worth: $11,338,000
Earnings: ($3,324,000)
Emp.: 69
Fiscal Year-end: 09/30/23
Telephone Apparatus Manufacturing
N.A.I.C.S.: 334210
Mike Plumer (VP-Sls)
Shirley Sun (VP-R&D)
Paul Fullman (VP-Skype-Bus Solutions)
Jeremiah J. Fleming (Chm, Pres & CEO)

ALTIMETER GROWTH CORP.
2550 Sand Hill Rd Ste 150, Menlo
Park, CA 94025
Tel.: (650) 549-9145 Ky
Year Founded: 2020
AGCB—(NASDAQ)
Rev.: $28,148
Assets: $451,226,401
Liabilities: $466,610,671
Net Worth: ($15,384,270)
Earnings: ($1,099,494)

Emp.: 2
Fiscal Year-end: 12/31/21
Investment Services
N.A.I.C.S.: 523999
Hab Siam (Gen Counsel)
Brad Gerstner (Chm, Pres & CEO)

ALTIMMUNE, INC
910 Clopper Rd Ste 201 S, Gaithersburg, MD 20878
Tel.: (240) 654-1450 DE
Web Site:
https://www.altimmune.com
Year Founded: 1997
ALT—(NASDAQ)
Rev.: $2,870,000
Assets: $206,928,000
Liabilities: $21,635,000
Net Worth: $185,293,000
Earnings: ($84,713,000)
Emp.: 52
Fiscal Year-end: 12/31/22
Holding Company
N.A.I.C.S.: 551112
Mitchel B. Sayare (Chm)
Vipin K. Garg (Pres & CEO)
Scot Roberts (Chief Scientific Officer)
M. Scott Harris (Chief Medical Officer)
Bertrand Georges (CTO)
Sarah K. Browne (VP)
Randy Brown (VP)
Tony Blandin (VP)
Raymond Jordt (Chief Bus Officer)
Richard Eisenstadt (CFO)
Vyjayanthi Krishnan (VP)
Dakshina Reddy (VP)
Karen Smith (VP)
Jay Yang (VP)
Andrew Shutterly (Acting CFO, Principal Acctg Officer & Controller)

Subsidiaries:

PharmAthene US Corporation (1)
1 Park Pl Ste 450, Annapolis, MD 21401
Tel.: (410) 269-2600
Web Site: http://www.pharmathene.com
Sales Range: $75-99.9 Million
Emp.: 200
Biodefense Products & Services
N.A.I.C.S.: 325412

ALTISOURCE ASSET MANAGEMENT CORPORATION
5100 Tamarind Reef, Christiansted,
VI 00820
Tel.: (704) 275-9113 VI
Web Site:
https://www.altisourceamc.com
Year Founded: 2012
AAMC—(NYSEAMEX)
Rev.: $4,965,000
Assets: $117,647,000
Liabilities: $207,537,000
Net Worth: ($89,890,000)
Earnings: ($15,934,000)
Emp.: 55
Fiscal Year-end: 12/31/22
Real Estate Asset Management Services
N.A.I.C.S.: 531390
William Charles Erbey (Chm & CEO)
Richard G. Rodick (CFO)
Stephen H. Gray (Gen Counsel & Sec)

ALTITUDE ACQUISITION CORP.
400 Perimeter Ctr Ter Ste 151, Atlanta, GA 30346
Web Site: https://www.altitudeac.com
Year Founded: 2020 DE
ALTUU—(NASDAQ)
Rev.: $12,720,571
Assets: $16,977,371
Liabilities: $35,551,191
Net Worth: ($18,573,820)

Earnings: $9,342,644
Emp.: 2
Fiscal Year-end: 12/31/22
Investment Services
N.A.I.C.S.: 523999
Thomas Breitling (Vice Chm)
Gary Teplis (Pres & CEO)
Farris Griggs (CFO)
Adeel Rouf (Sr VP-Corp Fin)

ALTITUDE INTERNATIONAL HOLDINGS, INC.
4500 SE Pine Valley St, Port Saint
Lucie, FL 34952
Tel.: (772) 323-0625 NY
Web Site: https://www.altdintl.com
Year Founded: 1994
ALTD—(OTCIQ)
Rev.: $12,209,237
Assets: $101,017,623
Liabilities: $77,901,449
Net Worth: $23,116,174
Earnings: ($8,625,824)
Emp.: 70
Fiscal Year-end: 12/31/22
Workforce Management Services
N.A.I.C.S.: 541618
Greg Breunich (Chm, CEO & CFO)
Gabe Jaramillo (Sr Exec VP, Exec VP & Dir-Tennis Trng)
Amy Cheli (Controller)

ALTO INGREDIENTS, INC.
1300 S 2nd St, Pekin, IL 61554
Tel.: (916) 403-2123 DE
Web Site:
https://www.altoingredients.com
Year Founded: 2003
ALTO—(NASDAQ)
Rev.: $1,335,621,000
Assets: $478,321,000
Liabilities: $170,232,000
Net Worth: $308,089,000
Earnings: ($41,597,000)
Emp.: 439
Fiscal Year-end: 12/31/22
Methanol Mfr
N.A.I.C.S.: 325199
William L. Jones (Founder & Chm)
Bryon T. McGregor (Pres & CEO)
Jim Sneed (Chief Comml Officer)
Todd E. Benton (COO)
Auste Graham (Gen Counsel)
Robert R. Olander (CFO)

Subsidiaries:

Kinergy Marketing LLC (1)
424 NE Hazelfern Pl, Portland, OR 97232
Tel.: (503) 819-8125
Emp.: 2
Marketing Consulting Services
N.A.I.C.S.: 541613

PE Op Co. (1)
400 Capital Mall Ste 2060, Sacramento, CA
95814
Tel.: (916) 403-2123
Renewable Fuel Mfr
N.A.I.C.S.: 324199

Pacific Ag. Products, LLC (1)
31470 Avenue 12, Madera, CA 93638-8363
Tel.: (559) 674-6607
Marketing Consulting Services
N.A.I.C.S.: 541613

Pacific Ethanol Aurora East, LLC (1)
1205 S O Rd, Aurora, NE 68818 (100%)
Tel.: (402) 694-3655
Web Site: http://www.pacificethanol.net
Fuel Grade Ethanol & Dried Grains Producer
N.A.I.C.S.: 325193

Pacific Ethanol Central, LLC (1)
1300 S 2nd St, Pekin, IL 61554
Tel.: (309) 347-9200
Sales Range: $800-899.9 Million
Emp.: 348
Corn-Based Ethanol Mfr & Marketer
N.A.I.C.S.: 325193

Hunter McCormack (Plant Mgr)
Steve Antonacci (Mgr-Environmental)

Subsidiary (Domestic):

Illinois Corn Processing Holdings Inc. (2)
1301 S Frnt St, Pekin, IL 61554
Tel.: (309) 353-3990
Investment Management Service
N.A.I.C.S.: 551112

Subsidiary (Domestic):

Illinois Corn Processing, LLC (3)
1301 S Front St, Pekin, IL 61554
Tel.: (309) 353-3990
Alcoholic Beverages Mfr
N.A.I.C.S.: 722410
Charles Puent (Production Mgr)

Pacific Ethanol Columbia, LLC (1)
71335 Rail Loop Dr, Boardman, OR 97818
Tel.: (541) 481-2716
Emp.: 31
Renewable Fuel Mfr
N.A.I.C.S.: 324199
Wanliya Bittinger (Office Mgr)

Pacific Ethanol Madera LLC (1)
31470 Ave 12, Madera, CA 93638-8363
Tel.: (559) 662-0553
Renewable Fuel Mfr
N.A.I.C.S.: 324199
Brian Fish (Mgr-Production)

Pacific Ethanol Magic Valley, LLC (1)
2600 Washington Ave, Burley, ID 83318-5109
Tel.: (208) 678-9684
Renewable Fuel Mfr
N.A.I.C.S.: 324199

Pacific Ethanol Pekin, Inc. (1)
1300 S 2nd St, Pekin, IL 61554
Tel.: (309) 347-9200
Methanol Mfr
N.A.I.C.S.: 325193

ALTO NEUROSCIENCE, INC.
369 S San Antonio Rd, Los Altos, CA
94022
Tel.: (650) 200-0412 DE
Web Site:
https://www.altoneuroscience.com
Year Founded: 2019
ANRO—(NYSE)
Rev.: $1,504,000
Assets: $86,628,000
Liabilities: $158,300,000
Not Worth: ($71,672,000)
Earnings: ($36,305,000)
Emp.: 63
Fiscal Year-end: 12/31/23
Pharmaceutical Product Mfr & Distr
N.A.I.C.S.: 325412
Michael C. Hanley (COO)

ALTRIA GROUP, INC.
Tel.: (804) 484-8838 VA
Web Site: https://www.altria.com
Year Founded: 1920
MO—(NYSE)
Rev.: $24,483,000,000
Assets: $38,570,000,000
Liabilities: $42,060,000,000
Not Worth: ($3,400,000,000)
Earnings: $8,130,000,000
Emp.: 6,400
Fiscal Year-end: 12/31/23
Tobacco Mfr
N.A.I.C.S.: 551112
Steven D'Ambrosia (VP & Controller)
Charles N. Whitaker (Chief Compliance Officer, Chief HR Officer & Sr VP)
Daniel J. Bryant (Treas & VP)
Murray R. Garnick (Gen Counsel)
Sal Mancuso (CFO & Exec VP)
Bob McCarter (Gen Counsel & Exec VP)
William F. Gifford Jr. (CEO)

Heather Newman (Chief Strategy Officer, Chief Growth Officer & Sr VP)
Jody L. Begley (COO & Exec VP)
W. Hildebrandt Surgner Jr. (VP)

Subsidiaries:

Altria Client Services Inc. **(1)**
6601 W Broad St, Richmond, VA 23230
Tel.: (804) 274-2000
Web Site: https://www.altria.com
General Administrative, Financial, Technical, Legal & Regulatory Support Services
N.A.I.C.S.: 561110
Jennifer Hunter (Sr VP-Corp Citizenship)
Todd Walker (Sr VP-Govt Affairs)
Paige Magness (Sr VP-Regulatory Affairs)
Maria Gogova (Chief Scientific Officer & VP)
Mac Livingston (VP-IR)
Bob McCarter (Sr VP)
Michael Thorne-Begland (Chief Inclusion, Diversity & Equity Officer & VP)
Megan Witherspoon (VP-Comm)

Altria Consumer Engagement Services Inc. **(1)**
6601 W Broad St, Richmond, VA 23230-1723
Tel.: (804) 274-2000
Tobacco & Wine Marketing Services
N.A.I.C.S.: 541613

F.W. Rickard Seeds, Inc. **(1)**
4274 Colby Rd, Winchester, KY 40391
Tel.: (859) 744-4191
Web Site: http://www.rickardseed.com
Seed Producer & Distr
N.A.I.C.S.: 111910

International Wine & Spirits Ltd. **(1)**
14111 NE 145th St, Woodinville, WA 98072-1976 **(100%)**
Tel.: (425) 488-1133
Web Site: http://www.ste-michelle.com
Sales Range: $500-549.9 Million
Emp.: 1,500
Holding Company; Wineries & Wine Distr
N.A.I.C.S.: 551112

John Middleton Inc. **(1)**
475 N Lewis Rd, Limerick, PA 19468
Tel.: (610) 265-1400
Web Site: http://www.johnmiddletonco.com
Sales Range: $300-349.9 Million
Emp.: 550
Smoking Tobacco
N.A.I.C.S.: 312230

National Smokeless Tobacco Company Ltd. **(1)**
319-1000 St Jean Boulevard, Pointe-Claire, H9R 5P1, QC, Canada
Tel.: (514) 697-5577
Sales Range: $25-49.9 Million
Emp.: 15
Tobacco Products Whslr
N.A.I.C.S.: 424940
Jean Francois Purcotte (Pres)

Philip Morris Capital Corp. **(1)**
6601 W Broad St, Richmond, VA 23230-1723 **(100%)**
Tel.: (203) 348-1350
Web Site:
http://www.philipmorriscapitalcorp.com
Emp.: 56
Leased Asset Investment Management Services
N.A.I.C.S.: 523940

Philip Morris USA Inc. **(1)**
6601 W Broad St, Richmond, VA 23230
Tel.: (804) 274-2200
Web Site: http://www.philipmorrisusa.com
Cigarette Mfr & Whslr
N.A.I.C.S.: 312230
Jon Moore (Pres & CEO)
Sheila Freeman (VP-Mfg)
Michael Manson (VP-Heated Tobacco Products)
Michael Brace (VP & Gen Mgr-Marlboro)

Unit (Domestic):

Philip Morris USA **(2)**
4001 Commerce Rd, Richmond, VA 23234-2267
Tel.: (804) 274-2000
Web Site: http://www.altria.com

Sales Range: $300-349.9 Million
Emp.: 150
Mfr of Cigarettes
N.A.I.C.S.: 312230

Subsidiary (Domestic):

U.S. Smokeless Tobacco Company, LLC **(2)**
6601 W Broad St, Richmond, VA 23230
Tel.: (804) 274-2200
Web Site: http://www.ussmokeless.com
Smokeless Tobacco Products Mfr & Distr
N.A.I.C.S.: 312230

Profigen do Brazil LDTA **(1)**
Estrada Do Couto Km 03, Santa Cruz do Sul, 96800-000, Rio Grande Do Sul, Brazil
Tel.: (55) 5130561400
Web Site: https://www.profigen.com.br
Tobacco Product Merchants
N.A.I.C.S.: 424940

Ste. Michelle Wine Estates, LLC **(1)**
14111 NE 145th St, Woodinville, WA 98072
Tel.: (425) 488-1133
Web Site: http://www.ste-michelle.com
Wineries
N.A.I.C.S.: 312130
Jim Mortensen (Pres & CEO)
Shawn W. Conway (CEO)

Subsidiary (Domestic):

Patz & Hall Wine Company **(2)**
21200 8th St E, Sonoma, CA 95476
Tel.: (707) 265-7700
Web Site: http://www.patzhall.com
Wineries
N.A.I.C.S.: 312130
Anne Moses (Co-Founder)
James Hall (Co-Founder)

U.S. Smokeless Tobacco Manufacturing Company LLC **(1)**
11601 Copenhagen Ct, Franklin Park, IL 60131-1301
Tel.: (847) 957-8200
Tobacco Products Whslr
N.A.I.C.S.: 424940

ALTRUST FINANCIAL SERVICES, INC.
1912 Cherokee Ave SW, Cullman, AL 35055
Tel.: (256) 737-7000   **AL**
Web Site:
http://www.peoplesbankal.com
Year Founded: 1985
ATFS—(OTCIQ)
Bank Holding Company
N.A.I.C.S.: 551111
James Robin Cummings (CEO)
Tim Williams (Pres)
Jim Kinney (Chief Information Officer, COO & Exec VP)
David Patterson (CFO & Exec VP)

Subsidiaries:

Peoples Bank of Alabama **(1)**
1912 Cherokee Ave SW, Cullman, AL 35055
Tel.: (256) 737-7000
Web Site: http://www.peoplesbankal.com
Emp.: 75
Banking Services
N.A.I.C.S.: 522110
James Robin Cummings (CEO)
Tim Williams (Pres)

ALTUS POWER, INC.
2200 Atlantic St Fl 6, Stamford, CT 06902
Tel.: (203) 698-0090
Web Site:
https://www.altuspower.com
Year Founded: 2009
AMPS—(NYSE)
Rev.: $101,163,000
Assets: $1,376,888,000
Liabilities: $931,962,000
Net Worth: $444,926,000
Earnings: $55,437,000
Emp.: 59

Fiscal Year-end: 12/31/22
Investment Advice
N.A.I.C.S.: 523940
Gregg J. Felton (Co-Founder & CEO)
Lars R. Norell (Co-Founder)
Dan Alcombright (Chief Platform Officer)
Julia Sears (Chief Digital Officer)

ALUF HOLDINGS, INC.
4801 S University Dr Ste 227, Fort Lauderdale, FL 33328   **FL**
Web Site: https://www.aluf.com
Year Founded: 1977
AHIX—(OTCIQ)
Offices of Other Holding Companies
N.A.I.C.S.: 551112
Teresa McWilliams (Interim CEO, CFO & Sec)
Donald C. Bennett (Chm)
Ben Zandi (Vice Chm)

Subsidiaries:

Interaqt Corp. **(1)**
1 Gatehall Dr Ste 208, Parsippany, NJ 07054
Tel.: (973) 575-7997
Web Site: http://www.colotraq.com
Computer Integrated Systems Design
N.A.I.C.S.: 541512
Dany Bouchedid (Founder & CEO)

ALUMIFUEL POWER CORPORATION
7315 E Peakview Ave, Englewood, CO 80111
Tel.: (971) 285-4570   **WY**
Year Founded: 2000
AFPW—(OTCIQ)
Emp.: 1
Holding Company; Alternative Energy
N.A.I.C.S.: 551112
Pedro Villagran-Garcia (CEO)
Thomas B. Olson (Sec)

Subsidiaries:

Alumifuel Power International, Inc. **(1)**
7315 E Peakview Ave, Englewood, CO 80111
Tel.: (303) 769-8940
Hydrogen Generation Products Mfr & Distr
N.A.I.C.S.: 335999

ALX ONCOLOGY HOLDINGS INC.
323 Allerton Ave, South San Francisco, CA 94080
Tel.: (650) 466-7125   **DE**
Web Site:
https://www.alxoncology.com
Year Founded: 2020
ALXO—(NASDAQ)
Rev.: $4,278,000
Assets: $306,489,000
Liabilities: $43,025,000
Net Worth: $263,464,000
Earnings: ($123,482,000)
Emp.: 58
Fiscal Year-end: 12/31/22
Research & Development in Biotechnology (except Nanobiotechnology)
N.A.I.C.S.: 541714
Peter S. Garcia (CFO)
Jeanne Y. Jew (Chief Bus Officer)
Michael Chang (VP-Ops)
Hank Stern (VP-Chemistry, Mfg & Controls)
Michael Warner (Gen Counsel)
Corey Goodman (Co-Founder & Chm)
Shelly Pinto (Chief Acctg Officer & VP-Fin)
Susan Vermeir (VP-Regulatory Affairs)
K. Christopher Garcia (Co-Founder)

Jaume Pons (Co-Founder, Pres & Chief Scientific Officer)
Corey S. Goodman (Co-Founder & Exec Chm)
Jason Lettmann (CEO)

ALY ENERGY SERVICES, INC.
19450 Highway 249 Ste 200, Houston, TX 77070
Tel.: (713) 333-4000   **DE**
Web Site: http://www.alyenergy.com
Year Founded: 2012
ALYE—(OTCIQ)
Rev.: $6,731,000
Assets: $20,420,000
Liabilities: $8,821,000
Net Worth: $11,599,000
Earnings: ($13,050,000)
Emp.: 58
Fiscal Year-end: 12/31/20
Oilfield Mfr & Whslr Services
N.A.I.C.S.: 333132
Munawar H. Hidayatallah (Chm & CEO)
Alya H. Hidayatallah (CFO)

AMALGAMATED FINANCIAL CORP.
275 7th Ave, New York, NY 10001
Tel.: (212) 255-6200   **DE**
Web Site:
https://www.amalgamatedbank.com
Year Founded: 2020
AMAL—(NASDAQ)
Rev.: $282,386,000
Assets: $7,843,124,000
Liabilities: $7,334,169,000
Net Worth: $508,955,000
Earnings: $81,477,000
Emp.: 409
Fiscal Year-end: 12/31/22
Bank Holding Company
N.A.I.C.S.: 551111
Priscilla Sims Brown (Pres & CEO)
Jason Darby (CFO & Sr Exec VP)
Leslie Veluswamy (Chief Acctg Officer & Exec VP)
Sean Searby (COO & Exec VP)
Mandy Tenner (Chief Legal Officer & Exec VP)
Tye Graham (Chief HR Officer & Exec VP)
Kenneth Schmidt (Exec VP-Finance)
Margaret Lanning (Chief Credit Risk Officer & Exec VP)
John Saltos (Exec VP & Dir-Commercial Banking)
Ina Narula (Chief Risk Officer & Exec VP)
Ivan Frishberg (Chief Sustainability Officer & Sr VP)
Adrian Glace (CTO & Sr VP)

Subsidiaries:

Amalgamated Bank **(1)**
275 7th Ave, New York, NY 10001
Tel.: (212) 255-6200
Web Site:
https://www.amalgamatedbank.com
Sales Range: $100-124.9 Million
Emp.: 409
Provider of Banking Services
N.A.I.C.S.: 522110
Priscilla Sims Brown (Pres & CEO)
Sam Brown (Chief Banking Officer, Sr Exec VP & Exec VP-Bus Dev)
Ivan Frishberg (Chief Sustainability Officer & Sr VP)
Adrian Glace (CTO)
Ina Narula (Chief Risk Officer)
John Saltos (Exec VP)
Margaret Lanning (Chief Credit Risk Officer)
Kenneth Schmidt (Exec VP-Finance)
Tye Graham (Chief HR Officer)
Mandy Tenner (Chief Legal Officer)
Sean Searby (COO)
Jason Darby (CFO)

Amalgamated Financial Corp.—(Continued)

AMANASU ENVIRONMENT CORPORATION

224 5th Ave 2nd Fl, New York, NY 10001
Tel.: (604) 790-8799   NV
Year Founded: 1999
AMSU—(NASDAQ)
Assets: $25,121
Liabilities: $800,741
Net Worth: ($775,620)
Earnings: ($78,993)
Fiscal Year-end: 12/31/21
Environmental Technology Researcher & Developer
N.A.I.C.S.: 541715
Atsushi Maki (*Chm, Pres, CEO, CFO & Principal Acctg Officer*)

AMANASU TECHNO HOLDINGS CORPORATION

445 Park Ave Ctr 10th Fl, New York, NY 10022
Tel.: (646) 274-1274   NV
Web Site: https://www.amanasu.net
Year Founded: 1997
ANSU—(OTCIQ)
Assets: $64,519
Liabilities: $872,962
Net Worth: ($808,443)
Earnings: ($79,970)
Fiscal Year-end: 12/31/21
Environmental Research & Development Services
N.A.I.C.S.: 541720
Atsushi Maki (*Chm & CEO*)

AMARANTUS BIOSCIENCE HOLDINGS, INC.

45 Wall St Ste 920, New York, NY 10005
Tel.: (650) 862-5391   DE
Web Site: http://www.amarantus.com
Year Founded: 2007
AMBS—(OTCEM)
Emp.: 12
Pharmaceuticals Mfr
N.A.I.C.S.: 325412
Tiffini Clark (*Head-Ops & Regulatory Affairs*)
Rongguo Wei (*CFO*)
Marc E. Faerber (*VP-Ops & Controller*)
Kerry Segal (*Head-Bus Dev*)
Aimee Boutcher (*Dir-IR*)
Charlotte Keywood (*Chief Medical Officer-Therapeutics Div*)
Mark Wakefield (*Head-Clinical Dev*)
F. Randall Grimes (*Head-Sponsored Res*)
Paul Jorgensen (*Head-Diagnostics Product Dev*)
Elise Brownell (*Sr VP-Ops & Project Mgmt*)
Barney Monte (*CFO & COO-Interim*)
John W. Commissiong (*Chief Scientific Officer*)

AMAYA GLOBAL HOLDINGS CORP.

225 Grand St, New York, NY 10013
Tel.: (212) 219-7783   DE
Year Founded: 2010
AYAG—(OTCIQ)
Holding Company
N.A.I.C.S.: 551112
Jin Rong (*Vice Chm*)
Bin Zhou (*Gen Counsel*)
Mann C. Yam (*Chm, Pres, CEO & CFO*)

AMAZON.COM, INC.

410 Terry Ave N, Seattle, WA 98109-5210
Tel.: (206) 266-1000   DE

Web Site: http://www.amazon.com
Year Founded: 1994
AMZN—(NASDAQ)
Rev.: $574,785,000,000
Assets: $527,854,000,000
Liabilities: $325,979,000,000
Net Worth: $201,875,000,000
Earnings: $30,425,000,000
Emp.: 1,525,000
Fiscal Year-end: 12/31/23
Books, CDs, Videos, DVDs, Magazines, Audiotapes, Apparel, Sporting Goods, Toys, Software, Phones, Office Products, Electronics, Garden Equipment & Supplies Online Retailer
N.A.I.C.S.: 449210
Jeffrey Preston Bezos (*Founder & Exec Chm*)
Shelley L. Reynolds (*Principal Acctg Officer, VP & Worldwide Controller*)
David A. Zapolsky (*Gen Counsel, Sec & Sr VP*)
Brian T. Olsavsky (*CFO & Sr VP*)
Sarah C. Rhoads (*VP-Amazon Global Air*)
Mike Hopkins (*Sr VP-Studios & Prime Video*)
William F. Lacey (*VP-Fin-Books & Kindle Content*)
Douglas J. Herrington (*CEO-Worldwide Amazon Stores & Sr VP-North America Consumer*)
Hao Tian (*Mgr-Risk*)
Natasha C. Chand (*Co-Founder-Softlines Private Brands*)
Peter Krawiec (*Sr VP-Corporate & Bus Dev-Worldwide*)
Andrew R. Jassy (*Pres & CEO*)

Subsidiaries:

1Life Healthcare, Inc.   (1)
1 Embarcadero Ctr Ste 1900, San Francisco, CA 94111
Tel.: (415) 814-0927
Web Site: https://www.onemedical.com
Rev.: $623,315,000
Assets: $2,627,032,000
Liabilities: $898,449,000
Net Worth: $1,728,583,000
Earnings: ($254,641,000)
Emp.: 3,090
Fiscal Year-end: 12/31/2021
Health Care Srvices
N.A.I.C.S.: 621610

Subsidiary (Domestic):

Iora Health, Inc.   (2)
1 Lincoln St 24th Fl, Boston, MA 02111
Web Site: https://www.iorahealth.com
Healtcare Services
N.A.I.C.S.: 621112

Abebooks Inc.   (1)
655 Tyee Rd Ste 500, Victoria, V9A 6X5, BC, Canada
Tel.: (250) 475-6013
Web Site: http://www.abebooks.com
Sales Range: $75-99.9 Million
Emp.: 107
Online Marketplace For New & Used Books
N.A.I.C.S.: 459210

Alexa Internet, Inc.   (1)
Presidio of San Francisco Bldg 37, San Francisco, CA 94129
Tel.: (415) 561-6900
Web Site: http://www.alexa.com
Sales Range: $10-24.9 Million
Emp.: 25
Internet-Traffic Measurement Services
N.A.I.C.S.: 541910
Dave Sherfesee (*VP-Strategic Infrastructure*)
Ron Shalhoup (*Sr Mgr-Ops*)
Steve Dawson (*Dir-Software Engrg*)
Andrew Ramm (*Pres & Gen Mgr*)

Amazon EU Sarl   (1)
5 Rue Plaetis, Luxembourg, 2338, Luxembourg   (100%)
Tel.: (352) 26733000
Sales Range: $250-299.9 Million
Holding Company
N.A.I.C.S.: 551112

Raimund Paetzmann (*Sr Mgr*)
Stuart Jackson (*Dir-Comm-Europe*)
Ty Rogers (*Dir-Corp Comm-Europe*)

Subsidiary (Non-US):

Amazon.co.uk Ltd.   (2)
1 Principal Place, London, EC2A 2FA, Berkshire, United Kingdom
Tel.: (44) 2086369200
Web Site: https://www.aboutamazon.co.uk
Sales Range: $150-199.9 Million
Emp.: 900
Online Retail Services
N.A.I.C.S.: 425120

Amazon.de GmbH   (2)
Moosacher Strasse 51, 80809, Munich, Germany
Tel.: (49) 89358030
Web Site: http://www.amazon.de
Sales Range: $150-199.9 Million
Electronic Shopping Services
N.A.I.C.S.: 455219

LOVEFiLM UK Ltd.   (2)
No 9 6 Portal Way, London, W3 6RU, United Kingdom
Tel.: (44) 2088968000
Web Site: http://www.lovefilm.com
Sales Range: $100-124.9 Million
Emp.: 346
Online Movie Rental Services
N.A.I.C.S.: 532282

Amazon Japan K.K.   (1)
1 8 1 Shimomeguro Arco Tower Annex, Meguro ku, Tokyo, 153-0064, Japan
Tel.: (81) 363674000
Web Site: http://www.amazon.co.jp
Sales Range: $150-199.9 Million
Online Retail Services
N.A.I.C.S.: 425120

Amazon Robotics LLC   (1)
300 Riverpark Dr, North Reading, MA 01864-2622
Tel.: (781) 221-4640
Web Site: http://www.amazonrobotics.com
Logistics & Transportation Services
N.A.I.C.S.: 541614
Joseph Quinlivan (*Pres & COO*)

Amazon Web Services, Inc.   (1)
410 Terry Ave N, Seattle, WA 98109-5210
Tel.: (206) 266-4064
Web Site: https://aws.amazon.com
Web Related Services
N.A.I.C.S.: 541519
Andrew R. Jassy (*Founder*)
Terry Wise (*VP-Worldwide Partners & Sls-West*)
Dominic Delmolino (*VP-Worldwide Pub Sector Tech & Innovation*)
Phoebe L. Yang (*Gen Mgr-Healthcare*)

Subsidiary (Domestic):

Sqrrl Data, Inc.   (2)
125 Cambridge Park Dr Ste 401, Cambridge, MA 02140
Tel.: (617) 902-0784
Cybersecurity Software Publishers
N.A.I.C.S.: 513210
Mark Terenzoni (*CEO*)

Amazon.ca, Inc.   (1)
410 Terry Ave N, Seattle, WA 98109-5210
Tel.: (206) 266-1000
Web Site: http://www.amazon.ca
Sales Range: $100-124.9 Million
Emp.: 200
Online Shopping Services
N.A.I.C.S.: 425120

Amazon.com.dedc, LLC   (1)
1 Centerpoint Blvd, New Castle, DE 19720   (100%)
Tel.: (302) 395-7440
Sales Range: $150-199.9 Million
Warehouse & Storage
N.A.I.C.S.: 493110

Audible, Inc.   (1)
1 Washington Park, Newark, NJ 07102
Tel.: (973) 820-0400
Web Site: http://www.audible.com
Sales Range: $50-74.9 Million
Emp.: 172
Online Audio Book Retailer
N.A.I.C.S.: 516210

Cynthia Chu (*CFO*)

Subsidiary (Non-US):

Audible GmbH   (2)
Schumannstr 6, 10117, Berlin, Germany
Tel.: (49) 8005890073
Web Site: https://www.audible.de
Online Audio Book Retailer
N.A.I.C.S.: 459210

Audible Limited   (2)
26-28 Glasshouse Yard, London, EC1A 4JU, United Kingdom
Tel.: (44) 8000825100
Web Site: http://www.audible.co.uk
Online Audio Book Retailer
N.A.I.C.S.: 424920

Brilliance Publishing, Inc   (1)
1704 Eaton Dr, Grand Haven, MI 49417
Tel.: (616) 846-5256
Web Site:
    https://www.brilliancepublishing.com
Audiobook Publishing
N.A.I.C.S.: 334610

Fabric Com, Inc.   (1)
4190 Jiles Rd, Kennesaw, GA 30144
Tel.: (770) 794-7071
Web Site: http://www.fabric.com
Sewing, Needlework & Fabric Mfr
N.A.I.C.S.: 459130

IVONA Software Sp. z o.o.   (1)
Aleja Zwyciestwa 96/98, 81-451, Gdynia, Poland
Tel.: (48) 587834951
Web Site: http://www.ivona.com
Text-to-Speech Software Developer
N.A.I.C.S.: 513210

Immedia Semiconductor, Inc.   (1)
100 Burtt Rd Ste 100, Andover, MA 01810
Tel.: (781) 332-5465
Web Site: http://www.blinkforhome.com
Security Camera Mfr
N.A.I.C.S.: 333310
Michael Solt (*Mgr-Engrg*)

Metro-Goldwyn-Mayer Studios, Inc.   (1)
245 N Beverly Dr, Beverly Hills, CA 90210
Tel.: (310) 449-3000
Web Site: http://www.mgm.com
Motion Picture Production
N.A.I.C.S.: 512110

Subsidiary (Domestic):

MGM Networks Inc.   (2)
245 N Beverly Dr, Beverly Hills, CA 90210
Tel.: (310) 449-3000
Web Site: http://www.mgm.com
Cable & Satellite Television Programming Production, Distribution & Broadcasting Services
N.A.I.C.S.: 517111
Bruce Tuchman (*Pres*)
Matthew Baxter (*VP-Distr-Global*)
Elizabeth Squires (*VP-Programming, Distr & Mktg*)

MGM Television Entertainment Inc.   (2)
245 N Beverly Dr, Beverly Hills, CA 90210
Tel.: (310) 449-3000
Web Site: http://www.mgm.com
Sales Range: $150-199.9 Million
Television Programs & Specials Production & Distribution
N.A.I.C.S.: 512110
Max Kisbye (*Exec VP-Television Production & Dev*)
Nathan Taylor (*Dir-Dev*)
Andrew Mittman (*Sr VP-Television Production & Dev*)
Brian Edwards (*Pres*)
Barry Poznick (*Pres-Unscripted & Alternative Television*)
Tess Charman (*Interim Exec Dir-EMEA*)

Metro-Goldwyn-Mayer Distribution Co.   (2)
245 N Beverly Dr, Beverly Hills, CA 90210
Tel.: (310) 449-3000
Web Site: http://www.mgm.com
Motion Picture Distr
N.A.I.C.S.: 512120

Metro-Goldwyn-Mayer Home Enter-
tainment LLC (2)
245 N Beverly Dr, Beverly Hills, CA 90210
Tel.: (310) 449-3000
Web Site: http://www.mgm.com
Emp.: 500
Home Video & DVD Production & Marketing
N.A.I.C.S.: 512110

Metro-Goldwyn-Mayer Pictures
Inc. (2)
10250 Constellation Blvd, Los Angeles, CA
90067
Tel.: (310) 449-3000
Motion Picture Production
N.A.I.C.S.: 512110
Paul Bischoff (VP-Subscription Television &
Bus Dev)

United Artists Corporation (2)
10250 Constellation Blvd, Los Angeles, CA
90067-3065
Tel.: (310) 449-3000
Web Site: http://www.unitedartists.com
Sales Range: $25-49.9 Million
Emp.: 40
Movie Production Services
N.A.I.C.S.: 512120

On-Demand Publishing, LLC (1)
410 Terry Ave N, Seattle, WA
98109 (100%)
Tel.: (206) 266-4064
Web Site: http://www.createspace.com
Sales Range: $50-74.9 Million
Publishing & Manufacturing for Independent
Content Creators, Publishers, Film Studios
& Music Labels
N.A.I.C.S.: 513130

Shopbop.com (1)
1245 E Washington Ave Ste 300, Madison,
WI 53703
Tel.: (608) 270-3900
Web Site: http://www.shopbop.com
Sales Range: $75-99.9 Million
Online Retailer of Women's Apparel, Shoes
& Accessories
N.A.I.C.S.: 458210
Shira Suveyke (Pres-Brand)

Twitch Interactive, Inc. (1)
350 Bush St 2nd Fl, San Francisco, CA
94104
Tel.: (415) 684-7494
Web Site: http://www.twitch.tv
Gaming Video Platform & Chat Community
Website Publisher
N.A.I.C.S.: 541511
Emmett Shear (CEO)
Laura Lee (Chief Content Officer)
Laura Lee (Chief Content Officer)
Dan Clancy (Pres)

Subsidiary (Domestic):

Bebo, Inc. (2)
387 Tehama St, San Francisco, CA 94103
Tel.: (415) 243-4800
Web Site: http://www.bebo.com
Sales Range: $25-49.9 Million
Social Networking Website Operator
N.A.I.C.S.: 516210

Whole Foods Market, Inc. (1)
550 Bowie St, Austin, TX 78703
Tel.: (512) 477-4455
Web Site:
  http://www.wholefoodsmarket.com
Natural & Organic Food Supermarket Op-
erator
N.A.I.C.S.: 445110
John P. Mackey (Founder)
James P. Sud (Exec VP)
Bart Beilman (Sr VP-Suply Chain & Retail
Ops)
Christina Minardi (Exec VP-Ops)
Brian O'Connell (VP-Team Member Svcs-
Global)
Jeff Turnas (Sr VP-Global Culinary Procure-
ment & Ops)
Robert M. Twyman (Exec VP-Ops)
Jason J. Buechel (CEO)
Sonya Gafsi Oblisk (CMO)
Keith Manbeck (CFO & Chief Admin Officer)
Heather Stern (Gen Counsel, Sec & Sr VP-
Legal Affairs-Global)
Karen Christensen (Sr VP-Perishable Mdsg)
Robert Fraser (Sr VP-Operational Fin)

Angela Lorenzen (Pres-Pacific Northwest
Reg)
Alyssa Vescio (Sr VP-Procurement-Non
Perishable)

Subsidiary (Domestic):

Allegro Coffee Co. (2)
12799 Claude Ct Bldg B, Thornton, CO
80241
Tel.: (303) 444-4844
Coffee Whslr
N.A.I.C.S.: 445110
Jeff Teter (Pres)

Mrs. Gooch's Natural Food Markets,
Inc. (2)
207 Goode Ave 7th Fl, Glendale, CA 91203
Tel.: (818) 501-8484
Natural & Organic Foods Retailer
N.A.I.C.S.: 445110

WFM Beverage Corp. (2)
11145 Westheimer Rd, Houston, TX 77042-
3207
Tel.: (713) 784-7776
Beverage Product Distr
N.A.I.C.S.: 424820

WFM Hawaii, LLC (2)
900 Fort St Mall Ste 1680, Honolulu, HI
96813
Tel.: (808) 738-0820
Web Site:
  http://www.wholefoodsmarket.com
Natural & Organic Foods Retailer
N.A.I.C.S.: 445110

WFM Medical & Wellness Centers,
Inc. (2)
800 N Central Ave Ste 203, Glendale, CA
91204
Tel.: (818) 844-2300
Web Site: http://www.wfmmedical.com
Health Care Srvices
N.A.I.C.S.: 621999

WFM Private Label, L.P. (2)
550 Bowie St, Austin, TX 78703
Tel.: (512) 542-0889
Supermarket Operating Services
N.A.I.C.S.: 445110

Branch (Domestic):

Whole Foods Market - Florida
Region (2)
2000 N Federal Hwy, Fort Lauderdale, FL
33305
Tel.: (954) 398-2000
Web Site:
  http://www.wholefoodsmarket.com
Natural & Organic Foods Supermarkets
N.A.I.C.S.: 445110
Juan Nunez (Reg Pres)

Whole Foods Market - Mid-Atlantic
Region (2)
11355 Woodglen Dr, Rockville, MD 20852
Tel.: (301) 984-4880
Web Site:
  http://www.wholefoodsmarket.com
Natural & Organic Foods Supermarkets
N.A.I.C.S.: 445110
Scott Allshouse (Reg Pres)

Whole Foods Market - Midwest
Region (2)
5118 S Lake Park Ave, Chicago, IL 60615
Tel.: (773) 819-1600
Web Site:
  http://www.wholefoodsmarket.com
Natural & Organic Foods Supermarkets
N.A.I.C.S.: 445110
David Schwartz (Reg Pres)

Whole Foods Market - North Atlantic
Region (2)
340 River St, Cambridge, MA 02139
Tel.: (617) 876-6990
Web Site:
  http://www.wholefoodsmarket.com
Sales Range: $50-74.9 Million
Emp.: 110
Natural & Organic Foods Supermarkets
N.A.I.C.S.: 445110
Rick Bonin (Reg Pres)

Whole Foods Market - Northeast
Region (2)

210 Hudson St Ste 700 Harborside 3, Jer-
sey City, NJ 17311-1208
Tel.: (201) 567-2090
Web Site:
  http://www.wholefoodsmarket.com
Natural & Organic Foods Supermarkets
N.A.I.C.S.: 445110
Nicole Wescoe (Reg Pres)

Whole Foods Market - Northern Cali-
fornia Region (2)
6401 Hollis St Ste 150, Emeryville, CA
94608
Tel.: (510) 428-7400
Web Site:
  http://www.wholefoodsmarket.com
Natural & Organic Foods Supermarkets
N.A.I.C.S.: 445110
Omar Gaye (Reg Pres)

Whole Foods Market - Rocky Moun-
tain Region (2)
2905 Pearl St, Boulder, CO 80301
Tel.: (303) 545-6611
Web Site:
  http://www.wholefoodsmarket.com
Natural & Organic Food Supermarkets
N.A.I.C.S.: 445110
Bill Jordan (Reg Pres)

Whole Foods Market - Southern Pa-
cific Region (2)
331 N Glendale Ave, Glendale, CA 91206
Tel.: (818) 548-3695
Web Site:
  http://www.wholefoodsmarket.com
Natural & Organic Foods Supermarkets
N.A.I.C.S.: 445110
Patrick Bradley (Pres)

Whole Foods Market - Southwest
Region (2)
901 E 5th St Ste 100, Austin, TX 78702
Tel.: (512) 884-5910
Web Site:
  http://www.wholefoodsmarket.com
Natural & Organic Foods Supermarkets
N.A.I.C.S.: 445110
Matt Ray (Reg Pres)

Subsidiary (Domestic):

Whole Foods Market California,
Inc. (2)
650 W Shaw Ave, Fresno, CA 93704
Tel.: (559) 241-0300
Natural & Organic Foods Retailer
N.A.I.C.S.: 445110

Subsidiary (Non-US):

Whole Foods Market Canada,
Inc. (2)
925 Main St, West Vancouver, V7T 2Z3,
BC, Canada
Tel.: (604) 678-0500
Supermarket Operating Services
N.A.I.C.S.: 445110

Subsidiary (Domestic):

Whole Foods Market Nebraska,
LLC (2)
10020 Regency Cir, Omaha, NE 68114
Tel.: (402) 393-1200
Supermarket Operating Services
N.A.I.C.S.: 445110

Whole Foods Market Pacific North-
west, Inc. (2)
888 116th Ave NE, Bellevue, WA 98004
Tel.: (425) 462-1400
Natural & Organic Foods Retailer
N.A.I.C.S.: 445110
Angela Lorenzen (Reg Pres)

Whole Foods Market Rocky
Mountain/Southwest, L.P. (2)
2905 Pearl St, Boulder, CO 80301
Tel.: (303) 545-6611
Supermarket Operating Services
N.A.I.C.S.: 445110

Whole Foods Market Services,
Inc. (2)
525 N Lamar Blvd, Austin, TX 78703-4644
Tel.: (512) 542-2200
Natural Food Retailer
N.A.I.C.S.: 445298

Zappos.com, Inc. (1)
400 E Stewart Ave, Las Vegas, NV
89101 (100%)
Tel.: (702) 943-7677
Web Site: http://www.zappos.com
Sales Range: $1-4.9 Billion
Emp.: 1,421
Online Shoe, Apparel & Accessories Re-
tailer
N.A.I.C.S.: 458210
Scott Schaefer (CEO)
Ginny McCormick (CMO)

a9.com, Inc. (1)
101 Lytton Ave, Palo Alto, CA
94301 (100%)
Tel.: (650) 331-2600
Web Site: http://www.a9.com
Sales Range: $10-24.9 Million
Emp.: 70
Electronic Commerce Search Processing
Services; Online Advertising Services
N.A.I.C.S.: 541890

dpreview.com Ltd. (1)
6 Effingham Road, Surbiton, KT6 5JY,
United Kingdom
Tel.: (44) 2083980138
Web Site: http://www.dpreview.com
Sales Range: $100-124.9 Million
Online Reviews & Information About Digital
Photography
N.A.I.C.S.: 513199

AMAZONAS FLORESTAL LTD
7922-7924 NW 67th St, Miami, FL
33166
Tel.: (305) 351-9851 NV
Web Site: http://www.amazonasf.com
AZFL—(OTCIQ)
Sales Range: Less than $1 Million
Forestry & Timber Operations
N.A.I.C.S.: 115310
Carlos Martinez (CFO)
Ricardo Cortez (Chm, Treas & Sec)

AMB FINANCIAL CORP.
7880 Wicker Ave, Saint John, IN
46373
Tel.: (219) 365-6700 DE
Web Site: https://www.acbanker.com
Year Founded: 1993
AMFC—(OTCIQ)
Offices of Bank Holding Companies
N.A.I.C.S.: 551111
Michael J. Mellon (Pres & CEO)
Ginger Watts (VP & Officer-
Compliance)
Mohammad Saleem (VP & CIO)
Clement B. Knapp Jr. (Chm)
Todd C. Williams (VP-Lending)
Steven A. Bohn (CFO & VP)

Subsidiaries:

American Community Bank of
Indiana (1)
7880 Wicker Ave, Saint John, IN 46373
Tel.: (219) 365-6700
Web Site: http://www.acbanker.com
Banking Services
N.A.I.C.S.: 522110
Michael J. Mellon (Pres & CEO)

AMBAC FINANCIAL GROUP,
INC.
1 World Trade Ctr 41st Fl, New York,
NY 10007
Tel.: (212) 658-7470 DE
Web Site: https://www.ambac.com
Year Founded: 1971
AMBC—(NYSE)
Rev.: $269,000,000
Assets: $8,428,000,000
Liabilities: $7,013,000,000
Net Worth: $1,415,000,000
Earnings: $5,000,000
Emp.: 168
Fiscal Year-end: 12/31/23
Holding Company; Financial Guaran-
tees & Financial Services to Public &
Private Sector Clients

Ambac Financial Group, Inc.—(Continued)

N.A.I.C.S.: 551112
Stephen M. Ksenak (Sr Mng Dir & Gen Counsel)
Robert B. Eisman (Sr Mng Dir, Chief Acctg Officer & Controller)
Michael Reilly (Sr Mng Dir, CIO & Chief Admin Officer)
David Barranco (Sr Mng Dir & Head-Risk Mgmt)
Jeffrey Scott Stein (Chm)
Naveen Anand (Pres-Cirrata Grp)
Charles Sebaski (Mng Dir-IR)
Kate Smith (Dir-Corp Comm)
Dan McGinnis (Sr Mng Dir & COO)

Subsidiaries:

All Trans Risk Solutions, LLC **(1)**
1200 MacArthur Blvd, Mahwah, NJ 07430
Tel.: (201) 482-5900
Web Site: https://www.alltransins.com
Vehicle Insurance Services
N.A.I.C.S.: 524126

Ambac Assurance Corp **(1)**
1 State St Plz, New York, NY, 10004-1505 **(100%)**
Tel.: (212) 668-0340
Web Site: http://www.ambac.com
Sales Range: $100-124.9 Million
Financial Services
N.A.I.C.S.: 523940

Ambac Assurance Corporation **(1)**
Level 31 88 Phillip Street, Sydney, 2000, NSW, Australia **(100%)**
Tel.: (61) 282110431
Web Site: http://www.ambac.com.au
Sales Range: $150-199.9 Million
Financial Services
N.A.I.C.S.: 523940

Ambac Assurance UK Limited **(1)**
Second Floor 21 Great Winchester Street, London, EC2N 2JA, United Kingdom **(100%)**
Tel.: (44) 2077864300
Web Site: https://www.ambac.com
Sales Range: $150-199.9 Million
Emp.: 13
Financial Services
N.A.I.C.S.: 525990
John Tisfi (CEO)

Ambac Assurance UK Limited-Milan Branch **(1)**
Via Monte di Pieta 21, 20121, Milan, Italy **(100%)**
Tel.: (39) 0286337642
Web Site: http://www.ambac.com
Sales Range: $150-199.9 Million
Financial Services
N.A.I.C.S.: 525990

Ambac Capital Corporation **(1)**
1 State St Plz, New York, NY 10004
Tel.: (212) 208-3259
Investment Management Service
N.A.I.C.S.: 523940

Capacity Marine Corporation **(1)**
1200 MacArthur Blvd Ste 302A, Mahwah, NJ 07430
Web Site: https://capacitymarine.com
Marine Insurance Services
N.A.I.C.S.: 524126
Walter Wynne (Pres)
Robert G. Lull (Dir)
Sally Fane (Mgr-Accounting)
Anne Crowe (Mgr-Administration)
Captain Thomas Bolcar (Reg VP-Loss Control)
Joyce Alimi (Mgr-New Bus Dev)
David O'Dowd (Reg VP)
John W. Moraites (Reg VP)
Mark Weinraub (Chm)

Xchange Benefits, LLC **(1)**
200 Business Park Dr Ste 303, Armonk, NY 10504 **(80%)**
Tel.: (917) 437-7359
Web Site: https://www.xbllc.com
Insurance & Reinsurance Underwriter
N.A.I.C.S.: 524298
Peter McGuire (Pres & CEO)
James Denison (Chief Underwriting Officer & Exec VP)

Ned Browne (CMO & Exec VP)
Kenneth Zieden-Weber (CFO, COO & Exec VP)
Lani M. McCann (Sr VP)
Chris LaDelfa (Sr VP-Captive Solutions)
Stephen Hitch (Sr VP-Underwriting)

AMBARELLA, INC.

3101 Jay St, Santa Clara, CA 95054
Tel.: (408) 734-8888 **Ky**
Web Site: https://www.ambarella.com
Year Founded: 2004
AMBA—(NASDAQ)
Rev.: $337,606,000
Assets: $710,195,000
Liabilities: $104,107,000
Net Worth: $606,088,000
Earnings: ($65,386,000)
Emp.: 937
Fiscal Year-end: 01/31/23
Semiconductor Components Mfr
N.A.I.C.S.: 334413
Feng-Ming Wang (Founder, Chm, Pres & CEO)
Leslie D. Kohn (CTO)
Christopher Day (VP-Mktg & Bus Dev)
Chan Lee (COO)
John Chi-Hong Ju (Sr VP-Sys & Gen Mgr-Design Centers-Asia)
Zemo Yang (VP-Ops)
Michael Morehead (Gen Counsel)
Michael Chen (VP-Bus Dev)
Brian C. White (CFO)
Amee Orozco-Guiriba (VP-HR)
Robert Bloomquist (VP-Automotive Bus Dev)
John Young (CFO)

Subsidiaries:

Ambarella Shanghai Co., Ltd. **(1)**
9th Floor Park Center 1088 Fangdian Road, Pudong New District, Shanghai, 201204, China
Tel.: (86) 2160880608
Electronic Control Equipment Mfr
N.A.I.C.S.: 334413
Yupeng Chang (Engr-Staff Sys Application)

Ambarella Taiwan Ltd. **(1)**
Suite C1 No 1 Li-Hsin Road 1, Science-Based Industrial Park, Hsinchu, 30078, Taiwan
Tel.: (886) 36668828
Electronic Control Equipment Mfr
N.A.I.C.S.: 334413

VisLab S.r.l. **(1)**
Parco Area delle Scienze 49, 43124, Parma, Italy
Tel.: (39) 052116023
Web Site: https://www.vislab.it
Computer Software Services
N.A.I.C.S.: 541511
Alberto Broggi (Founder, Pres, CEO & Gen Mgr)

AMBASE CORPORATION

7857 W Sample Rd Ste 134, Coral Springs, FL 33065
Tel.: (201) 265-0169 **DE**
Year Founded: 1975
ABCP—(OTCIQ)
Rev.: $9,000
Assets: $410,000
Liabilities: $1,484,000
Net Worth: ($1,074,000)
Earnings: ($3,473,000)
Emp.: 4
Fiscal Year-end: 12/31/22
Property & Casualty Insurance; Risk Management & Specialty Services
N.A.I.C.S.: 531120
Richard A. Bianco (Chm, Pres & CEO)
John P. Ferrara (CFO, VP & Controller)
Joseph R. Bianco (Treas)

AMC NETWORKS INC.

11 Penn Plz 15th Fl, New York, NY 10001
Tel.: (212) 324-8500 **NY**
Web Site:
https://www.amcnetworks.com
Year Founded: 1980
AMCX—(NASDAQ)
Rev.: $2,711,877,000
Assets: $4,969,787,000
Liabilities: $3,710,544,000
Net Worth: $1,259,243,000
Earnings: $215,464,000
Emp.: 1,900
Fiscal Year-end: 12/31/23
Holding Company for Cable Television Channels
N.A.I.C.S.: 516210
James L. Dolan (Executives, Bd of Dirs)
Kristin Aigner Dolan (CEO)
James G. Gallagher (Gen Counsel & Exec VP)
Georgia Juvelis (Exec VP-Corp Comm)
Jennifer Caserta (Chief Transformation & People Officer)
Aisha Thomas-Petit (Chief Diversity, Equity & Inclusion Officer)
Nicholas Seibert (VP-Corp Dev & IR)
Matt Blank (Interim CEO)
Len Fogge (Pres-Mktg)
Michael J. Sherin III (Chief Acctg Officer & Exec VP)
Patrick O'Connell (CFO & Exec VP)
Anne Kelly (Sec)

Subsidiaries:

AMC Networks Central Europe Kft **(1)**
Lomb u 23-27, 1139, Budapest, Hungary
Tel.: (36) 12369100
Cable & Other Subscription Programming Services
N.A.I.C.S.: 516210

American Movie Classics Company LLC **(1)**
11 Pen Plz 15th Fl, New York, NY 10001
Tel.: (212) 324-8500
Web Site: http://www.amctv.com
Rev.: $33,300,000
Emp.: 150
Cable Television Services
N.A.I.C.S.: 516210
Charles Collier (Pres)

IFC Companies **(1)**
11 Penn Plz 18th Fl, New York, NY 10001
Tel.: (212) 324-8500
Web Site: http://www.ifc.com
Sales Range: $50-74.9 Million
Emp.: 100
Independent Film & Television Production, Distribution & Financing
N.A.I.C.S.: 512110

RLJ Entertainment, Inc. **(1)**
8515 Georgia Ave Ste 650, Silver Spring, MD 20910 **(100%)**
Tel.: (301) 608-2115
Web Site: http://www.rljentertainment.com
Rev.: $86,304,000
Assets: $147,589,000
Liabilities: $132,046,000
Net Worth: $15,543,000
Earnings: ($30,120,000)
Emp.: 98
Fiscal Year-end: 12/31/2017
Holding Company; Entertainment Content & Programming Licenser & Distr
N.A.I.C.S.: 551112
Miguel Penella (Pres)
Sylvia George (Gen Mgr)
Mark Stevens (Chief Content Officer)
Mike Pears (Exec VP & Gen Mgr)
Mark Ward (Chief Acquisitions Officer)
Mark Nunis (Chief Acctg Officer)
Titus Bicknell (Chief Digital Officer & Exec VP-Ops)
Stuart Shaw (Mng Dir)
Matthew Graham (Gen Mgr)
Brett Dismuke (Chief Content Officer-UMC)
Robert L. Johnson (Chm)

Subsidiary (Domestic):

Acorn Media Group, Inc. **(2)**
8515 Georgia Ave Ste 650, Silver Spring, MD 20910
Tel.: (301) 608-2115
Web Site: http://www.acornmedia.com
British Entertainment DVD & Bluray Publisher & Distr
N.A.I.C.S.: 513199

Subsidiary (Non-US):

Acorn Productions Ltd **(2)**
55 Drury Lane, Covent Garden, London, WC2B 5SQ, United Kingdom
Tel.: (44) 2037348706
Web Site:
http://www.acornproductionsltd.com
Teleproduction & Other Postproduction Services
N.A.I.C.S.: 512191

Subsidiary (Domestic):

Image Entertainment, Inc. **(2)**
6320 Canoga Ave, Woodland Hills, CA 91367
Tel.: (818) 407-9100
DVD Licenser & Distr
N.A.I.C.S.: 334610

AMCON DISTRIBUTING COMPANY

7405 Irvington Rd, Omaha, NE 68122
Tel.: (402) 331-3727 **DE**
Web Site: https://www.amcon.com
Year Founded: 1986
DIT—(NYSEAMEX)
Rev.: $2,710,981,108
Assets: $374,107,310
Liabilities: $262,377,525
Net Worth: $111,729,785
Earnings: $4,336,489
Emp.: 1,362
Fiscal Year-end: 09/30/24
Groceries, Cigarettes & Beauty Care Products Distr
N.A.I.C.S.: 424410
Christopher H. Atayan (CEO & Chm)
Andrew C. Plummer (Pres & COO)
Charles J. Schmaderer (CFO, Sec & VP)

Subsidiaries:

AMCON Distributing Company, Inc. **(1)**
2517 Ellington Rd, Quincy, IL 62305 **(100%)**
Tel.: (217) 222-3355
Sales Range: $125-149.9 Million
Emp.: 200
Operates a Wholesale Distribution Services of Consumer Products
N.A.I.C.S.: 424210

AMCON Distributing Company-Crossville **(1)**
624 Industrial Blvd, Crossville, TN 38555
Tel.: (931) 484-5155
Sales Range: $75-99.9 Million
Emp.: 90
Wholesale Grocery Warehouse Services
N.A.I.C.S.: 424490

Burklund Distributors Inc. **(1)**
2500 N Main St, East Peoria, IL 61611-1787
Tel.: (309) 694-1900
Web Site: https://www.burklund.com
Rev.: $93,000,000
Emp.: 130
Tobacco & Tobacco Products Distr
N.A.I.C.S.: 424940
Jon Burklund (CEO)
Paul Benes (Controller)

Subsidiary (Domestic):

National Marine Sales Inc. **(2)**
5406 N Galena Rd, Peoria, IL 61616-5445 **(100%)**
Tel.: (309) 688-5513
Web Site:
http://www.nationalmarinesales.com

Sales Range: $10-24.9 Million
Emp.: 7
Boat Dealers
N.A.I.C.S.: 441222
Pate Ward (CEO)

Chamberlin Natural Foods Inc. (1)
4924 E Colonial Dr Shoppes of Baldwin
Park, Orlando, FL 32803
Tel.: (407) 228-1373
Web Site: https://www.chamberlins.com
Sales Range: $25-49.9 Million
Emp.: 65
Miscellaneous Food Stores
N.A.I.C.S.: 456191
Eric Hinkesent (Pres)

EOM Acquisition Corp. (1)
30555 US Hwy 19 N, Palm Harbor, FL
34684
Tel.: (727) 785-7951
Web Site:
    http://www.earthoriginsmarket.com
Grocery Product Whslr
N.A.I.C.S.: 424410

FortuNet, Inc. (1)
3901 Graphic Center Dr, Las Vegas, NV
89148
Tel.: (702) 796-9090
Web Site: https://www.fortunet.com
Sales Range: $10-24.9 Million
Emp.: 50
Electronic Gaming Systems Mfr
N.A.I.C.S.: 339930
Yuri Itkis (Chm, CEO & CFO)
Boris Itkis (CTO, Treas, Sec & VP- Engrg)

Subsidiary (Domestic):

Summit Amusement & Distributing
Ltd. (2)
2480 Overland Ave, Billings, MT
59102   (100%)
Tel.: (406) 652-3239
Web Site:
    https://www.summitgamingmt.com
Electronic Gambling Device Mfr
N.A.I.C.S.: 713290
Kelly Michalies (Mgr-Ops)

Health Food Associates, Inc. (1)
51st Memorial 7807 E 51st St, Tulsa, OK
74145
Tel.: (918) 663-4137
Web Site: https://akins.com
Supermarket Operating Services
N.A.I.C.S.: 445110

Henry's Foods, Inc. (1)
234 Mckay Ave N, Alexandria, MN 56308-
6308
Web Site: http://www.henrysfoods.com
Refrigerated Warehousing & Storage
N.A.I.C.S.: 493120
Bev Clausen-Kieffer (Controller)
Kellie Janssen (Pres)

Richmond Master Distributors
Inc. (1)
4202 Technology Dr, South Bend, IN
46628-9772
Tel.: (574) 239-0310
Web Site: http://www.richmondmaster.com
Sales Range: $25-49.9 Million
Emp.: 135
Provider of Tobacco Products, Confection-
ery & Groceries
N.A.I.C.S.: 424940
Patrick Carrico (CEO)
Brad Bohn (Coord-Reclamations)
Christine Markham (Mgr-IT)
Scott Carrico (COO)

Team Sledd, LLC (1)
100 E Cove Ave, Wheeling, WV 26003
Tel.: (304) 243-1820
Web Site: https://www.sleddco.com
Grocery Product Whslr
N.A.I.C.S.: 445110

AMEDISYS, INC.
3854 American Way Ste A, Baton
Rouge, LA 70816
Tel.: (225) 292-2031   DE
Web Site: https://www.amedisys.com
Year Founded: 1982
AMED—(NASDAQ)
Rev.: $2,236,382,000

Assets: $2,060,170,000
Liabilities: $940,387,000
Net Worth: $1,119,783,000
Earnings: ($9,747,000)
Emp.: 19,000
Fiscal Year-end: 12/31/23
Home Health Care & Hospice Ser-
vices
N.A.I.C.S.: 621610
Paul B. Kusserow (Chm & CEO)
Kendra Kimmons (VP-Mktg & Comm)
Denise Bohnert (Chief Compliance
Officer)
Nick Muscato (VP-Strategic Fin)
Jennifer Guckert Griffin (Interim Chief
Legal Officer)
Adam Holton (Chief People Officer)
Richard M. Ashworth (Pres & CEO)
Scott G. Ginn (CFO & COO)

Subsidiaries:

AMEDISYS ARIZONA, L.L.C. (1)
2971 Willow Creek Rd, Prescott, AZ 86301
Tel.: (928) 443-7663
Women Healthcare Services
N.A.I.C.S.: 621610

AMEDISYS DELAWARE, L.L.C. (1)
1201 College Park Dr Ste 101, Dover, DE
19904
Tel.: (302) 678-4764
Web Site: http://www.amdesys.com
Emp.: 30
Women Healthcare Services
N.A.I.C.S.: 621610

AMEDISYS FLORIDA, L.L.C. (1)
3927 Hwy 4 Ste 201, Jay, FL 32565-1752
Tel.: (850) 675-6505
Women Healthcare Services
N.A.I.C.S.: 621610

AMEDISYS HOME HEALTH, INC.
OF ALABAMA (1)
123 S Painter Ave Ste C, Ozark, AL 36360
Tel.: (334) 774-0370
Web Site: http://www.amedisys.com
Sales Range: $10-24.9 Million
Emp.: 15
Women Healthcare Services
N.A.I.C.S.: 621610

AMEDISYS HOME HEALTH, INC.
OF SOUTH CAROLINA (1)
208 Elm St, Conway, SC 29526
Web Site: https://www.amedisys.com
Emp.: 40
Women Healthcare Services
N.A.I.C.S.: 621610

AMEDISYS NEW HAMPSHIRE,
L.L.C. (1)
1E Commons Dr Unit 33, Londonderry, NH
03053
Tel.: (603) 437-9443
Web Site: https://www.amedisys.com
Emp.: 9
Women Healthcare Services
N.A.I.C.S.: 621610

AMEDISYS NEW JERSEY,
L.L.C. (1)
21 Main St Ste 253, Hackensack, NJ 07601
Tel.: (201) 342-7766
Web Site: http://www.amedisys.com
Emp.: 200
Women Healthcare Services
N.A.I.C.S.: 621610

AMEDISYS NORTH CAROLINA,
L.L.C. (1)
100 Europa Dr Ste 330, Chapel Hill, NC
27517
Tel.: (919) 401-3000
Web Site: http://www.amedisys.com
Sales Range: $10-24.9 Million
Emp.: 40
Women Healthcare Services
N.A.I.C.S.: 621610

AMEDISYS OKLAHOMA, L.L.C. (1)
2503 SE Washington Blvd Ste 4, Bartlesville, OK 74006-7606
Tel.: (918) 333-2802
Web Site: http://www.amedisys.com

Sales Range: $10-24.9 Million
Emp.: 30
Health Care Srvices
N.A.I.C.S.: 621610

AMEDISYS SP-IN, L.L.C. (1)
2200 Lk Ave Ste 150, Fort Wayne, IN
46805
Tel.: (260) 422-8900
Web Site: http://www.amedisys.com
Emp.: 24
Women Healthcare Services
N.A.I.C.S.: 621610

AMEDISYS SP-KY, L.L.C. (1)
2480 Fortune Dr Ste 120, Lexington, KY
40509
Tel.: (859) 271-0611
Health Care Srvices
N.A.I.C.S.: 621610

AMEDISYS SP-OH, L.L.C. (1)
9 Triangle Park Dr Ste 901, Cincinnati, OH
45246
Tel.: (513) 772-0111
Web Site: https://www.amedisys.com
Sales Range: $10-24.9 Million
Emp.: 25
Women Healthcare Services
N.A.I.C.S.: 621610

AMEDISYS SPECIALIZED MEDICAL
SERVICES, INC. (1)
1651 Louisville Ave Ste 118, Monroe, LA
71201
Tel.: (318) 324-0681
Women Healthcare Services
N.A.I.C.S.: 621610

AMEDISYS TENNESSEE, L.L.C. (1)
2601 Elm Hill Pike Ste A B C, Nashville, TN
37214
Tel.: (615) 313-7400
Web Site: https://www.amedisys.com
Sales Range: $10-24.9 Million
Emp.: 30
Women Healthcare Services
N.A.I.C.S.: 621610

ANGEL WATCH HOME CARE,
L.L.C. (1)
617 Houser St, Park Hills, MO 63601
Tel.: (573) 330-5213
Web Site: https://www.angelwatchhc.com
Women Healthcare Services
N.A.I.C.S.: 621610

Amedisys Home Health Care (1)
1007 W Thomas St Ste L, Hammond, LA
70401
Tel.: (985) 902-9922
Web Site: http://www.amedisys.com
Health Care Srvices
N.A.I.C.S.: 621610

Amedisys Home Health Care -
Gastonia (1)
1050 Xray Dr, Gastonia, NC 28054
Tel.: (704) 867-1141
Web Site: http://www.amedisys.com
Emp.: 30
Health Care Srvices
N.A.I.C.S.: 621610

Amedisys Home Health Care -
Wheeling (1)
1251 Warwood Ave, Wheeling, WV 26003
Tel.: (304) 277-1500
Web Site: http://www.amedisys.com
Emp.: 60
Health Care Srvices
N.A.I.C.S.: 621610

Amedisys Home Health Of Nebraska,
L.L.C. (1)
6415 2nd Ave Ste 3, Kearney, NE 68847
Tel.: (308) 698-0580
Web Site: https://www.amedisys.com
Health Care Srvices
N.A.I.C.S.: 621610

Associated Home Care, LLC (1)
500 Unicorn Park Dr Ste 105, Woburn, MA
01801
Tel.: (978) 922-0745
Web Site:
    https://www.associatedhomecare.com
Women Healthcare Services
N.A.I.C.S.: 621610
Michael Trigilio (CEO)

Beacon Hospice, Inc. (1)
245 Ctr St Ste 10A, Auburn, ME 04210-
6169
Tel.: (207) 784-4242
Web Site: http://www.amedisys.com
Emp.: 25
Women Healthcare Services
N.A.I.C.S.: 621610
Robin Turner (Dir Gen)

Compassionate Care Hospice of
Bryan Texas, LLC (1)
3833 S Texas Ave Ste 200, Bryan, TX
77802
Tel.: (979) 260-9700
Health Care Srvices
N.A.I.C.S.: 621610

Compassionate Care Hospice of Clif-
ton, LLC (1)
1373 Broad St Ste 306, Clifton, NJ 07013
Health Care Srvices
N.A.I.C.S.: 621610

Compassionate Care Hospice of
Houston, LLC (1)
2040 North Loop W Ste 320, Houston, TX
77018
Tel.: (713) 667-3247
Health Care Srvices
N.A.I.C.S.: 621610

Compassionate Care Hospice of Illi-
nois, LLC (1)
200 N Hammes Ste 3, Joliet, IL 60435
Tel.: (847) 470-9480
Health Care Srvices
N.A.I.C.S.: 621610

Compassionate Care Hospice of Kan-
sas, LLC (1)
8725 Rosehill Rd Ste 380, Lenexa, KS
66215
Tel.: (913) 671-6740
Health Care Srvices
N.A.I.C.S.: 621610

Compassionate Care Hospice of
Michigan, LLC (1)
5730 N Lilley Rd Ste A&B, Canton, MI
48187
Tel.: (734) 983-9050
Health Care Srvices
N.A.I.C.S.: 621610

Compassionate Care Hospice of Min-
nesota, LLC (1)
31361 St Hwy 266, Worthington, MN 56187
Health Care Srvices
N.A.I.C.S.: 621610

Compassionate Care Hospice of
Pittsburg, LLC (1)
1725 Washington Rd Ste 509, Pittsburgh,
PA 15241
Tel.: (412) 241-8240
Health Care Srvices
N.A.I.C.S.: 621610

Compassionate Care Hospice of The
Midwest, LLC (1)
6009 W 41st St Ste 4 Kirkwood Plz, Sioux
Falls, SD 57106
Tel.: (605) 338-2066
Health Care Srvices
N.A.I.C.S.: 621610

Compassionate Care Hospice of Wis-
consin, LLC (1)
16655 W Bluemound Rd Ste 275, Brookfield, WI 53005
Tel.: (414) 257-1708
Health Care Srvices
N.A.I.C.S.: 621610

Contessa Health Of Tennessee,
LLC (1)
49 Music Sq W Ste 401, Nashville, TN
37203
Web Site: https://contessahealth.com
Health Care Srvices
N.A.I.C.S.: 621610

ELDER HOME OPTIONS, L.L.C. (1)
10 Waldens Hill Dr, Peabody, MA 01960
Tel.: (978) 535-3866
Women Healthcare Services
N.A.I.C.S.: 621610

Evolution Health, LLC (1)

Amedisys, Inc.—(Continued)

13737 Noel Rd Ste 1200, Dallas, TX 75240
Tel.: (214) 712-2610
Web Site: http://www.evolution.net
Health Care Srvices
N.A.I.C.S.: 621610
Regina Caldwell (VP-Employee Engagement)
Mike Parsons (Pres)
Mike Rzendzian (CFO)
Kurt Baumgartel (COO)
Tom Wilken (VP-HR)
Jeanne Kalvaitis (Sr VP-Hospice Ops)
Bobi Rose (Sr VP)

FAMILY HOME HEALTH CARE, INC. (1)
2200 E Parrish Ave Ste 103E, Owensboro, KY 42303
Tel.: (270) 852-4811
Web Site: http://www.amedisys.org
Emp.: 15
Women Healthcare Services
N.A.I.C.S.: 621610
Marissa R. Ocariza (Pres & CEO)
Lorna P. Manasala (Dir-Patient Care Svcs)

HI-TECH CARE, INC. (1)
3854 American Way Ste A, Baton Rouge, LA 70816
Tel.: (225) 292-2031
Web Site: https://www.amedisys.com
Financial Investment Services
N.A.I.C.S.: 523940

HOME HEALTH OF ALEXANDRIA, L.L.C. (1)
4230 Parliament Dr, Alexandria, LA 71303-3578
Tel.: (318) 445-2846
Web Site: http://www.amedisys.com
Women Healthcare Services
N.A.I.C.S.: 621610

Homecare Preferred Choice, Inc. (1)
1201 College Pk Dr Ste 101, Dover, DE 19904
Tel.: (302) 678-4764
Web Site: https://www.amedisys.com
Health Care Srvices
N.A.I.C.S.: 621610

INFINITY HOME CARE, L.L.C. (1)
6700 Professional Pkwy W, Sarasota, FL 34240
Tel.: (941) 378-3703
Emp.: 500
Women Healthcare Services
N.A.I.C.S.: 621610

MARIETTA HOME HEALTH AND HOSPICE, L.L.C. (1)
450 Pike St Ste I-1, Marietta, OH 45750
Tel.: (740) 374-9100
Women Healthcare Services
N.A.I.C.S.: 621610

MORGANTOWN HOSPICE, LLC. (1)
3596 Collins Ferry Rd Ste 250, Morgantown, WV 26505
Tel.: (304) 285-2777
Women Healthcare Services
N.A.I.C.S.: 621610

NINE PALMS 1, LP (1)
5360 Discovery Park Blvd Ste 200, Williamsburg, VA 23188
Tel.: (757) 253-2536
Web Site: http://www.amedisys.com
Emp.: 100
Health Care Srvices
N.A.I.C.S.: 621610

NINE PALMS 2, LLP (1)
11010 Hwy 49 Ste 4, Gulfport, MS 39503-4191
Tel.: (228) 831-9821
Women Healthcare Services
N.A.I.C.S.: 621610

Staff Builders Home Health
3505 Duluth Park Ln Ste 300, Duluth, GA 30096
Tel.: (678) 417-1033
Web Site: http://www.amedisys.com
Women Healthcare Services
N.A.I.C.S.: 621610

TENDER LOVING CARE HEALTH CARE SERVICES OF ERIE NI-

AGARA, LLC (1)
1127 Wehrle Dr Ste 50, Amherst, NY 14221-7700
Tel.: (716) 632-6420
Web Site: http://www.amedisys.com
Women Healthcare Services
N.A.I.C.S.: 621610

TENDER LOVING CARE HEALTH CARE SERVICES OF GEORGIA, LLC (1)
3505 Duluth Park Ln Ste 300, Duluth, GA 30337
Tel.: (678) 417-1033
Web Site: https://www.amedisys.com
Emp.: 25
Women Healthcare Services
N.A.I.C.S.: 621610

TENDER LOVING CARE HEALTH CARE SERVICES OF LONG IS-LAND, LLC (1)
960 S Broadway Ste 110A, Hicksville, NY 11801
Tel.: (516) 935-3737
Web Site: http://www.amedisys.com
Health Care Srvices
N.A.I.C.S.: 621610

TRI-CITIES HOME HEALTH, LLC. (1)
8819 W Victoria Ave Ste 110, Kennewick, WA 99336
Tel.: (509) 783-1851
Women Healthcare Services
N.A.I.C.S.: 621610

AMEN PROPERTIES, INC.
PO Box 835451, Richardson, TX 75083
Tel.: (972) 999-0494   **DE**
Web Site:
https://www.amenproperties.com
Year Founded: 1993
AMEN—(OTCIQ)
Rev.: $3,065,000
Assets: $5,298,000
Liabilities: $497,000
Net Worth: $4,801,000
Earnings: $1,757,000
Fiscal Year-end: 12/31/21
Holding Company; Real Estate, Oil & Gas Assets & Energy Consulting Services
N.A.I.C.S.: 551112
Eric L. Oliver (Chm)
Kris Oliver (CEO & Sec)

Subsidiaries:

NEMA Properties, LLC (1)
2215-B Renaissance Dr #B2, Las Vegas, NV 89119-6163   (100%)
Tel.: (702) 967-2460
Holding Company; Real Estate Investment
N.A.I.C.S.: 551112

AMERAMEX INTERNATIONAL, INC.
3930 Esplanade, Chico, CA 95973
Tel.: (530) 895-8955
Web Site: https://www.ammx.net
Year Founded: 1990
AMMX—(OTCIQ)
Rev.: $24,721,838
Assets: $10,785,501
Liabilities: $7,505,824
Net Worth: $3,279,677
Earnings: $1,631,747
Emp.: 19
Fiscal Year-end: 12/31/21
Heavy Equipment Maintenance Services
N.A.I.C.S.: 811310
Lee R. Hamre (Chm, Pres & CEO)
Hope Stone (CFO)
Marty Tullio (Sec)

AMERANT BANCORP INC.
Tel.: (305) 460-4001   **FL**
Web Site:
https://www.amerantbank.com

Year Founded: 1979
AMTB—(NASDAQ)
Rev.: $406,053,000
Assets: $9,127,804,000
Liabilities: $8,422,078,000
Net Worth: $705,726,000
Earnings: $63,310,000
Emp.: 692
Fiscal Year-end: 12/31/22
Bank Holding Company
N.A.I.C.S.: 551111
Carlos Iafigliola (COO & Sr Exec VP)
Julio V. Pena (Sr VP & Asst Sec)
Gerald P. Plush (Chm, Pres & CEO)
Christine Esteve (CMO & Exec VP)
Sharymar Calderon (CFO & Exec VP)
Armando D. Fleitas (Principal Acctg Officer)
Juan Esterripa (Sr Exec VP)
Silvia Larrieu (Sr VP)
Howard Levine (Sr Exec VP)
S. Marshall Martin (Chief Legal Officer)
Jason Russek (Pres)
Mariola Sanchez (Chief People Officer)
Caroline Verot Moore (Exec VP)
Laura Rossi (Sr Exec VP)

Subsidiaries:

Amerant Bank, N.A. (1)
220 Alhambra Cir, Coral Gables, FL 33134
Tel.: (305) 460-4001
Web Site: https://www.amerantbank.com
Sales Range: $350-399.9 Million
Commercial Banking
N.A.I.C.S.: 522110
Jerry Plush (Vice Chm & CEO)
Frederick C. Copeland Jr. (Chm)

Amerant Mortgage, LLC (1)
220 Alhambra Cir Ste 310, Coral Gables, FL 33134-5174
Web Site:
https://www.amerantmortgage.com
Engineering Construction Services
N.A.I.C.S.: 541330

AMEREN CORPORATION
1901 Chouteau Ave, Saint Louis, MO 63103
Tel.: (314) 621-3222   **MO**
Web Site: https://www.ameren.com
Year Founded: 1997
AEE—(NYSE)
Rev.: $7,500,000,000
Assets: $40,830,000,000
Liabilities: $29,352,000,000
Net Worth: $11,478,000,000
Earnings: $1,152,000,000
Emp.: 18,744
Fiscal Year-end: 12/31/23
Electricity Distribution Services
N.A.I.C.S.: 237990
Martin J Lyons Jr. (Chm, Pres & CEO)
Martin J. Lyons Jr. (Pres & CEO)
Shawn E. Schukar (Chm-Ameren Transmission & Pres-Ameren Transmission)
Theresa A. Shaw (Chief Acctg Officer & Sr VP-Fin)
Chonda J. Nwamu (Gen Counsel, Sec & Sr VP)
Bhavani Amirthalingam (Chief Digital Info Officer & Officer & Sr VP-Ameren Services)
Fadi M. Diya (Chief Nuclear Officer & Sr VP-Missouri)
Ajay Arora (Chief Renewable Development Officer.)
Gwendolyn G. Mizell (Chief Philanthropy Officer, Chief Sustainability & Diversity Officer & Sr VP)

Subsidiaries:

Ameren Energy Fuels & Services Co. (1)

1901 Chouteau Ave, Saint Louis, MO 63103   (100%)
Tel.: (314) 621-3222
Sales Range: $200-249.9 Million
Electronic Services
N.A.I.C.S.: 221118

Ameren Illinois Company (1)
10 Richard Mark Way, Collinsville, IL 62234   (100%)
Tel.: (618) 343-8150
Web Site: https://www.amereninvestors.com
Rev.: $3,482,000,000
Assets: $18,122,000,000
Liabilities: $11,297,000,000
Net Worth: $6,825,000,000
Earnings: $607,000,000
Emp.: 3,280
Fiscal Year-end: 12/31/2023
Electric Power Distribution Services
N.A.I.C.S.: 221122
Theresa A. Shaw (Sr VP-Fin Svcs & Regulatory Affairs)
Michael L. Moehn (CFO & Exec VP)
David N. Wakeman (Sr VP-Ops & Technical Svcs)
Eric M. Kozak (VP-Gas Ops)
James C. Blessing (VP-Regulatory Policy & Energy Supply)
George T. Justice (VP-Electric Ops)
Robin Kies (VP-Fin Svcs & Performance Mgmt)
Leonard Singh (Chm & Pres)
Kristol Simms (VP)
Joseph Solari (VP)
Craig Gilson (VP)

Ameren Michigan Gas Storage, LLC (1)
1901 Chouteau Ave, Saint Louis, MO 63103-3003
Tel.: (314) 554-2715
Oil & Gas Field Services
N.A.I.C.S.: 213112

Ameren Services Inc. (1)
1901 Chouteau Ave, Saint Louis, MO 63103-3003
Tel.: (314) 621-3222
Web Site: https://www.ameren.com
Sales Range: $75-99.9 Million
Administrative Services
N.A.I.C.S.: 561110
Michael Moehn (Pres)

AmerenIP (1)
370 S Main St, Saint Louis, MO 62523
Tel.: (314) 554-2255
Sales Range: $1-4.9 Billion
Emp.: 1,900
Public Utility
N.A.I.C.S.: 221118
Freda Carney (Engr-Design)

Electric Energy, Inc. (1)
2100 Portland Rd, Joppa, IL 62953   (80%)
Tel.: (618) 543-7531
Sales Range: $75-99.9 Million
Emp.: 179
Generating Station
N.A.I.C.S.: 221118
Randy Harris (Supvr-Electrical Maintenance)
Chris Goebel (Supvr-Electrical)
Greg Russell (Plant Mgr)

Union Electric Company (1)
120 S Central Ave, Clayton, MO 63105
Tel.: (314) 621-3222
Web Site: https://www.ameren.com
Rev.: $3,859,000,000
Assets: $20,606,000,000
Liabilities: $13,643,000,000
Net Worth: $6,963,000,000
Earnings: $548,000,000
Emp.: 4,011
Fiscal Year-end: 12/31/2023
Wholesale Energy Services
N.A.I.C.S.: 221122
Martin J Lyons Jr. (Chm & Pres)
Martin J. Lyons Jr. (Chm & Pres)
Michael L. Moehn (CFO & Exec VP)

Subsidiary (Domestic):

STARS Alliance, LLC (2)
6751 N Sunset Blvd Ste E-460, Glendale, AZ 85305
Tel.: (623) 209-7549

Web Site: https://www.starsalliance.com
Electric Power Distribution Services
N.A.I.C.S.: 221122

AMERESCO, INC.
111 Speen St Ste 410, Framingham,
MA 01701
Tel.: (508) 661-2200   DE
Web Site: https://www.ameresco.com
Year Founded: 2000
AMRC—(NYSE)
Rev.: $1,824,422,000
Assets: $2,876,821,000
Liabilities: $2,003,790,000
Net Worth: $873,031,000
Earnings: $94,926,000
Emp.: 180
Fiscal Year-end: 12/31/22
Renewable Power Generation Assets
Developer, Owner & Operator
N.A.I.C.S.: 221114
George P. Sakellaris *(Chm, Pres & CEO)*
Nicole Allen Bulgarino *(Exec VP)*
Robert Georgeoff *(Exec VP-South Reg)*
Lauren Todd *(Sr VP-HR & Ops)*
Leila Dillon *(Sr VP-Corp Mktg & Comm)*
Peter Christakis *(Exec VP)*
Lenka Patten *(Chief HR Officer)*
David J. Corrsin *(Gen Counsel, Sec & Exec VP)*
Mark A. Chiplock *(CFO, Chief Acctg Officer & Exec VP)*

Subsidiaries:

Ameresco DMHS LLC   (1)
5301 Limestone Rd Ste 222, Wilmington,
DE 19808
Tel.: (302) 504-3070
Web Site: http://www.ameresco.com
Renewable Energy Consulting Services
N.A.I.C.S.: 541690

Ameresco Federal Solutions, Inc. (1)
101 Constitution Ave NW Ste 525 E, Washington, DC 20001
Tel.: (202) 650-6200
Web Site: http://www.ameresco.com
Energy Conservation & Power Generation Services
N.A.I.C.S.: 238210
Nicole Allen Bulgarino *(Exec VP & Gen Mgr)*
Nicole Allen Bulgarino *(Exec VP & Gen Mgr)*

Ameresco Georgia LLC   (1)
120 W Trinity Pl 4th Fl, Decatur, GA 30030
Tel.: (404) 812-5350
Web Site: http://www.ameresco.com
Renewable Energy Consulting Services
N.A.I.C.S.: 541690

Ameresco Limited   (1)
Halkin Building 4th Floor 1-2 Paris Garden,
Southwark, London, SE1 8ND, United Kingdom
Tel.: (44) 2035428300
Web Site: https://uk.ameresco.com
Energy Services
N.A.I.C.S.: 238210

Ameresco Select, Inc.   (1)
111 Speen St Ste 410, Framingham, MA
01701-2090
Tel.: (508) 653-0456
Web Site: http://www.ameresco.com
Emp.: 50
Energy Distr
N.A.I.C.S.: 221122

Ameresco Solar - Solutions Inc. (1)
42261 Zevo Dr, Temecula, CA 92590
Tel.: (619) 764-6023
Energy Management Services
N.A.I.C.S.: 221114
Michael Russell *(Mgr-Pur & Supply Chain)*

Ameresco Southwest, Inc.   (1)
120 E Corporate Pl, Chandler, AZ 85225
Tel.: (480) 760-2500
Web Site: http://southwest.ameresco.com

Sales Range: $25-49.9 Million
Emp.: 55
Electricity & Energy Usage Management &
Solutions
N.A.I.C.S.: 221122

Ameresco Stafford LLC   (1)
4701 Cox Rd Ste 285, Glen Allen, VA
23060
Tel.: (540) 288-3248
Energy Services
N.A.I.C.S.: 238210

AmerescoSolutions, Inc.   (1)
5550 77 Ctr Dr Ste 380, Charlotte, NC
28217
Tel.: (704) 916-3500
Web Site: http://www.ameresco.com
Sales Range: $25-49.9 Million
Emp.: 30
Utilities Construction Services
N.A.I.C.S.: 237130

Applied Energy Group, Inc.   (1)
1377 Motor Pkwy Ste 401, Islandia, NY
11749
Tel.: (631) 434-1414
Web Site:
    https://www.appliedenergygroup.com
Sales Range: $150-199.9 Million
Emp.: 750
Scientific & Technical Consulting Services
N.A.I.C.S.: 541690
Ingrid Rohmund *(Sr VP, Sr VP & Mgr)*
Eddy Saleh *(Sr VP-Strategy & Business Development)*
Kenny Maslak *(VP-Product Mgmt & Development)*
Eli Morris *(Sr Mng Dir-Consulting Svcs)*
Jamie Nerys *(Mng Dir-Implementation Svcs)*
Peter Gazzo *(Sr Mng Dir-Vision DSM Delivery Svcs)*
Joe Giarrusso *(Dir-Bus Ops)*
Kenin O'Connor *(Dir-Bus & Solution Integration)*

Green Wave LLC   (1)
700 N Brand Blvd Ste 640, Glendale, CA
91203
Tel.: (818) 507-4732
Web Site: https://www.greenwavellc.com
Energy Services
N.A.I.C.S.: 238210

Montevue Lane Solar LLC   (1)
111 Speen St Ste 410, Framingham, MA
01701
Tel.: (508) 661-2200
Eletric Power Generation Services
N.A.I.C.S.: 221111
George Sakellaris *(CEO)*

TerraNavigator, LLC   (1)
888 Prospect St Ste 200, La Jolla, CA
92037
Tel.: (858) 263-2889
Web Site: http://www.terranavigator.com
Renewable Energy Services
N.A.I.C.S.: 221118

AMERGENT HOSPITALITY GROUP, INC.
Tel.: (704) 366-5122   DE
Web Site:
    https://www.amergenthg.com
Year Founded: 2020
AMHG—(OTCIQ)
Rev.: $21,294,000
Assets: $19,185,000
Liabilities: $28,489,000
Net Worth: ($9,304,000)
Earnings: ($3,013,000)
Emp.: 319
Fiscal Year-end: 12/31/22
Restaurant Operators
N.A.I.C.S.: 722511
Stephen J. Hoelscher *(CFO)*
Michael D. Pruitt *(Chm & CEO)*

AMERICA GREAT HEALTH
1609 W Valley Blvd Ste 338, Alhambra, CA 91803   WY
Web Site: https://aaghus.com
Year Founded: 2009
AAGH—(OTCIQ)
Rev.: $204,308

Assets: $299,129
Liabilities: $4,824,965
Net Worth: ($4,525,836)
Earnings: ($761,420)
Emp.: 7
Fiscal Year-end: 06/30/23
Pharmaceuticals Distr
N.A.I.C.S.: 424210
Mike Q. Wang *(Pres & CEO)*

AMERICA'S CAR-MART, INC.
1805 N 2nd St Ste 401, Rogers, AR
72756
Tel.: (479) 464-9944   TX
Web Site: https://www.car-mart.com
Year Founded: 1983
CRMT—(NASDAQ)
Rev.: $1,393,894,000
Assets: $1,477,644,000
Liabilities: $1,006,894,000
Net Worth: $470,750,000
Earnings: ($31,393,000)
Emp.: 2,280
Fiscal Year-end: 04/30/24
Holding Company; Used Car Dealerships Owner & Operator
N.A.I.C.S.: 551112
Douglas W. Campbell *(Pres & CEO)*
Vickie D. Judy *(CFO)*
Joshua G. Welch *(Chm)*
Douglas Campbell *(Pres)*
Holly Thomson *(Chief Digital Officer)*

Subsidiaries:

America's Car Mart, Inc.   (1)
1805 N 2nd St Ste 401, Rogers, AR 72756
Tel.: (479) 464-9944
Web Site: https://www.car-mart.com
Sales Range: $1-9.9 Million
Emp.: 24
Used Car Dealership Operator
N.A.I.C.S.: 441120
Douglas W. Campbell *(Pres & CEO)*
Barry Baggett *(Sr Mgr-Mktg)*
Curtis Valentine *(Gen Mgr-Car Mart of Rogers)*

Colonial Auto Finance, Inc.   (1)
802 SE Plz Ave Ste 200, Bentonville, AR
72712
Tel.: (479) 464-9944
Emp.: 200
Consumer Lending Services
N.A.I.C.S.: 522291
Hank Henderson *(Pres)*
Jeffrey Williams *(CFO)*

Texas Car-Mart, Inc.   (1)
2300 W Ferguson Rd, Mount Pleasant, TX
75455
Tel.: (903) 572-9400
Web Site: http://www.car-mart.com
Emp.: 11
Used Car Dealers
N.A.I.C.S.: 441120
Angel Carrillo *(Gen Mgr)*

AMERICAN ACQUISITION OPPORTUNITY, INC.
12115 Visionary Way, Fishers, IN
46038
Tel.: (317) 855-9926   DE
Year Founded: 2021
AMAO—(NASDAQ)
Rev.: $22,729
Assets: $7,790,834
Liabilities: $11,725,680
Net Worth: ($3,934,846)
Earnings: $3,888,708
Fiscal Year-end: 12/31/22
Investment Services
N.A.I.C.S.: 523999
Mark C. Jensen *(Chm & CEO)*
Kirk P. Taylor *(Pres & CFO)*

Subsidiaries:

Royalty Management Holding
Corporation   (1)
12115 Visionary Way Ste 174, IN 46038
Tel.: (317) 855-9926

Financial Services
N.A.I.C.S.: 523999

AMERICAN AIRLINES GROUP INC.
1 Skyview Dr, Fort Worth, TX 76155
Tel.: (682) 278-9000   DE
Web Site: https://www.aa.com
Year Founded: 1982
AAL—(NASDAQ)
Rev.: $52,788,000,000
Assets: $63,058,000,000
Liabilities: $68,260,000,000
Net Worth: ($5,202,000,000)
Earnings: $822,000,000
Emp.: 132,100
Fiscal Year-end: 12/31/23
Holding Company; Air Transportation
Services
N.A.I.C.S.: 551112
Elise R. Eberwein *(Exec VP-People & Global Engagement)*
Robert D. Isom Jr. *(Pres & CEO)*
Devon E. May *(CFO & Exec VP)*
Stephen L. Johnson *(Exec VP-Corp Affairs)*
Devon E. May *(CFO)*
Angela K. Owens *(VP)*

Subsidiaries:

American Airlines, Inc.   (1)
1 Skyview Dr, Fort Worth, TX
76155   **(100%)**
Tel.: (682) 278-9000
Web Site: https://www.aa.com
Rev.: $48,965,000,000
Assets: $70,324,000,000
Liabilities: $64,731,000,000
Net Worth: $5,593,000,000
Earnings: $338,000,000
Emp.: 129,699
Fiscal Year-end: 12/31/2022
Air Transportation
N.A.I.C.S.: 488119
William Douglas Parker *(Chm)*
Elise R. Eberwein *(Exec VP-People & Comm-American Airlines Group Inc.)*
Devon E. May *(CFO & Exec VP)*
Stephen L. Johnson *(Exec VP-Corp Affairs-American Airlines Group Inc.)*
Ganesh Jayaram *(Chief Digital & Info Officer & Exec VP)*
Kyle Mabry *(VP-Ops & Comml-EMEA & APAC)*
Priya Aiyar *(Chief Legal Officer)*
Nate Gatten *(Chief Govt Affairs Officer)*
Vasu Raja *(Chief Comml Officer)*
David Seymour *(COO)*
Angela K. Owens *(VP)*

Subsidiary (Domestic):

Admirals Club, Inc.   (2)
4333 Amon Carter Blvd, Fort Worth, TX
76155-9616
Tel.: (817) 963-1234
Web Site: http://www.aa.com
Club Management Services
N.A.I.C.S.: 711211

Unit (Domestic):

American Airlines Cargo   (2)
4225 Amon Carter Blvd, Fort Worth, TX
76155-2603   **(100%)**
Tel.: (817) 355-6800
Web Site: https://www.aacargo.com
Sales Range: $100-124.9 Million
Emp.: 4,800
Provider of Freight & Mail Services
N.A.I.C.S.: 561599

Branch (Domestic):

American Airlines, Inc. - Puerto Rico
Office   (2)
Calle 1 Ste 100 15 Guaynabo, San Juan,
PR 00926-9633
Tel.: (787) 749-5050
Web Site: http://www.aa.com
Sales Range: $400-449.9 Million
Emp.: 30
Air Passenger Carrier
N.A.I.C.S.: 481111

American Airlines Group Inc.—(Continued)

Subsidiary (Domestic):

American Aviation Supply LLC   **(2)**
4333 Amon Carter Blvd, Fort Worth, TX
76155
Tel.: (817) 963-2214
Oil Transportation Services
N.A.I.C.S.: 481111

Envoy Aviation Group Inc.   **(1)**
4301 Regent Blvd, Irving, TX 75063
Tel.: (972) 374-5200
Web Site: http://www.envoyair.com
Holding Company; Airline Operator
N.A.I.C.S.: 551112

Subsidiary (Domestic):

Eagle Aviation Services, Inc.   **(2)**
2751 Airport Blvd, Abilene, TX 79602
Tel.: (325) 672-0983
Passenger Air Transportation Services
N.A.I.C.S.: 481111

Envoy Air Inc.   **(2)**
4301 Regent Blvd, Irving, TX 75063
Tel.: (972) 374-5200
Web Site: https://www.envoyair.com
Emp.: 18,000
Passenger Airline Operator
N.A.I.C.S.: 481111
Scott Trepinski (VP-Safety, Security, and
Environmental)
Mindi Kimmell (Mng Dir-Fin Svcs)
Chanen Lively (VP-HR & Employment
Counsel)
Jose Velez-Rubio (VP-Dallas & Fort Worth
Hub)
Frank Reynolds (VP-New York Hubs &
Northeast)
Migdoel Rosa (VP-Miami Hub)
Deesha Desai (VP-Los Angeles & West Re-
gion)
Christopher James (Dir-Legal, Labor & Em-
ployment)

**International Ground Services, S.A.
de C.V.**   **(1)**
Aeropuerto Intl Cancun, 77565, Cancun,
Quintana Roo, Mexico
Tel.: (52) 9988860263
Emp.: 100
Air Cargo Handling Services
N.A.I.C.S.: 488119
Patricia Oranday (Gen Mgr)

Material Services Company, Inc.   **(1)**
1000 Rosedale Ave, Middletown, PA 17057
Tel.: (717) 948-5500
Sales Range: $50-74.9 Million
Emp.: 10
Air Transport Services
N.A.I.C.S.: 424720

PSA Airlines, Inc.   **(1)**
3400 Terminal Dr, Vandalia, OH
45377   **(100%)**
Web Site: https://www.psaairlines.com
Sales Range: $400-449.9 Million
Emp.: 5,000
Aircraft Maintenance Services
N.A.I.C.S.: 488190
Dion J. Flannery (Pres)
Keith Stamper (VP-Flight Ops)
Michael Bruhn (VP-Fin)
Reddy Gumireddy (VP-Ops Plng & Perfor-
mance)
Christine Hollanshead (VP-)
Steve Kingsley (VP-)
Richard Ugarte (VP-)

Piedmont Airlines, Inc.   **(1)**
5443 Airport Terminal Rd, Salisbury, MD
21804   **(100%)**
Tel.: (410) 572-5100
Web Site: https://www.piedmont-
airlines.com
Sales Range: $200-249.9 Million
Emp.: 500
Scheduled Passenger Air Carrier; Freight
Forwarding Services
N.A.I.C.S.: 481112
Eric Morgan (Sr VP-Ground Handling)
William W. Arndt (VP-Engrg & Maintenance)
Lyle Hogg (Pres & CEO)
Julie Schell (VP-Regulatory Compliance &
Safety)

Perry Constant (VP-Fin)
Jackie Lanza Jennings (Dir-Corp Comm)
Jeff Garver (VP-)
Eddie Leverton (VP-)

AMERICAN ASSETS TRUST, INC.

3420 Carmel Mountain Rd Ste 100,
San Diego, CA 92121
Tel.: (858) 350-2600   **MD**
Web Site:
  https://www.americanassets
  trust.com
AAT—(NYSE)
Rev.: $422,648,000
Assets: $2,987,881,000
Liabilities: $1,802,356,000
Net Worth: $1,185,525,000
Earnings: $43,506,000
Emp.: 216
Fiscal Year-end: 12/31/22
Real Estate Investment Services
N.A.I.C.S.: 525990
Ernest Sylvan Rady (Chm & CEO)
Robert F. Barton (CFO, Treas & Exec
VP)
Adam Wyll (Pres & COO)
Emily Mandic (VP)

Subsidiaries:

American Assets Trust, L.P.   **(1)**
3420 Carmel Mountain Rd Ste 100, San
Diego, CA 92121
Tel.: (858) 350-2600
Web Site:
  https://www.americanassetstrust.com
Rev.: $422,647,999
Assets: $2,987,880,999
Liabilities: $1,802,355,999
Net Worth: $1,185,524,999
Earnings: $55,229,000
Emp.: 215
Fiscal Year-end: 12/31/2022
Real Estate Investment Services
N.A.I.C.S.: 531110
Ernest Sylvan Rady (Chm, Pres & CEO)
Sylvan Rady (Co-Founder & CFO)
Robert Barton (Co-Founder)
Adam Wyll (CTO)
Jerry Gammieri (Sr VP)
Steve Center (Sr VP)
Chris Sullivan (Sr VP)
Abigail Rex (VP)
Emily Mandic (VP)

AMERICAN AXLE & MANU-FACTURING HOLDINGS, INC.

1 Dauch Dr, Detroit, MI 48211-1198
Tel.: (313) 758-2000   **DE**
Web Site: https://www.aam.com
Year Founded: 1998
AXL—(NYSE)
Rev.: $5,802,400,000
Assets: $5,469,400,000
Liabilities: $4,842,100,000
Net Worth: $627,300,000
Earnings: $64,300,000
Emp.: 19,000
Fiscal Year-end: 12/31/22
Holding Company; Motor Vehicle
Driveline, Drivetrain, Chassis & Other
Automotive Components Designer &
Mfr
N.A.I.C.S.: 551112
David C. Dauch (Chm & CEO)
Michael J. Lynch (Pres & COO)
Christopher J. May (CFO & Exec VP)
David E. Barnes (Gen Counsel & VP)
James G. Zaliwski (Chief Acctg Offi-
cer)

Subsidiaries:

**American Axle & Manufacturing,
Inc.**   **(1)**
1 Dauch Dr, Detroit, MI
48211-1198   **(100%)**
Tel.: (313) 758-2000
Web Site: http://www.aam.com

Motor Vehicle Driveline, Drivetrain, Chassis
& Other Automotive Components Designer
& Mfr
N.A.I.C.S.: 336390

Subsidiary (Domestic):

AAM International Holdings, Inc.   **(2)**
One Dauch Dr, Detroit, MI
48211-1198   **(100%)**
Tel.: (313) 758-2000
Web Site: http://www.aam.com
Sales Range: $250-299.9 Million
Holding Company
N.A.I.C.S.: 551112
David C. Dauch (Chm & CEO)

Subsidiary (Non-US):

AAM Germany GmbH   **(3)**
Paul-Ehrlich-Strasse 10, 63225, Langen,
Germany
Tel.: (49) 6172 138 6000
Web Site: https://www.aam.com
Emp.: 300
Iron & Steel Forging Services
N.A.I.C.S.: 332111

**AAM Pantnagar Axle Private
Limited**   **(3)**
Plot No 36 A Sector 11 Sidcul, Rudrapur,
263 153, Uttarakhand, India
Tel.: (91) 59 44211007
Iron & Steel Forging Services
N.A.I.C.S.: 332111

AAM Poland Sp. z o. o.   **(3)**
ul Szarych Szeregow 16-18, 58-100, Swid-
nica, Poland
Tel.: (48) 746409300
Iron & Steel Forging Services
N.A.I.C.S.: 332111

AAM do Brasil Ltda.   **(3)**
Avenida das Nacoes 2051, Bairro Capela
Velha, Araucaria, 83705-335,
Brazil   **(99.23%)**
Tel.: (55) 412 141 1000
Web Site: https://www.aam.com
Sales Range: $250-299.9 Million
Emp.: 700
Motor Vehicle Parts Manufacturing, Engi-
neering, Sales & Customer Service
N.A.I.C.S.: 336390

**Albion Automotive (Holdings)
Limited**   **(3)**
1187 South Street, Scotstoun Glasgow,
Glasgow, G14 0DT, United Kingdom
Tel.: (44) 141 434 2400
Web Site: http://www.aem.com
Sales Range: $50-74.9 Million
Emp.: 100
Automotive Products Mfr & Distr
N.A.I.C.S.: 423120
Brian Mecleud (Plant Mgr)

Albion Automotive Limited   **(3)**
1187 South Street Scotstoun, Glasgow,
G14 0DT, United Kingdom   **(100%)**
Tel.: (44) 1419591261
Web Site: http://www.aam.com
Sales Range: $300-349.9 Million
Manufacture & Assembly of Commercial
Vehicle Axles, Transmission Components,
Chassis Components & Crankshafts
N.A.I.C.S.: 336390

Subsidiary (Domestic):

AccuGear, Inc.   **(2)**
6710 Innovation Blvd, Fort Wayne, IN
46818-1334
Tel.: (260) 497-6600
Iron & Steel Forging Services
N.A.I.C.S.: 332111

Subsidiary (Non-US):

**American Axle & Manufacturing de
Mexico Holdings S. de R.L. de
C.V.**   **(2)**
Av Comerciantes No 1300 Parque Industrial
Fipasi, Silao, 36100, Mexico   **(99.99%)**
Tel.: (52) 4727229500
Sales Range: $250-299.9 Million
Holding Company; Motor Vehicle Parts
Manufacturing
N.A.I.C.S.: 551112

Subsidiary (Domestic):

**American Axle & Manufacturing de
Mexico S. de R.L. de C.V.**   **(3)**
Comerciantes No 1300 Parque Industrial
FIPASI Carretera, Silao-Irapuato Km 5 3
Guanajuato, Silao, 36100, Mexico
Tel.: (52) 4727229500
Motor Vehicle Transmission Mfr
N.A.I.C.S.: 336350

**Guanajuato Gear & Axle de Mexico
S. de R.L. de C.V.**   **(3)**
Calle Sin Nombre Ste 1300 Parque Indus-
trial Fipasi, Unidades Economicas Grandes
Fuera De Localidad, Silao, 36100, Mexico
Tel.: (52) 4727229500
Web Site: http://www.aam.com
Axle Assemblies, Propeller Shafts & Driv-
eline Systems Mfr
N.A.I.C.S.: 336390

Subsidiary (Domestic):

Colfor Manufacturing, Inc.   **(2)**
3255 Alliance Rd NW, Malvern, OH
44644-0485   **(100%)**
Tel.: (330) 470-6207
Web Site:
  https://colformanufacturinginc.com
Sales Range: $150-199.9 Million
Emp.: 700
Iron & Steel Forging & Machining Services
N.A.I.C.S.: 332111

MSP Industries Corporation   **(2)**
45 W Oakwood Rd, Oxford, MI
48371-1631   **(100%)**
Tel.: (248) 628-4150
Web Site: http://www.aam.com
Mfr of Forgings of Ferrous & Non-Ferrous
Materials
N.A.I.C.S.: 332111

**Metaldyne Performance Group
Inc.**   **(2)**
1 Towne Sq Ste 550, Southfield, MI 48076
Tel.: (248) 727-1800
Web Site: http://www.aam.com
Engine, Transmission, Driveline, Chassis,
Suspension, Steering & Brake Components
Mfr
N.A.I.C.S.: 336310

Subsidiary (Domestic):

HHI Group Holdings, LLC   **(3)**
2727 W 14 Mile Rd, Royal Oak, MI 48073
Tel.: (248) 597-3800
Holding Company; Forged Automotive Parts
Mfr
N.A.I.C.S.: 551112

Subsidiary (Domestic):

HHI FormTech, LLC   **(4)**
2727 W Fourteen Mile Rd, Royal Oak, MI
48073-1712
Tel.: (248) 597-3800
Web Site: http://ww.forging.org
Forged Automotive Parts Mfr
N.A.I.C.S.: 332111

Impact Forge Group, LLC   **(4)**
2805 Norcross Dr, Columbus, IN 47201-
4911
Tel.: (812) 342-4437
Web Site: http://www.aam.com
Forged Mechanical Components Mfr
N.A.I.C.S.: 332111

Jernberg Industries, LLC   **(4)**
328 W 40th Pl, Chicago, IL 60609
Tel.: (773) 268-3004
Web Site: http://www.aam.com
Iron & Steel Forgings; Motorcycle Wheels &
Ring Gears Mfr
N.A.I.C.S.: 332111

Subsidiary (Domestic):

Jernberg Sales, LLC   **(5)**
328 W 40th Pl, Chicago, IL 60609
Tel.: (773) 268-3004
Web Site: http://www.aam.com
Forged & Machined Automotive Products
Mfr
N.A.I.C.S.: 336350

Subsidiary (Domestic):

Metaldyne, LLC   **(3)**
40600 Ann Arbor Rd #201,, Plymouth, MI
48170
Tel.: (734) 207-6200

Automotive Engine & Transmission Components & Assemblies Mfr
N.A.I.C.S.: 336350

Subsidiary (Non-US):

Metaldyne International (UK) Ltd. **(4)**
131 Parkinson Lane, Halifax, HX1 3RD, United Kingdom
Tel.: (44) 1422357234
Web Site: https://www.metaldyne.co.uk
Automotive Vibration Control Engine Components Mfr
N.A.I.C.S.: 336390
David A. Whitaker (Mgr-Sls & Svc)

Metaldyne Nurnberg GmbH **(4)**
Otto-Kraus-Strasse 11, 90411, Nuremberg, Germany
Tel.: (49) 91159810
Web Site: http://www.aam.com
Hot & Cold Forged, Machined & Annealed Automotive Engine & Transmission Components & Assemblies Mfr
N.A.I.C.S.: 332111

Metaldyne Oslavany, spol. s.r.o. **(4)**
Padochovska 1117/1, 664 12, Oslavany, Czech Republic
Tel.: (420) 515517153
Web Site: https://www.metaldyne.cz
Emp.: 200
Cold Forged & Machined Automotive Engine & Transmission Components & Assemblies Mfr
N.A.I.C.S.: 332111

Subsidiary (Domestic):

Metaldyne SinterForged Products, LLC **(4)**
3100 N Hwy Ste 3, North Vernon, IN 47265
Tel.: (812) 346-1566
Web Site: http://www.aam.com
Forged & Machined Motor Vehicle Connecting Rods Mfr
N.A.I.C.S.: 336390

Metaldyne Sintered Components, Inc. - St. Marys **(4)**
197 W Creek Rd, Saint Marys, PA 15857
Tel.: (814) 834-1222
Web Site: http://www.aam.com
Machined Motor Vehicle Components Mfr
N.A.I.C.S.: 336390

Metaldyne Sintered Ridgway, LLC **(4)**
1149 Rocky Rd, Ridgway, PA 15853
Tel.: (814) 776-1141
Web Site: http://www.aam.com
Sintered, Forged & Machined Automotive Components Mfr
N.A.I.C.S.: 332111

Subsidiary (Domestic):

Oxford Forge, Inc. **(2)**
2300 X-Celsior Dr, Oxford, MI 48371-1631
Tel.: (248) 628-1303
Web Site: http://www.aam.com
Emp.: 100
Iron & Steel Forging Services
N.A.I.C.S.: 332111

Jernberg Industries, LLC **(1)**
455 Gibraltar Dr, Bolingbrook, IL 60440
Tel.: (630) 972-7000
Motor Vehicle Parts Distr
N.A.I.C.S.: 423120
John Hieronymus (Sr Mgr-HR)

Metaldyne International France SAS **(1)**
33-35 Rue Roger Salengro, PO Box 227, 69200, Venissieux, Cedex, France
Tel.: (33) 478784678
Motor Vehicle Parts Distr
N.A.I.C.S.: 423120

Metaldyne Powertrain Mexico, S. de R.L. de C.V. **(1)**
Calzada Ermita Iztapalapa 1478 Colonia Barrio, Iztapalapa, San Miguel de Allende, 09360, Mexico
Tel.: (52) 5558043300
Motor Vehicle Parts Distr
N.A.I.C.S.: 423120

Punchcraft Machining and Tooling, LLC **(1)**

30500 Ryan Rd, Warren, MI 48092
Tel.: (586) 573-4840
Motor Vehicle Parts Distr
N.A.I.C.S.: 423120
Keith Jason (Ops Mgr)

AMERICAN BANCORP, INC.
307 E Landry St, Opelousas, LA 70570
Tel.: (337) 948-3056
Web Site:
http://www.americanbankand trust.net
ABNC—(OTCIQ)
Bank Holding Company
N.A.I.C.S.: 551111
Ronald J. Lashute (CEO & Sec)
Salvador L. Diesi (Pres)

Subsidiaries:

American Bank & Trust **(1)**
307 E Landry St, Opelousas, LA 70570
Tel.: (337) 948-3056
Web Site:
http://www.americanbankandtrust.net
Banking Services
N.A.I.C.S.: 522110
Ronald J. Lashute (Pres & CEO)

AMERICAN BANK INCORPORATED
4029 W Tilghman St, Allentown, PA 18104-1619
Tel.: (610) 366-1800   PA
Year Founded: 2001
AMBK—(OTCIQ)
Rev.: $27,404,000
Assets: $641,552,000
Liabilities: $580,891,000
Net Worth: $60,661,000
Earnings: $7,881,000
Emp.: 58
Fiscal Year-end: 12/31/19
Bank Holding Company
N.A.I.C.S.: 551111
Mark W. Jaindl (Chm, Pres & CEO)
Toney C. Horst (Treas)
Karina F. Behler (Sec)
Brian P. Farrell (Sr VP)
Kyle Beitzer (Controller)
Chris J. Persichetti (Chief Legal Officer & Exec VP)
Louis Monaco III (Sr VP & Reg Mgr)

Subsidiaries:

American Bank **(1)**
4029 W Tilghman St, Allentown, PA 18104   **(100%)**
Tel.: (610) 366-1800
Web Site: http://www.ambk.com
Sales Range: $25-49.9 Million
Commericial Banking
N.A.I.C.S.: 522110
Mehulkumar B. Patel (Owner)
Mark W. Jaindl (Chm, Pres & CEO)
Toney C. Horst (CFO & Sr VP)
Karina F. Behler (COO, Sec & Sr VP)
Chris J. Persichetti (Chief Lending Officer & Exec VP)
Robert W. Turner (CIO & Sr VP)
Brian P. Farrell (Chief Credit Officer, Chief Risk Officer & Sr VP)

Subsidiary (Domestic):

American Capital Trust I **(2)**
4029 W Tilghman St, Allentown, PA 18104
Tel.: (610) 366-1800
Financial Banking Services
N.A.I.C.S.: 522110
Mark W. Jaindl (Pres & CEO)
Harry Birkhimer (CFO & Sr VP)

AMERICAN BASKETBALL ASSOCIATION, INC.
9421 Holliday Dr, Indianapolis, IN 46260
Tel.: (317) 844-7502   UT
ABKB—(OTCIQ)
Sports Club Operator

N.A.I.C.S.: 711211
Joseph A. Newman (CEO)

AMERICAN BATTERY MATERIALS, INC.
500 W Putnam Ave Ste 400, Greenwich, CT 06830   DE
Web Site:
https://www.americanbatterymate rials.com
Year Founded: 2007
BLTH—(OTCIQ)
Rev.: $351,760
Assets: $205,299
Liabilities: $1,505,711
Net Worth: ($1,300,412)
Earnings: ($1,486,848)
Emp.: 1
Fiscal Year-end: 12/31/22
Vending Machine Operators
N.A.I.C.S.: 445132
Sebastian Lux (Interim CEO)
Patrick L. Avery (COO)

AMERICAN BATTERY METALS CORP.
401 S Ryland St Ste 138, Reno, NV 89502
Tel.: (775) 473-4744
Web Site:
http://www.americanbatterytech nology.com
Year Founded: 2016
ABML—(OTCIQ)
Rev.: $18,084
Assets: $21,263,103
Liabilities: $1,822,498
Net Worth: $19,440,605
Earnings: ($41,760,064)
Fiscal Year-end: 06/30/21
Metal Exploration Services
N.A.I.C.S.: 213114
Ryan Melsert (CEO & CTO)
Chuck Leber (Project Mgr-Onsite Construction & Dev)
Vickey Alvarez (Controller)
David Corsaut (CFO)
Doug Hamilton (Head-Policy)
Andres Meza (COO)

AMERICAN BATTERY TECHNOLOGY COMPANY
100 Washington St St Ste 100, Reno, NV 89503
Tel.: (775) 473-4744   NV
Web Site:
https://www.americanbatterytech nology.com
Year Founded: 2011
ABAT—(NASDAQ)
Rev.: $237,067
Assets: $74,658,652
Liabilities: $13,444,168
Net Worth: $61,214,484
Earnings: ($21,338,207)
Emp.: 54
Fiscal Year-end: 06/30/23
Other Metal Ore Mining
N.A.I.C.S.: 212290
Ryan Melsert (Chm, CEO & CTO)
Scott Jolcover (Chief Resource Officer)
Mitchell Dreier (Dir-Engrg)
Jesse Deutsch (CFO)

AMERICAN BILTRITE INC.
57 River St Ste 302, Wellesley Hills, MA 02481-2097
Tel.: (617) 237-6655   DE
Web Site: https://www.american-biltrite.com
Year Founded: 1908
ABLT—(OTCIQ)
Rev.: $162,477,000
Assets: $121,575,000
Liabilities: $99,767,000

Net Worth: $21,808,000
Earnings: ($14,111,000)
Emp.: 659
Fiscal Year-end: 12/31/20
Vinyl & Rubber Floor Tile, Hard Wood Floors, Rubber & Vinyl Tape, Protective Film Tape, Paper Tape & Other Pressure Sensitive Tape Mfr & Distr
N.A.I.C.S.: 326112
Roger A. Marcus (Chm & CEO)
Richard A. Marcus (Pres & COO)
Howard A. Feist III (CFO)

Subsidiaries:

ABItalia, Inc. **(1)**
Via Breda 11/B Zona Ind. A, Civitanova Marche, 62012, Macerata, MC, Italy
Tel.: (39) 0733801086
Web Site: http://www.abitape.com
Pressure Sensitive Tapes, Protective Films, Commercial Flooring & Performance Sheet Rubber Supplier & Mfr
N.A.I.C.S.: 326299

ABTRE, Inc. **(1)**
57 River St, Wellesley Hills, MA 02481   **(100%)**
Tel.: (781) 237-6655
Web Site: http://www.ambilt.com
Sales Range: $300-349.9 Million
Emp.: 10
Industrial Products
N.A.I.C.S.: 326299
Richard Marcus (Pres)

American Biltrite **(1)**
105 Whittendale Dr, Moorestown, NJ 08057-1364
Tel.: (856) 778-0700
Web Site: http://www.abitape.com
Sales Range: $125-149.9 Million
Emp.: 135
Electrical, Protective & Industrial Tapes
N.A.I.C.S.: 314910
Michael J. Merkx (VP & Gen Mgr-Tape Products Div)

American Biltrite Far East, Inc. **(1)**
17 Jo Koon Crescent, Singapore, 629016, Singapore   **(100%)**
Tel.: (65) 68978327
Web Site: http://www.abitape.com
Sales Range: $10-24.9 Million
Emp.: 17
Tape Products
N.A.I.C.S.: 322220
Irene Tan (Mng Dir)

American Biltrite Intellectual Properties Inc. **(1)**
103 Foulk Rd Ste 200, Wilmington, DE 19803
Tel.: (302) 656-1950
Sales Range: $100-124.9 Million
Pipe Fitting Mfr
N.A.I.C.S.: 332996

American Biltrite Ltd. **(1)**
200 Bank St, Sherbrooke, J1H 4K3, QC, Canada   **(100%)**
Tel.: (819) 829-3300
Web Site: http://www.american-biltrite.com
Sales Range: $50-74.9 Million
Emp.: 250
Footwear Products, Floor Coverings & Industrial Rubber & Plastic Products
N.A.I.C.S.: 326199

Ideal Tape Company **(1)**
1400 Middlesex St, Lowell, MA 01851-1222   **(100%)**
Tel.: (978) 458-6833
Web Site: http://www.idealtape.com
Sales Range: $10-24.9 Million
Emp.: 30
Shoe, Athletic & Electronic Tapes & Other Pressure Sensitive Tapes
N.A.I.C.S.: 322220
Bonnie Posnak (VP-HR)

Ideal Tape-Belgium **(1)**
Klein Frankrijkstraat 13, 9600, Ronse, Renaix, Belgium   **(100%)**
Tel.: (32) 55235151
Web Site: http://www.idealabi.com
Sales Range: $10-24.9 Million
Emp.: 30
Tape Products

American Biltrite Inc.—(Continued)

N.A.I.C.S.: 322220
Jacques Geigsan (Gen Mgr)

K&M Associates (1)
425 Dexter St, Providence, RI
02907-2814 (94.5%)
Tel.: (401) 461-4300
Web Site: http://www.kandmassociates.com
Sales Range: $25-49.9 Million
Emp.: 150
Mfr of Jewelry & Accessories
N.A.I.C.S.: 339910
Candy Heatherton (VP-Sls)
Greg Lamoreaux (VP-Strategic Bus Dev)

AMERICAN BIO MEDICA CORPORATION
122 Smith Rd, Kinderhook, NY 12106
Tel.: (518) 758-8158 NY
Web Site: http://www.abmc.com
Year Founded: 1986
ABMC—(OTCIQ)
Rev.: $913,000
Assets: $1,269,000
Liabilities: $3,608,000
Net Worth: ($2,339,000)
Earnings: ($1,410,000)
Emp.: 16
Fiscal Year-end: 12/31/22
Mfr, Developer & Marketer of Immunoassay Diagnostic Test Kits for Drug Abuse
N.A.I.C.S.: 541380
Melissa A. Waterhouse (Chief Acctg Officer)
Lawrence Ferringo (VP-Manufacturing-Research & Development)
Jean Neff (Sec)

AMERICAN BUSINESS BANK
400 S Hope St Ste 300, Los Angeles, CA 90071
Tel.: (213) 430-4000
Web Site:
https://www.americanbb.bank
Year Founded: 1998
AMBZ—(OTCIQ)
Rev.: $98,798,739
Assets: $3,454,261,682
Liabilities: $3,206,423,498
Net Worth: $247,838,184
Earnings: $28,772,824
Emp.: 192
Fiscal Year-end: 12/31/20
Business Banking Services
N.A.I.C.S.: 522110
Leon I. Blankstein (CEO)
Karen A. Schoenbaum (CFO & Exec VP)
Philip Fernando (Exec VP-Banking)
Jeff Munson (Reg Exec VP-San Fernando Valley)
Patti A. Vollmer (Chief Credit Officer & Exec VP)
Suzanne Dondanville (COO & Exec VP)
David A. Wolf (Exec VP)
Philip C. Feghali (Pres)
Gary Allen Cook (Officer-Real Estate & Sr VP)
David Kohn (Exec VP-Reg)
Sharon Hauptman (First VP & Sr Mgr-Relationship)
Simon Leyva (VP & Mgr-Relationship)
Ricardo Ceja (VP & Sr Mgr-Relationship)
Alfred Ayala (Mgr-Relationship)
Vahe Medzoyan (VP & Mgr-Credit & Portfolio)

AMERICAN CANNABIS COMPANY, INC.
200 Union St Ste 200, Lakewood, CO 80228
Tel.: (303) 974-4770 DE

Web Site:
https://www.americancannabisconsulting.com
Year Founded: 1983
AMMJ—(OTCQB)
Rev.: $18,808,545
Assets: $4,616,201
Liabilities: $2,746,579
Net Worth: $1,869,622
Earnings: ($633,192)
Emp.: 24
Fiscal Year-end: 12/31/22
Administrative Management & General Management Consulting Services
N.A.I.C.S.: 541611
Ellis Smith (Chm, Pres, CEO, CFO & Chief Dev Officer)

Subsidiaries:

Hollister & Blacksmith, Inc. (1)
200 Union St Ste 200, Lakewood, CO 80228
Tel.: (303) 974-4770
Web Site:
https://americancannabisconsulting.com
Management Consulting Services
N.A.I.C.S.: 541618

AMERICAN CHURCH MORTGAGE COMPANY
10400 Yellow Cir Dr Ste 102, Minnetonka, MN 55343
Tel.: (952) 945-9455 MN
Web Site: http://www.church-loans.squarespace.com
Year Founded: 1994
ACMC—(OTCIQ)
Rev.: $1,917,145
Assets: $30,697,781
Liabilities: $21,924,421
Net Worth: $8,773,360
Earnings: ($1,295,201)
Emp.: 2
Fiscal Year-end: 12/31/21
Real Estate Investment Trust
N.A.I.C.S.: 523999
Philip J. Myers (Chm, Pres, CEO, Co-CFO & Sec)
Scott J. Marquis (Co-CFO & Treas)

AMERICAN CLEAN RESOURCES GROUP, INC.
12567 W Cedar Dr, Lakewood, CO 80228-2039
Tel.: (720) 458-1124 NV
Web Site: https://acrgincorp.com
Year Founded: 1985
ACRG—(OTCQB)
Rev.: $8,396
Assets: $3,884,775
Liabilities: $22,351,299
Net Worth: ($18,466,524)
Earnings: ($1,052,640)
Fiscal Year-end: 12/31/22
Minerals Processing Services
N.A.I.C.S.: 212290
Sharon L. Ullman (CFO, Chief Admin Officer & Treas)
J. Bryan Read (Pres & Sec)
Tawana Bain (Chm & CEO)

AMERICAN COASTAL INSURANCE CORPORATION
800 2nd Ave S, Saint Petersburg, FL 33701
Tel.: (727) 633-0851 DE
Web Site:
https://www.amcoastal.com
Year Founded: 2007
ACIC—(NASDAQ)
Rev.: $455,422,000
Assets: $2,837,496,000
Liabilities: $3,019,535,000
Net Worth: ($182,039,000)
Earnings: ($469,855,000)
Emp.: 269

Fiscal Year-end: 12/31/22
Holding Company; Property & Casualty Insurance Products & Services
N.A.I.C.S.: 551112
Robert Daniel Peed (Chm & CEO)
Bennett Bradford Martz (Pres)
Brook Adler (Interim Gen Counsel)
Chris Griffith (COO & CIO)
Svetlana Castle (CFO)
Andy Gray (Chief Compliance Officer & Chief Risk Officer)
Antonio Gonzaiez (Sr VP-Sales & Agency Rels)

Subsidiaries:

American Coastal Insurance Company (1)
800 2nd Ave S, Saint Petersburg, FL 33701
Tel.: (727) 895-7737
Web Site: https://investors.amcoastal.com
Insurance Services
N.A.I.C.S.: 524298

Interboro Insurance Company (1)
PO Box 31309, Tampa, FL 33631-3309
Web Site:
https://www.interboroinsurance.com
Insurance Services
N.A.I.C.S.: 524126

United Insurance Management, L.C. (1)
800 2nd Ave S, Saint Petersburg, FL 33701
Tel.: (727) 895-7737
Web Site: http://www.tpcinsurance.com
Emp.: 175
Insurance Agencies & Brokerage Services
N.A.I.C.S.: 524210

AMERICAN CRYOSTEM CORPORATION
1 Meridian Rd Ste 5, Eatontown, NJ 07724
Tel.: (732) 747-1007 NV
Web Site:
http://www.americancryostem.com
Year Founded: 2009
CRYO—(OTCIQ)
Rev.: $557,903
Assets: $1,476,849
Liabilities: $1,898,048
Net Worth: ($421,199)
Earnings: ($1,179,285)
Emp.: 6
Fiscal Year-end: 09/30/20
Stem Cell Storage Services
N.A.I.C.S.: 325413
John S. Arnone (Chm, Pres & CEO)
Anthony F. Dudzinski (Founder, COO, Treas & Sec)
Ruth Goldman (VP & Dir-Laboratory)

AMERICAN CRYSTAL SUGAR COMPANY
101 N 3rd St, Moorhead, MN 56560-1952
Tel.: (218) 236-4400 MN
Web Site:
http://www.crystalsugar.com
Year Founded: 1899
ASCS—(OTCEM)
Sales Range: $1-4.9 Billion
Sugar Producer
N.A.I.C.S.: 311313

Subsidiaries:

Midwest Agri-Commodities (1)
999 5th Ave Ste 500, San Rafael, CA 94901
Tel.: (415) 259-2720
Web Site: http://www.mwagri.com
Sales Range: $250-299.9 Million
Emp.: 60
Sugar Beet Pulp, Molasses & Raffinates Whslr
N.A.I.C.S.: 424490
Jim Eichenberger (Pres)
Tim Klovstad (Mgr-Natl Sls)
Roger Roslund (Mgr-Sls)
Kevin Christensen (VP-Fin)

ProGold LLC (1)
18049 County Rd 8 E, Wahpeton, ND 58075 (51%)
Tel.: (701) 671-1600
Web Site: http://www.crystalsugar.com
Sales Range: $50-74.9 Million
Emp.: 160
Corn Wet Milling
N.A.I.C.S.: 311221
Pat Benedict (Chm)

Sidney Sugars Incorporated (1)
35140 County Rd 125, Sidney, MT 59270
Tel.: (406) 433-3301
Web Site: http://www.sidneysugars.com
Emp.: 300
Sugar Beet Production
N.A.I.C.S.: 311313
David Garland (Gen Mgr & Mgr-Tech Svcs)
Raymond Carlson (Mgr-Ops)
Kevin Roth (Controller)

United Sugars Corp. (1)
524 Center Ave, Moorhead, MN 56560
Tel.: (218) 236-4740
Web Site: http://www.unitedsugars.com
Rev.: $16,500,000
Emp.: 30
Beet Sugar Manufacturing
N.A.I.C.S.: 424590
Lee Glass (Dir-Transportation)
Christi Thielke (Mgr-Customer Svc)

AMERICAN DIVERSIFIED HOLDINGS CORPORATION
122 15th St Ste 2568, Del Mar, CA 92014
Tel.: (212) 537-5900 WY
Web Site:
http://www.adhcorporation.com
Year Founded: 2020
ADHC—(OTCIQ)
Assets: $61,000
Liabilities: $2,392,000
Net Worth: ($2,331,000)
Earnings: ($227,000)
Emp.: 3
Fiscal Year-end: 07/31/20
Holding Company; Executive Management, Corporate Governance, Administrative Support & Financial Advice
N.A.I.C.S.: 551112
John A. Cacchioli (CEO)

AMERICAN EAGLE OUTFITTERS, INC.
77 Hot Metal St, Pittsburgh, PA 15203-2329
Tel.: (412) 432-3300 DE
Web Site: https://www.aeo-inc.com
Year Founded: 1957
AEO—(NYSE)
Rev.: $4,989,833,000
Assets: $3,420,956,000
Liabilities: $1,821,793,000
Net Worth: $1,599,163,000
Earnings: $125,136,000
Emp.: 14,400
Fiscal Year-end: 01/28/23
Men's & Women's Outdoor Apparel Retailer
N.A.I.C.S.: 458110
Charles F Kessler (Pres-Brand-Global)
Michael R. Rempell (COO & Exec VP)
Michael A. Mathias (CFO & Exec VP)
James H. Keefer Jr. (Chief Acctg Officer & Sr VP)
Marisa Baldwin (Chief HR Officer & Sr VP)
Jennifer Foyle (Pres & Exec Creative Dir-AE & Aerie)
Sarah Clarke (Chief Supply Chain Officer & Exec VP)
Valerie van Ogtrop (Exec VP-Brand Ops)
Jay L. Schottenstein (Chm & CEO)

Subsidiaries:

AE Outfitters Retail Co.   **(1)**
8401 Gateway Blvd W, El Paso, TX 79925-5668
Tel.: (915) 772-8887
All Other Business Support Services
N.A.I.C.S.: 561499

AEO Foreign Hold Co LLC   **(1)**
77 Hot Metal St, Pittsburgh, PA 15203
Tel.: (412) 432-3300
Web Site: http://www.ae.com
Apparel & Accessory Online Distr
N.A.I.C.S.: 458110

American Eagle Outfitters Dutch Op Co B.V.   **(1)**
Evert van de Beekstraat 310, Schiphol, 1118 CX, Netherlands
Tel.: (31) 205214777
Apparel & Accessory Online Distr
N.A.I.C.S.: 458110

AMERICAN EDUCATION CENTER, INC.

630 5th Ave Ste 2338, New York, NY 10111
Tel.: (929) 923-2740   **NV**
Web Site: https://www.aec100.com
Year Founded: 1999
AMCT—(OTCIQ)
Rev.: $342,499
Assets: $2,824,098
Liabilities: $4,141,737
Net Worth: ($1,317,639)
Earnings: ($2,753,652)
Emp.: 21
Fiscal Year-end: 12/31/20
Educational Consulting Services
N.A.I.C.S.: 611710
Weihua Zhu *(COO)*
Christian Rockefeller *(Chm, CEO, CFO & Dir-Sole)*

Subsidiaries:

American Institute of Financial Intelligence LLC   **(1)**
200 Centennial Ave Ste 106, Piscataway, NJ 08854
Tel.: (848) 229-1678
Educational Support Services
N.A.I.C.S.: 611710
Xinyi Cindy Yu *(Co-Founder & Architect)*
Hong Zhang *(Co-Founder & Pres)*
Cindy Qiu *(COO)*
Anthony Santullo *(Editor-in-Chief)*

Shenzhen Zhongwei Technology Co., Ltd.   **(1)**
2408 C Baihexingcheng, Buji Longgang, Shenzhen, China
Tel.: (86) 75589979076
Web Site: http://www.szzwkeji.com
Electronics Repair & Maintenance Services
N.A.I.C.S.: 811210

AMERICAN ELECTRIC POWER COMPANY, INC.

1 Riverside Plz, Columbus, OH 43215-2372
Tel.: (614) 716-1000   **NY**
Web Site: https://www.aep.com
Year Founded: 1906
AEP—(NASDAQ)
Rev.: $18,982,300,000
Assets: $96,684,000,000
Liabilities: $71,398,100,000
Net Worth: $25,285,900,000
Earnings: $2,208,100,000
Emp.: 17,250
Fiscal Year-end: 12/31/23
Electric Utility Holding Company
N.A.I.C.S.: 221111
Greg B. Hall *(Chief Comml Officer, Exec VP, Exec VP-Energy Supply & VP-Energy Mktg)*
Melissa McHenry *(Sr VP-Comm & Mktg)*
Charles E. Zebula *(CFO & Exec VP)*

Julie Sherwood *(Sr VP-Treasury & Risk)*
Charles E. Zebula *(CFO & Exec VP)*
David M. Feinberg *(Gen Counsel, Sec & Exec VP)*
Therace M. Risch *(CIO, CTO & Exec VP)*
Raja Sundararajan *(Exec VP-External Affairs)*
Toby L. Thomas *(Pres/COO-Power-Indiana & Michigan)*
Matthew J. Satterwhite *(Regulatory Svcs)*
Therace Risch *(Chief Info & Tech Officer & Sr VP)*
Timothy J. Wells *(VP-Sls, Economic & Bus Dev)*
Greg Hall *(Chief Comml Officer & Exec VP)*
Kate Sturgess *(Chief Acctg Officer, Sr VP & Controller)*
Christian T. Beam *(Exec VP-Energy Svcs)*
Antonio P. Smyth *(Exec VP)*
Phil Ulrich *(Chief HR Officer)*
Emily Duncan *(Sr VP)*
Darcy Reese *(VP)*
Annie Pribisko *(Dir)*
Scott Blake *(Mgr)*
Holly Grimes *(Coord)*
Emily Smith *(Mgr)*
Kyle Vanderhoff *(Mgr)*
Barry Mosser *(Dir)*
Bud Clark *(Natl Mgr)*
Darren Kelsey *(Mgr)*
Anthony Hray *(Mgr)*
Scott Mann *(Natl Mgr)*
Mike Taylor *(Mgr)*
Michael Tyler *(Natl Mgr)*
Amy Koscielak *(Sr Mgr)*
Eric Basinger *(Mgr)*
Amanda Clark *(Mgr)*
Whitney Czelusniak *(Mgr)*
Dale Fowler *(Mgr)*
Shelley Klug *(Mgr)*
William J. Fehrman *(Pres & CEO)*
Peggy I. Simmons *(Chief Admin Officer & Exec VP-Regulatory)*

Subsidiaries:

AEP Energy Partners, Inc.   **(1)**
155 W Nationwide Blvd Ste 500, Columbus, OH 43215
Tel.: (614) 583-6408
Eletric Power Generation Services
N.A.I.C.S.: 221115

AEP Energy, Inc.   **(1)**
225 W Wacker Dr Ste 700, Chicago, IL 60606
Tel.: (312) 327-0090
Web Site: https://www.aepenergy.com
Sales Range: $200-249.9 Million
Emp.: 219
Electric Power Distribution Services
N.A.I.C.S.: 221122
Darren Beattie *(Sr Mgr-Channel)*
Kobe Chanthaboury *(Sr Mgr-Energy)*
Nick Labate *(Mgr-Energy)*
Michael Nault *(Sr Mgr-Energy)*
Matthew Schmitt *(Sr Mgr-Channel)*
Frank Willson *(VP-Residential & Small Bus Solution Sls)*

AEP Generating Company   **(1)**
1 Riverside Plz, Columbus, OH 43215-2355   **(100%)**
Tel.: (614) 716-1000
Web Site: http://www.aep.com
Sales Range: $350-399.9 Million
Emp.: 16,800
Generator & Whslr of Electric Power
N.A.I.C.S.: 221111

AEP River Transportation   **(1)**
Ohio River Rd, West Columbia, WV 25287
Tel.: (304) 675-6300
Sales Range: $75-99.9 Million
Emp.: 282
Moving Services
N.A.I.C.S.: 488999

AEP Texas Inc.   **(1)**
1 Riverside Plz, Columbus, OH 43215-2373
Tel.: (614) 716-1000
Web Site: https://www.aeptexas.com
Rev.: $1,846,800,000
Assets: $12,892,200,000
Liabilities: $8,987,900,000
Net Worth: $3,904,300,000
Earnings: $307,900,000
Emp.: 1,594
Fiscal Year-end: 12/31/2022
Electric Utilities
N.A.I.C.S.: 221122
Charles E. Zebula *(Exec VP)*
Therace M. Risch *(CIO)*
Ann P. Kelly *(CFO)*
Julia A. Sloat *(CFO & VP)*
Leigh Anne Strahler *(VP-Regulatory & Fin)*
Chris Beam *(Exec VP)*
Greg Hall *(Chief Comml Officer)*
Peggy I. Simmons *(Exec VP)*
Therace Risch *(CIO)*
Ann P. Kelly *(CFO)*
Charles E. Zebula *(Exec VP)*
Phil Ulrich *(Chief HR Officer)*
Antonio P. Smyth *(Exec VP)*
Matthew Satterwhite *(Sr VP)*
Melissa McHenry *(Sr VP)*
Emily Duncan *(Sr VP)*
Toby L. Thomas *(Sr VP)*
Julie Sherwood *(Sr VP)*
Marc Reitter *(Pres)*
Aaron Walker *(Pres)*
Steve Baker *(Pres)*
Brett Mattison *(Pres)*
Cindy Wiseman *(Pres)*

Subsidiary (Domestic):

AEP Texas Central Transition Funding II LLC   **(2)**
1 Riverside Pl, Columbus, OH 43215
Tel.: (614) 716-1000
Funding Services
N.A.I.C.S.: 522299
Brian X. Tierney *(Pres & Mgr)*
Victor A. Duva *(Mgr)*
Daniel P. McMahon *(Mgr)*

AEP Texas Central Transition Funding III LLC   **(2)**
539 N Carancahua St Ste 1700, Corpus Christi, TX 78401
Tel.: (361) 881-5399
Funding Services
N.A.I.C.S.: 522299
Brian X. Tierney *(Pres & Mgr)*
Brian X. Tierney *(Pres & Mgr)*

AEP Texas Central Transition Funding LLC   **(2)**
539 N Carancahua St Ste 1700, Corpus Christi, TX 78401
Tel.: (361) 881-5398
Funding Services
N.A.I.C.S.: 522299

AEP Transmission Company, LLC   **(1)**
1 Riverside Plz, Columbus, OH 43215-2373
Tel.: (614) 716-1000
Rev.: $1,672,000,000
Assets: $15,072,500,000
Liabilities: $8,739,200,000
Net Worth: $6,333,300,000
Earnings: $614,200,000
Emp.: 6,364
Fiscal Year-end: 12/31/2023
Electric Power Transmission Services
N.A.I.C.S.: 221121
Ann P. Kelly *(CFO)*
Joseph M. Buonaiuto *(Chief Acctg Officer & Controller)*
Ann P. Kelly *(CFO)*
Julia A. Sloat *(CEO)*

American Electric Power Service Corporation   **(1)**
1 Riverside Plz, Columbus, OH 43215-2355   **(100%)**
Tel.: (614) 716-1000
Web Site: http://www.aep.com
Sales Range: $1-4.9 Billion
Emp.: 2,300
Public Utilities Management Services
N.A.I.C.S.: 221118

Appalachian Power Company   **(1)**
1 Riverside Plz, Columbus, OH 43215   **(100%)**

Tel.: (304) 882-2126
Web Site: http://www.appalachianpower.com
Rev.: $3,519,900,000
Assets: $15,222,200,000
Liabilities: $10,246,800,000
Net Worth: $4,975,400,000
Earnings: $394,200,000
Emp.: 1,650
Fiscal Year-end: 12/31/2022
Electric Utility
N.A.I.C.S.: 221112
John Scalzo *(VP)*
Brad Hall *(VP)*
Mike Zwick *(VP)*
Jason Baker *(VP)*
Joseph M. Buonaiuto *(Chief Acctg Officer & Controller)*
Aaron Walker *(Pres & COO)*

Subsidiary (Domestic):

Appalachian Consumer Rate Relief Funding LLC   **(2)**
1 Riverside Plz, Columbus, OH 43215
Tel.: (614) 716-3627
Funding Services
N.A.I.C.S.: 522299
Brian X. Tierney *(Pres & Mgr)*
Julia A. Sloat *(Treas & Mgr)*

Cedar Coal Co.   **(1)**
7617 Upper Johns Creek Rd, Phelps, KY 41553-8775
Tel.: (606) 835-4562
Emp.: 3
Coal Mining Services
N.A.I.C.S.: 213113
Larry Phillips *(Pres)*

Columbus Southern Power Company   **(1)**
1 Riverside Plaza, Columbus, OH 43215   **(100%)**
Tel.: (614) 716-1000
Web Site: http://www.aepohio.com
Sales Range: $5-14.9 Billion
Emp.: 1,323
Electric Power Generator & Distr
N.A.I.C.S.: 221112

Subsidiary (Domestic):

Conesville Coal Preparation Co.   **(2)**
1 Riverside Plz, Columbus, OH 43215   **(100%)**
Tel.: (614) 716-1000
Web Site: http://www.aep.com
Sales Range: $600-649.9 Million
Electric Utility Services
N.A.I.C.S.: 212114

Indiana Michigan Power Company   **(1)**
1 Riverside Plz, Columbus, OH 43215-2373   **(100%)**
Tel.: (614) 716-1000
Web Site: https://www.indianamichiganpower.com
Rev.: $2,669,600,000
Assets: $12,118,900,000
Liabilities: $9,110,600,000
Net Worth: $3,008,300,000
Earnings: $324,700,000
Emp.: 16,974
Fiscal Year-end: 12/31/2022
Electric Power Distr
N.A.I.C.S.: 221122
Brian X. Tierney *(CFO & VP)*
Toby L. Thomas *(Pres & COO)*
Marc E. Lewis *(VP-Regulatory & External Affairs)*
Nicholas M. Elkins *(Dir-Customer Svcs & Bus Dev)*
David A. Lucas *(VP-Fin & Customer Experience)*
David S. Isaacson *(VP-Distr Reg Ops)*
Archie Pugh *(Mng Dir-Transmission Field Svcs)*
Brian Bergsma *(Dir-Govt Affairs)*
Andrew Williamson *(Dir-Regulatory Svcs)*
Tim Kerns *(VP-Generating Assets)*
Dona Seger-Lawson *(Dir-Regulatory Svcs)*
Subin Mathew *(Dir)*
Stephanny Smith *(Dir)*
Katie Davis *(VP)*
Steve Baker *(Pres)*

Indiana-Kentucky Electric Corporation   **(1)**

American Electric Power Company, Inc.—(Continued)

3932 US Route 23, Piketon, OH 45661
Tel.: (740) 289-7200
Sales Range: $75-99.9 Million
Emp.: 365
Electric Power Generation Equipment Mfr
N.A.I.C.S.: 335311
Clifford Carnes (Plant Mgr)

Kentucky Power Company (1)
855 Central Ave Ste 200, Ashland, KY
41101 (100%)
Web Site: https://www.kentuckypower.com
Rev.: $624,218,000
Assets: $1,615,578,000
Liabilities: $1,135,968,000
Net Worth: $479,610,000
Earnings: $50,978,000
Emp.: 447
Fiscal Year-end: 12/31/2012
Electric Power Generator & Distr
N.A.I.C.S.: 221112

Kingsport Power Company (1)
40 Franklin Rd SW, Roanoke, VA
24011-2404 (100%)
Tel.: (800) 956-4237
Web Site: http://www.appalachianpower.com
Electric Utility
N.A.I.C.S.: 221118

Ohio Power Company (1)
1 Riverside Plz, Columbus, OH 43215-2373
Tel.: (614) 716-1000
Web Site: https://www.aep.com
Rev.: $3,665,100,000
Assets: $10,003,100,000
Liabilities: $6,915,000,000
Net Worth: $3,088,100,000
Earnings: $287,800,000
Emp.: 1,713
Fiscal Year-end: 12/31/2022
Electric Power Distr
N.A.I.C.S.: 221122
Joseph M. Buonaiuto (Chief Acctg Officer & Controller)
Jon Williams (Mng Dir)
Lisa Kelso (VP)
Tom Kratt (VP)

Unit (Domestic):

AEP Ohio (2)
850 Tech Ctr Dr, Gahanna, OH 43230
Tel.: (614) 883-7999
Web Site: http://www.aepohio.com
Sales Range: $1-4.9 Billion
Emp.: 2,790
Regional Managing Office; Electric Power
Generator & Distr
N.A.I.C.S.: 551114
Marc Reitter (VP-Regulatory & Fin)
Raja Sundararajan (Pres & COO)
Jon Williams (Mng Dir-Customer Experience & Distr Tech)
Tom Kratt (VP-Distr Ops)
Scott S. Osterholt (Dir-Grid Modernization)

Subsidiary (Domestic):

Ohio Phase-In-Recovery Funding LLC (2)
1 Riverside Plz, Columbus, OH 43215
Tel.: (614) 716-3622
Funding Services
N.A.I.C.S.: 522299
Brian X. Tierney (Pres & Mgr)

Public Service Company of Oklahoma (1)
1 Riverside Plz, Columbus, OH
43215-2373 (100%)
Tel.: (614) 716-1000
Web Site: https://www.psoklahoma.com
Rev.: $1,874,700,000
Assets: $6,965,900,000
Liabilities: $4,546,800,000
Net Worth: $2,419,100,000
Earnings: $167,600,000
Emp.: 1,030
Fiscal Year-end: 12/31/2022
Electric Power Distr
N.A.I.C.S.: 221122
Tiffini Jackson (VP-External Affairs)
Matthew Horeled (VP-Regulatory & Fin)
Debbie Arwood (Reg Mgr-HR)
Steve Baker (VP-Distr Ops)
Whitney Emerick (Dir-Comm)

Judie Hackerott (Dir-Bus Ops Support)
Monte McMahon (VP-PSO Generating Assets)
Shawn Robinson (Mng Dir-Transmission Field Svcs-West)
Paul Avanessian (Dir-Transmission Field Svcs Construction-West)
Scott Ritz (Dir-Customer Svcs & Mktg)
Mary Williamson (Dir-Regulatory Svcs)
Chris Baucom (Mgr-Safety & Health)
Leigh Anne Strahler (Pres & COO)

Sempra Renewables, LLC (1)
488 8th Ave HQ12, San Diego, CA 92101
Tel.: (877) 855-7887
Web Site:
http://www.semprarenewables.com
Solar Electric Power Generation Services
N.A.I.C.S.: 221114
Larry Folks (VP-Renewables Dev)
Glen Donovan (VP-Bus Dev & Structuring)

Southwestern Electric Power Company (1)
428 Travis St, Shreveport, LA 71101
Tel.: (318) 673-3551
Web Site: http://www.swepco.com
Electric Utility
N.A.I.C.S.: 221118
Ann P. Kelly (CFO)
Ann P. Kelly (CFO)
Brian Bond (VP-External Affairs)
Joseph M. Buonaiuto (Chief Acctg Officer & Controller)
Brenda Meyers (Dir-Bus Ops)
Malcolm Smoak (Pres & COO)
Lynn Ferry Nelson (VP-Regulatory Svcs)
Drew Seidel (VP-Distr Reg Ops)
Paul Pratt (Dir-Customer Svcs & Mktg)
Peter Kimani (Dir)
Amanda Keeney (Dir)
Monte A. McMahon (VP)
Adam Keeth (Dir)
Ann P. Kelly (CFO)
Julia A. Sloat (CEO)
Thomas P. Brice Jr. (VP-Regulatory & Fin)
Peter Kimani (Dir)
Amanda Keeney (Dir)
Monte A. McMahon (VP)
Adam Keeth (Dir)
Julia A. Sloat (CEO)

Subsidiary (Domestic):

Dolet Hills Lignite Company (2)
377 Hwy 522, Mansfield, LA
71052 (100%)
Tel.: (318) 872-6300
Sales Range: $150-199.9 Million
Emp.: 240
Lignite Mining Services
N.A.I.C.S.: 212114

AMERICAN ENERGY PARTNERS, INC.
6000 Town Ctr Blvd Ste 210, Canonsburg, PA 15317
Tel.: (610) 217-3275　　CO
Web Site:
https://www.americanenergy-inc.com
Year Founded: 2004
AEPT—(OTCIQ)
Rev.: $23,812,000
Assets: $14,030,000
Liabilities: $18,175,000
Net Worth: ($4,145,000)
Earnings: ($22,708,000)
Fiscal Year-end: 12/31/23
Water Supply Services
N.A.I.C.S.: 221310
Brad J. Domitrovitsch (Chm & CEO)

AMERICAN ENVIRONMENTAL ENERGY, INC.
14 Wall St Office 2090, New York, NY
10005
Tel.: (212) 618-1315　　NV
Year Founded: 2008
AEEI—(OTCIQ)
Eletric Power Generation Services
N.A.I.C.S.: 221117
Wenyi Yu (Pres & CEO)
Scott D. Marchant (Treas & Sec)
Jonathan Jay Willard (CFO)

AMERICAN EXPRESS COMPANY
200 Vesey St, New York, NY 10285
Tel.: (212) 640-2000　　NY
Web Site:
https://www.americanexpress.com
Year Founded: 1850
AXP—(NYSE)
Rev.: $47,381,000,000
Assets: $261,108,000,000
Liabilities: $233,051,000,000
Net Worth: $28,057,000,000
Earnings: $8,374,000,000
Emp.: 74,600
Fiscal Year-end: 12/31/23
Diversified Financial & Travel; International Banking, Life Insurance, Publishing, Information Services, Asset Management Services & Consumer Lending
N.A.I.C.S.: 522291
Denise Pickett (Pres-Svcs Grp-Global)
Glenda G. McNeal (Pres-Enterprise Strategic Partnerships)
Monique Herena (Chief Colleague Experience Officer)
Jennifer Skyler (Chief Corp Affairs Officer)
Ravi Radhakrishnan (CIO & Exec VP)
Mohammed Badi (Pres-Network Svcs-Global)
Howard Grosfield (Pres-Consumer Svcs-US)
Rafael Marquez (Pres-Card Svcs-Intl)
Douglas E. Buckminster (Vice Chm)
Raymond Donald Joabar (Grp Pres-Merchant & Network Svcs-Global)
Stephen J. Squeri (Chm & CEO)
Anna Marrs (Grp Pres-Global)
Anre Williams (Grp Pres-Enterprise Svcs)
Christophe Le Caillec (CFO)
David Nigro (Chief Credit Officer-American Express & Chief Risk Officer)
Doug Tabish (Chief Risk Officer-American Express)
Nicole Hildebrandt (Chief Strategy Officer)
Alan Gallo (Exec VP)
Laureen E. Seeger (Chief Legal Officer)

Subsidiaries:

AMEX (Middle East) QFC LLC (1)
Al Jazeera Tower Ground Floor Conference Center Street, PO Box 17150, Diplomatic Area West Bay, Doha, Qatar
Tel.: (974) 44556888
Web Site:
https://secure.americanexpress.com.bh
Payment Card Processing Services
N.A.I.C.S.: 522320

Alpha Card S.C.R.L./C.V.B.A. (1)
100 Boulevard du Souverain, Brussels, 1170, Belgium
Tel.: (32) 26762181
Web Site: http://www.americanexpress.com
Financial Management Services
N.A.I.C.S.: 541611

American Express (Malaysia) SDN. BHD. (1)
Menara Weld Jalan Raja Chulan, 50250, Kuala Lumpur, Malaysia
Tel.: (60) 320500000
Credit Card Services
N.A.I.C.S.: 522210

American Express Argentina S.A. (1)
Arenales 707, C1061AAA, Buenos Aires, 1061, Argentina
Tel.: (54) 8004442450
Web Site:
https://www.americanexpress.com
Credit Card Processing Services

N.A.I.C.S.: 522320

American Express Austria Bank GmbH (1)
Karntner Strasse 21-23, 1010, Vienna, Austria
Tel.: (43) 15450110
Financial Banking Services
N.A.I.C.S.: 522210

American Express Brasil Assessoria Empresarial Ltda. (1)
Rua Joao Avelino Pine Mellao 599/PA 141, Paraisopolis, Sao Paulo, Brazil
Tel.: (55) 1135015392
Credit Card Services
N.A.I.C.S.: 522210

American Express Europe Limited (1)
200 Vesey St, New York, NY 10285-0002
Tel.: (212) 640-5130
Travel Management Services
N.A.I.C.S.: 561510

American Express France SAS (1)
4 Rue Louis Bleriot, Rueil-Malmaison, 92561, France
Tel.: (33) 147773545
Credit Card Services
N.A.I.C.S.: 522210

American Express Global Commercial Card Group (1)
3 World Financial Ctr, New York, NY 10281-1013
Tel.: (212) 640-2000
Web Site: http://www.americanexpress.com
Sales Range: $125-149.9 Million
Corporate Card Purchasing Solutions
N.A.I.C.S.: 522210

Subsidiary (Domestic):

Harbor Payments, Inc. (2)
400 Galleria Pkwy SE Ste 700, Atlanta, GA 30339
Tel.: (404) 267-5000
Sales Range: $10-24.9 Million
Emp.: 100
Electronic Outsourced Invoicing, Billing & Disbursement Solutions
N.A.I.C.S.: 541211

American Express Global Information Services (1)
2901 Wilcrest Dr Ste 600, Houston, TX 77042 (100%)
Tel.: (713) 954-2900
Web Site: http://www.americanexpress.com
Sales Range: $100-124.9 Million
Emp.: 400
Computer Software Development
N.A.I.C.S.: 541511

American Express Holdings (France) SAS (1)
4 Rue Louis Bleriot, 92500, Rueil-Malmaison, France
Tel.: (33) 147517572
Holding Company
N.A.I.C.S.: 551112

American Express Italia S.r.l. (1)
Viale Alexandre Gustave Eiffel 15, 00148, Rome, Italy
Tel.: (39) 0672280735
Web Site: http://www.americanexpress.com
Payment Card Processing Services
N.A.I.C.S.: 522320

American Express Nippon Travel Agency, Inc. (1)
SD Bldg 6F 4-chome-3-8 Taihei, Sumida-ku, Tokyo, 130-0012, Japan
Tel.: (81) 358191600
Web Site: https://www.gbtnta.com
Emp.: 250
Travel Management Services
N.A.I.C.S.: 561599
Shozo Azuma (Mgr-Travel Svc)
Makoto Arai (Mgr-Travel Svc)
Kyoko Okazaki (Mgr-Travel Svc)
Chihiro Sugiyama (Mgr-Travel Svc)

American Express TLS HK Limited (1)
Suites 1701-3 & 1712-14 17/F 12 TaiKoo Wan Rd, Taikoo Shing, China (Hong Kong)
Tel.: (852) 30017041

Banking Financial Services
N.A.I.C.S.: 522320

American Express Travel Related Services Company, Inc. (1)
200 Vesey St, New York, NY 10285 **(100%)**
Tel.: (212) 640-2000
Web Site: http://www.americanexpress.com
Sales Range: $100-124.9 Million
Travel Related Services
N.A.I.C.S.: 561599
Kenneth I. Chenault (Chm)
Nathan Blecharczyk (CEO)

Subsidiary (Domestic):

AMERICAN EXPRESS CREDIT CORPORATION (2)
200 Vesey St, New York, NY 10285 **(100%)**
Tel.: (212) 640-2000
Rev.: $830,000,000
Assets: $24,308,000,000
Liabilities: $21,413,000,000
Net Worth: $2,895,000,000
Earnings: $201,000,000
Emp.: 5
Fiscal Year-end: 12/31/2020
Non Interest Bearing Cardmember Receivables Financing Services
N.A.I.C.S.: 522210
David L. Yowan (CEO)
Anderson Y. Lee (CFO)

Subsidiary (Non-US):

American Express Overseas Credit Corporation Limited (3)
41/43 Lane Motte Street, Saint Helier, JE2 4SZ, Jersey
Tel.: (44) 87733
Sales Range: $150-199.9 Million
Emp.: 7
Credit Card Services
N.A.I.C.S.: 522210

Subsidiary (Domestic):

Credco Receivables Corp. (3)
301 N Walnut St Ste 1002, Wilmington, DE 19801
Tel.: (302) 594-3350
Sales Range: $10-24.9 Million
Credit Collection Services
N.A.I.C.S.: 561440

Subsidiary (Non-US):

AMEX Bank of Canada (2)
101 McNabb St, Markham, L3R 4H8, ON, Canada **(100%)**
Tel.: (905) 474-0870
Web Site:
   https://www.americanexpress.com
Emp.: 1,600
Charge & Credit Cards
N.A.I.C.S.: 522210
Rob McClean (Pres & CEO)

AMEX Canada Inc. (2)
101 McNabb Street, Markham, L3R 4H8, ON, Canada **(100%)**
Tel.; (905) 474-8000
Web Site: http://www.americanexpress.ca
Sales Range: $550-599.9 Million
Emp.: 2,000
Functions Related To Deposit Banking
N.A.I.C.S.: 522110
Rob McClean (Pres & Gen Mgr)

Affiliate (Non-US):

Alpha Card SCRL (2)
Blvd du Souverain 100, 1170, Brussels, Belgium **(50%)**
Tel.: (32) 26762525
Web Site: http://www.americanexpress.be
Sales Range: $25-49.9 Million
Emp.: 50
Credit Card & Travel Related Services
N.A.I.C.S.: 522210

Subsidiary (Non-US):

American Express Barcelo Viajes SL (2)
Calle de Albasanz 14, Madrid, 28037, Spain
Tel.:(34) 902300908
Web Site: http://www.amexbarcelo.com

Travel Management Services
N.A.I.C.S.: 561510

American Express Carte France SA (2)
Immeuble Voyager 8-10 rue Henri Sainte-Claire Deville, 92506, Rueil-Malmaison, Cedex, France
Tel.: (33) 14 777 3000
Web Site:
   https://www.americanexpress.com
Emp.: 900
Commercial Credit Services
N.A.I.C.S.: 522110

Subsidiary (Domestic):

American Express Centurion Bank (2)
4315 S 2700 W, Salt Lake City, UT 84184-0001
Tel.: (801) 945-3000
Web Site: http://www.americanexpress.com
Credit Cards
N.A.I.C.S.: 523940
Ashwini Gupta (Pres)

Subsidiary (Non-US):

American Express Change SAS (2)
4 rue Louis Bleriot, 92561, Rueil-Malmaison, France
Tel.: (33) 147773000
Web Site: http://www.americanexpress.com
Emp.: 500
Financial Management Services
N.A.I.C.S.: 522110

American Express Company (Mexico) S.A. de C.V. (2)
Sales Range: $25-49.9 Million
Emp.: 50
Travel & Financial Related Services
N.A.I.C.S.: 561599
Santiago Fernandez Vidal (CEO)

Subsidiary (Domestic):

American Express Servicios Profesionales, S. de R.L. de C.V. (3)
Av Patriotismo No 635, Mexico, 03710, Mexico
Tel.: (52) 5553262626
Credit Card Processing Services
N.A.I.C.S.: 522320

Subsidiary (Domestic):

American Express International, Inc. (2)
World Financial Ctr 200 Vesey St, New York, NY 10285
Tel.: (212) 640-2000
Web Site: http://www.americanexpress.com
Holding Company for International Operations
N.A.I.C.S.: 551112

Subsidiary (Non-US):

American Express (Thai) Company Limited (3)
SP Building 388 Phaholyothin Road, Samsennai Phayathai, Bangkok, 10400, Thailand
Tel.: (66) 22735500
Web Site:
   https://www.americanexpress.com
Credit Card Processing Services
N.A.I.C.S.: 522320

American Express Company AS (3)
Dronning Eufemias Gate 30, Oslo, 0191, Norway
Tel.: (47) 22960800
Web Site: http://www.americanexprss.no
Credit Card Services
N.A.I.C.S.: 522210
Inge Kjonnoy (Gen Mgr)

American Express Denmark A/S (3)
Turesensgade 22, 1368, Copenhagen, Denmark
Tel.: (45) 70230460
Emp.: 15
Travel Management Services
N.A.I.C.S.: 561510
Steve Ingham (Gen Mgr)

American Express Holding AB (3)

Tegeludsvagen 21, Stockholm, 106 82, Sweden
Tel.: (46) 84295000
Web Site: http://www.americanexpress.se
Travel & Credit Card Services
N.A.I.C.S.: 561599

Subsidiary (Non-US):

American Express Corporate Travel A/S (4)
Nansensgade 19 3rd fl, 1366, Copenhagen, Denmark
Tel.: (45) 70230460
Web Site:
   http://www.amexglobalbusinesstravel.com
Sales Range: $75-99.9 Million
Emp.: 100
Travel Related Services
N.A.I.C.S.: 488999

Subsidiary (Non-US):

American Express Hungary KFT (3)
Vaci Ut 47, 1133, Budapest, Hungary
Tel.: (36) 17779777
Web Site:
   https://www.americanexpress.com
Sales Range: $25-49.9 Million
Emp.: 65
Travel Related Services
N.A.I.C.S.: 561599

American Express International (Taiwan), Inc. (3)
12th Floor 363 Fuxing North Road, Taipei, 105, Taiwan
Tel.: (886) 227180504
Web Site: http://www.americanexpress.com
Emp.: 300
Credit Card Services
N.A.I.C.S.: 522210

American Express International SA (3)
318 Messoghion Avenue, Agia Paraskevi, 15341, Athens, Greece
Tel.: (30) 2106590700
Web Site:
   http://www.businesstravel.americanexpress.com
Emp.: 36
Travel Agency Services
N.A.I.C.S.: 561510
Dimitris Vernezos (Country Mgr)

American Express Locazioni Finanziarie S.r.l. (3)
Largo Dei Caduti di el Alamein 9, 173, Rome, Italy
Tel.: (39) 06722801
Web Site: http://www.americanexpress.com
Sales Range: $75-99.9 Million
Emp.: 3
Travel & Credit Card Services
N.A.I.C.S.: 561599

American Express Poland Sp z o o (3)
Chlodna 51, 00-867, Warsaw, Poland
Tel.: (48) 225815100
Sales Range: $25-49.9 Million
Emp.: 170
Travel Related Services
N.A.I.C.S.: 561599

American Express Reiseburo GmbH (3)
Karntner Strasse 21-23, Vienna, 1010, Austria
Tel.: (43) 1 51511 500
Web Site: http://www.americanexpress.at
Travel Management Services
N.A.I.C.S.: 561599

American Express Services Europe Limited (3)
Belgrave House 76 Buckingham Palace Road, London, SW1W 9AX, East Sussex, United Kingdom
Tel.: (44) 1293826704
Web Site:
   https://www.americanexpress.com
Travel & Credit Card Services
N.A.I.C.S.: 561599

American Express spol. s.r.o. (3)
Na Prikope 19, 117 19, Prague, Czech Republic
Tel.: (420) 22 280 0100

Web Site:
   https://www.americanexpress.com
International Banking Services
N.A.I.C.S.: 522390

Joint Venture (Non-US):

Swisscard AECS AG (3)
Neugasse 18, 8810, Horgen, Switzerland
Tel.: (41) 446596492
Web Site: https://www.swisscard.ch
Sales Range: $150-199.9 Million
Emp.: 400
Credit Cards
N.A.I.C.S.: 522210

Subsidiary (Non-US):

TransUnion Limited (3)
Suite 811 8th Floor Tower 5 The Gateway 15 Canton Road, Tsim Sha Tsui, Kowloon, China (Hong Kong)
Tel.: (852) 29793000
Web Site: https://www.transunion.hk
Emp.: 160
Financial Management Services
N.A.I.C.S.: 522110

Subsidiary (Domestic):

American Express National Bank (2)
PO Box 30384, Salt Lake City, UT 84130
Web Site: http://www.americanexpress.com
Commercial Banking Services
N.A.I.C.S.: 522110
Anre D. Williams (CEO)
Richard Petrino (COO)

Subsidiary (Non-US):

American Express Voyages SAS (2)
4 rue Louis Bleriot, 92561, Rueil-Malmaison, France
Tel.: (33) 1 46 96 33 00
Travel Management Services
N.A.I.C.S.: 561599

Amex Asesores de Seguros, S.A. (Sociedad Unipersonal) (2)
Calle Juan Ignacio Luca De Tena 17 - Planta 1a, Madrid, 28027, Spain
Tel.: (34) 902263399
International Banking Services
N.A.I.C.S.: 522390

BCC Corporate NV/SA (2)
Keizerinlaan 66 Boulevard de Iimperatrice, 1000, Brussels, Belgium
Tel.: (32) 22058787
Web Site: http://www.bcc-corporate.be
Credit Card Processing Services
N.A.I.C.S.: 522390

Resy Network, Inc. (2)
Web Site: http://resy.com
Travel Arrangement & Reservation Services
N.A.I.C.S.: 561599

Amex Agenzia Assicurativa S.r.l. (1)
Viale Alexandre Gustave Eiffel 15, 00148, Rome, Italy
Tel.: (39) 0672900347
Travel Agency Services
N.A.I.C.S.: 561510

Amex Al Omania LLC (1)
Building No 1022 Al Walaj Street Way No 1013, PO Box 260, Al Qurum, 118, Muscat, Oman
Tel.: (968) 24573555
Banking Financial Services
N.A.I.C.S.: 522320

Amex Asesores de Seguros, S.A. (1)
Avenida Partenon 12-14, 28042, Madrid, Spain
Tel.: (34) 90 226 3399
Web Site:
   http://www.seguros.americanexpress.es
Travel Agency Services
N.A.I.C.S.: 561510

Amex Card Services Company (1)
2401 W Behrend Dr Ste 5, Phoenix, AZ 85027
Tel.: (602) 537-5728
Web Site:
   http://www.amexcardservicescompany.com
Credit Card Services
N.A.I.C.S.: 522210

American Express Company—(Continued)

Amex Egypt Company Limited Liability Company (1)
American Express Cards - Heliopolis City Stars - Capital F2, 2nd Floor Office 22 Nasr City, Cairo, Egypt
Tel.: (20) 224801530
Banking Financial Services
N.A.I.C.S.: 522320

Asesorias e Inversiones American Express Chile Limitada (1)
Isidora Goyenechea 3621, Santiago, Chile
Tel.: (56) 27838700
Credit Card Processing Services
N.A.I.C.S.: 522320

Bansamex, S.A. (1)
Calle Juan Ignacio Luca De Tena 17, 28027, Madrid, Spain
Tel.: (34) 902375637
Emp.: 16
Credit Card Processing Services
N.A.I.C.S.: 522320

InAuth, Inc. (1)
376 Boylston St Ste 501, Boston, MA 02116
Web Site: http://www.inauth.com
Fraud Prevention Software Publisher
N.A.I.C.S.: 513210
Michael Lynch (Chief Strategy Officer)

LP Management Verwaltung GmbH (1)
Theresienhohe 12, Schwanthalerhoehe, 80339, Munich, Bavaria, Germany
Tel.: (49) 8999741202
Business Management Consulting Services
N.A.I.C.S.: 541611

Loyalty Partner GmbH (1)
Theresienhohe 12, 80339, Munich, Germany
Tel.: (49) 8999741420
Web Site: http://www.loyaltypartner.com
Credit Card Processing Services
N.A.I.C.S.: 522320
Bernhard Brugger (CEO)
Dominik Dommick (CMO)
Markus Knorr (CFO)
Alexander Rittweger (Founder)

Loyalty Partner Solutions GmbH (1)
Theresienhohe 12, 80339, Munich, Germany
Tel.: (49) 899616090
Web Site: https://www.lpsolutions.com
Information Technology Services
N.A.I.C.S.: 541511

Northwinds Marketing Group LLC (1)
211 North 1st St Ste 325, Minneapolis, MN 55401-1480 (50.1%)
Tel.: (612) 486-4100
Sales Range: $1-9.9 Million
Emp.: 4
Marketing
N.A.I.C.S.: 541820

Payback GmbH (1)
Theresienhohe 12, 80339, Munich, Germany
Tel.: (49) 89997410
Web Site: https://www.payback.group
Emp.: 1,000
Customer Management Consulting Services
N.A.I.C.S.: 541613
Bernhard Brugger (Member-Mgmt Bd)
Dominik Dommick (Member-Mgmt Bd)
Markus Knorr (Member-Mgmt Bd)
Rijish Raghavan (OOO-India)
Conrad Pozsgai (Member-Mgmt Bd)

Subsidiary (Non-US):

PAYBACK Austria GmbH (2)
Karntner Str 21 - 23, 1010, Vienna, Austria
Tel.: (43) 19622420
Web Site: https://www.payback.group
Online Shopping Services
N.A.I.C.S.: 541870

Revolution Money Inc. (1)
PO Box 1089, Saint Petersburg, FL 33731
Tel.: (866) 352-5919
Payment Processing Solutions
N.A.I.C.S.: 522320

Rexport, Inc. (1)

4200 Las Palmas Cir, Brownsville, TX 78521
Tel.: (956) 542-7495
Credit Card Processing Services
N.A.I.C.S.: 522320

Serve Virtual Enterprises, Inc. (1)
200 Central Ave 11th Fl, Saint Petersburg, FL 33701
Tel.: (727) 374-2105
Credit Card Services
N.A.I.C.S.: 522210

Sometrics, inc. (1)
909 N Sepulveda Blvd Ste 860, El Segundo, CA 90245
Tel.: (213) 814-1220
Web Site: http://www.sometrics.com
Online Game Publisher
N.A.I.C.S.: 513210
Ian Swanson (CEO)
Matthew Gray (CTO)

Swisscard AECS GmbH (1)
Neugasse 18, 8810, Horgen, Switzerland (50%)
Tel.: (41) 446596492
Web Site: https://www.swisscard.ch
Credit Card Providers
N.A.I.C.S.: 522210
Florence Schnydrig Moser (CEO)
Ozlem Civelek (Head-Risk)
Michael Marek (Head-Ops)
Marco Bazzani (Head-IT)
Barbara Allemann (Head-HR)
Enrico Salvadori (Head-Consumer Bus)
Alex Friedli (Head-Bus-to-Bus)

Uvet American Express Corporate Travel S.p.A. (1)
Via Ambrogio Binda 21, Milan, 20143, Italy
Tel.: (39) 02818381
Web Site: http://www.uvetamex.com
Business Travel & Tour Operating Services
N.A.I.C.S.: 561520
Mario Mazzei (Dir-Mktg & Comm)

emnos Iberia S.L (1)
Calle de Maria de, Molina 37, 28006, Madrid, Spain
Tel.: (34) 915017490
Web Site: http://www.emnos.com
Emp.: 22
Customer Management Consulting Services
N.A.I.C.S.: 541613

emnos S.a.r.l. (1)
97 Saint-Lazare Street, 75009, Paris, France
Tel.: (33) 173020200
Web Site: http://www.emnos.com
Emp.: 40
Customer Management Consulting Services
N.A.I.C.S.: 541613
Atessa Mohseni-Leroy (Mng Dir-Southern Europe)

emnos UK Ltd. (1)
Oriel House 26 the Quadrant, Richmond, TW9 1DL, Surrey, United Kingdom
Tel.: (44) 2086147700
Web Site: http://www.emnos.com
Emp.: 20
Customer Management Consulting Services
N.A.I.C.S.: 541613

emnos USA Corp. (1)
300 N LaSalle Ste 5575, Chicago, IL 60654
Tel.: (312) 880-1336
Customer Management Consulting Services
N.A.I.C.S.: 541613
Matthew Green (Mng Dir)

AMERICAN FILMS, INC.
7901 4th St N Ste 13245, Saint Petersburg, FL 33702
Tel.: (508) 259-6877 NV
Web Site: https://www.americanfilms.us
AMFL—(OTCIQ)
Media Production & Distribution Services
N.A.I.C.S.: 512110
Geoff Lee (Pres & CEO)
Jamie Warren (CFO & Treas)
David Tamaroff (Gen Counsel & VP-Legal Affairs)
Craig Campbell (Chm & CTO)

AMERICAN FINANCIAL GROUP, INC.
301 E 4th St, Cincinnati, OH 45202
Tel.: (513) 579-2121 OH
Web Site: https://www.afginc.com
Year Founded: 1940
AFG—(NYSE)
Rev.: $7,827,000,000
Assets: $29,787,000,000
Liabilities: $25,529,000,000
Net Worth: $4,258,000,000
Earnings: $852,000,000
Emp.: 8,500
Fiscal Year-end: 12/31/23
Holding Company; Insurance & Annuity Products & Services
N.A.I.C.S.: 551112
Carl H. Lindner III (Co-CEO)
S. Craig Lindner (Co-CEO)
Brian S. Hertzman (CFO & Sr VP)
Anthony W. Dunn (VP-Internal Audit)
Sue A. Erhart (VP)
Joseph C. Alter (Sec, VP & Deputy Gen Counsel)
Robert A. Dee (VP & Controller)
Annette D. Gardner (Treas & VP)
JD Rogers (Chief Information Security Officer & VP)

Subsidiaries:

American Financial Enterprises, Inc. (1)
301 E 4th St 27 FL, Cincinnati, OH 45202-3717 (100%)
Tel.: (513) 579-2172
Web Site: http://www.gaic.com
Sales Range: $1-4.9 Billion
Holding Company; Successor to The New York, New Haven & Hartford Railroad Companies
N.A.I.C.S.: 523999
Carl H. Lindner III (Co-Chm & Co-Pres)

American Money Management Corporation (1)
301 E 4th St, Cincinnati, OH 45202-3717 (100%)
Tel.: (513) 579-2121
Securities Management for AFC & Affiliates
N.A.I.C.S.: 523940
John B. Berding (Pres)
Jason J. Maney (Exec VP)

Bridgefield Casualty Insurance Company (1)
2310 Commerce Pt Dr, Lakeland, FL 33801-6880
Tel.: (863) 665-6060
Casualty Insurance Services
N.A.I.C.S.: 524126

Crop Risk Services, Inc. (1)
PO Box 1470, Decatur, IL 62524-1470
Tel.: (888) 523-6277
Direct Property & Casualty Insurance Services
N.A.I.C.S.: 524126

Great American Financial Resources, Inc. (1)
301 E 4th St, Cincinnati, OH 45202 (100%)
Tel.: (513) 579-2121
Holding Company; Annuities & Life Insurance
N.A.I.C.S.: 551112

Subsidiary (Domestic):

Central Reserve Life Insurance Company (2)
11200 Lakeline Blvd Ste100, Austin, TX 78717-5964
Tel.: (512) 531-1599
Web Site: http://www.mypolicyhq.com
Insurance Services
N.A.I.C.S.: 524298

Affiliate (Domestic):

Dempsey & Siders Insurance Agency (2)
6725 Miami Rd Ste 102, Cincinnati, OH 45243 (100%)

Tel.: (513) 891-4400
Web Site: http://www.dempsey-siders.com
Sales Range: $75-99.9 Million
Insurance Agents
N.A.I.C.S.: 524210
Casey W. Connor (Pres)
Nicole O'Brien (Ops Mgr)
Cheryl Creeden (Mgr-Comml Lines)
Casey Connor (Pres)

Great American Advisors, Inc. (2)
301 E 4th St, Cincinnati, OH 45202
Tel.: (513) 333-6030
Web Site: http://www.gaadvisors.com
Sales Range: $10-24.9 Million
Emp.: 3
Security Broker & Dealer
N.A.I.C.S.: 524126

Great American Holding, Inc. (1)
301 E Fourth St, Cincinnati, OH 45202
Tel.: (513) 369-3696
Web Site: https://www.greatamericaninsurance group.com
Property & Casualty Insurance, Specialty Insurance, Annuities & Commercial Insurance
N.A.I.C.S.: 524126

Subsidiary (Domestic):

ABA Insurance Services Inc. (2)
3401 Tuttle Rd Ste 300, Shaker Heights, OH 44122
Web Site: https://www.abais.com
Insurance Services
N.A.I.C.S.: 524210
Lisa Kelly (Sr VP & Dir-Bank Program)
Shawn McNamara (Sr VP-Fin)
Eric Steiner (Sr VP & Dir-Claims)
Todd Evans (VP-Ops)
John Wells (Pres-Div)
Michael Read (VP-Bus Dev)

American Empire Surplus Lines Insurance Company (2)
301 E 4th St 26th Fl, Cincinnati, OH 45202-4201 (100%)
Tel.: (513) 763-8400
Web Site: http://www.aeslic.com
Sales Range: $25-49.9 Million
Emp.: 48
Property & Casualty Insurance
N.A.I.C.S.: 524126

Subsidiary (Domestic):

American Empire Insurance Company (3)
515 Main St, Cincinnati, OH 45202-3207 (100%)
Tel.: (513) 369-3000
Web Site: https://www.aeslic.com
Sales Range: $25-49.9 Million
Emp.: 55
Casualty & Property Insurance
N.A.I.C.S.: 524126
T. Matthew Held (Treas & VP)

Subsidiary (Domestic):

American Empire Underwriters, Inc. (4)
3200 Wilcrest Ste 300, Houston, TX 77042 (100%)
Tel.: (713) 771-9800
Sales Range: Less than $1 Million
Emp.: 11
Insurance Underwriting
N.A.I.C.S.: 524210

Subsidiary (Domestic):

Mid-Continent Casualty Co. (2)
1437 S Boulder Ave W Ste 200, Tulsa, OK 74119-3609 (100%)
Tel.: (918) 587-7221
Web Site: https://www.mcg-ins.com
Property & Casualty Insurance
N.A.I.C.S.: 524126

Subsidiary (Domestic):

Mid-Continent Assurance Company (3)
1437 S Boulder Ave Ste 200, Tulsa, OK 74119 (100%)
Tel.: (918) 587-7221

Sales Range: $100-124.9 Million
Emp.: 230
Property & Casualty Insurance
N.A.I.C.S.: 524126

Mid-Continent Excess and Surplus Insurance Company (3)
1437 S Boulder Ave Ste 200, Tulsa, OK 74119
Tel.: (918) 587-7221
Property & Casualty Insurance Services
N.A.I.C.S.: 524126

Oklahoma Surety Company (3)
1437 S Boulder Ste 200, Tulsa, OK 74119-3693 (100%)
Tel.: (918) 587-7221
Sales Range: $100-124.9 Million
Property & Casualty Insurance
N.A.I.C.S.: 524126

Great American Insurance Company (1)
301 E 4th St, Cincinnati, OH 45202
Tel.: (513) 369-5000
Web Site:
https://www.greatamericaninsurance group.com
Sales Range: $150-199.9 Million
Emp.: 1,500
Property & Casualty Insurance
N.A.I.C.S.: 524126
Carol Sipe (Pres & CEO)
Kenneth B. Patrick (Pres-AgriBusiness)
Brian D. DeSoto (Pres-Great American Risk Solutions Div, Environmental Div, and Mid-Continent Grp)
Carrie A. Little (Pres-Specialty Human Svcs Div)
Richard L. Suter (Pres-Alternative Markets Div)

Subsidiary (Domestic):

Brothers Property Corporation (2)
1280 2 Alhambra Plz, Coral Gables, FL 33134 (80%)
Tel.: (305) 285-1035
Web Site: http://www.brothersproperty.com
Sales Range: $1-9.9 Million
Emp.: 22
Real Estate Managers
N.A.I.C.S.: 531210

Subsidiary (Non-US):

El Aguila, Compania de Seguros, S.A. de C.V. (2)
Av Insurgentes Sur 1106 1er Piso, Col Tlacoquemecatl Del Benito Juarez, CP 03200, Mexico, Mexico
Tel.: (52) 54888888
Web Site: https://www.elaguila.com.mx
Property & Casualty Insurance Services
N.A.I.C.S.: 524126

Subsidiary (Domestic):

Employer's Comp Associates, Inc. (2)
14350 Proton Rd, Dallas, TX 75244
Tel.: (972) 931-2026
Web Site: http://www.gaig.com
Sales Range: $10-24.9 Million
Emp.: 20
Insurance Agencies & Brokerages
N.A.I.C.S.: 524210

Farmers Crop Insurance Alliance, Inc. (2)
49 E 4th St, Cincinnati, OH 45202
Tel.: (800) 587-1553
Web Site:
https://www.greatamericancrop.com
Insurance Products & Services
N.A.I.C.S.: 524210

Subsidiary (Domestic):

FCIA Management Company Inc. (3)
125 Park Ave 14th Fl, New York, NY 10017
Tel.: (212) 885-1500
Web Site: http://www.fcia.com
Rev.: $8,000,000
Emp.: 35
Credit & Other Financial Responsibility Insurance
N.A.I.C.S.: 524126

Subsidiary (Domestic):

Great American Alliance Insurance Company (2)
301 E 4th St, Cincinnati, OH 45202-3110
Tel.: (513) 369-5000
Rev.: $940,189
Emp.: 700
Fire Marine & Casualty Insurance
N.A.I.C.S.: 524126

Great American Assurance Company (2)
301 E 4th St, Cincinnati, OH 45202 (100%)
Tel.: (513) 369-5000
Web Site: https://www.gaig.com
Sales Range: $150-199.9 Million
Property & Casualty Insurance
N.A.I.C.S.: 524126

Great American Casualty Insurance Company (2)
301 E 4th St, Cincinnati, OH 45202
Tel.: (513) 369-5000
Emp.: 7,000
Insurance Services
N.A.I.C.S.: 524298

Great American Contemporary Insurance Company (2)
580 Walnut St Ste 900, Cincinnati, OH 45202-3193
Tel.: (513) 369-5000
Insurance Services
N.A.I.C.S.: 524298

Great American Custom Insurance Services, Inc. (2)
725 S Figueroa St Ste 3400, Los Angeles, CA 90017
Tel.: (213) 430-4300
Web Site: http://www.gamcustom.com
Sales Range: Less than $1 Million
Emp.: 150
Insurance Agents & Brokers
N.A.I.C.S.: 524210

Great American Protection Insurance Company (2)
301 E 4th St, Cincinnati, OH 45202-3193
Tel.: (513) 369-5000
Insurance Agencies & Brokerages
N.A.I.C.S.: 524210

Great American Spirit Insurance Co. (2)
301 E 4th St, Cincinnati, OH 45202 (100%)
Tel.: (513) 369-5000
Web Site:
https://www.greatamericaninsurance group.com
Rev.: $320,000
Emp.: 4
Insurance Services
N.A.I.C.S.: 524126

National Interstate Corporation (2)
3250 Interstate Dr, Richfield, OH 44286-9000 (100%)
Tel.: (330) 659-8900
Web Site:
https://www.nationalinterstate.com
Sales Range: $600-649.9 Million
Emp.: 600
Property & Casualty Insurance Holding Company
N.A.I.C.S.: 551112

Subsidiary (Domestic):

American Highways Insurance Agency, Inc. (3)
3250 Interstate Dr, Richfield, OH 44286
Tel.: (800) 935-2442
Web Site: http://www.ahiains.com
Sales Range: $150-199.9 Million
Emp.: 500
Transportation Risk Management & Insurance Services
N.A.I.C.S.: 524126

Explorer RV Insurance Agency, Inc. (3)
3250 Interstate Dr, Richfield, OH 44286-0568
Tel.: (888) 352-5410
Web Site: http://www.explorerrv.com

Emp.: 3
Recreational Vehicle Insurance Services
N.A.I.C.S.: 524126

National Interstate Insurance Agency, Inc. (3)
3250 Interstate Dr, Richfield, OH 44286-9000
Tel.: (330) 659-8900
Web Site: http://www.natl.com
Emp.: 600
Insurance Brokerage Services
N.A.I.C.S.: 524210

National Interstate Insurance Company of Hawaii, Inc. (3)
Kapolei Bldg 1001 Kamokila Blvd Ste 201, Kapolei, HI 96707-2091
Tel.: (808) 536-3366
Web Site:
https://www.nationalinterstate.com
Sales Range: $150-199.9 Million
Insurance Products
N.A.I.C.S.: 524126

Safety, Claims & Litigation Services, LLC (3)
3250 Interstate Dr, Richfield, OH 44286-9000
Tel.: (866) 668-0192
Web Site: http://www.sclsonline.com
Transportation Risk Management & Insurance Services
N.A.I.C.S.: 524126

TransProtection Service Company (3)
1 Premier Dr, Saint Louis, MO 63026
Tel.: (800) 325-3619
Web Site: http://transprotection.vanliner.com
Transportation Risk Management & Insurance Services
N.A.I.C.S.: 524126

Vanliner Insurance Company (3)
1 Premier Dr, Fenton, MO 63026 (100%)
Web Site: http://www.vanliner.com
Sales Range: $100-124.9 Million
Insurance Services for Moving & Storage Industry
N.A.I.C.S.: 524210

Subsidiary (Domestic):

Summit Holding Southeast, Inc. (2)
PO Box 988, Lakeland, FL 33802-0988
Tel.: (863) 665-6060
Web Site: http://www.summitholdings.com
Sales Range: $350-399.9 Million
Holding Company; Insurance Products & Services
N.A.I.C.S.: 551112

Subsidiary (Domestic):

Bridgefield Employers Insurance Company (3)
117 N Massachusetts Ave, Lakeland, FL 33801-6880
Tel.: (863) 665-6060
Web Site: https://www.summitholdings.com
Sales Range: $150-199.9 Million
Emp.: 100
Insurance Underwriting Services
N.A.I.C.S.: 524210

BusinessFirst Insurance Company (3)
PO Box 988, Lakeland, FL 33802-0988
Tel.: (863) 665-6060
Web Site:
https://www.businessfirstinsurance.com
Workers' Compensation Insurance Administration Services
N.A.I.C.S.: 524292

Summit Consulting, LLC (3)
2310 Commerce Point Dr, Lakeland, FL 33801
Tel.: (863) 665-6060
Web Site: https://www.summitholdings.com
Rev.: $29,200,000
Emp.: 500
Insurance Services
N.A.I.C.S.: 524298
Carol P. Sipe (Pres & CEO)
Patrick Smyth (CFO & Sr VP-Fin)
Robert Grimm (Sr VP-Claims)

Subsidiary (Domestic):

Worldwide Casualty Insurance Company (2)

580 Walnut St, Cincinnati, OH 45202-3110 (100%)
Tel.: (513) 369-5000
Web Site: http://www.coverna.net
Personal Auto Insurance
N.A.I.C.S.: 524126

Neon Capital Limited (1)
8 Lloyds Ave, London, EC3N 3EL, United Kingdom (100%)
Tel.: (44) 2074887700
Investment Management Service
N.A.I.C.S.: 541618
Ian Martin (Mng Dir)
Mark Stockton (Head-Underwriting Performance)
Deepon Sen Gupta (Dir-Corp Strategy)
Scott Gregory (Dir-Comm & Mktg)
David Lednor (Chief Underwriting Officer)

Subsidiary (Domestic):

Marketform Holdings Limited (2)
8 Lloyd, London, EC3N 3EL, United Kingdom
Tel.: (44) 02074887700
Insurance Services
N.A.I.C.S.: 524298

Republic Indemnity Company of America (1)
4500 Park Granada Ste 300, Calabasas, CA 91302
Tel.: (818) 990-9860
Web Site:
https://www.republicindemnity.com
Insurance Services
N.A.I.C.S.: 524128
Sean Pepper (Sr VP-Underwriting)
Craig Borstelmann (CFO & Sr VP)
David Simmeth (CIO & Sr VP)
Gene Simpson (Pres)
Janet Miller (Sr VP-)
Jim Hurley (Sr VP-)

Subsidiary (Domestic):

Republic Indemnity Company of California (2)
PO Box 4275, Woodland Hills, CA 91365-4275 (100%)
Tel.: (818) 990-9860
Web Site: http://www.republicindemnity.com
Sales Range: $250-299.9 Million
Workers Compensation Insurance
N.A.I.C.S.: 524126

AMERICAN GREEN, INC.
2902 W Virginia Ave, Phoenix, AZ 85009
Tel.: (480) 443-1600
Web Site:
https://www.americangreen.com
ERBB—(OTCIQ)
Rev.: $1,273,000
Assets: $11,271,000
Liabilities: $19,530,000
Net Worth: ($8,259,000)
Earnings: ($3,036,000)
Fiscal Year-end: 06/30/19
Medicinal & Botanical Manufacturing
N.A.I.C.S.: 325411

Subsidiaries:

CannAwake Corporation (1)
HC1 Box 360 107355 Nipton Rd, Nipton, CA 92364
Tel.: (720) 573-0102
Web Site: http://www.deltaoilgas.com
Sales Range: Less than $1 Million
Emp.: 2
Oil & Gas Exploration & Production Services
N.A.I.C.S.: 211120
Scott Stoegbauer (Pres-Interim)
Malcolm W. Sherman (Chm & Sec)

Vendweb.com (1)
1735 Dameron Rd, Bessemer City, NC 28016-7700
Tel.: (704) 802-4394
Web Site: http://www.vendweb.com
Vending Machine Operators
N.A.I.C.S.: 445132
Lindel Creed (Owner)

American Homes 4 Rent—(Continued)

AMERICAN HOMES 4 RENT
280 Pilot Rd, Las Vegas, NV 89119
Tel.: (702) 847-7800
Web Site: https://www.amh.com
AMH—(NYSE)
Rev.: $1,623,605,000
Assets: $12,688,190,000
Liabilities: $5,035,307,000
Net Worth: $7,652,883,000
Earnings: $366,224,000
Emp.: 1,725
Fiscal Year-end: 12/31/23
Residential Home Investment, Renovation & Leasing
N.A.I.C.S.: 531390
Brian Reitz (Chief Acctg Officer & Exec VP)
Sara H. Vogt-Lowell (Chief Legal Officer)
Christopher C. Lau (CFO & Sr Exec VP)
B. Wayne Hughes (Founder)
Bryan Smith (CEO)

Subsidiaries:

AH4R Management-GA, LLC (1)
2 Sun Crt Ste 210, Norcross, GA 30092
Tel.: (404) 445-1814
Web Site:
http://www.americanhomes4rent.com
Commercial Property Rental Services
N.A.I.C.S.: 531110

AH4R Management-NC, LLC (1)
2700 Gateway Ctr Blvd Ste 600, Morrisville, NC 27560
Tel.: (919) 582-6197
Commercial Property Rental Services
N.A.I.C.S.: 531110

AH4R Management-TX, LLC (1)
19115 FM2252 Ste 15, San Antonio, TX 78266
Tel.: (210) 319-6009
Commercial Property Rental Services
N.A.I.C.S.: 531110

AH4R Properties, LLC (1)
30601 Agoura Rd ste 200, Agoura Hills, CA 91301
Tel.: (310) 774-5300
Web Site: http://www.ah4r.com
Emp.: 150
Commercial Property Rental Services
N.A.I.C.S.: 531110

AMH Portfolio One, LLC (1)
30601 Agoura Rd Ste 200, Agoura Hills, CA 91301
Tel.: (480) 921-4600
Commercial Property Rental Services
N.A.I.C.S.: 531110

American Homes 4 Rent, L.P. (1)
280 Pilot Rd, Las Vegas, NV 89119
Tel.: (702) 847-7800
Web Site: https://www.amh.com
Rev.: $1,623,604,999
Assets: $12,688,189,999
Liabilities: $5,035,306,999
Net Worth: $7,652,882,999
Earnings: $418,198,000
Emp.: 1,724
Fiscal Year-end: 12/31/2023
Residential Property Management Services
N.A.I.C.S.: 531311

AMERICAN INTERNATIONAL GROUP, INC.
1271 Ave of the Americas Fl 41, New York, NY 10020-1304
Tel.: (212) 770-7000   DE
Web Site: https://www.aig.com
Year Founded: 1919
AIG—(NYSE)
Rev.: $46,802,000,000
Assets: $539,306,000,000
Liabilities: $488,005,000,000
Net Worth: $51,301,000,000
Earnings: $3,614,000,000
Emp.: 25,200
Fiscal Year-end: 12/31/23

Holding Company; Insurance & Financial Services
N.A.I.C.S.: 551112
Edward L. Dandridge (Chief Mktg & Comm Officer & Exec VP)
Rose Marie E. Glazer (Gen Counsel)
Peter S. Zaffino (Chm & CEO)
Luciana Fato (Gen Counsel, Exec VP & Head-Comm & Govt Affairs-Global)
Roshan Navagamuwa (CIO & Exec VP)
Shane Fitzsimons (Exec VP & Head-Ops & FP&A-Global)
Claude Wade (Exec VP)
Charlie Fry (Exec VP-Reinsurance & Risk Capital Optimization)
Christopher T. Schaper (Chief Underwriting Officer-Global & Exec VP)
Melissa Twiningdavis (Chief Admin Officer & Exec VP)
Keith Walsh (CFO & Exec VP)
Kelly Lafnitzegger (Chief HR Officer, Chief Diversity Officer & Exec VP)
Ted Devine (Chief Admin Officer, Exec VP & Head-200-Global)
Don Bailey (CEO-North America Insurance, Exec VP & Head-Distr-Global)
Keith Walsh (CFO & Exec VP)

Subsidiaries:

AIG Asset Management (U.S.), LLC (1)
80 Pine St Ste 4, New York, NY 10005
Tel.: (212) 770-3980
Emp.: 3
Insurance & Brokerage Services
N.A.I.C.S.: 524210

AIG Capital Corporation (1)
70 Pine St Ste 11, New York, NY 10270
Tel.: (908) 679-3150
Emp.: 7,000
Insurance Services
N.A.I.C.S.: 524298

Subsidiary (Non-US):

AIG Credit Corp. (2)
666 Burrard St Ste 1100, Vancouver, V6C2X8, BC, Canada
Tel.: (604) 691-2918
Property & Casualty Insurance Services
N.A.I.C.S.: 524210
Alex Cano (Exec VP)

AIG Claims, Inc. (1)
5 Wood Hollow Rd Ste 3, Parsippany, NJ 07054-2832
Tel.: (973) 402-2800
Casualty Insurance Services
N.A.I.C.S.: 524126

AIG Consultants, Inc. (1)
70 Pine St, New York, NY 10270
Tel.: (212) 770-7000
Sales Range: $75-99.9 Million
Provider of Exposure & Risk Identifying Services
N.A.I.C.S.: 541690

AIG Consumer Finance Group, Inc. (1)
70 Pine St 11th Fl, New York, NY 10270
Tel.: (908) 679-3150
Web Site: http://www.chartisinsurance.com
Sales Range: $10-24.9 Million
Emp.: 70
Consumer Financial Products
N.A.I.C.S.: 921130
Richard Pfeiffer (Chm & CEO)

Subsidiary (Domestic):

AIG Financial Products Corp (2)
50 Danbury Rd, Wilton, CT 06897
Tel.: (203) 222-4700
Emp.: 175
Fire Insurance Services
N.A.I.C.S.: 524113

Subsidiary (Non-US):

AIG Management France S.A. (3)
Tour CB 21 16 place de l Iris, 92400,

Courbevoie, France
Tel.: (33) 149024222
Financial Management Services
N.A.I.C.S.: 541611

Subsidiary (Domestic):

AIG Matched Funding Corp. (3)
100 Nyala Farms Rd, Westport, CT 06880
Tel.: (203) 222-4700
Casualty Insurance Services
N.A.I.C.S.: 524126

Subsidiary (Non-US):

Banque AIG S.A. (3)
112 Ave Kleber CS 31603, 75773, Paris, France
Tel.: (33) 149523600
Commercial Banking Services
N.A.I.C.S.: 522110

AIG Europe (U.K.) Limited (1)
58 Fenchurch St, London, EC3M 4AB, United Kingdom (100%)
Tel.: (44) 2079547000
Sales Range: $10-24.9 Million
Emp.: 110
Insurance Company
N.A.I.C.S.: 524298

AIG Europe Limited (1)
30 North Wall Quay International Financial Services Centre, Dublin, D01 R8H7, Ireland (100%)
Tel.: (353) 12081400
Web Site: https://www.aig.ie
Sales Range: $25-49.9 Million
Emp.: 130
Insurance Services
N.A.I.C.S.: 524298

AIG Europe, SA (1)
Tour CBX 1 Passerelle des Reflets, 34-34 Place des Corolles, 92400, Courbevoie, France (100%)
Tel.: (33) 149024222
Web Site: https://www.aigassurance.fr
Provider of Asset Protection Services to Major & Multinational Companies in Europe
N.A.I.C.S.: 524128
Christophe Zaniewski (Mng Dir)

AIG Federal Savings Bank (1)
1 Alico Plz 600 King St, Wilmington, DE 19801-3722
Tel.: (302) 661-8998
Casualty Insurance Services
N.A.I.C.S.: 524126

AIG Insurance (Thailand) Public Company Limited (1)
989 Siam Piwat Tower 21st and 23rd Floor Rama I Road, Patumwan, Bangkok, 10330, Thailand
Tel.: (66) 26491999
Web Site: https://www.aig.co.th
Emp.: 2,800
Insurance Services
N.A.I.C.S.: 524210

AIG Insurance Company China Limited (1)
Room 501B 503B and 504 5th Floor No 1589 Century Avenue, Changtai International Financial Building Pudong New Area, Shanghai, 200122, China
Tel.: (86) 2138578000
Web Site: https://www.aiginsurance.com.cn
Casualty Insurance Services
N.A.I.C.S.: 524126
Lisa Sun (CEO)

Subsidiary (Domestic):

AIG Insurance Company of Canada (1)
2000 McGill College Avenue Suite 920, Montreal, H3A 3H3, QC, Canada
Tel.: (514) 842-0603
Web Site: http://www.aig.ca
Emp.: 425
Insurance Services
N.A.I.C.S.: 524298

AIG Insurance Company, JSC (1)
Floor 11 Building 3 72 Leningradsky Prospect Alcon Business Centre, 125315, Moscow, Russia
Tel.: (7) 4959358950
Web Site: http://www.aig.ru
Insurance Services

N.A.I.C.S.: 524126

AIG International Inc. (1)
180 Maiden Ln, New York, NY 10038-4925 (100%)
Tel.: (212) 770-7000
Web Site: http://www.aig.com
Sales Range: $1-4.9 Billion
Emp.: 7,000
Foreign Exchange Currency
N.A.I.C.S.: 523150

AIG Investments UK Limited (1)
The AIG Building 58 Fenchurch Street, London, EC3M 4AB, United Kingdom
Tel.: (44) 2079547000
Web Site: http://www.aig.co.uk
Emp.: 900
Property & Casualty Insurance Services
N.A.I.C.S.: 524126

AIG Israel Insurance Company Limited (1)
25 Fiber Street Kiryat Matalon, PO Box 535, Petach Tikva, 4910001, Israel
Tel.: (972) 39272300
Web Site: https://www.aig.co.il
Casualty Insurance Services
N.A.I.C.S.: 524126

AIG Japan Holdings Kabushiki Kaisha (1)
Kamiyacho MT Building 3-20 Toranomon 4-chome, Minato-ku, Tokyo, 105-0001, Japan
Tel.: (81) 354004000
Web Site: https://www-510.aig.co.jp
Insurance Services
N.A.I.C.S.: 551112

Subsidiary (Domestic):

AIG General Insurance Co., Ltd. (2)
Kamiyacho MT Building 3-20 Toranomon 4-chome, Minato-ku, Tokyo, 105-8403, Japan
Tel.: (81) 368488500
Web Site: https://www.aig.co.jp
Insurance Services
N.A.I.C.S.: 524126
James Nash (Pres)

Subsidiary (Non-US):

American Home Assurance Co., Ltd. (2)
The H Hotel Complex Trade Centre First 27th floor, PO Box 40569, Dubai, United Arab Emirates
Tel.: (971) 45096111
Web Site: https://www.aig.ae
Property & Casualty Insurance Services
N.A.I.C.S.: 524126

AIG Lebanon SAL (1)
Lebanon-Dbayeh Highway Le Mall building Regus office 7th Floor, PO Box 13-5459, Beirut Central District, Beirut, Lebanon
Tel.: (961) 199 0127
Web Site: https://www-152.aig.com
Insurance Services
N.A.I.C.S.: 524126

AIG Life & Retirement (1)
21650 Oxnard St Ste 750, Woodland Hills, CA 91367 (100%)
Tel.: (832) 242-1641
Web Site:
https://www.corebridgefinancial.com
Sales Range: $1-4.9 Billion
Emp.: 16,000
Holding Company, Life Insurance, Retirement Services, Consumer Lending & Investment Management
N.A.I.C.S.: 551112
Stasa Cushman (Dir-Comm)
Adam Winslow (CEO-Intl)
Kevin Hogan (CEO & Exec VP)

Subsidiary (Domestic):

American General Assurance Company (2)
1000 E Woodfield Rd Ste 300, Schaumburg, IL 60173 (100%)
Tel.: (847) 517-6000
Web Site: http://www.agfg.com
Rev.: $176,015,000
Emp.: 182

Credit Life Insurance & Disability Insurance
N.A.I.C.S.: 524113

**American General Life & Accident
Insurance Company** **(2)**
2000 American General Way, Brentwood,
TN 37027 **(100%)**
Tel.: (615) 749-2777
Web Site: http://www.agla.com
Sales Range: $700-749.9 Million
Emp.: 1,000
Life Insurance
N.A.I.C.S.: 524113
Joe Kelley (CEO)

Subsidiary (Domestic):

**American General Life & Accident
Insurance Company** **(3)**
American General Ctr, Nashville, TN
37250-0001 **(100%)**
Tel.: (615) 749-1000
Web Site: http://www.agla.com
Life & Health Insurance
N.A.I.C.S.: 524113

**American International Life Assurance
Company of New York** **(3)**
175 Water St, New York, NY
10038 **(77.52%)**
Tel.: (212) 770-6580
Sales Range: $150-199.9 Million
Emp.: 300
Provider of Commercial & Personal Life In-
surance Products
N.A.I.C.S.: 524126
Mary Andrews (Dir-Complex)

Subsidiary (Domestic):

**American General Life Companies -
Springfield** **(2)**
3051 Hollis Dr, Springfield, IL
62704 **(100%)**
Tel.: (217) 541-7700
Web Site: http://www.americangeneral.com
Sales Range: $350-399.9 Million
Emp.: 650
Whole Life & Disability Insurance
N.A.I.C.S.: 524113

Corebridge Financial, Inc. **(2)**
2919 Allen Parkway Woodson Tower, Hous-
ton, TX 77019
Tel.: (310) 772-6000
Web Site:
  https://www.corebridgefinancial.com
Rev.: $18,878,000,000
Assets: $379,270,000,000
Liabilities: $366,635,000,000
Net Worth: $12,635,000,000
Earnings: $1,104,000,000
Emp.: 5,700
Fiscal Year-end: 12/31/2023
Fire Insurance Services
N.A.I.C.S.: 524113
Peter S. Zaffino (Chm)

Subsidiary (Non-US):

AIG Life Limited **(3)**
The AIG Building 58 Fenchurch Street, Lon-
don, EC3M 4AB, United Kingdom
Tel.: (44) 3456006820
Insurance Services
N.A.I.C.S.: 524128

Subsidiary (Domestic):

**American General Life Insurance
Company** **(3)**
2727-A Allen Pkwy, Houston, TX
77019 **(100%)**
Tel.: (713) 522-1111
Web Site: http://www.americangeneral.com
Sales Range: $650-699.9 Million
Emp.: 993
Provider of Life Insurance Services
N.A.I.C.S.: 524113

Subsidiary (Domestic):

**SunAmerica Asset Management,
LLC** **(4)**
Harborside 5 185 Hudson St Ste 3300, Jer-
sey City, NJ 07311 **(100%)**
Tel.: (201) 324-6700
Web Site: http://www.sunamericafunds.com

Sales Range: $150-199.9 Million
Investment Advice & Mutal Funds
N.A.I.C.S.: 523150

Subsidiary (Domestic):

**SunAmerica Capital Services,
Inc.** **(5)**
Harborside 5 185 Hudson St Ste 3300, Jer-
sey City, NJ 07311 **(100%)**
Tel.: (201) 324-6537
Rev.: $37,840,229
Emp.: 100
Brokers Security
N.A.I.C.S.: 523150
John Genoy (CFO)
Peter Harbeck (Pres & CEO)

Subsidiary (Domestic):

**The United States Life Insurance
Company in the City of New
York** **(3)**
1 World Financial Ctr 200 Liberty St, New
York, NY 10281 **(100%)**
Tel.: (800) 487-5433
Fire Insurance Services
N.A.I.C.S.: 524113

**The Variable Annuity Life Insurance
Company** **(3)**
205 E 10th Ave, Amarillo, TX
79101 **(100%)**
Tel.: (877) 246-4501
Web Site: http://www.aigrs.com
Sales Range: $1-4.9 Billion
Financial & Retirement Services
N.A.I.C.S.: 524128
Robert Scheinerman (Pres)

**AIG Life Insurance Company (Swit-
zerland) Ltd.** **(1)**
Via Camara 19, 6932, Breganzona,
Switzerland **(100%)**
Tel.: (41) 919604848
Web Site: http://www.aslife.com
Sales Range: $25-49.9 Million
Emp.: 40
Provider of Investment Oriented & Insur-
ance Oriented Life Insurance Products
N.A.I.C.S.: 524128

AIG Marketing, Inc. **(1)**
70 Pine St, New York, NY 10005 **(100%)**
Tel.: (212) 770-7000
Web Site: http://www.aig.com
Sales Range: $250-299.9 Million
Provider of Marketing & Related Services
N.A.I.C.S.: 525910

AIG Markets, Inc. **(1)**
70 Pine St, New York, NY 10270
Tel.: (212) 770-6157
Business Consulting Services
N.A.I.C.S.: 541618

AIG Property Casualty Company **(1)**
1271 Ave of the Americas FL 41, New York,
NY 10020-1304 **(100%)**
Tel.: (212) 770-7000
Fire & Casualty Insurance
N.A.I.C.S.: 524126

AIG Property Casualty Inc. **(1)**
175 Water St 17th Fl, New York, NY 10038
Tel.: (212) 770-7000
Web Site: http://www.chartisinsurance.com
Sales Range: $5-14.9 Billion
Emp.: 34,000
Insurance Services
N.A.I.C.S.: 524126

Subsidiary (Domestic):

**AIG Insurance Company-Puerto
Rico** **(2)**
250 Munoz Rivera Ave American Interna-
tional Plz Ste 500, Hato Rey, PR 00918
Tel.: (787) 767-6400
Web Site: https://www.aig.com.pr
Property & Casualty Insurance Services
N.A.I.C.S.: 524126
Agnes B. Suarez (Pres & CEO)

**AIG Property Casualty International,
LLC** **(2)**
175 Water St 15th Fl, New York, NY 10038
Tel.: (212) 458-6091
Insurance Services
N.A.I.C.S.: 524126

Subsidiary (Non-US):

AIG APAC Holdings Pte. Ltd. **(3)**
78 Shenton Way 07-16, Singapore, 079120,
Singapore
Tel.: (65) 64193000
Web Site: http://www.aig.sg
Holding Company; Regional Managing Of-
fice
N.A.I.C.S.: 551112

Subsidiary (Domestic):

**AIG Asia Pacific Insurance Pte.
Ltd.** **(4)**
AIG Building 78 Shenton Way Level 1, Sin-
gapore, 079120, Singapore
Tel.: (65) 64193000
Web Site: https://www.aig.sg
Property & Casualty Insurance Services
N.A.I.C.S.: 524126

Subsidiary (Non-US):

**AIG Insurance Hong Kong
Limited** **(5)**
7/F One Island East 18 Westlands Road
Island East, Hong Kong, China (Hong
Kong)
Tel.: (852) 3 555 0000
Web Site: https://www.aig.com.hk
Property & Casualty Insurance Services
N.A.I.C.S.: 524126

**AIG Insurance New Zealand
Limited** **(5)**
Physical is 21 Queen Street Level 7, Auck-
land, 1010, New Zealand
Tel.: (64) 93553100
Web Site: https://www.aig.co.nz
Emp.: 60,000
Insurance Services
N.A.I.C.S.: 524126

AIG Korea Inc. **(5)**
27 Floor Two IFC 10 Gukjegeumyung-ro,
Youngdeungpo-gu, Seoul, 150-945, Korea
(South)
Tel.: (82) 222606800
Web Site: https://www.m.aig.co.kr
Insurance Services
N.A.I.C.S.: 524126

AIG Malaysia Insurance Berhad **(5)**
Level 18 Menara Worldwide 198, Jalan
Bukit Bintang, 55100, Kuala Lumpur, Malay-
sia
Tel.: (60) 321180188
Web Site: https://www.aig.my
Insurance Services
N.A.I.C.S.: 524298

AIG Philippines Insurance, Inc. **(5)**
30th Floor Philam Life Tower 8767 Paseo
de Roxas, Makati, 1226, Metro Manila, Phil-
ippines
Tel.: (63) 288153000
Web Site: https://www.aig.com.ph
Emp.: 80
Insurance Services
N.A.I.C.S.: 524210
Mark Lwin (Pres & CEO)
Ambassador Roberto R. Romulo (Chm)
Jeffrey Lacson (CFO & Sr VP)
Leilani T. Isidro (Head-Liabilities & Fin
Lines)
Iris B. Raymundo (Head-Marine-Southeast
Asia)
Michelle Annie Comia-Marasigan (Officer-
Compliance & Risk-Guam)
Cristopher Taguba (Head-Gen Svcs Dept)
Farah Repol (Gen Counsel)
Rogelio Ancheta (Partner-IT Bus)
Shelie Baydo (Treas)
Consuelo Villamor (VP)

AIG Re-Takaful (L) Berhad **(5)**
Level 11B Block 4 Office Tower Financial
Park Labuan Jalan Merdeka, 87000,
Labuan, Malaysia
Tel.: (60) 87417672
Web Site: http://www.aig.my
Insurance Services
N.A.I.C.S.: 524126

AIG Taiwan Insurance Co., Ltd. **(5)**
Taiwan Hsiao West Road Section 6 15 17
18 F, Taipei, Taiwan
Tel.: (886) 223161188
Web Site: http://www.aig.com.tw

Emp.: 200
Insurance Services
N.A.I.C.S.: 524298
Kian Tiong Lim (Mng Dir)

**AIG Vietnam Insurance Company
Limited** **(5)**
Tower 1 Floor 9 Saigon Center 65 Le Loi,
District 1, Ho Chi Minh City, Vietnam
Tel.: (84) 2839140065
Web Site: https://www.aig.com.vn
Insurance Services
N.A.I.C.S.: 524298

**Chartis Insurance Company China
Limited** **(5)**
5F Chamtime International Financial Center
1589 Century Avenue, Pu Dong District,
Shanghai, 200122, China
Tel.: (86) 2138578000
Web Site: http://www.aig.com.cn
Property & Casualty Insurance Services
N.A.I.C.S.: 524126

**Chartis Vietnam Insurance Company
Limited** **(5)**
Tower 1 Floor 9 Saigon Center 65 Le Loi
Street, District 1, Ho Chi Minh City, Vietnam
Tel.: (84) 2839140065
Web Site: https://www.aig.com.vn
Insurance Services
N.A.I.C.S.: 524126

PT AIG Insurance Indonesia **(5)**
Indonesia Stock Exchange Building Tower 2
Floor 3A, Jl Jend Sudirman Kav 52-53, Ja-
karta, 12190, Indonesia
Tel.: (62) 8001248888
Web Site: https://www.aig.co.id
Insurance Services
N.A.I.C.S.: 524126
Robert E. Logie (Chm)

Subsidiary (Non-US):

AIG Cyprus Limited **(3)**
26 Esperidon Street 2001 Strovolos, PO
Box 21745, CY-1512, Nicosia,
Cyprus **(100%)**
Tel.: (357) 22699999
Web Site: https://www.aig.com.cy
Sales Range: $25-49.9 Million
Emp.: 60
Insurance Services
N.A.I.C.S.: 524126
Stravus Florides (Gen Mgr)

AIG Life South Africa Limited **(3)**
 (100%)
Tel.: (27) 115518000
Web Site: https://www.aig.co.za
Insurance Management Services
N.A.I.C.S.: 524298

AIG MEA Holdings Limited **(3)**
The H Hotel Complex Trade Centre First
27th floor, Dubai, United Arab
Emirates **(100%)**
Tel.: (971) 45096111
Web Site: https://www.aig.ae
Holding Company; Property & Casualty In-
surance Services
N.A.I.C.S.: 551112

Subsidiary (Non-US):

**AIG Egypt Insurance Company
S.A.E.** **(4)**
44 Abdel Moniem Riad Street 1st floor Mo-
handessin, Giza, Egypt **(95.08%)**
Tel.: (20) 23 308 2000
Web Site: https://www.aig.eg
Insurance Services
N.A.I.C.S.: 524126

AIG Insurance Limited **(4)**
Level 17 BOC Merchant Tower 28 St Mi-
chaels Road, Colombo, 3, Sri Lanka
Tel.: (94) 112371000
Web Site: http://www.aig.lk
Insurance Services
N.A.I.C.S.: 524298

**AIG Kenya Insurance Company
Limited** **(4)**
Eden Square Complex Chiromo Road, PO
Box 49460, 00100, Nairobi, Kenya
Tel.: (254) 203676000
Web Site: https://www.aig.co.ke
Insurance Services

American International Group, Inc.—(Continued)

N.A.I.C.S.: 524298

Subsidiary (Domestic):

AIG MEA Limited **(4)**
The H Hotel Complex Trade Centre First
27th floor, PO Box 40569, Dubai, United
Arab Emirates
Tel.: (971) 45096111
Web Site: https://www.aig.ae
Casualty Insurance Services
N.A.I.C.S.: 524126

Subsidiary (Non-US):

AIG Uganda Limited **(4)**
Lotis Towers Ground Floor Plot 16 Mackin-
non Rd, PO Box 7077, Nakasero, Kampala,
Uganda
Tel.: (256) 31 221 1311
Web Site: https://www.aig.co.ug
Insurance Services
N.A.I.C.S.: 524298

Subsidiary (Non-US):

AIG Seguros Brasil S.A. **(3)**
Av Dr Chucri Zaidan 296-17th floor-Torre Z,
Vila Olimpia, Sao Paulo, 04583-110, SP,
Brazil
Tel.: (55) 1138092121
Web Site: https://www.aig.com.br
Insurance Services
N.A.I.C.S.: 524298

**AIG Seguros Mexico, S.A. de
C.V.** **(3)**
Insurgentes Sur 1136, Colonia del Valle,
03219, Mexico, Baja California,
Mexico **(100%)**
Tel.: (52) 5554884700
Web Site: https://www.aig.com.mx
Casualty Insurance Services
N.A.I.C.S.: 524126

**AIG Ukraine Insurance Company
PJSC** **(3)**
St Ilinskaya 8 Entrance No 10 1 Floor,
04070, Kiev, Ukraine
Tel.: (380) 444906550
Web Site: http://www.aig.ua
Property & Casualty Insurance Services
N.A.I.C.S.: 524126

**AIG-Metropolitana Cia de Seguros y
Reaseguros S.A.** **(3)**
Web Site: https://www.aig.com.ec
Property & Casualty Insurance Services
N.A.I.C.S.: 524126

**American International Reinsurance
Company, Ltd.** **(3)**
American International Building 29 Rich-
mond Road, Hamilton, HM 08, Bermuda
Tel.: (441) 2985227
Reinsurance Services
N.A.I.C.S.: 524130

**C.A. de Seguros American
International** **(3)**
Tel.: (58) 2123188300
Web Site: https://www.aig.com.ve
Property & Casualty Insurance Services
N.A.I.C.S.: 524126

CHARTIS Takaful-Enaya B.S.C. **(3)**
Suite 402 Al Moayyed Tower, PO Box
20107, Seef District, Manama, 10488, Bah-
rain
Tel.: (973) 17565999
Web Site: http://www.aig.com
Emp.: 10
Casualty Insurance Services
N.A.I.C.S.: 524126

**Chartis Kazakhstan Insurance
Company** **(3)**
5 Al-Farabi Str Business Centre Nurly Tau
Block 2A Office 202, PO Box 050059, Al-
maty, 50059, Kazakhstan
Tel.: (7) 7272599322
Web Site: http://www.aig.com.kz
Insurance Services
N.A.I.C.S.: 524126

Subsidiary (Domestic):

AIG Property Casualty U.S., Inc. **(2)**
175 Water St, New York, NY 10038

Tel.: (212) 770-7000
Insurance Services
N.A.I.C.S.: 524126

Subsidiary (Domestic):

**AIG Aerospace Insurance Services,
Inc.** **(3)**
1200 Abernasie Rd NE Bldg 600, Atlanta,
GA 30328
Tel.: (404) 249-1800
Web Site: http://www.aig.com
Emp.: 200
Aerospace Insurance Services
N.A.I.C.S.: 524128

**AIG Property Casualty Insurance
Agency, Inc.** **(3)**
Connell Corporate Ctr I 100 Connell Dr,
Berkeley Heights, NJ 07922
Tel.: (908) 679-4748
Web Site: http://www.aig.com
Insurance Services
N.A.I.C.S.: 524298

Subsidiary (Non-US):

**American Home Assurance
Company** **(3)**
(100%)
Tel.: (212) 770-7000
Web Site: http://www.aig.com
Sales Range: $125-149.9 Million
Provider of Commercial Umbrella/Excess
Liability & Primary & Excess Workers' Com-
pensation Insurance
N.A.I.C.S.: 524126

Subsidiary (Domestic):

**American International Realty
Corp.** **(4)**
70 Pine St Fl 1, New York, NY 10270
Tel.: (212) 770-7000
Commercial & Industrial Building Operation
N.A.I.C.S.: 531120

Subsidiary (Domestic):

NSM Holdings, Inc. **(3)**
1574 Gulf Rd, Point Roberts, WA 98281
Tel.: (604) 671-8780
Emp.: 8
Holding Company
N.A.I.C.S.: 551112

Service Net Warranty, LLC **(3)**
650 Missouri Ave, Jeffersonville, IN 47130
Web Site: https://www.servicenet.com
Insurance Services
N.A.I.C.S.: 524126

AIG Resseguros Brasil S.A. **(1)**
Ave Dr Chucri Zaidan 296 - 17th floor-
Torre Z, Sao Paulo, 04583-110, Brazil
Tel.: (55) 1138092121
Web Site: https://www.aig.com.br
Insurance Services
N.A.I.C.S.: 524128

AIG Risk Management, Inc. **(1)**
175 Water St 27th Fl, New York, NY
10038-4918 **(100%)**
Tel.: (212) 458-3085
Sales Range: $100-124.9 Million
Emp.: 500
Customized Primary Casualty Programs to
Large Commercial Companies
N.A.I.C.S.: 524210
Bill Rabl (CEO)
Joseph C. Smetana Jr. (CEO)

**AIG Shared Services
Corporation** **(1)**
70 Pine St, New York, NY
10270-0002 **(100%)**
Tel.: (212) 770-7000
Web Site: http://www.aig.com
Information Technology & Facilities Support
Services
N.A.I.C.S.: 561499
Peter P. Robertson (Pres & CEO)

AIG South Africa Limited **(1)**
1st Floor Sandown Mews West 88 Stella
Street Sandown 2196, PO Box 31983,
Braamfontein, 2017, South Africa
Tel.: (27) 115518000
Web Site: https://www.aig.co.za
Insurance Services

N.A.I.C.S.: 524128

**AIG Specialty Insurance
Company** **(1)**
500 W Madison St Ste 3000, Chicago, IL
60661-4576
Tel.: (212) 458-2521
Casualty Insurance Services
N.A.I.C.S.: 524126

AIG Trading Group Inc. **(1)**
175 Water St, New York, NY
10038 **(100%)**
Tel.: (212) 770-7000
Sales Range: $125-149.9 Million
Insurance Services
N.A.I.C.S.: 524126

AIG Travel Assist, Inc. **(1)**
2727 Allen Pkwy Ste A, Houston, TX 77019
Tel.: (713) 267-2550
Insurance Services
N.A.I.C.S.: 524298

Subsidiary (Domestic):

Travel Guard Group, Inc. **(2)**
3300 Business Park Dr, Stevens Point, WI
54482
Tel.: (715) 345-0505
Web Site: https://www.travelguard.com
Sales Range: $10-24.9 Million
Emp.: 312
Medical Insurance Services
N.A.I.C.S.: 524210
Jim Koziol (CFO)

Subsidiary (Domestic):

Travel Guard Americas LLC **(3)**
3300 Business Park Dr, Stevens Point, WI
54482
Tel.: (715) 345-0505
Web Site: https://www.travelguard.com
Travel Insurance Services
N.A.I.C.S.: 524298

Subsidiary (Domestic):

Livetravel, Inc. **(4)**
1814 Plover Rd, Plover, WI 54467
Tel.: (718) 343-0701
Travel Agency Operator
N.A.I.C.S.: 561510

Subsidiary (Domestic):

Travel Guard Worldwide, Inc. **(3)**
3300 Business Park Dr, Stevens Point, WI
54482
Tel.: (715) 345-0505
Web Site: http://www.travelguard.com
General Travel Insurance Services
N.A.I.C.S.: 524128

Subsidiary (Non-US):

Travel Guard EMEA Limited **(4)**
PO Box 60108, Hove, BN4 35FF, United
Kingdom
Tel.: (44) 1273749222
Travel Insurance Services
N.A.I.C.S.: 524126

AM Holdings LLC **(1)**
225 Grand Ave, Saint Louis, MO 63122
Tel.: (314) 568-0667
Casualty Insurance Services
N.A.I.C.S.: 524126

**American General Finance
Advisors** **(1)**
2727 Allen Pkwy, Houston, TX
77019-7100 **(100%)**
Tel.: (713) 522-1111
Web Site: http://www.americangeneral.com
Sales Range: $1-4.9 Billion
Emp.: 5,000
Personal Credit Institutions
N.A.I.C.S.: 524113

**American International Group UK
Limited** **(1)**
The AIG Building 58 Fenchurch Street, Lon-
don, EC3M 4AB, United Kingdom
Tel.: (44) 2079547000
Web Site: https://www.aig.co.uk
Insurance Services
N.A.I.C.S.: 524126
Hannah Scott (Mgr-External Comm)

**American International Insurance
Company of Puerto Rico** **(1)**
250 Ave Munoz Rivera Ste 500, San Juan,
PR 00918 **(100%)**
Tel.: (787) 767-6400
Rev.: $38,252,077
Emp.: 105
Property & Casualty Insuarance
N.A.I.C.S.: 524210
Sergio Carillo (Pres)

**American Security Life Insurance
Company** **(1)**
Zollstrasse 23, 9490, Schaan,
Liechtenstein **(100%)**
Tel.: (423) 2376888
Web Site: https://www.aslife.li
Sales Range: $10-24.9 Million
Emp.: 2
Provider of Investment Oriented & Insur-
ance Oriented Life Insurance Products
N.A.I.C.S.: 524128

**American Security Life Insurance
Company Limited** **(1)**
Zollstrasse 23, 9490, Schaan, Liechtenstein
Tel.: (423) 2376888
Web Site: http://www.aslife.li
Property & Casualty Insurance Services
N.A.I.C.S.: 524210

**Delaware American Life Insurance
Company** **(1)**
600 King St, Wilmington, DE
19801 **(100%)**
Tel.: (302) 594-2871
Sales Range: $750-799.9 Million
Emp.: 1,050
Life Insurance
N.A.I.C.S.: 524113

Glatfelter Insurance Group **(1)**
183 Leader Hts Rd, York, PA 17405
Tel.: (717) 741-0911
Web Site: http://www.glatfelters.com
Insurance & Brokerage Services
N.A.I.C.S.: 524210

Subsidiary (Domestic):

Arthur J. Glatfelter Agency Inc. **(2)**
221 W Philadelphia St Ste 400E, York, PA
17405
Tel.: (717) 852-8000
Sales Range: $100-124.9 Million
Emp.: 50
Insurance Agents, Brokers & Service
N.A.I.C.S.: 524210
Scott C. Rogers (Pres)
Hellen Edwards (Office Mgr)

Subsidiary (Domestic):

**Glatfelter Underwriting Services,
Inc.** **(3)**
183 Leader Heights Rd, York, PA 17402
Insurance Services
N.A.I.C.S.: 524210

Subsidiary (Domestic):

GIG of Missouri Inc. **(2)**
183 Leaders Heights Rd, York, PA
17402-4714 **(100%)**
Tel.: (800) 444-8675
Sales Range: $25-49.9 Million
Emp.: 35
Insurance Agents, Brokers & Services
N.A.I.C.S.: 524210

Glatfelter Brokerage Service **(2)**
52 Corporate Cir Ste 210, Albany, NY
12203
Tel.: (800) 833-8822
Web Site:
    http://www.glatfelterpublicpractice.com
Insurance Brokerage Services
N.A.I.C.S.: 524210

**Glatfelter Claims Management,
Inc.** **(2)**
183 Leaders Heights Rd, York, PA
17402-4714 **(100%)**
Tel.: (717) 741-0911
Web Site: http://www.vfis.com
Sales Range: $100-124.9 Million
Emp.: 400
Insurance Agents, Brokers & Service
N.A.I.C.S.: 524291

Robert S. Maxam Inc. **(2)**
822 Courtyard Dr, Hillsborough, NJ 08844
Tel.: (908) 707-0911
Web Site: http://www.vfis.com
Sales Range: $25-49.9 Million
Emp.: 4
Insurance Agents, Brokers & Service
N.A.I.C.S.: 524210

Division (Domestic):

The Insurancenter **(2)**
2901 Arizona Ave, Joplin, MO 64804
Tel.: (417) 623-7500
Web Site: https://www.theinsurancenter.com
Emp.: 27
Insurance Management Services
N.A.I.C.S.: 524298
J. Scott Brothers (Pres & CEO)

Subsidiary (Domestic):

Volunteer Firemen's Insurance Services, Inc. **(2)**
183 Leader Heights Rd, York, PA 17405
Tel.: (717) 741-0911
Web Site: https://www.vfis.com
Sales Range: $100-124.9 Million
Emp.: 420
Insurance Agents, Brokers & Service
N.A.I.C.S.: 524210
Troy Markel (Pres)
Dan Naylor (VP-Western Reg)
Joe Giorgi (Reg VP)
Tina Kerchner (Mgr-A&S Program)
Christine Einolf (Mgr-Underwriting)
Edmund Williams (Sr VP & Mgr-Program)
David Michaels (Exec VP-Education Trng & Consulting)
Scott Harkins (Sr VP-Client Risk Solutions)
Michael Baker (Dir-Client Risk Solutions)

Health Direct, Inc. **(1)**
74 Scott Swamp Rd, Farmington, CT 06032-2800
Tel.: (860) 677-2331
Property & Casualty Insurance Services
N.A.I.C.S.: 524126
Kathy Brandi (Mgr-Telephonic Nurse Case)

IC Guardia **(1)**
Leningradsky Prospekt 72 Bldg 2 3rd Floor BC Alkon, Moscow, 125315, Russia
Tel.: (7) 4959358950
Web Site: http://www.aig.ru
Insurance Services
N.A.I.C.S.: 524298

ILFC Holdings, Inc. **(1)**
10250 Constellation Blvd Ste 1500, Los Angeles, CA 90067
Tel.: (310) 788-1999
Sales Range: $50-74.9 Million
Emp.: 214
Holding Company
N.A.I.C.S.: 551112

Morefar Marketing, Inc. **(1)**
503 Carr Rd Fl 3, Wilmington, DE 19809-2800
Tel.: (212) 458-4581
Casualty Insurance Services
N.A.I.C.S.: 524126

National Union Fire Insurance Company of Pittsburgh, Pa. **(1)**
70 Pine St, New York, NY 10270 **(100%)**
Tel.: (877) 541-9748
Sales Range: $125-149.9 Million
Casualty Insurance Services
N.A.I.C.S.: 524126

Subsidiary (Domestic):

Lexington Insurance Company **(2)**
99 High St Fl 24, Boston, MA 02110-2378 **(100%)**
Tel.: (617) 330-1100
Web Site: https://www.lexingtoninsurance.com
Sales Range: $100-124.9 Million
Insurance Services
N.A.I.C.S.: 524126
John Artesani (Officer-Finance & Sr VP)
Lou Levinson (Pres & CEO)
Susan Chmieleski (Head)
John Flannery (Head-Communications)
Christopher Flatt (Exec VP & Head)
Clifton Hope (Head-Property)
Joanne Keating (Head)
Neil Smallcombe (Head-Casualty)
Deb Goldberg (Head)

Division (Domestic):

South East Risk Specialty Properties **(3)**
1200 Abernathy Rd NE, Atlanta, GA 30328-5662
Tel.: (770) 671-2000
Sales Range: $100-124.9 Million
Emp.: 300
Surplus Loan Brokers
N.A.I.C.S.: 524210
Gwen King (Mgr)

Risk Specialists Companies, Inc. **(1)**
99 High St Fl 26, Boston, MA 02110 **(100%)**
Tel.: (212) 770-7000
Rev.: $22,300,000
Emp.: 480
Insurance Agents
N.A.I.C.S.: 524210

Division (Domestic):

New England Risk Specialists **(2)**
99 High St, Boston, MA 02110-2320
Tel.: (617) 457-5853
Web Site: http://www.aig.com
Sales Range: Less than $1 Million
Emp.: 5
Insurance Brokers
N.A.I.C.S.: 524298

Southeastern Risk Specialists **(2)**
600 N Park Town 1200AB NE, Atlanta, GA 30328
Tel.: (770) 671-2000
Web Site: http://www.aig.com
Sales Range: $100-124.9 Million
Insurance Brokers
N.A.I.C.S.: 524210

The Insurance Company of the State of Pennsylvania **(1)**
1271 Ave of the Americas FL 41, New York, NY 10020-1304 **(100%)**
Tel.: (212) 770-7000
Sales Range: $125-149.9 Million
Provider of Casualty Insurance
N.A.I.C.S.: 524128

Validus Holdings, Ltd. **(1)**
29 Richmond Road, Pembroke, HM 08, Bermuda
Tel.: (441) 2789000
Web Site: http://www.validusholdings.com
Holding Company; Insurance Services
N.A.I.C.S.: 551112

Subsidiary (Domestic):

AlphaCat Managers Ltd. **(2)**
29 Richmond Road, Pembroke, HM 08, Bermuda
Tel.: (441) 2789000
Insurance Services
N.A.I.C.S.: 524298
Lixin Zeng (CEO)

Subsidiary (Non-US):

Talbot Underwriting Ltd. **(2)**
60 Threadneedle Street, London, EC2R 8HP, United Kingdom
Tel.: (44) 2075503500
Web Site: https://talbot.aig.com
Specialty Insurance Services
N.A.I.C.S.: 524298
Julian G. Ross (Chief Risk Officer)
Chris Rash (CEO)
Russell Bean (Chief Underwriting Officer)
Richard Cowling (CFO)
Diane Gallacher (Dir-HR)
Glen Browse (CIO)
Shalin Haria (Chief Actuary)
James Middleton (Gen Counsel)

Subsidiary (Non-US):

Talbot Risk Services (Labuan) Pte, Ltd. **(3)**
Brighton Place Ground Floor No U0215 Jalan Bahasa, Labuan, 87014, Malaysia
Tel.: (60) 87442899
Reinsurance Services
N.A.I.C.S.: 524130

Talbot Risk Services Pte Ltd. **(3)**
One George Street No 15-01/06, Singapore, 049145, Singapore
Tel.: (65) 65111400

Insurance Brokerage Services
N.A.I.C.S.: 524210

Talbot Underwriting (LATAM) S.A. **(3)**
Avenida Apoquindo 3650 Piso 8 Oficina 803, Las Condes, 7550, Chile
Tel.: (56) 227970300
Web Site: http://www.validusholdings.com
Reinsurance Services
N.A.I.C.S.: 524130

Talbot Underwriting (MENA) Ltd. **(3)**
Dubai International Financial Centre, PO Box 506809, Gate Village Building 10 Level 5, Dubai, 506809, United Arab Emirates
Tel.: (971) 4 448 7780
Web Site: http://www.validusholdings.com
Insurance Services
N.A.I.C.S.: 524298

Subsidiary (Domestic):

Talbot Underwriting Risk Services Ltd. **(3)**
60 Threadneedle Street, London, EC2R 8HP, United Kingdom
Tel.: (44) 2075503737
Insurance Underwriting Services
N.A.I.C.S.: 524298

Subsidiary (US):

Talbot Underwriting Services (US), Ltd. **(3)**
48 Wall St 17th Fl, New York, NY 10005
Tel.: (212) 785-2000
Reinsurance Services
N.A.I.C.S.: 524130

Subsidiary (Non-US):

Talbot Underwriting Services, Ltd. **(2)**
60 Threadneedle Street, London, EC2R 8HP, United Kingdom
Tel.: (44) 2075503500
Web Site: http://www.talbotuw.com
Reinsurance Services
N.A.I.C.S.: 524130

Subsidiary (Domestic):

Validus Reinsurance, Ltd. **(2)**
29 Richmond Rd, Pembroke, HM 08, Bermuda
Tel.: (441) 2789000
Web Site: http://www.validusholdings.com
Reinsurance Products & Services
N.A.I.C.S.: 524130
Kevin Downs (Chief Actuary)

Subsidiary (Non-US):

Talbot Underwriting (LATAM) S.A. **(3)**
Avenida Apoquindo 3650 Piso 8 Oficina 803, Las Condes, 7550, Chile
Tel.: (56) 2 2797 0300
Web Site: http://www.validusholdings.com
Emp.: 10
Insurance Services
N.A.I.C.S.: 524130

Underwriting Risk Services S.A. **(3)**
Avenida Apoquindo 3650, Piso 8 Oficina 803, Las Condes, Santiago, Chile
Tel.: (56) 27970300
Sales Range: $50-74.9 Million
Emp.: 6
Insurance Underwriter & Risk Management Services
N.A.I.C.S.: 524298

Subsidiary (US):

Validus Reaseguros, Inc. **(3)**
600 Brickell Ave Ste 1850, Miami, FL 33131
Tel.: (305) 631-7780
Reinsurance & Insurance Underwriting Services
N.A.I.C.S.: 524130

Subsidiary (Non-US):

Validus Reinsurance (Switzerland) Ltd **(3)**
Talstrasse 83 4th Floor, 8001, Zurich, Switzerland
Tel.: (41) 433447310
Reinsurance Services

N.A.I.C.S.: 524130
Florian Lutz (Dir-Underwriting)

Validus Research Inc. **(3)**
187 King Street South Suite 201, Waterloo, N2J 1R1, ON, Canada
Tel.: (519) 793-9100
Insurance Services
N.A.I.C.S.: 524298

Validus Risk Services (Ireland) Limited **(3)**
Unit 1E Paramont Court Corrig Road, Sandyford, Dublin, Ireland
Tel.: (353) 15387010
Reinsurance Services
N.A.I.C.S.: 524130

Subsidiary (US):

Western World Insurance Group, Inc. **(2)**
300 Kimball Dr Ste 500, Parsippany, NJ 07054
Tel.: (201) 847-8600
Web Site: http://www.westernworld.com
Sales Range: $100-124.9 Million
Emp.: 250
Holding Company; Insurance Products & Services
N.A.I.C.S.: 551112
Lisa A. Rosa (Sr VP)

Subsidiary (Domestic):

Stratford Insurance Company **(3)**
300 Kimball Dr Ste 500, Parsippany, NJ 07054
Tel.: (201) 847-8600
Sales Range: $50-74.9 Million
Emp.: 200
Insurance Services
N.A.I.C.S.: 524126

Tudor Insurance Company **(3)**
300 Kimball Drive Suite 500, Parsippany, NJ 07054
Tel.: (201) 847-8600
Web Site: http://www.westernworld.com
Sales Range: $50-74.9 Million
Emp.: 200
Insurance Services
N.A.I.C.S.: 524126

Westco Claims Management Services, Inc. **(3)**
400 Parsons Pond Dr, Franklin Lakes, NJ 07417
Tel.: (201) 847-8600
Reinsurance Services
N.A.I.C.S.: 524130

Western World Insurance Company **(3)**
300 Kimball Dr Ste 500, Parsippany, NJ 07054
Tel.: (201) 847-8600
Web Site: http://www.westernworld.com
Sales Range: $50-74.9 Million
Insurance Services
N.A.I.C.S.: 524126

AMERICAN INTERNATIONAL HOLDINGS CORP.
205S Bailey St, Electra, TX 76360
Tel.: (940) 495-2155 NV
Year Founded: 1986
AMIH—(OTCEM)
Rev.: $61,899
Assets: $343,335
Liabilities: $4,820,674
Net Worth: ($4,477,339)
Earnings: ($2,574,807)
Emp.: 1
Fiscal Year-end: 12/31/22
Holding Company; Oil & Gas Field Services
N.A.I.C.S.: 551112
James Pendergast (CFO)

AMERICAN INTERNATIONAL INDUSTRIES, INC.
601 Cien St Ste 235, Kemah, TX 77565-3077
Tel.: (281) 334-9479 NV
Web Site: http://www.americanii.com

American International Industries, Inc.—(Continued)

Year Founded: 1994
AMIN—(OTCEM)
Sales Range: Less than $1 Million
Emp.: 14
Holding Company; Real Estate, Intellectual Property & Petroleum Resources
N.A.I.C.S.: 551112
Daniel Dror (Chm, Pres & CEO)
Rebekah Laird-Ruthstrom (Treas & Sec)

AMERICAN INTERNATIONAL VENTURES, INC.

15105 Kestrelglen Way, Lithia, FL 33547
Tel.: (813) 944-2988   DE
Web Site: http://www.aivn.co
Year Founded: 1984
AIVN—(OTCIQ)
Assets: $456,000
Net Worth: $508,000
Earnings: ($517,000)
Emp.: 1
Fiscal Year-end: 05/31/20
Investment Services
N.A.I.C.S.: 523999

AMERICAN LEISURE HOLDINGS, INC.

3000 N Federal Hwy Ste 200W, Fort Lauderdale, FL 33306
Tel.: (561) 654-5722   CO
Year Founded: 2001
AMLH—(OTCIQ)
Hotel & Resort Operator
N.A.I.C.S.: 721110
Adrian Patasar (CEO)

AMERICAN NOBLE GAS, INC.

15612 College Blvd, Lenexa, KS 66219
Tel.: (913) 948-9512   DE
Web Site:
https://www.amnoblegas.com
Year Founded: 1987
AMNI—(OTCQB)
Rev.: $79,002
Assets: $1,105,601
Liabilities: $4,271,091
Net Worth: ($3,165,490)
Earnings: ($1,778,210)
Emp.: 3
Fiscal Year-end: 12/31/21
Oil & Gas Exploration & Development Services
N.A.I.C.S.: 213111
Stanton E. Ross (Pres & Co-COO)
Daniel F. Hutchins (CFO, Treas & Sec)

Subsidiaries:

Infinity Oil and Gas of Texas, Inc.   (1)
30010 Overland Pk, Overland Park, KS 66210
Tel.: (913) 948-9512
Web Site: http://www.infyoil.com
Sales Range: $250-299.9 Million
Oil & Gas Exploration & Development Services
N.A.I.C.S.: 213111
Stanton E. Ross (Chm & Pres)

AMERICAN ONCOLOGY NETWORK, INC.

14543 Global Pkwy Ste 110, Fort Meyers, FL 33913   DE
Web Site: https://www.aoncology.com
Year Founded: 2020
AONC—(NASDAQ)
Rev.: $13,948,974
Assets: $338,883,014
Liabilities: $353,086,564

Net Worth: ($14,203,550)
Earnings: $10,532,439
Emp.: 2
Fiscal Year-end: 12/31/22
Offices of Other Holding Companies
N.A.I.C.S.: 551112
David Afshar (CFO & COO)
Kevin Nazemi (Chm & CEO)
Kyle Francis (Sec)

Subsidiaries:

American Oncology Network, LLC   (1)
14543 Global Pkwy Ste 110, Fort Meyers, FL 33913
Web Site: https://www.aoncology.com
Oncology Services Network Operator
N.A.I.C.S.: 621111

AMERICAN OUTDOOR BRANDS, INC.

1800 N Route Z, Columbia, MO 65202   DE
Web Site: https://www.aob.com
Year Founded: 2020
AOUT—(NASDAQ)
Rev.: $201,099,000
Assets: $240,597,000
Liabilities: $62,672,000
Net Worth: $177,925,000
Earnings: ($12,248,000)
Emp.: 289
Fiscal Year-end: 04/30/24
Sport Accessories Mfr
N.A.I.C.S.: 339920
Andrew H. Fulmer (CFO)
Brian D. Murphy (Pres)
Elizabeth A. Sharp (VP)

AMERICAN POWER GROUP CORPORATION

Tel.: (781) 224-2411   DE
Web Site:
https://www.americanpowergroupinc.com
Year Founded: 1992
APGI—(OTCIQ)
Sales Range: Less than $1 Million
Emp.: 20
Alternative Fuel Solutions
N.A.I.C.S.: 333618
Charles E. Coppa (CEO, CFO, Treas & Sec)
Neil K. Braverman (Chm)
Dana Brewster (Reg Mgr-Bus Dev)

AMERICAN PREMIUM WATER CORPORATION

187 E Warm Springs Rd, Las Vegas, NV 89119
Tel.: (656) 333-9181   NV
Web Site:
https://www.newelectriccv.com
HIPH—(OTCIQ)
Consumer Good Mfr & Distr
N.A.I.C.S.: 311920
Melissa K. Sims (CEO)
Adam Tan (COO)
John Thatch (Chm)

AMERICAN PUBLIC EDUCATION, INC.

111 W Congress St, Charles Town, WV 25414
Tel.: (304) 724-3700   DE
Web Site: https://www.apei.com
Year Founded: 1991
APEI—(NASDAQ)
Rev.: $606,328,000
Assets: $615,056,000
Liabilities: $265,329,000
Net Worth: $349,727,000
Earnings: ($114,993,000)
Emp.: 2,357
Fiscal Year-end: 12/31/22

Online Post-Secondary Education for Military & Public Service Sectors
N.A.I.C.S.: 611310
Thomas A. Beckett (Gen Counsel, Sec & Sr VP)
Richard W. Sunderland Jr. (CFO & Exec VP)
Angela K. Selden (Pres & CEO)
Barbara Grace Fast (Executives)
Tanya Axenson (Chief HR Officer)
Melissa Frey (Sr VP & Controller)
Marcie Baetcke (VP-Mktg)
Jessica Jackson (VP-HR)
Nathan Linnell (VP-Mktg Intelligence)
Dan Lochner (VP-IT Bus Plng & Project Mgmt)
Angela K. Selden (Pres & CEO)
Jason Dom (VP-Classroom & Campus Technical Support)
Don Cox (Chief Information Security Officer & VP)
David Holcomb (Chief Data Officer & VP)
Steve Somers (Chief Strategy & Corp Dev Officer & Sr VP)
Frank Tutalo (Dir-PR)
Ryan Koren (Asst VP-Corp Dev & IR)
Craig MacGibbon (CIO)
Andy McShane (Sr VP)
Raja Patel (VP)

Subsidiaries:

American Public University System, Inc.   (1)
111 W Congress St, Charles Town, WV 25414
Tel.: (703) 330-5398
Web Site: https://www.apus.edu
Sales Range: $75-99.9 Million
Online Education Services
N.A.I.C.S.: 611310
Thomas A. Beckett (Gen Counsel & Sec)
Richard W. Sunderland Jr. (CFO & Exec VP)
Caroline Simpson (VP-Student Svcs)
Jennifer Stephens Helm (VP-Accreditation)
Keith Wellings (VP-Fin Aid & Compliance)
Frank Ball (Chm)
Brian Freeland (VP & Dean-Health Sciences)
Gregory Hill (VP-Admissions)
Carolyn Todaro (VP-Academic Advising)
Lori E. Reynolds (Vice Chm)
Nuno Fernandes (Pres)
Erika Orris (VP-Operations)
Mauricia Blackwell (VP-Human Resources)
Travis Durepo (VP-Student Support & Enrollment Ops)
Lindsey Larson (VP)
Jose G. Molleja (VP-APU Brand Expansion & Student Success)
Frank Tutalo (Assoc VP-Public Rels)

AMERICAN REALTY INVESTORS, INC.

1603 Lyndon B Johnson Fwy Ste 800, Dallas, TX 75234
Tel.: (469) 522-4200   NV
Web Site:
https://www.americanrealtyinvest.com
Year Founded: 1961
ARL—(NYSE)
Rev.: $37,544,000
Assets: $1,107,470,000
Liabilities: $385,311,000
Net Worth: $812,168,000
Earnings: $475,317,000
Fiscal Year-end: 12/31/22
Real Estate Investment Services
N.A.I.C.S.: 525990
Louis J. Corna (Gen Counsel, Sec & Exec VP)
Erik L. Johnson (Pres & CEO)
Henry A. Butler (Chm)
Bradley J. Kyles (Exec VP-Multifamily Ops)

Subsidiaries:

American Realty Trust, Inc.   (1)

1800 Valley View Ln Ste 300, Dallas, TX 75234-8922
Tel.: (469) 522-4200
Real Estate Investment Services
N.A.I.C.S.: 531110

Subsidiary (Domestic):

Denver Merchandise Mart, Inc.   (2)
451 E 58th Ave Unit 470 Ste 2490, Denver, CO 80216-8470
Tel.: (303) 292-6278
Web Site: http://www.denvermart.com
Sales Range: $50-74.9 Million
Emp.: 40
Real Estate Investment Services
N.A.I.C.S.: 531110

Transcontinental Realty Investors, Inc.   (1)
1603 LBJ Freeway Ste 800, Dallas, TX 75234
Tel.: (469) 522-4200
Web Site:
https://www.transconrealty-invest.com
Rev.: $49,905,000
Assets: $1,043,044,000
Liabilities: $196,090,000
Net Worth: $846,954,000
Earnings: $7,250,000
Fiscal Year-end: 12/31/2023
Provider of Real Estate Investment Trust Services
N.A.I.C.S.: 525990
Erik L. Johnson (Pres & CEO)
Henry A. Butler (Chm)
Alla Dzyuba (Chief Acctg Officer & VP)
Bradley J. Kyles (Exec VP-Multifamily Ops)

Subsidiary (Domestic):

Cascades Apartments, LTD   (2)
2518 Sheppard Access Rd, Wichita Falls, TX 76306
Tel.: (940) 723-6781
Apartment Building Rental & Leasing Services
N.A.I.C.S.: 531110

Dakota Arms, LTD   (2)
6703 82nd St, Lubbock, TX 79424
Tel.: (806) 203-6554
Web Site: https://www.dakotaarmsapts.com
Apartment Building Rental & Leasing Services
N.A.I.C.S.: 531110

El Paso Legends, LTD   (2)
200 Desert Pass St, El Paso, TX 79912
Tel.: (915) 245-2485
Web Site:
http://www.livelegendsofelpaso.com
Apartment Building Rental & Leasing Services
N.A.I.C.S.: 531110

Falcon Lakes, LTD   (2)
6504 Falcon River Way, Arlington, TX 76001
Tel.: (817) 572-5300
Web Site: http://www.falconlakesapt.com
Emp.: 6
Apartment Building Rental & Leasing Services
N.A.I.C.S.: 531110

Heather Creek Apartments Mesquite, LTD   (2)
1540 N Galloway Ave, Mesquite, TX 75149
Tel.: (972) 289-6622
Web Site: http://www.heathercreekapt.com
Emp.: 5
Apartment Building Rental & Leasing Services
N.A.I.C.S.: 531110

Lake Forest AM, LTD   (2)
19780 Atascocita Shores Dr, Humble, TX 77346
Tel.: (832) 445-0222
Web Site:
http://www.lakeforestapartments.com
Emp.: 4
Apartment Building Rental & Leasing Services
N.A.I.C.S.: 531110

Mason Park, LTD   (2)
222 Mason Creek Dr, Katy, TX 77450
Tel.: (346) 248-4011
Web Site: https://www.masonparkapts.com
Emp.: 9

Apartment Building Rental & Leasing Services
N.A.I.C.S.: 531110

Parc at Maumelle, LP (2)
100 Park Dr, Maumelle, AR 72113
Tel.: (501) 727-2313
Web Site:
  https://www.parcatmaumelleapts.com
Apartment Building Rental & Leasing Services
N.A.I.C.S.: 531110

Parc at Metro Center, LP (2)
377 Athens Way, Nashville, TN 37228
Tel.: (615) 437-9313
Web Site: http://www.parcatmetro.com
Emp.: 4
Apartment Building Rental & Leasing Services
N.A.I.C.S.: 531110

Parc at Rogers, LP (2)
513 S Dodson Rd, Rogers, AR 72758
Tel.: (479) 448-4418
Web Site: http://www.parcatrogers.com
Sales Range: $25-49.9 Million
Emp.: 6
Apartment Building Rental & Leasing Services
N.A.I.C.S.: 531110

Vistas of Vance Jackson, LTD (2)
12436 Vance Jackson Rd, San Antonio, TX 78230
Tel.: (210) 877-1195
Web Site: https://www.vancejackson.com
Emp.: 5
Apartment Building Rental & Leasing Services
N.A.I.C.S.: 531110

Wildflower Villas, LTD (2)
5227 W Adams Ave, Temple, TX 76502
Tel.: (254) 277-1854
Web Site: https://www.wildflowervillas.com
Apartment Building Rental & Leasing Services
N.A.I.C.S.: 531110

AMERICAN REBEL HOLDINGS, INC.
909 18th Ave S Ste A, Nashville, TN 37212
NV
Web Site:
  https://www.americanrebel.com
Year Founded: 2014
AREB—(NASDAQ)
Rev.: $8,449,800
Assets: $16,560,561
Liabilities: $5,207,442
Net Worth: $11,353,119
Earnings: ($7,143,153)
Fiscal Year-end: 12/31/22
Concealed Carry Goods & Apparel Mfr & Distr
N.A.I.C.S.: 315990
Corey A. Lambrecht (CEO)
Charles A. Ross Jr. (Founder, Chm, CEO, Treas & Sec)
Doug E. Grau (Pres & Interim Principal Acctg Officer)
John Garrison (CFO)

AMERICAN RESOURCES CORPORATION
12115 Visionary Way, Fishers, IN 46038
Tel.: (317) 855-9926
FL
Web Site:
  https://www.americanresources
  corp.com
Year Founded: 2013
AREC—(NASDAQ)
Rev.: $39,474,269
Assets: $55,916,349
Liabilities: $55,631,653
Net Worth: $284,696
Earnings: ($1,445,672)
Emp.: 17
Fiscal Year-end: 12/31/22
Holding Company; Coal Mining & Processing

N.A.I.C.S.: 551112
Mark C. Jensen (Chm & CEO)
Kirk P. Taylor (CFO)
Thomas M. Sauve (Pres)
Tarlis R. Thompson (COO)
Mark J. Laverghetta (VP-Corp Fin & Comm)
Gregory Q. Jensen (Gen Counsel)
Jeff Peterson (VP-Rare Earth Div)

AMERICAN RIVIERA BANK
1033 Anacapa St, Santa Barbara, CA 93101
Tel.: (805) 979-3545
Web Site:
  https://americanriviera.bank
Year Founded: 2006
ARBV—(OTCQX)
Rev.: $37,636,000
Assets: $971,623,000
Liabilities: $886,704,000
Net Worth: $84,919,000
Earnings: $7,378,000
Emp.: 121
Fiscal Year-end: 12/31/20
Retail & Commercial Banking
N.A.I.C.S.: 522110
Jeffrey B. DeVine (Pres & CEO)
Lawrence Koppelman (Bd of Dirs & Chm)
Darren D. Caesar (Chm & Vice Chm)
Michelle Martinich (CFO & Exec VP)
Joanne Funari (COO & Exec VP)
Paul Abramson (CTO & Exec VP)
Laurel Sykes (Chief Risk Officer, Chief Compliance & Risk Officer & Exec VP)
Elizabeth Cholawsky (Vice Chm)
Jason Kaufman (VP & Branch Mgr-Santa Barbara)
Holly Mislavsky (VP & Sr Branch Mgr-Atascadero)
Dustin Reese (VP & Branch Mgr-San Luis Obispo)
Julie Ezzo (Asst VP & Branch Mgr-Paso Robles)
Lisa French (Asst VP & Branch Mgr-Goleta)
Katie Stewart (Asst VP & Branch Mgr-Montecito)
Adriana Corona (Mgr-Svc-Santa Barbara)
Jessica Hernandez (Asst Mgr-Svc-Montecito)
Kindell Rucobo (Asst Mgr-Svc-Santa Maria)
Chymah Sadat (Asst Mgr-Svc-Paso Robles)
Quynh Schooter (Asst Mgr-Svc-Goleta)
Karin Smith (Mgr-Svc-Atascadero)
Steven Harding (Reg Pres & Exec VP-San Luis Obispo)
Barbara Caballero-Munoz (Sr VP & Mgr-Loan Admin-Santa Barbara)
Tony Meyer (Treas & Sr VP-Santa Barbara)
Jon Apilado (First VP & Controller-Santa Barbara)
Bobby Boyes (First VP & Mgr-Banking Relationship-Santa Barbara)
Holly Carroll (First VP & Dir-Operations-Paso Robles)
Heidi Cummings (First VP & Reg Mgr-Branch-Santa Barbara)
Yatzie Acosta (VP & Mgr-Human Resources-Santa Barbara)
Sandy Cocklin (VP & Reg Mgr-Svc-Santa Barbara)
Sandra Gallo (VP & Sr Mgr-Product-Santa Barbara)
Raul Hurtado (VP & Sr Mgr-Loan Svcs-Santa Barbara)
Eusebio Cordova Jr. (Chief Credit Officer & Exec VP)

AMERICAN SENIORS ASSO-

CIATION HOLDING GROUP, INC.
353 6th Ave W, Bradenton, FL 34205
Tel.: (941) 216-3805
GA
Web Site:
  http://www.americanseniors.org
AMSA—(OTCIQ)
Senior Advocacy Services
N.A.I.C.S.: 813319
Paul Cornell (CEO)

AMERICAN SHARED HOSPITAL SERVICES
601 Montgomery St Ste 1112, San Francisco, CA 94111
Tel.: (415) 788-5300
CA
Web Site: https://www.ashs.com
Year Founded: 1980
AMS—(NYSEAMEX)
Rev.: $21,325,000
Assets: $48,262,000
Liabilities: $21,983,000
Net Worth: $26,279,000
Earnings: $610,000
Emp.: 13
Fiscal Year-end: 12/31/23
Gamma Knife Stereotactic Radiosurgery Services
N.A.I.C.S.: 621511
Craig K. Tagawa (Pres & Asst Sec)
Ernest R. Bates (VP-Sls & Mktg-Intl)
Peter Gaccione (COO)
Raymond C. Stachowiak (Exec Chm & CEO)
Alexis Wallace (Chief Acctg Officer & Sec)
Peter Gaccione (COO)
Timothy J. Keel (VP-Sls & Mktg)
Robert Hiatt (CFO & Principal Acctg Officer)
Ernest A. Bates (Bd of Dirs, Executives)

Subsidiaries:

American Shared Radiosurgery Services (1)
2 Embarcadero Ctr Ste 410, San Francisco, CA 94111-4107 (100%)
Tel.: (415) 788-5300
Web Site: http://www.ashs.com
Sales Range: $1-9.9 Million
Leaser of Gamma Knife Medical Radiosurgery Equipment to Hospitals
N.A.I.C.S.: 621511

AMERICAN SILVER MINING CO.
3503 E 17th Ave, Spokane, WA 99223
Tel.: (509) 534-7277
ID
Year Founded: 1924
ASLM—(OTCIQ)
Silver Ore Mining Services
N.A.I.C.S.: 212220
E. Wafford Conrad (Pres)
Kay Conrad (Treas, Sec & VP)

AMERICAN SOFTWARE, INC.
470 E Paces Ferry Rd, Atlanta, GA 30305
Tel.: (404) 261-4381
GA
Web Site:
  https://www.amsoftware.com
Year Founded: 1970
AMSWA—(NASDAQ)
Rev.: $102,515,000
Assets: $192,444,000
Liabilities: $61,963,000
Net Worth: $130,481,000
Earnings: $11,373,000
Emp.: 331
Fiscal Year-end: 04/30/24
Business Application Software Developer, Marketer & Support
N.A.I.C.S.: 334610
Bryan L. Sell (Chief Acctg Officer & Controller)

Vincent C. Klinges (CFO & Treas)
H. Allan Dow (Pres & CEO)
James C. Edenfield (Founder)
Donald L. Thomas (CIO)

Subsidiaries:

ASI Properties, Inc. (1)
470 E Paces Ferry Rd NE, Atlanta, GA 30305-3301
Tel.: (404) 261-4381
Web Site: http://www.amsoftware.com
Sales Range: $100-124.9 Million
Computer Programming Services
N.A.I.C.S.: 541511

Demand Management, Inc. (1)
1 CityPlace Dr Ste 540, Saint Louis, MO 63141
Tel.: (314) 991-7100
Web Site: http://www.demandsolutions.com
Supply Chain & Logistics Management Software Publisher
N.A.I.C.S.: 513210
Bill Harrison (Pres)
Scott Tillman (Exec VP-R&D)
Dani Owen (VP-Cloud Svcs)
Marti Kirsch (VP-Mktg)
Randy Bartlett (VP-Customer Success)
Steve Cobham (Reg VP-Sls-APAC)
Alexander Price (Sr VP-Alliance Partners & Sls)

Logility NZ (UC) (1)
Massey University House Level 8 90 Symonds Street, Auckland, 1010, New Zealand
Tel.: (64) 93799099
Business Planning Software Development Services
N.A.I.C.S.: 541511

Logility Solutions Pvt. Ltd. (1)
Novel Tech Park 46/4 GB Palya Hosur Main Road, Bengaluru, 560 068, Karnataka, India
Tel.: (91) 9845879094
Software Development Services
N.A.I.C.S.: 513210

Logility, Inc. (1)
470 E Paces Ferry Rd NE, Atlanta, GA 30305 (88%)
Tel.: (404) 261-4381
Web Site: https://www.logility.com
Sales Range: $25-49.9 Million
Emp.: 141
Business Application Software Providing Supply Chain Managment Solutions
N.A.I.C.S.: 513210
Vincent C. Klinges (CFO-Logility)
H. Allan Dow (Pres)
Donald L. Thomas (CIO)
Vince C. Klinges (CFO)
Allan Dow (CEO)

New Generation Computing (1)
14900 NW 79th Ct Ste 100, Miami Lakes, FL 33106
Tel.: (305) 556-9122
Web Site: http://www.ngcsoftware.com
Sales Range: $50-74.9 Million
Emp.: 200
Provider of Development, Marketing & Support of Business Application Software
N.A.I.C.S.: 513210
James C. Edenfield (Co-Pres & CEO)
Mark Burstein (Co-Pres & Chief Strategy Officer)
Fred Isenberg (Pres-Consulting Svcs)
Benjamin Siegel (CTO)
Roger Mayerson (VP-Vendor & Product Compliance Solutions)
Jennifer Carter (Dir-Solutions Consulting)
Nelson Rodriguez (Dir-Application Design)
Lily Sabin (Dir-Customer Svc)

AMERICAN STATES WATER COMPANY
630 E Foothill Blvd, San Dimas, CA 91773-1212
Tel.: (909) 394-3600
CA
Web Site: https://www.aswater.com
Year Founded: 1929
AWR—(NYSE)
Rev.: $491,528,000
Assets: $2,034,374,000
Liabilities: $878,278,000

American States Water Company—(Continued)

Net Worth: $1,156,096,000
Earnings: $78,396,000
Emp.: 811
Fiscal Year-end: 12/31/22
Water Supply Services
N.A.I.C.S.: 221310
Robert J. Sprowls *(Pres & CEO)*
Eva G. Tang *(CFO, Treas, Sec & Sr VP-Fin)*
Gladys M. Farrow *(Asst Sec)*
Christopher H. Connor *(Sr VP)*
Sunil K. Pillai *(VP-Environmental Quality)*
David R. Schickling *(VP-Water Ops)*
Susan P. Miller *(VP-Operations)*

Subsidiaries:

American States Utility Services, Inc.　　　　　　　　　　(1)
630 E Foothill Blvd, San Dimas, CA 91773
Tel.: (909) 305-2400
Web Site: http://www.asusinc.com
Sales Range: $25-49.9 Million
Emp.: 14
Water & Sewer Line Management Services
N.A.I.C.S.: 237110
Robert J. Sprowls *(Executives, Bd of Dirs)*
Josh Hemus *(Controller-Div)*
Gabriel Willis *(VP)*
Greg Booker *(Mgr-Utility-TUS)*
Susan Miller *(Dir-Acting-Ops)*
Brannon Richards *(Dir)*
Rebecca Hooper *(Mgr-Subcontracts)*
Zbigniew Resiak *(Mgr-Utility-ECUS)*
Gilbert Mesa *(Mgr-Utility-FBWSC)*
Timothy Loughman *(Mgr-Utility-ONUS)*
Emily Stewart *(Dir-Business Development)*
Stuart Harrison *(Sr VP)*
Michael Munns *(Mgr-Utility-FRUS)*
Chris Connor *(Sr VP)*

Subsidiary (Domestic):

Emerald Coast Utility Services, Inc.　　　　　　　　　　(2)
PO Box 1869, Eglin AFB, FL 32542
Tel.: (850) 389-8773
Water Supply & Irrigation System Services
N.A.I.C.S.: 221310

Fort Bliss Water Services Company　　　　　　　　　　(2)
Bldg 516A Pleasanton, Fort Bliss, TX 79906
Tel.: (915) 564-1332
Web Site: https://www.asusinc.com
Water & Sewer Line Management Services
N.A.I.C.S.: 237110

Fort Riley Utility Services, Inc.　(2)
PO Box 2386, Fort Riley, KS 66442
Tel.: (785) 717-3083
Web Site: https://www.asusinc.com
Water Supply & Irrigation System Services
N.A.I.C.S.: 221310

Old Dominion Utility Services, Inc.　　　　　　　　　　(2)
2023 Harrison Rd, Fort Eustis, VA 23604
Tel.: (757) 888-0485
Web Site: https://www.asusinc.com
Water & Sewer Line Management Services
N.A.I.C.S.: 237110

Old North Utility Services, Inc.　(2)
2941 Logistics St Bldg N-6307, Fort Bragg, NC 28310
Tel.: (910) 495-1311
Web Site: http://www.asus.com
Emp.: 60
Power & Communication Structure Construction Services
N.A.I.C.S.: 237130
Timothy Loughman *(Mgr-Utility)*

Palmetto State Utility Services, Inc.　　　　　　　　　　(2)
F1000 Ivy Rd, Fort Jackson, SC 29207
Tel.: (803) 790-7288
Web Site: https://www.asusinc.com
Water & Sewer Line Management Services
N.A.I.C.S.: 237110

Terrapin Utility Services, Inc.　(2)
3414 Pennsylvania Ave, Andrews AFB, MD 20762

Tel.: (301) 735-4101
Web Site: https://www.asusinc.com
Emp.: 12
Water Treatment Equipment Supplier
N.A.I.C.S.: 423830

Bear Valley Electric Service, Inc.　(1)
42020 Garstin Dr, Big Bear Lake, CA 92315
Web Site: https://www.bvesinc.com
Electric Power Distribution Services
N.A.I.C.S.: 221122

California Cities Water Company, Inc.　　　　　　　　　　(1)
1140 Los Olivos Ave, Los Osos, CA 93402
Tel.: (805) 528-1626
Water Supply & Irrigation Services
N.A.I.C.S.: 221310

Golden State Water Company　(1)
630 E Foothill Blvd, San Dimas, CA 91773-1212
Tel.: (909) 394-3600
Web Site: http://www.gswater.com
Rev.: $433,473,000
Assets: $1,916,155,000
Liabilities: $671,589,000
Net Worth: $1,244,566,000
Earnings: $102,708,000
Emp.: 506
Fiscal Year-end: 12/31/2023
Water & Electric Production & Distribution
N.A.I.C.S.: 221310
Robert J. Sprowls *(Pres & CEO)*
Anne M. Holloway *(Chm)*
Eva G. Tang *(CFO, Chief Acctg Officer, Sec & Sr VP-Fin)*

AMERICAN SUPERCONDUCTOR CORPORATION

114 E Main St, Ayer, MA 01432
Tel.: (978) 842-3000　　　　DE
Web Site: https://www.amsc.com
Year Founded: 1987
AMSC—(NASDAQ)
Rev.: $108,435,000
Assets: $173,887,000
Liabilities: $64,498,000
Net Worth: $109,389,000
Earnings: ($19,193,000)
Emp.: 326
Fiscal Year-end: 03/31/22
Motor & Generator Manufacturing
N.A.I.C.S.: 335312
Daniel P. McGahn *(Pres, CEO & Chm)*
John W. Kosiba Jr. *(CFO, Treas & Sr VP)*

Subsidiaries:

AMSC Austria GmbH　　　　(1)
Feldkirchner Strasse 138, Worthersee, 9020, Klagenfurt, Carinthia, Austria
Tel.: (43) 4634446040
Emp.: 75
Power & Energy Structures Construction Services
N.A.I.C.S.: 237130

AMSC India Private Limited　(1)
C-42 Sector-81, Nehru Place Greens, Noida, 201 305, Uttar Pradesh, India
Tel.: (91) 9810811180
Emp.: 10
Power & Energy Structures Construction Services
N.A.I.C.S.: 237130

AMSC Windtec GmbH　　　(1)
Lakeside B08 9020, Surk, 9020, Klagenfurt, Austria
Tel.: (43) 463 444 6040
Web Site: http://www.amsc-amsc.com
Sales Range: $125-149.9 Million
Emp.: 100
Wind Turbine Electrical System Mfr
N.A.I.C.S.: 333611
Michael Nessner *(VP-Wind Products)*

Megatran Industries Inc.　　(1)
312 Rising Sun Rd, Bordentown, NJ 08505-9626
Tel.: (609) 298-7300
Web Site: http://www.nwl.com
Sales Range: $25-49.9 Million
Emp.: 250

Power, Distribution & Specialty Transformer Mfr
N.A.I.C.S.: 335311
David Seitz *(Pres)*
Tom Thorne *(Sec)*

Subsidiary (Domestic):

Hunter Industries Inc.　　　(2)
312 Rising Sun Rd, Bordentown, NJ 08505-9626　　　　　　　　　(100%)
Tel.: (609) 298-7300
Web Site: http://www.nwl.com
Sales Range: $10-24.9 Million
Emp.: 2
Real Estate Services
N.A.I.C.S.: 531210
Dave Seitz *(Pres & CEO)*

NWL Transformers Inc.　　(1)
312 Rising Sun Rd, Bordentown, NJ 08505
Tel.: (609) 298-7300
Web Site: http://www.nwl.com
Sales Range: $25-49.9 Million
Emp.: 200
Power, Distribution & Specialty Transformers Mfr
N.A.I.C.S.: 335311
Rodger Zara *(Mgr-IT)*
Brooke Brennan *(Dir-HR)*

Neeltran, Inc.　　　　　　　(1)
71 Pickett District Rd, New Milford, CT 06776
Tel.: (860) 350-5964
Web Site: https://www.neeltran.com
Transformers & Power Systems Mfr
N.A.I.C.S.: 335311
Antonio Capanna Jr. *(Pres & COO)*

Northeast Power Systems, Inc.　(1)
66 Carey Rd, Queensbury, NY 12804
Tel.: (518) 792-4776
Web Site: http://www.nepsi.com
Sales Range: $1-9.9 Million
Emp.: 10
Electrical Apparatus & Equipment Mfr
N.A.I.C.S.: 423610
John Steciuk *(Engr-Automation)*

Tres Amigas, LLC　　　　　(1)
119 E Marcy St Ste 104, Santa Fe, NM 87501
Tel.: (505) 428-6374
Web Site: http://www.tresamigasllc.com
Electric Power Transmission Services
N.A.I.C.S.: 221121
Russell M. Stidolph *(Bd of Dirs, Executives)*
Russell Stidolph *(CFO & Sr VP)*
Phillip G. Harris *(Chm, Pres & CEO)*
Russell Stidolph *(Mng Partner)*
Ziad Alaywan *(COO)*

AMERICAN TOWER CORPORATION

116 Huntington Ave 11th Fl, Boston, MA 02116
Tel.: (617) 375-7500　　　DE
Web Site: https://www.americantower.com
Year Founded: 1995
AMT—(NYSE)
Rev.: $11,144,200,000
Assets: $66,027,600,000
Liabilities: $55,162,200,000
Net Worth: $10,865,400,000
Earnings: $1,483,300,000
Emp.: 5,643
Fiscal Year-end: 12/31/23
Real Estate Investment Trust
N.A.I.C.S.: 525990
Ruth Dowling *(Chief Admin Officer, Gen Counsel, Sec & Exec VP)*
Steven O. Vondran *(Pres & CEO)*
Olivier Puech *(Pres-Latin America & EMEA & Exec VP)*
Rodney M. Smith *(CFO, Treas & Exec VP)*
Robert Joseph Meyer Jr. *(Chief Acctg Officer & Sr VP)*

Subsidiaries:

ACC Tower Sub, LLC　　　(1)
750 Park of Commerce Blvd Ste 300, Boca Raton, FL 33487-3612

Tel.: (561) 886-3919
Broadcast Communication Services
N.A.I.C.S.: 517410

ATC Fibra de Colombia, S.A.S.　(1)
CCarrera 11A 93-35 Piso 2, Bogota, Colombia
Tel.: (57) 6015147690
Web Site: https://atcsitios.com.co
Wireless Communication Equipment Mfr
N.A.I.C.S.: 334220

ATC France Holding S.A.S.　(1)
1 rue Eugene Varlin, 92240, Malakoff, France
Tel.: (33) 145365080
Web Site: https://www.atcfrance.fr
Wireless Telecommunication Services
N.A.I.C.S.: 517112

ATC Germany Holdings GmbH　(1)
Balcke-Durr-Allee 2, 40882, Ratingen, Germany
Tel.: (49) 21025390800
Holding Company
N.A.I.C.S.: 551112

ATC Germany Operating 1 GmbH　　　　　　　　　　(1)
Balcke-Durr-Allee 2, Ratingen, 40882, Germany
Tel.: (49) 2102539080
Broadcast Communication Services
N.A.I.C.S.: 517410

ATC Germany Services GmbH　(1)
Balcke-Durr-Allee 2, 40882, Ratingen, Germany
Tel.: (49) 2102539080
Telecommunication Servicesb
N.A.I.C.S.: 517112

ATC Marketing (Uganda) Limited　(1)
Rwenzori Towers 6th Floor Plot 6 Nakasero Road, PO Box 7275, Kampala, Uganda
Tel.: (256) 312132700
Web Site: https://atcuganda.ug
Wireless Telecommunication Services
N.A.I.C.S.: 517112

ATC Paraguay S.R.L.　　　(1)
Avenida Santa Teresa entre Avenida Aviadores del Chaco y Herminio, Maldonado Paseo la Galeria Torre 2 Piso 14 Oficinas 9 12 14 16 y 18, Asuncion, Paraguay
Tel.: (595) 21 659 4400
Web Site:
　https://www.americantower.com.py
Wireless Telecommunication Services
N.A.I.C.S.: 517112

ATC Sequoia LLC　　　　　(1)
116 Huntington Ave, Boston, MA 02116-5749
Tel.: (781) 926-4628
Wired Telecommunication Services
N.A.I.C.S.: 517111

ATC South Africa Services Pty Ltd　　　　　　　　　　(1)
Suite 11 & 12 Building C Monte Circle 64 Montecasino Boulevard, Fourways, South Africa
Tel.: (27) 100038800
Web Site: https://www.atcsouthafrica.co.za
Wireless Communication Tower Services
N.A.I.C.S.: 517112
Tom Bartlett *(Pres & CEO)*
Ed DiSanto *(Chief Admin Officer, Gen Counsel, Sec & Exec VP)*

ATC Tower (Ghana) Limited　(1)
2nd Floor 5th Avenue Corporate Offices Plot 32, Osu Avenue Extension Cantonments, Accra, Ghana
Tel.: (233) 30 265 2901
Web Site:
　https://www.americantower.com.gh
Wireless Telecommunication Services
N.A.I.C.S.: 517112

American Tower International, Inc.　　　　　　　　　　(1)
116 Huntington Ave 11th Fl, Boston, MA 02116
Tel.: (617) 375-7500
Web Site: https://www.americantower.com
Wireless Telecommunication Services
N.A.I.C.S.: 517112

American Tower Investments LLC　　　　　　　　　　　(1)

116 Huntington Ave Ste 1100, Boston, MA
02116
Tel.: (617) 375-7500
Emp.: 126
Holding Company
N.A.I.C.S.: 551112

Subsidiary (Domestic):

CoreSite Realty Corporation   **(2)**
1001 17th St Ste 500, Denver, CO 80202
Tel.: (303) 405-1000
Web Site: http://www.coresite.com
Rev.: $606,824,000
Assets: $2,176,273,000
Liabilities: $2,103,795,000
Net Worth: $72,478,000
Earnings: $79,309,000
Emp.: 481
Fiscal Year-end: 12/31/2020
Real Estate Investment Trust
N.A.I.C.S.: 525990
Robert G. Stuckey *(Chm)*
Paul E. Szurek *(Pres & CEO)*
Jeffrey S. Finnin *(CFO)*
Derek McCandless *(Gen Counsel, Sec & Sr VP-Legal)*
Steven Smith *(Chief Revenue Officer)*
Brian Warren *(Sr VP-Dev & Product Engrg)*
Mark R. Jones *(Chief Acctg Officer)*
Maile Kaiser *(Sr VP-Sls)*
Juan Font *(Sr VP-Gen Mgmt)*
Anthony Hatzenbuehler *(Sr VP-Data Center Ops)*
Aleks Krusko *(VP-IT & Digitization)*
Leslie McIntosh *(VP-HR)*

Subsidiary (Domestic):

CoreSite Denver, L.L.C.   **(3)**
1001 17th St Ste 500, Denver, CO 80202
Tel.: (303) 405-1000
Data Processing Services
N.A.I.C.S.: 518210

CoreSite, L.P.   **(3)**
900 N Alameda St, Los Angeles, CA 90012
Web Site: https://www.coresite.com
Property Management Services
N.A.I.C.S.: 531110

U.S. Colo, LLC   **(3)**
1 Wilshire Bldg 624 S Grand Ave Ste 1810,
Los Angeles, CA 90017
Tel.: (213) 689-4600
Web Site: https://www.uscolo.com
Wired Telecommunications Carriers
N.A.I.C.S.: 517111

Subsidiary (Domestic):

InSite Wireless Group, LLC   **(2)**
1199 N Fairfax St Ste 700, Alexandria, VA
22314-1437
Tel.: (703) 535-3009
Web Site: http://www.insitewireless.com
Wireless Telecommunications
N.A.I.C.S.: 517112
David E. Weisman *(Co-Founder & CEO)*
Roni D. Jackson *(Gen Counsel)*
Lance C. Cawley *(Co-Founder & CFO)*
Bob Johnson *(COO)*
Joseph F. Mullin *(CTO)*
Todd Weller *(Sr VP-DAS Bus Dev & Sls)*
David Denton *(Sr VP-Brdcst, Caribbean Portfolio & New Tower Dev)*
Max Lind *(VP-Tower Sls & Mktg)*
Christian Carmody *(VP-Tower Ops)*
Robb Alarcon *(VP-DAS Engrg & Ops)*
Timothy O'Connor *(VP-IT)*
Tony Sabatino *(Pres & Chief Strategy Officer)*

Blue Sky Towers Pty Ltd   **(1)**
Unit 1 Excalibur Park Buketraube Crescent
Saxenburg Park 2, Blackheath, Johannesburg, 7580, South Africa
Tel.: (27) 219057165
Web Site: http://www.blueskytowers.com
Mobile Network Tower Construction Services
N.A.I.C.S.: 237130
Antony Moller *(Exec Dir)*
Ian Moller *(Exec Dir)*
Ken Jensen *(Exec Dir)*

Colo ATL, LLC   **(1)**
55 Marietta St Ste 570 and 800, Atlanta,
GA 30303
Tel.: (404) 355-2212

Web Site: http://www.coloatl.com
Telecommunication Servicesb
N.A.I.C.S.: 517810
John J. Ghirardelli *(Gen Mgr)*
Butch Bolling *(Mgr-Site)*
Scott Anderson *(Mgr-Site)*
Nick Neuhart *(Mgr-Site)*
Jim Leifer *(Dir-Site)*

DCS Tower Sub, LLC   **(1)**
750 Park Of Commerce Blvd Ste 300, Boca
Raton, FL 33487-3605
Tel.: (561) 886-3909
Emp.: 4
Wireless Telecommunication Services
N.A.I.C.S.: 517112

GTP South Acquisitions II, LLC   **(1)**
750 Park of Commerce Blvd Ste 300, Boca
Raton, FL 33487-3612
Tel.: (561) 886-3953
Broadcast Communication Services
N.A.I.C.S.: 517410

Global Tower Services, LLC   **(1)**
111 Catherine Dr, Woodland, WA 98674
Tel.: (360) 225-8800
Web Site:
https://www.globaltowerservice.com
Emp.: 20
Broadcast Communication Services
N.A.I.C.S.: 517410
Jeff Hahn *(Pres)*
Matt Halpin *(VP)*

Global Tower Sites I, LLC   **(1)**
750 Park of Commerce Blvd Ste 300, Boca
Raton, FL 33487-3612
Tel.: (561) 886-5854
Broadcast Communication Services
N.A.I.C.S.: 517410

Global Tower, LLC   **(1)**
2503 Scenic Dr SE, Huntsville, AL 35801
Tel.: (256) 337-8514
Wireless Telecommunication Services
N.A.I.C.S.: 517112

**MATC Infraestructura, S. de R.L. de
C.V.**   **(1)**
Av Juan Vazquez De Mella No 481 Piso 5
Ciudad de, Mexico, 11510, Distrito Federal,
Mexico
Tel.: (52) 51331111
Broadcast Communication Services
N.A.I.C.S.: 517410

**Mid-Atlantic Tower Management,
LLC**   **(1)**
38974 Old Stage Pl, Waterford, VA 20197
Tel.: (540) 924-8400
Emp.: 3
Land Subdivision Services
N.A.I.C.S.: 237210

New Towers LLC   **(1)**
5809 Fox Chapel Dr, Austin, TX 78746
Tel.: (512) 732-0658
Emp.: 3
Broadcast Communication Services
N.A.I.C.S.: 517410

RSA Media, Inc.   **(1)**
1 Huntington Ave Ste 1104, Boston, MA
02116
Tel.: (617) 227-4858
Web Site: http://www.rsamedia.com
Billboard Advertising Services
N.A.I.C.S.: 541850

**Repeater Communications Group,
LLC**   **(1)**
6 Grace Ave Ste 300, Great Neck, NY
11021
Tel.: (646) 300-9011
Web Site: http://www.rfsites.com
Tower Communication Operator
N.A.I.C.S.: 517810
Paul Eisenberg *(Co-Pres)*
Michael Lifland *(Co-Pres)*
Robyn Lifland *(Sr Dir-Ops Mgmt)*
Jessalyn Gerbholz *(Dir-Site Acquisitions)*

**Richland Towers - Kansas City,
LLC**   **(1)**
6309 E 56th St, Kansas City, MO 64129
Tel.: (813) 579-4481
Emp.: 3
Fraternal Association Management Services
N.A.I.C.S.: 813990

Richland Towers - Orlando, LLC   **(1)**
400 N Ashley Dr Ste 3010, Tampa, FL
33602-4354
Tel.: (813) 490-4354
Telecommunication Servicesb
N.A.I.C.S.: 517121

**Richland Towers - San Antonio,
LLC**   **(1)**
3161 Michelson Dr Ste 425, Irvine, CA
92612
Tel.: (949) 261-7010
Real Estate Management Services
N.A.I.C.S.: 531210

**Richland Towers Management,
LLC**   **(1)**
4001 Nebraska Ave NW, Washington, DC
20016
Tel.: (813) 579-4241
Fabricated Structural Metal Mfr
N.A.I.C.S.: 332312

**SpectraSite Communications,
LLC**   **(1)**
100 Regency Forest Dr Ste 400, Cary, NC
27511-8598
Tel.: (919) 468-0112
Web Site: http://www.americantower.com
Sales Range: $300-349.9 Million
Emp.: 512
Wireless Telecommunication Services
N.A.I.C.S.: 517112

Transcend Infrastructure Limited   **(1)**
S2 Level Upper Ground Floor Block F International Trade Tower, Nehru Place, New
Delhi, 110019, India
Tel.: (91) 11 46705600
Web Site: http://www.americantower.com
Emp.: 4
Wireless Infrastructure Operator
N.A.I.C.S.: 237130
Johann-Philipp Bruns *(Pres & VP-Education)*

**Transcend Infrastructure Private
Limited**   **(1)**
145 Rashbehari Avenue 4th Floor, Kolkata,
700029, India
Tel.: (91) 3340223000
Tower Installation Services
N.A.I.C.S.: 237130

AMERICAN VANGUARD CORPORATION

4695 MacArthur Ct, Newport Beach,
CA 92660
Tel.: (949) 260-1200   DE
Web Site: https://www.amvac.com
Year Founded: 1969
AVD—(NYSE)
Rev.: $609,615,000
Assets: $726,313,000
Liabilities: $356,334,000
Net Worth: $369,979,000
Earnings: $27,404,000
Emp.: 822
Fiscal Year-end: 12/31/22
Holding Company;Agricultural Chemicals Developer & Marketer
N.A.I.C.S.: 551112
Eric G. Wintemute *(Chm & CEO)*
David T. Johnson *(CFO & Chief Acctg
Officer)*
Mason Bennett *(VP-North American
Crop)*
Peter E. Eilers *(Mng Dir-AMVAC
Netherlands BV)*

Subsidiaries:

AMVAC Chemical Corporation   **(1)**
4695 MacArthur Ct Ste 1200, Newport
Beach, CA 92660
Tel.: (949) 260-1200
Web Site: https://www.amvac.com
Sales Range: $25-49.9 Million
Emp.: 100
Holding Company
N.A.I.C.S.: 325320
Peter Porpiglia *(VP-Product Dev-Global)*
Eric Wintemute *(Chm)*
David T. Johnson *(CFO)*
Timothy J. Donnelly *(Chief Admin Officer)*

Shirin Khosravi *(Sr VP-Human Resources)*
Suneet Ranganath *(VP-Global Supply
Chain & Operations)*
Anne Turnbough *(VP-Regulatory Affairs)*
Andrew Naughton *(VP-Technology)*
Don Gualdoni *(Chief Transformation Officer)*
Anthony Young *(Dir-Investor Relations)*

Plant (Domestic):

AMVAC Chemical Corporation   **(2)**
4100 E Washington Blvd, Los Angeles, CA
90023
Tel.: (323) 264-3910
Web Site: http://www.amvac-chemical.com
Agricultural Pesticides Developer, Distr &
Mfr
N.A.I.C.S.: 325320
David T. Johnson *(CFO & VP)*
Ulrich Trogele *(COO & Exec VP)*
Timothy J. Donnelly *(Chief Admin Officer,
Gen Counsel, Sec & VP)*
Johann Venter *(VP & Dir-Tech)*
Anne Turnbough *(VP-Regulatory Affairs)*
William A. Kuser *(Dir-IR & Corp Comm)*
Suneet Ranganath *(VP-Supply Chain &
Ops)*
Peter Porpiglia *(VP-Global Product Dev &
Technical Support)*
Scott Hendrix *(Sr VP)*

Subsidiary (Non-US):

AMVAC Chemical UK Ltd.   **(2)**
Surrey Technology Centre 40 Occam Rd,
The Surrey Research Park, Guildford, GU2
5YG, Surrey, United Kingdom   **(100%)**
Tel.: (44) 1483295780
Web Site: http://www.amvac-chemical.com
Sales Range: $25-49.9 Million
Emp.: 2
Chemical Retailer & Distr
N.A.I.C.S.: 424690

AMVAC Netherlands BV   **(2)**
Kokermolen 5, 3994 DG, Houten, Netherlands
Tel.: (31) 852731600
Web Site: http://www.amvac.com
Agricultural Chemical Mfr
N.A.I.C.S.: 325320

Subsidiary (Domestic):

OHP, Inc.   **(2)**
PO Box 746, Bluffton, SC 29910-0746
Tel.: (800) 356-4647
Web Site: http://www.ohp.com
Chemical Mfr Company
N.A.I.C.S.: 325320
Dan Stahl *(VP & Gen Mgr)*
Rick Meck *(Mgr-Ops)*
Janet Bossak *(Mgr-Acctg)*
Troy Bettner *(Head-Sls & Mktg)*

**AMVAC Mexico S. De R.L. De
C.V.**   **(1)**
Av Vallarta No 6503 Col Cd Granja CP
Plaza Concentro Loc B-17, CP 45010, Zapopan, Jalisco, Mexico
Tel.: (52) 3331101936
Web Site: https://www.amvac.com.mx
Chemical Retailer & Distr
N.A.I.C.S.: 424690

AgNova Technologies Pty Ltd   **(1)**
PO Box 736, Hamilton, 4007, QLD, Australia
Tel.: (61) 398998100
Web Site: http://www.agnova.com.au
Agricultural Crop Farming Services
N.A.I.C.S.: 111998

Agrinos India Private Limited   **(1)**
308-310 3rd Floor DLF Tower A, Jasola District Centre, New Delhi, 110025, India
Tel.: (91) 1149204700
Agricultural Crop Farming Services
N.A.I.C.S.: 111998

Agrinos Ukraine LLC   **(1)**
St Petra Bolbochana 4-A, Kiev, Ukraine
Tel.: (380) 674099903
Web Site: http://www.agrinos.com.ua
Agricultural Crop Farming Services
N.A.I.C.S.: 111998

Agrinos do Brazil Fertilizantes Biologicos Ltda   **(1)**

American Vanguard Corporation—(Continued)

Avenida Andromeda 885 - 24 Andar Sala 2401 - Bloco B Edificio Brascan, Century Plaza Alphaville, Barueri, 06473 000, Sao Paulo, Brazil
Tel.: (55) 1124248600
Agricultural Crop Farming Services
N.A.I.C.S.: 111998

GemChem, Inc.   (1)
95 River Rd Ste B, Canton, CT 06019   (100%)
Tel.: (860) 693-1331
Web Site:
   http://www.americanvanguard.com
Sales Range: $50-74.9 Million
Emp.: 4
Chemical Retailer & Distr
N.A.I.C.S.: 424210

TyraTech, Inc.   (1)
5151 McCrimmon Pkwy Ste 275, Morrisville, NC 27560   (100%)
Tel.: (919) 415-4300
Web Site: https://www.tyratech.com
Insecticide & Parasiticide Products Mfr
N.A.I.C.S.: 325320

AMERICAN VIDEO TELECONFERENCING CORP.
11226 Pentland Downs St, Las Vegas, NV 89141
Tel.: (407) 489-3736   NY
Year Founded: 1981
AVOT—(OTCIQ)
Business Services
N.A.I.C.S.: 561499
Arnulfo Saucedo-Bardan (Chief Admin Officer)
Brian D. Colvin (Chm)
Willy A. Saint-Hilaire (Pres & CEO)

AMERICAN VIRTUAL CLOUD TECHNOLOGIES, INC.
1720 Peachtree St Ste 629, Atlanta, GA 30309
Tel.: (404) 239-2863   DE
Web Site:
   https://www.avctechnologies.com
Year Founded: 2016
AVCTQ—(NASDAQ)
Rev.: $16,811,000
Assets: $31,909,000
Liabilities: $13,418,000
Net Worth: $18,491,000
Earnings: ($39,799,000)
Emp.: 127
Fiscal Year-end: 12/31/22
Investment Services
N.A.I.C.S.: 523999
Darrell J. Mays (Vice Chm)
Robert Willis (Vice Chm-Capital Markets)
Jay Patel (Chief Product Officer)
Thomas H. King (Interim Head-Staff)
Kevin Keough (CEO)
Adrian Foltz (CFO)
Onex Evans (Chief Acctg Officer)
Chris Koeneman (Chief Revenue Officer)
Lawrence E. Mock Jr. (Chm)

AMERICAN WATER WORKS COMPANY, INC.
1 Water St, Camden, NJ 08102-1658
Tel.: (856) 566-4005   DE
Web Site: https://ir.amwater.com
Year Founded: 1886
AWK—(NYSE)
Rev.: $4,234,000,000
Assets: $30,298,000,000
Liabilities: $8,783,000,000
Net Worth: $21,515,000,000
Earnings: $944,000,000
Emp.: 6,500
Fiscal Year-end: 12/31/23
Water Utility Holding Company
N.A.I.C.S.: 221310

Maureen Duffy (Sr VP-Comm & External Affairs)
Melanie M. Kennedy (Chief HR Officer & Sr VP)
Kevin B. Kirwan (Chief Operational Excellence & Safety Officer & Sr VP)
Karen Cotton (Sr Mgr-External Comm)
M. Susan Hardwick (Pres & CEO)
John C. Griffith (CFO & Exec VP)
Aaron Musgrave (VP-IR)
Lori Sutton (Chief Inclusion, Diversity & Equity Officer)
Ruben Rodriguez (Sr Dir-External Comm)
David Bowler (CFO)

Subsidiaries:

American Water Acciona Agua LLC   (1)
13041 Wyandotte Rd, Gibsonton, FL 33534
Tel.: (813) 671-9992
Waste Water Treatment Services
N.A.I.C.S.: 221320

American Water Capital Corporation   (1)
1025 Laurel Oak Rd, Voorhees, NJ 08043   (100%)
Tel.: (856) 346-8200
Web Site: http://www.amwater.com
Sales Range: $1-4.9 Billion
Financial Services
N.A.I.C.S.: 525990

Aqua New York, Inc.   (1)
762 W Lancaster Ave, Bryn Mawr, PA 19010-3402
Tel.: (610) 645-1126
Web Site: http://www.aquaamerica.com
Sales Range: $200-249.9 Million
Water Utility Services
N.A.I.C.S.: 221310

California American Water Company   (1)
1025 Palm Ave, Imperial Beach, CA 91932
Tel.: (619) 446-5700
Water & Water Waste Utility
N.A.I.C.S.: 924110
Kevin Tilden (Pres)

Subsidiary (Domestic):

East Pasadena Water Co.   (2)
3725 Mountain View Ave, Pasadena, CA 91107-4981
Tel.: (626) 793-6189
Web Site: http://www.epwater.com
Sales Range: $1-9.9 Million
Emp.: 7
Waste Treatment Services
N.A.I.C.S.: 221310
Lawrence Morales (VP & Gen Mgr)
Patti Latourelle (Office Mgr)

Environmental Management Corporation   (1)
1001 Boardwalk Springs Pl, O'Fallon, MO 63368
Tel.: (636) 561-9400
Waste Water Treatment Services
N.A.I.C.S.: 221320

Fruitridge Vista Water Co.   (1)
1108 2nd St, Sacramento, CA 95814
Tel.: (916) 443-2607
Water Supply & Irrigation Systems
N.A.I.C.S.: 221310
Stephen W. Cook (Mgr-Ops)

Illinois American Water   (1)
PO Box 6029, Carol Stream, IL 60197-6029
Tel.: (618) 239-3266
Web Site: https://www.amwater.com
Sales Range: $300-349.9 Million
Water Utility
N.A.I.C.S.: 221310
Stan Scott (Superintendent-Operations)
Rhonda Carter Adams (Program Mgr)
Rachel Bretz (Dir)
Bernie Sebold (Sr Program Mgr-Safety)
Beth Matthews (VP-Ops)

Indiana American Water   (1)
153 N Emerson Ave, Greenwood, IN 46143
Tel.: (317) 885-2400

Web Site: http://www.indiana-american.com
Sales Range: $25-49.9 Million
Emp.: 30
Water Utility
N.A.I.C.S.: 221310
Deborah Dewey (Pres)

Indiana-American Water Company, Inc.   (1)
555 E County Line Rd Ste 201, Greenwood, IN 46143
Tel.: (317) 885-2400
Web Site: https://www.amwater.com
Waste Water Treatment Services
N.A.I.C.S.: 221320
Justin Schneider (Dir-Consumer Affairs)

Kentucky American Water   (1)
2300 Richmond Rd, Lexington, KY 40502-1308
Tel.: (859) 269-2386
Web Site: http://www.amwater.com
Sales Range: $50-74.9 Million
Water Utility
N.A.I.C.S.: 221310
Adam Caswell (Dir-Govt Affairs)

Maryland-American Water Company   (1)
212 Archer St Ste B & C, Bel Air, MD 21014
Emp.: 13
Water Distr
N.A.I.C.S.: 221310
Barry Suits (Pres)

Michigan-American Water Company   (1)
311 5th St, Calumet, MI 49913
Tel.: (906) 337-3502
Web Site:
   https://www.uppermichiganwater.com
Water Distr
N.A.I.C.S.: 221310

Missouri-American Water Company   (1)
727 Craig Rd, Saint Louis, MO 63141
Tel.: (314) 991-3404
Web Site: https://www.amwater.com
Sales Range: $50-74.9 Million
Water Utilities
N.A.I.C.S.: 221310
Jeffrey T. Kaiser (VP-Ops)

Subsidiary (Domestic):

Tri-State Utility Products Inc.   (2)
1030 Atlanta Industrial Dr, Marietta, GA 30066-6601
Tel.: (770) 427-3119
Web Site: https://www.tsup.com
Sales Range: $25-49.9 Million
Emp.: 27
Electrical Apparatus & Equipment
N.A.I.C.S.: 423610

New Jersey American Water   (1)
1 Water St, Camden, NJ 08102
Tel.: (856) 346-8200
Web Site: http://www.amwater.com
Sales Range: $75-99.9 Million
Emp.: 250
Water Utility
N.A.I.C.S.: 221310
Michael A. Sgro (Gen Counsel, Sec & Exec VP)
Denise Venuti Free (Dir-Communications)

New Jersey-American Water Company, Inc.   (1)
1 Water St, Camden, NJ 08102
Tel.: (856) 346-8200
Web Site: http://www.amwater.com
Waste Water Treatment Services
N.A.I.C.S.: 221320

Pennsylvania American Water   (1)
852 Wesley Dr, Mechanicsburg, PA 17055
Tel.: (717) 790-3024
Web Site: http://www.amwater.com
Emp.: 1,100
Water Utility Services
N.A.I.C.S.: 221310
Robert Burton (Pres)
Maggie Sheely (Mgr-Southeast,Central PA)
Bernie Grundusky (VP)

Pivotal Home Solutions, LLC   (1)

1751 W Diehl Rd Ste 200, Naperville, IL 60563
Web Site:
   https://www.yourhomesolutions.com
Appliance Repair Services
N.A.I.C.S.: 811412
Pam Watkins (Dir-Operations)

Tennessee American Water   (1)
109 Wiehl St, Chattanooga, TN 37403
Tel.: (423) 771-4750
Web Site: http://www.tawc.com
Sales Range: $50-74.9 Million
Water Utility Services
N.A.I.C.S.: 221310

Virginia American Water Co.   (1)
2223 Duke St, Alexandria, VA 22314
Tel.: (703) 549-7080
Web Site: http://www.amwater.com
Sales Range: $25-49.9 Million
Water Utility
N.A.I.C.S.: 221310
Jeffrey L. McIntyre (Pres-Pennsylvania)

Water Solutions Holdings LLC   (1)
34 NE Dr, Hershey, PA 16801
Tel.: (717) 508-0550
Web Site: http://www.keystoneclear.com
Water Management Solutions
N.A.I.C.S.: 221310

AMERICAN WELL CORPORATION
75 State St 26th Fl, Boston, MA 02109
Tel.: (617) 204-3500   DE
Web Site:
   https://business.amwell.com
Year Founded: 2006
AMWL—(NYSE)
Rev.: $277,190,000
Assets: $1,217,557,000
Liabilities: $133,706,000
Net Worth: $1,083,851,000
Earnings: ($270,429,000)
Emp.: 1,035
Fiscal Year-end: 12/31/22
Software Publisher
N.A.I.C.S.: 513210
Bradford Gay (Gen Counsel & Sr VP)
Kurt Knight (COO)
Paul McNeice (VP-Acctg)
Serkan Kutan (CTO)
Amber Howe (Chief People Officer)
Dan Olson (Sr VP-Provider Solutions)
Tim Conway (CIO)
Vaughn Paunovich (Exec VP)
Matthew McAllister (Chief Product Officer)
Carrie Nelson (Chief Medical Officer)
Murray Brozinsky (Chief Strategy Officer)
Ken Cahill (Chief Behavioral Health Officer)
Phyllis Gotlib (Pres-Intl)
Kathy Weiler (Chief Comml & Growth Officer & Exec VP)
Ido Schoenberg (Co-Founder, Chm & CEO)
Roy Schoenberg (Co-Founder, Vice Chm & Co-CEO)

Subsidiaries:

Avizia Inc.   (1)
12018 Sunrise Valley Dr Ste 315, Reston, VA 20191
Tel.: (571) 267-2999
Web Site: http://www.avizia.com
Technology Services for Healthcare Industry
N.A.I.C.S.: 513210
Mike Baird (Co-Founder)
Luke Leininger (Co-Founder)
Cory Costley (Co-Founder)

AMERICAN WOODMARK CORPORATION
561 Shady Elm Rd, Winchester, VA 22602
Tel.: (540) 665-9100   VA

Web Site: https://www.americanwood
mark.com
Year Founded: 1980
AMWD—(NASDAQ)
Rev.: $1,847,502,000
Assets: $1,593,865,000
Liabilities: $683,489,000
Net Worth: $910,376,000
Earnings: $116,216,000
Emp.: 8,600
Fiscal Year-end: 04/30/24
Kitchen Cabinets & Vanities Mfr &
Distr
N.A.I.C.S.: 423310
Vance W. Tang (Chm)
Kevin Dunnigan (Treas & VP)
Paul Joachimczyk (CFO & VP)
M. Scott Culbreth (Pres & CEO)
Robert J. Adams Jr. (Sr VP-Mfg &
Technical Ops)

Subsidiaries:

Professional Cabinet Solutions (1)
11350 Riverside Dr, Mira Loma, CA 91752
Tel.: (909) 614-2900
Web Site: http://www.pcscabinetry.com
Furniture Installation Services
N.A.I.C.S.: 238350

AMERICANN INC.
1550 Wewatta St 2nd Fl, Denver, CO
80202
Tel.: (303) 862-9000 DE
Web Site: https://www.americann.co
ACAN—(OTCQB)
Rev.: $2,552,200
Assets: $15,154,894
Liabilities: $9,447,537
Net Worth: $5,707,357
Earnings: ($94,755)
Emp.: 3
Fiscal Year-end: 09/30/23
Cannabis Industry Services
N.A.I.C.S.: 561499
Timothy Ryan Keogh (Pres & CEO)
Benjamin J. Barton (Founder, CFO &
Chief Acctg Officer)

AMERICAS TECHNOLOGY ACQUISITION CORP.
16400 Dallas Pkwy Ste 305, Dallas,
TX 75248
Tel.: (303) 885-8688 Ky
Year Founded: 2020
ATA—(NYSE)
Rev.: $3,079,349
Assets: $116,983,152
Liabilities: $118,891,790
Net Worth: ($1,908,638)
Earnings: $1,962,680
Emp.: 2
Fiscal Year-end: 12/31/21
Investment Services
N.A.I.C.S.: 523999
Lisa Harris (Chm)
Jorge Marcos (CEO)
Juan Pablo Visoso (CFO)

AMERICOLD REALTY TRUST, INC.
10 Glenlake Pkwy Ste 600 S Tower,
Atlanta, GA 30328
Tel.: (678) 441-1400 MD
Web Site: https://www.americold.com
Year Founded: 2002
COLD—(NYSE)
Rev.: $2,673,329,000
Assets: $7,869,252,000
Liabilities: $4,234,665,000
Net Worth: $3,634,587,000
Earnings: ($336,269,000)
Emp.: 14,706
Fiscal Year-end: 12/31/23
Real Estate Investment Trust
N.A.I.C.S.: 525990
E. Jay Wells (CFO & Exec VP)
George F. Chappelle Jr. (CEO)

James C. Snyder Jr. (Chief Legal Officer, Sec & Exec VP)
Robert S. Chambers (Pres-Americas)
Richard C. Winnall (Pres-Intl)
R. Scott Henderson (Chief Investment Officer & Exec VP)
Samantha L. Charleston (Chief HR Officer & Exec VP)
Michael Spires (CIO)
Bryan Verbarendse (COO-North America & Exec VP)
George F. Chappelle Jr. (CEO)

Subsidiaries:

AGRO Merchants North America
Holdings LLC (1)
1150 Sanctuary Pkwy Ste 125, Alpharetta,
GA 30009
Tel.: (888) 599-5512
Web Site: http://www.agromerchants.com
Cold Storage & Warehousing, Freight Forwarding & Packaging Services
N.A.I.C.S.: 493190
Carlos Rodriguez (CEO)

Subsidiary (Domestic):

Cool-Pak Solutions LP (2)
1071 E 233rd St, Carson, CA 90745-6206
Tel.: (201) 986-7990
Refrigerated Warehousing & Storage Services
N.A.I.C.S.: 493120
Steve Karo (Founder)

Americold Barcelona Palau S.A. (1)
Carrer de Santa Margarida de Boada Vell 1,
Palau Solita I Plegamans, 08184, Barcelona, Spain
Tel.: (34) 938649258
Food Product Mfr & Distr
N.A.I.C.S.: 311919

Americold Cascade Cold Inc. (1)
406 2nd St, Lynden, WA 98264
Tel.: (360) 354-2138
Sales Range: $10-24.9 Million
Emp.: 20
Refrigerated Warehousing & Storage
N.A.I.C.S.: 493120
Rick Nelson (Mgr-Ops)

Americold Forwarding Agency
B.V. (1)
Van Riemsdijkweg 78, 3088 HD, Rotterdam,
Netherlands
Tel.: (31) 854848575
Food Product Mfr & Distr
N.A.I.C.S.: 311919

Americold Leixoes Unipessoal
LDA (1)
Lote 3 Platforma Logistica do Porto de
Leixoes Polo 1, 4455-846, Santa Cruz, Portugal
Tel.: (351) 220998463
Food Product Mfr & Distr
N.A.I.C.S.: 311919

Americold Logistics, LLC (1)
10 Glenlake Pkwy Ste 600 S Tower, Atlanta, GA 30328-7250
Tel.: (678) 441-1400
Web Site: https://www.americold.com
Sales Range: $75-99.9 Million
Public Refrigerated Warehousing, Refrigerated Transportation, Logistics & Consulting
N.A.I.C.S.: 493120
Fred Walker (VP-Facility Svcs)
Neal J. Rider (Pres-Ops-Intl)
Carl Fowler (Sr VP-Bus Dev-Reg Accts)

Subsidiary (Domestic):

Versacold Logistics, LLC (2)
19840 South Rancho Way, Compton, CA
90220
Tel.: (310) 632-6265
Sales Range: $25-49.9 Million
Emp.: 60
Refrigerated Warehousing & Storage
N.A.I.C.S.: 493120
Jack Rudolph (Chief Engr)

Americold Maasvlakte B.V. (1)
Malakkastraat 15, Maasvlakte, 3199 LK,
Rotterdam, Netherlands
Tel.: (31) 850436400

Food Product Mfr & Distr
N.A.I.C.S.: 311919

Americold Realty LLC (1)
10 Glenlake Pkwy Ste 600 S Tower, Atlanta, GA 30328
Tel.: (678) 441-1400
Web Site: https://www.americold.com
Refrigerated Warehouses
N.A.I.C.S.: 493120

Americold Sines Unipessoal
LDA. (1)
ZAL Sina Zona B, 7520-203, Sines, Portugal
Tel.: (351) 269098157
Food Product Mfr & Distr
N.A.I.C.S.: 311919

Americold Urk B.V. (1)
Abbert 10, 8321 WN, Urk, Netherlands
Tel.: (31) 527686403
Food Product Mfr & Distr
N.A.I.C.S.: 311919

Americold Valencia S.L.U. (1)
Ampliacion Muelle Sur, 46024, Valencia,
Spain
Tel.: (34) 963673515
Food Product Mfr & Distr
N.A.I.C.S.: 311919

Cloverleaf Cold Storage Co. Inc. (1)
401 Douglas St Ste 406, Sioux City, IA
51101
Tel.: (712) 279-8000
Web Site: http://www.cloverleaf.com
Sales Range: $25-49.9 Million
Emp.: 400
Refrigerated Warehousing & Storage
N.A.I.C.S.: 493120
Bill Feiges (CEO)

Plant (Domestic):

Cloverleaf Cold Storage Co. Inc. -
Plant 1 (2)
2900 Murray St, Sioux City, IA 51111
Tel.: (712) 279-0918
Cold Storage Warehousing Services
N.A.I.C.S.: 493120
Doug Stewart (Plant Mgr)
Ron Graham (Reg VP)

Cloverleaf Cold Storage Co. Inc. -
Plant 6 (2)
2640 Murray St, Sioux City, IA 51111
Tel.: (712) 279-8022
Cold Storage Warehousing Services
N.A.I.C.S.: 493120
Ron Graham (Reg VP)

Subsidiary (Domestic):

Steffen Midwest Inc. (2)
404 Admiral Blvd, Kansas City, MO 64106-1508
Tel.: (816) 421-3229
Web Site: http://www.steffeninc.com
Sales Range: $10-24.9 Million
Emp.: 25
Industrial Machinery & Equipment
N.A.I.C.S.: 423830
David Kaplan (Pres)

Steffen, Inc. (2)
623 W Seventh St, Sioux City, IA 51103-4339
Tel.: (712) 279-8080
Web Site: http://www.steffensystems.com
Sales Range: $10-24.9 Million
Emp.: 20
Motor Vehicle Supplies & New Parts
N.A.I.C.S.: 423120
Michael Heathers (Gen Mgr)

Zero Mountain, Inc. (2)
8425 Hwy 45 S, Fort Smith, AR 72916
Tel.: (479) 646-7767
Web Site: http://www.zeromtn.com
Sales Range: $25-49.9 Million
Emp.: 90
Refrigerated Storage Services
N.A.I.C.S.: 493120
Andy Sudigala (CIO & VP)
Mark Rumsey (Chm)
Tony Bell (CFO & VP)

KMT Brrr! (1)
1145 Commerce Blvd, Swedesboro, NJ
08015-8015

Tel.: (856) 455-0031
Web Site: http://www.kmtbrrr.com
Specialized Freight Trucking
N.A.I.C.S.: 484230
Allen Wronko (Dir-Transportation)

Newport-St. Paul Cold Storage
Co. (1)
2233 Maxwell Ave, Newport, MN 55055
Tel.: (651) 459-5555
Web Site: http://www.newportcold.com
Refrigerated Warehousing & Storage
N.A.I.C.S.: 493120
Randy Lewis (VP-Ops)
Drew Greenberg (Pres & CEO-New Bus
Dev)
Lindsey Arens (Mgr-Customer Svc)
Russ Stevens (Mgr-Compliance & Quality
Assurance)
Craig Lengsfeld (Mgr-Facilities & Refrigeration)

Superfrio Armazens Gerias S.A. (1)
Av Luiz Eduardo Toledo Prado n 800 - 1st
floor - Tower I, Ribeirao Preto, 14027-250,
Sao Paulo, Brazil
Tel.: (55) 16997755603
Web Site: https://superfrio.com.br
Freight & Logistics Services
N.A.I.C.S.: 541614

AMERICREW INC.
21 Omaha St, Dumont, NJ 07628
Tel.: (201) 387-7700 NJ
Web Site: https://americrew.com
Year Founded: 2007
ACRU—(OTCIQ)
Rev.: $5,512,368
Assets: $2,520,475
Liabilities: $4,901,697
Net Worth: ($2,381,222)
Earnings: ($1,889,214)
Emp.: 57
Fiscal Year-end: 12/31/21
Telecommunication Servicesb
N.A.I.C.S.: 517112
P. Kelley Dunne (CEO)
Brian Weis (COO)
Ross DiMaggio (CFO)

AMERIGUARD SECURITY SERVICES, INC.
5470 W Spruce Ave Ste 102, Fresno,
CA 93722
Tel.: (559) 271-5984
Web Site:
https://www.ameriguardsecurity.com
AGSS—(OTCIQ)
Rev.: $24,947,401
Assets: $3,809,252
Liabilities: $5,798,392
Net Worth: $1,989,140
Earnings: ($428,458)
Emp.: 315
Fiscal Year-end: 12/31/22
Investigation & Personal Background
Check Services
N.A.I.C.S.: 561611
Lawrence Garcia (Pres)
Leo Reijnders (Bus Mgr)
Harlan Hartman (Mgr-Ops)

AMERIPRISE FINANCIAL, INC.
1099 Ameriprise Financial Ctr, Minneapolis, MN 55474
Tel.: (612) 671-3131 DE
Web Site:
https://www.ameriprise.com
Year Founded: 1894
AMP—(NYSE)
Rev.: $16,096,000,000
Assets: $175,191,000,000
Liabilities: $170,462,000,000
Net Worth: $4,729,000,000
Earnings: $2,556,000,000
Emp.: 13,800
Fiscal Year-end: 12/31/23
Financial Planning, Products & Services for Individual, Business & Institutional Clients

Ameriprise Financial, Inc.—(Continued)
N.A.I.C.S.: 523940
Deirdre Davey McGraw *(Exec VP-Mktg, Corp Comm & Community Rels)*
James M. Cracchiolo *(Chm & CEO)*
Kelli Hunter Petruzillo *(Exec VP-HR)*
Walter S. Berman *(CFO & Exec VP)*
William Davies *(Chief Investment Officer)*
Gumer Alvero *(Pres & Pres-Insurance & Annuities)*
Joseph E. Sweeney *(Pres & Pres-Advice, Wealth Mgmt, Products, and Svc Delivery)*
David Logan *(Head-EMEA & Global Bus Dev)*
Heather Melloh *(Gen Counsel-Ameriprise Fin & Exec VP)*
Dawn Brockman *(Principal Acctg Officer & Interim Controller)*

Subsidiaries:

American Enterprise Investment Services, Inc.   **(1)**
802 Ameriprise Financial Ctr 707 2nd Ave S, Minneapolis, MN 55474
Tel.: (612) 671-2523
Web Site:
  https://www.ameriprisefinancial.com
Sales Range: $650-699.9 Million
Clearing & Trade Execution Services for Investors
N.A.I.C.S.: 523999
James M. Cracchiolo *(Chm & CEO)*

Ameriprise Advisor Services, Inc.   **(1)**
719 Griswold St Ste 1700, Detroit, MI 48226
Tel.: (313) 961-6666
Sales Range: $150-199.9 Million
Emp.: 2,000
Investment Services
N.A.I.C.S.: 523940

Ameriprise Certificate Company   **(1)**
1099 Ameriprise Financial Ctr, Minneapolis, MN 55474   **(100%)**
Tel.: (612) 671-3131
Web Site: http://www.ameriprise.com
Rev.: $660,113,000
Assets: $14,249,353,000
Liabilities: $13,559,995,000
Net Worth: $689,358,000
Earnings: $102,117,000
Fiscal Year-end: 12/31/2023
Investment Services
N.A.I.C.S.: 523999
Abu M. Arif *(Pres & CEO)*
James R. Hill *(CFO)*
Brian L. Granger *(Chief Acctg Officer)*

Ameriprise Financial Services, Inc.   **(1)**
55 Ameriprise Financial Ctr, Minneapolis, MN 55474
Tel.: (612) 671-3131
Web Site: https://www.ameriprise.com
Brokerage, Investment & Financial Advisory Services
N.A.I.C.S.: 523999
James M. Cracchiolo *(Chm & CEO)*

Ameriprise Trust Company   **(1)**
707 2nd Ave S, Minneapolis, MN 55402-2405
Tel.: (612) 671-3131
Insurance Brokerage Services
N.A.I.C.S.: 524210

Columbia Threadneedle Investments (ME) Limited   **(1)**
Level 2 Gate Village Building 5 Dubai International Financial Centre, Dubai, United Arab Emirates
Tel.: (971) 44254702
Financial Planning Services
N.A.I.C.S.: 523940
Raymundo Yu *(Chm-Asia Pacific)*
Jon Allen *(Head-Distr-Asia Pacific)*
Glen Giddings *(Head-Institutional-Australia & New Zealand)*
Kelly-Ann Cavagnaro *(Head-Consultant Rels-North America Institutional Bus)*
Scott Couto *(Head-North America)*

Columbia Wanger Asset Management, LLC   **(1)**
227 W Monroe St Ste 3000, Chicago, IL 60606-5018   **(100%)**
Tel.: (312) 634-9200
Web Site: http://www.wanger.com
Sales Range: $125-149.9 Million
Emp.: 85
Investment Advisory Services
N.A.I.C.S.: 523150

IDS Management Corporation   **(1)**
220 S 6th St Ste 700, Minneapolis, MN 55402
Tel.: (612) 851-3200
Web Site: http://www.idsgrp.com
Sales Range: $75-99.9 Million
Management Consulting Services
N.A.I.C.S.: 541611

IDS Property Casualty Insurance Company   **(1)**
3500 Packerland Dr, De Pere, WI 54115-9070
Tel.: (920) 330-5100
Web Site: http://www.ampf.com
Property & Casualty Insurance Services
N.A.I.C.S.: 524126

Investment Professionals, Inc.   **(1)**
16414 San Pedro Ave Ste 300, San Antonio, TX 78232
Tel.: (210) 308-8800
Security Brokers & Dealers
N.A.I.C.S.: 523150
Jay McAnelly *(Pres & CEO)*
Suzanne Fancher *(Sr VP-Ops)*
Brian Surovik *(Chief Compliance Officer & Sr VP)*
Lee Whiteley *(VP & Dir-IT)*
Christine Walters *(Controller)*

Lionstone Partners, LLC   **(1)**
712 Main St Ste 2500, Houston, TX 77002
Tel.: (713) 533-5860
Web Site:
  https://www.lionstoneinvestments.com
Financial Planning Services
N.A.I.C.S.: 523940

RiverSource Distributors, Inc.   **(1)**
100 S 5th St Ste 1075, Minneapolis, MN 55402
Tel.: (612) 671-5510
Business Management Consulting Services
N.A.I.C.S.: 541611

RiverSource Life Insurance Company   **(1)**
70100 Ameriprise Financial Ctr, Minneapolis, MN 55474
Tel.: (612) 671-3131
Web Site: http://www.riversource.com
Rev.: $4,292,000,000
Assets: $123,885,000,000
Liabilities: $122,728,000,000
Net Worth: $1,157,000,000
Earnings: $394,000,000
Fiscal Year-end: 12/31/2023
Fire Insurance Services
N.A.I.C.S.: 524113
John R. Woerner *(Pres-Insurance and Annuities & Chief Strategy Officer-Ameriprise)*
Brian J. McGrane *(CFO & Exec VP)*
Gumer C. Alvero *(Interim Chm & Exec VP-Annuities)*
Brian E. Hartert *(CFO)*

Subsidiary (Domestic):

RiverSource Life Insurance Co. of New York   **(2)**
70500 Ameriprise Financial Ctr, Minneapolis, MN 55474
Tel.: (518) 869-8613
Web Site: http://www.riversource.com
Fire Insurance Services
N.A.I.C.S.: 524113

Threadneedle Asset Management Holdings Limited   **(1)**
78 Cannon Street, London, EC4N 6AG, United Kingdom
Tel.: (44) 2074645000
Sales Range: $250-299.9 Million
Emp.: 250
Asset Management Services
N.A.I.C.S.: 523999

Affiliate (Domestic):

EMX Company Ltd.   **(2)**

33 Cannon Street, London, EC4M 5SB, United Kingdom   **(22.5%)**
Tel.: (44) 1279858300
Monetary Funds Automation Technology Services
N.A.I.C.S.: 541519

Subsidiary (Domestic):

Sackville TPEN Property (GP) Ltd.   **(2)**
78 Cannon St, London, ec4n 6ag, United Kingdom
Tel.: (44) 02074645000
Sales Range: $300-349.9 Million
Emp.: 500
Investment Services
N.A.I.C.S.: 523999

Sackville TSP Property (GP) Ltd.   **(2)**
78 cannon street london, London, ec4n 6ag, United Kingdom
Tel.: (44) 2074645000
Sales Range: $300-349.9 Million
Emp.: 300
Investment Services
N.A.I.C.S.: 523999

Threadneedle Asset Management Ltd.   **(2)**
Cannon Place 78 Cannon Street, London, EC4N 6AG, United Kingdom
Tel.: (44) 2074645667
Web Site:
  http://www.columbiathreadneedle.com
Sales Range: $250-299.9 Million
Emp.: 700
Asset Management Services
N.A.I.C.S.: 523999

Threadneedle International Ltd.   **(2)**
Cannon Pl 78 Cannon St, London, EC4N 6AG, United Kingdom
Tel.: (44) 02074645000
Web Site:
  http://www.columbiathreadneedle.com
Sales Range: $300-349.9 Million
Investment Services
N.A.I.C.S.: 523999

Subsidiary (Non-US):

Threadneedle Investment Services GmbH   **(2)**
An der Welle 5, 60322, Frankfurt am Main, Germany
Tel.: (49) 692972990
Sales Range: $650-699.9 Million
Emp.: 10
Investment Services
N.A.I.C.S.: 523999

Subsidiary (Domestic):

Threadneedle Investment Services Ltd.   **(2)**
PO Box 10033, Chelmsford, CM99 2AL, Essex, United Kingdom
Tel.: (44) 8009530134
Web Site:
  http://www.columbiathreadneedle.com
Sales Range: $300-349.9 Million
Emp.: 600
Investment & Fund Management Services
N.A.I.C.S.: 523999

Threadneedle Management Services Ltd.   **(2)**
Cannon Pl 78 Cannon St, London, EC4N 6AG, United Kingdom
Tel.: (44) 02074645000
Sales Range: $300-349.9 Million
Investment Services
N.A.I.C.S.: 523999

Threadneedle Pensions Ltd.   **(2)**
Cannon Place 78 Cannon Street, London, EC4N 6AG, United Kingdom
Tel.: (44) 02074645000
Web Site:
  http://www.threadneedlepensions.co.uk
Sales Range: $200-249.9 Million
Pension Investment Services
N.A.I.C.S.: 524292

Threadneedle Capital Management Ltd.   **(1)**
Cannon Place 78 Cannon Street, London, EC4N 6AG, United Kingdom
Tel.: (44) 2074645000

Property Leasing Services
N.A.I.C.S.: 531190

Threadneedle Portfolio Services Hong Kong Ltd.   **(1)**
Unit 3004 Two Exchange Square 8 Connaught Place, Hong Kong, China (Hong Kong)
Tel.: (852) 37981212
Web Site: http://www.threadneedle.hk
Emp.: 9
Investment Management Service
N.A.I.C.S.: 523940

Threadneedle Property Investments Ltd.   **(1)**
60 Saint Mary Axe, London, EC3A 8JQ, United Kingdom
Tel.: (44) 2074378000
Investment Management Service
N.A.I.C.S.: 523940
Alan Kaye *(Sec)*

AMERIS BANCORP

3490 Piedmont Rd NE Ste 1550, Atlanta, GA 30305
Tel.: (404) 639-6500   **GA**
Web Site:
  https://www.amerisbank.com
Year Founded: 1980
ABCB—(NASDAQ)
Rev.: $1,178,310,000
Assets: $25,053,286,000
Liabilities: $21,855,886,000
Net Worth: $3,197,400,000
Earnings: $346,540,000
Emp.: 2,847
Fiscal Year-end: 12/31/22
Bank Holding Company
N.A.I.C.S.: 551111
H. Palmer Proctor Jr. *(Vice Chm & CEO)*
William D. McKendry *(Chief Risk Officer & Exec VP)*
Nicole S. Stokes *(CFO & Exec VP)*
Doug Strange *(Chief Credit Officer & Exec VP)*
Lawton E. Bassett III *(Pres-Banking Grp)*
James Allan LaHaise III *(Chief Strategy Officer & Exec VP)*
Jody L. Spencer *(Chief Legal Officer & Exec VP)*
Ross L. Creasy *(Chief Innovation Officer & Exec VP)*
H. Palmer Proctor Jr. *(CEO)*

Subsidiaries:

Ameris Bank   **(1)**
3490 Piedmont Rd NE, Atlanta, GA 30305   **(100%)**
Tel.: (229) 985-4040
Web Site: http://www.amerisbank.com
Commercial Banking
N.A.I.C.S.: 522110
H. Palmer Proctor Jr. *(Vice Chm & CEO)*
Cindi H. Lewis *(Chief Admin Officer, Sec & Exec VP)*
William D. McKendry *(Chief Risk Officer & Exec VP)*
Nicole S. Stokes *(CFO & Exec VP)*
Doug Strange *(Chief Credit Officer & Exec VP)*
James Allan LaHaise III *(Chief Strategy Officer & Exec VP)*
Lawton E. Bassett III *(Pres)*
Ross L. Creasy *(Chief Innovation Officer)*
Michael T. Pierson *(Chief Governance Officer)*
Jody L. Spencer *(Chief Legal Officer)*
Ross McWilliams *(Exec VP & Mng Dir-Homebuilder Div)*

Subsidiary (Domestic):

Fountain Financial, Inc.   **(2)**
1301 Riverplace Blvd, Jacksonville, FL 32207
Tel.: (904) 486-7238
Insurance Agents
N.A.I.C.S.: 524210

LionMark Insurance Company   **(1)**

3490 Piedmont Rd NE Ste 1550, Atlanta, GA 30305
Tel.: (404) 240-1504
Web Site: http://www.amerisbank.com
Credit Loss Protection Insurance Services
N.A.I.C.S.: 524298
H. Palmer Proctor Jr. *(Treas & Sec)*

US Premium Finance, Inc. **(1)**
280 Technology Pkwy Ste 200, Norcross, GA 30092
Tel.: (770) 446-8773
Web Site:
    https://www.uspremiumfinance.com
Insurance Premium Financing Services
N.A.I.C.S.: 522220
Curren Coco *(Pres)*

AMERISAFE, INC.
2301 Hwy 190 W, Deridder, LA 70634
Tel.: (337) 463-9052 TX
Web Site: https://www.amerisafe.com
Year Founded: 1985
AMSF—(NASDAQ)
Rev.: $294,737,000
Assets: $1,269,279,000
Liabilities: $951,847,000
Net Worth: $317,432,000
Earnings: $55,602,000
Emp.: 354
Fiscal Year-end: 12/31/22
Insurance Holding Company; Workers Compensation Insurance
N.A.I.C.S.: 551112
Ray Wise *(Chief Sls Officer & Exec VP)*
Jared A. Morris *(Chm)*
G. Janelle Frost *(Pres & CEO)*
Vincent J. Gagliano *(Chief Risk Officer & Exec VP)*
Kathryn H. Shirley *(Chief Admin Officer, Sec & Exec VP)*
Barbra E. McCrary *(Sr VP-Policyholder Svcs)*
Anastasios Omiridis *(CFO & Exec VP)*
Garrett S. Little *(Sr VP-Safety Ops)*
Angela W. Pearson *(Sr VP & Controller)*
Nancy E. Hunt *(Sr VP)*
Henry O. Lestage IV *(Sr VP-Claims Ops)*

Subsidiaries:

American Interstate Insurance Company Inc. **(1)**
2301 Hwy 190 W, Deridder, LA 70634-6004
Tel.: (337) 463-9052
Web Site: https://www.amerisafe.com
Rev.: $92,847,000
Emp.: 300
Insurance Agents & Brokerage Services
N.A.I.C.S.: 524210

Amerisafe Risk Services, Inc. **(1)**
2301 Hwy 190 W, Deridder, LA 70634
Tel.: (337) 463-9052
Insurance Related Services
N.A.I.C.S.: 524298

Silver Oak Casualty, Inc. **(1)**
2301 Hwy 190 W, Deridder, LA 70634 **(100%)**
Tel.: (337) 463-9052
Sales Range: $10-24.9 Million
Emp.: 300
Insurance Agents & Brokerage Services
N.A.I.C.S.: 524210
Clifford Allen Bradley Jr. *(Chm)*

AMERISERV FINANCIAL, INC.
216 Franklin St, Johnstown, PA 15901
Tel.: (814) 533-5300 PA
Web Site: https://www.ameriserv.com
Year Founded: 1983
ASRV—(NASDAQ)
Rev.: $7,767,000
Assets: $134,585,000
Liabilities: $28,407,000
Net Worth: $106,178,000

Earnings: $7,448,000
Emp.: 329
Fiscal Year-end: 12/31/22
Bank Holding Company
N.A.I.C.S.: 551111
Jeffrey A. Stopko *(Pres & CEO)*
Michael D. Lynch *(CFO, Chief Investment Officer, Chief Risk Officer & Sr VP)*
Bettina D. Fochler *(Chief Credit Officer & Sr VP)*
Michael R. Baylor *(Chief Comml Banking Officer & Exec VP)*
Kerri L. Mueller *(Sr VP-Retail Banking--AmeriServ Financial Bank)*
Laura L. Fiore *(Sr VP)*
Wendy M. Gressick *(Chief Loan Review Officer & Sr VP)*
Anthony M. Gojmerac *(Officer-Pur & Facilities & VP)*
Jessica L. Johnson *(VP & Mgr-Regulatory Acctg)*
Tammie L. Slavick *(VP-Fin & Profitability Analysis)*

Subsidiaries:

AmeriServ Financial Bank **(1)**
216 Franklin St, Johnstown, PA 15901
Tel.: (620) 672-5611
Sales Range: $125-149.9 Million
Emp.: 250
Commericial Banking
N.A.I.C.S.: 522110
Jeffrey A. Stopko *(Pres & CEO)*

Ameriserv Trust & Financial Services Co. **(1)**
216 Franklin St, Johnstown, PA 15901-1911 **(100%)**
Tel.: (814) 533-5397
Web Site: http://www.ameriservfinancial.com
Sales Range: $150-199.9 Million
Emp.: 400
Provides Trust Services
N.A.I.C.S.: 525990
Diana M. Hipp *(Asst VP & Ops Mgr)*
Timothy E. Walters *(Sr VP)*
Stephanie G. Bassett *(Accountant-Trust)*
Christopher C. Sheedy *(Sr VP & Dir-Specialty Real Estate)*
David A. Finui *(Exec VP & Dir-Wealth & Capital Mgmt)*
Scott D. Porterfield *(VP)*
Christiana Chmielewski *(Officer-Personal Trust & Asst VP)*
Marie A. Mock *(Officer-Personal Trust & Asst VP)*
Roberta K. Ream *(Officer-Personal Trust & Asst VP)*
Nicholas A. Urban *(Officer-Personal Trust & Asst VP)*
Kathleen M. Wallace *(Sr VP & Mgr-Retirement Svcs)*
Dennis E. Hunt *(Officer-Retirement Svcs & VP)*
Sharon E. Delic *(Officer-Retirement Svcs & VP)*
Michele Komara-Czyrnik *(Officer-Retirement Svcs & Asst VP)*
Mary Lou Mandichak *(Officer-Retirement Svcs & Asst VP)*
Ricky A. Kalanish *(Asst VP)*
Nicholas E. Debias Jr. *(Sr VP-Retirement Svcs)*
Ernest L. Petersen III *(Sr VP & Mgr-Diversified Svcs)*

AMERISTAR NETWORK, INC.
784 N 2460 W, Hurricane, UT 84737
Tel.: (435) 229-1955 DE
Web Site:
    https://ameristarnetwork.com
Year Founded: 1997
AMWK—(OTCIQ)
Software Development Services
N.A.I.C.S.: 541511
Bruce Magown *(CEO)*
William Noe *(Pres)*
O. Russell Crandall *(Chm & Sec)*

AMERITEK VENTURES

1980 Festival Plaza Dr Ste 530, Las Vegas, NV 89135
Tel.: (877) 571-1776 NV
Web Site:
    http://www.ameritekventures.com
Year Founded: 2010
ATVK—(OTCQB)
Assets: $40,578
Liabilities: $635,854
Net Worth: ($595,276)
Earnings: ($606,506)
Emp.: 5
Fiscal Year-end: 05/31/18
Optical Fiber Cable Mfr
N.A.I.C.S.: 335921
Shaun Passley *(Chm & CEO)*

Subsidiaries:

VW Win Century Inc. **(1)**
2575 McCabe Way Ste 100, Irvine, CA 92614
Tel.: (415) 250-4566
Web Site: http://www.flexfridge.com
Mini-Fridge Mfr
N.A.I.C.S.: 335210
TeikKeng Goh *(Chm)*
SeeKuy Tan *(Pres & Treas)*
Kathleen Mary Johnston *(Sec)*

AMERITRANS CAPITAL CORPORATION
50 Jericho Quadrangle Ste 109, Jericho, NY 11753
Tel.: (212) 355-2449 DE
Web Site:
    http://www.ameritranscapital.com
AMTC—(OTCIQ)
Sales Range: $1-9.9 Million
Lending & Investment Services
N.A.I.C.S.: 523999

Subsidiaries:

Elk Associates Funding Corporation **(1)**
747 3rd Ave 4th Fl, New York, NY 10017 **(100%)**
Tel.: (212) 355-2449
Provider of Specialty Finance Services
N.A.I.C.S.: 522299

Subsidiary (Domestic):

Medallion Auto Management LLC **(2)**
747 Third Ave 4th Fl, New York, NY 10017 **(100%)**
Tel.: (212) 355-2449
Automobile Leasing
N.A.I.C.S.: 532112

Elk Capital Corporation **(1)**
747 3rd Ave, New York, NY 10017 **(100%)**
Tel.: (212) 355-2449
Provider of Funding & Management Services
N.A.I.C.S.: 522299

AMERITRUST CORPORATION
1712 Pioneer Ave Ste 500, Cheyenne, WY 82001
Tel.: (475) 217-6124 NV
Web Site:
    https://www.gryphonresourcesinc.com
Year Founded: 2006
ATCC—(OTCIQ)
Rev.: $31,783
Assets: $4,225,653
Liabilities: $75,469
Net Worth: $4,150,184
Earnings: ($750,217)
Fiscal Year-end: 09/30/20
Oil & Gas Exploration Services
N.A.I.C.S.: 211120

AMERITYRE CORPORATION
1501 Industrial Rd, Boulder City, NV 89005
Tel.: (702) 293-1930 NV
Web Site: https://www.amerityre.com
Year Founded: 1995

AMTY—(OTCIQ)
Rev.: $6,495,530
Assets: $3,318,755
Liabilities: $1,172,632
Net Worth: $2,146,123
Earnings: $431,887
Emp.: 16
Fiscal Year-end: 06/30/22
Polyurethane Tire Mfr
N.A.I.C.S.: 326211
Michael Francis Sullivan *(Chm, CEO & COO)*
Lynda R. Keeton-Cardno *(CFO)*
David S. Clark *(Sec-Board)*

AMERIWORKS FINANCIAL SERVICES, INC.
1 Linden Ct, Sciota, PA 18354
Year Founded: 1997
AWKS—(OTCIQ)
Debt Collection Services
N.A.I.C.S.: 561440
Matthew Perosi *(Mng Dir-IT & Ops)*

AMES NATIONAL CORPORATION
323 6th St, Ames, IA 50010
Tel.: (515) 232-6251 IA
Web Site:
    https://www.amesnational.com
Year Founded: 1975
ATLO—(NASDAQ)
Rev.: $74,301,000
Assets: $2,155,481,000
Liabilities: $1,989,693,000
Net Worth: $165,788,000
Earnings: $10,817,000
Emp.: 273
Fiscal Year-end: 12/31/23
Multi-Bank Holding Company
N.A.I.C.S.: 551111
John P. Nelson *(Pres & CEO)*
Justin C. Clausen *(CFO & Chief Acctg Officer)*
Michael A. Wilson *(Chief Lending Officer & Exec VP)*

Subsidiaries:

Boone Bank and Trust Co. **(1)**
716 8th St, Boone, IA 50036
Tel.: (515) 432-6200
Web Site: https://www.boonebankiowa.com
Sales Range: $1-9.9 Million
Emp.: 25
Commericial Banking
N.A.I.C.S.: 522110
Nancy Hager *(Officer-Mortgage Loan & VP)*

First National Bank, Ames, Iowa **(1)**
405 5th St, Ames, IA 50010
Tel.: (515) 232-5561
Web Site: https://www.fnb247.com
Sales Range: $125-149.9 Million
Emp.: 55
Commericial Banking
N.A.I.C.S.: 522110
Thomas H. Pohlman *(Chm)*
Scott T. Bauer *(Pres)*
John R. Linch *(Chief Credit Officer & Exec VP)*
Brian E. Vahle *(Sr VP-Johnston)*
Rod A. West *(Sr VP-Ankeny)*
Zack Ray *(VP-West Des Moines)*

Iowa State Savings Bank **(1)**
401 W Adams St, Creston, IA 50801 **(100%)**
Tel.: (641) 782-1000
Web Site: https://www.issbbank.com
Sales Range: $1-9.9 Million
Emp.: 42
Commericial Banking
N.A.I.C.S.: 522110
Adam Snodgrass *(Pres & CEO)*

Reliance State Bank **(1)**
606 Broad St, Story City, IA 50248 **(100%)**
Tel.: (515) 733-4396
Web Site: https://www.rsbiowa.com
Sales Range: $1-9.9 Million
Emp.: 32
Commericial Banking

Ames National Corporation—(Continued)

N.A.I.C.S.: 522110
Richard J. Schreier *(Pres & CEO)*

State Bank & Trust Co. **(1)**
1025 6th St, Nevada, IA 50201
Tel.: (515) 382-2191
Web Site: https://www.banksbt.com
Sales Range: $1-9.9 Million
Emp.: 24
Commercial Banking
N.A.I.C.S.: 522110

United Bank & Trust NA **(1)**
2101 S Ctr St, Marshalltown, IA
50158 **(100%)**
Tel.: (641) 753-5900
Web Site: https://www.bankubt.com
Sales Range: $1-9.9 Million
Emp.: 8
Savings Bank
N.A.I.C.S.: 522180
Curt Hoff *(Pres)*
Robert Thomas *(Sr VP)*

AMESITE INC.
607 Shelby St Ste 700 PMB 214, Detroit, MI 48226
Tel.: (734) 876-8141 **DE**
Web Site: https://amesite.com
Year Founded: 2017
AMST—(NASDAQ)
Rev.: $166,881
Assets: $3,314,177
Liabilities: $798,465
Net Worth: $2,515,712
Earnings: ($4,403,182)
Emp.: 9
Fiscal Year-end: 06/30/24
Educational Software Development
Services
N.A.I.C.S.: 541511
Ann Marie Sastry *(Pres, CEO & Chm)*
Sherlyn W. Farrell *(CFO)*

AMETEK, INC.
1100 Cassatt Rd, Berwyn, PA 19312-
1177
Tel.: (610) 647-2121 **DE**
Web Site: https://www.ametek.com
Year Founded: 1930
AME—(NYSE)
Rev.: $6,596,950,000
Assets: $15,023,533,000
Liabilities: $6,293,342,000
Net Worth: $8,730,191,000
Earnings: $1,313,188,000
Emp.: 21,500
Fiscal Year-end: 12/31/23
Electronic Instruments & Electrome-
chanical Devices Mfr
N.A.I.C.S.: 335312
Dalip M. Puri *(CFO & Exec VP)*
David A. Zapico *(Chm & CEO)*
Tony J. Ciampitti *(Pres-Electronic In-
struments)*
Ronald J. Oscher *(Chief Admin Offi-
cer)*
Emanuela Speranza *(Chief Comml
Officer)*
David F. Hermance *(Pres-
Electromechanical Grp)*

Subsidiaries:

AMETEK Aegis, Inc. **(1)**
50 Welby Rd, New Bedford, MA 02745
Tel.: (508) 998-3141
Web Site: https://www.ametekaegis.com
Metal Seal Mfr & Distr
N.A.I.C.S.: 332322

**AMETEK Airtechnology Group
Ltd.** **(1)**
111 Windmill Road, Sunbury-on-Thames,
TW16 7EF, Middlesex, United Kingdom
Tel.: (44) 193 276 5822
Web Site: https://www.ametek-
airtechnology.com
Emp.: 300

Electronic instruments & Electromechanical
Components Mfr
N.A.I.C.S.: 334514

AMETEK CTS Europe GmbH **(1)**
Lunener Strasse 211, 59174, Kamen, Ger-
many
Tel.: (49) 2307260700
Power Amplifier Mfr & Distr
N.A.I.C.S.: 335999

AMETEK Canada, LLC **(1)**
5309 Forest Hill Dr, Mississauga, L5M 5B8,
ON, Canada
Tel.: (905) 813-0885
Wiring Device Mfr
N.A.I.C.S.: 335932

AMETEK Denmark **(1)**
Gydevang 32, 3450, Allerod,
Denmark **(100%)**
Tel.: (45) 48168000
Web Site: http://www.ametek.dk
Sales Range: $10-24.9 Million
Mfr of Temperature Calibration
Equipment/Jofra Temperature Calibrators
N.A.I.C.S.: 334515

**AMETEK Electromechanical
Group** **(1)**
1100 Cassatt Rd, Berwyn, PA 19312
Tel.: (610) 647-2121
Web Site: http://www.ametek.com
Electrical Interconnect System & Motor
Component Mfr
N.A.I.C.S.: 335312
Dave Hermance *(Pres)*

Division (Domestic):

**AMETEK Floorcare Specialty Motors
Division** **(2)**
627 Lake St, Kent, OH 44240
Tel.: (330) 673-3786
Web Site: http://www.gselectric.com
Sales Range: $250-299.9 Million
Specialty Motor Mfr
N.A.I.C.S.: 335312

Subsidiary (Domestic):

AMETEK Hughes-Treitler **(2)**
300 Endo Blvd, Garden City, NY 11530
Tel.: (516) 832-8811
Web Site: https://www.hughes-treitler.com
Heat Transfer Equipment Mfr
N.A.I.C.S.: 333415

Division (Domestic):

AMETEK Lamb Electric Division **(2)**
100 E Erie St, Kent, OH 44240
Tel.: (330) 673-3452
Web Site: https://www.ametekdfs.com
Sales Range: $50-74.9 Million
Electric Motors & Blowers Mfr
N.A.I.C.S.: 335312

**AMETEK Specialty Metal Products
Division** **(2)**
21 Toelles Rd, Wallingford, CT 06492-4449
Tel.: (610) 489-5260
Web Site: https://www.ametek-ct.com
Sales Range: $50-74.9 Million
Mfr of High Purity Metals & Alloys in Pow-
dered & Strip Form for Use In Electronics &
Metal Fabrication
N.A.I.C.S.: 335312

Unit (Domestic):

Coining, Inc. **(2)**
15 Mercedes Dr, Montvale, NJ 07645
Tel.: (201) 791-4020
Web Site: https://www.ametek-coining.com
Bonding Wire & Brazing & Soldering Pre-
form Mfr
N.A.I.C.S.: 332119

Subsidiary (Domestic):

HCC Industries International **(2)**
4232 Temple City Blvd, Rosemead, CA
91770-1552
Tel.: (626) 443-8933
Web Site: http://www.hccindustries.com
Hermetic Seals & Connectors Mfr
N.A.I.C.S.: 334419

Subsidiary (Domestic):

AMETEK Ceramics, Inc. **(3)**

4501 N Arden Dr, El Monte, CA 91731
Tel.: (626) 258-3600
Electronic Instruments & Electromechanical
Components Mfr
N.A.I.C.S.: 334514

Glasseal Products **(3)**
485 Oberlin Ave S, Lakewood, NJ 08701-
0978
Tel.: (732) 370-9100
Web Site: http://www.glasseal.com
Sales Range: $50-74.9 Million
Glass to Metal Seals Mfr
N.A.I.C.S.: 339991

Subsidiary (Domestic):

Sealtron Acquisition Corp. **(4)**
9705 Reading Rd, Cincinnati, OH 45215
Tel.: (513) 733-8400
Web Site: http://www.ametek.com
Sales Range: $25-49.9 Million
Electronic instruments & Electromechanical
Components Mfr
N.A.I.C.S.: 334514

Sealtron Inc. **(4)**
9705 Reading Rd, Cincinnati, OH 45215
Tel.: (513) 733-8400
Web Site: https://www.sealtron.com
Sales Range: $10-24.9 Million
Hermetically Sealed Connectors Mfr
N.A.I.C.S.: 334417

Subsidiary (Domestic):

HCC Aegis Inc. **(3)**
50 Welby Rd, New Bedford, MA 02745
Tel.: (508) 998-3141
Web Site: http://www.hccindustries.com
Sales Range: $75-99.9 Million
Electronics Instrument Mfr
N.A.I.C.S.: 334419

HCC Industries International **(3)**
4232 Temple City Blvd, Rosemead, CA
91770
Tel.: (626) 443-8933
Electronic instruments & Electromechanical
Components Mfr
N.A.I.C.S.: 334419

Hermetic Seal **(3)**
4232 Temple City Blvd, Rosemead, CA
91770-1552
Tel.: (626) 443-8931
Web Site: https://www.hermeticseal.com
Sales Range: $50-74.9 Million
Emp.: 200
Hermetic Sub-Miniature Rectangular Con-
nectors Mfr
N.A.I.C.S.: 334419

Sealtron Inc. **(3)**
9705 Reading Rd, Cincinnati, OH 45215
Tel.: (513) 733-8400
Web Site: http://www.sealtron.com
Sales Range: $25-49.9 Million
Emp.: 150
Hermetic Sub-Miniature Rectangular Con-
nectors Mfr
N.A.I.C.S.: 334417

Subsidiary (Domestic):

Hamilton Precision Metals, Inc. **(2)**
1780 Rohrerstown Rd, Lancaster, PA 17601
Tel.: (610) 489-5260
Web Site: http://www.hpmetals.com
Sales Range: $25-49.9 Million
Metal Strips & Foils Mfr
N.A.I.C.S.: 331221
Robert Crawford *(Mgr-Bus Dev)*

**Haydon Kerk Motion Solutions, Inc.-
Haydon Products Division** **(2)**
1500 Meriden Rd, Waterbury, CT 06705
Tel.: (203) 756-7441
Web Site: http://www.haydonkerk.com
Sales Range: $25-49.9 Million
Electric Motors, Actuators & Switch Compo-
nents Mfr
N.A.I.C.S.: 335999
Hal Zimmermann *(Pres)*

Subsidiary (Domestic):

**Haydon Kerk Motion Solutions, Inc.-
Kerk Products Division** **(3)**
56 Meadowbrook Dr, Milford, NH 03055
Tel.: (603) 213-6290

Web Site: http://www.haydonkerk.com
Sales Range: $25-49.9 Million
Motion Control Parts
N.A.I.C.S.: 334513

Subsidiary (Domestic):

Pacific Design Technologies, Inc. **(2)**
59 S La Patera Ln, Goleta, CA 93117
Tel.: (805) 961-9110
Web Site: https://www.pd-tech.com
Search, Detection, Navigation, Guidance,
Aeronautical & Nautical System & Instru-
ment Mfr
N.A.I.C.S.: 334511
Mike Brown *(VP-)*

Pittman **(2)**
343 Godshall Dr, Harleysville, PA 19438
Tel.: (215) 256-6601
Web Site: http://www.ametek.com
Electric Motor Mfr
N.A.I.C.S.: 335312

Reichert, Inc. **(2)**
3362 Walden Ave Ste 100, Depew, NY
14043
Tel.: (716) 686-4500
Web Site: https://www.reichert.com
Sales Range: $50-74.9 Million
Opthalmic & Analytical Refractometer In-
struments Mfr
N.A.I.C.S.: 333310

Division (Domestic):

Reichert Microscope Services **(3)**
3362 Walden Ave, Depew, NY
14043 **(100%)**
Tel.: (716) 686-3166
Web Site: http://www.reichertms.com
Sales Range: $50-74.9 Million
Emp.: 120
Microscope Equipment & Parts Retailer
N.A.I.C.S.: 423490

Subsidiary (Domestic):

Superior Tube Company Inc. **(2)**
3900 Germantown Pike, Collegeville, PA
19426-3112
Tel.: (610) 489-5200
Web Site: https://www.superiortube.com
Small Metal Tubing Mfr
N.A.I.C.S.: 331210
Dirk Fanning *(Reg Sls Mgr-Western US)*
Devyn Reese *(Sls Mgr-Inside)*

**AMETEK Electronic Instruments
Group** **(1)**
1100 Cassatt Rd, Berwyn, PA 19312
Tel.: (610) 647-2121
Web Site: https://www.ametek.com
Sales Range: $1-4.9 Billion
Emp.: 15,000
Aerospace & Industrial Testing, Monitoring
& Calibration Equipment Mfr
N.A.I.C.S.: 334513
John W. Hardin *(Pres)*
David A. Zapico *(CEO)*
William J. Burke *(CFO)*
Ronald J. Oscher *(Chief Admin Officer)*
Emanuela Speranza *(Chief Comml Officer)*

Division (Domestic):

**AMETEK Aerospace & Defense
Division** **(2)**
60 Fordham Rd, Wilmington, MA
01887-2177 **(100%)**
Tel.: (978) 988-4101
Web Site: http://www.aapi.com
Sales Range: $150-199.9 Million
Emp.: 550
Designer & Developer of Aircraft & Propul-
sion Subsystems, Turbine Engine Sensors,
Electronics & Cockpit Instrumentation
N.A.I.C.S.: 334511

Subsidiary (Non-US):

AEM Limited **(3)**
Taylor's End Stansted Airport, Stansted,
CM24 1RB, Essex, United Kingdom
Tel.: (44) 1279680030
Web Site: https://www.aem.co.uk

Sales Range: $50-74.9 Million
Emp.: 70
Aircraft Component Repair & Overhaul Service
N.A.I.C.S.: 811210

Subsidiary (Domestic):

AMETEK Advanced Industries, Inc. (3)
4550 S Southeast Blvd, Wichita, KS 67210-1623
Tel.: (316) 522-0424
Web Site: https://www.mtek.com
Industrial Product Whslr
N.A.I.C.S.: 423830

AMETEK Aircraft Parts & Accessories, Inc. (3)
1414 S Mosley St, Wichita, KS 67211
Tel.: (316) 264-2397
Web Site: http://www.bsaircraft.com
Sales Range: $25-49.9 Million
Emp.: 50
Aircraft Repair & Maintenance Services
N.A.I.C.S.: 488190

AMETEK Ameron, LLC (3)
4750 Littlejohn St, Baldwin Park, CA 91706
Tel.: (626) 337-4640
Web Site: http://www.ameronglobal.com
Rev.: $11,500,000
Emp.: 12
Aircraft/Aerospace Flight Instruments & Guidance Systems
N.A.I.C.S.: 334511

Unit (Domestic):

Mass Systems Ameron Global, Inc. (4)
4601 Littlejohn St, Baldwin Park, CA 91706
Tel.: (626) 337-4640
Web Site: http://ameronglobal.com
Sales Range: $25-49.9 Million
Aviation Equipment Mfr
N.A.I.C.S.: 336413

Subsidiary (Domestic):

AMETEK HSA, Inc. (3)
7841 NW 56th St, Miami, FL 33166
Tel.: (305) 599-8855
Electronic instruments & Electromechanical Components Mfr
N.A.I.C.S.: 334514

AMETEK MRO Florida, Inc. (3)
7370 NW 35th St, Miami, FL 33122 (100%)
Tel.: (305) 640-0265
Web Site: http://www.ametekmroflorida.com
Aircraft Repair & Maintenance Services
N.A.I.C.S.: 488190

AMETEK Rotron (3)
55 Hasbrouck Ln, Woodstock, NY 12498
Tel.: (845) 679-2401
Web Site: http://www.ametekaerodefense.com
Sales Range: $100-124.9 Million
Emp.: 250
Cooling Equipment Mfr
N.A.I.C.S.: 333413

Unit (Domestic):

AMETEK Rotron - El Cajon (4)
474 Raleigh Ave, El Cajon, CA 92020
Tel.: (619) 593-7400
Web Site: http://www.rotron.com
Sales Range: $10-24.9 Million
Emp.: 15
Mfr of Heat Exchangers & Air Movers for Cooling Electronic Systems, Primarily for Military Applications
N.A.I.C.S.: 333413

Subsidiary (Non-US):

Airscrew Limited (3)
111 Windmill Road, Sunbury-on-Thames, TW16 7EF, Middlesex, United Kingdom (100%)
Tel.: (44) 1932765822
Web Site: http://www.ametek.co.uk
Sales Range: $75-99.9 Million
Emp.: 150
Axial Flow Fans Mfr
N.A.I.C.S.: 336411

Subsidiary (Domestic):

Drake Air, Inc. (3)
4085 Southwest Blvd, Tulsa, OK 74107
Tel.: (918) 445-3500
Web Site: https://www.drakeair.com
Sales Range: $25-49.9 Million
Emp.: 60
Aircraft Repair & Maintenance Services
N.A.I.C.S.: 488190

Subsidiary (Non-US):

Muirhead Aerospace (3)
33 Oakfield Road, Penge, London, SE20 8EW, United Kingdom
Tel.: (44) 2086599090
Web Site: https://www.ametek.co.uk
Sales Range: $50-74.9 Million
Emp.: 100
Electric Motors & Generators Mfr
N.A.I.C.S.: 335312

Subsidiary (Domestic):

Southern Aero Partners, Inc. (3)
4085 SW Blvd, Tulsa, OK 74107
Tel.: (918) 437-7676
Web Site: http://www.southernaeroparts.com
Sales Range: $25-49.9 Million
Emp.: 100
Industrial Product Whslr
N.A.I.C.S.: 488210

Southern Aeroparts, Inc. (3)
4085 SW Blvd, Tulsa, OK 74107
Tel.: (918) 437-7676
Web Site: http://www.southernaeroparts.com
Sales Range: $25-49.9 Million
Emp.: 80
Aircraft Repair & Maintenance Services
N.A.I.C.S.: 488190

Unit (Domestic):

AMETEK Automation & Process Technologies (2)
1080 N Crooks Rd, Clawson, MI 48017 (100%)
Tel.: (248) 435-0700
Web Site: http://www.ametekapt.com
Sales Range: $10-24.9 Million
Emp.: 15
Mfr of Position Sensors, Programmable Limit Switches, Linear Displacement Transducers, Rotary Encoders & Point Level & Continuous Level Measurement Devices
N.A.I.C.S.: 335314

AMETEK Chemical Products (2)
455 Corporate Blvd, Newark, DE 19702-3331 (100%)
Tel.: (302) 456-4400
Web Site: http://www.ametekfpp.com
Sales Range: $25-49.9 Million
Emp.: 2
Corrosion Resistant Fluoropolymer Heat Exchangers, Fluoropolymer Tubing & Refractory Filters
N.A.I.C.S.: 325998

Division (Domestic):

AMETEK Measurement & Calibration Technologies (2)
8600 Somerset Dr, Largo, FL 33773
Tel.: (727) 538-6000
Web Site: http://www.ametek.com
Sensors & Sensor-Based Instruments & Calibration Systems Mfr
N.A.I.C.S.: 334519

Subsidiary (Domestic):

AMETEK Chatillon Force Measurement Products (3)
8600 Somerset Dr, Largo, FL 33773 (100%)
Tel.: (727) 538-6000
Web Site: http://www.chatillon.com
Sales Range: $25-49.9 Million
Emp.: 75
Mfr of Scientific Equipment
N.A.I.C.S.: 333998

AMETEK Drexelbrook (3)
205 Keith Vly Rd, Horsham, PA 19044
Tel.: (215) 674-1234

Web Site: http://www.drexelbrook.com
Sales Range: $25-49.9 Million
Emp.: 80
Mfr of Process Control Instruments
N.A.I.C.S.: 334513

Atlas Material Testing Technology LLC (3)
1500 Bishop Ct, Mount Prospect, IL 60056
Tel.: (773) 327-4520
Web Site: https://www.atlas-mts.com
Sales Range: $50-74.9 Million
Emp.: 200
Artificial Weathering Chambers, Flammability Chambers, Polymer Evaluation Products & Textile Testing Instruments
N.A.I.C.S.: 541990

Subsidiary (Non-US):

Atlas Material Testing Technology GmbH (4)
Vogelsbergstrasse 22, Altenhasslau, 63589, Linsengericht, Germany
Tel.: (49) 6051707140
Web Site: https://www.atlas-mts.com
Sales Range: $25-49.9 Million
Designer & Mfr of Testing Instruments & Testing Solutions for Products
N.A.I.C.S.: 541380
Jorn Jahnke (Mng Dir)
Wiebke Rumpf (Mng Dir)

Subsidiary (Domestic):

Atlas Weathering DSET Laboratories (4)
45601 N 47th Ave, Phoenix, AZ 85087-7042
Tel.: (623) 465-7356
Web Site: http://www.atlas-mts.com
Sales Range: $25-49.9 Million
Emp.: 30
Materials Durability Testing Services
N.A.I.C.S.: 541380

Subsidiary (Domestic):

Crystal Engineering Corporation (3)
708 Fiero Ln Ste 9, San Luis Obispo, CA 93401
Tel.: (805) 595-5477
Web Site: https://www.ametek.com
Sales Range: $25-49.9 Million
Emp.: 25
Digital Pressure Gauge & Calibrator Mfr
N.A.I.C.S.: 334519

Subsidiary (Non-US):

Lloyd Materials Testing (3)
Steyning Way, Bognor Regis, PO22 9ST, West Sussex, United Kingdom (100%)
Tel.: (44) 1243833389
Web Site: http://www.ametektest.com
Sales Range: $25-49.9 Million
Emp.: 15
Mfr of Machines for Tensile Compression & Flexural Testing
N.A.I.C.S.: 333998

Subsidiary (Domestic):

Newage Testing Instruments, Inc. (3)
8600 Somerset Dr, Largo, FL 33773
Tel.: (727) 538-6127
Web Site: http://www.hardnesstesters.com
Sales Range: $10-24.9 Million
Hardness Testers Mfr
N.A.I.C.S.: 334519

Unit (Domestic):

AMETEK Panalarm Products (2)
1725 Western Dr, West Chicago, IL 60185-1880
Tel.: (630) 231-5900
Web Site: http://www.panalarm.com
Sales Range: $75-99.9 Million
Emp.: 9
Monitoring Products Mfr
N.A.I.C.S.: 423690

AMETEK Power Instruments (2)
255 N Union St, Rochester, NY 14605
Tel.: (585) 263-7700
Web Site: http://www.ametekpower.com
Electric Power Generation Sensor, Instrument & Monitoring Systems Mfr
N.A.I.C.S.: 334513

AMETEK Precision Motion Control - Rotron/Nautilair Blowers (2)
75 North St, Saugerties, NY 12477
Tel.: (845) 246-3401
Web Site: http://www.ametek.com
Sales Range: $100-124.9 Million
Emp.: 250
Air Purification Equipment Mfr
N.A.I.C.S.: 333413

Division (Domestic):

AMETEK Process & Analytical Instruments Division (2)
150 Freeport Rd, Pittsburgh, PA 15238
Tel.: (412) 828-9040
Web Site: https://www.ametekpi.com
Sales Range: $50-74.9 Million
Emp.: 100
Supplies Merchant Whslr
N.A.I.C.S.: 423490
Frank Donnelly (CFO)

Subsidiary (Non-US):

AMETEK Solartron ISA (3)
Hackworth Industrial Park, Shildon, DL4 1LH, United Kingdom
Tel.: (44) 1388773065
Web Site: https://www.solartronisa.com
Sales Range: $10-24.9 Million
Emp.: 65
Temperature Measurement Products Mfr
N.A.I.C.S.: 334513
Alan Downing (Dir-Sls)

CAMECA S.A.S. (3)
29 quai des Gresillons, 92230, Gennevilliers, Cedex, France
Tel.: (33) 143346200
Web Site: http://www.cameca.com
Sales Range: $50-74.9 Million
Scientific Instrument Mfr
N.A.I.C.S.: 334516

Subsidiary (Non-US):

CAMECA GmbH (4)
Edisonstr 3, Unterschleissheim, 85716, Munich, Germany
Tel.: (49) 893158910
Web Site: http://www.cameca.com
Emp.: 9
Metrology Services
N.A.I.C.S.: 541715

Subsidiary (US):

CAMECA Instruments, Inc. (4)
5470 Nobel Dr, Madison, WI 53711
Tel.: (608) 274-6880
Web Site: http://www.cameca.com
Sales Range: $25-49.9 Million
Analytical Instrument Mfr
N.A.I.C.S.: 334516

Subsidiary (Non-US):

CAMECA Taiwan Corp. Ltd. (4)
A2 10F-65 No 120 Sector 2 GongDaoWu Rd, Hsin-chu, 30072, Taiwan
Tel.: (886) 35750099
Web Site: http://www.cameca.com
Semiconductor Mfr
N.A.I.C.S.: 334413

Subsidiary (Domestic):

Chandler Engineering Company LLC (3)
2001 N Indianwood Ave, Broken Arrow, OK 74012-1163
Tel.: (918) 250-7200
Web Site: https://www.chandlereng.com
Sales Range: $100-124.9 Million
Emp.: 100
Industrial Instrument Mfr
N.A.I.C.S.: 334513
Robert MacLeod (Mgr-Bus Dev)

EDAX (3)
91 McKee Dr, Mahwah, NJ 07430-2105
Tel.: (201) 529-4880
Web Site: http://www.edax.com
Sales Range: $25-49.9 Million
Emp.: 100
Mfr of X-Ray Flourescent Analyzers
N.A.I.C.S.: 334516

AMETEK, Inc.—(Continued)

Subsidiary (Non-US):

Land Instruments International   (3)
Stubley Lane, Dronfield, S18 1DJ, United Kingdom
Tel.: (44) 1246417691
Web Site: http://www.ametek-land.com
Sales Range: $25-49.9 Million
Industrial Instrument Mfr
N.A.I.C.S.: 334513
Justin Smith *(Mng Dir)*
Phil Doyle *(Dir-Customer Svc)*
Peter Drogmoller *(Dir-Innovation & Tech)*
Colin Mearns *(Dir-Fin)*
Alan Tarry *(Dir-Ops)*
David Primhak *(Dir-Dev & Product Mgmt)*
Peter Unwin *(Mgr-Global Industry-Metals)*
Philippe Kerbois *(Mgr-Global Industry-Glass)*
James Cross *(Mgr-Global Industry)*
Manfred Hayk *(Mgr-Global Infrared Product)*
Derek Stuart *(Mgr-Global Product-Power, Combustion & Environmental)*

Subsidiary (US):

AMETEK Land, Inc.   (4)
150 Freeport Rd, Pittsburgh, PA 15238
Tel.: (412) 826-4444
Web Site: http://www.ametek-land.com
Sales Range: $10-24.9 Million
Temperature Measuring Instruments Mfr
N.A.I.C.S.: 334513

Subsidiary (Domestic):

Nu Instruments Limited   (4)
Unit 74 - Clywedog Road South, Wrexham, LL13 9XS, United Kingdom
Tel.: (44) 1978661304
Web Site: https://www.nu-ins.com
Mass Spectrometer Mfr
N.A.I.C.S.: 334516

Subsidiary (Non-US):

SPECTRO Analytical Instruments GmbH   (3)
Böschstr 10, 47533, Kleve, Germany
Tel.: (49) 28218920
Web Site: https://www.spectro.com
Emp.: 600
Scientific Instrument Mfr
N.A.I.C.S.: 334516
Michael Privik *(Mng Dir)*
Wiebke Rumpf *(Mng Dir)*

Subsidiary (Non-US):

SPECTRO Analytical Instruments (Asia-Pacific) Ltd.   (4)
Unit 1603 16/F Tower III Enterprise Square No 9 Sheung Yuet Road, Kowloon, Hong Kong, China (Hong Kong)
Tel.: (852) 29769162
Electronic Instrument & Electromechanical Device Mfr
N.A.I.C.S.: 334513

Subsidiary (US):

Spectro Analytical Instruments Inc.   (4)
91 McKee Dr, Mahwah, NJ 07430
Tel.: (201) 642-3000
Web Site: http://www.spectro.com
Sales Range: $10-24.9 Million
Emp.: 35
Electronics Instrument Mfr
N.A.I.C.S.: 334419

Subsidiary (Non-US):

Solartron Metrology Ltd.   (3)
Steyning Way, Bognor Regis, PO22 9ST, West Sussex, United Kingdom
Tel.: (44) 1243833333
Web Site: https://www.solartronmetrology.com
Sales Range: $10-24.9 Million
Measurement & Control Equipment Mfr
N.A.I.C.S.: 334519

Taylor Hobson Holdings Ltd.   (3)
2 New Star Rd, PO Box 36, Leicester, LE4 9JQ, United Kingdom
Tel.: (44) 1162763771
Web Site: https://www.taylor-hobson.com

Sales Range: $25-49.9 Million
Mfr of Form & Surface Measurement Devices
N.A.I.C.S.: 334519

Subsidiary (US):

Precitech, Inc.   (4)
44 Black Brook Rd, Keene, NH 03431
Tel.: (603) 357-2511
Web Site: https://www.precitech.com
Design & Manufacture Ultra Precision Machine & Metrology Systems For Global Markets; Mfr of Standard Customized Air Bearing Components & Modular Geometry & Metology Systems
N.A.I.C.S.: 332216

Subsidiary (Domestic):

Vision Research, Inc.   (3)
100 Dey Rd, Wayne, NJ 07470
Tel.: (973) 696-4500
Web Site: https://www.phantomhighspeed.com
Sales Range: $25-49.9 Million
High-Speed Digital Imaging System Mfr
N.A.I.C.S.: 333310

Subsidiary (Domestic):

AMETEK Programmable Power, Inc.   (2)
9250 Brown Deer Rd, San Diego, CA 92121-2267
Tel.: (858) 450-0085
Web Site: https://www.programmablepower.com
Sales Range: $50-74.9 Million
Programmable Power Supply System Developer & Mfr
N.A.I.C.S.: 334220

Subsidiary (Domestic):

California Instruments Corporation   (3)
9250 Brown Deer Rd, San Diego, CA 92121-2267
Tel.: (858) 677-9040
Web Site: http://www.calinst.com
Sales Range: $10-24.9 Million
Emp.: 85
AC & DC Power Sources Mfr & Supplier
N.A.I.C.S.: 334515

Unit (Domestic):

AMETEK Solid State Controls   (2)
875 Dearborn Dr, Columbus, OH 43085   **(100%)**
Tel.: (614) 846-7500
Web Site: http://www.solidstatecontrolsinc.com
Rev.: $37,338,000
Emp.: 200
Provider of Electrical Industrial Apparatus
N.A.I.C.S.: 335999

AMETEK U.S. Gauge   (2)
205 Keith Valley Rd, Horsham, PA 19044
Tel.: (215) 674-1234
Web Site: https://www.ametekusg.com
Sales Range: $25-49.9 Million
Emp.: 60
Industrial Gauges Mfr
N.A.I.C.S.: 335312

AMETEK Vehicular Infstrumentation Systems   (2)
287 27 Rd, Grand Junction, CO 81503   **(100%)**
Tel.: (970) 242-8863
Web Site: http://www.ametekvis.com
Sales Range: $25-49.9 Million
Emp.: 60
Measuring & Controlling Devices
N.A.I.C.S.: 335312

Division (Domestic):

Advanced Measurement Technology, Inc.   (2)
801 S Illinois Ave, Oak Ridge, TN 37830
Tel.: (865) 388-4573
Measurement Technology Mfr
N.A.I.C.S.: 334519

Subsidiary (Non-US):

Solartron Analytical   (3)

5 Ashville Way Molly Millars Lane, Southwood Business Park, Wokingham, RG41 2PL, Hampshire, United Kingdom
Tel.: (44) 1252556800
Web Site: http://www.solartronanalytical.com
Sales Range: $10-24.9 Million
Emp.: 35
Measuring Instrumentation & Software Mfr
N.A.I.C.S.: 334513

Subsidiary (Non-US):

Sunpower, Inc.   (3)
2005 E State St Ste 104, Athens, OH 45701-2125
Tel.: (740) 594-2221
Web Site: https://www.sunpowerinc.com
Sales Range: $25-49.9 Million
Engine Equipment Mfr
N.A.I.C.S.: 333618

Subsidiary (Domestic):

Controls Southeast Inc.   (2)
12201 Nations Ford Rd, Pineville, NC 28134
Tel.: (704) 644-5000
Web Site: https://www.csiheat.com
Sales Range: $50-74.9 Million
Piping Systems Mfr & Engineering Services
N.A.I.C.S.: 332996

Micro-Poise Measurement Systems, LLC   (2)
555 Mondial Pkwy, Streetsboro, OH 44241-4510
Tel.: (330) 541-9100
Web Site: https://www.micropoise.com
Sales Range: $125-149.9 Million
Precision Measurement & Inspection Systems for Tire & Automobile Industries
N.A.I.C.S.: 333248

Division (Domestic):

MP Balance Engineering   (3)
1731 Thorncroft Dr, Troy, MI 48084   **(100%)**
Tel.: (248) 643-2800
Web Site: http://www.balanceengineering.com
Sales Range: $25-49.9 Million
Emp.: 75
Industrial Balancing Machines Mfr
N.A.I.C.S.: 333248

Subsidiary (Non-US):

Micro-Poise Industrial Equipment (Beijing) Co., Ltd   (3)
Rising International Industrial Park #1 Building 29 Jinghai 3rd R, Beijing, 100023, China
Tel.: (00) 10 0709 2171
Precision Measurement & Inspection Systems for Tire & Automobile Industries
N.A.I.C.S.: 333248

MicroPoise Measurement Systems Europe GmbH   (3)
Kruppstr 10, 23560, Lubeck, Germany
Tel.: (49) 451890960
Web Site: https://www.micropoise.com
Emp.: 50
Precision Measurement & Inspection Systems for Tire & Automobile Industries
N.A.I.C.S.: 333248
Emanuela Speranza *(Mng Dir)*

Subsidiary (Domestic):

O'Brien Corporation   (2)
1900 Crystal Industrial Ct, Saint Louis, MO 63114
Tel.: (314) 236-2020
Web Site: http://www.obcorp.com
Sales Range: $75-99.9 Million
Emp.: 180
Insulated Tubing & Heat Enclosures Mfr
N.A.I.C.S.: 335932

Subsidiary (Domestic):

Cardinal UHP LLC   (3)
1900 Crystal Industrial Ct, Saint Louis, MO 63114-6020
Tel.: (314) 236-2020
Web Site: https://www.cardinaluhp.com
Emp.: 20
Tubing & Fitting Components Mfr

N.A.I.C.S.: 331210

Universal Analyzers Inc.   (3)
5200 Convair Dr, Carson City, NV 89706
Tel.: (775) 883-2500
Web Site: https://www.universalanalyzers.com
Laboratory Equipment Mfr
N.A.I.C.S.: 334516

Subsidiary (Domestic):

Barben Analyzer Technology, LLC   (4)
5200 Convair Dr, Carson City, NV 89706
Tel.: (755) 883-2500
Electronic Instrument & Electromechanical Device Mfr
N.A.I.C.S.: 334513
Melvin Thweatt *(VP-Sls)*
Steve Hammond *(Product Mgr)*
Jamie Biederman *(Acct Mgr-Inside Sls)*

Subsidiary (Domestic):

Powervar Inc.   (2)
1450 S Lakeside Dr, Waukegan, IL 60085
Tel.: (847) 596-7000
Web Site: https://www.powervar.com
Sales Range: $50-74.9 Million
Emp.: 100
Mfr of Electronic Generation Equipment
N.A.I.C.S.: 335999

Subsidiary (Non-US):

Powervar Canada Inc.   (3)
700 Finley Ave Unit 4, Ajax, L1S 3Z2, ON, Canada
Tel.: (905) 239-9284
Web Site: http://www.powervar.com
Emp.: 1
Electronic Instrument & Electromechanical Device Mfr
N.A.I.C.S.: 334513

Division (Non-US):

Powervar, Ltd.   (3)
Unit 5 Birch Kembrey Pk Swindon, Swindon, SN2 8UU, United Kingdom   **(100%)**
Tel.: (44) 1793553980
Web Site: http://www.powervar.com
Sales Range: $10-24.9 Million
Emp.: 9
Mfr of Industrial Products
N.A.I.C.S.: 334513

Subsidiary (Non-US):

Powervar Deutschland GmbH   (4)
Melkweg 16, 33106, Paderborn, Germany
Tel.: (49) 52513906364
Electronic Instrument & Electromechanical Device Mfr
N.A.I.C.S.: 334513
Werner Karau *(Country Mgr)*

Subsidiary (Domestic):

Rauland-Borg Corporation   (2)
1802 W Central Ave, Mount Prospect, IL 60056
Tel.: (847) 590-7100
Web Site: https://www.rauland.com
Communication Systems for Health Care, Education & Corrections Fields Designer & Mfr; Professional Sound Reinforcement Systems
N.A.I.C.S.: 334210

Subsidiary (Domestic):

Biamp Systems, LLC   (3)
9300 SW Gemini Dr, Beaverton, OR 97008
Tel.: (503) 641-7287
Web Site: https://www.biamp.com
Networked Digital Audio & Video, Networked Public Address & Voice Evacuation & Distance Conferencing
N.A.I.C.S.: 334310
Alex Buchanan-Munro *(CFO & VP)*
Rashid Skat *(Chm, Pres & CEO)*
Joe Andrulis *(Exec VP-Corp Dev)*

Subsidiary (Domestic):

Cambridge Sound Management Inc.   (4)
404 Wyman St Ste 200, Waltham, MA 02451

Tel.: (617) 349-3779
Web Site: http://www.cambridgesound.com
Rev.: $1,900,000
Emp.: 11
Music & Sound Masking Technology
N.A.I.C.S.: 541990

Subsidiary (Domestic):

Dynasound, Inc. (5)
6439 Atlantic Blvd, Norcross, GA 30071
Tel.: (770) 242-8176
Web Site: http://www.soundmasking.com
Rev.: $1,800,000
Emp.: 19
All Other Miscellaneous Electrical Equipment & Component Mfr
N.A.I.C.S.: 335999

Subsidiary (Domestic):

Rauland-Borg Corporation of Florida (3)
620 Douglas Ave Ste 1316, Altamonte Springs, FL 32714 (100%)
Tel.: (407) 830-6175
Web Site: http://www.rauland-fl.com
Waste Water Treatment Services
N.A.I.C.S.: 221320
Nardo Bosque (Pres & CEO)
Shawn Hunter (Dir-Tech & Engrg)
Clay Littleton (Dir-Sls & Mktg)
Isaac Molina (Reg Mgr-West)
Gary Ward (Reg Mgr-South)
Ariane Ortiz (Controller)
Jamie Ball (Gen Mgr-Ft. Myers-West)
Cody Lee Hebner (Mgr-Tech Integration)
David Woodby (Engr-Project Tech-North & Central)
Alan Hancock (Engr-Product Tech-North & Central)
Al Prince (Engr-Product Tech-South)
Jessica Munro (Acct Mgr-North & Central)
Joanne Aczualdez (Acct Mgr-South)
Althea Beaton (Mgr-Svc Solution)
Brandon Ridinger (Mgr-Ops-North & Central)
Edwin Rivas (Mgr-Ops-West)
James Ross (Mgr-Education Div-West Reg)
Michael Taylor (Dir-Support Svcs)
James Harvey (Engr-Product Tech)
Breet Criscione (Engr-IT Project)
Sawyer Bartell (Engr-IT Project)
Bryan Bosque (Acct Mgr-South)
Ashley Strein (Acct Mgr-West)

Subsidiary (Non-US):

Teseq Holding AG (2)
Sternenhofstrasse 15, 4542, Reinach, Switzerland
Tel.: (41) 326814040
Web Site: http://www.teseq.com
Sales Range: $50-74.9 Million
Emp.: 250
Holding Company; EMC Emission & Immunity Testing Instrument & Systems Mfr & Distr
N.A.I.C.S.: 551112

Subsidiary (US):

Instruments for Industries, Inc. (3)
903 S 2nd St, Ronkonkoma, NY 11779
Tel.: (631) 467-8400
Web Site: http://www.ifi.com
RF Microwave Solid State & Traveling Wave Tube Amplifiers Designer & Mfr
N.A.I.C.S.: 334220

Subsidiary (Non-US):

Teseq (Taiwan) Ltd. (3)
3F-2 No 92 Baozhong Road, Xindian District, New Taipei City, 00231, Taiwan
Tel.: (886) 229178080
Web Site: http://www.teseq.ch
Electronic Instrument & Electromechanical Device Mfr
N.A.I.C.S.: 334513

Subsidiary (Domestic):

Teseq AG (3)
Nordstrasse 11F, 4542, Luterbach, Switzerland
Tel.: (41) 326814040
Web Site: http://www.teseq.ch
Emp.: 50

EMC Emission & Immunity Testing Instrument & Systems Mfr & Distr
N.A.I.C.S.: 334419

Subsidiary (Non-US):

Teseq Company Ltd. (3)
Office1001 Sky Plaza No 46 Dongzhienwai Str, Beijing, 100027, China
Tel.: (86) 1084608080
Web Site: http://www.teseq.com.cn
Electronic Instrument & Electromechanical Device Mfr
N.A.I.C.S.: 334513

Teseq GmbH (3)
Lunener Strasse 211, 59174, Kamen, Germany
Tel.: (49) 2307260700
Electronic Instrument & Electromechanical Device Mfr
N.A.I.C.S.: 334513

Subsidiary (US):

Teseq Inc. (3)
52 Mayfield Ave, Edison, NJ 08837
Tel.: (732) 417-0501
Web Site: http://www.teseq.us
EMC Emission & Immunity Testing Instrument & Systems Distr
N.A.I.C.S.: 423690

Subsidiary (Non-US):

Teseq K.K. (3)
6F Nakameguro NK Bldg 2-10-5 Nakameguro Meguro, Meguro-ku, Tokyo, 153-0061, Japan
Tel.: (81) 3 5725 9460
Web Site: http://www.teseq.jp
EMC Emission & Immunity Testing Instrument & Systems Distr
N.A.I.C.S.: 423690

Unit (Domestic):

Westchester Plastics (2)
42 Mtn Ave, Nesquehoning, PA 18240
Tel.: (570) 645-6900
Web Site: http://www.ametek.com
Sales Range: $50-74.9 Million
Emp.: 180
Custom Coloring & Compounding of Elastomers, Engineering Resins & Thermoplastics
N.A.I.C.S.: 335312

Subsidiary (Domestic):

Zygo Corporation (2)
Laurel Brook Rd, Middlefield, CT 06455-1291
Tel.: (860) 347-8506
Web Site: https://www.zygo.com
Sales Range: $125-149.9 Million
Emp.: 300
Mfr of Metrology, Optical & System Solutions for Semiconductor, Telecommunications & Industrial Markets
N.A.I.C.S.: 333310

Branch (Domestic):

Zygo Corporation - Western Regional Office (3)
3350 Scott Blvd, Santa Clara, CA 95054
Tel.: (408) 434-1000
Web Site: http://www.zygo.com
Semiconductors Sales
N.A.I.C.S.: 423690

Unit (Domestic):

Zygo Electro-Optics Group Manufacturing Center (3)
2650 E Elvira Rd, Tucson, AZ 85756
Tel.: (520) 295-8900
Web Site: http://www.zygo.com
Electro-Optics Products Mfr
N.A.I.C.S.: 333310

Subsidiary (Non-US):

Zygo K.K. (3)
Ueno Sanwa Bldg 1-14-4 Higashiueno, 1-1-30 Shibadaimon Minato-ku, Tokyo, 110-0015, Japan (100%)
Tel.: (81) 358126051
Web Site: http://www.zygokk.co.jp
Emp.: 7
Electro-Optics Products Sales & Service

N.A.I.C.S.: 423690
Egashira Yoshiya (Gen Mgr)

Zygo Pte. Ltd. (3)
20 Changi Business Park Central 2 04-03/04, Singapore, 486031, Singapore
Tel.: (65) 64842388
Web Site: https://www.zygo.com
Electronics Instrument Mfr
N.A.I.C.S.: 334419

Subsidiary (Non-US):

ZygoLamda Metrology Instrument (Shanghai) Co., Ltd. (4)
Building 1 No 552 Lian Cao Road, Shanghai, 201108, China (66%)
Tel.: (86) 21 6434 6150
Electro-Optics Products Sales & Service
N.A.I.C.S.: 423690

Subsidiary (Domestic):

Zygo Richmond, Inc. (3)
3900 Lakeside Dr, Richmond, CA 94806
Tel.: (510) 222-2310
Web Site: https://www.zygo.com
Emp.: 90
Optical Component Mfr
N.A.I.C.S.: 333310

Subsidiary (Non-US):

Zygo Taiwan Co., Ltd. (3)
1F No 26 Chuangye Road, Tainan Science Park Xinshi District, T'ainan, 741, Taiwan
Tel.: (886) 65051339
Web Site: https://www.zygo.com.tw
Optical Components & Complex Electro Optical Systems Sales & Service
N.A.I.C.S.: 423690

ZygoLOT GmbH (3)
Rudolf Diesel Str 16, 64331, Weiterstadt, Germany
Tel.: (49) 61505437064
Web Site: https://www.zygo.de
Emp.: 17
Optical Components & Electro-Optical Systems Sales & Service
N.A.I.C.S.: 423690

AMETEK GmbH (1)
Rudolf Diesel Str 16, 40670, Meerbusch, Germany
Tel.: (49) 215991360
Web Site: http://www.ametek.de
Sales Range: $1-9.9 Million
Emp.: 80
Mfr of Motors
N.A.I.C.S.: 335312

Subsidiary (Non-US):

AMETEK Nordic AB (2)
Krossgatan 36, 162 50, Vallingby, Sweden
Tel.: (46) 851906031
Electronic instruments & Electromechanical Components Mfr
N.A.I.C.S.: 334419

Subsidiary (Domestic):

Creaform Deutschland GmbH (2)
Meisenweg 37, 70771, Leinfelden-Echterdingen, Germany
Tel.: (49) 71118568030
Web Site: http://www.creaform3d.com
Optical Measurement Technology Services
N.A.I.C.S.: 541715

AMETEK HDR Power Systems, Inc. (1)
530 Ste CLakeview Plz Blvd, Worthington, OH 43085
Tel.: (614) 308-5500
Web Site: https://www.hdrpower.com
Sales Range: $25-49.9 Million
Emp.: 25
Process Equipment & Component Mfr
N.A.I.C.S.: 335314

AMETEK Italia (1)
Via De Barzi, Robecco Sul Naviglio, 20087, Milan, Italy (100%)
Tel.: (39) 02946931
Web Site: http://www.ametek.it
Sales Range: $25-49.9 Million
Emp.: 100
Mfr of Small Diameter Motors
N.A.I.C.S.: 335312

AMETEK Lamb Motores de Mexico, S. de R.L. de C.V. (1)
AV Rio San Juan S/N Parque Industrial del Norte, Reynosa, 88730, Tamaulipas, Mexico
Tel.: (52) 9568434500
Web Site: https://www.ametekfsm.com
Drive & Vacuum Motors Mfr
N.A.I.C.S.: 336310

AMETEK Material Analysis Holdings GmbH (1)
Boschstr 10, Kleve, 47533, Germany
Tel.: (49) 28218920
Holding Company
N.A.I.C.S.: 551112

AMETEK Middle East FZE (1)
Jafza Liu Fzs1-BA03, PO Box 261454, Jebel Ali, Dubai, United Arab Emirates
Tel.: (971) 48806345
Engineeering Services
N.A.I.C.S.: 541330

AMETEK Motors (Shanghai) Co., Ltd. (1)
155 Puhui Road Jiuting Town Songjiang District, Shanghai, 201615, China
Tel.: (86) 2137632111
Web Site: http://www.ametek.com.cn
Sales Range: $100-124.9 Million
Emp.: 500
Electronic instruments & Electromechanical Components Mfr
N.A.I.C.S.: 334419

AMETEK S.r.l. (1)
Via della Liberazione 24, Robecco sul Vaviglio, 20068, Peschiera Borromeo, Italy
Tel.: (39) 02946931
Electronic instruments & Electromechanical Components Mfr
N.A.I.C.S.: 334514

AMETEK SCP, Inc. (1)
52 Airport Rd, Westerly, RI 02891
Tel.: (401) 596-6658
Web Site: https://www.ametekscp.com
Emp.: 68
Electronic instruments & Electromechanical Components Mfr
N.A.I.C.S.: 334514

AMETEK Thermal Systems, Inc (1)
300 Endo Blvd, Garden City, NY 11530-6708
Tel.: (516) 832-8811
Web Site: https://www.hughes-treitler.com
Emp.: 180
Heating Equipment Mfr
N.A.I.C.S.: 333415
Robert J. Vogel (Pres)

Abaco Systems Inc. (1)
Redstone Gateway SW Ste 200, Huntsville, AL 35808
Tel.: (256) 880-0444
Web Site: https://www.abaco.com
Aerospace & Defense Computer & Electronic Systems
N.A.I.C.S.: 541519
Bernie Anger (Pres)
Chris Lever (VP-Corporate Development)
Rich Sorelle (CEO)
William Read (CFO)
Ian McMurray (Mgr-Communications)
Christopher G. Cummins (COO)
John Muller (Chief Growth Officer)
Lorne Graves (CTO)

Subsidiary (Domestic):

4DSP LLC (2)
3101 Bee Caves Rd Ste 350, Austin, TX 78746
Web Site: https://www.4dsp.com
Sales Range: $50-74.9 Million
Emp.: 22
Electronic Communication Circuit Boards Mfr
N.A.I.C.S.: 334412

Abaco Systems Limited (1)
Tove Valley Business Park Old Tiffield Rd, Towcester, NN12 6PF, Northamptonshire, United Kingdom
Tel.: (44) 1327359444
Digital Electronic Component Mfr
N.A.I.C.S.: 334111

Alphasense Limited (1)

AMETEK, Inc.—(Continued)

Sensor Technology House 300 Avenue West Skyline 120, Great Notley, Braintree, CM77 7AA, Essex, United Kingdom
Tel.: (44) 1376556700
Web Site: https://www.alphasense.com
Electro Medical & Control Machinery Mfr
N.A.I.C.S.: 334510

Alphasense USA, Inc. (1)
24 Union Sq E 5th Fl, New York, NY 10003
Tel.: (646) 783-1995
Web Site: https://www.alpha-sense.com
Market Intelligence Services
N.A.I.C.S.: 541910

Amekai Meter (Xiamen) Co.,Ltd. (1)
1-2F Torch Hi-Tech, Innovate City, Xiamen, 361006, China
Tel.: (86) 5926030566
Web Site: https://www.amekai.com
Electronic instruments & Electromechanical Components Mfr
N.A.I.C.S.: 334514
David Chen (Mgr-Sales)

Amplifier Research Corp. (1)
160 Schoolhouse Rd, Souderton, PA 18964-9990
Tel.: (215) 723-8181
Web Site: https://www.arworld.us
Sales Range: $25-49.9 Million
Emp.: 130
Amplifiers
N.A.I.C.S.: 334220

Amptek, Inc. (1)
14 DeAngelo Dr, Bedford, MA 01730
Tel.: (781) 275-2242
Web Site: https://www.amptek.com
Electronics Instrument Mfr
N.A.I.C.S.: 334419

Avicenna Technology, Inc. (1)
1602 Benson Rd, Montevideo, MN 56265
Tel.: (612) 426-3555
Web Site: https://www.ametekmc.com
Medical Device Components Mfr
N.A.I.C.S.: 339999

**Bison Gear & Engineering
Corporation** (1)
3850 Ohio Ave, Saint Charles, IL 60174-5462
Tel.: (630) 377-4327
Web Site: https://www.bisongear.com
Rev.: $37,000,000
Emp.: 230
Mfr of Speed Changers Drives & Gears
N.A.I.C.S.: 333612
George Thomas (Sr VP-Ops)
Martin Swarbrick (Pres & COO)
Robert Armstrong (Mgr-IT & IS)
Clayton Hinkle (Reg Mgr-Sls)
Sylvia Wetzel (Chief Learning Officer)
Peter Mattio (Dir-Matls)
Nataly Dvoretsky (Engr-Design)
Ted Lat (Engr-Mfg)

**Brookfield Engineering Laboratories,
Inc.** (1)
11 Commerce Blvd, Middleboro, MA 02346
Tel.: (508) 946-6200
Web Site:
http://www.brookfieldengineering.com
Sales Range: $150-199.9 Million
Emp.: 165
Viscosity Measuring Instruments Mfr
N.A.I.C.S.: 334516

Subsidiary (Non-US):

AMETEK Germany GmbH (2)
Schutterwaelder Strasse 23, Ottendorf-Okrilla, 1458, Bautzen, Germany
Tel.: (49) 3520 559 670
Web Site: http://www.rheotec.de
Viscometer & Rheometer Mfr
N.A.I.C.S.: 334519

Brookfield Viscometers, Ltd. (2)
Brookfield Technical Centre, Stadium Way, Harlow, CM19 5GX, Essex, United Kingdom (100%)
Tel.: (44) 1279451774
Web Site:
https://www.brookfieldengineering.com
Sales Range: $10-24.9 Million
Emp.: 9

Meter Measurements for On-Line Process Control & Applications
N.A.I.C.S.: 334516

CARDINALUHP LLC (1)
1900 Crystal Industrial Ct, Saint Louis, MO 63114
Tel.: (314) 473-2145
Web Site: http://www.cardinaluhp.com
Electronics Instrument Mfr
N.A.I.C.S.: 334419

Crank Software ULC (1)
1000 Innovation Drive Suite 100, Ottawa, K2K 3E7, ON, Canada
Tel.: (613) 595-1999
Web Site: https://www.cranksoftware.com
Software Development Services
N.A.I.C.S.: 541511

Creaform Inc. (1)
4700 rue de la Pascaline, Levis, G6W 0L9, QC, Canada
Tel.: (418) 833-4446
Web Site: https://www.creaform3d.com
Sales Range: $10-24.9 Million
3D Digital Equipment & Solutions
N.A.I.C.S.: 334519
Martin Lamontagne (Founder)
Fanny Truchon (Pres & CEO)
Daniel Rivard (VP-Operations)
Pierre-Hugues Allard (VP-Sales)

Subsidiary (Non-US):

Creaform France S.A.S. (2)
24 Rue Jean-Pierre Timbaud, 88600, Fontaine, France
Tel.: (33) 457383150
Web Site: http://www.creaform3d.com
Electronic Instrument & Electromechanical Device Mfr
N.A.I.C.S.: 334513

Creaform Japan K.K. (2)
3F Shiba NBF Tower 1-1-30 Shibadaimon, Minatoku, Tokyo, 105-0012, Japan
Tel.: (81) 344002460
Optical Measurement Technology Services
N.A.I.C.S.: 541715

Creaform Shanghai Ltd. (2)
Part A1 A4 2/F Building No 1 No 526 Fute 3rd Road, East Pilot Free Trade Zone, Shanghai, 200131, China
Tel.: (86) 2160905288
Electronic Instrument & Electromechanical Device Mfr
N.A.I.C.S.: 334513

Creaform USA, Inc. (1)
2031 Main St, Irvine, CA 92614
Tel.: (302) 444-6696
Optical Measurement Technology Services
N.A.I.C.S.: 541715

Dansensor Espana, S.L. (1)
Ronnedevej 18, DK-4100, Ringsted, Denmark
Tel.: (45) 57660088
Web Site: http://www.dansensor.com
Laboratory Equipment Mfr & Distr
N.A.I.C.S.: 334519

Dunkermotoren France SAS (1)
Ronnedevej 18, Cailloux-sur-Fontaines, 69270, Lyon, France
Tel.: (33) 472292290
Web Site: http://www.dunkermotoren.com
Electronic Instrument & Electromechanical Device Mfr
N.A.I.C.S.: 334513

Dunkermotoren Italia s.r.l. (1)
Via De Barzi, 20087, Robecco sul Naviglio, Italy
Tel.: (39) 0294693233
Electronic Instrument & Electromechanical Device Mfr
N.A.I.C.S.: 334513

Dunkermotoren Subotica d.o.o. (1)
Batinska 94, Subotica, 24000, Serbia
Tel.: (381) 24630100
Electronic Instrument & Electromechanical Device Mfr
N.A.I.C.S.: 334513

Dunkermotoren Taicang Co., Ltd. (1)
No 9 Workshop No 111 Dongting N, Taicang Economy Development Area, Taicang,

215400, China
Tel.: (86) 51288898889
Electronic Instrument & Electromechanical Device Mfr
N.A.I.C.S.: 334513

Dunkermotoren USA Inc. (1)
1210 NC Hwy 61, Whitsett, NC 27377
Tel.: (336) 449-7909
Web Site: https://www.dunkermotoren.com
Electronic Instrument & Electromechanical Device Mfr
N.A.I.C.S.: 334513

EGS Automation GmbH (1)
Raiffeisenstrasse 2, D- 78166, Donaueschingen, Germany
Tel.: (49) 7718986060
Web Site: https://www.egsautomation.de
Plastics Product Mfr
N.A.I.C.S.: 326199
Oliver Kupper (Mng Dir)
Emanuela Speranza (Mng Dir)

EM Test (Switzerland) GmbH (1)
Sternenhofstrasse 15, 4153, Reinach, Switzerland
Tel.: (41) 617179191
Web Site: http://www.emtest.com
Emp.: 100
Electronic instruments & Electromechanical Components Mfr
N.A.I.C.S.: 334419

Subsidiary (Non-US):

AMETEK CTS Germany GmbH (2)
Lunener Strasse 211, 59174, Kamen, Germany
Tel.: (49) 2307260700
Web Site: http://www.ametekcts.com
Emp.: 35
Electronic instruments & Electromechanical Components Mfr
N.A.I.C.S.: 334514

Subsidiary (US):

EM Test (USA), Inc. (2)
9250 Brown Deer Rd, San Diego, CA 92121
Tel.: (603) 769-3477
Sales Range: $100-124.9 Million
Electronic instruments & Electromechanical Components Mfr
N.A.I.C.S.: 334419

Subsidiary (Domestic):

**Luthi Elektronik-Feinmechanik
AG** (2)
Sternenhofstrasse 15, 4153, Reinach, Switzerland
Tel.: (41) 61 7179191
Web Site: http://www.luethi-ag.ch
Electronic instruments & Electromechanical Components Mfr
N.A.I.C.S.: 334419

FMH Aerospace Corp. (1)
17072 Daimler St, Irvine, CA 92614
Tel.: (714) 751-1000
Web Site: https://www.fmhaerospace.com
Flexible Metal Hose Mfr
N.A.I.C.S.: 332999

Forza Silicon Corporation (1)
2947 Bradle St Ste 130, Pasadena, CA 91107
Tel.: (626) 796-1182
Web Site: https://www.forzasilicon.com
Semiconductor Devices Mfr
N.A.I.C.S.: 334413
Barmak Mansoorian (Co-Founder & Pres)
Daniel Van Blerkom (Co-Founder & CTO)
Anders Andersson (VP-Engineering)

Gatan, Inc. (1)
5794 W Las Positas Blvd, Pleasanton, CA 94588
Tel.: (925) 463-0200
Web Site: http://www.gatan.com
Instrumentation & Software Used to Enhance Performance of Electron Microscopes Mfr
N.A.I.C.S.: 334516

Branch (Domestic):

Gatan, Inc. (2)

780 Commonwealth Dr, Warrendale, PA 15086
Tel.: (724) 776-5260
Web Site: http://www.gatan.com
Electron Microscope Instrument Mfr
N.A.I.C.S.: 334516

**Haydon Linear Motors (Changzhou)
Co., Ltd.** (1)
99 Chuangxin Avenue, Xinbei District, Changzhou, 213031, Jiangsu, China
Tel.: (86) 400 001 3059
Web Site:
https://www.haydonkerkpittman.com.cn
Sales Range: $25-49.9 Million
Electronic Components Mfr
N.A.I.C.S.: 334419

Instruments for Industry, Inc. (1)
903 S 2nd St, Ronkonkoma, NY 11779
Tel.: (631) 467-8400
Web Site: http://www.ifi.com
Emp.: 30
Electronic Instrument & Electromechanical Device Mfr
N.A.I.C.S.: 334513

Intellipower, Inc. (1)
1746 N Saint Thomas Cir, Orange, CA 92865
Tel.: (714) 921-1580
Web Site: http://www.intellipower.com
Mfg Transformers
N.A.I.C.S.: 335311

Keimos 1988 U.S. Inc. (1)
27 Renmar Ave, Walpole, MA 02081
Tel.: (508) 921-4600
Web Site: http://www.ueidaq.com
Rev.: $3,666,666
Emp.: 20
Electronic Products Mfr
N.A.I.C.S.: 423690
Dennis Kraplin (Dir-Engrg)
Michael Tiemann (CTO)
Shaun Miller (Dir)

Laserage Technology Corp. (1)
3021 N Delaney Rd, Waukegan, IL 60087
Tel.: (847) 249-5900
Web Site: http://www.laserage.com
Laser Processing Services
N.A.I.C.S.: 332710

MOCON Italia S.R.L. (1)
Centro Commerciale 43, 20090, Milan, Italy
Tel.: (39) 0270300807
Electronic Instrument Distr
N.A.I.C.S.: 423690

MOCON, Inc. (1)
7500 Mendelssohn Ave N, Brooklyn Park, MN 55428
Tel.: (763) 493-6370
Web Site: http://www.ametekmocon.com
Sales Range: $50-74.9 Million
Instrumentation, Consulting & Laboratory Services to Medical, Pharmaceutical, Food & Other Industries Worldwide
N.A.I.C.S.: 334519

Subsidiary (Domestic):

Baseline-MOCON, Inc. (2)
19661 US Hwy 36, Lyons, CO 80540
Tel.: (303) 823-6661
Web Site: http://www.baseline-mocon.com
Gas Detection Equipment Mfr
N.A.I.C.S.: 334516

Subsidiary (Non-US):

MOCON Europe A/S (2)
Ronnedevej 18, 4100, Ringsted, Denmark
Tel.: (45) 57660088
Web Site: http://www.dansensor.com
Gas Measurement & Testing System Mfr & Distr
N.A.I.C.S.: 541380
Erik Borgesen (Mng Dir-PTPS Products)
Morten Torngaard (Sls Mgr)

Subsidiary (Non-US):

AMETEK Instrumentos, S.L. (3)
Esteve Terradas 31-Local 9, 08023, Barcelona, Spain
Tel.: (34) 932052286
Gas Analyzer Mfr
N.A.I.C.S.: 334513

Magnetrol International Inc. **(1)**
705 Enterprise St, Aurora, IL 60515-8149
Tel.: (630) 969-4000
Web Site: http://www.magnetrol.com
Sales Range: $150-199.9 Million
Emp.: 400
Liquid Level & Flow Instrumentation Mfr
N.A.I.C.S.: 334513
Mike Hojnacki (Engr-Mfg)
Bill Sujak (Mgr)
Alice Angelini (Project Coord)
Ethan Crooks (Assoc Gen Counsel)
Catie Rizzo (Dir-Fin)
Chris Diviak (Engr-Applications)
Han Wang (Engr-Inside Sls)
Eivydas Drulia (Engr-Welding)
Darren Meyer (Mgr-Application Engrg, Inside Sls & Project Quotations)
Jay Bosserman (Mgr-Production & Facility)
Denny Frantzen (Mgr-Sls)
Marlin Underwood (CFO & VP)
Pat Jennings (Coord-Inspections)
Kurt E. Flowers (Engr-Design)
Kevin Costello (Mgr-Matls)
Steve Reynolds (Mgr-Sustaining Engrg & Evaluation Engrg)
Thomas Kemme (Product Mgr)

Unit (Domestic):

Introtek International **(2)**
150 Executive Dr, Edgewood, NY 11717-8323 **(100%)**
Tel.: (631) 242-5425
Web Site: https://www.introtek.com
Sales Range: $10-24.9 Million
Emp.: 20
Special Ultrasonic Sensors
N.A.I.C.S.: 541715
Deb Corwin (Gen Mgr)

Subsidiary (Domestic):

Magnetrol Environmental, L.P. **(2)**
5300 Belmont Rd, Downers Grove, IL 60515-4499
Tel.: (630) 969-4028
Web Site:
   http://www.magnetrolenvironmental.com
Flow Control Switch & Transmitter Mfr
N.A.I.C.S.: 335314

Subsidiary (Non-US):

Magnetrol Instrumentation Industrial Ltda. **(2)**
Av Dr Mauro Lindemberg Monteiro 185 Quadrante 16, Osasco, Sao Paulo, 06278-010, Brazil **(100%)**
Tel.: (55) 11 3381 8100
Web Site: http://www.magnetrol.com
Level & Flow Instrumentation Solutions
N.A.I.C.S.: 334513

Magnetrol International **(2)**
C-20 Community Centre, Janakpuri, New Delhi, 110 058, India **(100%)**
Tel.: (91) 11 41661840
Web Site: http://www.magnetrol.com
Sales Range: Less than $1 Million
Emp.: 8
Sales of Liquid Level & Flow Instrumentation
N.A.I.C.S.: 334513

Magnetrol International **(2)**
Plant 6 No 191 Huajin Road Minhang, Minhang, Shanghai, 201108, China **(100%)**
Tel.: (86) 2162491350
Sales Range: $10-24.9 Million
Emp.: 8
Liquid Level & Flow Instrumentation Mfr
N.A.I.C.S.: 334513

Magnetrol International **(2)**
20 Changi Business Park Central 2 04-03, Singapore, 486031, Singapore **(100%)**
Tel.: (65) 66340581
Web Site: https://www.magnetrol.com
Sales Range: $10-24.9 Million
Emp.: 5
Mfr of Liquid Level & Flow Instrumentation
N.A.I.C.S.: 334513

Magnetrol International **(2)**
Regent Business Centre Jubilee Road, Burgess Hill, RH15 9TL, West Sussex, United Kingdom **(100%)**
Tel.: (44) 1444 871313
Web Site: http://www.magnetrol.be

Sales Range: $10-24.9 Million
Emp.: 5
Sales of Liquid Level & Flow Instrumentation
N.A.I.C.S.: 334513
Richard Jeynes (Country Mgr)

Magnetrol International **(2)**
Via Arese 12, 20159, Milan, Italy **(100%)**
Tel.: (39) 0026072298
Web Site: http://www.magnetrol.com
Sales Range: $1-9.9 Million
Emp.: 6
Sales of Liquid Level & Flow Instrumentation
N.A.I.C.S.: 334513

Magnetrol International N.V. **(2)**
Heikensstraat 6, 9240, Zele, Belgium **(100%)**
Tel.: (32) 52451111
Web Site: https://www.magnetrol.com
Sales Range: $10-24.9 Million
Emp.: 120
Marketing & Sales of Liquid Level & Flow Instrumentation
N.A.I.C.S.: 334513

Magnetrol International, Inc. **(2)**
145 Jardin Drive Unit 1& 2, Concord, L4K 1X7, ON, Canada **(100%)**
Tel.: (905) 738-9600
Web Site: http://www.magnetrol.com
Sales Range: $10-24.9 Million
Emp.: 6
Technical Services for Liquid Level & Flow Instrumentation
N.A.I.C.S.: 334513
Kevin Martyn (Gen Mgr)

Subsidiary (Domestic):

Orion Instruments, LLC. **(2)**
2105 Oak Villa Blvd, Baton Rouge, LA 70815
Tel.: (225) 906-2343
Web Site: http://www.orioninstruments.com
Emp.: 122
Measuring Equipment Mfr
N.A.I.C.S.: 333914
Don Sanders (Gen Mgr & Dir)

STI Controls, L.P. **(2)**
705 Enterprise, Aurora, IL 60504 **(100%)**
Tel.: (630) 969-4000
Sales Range: $25-49.9 Million
Emp.: 300
Liquid Level & Flow Control Systems for the Municipal Water & Waste Water Market
N.A.I.C.S.: 334513
Jeffrey K. Swallow (VP-Admin)

Milmega Limited **(1)**
Park Road, Ryde, PO33 2BE, Isle of Wight, United Kingdom
Tel.: (44) 1983618000
Web Site: https://www.milmega.co.uk
Emp.: 30
Electronic Instrument & Electromechanical Device Mfr
N.A.I.C.S.: 334513

Motec GmbH **(1)**
Oberweyerer Strasse 21, Hadamar, 65589, Steinbach, Germany
Tel.: (49) 643391450
Web Site: https://www.motec-cameras.com
Camera Monitor System Distr
N.A.I.C.S.: 449210
Emanuela Speranza (Mng Dir)

NSI-MI Technologies, LLC **(1)**
1125 Satellite Blvd NW Ste 100, Suwanee, GA 30024-4629
Tel.: (678) 475-8300
Web Site: https://www.nsi-mi.com
Holding Company; Microwave Measurement Products Mfr
N.A.I.C.S.: 551112
John E. Breyer (Pres & CEO)
Jeffrey A. Fordham (VP)
John Wilber (Sr VP)
John Hatzis (VP)
Mike Murphy (VP-Sales-Marketing)
Daniel Janse van Rensburg (CTO & VP-Field Sys)
John Demas (VP-Field Sys)
Dave Wayne (VP-Quality)
John Ward (VP-Operations)
Stephen Blalock (VP-Engineering)

Larry Cohen (Dir & Acct Mgr)
Larry Cohen (Dir & Acct Mgr)
Charles R. Smith III (Mgr & VP)

Subsidiary (Domestic):

Nearfield Systems, Inc. **(2)**
19730 Magellan Dr, Torrance, CA 90502
Tel.: (310) 525-7000
Web Site: https://www.nearfield.com
Sales Range: $1-9.9 Million
Emp.: 42
Antenna Measurement System Mfr
N.A.I.C.S.: 334515
Greg Hindman (Pres)
Lauretta McKie (Mgr-HR)
John Demas (Grp VP-Near Field)
John Hatzis (Grp VP-Customer Support)

NSI-MI UK Limited **(1)**
Unit 51 Harley Road, Sheffield, S11 9SE, United Kingdom
Tel.: (44) 114 235 3507
Web Site: https://nsi-mi.co.uk
Electrical Equipment & Component Mfr
N.A.I.C.S.: 335999

Navitar, Inc. **(1)**
200 Commerce Dr, Rochester, NY 14623
Tel.: (585) 359-4000
Web Site: http://www.navitar.com
Laser Systems & Equipment Mfr
N.A.I.C.S.: 335999
Julian Goldstein (Co-CEO)
Thomas Mccune (COO)
Michael Thomas (Pres)
Jeremy Goldstein (Co-CEO)
Russ Hudyma (CTO)

Subsidiary (Domestic):

Navitar Coating Labs, Inc. **(2)**
882 Production Pl, Newport Beach, CA 92663-2810
Tel.: (949) 642-5446
Web Site: http://www.navitar.com
Sales Range: $10-24.9 Million
Producer of Vacuum Deposited & Sputtered Coatings for UV, Visible & IR Applications
N.A.I.C.S.: 333310

Navitar Industries, LLC **(2)**
30 Nashua Street, Woburn, MA 01801
Tel.: (781) 933-6125
Web Site: http://www.navitarindustries.com
Optical Instrument & Lens Mfr
N.A.I.C.S.: 333310

PicturePhone, Inc. **(2)**
200 Commerce Dr, Rochester, NY 14623
Tel.: (585) 334-9040
Web Site: http://www.picturephone.com
Videoconferencing Products & Accessories Distr
N.A.I.C.S.: 423690
Tom Jerzak (Reg Mgr-Sls)
John Ryan (Mgr-Technical Svcs)
Rob Kramer (Reg Sls Mgr)
Rob Brown (Dir-Sls & Technical Svcs)
Dave Weber (Exec VP)
John Wilcoxen (Mgr-Pur)
Pete Mancuso (Engr-Sls)

Special Optics, Inc. **(2)**
3 Stewart Ct, Denville, NJ 07834
Tel.: (973) 366-7289
Web Site: https://www.specialoptics.com
Sales Range: $1-9.9 Million
Emp.: 2
Optical Lens Mfr
N.A.I.C.S.: 339115
Steven Morales (Mgr-Sls)

OBCORP LLC **(1)**
1900 Crystal Industrial Ct, Saint Louis, MO 63114
Tel.: (314) 236-2020
Web Site: https://www.obcorp.com
Electronic Instrument & Electromechanical Device Mfr
N.A.I.C.S.: 334513

Subsidiary (Non-US):

O'Brien BVBA **(2)**
Flor Alpaertsstraat 63, 2600, Berchem, Belgium
Tel.: (32) 33349645
Web Site: http://www.obcorp.com
Electronic Instrument & Electromechanical Device Mfr

N.A.I.C.S.: 334513

Paragon Medical Europe Sarl **(1)**
Av de l Avant-Poste 4, 1005, Lausanne, Switzerland
Tel.: (41) 213203785
Medical Equipment Mfr & Distr
N.A.I.C.S.: 339112

Paragon Medical International, Inc. **(1)**
8 Matchett Dr, Pierceton, IN 46562
Tel.: (574) 594-2140
Web Site: https://www.paragonmedical.com
Medical Equipment Mfr & Distr
N.A.I.C.S.: 339112

Paragon Medical, Device (Changzhou) Co., Ltd. **(1)**
10B GDH Industrial Park No 16 Chuangye Road Xinbei Zone, Changzhou, 213033, China
Tel.: (86) 51989890066
Medical Equipment Mfr & Distr
N.A.I.C.S.: 339112

Paragon Medical, Inc. **(1)**
8 Matchet Dr, Pierceton, IN 46562
Tel.: (574) 594-2140
Web Site: https://www.paragonmedical.com
Customized Polymer Surgical Instrument Cases & Trays Mfr
N.A.I.C.S.: 326199
Simon J. Newman (Chm)

Paragon Siechnice Sp. z o.o. **(1)**
Ul Staszica 5, 55-011, Siechnice, Poland
Tel.: (48) 717258063
Medical Equipment Mfr & Distr
N.A.I.C.S.: 339112

Pixelink, Inc. **(1)**
1000 Innovation Drive Suite 100, Ottawa, K2K 3E7, ON, Canada
Tel.: (613) 247-1211
Web Site: https://pixelink.com
Camera Hardware Mfr & Distr
N.A.I.C.S.: 334310

RTDS Technologies Inc. **(1)**
150 Innovation Drive, Winnipeg, R3T 2E1, MB, Canada
Tel.: (204) 989-9700
Web Site: https://www.rtds.com
Hardware & Software Development Services
N.A.I.C.S.: 541511

Responder Systems Corporation **(1)**
16810 Valley View Ave, La Mirada, CA 90638-5825
Tel.: (714) 367-1124
Web Site: https://www.rauland-ca.com
Electronics Instrument Mfr
N.A.I.C.S.: 334513

Solidstate Controls, LLC **(1)**
875 Dearborn Dr, Columbus, OH 43085-1596
Tel.: (614) 846-7500
Web Site:
   https://www.solidstatecontrolsinc.com
Sales Range: $25-49.9 Million
Electronic instruments & Electromechanical Components Mfr
N.A.I.C.S.: 334419

Subsidiary (Non-US):

Solidstate Controls Mexico, S.A. de C.V. **(2)**
Camino a La Montana No 178-101 Fracc Industrial La Perla, 53340, Naucalpan, Mexico
Tel.: (52) 555 250 1232
Web Site:
   https://www.solidstatecontrolsinc.com
Emp.: 7
Electronic instruments & Electromechanical Components Mfr
N.A.I.C.S.: 334419

Solidstate Controls, Inc. de Argentina S.R.L. **(2)**
Olive 1954, Santa Fe, S2013BMZ, Rosario, Argentina
Tel.: (54) 341 455 3332
Web Site:
   https://www.solidstatecontrolsinc.com
Emp.: 6

AMETEK, Inc.—(Continued)

Electronic Instruments & Electromechanical Components Mfr
N.A.I.C.S.: 334514

Sound Com Corporation (1)
227 Depot St, Berea, OH 44017-1899
Tel.: (440) 234-2604
Web Site: https://www.soundcom.net
Communication Equipment Installation Services
N.A.I.C.S.: 238210
Jeff Rollins (Dir-AV Ops)
Mary Rogers (Controller)
Nenad Bjelanovic (Mgr-Healthcare Integrations)

Spectro Scientific Inc. (1)
One Executive Dr Ste 101, Chelmsford, MA 01824-2563
Tel.: (978) 486-0123
Web Site: http://www.spectrosci.com
Analytical Instrumentation Mfr
N.A.I.C.S.: 334516

Subsidiary (Domestic):

Wilks Enterprise Inc. (2)
25 Van Zant St Ste 8F, Norwalk, CT 06855
Tel.: (203) 855-9136
Web Site: http://www.wilksir.com
Emp.: 10
Analytical Laboratory Instrument Mfr
N.A.I.C.S.: 334516

Taylor Hobson Ltd. (1)
2 New Star Road, PO Box 36, Leicester, LE4 9JQ, United Kingdom
Tel.: (44) 116 276 3771
Web Site: https://www.taylor-hobson.com
Emp.: 187
Electronic Inspection & Monitoring Instrument Mfr
N.A.I.C.S.: 334513
Craig Howarth (Mng Dir & VP-Div)
Tim Garner (Dir-Ops)
Bob Bennett (Dir-Technical)
Jurgen Petter (Dir-Optics Metrology)

Telular Corporation (1)
311 S Wacker Dr Ste 4300, Chicago, IL 60606
Tel.: (312) 379-8397
Web Site: http://www.telular.com
Telecommunications Equipment Mfr
N.A.I.C.S.: 334210
Henry Popplewell (Chief Comml Officer-IoT Telematics)

Subsidiary (Domestic):

SkyBitz Tank Monitoring Corporation (2)
1500 Bishop Ct Mt Prospect, Chicago, IL 60056-6039
Web Site: https://www.skybitz.com
Chemicals Mfr
N.A.I.C.S.: 325180

SkyBitz, Inc. (2)
2300 Dulles Station Blvd Fl 6, Herndon, VA 20171
Tel.: (703) 478-3340
Web Site: https://www.skybitz.com
Sales Range: $25-49.9 Million
Mobile Asset Management & Tracking Services
N.A.I.C.S.: 541614

Subsidiary (Domestic):

SkyBitz Petroleum Logistics LLC (3)
10306 Barberville Rd, Fort Mill, SC 29707
Tel.: (980) 244-3455
Chemicals Mfr
N.A.I.C.S.: 325180

Subsidiary (Non-US):

TankLink Corporation (2)
Tel.: (847) 882-0060
Inventory Management Services
N.A.I.C.S.: 541614

Tritex Corporation (1)
1390 Holly Ave, Columbus, OH 43212
Tel.: (614) 294-8511
Web Site: https://www.tritexcorp.com
Upholstery Services
N.A.I.C.S.: 811121

Russ Moseley (Co-Owner & Pres)
Kathy Stanley (Bus Mgr)
Justin Hahn (Co-Owner & VP)
Tyler Dalgarn (Mgr-Svc)

VTI Instruments Corporation (1)
2031 Main St, Irvine, CA 92614-6509
Tel.: (949) 955-1894
Web Site: http://www.vtiinstruments.com
Sales Range: $25-49.9 Million
Emp.: 50
Testing & Measurement Instrument Mfr
N.A.I.C.S.: 334515

VTI Instruments Private Limited (1)
4th Floor Block A Divyashree NR Enclave, EPIP Industrial Area Whitefield, Bengaluru, 560066, India
Tel.: (91) 804 040 7900
Web Site: https://www.vtiinstruments.com
Electronic Instrument & Electromechanical Device Mfr
N.A.I.C.S.: 334513

innoRIID GmbH (1)
Merowinger Platz 1, 40225, Dusseldorf, Germany
Tel.: (49) 15142538786
Web Site: https://www.innoriid.eu
Software & Hardware Development Services
N.A.I.C.S.: 541511

AMEXDRUG CORPORATION
369 S Doheny Dr Ste 326, Beverly Hills, CA 90211
Tel.: (323) 725-3100   NV
Web Site: https://www.amexdrug.com
Year Founded: 2000
AXRX—(OTCIQ)
Sales Range: $10-24.9 Million
Emp.: 9
Holding Company
N.A.I.C.S.: 551112
Jack Amin (Pres & CEO)
Rodney S. Barron (Bd of Dirs & Mng Dir)

AMFIN FINANCIAL CORP.
1999 Circle Dr Ste B, Cleveland, OH 44106
Tel.: (216) 896-9418   OH
Web Site:
   https://www.amfinfinancialcorp.com
AFNL—(OTCIQ)
Offices of Bank Holding Companies
N.A.I.C.S.: 551111
Frank Bolognia (Chm)
Michael Attias (CFO)
Brett Levy (Sr VP)
Zac Ponsky (CEO)
David Goldberg (VP)

AMGEN INC.
1 Amgen Center Dr, Thousand Oaks, CA 91320-1799
Tel.: (805) 447-1000   DE
Web Site: https://www.amgen.com
Year Founded: 1980
AMGN—(NASDAQ)
Rev.: $28,190,000,000
Assets: $97,154,000,000
Liabilities: $90,922,000,000
Net Worth: $6,232,000,000
Earnings: $6,717,000,000
Emp.: 26,700
Fiscal Year-end: 12/31/23
Human Therapeutics Developer, Mfr & Marketer
N.A.I.C.S.: 325414
Elizabeth H. Z. Thompson (Exec VP-R&D-Rare Disease)
Esteban Santos (Exec VP-Ops)
Jonathan P. Graham (Gen Counsel, Sec & Exec VP)
Raymond J. Deshaies (Sr VP-Global Res)
Gilles Marrache (Sr VP & Gen Mgr-Europe)
Annalisa Pizzarello (Sr VP-Results Delivery Office)

David M. Reese (CTO & Exec VP)
Murdo Gordon (Exec VP-Global Comml Ops)
Jerry Murry (Sr VP-Process Dev)
Arleen Paulino (Sr VP-Mfg)
Ian Thompson (Sr VP & Reg Gen Mgr)
Peter H. Griffith (CFO & Exec VP)
Susan Sweeney (Sr VP-Global Mktg, Access & Capabilities)
Nancy Grygiel (Chief Compliance Officer & Sr VP-Worldwide Compliance & Bus Ethic)
Rachna Khosla (Sr VP-Business Development)
Derek Miller (Sr VP-Human Resources)
Greg Portner (Sr VP-Global Govt Affairs & Policy)
Emily Razaqi (Sr VP-Obesity & Related Conditions)
Jean-Charles Soria (Sr VP-Research & Development)
Mark J. Taisey (Sr VP-Global Regulatory Affairs & Strategy)
Matthew C. Busch (Chief Acctg Officer & VP-Fin)
Robert A. Bradway (Chm & CEO)
Sam Guhan (Sr VP-Global Engrg)
Narimon Honarpour (Sr VP-Global Dev)
James E. Bradner (Chief Scientific Officer & Exec VP-R&D)
Sean Bruich (Sr VP-Artificial Intelligence & Data)
Paul Burton (Chief Medical Officer & Sr VP)
Jackie Elbonne (Chief Quality Officer & Sr VP-Quality)
Scott Skellenger (CIO & Sr VP)
Brenda Torres (Sr VP-Global Supply Chain)
Alper Ureten (VP-Commercialization & Program Mgmt)
Jasper van Grunsven (Sr VP-Rare Disease)
Kave Niksefat (Sr VP-Global Mktg & Access)
Susie Tappouni (Head-Corp Affairs)

Subsidiaries:

Amgen Australia Pty Ltd. (1)
Level 11 10 Carrington Street, Sydney, 2000, NSW, Australia   (100%)
Tel.: (61) 290701300
Web Site: http://www.amgen.com.au
Sales Range: $50-74.9 Million
Emp.: 100
Sales & Marketer of Pharmaceutical Products
N.A.I.C.S.: 424210
Troels Wolthers (Exec Dir-Medical)
Haydn Smyth (Dir-Haematology & Oncology)
Belinda Hansen (Dir-HR)
Alastair Lomas (Dir-Fin & Ops)
Ciara McKenna (Dir-Bone)
Shannon Sullivan (Mng Dir & VP)
Paul Silveri (Dir-Specialty)
Tracey Trass (Dir-Centre of Excellence)
Ian Noble (Dir-Value, Access & Policy)
Reena Patel (Dir-Regulatory Affairs)
Lisa Kurian (Sec & Dir-Legal)
Susan Dean (Officer-Data Privacy & Sr Mgr-Compliance)

Branch (Domestic):

Amgen Australia Pty Ltd. (2)
Mezzanine Level 115 Cotham Rd Kew, Melbourne, 3101, VIC, Australia   (100%)
Tel.: (61) 398549800
Web Site: http://www.amgen.com.au
Sales Range: $25-49.9 Million
Emp.: 55
Packager & Labeler of Pharmaceutical Products
N.A.I.C.S.: 456191

Amgen Canada Inc. (1)
6775 Financial Drive Suite 100, Missis-

sauga, L5N 0A4, ON, Canada   (100%)
Tel.: (905) 285-3000
Web Site: https://www.amgen.ca
Sales Range: $150-199.9 Million
Emp.: 300
Marketing & Sales of Pharmaceutical Products
N.A.I.C.S.: 424210

Amgen Colorado, Inc. (1)
4000 Nelson Rd, Longmont, CO 80503-9004
Tel.: (303) 401-1000
Web Site: http://www.amgen.com
Sales Range: $250-299.9 Million
Emp.: 600
Protein Pharmaceuticals Mfr to Treat Inflammatory Diseases, Skin Ulcers & Neurological Disorders
N.A.I.C.S.: 325412
Michael Bevilcqua (Pres-Amgen Boulder)

Amgen Development Corporation (1)
1 Amgen Ctr Dr, Thousand Oaks, CA 91320-1701   (100%)
Tel.: (805) 447-1000
Web Site: http://www.amgen.com
Sales Range: $1-4.9 Billion
Emp.: 13,000
Pharmaceuticals Product Mfr
N.A.I.C.S.: 325412

Amgen Europe B.V. (1)
Minervum 7061, 4817 ZK, Breda, Netherlands   (100%)
Tel.: (31) 765732000
Web Site: https://www.amgen.nl
Sales Range: $150-199.9 Million
Emp.: 500
Marketer & Sales of Pharmaceutical Products
N.A.I.C.S.: 424210

Subsidiary (Non-US):

Amgen (Europe) GmbH (2)
Suurstoffi 22, PO Box 94, 6343, Rotkreuz, Switzerland   (100%)
Tel.: (41) 413690300
Web Site: http://www.amgen.ch
Sales Range: $50-74.9 Million
Sales & Marketer of Pharmaceutical Products
N.A.I.C.S.: 424210

Amgen AB (2)
Gustav III s Boulevard 54, PO Box 706, 169 27, Solna, Sweden   (100%)
Tel.: (46) 86951100
Web Site: http://www.amgen.se
Sales Range: $75-99.9 Million
Emp.: 100
Sales & Marketer of Pharmaceutical Products
N.A.I.C.S.: 424210

Subsidiary (Domestic):

Amgen B.V. (2)
Minervum 7061, 4817 ZK, Breda, Netherlands   (100%)
Tel.: (31) 765732000
Web Site: https://www.amgen.nl
Sales Range: $400-449.9 Million
Marketer & Sales of Pharmaceutical Products
N.A.I.C.S.: 424210

Subsidiary (Non-US):

Amgen Belgium S.A. N.V. (2)
The Lighthouse Building Telecomlaan 5-7, Ave, 1831, Diegem, Belgium   (100%)
Tel.: (32) 27752711
Web Site: http://www.amgen.com
Sales Range: $75-99.9 Million
Emp.: 85
Marketer & Sales of Pharmaceutical Products
N.A.I.C.S.: 424210

Amgen GmbH (2)
Riesstrasse 24, 80992, Munich, Germany   (100%)
Tel.: (49) 891490960
Web Site: http://www.amgen.de
Sales Range: $75-99.9 Million
Marketer & Sales of Pharmaceutical Products

N.A.I.C.S.: 424210

Amgen GmbH (2)
Franz Josefs-Kai 47, 1010, Vienna,
Austria (100%)
Tel.: (43) 1502170
Web Site: http://www.amgen.at
Sales Range: $150-199.9 Million
Marketer & Sales of Pharmaceutical Products
N.A.I.C.S.: 424210

Amgen Limited (2)
216 Cambridge Science Park Milton Road,
Cambridge, CB4 0WA, United
Kingdom (100%)
Tel.: (44) 1223420305
Web Site: http://www.amgen.co.uk
Sales Range: $300-349.9 Million
Emp.: 400
Marketer & Sales of Pharmaceutical Products
N.A.I.C.S.: 424210

**Amgen Research (Munich)
GmbH** (2)
Staffelseestr 2, 81477, Munich,
Germany (100%)
Tel.: (49) 898952770
Web Site: http://www.amgen.de
Sales Range: $150-199.9 Million
Research & Development of Biological
Products in the Treatment of Cancer, Inflammatory & Autoimmune Diseases
N.A.I.C.S.: 325414
Robert Saller (Exec Dir-Project Mgmt)

Amgen S.A. (2)
Placa del Gas 1 Marenostrum Tower Tower
A floor 20, Edifici Sud Planta7, 08003, Barcelona, Spain (100%)
Tel.: (34) 936001900
Web Site: https://www.amgen.es
Sales Range: $75-99.9 Million
Emp.: 260
Marketer & Sales of Pharmaceutical Products
N.A.I.C.S.: 424210
Maria Gesti (Sec)

Amgen S.A. (2)
62 boulevard Victor Hugo, 92523, Neuillysur-Seine, France (100%)
Tel.: (33) 140882700
Web Site: http://www.amgen.fr
Sales Range: $50-74.9 Million
Emp.: 50
Sales & Marketer of Pharmaceutical Products
N.A.I.C.S.: 424210

Amgen S.p.A. (2)
Via Tazzoli 6, 20154, Milan, Italy (100%)
Tel.: (39) 026241121
Web Site: https://www.amgen.it
Sales Range: $50-74.9 Million
Emp.: 66
Pharmaceutical Products Distr
N.A.I.C.S.: 424210

Amgen-Bio-Farmaceutica, Lda. (2)
Avenida Jose Malhoa 19 - Floor 5, Paco De
Arcos, 1070-157, Lisbon, Portugal (100%)
Tel.: (351) 214220550
Web Site: https://www.amgen.pt
Sales & Marketer of Pharmaceutical Products
N.A.I.C.S.: 424210

Amgen Fremont Inc. (1)
6701 Kaiser Dr, Fremont, CA 94555-3659
Tel.: (510) 608-6500
Pharmaceuticals Product Mfr
N.A.I.C.S.: 325412

Amgen Global Finance B.V. (1)
Minervum 7061, 4817 ZK, Breda, Netherlands
Tel.: (31) 765732000
Web Site: https://www.amgen.nl
Pharmaceuticals Product Mfr
N.A.I.C.S.: 325412

Amgen Holding, Inc. (1)
1 Amgen Ctr Dr, Thousand Oaks, CA
91320 (100%)
Tel.: (805) 447-1000
Web Site: http://www.amgen.com
Holding Company
N.A.I.C.S.: 325412

**Amgen Inc. - Government Affairs
Office** (1)
601 13th St NW 12th Fl, Washington, DC
20005
Tel.: (202) 585-9500
Web Site: http://www.amgen.com
Sales Range: $10-24.9 Million
Emp.: 45
Provider of Business Services
N.A.I.C.S.: 541618

Amgen Inc. - San Francisco (1)
1120 Veterans Blvd, South San Francisco,
CA 94080
Tel.: (650) 244-2000
Sales Range: $75-99.9 Million
Emp.: 406
Pharmaceuticals Mfr
N.A.I.C.S.: 541715

Amgen Manufacturing, Limited (1)
PO Box 4060, Juncos, PR 00777 (100%)
Tel.: (787) 656-2000
Sales Range: $150-199.9 Million
Global Biotechnology
N.A.I.C.S.: 325414

Amgen Rockville, Inc. (1)
9201 Corporate Blvd Ste 400, Rockville,
MD 20850
Tel.: (240) 752-1420
Sales Range: $50-74.9 Million
Emp.: 215
Holding Company; Cancer Treatment &
Control Biological Products Research, Development & Commercialization Services
N.A.I.C.S.: 551112

Amgen S.A.S. (1)
Arcs de Seine 18-20 Quai du Point du Jour,
PO Box 10096, 92650, BoulogneBillancourt, France
Tel.: (33) 170289000
Web Site: http://www.amgen.fr
Healtcare Services
N.A.I.C.S.: 621491

**Amgen Singapore Manufacturing Pte.
Ltd.** (1)
1 Tuas View Drive, Singapore, 637026,
Singapore
Tel.: (65) 66750600
Web Site: https://www.amgen.com.sg
Blood Derivative & Antiserum Mfr
N.A.I.C.S.: 325414

Amgen USA Inc. (1)
1 Amgen Ctr Dr, Thousand Oaks, CA
91320-1799
Tel.: (805) 447-1000
Web Site: https://www.amgen.com
Human Therapeutic Products Mfr
N.A.I.C.S.: 325412

ChemoCentryx, Inc. (1)
850 Maude Ave, Mountain View, CA 94043
Tel.: (650) 210-2900
Web Site: http://www.chemocentryx.com
Rev.: $32,224,000
Assets: $425,652,000
Liabilities: $139,532,000
Net Worth: $286,120,000
Earnings: ($131,755,000)
Emp.: 178
Fiscal Year-end: 12/31/2021
Autoimmune Diseases, Inflammatory Disorders & Cancer Clinical Researcher & Pharmacautical Mfr
N.A.I.C.S.: 541715
Thomas J. Schall (Founder)
Markus J. Cappel (Chief Bus Officer &
Treas)
Pui San Kwan (VP-Fin)
Yi Ching Yau (Principal Acctg Officer & Sr
VP-Fin)
Dalia R. Rayes (Sr VP & Head-Comml)
Sangita Ghosh (Sr VP-Technical Ops)
Kari E. Leetch (Sr VP-HR)
Tausif Butt (COO & Exec VP)

Five Prime Therapeutics, Inc. (1)
111 Oyster Point Blvd, South San Francisco, CA 94080
Tel.: (415) 365-5600
Web Site: http://www.amgen.com
Rev.: $13,178,000
Assets: $331,650,000
Liabilities: $66,550,000
Net Worth: $265,100,000
Earnings: ($84,328,000)

Emp.: 51
Fiscal Year-end: 12/31/2020
Pharmaceuticals Mfr
N.A.I.C.S.: 325412
William R. Ringo Jr. (Chm)

**Gensenta Ilac Sanayi ve Ticaret
Anonim Sirketi** (1)
Levent Mah Meltem Sok is Kuleleri Kule 2
K 24 No 10 4, Levent Besiktas, Istanbul,
Turkiye
Tel.: (90) 2123373800
Web Site: http://www.gensenta.com.tr
Pharmaceuticals Product Mfr
N.A.I.C.S.: 325412

Horizon Therapeutics plc (1)
70 St Stephens Green Saint Kevins, Dublin,
Ireland
Tel.: (353) 17722100
Web Site:
   https://www.horizontherapeutics.com
Rev.: $3,629,044,000
Assets: $9,114,616,000
Liabilities: $4,042,442,000
Net Worth: $5,072,174,000
Earnings: $521,482,000
Emp.: 2,115
Fiscal Year-end: 12/31/2022
Holding Company; Biopharmaceutical Developer, Mfr & Marketer
N.A.I.C.S.: 551112
Jeffrey W. Sherman (Chief Medical Officer
& Exec VP-Dev & Regulatory Affairs)

Subsidiary (Non-US):

**Horizon Pharma Switzerland
GmbH** (2)
Kagenstrasse 17, 4153, Reinach, Switzerland
Tel.: (41) 617152040
Medicine Mfr
N.A.I.C.S.: 325412

Co-Headquarters (US):

Horizon Pharma, Inc. (2)
1 Horizon Way, Deerfield, IL 60015
Tel.: (224) 383-3000
Web Site: http://www.horizonpharma.com
Sales Range: $100-124.9 Million
Emp.: 304
Pharmaceutical Products Distr
N.A.I.C.S.: 424210
Timothy P. Walbert (Chm, Pres & CEO)
Jeffrey W. Sherman (Chief Medical Officer
& Exec VP-R&D)
Jeffrey W. Sherman (Chief Medical Officer
& Exec VP-R&D)
Jeffrey W. Sherman (Chief Medical Officer
& Exec VP-R&D)
Kelley Allison (Sr VP)
Sean Clayton (Exec VP)
Aaron Cox (Exec VP)
Geoffrey M. Curtis (Exec VP)
Jack Danilkowicz (Exec VP)
Michael DesJardin (Exec VP)
Eric Foster (Sr VP)
Jane Gonnerman (Sr VP)
Irina Konstantinovsky (Exec VP)
Andy Pasternak (Exec VP)
Tina Ventura (Sr VP)
Keli Walbert (Chief Marketing Officer-
Comml-U.S)

Subsidiary (Domestic):

HZNP USA LLC (3)
1000 Holcomb Woods Pkwy Ste 270, Roswell, GA 30076
Tel.: (678) 205-5444
Pharmaceutical Products Distr
N.A.I.C.S.: 424210

Subsidiary (Non-US):

Horizon Pharma AG (3)
Kagenstrasse 17, 4153, Reinach, Switzerland
Tel.: (41) 617152040
Web Site: http://www.horizonpharma.com
Biopharmaceutical Marketer
N.A.I.C.S.: 424210

Horizon Pharma GmbH (3)
Joseph-Meyer-Str 13-15, 68167, Mannheim,
Germany
Tel.: (49) 6214385020
Web Site: http://www.horizonpharma.com

Biopharmaceutical Marketer
N.A.I.C.S.: 424210

Subsidiary (Domestic):

Horizon Pharma USA, Inc. (3)
150 Saunders Rd Ste 130, Lake Forest, IL
60045
Tel.: (224) 383-3000
Web Site: http://www.horizonpharma.com
Emp.: 50
Pharmaceutical Products Distr
N.A.I.C.S.: 424210
Jeffrey W. Sherman (Chief Medical Officer)

Plant (Domestic):

**Horizon Pharma USA, Inc. - Roswell,
Georgia Office** (4)
1000 Holcomb Woods Pkwy Ste 270, Roswell, GA 30076
Tel.: (678) 205-5444
Web Site: http://www.horizonpharma.com
Biopharmaceutical Developer, Mfr & Marketer
N.A.I.C.S.: 325412

Subsidiary (Domestic):

Horizon Pharmaceutical LLC (3)
7 Hamilton Landing Ste 100, Novato, CA
94949
Tel.: (415) 408-6200
Emp.: 100
Pharmaceutical Preparation Mfr
N.A.I.C.S.: 325412
Eric B. Mosbrooker (VP-Comml Ops)

Subsidiary (US):

Viela Bio, Inc. (2)
1 MedImmune Way 1st Fl Area Two, Gaithersburg, MD 20878
Tel.: (240) 558-0038
Web Site: http://www.vielabio.com
Rev.: $50,000,000
Assets: $384,054,000
Liabilities: $29,543,000
Net Worth: $354,511,000
Earnings: ($86,429,000)
Emp.: 139
Fiscal Year-end: 12/31/2019
Biotechnology Research & Development
Services
N.A.I.C.S.: 541714
Zhengbin Yao (CEO)

KAI Pharmaceuticals, Inc. (1)
270 Littlefield Ave, South San Francisco,
CA 94080
Tel.: (650) 244-1100
Web Site: http://www.kaipharma.com
Pharmaceutical Developer
N.A.I.C.S.: 541715

**Mustafa Nevzat Ilac Sanayii Anonim
Sirketi** (1)
Levent Mah Meltem Sok is Kuleleri Kule 2
K 24 No 10 4 Levent Besiktas, Istanbul,
Turkiye
Tel.: (90) 2123373800
Web Site: http://www.mn.com.tr
Blood Derivative & Antiserum Mfr
N.A.I.C.S.: 325414

deCODE Genetics, Inc. (1)
Sturlugata 8, 101, Reykjavik, Iceland
Tel.: (354) 5701900
Web Site: http://www.decode.com
Sales Range: $25-49.9 Million
Emp.: 200
Gene Technology & Database & Information
Technology Products Developer for Healthcare Industry
N.A.I.C.S.: 541715
Unnur Thorsteinsdottir (VP-Res)
Daniel Gudbjartsson (VP-Applied Statistics)
Patrick Sulem (Head-Clinical Sequencing)
Gisli Masson (VP-Informatics)
Thorunn Rafnar (Head-Oncology)
Hreinn Stefansson (Head-CNS)
Ingileif Jonsdottir (Head-Infectious & Inflammatory Diseases)
Johann Hjartarson (Chief Compliance Officer, Officer-Data Protection & Gen Counsel)
Agnar Helgason (Head-Anthropology)
Bjarni V. Halldorsson (Head-Sequence
Analysis)

Amgen Inc.—(Continued)

Gudmundur L. Norddahl *(Head-Functional Genomics)*
Pall Melsted *(Head-RNA Sequencing Data)*
Magnus Orn UlFarsson *(Head-Artificial Intelligence)*
Lara Ingolfsdottir *(CFO)*

Subsidiary (US):

deCODE Genetics, Inc. (2)
2501 Davey Rd, Woodridge, IL 60517
Tel.: (630) 783-4600
Web Site: http://www.medichem.com
Sales Range: $10-24.9 Million
Emp.: 125
Provider of Drug Discovery Technology & Reserarch Services to Pharmaceutical & Biotechnology Companies
N.A.I.C.S.: 541720

AMICUS THERAPEUTICS, INC.
3675 Market St, Philadelphia, PA 19104
Tel.: (215) 921-7600 DE
Web Site: https://www.amicusrx.com
Year Founded: 2002
FOLD—(NASDAQ)
Rev.: $329,233,000
Assets: $724,167,000
Liabilities: $601,120,000
Net Worth: $123,047,000
Earnings: ($236,568,000)
Emp.: 484
Fiscal Year-end: 12/31/22
Pharmaceutical Preparation Manufacturing
N.A.I.C.S.: 325412
Simon N. R. Harford *(CFO)*
David Clark *(Chief People Officer)*
Bradley L. Campbell *(Pres & CEO)*
Jeffrey P. Castelli *(Chief Dev Officer)*
Ellen S. Rosenberg *(Chief Legal Officer)*
Patrik S. Florencio *(Chief Compliance & Risk Officer-Global & Sr VP)*
Samantha Prout *(Chief Acctg Officer & Controller)*
Sebastien Martel *(Chief Bus Officer)*
Jill Weimer *(Chief Science Officer)*
Mitchell Goldman *(Chief Medical Officer)*
Pat O'Sullivan *(Chief Technical Ops Officer)*
Diana Moore *(Head-Global Corp Comm)*
Andrew Faughnan *(VP-IR)*

Subsidiaries:

Amicus Therapeutics B.V. (1)
Science Park 402, 1098 XH, Amsterdam, Netherlands
Tel.: (31) 202358510
Web Site: https://www.amicusrx.nl
Infusion Therapy Center Operator
N.A.I.C.S.: 621498

Amicus Therapeutics Canada Inc. (1)
Suite 1600 1 First Canadian Place 100 King Street West, Toronto, M5X 1G5, ON, Canada
Tel.: (514) 426-6261
Web Site: http://www.amicustherapeutics.ca
Pharmaceuticals Product Mfr
N.A.I.C.S.: 325412
Claude Perron *(Gen Mgr)*

Amicus Therapeutics GmbH (1)
Willy-Brandt-Platz 3, 81829, Munich, Germany
Tel.: (49) 89248879810
Web Site: https://www.amicusrx.de
Infusion Therapy Center Operator
N.A.I.C.S.: 621498

Amicus Therapeutics K.K. (1)
19th floor Shin-Marunouchi Center Building 1-6-2 Marunouchi, Chiyoda-ku, Tokyo, 100-0005, Japan
Tel.: (81) 12 090 7477
Web Site: https://www.amicusrx.jp
Pharmaceutical Products Distr

Kurt Rimkus *(VP & Gen Mgr)*

Amicus Therapeutics S.L. (1)
Paseo de la Castellana 55 planta 1, 28046, Madrid, Spain
Tel.: (34) 917376973
Web Site: https://amicusrx.com
Infusion Therapy Center Operator
N.A.I.C.S.: 621498

Amicus Therapeutics S.L.U. (1)
Paseo de la Castellana 55 planta 1, 28046, Madrid, Spain
Tel.: (34) 917376973
Web Site: https://www.amicusrx.es
Pharmaceuticals Product Mfr
N.A.I.C.S.: 325412
Fermin Rivas *(Gen Mgr)*

Amicus Therapeutics S.r.l. (1)
Via Giovanni Boccaccio 11, 20123, Milan, Italy
Tel.: (39) 0291578175
Web Site: http://www.amicusrx.it
Infusion Therapy Center Operator
N.A.I.C.S.: 621498
David Allsop *(Sr VP & Head-Intl)*

Amicus Therapeutics SAS (1)
Opera E Les Collines de l'Arche 76 route de la Demi-Lune, La Defense, 92057, Paris, Cedex, France
Tel.: (33) 172757254
Web Site: https://www.amicusrx.fr
Infusion Therapy Center Operator
N.A.I.C.S.: 621498

Amicus Therapeutics UK Operations Limited (1)
One Globeside Fieldhouse Lane, Marlow, SL7 1HZ, United Kingdom
Tel.: (44) 175 388 8567
Web Site: https://www.amicusrx.co.uk
Biotechnology Research & Development Services
N.A.I.C.S.: 541714
Simon Jordon *(Sr VP)*
Simon Collins *(VP)*
Carlie Crowley *(Head-HR)*
Lori Mochon *(Head-Fin)*
David Jones *(Head-Quality)*

AMINCOR, INC.
365 W Passaic St Ste 525, Rochelle Park, NJ 07662
Tel.: (347) 821-3452 NV
Web Site: http://www.amincorinc.com
Year Founded: 1997
AMNC—(OTCIQ)
Investment Management Service
N.A.I.C.S.: 523940
Joseph F. Ingrassia *(CFO-Interim)*
Thomas Ingrassia *(Dir-Fin)*
Ruth Abady *(Controller)*
Stephen D'Angelo *(Pres)*
Steven L. Siskind *(Sec)*
John R. Rice III *(Pres)*

AMJ GLOBAL TECHNOLOGY
Tel.: (818) 853-7033 NV
Year Founded: 2013
AMJT—(OTCQB)
Assets: $9,140
Liabilities: $127,215
Net Worth: ($118,075)
Earnings: ($136,789)
Fiscal Year-end: 11/30/23
Mobile Software Products
N.A.I.C.S.: 513210
Arthur Malone Jr. *(CEO, CFO, Treas & Sec)*

AMKOR TECHNOLOGY, INC.
2045 E Innovation Cir, Tempe, AZ 85284
Tel.: (480) 821-5000 DE
Web Site: https://www.amkor.com
Year Founded: 1968
AMKR—(NASDAQ)
Rev.: $7,091,585,000
Assets: $6,821,757,000
Liabilities: $3,122,056,000

Net Worth: $3,699,701,000
Earnings: $765,823,000
Emp.: 31,300
Fiscal Year-end: 12/31/22
Semiconductor Packaging & Test Services
N.A.I.C.S.: 333242
Joanne Solomon *(CFO)*
Guillaume Marie Jean Rutten *(Pres & CEO)*
Megan Faust *(CFO, Exec VP & Controller)*
Mark N. Rogers *(Gen Counsel, Sec & Exec VP)*
Kevin Engel *(Exec VP)*
James J. Kim *(Founder)*

Subsidiaries:

ATEP - Amkor Technology Portugal, S.A. (1)
Avenida Primeiro de Maio 801, 4485-629, Vila do Conde, Portugal
Tel.: (351) 252246000
Semiconductor Packaging Product Distr
N.A.I.C.S.: 423690

Amkor Advanced Technology Taiwan, Inc. (1)
39 Guangfu North Road, Hsinchu Industrial Park Hukou Township, Hukou, 303, Hsinchu, Taiwan
Tel.: (886) 3 597 2777
Web Site: https://www.amkor.com
Semiconductor Mfr
N.A.I.C.S.: 334413

Amkor Assembly & Test (Shanghai) Co., Ltd. (1)
111 Yinglun Road Waigaoqiao Free Trade Zone, Pudong, Shanghai, 200131, China
Tel.: (86) 2150644590
Semiconductor Assembly & Test Services
N.A.I.C.S.: 334413

Amkor Technology Euroservices, S.A.R.L. (1)
Archamps Technopole 60 Avenue Marie Curie, 74160, Archamps, France
Tel.: (33) 4 50 31 88 00
Web Site: http://www.amkor.com
Semiconductor Assembly & Test Services
N.A.I.C.S.: 423690

Amkor Technology Germany GmbH (1)
Werner-Eckert-Strasse 8, 81829, Munich, Germany
Tel.: (49) 89124149840
Semiconductor Mfr & Distr
N.A.I.C.S.: 334413

Amkor Technology Japan, K.K. (1)
Shiba Kouen Front Tower 14F 2-6-3 Shibakoen, Minato-ku, Tokyo, 105-0011, Japan
Tel.: (81) 354252830
Emp.: 60
Semiconductor Sales & Service
N.A.I.C.S.: 423690
Yoshio Yoshimura *(Gen Mgr)*

Subsidiary (Domestic):

J-Devices Corporation (2)
1913-2 Takegashita Fukura, Kitsuki-ku, Usuki, 875-0053, Oita, Japan
Tel.: (81) 5031614938
Web Site: http://www.j-devices.co.jp
Emp.: 4,700
Semiconductor Mfr
N.A.I.C.S.: 334413
Hidenori Homma *(Pres)*

Amkor Technology Korea, Inc. (1)
Songdo 150 Songdomirae-ro, Yeonsu-gu, Incheon, 21991, Korea (South)
Tel.: (82) 32 728 4114
Web Site: http://www.amkor.com
Semiconductor Mfr & Sales
N.A.I.C.S.: 334413

Amkor Technology Malaysia Sdn. Bhd. (1)
15Km Jalan Klang-Banting, Telok Panglima Garang, 42507, Kuala Langat, Selangor, Malaysia (100%)
Tel.: (60) 33 122 6001
Web Site: http://www.amkor.com

Sales Range: $300-349.9 Million
Semiconductors, Transistors & Microcontrollers Mfr
N.A.I.C.S.: 334413

Amkor Technology Philippines, Inc. (1)
KM 22 East Service Road Special Economic Zone, Cupang, Muntinlupa, 1771, Philippines
Tel.: (63) 288507000
Web Site: http://www.amkor.com
Emp.: 500
Semiconductor Mfr & Sales
N.A.I.C.S.: 334413

Amkor Technology Singapore Holding Pte. Ltd. (1)
491B River Valley Road 12-03 Valley Point Office Tower, Singapore, 248373, Singapore
Tel.: (65) 6 211 3333
Web Site: https://www.amkor.com
Semiconductor Sales & Service
N.A.I.C.S.: 423690

Amkor Technology Taiwan Ltd. (1)
1F No 1 Kao-Ping Sec Chung-Feng Road, Longtan District, Taoyuan, 325, Taiwan
Tel.: (886) 3 411 6000
Web Site: http://www.amkor.com
Semiconductor Mfr & Sales
N.A.I.C.S.: 334413

AMMO, INC.
7681 E Gray Rd, Scottsdale, AZ 85260
Tel.: (480) 947-0001 DE
Web Site: https://www.ammoinc.com
Year Founded: 2016
POWW—(NASDAQ)
Rev.: $145,054,572
Assets: $399,902,216
Liabilities: $43,345,187
Net Worth: $356,557,029
Earnings: ($15,565,200)
Emp.: 374
Fiscal Year-end: 03/31/24
Ammunition Mfr & Distr
N.A.I.C.S.: 332993
Fred W. Wagenhals *(Founder & Exec Chm)*
Mark Hanish *(Pres-Mktg & Comml Sls-Global)*
Tod Wagenhals *(Exec VP)*
Jared R. Smith *(CEO)*
Anthony Tate *(VP-Sales & Marketing)*
Beth Cross *(COO)*

AMN HEALTHCARE SERVICES, INC.
2999 Olympus Blvd Ste 500, Dallas, TX 75019 DE
Web Site: https://www.amnhealthcare.com
Year Founded: 1981
AMN—(NYSE)
Rev.: $3,789,254,000
Assets: $2,924,394,000
Liabilities: $2,093,138,000
Net Worth: $831,256,000
Earnings: $210,679,000
Emp.: 3,585
Fiscal Year-end: 12/31/23
Temporary & Permanent Healthcare Staffing Services
N.A.I.C.S.: 561320
Cary Grace *(Pres & CEO)*
Landry Seedig *(Pres-Grp & COO-Nursing & Allied Solutions)*
Jeff Decker *(Pres-Locum Tenens Div)*
Robin Johnson *(Pres-Allied Div)*
Jeffrey R. Knudson *(CFO & Chief Acctg Officer)*
Cole Edmonson *(Chief Experience & Clinical Officer)*
Mark Hagan *(Chief Information & Digital Officer)*
Kelly E. Rakowski *(Pres-Grp & COO-Strategic Talent Solutions)*

James Taylor *(Pres-Grp, COO, Leadership Solutions & Physician)*
Cody Burch *(Pres-Interim-Leadership & Search)*
Jeffrey R. Knudson *(CFO)*
Whitney M. Laughlin *(Chief Legal Officer & Sec)*
Carolyn Kenny *(Chief People Officer)*
Kimberly Martini *(Pres)*
Julie Purinton *(Pres)*

Subsidiaries:

AMN Allied Services, LLC (1)
5001 Statesman Dr, Irving, TX 75063-2414
Tel.: (858) 314-7443
Healthcare Staffing Services
N.A.I.C.S.: 561320

AMN Healthcare Allied, Inc. (1)
8840 Cypress Waters Blvd, Coppell, TX 75019
Tel.: (469) 524-1473
Web Site: https://www.amnhealthcare.com
Emp.: 700
Healthcare Staffing Services
N.A.I.C.S.: 561320

AMN Healthcare, Inc. (1)
12400 High Bluff Dr, San Diego, CA 92130
Healthcare Staffing Services
N.A.I.C.S.: 561320

AMN Services, LLC (1)
12400 High Bluff Dr Ste 500, San Diego, CA 92130-3077
Tel.: (858) 720-6210
Emp.: 1,000
Healthcare Staffing Services
N.A.I.C.S.: 561320

AMN Staffing Services, LLC (1)
12400 High Bluff Dr Ste 500, San Diego, CA 92130
Tel.: (858) 792-0711
Healthcare Staffing Services
N.A.I.C.S.: 561320

Advanced Medical Personnel Services, Inc. (1)
5535 S Williamson Blvd Ste 774, Port Orange, FL 32128
Tel.: (386) 756-4395
Web Site: http://www.advanced-medical.net
Sales Range: $25-49.9 Million
Emp.: 300
Healthcare & Education Employment Placement Services
N.A.I.C.S.: 561311

Subsidiary (Domestic):

Advanced Travel Nursing (2)
14701 Cumberland Rd Ste 500, Noblesville, IN 46060
Tel.: (800) 322-9796
Web Site:
    http://www.innovativeplacements.com
Employment Agencies
N.A.I.C.S.: 561311

Rise Medical Staffing, LLC (2)
2525 Natomas Park Dr Ste 140, Sacramento, CA 95833
Tel.: (888) 585-0455
Offices of Other Health Practitioners
N.A.I.C.S.: 621399

American Mobile Healthcare (1)
8840 Cypress Waters Blvd, Dallas, TX 75019
Tel.: (858) 792-0711
Web Site: https://www.americanmobile.com
Sales Range: $250-299.9 Million
Emp.: 800
Temporary Healthcare Staffing Services
N.A.I.C.S.: 423450

Avantas, LLC (1)
2121 N 117th Ave Ste 300, Omaha, NE 68164
Tel.: (402) 717-7770
Web Site: https://www.avantas.com
Sales Range: $1-9.9 Million
Clinical Labor Management Software
N.A.I.C.S.: 513210
Holly Holz *(Sr Dir-Client Engagement & Optimization)*

B. E. Smith, LLC (1)

8840 Cypress Waters Blvd, Dallas, TX 75019
Web Site: https://www.besmith.com
Health Care Srvices

Bryan Christianson *(Sr VP-Strategic Accounts)*
Lisa Carr *(Sr VP-Talent Strategies)*
Deon Barber *(Sr VP-Sr Exec Search)*
Ben Harber *(VP)*
Christine Mackey-Ross *(Pres)*
Cecilia Beard *(VP)*
Jennifer Schaulin *(VP)*
River Meisinger *(Sr VP)*
Beth Harhai *(Sr VP)*

B.E. Smith, Inc. (1)
8840 Cypress Waters Blvd, Dallas, TX 75019
Web Site: https://www.besmith.com
Healthcare Industry Executive Search & Consulting Services
N.A.I.C.S.: 561312
Cecilia Beard *(VP)*
Deon Barber *(Sr VP)*
Jennifer Schaulin *(VP)*

B4Health, LLC (1)
4800 Hamden Ln Ste 200, Bethesda, MD 20814
Tel.: (301) 652-0444
Web Site: https://www.b4health.com
Health Care Srvices
N.A.I.C.S.: 621610
Michael Wheeden *(Mng Partner)*

Club Staffing (1)
8840 Cypress Waters Blvd, Dallas, TX 75019
Healthcare Staffing Services
N.A.I.C.S.: 561311
Nancy S. *(Clinic Mgr)*

HealthSource Global Staffing, Inc. (1)
12400 High Bluff Dr, San Diego, CA 92130
Web Site: https://www.hsgstaffing.com
Health Professional Services
N.A.I.C.S.: 813920

MedPartners HIM, LLC (1)
2999 Olympus Blvd Ste 500, Dallas, TX 75019
Tel.: (813) 418-3800
Web Site: http://www.medpartners.com
Health Care Srvices
N.A.I.C.S.: 622110

Medefis, Inc. (1)
2121 N 117th Av Ste 200, Omaha, NE 68164
Tel.: (402) 393-6333
Web Site: https://www.medefis.com
Software Programming Services
N.A.I.C.S.: 541511

Medical Express (1)
2601 Blake St Ste 400, Denver, CO 80205
Tel.: (303) 524-6150
Web Site: http://www.medicalexpress.com
Sales Range: $25-49.9 Million
Emp.: 200
Temporary Help Services for Healthcare Industry
N.A.I.C.S.: 561499

Merritt, Hawkins & Associates (1)
8840 Cypress Waters Blvd Ste 300, Dallas, TX 75019
Tel.: (469) 524-1400
Web Site: https://www.merritthawkins.com
Sales Range: $150-199.9 Million
Staffing Services
N.A.I.C.S.: 561320
Kurt Mosley *(VP-Strategic Alliances)*
James Merritt *(Founder)*
Travis Singleton *(Exec VP-Mktg & Sls)*
Tom Florence *(Exec VP-Recruiting)*

MillicanSolutions, LLC (1)
552 Silicon Dr Ste 101, Southlake, TX 76092
Tel.: (817) 421-5800
Web Site: http://www.millicansolutions.com
Health Care Srvices
N.A.I.C.S.: 621610

Nursefinders, LLC (1)
12400 High Bluff Dr Ste 100, San Diego, CA 92130

Tel.: (630) 353-2410
Web Site: http://www.nursefinders.com
Healthcare Staffing Services
N.A.I.C.S.: 561320

NursesRX (1)
12400 High Bluff Dr, San Diego, CA 92130
Web Site: http://www.nursesrx.com
Travel Nursing Staffing Agency
N.A.I.C.S.: 561599

O'Grady-Peyton International (USA), Inc. (1)
8840 Cypress W Blvd Ste 300, Dallas, TX 75019
Tel.: (912) 352-0684
Web Site: http://www.ogradypeyton.com
Sales Range: $10-24.9 Million
Temporary Healthcare Staffing Services
N.A.I.C.S.: 561320

Peak Health Solutions, Inc. (1)
725 Cool Springs Blvd Ste 100, Franklin, TN 37067
Web Site: http://www.peakhs.com
Emp.: 500
Health Information Management Services
N.A.I.C.S.: 519290
Gabe Stein *(Co-Founder)*
Justin Schmidt *(Co-Founder, Pres & Sr VP)*
Peder Christensen *(VP-Sls)*
Laura Pait *(VP-HIM & Consulting Ops)*
Teresa Carter *(VP-Talent Acquisition)*
Todd Ryan *(Assoc VP-Sls & Strategic Partnerships)*
Melissa McLeod-Seyfert *(Sr Dir-Consulting)*
Bryanna Bone *(Dir-Ops & Bus Dev)*
Susan Griffin *(Dir-Coding Svcs-VA & Indian Health)*
Jeanne Castellano *(Mgr-Acctg)*

ShiftWise, Inc. (1)
200 SW Market St Ste 700, Portland, OR 97201
Tel.: (503) 548-2030
Web Site: https://www.shiftwise.com
Health Care Srvices
N.A.I.C.S.: 621610

Silversheet Inc. (1)
1950 Sawtelle Blvd Ste 120, Los Angeles, CA 90025
Web Site: https://www.silversheet.com
Health Care Srvices
N.A.I.C.S.: 621610
Miles Beckett *(Founder & CEO)*

Staff Care, Inc. (1)
5001 Statesman Dr, Irving, TX 75063
Web Site: http://www.staffcare.com
Healthcare Staffing Services
N.A.I.C.S.: 561320
Rob Romaine *(Sr VP-Delivery)*

The First String Healthcare, Inc. (1)
9 Executive Cir Ste 225, Irvine, CA 92614
Tel.: (949) 574-5999
Web Site: http://www.thefirststring.com
Health Care Srvices
N.A.I.C.S.: 621610

The MHA Group, Inc. (1)
5001 Statesman Dr, Irving, TX 75063
Tel.: (469) 524-1400
Web Site: http://www.mha-group.com
Healthcare Staffing Services
N.A.I.C.S.: 561320

AMNEAL PHARMACEUTICALS, INC.
400 Crossing Blvd 3rd Fl, Bridgewater, NJ 08807
Tel.: (908) 947-3120   DE
Web Site: https://www.amneal.com
Year Founded: 2017
AMRX—(NYSE)
Rev.: $2,212,304,000
Assets: $3,799,341,000
Liabilities: $3,615,362,000
Net Worth: $183,979,000
Earnings: ($129,986,000)
Emp.: 7,750
Fiscal Year-end: 12/31/22
Offices of Other Holding Companies
N.A.I.C.S.: 551112
Gustavo J. Pesquin *(Chief Comml Officer-Specialty & Exec VP)*

Andrew S. Boyer *(Chief Comml Officer-Generics & Exec VP)*
Chirag K. Patel *(Co-Founder, Pres & Co-CEO)*
Chintu Patel *(Co-Founder & Co-CEO)*
Anastasios G. Konidaris *(CFO & Exec VP)*
Stephen J. Manzano *(Gen Counsel, Sec & Sr VP)*
Nikita Shah *(Chief HR Officer, Officer-Strategic Plng & Exec VP)*
Joseph Todisco *(Chief Comml Officer-Specialty & Exec VP)*

Subsidiaries:

Amneal Pharmaceuticals Company GmbH (1)
Turmstrasse 30, 6312, Steinhausen, Switzerland
Tel.: (41) 417492900
Pharmaceuticals Product Mfr
N.A.I.C.S.: 325412
Hanumantha Rao Kamma *(Sr Dir-Bus Dev & Strategy-Global)*

Amneal Pharmaceuticals LLC (1)
400 Crossing Blvd 3 Fl, Bridgewater, NJ 08807
Tel.: (908) 947-3120
Web Site: https://www.amneal.com
Pharmaceuticals Mfr & Whslr
N.A.I.C.S.: 325412
Andrew S. Boyer *(Chief Comml Officer-Generics & Exec VP)*
Chirag K. Patel *(Co-Founder, Pres & Co-CEO)*
Chintu Patel *(Co-Founder & Co-CEO)*
Nikita Shah *(Chief HR Officer, Officer-Strategic Plng & Exec VP)*
Sanjay Kumar Jain *(Pres-India)*
Anastasios G. Konidaris *(CFO & Exec VP)*
Srinivas Kone *(Sr VP-Generic R&D-Global)*
Jason B. Daly *(Chief Legal Officer)*
Gregory Sgammato *(Sr VP)*
Joe Renda *(Chief Comml Officer)*
Harsher Singh *(Sr VP)*

Subsidiary (Domestic):

Amneal Pharmaceuticals of New York LLC (2)
28 Liberty St, New York, NY 10005
Tel.: (908) 231-1911
Web Site: http://www.amneal.com
Pharmaceuticals Mfr
N.A.I.C.S.: 325412

AvKARE, Inc. (1) **(65.1%)**
615 N 1st St, Pulaski, TN 38478
Tel.: (931) 292-6222
Web Site: http://www.avkare.com
Durable Goods Merchant Whslr
N.A.I.C.S.: 423990

Dixon-Shane LLC (1)
8407 Austin Tracy Rd, Fountain Run, KY 42133
Web Site: https://www.rsnortheast.com
Healthcare Product Distr
N.A.I.C.S.: 423450
Ted McMurtrey *(Dir-Vendor Rels)*
Billie Fraley *(Controller)*
Timi Smith *(Exec VP)*
Steve Wilhelm *(VP-Ops)*
Rick Devey *(VP-IT)*

Impax Laboratories, LLC (1)
30831 Huntwood Ave, Hayward, CA 94544
Tel.: (510) 476-2000
Pharmaceuticals Mfr & Marketer
N.A.I.C.S.: 325412
Luis Kolb *(VP-Global Supply Chain & Mfg)*

Subsidiary (Domestic):

Tower Holdings, Inc. (2)
30831 Huntwood Ave, Hayward, CA 94544
Tel.: (510) 240-6000
Holding Company
N.A.I.C.S.: 551112

RAKS Pharma Pvt. Ltd. (1)
Plot No 68 Survey No 60 62 63 Jawaharlal Nehru Pharma City, E-Bonangi Revenue Village Parawada Mandal, Visakhapatnam, 530012, Andhra Pradesh, India
Tel.: (91) 891 308 1555

Amneal Pharmaceuticals, Inc.—(Continued)

Web Site: https://www.rakspharma.com
Pharmaceuticals Product Mfr
N.A.I.C.S.: 325412
Venkata Kiran Yandamuri (Mgr-HR & Admin)

AMPCO-PITTSBURGH CORPORATION

726 Bell Ave Ste 301, Carnegie, PA
15106
Tel.: (412) 456-4400   PA
Web Site: https://ampcopgh.com
Year Founded: 1929
AP—(NYSE)
Rev.: $390,189,000
Assets: $502,774,000
Liabilities: $389,378,000
Net Worth: $113,396,000
Earnings: $3,416,000
Emp.: 1,565
Fiscal Year-end: 12/31/22
Forged Hardened Steel Rolls & Centrifugal Pumps Mfr
N.A.I.C.S.: 332111
Michael G. McAuley (CFO, Treas & Sr VP)
Roscoe Carrier (CIO)
Keith A. Zatawski (Chief Risk Officer & Dir-Benefits)
Nancy Woods (Mgr-Benefits Admin)
Samuel C. Lyon (Pres-Union Electric Steel Corporation)
J. Brett McBrayer (CEO)

Subsidiaries:

Aerofin Corp.   (1)
4621 Murray Pl, Lynchburg, VA
24506   (100%)
Tel.: (434) 845-7081
Web Site: https://www.aerofin.com
Sales Range: $100-124.9 Million
Emp.: 215
Heating & Cooling Coils Mfr
N.A.I.C.S.: 333415
Gavin Divers (Pres)

Air & Liquid Systems
Corporation   (1)
1680 S Livernois, Rochester, MI 48307
Tel.: (248) 656-3610
Web Site: https://www.airliquidsystems.com
Emp.: 15
Liquid Filtration Equipment Mfr
N.A.I.C.S.: 333998

Akers Valji Ravne d.o.o.   (1)
Koroska c 14, 2390, Ravne na Koroskem,
Slovenia
Tel.: (386) 28707846
Steel Roll Mfr
N.A.I.C.S.: 423390
Nina Kotnik (Controller)

Alloys Unlimited Processing   (1)
3760 Oakwood Ave, Austintown, OH 44515
Tel.: (330) 544-3095
Web Site: https://www.alloysunlimited.com
Fabricated Structural Metal Mfr
N.A.I.C.S.: 332312

Buffalo Air Handling   (1)
467 Zane Snead Dr, Amherst, VA
24521   (100%)
Tel.: (434) 946-7455
Web Site: https://www.buffaloair.com
Sales Range: $75-99.9 Million
Emp.: 140
Air Handling Equipment for Commercial,
Construction & Industrial Applications
N.A.I.C.S.: 333413
Ted Krueger (Pres)

Buffalo Pumps, Inc.   (1)
874 Oliver St, North Tonawanda, NY
14120-3298   (100%)
Tel.: (716) 693-1850
Web Site: https://www.buffalopumps.com
Sales Range: $50-74.9 Million
Emp.: 120
Mfr of Pumps
N.A.I.C.S.: 333914

Shanxi Akers TISCO Roll Co.
Ltd.   (1)

No 2 JianCaoPing, Taiyuan, 030003,
Shanxi, China
Tel.: (86) 3513131696
Iron Casting Mfr
N.A.I.C.S.: 331511

Union Electric Steel Corp.   (1)
726 Bell Ave Ste 101, Carnegie, PA
15106-0465   (100%)
Tel.: (412) 429-7655
Web Site: https://www.uniones.com
Sales Range: $50-74.9 Million
Emp.: 150
Mfr of Forged Hardened Steel Rolls, Ingots
& Other Forgings
N.A.I.C.S.: 331513

Subsidiary (Non-US):

Union Electric Steel BVBA   (2)
Bosstraat, B 3560, Lummen,
Belgium   (100%)
Tel.: (32) 13661711
Web Site: http://www.uniones.com
Sales Range: $10-24.9 Million
Emp.: 3
Forged Steel Machinery & Equipment Mfr
N.A.I.C.S.: 333519

Plant (Domestic):

Union Electric Steel Corp.   (2)
PO Box 29, Valparaiso, IN 46384   (100%)
Tel.: (219) 464-0587
Web Site: http://www.uniones.com
Sales Range: $25-49.9 Million
Emp.: 100
Mfr of Hardened Steel Rolls
N.A.I.C.S.: 331513
Kevin Papich (VP-Mfg)
Edward J. Siddons (VP-Supply Chain &
Procurement-Global)
Jason B. Sychterz (VP-Tech European &
Ops Asian)
Dave Anderson (VP-Fin)
Lew Prenni (VP-Tech Ops-North American)
Charles Reinert Jr. (VP-Sls-Global)

Subsidiary (Non-US):

Union Electric Steel UK Limited   (2)
Coulthards Lane, PO Box 21, Gateshead,
NE8 3DX, Tyne & Wear, United
Kingdom   (100%)
Tel.: (44) 1914025200
Web Site: http://www.unionesuk.co.uk
Sales Range: $50-74.9 Million
Emp.: 250
Hardened Steel Roll Mfr
N.A.I.C.S.: 331318

AMPHASTAR PHARMACEUTICALS, INC.

11570 6th St, Rancho Cucamonga,
CA 91730
Tel.: (909) 980-9484   DE
Web Site:
    https://www.amphastar.com
Year Founded: 1996
AMPH—(NASDAQ)
Rev.: $498,987,000
Assets: $741,987,000
Liabilities: $213,329,000
Net Worth: $528,658,000
Earnings: $91,386,000
Emp.: 1,615
Fiscal Year-end: 12/31/22
Pharmaceutical Preparation Manufacturing
N.A.I.C.S.: 325412
William J. Peters (CFO, Treas & Exec
VP-Fin)
Mary Ziping Luo (Chm & COO)
Jack Yongfeng Zhang (Co-Founder,
Pres, CEO & Chief Science Officer)
Jacob Liawatidewi (Sec & Exec VP-
Mktg, Sls, and Corp Admin Center)
William J. Peters (CFO, Treas & Exec
VP-Fin)
Dan Dischner (Sr VP)

Subsidiaries:

Armstrong Pharmaceuticals, Inc.   (1)
11570 6th St, Rancho Cucamonga, CA
91730

Tel.: (617) 323-7404
Web Site: https://amphastar.com
Pharmaceutical Products Mfr; Injectable,
Intranasal & Inhalation Products
N.A.I.C.S.: 325412

International Medication Systems,
Limited   (1)
1886 Santa Anita Ave, South El Monte, CA
91733
Tel.: (626) 442-6757
Pharmaceuticals Mfr
N.A.I.C.S.: 325412
Mau Hung Chuang (Supvr-Software Grp)

AMPHENOL CORPORATION

358 Hall Ave, Wallingford, CT 06492
Tel.: (203) 265-8900   IL
Web Site: https://www.amphenol.com
Year Founded: 1932
APH—(NYSE)
Rev.: $12,554,700,000
Assets: $16,526,400,000
Liabilities: $8,130,600,000
Net Worth: $8,395,800,000
Earnings: $1,928,000,000
Emp.: 95,000
Fiscal Year-end: 12/31/23
Cable & Connector Mfr
N.A.I.C.S.: 334417
Peter J. Straub (Pres-Interconnect &
Sensor Sys Div)
Richard Adam Norwitt (Pres & CEO)
Craig A. Lampo (CFO & Sr VP)
Lance E. D'Amico (Gen Counsel, Sec
& Sr VP)
Dietrich Ehrmanntraut (VP & Gen
Mgr-Automotive Products Grp)
Linda Chan (VP-IT)
Stephen Dorrough (Asst Sec, VP &
Deputy Gen Counsel)
Patrick J. Gillard (VP-Bus Dev)
Michael R. Ivas (VP & Controller)
Pedro T. Lay (VP-Internal Audit)
Lily Mao (VP-HR)
Sherri Scribner (VP-Strategy & IR)
Mark C. Turner (Treas & VP)
Gary C. Voccio (VP-Tax)
David M. Silverman (Sr VP)
David C. Abbott (VP)
Richard Gu (VP)
Philippe John Lantin (VP)
Ursula Nadeau (VP)
Peter J. Straub (VP)

Subsidiaries:

AUXEL FTG Shanghai Co., Ltd.   (1)
Tel.: (86) 2158594088
Electronic Product Distr
N.A.I.C.S.: 423690

Airmar EMEA EURL   (1)
9 Bis Rue De Grand Jardin Zi Sud, 35400,
Saint-Malo, France
Tel.: (33) 223520648
Web Site: https://www.airmar-emea.com
Marine Transducer Parts Mfr & Distr
N.A.I.C.S.: 334419

All Sensors Asia Pacific K.K.   (1)
Venture Plaza Funabashi 222 1-17-25
Kitamoto-cho, Funabashi, 273-0864, Chiba,
Japan
Tel.: (81) 474895939
Web Site: http://www.allsensors-apac.com
Pressure Sensor Mfr
N.A.I.C.S.: 334519

All Sensors GmbH   (1)
Am Weidegrund 8, 82194, Grobenzell, Germany
Tel.: (49) 81424219770
Pressure Sensor Mfr & Distr
N.A.I.C.S.: 334512

Alturna Direct N.V.   (1)
Veluwezoom 15F 5th Floor, 1327 AE, Almere, Netherlands
Tel.: (31) 882347500
Web Site: https://alturna.direct
Electric Component Whslr
N.A.I.C.S.: 423690

Alturna Integration Services N.V.   (1)
De Huchtstraat 35, 1327 EC, Almere, Netherlands
Tel.: (31) 88 258 8762
Web Site:
    https://www.alturnaintegrationservices.com
Network Design Services
N.A.I.C.S.: 541512

Alturna Networks N.V.   (1)
De Huchtstraat 35, 1327 EC, Almere, Netherlands
Tel.: (31) 882588762
Web Site: https://www.alturnanetworks.com
Network Equipment Whslr
N.A.I.C.S.: 423430

American Conec Corporation   (1)
343 Technology Dr, Garner, NC 27529
Tel.: (919) 460-8800
Rev.: $8,080,000
Emp.: 8
Electronic Parts Whslr
N.A.I.C.S.: 423690
Duane Harrison (Mng Dir)

Amphenol (Changzhou) Advanced
Connector Co. Ltd.   (1)
No 6 Fengxi Rd South District Wujin Hi-
Tech Industrial Zone, Wujin, Changzhou,
213164, Jiangsu, China
Tel.: (86) 51986526988
Electronic Connector Mfr
N.A.I.C.S.: 334417

Amphenol (Xiamen) High Speed
Cable Co., Ltd.   (1)
2nd-4th Floor No 176 Xinfeng Road Xiamen
Torch Hi-Tech Zone, Xiamen, 361009, Fujian, China
Tel.: (86) 5925695266
Electronic Components Distr
N.A.I.C.S.: 423690
Cathy Zhang (Mgr-HR)

Amphenol Advanced Sensors   (1)
Sinsheimer Strasse 6, 75179, Pforzheim,
Germany
Tel.: (49) 7231143350
Web Site: http://www.amphenol-
    sensors.com
Sensor Mfr
N.A.I.C.S.: 334413

Amphenol Advanced Sensors Puerto
Rico, LLC   (1)
Rd 402 KM1 3 Industrial Park, Anasco, PR
00610
Tel.: (787) 826-0222
Web Site: http://www.amphenol-
    sensors.com
Emp.: 200
Sensor Mfr
N.A.I.C.S.: 334413

Amphenol Aerospace & Industrial
Operations   (1)
40-60 Delaware Ave, Sidney, NY 13838
Tel.: (607) 563-5011
Web Site: http://www.amphenol-
    aerospace.com
Sales Range: $450-499.9 Million
Emp.: 1,400
Electrical Equipment for Internal Combustion Engines
N.A.I.C.S.: 334417

Subsidiary (Domestic):

Amphenol Borisch Technologies,
Inc   (2)
4511 E Paris Ave, Grand Rapids, MI 49512
Tel.: (616) 554-9820
Web Site: http://www.borisch.com
Aircraft Electronic Component Mfr
N.A.I.C.S.: 336411

Amphenol Printed Circuits, Inc.   (2)
91 Northeastern Blvd, Nashua, NH 03062
Tel.: (603) 324-4500
Web Site: https://www.amphenol-apc.com
Electronic Components Mfr
N.A.I.C.S.: 334419

Amphenol Steward Enterprises,
Inc.   (2)
1921 Alta Vista Dr, Midland, TX 79707
Tel.: (432) 687-2553
Sales Range: $10-24.9 Million
Emp.: 90

Seismic Cable, Wire & Connector Products
Mfr & Distr
N.A.I.C.S.: 332618

Unit (Non-US):

**Amphenol Technical Products
International** (2)
2110 Notre Dame Avenue, Winnipeg, R3H
0K1, MB, Canada
Tel.: (204) 697-2222
Web Site: http://www.tpil.com
Sales Range: $25-49.9 Million
Filtered Connectors & Specialty Intercon-
nect Devices
N.A.I.C.S.: 334290
Andrew Schofield (Gen Mgr)

Subsidiary (Non-US):

**Amphenol Technology (Shenzhen)
Co. Ltd.** (1)
Building C 2nd Industrial Zone of Xia Shi
Jia, Gongming sub-district Guangming New
district, Shenzhen, 518106, Guangdong,
China
Tel.: (86) 75529918389
Web Site: http://www.amphenol.com
Sales Range: $100-124.9 Million
Cable & Connector Mfr
N.A.I.C.S.: 334417

**Guangzhou Amphenol Sincere Flex
Circuits Co. Ltd.** (2)
A WanAn Ind Park, LanHe Town Nansha
Dist, Guangzhou, 511480, China
Tel.: (86) 203 483 9801
Web Site: https://www.amphenol-gasf.com
Electronic & Fiber Optic Connectors, Inter-
connect Systems & Coaxial & Flat-ribbon
Cable Designer & Mfr
N.A.I.C.S.: 334417

**Amphenol Antenna Solutions,
Inc.** (1)
1300 Capital Dr, Rockford, IL 61109
Tel.: (815) 399-0001
Web Site: http://www.amphenol-
antennas.com
Antenna Mfr
N.A.I.C.S.: 334220

Division (Domestic):

C&S Antennas, Inc. (2)
123 Industrial Dr SW, Conover, NC 28613
Tel.: (828) 324-2454
Web Site: http://www.csantennas.com
Antenna Mfr
N.A.I.C.S.: 334220

Amphenol Bar-Tec, LTD (1)
3 Hagavish St, PO Box 2479, Kfar Saba,
44641, Israel
Tel.: (972) 97644100
Web Site: http://www.bar-tec.com
Connector Distr
N.A.I.C.S.: 423610
Orit Rapaport (Mng Dir)
Avi Inbar (Founder)

Amphenol Benelux B.V. (1)
Hoofdveste 19, 3992 DH, Houten, Nether-
lands
Tel.: (31) 306358000
Web Site: http://www.amphenolinfocom.eu
Electronic Component Mfr & Whslr
N.A.I.C.S.: 423690

**Amphenol CNT (Xian) Technology
Co., Ltd.** (1)
Bldg A 181 South Tai Bai Road, Xi'an,
710065, Shaanxi, China
Tel.: (86) 298 825 3388
Web Site: http://www.amphenol.com
Cable & Connector Mfr
N.A.I.C.S.: 334417

**Amphenol Cables On Demand
Corp.** (1)
20 Valley St, Endicott, NY 13760-3600
Tel.: (607) 321-2115
Web Site: http://www.cablesondemand.com
Fiber Optic Cable Mfr
N.A.I.C.S.: 335921

Amphenol Canada Corp. (1)
5950 14th Ave, Markham, L3S 4M4, ON,
Canada
Tel.: (416) 291-4401

Web Site:
https://www.amphenolcanada.com
Sales Range: $25-49.9 Million
Filtered Connectors & Specialty Intercon-
nect Devices
N.A.I.C.S.: 334290

**Amphenol Commercial Interconnect
Korea Co. Ltd.** (1)
66 Saneop-Ro 92 Beon-gil, Gwonseon-gu,
Suwon, 016-643, Gyeonggi-do, Korea
(South)
Tel.: (82) 312902600
Electronic Component Mfr & Distr
N.A.I.C.S.: 334419

**Amphenol Commercial Products
(Chengdu) Co. Ltd.** (1)
Block D3 Molding Tool Industry Park, Hong-
Guang Town West District of Gaoxin,
Chengdu, 611743, China
Tel.: (86) 288 798 8678
Web Site: http://www.amphenol.com.cn
Sales Range: $10-24.9 Million
Emp.: 1,000
Cable & Connector Mfr
N.A.I.C.S.: 334417

**Amphenol Commercial and Industrial
UK, Limited** (1)
Thanet Way, Whitstable, CT5 3JF, Kent,
United Kingdom
Tel.: (44) 1227773200
Electronic Component & Industrial Connec-
tor Mfr
N.A.I.C.S.: 334419

Amphenol ConneXus Ou (1)
Sundbybergsvagen 1, 171 73, Solna, Swe-
den
Tel.: (46) 854547070
Web Site: https://amphenol.ee
Cable Mfr
N.A.I.C.S.: 334417

Amphenol Custom Cable, Inc. (1)
3221 Cherry Palm Dr, Tampa, FL 33619-
8334
Web Site: https://www.customcable.com
Cable Mfr
N.A.I.C.S.: 334417

Amphenol DC Electronics (1)
1870 Little Orchard St, San Jose, CA 95125
Tel.: (408) 947-4500
Web Site: http://www.dcelectronics.com
Cable & Wire Mfr
N.A.I.C.S.: 332618
Ruben Macias Jr. (Gen Mgr)

**Amphenol DaeShin Electronic & Pre-
cision Co., Ltd.** (1)
Songnae-dong 14 Gyeonggin-ro 133 Beon-
gil, Sosa-gu, Bucheon, Gyeonggi-do, Korea
(South)
Tel.: (82) 326103800
Web Site: http://www.amphenol.co.kr
Sales Range: $100-124.9 Million
Cable & Connector Mfr
N.A.I.C.S.: 334417

Amphenol EEC, Inc. (1)
4050 N Rockwell St, Chicago, IL 60618
Tel.: (773) 463-8343
Web Site: https://www.elecquip.com
Electrical Component Mfr
N.A.I.C.S.: 335999

**Amphenol East Asia Elect. Tech.
Shenzhen Co., Ltd.** (1)
Building AM1 AM2 AM3 BM2 BM3 Tangwei
Industrial Zone Gongming office, Tangwei
Community Industrial Corporation Guang-
ming New District, Shenzhen, 518132,
China
Tel.: (86) 75527177945
Web Site: https://www.amphenol.com.cn
Sales Range: $100-124.9 Million
Emp.: 1,000
Cable & Connector Mfr
N.A.I.C.S.: 334417

**Amphenol East Asia Electronic Tech-
nology (Shenzhen) Co. Ltd.** (1)
Building AM1 AM2 AM3 BM2 BM3 Tangwei
Industrial Zone Gongming office, Tangwei
Community Industrial Corporation Guang-
ming New District, Shenzhen, 518132,
China
Tel.: (86) 75527177945

Electronic Connector & Cable Mfr
N.A.I.C.S.: 334417

Amphenol FCI Asia Pte. Ltd. (1)
159 Kampong Ampat KA Place 04-01/04,
Singapore, 368328, Singapore
Tel.: (65) 6 549 6666
Web Site: https://www.fci.com
Connector Mfr & Whslr
N.A.I.C.S.: 334417
Thierry Lacarne (VP-HR)

Subsidiary (Non-US):

Amphenol FCI Besancon SA (2)
2 Rue la Fayette, 25050, Besancon, France
Tel.: (33) 381545454
Web Site: https://amphenol-fci-
besancon.com
Electronic Connector Mfr
N.A.I.C.S.: 334417
Nathalie Pepe-Aubry (Dir-HR)

Subsidiary (Domestic):

**Amphenol FCI Connectors Singapore
Pte. Ltd.** (2)
159 Kampong Ampat KA Place 04-01/04,
Singapore, 368328, Singapore
Tel.: (65) 6549 6666
Web Site: http://www.amphenol-icc.com
Electronic Components Mfr
N.A.I.C.S.: 334419

Branch (Non-US):

**Amphenol FCI Connectors Singapore
Pte Ltd - Thailand Representative
Office** (3)
Unit 6 11th Fl Rasa Tower, 555 Phaholy-
othin Road, Chatuchak, Bangkok, 10900,
Thailand
Tel.: (66) 29370072
Electronic Connector Mfr
N.A.I.C.S.: 334417

Subsidiary (Non-US):

**FCI Connector Malaysia Sdn.
Bhd.** (2)
Plot 88A Jalan Perindustrian Bukit Minyak
Kawasan, Perindustrian Bukit Minyak
MK13, Penang, 14000, Malaysia
Tel.: (60) 45038236
Electronic Connector Mfr
N.A.I.C.S.: 334417

FCI Connectors Hong Kong Ltd. (2)
Office B 27th Floor 39 Chatham Road
South, Kowloon, China (Hong Kong)
Tel.: (852) 25108131
Electronic Connector Mfr
N.A.I.C.S.: 334417

FCI Connectors Korea Ltd. (2)
66 Saneop-ro 92beon-gil, Gwonseon-gu,
Suwon, 16643, Gyeonggi-do, Korea (South)
Tel.: (82) 312786253
Electronic Components Mfr
N.A.I.C.S.: 334419

**FCI Connectors Shanghai Co.
Ltd.** (2)
Room 6N 360 South Pu Dong Road New
Shanghai Industrial Mansion, 6th Floor Pu-
dong, Shanghai, 200122, China
Tel.: (86) 2158365500
Web Site: http://www.amphenol-icc.com
Electronic & Allied Component Mfr
N.A.I.C.S.: 334419

FCI Connectors Sweden AB (2)
Knararrnasgatan 7 Kista Entre, 164 40,
Stockholm, Sweden
Tel.: (46) 852291848
Web Site: http://www.amphenol-icc.com
Electronic Connector Mfr
N.A.I.C.S.: 334417

FCI Deutschland GmbH (2)
Obere Zeil 2, 61440, Oberursel, Germany
Tel.: (49) 61718860
Web Site: https://www.fci.com
Electronic Connector Mfr
N.A.I.C.S.: 334417

FCI Electronics Hungary Kft (2)
Fo ter 30 2/A, 2800, Tatabanya, Hungary
Tel.: (36) 34814671
Web Site: http://www.amphenol-icc.com
Electronic Components Mfr

N.A.I.C.S.: 334419

FCI Japan K. K. (2)
2F NT Building 1-47-1 Ooi, Shinagawa-ku,
Tokyo, 140-0014, Japan
Tel.: (81) 34 334 5000
Web Site: https://www.amphenol-cs.com
Electronic Components Mfr
N.A.I.C.S.: 334419

FCI OEN Connectors Ltd (2)
29/2089 Tripunithura Road Thykoodam Vyt-
tila, PO Box 1958, Kochi, 682 019, Kerala,
India
Tel.: (91) 4844090700
Web Site: https://www.fcoen.com
Electronic Connector Mfr
N.A.I.C.S.: 334417
G. Rajamani (CFO)

FCI Taiwan Ltd (2)
23F 99 Xin-Pu 6th street, Taoyuan, 33044,
Taiwan
Tel.: (886) 3 341 5521
Web Site: http://www.amphenol-icc.com
Electronic Components Mfr
N.A.I.C.S.: 334419

Subsidiary (US):

FCI USA LLC (2)
825 Old Trail, Etters, PA 17319
Tel.: (717) 938-7200
Web Site: http://www.amphenol-icc.com
Electronic Electrical & Automotive Connec-
tor Mfr
N.A.I.C.S.: 334417

Unit (Domestic):

FCI USA LLC - Automotive (3)
28100 Cabot Dr #100, Novi, MI 48377
Tel.: (248) 592-2700
Electronic Connector Mfr
N.A.I.C.S.: 334417

**Amphenol Fiber Optic Technology
(Shenzhen) Co., Ltd.** (1)
Shigu Road, Nanshan, Shenzhen, 518055,
China
Tel.: (86) 75526756086
Electronic Components Mfr
N.A.I.C.S.: 334419

**Amphenol Fiber Technology (Shen-
zhen) Co., Ltd.** (1)
2 Changfeng Rd Dongkeng Community
Gongming Town, Xili town Nanshan District,
Shenzhen, 518106, Guangdong, China
Tel.: (86) 75527177945
Web Site: http://www.amphenol.com
Sales Range: $50-74.9 Million
Emp.: 300
Cable & Connector Mfr
N.A.I.C.S.: 334417

Amphenol Filec, S.A.S. (1)
40 Rue de Disse, PO Box 40, Airvault,
79600, France
Tel.: (33) 549708570
Sales Range: $25-49.9 Million
Emp.: 100
Cable & Connector Mfr
N.A.I.C.S.: 334417
Yannitk Taitrault (Mgr)

Amphenol Finland OY (1)
Kutojantie 2C, 02630, Espoo, Finland
Tel.: (358) 2 085 0600
Web Site: http://www.amphenol.com
Cable Mfr
N.A.I.C.S.: 335929

Amphenol Gesellschaft m.b.H. (1)
Hietzinger Kai 133, Vienna, 1130, Austria
Tel.: (43) 19713759
Electronic Component Mfr & Distr
N.A.I.C.S.: 334419

**Amphenol Global Interconnect
Systems** (1)
200 Innovative Way Ste 201, Nashua, NH
03062
Tel.: (603) 879-3000
Web Site: http://www.amphenol-tcs.com
Emp.: 200
Group Managing Office; Fiber Optic & Wire
Cables, Assemblies & Connectors Mfr
N.A.I.C.S.: 551114

Amphenol Corporation—(Continued)

Subsidiary (Non-US):

Amphenol AssembleTech (Xiamen) Co., Ltd. **(2)**
39B Qianpu Industrial Estate, Xiamen, 361009, Fujian, China
Tel.: (86) 5925936666
Web Site: http://www.amphenol-china.com
Cable & Connector Mfr
N.A.I.C.S.: 334417

Amphenol ConneXus AB **(2)**
Sundbybergsvagen 1, 171 73, Solna, Sweden
Tel.: (46) 854547070
Web Site: http://www.amphenol.ee
Cable & Connector Mfr
N.A.I.C.S.: 334417

Amphenol ConneXus AEOU **(2)**
Laanemere tee 72 A, 13914, Tallinn, Estonia
Tel.: (372) 5 890 9525
Web Site: https://www.amphenol-gcs.eu
Emp.: 200
Cable & Connector Mfr
N.A.I.C.S.: 334417

Subsidiary (Domestic):

Amphenol Interconnect Products Corporation **(2)**
20 Valley St, Endicott, NY 13760
Tel.: (607) 754-4444
Web Site: https://amphenol-ipc.com
Fiber Optic Cable Mfr
N.A.I.C.S.: 335921

Amphenol Griffith Enterprises, LLC **(1)**
6000 E Coury Dr, Cottonwood, AZ 86326-9202
Tel.: (928) 851-7955
Web Site: http://www.griffithent.com
Electronic Components Mfr
N.A.I.C.S.: 334419

Amphenol Intercon Systems, Inc. **(1)**
825 Old Trial Rd Ste A, Etters, PA 17319
Tel.: (717) 915-1400
Web Site: http://www.interconsystems.com
Data Processing Services
N.A.I.C.S.: 518210

Amphenol International Military Aerospace & Industrial Operations **(1)**
Immeuble Le Doublon 11 Avenue Dubonnet, Courbevoie, 92407, France
Tel.: (33) 149053000
Web Site: http://www.amphenol.com
Sales Range: $100-124.9 Million
Emp.: 10
Cable & Connector Mfr
N.A.I.C.S.: 334417

Subsidiary (Non-US):

Amphenol Air LB GmbH **(2)**
Am Kleinbahnhof 4, 66740, Saarlouis, Germany
Tel.: (49) 683198100
Web Site: http://www.amphenol-airlb.de
Sales Range: $10-24.9 Million
Cable & Connector Mfr
N.A.I.C.S.: 334417

Amphenol Air LB North America, Inc. **(2)**
3600 Matter Boulevard Suites H-22 and J, Brossard, J4Y 2Z2, QC, Canada
Tel.: (450) 444-1266
Web Site: http://www.amphenolpcd.com
Fiber Optic Systems
N.A.I.C.S.: 335921

Subsidiary (US):

Amphenol Alden Products Company **(2)**
117 N Main St, Brockton, MA 02301
Tel.: (508) 427-7000
Web Site: http://www.amphenolalden.com
Electronic Component Mfr & Distr
N.A.I.C.S.: 334419

Subsidiary (Non-US):

Amphenol Alden Products Mexico, S.A. de C.V. **(3)**

Severiano Talamante 6B, Dynatech Industrial Park, 83170, Hermosillo, Sonora, Mexico
Tel.: (52) 15084277000
Electronic Components Mfr
N.A.I.C.S.: 334419

Subsidiary (Non-US):

Amphenol Australia Pty. Ltd. **(2)**
22 Industry Boulevard, Carrum Downs, 3201, VIC, Australia
Tel.: (61) 387968888
Web Site: http://www.amphenol.com.au
Sales Range: $100-124.9 Million
Cable & Connector Mfr
N.A.I.C.S.: 334417

Amphenol Interconnect India Private Limited **(2)**
105 Bhosari Industrial Area, Pune, 411 026, India
Tel.: (91) 2067360304
Web Site: http://www.amphenol-in.com
Cable & Connector Mfr
N.A.I.C.S.: 334417
V. G. Kadam (Mgr-Factory)
Vijay Bhavsar (Gen Mgr-Mktg & Sls)
Anant Joshi (Sr Mgr-Industrial Mktg)
S. V. Patil (Asst Gen Mgr-Exports)
K. Manoj (Mgr-Southern)
P. R. Prasad (Mgr-Central)
Sunil Patil (Mgr-Western)
Shrikant Gramopadhye (Mgr-Ops)

Amphenol Limited **(2)**
Thanet Way, Whitstable, CT5 3JF, Kent, United Kingdom
Tel.: (44) 1227773200
Web Site: https://www.amphenol.co.uk
Emp.: 300
Cable & Connector Mfr
N.A.I.C.S.: 334417
Steve Fowler (Dir-Technical)
Steve Roberts (Gen Mgr)
Paula Savage (Coord-Sls & Product Support-Nottingham)
Suzanne Butcher (Controller-Fin)
Karen Perry (Coord-Distr)

Subsidiary (US):

Amphenol PCD Inc. **(2)**
72 Cherry Hill Dr, Beverly, MA 01915-1065
Tel.: (978) 624-3400
Web Site: http://www.amphenolpcd.com
Sales Range: $75-99.9 Million
Electronic Connector Mfr
N.A.I.C.S.: 334417

Subsidiary (Non-US):

Amphenol PCD (Shenzhen) Co., Ltd. **(9)**
Building C Da Gang Industrial Zone Yu Tang Street, Guang Ming District, Shenzhen, 518132, China
Tel.: (86) 75581738000
Web Site: https://www.amphenolpcd.com.cn
Sales Range: $75-99.9 Million
Cable & Connector Mfr
N.A.I.C.S.: 334417

Subsidiary (US):

Fiber Systems International, Inc. **(2)**
1300 Central Expy N Ste 100, Allen, TX 75013
Tel.: (214) 547-2400
Web Site: http://www.fibersystems.com
Emp.: 100
Fiber Optic Systems
N.A.I.C.S.: 335921

Amphenol Invotec Limited **(1)**
Unit 1-3 Hedging Lane Industrial Estate, Dosthill, Tamworth, B77 5HH, United Kingdom
Tel.: (44) 1827263000
Web Site: http://www.amphenol-invotec.com
Printed Circuit Board Mfr
N.A.I.C.S.: 334412

Amphenol Japan, Ltd. **(1)**
471-1 Deba, Ritto, 520-3041, Shiga, Japan
Tel.: (81) 775538501
Web Site: http://www.amphenol.co.jp
Sales Range: $100-124.9 Million
Cable & Connector Mfr
N.A.I.C.S.: 334417

Amphenol Kai Jack (Shenahen) Co. Ltd. **(1)**
Block DM 2 Tong Wei Industrial District Gong Ming Town, Bao An District, Shenzhen, 518132, China
Tel.: (86) 75527177843
Sales Range: $100-124.9 Million
Cable & Connector Mfr
N.A.I.C.S.: 334417

Amphenol LTW Technology Co., Ltd **(1)**
5F-3 No 51 Sec 4 Zhongyang Rd, Tucheng Dist, New Taipei City, 23675, Taiwan
Tel.: (886) 277416888
Web Site: https://amphenolltw.com
Cable Mfr
N.A.I.C.S.: 335929

Amphenol Malaysia Sdn Bhd **(1)**
156 Banyan Lepas Free Ind Zone 1, Penang, 11900, Malaysia
Tel.: (60) 46448628
Sales Range: $100-124.9 Million
Emp.: 150
Cable & Connector Mfr
N.A.I.C.S.: 334417
Adam Norwitt (Pres)

Amphenol Mobile Connector Solutions (Changzhou) Co., Ltd. **(1)**
No 28 XinSi Road, New North District, Changzhou, 213031, Jiangsu, China
Tel.: (86) 51985601866
Electronic Connector & Cable Mfr
N.A.I.C.S.: 334417

Amphenol Mobile Consumer Products Group **(1)**
Room 2604 Railway Plaza 39 Chatham Road South, Tsim Sha Tsui, Kowloon, China (Hong Kong)
Tel.: (852) 26992663
Web Site: http://www.amphenol-mcp.com
Cable & Connector Mfr
N.A.I.C.S.: 334417

Subsidiary (Non-US):

Amphenol MCP Korea Limited **(2)**
640-23 Juseok-ro BiBong-myun, Hwaseong, 018-293, Gyeonggi-do, Korea (South)
Tel.: (82) 313552222
Web Site: https://www.amphenolmcpkorea.com
Sales Range: $100-124.9 Million
Cable & Connector Mfr
N.A.I.C.S.: 334417

Subsidiary (US):

Amphenol T&M Antennas, Inc. **(2)**
100 Tri-State International Ste 255, Lincolnshire, IL 60069
Tel.: (847) 478-5600
Web Site: http://www.amphenol-tm.com
Antenna Mfr
N.A.I.C.S.: 334220

Subsidiary (Non-US):

Amphenol Taiwan Corp. **(2)**
5F No 361 Fusing 1st Rd, Gueishan Dist, Taoyuan, 33375, Taiwan
Tel.: (886) 32647200
Web Site: http://www.amphenol.com.tw
Cable & Connector Mfr
N.A.I.C.S.: 334417

Hangzhou Amphenol Phoenix Telecom Parts Co., Ltd. **(2)**
No 98-5 South Road 19, Hangzhou Economic and Technological Development Zone, Hangzhou, China
Tel.: (86) 5718 671 4425
Web Site: https://www.amphenol-hzp.com
Cable & Connector Mfr
N.A.I.C.S.: 334417

Shanghai Amphenol Airwave Communication Electronic Co., Ltd. **(2)**
No 689 Shennan Road, Xinzhuang Industry Park, Shanghai, 201108, China
Tel.: (86) 2161255222
Web Site: http://www.amphenol-saa.com
Sales Range: $25-49.9 Million
Cable & Connector Mfr
N.A.I.C.S.: 334417

Amphenol Nelson Dunn Technologies, Inc. **(1)**
17719 Valley View Ave, Cerritos, CA 90703
Tel.: (714) 249-7700
Web Site: http://www.amphenol-ecs.com
Electrical & Hose Valve Mfr
N.A.I.C.S.: 332912

Amphenol Network Solutions, Inc. **(1)**
22425 E Appleway Ave Ste 11, Liberty Lake, WA 99019
Tel.: (509) 926-6000
Web Site: http://amphenol-ns.com
Develops & Produces Fiber Optic, Digital & Analog Communication Connectivity Products & Power Distribution Panels
N.A.I.C.S.: 334210

Amphenol Omniconnect Indai Private Limited **(1)**
Plot 3/4B & 5A CMDAs Industrial Area Maraimalai Nagar, Kilkaranai Village Chengleput Taluk Kancheepuram District, Chennai, 603 209, India
Tel.: (91) 4467405750
Web Site: http://www.amphenol-omni.com
Sales Range: $50-74.9 Million
Cable & Connector Mfr
N.A.I.C.S.: 334417

Amphenol Optimize Mexico S.A. de C.V. **(1)**
Carretera Internacional Km 6 5 Col Parque Industrial, 84094, Nogales, Sonora, Mexico
Tel.: (52) 6313111600
Web Site: http://www.amphenol-optimize.com
Electronic Components Mfr
N.A.I.C.S.: 334419
Frank M. Jaehnert (Gen Mgr)

Amphenol Phitek Limited **(1)**
Level 4 2 Kingdon Street, Newmarket, Auckland, 1023, New Zealand
Tel.: (64) 95242984
Web Site: http://www.phitek.com
Electro-Acoustic Technologies
N.A.I.C.S.: 334419

Amphenol Procom, Inc. **(1)**
1300 Capital Dr, Rockford, IL 61109
Tel.: (815) 980-0809
Web Site: http://www.amphenolprocom.com
Emp.: 180
Antenna Product Mfr
N.A.I.C.S.: 334220

Amphenol Provens SAS **(1)**
Promenade de la Arve, Thyez, 74300, France
Tel.: (33) 442747055
Electronic Components Mfr
N.A.I.C.S.: 334419

Amphenol RF **(1)**
4 Old Newtown Rd, Danbury, CT 06810
Tel.: (203) 743-9272
Web Site: http://www.amphenolrf.com
Cable Mfr
N.A.I.C.S.: 335929

Amphenol RF Asia Limited **(1)**
BLk DM 2 Tong Wei Ind dist, Gong Ming Town Bao An District, Shenzhen, 518132, China
Tel.: (86) 75527177843
Electronic Connector Mfr
N.A.I.C.S.: 335931
Sam Lau (Gen Mgr)

Amphenol Sensing Korea Company Limited **(1)**
23 Hasan-gil, Chungbuk-myum, Pyeongtaek, Korea (South)
Tel.: (82) 316800600
Electronic Components Mfr
N.A.I.C.S.: 334419

Amphenol Shouh Min Industry (Shenzhen) Company **(1)**
Bao an District Shajing Town Dawangshan fourth industrial zone 6, Shajing Town Baoan District, Shenzhen, 518132, China
Tel.: (86) 75581490081
Web Site: http://www.amphenol-shuomin.com
Electronic Connector Mfr
N.A.I.C.S.: 335931

Amphenol TCS (1)
200 Innovative Way Ste 201, Nashua, NH 03062
Tel.: (603) 879-3000
Web Site: http://www.amphenol-tcs.com
Rev.: $373,051,008
Emp.: 7,000
Electronic Connector, High Performance Circuit & Backplane Mfr
N.A.I.C.S.: 334417
Richard E. Schneider (Pres)

Subsidiary (Non-US):

Amphenol TCS Ireland Ltd. (2)
The Mill Enterprise Hub Newtown Link Road Greenhills, Drogheda, A92 CD3D, Co Louth, Ireland
Tel.: (353) 419806970
Web Site: http://www.amphenol.com
Cable & Connector Mfr
N.A.I.C.S.: 334417

Amphenol TCS Sdn Bhd (2)
Plot 88A Jalan Perindustrian Bukit Minyak, Kawasan Perindustrian Bukit Minyak MK 13, 14000, Penang, Malaysia
Tel.: (60) 45038200
Web Site: http://www.amphenol-tcs.com
Sales Range: $100-124.9 Million
Emp.: 300
Connector Molding & Stamping Mfr
N.A.I.C.S.: 334417

Amphenol TCS de Mexico S.A. de C.V. (2)
El Dorado 65 Colorado 2, Parque Industrial El Dorado, 21190, Mexicali, Mexico
Tel.: (52) 6865595700
Sales Range: $350-399.9 Million
Emp.: 1,000
Cable & Connector Mfr
N.A.I.C.S.: 334417

Amphenol TCS (Malaysia) Sdn Bhd (1)
Plot 88A Jalan Perindustrian Bukit Minyak, Kawasan Perindustrian Bukit Minyak MK 13, 14000, Penang, Malaysia
Tel.: (60) 45013399
Connector Molding & Stamping Mfr
N.A.I.C.S.: 334417

Amphenol Technology Macedonia (1)
Ungarska 9, 2300, Kocani, North Macedonia
Tel.: (389) 33270433
Electronic Components Mfr
N.A.I.C.S.: 334419

Amphenol Tecvox LLC (1)
4900 Bradford Dr, Huntsville, AL 35805
Tel.: (256) 417-4338
Web Site: https://tecvox.com
Emp.: 45
Automotive Electronic Parts Mfr & Distr
N.A.I.C.S.: 334417

Amphenol Tel-Ad Limited (1)
13 Atir Yeda st, PO Box 2408, Kfar Saba, 44641, Israel
Tel.: (972) 97634111
Web Site: http://www.tel-ad.co.il
Electronic Component Mfr Mfr & Distr
N.A.I.C.S.: 334419

Amphenol Thermometrics (UK) Limited (1)
Crown Industrial Estate Priorswood Road, Taunton, TA2 8QY, United Kingdom
Tel.: (44) 182 333 5200
Web Site: http://www.amphenol.com
Electronic Components Mfr
N.A.I.C.S.: 334419

Amphenol Thermometrics (UK) Limited (1)
Crown Industrial Estate Priorswood Rd, Taunton, TA2 8QY, Somerset, United Kingdom
Tel.: (44) 1823335200
Web Site: http://www.amphenol-sensors.com
Thermistors Mfr
N.A.I.C.S.: 334416

Amphenol Thermometrics, Inc. (1)
967 Windfall Rd, Saint Marys, PA 15857-3333
Tel.: (814) 834-9140
Electronic Components Mfr
N.A.I.C.S.: 334419

Amphenol Tianjin Co. Ltd. (1)
Wujing Road 17 Dongli Development District, Tianjin, 300300, China
Tel.: (86) 22 2498 3815
Web Site: http://www.amphenol-tcs.com
Sales Range: $100-124.9 Million
Cable & Connector Mfr
N.A.I.C.S.: 334417

Amphenol Trackwise Designs Limited (1)
1 Ashvale Alexandra Way, Tewkesbury, Gloucester, GL20 8NB, United Kingdom
Tel.: (44) 1684299930
Web Site: https://www.trackwise.co.uk
Printed Circuit Board Mfr & Distr
N.A.I.C.S.: 334412

Amphenol Tuchel Industrial GmbH (1)
August-Haeusser-Strasse 10, 74080, Heilbronn, Germany
Tel.: (49) 71319290
Web Site: http://www.amphenol.de
Electronic Components Mfr
N.A.I.C.S.: 334419

Amphenol Turkey Baglanti Cozumleri Limited Sirketi (1)
Sun Plaza Kat 19 Maslak Mh Bilim Sk No 5, Sisli, 34398, Istanbul, Turkiye
Tel.: (90) 2123679220
Web Site: https://amphenol.com.tr
Electrical Component Mfr & Distr
N.A.I.C.S.: 335921

Amphenol do Brasil Ltda. (1)
Rua Diogo Moreira 132 20 th Floor, Charcaras Reunidas, Sao Paulo, 05423-010, SP, Brazil
Tel.: (55) 1138151003
Web Site: http://www.amphenol.com.br
Cable & Connector Mfr
N.A.I.C.S.: 334417

Amphenol-Tuchel Electronics GmbH (1)
August-Haeusser-Str 10, 74080, Heilbronn, Germany
Tel.: (49) 71319290
Web Site: http://www.amphenol-automotive.de
Sales Range: $100-124.9 Million
Cable & Connector Mfr
N.A.I.C.S.: 334417
Ulrich Troster (Mng Dir)

Anytek Technology Corporation Ltd (1)
5F-6 No 77 Sec 1 Xintai 5th Rd, Xizhi Dist, New Taipei City, 22175, Taiwan
Tel.: (886) 26980366666
Web Site: http://www.anytek.com.tw
Electronic Product Mfr & Distr
N.A.I.C.S.: 334417

Ardent Concepts, Inc. (1)
4 Merrill Industrial Dr, Hampton, NH 03842
Tel.: (603) 474-1760
Web Site: http://www.ardentconcepts.com
Semiconductor & Related Device Mfr
N.A.I.C.S.: 334413
Steve Cleveland (Co-Founder)
Gordon Vinther (Co-Founder, Pres & CTO)
Sergio Diaz (Dir-Engrg)
David Emma (Exec VP-Sls, Mktg & Bus Dev)

Bernd Richter GmbH (1)
Hansestrasse 4, 51688, Wipperfurth, Germany
Tel.: (49) 2267881980
Web Site: https://www.bernd-richter-gmbh.com
Emp.: 130
Electronic Connector & Cable Mfr
N.A.I.C.S.: 334417
Thomas Grimm (VP-Ops)

Bernd Richter U.S.A., Inc. (1)
413 Wacouta St Ste 420, Saint Paul, MN 55101
Tel.: (651) 602-0087
Electronic Connector & Cable Mfr
N.A.I.C.S.: 334417

C.M.R. U.S.A., Inc. (1)
940 Riverside Pl, Leetsdale, PA 15056
Tel.: (724) 452-2200
Automotive Sensor Mfr & Distr
N.A.I.C.S.: 334413

CMR Group Ltd. (1)
Technopole de Chateau Gombert 7 rue John Maynard Keynes, CS 80012, 13388, Marseilles, Cedex 13, France
Tel.: (33) 491113700
Web Site: https://www.cmr-group.com
Automotive Sensor Mfr & Distr
N.A.I.C.S.: 334413

CMR Philippines, Inc. (1)
2QA 2F ODC International Plaza 219 Salcedo Street, Legaspi Village, Makati, 1229, Philippines
Tel.: (63) 9178121571
Communication Product Mfr & Distr
N.A.I.C.S.: 334210

CTI Industries (1)
5621 Finch Ave E, Toronto, M1B 2T9, ON, Canada
Tel.: (416) 297-8738
Web Site: http://www.ctiind.com
Wiring Device Mfr
N.A.I.C.S.: 339999

Cablescan B.V. (1)
Hakstraat 24A, 8308 AH, Nagele, Netherlands
Tel.: (31) 527652873
Web Site: https://cablescan.nl
Electronic Connector & Cable Mfr
N.A.I.C.S.: 334417
Ton Van Den Berg (Mgr-Project Bus Dev)

Cablescan Limited (1)
Building No 55A Humber Enterprise Park Cirrus Way Saltgrounds Road, Brough, HU15 1XW, East Yorkshire, United Kingdom
Tel.: (44) 1482873073
Web Site: http://www.cablescan.co.uk
Electronic Connector & Cable Mfr
N.A.I.C.S.: 334417

Carlisle Interconnect Technologies, Inc. (1)
100 Tensolite Dr, Saint Augustine, FL 32092-0590
Tel.: (904) 829-5600
Web Site: https://www.carlisleit.com
Sales Range: $125-149.9 Million
Specialty Insulated Wire & Cable Mfr
N.A.I.C.S.: 332618

Branch (Domestic):

Carlisle Interconnect Technologies (2)
22412 66th Ave S Bldg B Ste C, Kent, WA 98032
Tel.: (425) 251-0700
Web Site: http://www.carlisleit.com
Sales Range: $200-249.9 Million
Cable & Wire Mfr
N.A.I.C.S.: 335931

Subsidiary (Non-US):

Carlisle Interconnect Technologies de Mexico (2)
Blvd Luis Donaldo Colosio M 1195Colonia Obrera, 84048, Nogales, Sonora, Mexico
Tel.: (52) 6313146105
Medical Cable Mfr
N.A.I.C.S.: 332618

Subsidiary (Domestic):

Micro-Coax, Inc. (2)
206 Jones Blvd, Pottstown, PA 19464-3465
Tel.: (610) 495-0110
Web Site: http://www.micro-coax.com
Electronic Components Mfr
N.A.I.C.S.: 334419
Drew Freed (CEO)

MicroConnex Corporation (2)
34935 SE Douglas St Ste 200, Snoqualmie, WA 98065-9228
Tel.: (425) 396-5707
Web Site: http://www.microconnex.com
Radio, Television Broadcasting & Wireless Communications Equipment Mfr
N.A.I.C.S.: 334220

Wayne Van Zandt (Dir-Sales-Marketing)
Sam Ishizaka (Dir-Manufacturing)
Steve Leith (Dir-Engineering-Technology)
Paul Henwood (Dir)
Thomas Clary (Co-Founder)
Scott Corbett (Co-Founder)
Thomas Clary (Co-Founder)
Scott Corbett (Co-Founder)

Star Aviation, Inc. (2)
2150 Michigan Ave Brookley Complex, Mobile, AL 36615
Tel.: (251) 650-0600
Web Site: http://www.carlisleit.com
Specializes in Post-Delivery Modification of Commercial & General Aircraft Certification & Engineering Services
N.A.I.C.S.: 336412

Casco Automotive Singapore Pte., Ltd. (1)
159 Kampong Ampat 04-01 KA Place, Singapore, 368328, Singapore
Tel.: (65) 65496551
Automotive Electronic Parts Mfr
N.A.I.C.S.: 334417

Casco Holdings GmbH (1)
Zuricher Strasse 3, 60437, Frankfurt am Main, Hessen, Germany
Tel.: (49) 6975938276
Holding Company
N.A.I.C.S.: 551112

Casco Imos Italia S.r.l. (1)
Via Enrico Fermi 3/5, Turin, 10091, Italy
Tel.: (39) 0119670311
Motor Vehicle Parts Mfr
N.A.I.C.S.: 336390

Casco Schoeller GmbH (1)
Zuricher Strasse 3, 60437, Frankfurt am Main, Germany
Tel.: (49) 6950064100
Automotive Electric Parts Distr
N.A.I.C.S.: 423690
Scott Brown (Gen Mgr)

Casco do Brasil Ltda (1)
R Arthur Barbarini 399 Park Comercial de Indaiatuba, Joao Narezzi Industrial District, Indaiatuba, 13347-444, Sao Paulo, Brazil
Tel.: (55) 1933856100
Web Site: http://www.casco-cpcn.com
Automotive Electronic Parts Mfr
N.A.I.C.S.: 334417
Paulo Medeiros (Mgr-HR)

Cemm-Mex, S.A. de C.V. (1)
Iris 105 Col 29 De Julio Parque Industrial Kalos Guadalupe, 67205, Guadalupe, Nuevo Leon, Mexico
Tel.: (52) 8188659200
Sales Range: $100-124.9 Million
Emp.: 50
Automobile Parts Mfr
N.A.I.C.S.: 336390
Jose Luis (Plant Mgr)

Changzhou Amphenol Fuyang Communication Equipment Company Limited (1)
No 6 Fengqi Road, Wujin High-Tech District, Changzhou, Jiangsu, China
Tel.: (86) 51986520303
Web Site: http://www.amphenol-fuyang.com
Electronic Connector Mfr
N.A.I.C.S.: 335931

Charles Industries, Ltd. (1)
1450 American Ln 20th Fl, Schaumburg, IL 60173-5492
Tel.: (847) 806-6300
Web Site: http://www.charlesindustries.com
Diversified Manufacturing & Technology Services
N.A.I.C.S.: 339999
John Sieber (Gen Mgr)

Conec Corporation (1)
125 Sun Pac Blvd, Brampton, L6S 5Z6, ON, Canada
Tel.: (905) 790-2200
Electronic Connector & Cable Distr
N.A.I.C.S.: 423610
Nicholas Diamandas (Mng Dir)

Conec Elektronische Bauelemente GmbH (1)
Ostenfeldmark 16, 59557, Lippstadt, Germany

Amphenol Corporation—(Continued)

Tel.: (49) 29417650
Web Site: https://conec.com
Electronic Connector & Cable Distr
N.A.I.C.S.: 423610
Lutz Detro *(Mgr-Distr & Internal Sls)*
Katja Schade *(Mgr-Mktg)*

Conec Polska Sp. z o.o. (1)
Ul Szmaragdowa 10, 52-215, Wroclaw,
Poland
Tel.: (48) 713744045
Electronic Connector & Cable Distr
N.A.I.C.S.: 423610

**Conec Shanghai International Co.,
Ltd.** (1)
Rm 718 Yongding Bldg No 3388 Gong He
Xin Rd, Shanghai, 200436, China
Tel.: (86) 2166300930
Electronic Connector & Cable Distr
N.A.I.C.S.: 423610

Conec s.r.o. (1)
Loucka 137, 763 25, Ujezd, Czech Republic
Tel.: (420) 577350132
Electronic Connector & Cable Distr
N.A.I.C.S.: 423610
Ladislav Koncicky *(Mgr)*

**Connor Manufacturing (SuZhou) Co.,
Ltd.**
Export Processing Zone SMD-Unit B Centre
Suhong Rd, Suzhou Industrial Park, Su-
zhou, 215021, China
Tel.: (86) 51262588188
Metal Stamping Product Mfr & Distr
N.A.I.C.S.: 336370

**Connor Manufacturing Service (Asia)
Pte Ltd.** (1)
2 Venture Drive Vision Exchange 24-01 to
24-32 Suite 24050, Singapore, 608526,
Singapore
Tel.: (65) 68541661
Metal Stamping Product Mfr & Distr
N.A.I.C.S.: 336370

**Connor Manufacturing Services (JB)
Sdn. Bhd.** (1)
No 24 Jalan I-Park Kawasan Perindustrian
I-Park, Bandor Indahpura Kulaijaya, 81000,
Johor, Malaysia
Tel.: (60) 76608198
Metal Stamping Product Mfr & Distr
N.A.I.C.S.: 336370

**Connor Manufacturing Services
(Kushan) Co., Ltd.** (1)
No 33 Yuanfeng Road, Yushan Town, Kun-
shan, 215300, Jiangsu, China
Tel.: (86) 51262588188
Metal Stamping Product Mfr & Distr
N.A.I.C.S.: 336370

**Connor Metal Stamping de Mexico S.
DE R.L. DE C.V.** (1)
Avenida Las Americas 72-A, Fracciona-
miento Las Americas Parque Industrial Gar-
cia, 66023, Nuevo Leon, Mexico
Tel.: (52) 8153500680
Metal Stamping Product Mfr & Distr
N.A.I.C.S.: 336370

**Control Mesure Regulation (UK)
Limited** (1)
New York Way New York Industrial Park,
Tyne and Wear, Wallsend, NE27 0QF,
United Kingdom
Tel.: (44) 1912585222
Automotive Sensor Mfr & Distr
N.A.I.O.C.: 004410

Costronic S.A. (1)
Rue de IIndustrie 58, CH-1030, Bussigny-
pres-Lausanne, Switzerland
Tel.: (41) 218045020
Web Site: https://www.costronic.ch
Automotive Sensor Mfr & Distr
N.A.I.C.S.: 334413

ED Products Ltd. (1)
90 Atlas Avenue, Welland, L3B 6H5, ON,
Canada
Tel.: (905) 732-9473
Cable & Connector Mfr
N.A.I.C.S.: 334417

**Edwin Deutgen, Kunstofftechnik
GmbH** (1)

Kumpenkampsheide 1, Hermannsburg,
29320, Sudheide, Germany
Tel.: (49) 5052988880
Web Site: http://www.deutgen-kt.de
Emp.: 130
Automotive Electronic Parts Mfr
N.A.I.C.S.: 334417

**Ehrlich Werkzeug & Geratebau
GmbH** (1)
Gewerbering 16, Leupoldishain, 01824,
Konigstein, Germany
Tel.: (49) 350 219 8990
Web Site: https://www.ehrlich-gmbh.de
Automotive Plastic Parts Mfr
N.A.I.C.S.: 326199

**Exa Thermometrics India Private
Limited** (1)
181 Lake Shore Road BTM Layout IInd
Stage, Bengaluru, 560 076, India
Tel.: (91) 8040698200
Web Site:
    http://www.exathermometrics.co.in
Thermistors Mfr
N.A.I.C.S.: 334416

**FCI Connectors Malaysia Sdn.
Bhd.** (1)
PLO 205 Jalan Cyber 14 Kawasan, Perin-
dustrian Senai IV Takzim, 81400, Senai,
Johor Darul, Malaysia
Tel.: (60) 75977200
Electronic Connector Mfr
N.A.I.C.S.: 334417

**FEP Fahrzeugelektrik Pirna
GmbH** (1)
Hugo-Kuttner-Strasse 8, 01796, Pirna, Ger-
many
Tel.: (49) 35015140
Web Site: http://www.fepz.de
Sales Range: $100-124.9 Million
Electronic Components Mfr
N.A.I.C.S.: 334419
Evelyn Duarte Martinez *(Member-Mgmt Bd
& Gen Mgr)*
Daniel Rabe *(Member-Mgmt Bd & Head-HR
& Legal Affairs)*
Franziska Kohler *(Member-Mgmt Bd &
Head-Order Disposition)*
Andre Wiemann *(Member-Mgmt Bd &
Head-Quality)*
Guido Glinski *(Chm-Mgmt Bd & Gen Mgr)*

Filec-Lectric SARL (1)
ZI El Fahs, PO Box 75, El Fahs, 1140, Tu-
nisia
Tel.: (216) 72670211
Web Site: http://www.amphenol.com
Cable & Connector Mfr
N.A.I.C.S.: 334417

Flexus Electronic Inc. (1)
95 Hines Road, Kanata, K2K 2M5, ON,
Canada
Tel.: (613) 591-0768
Cable & Connector Mfr
N.A.I.C.S.: 334417

**Friedrich Gohringer Elektrotechnik
GmbH** (1)
Gerwigstrasse 8, 78098, Triberg, Germany
Tel.: (49) 772296360
Web Site: http://www.ftg-germany.de
Plug Connection Mfr
N.A.I.C.S.: 335931

**Guangzhou Amphenol Electronics
Co., Ltd.** (1)
No 5 Jian Ta Shan Road, Guangzhou,
510000, China
Tel.: (86) 2032106099
Electronic Components Mfr
N.A.I.C.S.: 334419
Linda Chen *(Dir-Sls)*

**Hangzhou Amphenol JET Intercon-
nect Technology Co. Ltd.** (1)
29 Futai Road ZhongTai industrial park, Yu-
Hang Town, Hangzhou, 311121, China
Tel.: (86) 5718 865 2006
Web Site: https://www.amphenol-jet.com
Stamping & Inserting Molding Mfr
N.A.I.C.S.: 333511

**Hangzhou Amphenol Phoenix Tele-
com Parts Co. Ltd.** (1)
No 98-5 South Rd 19, Hangzhou Economic

and Technological Development Zone,
Hangzhou, 310018, Zhejiang, China
Tel.: (86) 57186714425
Web Site: http://www.amphenol-hzp.com
Telecommunication Servicesb
N.A.I.C.S.: 517810

Holland Electronics, Inc. (1)
2935 Golf Course Dr, Ventura, CA 93003
Tel.: (805) 339-9060
Web Site: http://www.hollandelectronics.com
Electronic Product Mfr & Distr
N.A.I.C.S.: 334417
Michael Francis Holland *(Owner)*

ICA Midwest, Inc. (1)
N1043 Quality Dr, Greenville, WI 54942-
8625
Tel.: (920) 757-0730
Wire Product Mfr & Distr
N.A.I.C.S.: 335929

**Intelligente Sensorsysteme Dresden
GmbH** (1)
Zur Wetterwarte 50, 01109, Dresden, Ger-
many
Tel.: (49) 351885960
Web Site: http://www.i2s-sensors.de
Sensor System Instrument Mfr
N.A.I.C.S.: 334513
Wolfram Beyer *(Mng Dir)*

Ionix Aerospace Limited (1)
Green Fold Way, Leigh, WN7 3XJ, United
Kingdom
Tel.: (44) 1942685200
Electronic Connector Mfr
N.A.I.C.S.: 334417

Ionix Systems Ou (1)
Pikk 59b, 93815, Kuressaare, Maakond,
Estonia
Tel.: (372) 4521780
Web Site: http://www.ionixsystems.com
Automotive Electronic Parts Mfr
N.A.I.C.S.: 334417

Jaybeam Limited (1)
Rutherford Drive Park Farm South, Welling-
borough, NN8 6AX, Northamptonshire,
United Kingdom
Tel.: (44) 1933408408
Telecommunication Antennas, Masts & Re-
lated Products Mfr
N.A.I.C.S.: 334220

Jaybeam Wireless SAS (1)
ZI La De BoitardiAcre Chemin du Roy,
37400, Amboise, France
Tel.: (33) 247306970
Electronic Components Mfr
N.A.I.C.S.: 334419
Erik Thijssen *(Project Mgr-RF)*

KE Elektronik GmbH (1)
Im Klingenfeld 21, Kressberg, 74594, Markt-
lustenau, Germany
Tel.: (49) 795798860
Web Site: https://www.ke-elektronik.de
Electronic Components Mfr
N.A.I.C.S.: 334419

KE Elektronik GmbH (1)
Im Klingenfeld 21, Kressberg, 74594, Markt-
lustenau, Germany
Tel.: (49) 795798860
Web Site: http://www.ke-elektronik.de
Electronic Products Mfr
N.A.I.C.S.: 334417

KE Ostrov-Elektrik s.r.o. (1)
Prumyslova 1471, 363 01, Ostrov, Czech
Republic
Tel.: (420) 359900111
Web Site: http://www.konfektion-e.de
Sales Range: $100-124.9 Million
Emp.: 250
Cable & Connector Mfr
N.A.I.C.S.: 334417

Plant (Domestic):

KE Ostrov Elektrik s.r.o. (2)
Prumyslova 1471, 363 01, Ostrov, Czech
Republic
Tel.: (420) 359 900111
Web Site: http://www.ke-elektronik.de
Cable & Connector Mfr
N.A.I.C.S.: 334417

KE Ostrov Elektrik s.r.o. (2)

Prumyslova 1471, 363 01, Ostrov, Czech
Republic
Tel.: (420) 35 990 0111
Web Site: https://www.ke-elektronik.de
Cable & Connector Mfr
N.A.I.C.S.: 334417

KE Presov Elektrik, s.r.o. (1)
Jilemnickeho 5, 080 01, Presov, Slovakia
Tel.: (421) 517470777
Web Site: http://www.ke-elektronik.de
Cable & Connector Mfr
N.A.I.C.S.: 334417

Konfektion E Electronik GmbH (1)
Im Klingenfeld 21 Kressberg-Marktlustenau,
74594, Aalen, Germany
Tel.: (49) 795798860
Web Site: https://www.ke-elektronik.de
Sales Range: $100-124.9 Million
Emp.: 1,200
Cable & Connector Mfr
N.A.I.C.S.: 334417
Gerhard Hammer *(Mng Dir)*
Armin Dollinger *(Mng Dir)*
R. Adam Norwitt *(Mng Dir)*
Dietrich Ehrmanntraut *(Mng Dir)*

LID Technologies Inc. (1)
3 rue Giotto, 31520, Ramonville-Saint-Agne,
France
Tel.: (33) 534504092
Web Site: https://www.lid.tech
Automotive Sensor Mfr & Distr
N.A.I.C.S.: 334413

LinxIT LLC (1)
15151 Woodlawn Ave, Tustin, CA 92780
Web Site: https://www.linxit.com
Fiber Optic Network Component Mfr
N.A.I.C.S.: 335921

MSI Transducers Corp. (1)
543 Great Rd, Littleton, MA 01460
Tel.: (978) 486-0404
Web Site: https://www.msitransducers.com
Transducer Material Mfr & Distr
N.A.I.C.S.: 334419

MTS Systems Corporation (1)
14000 Technology Dr, Eden Prairie, MN
55344
Tel.: (952) 937-4000
Web Site: http://www.mts.com
Rev.: $828,586,000
Assets: $1,150,231,000
Liabilities: $929,048,000
Net Worth: $221,183,000
Earnings: ($272,051,000)
Emp.: 3,600
Fiscal Year-end: 10/03/2020
Testing & Sensing Solutions
N.A.I.C.S.: 334519
Randy J. Martinez *(Pres & CEO)*
Steven B. Harrison *(Pres-Test & Simulation
& Exec VP)*
Mark D. Losee *(CIO & Sr VP)*
Brian T. Ross *(CFO & Exec VP)*
Todd J. Klemmensen *(Gen Counsel, Sec &
Sr VP)*
Phyllis B. Nordstrom *(Chief Compliance Of-
ficer, Chief Risk Officer & Sr VP)*
Amanda R. Daniel *(Chief HR Officer & Sr
VP)*
David T. Hore *(Pres-Sensors & Exec VP)*

Subsidiary (Domestic):

Accumetrics, Inc. (2)
6 British American Blvd Ste 103-F, Latham,
NY 12110
Tel.: (518) 393-2200
Web Site: https://www.accumetrix.com
Rotor Telemetry Technology Design & As-
semble Mfr
N.A.I.C.S.: 334513

Subsidiary (Non-US):

Denison Mayes Group Ltd. (2)
98 Church Street, Hunslet, Leeds, LS10
2AZ, United Kingdom
Tel.: (44) 1132708011
Web Site:
    http://www.denisonmayesgroup.com
Fatigue Frame & Creep Mfr
N.A.I.C.S.: 339999

E2M Technologies B.V. (2)
Pedro de Medinalaan 17, 1086 XP, Amsterdam, Netherlands

Tel.: (31) 207070901
Web Site: http://www.e2mtechnologies.eu
Electric Motion System Services
N.A.I.C.S.: 561621

Subsidiary (Domestic):

E2M Technologies Inc. (2)
3259 Progress Dr, Orlando, FL 32826
Tel.: (512) 554-8844
Web Site: http://www.e2mtechnologies.com
Electric Motion System Services
N.A.I.C.S.: 561621

Subsidiary (Non-US):

MTS (Japan) Ltd. (2)
Raiden Bldg 3F 3-22-6 Ryogoku, Sumida-
ku, Tokyo, 130-0026, Japan **(100%)**
Tel.: (81) 356380850
Web Site: http://www.mts.com
Sales Range: $10-24.9 Million
Emp.: 60
Sales & Servicer of Measurement, Automa-
tion & Control Systems
N.A.I.C.S.: 541618

Subsidiary (Domestic):

MTS Sensor Technology Corp (3)
1-6 Yaesu 1-chome, Chuo-ku, Tokyo, 103-
8284, Japan
Tel.: (81) 332790771
Web Site: http://www.mtssensor.com
Emp.: 60
Testing & Sensing Equipment Mfr
N.A.I.C.S.: 334519

Subsidiary (Non-US):

MTS Korea, Inc. (2)
5th Fl Core Bldg 8-1 Sunae-Dong Bundang-
Gu, Songnam, 463 825, Korea (South)
Tel.: (82) 317147151
Web Site: http://www.mts.com
Sales Range: $10-24.9 Million
Emp.: 30
Sales & Service of Measurement, Automa-
tion & Control Systems
N.A.I.C.S.: 541511
Chang Won Lee (Pres)

**MTS Sensor Technologie und
Verwaltungs-GmbH** (2)
Auf dem Schuffel 9, Ludenscheid, 58513,
Germany
Tel.: (49) 235195870
Web Site: http://www.mtssensor.de
Emp.: 200
Testing & Sensing Equipment Distr
N.A.I.C.S.: 334519

MTS Sensors Technology K.K. (2)
737 Aihara-cho, Machida, 194-0211, Japan
Tel.: (81) 427753838
Web Site: http://www.mtssensor.co.jp
Sales Range: $10-24.9 Million
Emp.: 60
Mechanical Testing Systems & Position
Sensors Mfr & Supplier
N.A.I.C.S.: 334519

MTS Systems (China) Ltd. (2)
Tower B Gemdale Plaza RM 1515 - 1518
No 91 Jianguo Road, Chaoyang District,
Beijing, 100022, China
Tel.: (86) 1065876888
Web Site: http://www.compositesworld.com
Sales Range: $75-99.9 Million
Sales & Service of Measurement, Automa-
tion & Control Systems
N.A.I.C.S.: 541618

MTS Systems (Hong Kong) Inc. (2)
Rm 602 Golden Gate Comml Bldg 136-8
Austin Rd, Tsim Sha Tsui, Kowloon, China
(Hong Kong)
Tel.: (852) 23012200
Web Site: http://www.kao-hk.com
Sales Range: $100-124.9 Million
Emp.: 5
Hardware & Software Products Mfr & Pro-
gramming Services
N.A.I.C.S.: 541511
Anthony Poon (Gen Mgr)

MTS Systems GmbH (2)
Hohentwielsteig 3, 14163, Berlin, Germany
Tel.: (49) 30810020
Web Site: http://www.mts.com

Sales Range: $100-124.9 Million
Emp.: 70
Sales & Service of Measurement, Automa-
tion & Control Systems
N.A.I.C.S.: 444180

Subsidiary (Non-US):

MTS Holdings France, SARL (3)
12 Rue Auguste Dupuis, Creteil, 94046,
France
Tel.: (33) 158439000
Web Site: http://www.mts.com
Holding Company
N.A.I.C.S.: 551112

Subsidiary (Domestic):

**MTS Sensor Technologie GmbH and
Co. KG** (3)
Auf dem Schuffel 9, 58513, Ludenscheid,
Germany
Tel.: (49) 235195870
Web Site: https://www.temposonics.com
Testing & Sensing Equipment Distr
N.A.I.C.S.: 334519

Subsidiary (Non-US):

MTS Systems Ltd. (2)
98 Church Street, Hunslet, Leeds, LS10
2AZ, Surrey, United Kingdom **(100%)**
Tel.: (44) 1132708011
Testing & Sensing Product Mfr
N.A.I.C.S.: 334519
Susan E. Knight (CFO & VP)

MTS Systems Norden AB (2)
Datavagen 37b, Askim, 436 32, Gothen-
burg, Sweden
Tel.: (46) 31686999
Web Site: http://www.mts.com
Sales Range: $25-49.9 Million
Emp.: 100
Sales & Service of Measurement, Automa-
tion & Control Systems
N.A.I.C.S.: 541618
Martin Augustsson (Gen Mgr & Mgr-Svc)
Anna Nogander (Coord-European Mktg)
Mia Voll Hansen (Acct Mgr-Inside-Svc)

MTS Systems SA (2)
BAT EXA 16 16/18 rue Eugene Dupuis,
94046, Creteil, France **(100%)**
Tel.: (33) 158439000
Web Site: http://www.mts.com
Sales Range: $1-9.9 Million
Emp.: 40
Sales & Service of Measurement, Automa-
tion & Control Systems
N.A.I.C.S.: 541618

MTS Systems srl (2)
Strada Pianezza 289, 10151, Turin,
Italy **(100%)**
Tel.: (39) 0114517511
Sales Range: $75-99.9 Million
Emp.: 40
Mfr of Hardware & Software Products &
Provider of Services Used to Improve Prod-
uct Quality, Stimulate Innovation & Increase
Productivity
N.A.I.C.S.: 332618

**MTS Testing Systems (Canada)
Ltd.** (2)
Plaza 4 2000 Argantia Rd Suite 100, Mis-
sissauga, L5N 1P7, ON, Canada
Tel.: (905) 821-7811
Sales Range: $50-74.9 Million
Sales & Service of Measurement, Automa-
tion & Control Systems
N.A.I.C.S.: 611710

Subsidiary (Domestic):

Meggitt (Orange County), Inc. (2)
14600 Myford Rd, Irvine, CA 92606
Tel.: (949) 493-8181
Web Site: http://www.meggitt.com
Accelerometer Devices & Shock Sensor
Product Mfr
N.A.I.C.S.: 334519

PCB Group, Inc. (2)
3425 Walden Ave, Depew, NY 14043-2495
Tel.: (716) 684-0001
Web Site: http://www.pcb.com
Provider of Electronic Components Services

Subsidiary (Domestic):

PCB Piezotronics Inc. (3)
3425 Walden Ave, Depew, NY 14043-2495
Tel.: (716) 684-0001
Web Site: https://www.pcb.com
Emp.: 500
Provider of Electronic Component Services
N.A.I.C.S.: 334419

Subsidiary (Domestic):

PCB Load & Torque, Inc. (4)
24350 Indoplex Cir, Farmington Hills, MI
48335
Tel.: (716) 684-0001
Web Site: http://www.pcbloadtorque.com
Motor Vehicle Transmission Parts Mfr
N.A.I.C.S.: 336350

Subsidiary (Non-US):

PCB Piezotronics Ltd (4)
Business and Technology Centre Bessemer
Drive, Stevenage, SG1 2DX, Hertfordshire,
United Kingdom
Tel.: (44) 1438908908
Web Site: http://www.pcb.com
Emp.: 4
Accelerometer Whslr
N.A.I.C.S.: 423830
Graham Turgoose (Mng Dir)

PCB Piezotronics S.A. (4)
Immeuble Discovery Parc Technologique -
Route de l'Orme, 91190, Saint Aubin,
France
Tel.: (33) 169331960
Web Site: https://www.pcbpiezotronics.fr
Accelerometer Whslr
N.A.I.C.S.: 423830

PCB Piezotronics Srl (4)
Centro Direzionale Rondo di Curnasco Via
F lli Bandiera 2, 24048, Treviolo, BG, Italy
Tel.: (39) 03 520 1421
Web Site: http://www.pcbpiezotronics.it
Accelerometer Whslr
N.A.I.C.S.: 423830

Subsidiary (Domestic):

Simutech Group, Inc. (3)
500 Parker Hill Dr, Rochester, NY 14625
Tel.: (585) 424-2010
Web Site: http://www.simutechgroup.com
Electrical Engineering Services
N.A.I.C.S.: 541511
Dennis M. Peel (VP-Turbomachinery &
Testing Svcs)
Rick James (Pres)
John Ilijevski (CFO)
Jim Radochia (CIO)
Butch Vision (VP-Engrg)
Alan McKim (VP-Test Engrg & QA)
Katie Lally (Owner & Dir-Mktg & Sls En-
ablement)
Brent Mattson (VP-Sls)
Victoria Cone (Mgr-HR & Recruiting)

Subsidiary (Non-US):

SimuTech Group - Toronto (4)
50 Ronson Drive Suite 120, Toronto, M9W
1B3, ON, Canada
Tel.: (416) 249-1471
Web Site: http://www.simutechgroup.com
Emp.: 14
Electrical Engineering Services
N.A.I.C.S.: 541330
Alan McKim (VP-Test Engrg & QA)

Subsidiary (Domestic):

The Modal Shop Inc. (3)
10310 Aerohub Blvd, Cincinnati, OH 45215
Tel.: (513) 351-9919
Web Site: https://www.modalshop.com
Emp.: 25
Provider of Equipment Rental & Leasing
Services
N.A.I.C.S.: 532210

Subsidiary (Non-US):

PCB Piezotronics BVBA (2)
Corporate Village building A Da Vincilaan 1
9th Floo, 1930, Zaventem, Belgium
Tel.: (32) 28011354
Web Site: https://www.pcb.com
Pressure Measurement Device Mfr

N.A.I.C.S.: 334419

PCB Piezotronics Europe GmbH (2)
Porschestrasse 20-30, 41836, Huckel-
hoven, Germany
Tel.: (49) 243344444080
Web Site: https://www.pcb.com
Pressure Measurement Device Mfr
N.A.I.C.S.: 334419

PCB Synotech GmbH (2)
Porschestrasse 20-30, 41836, Huckel-
hoven, Germany
Tel.: (49) 2433 444 4400
Web Site: https://www.synotech.de
Measuring Sensor Calibration Mfr
N.A.I.C.S.: 334519

Marport Americas, Inc. (1)
12123 Harbour Reach Dr Ste 100, Mukilteo,
WA 98275
Tel.: (360) 568-5270
Monitoring Sensor Mfr & Distr
N.A.I.C.S.: 334413

Marport Ehf (1)
Tonahvarf 7, 203, Kopavogur, Iceland
Tel.: (354) 5333838
Monitoring Sensor Mfr & Distr
N.A.I.C.S.: 334413

Marport France SAS (1)
8 Rue Maurice Le Leon, 56100, Lorient,
France
Tel.: (33) 297887774
Monitoring Sensor Mfr & Distr
N.A.I.C.S.: 334413

Marport Norge AS (1)
Breivika Industrivei 69, 6018, Alesund, Nor-
way
Tel.: (47) 46536949
Monitoring Sensor Mfr & Distr
N.A.I.C.S.: 334413

Marport South Africa (Pty) Ltd. (1)
11 Paarden Eiland Road, Cape Town, 7405,
Western Cape, South Africa
Tel.: (27) 795198318
Monitoring Sensor Mfr & Distr
N.A.I.C.S.: 334413

Marport Spain SL (1)
Camino Do Chouzo No 1 Acceso Plaza Eu-
genio Fadrique, 36208, Vigo, Pontevedra,
Spain
Tel.: (34) 986117310
Monitoring Sensor Mfr & Distr
N.A.I.C.S.: 334413

Marport UK Ltd. (1)
32 Wilson Street, Peterhead, Aberdeen,
AB42 1UD, United Kingdom
Tel.: (44) 7801678709
Monitoring Sensor Mfr & Distr
N.A.I.C.S.: 334413

Martec Limited (1)
Thanet Way, Whitstable, CT5 3JF, Kent,
United Kingdom
Tel.: (44) 1227287781
Web Site: https://martec.solutions
Power Connector Mfr
N.A.I.C.S.: 335313

NPI Solutions, Inc. (1)
685 Jarvis Dr, 95037, Morgan Hill, CA
Tel.: (408) 944-9178
Web Site: http://www.npisolutions.com
Design & Engineering Services
N.A.I.C.S.: 541490
Dawn Goodrich (CFO & Controller)
John Wells (Coord-RMA)

**Nantong Docharm Amphenol Automo-
tive Electronics Co., Ltd.** (1)
No 599 Hehai West Road Haimen Eco-
nomic Development Zone, Jiangsu, 226103,
China
Tel.: (86) 51389282507
Web Site: https://www.docharm.com
Plastics Product Mfr
N.A.I.C.S.: 326199

**New Product Integration Solutions,
Inc.** (1)
685 Jarvis Dr, Morgan Hill, CA 95037
Tel.: (408) 944-9178
Web Site: https://www.npisolutions.com
Electronic Components Mfr
N.A.I.C.S.: 334419

Amphenol Corporation—(Continued)

Onanon Inc. (1)
720 S Milpitas Blvd, Milpitas, CA 95035
Tel.: (408) 262-8990
Web Site: http://www.onanon.com
Cable Assembly Mfr
N.A.I.C.S.: 335929

PCB Piezotronics GmbH (1)
Porschestrasse 20-30, 41836, Huckel-
hoven, Germany
Tel.: (49) 24334444400
Pressure Sensor Mfr & Distr
N.A.I.C.S.: 334512

PCTEL Europe AB (1)
Kronborgsgrand 7, 164 46, Kista, Sweden
Tel.: (46) 87929200
Wireless Testing Product Mfr & Distr
N.A.I.C.S.: 334513

PCTEL, Inc. (1)
471 Brighton Dr, Bloomingdale, IL 60108
Tel.: (630) 372-6800
Web Site: https://www.pctel.com
Rev.: $99,428,000
Assets: $89,875,000
Liabilities: $20,877,000
Net Worth: $68,998,000
Earnings: $2,869,000
Emp.: 213
Fiscal Year-end: 12/31/2022
Wireless Propagation & Optimization Prod-
ucts & Solutions
N.A.I.C.S.: 517112
David A. Neumann (Pres & Gen Mgr)

Subsidiary (Domestic):

Network Engineering Services (2)
101 Crawfords Corner Rd Ste 3400,
Holmdel, NJ 07733
Tel.: (732) 383-1950
Web Site: https://colliersengineering.com
Sales Range: $1-9.9 Million
Emp.: 15
Communications Engineering Services
N.A.I.C.S.: 541330

Subsidiary (Non-US):

**PCTEL (Tianjin) Electronics Company
Ltd.** (2)
PengAn Road 3 Pengan Industrial Park Be-
ichen, Tianjin, China
Tel.: (86) 2226666741
Web Site: http://www.pctel.com
Electronic Products Mfr
N.A.I.C.S.: 334419

Subsidiary (Domestic):

PCTEL RF Solutions Inc. (2)
20410 Observation Dr, Germantown, MD
20876
Tel.: (301) 515-0036
Web Site: http://rfsolutions.pctel.com
Sales Range: $150-199.9 Million
Emp.: 200
Scanning Receivers & Interference Man-
agement Solutions for Wireless Operations
N.A.I.C.S.: 423430

PT Plasmotech Batam (1)
Executive Industrial Park Block D4 No 17
and 18, JL Engku Putri Batam Centre,
Batam, 29400, Indonesia
Tel.: (62) 7787482300
Plastic Component Mfr
N.A.I.C.S.: 326199

Piezotech, LLC (1)
8431 Georgetown Rd Ste 300, Indianapolis,
IN 46268
Tel.: (317) 876-4670
Web Site: http://www.piezotechnologies.com
Piezoelectric Ceramic Mfr
N.A.I.C.S.: 327910

Piher Sensors & Controls S.A. (1)
Poligono Industrial Municipal Vial T2 22,
31500, Tudela, Spain
Tel.: (34) 948820450
Web Site: http://www.piher.net
Cable Mfr
N.A.I.C.S.: 334417

Plasmotech Pte. Ltd. (1)
3014A Ubi Road 1 02-09/12 Kampong Ubi

Industrial Estate, Singapore, 408703, Sin-
gapore
Tel.: (65) 67435488
Web Site: https://plasmotech.com
Plastic Component Mfr
N.A.I.C.S.: 326199

Precision Wireless LLC (1)
Block K2 Hai Tai Green Industry Base Bin-
hai High-tech Industry Park, Tianjin, China
Tel.: (86) 2283726892
Microwave Component Mfr & Distr
N.A.I.C.S.: 334419

Procaly SAS (1)
Parc des Plattes 12 Chemin des Ronzieres,
69390, Vourles, France
Tel.: (33) 478828200
Web Site: https://www.procaly.com
Electronic Component Mfr & Distr
N.A.I.C.S.: 334416

Procom A/S (1)
Smedetoften 12, 3600, Frederikssund, Den-
mark
Tel.: (45) 48278484
Web Site: http://www.procom.dk
Electrical Interconnect Product Mfr & Distr
N.A.I.C.S.: 334417
Adnan Ahmad (Dir-Engrg)

Procom Antennas AB (1)
Kanalvagen 17, 183 30, Taby, Sweden
Tel.: (46) 709323236
Web Site: http://www.procom.se
Antenna Distr
N.A.I.C.S.: 423690

Procom Deutschland GmbH (1)
Feldstrasse 1, 24983, Handewitt, Germany
Tel.: (49) 461957722
Web Site: http://www.procom-
deutschland.de
Antenna Mfr & Distr
N.A.I.C.S.: 334220

Procom France SARL (1)
128 Bis Avenue Jean Jaures Parc Mure -
Lot J10, 94200, Ivry-sur-Seine, France
Tel.: (33) 149803200
Web Site: http://www.procom.fr
Electronic Components Distr
N.A.I.C.S.: 423690

RFS Technologies, Inc. (1)
200 Pond View Dr, Meriden, CT 06450
Web Site: https://www.rfstechnologies.com
Cable Product Mfr & Distr
N.A.I.C.S.: 335929

SGX Europe SP. z.o.o. (1)
Ligocka Street, 40-568, Katowice, Poland
Tel.: (48) 324384780
Web Site: http://www.sgxsensortech.com
Sensor & Detector Device Mfr & Distr
N.A.I.C.S.: 334511

SGX Sensortech China Limited (1)
Building D No 4997 Bao An Road, Jiading
District, Shanghai, 201805, China
Tel.: (86) 2159571502
Web Site: http://www.sgxsensortech.com
Sensor & Detector Device Distr
N.A.I.C.S.: 423830

SGX Sensortech GmbH (1)
Sudwestpark 37-41, 90449, Nuremberg,
Germany
Tel.: (49) 91121714440
Web Site: http://www.sgxsensortech.com
Sensor & Detector Device Distr
N.A.I.C.S.: 423830

SGX Sensortech SA (1)
Courtils 1, Cormondreche, 2035, Corcelles,
Switzerland
Tel.: (41) 327321670
Web Site: http://www.sgxsensortech.com
Sensor & Detector Device Distr
N.A.I.C.S.: 423830

SSI Technologies GmbH (1)
Chiemgaustrasse 148, 81549, Munich, Ger-
many
Tel.: (49) 89716777910
Electronic Connector & Cable Mfr
N.A.I.C.S.: 334417

SSI Technologies s.r.o (1)
VGP Park Usti nad Labem cp 113, Pres-

tanov, 403 17, Usti nad Labem, Czech Re-
public
Tel.: (420) 602267691
Automotive Sensor Product Mfr
N.A.I.C.S.: 334519

Sarl Conec France (1)
202 Rue des Chevreuils, Poulx, 30320,
Nimes, France
Tel.: (33) 975267217
Electronic Connector & Cable Distr
N.A.I.C.S.: 423610

Skylane Optics SA (1)
Rue du Moulin 18, Fraire, 5650, Namur,
Belgium
Tel.: (32) 71610640
Web Site: https://www.skylaneoptics.com
Telecommunication Equipment Distr
N.A.I.C.S.: 423690

**Societe d'Etudes et de Fabrications
Electroniques et Electriques** (1)
Z I des Cazes, BP 243, 12402, Saint-
Affrique, Cedex, France
Tel.: (33) 565981100
Web Site: http://www.sefee.com
Electric Equipment Mfr
N.A.I.C.S.: 334511

Solid Optics EU N.V. (1)
Veluwezoom 15e, 1327 AE, Almere, Nether-
lands
Tel.: (31) 883423776
Web Site: https://www.solid-optics.com
Telecommunication Equipment Distr
N.A.I.C.S.: 423690

Solid Optics LLC (1)
10575B Virginia Ave, Culver City, CA 90232
Web Site: https://www.solid-optics.com
Telecommunication Equipment Distr
N.A.I.C.S.: 423690

Spectra Strip Cable Products (1)
720 Sherman Ave, Hamden, CT 06514
Tel.: (203) 281-3200
Sales Range: $25-49.9 Million
Emp.: 100
Cable & Connector Mfr
N.A.I.C.S.: 334417

Subsidiary (Non-US):

Spectra Strip Ltd. (2)
Units 212-23 Romsey Ind Estate Great-
bridge Road, Romsey, SO51 0HR, Hamp-
shire, United Kingdom
Tel.: (44) 1794517575
Sales Range: $100-124.9 Million
Cable & Connector Mfr
N.A.I.C.S.: 334417

**Staku Stanz und Kunsstoff Technik
GmbH** (1)
Ostenfeldmark 16, 59557, Lippstadt, Ger-
many
Tel.: (49) 2941765710
Web Site: http://www.staku.de
Metal Parts Mfr
N.A.I.C.S.: 332313

**Suzhou CMR Electronic Devices Co.,
Ltd.** (1)
Workshop 2 128 Fangzhou Road Suzhou
Industrial Park, Suzhou, 215024, China
Tel.: (86) 51262890311
Electronic Device Mfr & Distr
N.A.I.C.S.: 334419

**TPCW Mexico, S. de R.L. de
C.V.** (1)
Campo Real 121 Col Valle Real, 25198,
Saltillo, Coahuila, Mexico
Tel.: (52) 18772831696
Cable Product Mfr & Distr
N.A.I.C.S.: 335929

Tecvox OEM Solutions, LLC (1)
650 Sun Temple Dr Ste 101, Madison, AL
35758
Tel.: (256) 417-4341
Emp.: 39
Engineeering Services
N.A.I.C.S.: 541330
Ryan Brown (Mgr-Fin)
Raj Khanijow (Pres)

**Telect de Mexico S. de R.L. de
C.V.** (1)
Calzada Juan Gil Preciado 2450 - 1 Y 2 Col

Los Robles, 45134, Zapopan, Mexico
Tel.: (52) 5099216067
Fiber Optic Connector Mfr
N.A.I.C.S.: 334417

Temposonics GmbH & Co. KG (1)
Auf dem Schuffel 9, 58513, Ludenscheid,
Germany
Tel.: (49) 23 519 5870
Web Site: https://www.temposonics.com
Automation Machinery Mfr
N.A.I.C.S.: 333998

Tianjin Amphenol KAE Co., Ltd. (1)
Dongli Economic Dev Area, 27 Yijin Road,
Tianjin, 300300, China
Tel.: (86) 2224983820
Web Site: http://www.amphenolcanada.com
Cable & Connector Mfr
N.A.I.C.S.: 334417

**Times Fiber Communications,
Inc.** (1)
358 Hall Ave, Wallingford, CT 06492
Tel.: (434) 432-1800
Web Site: https://www.timesfiber.com
Sales Range: $200-249.9 Million
Emp.: 90
Coaxial Cable Mfr
N.A.I.C.S.: 335929

Subsidiary (Non-US):

Amphenol TFC do Brasil Ltda. (2)
Rodovia Governador, Adhemar Pereira de
Barros Km 121 5 S/N, Campinas, 13098-
396, Sao Paulo, Brazil
Tel.: (55) 1138151003
Sales Range: $25-49.9 Million
Emp.: 145
Cable & Connector Mfr
N.A.I.C.S.: 334417
Marialusa Ferltrin (Mgr-HR)

**Amphenol-TFC (Changzhou) Com-
munications Equipment Co., Ltd.** (2)
100 Hehai Road, Changzhou, 213022,
China
Tel.: (86) 51985103918
Web Site: https://www.timesfiber.com.cn
Cable & Connector Mfr
N.A.I.C.S.: 334417

TFC South America S.A. (2)
Av Callao 966-7mo Piso A, Buenos Aires,
C1023 AAP, Argentina
Tel.: (54) 1148156979
Web Site: http://www.amphenol.com.ar
Sales Range: $100-124.9 Million
Emp.: 5
Cable & Connector Mfr
N.A.I.C.S.: 334417

Times Fiber Canada Ltd. (2)
580 O Brien Road, Renfrew, K7V 3Z2, ON,
Canada
Tel.: (613) 432-8566
Web Site: http://www.timesfiber.com
Sales Range: $25-49.9 Million
Cable Fiber
N.A.I.C.S.: 335921

U-JIN Cable Industrial Co., Ltd. (2)
Cheongyeon-ro Yeondong-myeon, 442-23,
Sejong, Korea (South)
Tel.: (82) 448640858
Web Site: http://www.u-jincable.com
Sales Range: $100-124.9 Million
Cable & Connector Mfr
N.A.I.C.S.: 334417
Tae-Bong Jeong (CEO)

**Xgiga Communication Technology
Co., Ltd.** (1)
Bld A1 Junfeng Innovation Park, Fuyong
Baoan District, Shenzhen, 518103, China
Tel.: (86) 75526063636
Web Site: http://www.xgiga.com
Optical Transceiver Mfr
N.A.I.C.S.: 333310
Richard Sun (Dir-Sls)

**AMPIO PHARMACEUTICALS,
INC.**
9800 Mount Pyramid Ct Ste 400,
Englewood, CO 80112
Tel.: (720) 437-6500 DE
Web Site:
https://www.ampiopharma.com

AMPE—(NYSEAMEX)
Rev.: $5,981,000
Assets: $13,588,000
Liabilities: $1,799,000
Net Worth: $11,789,000
Earnings: ($16,337,000)
Emp.: 5
Fiscal Year-end: 12/31/22
Pharmaceuticals Mfr
N.A.I.C.S.: 325412
J. Kevin Buchi (Chm)
Michael A. Martino (CEO)
Michael E. Macaluso (Founder)
Daniel G. Stokely (CFO & Sec)

AMPLIFY ENERGY CORP.

500 Dallas St Ste 1700, Houston, TX
77002
Tel.: (832) 219-9001   DE
Web Site:
   https://www.amplifyenergy.com
Year Founded: 2011
AMPY—(NYSE)
Rev.: $458,456,000
Assets: $459,478,000
Liabilities: $464,043,000
Net Worth: ($4,565,000)
Earnings: $57,875,000
Emp.: 208
Fiscal Year-end: 12/31/22
Oil & Gas Exploration
N.A.I.C.S.: 211120
Martyn Willsher (Pres & CEO)
Eric Dulany Eric Dulany (Chief Acctg
Officer & VP)
Christopher W. Hamm (Chm)
Tony Lopez (Sr VP-Engrg & Exploita-
tion)
Michael Jordan (Treas & Dir-Fin)

Subsidiaries:

Amplify Energy Holdings LLC   (1)
500 Dallas St Ste 1800, Houston, TX 77002
Tel.: (713) 490-8900
Web Site: http://www.amplifyenergy.com
Rev.: $340,144,000
Assets: $836,843,000
Liabilities: $420,285,000
Net Worth: $416,558,000
Earnings: $54,609,000
Emp.: 222
Fiscal Year-end: 12/31/2018
Holding Company; Oil & Natural Gas Explo-
ration & Extraction Services
N.A.I.C.S.: 551112
Martyn Willsher (Pres)
Christopher W. Hamm (Chm)
Jason McGlynn (CFO & Sr VP)
Denise Dubard (Chief Acctg Officer & VP)
Eric Chang (Treas)

Subsidiary (Domestic):

Columbus Energy, LLC   (2)
6189 Hwy 359, Laredo, TX 78042
Tel.: (956) 722-5239
Sales Range: $50-74.9 Million
Emp.: 25
Crude Petroleum & Natural Gas Extraction
Services
N.A.I.C.S.: 211120
Billy Granger (Superintendent)

San Pedro Bay Pipeline
Company   (2)
160 S Pico Ave, Long Beach, CA 90802
Tel.: (562) 436-0521
Crude Petroleum & Natural Gas Extraction
Services
N.A.I.C.S.: 211120

AMPLITECH GROUP, INC.

155 Plant Ave, Hauppauge, NY
11788
Tel.: (631) 521-7831   NV
Web Site:
   https://www.amplitechgroup.com
Year Founded: 2002
AMPG—(NASDAQ)
Rev.: $19,394,492
Assets: $36,679,634

Liabilities: $7,924,122
Net Worth: $28,755,512
Earnings: ($677,107)
Emp.: 36
Fiscal Year-end: 12/31/22
Radio & Television Broadcasting &
Wireless Communications Equipment
Manufacturing
N.A.I.C.S.: 334220
Fawad Maqbool (Founder, Chm,
Pres, CEO, CTO & Treas)
Louisa Sanfratello (CFO & Sec)
Don Sartorius (Mgr-Quality Assur-
ance)
John P. Pastore (Dir-Sls)
Brandon Worster (Dir-Engrg)
Chris Baars (Sr Engr)
Ewa Polubiak (Supvr-Assembly &
Production)
Jorge Flores (COO)

Subsidiaries:

Specialty Microwave Corp.   (1)
120 Raynor Ave, Ronkonkoma, NY 11779
Tel.: (631) 737-1919
Web Site:
   http://www.specialtymicrowave.com
Radio & Television Broadcasting & Wireless
Communications Equipment Mfr
N.A.I.C.S.: 334220

AMPLITUDE, INC.

201 3rd St Ste 200, San Francisco,
CA 94103
Tel.: (415) 231-2353   DE
Web Site: https://www.amplitude.com
Year Founded: 2011
AMPL—(NASDAQ)
Rev.: $276,284,000
Assets: $433,684,000
Liabilities: $138,931,000
Net Worth: $294,753,000
Earnings: ($90,363,000)
Emp.: 675
Fiscal Year-end: 12/31/23
Software Development Services
N.A.I.C.S.: 541511
Thomas Hansen (Pres)
Liz Fisher (Gen Counsel)
Thomas Hansen (Pres)
Spenser Skates (Co-Founder & CEO)
Jeffrey Wang (Co-Founder)
Curtis Liu (Co-Founder & CTO)
Kristina Johnson (Chief HR Officer)
Francois Ajenstat (Chief Product Offi-
cer)
Shadi Rostami (Sr VP-Engrg)
Andrew Casey (CFO)
Nate Crook (Chief Revenue Officer)
Jenna Elliott (VP-Global Customer
Success)
Andrew Casey (CFO)

AMPRIUS TECHNOLOGIES, INC.

1180 Page Ave, Fremont, CA
94538   DE
Web Site: https://www.amprius.com
Year Founded: 2008
AMPX—(NYSE)
Rev.: $4,409,000
Assets: $83,171,000
Liabilities: $10,138,000
Net Worth: $73,033,000
Earnings: ($17,332,000)
Emp.: 59
Fiscal Year-end: 12/31/22
Battery Manufacturing
N.A.I.C.S.: 335910
Aaron Bakke (VP)
Jon Bornstein (COO)
Kang Sun (CEO)
Kang Sun (CEO)

AMREP CORPORATION

850 W Chester Pike Ste 205, Havertown, PA 19083

Tel.: (610) 487-0905   OK
Web Site:
   https://www.amrepcorp.com
Year Founded: 1961
AXR—(NYSE)
Rev.: $51,369,000
Assets: $122,830,000
Liabilities: $4,780,000
Net Worth: $118,050,000
Earnings: $6,690,000
Emp.: 42
Fiscal Year-end: 04/30/24
Land Developer & Magazine Distr
N.A.I.C.S.: 237210
Christopher V. Vitale (Pres & CEO)
Adrienne M. Uleau (VP-Fin & Acctg)
Edward B. Cloues II (Chm)

Subsidiaries:

AMREP Southwest, Inc.   (1)
303 Rio Rancho Blvd NE Ste 202, Rio Ran-   (100%)
cho, NM 87124-1450
Tel.: (505) 892-9200
Web Site: http://www.amrepsw.com
Sales Range: Less than $1 Million
Emp.: 5
Community Development
N.A.I.C.S.: 237210
Carey A. Plant (VP)
Al Salas (Dir-Field Ops)
Jarrod Likar (VP-Land Dev)

Subsidiary (Domestic):

Eldorado at Santa Fe   (2)
309 W San Francisco St, Santa Fe, NM   (100%)
87501
Tel.: (505) 988-4455
Web Site: http://www.eldoradohotel.com
Real Estate Development
N.A.I.C.S.: 531110
Mark Krumback (Dir-Grp Sls)

American Republic Investment
Co.   (2)
103 Foulk Rd, Wilmington, DE 19803-3742
Tel.: (302) 691-6414
Investment Banking Services
N.A.I.C.S.: 523150

Subsidiary (Non-US):

Kable Media Services, Inc.   (2)
Tel.: (212) 705-4600
Web Site: http://www.kable.com
Emp.: 30
Magazine Distr
N.A.I.C.S.: 424920

Subsidiary (Non-US):

Kable Distribution Services, Inc.   (3)
Tel.: (212) 705-4613
Magazine Distr
N.A.I.C.S.: 424920

Subsidiary (Domestic):

Palm Coast Data Holdco, Inc.   (2)
11 Commerce Blvd, Palm Coast, FL 32164-
4500
Tel.: (386) 445-4662
Web Site: http://www.palmcoastdata.com
Process & Logistics Consulting Services
N.A.I.C.S.: 541614

El Dorado Utilities, Inc.   (1)
1 Caliente Rd Ste B, Santa Fe, NM 87508-
8162
Tel.: (505) 466-4749
Water Supply & Irrigation Systems
N.A.I.C.S.: 221310

Kable News Co., Inc.   (1)
14 Wall St, New York, NY 10005   (100%)
Tel.: (212) 705-4600
Web Site: http://www.kable.com
Sales Range: $50-74.9 Million
Emp.: 32
Magazine & Book Distributors
N.A.I.C.S.: 424920

Kable News Company   (1)
16 S Wesley Ave, Mount Morris, IL 61054-
1449
Tel.: (815) 734-4151
Web Site: http://www.kable.com

Sales Range: $350-399.9 Million
Emp.: 70
Magazine Distribution
N.A.I.C.S.: 424920
Bruce Obendorf (Sr VP-Fin)

AMTECH SYSTEMS, INC.

58 S River Dr Ste 370, Tempe, AZ
85288
Tel.: (480) 967-5146   AZ
Web Site:
   https://www.amtechsystems.com
Year Founded: 1981
ASYS—(NASDAQ)
Rev.: $101,214,000
Assets: $118,953,000
Liabilities: $36,595,000
Net Worth: $82,358,000
Earnings: ($8,486,000)
Emp.: 328
Fiscal Year-end: 09/30/24
Mfr & Marketer of Equipment Used in
Semiconductors
N.A.I.C.S.: 333242
Jong S. Whang (Founder)
Lisa D. Gibbs (CFO, Sec & VP)
Paul Lancaster (VP-Sls & Customer
Svc)
Robert C. Daigle (Chm, Pres & CEO)
Louis M. Golato (VP)

Subsidiaries:

BTU International, Inc.   (1)
23 Esquire Rd, North Billerica, MA 01862
Tel.: (978) 667-4111
Web Site: http://www.btu.com
Emp.: 250
Holding Company; Thermal Processing
Equipment Mfr & Whslr
N.A.I.C.S.: 551112

Subsidiary (Non-US):

BTU (France)   (2)
6 allee Saint Exupery, Montmorency,
95230, France
Tel.: (33) 139348535
Web Site: http://www.btu.com
Industrial Process Furnaces & Ovens Mfr
N.A.I.C.S.: 333994
Oliver Wehner (Sls Mgr-Europe)

BTU Europe Ltd.   (2)
Unit 13 LDL Business Centre Station Road
West, Ash Vale, Guildford, GU12 5RT, Sur-
rey, United Kingdom   (100%)
Tel.: (44) 1252660010
Web Site: http://www.btu.com
Sales Range: $1-9.9 Million
Emp.: 11
Supplier of Thermal Processing Systems
N.A.I.C.S.: 334513
Peter Franklin (Mng Dir)

BTU Ltd.   (2)
Tel.: (86) 2158669098
Web Site: http://www.btu.com
Thermal Processing Equipment Mfr & Sup-
plier
N.A.I.C.S.: 333994

BTU Overseas, Ltd.   (2)
Block 5Block 5 Ang Mo Kio Industrial Park
2A #05-16, Singapore, 567760, Singapore
Tel.: (65) 67414567
Web Site: http://www.btu.com
Engineering Services
N.A.I.C.S.: 541330

Bruce Technologies Europe
GmbH   (1)
Telemannstrasse 24, 93133, Burglengen-
feld, Germany
Tel.: (49) 94715878
Semiconductor Equipment Distr
N.A.I.C.S.: 423690

Bruce Technologies, Inc   (1)
23 Esquire Rd, North Billerica, MA 01862
Tel.: (978) 670-5501
Web Site:
   https://www.brucetechnologiesinc.com
Semiconductor Equipment Mfr & Distr
N.A.I.C.S.: 333242

Entrepix Asia Ptd., Ltd.   (1)

Amtech Systems, Inc.—(Continued)

21 Woodlands Close 08-40 Primz Bizhub,
Singapore, 737854, Singapore
Tel.: (65) 62503328
Semiconductor Wafer Processing Equip-
ment Mfr & Distr
N.A.I.C.S.: 333242

P.R. Hoffman Machine Products,
Inc. (1)
453 Lincoln St, Carlisle, PA 17013
Tel.: (717) 243-9900
Web Site: https://www.prhoffman.com
Sales Range: $25-49.9 Million
Emp.: 30
Mfr & Marketer of Equipment Used in the
Manufacture of Semiconductors
N.A.I.C.S.: 333517
Kerry Woods *(Mgr-Sls)*
Fang Huang *(Engr-Sls & Quality)*

R2D Automation SAS (1)
8 Rue Georges Besse, 34830, Clapiers,
France
Tel.: (33) 467594808
Web Site: http://www.r2d-automation.com
Semiconductor Equipment Mfr & Distr
N.A.I.C.S.: 333242

SoLayTec B.V. (1)
Dillenburgstraat 9G, 5652 AM, Eindhoven,
Netherlands
Tel.: (31) 402380500
Web Site: http://www.solaytec.com
Industrial Machinery Products Mfr
N.A.I.C.S.: 333998

Tempress Systems B.V. (1)
Radeweg 31, Vaassen, 8171 MD, Gelder-
land, Netherlands
Tel.: (31) 578699200
Web Site: http://www.tempress.nl
Holding Company
N.A.I.C.S.: 551112

Tempress Systems, Inc. (1)
Radeweg 31, 8171 MD, Vaassen,
Netherlands (100%)
Tel.: (31) 578699200
Web Site: https://www.tempress.nl
Sales Range: $10-24.9 Million
Emp.: 100
Diffusion Furnaces & Semiconductor Pro-
cesses
N.A.I.C.S.: 334413

AMYLYX PHARMACEUTICALS,
INC.
43 Thorndike St, Cambridge, MA
02141
Tel.: (617) 682-0917   **DE**
Web Site: https://www.amylyx.com
Year Founded: 2014
AMLX—(NASDAQ)
Rev.: $380,786,000
Assets: $517,454,000
Liabilities: $84,022,000
Net Worth: $433,432,000
Earnings: $49,271,000
Emp.: 384
Fiscal Year-end: 12/31/23
Biotechnology Research & Develop-
ment Services
N.A.I.C.S.: 541714
James M. Frates *(CFO)*
Debra Canner *(Chief HR Officer &*
Head-Human Resources)
Gina M. Mazzariello *(Chief Legal Offi-*
cer & Gen Counsel)
Tom Holmes *(Chief Technical Ops*
Officer)
Linda A. Arsenault *(Chief HR Officer)*
Josh Cohen *(Co-Founder & Co-CEO)*
Justin Klee *(Co-Founder & Co-CEO)*
Camille L. Bedrosian *(Chief Medical*
Officer)

AMYRIS, INC.
5885 Hollis St Ste 100, Emeryville,
CA 94608
Tel.: (510) 450-0761   **DE**
Web Site: https://www.amyris.com
Year Founded: 2003

AMRS—(NASDAQ)
Rev.: $269,847,000
Assets: $824,932,000
Liabilities: $1,326,534,000
Net Worth: ($501,602,000)
Earnings: ($528,510,000)
Emp.: 1,598
Fiscal Year-end: 12/31/22
Biotechnology Chemical Products
Researcher, Developer & Mfr
N.A.I.C.S.: 541714
Geoffrey M. Duyk *(Interim Chm)*
Charles Kraft *(Sr VP-Mfg-Global &*
Process Dev)
Christine Ofori *(Chief People Officer)*
Beth Baker Bannerman *(Chief En-*
gagement & Sustainability Officer)
Han Kieftenbeld *(Interim CEO &*
CFO)
Catherine Gore *(Pres-Biossance)*
Kathy L. Fortmann *(CEO)*
Annie Tsong *(Chief Strategy & Prod-*
uct Officer)
Francisco Costa *(Chief Creative Offi-*
cer)
Deb Millard *(Pres)*
Mike Rytokoski *(Pres)*
Lee Tappenden *(Pres)*
Sola Biu *(VP)*
Teresa Lo *(VP)*
Mike Thompson *(VP)*

Subsidiaries:

Aprinnova, LLC (1)
5885 Hollis St Ste 100, Emeryville, CA
94608
Tel.: (510) 450-0761
Web Site: http://www.aprinnova.com
Biotechnology Chemical Product Mfr
N.A.I.C.S.: 325414

AN2 THERAPEUTICS, INC.
1800 El Camino Real Ste D, Menlo
Park, CA 94027
Tel.: (650) 331-9090   **DE**
Web Site:
https://www.an2therapeutics.com
Year Founded: 2017
ANTX—(NASDAQ)
Rev.: $1,351,000
Assets: $102,560,000
Liabilities: $7,188,000
Net Worth: $95,372,000
Earnings: ($42,776,000)
Emp.: 35
Fiscal Year-end: 12/31/22
Biotechnology Research & Develop-
ment Services
N.A.I.C.S.: 541714
Eric Easom *(Co-Founder, Chm, Pres*
& CEO)
Sanjay Chanda *(Chief Dev Officer)*
Lucy O. Day *(CFO, Principal Acctg*
Officer, Treas & Sec)
Joseph Zakrzewski *(Co-Founder &*
Chm)
Paul Eckburg *(Chief Medical Officer)*
Kevin Krause *(Chief Strategy Officer)*
Jennifer Huber *(Sr VP-Regulatory*
Affairs & Quality)
George H. Talbot *(Co-Founder)*
Josh Eizen *(Chief Legal Officer &*
Sec)
Michael R. K. Alley *(Co-Founder &*
Head)

ANACOMP, INC.
13800 Coppermine Rd Ste 100,
Herndon, VA 20171
Tel.: (703) 234-3910   **DE**
Web Site: https://www.anacomp.com
Year Founded: 1968
ANMP—(OTCIQ)
Sales Range: $1-9.9 Million
Emp.: 1,200

Document-Management Outsourcing
Services, Field Maintenance Services
& Document-Management Systems &
Supplies
N.A.I.C.S.: 561410
Thomas P. Cunningham *(CEO)*
William Keller *(Dir-Product Mgmt)*
Kimberly Roeh *(Dir-HR)*
Isabella Janovick *(Dir-Mktg)*

Subsidiaries:

Anacomp (Nederland) B.V. (1)
Telecisie St 15, 1322 AC, Almere,
Netherlands (100%)
Tel.: (31) 365381811
Web Site: http://www.anacomp.nl
Sales Range: $10-24.9 Million
Emp.: 13
Marketing of Computer Equipment & Sup-
plies, Maintenance Services
N.A.I.C.S.: 449210

ANALOG DEVICES, INC.
1 Analog Way, Wilmington, MA 01887
Tel.: (781) 935-5565   **MA**
Web Site: https://www.analog.com
Year Founded: 1965
ADI—(NASDAQ)
Rev.: $12,305,539,000
Assets: $48,794,478,000
Liabilities: $13,229,356,000
Net Worth: $35,565,122,000
Earnings: $3,314,579,000
Emp.: 26,000
Fiscal Year-end: 10/28/23
Analog, Mixed-Signal & Digital Signal
Processing Integrated Circuits De-
signer, Mfr & Whslr
N.A.I.C.S.: 334413
Raymond S. Stata *(Co-Founder)*
John Hassett *(COO-Maxim Bus & Sr*
VP)
Margaret K. Seif *(Chief People Offi-*
cer)
Martin Cotter *(Sr VP-Industrial &*
Multi-Markets)
Patrick O'Doherty *(Sr VP-Digital*
Healthcare)
Gregory M. Bryant *(Pres-Bus Units &*
Exec VP)
Jerry Jian Ren Fan *(Mng Dir, Corpo-*
rate & Country Mgr)
Gregory N. Henderson *(Sr VP-*
Comm, Automotive, Energy, and
Aerospace Grp)
Michael Lucarelli *(VP-IR & FP&A)*
Michael Sondel *(Chief Acctg Officer &*
VP)
Dan Leibholz *(Sr VP-Digital Bus)*
Janene I. Asgeirsson *(Chief Legal*
Officer, Sec & Sr VP)
Anelise Sacks *(Chief Customer Offi-*
cer & Sr VP)
Bruno Kranzen *(Sr VP-Consumer &*
Cloud Infrastructure Grp)
Vivek Jain *(Sr VP-Tech & Ops-*
Global)
Michael Schneider *(Chief Comm Offi-*
cer)
Alan Lee *(CTO)*
Duncan Bosworth *(Acting VP)*
Rob Oshana *(Sr VP)*
Mariya Trickett *(Chief HR Officer)*
Vincent T. Roche *(Chm & CEO)*

Subsidiaries:

Analog Devices (China) Co. Ltd. (1)
5/F Block B Jing Meng Gao Ke Building,
Hai dian District, Beijing, 100085, China
Tel.: (86) 1059871000
Semiconductor Devices Mfr
N.A.I.C.S.: 334413

Analog Devices (Shanghai) Co.
Ltd. (1)
5F Sandhill Plaza 2290 ZuChongzhi Road,
Zhangjiang Hi-Tech Park Pudong New District, Shanghai, 201203, China

Tel.: (86) 2123208000
Semiconductor & Related Device Mfr
N.A.I.C.S.: 334413

Analog Devices AB (1)
Kistagangen 26 3rd Floor, 164 40, Kista,
Sweden (100%)
Tel.: (46) 856421160
Sales Range: $10-24.9 Million
Emp.: 8
Sales & Marketing
N.A.I.C.S.: 449210

Analog Devices AS (1)
Diplomvej 381, 2800, Kongens Lyngby,
Denmark (100%)
Tel.: (45) 48107777
Sales Range: $10-24.9 Million
Electronic Devices Whslr & Distr
N.A.I.C.S.: 423690

Analog Devices Australia Pty.
Ltd. (1)
Unit 3 97 Lewis Rd, Wantirna, 3152, VIC,
Australia (100%)
Tel.: (61) 398819999
Sales Range: $10-24.9 Million
Emp.: 20
Design, Mfr & Marketing of Analog, Mixed
Signal & Digital Signal Processing (DSP)
Integrated Circuits
N.A.I.C.S.: 334515
Zuhra Ruzicka *(Controller-Fin)*

Analog Devices GmbH (1)
Otl-Aicher Strasse 60-64, 80807, Munich,
Germany (100%)
Tel.: (49) 89769030
Web Site: http://www.analog.com
Sales Range: $10-24.9 Million
Emp.: 50
Sales & Marketing
N.A.I.C.S.: 449210

Branch (Domestic):

Analog Devices GmbH-Technisches
Buro West (2)
Ogl-Aicher-str, D 63264, Munich,
Germany (100%)
Tel.: (49) 89769030
Web Site: http://www.analog.com
Sales Range: $10-24.9 Million
Emp.: 6
Sales & Marketing
N.A.I.C.S.: 449210

Analog Devices GmbH (1)
Europaring A03 401, Brunn am Gebirge,
2345, Vienna, Austria
Tel.: (43) 2236377123
Web Site: http://www.analog.com
Sales & Marketing; Conversion Technolo-
gies
N.A.I.C.S.: 449210

Analog Devices India Pvt. Ltd. (1)
Salarpuria Nova No 1 Varthur Road Naga-
varpalya Old Madras Road, Tower D Level
6, Bengaluru, 560093, India
Tel.: (91) 804 300 2000
Web Site: https://www.analog.com
Sales Range: $100-124.9 Million
Developing Technology DSP Analog De-
vices
N.A.I.C.S.: 334513

Analog Devices International Finan-
cial Services Limited (1)
Raheen Business Park, Raheen, Limerick,
Ireland
Tel.: (353) 61495128
Sales Range: $350-399.9 Million
Emp.: 1,200
Investment Management Service
N.A.I.C.S.: 523940
Gennis Toyle *(Gen Mgr)*

Analog Devices International
U.C. (1)
Raheen Industrial Estate, Limerick, Ireland
Tel.: (353) 61302263
Electronic Parts & Equipment Whslr
N.A.I.C.S.: 423690

Analog Devices Ireland Ltd. (1)
Raheen Business Park Raheen, Limerick,
Ireland (100%)
Tel.: (353) 61229011
Web Site: http://www.analog.ie

Sales Range: $450-499.9 Million
Emp.: 1,200
Mfr, Designer & Marketer of Electronic Components
N.A.I.C.S.: 334419

Analog Devices K.K. **(1)**
(100%)
Tel.: (81) 354028200
Web Site: http://www.analog.co.jp
Sales Range: $25-49.9 Million
Emp.: 100
Sales & Marketing of High Performance Signal Processing Devices
N.A.I.C.S.: 334515

Subsidiary (Domestic):

Analog Tech KK **(2)**
BC Plz 2-3-10 Kudan Minami, Chiyoda Ku, Tokyo, 102 0074, Japan **(100%)**
Tel.: (81) 332652801
Web Site: http://www.analogtech.co.jp
Sales Range: $100-124.9 Million
Mfr of Analog Devices & IPC's
N.A.I.C.S.: 334118

Analog Devices Korea, Ltd. **(1)**
7F West Tower POSCO Center B/D 440 Teheran-Ro, Gangnam-gu, Seoul, 6194, Korea (South) **(100%)**
Tel.: (82) 23682500
Web Site: http://www.analog.com
Sales Range: $10-24.9 Million
Emp.: 20
Distr of Electronic Components
N.A.I.C.S.: 449210

Analog Devices Ltd. **(1)**
4th Floor The Record Store 15 Pressing Lane, Hayes, UB3 1EP, United Kingdom **(100%)**
Tel.: (44) 1932358530
Web Site: http://www.analog.com
Semiconductor Whslr
N.A.I.C.S.: 423610

Analog Devices Nederland B.V. **(1)**
High Tech Campus 41, 5656 AE, Eindhoven, Netherlands **(100%)**
Tel.: (31) 404016000
Emp.: 6
Analog, Mixed-Signal & Digital Signal Processing Integrated Circuits Whslr
N.A.I.C.S.: 423690

Analog Devices S.A.S **(1)**
3 rue Jeanne Garnerin, 91320, Wissous, France
Tel.: (33) 169939700
Sales Range: $25-49.9 Million
Emp.: 17
Electric Component Whslr
N.A.I.C.S.: 423690

Analog Devices S.L. **(1)**
Parc Cientific Universitat de Valencia C/ Catedratico Agustin, Escardino 9 Paterna, 46980, Valencia, Spain
Tel.: (34) 911624259
Sales Range: $25-49.9 Million
Emp.: 45
Semiconductor & Related Device Mfr
N.A.I.C.S.: 334413
Javier Calpe (Gen Mgr)

Analog Devices SRL **(1)**
Energy Park - Building 03 Sud Via Energy Park 6, 20871, Vimercate, MI, Italy **(100%)**
Tel.: (39) 039684891
Web Site: http://www.analog.com
Sales Range: $25-49.9 Million
Emp.: 100
Sales & Marketing
N.A.I.C.S.: 449210

Analog Devices Taiwan, Ltd. **(1)**
5F-1 No 408 Rui Guang Road, Neihou, Taipei, 11492, Taiwan
Tel.: (886) 226502888
Web Site: http://www.analog.com
Mfr & Marketing of Analog, Mixed Signal & Digital Signal Processing (DSP) Integrated Circuits.
N.A.I.C.S.: 334515

Analog Devices, (Israel) Ltd. **(1)**
2 Ha'Pnina Street, Ra'anana, 43215, Israel **(100%)**
Tel.: (972) 97774300
Web Site: http://www.analog.com

Sales Range: $10-24.9 Million
Emp.: 15
Sales &Marketing Office
N.A.I.C.S.: 449210

Analog Devices, Inc. - Greensboro **(1)**
7910 Triad Center Dr, Greensboro, NC 27409-9758
Tel.: (336) 668-9511
Web Site: http://www.analog.com
Sales Range: $10-24.9 Million
Emp.: 15
Analog, Mixed-Signal & Digital Signal Processing Integrated Circuits Engineering Services
N.A.I.C.S.: 334413

Analog Devices, Inc. - San Jose **(1)**
3550 N 1st St, San Jose, CA 95134
Tel.: (408) 727-9222
Web Site: http://www.analog.com
Sales Range: $250-299.9 Million
Emp.: 850
Analog, Mixed-Signal & Digital Signal Processing Integrated Circuits Engineering Services
N.A.I.C.S.: 334413

Analog Devices, Inc. - Wilmington **(1)**
804 Woburn St, Wilmington, MA 01887-3494
Tel.: (781) 935-5565
Web Site: http://www.analog.com
Analog, Mixed-Signal & Digital Signal Processing Integrated Circuits Mfr, Testing Services & Whslr
N.A.I.C.S.: 334413

Innovasic, Inc. **(1)**
5635 Jefferson St NE Suite A, Albuquerque, NM 87109 **(100%)**
Tel.: (505) 883-5263
Web Site: http://www.innovasic.com
Sales Range: $1-9.9 Million
Emp.: 33
Mfr of Silicon & Software Solutions
N.A.I.C.S.: 541512

Linear Technology (Italy) S.r.l. **(1)**
Via Torri Bianche 3-Palazzo Larice, 20871, Vimercate, MB, Italy
Tel.: (39) 039 596 5080
Web Site: http://www.analog.com
Integrated Circuits Mfr
N.A.I.C.S.: 334413

Linear Technology (Taiwan) Corporation **(1)**
5F-1 No 408 Ruiguang Rd, Neihu District, Taipei, 11492, Taiwan
Tel.: (886) 2 2650 2888
Web Site: http://www.analog.com
Semiconductor Device Distr
N.A.I.C.S.: 423690

Linear Technology (U.K.) Ltd. **(1)**
3 The Listons Liston Road, Marlow, SL7 1FD, Bucks, United Kingdom
Tel.: (44) 1628477066
Semiconductors & Related Devices Mfr
N.A.I.C.S.: 334413

Linear Technology AB **(1)**
Kistagangen 26 3rd Floor, SE-164 40, Kista, Sweden
Tel.: (46) 8 564 211 60
Semiconductors & Related Devices Mfr
N.A.I.C.S.: 334413

Linear Technology Corporation Limited **(1)**
Units 1503-04 Metroplaza Tower 2 223 Hing Fong Road, Kwai Fong, Hong Kong, China (Hong Kong)
Tel.: (852) 24280303
Semiconductors & Related Devices Whslr
N.A.I.C.S.: 423690
Sam Koh (Head-Greater China)

Linear Technology GK **(1)**
8F Kioicho Park Bldg 3-6 Kioicho, Chiyoda-ku, Tokyo, 102-0094, Japan
Tel.: (81) 352267291
Web Site: http://www.analog.com
Semiconductor Device Mfr & Distr
N.A.I.C.S.: 334413

Linear Technology GmbH **(1)**

Osterfeldstrasse 84 Haus C, Ismaning, D-85737, Munich, Germany
Tel.: (49) 899624550
Web Site: http://www.analog.com
Semiconductors & Related Devices Whslr
N.A.I.C.S.: 423690

Linear Technology K.K. **(1)**
Shin-Osaka Trust Tower 3-5-36 Miyahara, Yodogawa-ku, Osaka, 532-0003, Japan
Tel.: (81) 6 6350 6868
Semiconductors & Related Devices Mfr
N.A.I.C.S.: 334413
Hiroshi Ishida (Branch Mgr)

Linear Technology Pte. Ltd. **(1)**
507 Yishun Industrial Park A, Singapore, 768734, Singapore
Tel.: (65) 67532692
Web Site: http://www.analog.com
Semiconductor & Related Devices Distr
N.A.I.C.S.: 423690

Linear Technology S.A.R.L. **(1)**
Parc Tertiaire SILIC 2 Rue de la Couture, BP 10217, Rungis, 94518, Paris, Cedex, France
Tel.: (33) 156701990
Web Site: http://www.analog.com
Semiconductors & Related Devices Mfr
N.A.I.C.S.: 334413

Linear Technology Semiconductor Mexico S. de R.L. de C.V. **(1)**
Periferico Sur 7999-A, Piso, 45601, Jalisco, Mexico
Tel.: (52) 13315208319
Digital Signal Processing Integrated Circuit Mfr
N.A.I.C.S.: 334413

Maxim Integrated Products, Inc. **(1)**
160 Rio Robles, San Jose, CA 95134
Tel.: (408) 601-1000
Web Site: https://www.maximintegrated.com
Rev.: $2,632,529,000
Assets: $4,523,099,000
Liabilities: $2,107,159,000
Net Worth: $2,415,940,000
Earnings: $827,261,000
Emp.: 7,100
Fiscal Year-end: 06/26/2021
Analog & Mixed-Signal Integrated Circuits Mfr & Sales
N.A.I.C.S.: 334413
Theodore L. Tewksbury (Founder)
Christopher J. Neil (Sr VP-New Ventures)
Edwin B. Medlin (Chief Legal, Admin & Compliance Officer, Gen Counsel & Sr VP)
Rob Georges (VP-Central Engrg Grp)
Bryan J. Preeshl (Sr VP-Quality)
David Dwelley (Chief Technical Officer & VP)
Laura M. Owen (Chief HR Officer)
Kathy Ta (VP-IR)
Jon Imperato (Sr VP-Worldwide Sls & Mktg)
Evan Wang (Sr Mgr-IR)
Eric Chow (Mgr-IR)
Sophie Han (Mng Dir/Country Mgr-Korea)

Subsidiary (Domestic):

Bedrock Automation Platforms, Inc. **(2)**
275 Turnike St Canton, Canton, MA 02021
Tel.: (781) 821-0280
Web Site:
    http://www.bedrockautomation.com
Emp.: 12
Industrial Measuring & Controlling Equipment Mfr
N.A.I.C.S.: 333310
Paul Tornabene (Dir-Sls)

Subsidiary (Non-US):

Calvatec Limited **(2)**
4 Jamaica Street, Edinburgh, EH3 6HH, United Kingdom
Tel.: (44) 1315167800
Sales Range: $25-49.9 Million
Emp.: 25
Analog & Mixed Signal Integrated Circuits Mfr
N.A.I.C.S.: 334413

Icron Technologies Corporation **(2)**
4664 Lougheed Highway Suite 221, Burnaby, V5C 5T5, BC, Canada
Tel.: (604) 638-3920

Web Site: http://www.icron.com
USB & DVI Extension Products Designer, Mfr & Marketer
N.A.I.C.S.: 423430
Todd Hamel (VP-Fin)
Brian Donnelly (VP-Mktg & Bus Dev)
Sukhdeep Hundal (VP-Engrg & Tech)
Glenn Antonelli (Dir-Mktg)

Maxim Direct **(2)**
150 Joseph Kessel Ave, 78960, Voisins-le-Bretonneux, France
Tel.: (33) 1 39 301900
Web Site: http://www.maxim-ic.com
Sales Range: $100-124.9 Million
Semiconductor Distr
N.A.I.C.S.: 334413

Maxim India Integrated Circuit Design Pvt Ltd **(2)**
4Th Floor Tower B Commercio At Mantri Survey No 51/2, Kariyammana Agrahara Off Outer Ring Road, Bengaluru, 560103, Karnataka, India
Tel.: (91) 8061535800
Sales Range: $10-24.9 Million
Emp.: 124
Mfr of Semiconductors
N.A.I.C.S.: 334413
Gopal Krishna (Mng Dir)

Maxim Integrated Products (Ireland) Holdings Limited **(2)**
25/28 North Wall Quay, Dublin, 1, Ireland
Tel.: (353) 12235500
Holding Company
N.A.I.C.S.: 551114

Maxim Integrated Products (Thailand) Co., Ltd. **(2)**
Amata Nakorn Industrial Estate 700 /114 Moo 5, Muang District, Tambol, 20000, Chonburi, Thailand
Tel.: (66) 38468340
Sales Range: $150-199.9 Million
Emp.: 750
Analog & Mixed Signal Integrated Circuits Mfr
N.A.I.C.S.: 334413

Maxim Integrated Products GmbH **(2)**
Landsberger Str 300, 80687, Munich, Germany
Tel.: (49) 8001824943
N.A.I.C.S.: 334413

Maxim Integrated Products India Sales Pvt Ltd. **(2)**
Unit 2, 16th Floor, Gift 1 Tower, Road 5C, Zone 5, Fift city, Gandhinagar, 382355, Gujarat, India
Tel.: (91) 7961701400
Sales Range: $25-49.9 Million
Emp.: 57
Integrated Circuits Whslr
N.A.I.C.S.: 423690
Vimal Bhatt (Gen Mgr)

Maxim Integrated Products International Sales Japan GK **(2)**
Midosuji Daiwa Building 10F 3-6-8 Kyutaromachi, Chuo-ku, Osaka, 541-0056, Japan
Tel.: (81) 647043106
Sales Range: $25-49.9 Million
Emp.: 70
Integrated Circuits Whslr
N.A.I.C.S.: 423690

Maxim Integrated Products International Sales Limited **(2)**
25/28 North Wall Quay, Dublin, D01 H104, Ireland
Tel.: (353) 12235500
General Management Consulting Services
N.A.I.C.S.: 541611

Maxim Integrated Products Netherlands B.V. **(2)**
Delftechpark 37C-D, Delft, 2628 XJ, Netherlands
Tel.: (31) 152629426
Web Site: http://www.maximintegrated.com
Emp.: 30
Integrated Circuits Mfr
N.A.I.C.S.: 334413

Maxim Integrated Products UK Limited **(2)**

Analog Devices, Inc.—(Continued)

612 Reading Road Winnersh, Wokingham,
RG41 5HE, United Kingdom
Tel.: (44) 1189006300
Web Site: http://www.maxim-ic.com
Sales Range: $10-24.9 Million
Emp.: 60
Distr Semiconductors
N.A.I.C.S.: 334413

Maxim Integrated S.A. (2)
ZI Athelia IV Le Forum Bat A Quartier Rou-
magoua, La Ciotat, 13600, France
Tel.: (33) 442981480
Web Site: http://www.maximintegrated.com
Sales Range: $10-24.9 Million
Emp.: 20
Integrated Microcircuit Mfr
N.A.I.C.S.: 334413

Maxim Japan Co., Ltd. (2)
Osaki New City Building 4 20F 1-6-4 Osaki,
Shinagawa-ku, Tokyo, 141-0032, Japan
Tel.: (81) 368936600
Web Site: http://japan.maximintegrated.com
Sales Range: $25-49.9 Million
Emp.: 70
Integrated Circuits Whslr
N.A.I.C.S.: 423690

**Maxim Philippines Operating
Corporation** (2)
Gateway Business Park Special Export Pro-
cessing Zone Brgy Javalera, General Trias,
Cavite, Philippines
Tel.: (63) 464330346
Semiconductor Devices Mfr
N.A.I.C.S.: 334413
Francis Dar (Engr-Test Dev)

**Trinamic Motion Control GmbH & Co.
KG** (2)
Waterloohain 5, 22769, Hamburg, Germany
Tel.: (49) 405148060
Web Site: http://www.trinamic.com
Integrated Circuit & Semiconductor Mfr
N.A.I.C.S.: 334412
James Michael Mollica (Mng Dir)

Subsidiary (Domestic):

Trinamic, Inc. (2)
405 W Superior St Office 702, Chicago, IL
60654
Tel.: (630) 626-4802
Integrated Circuit & Semiconductor Mfr
N.A.I.C.S.: 334412

OneTree Microdevices, Inc. (1)
3843 Brickway Blvd Ste 206, Santa Rosa,
CA 95403
Tel.: (707) 890-8930
Web Site: https://www.onetreemicro.com
Digital Processing Integrated Circuit Mfr
N.A.I.C.S.: 334413

OtoSense Inc. (1)
3239 El Camino Real, Palo Alto, CA 94306
Tel.: (857) 204-5346
Web Site: http://www.otosense.com
Semiconductor Devices Mfr
N.A.I.C.S.: 334413

Symeo GmbH (1)
Prof-Messerschmitt-Str 3, Neubiberg,
85579, Munich, Germany
Tel.: (49) 896 607 7960
Web Site: https://www.symeo.com
Electronic Components Mfr
N.A.I.C.S.: 334220
Stephan Goldmann (CFO & Head-HR)

Symeo Sp. z o.o. (1)
Al Rozdzienskiego 188C, 40-203, Katowice,
Poland
Tel.: (48) 327456060
HF Radio Sensor Component Mfr
N.A.I.C.S.: 334220

ANAPLAN, INC.
50 Hawthorne St, San Francisco, CA
94105
Tel.: (415) 742-8199　　　　DE
Web Site: http://www.anaplan.com
Year Founded: 2008
PLAN—(NYSE)
Rev.: $592,176,000
Assets: $832,635,000

Liabilities: $569,934,000
Net Worth: $262,701,000
Earnings: ($203,599,000)
Emp.: 2,200
Fiscal Year-end: 01/31/22
Computer Technology Development
Services
N.A.I.C.S.: 541511
Charles E. Gottdiener (CEO)
Simon Tucker (Chief Plng Officer)
Vivie Y. Y. Lee (Chief Strategy Officer
& Sr VP)
Marilyn Miller (Chief People Officer)
Parvesh Sethi (Sr VP-Emerging
Technologies Incubation)
Bill Schuh (Chief Revenue Officer)
Ana G. Pinczuk (Sr VP & Chief
Transformation Officer)
Linda Lee (VP-Exec Comm & Cul-
ture)
Osvaldo Bianchi (Sr VP-Go-to-
Market)
Sue McKinney (Sr VP-Platform En-
grg)
John Nassar (Mng Dir)
Jacob Shama (Gen Mgr-Plng AI)
Rohit Shrivastava (Sr VP-Product &
UX)
Erin Siemens (Chief Customer Offi-
cer)
Gary Spiegel (Gen Counsel & Sr VP)
Charles Goodman (Chm)
Carla A. Moradi (Sr VP-Go-To,Market
Transformation)

ANAPTYSBIO, INC.
10770 Wateridge Cir Ste 210, San
Diego, CA 92121-5801
Tel.: (858) 362-6295　　　DE
Web Site:
　https://www.anaptysbio.com
Year Founded: 2005
ANAB—(NASDAQ)
Rev.: $17,157,000
Assets: $452,389,000
Liabilities: $364,286,000
Net Worth: $88,103,000
Earnings: ($163,619,000)
Emp.: 117
Fiscal Year-end: 12/31/23
Pharmaceuticals Mfr
N.A.I.C.S.: 325412
Paul F. Lizzul (Chief Medical Officer)
Dennis M. Mulroy (CFO)
Lewis Gryziewicz (VP-Regulatory Af-
fairs)
Beth Mueller (Sr VP-HR)
Angela Stambaugh (VP)
Bart Burington (VP)
Ben Stone (Sr VP)
Ellen Zigmont (VP)
Kenneth Luu (VP)
Monique D. A. Silva (VP)
Pejman Soroosh (VP)
Priya Raina (VP)
Nick Montemarano (Sr Dir-IR & Stra-
tegic Comm)
Daniel R. Faga (Pres & CEO)

**ANAVEX LIFE SCIENCES
CORP.**
630 5th Ave 20th Fl, New York, NY
10111
Web Site: https://www.anavex.com
Year Founded: 2004
AVXL—(NASDAQ)
Rev.: $8,258,000
Assets: $154,386,000
Liabilities: $12,534,000
Net Worth: $141,852,000
Earnings: ($47,505,000)
Emp.: 40
Fiscal Year-end: 09/30/23
Biotechnology Research & Develop-
ment Services
N.A.I.C.S.: 541714

Christopher U. Missling (Pres, CEO &
Sec)
Athanasios Skarpelos (Founder)
Sandra Boenisch (CFO & Treas)
Emmanuel O. Fadiran (Sr VP-
Regulatory Affairs)
Daniel Klamer (VP-Bus Dev & Scien-
tific Strategy)
Walter E. Kaufmann (Chief Medical
Officer)
Stephan Toutain (Sr VP-Ops)
Adebayo Laniyonu (Sr VP-Nonclinical
Dev)
Edward Hammond (CMO)
David Goldberger (Sr VP-Regulatory
Affairs)
Jiong Ma (Chm)

ANDES GOLD CORP.
1200 N Federal Hwy Ste 200, Boca
Raton, FL 33432-2813
Tel.: (561) 210-8496　　　FL
Year Founded: 1996
AGCZ—(OTCIQ)
Gold Mining
N.A.I.C.S.: 212220
Robert Talbot (Pres, Treas & Sec)
Henry Andrews (VP)

ANDIAMO CORPORATION
129E13800SoSteB2241, Draper, UT
84020
Tel.: (517) 227-2350　　　NV
Web Site: http://www.andiamo-
　corp.com
ANDI—(OTCIQ)
Sales Range: Less than $1 Million
Emp.: 8
Investment Holding Company
N.A.I.C.S.: 551112
Michael McDonald (CEO)

ANDOVER BANCORP, INC.
600 E Main St, Andover, OH 44003
Tel.: (440) 293-7605　　　OH
Web Site:
　https://www.andoverbancorp.com
ANDC—(OTCIQ)
Rev.: $17,581,709
Assets: $526,748,952
Liabilities: $477,944,117
Net Worth: $48,804,835
Earnings: $4,258,282
Emp.: 88
Fiscal Year-end: 12/31/20
Bank Holding Company
N.A.I.C.S.: 551111
Martin R. Cole (Chm)
Nancy C. Cook (Sr VP-HR & VP)
Kimberly A. Giddings (Sr VP-Ops)
Edward B. Debevec (Treas & Sr VP)
Richard B. Kotila (Gen Counsel, Sec
& Sr VP)
Craig A. Cumberworth (Sr VP-Retail
Banking & VP)
Daniel J. Weber (Sr VP-Lending &
VP)

Subsidiaries:

Andover Bank (1)
600 E Main St, Andover, OH 44003
Tel.: (440) 293-7256
Web Site: http://www.andoverbankohio.com
Emp.: 50
Banking Services
N.A.I.C.S.: 522110
Martin R. Cole (Chm)
Donna Shaw (Mgr-Loan Admin)
Diane M. Brunell (Sls Mgr-Community-
Banking Center-Austinburg)
Stephen Varckette (Pres & CEO)

**ANDREA ELECTRONICS COR-
PORATION**
620 Johnson Ave Ste 1B, Bohemia,
NY 11716
Tel.: (631) 719-1800　　　NY

Web Site:
　https://www.andreaelectronics.com
Year Founded: 1934
ANDR—(OTCIQ)
Rev.: $1,961,796
Assets: $877,881
Liabilities: $3,326,676
Net Worth: ($2,448,795)
Earnings: ($288,179)
Emp.: 8
Fiscal Year-end: 12/31/22
Hardware & Software Microphone
Technologies Developer
N.A.I.C.S.: 334220

**ANEBULO PHARMACEUTI-
CALS, INC.**
1017 Ranch Rd 620 S Ste 107, Lake-
way, TX 78734
Tel.: (512) 598-0931　　　DE
Web Site: https://www.anebulo.com
Year Founded: 2020
ANEB—(NASDAQ)
Rev.: $249,022
Assets: $4,073,114
Liabilities: $260,583
Net Worth: $3,812,531
Earnings: ($8,201,703)
Emp.: 2
Fiscal Year-end: 06/30/24
Research & Development in Biotech-
nology (except Nanobiotechnology)
N.A.I.C.S.: 541714
Kenneth C. Cundy (Chief Scientific
Officer)
Richard Anthony Cunningham (CEO)
Joseph F. Lawler (Founder & Chm)
Linda Klumpers (Chief Scientific Offi-
cer)
Dan George (Acting CFO)
Richie Cunningham (CEO)

**ANGEL OAK MORTGAGE
REIT, INC.**
3344 Peachtree Rd NE Ste 1725,
Atlanta, GA 30326
Tel.: (404) 953-4900　　　MD
Web Site:
　https://www.angeloakreit.com
Year Founded: 2018
AOMR—(NYSE)
Rev.: $115,544,000
Assets: $2,946,212,000
Liabilities: $2,709,733,000
Net Worth: ($236,479,000)
Earnings: ($187,833,000)
Emp.: 400
Fiscal Year-end: 12/31/22
Offices of Real Estate Agents & Bro-
kers
N.A.I.C.S.: 531210
Sreeni Prabhu (Pres & CEO)
Brandon Filson (CFO & Treas)
David Gordon (Sec)

**ANGEL POND HOLDINGS
CORPORATION**
950 3rd Ave 25th Fl, New York, NY
10022
Tel.: (212) 878-3702　　　Ky
Web Site: http://www.angelpond.com
Year Founded: 2021
POND—(NYSE)
Investment Services
N.A.I.C.S.: 523999
Theodore T. Wang (Co-Founder, Chm
& CEO)
Shihuang Xie (Co-Founder)
Hanchen Jin (CFO)
Pearl Yuan-Garg (Gen Counsel &
VP)
Kirtiraj Chauhan (VP)

ANGIODYNAMICS, INC.
14 Plaza Dr, Latham, NY 12110
Tel.: (518) 798-1215　　　DE

Web Site:
https://www.angiodynamics.com
Year Founded: 1988
ANGO—(NASDAQ)
Rev.: $303,914,000
Assets: $317,671,000
Liabilities: $112,085,000
Net Worth: $205,586,000
Earnings: ($184,349,000)
Emp.: 748
Fiscal Year-end: 05/31/24
Vascular Disease Treatment Devices
Mfr
N.A.I.C.S.: 339112
James C. Clemmer (Pres & CEO)
Scott Centea (Sr VP & Gen Mgr-VIT)
Saleem M. Cheeks (VP-Comm)
Richard Rosenzweig (Gen Counsel, Sec & Sr VP)
Howard W. Donnelly (Chm)
Stephen A. Trowbridge (Exec VP)
Chad T. Campbell (Sr VP & Gen Mgr-Vascular Access)

Subsidiaries:

AngioDynamics Canada Inc. (1)
2275 Upper Middle Road East 101, Oakville, L6H 0C3, ON, Canada
Tel.: (905) 491-6981
Medical Equipment Mfr & Distri
N.A.I.C.S.: 334510

AngioDynamics Netherlands B.V. (1)
Haaksbergweg 75 Margriettoren, 1101 BR, Amsterdam, Netherlands
Tel.: (31) 207532949
Web Site: http://www.angiodynamics.com
Emp.: 50
Surgical & Medical Instrument Mfr
N.A.I.C.S.: 339112

AngioDynamics UK Limited (1)
Building 2000 Beach Drive Cambridge Research Park, Waterbeach, Cambridge, CB25 9TE, United Kingdom
Tel.: (44) 1223729300
Surgical & Medical Instrument Mfr
N.A.I.C.S.: 339112

Eximo Medical, Ltd. (1)
3 Pekeris Einstein building, Tamar Park, Rehovot, 7670203, Israel
Tel.: (972) 86307630
Web Site: http://www.eximomedical.com
Medical Device Mfr & Distr
N.A.I.C.S.: 339112
Yoel Zabar (CEO)

Navilyst Medical, Inc. (1)
26 Forest St, Marlborough, MA 01752
Tel.: (508) 658-7990
Web Site: http://www.navilystmedical.com
Medical Device Mfr
N.A.I.C.S.: 339113

Branch (Domestic):

Navilyst Medical, Inc. - New York (2)
10 Glens Falls Technical Park, Glens Falls, NY 12801
Tel.: (518) 792-4112
Web Site: http://www.navilystmedical.com
Medical Device Mfr
N.A.I.C.S.: 339113

RadiaDyne, LLC (1)
10801 Hammerly Blvd APT 220, Houston, TX 77043
Tel.: (281) 759-9600
Medical, Dental & Hospital Equipment & Supplies Merchant Whslr
N.A.I.C.S.: 423450

Vortex Medical (1)
14 Plaza Dr, Latham, NY 12110
Tel.: (518) 798-1215
Health Care Srvices
N.A.I.C.S.: 621610

ANGIOGENEX, INC.
425 Madison Ave Ste 902, New York, NY 10017
Tel.: (347) 468-6799   NV

Web Site:
http://www.angiogenex.com
Year Founded: 1999
AGGX—(OTCIQ)
Sales Range: Less than $1 Million
Biopharmaceutical Product Mfr & Distr
N.A.I.C.S.: 325412
Michael M. Strage (COO)
Robert Benezra (Founder)
Martin Murray (CFO)
Michael C. Aronstein (Chm, Pres & CEO)

ANGO WORLD HOLDINGS, INC.
16700 Creek Bend Dr Ste 204, Sugar Land, TX 77478
Year Founded: 1984
AWHI—(OTCIQ)
Investment Banking Services
N.A.I.C.S.: 523150
A. Ricardo Sachango (CEO)

ANGSTROM TECHNOLOGIES INC.
7880 Foundation Dr, Florence, KY 41042
Tel.: (859) 282-0020   DE
Web Site: https://www.angtech.com
Year Founded: 1983
AGTT—(OTCIQ)
Sales Range: $10-24.9 Million
Emp.: 10
Mfr & Developer of UV Chemical Compounds & UV Detection Equipment
N.A.I.C.S.: 325998
Cristine Andrea Peila Koock (Chm)

ANI PHARMACEUTICALS, INC.
210 Main St W, Baudette, MN 56623
Tel.: (218) 634-3500   DE
Web Site:
https://www.anipharmaceuticals.com
ANIP—(NASDAQ)
Rev.: $316,385,000
Assets: $760,087,000
Liabilities: $446,397,000
Net Worth: $313,690,000
Earnings: ($47,896,000)
Emp.: 600
Fiscal Year-end: 12/31/22
Prescription Pharmaceuticals Developer, Mfr & Marketer
N.A.I.C.S.: 325412
James G. Marken (Sr VP-Ops & Product Dev)
Nikhil Lalwani (Pres & CEO)
Ori Gutwerg (Sr VP-Generics)
Meredith W. Cook (Gen Counsel, Sec & Sr VP)
Muthusamy Shanmugam (COO-Ops-New Jersey & Head-R&D)
Chad Gassert (Sr VP)
Krista Davis (Chief HR Officer)
Stephen P. Carey (CFO & Sr VP)

Subsidiaries:

Alimera Sciences, Inc. (1)
6310 Town Square Ste 400, Alpharetta, GA 30005
Tel.: (678) 990-5740
Web Site: https://www.alimerasciences.com
Rev.: $54,129,000
Assets: $42,602,000
Liabilities: $63,410,000
Net Worth: ($20,808,000)
Earnings: ($18,107,000)
Emp.: 150
Fiscal Year-end: 12/31/2022
Prescription Ophthalmic Pharmaceuticals Researcher, Developer & Marketer
N.A.I.C.S.: 325412
Todd Wood (Pres-Ops-U.S.)
Charles Daniel Myers (Co-Founder)
Richard S. Eiswirth Jr. (Pres & CEO)

Philip Ashman (Pres-Intl Ops)
David R. Holland (Co-Founder, CMO & Sr VP-Corp Comm & Managed Markets)
Jason Werner (COO)
Elliot Maltz (CFO)

Subsidiary (Non-US):

Alimera Sciences Europe Limited (2)
77 Sir John Rogerson's Quay, Dublin, D02 VK60, Ireland
Tel.: (353) 15530215
Web Site: https://www.alimerasciences.ie
Pharmaceuticals Product Mfr
N.A.I.C.S.: 325412
Dan Myers (Founder & Chm)

Alimera Sciences Limited (2)
Royal Pavilion Wellesley Road, Aldershot, GU11 1PZ, Hampshire, United Kingdom
Tel.: (44) 1252354000
Web Site:
https://www.alimerasciences.co.uk
Pharmaceuticals Product Mfr
N.A.I.C.S.: 325412

Alimera Sciences Opthamologie GmbH (2)
Cicerostrasse 21, 10709, Berlin, Germany
Tel.: (49) 3081096010
Web Site: https://www.alimerasciences.de
Research & Development Services
N.A.I.C.S.: 541714
Philip Ashman (COO & Sr VP-Comml Ops-Europe)

ANIKA THERAPEUTICS, INC.
32 Wiggins Ave, Bedford, MA 01730
Tel.: (781) 457-9000   MA
Web Site:
https://www.clinicaltrials.gov
ANIK—(NASDAQ)
Rev.: $156,236,000
Assets: $349,128,000
Liabilities: $63,565,000
Net Worth: $285,563,000
Earnings: ($14,859,000)
Emp.: 345
Fiscal Year-end: 12/31/22
Therapeutic Products Mfr for Treatment of Bone, Cartilage & Soft Tissue
N.A.I.C.S.: 325414
Mira Leiwant (VP-Regulatory Affairs, Quality & Clinical Affairs)
David Colleran (Gen Counsel, Sec & Exec VP)
Stephen D. Griffin (CFO, Treas & Exec VP)
Steven Ek (VP-R&D)
Robert Delp (VP)
Lisa Funiciello (VP)
Anne Nunes (VP)
Cheryl Renee Blanchard (Pres)

Subsidiaries:

ArthroSurface Incorporated (1)
28 Forge Pkwy, Franklin, MA 02038
Tel.: (508) 520-3003
Web Site: http://www.arthrosurface.com
Orthopaedic Product Mfr
N.A.I.C.S.: 339113
Steve Ek (CEO)

Parcus Medical, LLC (1)
6423 Parkland Dr, Sarasota, FL 34243
Tel.: (941) 755-7965
Web Site: http://www.parcusmedical.com
Sales Range: $1-9.9 Million
Emp.: 20
Medical Products Mfr & Sales
N.A.I.C.S.: 339112
Mark Brunsvold (Co-Founder & Pres)
Bart Bracy (Co-Founder & VP)
Dan Hauert (Mgr-Sls-Natl)

ANIXA BIOSCIENCES, INC.
3150 Almaden Expy Ste 250, San Jose, CA 95118
Tel.: (408) 708-9808   DE
Web Site: https://www.anixa.com
Year Founded: 1982
ANIX—(NASDAQ)
Rev.: $210,000

Assets: $25,522,000
Liabilities: $2,151,000
Net Worth: $23,371,000
Earnings: ($9,811,000)
Emp.: 4
Fiscal Year-end: 10/31/23
Flat Panel, Video Display & Encryption Device Mfr
N.A.I.C.S.: 334118
Amit Kumar (Chm & CEO)
Arnold M. Baskies (Executives, Bd of Dirs)
Michael J. Catelani (Pres, CFO & COO)
Pamela D. Garzone (Chief Dev Officer)

ANKAM INC.
5348 Vegas Dr, Las Vegas, NV 89108
Tel.: (361) 232-5001   NV
Year Founded: 2018
ANKM—(OTCQB)
Rev.: $1,760
Assets: $446,030
Liabilities: $492,176
Net Worth: ($46,146)
Earnings: ($55,291)
Fiscal Year-end: 11/30/22
Investment Services
N.A.I.C.S.: 523999
Georgii Salbie (Pres, CEO, CFO, Chief Acctg Officer, Treas & Sec)

ANNABIDIOL CORP.
PO Box 174, Marblehead, MA 01945
Tel.: (617) 517-6310
Year Founded: 2009
ACBD—(OTCIQ)
Emp.: 2
Business Support Services
N.A.I.C.S.: 561499
Chris Kohler (CFO)

ANNALY CAPITAL MANAGEMENT, INC.
1211 Avenue of the Americas, New York, NY 10036
Tel.: (212) 696-0100   MD
Web Site: https://www.annaly.com
Year Founded: 1996
NLY—(NYSE)
Rev.: $3,731,581,000
Assets: $93,227,236,000
Liabilities: $81,882,145,000
Net Worth: $11,345,091,000
Earnings: ($1,643,171,000)
Emp.: 187
Fiscal Year-end: 12/31/23
Mortgage-Backed Securities Investment Management Services
N.A.I.C.S.: 523150
Wellington Jamie Denahan-Norris (Founder)
Michael Edward Haylon (Chm)
Steven F. Campbell (Pres & COO)
David L. Finkelstein (CEO & Chief Investment Officer)
Anthony C. Green (Chief Corp Officer, Chief Legal Officer & Sec)
Serena Wolfe (CFO)
Peter Koukouras (Treas)
Ken Adler (Head)
Don Choe (CTO)
Seana Gormley (Head)
Tanya Rakpraja (Head)
V. S. Srinivasan (Head)

Subsidiaries:

Annaly Commercial Real Estate Group, Inc. (1)
1211 Ave of the Americas Site 2902, New York, NY 10036
Tel.: (646) 829-0160
Web Site: http://www.annaly.com
Rev.: $86,893,000
Assets: $973,999,000
Liabilities: $66,126,000

Annaly Capital Management, Inc.—(Continued)

Net Worth: $907,873,000
Earnings: $71,032,000
Fiscal Year-end: 12/31/2012
Real Estate Investment Services
N.A.I.C.S.: 523999

Merganser Capital Management, Inc.   (1)
99 High St, Boston, MA 02110
Tel.: (617) 528-4863
Web Site: http://www.merganser.com
Sales Range: $25-49.9 Million
Investment Management Service
N.A.I.C.S.: 523940
Jeffery Addis (Pres)
Mark Nasser (CTO)
Andrew Smock (CEO & Chief Investment Officer)
Adam Ware (Portfolio Mgr)
Jennifer Wynn (Portfolio Mgr)
Richard McGowan (Mgr-Ops)
Peter Kaplan (Head-Structured Products & Portfolio Mgr)
Todd Copenhaver (Head-Credit Res & Portfolio Mgr)

Onslow Bay Financial LLC   (1)
1211 Avenue of the Americas Ste 4100, New York, NY 10036
Tel.: (646) 979-1460
Web Site:
  https://www.onslowbayfinancial.com
Financial Investment Services
N.A.I.C.S.: 523999

RCap Securities, Inc.   (1)
1211 Avenue of the Americas Ste 2902, New York, NY 10036
Tel.: (646) 829-0141
Web Site: http://www.rcapsecurities.com
Real Estate Investment Trust
N.A.I.C.S.: 525990
Thomas Murphy (Pres)
Jon Hunt (Mng Dir)
William Clark (Sr VP)
Thomas Mullane (Exec VP)
John Frost (Exec VP)
Mike Hernandez (CFO)

Shannon Funding LLC   (1)
1211 Ave of the Americas Ste 4100, New York, NY 10036
Tel.: (646) 728-7982
Web Site: http://www.shannonfunding.com
Mortgage Financing Services
N.A.I.C.S.: 522310

ANNEXON, INC.
1400 Sierra Point Pkwy Bldg C 2nd Fl, Brisbane, CA 94005
Tel.: (650) 822-5500   DE
Web Site:
  https://www.annexonbio.com
Year Founded: 2011
ANNX—(NASDAQ)
Rev.: $3,652,000
Assets: $285,096,000
Liabilities: $53,902,000
Net Worth: $231,194,000
Earnings: ($141,947,000)
Emp.: 80
Fiscal Year-end: 12/31/22
Research & Development in Biotechnology (except Nanobiotechnology)
N.A.I.C.S.: 541714
Ted Yednock (Chief Innovation Officer)
Ben Barres (Co-Founder)
Sanjay Keswani (Chief Medical Officer & Exec VP)
Jennifer Lew (CFO & Exec VP)
Michael Overdorf (Chief Bus Officer & Exec VP)
Douglas Love (Pres & CEO)

ANNOVIS BIO, INC.
101 Lindenwood Dr Ste 225, Malvern, PA 19355
Tel.: (484) 875-3192   DE
Web Site:
  https://www.annovisbio.com
Year Founded: 2008

ANVS—(NYSE)
Rev.: $182,712
Assets: $36,022,069
Liabilities: $7,698,539
Net Worth: $28,323,530
Earnings: ($25,328,567)
Emp.: 5
Fiscal Year-end: 12/31/22
Research & Development in Biotechnology (except Nanobiotechnology)
N.A.I.C.S.: 541714
Maria Luisa Maccecchini (Founder, Pres, CEO & Interim CFO)
Maria L. Maccecchini (Founder, Pres, CEO & Interim CFO)
Michael B. Hoffman (Chm)

ANSYS, INC.
2600 ANSYS Dr, Canonsburg, PA 15317
Tel.: (724) 746-3304   DE
Web Site: https://www.ansys.com
Year Founded: 1970
ANSS—(NASDAQ)
Rev.: $2,269,949,000
Assets: $7,322,875,000
Liabilities: $1,932,511,000
Net Worth: $5,390,364,000
Earnings: $500,412,000
Emp.: 6,200
Fiscal Year-end: 12/31/23
Develops, Markets & Supports Software Solutions for Design Analysis & Optimization
N.A.I.C.S.: 513210
Ajei S. Gopal (Pres & CEO)
Shane R. Emswiler (Sr VP-Products)
Ajei S. Gopal (Pres & CEO)
Janet Lee (Gen Counsel, Sec & VP)
Prith Banerjee (CTO)
John Lee (VP-Electronics & Semiconductor & Gen Mgr)
Walt Hearn (Sr VP)
Andy Kincheloe (VP)

Subsidiaries:

ANSYS Belgium SA   (1)
Avenue Pasteur 4, 1300, Wavre, Belgium
Tel.: (32) 1 045 2861
Web Site: https://www.ansys.com
Sales Range: $10-24.9 Million
Develops, Markets & Supports Software Solutions for Design Analysis & Optimization
N.A.I.C.S.: 513210

ANSYS Canada Ltd.   (1)
283 Northfield Drive E Unit 21, Waterloo, N2J 4G8, ON, Canada
Tel.: (519) 886-8000
Sales Range: $25-49.9 Million
Develops, Markets & Supports Software Solutions for Design Analysis & Optimization
N.A.I.C.S.: 513210

ANSYS China   (1)
Rm 1509 South Building Raycom Infotech Park Tower B, No 2 Science Institute South Road, Beijing, 100190, China   (100%)
Tel.: (86) 1082861715
Web Site: http://www.ansys.com.cn
Sales Range: $10-24.9 Million
Emp.: 33
N.A.I.C.S.: 541511

ANSYS Fluent India Pvt. Ltd.   (1)
34/1 Rajiv Gandhi Infotech Park MIDC Hinjewadi, MIDC Hinjewadi, Pune, 411057, India
Tel.: (91) 2066522500
Web Site: http://www.ansys.com
Sales Range: $50-74.9 Million
Emp.: 250
Develops, Markets & Supports Software Solutions for Design Analysis & Optimization
N.A.I.C.S.: 513210

ANSYS Fluent Shanghai Engineering Software Trading Company Ltd.   (1)
20F Verdant Place No 128 West Nan Jing Road, Huang Pu District, Shanghai, 200003, China
Tel.: (86) 2163351885
Web Site: http://www.ansys.com
Develops, Markets & Supports Software Solutions for Design Analysis & Optimization
N.A.I.C.S.: 513210

ANSYS France SAS   (1)
15 Place Georges Pompidou, 78180, Montigny-le-Bretonneux, France
Tel.: (33) 13 060 1500
Web Site: https://www.ansys.com
Develops, Markets & Supports Software Solutions for Design Analysis & Optimization
N.A.I.C.S.: 513210

ANSYS Germany GmbH   (1)
Birkenweg 14a, 64295, Darmstadt, Germany
Tel.: (49) 61512776659
Web Site: http://www.ansys-germany.com
Sales Range: $25-49.9 Million
Develops, Markets & Supports Software Solutions for Design Analysis & Optimization
N.A.I.C.S.: 513210

ANSYS Hong Kong Ltd.   (1)
1604 Lyndhurst Tower 1 Lyndhurst Terrace, Central, China (Hong Kong)
Tel.: (852) 25259400
Design Analysis & Optimization Software & Solutions Provider
N.A.I.C.S.: 513210

ANSYS Horsham   (1)
Springfield House, Springfield Rd, Horsham, RH12 2RG, West Sussex, United Kingdom   (100%)
Tel.: (44) 1403270066
Web Site: http://www.ansys.com
Sales Range: $10-24.9 Million
Emp.: 30
Custom Computer Programming Services
N.A.I.C.S.: 541511

ANSYS ICEM CFD Inc.   (1)
900 Victors Way Atrium 1 Ste 350, Ann Arbor, MI 48108-5213
Tel.: (734) 213-6821
Web Site: http://www.ansys.com
Sales Range: $10-24.9 Million
Emp.: 14
N.A.I.C.S.: 541511
James E. Cashman III (Pres & CEO)

ANSYS Iberia S.L.   (1)
Paseo de la Castellana 81 Planta 9, 28046, Madrid, Spain
Tel.: (34) 91 789 4900
Web Site: http://www.ansys-iberia.com
Emp.: 20
Design, Analysis & Optimization Software Mfr
N.A.I.C.S.: 513210

ANSYS Italia, S.r.l   (1)
Via G B Pergolesi 25, 20124, Milan, Italy
Tel.: (39) 028 901 3378
Web Site: https://www.ansys.com
Design Analysis & Optimization Software Provider
N.A.I.C.S.: 513210

ANSYS Japan K.K.   (1)
Nittochi Nishishinjuku Building 18F 6-10-1, Nishishinjuku Shinjuku-ku, Tokyo, 160-0023, Japan   (100%)
Tel.: (81) 353247301
Web Site: http://www.ansys.com
Sales Range: $1-9.9 Million
Develops, Markets & Supports Software Solutions for Design Analysis & Optimization
N.A.I.C.S.: 541511
Hotsumi Baba (Mng Dir)

ANSYS Korea LLC   (1)
20F State Tower Namsan 100, Toegye-ro Jung-gu, Seoul, 04631, Republic of Korea, Korea (South)
Tel.: (82) 60090500
Software Development Services
N.A.I.C.S.: 541511
Soyeon Kim (Mgr-Sls Operation)

ANSYS OOO   (1)
Tel.: (7) 4955102538

Optimization Software Publisher
N.A.I.C.S.: 513210

ANSYS Software Pvt. Ltd.   (1)
Prestige Tech Park 2nd floor Mercury Block, Kadubeesanahalli Village Varthur Hobli Outer Ring Road, Bengaluru, 560 103, India
Tel.: (91) 8049010800
Sales Range: $10-24.9 Million
Emp.: 28
Develops, Markets & Supports Software Solutions for Design Analysis & Optimization
N.A.I.C.S.: 513210

ANSYS Sweden AB   (1)
Anders Personsgatan 14, Goteborg, 416 64, Gothenburg, Sweden
Tel.: (46) 10 516 4900
Web Site: http://www.ansys.com
Develops, Markets & Supports Software Solutions for Design Analysis & Optimization
N.A.I.C.S.: 513210

ANSYS Switzerland GmbH   (1)
Technoparkstrasse 1, 8005, Zurich, Switzerland
Tel.: (41) 445009384
Software Development Services
N.A.I.C.S.: 541511
Nino Zehnder (Dir-Engrg)

ANSYS Technology (Shanghai) Co., Ltd.   (1)
20F Verdant Place No 128 West NanJing Road, Huang Pu District, Shanghai, China
Tel.: (86) 2163351885
Computer Software Services
N.A.I.C.S.: 541511

ANSYS UK, Ltd.   (1)
3 St Paul's Place 129 Norfolk Street, Sheffield, S1 2JE, United Kingdom
Tel.: (44) 1142818888
Web Site: http://www.ansys-uk.com
Sales Range: $10-24.9 Million
N.A.I.C.S.: 541511

ANSYS, Inc.   (1)
900 Victors Way Ste 350, Ann Arbor, MI 48108
Tel.: (734) 213-6821
Web Site: https://www.ansys.com
Sales Range: $100-124.9 Million
Emp.: 30
N.A.I.C.S.: 541511

Analytical Graphics Inc.   (1)
220 Valley Creek Blvd, Exton, PA 19341
Tel.: (610) 981-8000
Web Site: http://www.agi.com
Sales Range: $50-74.9 Million
Computer Software Development & Applications
N.A.I.C.S.: 541511
Paul L. Graziani (Co-Founder & CEO)
Francesco Linsalata (Gen Mgr)
William Broderick (CFO)
Scott A. Reynolds (Co-Founder)
Joe Sheehan (Pres)
Peter Sardella (CIO)
Kevin Flood (Co-Chief Revenue Officer & VP-Engrg)
Doug Cather (Dir-Space Ops Technical)
Vince Coppola (Dir-Technical Project Mgmt)
Sylvain Dupont (Dir-Software Architecture)
Tom Johnson (Sr VP-Innovation)
Haroon Rashid (Sr Engr-Advisory)
Cody Short (Engr-Astrodynamics Software)
Frank Stoner (Engr-Advisory Software)
Sunny Wong (Dir-Enterprise Dev)

Ansoft Corporation   (1)
225 W Station Sq Dr Ste 200, Pittsburgh, PA 15219
Tel.: (412) 261-3200
Sales Range: $100-124.9 Million
Emp.: 314
Develops, Markets & Supports EDA Software Solutions
N.A.I.C.S.: 334610
Shane R. Emswiler (VP & Gen Mgr-Electronics Bus Unit)

Ansys Government Initiatives, Inc. AGI   (1)
220 Valley Creek Blvd, Exton, PA 19341
Tel.: (610) 981-8000

Web Site: https://www.agi.com
Software Analysis & Digital Engineering Services
N.A.I.C.S.: 541512

Apache Design Solutions Inc. (1)
9F No 8 Ln 32 Xianzheng 5th St, Jhubei, 30268, Taiwan
Tel.: (886) 35536107
Web Site: http://www.apache-da.com
Sales Range: $25-49.9 Million
Emp.: 19
Computer Software Development Services
N.A.I.C.S.: 541511

Apache Design Solutions K.K. (1)
3-19-1 Shinyokohama, Kohokuku, Yokohama, 222-0033, Kanagawa, Japan
Tel.: (81) 454786360
Web Site: http://www.apache-da.com
Design Analysis & Optimization Software Solutions
N.A.I.C.S.: 513210

Apache Design Solutions Yuhan Hoesa (1)
608 6F Kofomo Tower 16-3 Sunae-Dong Bundang-Gu Kyunggi-Do, Kangnam-gu, Seongnam, 463-825, Korea (South)
Tel.: (82) 7075098032
Software Support Design Services
N.A.I.C.S.: 541511

Apache Design Solutions, Inc. (1)
1307-1310 Room No 899 Dong Fang Road, Pudong, Shanghai, 200122, China
Tel.: (86) 2150817965
Software Development Services
N.A.I.C.S.: 541511
Zhanbo Su (Engr-Software)

Apache Design, Inc. (1)
2645 Zanker Rd, San Jose, CA 95134
Tel.: (408) 457-2000
Web Site: http://www.apache-da.com
Sales Range: $25-49.9 Million
Emp.: 257
Power & Noise Solutions for Chip-Package-System Convergence
N.A.I.C.S.: 334419

Apache Power Solutions Israel Ltd. (1)
6th Floor 91 Hertzel Street Lot 561, Rishon le Zion, 3926, Israel
Tel.: (972) 528531444
Software Publisher
N.A.I.C.S.: 513210
Ronen Stilkol (Gen Mgr)

CERTIF-ICE, Inc. (1)
2385 Chemin Du Bord-Du-Lac/Lakeshore, Dorval, H9S 2G7, QC, Canada
Tel.: (514) 592-8163
Web Site: http://certifice.com
Computational Fluid Dynamics (CFD) Software Developer
N.A.I.C.S.: 513210
Wagdi G. Habashi (Pres)

Computational Engineering International, Inc. (1)
2166 N Salem St Ste 101, Apex, NC 27523-6456
Tel.: (919) 363-0883
Web Site: http://www.ensight.com
Software Publisher & Developer
N.A.I.C.S.: 513210

DYNARDO (Dynamic Software & Engineering) GmbH (1)
Steubenstrasse 25, 99423, Weimar, Germany
Tel.: (49) 364 390 0830
Web Site: https://www.dynardo.de
Emp.: 2
Software Services
N.A.I.C.S.: 541511,
Johannes Will (Mng Dir)

DYNARDO Austria GmbH (1)
Wagenseilgasse 14, 1120, Vienna, Austria
Tel.: (43) 1997120710
Software Services
N.A.I.C.S.: 541511,

DYNAmore Nordic AB (1)
Brigadgatan 5, 58758, Linkoping, Sweden
Tel.: (46) 13236680
Web Site: https://www.dynamore.se

Emp.: 26
Software Development & Computer System Services
N.A.I.C.S.: 541512

DfR Solutions, LLC (1)
9000 Virginia Manor Rd Ste 290, Beltsville, MD 20705
Tel.: (301) 474-0607
Web Site: http://www.dfrsolutions.com
Engineeering Services
N.A.I.C.S.: 541330
Craig Hillman (CEO)
Ed Dodd (Mgr-Bus Dev)
Mark Musitano (Acct Mgr)
Gilad Sharon (Sr Engr-Application)
Natalie Hernandez (Sr Product Mgr)
Billie Early (Program Mgr)
Vidyu Challa (Mgr-Consulting)
Michael Howard (Sr Mgr-Consulting)
Chris Montgomery (Reg Dir-Sls)
Ashok Alagappan (Sys Engr)
Dock Brown (Sys Engr)
Greg Caswell (Sys Engr)

Diakopto Inc. (1)
4010 Moorpark Ave Ste 204, San Jose, CA 95117
Tel.: (408) 345-5909
Web Site: https://diakopto.com
Semiconductor Design Mfr
N.A.I.C.S.: 334413

Esterel Technologies, S.A. (1)
15 Place Georges Pompidou, 78180, Montigny-le-Bretonneux, France **(100%)**
Tel.: (33) 1 30 68 61 60
Web Site: http://www.esterel-technologies.com
Sales Range: $10-24.9 Million
Emp.: 100
Develops & Produces Software Development Tools for Embedded Systems
N.A.I.C.S.: 513210
Marie-Aude De Bonnieres (CFO)

Subsidiary (Non-US):

Esterel Technologies GmbH (2)
Otto-Hahn-Strasse 13b, 85521, Ottobrunn, Germany
Tel.: (49) 8960875537
Web Site: http://www.esterel-technologies.com
Computer Software Sales
N.A.I.C.S.: 423430

Subsidiary (US):

Esterel Technologies, Inc. (2)
1802 N Alafaya Trl Ste 124, Orlando, FL 32826
Tel.: (724) 746-3304
Web Site: http://www.esterel-technologies.com
Sales Range: $10-24.9 Million
Emp.: 10
Develops & Produces Software Development Tools for Embedded Systems
N.A.I.C.S.: 513210

Gear Design Solutions, Inc. (1)
1762 Technology Dr Ste 118, San Jose, CA 95138
Tel.: (408) 219-0344
Emp.: 3
Software Development Services
N.A.I.C.S.: 541511

Granta Design Limited (1)
300 Rustat House 62 Clifton Road, Cambridge, CB1 7EG, United Kingdom
Tel.: (44) 1223218000
Web Site: http://www.grantadesign.com
Software Services
N.A.I.C.S.: 541511
Wen Zhao (Mgr-Bus Dev)

Livermore Software Technology Corp. (1)
7374 Las Positas Rd, Livermore, CA 94551
Tel.: (925) 449-2500
Web Site: https://www.lstc.com
Software Development Support & Consulting Services
N.A.I.C.S.: 541511

OPTIS CN Limited (1)
Room 2003, No. 1 building Green Land Central Plaza Lane 1377, Jiangchang Road

Jing'an District, Shanghai, China
Tel.: (86) 4008198999
Software Development Services
N.A.I.C.S.: 541511

OPTIS Japan K.K. (1)
Pacific Century Place Marunouchi 16F 1-11-1 Marunouchi, Chiyoda-ku, Tokyo, 100-6216, Japan
Tel.: (81) 362680047
Software Development Services
N.A.I.C.S.: 541511
Taka Yoshimura (Owner)

OPTIS Korea Co., Ltd (1)
1908 A-dong 17 Gosan-ro 148beon-gil, Gunpo, Gyeonggi, Korea (South)
Tel.: (82) 314555422
Software Development Services
N.A.I.C.S.: 541511
Justin Son (Sls Mgr)

OPTIS North America Inc. (1)
3001 W Big Beaver Rd Ste 404, Troy, MI 48084-3105
Tel.: (248) 251-0128
Software Development Services
N.A.I.C.S.: 513210

OPTIS Pristine Limited (1)
Suite G39 Daresbury Innovation Centre, Daresbury Science and Innovation Campus Keckwick Lane, Daresbury, WA4 4FS, United Kingdom
Tel.: (44) 1925607295
Software Development Services
N.A.I.C.S.: 541511

OPTIS SAS (1)
WTC Les Deux Arcs Bat C 1800 Route des Cretes, Sophia-Antipolis, 6560, Valbonne, France
Tel.: (33) 494087745
Software Development Services
N.A.I.C.S.: 541511

Phoenix Integration, Inc. (1)
1275 Drummers Ln Ste 105, Wayne, PA 19087
Tel.: (610) 971-9603
Web Site: http://stingray.phoenix-int.com
Sales Range: $10-24.9 Million
Emp.: 30
Computer System Design Services
N.A.I.C.S.: 541512
Chris Randazzo (VP-Sls & Mktg)
Scott Woyak (Founder)
Alan Arico (Dir-Sls & Mktg)
Jane Trenaman (CEO)
Yvain Ballini (Mgr-Sls-European Territory)

Unit (Domestic):

Phoenix Integration, Inc. - North America (2)
1715 Pratt Dr Ste 2000, Blacksburg, VA 24060
Tel.: (540) 961-7215
Web Site: https://www.phoenix-int.com
Sales Range: $10-24.9 Million
Computer System Design Services
N.A.I.C.S.: 541512
Chris Randazzo (VP-Sls & Mktg)

Reaction Design, Inc. (1)
5930 Cornerstone Ct W Ste 230, San Diego, CA 92121
Tel.: (858) 550-1920
Web Site: http://www.reactiondesign.com
Sales Range: $1-9.9 Million
Emp.: 25
Engineering Simulation Software Developer
N.A.I.C.S.: 513210

SpaceClaim Corporation (1)
150 Baker Ave Ext, Concord, MA 01742
Tel.: (978) 482-2100
Web Site: http://www.spaceclaim.com
Software Development Services
N.A.I.C.S.: 541511

SpaceClaim Japan, K.K. (1)
Day land Nishi building 18F 6-10-1 Nishishinjuku, Shinjuku-ku, Tokyo, 160-0023, Japan
Tel.: (81) 353247653
Web Site: http://www.spaceclaim.com
Software Development Services
N.A.I.C.S.: 541511

Zemax Europe Limited (1)

Unit 6 and 8 Riverside Business Park Stoney Common Road, Stansted, CM24 8PL, Essex, United Kingdom
Tel.: (44) 127 981 0911
Software Development Services
N.A.I.C.S.: 541512

Zemax Japan K.K. (1)
AD Ichigaya Building 4th Floor 2-5 Ichigaya Honmura-cho, Shinjuku-ku, Tokyo, 162-0845, Japan
Tel.: (81) 34 405 6085
Software Development Services
N.A.I.C.S.: 541512

Zemax Optical Technology Consulting (Shanghai) Co., Ltd. (1)
Room 1806 Donghai SOHO Square No 299 Tongren Road, Jingan District, Shanghai, 200040, China
Tel.: (86) 216 271 3200
Software Development Services
N.A.I.C.S.: 541512

ANTERIX INC.
3 Garret Mountain Plz Ste 401, Woodland Park, NJ 07424
Tel.: (973) 771-0300   DE
Web Site: https://www.anterix.com
Year Founded: 1997
ATEX—(NASDAQ)
Rev.: $4,191,000
Assets: $324,894,000
Liabilities: $163,862,000
Net Worth: $161,032,000
Earnings: ($9,128,000)
Emp.: 86
Fiscal Year-end: 03/31/24
Computer System Design Services
N.A.I.C.S.: 541512
Gena L. Hudgins-Ashe (Chief Legal Officer & Sec)
Robert H. Schwartz (Pres & CEO)
Thomas R. Kuhn (Vice Chm)
Natasha Vecchiarelli (Dir-IR & Corp Comm)
Gena L. Ashe (Chief Legal Officer & Sec)
Morgan E. O'Brien (Chm)
Timothy A. Gray (CFO)
Ryan Gerbrandt (COO)
Carlos L'Abbate (CTO & Chief Engrg Officer)
Chris Guttman-McCabe (Chief Regulatory & Comm Officer)
Wassim Akhdar (Sr VP-Product & Innovation)
Alice Moy-Gonzalez (Sr VP-Strategic Development)
Gretchen Starcher (Chief People Officer)

ANTERO MIDSTREAM CORPORATION
1615 Wynkoop St, Denver, CO 80202
Tel.: (303) 357-7310   DE
Web Site:
https://www.anteromidstream.com
Year Founded: 2013
AM—(NYSE)
Rev.: $1,041,771,000
Assets: $5,737,618,000
Liabilities: $3,585,887,000
Net Worth: $2,151,731,000
Earnings: $371,786,000
Emp.: 604
Fiscal Year-end: 12/31/23
Natural Gas Distr
N.A.I.C.S.: 221210
Paul M. Rady (Chm, Pres & CEO)
Steven M. Woodward (Sr VP-Bus Dev)
J. Kevin Ellis (Sr VP-Reg)
Sheri L. Pearce (Chief Acctg Officer & Sr VP-Acctg)
Michael N. Kennedy (Sr VP-Fin)
W. Patrick Ash (Sr VP-Reserves, Plng, and Midstream)

Antero Midstream Corporation—(Continued)

Jennifer A. Hornemann *(VP)*
Jeremy D. Jones *(VP)*
Jon S. McEvers *(Sr VP-Ops)*

Subsidiaries:

Antero Midstream Partners LP **(1)**
1615 Wynkoop St, Denver, CO 80202
Tel.: (303) 357-7310
Web Site: https://www.anteromidstream.com
Rev.: $1,028,522,000
Assets: $3,546,417,000
Liabilities: $1,854,909,000
Net Worth: $1,691,508,000
Earnings: $585,944,000
Fiscal Year-end: 12/31/2018
Midstream Energy Assets Owner, Operator
& Developer
N.A.I.C.S.: 237130
Alvyn A. Schopp *(Chief Admin Officer, Treas & Reg Sr VP)*
Kevin J. Kilstrom *(Sr VP)*
Steven M. Woodward *(Sr VP-Bus Dev)*
Aaron S. G. Merrick *(Chief Admin Officer)*
W. Patrick Ash *(Sr VP-Planning)*
Maria Wood Henry *(Sr VP)*
Jeremy D. Jones *(VP)*
Jen A. Hornemann *(VP)*
Jeremy D. Jones *(VP)*
Jen A. Hornemann *(VP)*
Jeremy D. Jones *(VP)*
Jen A. Hornemann *(VP)*
Brendan E. Krueger *(CFO)*
Yueete K. Schultz *(Sec)*
Sheri L. Pearce *(Chief Acctg Officer)*
David A. Cannelongo *(Sr VP)*
Justin B. Fowler *(Sr VP)*
Robert H. Krcek *(Sr VP)*
Jon S. McEvers *(Sr VP)*

**ANTERO RESOURCES COR-
PORATION**
1615 Wynkoop St, Denver, CO 80202
Tel.: (303) 357-7310　　DE
Web Site:
https://www.anteroresources.com
Year Founded: 2002
AR—(NYSE)
Rev.: $4,681,972,000
Assets: $13,619,414,000
Liabilities: $6,405,312,000
Net Worth: $7,214,102,000
Earnings: $242,919,000
Emp.: 604
Fiscal Year-end: 12/31/23
Oil & Natural Gas Services
N.A.I.C.S.: 213112
Paul M. Rady *(Co-Founder, Chm, Pres & CEO)*
Steven M. Woodward *(Sr VP-Bus Dev)*
W. Patrick Ash *(Sr VP-Reserves, Plng, and Midstream)*
Brendan E. Krueger *(Treas & VP-Fin)*
Dan Katzenberg *(Dir-Fin)*
Jon S. McEvers *(Sr VP)*

Subsidiaries:

Antero Midstream LLC **(1)**
1615 Wynkoop St, Denver, CO 80202
Tel.: (303) 357-7310
Natural Gas Extraction Services
N.A.I.C.S.: 211130

Monroe Pipeline LLC **(1)**
46678 Swazey Rd, Monroe, OH 43754
Tel.: (740) 838-1148
Crude Oil Transportation Services
N.A.I.C.S.: 486110

**ANTHERA PHARMACEUTI-
CALS, INC.**
25801 Industrial Blvd Ste B, Hay-
ward, CA 94545
Tel.: (510) 856-5600　　DE
Web Site: http://www.anthera.com
Year Founded: 2004
ANTH—(OTCIQ)
Sales Range: $1-9.9 Million

Emp.: 21
Pharmaceuticals Mfr
N.A.I.C.S.: 325412
May Liu *(Sr VP-Fin & Admin)*
Craig B. Thompson *(Pres & CEO)*

ANTHROPOS CAPITAL CORP.
201 Broad St 14th Fl, Stamford, CT 06901
Tel.: (216) 408-0134　　Ky
Year Founded: 2021
HUMCU—(NASDAQ)
Investment Services
N.A.I.C.S.: 523999
John Megrue *(Co-CEO)*
Fred Crawford *(Co-CEO)*
Benjamin Pinkas *(CFO)*

**ANTIAGING QUANTUM LIVING
INC.**
1345 Avenue of the Americas 33rd Fl,
New York, NY 10105
Tel.: (917) 470-5393　　NY
Year Founded: 2014
AAQL—(OTCIQ)
Rev.: $13,600
Assets: $894
Liabilities: $87,001
Net Worth: ($86,107)
Earnings: ($36,630)
Fiscal Year-end: 03/31/23
Investment Services
N.A.I.C.S.: 523999
Barry Wan *(Chm & CEO)*

**ANVIA HOLDINGS CORPORA-
TION**
100 Challenger Rd Ste 830, Ridge-
field Park, NJ 07660
Tel.: (323) 713-3244　　DE
Web Site:
http://www.anviaholdings.com
Year Founded: 2016
ANVV—(OTCIQ)
Rev.: $14,245,425
Assets: $20,722,373
Liabilities: $20,116,894
Net Worth: $605,479
Earnings: ($3,386,248)
Emp.: 84
Fiscal Year-end: 12/31/19
Education Training Services
N.A.I.C.S.: 611710
Ali Kasa *(Pres, CFO, CEO & Sec)*

**ANYWHERE REAL ESTATE
INC.**
175 Park Ave, Madison, NJ 07940
Tel.: (973) 407-2000　　DE
Web Site: https://anywhere.re
Year Founded: 2006
HOUS—(NYSE)
Rev.: $6,908,000,000
Assets: $6,383,000,000
Liabilities: $4,616,000,000
Net Worth: $1,767,000,000
Earnings: ($287,000,000)
Emp.: 8,890
Fiscal Year-end: 12/31/22
Holding Company; Real Estate Bro-
kerage Services
N.A.I.C.S.: 551112
Marilyn J. Wasser *(Gen Counsel, Sec & Exec VP)*
Timothy B. Gustavson *(Chief Acctg Officer, Sr VP & Controller)*
Ryan M. Schneider *(Pres & CEO)*
Charlotte C. Simonelli *(CFO, Treas & Exec VP)*
Tanya Reu-Narvaez *(Chief People Officer & Exec VP)*
Caitlin McCrory *(VP-Industry Rels)*
Trey Sarten *(Chief Comm Officer)*
Shacara Delgado *(Chief Ethics Offi-
cer)*

Peter J. Sobeck *(Exec VP)*
Rebecca Jensen Tallent *(VP)*
Rudy Wolfs *(CTO & Exec VP)*

Subsidiaries:

Anywhere Real Estate Group
LLC **(1)**
175 Park Ave, Madison, NJ 07940
Tel.: (973) 407-2000
Web Site: https://www.anywhere.re
Rev.: $5,635,999,999
Assets: $5,838,999,999
Liabilities: $4,157,999,999
Net Worth: $1,680,999,999
Earnings: ($96,999,999)
Emp.: 7,964
Fiscal Year-end: 12/31/2023
Real Estate & Relocation Services
N.A.I.C.S.: 531390
Michael J. Williams *(Chm)*

Subsidiary (Domestic):

Better Homes & Gardens Real Estate
LLC **(2)**
175 Park Ave, Madison, NJ 07940
Tel.: (973) 407-6880
Web Site: https://www.bhgre.com
Real Estate Agencies & Brokerage Services
N.A.I.C.S.: 531210
Sherry Chris *(Pres & CEO)*

Subsidiary (Domestic):

GH LII Management, LLC **(3)**
5120 Woodway Dr Ste 5020, Houston, TX 77056
Tel.: (713) 465-6644
Web Site: http://www.garygreene.com
Emp.: 1,100
Real Estate Agency
N.A.I.C.S.: 531210
John Stoever *(CFO)*
Chaille Ralph *(VP-Ops)*
Toni Nelson *(Dir-Competitive Intelligence)*
Dianne McCoy *(Dir-Education & Compli-
ance)*
Terri McGowan *(VP-Sls Growth)*
Kristen Brown *(Dir-Relocation)*

Subsidiary (Domestic):

Heritage Texas Properties, LLC **(4)**
14340 Memorial Dr, Houston, TX 77079
Tel.: (281) 493-3880
Web Site: http://www.heritagetexas.com
Sales Range: $25-49.9 Million
Emp.: 300
Real Estate Broker Services
N.A.I.C.S.: 531210
Robin Mueck *(CEO)*
Chaille G. Ralph *(VP-Ops)*
John McFarlin *(Mng Dir-Comml Svcs)*

Subsidiary (Domestic):

CGRN, Inc. **(2)**
175 Park Ave, Madison, NJ 07940
Tel.: (973) 407-6880
Real Estate Agencies & Brokerage Services
N.A.I.C.S.: 531210

Subsidiary (Non-US):

Cartus B.V. **(2)**
Cuserstraat 93 Floor 2 and 3, 1081 CN,
Amsterdam, Netherlands
Tel.: (31) 205736070
Real Estate Agencies & Brokerage Services
N.A.I.C.S.: 531210

Subsidiary (Domestic):

Cartus Corporation **(2)**
100 Reserve Rd, Danbury, CT 06810
Tel.: (203) 205-3400
Web Site: https://cartus.com
Sales Range: $550-599.9 Million
Emp.: 2,700
Relocation Management Services
N.A.I.C.S.: 561990

Subsidiary (Non-US):

Cartus Corporation Pte. Ltd. **(3)**
4 Shenton Way 09-01/04 SGX Centre 2,
Singapore, 068807, Singapore
Tel.: (65) 6 880 5800
Web Site: http://www.cartus.com

Sales Range: $50-74.9 Million
Emp.: 175
Relocation Management Services
N.A.I.C.S.: 561990

Cartus UK plc **(3)**
Frankland Rd, Blagrove, Swindon, SN5
8RS, United Kingdom
Tel.: (44) 1793756000
Web Site: http://www.cartus.com
Relocation Management Services
N.A.I.C.S.: 561990

Subsidiary (Domestic):

Century 21 Real Estate LLC **(2)**
175 Park Ave, Madison, NJ 07940
Tel.: (973) 407-5296
Web Site: https://www.century21.com
Sales Range: $25-49.9 Million
Emp.: 155
Franchisor of Real Estate Agencies
N.A.I.C.S.: 533110
Michael Miedler *(Pres & CEO)*
Christy Torian *(VP--Field Svcs)*

Subsidiary (Non-US):

Coldwell Banker Canada Operations
ULC **(2)**
5500 N Service Rd Ste 1001, Burlington,
L7L 6W6, ON, Canada
Tel.: (905) 331-7556
Real Estate Agencies & Brokerage Services
N.A.I.C.S.: 531210
Andy Puthon *(Pres)*
John Alexander *(Dir-Franchise Sls)*

Subsidiary (Domestic):

Coldwell Banker LLC **(2)**
265 Baldwin Rd, Parsippany, NJ 07054
Tel.: (973) 428-9700
Real Estate Agencies & Brokerage Services
N.A.I.C.S.: 531210
Mike James *(Pres-San Francisco Bay Reg)*
Judy Carr *(VP-Sls-Tomball)*

Coldwell Banker Real Estate
LLC **(2)**
175 Park Ave, Madison, NJ 07940
Tel.: (973) 407-4300
Web Site: http://www.coldwellbanker.com
Sales Range: $75-99.9 Million
Emp.: 200
Real Estate Services
N.A.I.C.S.: 531210
David C. Marine *(CMO)*
Liz Gehringer *(COO)*
M. Ryan Gorman *(Co-Pres & Co-CEO)*

Division (Domestic):

Coldwell Banker **(3)**
100 N Crescent Dr Ste 324, Beverly Hills,
CA 90210-5411
Tel.: (310) 820-6811
Web Site: http://www.coldwellbanker.com
Full Service Residential Real Estate Broker-
age & Development Company
N.A.I.C.S.: 531210

Subsidiary (Domestic):

Coldwell Banker Bain Associates,
Inc. **(3)**
15410 Manion Way NE Ste E, Duvall, WA 98019
Tel.: (425) 788-1547
Web Site: http://www.cbbain.com
Sales Range: $1-9.9 Million
Emp.: 26
Lessors of Nonresidential Buildings (except
Miniwarehouses)
N.A.I.C.S.: 531120
Bill Riss *(Owner & CEO)*
Linda Aaron *(Dir-Trng & Coord-Ops)*
Kimberly Brangwin *(Sr Mgr)*
Leslie Colantuono *(VP-Fin)*
Mike Grady *(Pres & COO)*
Kim Gray *(Dir-HR)*
Kim Hart *(VP-Corp Bus Dev)*
Adam Jundt *(CIO)*
Suzanne Mueller *(CMO)*
Susan Stockmann *(Mgr-CRM)*
Rob Wachter *(Mgr-Inbound Mktg)*
Peggy Au-Yeung *(Dir-Intl)*
Ryan Ackley *(Mgr-Mktg-Madison Park)*
Shannon Bates *(Mgr-Madison Park)*

Coldwell Banker Commercial Affiliates (3)
1 Campus Dr, Parsippany, NJ 07054-0642
Tel.: (973) 407-7651
Web Site: http://www.cbcworldwide.com
Sales Range: $25-49.9 Million
Emp.: 15
Commercial Real Estate Services
N.A.I.C.S.: 531190
M. Ryan Gorman (Pres & CEO)
Elisabeth Gehringer (COO)
David Marine (CMO)
Dan Spiegel (Mng Dir)

Subsidiary (Domestic):

Coldwell Banker Real Estate Services LLC (2)
9600 Perry Hwy Ste 100, Pittsburgh, PA 15237-5552
Tel.: (412) 366-1600
Web Site:
    http://www.coldwellbankerhomes.com
Sales Range: $25-49.9 Million
Emp.: 35
Real Estate Agency & Brokerage Services
N.A.I.C.S.: 531210
Amber Housholder (VP-Mortgage Lending)
Ken Hoffert (Gen Counsel & Sr VP)
Peter J. Sobeck (Chief Recruiting Officer)
Roger Lepage (VP-)

ERA Franchise Systems LLC (2)
113 Parsippany Rd, Parsippany, NJ 07054
Tel.: (973) 887-1560
Web Site: http://www.era.com
International Residential Franchise Brokerage Services; Home Warranties, Referral & Relocations Services; Sellers Security & Buyers Protection Plan
N.A.I.C.S.: 533110

Global Client Solutions LLC (2)
4500 S 129th E Ave Ste 170, Tulsa, OK 74134-5801
Tel.: (918) 492-0386
Web Site:
    http://www.globalclientsolutions.com
Office Administrative Services
N.A.I.C.S.: 561110
Robert Merrick (Co-Founder & Exec VP-Sls)
Allison Newfield (Chief Acctg Officer)
Brent Hampton (Gen Counsel & VP)
Darren Parsons (VP-Ops)
Jeff Boatman (Co-Founder & Mng Partner)
Kristie L. Medlen (VP-Sls & Bus Dev)
Michael Hendrix (Co-Founder)
Mike Riggin (Chief Compliance Officer, Chief Risk Officer & VP-Banking)
Steve Kramer (CFO)
Timothy L. Merrick (Co-Founder & CEO)

Guardian Title Agency, LLC (2)
2700 Canyon Blvd Ste 205, Boulder, CO 80302
Tel.: (303) 413-2384
Web Site:
    http://www.guardiantitleagency.com
Title Insurance Services
N.A.I.C.S.: 541191
Noelle Lovato (Pres)

Keystone Closing Services LLC (2)
2605 Nicholson Rd Ste 3240, Sewickley, PA 15143
Tel.: (412) 922-8500
Web Site: http://www.keystoneclosing.com
Title Insurance Services
N.A.I.C.S.: 541191
Scott Storck (Pres)

NRT LLC (2)
175 Park Ave, Madison, NJ 07940
Tel.: (973) 407-5296
Web Site: http://www.nrtllc.com
Sales Range: $150-199.9 Billion
Emp.: 5,100
Real Estate Agents & Managers
N.A.I.C.S.: 531210
M. Ryan Gorman (Pres & CEO)

Subsidiary (Domestic):

Coldwell Banker Burnet Resource Center (3)
7550 France Ave S Ste 300, Edina, MN 55435-4765
Tel.: (952) 844-6000

Web Site: http://www.coldwellbanker.com
Sales Range: $100-124.9 Million
Emp.: 350
Real Estate Agents & Managers
N.A.I.C.S.: 531210

Coldwell Banker Commercial Pacific Properties LLC (3)
1314 S King St Fl 2nd, Honolulu, HI 96814
Tel.: (808) 596-0456
Real Estate Agencies & Brokerage Services
N.A.I.C.S.: 531210
Ron B. Teves (Pres)

Coldwell Banker Pacific Properties LLC (3)
98-211 Pali Momi Unit 411, Aiea, HI 96701
Tel.: (808) 488-1991
Web Site:
    http://www.coldwellbankerhomes.com
Sales Range: $50-74.9 Million
Emp.: 100
Real Estate Agency & Brokerage Services
N.A.I.C.S.: 531210

Coldwell Banker Residential Brokerage of Utah (3)
9350 S 150 E Ste 500, Sandy, UT 84070
Tel.: (801) 563-7600
Web Site: http://www.utahhomes.com
Sales Range: $450-499.9 Million
Emp.: 1,200
Residential Real Estate Brokerage Firm
N.A.I.C.S.: 531210

Coldwell Banker Residential Brokerage, Inc. (3)
7 Mount Bethel Rd, Warren, NJ 07059
Tel.: (908) 754-7511
Web Site:
    http://www.coldwellbankerhomes.com
Offices of Real Estate Agents & Brokers
N.A.I.C.S.: 531210

Coldwell Banker Residential Real Estate Inc. (3)
5965 Red Bug Lk Rd 101 unit, Winter Springs, FL 32708-5080
Tel.: (407) 696-8000
Web Site: http://www.lauranbeasley.com
Sales Range: $50-74.9 Million
Emp.: 95
Real Estate Brokerage
N.A.I.C.S.: 531210

Coldwell Banker Residential Real Estate LLC (3)
27742 Vista Del Lago Ste J1, Mission Viejo, CA 92692
Tel.: (949) 837-5700
Rev.: $81,000,000
Emp.: 500
Real Estate Agents & Managers
N.A.I.C.S.: 531210

Coldwell Banker Residential Real Estate Services Inc. (3)
6285 NE Barfield Rd Ste 100, Atlanta, GA 30328-4322
Tel.: (404) 705-1500
Web Site:
    http://www.coldwellbankeratlanta.com
Sales Range: $50-74.9 Million
Emp.: 70
Real Estate Agents & Managers
N.A.I.C.S.: 531210
Laura L. Rittenberg (Pres-Residential)

Coldwell Banker United, Realtors (3)
3701 Executive Center Dr, Austin, TX 78731
Tel.: (512) 691-1960
Web Site: http://www.coldwellbanker.com
Sales Range: $5-14.9 Billion
Emp.: 10
Real Estate Agency
N.A.I.C.S.: 531210
Richard Smith (Founder)

NRT Arizona LLC (3)
7975 N Hayden Rd Ste D105, Scottsdale, AZ 85258
Tel.: (480) 951-1010
Title Insurance Services
N.A.I.C.S.: 541191

NRT Development Advisors LLC (3)
2170 W State Rd 434 Ste 450, Longwood, FL 32779
Tel.: (407) 712-7070

Web Site:
    http://www.webapps2.planetrealtor.com
Emp.: 55
Real Estate Services
N.A.I.C.S.: 531390

NRT Missouri LLC (3)
2458 Old Dorsett Rd Ste 100, Maryland Heights, MO 63043
Tel.: (314) 298-5200
Web Site: http://www.cbgundaker.com
Sales Range: $200-249.9 Million
Emp.: 50
Real Estate Agency
N.A.I.C.S.: 531210
Ken Hoffert (Gen Counsel & Sr VP)
Peter J. Sobeck (Chief Recruiting Officer)
Thomas N. Rispoli (Co-CFO)
Andy House (VP-)
Simeon Williams (VP-)

NRT Missouri Referral Network LLC (3)
1 Campus Dr, Parsippany, NJ 07054
Tel.: (973) 407-6880
Real Estate Services
N.A.I.C.S.: 531390

NRT Pittsburgh LLC (3)
9600 Perry Hwy Ste 200, Pittsburgh, PA 15237
Tel.: (412) 367-3050
Web Site: http://www.nrtpittsburgh.com
Emp.: 100
Real Estate Agencies & Brokerage Services
N.A.I.C.S.: 531210
Amber Housholder (VP-)
Roger LePage (VP-)

NRT Property Management Arizona LLC (3)
3337 N Miller Rd Ste 105, Scottsdale, AZ 85251
Tel.: (480) 970-1999
Web Site:
    http://www.propertyframeworks.com
Residential Property Management Services
N.A.I.C.S.: 531311

NRT Property Management Florida LLC (3)
6365 NW 6th Way Ste 200, Fort Lauderdale, FL 33309
Web Site:
    http://www.propertyframeworks.com
Residential Property Management Services
N.A.I.C.S.: 531311

NRT Property Management Texas LLC (3)
9840 N Central Expwy Ste 300, Dallas, TX 75231
Tel.: (214) 522-5700
Web Site:
    http://www.propertyframeworks.com
Residential Property Management Services
N.A.I.C.S.: 531311

NRT REOExperts LLC (3)
6365 NW 6th Way Ste 300, Fort Lauderdale, FL 33309
Web Site: http://www.reoexperts.net
Real Estate Agencies & Brokerage Services
N.A.I.C.S.: 531210

Real Services, Inc. (3)
1732 London Rd, Duluth, MN 55812
Tel.: (218) 728-5161
Sales Range: $1-9.9 Million
Emp.: 45
Offices of Real Estate Agents & Brokers
N.A.I.C.S.: 531210
Greg Kamp (Pres)

Sotheby's International Realty, Inc. (3)
38 E 61st St, New York, NY 10065
Tel.: (212) 606-7660
Web Site: http://www.sothebysrealty.com
Residential Real Estate Brokerage Firm
N.A.I.C.S.: 531210
Philip White (Pres & CEO)

Subsidiary (Domestic):

Martha Turner Sotheby's International Realty (4)
50 Briar Hollow LN Ste 700W, Houston, TX 77027
Tel.: (713) 520-1981

Web Site: http://www.marthaturner.com
Real Estate Agents & Brokers
N.A.I.C.S.: 531210
Robin Suter (Co-Pres)
Robin Conner (Co-Pres)

Branch (Domestic):

Sotheby's International Realty (4)
9665 Wilshire Blvd Ste 400, Beverly Hills, CA 90212
Tel.: (310) 724-7000
Web Site: http://www.sothebyshomes.com
Residential Real Estate Brokerage Firm
N.A.I.C.S.: 524210
Frank G. Symons Jr. (Exec VP-Northern California, Santa Barbara & Santa Fe)
Jeffrey G. Gibson (Sr VP & Mgr-Brokerage-San Francisco)
Clifford Siegel (CFO, COO & Exec VP)
Bradley Nelson (CMO)
Christine Montalvo (VP-Mktg)
Sanoj Stephen (Gen Counsel & Sr VP)
Ronald Lipstone (VP-Western Reg & Asst Mgr)
Julia Paridis (Corp Counsel)
Kevin Ilarraza (Dir-HR)
Candace Chan (Fin Dir & Controller)
Kristina Helb (Sr Dir-Strategic Comm)
Lauren Stewart (Mgr-Creative)
Philip A. White Jr. (Pres & CEO)

Sotheby's International Realty (4)
185 W Broadway, Jackson, WY 83001
Tel.: (307) 733-9009
Web Site: http://www.sothebysrealty.com
Rev.: $325,000,000
Emp.: 10
Real Estate Brokerage Services
N.A.I.C.S.: 531210

Subsidiary (Domestic):

The Corcoran Group (3)
660 Madison Ave, New York, NY 10065
Tel.: (212) 355-3550
Web Site: http://www.corcoran.com
Sales Range: $25-49.9 Million
Emp.: 2,000
Upscale Residential Real Estate Broker
N.A.I.C.S.: 531210
Pamela Liebman (Pres & CEO)
Ernest Cervi (Sr VP-East End)
Christina Lowris Panos (CMO)
Terence L. Thomas (Dir-IT)
Linda T. Honan (Sr Mng Dir-Union Square)
Ellen K. Leon (Sr Mng Dir-Westside)
Gary L. Malin (COO)
Juliana Brown (Sr Mng Dir-Bedford Stuyvesant & Fort Greene)
Tim Cass (Sr Mng Dir-Park Avenue South)
Alex Cho (Sr Mng Dir-Park Avenue South)
Robert Doernberg (Sr Mng Dir-East Side)
Joel Dommel (Mng Dir-West Side)
Ben Elesh (Sr Mng Dir-Park Slope)
Ryan Fitzpatrick (Sr Mng Dir-Chelsea & Flatiron)
Eric Hamm (Sr Mng Dir-West Side-Columbus)
Janet Lowry (Sr Mng Dir-West Side-Gallery)
Paula Manikowski (Sr Mng Dir-Soho)
Helen Monti (Sr Mng Dir-East Side)
Ayumi Otaki (Sr Mng Dir-Long Island City & Williamsburg Bedford)
Kimberly Pickard (Mng Dir-Park Avenue South)
Tim Rettaliata (Mng Dir-Brooklyn Heights)
Alex Saltalamacchia (Sr Mng Dir-Williamsburg-Driggs)
Yael Streit (Sr Mng Dir-Brooklyn Heights)
Brian Ullman (Sr Mng Dir-East Side)
Andrew Levinson (Gen Counsel & Sr VP)
John Felicetti (VP-New Dev)
Ryan Schleis (Sr VP-Res & Analytics)
Marc C. Alter (Sr VP-Learning & Dev)
Ida Fields (VP-Agent Mktg & Bus Dev)
Luke Barton (VP-Franchise Ops)
Alisande Heriyanto (VP-Technical Support & Svcs)
Sheri Imperiali (CFO)
Michael Sorrentino (Sr VP & Gen Sls Mgr)
Jennifer Kaplow (Reg Dir-HR)
Jodi Stasse (Exec VP-New Dev)
David J. Maundrell III (Exec VP-New Dev)

Subsidiary (Domestic):

Citi Habitats (4)
387 Park Ave S 4th Fl, New York, NY 10016

Anywhere Real Estate Inc.—(Continued)

Tel.: (212) 685-7777
Web Site: http://www.citihabitats.com
Sales Range: $50-74.9 Million
Emp.: 50
Real Estate Sales & Rental Services
N.A.I.C.S.: 531210

Division (Domestic):

Corcoran Sunshine Marketing Group (4)
888 7th Ave, New York, NY 10106
Tel.: (212) 634-6500
Web Site:
   https://www.corcoransunshine.com
Sales Range: $50-74.9 Million
Emp.: 60
Property Developer & Marketer
N.A.I.C.S.: 531390
Kelly Kennedy Mack (Pres)

Subsidiary (Domestic):

ZapLabs LLC (3)
2000 Powell St Ste 700, Emeryville, CA 94608
Tel.: (510) 735-2600
Web Site: http://www.ziplabs.com
Residential Real Estate Brokerage Software Network Developer & Operator
N.A.I.C.S.: 518210

Subsidiary (Domestic):

ONCOR International LLC (2)
175 Park Ave, Madison, NJ 07940
Tel.: (973) 407-7424
Web Site: http://www.oncorintl.com
Emp.: 400
Commercial Real Estate Brokerage
N.A.I.C.S.: 531210

Quality Choice Title LLC (2)
4535 W Dublin Granville Rd, Dublin, OH 43017
Tel.: (614) 799-2833
Web Site: https://www.qualitychoicetitle.com
Sales Range: $25-49.9 Million
Emp.: 8
Real Estate Agencies & Brokerage Services
N.A.I.C.S.: 531210

Real Estate Referrals LLC (2)
19400 108th Ave SE, Kent, WA 98031
Tel.: (206) 954-4038
Real Estate Agencies & Brokerage Services
N.A.I.C.S.: 531210

Realogy Franchise Group LLC (2)
175 Park Ave, Madison, NJ 07940
Tel.: (973) 407-2000
Web Site: http://www.realogy.com
Real Estate Agencies & Brokerage Services
N.A.I.C.S.: 531210
Susan Yannaccone (Pres & CEO)

Referral Network Plus, Inc. (2)
27271 Las Ramblas, Mission Viejo, CA 92691
Tel.: (973) 407-2000
Real Estate Agencies & Brokerage Services
N.A.I.C.S.: 531210

Riverbend Title, LLC (2)
11625 Coldwater Rd, Fort Wayne, IN 46845
Tel.: (260) 416-5179
Web Site: http://www.riverbendtitlellc.com
Real Estate Agencies & Brokerage Services
N.A.I.C.S.: 531210

St. Mary's Title Services, LLC (2)
200 McGregor St, Manchester, NH 03102
Tel.: (603) 669-4600
Web Site: https://www.stmarysbank.com
Sales Range: $25-49.9 Million
Emp.: 6
Real Estate Settlement Services
N.A.I.C.S.: 541191
Karen Hegner (Mgr-Customer Rels)

The Sunshine Group, Ltd. (2)
595 Madison Ave, New York, NY 10022
Tel.: (212) 750-0500
Real Estate Agencies & Brokerage Services
N.A.I.C.S.: 531210

Title Resource Group LLC (2)
3001 Leadenhall Rd, Mount Laurel, NJ 08054

Tel.: (856) 914-8500
Web Site: https://www.anywhereis.re
Sales Range: $450-499.9 Million
Emp.: 2,800
Title, Escrow & Other Settlement Services
N.A.I.C.S.: 541191
Donald J. Casey (Pres & CEO)

Subsidiary (Domestic):

American Title Company of Houston (3)
2603 Augusta Dr Ste 1125, Houston, TX 77057
Tel.: (713) 965-9777
Web Site:
   http://www.americantitlehouston.com
Emp.: 50
Title Insurance Services
N.A.I.C.S.: 541191

Burnet Title LLC (3)
7550 France Ave So Ste 300, Edina, MN 55435
Tel.: (952) 844-6200
Web Site: https://www.burnettitle.com
Rev.: $6,000,000
Emp.: 60
Title Insurance
N.A.I.C.S.: 524127
Ronnie Semlak (Pres)

Burnet Title of Indiana, LLC (3)
14 E US Hwy 30, Schererville, IN 46375-2105
Tel.: (219) 322-2257
Web Site: http://www.burnettitlein.com
Title Insurance Services
N.A.I.C.S.: 541191

Cornerstone Title Company (3)
19330 Stevens Creek Blvd, Cupertino, CA 95014
Tel.: (408) 973-1410
Web Site: http://www.cornerstonetitleco.com
Title Insurance Services
N.A.I.C.S.: 541191
Patrick Frasier (Pres)
Rod Huddleston (Chief Title Officer-)

Equity Title Company (3)
801 N Brand Blvd Ste 400, Glendale, CA 91203
Tel.: (818) 291-4400
Web Site: https://www.equitytitle.com
Emp.: 80
Title Insurance Services
N.A.I.C.S.: 541191
Michelle Debardas (Dir-Sls Admin & Office Ops)
Kevin M. Razban (Chief Title Officer)
Patrick Frasier (Pres)

First Advantage Title, LLC (3)
2301 N Burkhardt Rd, Evansville, IN 47715
Tel.: (812) 490-8485
Web Site: https://www.fa-title.com
Title Insurance Services
N.A.I.C.S.: 541191

First California Escrow Corporation (3)
1110 Camino Del Mar Ste G, Del Mar, CA 92014
Tel.: (858) 793-0502
Web Site:
   http://www.firstcaliforniaescrow.com
Title Insurance Services541191
N.A.I.C.S.: 541191
Nancy Closson (Pres)
Staci Pawlowski (Dir-Bus Dev-Southern California Escrow)
Dee Anna Pope (Mgr)

Market Street Settlement Group LLC (3)
803 Elm St, Manchester, NH 03101
Tel.: (603) 624-1303
Web Site: http://www.mssg.com
Title Insurance Services
N.A.I.C.S.: 541191
Michael R. Maloney (Pres)

Mercury Title LLC (3)
3595 N College Ave, Fayetteville, AR 72703
Tel.: (479) 582-5673
Web Site: https://www.mercurytitlear.com
Emp.: 4
Title Insurance Services
N.A.I.C.S.: 541191

Jennifer A. Battista (VP)

Mid-Atlantic Settlement Services LLC (3)
4 N Park Dr Ste 205, Hunt Valley, MD 21030
Tel.: (410) 252-1208
Web Site: http://www.masettlement.com
Title Insurance Services
N.A.I.C.S.: 541191
Richard Hearn (Pres)

Secured Land Transfers LLC (3)
485 Saint Johns Church Rd, Shiremanstown, PA 17011
Tel.: (717) 901-8342
Web Site: http://www.securedland.com
Real Estate Agency & Brokerage Services
N.A.I.C.S.: 531210
Scott Storck (Pres)
Stephanie Witmer (VP)
Heather Jones (Mgr-Sls)

Texas American Title Company (3)
2603 Augusta Dr Ste 1125, Houston, TX 77057
Tel.: (713) 988-9999
Web Site: https://www.texasamerican.com
Sales Range: $50-74.9 Million
Emp.: 80
Title Insurance & Settlement Services
N.A.I.C.S.: 524127
Jeanette Fraley (Sr VP-Houston Div)
Stacey Kuithe (VP-Mktg-Houston Div)

TitleOne Corp. (3)
1101 W River St Ste 201, Boise, ID 83702
Tel.: (208) 424-8511
Web Site: http://www.titleonecorp.com
Insurance Related Activities
N.A.I.C.S.: 524298
Ryan Taylor (VP-Eastern Idaho)
Jason Vickrey (Pres)
Cameron McFaddan (Sr VP-Comml & Title)
Randy Rabehl (CFO)
Jacqui Porter (Asst VP)
Laura Page (Dir-Trng & Escrow Dev)
Scott Darling (Co-Founder & Officer-Comml Escrow)
Anna Hunt (Coord-Mktg Comm)
Logan Coulter (Sr VP-Strategic Growth)
David Gerber (VP-IT Dir)
Deedra Stith (VP-Customer Experience & Builder Svcs)
Michelle Wood (VP & Dir-Mktg)
Jake Proffitt (VP-Strategic Dev)
Scott Thiel (Co-Founder & Chief Title Officer)

U.S. Title Guaranty Company (3)
7930 Clayton Rd Ste 320, Saint Louis, MO 63117
Tel.: (314) 727-2900
Web Site: http://www.us-title.com
Sales Range: $75-99.9 Million
Emp.: 250
Title, Escrow & Other Settlement Services
N.A.I.C.S.: 541191
Steven L. Dieckmann (Exec VP)
John R. Winkler (Sr VP-Production)
Kellie Meyer (VP-Bus Dev)
Brenda Brugger (VP-Escrow Ops)
Stacy Burton (VP-Escrow Ops)
Danielle Gleason (Supvr-Acctg Dept)

West Coast Escrow Company (3)
27742 Vista Del Lago Ste 1, Mission Viejo, CA 92692
Tel.: (949) 707-0241
Web Site: http://www.westcoastescrow.com
Sales Range: $25-49.9 Million
Emp.: 3
Real Estate Escrow Services
N.A.I.C.S.: 531390

Subsidiary (Domestic):

Equity Title Co. Inc. (4)
801 N Brand Blvd Ste 400, Glendale, CA 91203
Tel.: (818) 291-4400
Web Site: https://www.equitytitle.com
Sales Range: $50-74.9 Million
Title Insurance
N.A.I.C.S.: 524127

Subsidiary (Domestic):

Title Resource Group Settlement Services, LLC (2)

3001 Leadenhall Rd, Mount Laurel, NJ 08054
Tel.: (856) 914-8500
Web Site: http://www.trgc.com
Title Insurance Services
N.A.I.C.S.: 541191

Broker Technology Solutions LLC (1)
105 Frederick Ave, Frederick, MD 21701
Tel.: (301) 789-1101
Computer Consulting Services
N.A.I.C.S.: 541512

Cartus Brasil Servicos de Relocacao Ltda. (1)
Al Santos 2313 EN 2315 Conj 111 A 115 Pavmto11 Cerqueira Cesar, Sao Paulo, 01419-101, Brazil
Tel.: (55) 30987474
Business Management Consulting Services
N.A.I.C.S.: 541611

Corcoran Group LLC (1)
1241 Wheatfield Way, Oshkosh, WI 54904
Tel.: (920) 216-2742
Web Site: https://www.corcorangroupllc.com
Event & Meeting Planning Services
N.A.I.C.S.: 561920

Cypress Title Corporation (1)
1200 E Orangeburg Ave Ste 101, Modesto, CA 95350
Tel.: (209) 523-2694
Emp.: 64
Real Estate Management Services
N.A.I.C.S.: 531210
Eddie Zuniga (Gen Mgr)

Estately, Inc. (1)
PO Box 23181, Seattle, WA 98102
Web Site: https://www.estately.com
Real Estate Services
N.A.I.C.S.: 531390

Guardian Title Company (1)
1451 W Business 380 Bldg 1, Decatur, TX 76234
Tel.: (940) 627-5888
Web Site: https://www.guardiantitleco.com
Title Insurance Services
N.A.I.C.S.: 524127
Anthony J. Asher (Founder)
Shanna Mowery (Pres & Mgr-Title)
Amy Ingram (VP & Mgr-Escrow)

HFS.com Real Estate Incorporated (1)
450 Exchange, Irvine, CA 92602
Tel.: (949) 385-8927
Web Site:
   http://hfscomrealestateincorporated.metro listpro.com
Real Estate Management Services
N.A.I.C.S.: 531210

HFS.com Real Estate LLC (1)
175 Park Ave, Madison, NJ 07940
Tel.: (973) 407-5225
Real Estate Management Services
N.A.I.C.S.: 531210

Land Title and Escrow, Inc. (1)
111 E George Hopper Rd, Burlington, WA 98233
Tel.: (360) 707-2158
Web Site: https://www.ltco.com
Emp.: 50
Real Estate Services
N.A.I.C.S.: 531390

NRT Devonshire West LLC (1)
1061 Tierra Del Rey Ste 302, Chula Vista, CA 91910
Tel.: (619) 934-8802
Web Site: http://www.coldwellwest.com
Real Estate Management Services
N.A.I.C.S.: 531210

NRT ZipRealty LLC (1)
200 W Mercer St Ste 502, Seattle, WA 98119
Tel.: (425) 522-1328
Web Site: http://www.nrtziprealtyagents.com
Real Estate Management Services
N.A.I.C.S.: 531210

On Collaborative LLC (1)
676 N Michigan Ave Ste 3010, Chicago, IL 60611
Tel.: (312) 799-2800
Web Site: http://www.oncollaborative.com

Real Estate Services
N.A.I.C.S.: 531390
David Wolf (Pres)
Christine Lutz (VP-Sls)
Kellie Kao Miles (VP-Strategy)

REALtech Title LLC (1)
3001 Leadenhall Rd, Mount Laurel, NJ 08054
Web Site: https://www.realtechtitle.com
Residential Property Management Services
N.A.I.C.S.: 531311
Jennifer A. Battista (Sr VP-Bus Ops)

Realogy Brokerage Group LLC (1)
100 5th Ave, Waltham, MA 02451
Tel.: (781) 684-5462
Real Estate Manangement Services
N.A.I.C.S.: 531210
Roni Boyles (Dir-PR-Natl)
Brian Lynch (VP-IT)

Realogy Title Group LLC (1)
3001 Leadenhall Rd, Mount Laurel, NJ 08054
Tel.: (856) 914-8848
Real Estate Agency Services
N.A.I.C.S.: 531210
Jon McGrain (VP-Mktg & Comm)

Terra Coastal Escrow, Inc. (1)
23805 Stuart Ranch Rd Ste 200, Malibu, CA 90265
Tel.: (310) 456-6434
Web Site: https://www.terracoastal.com
Real Estate Services
N.A.I.C.S.: 531390

TitleOne Exchange Company (1)
Golden Eagle Bldg 1101 W River St Ste 201, Boise, ID 83702
Tel.: (208) 424-8511
Web Site: http://www.titleonecorp.com
Real Estate Services
N.A.I.C.S.: 531390

Upward Title & Closing Texas LLC (1)
2603 Augusta Dr Ste 1125, Houston, TX 77057
Tel.: (346) 389-7921
Web Site: https://upwardtitle.com
Real Estate Manangement Services
N.A.I.C.S.: 531210

Upward Title & Escrow Co., Ltd. (1)
45 Sugar Sand Ln Ste B, Santa Rosa Beach, FL 32459
Tel.: (850) 952-9718
Web Site: https://upwardtitle.com
Real Estate Development Services
N.A.I.C.S.: 531390

Upward Title Co., Ltd. (1)
801 N Brand Blvd Ste 420, Glendale, CA 91203
Real Estate Development Services
N.A.I.C.S.: 531390

APA CORPORATION
2000 W Sam Houston Pkwy S Ste 200, Houston, TX 77042
Tel.: (713) 296-6000 DE
Web Site: https://www.apacorp.com
Year Founded: 2021
APA—(NASDAQ)
Rev.: $8,279,000,000
Assets: $15,244,000,000
Liabilities: $11,553,000,000
Net Worth: $3,691,000,000
Earnings: $2,855,000,000
Emp.: 2,271
Fiscal Year-end: 12/31/23
Holding Company; Natural Gas & Crude Oil Exploration, Development & Production
N.A.I.C.S.: 551112
John J. Christmann IV (CEO)
Stephen J. Riney (Pres & CFO)
Clay Bretches (Exec VP-Ops)
P. Anthony Lannie (Exec VP & Gen Counsel)
Mark J. Bright (Sr VP-Plng)
Timothy R. Custer (Sr VP-Land)
W. Brad Eubanks (Sr VP-Production Ops)

Tracey K. Henderson (Sr VP-Exploration)
Rebecca A. Hoyt (Chief Acctg Officer, Sr VP & Controller)
Mark D. Maddox (Sr VP-Admin)
Ben C. Rodgers (Treas & Sr VP)
Gary T. Clark (VP-IR)
Jeremy Hill (VP-Supply Chain-Global)
Jessica Jackson (VP-Environment, Health & Safety)
Brandy Jones (VP-HR)
Castlen M. Kennedy (VP-Corp Comm & Pub Affairs)
Travis Osborne (VP-IT)
Rajesh Sharma (Sec & Asst Gen Counsel-Governance)
Carla Tharp (VP-Corp Dev)
Eric Vosburgh (VP-Portfolio Mgmt & Geoscience-Global)
John J. Christmann IV (Pres & CEO)

Subsidiaries:

Apache Corporation (1)
1 Post Oak Central 2000 Post Oak Blvd Ste 100, Houston, TX 77056-4400 **(100%)**
Tel.: (713) 296-6000
Web Site: https://www.apacorp.com
Rev.: $10,883,000,000
Assets: $14,255,000,000
Liabilities: $11,013,000,000
Net Worth: $3,242,000,000
Earnings: $3,536,000,000
Emp.: 3,163
Fiscal Year-end: 12/31/2022
Natural Gas & Crude Oil Exploration, Development & Production
N.A.I.C.S.: 211130
John J. Christmann IV (Pres & CEO)
Stephen J. Riney (CFO & Exec VP)
Rebecca A. Hoyt (Chief Acctg Officer, Sr VP & Controller)
Tracey K. Henderson (Exec VP)
W. Brad Eubanks (Sr VP)
Travis Osborne (CIO)
Jeremy Hill (VP)
Jessica Jackson (VP)
Brandy Jones (VP)
Carla Tharp (VP)
Gary T. Clark (VP-IR)

Subsidiary (Domestic):

Apache Crude Oil Marketing, Inc. (2)
2000 Post Oak Blvd Ste 100, Houston, TX 77056-4499
Tel.: (713) 296-6000
Emp.: 10
Petroleum Product Whslr
N.A.I.C.S.: 424720

Apache Delaware Investment LLC (2)
103 Foulk Rd, Wilmington, DE 19803
Tel.: (302) 691-6329
Investment Management Service
N.A.I.C.S.: 523940

Unit (Non-US):

Apache Egypt Companies (2)
11 Street 281 New Maadi, Cairo, Egypt
Tel.: (20) 225193835
Web Site: http://www.apachecorp.com
Sales Range: $150-199.9 Million
Oil & Gas Exploration & Production
N.A.I.C.S.: 211120

Subsidiary (Non-US):

Apache Finance Canada Corporation (2)
2800 421 7th Ave SW, Calgary, T2P 4K9, AB, Canada
Tel.: (403) 261-1200
Web Site: https://www.apachecorp.com
Sales Range: $400-449.9 Million
Emp.: 800
Oil & Gas Exploration Services
N.A.I.C.S.: 213112

Subsidiary (Domestic):

Apache International, Inc. (2)
2000 Post Oak Blvd Ste 100, Houston, TX 77056-4497

Tel.: (713) 296-6000
Web Site: http://www.apachecorp.com
Sales Range: $650-699.9 Million
Emp.: 1,000
Development & Production of Natural Gas & Crude Oil
N.A.I.C.S.: 213112

Apache Louisiana Minerals LLC (2)
1913 La Terre Ct, Houma, LA 70363-7525
Tel.: (985) 879-3528
Web Site: http://www.apache.com
Natural Gas Exploration Service
N.A.I.C.S.: 211130

Subsidiary (Non-US):

Apache North Sea Limited (2)
Tel.: (44) 1224505000
Web Site: http://www.apachecorp.com
Sales Range: $150-199.9 Million
Emp.: 180
Oil & Gas Exploration & Production
N.A.I.C.S.: 211120

Subsidiary (Domestic):

Apache North Sea Investment (3)
Alba Gate Stoneywood Park Stoneywood Road, Dyce, AB21 7DZ, Aberdeen, United Kingdom
Tel.: (44) 1224756400
Natural Gas Exploration Service
N.A.I.C.S.: 213112

Subsidiary (Domestic):

Apache Offshore Investment Partnership (2)
1 Post Oak Central 2000 Post Oak Blvd Ste 100, Houston, TX 77056-4400
Tel.: (713) 296-6000
Web Site: https://apacorp.com
Rev.: $1,802,675
Assets: $8,639,782
Liabilities: $1,548,151
Net Worth: $7,091,631
Earnings: $575,216
Fiscal Year-end: 12/31/2022
Venture Capital Services
N.A.I.C.S.: 523910
John J. Christmann IV (Pres & CEO)

Subsidiary (Non-US):

Apache Suriname 58 Holdings Corporation LDC (2)
Kromme Elleboogstraat 9, Paramaribo, Suriname
Tel.: (597) 425072
Natural Gas Extraction Services
N.A.I.C.S.: 211130
Ian Roberts (Country Mgr)

Subsidiary (Domestic):

Clear Creek Hunting Preserve, Inc. (2)
2000 Post Oak Blvd Ste 100, Houston, TX 77056-4400
Tel.: (307) 737-2237
Sales Range: $50-74.9 Million
Emp.: 2
Oil & Gas Exploration Services
N.A.I.C.S.: 213112
John Christman (CEO)

Granite Operating Company (2)
8450 E Crescent Pkwy St, Canadian, TX 79014
Tel.: (806) 323-9118
Oil & Gas Exploration Services
N.A.I.C.S.: 213112

Subsidiary (Non-US):

Harriet (Onyx) Pty Ltd (2)
L 1 47 Colin St, West Perth, 6005, WA, Australia
Tel.: (61) 894851000
Oil & Gas Exploration Services
N.A.I.C.S.: 213112

APARTMENT INVESTMENT AND MANAGEMENT COMPANY
4582 S Ulster St Ste 1450, Denver, CO 80237
Tel.: (303) 224-7900 MD

Web Site: https://www.aimco.com
Year Founded: 1994
AIV—(NYSE)
Rev.: $190,344,000
Assets: $2,181,223,000
Liabilities: $1,555,865,000
Net Worth: $625,358,000
Earnings: $75,726,000
Emp.: 62
Fiscal Year-end: 12/31/22
Other Financial Vehicles
N.A.I.C.S.: 525990
H. Lynn Stanfield (CFO & Exec VP)
Wesley W. Powell (Pres & CEO)
R. Dary Stone (Chm)
Matt Foster (Sr Dir-Capital Markets & IR)
Jennifer Johnson (Chief Admin Officer)
Kellie Dreyer (Chief Acctg Officer)
Lee Hodges (Sr VP)
Matt Hopkins (Sr VP)
Matt Konrad (Sr VP)
Elizabeth Likovich (Sr VP)
Tom Marchant (Sr VP)
John Nicholson (Treas)
Derek Ullian (Sr VP)

Subsidiaries:

1001 Brickell Bay Drive, LLC (1)
4582 S Ulster St Ste 1450, Denver, CO 80237
Tel.: (305) 536-1001
Real Estate Investment Management Services
N.A.I.C.S.: 531390

AIMCO ANGELES GP, LLC (1)
4582 S Ulster St Ste 1100, Denver, CO 80237
Tel.: (303) 757-8101
Web Site: http://www.aimco.com
Emp.: 300
Property Rental & Leasing Services
N.A.I.C.S.: 531110

AIMCO ANTIOCH, L.L.C. (1)
100 Chimneytop Dr, Antioch, TN 37013
Tel.: (615) 731-1528
Property Rental & Leasing Services
N.A.I.C.S.: 531110

AIMCO EQUITY SERVICES, LLC (1)
3100 S Vermont Ave, Los Angeles, CA 90007-3044
Tel.: (323) 734-1664
Financial Services
N.A.I.C.S.: 541611

AIMCO ESPLANADE AVENUE APARTMENTS, LLC (1)
380 Esplanade Ave, Pacifica, CA 94044
Tel.: (650) 355-3418
Property Rental & Leasing Services
N.A.I.C.S.: 531110

AIMCO KEY TOWERS, L.P. (1)
6060 Tower Ct, Alexandria, VA 22304-3205
Tel.: (571) 403-5371
Property Rental & Leasing Services
N.A.I.C.S.: 531110

AIMCO PARK AND 12TH, LLC (1)
1045 Piedmont Ave NE, Atlanta, GA 30309-3747
Tel.: (404) 347-2262
Apartment Community Management Services
N.A.I.C.S.: 531311

AIMCO SAN MELIA, LLC (1)
14435 S 48th St, Phoenix, AZ 85044
Tel.: (480) 454-4115
Web Site: http://www.sanmelialiving.com
Apartment Community Management Services
N.A.I.C.S.: 531311

AIMCO WARWICK, L.L.C. (1)
42 Cedar Pond Dr Ste 41, Warwick, RI 02886-6614

Apartment Investment and Management Company—(Continued)

Tel.: (401) 828-7444
Web Site: http://www.aimco.com
Emp.: 12
Property Rental & Leasing Services
N.A.I.C.S.: 531110

AIMCO/BETHESDA GP, L.L.C. (1)
2711 Centerville Rd, Wilmington, DE 19808
Tel.: (303) 757-8101
Emp.: 50
Property Rental & Leasing Services
N.A.I.C.S.: 531110

ARVADA HOUSE PRESERVATION LIMITED PARTNERSHIP (1)
10175 W 58th Pl, Arvada, CO 80004
Tel.: (303) 424-6592
Property Rental & Leasing Services
N.A.I.C.S.: 531110

Aimco Southstar Lofts, LLC (1)
521 S Broad St, Philadelphia, PA 19147
Tel.: (267) 296-9680
Web Site: https://www.southstarlofts.com
Real Estate Services
N.A.I.C.S.: 531390

BEDFORD HOUSE, LTD. (1)
301 Licking St, Falmouth, KY 41040
Tel.: (859) 654-3957
Property Rental & Leasing Services
N.A.I.C.S.: 531110

BILTMORE APARTMENTS, LTD. (1)
418 E Loretta Pl, Seattle, WA 98102
Tel.: (206) 709-2866
Real Estate Agents & Brokerage Services
N.A.I.C.S.: 531210

BURLINGTON RIVER APARTMENTS, LIMITED PARTNERSHIP (1)
611 W Van Weiss Blvd, West Burlington, IA 52655
Tel.: (319) 752-7578
Real Estate Agents & Brokerage Services
N.A.I.C.S.: 531210

CAMBRIDGE HEIGHTS APARTMENTS LIMITED PARTNERSHIP (1)
311 Dumas St, Natchez, MS 39120-2681
Tel.: (601) 442-7830
Property Rental & Leasing Services
N.A.I.C.S.: 531110

CCIP STERLING, L.P. (1)
1815 John F Kennedy Blvd, Philadelphia, PA 19103-1731
Tel.: (267) 776-2169
Web Site: http://www.sterlingapthomes.com
Sales Range: $25-49.9 Million
Emp.: 20
Real Estate Agents & Brokerage Services
N.A.I.C.S.: 531210

DARBY TOWNHOUSES PRESERVATION, LP (1)
1011 Burton Ave, Sharon Hill, PA 19079-2401
Tel.: (610) 522-1131
Property Rental & Leasing Services
N.A.I.C.S.: 531110

DAVIDSON PROPERTIES, INC. (1)
8151 Broadway St, San Antonio, TX 78209
Tel.: (210) 826-1616
Web Site:
    https://www.davidsonproperties.com
Sales Range: $25-49.9 Million
Emp.: 6
Property Rental & Leasing Services
N.A.I.C.S.: 531110
Dylan Thomas (Owner & Pres)
Ken Southwell (Dir-Maintenance)

DIXON RIVER APARTMENTS, L.P. (1)
624 Marclare St, Dixon, IL 61021
Tel.: (815) 284-6782
Emp.: 3
Property Rental & Leasing Services
N.A.I.C.S.: 531110
Nicole Miller (Mgr-Property)

FOX RUN APARTMENTS, LTD. (1)
2900 Fox Lair Dr, Woodbridge, VA 22191
Tel.: (703) 221-2700

Emp.: 8
Property Rental & Leasing Services
N.A.I.C.S.: 531110
Rossa Coello (Gen Mgr)

GATE MANOR APARTMENTS, LTD., A TENNESSEE LIMITED PARTNERSHIP (1)
1200 Fowler Ln Ofc, Clinton, TN 37716
Tel.: (865) 457-7651
Property Rental & Leasing Services
N.A.I.C.S.: 531110

GEORGETOWN WOODS SENIOR APARTMENTS, L.P. (1)
5360 Georgetown Rd, Indianapolis, IN 46254
Tel.: (317) 388-9513
Web Site:
    https://www.georgetownwoodsin.com
Property Rental & Leasing Services
N.A.I.C.S.: 531110

GOTHAM APARTMENTS, LIMITED PARTNERSHIP (1)
2718 E Linwood Blvd, Kansas City, MO 64128
Tel.: (816) 921-0652
Property Rental & Leasing Services
N.A.I.C.S.: 531110

HISTORIC PROPERTIES INC. (1)
5333 Senseny Rd, Berryville, VA 22611
Tel.: (540) 955-1055
Web Site:
    https://www.historicproperties.com
Real Estate Agents & Brokerage Services
N.A.I.C.S.: 531210

HOUSING ASSISTANCE OF ORANGE CITY, LTD. (1)
2515 Enterprise Rd, Orange City, FL 32763-7949
Tel.: (386) 775-2697
Real Estate Agents & Brokerage Services
N.A.I.C.S.: 531210

INGRAM SQUARE PRESERVATION, L.P. (1)
5901 Flynn Dr, San Antonio, TX 78228-2668
Tel.: (210) 436-1644
Property Rental & Leasing Services
N.A.I.C.S.: 531110

INTEGRATED PROPERTIES, INC. (1)
75 Union Ave, Sudbury, MA 01776
Web Site: https://www.itgprop.com
Property Rental & Leasing Services
N.A.I.C.S.: 531110
Robert Prendergast (Co-Founder)

LA INDIAN OAKS QRS INC. (1)
4582 S Ulster St Ste 1100, Denver, CO 80237-2662
Tel.: (303) 825-3434
Apartment Community Management Services
N.A.I.C.S.: 531311

LEWISBURG ASSOCIATES LIMITED PARTNERSHIP (1)
1230 S Ellington Pkwy Ste 2400, Lewisburg, TN 37091-4330
Tel.: (931) 359-6735
Property Rental & Leasing Services
N.A.I.C.S.: 531110

M & P DEVELOPMENT COMPANY (1)
26 Woodside St, Stamford, CT 06902
Tel.: (203) 324-3932
Property Rental & Leasing Services
N.A.I.C.S.: 531110

MONTICELLO MANOR, LTD. (1)
5518 Culebra Rd Apt 1622, San Antonio, TX 78228
Tel.: (210) 434-2107
Web Site: http://www.monticellomanor.com
Sales Range: $25-49.9 Million
Emp.: 4
Property Rental & Leasing Services
N.A.I.C.S.: 531110

PEPPERTREE VILLAGE OF AVON PARK, LIMITED (1)
904 S Florida Ave, Avon Park, FL 33825-5002

Tel.: (863) 452-1552
Property Rental & Leasing Services
N.A.I.C.S.: 531110

PINEWOOD PARK APARTMENTS, A LIMITED PARTNERSHIP (1)
1600 Windmill Way, Republic, MO 65738
Tel.: (417) 732-9600
Emp.: 2
Property Rental & Leasing Services
N.A.I.C.S.: 531110
Cheryl Roderick (Gen Mgr)

RIVERWOODS PRESERVATION, L.P. (1)
300 E River St, Kankakee, IL 60901-5160
Tel.: (815) 939-1500
Web Site: http://www.aimco.com
Emp.: 3
Real Estate Agents & Brokerage Services
N.A.I.C.S.: 531210

Rosewood Apartments Corporation (1)
216 W Forest Ave Ste 100, Round Lake, IL 60073-3534
Tel.: (847) 546-6800
Real Estate Agents & Brokerage Services
N.A.I.C.S.: 531210

UNIVERSAL BOOT SHOPS, A CALIFORNIA GENERAL PARTNERSHIP (1)
555 Broadway Ste 1030, Chula Vista, CA 91910
Tel.: (619) 422-4641
Leather Goods Distr
N.A.I.C.S.: 458210

VERDES DEL ORIENTE PRESERVATION, L.P. (1)
360 W 3rd St, San Pedro, CA 90731
Tel.: (310) 832-4501
Web Site: http://www.aimco.com
Sales Range: $25-49.9 Million
Emp.: 4
Property Rental & Leasing Services
N.A.I.C.S.: 531110

Van Nuys Apartments (1)
210 W 7th St Ofc, Los Angeles, CA 90014-1541
Tel.: (213) 627-5286
Web Site: http://www.aimco.com
Sales Range: $25-49.9 Million
Emp.: 8
Property Rental & Leasing Services
N.A.I.C.S.: 531110

WALNUT HILLS PRESERVATION, L.P. (1)
1137 1175 Walpert St, Hayward, CA 94541
Tel.: (510) 581-8484
Web Site: https://www.walnuthills-apartments.com
Emp.: 6
Property Rental & Leasing Services
N.A.I.C.S.: 531110

WILKES TOWERS LIMITED PARTNERSHIP (1)
830 Main St Ofc 200, North Wilkesboro, NC 28659-4158
Tel.: (336) 838-8552
Web Site: http://www.wilkestowers.monroegroup.com
Emp.: 4
Property Rental & Leasing Services
N.A.I.C.S.: 531110

WINTER GARDEN PRESERVATION, L.P. (1)
5708 Kingsbury Pl, Saint Louis, MO 63112-1641
Tel.: (314) 361-7225
Web Site: http://www.aimco.com
Emp.: 3
Property Rental & Leasing Services
N.A.I.C.S.: 531110

Wasco Arms (1)
2617 Poso Dr, Wasco, CA 93280
Tel.: (661) 758-4289
Web Site: https://www.wascoarms.com
Property Rental & Leasing Services
N.A.I.C.S.: 531110

APEIRON CAPITAL INVESTMENT CORP.

175 Federal St Ste 875, Boston, MA 02110
Tel.: (617) 279-0045 DE
Year Founded: 2020
APNC—(OTCIQ)
Rev.: $8,375,006
Assets: $17,454,016
Liabilities: $29,116,458
Net Worth: ($11,662,442)
Earnings: $6,582,898
Emp.: 3
Fiscal Year-end: 12/31/22
Investment Services
N.A.I.C.S.: 523999
Joel Shulman (Chm & CEO)
Eva Adosoglou (COO)
Grant Grigorian (CFO)

APELLIS PHARMACEUTICALS, INC.
100 5th Ave, Waltham, MA 02451
Tel.: (617) 977-5700 DE
Web Site: https://www.apellis.com
Year Founded: 2009
APLS—(NASDAQ)
Rev.: $396,591,000
Assets: $788,730,000
Liabilities: $594,209,000
Net Worth: $194,521,000
Earnings: ($528,628,000)
Emp.: 702
Fiscal Year-end: 12/31/23
Developer of Therapeutics & Drug Delivery Technologies of Chronic Inflammatory Diseases
N.A.I.C.S.: 325412
Alec Machiels (Executives, Bd of Dirs)
Cedric Francois (Co-Founder, Pres & CEO)
Pascal Deschatelets (Co-Founder & Chief Scientific Officer)
David Watson (Gen Counsel)
Timothy E. Sullivan (CFO & Treas)
Adam Townsend (COO)
James G. Chopas (Chief Acctg Officer, VP & Controller)
Karen Lewis (Chief People Officer)
Nur Nicholson (Chief Technical Ops Officer)
Caroline Baumal (Chief Medical Officer)
Mark DeLong (Chief Bus Officer)
Jeffrey Eisele (Chief Dev Officer)
Gerald Lokchung Chan (Chm)

Subsidiaries:

Potentia Pharmaceuticals, Inc. (1)
6400 Westwind Way Suite A, Crestwood, KY 40014
Tel.: (502) 241-4114
Web Site: http://www.potentiapharma.com
Biotechnology Drug Developer of Chronic Inflammatory Diseases Therapy
N.A.I.C.S.: 325412

APERTURE ACQUISITION CORP.
747 3rd Ave 19th Fl, New York, NY 10017
Tel.: (212) 970-2100 Ky
Year Founded: 2021
APCPU—(NYSE)
Investment Services
N.A.I.C.S.: 523999
Lance West (Chm & CEO)
Jeffrey Gelfand (CFO)

APHEX BIOCLEANSE SYSTEMS, INC
1820 State Road13 Ste 11-43, Saint Johns, FL 32259
Tel.: (585) 798-7775
Web Site:
    http://www.sunsetcapitalassets.com
Year Founded: 2012

SNST—(OTCIQ)
Sales Range: Less than $1 Million
Diversified Financial Services
N.A.I.C.S.: 525990
Lewis Brine (Mng Dir)

APOGEE ENTERPRISES, INC.
4400 W 78th St Ste 520, Minneapolis, MN 55435
Tel.: (952) 835-1874   MN
Web Site: https://www.apog.com
Year Founded: 1949
APOG—(NASDAQ)
Rev.: $1,440,696,000
Assets: $915,365,000
Liabilities: $518,957,000
Net Worth: $396,408,000
Earnings: $104,107,000
Emp.: 4,900
Fiscal Year-end: 02/25/23
Architectural & Building Products & Services
N.A.I.C.S.: 327211
Ty R. Silberhorn (CEO)
Gary R. Johnson (Treas & Sr VP)
Brent C. Jewell (Pres-Architectural Glass Segment)
Meghan M. Elliott (Gen Counsel, Sec & VP)
Mark Augdahl (Interim CFO & VP-Fin-Architectural Glass Segment)
Matthew James Osberg (CFO & Exec VP)
Nick C. Longman (Pres-Architectural Framing Sys Segment)
Jeff Huebschen (VP-IR & Comm)
Michelle Roemer (CIO & Sr VP)
Greg J. Sachs (Chief Procurement Officer)
Raelyn A. Trende (Chief HR Officer & Exec VP)

Subsidiaries:

Alumicor Limited   (1)
290 Humberline Drive, Toronto, M9W 5S2, ON, Canada
Tel.: (416) 745-4222
Web Site: https://www.alumicor.com
Architectural Equipment Mfr & Whslr
N.A.I.C.S.: 332323

EFCO Corporation   (1)
1000 County Rd, Monett, MO 65708-9214
Tel.: (417) 235-3193
Web Site: http://www.efcocorp.com
Emp.: 2,000
Aluminum Windows, Custom Curtainwalls, Store Fronts & Entry Doors Mfr
N.A.I.C.S.: 332321

Harmon, Inc.   (1)
1650 W 82nd St Ste 1100, Bloomington, MN 55431-1159
Tel.: (905) 846-3177
Web Site: https://harmoninc.com
Sales Range: $150-199.9 Million
Emp.: 24
Exterior Cladding Services
N.A.I.C.S.: 238150
Troy Johnson (Pres)
Beth Dienst (VP-HR)
Brian Clark (VP-Ops-Natl)
Jeff Jansen (VP-Manufacturing)
Andy Lawson (VP-Finance)
Ryan Cogan (Sr Dir-Engrg And Design)
Jon Liesmaki (Dir-Safety)
Mersea Kidan (Dir-Continuous Improvement)

Subsidiary (Domestic):

Harmon, Inc.   (2)
100 E Crossroads Pkwy Ste B, Bolingbrook, IL 60440
Tel.: (630) 759-8060
Web Site: http://www.harmoninc.com
Sales Range: $25-49.9 Million
Emp.: 17
Commercial Glass Installation Services
N.A.I.C.S.: 332321

Linetec   (1)
7500 Stewart Ave, Wausau, WI 54401

Tel.: (715) 843-4100
Web Site: http://www.linetec.com
Sales Range: $50-74.9 Million
Emp.: 330
Mfr of Architectural Paint: Paint & Anodize Finisher
N.A.I.C.S.: 332321

Sotawall Limited   (1)
80 Van Kirk Drive, Brampton, L7A 1B1, ON, Canada
Tel.: (905) 846-3177
Web Site: https://www.sotawall.com
Flat Glass Mfr
N.A.I.C.S.: 327211

Tru Vue, Inc.   (1)
9400 W 55th St, McCook, IL 60525
Tel.: (708) 485-5080
Web Site: https://tru-vue.com
Sales Range: $100-124.9 Million
Emp.: 225
Glass Mfr
N.A.I.C.S.: 325612

Plant (Domestic):

Tru Vue, Inc.   (2)
2150 Airport Dr, Faribault, MN 55021-7798
Tel.: (507) 334-0051
Web Site: http://www.tru-vue.com
Sales Range: $50-74.9 Million
Emp.: 115
Mfr of Optical Thin Film Coatings
N.A.I.C.S.: 327215

Tubelite Inc.   (1)
3056 Walker Ridge Dr NW Ste G, Walker, MI 49544
Tel.: (616) 301-0056
Web Site: http://www.tubeliteinc.com
Emp.: 300
Commercial Building Services & Product Distr
N.A.I.C.S.: 327211
Steve Green (Pres)

Viracon, Inc.   (1)
800 Park Dr, Owatonna, MN 55060   (100%)
Tel.: (507) 451-9555
Web Site: https://www.viracon.com
Rev.: $13,692,000
Emp.: 1,750
Architectural Glass Product Mfr
N.A.I.C.S.: 325612
Nick C. Longman (Pres)
Mark R. Augdahl (VP-Fin)

Subsidiary (Non-US):

Glassec Vidros de Seguranca Ltd.   (2)
Tel.: (55) 1145978100
Web Site:
https://www.glassecviracon.com.br
Emp.: 210
Glass Products Designer & Developer
N.A.I.C.S.: 327211

Subsidiary (Domestic):

Viracon Georgia, Inc.   (2)
8373 Zell Miller Pkwy, Statesboro, GA 30458
Tel.: (912) 871-3500
Web Site: http://www.viracon.com
Emp.: 378
Architectural Glass Mfr
N.A.I.C.S.: 327211

Wausau Window & Wall Systems   (1)
7800 International Dr, Wausau, WI 54401   (100%)
Tel.: (715) 845-2161
Web Site: http://www.wausauwindow.com
Sales Range: $50-74.9 Million
Emp.: 500
Custom Aluminum Window & Curtain Wall Systems Mfr
N.A.I.C.S.: 332321

APOGEE THERAPEUTICS, INC.
221 Crescent St, Waltham, MA 02453
Tel.: (650) 394-5230   DE

Web Site:
https://www.apogeetherapeutics.com
Year Founded: 2023
APGE—(NASDAQ)
Emp.: 25
Research & Development in Biotechnology (except Nanobiotechnology)
N.A.I.C.S.: 541714
Jane Pritchett Henderson (CFO)
Mark C. McKenna (Chm)
Rebecca Dabora (CTO)
Noel Kurdi (VP-IR)
Carl Dambkowski (Chief Medical Officer)
Michael Henderson (CEO)

APOLLO BANCORP, INC.
201 N Warren Ave, Apollo, PA 15613
Tel.: (724) 478-3151
Web Site:
https://www.apollotrust.com
APLO—(OTCIQ)
Rev.: $7,712,230
Assets: $166,592,606
Liabilities: $144,291,159
Net Worth: $22,301,447
Earnings: $1,740,454
Fiscal Year-end: 12/31/20
Bank Holding Company
N.A.I.C.S.: 551111
Nelson L. Person (Pres & CEO)
George B. Davis (VP-Comml Lending)
Julia M. Holmes (Sec & VP-Risk Mgmt)
Robert B. Kastan (CFO, Treas & VP)
Robert J. Kopec (VP-Residential Lending)
Christopher Martin (Chief Banking Officer & VP)
Kirk S. Montgomery (CIO & VP-Ops)
Sara J. Copeland (Asst VP-Ops)
Joyce M. Corbin (Asst Treas & Asst Sec)
Linda M. Daley (Asst VP-Retail Banking)

Subsidiaries:

Apollo Trust Company   (1)
201 N Warren Ave, Apollo, PA 15613
Tel.: (724) 478-3151
Web Site: http://www.apollotrust.com
Commericial Banking
N.A.I.C.S.: 522110
Barbara Calizzi (COO, Sec & Exec VP)
Carolyn R. Bash (Sec & Asst Treas)
Brian Hulme (VP-Comml Lending)
Kevin Butler (VP-Comml Lending)
Robert Kastan (CFO, Treas & VP)

APOLLO GLOBAL MANAGEMENT, INC.
9 W 57th St 42nd Fl, New York, NY 10019
Tel.: (212) 515-3200   DE
Web Site: https://www.apollo.com
Year Founded: 2021
APO—(NYSE)
Rev.: $32,644,000,000
Assets: $313,488,000,000
Liabilities: $288,243,000,000
Net Worth: $25,245,000,000
Earnings: $6,509,000,000
Emp.: 2,903
Fiscal Year-end: 12/31/23
Holding Company; Investment Services
N.A.I.C.S.: 551112
Reed B. Rayman (Partner-Private Equity)
Marc J. Rowan (Founder & CEO)
Stuart A. Rothstein (COO-Asset Backed Fin)
Christine Cahill (Principal)
Katherine G. Newman (Partner-Senior Tax Counsel)

Subsidiaries:

Apollo Asset Management, Inc.   (1)
9 W 57th St 42nd Fl, New York, NY 10019
Tel.: (212) 515-3200
Web Site: https://www.apollo.com
Rev.: $3,551,356,000
Assets: $13,793,947,000
Liabilities: $10,326,960,000
Net Worth: $3,466,987,000
Earnings: $933,867,000
Emp.: 2,540
Fiscal Year-end: 12/31/2022
Private Equity, Capital Markets & Real Estate Investment Advisory & Management Services
N.A.I.C.S.: 523999
Sanjay Hiralal Patel (Sr Partner & Chm-Intl)
Michael S. Downing (Partner)
Scott M. Kleinman (Co-Chm & Co-Pres)
Marc E. Becker (Sr Partner-Private Equity)
Marc E. Becker (Sr Partner-Private Equity)
Reed B. Rayman (Partner-Private Equity)
Marc J. Rowan (Co-Founder)
James Charles Zelter (Co-Chm & Co-Pres)
Matthew H. Nord (Partner & Co-Head)
Lee J. Solomon (Partner-Private Equity)
Nicole Bonsignore (Mng Dir-Human Capital)
Johannes H. Worsoe (Partner & CFO)
Joshua J. Harris (Sr Mng Dir)
Stephanie Drescher (Chief Client & Product Dev Officer & Officer-Client & Product Dev)
Byron C. Vielehr (Partner & Co-COO)
Martin Bernard Kelly (Co-COO)
Vikram Mahidhar (Ops Partner)
Gernot Lohr (Sr Partner & Head-Fin Institutions Grp)
Gary Parr (Sr Mng Dir)
Samuel Feinstein (Partner-Private Equity)
David Kuritsky (Mng Dir-Credit)
Gary Albelli (Mng Dir-Tech-Global)
Robert Azerad (Mng Dir-Fin)
Andrew Berg (Mng Dir-Credit)
Ramona Boston (Mng Dir-Client & Product Solutions)
Daniel Castaline (Mng Dir-Credit)
Ryan Crum (Mng Dir-Tech-Global)
John DeRosa (Mng Dir-Fin)
Jeremy Ellermeyer (Mng Dir-Credit)
Richard Frank (Mng Dir-Credit)
Jaime Fuertes (Mng Dir-Corp Svcs)
Adam Biren (Mng Dir-Client & Product Solutions)
Abhijit Choudhary (Mng Dir-Ops)
Lauren Coape-Arnold (Head-Human Capital-Citizenship-Global)
Jason D'Silva (Mng Dir-Tech-Global)
Wilson Handler (Partner-Private Equity)
Christine Hommes (Partner-Private Equity)
Earl Hunt (Partner-Credit)
Gregory Hunt (Mng Dir-Fin)
Bogdan Ignaschenko (Partner-Private Equity)
Vikram Mahidhar (Ops Partner)
Noah Gunn (Head-IR-Global)
Joanna Rose (Head-Corp Comm-Global)
Reed Rayman (Partner-Private Equity)
Jose A. Briones Jr. (Partner)
Louis-Jacques Tanguy (Chief Acctg Officer)
Andy Jhawar (Partner)
Theo Kwon (Partner)
Antoine Munfakh (Partner)
Danielle Thorsen (Partner)
Itai Wallach (Partner)
Rajesh Jegadeesh (Principal)
Paulomi Shah (Partner)
Ben Eppley (Partner)
Seda Yalcinkaya (Partner)
Jordan Lubkeman (Principal)
Heather Berger (Partner)
Brian Laureano (Principal)
Neil Mehta (Partner)
Salim Hirji (Partner)
Matthew Michelini (Partner)
Akila Grewal (Partner)
Marsha Alexander (Mng Dir)
Jeffrey Arek (Mng Dir)
Shahriar Azizpour (Mng Dir)
Johnathon Baker (Mng Dir)
Virender Bedi (Mng Dir)
Demetri Bouras (Mng Dir)
Mickey Brennan (Partner)
Matthew Brody (Mng Dir)
Scott Browning (Partner)
Brian Carney (Mng Dir)
James Caruso (Mng Dir)
Alexander Chastain-Chapman (Mng Dir)
Daniel Cohen (Partner)

Apollo Global Management, Inc.—(Continued)

John Cortese (Partner)
Derek Dillon (Mng Dir)
Diego Donoso (Mng Dir)
Daniel Duval (Mng Dir)
Benjamin Eason (Mng Dir)
Obinna Eke (Mng Dir)
James Elworth (Mng Dir)
Kristen Hester (Mng Dir)
Veena Isaac (Partner)
Robert Kalsow-Ramos (Partner)
David B. Sambur (Sr Partner & Co-Head-Private Equity)
John J. Suydam (Sr Partner & Chief Legal Officer)
John J. Hannan (Sr Partner-Credit)
Itai Wallach (Partner)
Alex van Hoek (Partner)

Holding (Non-US):

ABC Technologies Holdings Inc.　(2)
2 Norelco Drive, Toronto, M9L 2X6, ON, Canada　　(65.1%)
Tel.: (416) 246-1782
Web Site: https://abctechnologies.com
Emp.: 100
Automotive Systems & Components Mfr
N.A.I.C.S.: 336330
Terry Campbell (Pres)
Scott Roggenbauer (CFO)
Philip Grella (Exec VP)
Leonard Roelant (Exec VP)
Mike Fritts (Exec VP)
Mark Decker (Chief HR Officer)
Ryan Conacher (Gen Counsel)

Subsidiary (US):

dlhBOWLES, Inc.　(3)
2422 Leo Ave SW, Canton, OH 44706
Tel.: (330) 478-2503
Web Site: http://www.dlhbowles.com
Sales Range: $10-24.9 Million
Plastic Injection Molding Products Mfr
N.A.I.C.S.: 326199
John Saxon (Pres & CEO)
David O'Neal (Dir-Engrg)

Holding (Domestic):

ADSG, Inc.　(2)
10131 FM 2920, Tomball, TX 77375
Tel.: (281) 225-4881
Web Site:
　http://www.accentfamilyofcompanies.com
Sales Range: $25-49.9 Million
Building Materials Distr
N.A.I.C.S.: 423390
Bill Sims (Pres & CEO)

ADT Inc.　(2)
1501 Yamato Rd, Boca Raton, FL 33431　　(74.6%)
Tel.: (561) 404-0338
Web Site: https://www.adt.com
Rev.: $4,982,659,000
Assets: $15,964,094,000
Liabilities: $12,175,448,000
Net Worth: $3,788,646,000
Earnings: $463,009,000
Emp.: 14,300
Fiscal Year-end: 12/31/2023
Holding Company; Security Systems & Monitoring Services
N.A.I.C.S.: 551112
James David DeVries (Chm, Pres & CEO)
Jamie E. Haenggi (COO/Exec VP-Solar)
Jeffrey A. Likosar (CFO, Chief Transformation Officer & Pres-Corp Dev)
Jamie E. Haenggi (COO/Exec VP-Solar)
Donald M. Young (COO & Exec VP)
David Smail (Chief Legal Officer, Sec & Exec VP)
Zachary Susil (Chief Acctg Officer, CFO-ADT Solar, Sr VP-ADT Solar, VP & Controller)
Steven Burzo (Chief Acctg Officer)
Harriet Harty (Chief Admin Officer)
DeLu Jackson (CMO)
Wayne Thorsen (Chief Bus Officer)
DeLu Jackson (CMO & Exec VP)

Subsidiary (Domestic):

Alliant Integrators, Inc.　(3)
2700 Diode Ln, Louisville, KY 40299-0299
Tel.: (502) 363-8633
Web Site: http://www.alliantintegrators.com

Electrical Contractor
N.A.I.C.S.: 238210

Safe Electronics, Inc.　(3)
2441 Western Ave, Las Vegas, NV 89109
Tel.: (702) 367-8959
Sales Range: $1-9.9 Million
Emp.: 50
Security Systems Services (except Locksmiths)
N.A.I.C.S.: 561621
Bruce Boles (Pres)
Robert Miller (Project Mgr)

The ADT Security Corporation　(3)
1501 Yamato Rd, Boca Raton, FL 33431
Tel.: (561) 404-0338
Holding Company; Security Systems Services
N.A.I.C.S.: 551112

Subsidiary (Domestic):

ADT LLC　(4)
1501 Yamato Rd, Boca Raton, FL 33431
Tel.: (564) 404-0338
Web Site: http://www.adt.com
Residential & Commercial Security Systems Services
N.A.I.C.S.: 561621
James David DeVries (Co-Pres & Co-CEO)
Jim D. DeVries (Co-Pres & Co-CEO)
Jamie E. Haenggi (Chief Customer Officer)
Jeffrey A. Likosar (CFO)
Jamie E. Haenggi (Chief Customer Officer)
Kenneth J. Porpora (Chief Growth Officer)
Jeff Likosar (CFO)
Ken Porpora (Chief Growth Officer)

Branch (Domestic):

ADT LLC - Carrollton Office　(5)
3220 Keller Springs Rd, Carrollton, TX 75006
Tel.: (972) 535-8340
Web Site: http://www.adt.com
Security Services
N.A.I.C.S.: 561621

ADT LLC - Louisville Office　(5)
2115 Stanley Gault Pkwy Ste 100, Louisville, KY 40223
Tel.: (502) 785-3045
Web Site: http://www.adt.com
Safety & Security Services
N.A.I.C.S.: 561621

ADT LLC - Melville Office　(5)
50 Republic Rd, Melville, NY 11747
Tel.: (516) 986-2349
Web Site: http://www.adt.com
Security Services
N.A.I.C.S.: 561621

ADT LLC - New York Office　(5)
350 7th Ave, New York, NY 10001
Tel.: (646) 233-1834
Web Site: http://www.adt.com
Burglar Alarms, Fire Alarms, Access Control & Closed Circuit Television Systems Installation & Monitoring Services
N.A.I.C.S.: 561621

ADT LLC - San Antonio Office　(5)
814 Arion Pkwy, San Antonio, TX 78216
Tel.: (210) 468-1420
Web Site: http://www.adt.com
Security Services
N.A.I.C.S.: 561621

ADT LLC - Totowa Office　(5)
20 Commerce Way, Totowa, NJ 07512
Tel.: (973) 239-7044
Web Site: http://www.adt.com
Security Systems
N.A.I.C.S.: 561621

ADT Security Services, LLC - Aurora Office　(5)
3190 S Vaughn Way, Aurora, CO 80014
Tel.: (303) 857-5463
Web Site: http://www.adt.com
Security System Services
N.A.I.C.S.: 561621

Subsidiary (Domestic):

CAM Connections, Inc.　(5)
3970 S Pipkin Rd, Lakeland, FL 33811
Tel.: (863) 583-3343
Web Site: https://www.camconn.com

Security Products & Services
N.A.I.C.S.: 561621
Robert W. Bull Jr. (Pres & CEO)

Datashield LLC　(5)
1475 N Scottsdale Rd Ste 410, Scottsdale, AZ 85257
Tel.: (866) 428-4567
Web Site: http://www.datashieldprotect.com
Data Security Services
N.A.I.C.S.: 518210
Joel Menk (Founder & COO)
James Treuting (Pres & Gen Mgr)
Dave Norlin (Chief Information & Security Officer)
Alex Achs (Dir-Security Ops)
Clayton Paplaczyk (Mgr-Security Engrg)
Chris Tunks (Sr Engr-Security)
Mike Heller (Dir-Product Mgmt)
Justin Bahr (Product Mgr)
Elijah Penney (Mgr-R&D)
Chase Hall (Dir-Engagement Mgmt)
Juan Wilbur (Mgr-Engagement)
Adam Merkley (Mgr-Engagement)
Shana Gold (Mgr-Engagement)
Doug Roberts (Reg Dir-Sls)
Michael Londino (Reg Dir-Sls)
German Sanchez (Mgr-Channel Sls)
Chris Vincent (Dir-Demand Generation)
D. J. Jones (Sls Dir-West)
Kurt Rogers (Sls Dir-West)

Subsidiary (Domestic):

Integrated Business Solutions, Inc.　(6)
455 E 200 S Ste 100, Salt Lake City, UT 84111-2140
Tel.: (801) 328-4567
Information Technology Consulting Services
N.A.I.C.S.: 423430

Subsidiary (Domestic):

Gaston Security Inc.　(5)
115 N Main St, Emporia, VA 23847
Tel.: (800) 965-1266
Web Site: http://www.gastonsecurity.com
Sales Range: $1-9.9 Million
Emp.: 7
Electronic Security Services
N.A.I.C.S.: 423610
Greg Burns (VP)

Protec, Inc.　(5)
720 NE Flanders St, Portland, OR 97232-2763
Tel.: (503) 235-4000
Web Site: http://www.protecsecurity.com
Security System Services
N.A.I.C.S.: 561621
Andy Schwartz (Pres)

Subsidiary (Non US):

AGM India Advisors Private Limited　(2)
The Grand Hyatt Complex Suite F-11, Mumbai, 400 055, India
Tel.: (91) 2239571400
Emp.: 15
Investment Advisory Services
N.A.I.C.S.: 523940
Mintoo Bhandari (Mng Dir)

Holding (Domestic):

AMI (Holdings), LLC　(2)
725 Arizona Ave Ste 200, Santa Monica, CA 90401
Tel.: (310) 458-1384
Web Site: https://www.amigrp.com
Holding Company
N.A.I.C.S.: 551111

Affiliate (Domestic):

Apollo Commercial Real Estate Finance, Inc.　(2)
9 W 57th St 42nd Fl, New York, NY 10019
Tel.: (212) 515-3200
Web Site: https://www.apollocref.com
Rev.: $701,002,000
Assets: $9,296,730,000
Liabilities: $7,087,997,000
Net Worth: $2,208,733,000
Earnings: $45,855,000
Fiscal Year-end: 12/31/2023
Real Estate Investment Trust
N.A.I.C.S.: 525990

Stuart A. Rothstein (Pres & CEO)
Anastasia Mironova (CFO, Treas & Sec)

Joint Venture (Domestic):

Apollo Education Group, Inc.　(2)
4025 S Riverpoint Pkwy, Phoenix, AZ 85040
Tel.: (480) 966-5394
Web Site: http://www.apollo.edu
Holding Company; Online Higher Education Program Services
N.A.I.C.S.: 551112
Gregory W. Cappelli (CEO)
Anthony Miller (Chm)

Subsidiary (Domestic):

Institute for Professional Development　(3)
17 Hathaway Pl, Glen Ridge, NJ 07028
Tel.: (973) 777-4200
Web Site: https://www.ipd2.com
Educational Consulting Services
N.A.I.C.S.: 541618

University of Phoenix, Inc.　(3)
4035 S Riverpoint Pkwy, Phoenix, AZ 85040
Tel.: (602) 254-0086
Web Site: https://www.phoenix.edu
Colleges & Universities
N.A.I.C.S.: 611310
Steve Gross (CMO)
Raghu Krishnaiah (COO)
Srini Medi (Gen Counsel & Sr VP)
Cheryl Naumann (Chief HR Officer)
Eric Rizzo (Sr VP-Govt Affairs)
Jamie Smith (CIO)
Ruth Veloria (Chief Strategy Officer & Chief Customer officer)
John Woods (Chief Academic Officer)
Blair Westblom (CFO)

Western International University, Inc.　(3)
1601 W Fountainhead Pkwy, Tempe, AZ 85282
Investment Services
N.A.I.C.S.: 523999

Subsidiary (Domestic):

Apollo Global Real Estate Management, L.P　(2)
9 W 57th St Ste 4100, New York, NY 10019
Tel.: (212) 515-3200
Web Site: http://www.agm.com
Real Estate Investment Services
N.A.I.C.S.: 525990

Apollo International Management, L.P.　(2)
9 W 57th St Fl 43, New York, NY 10019
Tel.: (212) 515-3400
Emp.: 1
Business Support Services
N.A.I.C.S.: 561499

Apollo Investment Management, L.P.　(2)
609 Main St Ste 2750, Houston, TX 77002
Tel.: (832) 708-2000
Web Site: https://www.agm.com
Investment Advisory Services
N.A.I.C.S.: 523940

Subsidiary (Non-US):

Apollo Management International LLP　(2)
25 St George Street, London, W1S 1FS, United Kingdom
Tel.: (44) 2070165000
Web Site: http://www.agm.com
Investment Advisory Services
N.A.I.C.S.: 523940

Subsidiary (Domestic):

Apollo ST Debt Advisors LLC　(2)
152 W 57th St, New York, NY 10019-3386
Tel.: (212) 258-0940
Investment Advisory Services
N.A.I.C.S.: 523940

Affiliate (Domestic):

Apollo Senior Floating Rate Fund Inc.　(2)

9 W 57th St 43rd Fl, New York, NY 10019
Tel.: (212) 515-3200
Web Site: http://www.agm.com
Sales Range: Less than $1 Million
Investment Services
N.A.I.C.S.: 523999
Cindy Z. Michel *(Chief Compliance Officer)*
Joseph Moroney *(Head-Performing Credit-Global)*
Barry J. Cohen *(Chm)*

Apollo Tactical Income Fund Inc. (2)
9 W 57th St, New York, NY 10019
Tel.: (212) 515-3200
Sales Range: $25-49.9 Million
Closed-End Investment Fund
N.A.I.C.S.: 525990
Cindy Z. Michel *(Chief Compliance Officer)*
Joseph D. Glatt *(Chief Legal Officer & Sec)*
Barry J. Cohen *(Chm)*

Holding (Non-US):

Aspen Insurance Holdings Limited (2)
141 Front Street, Hamilton, HM 19, Bermuda
Tel.: (441) 2958201
Web Site: https://www.aspen.co
Rev.: $2,890,000,000
Assets: $15,157,300,000
Liabilities: $12,799,300,000
Net Worth: $2,358,000,000
Earnings: $51,100,000
Emp.: 946
Fiscal Year-end: 12/31/2022
Insurance Services
N.A.I.C.S.: 524126
Christian Dunleavy *(CEO/Chief Underwriting Officer-Aspen Bermuda Limited)*
Cecile M. Locurto *(VP-Grp Comm)*
Mark Cloutier *(Chm & Grp CEO)*
Jonny Atkinson *(Chief Bus Dev Officer)*
Mohinder Kang *(Chief People & Transformation Officer)*
Brian Tobben *(CEO-Aspen Capital Partners)*
Scott Kreuzer *(Sr Mng Dir-Aspen Re America)*
William Miller *(Grp Chief Actuarial Officer)*
Mark Pickering *(Chief Capital Mgmt Officer & Treas)*
Josh Brekenfeld *(Dir-Comm & Dev)*
Chris Coleman *(CFO)*
Rob Houghton *(Grp COO)*
Aileen Mathieson *(Chief Investment Officer)*

Subsidiary (Non-US):

APJ Asset Protection Jersey Limited (3)
Ogier House The Esplanade, Saint Helier, JE4 9WG, Jersey
Tel.: (44) 1534832366
Web Site: http://www.aspen-apj.com
Financial Services
N.A.I.C.S.: 523940
Henry MacHale *(Head-Crisis Mgmt-Global)*

Subsidiary (US):

AgriLogic Consulting, LLC (3)
1700 Research Pkwy Ste 290 Texas A M University, College Station, TX 77845
Tel.: (979) 267-6971
Web Site:
    https://www.agrilogicconsulting.com
Group Insurance Services
N.A.I.C.S.: 524126
S. Clifton Parks *(Pres)*
Bill Smith *(VP-Policy & Procedure)*
Keith Schumann *(Sr VP-Quantitative Analysis)*

Aspen Capital Advisors Inc. (3)
1740 Persimmon Dr, Naples, FL 34109
Tel.: (239) 594-0766
Investment Advisory Services
N.A.I.C.S.: 523940

Aspen Insurance U.S. Services Inc. (3)
600 Atlantic Ave Ste 2100, Boston, MA 02110-2320
Tel.: (617) 531-5100
Sales Range: $50-74.9 Million
Emp.: 50
Insurance Agencies & Brokerages
N.A.I.C.S.: 524210
Grace W. Fortune *(Sr VP)*
Bob Rheel *(Exec VP & Head-Property & Casualty Insurance)*

Russell Brown *(Sr VP & Head-Distr)*
Dominick Tassone *(Exec VP-Programs)*
Sean McPhillips *(Sr VP & Head-Primary Casualty-New York)*
Nicky Alexandru *(Head-Crisis Mgmt-New York)*
Henry MacHale *(Global Head-Crisis Mgmt)*

Subsidiary (Non-US):

Aspen Insurance UK Limited (3)
Plantation Pl 30 Fenchurch St, London, EC3M 3BD, United Kingdom
Tel.: (44) 2071848000
Property & Casualty Insurance Services
N.A.I.C.S.: 524126

Aspen Risk Management Limited (3)
Waterhouse Business Centre Cromar Way, Chelmsford, CM1 2QE, United Kingdom
Tel.: (44) 1245392131
Web Site:
    http://www.aspenriskmanagement.co.uk
Insurance & Reinsurance Services
N.A.I.C.S.: 524130

Aspen Singapore Pte. Ltd. (3)
138 Market Street 04-04 CapitaGreen, Singapore, 048946, Singapore
Tel.: (65) 64081006
Property & Casualty Insurance Services
N.A.I.C.S.: 524126

Subsidiary (US):

Aspen Specialty Insurance Company (3)
155 Federal St Ste 602, Boston, MA 02110-2320
Tel.: (617) 532-7300
Sales Range: $50-74.9 Million
Emp.: 50
Insurance Agencies & Brokerages
N.A.I.C.S.: 524210

Aspen Specialty Insurance Solutions, LLC (3)
777 S Figueroa St Ste 3650, Los Angeles, CA 90017
Tel.: (626) 463-7628
General Insurance Services
N.A.I.C.S.: 524298

Holding (Non-US):

Athene Holding Ltd. (2)
Tel.: (441) 2798400
Web Site: http://www.athene.com
Rev.: $28,494,000,000
Assets: $300,579,000,000
Liabilities: $279,344,000,000
Net Worth: $21,235,000,000
Earnings: $4,484,000,000
Emp.: 1,976
Fiscal Year-end: 12/31/2023
Holding Company; Reinsurance
N.A.I.C.S.: 551112
Michael S. Downing *(COO, Chief Actuary & Exec VP)*
James R. Belardi *(Co-Founder, Chm, CEO & Chief Investment Officer)*
Randall William Epright *(CIO & Exec VP)*
Sarah VanBeck *(Principal Acctg Officer, Sr VP & Controller)*
Grant Kvalheim *(Pres & Exec VP)*
William J. Wheeler *(Vice Chm)*
Martin P. Klein *(CFO & Exec VP)*
Sean C. Brennan *(Exec VP-Pension Risk Transfer & Flow Reinsurance)*
Katherine A. Daly *(Exec VP-Corp Dev)*
Doug Niemann *(Chief Risk Officer & Exec VP)*
Joseph Cohen *(Gen Counsel)*
Rebecca H. Tadikonda *(Exec VP)*
Christopher Grady *(Exec VP)*
Christopher R. Welp *(Exec VP)*

Subsidiary (US):

Athene Annuity & Life Assurance Company (3)
2000 Wade Hampton Blvd, Greenville, SC 29615 (100%)
Tel.: (864) 609-1000
Web Site: http://www.atheneannuity.com
Sales Range: $75-99.9 Million
Emp.: 200
Annuity Products & Services
N.A.I.C.S.: 524113

Athene Annuity & Life Assurance Company of New York (3)
200 Wade Hampton Blvd, Greenville, SC 29615
Tel.: (845) 358-2300
Web Site: http://www.presidentiallife.com
Sales Range: $250-299.9 Million
Emp.: 100
Life Insurance & Annuities
N.A.I.C.S.: 524113

Athene Asset Management, L.P. (3)
2121 Rosecrans Ave Ste 5300, El Segundo, CA 90245
Tel.: (310) 698-4444
Web Site: http://www.athenelp.com
Investment Advisory Services
N.A.I.C.S.: 523940
James R. Belardi *(Chm, CEO & Chief Investment Officer)*

Subsidiary (Domestic):

Athene Life Re Ltd. (3)
Second Floor Washington House 16 Church Street, Hamilton, HM 11, Bermuda
Tel.: (441) 2798400
Web Site: https://www.athenelifere.bm
Emp.: 30
Fixed Annuity Reinsurance
N.A.I.C.S.: 524130
Fergus Daly *(CFO)*
Devin Mullan *(Sr VP)*
Eric Henderson *(Sr VP)*
Janine Carey *(Chief Compliance Officer)*

Subsidiary (US):

Athene USA Corporation (3)
7700 Mills Civic Pkwy, West Des Moines, IA 50266
Tel.: (515) 362-3600
Web Site: http://www.athene.com
Sales Range: $700-749.9 Million
Emp.: 1,800
Annuity Insurance Services
N.A.I.C.S.: 524298
Grant Kvalheim *(Pres & CEO)*

Donlen Corporation (3)
3000 Lakeside Dr, Bannockburn, IL 60015
Tel.: (847) 714-1400
Web Site: http://www.donlen.com
Sales Range: $350-399.9 Million
Emp.: 250
Fleet Leasing & Management Services
N.A.I.C.S.: 532112
Tom Callahan *(Pres)*
Dennis Straight *(CTO & Sr VP)*
Eric Hiller *(CFO & Sr VP)*
Jeff Lucas *(Sr VP-Customer Experience & Contact Center Ops)*
Jim Wohlever *(VP-Sls & Client Rels)*
Ilese Flamm *(Gen Counsel, Sec & Sr VP)*
Sharon Peete *(Sr Dir-HR)*
Khalid Latif *(Sr VP-Ops & Supply Chain)*

Petros PACE Finance, LLC (3)
300 W 6th St Ste 1540, Austin, TX 78701
Tel.: (512) 599-9037
Web Site: http://www.petros-pace.com
Commercial Financing Services
N.A.I.C.S.: 522320
Mansoor Ghori *(Founder & CEO)*
Jim Stanislaus *(Founder & CFO)*
Tommy Deavenport *(COO)*
Andy Meyer *(Mng Dir-Originations)*

Holding (Non-US):

Athora Holding Ltd. (2)
First Floor Swan Building 26 Victoria Street, Hamilton, HM12, Bermuda
Tel.: (441) 2788600
Web Site: https://www.athora.com
Acquisition, Portfolio Transfer & Reinsurance Solutions Services
N.A.I.C.S.: 524130

Subsidiary (Non-US):

Athene Lebensversicherung AG (3)
Abraham-Lincoln-Park 1, 65189, Wiesbaden, Germany
Tel.: (49) 611 2908 7862
Web Site: http://www.athora.com
Life Insurance, Pension, Investment Banking & Mortgage Products & Services
N.A.I.C.S.: 524298

Generali Belgium S.A. (3)
Av Louise 149, Brussels, 1050, Belgium (100%)
Tel.: (32) 2403 87 00
Web Site: http://www.generali.be
Insurance Company
N.A.I.C.S.: 524128

Subsidiary (Domestic):

Bureau d'Assurances et dePrets (4)
Avenue De La Salm 9, 6690, Vielsalm, Belgium
Tel.: (32) 80217171
Insurance Brokerage Services
N.A.I.C.S.: 524210

Subsidiary (Non-US):

Dedale S.A. (4)
15 Place de la Nation, 75011, Paris, France
Tel.: (33) 1 58 39 30 90
Web Site: http://www.dedale.net
Sales Range: $25-49.9 Million
Emp.: 14
Human Resource Consulting Services
N.A.I.C.S.: 541612
Jean Paries *(Pres)*
Veronique Moulin *(Office Mgr)*

GENERALI Real Estate Investments B.V. (4)
Diemerhof 42, Diemen, 1112 XN, Noord-Holland, Netherlands
Tel.: (31) 206601802
Real Estate Investment Services
N.A.I.C.S.: 531390

Subsidiary (Non-US):

MRS Bioul S.A. (5)
Avenue Louise 149, 1050, Brussels, Belgium
Tel.: (32) 71 79 70 00
Real Estate Manangement Services
N.A.I.C.S.: 531390

Subsidiary (Domestic):

Soenen Verzekeringskantoor nv (4)
Gasthuisstraat 81, 8970, Poperinge, Belgium
Tel.: (32) 57 33 41 41
Web Site: http://www.soenen-verzekeringen.be
General Insurance Services
N.A.I.C.S.: 524210

Webbroker S.A. (4)
Rue Defacqz 6, 1050, Brussels, Belgium
Tel.: (32) 25334030
Web Site: http://www.mefirst.be
Sales Range: $50-74.9 Million
Emp.: 4
Insurance Management Services
N.A.I.C.S.: 524298

Subsidiary (Non-US):

Vivat N.V. (3)
Burgemeester Rijnderslaan 7, 1185 MD, Amstelveen, Netherlands (100%)
Tel.: (31) 20 543 6 543
Web Site: http://vivat.nl
Sales Range: $1-4.9 Billion
Emp.: 3,006
Holding Company; Insurance Products & Services
N.A.I.C.S.: 551112
Ron van Oijen *(Chm)*
Yinhua Cao *(CFO)*
Lan Tang *(Chief Risk Officer)*
Wendy de Ruiter-Lorx *(Chief Comml Officer)*
Xiao Wei Wu *(Chief Transformation Officer)*
Jeroen Potjes *(COO)*
Maarten Dijkshoorn *(Chm-Supervisory Bd)*

Subsidiary (Domestic):

Proteq Levensverzekeringen N.V. (4)
Burgemeester Rijnderslaan 7, 1800 BH, Amstelveen, Netherlands
Tel.: (31) 725180180
Web Site: http://www.proteq.nl
Direct Life Insurance Carriers
N.A.I.C.S.: 524126

REAAL Schadeverzekeringen N.V. (4)

Apollo Global Management, Inc.—(Continued)

Postbus 274, 1800 BH, Alkmaar, Netherlands
Tel.: (31) 72 519 4000
Web Site: http://www.reaal.nl
Insurance Products & Services
N.A.I.C.S.: 524298

Division (Domestic):

Route Mobiel **(5)**
Burgemeester Rijnderslaan 7, 1185 MD, Amstelveen, Netherlands
Tel.: (31) 72 5185640
Web Site: http://www.routemobiel.nl
Car Insurance Roadside Assistance & Breakdown Services
N.A.I.C.S.: 524298

Joint Venture (Domestic):

Atlas Air Worldwide Holdings, Inc. **(2)**
2000 Westchester Ave, Purchase, NY 10577
Tel.: (914) 701-8000
Rev.: $4,549,104,000
Assets: $6,696,316,000
Liabilities: $3,631,540,000
Net Worth: $3,064,776,000
Earnings: $355,880,000
Emp.: 4,500
Fiscal Year-end: 12/31/2022
Holding Company; Airline Transportation Services
N.A.I.C.S.: 551112
Adam R. Kokas (Gen Counsel, Sec & Exec VP)
Michael T. Steen (CEO)
James A. Forbes (COO & Exec VP)
Spencer Schwartz (CFO & Exec VP)
Keith H. Mayer (Chief Acctg Officer, Sr VP & Controller)
Martin Drew (Chief Strategy & Transformation Officer)
Artem Gonopolskiy (CFO & Exec VP)
Patricia Goodwin-Peters (Sr VP-HR)
David Siegel (Chm)

Subsidiary (Domestic):

Atlas Air, Inc. **(3)**
2000 Westchester Ave, Purchase, NY 10577-2543
Tel.: (914) 701-8000
Web Site: https://www.atlasair.com
Sales Range: $250-299.9 Million
Emp.: 450
Airport-to-Airport Cargo Transportation Services
N.A.I.C.S.: 481112

Polar Air Cargo Worldwide, Inc. **(3)**
2000 Westchester Ave, Purchase, NY 10577 **(51%)**
Tel.: (914) 701-8000
Web Site: https://www.polaraircargo.com
Sales Range: $250-299.9 Million
Emp.: 500
Air Cargo Carriers Nonscheduled
N.A.I.C.S.: 481212
William J. Flynn (Pres & CEO)
Adam R. Kokas (Gen Counsel, Exec VP & Asst Sec)
Jeffrey Carlson (VP-Flight Ops)
Thomas Betenia (VP-Sales-Marketing-Americas)
Kersti Krepp (VP-Sls & Mktg-Asia-Pacific)
Sylvie Blondeel (CFO & Sr VP)
Abilash Kurien (VP-Marketing)
Carlton Llewellyn (VP-Quality-Worldwide)
Jon Olin (COO & Exec VP)
Ingrid Chariah (Sr Dir)
Drew McGee (Sr Dir)
Jon Olin (COO & Exec VP)
Ingrid Chariah (Sr Dir)
Drew McGee (Sr Dir)

Division (Domestic):

Polar Air Cargo Inc. **(4)**
5761 W Imperial Hwy Los Angeles International Airport, Los Angeles, CA 90045
Tel.: (310) 730-7112
Web Site: https://www.polaraircargo.com
Sales Range: $550-599.9 Million
Air Cargo Carriers Nonscheduled
N.A.I.C.S.: 481112
William J. Flynn (Pres & CEO)

Subsidiary (Domestic):

Worldwide Air Logistics Group, Inc. **(3)**
2000 Westchester Ave, Purchase, NY 10577 **(100%)**
Tel.: (914) 701-8000
Air Cargo Services
N.A.I.C.S.: 481112

Joint Venture (Non-US):

Bremer Kreditbank AG **(2)**
Wachtstrasse 16, 28195, Bremen, Germany
Tel.: (49) 42136840
Web Site: http://www.bkb-bank.com
Commercial Banking Asset Management & Investment Banking Services
N.A.I.C.S.: 522110
Jutta Nikolic (Sr VP)

Subsidiary (Domestic):

Oldenburgische Landesbank AG **(3)**
Stau 15/17, 26122, Oldenburg, Germany
Tel.: (49) 4412210
Web Site: https://www.olb.de
Sales Range: $400-449.9 Million
International Banking
N.A.I.C.S.: 522299

Subsidiary (Domestic):

Degussa Bank AG **(4)**
Theodor Heuss Allee 74, 60486, Frankfurt am Main, Germany
Tel.: (49) 6936005555
Web Site: http://www.degussa-bank.de
Sales Range: $50-74.9 Million
Emp.: 400
Banking Services
N.A.I.C.S.: 522299

Holding (Domestic):

CEC Entertainment, Inc. **(2)**
1707 Market Pl Blvd Ste 200, Irving, TX 75063
Tel.: (972) 258-8507
Web Site: https://www.chuckecheese.com
Rev.: $912,865,000
Assets: $2,119,549,000
Liabilities: $1,905,763,000
Net Worth: $213,786,000
Earnings: ($28,923,000)
Emp.: 16,400
Fiscal Year-end: 12/29/2019
Holding Company; Restaurant & Entertainment Centers Operator & Franchisor
N.A.I.C.S.: 551112
Andrew S. Jhawar (Chm)
John R. Cardinale (Pres)
David McKillips (CEO)
Rudy Rodriguez Jr. (Chief Legal & HR Officer & Exec VP)

Subsidiary (Domestic):

Peter Piper, Inc. **(3)**
4745 N 7th St Ste 350, Phoenix, AZ 85014
Tel.: (480) 609-6400
Web Site: http://www.peterpiperpizza.com
Sales Range: $50-74.9 Million
Emp.: 1,700
Pizza Restaurants Owner, Operator & Franchiser
N.A.I.C.S.: 722511
Bill Toole (COO)
Genaro Perez (CMO)

Holding (Domestic):

CORE Media Group., Inc. **(2)**
1071 Ave of the Americas, New York, NY 10018
Tel.: (212) 784-7770
Web Site: http://www.coremediagroup.com
Sales Range: $250-299.9 Million
Emp.: 310
Entertainment Holding Company; Entertainment & Commercial Content Developer
N.A.I.C.S.: 512110
Anoop Mathur (Founder & Pres)
Sudhir Kamath (Country Dir)
Sneha Jha (Mng Editor)
Aditya Sawant (Head-Strategic Accounts)
Sadanand Manda (Head-Sls & Event Ops)

Subsidiary (Non-US):

19 Entertainment Limited **(3)**

Unit 33 Ransomes Dock Business Center 35-37 Parkgate Road, London, SW11 4NP, United Kingdom **(100%)**
Tel.: (44) 2078011919
Web Site: http://www.19.co.uk
Sales Range: $50-74.9 Million
Emp.: 111
Television, Music, Artist Management, Touring, Sponsorship & Merchandising Services
N.A.I.C.S.: 711410

Subsidiary (Domestic):

Storm Model Management Ltd. **(4)**
5 Jubilee Place, London, SW3 3TD, United Kingdom
Tel.: (44) 2073689967
Web Site: http://www.stormmodels.com
Sales Range: $1-9.9 Million
Emp.: 25
Modeling Agency
N.A.I.C.S.: 711410
Sarah N. Doukas (Founder)

Subsidiary (Domestic):

Elvis Presley Enterprises, Inc. **(3)**
3734 Elvis Presley Blvd, Memphis, TN 38116 **(85%)**
Tel.: (901) 332-3322
Web Site: https://www.graceland.com
Sales Range: $75-99.9 Million
Restaurant & Hotel Owner; Tour Operator; Gift & Novelty Sales
N.A.I.C.S.: 712110

Holding (Non-US):

Catalina Holdings (Bermuda) Ltd. **(2)**
The Belvedere Building 2nd Floor 69 Pitts Bay Road, Pembroke, HM 08, Bermuda
Tel.: (441) 2946350
Web Site: https://www.catalinare.com
Holding Company; Non-Life Insurance & Reinsurance Companies
N.A.I.C.S.: 551112
Chris Fagan (Chm & CEO)
Dean Dwonczyk (Grp Dir-Liabilities & Risk Mgmt)
Keith Lyon (Gen Counsel)
Campbell McBeath (Grp Treas)

Subsidiary (Non-US):

Catalina Holdings UK Limited **(3)**
1 Alie Street, London, E1 8DE, United Kingdom
Tel.: (44) 2072655000
Web Site: http://www.catalina.com
Holding Company; Insurance Related Activities
N.A.I.C.S.: 551112

Subsidiary (Domestic):

Catalina Worthing Insurance Limited **(4)**
1 Alie Street, London, E1 8DE, United Kingdom
Tel.: (44) 1903836930
Web Site: https://catalinaworthing.co.uk
Insurance Services
N.A.I.C.S.: 524298

Downlands Liability Management Ltd. **(4)**
Unit B/C Downlands Business Park, Lyons Way, Worthing, BN14 9RX, West Sussex, United Kingdom
Tel.: (44) 1903836822
Web Site: http://www.downlandsliability.com
Insurance Services
N.A.I.C.S.: 524210

Holding (US):

SPARTA Insurance Holdings, Inc. **(3)**
CityPl II 185 Asylum St, Hartford, CT 06103
Tel.: (860) 275-6500
Web Site: http://www.spartainsurance.com
Insurance Services
N.A.I.C.S.: 524210

Holding (Domestic):

Claire's Inc. **(2)**
2400 W Central Rd, Hoffman Estates, IL 60192

Tel.: (847) 765-1100
Rev.: $910,341,000
Assets: $1,723,243,000
Liabilities: $1,433,032,000
Net Worth: $290,211,000
Earnings: ($235,968,000)
Emp.: 13,100
Fiscal Year-end: 01/30/2021
Holding Company
N.A.I.C.S.: 551112
Kristin Patrick (CMO & Exec VP)
Ryan Vero (CEO)
Colleen Collins (Exec VP-Stores)
Richard Flint (Pres-Europe & Exec VP)
Jordana Kammerud (Chief HR Officer & Exec VP)
Brendan McKeough (Gen Counsel, Sec & Exec VP)
Beth Moeri (Chief Mdsg Officer & Exec VP)
Kristin Patrick (CMO & Exec VP)
Marc Saffer (CIO & Exec VP)
Michael Schwindle (CFO & Exec VP)
Samantha Algaze (Chm)

Subsidiary (Domestic):

Claire's Stores, Inc. **(3)**
2400 W Central Rd, Hoffman Estates, IL 60192
Tel.: (847) 765-1100
Web Site: https://corporate.claires.com
Sales Range: $1-4.9 Billion
Emp.: 17,300
Women's Fashion Accessories & Apparel Retailer
N.A.I.C.S.: 458110
Kristin Patrick (CMO)
Colleen Collins (Exec VP-Stores)
Michael Schwindle (CFO & Exec VP)
Jordana Kammerud (Chief HR Officer & Exec VP)
Brendan McKeough (Gen Counsel, Sec & Exec VP)
Kristin Patrick (CMO)
Rohit Kapoor (Exec VP)

Subsidiary (Non-US):

Claire's Accessories UK Ltd. **(4)**
Unit 4 Bromford Gate Bromford Ln, Birmingham, B24 8DW, United Kingdom
Tel.: (44) 1216828000
Web Site: http://www.claires.com
Emp.: 260
Provider of Girls' & Women's Accessories
N.A.I.C.S.: 424350

Claire's Austria GmbH **(4)**
Industriestrasse B 13, 2345, Brunn, Austria
Tel.: (43) 2236327170
Web Site: http://www.claires.at
Sales Range: $25-49.9 Million
Emp.: 8
Provider of Girls' & Women's Accessories
N.A.I.C.S.: 424350

Subsidiary (Domestic):

Claire's Boutiques, Inc. **(4)**
3 SW 129th Ave, Pembroke Pines, FL 33027-1775
Tel.: (954) 433-3900
Web Site: http://www.claires.com
Sales Range: $50-74.9 Million
Emp.: 250
Retailer of Women's Fashion Accessories
N.A.I.C.S.: 458110

Subsidiary (Non-US):

Claire's Canada Corp. **(4)**
477 Paul St, Dieppe, E1A 4X5, NB, Canada
Tel.: (506) 854-7050
Web Site: http://www.claires.com
Sales Range: $25-49.9 Million
Emp.: 5
Provider of Girls' & Women's Accessories
N.A.I.C.S.: 424350

Claire's France S.A.S. **(4)**
10 Avenue Kleber, 75116, Paris, France
Tel.: (33) 184880345
Web Site: http://www.claires.co.uk
Sales Range: $350-399.9 Million
Emp.: 900
Provider of Girls' & Women's Accessories
N.A.I.C.S.: 424350

Claire's Nippon Co., Ltd. **(4)**
2nd Floor Ningyocho Building 1-1-11 Ni-

hombashi, Chuo-ku, Tokyo, 1030013,
Japan   **(100%)**
Tel.: (81) 368610005
Web Site: http://www.clairesn.co.jp
Women's Accessories Retailer
N.A.I.C.S.: 424350
Yoshitaka Yamaguchi *(Pres)*

Claire's Switzerland GmbH   **(4)**
Quellenstrasse 29, 8005, Zurich, Switzerland
Tel.: (41) 442768888
Web Site: http://www.claires.com
Sales Range: $25-49.9 Million
Emp.: 35
Provider of Girls' & Women's Accessories
N.A.I.C.S.: 424350

Holding (Domestic):

Classic Party Rentals, Inc.   **(2)**
901 W Hillcrest Blvd, Inglewood, CA 90301
Tel.: (310) 535-3660
Web Site:
    http://www.classicpartyrentals.com
Sales Range: $125-149.9 Million
Emp.: 1,000
Party & Event Rentals
N.A.I.C.S.: 532289

Branch (Domestic):

**Classic Party Rentals, Inc. -
Dallas**   **(3)**
3200 Belmeade Dr Ste 130, Carrollton, TX
75006-2552
Tel.: (972) 381-8000
Web Site: http://classicpartyrentals.com
Sales Range: $25-49.9 Million
Emp.: 125
Party & Tent Rental
N.A.I.C.S.: 532289

**Classic Party Rentals, Inc. - El
Segundo**   **(3)**
2310 E Imperial Hwy, El Segundo, CA
90245
Tel.: (310) 535-3660
Web Site:
    http://elsegundo.classicpartyrentals.com
Sales Range: $25-49.9 Million
Emp.: 200
Silverware & Glassware & Other Party
Products Rental
N.A.I.C.S.: 532289
Michael Stern *(Exec VP)*

**Classic Party Rentals, Inc. -
Phoenix**   **(3)**
3103 E Broadway Rd Ste 400, Phoenix, AZ
85040
Tel.: (602) 232-9900
Web Site: http://classicpartyrentals.com
Sales Range: $25-49.9 Million
Emp.: 100
Party Equipment Rental
N.A.I.C.S.: 532289

**Classic Party Rentals, Inc. - San
Diego**   **(3)**
7069 Consolidated Way Ste 300, San Diego, CA 92121
Tel.: (858) 496-9700
Web Site:
    http://sandiego.classicpartyrentals.com
Sales Range: $10-24.9 Million
Emp.: 100
Party Equipment Rental
N.A.I.C.S.: 532289

Holding (Domestic):

ClubCorp Holdings, Inc.   **(2)**
3030 LBJ Fwy Ste 500, Dallas, TX 75234
Tel.: (972) 243-6191
Web Site: http://www.clubcorp.com
Holding Company; Golf, Country, Business,
Sports & Alumni Clubs Owner & Operator
N.A.I.C.S.: 551112
Dilliana Stewart *(VP-Technical Acctg & Fin
Reporting)*
Robert Morse *(Pres & COO)*
David Pillsbury *(CEO)*
Tom Bennison *(Chief Dev Officer)*
Andrew Lacko *(CFO & Treas)*
Chuck Feddersen *(Exec VP-Club Ops)*
Emily Decker *(Chief Legal Officer)*
Ken Guerra *(Chief Revenue Officer)*
Meg Tollison *(Chief Membership Officer)*
Jim Berra *(Chief Mktg & Innovation Officer)*

Sherry Vidal-Brown *(Chief People Officer)*
Brian Koch *(CIO)*
Vladimir Anokhin *(Chief Strategy Officer)*
Ron Vlasic *(Exec VP)*

Subsidiary (Domestic):

ClubCorp USA, Inc.   **(3)**
3030 LBJ Fwy Ste 500, Dallas, TX
75234-7743   **(100%)**
Tel.: (972) 243-6191
Web Site: http://www.clubcorp.com
Private Clubs, Resorts & Golf Courses Operator
N.A.I.C.S.: 713910
Tom Bennison *(Chief Dev Officer)*
Meg Tollison *(CMO)*
Ken Guerra *(Chief Revenue Officer)*
Emily Decker *(Chief Legal Officer)*
Chuck Feddersen *(Exec VP-Club Ops)*
Andrew Lacko *(CFO & Treas)*
Robert Morse *(Pres & COO)*
David Pillsbury *(CEO)*
Peter Kent *(Chief Comml Officer)*
Brian Koch *(CIO)*
Vladimir Anokhin *(Chief Strategy Officer)*
Ron Vlasic *(Exec VP)*

Unit (Domestic):

Aliso Viejo Country Club   **(4)**
33 Santa Barbara Dr, Aliso Viejo, CA 92656
Tel.: (949) 598-9200
Web Site: http://www.alisogolf.com
Private Membership Golf Course & Country
Club Operator
N.A.I.C.S.: 713910
Paulina James *(Dir-Membership)*

Anthem Golf & Country Club   **(4)**
2708 W Anthem Club Dr, Anthem, AZ
85086
Tel.: (623) 742-6200
Web Site: http://www.clubcorp.com
Golf Courses & Country Clubs
N.A.I.C.S.: 713910
Brad Harrington *(Gen Mgr)*

Aspen Glen Club   **(4)**
0545 Bald Eagle Way, Carbondale, CO
81623
Tel.: (970) 704-1905
Web Site: http://www.aspen-glen.com
Private Membership Golf Course & Country
Club Operator
N.A.I.C.S.: 713910
Jake Falke *(Superintendent)*
Dave Thompson *(Head-Golf Professional)*

Subsidiary (Domestic):

Belmont Country Club   **(4)**
19661 Belmont Manor Ln, Ashburn, VA
20147
Tel.: (703) 723-5330
Web Site:
    http://www.belmontcountryclub.com
Golf Club
N.A.I.C.S.: 713910

Unit (Domestic):

Braemar Country Club   **(4)**
4001 Reseda Blvd, Tarzana, CA 91356
Tel.: (818) 345-6520
Web Site: http://www.braemarclub.com
Private Membership Golf Course & Country
Club Operator
N.A.I.C.S.: 713910
Janine Walker *(Dir-Membership)*
Alex Guzman *(Dir-Maintenance)*
Susan Pendo *(Dir-Tennis)*

Subsidiary (Domestic):

Brier Creek Country Club   **(4)**
9400 Club Hill Dr, Raleigh, NC 27617
Tel.: (919) 206-4600
Web Site: http://www.clubcorp.com
Country Club Operator
N.A.I.C.S.: 713910
Ron Woolard *(Gen Mgr)*
John Rodriguez *(Mgr-Club)*

Unit (Domestic):

Brookhaven Country Club   **(4)**
3333 Golfing Green Dr, Farmers Branch,
TX 75234
Tel.: (972) 243-6151
Web Site: http://www.brookhavenclub.com

Private Membership Golf Course & Country
Club Operator
N.A.I.C.S.: 713910
Jeff Anderson *(Dir-Golf)*
Dave Ware *(Dir-Racquet Sports)*
Harrison Sluice *(Dir-Fitness & Wellness)*

Canyon Creek Country Club   **(4)**
625 W Lookout Dr, Richardson, TX 75080
Tel.: (972) 231-1466
Web Site: http://www.canyoncreekclub.com
Private Membership Golf Course & Country
Club Operator
N.A.I.C.S.: 713910
Lisa Neel *(Gen Mgr)*
Heather Stewart *(Head-Golf Professional)*
Craig Loving *(Dir-Agronomy)*
Rob Van Der Schans *(Dir-Tennis)*

Canyon Crest Country Club   **(4)**
975 Country Club Dr, Riverside, CA 92506
Tel.: (951) 274-7900
Web Site:
    https://www.canyoncrestcountryclub.com
Private Membership Golf Course & Country
Club Operator
N.A.I.C.S.: 713910
Brett Kimura *(Gen Mgr)*

Canyon Gate Country Club   **(4)**
2001 Canyon Gate Dr, Las Vegas, NV
89117
Tel.: (702) 363-0303
Web Site: http://www.canyon-gate.com
Private Membership Golf Course & Country
Club Operator
N.A.I.C.S.: 713910
Allen Fredrickson *(Gen Mgr)*
Vince Brown *(Dir-Fitness)*
Celeste Alvarado *(Office Mgr)*

Carolina Club   **(4)**
150 Stadium Dr, Chapel Hill, NC 27514
Tel.: (919) 962-1101
Web Site: http://www.carolina-club.com
Private Membership Club & Restaurant
Operator
N.A.I.C.S.: 813410
Elizabeth Cheek *(Gen Mgr)*

City Club LA   **(4)**
555 Flower St 51st Fl, Los Angeles, CA
90071
Tel.: (213) 620-9662
Web Site: http://www.clubcorp.com
Private Membership Club & Restaurant
Operator
N.A.I.C.S.: 813410
Alex Thapar *(Gen Mgr)*

Country Club of Hilton Head   **(4)**
70 Skull Creek Dr, Hilton Head Island, SC
29926
Tel.: (843) 681-2582
Web Site: http://www.hiltonheadclub.com
Private Membership Golf Course & Country
Club Operator
N.A.I.C.S.: 713910
Dori Palchak *(Dir-Fitness)*

DeBary Golf & Country Club   **(4)**
300 Plantation Club Dr, Debary, FL 32713
Tel.: (386) 668-1705
Web Site: https://www.debarycc.com
Private Membership Golf Course & Country
Club Operator
N.A.I.C.S.: 713910
Shawn McGuigan *(Gen Mgr)*

Deercreek Country Club   **(4)**
7816 McLaurin Rd N, Jacksonville, FL
32256
Tel.: (904) 363-1604
Web Site:
    https://www.deercreekcountryclub.com
Private Membership Golf Course & Country
Club Operator
N.A.I.C.S.: 713910

Subsidiary (Domestic):

Dominion Vallley Country Club   **(4)**
15200 Arnold Palmer Dr, Haymarket, VA
20169
Tel.: (571) 222-6900
Web Site:
    http://www.dominionvalleycountryclub.com
Golf Club
N.A.I.C.S.: 713910
Andy Salguero *(Gen Mgr)*

Unit (Domestic):

Firestone Country Club   **(4)**
452 E Warner Rd, Akron, OH 44319
Tel.: (330) 644-8441
Web Site:
    http://www.firestonecountryclub.com
Private Membership Golf Course & Country
Club Operator
N.A.I.C.S.: 713910
Jay Walkinshaw *(Gen Mgr)*
Kendle Deaderick *(Mgr-Club)*

Gleneagles Country Club   **(4)**
5401 W Park Blvd, Plano, TX 75093
Tel.: (972) 867-6666
Web Site: http://www.gleneaglesclub.com
Private Membership Golf Course & Country
Club Operator
N.A.I.C.S.: 713910
Kim Kantor *(Dir-Membership)*
Bryant Early *(Gen Mgr)*

**Golden Bear Golf Club at Indigo
Run**   **(4)**
72 Golden Bear Way, Hilton Head Island,
SC 29926
Tel.: (843) 689-2200
Web Site: http://www.goldenbear-
indigorun.com
Private Membership Golf Course & Country
Club Operator
N.A.I.C.S.: 713910
Mark Turner *(Gen Mgr)*
Jessa Burt *(Mgr-Club)*

Granite Bay Golf Club   **(4)**
9600 Golf Club Dr, Granite Bay, CA 95746
Tel.: (916) 791-7578
Web Site: https://www.invitedclubs.com
Private Membership Golf Course & Country
Club Operator
N.A.I.C.S.: 713910
Kelle Collier *(Dir-Private Event)*
Michael Peabody *(Gen Mgr)*
Matt Dillon *(Superintendent-Golf Course)*
Ryan Toms *(Dir-Food & Beverage)*

Subsidiary (Domestic):

Hasentree   **(4)**
7305 Village Club Dr, Wake Forest, NC
27587
Tel.: (919) 375-7000
Web Site:
    http://www.hasentreecountryclub.com
Country Club Operator
N.A.I.C.S.: 713910
Scott Campbell *(Gen Mgr)*

Unit (Domestic):

Hunter's Green Country Club   **(4)**
18101 Longwater Run Dr, Tampa, FL
33647-2309
Tel.: (813) 973-1000
Web Site: http://www.huntersgreencc.com
Private Membership Golf Course & Country
Club Operator
N.A.I.C.S.: 713910
Allegra Campos *(Dir-Tennis)*
Greg Lauzier *(Gen Mgr)*
Kelsey Jakubiak *(Dir-Private Event)*
Matt Hilts *(Dir-Youth)*
Jason Pellin *(Dir-Facilities Maintenance)*
Cory Wood *(Superintendent-Golf Course)*
Stew McComb *(Dir-Golf)*
Dustin Pugliese *(Dir-Food & Beverage)*

Subsidiary (Domestic):

Jupiter Country Club, Inc.   **(4)**
300 Marsala Ct, Jupiter, FL 33478
Web Site:
    http://www.thejupitercountryclub.com
Golf Course & Club Management Services
N.A.I.C.S.: 713910
Frank Petitti *(Gen Mgr)*
Mike Bronkema *(Mgr-Club)*
Scott Lefevre *(Dir-Instruction)*
Ben Derauf *(Dir-Membership & Mktg)*
Beth Gili *(Office Mgr)*
Zack Campbell *(Dir-Tournament)*
Jim Moore *(Superintendent-Golf Course)*
Lisa Williams *(Coord-Spa & Fitness)*
Shakeera Thomas *(Coord-Spa & Fitness)*
Kasie Agarwal *(Dir-Fitness)*
Heinrich Zondagh *(Dir-Food & Beverage)*

Apollo Global Management, Inc.—(Continued)

Unit (Domestic):

Medina Golf & Country Club **(4)**
400 Evergreen Rd, Medina, MN 55340-
2106
Tel.: (763) 478-6021
Web Site: http://www.clubcorp.com
Country Club Operator
N.A.I.C.S.: 713910

Mission Hills Country Club **(4)**
34-600 Mission Hills Dr, Rancho Mirage,
CA 92270
Tel.: (760) 324-9400
Web Site: http://www.clubcorp.com
Private Membership Golf Course & Country
Club Operator
N.A.I.C.S.: 713910
Dan Hewitson *(Sr VP)*

Subsidiary (Domestic):

Norbeck Country Club, Inc. **(4)**
17200 Cashell Rd, Rockville, MD 20853
Tel.: (301) 774-7700
Web Site: http://www.clubcorp.com
Country Club Operator
N.A.I.C.S.: 713910
Patrick Ellis *(Gen Mgr)*

Oak Creek Golf Club **(4)**
600 Bowieville Manor Ln, Upper Marlboro,
MD 20774
Tel.: (301) 249-0809
Golf Club
N.A.I.C.S.: 713910
William Fritz *(Pro Mgr)*

Oro Valley Country Club, Inc. **(4)**
300 W Greenock Dr, Oro Valley, AZ 85737
Tel.: (520) 297-1121
Web Site:
   http://www.orovalleycountryclub.com
Country Club
N.A.I.C.S.: 713910
Linda DeWilde *(Coord-Member Rels & Private Events)*

Prestonwood Golf Club LLC **(4)**
15909 Preston Rd, Dallas, TX 75248-3550
Tel.: (972) 239-7111
Web Site: http://www.clubcorp.com
Golf Course & Country Club Operator
N.A.I.C.S.: 713910
Scott Hajdu *(Gen Mgr)*

**Queens Harbour Yacht & Country
Club, Ltd.** **(4)**
13361 Atlantic Blvd, Jacksonville, FL 32225
Tel.: (904) 221-2605
Web Site: http://www.qhycc.com
Land Subdivision
N.A.I.C.S.: 237210

Unit (Domestic):

Ravinia Green Country Club **(4)**
1200 Saunders Rd, Riverwoods, IL 60015
Tel.: (847) 945-6200
Web Site: http://www.clubcorp.com
Country Club Operator
N.A.I.C.S.: 713910
Tony Rizzo *(Gen Mgr)*
Trinidad Vega *(Chief Engr)*

Subsidiary (Domestic):

Regency at Dominion Valley LLC **(4)**
15351 Championship Dr, Haymarket, VA
20169
Tel.: (571) 261-3335
Web Site: https://regencydvonline.com
Residential Building Construction Services
N.A.I.C.S.: 236117

Unit (Domestic):

Seville Golf & Country Club **(4)**
6683 S Clubhouse Dr, Gilbert, AZ 85298
Tel.: (480) 722-8100
Web Site: http://www.sevillegcc.com
Private Membership Golf Course & Country
Club Operator
N.A.I.C.S.: 713910
Stephanie Beach *(Dir-Membership)*
John Peterson *(Dir-Membership & Mktg)*

The Club at Falcon Point **(4)**
24503 Falcon Point Dr, Katy, TX 77494

Tel.: (281) 392-7888
Web Site: http://www.clubcorp.com
Private Membership Golf Course & Country
Club
N.A.I.C.S.: 713910
Monica Cotton *(Dir-Membership)*
Joey Perez *(Head-Golf Professional)*
Todd Folsom *(Dir-Tennis)*
Linda Bowles *(Office Mgr-Acctg)*

Holding (Domestic):

Coinstar, LLC **(2)**
330 120th Ave NE, Bellevue, WA 98005
Tel.: (425) 943-8000
Web Site: https://www.coinstar.com
Coin Counting & Processing Machines Mfr,
Owner & Operator
N.A.I.C.S.: 445132

Subsidiary (Non-US):

Coinstar Limited **(3)**
16-17 Old Bond Street, Bath, BA1 1BP,
United Kingdom
Tel.: (44) 8003282274
Web Site: http://www.coinstar.co.uk
Currency Exchange Vending Machinery
Operator
N.A.I.C.S.: 445132

Subsidiary (Domestic):

Redbox Automated Retail, LLC **(3)**
1 Tower Ln Ste 900, Oakbrook Terrace, IL
60181
Tel.: (866) 733-2693
Web Site: http://www.redbox.com
Automated Video Rental Machine Operator
N.A.I.C.S.: 445132
Jason Kwong *(Chief Strategy Officer &
Chief Bus Dev Officer)*
Galen Smith *(CEO)*

ecoATM, LLC **(3)**
10121 Barnes Canyon Rd, San Diego, CA
92121-4340
Tel.: (858) 766-7249
Web Site: https://www.ecoatm.com
Research & Development in Biotechnology
N.A.I.C.S.: 541714
David B. Sambur *(Chm)*

Holding (Non-US):

Companhia de Seguros Tranquilidade, S.A. **(2)**
Avenida da Liberdade 242, 1250-149, Lisbon, Portugal   **(100%)**
Tel.: (351) 211520310
Web Site: http://www.tranquilidade.pt
Sales Range: $75-99.9 Million
Emp.: 100
Non-Life Insurance Products & Services
N.A.I.C.S.: 524126

Subsidiary (Domestic):

Seguros LOGO S.A. **(3)**
Rua Dom Manuel Ii 290, 4050-344, Porto,
Portugal   **(100%)**
Tel.: (351) 915737100
Web Site: http://www.logo.pt
Home & Automotive Insurance Products &
Services
N.A.I.C.S.: 524126

Holding (Domestic):

Constellis Holdings, Inc. **(2)**
12018 Sunrise Vly Dr Ste 140, Reston, VA
20191
Tel.: (703) 673-5000
Web Site: http://constellis.com
Holding Company
N.A.I.C.S.: 551112
Gearoid Moore *(Chief Legal Officer)*
Rick Tye *(Pres-Crisis Mitigation)*
Beth Skoletsky *(Chief HR Officer)*
Richard Hozik *(CFO)*
Darryle Conway *(Chief Growth Officer)*
Terry Ryan *(Chm & CEO)*
Todd Wallace *(CIO)*
Andrew Hartsog *(VP-Special Projects)*

Subsidiary (Domestic):

Centerra Group, LLC **(3)**
7121 Fairway Dr Ste 301, Palm Beach Gardens, FL 33418
Tel.: (561) 406-7193

Web Site: http://www.centerragroup.com
Security Risk Management & Operational
Support Services
N.A.I.C.S.: 561612

Constellis, LLC **(3)**
12018 Sunrise Vly Dr Ste 140, Reston, VA
20191
Tel.: (703) 673-5000
Web Site: http://constellis.com
Security, Support & Advisory Services
N.A.I.C.S.: 561612
Emily Peterson Alva *(CEO)*
Gearoid Moore *(Chief Legal Officer)*
Rick Tye *(Pres-Crisis Mitigation)*
Jim Noe *(Pres-Ops-Global)*
Paul Donahue *(COO)*
David G. Mathews *(Pres-Natl Security Ops)*
Gerard Neville *(Pres-Ops-North American)*

Subsidiary (Domestic):

ACADEMI LLC **(4)**
PO Box 1029, Moyock, NC 27958
Tel.: (252) 435-2488
Web Site: http://www.academi.com
Emp.: 450
Military & Defense Training Services
N.A.I.C.S.: 561612

Triple Canopy, Inc. **(4)**
12018 Sunrise Vly Dr, Reston, VA 20191
Tel.: (703) 673-5000
Safety, Training, Crisis Management & Protective Services
N.A.I.C.S.: 561621

Joint Venture (Domestic):

**Diamond Resorts International,
Inc.** **(2)**
10600 W Charleston Blvd, Las Vegas, NV
89135
Tel.: (702) 823-7534
Web Site: http://www.diamondresorts.com
Holding Company; Hotel & Resort Owner &
Operator
N.A.I.C.S.: 551112
Michael Flaskey *(CEO)*
Jim Mikolaichik *(CFO)*
Kenneth S. Siegel *(Pres, Chief Admin Officer & Gen Counsel)*

Affiliate (Domestic):

Diamond Resorts Corporation **(3)**
10600 W Charleston Blvd, Las Vegas, NV
89135
Tel.: (702) 684-8000
Hotel Properties Management Services
N.A.I.C.S.: 721110
Lisa Gann *(Controller)*
Jim Mikolaichik *(CFO)*

Subsidiary (Domestic):

Diamond Resorts Holdings, LLC **(3)**
10600 W Charleston Blvd, Las Vegas, NV
89135
Tel.: (702) 823-7534
Web Site: http://www.diamondresorts.com
Holding Company
N.A.I.C.S.: 551112
Jim Mikolaichik *(CFO)*
Michael Flaskey *(CEO)*

Unit (Domestic):

Kohl's Ranch Lodge **(4)**
202 S Kohls Ranch Lodge Rd, Payson, AZ
85541
Tel.: (928) 478-4211
Web Site:
   http://www.diamondresortsandhotels.com
Hotel & Resort Operator
N.A.I.C.S.: 721110

Los Abrigados Resort & Spa **(4)**
160 Portal Ln, Sedona, AZ 86336
Tel.: (928) 282-1777
Web Site:
   http://www.diamondresortsandhotels.com
Hotel, Resort & Spa Operator
N.A.I.C.S.: 721110

Mystic Dunes Resort & Golf Club **(4)**
7600 Mystic Dunes Ln, Celebration, FL
34747
Tel.: (407) 396-1311
Web Site:
   http://www.diamondresortsandhotels.com

Hotel & Resort Operator & Time-Share
Condominium Exchange Services
N.A.I.C.S.: 721110

Subsidiary (Domestic):

Potter's Mill, Inc. **(4)**
300 Potter Dr, Bellevue, IA 52001
Tel.: (563) 872-3838
Web Site: https://www.pottersmill.net
Full-Service Restaurants
N.A.I.C.S.: 722511

Unit (Domestic):

The Historic Crags Lodge **(4)**
300 Riverside Dr, Estes Park, CO 80517
Tel.: (970) 586-6066
Web Site:
   http://www.diamondresortsandhotels.com
Hotel & Resort Operator
N.A.I.C.S.: 721110

**Varsity Clubs of America - South
Bend** **(4)**
3800 N Main St, Mishawaka, IN 46545
Tel.: (574) 277-0500
Web Site:
   http://www.diamondresortsandhotels.com
Hotel & Resort Operator
N.A.I.C.S.: 721110

**Varsity Clubs of America -
Tucson** **(4)**
3855 E Speedway Blvd, Tucson, AZ 85716
Tel.: (520) 318-3777
Web Site:
   http://www.diamondresortsandhotels.com
Hotel & Resort Operator
N.A.I.C.S.: 721110
Aldo Dioverti *(Mgr-Resort)*

Holding (Domestic):

Direct ChassisLink, Inc. **(2)**
3525 White Hall Prk Dr, Charlotte, NC
28273-8136
Tel.: (704) 594-3800
Web Site: http://www.dcli.com
Chassis Whslr
N.A.I.C.S.: 423110
Esposito Dave *(Gen Mgr-Tech Dept)*
Ron Joseph *(COO)*
Ryan Houfek *(CMO & Chief Sls Officer)*
Brian Taylor *(Pres)*
Bill Shea *(CEO)*
Stacy Kirincic *(Dir-Mktg)*
Lee Newitt *(CFO)*
Steve Park *(Area Mgr-Sls-Northeast)*
Bill Monahan *(Area Mgr-Sls-Southeast)*
Ruben Quezada *(Area Mgr-Sls-West Coast)*
Lee Mauney *(Area Mgr-Sls-Gulf & Midwest)*
David Arsenault *(Chief Strategy Officer)*

Subsidiary (Domestic):

REZ 1, Inc. **(3)**
100 William St Ste 100, Wellesley, MA
02481
Tel.: (781) 263-0200
Web Site: http://www.rez1.com
Emp.: 200
Intermodal Equipment Management & Services
N.A.I.C.S.: 541618
Marie Colbert *(Pres)*
Jim Glatiotis *(CTO & Exec VP)*
Mike Davis *(Mgr-Software Dev)*
Scott Dipippo *(Dir-Bus Intelligence)*
Steve Dowse *(Sr VP-Product Mgmt)*
Debra Garverich *(VP-Fin & Admin)*
Nick Goldman *(Mgr-Software Dev)*
Rachel Gordon *(Dir-HR)*
Steve Ledbury *(Dir-Sys Architecture)*
James Miller *(Sls Dir)*
Blair Peterson *(VP-Comml)*
Heather Reynolds *(Mgr-IT Project Mgmt)*
Paul Vangundy *(Mgr-Tech Ops)*
Mike Wynne *(Controller)*
Ellie Hiller *(VP-Sls)*
Pervinder Johar *(CEO)*

Joint Venture (Domestic):

EP Energy Corporation **(2)**
601 Travis St Ste 1400, Houston, TX
77002   **(44.7%)**
Tel.: (713) 997-1000
Web Site: http://www.epenergy.com

Sales Range: $1-4.9 Billion
Emp.: 372
Holding Company; Oil & Natural Gas Exploration, Development & Production Services
N.A.I.C.S.: 551112
Jace D. Locke *(Gen Counsel, Sec & VP)*
Kyle A. McCuen *(CFO, Chief Acctg Officer, Treas & Sr VP)*
Raymond J. Ambrose *(Sr VP-Engrg & Subsurface)*
Chad D. England *(Sr VP-Ops)*
Peter D. Addison *(VP-Land & Land Admin)*
Mark E. Hargis *(VP-Geoscience)*
Dennis M. Price *(VP-Mktg)*
Alan R. Crain Jr. *(Chm)*

Subsidiary (Domestic):

EP Energy LLC **(3)**
1001 Louisiana St, Houston, TX 77002
Tel.: (713) 997-1200
Web Site: http://www.epenergy.com
Rev.: $1,323,999,999
Assets: $4,180,999,999
Liabilities: $4,779,999,999
Net Worth: ($599,000,000)
Earnings: ($1,002,999,999)
Emp.: 991
Fiscal Year-end: 12/31/2018
Oil & Natural Gas Exploration & Production
N.A.I.C.S.: 211120
Kyle McCuen *(CFO, Treas & Sr VP)*

Holding (Domestic):

EmployBridge, LLC **(2)**
1040 Crown Pointe Pkwy Ste 1040, Atlanta, GA 30338
Tel.: (770) 671-1900
Web Site: http://www.employbridge.net
Personnel Staffing Services
N.A.I.C.S.: 561320
Sharon Greenbaum *(Gen Counsel)*
Shawn W. Poole *(Founder)*
Mike Baer *(Chief People Officer)*
Paul Seymour *(Pres-Western Reg)*
Craig Kirby *(VP-Fin-Strategic Relationships & Risk)*
Chris Loope *(VP-Ops)*
Doni McDermott *(Treas)*
Carolyn Silvey *(Reg Pres-Southeast Reg)*
Dan Lieblich *(VP-Central Reg)*
Al Aguirre *(Chm)*
Chi Nguyen *(CFO & Exec VP)*
Doug Dandurand *(Partner & Pres-East)*
Colin S. Mooney *(Chief Transformation Officer)*
Billy Milam *(CEO)*
Don Sloan *(Chief Digital Officer)*
Bill Ravenscroft *(Chief Revenue Officer)*
Janelle Bieler *(Pres-West)*
Skip Wood *(Pres-Comml)*
Whitney Woodward *(Chief People Officer)*
Evan White *(Mgr-PR)*
Chris Campbell *(Chief Product Officer)*

Subsidiary (Domestic):

Hire Dynamics, LLC. **(3)**
1845 Satellite Blvd Ste 800, Duluth, GA 30097
Tel.: (678) 482-8041
Web Site: http://www.hiredynamics.com
Sales Range: $50-74.9 Million
Emp.: 80
Human Resource Consulting Services
N.A.I.C.S.: 541612
Jeannette Blake *(VP-Atlanta Ops)*
Jon Neff *(Co-Founder & COO)*
Kim Wallace *(Exec VP)*
Dan Campbell *(Co-Founder & Chm)*
Sonya Buckley *(Chief People Officer)*
Andi Haynes *(Dir-On-sites)*
Ramona Burle *(Mgr-Area)*
Billy Milam *(CEO)*

Holding (Domestic):

Hexion TopCo, LLC **(2)**
180 E Broad St, Columbus, OH 43215-3799
Tel.: (614) 986-2497
Web Site: http://www.hexion.com
Sales Range: $1-4.9 Billion
Emp.: 4,300
Holding Company; Specialty Chemical Products Mfr
N.A.I.C.S.: 551112
George F. Knight III *(CFO & Exec VP)*

Holding (Non-US):

Ingenico Group S.A. **(2)**
28-32 boulevard de Grenelle, 75015, Paris, France
Tel.: (33) 158018000
Web Site: http://www.ingenico.com
Rev.: $3,774,040,186
Assets: $8,473,868,634
Liabilities: $5,659,772,440
Net Worth: $2,814,096,194
Earnings: $242,449,690
Emp.: 8,869
Fiscal Year-end: 12/31/2019
Electronic Payment & Credit Authorization Systems Developer
N.A.I.C.S.: 522320
Matthieu Destot *(CEO)*
Catherine Guillouard *(Chm)*

Subsidiary (Non-US):

Airlink Technology Co., Ltd. **(3)**
Rm D 11F No 44 Sec 2 Zhongshan N Rd, Zhongshan Dist, Taipei, 104, Taiwan
Tel.: (886) 225236706
Web Site: http://www.airlinktech.com.tw
Credit Card Payment & Banking Services
N.A.I.C.S.: 522210

Bambora Group AB **(3)**
Vasagatan 16, 111 20, Stockholm, Sweden
Tel.: (46) 101066000
Holding Company; Payment & Financial Transaction Processing Services
N.A.I.C.S.: 551112
Johan Tjarnberg *(Founder & CEO)*

Subsidiary (Domestic):

Bambora AB **(4)**
Magnus Ladulasgatan 2, 118 66, Stockholm, Sweden
Tel.: (46) 8146914
Payment Card Services
N.A.I.C.S.: 522320
Johan Tjarnberg *(CEO)*

Subsidiary (Non-US):

Bambora Inc. **(4)**
Suite 200 - 1803 Douglas Street, Victoria, V8T 5C3, BC, Canada
Tel.: (250) 472-2326
Web Site: http://www.bambora.com
Electronic Payment Processing
N.A.I.C.S.: 522320

Subsidiary (Non-US):

Fujian Landi Commercial Equipment Co., Ltd. **(3)**
Room 1203 Tower C Beijing Global Trade Center 36 North Third Ring Road, Dongcheng District, Beijing, 100013, China
Tel.: (86) 1059575002
Web Site: http://www.landicorp.com
Emp.: 1,600
Secure Electronic Payment Services
N.A.I.C.S.: 522320

Ingenico (Thailand) Co., Ltd. **(3)**
No 253 19th Floor Sukhumvit 21 Road, Khlong Toei Nuea Sub-District Watthana District, 10110, Bangkok, Thailand
Tel.: (66) 26408240
Payment Solution Banking Services
N.A.I.C.S.: 522320

Ingenico (UK) Ltd. **(3)**
17 Ridge Way, Donibristle Industrial Park, Dalgety Bay, KY11 9JU, Fife, United Kingdom **(100%)**
Tel.: (44) 1314598800
Web Site: http://www.ingenico.co.uk
Sales Range: $50-74.9 Million
Emp.: 200
Electronic Payment Systems
N.A.I.C.S.: 333310

Representative Office (Non-US):

Ingenico Argentina **(3)**
Florida 375 FL 5 C, C1005AAG, Buenos Aires, Argentina **(100%)**
Tel.: (54) 1143941046
Sales Range: $25-49.9 Million
Emp.: 50
Electronic Payment Systems
N.A.I.C.S.: 333310

Subsidiary (Domestic):

Ingenico Business Support SAS **(3)**
28/32 Boulevard De Grenelle, 75015, Paris, France
Tel.: (33) 158018000
Payment Solution Banking Services
N.A.I.C.S.: 522320

Subsidiary (Non-US):

Ingenico CZ s.r.o. **(3)**
Lazarska 11/6, 120 00, Prague, Czech Republic
Tel.: (420) 225996701
Sales Range: $50-74.9 Million
Emp.: 5
Financial Transaction Services
N.A.I.C.S.: 522320
Nadia Mrnousova *(Gen Mgr)*

Subsidiary (US):

Ingenico Corp. **(3)**
3025 Windward Plz Ste 600, Alpharetta, GA 30005
Tel.: (678) 456-1200
Web Site: http://www.ingenico-us.com
Rev.: $13,000,000
Emp.: 240
Mfr of Point of Sale Products
N.A.I.C.S.: 334118
Bernie Frey *(Sr VP-Acquirer Sls)*

Subsidiary (Domestic):

Global Collect Services USA, Inc. **(4)**
One California St 22 Fl, San Francisco, CA 94111
Tel.: (415) 975-0969
Web Site: http://www.globalcollect.com
Payment Processing Services
N.A.I.C.S.: 522320
Benjamin Mieremet *(VP-Merchant Acctg)*
Shawna Harris *(Mgr-Acct)*
Daphne Tay *(Mgr-Vendor Application)*
Mirelle Cuvelier *(VP-Merchant Svcs)*

Subsidiary (Non-US):

Ingenico Canada Ltd. **(4)**
5180 Orbitor Drive 2nd Floor, Mississauga, L4W 5L9, ON, Canada **(100%)**
Tel.: (905) 212-9464
Web Site: http://www.ingenicoca.com
Sales Range: $50-74.9 Million
Emp.: 60
Financial Transaction Solutions
N.A.I.C.S.: 522320
Suzan Denoncourt *(Mng Dir)*

Subsidiary (Domestic):

e-Concert Solutions **(4)**
1003 Mansell Rd, Atlanta, GA 30076-1507
Tel.: (770) 594-6000
Sales Range: $50-74.9 Million
Emp.: 160
Electronic Payment Solutions
N.A.I.C.S.: 459999

Branch (Domestic):

e-Concert Solutions **(5)**
420 Maples St, Marlborough, MA 01752 **(100%)**
Tel.: (508) 229-2261
Electronic Payment Solutions
N.A.I.C.S.: 541690

Subsidiary (Non-US):

Ingenico Financial Solutions SA **(3)**
Leonardo Da Vincilaan/Avenue Leonardo Da Vinci 3, 1930, Zaventem, Belgium
Tel.: (32) 23180110
Payment Solution Banking Services
N.A.I.C.S.: 522320
Arnaud Schvartz *(Mng Dir)*
Daniel Nordholm *(Mng Dir)*

Subsidiary (Domestic):

Ingenico France SAS **(3)**
13/17 Rue Pages, 92150, Suresnes, France
Tel.: (33) 158018000
Payment Solution Banking Services
N.A.I.C.S.: 522320

Subsidiary (Non-US):

Ingenico GmbH **(3)**
Daniel-Goldbach-Strasse 17-19, 40880, Ratingen, Germany
Tel.: (49) 21029979260
Web Site: https://ingenico.com
Electronic Payment Systems
N.A.I.C.S.: 333310

Ingenico Healthcare GmbH **(3)**
Daniel-Goldbach-Strasse 17-19, 40880, Ratingen, Germany
Tel.: (49) 21029979260
Payment Solution Banking Services
N.A.I.C.S.: 522320

Ingenico Hungary Kft. **(3)**
Vaci Ut 19 Panorama Irodahaz III emelet, 1134, Budapest, Hungary
Tel.: (36) 19991775
Web Site: https://ingenico.com
Financial Transaction Processing Services
N.A.I.C.S.: 522320

Ingenico Iberia, SL **(3)**
Paseo de las 12 estrellas 2 Planta 1 Oficina C, 28042, Madrid, Spain **(100%)**
Tel.: (34) 619587328
Web Site: http://www.ingenico.com
Sales Range: $25-49.9 Million
Emp.: 50
Electronic Payment Systems
N.A.I.C.S.: 333310

Subsidiary (Domestic):

Ingenico Telesincro **(4)**
Augusta 15 Bldg 1 Fl 5, 8170, Cerdanyola del Valles, Barcelona, Spain **(100%)**
Tel.: (34) 935802227
Web Site: http://www.es.engenico.com
Sales Range: $25-49.9 Million
Electronic Payment Systems Mfr
N.A.I.C.S.: 336320

Subsidiary (Non-US):

Ingenico International (Pacific) Pty. Ltd. **(3)**
Level 14 Suite 1 / 309 Kent Street, Sydney, 2000, NSW, Australia
Tel.: (61) 299970900
Sales Range: $50-74.9 Million
Emp.: 7
Financial Transaction Processing Services
N.A.I.C.S.: 522320
John Pait *(Gen Mgr)*

Ingenico International (Singapore) Pte. Ltd. **(3)**
152 Beach Road 36-01/08 Gateway East, Singapore, 189721, Singapore
Tel.: (65) 63457022
Web Site: http://www.ingenico.com
Sales Range: $50-74.9 Million
Emp.: 65
Financial Transaction Processing Services
N.A.I.C.S.: 522320

Ingenico Italia SpA **(3)**
Via Giorgio Stephenson 43/A, 20157, Milan, Italy
Tel.: (39) 023320361
Web Site: http://www.ingenico.it
Sales Range: $25-49.9 Million
Emp.: 36
Electronic Payment Systems
N.A.I.C.S.: 333310

Ingenico LLC **(3)**
Godovikova str 9 bld 16, 129085, Moscow, Russia
Tel.: (7) 4959806855
Financial Transaction Services
N.A.I.C.S.: 522320

Ingenico Marketing Solutions GmbH **(3)**
Hugh Greene Way 2, 22529, Hamburg, Germany
Tel.: (49) 4073440401
Web Site: https://www.knistr.com
Emp.: 98
Internet Marketing Services
N.A.I.C.S.: 541613
Michael Bregulla *(Head-Client Dev)*

Ingenico Mexico S.A. de C.V. **(3)**

Apollo Global Management, Inc.—(Continued)

Calle Andres Bello No 10 17th floor Colonia Polanco, Chapultepec Miguel Hidalgo Delegation, 11560, Mexico, Mexico
Tel.: (52) 5559053400
Web Site: https://ingenico.com
Payment Solution Banking Services
N.A.I.C.S.: 522320

Ingenico Odeme Sistem Cozumleri A.S. (3)
ITU Ayazaga Kampusu ARI 2 Binas B Blok 6-1 Koru Yolu, Maslak, 34469, istanbul, Turkiye   (100%)
Tel.: (90) 2123664800
Financial Transaction Services
N.A.I.C.S.: 522320

Ingenico Polska Sp. z o.o (3)
st Emilii Plater 28 V p, 00-688, Warsaw, Poland
Tel.: (48) 226303268
Payment Solution Banking Services
N.A.I.C.S.: 522320

Ingenico Solutions (Malaysia) Sdn. Bhd. (3)
506 - 508 5th Floor Tower 2 Faber Towers Jalan Desa Bahagia, Taman Desa, 58100, Kuala Lumpur, Malaysia
Tel.: (60) 376102121
Payment Solution Banking Services
N.A.I.C.S.: 522320

Ingenico Switzerland SA (3)
56 Impasse des Ecureuils 2, 1763, Granges-Paccot, Switzerland
Tel.: (41) 264605520
Web Site: http://www.ingenico.ch
Financial Transaction Services
N.A.I.C.S.: 522320

Subsidiary (Domestic):

Ingenico Terminals SAS (3)
28/32 Boulevard De Grenelle, 75015, Paris, France
Tel.: (33) 158018000
Payment Solution Banking Services
N.A.I.C.S.: 522320

Ingenico Ventures SAS (3)
28 Boulevard de grenell, 75015, Paris, France
Tel.: (33) 146258200
Investment Holding Company
N.A.I.C.S.: 551112
Martin Rutar (Gen Mgr)

Subsidiary (Non-US):

Ingenico Vietnam Co., Ltd. (3)
Unit 1102 11th floor Daeha Business Centre 360 Kim Ma street, Ba Dinh Dist, Hanoi, 10000, Vietnam
Tel.: (84) 2432181367
Payment Solution Banking Services
N.A.I.C.S.: 522320

Ingenico do Brasil Ltda. (3)
R Olimpiadas 134-3, Sao Paulo, 04551-000, Brazil
Tel.: (55) 1126782200
Payment Solution Banking Services
N.A.I.C.S.: 522320

Ingenico e-Commerce Solutions BV (3)
Neptunusstraat 41-63, 2132 JA, Hoofddorp, Netherlands
Tel.: (31) 237524200
Payment Solution Banking Services
N.A.I.C.S.: 522320

Ingenico e-Commerce Solutions BVBA (3)
Da Vincilaan 3, 1930, Zaventem, Belgium
Tel.: (32) 22869611
Payment Solution Banking Services
N.A.I.C.S.: 522320
William Grant (Mng Dir)
Charles Mahaut (Mng Dir)
Benoit Boudier (Mng Dir)

Ingenico e-Commerce Solutions Ltd. (3)
20 Eastbourne Terrace, London, W2 6LG, United Kingdom
Tel.: (44) 2031474966
Web Site: http://www.ingenico.co.uk

Payment Solution Banking Services
N.A.I.C.S.: 522320

Subsidiary (Domestic):

Ingenico e-Commerce Solutions SAS (3)
28/32 Boulevard De Grenelle, 75015, Paris, France
Tel.: (33) 158018000
Payment Solution Banking Services
N.A.I.C.S.: 522320

Holding (Domestic):

Intrado Corporation (2)
11808 Miracle Hills Dr, Omaha, NE 68154
Tel.: (402) 702-2390
Web Site: http://www.intrado.com
Communication & Network Infrastructure Services
N.A.I.C.S.: 517810
John Shlonsky (Pres & CEO)
Anup Nair (CIO)
Louis Brucculeri (Gen Counsel & Exec VP)
Steve Cadden (COO)
Ben Chodor (Pres-Digital Media)
Matt Carter (CEO)

Subsidiary (Domestic):

Callpointe.com, Inc. (3)
3444 N Country Club Rd Ste 200, Tucson, AZ 85716
Tel.: (866) 402-6500
Web Site: http://www.callpointe.com
Web-based Services
N.A.I.C.S.: 541519

Subsidiary (Non-US):

Conferencecall Services India Private Limited (3)
309-311 Aditya Heritage Mindspace Of New Link Rd Maled W, Mindspace Link Road Malad, Mumbai, 400064, Maharashtra, India
Tel.: (91) 2240237211
Web Site: http://www.intrado.com
Telecommunication Servicesb
N.A.I.C.S.: 517810

GlobeNewswire, Inc. (3)
25 York Street Suite 900 CP 403, Toronto, M5J 2V5, ON, Canada
Tel.: (416) 362-0885
Web Site: http://w.globenewswire.com
Social Communication Services
N.A.I.C.S.: 516210

Subsidiary (Non-US):

GlobeNewswire UK Limited (4)
Dauntsey House 4B Frederick's Place, London, EC2R 8AB, United Kingdom
Tel.: (44) 2035148201
Web Site: http://www.globenewswire.com
Press Release Distribution Services
N.A.I.C.S.: 513199

Marketwired China Ltd. (4)
66/F The Centre 99 Queens Road, Central, China (Hong Kong)
Tel.: (852) 22735938
Web Site: http://www.marketwired.com
Social Communication Services
N.A.I.C.S.: 516210

Subsidiary (Domestic):

Holly Connects, Inc. (3)
75 Arlington St Fl 5, Boston, MA 02116
Tel.: (617) 861-4555
Telecommunication Servicesb
N.A.I.C.S.: 517810

Hubb, Inc. (3)
1012 Washington St, Vancouver, WA 98660
Tel.: (360) 949-7800
Web Site: http://www.hubb.me
Sales Range: $1-9.9 Million
Emp.: 50
Software Development Services
N.A.I.C.S.: 541511
Allison Magyar (Pres & CEO)
Kiki Grant (Mgr-Customer Success)

INXPO Inc. (3)
770 N Halsted St Ste 6S, Chicago, IL 60642
Tel.: (312) 962-3700

Web Site: http://www.inxpo.com
Sales Range: $10-24.9 Million
Emp.: 100
Advertising Related Services
N.A.I.C.S.: 541810
Drew VanVooren (Founder)

Subsidiary (Non-US):

Intercall De Mexico S De Rl De Cv (3)
Gral. Benjamin Hill 229 Hipodromo, Cuauhtemoc, Mexico, 06100 Ciudad de, Mexico
Tel.: (52) 3330025200
Telecommunication Servicesb
N.A.I.C.S.: 517810

Subsidiary (Domestic):

Intrado Communications LLC (3)
3200 W Pleasant Run Rd Ste 300, Lancaster, TX 76050
Tel.: (469) 727-1622
Web Site: http://intrado.me
Data Processing, Hosting & Related Services
N.A.I.C.S.: 518210

West Notification, Inc. (3)
11650 Miracle Hills Dr, Omaha, NE 68154
Telecommunication Servicesb
N.A.I.C.S.: 517810

West Safety Services, Inc. (3)
1601 Dry Creek Dr, Longmont, CO 80503
Tel.: (720) 494-5800
Web Site: https://www.intrado.com
Emergency Communication Services
N.A.I.C.S.: 517810

West Unified Communications Services, Inc. (3)
8420 W Bryn Mawr Ste 1100, Chicago, IL 60631
Tel.: (773) 399-1600
Web Site: http://www.intrado.com
Audio, Video & Web Conferencing Services
N.A.I.C.S.: 517112

Subsidiary (Non-US):

InterCall Asia Pacific Holdings Pte. Ltd. (4)
600 N Bridge Rd Ste 23-01 Parkview Square, 20-01/02 Tower Fifteen, Singapore, 188778, Singapore
Tel.: (65) 64682255
Web Site: http://www.westuc.com
Investment Management Service
N.A.I.C.S.: 551112

InterCall De Mexico, S. de R.L. de C.V. (4)
Gral Benjamin Hill 229 Hipodrom, Cuauhtemoc, Mexico, 06100, Mexico
Tel.: (52) 55 3600 3200
Web Site: http://www.intrado.com
Telecommunication Servicesb
N.A.I.C.S.: 517810

Intrado Belgium (4)
Avenue Louise 475, 1050, Brussels, Belgium
Tel.: (32) 24017039
Web Site: http://www.intrado.com
Telecommunication Servicesb
N.A.I.C.S.: 517810

Intrado EC Services Spain SA (4)
Carretera de Fuencarral a Alcobendas 14C Bajo C, 28049, Madrid, Spain
Tel.: (34) 914146268
Web Site: http://www.intrado.com
Telecommunication Servicesb
N.A.I.C.S.: 517810

Intrado EC Singapore Private Limited (4)
15 Hoe Chiang Rd 20-01/02 Tower Fifteen, Singapore, 089316, Singapore
Tel.: (65) 6468 2255
Web Site: http://www.intrado.com
Call Center Operations
N.A.I.C.S.: 517112

Intrado Ec India Private Limited (4)
No 11 Adam Chambers Level 2 Richmond Road, Bengaluru, 560025, Karnataka, India
Tel.: (91) 8006105047
Web Site: http://www.intrado.com
Call Center

N.A.I.C.S.: 517112

Intrado Hong Kong Limited (4)
Suite 1905 Lippo Centre Tower Two 89 Queensway Admiralty, Hong Kong, China (Hong Kong)
Tel.: (852) 3018 6882
Web Site: http://www.intrado.com
Call Center Operations
N.A.I.C.S.: 517112

Intrado Italy S.R.L. (4)
Via Montebello 14, 20121, Milan, Italy
Tel.: (39) 03381414838
Web Site: https://www.intrado.it
Telecommunication Servicesb
N.A.I.C.S.: 517810

Intrado Japan K.K (4)
1-20-3 Nishinjuku, Shinjuku-ku, Tokyo, 160-0023, Japan
Tel.: (81) 3 6757 4891
Web Site: http://www.intrado.com
Call Center Operations
N.A.I.C.S.: 517112

West UC Australia Pty Ltd. (4)
Level 6 171 Clarence Street, Sydney, 2000, NSW, Australia
Tel.: (61) 282959000
Web Site: http://www.intrado.com
Call Center Operations
N.A.I.C.S.: 517112

West UC Germany GmbH (4)
Herriotstrasse 1, 60528, Frankfurt am Main, Germany
Tel.: (49) 69427237500
Web Site: http://www.intrado.com
Telecommunication Servicesb
N.A.I.C.S.: 517810

West UC Sweden AB (4)
Wallingatan 12, 111 60, Stockholm, Sweden
Tel.: (46) 856210200
Web Site: http://www.intrado.com
Telecommunication Servicesb
N.A.I.C.S.: 517810

West Unified Communications Services Canada, Inc. (4)
40 Hyperion Court, Kingston, K7K 7K2, ON, Canada
Tel.: (780) 414-6741
Web Site: http://www.intrado.com
Telecommunication Servicesb
N.A.I.C.S.: 517810

Joint Venture (Non-US):

JSW Ispat Special Products Limited. (2)
Bandra Kurla Complex, Bandra, Mumbai, 400051, India
Tel.: (91) 2242861000
Web Site: https://www.aionjsw.in
Rev.: $273,379,194
Assets: $670,998,714
Liabilities: $428,071,944
Net Worth: $242,926,770
Earnings: ($509,391,216)
Emp.: 2,295
Fiscal Year-end: 03/31/2019
Minerals Product Mfr
N.A.I.C.S.: 327999
Ravichandar Moorthy Dhakshana (Exec Dir)
J. Nagarajan (CFO)
Ajay Kadhao (Compliance Officer & Sec)

Subsidiary (Domestic):

MPDL Ltd. (3)
Monnet House 11 Masjid Moth, Greater Kailash Part - II, New Delhi, 110048, India
Tel.: (91) 1129223112
Web Site: https://www.monnetgroup.com
Rev.: $1,880,115
Assets: $23,944,344
Liabilities: $10,018,764
Net Worth: $13,925,580
Earnings: ($461,171)
Emp.: 11
Fiscal Year-end: 03/31/2023
Sugar Mfr
N.A.I.C.S.: 311313
Subhash Kumar Singh (CFO)
Braham Dutt Bhardwaj (Exec Dir)
Anurag Singh Rathore (Compliance Officer & Sec)

Monind Ltd. (3)

Urla Industrial Complex Plot No 216
Sector-C, Raipur, 493221, Chattisgarh, India
Tel.: (91) 1129218542
Web Site: http://www.monnetgroup.com
Rev.: $996
Assets: $3,700,925
Liabilities: $21,187,639
Net Worth: ($17,486,715)
Earnings: ($233,947)
Emp.: 2
Fiscal Year-end: 03/31/2021
Iron & Steel Products Mfr
N.A.I.C.S.: 331210
Mahesh Kumar Sharma *(CFO)*

Monnet Industries Ltd. **(3)**
Monnet House 11 Masjid Moth Greater
Kailash Part-2, New Delhi, 110 048, India
Tel.: (91) 1129218542
Steel Products Mfr
N.A.I.C.S.: 331110

Rameshwaram Steel & Power Pvt.
Ltd. **(3)**
Indira Chowk Bailadula, Raigarh, 496 001,
Chhattisgarh, India
Tel.: (91) 9893629840
Sponge Iron Mfr
N.A.I.C.S.: 331110

Holding (Domestic):

Jimmy Sanders, Inc. **(2)**
518 N Sharpe Ave, Cleveland, MS 38732
Tel.: (662) 843-3626
Web Site: https://www.jsanders.com
Rev.: $200,000,000
Emp.: 30
Agricultural Input Supplies & Distribution
N.A.I.C.S.: 424910
Chuck Williamson *(Mgr-Retail)*

Joint Venture (Non-US):

Leighton Contractors Pty. Limited **(2)**
Level 8 Tower 1, 495 Victoria Avenue,
Chatswood, 2067, NSW, Australia **(50%)**
Tel.: (61) 286686000
Web Site: http://www.broad.com.au
Sales Range: $100-124.9 Million
Emp.: 500
Contractor Services
N.A.I.C.S.: 236220
Roman Garrido *(Acting Mng Dir)*

Holding (Domestic):

Lumileds LLC **(2)**
370 W Trimble Rd, San Jose, CA
95131 **(80.1%)**
Tel.: (408) 964-2900
Web Site: https://www.lumileds.com
Emp.: 7,000
Light Emitting Diode Products Mfr & Whslr
N.A.I.C.S.: 334413
Steve Barlow *(Pres-Automotive Bus Unit)*
Steve Landau *(Dir-Mktg Comm)*
Mircea Buzgar-Nazare *(Sr VP-Bus Transformation)*
Megan Giannini *(Chief HR Officer)*
Cheree McAlpine *(Chief Legal Officer)*
Matt Roney *(CEO)*
Jan Paul Teuwen *(CFO)*
Sridhar Vajapey *(Sr VP-R&D)*

Subsidiary (Non-US):

Lumileds Netherlands B.V. **(3)**
Beemdstraat 42, 5652 AB, Eindhoven,
Netherlands
Tel.: (31) 402740204
Web Site: http://www.lumileds.com
Light Emitting Diode Products Whslr
N.A.I.C.S.: 423690

Philips LumiLeds Lighting Company
Sdn. Bhd. **(3)**
Lebuh Kampung Jawa Bayan Lepas FIZ
Phase 3, Penang, 11900, Malaysia
Tel.: (60) 4 642 6868
Web Site: http://www.lumileds.com
Light Emitting Diode Products Whslr
N.A.I.C.S.: 423690

Holding (Domestic):

Maxim Crane Works, L.P. **(2)**
1225 Washington Pike, Bridgeville, PA
15017
Tel.: (412) 504-0200

Web Site: https://www.maximcrane.com
Crane, Truck & Industrial Equipment Rental
Services
N.A.I.C.S.: 532490
Ryan R. Gutwald *(VP-Risk Mgmt)*
Paul McDonnell *(CEO)*
Sean Collopy *(CFO)*
Don Goebel *(Chief Legal Officer & Chief Tax Officer)*
Larry Lis *(VP-Fleet)*

Division (Domestic):

AmQuip Crane **(3)**
2500A State Rd, Bensalem, PA 19020
Tel.: (215) 639-9200
Web Site: http://www.amquip.com
Crane Rentals & Related Services
N.A.I.C.S.: 532412

Subsidiary (Domestic):

B&G Crane Service, LLC **(3)**
725 Central Ave, Jefferson, LA 70121
Tel.: (504) 733-9400
Web Site: http://www.bgcrane.com
Sales Range: $50-74.9 Million
Emp.: 250
Rental & Leasing of Cranes & Aerial Lift
Equipment
N.A.I.C.S.: 532412
Trip Grilleta *(VP-Ops)*
Ted Redmond *(CEO)*
Gawain Grilletta *(VP & Gen Mgr)*
Rich Haggard *(VP-Sls & Mktg)*
Xavier Grilleta III *(Gen Mgr-Texas)*

Maxim Crane Works, L.P. -
Seattle **(3)**
1124 112th St E, Tacoma, WA 98445
Tel.: (206) 622-1151
Specialty Lift Services & Crane Equipment
Rental
N.A.I.C.S.: 541990

Branch (Domestic):

Coast Crane Co. **(4)**
1110 Lake Cook Road Suite 220, Buffalo
Grove, IL 60089-1974
Tel.: (509) 535-4266
Web Site: http://www.coastcrane.com
Sales Range: $10-24.9 Million
Emp.: 8
Specialty Lift Services & Crane Equipment
Rental
N.A.I.C.S.: 541990

Coast Crane Co.-Bakersfield **(4)**
6615 Rosedale Hwy, Bakersfield, CA 93308
Tel.: (661) 589-7770
Web Site: http://www.coastcrane.com
Sales Range: $10-24.9 Million
Emp.: 10
Specialty Lift Services & Crane Equipment
Rental
N.A.I.C.S.: 541990

Coast Crane Co.-City of Industry **(4)**
19062 E San Jose Ave, City of Industry, CA
91748
Tel.: (626) 810-1870
Web Site: http://www.coastcrane.com
Sales Range: $25-49.9 Million
Emp.: 14
Specialty Lift Services & Crane Equipment
Rental
N.A.I.C.S.: 541990

Coast Crane Co.-Pasco **(4)**
525 S Oregon Ave, Pasco, WA 99301-4318
Tel.: (509) 545-9138
Web Site: http://www.coastcrane.com
Sales Range: $10-24.9 Million
Emp.: 9
Specialty Lift Services & Crane Equipment
Rental
N.A.I.C.S.: 423810

Coast Crane Co.-Portland **(4)**
6654 NE 47th Ave, Portland, OR 97218
Tel.: (503) 288-8100
Web Site: http://www.coastcrane.com
Sales Range: $25-49.9 Million
Emp.: 40
Specialty Lift Services & Crane Equipment
Rental
N.A.I.C.S.: 541990

Coast Crane Co.-San Leandro **(4)**

14951 Catalina St, San Leandro, CA 94577-6613
Tel.: (510) 352-0123
Web Site: http://www.coastcrane.com
Sales Range: $25-49.9 Million
Emp.: 15
Specialty Lift Services & Crane Equipment
Rental
N.A.I.C.S.: 541990

Coast Crane Co.-Tacoma **(4)**
1124 112th St E, Tacoma, WA 98445-3710
Tel.: (206) 622-1151
Web Site: http://www.coastcrane.com
Sales Range: $10-24.9 Million
Emp.: 5
Specialty Lift Services & Crane Equipment
Rental
N.A.I.C.S.: 541990

Subsidiary (Non-US):

Coast Crane Ltd. **(4)**
9538 195th Street, Surrey, V4N 4G2, BC,
Canada
Tel.: (604) 888-8474
Web Site: http://www.coastcrane.com
Sales Range: $25-49.9 Million
Emp.: 10
Specialty Lift Services & Crane Equipment
Rental
N.A.I.C.S.: 541990

Subsidiary (Domestic):

Shaughnessy And Ahern
Company **(3)**
346 D St, Boston, MA 02127
Tel.: (617) 269-6600
Crane Services
N.A.I.C.S.: 238910

Affiliate (Domestic):

MidCap Financial Investment
Corporation **(2)**
9 W 57th St 37th Fl, New York, NY 10019
Tel.: (212) 515-3450
Web Site: http://www.apolloic.com
Rev.: $213,155,000
Assets: $2,600,121,000
Liabilities: $1,595,289,000
Net Worth: $1,004,832,000
Earnings: $95,961,000
Fiscal Year-end: 03/31/2022
Closed-End Management Investment Fund
N.A.I.C.S.: 525990
Gregory William Hunt *(CFO & Treas)*
Howard T. Widra *(CEO)*
Tanner Powell *(Pres)*
Isabelle R. Gold *(Chief Compliance Officer)*
John J. Hannan *(Chm)*
Joseph D. Glatt *(Chief Legal Officer, Sec & VP)*
Ryan Del Giudice *(Chief Compliance Officer)*

Holding (Domestic):

Novolex Holdings, LLC **(2)**
101 E Carolina Ave, Hartsville, SC 29550
Tel.: (843) 857-4800
Web Site: http://www.novolex.com
Emp.: 10,000
Paper & Plastic Packaging Services
N.A.I.C.S.: 561910
Janet Gibbons *(Treas & VP)*
Adrianne Tipton *(CTO)*
Matthew Winokur *(Sr VP-Corp Affairs)*

Subsidiary (Domestic):

B&H Bag Company **(3)**
6002 Osborn St, Houston, TX 77033
Tel.: (713) 641-0921
Web Site: http://www.bhbag.com
Sales Range: $1-9.9 Million
Emp.: 30
Mfg Bags-Uncoated Paper
N.A.I.C.S.: 322220
Buddy Robson *(Co-Founder)*
Happy Robson *(Co-Founder)*

Bagcraft Papercorn I, LLC **(3)**
3900 W 43rd St, Chicago, IL
60632 **(100%)**
Tel.: (773) 254-8000
Web Site: http://www.bagcraft.com
Paper & Foil Food Packaging Products Mfr
N.A.I.C.S.: 322220

Chuck Hathaway *(VP-Comml Paper Sls)*

Subsidiary (Non-US):

De Luxe Group Inc. **(3)**
200 Marien Ave, Montreal, H1B4V2, QC,
Canada
Tel.: (514) 645-4571
Web Site: http://www.deluxegrp.com
Paper Products Mfr
N.A.I.C.S.: 322299

Direct Plastics Group, Ltd. **(3)**
20 Stewart Court, Orangeville, L9W 3Z9,
ON, Canada
Tel.: (519) 942-8511
Plastic Flexible Packaging Products Mfr &
Distr
N.A.I.C.S.: 326112
Tom Cook *(Plant Mgr)*
Colleen Mackenzie *(Mgr-HR)*

Subsidiary (Domestic):

Duro Bag Manufacturing
Company **(3)**
7600 Empire Dr, Florence, KY 41042
Tel.: (859) 371-2150
Web Site: https://novolex.com
Paper Bag Mfr
N.A.I.C.S.: 322220
Jim Eaton *(Exec VP)*

Plant (Domestic):

Duro Bag Manufacturing Co. -
Brownsville **(4)**
3401 David Shor Dr Port of Brownsville,
Brownsville, TX 78520
Tel.: (956) 831-4209
Paper Bag Mfr
N.A.I.C.S.: 322220

Duro Bag Manufacturing Co. -
Elizabeth **(4)**
750 Dowd Ave, Elizabeth, NJ 07201-2108
Tel.: (908) 351-2400
Paper Bag Mfr
N.A.I.C.S.: 322220

Duro Bag Manufacturing Co. -
Richwood **(4)**
1 Duro Way, Walton, KY 41094
Tel.: (859) 485-6660
Paper Bag Mfr
N.A.I.C.S.: 322220

Subsidiary (Domestic):

Heritage Bag Company **(3)**
501 Gateway Pkwy, Roanoke, TX 76262
Tel.: (972) 241-5525
Web Site: https://www.heritage-bag.com
Plastic Can Liners & Packaging Products
Mfr
N.A.I.C.S.: 326112
Tim Rechner *(VP-Sls-Central)*
Don Ricks *(Reg Mgr)*
Jerry Ostmeyer *(Reg Mgr)*
Lauren Miller *(Reg Mgr)*

Subsidiary (Domestic):

Heritage Bag Company -
Fairfield **(4)**
4225 Thunderbird Ln, Fairfield, OH 45014
Tel.: (513) 814-3311
Trash Can Liners Mfr
N.A.I.C.S.: 326111
Chris Butterfield *(VP-Sls)*
Wesley Boals *(Territory Mgr)*
Ed Campbell *(Territory Mgr)*
John Krafft *(Territory Mgr)*
Dan Pfeiffer *(Territory Mgr)*
Jason Schreiber *(Territory Mgr)*

Heritage Bag Company - Logan
Township **(4)**
2321 High Hill Rd, Logan Township, NJ
08085
Tel.: (856) 467-2247
Trash Can Liners Mfr
N.A.I.C.S.: 326111
Ted Wells *(VP-Sls-Northeast Div)*
Patrick Bush *(Territory Mgr)*
Tom Ripple *(Territory Mgr)*

Heritage Bag Company - Rancho
Cucamonga **(4)**

Apollo Global Management, Inc.—(Continued)

12320 4th St, Rancho Cucamonga, CA
91730
Tel.: (909) 899-5554
Trash Can Liners Mfr
N.A.I.C.S.: 326111
Tony Scibilia (Sr VP-Can Liner)
Matt Franz (Territory Mgr)
Brian McCarville (VP-Sls)
Scott McKelvey (Reg Sls Mgr)

Heritage Bag Company - Villa
Rica   (4)
8096 E Hwy 78, Villa Rica, GA 30180
Tel.: (770) 942-0025
Trash Can Liners Mfr
N.A.I.C.S.: 326111
Brian Brewer (VP-Sls-Southeast Div)
Jim Campbell (Mgr-Corp Acct)
Tim Youngblood (Territory Mgr)

Subsidiary (Domestic):

Hilex Poly Co. LLC   (3)
101 E Carolina Ave, Hartsville, SC 29550
Tel.: (843) 857-4800
Emp.: 10,000
Plastics Bag & Pouch Manufacturing
N.A.I.C.S.: 326111

Subsidiary (Domestic):

Accutech Films, Inc.   (4)
620 Hardin St, Coldwater, OH 45828
Tel.: (419) 678-8700
Plastic Flexible Packaging Products Mfr &
Distr
N.A.I.C.S.: 326112

Plant (Domestic):

Hilex Poly Co. LLC - North
Vernon   (4)
1001 N 2nd St, North Vernon, IN 47265-
6518
Tel.: (812) 346-1066
High Density Film Mfr
N.A.I.C.S.: 326111

Subsidiary (Domestic):

International Converter LLC   (3)
17153 Industrial Hwy, Caldwell, OH 43724
Tel.: (740) 732-3060
Web Site: http://www.i-convert.com
Packaging Services
N.A.I.C.S.: 561910

Subsidiary (Domestic):

Pac Paper, LLC   (3)
6416 NW Whitney Rd, Vancouver, WA
98665-7016
Tel.: (360) 695-7771
Paper Products Mfr
N.A.I.C.S.: 322299
David Morgan (Sr Dir-Natl Sls)

Waddington Group, Inc.   (3)
50 E RiverCenter Blvd Ste 650, Covington,
KY 41011
Tel.: (859) 292-8028
Holding Company; Disposable Plastic Pack-
aging Products Mfr & Whslr
N.A.I.C.S.: 551112

Subsidiary (Non-US):

Deltaform Ltd   (4)
Brue Avenue Colley Lane Industrial Estate,
Bridgwater, TA6 5YE, Somerset, United
Kingdom
Tel.: (44) 1278 410160
Plastic Packaging Container Mfr
N.A.I.C.S.: 326199
Neil Richards (Mgr-Pur)

Polar Pak Inc.   (4)
26 Victoria Crescent, Brampton, L6T 1E5,
ON, Canada
Tel.: (905) 792-3000
Web Site: http://polarpak.ca
Plastic Packaging Mfr
N.A.I.C.S.: 326112
Alain Roucau (Mgr-Maintenance)

Subsidiary (Domestic):

Waddington North America, Inc.   (4)
6 Stuart Rd, Chelmsford, MA 01824-4108
Web Site: https://www.wna.biz
Cutlery Mfr

N.A.I.C.S.: 326199

Subsidiary (Domestic):

Eco-Products, Inc.   (5)
4755 Walnut St, Boulder, CO 80301
Tel.: (303) 449-1876
Web Site: http://www.ecoproducts.com
Food Service Products Mfr
N.A.I.C.S.: 322220
Ian Jacobson (Pres)

Subsidiary (Domestic):

Wisconsin Film & Bag, Inc.   (3)
3100 E Richmond St, Shawano, WI 54166
Tel.: (715) 524-2565
Web Site: http://www.wifb.com
Plastic Bags & Film Mfr
N.A.I.C.S.: 326111
Greg Greene (VP-Sls & Sustainable Pkg
Solutions)

Zenith Specialty Bag Co. Inc.   (3)
17625 E Railroad St, City of Industry, CA
91748
Tel.: (626) 912-2481
Web Site: http://www.zbags.com
Rev.: $27,700,000
Emp.: 200
Plastic Bags
N.A.I.C.S.: 322220
Scott Anderson (Pres)
Jack Grave (CFO)
Ron Anderson (VP)

Subsidiary (Non-US):

PK Air Finance France SAS   (2)
17 Avenue Didier Daurat 4th Floor Im-
meuble Socrate, Blagnac, Toulouse, 31700,
France
Tel.: (33) 3523420301
Asset Management Services
N.A.I.C.S.: 523940
Guillaume Degemard (VP-Mktg)

PK AirFinance Japan G.K.   (2)
Okura Prestige Tower 2-10-4 Toranomon,
Minato-Ku, Tokyo, 107-6112, Japan
Tel.: (81) 335886155
Asset Management Services
N.A.I.C.S.: 523940
Shinji Sato (Exec Mgr)

Holding (Domestic):

Rackspace Hosting, Inc.   (2)
1 Fanatical Pl City of Windcrest, San Anto-
nio, TX 78218
Tel.: (513) 999-2741
Web Site: https://www.rackspace.com
Website Hosting & Other IT Services
N.A.I.C.S.: 518210
Michael Bross (Chief Legal Officer)
Holly Windham (Chief Legal & People Offi-
cer & Exec VP)
Amar Maletira (CEO)
Rodrigo Martineli (VP/Gen Mgr-Latin
America)
Kellie Teal-Guess (Chief HR Officer)
Naushaza Molu (CTO)
Casey Shilling (CMO)
Brian Lillie (Pres)
Srini Koushik (CTO)
Salil Jain (Chief Bus Officer)

Subsidiary (Domestic):

DataPipe, Inc.   (3)
10 Exchange Pl, Jersey City, NJ 07302
Tel.: (201) 792-4847
Web Hosting
N.A.I.C.S.: 518210
Richard Lawrence (Mgr-Technical Escala-
tions)

Subsidiary (Non-US):

Adapt Group Limited   (4)
20-22 Commercial Street, London, E1 6LP,
United Kingdom
Tel.: (44) 8453043044
IT Network & Managed Hosting Services
N.A.I.C.S.: 518210

Subsidiary (Domestic):

Jungle Disk LLC   (3)
21750 Hardy Oak Blvd Ste 104, San Antonio, TX 78258

Web Site: https://cyberfortress.com
Emp.: 50
Online Data Storage & Backup Services
N.A.I.C.S.: 518210
Bret Piatt (Chm, Pres & CEO)
Huw Edwards (CFO & Chief Strategy Offi-
cer)
Seema Chacko (CFO)
Scott Graham (VP)

Subsidiary (Non-US):

Rackspace Ltd.   (3)
5 Millington Road, Hyde Park, Hayes, UB3
4AZ, Middlesex, United Kingdom
Tel.: (44) 2087348107
Web Site: http://www.rackspace.com
Website Hosting & IT Services
N.A.I.C.S.: 518210

Subsidiary (US):

TriCore Solutions LLC   (4)
141 Longwater Dr Ste 100, Norwell, MA
02061
Tel.: (888) 239-7775
Web Site: http://www.tricoresolutions.com
Software Publisher
N.A.I.C.S.: 513210

Holding (Domestic):

RegionalCare Hospital Partners,
Inc.   (2)
103 Continental Pl Ste 200, Brentwood, TN
37027
Tel.: (615) 844-9800
Holding Company; Hospital Operator
N.A.I.C.S.: 551112
Judy Gibson (Dir-Reimbursement)

Unit (Domestic):

Capital Medical Center   (3)
3900 Capitol Mall Dr SW, Olympia, WA
98502
Tel.: (360) 754-5858
Web Site: http://capitalmedical.com
Sales Range: $25-49.9 Million
Hospital Operator
N.A.I.C.S.: 622110
Colleen Gillespie (Chm)
Doug Mah (Vice Chm)
Mark Turner (CEO)
Chris Sloan (COO)
Becky Means (Chief Nursing Officer)
Kathleen Boswell-Gregg (Chief Quality Offi-
cer)
Jennifer Weldon (CFO)
John Masterson (Vice Chm)

Subsidiary (Domestic):

Community Medical Center, Inc.   (3)
2827 Fort Missoula Rd, Missoula, MT
59804
Tel.: (406) 728-4100
Web Site: https://www.communitymed.org
Emp.: 1,100
Hospital Operator
N.A.I.C.S.: 622110
Barb Jones (Chief Nursing Officer)
Sandee Mahoney (Co-CEO)
Jim Gillhouse (COO)
Bonnie Stephens (Chief Medical Officer)

Hartsville HMA, Inc.   (3)
1304 W Bobo Newsom Hwy, Hartsville, SC
29550
Tel.: (843) 339-2100
Web Site: https://www.cprmc.com
Sales Range: $50-74.9 Million
Hospital Services
N.A.I.C.S.: 622110
Bill Little (CEO)
Rodney Van Donkelaar (CFO)
Brian Sponseller (Chief Medical Officer)
Christy Moody (Chief Nursing Officer)

LifePoint Health, Inc.   (3)
330 Seven Springs Way, Brentwood, TN
37027
Tel.: (615) 920-7000
Web Site: http://www.lifepointhealth.net
Sales Range: $5-14.9 Billion
Holding Company; General Medical Hospi-
tal Owner & Operator
N.A.I.C.S.: 551112
David M. Dill (Chm & CEO)
Michael S. Coggin (CFO & Exec VP)

Jennifer Peters (Gen Counsel & Exec VP)
Michelle Augusty (VP-Comm)
Rob Jay (Exec VP-Integrated Ops)
Cherie Sibley (Pres-Central)
Sonny Terrill (Exec VP-HR)
Jamie Carter (Pres-Eastern Div)
Sandra C. Podley (Pres-Western Div)
Robert B. Wampler (Pres-Mountain Div)
Jason Zachariah (COO & Exec VP)
Aaron Lewis (Exec VP-Growth & Integrated
Solutions)
Elmer Polite (Pres-East)

Subsidiary (Domestic):

AMG-Livingston, LLC   (4)
529 Medical Dr, Livingston, TN 38570
Tel.: (931) 823-2854
General Medical Services
N.A.I.C.S.: 622110
Vicki Smith (Mgr)

AMG-Southern Tennessee, LLC   (4)
15 S Central Ave, Monteagle, TN 37356-
3074
Tel.: (931) 924-4045
General Medical Services
N.A.I.C.S.: 622110

Acquisition Bell Hospital, LLC   (4)
901 Lakeshore Dr, Ishpeming, MI 49849-
1367
Tel.: (906) 485-2797
Web Site: http://www.bellhospital.org
General Medical & Surgical Services
N.A.I.C.S.: 622110
Mitch Leckelt (CEO & Sec)
Teresa Perry (CFO)
Douglas LaBelle (Chief Medical Officer)

Ashley Valley Medical Center,
LLC   (4)
150 W 100 N, Vernal, UT 84078
Tel.: (435) 789-3342
Web Site: https://www.ashleyregional.com
General Medical Services
N.A.I.C.S.: 622110

Athens Surgery Center Partner,
LLC   (4)
330 Seven Springs Way, Brentwood, TN
37027
Tel.: (615) 920-7646
General Medical & Surgical Services
N.A.I.C.S.: 622110

Athens Surgery Center, LLC   (4)
75 Hospital Dr Ste 100, Athens, OH 45701
Tel.: (740) 566-4500
Web Site:
https://www.athenssurgerycenter.com
Ambulatory Surgical Services
N.A.I.C.S.: 621403
Heather Akers (Bus Office Mgr)

Bell Physician Practices, Inc.   (4)
901 Lakeshore Dr, Ishpeming, MI 49849
Tel.: (906) 485-7777
Web Site: http://www.bellhospital.org
Emp.: 3
General Medical & Surgical Services
N.A.I.C.S.: 622110

Bolivar Medical Center   (4)
901 HWY 8 E, Cleveland, MS 38732
Tel.: (662) 846-0061
Web Site: https://www.bolivarmedical.com
General Medical Services
N.A.I.C.S.: 622110

Bourbon Community Hospital,
LLC   (4)
9 Linville Dr, Paris, KY 40361
Tel.: (859) 987-3600
Web Site: https://www.bourbonhospital.com
General Medical Services
N.A.I.C.S.: 622110
Joe Koch (CEO)
Allyson Eads (Chm)

Castleview Hospital, LLC   (4)
300 N Hospital Dr, Price, UT 84501
Tel.: (435) 637-4800
Web Site: https://www.castleviewhospital.net
Sales Range: $25-49.9 Million
Emp.: 340
General Medical & Surgical Hospital Ser-
vices
N.A.I.C.S.: 622110

Greg Cook *(CEO)*
Jay Noyes *(CFO)*

Clark Regional Physician Practices, LLC (4)
225 Hospital Dr Ste 315, Winchester, KY 40391
Tel.: (859) 737-6488
Emp.: 20
General Medical & Surgical Services
N.A.I.C.S.: 622110
Breanne Cole *(Mgr-Practice)*

Clinch Valley Medical Center, Inc. (4)
6801 Governor GC Peery Hwy, Richlands, VA 24641
Tel.: (276) 596-6000
Web Site:
https://www.clinchvalleyhealth.com
Sales Range: $75-99.9 Million
Emp.: 1,975
Hospital Services
N.A.I.C.S.: 622110

Clinch Valley Physicians Associates, LLC (4)
1 Clinic Rd, Cedar Bluff, VA 24609
Tel.: (276) 964-6771
General Medical & Surgical Services
N.A.I.C.S.: 622110
Melissa Robinette *(Gen Mgr)*

Colorado Plains Physician Practices, LLC (4)
1000 Lincoln St Ste 101, Fort Morgan, CO 80701
Tel.: (970) 522-7195
Web Site:
http://www.coloradoplainsphysicianprac
tices.com
Sales Range: $50-74.9 Million
Emp.: 250
Hospital
N.A.I.C.S.: 622110
Dene Ohara *(CEO)*

Crockett Hospital, LLC (4)
1607 S Locust Ave Hwy 43, Lawrenceburg, TN 38464
Tel.: (931) 762-6571
Web Site:
https://www.southerntnlawrenceburg.com
Sales Range: $25-49.9 Million
Emp.: 250
General Medical Services
N.A.I.C.S.: 622110

DLP Cardiology Associates, LLC (4)
2660 Tate Blvd SE, Hickory, NC 28602-1465
Tel.: (615) 920-7000
Health Care Srvices
N.A.I.C.S.: 621610

DLP Central Carolina Family Medicine, LLC (4)
2412 Wilkins Dr, Sanford, NC 27330-7268
Tel.: (919) 776-6000
Health Care Srvices
N.A.I.C.S.: 621610

DLP Conemaugh Memorial Medical Center, LLC (4)
1086 Franklin St, Johnstown, PA 15905
Tel.: (814) 534-9000
Emp.: 1,016
Health Care Srvices
N.A.I.C.S.: 621610

DLP Conemaugh Miners Medical Center, LLC (4)
290 Haida Ave, Hastings, PA 16646-0689
Tel.: (814) 247-3100
General Medical Services
N.A.I.C.S.: 621111

DLP Frye Regional Medical Center, LLC (4)
415 N Center St, Hickory, NC 28601-5057
Tel.: (828) 323-8281
General Medical Services
N.A.I.C.S.: 621111

DLP Harris Regional Hospital, LLC (4)
68 Hospital Rd, Sylva, NC 28779-2722
Tel.: (828) 586-7000
Health Care Srvices
N.A.I.C.S.: 621610

DLP Healthcare, LLC (4)
330 7 Springs Way, Brentwood, TN 37027
Tel.: (615) 920-7000
Web Site:
http://www.dukelifepointhealthcare.com
Holding Company; Healthcare Services
N.A.I.C.S.: 551112

Subsidiary (Domestic):

Central Carolina Ambulatory Surgery Center, LLC (5)
1135 Carthage St, Sanford, NC 27330
Tel.: (919) 774-2100
Web Site:
https://www.centralcarolinahosp.com
Medical Services & Hospital Operator
N.A.I.C.S.: 622110

Affiliate (Domestic):

Central Carolina-CIM, L.L.C. (6)
4546 Highway 87 S, Sanford, NC 27332
Tel.: (919) 499-5151
Web Site:
http://centralcarolinainternalmed.com
Health Care Srvices
N.A.I.C.S.: 621999

Central Carolina-IMA, L.L.C. (6)
1139 Carthage St Ste 110-A, Sanford, NC 27330-4111
Tel.: (919) 774-2195
Web Site:
http://internalmedicineofsanford.com
Health Care Srvices
N.A.I.C.S.: 621999

Subsidiary (Domestic):

DLP Cardiac Partners, LLC (5)
3700 Arco Corporate Dr Ste 450, Charlotte, NC 28273
Tel.: (704) 714-8858
Web Site:
http://www.dlpcardiacpartners.com
Sales Range: $10-24.9 Million
Emp.: 30
General Medical Services
N.A.I.C.S.: 622110
Todd Williamson *(Exec Dir)*
Russ Bryant *(Mgr-Interim Mobile Labs)*

DLP Maria Parham Medical Center, LLC (5)
566 Ruin Creek Rd, Henderson, NC 27536
Tel.: (252) 438-4143
Web Site: http://www.mariaparham.org
General Medical Services
N.A.I.C.S.: 622110

Subsidiary (Domestic):

DLP Maria Parham Physician Practices, LLC (6)
568 Ruin Creek Rd Ste 003, Henderson, NC 27536
Tel.: (252) 436-1080
General Medical Services
N.A.I.C.S.: 622110

Subsidiary (Domestic):

Frye Regional Medical Center, Inc. (5)
420 N Center St, Hickory, NC 28601
Tel.: (828) 322-5000
Web Site: https://www.fryemedctr.com
General Medical Hospital
N.A.I.C.S.: 622110

Subsidiary (Domestic):

Guardian Health Services, L.L.C. (6)
100 Main Ave NW Ste 200, Hickory, NC 28601
Tel.: (828) 324-3025
Web Site: http://www.ghsnc.com
Health Care Srvices
N.A.I.C.S.: 621610

Viewmont Surgery Center, L.L.C. (6)
50 13th Ave NE Ste 1, Hickory, NC 28601
Tel.: (828) 624-1250
Web Site:
https://www.viewmontsurgerycenter.com
Medical Devices
N.A.I.C.S.: 622110

Subsidiary (Domestic):

DLP Marquette General Hospital, LLC (4)
580 W College Ave, Marquette, MI 49855
Tel.: (906) 228-9440
Health Care Srvices
N.A.I.C.S.: 621610
Trent Crable *(CEO)*
Jeff Perry *(COO)*
Steve Embree *(CFO)*
Wael Khouli *(CMO)*
Fran Finley *(VP-Physician Practices)*

DLP Marquette Physician Practices, Inc. (4)
107 W Main St, Marquette, MI 49855
Tel.: (906) 225-7188
General Medical Services
N.A.I.C.S.: 621111

DLP Person Urgent Care, LLC (4)
3762 Durham Rd Ste A, Roxboro, NC 27573-2741
Tel.: (336) 330-0400
Healtcare Services
N.A.I.C.S.: 621491

DLP Rutherford Physician Practices, LLC (4)
139 Doctor Henry Norris Dr, Rutherfordton, NC 28139-3176
Tel.: (828) 287-9260
Health Care Srvices
N.A.I.C.S.: 621610

DLP Rutherford Regional Health System, LLC (4)
2270 Us Hwy 74a Byp, Forest City, NC 28043-2434
Tel.: (828) 245-3575
Women Healthcare Services
N.A.I.C.S.: 621610

DLP Swain County Hospital, LLC (4)
45 Plateau St, Bryson City, NC 28713-6784
Tel.: (828) 488-2155
Health Care Srvices
N.A.I.C.S.: 621610

DLP Western Carolina Physician Practices, LLC (4)
98 Doctors Dr, Sylva, NC 28779-4501
Tel.: (828) 586-8971
Health Care Srvices
N.A.I.C.S.: 621610

DLP WilMed Nursing Care and Rehabilitation Center, LLC (4)
1705 Tarboro St SW, Wilson, NC 27893-3428
Tel.: (252) 399-8040
Nursing Care Facility Operator
N.A.I.C.S.: 623110

DLP Wilson Physician Practices, LLC (4)
1700 Tarboro St W Ste 100, Wilson, NC 27893-3481
Tel.: (252) 399-5300
Health Care Srvices
N.A.I.C.S.: 621610

Danville Diagnostic Imaging Center, LLC (4)
125 Executive Dr, Danville, VA 24541-4155
Tel.: (434) 793-1043
Emp.: 42
General Medical Services
N.A.I.C.S.: 622110

Danville Physician Practices, LLC (4)
305 N Main St, Gretna, VA 24557
Tel.: (434) 656-2224
Emp.: 6
General Medical Services
N.A.I.C.S.: 622110
June Hill *(Mgr)*

Danville Regional Medical Center School of Health Professions, LLC (4)
142 S Main St, Danville, VA 24541
Tel.: (434) 799-2271
General Medical Services
N.A.I.C.S.: 622110

Danville Regional Medical Center, LLC (4)
142 S Main St, Danville, VA 24541
Tel.: (434) 799-2100
Web Site: http://www.danvilleregional.com
Emp.: 1,300
General Medical Services
N.A.I.C.S.: 622110

Dlp Conemaugh Physician Practices, Llc (4)
225 Keystone Ave, Cresson, Pa 16630-1214
Tel.: (814) 886-2911
General Medical Services
N.A.I.C.S.: 621111

Fauquier Long-Term Care, LLC (4)
360 Hospital Dr, Warrenton, VA 20186-3006
Tel.: (540) 316-5500
Web Site: http://www.fauquierhospital.org
Emp.: 120
Nursing Services
N.A.I.C.S.: 623110
Roger Baker *(CEO)*

Fauquier Medical Center, LLC (4)
500 Hospital Dr, Warrenton, VA 20186-2639
Tel.: (540) 316-5000
Web Site: https://www.fauquierhealth.org
General Medical & Surgical Services
N.A.I.C.S.: 622110

Fleming Medical Center, LLC (4)
55 Foundation Dr, Flemingsburg, KY 41041-1141
Tel.: (606) 849-5000
Health Care Srvices
N.A.I.C.S.: 621610

Gateway Health Alliance, Inc. (4)
341 Main St Ste 301, Danville, VA 24541
Tel.: (434) 799-3838
Web Site: https://www.gatewayhealth.com
Medical Management Services
N.A.I.C.S.: 621999

Georgetown Community Hospital, LLC (4)
1140 Lexington Rd, Georgetown, KY 40324
Tel.: (502) 868-1100
Web Site:
http://www.georgetowncommunityhos
pital.com
Sales Range: $25-49.9 Million
Emp.: 226
General Medical Services
N.A.I.C.S.: 622110
William Haugh *(CEO)*
Dallas Blankenship *(Chm)*
Richard Snapp *(CFO)*
Cliff Wilson *(Pres)*
Barbara Kinder *(Chief Nursing Officer)*

Havasu Regional Medical Center, LLC (4)
101 Civic Ctr Ln, Lake Havasu City, AZ 86403
Tel.: (928) 855-8185
Web Site: https://www.havasuregional.com
Sales Range: $25-49.9 Million
Emp.: 500
General Medical Services
N.A.I.C.S.: 622110

Havasu Surgery Center, Inc. (4)
1775 McCulloch Blvd N, Lake Havasu City, AZ 86403
Tel.: (928) 453-4200
Rev.: $5,500,000
Emp.: 30
Surgical Hospital Services
N.A.I.C.S.: 622110

Hillside Hospital, LLC (4)
1265 E College St, Pulaski, TN 38478
Tel.: (931) 363-7531
Web Site: https://www.hillsidehospital.com
Health Care Srvices
N.A.I.C.S.: 621610
Jim Edmondson *(CEO)*
Donald Gavin *(CFO)*
Tammy Brenner *(Dir-Bus Office)*
Edith Niles *(Mgr-Materials)*
Gwen Black *(Mgr-Case)*

Kentucky Physician Services, Inc. (4)
400 Gatlin Ave Orlando, Orlando, FL 32806
Tel.: (859) 514-5547
Web Site: http://www.vaxcare.com
General Medical Services
N.A.I.C.S.: 622110

Apollo Global Management, Inc.—(Continued)

Kindred Healthcare, LLC (4)
680 S Fourth St, Louisville, KY 40202-2412
Tel.: (502) 596-7300
Web Site: http://www.kindredhealthcare.com
Hospitals, Nursing Centers & Rehabilitation
Service Facilities Operator
N.A.I.C.S.: 623110
Kent H. Wallace (Exec VP)
Benjamin A. Breier (CEO)
David A. Causby (Pres-Kindred At Home &
Exec VP)
William M. Altman (Exec VP-Strategy)
John J. Lucchese (CFO)
Joseph L. Landenwich (Gen Counsel &
Sec)
Stephen R. Cunanan (Chief Admin Officer &
Chief People Officer)
Peter K. Kalmey (Pres-Hospital Div & Exec
VP)
Jason Zachariah (Pres)
Linn P. Billingsley (VP-Reg Ops)

Subsidiary (Domestic):

Alta Vista Healthcare (5)
9020 Garfield St, Riverside, CA 92503-3903
Tel.: (951) 688-8200
Sales Range: $25-49.9 Million
Emp.: 110
Skilled Nursing Facility
N.A.I.C.S.: 623311
Oscar Garcia (Gen Mgr)

Avery Manor Nursing, L.L.C. (5)
100 W St, Needham, MA 02494-1319
Tel.: (781) 234-6300
Web Site: http://www.averymanor.com
Nursing Care Facility Services
N.A.I.C.S.: 623110
Mark Roher (Dir-Medical)

**BWB Sunbelt Home Health Services,
LLC** (5)
7500 Viscount Blvd Ste 156, El Paso, TX
79925-5638
Tel.: (915) 629-8408
Health Care Srvices
N.A.I.C.S.: 621610

**Bethany Hospice and Palliative
Care** (5)
2700 N Oak St Bldg B, Valdosta, GA 31602
Tel.: (229) 588-2339
Web Site: http://www.bethany-hospice.com
Health Care Srvices
N.A.I.C.S.: 622110

**Blueberry Hill Healthcare Nursing
Home** (5)
75 Brimbal Ave, Beverly, MA 01915
Tel.: (070) 927 2020
Web Site:
https://www.blueberryhillrehab.com
Sales Range: $25-49.9 Million
Emp.: 200
Nursing Care Facility
N.A.I.C.S.: 623311

Care Center of Rossmoor, L.L.C. (5)
1224 Rossmoor Pkwy, Walnut Creek, CA
94595-2501
Tel.: (925) 937-7450
Web Site:
http://www.kindredwalnutcreek.com
Nursing Care Facility Services
N.A.I.C.S.: 623110

**Colony House Nursing and Rehabili-
tation Center** (5)
277 Washington St, Abington, MA 02351-
2489
Tel.: (781) 871-0200
Web Site: http://www.kindredhealthcare.com
Sales Range: $25-49.9 Million
Emp.: 110
Rehabilitation & Nursing Care Facility
N.A.I.C.S.: 623110
Emily Felix (Exec Dir)

Compass Hospice, Inc (5)
3001 W Illinois Ave Ste 3A, Midland, TX
79701
Tel.: (432) 704-5210
Nursing Center & Rehabilitation Services
N.A.I.C.S.: 623110

Curo Health Services, LLC (5)

655 Brawley School Rd Ste 200, Moores-
ville, NC 28117
Tel.: (704) 664-2876
Web Site:
https://www.curohealthservices.com
Hospice Healthcare Services
N.A.I.C.S.: 621610
Larry Graham (CEO)

**Cypress Point Rehabilitation & Health
Care Center** (5)
2006 S 16th St, Wilmington, NC 28401-
6613
Tel.: (910) 736-6271
Web Site:
https://www.cypresspointerehab.com
Sales Range: $25-49.9 Million
Emp.: 150
Rehabilitation & Nursing Care Facility Op-
erator
N.A.I.C.S.: 623110

**Dover Rehabilitation & Living
Center** (5)
307 Plz Dr, Dover, NH 03820-2455
Tel.: (603) 742-2676
Web Site: http://www.doverrehab.com
Sales Range: $25-49.9 Million
Emp.: 150
Nursing & Rehabilitation Facility
N.A.I.C.S.: 623110

EmpRes at Rock Springs, LLC (5)
1325 Sage St, Rock Springs, WY 82901
Tel.: (307) 362-3780
Web Site: https://www.empres.com
Nursing Care Facility
N.A.I.C.S.: 623110

Fifth Avenue Healthcare Center (5)
1601 5th Ave, San Rafael, CA 94901-1808
Tel.: (415) 456-7170
Sales Range: $10-24.9 Million
Nursing Care Facility
N.A.I.C.S.: 623311

**Foothill Nursing Company
Partnership** (5)
401 W Ada Ave, Glendora, CA 91741-4241
Tel.: (626) 335-9810
Health Care Srvices
N.A.I.C.S.: 621610

Forestview Nursing, L.L.C. (5)
50 Indian Neck Rd, Wareham, MA 02571-
2174
Tel.: (302) 658-7581
Web Site:
http://www.forestviewwareham.com
Nursing Care Facility Services
N.A.I.C.S.: 623110

Fox Hill Village Partnership (5)
10 Longwood Dr, Westwood, MA 02090
Tel.: (781) 329-4433
Web Site: http://www.foxhillvillage.com
Hospitality Services
N.A.I.C.S.: 621610
Barbara Clark (Pres)
Felix Rosenwasser (CEO)

**Franklin Skilled Nursing & Rehabilita-
tion Center** (5)
130 Chestnut St, Franklin, MA 02038-3903
Tel.: (508) 528-4600
Web Site: http://www.franklin-help.com
Sales Range: $25-49.9 Million
Emp.: 120
Nursing Care Facility
N.A.I.C.S.: 623110

Gentiva Health Services, Inc. (5)
3350 Riverwood Pkwy, Atlanta, GA 30339-
3314
Tel.: (855) 488-7026
Web Site: https://www.gentivahs.com
Home Health Care, Hospice & Community
Care Services
N.A.I.C.S.: 621610
David A. Causby (Pres & CEO)

Subsidiary (Domestic):

Gentiva Hospice (6)
3508 Professional Cir A, Augusta, GA
30907
Tel.: (706) 210-5900
Health Care Srvices
N.A.I.C.S.: 621610

**Odyssey HealthCare of South Texas,
LLC** (6)
410 Sta A, Arlington, TX 78550
Tel.: (956) 423-1101
Health Care Srvices
N.A.I.C.S.: 621610
Josh Lasater (Exec Dir)

Subsidiary (Domestic):

Golden Gate Healthcare Center (5)
2707 Pine St, San Francisco, CA 94115
Tel.: (415) 563-7600
Web Site: http://www.goldengatehcc.com
Sales Range: $10-24.9 Million
Emp.: 130
Nursing Care Facility
N.A.I.C.S.: 621999
Christine Pelgone (Exec Dir)

**Great Barrington Rehabilitation and
Nursing Center** (5)
148 Maple Ave, Great Barrington, MA
01230-1906
Tel.: (413) 528-3320
Web Site:
http://www.greatbarringtonrnc.com
Sales Range: $25-49.9 Million
Emp.: 100
Nursing Care Facility
N.A.I.C.S.: 623110
Kathie Coburn (Mgr-HR)

Greenbriar Operations, LLC (5)
55 Harris Rd, Nashua, NH 03062-2145
Tel.: (603) 888-1573
Web Site: http://premiernursinghome.com
Nursing Care Facility
N.A.I.C.S.: 623110

Guardian Care of Ahoskie (5)
604 Stokes St E, Ahoskie, NC 27910
Tel.: (252) 332-2126
Nursing Care Facility
N.A.I.C.S.: 623110

**Guardian Care of Roanoke
Rapids** (5)
305 E 14th St, Roanoke Rapids, NC 27870-
4430
Tel.: (252) 537-6181
Healthcare & Nursing Facility
N.A.I.C.S.: 623110

**Home Health of Rural Texas,
Inc.** (5)
108 E Morris St, Seymour, TX 76380
Tel.: (940) 888-3744
Health Care Srvices
N.A.I.C.S.: 621610

IntegraCare of Abilene, LLC (5)
1665 Antilley Rd Ste 100, Abilene, TX
79606-5268
Tel.: (325) 691-9948
Health Care Srvices
N.A.I.C.S.: 621610

IntegraCare of Albany, LLC (5)
124 Hill St, Albany, TX 76430
Tel.: (325) 762-2854
Health Care Srvices
N.A.I.C.S.: 621610

IntegraCare of Granbury, LLC (5)
1715 S Morgan St, Granbury, TX 76048
Tel.: (817) 573-7830
Health Care Srvices
N.A.I.C.S.: 621610

**IntegraCare of Olney Home Health,
LLC** (5)
104 North Ave E, Olney, TX 76374
Tel.: (940) 564-4696
Health Care Srvices
N.A.I.C.S.: 621610

**IntegraCare of Wichita Falls,
LLC** (5)
4309 Jacksboro Hwy, Wichita Falls, TX
76308
Tel.: (940) 720-0514
Health Care Srvices
N.A.I.C.S.: 621610

**Kindred Healthcare of Elizabeth
City** (5)
901 S Halstead Blvd, Elizabeth City, NC
27909-6920
Tel.: (252) 338-0137

Web Site: http://www.gcelizabeth.com
Sales Range: $100-124.9 Million
Emp.: 170
Nursing Care Facility
Erikka Hallback (Exec Dir)

Kindred Hospital - Atlanta (5)
1303 Hightower Trl Ste 105, Atlanta, GA
30350
Tel.: (770) 998-1393
Web Site: http://www.kindredatlanta.com
Sales Range: $50-74.9 Million
Acute Care Hospital Services
N.A.I.C.S.: 622310

**Kindred Hospital - Bay Area -
Tampa** (5)
4555 S Manhattan Ave, Tampa, FL 33611
Tel.: (813) 839-6341
Nursing & Hospital Services
N.A.I.C.S.: 623110

Kindred Hospital - Cleveland (5)
2351 E 22nd St 7th Fl, Cleveland, OH
44115
Tel.: (216) 592-2830
Web Site: http://www.kindredcleveland.com
Sales Range: $50-74.9 Million
Emp.: 150
Specialty Hospitals
N.A.I.C.S.: 622110

Kindred Hospital - Louisville (5)
1313 St Anthony Pl, Louisville, KY 40204
Tel.: (502) 587-7001
Hospital Facility
N.A.I.C.S.: 623110

Kindred Hospital - San Diego (5)
1940 El Cajon Blvd, San Diego, CA 92104
Tel.: (619) 543-4500
Web Site: https://www.kindredhospitals.com
Hospital Facility
N.A.I.C.S.: 622310
Kerry Ashment (CEO)

**Kindred Hospital Palm Beach,
L.L.C.** (5)
5555 W Blue Heron Blvd, Riviera Beach, FL
33418
Tel.: (561) 840-0754
Web Site: https://www.kindredhospitals.com
Hospital Management Services
N.A.I.C.S.: 622110

Kindred Hospital Tucson (5)
355 N Wilmot Rd, Tucson, AZ 85711
Tel.: (520) 584-4500
Web Site: http://www.khtucson.com
Hospital Operations
N.A.I.C.S.: 622110
Diane Chartier (CEO)

**Kindred Hospital-Pittsburgh-North
Shore, L.L.C.** (5)
1004 Arch St, Pittsburgh, PA 15212
Tel.: (412) 323-5800
Web Site: http://www.kindrednorthshore.com
Hospital Management Services
N.A.I.C.S.: 622110

**Kindred Nursing Centers Limited
Partnership** (5)
853 Lexington Rd, Harrodsburg, KY 40330
Tel.: (859) 734-7791
Web Site:
http://www.harrodsburghealthandrehab.com
Nursing Care Facility Operator
N.A.I.C.S.: 623110

**Kindred Nursing Centers West,
L.L.C.** (5)
3128 Boxelder St, Cheyenne, WY 82001-
5803
Tel.: (307) 634-7901
Web Site: http://www.mttowersrehab.com
Sales Range: $25-49.9 Million
Emp.: 100
Nursing & Hospice Facility
N.A.I.C.S.: 621111
Dan Stackis (Gen Mgr)

**Kindred Nursing Centers West,
LLC** (5)
49 Lyme Rd, Hanover, NH 03755-1205
Tel.: (603) 643-2854
Web Site: https://www.bearmountainhc.com
Nursing Care Facility
N.A.I.C.S.: 623110

Kindred Nursing and Rehabilitation - Braintree (5)
1102 Washington St, Braintree, MA 02184-5438
Tel.: (781) 848-3100
Web Site: http://www.braintreemanor.com
Nursing Care Facility Services
N.A.I.C.S.: 623110

Lafayette Health Care Center, Inc. (5)
110 Brandywine Blvd, Fayetteville, GA 30214
Tel.: (770) 461-2928
Health Care Srvices
N.A.I.C.S.: 621610

Lafayette Specialty Hospital, LLC (5)
204 Energy Pkwy, Lafayette, LA 70508
Tel.: (337) 232-1905
Nursing Care Facility Services
N.A.I.C.S.: 623110

Subsidiary (Domestic):

Greater Peoria Specialty Hospital, LLC (6)
500 W Romeo B Garrett Ave, Peoria, IL 61605
Tel.: (309) 680-1500
Web Site: https://www.osftch.com
Hospital Management Services
N.A.I.C.S.: 622110

Northland LTACH, LLC (6)
500 NW 68th St, Kansas City, MO 64118
Tel.: (816) 420-6300
Web Site: https://www.kindredhospitals.com
Health Care Srvices
N.A.I.C.S.: 621610

The Specialty Hospital, L.L.C. (6)
304 Turner McCall Blvd, Rome, GA 30162-1566
Tel.: (706) 509-4100
Health Care Srvices
N.A.I.C.S.: 621610

Triumph Hospital Northwest Indiana, LLC (6)
5454 Hohman Ave, Hammond, IN 46320
Tel.: (800) 259-9839
Health Care Srvices
N.A.I.C.S.: 621610

Triumph Rehabilitation Hospital of Northeast Houston, LLC (6)
18839 McKay Blvd, Humble, TX 77338
Tel.: (281) 964-6600
Nursing Care & Rehabilitation Services
N.A.I.C.S.: 623110

Subsidiary (Domestic):

Las Vegas Healthcare and Rehabilitation Center (5)
2832 S Maryland Pkwy, Las Vegas, NV 89109-1502
Tel.: (702) 735-5848
Web Site: http://www.lasvegaskindred.com
Sales Range: $25-49.9 Million
Emp.: 100
Rehabilitation & Healthcare Facility
N.A.I.C.S.: 623110

Lawton Healthcare Center (5)
1575 7th Ave, San Francisco, CA 94122-0249
Tel.: (415) 566-1200
Web Site: http://www.lawtonhealthcare.com
Sales Range: $10-24.9 Million
Emp.: 70
Nursing Care Facility
N.A.I.C.S.: 623311

Ledgewood Health Care Corporation (5)
87 Herrick St, Beverly, MA 01915-2773
Tel.: (978) 921-1392
Web Site: https://www.banecare.com
Nursing Care Facility Services
N.A.I.C.S.: 623110

Ledgewood Rehabilitation and Skilled Nursing Center (5)
87 Herrick St, Beverly, MA 01915
Tel.: (978) 921-1392
Web Site: https://www.banecare.com
Rehabilitation & Nursing Care Facility
N.A.I.C.S.: 623110

Maine Assisted Living, L.L.C. (5)
78 Scott Dyer Rd, Cape Elizabeth, ME 04107-2200
Tel.: (207) 799-7332
Web Site: https://www.thelandingatcapeelizabeth.com
Nursing Care Facility & Care Retirement Community Services
N.A.I.C.S.: 623110

Maywood Acres Healthcare (5)
2641 S C St, Oxnard, CA 93033-4502
Tel.: (805) 487-7840
Web Site: http://maywoodacres.com
Nursing Care Facility
N.A.I.C.S.: 623110
Girlie Rozario *(Office Mgr-Bus)*

Med Tech Services of Palm Beach, Inc. (5)
525 NW Lake Whitney Pl, Port Saint Lucie, FL 34986
Tel.: (772) 223-2116
Health Care Srvices
N.A.I.C.S.: 621610

Med. Tech. Services of South Florida, Inc. (5)
8198 Jog Rd # 101, Boynton Beach, FL 33472
Tel.: (561) 886-1500
Health Care Srvices
N.A.I.C.S.: 621610

MedTech Services of Dade, Inc. (5)
14400 NW 77th Ct Ste 106, Miami Lakes, FL 33016
Tel.: (305) 821-5553
Health Care Srvices
N.A.I.C.S.: 621610

Mills Medical Practices, LLC (5)
9293 State Route 43 Ste B, Streetsboro, OH 44241
Tel.: (330) 626-1113
Health Care Srvices
N.A.I.C.S.: 621610

Nutmeg Pavilion Healthcare (5)
78 Viets St, New London, CT 06320-3354
Tel.: (860) 447-1416
Web Site: http://www.nutmegpavilion.com
Nursing Care Facility
N.A.I.C.S.: 623110

Orange Health Care Center (5)
920 W La Veta Ave, Orange, CA 92868-4302
Tel.: (714) 633-3568
Sales Range: $25-49.9 Million
Emp.: 100
Healthcare Facility
N.A.I.C.S.: 621498

Outreach Health Services of North Texas, LLC (5)
251 Renner Pkwy, Richardson, TX 75080
Tel.: (972) 840-7360
Web Site: https://www.outreachhealth.com
Health Care Srvices
N.A.I.C.S.: 621610

Pacific Coast Care Center, L.L.C. (5)
720 E Romie Ln, Salinas, CA 93901-4208
Tel.: (831) 424-8072
Nursing Care Facility Services
N.A.I.C.S.: 623110

Parkview Acres Cure & Rehabilitation Center (5)
200 N Oregon St, Dillon, MT 59725-3624
Tel.: (406) 683-5105
Web Site: http://www.parkviewacres.com
Sales Range: $25-49.9 Million
Emp.: 93
Rehabilitation & Specialty Hosptial Facility
N.A.I.C.S.: 623311
Claire Miller *(Exec Dir)*

Parkway Pavilion Healthcare (5)
1157 Enfield St, Enfield, CT 06082-4329
Tel.: (860) 745-1641
Web Site: https://www.parkwaypavilion-health.com
Sales Range: $25-49.9 Million
Emp.: 180
Nursing Care Facility Operator
N.A.I.C.S.: 623110

PeopleFirst HomeCare & Hospice of Indiana, LLC (5)
5250 E US Hwy 36 Ste 850, Avon, IN 46123
Tel.: (317) 481-2281
Health Care Srvices
N.A.I.C.S.: 621610
Donald Gaddy *(Sr VP-Sls)*
Selece Beasley *(Officer-Clinical & Sr VP)*
David Gieringer *(Mgr)*
Todd Sexe *(Pres-North Central Reg)*
Paul VerHoeve *(Pres-West Reg)*
Susan Benoit *(Pres-Mid-Atlantic Reg)*
John Aurelio *(Pres-South Central Reg & Community Care)*

PeopleFirst HomeCare & Hospice of Ohio, LLC (5)
112 Harcourt Rd Ste 3, Mount Vernon, OH 43050
Tel.: (740) 263-2248
Web Site: http://www.kindredhospice.com
Health Care Srvices
N.A.I.C.S.: 621610

PeopleFirst Virginia, LLC (5)
110 Lauck Dr, Winchester, VA 22603
Tel.: (540) 667-7830
Health Care Srvices
N.A.I.C.S.: 621610

PersonaCare of Ohio, LLC (5)
70 Normandy Dr, Painesville, OH 44077
Tel.: (440) 357-1311
Nursing Care Facility Services
N.A.I.C.S.: 623110

Pettigrew Rehabilitation & Healthcare Center (5)
1515 W Pettigrew St, Durham, NC 27705
Tel.: (919) 286-0751
Web Site: http://www.pettigrewhc.com
Sales Range: $25-49.9 Million
Emp.: 100
Rehabilitation & Healthcare Facility
N.A.I.C.S.: 623110
Michael McOrris Jr. *(VP)*

Promise Hospital of East Los Angeles, L.P. (5)
16453 S Colorado Ave, Paramount, CA 90723
Tel.: (562) 531-3110
Hospital Operator
N.A.I.C.S.: 622110
Mark Apodaca *(CEO)*
Nikki Cunningham *(Chief Clinical Officer)*

Quince Holdings, LLC (5)
5545 E Lee St, Tucson, AZ 85712
Tel.: (520) 296-2306
Web Site: https://pueblosprings.com
Nursing Care & Rehabilitation Services
N.A.I.C.S.: 623110

Santa Cruz Healthcare Center (5)
1115 Capitola Rd, Santa Cruz, CA 95062-2844
Tel.: (831) 475-4055
Web Site: http://www.kindred.com
Sales Range: $25-49.9 Million
Emp.: 150
Nursing Care Facility
N.A.I.C.S.: 623110
Raeann Radford *(Gen Mgr)*

Senior Home Care, Inc. (5)
380 Park Pl Blvd Ste 100, Clearwater, FL 33759
Tel.: (727) 531-0300
Web Site: http://www.kindredhealthcare.com
Women Healthcare Services
N.A.I.C.S.: 621610

Silas Creek Manor (5)
3350 Silas Creek Pkwy, Winston Salem, NC 27103-3014
Tel.: (336) 765-0550
Web Site: http://www.kindredhealthcare.com
Sales Range: $25-49.9 Million
Emp.: 80
Nursing Care Facility
N.A.I.C.S.: 621610

Silver State ACO, LLC (5)
801 S Rancho Ste C1, Las Vegas, NV 89106
Tel.: (702) 800-7084
Web Site: http://www.silverstateaco.com
Health Care Srvices

N.A.I.C.S.: 621610
Linn Billingsley *(Vice Chm)*
Wayne P. Salem *(CFO)*
Lawrence M. Preston *(CEO)*
Leslie C. Jacobs *(Chief Medical Officer)*
Karla Perez *(VP)*
Rhonda Hamilton *(COO)*

Smith Ranch Care Center, L.L.C. (5)
1550 Silveira Pkwy, San Rafael, CA 94903
Tel.: (415) 499-1000
Nursing Care Facility Services
N.A.I.C.S.: 623110

South Central Wyoming Healthcare & Rehabilitation (5)
542 16th St, Rawlins, WY 82301
Tel.: (307) 324-2759
Web Site: http://www.KindredHealthcare.com
Sales Range: $10-24.9 Million
Emp.: 70
Nursing Care Facility
N.A.I.C.S.: 623110

Southern Utah Home Oxygen (5)
640 E 700 S Ste 102, Saint George, UT 84770
Tel.: (435) 674-5488
Health Care Srvices
N.A.I.C.S.: 621610

Specialty Healthcare Services, Inc. (5)
305 W Harriet St, Leesville, LA 71446
Tel.: (337) 238-4449
Hospital Management Services
N.A.I.C.S.: 622110

Subsidiary (Domestic):

Southern California Specialty Care, LLC (6)
1901 N College Ave, Santa Ana, CA 92706
Tel.: (714) 564-7800
Web Site: https://www.kindredhospitals.com
Nursing Care Facility Services
N.A.I.C.S.: 623110

Subsidiary (Domestic):

Springfield Park View Hospital, L.L.C. (5)
1400 State St, Springfield, MA 01109
Tel.: (413) 787-6700
Sales Range: $10-24.9 Million
Emp.: 10
Hospital Management Services
N.A.I.C.S.: 622110

St. Luke's Rehabilitation Hospital, LLC (5)
14709 Olive Blvd, Chesterfield, MO 63017
Tel.: (314) 317-5700
Web Site: https://pamhealth.com
Health Care Srvices
N.A.I.C.S.: 621610

Subsidiary (Non-US):

Starr Farm Partnership (5)
Tel.: (802) 658-6717
Web Site: http://www.starrfarmnc.com
Health Care Srvices
N.A.I.C.S.: 621610

Subsidiary (Domestic):

Synergy Home Care Capitol Region, Inc. (5)
58725 Belleview Dr Ste A3, Plaquemine, LA 70764-3948
Tel.: (225) 687-8188
Health Care Srvices
N.A.I.C.S.: 621610

Synergy Home Care Central Region, Inc. (5)
137 Yorktown Dr, Alexandria, LA 71303
Tel.: (318) 487-6700
Health Care Srvices
N.A.I.C.S.: 621610

Synergy Home Care Northeastern Region, Inc. (5)
1605 Stubbs Ave, Monroe, LA 71201
Tel.: (318) 805-0106
Health Care Srvices
N.A.I.C.S.: 621610

Apollo Global Management, Inc.—(Continued)

Synergy Home Care Northshore Region, Inc. (5)
200 Derek Dr Ste 202, Hammond, LA 70403
Tel.: (985) 429-9040
Health Care Srvices
N.A.I.C.S.: 621610

Synergy Home Care Northwestern Region, Inc. (5)
622 Rush St, Coushatta, LA 71019
Tel.: (318) 932-4442
Health Care Srvices
N.A.I.C.S.: 621610

Synergy Home Care Southeastern Region, Inc. (5)
216 Mystic Blvd Ste H, Houma, LA 70360-2870
Tel.: (985) 223-4321
Health Care Srvices
N.A.I.C.S.: 621610

The Therapy Group, Inc. (5)
144 Valhi Lagoon Crossing, Houma, LA 70360
Tel.: (985) 876-5322
Health Care Srvices
N.A.I.C.S.: 621610

Torrey Pines Care Center (5)
1701 S Torrey Pines Dr, Las Vegas, NV 89146-2999
Tel.: (702) 871-0005
Web Site: https://www.torreypinescare.com
Sales Range: $25-49.9 Million
Emp.: 200
Nursing Care Facility
N.A.I.C.S.: 623110
Nancy Webster (Coord-Dev)

Trinity Hospice of Texas, LLC (5)
1101 W Henderson St, Cleburne, TX 76033
Tel.: (817) 354-7200
Health Care Srvices
N.A.I.C.S.: 621610

Tucker Nursing Center, LLC (5)
2165 Idlewood Rd, Tucker, GA 30084
Tel.: (770) 934-3172
Web Site: https://www.tuckerctr.com
Nursing Care Facility Services
N.A.I.C.S.: 623110

VTA Management Services, LLC (5)
2275 Coleman St Ste 4, Brooklyn, NY 11234
Tel.: (718) 615-0049
Nursing Care Facility Services
N.A.I.C.S.: 623110

Subsidiary (Non-US):

Wasatch Valley Rehabilitation (5)
Tel.: (801) 486-2096
Sales Range: $25-49.9 Million
Emp.: 110
Nursing Care & Rehabilitation Facility
N.A.I.C.S.: 623110

Subsidiary (Domestic):

Wind River Health Care & Rehabilitation Center (5)
1002 Forest Dr, Riverton, WY 82501
Tel.: (307) 856-9471
Web Site: http://www.windriverhealthcare.com
Sales Range: $25-49.9 Million
Emp.: 100
Rehabilitation & Nursing Facility
N.A.I.C.S.: 623110
Joanne Aldrich (Exec Dir)

Subsidiary (Domestic):

Lake Cumberland Cardiology Associates, LLC (4)
120 Tradepark Dr Ste B, Somerset, KY 42503-3454
Tel.: (606) 678-0599
Emp.: 7
General Medical Services
N.A.I.C.S.: 622110
Rick Wesley (Gen Mgr)

Lake Cumberland Regional Hospital, LLC (4)
305 Langdon St, Somerset, KY 42503

Tel.: (606) 679-7441
Web Site: https://www.lakecumberlandhospital.com
Sales Range: $200-249.9 Million
Emp.: 1,200
Women Healthcare Services
N.A.I.C.S.: 622110
Robert Parker (CEO)
Allen Crawford (Chm)
Dana Speck (Vice Chm)
Michael Citak (Chief Medical Officer)
Steve Sloan (CFO)
J. Barry Dixon (Pres-Physician Practices)
Brian Springate (COO)
Pam Booker (Chief Nursing Officer)

Lake Cumberland Surgery Center, LP (4)
301 Langdon St, Somerset, KY 42503
Tel.: (606) 678-9688
Web Site: http://www.lakecumberlandsurgerycenter.com
Sales Range: $10-24.9 Million
Emp.: 35
General Medical Services
N.A.I.C.S.: 622110

Lander Valley Physician Practices, LLC (4)
830 Lincoln St, Lander, WY 82520-3736
Tel.: (307) 332-9577
General Medical Services
N.A.I.C.S.: 622110

LifePoint Corporate Services, General Partnership (4)
330 Seven Springs Way, Brentwood, TN 37027
Tel.: (615) 920-7000
Web Site: http://www.lifepointhealth.net
Sales Range: $100-124.9 Million
Emp.: 484
Administrative Management & General Management Consulting Services
N.A.I.C.S.: 541611

LifePoint of Lake Cumberland, LLC (4)
305 Langdon St, Somerset, KY 42503
Tel.: (606) 679-7441
Web Site: http://www.lakecumberlandhospital.com
General Medical Services
N.A.I.C.S.: 622110

Livingston Regional Hospital, LLC (4)
315 Oak St, Livingston, TN 38570
Tel.: (931) 823-5611
Web Site: https://www.mylivingstonhospital.com
Sales Range: $50-74.9 Million
Emp.: 330
General Medical & Surgical Hospitals
N.A.I.C.S.: 622110

Logan General Hospital, LLC (4)
20 Hospital Dr, Logan, WV 25601
Tel.: (304) 831-1101
Web Site: http://www.loganregionalmedicalcenter.com
General Medical Services
N.A.I.C.S.: 622110
Simon Ratliff (CEO)

Memorial Hospital of Martinsville & Henry County Ambulatory Surgery Center, LLC (4)
320 Hospital Dr, Martinsville, VA 24112-0000
Tel.: (276) 666-7200
Web Site: http://www.martinsvillehospital.com
General Medical Services
N.A.I.C.S.: 622110

Mexia Principal Healthcare Limited Partnership (4)
600 S Bonham St, Mexia, TX 76667
Tel.: (254) 562-5332
Web Site: http://www.parkviewregional.com
Sales Range: $25-49.9 Million
Emp.: 193
General Medical Services
N.A.I.C.S.: 622110
Jack Wilcox (CFO)
John Stubbs (Chm)
Edwina Miner (Chief Nursing Officer)

Minden Physician Practices, LLC (4)
103 Powell Ct Ste 200, Brentwood, TN 37027-5079
Tel.: (615) 372-8500
Healtcare Services
N.A.I.C.S.: 621491

NWMC-Winfield Anesthesia Physicians, LLC (4)
1530 US Hwy 43, Winfield, AL 35594-5056
Tel.: (205) 487-7979
General Medical Services
N.A.I.C.S.: 622110

Nason Hospital (4)
105 Nason Dr, Roaring Spring, PA 16673
Tel.: (814) 224-2141
Web Site: http://www.nasonhospital.com
Hospital Operator
N.A.I.C.S.: 622110

Nason Physician Practices, LLC (4)
104 Hillcrest Dr, Roaring Spring, PA 16673-1210
Tel.: (814) 224-5455
General Medical & Surgical Services
N.A.I.C.S.: 622110

PH Copper Country Apothecaries, LLC (4)
500 Campus Dr, Hancock, MI 49930-1452
Tel.: (906) 483-1901
General Medical & Surgical Services
N.A.I.C.S.: 622110

PHC-Fort Mohave, Inc. (4)
5330 S Hwy 95, Fort Mohave, AZ 86426
Tel.: (928) 788-2273
Web Site: http://www.valleyviewmedicalcenter.net
General Medical Services
N.A.I.C.S.: 622110

PHC-Los Alamos, Inc. (4)
3917 W Rd, Los Alamos, NM 87544-2275
Tel.: (505) 662-3452
General Medical Services
N.A.I.C.S.: 622110

PHC-Minden, L.P. (4)
1 Medical Plz Pl, Minden, LA 71055-3330
Tel.: (318) 377-2321
Web Site: http://www.mindenmedicalcenter.com
Sales Range: $50-74.9 Million
Emp.: 550
General Medical Services
N.A.I.C.S.: 622110

PRHC-Alabama, LLC (4)
1015 Medical Ctr Pkwy, Selma, AL 36701-6748
Tel.: (334) 418-4100
General Medical Services
N.A.I.C.S.: 622110

Providence Hospital, LLC (4)
2435 Forest Dr, Columbia, SC 29204-2026
Tel.: (803) 256-5300
Healtcare Services
N.A.I.C.S.: 621491

Providence Imaging Center, LLC (4)
11011 Haskell Ave Wyandotte, Kansas City, KS 66109-8500
Tel.: (913) 667-5600
Healtcare Services
N.A.I.C.S.: 621491

Putnam Community Medical Center, LLC (4)
611 Zeagler Dr, Palatka, FL 32177
Tel.: (386) 328-5711
Web Site: http://www.pcmcfl.com
Sales Range: $25-49.9 Million
Emp.: 421
General Medical Services
N.A.I.C.S.: 622110

RHN Clark Memorial Hospital, LLC (4)
1220 Missouri Ave, Jeffersonville, IN 47130
Tel.: (812) 282-6631
Web Site: https://www.clarkmemorial.org
General Healthcare Services
N.A.I.C.S.: 622110
Klaus Boel (Chief Medical Officer)
Jason Schmiedt (CFO)
Michelle England (Chief Nursing Officer)
Joey Waddell (COO)
Tiffany Hannigan (Chief Medical Officer)

RHN Clark Memorial Physician Practices, LLC (4)
130 Hunter Station Way, Sellersburg, IN 47172-8930
Tel.: (812) 246-4808
Ambulatory Health Care Services
N.A.I.C.S.: 621493

RHN Scott Physician Practices, LLC (4)
1451 N Gardner St, Scottsburg, IN 47170-7751
Tel.: (502) 868-5618
General Medical & Surgical Services
N.A.I.C.S.: 622110

Raleigh General Hospital, LLC (4)
1710 Harper Rd, Beckley, WV 25801-3357
Tel.: (304) 256-4100
Web Site: https://www.raleighgeneral.com
Sales Range: $150-199.9 Million
Emp.: 1,000
General Medical Hospital
N.A.I.C.S.: 622110

River Parishes Hospital, LLC (4)
500 Rue De Sante, La Place, LA 70068
Tel.: (985) 652-7000
Web Site: http://www.riverparisheshospital.com
Sales Range: $50-74.9 Million
Emp.: 450
General Medical & Surgical Hospital
N.A.I.C.S.: 621111

River Parishes Physician Practices, LLC (4)
429 W Airline Hwy Ste B, La Place, LA 70068-3817
Tel.: (985) 652-5052
General Medical Services
N.A.I.C.S.: 622110

Riverton Memorial Hospital LLC (4)
2100 W Sunset Dr, Riverton, WY 82501
Tel.: (307) 856-4161
Web Site: https://www.sagewesthealthcare.com
Rev.: $10,000,000
Emp.: 225
General Medical & Surgical Hospitals
N.A.I.C.S.: 621111
Jennifer Hamilton (CFO)
Mel Meyer (Chm)
John Ferrelli (CEO)

Riverview Medical Center, LLC (4)
158 Hospital Dr, Carthage, TN 37030
Tel.: (615) 735-1560
Web Site: http://www.myriverviewmedical.com
General Medical Services
N.A.I.C.S.: 622110
Patricia Anderson (Chief Nursing Officer)
Mike Herman (CEO)

Southern Tennessee Regional Health System (4)
1265 E College St, Pulaski, TN 38478
Tel.: (931) 363-7531
Web Site: https://www.southerntennessee.com
Emp.: 200
General Medical Services
N.A.I.C.S.: 622110

Spring View Hospital, LLC (4)
320 Loretto Rd, Lebanon, KY 40033
Tel.: (270) 692-3161
Web Site: https://www.springviewhospital.com
Emp.: 270
General Medical Services
N.A.I.C.S.: 622110
Reba Celsor (CEO)
Denise Thomas (CFO)
Tonia McCarthy (Chief Nursing Officer)

Springstone, Inc. (4)
101 S 5th St Ste 3850, Louisville, KY 40202
Tel.: (502) 587-1007
Web Site: http://www.springstone.com
Behavioral Healthcare Services
N.A.I.C.S.: 623220

St. Francis Affiliated Services, LLC (4)
3465 Macon Rd Ste D, Columbus, GA 31907
Tel.: (706) 243-3051

Ambulatory Health Care Services
N.A.I.C.S.: 621493

St. Francis Health, LLC (4)
1700 SW 7th St, Topeka, KS 66606-1674
Tel.: (785) 295-8000
General Healthcare Services
N.A.I.C.S.: 622110

St. Francis Physician Practices, LLC (4)
2122 Manchester Expy, Columbus, GA 31904-6878
Tel.: (706) 354-5724
Emergency Health Care Services
N.A.I.C.S.: 621493

Sumner Regional Medical Center, LLC (4)
555 Hartsville Pike, Gallatin, TN 37066
Tel.: (615) 328-8888
Web Site:
http://www.mysumnermedical.com
General Medical Services
N.A.I.C.S.: 622110
Geoffrey Lifferth *(Chief Medical Officer)*
Evan Nushart *(CFO-Interim-Market)*

Teche Regional Physician Practices, LLC (4)
429 W Airline Hwy Ste N, La Place, LA 70068-3817
Tel.: (985) 652-5052
Health Care Srvices
N.A.I.C.S.: 621610

Trousdale Medical Center, LLC (4)
500 Church St, Hartsville, TN 37074
Tel.: (615) 374-2221
Web Site:
https://www.mytrousdalemedical.com
Emp.: 70
General Medical Services
N.A.I.C.S.: 622110
Carolyn Sparks *(CEO)*
Rod Harkleroad *(Pres)*
John Doyle *(CFO)*
Geoff Lifferth *(Chief Medical Officer)*

Two Rivers Physician Practices, LLC (4)
1499 Main St, Yanceyville, NC 27379-8793
Tel.: (336) 694-6969
Emp.: 4
General Medical & Surgical Services
N.A.I.C.S.: 622110
Vicki Henderson *(Coord-Office)*

UP Imaging Management Services, LLC (4)
420 W Magnetic St, Marquette, MI 49855
Tel.: (906) 225-4854
Hotel & Club Management Services
N.A.I.C.S.: 561110

Vaughan Regional Medical Center, LLC (4)
1015 Medical Ctr Pkwy, Selma, AL 36701
Tel.: (334) 418-4100
Web Site: http://www.vaughanregional.com
Emp.: 600
General Medical Services
N.A.I.C.S.: 622110

Watertown Medical Center, LLC (4)
125 Hospital Dr, Watertown, WI 53098-3303
Tel.: (920) 261-4210
Health Care Srvices
N.A.I.C.S.: 621610

Watertown Physician Practices, LLC (4)
125 Hospital Dr, Watertown, WI 53098-3303
Tel.: (920) 252-4800
Health Care Srvices
N.A.I.C.S.: 621610

Western Plains Medical Complex (4)
3001 Ave A, Dodge City, KS 67801
Tel.: (620) 225-8400
Web Site: http://www.westernplainsmc.com
Emp.: 293
General Medical Services
N.A.I.C.S.: 622110

Wythe County Community Hospital, LLC (4)
600 W Ridge Rd, Wytheville, VA 24382

Tel.: (276) 228-0200
Web Site: https://www.wcch.org
Sales Range: $25-49.9 Million
Emp.: 350
General Medical Services
N.A.I.C.S.: 622110
Vicki Parks *(CEO)*
Donad Hayes *(CFO)*

Subsidiary (Domestic):

Ottumwa Regional Health Center, Inc. (3)
1001 Pennstivania Ave, Ottumwa, IA 52501
Tel.: (641) 684-2300
Web Site:
https://www.ottumwaregionalhealth.com
Emp.: 689
Hospital Operator
N.A.I.C.S.: 622110

Unit (Domestic):

Southwestern Medical Center (3)
5602 SW Lee Blvd, Lawton, OK 73505
Tel.: (580) 531-4700
Web Site: https://www.swmconline.com
Sales Range: $25-49.9 Million
Hospital Operator
N.A.I.C.S.: 622110
Jayne Thomas *(Chief Nursing Officer)*
Elizabeth Jones *(CEO)*
Dinah Lazarte *(Chief Quality Officer)*
James R. Huffines *(Chm)*

Holding (Non-US):

Reno de Medici S.p.A. (2)
Viale Isonzo 25, 20135, Milan, Italy (67%)
Tel.: (39) 0289966111
Web Site: http://www.renodemedici.it
Rev.: $785,683,697
Assets: $577,222,878
Liabilities: $347,116,285
Net Worth: $230,106,593
Earnings: $17,466,456
Emp.: 1,766
Fiscal Year-end: 12/31/2019
Cardboard Mfr
N.A.I.C.S.: 322299
Michele Bianchi *(CEO)*
Eric Laflamme *(Chm)*

Subsidiary (Non-US):

Barcelona Cartonboard, S.A.U. (3)
Potassi 7, 08755, Castellbisbal, Spain
Tel.: (34) 936 311 000
Web Site: http://www.bcncarton.com
Recycled Paper Carton Board Mfr
N.A.I.C.S.: 322130
Juan Torras *(Sls Dir)*
Nuria Ayats *(Head-Sustainability)*
Miguel Sanchez *(CEO & Mng Dir)*
Jose Antonio Campo *(Dir-Technical)*
Julio Lopez *(Dir-Pur & Logistics)*
Juan Navarrete *(Dir-HR)*
David Sanchez *(Dir-Fin & IT)*
Nuria Canals *(Head-Sls Export)*

Subsidiary (Domestic):

Careo S.r.l. (3)
Via Durini 18, IT-20122, Milan, Italy (70%)
Tel.: (39) 02 8996 6411
Web Site: http://www.careo.biz
Sales Range: $400-449.9 Million
Emp.: 2,400
Recycled Cartonboard & Folding Carton Mfr & Whslr
N.A.I.C.S.: 322212

Subsidiary (Non-US):

Careo Kft (4)
Otvos Janos u 3, 1119, Budapest, Hungary
Tel.: (36) 13927259
Web Site: http://www.careo.biz
Sales Range: $100-124.9 Million
Emp.: 3
Cartons & Packaging Materials Whslr
N.A.I.C.S.: 424130

Careo Limited (4)
Careo Unit 7 Hill Top Industrial Estate Shaw Street, West Bromwich, B70 0TX, W Midlands, United Kingdom
Tel.: (44) 121 505 9810
Web Site: http://www.careo.biz

Sales Range: $75-99.9 Million
Emp.: 7
Cartons & Packaging Materials Whslr
N.A.I.C.S.: 424130

Careo Sp. z o.o. (4)
Altowa 6, PL 02-386, Warsaw, Poland
Tel.: (48) 225898700
Web Site: http://www.careo.biz
Sales Range: $75-99.9 Million
Emp.: 4
Cartons & Packaging Materials Whslr
N.A.I.C.S.: 424130

Careo s.r.o. (4)
Jinonicka 80, Prague, 15800, Czech Republic
Tel.: (420) 257290298
Web Site: http://www.careo.biz
Sales Range: $100-124.9 Million
Emp.: 4
Cartons & Packaging Materials Whslr
N.A.I.C.S.: 424130

Subsidiary (Domestic):

Emmaus Pack S.r.L. (3)
via Rome 151, Marcallo Con Casone, 20010, Milan, Italy (51.39%)
Tel.: (39) 029760644
Cardboard Mfr & Distr
N.A.I.C.S.: 322299

R.D.M. Ovaro (3)
Via della Cartiera 27, 33025, Udine, Ovaro, Italy
Tel.: (39) 043367241
Web Site: http://borntobeconverted.com
Emp.: 150
Mfr & Distr of Ovaro Paper & Cardboard Products
N.A.I.C.S.: 322120

Subsidiary (Non-US):

Reno de Medici Almazan (3)
Carretera de Gomara km 14, 2200, Soria, Almazan, Spain (100%)
Tel.: (34) 975 310144
Web Site: http://borntobeconverted.com
Sales Range: $25-49.9 Million
Emp.: 93
Cardboard Distr
N.A.I.C.S.: 424130

Reno de Medici Arnsberg (3)
51 Hellefelder Strasse, 59821, Arnsberg, Germany
Tel.: (49) 29 31 851
Web Site: http://borntobeconverted.com
Emp.: 315
Mfr & Distr of Contiboard, Flexoliners, Serviboard, Servifreeze, Serviliners & Servisoaps
N.A.I.C.S.: 322219
Dirk Verschueren *(Co-Mng Dir)*
Thomas Bock *(Co-Mng Dir)*

Reno de Medici Blendecques (3)
BP 53006, Blendecques, 62501, Saint-Omer, Cedex, France
Tel.: (33) 3 21 38 80 20
Web Site: http://borntobeconverted.com
Emp.: 197
Mfr & Distr of Blanc II, Hermicoat, Hermifood & Hermiwhite Paper Products
N.A.I.C.S.: 322120

Subsidiary (Domestic):

Reno de Medici Santa Giustina (3)
Localita Campo, 32035, Belluno, Santa Giustina, Italy
Tel.: (39) 04378811
Web Site: http://borntobeconverted.com
Emp.: 288
Mfr & Distr of Vinci Avana, Vincicoat, Vincifood & Vincistar Paper Products
N.A.I.C.S.: 322120

Reno de Medici Villa Santa Lucia (3)
Via Casilina km 134 5, 03030, Frosinone, Villa Santa Lucia, Italy
Tel.: (39) 077637091
Web Site: http://borntobeconverted.com
Emp.: 214
Mfr & Distr of Vincicoat, Vinciflexo & Vinciliner Paper Products
N.A.I.C.S.: 322219

Holding (Domestic):

Shutterfly, Inc. (2)
2800 Bridge Pkwy, Redwood City, CA 94065
Tel.: (650) 610-5200
Web Site: http://www.shutterflyinc.com
Online Digital Photo Printing Services
N.A.I.C.S.: 812921
Maureen Mericle *(CMO)*
Hilary A. Schneider *(Chm & Pres)*
Eva Manolis *(Co-Founder)*
David B. Sambur *(Chm)*
Sally Pofcher *(CEO)*
Dwayne A. Black *(COO & Sr VP)*
Jason Sebring *(Gen Counsel & Sr VP)*
Moudy Elbayadi *(CTO & Sr VP)*
Jennifer George Caligiuri *(VP-Comm)*

Subsidiary (Domestic):

Lifetouch, Inc. (3)
11000 Viking Dr Ste 400 W, Eden Prairie, MN 55344-7294
Tel.: (952) 826-4000
Web Site: http://www.lifetouch.com
Photographic Studios
N.A.I.C.S.: 541921
Michael Meek *(CEO)*
Tom Booth *(VP-IT)*
Dave Potente *(COO & Exec VP)*
Stephanie Schmid *(VP-Enterprise Mktg & Bus Dev)*
Agnes Semington *(VP-HR)*
Tom Wargolet *(COO-Schools & Exec VP)*
Greg Hintz *(Pres)*

Subsidiary (Non-US):

Lifetouch Canada Inc. (4)
1410 Mountain Ave Ste 1, Winnipeg, R2X0A4, MB, Canada
Tel.: (204) 977-3475
Web Site: http://www.lifetouch.ca
Photography Developing Services
N.A.I.C.S.: 812921
Maureen Drummond *(Dir-HR)*

Subsidiary (Domestic):

Lifetouch Church Directories and Portraits Inc. (4)
11000 Viking Dr, Eden Prairie, MN 55344
Tel.: (800) 736-4753
Web Site:
http://churchdirectories.lifetouch.com
Photography Developing Services
N.A.I.C.S.: 541921

Shutterfly Lifetouch, LLC (4)
11000 Viking Dr, Eden Prairie, MN 55344
Tel.: (757) 420-7780
Web Site: http://www.lifetouch.com
Individual Portrait & Yearbook Requirements For Public & Private Schools
N.A.I.C.S.: 541921

Subsidiary (Domestic):

R & R Images, Inc. (3)
3602 E La Salle St, Phoenix, AZ 85040
Tel.: (602) 437-4545
Web Site: http://www.randrimages.com
Sales Range: $1-9.9 Million
Emp.: 48
Cross-Media Marketing, Photography & Printing Services
N.A.I.C.S.: 541922

Spoonflower, Inc. (3)
2810 Meridian Pkwy Ste 176, Durham, NC 27713
Tel.: (919) 886-7885
Web Site: http://www.spoonflower.com
Sales Range: $10-24.9 Million
Emp.: 110
Digital Marketing; Custom Fabric, Wallpaper & Home Decor
N.A.I.C.S.: 444180
Marlo Wilcox *(Dir-HR)*
Gart Davis *(Co-Founder & COO)*
Michael Jones *(CEO)*
Stephen Fraser *(Co-Founder)*
Allison Polish *(Pres)*
Sarah Ward *(Sr VP-Mktg)*
Brad Schomber *(CFO)*
Jessica Lesesky *(Chief Revenue Officer)*
David Laboy *(Head-Diversity, Equity, Inclusion & Sustainability)*
Dee Worley *(Dir-PR)*

Apollo Global Management, Inc.—(Continued)

Holding (Domestic):

Smart & Final Stores, LLC **(2)**
600 Citadel Dr, Commerce, CA 90040
Tel.: (323) 869-7500
Web Site: http://www.smartandfinal.com
Rev.: $4,741,772,000
Assets: $1,711,918,000
Liabilities: $1,403,763,000
Net Worth: $308,155,000
Earnings: ($112,155,000)
Emp.: 3,610
Fiscal Year-end: 12/31/2018
Grocery Stores
N.A.I.C.S.: 445110
Scott R. Drew (COO)
David G. Hirz (CEO)

Subsidiary (Domestic):

Smart & Final, Inc. **(3)**
600 Citadel Dr, City of Commerce, CA 90040
Tel.: (323) 869-7500
Web Site: http://www.smartandfinal.com
Sales Range: $1-4.9 Billion
Emp.: 6,000
Wholesale Grocers & Restaurant & Grocery Items Supplier
N.A.I.C.S.: 445110
David B. Kaplan (Chm)
David B. Kaplan (Chm)

Holding (Domestic):

Snapfish LLC **(2)**
100 Montgomery St Ste 1000, San Francisco, CA 94107
Tel.: (800) 558-8224
Web Site: http://www.snapfish.com
Online Film & Digital Photography Services
N.A.I.C.S.: 812921
Jasbir Patel (Pres & CEO)

Tenneco, Inc. **(2)**
500 N Field Dr, Lake Forest, IL 60045
Tel.: (847) 482-5000
Web Site: https://www.tenneco.com
Rev.: $18,035,000,000
Assets: $11,622,000,000
Liabilities: $11,226,000,000
Net Worth: $396,000,000
Earnings: $100,000,000
Emp.: 71,000
Fiscal Year-end: 12/31/2021
Motor Vehicle Electrical & Electronic Equipment Manufacturing
N.A.I.C.S.: 336320
Jeffrey M. Stafeil (CFO & Exec VP)
Patrick Guo (Pres-Clean Air & Exec VP)
Rusty Patel (CIO & Sr VP)
Linae Golla (VP-IR)
Kaled Awada (Chief HR Officer & Sr VP)
Scott Usitalo (Pres-Motorparts & Exec VP)
Brad Norton (Pres-OE Ride Performance & Exec VP)
Chris Brathwaite (Chief Comm Officer & Sr VP)
Rich Kwas (VP-IR)
Ernie Keith (Chief Supply Chain Officer & Sr VP)
Kevin W. Baird (COO & Exec VP)
Jim Voss (CEO)

Subsidiary (Non-US):

Anand I-Power Limited **(3)**
20 MIDC Estate Satpur, Nashik, 422007, Maharashtra, India
Tel.: (91) 142092300
Web Site: http://www.anandgroupindia.com
Piston Ring & Clutch Plate Mfr
N.A.I.C.S.: 336310

Armstrong Hydraulics South Africa (Pty.) Ltd. **(3)**
267 Grahamstown Rd, Deal Party, 6012, Port Elizabeth, South Africa
Tel.: (27) 414017200
Web Site: http://www.tenneco.com
Motor Vehicle Parts & Accessories Mfr
N.A.I.C.S.: 336390
Justin Toth (Gen Mgr)

CATAI s.r.l.
Via Giovanni Prati 47, 20092, Cinisello Balsamo, MI, Italy
Tel.: (39) 026128831

Web Site: https://www.cataisrl.com
Friction Material & Braking System Mfr
N.A.I.C.S.: 327999

Subsidiary (Domestic):

CEDS Inc. **(3)**
21520 84th Pl S, Kent, WA 98031
Tel.: (215) 843-2825
Web Site: https://www.cednw.com
Streetlight Mfr
N.A.I.C.S.: 336320

Subsidiary (Non-US):

Componentes Venezolanos de Direccion, S.A. **(3)**
Carretera Nacional Los Guayos entre Av 67 y 73 Urbanizacion, Industrial Carabobo, Valencia, Estado Carabobo, Venezuela
Tel.: (58) 2418386093
Web Site: http://www.covendisa.com
Steering & Suspension Component Mfr
N.A.I.C.S.: 336330

FM PBW Bearings Private Limited **(3)**
Plot No G-515 G-516 G-517 Gate No 3 Kishan Gate Road Lodhika Gidc, Metoda, Rajkot, 360021, Gujarat, India
Tel.: (91) 2827286271
Web Site: https://www.fmpbw-india.com
Casting & Brass Component Mfr
N.A.I.C.S.: 331523
Ramesh Patel (Chm)
Mahesh Patel (Vice Chm)
Naresh Patel (Mng Dir)
Kiran Patel (Dir-EDP)
Anand Patel (Dir-Technical & Sys)
Shivraj Patel (Dir-Mktg & Fin)

Federal Mogul Powertrain Otomotiv Anonim Sirketi **(3)**
Cumhuriyet Mahallesi Muammer Dereli Sok No 2-A, 41100, Izmit, Turkiye
Tel.: (90) 2622260820
Web Site: https://www.federalmogulpowertrain.com.tr
Piston & Pin Mfr
N.A.I.C.S.: 336310

Subsidiary (Domestic):

Federal-Mogul Holdings LLC **(3)**
26555 Northwestern Hwy, Southfield, MI 48033
Tel.: (248) 354-7700
Web Site: http://www.federalmogul.com
Holding Company; Motor Vehicle Parts Mfr & Whslr
N.A.I.C.S.: 551112

Subsidiary (Domestic):

Beck Arnley Holdings LLC **(4)**
27300 West 11 Mile Rd Tower 300, Southfield, MI 48034
Tel.: (833) 897-0456
Web Site: http://www.beckarnley.com
Metal Coating, Engraving & Allied Services Mfr
N.A.I.C.S.: 332812

Subsidiary (Non-US):

Daros Piston Rings AB **(4)**
Teknologivagen 5, PO Box 138, 435 23, Molnlycke, Sweden
Tel.: (46) 313384000
Web Site: http://www.daros.se
Sales Range: $50-74.9 Million
Emp.: 220
Piston Rings Mfr
N.A.I.C.S.: 336310

Subsidiary (Domestic):

FM International, LLC **(4)**
26555 Northwestern Hwy, Southfield, MI 48033
Tel.: (248) 354-7700
Web Site: http://www.federalmogul.com
Sales Range: $125-149.9 Million
Emp.: 700
Holding Company
N.A.I.C.S.: 339991

Subsidiary (Non-US):

Federal Mogul Argentina SA. **(4)**
Cno Gral Belgrano Km 6 5, 1897, La Plata,

Buenos Aires, Argentina
Tel.: (54) 2320490000
Web Site: http://www.federalmogul.com.ar
Sales Range: $50-74.9 Million
Emp.: 180
Financial Investment Services
N.A.I.C.S.: 523999

Federal Mogul Japan K.K. **(4)**
3-9-13 Moriyacho, Kanagawa-Ku, Yokohama, 221-0022, Japan
Tel.: (81) 454790220
Financial Investment Services
N.A.I.C.S.: 523999

Federal-Mogul (China) Co., Ltd. **(4)**
118 Jiqiao Road, Pudong District, Shanghai, 201206, China
Tel.: (86) 2161827688
Motor Vehicle Part Research & Development Services
N.A.I.C.S.: 541330

Federal-Mogul Aftermarket Espana, SA **(4)**
Calle Mario Roso De Luna 41, Madrid, 28022, Spain
Tel.: (34) 917475597
Sales Range: $25-49.9 Million
Emp.: 45
Financial Investment Services
N.A.I.C.S.: 523999
David Zapata (Gen Mgr)

Federal-Mogul Aftermarket GmbH **(4)**
Albert-Ruprecht-Strasse 2, 71636, Ludwigsburg, Germany
Tel.: (49) 7141648650
Automotive Part Whslr
N.A.I.C.S.: 423120

Federal-Mogul Anand Sealings India Limited **(4)**
152/223 Mahalunge Chakan Talegaon Road Tal Khed, Pune, 410501, Maharashtra, India
Tel.: (91) 2135677300
Automotive Part Whslr
N.A.I.C.S.: 423120

Federal-Mogul Asia Investments Limited **(4)**
Suite 11A Manchester International Office Center Styal Road, Lancashire, Manchester, M22 5TN, United Kingdom
Tel.: (44) 1614904000
Holding Company; Financial Investment Services
N.A.I.C.S.: 551112

Unit (Domestic):

Federal Mogul Automotive **(4)**
1072 Progress Way, Maysville, KY 41056-9685
Tel.: (606) 759-4220
Sales Range: $125-149.9 Million
Emp.: 300
Automotive Components
N.A.I.C.S.: 441330

Subsidiary (Non-US):

Federal-Mogul Automotive Pty Ltd. **(4)**
29 Anvil Rd, Seven Hills, 2147, NSW, Australia
Tel.: (61) 296749855
Sales Range: $10-24.9 Million
Emp.: 10
Financial Investment Services
N.A.I.C.S.: 523999

Federal-Mogul Bearings India Limited **(4)**
Plot no 5 sector - 2, Parwanoo, 173220, India
Tel.: (91) 1792281340
Automotive Part Whslr
N.A.I.C.S.: 423120

Federal-Mogul Burscheid GmbH **(4)**
Bugermeister Schmidt Strasse 17, Burscheid, 51399, Germany
Tel.: (49) 2174690
Sales Range: $450-499.9 Million
Emp.: 1,500
Mfr & Sales of Piston Rings
N.A.I.C.S.: 336310

Michael Hedderich (Mng Dir)

Subsidiary (Domestic):

Federal-Mogul Burscheid Beteiligungs GmbH **(5)**
Burgermeister Schmidt Strasse 17, 51399, Burscheid, Germany **(100%)**
Tel.: (49) 2174690
Web Site: http://www.federalmogul.com
Sales Range: $500-549.9 Million
Emp.: 1,800
Financial Investment Services
N.A.I.C.S.: 523999

Subsidiary (Non-US):

Federal-Mogul Canada Limited **(4)**
59 Administration Rd, Concord, L4K 2R8, ON, Canada
Tel.: (905) 761-5400
Web Site: http://www.federalmogul.com
Sales Range: $75-99.9 Million
Emp.: 200
Financial Investment Services
N.A.I.C.S.: 523999

Subsidiary (Domestic):

Federal-Mogul Chassis LLC **(4)**
27300 W 11 Mile Rd, Southfield, MI 48034
Tel.: (219) 243-7128
Emp.: 100
Automotive Parts Holding Company Services
N.A.I.C.S.: 551112

Subsidiary (Non-US):

Federal-Mogul Controlled Power Limited **(4)**
2-4 Westmayne Industrial Park, Bramston Way, Basildon, SS15 6TP, United Kingdom
Tel.: (44) 1268564800
Automotive Part Whslr
N.A.I.C.S.: 423120

Federal-Mogul Deva GmbH **(4)**
Schulstr 20, 35260, Stadtallendorf, Germany
Tel.: (49) 64287010
Web Site: http://www.deva.de
Bearing Products Mfr
N.A.I.C.S.: 332991
Olaf Weidlich (Co-Mng Dir)
Hendryk Pfeuffer (Co-Mng Dir)

Federal-Mogul Dongsuh (Qingdao) Pistons Co., Ltd. **(4)**
14 Jiangshan Middle Road Qingdao Econ Tech Dev Zone, Qingdao, 266510, Shandong, China
Tel.: (86) 53286763211
Financial Investment Services
N.A.I.C.S.: 523999

Subsidiary (Domestic):

Federal-Mogul Dutch Holdings Inc. **(4)**
26555 Northwestern Hwy, Southfield, MI 48034
Tel.: (248) 354-7700
Web Site: http://www.federalmogul.com
Sales Range: $250-299.9 Million
Emp.: 1,000
Holding Company
N.A.I.C.S.: 339991

Subsidiary (Non-US):

Federal Mogul EMEA Distribution Services, BVBA **(4)**
Schoondonkweg 17, 2830, Willebroek, Belgium
Tel.: (32) 34508310
Financial Investment Services
N.A.I.C.S.: 523999

Federal-Mogul Financial Services SAS **(4)**
205 Rue De lEurope, 60403, Noyon, Cedex, France
Tel.: (33) 344098500
Sales Range: $75-99.9 Million
Emp.: 220
Financial Investment Services
N.A.I.C.S.: 523999
Kamal Aqaidi (Mng Dir)

Unit (Domestic):

Federal-Mogul Friction Products **(4)**
300 Wagner Dr, Boaz, AL 35957
Tel.: (256) 505-6224
Sales Range: $50-74.9 Million
Emp.: 175
Automotive Components Mfr
N.A.I.C.S.: 339991
Rick Owens *(Dir-Quality)*

Federal-Mogul Friction Products **(4)**
2084 Rowesville Rd, Orangeburg, SC
29115
Tel.: (803) 535-3643
Web Site: http://www.federalmogul.com
Sales Range: $125-149.9 Million
Emp.: 350
Automotive Components
N.A.I.C.S.: 336390

Subsidiary (Non-US):

Federal-Mogul Friction Products
(Thailand) Ltd **(4)**
1/6 Moo 5 Rojana Industrial Park Rojana
Rd Tambon Khanham, 13210, Ayutthaya,
Uthai Thani, Thailand
Tel.: (66) 35226062
Web Site: http://www.federalmogul.com
Sales Range: $25-49.9 Million
Emp.: 130
Motor Vehicle Parts & Accessories
N.A.I.C.S.: 336390

Federal-Mogul Friction Products
A.S. **(4)**
Jircharska 233, Prague, 51741, Kostelec
nad Orlici, Czech Republic
Tel.: (420) 494333222
Automotive Aftermarket Products & Services
vices
N.A.I.C.S.: 336110

Federal-Mogul Friction Products Bar-
celona S.L. **(4)**
Pol Ind Zona Franca 14 B, 08040, Barce-
lona, Spain
Tel.: (34) 932642060
Automotive Parts & Accessories Store
N.A.I.C.S.: 441330

Federal-Mogul Friction Products Inter-
national GmbH **(4)**
Glinder Weg 1, 21509, Glinde, Germany
Tel.: (49) 4072710
Holding Company; Brake Pads & Braking
System Components Mfr & Distr
N.A.I.C.S.: 551112

Federal-Mogul Friction Products
SA **(4)**
Calle Progreso 394, Badalona, 08918, Bar-
celona, Spain
Tel.: (34) 934602470
Web Site: http://www.federalmogul.com
Sales Range: $25-49.9 Million
Emp.: 169
Financial Investment Services
N.A.I.C.S.: 523999

Federal-Mogul Global Aftermarket
EMEA, BVBA **(4)**
Prins Boudewijnlaan 5, 2550, Kontich, Bel-
gium
Tel.: (32) 34519711
Web Site: http://www.drivparts.com
Emp.: 300
Financial Investment Services
N.A.I.C.S.: 523999

Subsidiary (Domestic):

Federal-Mogul Global Inc. **(4)**
27300 W 11 Mile Rd, Southfield, MI 48034
Tel.: (248) 354-7700
Web Site: http://www.federalmogul.com
Sales Range: $25-49.9 Million
Emp.: 800
Holding Company
N.A.I.C.S.: 339991

Subsidiary (Non-US):

Federal-Mogul GmbH **(4)**
Steinackerstrasse 9, Kusnacht, 8700, Zu-
rich, Switzerland
Tel.: (41) 229497411
Financial Investment Services
N.A.I.C.S.: 523999

Federal-Mogul Goetze (India) Ltd **(4)**
DLF Prime Towers 10 Ground Floor F 79
and 80 Okhla Phase - I, Delhi, 110 020,
India
Tel.: (91) 1149057597
Web Site:
https://www.federalmogulgoetzeindia.net
Rev.: $152,640,879
Assets: $180,032,676
Liabilities: $58,968,505
Net Worth: $121,064,171
Earnings: $674,051
Emp.: 3,133
Fiscal Year-end: 03/31/2021
Piston Mfr
N.A.I.C.S.: 336310
Krishnamurthy Naga Subramaniam *(Chm)*
Khalid I. Khan *(Compliance Officer, Compli-*
ance Officer, Sec, Sec & Exec Dir/Exec Dir-
Legal)
Rajesh Sinha *(Exec Dir-Ops, Rings, and*
Liners)
Vinod Kumar Hans *(Mng Dir)*
Manish Chadha *(CFO & Dir-Fin)*

Federal-Mogul Gorzyce SA **(4)**
Odlewnikow 52, 39-0432, Gorzyce, Poland
Tel.: (48) 158360100
Web Site: https://www.fmgorzyce.pl
Sales Range: $200-249.9 Million
Emp.: 2,400
Motor Vehicle Parts & Accessories
N.A.I.C.S.: 336390

Federal-Mogul Holdings Deutschland
GmbH **(4)**
Stielstr 11, Wiesbaden, 65201, Germany
Tel.: (49) 6112010
Sales Range: $650-699.9 Million
Emp.: 1,500
Holding Company
N.A.I.C.S.: 551112

Subsidiary (Domestic):

Federal-Mogul Friedberg GmbH **(5)**
Engelschalkstr 1, PO Box 1261, Friedberg,
86316, Germany **(100%)**
Tel.: (49) 82160010
Web Site: http://www.federalmogul.com
Sales Range: $200-249.9 Million
Emp.: 1,200
Financial Investment Services
N.A.I.C.S.: 523999
Peter Kienast *(Mng Dir)*

Federal-Mogul Sealing Systems
GmbH **(5)**
Hermann-Goetze-Strasse 8, Herdorf,
57562, Altenkirchen, Germany
Tel.: (49) 2744501
Automobile Product Distr
N.A.I.C.S.: 423110

Federal-Mogul TP Piston Rings
GmbH **(5)**
Burgermeister-Schmidt Strasse 17, 51399,
Burscheid, Germany
Tel.: (49) 2174690
Piston Rings Mfr
N.A.I.C.S.: 336310

Subsidiary (Non-US):

Federal-Mogul Hungary Kft. **(4)**
Fo utca 51, 9184, Kunsziget, Hungary
Tel.: (36) 96552050
Automotive Components Mfr
N.A.I.C.S.: 336390

Federal-Mogul Industria de Autope-
cas Ltda. **(4)**
Av Of Oitis 235, Industrial District, Manaus,
69075-842, Brazil
Tel.: (55) 9238783713
Financial Investment Services
N.A.I.C.S.: 523999

Federal-Mogul Italy S.r.l. **(4)**
Corso Inghilterra 2, Mondovi, 12084, Cu-
neo, Italy
Tel.: (39) 059638411
Web Site: http://www.fmitaly.com
Financial Investment Services
N.A.I.C.S.: 523999

Subsidiary (Domestic):

Federal-Mogul LLC **(4)**
27300 W 11 Mile Rd, Southfield, MI 48034

Tel.: (248) 354-7700
Web Site: http://www.federalmogul.com
Motor Vehicle Parts Mfr & Whslr
N.A.I.C.S.: 336350
Rainer Jueckstock *(CEO-Powertrain)*

Plant (Domestic):

Federal-Mogul Corp. - Frankfort **(5)**
2845 W State Rd 28, Frankfort, IN 46041
Tel.: (765) 659-5550
Web Site: http://www.federal-mogul.com
Sales Range: $75-99.9 Million
Emp.: 450
Automotive Components Mfr
N.A.I.C.S.: 339991

Federal-Mogul Corp. - Skokie **(5)**
7450 McCormick Blvd, Skokie, IL 60076
Tel.: (847) 674-7700
Web Site: http://www.federal-mogul.com
Sales Range: $400-449.9 Million
Emp.: 1,600
Automotive Components Mfr
N.A.I.C.S.: 339991

Federal-Mogul Corp. -
Summerton **(5)**
9104 Alex Harvin Hwy, Summerton, SC
29148
Tel.: (803) 478-2382
Sales Range: $125-149.9 Million
Emp.: 600
Automotive Components Mfr
N.A.I.C.S.: 339991
Robbie Day *(Plant Mgr)*

Subsidiary (Non-US):

Federal-Mogul Motorparts (Singa-
pore) Pte. Ltd. **(4)**
3 Tampines Central 1 Suite 02-02 Abacus
Plaza, Singapore, 529540, Singapore
Tel.: (65) 68059432
Automotive Part Whslr
N.A.I.C.S.: 423120

Federal-Mogul Motorparts Minority
Holding B.V. **(4)**
Keplerstraat 34, 1171CD, Badhoevedorp,
Netherlands
Tel.: (31) 203055700
Emp.: 100
Automotive Parts Holding Company Ser-
vices
N.A.I.C.S.: 551112

Federal-Mogul Operations Italy
S.r.l. **(4)**
Corso Inghilterra 2, 12084, Mondovi, Italy
Tel.: (39) 0174562211
Sales Range: $125-149.9 Million
Emp.: 300
Automotive Products Mfr
N.A.I.C.S.: 336340
Dario Borghesa *(Mng Dir)*

Subsidiary (Domestic):

Federal-Mogul Piston Rings, Inc. **(4)**
26555 Northwestern Hwy, Southfield, MI
48034
Tel.: (248) 354-7700
Web Site: http://www.federalmogul.com
Sales Range: $300-349.9 Million
Emp.: 900
Mfr of Piston Rings
N.A.I.C.S.: 336310

Subsidiary (Non-US):

Federal-Mogul Powertrain Italy
S.r.l **(4)**
6 Via Scienza, 41012, Carpi, MO, Italy
Tel.: (39) 059638411
Emp.: 100
Automotive Parts Holding Company Ser-
vices
N.A.I.C.S.: 551112

Federal-Mogul Powertrain Solutions
India Private Limited **(4)**
Plot No A 118 & A-119 RIICO Industrial
Area, 301019, 301019, Rajasthan, India
Tel.: (91) 8440046052
Emp.: 100
Automotive Parts Holding Company Ser-
vices
N.A.I.C.S.: 441330

Federal-Mogul Powertrain Systems
SA (Pty) Ltd **(4)**
15 Alexander Rd, Westmead, Pinetown,
3610, South Africa
Tel.: (27) 317173300
Emp.: 100
Automotive Parts Holding Company Ser-
vices
N.A.I.C.S.: 441330

Subsidiary (Domestic):

Federal-Mogul Powertrain, LLC **(4)**
27300 W 11 Mile Rd, Southfield, MI 48034
Tel.: (248) 354-7700
Motor Vehicle Parts Mfr & Distr
N.A.I.C.S.: 336390
Rainer Jueckstock *(CEO & Pres-*
Powertrain)

Branch (Domestic):

Federal-Mogul Powertrain, LLC **(5)**
5200 Willson Road Ste 150, Edina, MN
55424 **(100%)**
Tel.: (651) 345-4541
Automotive Components Mfr
N.A.I.C.S.: 331511

Subsidiary (Non-US):

Federal-Mogul Valvetrain GmbH **(5)**
Hannoversche Strasse 72, 30890, Barsing-
hausen, Germany
Tel.: (49) 51055180
Financial Investment Services
N.A.I.C.S.: 523999

Subsidiary (Non-US):

Federal-Mogul Pty. Ltd. **(4)**
29 Anvil Rd, Seven Hills, 2147, NSW, Aus-
tralia
Tel.: (61) 296749855
Web Site: http://www.federalmogul.com
Sales Range: $10-24.9 Million
Automotive Aftermarket Sales & Distribution
Services
N.A.I.C.S.: 336110

Federal-Mogul S.A. **(4)**
Kontichsesteenweg 67/1, 2630, Aartselaar,
Belgium
Tel.: (32) 34519711
Web Site: http://www.federalmogul.com
Automotive Aftermarket Sales & Distribution
Services
N.A.I.C.S.: 336110

Federal-Mogul SA de CV **(4)**
Calzada Ignacio Zaragoza 420, 72210,
Puebla, Mexico
Tel.: (52) 2222221335
Web Site: http://www.federalmogul.com
Sales Range: $75-99.9 Million
Emp.: 410
Mfr of Ball & Roller Bearing
N.A.I.C.S.: 332991

Federal-Mogul SAS **(4)**
Pl Paul Bert, BP 39, Saint Jean-de-la-
Ruelle, 45141, France
Tel.: (33) 238229200
Web Site: http://www.federalmogul.com
Sales Range: $50-74.9 Million
Emp.: 243
Holding Company; Automotive Aftermarket
Parts Mfr
N.A.I.C.S.: 551112

Subsidiary (Domestic):

Federal-Mogul Friction Products **(5)**
Industrielle Zone 205 Rue de l'Europe,
Noyon, 60400, France **(100%)**
Tel.: (33) 344098500
Sales Range: $50-74.9 Million
Original & Aftermarket Automotive Parts Mfr
N.A.I.C.S.: 336110

Federal-Mogul Operations France
SAS **(5)**
Place Paul Bert, 45140, Saint-Jean-de-la-
Ruelle, France
Tel.: (33) 238229200
Fabricated Metal Products Mfr
N.A.I.C.S.: 332999

Unit (Non-US):

Federal-Mogul Sealing Systems **(4)**

Apollo Global Management, Inc.—(Continued)

25 Rue Aristide Briand, Saint Priest, 69800, France
Tel.: (419) 238-0030
Sales Range: $300-349.9 Million
Emp.: 700
Automotive Components
N.A.I.C.S.: 441330

Subsidiary (Non-US):

Federal-Mogul Shanghai Bearing Co., Ltd. (4)
301 Jianlin Road Zhoupu Industry Park, Pudong District, Shanghai, 201318, China
Tel.: (86) 2156650266
Automobile Parts Mfr
N.A.I.C.S.: 423110

Federal-Mogul Sintertech, SAS (4)
Place Paul Bert, 45140, Saint Jean-de-la-Ruelle, France
Tel.: (33) 238229200
Web Site: http://www.federalmogul.com
Emp.: 243
Automobile Component & Sub Systems Distr
N.A.I.C.S.: 336390

Federal-Mogul Sorocaba-Holding Ltda (4)
Av Jaragua 89 Aparecida Room, Sorocaba, 18087-380, SP, Brazil
Tel.: (55) 6112019190
Emp.: 100
Automotive Parts Holding Company Services
N.A.I.C.S.: 551112

Subsidiary (Domestic):

Federal-Mogul Technical Center, LLC (4)
47001 Port St, Plymouth, MI 48170
Tel.: (734) 254-0100
Technical Research & Development
N.A.I.C.S.: 541715

Subsidiary (Non-US):

Federal-Mogul Technology Limited (4)
Suite 14 Manchester International Office Centre Styal Rd, Manchester, M22 5TN, United Kingdom
Tel.: (44) 1614904000
Motor Vehicle Parts Mfr
N.A.I.C.S.: 336390

Federal-Mogul UK Holding Ltd. (4)
Styal Rd, Manchester, M22 5TN, United Kingdom
Tel.: (44) 1200011300
Web Site: http://www.federalmogul.com
Sales Range: $250-299.9 Million
Holding Company
N.A.I.C.S.: 551112

Subsidiary (Domestic):

F-M Trademarks Ltd. (5)
Manchester International Centre, Styal Road, Manchester, M22 5TN, United Kingdom **(100%)**
Tel.: (44) 1614904000
Web Site: http://www.federalmogul.com
Sales Range: $250-299.9 Million
Holding Company; Trademark Patent Owner
N.A.I.C.S.: 551112

Federal-Mogul Acquisition Company Limited (5)
Manchester International Office Ctr, Styal Rd, Manchester, M22 5TN, United Kingdom **(100%)**
Tel.: (44) 1619555200
Web Site: http://www.federalmogul.com
Sales Range: $50-74.9 Million
Emp.: 150
Holding Company
N.A.I.C.S.: 551112

Federal-Mogul Aftermarket UK Limited (5)
Greyhound Drive Legrams Lane, Bradford, BD7 1NQ, West Yorkshire, United Kingdom
Tel.: (44) 8009700203
Web Site: http://www.federal-mogul.com

Sales Range: $25-49.9 Million
Emp.: 100
Financial Investment Services
N.A.I.C.S.: 523999
Michael T. Broderick *(CEO)*

Federal-Mogul Bradford Limited (5)
Neville Rd, Bradford, BD4 8TU, West Yorkshire, United Kingdom
Tel.: (44) 8009700203
Web Site: http://www.federalmogul.com
Sales Range: $25-49.9 Million
Emp.: 150
Financial Investment Services
N.A.I.C.S.: 523999

Federal-Mogul Engineering Limited (5)
Manchester International Office Centre Styal Rd, Manchester, M22 5TN, United Kingdom
Tel.: (44) 1614904000
Engineeering Services
N.A.I.C.S.: 541330

Federal-Mogul Friction Products Limited (5)
Hayfield Road, High Peak, Chapel-en-le-Frith, SK23 0JP, Derbyshire, United Kingdom
Tel.: (44) 1298811200
Emp.: 400
Financial Investment Services
N.A.I.C.S.: 523999
Paul G. Underhill *(Product Mgr)*

Federal-Mogul Limited (5)
Suite 14 Manchester International Office Ctr, Styal Road, Manchester, M22 5TN, United Kingdom
Tel.: (44) 1619555200
Web Site: http://www.federalmogul.com
Financial Investment Services
N.A.I.C.S.: 523999

Subsidiary (Domestic):

Federal-Mogul UK Holdings Inc. (4)
26555 Nwestern Hwy, Southfield, MI 48034
Tel.: (248) 354-7700
Web Site: http://www.federalmogul.com
Sales Range: $150-199.9 Million
Emp.: 800
Holding Company
N.A.I.C.S.: 339991

Federal-Mogul Valve Train International LLC (4)
1035 Western Dr, Brunswick, OH 44212
Tel.: (216) 332-7100
Motor Vehicle Parts Mfr
N.A.I.C.S.: 336390

Subsidiary (Non-US):

Federal-Mogul Valvetrain La Source SAS (4)
15 Avenue Buffon, Orleans, 45100, France
Tel.: (33) 238495656
Automotive Parts Holding Company Services
N.A.I.C.S.: 551112

Federal-Mogul Valvetrain Schirmeck SAS (4)
31 Rue Des Forges, Schirmeck, Dijon, 67130, France
Tel.: (33) 388496060
Emp.: 100
Automotive Parts Holding Company Services
N.A.I.C.S.: 551112

Federal-Mogul Wiesbaden GmbH (4)
Stielstrasse 11, 65201, Wiesbaden, Germany
Tel.: (49) 6112011001
Sales Range: $350-399.9 Million
Emp.: 1,500
Bearings, Bushings, Washers, Sputter Bearings, Glycodur Bushings & Lead-Free Overlays
N.A.I.C.S.: 326199

Federal-Mogul World Trade (Asia) Limited (4)
625 Nathan Rd, Mong Kok, Kowloon, Mong Kok, China (Hong Kong)
Tel.: (852) 24276391

Web Site: http://www.federalmogul.com
Sales Range: $200-249.9 Million
Financial Investment Services
N.A.I.C.S.: 523999

Subsidiary (Domestic):

Federal-Mogul World Wide, Inc. (4)
26555 Northwestern Hwy, Southfield, MI 48033-2146
Tel.: (248) 354-7700
Web Site: http://www.federalmogul.com
Sales Range: $150-199.9 Million
Emp.: 700
Holding Company
N.A.I.C.S.: 551112

Subsidiary (Non-US):

Federal-Mogul de Mexico S.A. de C.V. (4)
Av Radial Toltecas No 2, Col Tequexquinahauc, 02300, Tlalnepantla, Mexico
Tel.: (52) 5553212800
Financial Investment Services
N.A.I.C.S.: 523999

Subsidiary (Domestic):

Felt Products Manufacturing Co. (4)
26555 Northwestern Hwy, Southfield, MI 48033
Tel.: (248) 354-7700
Web Site: http://www.federalmogul.com
Sales Range: $50-74.9 Million
Emp.: 150
Mfr of Gaskets & Sealing Devices
N.A.I.C.S.: 339991

Subsidiary (Non-US):

JFK Rings GmbH (4)
Leibnizstrasse 52, 07548, Gera, Germany
Tel.: (49) 36520190
Web Site: https://jfk-rings.com
Metal Piston Rings & Gaskets Supplier
N.A.I.C.S.: 336310

Servicios Administrativos Industriales SA de CV (4)
Radial Tolteca No 2, Tequesquinahuac, Tlalnepantla, 54020, Mexico
Tel.: (52) 5553212800
Web Site: http://www.federalmogul.com
Sales Range: $50-74.9 Million
Emp.: 180
Motor Vehicle Supplies & New Parts
N.A.I.C.S.: 423120

Subensambles Internacionales SA de CV (4)
Prolongacion Hermanos Escobar No 7151-C Parque Industrial Omega, Ciudad Juaroz, 32320, Chihuahua, Juaroz, Moxioo
Tel.: (52) 6566270754
Web Site: http://www.federalmogul.com
Sales Range: $10-24.9 Million
Emp.: 700
Financial Investment Services
N.A.I.C.S.: 523999

T&N De Mexico SA de CV (4)
Radial Toltecas Valle Dorado, 54020, Mexico, Mexico
Tel.: (52) 5553212800
Web Site: http://www.federalmogul.com
Gaskets, Packing & Sealing Devices
N.A.I.C.S.: 339991

Subsidiary (Non-US):

Federal-Mogul Izmit Piston ve Pim Uretim Tesisleri A.S. (0)
Cumhuriyet Mahallesi Muammer Dereli Sok No 2-A, 41100, Izmit, Turkiye
Tel.: (90) 2622260820
Web Site: https://www.fmizp.com
Piston & Pin Mfr
N.A.I.C.S.: 336310
Frederic Robert Colley *(Chm)*
Ergin Erkek *(Vice Chm)*

Frenos Hidraulicos Automotrices, S.A. de C.V. (3)
Av La Presa No 6 Colonia, San Juan Ixhuatepec, Tlalnepantla, Mexico
Tel.: (52) 5555862333
Web Site: http://www.fhasa-w.com
Brake Fluid & Ring Motor Mfr
N.A.I.C.S.: 336310

Fric-Rot S.A.I.C. (3)
Eastern Republic Of Uruguay 2627, Rosario, Argentina
Tel.: (54) 3415223200
Motor Vehicle Parts Mfr
N.A.I.C.S.: 336390

Joint Venture (Non-US):

Futaba Tenneco U.K. Limited (3)
Liverpool Road Rosegrove, Burnley, BB12 6HJ, Lancashire, United Kingdom
Tel.: (44) 1282433171
Web Site: https://www.fmuk.ltd
Sales Range: $125-149.9 Million
Emp.: 300
Automobile Parts Mfr
N.A.I.C.S.: 336390
Kevin Schofield *(Mng Dir)*

Subsidiary (Non-US):

Gillet Tubes Technologies S.A.S. (3)
6 Rue des Fontangues, 55400, Etain, France
Tel.: (33) 329832250
Emp.: 70
Exhaust Pipe Tube Mfr
N.A.I.C.S.: 334419
Christopher Buvejnear *(Gen Mgr)*

Monroe Australia Pty. Limited (3)
1326 - 1378 South Road, Clovelly Park, 5042, SA, Australia
Tel.: (61) 883745222
Web Site: http://www.monroe.com.au
Motor Vehicle Parts & Accessories Mfr
N.A.I.C.S.: 336390
Robert Backhouse *(Sec)*

Monroe Packaging BVBA (3)
Industriezone Schurhovenveld 1037IZ, Saint Truiden, 3800, Limburg, Belgium
Tel.: (32) 11703111
Web Site: http://www.tenneco.com
Emp.: 1,500
General Freight Trucking, Long-Distance, Truckload
N.A.I.C.S.: 484121

Subsidiary (Domestic):

Ohlins USA, Inc. (3)
703 S Grove St, Hendersonville, NC 28792-4370
Tel.: (828) 692-4525
Web Site: https://www.ohlinsusa.com
Motor Cycle Distr
N.A.I.C.S.: 441227

Subsidiary (Non-US):

TM S.r.l. (3)
Via Cicogna 12-14, Can Lazzaro di Cavena, 40068, Bologna, Italy
Tel.: (39) 0516511012
Web Site: https://www.tm-italia.it
Pharmaceuticals Merchant Whslr
N.A.I.C.S.: 424210

Tenneco Automotive Deutschland GmbH (3)
Luitpoldstrasse 83, Edenkoben, 67480, Ludwigshafen, Germany
Tel.: (49) 6323470
Motor Vehicle Parts Mfr
N.A.I.C.S.: 336390

Tenneco Automotive Eastern Europe Sp. zo.o. (3)
Bojkowska 59b, 44-100, Gliwice, Poland
Tel.: (48) 323385291
Web Site: http://www.tenneco.com
Emp.: 1,000
Motor Vehicle Parts Mfr
N.A.I.C.S.: 336390

Tenneco Automotive Europe Coordination Center BVBA (3)
Ave Du Bourget 50, Brussels, 1130, Belgium
Tel.: (32) 22081492
Automotive & Motor Vehicle Parts Mfr
N.A.I.C.S.: 336390

Tenneco Automotive Europe, Ltd. (3)
50 Avenue du Bourget, Brussels, 1130, Belgium **(100%)**
Mfr of Automotive Parts
N.A.I.C.S.: 336340

Subsidiary (Non-US):

Tenneco Automotive Italia S.r.l. (4)
Via Walter Tobagi 13, Milan, 20068, Italy
Web Site: http://www.tenneco.com
Sales Range: $75-99.9 Million
Emp.: 7
Automotive Emissions Control Mfr
N.A.I.C.S.: 811198

Subsidiary (Non-US):

Tenneco Automotive Holdings South Africa Pty. Ltd (3)
267-275 Grahamstown Rd Deal Party, Port Elizabeth, 6001, Eastern Cape, South Africa
Tel.: (27) 414017200
Web Site: http://www.tenneco.com
Emp.: 478
Motor Vehicle Parts Mfr
N.A.I.C.S.: 336390

Subsidiary (Domestic):

Tenneco Automotive Operating Company Inc (3)
500 N Field Dr, Lake Forest, IL 60045
Tel.: (847) 482-5000
Web Site: http://www.tenneco.com
Sales Range: $75-99.9 Million
Automotive Emissions Control Mfr
N.A.I.C.S.: 811198

Subsidiary (Non-US):

Tenneco Automotive Polska Sp. z.o.o. (3)
Ul Przemyslowa 2 C, 44-203, Rybnik, Poland
Tel.: (48) 324294100
Automobile Product & System Retailer
N.A.I.C.S.: 441330

Tenneco Automotive Port Elizabeth (Pty) Limited (3)
12 Libertas Rd, Port Elizabeth, 6001, Eastern Cape, South Africa
Tel.: (27) 414015000
Web Site: http://www.tenneco.com
Emp.: 200
Motor Vehicle Parts Mfr
N.A.I.C.S.: 336390

Tenneco Automotive Sverige A.B. (3)
Rosendalsvagen 5, Vittaryd, 340 15, Kronoberg, Sweden
Tel.: (46) 37270500
Web Site: http://www.tenneco.com
Sales Range: $25-49.9 Million
Emp.: 35
Motor Vehicle Parts Mfr
N.A.I.C.S.: 336390
Mats Wilhelmsson (CEO)

Subsidiary (Domestic):

Tenneco Automotive Walker (3)
590 Work St, Salinas, CA 93901
Tel.: (831) 422-7824
Rev.: $25,000,000
Emp.: 130
Machine Shop, Jobbing & Repair
N.A.I.C.S.: 332710

Subsidiary (Non-US):

Tenneco Canada Inc (3)
1800 17th St E, Owen Sound, N4K 5Z9, ON, Canada
Sales Range: $750-799.9 Million
Emp.: 600
Automotive Emissions Control Mfr
N.A.I.C.S.: 811198

Tenneco Marzocchi Asia Ltd. (3)
25F-A2 No 760 Chung Ming South Rd, Taichung, Taiwan
Tel.: (886) 422634382
Motor Vehicle Parts Mfr
N.A.I.C.S.: 336390

Tenneco Marzocchi S.r.l. (3)
2 Via Amleto Grazia, Zola Predosa, 40069, Italy
Tel.: (39) 0516168711
Motor Vehicle Parts Mfr
N.A.I.C.S.: 336390

Tenneco Zwickau GmbH (3)

Hilferdingstrasse 8, 08056, Zwickau, Germany
Tel.: (49) 3758250
Web Site: http://www.tenneco-cleanair.com
Motor Vehicle Parts Mfr
N.A.I.C.S.: 336390

Subsidiary (Domestic):

The Pullman Company (3)
500 N Field Dr, Lake Forest, IL 60045
Tel.: (847) 482-5000
Sales Range: $75-99.9 Million
Automotive Emission Control & Ride Control Products Mfr
N.A.I.C.S.: 811198
Kenneth R. Trammell (CFO & Exec VP)

Subsidiary (Non-US):

Autopartes Walker, S. de R.L. de C.V (4)
Carill Norte San Felipe, Puebla, 72900, Mexico
Tel.: (52) 2222298633
Automobile Repair Shops
N.A.I.C.S.: 811198

Subsidiary (Domestic):

Monroe Mexico S.A. DE C.V. (5)
Av Poniente 4 Ste 118 CD Industrial, 38010, Celaya, GTO, Mexico
Tel.: (52) 4616186500
Web Site: http://www.monroe.com
Sales Range: $50-74.9 Million
Emp.: 200
Automotive Emissions Control Mfr
N.A.I.C.S.: 811198

Subsidiary (Non-US):

Walker Australia Pty. Limited (3)
1326-1378 South Rd, Clovelly Park, 5042, SA, Australia
Tel.: (61) 883745222
Sales Range: $125-149.9 Million
Emp.: 736
Motor Vehicle Parts Mfr
N.A.I.C.S.: 336390
Trevor King (DIR)
Timothy Donovan (DIR)
Robert Backhouse (SEC)

Walker Danmark ApS. (3)
Sjallandsvej 2, 5500, Middelfart, Fyn, Denmark
Tel.: (45) 63413300
Web Site: https://www.walker.dk
Emp.: 14
Motor Vehicle Parts & Accessories Mfr
N.A.I.C.S.: 336390

Walker Exhaust (Thailand) Co. Ltd. (3)
700/701-702 700/757 Moo1, Panthong District, Chon Buri, 20160, Thailand
Tel.: (66) 384475009
Exhaust Systems Mfr
N.A.I.C.S.: 339999

Holding (Domestic):

Terrier Media Buyer, Inc. (2)
6205 Peachtree Dunwoody Rd, Atlanta, GA 30328
Tel.: (678) 645-0816
Web Site: https://www.cmg.com
Holding Company; Media Assets Operator
N.A.I.C.S.: 551112
Daniel York (Pres & CEO)
Joseph P. Hannan (CFO & Exec VP)

Subsidiary (Domestic):

Cox Media Group, LLC (3)
6205 Peachtree Dunwoody Rd, Atlanta, GA 30328
Tel.: (678) 645-0816
Web Site: http://www.coxmediagroup.com
Sales Range: $1-4.9 Billion
Emp.: 9,000
Broadcasting, Publishing, Direct Marketing & Digital Media Services
N.A.I.C.S.: 334220
Ben Reed (VP & Gen Mgr-San Antonio)
Jane Williams (Exec VP)
Marian Pittman (Exec VP-Content, Product & Innovation)
Moya Neville (VP-Sls)
Mike Dreaden (VP-News & Mktg-Television)

Jodi Rainey (Dir-Natl Sls-Radio)
Bill Hendrich (Exec VP-Radio)
Ashley Peterson (Sr Dir-HR)
Mary Ellen Marcilliat-Falkner (Chief People Officer & Exec VP)
Donna Hall (VP-Mktg)
Mark Medici (VP-Audience & Newspaper Ops)
Paul Briggs (VP-Content & Brdcst Ops)
Maryann Balbo (VP-Kansas & Arkansas)
David Abel (VP-Mkt Mgr Radio-San Antonio)
Heidi Eddy-Dorn (Chief Compliance Officer, Gen Counsel & Corp Sec)
Zac Morgan (Mgr-Digital Audience Dev)
Ken Newman (Dir-Sls-San Antonio)
Katie Reid (VP & Gen Mgr-Radio Stations-Jacksonville)
Paul Curran (VP-Jacksonville)
Steve Pruett (Chm)
Daniel York (Pres & CEO)
Cathy Gunther (VP)
Cody Welling (Dir-Sls)
Joseph P. Hannan (CFO & Exec VP)
Eric Dodson Greenberg (Gen Counsel, Sec & Exec VP)

Subsidiary (Domestic):

Cox Newspapers, Inc. (4)
6205 Peachtree Dunwoody Rd, Atlanta, GA 30328-1464 (100%)
Tel.: (678) 645-0000
Web Site: http://www.coxnewspapers.com
Sales Range: $400-449.9 Million
Emp.: 2,500
Newspaper Operations
N.A.I.C.S.: 513110
Sharon Hartnett (Sr Acct Exec)

Subsidiary (Domestic):

Cox Custom Media Inc. (5)
10983 Granada Ln Ste 300, Leawood, KS 66211-1441 (100%)
Tel.: (864) 297-7771
Web Site: http://www.coxcustommedia.com
Sales Range: $10-24.9 Million
Emp.: 100
Publisher of Newsletters
N.A.I.C.S.: 513199

Dayton Newspapers, Inc. (5)
1611 S Main St, Dayton, OH 45409-1810 (100%)
Tel.: (937) 225-2000
Web Site: http://www.daytondailynews.com
Sales Range: $100-124.9 Million
Emp.: 1,300
Newspaper Publishing
N.A.I.C.S.: 513110
John Boyle (VP-Circulation)

Grand Junction Newspapers, Inc. (5)
734 S 7th St, Grand Junction, CO 81501-7737
Tel.: (970) 242-5050
Web Site: http://www.gjsentinel.com
Sales Range: $25-49.9 Million
Emp.: 185
Newspaper Publishing
N.A.I.C.S.: 513110
Jay Seaton (Publr)
Bob Eicher (Mgr-IT)
Bud Winslow (Dir-Ops)
Cathy Harlan (Mgr-Credit)
Darrel Allen (Dir-Bus Dev)
Karan Brickey (Mgr-Circulation)
Lori Henricksen (Dir-Adv)
Sandra Rogers (Dir-HR)
Sheryl Huffaker (CFO & Controller)
Tim Jackson (Mgr-Single Copy)
Tracy Gettman (Dir-Circulation)

Springfield Newspapers, Inc. (5)
202 N Limestone St, Springfield, OH 45503-4202 (100%)
Tel.: (937) 328-0372
Web Site: http://www.springfieldnewssun.com
Sales Range: $10-24.9 Million
Emp.: 90
Publisher of Newspapers
N.A.I.C.S.: 513110

Unit (Domestic):

The Atlanta Journal-Constitution (5)

223 Perimeter Ctr Pkwy NE, Atlanta, GA 30346
Tel.: (404) 526-5151
Web Site: http://www.ajc.com
Newspapers
N.A.I.C.S.: 513110
Bert Roughton (Mng Editor)
Jim Kennedy (CEO)
Amy Chown (VP-Mktg)
Amy Glennon (Publr)
Andre Jackson (Editor-Editorial)
Kevin Riley (Editor-in-Chief-Dayton Daily News)
Jason Smith (Sr Dir-HR)
Brian Cooper (Sr VP-Fin & Bus Ops)
Joe McKinnon (VP-Fulfillment)

Subsidiary (Domestic):

Cox Radio, Inc. (4)
6205 Peachtree Dunwoody Rd, Atlanta, GA 30319-1464 (69%)
Tel.: (678) 645-0000
Web Site: http://www.coxradio.com
Sales Range: $400-449.9 Million
Emp.: 1,375
Radio Broadcasting Stations
N.A.I.C.S.: 516110
Kimberly Guthrie (Reg VP)
Robert B. Reed (Reg VP)

Unit (Domestic):

KKBQ-FM (5)
1990 Post Oak Blvd, Houston, TX 77056 (100%)
Tel.: (713) 963-1200
Web Site: http://www.thenew93q.com
Sales Range: $25-49.9 Million
Emp.: 200
Radio Broadcasting
N.A.I.C.S.: 516110
John Chiang (Dir-Programming)

Division (Domestic):

Cox Reps (4)
885 2nd Ave 24th Fl, New York, NY 10017
Tel.: (212) 759-8787
Web Site: https://www.coxreps.com
Emp.: 300
Media Advertising & Marketing Services
N.A.I.C.S.: 541840
Ann Pero Hailer (Pres)
John DeWan (Exec VP)
Ray Karczewski (Exec VP)
K. J. Anand (Sr VP)
Dean Halvatzis (Sr VP)
John McMorrow (Sr VP)
Peter Insley (Sr VP)
John Sommese (Sr VP)
Jennifer Shapiro (Sr VP)
Mica Hansen (Sr VP)
Joe Knauer (VP)

Subsidiary (Domestic):

Cox Digital Solutions, LLC (5)
1 Dag Hammarskjold Plz 885 2nd Ave 25th Fl, New York, NY 10017
Tel.: (212) 588-2800
Web Site: http://www.gamut.media
Sales Range: $25-49.9 Million
Emp.: 45
Online Advertising Services
N.A.I.C.S.: 541870
David Koch (VP-Media Ops)
Gene Pizzolato (Pres & Gen Mgr)

Unit (Domestic):

Cox Cross Media (6)
1 Dag Hammarskjold Plz, New York, NY 10017
Tel.: (212) 588-2680
Cross Platform Advertising Sales & Marketing Services
N.A.I.C.S.: 541840

Subsidiary (Domestic):

Harrington, Righter & Parsons, LLC (5)
1 Dag Hammarskjold Plz, New York, NY 10017
Tel.: (212) 756-3600
Web Site: http://www.hrprep.com
Sales Range: $50-74.9 Million
Media Advertising & Marketing Services
N.A.I.C.S.: 541840

Apollo Global Management, Inc.—(Continued)

David Palmer *(Pres & Gen Mgr)*
Ray Karczewski *(Sr VP & Dir-Sls)*
Mark Marino *(Sr VP & Dir-Sls)*
John McMorrow *(VP & Dir-Programming & Res)*
Ann Pero Hailer *(Sr VP & Gen Mgr-Sls)*

MMT Sales, LLC (5)
1 Dag Hammarskjold Plz Ste 30, New York, NY 10017
Tel.: (212) 319-8008
Web Site: http://www.mmtsales.com
Sales Range: $1-9.9 Million
Emp.: 80
Media Marketing & Advertising Services
N.A.I.C.S.: 541840
Jay Isabella *(Sr VP)*

Subsidiary (Domestic):

TeleRep, LLC (5)
1 Dag Hammarskjold Plz 885 2nd Ave, New York, NY 10017 (100%)
Tel.: (212) 759-8787
Web Site: http://www.telerepinc.com
Sales Range: $25-49.9 Million
Emp.: 204
Radio & Television Advertising Representative Services
N.A.I.C.S.: 541840
John Dewan *(Sr VP & Dir-Sls)*
Gib Gibson *(Sr VP & Dir-Sls)*
Jim Hughes *(Pres & Gen Mgr)*
Jason Morrow *(Sr VP & Dir-Sls)*
Joe Dudek *(VP & Dir-Sls)*

Subsidiary (Domestic):

Georgia Television Company (4)
1601 W Peachtree St NE, Atlanta, GA 30309-2641 (100%)
Tel.: (404) 897-7000
Web Site: https://www.wsbtv.com
Sales Range: $50-74.9 Million
Emp.: 500
Television Broadcasting
N.A.I.C.S.: 516120

KTVU, Inc. (4)
2 Jack London Sq, Oakland, CA 94607-3727 (100%)
Tel.: (510) 834-1212
Web Site: https://www.ktvu.com
Sales Range: $25-49.9 Million
Emp.: 200
Holding Company; Television Broadcasting Stations
N.A.I.C.S.: 551112

Subsidiary (Domestic):

KTVU, LLC (5)
2 Jack London Sq NW, Oakland, CA 94607
Tel.: (510) 834-1212
Web Site: http://www.ktvu.com
Television Broadcasting Services
N.A.I.C.S.: 516120

Unit (Domestic):

KICU-TV (6)
2 Jack London Sq, Oakland, CA 94607
Tel.: (510) 834-1212
Web Site: http://www.ktvu.com
Television Broadcasting Station
N.A.I.C.S.: 516120
Lisa Yokota *(Dir-Community & Pub Affairs)*

Subsidiary (Domestic):

Miami Valley Broadcasting Corporation (4)
1611 S Main St, Dayton, OH 45409-2547 (100%)
Tel.: (937) 259-2111
Web Site: http://www.whiotv.com
Sales Range: $25-49.9 Million
Emp.: 110
Television Broadcasting Station
N.A.I.C.S.: 516120
James Cosby *(VP-Brdcst Sls)*
Sean Dunster *(Dir-News)*
Brittany Otto *(Dir-News)*

WFTV, Inc. (4)
490 E S St, Orlando, FL 32801 (100%)
Tel.: (407) 841-9000
Web Site: http://www.wftv.com
Sales Range: $25-49.9 Million
Emp.: 50
Television Broadcasting

N.A.I.C.S.: 516120
Paul Curran *(VP & Gen Mgr)*

WFXT-TV FOX25 (4)
25 Fox Dr, Dedham, MA 02027-9125
Tel.: (781) 467-1020
Web Site: http://www.fox25boston.com
Television Broadcasting Station
N.A.I.C.S.: 516120

WGAU Radio (4)
1010 Tower Pl, Bogart, GA 30622
Tel.: (706) 549-6222
Web Site: https://www.wgauradio.com
Radio Stations
N.A.I.C.S.: 516110
Pete de Graaff *(Mgr-Ops)*

WPXI, Inc. (4)
4145 Evergreen Rd, Pittsburgh, PA 15214 (100%)
Tel.: (412) 237-1100
Web Site: https://www.wpxi.com
Sales Range: $25-49.9 Million
Emp.: 200
Television Broadcasting
N.A.I.C.S.: 516120
Rob Deli *(Controller)*

WSOC Television, Inc. (4)
235 W 23rd St, Charlotte, NC 28206-2733 (100%)
Tel.: (704) 335-4738
Web Site: https://www.wsoctv.com
Sales Range: $25-49.9 Million
Emp.: 200
Television Broadcasting Services
N.A.I.C.S.: 516120

Holding (Domestic):

The Fresh Market, Inc. (2)
300 N Greene St Ste 1100, Greensboro, NC 27401
Tel.: (336) 389-5795
Web Site: https://www.thefreshmarket.com
Sales Range: $1-4.9 Billion
Emp.: 300
Grocery Store Owner & Operator
N.A.I.C.S.: 445110
Dan Portnoy *(Chief Mdsg Officer)*
Jason Potter *(Pres & CEO)*
Kevin Miller *(CMO)*
Brian Johnson *(Sr VP-Store Ops)*
Carlos Clark *(Gen Counsel, Corp Sec & Sr VP)*
Jim Heaney *(CFO)*
Gerald Walden *(VP)*
Diane Cleven *(Dir-Deli, CMS & Bakery)*
David Cummings *(Dir-Bakery)*
Ted Frumkin *(Grp VP-Real Estate, Dev & Construction)*
Peter Mayes *(Grp VP-Mdsg)*
Wade Yenny *(VP-Center Store)*

The Michaels Companies, Inc. (2)
3939 W John Carpenter Fwy, Irving, TX 75063
Tel.: (972) 409-1300
Web Site: http://www.michaels.com
Rev.: $5,271,112,000
Assets: $4,528,405,000
Liabilities: $5,725,575,000
Net Worth: ($1,197,170,000)
Earnings: $294,935,000
Emp.: 11,000
Fiscal Year-end: 01/30/2021
Holding Company; Arts & Crafts Stores Operator
N.A.I.C.S.: 551112
James E. Sullivan *(Chief Acctg Officer, Sr VP & Controller)*
Ashley Buchanan *(CEO)*
Tim Cheatham *(Chief Compliance Officer, Gen Counsel, Sec & Exec VP)*
Heather Bennett *(Exec VP-Mktg & ECommerce)*
Brynn Evanson *(Chief HR Officer)*
Patrick Joe Venezia *(COO-Stores & Exec VP)*

Subsidiary (Domestic):

Michaels Stores, Inc. (3)
3939 W John Carpenter FWY, Irving, TX 75063 (100%)
Tel.: (972) 409-1300
Web Site: https://www.michaels.com
Arts & Crafts Retailer
N.A.I.C.S.: 459130

Michael J. Veitenheimer *(Gen Counsel, Sec & Sr VP)*
Carl S. Rubin *(Chm & CEO)*
Nicholas E. Crombie *(Exec VP-Store Ops)*

Subsidiary (Domestic):

Aaron Brothers, Inc. (4)
1221 S Beltline Rd Ste 500, Coppell, TX 75019
Tel.: (214) 492-6200
Web Site: http://www.aaronbrothers.com
Sales Range: $75-99.9 Million
Custom Framing, Oil Paintings, Art Supplies, Easels & Art Studio Furniture, Framed Mirrors & Decorator Items
N.A.I.C.S.: 459120
Shawn Hearn *(VP-HR)*

Holding (Domestic):

The New Home Company Inc. (2)
15231 Laguna Canyon Rd Ste 250, Irvine, CA 92618
Tel.: (949) 382-7800
Web Site: http://www.nwhm.com
Rev.: $507,411,000
Assets: $495,699,000
Liabilities: $298,257,000
Net Worth: $197,442,000
Earnings: ($32,819,000)
Emp.: 209
Fiscal Year-end: 12/31/2020
Residential Construction
N.A.I.C.S.: 236115
Matthew R. Zaist *(CEO)*
H. Lawrence Webb *(Chm)*
John M. Stephens *(CFO & Exec VP)*
Leonard S. Miller *(Pres)*
Miek Harbur *(Gen Counsel, Sec & Sr VP)*

Subsidiary (Domestic):

The New Home Company Northern California LLC (3)
1990 N California Blvd Ste 650, Walnut Creek, CA 94596
Tel.: (925) 244-0700
Web Site: http://www.nwhm.com
New Single Family Housing Construction Services
N.A.I.C.S.: 236115
Kevin Carson *(Pres)*

Holding (Non-US):

The Restaurant Group plc (2)
5 7 Marshalsea Road, London, SE1 1EP, United Kingdom
Tel.: (44) 2031175001
Web Site: http://www.trgplc.com
Rev.: $864,324,552
Assets: $1,837,945,564
Liabilities: $1,240,056,080
Net Worth: $596,989,484
Earnings: ($52,136,448)
Emp.: 14,771
Fiscal Year-end: 01/02/2022
Casual Dining Restaurant Operator
N.A.I.C.S.: 722511
Andy Hornby *(CEO)*
Jean-Paul Rabin *(Sec)*
Mark Chambers *(CFO)*

Subsidiary (Domestic):

Blubeckers Limited (3)
The Old Barn Hook Road, North Warnborough, Oldham, RG291ET, United Kingdom (100%)
Tel.: (44) 1256702935
Web Site: http://www.blubeckers.co.uk
Restaurant
N.A.I.C.S.: 722511

Brunning and Price Limited (3)
First Floor Rake Hall Rake Lane, Little Stanney, Chester, CH2 4HS, Cheshire, United Kingdom
Tel.: (44) 1244333100
Web Site:
　https://www.brunningandprice.co.uk
Sales Range: $10-24.9 Million
Pubs Management & Operation Services
N.A.I.C.S.: 722410
Mary Willcock *(Mng Dir)*
Tom Fletcher *(Dir-South)*
Stephen Butt *(Mgr-Ops)*
James Killick *(Mgr-Ops)*
Tamsyn Little *(Mgr-Ops)*

Paul Morris *(Mgr-Fin)*
Andrew Beighton-Butler *(Mgr-Payroll)*
Aimee Meredith-Jones *(Controller-Payroll)*
Suzy Turner *(Mgr-Trng)*
Beth Collins *(Mgr-HR)*
Irene Adam *(Mgr-HR)*
Jan Bullen *(Mgr-HR)*
Caroline Wiltshire *(Mgr-HR)*

Chiquito Limited (3)
20/21 Leicester Square, London, WC2H 7LE, United Kingdom
Tel.: (44) 2073216070
Web Site: http://www.chiquito.co.uk
Sales Range: $25-49.9 Million
Mexican Restaurant Operation Services
N.A.I.C.S.: 722511

City Centre Restaurants (UK) Limited (3)
Cuxton Road Medway Valley Leisure Park, Rochester, ME2 2FF, Kent, United Kingdom
Tel.: (44) 1634739670
Sales Range: $10-24.9 Million
Emp.: 20
Restaurant Operating Services
N.A.I.C.S.: 722511

DPP Restaurants Limited (3)
71-81 Church St, FY11HU, Blackpool, United Kingdom (100%)
Tel.: (44) 8456125001
Restaurant
N.A.I.C.S.: 722511

Subsidiary (Non-US):

Frankie & Bennys Limited (3)
Avenida Bruselas 21 local 16, Alcobendas, Madrid, Spain (100%)
Tel.: (34) 916623860
Web Site: http://www.frankieandbennys.com
Sales Range: $10-24.9 Million
Emp.: 100
Restaurant
N.A.I.C.S.: 722511

Subsidiary (Domestic):

U.S. Silica Holdings, Inc. (2)
24275 Katy Fwy Ste 600, Katy, TX 77494
Tel.: (281) 258-2170
Web Site: https://www.ussilica.com
Rev.: $1,525,147,000
Assets: $2,214,580,000
Liabilities: $1,509,886,000
Net Worth: $704,694,000
Earnings: $78,176,000
Emp.: 2,013
Fiscal Year-end: 12/31/2022
Commercial Silica Producer
N.A.I.C.S.: 325998
Bryan A. Shinn *(CEO)*
Eugene Padgett *(Chief Acctg Officer, VP & Controller)*
Jay Moreau *(COO & Exec VP)*
Stacy Russell *(Gen Counsel, Sec & Sr VP)*
Patricia Gil *(VP-IR & Sustainability)*
Ida Ashley *(VP)*
Alan Schultz *(CFO, Exec VP & Sr VP-Strategy)*

Subsidiary (Domestic):

Cadre Services Inc. (3)
11757 Katy Freeway Ste 1050, Houston, TX 77079
Tel.: (281) 531-2100
Oil & Gas Field Services
N.A.I.C.S.: 213112

Coated Sand Solutions, LLC (3)
8490 Progress Dr Ste 300, Frederick, MD 21701-4996
Tel.: (815) 997-7380
Silica Mining Services
N.A.I.C.S.: 212322

Plant (Domestic):

Cadre Proppants - Voca Plant (4)
153 County Rd 220, Voca, TX 76887
Tel.: (325) 400-2793
Sand Proppant Mfr
N.A.I.C.S.: 212322

Subsidiary (Domestic):

EP Engineered Clays Corporation (3)
600 E McDowell Rd, Jackson, MS 39204

Tel.: (601) 948-3966
Web Site:
    https://www.epengineeredclays.com
Bleaching Clay & Mineral Adsorbent Product Mfr
N.A.I.C.S.: 327999

EP Management Corporation (3)
7 Tozer Rd, Beverly, MA 01915-1091
Tel.: (978) 232-1126
Web Site: https://www.epmanagement.com
Property Management Services
N.A.I.C.S.: 531311

Subsidiary (Non-US):

EP Minerals Europe GmbH & Co. KG (3)
Rehrhofer Weg 115, 29633, Munster, Germany
Tel.: (49) 519298970
Paint Pigment Mfr
N.A.I.C.S.: 325510

Subsidiary (Domestic):

EP Minerals, LLC (3)
9785 Gateway Dr, Reno, NV 89521
Tel.: (775) 824-7600
Web Site: https://www.epminerals.com
Diatomaceous Earth Filter Aids, Aggregates, Absorbents, Catalyst Supports Mfr
N.A.I.C.S.: 212390
Al Kaczanowski (VP-Global Sls & Mktg)
J.P. Blanchard (Sr VP & Pres-Performance Materials)
Larry Clawson (CFO)
Drew Shaver (VP-Ops)

Hourglass Acquisition I, LLC (3)
1 Riverchase Pkwy S, Birmingham, AL 35244
Tel.: (205) 987-5500
Silica Mining Services
N.A.I.C.S.: 212322

Pennsylvania Glass Sand Corporation (3)
Route 522 N, Berkeley Springs, WV 25411
Tel.: (304) 258-2500
Web Site: https://www.ussilica.com
Sales Range: $50-74.9 Million
Emp.: 70
Silica Mining Services
N.A.I.C.S.: 212322

Sandbox Logistics, LLC (3)
1301 McKinney St Ste 2400, Houston, TX 77010
Tel.: (281) 949-8400
Logistics & Transportation Services
N.A.I.C.S.: 541614

U.S. Silica Company (3)
2496 Hancock Rd, Berkeley Springs, WV 25411
Tel.: (304) 258-2500
Web Site: https://www.ussilica.com
Sales Range: $100-124.9 Million
Emp.: 700
Industrial Minerals Supplier
N.A.I.C.S.: 212322

USS Holdings, Inc. (3)
8490 Progress Dr, Frederick, MD 21701
Tel.: (301) 682-0600
Investment Management Service
N.A.I.C.S.: 551112

Holding (Domestic):

Univar Solutions Inc. (2)
3075 Highland Pkwy Ste 200, Downers Grove, IL 60515
Tel.: (331) 777-6000
Web Site: https://www.univarsolutions.com
Rev.: $11,475,300,000
Assets: $7,145,700,000
Liabilities: $4,651,500,000
Net Worth: $2,494,200,000
Earnings: $545,300,000
Emp.: 9,746
Fiscal Year-end: 12/31/2022
Offices of Other Holding Companies
N.A.I.C.S.: 551112
David Jukes (CEO)

Subsidiary (Non-US):

BDI Distribution West Inc. (3)
555 Hervo Street Suite 240, Winnipeg, R3T

3L6, MB, Canada
Tel.: (204) 474-2546
Chemical Distr
N.A.I.C.S.: 424690

Bluestar Distribution Inc. (3)
55187 Talbot Line, Aylmer, N5H 2R3, ON, Canada
Tel.: (519) 866-3446
Logistic Services
N.A.I.C.S.: 541614

ChemPoint.com-EMEA B.V. (3)
Renier Nafzgerstraat 114, 6221 KL, Maastricht, Netherlands
Tel.: (31) 437110100
Web Site: https://www.chempoint.com
Chemical Product Whslr
N.A.I.C.S.: 424690
Frank Speetjens (Dir-Bus-EMEA)

Cravenhurst Properties Limited (3)
Aquarius House 6 Mid Point Buisness Park, Bradford, BD3 7AY, West Yorkshire, United Kingdom
Tel.: (44) 1274377001
Real Estate Services
N.A.I.C.S.: 531210

Future Transfer Co. Inc. (3)
281 Tillson Ave, Tillsonburg, N4G 5X2, ON, Canada
Tel.: (519) 842-7600
Web Site: http://www.univarsolutions.com
Logistic Services
N.A.I.C.S.: 541614
John Lansink (Pres)
Chan Perera (VP)

Subsidiary (Domestic):

Magnablend, Inc. (3)
326 N Grand Ave, Waxahachie, TX 75165
Tel.: (972) 938-2028
Chemical Product Whslr
N.A.I.C.S.: 424690

Nexeo Solutions, Inc. (3)
3 Waterway Sq Pl Ste 1000, The Woodlands, TX 77380
Tel.: (281) 297-0700
Web Site: http://www.nexeosolutions.com
Rev.: $4,034,200,000
Assets: $2,243,600,000
Liabilities: $1,429,100,000
Net Worth: $814,500,000
Earnings: $29,400,000
Fiscal Year-end: 09/30/2018
Holding Company; Chemicals, Plastics & Composites Distr; Environmental Services
N.A.I.C.S.: 551112

Subsidiary (Domestic):

Nexeo Solutions Holdings, LLC (4)
3 Waterway Sq Pl Ste 1000, The Woodlands, TX 77380 (100%)
Tel.: (281) 297-0700
Web Site: http://www.nexeosolutions.com
Emp.: 2,450
Fiscal Year-end: 09/30/2015
Holding Company
N.A.I.C.S.: 551112

Subsidiary (Non-US):

Accolade Finland Oy (5)
Fredrikinkatu 61, 00100, Helsinki, Finland
Tel.: (358) 942450272
Web Site: http://www.accolade.fi
Digital Commerce Design Services
N.A.I.C.S.: 541430
Kim Dannholm (Owner & CEO)

Accolade France SAS (5)
Immeuble Debussy 77/81 Boulevard de la Republique, 92250, La Garenne-Colombes, France
Tel.: (33) 141192939
Chemical Products Distr
N.A.I.C.S.: 424690

Nexeo Plaschem (Shanghai) Co., Ltd. (5)
Rm 2702 BM Inter Continental Business Center No 100 Yutong Rd, Shanghai, 200070, China
Tel.: (86) 2132528899
Chemical Products Distr
N.A.I.C.S.: 424690

Nexeo Solutions Germany GmbH (5)
Curiestr 2, 70563, Stuttgart, Germany
Tel.: (49) 71149096087
Chemical Products Distr
N.A.I.C.S.: 424690

Nexeo Solutions Italy SRL (5)
Strada 4-Palazzo A5 Milano Fiori, 20090, Assago, Italy
Tel.: (39) 0225547050
Chemical Products Distr
N.A.I.C.S.: 424690

Nexeo Solutions Mexico S. de R.L. de C.V. (5)
Av Santa Fe 170 Suite 3-4-14 Col Lomas de Santa FE Alvaro Obregon, Mexico, 01210, Mexico
Tel.: (52) 5547491710
Chemical Products Distr
N.A.I.C.S.: 424690

Nexeo Solutions Plastics UK Limited (5)
Unit 6 - Swanwick Court, Alfreton, DE55 7AS, Derbyshire, United Kingdom
Tel.: (44) 1773520666
Chemical Products Distr
N.A.I.C.S.: 424690

Nexeo Solutions Poland Sp. z o.o. (5)
Ul Ruchliwa 15, 02-182, Warsaw, Poland
Tel.: (48) 225755600
Chemical Products Distr
N.A.I.C.S.: 424690

Nexeo Solutions RUS LLC (5)
Savushkina St 126 BC Atlantic City of 20N, 197342, Saint Petersburg, Russia
Tel.: (7) 8127777957
Chemical Products Distr
N.A.I.C.S.: 424690

Nexeo Solutions Spain SLU (5)
Carrer Luis Muntadas 5, Cornella de Llobregat, 08940, Barcelona, Spain
Tel.: (34) 934809125
Chemical Products Distr
N.A.I.C.S.: 424690

Nexeo Solutions Sweden AB (5)
Vastanvindsgatan 8, 444 30, Stenungsund, Sweden
Tel.: (46) 303729500
Chemical Products Distr
N.A.I.C.S.: 424690

Subsidiary (Domestic):

Startex Chemical, LLC (5)
6000 Parkwood Pl, Dublin, OH 43016
Web Site: https://www.startexchemicals.com
Chemical Products Distr
N.A.I.C.S.: 424690

Subsidiary (Non-US):

SCI Jacquot (5)
3 rue Franklin Immeuble, Cityscope Montreuil, 93108, Montreuil, France
Tel.: (33) 384673159
Chemical Product Whslr
N.A.I.C.S.: 424690

Servitas Calidad SA de CV (3)
Plum Forest No 180 Bosque de las Lomas, 01170, Mexico, Mexico
Tel.: (52) 5555965700
Emp.: 16
Business Management Services
N.A.I.C.S.: 541611

Univar AB (3)
Kungsgatan 6, PO Box 4072, 211 49, Malmo, Sweden
Tel.: (46) 40352801
Chemical Distr
N.A.I.C.S.: 424690

Univar BV (3)
Schouwburgplein 30-34, PO Box 21407, 3012 CL, Rotterdam, Netherlands
Tel.: (31) 102757800
Chemical Product Whslr
N.A.I.C.S.: 424690
Merel Ritsma (Dir-Process Improvement-EMEA)

Univar Belgium NV (3)

Riverside Business Park Building G Internationalelaan 55, Brussels, 1070, Belgium
Tel.: (32) 25250511
Chemical Product Whslr
N.A.I.C.S.: 424690
Rebecca De Smedt (Mgr-HR)

Univar Brasil Ltda. (3)
Rua Arinos 15 Parque Industrial, Osasco, 06276-032, Sao Paulo, Brazil
Tel.: (55) 1136027222
Chemical Product Whslr
N.A.I.C.S.: 424690
Michele Carvalho (Project Mgr, Mgr-Supply Chain & Coord-New Bus)

Univar Canada Ltd. (3)
9800 Van Horne Way, Richmond, V6X 1W4, BC, Canada
Tel.: (604) 273-1441
Web Site: http://www.univarcanada.com
Sales Range: $1-4.9 Billion
Emp.: 100
Chemical Distr
N.A.I.C.S.: 424690

Univar Czech sro (3)
Belgicka 642/15, 120 00, Prague, Czech Republic
Tel.: (420) 230234953
Chemical Product Whslr
N.A.I.C.S.: 424690

Univar Egypt LLC (3)
Sabra Tower 2nd Floor Office 22 3/1 El-laselky St Estate No 9, New Maadi, Cairo, Egypt
Tel.: (20) 225177216
Chemical Product Whslr
N.A.I.C.S.: 424690
Ahmed Fakhr (Country Mgr)

Univar Europe Holdings B.V. (3)
Blvd International 55 Bldg G, 1070, Brussels, Belgium (100%)
Tel.: (32) 25250511
Web Site: http://www.univareurope.com
Sales Range: $1-4.9 Billion
Holding Company; Regional Managing Office
N.A.I.C.S.: 551112
John van Osch (Pres-EMEA)

Subsidiary (Non-US):

Univar AG (4)
Scharenmoosstrasse 77, 8052, Zurich, Switzerland
Tel.: (41) 583607272
Web Site: http://www.univareurope.com
Sales Range: $100-124.9 Million
Emp.: 60
Chemical Distr
N.A.I.C.S.: 424690

Subsidiary (Domestic):

Univar Benelux (4)
Rue de la petite Ile 4 Klein-Eiland 4, Anderlecht, Brussels, 1070, Belgium
Tel.: (32) 25250511
Web Site: http://www.univar.com
Sales Range: $150-199.9 Million
Emp.: 160
Chemical Distr
N.A.I.C.S.: 424690

Subsidiary (Non-US):

Univar France (4)
17 avenue Louison Bobet, 94132, Fontenay-sous-Bois, France
Tel.: (33) 149748080
Web Site: http://www.univar.com
Sales Range: $100-124.9 Million
Emp.: 100
Chemical Distr
N.A.I.C.S.: 424690

Univar GmbH (4)
Hinsbecker Loh 10c, 45257, Essen, Germany
Tel.: (49) 20189590
Web Site: http://www.univar.com
Sales Range: $100-124.9 Million
Emp.: 60
Chemical, Food Ingredient & Polymer Distr
N.A.I.C.S.: 424690

Univar Iberia S.A. (4)
C/Goya 115 Planta 6, 28009, Madrid, Spain

Apollo Global Management, Inc.—(Continued)

Tel.: (34) 913096363
Web Site: http://www.univariberia.com
Chemical Distr
N.A.I.C.S.: 424690

Univar Ireland　(4)
Greenogue Business Park 536 Grants
Crescent, Rathcoole, Dublin, Ireland
Tel.: (353) 14019800
Web Site: http://www.univareurope.com
Sales Range: $75-99.9 Million
Emp.: 40
Chemical Distr
N.A.I.C.S.: 424690
Nigel Hayes (Reg VP)

Univar Nordic　(4)
Marieholmsgatan 56, PO Box 48, Gothen-
burg, 401 20, Sweden
Tel.: (46) 31838000
Web Site: http://www.univar.com
Sales Range: $150-199.9 Million
Emp.: 200
Chemical Distr
N.A.I.C.S.: 424690

Univar S.p.A.　(4)
Via Caldera 21, 20153, Milan, Italy
Tel.: (39) 02452771
Web Site: http://www.univareurope.com
Sales Range: $150-199.9 Million
Emp.: 214
Chemical Distr
N.A.I.C.S.: 424690

Univar UK Limited　(4)
Hale Road Industrial Estate Pickerings
Road, Thornbury, Widnes, WA8 8XW,
United Kingdom　(100%)
Tel.: (44) 1514226240
Web Site: http://www.univarsolutions.com
Wholesale Chemical Distribution
N.A.I.C.S.: 424690
Nigel Hayes (Reg VP)

Subsidiary (Non-US):

Univar France SNC　(3)
3 rue Franklin - Immeuble Cityscope,
93108, Montreuil, France
Tel.: (33) 185574598
Chemical Distr
N.A.I.C.S.: 424690

**Univar Hungary Sales Limited Liabil-
ity Co**　(3)
Retkoz u 5, Budapest, 1118, Hungary
Tel.: (36) 12480747
Chemical Product Whslr
N.A.I.C.S.: 424690

Univar Limited　(3)
Aquarius House 6 Mid Point Business Park
Thornbury, Bradford, BD3 7AY, United
Kingdom
Tel.: (44) 1274267300
Chemical Distr
N.A.I.C.S.: 424690

Univar Middle East-Africa FZE　(3)
Jebel Ali Free Zone, PO Box 262432,
Dubai, FZS1 BP01, United Arab Emirates
Tel.: (971) 48894818
Chemical Product Whslr
N.A.I.C.S.: 424690

Univar Poland Sp.zo.o　(3)
70 Polczynka St, 01-337, Warsaw, Poland
Tel.: (48) 222793571
Web Site: https://www.univar.pl
Chemical Product Whslr
N.A.I.C.S.: 424690
Zbigniew Chruscicki (Acct Mgr)

Univar Singapore PTE LTD　(3)
8 Boon Lay Way 03-09 8 Tradehub 21, Sin-
gapore, 609964, Singapore
Tel.: (65) 67159520
Chemical Product Whslr
N.A.I.C.S.: 424690
Lim Chee Khan (Dir-Comml)

Univar Solutions AS　(3)
Rosenholmveien 25, 1414, Trollasen, Nor-
way
Tel.: (47) 22881600
Shell Lubricant Distr
N.A.I.C.S.: 457210

Geir Eikemo (Sls Mgr)
Lisbeth Haugan (Mgr-Key Acct)
Thomas Kristensen (Acct Mgr-Aviation
Lubricants-Nordic)
Rune Wike (Mgr-Key Acct)
Borge Skagen (Acct Mgr-Marine)

Univar Solutions China Ltd.　(3)
2290 Zuchongzhi Road Building 3 Sandhill
Plaza, Pudong New District, Shanghai,
201203, China
Tel.: (86) 2161932700
Chemical Product Whslr
N.A.I.C.S.: 424690

Univar Solutions Denmark A/S　(3)
Islands Brygge 43, 2300, Copenhagen,
Denmark
Tel.: (45) 35371244
Shell Lubricant Distr
N.A.I.C.S.: 457210
Thomas Lausen (Sls Mgr-B2C)
Morten Hersoug (Mgr-Bus Dev)
Kim Larsen (Acct Mgr)
Thomas Kristensen (Acct Mgr-Aviation
Lubricants-Nordic)
Kenth Pedersen (Acct Mgr-Transport)

Univar Solutions Hellas EPE　(3)
Vouliagmenis Avenue 591, Argyroupolis,
16452, Athens, Greece
Tel.: (30) 2109739973
Chemical Product Whslr
N.A.I.C.S.: 424690

**Univar Solutions Kimya Sanayi ve Dis
Ticaret Limited**　(3)
RuzgarliBahce Mah Sehit Sinan Eroglu Cad
No 3/7, Kavacik-Beykoz, 34805, Istanbul,
Turkiye
Tel.: (90) 2164254030
Chemical Product Whslr
N.A.I.C.S.: 424690

Univar Solutions LLC　(3)
Mendeleev Street 145, 450022, Ufa, Russia
Tel.: (7) 3472861062
Chemical Product Whslr
N.A.I.C.S.: 424690

Univar Solutions Oy　(3)
Ayritie 12 B, 01510, Vantaa, Finland
Tel.: (358) 93508650
Shell Lubricant Distr
N.A.I.C.S.: 457210
Paivi Kimpimaki (Acct Mgr)
Thomas Kristensen (Acct Mgr-Aviation
Lubricants-Nordic)

Univar Solutions Portugal SA　(3)
Zone Ind da Maia I Sector VII Rua de
Delfim Ferreira Lotes 100 e 101, 4470-436,
Moreira, Portugal
Tel.: (351) 214267100
Chemical Product Whslr
N.A.I.C.S.: 424690

Univar Solutions SAS　(3)
17 Avenue Louison Bobet, 94120,
Fontenay-sous-Bois, France
Tel.: (33) 149748080
Chemical Product Whslr
N.A.I.C.S.: 424690

**Univar Solutions Singapore Pte
Ltd**　(3)
8 Boon Lay Way 03-09 8 Tradehub 21, Sin-
gapore, 609964, Singapore
Tel.: (65) 67159520
Chemical Product Whslr
N.A.I.C.S.: 424690

Univar Solutions Spain SA　(3)
Avenida Gran Via 16-20 Planta 3a, Hospita-
let de Llobregat, 08902, Barcelona, Spain
Tel.: (34) 932291005
Chemical Product Whslr
N.A.I.C.S.: 424690

Univar Solutions UK Ltd.　(3)
Pickerings Road, Hale Road Industrial Es-
tate, Widnes, WA8 8XW, United Kingdom
Tel.: (44) 1514226240
Chemical Product Whslr
N.A.I.C.S.: 424690

Subsidiary (Domestic):

Univar Solutions USA Inc.　(3)
17411 NE Union Hill Rd, Redmond, WA
98052-3375　(100%)

Tel.: (425) 889-3400
Web Site: http://www.univarusa.com
Chemical Distr
N.A.I.C.S.: 424690

Subsidiary (Non-US):

Univar South-East Europe S.r.l.　(3)
Strada Poterasi Nr 10, 040265, Bucharest,
Romania
Tel.: (40) 314379971
Chemical Product Whslr
N.A.I.C.S.: 424690
Virgil Chindle (Mgr-Sls)

**Univar Specialty Consumables
Limited**　(3)
USC House Tame Park, Wilnecote, Tam-
worth, B77 5DY, Staffordshire, United King-
dom
Tel.: (44) 1827255200
Web Site: http://www.univarsc.com
Chemical Product Whslr
N.A.I.C.S.: 424690

Univar Zwijndrecht N.V.　(3)
Noordweg 3, 3336 LH, Zwijndrecht, Nether-
lands
Tel.: (31) 786250000
Chemical Product Whslr
N.A.I.C.S.: 424690
Guus Carbaat (Gen Mgr)

Subsidiary (Domestic):

Valley Solvent Company, Inc.　(3)
15281 State Highway 107, Harlingen, TX
78552
Tel.: (956) 423-2791
Web Site: http://www.valleysolvents.com
Sales Range: $1-9.9 Million
Emp.: 40
Chemicals And Allied Products, Nec
N.A.I.C.S.: 424690
June Davis (Sec & VP)

Subsidiary (Non-US):

Van Eyck Chemie NV　(3)
Internationalelaan 55, 1070, Anderlecht,
Belgium
Tel.: (32) 23323080
Chemical Product Whslr
N.A.I.C.S.: 424690

Holding (Domestic):

Vectra Co.　(2)
120 S Central Ave Ste 200, Saint Louis,
MO 63017
Tel.: (216) 781-0083
Web Site: http://www.vectraco.com
Holding Company; Battery Technologies,
Magnetic Technologies & Organic Materials
Mtr
N.A.I.C.S.: 551112
Edward Yocum (Chief Compliance Officer,
Gen Counsel, Sec & Exec VP)
Ronald W. LeBaube (Project Mgr-IT)

Subsidiary (Domestic):

OMG Americas, Inc.　(3)
811 Sharon Dr, Westlake, OH 44145
Tel.: (440) 899-2950
Specialty Chemicals Mfr
N.A.I.C.S.: 325998

Holding (Non-US):

Ventia Pty Ltd　(2)
495 Victoria Ave, Chatswood, 2067, NSW,
Australia
Tel.: (61) 1300836842
Web Site: http://www.ventia.com
Emp.: 4,500
Infrastructure Services
N.A.I.C.S.: 541330
David Moffatt (Chm & CEO)

Subsidiary (Domestic):

Broadspectrum Pty. Ltd.　(3)
Level 8 80 Pacific Hwy, North Sydney,
2060, NSW, Australia
Tel.: (61) 294641000
Web Site: http://www.broadspectrum.com
Holding Company; Maintenance, Engineer-
ing, Construction & Technical Consulting
Services
N.A.I.C.S.: 551112

Subsidiary (Domestic):

**Broadspectrum (Australia) Pty.
Ltd.**　(4)
Level 8 80 Pacific HWY, North Sydney,
2060, NSW, Australia
Tel.: (61) 2 9464 1000
Web Site: http://www.broadspectrum.com
Maintenance, Engineering, Construction &
Technical Consulting Services
N.A.I.C.S.: 541330

Subsidiary (Non-US):

**Broadspectrum (New Zealand)
Limited**　(4)
Level 2 Building C 600- 602 Great South
Road, Ellerslie, Auckland, 1051, New Zea-
land
Tel.: (64) 9 523 9900
Web Site: http://www.broadspectrum.com
Construction Engineering Services
N.A.I.C.S.: 541330

Subsidiary (Domestic):

Broadspectrum (WA) Pty Limited　(4)
Level 5 181 Adelaide Terrace, Perth, 6004,
WA, Australia
Tel.: (61) 8 9422 3100
Web Site: http://www.broadspectrum.com
Construction Engineering Services
N.A.I.C.S.: 541330

**Broadspectrum Australia (QLD) Pty
Limited**　(4)
Level 4 52 Merivale Street, Brisbane, 4101,
QLD, Australia
Tel.: (61) 732488700
Web Site: http://www.broadspectrum.com
Construction Engineering Services
N.A.I.C.S.: 541330

CI Australia Pty Limited　(4)
Level 4 35 Clarence Street, Sydney, 2000,
NSW, Australia
Tel.: (61) 282380000
Web Site: https://www.ciaustralia.com.au
Real Estate Consulting Service
N.A.I.C.S.: 531390

Easternwell Group Pty Limited　(4)
Level 8 80 Pacific Highway, North Sydney,
2060, NSW, Australia
Tel.: (61) 1300662819
Oil & Gas Well Drilling Services
N.A.I.C.S.: 213111
Marco Waanders (Gen Mgr-Comml)
Kyle Koziol (Gen Mgr)

Subsidiary (Domestic):

Easternwell WA Pty Limited　(5)
Level 5 101 Adelaide Terrace, Perth, 0000,
WA, Australia
Tel.: (61) 1300662819
Oil & Gas Well Drilling Services
N.A.I.C.S.: 213111

Subsidiary (US):

Ferrovial Services US, Inc.　(4)
10814 Jollyville Rd Bldg 4 Ste 160, Austin,
TX 78759
Tel.: (713) 964-2800
Web Site:
　http://www.ferrovialservicesna.com
Maintenance, Engineering, Construction &
Technical Consulting Services
N.A.I.C.S.: 541330
Marilyn King (Exec VP)

Subsidiary (Non-US):

**Ferrovial Servicios Ambientales
S.A.**　(4)
Avenida El Golf 40 Oficina 702, Santiago,
Chile
Tel.: (56) 2 2233 7485
Web Site: http://www.ferrovialservicios.cl
Construction Engineering Services
N.A.I.C.S.: 541330

Subsidiary (US):

HRI, Inc.　(4)
1750 W College Ave, State College, PA
16801
Tel.: (814) 238-5071
Web Site: https://www.hriinc.com

Industrial Equipment Repair & Maintenance Services
N.A.I.C.S.: 811310

Subsidiary (Domestic):

ICD (Asia Pacific) Pty Limited (4)
Level 8 80 Pacific Highway North, Norwest Business Park, Sydney, 2060, NSW, Australia
Tel.: (61) 300836842
Web Site: http://www.icdasiapacific.com.au
Construction Engineering Services
N.A.I.C.S.: 541330

Subsidiary (Non-US):

Inser-Transfield Services S.A. (4)
Jose Toribio Medina 094, Antofagasta, Chile
Tel.: (56) 552533693
Web Site: http://www.ferrovialservicios.cl
Construction Engineering Services
N.A.I.C.S.: 541330

Subsidiary (Domestic):

Silver City Drilling (QLD) Pty Limited (4)
66 Smith Street, Alice Springs, 0870, NT, Australia
Tel.: (61) 889522966
Web Site:
    http://www.silvercitydrilling.com.au
Oil & Gas Well Drilling Services
N.A.I.C.S.: 213111

Subsidiary (US):

Steier Oil Field Service Inc. (4)
4637 W Villard, Dickinson, ND 58601
Tel.: (701) 483-8245
Web Site:
    http://www.ferrovialservicesna.com
Oil & Gas Well Drilling Services
N.A.I.C.S.: 213111

Holding (Non-US):

Verallia France (2)
Carpe Diem 31 place des Corolles, 92400, Courbevoie, France (90%)
Tel.: (33) 171131100
Web Site: http://www.verallia.com
Glass Containers Mfr & Distr
N.A.I.C.S.: 327213
Wendy Kool-Foulon *(Gen Counsel-Verallia Grp)*

Subsidiary (Non-US):

Verallia Argentina (3)
Carril Nacional 6070 Rodeo de la Cruz CP 5525, Mendoza, Argentina
Tel.: (54) 261 4130200
Web Site: http://www.verallia.com
Glass Container Mfr
N.A.I.C.S.: 327213

Verallia Chile (3)
Camino Rosario a Quinta de Tilcoco 1650, Rengo, Chile
Tel.: (56) 72959 100
Web Site: http://www.verallia.com
Glass Container Mfr
N.A.I.C.S.: 327213

Holding (Non-US):

Watches of Switzerland Operations Limited (2)
Aurum House 2 Elland Road, Braunstone, Leicester, LE3 1TT, Leics, United Kingdom
Tel.: (44) 1162322000
Web Site: http://ukcareers.thewosgroup.com
Holding Company; Jewellery Retailer
N.A.I.C.S.: 551112
Brian Duffy *(CEO)*

Subsidiary (Domestic):

Aurum Group Limited (3)
Aurum House 2 Elland Road, Braunstone, Leicester, LE3 1TT, Leicestershire, United Kingdom
Tel.: (44) 8008495051
Web Site: http://www.goldsmiths.co.uk
Jewelry Retailer
N.A.I.C.S.: 458310

Subsidiary (US):

Mayor's Jewelers, Inc. (3)

3440 NW 53rd StSte 402, Fort Lauderdale, FL 33309 (100%)
Tel.: (954) 590-9000
Web Site: http://www.mayors.com
Holding Company; Fine Jewelry, Watches & Gift Items Retailer & Whslr
N.A.I.C.S.: 551112

Subsidiary (Domestic):

Mayor's Jewelers of Florida, Inc. (4)
5870 N Hiatus Rd, Tamarac, FL 33321
Tel.: (954) 590-9000
Web Site: http://www.mayors.com
Fine Jewelry, Watches & Gift Items Retailer & Whslr
N.A.I.C.S.: 458310

Holding (Domestic):

Yahoo, Inc. (2)
770 Broadway, New York, NY 10003
Tel.: (212) 652-6400
Web Site: https://www.yahoo.com
Internet Advertising, Entertainment & Information Services; Internet Access Services
N.A.I.C.S.: 517810
Jim Lanzone *(CEO)*

Subsidiary (Non-US):

AOL Deutschland Medien GmbH (3)
Neuer Wall 50, 20357, Hamburg, Germany
Tel.: (49) 40361590
Web Site: http://www.aol.de
Internet Advertising, Entertainment & Information Services
N.A.I.C.S.: 519290
Donald D'Anna Jr. *(Mng Dir)*

Subsidiary (Domestic):

MapQuest, Inc. (3)
1555 Blake St, Denver, CO 80202
Tel.: (303) 486-4000
Web Site: http://www.mapquest.com
Emp.: 136
Online Mapping, Directions & Local Searches
N.A.I.C.S.: 519290

Millennial Media LLC (3)
2400 Boston St Ste 300, Baltimore, MD 21224
Tel.: (410) 522-8705
Web Site: http://www.millennialmedia.com
Emp.: 575
Mobile Advertising Services
N.A.I.C.S.: 541890

Oath (Americas) Inc. (3)
770 Broadway, New York, NY 10003
Tel.: (212) 652-6400
Web Site: http://www.oath.com
Emp.: 4,500
Internet Advertising & Publishing Services
N.A.I.C.S.: 541890

Subsidiary (Non-US):

Oath (Canada) Corp. (3)
99 Spadina Ave, Toronto, M5V 3P8, ON, Canada
Tel.: (416) 263-8100
Web Site: http://www.aol.ca
Internet Advertising, Entertainment & Information Services
N.A.I.C.S.: 519290

Oath (UK) Limited (3)
Shropshire House, 11-20 Capper St, London, WC1E 6JA, United Kingdom
Tel.: (44) 8082349279
Web Site: http://www.aol.co.uk
Internet Advertising, Entertainment & Information Services
N.A.I.C.S.: 519290

Oath Denmark ApS (3)
Sundkrogsgade 21, 2100, Copenhagen, Denmark
Tel.: (45) 70274527
Advertisement Agency
N.A.I.C.S.: 541810

Oath Japan KK (3)
3-20-2 Nishishinjyuku, Operacity 16th Floor, Shinuku-Ku, Tokyo, 16314, Japan
Tel.: (81) 353539400

News, Travel & Restaurant Guides Online; Joint Venture of Nihon Keizai Shimbun, Inc., America Online Incorporated & Mitsui & Co.
N.A.I.C.S.: 517810

Subsidiary (Domestic):

Verizon Digital Media Services Inc. (3)
13031 W Jefferson Blvd Bldg 900, Los Angeles, CA 90094
Tel.: (877) 334-3236
Web Site:
    http://www.verizondigitalmedia.com
Emp.: 849
Computer System Design Services
N.A.I.C.S.: 541512
Mary Kay Evans *(Chief Mktg Officer)*
Ariff Sidi *(Chief Product Officer)*
Rick Capstraw *(Chief Revenue Officer & Head-Sls-Global)*

Subsidiary (Domestic):

Volicon Inc. (4)
99 S Bedford St, Burlington, MA 01803
Tel.: (781) 221-7400
Web Site: http://www.volicon.com
Emp.: 200
Enterprise Media Intelligence Solutions
N.A.I.C.S.: 541830

Subsidiary (Domestic):

Yahoo Holdings, Inc. (3)
701 1st Ave, Sunnyvale, CA 94089
Tel.: (408) 349-3300
Web Site: http://www.yahoo.com
Holding Company; Web Search Portal & Other Related Internet Content Publishing
N.A.I.C.S.: 551112

Subsidiary (Domestic):

Genome, Inc. (4)
11 W 19th St 10th Fl 10, New York, NY 10011-4343
Tel.: (646) 722-6260
Integrated Multi-Channel Internet Advertising Solutions
N.A.I.C.S.: 541890

Unit (Domestic):

Participant Media, LLC (4)
3520 Wesley St., Culver City, CA 90232
Tel.: (310) 550-5100
Web Site: http://www.participantmedia.com
Internet Publishing
N.A.I.C.S.: 513199
Jeff Skoll *(Founder & Chm)*
David Linde *(CEO)*
Gabriel Brakin *(COO)*
Andy Kim *(CFO)*
Robert Kessel *(Exec VP-Narrative Film)*
Anikah McLaren *(Exec VP-Narrative Film)*
Jeannine Tang *(Gen Counsel)*

Subsidiary (Domestic):

Tumblr, Inc. (4)
35 E 21st St Ground Fl, New York, NY 10010
Tel.: (678) 439-8862
Web Site: http://www.tumblr.com
Social Networking Website Operator
N.A.I.C.S.: 516210
Jeff D'Onofrio *(CEO)*

Subsidiary (Non-US):

Yahoo Software Development India Private Limited (4)
Torrey Pines EGL Business Park, Intermediate Ring Road 2nd Floor Challaghatta, Bengaluru, 560071, Karnataka, India
Tel.: (91) 80255837
Data Processing Hosting Related Services
N.A.I.C.S.: 518210

Yahoo! 350 SAS (4)
17 Rue Guillaume Tell, Paris, 75017, France
Tel.: (33) 170912000
Data Processing Hosting Related Services
N.A.I.C.S.: 518210

Yahoo! Canada Co. (4)
100 University Ave, Toronto, M5V 3P8, ON, Canada (100%)
Tel.: (416) 341-8605

Web Site: https://ca.yahoo.com
Provider of Comprehensive Online Products & Services to Consumers & Businesses
N.A.I.C.S.: 561499

Group (Domestic):

Yahoo! Connected Life (4)
701 1st Ave, Sunnyvale, CA 94089
Tel.: (408) 349-3300
Mobile, Broadband & Digital Wireless Services
N.A.I.C.S.: 517810

Subsidiary (Non-US):

Yahoo! France S.A.S. (4)
18 Boulevard Malesherbes 3rd Floor, 75008, Paris, France (70%)
Tel.: (33) 170912000
Web Site: http://www.yahoo.fr
Online Products & Services to Consumers & Businesses
N.A.I.C.S.: 519290

Group (Domestic):

Yahoo! Global Partner Solutions (4)
701 1st Ave, Sunnyvale, CA 94089
Tel.: (408) 349-3300
Internet Advertising & Sales
N.A.I.C.S.: 541810

Subsidiary (Non-US):

Yahoo! Hungary Labs Kft. (4)
Reitter Ferenc u 132, Budapest, 1131, Hungary
Tel.: (36) 303871432
Developer of Web Analytics Software
N.A.I.C.S.: 513210

Group (Domestic):

Yahoo! Network (4)
701 1st Ave, Sunnyvale, CA 94089
Tel.: (408) 349-3300
Consumer Web Products & Services
N.A.I.C.S.: 519290

Division (Domestic):

Yahoo! Communications & Communities (5)
701 1st Ave, Sunnyvale, CA 94089
Tel.: (408) 349-3300
Internet Marketing & Services
N.A.I.C.S.: 519290

Unit (Domestic):

Yahoo! Groups (6)
701 1st Ave, Sunnyvale, CA 94089
Tel.: (408) 349-3300
Web Site: http://www.yahoo.com
E-mail ListServ Services
N.A.I.C.S.: 519290

Yahoo! Mail (6)
701 1st Ave, Sunnyvale, CA 94089
Tel.: (408) 349-3300
Web Site: https://login.yahoo.com
Email Services
N.A.I.C.S.: 519290

Division (Domestic):

Yahoo! Media (5)
701 1st Ave, Sunnyvale, CA 94089
Tel.: (408) 349-3300
Web Site: http://www.yahoo.com
Internet Publishing Services
N.A.I.C.S.: 519290

Unit (Domestic):

Yahoo! Entertainment (6)
701 1st Ave, Sunnyvale, CA 94089
Tel.: (408) 349-3300
Online Entertainment News Coverage
N.A.I.C.S.: 516210

Yahoo! Finance (6)
701 1st Ave, Sunnyvale, CA 94089
Tel.: (408) 349-3300
Web Site: https://finance.yahoo.com
Online Business Information Services
N.A.I.C.S.: 519290

Yahoo! News (6)
701 1st Ave, Sunnyvale, CA 94089
Tel.: (408) 349-3300

Apollo Global Management, Inc.—(Continued)

Provider of Comprehensive Online News
Service
Web Site: https://news.yahoo.com
Online News Service
N.A.I.C.S.: 516210

Yahoo! Sports　　　　　　　　　　(6)
701 First Ave, Sunnyvale, CA 94089-1019
Tel.: (408) 349-3300
Web Site: http://www.sports.yahoo.com
Online Sports News Services
N.A.I.C.S.: 516210
Raj Mannick (Head-Sport)

Division (Domestic):

Yahoo! Search　　　　　　　　　　(5)
701 1st Ave, Sunnyvale, CA 94089
Tel.: (408) 349-3300
Internet Search Engine & Marketing Services
N.A.I.C.S.: 519290

Unit (Domestic):

Yahoo! Local　　　　　　　　　　(6)
701 1st Ave, Sunnyvale, CA 94089
Tel.: (408) 349-3300
Regional Online Marketing Services
N.A.I.C.S.: 519290

Group (Domestic):

**Yahoo! Research & Strategic Data
Solutions**　　　　　　　　　　(4)
701 1st Ave, Sunnyvale, CA 94089
Tel.: (408) 349-3300
Data Mining & Knowledge Discovery Services
N.A.I.C.S.: 541715

Unit (Domestic):

Yahoo! Research　　　　　　　　　　(5)
701 1st Ave, Sunnyvale, CA 94089
Tel.: (408) 349-3300
Web Site: https://research.yahoo.com
Engineeering Services
N.A.I.C.S.: 541715

Subsidiary (Non-US):

Yahoo! Technologies Norway AS　(4)
Prinsens Gate 49 3rd Floor, 7011, Trondheim, Norway
Tel.: (47) 73201200
Data Processing Hosting Related Services
N.A.I.C.S.: 518210

Yahoo! de Mexico, S.A. de C.V.　(4)
Paseo De Las Palmas Num 330 Piso 2,
Mexico, 11000, Mexico　　　　　(100%)
Tel.: (52) 5530031900
Web Site: http://www.yahoo.com.mx
Provider of Comprehenoivo Online Producto
& Services to Consumers & Businesses
N.A.I.C.S.: 561499

Yahoo! do Brasil Internet Ltda.　(4)
Av Brg Faria Lima No 3600, Itaim Bibi, Sao
Paulo, SP, Brazil　　　　　　　　(100%)
Tel.: (55) 1130545200
Web Site: http://br.yahoo.com
Provider of Comprehensive Online Products
& Services to Consumers & Businesses
N.A.I.C.S.: 561499

**Cengage Learning Holdings II,
Inc.**　　　　　　　　　　(1)
3 Ctr Plz Ste 700, Boston, MA 02108
Tel.: (513) 229-1000
Web Site: https://www.cengagegroup.com
Rev.: $1,502,700,000
Assets: $2,600,100,000
Liabilities: $2,485,700,000
Net Worth: ($389,400,000)
Earnings: ($80,900,000)
Emp.: 4,400
Fiscal Year-end: 03/31/2024
Holding Company; Library Reference &
Educational Materials Publishing & Learning
Solutions
N.A.I.C.S.: 551112
Michael E. Hansen (CEO)
Jim Chilton (CTO)
Darren Person (Chief Digital Officer)
Michael E. Hansen (CEO)
Bob Munro (CFO)
Alexander Broich (Pres-Cengage Select &
Gen Mgr-English Language Teaching &
Cengage Work)

Jeri Herman (Chief People Officer)
Brooke Carey (Chief Comm Officer)
Dawn Ehlers (Gen Counsel)
Morgan Wolbe (Exec VP-Ops-Global &
Chief Transformation Officer)

Subsidiary (Domestic):

Cengage Learning, Inc.　　　　(2)
3 Ctr Plz Ste 700, Boston, MA 2108
Tel.: (513) 229-1000
Web Site: http://www.cengage.com
Library Reference & Educational Materials
Publishing & Learning Solutions
N.A.I.C.S.: 513130
Michael E. Hansen (CEO)
Sean Chamberland (Sr Dir-Mktg-Cengage
Canada)
Julianne Isaac (Gen Mgr)

Subsidiary (Domestic):

**Advanced Instructional Systems,
Inc.**　　　　　　　　　　(3)
1791 Varsity Dr Ste 200, Raleigh, NC
27606
Tel.: (919) 829-8181
Web Site: https://www.webassign.com
Sales Range: $1-9.9 Million
Emp.: 25
Online Software Solutions Services
N.A.I.C.S.: 513210
Rob Simora (CTO)

Division (Domestic):

Cengage Higher Education　　　(3)
20 Davis Dr, Belmont, CA 94002
Tel.: (650) 595-2350
Web Site:
　http://www.academic.cengage.com
Educational Book Publishing
N.A.I.C.S.: 513130

Unit (Domestic):

**South-Western Cengage
Learning**　　　　　　　　　　(4)
5191 Natorp Blvd, Mason, OH 45040
Tel.: (513) 229-1000
Web Site: http://www.cengagelearning.com
Sales Range: $200-249.9 Million
Accounting, Marketing & Management Education Book Publisher
N.A.I.C.S.: 513130

Wadsworth Cengage Learning　(4)
10 Davis Dr, Belmont, CA 94002-3002
Tel.: (650) 595-2350
Web Site:
　http://www.academic.cengage.com
Educational Software & Textbook Publisher
N.A.I.C.S.: 513130

Subsidiary (Non-US):

Cengage Learning Asia　　　　(3)
30A Kallang Place 12-06, UIC Bldg, Singapore, 339213, Singapore
Tel.: (65) 64101200
Web Site: https://www.cengageasia.com
Sales Range: $50-74.9 Million
Emp.: 70
Educational & Reference Book Publisher
N.A.I.C.S.: 513130

**Cengage Learning Australia Pty.
Limited**　　　　　　　　　　(3)
80 Dorcas St Level 7, Victoria, 3205, VIC,
Australia
Tel.: (61) 396854111
Web Site: http://www.cengage.com.au
Sales Range: $50-74.9 Million
Emp.: 200
Educational & Reference Book Publishing
N.A.I.C.S.: 513130
Tamara Silver (Mgr-HR)
Paul Petrulis (VP-Higher Education)
Nicole McCarten (VP-Schools Div)
John Durow (Fin Dir & COO)
Paul Brady (Dir-Technologies)
Nigel Matai (Head-Production)

Subsidiary (Domestic):

Delmar Cengage Learning　　　(3)
5 Maxwell Dr Executive Woods, Clifton
Park, NY 12065-2919
Tel.: (518) 348-2300
Web Site: http://www.cengage.com

Sales Range: $100-124.9 Million
Emp.: 294
Educational, Technical & Vocational Publishers
N.A.I.C.S.: 513130

Subsidiary (Non-US):

Gale Group Inc.　　　　　　　　(3)
Tel.: (248) 699-4253
Web Site: http://www.gale.com
Sales Range: $300-349.9 Million
Reference Book & Electronic Reference
Materials Publisher
N.A.I.C.S.: 513140
Paul Gazzolo (Sr VP & Gen Mgr)
Brian McDonough (Sr VP-Sls-North
America)
Terry Robinson (Mng Dir-Intl & Sr VP)

Division (Domestic):

Macmillan Reference USA　　　(4)
12 Lunar Dr, Woodbridge, CT 06525-2322
Tel.: (203) 397-2600
Web Site: http://gale.cengage.com
Sales Range: $25-49.9 Million
Emp.: 55
Publisher of Academic & Professional Reference Materials, Newspapers & U.S. &
Foreign Patents
N.A.I.C.S.: 513130

Subsidiary (Domestic):

Learning Objects, Inc.　　　　(3)
1528 Connecticut Ave NW, Washington, DC
20036
Tel.: (202) 265-3276
Web Site: https://www.learningobjects.com
Education Technology Software Publisher
N.A.I.C.S.: 513210

Subsidiary (Non-US):

Nelson Education Ltd.　　　　(3)
1120 Birchmount Rd, Scarborough, M1K
5G4, ON, Canada
Tel.: (416) 752-9448
Web Site: http://www.nelson.com
Sales Range: $100-124.9 Million
Education & Reference Book Publisher
N.A.I.C.S.: 513130
Steve Brown (Pres & CEO)
Claudine O'Donnell (Sr VP)
Ryan Anklesaria (Sr VP)

APOLLOMICS INC.
989 E Hillsdale Blvd Ste 220, Foster
City, CA 94404
Tel.: (650) 209-4055　　　　Ky
Web Site:
　https://www.apollomicsinc.com
Year Founded: 2015
APLM—(NASDAQ)
Rev.: $1,447,000
Assets: $76,475,000
Liabilities: $524,595,000
Net Worth: ($448,120,000)
Earnings: ($240,811,000)
Emp.: 43
Fiscal Year-end: 12/31/22
Research & Development in Biotechnology (except Nanobiotechnology)
N.A.I.C.S.: 541714
Brianna MacDonald (Gen Counsel)
Jane Wang (Chief Scientific Officer)
Sanjeev Redkar (Pres)

Subsidiaries:

Apollomics (Australia) Pty. Ltd.　(1)
Level 19 HWT Tower 40 City Road, Southbank, 3006, VIC, Australia
Tel.: (61) 398695900
Biotechnology Research & Development
Services
N.A.I.C.S.: 541714

APPFOLIO, INC.
70 Castilian Dr, Goleta, CA 93117
Tel.: (805) 364-6093　　　　DE
Web Site: https://www.appfolio.com
Year Founded: 2006
APPF—(NASDAQ)
Rev.: $620,445,000

Assets: $408,889,000
Liabilities: $111,577,000
Net Worth: $297,312,000
Earnings: $2,702,000
Emp.: 1,504
Fiscal Year-end: 12/31/23
Software Publisher
N.A.I.C.S.: 513210
Klaus Schauser (Co-Founder)
Andreas von Blottnitz (Chm)
Amy Meyer (Chief People Officer)
Fay Sien Goon (CFO)
William Shane Trigg (Pres & CEO)
Jon Walker (Co-Founder)

APPGATE, INC.
2 Alhambra Plz Ste PH-1-B, Coral
Gables, FL 33134　　　　　　　　DE
Web Site: https://www.appgate.com
Year Founded: 2005
APGT—(OTCIQ)
Rev.: $42,664,000
Assets: $138,824,000
Liabilities: $162,910,000
Net Worth: ($24,086,000)
Earnings: ($30,085,000)
Emp.: 415
Fiscal Year-end: 12/31/22
Offices of Other Holding Companies
N.A.I.C.S.: 551112
Jonathan J. Ledecky (Pres & CFO)

APPHARVEST, INC.
500 Appalachian Way, Morehead, KY
40351
Tel.: (606) 653-6100　　　　DE
Web Site:
　https://www.appharvest.com
Year Founded: 2018
APPH—(NASDAQ)
Rev.: $9,050,000
Assets: $554,064,000
Liabilities: $166,424,000
Net Worth: $387,640,000
Earnings: ($166,186,000)
Emp.: 500
Fiscal Year-end: 12/31/21
Farming Services
N.A.I.C.S.: 111219
Anthony Martin (CEO)
Jonathan Webb (Founder & Chief
Strategy Officer)
Gary Broadbent (Chief Legal Officer,
Chief Restructuring Officer & Sec)
David Lee (Pres)
Loren Eggleton (CFO)

APPIAN CORPORATION
7950 Jones Branch Dr, McLean, VA
22102
Tel.: (703) 442-8844　　　　DE
Web Site: https://www.appian.com
Year Founded: 1999
APPN—(NASDAQ)
Rev.: $467,991,000
Assets: $594,214,000
Liabilities: $448,514,000
Net Worth: $145,700,000
Earnings: ($150,920,000)
Emp.: 2,307
Fiscal Year-end: 12/31/22
Custom Computer Programming Services
N.A.I.C.S.: 541511
Christopher Winters (Gen Counsel)
Myles Weber (CIO)
Pavel Zamudio-Ramirez (Chief Customer Officer)
Mark Matheos (CFO & Chief Acctg
Officer)
Susan Charnaux (Chief People Officer)
Sanat Joshi (Sr VP)
Matthew W. Calkins (Co-Founder,
Chm, Pres & CEO)

Robert C. Kramer *(Co-Founder & Gen Mgr)*
Michael Beckley *(Co-Founder & CTO)*

Subsidiaries:

Appian Europe Ltd. (1)
24 Martin Lane, London, EC4R 0DR, United Kingdom
Tel.: (44) 2035142838
Software Development Services
N.A.I.C.S.: 541511

Appian France Sarl (1)
Tour Trinity 1 bis Pl de la Defense 19 Av de la Division Leclerc, Puteaux, 92800, Paris, Cedex, France
Tel.: (33) 186527402
Software Development Services
N.A.I.C.S.: 541511

Appian Netherlands BV (1)
Barbara Strozzilaan 101, 1083 HN, Amsterdam, Netherlands
Tel.: (31) 202993350
Software Development Services
N.A.I.C.S.: 541511

Appian Singapore Pte. Ltd. (1)
Level 42 6 Battery Road, Singapore, Singapore
Tel.: (65) 283176698
Software Development Services
N.A.I.C.S.: 541511

Appian Software Germany GmbH (1)
Muskauer Str 43, 10997, Berlin, Germany
Tel.: (49) 6950607686
Software Development Services
N.A.I.C.S.: 541511

Appian Software International GmbH (1)
Baarerstrasse 21, 6300, Zug, Switzerland
Tel.: (41) 435085339
Software Development Services
N.A.I.C.S.: 541511

Appian Software Switzerland LLC (1)
Baarerstrasse 21, 6300, Zug, Switzerland
Tel.: (41) 435085339
Software Development Services
N.A.I.C.S.: 541511

Appian Spain, S.L. (1)
Calendula 93 - Miniparc III Edif E, 28109, Alcobendas, Madrid, Spain
Tel.: (34) 911234782
Software Development Services
N.A.I.C.S.: 541511

APPLE INC.

1 Apple Pkwy, Cupertino, CA 95014
Tel.: (408) 996-1010   CA
Web Site: https://www.apple.com
Year Founded: 1977
AAPL—(NASDAQ)
Rev.: $391,035,000,000
Assets: $364,980,000,000
Liabilities: $308,030,000,000
Net Worth: $56,950,000,000
Earnings: $93,736,000,000
Emp.: 164,000
Fiscal Year-end: 09/28/24
Software Development Services
N.A.I.C.S.: 334118
Arthur D. Levinson *(Chm)*
Jeffrey E. Williams *(COO)*
Eddy Cue *(Sr VP-Svcs)*
Lisa Jackson *(VP-Environment, Policy & Social Initiatives)*
Johny Srouji *(Sr VP-Hardware Technologies)*
Jennifer Bailey *(VP-Internet Svcs)*
Philip W. Schiller *(Sr VP-Mktg-Worldwide)*
Isabel Ge Mahe *(Mng Dir-Greater China & VP)*
Deirdre O'Brien *(Sr VP-Retail & People)*
Tor Myhren *(VP-Mktg Comm)*

Katherine L. Adams *(Gen Counsel & Sr VP)*
John Giannandrea *(Sr VP-Machine Learning & Artificial Intelligence Strategy)*
Adrian Perica *(VP-Corp Dev)*
Sabih Khan *(Sr VP-Ops)*
Barbara H. Whye *(VP-Inclusion & Diversity)*
John Ternus *(Sr VP-Hardware Engrg)*
Kristin Huguet Quayle *(Head-PR)*
Sashi Ramani *(Head-Ad Platform Partnerships-Global)*
Greg Joswiak *(Sr VP-Mktg-Worldwide)*
Timothy D. Cook *(CEO)*
Isabel Ge Mahe *(Mng Dir-Greater China & VP)*
Craig Federighi *(Sr VP-Software Engrg)*
Craig Federighi *(Sr VP-Software Engrg)*

Subsidiaries:

Apple Asia Limited (1)
2401 Tower One Times Square, Causeway Bay, China (Hong Kong)   (100%)
Tel.: (852) 21120099
Web Site: https://www.apple.com
Sales Range: $25-49.9 Million
Earnings: $56,000,000
Emp.: 100
Mfr of Personal Computers
N.A.I.C.S.: 334111

Apple Canada Inc. (1)
120 Bremner Boulevard Suite 1600, Toronto, M5J 0A8, ON, Canada
Tel.: (647) 943-4400
Web Site: http://www.apple.ca
Sales Range: $50-74.9 Million
Emp.: 120
Retailer of Personal Computers, Portable Digital Music Players & Mobile Communication Devices
N.A.I.C.S.: 551114

Apple Computer Mexico S.A. de C.V. (1)
Paseo de La Reforma 600 Suite 132 Colonia Pena Blanca Santa Fe, Delegacion Alvaro Obregon, CP 01210, Mexico, DF, Mexico
Tel.: (52) 5552091200
Web Site: http://www.apple.com.mx
Sales Range: $25-49.9 Million
Earnings: $25,000,000
Emp.: 25
Distr & Marketing of Apple Branded Computers & Related Accessories
N.A.I.C.S.: 334111

Apple India Private Limited (1)
19th Floor Concorde Tower C UB City No 24 Vittal Mallya Road, Bengaluru, 560001, India
Tel.: (91) 8040455150
Personal Computer & Mobile Communication Device Distr
N.A.I.C.S.: 334111

Apple Japan, Inc. (1)
Roppongi Hills 6-10-1 Roppongi, Minato-ku, Tokyo, 106-6140, Yubinbango, Japan
Tel.: (81) 120277535
Web Site: https://www.apple.com
Sales Range: $125-149.9 Million
Mfr & Sales of Personal Computers, Computers & iPhones
N.A.I.C.S.: 334111

Apple Operations Europe (1)
Hollyhill Industrial Estate, Hollyhill, Cork, Ireland
Tel.: (353) 214284000
Web Site: http://www.apple.com
Emp.: 4,000
Computer Peripheral Mfr & Distr
N.A.I.C.S.: 334118

Apple Operations International (1)
Hollyhill Industrial Estate, Cork, T23 YKH4, Ireland
Tel.: (353) 214284000
Sales Range: $900-999.9 Million
Emp.: 3,000
Consumer Electronics Distr

N.A.I.C.S.: 423620

Apple Pty. Limited (1)
Level 3 20 Martin Place, Sydney, 2000, NSW, Australia   (100%)
Tel.: (61) 133511
Web Site: https://www.apple.com
Sales Range: $100-124.9 Million
Emp.: 300
Mfr of Personal Computers
N.A.I.C.S.: 334111

Apple Sales International (1)
Hollyhill Industrial Estate, Cork, T23YKH4, Ireland
Tel.: (353) 214392088
Web Site: http://www.apple.com
Rev.: $1,305,256,704
Emp.: 4,000
Mfr of Personal Computers, Portable Digital Music Players & Mobile Communication Devices
N.A.I.C.S.: 334111

Subsidiary (Non-US):

Apple AB (2)
(100%)
Tel.: (46) 87033000
Web Site: http://www.apple.com
Sales Range: $25-49.9 Million
Emp.: 50
Retailer of Personal Computers, Portable Digital Music Players & Mobile Communication Devices
N.A.I.C.S.: 551114

Apple Benelux B.V. (2)
Leidseplein 29, 1017 PS, Amsterdam, Netherlands
Tel.: (31) 205302200
Web Site: http://www.apple.com
Sales Range: $25-49.9 Million
Emp.: 100
Personal Computers Mfr & Whslr
N.A.I.C.S.: 334111

Branch (Non-US):

Apple Benelux B.V. - Belgium Office (3)
Buru And Design Ctr 5th Fl Heizel Esplanade Heizel 1, PO Box 100, 1020, Brussels, Belgium
Tel.: (32) 24744211
Web Site: http://www.apple.com
Sales Range: $10-24.9 Million
Emp.: 20
Mfr of Personal Computers
N.A.I.C.S.: 334111

Subsidiary (Non-US):

Apple France SARL (2)
12 Ave De Oceanie, Courtaboeus, 91956, Les Ulis, Cedex, France
Tel.: (33) 169863400
Web Site: http://www.apple.com
Sales Range: $75-99.9 Million
Emp.: 200
Personal Computer Mfr
N.A.I.C.S.: 334111

Apple Ges.mbH (2)
Landstrasser Hauptstrasse 71, 1030, Vienna, Austria   (100%)
Tel.: (43) 1711820
Web Site: http://www.apple.com
Sales Range: $1-4.9 Billion
Mfr of Personal Computers
N.A.I.C.S.: 334111

Apple GmbH (2)
Arnunfstrasse 19, Munich, 80335, Germany   (100%)
Tel.: (49) 89996400
Web Site: http://www.apple.com
Sales Range: $25-49.9 Million
Emp.: 100
Microcomputers, Software & Peripherals Distr
N.A.I.C.S.: 334111

AuthenTec (Shanghai) Co., Ltd (1)
Shanghai Multimedia Park Room 1101-1102, 1027 Changning Road, Shanghai, 200050, China
Tel.: (86) 2152418800
Mobile & Network Security Services
N.A.I.C.S.: 541512

AuthenTec K.K. (1)
White Akasaka Bldg 5F 5-4-13 Akasaka, Minato-ku, Tokyo, 107 0052, Japan
Tel.: (81) 3 5114 5688
Web Site: http://www.authentec.com
Fingerprint Sensors Sales
N.A.I.C.S.: 423690

Beats Electronics, LLC (1)
8600 Hayden Pl, Culver City, CA 90232
Tel.: (424) 326-4679
Web Site: http://www.beatsbydre.com
Sales Range: $1-4.9 Billion
Audio Equipment Mfr, Whslr & Online Retailer
N.A.I.C.S.: 334310
Andre Romelle Young *(Co-Founder)*

FileMaker, Inc. (1)
5201 Patrick Henry Dr, Santa Clara, CA 95054   (100%)
Tel.: (408) 987-7000
Web Site: http://www.filemaker.com
Sales Range: $75-99.9 Million
Emp.: 200
Database Software Development Services
N.A.I.C.S.: 513210
Ryan Rosenberg *(VP-Mktg & Svcs)*
Brad Freitag *(VP-Sls-Americas)*
Ann Monroe *(VP-Mktg)*
Frank Lu *(VP-Engrg)*
Sophia Yungen *(Sec & Corp Counsel)*
Peter Nelson *(VP)*

Subsidiary (Non-US):

FileMaker Japan Inc. (2)
Roppongi Hills Mori Tower 6-10-1 Roppongi, Minato-ku, Tokyo, 106-6140, Japan
Tel.: (81) 343453333
Sales Range: $75-99.9 Million
Database Software Development Services
N.A.I.C.S.: 513210

Shazam Entertainment Ltd. (1)
26 28 Hammersmith Grove, London, W6 7HA, United Kingdom
Tel.: (44) 20 8742 6820
Web Site: http://www.shazam.com
Mobile Device Application Developer
N.A.I.C.S.: 513210

iFixit, Inc. (1)
1330 Monterey Street, San Luis Obispo, CA 93401
Tel.: (805) 464-0573
Web Site: http://www.ifixit.com
Sales Range: $1-9.9 Million
Emp.: 14
Computer Maintenance & Repair
N.A.I.C.S.: 811210

APPLE RUSH CO, INC.

1419 Chaffee Drive Suite 2A, Titusville, FL 32780
Tel.: (88-) 74-1377
Web Site: https://aprubrands.com
APRU—(OTCIQ)
Rev.: $502,000
Assets: $1,401,000
Liabilities: $815,000
Net Worth: $586,000
Earnings: ($2,968,000)
Fiscal Year-end: 12/31/19
Food Products Mfr
N.A.I.C.S.: 311999
Tony Torgerud *(CEO)*

APPLIED BIOCODE CORP.

12130 Mora Dr Unit 2, Santa Fe Springs, CA 90670
Tel.: (562) 777-9800
Web Site:
https://www.apbiocode.com
6598—(TPE)
Rev.: $3,481,076
Assets: $23,906,983
Liabilities: $6,262,870
Net Worth: $17,644,113
Earnings: ($9,312,427)
Emp.: 60
Fiscal Year-end: 12/31/19
Clinical Product Mfr
N.A.I.C.S.: 325414

Applied BioCode Corp.—(Continued)

Winston Z. Ho *(Founder, Pres & CTO)*

APPLIED BIOSCIENCES CORP.

9701 Wilshire Blvd Ste 1000, Beverly Hills, CA 90212
Tel.: (310) 356-7374   NV
Web Site: https://appbiocorp.com
Year Founded: 2014
APPB—(OTCEM)
Rev.: $707,062
Assets: $3,651,448
Liabilities: $374,266
Net Worth: $3,277,182
Earnings: ($2,629,327)
Emp.: 25
Fiscal Year-end: 03/31/19
Research & Development in Biotechnology
N.A.I.C.S.: 541714

APPLIED DIGITAL CORPORATION

3811 Turtle Creek Blvd Ste 2100, Dallas, TX 75219
Tel.: (214) 427-1704   NV
Web Site:
https://www.applieddigital.com
Year Founded: 2001
APLD—(NASDAQ)
Rev.: $55,392,000
Assets: $263,957,000
Liabilities: $194,278,000
Net Worth: $69,679,000
Earnings: ($44,646,000)
Emp.: 121
Fiscal Year-end: 05/31/23
Software Development Services
N.A.I.C.S.: 541511
Wesley Theta Carl Cummins *(Chm, CEO, Treas & Sec)*
Wes Cummins *(CEO, Chm, Treas & Sec)*
David Rench *(CFO)*
Michael Maniscalco *(CTO)*

Subsidiaries:

Gigawatts, LLC   (1)
1630 S Sunkist St Ste E & F, Anaheim, CA 92806
Web Site: https://www.gigawattinc.com
Solar Power Installation Services
N.A.I.C.S.: 221114

APPLIED DNA SCIENCES, INC.

50 Health Sciences Dr, Stony Brook, NY 11790
Tel.: (631) 240-8800   DE
Web Site: https://www.adnas.com
APDN—(NASDAQ)
Rev.: $3,431,420
Assets: $12,789,040
Liabilities: $3,820,955
Net Worth: $8,968,085
Earnings: ($7,088,306)
Emp.: 46
Fiscal Year-end: 09/30/24
Anti-Counterfeiting & Product Authentication Solutions
N.A.I.C.S.: 561621
James A. Hayward *(Chm, Pres & CEO)*
Wayne Buchen *(VP-Strategic Sls)*
Clay Shorrock *(Chief Legal Officer & Exec Dir-Bus Dev)*
Beth M. Jantzen *(CFO)*
Judith Murrah *(COO)*
Sanjay M. Hurry *(Exec Dir-IR & Corp Comm)*

Subsidiaries:

Linearx, Inc.   (1)
50 Health Sciences Dr, Stony Brook, NY 11790

Tel.: (631) 240-8877
Web Site: https://www.linearxdna.com
DNA Production Services
N.A.I.C.S.: 339112

Subsidiary (Domestic):

Vitatex Inc.   (2)
25 Health Sciences Dr Ste 220, Stony Brook, NY 11790-3384
Tel.: (631) 444-8482
Web Site: http://www.vitatex.com
Chemicals Mfr
N.A.I.C.S.: 325413
Wen-Tien Chen *(Founder & Pres)*
Qiang Zhao *(Mng Dir & Dir-Res)*
Huan Dong *(Dir-Product Res)*
Shaun Tulley *(Dir-Quality Mgmt)*
Che Chen *(Dir-Ops)*

APPLIED ENERGETICS, INC.

9070 S Rita Rd Ste 1500, Tucson, AZ 85747
Tel.: (520) 628-7415   DE
Web Site:
https://www.appliedenergetics.com
Year Founded: 2002
AERG—(OTCQB)
Rev.: $1,307,757
Assets: $6,728,227
Liabilities: $1,150,241
Net Worth: $5,577,986
Earnings: ($5,805,647)
Emp.: 14
Fiscal Year-end: 12/31/22
Directed-Energy Weapon Systems Developer
N.A.I.C.S.: 334511
Stephen W. McCahon *(Founder & Chief Science Officer)*
Bradford T. Adamczyk *(Exec Chm)*
Gregory J. Quarles *(Pres & CEO)*
Mary P. O'Hara *(Chief Legal Officer, Gen Counsel & Sec)*
Christopher Donaghey *(CFO & COO)*

APPLIED INDUSTRIAL TECHNOLOGIES, INC.

1 Applied Plz, Cleveland, OH 44115
Tel.: (216) 426-4000   OH
Web Site: https://www.applied.com
Year Founded: 1923
AIT—(NYSE)
Rev.: $4,479,406,000
Assets: $2,951,910,000
Liabilities: $1,263,129,000
Net Worth: $1,688,781,000
Earnings: $385,762,000
Emp.: 6,500
Fiscal Year-end: 06/30/24
Industrial Fluid Power & Engineered Products & Systems Distr
N.A.I.C.S.: 423840
Christopher Macey *(Controller)*
Warren E. Hoffner *(VP & Gen Mgr-Fluid Power & Flow Control)*
Ryan D. Cieslak *(Dir-IR & Treasury)*
Neil A. Schrimsher *(Pres & CEO)*
David K. Wells *(CFO, Principal Acctg Officer, Treas & VP)*
Kurt W. Loring *(Chief HR Officer & VP)*
Peter C. Wallace *(Chm)*

Subsidiaries:

Advanced Control Solutions   (1)
119 SE Pkwy Ct Ste 250, Franklin, TN 37064-3967
Tel.: (615) 595-6770
Web Site: http://www.advanced-control-inc.com
Engineering Services
N.A.I.C.S.: 541330
Rick Lynch *(Acct Mgr)*

Advanced Motion Systems Inc.   (1)
3800 Monroe Ave, Pittsford, NY 14534
Tel.: (585) 381-9320
Web Site: http://www.allaboutmotion.com
Rev.: $6,104,000
Emp.: 8

Electrical Apparatus & Equipment, Wiring Supplies & Related Equipment Merchant Whslr
N.A.I.C.S.: 423610
David Overy *(Pres)*

Air Draulics Engineering Co.   (1)
4250 Pilot Dr, Memphis, TN 38118-6932   (100%)
Tel.: (901) 794-4300
Web Site: http://www.airdraulic.com
Sales Range: $25-49.9 Million
Emp.: 15
Hydraulic Systems Equipment & Supplies Distr
N.A.I.C.S.: 423830

Air-Hydraulic Systems Inc.   (1)
6055 Nathen Ln Ste 100, Plymouth, MN 55402
Tel.: (612) 374-2100
Rev.: $17,000,000
Emp.: 40
Industrial Machinery & Equipment
N.A.I.C.S.: 423830

Applied Canada, ULC   (1)
100 Wright Ave Unit 17, Dartmouth, B3B 1L2, NS, Canada
Tel.: (902) 468-4300
Web Site: http://www.appliedcanada.com
Emp.: 9
Industrial Machinery Parts Mfr & Distr
N.A.I.C.S.: 333248

Applied Industrial Technologies - CA LLC   (1)
255 E Brokaw Rd, San Jose, CA 95112-4206
Tel.: (408) 436-5464
Web Site: http://www.applied.com
Industrial Equipment Distr
N.A.I.C.S.: 423610

Applied Industrial Technologies - DBB, Inc.   (1)
5454 Havana St Unit 714, Denver, CO 80239-2001
Tel.: (303) 375-9696
Web Site: http://www.applied.com
Sales Range: $25-49.9 Million
Emp.: 15
Industrial Equipment Whsr
N.A.I.C.S.: 423840

Applied Industrial Technologies - Indiana LLC   (1)
2628 N Cullen Ave Ste A, Evansville, IN 47715-2170
Tel.: (812) 473-2529
Web Site: http://www.applied.com
Sales Range: $25-49.9 Million
Emp.: 10
Industrial Equipment Whsr
N.A.I.C.S.: 423840

Applied Industrial Technologies - MBC, Inc.   (1)
1517 Main Ave, Fargo, ND 58103-1529
Tel.: (701) 237-4110
Web Site: http://www.applied.com
Emp.: 1
Industrial Equipment Whsr
N.A.I.C.S.: 423840

Applied Industrial Technologies - PA LLC   (1)
1727 Whiteford Rd, York, PA 17402-2207
Tel.: (717) 755-1902
Web Site: http://www.applied.com
Emp.: 10
Hydraulic Systems Equipment Whslr
N.A.I.C.S.: 423830

Applied Industrial Technologies - TX LP   (1)
7198 Merchant Ave Ste A3, El Paso, TX 79915-1221
Tel.: (915) 771-7481
Web Site: http://www.applied.com
Emp.: 4
Power Tools & Accessories Whslr
N.A.I.C.S.: 423710

Applied Industrial Technologies Pty Ltd.   (1)
22 Stamford Rd, Oakleigh, 3166, VIC, Australia
Tel.: (61) 395678700
Emp.: 37

Industrial Machinery Parts Distr
N.A.I.C.S.: 423830
Ashok Kapoor *(SEC & Dir)*

Applied Industrial Technologies, Inc. - London   (1)
337 Sovereign Road, London, N6M 1A6, ON, Canada
Tel.: (519) 686-2650
Web Site: http://www.appliedcanada.com
Power Transmission Equipment Whslr
N.A.I.C.S.: 423840

Applied Industrial Technologies, LP   (1)
124 Oakdale Road Unit A, Downsview, M3N 1V9, ON, Canada
Tel.: (416) 743-5713
Web Site: http://www.appliedcanada.com
Emp.: 18
Industrial Machinery Parts Mfr & Distr
N.A.I.C.S.: 333248

Applied Industrial Technologies, Ltd.   (1)
143 Wheeler St, Saskatoon, S7P 0A4, SK, Canada   (100%)
Tel.: (306) 931-0888
Web Site: http://www.aitcanada.com
Sales Range: $150-199.5 Million
Emp.: 500
Industrial Supplies Whslr

Applied Maintenance Supplies & Solutions   (1)
14790 Foltz Pkwy, Strongsville, OH 44149
Tel.: (216) 456-3600
Web Site: http://www.appliedmss.com
C Class Maintenance, Repair, Operating & Production (MROP) Supplies Distr
N.A.I.C.S.: 423840

Applied Maintenance Supplies & Solutions, LLC   (1)
14790 Foltz Pkwy, Strongsville, OH 44149
Tel.: (216) 456-3600
Web Site: http://www.appliedmss.com
Industrial Machinery Parts Mfr & Distr
N.A.I.C.S.: 333248

Applied Mexico Holdings, S.A. de C.V.   (1)
Av Silvestre Terrazas Enriquez No 8816, Col Sector 12 Campesina, Chihuahua, Mexico
Tel.: (52) 6144323550
Web Site: http://www.applied.com.mx
Holding Company
N.A.I.C.S.: 551112

Subsidiary (Domestic):

Applied Mexico, S.A. de C.V.   (2)
Av Silvestre Terrazas 8816-Sector 12 Campesina Nueva, 31410, Chihuahua, Mexico
Tel.: (52) 6144323550
Web Site: http://appliedmexico.net
Sales Range: $25-49.9 Million
Emp.: 50
Industrial Supplies Whslr
N.A.I.C.S.: 423840

VYCMEX Mexico, S.A. de C.V.   (2)
Av Colon 1500 Poniente Col Centro, 64000, Monterrey, Mexico
Tel.: (52) 18112330533
Web Site: http://vycmex.net
Sales Range: $150-199.9 Million
Industrial Supplies Whslr
N.A.I.C.S.: 423840

Atelier P.V. Hydraulique 2004 Inc.   (1)
34 Av Babin, Baie Comeau, G4Z 3A6, QC, Canada
Tel.: (418) 296-6155
Web Site: http://www.pvhydraulique.com
Emp.: 50
Commercial Equipment & Repair Services
N.A.I.C.S.: 811310

Atlantic Fasteners Co., Inc.   (1)
92 Almgren Dr, Agawam, MA 01001
Tel.: (413) 785-1687
Web Site: http://www.atlanticfasteners.com
Rev.: $10,000,000
Emp.: 48
Industrial Supplies Merchant Whslr
N.A.I.C.S.: 423840

Norman Fortini *(Mgr-Warehouse)*

Automation, Inc. **(1)**
4830 Azelia Ave N, Minneapolis, MN 55429-3915
Tel.: (763) 571-3336
Sales Range: $1-9.9 Million
Emp.: 30
Industrial Machinery Whslr
N.A.I.C.S.: 423830
Henry O'Donnell *(Pres)*

Basin Engine & Pump, Inc. **(1)**
1914 S County Rd 1083, Midland, TX 79706
Tel.: (432) 570-1114
Web Site: http://www.basinengine.com
Industrial Machinery & Equipment Whslr
N.A.I.C.S.: 423830
Mark Hill *(CFO)*

Bearing Distributors, Inc. **(1)**
930 S Stadium Rd, Columbia, SC 29201-4725
Tel.: (803) 799-0834
Web Site:
   https://www.bearingdistributors.com
Sales Range: $75-99.9 Million
Emp.: 100
Wholesale Distributor of Bearings, Power Transmission Equipment & Apparatus
N.A.I.C.S.: 423840

Subsidiary (Domestic):

Bearing Distributors and Drives, Inc. **(2)**
1036 Upper Asbury Ave, Charlotte, NC 28206
Tel.: (704) 375-0061
Bearing Distr
N.A.I.C.S.: 423830
Brian Odom *(Branch Mgr)*

Bearings & Oil Seals Specialists Inc. **(1)**
510 Beach Rd, Hamilton, L8H 7R4, ON, Canada
Tel.: (905) 545-2677
Web Site: http://www.bossinc.com
Industrial Machinery Parts Distr
N.A.I.C.S.: 423830

Cangro Industries Inc. **(1)**
495 Smith St, Farmingdale, NY 11735
Tel.: (631) 454-9000
Web Site: http://www.cangroindustries.com
Sales Range: $10-24.9 Million
Emp.: 20
Provider of Control Solutions to Manufacturers
N.A.I.C.S.: 423610
Victor Cangro *(Pres)*
Scott Vidiri *(Mgr-Sls)*

Disenos Construcciones y Fabricaciones Hispanoamericanas, S.A. **(1)**
Calle 24 Sur No 3908 Col Alseseca, Puebla, 72543, Mexico, Mexico
Tel.: (52) 2222821384
Web Site: https://www.dicofasa.mx
Industrial Machinery & Equipment Distr
N.A.I.C.S.: 423830

ESI Acquisition Corporation **(1)**
18 Progress PKWY, Maryland Heights, MO 63043-3706
Tel.: (314) 878-4500
Web Site: https://www.engineeredsales.com
Sales Range: $25-49.9 Million
Emp.: 30
Mfr of Industrial Machinery & Equipment
N.A.I.C.S.: 423830
Warren E. Hoffner *(VP & Gen Mgr)*

Eads Distribution, LLC **(1)**
13843 N Promenade Blvd Ste 100, Stafford, TX 77477
Tel.: (281) 243-2900
Web Site: http://www.eadsdistribution.com
Industrial Machinery & Equipment Whslr
N.A.I.C.S.: 423830

FCX Performance, Inc. **(1)**
3000 E 14th Ave, Columbus, OH 43219
Tel.: (614) 253-1996
Web Site: http://www.fcxperformance.com
Process Flow Products Mfr
N.A.I.C.S.: 423830
Jody Linnig *(Sr VP-Sls)*

Subsidiary (Domestic):

Baro Companies **(2)**
4655 Wright Rd, Stafford, TX 77477
Tel.: (281) 561-0900
Web Site: https://www.barocompanies.com
Industrial Equipment Whsr
N.A.I.C.S.: 423830

Florida Sealing Products **(2)**
3810 Drane Filed Rd Ste 16, Lakeland, FL 33811
Tel.: (863) 425-9611
Web Site: http://www.solarescontrols.com
Seal & Coating Whslr
N.A.I.C.S.: 423840

Massey-Chesson, Inc. **(2)**
9006-A Perimeter Woods Dr, Charlotte, NC 28216
Tel.: (704) 827-9661
Web Site:
   http://www.themasseycompany.com
Industrial Machinery & Equipment Merchant Whslr
N.A.I.C.S.: 423830

Pierce Pump **(2)**
9010 John W Carpenter Frwy, Dallas, TX 75247-4520
Tel.: (214) 320-3604
Web Site: http://www.piercepump.com
Pump & Compressor Distr
N.A.I.C.S.: 423830

Process Control Services, Inc. **(2)**
24450 Indoplex Cir, Farmington Hills, MI 48335
Tel.: (734) 453-0620
Web Site:
   http://www.processcontrolservices.com
Industrial Automation & Instrumentation Design, Repair, Installation & Calibration Services
N.A.I.C.S.: 334513

Pump Pro's, Inc. **(2)**
7601 Innovation Way, Mason, OH 45040
Tel.: (513) 860-9771
Web Site: http://www.pumppros.com
Industrial Pumps, Mechanical Seals & Mixers Mfr & Distr
N.A.I.C.S.: 332912

Solares Controls **(2)**
3810 Drane Field Rd Ste 5, Lakeland, FL 33811
Tel.: (863) 607-6623
Web Site: http://www.solarescontrols.com
Pump & Pumping Equipment Mfr
N.A.I.C.S.: 333914

Fluid Power Sales, Inc. **(1)**
8257 Loop Rd, Baldwinsville, NY 13027
Tel.: (315) 487-7111
Web Site: http://www.fluidpowersales.com
Industrial Machinery & Equipment Merchant Whslr
N.A.I.C.S.: 423830
Mark Townsend *(Pres)*

Gibson Engineering Company, Inc. **(1)**
90 Broadway, Norwood, MA 02062-3519
Tel.: (781) 769-3600
Web Site:
   http://www.gibsonengineering.com
Engineered Solutions & Automation Services
N.A.I.C.S.: 541330
Dan O'Brien *(Pres)*

Hydradyne, LLC **(1)**
15050 FAA Blvd, Fort Worth, TX 76155
Tel.: (817) 391-1547
Web Site: http://www.hydradynellc.com
Emp.: 500
Industrial Machinery & Equipment Mfr
N.A.I.C.S.: 423830
Chris Raschke *(Gen Mgr)*
Cody Burk *(Gen Mgr)*
Jim Markum *(Gen Mgr)*
Parker Cook *(Gen Mgr)*
Tim Gallaway *(Gen Mgr)*
Nestor Rivera *(Gen Mgr)*

Subsidiary (Domestic):

Baumgardner Services Inc. **(2)**
120 Belcher Rd, Boiling Springs, SC 29316
Tel.: (864) 599-6655

Web Site:
   http://www.baumgarnerservice.com
Site Preparation Contractor
N.A.I.C.S.: 238910

Gatlin Corporation **(2)**
58 Highway 84 E, Brookhaven, MS 39601
Tel.: (601) 833-9475
Web Site: http://www.gatlincorp.com
Rev: $8,587,600
Emp.: 70
All Other Miscellaneous General Purpose Machinery Mfr
N.A.I.C.S.: 333998
Bob Roberts *(Mgr-Sls)*
Gene McNeer *(Territory Mgr)*

Hydro Air LLC **(1)**
243 State St, North Haven, CT 06473
Tel.: (203) 248-8863
Web Site: http://www.hydroair.net
Sales Range: $25-49.9 Million
Emp.: 60
Provider of Hydraulic & Pneumatic Components
N.A.I.C.S.: 423830
Gary Rogers *(Pres)*

HydroAir Hughes, LLC **(1)**
9685 Main St, Clarence, NY 14031-2036
Tel.: (716) 759-8374
Web Site: https://www.hydroair.net
Sales Range: $25-49.9 Million
Emp.: 30
Hydraulic Systems Equipment Whslr
N.A.I.C.S.: 423830

Hyquip, LLC **(1)**
1811 Dolphin Dr, Waukesha, WI 53186
Tel.: (262) 521-2170
Web Site: https://www.hyquip.net
Sales Range: $1-9.9 Million
Emp.: 20
Industrial Supplies
N.A.I.C.S.: 423840

Knox Oil Field Supply, Inc. **(1)**
6328 US Hwy 277 S, San Angelo, TX 76904
Tel.: (325) 651-6818
Web Site: http://www.knoxsupplyinc.com
Sales Range: $100-124.9 Million
Emp.: 8
Oil Field Production Equipment Mfr
N.A.I.C.S.: 423830
Nathan Smith *(Dir-Ops)*

Olympus Controls Corp. **(1)**
13633 SW Industry Ln Ste 100, Sherwood, OR 97140
Tel.: (503) 582-8100
Web Site: https://www.olympus-controls.com
Engineeering Services
N.A.I.C.S.: 541330
Scott Hendrickson *(Founder & CEO)*
Nick Armenta *(Sls Engr)*
Jakob Bahner *(Sls Engr)*
Jason Brickner *(Sls Engr)*
Lance Douglas *(Sls Engr)*
Lanz Fritz *(Pres)*

Power Systems, LLC **(1)**
8325 Commerce Dr, Chanhassen, MN 55317
Tel.: (952) 361-6800
Web Site: http://www.powersystems.mn.com
Sales Range: $25-49.9 Million
Emp.: 50
Hydraulic Fluid Power Equipment Distr
N.A.I.C.S.: 423830

R. L. Stone Company, Inc. **(1)**
8257 Loop Rd, Baldwinsville, NY 13027
Tel.: (315) 479-7979
Web Site: http://www.rl-stone.com
Industrial Equipment Mfr
N.A.I.C.S.: 334512
Louis Betrus *(CEO)*

R. R. Floody Company, Inc. **(1)**
5065 - 27th Ave, Rockford, IL 61109
Tel.: (815) 399-1931
Web Site: https://www.rrfloody.com
Automation Control Product Mfr & Retailer
N.A.I.C.S.: 335314

Rafael Benitez Carrillo, Inc. **(1)**
Calle Estado 715 Miramar, San Juan, PR 00907
Tel.: (787) 725-7635
Web Site: http://www.appliedindustrial.com

Sales Range: $25-49.9 Million
Emp.: 20
Power Transmission Products Supplier
N.A.I.C.S.: 423120
Ivan Batista *(Gen Dir)*

Reliance Industrial Products USA, Ltd. **(1)**
2030 E-8 St Ste B, Greeley, CO 80631
Tel.: (970) 346-3751
Industrial Machinery Parts Mfr & Distr
N.A.I.C.S.: 333248
Richard Lietz *(Branch Mgr)*

S.G. Morris Co., LLC **(1)**
699 Miner Rd, Highland Heights, OH 44143
Tel.: (440) 473-1640
Web Site: http://www.sgmorris.com
Industrial Machinery & Equipment Mfr
N.A.I.C.S.: 423830

Seals Unlimited Holding Co., Inc. **(1)**
1177 King Road, Burlington, L7T 0B7, ON, Canada
Tel.: (905) 278-1326
Web Site: https://www.sealsunlimited.ca
Industrial Machinery & Equipment Whslr
N.A.I.C.S.: 423830

Sentinel Fluid Controls, LLC **(1)**
5702 Opportunity Dr, Toledo, OH 46312
Tel.: (419) 478-9086
Web Site:
   https://www.sentinelfluidcontrols.com
Industrial Machinery & Equipment Whslr
N.A.I.C.S.: 423830

Servco Oilfield Supply Canada Ltd. **(1)**
606 19 Avenue, Nisku, T9E 7W1, AB, Canada
Tel.: (780) 955-7444
Web Site: http://www.servcooilfield.com
Emp.: 12
Industrial Machinery Parts Distr
N.A.I.C.S.: 423830

Solutions Industrielles ULC **(1)**
1932 St-Paul Boulevard, Chicoutimi, G7K 1H2, QC, Canada
Tel.: (418) 690-1441
Web Site:
   http://www.appliedindustiraltechnologies.com
Emp.: 20
Industrial Machinery Parts Distr
N.A.I.C.S.: 423830

Specialites Industrielles Harvey ULC **(1)**
6600 Boul Pierre-Bertrand Nord, Quebec, G2J 1S7, QC, Canada
Tel.: (418) 628-2255
Web Site: http://www.siharvey.com
Emp.: 20
Bearing & Power Transmission Product Distr
N.A.I.C.S.: 423840

Spencer Fluid Power **(1)**
19308 68th Ave S, Kent, WA 98032
Tel.: (253) 796-1100
Web Site: http://www.spencerfluidpower.com
Sales Range: $25-49.9 Million
Emp.: 39
Hydraulic Components & Systems Whslr & Distr
N.A.I.C.S.: 423830

Stanley M. Proctor Company, LLC **(1)**
2016 Midway Dr, Twinsburg, OH 44087
Tel.: (330) 425-7814
Web Site: http://www.stanleyproctor.com
Sales Range: $10-24.9 Million
Emp.: 25
Industrial Machinery & Equipment Merchant Whslr
N.A.I.C.S.: 423830
John D. Proctor *(Pres & CEO)*

Texas Oilpatch Services, LLC **(1)**
3515 Vista Rd, Pasadena, TX 77504
Tel.: (713) 946-1030
Web Site: https://www.texasoilpatch.com
Industrial Machinery Parts Mfr & Distr
N.A.I.C.S.: 333248

Total Machine Solutions, Inc. **(1)**
16 Spielman Rd, Fairfiled, NJ 07004
Tel.: (516) 942-5125

Applied Industrial Technologies,
Inc.—(Continued)

Web Site: http://www.tmsny.com
Sales Range: $1-9.9 Million
Emp.: 14
Electrical Apparatus And Equipment, Nsk
N.A.I.C.S.: 423610
Kevin Orlofski (Mgr-Sls)
Christina Doner (Office Mgr-Plainview)
James Fuoco (Mgr-Warehouse-Plainview)
Joe Vazquez (Mgr-Warehouse-Fairfield)
Marvin Goldman (Pres-Plainview)

APPLIED MATERIALS, INC.
3050 Bowers Ave, Santa Clara, CA
95052-8039
Tel.: (408) 727-5555   **DE**
Web Site:
https://www.appliedmaterials.com
Year Founded: 1967
AMAT—(NASDAQ)
Rev.: $27,176,000,000
Assets: $34,409,000,000
Liabilities: $15,408,000,000
Net Worth: $19,001,000,000
Earnings: $7,177,000,000
Emp.: 35,700
Fiscal Year-end: 10/27/24
Supplier of Wafer Fabrication Sys-
tems & Services to the Global Semi-
conductor Industries; Plasma Etch
Systems & Chemical Vapor Deposi-
tion (CVD) Systems
N.A.I.C.S.: 333242
Brice C. Hill (CFO & Sr VP)
Thomas J. Iannotti (Chm)
Omkaram Nalamasu (CTO & Sr VP)
Gary E. Dickerson (Pres & CEO)
Charles W. Read (CFO-Ops & VP-
Bus Units)
Prabu G. Raja (Sr VP-Semiconductor
Products Grp)
Susan Schmitt Winchester (Grp VP &
Head-HR)
Alex Belogolovsky (VP & Gen Mgr-
Common Sys Software Corp Engrg)
Mei Chang (Mng Dir-Chemistry Cen-
ter of Excellence-New Markets & Alli-
ances)
Ken Collins (VP-Disruptive Tech &
Enrgrg-Semiconductor Products Grp)
Tza-Jing Gung (VP & Gen Mgr-
Dielectric CVD Products-
Semiconductor Products Grp)
Shinichi Kurita (VP & Head-Thin Film
Engrg-Display & Flexible Tech Grp)
Ron Naftali (CTO-Process Diagnos-
tics & Control-Silicon Sys Grp)
Nick Parisi (Mng Dir-Software Engrg-
Implant Bus Unit-Semiconductor
Products)
Hari Ponnekanti (VP & Gen Mgr-
Dielectric CVD Products-
Semiconductor Products Grp)
John White (VP-Engrg & Product
Tech Dev-Display & Flexible Tech
Bus Grp)
Ellie Yieh (VP-Advanced Product
Tech Dev-New Markets & Alliances
Grp)
Teri Little (Chief Legal Officer, Sec &
Sr VP)
Chris Librie (Dir-ESG, Corp Sustain-
ability & Reporting)
Keith Wells (VP-Grp & Gen Mgr-
Imaging & Process Control Grp)
Raman Achutharaman (Grp VP)
Timothy M. Deane (Grp VP)
K. C. Ong (VP)
Robert J. Halliday (VP)

Subsidiaries:

AKT America, Inc.   (1)
3101 Scott Blvd Bldg 91, Santa Clara, CA
95054-3318
Tel.: (408) 563-5455
Web Site: http://www.appliedmaterials.com

Electronic Components Mfr
N.A.I.C.S.: 334419

Applied Materials (China) Holdings,
Ltd.   (1)
F18 Bldg 40 1 North Disheng Street,
Economic-Technological Development
Zone, Beijing, 100176, China
Tel.: (86) 1087859500
Web Site: http://www.appliedmaterial.com
Semiconductor Product Mfr
N.A.I.C.S.: 334413

Subsidiary (Domestic):

Applied Materials (Xian), Ltd.   (2)
28 Xinxi Road, Xi'an Hi-Tech Industrial De-
velopment Zone, Xi'an, 710119, Shaanxi,
China
Tel.: (86) 296 891 7000
Web Site: http://www.appliedmaterials.com
Commercial Physical Research Services
N.A.I.C.S.: 541715
Roger Chant (Pres)

Applied Materials (China), Inc.   (1)
Building 22/23/26 1388 Zhangdong Road,
Zhangjiang Hi-Tech Park Pudong New Area,
Shanghai, 201203, China
Tel.: (86) 2138616000
Semiconductors & Related Devices Mfr
N.A.I.C.S.: 334413

Applied Materials Canada, Inc.   (1)
170 University Ave Suite 1200, Toronto,
M5H 3B3, ON, Canada
Tel.: (416) 977-0599
Web Site: http://www.appliedmaterials.com
Sales Range: $25-49.9 Million
Computer Softwares Mfr
N.A.I.C.S.: 541512

Applied Materials Corp.   (1)
3050 Bowers Ave S, Santa Clara, CA
95054-3201
Tel.: (408) 727-5555
Web Site: http://www.appliedmaterials.com
Rev.: $40,635,000
Emp.: 270
Designer, Retailer & Mfr of Execution Sys-
tem Software
N.A.I.C.S.: 333242

Applied Materials Deutschland Hold-
ing GmbH   (1)
Siemensstrasse 100, 63755, Alzenau, Ger-
many
Tel.: (49) 6023926000
Web Site: http://www.appliedmaterials.com
Emp.: 300
Investment Consulting Services
N.A.I.C.S.: 523940

Applied Materials Europe BV   (1)
Spicalaan 57, 2132 JG, Hoofddorp,
Netherlands   (100%)
Tel.: (31) 23 565 6111
Web Site: http://www.appliedmaterials.com
Sales Range: $25-49.9 Million
Emp.: 45
Sales & Service
N.A.I.C.S.: 333310

Subsidiary (Non-US):

Applied Materials France SARL   (2)
864 Chemin des Fontaines, 38190, Bernin,
France
Tel.: (33) 47 604 2900
Web Site: https://www.appliedmaterials.com
Sales Range: $50-74.9 Million
Electronic Components
N.A.I.C.S.: 334419

Applied Materials GmbH   (2)
Buchenstrasse 16b, 01097, Dresden, Ger-
many
Tel.: (49) 351 800 2300
Web Site: http://www.appliedmaterials.com
Sales Range: $100-124.9 Million
Electronic Components
N.A.I.C.S.: 334419

Applied Materials Ireland Ltd.   (2)
Block A Maynooth Business Campus, May-
nooth, Kildare, Ireland
Tel.: (353) 1 505 2600
Web Site: https://www.appliedmaterials.com
Sales Range: $25-49.9 Million
Electronic Components
N.A.I.C.S.: 334419

Michael Hill (Pres)

Applied Materials Italia S.r.l.   (2)
Via Della Vignolina 2, 20864, Agrate Bri-
anza, MB, Italy
Tel.: (39) 039 634 0001
Web Site: http://www.appliedmaterials.com
Sales Range: $100-124.9 Million
Electronic Components
N.A.I.C.S.: 334419

Applied Materials GmbH & Co.,
KG   (1)
Siemensstrasse 100, 63755, Alzenau, Ger-
many
Tel.: (49) 6023926000
Semiconductor Machinery Mfr
N.A.I.C.S.: 333242

Applied Materials India Private
Limited   (1)
Unit 5 Third Floor Explorer Building, Inter-
national Technology Park Whitefield Road,
Bengaluru, 560 066, Karnataka, India
Tel.: (91) 8066283000
Semiconductor Machinery Mfr
N.A.I.C.S.: 333242

Applied Materials Israel, Ltd.   (1)
9 Oppenheimer Street, Rehovot, 76705,
Israel
Tel.: (972) 89488888
Sales Range: $350-399.9 Million
Electronic Components
N.A.I.C.S.: 334419

Applied Materials Japan, Inc.   (1)
Yokoso Rainbow Tower 3-20-20 Kaigan,
Minato-ku, Tokyo, 108-8444, Japan
Tel.: (81) 36 812 6800
Sales Range: $100-124.9 Million
Emp.: 568
Electronic Components
N.A.I.C.S.: 334419

Subsidiary (Domestic):

Sigmameltec Ltd.   (2)
3-37-7 Shimoasao, Asao-ku, Kawasaki,
215-0022, Kanagawa, Japan
Tel.: (81) 449879381
Web Site: http://www.sigmameltec.co.jp
Semiconductor Machinery Mfr & Distr
N.A.I.C.S.: 333242
Yutaka Tanaka (Pres)

Applied Materials Korea, Ltd.   (1)
5th FL Korea Design Center Bldg 322,
Yanghyeon-ro Bundang-gu, Seongnam,
13496, Gyeonggi, Korea (South)
Tel.: (82) 317247000
Semiconductor Machinery Mfr
N.A.I.C.S.: 333242

Applied Materials SPV2, Inc.   (1)
3050 Bowers Ave, Santa Clara, CA 95054
Tel.: (408) 727-5555
Semiconductor Machinery Mfr
N.A.I.C.S.: 333242

Applied Materials Singapore Technology Pte. Ltd.   (1)
10 Science Park Rd 1-01B, The Alpha Science Park II, Singapore, 117684, Singapore
Tel.: (65) 64304180
Semiconductor Machinery Mfr
N.A.I.C.S.: 333242

Applied Materials South East Asia
Pte. Ltd.   (1)
8 Upper Changi Road North, Singapore,
506906, Singapore
Tel.: (65) 63117000
Sales Range: $100-124.9 Million
Emp.: 50
Electronic Parts & Equipment Mfr
N.A.I.C.S.: 334419
Jackie Tan (Gen Mgr)

Subsidiary (Non-US):

Perceptive Engineering Limited   (2)
Vanguard House Keckwick Lane Sci Tech,
Daresbury, WA4 4AB, Cheshire, United
Kingdom
Tel.: (44) 1925607150
Web Site: https://www.perceptiveapc.com
Software Development Services
N.A.I.C.S.: 541511
David Lovett (Founder & Mng Dir)
John Mack (Dir-Engineering)

Matthew McEwan (Sys Engr)
Keith Smith (Sys Engr)
Simon Mazier (Mktg Dir)

Applied Materials Taiwan, Ltd.   (1)
No 32 R and D Road II Hsinchu Science
Park, Hsin-chu, 30076, Taiwan
Tel.: (886) 35798888
Electronic Components Mfr
N.A.I.C.S.: 335999

Applied Materials UK Limited   (1)
200 Brook Drive Green Park, Reading, RG2
6UB, Berks, United Kingdom   (100%)
Tel.: (44) 1189315600
Web Site: http://www.appliedmaterials.com
Sales Range: $50-74.9 Million
Emp.: 15
Retailer & Marketer of Computer Software
N.A.I.C.S.: 423430

Applied Materials WEB Coating
GmbH   (1)
Tel.: (49) 6023926000
Semiconductor Equipment Mfr
N.A.I.C.S.: 334413

Applied Materials, Inc.   (1)
9700 290 E, Austin, TX 78724
Tel.: (512) 272-1000
Web Site: http://www.appliedmaterials.com
Sales Range: $500-549.9 Million
Emp.: 2,200
Data Mining Services for the Semiconductor
Mfr Industry
N.A.I.C.S.: 561499

Applied Ventures, LLC   (1)
3050 Bowers Ave, Santa Clara, CA 95054-
3299
Tel.: (408) 986-3317
Web Site: http://www.appliedventures.com
Semiconductor Solar Photovoltaic Products
Mfr
N.A.I.C.S.: 334413

ICT Integrated Circuit Testing
GmbH   (1)
Ammerthalstrasse 20, 85551, Heimstetten,
Germany
Tel.: (49) 896933090
Electrical Component Mfr
N.A.I.C.S.: 335999

Perceptive Engineering Pte. Ltd.   (1)
8 Upper Changi Road North, Singapore,
506906, Singapore
Tel.: (65) 63117000
Web Site: https://www.perceptiveapc.com
Software Development Services
N.A.I.C.S.: 541511

PineBrook Imaging, Inc.   (1)
3511 Thomas Rd Ste 1, Santa Clara, CA
95054
Tel.: (408) 988-1008
Emp.: 5
Software Publishing Services
N.A.I.C.S.: 513210

Tango System LLC   (1)
2620 Regatta Dr Ste 102, Las Vegas, NV
89124
Web Site: http://www.tangosys.com
Application Design Services
N.A.I.C.S.: 541490

Think Silicon Research & Technology
Single Member S.A.
Patras Science Park, Rion Achaias, 265 04,
Patras, Greece
Tel.: (30) 2610910650
Web Site: http://www.think-silicon.com
Semiconductor Product Mfr
N.A.I.C.S.: 334413
George Sidiropoulos (Co-Founder & CEO)
Lakovos Stamoulis (Co-Founder & CTO)
Georgios Keramidas (Chief Scientific Offi-
cer)
Ulli Mueller (VP-Bus Dev & Mktg)

Think Silicon Single Member
P.C.   (1)
Patras Science Park, 26504, Rion Achaias,
Greece
Tel.: (30) 2610910650
Web Site: https://www.think-silicon.com
Software Design & Development Services
N.A.I.C.S.: 541511

Varian Semiconductor Equipment Associates PacRim Pte. Ltd.   (1)

10 Upper Aljunied Link 04-09 York International Industria, Singapore, 367904, Singapore
Tel.: (65) 63117000
Semiconductor Equipment Mfr
N.A.I.C.S.: 334413

Varian Semiconductor Equipment Associates, Inc.   **(1)**
35 Dory Rd, Gloucester, MA 01930-2236
Tel.: (978) 282-2000
Web Site: http://www.amat.com
Sales Range: $800-899.9 Million
Emp.: 1,500
Semiconductor Equipment Mfr
N.A.I.C.S.: 333242

Subsidiary (Non-US):

Varian Korea Ltd.   **(2)**
433-1 Mogkok-dong, Gyeonggi-do, Pyeong-taek, 459-040, Korea (South)
Tel.: (82) 31 6107114
Sales Range: $100-124.9 Million
Semiconductor Parts & Equipment Mfr
N.A.I.C.S.: 334413

APPLIED MINERALS, INC.
55 Washington St Ste 301, Brooklyn, NY 11201
Tel.: (435) 433-2059   DE
Web Site:
  https://www.appliedminerals.com
AMNL—(OTCIQ)
Rev.: $1,409,019
Assets: $1,177,821
Liabilities: $51,578,703
Net Worth: ($50,400,882)
Earnings: ($3,563,360)
Emp.: 7
Fiscal Year-end: 12/31/21
Kaolinite Clay Production & Mining Services
N.A.I.C.S.: 327120
John F. Levy *(Vice Chm)*
Mario Concha *(Chm)*
Christopher T. Carney *(Pres & CEO)*
Sharad Mathur *(CTO)*

APPLIED OPTOELECTRON-ICS, INC.
13139 Jess Pirtle Blvd, Sugar Land, TX 77478
Tel.: (281) 295-1800   DE
Web Site: https://www.ao-inc.com
Year Founded: 1997
AAOI—(NASDAQ)
Rev.: $222,818,000
Assets: $408,263,000
Liabilities: $223,593,000
Net Worth: $184,670,000
Earnings: ($66,397,000)
Emp.: 2,213
Fiscal Year-end: 12/31/22
Optical Semiconductor Devices, Packaged Optical Components, Optical Subsystems, Laser Transmitters & Fiber Optic Transceivers Mfr
N.A.I.C.S.: 334413
Stefan J. Murry *(CFO & Chief Strategy Officer)*
Fred Hung-Lun Chang *(Sr VP-Optical Components Bus Unit & Gen Mgr-North America)*
Klaus Alexander Anselm *(VP-Semiconductor Products)*
Shu-Hua Yeh *(Sr VP-Network Equipment Module Bus Unit & Gen Mgr-Asia)*
David C. Kuo *(Chief Compliance Officer, Gen Counsel, Sec & VP)*
Michael Ballard *(Sr Dir-Mktg-Broadband Access)*
Todd McCrum *(Sr VP/Gen Mgr-Broadband Access)*
Chih-Hsiang Lin *(Founder, Chm, Pres & CEO)*

APPLIED THERAPEUTICS, INC.

545 5th Ave Ste 1400, New York, NY 10017
Tel.: (212) 220-9226   DE
Web Site:
  https://www.appliedtherapeutics.com
Year Founded: 2016
APLT—(NASDAQ)
Rev.: $442,000
Assets: $38,363,000
Liabilities: $34,302,000
Net Worth: $4,061,000
Earnings: ($82,508,000)
Emp.: 27
Fiscal Year-end: 12/31/22
Biotechnology Research & Development Services
N.A.I.C.S.: 541714
Riccardo Perfetti *(Chief Medical Officer)*
Catherine Thorpe *(Chief Acctg Officer & Interim Principal Fin Officer)*
Les Funtleyder *(CFO)*
Shoshana Shendelman *(Founder, Chm, Pres, CEO & Sec)*

APPLIED UV, INC.
150 N Macquesten Pkwy, Mount Vernon, NY 10550
Tel.: (720) 531-4152   DE
Web Site:
  https://www.applieduvinc.com
Year Founded: 2019
AUVI—(NASDAQ)
Rev.: $11,667,579
Assets: $38,525,992
Liabilities: $5,860,232
Net Worth: $32,665,760
Earnings: ($7,390,355)
Emp.: 61
Fiscal Year-end: 12/31/21
Holding Company
N.A.I.C.S.: 551112
John J. Hayman III *(Interim COO)*
Max Munn *(Pres & CEO)*
Mike Riccio *(CFO)*
Brett Maas *(Mng Principal)*

Subsidiaries:

LED Supply Co.   **(1)**
747 Sheridan Blvd Unit 8E, Lakewood, CO 80214
Web Site: http://www.ledsupplyco.com
Sales Range: $1-9.9 Million
Emp.: 6
Electronic Product Distr
N.A.I.C.S.: 423610
Brian Stern *(Founder & Pres)*
Webb Lawrence *(Exec VP)*

Munn Works LLC   **(1)**
150 N Macquesten Pkwy, Mount Vernon, NY 10550
Tel.: (914) 665-6100
Web Site: https://www.munnworks.com
Mirror & Framed Art Work Mfr
N.A.I.C.S.: 327215
Max Munn *(Pres & CEO)*
Molly Munn *(Project Mgr)*

SteriLumen, Inc.   **(1)**
150 N Macquesten Pkwy, Mount Vernon, NY 10550
Tel.: (914) 665-6100
Web Site: https://www.sterilumen.com
Emp.: 30
Hardware Services
N.A.I.C.S.: 541512
Rhonda A. Wallen *(VP-Mktg & Corp Dev)*

Subsidiary (Domestic):

KES Science & Technology, Inc.   **(2)**
3625 Kennesaw N Ind Pkwy, Kennesaw, GA 30144
Tel.: (770) 427-6500
Web Site: http://www.kesscience.com
Rev.: $6,300,000
Emp.: 34
Farm & Garden Machinery & Equipment Merchant Whslr
N.A.I.C.S.: 423820
John J. Hayman III *(Chm, Pres & CEO)*

APPLIED VISUAL SCIENCES, INC.
525K E Market St 116, Leesburg, VA 20176
Tel.: (703) 539-6190   DE
Web Site: http://www.appliedvs.com
Year Founded: 1989
APVS—(OTCEM)
Sales Range: Less than $1 Million
Emp.: 3
Image Analysis Software & Equipment
N.A.I.C.S.: 513210
Gregory E. Hare *(CFO & Sec)*
William J. Donovan *(Chm & CEO)*

APPLIFE DIGITAL SOLUTIONS, INC.
50 California St Ste 1500, San Francisco, CA 94111
Tel.: (415) 439-5260   NV
Web Site:
  https://www.applifedigital.com
Year Founded: 2018
ALDS—(OTCQB)
Rev.: $46,879
Assets: $158,264
Liabilities: $1,594,325
Net Worth: ($1,436,061)
Earnings: ($3,496,573)
Emp.: 1
Fiscal Year-end: 06/30/23
Software Development Services
N.A.I.C.S.: 541511
Matthew Reid *(Pres, CEO, CFO, Principal Acctg Officer & Sec)*
Michael Kaniela Wheeler *(Chief Legal Officer)*
Lesly Bernard *(Project Dir)*

Subsidiaries:

Rooster Essentials APP SPV, LLC   **(1)**
50 California St Ste 1500, San Francisco, CA 94111
Web Site: https://www.roosteressentials.com
Grooming Product Distr
N.A.I.C.S.: 423850

APPLIQATE, INC.
30 N Gould St Ste 4000, Sheridan, WY 82801
Tel.: (305) 507-3335   WY
Web Site: http://www.appliqate.com
Year Founded: 2015
APQT—(OTCIQ)
Rev.: $44,000
Assets: $1,393,000
Liabilities: $4,000
Net Worth: $1,389,000
Earnings: ($40,000)
Fiscal Year-end: 01/31/19
Marketing & Technology Services
N.A.I.C.S.: 541613
Una Taylor *(Chm, Pres & CEO)*

APPLOVIN CORP.
1100 Page Mill Rd, Palo Alto, CA 94304
Tel.: (650) 453-8486   DE
Web Site: https://www.applovin.com
Year Founded: 2012
APP—(NASDAQ)
Rev.: $3,283,087,000
Assets: $5,359,187,000
Liabilities: $4,102,858,000
Net Worth: $1,256,329,000
Earnings: $356,711,000
Emp.: 1,717
Fiscal Year-end: 12/31/23
Mobile Games Studios & Marketing Technology
N.A.I.C.S.: 513210
Andrew Karam *(VP-Product & Co-Founder)*
Katie Jansen *(CMO)*
Rafael Vivas *(Pres-Lion Studios)*

Basil Shikin *(CTO)*
Omer Hasan *(VP-Ops)*
Jordan Satok *(VP-Corp Dev)*
Barry Dilouya *(VP-Global Bus Ops)*
Christina Seafort *(Chief People Officer)*
Adam Foroughi *(Co-Founder, Chm & CEO)*

Subsidiaries:

MoPub, Inc.   **(1)**
245 W 17th St Fl 5, New York, NY 10011   **(100%)**
Tel.: (415) 426-4200
Web Site: http://www.mopub.com
Mobile Advertising Platform Services
N.A.I.C.S.: 513210

WURL, Inc.   **(1)**
550 Lytton Ave 2nd Fl, Palo Alto, CA 94301
Tel.: (650) 470-7550
Web Site: http://www.wurl.com
Online Video Streaming & Hosting Services
N.A.I.C.S.: 541519
Sean Doherty *(Co-Founder & CEO)*
David Martinez *(Co-Founder & Head-Engrg)*
Joe Stockwell *(Head-Corp Dev)*
Rich Saffir *(Gen Counsel)*
Ron Gutman *(VP-Broadcast Engrg)*
Kris Johns *(VP-User Experience)*
Mike Woods *(Sr VP-Product)*
Craig Heiting *(Sr VP-Worldwide Bus Dev)*

APPRECIATE HOLDINGS, INC.
6101 Baker Rd Ste 200, Minnetonka, MN 55345
Tel.: (952) 470-8888   DE
Web Site: https://www.appreciate.rent
SFRT—(OTCQB)
Holding Company; Real Estate Services
N.A.I.C.S.: 551112

Subsidiaries:

RW National Holdings, LLC   **(1)**
6101 Baker Rd Ste 200, Minnetonka, MN 55345
Tel.: (952) 470-8888
Real Estate Services
N.A.I.C.S.: 531390

Subsidiary (Domestic):

Renters Warehouse   **(2)**
6101 Baker Rd Ste 200, Minnetonka, MN 55345
Tel.: (952) 470-8888
Web Site: http://www.renterswarehouse.com
Rev.: $33,000,000
Emp.: 39
Real Estate Services
N.A.I.C.S.: 531210
Brenton Hayden *(Founder)*
Kevin Ortner *(CEO)*
Jonathan Confeld *(CFO)*
Caleb Gilbertson *(VP-Mktg & Adv)*
Jesse Evans *(Reg VP)*
Steven Walters *(Mgr-Rent Collection Property)*
Dave Thompson *(Chief Legal Officer)*
Pam Kosanke *(CMO)*
Emily Doe *(Controller)*
Trevor Brace *(CTO)*
Bill Bump *(Dir-Customer Svc)*
Shay Guldberg *(Dir-Digital Mktg)*
Tiffany Haun *(Dir-Fin)*
Josh Zupfer *(Dir-Maintenance)*
Nate Uher *(VP-Property Mgmt)*
Anthony Cazazian *(Chief Investment Officer & Pres-Portfolio Svcs)*
Jonathan Ortner *(VP-Portfolio Svcs)*
Charles Wyatt *(CFO)*
David Sommer *(COO)*
Mitch Bowling *(COO)*

APPSOFT TECHNOLOGIES, INC.
1225 Franklin Ave Ste 325, Garden City, NY 11530
Tel.: (516) 224-7717   NV
Web Site:
  https://www.appsofttechnologies.com
Year Founded: 2015

AppSoft Technologies, Inc.—(Continued)

ASFT—(OTCIQ)
Assets: $6
Liabilities: $369,938
Net Worth: ($369,932)
Earnings: ($31,439)
Emp.: 1
Fiscal Year-end: 12/31/22
Mobile Application Development Services
N.A.I.C.S.: 541511
Brian Kupchik *(Pres, CEO, CFO, Chief Acctg Officer & Sec)*

APPSWARM, INC.
401 S Boston Ste 500, Tulsa, OK 74103
Tel.: (918) 706-5497
Web Site: https://www.app-swarm.com
SWRM—(OTCIQ)
Rev.: $25,000
Assets: $592,000
Liabilities: $440,000
Net Worth: $152,000
Earnings: ($59,000)
Fiscal Year-end: 12/31/19
Custom Computer Programming Services
N.A.I.C.S.: 541511
Ron Brewer *(CEO)*

APPTECH PAYMENTS CORP.
5876 Owens Ave Ste 100, Carlsbad, CA 92008
Tel.: (760) 707-5959
Web Site:
https://www.apptechcorp.com
APCX—(NASDAQ)
Rev.: $450,000
Assets: $12,519,000
Liabilities: $5,095,000
Net Worth: $7,424,000
Earnings: ($16,281,000)
Emp.: 23
Fiscal Year-end: 12/31/22
Financial Services & Information Technology
N.A.I.C.S.: 522320
Luke D'Angelo *(Chm, CEO & Chief Investment Officer)*
Virgilio Llapitan *(Pres & COO)*
Meilin Yu *(CFO, Principal Acctg Officer & Treas)*
Marc Evans *(Sec)*
Julia Yu *(Sr VP)*

APPYEA, INC.
447 Broadway 2nd FL, New York, NY 10013
Tel.: (817) 887-8142   SD
Web Site: https://www.appyea.com
Year Founded: 2012
APYP—(OTCQB)
Assets: $474,000
Liabilities: $3,027,000
Net Worth: ($2,553,000)
Earnings: ($1,817,000)
Emp.: 9
Fiscal Year-end: 12/31/23
Mobile Software Applications
N.A.I.C.S.: 513210
Keri R. Williams *(Sec)*
Todd Violette *(Chm)*
Adi Shemer *(CEO)*

APREA THERAPEUTICS, INC.
3805 Old Eon Rd, Doylestown, PA 18902
Tel.: (617) 463-9385   DE
Web Site: https://www.aprea.com
Year Founded: 2019
APRE—(NASDAQ)
Rev.: $730,201
Assets: $30,155,827
Liabilities: $4,512,149

Net Worth: $25,643,678
Earnings: ($112,662,027)
Emp.: 9
Fiscal Year-end: 12/31/22
Research & Development in Biotechnology (except Nanobiotechnology)
N.A.I.C.S.: 541714
Lars Abrahmsen *(Chief Scientific Officer & Sr VP)*
Gregory A. Korbel *(Chief Bus Officer)*
Klas Wiman *(Co-Founder)*
Galina Selivanova *(Co-Founder)*
Vladimir Bykov *(Co-Founder)*
Staffan Stromblad *(Co-Founder)*
Wenjie Bao *(Co-Founder)*
Natalia Issaeva *(Co-Founder)*
Oren Gilad *(CEO)*
John P. Hamill *(CFO, Principal Acctg Officer & Sr VP)*
John P. Hamill *(CFO, Principal Acctg Officer & Sr VP)*

APT MOTO VOX GROUP, INC.
8844 Hillcrest Rd, Kansas City, MO 64138
Tel.: (816) 767-8783   DE
MTVX—(OTCIQ)
Motorcycle & Parts Mfr
N.A.I.C.S.: 336991
Troy Covey *(Pres)*
William Maher *(Acting CFO, Sr VP & VP-Corp & Legal Affairs)*

APT SYSTEMS, INC.
505 Montgomery St 11th Fl, San Francisco, CA 94111
Tel.: (415) 200-1105   DE
Web Site:
https://www.aptsystemsinc.com
Year Founded: 2010
APTY—(OTCIQ)
Sales Range: Less than $1 Million
Emp.: 3
Software Publisher
N.A.I.C.S.: 513210
Glenda M. Dowie *(Founder, Pres & CEO)*
Joseph James Gagnon *(Sec)*
Carl Hussey *(CFO & Treas)*

APTARGROUP, INC.
265 Exchnage Dr Ste 301, Crystal Lake, IL 60014
Tel.: (815) 477-0424   DE
Web Site: https://www.aptar.com
Year Founded: 1992
ATR—(NYSE)
Rev.: $3,487,450,000
Assets: $4,451,890,000
Liabilities: $2,130,592,000
Net Worth: $2,321,298,000
Earnings: $284,487,000
Emp.: 13,800
Fiscal Year-end: 12/31/23
Convenience Dispensing Products & Systems for the Fragrance, Cosmetics, Personal Care, Pharmaceutical, Household Product & Food Industries
N.A.I.C.S.: 456199
Stephan B. Tanda *(Pres & CEO)*
Shiela Vinczeller *(Chief HR Officer)*
Xiangwei Gong *(Pres-Asia)*
Vanessa Kanu *(CFO & Exec VP)*

Subsidiaries:

Aptar (Thailand) Ltd.   (1)
700 / 252-253 Moo 1 Amata Industrial Estate, Bankaow Sub-district Panthong District, 20160, Chon Buri, Thailand
Tel.: (66) 384682069
Web Site: http//www.aptar.com
Commercial Stationery Supplies
N.A.I.C.S.: 424120

Aptar Ballinasloe Limited   (1)
Ballinasloe Business Park Creagh, Ballinasloe, County Gallway, Ireland
Tel.: (353) 909646033

Web Site: http://www.aptar.com
Emp.: 116
Pharmaceutical Product Whslr
N.A.I.C.S.: 424210

Aptar CSP Technologies, Inc.   (1)
960 W Veterans Blvd, Auburn, AL 36832
Tel.: (334) 887-8300
Web Site: https://www.csptechnologies.com
Plastic Packaging Products Mfr & Whslr
N.A.I.C.S.: 326112

Subsidiary (Domestic):

Maxwell Chase Technologies, LLC.   (2)
125 Westlake Pkwy SW, Atlanta, GA 30336
Tel.: (404) 344-0796
Web Site: http://www.maxwellchase.com
Rev.: $9,700,000
Emp.: 38
Urethane & Other Foam Product, except Polystyrene, Mfr
N.A.I.C.S.: 326150
Tom Gautreaux *(Dir-Sales-Natl)*
Schmidt Bill *(Project Mgr)*

Aptar Cali SAS   (1)
Valle del Cauca, Cantarrana, 763537, Cali, Colombia
Tel.: (57) 25540811
Parcel Delivery Services
N.A.I.C.S.: 561431

Aptar France S.A.S.   (1)
place called the Priory, 27110, Le Neubourg, France
Tel.: (33) 130084150
Pharmaceutical Product Whslr
N.A.I.C.S.: 424210

Aptar Freyung GmbH   (1)
1 Lofflerstrasse, PO Box 1306, 94078, Freyung, Germany
Tel.: (49) 85519750
Pharmaceutical Product Whslr
N.A.I.C.S.: 424210

Subsidiary (Non-US):

Aptar Ckyne s.r.o.   (2)
Ckyne 299 Okres Prachatice, 384 81, Ckyne, Czech Republic
Tel.: (420) 388405111
Web Site: http://www.aptar.com
Emp.: 300
Pharmaceutical Product Whslr
N.A.I.C.S.: 424210

Aptar Italia S.p.A.   (1)
49-32 Via Po, Zona Industriale Val Pescara, 66020, Chieti, CH, Italy
Tel.: (39) 08544421
Pharmaceutical Product Whslr
N.A.I.C.S.: 424210

Aptar Mezzovico S.A.   (1)
Via Cantonale, 6805, Mezzovico-Vira, 6805, Switzerland
Tel.: (41) 919359090
Web Site: http://www.aptar.com
Emp.: 164
Pharmaceutical Product Whslr
N.A.I.C.S.: 424210

Aptar Radolfzell GmbH   (1)
54-56 Oschlestrasse, Bodensee, 78315, Radolfzell, Germany
Tel.: (49) 77328010
Emp.: 250
Pharmaceutical Product Whslr
N.A.I.C.S.: 424210

Aptar Torello, S.A.   (1)
10 Carrer el Gorg Negre, Torello, 08570, Barcelona, Spain
Tel.: (34) 938594500
Pharmaceutical Products Distr
N.A.I.C.S.: 424210

Aptar Villingen GmbH   (1)
36 Auf Herdenen, 78052, Villingen-Schwenningen, Germany
Tel.: (49) 772191940
Pharmaceutical Products Distr
N.A.I.C.S.: 424210

Capitol Dairy Solutions   (1)
9 rue du Sandholz, Niederbronn-les- Bains, 67110, Strasbourg, France
Tel.: (33) 388098900

Milk Production Services
N.A.I.C.S.: 112120

Capitol Plastic Products, LLC   (1)
1549 St Hwy 5S, Amsterdam, NY 12010
Tel.: (518) 627-0051
Web Site:
http://www.capitolplasticproducts.com
Plastic Product Mfr & Distr
N.A.I.C.S.: 326191

Fusion Packaging I, LLC   (1)
2608 Inwood Rd Ste 200, Dallas, TX 75235
Tel.: (214) 747-2004
Web Site: http://www.fusionpkg.com
Skincare Product Packaging Services
N.A.I.C.S.: 561910

Gateway Analytical LLC   (1)
5316 William Flynn Hwy Ste 303, Gibsonia, PA 15044-9697
Tel.: (724) 443-1900
Web Site: http://www.gatewayanalytical.com
Testing Laboratories
N.A.I.C.S.: 541380
David Exline *(Pres & Founder)*
Rebekah Byrne *(Mgr-Quality)*
Paige Cohen *(Coord-Business Development)*
Antonio Scatena *(Dir-Sales-Marketing)*
Danielle Reifer *(Mgr-Quality)*
Cara Plese *(Mgr)*
Jennifer Flaherty *(Dir)*
Kylie Liebdzinski *(Program Mgr)*
Michael Litwin *(Acct Mgr)*
Mike Gorski *(Program Mgr)*
Pat Dayton *(Project Mgr)*

Gulf Closures W.L.L.   (1)
PO Box 2715, Manama, Bahrain
Tel.: (973) 17735565
Sales Range: $10-24.9 Million
Aluminum & Plastic Closure Mfr; Owned by Closure Systems International, Inc. & by Al Zayani Investments WLL
N.A.I.C.S.: 331318

LMS, Inc.   (1)
2202 Ridgewood Dr, Midland, MI 48642-5701
Tel.: (989) 631-8030
Web Site: http://www.lmsvalves.com
Molded Silicone Rubber Components Mfr
N.A.I.C.S.: 326299

MBF Embalagens Ltda.   (1)
Rua Pioneira Maria 1449, Cavalcante Ruy, Maringa, 87065-090, Brazil
Tel.: (55) 4432206688
Web Site: http://www.aptar.com
Emp.: 50
Commercial Stationery Supplies
N.A.I.C.S.: 424120

NanoPharm Ltd.   (1)
Cavendish House, Newport, NP10 8FY, United Kingdom
Tel.: (44) 1633504776
Web Site: https://www.nanopharm.co.uk
Pharmaceuticals Product Mfr
N.A.I.C.S.: 325412
Rob Price *(Founder & Chief Scientific Officer)*
Jag Shur *(CEO)*
Sarah Brooks *(Mgr-Human Resources)*

OOO Seaquist Closures   (1)
Tverskaya Street 16 Building 1, Moscow, 125009, Russia
Tel.: (7) 4957370796
Commercial Stationery Supplies
N.A.I.C.S.: 424120

PT. Aptar B&H Indonesia   (1)
Kawasan Industri Jababeka Jalan Jababeka IV SFB Blok B 11 U, Cikarang, 17530, Bekasi, Indonesia
Tel.: (62) 218936476
Beauty Supply Distr
N.A.I.C.S.: 456120

Philson, Inc.   (1)
1465 Main St, Watertown, CT 06795   (100%)
Tel.: (860) 274-8811
Web Site: http://www.philsoninc.com
Sales Range: $50-74.9 Million
Emp.: 25
Plastic Mfr

N.A.I.C.S.: 326199
Mike Smegielski *(Mgr)*
Lise Fitzpatrick *(Office Mgr)*

REBOUL SAS (1)
21 Rue Grignan, Chavanod, 13006, Marseilles, France
Tel.: (33) 457090200
Web Site: http://www.reboulsas.com
Cosmetic Product Distr
N.A.I.C.S.: 456120
Sandrine Brechon *(Mgr-Innovation & Dev)*

Total Innovative Packaging, Inc. (1)
1214 W Catawba Ave, Mount Holly, NC 28120
Tel.: (704) 867-5999
Web Site:
   http://www.totalpackagingcompany.com
Packaging Services
N.A.I.C.S.: 561910
Brian Schneider *(Pres)*
Kent Schneider *(VP-Ops)*
Tabatha Connard *(Mgr-Customer Svcs)*
Bill Schneider *(Acct Mgr)*
Kam McGillicuddy *(Ops Mgr)*

Valois (Ireland) Limited (1)
IDA Business Park, Ballinasloe, Galway, Ireland
Tel.: (353) 909646033
Web Site: http://www.aptar.com
Sales Range: $25-49.9 Million
Emp.: 110
Commercial Stationery Supplies
N.A.I.C.S.: 424120

Valois S.A.S. (1)
Lieu-Dit le Prieure - BPG, Le Neubourg, 27110, Evreux, France (100%)
Tel.: (33) 232248484
Web Site: http://wwwtest.valois.com
Emp.: 200
Nasal & Pulmonary Drug Mfr & Distr
N.A.I.C.S.: 325412

Subsidiary (Non-US):

Aptar Leeds (2)
5 Bruntcliffe Avenue, Morley, Leeds, LS27 0SS, West Yorkshire, United Kingdom (100%)
Tel.: (44) 1132203200
Web Site: http://www.aptar.com
Sales Range: $50-74.9 Million
Emp.: 60
Mfr & Distr of Bottle Closures
N.A.I.C.S.: 332119

Aptar Mezzovico S.A. (2)
Via Cantonale, Mezzovico-Vira, 6805, Lugano, TI, Switzerland (100%)
Tel.: (41) 919359090
Web Site: http://www.valoisbeauty.com
Cosmetic Packaging Services
N.A.I.C.S.: 561910

Subsidiary (US):

AptarGroup, Inc.- Congers (2)
250 New York 303, Congers, NY 10920-1408 (100%)
Tel.: (845) 639-3700
Web Site: http://www.aptar.com
Sales Range: $75-99.9 Million
Pumps for the Fragrance Cosmetics & Pharmaceutical Markets & Sells Aerosol Valves for the Pharmaceutical Market
N.A.I.C.S.: 333914

Subsidiary (Domestic):

Seaquist General Plastics (2)
44 Ave de Meaux, 77270, Poincy, France (100%)
Tel.: (33) 160411200
Web Site: http://www.aptar.com
Sales Range: $25-49.9 Million
Emp.: 130
Mfr & Distributor of Lotion Pumps
N.A.I.C.S.: 333914
Claiys Chrystopher *(Pres)*

Subsidiary (Non-US):

Valois Espana S.A. (2)
Calle Jorge Juan 72 1, 28009, Madrid, Spain (100%)
Tel.: (34) 917814360
Web Site: http://www.valois.com

Sales Range: $10-24.9 Million
Emp.: 20
Mfr of Cosmetic Products
N.A.I.C.S.: 325620

Voluntis SA (1)
22 quai Gallieni, Paris, 92150, France (64.6%)
Tel.: (33) 141383920
Sales Range: Less than $1 Million
Software Development Services
N.A.I.C.S.: 541511
Pierre Leurent *(Co-Founder & CEO)*
Eric Eliott *(Chm)*
Romain Marmot *(Co-Founder & Chief Bus Officer)*
Etienne Vial *(Co-Founder & CTO)*
Genevieve D'Orsay *(Chief Medical Officer)*
Guillaume Floch *(CFO)*
Aurore Beaume *(Sr VP-Bus Dev-Global)*
Damien McKeon *(Sr VP-Strategic Alliances-Global)*
Eric Baviere *(Sr VP-Solution Design & Delivery)*
Raffi Krikorian *(Sr VP-Quality Assurance & Regulatory Affairs-Global)*
Adeline Jospe *(VP-HR)*
Guillaume Moucheroud *(VP-Performance, Safety & Architecture)*
Sai Shankar *(Deputy CEO)*

APTEVO THERAPEUTICS INC.
2401 4th Ave Ste 1050, Seattle, WA 98121
Tel.: (206) 838-0500   DE
Web Site:
   https://www.aptevotherapeutics.com
APVO—(NASDAQ)
Assets: $24,842,000
Liabilities: $12,621,000
Net Worth: $12,221,000
Earnings: ($17,411,000)
Emp.: 40
Fiscal Year-end: 12/31/23
Pharmaceuticals Product Mfr
N.A.I.C.S.: 325412
Daphne L. Taylor *(CFO & Sr VP)*
Jeffrey G. Lamothe *(COO & Exec VP)*
SoYoung Kwon *(Gen Counsel-Corp Affairs & HR & Sr VP)*
Censia Pottorf *(VP-HR)*
Marvin L. White *(Pres & CEO)*

APTINYX, INC.
909 Davis St Ste 600, Evanston, IL 60201
Tel.: (847) 871-0377
Web Site: https://www.aptinyx.com
APTX—(NASDAQ)
Rev.: $737,000
Assets: $66,684,000
Liabilities: $28,399,000
Net Worth: $38,285,000
Earnings: ($64,849,000)
Emp.: 12
Fiscal Year-end: 12/31/22
Pharmaceuticals Product Mfr
N.A.I.C.S.: 325412
Norbert G. Riedel *(Chm)*
Andy Kidd *(Pres & CEO)*
Ashish Khanna *(CFO & Chief Bus Officer)*
Molly Dir *(VP-HR)*
Juan Estupinan *(VP-Fin & Acctg & Controller)*
M. Amin Khan *(VP-Chemistry R&D)*
Kathryn King *(Sr VP-Clinical Dev)*
Harald Murck *(VP-Medical & Pharmacovigilance)*
Nick Smith *(VP-Corp Dev & IR)*

APYX MEDICAL CORPORATION
5115 Ulmerton Rd, Clearwater, FL 33760-4004
Tel.: (727) 384-2323   DE
Web Site:
   https://www.apyxmedical.com

APYX—(NASDAQ)
Rev.: $44,510,000
Assets: $51,775,000
Liabilities: $13,982,000
Net Worth: $37,793,000
Earnings: ($23,184,000)
Emp.: 276
Fiscal Year-end: 12/31/22
Surgical & Medical Instruments Mfr & Marketer
N.A.I.C.S.: 339112
Matthew C. Hill *(CFO)*
Moshe Citronowicz *(Sr VP)*
Todd Hornsby *(Exec VP)*
John C. Andres *(Vice Chm)*
Charles D. Goodwin II *(Pres & CEO)*

Subsidiaries:

Bovie Canada ULC (1)
4056 North Service Road, Windsor, N8W 5X2, ON, Canada (100%)
Tel.: (519) 251-0668
Sales Range: $10-24.9 Million
Emp.: 20
Medical & Surgical Equipment Mfr
N.A.I.C.S.: 339112

AQUA METALS, INC.
5370 Kietzke Ln Ste 201, Reno, NV 89511
Tel.: (775) 446-4418   DE
Web Site:
   https://www.aquametals.com
Year Founded: 2013
AQMS—(NASDAQ)
Rev.: $4,000
Assets: $33,502,000
Liabilities: $12,586,000
Net Worth: $20,916,000
Earnings: ($15,431,000)
Emp.: 30
Fiscal Year-end: 12/31/22
Secondary Smelting, Refining & Alloying of Nonferrous Metal (except Copper & Aluminum)
N.A.I.C.S.: 331492
Dave McMurtry *(Chief Bus Officer)*
Stephen Cotton *(Pres & CEO)*
Judd B. Merrill *(CFO)*
Benjamin Taecker *(Chief Engrg & Operating Officer)*

AQUABOUNTY TECHNOLOGIES, INC.
233 Ayer Rd Unit 4, Harvard, MA 01451
Tel.: (978) 648-6000   DE
Web Site:
   https://www.aquabounty.com
Year Founded: 1991
AQB—(NASDAQ)
Rev.: $2,472,659
Assets: $187,551,428
Liabilities: $22,534,710
Net Worth: $165,016,718
Earnings: ($27,557,901)
Emp.: 104
Fiscal Year-end: 12/31/23
Biotechnology & Medical Research Services
N.A.I.C.S.: 541714
David A. Frank *(CFO & Treas)*
Alejandro Rojas *(COO)*
Angela M. Olsen *(Gen Counsel & Sec)*
Chris Beattie *(Chief Scientific Officer)*
Melissa Daley *(Chief People Officer)*
Chris Bucich *(VP)*
David F. Melbourne Jr. *(Pres & CEO)*

AQUARON ACQUISITION CORP.
515 Madison Ave 8th Fl, New York, NY 10022
Tel.: (646) 970-2181   DE
Year Founded: 2021

AQU—(NASDAQ)
Rev.: $259,976
Assets: $55,700,859
Liabilities: $50,402,119
Net Worth: $5,298,740
Earnings: $164,068
Emp.: 2
Fiscal Year-end: 12/31/22
Investment Services
N.A.I.C.S.: 523999
Qingze Zhao *(CFO)*
Yi Zhou *(Chm, Pres & CEO)*

ARADIGM CORPORATION
3929 Point Eden Way, Hayward, CA 94545
Tel.: (510) 265-9000   CA
Web Site: http://www.aradigm.com
ARDMQ—(OTCIQ)
Sales Range: $10-24.9 Million
Emp.: 14
Pulmonary Drug Delivery Systems Developer
N.A.I.C.S.: 334510
David Cipolla *(VP-Preclinical R&D)*
Janice Dahms *(VP-Project Mgmt)*
John M. Siebert *(Interim CEO & Interim CFO)*

ARAMARK
2400 Market St, Philadelphia, PA 19103
Tel.: (215) 238-3000   DE
Web Site: https://www.aramark.com
Year Founded: 2007
ARMK—(NYSE)
Rev.: $17,400,701,000
Assets: $12,674,371,000
Liabilities: $9,635,397,000
Net Worth: $3,038,974,000
Earnings: $261,893,000
Emp.: 266,680
Fiscal Year-end: 09/27/24
Holding Company; Food, Facilities & Uniform Services
N.A.I.C.S.: 551112
John J. Zillmer *(CEO)*
Abigail Charpentier *(Chief HR Officer & Sr VP)*
Marc A. Bruno *(COO-Food & Facilities-US)*
Lauren A. Harrington *(Gen Counsel & Sr VP)*
Carl Mittleman *(COO-Intl)*
Ashwani Hanson *(Chief Diversity & Sustainability Officer)*
Debbie Albert *(Sr VP-Comm)*
Kim Scott *(Pres/CEO-Aramark Uniform Svcs)*
Christopher T. Schilling *(Chief Acctg Officer, Sr VP & Controller)*
John M. Orobono *(Sr VP-Supply Chain-Global)*
Kimberly Scott *(Pres/CEO-Uniform Svcs)*
Abigail Charpentier *(Chief HR Officer & Sr VP)*
James Tarangelo *(CFO & Sr VP)*

Subsidiaries:

ARAMARK Intermediate Holdco Corporation (1)
1101 Market St, Philadelphia, PA 19107
Tel.: (215) 238-3000
Web Site: http://www.aramark.com
Holding Company
N.A.I.C.S.: 551112
Eric Foff *(CEO)*

Subsidiary (Domestic):

ARAMARK Corporation (2)
2400 Market St, Philadelphia, PA 19103
Tel.: (215) 238-3000
Web Site: http://www.aramark.com

Aramark—(Continued)

Holding Company; Food Services, Uniforms & Facility Management Services
N.A.I.C.S.: 551112
Autumn R. Bayles (Sr VP-Global Supply Chain)

Subsidiary (Domestic):

1ST & Fresh, LLC **(3)**
1101 Market St, Philadelphia, PA 19107
Tel.: (215) 232-3762
Catering Services
N.A.I.C.S.: 722320
Carl Rogler (Office Mgr)

Subsidiary (Non-US):

ARAMARK China **(3)**
Room 703 Bldg A Beijing Global Trade Ct No 36 N Third Ring Rd, E Dong Cheng Dist, Beijing, 100013, China **(100%)**
Tel.: (86) 1058257010
Web Site: http://www.aramark.cn
Sales Range: $700-749.9 Million
Emp.: 12,000
Managed Services in Healthcare, Education & Business & Industry Sectors
N.A.I.C.S.: 561499

Group (Domestic):

ARAMARK Food and Support Services Group, Inc. **(3)**
1101 Market St, Philadelphia, PA 19107
Tel.: (215) 238-3000
Web Site: http://www.aramark.com
Sales Range: $900-999.9 Million
Emp.: 2,000
Holding Company
N.A.I.C.S.: 551112

Subsidiary (Non-US):

ARAMARK Canada Ltd. **(4)**
811 Islington Ave, Toronto, M8Z 5W8, ON, Canada **(66%)**
Tel.: (416) 255-1331
Web Site: http://www.aramark.ca
Sales Range: $200-249.9 Million
Emp.: 14,000
Service Management Company; Food Service, Vending, Office Coffee & Cleaning, Laundry & Housekeeping Services
N.A.I.C.S.: 561210
Andy Siklos (Pres)
Ali Adat (Reg VP-West)
Brett Bottyan (VP-Remote Workplace Svcs)
Brian Emmerton (VP & Gen Mgr-Complete Pur Svcs)
Deborah Heiser (VP-Fin)
Louise Hudson (VP-Mktg Ops)
Greg Lawrie (VP-Growth)
Glenn Livingston (Assoc VP-Ops)
Kathy Mah (Sec, Head-Legal, Assoc VP & Asst Gen Counsel)
Steven Prisco (Reg VP-Central)
Nicolas Seguier (Reg VP-East)
Karen Williams (VP-Mktg & Culinary Dev)
Faybian Palmer (Dir-Strategic Dev)
Adelia Marchese (Mgr-Health & Safety)
Kevin Hamer (Dir-Culinary Dev)

Subsidiary (Domestic):

ARAMARK Canada Ltd. **(5)**
105 The East Mall, Toronto, M8Z 5X9, ON, Canada **(100%)**
Tel.: (902) 468-8877
Web Site: http://www.aramark.com
Emp.: 15
Food Service & Vending Machine Operations
N.A.I.C.S.: 445132

ARAMARK Entertainment Services (Canada), Inc. **(5)**
1015 Bank St, Ottawa, K1S 3W7, ON, Canada
Tel.: (613) 563-0625
Emp.: 100
Entertainment Management Services
N.A.I.C.S.: 561499

ARAMARK Quebec, Inc. **(5)**
2425-46th avenue, Lachine, H8T 3C9, QC, Canada **(100%)**
Tel.: (514) 341-7770
Web Site: http://www.aramark.qc.ca

Emp.: 25
Food Services & Vending Machines
N.A.I.C.S.: 445132

Travers Food Service Ltd. **(5)**
9647 45th Ave, Edmonton, T6E 5Z8, AB, Canada **(100%)**
Tel.: (780) 437-5665
Web Site: http://www.traversltd.com
Emp.: 30
Catering & Camp Services for Field Workers
N.A.I.C.S.: 722320
John Dampf (Pres)

Subsidiary (Domestic):

ARAMARK Educational Group, LLC **(4)**
1101 Market St, Philadelphia, PA 19107
Tel.: (215) 238-3000
Web Site: http://www.aramark.com
Facility & Dining Services for Higher Education
N.A.I.C.S.: 722511

ARAMARK FHC Business Services, LLC **(4)**
Aramark Twr 1101 Market St, Philadelphia, PA 19107
Tel.: (215) 238-3000
Sales Range: $200-249.9 Million
Emp.: 1,700
Business Services
N.A.I.C.S.: 722310

ARAMARK Facility Services, LLC **(4)**
2300 Warrenville Rd, Downers Grove, IL 60515
Tel.: (630) 271-2000
Sales Range: $125-149.9 Million
Emp.: 400
Food Service
N.A.I.C.S.: 541611
Eric J. Foss (Pres)
Eric Foss (Pres)

Branch (Domestic):

ARAMARK Facility Services **(5)**
1101 Market St, Philadelphia, PA 19107
Tel.: (215) 413-8529
Web Site: http://www.aramark.com
Janitorial Services
N.A.I.C.S.: 561720

Subsidiary (Domestic):

ARAMARK Healthcare Support Services, LLC **(4)**
1101 Market St Aramark Tower, Philadelphia, PA 19107
Tel.: (215) 238-3000
Web Site: http://www.aramarksports.com
Food, Facility & Clinical Technology Services
N.A.I.C.S.: 722310

Subsidiary (Non-US):

ARAMARK Mexico S.A. de C.V. **(4)**
Ejercito Nacional No 425 6 piso, Col Granada, 11520, Mexico, Mexico
Tel.: (52) 5585036100
Web Site: http://www.aramark.com.mx
Sales Range: $800-899.9 Million
Emp.: 3,500
Business Support Services
N.A.I.C.S.: 561499

Subsidiary (Domestic):

ARAMARK Refreshment Services, LLC **(4)**
Aramark Tower 1101 Market St, Philadelphia, PA 19107-2934 **(100%)**
Tel.: (215) 238-3000
Web Site: http://www.aramarkrefreshments.com
Sales Range: $50-74.9 Million
Emp.: 150
Refreshment Services for the Workplace
N.A.I.C.S.: 722330

Subsidiary (Domestic):

ARAMARK Refreshment Services, Inc. **(5)**

1665 Townhurst Ste 160, Houston, TX 77043
Tel.: (713) 932-0093
Web Site: http://www.aramarkrefreshments.com
Emp.: 55
Managed Care Food & Cleaning Services
N.A.I.C.S.: 561990

Subsidiary (Domestic):

ARAMARK Services of Puerto Rico, Inc. **(4)**
1590 Avenue Ponce De Leon Ste 212, San Juan, PR 00926-2722 **(100%)**
Tel.: (787) 751-6525
Web Site: http://www.aramark.net
Sales Range: $50-74.9 Million
Emp.: 300
Restaurant Management
N.A.I.C.S.: 561110
Maria Pabon (Mng Dir)

ARAMARK Sports & Entertainment Services, LLC **(4)**
1101 Market St, Philadelphia, PA 19107-2934
Tel.: (215) 238-3000
Web Site: https://www.aramark.com
Food & Beverage Concession Consulting Services
N.A.I.C.S.: 541618
Amy Cross (CIO)

Aramark American Food Services, LLC **(4)**
1101 Market St, Philadelphia, PA 19107
Tel.: (215) 238-3000
Food Service Contractors
N.A.I.C.S.: 722310

Aramark FHC, LLC **(4)**
801 Front Ave, Columbus, GA 31901
Tel.: (706) 225-3713
Emp.: 60
Restaurant Service Provider
N.A.I.C.S.: 722511

Aramark Facilities Management, LLC **(4)**
941 W 35th St, Los Angeles, CA 90007
Tel.: (213) 740-8968
Building Cleaning & Janitorial Services
N.A.I.C.S.: 561720
Ron Cote (Mgr)

Aramark Refreshment Services of Tampa, LLC **(4)**
8723 Florida Mining Blvd, Tampa, FL 33634
Tel.: (813) 885-3760
Web Site: http://www.aramarkrefreshments.com
Emp.: 10
Business Support Services
N.A.I.C.S.: 541611

Corporate Coffee Systems, LLC **(4)**
745 Summa Ave, Westbury, NY 11590
Tel.: (516) 371-4800
Web Site: http://www.corpcofe.com
Emp.: 90
Electronic Equipment Mfr & Distr
N.A.I.C.S.: 334310
David Henchel (Co-Founder, Pres & CEO)
Donn Luti (Co-Founder)
Gregg Henchel (Co-Founder)

Subsidiary (Domestic):

ARAMARK Harrison Lodging **(3)**
135 New Rd, Madison, CT 06443
Tel.: (203) 318-2102
Operator of Conference Centers, Corporate Training Centers & Specialty Hotels
N.A.I.C.S.: 722310

Subsidiary (Domestic):

Lake Tahoe Cruises, Inc. **(4)**
900 Ski Run Blvd, South Lake Tahoe, CA 96150-3364
Tel.: (775) 588-1881
Web Site: http://www.laketahoecruises.com
Cruise Services
N.A.I.C.S.: 483114

Mesa Verde Company **(4)**
34879 US Hwy 160, Mancos, CO 81328 **(100%)**
Tel.: (970) 533-7731

Web Site: http://www.visitmesaverde.com
Sales Range: $25-49.9 Million
Emp.: 250
Hotel
N.A.I.C.S.: 721110

Zephyr Cove Resort **(4)**
760 US Hwy 50, Zephyr Cove, NV 89448
Tel.: (775) 589-4906
Web Site: http://www.tahoedixie2.com
Sales Range: $125-149.9 Million
Emp.: 380
Sight Seeing Boats & Resorts
N.A.I.C.S.: 487210

Subsidiary (Non-US):

ARAMARK Holdings GmbH & Co. KG **(3)**
Martin Behaim Str 6, PO Box 1163, Neu-Isenburg, 63263, Germany **(100%)**
Tel.: (49) 61027450
Web Site: http://www.aramark.de
Sales Range: $1-4.9 Billion
Emp.: 6,000
Holding Company
N.A.I.C.S.: 551112
Peter Amon (Pres)

Subsidiary (Domestic):

ARAMARK GmbH **(4)**
Martin-Behaim-Str 6, 63263, Neu-Isenburg, Germany **(100%)**
Tel.: (49) 61027450
Web Site: http://www.aramark.de
Sales Range: $50-74.9 Million
Emp.: 600
Vending Machine Operators
N.A.I.C.S.: 445132

Aramark Restaurations GmbH **(4)**
Martin-Behaim-Str 6, 63263, Neu-Isenburg, Germany **(100%)**
Tel.: (49) 61027450
Food Contractor Services
N.A.I.C.S.: 722310
Udo Luerssen (Pres)

Subsidiary (Non-US):

ARAMARK Limited **(3)**
250 Fowler Avenue, IQ Business Park Farnborough, London, GU14 7JP, Hampshire, United Kingdom **(100%)**
Tel.: (44) 1252529000
Web Site: http://northerneurope.aramark.com
Sales Range: $10-24.9 Million
Emp.: 60
Catering & Janitorial Services
N.A.I.C.S.: 722320

Division (Domestic):

ARAMARK Catering Limited **(4)**
Millbank Tower 21-24 Millbank, London, SW1P 4QP, United Kingdom **(100%)**
Tel.: (44) 2079630000
Web Site: http://www.aramark.co.uk
Catering Services
N.A.I.C.S.: 722320

ARAMARK Manning Services Limited **(4)**
Millbank Tower 21 24 Millbank, London, SW1P 4QP, United Kingdom **(100%)**
Tel.: (44) 2079630000
Web Site: http://www.aramark.co.uk
Business Services
N.A.I.C.S.: 561499

Subsidiary (Non-US):

ARAMARK Nederland **(3)**
Prins Bernhardplein 200, 1097 JB, Amsterdam, Netherlands
Tel.: (31) 205214777
Web Site: http://www.aramark.be
Catering & Vending Services
N.A.I.C.S.: 445132

ARAMARK S.A. **(3)**
Chaussee de Wavre 1110, 1160, Brussels, Belgium **(100%)**
Tel.: (32) 26634940
Web Site: http://www.aramark.be
Sales Range: $50-74.9 Million
Emp.: 900
Vending Machine Operators
N.A.I.C.S.: 445132

ARAMARK Servicios de Catering, S.L. (3)
Aribau 200-210, 08036, Barcelona, Spain (100%)
Tel.: (34) 932402141
Web Site: http://www.aramark.es
Emp.: 100
Catering Services
N.A.I.C.S.: 722320
Pablo Alcala *(Pres)*

Joint Venture (Non-US):

ARAMARK Uniform Services Japan Corporation (3)
Tornare Nihonbashi Hamacho 8Floor 3-3-2 Nihonbashi Hamacho, Chuo-ku, Tokyo, 103-0007, Japan
Tel.: (81) 358470930
Web Site: https://www.aramark-uniform.co.jp
Emp.: 1,506
Uniform Rentals, Sales & Cleaning Services
N.A.I.C.S.: 812331
Akihiro Nishimura *(Pres)*

Subsidiary (Non-US):

ARAMARK/Campbell Catering (3)
Northern Cross Malahide Rd, 17, Dublin, Ireland (100%)
Tel.: (353) 18160700
Web Site: http://www.aramark.ie
Sales Range: $400-449.9 Million
Emp.: 4,100
Food Services & Facilities Management in Healthcare, Education, Business & Industry & Government Sectors
N.A.I.C.S.: 311999
Conal Oberin *(CEO)*

Joint Venture (Non-US):

Aim Services Co., Ltd. (3)
Ark Hills Front Tower 2-23-1, Akasaka Minato-ku, Tokyo, 107-0052, Japan (50%)
Tel.: (81) 362357500
Web Site: http://www.aimservices.co.jp
Sales Range: $10-24.9 Million
Emp.: 200
Food & Support Services; Joint Venture by Aramark Corporation & by Mitsui & Co., Ltd
N.A.I.C.S.: 445132

Subsidiary (Domestic):

AmeriPride Services Inc. (3)
10801 Wayzata Blvd, Minnetonka, MN 55305-5510
Tel.: (952) 738-4200
Web Site: http://www.ameripride.com
Linen, Work Apparel & Industrial Supplies
N.A.I.C.S.: 812331
Al Ertz *(VP-Production)*
Steven John *(VP-IT)*

Subsidiary (Domestic):

AmeriPride Linen & Uniform Services, Inc. (4)
398 Great Oak Dr, Canton, NC 28716-1188
Tel.: (828) 648-2384
Web Site: http://www.ameripride.com
Linen & Uniform Services
N.A.I.C.S.: 812331

Subsidiary (Non-US):

Arakor Co. Ltd. (3)
17th Fl Daewoo Foundation 526 Namdaemunno 5-ga, Jung-gu, Seoul, Korea (South) (100%)
Tel.: (82) 27788797
Web Site: http://www.arakor.co.kr
Food Business Services
N.A.I.C.S.: 561499

Aramark China Holdings Limited (3)
Rm B 32/f Lippo Centre Tower 1 89 Queensway, Hong Kong, China (Hong Kong)
Tel.: (852) 28016031
Holding Company
N.A.I.C.S.: 551112

Subsidiary (Domestic):

Aramark Chugach Alaska Services, LLC (3)
3800 Centerpoint Dr Ste 1200, Anchorage, AK 99503

Tel.: (907) 261-0391
Web Site: http://www.chugach.com
Construction Management Services
N.A.I.C.S.: 236220

Subsidiary (Non-US):

Aramark Co. Ltd. (3)
137 KPX Building Mapo-dong Mapo-gu, Seoul, 121-805, Korea (South)
Tel.: (82) 232788000
Catering Services
N.A.I.C.S.: 722320

Aramark Colombia SAS (3)
Av 19 N 96-07 Palo Verde Office Building 301, Bogota, Colombia
Tel.: (57) 17427142
Catering Services
N.A.I.C.S.: 722320

Aramark Denmark ApS (3)
John Tranums Vej 23 2 East, 6705, Esbjerg, Denmark
Tel.: (45) 75156004
Food & Beverage Distr
N.A.I.C.S.: 424490

Subsidiary (Domestic):

Aramark Entertainment, LLC (3)
2000 E Gene Autry Way, Anaheim, CA 92806
Tel.: (714) 940-2499
Business Consulting Services
N.A.I.C.S.: 541611

Subsidiary (Non-US):

Aramark India Private Limited (3)
Andheri - Kurla Rd J B Nagar, Andheri East, 400059, Mumbai, India
Tel.: (91) 9619928246
Employee Recruitment Services
N.A.I.C.S.: 561311
Ravi Manchandani *(CEO)*

Aramark Ireland Holdings Limited (3)
Northern Cross Malahide Road, Dublin, Ireland
Tel.: (353) 18160700
Web Site: http://www.aramark.ie
Emp.: 100
Holding Company
N.A.I.C.S.: 551112

Aramark Management GmbH (3)
Martin-Behaim-Str 6, 63263, Neu-Isenburg, Germany
Tel.: (49) 61027450
Catering Services
N.A.I.C.S.: 722320

Aramark Peru, S.A.C. (3)
Recavarren Street No 111, Lima, 15074, Lima, Peru
Tel.: (51) 14889900
Catering Services
N.A.I.C.S.: 722320
Carlos Lopez *(Mgr-Contract)*

Aramark Property Services Limited (3)
5th Floor St Stephens Green House, Earlsfort Terrace, Dublin, D17 HR92, Ireland
Tel.: (353) 18715400
Web Site: http://aramarkproperty.ie
Emp.: 140
Property Management Services
N.A.I.C.S.: 531311
Deirdre Coker *(Mgr-Bldg)*

Aramark Remote Workplace Services Ltd. (3)
9647 45 Ave NW, Edmonton, T6E 5Z8, AB, Canada
Tel.: (780) 437-5665
Web Site: http://www.aramark.com
Emp.: 40
Catering Services
N.A.I.C.S.: 722310

Aramark SARL (3)
Rue des Trois Cantons 57, Ehlange Sur Mess, 3961, Luxembourg, Luxembourg
Tel.: (352) 26305099
Web Site: http://www.aramark.be
Catering Services
N.A.I.C.S.: 722320

Aramark Service Industries (China) Co., Ltd. (3)
11th Floor Min Sheng Plaza, Building 2 No 38 East Third Ring Road North Chaoyang Dist, Beijing, 100026, China
Tel.: (86) 1085870936
Commercial Property Management Services
N.A.I.C.S.: 531312

Aramark Servicios Integrales, S.A. (3)
C/Aribau 200-210, 08036, Barcelona, Spain
Tel.: (34) 932402141
Catering Services
N.A.I.C.S.: 722310

Aramark Servicios SRL (3)
Dr Nicolas Repetto 3656 1st Floor, B1636CTL, Buenos Aires, Argentina
Tel.: (54) 1151717700
Food Contractor Services
N.A.I.C.S.: 722310

Aramark Uniform Services (Canada) Ltd. (3)
2390 Winston Park Blvd - Unit 2, Oakville, L6H 0G7, ON, Canada
Tel.: (905) 829-8770
Laundry Services
N.A.I.C.S.: 812320

Aramark Workplace Solutions (UK) Ltd. (3)
250 Fowler Avenue Farnborough Business Park, Farnborough, GU14 7JP, Hampshire, United Kingdom
Tel.: (44) 1252529092
Catering Services
N.A.I.C.S.: 722320
Gavin Vaughan *(Mgr-Ops)*

Aramark Workplace Solutions Yonetim Hizmetleri Limited Sirketi (3)
Obelisks Mh Ayazmader Cd Tellioglu Plz N 6 K4 1D Odan 1 Besiktas, Istanbul, Türkiye
Tel.: (90) 2123470647
Building Construction Services
N.A.I.C.S.: 236115

Aramark, S.R.O. (3)
Pekarska 628/14, Michle, 155 00, Prague, Czech Republic
Tel.: (420) 286014111
Web Site: http://www.aramark.cz
Catering Services
N.A.I.C.S.: 722320

Subsidiary (Domestic):

Avendra, LLC (3)
540 Gaither Rd Ste 200, Rockville, MD 20850
Tel.: (301) 825-0500
Web Site: http://www.avendra.com
Hospitality Procurement Services
N.A.I.C.S.: 561499
Robert J. McCarthy *(Founder & Chm)*
Heather Altieri *(VP)*
Cory Dellinger *(VP)*
Jesse Messitte *(VP)*
Patrick Poncet *(VP)*
Leonard Queiroz *(VP)*
Eleanor Waddell *(VP)*
Steven Werner *(VP)*
Susan Weber *(VP)*

Subsidiary (Non-US):

Avoca Handweavers Limited (3)
Kilmacanogue Bray, Wicklow, Ireland
Tel.: (353) 12746902
Web Site: http://www.avocahandweavers.com
Clothing & Accessory Merchant Whslr
N.A.I.C.S.: 424350

Avoca Handweavers Shops Limited (3)
Unit 1 Riverside Business Park, Rathnew, Wicklow, Ireland
Tel.: (353) 12746996
Web Site: http://www.avoca.com
Clothing & Accessory Merchant Whslr
N.A.I.C.S.: 424350

Campbell Catering (Belfast) Ltd. (3)
150 Holywood Rd, Belfast, BT4 1NY, United Kingdom
Tel.: (44) 2890474480

Catering Services
N.A.I.C.S.: 722310

Subsidiary (Domestic):

Carter Brothers Aramark Integrated Facilities Management, LLC (3)
950 Eagles Landing Pkwy Ste 349, Stockbridge, GA 30281
Tel.: (770) 954-7010
Web Site: http://www.cbaramarkifm.com
Integrated Facility Management Services
N.A.I.C.S.: 811210

Subsidiary (Non-US):

Central Multiservicios S.R.L. (3)
Calle Moreno 651 1091, Buenos Aires, Argentina
Tel.: (54) 1151717700
Hotel & Restaurant Management Services
N.A.I.C.S.: 721110

Central de Abastecimiento Limitada (3)
Calle Los Espinos Macul 2681, Santiago, Chile
Tel.: (56) 222382471
Textile Products Mfr
N.A.I.C.S.: 314999

Central de Restaurantes Aramark Limitada (3)
Avda del Condor 760 Ciudad Empresarial, Huechuraba, Santiago, Chile
Tel.: (56) 223851000
Web Site: http://www.aramark.cl
Catering Services
N.A.I.C.S.: 722320

Centrapal S.R.L. (3)
Moreno 651, Buenos Aires, C1091AAM, Argentina
Tel.: (54) 1151717700
Financial Software Development Services
N.A.I.C.S.: 541511

Complete Purchasing Services Inc. (3)
5150 Spectrum Way Suite 200, Mississauga, L4W 5G2, ON, Canada
Tel.: (416) 253-3180
Web Site: https://www.portal.ecps.ca
Business Support Services
N.A.I.C.S.: 561499

GTB Gastro Team Bremen GmbH (3)
Am Winterhafen 3, 28217, Bremen, Germany
Tel.: (49) 421320915
Web Site: http://www.gastro-team-bremen.de
Event Management Services
N.A.I.C.S.: 722320

Glenrye Properties Services Limited (3)
67 Park St, Co Louth, Dundalk, Ireland
Tel.: (353) 429351966
Commercial Property Management Services
N.A.I.C.S.: 531312

Subsidiary (Domestic):

HPSI Purchasing Services, LLC (3)
1 Ada Ste 150, Irvine, CA 92618
Web Site: http://www.hpsionline.com
Software Development Services
N.A.I.C.S.: 541511
Dean Hansen *(Mng Dir-Supply Chain)*
Kirk Hess *(Mng Dir)*
Greg Perron *(Mng Dir)*

Institutional Processing Services, LLC (3)
10700 Meridian Ave N Ste 506, Seattle, WA 98133
Web Site: http://www.ipsrebates.com
School & Camp Food Services
N.A.I.C.S.: 722310
Jeff Herman *(Mgr-Mktg)*

Subsidiary (Non-US):

Irish Estates (Facilities Management) Limited (3)
Beresford Court 16 Beresford Place, Dublin, Ireland
Tel.: (353) 17041400

Aramark—(Continued)

Commercial Real Estate Consulting Services
N.A.I.C.S.: 531210

Subsidiary (Domestic):

Lifeworks Restaurant Group, LLC (3)
500 S Buena Vista St, Burbank, CA 91521
Tel.: (818) 560-7918
Restaurant Service Provider
N.A.I.C.S.: 722511

Subsidiary (Non-US):

Nissho Linen (3)
777 Yamagawacho, Ashikaga, 326-0021, Japan
Tel.: (81) 284416481
Textile Products Mfr
N.A.I.C.S.: 314999

Orange Support Services Limited (3)
Principle House, Fleet, GU51 3PD, Hampshire, United Kingdom
Tel.: (44) 8704170002
Engineering Support Services
N.A.I.C.S.: 541330

Pelican Procurement Services Limited (3)
Ash House Tanshire Park Shackleford Road, Elstead, GU8 6LB, Surrey, United Kingdom
Tel.: (44) 1252705200
Web Site:
http://www.pelicanprocurement.co.uk
Goods Procurement Services
N.A.I.C.S.: 541614

Subsidiary (Domestic):

Sun Office Service, Inc. (3)
10015 Lickinghole Rd, Ashland, VA 23005
Tel.: (804) 496-6723
Web Site: http://www.sunofficeservices.com
Book Import & Distr
N.A.I.C.S.: 424920

Tarrant County Concessions, LLC (3)
13960 Trinity Blvd, Euless, TX 76040
Tel.: (817) 858-0078
Restaurant Service Provider
N.A.I.C.S.: 722511

Subsidiary (Non-US):

Twose of Tiverton Ltd. (3)
Chinon Court Unit 6 Lower Moor Way, Tiverton, EX16 6SS, United Kingdom
Tel.: (44) 1884253691
Web Site: http://www.twose.com
Sales Range: $10-24.9 Million
Emp.: 7
Machinery Equipment Mfr
N.A.I.C.S.: 333111

Vector Environmental Services Limited (3)
50 Bedford Street, Belfast, BT2 7FW, United Kingdom
Tel.: (44) 2838393811
Health & Safety Certification Services
N.A.I.C.S.: 541611

Vector Workplace and Facility Management Limited (3)
Novum Building Clonshaugh Industrial Estate, Dublin, Ireland
Tel.: (353) 18022240
Management Consulting Services
N.A.I.C.S.: 541611

Subsidiary (Domestic):

Wilderness River Adventures, LLC (3)
199 Kaibab Rd, Page, AZ 86040
Tel.: (928) 645-3296
Web Site: http://www.riveradventures.com
River Rafting Operator
N.A.I.C.S.: 713990

Subsidiary (Non-US):

Avoca Handweavers Designs Limited (1)
Kilmacanogue, Bray County, Wicklow, Ireland
Tel.: (353) 12746902

Web Site:
http://www.avocahandweavers.com
Home Furnishing Merchant Whslr
N.A.I.C.S.: 423220

By Word of Mouth Limited (1)
19-26 Glenville Mews Kimber Road, London, SW18 4NJ, United Kingdom
Tel.: (44) 2088719566
Web Site: https://bywordofmouth.co.uk
Catering & Event Management Services
N.A.I.C.S.: 722320

First Choice Purchasing Limited (1)
Suite 317 1 Horgans Quay Waterfront Square, Cork, T23 PPT8, Ireland
Tel.: (353) 212390060
Web Site: https://firstchoicepurchasing.com
Health Care Consultancy Services
N.A.I.C.S.: 541611

Landsea Camp and Catering Services Ltd. (1)
7-38921 Progress Way, Squamish, V8B 0K6, BC, Canada
Tel.: (604) 815-4500
Web Site: https://landseacamps.com
Camp Management Services
N.A.I.C.S.: 721214

Next Level Hospitality Services, LLC (1)
100 Challenger Rd Ste 105, Ridgefield Park, NJ 07660
Tel.: (551) 225-8320
Web Site: https://nextlevelhs.net
Culinary & Environmental Services
N.A.I.C.S.: 722310

Union Supply Group, Inc. (1)
2500 Regent Blvd, Dallas, TX 75261
Web Site: https://www.unionsupply.com
Grocery Product Distr
N.A.I.C.S.: 424410

Wilson Vale Catering Management Limited (1)
Ivanhoe Office Park, Ashby de la Zouch, LE65 2AB, Leicestershire, United Kingdom
Tel.: (44) 1530563100
Web Site: https://wilsonvale.co.uk
Catering Contract Services
N.A.I.C.S.: 722310

Word on the Street (UK Events) Limited (1)
24 Glenville Mews Kimber Road, London, SW18 4NJ, United Kingdom
Tel.: (44) 2030721921
Web Site:
https://www.wordonthestreet.uk.com
Event Management Services
N.A.I.C.S.: 561920

ARAVIVE, INC.
3730 Kirby Dr Ste 1200, Houston, TX 77098
Tel.: (936) 355-1910 DE
Web Site: https://www.aravive.com
Year Founded: 2008
ARAV—(NASDAQ)
Rev.: $9,137,000
Assets: $62,153,000
Liabilities: $51,496,000
Net Worth: $10,657,000
Earnings: ($76,322,000)
Emp.: 23
Fiscal Year-end: 12/31/22
Pharmaceuticals Mfr
N.A.I.C.S.: 325412
Leonard Scott Dove (COO)
Maria Carolina Petrini (Chief Comml Officer)
Rudy C. Howard (CFO & Principal Acctg Officer)
Fredric N. Eshelman (Chm)
Gail F. McIntyre (Pres & CEO)
Robert B. Geller (Chief Medical Officer)

ARBOR REALTY TRUST, INC.
333 Earle Ovington Blvd Ste 900, Uniondale, NY 11553
Tel.: (516) 506-4200 MD
Web Site: https://www.arbor.com

Year Founded: 2003
ABR—(NYSE)
Rev.: $948,401,000
Assets: $17,038,985,000
Liabilities: $13,967,106,000
Net Worth: $3,071,879,000
Earnings: $284,829,000
Emp.: 630
Fiscal Year-end: 12/31/22
Real Estate Investment Trust; Multifamily, Commercial Real Estate Equity Investments & Mortgage Related Securities
N.A.I.C.S.: 525990
Fred Weber (Exec VP & Mng Dir-Structured Fin & Principal Transactions)
Gene Kilgore (Exec VP-Structured Securitization)
Paul Elenio (CFO & Exec VP)
Andrew G. Guziewicz (Mng Dir & Chief Credit Officer-Structured Fin)
John G. Caulfield (COO-Agency Lending & Exec VP)
John Natalone (Exec VP-Treasury & Servicing)
Frank Maniglia (Mng Dir-Agency Lending Ops)
Peter Reisert (Mng Dir-Capital Markets & Agency Lending)
Garth Davis (Sr VP/Dir-Western Region-San Francisco)
Gary DeSimone (Sr VP-Fin)
Annette Givelekian (Sr VP-HR)
Joan Gredys (Sr VP-Corp Facilities)
Peter Kempton (Sr VP-Talent Acquisition)
Howard Leiner (CTO & Exec VP)
Steven Katz (Chief Investment Officer-Residential Financing & Exec VP)
RoseElla Frankiewich (Sr VP-Servicing Ops)
John Richardson (Mng Dir)
Ken Dowling (Sr VP-Capital Markets)
Ramandeep Walia (Sr VP-Solutions Delivery)
William Foster (Exec VP-Tax & Strategic Plng)
Arthanais Williams (Mng Dir-Affordable Housing)
Alex Bord (Sr VP-IT Infrastructure)
James Kresl (Sr VP-Single-Family Rental Underwriting)
Ryan Nichols (Sr VP)
David E. Friedman (Exec VP)
Maysa Vahidi (Gen Counsel)
Brian Blue (Mng Dir)
Charles Marino (Mng Dir)
Jean-Laurent Pouliot (Mng Dir)
Juli Achee (Sr VP)
Mario Arena (Sr VP)
Brett Neely (Sr VP)
Dana Caragine (Sr VP)
Matthew Chase (Sr VP)
Sean Coon (Sr VP)
William Correa (Sr VP)
James Devlin (Sr VP)
Adam Dratch (Sr VP)
Chris Femino (Sr VP)
Joyce Figueroa (Sr VP)
Timothy D. Finucane (Sr VP)
Breandan Fisher (Sr VP)
Leah Fisher (Sr VP)
Michael Franzoni (Sr VP)
Gillian Harrington (Sr VP)
Ivan Kaufman (Founder, Chm, Pres & CEO)

Subsidiaries:

Arbor Realty Funding, LLC (1)
333 Earle Ovington Blvd Ste 900, Uniondale, NY 11553
Tel.: (516) 506-4200
Real Estate Management Services
N.A.I.C.S.: 531390

Arbor Realty SR, Inc. (1)
333 Earle Ovington Blvd Ste 900, Uniondale, NY 11553
Tel.: (516) 832-8002
Sales Range: $50-74.9 Million
Real Estate Management Services
N.A.I.C.S.: 531390
John Dredys (Office Mgr)

ARBUTUS BIOPHARMA CORPORATION
701 Veterans Cir, Warminster, PA 18974
Tel.: (267) 469-0914 BC
Web Site:
https://www.arbutusbio.com
Year Founded: 1992
ABUS—(NASDAQ)
Rev.: $39,019,000
Assets: $195,419,000
Liabilities: $58,567,000
Net Worth: $136,852,000
Earnings: ($69,456,000)
Emp.: 96
Fiscal Year-end: 12/31/22
Pharmaceutical Preparation Manufacturing
N.A.I.C.S.: 325412
Michael J. McElhaugh (Co-Founder, Interim Pres & Interim CEO)
J. Christopher Naftzger (Chief Compliance Officer & Gen Counsel)
Lisa M. Caperelli (VP-IR)
Karen Sims (Chief Medical Officer)
Shannon Briscoe (VP)
David C. Hastings (CFO)

Subsidiaries:

Enantigen Therapeutics, Inc. (1)
3805 Old E Rd, Doylestown, PA 18902
Tel.: (215) 589-6350
Pharmaceuticals Product Mfr
N.A.I.C.S.: 325412

Protiva Biotherapeutics (USA), Inc. (1)
1127 41st Ave E, Seattle, WA 98112
Tel.: (604) 419-3200
Emp.: 81
Biotechnology Research & Development Services
N.A.I.C.S.: 541714

ARC DOCUMENT SOLUTIONS, INC.
12657 Alcosta Blvd Ste 200, San Ramon, CA 94583
Tel.: (925) 949-5100 DE
Web Site: https://www.e-arc.com
Year Founded: 2004
ARC—(NYSE)
Rev.: $286,010,000
Assets: $307,315,000
Liabilities: $151,025,000
Net Worth: $156,290,000
Earnings: $11,094,000
Emp.: 1,800
Fiscal Year-end: 12/31/22
Holding Company; Specialized Document Services
N.A.I.C.S.: 551112
Rahul K. Roy (CTO)
Kumarakulasingam Suriyakumar (Founder, Chm & CEO)
Jorge Avalos (CFO)
Dilantha Wijesuriya (Pres & COO)
David Stickney (VP-Corp Comm & IR)
Srinivas Mukkamala (Dir-Engrg & R&D & Gen Mgr)
Tracey Luttrell (Corp Counsel & Sec)
John Zulli (Exec VP)
Theodore Carlson (Sr VP)

Subsidiaries:

ARC Document Solutions - Texas (1)

2220 W Peter Smith St Ste 100, Fort Worth, TX 76102
Tel.: (817) 332-9704
Web Site: http://www.e-arc.com
Graphic Design Services
N.A.I.C.S.: 541430
Stokely Lee (Mgr)

ARC Document Solutions, Inc. (1)
1850 130th Ave NE Ste 6, Bellevue, WA 98005 (100%)
Tel.: (425) 883-1110
Web Site: https://www.e-arc.com
Sales Range: $10-24.9 Million
Emp.: 3
Reprographic Services
N.A.I.C.S.: 323111

ARC Document Solutions, Inc. (1)
819 State St, Cayce, SC 29033
Tel.: (803) 254-2561
Web Site: http://www.e-arc.com
Sales Range: $10-24.9 Million
Emp.: 11
Imaging & Lamination Services
N.A.I.C.S.: 323111
Lisa Beaty (Mgr)

ARC Document Solutions, Inc. (1)
2730 Occidental Ave S, Seattle, WA 98134 (100%)
Tel.: (206) 622-6000
Web Site: http://www.e-arc.com
Rev.: $180,000
Emp.: 100
Photocopying & Duplicating Services
N.A.I.C.S.: 323111
Ann Eng (Mgr-Managed Print Svcs)

ARC Document Solutions, Inc. (1)
945 Bryant St, San Francisco, CA 94103
Tel.: (415) 495-8700
Web Site: http://www.e-arc.com
Photocopying & Duplicating Services
N.A.I.C.S.: 323111

ARC Document Solutions, Inc. - Atlanta (1)
640 10th St NW, Atlanta, GA 30318
Tel.: (404) 873-5911
Web Site: http://www.e-arc.com
Document Services
N.A.I.C.S.: 323111
John Duncan (Mgr)

ARC Document Solutions, LLC (1)
6300 Gulfton St, Houston, TX 77081-1108
Tel.: (713) 782-8580
Web Site: http://www.e-arc.com
Reprographic & Printing Services
N.A.I.C.S.: 323113
Dilo Wijesuriya (Pres)
Tracey Luttrell (Corp Counsel)
Srinivas Mukkamala (Gen Mgr)
Jorge Avalos (CFO)
Rahul Roy (CTO)
Suri Suriyakumar (Chm)
David Stickney (VP-Corporate Communications & Investor Relations)
Greg Schiemann (VP-Technical Services)
John Herb (VP-Human Resources)
John Zulli (Exec VP-North America Ops)
Ken Gini (Sr VP-Admin Ops Procurement)
Kumar Wiratunga (VP-Strategic Partnerships)
Ted Buscaglia (Exec VP-Global Svcs)
Theodore Carlson (Sr VP-Mergers & Acquisitions)

ARC Midco L.L.C. (1)
700 N Central Ave Ste 550, Glendale, CA 91203-3299
Tel.: (818) 500-0225
Web Site: http://www.arc.com
Rev.: $140,438,000
Emp.: 30
Provider of Photocopying & Duplicating Services
N.A.I.C.S.: 561499

ARC Philadelphia
417 N 8th St Ste 402, Philadelphia, PA 19123
Tel.: (215) 563-7600
Web Site: http://www.e-arc.com
Sales Range: $75-99.9 Million
Emp.: 17
Full Service Document Production
N.A.I.C.S.: 323120
Donald Castignani (Mgr)

American Reprographics Company, LLC (1)
1981 N Broadway Ste 385, Walnut Creek, CA 94596
Tel.: (925) 949-5100
Web Site: http://www.e-arc.com
Specialized Document Services
N.A.I.C.S.: 561499
Kumarakulasingam Suriyakumar (Chm, Pres & CEO)

Arc Document Solutions, Inc. (1)
1421 N El Dorado St, Stockton, CA 95202-1018 (100%)
Tel.: (209) 464-8724
Web Site: http://www.e-arc.com
Provider of Photocopying & Duplicating Services
N.A.I.C.S.: 323111
Don Rader (Branch Mgr)

BPI Repro, LLC (1)
87 Taylor Ave, Norwalk, CT 06854-2038
Tel.: (203) 866-5600
Web Site: http://www.bpirepro.com
Digital Flex Printing Services
N.A.I.C.S.: 323111
Sam Wexler (Pres)

ERS Digital, Inc. (1)
4730 Park Glen Rd, Saint Louis Park, MN 55416
Tel.: (763) 694-5900
Emp.: 30
Other Miscellaneous Nondurable Goods Merchant Wholesalers
N.A.I.C.S.: 424990
Todd Peterson (Gen Mgr)

Inprint Corporation (1)
1161 N Fair Oaks Ave, Sunnyvale, CA 94089 (100%)
Tel.: (408) 400-0490
Web Site: http://www.inprintcorp.com
Rev.: $10,902,969
Emp.: 50
Provider of Electrical Equipment & Supplies
N.A.I.C.S.: 334419

Mirror Plus Technologies, Inc. (1)
45545 Northport Loop E, Fremont, CA 94538-6461
Tel.: (510) 403-2400
Graphic Design Services
N.A.I.C.S.: 541430

Planwell, LLC (1)
45535 Northport Loop E, Fremont, CA 94538
Tel.: (925) 658-0200
Web Site: http://www.planwell.com
Construction Management Software Developer & Publisher
N.A.I.C.S.: 513210

The Blue Print Independence (1)
295 Madison Ave, New York, NY 10017-6304
Tel.: (212) 686-2436
Web Site: http://www.e-arc.com
Rev.: $5,000,000
Emp.: 30
Provider of Photocopying & Duplicating Services
N.A.I.C.S.: 323111

ARC GROUP WORLDWIDE, INC.

810 Flightline Blvd, Deland, FL 32724
Tel.: (386) 736-4890   UT
Web Site: http://www.arcw.com
ARCW—(OTCIQ)
Rev.: $48,526,000
Assets: $54,281,000
Liabilities: $50,308,000
Net Worth: $3,973,000
Earnings: ($5,287,000)
Emp.: 412
Fiscal Year-end: 06/30/20
Holding Company
N.A.I.C.S.: 551112
Alan Grant Quasha (Chm)
Cheryl Reynolds (CFO)
Jedidiah Rust (CEO)

Subsidiaries:

AFT-Hungary Kft. (1)

Ipari Park, Retsag, 2651, Hungary
Tel.: (36) 35551000
Web Site: http://www.aftmimhu.com
Industrial Mold Mfr
N.A.I.C.S.: 333511

ARC Wireless, Inc. (1)
810 FlightLine Blvd, Deland, FL 32724
Tel.: (321) 446-2961
Web Site: http://www.antennas.com
Wireless Equipment Mfr & Distr
N.A.I.C.S.: 334220

ARC Wireless, LLC (1)
6330 N Washington St Ste 13, Denver, CO 80216-1146 (100%)
Tel.: (303) 467-5236
Web Site: http://www.antennas.com
Wireless Network Communications Equipment Mfr & Services
N.A.I.C.S.: 334220

Advance Tooling Concepts, LLC (1)
33 S Pratt Pkwy, Longmont, CO 80501-6256
Tel.: (303) 772-2525
Web Site: http://www.atcmold.com
Emp.: 35
Plastics Product Mfr
N.A.I.C.S.: 326199

Advanced Forming Technology, Inc. (1)
7040 Weld County Rd 20, Longmont, CO 80504-9423 (100%)
Tel.: (303) 833-6000
Web Site: http://www.aftmim.com
Sales Range: $75-99.9 Million
Emp.: 360
Metal Injection Molding & Metal Matrix Composites Mfr
N.A.I.C.S.: 331110

Subsidiary (Non-US):

AFT Europa Kft (2)
Ipari Park 5, H 2651, Retsag, Hungary
Tel.: (36) 35 551 009
Web Site: http://www.aftmimhu.com
Sales Range: $25-49.9 Million
Emp.: 184
Metal Injection Molding
N.A.I.C.S.: 332999
Aniko Sipos (Head-HR)

Quadrant Metals Technologies, LLC (1)
810 Flightline Blvd, Deland, FL 32724 (100%)
Tel.: (386) 736-4890
Web Site: http://www.quadrantmetals.com
Sales Range: $25-49.9 Million
Holding Company
N.A.I.C.S.: 551112

Subsidiary (Domestic):

FloMet LLC (2)
810 Flightline Blvd, Deland, FL 32724 (95.6%)
Tel.: (386) 736-4890
Web Site: http://www.flomet.com
Sales Range: $25-49.9 Million
Emp.: 150
Metal Injection Molding
N.A.I.C.S.: 332999
Ashley Nichols (VP-Tech & Engrg)
Tom Houck (VP-Mfg)
Daniel Tasseff (Dir-Sls & Mktg)
Alan Miles (Mgr-Mfg)

Thixoforming LLC (1)
8906 Frontier St, Firestone, CO 80504
Tel.: (303) 833-6000
Web Site: http://www.thixoworks.com
Injection Mold Product Mfr
N.A.I.C.S.: 333248

ARC GROUP, INC.

1409 Kingsley Ave Ste 2, Orange Park, FL 32073
Tel.: (904) 741-5500   FL
Web Site: http://www.arcgrpinc.com
Year Founded: 2000
ARCK—(OTCIQ)
Sales Range: $1-9.9 Million
Emp.: 1,022

Holding Company; Restaurant Franchisor & Operator
N.A.I.C.S.: 551112
Ketan B. Pandya (VP-Mktg)
Yannick Bastien (CFO & Chief Admin Officer)
Richard W. Akam (COO & Sec)
Seenu G. Kasturi (Chm, CEO & CTO)

Subsidiaries:

Fat Patty's (1)
1442 Winchester Ave, Ashland, KY 41101
Tel.: (606) 325-7287
Web Site: http://www.fatpattysonline.com
Full-Service Restaurants
N.A.I.C.S.: 722511

ARCA BIOPHARMA, INC.

10170 Church Ranch Way Ste 100, Westminster, CO 80021
Tel.: (720) 940-2100   DE
Web Site: https://arcabio.com
Year Founded: 1992
ABIO—(NASDAQ)
Rev.: $1,957,000
Assets: $37,861,000
Liabilities: $841,000
Net Worth: $37,020,000
Earnings: ($5,339,000)
Emp.: 4
Fiscal Year-end: 12/31/23
Gene-Based Products & Tests Developer
N.A.I.C.S.: 325413
Michael R. Bristow (Co-Founder)
Thomas A. Keuer (Pres, COO & Principal Exec Officer)
Robert Liscouski (Co-Founder)
Sharon Perry (VP-Regulatory Affairs & Quality)
C. Jeffrey Dekker (CFO & Principal Acctg Officer)

ARCADIA BIOSCIENCES, INC.

5950 Sherry Ln Ste 215, Dallas, TX 75225
Tel.: (214) 974-8921   AZ
Web Site: https://www.arcadiabio.com
Year Founded: 2002
RKDA—(NASDAQ)
Rev.: $5,330,000
Assets: $19,705,000
Liabilities: $7,002,000
Net Worth: $12,703,000
Earnings: ($13,986,000)
Emp.: 21
Fiscal Year-end: 12/31/23
Agricultural Biotechnology Mfr
N.A.I.C.S.: 325320
Eric J. Rey (Founder)
Kevin J. Comcowich (Chm)
Tracy Baker (VP-Product Innovation)
Brett Michel (Gen Mgr-The Life Portfolio-CBD & Wellness Brands)
Belinda Yao (VP-Ops)
Thomas J. Schaefer (Pres & CEO)

ARCBEST CORPORATION

8401 McClure Dr, Fort Smith, AR 72916
Tel.: (479) 785-6000   DE
Web Site: https://www.arcb.com
Year Founded: 1923
ARCB—(NASDAQ)
Rev.: $4,427,443,000
Assets: $2,485,094,000
Liabilities: $1,242,731,000
Net Worth: $1,242,363,000
Earnings: $195,433,000
Emp.: 15,000
Fiscal Year-end: 12/31/23
Diversified Holding Company Engaged in Motor Freight Transportation, Computer Services & Truck Tire Retreading

ArcBest Corporation—(Continued)
N.A.I.C.S.: 484210
Jason Turner *(VP-Talent & Growth Initiatives)*
Judy R. McReynolds *(Chm & CEO)*
Steven Leonard *(Chief Sls & Customer Engagement Officer)*
Erin K. Gattis *(Chief HR Officer)*
Barry Hunter *(VP-Fin Svcs & Risk Mgmt)*
David Humphrey *(VP-IR)*
Traci L. Sowersby *(Chief Acctg Officer, VP & Controller)*
Laura Bogner *(VP-Internal Audit)*
Cheryl Harper *(VP-Tax)*
Christopher Adkins *(VP-Yield Strategy & Mgmt)*
Dennis L. Anderson II *(Chief Strategy Officer)*
Matt Beasley *(VP)*
Jason Parks *(Chief Acctg Officer)*
Seth Runser *(Pres)*
David R. Cobb *(CFO)*

Subsidiaries:

ABF Freight System Canada, Ltd. **(1)**
15 Strathearn Avenue, Brampton, L6T 4P1, ON, Canada
Tel.: (905) 458-5888
Freight Transportation Services
N.A.I.C.S.: 484122

ABF Freight System, Inc. **(1)**
3801 Old Greenwood Rd, Fort Smith, AR 72903-5937 **(100%)**
Tel.: (479) 785-8900
Web Site: http://www.arcb.com
Sales Range: $1-4.9 Billion
Freight Services
N.A.I.C.S.: 484121

Subsidiary (Non-US):

ABF Freight System (B.C.), Ltd. **(2)**
17735 1st Avenue 174, Surrey, V3Z 9S1, BC, Canada
Tel.: (604) 542-0727
Web Site: https://www.arcb.com
Freight Transportation Services
N.A.I.C.S.: 484122

ABF Logistics II, Inc. **(1)**
6201 Rogers Ave Ste J, Fort Smith, AR 72903
Tel.: (479) 785-6000
Logistics Management Services
N.A.I.C.S.: 541614

Subsidiary (Domestic):

ABF Global Supply Chain, Inc. **(2)**
3801 Old Greenwood Rd, Fort Smith, AR 72903
Tel.: (479) 785-6000
Freight Transportation Services
N.A.I.C.S.: 484110
Gunnar Gose *(Dir-Ops)*

ABF Logistics, Inc. **(2)**
3801 Old Greenwood Rd, Fort Smith, AR 72903
Tel.: (479) 434-9540
Logistics Management Services
N.A.I.C.S.: 541614
Matt Meeks *(VP-Div)*

Subsidiary (Domestic):

Bear Transportation Services, L.P. **(3)**
5340 Legacy Dr Ste 200, Plano, TX 75024
Tel.: (800) 527-5380
Web Site: http://www.arcb.com
Truck Transportation Brokers
N.A.I.C.S.: 488510

Albert Companies, Inc. **(1)**
3801 Old Greenwood Rd, Fort Smith, AR 72903-5937 **(100%)**
Tel.: (479) 785-6000
Web Site: http://arcb.com
Freight Transportation Services
N.A.I.C.S.: 481212

ArcBest International, Inc. **(1)**

8401 McClure Dr, Fort Smith, AR 72916
Tel.: (479) 785-8900
Web Site: http://www.arcb.com
Freight Transportation Services
N.A.I.C.S.: 488510
Judy R. McReynolds *(Chm, Pres & CEO)*

ArcBest Logistics, Inc. **(1)**
3801 Old Greenwood Rd, Fort Smith, AR 72903
Tel.: (877) 279-8090
Transportation Management Consulting Services
N.A.I.C.S.: 541614

ArcBest Technologies, Inc. **(1)**
3801 Old Greenwood Rd, Fort Smith, AR 72917 **(100%)**
Tel.: (479) 494-6654
Web Site: https://jobs.arcbtech.com
Emp.: 375
Business Software Design, Maintenance & Programming Services
N.A.I.C.S.: 518210

Expedited Solutions, Inc. **(1)**
3801 Old Greenwood Rd, Fort Smith, AR 72903
Tel.: (479) 785-8700
Web Site: http://www.abfs.com
Logistics Management Services
N.A.I.C.S.: 541614

FTI Groups, Inc. **(1)**
PO Box 2349, Keller, TX 76244
Web Site: https://fleet.sureecosystem.com
Software Development Services
N.A.I.C.S.: 513210

Freightvalue Inc. **(1)**
3801 Old Greenwood Rd, Fort Smith, AR 72903-5937
Tel.: (479) 785-8700
Web Site: http://www.freightvalue.com
Sales Range: $1-9.9 Million
Emp.: 75
Trucking Service
N.A.I.C.S.: 484122

Land-Marine Cargo, Inc. **(1)**
Rd-165 KM 2.4 Freetrade Zone 61 Bldg 7, Guaynabo, PR 00965
Tel.: (787) 788-4747
Freight Transportation Services
N.A.I.C.S.: 481212
Luis Milian *(Gen Mgr)*

Moving Solutions, Inc. **(1)**
8401 McClure Dr, Fort Smith, AR 72903
Web Site: https://www.upack.com
Freight Transportation Services
N.A.I.C.S.: 481212

Panther Expedited Services, Inc. **(1)**
84 Medina Rd, Medina, OH 44256
Tel.: (330) 769-5830
Web Site: http://www.pantherexpedite.com
Sales Range: $150-199.9 Million
Emp.: 384
Single-Source Ground, Air & Ocean Shipping Services
N.A.I.C.S.: 488510

Panther II Transportation, Inc. **(1)**
84 Medina Rd, Medina, OH 44256
Tel.: (330) 769-5830
Motor Freight Transportation Services
N.A.I.C.S.: 484110

Panther Premium Logistics, Inc. **(1)**
84 Medina Rd, Medina, OH 44256
Tel.: (330) 769-5830
Web Site: http://www.arcb.com
Emp.: 004
Freight Transportation Services
N.A.I.C.S.: 484110

ARCELLX, INC.
800 King Farm Blvd Ste 600, Rockville, MD 20850
Tel.: (240) 327-0630   **DE**
Web Site: https://www.arcellx.com
Year Founded: 2014
ACLX—(NASDAQ)
Rev.: $2,580,000
Assets: $313,817,000
Liabilities: $108,863,000
Net Worth: $204,954,000
Earnings: ($188,679,000)

Emp.: 98
Fiscal Year-end: 12/31/22
Biotechnology Research & Development Services
N.A.I.C.S.: 541714
Rami Elghandour *(CEO & Chm)*
Kate Aiken *(Chief HR Officer)*
Christopher Heery *(Chief Medical Officer)*
Neeraj Teotia *(Chief Comml Officer)*
Michelle Gilson *(CFO)*
Doug Alleavitch *(VP-Quality)*
Aileen Fernandes *(Chief Bus Officer)*
Brad Gliner *(VP-Clinical Research & Regulatory Affairs)*
Brian Murphy *(VP-Cell Process Sciences)*
Narinder Singh *(Chief Technical Officer)*
David Tice *(Chief Scientific Officer)*
Maryam Abdul-Kareem *(Chief Legal Officer & Gen Counsel)*
Myesha Lacy *(Chief Comm Officer & Chief Investor Officer)*

ARCH RESOURCES, INC.
1 City Pl Dr Ste 300, Saint Louis, MO 63141
Tel.: (314) 994-2700   **DE**
Web Site: https://www.archrsc.com
Year Founded: 1969
ARCH—(NYSE)
Rev.: $3,145,843,000
Assets: $2,484,173,000
Liabilities: $1,004,717,000
Net Worth: $1,479,456,000
Earnings: $464,038,000
Emp.: 3,400
Fiscal Year-end: 12/31/23
Coal Mining Services
N.A.I.C.S.: 212114
Paul A. Lang *(CEO)*
Deck S. Slone *(Sr VP-Strategy & Pub Policy)*
John T. Drexler *(Pres)*
Matthew C. Giljum *(CFO & Sr VP)*
Paul T. Demzik *(Chief Comml Officer & Sr VP)*
George J. Schuller Jr. *(COO & Sr VP)*
Rosemary L. Klein *(Gen Counsel, Sec & Sr VP-Law)*
John A. Ziegler Jr. *(Chief Admin Officer & Sr VP)*

Subsidiaries:

Arch Coal Terminal, Inc. **(1)**
US 23 S, Catlettsburg, KY 41129
Tel.: (606) 739-8499
Emp.: 16
Coal Mining Services
N.A.I.C.S.: 212114
Dewey Webb *(Gen Mgr)*

Arch Coal, Inc. **(1)**
1 CityPlace Dr Ste 300, Saint Louis, MO 63141
Tel.: (314) 994-2700
Web Site: https://www.archrsc.com
Sales Range: $75-99.9 Million
Emp.: 20
Mining of Low-Sulfur Central Appalachian Coal
N.A.I.C.S.: 213113

Arch of Wyoming, LLC **(1)**
County Rd 291, Hanna, WY 82327
Tel.: (307) 325-6581
Coal Mining Services
N.A.I.C.S.: 212114

Coal-Mac, Inc. **(1)**
Harless Wood Industrial Park 22 Mine Rd, Holden, WV 25625-3009
Tel.: (304) 792-8400
Sales Range: $150-199.9 Million
Emp.: 300
Coal Mining Services
N.A.I.C.S.: 212114
M. Lynn Parrish *(Co-Founder & Pres)*

Hawthorne Coal Company, Inc. **(1)**
Sago Rd, Buckhannon, WV 26201
Tel.: (304) 472-3400
Nonmetallic Mineral Mining Services
N.A.I.C.S.: 212390

Otter Creek Coal, LLC **(1)**
401 N 31st St, Billings, MT 59101-1200
Tel.: (406) 245-0992
Coal Mining Services
N.A.I.C.S.: 212114

Patriot Mining Company Inc. **(1)**
2708 Cranberry Sq, Morgantown, WV, 26508-9286
Tel.: (304) 594-1616
Sales Range: $50-74.9 Million
Emp.: 45
Coal Mining
N.A.I.C.S.: 212114

Upshur Property LLC **(1)**
300 Corporate Ctr Dr, Scott Depot, WV 25560
Tel.: (304) 472-9272
Coal Mining
N.A.I.C.S.: 212114

ARCH THERAPEUTICS, INC.
235 Walnut St Ste 6, Framingham, MA 01702
Tel.: (617) 431-2313   **NV**
Web Site:
  https://www.archtherapeutics.com
Year Founded: 2009
ARTH—(OTCQB)
Rev.: $11,565
Assets: $3,676,485
Liabilities: $4,702,159
Net Worth: ($1,025,674)
Earnings: ($6,240,482)
Emp.: 10
Fiscal Year-end: 09/30/21
Medical Device Developer
N.A.I.C.S.: 339112
Terrence W. Norchi *(Founder, Chm, Pres & CEO)*
Daniel C. Wadsworth *(VP-Dermal Sciences)*
Michael S. Abrams *(CFO)*

ARCHER AVIATION INC.
190 W Tasman Dr, San Jose, CA 95134
Tel.: (650) 272-3233   **DE**
Web Site: https://www.archer.com
Year Founded: 2018
ACHR—(NYSE)
Rev.: $27,800,000
Assets: $573,300,000
Liabilities: $80,500,000
Net Worth: $493,300,000
Earnings: ($317,300,000)
Emp.: 390
Fiscal Year-end: 12/31/22
Aircraft Engine & Engine Parts Mfr
N.A.I.C.S.: 336412
Mark Mesler *(CFO)*
Adam Goldstein *(Founder & CEO)*
Tom Muniz *(CTO)*
Geoff Bower *(Chief Engr)*
Tosha Perkins *(Chief People Officer & Chief Partnerships Officer)*
Eric Lentell *(Gen Counsel)*

Subsidiaries:

Archer Aviation Operating Corp. **(1)**
190 West Tasman Dr, San Jose, CA 95134
Tel.: (650) 272-3233
Web Site: https://www.archer.com
Emp.: 100
Aircraft Engine & Engine Parts Mfr
N.A.I.C.S.: 336412

ARCHER-DANIELS-MIDLAND COMPANY
77 W Wacker Dr Ste 4600, Chicago, IL 60601
Tel.: (312) 634-8100   **DE**
Web Site: https://www.adm.com

Year Founded: 1902
ADM—(NYSE)
Rev.: $93,935,000,000
Assets: $54,631,000,000
Liabilities: $30,486,000,000
Net Worth: $24,145,000,000
Earnings: $3,483,000,000
Emp.: 630
Fiscal Year-end: 12/31/23
Food Products Distr
N.A.I.C.S.: 424420
Monish Patolawala *(CFO & Exec VP)*
Ray G. Young *(CFO, Exec VP & Vice Chm)*
Vikram Luthar *(Sr VP)*
Todd A. Werpy *(Chief Science Officer & Sr VP)*
Gregory A. Morris *(Pres-Oilseeds & Agricultural Svcs & Sr VP)*
Christopher M. Cuddy *(Pres-Carbohydrate Solutions & Sr VP)*
Ian Pinner *(Chief Sls & Mktg Officer, Pres-Nutrition & Sr VP)*
Thuy-Nga T. Vo *(Asst Sec)*
Kristy J. Folkwein *(CIO & Sr VP)*
Molly Strader Fruit *(Chief Acctg Officer, VP & Controller)*
Ron Bandler *(Treas)*
Joseph Taets *(Sr VP)*
Regina Bynote Jones *(Gen Counsel, Sec & Sr VP)*
Ismael Roig *(Pres-Animal Nutrition & Pres-EMEA)*
Leticia Goncalves *(Pres-Foods-Global)*
Leticia Goncalves *(Pres-Specialty Ingredients-Global)*
Juan R. Luciano *(Chm, Pres & CEO)*

Subsidiaries:

ADM (Shanghai) Management Co., Ltd. (1)
B5 Building 180 Yizhou Road, Xuhui District, Shanghai, 200233, China
Tel.: (86) 2160603099
Food Ingredient Distr
N.A.I.C.S.: 424590

ADM (Thailand) Ltd. (1)
173/20 Asia Centre Building 19th Floor South Sathorn Road, Thungmahamek Sathorn, Bangkok, 10120, Thailand
Tel.: (66) 22850704
Confectionery Ingredient Mfr
N.A.I.C.S.: 311352

ADM ANTWERP NV (1)
Rostockweg 17 Kaai 312a, 2030, Antwerp, Belgium
Tel.: (32) 35413807
Web Site: http://www.oilio.com
Package Cooking Oil Mfr
N.A.I.C.S.: 311224

ADM Agriculture Limited (1)
Lindsey House, Hemswell Cliff, Gainsborough, DN21 5TH, Lincolnshire, United Kingdom
Tel.: (44) 142 742 1200
Web Site: https://adm-agri.co.uk
Farm Management Services
N.A.I.C.S.: 115116

ADM Agro Iberica S.L.U. (1)
C/ Arturo Soria 336 7 Plta, 28033, Madrid, Spain
Tel.: (34) 914584700
Food Ingredient Distr
N.A.I.C.S.: 424590

ADM Agro Industries India Private Limited (1)
Plot No J-97 MIDC Tarapur Industrial Area Doripuja Road, Near Mahavir Chambers Boisar Palghar, Thane, 401 506, MH, India
Tel.: (91) 1244937800
Agricultural Services
N.A.I.C.S.: 926140

ADM Agro Industries Kota & Akola Private Limited (1)
807 New Delhi House Barakhamba Road Connaught Place, New Delhi, 110 001, India

Tel.: (91) 1244937800
Confectionery Ingredient Mfr
N.A.I.C.S.: 311352

ADM Agro Industries Latur & Vizag Private Limited (1)
Plot No G 75 TO G 86 MIDC, Latur, 413531, Maharashtra, India
Tel.: (91) 1244937800
Food Ingredient Distr
N.A.I.C.S.: 424590

ADM Alliance Nutrition, Inc. (1)
1000 N 30th St, Quincy, IL 62301-3400 (100%)
Tel.: (217) 222-7100
Web Site: https://www.admanimalnutrition.com
Sales Range: $200-249.9 Million
Emp.: 250
Feeds for Livestock; Livestock Equipment
N.A.I.C.S.: 311611

Plant (Domestic):

ADM Alliance Nutrition (2)
208 E 2nd St, Hoffman, IL 62250
Tel.: (618) 495-2202
Web Site: http://www.adm.com
Sales Range: $1-9.9 Million
Emp.: 2
Animal Feed
N.A.I.C.S.: 311611

ADM Alliance Nutrition (2)
2174 E 59th Ave, Columbus, NE 68601
Tel.: (402) 564-3155
Web Site: http://www.e-adm.com
Sales Range: Less than $1 Million
Emp.: 30
Prepared Feeds
N.A.I.C.S.: 311611

ADM Alliance Nutrition (2)
1800 W Western Ave, Bluffton, IN 46714
Tel.: (260) 824-0079
Web Site: http://www.moormans.com
Sales Range: $25-49.9 Million
Emp.: 34
Mfr Livestock Feed Supplements
N.A.I.C.S.: 311119

ADM Alliance Nutrition (2)
1501 New Columbia Rd, Campbellsville, KY 42718
Tel.: (270) 789-2780
Web Site: http://www.adm.com
Sales Range: $50-74.9 Million
Emp.: 10
Provider of Farm Supplies
N.A.I.C.S.: 424910

ADM Alliance Nutrition (2)
554 Pleasant Vly Rd, Sugarcreek, OH 44681 (100%)
Tel.: (330) 852-3025
Web Site: http://www.e-adm.com
Sales Range: $10-24.9 Million
Emp.: 10
Prepared Feeds
N.A.I.C.S.: 311119

Subsidiary (Domestic):

ADM Alliance Nutrition of Puerto Rico, LLC (2)
Carr 2 KM 83 Bo Carrizales St CA, Hatillo, PR 00659
Tel.: (787) 878-7474
Web Site: http://www.adm.com
Sales Range: $1-9.9 Million
Emp.: 6
Animal Food Product Mfr
N.A.I.C.S.: 311119

ADM Animal Nutrition (Cambodia) Co., Ltd. (1)
Building F Room 169 1st Floor Phnom Penh Center, Sihanouk Blvd St 274 Corner Sangkat Tonle Basak Khan Chamkarmon, Phnom Penh, Cambodia
Tel.: (855) 2 398 3323
Agricultural Raw Material Distr
N.A.I.C.S.: 424910

ADM Asia-Pacific Trading Pte. Ltd. (1)
230 Victoria Street 11-08 Bugis Junction Towers, Singapore, 188024, Singapore
Tel.: (65) 66222400

Emp.: 300
Food Ingredient Distr
N.A.I.C.S.: 424590

ADM Australia Pty. Limited (1)
Suite 1 Ground Floor 10A Julius Ave, North Ryde, 2113, NSW, Australia
Tel.: (61) 288794800
Agricultural Services
N.A.I.C.S.: 926140

ADM Bazancourt SASU (1)
114 rue de Pomacle, CS 30004, 51110, Bazancourt, Cedex, France
Tel.: (33) 326895950
Emp.: 1,400
Food Products Mfr
N.A.I.C.S.: 311221

ADM Benson Inc. (1)
301 S Fourth Ave Ste 960, Minneapolis, MN 55415 (100%)
Tel.: (612) 340-5905
Web Site: http://www.bqci.com
Sales Range: $50-74.9 Million
Emp.: 1
Futures Brokers & Dealers Commodity
N.A.I.C.S.: 523160

Subsidiary (Domestic):

ADM Benson-Quinn Company (2)
100 Railroad Ave, Rogers, ND 58479-4016 (100%)
Tel.: (701) 646-6310
Sales Range: $50-74.9 Million
Emp.: 15
Elevator & Fertilizers
N.A.I.C.S.: 424510
Travis Zerface *(Mgr)*

Benson-Quinn Commodities Inc. (2)
121 S 8th St Ste 1700, Minneapolis, MN 55402 (100%)
Tel.: (612) 340-5905
Web Site: https://www.bqci.com
Future Brokers & Dealers Commodity
N.A.I.C.S.: 523160

ADM Bio-Productos, S.A. de C.V. (1)
Boulevard Miguel Aleman Km 11-40 Sector Centro, Gomez Palacio, 35000, Mexico
Tel.: (52) 8717490715
Vegetable Oil Mfr
N.A.I.C.S.: 311224

ADM Clinton BioProcessing, Inc. (1)
410 18th Ave S, Clinton, IA 52732-5908
Tel.: (217) 424-5200
Emp.: 19
Food Ingredient Mfr
N.A.I.C.S.: 311221

ADM Czernin S.A. (1)
Ul B Chrobrego 29, 64-500, Szamotuly, Poland
Tel.: (48) 612929300
Agricultural Services
N.A.I.C.S.: 926140

ADM Direct Polska Sp. z o.o. (1)
Ul B Chrobrego 29, 64-500, Szamotuly, Poland
Tel.: (48) 612929300
Agricultural Services
N.A.I.C.S.: 926140

ADM Edible Bean Specialties, Inc. (1)
1804 Front St, Casselton, ND 58012 (100%)
Tel.: (701) 347-5321
Web Site: http://www.adm.com
Sales Range: $50-74.9 Million
Emp.: 7
Distribution of Edible Beans
N.A.I.C.S.: 424510

Plant (Domestic):

ADM Edible Bean Specialties, Inc. (2)
2385 Wright Ave, Twin Falls, ID 83301
Tel.: (208) 734-2550
Web Site: http://www.adm.com
Sales Range: $1-9.9 Million
Emp.: 10
Bean Cleaning Services
N.A.I.C.S.: 115114

ADM Edible Bean Specialties, Inc. (2)
PO Box 1470, Decatur, IL 62525
Tel.: (208) 423-5531
Web Site: http://www.adm.com
Sales Range: $25-49.9 Million
Grain & Field Beans
N.A.I.C.S.: 444240

ADM Edible Bean Specialties, Inc. (2)
2150 22nd St N, Olivia, MN 56277
Tel.: (320) 523-1637
Sales Range: $25-49.9 Million
Emp.: 6
Wholesale of Field Beans
N.A.I.C.S.: 493130

ADM Germany GmbH (1)
Ferdinandstrasse 5, Hamburg, 20095, Germany
Tel.: (49) 4030130
Food Ingredient Distr
N.A.I.C.S.: 424590

ADM Grain Company (1)
4666 Faries Pkwy, Decatur, IL 62526
Tel.: (217) 424-5200
Web Site: http://www.adm.com
Sales Range: $50-74.9 Million
Emp.: 6
Grains Industry
N.A.I.C.S.: 424510
Chris Boerm *(Pres)*

Subsidiary (Domestic):

ADM Collingwood Grain, Inc. (2)
8000 W 110th St Ste 220, Overland Park, KS 66210
Tel.: (913) 266-5070
Web Site: http://www.adm.com
Emp.: 150
Agricultural Services
N.A.I.C.S.: 444240

Plant (Domestic):

ADM Collingwood Grain Inc. (3)
304 Grand Ave, Plains, KS 67869-9704
Tel.: (620) 563-7218
Web Site: http://www.adm.com
Sales Range: $75-99.9 Million
Emp.: 30
Feed And Farm Supply
N.A.I.C.S.: 459910

ADM-Collingwood Grain (3)
181 N Front St, Scott City, KS 67871
Tel.: (620) 872-2174
Web Site: http://www.adm.com
Sales Range: $50-74.9 Million
Emp.: 5
Grains
N.A.I.C.S.: 424510

Collingwood Grain Inc. (3)
17 Wyoming, Goodland, KS 67735
Tel.: (785) 899-3636
Sales Range: $125-149.9 Million
Emp.: 210
Grain & Field Beans
N.A.I.C.S.: 424510

Plant (Domestic):

ADM Grain (2)
1301 N 4th St, Enid, OK 73701-8709
Tel.: (580) 233-5100
Web Site: http://www.admworld.com
Sales Range: $25-49.9 Million
Grains
N.A.I.C.S.: 311211

ADM Grain Co (2)
1700 N Halstead St, Hutchinson, KS 67501
Tel.: (620) 663-7957
Web Site: http://www.e-adm.com
Sales Range: $50-74.9 Million
Grain Elevators
N.A.I.C.S.: 424510

ADM Grain Co. (2)
8000 W 110th St Ste 220, Shawnee Mission, KS 66210 (100%)
Tel.: (913) 266-6300
Web Site: http://www.adm.com
Sales Range: $75-99.9 Million
Grains
N.A.I.C.S.: 424910

Archer-Daniels-Midland Company—(Continued)

ADM Grain Co. - Mendota (2)
110 E 12th St, Mendota, IL 61342
Tel.: (815) 539-7491
Web Site: http://www.adm.com
Grain Harvesting, Processing & Storage
N.A.I.C.S.: 424510

ADM Grain Company (2)
1901 S Sherman Dr, Indianapolis, IN
46203-3308 **(100%)**
Tel.: (317) 784-2200
Web Site: http://www.e-adm.com
Sales Range: $50-74.9 Million
Grain Elevators
N.A.I.C.S.: 424510

Subsidiary (Domestic):

ADM Grain River System, Inc. (2)
4666 E Faries Pkwy, Decatur, IL 62526-
5666
Tel.: (217) 424-5200
Web Site: http://www.adm.com
Sales Range: $125-149.9 Million
Grains
N.A.I.C.S.: 424510

Plant (Domestic):

ADM Grain River System, Inc. (3)
Broadway St, Carman, IL 61425
Tel.: (309) 873-2541
Sales Range: Less than $1 Million
Emp.: 15
Grain Elevators
N.A.I.C.S.: 115114

ADM Grain River System, Inc. (3)
2032 Hwy 44, Reserve, LA 70084-6325
Tel.: (985) 536-1151
Web Site: http://www.adm.com
Sales Range: $50-74.9 Million
Emp.: 42
Grain & Field Beans
N.A.I.C.S.: 424510

Plant (Domestic):

ADM-Grain (2)
492 WW Rd, Copeland, KS 67837 **(100%)**
Tel.: (620) 668-5531
Web Site: http://www.admworld.com
Sales Range: $25-49.9 Million
Supplier Of Grains
N.A.I.C.S.: 493130

**ADM Hamburg
Aktiengesellschaft** (1)
Nippoldstrasse 117, 21107, Hamburg, Germany
Tel.: (49) 40751940
Web Site: https://www.oelag.de
Agricultural Services
N.A.I.C.S.: 926140

ADM Hungary Agro Trading LLC (1)
Edison U 2 B/E/II, H-2040, Budaors, Hungary
Tel.: (36) 23445430
Emp.: 20
Food Ingredient Distr
N.A.I.C.S.: 424590

ADM Investor Services Inc. (1)
141 W Jackson Blvd Ste 2100A, Chicago,
IL 60604-2929
Tel.: (312) 242-7000
Web Site: http://www.admis.com
Sales Range: $150-199.9 Million
Financial Services
N.A.I.C.S.: 523160
John M. Walls (CIO & Sr VP)
Thomas J. Anderson (Sr VP)
Kurt Johnson (VP-Business Development)
Simta Gupta (VP-Operations)
Greg Hostetler (Chief Compliance Officer)

Division (Non-US):

**ADM Investor Services International
Limited** (2)
The Minster Building 3rd Floor 21 Mincing
Lane, London, EC3R 7AG, United
Kingdom **(100%)**
Tel.: (44) 2077168000
Web Site: https://www.admisi.com
Full Service Brokerage House to Institutions, Corporate & Retail Customers
N.A.I.C.S.: 523160

Fabian Somerville-Cotton (Mng Dir)

ADMIS Hong Kong Limited (2)
Unit 303 3 Floor Oxford House Taikoo
Place 979 King's Road, Quarry Bay, China
(Hong Kong)
Tel.: (852) 25373770
Web Site: https://www.admis.com.hk
Sales Range: $75-99.9 Million
Execution & Clearing Services for
Exchange-Traded Derivatives & Prime Brokerage Services in the Fixed Income & Foreign Exchange Markets
N.A.I.C.S.: 211130
Eric Wong (Mng Dir)

Subsidiary (Domestic):

**Archer Financial Services, Inc.
(AFS)** (2)
Chicago Board of Trade Bldg 141 W Jackson Blvd Ste 2100A, Chicago, IL
60604 **(100%)**
Tel.: (312) 242-7990
Web Site: https://www.archerfinancials.com
Sales Range: $650-699.9 Million
Emp.: 30
Brokerage Services to Individual Customers
& Independent Brokers
N.A.I.C.S.: 523160
Kurt M. Johnson (Pres)
Melanie O'Brien (VP)

ADM Italia S.r.l. (1)
Via Stazione 1a, Laives, 39055, Bolzano,
BZ, Italy
Tel.: (39) 047 195 5530
Web Site: https://admitalia.com
Business Support Services
N.A.I.C.S.: 561499

ADM Japan Ltd. (1)
Nihonbashi Central Square 4F 2-16-11 Nihombashi, Chuo, 103-0027, Japan
Tel.: (81) 362555800
Emp.: 60
Food Ingredient Distr
N.A.I.C.S.: 424590

ADM Mainz GmbH (1)
Dammweg 2, 55130, Mainz, 55130, Germany
Tel.: (49) 6131895238
Food Ingredient Distr
N.A.I.C.S.: 424590

ADM Malbork S.A. (1)
Ul Daleka 110, 82-200, Malbork, Poland
Tel.: (48) 552731218
Food Ingredient Distr
N.A.I.C.S.: 424590

ADM Milling Co. (1)
0000 W 110th St, Overland Park, KS
66210-2312
Tel.: (913) 491-9400
Web Site: http://www.adm.com
Sales Range: $50-74.9 Million
Flour; Dry Milling of Grains Mfr
N.A.I.C.S.: 311211

Plant (Domestic):

ADM Milling Co. (2)
1301 N 4th St, Enid, OK 73701
Tel.: (580) 237-8000
Web Site: http://www.questmedical.com
Sales Range: $10-24.9 Million
Emp.: 65
Mfr of Flour & Other Grain Mill Products
N.A.I.C.S.: 115114

ADM Milling Co. (2)
2301 E Trent Ave, Spokane, WA 99202-
2100
Tel.: (509) 535-2995
Web Site: http://www.adm.com
Sales Range: $25-49.9 Million
Emp.: 30
Prepared Cake & Doughnut Mixes
N.A.I.C.S.: 311824

ADM Milling Co. (2)
8000 W 110th St, Overland Park, KS
66210-2312 **(100%)**
Tel.: (913) 491-9400
Web Site: http://www.adm.com
Sales Range: $25-49.9 Million
Flour Mills
N.A.I.C.S.: 311211

ADM Milling Co. (2)
540 S St, Lincoln, NE 68502-1940 **(100%)**
Tel.: (402) 477-4161
Web Site: http://www.e-adm.com
Sales Range: $50-74.9 Million
Flour Producer
N.A.I.C.S.: 311211

ADM Milling Co. (2)
614 W 2nd St, Mount Vernon, IN 47620
Tel.: (812) 838-4445
Web Site: http://www.adm.com
Sales Range: $50-74.9 Million
Emp.: 100
Prepared Feeds
N.A.I.C.S.: 311119

ADM Milling Co. (2)
Spangler Rd, Camp Hill, PA 17011 **(100%)**
Tel.: (717) 737-0529
Web Site: http://www.e-adm.com
Sales Range: $50-74.9 Million
Emp.: 100
Blended, Prepared & Self-Rising Flour
N.A.I.C.S.: 311211

ADM Milling Co. (2)
8000 W 110th St, Overland Park, KS 67210
Tel.: (913) 491-9400
Web Site: http://www.admmilling.com
Sales Range: $50-74.9 Million
Emp.: 20
Grain Elevators
N.A.I.C.S.: 424510

ADM Milling Co. (2)
250 Ganson St, Buffalo, NY, 14203-3048
Tel.: (716) 849-7333
Web Site: http://www.adm.com
Flour & other Grain Mill Products
N.A.I.C.S.: 311211

ADM Milling Limited (1)
Hyatt Place 50-60 Broomfield Road,
Chelmsford, CM1 1SW, Essex, United Kingdom
Tel.: (44) 127 726 2525
Web Site: https://www.4flour.co.uk
Bakery Ingredient Mfr
N.A.I.C.S.: 311821

ADM Myanmar Company Limited (1)
402-A Level 4 Strand Square No 53 Strand
Road, Pabedan Township, Yangon, 11141,
Myanmar
Tel.: (95) 9 514 5409
Agricultural Raw Material Distr
N.A.I.C.S.: 424910

ADM Natural Health & Nutrition (2)
4666 Faries Pkwy, Decatur, IL 62526-5666
Tel.: (217) 451-4450
Web Site: http://www.adm.com
Sales Range: $350-399.9 Million
Isolated Soy Proteins
N.A.I.C.S.: 311221

ADM New Zealand Ltd. (1)
PO Box 4079, PO Box 4079, Mount Maunganui, 3149, New Zealand
Tel.: (64) 80 012 3753
Web Site:
    https://www.admnewzealand.co.nz
Food Ingredient Mfr
N.A.I.C.S.: 311221
Tina Thomas (Sls Mgr-Waikato)
Grant Gibson (Sls Mgr)
Brenda Gerken (Sls Mgr)

ADM North American Oilseed Processing Division (1)
5525 136th Ave SE, Enderlin, ND 58027
Tel.: (701) 437-3000
Web Site: http://www.adm.com
Sales Range: $350-399.9 Million
Emp.: 600
Oil Processing
N.A.I.C.S.: 311221

ADM Olomouc S.R.O. (1)
Heroes House Lomnickeho 1705/9, 140 00,
Prague, Czech Republic
Tel.: (420) 261399230
Confectionery Ingredient Mfr
N.A.I.C.S.: 311352

ADM Paraguay SRL (1)
Aviadores Del Chaco 1669 C/ San Martin
Edficio Aymac 6 piso, Asuncion, Paraguay
Tel.: (595) 216195000
Food Ingredient Distr

N.A.I.C.S.: 424590

ADM Portugal, SA (1)
Murtede Industrial Zone, Murtede, 3060-
372, Cantanhede, Portugal
Tel.: (351) 23 120 9900
Web Site: https://www.pt.wisium.com
Animal Feed Mfr
N.A.I.C.S.: 311119

ADM Protexin Limited (1)
Lopen Head, Somerset, TA13 5JH, United
Kingdom
Tel.: (44) 1460243230
Web Site: https://www.protexin.com
Confectionery Ingredient Mfr
N.A.I.C.S.: 311352
Toby Lewis (Founder)

ADM Pura Limited (1)
Church Manorway, Erith, DA8 1DL, United
Kingdom
Tel.: (44) 1322443000
Food Ingredient Distr
N.A.I.C.S.: 424590

ADM Razgrad EAD (1)
PO Box 239, North Industrial Area, 7200,
Razgrad, Bulgaria
Tel.: (359) 84619320
Emp.: 360
Wet Corn Mfr
N.A.I.C.S.: 311221

**ADM Rothensee GmbH & Co.
KG** (1)
Glockengiesserwall 22, Hamburg, 20095,
Germany
Tel.: (49) 405330260
Food Ingredient Distr
N.A.I.C.S.: 424590
Andre Berteit (Head-Logistics)

ADM STF Pte. Ltd. (1)
230 Victoria Street 11-08 Bugis Junction
Towers, Singapore, 188024, Singapore
Tel.: (65) 6 622 2400
Agricultural Raw Material Distr
N.A.I.C.S.: 424910

ADM STF Switzerland Sarl (1)
A One Business Center La Piece 3, 1180,
Rolle, Switzerland
Tel.: (41) 21 702 8000
Agricultural Raw Material Distr
N.A.I.C.S.: 424910

ADM Southern Cellulose (1)
103 W 45th St, Chattanooga, TN
37410 **(100%)**
Tel.: (423) 821-1561
Web Site: http://www.adm.com
Sales Range: $25-49.9 Million
Emp.: 150
Pulp Mfr
N.A.I.C.S.: 541618

ADM Specialty Ingredients (1)
4666 Faries Pkwy, Decatur, IL 62526-1820
Tel.: (217) 424-5200
Web Site: http://www.adm.com
Sales Range: $50-74.9 Million
Emp.: 3,000
Biochemical Food Additives Mfr
N.A.I.C.S.: 311221

Subsidiary (Domestic):

Specialty Commodities, Inc. (2)
1530 47th St N, Fargo, ND 58102
Tel.: (701) 282-8222
Web Site:
    http://www.specialtyfoodingredients.com
Sales Range: $10-24.9 Million
Emp.: 60
Miscellaneous Food Mfr
N.A.I.C.S.: 311999

ADM Stanley (1)
105 McKnight St, Stanley, WI 54768-0157
Tel.: (715) 644-5827
Web Site: http://www.e-adm.com
Sales Range: Less than $1 Million
Emp.: 20
Wholesale of Custom Drying
N.A.I.C.S.: 115114

ADM Trading Australia Pty. Ltd. (1)
Naylor House Level 4 191 Pulteney Street,
Adelaide, 5000, SA, Australia
Tel.: (61) 882109000

Web Site: https://www.admgrain.com.au
Food Ingredient Mfr
N.A.I.C.S.: 311221
Zac Ellis *(Mgr)*

ADM Trucking Company (1)
2501 N Brush College Rd, Decatur, IL
62526
Tel.: (217) 424-2651
Web Site: http://www.adm.com
Sales Range: $1-4.9 Billion
Emp.: 1,200
Truck Leasing
N.A.I.C.S.: 484121

Branch (Domestic):

ADM Trucking Inc. (2)
2501 N Brush College Rd, Decatur, IL
62526-5523
Tel.: (217) 451-7449
Web Site: http://www.admworld.com
Sales Range: $75-99.9 Million
Emp.: 171
Trucking Local & Long Distance
N.A.I.C.S.: 484121

ADM Vietnam Co., Ltd. (1)
Level 7 Saigon Centre Building 65 Le Loi
Boulevard, Ben Nghe Ward District 1, Ho
Chi Minh City, 70000, Vietnam
Tel.: (84) 2838217623
Animal Feed Whslr
N.A.I.C.S.: 424910

**ADM WILD Europe GmbH & Co.
KG** (1)
Rudolf-Wild-Strasse 107-115, 69214, Eppel-
heim, Germany
Tel.: (49) 62217990
Web Site: http://www.wildflavors.com
Flavor Ingredient Mfr
N.A.I.C.S.: 311930
Markus Lotsch *(Mng Dir)*
Jorg Bornhoft *(Mng Dir)*
Hans Christian Jensen *(Mng Dir)*
Martin Steinmann *(Mng Dir)*
Abraham van Hulsen *(Mng Dir)*
Burkhard Oesting *(Mng Dir)*
Erdal Kurban *(Mng Dir)*
Burkhard Oesting *(Mng Dir)*
Erdal Kurban *(Mng Dir)*

ADM WILD Nauen GmbH (1)
Berliner Str 119, 14641, Nauen, Germany
Tel.: (49) 332144840
Bakery Ingredient Mfr
N.A.I.C.S.: 311821

ADM WILD Valencia (1)
Partida La Coma S/n, 46740, Valencia,
Spain
Tel.: (34) 962467150
Food Ingredient Mfr
N.A.I.C.S.: 311221

ADMIS Singapore Pte. Limited (1)
230 Victoria Street 11-06 Bugis Junction
Towers, Singapore, 188024, Singapore
Tel.: (65) 66323000
Web Site: http://www.admis.com.sg
Agriculture Product Distr
N.A.I.C.S.: 424910

Agri Port Services, LLC (1)
120 Mallard St Ste 150, Saint Rose, LA
70087
Tel.: (985) 764-1105
Shipping Agency Services
N.A.I.C.S.: 488510

Agrinational Insurance Company (1)
76 Saint Paul St, Burlington, VT
05401   (100%)
Tel.: (802) 862-4400
Sales Range: $25-49.9 Million
Emp.: 60
Wet Corn Mfr
N.A.I.C.S.: 311221
Nancy Gray *(Office Mgr)*

Alfrebro, LLC (1)
1055 Reed Rd, Monroe, OH 45050
Tel.: (513) 539-7373
Web Site: http://www.alfrebro.com
Natural Extract & Aroma Chemical Mfr
N.A.I.C.S.: 325194

**American River Transportation
Company** (1)
4666 Faries Pkwy, Decatur, IL 62526

Tel.: (217) 451-7231
Web Site: http://www.adm.com
Grain Barge Operations
N.A.I.C.S.: 483211

Amylum Bulgaria EAD (1)
PO Box 239, North Industrial Area, 7200,
Razgrad, Bulgaria
Tel.: (359) 84619320
Emp.: 330
Wet Corn Milling Mfr
N.A.I.C.S.: 311221

**Amylum Nisasta Sanayi Ticaret
Anonim Sirketi** (1)
Adana Haci Sabanci Organize Sanayi
Bolgesi-5, Ocak Caddesi Numara 2 Sari-
cam, 01350, Adana, Turkiye
Tel.: (90) 3223554073
Corn Wet Mill Mfr
N.A.I.C.S.: 311221

**Amylum Nisasta Sanayi Ve Ticaret
Anonim Sirketi** (1)
Adana Haci Sabanci Organize Sanayi
Bolgesi-5 Ocak Caddesi Numara 2, Sari-
cam, 01350, Adana, Turkiye
Tel.: (90) 3223554073
Confectionery Ingredient Mfr
N.A.I.C.S.: 311352

**Anco Animal Nutrition Competence
GmbH** (1)
Linzer Strasse 55, 3100, Saint Polten, Aus-
tria
Tel.: (43) 27 429 0502
Web Site: https://www.anco.net
Animal Feed Mfr
N.A.I.C.S.: 311119

**Archer Daniels Midland Asia Pacific,
Limited** (1)
Rm 1401 Hutchison Hse 10 Harcourt Rd,
Central, China (Hong Kong)
Tel.: (852) 28611828
Grocery Product Distr
N.A.I.C.S.: 492210

Archer Daniels Midland Co. (1)
Foot Of E Ninth St, Little Rock, AR
72202   (100%)
Tel.: (501) 372-0277
Sales Range: $25-49.9 Million
Emp.: 42
Soybean Oil Seed Processing
N.A.I.C.S.: 493130

Archer Daniels Midland Co. (1)
1841 Clay Rd, Valdosta, GA 31601
Tel.: (229) 242-0100
Web Site: http://www.admworld.com
Sales Range: $75-99.9 Million
Emp.: 200
Soybean Oil Mills
N.A.I.C.S.: 311224

Archer Daniels Midland Co. (1)
Hwy 15 Rte K, Baring, MO 63531   (100%)
Tel.: (660) 892-4411
Sales Range: $25-49.9 Million
Emp.: 2
Grain Handling
N.A.I.C.S.: 424910

Archer Daniels Midland Co. (1)
126 La Grange, Red Wing, MN
55066   (100%)
Tel.: (651) 388-7111
Web Site: http://www.admworld.com
Sales Range: $25-49.9 Million
Emp.: 70
Oils & Greases Blending & Compounding
N.A.I.C.S.: 324191

Archer Daniels Midland Co. (1)
7800 Thayer St, Lincoln, NE 68507-1082
Tel.: (402) 464-9131
Web Site: http://www.adm.com
Sales Range: $75-99.9 Million
Emp.: 150
Soybean Oil Mills
N.A.I.C.S.: 311224

Archer Daniels Midland Co. (1)
1 Edmund St, Peoria, IL 61602   (100%)
Tel.: (309) 673-1724
Web Site: http://www.adm.com
Sales Range: $50-74.9 Million
Emp.: 180
Non-Alcoholic Beverages

N.A.I.C.S.: 325199

Archer Daniels Midland Co. (1)
250 Ganson St, Buffalo, NY
14203-3048   (100%)
Tel.: (716) 849-7333
Sales Range: $50-74.9 Million
Emp.: 100
Flour & Other Grain Products
N.A.I.C.S.: 311211
George Siradis *(Plant Mgr)*

Archer Daniels Midland Co. (1)
413 N Hampton St, Kershaw, SC 29067-
1139
Tel.: (803) 475-3751
Web Site: http://www.adm.com
Sales Range: $25-49.9 Million
Emp.: 40
Soybean Oil Mills
N.A.I.C.S.: 311224

Archer Daniels Midland Co. (1)
1730 E Moore St, Southport, NC
28461-9418   (100%)
Tel.: (910) 457-5011
Sales Range: $50-74.9 Million
Emp.: 150
Food Ingredients
N.A.I.C.S.: 325412
Eric Warner *(Plant Mgr)*

Archer Daniels Midland Co. (1)
1543 Calada St, Los Angeles, CA
90023   (100%)
Tel.: (323) 266-2750
Web Site: http://www.adm.com
Sales Range: $25-49.9 Million
Emp.: 40
Cereal Flour Mills
N.A.I.C.S.: 311211

Archer Daniels Midland Co. (1)
9808 S Wood St White, Brookston, IN
47923   (100%)
Tel.: (765) 563-3181
Web Site: http://www.e-ads.com
Sales Range: $50-74.9 Million
Emp.: 15
Service of Grain Elevator
N.A.I.C.S.: 424510

Archer Daniels Midland Co. (1)
1 E Grand Ave, Saint Louis, MO 63147-
2912
Tel.: (314) 241-9113
Web Site: http://www.adm.com
Sales Range: $50-74.9 Million
Emp.: 30
Grains
N.A.I.C.S.: 424510

Archer Daniels Midland Co. (1)
6801 Memorial Hwy, Ottawa Lake, MI
49267
Tel.: (734) 856-3667
Web Site: http://www.adm.com
Sales Range: Less than $1 Million
Emp.: 25
Grain Milling Custom Services
N.A.I.C.S.: 115114

Archer Daniels Midland Co. (1)
1350 Waconia Ave SW, Cedar Rapids, IA
52404-4322   (100%)
Tel.: (319) 398-0600
Web Site: http://www.adm.com
Sales Range: $150-199.9 Million
Emp.: 300
Dried or Unmixed Corn Syrup
N.A.I.C.S.: 311221

Archer Daniels Midland Co. (1)
240 Preston St, Jackson, TN
38301   (100%)
Tel.: (731) 424-3535
Web Site: http://www.admworld.com
Sales Range: $50-74.9 Million
Emp.: 100
Prepared Flour Mixes & Doughs
N.A.I.C.S.: 311824

Archer Daniels Midland Co. (1)
1050 S Airport Rd, Decatur, IL 62521-8768
Tel.: (217) 424-5521
Web Site: http://www.adm.com
Sales Range: $350-399.9 Million
Emp.: 22
Aircraft Servicing & Repairing
N.A.I.C.S.: 488190

Archer Daniels Midland Co. (1)
PO Box 15226, Minneapolis, MN 55415
Tel.: (612) 340-5900
Web Site: http://www.adm.com
Sales Range: $50-74.9 Million
Emp.: 80
Grain & Field Beans
N.A.I.C.S.: 444240

Archer Daniels Midland Co. (1)
4666 Faries Pkwy, Decatur, IL 62526
Tel.: (217) 424-5200
Web Site: http://www.adm.com
Sales Range: $150-199.9 Million
Emp.: 4,200
Packing & Crating
N.A.I.C.S.: 311221

Archer Daniels Midland Co. (1)
2800 Refinery Rd, Quincy, IL 62301
Tel.: (217) 224-1875
Sales Range: $50-74.9 Million
Emp.: 80
Vegetable Refined Oils
N.A.I.C.S.: 493130
Mike Pulliam *(Mgr-ADM Refinery)*

Archer Daniels Midland Co. (1)
5525 136th Ave SE, Enderlin, ND
58027-9771   (100%)
Tel.: (701) 437-3000
Web Site: http://www.adm.com
Sales Range: $50-74.9 Million
Emp.: 100
Vegetable Oil Mills
N.A.I.C.S.: 311225
Ellen Checkwood *(Sec)*

Archer Daniels Midland Co. (1)
575 Drake St, Saint Paul, MN
55102-3830   (100%)
Tel.: (651) 292-9796
Web Site: http://www.adm.com
Sales Range: $50-74.9 Million
Emp.: 12
Grain & Field Beans
N.A.I.C.S.: 424510

Archer Daniels Midland Co. (1)
5020 Shreve Ave, Saint Louis, MO 63115-
2226
Tel.: (314) 385-9100
Web Site: http://www.adm.com
Sales Range: $75-99.9 Million
Emp.: 100
Flour & Other Grain Mill Products
N.A.I.C.S.: 424510

Archer Daniels Midland Co. (1)
1388 Hwy 97, Velva, ND
58790-9003   (100%)
Tel.: (701) 338-2075
Web Site: http://www.adm.com
Sales Range: $25-49.9 Million
Emp.: 40
Edible Fats & Oils
N.A.I.C.S.: 311225

Archer Daniels Midland Co. (1)
W Main St, Oakland, IL 61943
Tel.: (217) 837-2432
Sales Range: $1-9.9 Million
Emp.: 5
Producer of Corn
N.A.I.C.S.: 115114
Brian Wiggin *(Mgr)*

Archer Daniels Midland Co. (1)
2620 Henkel Rd, Keokuk, IA 52632-2203
Tel.: (319) 524-2323
Web Site: http://www.admworld.com
Sales Range: $125-149.9 Million
Emp.: 150
Mfr of Wheat Starch
N.A.I.C.S.: 311221

Archer Daniels Midland Co. (1)
16994 Wright Rd, Grand Ledge, MI
48837   (100%)
Tel.: (517) 627-4017
Web Site: http://www.e-adm.com
Sales Range: $50-74.9 Million
Emp.: 20
Grain Elevators
N.A.I.C.S.: 424510

Archer Daniels Midland Co. (1)
620 W 10th St, Charlotte, NC 28202-1430
Tel.: (704) 332-3165
Sales Range: $25-49.9 Million
Emp.: 50
Flour Mills

Archer-Daniels-Midland Company—(Continued)

N.A.I.C.S.: 311211
David Saestokes *(Plant Mgr)*

Archer Daniels Midland Co. (1)
1155 Riverview Dr, Winona, MN 55987-2229
Tel.: (507) 452-3562
Web Site: http://www.adm.com
Sales Range: $50-74.9 Million
Emp.: 5
Janitorial Services
N.A.I.C.S.: 424510

Archer Daniels Midland Co. (1)
2191 W County Rd, Frankfort, IN 46041
Tel.: (765) 654-4411
Web Site: http://www.admfarmview.com
Sales Range: $75-99.9 Million
Emp.: 55
Soybean Oil Mills
N.A.I.C.S.: 311225

Archer Daniels Midland Co. (1)
601 W Division St, Altamont, IL 62411 **(100%)**
Tel.: (618) 483-6171
Web Site: http://www.e-adm.com
Sales Range: $25-49.9 Million
Emp.: 6
Grain Elevators
N.A.I.C.S.: 424510

Archer Daniels Midland Co. (1)
2301 Trent Ave, Spokane, WA 99202 **(100%)**
Tel.: (509) 534-2636
Sales Range: $25-49.9 Million
Emp.: 50
Flour Mills Cereal
N.A.I.C.S.: 311211

Archer Daniels Midland Co. (ADM) (1)
430 N Hampton St, Carrboro, NC 28110-8188 **(100%)**
Tel.: (704) 233-4051
Web Site: http://www.adm.com
Sales Range: $25-49.9 Million
Emp.: 3
Whslr of Grain Elevators
N.A.I.C.S.: 424510

Archer Daniels Midland Co.-West Plant (1)
3883 Faries Pkwy, Decatur, IL 62526-5656 **(100%)**
Tel.: (217) 424-5856
Web Site: http://www.adm.com
Sales Range: $150-199.9 Million
Emp.: 300
Process Soybean & Corn
N.A.I.C.S.: 311119

Archer Daniels Midland Compnay - Clinton (1)
1251 Beaver Channel Pkwy, Clinton, IA 52732
Tel.: (563) 242-1121
Emp.: 31,000
Wet Corn Milling
N.A.I.C.S.: 311221
Jim Woll *(Reg Mgr-Corn Processing Div)*
Dean Brainerd *(Plant Superintenden)*

Archer Daniels Midland Europe BV (1)
Kingsfordweg 43-117, 1043 GP, Amsterdam, Netherlands
Tel.: (31) 202195353
Web Site: http://www.adm.com
Food Ingredients & Animal Feeds Mfr
N.A.I.C.S.: 311999

Subsidiary (Non-US):

ADM Agri-Industries Company (2)
2089 Naylor Side Rd, Essex, N8M 2Y1, ON, Canada **(100%)**
Tel.: (519) 776-4208
Web Site: http://www.adm.com
Sales Range: $10-24.9 Million
Emp.: 10
Edible Fats & Oils
N.A.I.C.S.: 311224

Plant (Domestic):

ADM Agri-Industries Company (3)
5550 Maplewood Drive, Windsor, N9C 0B9,

ON, Canada
Tel.: (519) 972-8100
Crop Preparation Services
N.A.I.C.S.: 115112

ADM Agri-Industries Company (3)
R R 1, PO Box 820, Watson, S0K 4V0, SK, Canada **(100%)**
Tel.: (306) 287-3100
Web Site: http://www.adm.com
Sales Range: Less than $1 Million
Emp.: 5
Sales of Edible Fats & Oils
N.A.I.C.S.: 311224

ADM Agri-Industries Company (3)
4002 Bonnybrook Rd SE, Calgary, T2G 4M9, AB, Canada
Tel.: (403) 267-5600
Web Site: http://www.adm.com
Sales Range: $10-24.9 Million
Emp.: 75
Crop Preparation Services for Market
N.A.I.C.S.: 115112

ADM Agri-Industries Company (3)
300 Industrial Dr, Blenheim, N0P 1A0, ON, Canada
Tel.: (519) 676-8989
Web Site: http://www.adm.com
Research on Crop Grains
N.A.I.C.S.: 111998

ADM Agri-Industries Company (3)
Se 30-10-14 W, Carberry, R0K 0H0, MB, Canada **(100%)**
Tel.: (204) 834-2980
Web Site: http://www.e-adm.com
Sales Range: $1-9.9 Million
Emp.: 5
Crop Preparation Services for Market
N.A.I.C.S.: 115112

ADM Agri-Industries Company (3)
4805 6 2nd Ave, Lloydminster, T9V 3E7, AB, Canada **(100%)**
Tel.: (780) 875-5554
Web Site: http://www.adm.com
Edible Fats & Oils
N.A.I.C.S.: 311224

ADM Agri-Industries Company (3)
305 Caradoc St S, Strathroy, N7G 2P3, ON, Canada
Tel.: (519) 245-9014
Web Site: http://www.e-adm.com
Grain Merchandisers
N.A.I.C.S.: 424510

ADM Agri-Industries Company (3)
155 Iberia Ave, Candiac, J5R 3H1, QC, Canada
Tel.: (450) 659-1911
Web Site: http://www.adm.com
Wet Corn Milling
N.A.I.C.S.: 311221

ADM Agri-Industries Company (3)
5550 Maplewood Dr, PO Box 7128, Windsor, N9C 4G9, ON, Canada **(100%)**
Tel.: (519) 972-8100
Web Site: http://www.adm.com
Edible Fats & Oils
N.A.I.C.S.: 311224

Subsidiary (Non-US):

ADM Do Brasil LTDA (3)
Av Roque Petroni Jr 999 9 Andar, Sao Paulo, 04707-000, SP, Brazil
Tel.: (55) 1151853500
Web Site: http://www.adm.com
Edible Oil Mfr
N.A.I.C.S.: 311225

Subsidiary (Domestic):

ADM Milling Company (3)
1222 Allowance Ave SE, Medicine Hat, T1A 3H1, AB, Canada **(100%)**
Tel.: (403) 526-2876
Web Site: http://www.adm.com
Flour & Other Grain Mill Products
N.A.I.C.S.: 311211

Plant (Domestic):

ADM Milling Co. (4)
202 First St, PO Box 369, Midland, L4R 4L1, ON, Canada **(100%)**
Tel.: (705) 526-7861

Web Site: http://www.adm.com
Sales Range: $25-49.9 Million
Emp.: 68
Flour & other Grain Mill Products
N.A.I.C.S.: 311211

Subsidiary (Domestic):

ADM Alfred C. Toepfer International BV (2)
Boompjes 40, Rotterdam, 3011 XB, Netherlands
Tel.: (31) 102805500
Web Site: http://www.adm.com
Sales Range: $150-199.9 Million
Emp.: 6
Agricultural Product Trading
N.A.I.C.S.: 493130

Subsidiary (Non-US):

ADM International Sarl (2)
A One Business Center Z A Versde la Piece Route de l Etraz, 1180, Rolle, Switzerland
Tel.: (41) 217028000
Food & Beverage Mfr
N.A.I.C.S.: 311999

WILD Flavors GmbH (2)
Neugasse 22, 6300, Zug, Switzerland
Tel.: (41) 417287610
Web Site: http://www.wildflavors.com
Sales Range: $1-4.9 Billion
Emp.: 2,500
Food & Beverage Flavoring Syrups & Concentrates Developer & Mfr
N.A.I.C.S.: 311930
Hans-Peter Wild *(Chm)*

Subsidiary (Non-US):

Rudolf Wild GmbH & Co. KG (3)
Am Schlangengraben 3-5, 13597, Berlin, Germany
Tel.: (49) 30330870
Web Site: http://www.wildflavors.com
Food & Beverage Fruit Flavorings Mfr
N.A.I.C.S.: 311942

WILD Flavors (Canada) Inc. (3)
7315 Pacific Circle, Mississauga, L5T 1V1, ON, Canada
Tel.: (905) 670-1108
Web Site: http://www.wildflavors.com
Emp.: 50
Spray Dried Flavoring Powders & Dry Blended Seasonings Mfr
N.A.I.C.S.: 311942

Subsidiary (US):

WILD Flavors, Inc. (3)
1201 Pacific Ave, Erlanger, KY 41018
Tel.: (859) 342-3600
Web Site: https://www.wildflavors.com
Food & Beverage Flavorings, Colors & Other Ingredients Mfr
N.A.I.C.S.: 311942
Gary Massie *(CFO)*

Division (Domestic):

WILD Flavors and Specialty Ingredients Inc. - A.M. Todd Division (4)
1717 Douglas Ave, Kalamazoo, MI 49007
Tel.: (269) 343-2603
Web Site: http://www.wildflavors.com
Emp.: 50
Mint Oil Extraction Services
N.A.I.C.S.: 325998

Plant (Non-US):

WILD Flavors, Inc. - Tarapur Facility (4)
Plot Nr J-79 Midc Tarapur Doripuja Road, Boisar, Tarapur, 401 506, India
Tel.: (91) 2525274810
Web Site: http://www.wildflavors.com
Mint Oil Extraction Services
N.A.I.C.S.: 325998

Subsidiary (Non-US):

WILD Juice Services B.V. (3)
Capriweg 4, 1044 AL, Amsterdam, Netherlands
Tel.: (31) 204803711
Web Site: http://www.wildflavors.com

Fruit Concentrates, Fruit Purees & Fruit Concentrate Blends Mfr & Distr
N.A.I.C.S.: 311999

WILD Valencia S.A. (3)
Partida La Coma s/n, 46740, Carcaixent, Spain
Tel.: (34) 962467150
Web Site: http://www.wildflavors.com
Natural Sweetener, Concentrate, Coloring, Flavoring & Other Fruit Extracts Mfr
N.A.I.C.S.: 311930

Archer Daniels Midland Korea LLC (1)
2nd Floor KT and G Kosmo Daechi Tower Tehran-ro 98 Gil 8, Kangnam-gu, Seoul, 06181, Korea (South)
Tel.: (82) 23 440 6702
Agricultural Raw Material Distr
N.A.I.C.S.: 424910

Archer Daniels Midland Singapore, Pte. Ltd. (1)
230 Victoria Street 11-08 Bugis Junction Towers, Singapore, 188024, Singapore
Tel.: (65) 66222400
Agricultural Services
N.A.I.C.S.: 926140

Archer-Daniels-Midland Company - Corn Processing (1)
4666 E Faries Pkwy, Decatur, IL 62526
Tel.: (217) 424-5200
Web Site: http://www.adm.com
Sales Range: $5-14.9 Billion
Emp.: 26,000
Corn Milling & Products Mfr
N.A.I.C.S.: 311221

Archer-Daniels-Midland Philippines, Inc. (1)
4th Floor Pacific Star Building Gil Puyat corner Makati Avenue, Makati, 1200, Philippines
Tel.: (63) 88921516
Agricultural Services
N.A.I.C.S.: 926140

BIOPOLIS, S.L. (1)
Catedratico Agustin Escardino 9, Paterna, 46980, Valencia, Spain
Tel.: (34) 963160299
Web Site: http://www.biopolis-microbiome.com
Food Testing Laboratory Services
N.A.I.C.S.: 541380

Balanceados Nova SA Balnova (1)
Via a la costa Km 15 5, Guayaquil, Ecuador
Tel.: (593) 4 204 6394
Web Site: https://www.balnova.com
Animal Feed Mfr
N.A.I.C.S.: 311119

Bern Aqua (1)
Hagelberg 3, 2250, Olen, Belgium
Tel.: (32) 1 428 2520
Web Site: https://www.bernaqua.com
Fish Feed Producing Services
N.A.I.C.S.: 112511

Chamtor - Legal (1)
114 rue de Pomacle, CS 30004, 51110, Bazancourt, Cedex, France
Tel.: (33) 326895950
Wheat Farming Services
N.A.I.C.S.: 111140

Crosswind Industries, Inc. (1)
6300 NW Kelly Dr, Parkville, MO 64152
Tel.: (816) 891-7979
Holding Company; Pet Food Mfr
N.A.I.C.S.: 551112
Kenneth E. Matson *(Pres)*

Subsidiary (Domestic):

Crosswind Petfoods, Inc. (2)
6300 NW Kelly Dr, Parkville, MO 64152
Tel.: (816) 891-7979
Pet Food Mfr
N.A.I.C.S.: 311111

Daavision BV (1)
Lekstraat 14a, 5347 KV, Oss, Netherlands
Tel.: (31) 41 240 5760
Web Site: https://www.daavision.com
Animal Feed Mfr
N.A.I.C.S.: 311999

Erich Ziegler GmbH **(1)**
Am Weiher 133, Aufsess, 91347, Bayreuth, Germany
Tel.: (49) 91 989 2940
Web Site: https://www.erich-ziegler.com
Animal Feed Mfr
N.A.I.C.S.: 311999

Evialis France **(1)**
Talhouet, 56250, Saint Nolff, France
Tel.: (33) 297485454
Web Site: http://www.evialis.fr
Animal Feed Mfr
N.A.I.C.S.: 311119

Evialis Galicia S.A. **(1)**
Holy Spirit 29-30, Soneiro Sada, 15168, A Coruna, Spain
Tel.: (34) 98 163 1300
Web Site: https://evialis.es
Dog & Cat Food Mfr
N.A.I.C.S.: 311111

FISA Andina S.A.S. **(1)**
Zona Franca Palmaseca bodega A1 Valle del Cauca, Palmira, Colombia
Tel.: (57) 6028912799
Food Flavor Mfr
N.A.I.C.S.: 311930

Federation Sahanala Vanille **(1)**
Lot II E 39 Bis Ankadivato, Antananarivo, 101, Analamanga, Madagascar
Tel.: (261) 20 222 5830
Web Site: https://sahanala.net
Emp.: 280
Agricultural Raw Material Distr
N.A.I.C.S.: 424910

Filozoo SRL **(1)**
Viale del Commercio 28/30, 41012, Carpi, MO, Italy
Tel.: (39) 059637314
Emp.: 70
Animal Feed Mfr
N.A.I.C.S.: 311119

Flavor Infusion International, S.A. **(1)**
Panamerica Corporate Center Blvd de Americas Blg 9090 Local 1, Panama Pacifico, Panama, Panama
Tel.: (507) 8306181
Web Site: https://flavorinfusion.com
Food Flavor Mfr
N.A.I.C.S.: 311930

Florida Chemical Company, Inc. **(1)**
351 Winter Haven Blvd NE, Winter Haven, FL 33881-9432
Tel.: (863) 294-8483
Web Site: http://www.floridachemical.com
Organic Chemical Mfr & Whslr
N.A.I.C.S.: 325199
Joshua A. Snively Sr. *(Pres)*

Golden Peanut & Tree Nuts S.A. **(1)**
Ruta A 171, 2686, Alejandro Roca, Cordoba, Argentina
Tel.: (54) 3584980514
Peanut & Nut Butter Whslr
N.A.I.C.S.: 424590

Golden Peanut Argentina S.A. **(1)**
Ruta A 171, 2686, Cordoba, Alejandro Roca, South Africa
Tel.: (27) 3584980514
Web Site: http://www.goldenpeanut.com.ar
Peanut Product Mfr
N.A.I.C.S.: 311911

Golden Peanut Company, LLC **(1)**
100 N Point Ctr E Ste 400, Alpharetta, GA 30022-8262 **(100%)**
Tel.: (770) 752-8160
Web Site: https://www.goldenpeanut.com
Sales Range: $600-649.9 Million
Emp.: 55
Raw & Processed Peanuts Mfr
N.A.I.C.S.: 111992

Golden Peanut and Tree Nut SA (Pty) Ltd. **(1)**
Farm 5J9, PO Box 2256, Hartswater, Northern Cape, South Africa
Tel.: (27) 534741345
Web Site: http://www.goldenpeanut.com
Peanut Product Mfr
N.A.I.C.S.: 311224

Groupe Pilardiere **(1)**

La Pilardiere, 85590, Saint-Mars-la-Reorthe, France
Tel.: (33) 251573102
Web Site: https://www.pilardiere.eu
Animal Nutrition Mfr
N.A.I.C.S.: 311119

Guyomarc'h - VCN Company Limited **(1)**
N5 Street Area B, Hoa Mac Industrial Park Duy Tien District, Ha Nam, Vietnam
Tel.: (84) 2263555111
Animal Food Distr
N.A.I.C.S.: 424910

Jamaica Flour Mills Limited **(1)**
209 Windward Road, Kingston, 2, Jamaica
Tel.: (876) 9287221
Emp.: 30
Flour Mill Distr
N.A.I.C.S.: 424490

Master Mix of Trinidad Limited **(1)**
48-50 Sackville Street, Port of Spain, Trinidad & Tobago
Tel.: (868) 6793333
Confectionery Ingredient Mfr
N.A.I.C.S.: 311352

Minmetal S.R.L. **(1)**
Incinta Port Constanta Dana Str No 45 Floor 2, Constanta, 900003, Romania
Tel.: (40) 241639035
Emp.: 175
Marine Cargo Handling Services
N.A.I.C.S.: 488320

Monti Foods (Pty) Ltd. **(1)**
Cambridge Goods Complex Western Ave, Cambridge Village, East London, 5201, South Africa
Tel.: (27) 43 726 5232
Animal Feed Mfr
N.A.I.C.S.: 311119

NEOVIA SAS **(1)**
Route de Talhouet, Saint Nolff, France
Tel.: (33) 2 97 48 54 54
Web Site:
http://www.global.adnimalnutrition.com
Biochemical Products Mfr
N.A.I.C.S.: 325998

Subsidiary (US):

Epicore BioNetworks Inc. **(2)**
4 Lina Ln, Eastampton, NJ 08060
Tel.: (609) 267-9118
Web Site:
http://www.epicorebionetworks.com
Biotechnology Products & Specialty Animal Feeds Mfr, Developer & Marketer
N.A.I.C.S.: 541714
Fernando Garcia Abad *(Dir-Bus Dev-Aquaculture)*
Samuel DeMore *(Production Mgr)*
Samuel DeMore *(Production Mgr)*

Subsidiary (Non-US):

Epicore Ecuador S.A. **(3)**
Km 11 Via La Costa - Solar No 5, Guayaquil, Ecuador
Tel.: (593) 42990663
Web Site:
http://www.epicorebionetworks.com
Biotechnology Products Mfr
N.A.I.C.S.: 325414

New Orleans Ship Yard **(1)**
8400 River Rd, Jefferson, LA 70094-2317
Tel.: (504) 431-9611
Web Site: http://www.adm.com
Sales Range: $25-49.9 Million
Emp.: 80
Building & Repairing Barges
N.A.I.C.S.: 336611

NutraDine, LLC **(1)**
4700 Innovation Dr Bldg B, Fort Collins, CO 80525
Web Site: https://nutradinellc.com
Pet Food Mfr
N.A.I.C.S.: 311111

Pabor Archer Daniels Midland Company **(1)**
Brunner St, Peru, IL 61354
Tel.: (815) 223-8000
Web Site: http://www.adm.com

Sales Range: $25-49.9 Million
Emp.: 15
Grains
N.A.I.C.S.: 493130

Pancosma SA **(1)**
Voie des Traz 6, Le Grand Saconnex, 1218, Geneva, Switzerland
Tel.: (41) 229298484
Commercial Trading Services
N.A.I.C.S.: 523160

PetDine, LLC **(1)**
4700 Innovation Dr Bldg B, Fort Collins, CO 80525
Web Site: https://petdinellc.com
Animal Feed Mfr
N.A.I.C.S.: 311119
Preston Munsch *(CEO)*
Justin Boling *(Mktg Dir)*
Suzy Ferrin *(Project Mgr)*
Benjamin Fletcher *(Project Mgr)*
Elizabeth Barth *(COO)*

Precision Microblenders Inc. **(1)**
8 Thomas Davila, Barceloneta, PR 00617
Tel.: (787) 846-3204
Sales Range: $10-24.9 Million
Emp.: 31
Feed Premixes Mfr
N.A.I.C.S.: 311611
Camilo Almeda *(Gen Mgr)*

Rodelle Inc. **(1)**
3461 Precision Dr, Fort Collins, CO 80528
Web Site: http://www.rodellekitchen.com
Dry Food Flavoring & Spice Mfr
N.A.I.C.S.: 311942

SORA Laboratories, LLC **(1)**
15366 US Hwy 160, Forsyth, MO 65653
Web Site: https://soralabs.com
Laboratory Testing Services
N.A.I.C.S.: 541380

Setna Nutricion SA **(1)**
C/Clavo 1 Pol ind Santa Ana, 28522, Rivas-Vaciamadrid, Madrid, Spain
Tel.: (34) 91 666 8500
Web Site: https://www.setna.com
Animal Feed Whslr
N.A.I.C.S.: 424910
Angel Lazaro *(Mng Dir)*

Silo P. Kruse Betriebs-GmbH & Co. KG **(1)**
Blumensand 31-33, Wilhelmsburg, 21107, Hamburg, Germany
Tel.: (49) 4 075 2060
Web Site: https://www.silo-p-kruse.com
Animal Feed Mfr
N.A.I.C.S.: 311119
Candy Siekmann *(CEO)*

Societe Industrielle des Oleagineux-SIO **(1)**
16 rue du General de Gaulle, 62223, Saint-Laurent-Blangy, France
Tel.: (33) 643022436
Agricultural Services
N.A.I.C.S.: 926140

Sojaprotein d.o.o. **(1)**
Industrijska 1, 21220, Becej, Serbia **(62.94%)**
Tel.: (381) 21 691 5311
Web Site: https://sojaprotein.rs
Emp.: 378
Soybean Products Mfr
N.A.I.C.S.: 311224
Aleksandra Petric *(Dir-Quality)*
Milan Sevo *(Dir-Production & Technical Dept)*
Milenko Tica *(Exec Dir-Sls)*
Petar Dolinka *(Exec Dir-Legal & Gen Affairs)*
Marko Abramovic *(Gen Mgr)*
Dragana Andelkovic *(Exec Dir-Fin)*

Southern Cellulose Products, Inc. **(1)**
105 W 45th St, Chattanooga, TN 37410
Tel.: (423) 821-1561
Emp.: 110
Pulp Mfr
N.A.I.C.S.: 322110

Upscience Italia S.R.L. **(1)**
Via Staffette Partigiane 44-46-48, 41122, Modena, MO, Italy

Tel.: (39) 05 931 0759
Web Site: https://www.upscience-labs.com
Medical Laboratory Services
N.A.I.C.S.: 621511

Wild Amazon Flavors Ltda. **(1)**
1695 Torquato Tapajos Avenue - Paz Flores, 69048-010, Manaus, Brazil
Tel.: (55) 9236541532
Flavor System Mfr
N.A.I.C.S.: 312111

Wild Flavors (Beijing) Ltd. **(1)**
No 19 Zhonghe Street Bda, Beijing, 100176, China
Tel.: (86) 1067874455
Flavor System Mfr & Distr
N.A.I.C.S.: 312111

Wild Juice B.V. **(1)**
Capriweg 4, 1044 AL, Amsterdam, Netherlands
Tel.: (31) 204803711
Farm Product Warehousing Services
N.A.I.C.S.: 493130

ARCHON CORPORATION
210 N Park Blvd Ste 100, Grapevine, TX 76051
Tel.: (214) 526-0731 **NV**
Web Site:
https://www.archoncorp.com
Year Founded: 1982
ARHN—(OTCIQ)
Sales Range: $10-24.9 Million
Emp.: 321
Holding Company; Hotels & Casinos
N.A.I.C.S.: 713990
Gary Wood *(Principal & Architect)*
Katie Wurst *(Principal & Architect)*
Pamela Mathis-Hernandez *(Project Mgr)*
Brandon Gallimore *(Project Mgr)*
Brian Hernandez *(Project Mgr)*
Joey DelPrincipe *(Project Mgr)*
Kyle Kittelson *(Project Mgr & Designer)*

Subsidiaries:

Pioneer Hotel Inc. **(1)**
2200 S Casino Dr, Laughlin, NV 89029-1515 **(100%)**
Tel.: (702) 298-2442
Web Site: http://www.pioneerlaughlin.com
Sales Range: $50-74.9 Million
Hotel
N.A.I.C.S.: 721120
Margarite Gabaldon *(Dir-Gaming Ops & Mgr-HR)*

Subsidiary (Domestic):

Casino Properties, Inc. **(2)**
4336 Losee Rd Ste 9, North Las Vegas, NV 89030-3380 **(100%)**
Tel.: (702) 658-4300
Holding Company; Hotels & Casinos
N.A.I.C.S.: 523999

ARCHROCK, INC.
9807 Katy Frwy Ste 100, Houston, TX 77024
Tel.: (281) 836-8000 **DE**
Web Site: https://www.archrock.com
Year Founded: 2007
AROC—(NYSE)
Rev.: $845,568,000
Assets: $2,598,750,000
Liabilities: $1,738,057,000
Net Worth: $860,693,000
Earnings: $44,296,000
Emp.: 1,100
Fiscal Year-end: 12/31/22
Holding Company; Petroleum & Natural Gas Processing Equipment & Facilities Design, Engineering, Construction & Maintenance Services
N.A.I.C.S.: 551112
D. Bradley Childers *(Pres & CEO)*
Donna A. Henderson *(Chief Acctg Officer & VP)*

Archrock, Inc.—(Continued)

Jason G. Ingersoll *(Sr VP-Sls & Ops Support)*
Stephanie C. Hildebrandt *(Gen Counsel, Sec & Sr VP)*
Douglas S. Aron *(CFO & Sr VP)*
Elspeth A. Inglis *(Chief HR Officer & Sr VP-HR)*
Eric W. Thode *(Sr VP-Ops)*

Subsidiaries:

EES Leasing LLC **(1)**
16666 Northchase Dr, Houston, TX 77060
Tel.: (281) 836-7055
Oil & Gas Processing Equipment Maintenance Services
N.A.I.C.S.: 213112
David Miller *(VP)*

EXH GP LP LLC **(1)**
103 Foulk Rd, Wilmington, DE 19803-3742
Tel.: (302) 691-6396
Oil & Natural Gas Processing Equipment Maintenance Services
N.A.I.C.S.: 213112

EXH MLP LP LLC **(1)**
103 Foulk Rd, Wilmington, DE 19803
Tel.: (302) 421-7361
Oil & Gas Processing Equipment Maintenance Services
N.A.I.C.S.: 213112

Elite Compression Services, LLC **(1)**
10375 Richmond Ste 450, Houston, TX 77042
Tel.: (281) 919-2384
Web Site: http://www.elite-compression.com
Natural Gas Distribution
N.A.I.C.S.: 221210

Exterran Energy Corp. **(1)**
12001 N Houston Rosslyn Rd, Houston, TX 77086
Tel.: (281) 921-9337
Web Site: http://www.exterran.com
Emp.: 8,300
Oil & Natural Gas Processing Equipment Maintenance Services
N.A.I.C.S.: 213112

Exterran GP LLC **(1)**
16666 Northchase Dr, Houston, TX 77060 **(100%)**
Tel.: (281) 836-7000
Web Site: http://www.exterran.com
Holding Company
N.A.I.C.S.: 551112

Subsidiary (Domestic):

Archrook Partners, L.P. **(2)**
9807 Katy Fwy Ste 100, Houston, TX 77024
Tel.: (281) 836-8000
Web Site: https://www.archrock.com
Rev.: $706,292,000
Assets: $2,734,711,000
Liabilities: $1,922,746,000
Net Worth: $811,965,000
Earnings: $60,621,000
Fiscal Year-end: 12/31/2019
Holding Company; Natural Gas Contract Compression Products & Services
N.A.I.C.S.: 551112

Exterran HL LLC **(1)**
300 Delaware Ave, Wilmington, DE 19801
Tel.: (302) 421-7361
Oil & Gas Processing Equipment Maintenance Services
N.A.I.C.S.: 213112

ARCIMOTO, INC.
2034 W 2nd Ave, Eugene, OR 97402
Tel.: (541) 683-6293 **OR**
Web Site: https://www.arcimoto.com
Year Founded: 2007
FUV—(NASDAQ)
Rev.: $6,557,526
Assets: $56,408,032
Liabilities: $25,042,087
Net Worth: $31,365,945
Earnings: ($62,879,398)
Emp.: 208
Fiscal Year-end: 12/31/22

Automobile Mfr & Distr
N.A.I.C.S.: 336110
Mark D. Frohnmayer *(Founder, Chm & Chief Vision Officer)*
Christopher W. Dawson *(Bd of Dirs, CEO, Interim CFO & Principal Acctg Officer)*

ARCOSA, INC.
500 N Akard St Ste 400, Dallas, TX 75201
Tel.: (972) 942-6500 **DE**
Web Site: https://www.arcosa.com
Year Founded: 2018
ACA—(NYSE)
Rev.: $2,242,800,000
Assets: $3,340,600,000
Liabilities: $1,156,200,000
Net Worth: $2,184,400,000
Earnings: $245,800,000
Emp.: 5,230
Fiscal Year-end: 12/31/22
Construction Products & Services
N.A.I.C.S.: 423390
Antonio Carrillo Rule *(Pres & CEO)*
Mary Elizabeth Henderson *(Sr VP-Corp Admin)*
Reid S. Essl *(Pres-Construction Products)*
Kerry S. Cole *(Pres-Energy Equipment)*
Jesse E. Collins *(Pres-Transportation Products)*
Bryan P. Stevenson *(Chief Legal Officer)*
Mary E. Henderson *(Chief Acctg Officer)*
Gail M. Peck *(CFO & Treas)*
Erin Drabek *(Dir-IR)*
Eric Hurst *(Principal Acctg Officer, VP & Controller)*

Subsidiaries:

Ameron Pole Products LLC **(1)**
1020 B St, Fillmore, CA 93015-1024
Tel.: (805) 524-0223
Web Site: http://www.ameronpoles.com
Sales Range: $50-74.9 Million
Lighting & Traffic Poles Mfr
N.A.I.C.S.: 327390

Arcosa Aggregates Gulf Coast, LLC **(1)**
130 Robin Hood Dr, Hammond, LA 70403
Tel.: (225) 667-5868
Construction Materials Distr
N.A.I.C.S.: 423390

Arcosa Aggregates Ohio River Valley, LLC **(1)**
800 Barge Point Rd, Clarksville, TN 37042
Tel.: (931) 572-0093
Construction Materials Distr
N.A.I.C.S.: 423390

Arcosa Aggregates Texas, LLC **(1)**
401 S 145, Ferris, TX 75125
Tel.: (972) 544-5930
Construction Materials Distr
N.A.I.C.S.: 423390

Arcosa Aggregates West, LLC **(1)**
16402 S Tuthill Rd, Buckeye, AZ 85326
Tel.: (480) 987-7917
Construction Materials Distr
N.A.I.C.S.: 423390

Arcosa Wind Towers, Inc. **(1)**
500 N Akard St Ste 400, Dallas, TX 75201 **(100%)**
Tel.: (972) 942-6500
Web Site: https://www.arcosatowers.com
Tubular Wind Tower Designer & Fabricator
N.A.I.C.S.: 332312

Cherry Companies Management, Inc. **(1)**
6131 Selinsky Rd, Houston, TX 77048
Tel.: (713) 987-0000
Web Site: https://cherrycompanies.com
Construction Services
N.A.I.C.S.: 236220

Diamond Gypsum, LLC **(1)**
1720 S Redhills Dr, Richfield, UT 84701
Tel.: (435) 896-8870
Web Site:
https://www.diamondkgypsum.com
Gypsum Mining Services
N.A.I.C.S.: 212390
Kris Allred *(Gen Mgr)*
Thomas Tankersley *(Sls Mgr)*

Harrison Gypsum, LLC **(1)**
1550 Double Dr, Norman, OK 73069
Tel.: (405) 366-9500
Web Site:
https://arcosaspecialtymaterials.com
Gypsum Mining & Processing Services
N.A.I.C.S.: 212390
John Todd *(Pres & CEO)*
Randy Pryor *(VP-Oklahoma & Corp Ops)*
Brian Dowden *(VP-Ops Arcosa Lightweight)*
Brody Oakley *(VP-Sales & Marketing)*
Steven Rowe *(VP-Sls Arcosa Lightweight)*
Thomas Walker *(VP-Finance)*

Subsidiary (Domestic):

Art Wilson Company **(2)**
5251 Brick Rd, Carson City, NV 89721
Tel.: (775) 882-0700
Web Site: http://www.awgypsum.com
Sales Range: $1-9.9 Million
Emp.: 100
Chemical & Fertilizer Mining
N.A.I.C.S.: 212390
John Todd *(Pres & CEO)*

J.A.Jack & Sons, Inc. **(2)**
5427 Ohio Ave S, Seattle, WA 98184
Tel.: (206) 762-7622
Web Site: http://www.jajack.com
Crushed & Broken Limestone Mining & Quarrying
N.A.I.C.S.: 212312
Brody A. Oakley *(Sls Dir)*

Kelly Limestone, LLC **(2)**
PO Box 708, Lake Ozark, MO 65049
Tel.: (573) 745-0897
Web Site: http://www.kellysgreenteam.com
Brick, Stone & Related Construction Material Merchant Whslr
N.A.I.C.S.: 423320
Douglas Kelly *(Co-Founder)*
Theresa Kelly *(Co-Founder)*
Richard B. Kelly *(Co-Founder)*
Cora C. Kelly *(Co-Founder)*

North Florida Rock, Ltd. **(2)**
1714 W 23Rd St Ste 0, Panama City, FL 32405
Tel.: (850) 762-4315
Web Site: http://www.acgmaterials.com
Sales Range: $1-9.9 Million
Emp.: 20
Crushed & Broken Limestone Mining & Quarrying
N.A.I.C.S.: 212312

McConway & Torley, LLC **(1)**
109 48th St, Pittsburgh, PA 15201-2755
Tel.: (412) 682-4700
Web Site: https://www.mcconway.com
Sales Range: $50-74.9 Million
Emp.: 167
Steel Foundries
N.A.I.C.S.: 331513

Recycled Aggregate Materials Company, Inc. **(1)**
2655 1st St Ste 210, Simi Valley, CA 93065
Tel.: (805) 522-1646
Web Site: https://www.ramco.us.com
Construction Materials Distr
N.A.I.C.S.: 423390

Southwest Rock Products, LLC **(1)**
39350 N Schnepf Rd, Queen Creek, AZ 85242
Tel.: (480) 987-7917
Web Site: http://www.swrpaz.com
Industrial Building Construction
N.A.I.C.S.: 236210
Christopher Reinesch *(Principal)*

Standard Forged Products, LLC **(1)**
75 Nichol Ave, McKees Rocks, PA 15136
Tel.: (412) 778-2033
Web Site:
https://www.standardforgedproducts
inc.com

Emp.: 220
Electronic Heat Controller & Treating Furnaces Mfr
N.A.I.C.S.: 333414

Strata Materials, LLC **(1)**
2100 N Hwy 360 Ste 401, Grand Prairie, TX 75050
Tel.: (214) 412-3586
Web Site: http://www.stratamaterials.com
Construction Materials Distr
N.A.I.C.S.: 423390
Jeff Roesler *(Pres)*
Gary Allen *(VP-Ops)*
Richard Bythewood *(VP & Controller)*
Ed Gerik *(Dir-Consulting)*

Washita Valley Logistics, LLC **(1)**
1550 Double C Dr, Norman, OK 73069
Web Site:
http://www.washitavalleylogistics.com
Logistic Services
N.A.I.C.S.: 488510

ARCPOINT INC.
101 N Main St Ste E, Greenville, SC 29601
Tel.: (864) 271-3210
Web Site:
https://www.arcpointlabs.com
Year Founded: 1978
ARC—(TSXV)
Assets: $4,153,480
Liabilities: $181,312
Net Worth: $3,972,168
Earnings: ($124,931)
Fiscal Year-end: 12/31/20
Medical Laboratory & Testing Facility
N.A.I.C.S.: 621511
John A. Constantine *(CEO)*

Subsidiaries:

ARCpoint Group LLC **(1)**
101 N Main St Ste 301, Greenville, SC 29601
Tel.: (864) 271-3210
Web Site: https://www.arcpointlabs.com
Medical Laboratory & Testing Facility
N.A.I.C.S.: 621511

Veratta Technologies Inc. **(1)**
117 - 949 West 3rd Street, North Vancouver, V7P 3P7, BC, Canada
Tel.: (604) 639-8867
Web Site: http://www.veratta.com
Web Design & Web Application Development Services
N.A.I.C.S.: 541511

ARCTOS NORTHSTAR ACQUISITION CORP.
2021 McKinney Ave Ste 200, Dallas, TX 75201
Tel.: (972) 918-3800 **Ky**
Web Site:
http://www.arctosnorthstar.com
Year Founded: 2020
ANAC—(NYSE)
Investment Services
N.A.I.C.S.: 523999
David O'Connor *(Chm)*
Theo Epstein *(CEO)*
John Vedro *(CFO)*

ARCTURUS THERAPEUTICS HOLDINGS INC.
10628 Science Ctr Dr Ste 250, San Diego, CA 92121
Tel.: (858) 900-2660 **DE**
Web Site: https://www.arcturusrx.com
ARCT—(NASDAQ)
Rev.: $205,999,000
Assets: $450,387,000
Liabilities: $180,075,000
Net Worth: $270,312,000
Earnings: $9,349,000
Emp.: 170
Fiscal Year-end: 12/31/22
Holding Company
N.A.I.C.S.: 551112
Andrew H. Sassine *(CFO)*
Peter C. Farrell *(Chm)*

Kelly A. Lindert (Chief Dev Officer-Vaccines)
Joseph E. Payne (Pres & CEO)
Padmanabh Chivukula (COO & Chief Scientific Officer)
Lance Kurata (Chief Legal Officer)
Nirdosh Jagota (Chief Regulatory Officer)
Dushyant B. Varshney (CTO)

Subsidiaries:

Arcturus Therapeutics Ltd.   (1)
10628 Science Ctr Dr Ste 250, San Diego, CA 92121
Tel.: (858) 900-2660
Web Site: https://www.arcturusrx.com
Sales Range: $10-24.9 Million
Emp.: 72
Pharmaceuticals Mfr
N.A.I.C.S.: 325412
Andrew H. Sassine (CFO)
Joseph E. Payne (Pres & CEO)
Kevin T. Skol (Sr VP-Bus Dev & Alliance Mgmt)
Suezanne Parker (VP-Translational Biology)

ARCUS BIOSCIENCES, INC.

3928 Point Eden Way, Hayward, CA 94545
Tel.: (510) 694-6200   DE
Web Site: https://www.arcusbio.com
Year Founded: 2015
RCUS—(NYSE)
Rev.: $117,000,000
Assets: $1,095,000,000
Liabilities: $633,000,000
Net Worth: $462,000,000
Earnings: ($307,000,000)
Emp.: 577
Fiscal Year-end: 12/31/23
Immunotherapy Development Services
N.A.I.C.S.: 541714
Terry J. Rosen (Co-Founder & CEO)
Juan Carlos Jaen (Co-Founder & Pres)
Robert C. Goeltz II (CFO)
Alexander Azoy (Principal Acctg Officer)
Jay Powers (Sr VP-Drug Discovery)
Steve Young (Sr VP-Tech & Quantitative Biology)
Nigel Walker (Sr VP-Protein Therapeutics)
Carolyn Tang (Gen Counsel)
Eric Matthews (Chief Comml Officer)
Dimitry S. A. Nuyten (Chief Medical Officer)
Arun Tholudur (Sr VP)
Jennifer Jarrett (COO)

ARCUTIS BIOTHERAPEUTICS, INC.

3027 Townsgate Rd Ste 300, Westlake Village, CA 91361
Tel.: (805) 418-5006   DE
Web Site: https://www.arcutis.com
Year Founded: 2016
ARQT—(NASDAQ)
Rev.: $3,686,000
Assets: $449,274,000
Liabilities: $239,693,000
Net Worth: $209,581,000
Earnings: ($311,458,000)
Emp.: 268
Fiscal Year-end: 12/31/22
Biotechnology Research & Development Services
N.A.I.C.S.: 541714
Bhaskar Chaudhuri (Founder)
L. Todd Edwards (Chief Comml Officer)
David J. Topper (CFO & Principal Acctg Officer)
Todd Franklin Watanabe (Pres & CEO)

David W. Osborne (Chief Technical Officer)
David Berk (VP-Clinical Dev)
Meg Elias (VP-Clinical Ops)
Keith L. Klein (Gen Counsel)
Charlotte Merritt (VP-Regulatory Affairs)
Lynn Navale (VP-Biometrics)
Frank Pompilio (VP-Medical Affairs)
Heather Rowe Armstrong (VP-IR & Corp Comm)
Kimberly Lathroum (VP-Mktg)
Patrick Burnett (Chief Medical Officer)
Bethany Dudek (VP-Quality)
Jay Ramsinghani (VP-Comml Strategy & Ops)
John W. Smither (Interim CFO)
Amanda Sheldon (Head-Corp Comm)
Eric McIntyre (Head-IR)
Ayisha Jeter (Sr VP-Mktg & Market Access)

ARDELYX, INC.

400 Fifth Ave Ste 210, Waltham, MA 02451
Tel.: (617) 675-2739   DE
Web Site: https://www.ardelyx.com
Year Founded: 2007
ARDX—(NASDAQ)
Rev.: $124,456,000
Assets: $297,579,000
Liabilities: $130,763,000
Net Worth: $166,816,000
Earnings: ($66,067,000)
Emp.: 267
Fiscal Year-end: 12/31/23
Pharmaceuticals Mfr
N.A.I.C.S.: 325412
Susan Rodriguez (Chief Comml Officer)
Michael G. Raab (Pres & CEO)
Elizabeth A. Grammer (Chief Legal Officer & Chief Admin Officer)
David P. Rosenbaum (Chief Dev Officer)
Robert Blanks (Chief Regulatory Affairs & Quality Assurance Officer)
Charon Spencer (Chief HR Officer)
David M. Mott (Chm)

ARENA FORTIFY ACQUISITION CORP.

405 Lexington Ave 59th Fl, New York, NY 10174
Tel.: (212) 612-3205   DE
Year Founded: 2021
AFACU—(NASDAQ)
Investment Services
N.A.I.C.S.: 523999
Daniel Zwirn (CEO)
Greg White (Pres)
Kieran Goodwin (CFO)
Bryan Fisher (COO)

ARES ACQUISITION CORPORATION

245 Park Ave 44th Fl, New York, NY 10167
Tel.: (310) 201-4100   Ky
Web Site:
https://www.aresacquisitioncorporation.com
Year Founded: 2020
AAC—(NYSE)
Rev.: $28,326,302
Assets: $1,013,478,050
Liabilities: $1,074,434,118
Net Worth: ($60,956,068)
Earnings: $20,983,590
Emp.: 4
Fiscal Year-end: 12/31/22
Investment Services
N.A.I.C.S.: 523999
Michael J. Arougheti (Co-Chm)
Jarrod Phillips (CFO)
David B. Kaplan (Co-Chm & CEO)

Michael J. Arougheti (Co-Chm)
Allyson Satin (COO)
Peter Ogilvie (Exec VP-Strategy)

ARES MANAGEMENT CORPORATION

2000 Ave of the Stars 12th Fl, Los Angeles, CA 90067
Tel.: (310) 201-4100   DE
Web Site: https://www.aresmgmt.com
Year Founded: 1997
ARES—(NYSE)
Rev.: $3,631,884,000
Assets: $24,730,500,000
Liabilities: $20,256,187,000
Net Worth: $4,474,313,000
Earnings: $474,326,000
Emp.: 2,850
Fiscal Year-end: 12/31/23
Privater Equity Firm
N.A.I.C.S.: 523940
Antony P. Ressler (Co-Founder & Exec Chm)
David B. Kaplan (Co-Founder & Partner)
David B. Kaplan (Co-Founder & Partner)
Michael J. Arougheti (Co-Founder, Pres & CEO)
Michael L. Smith (Partner-Credit Grp & Co-Head-Credit-New York)
Scott C. Lem (Partner/Chief Acctg Officer-Public Credit Funds-Fin & Acctg Dept)
David A. Sachs (Co-Founder & Partner)
Jarrod Phillips (CFO & Chief Acctg Officer)
Paul Cho (Chief Acctg Officer/Mng Dir-Fin & Acctg Dept)
Jana Markowicz (Partner, COO-Dir Lending strategy & Head-Product Mgmt & IR)
Robert Kipp deVeer Jr. (Partner & Head-Credit Grp)
Bennett Rosenthal (Co-Founder, Partner & Chm-Ares Private Equity Grp)
Rajat Dhanda (Partner-Wealth Mgmt Solutions & Head-Wealth Mgmt Solutions-Global)
Ryan Berry (Partner & Chief Mktg & Strategy Officer)
Natasha Li (Partner-Private Equity Grp-Los Angeles)
Naseem Sagati Aghili (Partner, Gen Counsel & Sec)
Indhira Arrington (Mng Dir & Chief Diversity, Equity & Inclusion Officer-Global)
Francisco L. Borges (Chm, Partner & Co-Head-Ares Secondary Solutions)

Subsidiaries:

Ares Administrative Services (DIFC) Limited   (1)
Office 40 Level 15 - East Wing Gate Building, PO Box 121208, Dubai International Financial Centre, Dubai, United Arab Emirates
Tel.: (971) 44019111
Investment Management Service
N.A.I.C.S.: 523940

Ares Asia Management (HK), Limited   (1)
16th Floor 3A Chater Road Central Centra, Hong Kong, China (Hong Kong)
Tel.: (852) 37579675
Investment Management Service
N.A.I.C.S.: 523940

Ares Capital Corporation   (1)
245 Park Ave 44th Fl, New York, NY 10167
Tel.: (212) 750-7300
Web Site: https://www.arescapitalcorp.com
Rev.: $2,614,000,000
Assets: $23,800,000,000
Liabilities: $12,599,000,000
Net Worth: $11,201,000,000

Earnings: $1,266,000,000
Fiscal Year-end: 12/31/2023
Investment Services
N.A.I.C.S.: 523999
Michael J. Arougheti (Chm & Exec VP)
Mitchell S. Goldstein (Co-Pres)
Michael L. Smith (Mgr-Investment)
Scott C. Lem (CFO & CFO/Treas-Ares Strategic Income Fund & Treas)
Joshua M. Bloomstein (Sec, VP & Gen Counsel)
Paul Cho (Chief Acctg Officer)
Miriam G. Krieger (VP)
Kort Schnabel (Co-Pres)
Jana Markowicz (COO)
Lisa Morgan (Chief Compliance Officer)
John Stilmar (Mng Dir-Pub IR & Comm)
Carl Drake (Partner & Head-Pub IR & Comm)
Naseem Sagati Aghili (VP)

Ares Capital Management LLC   (1)
245 Park Ave 44th Fl, New York, NY 10167
Tel.: (212) 710-2100
Web Site: http://www.arescapitalcorp.com
Emp.: 200
Investment Management Service
N.A.I.C.S.: 523940

Ares Commercial Real Estate Corporation   (1)
245 Park Ave 42nd Fl, New York, NY 10167
Tel.: (212) 750-7300
Web Site: https://www.arescre.com
Rev.: $92,926,000
Assets: $2,279,777,000
Liabilities: $1,653,928,000
Net Worth: $625,849,000
Earnings: $38,867,000
Fiscal Year-end: 12/31/2023
Real Estate Investment Trust
N.A.I.C.S.: 525990
Tae-Sik Yoon (CFO & Treas)
Anton Feingold (Gen Counsel, Sec & VP-Los Angeles)
Bryan P. Donohoe (CEO)
Steven Connell (VP)
Stephen Dawson (Principal)
Greg Birk (Principal)
Danielle Duenas (Principal)
Jeffrey Gonzales (Principal)
Marina Hartnett (Principal)
Brandon Heim (VP)
Annie Herman (Principal)
Samuel Kupersmith (Mng Dir)
Gregory Liguori (Principal)
Mark Liimatta (Principal)
Jared Marcus (Principal)
Zach Nash (Principal)
David Proctor (Mng Dir)
Daniel Rosen (Principal)
John Stilmar (Mng Dir)

Ares Insurance Solutions LLC   (1)
14140 Magnolia Blvd, Sherman Oaks, CA 91423
Tel.: (818) 986-4207
Web Site: https://www.aresins.com
Fire Insurance Services
N.A.I.C.S.: 524113

Ares Management LLC   (1)
2000 Ave of the Stars 12th Fl, Los Angeles, CA 90067
Tel.: (310) 201-4100
Web Site: http://www.aresmgmt.com
Private Equity & Investment Management Services
N.A.I.C.S.: 523999
David A. Sachs (Co-Founder & Partner)

Joint Venture (Domestic):

99 Cents Only Stores LLC   (2)
4000 Union Pacific Ave, City of Commerce, CA 90023
Tel.: (323) 980-8145
Web Site: https://www.99only.com
Sales Range: $1-4.9 Billion
Emp.: 17,000
All Other General Merchandise Retailers
N.A.I.C.S.: 455219

Holding (Domestic):

AAMCO Transmissions, Inc.   (2)
470 Easton Rd Rear, Horsham, PA 19044
Tel.: (215) 657-1221
Web Site: https://www.aamco.com

Ares Management Corporation—(Continued)

Automobile Transmission Repair Center
Franchiser
N.A.I.C.S.: 811114

Alcami Carolinas Corporation (2)
2320 Scientific Park Dr, Wilmington, NC
28405
Tel.: (910) 254-7000
Web Site: https://www.alcaminow.com
Pharmaceuticals Research & Development
N.A.I.C.S.: 325412
Patrick Walsh (Chm & CEO)
Louise Hall (VP)
Katie Schlipp (Pres)
Elliott Franco (VP)
Ryan Williams (VP)
Jamie Iudica (Chief Mfg Officer)
Jacques Martin (VP)
Chad Bovero (VP)
Katie Bialock (VP)
Jessica Cao (VP)

American Decorative Surfaces,
Inc. (2)
1188 Walters Way Ln, Saint Louis, MO
63132-2200
Tel.: (618) 286-6000
Sales Range: $50-74.9 Million
Emp.: 180
Coated & Saturated Printed Decorative Papers; Printed Decorative Film, Furniture &
Panel Papers Mfr
N.A.I.C.S.: 326113

Subsidiary (Non-US):

Ares Capital Europe Limited (2)
C/O Tmf Group 8th Floor 20 Farringdon
Street, London, EC4A 4AB, United Kingdom
Tel.: (44) 2074346400
Web Site: http://www.aresmgmt.com
Sales Range: $25-49.9 Million
Emp.: 100
Investment Activities
N.A.I.C.S.: 523999
Michael Dennis (Partner & Head-European
Credit-Credit Grp)

Joint Venture (Domestic):

Healthcare Locums Plc (3)
10 Old Bailey, London, EC4M 7NG, United
Kingdom
Tel.: (44) 2074511451
Web Site: http://www.hclwiforc.com
Sales Range: $350-399.9 Million
Emp.: 10
Holding Company; Healthcare Recruitment
& Employment Placement Services
N.A.I.C.S.: 551112
Andy McRae (Exec Dir)
Stephen Burke (CEO)

Subsidiary (Domestic):

Allied Health Professionals
Limited (2)
Garden Flat 28 Clifton Park Road, Bristol,
BS8 3HL, Essex, United Kingdom
Tel.: (44) 8453892299
Web Site: http://www.ahp-ltd.com
Medical Staff Recruitment Services
N.A.I.C.S.: 561311

HCL BBL Medical Limited (4)
10 Old Bailey, London, EC4M 7NG, United
Kingdom
Tel.: (44) 845 222 3223
Web Site: http://www.healthcarelocums.com
Doctor Recruitment Services
N.A.I.C.S.: 561311

HCL GPS Limited (4)
Nesfield House Broughton, Skipton, BD23
3AE, North Yorkshire, United Kingdom
Tel.: (44) 8453661133
Web Site: http://www.healthcarelocums.com
Medical Staff Recruitment Services
N.A.I.C.S.: 561311

HCL Healthcare Limited (4)
33 Soho Square, London, W1D 3QU,
United Kingdom
Tel.: (44) 8450639639
Medical Staff Recruitment Services
N.A.I.C.S.: 561311

HCL Thames Medics Limited (4)
Nesfield House Broughton Hall, Skipton,

BD23 3AN, North Yorkshire, United Kingdom
Tel.: (44) 8450613613
Medical Staff Recruitment Services
N.A.I.C.S.: 561311

Affiliate (Domestic):

Ares Dynamic Credit Allocation Fund,
Inc. (2)
2000 Avenue of the Stars 12th Fl, Los Angeles, CA 90067
Tel.: (310) 201-4100
Web Site: http://www.arespublicfunds.com
Sales Range: $25-49.9 Million
Closed-End Investment Fund
N.A.I.C.S.: 525990
Scott C. Lem (CFO)
Penelope F. Roll (CFO)
Seth J. Brufsky (Pres, CEO & Portfolio Mgr)
Daniel J. Hall (Chief Legal Officer, Gen
Counsel & Sec)
Brett A. Byrd (Chief Compliance Officer &
Officer-Anti-Money Laundering)
John Eanes (VP)
Jeff M. Moore (VP)
Darryl L. Schall (VP)
Charles Arduini (VP & Portfolio Mgr)
Samantha Milner (VP & Portfolio Mgr)
Jason Duko (VP)
Kapil Singh (VP)
Americo Cascella (VP)
Michael D. Weiner (VP & Asst Sec)
Keith Ashton (VP)

Group (Domestic):

Ares Management LLC-Capital Markets Group (2)
2000 Avenue of the Stars 12th Fl, Los Angeles, CA 90067
Tel.: (310) 201-4100
Web Site: http://www.aresmgmt.com
Sales Range: $300-349.9 Million
Emp.: 240
Investment Activities
N.A.I.C.S.: 523999
Seth J. Brufsky (Partner, Chm-Global Liquid
Credit & Portfolio Mgr)

Ares Management LLC-Private Debt
Group (2)
2000 Ave of the Stars 12th Fl, Los Angeles,
CA 90067
Tel.: (310) 201-4100
Web Site: http://www.aresmgmt.com
Sales Range: $300-349.9 Million
Emp.: 240
Investment Activities
N.A.I.C.S.: 523999
Michael J. Arougheti (Pres, Sr Partner &
Co-Head-Direct Lending Grp)
Michael I. Smith (Partner & Head-Credit
Grp-New York)
Kort Schnabel (Partner, Head-Direct Lending & Portfolio Mgr-Credit Grp)
Karen De Castro (Partner-Credit Grp-New
York)
Mark R. Affolter (Partner, Head-Direct Lending & Portfolio Mgr-Credit Grp-Chicago)
Jim Miller (Partner, Head-Direct Lending &
Portfolio Mgr-Credit Grp-New York)

Ares Management LLC-Private Equity
Group (2)
2000 Ave of the Stars 12th Fl, Los Angeles,
CA 90067
Tel.: (310) 201-4100
Web Site: http://www.aresmgmt.com
Sales Range: $300-349.9 Million
Emp.: 200
Investment Activities
N.A.I.C.S.: 523999
David B. Kaplan (Sr Partner & Co-Head)
David B. Kaplan (Sr Partner & Co-Head)
Bennett Rosenthal (Sr Partner)
Matthew D. Cwiertnia (Partner & Co-Head)
Brian Klos (Partner)
Andrew Jurkowski (Mng Dir)
Matthew Underwood (Executives)
Kyle Brazeal (VP)
Stephen Burhenn (Principal)
Amy Fujimoto (Partner)
Andrew Paik (Principal)
David Ricanati (Partner)
Kevin Ryan (Partner)
Eric Waxman (Partner)
Scott Graves (Partner)
Justin Anderson (VP)

Ryan Chuang (VP)
Kevin Cox (Principal)
Zack Gould (VP)
Nic Greer (VP)
Shakun Khanna (VP)
Steven Kutos (VP)
Jim McConeghy (VP)
Kirav Patel (VP)
Vishnu Reddy (VP)
Ryan Young (VP)
Abraham Zilkha (Partner)

Subsidiary (Domestic):

Ares EIF Management, LLC (3)
3 Charles River Pl 63 Kendrick St Ste 101,
Needham, MA 02494
Tel.: (781) 292-7000
Web Site: http://www.aresmgmt.com
Emp.: 40
Privater Equity Firm
N.A.I.C.S.: 523999

Holding (Domestic):

Paradigm Energy, Inc. (4)
20692 Corsair Blvd, Hayward, CA 94545
Tel.: (510) 785-9441
Electrical Contractor
N.A.I.C.S.: 238210

Group (Domestic):

Ares Management LLC-Real Estate
Group (2)
2000 Ave of the Stars 12th Fl, Los Angeles,
CA 90067
Tel.: (310) 201-4100
Web Site: http://www.aresmgmt.com
Real Estate Investment
N.A.I.C.S.: 523999

Subsidiary (Non-US):

Ares Management Limited (2)
C/O Tmf Group 8th Floor 20 Farringdon
Street, London, EC4A 4AB, United Kingdom
Tel.: (44) 2074346400
Web Site: http://www.aresmgmt.com
Emp.: 100
Investment Management Service
N.A.I.C.S.: 523940

Ares Management UK Limited (2)
10 New Burlington Street 6th Floor, London,
W1S 3BE, United Kingdom
Tel.: (44) 2074346400
Web Site: http://www.aresmgmt.com
Emp.: 100
Investment Management Service
N.A.I.C.S.: 523940

Holding (Domestic):

Aspen Dental Management, Inc. (2)
3590 W Genesee St, Syracuse, NY 13219
Tel.: (315) 505-2780
Web Site: https://www.aspendental.com
Dental Practice Management
N.A.I.C.S.: 541618
Doyle Williams (VP-Carrier Rels & Insurance Ops)

Holding (Non-US):

Blackbrush Oil & Gas, L.P. (2)
Tel.: (210) 495-5577
Web Site: http://www.blackbrushenergy.com
Sales Range: $1-9.9 Million
Emp.: 65
Petroleum & Natural Gas Extraction Services
N.A.I.C.S.: 211120
P. Scott Martin (CEO)
Philip M. Mezey (Founder & Chm)
Mark A. Norville (Pres)
Luis Mier (CFO)
Cole Newman (Mgr-Land)
Kevin DeLapp (VP-Reservoir Engrg)

Joint Venture (Domestic):

CHG Healthcare Services, Inc. (2)
7259 S Bingham Junction Blvd, Midvale, UT
84047
Tel.: (801) 930-3000
Web Site: https://www.chghealthcare.com
Sales Range: $400-449.9 Million
Temporary & Permanent Healthcare Staffing
Services
N.A.I.C.S.: 561311

Scott M. Beck (CEO)
Robert B. Millard (CFO)
Kerry Norman (Exec VP)
Bill Heller (Exec VP)

Subsidiary (Domestic):

CHG Management, Inc. (3)
7259 S Bingham Jct Blvd, Midvale, UT
84047
Tel.: (801) 930-3000
Web Site: http://www.chghealthcare.com
Sales Range: $125-149.9 Million
Healthcare Employment Services
N.A.I.C.S.: 561311
Mike Weinholtz (CEO)

Subsidiary (Domestic):

CHG Medical Staffing, Inc. (4)
4700 Exchange Ct Ste 125, Boca Raton,
FL 33431
Tel.: (561) 862-0011
Web Site: https://www.rnnetwork.com
Sales Range: $10-24.9 Million
Emp.: 100
Nursing Staffing Services
N.A.I.C.S.: 561311
Eric Darienzo (Pres)
Ann Smith (Mgr-Admin)

CompHealth Associates, Inc. (4)
7259 S Bingham Jct Blvd, Midvale, UT
84047
Tel.: (801) 930-3000
Web Site: http://www.comphealth.com
Sales Range: $25-49.9 Million
Emp.: 1,400
Physician Recruiters
N.A.I.C.S.: 541612
Scott Beck (CEO)

Weatherby Healthcare (4)
6451 N Federal Hwy Ste 700, Fort Lauderdale, FL 33308
Tel.: (954) 343-3050
Web Site:
https://www.weatherbyhealthcare.com
Sales Range: $10-24.9 Million
Emp.: 100
Physician Staffing Services
N.A.I.C.S.: 561311
Michael DePaolis (Sr VP)
Bev Leonard (Sr VP)
Warren Wooley (Sr VP)
Luke Woodyard (Pres)

Subsidiary (Domestic):

Global Medical Staffing Limited,
Inc. (3)
7259 Bingham Jct Blvd, Midvale, UT 84047
Tel.: (801) 365-0303
Web Site: https://www.gmedical.com
Emp.: 70
Medical Staffing Services
N.A.I.C.S.: 561320

Holding (Domestic):

Convergint Technologies, LLC (2)
1 Commerce Dr, Schaumburg, IL 60173
Tel.: (847) 229-0222
Web Site: http://www.convergint.com
Security, Fire Alarm & Safety Systems Designer & Installation Services
N.A.I.C.S.: 561621
Dan Moceri (Chm & Founder)
Barry Yatzor (VP-Fire Alarm & Life Safety)
Tony Varco (VP-Mktg & Security)
Ken Lochiatto (CEO)
Mike Mathes (Exec VP)
Sean Flint (Exec VP)
Alan Bergschneider (CFO & VP)
Mike Duncan (VP-Global Accts & EMEA)
Eric Yunag (VP-Tech)
Bhuvana Badrinathan (CIO)
Kathryn Ingraham (Gen Counsel, Sec &
VP)
Laura Mueller (Chief HR Officer)
Kevin Donegan (VP-Strategy & Cyber)
Yaruba Tate (VP-Inclusion & Diversity)
Paul Thomas (VP-Ops)

Subsidiary (Domestic):

Advantage Medical, Inc. (3)
32215 Dunlap Blvd Ste F, Yucaipa, CA
92399

Tel.: (909) 795-9791
Web Site: http://www.amihs.com
Sales Range: $1-9.9 Million
Emp.: 20
Medical, Dental & Hospital Equipment &
Supplies Merchant Whslr
N.A.I.C.S.: 423450
Daniel Rea *(Pres & CEO)*

Firstline Security Systems, Inc. (3)
2211 E Howell Ave, Anaheim, CA 92806
Tel.: (714) 937-1440
Security Integration Solution Services
N.A.I.C.S.: 561621
Steve Morefield *(Pres)*

Innovative Medical Systems, Inc. (3)
3075 N Wilson Ct NW, Grand Rapids, MI
49534
Web Site: http://www.innovative-
medical.com
Medical, Dental & Hospital Equipment &
Supplies Merchant Whslr
N.A.I.C.S.: 423450
Dan De Jong *(CEO)*

Integrated Security Systems (3)
1876 NW 7th St, Miami, FL 33125
Tel.: (305) 324-8800
Web Site: https://www.teamiss.com
Security System Services
N.A.I.C.S.: 561621
Jeffrey Nunberg *(Pres & CEO)*
Joe Graeber *(CTO)*
Maggie Wood *(CFO)*
Ronen Sarig *(Gen Mgr)*
Todd Galimidi *(Dir-Natl Sls)*

Ojo Technology, Inc. (3)
103 Hammond Ave, Fremont, CA 94539-
0000
Tel.: (510) 249-9540
Web Site: http://www.ojotech.com
Security System Services
N.A.I.C.S.: 561621
Angie Wong *(Pres & CEO)*

**Security Solutions & Management
LLC** (3)
2626 Glenwood Ave Ste 550, Raleigh, NC
27608
Tel.: (704) 545-9933
Security System Services
N.A.I.C.S.: 561621
Michael Gardner *(CEO)*
Shane Hamilton *(Gen Mgr)*

Total Recall Corporation (3)
17 Washington Ave, Suffern, NY 10901
Tel.: (845) 368-3700
Web Site: http://www.totalrecallcorp.com
Surveillance Products & Services
N.A.I.C.S.: 334310
Jordan Heilweil *(Pres-Sls)*

Holding (Domestic):

CoolSys, Inc. (2)
145 S State College Blvd Ste 200, Brea,
CA 92821
Tel.: (714) 701-8912
Web Site: http://coolsys.com
Refrigeration Products & Machinery Distr &
Whslr
N.A.I.C.S.: 423740
Anthony P. Tippins *(Pres-Professional Solu-
tions)*
Jay Parker *(Pres-Light Comml Solutions)*
Burton Hong *(Gen Counsel, Sec & Exec
VP)*
Mike Ochoa *(Exec VP-Sls & Mktg)*
Bryan Beitler *(VP-Engrg)*
Rich Wyckoff *(Pres & CEO)*

Subsidiary (Domestic):

**ABC Refrigeration & Air Conditioning,
Inc.** (3)
6619 Joy Rd, East Syracuse, NY 13057
Tel.: (315) 455-7083
Web Site: http://www.abcrefrigeration.com
Rev.: $10,400,000
Emp.: 100
Plumbing Heating & Air-Conditioning Con-
tractors
N.A.I.C.S.: 238220

Arjae Sheet Metal Company, Inc. (3)
8545 SE Mcloughlin Blvd, Milwaukie, OR
97222

Tel.: (503) 231-7717
Web Site: http://www.arjae.com
Plumbing, Heating & Air-Conditioning Ser-
vices
N.A.I.C.S.: 238220
Ken Klunder *(Gen Mgr)*

Building Air Services, Inc. (3)
10460 68th St N, Pinellas Park, FL 33782
Tel.: (727) 528-3688
Web Site:
http://www.buildingairservices.com
Refrigeration, Heating & Air-Conditioning
Maintenance Services
N.A.I.C.S.: 238220
Steve Boose *(Gen Mgr)*
Veronica Boose *(VP-Admin)*
Nick Fox *(Reg Dir-Field Ops-East Coast)*
Brandon Weiderhold *(Reg Dir-Field Ops-
West Coast)*
Mandi Fallon *(Coord)*

Eastern Refrigeration, Co. (3)
275 Old Hartford Rd, Colchester, CT 06415
Tel.: (860) 859-0016
Web Site: http://www.easternrefrig.com
Rev.: $2,900,000
Emp.: 25
Commercial & Institutional Building Con-
struction
N.A.I.C.S.: 236220
Pierre Belisle *(Founder)*
Stan Shumbo *(VP & Gen Mgr)*
Tom O'Meara *(Ops Mgr)*
Michael Belisle *(Ops Mgr)*

**Mechanical Engineering & Construc-
tion Corporation** (3)
2056 Lord Baltimore Dr, Baltimore, MD
21244
Tel.: (443) 200-1000
Web Site: http://www.m-corp.us
Rev.: $7,500,000
Emp.: 69
Site Preparation Contractor
N.A.I.C.S.: 238910
Richard Beattie *(Pres)*
Fred Kawa *(Principal)*

**Richmond Refrigeration Service,
Inc.** (3)
10984 Richardson Rd, Ashland, VA 23005
Tel.: (804) 798-9029
Web Site:
http://www.richmondrefrigeration.com
Rev.: $9,800,000
Emp.: 72
Plumbing, Heating & Air-Conditioning Con-
tractors
N.A.I.C.S.: 238220

Santapaul Corp. (3)
9050 State Rd, Philadelphia, PA 19136
Tel.: (215) 333-7500
Web Site: http://www.limacompany.net
Rev.: $3,500,000
Emp.: 45
Commercial & Institutional Building Con-
struction
N.A.I.C.S.: 236220
Robert A. Lima *(Pres)*

T&O Refrigeration, Inc. (3)
170 Walter Way, Fayetteville, GA 30214-
0000
Tel.: (770) 461-5217
Web Site: http://www.torefrig.com
Commercial Equipment Merchant Whslr
N.A.I.C.S.: 423440
Denese Tibbetts *(Treas & Sec)*

Tech Mechanical Inc. (3)
1490 E Highwood, Pontiac, MI 48340
Tel.: (248) 322-5600
Web Site: http://www.techmechanical.com
Heating, Ventilation, Air Conditioning & Re-
frigeration Services
N.A.I.C.S.: 238220
Michael Curi *(Founder & Pres)*

Triangle Refrigeration Co. (3)
3200 Oregon Pike, Leola, PA 17540
Tel.: (717) 656-2711
Web Site:
http://www.trianglerefrigeration.com
Rev.: $14,790,103
Emp.: 135
Warm Air Heating & Air Conditioning Con-
tractor
N.A.I.C.S.: 238220

Cleo W. Weaver *(CEO)*

Holding (Domestic):

**Cooper's Hawk Winery & Restaurant,
LLC** (2)
1801 Butterfield Rd, Downers Grove, IL
60515
Tel.: (331) 215-9463
Web Site: https://chwinery.com
Restaurant Operators
N.A.I.C.S.: 722511
Tim McEnery *(Founder & CEO)*

Fosbel, Inc. (2)
20600 Sheldon Rd, Cleveland, OH 44142
Tel.: (216) 362-3900
Web Site: https://www.fosbel.com
Furnace Refractory Maintenance Services
N.A.I.C.S.: 811310

Joint Venture (Domestic):

GNC Holdings Inc. (2)
300 6th Ave, Pittsburgh, PA 15222
Tel.: (412) 288-4600
Web Site: http://www.gnc.com
Rev.: $2,068,188,000
Assets: $1,650,587,000
Liabilities: $1,646,455,000
Net Worth: $4,132,000
Earnings: ($35,112,000)
Emp.: 4,400
Fiscal Year-end: 12/31/2019
Holding Company; Nutritional Supplements
Retailer
N.A.I.C.S.: 551112
Tricia K. Tolivar *(CFO)*
Kenneth A. Martindale *(Chm)*
Cameron W. Lawrence *(Chief Acctg Officer)*
Josh Burris *(CEO)*
Alan Chester *(Chief Supply Chain Officer)*

Subsidiary (Domestic):

GNC Parent LLC (3)
300 6th Ave, Pittsburgh, PA 15222
Tel.: (412) 288-4600
Web Site: http://www.gnc.com
Sales Range: $125-149.9 Million
Emp.: 600
Holding Company
N.A.I.C.S.: 551112

Subsidiary (Domestic):

GNC Corporation (4)
300 6th Ave, Pittsburgh, PA 15222
Tel.: (412) 288-4600
Web Site: http://www.gnc.com
Holding Company; Vitamins & Nutritional
Supplements Mfr, Distr & Retailer
N.A.I.C.S.: 551112

Subsidiary (Non-US):

GNC Hong Kong Limited (5)
8/F Devon House Taikoo Place 979 King's
Road, Quarry Bay, China (Hong Kong)
Tel.: (852) 22993390
Web Site: https://gnclivewell.com.hk
Health Supplements Distr
N.A.I.C.S.: 424210

Subsidiary (Domestic):

General Nutrition Centers, Inc. (5)
300 6th Ave, Pittsburgh, PA 15222
Tel.: (412) 288-4600
Web Site: http://www.gnc.com
Sales Range: $1-4.9 Billion
Nutritional Supplements Mfr, Distr & Retailer
N.A.I.C.S.: 456191
Thomas Dowd *(Exec VP-Store Ops & Dev)*
Guru Ramanathan *(Chief Innovation Officer
& Sr VP)*
Michael Locke *(Sr VP-Mfg)*
Lee Karayusuf *(Sr VP-Distr & Transporta-
tion)*

Subsidiary (Non-US):

**General Nutrition Centres
Company** (5)
6299 Airport Rd Suite 201, Mississauga,
L4V 1N3, ON, Canada
Tel.: (905) 612-1016
Web Site: http://www.gnc.ca
Nutritional Supplements Retailer
N.A.I.C.S.: 456191

Subsidiary (Domestic):

**General Nutrition Investment
Company** (5)
1011 Centre Rd, Wilmington, DE 19805
Tel.: (302) 573-3895
Investment Management Service
N.A.I.C.S.: 523940

Nutra Manufacturing, Inc. (5)
1050 Woodruff Rd, Greenville, SC 29607
Tel.: (864) 987-3400
Web Site: https://www.nutramfg.com
Sales Range: $25-49.9 Million
Emp.: 600
Vitamins & Nutritional Supplement Mfr
N.A.I.C.S.: 325411
Joseph M. Fortunato *(CEO)*

Holding (Domestic):

Gastar Exploration LLC (2)
1331 Lamar St Ste 650, Houston, TX 77010
Tel.: (713) 739-1800
Web Site: http://www.gastar.com
Oil & Gas Exploration Services
N.A.I.C.S.: 213112
Michael A. Gerlich *(CFO, Sec & Sr VP)*
Stephen P. Roberts *(COO & Sr VP)*
Keith R. Blair *(VP & Mgr-Exploration)*
Trent J. Determann *(VP-Fin)*
Henry J. Hansen *(VP-Land)*

Keltic Financial Services, LLC (2)
558 Miller Ct, Wyckoff, NJ 07481
Tel.: (914) 418-1200
Web Site: http://www.kelticfinancial.com
Emp.: 15
Business Support Services
N.A.I.C.S.: 561499
Paul Donlin *(Partner)*

Landmark Partners, LLC (2)
10 Mill Pond Ln, Simsbury, CT
06070-2429 (60%)
Tel.: (860) 651-9760
Web Site: http://www.landmarkpartners.com
Real Estate Investment & Private Equity
Investment Firm
N.A.I.C.S.: 523910
Timothy L. Haviland *(Pres & Mng Partner)*
Chad S. Alfeld *(Partner)*
Robert J. Shanfield *(Partner)*
Scott N. Humber *(Partner)*
R. Paul Mehlman *(Partner)*
Barry M. Miller *(Partner)*
Paul E. Parker *(Partner)*
Tina Pierre *(Partner)*
James J. Sunday *(Partner)*
Charles H. Tingue *(Partner)*
Kathryn M. Regan *(Partner)*
Antoinette C. Lazarus *(Chief Compliance &
Risk Officer)*
Michelle L. Creed *(Partner)*
Barry E. Griffiths *(Partner)*
John B. Slott *(Partner)*
Avi Turetsky *(Partner)*
Josh Gleason *(CTO)*
Edward C. Keith III *(Partner)*

Marietta Corporation (2)
37 Huntington St, Cortland, NY 13045
Tel.: (607) 753-6746
Web Site: https://www.mariettacorp.com
Sales Range: $150-199.9 Million
Personal Care Amenity Supplier
N.A.I.C.S.: 325611

Branch (Domestic):

Marietta Corp. - Los Angeles (3)
4633 S Downey Rd, Vernon, CA 90058-
2511
Tel.: (323) 589-8181
Web Site: http://www.mariettacorp.com
Sales Range: $50-74.9 Million
Emp.: 450
Packaging of Shampoos & Body Wash
N.A.I.C.S.: 325611

Marietta Corp. - Olive Branch (3)
11170 Green Valley Dr, Olive Branch, MS
38654-3822
Tel.: (662) 895-4500
Web Site: http://www.mariettacorp.com
Sales Range: $75-99.9 Million
Emp.: 220
Mfr of Bar Soaps for the Lodging & Cos-
metic Industries
N.A.I.C.S.: 325611

Ares Management Corporation—(Continued)

Holding (Non-US):

Modular Automation Ireland Ltd. (2)
Smithstown Indus Estate, Shannon, Clare, Ireland
Tel.: (353) 61363077
Web Site: http://www.modular-global.com
Sales Range: $10-24.9 Million
Emp.: 100
Designs, Manufactures & Builds Special Purpose Machines & Automation Equipment
N.A.I.C.S.: 333248
Mike Lane (CEO)
Martin Dolan (Chief Bus Dev Officer)
Vivan Farrell (Chief Comml Officer)

Joint Venture (Domestic):

National Bedding Co. (2)
2600 Forbs Ave, Hoffman Estates, IL 60192
Tel.: (847) 645-0200
Web Site: http://www.serta.com
Sales Range: $1-4.9 Billion
Emp.: 125
Holding Company; Mattress Mfr & Whslr
N.A.I.C.S.: 551112
Burton Kaplan (Co-Founder)
Kelly Ellis (Dir-Integrated Mktg-Serta)
David Swift (Chm)
Michael Traub (CEO-Serta Simmons Bedding)
Daren Couture (Exec VP-Ops-Serta Simmons Bedding)

Subsidiary (Domestic):

Serta, Inc. (3)
2600 Forbs Ave, Hoffman Estates, IL 60192
Tel.: (847) 645-0200
Web Site: http://www.serta.com
Sales Range: $25-49.9 Million
Mattress Mfr
N.A.I.C.S.: 337911
Kevin Bayer (Dir-Acctg)

Subsidiary (Domestic):

Serta Mattress Company (4)
61 Leona Dr, Middleboro, MA 02346-1404
Tel.: (508) 946-4700
Web Site: http://www.serta.com
Sales Range: $25-49.9 Million
Emp.: 120
Mattress Mfr
N.A.I.C.S.: 337910
Tom McCue (VP & Controller)

Plant (Domestic):

Serta Mattress Company (5)
2050 Cessna Dr, Vacaville, CA 95688-8712
Tel.: (707) 446-7999
Web Site: http://www.serta.com
Sales Range: $25-49.9 Million
Emp.: 100
Mattress Mfr
N.A.I.C.S.: 337910

Subsidiary (Domestic):

Simmons Company (3)
1 Concourse Pkwy Ste 800, Atlanta, GA 30328-6188
Tel.: (770) 512-7700
Web Site: http://www.simmons.com
Sales Range: $1-4.9 Billion
Bed & Mattress Mfr & Retailer
N.A.I.C.S.: 337910

Joint Venture (Domestic):

Neiman Marcus Group, Inc. (2)
1618 Main St, Dallas, TX 75201
Tel.: (214) 741-6911
Web Site: https://www.neimanmarcus.com
Sales Range: $1-4.9 Billion
Emp.: 10,000
Offices of Other Holding Companies
N.A.I.C.S.: 551112
T. Dale Stapleton (Chief Acctg Officer & Sr VP)
Geoffroy van Raemdonck (CEO)
Alan Morrell (VP/Gen Mgr-NorthPark Center)

Subsidiary (Domestic):

Neiman Marcus Group LTD LLC (3)

1 Marcus Sq 1618 Main St, Dallas, TX 75201
Tel.: (214) 743-7600
Web Site: http://www.neimanmarcusgroup.com
Rev.: $4,900,444,000
Assets: $7,545,903,000
Liabilities: $6,786,722,000
Net Worth: $759,181,000
Earnings: $251,131,000
Emp.: 13,500
Fiscal Year-end: 07/28/2018
Holding Company; Online & Specialty Store Fashion & Gift Retailer
N.A.I.C.S.: 551112
David B. Kaplan (Chm)
T. Dale Stapleton (Chief Acctg Officer & Sr VP)
Joseph Weber (Chief HR Officer & Sr VP)
Tracy M. Preston (Gen Counsel & Sr VP)
Geoffroy Van Raemdonck (CEO)
Sarah W. Miller (CIO & Sr VP)
Liz Allison (Sr VP-Last Call)
Brent Laffere (Sr VP-Properties, Plng & Spend Mgmt)
Willis Weirich (Sr VP-Supply Chain)
Natalie Lockhart (Sr VP-Strategy & Execution)
Chris Demuth (Sr VP-People Svcs, ESG, Belonging & Corp Philanthropy)
Eric Severson (Chief People & Belonging Officer & Exec VP)

Subsidiary (Domestic):

Bergdorf Goodman, Inc. (4)
754 5th Ave, New York, NY 10019
Tel.: (212) 753-7300
Web Site: https://www.bergdorfgoodman.com
Sales Range: $150-199.9 Million
Men's & Women's Clothing Retailer
N.A.I.C.S.: 458110
Darcy Penick (Pres)

Unit (Domestic):

Neiman Marcus Stores (4)
1618 Main St, Dallas, TX 75201
Tel.: (214) 741-6911
Web Site: http://www.neimanmarcus.com
Sales Range: $1-4.9 Billion
Speciality Retailing Men's, Women's & Children's Clothing & Accessories
N.A.I.C.S.: 455110
Tim Adair (VP & Gen Mgr)

Holding (Domestic):

New England Confectionery Company Inc. (2)
135 American Legion Hwy, Revere, MA 02151
Tel.: (781) 485-4500
Candy Mfr
N.A.I.C.S.: 311340
Michael McGee (CEO)

Joint Venture (Domestic):

Press Ganey Holdings, Inc. (2)
53 State St Ste 2101, Boston, MA 02109
Tel.: (781) 295-5000
Web Site: http://www.pressganey.com
Holding Company; Healthcare Advisory & Consulting
N.A.I.C.S.: 551112
Patrick T. Ryan (Chm & CEO)
Joseph Greskoviak (Vice Chm)
Thomas H. Lee (Chief Medical Officer)
Devin J. Anderson (Gen Counsel & Sec)
Nell Buhlman (Chief Strategy Officer)
Jeffrey N. Doucette (Chief Nursing Officer)
David Shapiro (Sr VP/Gen Mgr-Member Experience)
Darren Dworkin (Pres & COO)
Noel Hamill (CMO)

Subsidiary (Domestic):

Bivarus, Inc. (3)
2525 Meridian Pkwy Ste 460, Durham, NC 27713
Tel.: (919) 336-9142
Web Site: http://www.pressganey.com
Analytics & Consulting Services for Healthcare Industry
N.A.I.C.S.: 541618

Subsidiary (Domestic):

The Jackson Group Inc. (4)

219 1st Ave SW, Hickory, NC 28602
Tel.: (828) 328-8968
Analytics & Consulting Services to Healthcare Organizations
N.A.I.C.S.: 541618
Alan K. Jackson (Dir)

Subsidiary (Domestic):

Forsta Inc. (3)
330 7th Ave Floor 3, 10001, New York, NY
Tel.: (212) 660-1800
Web Site: https://www.forsta.co
Software Development Company
N.A.I.C.S.: 513210
Kyle Ferguson (CEO)
Henry Pooley (Mng Dir-Asia Pacific)

Subsidiary (Domestic):

Rio SEO, Inc. (4)
8080 Dagget St Ste 220, San Diego, CA 92111
Tel.: (858) 397-1500
Web Site: http://www.rioseo.com
Data Processing, Hosting & Related Services
N.A.I.C.S.: 518210
Bill Connard (VP-Local Search)
Mick Wilson (VP-Customer Success)

Subsidiary (Domestic):

Press Ganey Associates, Inc. (3)
404 Columbia Pl, South Bend, IN 46601
Tel.: (800) 232-8032
Web Site: http://www.pressganey.com
Health Care Srvices
N.A.I.C.S.: 621999
Patrick T. Ryan (Chm & CEO)
Nell Buhlman (Press & COO)

Subsidiary (Domestic):

Binary Fountain Inc. (4)
1660 International Dr Ste 225, McLean, VA 22102
Tel.: (404) 526-8301
Web Site: http://www.binaryfountain.com
Healthcare Advisory & Consulting Services
N.A.I.C.S.: 541618
Aaron Clifford (Sr VP-Mktg)
Ramu Potarazu (Pres & CEO)

Strategic Management Decisions LLC (4)
2472 Jett Ferry Rd Ste 400-107, Atlanta, GA 30338
Tel.: (404) 808-4730
Web Site: http://www.smdhr.com
Sales Range: $1-9.9 Million
Emp.: 7
Marketing Analysis Services
N.A.I.C.S.: 541910
Hannah Spell (Dir-Res & Analytics)
Holly Bossert (VP-Sls)
Natalie Ollinger (Dir-Mktg & Project Mgmt)
Scott Mondore (Co-Founder & Mng Partner)
Shane Douthitt (Co-Founder & Mng Dir)

Subsidiary (Domestic):

Soyring Consulting, Inc. (3)
880 21st Ave N, Saint Petersburg, FL 33704
Tel.: (727) 822-8774
Web Site: http://www.soyringconsulting.com
Healthcare Management & Consulting Services
N.A.I.C.S.: 541618
Lucas Higman (Partner)
Adam Higman (Partner)
Charles Hagood (Partner)
Dragan Gough (Dir)
Jerzy Kaczor (Sr Mgr)
Charles Demanche (Project Dir & Mgr)
Shelly Turner (Mgr)

Symphony Performance Health, Inc. (3)
11605 Haynes Bridge Rd Ste 400, Alpharetta, GA 30009
Tel.: (866) 460-5681
Web Site: http://www.sphanalytics.com
Health Care Data, Analytics & Consulting Services
N.A.I.C.S.: 518210
Amy Amick (CEO)
Matthew Fusan (Gen Mgr-Population Health)
Kevin Weinstein (Pres)

Holding (Domestic):

Resource Label Group, LLC (2)
147 Seaboard Ln, Franklin, TN 37067
Tel.: (615) 661-5900
Web Site: http://www.resourcelabel.com
Pressure Sensitive Label, Shrink Sleeve & RFID/NFC Mfr
N.A.I.C.S.: 323111
Mike Apperson (Pres & CEO)

Subsidiary (Domestic):

Advanced Labels N. W. (3)
2100 196th St SW Ste 131, Lynnwood, WA 98036
Tel.: (425) 776-4315
Web Site: http://www.advancedlabelsnw.com
Custom Printed Labels & Tags
N.A.I.C.S.: 561910
Joseph Thompson (Gen Mgr)

Ample Industries, Inc. (3)
1101 Eaglecrest St, Nixa, MO 65714
Tel.: (417) 725-2657
Web Site: http://www.amplelabels.com
Sales Range: $1-9.9 Million
Emp.: 49
Flexible Packaging & Food & Beverage Labeling Services
N.A.I.C.S.: 561910
David Menzies (Founder)

Axiom Label, LLC (3)
1360 W Walnut Pkwy, Compton, CA 90220
Tel.: (310) 603-8910
Web Site: http://www.axiomlabel.com
Sales Range: $10-24.9 Million
Emp.: 44
Label Printing Services
N.A.I.C.S.: 561910
Kieron Delahunt (Owner & Pres)

Best Label Company Inc. (3)
13260 Moore St, Cerritos, CA 90703
Tel.: (562) 926-1432
Web Site: http://www.bestlabel.com
Label Printing Services
N.A.I.C.S.: 323111
Ernest Wong (Chm & CEO)
Dora Lau (Mgr-Acctg)

Cellotape, Inc. (3)
39611 Eureka Dr, Newark, CA 94560
Tel.: (510) 651-5551
Web Site: http://www.cellotape.com
Digital, Screen & Flexographic Printing
N.A.I.C.S.: 323111
Jim Doss (Acct Mgr-Medical & Tech)

Coast Label Company (3)
17406 Mount Cliffwood Cir, Fountain Valley, CA 92708
Tel.: (714) 426-1410
Web Site: http://www.coastlabel.com
Rev.: $3,146,000
Emp.: 22
Commercial Flexographic Printing
N.A.I.C.S.: 323111
Craig Mooreland (Pres)

Gintzler Graphics, Inc. (3)
147 Seaboard Ln, Franklin, TN 37067
Tel.: (716) 631-9700
Web Site: http://www.gintzlerinternational.com
Printing Services; Pressure Sensitive & Shrink Labels & Sleeves
N.A.I.C.S.: 323111
Carrie Meidenbauer (Exec VP-Sls)

Labels West, Inc. (3)
17629 130th Ave NE, Woodinville, WA 98072
Tel.: (425) 486-8484
Web Site: http://www.labelswest.com
Rev.: $10,000,000
Emp.: 45
Coated & Laminated Paper Mfr
N.A.I.C.S.: 322220
Lance Wilson (Dir-Sls)

Medlit Solutions, LLC (3)
191 Technology Dr, Garner, NC 27529-7940

Tel.: (919) 878-6789
Web Site: https://medlitsolutions.com
Pharmaceutical Printing, Packaging & Marketing Services
N.A.I.C.S.: 323111
Kevin Grogan *(CEO)*

Pharmaceutic Litho & Label Company, Inc. (3)
3990 Royal Ave, Simi Valley, CA 93063
Tel.: (805) 285-5162
Web Site: http://www.pharmaceuticlitho.com
Printing
N.A.I.C.S.: 323113
Trent Machale *(VP-Ops)*

Raypress Corp. (3)
380 Riverchase Pkwy E, Birmingham, AL 35244
Tel.: (205) 989-3731
Web Site: http://www.resourcelabel.com
Commercial Gravure Printing
N.A.I.C.S.: 323111

Spectrum Label Corporation (3)
30803 San Clemente St, Hayward, CA 94544
Tel.: (510) 477-0707
Web Site: http://www.spectrumlabel.com
Commercial Flexographic Printing Services
N.A.I.C.S.: 323111

Taylor Made Labels (3)
17252 Pilkington Rd, Lake Oswego, OR 97035
Tel.: (503) 699-5000
Web Site: http://www.resourcelabel.com
Coated & Laminated Paper Mfr
N.A.I.C.S.: 322220

Tek Label and Printing, Inc. (3)
472 Vista Way, Milpitas, CA 95035
Tel.: (408) 586-8107
Web Site: http://www.teklabel.com
Printing
N.A.I.C.S.: 323120
James DiBona *(Co-Founder)*
David Hinds *(Co-Founder)*

Holding (Domestic):

Rug Doctor, LLC (2)
2201 W Plano Pkwy Ste 100, Plano, TX 75075
Tel.: (972) 673-1400
Web Site: https://www.rugdoctor.com
Water Extraction Carpet Cleaning Machines & Related Products
N.A.I.C.S.: 333310

WIS International (2)
2000 Taylor Rd, Auburn Hills, MI 48326
Tel.: (858) 565-8111
Web Site: https://www.wisusa.com
Emp.: 15,000
Retail Inventory Services
N.A.I.C.S.: 561499
Bill McDonald *(CIO)*
Richard Baxter *(CFO)*
Waseem Bawa *(COO)*
Russ Silber *(Chief Revenue Officer)*

Front Yard Residential Corporation (1)
5100 Tamarind Reef, Christiansted, VI 00820
Tel.: (340) 692-0525
Web Site:
   http://www.frontyardresidential.com
Sales Range: $200-249.9 Million
Real Estate Management Services
N.A.I.C.S.: 531390
Brian Chappell *(VP-Fin Reporting)*

Subsidiary (Domestic):

ARNS, Inc. (2)
640 Main St, Northport, NY 11768
Tel.: (631) 757-7959
Residential Building Leasing Services
N.A.I.C.S.: 531110

Hyatt Regency Orlando (1)
9801 International Dr, Orlando, FL 32819
Tel.: (407) 284-1234
Web Site:
   http://www.orlando.regency.hyatt.com
Hotel Operations
N.A.I.C.S.: 721110

TricorBraun Inc. (1)

6 City Pl Dr St 1000, Saint Louis, MO 63141
Tel.: (855) 754-3728
Web Site: http://www.tricorbraun.com
Plastic, Glass & Metal Rigid Packaging Product Services
N.A.I.C.S.: 423990
Keith Strope *(Chm)*
Brett J. Binkowski *(Chief Comml Officer)*
Court D. Carruthers *(Pres & CEO)*
Becky Giessel *(Chief People Officer & Sr VP-HR)*
Susan Bergethon *(Gen Counsel & Sr VP)*
Brandi Mathews *(CFO)*

Subsidiary (Domestic):

CanSource, LLC (2)
2120 Miller Dr Ste G, Longmont, CO 80501
Web Site: http://www.cansource.com
Sales Range: $1-9.9 Million
Emp.: 200
Beverage Product Mfr
N.A.I.C.S.: 312140
Paige Sopcic *(CEO)*

Package All Corp. (2)
655 Church St, Bayport, NY 11705
Tel.: (631) 472-7200
Web Site: https://www.packageall.com
Packaging Industry Services
N.A.I.C.S.: 561910

Price Container & Packaging Corporation (2)
8850 S Hwy 89, Willard, UT 84340
Tel.: (801) 786-1509
Web Site: http://www.pricecontainers.com
Sales Range: $1-9.9 Million
Emp.: 22
Plastic Container, Bottle & Jar Distr
N.A.I.C.S.: 423840
Ryan Price *(Pres)*

SGB Packaging Group, Inc. (2)
401 Hackensack Ave Ste 7 Fl, Hackensack, NJ 07601-6426
Tel.: (201) 488-3030
Web Site: http://www.sgbpackaging.com
Landscape Architectural Services
N.A.I.C.S.: 541320
Shoshanna Gibli *(Founder & Pres)*
Lauren Gibli *(Exec VP & Dir-Sales & Ops)*
Julie Gibli *(VP-Acct Mgmt & Dev)*

Division (Domestic):

TricorBraun Design & Engineering (2)
3011 Butterfield Rd Ste 200, Oak Brook, IL 60523
Tel.: (630) 645-1200
Rigid Packaging Design Services
N.A.I.C.S.: 541490

ARETE INDUSTRIES, INC.
13209 Byrd Dr, Odessa, FL 33556
Tel.: (813) 865-0208   CO
Web Site: https://areteindustries.us
Year Founded: 1987
ARET—(OTCEM)
Rev.: $953,021
Assets: $6,276,868
Liabilities: $2,969,828
Net Worth: $3,307,040
Earnings: ($4,747,053)
Fiscal Year-end: 12/31/15
Holding Company; Oil & Gas Exploration & Asset Development
N.A.I.C.S.: 551112

ARGAN, INC.
1 Church St Ste 201, Rockville, MD 20850
Tel.: (301) 315-0027   DE
Web Site: https://www.arganinc.com
AGX—(NYSE)
Rev.: $455,040,000
Assets: $489,487,000
Liabilities: $208,590,000
Net Worth: $280,897,000
Earnings: $33,098,000
Emp.: 985
Fiscal Year-end: 01/31/23

Holding Company; Power Plant Engineering, Design, Procurement & Construction Services; Wiring & Telecommunication Construction Services; Nutraceutical Mfr & Distr
N.A.I.C.S.: 551112
Rainer H. Bosselmann *(Founder, Chm & CEO)*
David H. Watson *(Pres & CEO)*
William F. Leimkuhler *(Chm)*

Subsidiaries:

Atlantic Projects Company Limited (1)
Bedford Place Howley's Quay Henry Street, Limerick, V94 K6YY, Co Dublin, Ireland
Tel.: (353) 61535763
Web Site: http://www.atlanticprojects.com
Engineering Services
N.A.I.C.S.: 541330

Atlantic Projects Company, Inc. (1)
5 Southside Dr Bldg 11 Ste 229, Clifton Park, NY 12065
Tel.: (802) 362-2114
Web Site: http://www.atlanticprojects.com
Engineeering Services
N.A.I.C.S.: 541330

Gemma Power Systems, LLC (1)
769 Hebron Ave, Glastonbury, CT 06033   **(100%)**
Tel.: (860) 659-0509
Web Site: https://www.gemmapower.com
Rev.: $200,000,000
Emp.: 50
Power Plant Operation & Maintenance Services
N.A.I.C.S.: 236210
Terrence Colin Trebilcock *(Co-Pres)*
Christopher J. Kollmer *(Sr VP)*
Adam A. Malinowski *(CFO & VP)*
Robert J. Haupt *(Sr VP)*
Richard P. Poulin *(VP)*
Charles E. Collins IV *(Co-Pres)*

Subsidiary (Domestic):

Gemma Plant Operations, LLC (2)
1580 County Rd 1020, Woodville, TX 75979
Tel.: (860) 659-0509
Engineeering Services
N.A.I.C.S.: 541330

Southern Maryland Cable, Inc. (1)
5932 Old Solomons Is Rd, Tracys Landing, MD 20779
Tel.: (410) 867-7577
Web Site: https://www.smcis.com
Sales Range: $200-249.9 Million
Emp.: 50
Power Distribution & Construction Services
N.A.I.C.S.: 541330

TRC Acquisition, LLC (1)
176 Laurie Ellis Rd, Winterville, NC 28590
Tel.: (252) 355-9353
Industrial Building Construction Services
N.A.I.C.S.: 237990

Subsidiary (Domestic):

The Roberts Company Fabrication Services, Inc. (2)
176 Laurie Ellis Rd, Winterville, NC 28590
Tel.: (252) 355-9353
Web Site: https://www.robertscompany.com
Emp.: 220
Engineering Related Services
N.A.I.C.S.: 541330

The Roberts Company, Inc. (1)
176 Laurie Ellis Rd, Winterville, NC 28590
Tel.: (252) 355-9353
Civil Engineering Construction Services
N.A.I.C.S.: 237990

ARGONAUT GOLD INC.
9600 Prototype Ct, Reno, NV 89521
Tel.: (775) 284-4422   ON
Web Site:
   http://www.argonautgold.com
Year Founded: 2007
AGREF—(OTCIQ)
Rev.: $319,692,000
Assets: $1,053,410,000
Liabilities: $281,232,000

Net Worth: $772,178,000
Earnings: $14,211,000
Emp.: 901
Fiscal Year-end: 12/31/20
Gold Exploration, Mine Development & Production
N.A.I.C.S.: 212220
James E. Kofman *(Chm)*
David A. Ponczoch *(CFO)*
W. Robert Rose *(VP-Technical Svcs)*
Daniel A. Symons *(VP-Corp Dev & IR)*
Brian Arkell *(VP-Exploration)*
Lowe Billingsley *(Sr VP-Ops)*
Peter C. Dougherty *(Pres & CEO)*

Subsidiaries:

Alio Gold Inc. (1)
700 West Pender Street Suite 507, Vancouver, V6C 1G8, BC, Canada
Tel.: (604) 682-4002
Web Site: http://www.aliogold.com
Rev.: $111,541,000
Assets: $251,284,000
Liabilities: $132,673,000
Net Worth: $118,611,000
Earnings: ($136,223,000)
Emp.: 250
Fiscal Year-end: 12/31/2019
Gold Mining Services
N.A.I.C.S.: 212220
Miguel Bonilla *(Mgr-Mexico)*
Paul Jones *(Sr VP-Corp Dev)*

Subsidiary (US):

Rye Patch Gold US Inc. (2)
Ste 9 220 S Rock Blvd, Reno, NV 89502
Tel.: (775) 856-4900
Gold & Silver Mining
N.A.I.C.S.: 212220

Subsidiary (Non-US):

Timmins Gold Corp Mexico S.A de C.V (2)
Boulevard Soliearize, Hermosillo, 83270, Sonora, Mexico
Tel.: (52) 662 218 1067
Web Site: http://www.timminsgold.com
Gold Ore Mining Services
N.A.I.C.S.: 212220

Compania Minera Pitalla, S.A. de C.V. (1)
Carlos Quintero Arce 24SurB, Local 12 Col, Sonora, 83247, Mexico
Tel.: (52) 6621368080
Sales Range: $50-74.9 Million
Mineral Mining Services
N.A.I.C.S.: 212323

ARGUS CAPITAL CORP.
3 Columbus Cir 24th Fl, New York, NY 10019
Tel.: (212) 812-7702   DE
Web Site:
   http://www.arguscapitalcorp.com
Year Founded: 2021
ARGU—(NASDAQ)
Investment Management Service
N.A.I.C.S.: 523999
Joseph R. Ianniello *(Chm & CEO)*
Marc DeBevoise *(Vice Chm & Pres)*
Saif Rahman *(CFO)*
Maria Corsaro Charon *(Sr VP-Mergers & Acquisitions)*
Dana McClintock *(Chief Comm Officer)*
Stephen D. Mirante *(Chief Admin Officer)*
Charles Pavlounis *(Chief Bus Dev Officer)*
Kelli Raftery *(CMO)*
Gautam Ranji *(Chief Strategy Officer)*

ARGUS WORLDWIDE CORP.
1712 Pioneer Ave Ste 500, Cheyenne, WY 82001
Tel.: (613) 731-5935
ARGW—(NASDAQ)

Argus Worldwide Corp.—(Continued)

Mobile Applications
N.A.I.C.S.: 513210

ARION GROUP CORP.
16839 Gale Ave Ste 210, City of Industry, CA 91745 **NV**
Year Founded: 2016
ARGC—(OTCIQ)
Rev.: $20,818
Assets: $33,902
Liabilities: $259,784
Net Worth: ($225,882)
Earnings: ($81,923)
Emp.: 1
Fiscal Year-end: 01/31/23
Cedar Phyto Barrel Distr
N.A.I.C.S.: 423840
Mingyong Huang *(Sec)*
Jay Hamilton *(Pres & CEO)*
Brenda Bin Wang *(CFO)*

ARIS WATER SOLUTIONS, INC.
9811 Katy Fwy Ste 700, Houston, TX 77024
Tel.: (832) 304-7003 **DE**
Web Site: https://www.ariswater.com
Year Founded: 2021
ARIS—(NYSE)
Rev.: $321,001,000
Assets: $1,303,366,000
Liabilities: $646,279,000
Net Worth: $657,087,000
Earnings: $4,797,000
Emp.: 196
Fiscal Year-end: 12/31/22
Offices of Other Holding Companies
N.A.I.C.S.: 551112
William A. Zartler *(Founder & Exec Chm)*
Amanda M. Brock *(Pres & CEO)*
Stephan E. Tompsett *(CFO)*
William A. Zartler *(Founder & Chm)*
Amanda M. Brock *(Pres & CEO)*
Adrian Milton *(Chief Admin Officer, Gen Counsel & Sec)*
David Tuerff *(Sr VP-Fin & IR)*
Dylan Van Brunt *(COO)*
Gregory Mullin *(Sr VP-Comml)*
Jon Ricker *(Sr VP-Ops & Engrg)*
Michael Incerto *(Sr VP-Water Resources)*
William Harvey *(Sr VP-Corp Dev)*
Jeffrey K. Hunt *(Chief Acctg Officer)*
Nick Patterson *(Chief Comml Officer)*

ARISTA NETWORKS, INC.
5453 Great America Pkwy, Santa Clara, CA 95054
Tel.: (408) 547-5500 **DE**
Web Site: https://www.arista.com
Year Founded: 2004
ANET—(NYSE)
Rev.: $5,860,168,000
Assets: $9,946,806,000
Liabilities: $2,727,747,000
Net Worth: $7,219,059,000
Earnings: $2,087,321,000
Emp.: 4,023
Fiscal Year end: 12/31/23
Cloud Networking Solutions
N.A.I.C.S.: 513210
Jayshree V. Ullal *(Pres & CEO)*
John F. McCool *(Chief Platform Officer & Sr VP-Engrg & Ops)*
Jayshree V. Ullal *(Chm, Pres & CEO)*
Marc Taxay *(Gen Counsel & Sr VP)*
Andreas B. Bechtolsheim *(Co-Founder)*
Mark Foss *(Sr VP-Global Ops & Mktg)*
Ed Chapman *(VP-Bus Dev & Strategic Alliances)*
Douglas Gourlay *(VP/Gen Mgr-Cloud Networking Software)*

Hugh Holbrook *(Chief Dev Officer)*
Ashwin Kohli *(Chief Customer Officer)*
Jeff Raymond *(VP-EOS Software & Svcs)*
Christopher Schmidt *(Chief Sls Officer)*
Chantelle Breithaupt *(CFO & Sr VP)*
Kumar Srikantan *(VP)*
Kenneth Duda *(Co-Founder, CTO & Sr VP-Software Engrg)*

Subsidiaries:

Arista Networks Australia Pty Ltd (1)
Wynyard Green Level 5 11 York Street, Sydney, 2000, NSW, Australia
Tel.: (61) 283104383
Software Development Services
N.A.I.C.S.: 541511

Arista Networks EURL (1)
52 R Victoire, 75009, Paris, France
Tel.: (33) 175909017
Software Development Services
N.A.I.C.S.: 541511

Arista Networks GmbH (1)
Innere Kanalstr 15, 50823, Cologne, Germany
Tel.: (49) 22151084000
Software Development Services
N.A.I.C.S.: 541511

Arista Networks India Private Limited (1)
Global Tech Park Tower A & B 11th Floor Marathahalli Outer Ring Road, Devarabeesanahalli Village Varthur Hobli, Bengaluru, 560 103, India
Tel.: (91) 8049096000
Software Development Services
N.A.I.C.S.: 541511
Deepti B. *(Engr-Software)*

Arista Networks Singapore Private Ltd. (1)
9 Temasek Boulevard 29-01 Suntec Tower Two, Singapore, 038989, Singapore
Tel.: (65) 31571367
Software Development Services
N.A.I.C.S.: 541511

Awake Security LLC (1)
5453 Great America Pkwy, Santa Clara, CA 95054
Web Site: http://www.awakesecurity.com
Network Security Services
N.A.I.C.S.: 561612
Rahul Kashyap *(Pres & CEO)*
Keith Amidon *(Co-Founder)*
Rudolph Araujo *(VP-Security Strategy, Bus Dev & Mktg)*
Jason Bevis *(VP-Awake Labs)*
Debabrata Dash *(Co-Founder)*

Big Switch Networks, Inc. (1)
311 Coronado Dr Bldg A, Santa Clara, CA 95054
Tel.: (650) 322-6510
Web Site: http://www.bigswitch.com
Emp.: 51
Software Development Services
N.A.I.C.S.: 541511
Douglas Murray *(CEO)*

ARISTA POWER, INC.
1000 Mt Rd Blvd, Rochester, NY 14615
Tel.: (585) 243-4040 **NY**
Web Site:
https://www.aristapower.com
Year Founded: 2001
ASPW—(OTCEM)
Sales Range: $1-9.9 Million
Emp.: 7
Wind Turbine Technology Developer & Mfr
N.A.I.C.S.: 333611
Amy Collins *(CFO & Sec)*
Phill Dokins *(COO)*
Carl Weathers *(CEO)*

ARISTOCRAT GROUP CORP.
4701 Pine Cir Dr, Bellaire, TX 77401

Tel.: (832) 302-0600 **FL**
Year Founded: 2015
ASCC—(OTCIQ)
Personal Services
N.A.I.C.S.: 812990
Mark Corwin *(CFO)*
Derek K. Sisson *(Founder, Pres, CEO, Treas & Sec)*
Gilbert Audet *(Dir-Research & Development)*

ARISZ ACQUISITION CORP.
199 Water St 31st Fl, New York, NY 10038
Tel.: (212) 845-9945 **DE**
Year Founded: 2021
ARIZ—(NASDAQ)
Rev.: $2,386,358
Assets: $34,344,418
Liabilities: $40,025,357
Net Worth: ($5,680,939)
Earnings: $1,216,880
Fiscal Year-end: 09/30/23
Investment Management Service
N.A.I.C.S.: 523999

ARK RESTAURANTS CORP.
85 5th Ave 14th Fl, New York, NY 10003
Tel.: (212) 206-8800 **NY**
Web Site:
https://www.arkrestaurants.com
Year Founded: 1985
ARKR—(NASDAQ)
Rev.: $183,545,000
Assets: $156,041,000
Liabilities: $112,400,000
Net Worth: $43,641,000
Earnings: ($3,745,000)
Emp.: 1,246
Fiscal Year-end: 09/28/24
Holding Company; Restaurant & Bar Owner & Operator
N.A.I.C.S.: 551112
Michael S. Weinstein *(Founder, Chm & CEO)*
John Oldweiler *(Dir-Pur)*
Jennifer Jordan *(Co-COO)*
Walter Rauscher *(VP-Corp Sls & Catering)*
Nancy Alvarez *(Controller)*
Evyette Ortiz *(Dir-Mktg)*
Linda Clous *(Dir-Capital Projects & Facilities)*
Anthony J. Sirica *(Pres & CFO)*
Jeff Isaacson *(Dir-Bars & Beverage)*
Sonal Shah *(Gen Counsel)*
Guisela Nunez *(Dir, Dir, Pres, Pres, Pres, CFO, Exec VP & Sr VP)*
Michelle Dudenake *(Dir)*
Paul Gordon *(Sr VP)*

Subsidiaries:

Ark AC Burger Bar LLC (1)
2801 Pacific Ave, Atlantic City, NJ 08401
Tel.: (609) 317-4660
Web Site: https://broadwayburgerbarac.com
Restaurant Operators
N.A.I.C.S.: 722511

Ark Atlantic City Corp. (1)
1133 Boardwalk, Atlantic City, NJ 08401
Tel.: (609) 340-6555
Web Site: http://www.arkrestaurants.com
Restaurant Operators
N.A.I.C.S.: 722511

Ark Atlantic City Restaurant Corp. (1)
228 W 52nd St, New York, NY 10019
Tel.: (212) 586-5000
Web Site:
https://www.gallaghersnysteakhouse.com
Restaurant Operators
N.A.I.C.S.: 722511

Ark Bryant Park Corp. (1)
25 W 40th St, New York, NY 10018-2601 **(100%)**
Tel.: (212) 840-6500

Web Site: http://www.arkrestaurants.com
Sales Range: $25-49.9 Million
Restaurant Operators
N.A.I.C.S.: 722511

Ark Bryant Park Southwest LLC (1)
41 W 40th St, New York, NY 10018
Tel.: (212) 840-0324
Web Site: http://www.arkrestaurants.com
Restaurant Services
N.A.I.C.S.: 722511

Ark Connecticut Branches Corp. (1)
240 Indiantown Rd, Ledyard, CT 06338
Tel.: (860) 312-4087
Restaurant Operators
N.A.I.C.S.: 722511

Ark D.C. Kiosk, Inc. (1)
Union Sta 50 Massachusettes Ave NE, Washington, DC 20002 **(100%)**
Tel.: (202) 682-0143
Web Site: http://www.arkrestaurants.com
Sales Range: $50-74.9 Million
Restaurant Featuring Light Entrees, Sandwiches & Salads
N.A.I.C.S.: 722511

Ark Island Beach Resort LLC (1)
9800 S Ocean Dr, Jensen Beach, FL 34957
Tel.: (772) 229-3006
Web Site:
https://www.islandbeachresort.com
Restaurant Services
N.A.I.C.S.: 722511

Ark Jupiter RI, LLC (1)
1065 N Highway A1A, Jupiter, FL 33477
Tel.: (561) 320-9130
Restaurant Services
N.A.I.C.S.: 722511

Ark Las Vegas Restaurant Corp. (1)
3790 S Las Vegas Blvd 11, Las Vegas, NV 89109
Tel.: (702) 740-6454
Web Site: https://arkvegas.com
Restaurant Operating Services
N.A.I.C.S.: 722511

Ark Meadowlands LLC (1)
1 Racetrack Dr, Rutherford, NJ 07073
Tel.: (201) 843-2446
Restaurant Services
N.A.I.C.S.: 722511

Ark Operating Corp. (1)
160 E 38th St, New York, NY 10016-2651
Tel.: (212) 867-0922
Web Site: http://www.elriograndenyc.com
Sales Range: $10-24.9 Million
Mexican Restaurant
N.A.I.C.S.: 722511

Ark Oyster House Gulf Shores I, LLC (1)
701 Gulf Shores Pkwy, Gulf Shores, AL 36542-6471
Tel.: (251) 948-2445
Web Site:
http://www.originaloysterhouse.com
Emp.: 130
Restaurant Operators
N.A.I.C.S.: 722511

Ark Potomac Corporation (1)
3000 K St NW, Washington, DC 20007
Tel.: (202) 944-4200
Web Site: https://sequoiadc.com
Sales Range: $125-149.9 Million
Emp.: 350
Restaurant Operators
N.A.I.C.S.: 722511

Ark Southwest D.C. Corp. (1)
50 Massachusetts Ave NE, Washington, DC 20002
Tel.: (202) 333-3011
Restaurant Operators
N.A.I.C.S.: 722511

Ark Union Station, Inc. (1)
Union Station 50 Massachusetts Ave NE, Washington, DC 20002 **(100%)**
Tel.: (202) 682-9555
Sales Range: $50-74.9 Million
Emp.: 80
Restaurant Specializing in Ethnic & Regional Dishes
N.A.I.C.S.: 722511

Chefmod LLC (1)
85 5th Ave 14th Fl, New York, NY 10003
Tel.: (646) 651-1120
Web Site: https://www.chefmod.com
Food Service Provider
N.A.I.C.S.: 624210
John Oldweiler (Co-Founder & Pres)
Eduard Spivak (Co-Founder & CTO)

Clyde Ark LLC (1)
485 W 37th St, New York, NY 10018
Tel.: (212) 784-0009
Web Site: http://www.arkrestaurants.com
Restaurant Operators
N.A.I.C.S.: 722511

Las Vegas America Corp. (1)
3790 Las Vegas Blvd S New York-New York
Hotel and Casino, Las Vegas, NV 89109
Tel.: (702) 740-6451
Web Site: https://americalv.com
Sales Range: $50-74.9 Million
Restaurant
N.A.I.C.S.: 722511

Las Vegas Festival Food Corp. (1)
3790 Las Vegas Blvd S, Las Vegas, NV
89109
Tel.: (702) 740-6455
Restaurant Operators
N.A.I.C.S.: 722511

Las Vegas Venice Deli Corp. (1)
3377 Las Vegas Monorail, Las Vegas, NV
89109
Tel.: (702) 414-3626
Restaurant Operators
N.A.I.C.S.: 722511

MEB On First, Inc. (1)
1470 1st Ave, New York, NY 10021-3175
Tel.: (212) 734-1600
Sales Range: $10-24.9 Million
Emp.: 27
Restaurant Operators
N.A.I.C.S.: 722511
Ruperto Ramirez (Gen Mgr)

ARKANOVA ENERGY CORPO-
RATION
3809 Juniper Trace Ste 201, Austin,
TX 78738
Tel.: (512) 222-0975   NV
Web Site:
    https://www.arkanovaenergy.com
Year Founded: 2001
AKVA—(OTCIQ)
Sales Range: Less than $1 Million
Emp.: 7
Crude Petroleum Extraction Services
N.A.I.C.S.: 211120
Pierre G. Mulacek (Pres & CEO)
Reginald Denny (CFO)

ARKOSE ENERGY CORP.
1773 Westborough Dr Ste 100, Katy,
TX 77449
Tel.: (832) 487-7800   NV
Web Site: https://arkoseenergy.com
Year Founded: 2006
RKOS—(OTCIQ)
Oil & Gas Exploration
N.A.I.C.S.: 211120
Amzy Hibler (CFO)
Gavin Clarkson (Gen Counsel & Dir)
Daniel Lee Ritz Jr. (Pres & CEO)

ARLO TECHNOLOGIES, INC.
2200 Faraday Ave, Carlsbad, CA
92008
Tel.: (408) 890-3900   DE
Web Site: https://www.arlo.com
Year Founded: 2018
ARLO—(NYSE)
Rev.: $490,414,000
Assets: $272,201,000
Liabilities: $184,506,000
Net Worth: $87,695,000
Earnings: ($56,626,000)
Emp.: 343
Fiscal Year-end: 12/31/22
Security Control Device Mfr & Distr
N.A.I.C.S.: 334290

Kurtis J. Binder (CFO & COO)
Brian Busse (Gen Counsel & Sec)
Lily Knowles (Sr VP-Sls, Mktg & Cus-
tomer Care)
Scott McManigal (Sr VP-Design &
Experience)
Antoinette Switzer (Sr VP-HR-
Worldwide)
Gordon Mattingly (CFO & Principal
Acctg Officer)
Matthew McRae (CEO)

Subsidiaries:

Arlo Technologies International
Ltd.   (1)
Building 3 University Technology Centre
Curraheen Road, Cork, Ireland
Tel.: (353) 800949252
Smart Home Electronic Equipment Mfr
N.A.I.C.S.: 334310
Dan Mannix (Mng Dir)

ARMA SERVICES, INC.
7260 W Azure Dr Ste 140-928, Las
Vegas, NV 89130
Tel.: (702) 659-9321   NV
Web Site: https://armaoffsets.com
Year Founded: 2014
ARMV—(NASDAQ)
Liabilities: $41,804
Net Worth: ($41,804)
Earnings: ($9,659)
Fiscal Year-end: 10/31/22
Destination & Event Management
Services
N.A.I.C.S.: 561599
Eric Nixon (Pres, CEO & CFO)

ARMADA HOFFLER PROPER-
TIES, INC.
222 Central Park Ave Ste 2100, Vir-
ginia Beach, VA 23462
Tel.: (757) 366-4000   MD
Web Site:
    https://www.armadahoffler.com
AHH—(NYSE)
Rev.: $667,158,000
Assets: $2,562,898,000
Liabilities: $1,757,720,000
Net Worth: $805,178,000
Earnings: $8,287,000
Emp.: 164
Fiscal Year-end: 12/31/23
Real Estate Investment Services
N.A.I.C.S.: 523999
Alan R. Hunt (Exec VP-Construction)
W. Christopher Harvey (Exec VP-
Construction & Bus Dev)
Shawn J. Tibbetts (Pres & COO)
Matthew T. Barnes-Smith (CFO)
Louis S. Haddad (Vice Chm & CEO)
Daniel A. Hoffler (Exec Chm)

ARMADA MERCANTILE LTD.
9575 Pinehurst Dr, Roseville, CA
95747
Tel.: (916) 746-0029   BC
Web Site:
    https://www.armadamercantile.com
Year Founded: 1987
AAMTF—(OTCIQ)
Miscellaneous Financial Investment
Activities
N.A.I.C.S.: 523999
Patrick Cole (Pres)
Philip J. Skinder (CFO)

ARMANINO FOODS OF DIS-
TINCTION, INC.
5976 W Las Positas Blvd Ste 200,
Pleasanton, CA 94588
Tel.: (510) 441-9300   CO
Web Site:
    https://www.armaninofoods.com
Year Founded: 1998

AMNF—(OTCIQ)
Rev.: $31,815,652
Assets: $26,329,461
Liabilities: $5,468,558
Net Worth: $20,860,903
Earnings: $2,022,458
Emp.: 37
Fiscal Year-end: 12/31/20
Italian-Style Frozen Food Mfr
N.A.I.C.S.: 311412

ARMATA PHARMACEUTICALS,
INC.
5005 McConell Ave, Los Angeles, CA
90066
Tel.: (310) 665-2928   WA
Web Site:
    https://www.armatapharma.com
Year Founded: 1989
ARMP—(NYSEAMEX)
Rev.: $5,508,000
Assets: $95,834,000
Liabilities: $59,754,000
Net Worth: $36,080,000
Earnings: ($36,917,000)
Emp.: 72
Fiscal Year-end: 12/31/22
Pharmaceutical Preparation Manufac-
turing
N.A.I.C.S.: 325412
Robin C. Kramer (Chm)
Deborah L. Birx (CEO)
Bryan Kadotani (VP)

Subsidiaries:

Genovo, Inc.   (1)
512 Elmwood Ave Elmwood Ct Two, Sharon Hill, PA 19079
Tel.: (206) 623-7612
Sales Range: $75-99.9 Million
Developer & Marketer of Therapeutic & Diagnostic Products for Treatment of Diseases Related to Malfunctions of the Immune System
N.A.I.C.S.: 541720

Special Phage Holdings Pty Ltd   (1)
U 7 27 Dale St, Brookvale, 2100, NSW,
Australia
Tel.: (61) 299057634
Emp.: 12
Holding Company
N.A.I.C.S.: 551112

ARMOUR RESIDENTIAL REIT,
INC.
3001 Ocean Dr Ste 201, Vero Beach,
FL 32963
Tel.: (772) 617-4340   MD
Web Site:
    https://www.armourreit.com
Year Founded: 2008
ARR—(NYSE)
Rev.: $228,432,000
Assets: $9,437,047,000
Liabilities: $8,324,675,000
Net Worth: $1,112,372,000
Earnings: ($229,930,000)
Emp.: 21
Fiscal Year-end: 12/31/22
Real Estate Investment Trust
N.A.I.C.S.: 525990
Scott J. Ulm (Vice Chm & CEO)
Marc H. Bell (Founder)
Desmond E. Macauley (Co-Chief In-
vestment Officer & Head-Risk Mgmt)
Sergey Losyev (Co-Chief Investment
Officer)

Subsidiaries:

JAVELIN Mortgage Investment
Corp.   (1)
3001 Ocean Dr Ste 201, Vero Beach, FL
32963   (100%)
Tel.: (772) 617-4340
Web Site: http://investor.armourreit.com
Real Estate Investment Trust
N.A.I.C.S.: 525990

ARMSTRONG FLOORING, INC.
2500 Columbia Ave, Lancaster, PA
17604
Tel.: (717) 672-9611
Web Site:
    http://www.armstrongflooring.com
AFI—(NYSE)
Rev.: $649,900,000
Assets: $517,000,000
Liabilities: $317,800,000
Net Worth: $199,200,000
Earnings: ($53,000,000)
Emp.: 1,568
Fiscal Year-end: 12/31/21
Wood & Vinyl Flooring Product Mfr
N.A.I.C.S.: 321918
Larry S. McWilliams (Chm)
John C. Bassett (Chief HR Officer &
Sr VP)
Christopher S. Parisi (Chief Compli-
ance Officer, Gen Counsel, Sec & Sr
VP)
Scott W. Hess (CIO & Sr VP)
Brent A. Flaharty (Chief Customer
Experience Officer & Sr VP)
Michel S. Vermette (Pres & CEO)
Amy Peacock Trojanowski (CFO & Sr
VP)
Phillip J. Gaudreau (VP & Controller)
Sonya Zook (VP-Bus Transformation)
Dave Thoresen (Sr VP-Product & In-
novation)
Patrick Bargiel (VP-Supply Chain)

Subsidiaries:

Armstrong Flooring Hong Kong
Limited   (1)
Rm 901-903 9/F Siu On Centre 188 Lock-
hart Road, Wanchai, China (Hong Kong)
Tel.: (852) 25857821
Web Site: http://www.armstrongflooring.com
Wood Flooring Product Whslr
N.A.I.C.S.: 423310

Armstrong Flooring Pty. Ltd.   (1)
29-39 Mills Road, Braeside, 3195, VIC,
Australia
Tel.: (61) 395865500
Millwork Flooring Product Distr
N.A.I.C.S.: 423310

ARMSTRONG WORLD INDUS-
TRIES, INC.
2500 Columbia Ave, Lancaster, PA
17603
Tel.: (717) 397-0611   PA
Web Site:
    https://www.armstrongceilings.com
Year Founded: 1860
AWI—(NYSE)
Rev.: $1,295,200,000
Assets: $1,672,400,000
Liabilities: $1,080,600,000
Net Worth: $591,800,000
Earnings: $223,800,000
Emp.: 3,100
Fiscal Year-end: 12/31/23
Flooring, Ceiling & Cabinet Products
Designer, Mfr & Distr
N.A.I.C.S.: 326199
Victor D. Grizzle (Pres & CEO)
Mark A. Hershey (Sr VP-Americas)
James T. Burge (Principal Acctg Offi-
cer, VP & Controller)
Austin K. So (Gen Counsel, Sec & Sr
VP)
Christopher P. Calzaretta (CFO & Sr
VP)
Jill A. Crager (Sr VP-Sls Ops)
Dawn Kirchner-King (CIO)
Monica Maheshwari (Sr VP)

Subsidiaries:

3form LLC   (1)
2300 S 2300 W, Salt Lake City, UT 84119

Armstrong World Industries, Inc.—(Continued)

Tel.: (801) 694-2500
Web Site: http://www.3-form.com
Architectural Product Mfr
N.A.I.C.S.: 332323

AWI Licensing Company (1)
2500 Columbia Ave, Lancaster, PA
17603 (100%)
Tel.: (717) 397-0611
Web Site: https://www.armstrong.com
Sales Range: $250-299.9 Million
Product & Trademark Licensing Services
N.A.I.C.S.: 533110

**Architectural Components Group,
Inc.** (1)
900 George St, Marshfield, MO 65706
Tel.: (417) 630-3239
Web Site: http://www.acgiwood.com
Specialty Wood Ceiling & Wall Designer &
Mfr
N.A.I.C.S.: 321999

**Armstrong Building Products
B.V.** (1)
Bijster 37, 4817 HZ, Breda, Netherlands
Tel.: (31) 765230200
Web Site: http://www.armstrong.nl
Sales Range: $50-74.9 Million
Emp.: 25
Commercial Ceiling Products Mfr & Distr
N.A.I.C.S.: 327999

**Armstrong China Holdings,
Limited** (1)
19/F No 88 Gloucester Road, Wanchai,
Hong Kong, China (Hong Kong)
Tel.: (852) 25857828
Web Site: http://www.armstrong.com
Emp.: 10
Holding Company
N.A.I.C.S.: 551112

Armstrong Cork Finance LLC (1)
2500 Columbia Ave, Lancaster, PA
17603 (100%)
Tel.: (717) 397-0611
Web Site: https://www.armstrong.com
Sales Range: $125-149.9 Million
Emp.: 1,300
Financial Services
N.A.I.C.S.: 522299

Armstrong DLW AG (1)
Stuttgarter Str 75, D-74321, Bietigheim-
Bissingen, Germany
Tel.: (49) 7142710
Web Site: http://www.armstrong.de
Sales Range: $25-49.9 Million
Emp.: 100
Resilient Flooring Products Mfr & Distr
N.A.I.C.S.: 326199

**Armstrong Metalldecken Holdings
AG** (1)
Breitfeldstrasse 8, Saint Gallen, 9015, Swit-
zerland
Tel.: (41) 713136363
Web Site: http://www.gema.biz
Sales Range: $200-249.9 Million
Emp.: 40
Holding Company; Metal Ceiling Systems
Mfr & Distr
N.A.I.C.S.: 551112
Derk Wellmann (CFO)

Subsidiary (Domestic):

Phonex-Gema AG (2)
Raffelstrasse 29, 8045, Zurich, Switzerland
Tel.: (41) 444544444
Sales Range: $150-199.9 Million
Metal Ceiling System Planning, Installation
& Maintenance Services
N.A.I.C.S.: 238990

**Armstrong World Industries (Austra-
lia) Pty. Ltd.** (1)
29-39 Mills Rd, Braeside, 3195, VIC, Aus-
tralia
Tel.: (61) 800632624
Web Site: https://www.armstrongflooring.au
Sales Range: $25-49.9 Million
Emp.: 100
Resilient Flooring Products Mfr & Distr
N.A.I.C.S.: 326199

**Armstrong World Industries (H.K.)
Limited** (1)

19/F No 88 Gloucester Road, 128 Glouces-
ter Road, Wanchai, 200001, China (Hong
Kong)
Tel.: (852) 25857800
Web Site: http://www.armstrong.hk
Sales Range: $25-49.9 Million
Emp.: 200
Resilient Flooring Distr; Ceiling Products
Mfr & Distr
N.A.I.C.S.: 444180

**Armstrong World Industries Canada
Ltd.** (1)
255 Montpellier Blvd, 3rd Floor Suite 300,
Saint Laurent, H4N 2G3, QC, Canada
Tel.: (514) 744-3323
Web Site: http://www.armstrong.com
Sales Range: $50-74.9 Million
Emp.: 200
Resilient Flooring & Ceiling Products Mfr &
Distr
N.A.I.C.S.: 326199

**HomerWood Hardwood Flooring
Company** (1)
1026 Industrial Dr, Titusville, PA 16354
Tel.: (814) 827-3855
Web Site: http://www.homerwood.com
Sales Range: $25-49.9 Million
Emp.: 100
Floor Covering Mfr
N.A.I.C.S.: 326199

MRK Industries, Inc. (1)
1821 Industrial Dr, Libertyville, IL 60048
Tel.: (847) 362-8720
Web Site:
https://www.armstrongceilings.com
Specialty Metal Ceilings & Walls Mfr
N.A.I.C.S.: 332312

Moz Designs, Inc. (1)
711 Kevin Ct, Oakland, CA 94621
Tel.: (510) 632-0853
Web Site: http://www.mozdesigns.com
Rev.: $1,764,000
Emp.: 12
Structural Steel & Precast Concrete Con-
tractors
N.A.I.C.S.: 238120
Murray Sandford (Pres)
Ernie Ngo (Gen Mgr)
Linda Gutierrez (Dir-Sls & Mktg)
Luis Aguilar (Supvr-Fabrication Dept)
Tripp Sandford (Exec VP)
Anita Eramela (Controller)
Jun Gasgonia (Sr Project Mgr)
Juan Alatorre (Project Mgr)
Jing Soto (Project Mgr)
Deandre Montgomery (Project Mgr)
Heriberto Gutierrez (Production Mgr)
Dylan Odom (Supvr-Graphic Print & CNC)

Tootum, Inc. (1)
105 S 6th St, Newark, OH 43055
Tel.: (740) 345-9691
Web Site: http://www.tectum.com
Reconstituted Wood Product Mfr
N.A.I.C.S.: 321219

Worthington Armstrong Venture (1)
101 Lindenwood Dr Ste 350, Malvern, PA
19355 (50%)
Tel.: (610) 722-1200
Web Site:
https://worthingtonarmstrongventure.com
Sales Range: $25-49.9 Million
Emp.: 40
Steel Ceiling Suspension Grid Mfr
N.A.I.C.S.: 332311
Douglas D. Cadle (Pres)
Doug Wisel (CFO)
Kimberly Sims (VP)
Bill Stoots (VP)
Darren R. Semple (VP)
Kathy E. Herman (VP)

ARNO THERAPEUTICS, INC.
200 Route 31 N Ste 104, Flemington,
NJ 08822
Tel.: (862) 703-7175 DE
Web Site: http://www.arnothera.com
ARNI—(OTCIQ)
Sales Range: $1-9.9 Million
Emp.: 4
Cancer Treatment Biopharmaceuti-
cals Developer
N.A.I.C.S.: 541715

Arie S. Belldegrun (Chm)
David M. Tanen (Sec)
Stefan Proniuk (Chief Dev Officer)
Alexander A. Zukiwski (CEO, Chief
Medical Officer & VP)
David M. Jackson (VP-Diagnostics)

**AROGO CAPITAL ACQUISI-
TION CORP.**
848 Brickell Ave Penthouse 5, Miami,
FL 33131
Tel.: (786) 442-1482 DE
Web Site: https://arogocapital.com
Year Founded: 2021
AOGO—(NASDAQ)
Rev.: $1,102,445
Assets: $106,076,198
Liabilities: $110,555,754
Net Worth: ($4,479,556)
Earnings: ($726,312)
Emp.: 3
Fiscal Year-end: 12/31/22
Investment Services
N.A.I.C.S.: 523999
Suradech Taweesaengsakulthai
(CEO)
Chee Han Wen (Chief Strategy Offi-
cer)
Suthee Chivaphongse (CFO)
Tunku Naquiyuddin ibni Tuanku
Ja'afar (Chm)

ARRAY TECHNOLOGIES, INC.
3901 Midway Pl NE, Albuquerque,
NM 87109
Tel.: (505) 881-7567 DE
Web Site:
https://www.arraytechinc.com
Year Founded: 2018
ARRY—(NASDAQ)
Rev.: $1,637,546,000
Assets: $1,706,052,000
Liabilities: $1,581,771,000
Net Worth: $124,281,000
Earnings: $4,432,000
Emp.: 1,082
Fiscal Year-end: 12/31/22
Holding Company
N.A.I.C.S.: 551112
James Zhu (Chief Acctg Officer)
Kevin G. Hostetler (CEO)
Ron P. Corio (Founder)
Thierry Marin-Martinod (CTO)
Erica Brinker (Chief Comml Officer)
Kevin Hostetler (CEO)
Aaron Gabelnick (Chief Strategy &
Tech Officer)
Jessica Lawrence-Vaca (Sr VP-Policy
& External Affairs)
Neil Manning (Pres & COO)
Terrance L. Collins (Chief HR Officer)
Travis Rose (Chief Revenue Officer)
Tyson Hottinger (Chief Legal Officer)

ARRAYIT CORP.
927 Thompson Pl, Sunnyvale, CA
94085
Tel.: (408) 744-1331 DE
Web Site: https://www.arrayit.com
Year Founded: 1993
ANYC (OTCQD)
Sales Range: $1-9.9 Million
Emp.: 7
Microarray Mfr, Researcher & Devel-
oper
N.A.I.C.S.: 334516
Mark Schena (Pres & Chief Science
Officer)
Todd J. Martinsky (Founder & Exec
VP)
Rene A. Schena (Chm, Chm & CEO)

Subsidiaries:

Arrayit Diagnostics, Inc. (1)
1950 Cinnamon Teal Dr, Redmond, OR
97756

Tel.: (916) 599-3138
Genetic Researcher
N.A.I.C.S.: 541715
Steven Scott (Pres & CEO)

ARRIVENT BIOPHARMA, INC.
18 Campus Blvd Ste 100, Newtown
Square, PA 19073
Tel.: (628) 277-4836 DE
Web Site: https://www.arrivent.com
Year Founded: 2021
AVBP—(NASDAQ)
Rev.: $5,257,000
Assets: $163,098,000
Liabilities: $316,291,000
Net Worth: ($153,193,000)
Earnings: ($69,333,000)
Emp.: 40
Fiscal Year-end: 12/31/23
Biotechnology Research & Develop-
ment Services
N.A.I.C.S.: 541714
Winston W. Kung (CFO & Treas)

ARROW ELECTRONICS, INC.
9201 E Dry Creek Rd, Centennial,
CO 80112
Tel.: (303) 824-4000 NY
Web Site: https://www.arrow.com
Year Founded: 1935
ARW—(NYSE)
Rev.: $33,107,120,000
Assets: $21,726,168,000
Liabilities: $15,848,861,000
Net Worth: $5,877,307,000
Earnings: $903,505,000
Emp.: 22,100
Fiscal Year-end: 12/31/23
Electronic Components & Computer
Products Mfr & Distr
N.A.I.C.S.: 423690
Michael J. Long (Chm, Pres & CEO)
Richard J. Marano (Pres-Global Com-
ponents)
M. Catherine Morris (Chief Strategy
Officer & Sr VP)
Rajesh K. Agrawal (CFO & Sr VP)
Kim Brown Wilmsen (CIO & Sr VP)
Sean J. Kerins (Pres & CEO)
Chris D. Stansbury (CFO & Sr VP)
Shantnu Sharma (Sr VP)
Anthony Bencivenga (VP-IR)
John Hourigan (VP-Pub Affairs &
Corp Mktg)
Kirk Schell (Pres)

Subsidiaries:

A.E. Petsche Belgium BVBA (1)
Visbeekstraat 11 F, 2300, Turnhout, Bel-
gium
Tel.: (32) 14445800
Web Site: http://www.aepetsche.com
Electronic Equipment & Component Distr
N.A.I.C.S.: 423690

A.E. Petsche Canada, Inc. (1)
16643 Hymus, Kirkland, H9H 4R9, QC,
Canada
Tel.: (514) 426-9405
Web Site: http://www.aepetsche.com
Sales Range: $25-49.9 Million
Emp.: 10
Electronic Components & Suppliers
N.A.I.C.S.: 423690
John Drabik (Pres)

A.E. Petsche Company Inc. (1)
1501 Nolan Ryan Expy, Arlington, TX 76011
Tel.: (817) 459-7511
Web Site: http://www.aepetsche.com
Sales Range: $200-249.9 Million
Wire & Cable Mfr
N.A.I.C.S.: 331491

Subsidiary (Non-US):

A.E. Petsche SAS (2)
146 Avenue Des Freres Lumiere, 78190,
Trappes, France
Tel.: (33) 130131570

Sales Range: $25-49.9 Million
Emp.: 1
Wire & Cable Mfr
N.A.I.C.S.: 423610

A.E. Petsche UK Limited (1)
Unit 37 Suttons Business Park Earley,
Reading, RG6 1AZ, Berks, United Kingdom
Tel.: (44) 7961721648
Web Site: http://www.aepetsche.com
Electronic Equipment Whslr
N.A.I.C.S.: 423690

ALTIMATE Group SAS (1)
34 Avenue de l'Europe, 78140, Velizy-
Villacoublay, France
Tel.: (33) 134584740
Web Site: http://www.altimate-group.com
Sales Range: $25-49.9 Million
Emp.: 100
Distr of Enterprise IT Solutions Products &
Services
N.A.I.C.S.: 513210

**ARROWECS Portugal Sociedade
Unipessoal Lda.** (1)
Avenida D Joao II n 45 2 C/D, Edificio Cen-
tral Office Parque das Nacoes, 1990-084,
Lisbon, Portugal
Tel.: (351) 218933100
Web Site: http://www.arrowecs.pt
Optoelectronic Parts Whslr
N.A.I.C.S.: 423690

ATM Electronic Corp. (1)
14F-2 No 402 Shizheng Rd, Xitun Dist, Tai-
chung, 407, Taiwan
Tel.: (886) 422522415
Web Site: http://www.atm-tw.com
Electronic Components Distr
N.A.I.C.S.: 423690

**ATM Electronic Corporation (HK)
Limited** (1)
Room 3611-3622 Changping No 99 Hon-
ghua Road, Futian Free Trade Zone, Shen-
zhen, 518038, China
Tel.: (86) 75583867935
Web Site: http://www.atm-tw.com
Optoelectronic Parts Whslr
N.A.I.C.S.: 423690

**ATM Electronics Technology (Shen-
zhen) Co. Ltd.** (1)
Floor 24 25 Building T1 Upper Hills No
5001 Huang Gang Road, Futian District,
Shenzhen, 518038, China
Tel.: (86) 75588367918
Electronic Components Distr
N.A.I.C.S.: 423690

Altimate Belgium BVBA (1)
Woluwedal 30a, Saint-Stevens-Woluwe,
1932, Belgium
Tel.: (32) 23703911
Web Site: http://www.arrowecs.be
Emp.: 50
Information Technology Solutions Services
N.A.I.C.S.: 541511

Altimate ND Belgium BVBA (1)
Woluwedal 30a, Saint-Stevens-Woluwe,
1932, Belgium
Tel.: (32) 27216137
Emp.: 60
Information Technology Solutions Services
N.A.I.C.S.: 423420

Altimate UK Distribution Limited (1)
Lansdowne Ho, Stockport, SK2 6LR, United
Kingdom
Tel.: (44) 1614740444
Emp.: 15
Software Distr
N.A.I.C.S.: 513210

**Arrow (China) Electronics Trading Co.
Ltd.** (1)
11/F BM Intercontinental Business Center
100 Yu Tong Road, Shanghai, 200070,
China
Tel.: (86) 2122152000
Electronic Components Distr
N.A.I.C.S.: 423690

**Arrow Altech Distribution (Pty)
Ltd.** (1)
53-57 Yaldwyn Road, Hughes Ext Jet Park,
Johannesburg, 1459, South Africa
Tel.: (27) 119239600

Web Site: http://www.arrow.altech.co.za
Sales Range: $50-74.9 Million
Emp.: 150
Electronic Equipment & Component Distr
N.A.I.C.S.: 423690
Stephan Martinussen *(Mng Dir-Acting &
Gen Mgr-Fin & Admin)*
Renato Martins *(Gen Mgr-Sls)*

Arrow Altech Holdings (Pty) Ltd. (1)
53 Yaldwyn Road, Boksburg, 1469, Gau-
teng, South Africa
Tel.: (27) 119239600
Web Site: http://www.altech.co.za
Holding Company
N.A.I.C.S.: 551112
Peter Griffiths *(Mng Dir)*

Arrow Argentina S.A. (1)
La Pampa 1391 6P of 1, Buenos Aires,
C1428DZA, Argentina
Tel.: (54) 1153656950
Home Electronic Component Mfr
N.A.I.C.S.: 334419

Arrow Asia Pac Ltd. (1)
2/F Green 18 Phase 2 Science Park, Pak
Shek Kok, Hong Kong, China (Hong Kong)
Tel.: (852) 24842484
Web Site: http://www.arrowasia.com.hk
Sales Range: $700-749.9 Million
Emp.: 1,374
Electronic Components Distr
N.A.I.C.S.: 423690
Grace Kung *(Sr Mgr-Mktg Comm)*

Subsidiary (Non-US):

Arrow Components (M) Sdn Bhd (2)
No 608 Block A Kelana Business Centre 97
Jalan SS 7/2, Kelana Jaya, 47301, Petaling
Jaya, Selangor, Malaysia
Tel.: (60) 378046313
Electronic Equipment & Component Distr
N.A.I.C.S.: 423690
Andrew S. Bryant *(COO)*

Arrow Electronics (S) Pte Ltd. (2)
750E Chai Chee Road 07-01/02 Tech-
nopark Chai Chee, Singapore, 469005,
Singapore
Tel.: (65) 65598388
Web Site: http://www.arrow.com
Sales Range: $25-49.9 Million
Emp.: 150
Electronic Components Mfr
N.A.I.C.S.: 334419

**Arrow Electronics Asia (S) Pte
Ltd.** (2)
750E Chai Chee Road, 07 01/02 Tech-
nopark, Singapore, 469005, Singapore
Tel.: (65) 65598388
Web Site: http://www.arroeasia.com
Electronic Components Distr
N.A.I.C.S.: 334419

**Arrow Electronics India Private
Ltd.** (2)
Unit No 306 Corporate 1 Plot No 5 Jasola
District Center Jasola, New Delhi, 110 025,
India
Tel.: (91) 1149202800
Sales Range: $50-74.9 Million
Emp.: 100
Electronic Components Distr
N.A.I.C.S.: 334419
Sanjeev Keskar *(Mng Dir)*

Arrow Electronics Korea Ltd. (2)
Dadong 4403-1/2 4F Joongang Circulation
Complex 1258 Kurobon-Dong, Kurogu,
Seoul, 08217, Korea (South)
Tel.: (82) 226118400
Web Site: http://www.arrowasia.com
Sales Range: $50-74.9 Million
Electronic Components Mfr
N.A.I.C.S.: 334220

Subsidiary (Domestic):

Excel Tech, Inc. (3)
7/F Soahm Building 208 Bangbae-Ro,
Seocho-gu, Seoul, 06585, Korea (South)
Tel.: (82) 23357823
Web Site: http://www.excelt.co.kr
Electronic Equipment & Component Distr
N.A.I.C.S.: 423690

Subsidiary (Non-US):

Arrow Electronics Taiwan Ltd. (2)

17F 13F-1 No 150 Jian 1st Road, Zhonghe
Dist, New Taipei City, 235603, Taiwan
Tel.: (886) 27 722 5168
Web Site: http://www.arrow.com
Sales Range: $100-124.9 Million
Emp.: 400
Electronic Components Mfr
N.A.I.C.S.: 334419

Arrow Brasil S.A. (1)
Rua Jose Gomes Falcao 111 Barra Fund,
Sao Paulo, 01139-010, SP, Brazil
Tel.: (55) 1151080880
Web Site: http://www.arrowbrasil.com.br
Electronic Equipment & Component Distr
N.A.I.C.S.: 423690

Arrow Central Europe GmbH (1)
Dieselstr 13, 63303, Dreieich, Germany
Tel.: (49) 61033040
Web Site: http://www.arrow.com
Electronic Computing Solutions Services
N.A.I.C.S.: 541513
Robert Schickhoff *(Mng Dir & VP-Fin-
EMEA)*

Subsidiary (Non-US):

Arrow ECS, SAS (2)
38 rue Victor Hugo, 92400, Courbevoie,
France
Tel.: (33) 149975000
Web Site: http://www.arrow.com
Sales Range: $25-49.9 Million
Data Storage & Channel Development
Products Distr
N.A.I.C.S.: 518210

**Arrow Electronics Poland
Sp.z.o.o.** (2)
ul Sosnowiecka 79, 31-345, Krakow, Poland
Tel.: (48) 126164300
Web Site: http://www.arrow.com
Electronic Equipment & Component Distr
N.A.I.C.S.: 423690

**Arrow Central Europe Holding Munich
GmbH** (1)
Frankfurter Strasse 211, 63263, Neu-
Isenburg, Germany
Tel.: (49) 81412283210
Holding Company
N.A.I.C.S.: 551112

Arrow Components (1)
8A Sheffield Crescent, Burnside,
Christchurch, 8053, New Zealand
Tel.: (64) 33662000
Electronic Components Distr
N.A.I.C.S.: 423690
Sharmalee Panagoda *(Engr-Field Applica-
tions)*

Arrow Components (NZ) (1)
Penrose Business Plz Ste 3 Level 7 45 O
Rorke Rd, Penrose, 1061, New Zealand
Tel.: (64) 92722940
Web Site: http://www.arrowiz.com
Sales Range: $25-49.9 Million
Emp.: 4
Electronic Equipment & Component Distr
N.A.I.C.S.: 423690

Arrow Components Sweden AB (1)
Kronborgsgrand 7, 164 46, Kista, Sweden
Tel.: (46) 855518800
Web Site: https://www.arrow.com
Sales Range: $50-74.9 Million
Emp.: 120
Electronic Equipment & Component Distr
N.A.I.C.S.: 423690

Arrow Denmark, ApS (1)
Marielundvej 29, 2730, Herlev, Denmark
Tel.: (45) 70102211
Web Site: http://www.arrow.com
Emp.: 60
Electronic Equipment & Component Distr
N.A.I.C.S.: 423690

Arrow ECS (Ireland) Limited (1)
19A Rosemount Business Park, Dublin, D11
HT35, Ireland
Tel.: (353) 18610500
Software Development Services
N.A.I.C.S.: 541511
Mark McHale *(VP-UK & Ireland)*

Arrow ECS (NI) Limited (1)
Ground Floor 34A Alfred Street, Belfast,
BT2 8EP, United Kingdom

Tel.: (44) 8455912800
Electronic Components Distr
N.A.I.C.S.: 423690

Arrow ECS AG (1)
Elsenheimerstrasse 1, 80687, Munich, Ger-
many
Tel.: (49) 89930990
Web Site: https://www.arrow.com
Software Development Services
N.A.I.C.S.: 541511
Eric Nowak *(Chm)*

Arrow ECS AG (1)
Ruchstuckstrasse 6, 8306, Bruttisellen,
Switzerland
Tel.: (41) 432228000
Web Site: http://www.arrowecs.ch
Information Technology Security Services
N.A.I.C.S.: 541512
Paul Karrer *(Mng Dir)*
Marco Pierro *(Country Mgr)*
Julia Stoger *(Sls Mgr-Ops)*
Julian Forstner *(Sls Mgr-Ops)*
Sarah Hauser *(Sls Mgr-Ops)*
Sebastian Jamnig *(Sls Mgr-Ops)*
Sabrina Kern *(Sls Mgr-Ops)*
Eva Mai *(Sls Mgr-Ops)*
Martin Peter *(Sls Mgr-Ops)*
Verena Pirerfellner *(Sls Mgr-Ops)*
Diana Reps *(Sls Mgr-Ops)*
Dominic Wukonig *(Sls Mgr-Ops)*
Madlen Zeller *(Sls Mgr-Ops)*
Emir Malkic *(Sls Mgr-Ops)*
Sarah Leonhartsberger *(Sls Mgr-Ops)*
Andrea Egger *(Sls Mgr-Operation)*
Sarah Rezaik *(Mgr-Enterprise Bus Dev)*
Roberto Troisi *(Mgr-Customer Experience)*
Gianluca Urbano *(Mgr-Bus Unit & Security-
Networks)*
Borce Nikolovski *(Mgr-Bus Dev & Security-
Networks)*
Mirko Medojevic *(Mgr-Bus Dev & Security-
Networks)*
Simona Genova *(Head-Mktg)*
Elio Di Maggio *(Head-Inside Sls & Security-
Networks)*
Markus Gysel *(Engr-Enterprise Sys)*
Roger Christen *(Acct Mgr)*

Arrow ECS ANZ Limited (1)
Level 2 318 Lambton Quay, Wellington,
6011, New Zealand
Tel.: (64) 800322255
Web Site: https://www.arrow.com
Computer Peripheral Equipment Distr
N.A.I.C.S.: 423430
Daniela Figueiredo *(Sr Mgr-HR)*
Karolina Mikita *(Mgr-Sls Support)*
Joseph Knock *(Mgr-Ops)*
Nick Payne *(Mgr-IT)*
Andrew Assad *(Gen Mgr)*
Lisa Stockwell *(Dir-Vendor Alliance)*
John Marshall *(Dir-Sls)*
Carineh Grigorian *(Dir-Mktg)*
Andrew Vaughan *(Dir-Fin & Ops)*
Scott Hayman *(Dir-Engrg & Svcs)*

Arrow ECS ANZ Pty Ltd (1)
Unit 6 39 Herbert Street, Saint Leonards,
2065, NSW, Australia
Tel.: (61) 290925000
Web Site: http://ecs-anz.arrow.com
Computer Peripheral Equipment Distr
N.A.I.C.S.: 423430

Arrow ECS Asia PTE. Ltd (1)
750E Chai Chee Road 07-01/02, Viva Busi-
ness Park, Singapore, 469005, Singapore
Tel.: (65) 65598388
Computer Peripheral Equipment Distr
N.A.I.C.S.: 423430

Arrow ECS Australia Pty. Limited (1)
6/39 Herbert St, Saint Leonards, 2065,
NSW, Australia
Tel.: (61) 130 067 3506
Web Site: https://www.arrow.com
Optoelectronic Parts Whslr
N.A.I.C.S.: 423690
Andrew Assad *(Gen Mgr)*
Andrew Vaughan *(Dir-Fin & Ops)*
Lisa Stockwell *(Dir-Vendor Alliance)*
John Marshall *(Dir-Sls)*
Carineh Grigorian *(Dir-Mktg)*
Nick Payne *(Mgr-IT)*
Daniela Figueiredo *(Sr Mgr-HR)*
Joseph Knock *(Ops Mgr)*
Karolina Mikita *(Mgr-Sls Support)*
Scott Hayman *(Dir-Engrg & Svcs)*

Arrow Electronics, Inc.—(Continued)

Arrow ECS B.V. (1)
Waanderweg 22, Emmen, 7812 HZÂ ,
Netherlands
Tel.: (31) 591855855
Web Site: http://www.arrowecs.nl
Information Technology Solutions Services
N.A.I.C.S.: 541511

Arrow ECS B.V. (1)
Elzenkade 1, 3992 AD, Houten, Nether-
lands
Tel.: (31) 88 024 2900
Web Site: https://www.arrow.com
Computer Peripheral & Software Whslr
N.A.I.C.S.: 423430

Arrow ECS Baltic OU (1)
Sopruse pst 145 B-entrance 3rd floor,
13417, Tallinn, Estonia
Tel.: (372) 6618059
Web Site: https://www.arrow.com
Information Technology Solutions Services
N.A.I.C.S.: 541511
Sigrid Raudsep *(Mgr-Nordic Bus Svc Cen-
ter)*
Raido Orumets *(Mgr-Bus Dev)*
Hannele Saar *(Coord-Mktg)*

Arrow ECS Belgium (1)
Woluwedal 30, 1932, Saint-Stevens-
Woluwe, Belgium
Tel.: (32) 23703911
Web Site: http://www.arrowecs.be
Sales Range: $10-24.9 Million
Emp.: 25
Computer Related Services
N.A.I.C.S.: 541519

**Arrow ECS Brasil Distribuidora
Ltda.** (1)
Av Ribeirao dos Cristais G Preto 800
Modulo E sala 4 Jordanesia, 07775-240,
Cajamar, Brazil
Tel.: (55) 1135493155
Web Site: http://www.arrowecs.com.br
Optoelectronic Parts Distr
N.A.I.C.S.: 423690

Arrow ECS FZCO (1)
Dubai Silicon Oasis E wing Office 301 306,
PO Box 341027, Dubai, United Arab Emir-
ates
Tel.: (971) 45015814
Web Site: http://www.arrowecs.ae
Computer Peripheral Equipment Distr
N.A.I.C.S.: 423430

Arrow ECS GmbH (1)
Elsenheimerstrasse 1, 80687, Munich, Ger-
many
Tel.: (49) 8 993 0990
Web Site: https://www.arrow.com
Computer Equipment & Software Distr
N.A.I.C.S.: 423430

Arrow ECS Internet Security AG (1)
Freistadterstrasse 236, 4040, Linz, Austria
Tel.: (43) 732757168
Web Site: http://www.arrow.com
Sales Range: $10-24.9 Million
Data Storage & Channel Development
Products Distr
N.A.I.C.S.: 518210

**Arrow ECS Internet Security AG -
Bruttisellen** (1)
Richtistrasse 11, 8304, Wallisellen, Switzer-
land
Tel.: (41) 432228000
Web Site: http://www.arrow.com.ch
Information Technology Security Services
N.A.I.C.S.: 541519

**Arrow ECS Internet Security,
S.L.** (1)
Avenida de Europa 21, Parque Empresarial
La Moraleja Alcobendas, 28108, Madrid,
Spain
Tel.: (34) 917612121
Office Machinery & Equipment Whslr
N.A.I.C.S.: 423420

Arrow ECS Kft. (1)
Infopark Setany 3 B epulet 5 emelet, 1117,
Budapest, Hungary
Tel.: (36) 1 371 2370
Web Site: https://www.arrow.com
Software Distr

N.A.I.C.S.: 423430

Arrow ECS Ltd. (1)
2 haNagar Street, Kfar Saba, 4442532,
Israel
Tel.: (972) 97645700
Electronic Components Distr
N.A.I.C.S.: 423690

Arrow ECS Ltd. (1)
2 haNagar Street, Kfar Saba, 4442532,
Israel
Tel.: (972) 97645700
Web Site: http://www.arrowecs.co.il
Emp.: 30
Computer Hardware & Software Distr
N.A.I.C.S.: 423430

**Arrow ECS Network & Security
SAS** (1)
38-40 rue Victor Hugo, Furuset, 92400,
Courbevoie, France
Tel.: (33) 149974911
Web Site: http://www.ip.arrowecs.fr
Sales Range: $25-49.9 Million
Emp.: 4
Network & Security Management Services
N.A.I.C.S.: 541618

Arrow ECS Nordic A/S (1)
Jens Juuls Vej 42, 8260, Viby, Denmark
Tel.: (45) 7 025 4500
Web Site: https://www.arrow.com
Data Storage & Channel Development
Products Distr
N.A.I.C.S.: 518210

Subsidiary (Domestic):

Arrow ECS Denmark A/S (2)
Jens Juuls Vej 42, Viby, 8260, Denmark
Tel.: (45) 70254500
Web Site: http://www.ecs-dk.arrow.com
Information Technology Solutions Services
N.A.I.C.S.: 541511

Subsidiary (Non-US):

Arrow ECS Finland OY (2)
Lars Sonckin Kaari 16, Stella Business Park
/ Terra-talo, 02600, Espoo, Finland
Tel.: (358) 207656600
Web Site: http://www.arrowecs.fi
Data Storage & Channel Development
Products Distr
N.A.I.C.S.: 518210

Arrow ECS Norway AS (2)
Innspurten 1A, 0663, Oslo, Norway
Tel.: (47) 22028100
Web Site: https://www.arrow.com
Data Storage & Channel Development
Products Distr
N.A.I.C.S.: 518210
Thor Egil Stangenes *(Dir-Bus Unit)*
Cathrine Rosen Olsen *(Mgr-Mktg)*

Arrow ECS Sweden AB (2)
Kronborgsgrand 7, 164 46, Kista, Sweden
Tel.: (46) 855518800
Web Site: https://www.arrow.com
Sales Range: $25-49.9 Million
Data Storage & Channel Development
Products Distr
N.A.I.C.S.: 518210
Jes Kongsmark *(Mng Dir)*

Arrow ECS Pty Ltd. (1)
Ground Floor 30 Alfred St Sth, Milsons
Point, 2061, NSW, Australia
Tel.: (61) 294327849
Web Site: http://www.arrowecs.com.au
Computer Peripheral Equipment Distr
N.A.I.C.S.: 423430

Arrow ECS SA NV (1)
Woluwedal 30, 1932, Saint-Stevens-
Woluwe, Belgium
Tel.: (32) 27167330
Web Site: http://www.arrowecs.be
Sales Range: $10-24.9 Million
IT Products Distr
N.A.I.C.S.: 518210
Bart Van Rheenen *(Mng Dir)*

Arrow ECS SARL (1)
Technopark Bureau 502, 13203, Casa-
blanca, Morocco
Tel.: (212) 52 252 9260
Web Site: https://www.arrow.com
Information Technology Solutions Services

N.A.I.C.S.: 541511

Arrow ECS SPA (1)
Via Lancia 6/A, 39100, Bolzano, Italy
Tel.: (39) 0471099100
Web Site: http://www.arrowecs.it
Computer Peripheral Equipment Distr
N.A.I.C.S.: 423430
Michele Puccio *(Dir-Sls)*
Alessandro Ricci *(Product Mgr)*

Arrow ECS Services Sp.z.o.o. (1)
Ul Jasnogorska 23, Krakow, 31-358, Poland
Tel.: (48) 126228800
Web Site: http://www.arrowecsservices.pl
Data Storage & Channel Development
Products Distr
N.A.I.C.S.: 518210

Arrow ECS Sp.z.o.o. (1)
ul Sosnowiecka 79, 31-345, Krakow, Poland
Tel.: (48) 126164300
Web Site: https://www.arrow.com
Data Storage & Channel Development
Products Distr
N.A.I.C.S.: 518210

Arrow ECS a.s. (1)
Tel.: (420) 596488811
Web Site: https://www.arrow.com
Information Technology Solutions Services
N.A.I.C.S.: 541511

Arrow ECS d.o.o. (1)
Tehnoloski park 24, 1000, Ljubljana, Slove-
nia
Tel.: (386) 1620 45 41
Web Site: http://www.arrow.si
Sales Range: $10-24.9 Million
Emp.: 6
Data Storage & Channel Development
Products Distr
N.A.I.C.S.: 518210

Arrow ECS s.r.o. (1)
Roznicka 24, 821 04, Bratislava, Slovakia
Tel.: (421) 903224888
Electronic Components Distr
N.A.I.C.S.: 423690

Arrow Electronice S.R.L. (1)
Calea Dorobantilor Nr 14-16, 400439, Cluj-
Napoca, Romania
Tel.: (40) 264417251
Web Site: http://www.arrow.com
Emp.: 10
Electronic Equipment & Component Distr
N.A.I.C.S.: 423690

Arrow Electronics (1)
2900 Westchester Ave Ste 401, Purchase,
NY 10577-2552
Tel.: (914) 701-7400
Web Site: http://www.arrow.com
Sales Range: $25-49.9 Million
Emp.: 17
Overseas Component Sales
N.A.I.C.S.: 423690

**Arrow Electronics (Shanghai) Co.
Ltd.** (1)
Room 602 Flat B Far East International
Plaza No 317 Xianxia Road, Shanghai,
200051, China
Tel.: (86) 2162351788
Electronic Components Distr
N.A.I.C.S.: 423690

**Arrow Electronics (Shenzhen) Co.
Ltd.** (1)
Room 2905 Flat A Jiangsu Tower Yitian
Road, Futian District, Shenzhen, 518026,
China
Tel.: (86) 75582943736
Electronic Components Distr
N.A.I.C.S.: 423690

Arrow Electronics (Sweden) KB (1)
Kronborgsgrand 7, Box 67, 164 94, Kista,
Sweden
Tel.: (46) 856265500
Web Site: http://www.arroweuro.com
Emp.: 100
Electronic Equipment & Component Distr
N.A.I.C.S.: 423690
Eric Hansen *(VP)*

**Arrow Electronics (Thailand)
Limited** (1)
Unit 803 8/F Le Concorde Tower 202
Ratchadapisek Road Kwaeng, Huay-Kwang,

Khet Huay-kwang, Bangkok, 10310, Thai-
land
Tel.: (66) 26942332
Electronic Components Distr
N.A.I.C.S.: 423690

**Arrow Electronics (Thailand)
Limited** (1)
Unit 803 8/F Le Concorde Tower 202
Ratchadapisek Road, Kwaenghuay-Kwang
Khet Huay-kwang, Bangkok, 10310, Thai-
land
Tel.: (66) 26942332
Web Site: http://www.arrowasia.com
Emp.: 30
Electronic Components Distr
N.A.I.C.S.: 423690

Arrow Electronics (UK) Ltd. (1)
Kao 1 Kao Park Hockham Way, Harlow,
CM17 9NA, Essex, United Kingdom
Tel.: (44) 1279441144
Electronic Equipment & Component Distr
N.A.I.C.S.: 423690

**Arrow Electronics ANZ Holdings Pty
Ltd.** (1)
Level 8 492 St Kilda Road, Melbourne,
3004, VIC, Australia
Tel.: (61) 392904800
Web Site: https://www.arrow.com
Holding Company
N.A.I.C.S.: 551112

**Arrow Electronics Asia (S) Pte
Ltd.** (1)
750E Chai Chee Road 07-01/02, Viva Busi-
ness Park, Singapore, 469005, Singapore
Tel.: (65) 65598388
Electronic Components Distr
N.A.I.C.S.: 423690

**Arrow Electronics Australia Pty
Ltd.** (1)
12 Eton Road, Keswick, 5035, SA, Australia
Tel.: (61) 881932400
Electronic Components Distr
N.A.I.C.S.: 423690

**Arrow Electronics Australia Pty
Ltd.** (1)
14 Nicole Close, Bayswater, 3153, VIC,
Australia
Tel.: (61) 397374900
Electrical Contractor Services
N.A.I.C.S.: 238210

Arrow Electronics Canada Ltd. (1)
171 Superior Blvd, Mississauga, L5T 2L1,
ON, Canada
Tel.: (905) 670-7769
Web Site: http://www.arrowelectronics.com
Sales Range: $50-74.9 Million
Electronic Parts Whslr
N.A.I.C.S.: 423690

Subsidiary (Domestic):

Richardson RFPD Canada, Inc. (2)
171 Superior Blvd Unit 1, Mississauga, L5T
2L6, ON, Canada
Tel.: (905) 565-4450
Web Site: http://www.richardsonrfpd.com
Sales Range: $25-49.9 Million
Emp.: 6
Electronic Equipment & Component Distr
N.A.I.C.S.: 423690

Arrow Electronics China Ltd. (1)
R1229 F12 No 2 Building Central Fifth
Street No 360 Gongye Road, Taijiang, Fu-
zhou, 350001, China
Tel.: (86) 59187845282
Electronic Components Distr
N.A.I.C.S.: 423690

Arrow Electronics Components (1)
9500 SW Nimbus Ave Bldg E, Beaverton,
OR 97008-7163 **(100%)**
Tel.: (503) 614-3300
Web Site: http://www.arrow.com
Sales Range: $10-24.9 Million
Emp.: 45
Electric Component Whslr
N.A.I.C.S.: 423690

Arrow Electronics Components (1)
2440 S 1070 W Ste A, Salt Lake City, UT
84116 **(100%)**
Tel.: (801) 973-8555

Web Site: http://www.arrow.com
Sales Range: $25-49.9 Million
Emp.: 22
Electronic Components Distr
N.A.I.C.S.: 423690

Arrow Electronics Components (1)
3380 146th Pl SE, Bellevue, WA 98007-6462
Tel.: (425) 643-9992
Web Site: http://www.arrow.com
Sales Range: $25-49.9 Million
Emp.: 25
Electronic Components Distr
N.A.I.C.S.: 423690

Arrow Electronics Components (1)
960 W 124th Ave Ste 100, Westminster, CO 80234 **(100%)**
Tel.: (303) 254-2900
Web Site: http://www.arrow.com
Sales Range: $10-24.9 Million
Emp.: 18
Electric Component Whslr
N.A.I.C.S.: 423690

Arrow Electronics Components (1)
6340 International Pkwy Ste 100, Plano, TX 75093
Tel.: (972) 447-8000
Web Site: http://www.arrow.com
Sales Range: $25-49.9 Million
Emp.: 63
Electronic Components Distr
N.A.I.C.S.: 423690

Arrow Electronics Components (1)
2998 Douglas Blvd Ste 320, Roseville, CA 95661 **(100%)**
Tel.: (916) 797-3200
Web Site: http://www.arrow.com
Sales Range: $25-49.9 Million
Emp.: 20
Electric Component Whslr
N.A.I.C.S.: 423690

Arrow Electronics Components (1)
20935 Warner Center Ln, Woodland Hills, CA 91367-6511
Tel.: (818) 932-1020
Web Site: http://www.arrow.com
Sales Range: $25-49.9 Million
Emp.: 75
Electric Component Whslr
N.A.I.C.S.: 423690

Arrow Electronics Components (1)
2901 Wilcrest Ste 120, Houston, TX 77042
Tel.: (713) 784-9953
Web Site: http://www.arrow.com
Sales Range: $25-49.9 Million
Emp.: 15
Electronic Components Distr
N.A.I.C.S.: 423690

Arrow Electronics Components (1)
3000 Bowers Ave, Santa Clara, CA 95051 **(100%)**
Tel.: (408) 727-2500
Web Site: http://www.arrow.com
Sales Range: $50-74.9 Million
Emp.: 123
Electric Component Whslr
N.A.I.C.S.: 423690

Arrow Electronics Components (1)
2950 Expressway Dr S, Islandia, NY 11749 **(100%)**
Tel.: (631) 851-2300
Web Site: http://www.arrow.com
Sales Range: $25-49.9 Million
Emp.: 50
Distr of Electronics
N.A.I.C.S.: 423690

Arrow Electronics Components (1)
27121 Towne Ctr Dr Ste 100, Foothill Ranch, CA 92610
Tel.: (949) 380-4700
Web Site: http://www.arrow.com
Sales Range: $75-99.9 Million
Emp.: 200
Specializes in the Distribution of Interconnect, Electromechanical & Passive Electronic Components & Related Value-Added Services
N.A.I.C.S.: 423690
Chuck Mann *(Pres)*

Arrow Electronics Components (1)

7459 S Lima St Bldg 1, Englewood, CO 80112-5816 **(100%)**
Tel.: (303) 645-8999
Web Site: http://www.arrow.com
Sales Range: $300-349.9 Million
Emp.: 900
Distr of Electromechanical & Connector Components & Services
N.A.I.C.S.: 423690

Arrow Electronics Components (1)
35 Upton Dr, Wilmington, MA 01887-1018
Tel.: (978) 658-7920
Web Site: http://www.arrow.com
Sales Range: $100-124.9 Million
Emp.: 250
Distr of Computers & Peripherals
N.A.I.C.S.: 423690

Arrow Electronics Components (1)
44720 Helm St, Plymouth, MI 48170-6019 **(100%)**
Tel.: (734) 335-9260
Web Site: http://www.arrow.com
Sales Range: $10-24.9 Million
Emp.: 13
Distribution of Semiconductor & OEM Computer Products
N.A.I.C.S.: 423690

Arrow Electronics Components (1)
2915 Premiere Pkwy Ste 150, Duluth, GA 30097
Tel.: (770) 495-5200
Web Site: http://www.arrow.com
Sales Range: $150-199.9 Million
Emp.: 30
Semiconductor & OEM Computer Products Distr
N.A.I.C.S.: 423690

Arrow Electronics Components (1)
7067 Columbia Gateway Dr, Columbia, MD 21046 **(100%)**
Tel.: (410) 312-4600
Web Site: http://www.arrow.com
Sales Range: $25-49.9 Million
Emp.: 25
Distribution of Semiconductor & OEM Computer Products
N.A.I.C.S.: 423430

Arrow Electronics Components (1)
9975 Parkland Blvd, Solon, OH 44139-2761
Tel.: (440) 248-9996
Web Site: http://www.arrow.com
Sales Range: $200-249.9 Million
Emp.: 200
Distribution of Semiconductor & OEM Computer Products
N.A.I.C.S.: 423690

Arrow Electronics Components (1)
7677 Paragon Rd Ste A, Dayton, OH 45459 **(100%)**
Tel.: (937) 428-7300
Web Site: http://www.arrow.com
Sales Range: $25-49.9 Million
Emp.: 22
Distribution of Semiconductor & OEM Computer Products
N.A.I.C.S.: 423690

Arrow Electronics Components (1)
800 Fairway Dr Ste 150, Deerfield Beach, FL 33441
Tel.: (954) 429-8200
Web Site: http://www.arrow.com
Sales Range: $25-49.9 Million
Emp.: 45
Distribution of Semiconductor & OEM Computer Products
N.A.I.C.S.: 423690

Arrow Electronics Components (1)
3077 E 98th St, Indianapolis, IN 46280
Tel.: (317) 810-6250
Web Site: http://www.arrow.com
Sales Range: $25-49.9 Million
Emp.: 30
Distribution of Semiconductor & OEM Computer Products
N.A.I.C.S.: 423690

Arrow Electronics Components (1)
100 Colonial Center Pkwy, Lake Mary, FL 32746 **(100%)**
Tel.: (321) 233-8800
Web Site: http://www.arrow.com
Sales Range: $10-24.9 Million
Emp.: 50

Distr of Electronic Components & OEM Computer Products
N.A.I.C.S.: 423690

Arrow Electronics Components (1)
1160 Spring Lake Dr, Itasca, IL 60143-2062
Tel.: (630) 250-0500
Web Site: http://www.arrow.com
Sales Range: $50-74.9 Million
Emp.: 75
Distr of Semiconductor & OEM Computer Products
N.A.I.C.S.: 423690

Arrow Electronics Components (1)
2 Barnes Industrial Rd S, Wallingford, CT 06492
Tel.: (203) 265-7741
Web Site: http://www.arrow.com
Sales Range: $25-49.9 Million
Emp.: 42
Distr of Semiconductor & OEM Computer Products
N.A.I.C.S.: 423690

Arrow Electronics Components (1)
10900 Nesbitt Ave S, Bloomington, MN 55438
Tel.: (952) 828-5350
Web Site: http://www.arrow.com
Sales Range: $150-199.9 Million
Emp.: 250
Distribution of Semiconductor & OEM Computer Products
N.A.I.C.S.: 423690

Arrow Electronics Components (1)
200 Perimeter Park Dr Ste D, Morrisville, NC 27560 **(100%)**
Tel.: (919) 388-6000
Web Site: http://www.arrow.com
Sales Range: $25-49.9 Million
Emp.: 30
Distribution of Semiconductor & OEM Computer Products
N.A.I.C.S.: 423690

Arrow Electronics Components (1)
1955 E Sky Harbor Cir N, Phoenix, AZ 85034
Tel.: (602) 495-9953
Web Site: http://www.arrowelectronics.com
Sales Range: $50-74.9 Million
Emp.: 178
Distr of Semiconductor & OEM Computer Products
N.A.I.C.S.: 423690

Arrow Electronics Components (1)
2165 Brighton-Henrietta Townline Rd, Rochester, NY 14623 **(100%)**
Tel.: (585) 427-0300
Web Site: http://www.arrow.com
Sales Range: $10-24.9 Million
Emp.: 40
Distribution of Semiconductor & OEM Computer Products
N.A.I.C.S.: 423690

Arrow Electronics Components (1)
514 Earth City Expy, Saint Louis, MO 63045
Tel.: (314) 567-6888
Web Site: http://www.arrow.com
Sales Range: $25-49.9 Million
Emp.: 25
Distribution of Semiconductor & OEM Computer Products
N.A.I.C.S.: 423690

Arrow Electronics Components (1)
7633 E 63rd Pl Ste 300, Tulsa, OK 74133
Tel.: (918) 986-1581
Web Site: http://www.arrow.com
Semiconductor & OEM Computer Products Distr
N.A.I.C.S.: 423690

Arrow Electronics Components (1)
400 N Executive Dr, Brookfield, WI 53005
Tel.: (262) 879-7200
Web Site: http://www.arrow.com
Sales Range: $10-24.9 Million
Emp.: 50
Distribution of Semiconductor & OEM Computer Products
N.A.I.C.S.: 449210

Arrow Electronics Czech Republic **s.r.o.** (1)

Hvezdova 1716/2b, 140 78, Prague, 4, Czech Republic
Tel.: (420) 222755420
Web Site: http://www.arrow.com
Sales Range: $25-49.9 Million
Emp.: 20
Electronic Equipment & Component Distr
N.A.I.C.S.: 423690

Arrow Electronics D.O.O. (1)
Ukmarjeva Ulica 2, Ljubljana, 1000, Slovenia
Tel.: (386) 12835604
Electronic Components Distr
N.A.I.C.S.: 423690

Arrow Electronics EMEASA S.r.l. (1)
Via Pietro Mascagni 14, Milan, 20122, Italy
Tel.: (39) 0276014181
Electronic Components Distr
N.A.I.C.S.: 423690

Arrow Electronics Estonia OU (1)
Sopruse Pst 145 Section A floor 5, Tallinn, EE-13417, Estonia
Tel.: (372) 6 774 250
Web Site: http://www.arroweurope.com
Sales Range: $25-49.9 Million
Emp.: 15
Electronic Equipment & Component Distr
N.A.I.C.S.: 423690

Arrow Electronics GK (1)
Tomitacho Park Building 5-6-10 Nishitenmay, Kita-ku, Osaka, 530-0047, Japan
Tel.: (81) 663145557
Electronic Components Distr
N.A.I.C.S.: 423690

Arrow Electronics Hellas S.A. (1)
Vouliagmenis Avenue 99, 11636, Athens, Greece
Tel.: (30) 2109020165
Home Electronic Component Mfr
N.A.I.C.S.: 334419

Arrow Electronics Holdings Pty Ltd. (1)
14 Nicole Cl, Bayswater North, Melbourne, 3153, VIC, Australia
Tel.: (61) 397374900
Web Site: http://www.arrowasia.com
Emp.: 50
Computer Related Products Distr
N.A.I.C.S.: 449210
Stewart Booth *(Gen Mgr)*

Arrow Electronics India Ltd. (1)
4th Floor House' 11/A-B Chandra Colony B/H Cargo Motors Off C G Road, Ahmedabad, 380 009, Gujarat, India
Tel.: (91) 7926563705
Electronic Components Distr
N.A.I.C.S.: 423690

Arrow Electronics International, Inc. (1)
100 Baylis Rd, Melville, NY 11747-3102
Tel.: (631) 847-2000
Electronic Equipment & Component Distr
N.A.I.C.S.: 423690

Arrow Electronics Italia S.r.l (1)
Viale dell Innovazione 3, 20126, Milan, Italy
Tel.: (39) 02661251
Web Site: http://www.arrow.com
Electronic Components Distr
N.A.I.C.S.: 423690

Arrow Electronics Japan K.K. (1)
Atago Green Hills MORI Tower 35F 2-5-1, Atago Minato-ku, Tokyo, 105-6235, Japan
Tel.: (81) 354251531
Web Site: https://www.arrowjapan.com
Home Electronic Component Mfr
N.A.I.C.S.: 334419

Arrow Electronics Mexico, S. de R.L. de C.V. (1)
Av Aviacion No 3800, Zapopan, Jalisco, Mexico **(100%)**
Tel.: (52) 3337773100
Electronic Equipment & Component Distr
N.A.I.C.S.: 423690

Arrow Electronics Norwegian Holdings AS (1)
Amsosen, Nedre Vats, 5578, Norway
Tel.: (47) 52763000
Holding Company
N.A.I.C.S.: 551112

Arrow Electronics, Inc.—(Continued)

Arrow Electronics Slovakia s.r.o **(1)**
Roznavska 24, 101 00, Bratislava, Slovakia
Tel.: (421) 232604300
Web Site: http://www.arrow.com
Sales Range: $25-49.9 Million
Emp.: 8
Electronic Equipment & Component Distr
N.A.I.C.S.: 423690

Arrow Electronics Ukraine, LLC **(1)**
Garmatna str 21/30, 03067, Kiev, Ukraine
Tel.: (380) 444564726
Electronic Components Distr
N.A.I.C.S.: 423690

Arrow Electronics Ukraine, LLC **(1)**
Garmatna str 21/30, Kiev, 03067, Ukraine
Tel.: (380) 444564726
Electronic Components Distr
N.A.I.C.S.: 423690

Arrow Electronics, Inc. **(1)**
90 E Halsey Rd, Parsippany, NJ 07054
Tel.: (973) 560-3820
Web Site: http://www.arrow.com
Semiconductor & OEM Computer Products
Distr
N.A.I.C.S.: 423690

Arrow Electronics, Ltd. **(1)**
Unit 3A Stephenson Court, Priory Business
Park, Bedford, MW44 3WJ, United Kingdom
Tel.: (44) 1234224050
Emp.: 20
Computer Peripheral Equipment Distr
N.A.I.C.S.: 423430
Will Orr (Mgr-Sls)

Arrow Elektronik Ticaret, A.S. **(1)**
Elbistan Sokak Pekiz Plaza No 5 Kat 6, Ka-
vacik Beykoz, 34810, Istanbul, Turkiye
Tel.: (90) 2165381200
Electronic Equipment & Component Distr
N.A.I.C.S.: 423690

**Arrow Enterprise Computing Solu-
tions Ltd.** **(1)**
Nidderdale House Beckwith Knowle Otley
Road, Harrogate, HG3 1SA, United King-
dom
Tel.: (44) 1423519000
Web Site: http://www.arrow.com
Sales Range: $25-49.9 Million
Data Storage & Channel Development
Products Distr
N.A.I.C.S.: 518210
Mark McHale (VP-Sls-EMEA)
Dan Waters (Country Mgr)

Branch (Domestic):

**Arrow Enterprise Computing Solu-
tions Ltd. - Nottingham Office** **(2)**
Woodside House Osier Drive Sherwood
Park, Nottingham, NG15 0DS, United King-
dom
Tel.: (44) 1623 500200
Web Site: http://www.arrowecs.co.uk
Sales Range: $10-24.9 Million
Emp.: 6
Information Technology Distr
N.A.I.C.S.: 541511

**Arrow Enterprise Computing Solu-
tions Ltd.** **(1)**
Carpenter 2, Kfar Saba, Israel
Tel.: (972) 97645700
Electronic Components Distr
N.A.I.C.S.: 423690

**Arrow Enterprise Computing Solu-
tions, Inc.** **(1)**
9201 E Dry Creek Rd, Centennial, CO
80112
Tel.: (303) 824-4000
Web Site: http://www.arrow.com
Sales Range: $650-699.9 Million
Supplier of Enterprise & Midrange Computing Products, Services & Solutions for Resellers, System Integrators & Software Vendors
N.A.I.C.S.: 423430
Kristin D. Russell (Pres-Global)

Subsidiary (Non-US):

Arrow ECS Canada Ltd. **(2)**
171 Superior Blvd, Mississauga, L5T 2L1,

ON, Canada
Tel.: (905) 565-4405
Web Site: http://www.arrow.com
Electronic Equipment & Component Distr
N.A.I.C.S.: 423690

Unit (Domestic):

**Arrow Enterprise Computing Solu-
tions S3** **(2)**
10900 Nesbitt Ave S, Bloomington, MN
55437
Tel.: (952) 828-5350
Web Site: http://www.arrowssi.com
Sales Range: $250-299.9 Million
Emp.: 150
Business Communications Solutions & Ser-
vices
N.A.I.C.S.: 517810

Branch (Domestic):

**Arrow Enterprise Computing Solu-
tions S3** **(3)**
10900 Nesbitt Ave S, Bloomington, MN
55437-3124
Tel.: (952) 828-3500
Web Site: http://www.crosstelecom.com
Sales Range: $100-124.9 Million
Emp.: 250
Business Communications Solutions & Ser-
vices
N.A.I.C.S.: 517810
Mike Bevilacqua (Pres)

**Arrow Enterprise Computing Solu-
tions, S.A.** **(1)**
Avenida de Europa 21 1 Izq Parque Empre-
sarial La Moraleja, 28108, Alcobendas,
Spain
Tel.: (34) 913043040
Web Site: http://www.arrowecs.es
Software Development Services
N.A.I.C.S.: 541511

Arrow Finland OY **(1)**
Stella Business Park / Terra-talo Lars Son-
ckin Kaari 16, 02600, Espoo, Finland
Tel.: (358) 207656600
Web Site: http://www.arrow.com
Sales Range: $25-49.9 Million
Emp.: 60
Electronic Equipment & Component Distr
N.A.I.C.S.: 423690

Arrow Iberia Electronica, S.L.U. **(1)**
La Avenida de Europa 21 1 Izq, Parque
Empresarial La Moraleja, 28108, Madrid,
Spain
Tel.: (34) 913043040
Electronic Components Distr
N.A.I.C.S.: 423690
Manuel Michelena (Acct Mgr)

Arrow Nordic Components AB **(1)**
Kronborgsgraend 19, Kista, 164 94, Swe-
den
Tel.: (46) 856265700
Web Site: http://www.planet-arrow.com
Sales Range: $50-74.9 Million
Emp.: 100
Electronic Equipment & Component Distr
N.A.I.C.S.: 423690
Erik Hansen (CEO)

Arrow Norway A/S **(1)**
Reidar Berges gt 7, 4013, Stavanger, Nor-
way
Tel.: (47) 52763000
Electronic Equipment & Component Distr
N.A.I.C.S.: 423690

Arrow S-Tech Norway AS **(1)**
Arrow Value Recovery Fokserodveien 31,
3241, Sandefjord, Norway
Tel.: (47) 33491600
Home Electronic Component Mfr
N.A.I.C.S.: 334419

Arrow UEC Japan, KK **(1)**
1-12-22 Tsukiji Chuo, Tokyo, 104-0045,
Japan
Tel.: (81) 335471861
Web Site: http://www.arrowuec.co.jp
Electronic Components Distr
N.A.I.C.S.: 423690

**Arrow Value Recovery Belgium
BVBA** **(1)**
Generaal De Witte Laan 7A, 2800,

Mechelen, Belgium
Tel.: (32) 15287930
Web Site:
http://www.arrowvaluerecovery.com
Emp.: 13
Computer Peripheral Equipment Mfr
N.A.I.C.S.: 334118

**Arrow Value Recovery Czech Repub-
lic sro** **(1)**
Na Rovince 873 CT Park Building O1,
Hrabova, Ostrava, 720 00, Czech Republic
Tel.: (420) 552302505
Computer Peripheral Equipment Mfr
N.A.I.C.S.: 334118

**Arrow Value Recovery Denmark
ApS** **(1)**
Lysholt Alle 10, 7100, Vejle, Denmark
Tel.: (45) 69663320
Electronic Components Distr
N.A.I.C.S.: 423690

Arrow Value Recovery EMEA BV **(1)**
Pascalweg 13, 4104 BE, Culemborg, Neth-
erlands
Tel.: (31) 345512380
Computer Peripheral Equipment Mfr
N.A.I.C.S.: 334118
Sander Onstenk (Acct Mgr)

**Arrow Value Recovery France
SAS** **(1)**
103-105 Rue Charles Michels, 93200, Saint
Denis, France
Tel.: (33) 185087109
Computer Peripheral Equipment Mfr
N.A.I.C.S.: 334118

**Arrow Value Recovery Germany
GmbH** **(1)**
Am Borsigturm 100, 13507, Berlin, Ger-
many
Tel.: (49) 304360270
Computer Peripheral Equipment Mfr
N.A.I.C.S.: 334118

**Arrow Value Recovery Netherlands
BV** **(1)**
Pascalweg 13, 4104 BE, Culemborg, Neth-
erlands
Tel.: (31) 345512380
Computer Peripheral Equipment Mfr
N.A.I.C.S.: 334118

**Arrow Value Recovery Norway
AS** **(1)**
Fokserodveien 31, 3241, Sandefjord, Nor-
way
Tel.: (47) 33491600
Web Site: http://www.arrowdirect.no
Computer Peripheral Whslr
N.A.I.C.O.: 420400

Arrow Value Recovery UK LTD **(1)**
Hirwaun Industrial Estate, Aberdare, CF44
9UP, Mid Glamorgan, United Kingdom
Tel.: (44) 1685814627
Computer Peripheral Equipment Mfr
N.A.I.C.S.: 334118

Arrow-Intechra LLC **(1)**
713 S Pear Orchard Rd, Ridgeland, MS
39157 **(100%)**
Tel.: (601) 981-5448
Web Site: http://www.intechra.com
Sales Range: $50-74.9 Million
Emp.: 300
Holding Company; Information Technology
Asset Disposition & Waste Management
Services
N.A.I.C.S.: 551112

Arrow/Rapac, Ltd. **(1)**
Ram House 3rd Entrance 5th Floor 36 Ha-
shacham Street, PO Box 7240, Ramat Siv,
Petah Tiqwa, 49250, Israel
Tel.: (972) 39203456
Web Site: http://www.arrow-israel.co.il
Electronic Equipment & Component Distr
N.A.I.C.S.: 423690

Artlink Technology Co. Ltd. **(1)**
7F-4 No 171 Sung Te Rd, Taipei, 11085,
Taiwan
Tel.: (886) 223462888
Emp.: 58
Electronic Equipment Whslr
N.A.I.C.S.: 423690

Aspencore Media GmbH **(1)**
Rauwagnerstrasse 5, 85560, Ebersberg,
Germany
Tel.: (49) 8092247740
Web Site: http://www.aspencore-media.eu
Advertising Services
N.A.I.C.S.: 541810

Aspencore, LLC **(1)**
245 Main St 2 Fl, Cambridge, MA 02142
Tel.: (617) 798-6340
Web Site: https://aspencore.com
Emp.: 650
Electronic Components Distr
N.A.I.C.S.: 423690

B.V. Arrow Electronics DLC **(1)**
Maarten de Vriesstraat 2, Sevenum, 5975
RW, Venlo, Netherlands
Tel.: (31) 205826200
Web Site: http://www.arrowdlc.com
Sales Range: $150-199.9 Million
Electronic Equipment & Component Distr
N.A.I.C.S.: 423690

CNT Brasil Servicos Ltda. **(1)**
Avenida Paulista 925, Sao Paulo, Bela
Vista, 01311-100, Brazil
Tel.: (55) 1135493151
Web Site: http://www.cntbrasil.com.br
Computer Peripheral Equipment Distr
N.A.I.C.S.: 423430

**COMPUTERLINKS (Aust) Pty
Ltd.** **(1)**
L 4 53 Walker St, North Sydney, 2060,
NSW, Australia
Tel.: (61) 285242100
Computer Peripheral & Software Distr
N.A.I.C.S.: 423430

COMPUTERLINKS Denmark A/S **(1)**
Jens Juuls Vej 42 Viby J, 8260, Arhus, Den-
mark
Tel.: (45) 70231600
Computer Peripheral & Software Whslr
N.A.I.C.S.: 423430

COMPUTERLINKS FZCO **(1)**
Block E, Silicon Oasis HQ, office 301,
Dubai, United Arab Emirates
Tel.: (971) 45015814
Computer Peripheral & Software Whslr
N.A.I.C.S.: 423430

COMPUTERLINKS Kft. **(1)**
Koztelek street 6th, 1092, Budapest, Hun-
gary
Tel.: (36) 612993080
Web Site: https://computerlinks-
kft.cegteszt.eu
Computer Peripheral & Software Whslr
N.A.I.C.S.: 423430

**COMPUTERLINKS North America
Inc.** **(1)**
11500 Metric Blvd Ste 300, Austin, TX
78758
Tel.: (512) 672-8900
Emp.: 15
Computer Software Distr
N.A.I.C.S.: 423430

COMPUTERLINKS SpA **(1)**
Via Lancia 6, 39100, Bolzano, Italy
Tel.: (39) 0471099100
Web Site: http://www.arrowecs.it
Computer Peripheral & Software Distr
N.A.I.C.S.: 423430

COMPUTERLINKS Sweden AB **(1)**
Kronborgsgrand 23, 164 46, Kista, Sweden
Tel.: (46) 855518500
Web Site: http://www.ecs-se.arrow.com
Computer Peripheral & Software Distr
N.A.I.C.S.: 423430

Chip One Stop, Inc. **(1)**
LIVMO Rising Building 10F 3-19-1 Shin,
Kouhoku-ku, Yokohama, 222-8525, Kana-
gawa, Japan
Tel.: (81) 454708750
Web Site: http://www.chip1stop.com
Emp.: 219
Semiconductor & Electronic Component
Distr
N.A.I.C.S.: 423690
Mark Kojo (Founder, Pres & CEO)
Tetsuya Umeki (CFO & Exec Dir)
Wai Fan Hung (Auditor)

Converge (1)
4 Technology Dr, Peabody, MA 01960
Tel.: (978) 538-8000
Web Site: http://www.converge.com
Sales Range: $25-49.9 Million
Emp.: 350
Semiconductors, Electronic Components,
Computer Products & Networking Equipment Distr
N.A.I.C.S.: 423690

Converge Netherlands BV. (1)
Q-Port Building Kingsfordweg 111-113 14th
Fl, 1043 GP, Amsterdam, Netherlands
Tel.: (31) 205826200
Web Site: http://www.converge.com
Sales Range: $25-49.9 Million
Emp.: 8
Electronic Equipment & Component Distr
N.A.I.C.S.: 423690

**Data Modul Electronics Technology
(Shanghai) Co. Ltd.** (1)
177 Jiang kai Road Room 202 Building 2,
Xinguang Park Minhang Qu, Shanghai,
201114, China
Tel.: (86) 2150313935
Electronic Components Distr
N.A.I.C.S.: 423690

Data Modul FZE (1)
Unit 7WA 3001 Building 7WA West Wing
Dubai Airport Freezone, PO Box 54592,
Dubai, United Arab Emirates
Tel.: (971) 42994009
Flat Glass Product Mfr & Distr
N.A.I.C.S.: 327211
Florian Pesahl (Chm-Exec Bd)

Data Modul France S.a r.l (1)
16 Rue Auber, 75009, Paris, France
Tel.: (33) 344549699
Electronic Components Distr
N.A.I.C.S.: 423690

Data Modul Hong Kong Ltd. (1)
262 Gloucester Road 10/F COFCO Tower,
Hong Kong Island, Hong Kong, 999077,
China (Hong Kong)
Tel.: (852) 75583292356
Electronic Components Distr
N.A.I.C.S.: 423690

Data Modul Italia S.r.l. (1)
Viale Cooperazione 15, 20095, Cusano
Milanino, MI, Italy
Tel.: (39) 0266409868
Electronic Components Distr
N.A.I.C.S.: 423690

Data Modul Weikersheim GmbH (1)
Lindenstrasse 8, D-97990, Weikersheim,
Germany
Tel.: (49) 79341010
Electronic Components Distr
N.A.I.C.S.: 423690

Dicopel, Inc. (1)
8695 Avenida Costa Blanca, San Diego, CA
92154
Tel.: (619) 423-3392
Electronic Equipment & Component Distr
N.A.I.C.S.: 423690

E-InfoChips KK (1)
Tel.: (81) 358160220
Computer Integrated Design Services
N.A.I.C.S.: 541512

**ETEQ Components International PTE
Ltd.** (1)
Mapletree 03 35 Marsiling Industrial Estate
Road 3, Singapore, 739257, Singapore
Tel.: (65) 63697271
Electronic Equipment & Component Distr
N.A.I.C.S.: 423690

ETEQ Components PTE Ltd. (1)
750E Chai Chee Road 07-01/02, Technopark Chai Chee, Singapore, 469005,
Singapore
Tel.: (65) 65598388
Electronic Components Distr
N.A.I.C.S.: 423690

ETEQ Components PTE Ltd. (1)
750E Chai Chee Road 07-01/02, Technopark Chai Chee, Singapore, 469005,
Singapore
Tel.: (65) 65598388
Web Site: http://www.arrow.com

Electronic Components Distr
N.A.I.C.S.: 423690

Elko C.E., S.A. (1)
Constitucion 3040, Buenos Aires, 1093,
Argentina
Tel.: (54) 1167773500
Web Site: http://www.elkonet.com
Sales Range: $25-49.9 Million
Emp.: 60
Electronic Equipment & Component Distr
N.A.I.C.S.: 423690

Eshel Technology Group, Inc. (1)
20935 Warner Ctr Ln, Woodland Hills, CA
91367
Tel.: (818) 932-1020
Web Site: http://www.etgtech.com
Sales Range: $25-49.9 Million
Emp.: 8
Electronic Equipment & Component Distr
N.A.I.C.S.: 423690

Eurocomponentes, S.A. (1)
4067 Rep Of Mexico, Capital Federal, Buenos Aires, C1223ACE, Argentina
Tel.: (54) 1149573820
Electricity Distribution Services
N.A.I.C.S.: 221122

Flection France SAS (1)
13/21 Quai desÂ Gresillions Pont de Saint
Quen, Gennevilliers, 9230, France
Tel.: (33) 689627779
Computer Peripheral & Software Distr
N.A.I.C.S.: 423430

Flection Germany GmbH (1)
Am Borsigturm 100, 13507, Berlin, Germany
Tel.: (49) 304360270
Computer Peripheral & Software Distr
N.A.I.C.S.: 423430

Flection United Kingdom Ltd. (1)
Hirwaun Industrial Estate, Aberdare, CF44
9UP, Mid Glamorgan, United Kingdom
Tel.: (44) 1685814627
Information Technology Security Services
N.A.I.C.S.: 541519

Greentech Denmark ApS (1)
Industrihegnet 9, 4030, Tune, Denmark
Tel.: (45) 69663320
Web Site: http://www.shop.greentech.as
Computer Peripheral Whslr
N.A.I.C.S.: 423430

Greentech Sweden AB (1)
Blockvagen 5, 352 45, Vaxjo, Sweden
Tel.: (46) 470703500
Web Site: http://www.greentech.se
Computer Peripheral Whslr
N.A.I.C.S.: 423430

IPVista A/S (1)
Jens Juuls Vej 42, 8260, Viby, Denmark
Tel.: (45) 70254500
Web Site: http://www.ipvista.dk
Marketing & Advertising Services
N.A.I.C.S.: 541810

LOGIX S.A. (1)
38-40 rue Victor Hugo, 92400, Courbevoie,
France
Tel.: (33) 149975000
Web Site: http://www.groupe-arrow.com
Rev.: $730,056,000
Emp.: 2,000
Computer Related Services
N.A.I.C.S.: 541519
Sadoun Laurent (Pres)

Subsidiary (Non-US):

Four Leaf Technologies A/S (2)
Jens Juuls Vej 42, 8260, Viby, Denmark
Tel.: (45) 70254500
Computer Related Services
N.A.I.C.S.: 541519

**Marubun-Arrow Mexico, S. de R.L. de
C.V.** (1)
Francisco Pimentel No 98 Col San Rafael
Deleg Cuauhtemoc, 06470, Mexico, Distrito
Federal, Mexico
Tel.: (52) 5551411680
Web Site: http://www.marubun.co.jp
Computer Peripheral Equipment Distr
N.A.I.C.S.: 423430

Marubun/Arrow (HK) Limited (1)

Units 1507 15/F Ofc Tower 1 the Harbourfront 18 Tak Fung st, Hunghom, Kowloon,
China (Hong Kong)
Tel.: (852) 23751126
Web Site: http://www.marubunarrow.com
Sales Range: $25-49.9 Million
Emp.: 40
Electronic Equipment & Component Distr
N.A.I.C.S.: 423690

Marubun/Arrow (M) Sdn. Bhd (1)
Tel.: (60) 378051518
Sales Range: $25-49.9 Million
Emp.: 9
Electronic Equipment & Component Distr
N.A.I.C.S.: 423690

Marubun/Arrow (Philippines) Inc. (1)
2/F MDD Building 121 East Science Avenue, Laguna Technopark Special Economic Zone, Binan, 4024, Laguna, Philippines
Tel.: (63) 495413356
Sales Range: $25-49.9 Million
Emp.: 8
Electronic Equipment & Component Distr
N.A.I.C.S.: 327910
Takao Sakurai (Gen Mgr)

Marubun/Arrow (S) Pte Ltd. (1)
18 Howard Road 10-10, Novelty BizCentre,
Singapore, 369585, Singapore
Tel.: (65) 6360050
Web Site: http://www.marubunarrow.com
Sales Range: $25-49.9 Million
Emp.: 15
Electronic Equipment & Component Distr
N.A.I.C.S.: 423690

Marubun/Arrow (Shanghai) Co. (1)
Unit 203 Tower 1 Lihpao Plaza No 189
Shenwu Road, Minhang District, Shanghai,
China
Tel.: (86) 2160812188
Electronic Equipment & Component Distr
N.A.I.C.S.: 423690

Marubun/Arrow (Thailand) Co. (1)
Empire Tower Unit 2907 29th floor 1 South
Sathorn Road, Yannawa Sathorn, Bangkok,
10120, Thailand
Tel.: (66) 2670077073
Electronic Components Distr
N.A.I.C.S.: 423690

**Marubun/Arrow (Thailand) Co.,
Ltd.** (1)
Empire Tower Unit 2907 29th floor 1 South
Sathorn Road, Yannawa Sathorn, Bangkok,
10120, Thailand
Tel.: (66) 2670077073
Electronic Components Distr
N.A.I.C.S.: 423690
Varaporn Huaysrichan (Accountant-Fin)

Microtronica Ltd. (1)
Unit 3 Bennet Court, Reading, RG2 0QX,
Berkshire, United Kingdom
Tel.: (44) 1189633870
Web Site: http://www.microtronica.com
Electronic Equipment & Component Distr
N.A.I.C.S.: 423690

NIC Components Asia PTE Ltd. (1)
50 Kallang Avenue 06-01 Noel Corporate
Building, Singapore, 339505, Singapore
Tel.: (65) 68441575
Electronic Components Mfr
N.A.I.C.S.: 334419

NIC Components Corp. (1)
100 Baylis Rd, Melville, NY 11747
Tel.: (631) 396-7500
Web Site: http://www.niccomp.com
Electrical Component Mfr & Distr
N.A.I.C.S.: 334416
Jim Wright (VP-Engrg & Quality)

NUHC, Inc. (1)
8555 Jane St, Concord, L4K 5N9, ON,
Canada
Tel.: (905) 761-1911
Electronic Appliance Whslr
N.A.I.C.S.: 423620

Nu Horizons Electronics A/S (1)
Savsvinget 7, 2970, Horsholm, Denmark
Tel.: (45) 70104888
Semiconductor & Electronic Component
Distr
N.A.I.C.S.: 423430

Nu Horizons Electronics Pty Ltd. (1)
U 11 42 Stud Rd, Bayswater, 3153, VIC,
Australia
Tel.: (61) 397206444
Emp.: 6
Electronic Equipment Whslr
N.A.I.C.S.: 423690

Openway SAS (1)
38-41 Av Rue VictorÂ Hugo, Courbevoie,
92411, France
Tel.: (33) 149975000
Data Processing & Hosting Services
N.A.I.C.S.: 518210

PCG Parent Corp. (1)
4 Technology Dr, Peabody, MA 01960
Tel.: (978) 538-8000
Web Site: http://www.converge.com
Electronic Components Distr
N.A.I.C.S.: 423690

PCG Trading, LLC (1)
4 Technology Dr, Peabody, MA 01960
Tel.: (978) 538-8000
Web Site: http://www.converge.com
Electronic Equipment & Component Distr
N.A.I.C.S.: 423690

PT Marubun Arrow Indonesia (1)
The Manor Office Park 7th Fl Unit L7-E,
Suryacipta Square Jl Surya Utama Kav C 1,
Karawang, 41363, Indonesia
Tel.: (62) 2678638030
Semiconductor & Electronic Component
Distr
N.A.I.C.S.: 423430

Pansystem S.r.l. (1)
Via Colleverde 16, 00131, Rome, Italy
Tel.: (39) 0688807500
Web Site: http://www.pansystem.com
Electronic Component & Cable Distr
N.A.I.C.S.: 423610

Pax8, Inc. (1)
5500 S Quebec St Ste 350, Greenwood
Village, CO 80111
Web Site: http://www.pax8.com
Data Cloud Services
N.A.I.C.S.: 518210
Ryan Walsh (Chief Product Officer)
Jennifer Bodell (VP-Channel)
Nick Heddy (Chief Revenue Officer)
John Street (CEO)
Don Jeter (VP-Mktg)
Klaus Dimmler (Chief Technical Officer)
Michael Dehmlow (COO)
Jefferson Keith (Sr VP-Corp Dev)
Brad Fugitt (CIO & Chief Security Officer)
Susan Mitnick (Chief HR Officer)
Aaron Garza (Sr VP-Bus Dev)
Jesse Taylor (VP-Developer Ops)
Cleve Lewis (VP-Empowerment Programs)
Ryan Burton (VP-Product Strategy)
Jared Pangretic (Sr VP-Sls)
Craig Donovan (VP-Partner Solutions)
Tony Ceravolo (VP-Engrg)
Derek Mapes (VP-Technical Support)
Lynn Leadley (VP-Pax8 University)
Jessica Maria (VP-Market Dev)
Sandi Rosenau (VP-Internal Ops)
Kelly Modert (VP-Fin)
Anna Weisbrodt (Corp Counsel & VP)
Amanda Lee (Sr VP-Global Comm)
Samantha Nelson (VP-Channel Dev)
Andrew Pryfogle (Chief Market Dev Officer)
Michael Lipfield (VP-Fin Ops)
David James (Chief Data Officer)
Natasha Wright (VP-Global Demand Center)
Aaron Watts (VP-Sls-Intl)
Puneet Pamnani (CFO)
Lori Frasier (Chief People Officer-Americas)
Robert Belgrave (Chief People Officer-Global)
Melissa Gallegos (Dir-Comm)
Carrie Schiff (Chief Legal Officer)
Mary Gill (Chief Compliance Officer)

Power and Signal Group GmbH (1)
Balcke-Duerr-Allee 2, 40882, Ratingen,
Germany
Tel.: (49) 210216770
Web Site: http://www.powerandsignal.eu
Emp.: 2
N.A.I.C.S.: 423120
Volker Strauss (Mng Dir)

Red Education Pty. Ltd. (1)

Arrow Electronics, Inc.—(Continued)

Suite 803 50 Berry Street, North Sydney, 2060, NSW, Australia
Tel.: (61) 1300651917
Electronic Components Distr
N.A.I.C.S.: 423690

Richardson RFPD (Thailand) Limited (1)
92/5 Sathorn Thani 2 Building 2nd Floor North Sathorn Road Silom, Bangkrak, Bangkok, 10500, Thailand
Tel.: (66) 21099642
Electronic Components Distr
N.A.I.C.S.: 423690

Richardson RFPD Australia Pty. Ltd. (1)
Unit 6 39 Herbert Street, Saint Leonards, 2065, NSW, Australia
Tel.: (61) 412362718
Electronic Components Distr
N.A.I.C.S.: 423690

Richardson RFPD Canada Ltd. (1)
171 Superior Blvd Unit 1, Mississauga, L5T 2L6, ON, Canada
Tel.: (905) 965-4450
Web Site: http://www.richardsonrfpd.com
Sales Range: $10-24.9 Million
Emp.: 5
Electronic Components Mfr
N.A.I.C.S.: 449210

Richardson RFPD France SAS (1)
Eco River Parc Bat A 30 rue des Peupliers, 92752, Nanterre, Cedex, France
Tel.: (33) 141321550
Web Site: http://www.richardsonrfpd.com
Sales Range: $25-49.9 Million
Emp.: 12
Electronic Equipment & Component Distr
N.A.I.C.S.: 423690

Richardson RFPD Germany GmbH (1)
Boschstr 1, Puchheim, 82178, Germany
Tel.: (49) 8989021451
Sales Range: $25-49.9 Million
Emp.: 15
Electronic Equipment & Component Distr
N.A.I.C.S.: 423690

Richardson RFPD Israel Ltd. (1)
Ram House Entrance A 5th Floor, 36 Ha-shacham Street Ramat Siv, Petach Tikva, 49250, Israel
Tel.: (972) 97483232
Electronic Equipment & Component Distr
N.A.I.C.S.: 423690

Richardson RFPD Italy Srl (1)
Via Sandro Pertini 95, 50019, Sesto Fioren-tino, Firenze, Italy
Tel.: (39) 055459241
Sales Range: $25-49.9 Million
Emp.: 12
Electronic Equipment & Component Distr
N.A.I.C.S.: 423690

Richardson RFPD Japan KK (1)
Tel.: (81) 364529811
Web Site: http://www.richardsonrfpd.co.jp
Emp.: 20
Electronic Component & Cable Distr
N.A.I.C.S.: 423610

Richardson RFPD Korea Ltd. (1)
5F 554 Samseong-Ro, Gangnam-gu, Seoul, 06165, Korea (South)
Tel.: (82) 25394731
Electronic Component & Cable Distr
N.A.I.C.S.: 423610

Richardson RFPD Netherlands BV (1)
Kruisweg 811 Breguetlaan 9, Hoofddorp, 2132 NG, Netherlands
Tel.: (31) 235560490
Electronic Equipment & Component Distr
N.A.I.C.S.: 423690
Philip Vale (VP)

Richardson RFPD Singapore (1)
750E Chai Chee Rd 07-01/02, ESR BizPark Chai Chee, Singapore, 469005, Singapore
Tel.: (65) 64875995
Web Site: http://www.richardsonrfpd.com
Sales Range: $25-49.9 Million
Emp.: 16
Electronic Equipment & Component Distr

N.A.I.C.S.: 423690

Richardson RFPD Spain SL (1)
Margarita Salas No16-1a Planta-oficina D Technologico De Legatec, 28919, Leganes, Madrid, Spain
Tel.: (34) 912968780
Electronic Components Distr
N.A.I.C.S.: 423690

Richardson RFPD Sweden AB (1)
Girovagen 13, Jarfalla, 175 62, Sweden
Tel.: (46) 856470590
Sales Range: $25-49.9 Million
Emp.: 5
Electronic Equipment & Component Distr
N.A.I.C.S.: 423690

Richardson RFPD Taiwan (1)
11F No 77 Sec 1 Xin-Tai 5 Rd, Xizhi Dist, New Taipei City, 22101, Taiwan
Tel.: (886) 226983288
Electronic Component & Cable Distr
N.A.I.C.S.: 423610

Richardson RFPD UK Ltd. (1)
226 Berwick Avenue, Slough, SL1 4QT, Berks, United Kingdom
Tel.: (44) 1753733010
Web Site: http://www.richardsonrfpd.com
Sales Range: $25-49.9 Million
Emp.: 15
Electronic Equipment & Component Distr
N.A.I.C.S.: 423690

Richardson RFPD do Brasil Ltda (1)
Rua Jose Gomes Falcao 111, Sao Paulo, 00139-010, SP, Brazil
Tel.: (55) 1136139375
Web Site: http://www.richardsonrfpd.com
Emp.: 8
Computer Peripheral Equipment Distr
N.A.I.C.S.: 423430

Richardson RFPD, Inc. (1)
1950 S Batavia Ave Ste 100, Geneva, IL 60134
Tel.: (630) 262-6800
Web Site: https://www.richardsonrfpd.com
Emp.: 400
Electronic Equipment & Component Distr
N.A.I.C.S.: 423690
Georg Bruderl (Mng Dir-EMEA)

SiliconExpert Technologies, Inc. (1)
9151 E Panorama Cir, Centennial, CO 80112
Tel.: (408) 330-7575
Web Site: https://www.siliconexpert.com
Emp.: 350
Computer Software Distr
N.A.I.C.S.: 423430
Esam Elashmawi (Co-Founder)
Ecam Elashmawi (Founder)

Sun Chain Technology Corp. (1)
1f 9 Alley 2 Lane 35 Chi Hu Rd, Neihu, Tai-pei, 11492, Taiwan
Tel.: (886) 287975177
Web Site: http://www.sun-chain.com.tw
Electronic Components Distr
N.A.I.C.S.: 423690

TechTurn, Inc. (1)
2214 W Braker Ln, Austin, TX 78758
Tel.: (512) 997-7974
Web Site: http://www.techturn.com
Sales Range: $50-74.9 Million
Emp.: 135
Information Technology Asset Recovery Services
N.A.I.C.S.: 541511

Transim Technology Corporation (1)
1455 NW Irving St Ste 200, Portland, OR 97209
Tel.: (503) 450-1355
Web Site: http://www.transim.com
Sales Range: $25-49.9 Million
Emp.: 40
Internet Software & Services
N.A.I.C.S.: 423430

U.S. Micro Operating Company, LLC (1)
7608 W Teco Ave, Las Vegas, NV 89113
Tel.: (702) 998-7900
Web Site: http://www.usmicrocorp.com
Waste Management Services
N.A.I.C.S.: 562119

Ultra Source Electronics (SZ) Co, LTD (1)
Floor 24 25 Building T1 Upper Hills No 5001 Huang Gang Road, Futian District, Shenzhen, 518038, China
Tel.: (86) 75588367918
Electronic Components Distr
N.A.I.C.S.: 423690

Ultra Source Technology Corp. (1)
17F 13F-1 No 150 Jian 1st Road, Zhonghe Dist, New Taipei City, 23511, Taiwan
Tel.: (886) 282263168
Web Site: http://www.arrow.com
Electronic Equipment & Component Distr
N.A.I.C.S.: 423690

e-InfoChips Private Limited (1)
2 Aryan Park complex Nr Shilaj Railway Crossing Thaltej, Ahmedabad, 380 054, India
Tel.: (91) 7967128700
Electronic Components Distr
N.A.I.C.S.: 423690

immixGroup, Inc. (1)
8444 Westpark Dr Ste 200, McLean, VA 22102
Tel.: (703) 752-0610
Web Site: http://www.immixgroup.com
Contract Management & IT Solutions
N.A.I.C.S.: 541618
Troy Fortune (VP & Gen Mgr)
Vaughn Harman (Sr Dir-Enterprise Solu-tions)
David Tong (Sr Dir-Sls)
Lars McCulloch (Sr Dir-Bus & Corp Dev)

Subsidiary (Domestic):

EC America, Inc. (2)
8444 Westpark Dr Ste 200, McLean, VA 22102 (100%)
Tel.: (703) 752-0610
Government Agency Vendor Contract Man-agement & Consulting Services
N.A.I.C.S.: 541618

immixSolutions, Inc. (1)
8444 Westpark Dr Ste 200, McLean, VA 22102-5112
Tel.: (703) 752-0614
Emp.: 12
Electronic Components Distr
N.A.I.C.S.: 423690

immixTechnology, Inc. (1)
8444 Westpark Dr Ste 200, McLean, VA 22102
Tel.: (703) 752-0610
Electronic Components Distr
N.A.I.C.S.: 423690

ARROW FINANCIAL CORPO-RATION
250 Glen St, Glens Falls, NY 12801
Tel.: (518) 415-4307 NY
Web Site:
https://www.arrowfinancial.com
Year Founded: 1983
AROW—(NASDAQ)
Rev.: $160,549,000
Assets: $3,969,509,000
Liabilities: $3,615,971,000
Net Worth: $353,538,000
Earnings: $48,799,000
Emp.: 502
Fiscal Year-end: 12/31/22
Bank Holding Company
N.A.I.C.S.: 551111
Penko Krassimir Ivanov (CFO, Chief Acctg Officer, Treas & Exec VP)
David S. DeMarco (Pres & CEO)
Andrew J. Wise (COO & Sr VP)

Subsidiaries:

Glens Falls National Bank & Trust Company (1)
250 Glen St, Glens Falls, NY 12801 (100%)
Tel.: (518) 793-4121
Web Site: https://www.gfnational.com
Sales Range: $150-199.9 Million
Emp.: 300
Banking Services
N.A.I.C.S.: 522110

Penko Krassimir Ivanov (CFO, Chief Acctg Officer, Treas & Exec VP)
David S. DeMarco (Pres & CEO)
Thomas L. Hoy (Chm)
Tracey Norman (VP & Dir-Wealth Mgmt)

Subsidiary (Domestic):

Capital Financial Group, Inc. (2)
89 Saratoga Ave PO Box 1265, South Glens Falls, NY 12803 (100%)
Tel.: (518) 793-2885
Web Site:
http://www.capitalfinancialgroupinc.com
Sales Range: $10-24.9 Million
Emp.: 15
Portfolio Management
N.A.I.C.S.: 523940

Loomis & LaPann, Inc. (2)
228 Glen St, Glens Falls, NY 12801 (100%)
Tel.: (518) 792-6561
Web Site: https://www.loomislapann.com
Sales Range: $25-49.9 Million
Emp.: 3
General Insurance Services
N.A.I.C.S.: 524210
Gregory J. Joly (Sr VP-Sports)
Karen Boller (Acct Mgr-Sports-Comml Lines)
Lori George (Acct Mgr-Sports-Comml Lines)
Chuck Gohn (Pres)
Jason Pirozzolo (VP)
Joseph Place (VP)

Upstate Agency, LLC (2)
6353 State Route 9, Chestertown, NY 12817 (100%)
Tel.: (518) 494-2417
Web Site: https://www.upstateagency.com
Sales Range: $25-49.9 Million
Emp.: 26
Insurance Services
N.A.I.C.S.: 524210

W. Joseph McPhillips, Inc. (2)
20 E Washington St, Glens Falls, NY 12801
Tel.: (518) 792-5841
Sales Range: $25-49.9 Million
Emp.: 27
Insurance Agencies & Brokerages
N.A.I.C.S.: 524210
James Goodspeed (VP)

Saratoga National Bank & Trust Company (1)
171 S Broadway, Saratoga Springs, NY 12866-8002 (100%)
Tel.: (518) 583-3114
Web Site: https://www.saratoganational.com
Sales Range: $1-9.9 Million
Emp.: 30
Banking Serviooc
N.A.I.C.S.: 522110
Penko Krassimir Ivanov (CFO, Chief Acctg Officer, Treas & Exec VP)
David S. DeMarco (Pres & CEO)
Raymond F. O'Conor (Chm)
Billie Marie Taft-Sitler (VP-Corp Banking-Saratoga Reg)
Kurt Moser (Sr VP & Mgr-Corp Banking)
Jenifer Marten (VP-Corp Banking)
Chad Stoffer (VP-Corp Banking)
Marc Yrsha (Sr VP-Corp Dev)
Tracey Norman (VP & Dir-Wealth Mgmt)
Marilyn Kraus (VP-Trust & Wealth Mgmt)
Michael Mihaly (VP-Investment Svcs)
Mary Pat Rabin (VP-Retirement Plan Svcs)

ARROWHEAD PHARMACEUTI-CALS, INC.
177 E Colorado Blvd Ste 700, Pasa-dena, CA 91105
Tel.: (626) 304-3400 DE
Web Site:
https://www.arrowheadpharma.com
ARWR—(NASDAQ)
Rev.: $3,551,000
Assets: $1,139,802,000
Liabilities: $948,739,000
Net Worth: $191,063,000
Earnings: ($599,493,000)
Emp.: 609
Fiscal Year-end: 09/30/24
Nanotechnology Products Developer & Mfr

N.A.I.C.S.: 325414
Christopher R. Anzalone (Pres & CEO)
Kenneth A. Myszkowski (CFO)
Douglass B. Given (Chm)
Bruce D. Given (Chief Scientist-Medical)
Thomas Schluep (VP-Program Mgmt)
Vincent Anzalone (VP & Head-IR)
Robert Teigen (VP-Intellectual Property & Assoc Gen Counsel)
Randy Steiner (VP-Regulatory Affairs)
Dave Bormett (VP-Quality Assurance)
Erik Bush (Grp VP-Biology)
Caroline LaPlaca Davis (VP-Clinical Ops)
Zhi-Ming Ding (VP-Biology)
Christine Esau (VP-Biology)
Fred Fleitz (Grp VP-Chemistry, Mfg & Controls)
Tao Pei (Grp VP-Chemistry)
Jack Shi (VP-Clinical Pharmacology)
Tracie Oliver (Chief Comml Officer)
Peter Carignan (VP)
Leslie Lemke-Boutcher (VP)
Nadia Meshkova (Treas)
Matt Pulisic (VP)
Aaron Tan (Head)

Subsidiaries:

Arrowhead Madison, Inc.   (1)
465 Science Dr Ste C, Madison, WI 53711
Tel.: (608) 316-3890
Web Site: http://www.rocheusa.com
Sales Range: $25-49.9 Million
Emp.: 45
RNA Interference & Gen Therapy Solutions Research & Development
N.A.I.C.S.: 541715

ARROWMARK FINANCIAL CORP.

100 Fillmore St Ste 325, Denver, CO 80206
Tel.: (212) 468-5441   DE
Web Site:
   https://ir.arrowmarkfinancial
   corp.com
Year Founded: 2013
BANX—(NASDAQ)
Rev.: $16,653,813
Assets: $188,360,866
Liabilities: $47,571,734
Net Worth: $140,789,132
Earnings: $7,780,414
Fiscal Year-end: 12/31/20
Financial Investment Services
N.A.I.C.S.: 523999
Sanjai Bhonsle (Chm & CEO)
Rick Grove (Chief Compliance Officer)
Dana Staggs (Pres)

ARS PHARMACEUTICALS, INC.

11682 El Camino Real Ste 120, San Diego, CA 92130
Tel.: (858) 771-9307   DE
Web Site: https://www.ars-pharma.com
Year Founded: 2016
SPRY—(NASDAQ)
Rev.: $1,316,000
Assets: $281,435,000
Liabilities: $8,549,000
Net Worth: $272,886,000
Earnings: ($34,682,000)
Emp.: 17
Fiscal Year-end: 12/31/22
Research & Development in Biotechnology (except Nanobiotechnology)
N.A.I.C.S.: 541714
Alexander A. Fitzpatrick (Chief Legal Officer)
Brian T. Dorsey (COO)
Kathleen Scott (CFO)
Richard Lowenthal (Pres & CEO)

Sarina Tanimoto (Chief Medical Officer)
Eric Karas (Chief Comml Officer)
Justin Chakma (Chief Bus Officer)
Harris Kaplan (Exec VP-Comml Strategy)
Robert Bell (Chief Science Officer)
Daniel Relovsky (Sr VP-Mktg)
Richard E. Lowenthal (Pres & CEO)

ART'S-WAY MANUFACTURING CO., INC.

5556 Hwy 9, Armstrong, IA 50514
Tel.: (712) 208-8467   DE
Web Site: https://www.artsway-mfg.com
Year Founded: 1956
ARTW—(NASDAQ)
Rev.: $24,965,086
Assets: $20,854,048
Liabilities: $10,499,601
Net Worth: $10,354,447
Earnings: $212,631
Emp.: 131
Fiscal Year-end: 12/31/21
Agricultural Equipment Mfr
N.A.I.C.S.: 333111
Michael W. Woods (CFO)
David King (CEO & Exec VP)
David A. King (Pres)
Mike Loux (Sls Dir)
Emily Bailey (Mktg Mgr)
Travis Hawkins (Mgr)
Brianne Anderson (Mgr)
Mark Tschirgi (Gen Mgr)
Mark Bresson (Gen Mgr)
Bryan Heuer (Production Mgr)
Travis Horton (Sls Dir)
Karen Tolbert (Mgr)

Subsidiaries:

Art's Way Scientific, Inc.   (1)
203 Oak St, Monona, IA 52159-0878
Tel.: (563) 276-5600
Web Site: https://www.artsway-scientific.com
Sales Range: $50-74.9 Million
Produces & Sells Modular Buildings
N.A.I.C.S.: 321992
Mark Tschirgi (Gen Mgr)
Bryan Streicher (Project Mgr)
Dave Tesar (Supvr)
Paula Keehner (Mgr-Purchasing)
Daniel Palmer (Pres)

Art's Way Vessels, Inc.   (1)
7010 Chavanelle Rd, Dubuque, IA 52002
Tel.: (563) 557-8265
Web Site: http://www.artsway-vessels.com
Sales Range: $10-24.9 Million
Emp.: 15
Precision Industrial Vessels Mfr
N.A.I.C.S.: 333248

Arts-Way Manufacturing International LTD   (1)
12 Mill Street, PO Box 374, Clifford, Minto, N0G 1M0, ON, Canada
Tel.: (519) 327-8005
Web Site:
   http://www.artswayinternational.com
Emp.: 1,956
Agricultural Machinery Mfr
N.A.I.C.S.: 333111

Ohio Metal Working Products Co., Inc.   (1)
3620 Progress St NE, Canton, OH 44705
Tel.: (330) 453-8438
Web Site:
   http://www.americancarbidetool.com
Sales Range: $1-9.9 Million
Emp.: 20
Cutting Tool & Machine Tool Accessory Mfr
N.A.I.C.S.: 333515

Universal Harvester Co., Inc.   (1)
101 N Dayton Ave, Ames, IA 50010
Tel.: (515) 233-3121
Web Site: http://www.uhcreels.com
Sales Range: $1-9.9 Million
Emp.: 15
Farm Machinery & Equipment Mfr

N.A.I.C.S.: 333111

ARTEC GLOBAL MEDIA, INC.

1000 E William St Ste 204, Carson City, NV 89701
Year Founded: 2012
ACTL—(OTCEM)
Marketing Consulting Services
N.A.I.C.S.: 541613
Timothy Honeycutt (COO & VP)

ARTELO BIOSCIENCES, INC.

505 Lomas Santa Fe Ste 160, Solana Beach, CA 92075
Tel.: (858) 925-7049   NV
Web Site: https://www.artelobio.com
Year Founded: 2011
ARTL—(NASDAQ)
Rev.: $204,000
Assets: $20,424,000
Liabilities: $1,021,000
Net Worth: $19,403,000
Earnings: ($10,083,000)
Emp.: 7
Fiscal Year-end: 12/31/22
Pharmaceutical Preparation Manufacturing
N.A.I.C.S.: 325412
Gregory D. Gorgas (Pres, CEO, CFO, Treas & Sec)
Steven D. Reich (Chief Medical Officer)
Jason Baybutt (Sr VP-Fin)
Randy Schreckhise (VP-Fin & Ops)
Andrew Yates (Chief Scientific Officer & Sr VP)
Saoirse Elizabeth O'Sullivan (VP-Translational Sciences)

ARTEMIS ACQUISITION CORP.

734 Placid Cove Way, Salem, SC 29676
Tel.: (203) 450-6657   DE
Year Founded: 2021
ARACU—(NASDAQ)
Investment Services
N.A.I.C.S.: 523999
Steve Wiggins (CEO & Chm)
James Cardwell (CFO)
Joseph Nelson (COO)

ARTEMIS STRATEGIC INVESTMENT CORPORATION

3310 E Corona Ave, Phoenix, AZ 85040
Tel.: (602) 346-0329   DE
Year Founded: 2021
ARTE—(NASDAQ)
Rev.: $10,540,962
Assets: $208,511,564
Liabilities: $216,424,089
Net Worth: ($7,912,525)
Earnings: $3,479,590
Emp.: 4
Fiscal Year-end: 12/31/22
Investment Services
N.A.I.C.S.: 523999
Holly Gagnon (Chm & Co-CEO)
Philip Kaplan (Pres, Co-CEO & Principal Fin Officer)
Scott Shulak (Sr VP-Acquisitions and Acctg)

ARTEMIS THERAPEUTICS, INC.

18 E 16th St Ste 307, New York, NY 10003
Tel.: (646) 233-1454   DE
Web Site: http://www.artemis-therapeutics.com
Year Founded: 2003
ATMS—(OTCIQ)
Rev.: $311,000
Assets: $265,000
Liabilities: $1,291,000
Net Worth: ($1,026,000)

Earnings: ($1,355,000)
Emp.: 4
Fiscal Year-end: 12/31/22
Investment Services
N.A.I.C.S.: 523999
Brian Culley (CEO)
David Dana (CFO)

ARTERIS, INC.

900 E Hamilton Ave Ste 300, Campbell, CA 95008
Tel.: (408) 470-7300
Web Site: https://www.arteris.com
Year Founded: 2003
AIP—(NASDAQ)
Rev.: $53,666,000
Assets: $102,801,000
Liabilities: $87,698,000
Net Worth: $15,103,000
Earnings: ($36,869,000)
Emp.: 243
Fiscal Year-end: 12/31/23
Network-on-Chip Interconnect IP Solutions
N.A.I.C.S.: 334413
Laurent Moll (COO)
Christel Mauffet-Smith (Exec VP-Global Sls)
Nicholas B. Hawkins (CFO)
Michal Siwinski (CMO)
Paul L. Alpern (Gen Counsel)
K. Charles Janac (Chm, Pres & CEO)

Subsidiaries:

Arteris S.A.   (1)
6 Parc Ariane Immeuble Mercure Boulevard des Chenes, 78284, Guyancourt, France
Tel.: (33) 1 61 37 38 40
Web Site: http://www.arteris.com
Network-on-Chip Interconnect IP Solutions
N.A.I.C.S.: 334413

ARTESIAN RESOURCES CORPORATION

664 Churchmans Rd, Newark, DE 19702
Tel.: (302) 453-6900   DE
Web Site:
   https://www.artesianwater.com
Year Founded: 1905
ARTNA—(NASDAQ)
Rev.: $98,897,000
Assets: $719,791,000
Liabilities: $356,241,000
Net Worth: $363,550,000
Earnings: $17,998,000
Emp.: 252
Fiscal Year-end: 12/31/22
Utilities & Land Development
N.A.I.C.S.: 221310
Karl G. Randall (Asst Sec)
John M. Thaeder (Sr VP-Ops)
David B. Spacht (CFO)
Dian C. Taylor (Chm, Pres & CEO)
Jennifer L. Finch (Treas & Sr VP-Fin)

Subsidiaries:

Artesian Development Corporation   (1)
664 Churchmans Rd, Newark, DE 19702
Tel.: (302) 453-6900
Web Site: http://www.artesianwater.com
Sales Range: $200-249.9 Million
Emp.: 200
Real Estate Management
N.A.I.C.S.: 237210
Karl G. Randall (Gen Counsel & Asst Sec)
Dian C. Taylor (Pres & CEO)
Pierre A. Anderson (VP-IT)
Joseph A. DiNunzio (Sec & Exec VP)
Jennifer L. Finch (VP & Asst Treas)
David B. Spacht (CFO & Treas)
John M. Thaeder (Sr VP)

Artesian Wastewater Management, Inc.   (1)
664 Churchmans Rd, Newark, DE 19702   (100%)
Tel.: (302) 453-6900

Artesian Resources Corporation—(Continued)

Web Site: http://www.artesianwater.com
Wastewater Treatment Facilities Services
N.A.I.C.S.: 221310
Joseph A. DiNunzio (Exec VP)
David B. Spacht (Pres)
Nicholle R. Taylor (COO)
Rodney Wyatt (VP)

Subsidiary (Domestic):

Tidewater Environmental Services, Inc. (2)
1100 S Little Creek Rd, Dover, DE 19901
Environmental Engineering Consulting Services
N.A.I.C.S.: 541620

Artesian Water Company, Inc. (1)
664 Churchmans Rd, Newark, DE
19702-1934 (100%)
Tel.: (302) 453-6900
Web Site: https://www.artesianwater.com
Sales Range: $50-74.9 Million
Emp.: 175
Public Water Utility
N.A.I.C.S.: 221310

Artesian Water Maryland, Inc. (1)
664 Churchmans Rd, Newark, DE 19702
Tel.: (302) 453-6900
Water Distribution Services
N.A.I.C.S.: 221310
Joseph A. DiNunzio (Pres)

Artesian Water Pennsylvania, Inc. (1)
664 Churchmans Rd, Newark, DE
19702 (100%)
Tel.: (302) 453-6900
Web Site: http://www.artesianwater.com
Utility Company
N.A.I.C.S.: 221310

ARTHUR J. GALLAGHER & CO.

2850 Golf Rd, Rolling Meadows, IL
60008-4050
Tel.: (630) 773-3800 DE
Web Site: https://www.ajg.com
Year Founded: 1927
AJG—(NYSE)
Rev.: $10,071,900,000
Assets: $51,615,800,000
Liabilities: $40,800,500,000
Net Worth: $10,815,300,000
Earnings: $969,500,000
Emp.: 52,000
Fiscal Year-end: 12/31/23
Holding Company; Insurance Brokerage, Risk Management & Human Resources Consulting Services
N.A.I.C.S.: 551112
Thomas J. Gallagher (Pres)
Douglas K. Howell (CFO & VP)
William F. Ziebell (Pres-Employee Benefit Consulting & Brokerage & VP)
Scott R. Hudson (Pres/CEO-Risk Mgmt Svcs & VP)
Vishal Jain (Chief Svc Officer-Global & VP)
Raymond Iardella (VP-IR)
Susan E. Pietrucha (Chief HR Officer & VP)
Christopher E. Mead (CMO & VP)
Patrick M. Gallagher (COO)
Mark H. Bloom (CIO-Global)
Michael R. Pesch (CEO-Global Brokerage-Americas,Corp & VP)

Subsidiaries:

AJG Financial Services, LLC (1)
2 Pierce Pl, Itasca, IL 60143-3141 (100%)
Tel.: (630) 773-3800
Web Site: http://www.ajg.com
Sales Range: $25-49.9 Million
Emp.: 120
Financial Services
N.A.I.C.S.: 561499

Subsidiary (Domestic):

AJG Capital, Inc. (2)

2 Pierce Pl, Itasca, IL 60143-3141
Tel.: (630) 773-3800
Web Site: http://www.ajg.com
Financial Services
N.A.I.C.S.: 561499

AJG Two Pierce, Inc. (1)
The Gallagher Ctr 2 Pierce Pl, Itasca, IL
60143-3141 (100%)
Tel.: (630) 773-3800
Web Site: http://www.agj.com
Sales Range: $200-249.9 Million
Emp.: 1,000
Insurance Services
N.A.I.C.S.: 561499

Abram Interstate Insurance Services, Inc. (1)
2211 Plz Dr Ste 100, Rocklin, CA 95765
Tel.: (916) 780-7000
Web Site: http://www.abraminterstate.com
Insurance Agencies & Brokerages
N.A.I.C.S.: 524210

Advanced Energy Systems, LLC (1)
65 Centennial Loop, Eugene, OR 97401
Tel.: (541) 683-2345
Web Site: https://www.aesrenew.com
Solar Energy Equipment Mfr & Distr
N.A.I.C.S.: 333414

Air-Sur, Inc. (1)
141 Sagebrush Trl, Ormond Beach, FL
32174
Web Site: http://www.air-sur.com
Insurance Agencies & Brokerages
N.A.I.C.S.: 524210
Thomas K. Coughlin (Pres & CEO)
Carma Y. Dougherty (Controller)
Cheryl A. Longino (Coord-Administration)
Dorothy L. Sanders (Acct Mgr)

Andrew Insurance Associates, Inc. (1)
9912 Brewster Ln, Powell, OH 43065
Tel.: (614) 336-8030
Insurance Agency Services
N.A.I.C.S.: 524210

Anthony Hodges Consulting Limited (1)
Heath Hall Heath, Wakefield, WF1 5SL,
West Yorkshire, United Kingdom
Tel.: (44) 1924203900
Web Site: http://www.ahc.com
Management Consulting Services
N.A.I.C.S.: 541618
Sam Charles (Head-Development)
Emma Pytches (Project Mgr)
John Laycock (Mgr)
Trevor Posliff (Head-Finance)
Julie Powell (Mgr-Human Resources)

Artex Risk Solutions (Gibraltar) Limited (1)
1st Floor Grand Ocean Plaza, PO Box
1338, Ocean Village, GX11 1AA, Gibraltar,
Gibraltar
Tel.: (350) 20074570
Insurance Services
N.A.I.C.S.: 524210
Marcus Hayday (Fin Dir)

Artex Risk Solutions (Malta) Limited (1)
The LandMark Level 1 Suite 2 Triq L-Iljun,
Qormi, QRM 3800, Malta
Tel.: (356) 22489100
Insurance Services
N.A.I.C.S.: 524210
Stuart Ciappara (Mng Dir)

Artex Risk Solutions (Singapore) Pte. Ltd. (1)
3 Anson Road 10-03 Springleaf Tower, Singapore, 079909, Singapore
Tel.: (65) 64227315
Insurance Services
N.A.I.C.S.: 524114
Vic Pannuzzo (CEO)

Arthur J. Gallagher & Co. (Bermuda) Limited (1)
26 Victoria Street, Hamilton, HM12, Pembroke Parish, Bermuda (100%)
Tel.: (441) 2944321
Sales Range: $75-99.9 Million
Emp.: 16
Insurance Services
N.A.I.C.S.: 524298

Subsidiary (Domestic):

Artex Risk Solutions, Inc. (2)
3rd Floor Wessex House 45 Reid Street, 26
Victoria Street, HM 12, Hamilton, Bermuda
Tel.: (441) 2927505
Web Site: https://www.artexrisk.com
Sales Range: $75-99.9 Million
Risk Managemeng Srvices
N.A.I.C.S.: 524298

Subsidiary (US):

Risk International Services Inc. (3)
4055 Embassy Pkwy Ste 100, Fairlawn, OH
44333-1781
Tel.: (216) 255-3400
Web Site: http://www.riskinternational.com
Rev.: $3,000,000
Emp.: 25
All Other Insurance Related Activities
N.A.I.C.S.: 524298
Douglas Talley (Chief Legal Officer & Exec VP)
Michael Davis (CEO)

Subsidiary (Domestic):

Arthur J. Gallagher Intermediaries (Bermuda) Limited (2)
Swan Buliding 26 Victoria St 48 Church
Street, HM 12, Hamilton, Bermuda (100%)
Tel.: (441) 2924654
Web Site: http://www.artexrisk.com
Sales Range: $75-99.9 Million
Provider of Insurance Services
N.A.I.C.S.: 524298

Arthur J. Gallagher Management (Bermuda) Limited (2)
Swan Building, 26 Victoria Street, HM 12,
Hamilton, Bermuda (100%)
Tel.: (441) 2924654
Sales Range: $75-99.9 Million
Emp.: 16
Provider of Insurance Services
N.A.I.C.S.: 524298

Arthur J. Gallagher & Co. (Illinois) (1)
2850 Golf Rd, Rolling Meadows, IL
60008 (100%)
Tel.: (630) 773-3800
Web Site: https://www.ajg.com
Sales Range: $50-74.9 Million
Emp.: 1,100
Insurance Services
N.A.I.C.S.: 524210
Patt Gallagher (Pres)
Kelli Murray (Dir)

Arthur J. Gallagher & Co. Insurance Brokers of California, Inc. (1)
1255 Battery St Ste 450, San Francisco,
CA 94111 (100%)
Tel.: (415) 546-9300
Web Site: http://www.ajg.com
Sales Range: $75-99.9 Million
Emp.: 200
Insurance Services
N.A.I.C.S.: 524210
Doug Bowring (Exec VP-Construction, Insurance & Risk Mgmt)

Subsidiary (Domestic):

Charity First Insurance Services, Inc. (2)
595 Market St Ste 2100, San Francisco, CA
94105 (100%)
Tel.: (415) 546-9300
Web Site: http://www.charityfirst.com
Sales Range: $50-74.9 Million
Provider of Insurance to Non-Profit Organizatons
N.A.I.C.S.: 524210

Arthur J. Gallagher & Co. Newport Beach (1)
1201 Dove St Ste 240, Newport Beach, CA
92660
(949) 724-1964
Web Site: http://www.ajg.com
Insurance Agencies & Brokerages
N.A.I.C.S.: 524210
Michael Rankin (Principal)

Arthur J. Gallagher (UK) Limited (1)
Wilcrok London, London, EC4 N8W, United
Kingdom (100%)

Tel.: (44) 2072046000
Web Site: http://www.ajginternational.com
Sales Range: $100-124.9 Million
Emp.: 300
Insurance Services
N.A.I.C.S.: 524298
Tim Devine (Mng Dir)
Carol Richmond (Chief Risk & Compliance Officer)
Charles Crawford (COO)
Claire Davies (Dir-Human Resources)
Charlie Scott (CFO)
Jonathan Turner (CEO)
Michael Rea (CEO-Retail-UK)
Tom Downey (CEO)
Bridget Lambie (Gen Counsel)

Subsidiary (Domestic):

Alesco Risk Management Services Limited (2)
25 Walbrook, London, EC4N 8AF, United
Kingdom
Tel.: (44) 2072048999
Web Site: https://www.alescorms.com
Risk Management Consultancy Services
N.A.I.C.S.: 522320
Ken Kavanagh (Partner)
Jonathan Turner (CEO)
Graeme Dean (Partner)
Bill Dyer (Partner)

Arthur J. Gallagher Housing Limited (2)
27-30 Railway Street, Chelmsford, CM1
1QS, United Kingdom
Tel.: (44) 1245341200
General Insurance Services
N.A.I.C.S.: 524210
Chris Matthews (Head-Acct Mgmt)

Arthur J. Gallagher Middle East BSC (2)
133 Houndsditch, London, EC3A 7AH,
United Kingdom
Tel.: (44) 2072046000
Sales Range: $100-124.9 Million
Emp.: 400
Insurance Services
N.A.I.C.S.: 524298
Stuart Hill (Dir-Mining & Property-Global)
Neil Stewart (Mng Dir-Corp & Global)

Contego Underwriting Limited (2)
133 Houndsditch, London, EC3A 7AH,
United Kingdom
Tel.: (44) 2072048302
Web Site:
http://www.contegounderwriting.com
General Insurance Services
N.A.I.C.S.: 524210

Gallagher Communication (2)
Liss Mill Mill Road, Liss, GU33 7BD, United
Kingdom
Tel.: (44) 1730891212
Web Site: http://www.shilling.co.uk
Business Consulting Services
N.A.I.C.S.: 541611
Ben Reynolds (Mng Dir)
Guy Etherington (Controller-Finance)
Howard Fry (Dir-Creative)
Matt Frost (Dir-Business Development)
Neil Strong (Dir)
Samantha Healey (Sr Principal)
Josephine Hallier (Dir)
Rhys Davies (Dir-Benefits)
Craig Pearce (Mgr-Creative Services)
Alexandra Houlden (Mgr-Client Service)
Ben Farnell (Mgr)
Kayleigh Grierson (Assoc Dir)
Nicole Eves (Dir)
Jon Hale (Gen Mgr)
Drew Munn (Head)
Kate Whitley (Dir)
Nick Jones (Head-Creative)
Chris Shawley (Dir-Art)
David Krieger (Sr VP-Communications)
Gianluca Pezzuti (Copywriter)
Maddison Grigsby (Dir)
Nathan Sait (Dir)
Sam Charles (Dir)
Karen Bolan (Dir)
Dan DiSciullo (Dir-Benefits)
Sam Charles (Dir)
Karen Bolan (Dir)
Dan DiSciullo (Dir-Benefits)

Giles Insurance Brokers Ltd. (2)

7th Floor Spectrum Building 55 Blythswood Street, Glasgow, G2 7AT, United Kingdom
Tel.: (44) 8443320529
Web Site: http://www.arthurjgallagher.co.uk
Sales Range: $350-399.9 Million
Emp.: 150
Insurance Brokerage Services
N.A.I.C.S.: 524210
Alister Hessecc (Gen Mgr)

Hill's Environmental Limited (2)
Gannaway Lane, Tewkesbury, Gloucestershire, United Kingdom
Tel.: (44) 1684296472
Environmental Consulting Services
N.A.I.C.S.: 541620

Insurance Dialogue Limited (2)
100 Holdenhurst Road, Bournemouth, BH8 8AQ, Dorset, United Kingdom
Tel.: (44) 8083018302
Web Site:
   http://www.insure4retirement.co.uk
Emp.: 200
General Insurance Services
N.A.I.C.S.: 524210

Morgan Insurance Services Limited (2)
9 Alie St, London, E1 8DE, United Kingdom (100%)
Tel.: (44) 72046000
Sales Range: $75-99.9 Million
Insurance Services
N.A.I.C.S.: 524298

OAMPS (UK) Limited (2)
Kings Court 41-51 Kingston Road, Leatherhead, KT22 7SL, Surrey, United Kingdom
Tel.: (44) 1372869700
Web Site: https://www.oamps.co.uk
Insurance Services
N.A.I.C.S.: 524210

Risk Management Partners Ltd. (2)
67 Lombard Street, London, EC3V 9LJ, United Kingdom
Tel.: (44) 2072041800
Web Site: https://www.rmpartners.co.uk
Sales Range: Less than $1 Million
Emp.: 20
Insurance Services
N.A.I.C.S.: 524298
Nick Colyer (CEO)
Mark Povey (Reg Dir-North)
Carl Dunckley (Mgr-Risk Control)
Ian Ross Bain (Mgr-Bus Dev)
Ashley Easen (Dir-Risk Control)
Joanne Seaward (Dir-Projects)
Michael Barnes (Dir-Education & Acct)
Philip Farrar (Dir-Dev-Natl)
Adrian Bloor (Dir-Claims)
Pam Savill (Dir-Area)
Paul Davison (Dir-Area)
Stephen Halsall (COO)
Roy Tapper (Co-Mng Dir)
Hayley Cray (Co-COO)
Adela Green (Acct Dir)
Catherine Starrs (Acct Dir)
Debbie Ball (Acct Dir)
Julian Cummings (Acct Dir)
Richard Blackwell (Acct Dir)
Peter Fulthorpe (Reg Dir)
Selina Walkley (Acct Dir)
Lisa Mills (Dir-Operations)
James Iles (Acct Dir)
Mark Stephens (Acct Dir)
Simon Johnson (Branch Mgr)
David Blackwell (Branch Mgr)
Lisa Mills (Dir-Operations)
James Iles (Acct Dir)
Mark Stephens (Acct Dir)
Simon Johnson (Branch Mgr)
David Blackwell (Branch Mgr)

Arthur J. Gallagher Australasia Holdings Pty. Ltd. (1)
Level 12 80 Pacific Highway, North Sydney, 2060, NSW, Australia (100%)
Tel.: (61) 292422000
Sales Range: $1-9.9 Million
Emp.: 30
Insurance Brokers
N.A.I.C.S.: 524210
Peter Kelly (Mng Dir)
Sarah Lyons (CEO)
Chris Ellis (CFO)
Lisbeth Rees (Dir-Human Resources)
Anthony Niardone (Gen Mgr-Risk-Compliance)

Robin Moore (Head-Marketing-Communications)
Paul Harvey (Mng Dir)
Mark Oatway (Mng Dir)
Paul Moorcroft (Mng Dir)
Andrew Whittle (Head)
Kylie Hull (Head)
Mark Saunderson (Head)
Sarah Lyons (CEO)
Chris Ellis (CFO)
Lisbeth Rees (Dir-Human Resources)
Anthony Niardone (Gen Mgr-Risk-Compliance)
Robin Moore (Head-Marketing-Communications)
Paul Harvey (Mng Dir)
Mark Oatway (Mng Dir)
Paul Moorcroft (Mng Dir)
Andrew Whittle (Head)
Kylie Hull (Head)
Mark Saunderson (Head)

Subsidiary (Domestic):

Arthur J. Gallagher & Co. (AUS) Ltd (2)
Level 4 289 Wellington Parade South, Melbourne, 3002, VIC, Australia
Tel.: (61) 394121555
General Insurance Services
N.A.I.C.S.: 524210
Sarah Lyons (CEO)
Chris Ellis (CFO)
Lisbeth Rees (Dir-Human Resources)
Anthony Niardone (Gen Mgr-Risk-Compliance)
Robin Moore (Head-Marketing-Communications)
Paul Harvey (Mng Dir)
Mark Oatway (Mng Dir)
Paul Moorcroft (Mng Dir)
Andrew Whittle (Head)
Kylie Hull (Head)
Mark Saunderson (Head)
Chris Ellis (CFO)
Lisbeth Rees (Dir-Human Resources)
Anthony Niardone (Gen Mgr-Risk-Compliance)
Robin Moore (Head-Marketing-Communications)
Paul Harvey (Mng Dir)
Mark Oatway (Mng Dir)
Paul Moorcroft (Mng Dir)
Andrew Whittle (Head)
Kylie Hull (Head)
Mark Saunderson (Head)

Subsidiary (Domestic):

Instrat Insurance Brokers Ltd (3)
Monash Corporate Centre 4/10 Duerdin Street, Clayton, 3168, VIC, Australia
Tel.: (61) 392447777
Web Site: http://www.imar.com.au
Emp.: 50
General Insurance Services
N.A.I.C.S.: 524210

Subsidiary (Domestic):

Arthur J. Gallagher (Aus) Pty. Ltd. (2)
Level 12 80 Pacific Highway, North Sydney, 2060, NSW, Australia (100%)
Tel.: (61) 292422000
Web Site: https://www.ajg.com
Insurance Brokerage Services
N.A.I.C.S.: 524210
Andrew Pytches (COO)

Arthur J. Gallagher Reinsurance Australasia Pty. Ltd. (2)
Level 8 Thakral House, 301 George Street, Sydney, 2000, NSW, Australia (100%)
Tel.: (61) 82430999
Insurance Brokers
N.A.I.C.S.: 524210

Subsidiary (Non-US):

Crombie Lockwood (NZ) Limited (2)
Level 4 Crombie Lockwood Centre 100 Beaumont Street, Mt Eden, Auckland, 1010, New Zealand
Tel.: (64) 9 623 9900
Web Site:
   https://www.crombielockwood.co.nz
Insurance Brokerage Services
N.A.I.C.S.: 524210

Carl O'Shea (Co-Founder & CEO)
Gillian Granger (COO)
Brord van der Kroft (CFO)
Greg Howarth (CIO)
Steve Lockwood (Co-Founder)
Mark Jones (Chief Broking Officer)

Elantis Premium Funding (NZ) Limited (2)
Swanson House Level 11 12 - 26 Swanson St, PO Box 2426, Auckland, 1010, New Zealand
Tel.: (64) 93081106
Web Site: https://www.elantis.com.au
Sales Range: $50-74.9 Million
Emp.: 11
Financial Management Services
N.A.I.C.S.: 523999

Fraser MacAndrew Ryan Limited (2)
Level 23 Swanson 191 Queen Street, Auckland, 1010, New Zealand
Tel.: (64) 93582258
Web Site:
   http://www.crombielockwood.co.nz
Emp.: 40
General Insurance Services
N.A.I.C.S.: 524210
Duane Duggan (Mgr-Ops)

Subsidiary (Domestic):

Penunderwriting Group Pty Ltd. (2)
Level 11 99 York Street, GPO Box 247, Sydney, 2000, NSW, Australia
Tel.: (61) 293235000
Web Site:
   https://www.penunderwriting.com.au
Insurance Agencies & Brokerage Services
N.A.I.C.S.: 524210
Ken Keenan (CEO)

Arthur J. Gallagher Brokerage & Risk Management Services, LLC (1)
2850 Golf Rd, Rolling Meadows, IL 60008
Tel.: (630) 773-3800
Web Site: http://www.ajg.com
Insurance Agencies & Brokerage Services
N.A.I.C.S.: 524210

Subsidiary (Domestic):

Artex Risk Solutions, Inc. (2)
2850 Golf Rd, Rolling Meadows, IL 60008-4050
Tel.: (630) 694-5050
Web Site: http://www.artexrisk.com
Risk Managemeng Srvices
N.A.I.C.S.: 541611
Simon Camilleri (Dir)
Jennifer Gallagher (Pres-North America)
Andy Atsaves (Exec VP-North America)
Chad Kunkel (Exec VP-Grp Captives-North America)
Martin Hughes (Exec VP-Underwriting-North America)
Andrew Parsons (Dir-HR)
Stephen Thompsett (COO)
Peter Mullen (CEO)
Brandon Marshall (CFO)

Subsidiary (Non-US):

Allied Risk Management Limited (3)
13 Fitzwilliam St Upper, Dublin, Ireland
Tel.: (353) 17645640
Web Site: http://www.alliedrisk.ie
Sales Range: $125-149.9 Million
Emp.: 300
Insurance Services
N.A.I.C.S.: 524298
Frank Coyle (CEO)

Bee Insurance Management Services Limited (3)
4th Floor Development House St Anne Street, Floriana, FRN 9010, Malta
Tel.: (356) 21235860
Web Site: http://www.bee.com.mt
Sales Range: $50-74.9 Million
Emp.: 10
Insurance Management Services
N.A.I.C.S.: 524298
Analise Attard (Acct Mgr)

Subsidiary (Domestic):

EWI RE, Inc. (3)
3 Lincoln Ctr Ste 1595, Dallas, TX 75240
Tel.: (972) 866-6815

Web Site: http://www.ewireinsurance.com
Sales Range: $50-74.9 Million
Emp.: 20
Insurance & Risk Management Services
N.A.I.C.S.: 524210
Steven M. McElhiney (Pres)
Toni Green (VP-Claims)
Lynn Carlisle Sheils (Gen Counsel & Sr VP)
Michael C. McKee (VP-Loss Control)
Joy Lin (Controller)
Abey Thomas (Asst Mgr-Risk)

Subsidiary (Domestic):

Arthur J. Gallagher Risk Management Services, Inc. (2)
The Gallagher Ctr 2 Pierce Pl, Itasca, IL 60143-3141 (100%)
Tel.: (630) 773-3800
Web Site: http://www.ajgrms.com
Insurance Brokers
N.A.I.C.S.: 524210
Scott R. Hudson (Pres & CEO)

Subsidiary (Domestic):

Arthur J. Gallagher Risk Management Services (Hawaii), Inc. (3)
Bishop Sq ASB Tower 1101 Bishop St, Honolulu, HI 96813 (100%)
Tel.: (808) 543-6376
Web Site: http://www.ajgrms.com
Sales Range: $10-24.9 Million
Emp.: 3
Insurance Brokers
N.A.I.C.S.: 524210

Subsidiary (Domestic):

Austin Consulting Group, Inc. (2)
240 Commerce Dr, Crystal Lake, IL 60014
Tel.: (720) 528-8900
Web Site: http://www.austincg.com
Insurance Agents
N.A.I.C.S.: 524210
W. Robert Messer (Owner & Pres)
Steve Graves (Mgr)
Shawn Dye (VP-Sls)
Keith Swearingen (Dir)
Glen King (Dir--Midwest)
Shannon Bennett (Mgr-)

The Presidio Group, Inc. (2)
6967 S River Gate Dr Ste 200, Salt Lake City, UT 84047
Tel.: (801) 924-1400
Web Site: http://www.presidio-group.com
Risk Management Consulting & Insurance Services
N.A.I.C.S.: 541618

Arthur J. Gallagher Sweden AB (1)
Tegnergatan 2C, Box 19572, 104 32, Stockholm, Sweden
Tel.: (46) 84418970
Web Site: http://www.ajg.com
Insurance Brokerage Services
N.A.I.C.S.: 524210
Frederick Enderlein (CEO & Mng Dir)
Ralph Winkler (Exec Dir)
Karl Lundell (Exec Dir-UAE)
Olle Lager (Gen Mgr-Norway & Exec Dir)
Martin Holdaas (Dir-Norway)

Atlas General Holdings, LLC (1)
4365 Executive Dr Ste 400, San Diego, CA 92121
Tel.: (858) 529-6700
Web Site: http://www.atlas.us.com
Sales Range: $50-74.9 Million
Insurance Agency Services
N.A.I.C.S.: 524210
Bill Trzos (Pres & CEO)
Ryan Clarkson (COO)
Mike Mathews (Pres-Workers Compensation Div)
Andrew Petersen (Chief Dev Officer)
Ryan Kirby (Chief Legal Officer & Gen Counsel)
Joe Zuk (Pres)
James Norris (Chief Actuarial Officer)
Mark Williams (Exec VP-Business Development)
Joe Ross (Pres)
Charles Lasher (Pres-Commercial)
Dayna Schneider (Sr VP)
Josh LaRiccia (VP)
Kristen Hakala (Asst VP)
Sarah Sloan (VP-Commercial)
Billy Garren (Program Mgr & Asst VP)

Arthur J. Gallagher & Co.—(Continued)

Jeff Hoffman *(VP)*
Pamela Flowers *(Asst VP)*
Joe Ross *(Pres)*
Charles Lasher *(Pres-Commercial)*
Dayna Schneider *(Sr VP)*
Josh LaRiccia *(VP)*
Kristen Hakala *(Asst VP)*
Sarah Sloan *(VP-Commercial)*
Billy Garren *(Program Mgr & Asst VP)*
Jeff Hoffman *(VP)*
Pamela Flowers *(Asst VP)*

BF&G Insurance Limited **(1)**
6380 Lady Hammond Rd, Nova Scotia, B3K
2S3, NS, Canada
Tel.: (902) 429-4150
General Insurance Services
N.A.I.C.S.: 524210

**Boley-Featherston-Huffman & Deal
Co.** **(1)**
701 Lamar St, Wichita Falls, TX 76301
Tel.: (940) 723-7111
Web Site: http://www.boleyfeatherston.com
Insurance Related Activities
N.A.I.C.S.: 524298

Brim AB **(1)**
Tegnergatan 2C, 104 32, Stockholm, Swe-
den
Tel.: (46) 84418970
Web Site: https://www.brim.se
Insurance Services
N.A.I.C.S.: 524210
Daniela Kruuse *(Controller)*
Peter Ringbom *(Mgr-Compliance)*

Buck Global LLC **(1)**
245 Park Ave, New York, NY 10167-0002
Tel.: (212) 330-1000
Web Site: http://www.buckglobal.com
Sales Range: $25-49.9 Million
Emp.: 120
Human Resource Consulting Services
N.A.I.C.S.: 541618

Subsidiary (Non-US):

Buck Consultants BV **(2)**
Beurs-World Trade Center, Beursplein 37,
Rotterdam, 3001, Netherlands
Tel.: (31) 102053500
Web Site: http://www.buckconsultants.nl
Sales Range: $10-24.9 Million
Emp.: 6
Human Resource Consulting Services
N.A.I.C.S.: 541612
Hans Veltkamp *(Gen Mgr)*

Buck Consultants Limited **(2)**
160 Queen Victoria Street, London, EC4V
4AN, United Kingdom
Tel.: (44) 2074291000
Web Site: http://www.buckconsultants.co.uk
Human Resource Consulting Services
N.A.I.C.S.: 541612

Subsidiary (Domestic):

**Buck Consultants (Administration &
Investment) Limited** **(3)**
160 Queen Victoria Street, London, EC4V
4AN, United Kingdom
Tel.: (44) 2074291000
Investment Management Service
N.A.I.C.S.: 523940

**Buck Consultants (Healthcare)
Limited** **(3)**
20 Wood Street, London, EC2V 7AF,
United Kingdom
Tel.: (44) 2074291000
Web Site: http://www.buckconsultants.com
Emp.: 42
Human Resource Consulting Services
N.A.I.C.S.: 541612
Paul Surprenant *(Mng Dir)*

Subsidiary (Non-US):

Buck Consultants NV/SA **(2)**
Park Hill E Mommaertslaan 16B, 1831, Di-
egem, Belgium
Tel.: (32) 27180660
Web Site: http://www.buckconsultants.de
Sales Range: $1-9.9 Million
Emp.: 9
Human Resource Consulting Services
N.A.I.C.S.: 541612

Buckman-Mitchell, Inc. **(1)**
500 N Santa Fe, Visalia, CA 93292
Tel.: (559) 733-1181
Web Site: http://www.bminc.com
General Insurance Agency
N.A.I.C.S.: 524210
Clifford H. Dunbar *(Chm & CEO)*
Brent E. Swanson *(Pres & COO)*
Judy A. Fussel *(Pres-Benefits Div)*
Todd C. Williams *(Exec VP)*
Stephan I. Chrisman *(Sr VP-Agri Bus)*
Linda N. Loflin *(Sr VP)*
Carolyn M. Cross *(Mgr-HR)*
Richard L. Nunes *(VP)*
JoeAnna D. Todd *(VP)*
Justin R. Workman *(VP)*
Donald P. Sharp *(VP)*
Luis Lopez *(Supvr-Client Svc)*
Ruth Bly *(Mgr-Client Svc)*
Julie McKinney *(Mgr-Client Svc)*
Jessica Weatherhead *(Mgr-Client Svc)*
Joanie Blackwell McLeod *(Dir-Client Svc)*
Joseph Orndoff *(Asst VP)*
James Smith *(Asst VP)*

C B S Insurance, L.L.P. **(1)**
3005 S Treadaway Blvd, Abilene, TX
79602-6729
Tel.: (325) 695-0222
Web Site: http://www.cbsins.com
Sales Range: $1-9.9 Million
Emp.: 30
Insurance Brokerage Services
N.A.I.C.S.: 524210
Eric Watson *(Partner)*
Mark Beale *(Partner)*

CG&B Investment Services, Inc. **(1)**
120 South Town Centre Blvd, Markham,
L6G 1C3, ON, Canada
Tel.: (905) 305-4306
Investment Banking Services
N.A.I.C.S.: 523150

**CGM Gallagher Insurance Brokers
(Barbados) Limited** **(1)**
Haggatt Hall, Saint Michael, BB11059, Bar-
bados
Tel.: (246) 4342200
Insurance Services
N.A.I.C.S.: 524210
John Rocheford *(Chm)*
Scott Stollmeyer *(Mng Dir)*
Karen Holder *(Sr VP-P&C)*
Tito Gulstone *(VP-Reg Claims)*
Stacey DaSilva *(VP-Fin)*

**CGM Gallagher Insurance Brokers
Jamaica Ltd.** **(1)**
27 Harbour Street, Kingston, Jamaica
Tel.: (876) 9486995
General Insurance Services
N.A.I.C.S.: 524210
Beulah Campbell *(VP-P&C & GEB)*
Camille Wilson *(VP-P&C & GEB)*
Ruth Preston *(Mgr-P&C & Mandeville)*
Careen Nolan *(Mgr-P&C)*
Maxine Finnikin *(Mgr-P&C)*

**CGM Gallagher Insurance Brokers
St. Kitts & Nevis Ltd.** **(1)**
E St John Payne Annex, PO Box 2410,
Basseterre, Saint Kitts & Nevis
Tel.: (869) 4653036
General Insurance Services
N.A.I.C.S.: 524210
Cedric Jeffers *(Branch Mgr)*

CJM Solutions Inc. **(1)**
88 Slayter Street, Dartmouth, B3A 2A6, NS,
Canada
Tel.: (002) 421 1000
Web Site: http://www.cjmsolutions.ca
Insurance & Retirement Planning Services
N.A.I.C.S.: 523940
Chris Matthews *(Partner)*
Jamie Spence *(Partner)*
Roger Sinclair *(Partner)*
Andrew MacKinnon *(Partner)*
Peter Thompson *(Partner)*

Cadence Insurance, Inc. **(1)**
4041 Essen Ln, Baton Rouge, LA 70809
Tel.: (281) 557-0344
Web Site:
http://www.cadenceinsurance.com
Insurance Agencies & Brokerages
N.A.I.C.S.: 524210
Stacey Voldt *(Mgr)*

**Capsicum Re Latin America Corre-
tora De Resseguros Ltda.** **(1)**
Rua Surubim 577 21st Floor Suite 211,
Brooklin Paulista Novo, 04571-050, Sao
Paulo, Brazil
Tel.: (55) 1132944040
Insurance Services
N.A.I.C.S.: 524210
Luiz Araripe *(CEO)*

Clements & Co. **(1)**
1660 L St NW Fl 9, Washington, DC 20036
Tel.: (202) 872-0060
Web Site: http://www.clements.com
Rev.: $4,000,000
Emp.: 49
Insurance Agencies & Brokerages
N.A.I.C.S.: 524210

**Commercial Insurance Underwriters,
Inc.** **(1)**
901 E Saint John St Ste 205, Springfield,
MO 65806-2537
Tel.: (417) 883-3277
Web Site: http://ciusgf.com
Sales Range: $1-9.9 Million
Emp.: 46
Insurance Agencies & Brokerages
N.A.I.C.S.: 524210

**Compass Point Retirement Planning,
Inc.** **(1)**
401 Edgewater Pl Ste 560, Wakefield, MA
01880-6231
Web Site: http://www.cprp.com
Investment Advice
N.A.I.C.S.: 523940

Complete Benefit Alliance, LLC **(1)**
2000 Morris Ave Ste 1400 14th Fl, Birming-
ham, AL 35203
Tel.: (205) 871-1082
Web Site: http://completebenefitalliance.com
Voluntary Benefits & Corporate Enrollment
Strategies
N.A.I.C.S.: 524210
Gina Gillilan *(Sr VP-Enrollment Svcs)*
James B. Kirke *(VP-Bus Dev)*
Steven R. Griffin *(CEO)*
Marc Koretzky *(COO)*
Julie Sailers *(Controller)*

Cool Insuring Agency, Inc. **(1)**
784 Troy-Schenectady Rd, Queensbury, NY
12804
Tel.: (518) 793-5133
Web Site: http://www.coolins.com
Insurance Services
N.A.I.C.S.: 524210
Anthony J. Mashuta *(Pres)*
John C. Bieniek *(Principal & VP)*
Mark E. Baker *(VP-Employee Benefits)*
Michael C. Plunkett *(VP)*
Gina M. Pasquini *(Mgr-Mktg)*
Dominic A. Gallo *(VP-Comml Lines Div)*
Robin M. Manell *(VP-Comml Lines Div)*
Ira D. Neifeld *(Sr VP)*
John F. Snow *(Sr VP)*
Michael J. Grasso *(Principal & VP)*
Kerry J. Furlong *(Treas & Sec)*
Brenda L. Osborne *(Mgr-Acctg Dept)*
Karen S. Camp *(Mgr-Personal Lines Div)*
Harry Ungeheuer *(Mgr-Bond)*
Matthew R. Webber *(VP)*
Paul J. Hennessey *(Asst VP-Comml Lines
Div)*
Joseph P. Tessitore *(Asst VP-Comml Lines
Div)*
Colleen Parmelee *(Asst VP-Comml Lines
Div)*
Ruth M. Yorker *(Mgr-HR Svcs)*

Coverdell Canada Corporation **(1)**
PO Box 1750, Station B, Montreal, H3B
3L3, QC, Canada
Web Site: http://www.lifestyleessentials.ca
Commercial Printing Mfr
N.A.I.C.S.: 323111

Cres Insurance Service, LLC **(1)**
PO Box 29502 #69121, Las Vegas, NV
89126-9502
Tel.: (858) 618-1648
Web Site: http://www.cresinsurance.com
Sales Range: $10-24.9 Million
Emp.: 45
Insurance Agencies & Brokerages
N.A.I.C.S.: 524210
Steven Sargenti *(Pres & CEO)*

DCP, Inc. **(1)**
215 Southwind Pl Ste 201, Manhattan, KS
66503
Tel.: (785) 537-0754
Pension Funds
N.A.I.C.S.: 525110

Denver Agency Company **(1)**
410 17th St Ste 1650, Denver, CO 80202
Tel.: (303) 892-6900
Web Site: http://www.denveragency.com
Sales Range: $1-9.9 Million
Emp.: 19
Insurance Agents, Brokers & Service, N
N.A.I.C.S.: 524210
Edwin A. Hyman *(Pres)*
Michelle Tremblay *(CMO)*

Eastern Insurance Group, LLC **(1)**
233 W Central St, Natick, MA 01760
Tel.: (508) 651-7700
Web Site:
https://www.easterninsurance.com
Insurance Agents
N.A.I.C.S.: 524210
Katie Pacione *(Mgr-Acct)*
Matthew F. Shadrick *(Exec VP-Eastern
Benefits Grp)*
Matthew F. Shadrick *(Exec VP-Benefits
Grp)*
Michael B. Uretsky *(Sr VP)*

Subsidiary (Domestic):

**Chase & Lunt Insurance Agency
LLC** **(2)**
65 Parker St, Newburyport, MA 01950
Tel.: (978) 462-4434
Insurance Services
N.A.I.C.S.: 524210

**Northbridge Insurance Agency
Inc.** **(2)**
1150 Main St Unit Ste 3, Concord, MA
01742
Tel.: (978) 369-5656
Web Site: http://www.northbridgeins.com
Insurance Agencies & Brokerages
N.A.I.C.S.: 524210
Carol Wilson *(Pres)*

Ericson Insurance Services, LLC **(1)**
PO Box 382, Washington Depot, CT 06794
Tel.: (860) 868-7361
Web Site: http://www.ericsoninsurance.com
Insurance Agencies & Brokerages
N.A.I.C.S.: 524210
Kurt Thoennessen *(VP-Mktg & Sls)*

**Evolution Technology Services
Limited** **(1)**
8 Lagonda Court Cowpen Lane Industrial
Estate, Billingham, TS23 4JF, United King-
dom
Tel.: (44) 3300011240
Web Site: https://www.evolutiontech.co.uk
Insurance Services
N.A.I.C.S.: 524210

**Financial Consultants of America,
Inc.** **(1)**
2104 W Laburnum Ave Ste 101, Richmond,
VA 23227-4357
Tel.: (804) 377-9498
Web Site: http://www.fcaretirement.com
Investment Advice
N.A.I.C.S.: 523940

Finergy Solutions Pty. Ltd. **(1)**
PO Box 1544, Milton, 4064, QLD, Australia
Tel.: (61) 1300071540
Insurance Services
N.A.I.C.S.: 524114

**Five Points Benefits Solutions,
LLC** **(1)**
377 Riverside Dr Ste 200, Franklin, TN
37064-5393
Tel.: (615) 791-7704
Web Site: http://www.fivepointsbenefits.com
Insurance Agencies & Brokerages
N.A.I.C.S.: 524210
Lisa Smith *(Mgr)*
Marisa Combs *(Gen Counsel & VP-Bus
Dev)*
Wes Dozier *(VP-Sls)*

Fleet Assistance Limited **(1)**
Tel.: (44) 1480813000
Web Site: http://www.fleetassist.co.uk

Fleet Consulting Services
N.A.I.C.S.: 541614
Karen Ewer (Head-Bus Dev)
Carl Blott (Fin Dir)
Mike Johnston (Mgr-Bus Dev)
Mark Davies (Mgr-Network Dev-North)
Vincent Saint Claire (Mng Dir)
Les Kerjenski (CTO)

Fortress Financial Solutions Pty. Ltd. (1)
15 Isabel Street, Toowoomba, 4350, QLD, Australia
Tel.: (61) 746464970
Web Site: http://www.fortressfinancialsolutions.com.au
Business Financial Services
N.A.I.C.S.: 541611
Ashley Gray (Mgr-Client Acct)

G.A. Mavon & Company (1)
10 W Chicago Ave, Hinsdale, IL 60521
Tel.: (630) 655-2400
Web Site: http://www.mavon.com
Insurance Related Activities
N.A.I.C.S.: 524298
Ian Kendall Snow (Mgr-Underwriting)

Gallagher Bassett Services, Inc. (1)
2850 Golf Rd, Rolling Meadows, IL 60008 (100%)
Tel.: (630) 773-3800
Web Site: http://www.artcobell.com
Rev.: $9,000,000
Emp.: 1,000
Insurance Services
N.A.I.C.S.: 524210
Scott R. Hudson (Pres & CEO)

Subsidiary (Non-US):

Gallagher Bassett Canada, Inc. (2)
4211 Young St 3404, Toronto, M2P 2A9, ON, Canada (100%)
Tel.: (416) 861-8212
Web Site: http://www.gallagherbassett.com
Sales Range: Less than $1 Million
Emp.: 20
Insurance Services
N.A.I.C.S.: 524298

Gallagher Bassett International Ltd. (UK) (2)
New Loom House, London, E1 1LU, United Kingdom (100%)
Tel.: (44) 2072088500
Web Site: http://www.gb.com
Sales Range: $1-9.9 Million
Emp.: 40
Insurance & Pension Services
N.A.I.C.S.: 524298

Subsidiary (Domestic):

HMG-PCMS Limited (3)
Unit 3 Amber Business Village Amber Close, Tamworth, B77 4RP, Staffordshire, United Kingdom
Tel.: (44) 1564730631
Web Site: http://www.hmg-pcms.com
Property Claim Management Services
N.A.I.C.S.: 524291

Strata Solicitors Ltd. (3)
Strata House Blisworth Hill Farm Stoke Road, Northampton, Blisworth, NN7 3DB, United Kingdom
Tel.: (44) 1604878880
Web Site: http://www.stratasolicitors.com
Legal Aid Services
N.A.I.C.S.: 541110

Subsidiary (Non-US):

Gallagher Bassett Services Pty. Ltd. (2)
Level 15 144 Edward Street, Brisbane, 4000, QLD, Australia (100%)
Tel.: (61) 730051900
Web Site: http://www.gallagherbassett.com.au
Sales Range: $1-9.9 Million
Emp.: 100
Insurance Services
N.A.I.C.S.: 524298
Damien Gilhooley (Gen Mgr-Integrated Claims Solutions)
Scott Newland (Gen Mgr-Govt & Long Tail Claims)

David Teall (Gen Mgr-Fin)
Andrew Spilsbury (VP-Brand Strategy, Mgmt & Growth)

Subsidiary (Domestic):

Gallagher Bassett Services Pty Ltd. (3)
20 Bond Street, Sydney, 2000, NSW, Australia (100%)
Tel.: (61) 294647111
Web Site: http://www.gallagherbassett.com.au
Insurance Services
N.A.I.C.S.: 524298
Scott Newland (Gen Mgr-Govt & Long Tail Claims)
Damien Gilhooley (Gen Mgr-Integrated Claims Solutions)

Gallagher Bassett Services Workers Compensation Victoria Pty. Ltd. (3)
Level 2 333 Collins Street, Locked Bag 3570, Melbourne, 3000, VIC, Australia (100%)
Tel.: (61) 392979000
Web Site: http://www.gallagherbassett.com.au
Insurance Services
N.A.I.C.S.: 524298

Gallagher Benefit Services, Inc. (1)
2850 Golf Rd, Rolling Meadows, IL 60008
Tel.: (630) 773-3800
Web Site: http://www.ajg.com
Employee Benefit & Human Resources Management & Consulting Services
N.A.I.C.S.: 541611

Subsidiary (Domestic):

AHC Digital LLC (2)
211 N 1st St Ste 240, Minneapolis, MN 55401
Tel.: (612) 443-4490
Web Site: http://www.lifetime.ahc.com
Financial Investment Services
N.A.I.C.S.: 523999

Division (Domestic):

Arthur J. Gallagher & Co. Rockville (2)
702 King Farm Blvd 2nd Fl, Rockville, MD 20850
Tel.: (301) 921-7804
Web Site: http://www.ajg.com
Independent Benefit Services
N.A.I.C.S.: 524210
Neil R. Simons (Pres-Benefits & HR Consulting)

Subsidiary (Domestic):

GBS Administrators, Inc. (2)
777 108th Ave NE, Bellevue, WA 98004
Tel.: (425) 454-8000
Web Site: http://www.ajg.com
Sales Range: $25-49.9 Million
Emp.: 50
Insurance Agencies & Brokerage Services
N.A.I.C.S.: 524210

GBS Insurance and Financial Services, Inc. (2)
1 Corporate Dr Ste 310, Shelton, CT 06484
Tel.: (203) 367-1322
Emp.: 50
Insurance Agencies & Brokerage Services
N.A.I.C.S.: 524210

GBS Retirement Services, Inc. (2)
2 Westchester Park Dr, White Plains, NY 10604 (100%)
Tel.: (914) 696-3700
Web Site: http://www.ajg.com
Pension Services
N.A.I.C.S.: 812990

Integrated Healthcare Strategies, LLC (2)
901 Marquette Ave S Ste 2100, Minneapolis, MN 55402
Tel.: (612) 339-0919
Web Site: http://www.integratedhealthcarestrategies.com
Healthcare Insurance & Employee Benefits Consulting Services
N.A.I.C.S.: 541612

Solid Benefit Guidance LLC (2)
85 Chestnut Rdg Rd Ste 214, Montvale, NJ 07645
Tel.: (201) 358-1132
Web Site: http://www.sbgbenefits.com
Pharmacy & Employee Benefits Management Services
N.A.I.C.S.: 541612
William Resnick (Founder)

Division (Domestic):

Worksite Communications (2)
800 Capital Cir SE Unit 2, Tallahassee, FL 32301
Tel.: (850) 521-0112
Web Site: https://www.enrollmentcompany.com
Sales Range: $1-9.9 Million
Emp.: 12
Employee Benefits Enrollment & Education Services
N.A.I.C.S.: 524292

Gallagher Construction Services (1)
1255 Battery St Ste 450, San Francisco, CA 94111
Tel.: (415) 391-1500
Web Site: http://www.ajgrms.com
Sales Range: $25-49.9 Million
Emp.: 200
Construction, Insurance, Surety & Risk Management Specialty Services
N.A.I.C.S.: 236220

Gallagher Healthcare Insurance Services, Inc. (1)
9821 Katy Freeway ste 700, Houston, TX 77024 (100%)
Tel.: (713) 461-4000
Web Site: http://www.ajgrms.com
Sales Range: $25-49.9 Million
Emp.: 130
Insurance Brokers
N.A.I.C.S.: 524210

Gallagher Insurance Brokers (St. Lucia) Limited (1)
2nd Floor Audi Building Choc Estate, PO Box Choc 8208, Castries, Saint Lucia
Tel.: (758) 4502410
Insurance Brokerage Services
N.A.I.C.S.: 524210
Camara Francois (Branch Mgr)

Gallagher Insurance Brokers (St. Vincent) Limited (1)
Villa Maria Building, PO Box 2149, Arnos Vale, Kingstown, Saint Vincent & the Grenadines
Tel.: (784) 4562120
Insurance Brokerage Services
N.A.I.C.S.: 524210

Garner & Glover Company (1)
135 S 8th Ave, Rome, GA 30161-5203
Tel.: (706) 291-7380
Web Site: http://www.garnerandglover.com
Sales Range: $1-9.9 Million
Emp.: 21
General Insurance Services
N.A.I.C.S.: 524210
Cindy Smith (Mgr-Operations)
Matt Sirmans (Pres & Owner)
Sue Jones (Mgr)
Tracy Mobley (Mgr)
Terri Scott (Mgr)

Garrett-Stotz Company, LLC (1)
1601 Alliant Ave, Louisville, KY 40299
Tel.: (502) 415-7000
Web Site: http://www.garrett-stotz.com
Insurance Agencies & Brokerages
N.A.I.C.S.: 524210
Don Mucci (Treas & Sec)
Tom Mitchell (VP)
Bill Kantlehner (Pres)
Ferren Meyer (Mgr)
Terri Hatfield (Mgr-Operations)
Roger Neal (Mgr)
Dallas Goodan (Controller)
Hunter Bowling (Acct Mgr)
Karen Cherry (Acct Mgr)
Julie Gentile (Acct Mgr)
Lois Kittel (Acct Mgr)
Kathy Martin (Acct Mgr)
Maureen Beyerle (Acct Mgr)
Becky Chowning (Acct Mgr)
Bobbie Fryrear (Acct Mgr)

Vicki George (Acct Mgr)
Donna Hellinger (Acct Mgr)
Colleen Hickman (Acct Mgr)
Beth Jost (Acct Mgr)
Melonie Smartt (Acct Mgr)
Brenda Trauth (Acct Mgr)
Andrea Cortes (Acct Mgr)
Liz Dawson (Acct Mgr)
Diane Phelps (Acct Mgr)
Sharon Gibson (Acct Mgr-Benefits)
Jinna Mills (Acct Mgr-Benefits)

Gatehouse Consulting Limited (1)
1 Vogans Mill Wharf 17 Mill Street, London, SE1 2BZ, United Kingdom
Tel.: (44) 2077543630
Web Site: http://www.gatehouse.co.uk
Public Relations Services
N.A.I.C.S.: 541820

General Southwest Insurance Agency, Inc. (1)
5628 E Thomas Rd, Phoenix, AZ 85018
Tel.: (480) 990-1900
Web Site: https://www.generalsouthwest.com
Sales Range: $1-9.9 Million
Emp.: 25
Insurance Agencies & Brokerages
N.A.I.C.S.: 524210
David Binsfeld (Exec VP)
Jay Binsfeld (Chm & CEO)
Joe Binsfeld (Pres)
John Binsfeld (VP-Ops)

Gillis, Ellis & Baker, Inc. (1)
1615 Poydras St Ste 700, New Orleans, LA 70112
Tel.: (504) 581-3334
Insurance Agencies & Brokerages
N.A.I.C.S.: 524210

HFG Benefits Corp. (1)
204-221 10th Ave SE, Calgary, T2G 0V9, AB, Canada
Tel.: (403) 231-8617
Web Site: http://www.hfgbenefits.com
Benefit Services
N.A.I.C.S.: 524292

HR Owen Insurance Services Limited (1)
Melton Court 25-27 Old Brompton Rd South Kensington, London, SW7 3TD, United Kingdom
Tel.: (44) 2033728382
Insurance Brokerage Services
N.A.I.C.S.: 524210

Hammerberg Investments, Inc. (1)
4101 Glass Rd NE, Cedar Rapids, IA 52402
Tel.: (319) 393-5262
Insurance Agencies & Brokerages
N.A.I.C.S.: 524210

Hanover Excess & Surplus, Inc. (1)
213 Racine Dr, Wilmington, NC 28403
Tel.: (910) 762-7109
Web Site: http://www.hanoverxs.com
Insurance Agencies & Brokerages
N.A.I.C.S.: 524210
Geoffrey Crater (VP-Underwriting)
Matthew Letson (Pres)
Dale Hart (Mgr)
Beth Rivenbark (Mgr)
Tina R. Foy (Mgr)
Jessica Wilson (Mgr-Accounting)

Harden & Associates, Inc. (1)
501 Riverside Ave Ste 1000, Jacksonville, FL 32202
Tel.: (904) 354-3785
Web Site: http://www.hardeninsight.com
Sales Range: $300-349.9 Million
Emp.: 130
Insurance Brokers
N.A.I.C.S.: 524210
Marvin Harden (Pres)
Natalie Johns (Acct Exec & VP)
Kurt Thoresen (Acct Exec-Marketing & VP)

Hartley Cylke Pacific Insurance Services, Inc. (1)
2747 University Ave, San Diego, CA 92104
Tel.: (619) 295-5155
Web Site: http://www.hcpacinsurance.com
Sales Range: $1-9.9 Million
Emp.: 50
Insurance Agencies & Brokerages
N.A.I.C.S.: 524210

Arthur J. Gallagher & Co.—(Continued)

Carrie Roda *(Sec)*
Michael E. Hartley *(Pres)*
John Cylke *(CEO)*

Hesse & Partner, AG (1)
Seefeldstrasse 15, 8008, Zurich,
Switzerland (100%)
Tel.: (41) 58 255 8188
Web Site: https://www.ajg.com
Insurance Services
N.A.I.C.S.: 524210
Guido Hesse *(Chm)*
Stephan Bachmann *(CEO)*

Subsidiary (Domestic):

Verbag AG (2)
Lettenstrasse 7, 6343, Rotkreuz, Switzerland
Tel.: (41) 417903980
Web Site: http://www.verbag.ch
Insurance Brokerage Services
N.A.I.C.S.: 524210

Home & Travel Limited (1)
Unit 4 46 Ilford Lane, Ilford, IG1 2JY, United Kingdom
Tel.: (44) 208 911 6194
Web Site: https://www.hometravelsltd.com
Flight Travel & Booking Services
N.A.I.C.S.: 561599

Horak Insurance, Inc (1)
115 E Washington St, Washington, IA 52353-2022
Tel.: (319) 653-2116
Web Site: http://www.horakinsurance.com
Insurance Related Activities
N.A.I.C.S.: 524298
Paul Horak *(Partner)*

Horseshoe Insurance Services Holdings Ltd. (1)
Wessex House 3rd Floor 45 Reid Street, HM 12, Hamilton, Bermuda
Tel.: (441) 2958478
Web Site: http://www.horseshoeglobal.com
Insurance & Reinsurance Professional Services
N.A.I.C.S.: 524130
Andre Perez *(Chm)*
Nigel Godfrey *(CFO & Exec VP)*
LaMel Burch *(COO)*
Rodney Davies *(CTO)*
Lola Myshketa *(Chief Bus Dev Officer)*
Kathleen Faries *(CEO)*
Jasmine DeSilva *(Sr VP-Business Development)*
Brian Desmond *(Chief Strategy Officer, Exec VP & Head)*
Scott Cobon *(Exec VP & Head)*
Paula Cox *(Gen Counsel)*
Yulanda Francis *(Exec VP & Head)*
Jane Lewis *(Compliance Officer)*
Gail Wright *(Head)*

Hughes Insurance Agency, Inc. (1)
328 Bay Rd, Queensbury, NY 12804
Tel.: (518) 793-3131
Web Site: http://www.hughesinsurance.com
Sales Range: $1-9.9 Million
Emp.: 15
Insurance Services
N.A.I.C.S.: 524210
Linda Abodeely *(Pres)*
Mark Abodeely *(VP)*
Joe Koncikowski *(VP)*

Insurance By Ken Brown, Inc. (1)
707 Pennsylvania Ave, Altamonte Springs, FL 32701
Tel.: (407) 849-0490
Web Site: http://www.insbykenbrown.com
Sales Range: $1-9.9 Million
Emp.: 20
Insurance Agencies & Brokerages
N.A.I.C.S.: 524210
Ken Brown *(Founder)*

Insure My Villa Limited (1)
30-34 Hounds Gate, Nottingham, NG1 7AB, United Kingdom
Tel.: (44) 1159505052
Web Site: http://www.insuremyvilla.com
Insurance Services
N.A.I.C.S.: 524126

Integrated Direct Marketing Solutions, Inc. (1)

820 A1A Hwy W18, Ponte Vedra Beach, FL 32082
Tel.: (904) 285-6020
Periodical Publishers
N.A.I.C.S.: 513120

JP Tech Insurance Services Inc. (1)
445 S Figueroa St Ste 3210, Los Angeles, CA 90071
Tel.: (213) 986-2560
Web Site: http://www.jptechinsurance.com
Insurance Agencies & Brokerages
N.A.I.C.S.: 524210
Joseph Plascencia *(Pres)*

Jones Brown Inc. (1)
145 Wellington Street West Suite 1200, Toronto, M5J 1H8, ON, Canada
Tel.: (416) 408-1920
Web Site: http://www.jonesbrown.com
Sales Range: $25-49.9 Million
Emp.: 100
Insurance Agents
N.A.I.C.S.: 524210
Peter Bryant *(Mng Dir & Head-Toronto Office)*
John Lindsay *(Vice Chm)*
David Gray *(VP-Calgary)*
Grant Robinson *(Mng Dir & Head-Calgary)*
Don Taylor *(VP-Comml)*
Bill Semrau *(VP-Vancouver)*
Wendy Sinclair *(Mng Dir & Head-Vancouver Office)*
Bradley Inkster *(VP-Comml)*
Jeffrey C. Charles *(Mng Dir-Intl Bus)*
Trevor Waldron *(Mng Dir & Head-Hamilton Office)*
Lola Thake *(VP)*
Sara Tanaka *(VP-Toronto)*
Linda Papadopoulos *(VP-Risk Mgmt-Hamilton)*
Nancy Au *(VP-Sports & Recreation-Hamilton)*
Jen Ormond *(Asst VP-Toronto)*
Michelle Laracy *(Mgr-Client-Toronto)*
Rutendo Chidovi *(Mgr-Client-Toronto)*
Emma McLachlan *(Mgr-Client-Toronto)*
Sarah Thomson *(Mgr-Client-Toronto)*
Emily Maganja *(Mgr-Client-Toronto)*
Donovan Crabtree *(Mgr-Client-Toronto)*
Claire Bourgard *(Mgr-Client-Toronto)*
Sylvia Lee *(Mgr-Client-Toronto)*
Kim Brandon *(Mgr-Client-Toronto)*
Natalee Sinclair *(VP-Private Client Svcs)*
John Federico *(VP-Comml)*
Brent Brandham *(VP-Comml)*
Holly Samson *(VP-Comml)*
David Kerr *(VP-Comml)*
David Lindsay *(VP-Comml)*
John Hawkrigg *(Sr Mgr-Bus Relationship)*
Leslie Ducommun *(Mgr-Client)*
Hanako van der Pol *(Mgr-Client)*
Karen Crippin *(Mgr-Client)*
Jennifer Lu *(Mgr-Client)*
Dustin Bunney *(Mgr-Client)*
Linda Cheong *(Mgr-Client)*
Roseanne Hoffart *(Mgr-Client)*
Kyle MacKellar *(Mgr-Client)*
Jessica Shuryn *(Mgr-Client)*
Helena Fan *(Mgr-Client)*
Arezoo Tarighati *(Mgr-Client)*
Debbie Amaral *(Mgr-Client)*
Amanda Tupper *(Mgr-Client)*
Michele Rotolo *(Mgr-Client)*
Jackie Cope *(Mgr-Bus Dev)*
John Edwards *(Asst VP-Comml)*
Mike Naughton *(Asst VP-Comml)*

Just Landlords Insurance Services Ltd. (1)
Spectrum Building 7th Floor 55 Blythswood Street, Glasgow, G2 7AT, United Kingdom
Tel.: (44) 8081689220
Web Site: https://www.justlandlords.co.uk
Insurance Services
N.A.I.C.S.: 524210

Kusske Financial Asset Management, Inc. (1)
11986 Portland Ave, Burnsville, MN 55337
Tel.: (952) 895-6963
Web Site: http://www.kusskefinancial.com
Investment Advice
N.A.I.C.S.: 523940

LSG Insurance Partners, Inc. (1)
2600 S Telegraph Rd Ste 100, Bloomfield Hills, MI 48302
Tel.: (248) 332-3100

Insurance Related Activities
N.A.I.C.S.: 524298

Lloyd Bedford Cox, Inc. (1)
325 Bedford Rd, Bedford Hills, NY 10507
Tel.: (914) 666-5121
Web Site: http://www.lbcinc.com
Sales Range: $1-9.9 Million
Emp.: 10
Insurance Agents, Brokers, And Service, N
N.A.I.C.S.: 524210
J. Cox *(Mgr)*
David Carlucci *(Acct Mgr)*
Greg Williams *(Chief Underwriting Officer)*
Lloyd Cox *(VP)*
Mark Mischenko *(COO)*

Mahowald Insurance Agency, LLC (1)
916 W Saint Germain St, Saint Cloud, MN 56301
Tel.: (320) 251-3751
Web Site: http://www.mahowald.net
Sales Range: $1-9.9 Million
Emp.: 20
Insurance Agencies & Brokerages
N.A.I.C.S.: 524210
Benjamin Thoele *(Coord-IT)*
Laura Tomczik *(Partner & Dir-Risk Mgmt)*
Greg Murray *(Partner)*
Robert W. Mahowald *(Mng Partner)*
David Mahowald *(Partner)*
Amanda Austin *(Acct Exec)*
Julie Kremer *(Acct Exec-Benefits)*

Mark J. Becker & Associates, LLC (1)
5501 NW 86th St Ste 700, Johnston, IA 50131
Web Site: http://www.mjbaconsulting.com
Leather Goods Mfr
N.A.I.C.S.: 315210
Mark J. Becker *(Pres)*

McLean Insurance Agency (1)
46179 Westlake Dr Ste 300, Potomac Falls, VA 20165
Tel.: (703) 790-5770
Web Site: http://www.mcleaninsurance.com
Insurance Related Activities
N.A.I.C.S.: 524298

Meadowbrook Insurance Agency, Inc. (1)
26255 American Dr, Southfield, MI 48034-6112
Web Site: http://www.meadowbrookagency.com
Direct Property & Casualty Insurance Services
N.A.I.C.S.: 524126
David N. Sheeran *(Pres)*
Matthew McGrail *(Sr VP-Ops)*

Subsidiary (Domestic):

Kleinschmidt Agency, Inc. (2)
305 E Eisenhower Pky Ste 200, Ann Arbor, MI 48108
Tel.: (734) 662-3100
Web Site: https://www.meadowbrookagency.com
Sales Range: $1-9.9 Million
Emp.: 14
Insurance Agencies & Brokerages
N.A.I.C.S.: 524210
Linda Kleinschmidt *(VP)*

MedInsights, Inc. (1)
377 River Side Sr Ste 400, Franklin, TN 37064
Tel.: (615) 778-5000
Web Site: http://www.medinsights.com
Emp.: 50
Insurance Agencies & Brokerage Services
N.A.I.C.S.: 524210

Meyers-Reynolds & Associates, Inc. (1)
615 E Britton Rd, Oklahoma City, OK 73114
Tel.: (405) 235-6633
Web Site: http://www.meyersreynolds.com
Sales Range: $25-49.9 Million
Emp.: 37
Insurance Agents & Brokerages
N.A.I.C.S.: 524210
Lee Reynolds *(Pres)*

Minvielle & Chastanet Insurance Brokers Limited (1)

9-11 Bridge Street, PO Box 99, Castries, Saint Lucia
Tel.: (758) 4588000
Web Site: https://themandcgroup.com
Holding Company; Retail, Wholesale, Distribution, Shipping, Insurance, Manufacturing, Tourism & IT Services
N.A.I.C.S.: 551112
Jonathan Powell *(CEO)*

Subsidiary (Domestic):

M&C Drugstore Ltd. (2)
Bridge Street, Castries, Saint Lucia
Tel.: (758) 4588147
Web Site: https://mandcdrugstore.com
Emp.: 130
Pharmacy & Drug Store Operator
N.A.I.C.S.: 456110
Fredreika Joseph-Leon *(Gen Mgr)*

M&C General Insurance Co. Ltd. (2)
9-11 Bridge Street, PO Box 99, Castries, LC04 101, Saint Lucia
Tel.: (758) 4588216
Web Site: https://mandcinsurance.net
Emp.: 17
Property & Casualty Insurance Products & Services
N.A.I.C.S.: 524126
Royer Felix *(Gen Mgr)*
Quincy Christophe *(Asst Mgr-Underwriting)*
Barbara Blasse *(Asst Mgr-Claims)*
Emily McFarlane *(Supvr-Underwriting)*
Emmalee Swanson *(Officer-Accounting)*
Dione Simon *(Supvr)*
Nichola Francis *(Mgr-Insurance)*
Johanne Hazell *(Officer-Insurance)*
Janet Quow *(Coord)*
Emily McFarlane *(Supvr-Underwriting)*
Emmalee Swanson *(Officer-Accounting)*
Dione Simon *(Supvr)*
Nichola Francis *(Mgr-Insurance)*
Johanne Hazell *(Officer-Insurance)*
Janet Quow *(Coord)*

M&C Home Depot Ltd. (2)
Vide Boutielle, Castries, LC01101, Saint Lucia
Tel.: (758) 4588300
Web Site: https://mandchomedepot.com
Emp.: 70
Hardware & Building Supplies Stores Operator
N.A.I.C.S.: 444140
Kernan Quinlan *(Mgr-Ops)*

M&C Shipping Department (2)
9-11 Bridge Street, PO Box 99, Castries, Saint Lucia
Web Site: http://www.mandcgroup.com
Deep-Sea Freight Shipping Arrangement Services
N.A.I.C.S.: 488510

NEK Insurance Inc. (1)
11481 San Pablo Ave, El Cerrito, CA 94530
Tel.: (510) 233-2600
Web Site: http://www.nekinsurance.com
Sales Range: $1-9.9 Million
Emp.: 22
Insurance Agencies & Brokerages
N.A.I.C.S.: 524210
Joan Kinsey *(Treas & Sec)*

Nordic Forsakring & Riskhantering AB (1)
Molndalsvagen 22, 412 63, Gothenburg, Sweden
Tel.: (46) 3 140 5370
Web Site: https://www.nordic.se
Claim Insurance Services
N.A.I.C.S.: 524291

PT IBS Insurance Broking Service (1)
Indonesia Stock Exchange Building Tower II 27th Floor, Jl Jenderal Sudirman Kav 52-53, Jakarta, 12190, Indonesia
Tel.: (62) 21 515 3131
Web Site: https://www.ibsrisk.com
Insurance Services
N.A.I.C.S.: 524210
Swandi Kendy *(Pres)*
Ani Kusharjati *(Bus Dir)*
Steve Raymond *(Asst VP-Business Development)*
Feter Kurniawan *(Bus Dir)*
Tedy Lesmana *(VP-Finance)*

Pen Underwriting Limited (1)
67 Lombard St, London, EC3V 9LJ, United Kingdom
Tel.: (44) 1403321196
Web Site:
https://www.penunderwriting.co.uk
Insurance Services
N.A.I.C.S.: 524210
Nick Wright (Chief Bus Dev Officer)
Jennifer Martin (Chief Underwriting Officer)
Steve Thornett (Mng Dir-Specialty)
Andy Westby (Mng Dir-e-SME & Personal Lines)
Nick Colyer (Mng Dir-Pub Sector)
Adrian Scott (Mng Dir-Fin Lines)
Sarah Breslin (CFO)
Matthew Lucas (COO)
Tom Downey (CEO)
Charles Manchester (CEO)

Potter-Holden & Co. (1)
900 Ashwood Pkwy Ste 100, Dunwoody, GA 30338
Tel.: (770) 399-6760
Web Site: http://www.potterholden.com
Sales Range: $25-49.9 Million
Emp.: 15
Insurance Agencies & Brokerages
N.A.I.C.S.: 524210

Premier Brokerage Services Inc. (1)
604 Harper Ave, Jenkintown, PA 19046-3207
Tel.: (215) 517-4080
Web Site: http://www.premierbrokerage.com
All Other Support Services
N.A.I.C.S.: 561990
Steven J. Katz (Sr VP-Area)
Lauren Shafer (Sr VP-Sls & Mktg)
Colette Tomeo (Sr VP-Ops)
Cheryl Visconti (Mktg Mgr)
Terri Funk (Mgr-New Bus)
Greg Rorer (VP-Underwriting)
Brenda Davis (Dir-Natl Accounts)
Lora Merlino (Mgr-Case)
Clara DiGiovannangelo (Sr Mgr-Case)
Karen White (Sr Mgr-Case)
Amy Garcia (Mgr-Case)
Giselle Gonzalez (Mgr-Case)
Andi Forman (Mgr-Case)
Michele Bonner (Mgr-Case)
Rachel Dubin (Mgr-Acctg)

Proinova AB (1)
Hamntorget 5, 252 21, Helsingborg, Sweden
Tel.: (46) 10 221 6670
Web Site: https://www.proinova.se
Insurance Brokerage Services
N.A.I.C.S.: 524210

Pronto General Agency , Ltd. (1)
PO Box 3267, Brownsville, TX 78523-3267
Tel.: (979) 202-4499
Web Site: https://www.prontoinsurance.com
Insurance Services
N.A.I.C.S.: 524126

RA Rossborough (Insurance Brokers) Ltd (1)
41 La Motte Street, PO Box 28, Saint Helier, Jersey
Tel.: (44) 1534500500
Web Site:
http://www.rossboroughgroup.co.uk
Emp.: 70
General Insurance Services
N.A.I.C.S.: 524210
Clive de la Cour (Chm)
James Anderson (Mng Dir)
Jennifer Gouyet (Mgr-Healthcare)
John Lowery (Dir)
Lee Refault (Comml Dir)
Mark Vautier (Head-Grp)
Rob Hewlett (Dir)
Nigel Lee-Briard (Dir-Commercial)
Richard Boddy (Acct Exec-Comml)
Tim Mitchell (Head-Grp)
Darren Wetheridge (Mgr)
Natasha Lucock (Head)
Gareth Wheatley (Mgr)
Steve Lindsay (Head-Commercial)
Tim Mitchell (Head-Grp)
Darren Wetheridge (Mgr)
Natasha Lucock (Head)
Gareth Wheatley (Mgr)
Steve Lindsay (Head-Commercial)

RGA Underwriting Limited (1)

27 Great West Road, Brentford, London, TW8 9BW, United Kingdom
Tel.: (44) 3330000173
Web Site: http://www.rgau.co.uk
Property & Commercial Insurance Services
N.A.I.C.S.: 531312
James Castell (CEO)
Xiao Cao (Dir-Operations)
Victor Wild (Dir)

Rentguard Limited (1)
27 Great West Road, Brentford, London, TW8 9BW, United Kingdom
Tel.: (44) 2085871060
Web Site: https://www.rentguard.co.uk
Property & Commercial Insurance Services
N.A.I.C.S.: 531312
Steve Jones (Mng Dir)
Kim O'Donnell (Dir-Human Resources)

Richter International Consulting, LLC (1)
317 NW Gilman Blvd Ste 51, Issaquah, WA 98027
Tel.: (425) 961-0446
Web Site: http://www.richterintl.com
Management Consulting Services
N.A.I.C.S.: 541618
David Richter (Founder & Pres)
Barbara Lee (Mgr-Client Rels)
Joe Roark (Dir-Bus Solutions-Global)
Nikki Hampton (Mgr-Acct)

Risk Placement Services, Inc. (1)
2850 Golf Rd, Rolling Meadows, IL 60008 (100%)
Tel.: (630) 773-3800
Web Site: https://www.rpsins.com
Sales Range: $75-99.9 Million
Provider of Insurance Services
N.A.I.C.S.: 541613
Russell Duffey (Pres-Program Admin-Signature Programs)
Joel Cavaness (Pres)

Subsidiary (Domestic):

McCloskey Surplus & Excess, Inc. (2)
245 Main St, Ridgefield Park, NJ 07660
Tel.: (201) 641-5100
Web Site: http://www.metcomexcess.com
Sales Range: $1-9.9 Million
Emp.: 50
Wholesale Insurance Broker
N.A.I.C.S.: 524210

RPS Excel (2)
200 American Metro Blvd Ste 104, Hamilton, NJ 08619
Tel.: (609) 530-0111
Web Site: http://www.rpsins.com
Wholesale Insurance Broker
N.A.I.C.S.: 524210

Seacoast Underwriters, Inc. (2)
1500 San Remo Ave Ste 214, Coral Gables, FL 33146
Tel.: (305) 774-9977
Web Site:
http://www.seacoastunderwriters.com
Sales Range: $1-9.9 Million
Emp.: 32
Insurance Agents, Brokers, And Service, N
N.A.I.C.S.: 524298
Yanay Blanco (Sr Mgr-Accounting)
Irma Marino (Mgr-Flood Underwriting)

Tejas American General Agency, LLC (2)
1620 La Jaita Dr Ste 300, Cedar Park, TX 78613
Tel.: (512) 346-0030
Web Site: http://www.taga1.com
Insurance Agents, Brokers, And Service, N
N.A.I.C.S.: 524210
Cindy Yurkovich (Mgr-Admin)

Risk Planners, Inc. (1)
3600 American Blvd W Ste 500, Bloomington, MN 55431 (100%)
Tel.: (800) 328-7475
Web Site: http://www.riskplanners.com
Sales Range: $1-9.9 Million
Emp.: 35
Property, Casualty & Life Insurance Services
N.A.I.C.S.: 524298

Robbi Davis Agency Inc. (1)

1909 Hinson Loop Rd Ste 102, Little Rock, AR 72212
Tel.: (501) 954-8100
Web Site: http://www.robbidavisagency.com
Insurance Agencies & Brokerages
N.A.I.C.S.: 524210
Robbi Davis (Pres & CEO)
Scott Davis (Product Mgr & CFO)
Kaleigh Marsh (Acct Mgr)
Tiffany Owens (Assoc Mgr)
Kelly Warner (Sr Acct Mgr)

Rosenzweig Insurance Agency, Inc. (1)
160 Herricks Rd, Mineola, NY 11501
Tel.: (516) 352-7495
Web Site:
http://www.rosenzweiginsurance.com
Sales Range: $1-9.9 Million
Emp.: 15
Insurance Agencies & Brokerages
N.A.I.C.S.: 524210

Rossborough Insurance (IOM) Ltd. (1)
New Wing Victory House Prospect Hill, IM1 1EQ, Douglas, Isle of Man
Tel.: (44) 1624631631
Web Site: https://www.rossborough.co.uk
General Insurance Services
N.A.I.C.S.: 524210
Simon Colquitt (Mgr)
Michael Sheeley (Mgr)
Gary Holdaway (Acct Mgr)
James Anderson (Mng Dir)
Ann Collins (Mng Dir)
Clive de la Cour (Chm)
James Hamlet (Head)
Lee Refault (Comml Dir)
Mark Vautier (Head-Grp)
James Anderson (Mng Dir)
Ann Collins (Mng Dir)
Clive de la Cour (Chm)
James Hamlet (Head)
Lee Refault (Comml Dir)
Mark Vautier (Head-Grp)

SP&G Insurance Brokers Sdn Bhd (1)
2nd Floor Bangunan KWSP No 3 Changkat Raja Chulan, 50200, Kuala Lumpur, Malaysia
Tel.: (60) 39 206 2200
Web Site: https://www.spgib.com.my
Insurance Services
N.A.I.C.S.: 524210
Zakaria Meranun (CEO & Chm)
Sudirman Hamzah (Deputy CEO)
Mohd Suhaimi Ahmad (Gen Mgr)

Serna Insurance Agency, Inc. (1)
9232 Will Clayton Pkwy, Humble, TX 77338
Tel.: (281) 812-9775
Insurance Agencies & Brokerages
N.A.I.C.S.: 524210

Stewart, Brimner, Peters & Company, Inc. (1)
3702 Rupp Dr, Fort Wayne, IN 46815
Tel.: (260) 482-6900
Web Site: http://www.sbpinsurance.com
Emp.: 40
Insurance Agents
N.A.I.C.S.: 524210
John Brimner (Mng Partner)
Jeff Peters (Mng Partner)
Tim Neuhauser (CFO)
Mick Stewart (Mng Partner)
Jason Brimmer (Mng Partner)
Angie Henn (Acct Mgr-Comml)
Tina Gibson (Acct Mgr-Comml)
Amy Pedersen (Acct Mgr-Comml)
Kelli Brimmer (Acct Mgr-Comml)
Colette Steigmeyer (Acct Mgr-Comml)
Connie Hawken (Mktg Mgr)

Strong Advisory Group, Inc. (1)
1611 10th St Ste A, Aurora, NE 68818
Tel.: (402) 694-6757
Web Site: https://www.strongag.com
Insurance Agents
N.A.I.C.S.: 524210
Chad Svoboda (Mgr)
Sara Strong (Office Mgr)

Surety Solutions, LLC (1)
4285 Commercial St SE Ste 110, Salem, OR 97302
Tel.: (866) 722-9239

Web Site: https://suretysolutions.com
Insurance Agencies & Brokerages
N.A.I.C.S.: 524210
Cory McDonald (VP)
Cryssi Brubaker (Mgr-Client Services)
Brian Radford (Mgr-Client Services)
Victoria Hatefi (Supvr-Client Service)
Katrina Fearn (Mgr-Client Service)
Beulah Hadley-Voth (Mgr)
Wendy Lewis (Acct Mgr-Surety)
Brett Feagans (Dir-IT)
Wendy Lewis (Acct Mgr)

Tave & Associates, LLC (1)
311 S Wacker Dr Ste 4525, Chicago, IL 60606
Tel.: (847) 267-0415
Web Site: http://www.taverm.com
Women's, Girls & Infants Cut & Sew Apparel Contractors
N.A.I.C.S.: 315210
Ruth Tave (Founder)

Texas Insurance Managers, Inc. (1)
418 E Tyler Ste B, Harlingen, TX 78550
Tel.: (956) 423-6986
Web Site: http://www.txinsmgr.com
Insurance Agents
N.A.I.C.S.: 524210
Richard W. May (CEO & Partner)

The Evans Agency, LLC (1)
1 Grimsby Dr Ste 200, Hamburg, NY 14075
Tel.: (716) 549-2000
Web Site: http://www.evansagencyins.com
Rev.: $120,000
Emp.: 20
Insurance Agents
N.A.I.C.S.: 524210
Mark Saint George (Pres)

The Human Capital Group, Inc. (1)
1612 Westgate Cir Ste 112, Brentwood, TN 37027
Tel.: (615) 371-0285
Web Site:
http://www.humancapitalgroupinc.com
Management Consulting Services
N.A.I.C.S.: 541611
Steve T. Hayes (Founder, Sr Partner & Sr Mng Dir)
Jamie Frame (Dir)
Paul Cleckner (Mng Dir)
David Alexander (Mng Dir)
Catherine Herro (Mgr)
Alex Petrini (Mgr-Marketing)

The Kirksey Agency, Inc. (1)
639 Commercial Pkwy Ste A, West Monroe, LA 71292
Tel.: (318) 323-2343
Web Site: http://www.thekirkseyagency.com
Insurance Related Activities
N.A.I.C.S.: 524298

Tyler Insurance Agency, LLC (1)
1225 W Main St, El Centro, CA 92243
Tel.: (760) 352-2611
Insurance Brokerage Services
N.A.I.C.S.: 524210

Uni-Care, Inc. (1)
233 S Wacker Dr, Chicago, IL 60606
Tel.: (312) 234-8000
Insurance Services
N.A.I.C.S.: 524114

United Dealer Services L.L.C. (1)
615 Route 32, Highland Mills, NY 10930
Professional, Scientific & Technical Services
N.A.I.C.S.: 541990

Vasek Insurance Services Limited (1)
30-34 Hounds Gate, Nottingham, NG1 7AB, United Kingdom
Tel.: (44) 1159505052
Web Site: https://www.vasek.co.uk
Insurance Services
N.A.I.C.S.: 524210
Sam Miles (Dir-Sls & Bus Dev)
Shauna Morlese (Mgr-Bus Dev)
Michael Czekalskyj (Mgr-Bus Dev)
James Collins (Mng Dir)

Viking Bond Service, Inc. (1)
22601 N 19th Ave Ste 210, Phoenix, AZ 85027
Tel.: (623) 933-9334

Arthur J. Gallagher & Co.—(Continued)

Web Site:
http://www.performancesuretybonds.com
Sales Range: $1-9.9 Million
Emp.: 10
Direct Property & Casualty Insurance Services
N.A.I.C.S.: 524126
Thomas Buckner *(Exec VP)*
William Belpedio *(VP)*
Sara McNeill *(Mgr-Ops)*
Jennifer Pixler *(Mgr-Clerical Dept)*

Walsdorf Agency, Inc. (1)
770 New York Ave, Huntington, NY 11743
Tel.: (631) 423-1140
Web Site:
http://www.walsdorfagency.greendays
group.com
Insurance Brokerage Services
N.A.I.C.S.: 524210

Western Litigation, Inc. (1)
1900 W Loop S Ste 1500, Houston, TX 77027
Tel.: (713) 468-0200
Web Site: https://www.gallagherbassett.com
Liability Claims Management & Risk Management Services
N.A.I.C.S.: 524292
Robert B. Blasio *(Pres & CEO)*

Wheatman Insurance Services, LLC (1)
5950 Canoga Ave Ste 600, Woodland Hills, CA 91367
Tel.: (818) 881-8900
Insurance Agencies & Brokerages
N.A.I.C.S.: 524210
Mark Wheatman *(Pres)*

Wigmore Insurance Agency, Inc. (1)
880 W. 19th St., Costa Mesa, CA 92627
Tel.: (714) 979-6543
Web Site: http://www.wigmoreins.com
Insurance Agencies & Brokerages
N.A.I.C.S.: 524210
Tim Wigmore *(Owner)*

Willis Re, Inc. (1)
200 Liberty St 3rd Fl, New York, NY 10281
Tel.: (212) 915-7600
Web Site: http://www.willisre.com
Reinsurance Broker
N.A.I.C.S.: 524210
Paddy Jago *(Co-Chm)*
Brian Ingle *(Chief Analytics Officer)*
Thomas Wafer *(Co-Chm)*
Jeffrey Livingston *(Vice Chm-North America)*
Mark E. Hansen *(COO)*
Charles Rumball *(Head-North America)*

Wrightman, Inc. (1)
5360 Jackson Dr, La Mesa, CA 91942-6002
Tel.: (619) 741-2872
Web Site: http://www.sascbonds.com
Insurance Agencies & Brokerages
N.A.I.C.S.: 524210
Cyndi Beilman *(Pres)*

ARTIFICIAL INTELLIGENCE TECHNOLOGY SOLUTIONS INC.
10800 Galaxie Ave, Ferndale, MI 48220
Tel.: (702) 990-3271　FL
Web Site: https://www.aitx.ai
Year Founded: 2010
AITX—(OTCIQ)
Rev.: $1,331,956
Assets: $6,296,858
Liabilities: $38,139,859
Net Worth: ($31,843,001)
Earnings: ($18,109,457)
Emp.: 70
Fiscal Year-end: 02/28/23
After Market Electronic, Audio & Video Upgrade Installation Services
N.A.I.C.S.: 811210
Steven Reinharz *(Pres, CEO, CFO & Sec)*

ARTISAN CONSUMER GOODS, INC.
999 N Northlake Way Ste 203, Seattle, WA 98103-3442
Tel.: (206) 517-7141　NV
Web Site:
http://www.artisanconsumer
goods.com
Year Founded: 2009
ARRT—(OTCIQ)
Rev.: $13,149
Assets: $2,920
Liabilities: $280,718
Net Worth: ($277,798)
Earnings: ($18,910)
Emp.: 1
Fiscal Year-end: 06/30/24
Consumer Packaged Goods Distr
N.A.I.C.S.: 423990
Amber Joy Finney *(Pres, CEO, Treas & Sec)*

ARTISAN PARTNERS ASSET MANAGEMENT INC.
875 E Wisconsin Ave Ste 800, Milwaukee, WI 53202
Tel.: (414) 390-6100　DE
Web Site:
https://www.artisanpartners.com
Year Founded: 1994
APAM—(NYSE)
Rev.: $975,131,000
Assets: $1,405,858,000
Liabilities: $1,054,507,000
Net Worth: $351,351,000
Earnings: $222,289,000
Emp.: 573
Fiscal Year-end: 12/31/23
Investment Management Service
N.A.I.C.S.: 523150
Eric Richard Colson *(Co-Chm & CEO)*
Andrew Arthur Ziegler *(Founder)*
Sarah A. Johnson *(Chief Legal Officer, Sec & Exec VP)*
Gregory K. Ramirez *(Exec VP)*
Stephanie G. DiMarco *(Co-Chm)*
Jason A. Gottlieb *(Pres)*
Christopher J. Krein *(Exec VP)*
Eileen L. Kwei *(Chief Admin Officer & Exec VP)*
Samuel B. Sellers *(COO & Exec VP)*
Charles J. Daley Jr. *(CFO)*

Subsidiaries:

Artisan Partners Holdings LP (1)
875 E Wisconsin Ave Ste 800, Milwaukee, WI 53202
Tel.: (414) 390-6100
Holding Company
N.A.I.C.S.: 551112

Artisan Partners Limited Partnership (1)
875 E Wisconsin Ave Ste 800, Milwaukee, WI 53202
Tel.: (414) 390-6100
Emp.: 375
Open-End Management Investment Operator
N.A.I.C.S.: 525910

Artisan Partners UK LLP (1)
25 St James's Street Tenth Floor, London, SW1A 1HA, United Kingdom
Tel.: (44) 2077667110
Emp.: 20
Business Management Consulting Services
N.A.I.C.S.: 541618

ARTISTMSS INTERNATIONAL GROUP, INC.
4055 Wilshire Blvd Ste 512, Los Angeles, CA 90010
Tel.: (213) 365-1880
Year Founded: 1984
AIGI—(OTCEM)
Clothing Product Retailer
N.A.I.C.S.: 458110

George Kim *(Pres)*
Sung Jung *(CMO, Officer-Administration, Chief Retail Officer & Asst Sec)*

ARTIVION, INC.
1655 Roberts Blvd NW, Kennesaw, GA 30144
Tel.: (770) 419-3355　FL
Web Site: https://www.artivion.com
Year Founded: 1984
AORT—(NYSE)
Rev.: $313,789,000
Assets: $762,798,000
Liabilities: $478,469,000
Net Worth: $284,329,000
Earnings: ($19,192,000)
Emp.: 1,300
Fiscal Year-end: 12/31/22
Implantable Medical Devices Developer & Marketer; Human Tissues for Cardiovascular, Vascular & Orthopaedic Transplant Applications Preserver & Distr
N.A.I.C.S.: 339113
Lance A. Berry *(CFO & Treas)*
Amy D. Horton *(Chief Acctg Officer & VP)*
James Patrick Mackin *(Chm, Pres & CEO)*
John E. Davis *(Sr VP-Global Sls & Mktg)*
Jean F. Holloway *(Chief Compliance Officer, Gen Counsel, Sec & Sr VP)*
Matthew A. Getz *(VP-HR)*
F. Peter Barthold *(VP-R&D)*
Marshall S. Stanton *(Chief Medical Officer)*
Andrew M. Green *(VP)*
Rochelle L. Maney *(VP)*

Subsidiaries:

CryoLife Asia Pacific, Pte. LTD. (1)
1 Marina Boulevard 28-00 One Marina Boulevard, Singapore, 018989, Singapore
Tel.: (65) 90307348
Medical Instrument Mfr
N.A.I.C.S.: 541715

CryoLife Europa, Ltd. (1)
Bramley House The Guildway Old Portsmouth Road, Old Portsmouth Road, Guildford, GU3 1LR, Surrey, United Kingdom (100%)
Tel.: (44) 1483441030
Web Site: http://www.cryolife.com
Sales Range: $25-40.0 Million
Emp.: 20
Preserved Tissue Products & Services Marketer & Distr
N.A.I.C.S.: 456199
David Feldman *(Country Mgr)*

JOTEC Cardiovascular S.L. (1)
Av Castilla 2 Edificio Europa - PB, 28830, San Fernando de Henares, Madrid, Spain
Tel.: (34) 916487020
Surgical Apparatus Whslr
N.A.I.C.S.: 423450

JOTEC GmbH (1)
Lotzenacker 23, 72379, Hechingen, Germany
Tel.: (49) 74719220
Web Site: https://www.jotec.com
Surgical Apparatus Whslr
N.A.I.C.S.: 423450
Christian Worne *(Dir)*
Manfred Engler *(Sls Dir)*
Ian Cunningham *(Sr Dir-Sales)*
Paolo Di Vincenzo *(Mgr-Information Technology)*
Steffen Rauschenberger *(Dir)*
Steven Ellis *(Dir-Information Technology-EMEA,APAC)*
Axel Grandt *(Dir-Research & Development)*
Cornelia Kuschel *(Dir-Regulatory Affairs)*
Thorve Raker *(Dir-Customer Service-EMEA)*
Manuel Schlenker *(Dir)*
Monika Schulze *(Dir-Quality)*
Steven Ellis *(Dir-Information Technology-EMEA,APAC)*

Axel Grandt *(Dir-Research & Development)*
Cornelia Kuschel *(Dir-Regulatory Affairs)*
Thorve Raker *(Dir-Customer Service-EMEA)*
Manuel Schlenker *(Dir)*
Monika Schulze *(Dir-Quality)*

JOTEC Polska Sp. z.o.o (1)
ul Bobrowiecka 8, 00-728, Warsaw, Poland
Tel.: (48) 222707010
Surgical Apparatus Whslr
N.A.I.C.S.: 423450

JOTEC Sales GmbH (1)
Tel.: (41) 792384411
Surgical Apparatus Whslr
N.A.I.C.S.: 423450

JOTEC UK Ltd. (1)
Bramley House The Guildway Old Portsmouth Road, Guildford, GU3 1LR, Surrey, United Kingdom
Tel.: (44) 1386429421
Surgical Apparatus Whslr
N.A.I.C.S.: 423450

JOTEC s.r.l. (1)
Via Thomas Alva Edison 110 Edison Center - Building A, 20099, Sesto San Giovanni, MI, Italy
Tel.: (39) 0291090491
Surgical Apparatus Whslr
N.A.I.C.S.: 423450

Jolly Buyer Acquisition GmbH (1)
Luzernerstrasse 91, 5630, Muri, Switzerland
Tel.: (41) 566759100
Surgical Apparatus Whslr
N.A.I.C.S.: 423450

On-X Life Technologies, Inc. (1)
1300 E Anderson Ln, Austin, TX 78752
Tel.: (512) 339-8000
Web Site: https://www.onxlti.com
Sales Range: $25-49.9 Million
Emp.: 70
Artificial Heart Valve Replacement & Repair Products Mfr
N.A.I.C.S.: 339112

ARVANA INC.
299 S Main St 13th Fl, Salt Lake City, UT 84111
Tel.: (801) 232-7395　NV
Web Site: https://arvana.us
Year Founded: 1977
AVNI—(OTCIQ)
Rev.: $24,276
Assets: $216,549
Liabilities: $1,178,675
Net Worth: ($962,126)
Earnings: ($1,010,579)
Emp.: 1
Fiscal Year-end: 12/31/23
Investment Services
N.A.I.C.S.: 523999
James Kim *(CEO)*

Subsidiaries:

Down 2 Fish Charters, LLC (1)
901 25th Ave W, Palmetto, FL 34221
Tel.: (801) 580-7172
Web Site: https://www.down2fishflorida.com
Fishing Charter Boat Services
N.A.I.C.S.: 713990

ARVINAS, INC.
5 Science Park 395 Winchester Ave, New Haven, CT 06511
Tel.: (203) 535-1456　DE
Web Site: https://www.arvinas.com
Year Founded: 2013
ARVN—(NASDAQ)
Rev.: $131,400,000
Assets: $1,268,800,000
Liabilities: $703,900,000
Net Worth: $564,900,000
Earnings: ($282,500,000)
Emp.: 415
Fiscal Year-end: 12/31/22
Biopharmaceutical Product Mfr & Distr
N.A.I.C.S.: 325412

Noah Berkowitz *(Chief Medical Officer)*
Timothy M. Shannon *(Chm)*
Kelly Page *(Sr VP & Head-Oncology Strategy & Program Leadership-Global)*
John G. Houston *(Pres & CEO)*
Achal Pashine *(VP-Oncology & Immuno-Oncology Res)*
Randy Teel *(Chief Bus Officer)*
Charlie Romano *(VP-Global Dev Ops)*
Alex Santini *(Sr VP-Global & US Market Access)*
Shiva Sekhar *(VP-Breast Cancer-Global,US Mktg)*
Janet Wang *(VP & Head-Translational Sciences & Oncology)*
Lisa Sinclair *(Sr VP-Corp Ops)*
Andrew Saik *(CFO)*
Yongqing Huang *(VP & Head-Nonclinical Sciences)*
Janice Kapty *(VP-Estrogen Receptor Global Asset Lead)*
John A. Grosso *(Sr VP-R&D Technical Ops & VP-Chemistry, Mfg, and Controls)*
Steve Weiss *(Chief HR Officer, Sr VP & VP-HR)*
Jared Freedberg *(Gen Counsel & Sec)*
Paul McInulty *(Sr VP-Regulatory Affairs)*
Sharvari Apte *(VP-Global & US Comml Analytics)*
Christopher Beck *(VP-Intellectual Property)*
Jeff Boyle *(VP-Investor Relations)*
Shelley Diaz *(VP-Quality, Environmental Health, and Safety)*
Michelle Edwards *(VP & Head-Medical Affairs)*
Brad Lanoue *(VP-Global, US Value, and Market Access Strategy)*
David Loomis *(Chief Acctg Officer, VP & Controller)*
Eric Masson *(Sr VP-Early Clinical Dev)*
Kimberly Wehger *(Sr VP-IT Sys & Security & VP-IT)*
Ian Taylor *(Pres-Research & Development)*
Angela M. Cacace *(Chief Scientific Officer)*
Andrew R. Saik *(CFO & Treas)*

AS-IP TECH, INC.

16 fl 100 Park Ave, New York, NY 10017
Tel.: (424) 888-2212   DE
Web Site: https://www.asiptech.com
Year Founded: 1998
IPTK—(OTCIQ)
Rev.: $73,837
Assets: $157,601
Liabilities: $1,474,847
Net Worth: ($1,317,246)
Earnings: ($1,370,828)
Fiscal Year-end: 06/30/21
In-Flight Communications
N.A.I.C.S.: 334220
Philip A. Shiels *(CFO)*
Ronald J. Chapman *(Chm)*
Adam Chapman *(VP-Mktg Svcs)*
Barry Chapman *(Pres, CEO & CMO)*

ASA GOLD & PRECIOUS METALS LTD.

3 Canal Plz, Portland, ME 04101
Tel.: (650) 376-3135   ZA
Web Site: https://www.asaltd.com
Year Founded: 1958
ASA—(NYSE)
Rev.: $2,371,123
Assets: $286,612,482
Liabilities: $733,262

Net Worth: $285,879,220
Earnings: ($1,111,296)
Fiscal Year-end: 11/30/19
Investment Services
N.A.I.C.S.: 523999
Mary Joan Hoene *(Chm)*
Jack P. Huntington *(Chief Compliance Officer)*
Peter Maletis *(Pres)*
Axel Merk *(COO)*
Karen Shaw *(Officer-Principal Fin)*
Zachary Tackett *(Sec)*

ASANA, INC.

633 Folsom St Ste 100, San Francisco, CA 94107
Tel.: (415) 525-3888   DE
Web Site: https://www.asana.com
Year Founded: 2008
ASAN—(NYSE)
Rev.: $547,212,000
Assets: $954,963,000
Liabilities: $598,389,000
Net Worth: $356,574,000
Earnings: ($407,768,000)
Emp.: 1,782
Fiscal Year-end: 01/31/23
Software Development Services
N.A.I.C.S.: 541511
Anne Raimondi *(COO & Head-Bus)*
Dustin Moskovitz *(CEO)*
Eleanor Lacey *(Gen Counsel & Sec)*
Anna Binder *(Head-People Ops)*
Alex Hood *(Head-Product)*
Oliver Jay *(Head-Sls & Bus Dev-Global)*
Dave King *(Head-Mktg)*
Prashant Pandey *(VP-Mktg)*
Justin Rosenstein *(Founder)*
Catherine Buan *(Head-IR)*
Ed McDonnell *(Chief Revenue Officer)*
Sonalee Parekh *(CFO & Head-Fin)*

ASBURY AUTOMOTIVE GROUP, INC.

2905 Premiere Pkwy NW Ste 300, Duluth, GA 30097
Tel.: (770) 418-8200   DE
Web Site:
  https://www.asburyauto.com
Year Founded: 1995
ABG—(NYSE)
Rev.: $14,802,700,000
Assets: $10,159,400,000
Liabilities: $6,915,300,000
Net Worth: $3,244,100,000
Earnings: $602,500,000
Emp.: 15,000
Fiscal Year-end: 12/31/23
Car Dealership Owner & Operator
N.A.I.C.S.: 441110
Jed M. Milstein *(Chief HR Officer & Sr VP)*
Michael D. Welch *(CFO & Sr VP)*
David W. Hult *(Pres & CEO)*
Daniel Clara *(Sr VP-Ops)*
Nathan Briesemeister *(Chief Acctg Officer, VP & Controller)*
Miran Maric *(Sr VP)*

Subsidiaries:

Asbury Atlanta AU L.L.C.   (1)
11505 Alpharetta Hwy, Roswell, GA 30076
Tel.: (404) 994-4327
Web Site: http://www.audinorthatlanta.com
New & Used Car Distr
N.A.I.C.S.: 441110
Andre Young *(Gen Mgr)*

Asbury Atlanta Toy 2 L.L.C.   (1)
7969 Mall Pkwy, Lithonia, GA 30038
Tel.: (770) 629-0279
Web Site: https://www.stonecresttoyota.com
New & Used Car Distr
N.A.I.C.S.: 441110

Asbury Automotive Jacksonville, L.P.   (1)

31200 US Hwy 19 N, Palm Harbor, FL 34684
Tel.: (727) 263-3103
Web Site: http://www.courtesycars.com
Sales Range: $25-49.9 Million
Emp.: 70
New & Used Car Dealer
N.A.I.C.S.: 441110
Charles R. Oglesby *(Owner)*

Asbury Ft. Worth Ford, L.L.C   (1)
2905 Premiere Pkwy Ste 300, Duluth, GA 30097
Tel.: (770) 418-8200
Web Site: http://www.asburyauto.com
Car Distr
N.A.I.C.S.: 441110

Asbury Jax Ford, LLC   (1)
9650 Atlantic Blvd, Jacksonville, FL 32225
Tel.: (904) 747-8996
Web Site:
  https://www.cogginfordjacksonville.com
New & Used Car Distr
N.A.I.C.S.: 441110

Coggin Automotive Corp.   (1)
4306 Pablo Oaks Ct, Jacksonville, FL 32224
Tel.: (904) 992-4110
Web Site: http://www.cogginauto.com
Rev.: $475,000,000
Emp.: 15
Automobile Dealership
N.A.I.C.S.: 441110

Unit (Domestic):

Coggin Ford   (2)
9650 Atlantic Blvd, Jacksonville, FL 32225
Tel.: (904) 747-8996
Web Site:
  https://www.cogginfordjacksonville.com
Emp.: 200
New & Used Car Dealer
N.A.I.C.S.: 441110
Ron Messinetti *(Gen Mgr)*
Robert Andrews *(Mgr-New Car)*
Shannon Dayton *(Mgr-Acctg)*

Subsidiary (Domestic):

KP Motors LLC   (2)
7245 Blanding Blvd, Jacksonville, FL 32244
Tel.: (904) 682-9278
Web Site: https://www.cogginbuickgmc.com
New & Used Automobile Dealerships
N.A.I.C.S.: 441110

Courtesy Quality Brandon   (1)
1207 E Brandon Blvd, Brandon, FL 33511
Tel.: (813) 324-2607
New & Used Car Distr
N.A.I.C.S.: 441110

Crown Auto Group   (1)
3902 W Wendover Ave, Greensboro, NC 27407
Tel.: (336) 203-1097
Web Site: https://www.crownauto.com
Sales Range: $550-599.9 Million
Emp.: 1,400
New & Used Car Dealerships
N.A.I.C.S.: 441110

Subsidiary (Domestic):

Crown Acura/Nissan, LLC   (2)
3908 W Wendover Ave, Greensboro, NC 27407-1903
Tel.: (336) 814-2554
Web Site:
  http://www.crownacuragreensboro.com
Sales Range: $25-49.9 Million
Emp.: 50
Automotive Products Whslr
N.A.I.C.S.: 441330

David McDavid Automotive Group   (1)
3600 W Airport Fwy, Irving, TX 75062-5906
Tel.: (972) 790-6100
Web Site: http://www.mcdavid.com
Sales Range: $450-499.9 Million
Emp.: 1,200
New & Used Car Dealer & Servicer
N.A.I.C.S.: 517112

Subsidiary (Domestic):

McDavid Austin-Acra, LLC   (2)

13553 Research Blvd, Austin, TX 78750
Tel.: (512) 643-6468
Web Site:
  https://www.davidmcdavidacuraofaustin.com
Automotive Products Whslr
N.A.I.C.S.: 441330

Gray-Daniels Auto Family   (1)
6060 I-55 N, Jackson, MS 39211
Tel.: (601) 899-6060
Web Site: http://www.graydaniels.com
Sales Range: $200-249.9 Million
New & Used Car Dealerships
N.A.I.C.S.: 441110

Jim Koons Management Company   (1)
2000 Chain Bridge Rd, Vienna, VA 22182-2531
Tel.: (703) 448-7000
Web Site: http://www.koons.com
Sales Range: $350-399.9 Million
Emp.: 1,500
Owner & Operator of Automobile Dealerships
N.A.I.C.S.: 561110
James E. Koons *(Founder & CEO)*
John Davis *(Dir-Art)*

Division (Domestic):

Koons of Tysons Corner Chevy Chrysler   (2)
2000 Chain Bridge Rd, Vienna, VA 22182-2531   (100%)
Tel.: (703) 356-0400
Web Site: http://www.koons.com
Sales Range: $25-49.9 Million
Emp.: 195
Automobile Dealership
N.A.I.C.S.: 441110
James E. Koons *(Owner)*
Bryan Murray *(Gen Mgr)*
Jim O'Connell *(Pres)*

Mike Shaw Subaru, Inc.   (1)
1650 W 104th Ave, Thornton, CO 80234
Tel.: (303) 782-4639
Web Site: http://www.mikeshawsubaru.com
Emp.: 120
Car Dealer
N.A.I.C.S.: 441110
Dominic Scrivner *(Gen Mgr)*
Dan Peeples *(Mgr-Svc)*
Dan Pham *(Gen Mgr-Sls)*
Paul Fischer *(Mgr-Parts)*
Josh Anderson *(Dir-Fin)*
Frank Cruz *(Mgr-Sls)*
Jonathan Susser *(Dir-Ops)*
Greg Kadnuck *(Mgr-Sls)*
Randon Givens *(Mgr-Customer Svc)*
Tien Tran *(Dir-Internet Sls)*
David Goad *(Asst Mgr-Parts)*
Alex Comar *(Mgr-Fin)*
Nastassia Rosa *(Mgr-Fin)*
Anthony Ulibarri *(Mgr-Fin)*
Chrystal Clapes *(Mgr-Acctg)*

Nalley Automotive Group   (1)
1235 Old Alpharetta Rd Ste 190, Alpharetta, GA 30005
Tel.: (770) 619-5000
Web Site: http://www.nalleycars.com
Holding Company; Regional Managing Office; New & Used Car Dealerships Operator
N.A.I.C.S.: 551112
Charles R. Oglesby *(Pres)*

Subsidiary (Domestic):

Asbury Atlanta Hon LLC   (2)
4197 Jonesboro Rd, Union City, GA 30291
Tel.: (770) 756-8717
Web Site: https://www.nalleyhonda.com
Sales Range: $10-24.9 Million
Emp.: 73
New & Used Car Dealer
N.A.I.C.S.: 441110

Asbury Atlanta Lex LLC   (2)
2750 Cobb Pkwy SE, Smyrna, GA 30080
Tel.: (770) 618-7908
Web Site:
  https://www.nalleylexussmyrna.com
Sales Range: $50-74.9 Million
Emp.: 97
New & Used Car Dealer
N.A.I.C.S.: 441110

Asbury Automotive Group, Inc.—(Continued)

Asbury Atlanta Nis LLC (2)
1625 Church St, Decatur, GA 30033
Tel.: (212) 885-2500
Web Site:
http://www.nalleynissanofatlanta.com
New & Used Car Dealer
N.A.I.C.S.: 441110

Asbury Atlanta Toy LLC (2)
11130 Alpharetta Hwy, Roswell, GA 30076
Tel.: (770) 763-7398
Web Site: https://www.toyotaofroswell.com
Sales Range: $50-74.9 Million
New & Used Car Dealer
N.A.I.C.S.: 441110

Unit (Domestic):

**Nalley Collision Center - Roswell
Body Shop** (2)
1000 Sun Valley Dr, Roswell, GA 30076
Tel.: (770) 343-4042
Web Site: https://www.nalleycollision.com
Sales Range: $1-9.9 Million
Emp.: 31
Automotive Body, Paint & Interior Repair &
Maintenance Services
N.A.I.C.S.: 811121

Precision Motorcars, Inc. (1)
4400 N Dale Mabry Hwy, Tampa, FL 33614
Tel.: (813) 543-8419
Web Site: https://www.mboftampabay.com
Sales Range: $10-24.9 Million
Emp.: 75
New & Used Car Dealer
N.A.I.C.S.: 441110
Bob Murray (Gen Mgr)

ASCEND WELLNESS HOLD-INGS, INC.
1411 Broadway 16th Fl, New York,
NY 10018
Tel.: (617) 453-4042   DE
Web Site:
https://www.awholdings.com
Year Founded: 2018
AAWH—(CNSX)
Rev.: $405,926,000
Assets: $872,160,000
Liabilities: $708,745,000
Net Worth: $163,415,000
Earnings: ($80,899,000)
Emp.: 2,200
Fiscal Year-end: 12/31/22
Holding Company
N.A.I.C.S.: 551112
John Hartmann (Co-CEO)
Abner Kurtin (Co-Founder & Exec
Chm)
Francis Perullo (Co-Founder & Exec
VP-Corporate Affairs)
Samuel Brill (Co-CEO)
Roman Nemchenko (CFO)
David Gacom (Chief Comml Officer)
Melissa Feck (Chief People Officer)
Rebecca Conti Koar (Exec VP-
Investor Relations & Strategy)

ASCENT INDUSTRIES CO.
20 N Martingale Rd Ste 430,
Schaumburg, IL 60173
Tel.: (630) 884-9181   DE
Web Site: https://www.synalloy.com
Year Founded: 1945
ACNT—(NASDAQ)
Rev.: $414,147,000
Assets: $269,043,000
Liabilities: $134,784,000
Net Worth: $134,259,000
Earnings: $22,066,000
Emp.: 698
Fiscal Year-end: 12/31/22
Stainless Steel Pipe & Fabrication;
Specialty Chemicals; Dyestuffs & Pig-
ments Mfr
N.A.I.C.S.: 331210
Michael Padden (Dir-IT)
J. Bryan Kitchen (CEO)
Benjamin L. Rosenzweig (Chm)

Subsidiaries:

American Stainless Tubing, Inc. (1)
123 Morehead Rd, Statesville, NC 28677
Tel.: (704) 878-8823
Web Site: http://www.asti-nc.com
Sales Range: $10-24.9 Million
Emp.: 200
Mechanical Tubing Mfr
N.A.I.C.S.: 331210

Bristol Metals, LLC (1)
390 Bristol Metals Rd, Bristol, TN
37620   (100%)
Tel.: (423) 989-4700
Web Site: https://www.brismet.com
Sales Range: $200-249.9 Million
Emp.: 357
Custom Stainless Steel Pipe & Fittings Mfr
N.A.I.C.S.: 331210
Rob Yepsen (VP-Tubular Products)
David C. Terrick (Reg Dir-Sls)
Parker Sword (Mgr-Intl & Special Alloy Sls)
Josh Ringley (VP-Bus Ops & Logistics)

CRI Tolling, LLC (1)
Woodfield Industrial Park 300 International
Blvd, Fountain Inn, SC 29644
Tel.: (864) 862-2399
Web Site: http://www.critoll.com
Chemical Products Mfr
N.A.I.C.S.: 325998

DanChem Technologies, Inc (1)
1975 Richmond Blvd, Danville, VA 24540-
3961
Tel.: (434) 797-8120
Web Site:
http://www.danchemtechnology.com
Specialty Fine Chemicals Mfr
N.A.I.C.S.: 325998
Jerry Cook (CFO)

Manufacturers Chemicals, LLC (1)
4325 Old Tasso Rd, Cleveland, TN
37320-2788   (100%)
Tel.: (423) 476-6518
Web Site:
http://www.manufacturerschemicals.com
Sales Range: $50-74.9 Million
Emp.: 63
Specialty Chemicals Mfr
N.A.I.C.S.: 314110

**Manufacturers Soap and Chemicals
Company** (1)
4325 Old Tasso Rd NE, Cleveland, TN
37312-5836
Tel.: (423) 476-6518
Web Site: http://www.synalloychemicals.com
Soap & Chemical Mfr
N.A.I.C.S.: 325611

Metchem, Inc. (1)
837 E 79th St, Cleveland, OH 44103-1817
Tel.: (216) 881-7900
Web Site: https://www.metchem.com
Wastewater Treatment Equipments Mfr
N.A.I.C.S.: 333310

Palmer of Texas Tanks, Inc. (1)
1701 N Hwy 385, Andrews, TX 79714
Tel.: (432) 523-5904
Web Site: http://www.palmeroftexas.com
Sales Range: $25-49.9 Million
Emp.: 137
Fiberglass & Steel Tank Mfr
N.A.I.C.S.: 332420

**Specialty Pipe & Tube Co. of Texas
Inc.** (1)
3838 Majestic Dr, Houston, TX 77026-4340
Tel.: (713) 676-2891
Web Site: https://www.specialtypipe.com
Sales Range: $25-49.9 Million
Emp.: 20
Metal Products Service & Mfr
N.A.I.C.S.: 423510

Specialty Pipe & Tube Inc. (1)
3600 Union St, Mineral Ridge, OH 44440-
0516
Tel.: (330) 505-8262
Web Site: http://www.specialtypipe.com
Metal Products Service & Mfr
N.A.I.C.S.: 423510

SynTrans, LLC (1)
2315 N Pearl St, Tacoma, WA 98406-2500
Tel.: (253) 266-3955

Welded Stainless Steel & Alloy Pipe Mfr
N.A.I.C.S.: 331110

ASCENT SOLAR TECHNOLO-GIES, INC.
12300 Grant St Ste 160, Thornton,
CO 80241
Tel.: (720) 872-5000   DE
Web Site:
https://www.ascentsolar.com
Year Founded: 2005
ASTI—(NASDAQ)
Rev.: $1,222,786
Assets: $18,676,702
Liabilities: $14,091,161
Net Worth: $4,585,541
Earnings: ($19,754,705)
Emp.: 60
Fiscal Year-end: 12/31/22
Photovoltaic Materials & Modules
Developer
N.A.I.C.S.: 334413
David Peterson (Chm)
Paul Warley Jr. (Pres & CEO)
Bobby Gulati (COO)
Jin Jo (CFO)

ASGN INCORPORATED
4400 Cox Rd Ste 110, Glen Allen, VA
23060   DE
Web Site: https://www.asgn.com
Year Founded: 1985
ASGN—(NYSE)
Rev.: $4,581,100,000
Assets: $3,585,700,000
Liabilities: $1,684,400,000
Net Worth: $1,901,300,000
Earnings: $268,100,000
Emp.: 4,000
Fiscal Year-end: 12/31/22
IT, Staffing, Recruitment & Profes-
sional Services
N.A.I.C.S.: 561320
Jennifer Hankes Painter (Chief Legal
Officer, Sec & Sr VP)
Theodore S. Hanson (CEO)
Rose Cunningham (Chief Acctg Offi-
cer, VP & Controller)
Randolph C. Blazer (Pres)
Marie L. Perry (CFO & Exec VP)

Subsidiaries:

Apex Systems, Inc. (1)
4400 Cox Rd Ste 100, Glen Allen, VA
23060
Tel.: (804) 254-2600
Web Site: http://www.apexsystems.com
Sales Range: $75-99.9 Million
Emp.: 700
Professional & Technical Staffing Services
N.A.I.C.S.: 561320

Creative Circle, LLC (1)
1180 Peachtree St NE Ste 1820, Atlanta,
GA 30309
Tel.: (404) 829-2769
Web Site: http://www.creativecircle.com
Temporary Staffing Services
N.A.I.C.S.: 561320

CyberCoders Inc. (1)
6591 Irvine Ctr Dr Ste 200, Irvine, CA
92618-2131
Tel.: (949) 885-5151
Web Site: https://www.cybercoders.com
Sales Range: $50-74.9 Million
Emp.: 190
Human Resources & Executive Search
Consulting Services
N.A.I.C.S.: 541612
Roy Monroy (VP-Recruiting)
Nitu Gulati-Pauly (VP-Recruiting)

ECS Federal, LLC (1)
2750 Prosperity Ave Ste 600, Fairfax, VA
22031
Tel.: (703) 270-1540
Web Site: https://www.ecstech.com
IT Services
N.A.I.C.S.: 541512
Shab Nassirpour (VP-Mktg & Comm)
Steve Hittle (CIO)

John Magee (Sr VP-Strategic Ops)
Marshall Thames (Sr VP-Mission Solutions)
Lindsey Reisinger (VP-HR)
John Heneghan (Pres)
Michael Perry (VP-Mission Solutions)
Luis Colon-Castro (VP-Navy & Marine Corp
Programs)
Deron Baker (VP-USPS & Commerce)
Keith Quigley (Sr VP-Enterprise Solutions)
Shayla Treadwell (VP-Governance, Risk,
and Compliance)
John Roman (VP-Contracts & Procurement)
Elise Walker (VP-Justice & Homeland Solu-
tions)
Martin Klein (VP-Analytics & Artificial Intelli-
gence)
Ryan Garner (CFO)
Kelly Demaitre (Sr VP-Human Capital)
Alex Lopez (VP-Business Development)
Steve Erickson (VP-Strategic Solutions)
Asad Akhtar (VP-Federal Health)
Martin Burke (VP-Integrated Solutions)
Joanna Dempsey (VP-Portfolio)
Stacey Donald (VP-VA & HHS Solutions)
Scott Fisher (VP-Natl Security & Intelli-
gence)
William Geimer (VP-Cybersecurity Solutions
Division)
Ian Keith (VP)
Kristin Lemus (VP-Health IT & Cyber)
Mark Maglin (VP-Department of Defense
Cybersecurity)
Joanne Morris (VP-Treasury & Energy)
Rob Mills (VP-Business Development)
J. David Sinniger (VP-Advanced Res & En-
grg Div)
Karthik Srinivasan (VP-Defense Solutions)
Jeff Urlwin (VP-Federal Managed Svcs)
Rob Warren (VP-Capture)
Andy Woods (VP-Enterprise Managed
Svcs)

Subsidiary (Domestic):

DHA Group Inc. (2)
1299 Pennsylvania Avenue NW Suite 425,
Washington, DC 20004
Tel.: (202) 347-9865
Management Consulting & Contracting Ser-
vices
N.A.I.C.S.: 541611

Indrasoft Inc. (2)
11150 Sunset Hills Rd Ste 120, Reston, VA
20190-5321
Tel.: (703) 435-9052
Web Site: http://www.indrasoft.com
Custom Computer Programming Services
N.A.I.C.S.: 541511
Neeraja Lingam (CEO)
Karthik Srinivasan (COO)

Iron Vine Security, LLC (2)
1029 Vermont Ave NW Ste 700, Washing-
ton, DC 20005-6323
Tel.: (202) 621-2344
Web Site: http://www.ivsec.com
Emp.: 230
Information Services
N.A.I.C.S.: 519290
William Geimer (CEO & COO)
Jim Brinkman (CFO)

**Enterprise Resource Performance,
Inc.** (1)
116K Edwards Ferry Rd NE, Leesburg, VA
20176
Tel.: (703) 441-4111
Rev.: $2,000,000
Emp.: 35
Custom Computer Programming Services
N.A.I.C.S.: 541511
Christopher Jones (Pres)

GlideFast Consulting LLC (1)
444 Washington St Ste 405, Woburn, MA
01801
Tel.: (339) 999-2190
Web Site: http://www.glidefast.com
Application Development Services
N.A.I.C.S.: 541511
Michael Lombardo (Co-Founder & CEO)
Lloyd Godson (Co-Founder & Pres)
Stephen Light (Chief Pub Sector Officer)

InterSys Consulting, Inc. (1)
505 Oakland Ave, Austin, TX 78703
Tel.: (512) 592-7171
Web Site: http://www.intersysconsulting.com
Business Software Consulting Services

N.A.I.C.S.: 541512

Lab Support, LLC (1)
2105 S Bascom Ave Ste 390, Campbell, CA
95008-3278
Tel.: (408) 371-8771
Web Site: http://www.labsupport.com
Human Resource Consulting Services
N.A.I.C.S.: 541612
Theodore S. Hanson (Pres)

Stratacuity Staffing Partners, Inc. (1)
1 Cate St Ste 200, Portsmouth, NH 03801-
3735
Tel.: (603) 766-0600
Web Site: http://www.stratacuity.com
Sales Range: $10-24.9 Million
Employment Placement & Staffing Agencies
N.A.I.C.S.: 561311
Robert Patten (Co-Founder)
Patrick Marshall (Co-Founder)
Aimee Turcotte (Head-Delivery & Ops)
Alex Temple (Partner-Client)
Amanda Sobel (Partner-Client)
Andrew Chan (Partner-Client)
Danny Hagenbuch (Partner-Client)
Jeff D'Italia (VP)
Jennifer Price (Sr Dir-Clinical & Regulatory
& Permanent Placement)
Nick Deal (Partner-Client)
Ryan March (Partner-Client)
Susi MacDonald (Dir-Mktg & Comm)
Todd Jamison (Dir-Technical Ops & Perma-
nent Placement)

Vista Staffing Services, Inc. (1)
275 E 200 S, Salt Lake City, UT 84111
Tel.: (801) 487-8190
Web Site: http://www.vistastaff.com
Human Resource Consulting Services
N.A.I.C.S.: 541612

ASHFORD HOSPITALITY
TRUST, INC.

14185 Dallas Pkwy Ste 1200, Dallas,
TX 75254
Tel.: (972) 490-9600   MD
Web Site: https://www.ahtreit.com
AHT—(NYSE)
Rev.: $1,240,859,000
Assets: $3,917,377,000
Liabilities: $4,067,766,000
Net Worth: ($150,389,000)
Earnings: ($139,825,000)
Fiscal Year-end: 12/31/22
Real Estate Investment Trust
N.A.I.C.S.: 525990
Deric S. Eubanks (CFO)
Mark L. Nunneley (Chief Acctg Offi-
cer)
Montgomery J. Bennett IV (Founder
& Chm)
Alex Rose (Gen Counsel, Sec &
Exec VP)

Subsidiaries:

Ashford Anchorage LP (1)
14185 Dallas Pkwy Ste 1100, Dallas, TX
75254-1319
Tel.: (972) 490-9600
Web Site: http://www.ahtreit.com
Sales Range: $25-49.9 Million
Emp.: 200
Home Management Services
N.A.I.C.S.: 721110

Ashford Pittsburgh Waterfront LP (1)
301 W Waterfront Dr, Homestead, PA
15120
Tel.: (412) 462-4226
Web Site:
    http://www.hamptoninn3.hilton.com
Hotel & Accommodation Services
N.A.I.C.S.: 721110

Ashford TRS Five LLC (1)
58 State Cir, Annapolis, MD 21401-1906
Tel.: (410) 263-2641
Web Site:
    https://www.historicinnsofannapolis.com
Casino & Gaming Services
N.A.I.C.S.: 721120

Ashford TRS Flagstaff LLC (1)
706 S Milton Rd, Flagstaff, AZ 86001
Tel.: (928) 774-4333

Hotel & Accommodation Services
N.A.I.C.S.: 721110

Ashford TRS Fort Tower I LLC (1)
815 Main St, Fort Worth, TX 76102
Tel.: (817) 870-2100
Hotel & Accommodation Services
N.A.I.C.S.: 721110
Cynthia Henderson (Mgr-Convention Svcs)

Ashford TRS Le Pavillon LLC (1)
833 Poydras St, New Orleans, LA 70112
Tel.: (504) 581-3111
Web Site: https://www.lepavillon.com
Hotel & Accommodation Services
N.A.I.C.S.: 721110

**Ashford TRS Minneapolis Airport
LLC** (1)
3800 American Blvd E, Bloomington, MN
55425
Tel.: (952) 854-2100
Hotel & Resort Services
N.A.I.C.S.: 721110
Lydia Zupancic (Mgr-Grp Sls)

**Ashford TRS Pittsburgh Southpointe
LLC** (1)
3000 Horizon Vue Dr, Canonsburg, PA
15317
Tel.: (724) 745-4663
Hotel & Accommodation Services
N.A.I.C.S.: 721110

Ashford TRS Pool A LLC (1)
50 Alhambra Plz, Coral Gables, FL 33134
Tel.: (305) 441-1234
Casino & Gaming Services
N.A.I.C.S.: 721120

Ashford TRS Pool C1 LLC (1)
11450 Marbella Palm Ct, Orlando, FL 32836
Tel.: (407) 465-0075
Hotel & Accommodation Services
N.A.I.C.S.: 721110

Ashford TRS Six LLC (1)
6425 S 3000 E, Salt Lake City, UT 84121
Tel.: (801) 453-0430
Hotel & Accommodation Services
N.A.I.C.S.: 721110
Alan Jacobson (Gen Mgr)

Ashford TRS Wichita LLC (1)
820 E 2nd St N, Wichita, KS 67202
Tel.: (316) 264-5300
Hotel & Accommodation Services
N.A.I.C.S.: 721110
Jovana Johnson (Dir-Sls)

HHC TRS Baltimore II LLC (1)
173 Jennifer Rd, Annapolis, MD 21401
Tel.: (410) 266-3131
Hotel & Resort Services
N.A.I.C.S.: 721110
Kourtney Turner (Supvr-Front Office)

ASHFORD INC.

14185 Dallas Pkwy Ste 1200, Dallas,
TX 75254
Tel.: (972) 490-9600   MD
Web Site:
    https://www.ashfordinc.com
Year Founded: 2014
AINC—(NYSEAMEX)
Rev.: $644,432,000
Assets: $482,356,000
Liabilities: $274,208,000
Net Worth: $208,148,000
Earnings: $3,646,000
Emp.: 7,827
Fiscal Year-end: 12/31/22
Asset Management Services
N.A.I.C.S.: 531390
Mark L. Nunneley (Sr Mng Dir)
Montgomery J. Bennett IV (Founder,
Chm & CEO)
Deric S. Eubanks (CFO)
Mark L. Nunneley (Chief Acctg Offi-
cer)
Alex Rose (Gen Counsel)

Subsidiaries:

Ashford Advisors, Inc. (1)
900 Ashwood Pkwy Ste 400, Atlanta, GA
30338

Tel.: (770) 390-2600
Web Site: https://www.ashfordadvisors.net
Emp.: 125
Real Estate Asset Management Services
N.A.I.C.S.: 531390
Patrick Martin (Principal)

Ashford Hospitality Advisors LLC (1)
14185 Dallas Pkwy Ste 1200, Dallas, TX
75254
Tel.: (972) 490-9600
Web Site: https://www.ahtreit.com
Asset Management Services
N.A.I.C.S.: 531390
J. Robison Hays (Pres)
Alex Rose (Exec VP)
Monty J. Bennett (Founder)
Amish V. Gupta (Dir)

**J&S Audio Visual Communications,
LLC** (1)
9150 N Royal Ln, Irving, TX 75063
Tel.: (972) 241-5444
Web Site: https://inspiresolutions.com
Audio Visual Equipment Leasing & Rental
Services
N.A.I.C.S.: 532289
Monroe Jost (Owner)

PURE Solutions NA, LLC (1)
5001 Genesee St, Buffalo, NY
14225   (70%)
Tel.: (716) 206-1200
Web Site: http://www.pureroom.com
Air Purification Services
N.A.I.C.S.: 561499
Brian Brault (CEO)

Project Management Group, LLC (1)
7040 Empire Central Dr, Houston, TX
77040
Tel.: (713) 880-2626
Web Site: https://www.pmgunited.com
Management Consulting Services
N.A.I.C.S.: 541618
Camila Bolivar (Dir-Mkg & Comm)

ASHLAND INC.

8145 Blazer Dr, Wilmington, DE
19808
Tel.: (859) 963-4704   DE
Web Site: https://www.ashland.com
Year Founded: 2016
ASH—(NYSE)
Rev.: $2,113,000,000
Assets: $5,645,000,000
Liabilities: $2,777,000,000
Net Worth: $2,868,000,000
Earnings: $169,000,000
Emp.: 3,200
Fiscal Year-end: 09/30/24
Holding Company; Specialty Additives
& Materials Mfr & Whslr
N.A.I.C.S.: 551112
Guillermo Novo (Chm & CEO)
J. Kevin Willis (CFO & Sr VP)
Eric T. Boni (Principal Acctg Officer &
VP-Fin)
Osama M. Musa (CTO & Sr VP)
Robin E. Lampkin (Gen Counsel, Sec
& Sr VP)
Jerome A. Peribere (CEO-Sealed Air
Corp)

Subsidiaries:

Ashland CZ s.r.o. (1)
Uzavrena 1, Prague, 18200, Czech Repub-
lic
Tel.: (420) 284680906
Web Site: http://www.ashland.com
Emp.: 10
Chemical Products Distr
N.A.I.C.S.: 424690

**Ashland Industries Europe
GmbH** (1)
Rheinweg 11, 8200, Schaffhausen, Switzer-
land
Tel.: (41) 525605552
Chemical Products Distr
N.A.I.C.S.: 424690

**Ashland International Holdings,
Inc.** (1)

50 E River Ctr Blvd, Covington, KY 41011-
1683
Tel.: (859) 815-3333
Web Site: http://www.ashland.com
Sales Range: $250-299.9 Million
Holding Company
N.A.I.C.S.: 551112

Subsidiary (Non-US):

**Ashland (China) Holdings Co.,
Ltd.** (2)
2/F Block B No 39 HongCao Road, Shang-
hai, 200233, China
Tel.: (86) 2160906606
Web Site: http://www.ashland.com
Specialty Ingredients Mfr
N.A.I.C.S.: 325998

Ashland Canada Corp. (2)
905 Winston Churchill Blvd, Mississauga,
L5J 4E7, ON, Canada   (100%)
Tel.: (905) 823-1800
Web Site: http://www.ashland.com
Sales Range: $75-99.9 Million
Emp.: 30
Oil & Chemicals Mfr
N.A.I.C.S.: 325998

Ashland Chemical Hispania, S.L. (2)
Partida Povet 37, 12580, Benicarlo, Castel-
lon, Spain   (100%)
Tel.: (34) 964467373
Web Site: http://www.ashland.com
Sales Range: $100-124.9 Million
Emp.: 120
Petroleum Refiner
N.A.I.C.S.: 324110

Ashland Danmark Aps (2)
Havnegade 39, Copenhagen, 1059, Den-
mark
Tel.: (45) 70215555
Web Site: http://www.ashland.com
Sales Range: $50-74.9 Million
Emp.: 11
Petroleum Products Distr & Sales
N.A.I.C.S.: 424720

Ashland Finland Oy (2)
Kilpilahden teollisuusalue, Porvoo, 6100,
Finland
Tel.: (358) 9228 420
Chemicals & Pharmaceuticals Products Mfr
N.A.I.C.S.: 325412

Ashland France SAS (2)
125 rue Casimir Perier, 95870, Bezons,
France   (100%)
Tel.: (33) 00134345454
Sales Range: $10-24.9 Million
Emp.: 50
Chemical Products Distr
N.A.I.C.S.: 325998

Ashland Services B.V. (2)
Shared Services Center, Pesetastraat 5,
2991 XT, Barendrecht,
Netherlands   (100%)
Tel.: (31) 104975000
Web Site: http://www.ashland.com
Rev.: $1,600,000,000
Emp.: 100
Specialty Chemicals & Resins Supplier &
Mfr; Construction, Infrastructure, Energy &
Transportation
N.A.I.C.S.: 325211

Ashland Performance Materials (1)
5200 Blazer Pkwy, Dublin, OH 43017-5309
Tel.: (614) 790-3333
Web Site: http://www.ashchem.com
Sales Range: $1-4.9 Billion
Emp.: 8,000
Specialty Chemicals Supplier for Construc-
tion, Packaging & Converting, Transporta-
tion & Marine & Metal Casting; High Perfor-
mance Adhesives & Specialty Resins Mfr
N.A.I.C.S.: 325998
Jose Armando Aguirre (Dir-Comml)
Andrew Beer (VP-Global Mktg & Bus Dev)
Bob Hall (Dir-Vinyl Ester & Specialty
Resins-Global)
Gary Landsettle (VP-North America)

Unit (Domestic):

**Ashland Performance Materials - Oak
Creek** (2)
7221 S 10th St, Oak Creek, WI 53154

Ashland Inc.—(Continued)

Tel.: (414) 762-3330
Sales Range: $25-49.9 Million
Emp.: 60
Adhesives & Resins Mfr
N.A.I.C.S.: 325520

Ashland Rhine Holdings B.V. (1)
Pesetastraat 5, 2991 XT, Barendrecht,
Netherlands
Tel.: (31) 104975000
Web Site: http://www.vv.ashland.com
Holding Company
N.A.I.C.S.: 551112

Ashland Rhone Holdings B.V. (1)
Pesetastraat 5, 2991 XT, Barendrecht,
Netherlands
Tel.: (31) 104975000
Chemical Products Distr
N.A.I.C.S.: 424690

**Ashland Specialties Belgium
BVBA** (1)
Geslecht 2 Haven 1920, Doel, Beveren,
9130, Belgium
Tel.: (32) 37300211
Web Site: http://www.ashland.com
Emp.: 165
Chemical Products Distr
N.A.I.C.S.: 424690

**Ashland Specialties Hispania
S.L.** (1)
Carretera Reial 137-139, 08960, Sant Just
Desvern, Spain
Tel.: (34) 932980700
Chemical Products Distr
N.A.I.C.S.: 424690

**Ashland Specialties South Africa Pro-
prietary Limited** (1)
1st Flr Lakeside 2 Ernest Oppenheimer Av
Bruma, Johannesburg, Gauteng, South
Africa
Tel.: (27) 116162200
Petroleum Refining Services
N.A.I.C.S.: 324110

Ashland Specialties Sverige AB (1)
Box 8619, 030 09, Rotterdam, Netherlands
Tel.: (31) 0701701990
Chemical Products Distr
N.A.I.C.S.: 424690

Ashland Specialties UK Limited (1)
Vale Industrial Estate, Kidderminster, DY11
7QU, Worcestershire, United Kingdom
Tel.: (44) 1562821300
Web Site: http://www.ashland.com
Emp.: 40
Chemical Products Distr
N.A.I.C.S.: 424600

**Ashland Switzerland Holdings
GmbH** (1)
C/O Ashland Industries Europe Gmbh,
Schaffhausen, 8200, Switzerland
Tel.: (41) 525605600
Web Site: http://www.ashland.com
Emp.: 40
Holding Company
N.A.I.C.S.: 551112

Hercules Argentina S.A. (1)
Av Cervino 4417 piso 7 Oficina A, Buenos
Aires, C1425AHB, Argentina
Tel.: (54) 1147793206
Chemical Products Distr
N.A.I.C.S.: 424690
Carlos Collado *(Gen Mgr)*

Hercules Chile Limitada (1)
Avenue Nueva Tajamar 481 Fl 11 Oficina,
Santiago, 1108, Las Condes, Chile
Tel.: (56) 22301110
Web Site: http://www.solenis.com
Emp.: 21
Chemical Products Distr
N.A.I.C.S.: 424690

**Hercules Holding Specialty Materials
B. V.** (1)
Pesetastraat 5, 2991 XT, Barendrecht,
Netherlands
Tel.: (31) 104975000
Emp.: 250
Financial Services
N.A.I.C.S.: 523999

Hercules Incorporated (1)
1313 N Market St, Wilmington, DE 19894-
0001
Tel.: (302) 594-5000
Sales Range: $1-4.9 Billion
Emp.: 4,660
Specialty Chemical Supplier; Papermaking,
Commercial, Institutional, Food & Beverage,
Mining & General Manufacturing Chemicals
N.A.I.C.S.: 325194

Subsidiary (Non-US):

Ashland Industries Austria GmbH (2)
Davidgasse 87 89, 1100, Vienna, Austria
Tel.: (43) 1 602 97 40
Web Site: http://www.ashland.com
Sales Range: $25-49.9 Million
Emp.: 10
Specialty Chemical Supplier & Mfr
N.A.I.C.S.: 325194

**Ashland Industries Belgium
BVBA** (2)
Industrieweg 150, Industriezone Raven-
shout 7/301, 3583, Beringen, Belgium
Tel.: (32) 1145 8590
Web Site: http://www.ashland.com
Sales Range: $50-74.9 Million
Emp.: 70
Specialty Chemical Supplier & Mfr
N.A.I.C.S.: 325194

**Ashland Industries Deutschland
GmbH** (2)
Paul Thomas Strasse 56, 40599, Dussel-
dorf, Germany
Tel.: (49) 21174910
Web Site: http://www.ashland.com
Sales Range: $1-4.9 Billion
Specialty Chemical Supplier; Papermaking,
Commercial, Institutional, Food & Beverage,
Mining & General Manufacturing Chemicals
N.A.I.C.S.: 325194

Ashland Industries Finland Oy (2)
Kolmihaarankatu 7, 33330, Tampere, Fin-
land
Tel.: (358) 207813700
Sales Range: $50-74.9 Million
Emp.: 40
Specialty Chemical Supplier; Papermaking,
Commercial, Institutional, Food & Beverage,
Mining & General Manufacturing Chemicals
N.A.I.C.S.: 325194

Ashland Industries France SAS (2)
Zone Industrielle, BP 12, 27460, Alizay,
France
Tel.: (33) 2 3298 9259
Web Site: http://www.ashland.com
Emp.: 120
Mfr of Water-Soluble Polymers
N.A.I.C.S.: 325998

Ashland Industries Italia S.R.L. (2)
Via Domenico Sansotta 97, Rome, RM 144,
Italy
Tel.: (39) 06526206300
Chemical Products Mfr
N.A.I.C.S.: 325998
Gabriella Gessini *(Gen Mgr)*

**Ashland Industries Nederland
B.V.** (2)
Pesetastraat 5, 2991 TX, Barendrecht,
Netherlands (100%)
Tel.: (31) 104975000
Web Site: http://www.ashland.com
Sales Range: $50-74.9 Million
Emp.: 100
Water Soluble Polymers & Coating Addi-
tives Mfr
N.A.I.C.S.: 325998

Ashland Industries Sweden AB (2)
Industrigatan 125, S 25106, Helsingborg,
Sweden
Tel.: (46) 42371000
Web Site: http://www.ashland.com
Sales Range: $75-99.9 Million
Emp.: 25
Specialty Chemical Supplier & Mfr
N.A.I.C.S.: 325194

Ashland Industries UK Limited (2)
Wimsey Way Alfreton Trading Estate, Alfreton, DE55 4LR, United Kingdom

Tel.: (44) 1773604321
Chemical Products Mfr
N.A.I.C.S.: 325998

Division (Domestic):

Ashland Specialty Ingredients (2)
1313 N Mkt St, Wilmington, DE 19894
Tel.: (302) 594-5000
Sales Range: $800-899.9 Million
Emp.: 1,000
Water Soluble Polymers & Coating Addi-
tives Mfr
N.A.I.C.S.: 325998
John E. Panichella *(Pres)*
Dale MacDonald *(VP-Coatings Additives
Indus Grp)*

Subsidiary (Non-US):

Aqualon France B.V. (3)
Zone Industrielle, 27460, Alizay, France
Tel.: (33) 232989203
Web Site: http://www.ashland.com
Sales Range: $25-49.9 Million
Emp.: 100
Mfr Water-Soluble Polymers
N.A.I.C.S.: 325211

Subsidiary (Non-US):

**Hercules Chemicals (Taiwan) Co.,
Ltd.** (2)
7/F No 37 Min Chuan E Road Section 3,
104, Taipei, Taiwan
Tel.: (886) 225002223
Sales Range: $25-49.9 Million
Emp.: 60
Mfr of Specialty Chemicals
N.A.I.C.S.: 325998

**Hercules Chemicals Solution Pte.
Ltd.** (2)
200 Pandan Loop #07-01 Pantech 21, Sin-
gapore, Singapore
Tel.: (65) 67755366
Web Site: http://www.ashland.com
Sales Range: $10-24.9 Million
Emp.: 60
Water Soluble Polymers & Coating Addi-
tives Mfr
N.A.I.C.S.: 325998

Hercules Doel BVBA (2)
Geslecht 2 Haven 1920, 9130, Doel, Bev-
eren, Belgium
Tel.: (32) 37300211
Web Site: http://www.ashland.com
Sales Range: $50-74.9 Million
Emp.: 190
Production of Water Soluble Polymers, Spe-
cialty Ingredients & Coating Additives
N.A.I.C.S.: 325998

Subsidiary (Domestic):

**Hercules Hydrocarbon Holdings,
Inc.** (2)
1313 N Market St, Wilmington, DE 19894
Tel.: (302) 594-5000
Chemical Products Distr
N.A.I.C.S.: 424690

Subsidiary (Non-US):

**Hercules do Brasil Produtos Quimi-
cos Ltda.** (2)
Rua dos Pinheiros 870 20 Andar Conj 203,
E 204, 05422 001, Sao Paulo, SP, Brazil
Tel.: (55) 1130899220
Sales Range: $10-24.9 Million
Emp.: 50
Mfr of Specialty Chemicals
N.A.I.C.S.: 325998

Pakistan Gum Industries Limited (2)
B/30 Estate Avenue Site, Karachi, 75700,
Pakistan
Tel.: (92) 2132574311
Web Site: http://www.pakgum.com
Sales Range: $125-149.9 Million
Guar Gum Mfr
N.A.I.C.S.: 325194

Quimica Hercules, S.A. de C.V. (2)
Saltillo 19 Piso 10, Mexico, 06140, Mexico
Tel.: (52) 5552110111
Sales Range: $1-9.9 Million
Emp.: 65
Mfr of Chemicals

N.A.I.C.S.: 325998

Hercules Portuguesa, Lda. (1)
Qta da Marquesa Pav IV Ed McClane Ca-
banas, Setubal, 2950-557, Quinta Do Anjo,
Portugal
Tel.: (351) 212108180
Web Site: http://www.ashland.com
Emp.: 2
Chemical Products Distr
N.A.I.C.S.: 424690

**Hercules Tianpu Chemicals Company
Limited** (1)
Gaoba, Luzhou, 646003, Sichuan, China
Tel.: (86) 8302796448
Web Site: http://www.hercules-tianpu.com
Chemical & Resin Mfr
N.A.I.C.S.: 325211

ISP Chemicals LLC (1)
Route 95 Industrial Area, Calvert City, KY
42029
Tel.: (270) 395-4165
Chemical Products Mfr
N.A.I.C.S.: 325998

**International Specialty Products,
Inc.** (1)
1361 Alps Rd, Wayne, NJ 07470
Tel.: (973) 628-4000
Web Site: http://www.ispcorp.com
Sales Range: $1-4.9 Billion
Emp.: 3,120
Holding Company; Chemicals & Mineral
Products Mfr & Supplier
N.A.I.C.S.: 551112

Plant (Domestic):

Ashland Specialty Ingredients (2)
Hwy 95 Industrial Complex, Calvert City, KY
42029
Tel.: (270) 395-4165
Sales Range: $150-199.9 Million
Emp.: 500
Industrial Organic Chemicals & Specialty
Chemicals Mfr
N.A.I.C.S.: 325199
Frank Stevens *(Plant Mgr)*

Subsidiary (Non-US):

ISP (Korea) Limited (2)
6th Floor Eunsung Building 601 18 Yeo-
ksam Dong, Kangnam-Ku, Seoul, 135-080,
Korea (South)
Tel.: (82) 25546622
Chemical Products Distr
N.A.I.C.S.: 424690

ISP (Polska) Sp.z o.o. (2)
ul Slaska 15, 40-741, Katowice, Poland
Tel.: (48) 326080110
Web Site: http://www.it-sp.pl
Emp.: 50
Data Processing & Automation Services
N.A.I.C.S.: 518210

ISP (Thailand) Co., Ltd (2)
Panavongs Building no 297 Suriwong Road
Bang rack, Bangkok, 10500, Thailand
Tel.: (66) 22678103
Web Site: http://www.ashland.com
Emp.: 15
Trading Speciality Chemicals
N.A.I.C.S.: 325199

ISP Argentina S.R.L. (2)
Paraguay 610, 1057, Buenos Aires, Argen-
tina
Tel.: (54) 1143140659
Chemical Products Mfr
N.A.I.C.S.: 325199

ISP Asia Pacific Pte. Ltd. (2)
200 Cantonment Rd No 06 05 Southpoint,
Singapore, 089763, Singapore
Tel.: (65) 62233778
Web Site: http://www.ispcorp.com
Sales Range: $25-49.9 Million
Emp.: 20
Specialty Chemical Whslr
N.A.I.C.S.: 424690

ISP Biochema Schwaben GmbH (2)
Luitpoldstrasse 32, Memmingen, 87700,
Germany
Tel.: (49) 833195800
Web Site: http://www.ashland.com
Emp.: 46

Chemical Products Mfr
N.A.I.C.S.: 325199

Subsidiary (Domestic):

ISP Chemical Products LLC **(2)**
1979 Atlas St, Columbus, OH 43228
Tel.: (614) 876-3637
Chemical Products Mfr
N.A.I.C.S.: 325199

Subsidiary (Non-US):

ISP France Marketing SARL **(2)**
Paris Nord 2 13 rue de la Perdrix Bat 3,
Roissy CDG, 95945, Paris, Cedex,
France **(100%)**
Tel.: (33) 149905800
Web Site: http://www.ispcorp.com
Sales Range: $25-49.9 Million
Emp.: 25
Specialty Chemical Sales
N.A.I.C.S.: 424690

ISP Global Technologies Deutschland
GmbH **(2)**
Emil-Hoffmann-Str 1 a, Cologne, 50996,
Germany
Tel.: (49) 223696490
Chemicals Mfr & Whslr
N.A.I.C.S.: 424690

Subsidiary (Domestic):

ISP Global Technologies Inc. **(2)**
1361 Alps Rd, Wayne, NJ 07470
Tel.: (973) 628-4000
Web Site: http://www.ispcorp.com
Sales Range: $150-199.9 Million
Emp.: 450
Industrial Organic Chemicals Mfr
N.A.I.C.S.: 325199

Subsidiary (Non-US):

ISP India Pvt. Ltd **(2)**
RVR Towers Level 4 6-3-1089/F Raj Bha-
wan Road, SomajiGuda, 500082, Hydera-
bad, India **(100%)**
Tel.: (91) 4044748888
Web Site: http://www.ispcorp.com
Sales Range: $25-49.9 Million
Emp.: 60
Specialty Chemical Sales & Research
N.A.I.C.S.: 325199
Dinesh Sharma *(Dir-Corp Support & Head-
HR)*

ISP Japan Ltd. **(2)**
Asteer Kayabacho Bldg 3rd Floor 161
chome Shinkawa, Chuo-ku, Tokyo, 104
0033, Japan **(100%)**
Tel.: (81) 355668661
Web Site: http://www.ispcorp.com
Sales Range: $25-49.9 Million
Emp.: 20
Specialty Chemical Sales
N.A.I.C.S.: 424690

Plant (Non-US):

ISP Marl GmbH **(2)**
Paul Baumann Str 1, Bldg 1878, 45764,
Marl, Germany
Tel.: (49) 236 549 6065
Web Site: http://www.ispcorp.com
Sales Range: $50-74.9 Million
Emp.: 225
Industrial Organic Chemicals Mfr
N.A.I.C.S.: 325199

Subsidiary (Non-US):

ISP Microcaps (U.K.) Limited **(2)**
8 9 Stepnell Reach 541 Blandford Road,
Poole, BH16 5BW, Dorsetshire, United
Kingdom
Tel.: (44) 1202627350
Industrial Water Treatment Services
N.A.I.C.S.: 221310

Subsidiary (Domestic):

ISP Synthetic Elastomers LLC **(2)**
1615 Main St, Port Neches, TX 77651-3039
Tel.: (409) 722-8321
Synthetic Rubber Mfr
N.A.I.C.S.: 325212

Plant (Domestic):

ISP Technologies Inc. **(2)**

4501 Attwater Ave & Hwy 146, Texas City,
TX 77590
Tel.: (973) 628-4000
Web Site: http://www.ispcorp.com
Sales Range: $50-74.9 Million
Emp.: 125
Specialty & Industrial Chemicals Mfr
N.A.I.C.S.: 325998

Subsidiary (Non-US):

ISP Turkey **(2)**
Ruzgarlibahce Mah Cumhuriyet Cad Asas
Pen Plaza Kat 1-2, Beykoz, 34810, Istan-
bul, Turkiye **(100%)**
Tel.: (90) 2165380800
Web Site: http://www.ispcorp.com
Sales Range: $25-49.9 Million
Emp.: 30
Specialty Chemical Research & Sales
N.A.I.C.S.: 424690
Philip Strenger *(Sr VP)*

ISP do Brasil Ltda. **(2)**
Av Embaixador Macedo Soares 10735 Conj
01 Bairro Vila Anastacio, Sao Paulo, 05095-
035, SP, Brazil
Tel.: (55) 11 3649 0455
Web Site: http://www.ashland.com
Chemical Product Mfr & Distr
N.A.I.C.S.: 424690

PT ISP Chemicals Indonesia **(2)**
J1 Letjen S Parman Kav 12 Wisma Slipi 8th
Floor, Jakarta, 11480, Indonesia
Tel.: (62) 2183700423
Emp.: 20
Chemical Products Mfr
N.A.I.C.S.: 325199
Chandra Ekaryana *(Mgr-HR)*

Pharmachem Laboratories, LLC **(1)**
265 Harrison Ave, Kearny, NJ 07032
Tel.: (201) 246-1000
Web Site: http://www.pharmachemlabs.com
Pharmaceutical Preparation Mfr
N.A.I.C.S.: 325412

Subsidiary (Domestic):

Avoca, Inc. **(2)**
841 Avoca Farm Rd, Merry Hill, NC 27957
Tel.: (252) 482-2133
Web Site: http://www.reducol.com
Botanical Extraction Services
N.A.I.C.S.: 325412

Techwax Limited **(1)**
Unit 4B Whinbank Park Whinbank Road
Newton Aycliffe, Durham, DL5 6AY, United
Kingdom
Tel.: (44) 1325301301
Web Site: http://www.ashland.com
Emp.: 25
Chemical Products Mfr
N.A.I.C.S.: 325199

ZAO Ashland MSP **(1)**
Ul Kirovogradskaya 16, Perm, 614101, Rus-
sia
Tel.: (7) 3422530146
Emp.: 70
Chemical Products Distr
N.A.I.C.S.: 424690
Alexe Yarefez *(Gen Mgr)*

ASIA BROADBAND, INC.

3753 Howard Hughes Pkwy Ste 200
738, Las Vegas, NV 89169
Tel.: (702) 866-9045
Web Site:
    https://www.asiabroadbandinc.com
AABB—(OTCIQ)
Rev.: $8,329,000
Assets: $24,708,000
Liabilities: $1,457,000
Net Worth: $23,251,000
Earnings: $5,355,000
Fiscal Year-end: 12/31/19
Jewelry, Watch, Precious Stone &
Precious Metal Merchant Whslr
N.A.I.C.S.: 423940
James Gilbert *(Pres & CEO)*

ASIA PROPERTIES, INC.

12707 High Bluff Dr 2nd Fl, San Diego, CA 92130

Tel.: (619) 350-4288   NV
ASPZ—(OTCIQ)
Real Estate Manangement Services
N.A.I.C.S.: 531390

ASPEN AEROGELS, INC.

30 Forbes Rd Bldg B, Northborough,
MA 01532
Tel.: (508) 691-1111   DE
Web Site: https://www.aerogel.com
Year Founded: 2001
ASPN—(NYSE)
Rev.: $180,364,000
Assets: $643,416,000
Liabilities: $195,981,000
Net Worth: $447,435,000
Earnings: ($82,738,000)
Emp.: 533
Fiscal Year-end: 12/31/22
Aerogel Insulation Blankets Mfr
N.A.I.C.S.: 325998
Donald R. Young *(Pres & CEO)*
George L. Gould *(CTO)*
Corby C. Whitaker *(Sr VP-Sls &
Mktg)*
Kelley W. Conte *(Sr VP-HR)*
Gregg R. Landes *(Sr VP-Ops & Stra-
tegic Dev)*
Ricardo C. Rodriguez *(CFO, Treas &
Sr VP)*
Keith L. Schilling *(Sr VP)*

ASPEN GROUP, INC.

276 5th Ave Ste 505, New York, NY
75093
Tel.: (480) 407-7365   DE
Web Site: https://www.aspu.com
Year Founded: 2010
ASPU—(NASDAQ)
Rev.: $76,694,366
Assets: $91,066,051
Liabilities: $48,520,327
Net Worth: $42,545,724
Earnings: ($9,585,781)
Emp.: 312
Fiscal Year-end: 04/30/22
Online Learning Services
N.A.I.C.S.: 923110
Michael Mathews *(CEO & Chm)*
Matthew Lavay *(CFO)*
Cheri St. Arnauld *(Chief Academic
Officer)*
Anne McNamara *(Chief Nursing Offi-
cer)*

Subsidiaries:

Aspen University Inc. **(1)**
1660 S Albion St Ste 525, Denver, CO
80222
Tel.: (303) 333-4224
Web Site: http://www.aspen.edu
Emp.: 306
University Operator
N.A.I.C.S.: 611310
Michael Mathews *(CEO)*
Anne McNamara *(Chief Nursing Officer)*
Jessica Peters *(Asst Dir-Student Svcs)*

United States University, Inc. **(1)**
7675 Mission Valley Rd, San Diego, CA
92108
Tel.: (619) 876-4250
Web Site: http://www.usuniversity.edu
University Operator
N.A.I.C.S.: 611310
Steven Stargardter *(Pres)*
Ming Tan *(CFO)*
Ken Cook *(Dir-Enrollment)*
Alyssa Hill *(Mgr-Faculty Support)*
Brandon Hughes *(Dir-Academic Advising)*

ASPEN INTERNATIONAL
HOLDINGS, INC.

12527 Kirkham Ct, Poway, CA 92064
Tel.: (305) 484-6656   NV
ASXH—(OTCIQ)
Metal Mining & Exploration Services
N.A.I.C.S.: 213114
Kerry Vinci *(Pres, CFO & Sec)*

ASPIRA WOMEN'S HEALTH
INC.

12117 Bee Caves Rd Bldg III Ste
100, Austin, TX 78738
Tel.: (512) 519-0400   DE
Web Site: https://www.aspirawh.com
Year Founded: 1993
AWH—(NASDAQ)
Rev.: $8,184,000
Assets: $17,373,000
Liabilities: $10,642,000
Net Worth: $6,731,000
Earnings: ($27,170,000)
Emp.: 85
Fiscal Year-end: 12/31/22
Protein Research Products Mfr
N.A.I.C.S.: 334516
Sandra Milligan *(Pres)*
Patrick Carpenter *(Gen Mgr-Aspira
Labs)*
Herbert A. Fritsche *(Dir-Lab-Aspira
Labs)*
Lesley Northrop *(Chief Scientific Offi-
cer)*
Kaile Zagger *(COO)*
Nicole Sandford *(Pres & CEO)*
Greg Richard *(Head-Corp Strategy,
Reimbursement & Managed Care)*
Tatiana Black *(Compliance Officer &
Sr Dir-Regulatory Affairs & Quality)*
Shieva Ghofrany *(Head-Global Clini-
cal Implementation)*
Tom Greco *(Head-Strategic Corp Dev
& Expansion)*
Kimberly Greene *(VP-Strategic Part-
nerships)*
Laura McPadden *(Head-People &
Culture)*
Stephanie Swenson *(Controller)*
Jennifer Van Aken *(Head-Mktg)*
Maxine Burns *(Mgr-Comml Ops)*
Justin Degrazia *(Sr Dir-R&D)*
Emily Granger *(Sr Dir-Mktg)*
Jessica Greenwood *(Sr Dir-Clinical
Implementation & Innovation)*
Cathy Minton *(Sr Dir-Revenue Cycle
Mgmt)*
April J. L. Pradier *(Dir-Program
Mgmt)*
Loreli Quintero-Jolliff *(Dir-Enterprise
Bus Activation)*
Ahmad Saleh *(Head-Hospital Sys)*
Tortsten Hombeck *(CFO, Principal
Acctg Officer & Sr VP)*
Michelle Snider *(Sr VP-Comml Strat-
egy & Ops)*

Subsidiaries:

ASPiRA Labs, Inc. **(1)**
12117 Bee Caves Rd Bldg III Ste 100, Aus-
tin, TX 78738
Tel.: (512) 519-0400
Web Site: http://www.aspiralab.com
Laboratory Testing Services
N.A.I.C.S.: 541380

ASPYRA, INC.

7400 Baymeadows Way Ste 101,
Jacksonville, FL 32256
Tel.: (818) 880-6700   CA
Web Site: https://www.aspyra.com
Year Founded: 1978
APYI—(OTCIQ)
Sales Range: $1-9.9 Million
Emp.: 69
Healthcare Industry Clinical Informa-
tion Systems Designer
N.A.I.C.S.: 541512
Dennis Prichard *(VP-LIS Dev & Ops)*
Bill Pratt *(Dir-Dev-Imaging Sys Solu-
tions)*
Gary W. Bennett *(Pres)*
Joy Wallace *(Mgr-Customer Care)*
Lisa Powell *(Mgr-Customer Care-LIS)*

Subsidiaries:

Aspyra Technologies Ltd. **(1)**

ASPYRA, INC.—(Continued)

The Center 201 203 London Road, East Grinstead, RH19 1HA, West Sussex, United Kingdom **(100%)**
Tel.: (44) 1923432610
Web Site: http://www.aspyra.com
Healthcare Technology Services
N.A.I.C.S.: 561499

Aspyra-East Coast Office **(1)**
9432 Baymetels Rd Ste 155, Jacksonville, FL 32256 **(100%)**
Tel.: (904) 731-1289
Web Site: http://www.aspyra.com
Help Desk Support Services
N.A.I.C.S.: 541519

ASSEMBLY BIOSCIENCES, INC.
2 Tower Pl 7 th Fl, South San Francisco, CA 94080
Tel.: (317) 210-9311   DE
Web Site:
    https://www.assemblybio.com
Year Founded: 2005
ASMB—(NASDAQ)
Rev.: $1,022,000
Assets: $101,794,000
Liabilities: $19,130,000
Net Worth: $82,664,000
Earnings: ($93,092,000)
Emp.: 68
Fiscal Year-end: 12/31/22
Pharmaceuticals Mfr
N.A.I.C.S.: 325412
William R. Ringo Jr. (Chm)
Derek A. Small (Founder)
Michele Anderson (Chief Dev Officer)
William Delaney (Chief Scientific Officer)
Jason A. Okazaki (Pres & CEO)
Nicole S. White (Chief Mfg Officer)
Jeanette M. Bjorkquist (Exec Dir)

Subsidiaries:

Assembly Pharmaceuticals, Inc. **(1)**
615 S Clifton Ave, Bloomington, IN 47401
Tel.: (812) 360-4416
Pharmaceuticals Product Mfr
N.A.I.C.S.: 325412
Derek A. Small (Co-Founder)

ASSERTIO HOLDINGS, INC.
100 S Saunders Rd Ste 300, Lake Forest, IL 60045
Tel.: (224) 419-7106   IL
Web Site: https://www.assertiotx.com
ASRT—(NASDAQ)
Rev.: $156,234,000
Assets: $413,913,000
Liabilities: $188,188,000
Net Worth: $225,725,000
Earnings: $109,625,000
Emp.: 30
Fiscal Year-end: 12/31/22
Drug Delivery Technologies Developer
N.A.I.C.S.: 325411
Brendan P. O'Grady (CEO)
Sam Schlessinger (Gen Counsel & Sr VP)
Ajay Patel (Chief Acctg Officer & Sr VP)
Paul Schwichtenberg (Sr VP-Market Access, Pricing, Trade, and Distr)
Jeff Christensen (Sr VP)
Vanessa Fox (VP)
Howard Franklin (Sr VP)
Bill Iskos (Sr VP)

Subsidiaries:

Spectrum Pharmaceuticals, Inc. **(1)**
11500 S Eastern Ave Ste 240, Henderson, NV 89052
Tel.: (702) 835-6300
Web Site: http://www.sppirx.com
Rev.: $10,114,000
Assets: $103,338,000
Liabilities: $75,450,000

Net Worth: $27,888,000
Earnings: ($75,401,000)
Emp.: 86
Fiscal Year-end: 12/31/2022
Early & Late-Stage Oncology & Other Drug Development Services
N.A.I.C.S.: 325412
Keith M. McGahan (Chief Legal Officer, Sec & Exec VP)
Nora E. Brennan (CFO & Exec VP)

Subsidiary (Non-US):

Spectrum Oncology Private Limited **(2)**
71 Free Press House Free Press Journal Marg Nariman Point, Mumbai, 400021, Maharashtra, India
Tel.: (91) 2222042380
Web Site: http://www.oncorxindia.com
Emp.: 10
Pharmaceuticals Product Mfr
N.A.I.C.S.: 325412

Zyla Life Sciences **(1)**
600 Lee Rd Ste 100, Wayne, PA 19087
Tel.: (610) 833-4200
Web Site: http://www.egalet.com
Sales Range: $25-49.9 Million
Holding Company; Pharmaceutical Mfr & Whslr
N.A.I.C.S.: 551112
Todd N. Smith (Pres & CEO)

ASSET ENTITIES INC.
100 Crescent Ct 7th Fl, Dallas, TX 75201
Tel.: (214) 459-3117   NV
Web Site:
    https://www.assetentities.com
Year Founded: 2020
ASST—(NASDAQ)
Rev.: $343,106
Assets: $373,021
Liabilities: $219,238
Net Worth: $153,783
Earnings: ($645,255)
Emp.: 7
Fiscal Year-end: 12/31/22
Digital Marketing Services
N.A.I.C.S.: 541810
Arshia Sarkhani (CEO)
Derek Dunlop (Chief Experience Officer)
Jackson Fairbanks (CMO)

ASSISTED 4 LIVING, INC.
5115 East State Rd 64, Bradenton, FL 34208
Tel.: (941) 758-4745   NV
Web Site:
    http://www.assisted4living.com
Year Founded: 2017
ASSF—(OTCIQ)
Rev.: $880,782
Assets: $264,810
Liabilities: $184,167
Net Worth: $80,643
Earnings: ($115,592)
Emp.: 1
Fiscal Year-end: 11/30/20
Health Care Consulting Services
N.A.I.C.S.: 524114
Roger Tichenor (CFO & Principal Acctg Officer)
Diane Harden (CTO, Principal Acctg Officer & Treas)
John Krusoe (Sec & Sr Exec VP)
Louis Collier Jr. (Pres & CEO)

ASSOCIATED BANC-CORP
433 Main St, Green Bay, WI 54301
Tel.: (920) 491-7500   WI
Web Site:
    https://www.associatedbank.com
Year Founded: 1861
ASB—(NYSE)
Rev.: $2,021,234,000
Assets: $41,015,855,000
Liabilities: $36,841,882,000
Net Worth: $4,173,973,000

Earnings: $171,456,000
Emp.: 4,100
Fiscal Year-end: 12/31/23
Bank Holding Company
N.A.I.C.S.: 551111
Randall J. Erickson (Gen Counsel, Sec & Exec VP)
Andrew J. Harmening (Pres & CEO)
David L. Stein (Exec VP & Head-Consumer & Bus Banking)
Phillip Trier (Exec VP)
Matthew R. Braeger (Exec VP)
Nicole M. Kitowski (Chief Risk Officer & Exec VP)
Angie M. DeWitt (Cheif HR Officer & Exec VP)
Bryan Carson (Chief Product & Mktg Officer)
Derek S. Meyer (CFO & Exec VP)
John Utz (Exec VP & Head-Corp Banking)

Subsidiaries:

Anderson Insurance & Investment Agency **(1)**
312 Central Ave SE, Minneapolis, MN 55414-1064
Tel.: (612) 331-3712
Web Site:
    http://www.andersonagencyins.com
Direct Property & Casualty Insurance Carriers
N.A.I.C.S.: 524126
Shaun Irwin (Pres)

Associated Bank, NA **(1)**
200 N Adams St, Green Bay, WI 54301
Tel.: (920) 433-3200
Web Site: http://www.associatedbank.com
Sales Range: $50-74.9 Million
Emp.: 150
Banking Services
N.A.I.C.S.: 522110

Associated Investment Services, Inc. **(1)**
2985 S Ridge Rd Ste C, Green Bay, WI 54304-5565
Tel.: (920) 327-5600
Web Site: http://www.associatedbank.com
Sales Range: $125-149.9 Million
Emp.: 60
Investment Consulting Services
N.A.I.C.S.: 523150

Associated Trust Company, NA **(1)**
401 E Kilbourn Ave, Milwaukee, WI 53202-3212 **(100%)**
Tel.: (414) 283-2230
Web Site: http://www.associatedtrust.com
Rev.: $2,599,760
Emp.: 20
Investment Services
N.A.I.C.S.: 523150
Andrew J. Harmening (Pres)

ASSOCIATED CAPITAL GROUP, INC.
191 Mason St, Greenwich, CT 06830
Tel.: (203) 629-9595   DE
Web Site: https://www.associated-capital-group.com
Year Founded: 2015
AC—(NYSE)
Rev.: $15,228,000
Assets: $927,690,000
Liabilities: $37,494,000
Net Worth: $890,196,000
Earnings: ($48,907,000)
Emp.: 24
Fiscal Year-end: 12/31/22
Portfolio Management & Investment Advice
N.A.I.C.S.: 523940
Mario J. Gabelli (Exec Chm)
Peter D. Goldstein (Chief Legal Officer)
Ian McAdams (CFO)
Douglas R. Jamieson (Pres & CEO)

ASSURANT, INC.

260 Interstate N Cir SE, Atlanta, GA 30339-2210
Tel.: (770) 763-1000   DE
Web Site: https://www.assurant.com
Year Founded: 1969
AIZ—(NYSE)
Rev.: $11,131,600,000
Assets: $33,635,200,000
Liabilities: $28,825,700,000
Net Worth: $4,809,500,000
Earnings: $642,500,000
Emp.: 13,600
Fiscal Year-end: 12/31/23
Specialized Insurance & Insurance-Related Products & Services
N.A.I.C.S.: 525190
Francesca L. Luthi (COO & Exec VP)
Keith R. Meier (CFO & Exec VP)
Michael P. Campbell (Pres-Global Housing)
Robert A. Lonergan (Chief Strategy & Risk Officer & Exec VP)
Keith W. Demmings (Pres & CEO)
Jay Rosenblum (Exec VP)
Biju Nair (Pres-Connected Living-Global)
Sean Moshier (VP-IR)
Rebekah Biondo (Deputy CFO)
Subhashish Sengupta (Chief People Officer)
Joseph A. Surber III (CTO)

Subsidiaries:

Alegre Pty Ltd **(1)**
Reply Paid 86913, Locked Bag 5103, Frenchs Forest, Sydney, 2086, NSW, Australia
Tel.: (61) 1300475275
Web Site: https://www.alegre.net.au
Smart Phone Distr
N.A.I.C.S.: 423690

American Bankers Life Assurance Company of Florida **(1)**
11222 Quail Roost Dr, Miami, FL 33157-6596
Tel.: (305) 252-6987
Emp.: 2,000
Fire Insurance Services
N.A.I.C.S.: 524113
Steven Lemasters (Pres & CEO)

American Financial & Automotive Services, Inc. **(1)**
1790 Hughes Landing Blvd Ste 700, The Woodlands, TX 77380
Web Site: http://www.afabno.com
Health & Medical Insurance Services
N.A.I.C.S.: 524114

American Financial Warranty Corporation **(1)**
PO Box 7719, The Woodlands, TX 77387
Warranty Claim Services
N.A.I.C.S.: 524128

American Memorial Life Insurance Company **(1)**
440 Mount Rushmore Rd, Rapid City, SD 57701
Tel.: (605) 719-0999
Web Site: https://www.trustage.com
Insurance Services
N.A.I.C.S.: 524210

American Title Inc. **(1)**
11010 Burdette St, Omaha, NE 68164-3801
Web Site: http://www.americantitleinc.com
Activities Related to Real Estate
N.A.I.C.S.: 531390
Scott McGregor (COO)
Josh Livingston (VP-Sls)
Ryan Lemmon (VP-Acct Mgmt)
Julie Matthes (VP-Centralized Svcs)
Shannon Fairchild (VP-Ops)
Kristy Kolivoski (VP-Ops)

Assurant Argentina Compania de Seguros Sociedad Anonima **(1)**
Ing Enrique Butty 240 Piso 15, C1001AFB, Buenos Aires, C1001AFB, Argentina
Tel.: (54) 1141218666
Insurance Services

N.A.I.C.S.: 524298

Assurant Consulting Company, Limited. (1)
Ocean International Center Suite 2401
2411Building A, No 56 4th East Ring Middle
Road Chaoyang District, Beijing, 100025,
China
Tel.: (86) 1065506999
Management Consulting Services
N.A.I.C.S.: 541611

Assurant Deutschland GmbH (1)
Fritz-Schaffer-Strasse 1, 53113, Bonn, Germany
Tel.: (49) 8002272772
Web Site: https://www.assurant.de
Insurance Services
N.A.I.C.S.: 524298
Andrew Morris (Mng Dir)
Christian Wesley Formby Hernandez (Mng Dir)
Alexander Hess (Mng Dir)
Andy Raymond Schaut (Mng Dir)

Assurant France (1)
45 Rue Denis Papin, 13290, Aix-en-Provence, 13290, France
Tel.: (33) 488055003
Flooded House & Expensive Car Repair Services
N.A.I.C.S.: 811198

Assurant Intermediary Ltd. (1)
Emerald Buildings Westmere Drive, Crewe,
CW1 6UN, Cheshire, United Kingdom
Tel.: (44) 333 200 0444
Web Site: https://assurantforadvisers.co.uk
Mortgage Broker Services
N.A.I.C.S.: 522310

Assurant Life of Canada (1)
5000 Yonge Street Suite 2000, Toronto,
M2N 7E9, ON, Canada
Tel.: (604) 736-2904
Web Site: http://www.assurantlife.ca
Sales Range: $25-49.9 Million
Insurance Services
N.A.I.C.S.: 524298

Assurant Services Canada, Inc. (1)
5000 Yonge St Suite 2000, Toronto, M2N
7E9, ON, Canada
Tel.: (416) 733-3360
Web Site: http://www.assurant.com
Sales Range: $50-74.9 Million
Emp.: 20
Insurance Services
N.A.I.C.S.: 524128

Assurant Services Ireland, Ltd. (1)
Cork Business & Technology Park, Model
Farm Road, Cork, Ireland
Tel.: (353) 214800300
Insurance Services
N.A.I.C.S.: 524298

Assurant Solutions (1)
11222 Quail Roost Dr, Miami, FL 33157
Tel.: (305) 252-6987
Web Site: http://www.assurantsolutions.com
Sales Range: $800-899.9 Million
Emp.: 3,000
Burial Insurance Services
N.A.I.C.S.: 524298

Division (Domestic):

**Assurant Solutions - Preneed
Division** (2)
260 Interstate North Cir SE, Atlanta, GA
30339-2210
Tel.: (770) 206-6400
Web Site: http://www.assurantpreneed.com
Rev.: $64,200,000
Emp.: 135
Burial Insurance Products & Services
N.A.I.C.S.: 524113
Tammy Lynn Schultz (Pres)

Assurant Solutions Spain, S.A. (1)
Avenida de Europa19Edif 2Pl 2ModC, Madrid, 28128, Spain
Tel.: (34) 91 2682900
Sales Range: $25-49.9 Million
Emp.: 2
Insurance Services
N.A.I.C.S.: 524298

Assurant Specialty Property (1)

260 Interstate N Cir SE, Atlanta, GA 30339-2110
Tel.: (770) 763-1000
Web Site: http://www.assurantspecialtyproperty.com
Sales Range: $350-399.9 Million
Emp.: 800
Homeowners Insurance Services
N.A.I.C.S.: 524298

Subsidiary (Domestic):

American Bankers Insurance Company of Florida (2)
11222 Quail Roost Dr, Miami, FL 33157
Tel.: (305) 253-2244
Emp.: 3,000
Specialty Property Insurance Products & Services
N.A.I.C.S.: 524126

eMortgage Logic, LLC (2)
9151 Blvd 26 Ste 400, North Richland Hills,
TX 76180
Tel.: (817) 581-2900
Web Site: http://www.emortgagelogic.com
Sales Range: $25-49.9 Million
Emp.: 71
Real Estate Property Valuation Services
N.A.I.C.S.: 531320
Ralph Sells (Pres)
Chris Santore (Exec VP)
Jennifer Sells (Exec VP-Ops & Client Rels)
Brandon Fox (VP-Client Rels)
Shane Martin (VP)
Anthony Di Staulo (Dir-Sls)
Tony Neveling (Chief Strategy Officer)
Bill Miller (CIO)

Axios Valuation Solutions, LLC (1)
9151 Blvd 26 Ste 400, North Richland Hills,
TX 76180
Tel.: (817) 581-2900
Web Site: http://www.myaxios.com
Emp.: 5
Professional Management Services
N.A.I.C.S.: 611430
Bill Miller (CIO)
Tony Neveling (Chief Strategy Officer)
Brandon Fox (VP-Client Rels)
Jennifer Sells (Exec VP-Ops & Client Rels)
Chris Santore (Exec VP)

CPR Strongsville LLC (1)
17270 Royalton Rd, Strongsville, OH 44136
Tel.: (440) 268-6627
Web Site: https://www.cellphonerepair.com
Electronic & Precision Equipment Maintenance Services
N.A.I.C.S.: 811210

Caribbean American Life Assurance Company (1)
350 Carlos Chardon St Ste 1101 Torre
Chardon, San Juan, PR 00918
Tel.: (787) 250-6470
Web Site: http://www.assurant.com
Sales Range: $50-74.9 Million
Emp.: 75
Specialty Insurance Services
N.A.I.C.S.: 524126

Caribbean American Property Insurance Company (1)
Torre Chardon 350 Carlos Chardon St Ste
1101, San Juan, PR 00918
Tel.: (787) 250-6470
Insurance Services
N.A.I.C.S.: 524114

Collateral Intelligence, LLC (1)
11 Huron Dr Ste 202, Natick, MA 01760-1336
Tel.: (508) 655-0342
Web Site: http://ativaluations.com
Real Estate Appraisal Management Services
N.A.I.C.S.: 531390

Field Asset Services, Inc (1)
101 W Louis Henna Blvd Ste 400, Austin,
TX 78728
Tel.: (512) 467-1537
Web Site: http://www.fieldassets.com
Emp.: 350
Asset Management Services
N.A.I.C.S.: 523940

Guardian Travel, Inc. (1)

1137 N Battlefield Blvd, Chesapeake, VA
23320
Tel.: (757) 312-8008
Web Site:
    https://www.guardiantravelonline.com
Travel Agency Services
N.A.I.C.S.: 561599
Janet Swinehart (Owner)

Hyla Mobile, Inc. (1)
Park W 1 & 2 1507 LBJ Fwy Ste 500,
Farmers Branch, TX 75234
Tel.: (972) 573-0300
Web Site: http://www.hylamobile.com
Wireless Communication Services
N.A.I.C.S.: 517112
Biju Nair (Pres & CEO)
Rebekah Griffiths (VP-Product Mgmt)
Shad Spears (CFO)
Scott Wagner (Chief Revenue Officer)
Bik Singh (VP-Software Dev)

I.Q. Data International, Inc. (1)
PO Box 340, Bothell, WA 98041-0340
Web Site: https://www.iqdata-inc.com
Collection Professional & Management Services
N.A.I.C.S.: 561110

**International Financial Group,
Inc.** (1)
238 International Rd, Burlington, NC 27215
Tel.: (336) 586-2500
Web Site: http://www.ifgcompanies.com
Insurance Services
N.A.I.C.S.: 524298
David McLeod (Pres)

LSG Insurance (1)
Dunrae House 12 Bell Crescent Westlake
Business Park 7945, PO Box 53038, Kenilworth, 7745, South Africa
Tel.: (27) 217010840
Web Site: http://www.lsginsurance.co.za
General Insurance Services
N.A.I.C.S.: 524210
Simon Griffiths (CEO)

Lifestyle Services Group Limited (1)
Emerald Buildings, Westmere Drive Crewe
Business Park, Crewe, CW1 6UN, Cheshire, United Kingdom
Tel.: (44) 1270413000
Web Site: http://www.lifestylegroup.co.uk
Sales Range: $350-399.9 Million
Mobile Phone Insurance, Identity Theft Protection & Specialized Insurance Services
N.A.I.C.S.: 524128

**London General Insurance Company
Limited** (1)
Fitzwilliam Business Centre 77 Sir John
Rogersons Quay, Dublin, 2, Ireland
Tel.: (353) 2696522
Administration & Marketing Services
N.A.I.C.S.: 524128

Mobile Defense, Inc. (1)
30400 Detroit Rd Ste 400, Westlake, OH
44145
Tel.: (440) 243-2520
Web Site: http://www.assurantlabs.com
Software Application Development Services
N.A.I.C.S.: 541511

National Insurance Agency (1)
14800 Quorum Dr Ste 500, Dallas, TX
75254-1496
Tel.: (214) 342-8588
Insurance & Brokerage Services
N.A.I.C.S.: 524210

**National Underwriting Agencies Pty.
Ltd.** (1)
Level 2 693 Burke Road, Camberwell,
3124, VIC, Australia
Tel.: (61) 1300654665
Web Site: https://www.nua.com.au
Third Party Administration & Claims Management Services
N.A.I.C.S.: 524292

North Star Marketing Corporation (1)
9050 Centre Pointe Dr Ste 120, West Chester, OH 45069
Tel.: (513) 563-7899
Web Site: http://www.assurant.com
Emp.: 13
Insurance Services
N.A.I.C.S.: 524210

Privowny France SAS (1)
Parc du Golf Bat 20/Safran 350 avenue
JRGG de la Lauziere, 13290, Aix-en-Provence, France
Tel.: (33) 75 682 4550
Web Site: https://privowny.app
Information Technology Consulting Services
N.A.I.C.S.: 541690

**Protecta Insurance New Zealand
Ltd.** (1)
PO-Box 37-371, Parnell, Auckland, 1151,
New Zealand
Tel.: (64) 800776832
Web Site:
    https://www.protectainsurance.co.nz
Vehicle Insurance Services
N.A.I.C.S.: 524210

Resource Automotive, Inc. (1)
175 W Jackson 11 th Fl, Chicago, IL 60604
Tel.: (312) 356-3000
Administration & Marketing Services
N.A.I.C.S.: 524128

STAMS Ltd. (1)
Hersham Place 41-61 Molesey Rd, Walton-on-Thames, KT12 4RS, United Kingdom
Tel.: (44) 1932891133
Web Site: http://www.stams.co.uk
General Insurance Services
N.A.I.C.S.: 524210

**Shipsurance Insurance Services,
Inc.** (1)
21900 Burbank Blvd Ste 100, Woodland
Hills, CA 91367
Tel.: (818) 444-8920
Web Site: https://www.shipsurance.com
Shipping Insurance & Cargo Insurance Services
N.A.I.C.S.: 525190

**Standard Guaranty Insurance
Company** (1)
260 Interstate N Cir Se, Atlanta, GA 30339
Tel.: (770) 763-1000
Emp.: 900
Insurance Services
N.A.I.C.S.: 524113

TWG Europe Limited (1)
Unit 10 Cable Court Pittman Way, Preston,
PR2 9YW, United Kingdom
Tel.: (44) 1772794704
Industries of Aerospace Construction & Design Mfr
N.A.I.C.S.: 336412

**TWG Repair Services (Shanghai)
Co., Ltd.** (1)
Suite 703-705 UC Tower No 500 Fushan
Road, Shanghai, 200122, China
Tel.: (86) 2138617666
Administration & Marketing Services
N.A.I.C.S.: 524128

TWG Services Limited (1)
The Aspen Building Floor 2 Vantage Point
Business Village, Gloucestershire,
Mitcheldean, GL17 0AF, United Kingdom
Tel.: (44) 1594863000
Administration & Marketing Services
N.A.I.C.S.: 524128

**The Warranty Group Australia Pty.
Ltd.** (1)
Level 2 74 Doncaster Road, Balwyn, 3104,
VIC, Australia
Tel.: (61) 398623200
Marketing & Administrative Management
Services
N.A.I.C.S.: 561110

**The Warranty Group Colombia
S.A.** (1)
Av Cll 100 No 19-54 of 302, Santa Fe, Bogota, Colombia
Tel.: (57) 16517800
Marketing & Administrative Management
Services
N.A.I.C.S.: 561110

The Warranty Group Korea, Inc. (1)
3rd Floor Choyang Building 50-10 Chungmuro 2-ga, Jung-gu, Seoul, Korea (South)
Tel.: (82) 222609910
Insurance & Third Party Claims Processing
Services
N.A.I.C.S.: 524292

Assurant, Inc.—(Continued)

The Warranty Group de Mexico S.A. de C.V. (1)
Av Paseo de la Reforma 115 Piso 14 despacho 1403, Mexico, 11000, Mexico
Tel.: (52) 53221900
Insurance & Third Party Claims Processing Services
N.A.I.C.S.: 524292
Marisol Trejo Arce *(Mgr-Treasury)*

Union Security Insurance Company (1)
2323 Grand Blvd, Kansas City, MO 64108
Tel.: (816) 474-2345
Rev.: $1,239,329,000
Assets: $7,575,490,000
Liabilities: $6,695,633,000
Net Worth: $879,857,000
Earnings: $69,178,000
Emp.: 1,737
Fiscal Year-end: 12/31/2014
Direct Life Insurance Carriers
N.A.I.C.S.: 524113
Miles B. Yakre *(Chm, Pres & CEO)*
Stacia N. Almquist *(Sr VP)*
Tamrha V. Mangelsen *(CFO & Treas)*
Kenneth D. Bowen *(Gen Counsel, Sr VP & Sec)*
Dianna D. Duvall *(Sr VP)*
Christopher J. Pagano *(Gen Mgr)*

Subsidiary (Domestic):

Dental Health Alliance, L.L.C. (2)
2323 Grand Blvd, Kansas City, MO 64108
Web Site: https://www.dha.com
Sales Range: $1-9.9 Million
Emp.: 35
Group Dental Insurance Services
N.A.I.C.S.: 524298

Union Security Life Insurance Company of New York (1)
212 Highbridge St Ste D, Fayetteville, NY 13066
Tel.: (315) 637-4232
Rev.: $30,718,000
Assets: $399,188,000
Liabilities: $343,473,000
Net Worth: $55,715,000
Earnings: $5,170,000
Emp.: 16
Fiscal Year-end: 12/31/2014
Insurance Services
N.A.I.C.S.: 524298
Miles B. Yakre *(Chm & CEO)*
Tamrha V. Mangelsen *(CFO & Treas)*
Paula M. SeGuin *(Pres & Asst Sec)*
Julie E. Cosio *(VP)*
Melissa J.T. Hall *(Asst Treas)*

United Service Protection, Inc. (1)
400 Carillon Pkwy Ste 300, Saint Petersburg, FL 33716-1290
Tel.: (727) 556-2900
Web Site: http://www.assurant.com
Direct Life Insurance Services
N.A.I.C.S.: 524113

Virginia Surety Company, Inc. (1)
175 W Jackson 11th Fl, Chicago, IL 60604
Tel.: (312) 356-3000
Property & Casualty Insurance Services
N.A.I.C.S.: 524126

ASSURE HOLDINGS CORP.
7887 E Belleview Ave Ste 240, Denver, CO 80111
Tel.: (720) 287-3093   NV
Web Site:
https://www.assureneuromonitoring.com
Year Founded: 2016
IONM—(NASDAQ)
Rev.: $10,976,000
Assets: $24,249,000
Liabilities: $18,784,000
Net Worth: $5,465,000
Earnings: ($30,112,000)
Emp.: 127
Fiscal Year-end: 12/31/22
Holding Company
N.A.I.C.S.: 551112
John A. Farlinger *(Exec Chm & CEO)*
Jerod Powell *(CIO)*

Paul Webster *(Sr VP-Managed Care & Revenue Cycle Mgmt)*
Sherri Wagner *(VP-Human Resources)*
Alex Rasmussen *(VP-Client Experience)*
Beth Lindstrom *(VP-Clinical Ops)*

AST SPACEMOBILE, INC.
6500 River Pl Blvd, Austin, TX 78730
Tel.: (917) 969-4834   DE
Year Founded: 2019
ASTS—(NASDAQ)
Rev.: $13,825,000
Assets: $438,372,000
Liabilities: $78,546,000
Net Worth: $359,826,000
Earnings: ($31,640,000)
Emp.: 342
Fiscal Year-end: 12/31/22
Investment Services
N.A.I.C.S.: 523999
Richard Mazer *(*)*
Abel Avellan *(Chm & CEO)*
Sean Wallace *(CFO & Exec VP)*
Brian Heller *(Gen Counsel, Sec & Exec VP)*
Shanti Gupta *(Chief Acctg Officer & Exec VP)*
Alexander Coleman *(Chm)*

ASTEC INDUSTRIES, INC.
1725 Shepherd Rd, Chattanooga, TN 37421
Tel.: (423) 899-5898   TN
Web Site:
https://www.astecindustries.com
Year Founded: 1972
ASTE—(NASDAQ)
Rev.: $1,274,500,000
Assets: $1,014,400,000
Liabilities: $387,500,000
Net Worth: $626,900,000
Earnings: ($600,000)
Emp.: 4,291
Fiscal Year-end: 12/31/22
Offices of Other Holding Companies
N.A.I.C.S.: 551112
Stephen C. Anderson *(Sr VP-Admin & IR)*
Jaco G. Van der Merwe *(Pres & CEO)*
Michael Norris *(Sr VP-Intl & Aftermarket Sls)*
Jamie E. Palm *(Chief Acctg Officer, VP & Controller)*
Rebecca A. Weyenberg *(CFO)*

Subsidiaries:

Allinov Inc. (1)
2333 rue St-Cesaire, Marieville, J3M 1E1, QC, Canada
Tel.: (450) 460-1011
Web Site: http://www.allinov.com
Concrete & Mining Equipment Mfr
N.A.I.C.S.: 333120

Astec Australia Pty Ltd (1)
13/243 Bradman Street, PO Box 142, Acacia Ridge, 4110, QLD, Australia
Tel.: (61) 737148800
Web Site: https://www.astecaustralia.com.au
Sales Range: $25-49.9 Million
Emp.: 35
Mining Equipment Mfr
N.A.I.C.S.: 333131

Astec Industries Africa Middle East (Pty) Ltd. (1)
57 Jansen Road, Boksburg, 1429, Gauteng, South Africa
Tel.: (27) 118207600
Concrete Batch Material Mfr
N.A.I.C.S.: 327320

Astec Mobile Machinery GmbH (1)
Freibusch 2-4, 31789, Hameln, Germany
Tel.: (49) 5151781050
Web Site: http://www.astec-europa.de
Emp.: 13

Industrial Equipment Mfr
N.A.I.C.S.: 333131

Astec Mobile Screens, Inc. (1)
2704 W LeFevre Rd, Sterling, IL 61081
Tel.: (815) 626-6374
Web Site: http://www.kpijci.com
Emp.: 100
Construction Machinery Mfr & Distr
N.A.I.C.S.: 333120

Astec, Inc. (1)
4101 Jerome Ave, Chattanooga, TN 37407-2915   (100%)
Tel.: (423) 867-4210
Sales Range: $200-249.9 Million
Emp.: 720
Asphalt Plants & Auxiliary Equipment
N.A.I.C.S.: 333120

B.M.H. Systems Inc. (1)
1395 Rue Rene Descartes, Saint-Bruno-de-Montarville, J3V 0B7, QC, Canada
Web Site: http://www.bmhsystems.com
Concrete Batch Material Mfr
N.A.I.C.S.: 327320

Breaker Technology Ltd (1)
35 Elgin St, PO Box 130, Thornbury, N0H 2P0, ON, Canada
Tel.: (519) 599-2015
Web Site: http://www.rockbreaker.com
Emp.: 140
Mining & Quarry Equipment Mfr
N.A.I.C.S.: 333131

Breaker Technology, Inc. (1)
30625 Solon Industrial Pkwy, Solon, OH 44139
Tel.: (440) 542-3720
Web Site: http://www.rockbreaker.com
Mining Machinery & Equipment Mfr
N.A.I.C.S.: 333131

CEI Enterprises, Inc. (1)
245 Woodward Rd SE, Albuquerque, NM 87102-5151   (100%)
Tel.: (505) 842-5556
Web Site: http://www.ceienterprises.com
Sales Range: $25-49.9 Million
Emp.: 86
Asphalt Forged Containers & Heaters Mfr
N.A.I.C.S.: 333415

Carlson Paving Products, Inc. (1)
800 Manufacturers Rd, Chattanooga, TN 37405
Tel.: (423) 265-0600
Web Site:
http://www.carlsonpavingproducts.com
Emp.: 120
Asphalt Paving Equipment Mfr
N.A.I.C.S.: 324121

Concrete Equipment Company, Inc. (1)
237 N 13th St, Blair, NE 68008-1673
Tel.: (402) 426-4181
Web Site: http://www.con-e-co.com
Emp.: 150
Concrete Batch Plants Mfr
N.A.I.C.S.: 327390

GEFCO, Inc. (1)
680 Conroe Park W Dr, Conroe, TX 77303   (100%)
Tel.: (713) 691-3000
Web Site: https://www.gefco.com
Sales Range: $50-74.9 Million
Emp.: 200
Mobile Rotary Drill Rigs & Seismic Vibrators for Oil & Mineral Exploration Mfr
N.A.I.C.S.: 333311

Heatec, Inc. (1)
5200 Wilson Rd, Chattanooga, TN 37410-2149   (100%)
Tel.: (423) 449-9523
Web Site: http://www.heatec.com
Sales Range: $50-74.9 Million
Emp.: 185
Hot Oil Heaters, Asphalt Heaters, Water Heaters & Heat Transfer Equipment
N.A.I.C.S.: 333994

Johnson Crushers International, Inc. (1)
86470 Franklin Blvd, Eugene, OR 97405
Tel.: (541) 736-1400
Web Site: http://www.kpijci.com

Sales Range: $50-74.9 Million
Emp.: 250
Aggregate Processing Equipment Mfr
N.A.I.C.S.: 333131

Kolberg-Pioneer, Inc. (1)
700 W 21st St, Yankton, SD 57078
Tel.: (605) 665-9311
Web Site: http://www.kpijci.com
Sales Range: $100-124.9 Million
Emp.: 370
Construction Machinery Mfr
N.A.I.C.S.: 333120

Peterson Pacific Corp. (1)
29408 Airport Rd, Eugene, OR 97402-9541
Tel.: (541) 689-6520
Web Site: http://www.petersoncorp.com
Industrial Machinery Mfr
N.A.I.C.S.: 333998

Power Flame Inc. (1)
2001 S 21st St, Parsons, KS 67357
Tel.: (620) 421-0480
Web Site: https://www.powerflame.com
Oil Burner Mfr
N.A.I.C.S.: 333414

RexCon, Inc. (1)
2841 Whiting Rd, Burlington, WI 53105
Tel.: (262) 539-4050
Web Site: http://www.rexcon.com
Construction Machinery Mfr
N.A.I.C.S.: 333120

RexCon, LLC (1)
2841 Whiting Rd, Burlington, WI 53105
Tel.: (262) 539-4050
Web Site: http://www.rexcon.com
Sales Range: $10-24.9 Million
Emp.: 60
Concrete Production Machinery Mfr
N.A.I.C.S.: 333120

Roadtec, Inc. (1)
800 Manufacturers Rd, Chattanooga, TN 37405-3706   (100%)
Tel.: (423) 265-0600
Web Site: http://www.roadtec.com
Sales Range: $100-124.9 Million
Mfr of Material Transfer Vehicles, Asphalt & Concrete Reclaiming Machines & Asphalt Paving Machines
N.A.I.C.S.: 333120

Telestack, Limited (1)
Bankmore Way East, Omagh, BT79 0NZ, Tyrone, United Kingdom
Tel.: (44) 2882251100
Web Site: https://www.telestack.com
Emp.: 140
Industrial Machinery Mfr
N.A.I.C.S.: 333998

ASTRA ENERGY INC.
1100 Benjamin Franklin Dr Unit 802, Sarasota, FL 34236
Web Site:
https://www.astraenergyinc.com
ASRE—(OTCQB)
Rev.: $750,100
Assets: $12,032,771
Liabilities: $11,672,216
Net Worth: $360,555
Earnings: ($3,487,467)
Fiscal Year-end: 08/31/24
N.A.I.C.S.:

ASTRANA HEALTH INC.
1668 S Garfield Ave 2nd Fl, Alhambra, CA 91801
Tel.: (626) 282-0288   DE
Web Site:
https://www.astranahealth.com
Year Founded: 1985
ASTH—(NASDAQ)
Rev.: $1,386,661,000
Assets: $933,361,000
Liabilities: $316,710,000
Net Worth: $616,651,000
Earnings: $60,717,000
Fiscal Year-end: 12/31/23
Health Care Center Operator
N.A.I.C.S.: 622110
Chan Basho *(CFO, COO & Chief Strategy Officer)*

Thomas S. Lam *(Co-Founder & Vice Chm)*
Albert Young *(Sr VP-Health Affairs)*
John Vong *(Chief Acctg Officer)*
Jeremy R. Jackson *(Chief Quality Officer)*
Paul Van Duine *(Sr VP-Contracting)*
Rita Pew *(VP-People & Operations)*
Kenneth T. Sim *(Co-Founder & Exec Chm)*
Dinesh Kumar *(Chief Medical Officer)*
Jaime Melkonoff *(Pres-AstranaCare-Texas)*
Marie Price *(Pres-AstranaCare-Nevada)*
Boon Chen *(Sr VP-Engineering)*

Subsidiaries:

APAACO, Inc. (1)
1668 S Garfield Ave 2nd Fl, Alhambra, CA 91801
Tel.: (626) 300-2855
Web Site: https://www.apaaco.net
Healtcare Services
N.A.I.C.S.: 621999
Thomas Lam *(Pres)*
Chan Basho *(CFO)*
Patrick Pham *(Dir-Medical)*
Anthony Hou *(Pres-Astrana Health)*
Kimberly Busenbark *(Dir-Provider Rels & Business Development)*
Brandon Sim *(CEO)*

Apollo Care Connect, Inc. (1)
700 N Brand Blvd Ste 1400, Glendale, CA 91203
Tel.: (818) 839-5208
Web Site: http://www.apollocareconnect.net
Health Care Srvices
N.A.I.C.S.: 622110

Apollo Medical Management, Inc. (1)
450 N Brand Blvd Ste 600, Glendale, CA 91203
Tel.: (818) 396-8050
Hospital Management Services
N.A.I.C.S.: 622110

ApolloMed Accountable Care Organization, Inc. (1)
700 N Brand Blvd Ste 1400, Glendale, CA 91203
Tel.: (818) 839-5200
Health Care Services
N.A.I.C.S.: 621999

Holistic Care Home Health Agency, Inc. (1)
11351-B James Watt Dr, El Paso, TX 79936
Tel.: (915) 855-2627
Web Site: http://www.holisticcareonline.net
Healtcare Services
N.A.I.C.S.: 621999

Network Medical Management, Inc. (1)
1668 S Garfield Ave, Alhambra, CA 91801
Tel.: (626) 282-0288
Web Site: https://www.networkmedicalmanagement.com
Health Care Management Services
N.A.I.C.S.: 541611

ASTREA ACQUISITION CORP.
55 Ocean Ln Dr Apt 3021, Key Biscayne, FL 33149
Tel.: (347) 607-8025 DE
Year Founded: 2020
ASAX—(NASDAQ)
Rev.: $61,090
Assets: $172,973,428
Liabilities: $1,552,178
Net Worth: $171,421,250
Earnings: ($1,632,762)
Emp.: 3
Fiscal Year-end: 12/31/21
Investment Services
N.A.I.C.S.: 523999
Catullus Helmer *(CEO)*
Nicolas Jacobson *(CFO)*

ASTRIA THERAPEUTICS, INC.
22 Boston Wharf Rd 10th Fl, Boston, MA 02210
Tel.: (617) 349-1971 DE
Web Site: https://www.astriatx.com
Year Founded: 2008
ATXS—(NASDAQ)
Rev.: $10,201,000
Assets: $254,666,000
Liabilities: $11,550,000
Net Worth: $243,116,000
Earnings: ($72,891,000)
Emp.: 59
Fiscal Year-end: 12/31/23
Pharmaceutical Preparation Mfr
N.A.I.C.S.: 325412
Andrea Matthews *(Chief Bus Officer)*
Andrew A. Komjathy *(Chief Comml Officer)*
Keri McGrail *(Sr VP-HR)*
Christopher Morabito *(Chief Medical Officer)*
John Ruesch *(Sr VP-Pharmaceutical Sciences & Technical Ops)*
Jill C. Milne *(Founder, Pres & CEO)*

ASTRO AEROSPACE LTD.
320 W Main St, Lewisville, TX 75057
Tel.: (469) 702-8344 NV
Web Site: http://www.flyastro.com
Year Founded: 2007
ASDN—(OTCIQ)
Assets: $1,003,423
Liabilities: $2,395,599
Net Worth: ($1,392,176)
Earnings: ($1,185,846)
Fiscal Year-end: 12/31/20
Holding Company; Manned & Cargo Drones Sercies
N.A.I.C.S.: 551112
Bruce Bent *(CEO)*

Subsidiaries:

Custom Pool & Spa Mechanics, Inc. (1)
2951 SE Waaler St, Stuart, FL 34997
Tel.: (772) 283-3332
Web Site: http://www.custompoolmechanics.com
Emp.: 40
Pool & Spa Maintenance Services
N.A.I.C.S.: 238990
Lawrence Calarco *(CEO)*
Loreen Calarco *(COO)*
Rachel Hotwagner *(Office Mgr-Custom Pool Plastering)*

ASTRONICS CORPORATION
130 Commerce Way, East Aurora, NY 14052
Tel.: (716) 805-1599 NY
Web Site: https://www.astronics.com
Year Founded: 1968
ATRO—(NASDAQ)
Rev.: $534,894,000
Assets: $615,031,000
Liabilities: $375,111,000
Net Worth: $239,920,000
Earnings: ($35,747,000)
Emp.: 2,400
Fiscal Year-end: 12/31/22
Aircraft External & Internal Lighting Systems & Power Generation & Distribution Technology Systems
N.A.I.C.S.: 335139
Peter J. Gundermann *(Pres & CEO)*
David C. Burney *(CFO & Exec VP)*
James F. Mulato *(Pres-Astronics Test Systems Inc & Exec VP)*
Mark A. Peabody *(Pres-Astronics Advanced Electronic Systems & Exec VP)*
Nancy L. Hedges *(Chief Acctg Officer & Controller)*

Subsidiaries:

Armstrong Aerospace, Inc. (1)
1437 Harmony Ct, Itasca, IL 60143
Tel.: (630) 285-0200
Web Site:
http://www.armstrongaerospace.com
Engineering Consulting Services
N.A.I.C.S.: 541330

Astronics Advanced Electronic Systems Corp. (1)
12950 Willows Rd NE, Kirkland, WA 98034 (100%)
Tel.: (425) 881-1700
Web Site: http://www.astronicsaes.com
Sales Range: $100-124.9 Million
Emp.: 500
Electrical Power Systems Mfr
N.A.I.C.S.: 335311
Dennis Markert *(Dir-Bus Dev, Sls, and Mktg-Global)*
Tom Howard *(Dir-Bus Dev-Boeing Comml)*
Randy Burnett *(Sr Mgr-Bus Dev-Bus Aircraft,VVIP)*
Michael Ballas *(Engr-Technical Mktg-Rotorcraft,Military,UAV)*
Ken Adwan *(Sr Mgr-Business Development)*
Ron Johnson *(Sr Mgr-Business Development)*
Alan Oka *(Sr Mgr-Business Development)*
Rotorcraft Military *(Sr Mgr-Business Development)*
Dirk De Vos *(Sr Mgr-Business Development)*

Astronics AeroSat Corporation (1)
220 Hackett Hill Rd, Manchester, NH 03102
Tel.: (603) 879-0205
Web Site: http://www.aerosat.com
Emp.: 100
Aeronautical Equipment Mfr
N.A.I.C.S.: 334511

Astronics Connectivity Systems & Certification Corp. (1)
804 S Northpoint Blvd, Waukegan, IL 60085
Tel.: (847) 244-4500
Web Site: http://www.astronics.com
Inflight Entertainment Connectivity Hardware for the Aerospace Industry
N.A.I.C.S.: 336413
Michael C. Kuehn *(Pres)*
Matt Wilken *(VP-Finance)*

Astronics Custom Controls Concepts Inc. (1)
6020 S 190th St, Kent, WA 98032
Tel.: (206) 575-0933
Web Site: http://www.custom-control.com
Lighting Equipment Mfr
N.A.I.C.S.: 335139
Bill Weaver *(Pres)*

Astronics Test Systems Inc. (1)
2652 McGaw Ave, Irvine, CA 92614
Tel.: (949) 859-8999
Web Site:
http://www.astronicstestsystems.com
Sales Range: $25-49.9 Million
Electronic Testing & Measurement Systems Mfr
N.A.I.C.S.: 334515
James F. Mulato *(Pres)*
Ted Baker *(VP-Ops & Gen Mgr)*
John Armstrong *(Sr Dir-HR, HR, HR, and HR)*
Lou Salzano *(Gen Mgr-Orlando)*
Stephanie Yuen *(Sr Dir-Fin)*
Haley Miller *(Gen Mgr-UK Bus)*
Carl Rosenblatt *(VP-Engineering)*
Arkesh Jaigeeshavya *(Mng Dir-India)*
Bernie Luciani *(Sr Dir-Mass Transit)*
Andy Jensen *(Sr Dir-Aerospace Defense & Government)*
Derek Holmes *(Sr Dir-Sls Bus Dev)*
Brian Huther *(Sr Dir-Contracts & Supply Chain)*
Wil Wilson *(Dir-Quality Assurance & Configuration Mgmt)*

Ballard Technology, Inc. (1)
11400 Airport Rd Ste 201, Everett, WA 98204
Tel.: (425) 339-0281
Web Site: http://www.ballardtech.com
Sales Range: $1-9.9 Million
Instrument Mfr for Measuring & Testing Electricity & Electrical Signals
N.A.I.C.S.: 334515

DME Corporation (1)

6830 NW 16th Ter, Fort Lauderdale, FL 33309 (100%)
Tel.: (954) 975-2100
Web Site: http://www.astronics.com
Sales Range: $75-99.9 Million
Emp.: 350
Designs, Develops & Manufactures Communications & Weapons Test Systems & Training & Simulation Devices; Aviation Safety & Survival Products Mfr; Airfield Lighting & Approach Systems Supplier
N.A.I.C.S.: 334511
Peter J. Gundermann *(CEO)*

Diagnosys Ferndown Limited (1)
Suite 19 Peartree Business Centre Cobham Road, Ferndown, Dorset, BH21 7PT, United Kingdom
Tel.: (44) 1202854000
Electronic Circuit Maintenance & Services
N.A.I.C.S.: 811210
Steve Young *(Coord-Sls & Applications)*

Diagnosys GmbH (1)
Prielmayerstrasse 3, 80335, Munich, Germany
Tel.: (49) 28418821560
Electronic Circuit Maintenance & Services
N.A.I.C.S.: 811210

Diagnosys Systems, Inc. (1)
5 Lan Dr, Westford, MA 01886
Tel.: (978) 392-0406
Web Site: https://www.diagnosys.com
Electronic Components Mfr
N.A.I.C.S.: 334413
Joe Dunne *(Engr-Electrical)*

Freedom Communication Technologies, Inc. (1)
2002 Synergy Blvd Ste 200, Kilgore, TX 75662
Tel.: (903) 985-8999
Web Site: https://www.freedomcte.com
Communication Test Equipment Mfr
N.A.I.C.S.: 334515
Shuntel Johnson *(Mgr-HR)*

Luminescent Systems, Inc. (1)
130 Commerce Way, East Aurora, NY 14052-2515 (100%)
Tel.: (716) 655-0800
Web Site: http://www.astronics.com
Sales Range: $50-74.9 Million
Emp.: 500
Film Electroluminescent Lamp Mfr
N.A.I.C.S.: 335139

Subsidiary (Non-US):

Luminescent Systems Canada, Inc. (2)
55 Lindsay Street, Dorval, H9P 2S6, QC, Canada (100%)
Tel.: (514) 636-9921
Mfr of Specialized Lighting & Electronics for Aircraft Industry
N.A.I.C.S.: 335139

Max-Viz, Inc. (1)
11241 SE Hwy 212, Clackamas, OR 97015
Tel.: (503) 968-3036
Web Site: http://www.max-vizastronics.com
Sales Range: $10-24.9 Million
Emp.: 19
Other Communications Equipment Mfr
N.A.I.C.S.: 334290

PECO, Inc. (1)
11241 SE Hwy 212, Clackamas, OR 97015
Tel.: (503) 233-6401
Web Site:
https://www.pecocontrolsystems.com
Sales Range: $75-99.9 Million
Aerospace Interior Components & Systems Mfr
N.A.I.C.S.: 336413

PGA Electronic s.a. (1)
ZI La Malterie Avenue Jean Monnet, 36130, Montierchaume, France
Tel.: (33) 254079090
Web Site: http://www.pga-avionics.com
Emp.: 190
Aeronautical Equipment Mfr
N.A.I.C.S.: 334511

ASTRONOVA, INC.

AstroNova, Inc.—(Continued)

600 E Greenwich Ave, West Warwick, RI 02893
Tel.: (401) 828-4000   RI
Web Site:
https://www.astronovainc.com
Year Founded: 1969
ALOT—(NASDAQ)
Rev.: $142,527,000
Assets: $139,207,000
Liabilities: $54,840,000
Net Worth: $84,367,000
Earnings: $2,661,000
Emp.: 394
Fiscal Year-end: 01/31/23
Hardware & Software Systems for Processing Data
N.A.I.C.S.: 334118
Stephen M. Petrarca (VP-Ops)
Thomas W. Carll (VP & Gen Mgr-Aerospace)
Michael J. Natalizia (CTO & VP-Tech Partner Alliances)
Gregory A. Woods (Pres & CEO)
Raj Ramasamy (CIO)
Matthew Cook (VP-HR & Organizational Dev)
Francois Lestage (VP)
Mikkel Wichmann (VP)
Thomas D. DeByle (CFO, Treas & VP)

Subsidiaries:

Astro Machine Corp.   (1)
630 Lively Blvd, Elk Grove Village, IL 60007-2016
Tel.: (847) 364-6363
Web Site: http://www.astromachine.com
Wholesale Trade Agents & Brokers
N.A.I.C.S.: 425120
Nancy Dedic (Mgr)
George Selak (Pres)

Astro-Med GmbH   (1)
Waldstrasse 70, 63128, Dietzenbach, Germany
Tel.: (49) 60743102500
Web Site: http://www.astro-med.de
Sales Range: $150-199.9 Million
Emp.: 20
Supplier of Hardware & Software Systems for Processing Data
N.A.I.C.S.: 423430

AstroNova (Shanghai) Trading Co., Ltd   (1)
Part D Building No 8 Plot Section No 81 Meiyue Road, Pilot Free Trade Zone, Shanghai, 200131, China
Tel.: (86) 2158681533
Printer Machinery Mfr
N.A.I.C.S.: 334118

AstroNova (Singapore) Pte Ltd.   (1)
1 Scott Road 24 10 Shaw Centre, Singapore, 228208, Singapore
Tel.: (65) 91412888
Web Site:
https://www.aerospace.astronovainc.com
Airborne Printer Mfr
N.A.I.C.S.: 334118

AstroNova GmbH   (1)
Waldstrasse 70, 63128, Dietzenbach, Germany
Tel.: (49) 60743102500
Printer Machinery Mfr
N.A.I.C.S.: 334118

Rugged Information Technology Equipment Corp.   (1)
25 E Easy St, Simi Valley, CA 93065
Tel.: (805) 577-9710
Web Site: https://www.ritecrugged.com
Sales Range: $1-9.9 Million
Emp.: 25
Computer Peripheral Equipment Mfr
N.A.I.C.S.: 334118

TrojanLabel ApS   (1)
Marielundvej 46A 2, 2730, Herlev, Denmark
Tel.: (45) 29640005
Web Site: http://www.trojanlabel.com
Printer Machinery Mfr

N.A.I.C.S.: 334118

ASTROTECH CORPORATION
2105 Donley Dr Ste 100, Austin, TX 78758
Tel.: (512) 485-9530   WA
Web Site:
https://www.astrotechcorp.com
Year Founded: 1984
ASTC—(NASDAQ)
Rev.: $1,664,000
Assets: $37,640,000
Liabilities: $2,833,000
Net Worth: $34,807,000
Earnings: ($11,666,000)
Emp.: 30
Fiscal Year-end: 06/30/24
Space Habitat Modules to Operate In the Cargo Bay of Space Shuttles
N.A.I.C.S.: 336414
Thomas Boone Pickens III (Chm & CEO)
Jaime Hinojosa (CFO, Treas & Sec)

Subsidiaries:

1st Detect Corporation   (1)
2105 Donley Dr Ste 100, Austin, TX 78758
Tel.: (512) 485-9530
Web Site: http://www.1stdetect.com
Mass Spectrometer Developer & Mfr
N.A.I.C.S.: 334516
Thomas Boone Pickens III (Chm & CEO)
Lee Drennan (VP-Engrg)
Raj Mellacheruvu (CEO)
Thomas B. Pickens III (Chm)

AgLAB, Inc.   (1)
Web Site: http://www.aglab.com
Mass Spectrometer Mfr
N.A.I.C.S.: 334516
Thomas Boone Pickens III (Chm & CEO)

Astral Images Corporation   (1)
3700 W Parmer Ln Ste 200, Austin, TX 78727
Tel.: (512) 960-4745
Web Site: http://www.astral-images.com
Commercial Photography Services
N.A.I.C.S.: 541922
Rob Hummel (Sr VP-Bus Dev)

BreathTech Corporation   (1)
2105 Donley Dr Ste 100, Austin, TX 78758
Tel.: (512) 485-9530
Web Site: https://www.breathtech.com
Medical Instrument Mfr
N.A.I.C.S.: 339112
Thomas Boone Pickens III (Chm & CEO)

Spacetech, Inc.   (1)
1535 E Marshall St, Tulsa, OK 74106
Tel.: (918) 582-2616
Industrial Equipment Mfr
N.A.I.C.S.: 333310
Roy Maxwell (Mgr-Site)

ASURE SOFTWARE, INC.
405 Colorado St Ste 1800, Austin, TX 78701
Tel.: (512) 437-2700   DE
Web Site:
https://www.asuresoftware.com
Year Founded: 1985
ASUR—(NASDAQ)
Rev.: $05,020,000
Assets: $419,908,000
Liabilities: $274,842,000
Net Worth: $145,066,000
Earnings: ($14,466,000)
Emp.: 493
Fiscal Year-end: 12/31/22
Software Developer
N.A.I.C.S.: 541512
Patrick F. Goepel (Chm & CEO)
Eyal Goldstein (Pres & Chief Revenue Officer)
John Pence (CFO)
Patrick McKillop (VP-IR)
Randal Rudniski (VP-IR, Fin Plng, and Analysis)

Subsidiaries:

Associated Data Services, Inc.   (1)
117 Gemini Cir Ste 416, Homewood, AL 35209
Tel.: (205) 942-4654
Data Processing & Payroll Services
N.A.I.C.S.: 541214

Asure Payroll Tax Management LLC   (1)
3700 N Capital of Texas Hwy Ste 350, Austin, TX 78746
Web Site: http://www.payrolltaxmgmt.com
Emp.: 430
Payroll Tax Processing Software Services
N.A.I.C.S.: 541214
Pat Goepel (Chm & CEO)
Eyal Goldstein (Pres & Chief Revenue Officer)
John Pence (CFO)

Compass HRM, Inc.   (1)
405 Colorado St Ste 1800, Austin, TX 78701
Tel.: (855) 777-2476
Software Development Services
N.A.I.C.S.: 513210

Mangrove COBRASource, LLC   (1)
945 Lakeview Pkwy Ste 170, Vernon Hills, IL 60061-1451
Tel.: (847) 223-1011
Insurance Agency & Brokerage Services
N.A.I.C.S.: 524210

Mangrove Software, Inc.   (1)
405 Colorado St Ste 1800, Austin, TX 78701
Tel.: (813) 387-3100
Fiscal Year-end: 12/31/2006
Software Development Services
N.A.I.C.S.: 541512

Pay Systems of America Inc.   (1)
1321 Murfreesboro Pike Ste 100, Nashville, TN 37217
Tel.: (615) 292-0000
Accounting Services
N.A.I.C.S.: 541219

Payroll Maxx, LLC   (1)
11248 John Galt Blvd, Omaha, NE 68137
Tel.: (402) 339-9700
Web Site: http://www.payrollmaxx.com
Sales Range: $1-9.9 Million
Emp.: 35
Payroll Processing Services
N.A.I.C.S.: 541214
Kenneth W. LaRose (Pres)
Bob Van Haute (VP-Sls)
Phil Cooney (COO)

Personnel Management Systems, Inc.   (1)
8259 122nd Ave NE Ste 300, Kirkland, WA 98033
Tel.: (425) 576-1900
Web Site: http://www.hrpmsi.com
Sales Range: $1-9.9 Million
Emp.: 40
Human Resources & Executive Search Consulting Services
N.A.I.C.S.: 541612

Telepayroll, Inc.   (1)
3631 S Harbor Blvd Ste 100, Santa Ana, CA 92704
Tel.: (562) 598-4993
Tax & Payroll Services
N.A.I.C.S.: 541214
Michael Gilberstadt (CEO)

USA Payrolls Inc.   (1)
405 Colorado St Ste 1800, Austin, TX 78701
Tel.: (888) 872-2432
Web Site: http://www.asuresoftware.com
Payroll Services
N.A.I.C.S.: 541214

AT&T INC.
208 S Akard St, Dallas, TX 75202
Tel.: (210) 821-4105   DE
Web Site: https://www.att.com
Year Founded: 1984
T—(NYSE)
Rev.: $122,428,000,000
Assets: $407,060,000,000

Liabilities: $289,618,000,000
Net Worth: $117,442,000,000
Earnings: $14,400,000,000
Emp.: 149,900
Fiscal Year-end: 12/31/23
Telecommunication Servicesb
N.A.I.C.S.: 551112
Matthew Grover (District Sls Mgr-New York, Acct Mgr-Global & Mgr-Acctg-Global)
John T. Stankey (CEO)
Jeff McElfresh (COO)
Joelle J. Phillips (Pres-Tennessee)
Jeff McElfresh (CEO-AT&T Comm)
Pascal Desroches (CFO & Sr Exec VP)
Jeremy Legg (CTO)
David R. McAtee II (Gen Counsel & Sr Exec VP)

Subsidiaries:

ACC Business   (1)
400 W Ave, Rochester, NY 14611-2538
Tel.: (585) 987-3000
Web Site: https://www.accbusiness.com
Rev.: $99,000,000
Emp.: 150
Business Telecommunication Services
N.A.I.C.S.: 517121
Ann-marie Dean (Dir-Ops)
Christopher R. Jones (Asst VP-Channels)
Jon White (Natl Dir-Sls)

AT&T   (1)
2600 Camino Ramon 2w856, San Ramon, CA 94583
Tel.: (925) 823-5388
Sales Range: $1-4.9 Billion
Emp.: 7,000
Regional Holding Company; Telecommunications Products & Services
N.A.I.C.S.: 517121

AT&T   (1)
220 Prospect Ave, Hot Springs National Park, AR 71901
Tel.: (501) 321-3201
Web Site: http://www.sbc.com
Sales Range: $1-9.9 Million
Emp.: 6
Telephone Communications
N.A.I.C.S.: 813110

AT&T   (1)
Fl 4 5130 Hacienda Dr, Dublin, CA 94568-7598   (100%)
Tel.: (800) 248-3632
Sales Range: $200-249.9 Million
Whslr of Communications Equipment
N.A.I.C.S.: 517121
Philip Dale (Engr-RF-V)
Mark Nagel (Exec Dir-Mktg-AT&T Foundry)
Bill Rehrmann (Mgr-Tech Security)
Daniel Madsen (Sr Dir-Tech-Security)

AT&T   (1)
96 Louise St, San Rafael, CA 94901
Tel.: (415) 454-0052
Sales Range: $1-9.9 Million
Emp.: 2
Local Telephone Communications
N.A.I.C.S.: 517111

AT&T   (1)
2525 N Watney Way, Fairfield, CA 94533-6725
Tel.: (707) 435-7400
Sales Range: $10-24.9 Million
Emp.: 36
Local Telephone Communications
N.A.I.C.S.: 517121

AT&T   (1)
11435 Quaker Ave Ste 300, Lubbock, TX 79423
Tel.: (806) 451-5008
Web Site: http://www.att.com
Sales Range: $75-99.9 Million
Emp.: 300
Local & Long Distance Telephone Communications
N.A.I.C.S.: 541870

AT&T   (1)
1270 Arroyo Way, Walnut Creek, CA 94596
Tel.: (510) 836-6889

Sales Range: $75-99.9 Million
Emp.: 300
Telephone Communications
N.A.I.C.S.: 561110

AT&T (1)
3368 Harding St, Carlsbad, CA 92008
Tel.: (760) 434-5081
Web Site: http://www.att.com
Sales Range: $1-9.9 Million
Emp.: 3
Telephone Communications
N.A.I.C.S.: 517121

AT&T Advanced Solutions, Inc. (1)
1010 N Saint Marys St Ste 13, San Antonio,
TX 78215-2109
Tel.: (210) 246-8151
Web Site: http://www.att.com
Sales Range: $75-99.9 Million
Emp.: 350
Retailer of DSL Transport Products & Services
N.A.I.C.S.: 517810

AT&T Communications Corp. (1)
1 AT&T Way, Bedminster, NJ 07921
Tel.: (908) 221-4191
Web Site: http://www.att.com
Sales Range: $200-249.9 Million
Voice, Data & Video Communications Services
N.A.I.C.S.: 517111
Jeremy Legg *(CTO & Exec VP)*
Kellyn Smith Kenny *(Chief Mktg & Growth Officer)*
Susan A. Johnson *(Exec VP/Gen Mgr-Wireline Transformation & Supply Chain)*
Susan Johnson *(Exec VP-Global Connections & Supply Chain)*

Representative Office (Non-US):

AT&T (2)
Highfield House Headless Cross Dr, Headless Cross, Redditch, B97 5EQ, Worcestershire, United Kingdom
Tel.: (44) 1527518181
Web Site: http://www.corp.att.com
Telecommunications
N.A.I.C.S.: 517810

Subsidiary (Non-US):

AT&T Enterprise Canada Co. (2)
55 Commerce Vly Dr W Ste 700, Thornhill,
L3T 7V9, ON, Canada (100%)
Tel.: (905) 762-7390
Rev.: $1,628,160
Emp.: 150
Communication & Data Management Services
N.A.I.C.S.: 425120

Subsidiary (Domestic):

AT&T Operations, Inc. (2)
530 McCullough Ave, San Antonio, TX
78215-2104
Tel.: (210) 229-2200
Web Site: http://www.att.com
Sales Range: $10-24.9 Million
Emp.: 8
Wired & Wireless Telecommunications Network Operator
N.A.I.C.S.: 517121

AT&T of Puerto Rico, Inc. (2)
996 San Roberto St Reparto Loyola, San
Juan, PR 00926
Tel.: (787) 717-9700
Web Site: http://www.engage.att.com
Telecommunication Servicesb
N.A.I.C.S.: 517121

AT&T Comunicaciones Digitales, S. de R.L. de C.V. (1)
Paseo de los Tamarindos No 90 24 Floor
Col Bosques de las Lomas, Delegation
Cuajimalpa de Morelos, Mexico, CP 05120,
DF, Mexico
Tel.: (52) 5510184000
Web Site: http://www.att.com.mx
Emp.: 20,000
Digital Wireless Communication Services
N.A.I.C.S.: 517112

AT&T Government Solutions (1)
1900 Gallows Rd, Vienna, VA
22182 (100%)
Tel.: (703) 506-5000

Web Site: http://www.att.com
Sales Range: $10-24.9 Million
Emp.: 1,109
Systems Integration Services to Government Agencies
N.A.I.C.S.: 541512

AT&T Messaging (1)
1000 S Fremont Ave, Alhambra, CA 91803-8800
Tel.: (626) 457-9707
Sales Range: $10-24.9 Million
Emp.: 10
Local & Long Distance Telephone Communications
N.A.I.C.S.: 517111

AT&T Mobility LLC (1)
Glenridge Highlands 2 5565 Glenridge Connector, Atlanta, GA 31132
Web Site: http://www.wireless.att.com
Sales Range: $25-49.9 Billion
Emp.: 69,876
Wireless Voice & Data Communications Services
N.A.I.C.S.: 517111
Barbara Roden *(VP)*

Branch (Domestic):

AT&T Mobility LLC (2)
555 Enterprise Dr, Rocky Hill, CT 06067-3913
Tel.: (860) 513-7600
Web Site: http://www.wireless.att.com
Sales Range: $400-449.9 Million
Emp.: 1,000
Mobile Telecommunications Services
N.A.I.C.S.: 517112

AT&T Mobility LLC (2)
7277 164th Ave NE, Redmond, WA 98052
Tel.: (425) 580-6000
Web Site: http://www.wireless.att.com
Sales Range: $1-4.9 Billion
Emp.: 5,000
Wireless Telecommunication Services
N.A.I.C.S.: 517112

AT&T Mobility LLC (2)
Appletree Business Park 2875 Union Rd
Ste 35U, Cheektowaga, NY 14227
Tel.: (716) 435-2000
Web Site: http://www.wireless.att.com
Sales Range: $50-74.9 Million
Emp.: 170
Wireless Telecommunication Services
N.A.I.C.S.: 517112

AT&T Mobility LLC (2)
15 E Midland Ave, Paramus, NJ 07652
Tel.: (201) 967-3000
Web Site: http://www.wireless.att.com
Rev.: $122,000,000,000
Assets: $407,000,000,000
Liabilities: $290,000,000,000
Net Worth: $117,000,000,000
Earnings: ($15,623,000,000)
Emp.: 149,900
Fiscal Year-end: 12/31/2023
Mobile Telecommunications Services
N.A.I.C.S.: 517112

AT&T Mobility LLC (2)
6294 Mayfield Rd, Cleveland, OH 44124
Tel.: (440) 605-0340
Web Site: http://www.wireless.att.com
Sales Range: $10-24.9 Million
Emp.: 43
Telephone Equipment & Systems
N.A.I.C.S.: 561110

AT&T Mobility LLC (2)
3300 Dallas Pkwy Ste 100, Plano, TX
75093
Tel.: (972) 403-1665
Web Site: http://www.wireless.att.com
Sales Range: $125-149.9 Million
Emp.: 4
Wireless Telecommunication Services
N.A.I.C.S.: 517112

AT&T Services Inc (1)
308 S Akard St Rm 1530, Dallas, TX
75202-5315
Tel.: (214) 464-6669
Sales Range: $10-24.9 Million
Emp.: 57
Telephone Communications
N.A.I.C.S.: 517111

AT&T Teleholdings, Inc (1)
205 W Monroe, Chicago, IL 60606
Tel.: (312) 920-0414
Sales Range: $200-249.9 Million
Regional Holding Company; Telephone & Cellular Telephone Services; Directory Publisher
N.A.I.C.S.: 517810

Subsidiary (Domestic):

AT&T Ohio (2)
150 E Gay St Rm 4-A, Columbus, OH
43215 (100%)
Tel.: (614) 223-7950
Web Site: http://www.wireless.att.com
Sales Range: $100-124.9 Million
Emp.: 450
Telecommunication Servicesb
N.A.I.C.S.: 517111

Branch (Domestic):

AT&T (3)
56 S Union St, London, OH 43140
Tel.: (740) 852-9960
Sales Range: $10-24.9 Million
Emp.: 10
Telecommunications
N.A.I.C.S.: 517111

AT&T (3)
7497 Sawmill Rd, Dublin, OH 43016
Tel.: (614) 610-4001
Web Site: http://www.att.com
Sales Range: $75-99.9 Million
Emp.: 250
Local Telephone Communications
N.A.I.C.S.: 517112

The Ohio Bell Telephone Company (3)
45 Erieview Plz, Cleveland, OH
44114 (100%)
Tel.: (216) 822-9700
Sales Range: $25-49.9 Million
Emp.: 100
Telecommunication Servicesb
N.A.I.C.S.: 517121

Subsidiary (Domestic):

BellSouth, LLC (2)
1025 Lenox Park Blvd NE, Atlanta, GA
30319
Tel.: (888) 722-1787
Web Site: http://www.bellsouth.com
Telecommunication Servicesb
N.A.I.C.S.: 517111

Division (Domestic):

AT&T Southeast (3)
1936 Blue Hills Dr NE, Roanoke, VA 24012-8608
Tel.: (540) 983-6000
Web Site: http://www.att.com
Sales Range: $25-49.9 Million
Emp.: 100
Customer Management Services
N.A.I.C.S.: 541611

AT&T Southeast (3)
1155 Peachtree St N E Room 15G03, Atlanta, GA 30309-3610
Tel.: (404) 249-2000
Sales Range: $400-449.9 Million
Long Distance Telephone Services
N.A.I.C.S.: 517121
Rob Eison *(Gen Mgr-Ops)*
Beth Shiroishi *(VP-Global Corp Social Responsibility Strategy & Insights)*
Bill Leahy *(Pres)*

Subsidiary (Domestic):

Michigan Bell Telephone Company (2)
444 Michigan Ave, Detroit, MI 48226-2517
Tel.: (313) 223-9900
Telecommunication & Internet Services
N.A.I.C.S.: 517111

Branch (Domestic):

AT&T (3)
1251 Lawson Dr, Howell, MI 48843
Tel.: (517) 997-1898
Web Site: http://www.att.com

Sales Range: $25-49.9 Million
Emp.: 70
Telephone Set Repair
N.A.I.C.S.: 517121

Subsidiary (Domestic):

Pacific Bell Telephone Company (2)
140 New Montgomery St, San Francisco,
CA 94105-3705
Tel.: (415) 542-9000
Sales Range: $75-99.9 Million
Telephone Communications
N.A.I.C.S.: 517121

Branch (Domestic):

AT&T West (3)
525 Market St, San Francisco, CA 94105
Tel.: (415) 778-1231
Web Site: http://www.att.com
Sales Range: $75-99.9 Million
Telecommunications & Internet Services
N.A.I.C.S.: 517111

Subsidiary (Domestic):

Southwestern Bell Telephone L.P. (2)
1 AT&T Plz 208 S Akard Rm 3700, Dallas,
TX 75202
Tel.: (214) 741-6655
Sales Range: $75-99.9 Million
Emp.: 117
Telecommunication Servicesb
N.A.I.C.S.: 517111

Division (Domestic):

AT&T Arkansas (3)
1111 W Capitol Ave Rm 605, Little Rock,
AR 72201-3005
Tel.: (501) 373-5127
Web Site: http://www.att.com
Sales Range: $125-149.9 Million
Emp.: 472
Telecommunication Servicesb
N.A.I.C.S.: 517111

AT&T Kansas (3)
220 SE Sixth Ave Rm 500, Topeka, KS
66603
Tel.: (785) 276-8201
Sales Range: $75-99.9 Million
Telecommunications & Internet Services
N.A.I.C.S.: 517111
Steve Hahn *(Pres)*
Mike Scott *(CEO)*

AT&T Missouri (3)
909 Chestnut St Rm 3516, Saint Louis, MO
63101
Tel.: (314) 244-9981
Web Site: http://www.att.com
Emp.: 9,200
Telecommunications & Internet Services
N.A.I.C.S.: 517111

Subsidiary (Domestic):

AT&T (4)
1497 St Louis Galleria, Saint Louis, MO
63117
Tel.: (314) 727-3303
Sales Range: $25-49.9 Million
Emp.: 80
Telecommunication Servicesb
N.A.I.C.S.: 517810

Division (Domestic):

AT&T Oklahoma (3)
405 N Broadway Ave, Oklahoma City, OK
73102
Tel.: (405) 236-6611
Sales Range: $75-99.9 Million
Emp.: 232
Local & Long Distance Telecommunications
& Broadband Internet Services
N.A.I.C.S.: 517111

AT&T Texas (3)
400 W 15th St, Austin, TX 78701
Tel.: (512) 870-3333
Sales Range: $75-99.9 Million
Telecommunications & Internet Services
N.A.I.C.S.: 517111

AlienVault, Inc. (1)
1875 S Grant St Ste 200, San Mateo, CA
94402

AT&T Inc.—(Continued)

Tel.: (650) 713-3333
Web Site: http://www.alienvault.com
Software & Technology Development Services; Cloud Security & Unified Security Management
N.A.I.C.S.: 513210

Cricket Wireless LLC (1)
12735 Morris Rd Ext Ste 300, Alpharetta, GA 30004-8904
Web Site: https://www.cricketwireless.com
Wireless Telecommunication Services
N.A.I.C.S.: 517112
John Dwyer (Pres)
Matt Haymons (CIO-AT&T Prepaid Portfolio & VP)
Kristi Turner (VP-Channel Ops)
Tony Mokry (CMO)
Lenny Rhee (VP)

DIRECTV, LLC (1)
2230 E Imperial Hwy, El Segundo, CA 90245 **(100%)**
Tel.: (310) 964-5000
Web Site: http://www.directv.com
Sales Range: $15-24.9 Billion
Emp.: 16,000
Satellite Television Transmission Services
N.A.I.C.S.: 517410

Subsidiary (Domestic):

California Broadcast Center, LLC (2)
2170 Bellflower Bl, Long Beach, CA 90815
Tel.: (562) 430-1200
Television Broadcasting Services
N.A.I.C.S.: 516120
Bruce Churchill (Pres)

DIRECTV Customer Services, Inc. (2)
4929 University Dr NW Ste G, Huntsville, AL 35816
Tel.: (256) 890-3700
Web Site: http://www.directv.com
Emp.: 5
Television Broadcasting Services
N.A.I.C.S.: 516120

DIRECTV Enterprises, LLC (2)
2230 E Imperial Hwy, El Segundo, CA 90245
Tel.: (310) 964-5106
Television Broadcasting Services
N.A.I.C.S.: 516120

DIRECTV Latin America, LLC (2)
14817 Oak Ln, Hialeah, FL 33016-1517
Tel.: (954) 958-3200
Web Site: http://www.directvla.com
Sales Range: $10-24.9 Million
Emp.: 50
Direct-to-Home Satellite Television Entertainment Services
N.A.I.C.S.: 516120

Subsidiary (Non-US):

DIRECTV Argentina, S.A. (3)
Sargento Juan B Cabral 3770, Munro, Buenos Aires1605, Argentina
Tel.: (54) 1137512500
Web Site: http://www.directv.com.ar
Cable Programming Services
N.A.I.C.S.: 516210

Subsidiary (Domestic):

Alpha Tel S.A. (4)
Capitan Justo G Bermudez 4547 Piso 1 Complejo, Panamericano-Torre I 1605 Buenos Aires, Munro, Argentina
Tel.: (54) 1137512500
Cable Programming Services
N.A.I.C.S.: 516210

Revistas Deportivas S.A. (4)
Balcarce 510, Buenos Aires, 1064, Argentina
Tel.: (54) 1152355100
Cable & Satellite Television Services
N.A.I.C.S.: 516210

Television Satelital Codificada S.A. (4)
Avenida San Juan 1130, 1147, Buenos Aires, Argentina
Tel.: (54) 1143003800
Web Site: http://www.tycsports.com.ar

Television Broadcasting Services
N.A.I.C.S.: 516120

Torneos y Competencias S.A. (4)
Balcarce 510, Buenos Aires, Argentina
Tel.: (54) 1152354800
Web Site: https://www.torneos.com
Cable & Satellite Television Programming
N.A.I.C.S.: 516210

Workjoy Argentina S.A. (4)
Fray J S De Oro Palermo - Ciudad de, 273004, Buenos Aires, Argentina
Tel.: (54) 1147027446
Television Broadcasting Services
N.A.I.C.S.: 516120

Subsidiary (Non-US):

DIRECTV Colombia, Ltda. (3)
Avenida Carrera 45, 103 60, Bogota, Colombia
Tel.: (57) 16516000
Television Broadcasting Services
N.A.I.C.S.: 516120

Subsidiary (Domestic):

Telecenter Panamericana Ltda. (4)
Cl 67 Norte 7 NRO 59 Pl 4-5, Cali, Colombia
Tel.: (57) 24897777
Television Broadcasting Services
N.A.I.C.S.: 516120

Win Sports S.A.S. (4)
Calle 11 65 51, Bogota, 110851, Colombia
Tel.: (57) 17956464
Web Site: https://www.winsports.co
Television Broadcasting Services
N.A.I.C.S.: 516120

Subsidiary (Non-US):

DIRECTV Peru S.r.L. (3)
Av 28 De Julio 150 of 401, Lima, 18, Peru
Tel.: (51) 17000300
Television Broadcasting Services
N.A.I.C.S.: 516120

DIRECTV Trinidad Limited (3)
31 Mulchan Seuchan Road, Chaguanas, Trinidad & Tobago
Tel.: (868) 672811
Television Broadcasting Services
N.A.I.C.S.: 516120

Subsidiary (Domestic):

DIRECTV Sports Net Pittsburgh, LLC (2)
323 N Shore Dr Ste 200, Pittsburgh, PA 15212-5320
Tel.: (412) 316-3800
Web Site: http://www.dirootv.com
Television Broadcasting Services
N.A.I.C.S.: 516210

DTV Network Systems, Inc. (2)
8830 Siempre Viva Rd, San Diego, CA 92154
Tel.: (858) 452-4601
Web Site: http://www.directv.com
Television Broadcasting Services
N.A.I.C.S.: 516120

INVIDI Technologies Corporation (1)
202 Carnegie Ctr Ste 204, Princeton, NJ 08540-5747
Tel.: (609) 951-3900
Web Site: https://www.invidi.com
Targeted Advertising Custom Software & Marketing Services
N.A.I.C.S.: 541000
David M. Downey (Co-CEO)
Bruce J. Anderson (Co-CEO & CTO)
Michael Kubin (Exec VP-Media)
Patrick Sheehan (CTO-Intl)
Ron Gravino (Sr VP-Fin & HR)
Chris O'Toole (Pres & CFO)
Howard Fiderer (COO)
Edward Thorn (Sr VP-Intl)
Dan Carella (COO)
Matt Perkins (Chief Compliance Officer & Gen Counsel)
Brian Lesser (Chm)
Niru Krishna (Chief Innovation Officer)
Prasad Sanagavarapu (Chief Bus Officer)
Matthew Hillary (Sr VP-Operations)
Marcelo Lechner (Sr VP)
Niru Krishna (Chief Innovation Officer)

Prasad Sanagavarapu (Chief Bus Officer)
Matthew Hillary (Sr VP-Operations)
Marcelo Lechner (Sr VP)
Niru Krishna (Chief Innovation Officer)
Prasad Sanagavarapu (Chief Bus Officer)
Matthew Hillary (Sr VP-Operations)
Marcelo Lechner (Sr VP)

New Cingular Wireless Services, Inc. (1)
7858 E 96th St, Fishers, IN 46037
Tel.: (317) 594-9400
Wireless Telecommunication Services
N.A.I.C.S.: 517112
Brian Bigelow (Principal)

SKY Brasil Servicos Ltda. (1)
Avenida Marcos Penteado de Ulhoa Rodrigues, 1000 Resid Tres, Santana de Parnaiba, 06543-900, Tambore, Brazil
Tel.: (55) 11 3003 7676
Televison & Satellite Programming
N.A.I.C.S.: 516120

Superclick, Inc. (1)
10222 St-Michel Blvd Suite 300, Montreal, H1H 5H1, QC, Canada
Tel.: (514) 847-0333
Web Site: http://www.superclick.com
Sales Range: $1-9.9 Million
Broadband High Speed Internet Connection Equipment
N.A.I.C.S.: 334220

Teleport Communications America, LLC (1)
2535 E 40th Ave, Denver, CO 80205
Tel.: (303) 299-5703
Telecommunication Servicesb
N.A.I.C.S.: 517810

Wayport, Inc. (1)
2105 Forest Trl, Austin, TX 78703-2931
Tel.: (469) 621-4600
Web Site: http://www.wayport.net
Sales Range: $50-74.9 Million
Data & Internet Services
N.A.I.C.S.: 541618

Xandr Inc. (1)
28 W 23rd St, New York, NY 10010
Tel.: (646) 825-6460
Web Site: http://www.xandr.com
Online Advertising Solutions Services
N.A.I.C.S.: 513210
Ben John (Head-Engineering-Customer Success-Operations)
Jason Brown (Chief Revenue Officer)
Ray Carpenter (CFO)
Lori Fink (Head)
Michele Golden (Chief HR Officer)
Amy Leifer (Exec VP-Operations)
Mike Welch (Exec VP & Gen Mgr)
Jennifer De La Torre (Head-Finance)
Doug Hurd (Head-Corporate Strategy-Business Development)
Dave Osborn (Head-Commercial-North America,Global Partnerships)
Andrew Rutledge (Head-Side Sls)
Jerome Underhill (Head)

ATACAMA RESOURCES INTERNATIONAL, INC.
1317 Edgewater Dr Ste 2510, Orlando, FL 32804
Tel.: (780) 512-3805   **FL**
Web Site: https://acrlintl.com
Year Founded: 2013
ACRL—(OTCIQ)
Mining Industry Consulting Services
N.A.I.C.S.: 541620
Glenn B. Grant (Pres & CEO)
Greg Praver (COO)
Brian Praver (VP-Business Development)
Thomas Moynihan (CFO)

ATARA BIOTHERAPEUTICS, INC.
2380 Conejo Spectrum St Ste 200, Thousand Oaks, CA 91320
Tel.: (805) 623-4211   **DE**
Web Site: https://www.atarabio.com
Year Founded: 2012

ATRA—(NASDAQ)
Rev.: $8,573,000
Assets: $165,504,000
Liabilities: $264,735,000
Net Worth: ($99,231,000)
Earnings: ($276,126,000)
Emp.: 225
Fiscal Year-end: 12/31/23
Biopharmaceutical Mfr
N.A.I.C.S.: 325412
Eric Hyllengren (CFO, Principal Acctg Officer & Sr VP)
Cokey Nguyen (Pres, CEO, Chief Scientific Officer & Chief Technical Officer)

Subsidiaries:

Atara Biotherapeutics Switzerland GmbH (1)
Zahlerweg 6, 6300, Zug, Switzerland
Tel.: (41) 415613210
Pharmaceutical Preparation Distr
N.A.I.C.S.: 424210

Nina Biotherapeutics, Inc (1)
3260 Bayshore Blvd, Brisbane, CA 94005
Tel.: (415) 287-2411
Pharmaceutical Drug Mfr
N.A.I.C.S.: 325412

ATEA PHARMACEUTICALS, INC.
225 Franklin St Ste 2100, Boston, MA 02110
Tel.: (857) 284-8891   **DE**
Web Site:
https://www.ateapharma.com
Year Founded: 2012
AVIR—(NASDAQ)
Assets: $666,708,000
Liabilities: $26,136,000
Net Worth: $640,572,000
Earnings: ($115,909,000)
Emp.: 70
Fiscal Year-end: 12/31/22
Biotechnology Research & Development Services
N.A.I.C.S.: 541714
Andrea Corcoran (CFO, Sec & Exec VP-Legal)
Wayne Foster (Sr VP-Fin & Admin)
Steven Good (Exec VP-Preclinical Science)
Janet Hammond (Chief Dev Officer)
Maria Arantxa Horga (Chief Medical Officer)
Adel Mousa (Exec VP-Chemistry)
Keith Pietropaolo (Sr VP-Clinical Sciences)
John Vavricka (Chief Comml Officer)
Xiao-Jian Zhou (Exec VP-Early Stage Dev)
Jonae Barnes (Sr VP-IR & Corp Comm)
Kai Lin (VP-Virology)
Jayanthi Wolf (Sr VP-Regulatory Affairs)
Claudio Avila (Sr VP-Medical Affairs)
Bruce Belanger (VP-Biostatistics)
Paul Fanning (Sr VP-HR)
Jean-Pierre Sommadossi (Founder, Chm, Pres & CEO)

ATERIAN, INC.
350 Springfield Ave Ste 200, Summit, NY 07901
Tel.: (347) 676-1681   **DE**
Web Site: https://www.aterian.io
Year Founded: 2014
ATER—(NASDAQ)
Rev.: $221,170,000
Assets: $156,439,000
Liabilities: $54,487,000
Net Worth: $101,952,000
Earnings: ($196,292,000)
Emp.: 178
Fiscal Year-end: 12/31/22

Holding Company
N.A.I.C.S.: 551112
William H. Kurtz (Chm)
Yaniv Sarig (Founder)
Michal Chaouat-Fix (Chief Product Officer)
Roi Zahut (CTO)
Phil Lepper (Chief Revenue Officer & Sr VP-Revenue)
Josh Feldman (CFO)
Arturo Rodriguez (CEO)

Subsidiaries:

Healing Solutions (Remedy) LLC **(1)**
4703 W Brill St Ste 101, Phoenix, AZ 85043
Web Site: https://www.healingsolutions.com
Online Shopping Services
N.A.I.C.S.: 456120

Sari Foods, LLC **(1)**
82 Nassau St Ste 60375, New York, NY 10038
Web Site: https://www.sarifoods.co
Online Shopping Services
N.A.I.C.S.: 311423

Sunlabz LLC **(1)**
222 Broadway, New York, NY 10038
Tel.: (830) 542-9303
Web Site: http://www.sunlabz.com
Accumulator & Battery Mfr
N.A.I.C.S.: 335910

Xtava LLC **(1)**
37 E 18th St, New York, NY 10003
Tel.: (646) 491-6500
Web Site: https://www.xtava.com
Hair Dryer Distr
N.A.I.C.S.: 456120

ATHENA BITCOIN GLOBAL
1 SE 3rd Ave Ste 2740, Miami, FL 33131
Tel.: (312) 690-4466   **NV**
Web Site: https://athenabitcoin.com
ABIT—(OTCIQ)
Holding Company; Bitcoin Trading Services
N.A.I.C.S.: 551112
Matias Goldenhorn (Co-CEO)
Sam Nazzaro (Chief Comml Officer)
Eric L. Gravengaard (Co-CEO)

ATHENA CONSUMER ACQUISITION CORP.
442 5th Ave, New York, NY 10018
Tel.: (970) 925-1572   **DE**
Year Founded: 2021
ACAQ—(NYSEAMEX)
Rev.: $2,959,199
Assets: $22,027,334
Liabilities: $35,478,983
Net Worth: ($13,451,649)
Earnings: ($2,246,145)
Emp.: 3
Fiscal Year-end: 12/31/22
Investment Services
N.A.I.C.S.: 523999
Isabelle Freidheim (Chm)
Jane Park (CEO)
Jennifer Carr-Smith (Pres, CFO & COO)
Jennifer C. Carr-Smith (Pres, CFO & COO)

ATHENA GOLD CORPORATION
2010A Harbison Dr Ste 312, Vacaville, CA 95687
Tel.: (707) 291-6198   **DE**
Web Site: https://athenagoldcorp.com
Year Founded: 2003
AHNR—(OTCQB)
Assets: $6,243,389
Liabilities: $1,279,975
Net Worth: $4,963,414
Earnings: ($683,658)
Fiscal Year-end: 12/31/22

Gold Ore Exploration & Mining Services
N.A.I.C.S.: 212220
John C. Power (CEO & Sec)
Tyler Minnick (CFO)
Brian Power (Dir)
John C. Power (Pres, CEO & Dir)

ATHENEX, INC.
1001 Main St Ste 600, Buffalo, NY 14203
Tel.: (716) 427-2950   **DE**
Year Founded: 2004
ATNX—(NASDAQ)
Rev.: $102,821,000
Assets: $204,055,000
Liabilities: $228,236,000
Net Worth: $24,181,000
Earnings: ($104,423,000)
Emp.: 269
Fiscal Year-end: 12/31/22
Holding Company; Cancer Treatment Biopharmaceutical Developer & Mfr
N.A.I.C.S.: 551112
Johnson Y. N. Lau (Chm & CEO)
Timothy Cook (Chief Bus & Comml Officer & Sr VP-Global Oncology)
Timothy Cook (Chief Bus & Comml Officer-Proprietary Drugs)
Nick Campbell (Chief Restructuring Officer)

Subsidiaries:

Athenex Pharma Solutions, LLC **(1)**
Conventus Bldg 1001 Main St Ste 600, Buffalo, NY 14203
Tel.: (716) 418-7274
Web Site: https://www.athenexpharma.com
Biopharmaceutical Mfr, Testing & Support Services
N.A.I.C.S.: 325412

Athenex Pharmaceutical Division, LLC **(1)**
1001 Main St Ste 600, Buffalo, NY 14203 **(100%)**
Tel.: (716) 427-2950
Web Site: http://www.athenex.com
Cancer Treatment Biopharmaceutical Developer, Mfr & Whslr
N.A.I.C.S.: 325412

Polymed Therapeutics, Inc. **(1)**
3040 Post Oak Blvd Ste 1110, Houston, TX 77056-6584 **(100%)**
Tel.: (713) 777-7088
Web Site: http://www.polymedt.com
Active Pharmaceutical Ingredients & Other Specialty Chemicals Mfr & Whslr
N.A.I.C.S.: 325412
William Zuo (Pres)

ATHIRA PHARMA, INC.
18706 N Creek Pkwy Ste 104, Bothell, WA 98011
Tel.: (425) 620-8501   **DE**
Web Site: https://www.athira.com
Year Founded: 2011
ATHA—(NASDAQ)
Rev.: $7,637,000
Assets: $160,245,000
Liabilities: $30,057,000
Net Worth: $130,188,000
Earnings: ($117,672,000)
Emp.: 65
Fiscal Year-end: 12/31/23
Biotechnology Research & Development Services
N.A.I.C.S.: 541714
Samantha Willing (Chief People Officer)
Leen Kawas (Founder)
Mark J. Litton (Pres & CEO)
Kevin Church (VP-Discovery)
Xue Hua (VP-Clinical Dev & Res)
Tadataka Yamada (Chm)
Rachel Lenington (CTO & Head-Product Dev Strategy)

Mark Worthington (Gen Counsel)
Robert Renninger (CFO, Principal Acctg Officer & VP-Fin)

ATHLON ACQUISITION CORP.
44 Brattle St, Cambridge, MA 02138
Tel.: (617) 855-6333   **DE**
Year Founded: 2020
SWET—(NASDAQ)
Rev.: $3,054,160
Assets: $276,980,380
Liabilities: $299,176,405
Net Worth: ($22,196,025)
Earnings: $1,715,748
Fiscal Year-end: 12/31/21
Investment Services
N.A.I.C.S.: 523999
Chris Hickey (CEO)
David Poltack (CFO)
Mark Wan (Chm)

ATI INC.
2021 McKinney Ave Ste 1100, Dallas, TX 75201
Tel.: (412) 394-2800   **DE**
Web Site:
  https://www.atimaterials.com
Year Founded: 1996
ATI—(NYSE)
Rev.: $3,836,000,000
Assets: $4,445,600,000
Liabilities: $3,288,400,000
Net Worth: $1,157,200,000
Earnings: $130,900,000
Emp.: 6,700
Fiscal Year-end: 12/31/22
Steel & Alloys Mfr
N.A.I.C.S.: 332312
Donald P. Newman (CFO & Sr VP-Fin)
Donald P. Newman (CFO, CFO & Exec VP/Sr VP-Fin)
Robert S. Wetherbee (Exec Chm)
Kevin B. Kramer (Chief Comml & Mktg Officer & Sr VP)
Scott A. Minder (Treas & VP-IR)
Kimberly A. Fields (Pres & CEO)
Kimberly A. Fields (Exec VP-Advanced Alloys & Solutions & High Performance Material)
Timothy J. Harris (Chief Digital & Information Officer & Sr VP)
Shelley L. Bias (VP-Internal Audit)
Michael B. Miller (Chief Acctg Officer, VP & Controller)

Subsidiaries:

ATI Casting Service **(1)**
300 Philadelphia St, La Porte, IN 46350
Tel.: (219) 362-1000
Web Site: http://www.castingservice.com
Sales Range: $50-74.9 Million
Emp.: 150
Machines & Metals Designer & Mfr
N.A.I.C.S.: 331511

ATI Flowform Products, LLC **(1)**
12 Suburban Park Dr, Billerica, MA 01821-3903
Tel.: (978) 667-0202
Web Site: http://www.flowform.com
Sales Range: $1-9.9 Million
Emp.: 45
Precision Machined Metal Product Mfr
N.A.I.C.S.: 332999

ATI Forged Products **(1)**
5481 S Packard Ave, Cudahy, WI 53110
Tel.: (414) 747-2611
Web Site: http://www.atimetals.com
Forged & Cast Metal Components Developer, Mfr & Marketer
N.A.I.C.S.: 332111

Division (Domestic):

ATI Ladish Diecast Tooling **(2)**
3001 Wolf St, Racine, WI 53404-1640
Tel.: (262) 632-7579
Sales Range: $150-199.9 Million
Emp.: 3

Aluminum Diecast Tooling Support Services & Mfr
N.A.I.C.S.: 331523

Subsidiary (Non-US):

ATI ZKM Forging Sp. z o.o. **(2)**
ul Wladyslawa Grabskiego 54, 37-450, Stalowa Wola, Poland
Tel.: (48) 126174141
Web Site: https://www.zkp.pl
Metal Forging & Heat Treating
N.A.I.C.S.: 332111

ATI Garryson Ltd. **(1)**
Spring Rd, Ibstock, LE67 6LR, Leicestershire, United Kingdom **(100%)**
Tel.: (44) 1530261145
Web Site: http://www.atagroup.co
Sales Range: $25-49.9 Million
Emp.: 80
Mfr & Distr of Abrasive & Solid Carbide Cutting Tools, Abrasive Flap Discs & Carbide Rotary Burrs
N.A.I.C.S.: 327910

Subsidiary (US):

ATI Garryson **(2)**
1 Teledyne Pl, La Vergne, TN 37086-3529
Tel.: (615) 641-4200
Web Site: http://www.atimetals.com
Mfr & Distr of Abrasive & Solid Carbide Cutting Tools, Abrasive Flap Discs & Carbide Rotary Burrs
N.A.I.C.S.: 423830

ATI Operating Holdings, LLC **(1)**
1000 6 Ppg Pl, Pittsburgh, PA 15222
Tel.: (412) 394-2800
Stainless Steel Mfr
N.A.I.C.S.: 331221

ATI Specialty Alloys and Components **(1)**
1600 Old Salem Rd NE, Albany, OR 97321-4548
Tel.: (541) 926-4211
Web Site: http://www.atimetals.com
Sales Range: $700-749.9 Million
Emp.: 1,000
Machines & Metals Designer & Mfr
N.A.I.C.S.: 331410

ATI Specialty Materials **(1)**
2600 E Roosevelt Blvd, Monroe, NC 28110
Tel.: (704) 289-4511
Web Site: http://www.atimetals.com
Metal Products Mfr
N.A.I.C.S.: 332322

ATI Stellram S.A **(1)**
Ave Du Mont Blanc 24, PO Box 339, Gland, 1196, Switzerland **(100%)**
Tel.: (41) 223549711
Web Site: http://www.atimetans.com
Sales Range: $50-74.9 Million
Emp.: 130
Metals Service Centers & Offices
N.A.I.C.S.: 423510

ATI Titanium, LLC **(1)**
1000 6 Ppg Pl, Pittsburgh, PA 15222
Tel.: (412) 394-2800
Iron & Steel Forging Services
N.A.I.C.S.: 332111

Allegheny Ludlum, LLC **(1)**
100 River Rd, Brackenridge, PA 15014
Tel.: (724) 226-5555
Web Site: https://www.atimaterials.com
Emp.: 960
Non Ferrous Metal Mfr
N.A.I.C.S.: 331491

Allegheny Rodney **(1)**
1357 E Rodney French Blvd, New Bedford, MA 02742
Tel.: (508) 996-5691
Web Site: http://www.atimetals.com
Sales Range: $150-199.9 Million
Emp.: 34
Stainless Steel & Specialty Metal Strip Products Processor & Distr
N.A.I.C.S.: 331221

Allegheny Technologies GmbH **(1)**
Heltorfer Strasse 1a, 40472, Dusseldorf, Germany **(100%)**
Tel.: (49) 2115135600
Web Site: http://www.atimetals.com

ATI Inc.—(Continued)

Sales Range: $1-9.9 Million
Emp.: 15
Metals Service Centers & Offices
N.A.I.C.S.: 423510

Allegheny Technologies Incorporated - Singapore (1)
8 Ubi Rd 2 06-18 Zervex Building, Singapore, 408538, Singapore (100%)
Tel.: (65) 68832577
Web Site:
    http://www.alleghenytechnologies.com
Sales Range: $25-49.9 Million
Emp.: 2
Wholesale Metal Merchants
N.A.I.C.S.: 423510

Allegheny Technologies Japan Ltd. (1)
Minami-Aoyama M-Square 5F 2-2-3 Minami-Aoyama, Minato-ku, Tokyo, 107-0062, Japan (100%)
Tel.: (81) 357703880
Web Site: http://www.atimetal.com
Sales Range: $25-49.9 Million
Emp.: 15
Stainless Steel & Nickel-Based Alloys
N.A.I.C.S.: 423510
Koji Tanaka (Pres & CEO)

Allegheny Technologies Korea (1)
Room 901 Jutaek Geonseol Hoegwan 25 Gukjegeumyung-Ro 8-gil, Yeoungdeungpo-Gu, 073-32, Seoul, Korea (South) (100%)
Tel.: (82) 27613961
Web Site: http://www.atimetals.com
Sales Range: $25-49.9 Million
Emp.: 7
Specialty Materials & Components Producer
N.A.I.C.S.: 332999
H. S. Hong (Mng Dir)

Allegheny Technologies Limited (1)
Granby Avenue, Garretts Green, Birmingham, B33 0SP, United Kingdom (100%)
Tel.: (44) 1217898030
Web Site: http://www.atieurope.eu
Sales Range: $10-24.9 Million
Emp.: 35
Metals Service Center
N.A.I.C.S.: 423510
Pam Broeker (Mng Dir)

Allegheny Technologies SAS (1)
Cap Mermoz 38 Rue Jean Mermoz, 78600, Maisons-Laffitte, France (100%)
Tel.: (33) 134938020
Web Site: http://www.atimetals.com
Sales Range: $10-24.9 Million
Emp.: 10
Specialty Metals Service Centers
N.A.I.C.S.: 423510

Aoovac Limited (1)
Atlas House Attercliffe Rd, Sheffield, S3 7UY, United Kingdom
Tel.: (44) 01142720081
Metals Service Centers & Offices
N.A.I.C.S.: 423510

International Hearth Melting, LLC (1)
3101 Kingsgate Way, Richland, WA 99354
Tel.: (509) 371-2500
Emp.: 70
Iron & Steel Forging Services
N.A.I.C.S.: 332111

Plant (Domestic):

Allegheny Ludlum-Vandergrift (2)
100 Lincoln Ave, Vandergrift, PA 15690 (100%)
Tel.: (724) 568-5224
Web Site: http://www.alleghenyludlum.com
Sales Range: $75-99.9 Million
Emp.: 300
Mfr & Distribution of Cold-Rolled Steel
N.A.I.C.S.: 331221

Oregon Metallurgical, LLC (1)
530 SW 34th Ave, Albany, OR 97322
Tel.: (541) 967-9000
Metal Ore Mining Services
N.A.I.C.S.: 212290

Shanghai STAL Precision Stainless Steel Company Limited (1)
No 291 Huajin Rd, Xinzhuang Industrial

Zone Minhang District, Shanghai, 201109, China (60%)
Tel.: (86) 2124087888
Web Site: https://www.stal.com.cn
Emp.: 500
Stainless Steel Mfr
N.A.I.C.S.: 331221

Teledyne Israel Composite Ltd. (1)
Shoam, PO Box 1751, Tel Aviv, 6082741, Israel
Tel.: (972) 39795135
Sales Range: $900-999.9 Million
Emp.: 5
N.A.I.C.S.: 425120
Ami Saban (Gen Mgr)

Teledyne Italy (1)
Via La Pira 25, 10028, Trofarello, Italy
Tel.: (39) 011 648 3111
Sales Range: $900-999.9 Million
N.A.I.C.S.: 425120

ATI NETWORKS INC
12482 Emerson Dr, Brighton, MI 48116
Tel.: (231) 518-0200   CO
Web Site:
    https://www.atinetworks.net
ATIW—(OTCIQ)
Media Services
N.A.I.C.S.: 541840
Lawrence Bestor (Chm & CEO)

ATLANTA BRAVES HOLDINGS, INC.
12300 Liberty Blvd, Englewood, CO 80112   NV
Web Site:
    https://www.bravesholdings.com
Year Founded: 2022
BATRA—(NASDAQ)
Offices of Other Holding Companies
N.A.I.C.S.: 551112
Terence F. McGuirk (Pres & CEO)
Brian J. Wendling (Chief Acctg Officer & Principal Fin Officer)

Subsidiaries:

Atlanta Braves, Inc. (1)
755 Battery Ave, Atlanta, GA 30339
Tel.: (404) 522-7630
Web Site: http://www.atlantabraves.com
Professional Baseball Team, Sports Arena & Affiliated Entities Operator
N.A.I.C.S.: 711211
Derek G. Schiller (Pres & CEO)
Rick Oehlesinger (Pres-Bus Ops)
David Stearns (Pres-Baseball Ops)
Matt Arnold (Sr VP & Gen Mgr)
Tyler Barnes (Sr VP-Comm & Affiliate Ops)
Steve Ethier (Sr VP-Stadium Ops)
Daniel Fumai (CFO)
Jason Hartlund (Chief Revenue Officer)
Marti Wronski (Gen Counsel & Sr VP-Admin)
Karl Mueller (Sr VP-Player Personnel)
Gord Ash (VP-Baseball Projects)
Tom Flanagan (VP-Minor League Ops)
Tod Johnson (VP-Domestic Scouting)
Matt Kleine (VP-Baseball Ops)
Brian Powalish (Mgr-Advance Scouting)
Kevin Ottsen (Coord-Baseball Ops)
Oscar Garcia (Coord-Scouting)

Subsidiary (Domestic):

Atlanta National League Baseball Club, LLC (2)
Turner Field 755 Hank Aaron Dr, Atlanta, GA 30315
Tel.: (404) 522-7630
Web Site: https://www.mlb.com
Professional Baseball Club & Sports Arena Operator
N.A.I.C.S.: 711211

Braves Productions LLC (2)
755 Hank Aaron Dr SW, Atlanta, GA 30315
Tel.: (404) 614-1331
Emp.: 6
Sports Teleproduction & Postproduction Services
N.A.I.C.S.: 512191

ATLANTIC ALLIANCE PARTNERSHIP CORP.
590 Madison Ave, New York, NY 10022
Tel.: (212) 409-2434   VG
Year Founded: 2015
AAPC—(NASDAQ)
Assets: $1,472
Liabilities: $295,458
Net Worth: ($293,986)
Earnings: ($71,592)
Emp.: 2
Fiscal Year-end: 12/31/19
Investment Services
N.A.I.C.S.: 523999
Jonathan Mitchell (CFO)
Iain Henry Abrahams (CEO)
Mark David Klein (Chm)

ATLANTIC AMERICAN CORPORATION
4370 Peachtree Rd NE, Atlanta, GA 30319
Tel.: (404) 266-5500   GA
Web Site: https://www.atlam.com
Year Founded: 1968
AAME—(NASDAQ)
Rev.: $187,851,000
Assets: $367,064,000
Liabilities: $264,871,000
Net Worth: $102,193,000
Earnings: $1,525,000
Emp.: 141
Fiscal Year-end: 12/31/22
Life, Health, Property & Casualty Insurance
N.A.I.C.S.: 524126
Hilton H. Howell Jr. (Chm, Pres & CEO)
Jeffrey Ross Franklin (CFO, Sec & VP)
John Dunbar (CIO & VP)
Bruce Snyder (Asst VP-Information Svcs)
Jake Gibson (Asst VP-Internal Audit)

Subsidiaries:

American Southern Insurance Company (1)
3715 Northside Pkwy Bldg 400 Ste 800, Atlanta, GA 30327 (100%)
Tel.: (404) 266-9599
Web Site: https://www.amsou.com
Rev.: $60,278,388
Emp.: 40
Properties & Casualties Insurance
N.A.I.C.S.: 524126
Scott G. Thompson (Pres & CEO)
Robert H. Knight (CFO & Exec VP)
Jerry A. Underwood (VP-Surety)
Constance B. Woods (VP-Legal)
Melonie Coppola (Sec)
Ray McGhie (Asst VP-IT)
Stu Holloway (VP-Marketing)
Laurie Brown (Asst VP-Claims)
Gregory Weaver (Partner-HR Bus)
Angi Mowens (Asst VP-Underwriting)
Scott Williams (Asst VP-Information Technology)

Subsidiary (Domestic):

American Safety Insurance Company (2)
3715 N Side Pkwy Bldg 400 8th Fl, Atlanta, GA 30327
Tel.: (404) 266-9599
Web Site: http://www.amsou.com
Sales Range: $25-49.9 Million
Emp.: 40
Property & Casualty Insurance
N.A.I.C.S.: 524126

Bankers Fidelity Life Insurance Company (1)
4370 Peachtree Rd NE, Atlanta, GA 30319-3054 (100%)
Tel.: (404) 266-5600
Web Site: https://bankersfidelity.com
Sales Range: $100-124.9 Million
Life & Supplemental Health Insurance Products

N.A.I.C.S.: 524113
Hilton H. Howell Jr. (Bd of Dirs, Executives)

xCalibre Risk Services, Inc. (1)
4370 Peachtree Rd NE, Atlanta, GA 30319 (100%)
Tel.: (404) 266-5781
Web Site: http://www.xcalibrebenefits.com
Sales Range: $10-24.9 Million
Emp.: 3
Third Party Administrator
N.A.I.C.S.: 541618

ATLANTIC AVENUE ACQUISITION CORP
2200 Atlantic St, Stamford, CT 06902
Tel.: (203) 989-9709   DE
Year Founded: 2020
ASAQU—(NYSE)
Rev.: $11,675,387
Assets: $251,209,708
Liabilities: $262,027,234
Net Worth: ($10,817,526)
Earnings: $9,589,773
Emp.: 5
Fiscal Year-end: 12/31/21
Investment Services
N.A.I.C.S.: 523999
Ashok Nayyar (Chm & CEO)

ATLANTIC INTERNATIONAL CORP.
3 Federal St, Billerica, MA 01821
Tel.: (781) 460-6016   DE
Web Site: https://www.seqll.com
Year Founded: 2014
ATLN—(NASDAQ)
Rev.: $78,659
Assets: $8,414,241
Liabilities: $4,047,355
Net Worth: $4,366,886
Earnings: ($4,094,833)
Emp.: 7
Fiscal Year-end: 12/31/22
Biotechnology Research & Development Services
N.A.I.C.S.: 541714
Frances Scally (CFO & Sec)
Daniel Jones (Co-Founder, Chm, Pres & CEO)
John W. Kennedy (CFO & Sec)
Erik Volke (Dir-Ops)
Abhijeet Shinde (Dir-Engrg)
William C. St Laurent (Co-Founder)

ATLANTIC SAPPHIRE ASA
22275 SW 272nd St, Homestead, FL 33031
Tel.: (786) 292-3632   NO
Web Site:
    https://www.atlanticsapphire.com
ASA—(OSL)
Seafood Product Preparation & Packaging
N.A.I.C.S.: 311710
Johan E. Andreassen (Founder & CEO)

ATLANTIC UNION BANKSHARES CORPORATION
1051 E Cary St Ste 103, Richmond, VA 23219
Tel.: (804) 633-5031   VA
Web Site:
    https://www.atlanticunionbank.com
Year Founded: 1993
AUB—(NYSE)
Rev.: $778,958,000
Assets: $20,461,138,000
Liabilities: $18,088,401,000
Net Worth: $2,372,737,000
Earnings: $234,510,000
Emp.: 1,877
Fiscal Year-end: 12/31/22
Bank Holding Company
N.A.I.C.S.: 551111
Robert Michael Gorman (CFO, Chief Acctg Officer & Exec VP)

John C. Asbury *(Pres & CEO)*
Maria P. Tedesco *(Executives)*
Shawn E. O'Brien *(Exec VP)*
Andrew Wexler *(Dir-Bus Dev)*
Patrick J. McCann *(Bd of Dirs & Vice Chm)*
Matthew L. Linderman *(CIO & Exec VP)*
Sherry Williams *(Chief Risk Officer & Exec VP)*
Maria P. Tedesco *(Pres, COO & Exec VP)*
Clare Miller *(Chief HR Officer & Exec VP)*

Subsidiaries:

American National Bankshares Inc. **(1)**
628 Main St, Danville, VA 24541
Tel.: (434) 792-5111
Rev.: $114,811,000
Assets: $3,065,902,000
Liabilities: $2,744,728,000
Net Worth: $321,174,000
Earnings: $34,428,000
Emp.: 343
Fiscal Year-end: 12/31/2022
Bank Holding Company
N.A.I.C.S.: 551111

Subsidiary (Domestic):

HomeTown Bankshares Corporation **(2)**
202 S Jefferson St, Roanoke, VA 24011
Tel.: (540) 345-6000
Web Site:
  http://investors.hometownbankva.com
Rev.: $22,490,000
Assets: $564,978,000
Liabilities: $511,279,000
Net Worth: $53,699,000
Earnings: $3,954,000
Emp.: 97
Fiscal Year-end: 12/31/2018
Bank Holding Company
N.A.I.C.S.: 551111
Laurie C. Hart *(Chief Retail & Deposit Officer & Exec VP)*
Terrance E. O'Shaughnessy *(Chief Lending Officer & Exec VP)*
William W. Budd Jr. *(Chief Credit Officer & Exec VP)*

Subsidiary (Domestic):

HomeTown Bank **(3)**
202 S Jefferson St, Roanoke, VA 24011
Tel.: (540) 345-6000
Web Site: http://www.hometownbankva.com
Commericial Banking
N.A.I.C.S.: 522110

Atlantic Union Bank **(1)**
3 James Ctr 1051 E Cary St Ste 103, Richmond, VA 23219
Tel.: (804) 327-5720
Web Site:
  https://www.atlanticunionbank.com
Commericial Banking
N.A.I.C.S.: 522110
John C. Asbury *(CEO)*
Maria P. Tedesco *(Pres & COO)*
Robert M. Gorman *(CFO)*
Matt Linderman *(CIO)*
Rachael Lape *(Gen Counsel)*
Clare Miller *(Chief HR Officer)*
Doug Woolley *(Chief Credit Officer)*
Sherry Williams *(Chief Risk Officer)*

Subsidiary (Domestic):

Dixon, Hubard, Feinour & Brown, Inc. **(2)**
601 S Jefferson St Ste 410, Roanoke, VA 24011
Tel.: (540) 343-9903
Web Site: http://www.dhfb.com
Investment Counseling Company
N.A.I.C.S.: 523150
Tracy L. Snyder *(Mgr-Data)*

Middleburg Investment Group, Inc. **(2)**
211 Fort Evans Rd NE, Leesburg, VA 20176
Tel.: (703) 737-3434

Full Range Financial Products & Investment Services
N.A.I.C.S.: 523999
David Hartley *(Pres & CEO)*

Subsidiary (Domestic):

Middleburg Trust Company **(3)**
1600 Forest Ave, Richmond, VA 23229
Tel.: (804) 644-2848
Web Site: http://www.middleburgtrust.com
Fiduciary & Investment Management Services
N.A.I.C.S.: 523991

Branch (Domestic):

Middleburg Trust Company **(4)**
1901 N Beauregard St Ste300, Alexandria, VA 22311
Tel.: (703) 931-1366
Web Site: http://www.middleburgtrust.com
Fixed Income Securities, Taxable & Tax-Exempt & Investment Services
N.A.I.C.S.: 523150

Middleburg Trust Company **(4)**
111 W Washington St, Middleburg, VA 20117
Tel.: (540) 687-4805
Web Site: http://www.middleburgtrust.com
Fiduciary & Investment Management Services
N.A.I.C.S.: 523150

Middleburg Trust Company **(4)**
5372 Discovery Park Blvd Ste 101, Williamsburg, VA 23188
Tel.: (757) 258-6878
Web Site: http://www.middleburgtrust.com
Fiduciary & Investment Management Services
N.A.I.C.S.: 523150

Subsidiary (Domestic):

Old Dominion Capital Management, Inc. **(2)**
200 Garrett St Ste L, Charlottesville, VA 22902
Tel.: (434) 977-1550
Web Site: http://www.odcm.com
Sales Range: $1-9.9 Million
Portfolio Management & Associated Financial Services
N.A.I.C.S.: 523940
J. Dawn Heneberry *(Mng Dir)*
Mauree L. Barrett *(Chief Compliance Officer & Mgr-Ops)*
Breanna R. Payne *(Compliance Officer)*
Benjamin J. Peress *(Reg Mng Dir & Chief Investment Officer)*
Esperanza D. Reyes *(Reg Mgr-Ops)*

Union Insurance Group, LLC **(1)**
1051 E Cary St Ste 1200, Richmond, VA 23219-0000
Tel.: (804) 633-5031
Insurance Agencies & Brokerage Services
N.A.I.C.S.: 524210

Union Mortgage Group, Inc. **(1)**
1051 E Cary St Ste 1200, Richmond, VA 23219-4044
Tel.: (703) 621-7900
Real Estate Credit Services
N.A.I.C.S.: 522292

ATLANTICA, INC.

11450 SE Dixie Hwy, Hobe Sound, FL 33455
Tel.: (772) 545-9002   **UT**
Year Founded: 1938
ALDA—(OTCIQ)
Liabilities: $4,874,214
Net Worth: ($4,874,214)
Earnings: ($1,494,848)
Fiscal Year-end: 12/31/22
Investment Services
N.A.I.C.S.: 523999
Alan D. Gordon *(Pres & CEO)*

ATLANTICUS HOLDINGS CORPORATION

5 Concourse Pkwy Ste 300, Atlanta, GA 30328
Tel.: (770) 828-2000

Web Site: https://www.atlanticus.com
ATLC—(NASDAQ)
Rev.: $1,046,913,000
Assets: $2,387,814,000
Liabilities: $2,062,774,000
Net Worth: $325,040,000
Earnings: $110,521,000
Emp.: 355
Fiscal Year-end: 12/31/22
Holding Company
N.A.I.C.S.: 551112
David G. Hanna *(Founder & Exec Chm)*
William R. McCamey *(CFO)*
Jeffrey A. Howard *(Pres & CEO)*

Subsidiaries:

CAR Financial Services, Inc. **(1)**
4850 Sugarloaf Pkwy Ste 211, Lawrenceville, GA 30044
Tel.: (678) 317-4364
Web Site: http://www.carfinancial.com
Automobile Financing Services
N.A.I.C.S.: 525990

ATLANTIS GLORY INC.

3773 Howard Hughes Pkwy Ste 500S, Las Vegas, NV 89169-6014
Tel.: (702) 960-0696   **NV**
Year Founded: 2016
AGLY—(OTCIQ)
Rev.: $8,333,679
Assets: $9,000
Liabilities: $71,923
Net Worth: ($62,923)
Earnings: $8,271,378
Emp.: 1
Fiscal Year-end: 12/31/22
Health Care Srvices
N.A.I.C.S.: 621498
Sau Heung Cheng *(Pres, CEO, Treas & Sec)*

ATLANTIS INTERNET GROUP CORP.

2831 St Rose Pkwy Suite 200, Henderson, NV 89052
Tel.: (702) 818-1052   **NV**
Web Site:
  https://www.atlantisgamingcorporation.com
ATIG—(OTCIQ)
Software Development Services
N.A.I.C.S.: 541511
Donald L. Bailey *(Pres & CEO)*
Linda I. Bailey *(Exec VP-Ops)*

ATLAS ENERGY GROUP, LLC

425 Houston St Ste 300, Fort Worth, TX 76102
Tel.: (412) 489-0006   **DE**
Web Site:
  http://www.atlasenergy.com
Year Founded: 2011
ATLS—(OTCIQ)
Sales Range: $1-9.9 Million
Emp.: 142
Energy Holding Company
N.A.I.C.S.: 551112
Edward E. Cohen *(CEO)*
Daniel C. Herz *(Pres)*
Jeffrey M. Slotterback *(CFO)*
Matthew Finkbeiner *(Chief Acctg Officer)*

Subsidiaries:

Atlas Resource Partners GP, LLC **(1)**
Park Pl Corporate Ctr 1 1000 Commerce Dr Ste 400, Pittsburgh, PA 15275
Web Site:
  http://www.atlasresourcepartners.com
Sales Range: $450-499.9 Million
Emp.: 640
Oil & Gas Exploration & Production Asset Management Services
N.A.I.C.S.: 523940

Jonathan Z. Cohen *(Chm)*
Edward E. Cohen *(Pres & Chm)*
Sean P. McGrath *(CFO)*
Mark D. Schumacher *(Pres)*
Freddie M. Kotek *(Sr VP-Investment Partnership Div)*
Freddie M. Kotek *(Sr VP-Investment Partnership Div)*
Matthew A. Jones *(Pres & Sr VP)*
Dave Leopold *(Sr VP-Ops)*
Jerry Dominey *(Sr VP-Exploration & Chief Geologist)*
Brad O. Eubanks *(Sr VP-Land)*

Affiliate (Domestic):

Titan Energy, LLC **(2)**
Park Pl Corporate Ctr 1 1000 Commerce Dr Ste 400, Pittsburgh, PA 15275 **(100%)**
Holding Company; Oil & Gas Exploration & Production
N.A.I.C.S.: 551112
Edward E. Cohen *(Chm)*
Jeffrey M. Slotterback *(CFO)*
Matthew J. Finkbeiner *(Chief Acctg Officer)*
Christopher Walker *(COO)*

Subsidiary (Domestic):

Anthem Securities, Inc **(3)**
311 Rouser Rd, Coraopolis, PA 15108-6801
Tel.: (412) 262-1680
Web Site: http://www.titinenergyllc.com
Emp.: 7
Investment Banking & Securities Dealing Services
N.A.I.C.S.: 523150

Joint Venture (Domestic):

Black Warrior Methane Corp. **(3)**
16243 Hwy 216, Brookwood, AL 35444-9801 **(50%)**
Tel.: (205) 554-6270
Web Site:
  http://www.blackwarriormethane.com
Sales Range: $25-49.9 Million
Emp.: 10
Methane Gas Extraction & Distr
N.A.I.C.S.: 211120
Charles Willlis *(Pres & Gen Mgr)*

Black Warrior Transmission Corp. **(3)**
16243 Hwy 216, Brookwood, AL 35444 **(50%)**
Tel.: (205) 481-6270
Sales Range: $10-24.9 Million
Emp.: 25
Transmission of Methane Gas Through Pipeline
N.A.I.C.S.: 486210
Charles Willis *(Pres)*

ATLAS ENERGY SOLUTIONS INC.

5918 W Courtyard Dr Ste 500, Austin, TX 78730
Tel.: (512) 220-1200   **DE**
Web Site: https://www.atlas.energy
Year Founded: 2022
AESI—(NYSE)
Emp.: 261
Oil & Gas Distribution Services
N.A.I.C.S.: 213112
Ben M. Brigham *(Founder & Exec Chm)*
Blake McCarthy *(CFO)*
Ben Brigham *(Founder & Exec Chm)*
John Turner *(Pres, CEO & CFO)*
Dathan Voelter *(Gen Counsel & Sec)*
Kirk Ginn *(VP-Human Resources & EHS)*
Shaam Farooq *(VP-Technology)*
Brian McConn *(Exec VP-Sales & Marketing)*
Kyle Turlington *(VP-Investor Relations)*
Chris Scholla *(COO)*
John Turner *(CEO)*

Subsidiaries:

Hi-Crush Inc. **(1)**
1330 Post Oak Blvd Ste 600, Houston, TX 77056
Tel.: (713) 980-6200

Atlas Energy Solutions Inc.—(Continued)

Web Site: http://www.hicrush.com
Rev.: $636,370,000
Assets: $1,111,137,000
Liabilities: $710,013,000
Net Worth: $401,124,000
Earnings: ($413,559,000)
Emp.: 747
Fiscal Year-end: 12/31/2019
Mineral Mining & Production Services
N.A.I.C.S.: 212390
Phil McCormick *(CFO & Principal Acctg Officer)*
Dirk Hallen *(CEO)*
Stephen White *(COO)*
William Barker *(Chief Comml Officer & Gen Counsel)*

Subsidiary (Domestic):

D&I Silica, LLC   (2)
7022 Route 6, Sheffield, PA 16347
Tel.: (814) 968-3327
Brick Stone & Related Construction Material Merchant Whlsr
N.A.I.C.S.: 423320

Subsidiary (Non-US):

FB Industries Inc.   (2)
PO Box 449, Winkler, R6W 4A6, MB, Canada
Tel.: (204) 325-7337
Web Site: http://www.fbindustriesinc.com
Industrial Equipment Whsr
N.A.I.C.S.: 423830
Henry Friesen *(Pres)*

Subsidiary (Domestic):

Hi-Crush Chambers LLC   (2)
3 Riverway Ste 1550, Houston, TX 77056
Tel.: (713) 960-4767
Sand Mining Services
N.A.I.C.S.: 212321

Hi-Crush Operating LLC   (2)
S11011 Cty Rd M, Augusta, WI 54722
Tel.: (715) 286-2079
Emp.: 40
Sand Mining Services
N.A.I.C.S.: 212321

ATLAS FINANCIAL HOLDINGS, INC.
953 American Ln 3rd Fl, Schaumburg, IL 60173
Tel.: (847) 472-6700   Ky
Web Site: https://www.atlas-fin.com
Year Founded: 2009
AFHIF—(OTCIQ)
Rev.. $4,838,000
Assets: $48,185,000
Liabilities: $73,687,000
Net Worth: ($25,502,000)
Earnings: ($5,668,000)
Emp.: 63
Fiscal Year-end: 12/31/21
Offices of Other Holding Companies
N.A.I.C.S.: 551112
Paul A. Romano *(CFO, Principal Acctg Officer & VP)*
Bruce Wayne Giles *(VP-Underwriting)*
Joseph Raymond Shugrue *(COO & VP)*
Scott David Wollney *(Chm, Pres & CEO)*

Subsidiaries.

American Insurance Acquisition Inc.   (1)
1209 Orange St, Wilmington, DE 19801
Tel.: (302) 658-7581
Insurance Related Services
N.A.I.C.S.: 524298

American Service Insurance Company   (1)
150 NW Point Blvd, Elk Grove Village, IL 60007-1015
Tel.: (847) 472-6700
Rev.: $43,000,000
Emp.: 10
Automobile Insurance
N.A.I.C.S.: 524126

ATLAS RESOURCES INTERNATIONAL, INC.
3060 W 3680 S Ste 92, West Valley City, UT 84119
Tel.: (801) 688-5194   FL
Year Founded: 1994
ALSI—(OTCIQ)
Nonwoven Fabric Product Mfr
N.A.I.C.S.: 313230

ATMOS ENERGY CORPORATION
1800 3 Lincoln Ctr 5430 LBJ Fwy, Dallas, TX 75240
Tel.: (972) 934-9227   TX
Web Site:
  https://www.atmosenergy.com
Year Founded: 1906
ATO—(NYSE)
Rev.: $4,099,690,000
Assets: $22,516,968,000
Liabilities: $5,007,693,000
Net Worth: $17,509,275,000
Earnings: $885,862,000
Emp.: 5,019
Fiscal Year-end: 09/30/23
Natural Gas Distribution Services
N.A.I.C.S.: 221210
Kim R. Cocklin *(Chm)*
Richard J. Gius *(CIO & VP)*
Christopher T. Forsythe *(CFO & Sr VP)*
Daniel M. Meziere *(Treas & VP-IR)*
John S. McDill *(Sr VP-Utility Ops)*
Kelli L. Martin *(VP-Workforce Dev)*
John Matt Robbins *(Sr VP-HR)*
J. Kevin Dobbs *(Pres-Kentucky & Mid-States Div)*
Karen E. Hartsfield *(Gen Counsel, Sec & Sr VP)*
Liz C. Beauchamp *(VP-Governmental & Pub Affairs)*
Jeff D. Martinez *(Pres-Atmos Pipeline-Texas)*
Becky Palmer *(Pres-West Texas Div)*
Jennifer G. Ries *(Pres-Louisiana Div)*
Jeffrey S. Knights *(Sr VP-Technical & Operating Svcs)*
Bart Armstrong *(Pres-Colorado & Kansas Div)*
Richard A. Mitschke *(VP-Customer Svc)*
Joel Multer *(VP-Tax)*
John Kevin Akers *(Pres & CEO)*
Richard M. Thomas *(VP-Fin Svcs)*

Subsidiaries:

ATMOS GATHERING COMPANY, LLC   (1)
13430 Northwest Fwy Ste 700, Houston, TX 77040
Tel.: (713) 316-8723
Natural Gas Distr
N.A.I.C.S.: 221210

Atmos Energy Holdings, Inc.   (1)
5420 LBJ Fwy Ste 1862, Dallas, TX 75240   **(100%)**
Tel.: (214) 206-2568
Web Site: http://www.atmosenergy.com
Sales Range: $350-399.9 Million
Emp.: 200
Holding Company
N.A.I.C.S.: 221210
Kim R. Cocklin *(Pres)*

Subsidiary (Domestic):

Atmos Energy Services, LLC   (2)
3 Lincoln Ctr Ste 160 5430 LBJ Frwy, Dallas, TX 75240   **(100%)**
Tel.: (972) 934-9227
Sales Range: $350-399.9 Million
Holding Company
N.A.I.C.S.: 221210

Atmos Pipeline and Storage, LLC   (2)
5420 LBJ Freeway, Dallas, TX 75240-2615   **(100%)**

Tel.: (972) 934-9227
Web Site: http://www.atmosenergy.com
Sales Range: $600-649.9 Million
Owner & Operator of Natural Gas Storage Facilities
N.A.I.C.S.: 221210

Atmos Power Systems, Inc.   (2)
13430 Northwest Fwy Ste 700, Houston, TX 77040   **(100%)**
Tel.: (713) 316-6622
Sales Range: $75-99.9 Million
Constructor & Operator of Electrical Power Generating Plants & Associated Facilities
N.A.I.C.S.: 221210

TRANS LOUISIANA GAS PIPELINE, INC.   (1)
1100 Poydras St Ste 3400, New Orleans, LA 70163-3400
Tel.: (504) 681-3100
Crude Petroleum Pipeline Services
N.A.I.C.S.: 486910

ATMUS FILTRATION TECHNOLOGIES INC.
26 Century Blvd, Nashville, TN 37214
Tel.: (615) 514-7339   DE
Web Site: https://www.atmus.com
Year Founded: 1958
ATMU—(NYSE)
Rev.: $1,562,100,000
Assets: $879,400,000
Liabilities: $429,900,000
Net Worth: $449,500,000
Earnings: $170,100,000
Emp.: 4,250
Fiscal Year-end: 12/31/22
Industrial & Commercial Fan & Blower & Air Purification Equipment Manufacturing
N.A.I.C.S.: 333413
Renee Swan *(Chief People Officer)*
Jack Kienzler *(CFO)*
Mark Osowick *(Chief HR Officer)*
Stephanie J. Disher *(CEO)*

ATN INTERNATIONAL, INC.
500 Cummings Ctr, Beverly, MA 01915
Tel.: (978) 619-1300   DE
Web Site: https://www.atni.com
ATNI—(NASDAQ)
Rev.: $725,745,000
Assets: $1,707,869,000
Liabilities: $1,031,040,000
Net Worth: $676,829,000
Earnings: ($5,645,000)
Emp.: 2,400
Fiscal Year-end: 12/31/22
Telecommunication Servicesb
N.A.I.C.S.: 517112
Michael T. Prior *(Exec Chm)*
Mary Mabey *(Gen Counsel, Sec & Sr VP)*
Brad W. Martin *(CEO)*
Justin Leon *(Sr VP)*

Subsidiaries:

Ahana Renewables, LLC   (1)
1 Sansome St Ste 730, San Francisco, CA 94104
Tel.: (628) 242-1386
Web Site: http://www.ahanarenewables.com
Energy Products Distr
N.A.I.C.S.: 541690
Jason Tai *(Co-Founder)*
Marvin Tien *(Co-Founder)*

Alaska Communications Systems Group, Inc.   (1)
600 E 36th Ave, Anchorage, AK 99503-6091
Tel.: (907) 297-3000
Web Site:
  http://www.alaskacommunications.com
Rev.: $240,569,000
Assets: $569,432,000
Liabilities: $403,513,000
Net Worth: $165,919,000
Earnings: ($1,073,000)
Emp.: 564

Fiscal Year-end: 12/31/2020
Telecommunications & Internet Services
N.A.I.C.S.: 517121
William H. Bishop *(Pres & CEO)*
Leonard A. Steinberg *(Sr VP-Legal, Regulatory & Govt Affairs)*
Laurie Butcher *(CFO)*
Diedre Williams *(Sr VP-Ops)*
Tiffany Hoogerhyde *(VP-Fin & Controller)*
Sandy Knechtel *(COO)*
Heather Marron *(Mgr-Corp Comm)*
Matthew McConnell *(CEO)*
Michael Prior *(Chm)*

Subsidiary (Domestic):

ACS Internet, Inc.   (2)
600 Telephone Ave, Anchorage, AK 99503
Tel.: (907) 565-2200
Sales Range: $100-124.9 Million
Provider of Computer Communications: Internet
N.A.I.C.S.: 517810

ACS Long Distance License Sub, Inc.   (2)
600 Telephone Ave, Anchorage, AK 99503
Tel.: (907) 297-3000
Sales Range: $400-449.9 Million
Telephone Communications
N.A.I.C.S.: 517121
Anand Vadapalli *(Pres & CEO)*

Alaska Communications Systems Holdings, Inc.   (2)
600 Telephone Ave, Anchorage, AK 99503
Tel.: (907) 297-3000
Telecommunication Services Provider
N.A.I.C.S.: 517121

TekMate, LLC   (2)
600 E 36th Ave, Anchorage, AK 99503
Tel.: (907) 297-3000
Web Site:
  https://www.alaskacommunications.com
Sales Range: $1-9.9 Million
Emp.: 60
Information Technology Services
N.A.I.C.S.: 541512
Shawn Fuller *(Pres & VP-Bus Dev)*

Commnet Four Corners, LLC   (1)
400 Northridge Rd Ste 1100, Atlanta, GA 30350
Tel.: (678) 338-5960
Web Site: http://www.commnetwireless.com
Emp.: 13
Wireless Telecommunication Services
N.A.I.C.S.: 518210

Commnet Wireless, LLC   (1)
400 Northridge Rd Ste 1100, Atlanta, GA 30350
Tel.: (678) 338-5960
Web Site: http://www.commnetwireless.com
Sales Range: $10-24.9 Million
Emp.: 30
Wireless Telecommunication Services
N.A.I.C.S.: 517112
John D. Champagne *(VP-Plng & Dev)*
Angela Flom *(VP-Sls Ops)*
Jeff Humiston *(Sr VP-Strategy & Comml Initiatives)*
Kevin Hayes *(VP-Sls & Distr)*
Ken Borner *(Sr VP-Network Ops)*
Leonard Westlake *(Sr VP-Network Engrg)*

Subsidiary (Domestic):

Commnet Broadband, LLC   (2)
1562 N Park St, Castle Rock, CO 80109
Tel.: (720) 733-8049
Web Site:
  https://www.commnetbroadband.com
Broadband Communication Services
N.A.I.C.S.: 517111
Tom Guthrie *(CEO)*

Subsidiary (Domestic):

Sacred Wind Enterprises, Inc.   (3)
5901 Wyoming Blvd NE, Albuquerque, NM 87109
Tel.: (505) 821-5080
Web Site: http://www.sacredwindcommunications.com

Sales Range: $1-9.9 Million
Emp.: 17
Telecommunication Servicesb
N.A.I.C.S.: 517121
John Badal (CEO)

Guyana Telephone & Telegraph Co (GT&T) (1)
55 Brickdam, Stabroek, Georgetown, Guyana (80%)
Tel.: (592) 2319541
Web Site: https://www.gtt.co.gy
Sales Range: $150-199.9 Million
Emp.: 640
Suppliers of all PublicTelecommunications Services in Guyana
N.A.I.C.S.: 517111
Cornelius B. Prior Jr. (Chm)

Mora Valley Wireless, LP (1)
400 Northridge Rd Ste 130, Atlanta, GA 30350
Tel.: (678) 338-5960
Telephone Communication Services
N.A.I.C.S.: 517121
Michael Prior (Pres)

One Communications, LLC (1)
30 Victoria Street 2nd Floor, Hamilton, HM 12, Bermuda
Tel.: (441) 7007300
Wireless Telecommunication Services
N.A.I.C.S.: 518210

ATOMERA INCORPORATED
750 University Ave Ste 280, Los Gatos, CA 95032
Tel.: (408) 442-5248   DE
Web Site: https://www.atomera.com
Year Founded: 2001
ATOM—(NASDAQ)
Rev.: $382,000
Assets: $26,729,000
Liabilities: $6,415,000
Net Worth: $20,314,000
Earnings: ($17,441,000)
Emp.: 21
Fiscal Year-end: 12/31/22
Engineered Silicon Semiconductor Products Developer & Mfr
N.A.I.C.S.: 334413
Scott A. Bibaud (Pres & CEO)
Francis B. Laurencio (CFO)
Hideki Takeuchi (VP)

ATOSSA THERAPEUTICS, INC.
10202 5th Ave NE Ste 200, Seattle, WA 98125
Tel.: (206) 588-0256   DE
Web Site:
   https://www.atossatherapeutics.com
Year Founded: 2009
ATOS—(NASDAQ)
Rev.: $877,000
Assets: $123,532,000
Liabilities: $5,568,000
Net Worth: $117,964,000
Earnings: ($26,960,000)
Emp.: 9
Fiscal Year-end: 12/31/22
Breast Cancer Pharmaceuticals Developer & Mfr
N.A.I.C.S.: 325412
Steven C. Quay (Chm, Pres & CEO)
Shu-Chih Chen (Founder)
B. Heather Fraser (VP-Clinical, Regulatory, and CMC)
Delly Behen (VP-Admin & HR)
Eric Van Zanten (VP)
Heather Rees (CFO & Principal Acctg Officer)

ATRECA, INC.
835 Industrial Rd Ste 400, San Carlos, CA 94070
Tel.: (650) 595-2595   DE
Web Site: https://www.atreca.com
Year Founded: 2010
BCEL—(NASDAQ)
Rev.: $817,000
Assets: $155,030,000

Liabilities: $76,624,000
Net Worth: $78,406,000
Earnings: ($97,157,000)
Emp.: 90
Fiscal Year-end: 12/31/22
Biotechnology Research & Development Services
N.A.I.C.S.: 541714
John A. Orwin (Pres, CEO & Principal Fin Officer)
Brian G. Atwood (Chm)
Tito A. Serafini (Co-Founder)
Jonathan Benjamin (Sr VP-Clinical Res)
Guy Cavet (Co-Founder)
Daniel Emerling (Sr VP-Res)
William H. Robinson (Co-Founder)
Courtney Phillips (Gen Counsel & Sec)
Rick Ruiz (Principal Acctg Officer & VP-Fin)

ATRICURE, INC.
7555 Innovation Way, Mason, OH 45040
Tel.: (513) 755-4100   DE
Web Site: https://www.atricure.com
Year Founded: 2000
ATRC—(NASDAQ)
Rev.: $399,245,000
Assets: $613,932,000
Liabilities: $147,764,000
Net Worth: $466,168,000
Earnings: ($30,438,000)
Emp.: 1,200
Fiscal Year-end: 12/31/23
Medical Device Mfr & Developer
N.A.I.C.S.: 339112
Vinayak Doraiswamy (Chief Scientific Officer)
Douglas J. Seith (COO)
Karl Dahlquist (Chief Legal Officer)
Justin Noznesky (Chief Mktg & Strategy Officer)
Valerie Storch-Willhaus (VP-Comm & Corp Mktg)
Michael H. Carrel (Pres & CEO)
Angela L. Wirick (CFO)
Deborah Yount (Chief HR Officer)

Subsidiaries:

AtriCure Europe, B.V. (1)
De entree 260, 1101 EE, Amsterdam, Netherlands
Tel.: (31) 207005560
Web Site: http://www.atricure.com
Sales Range: $100-124.9 Million
Medical & Surgical Device Mfr
N.A.I.C.S.: 339112

AtriCure Hong Kong Limited, (1)
Level 16 The Hong Kong Club Building 3A Chater Road, Central, China (Hong Kong)
Tel.: (852) 39748573
Surgical Equipment Distr
N.A.I.C.S.: 423450

Endoscopic Technologies, LLC (1)
31308 Via Colinas Unit 104, Westlake Village, CA 91362
Tel.: (818) 865-0270
Web Site: https://www.endoscopic.us
Surgical & Medical Instrument Mfr
N.A.I.C.S.: 339112

Ncontact Surgical Inc. (1)
1001 Aviation Pkwy Ste 400, Morrisville, NC 27560-9135
Tel.: (919) 466-9810
Web Site: http://www.ncontact.us
Medical, Dental & Hospital Equipment & Supplies Merchant Whslr
N.A.I.C.S.: 423450

SentreHEART, Inc. (1)
3875 Hopyard Rd 160 Unit, 94588, Pleasanton, CA
Tel.: (650) 354-1200
Web Site: http://www.sentreheart.com
Surgical Device Mfr
N.A.I.C.S.: 339112

Robert Strasser (VP-Operations)
Greg Fung (VP-Research & Development)
Russell A. Seiber (Pres, CEO & Founder)
Richard M. Ferrari (Chm)
Chris Lowe (CFO)
Pam Simons (VP-Clinical Affairs)

ATWEC TECHNOLOGIES, INC.
3147 Players Club Pkwy, Memphis, TN 38125
Tel.: (901) 289-2621   NV
Web Site: https://www.atwec.com
Year Founded: 2000
ATWT—(OTCIQ)
Security Systems Services (except Locksmiths)
N.A.I.C.S.: 561621
Alex T. Wiley (Pres & CEO)
George A. Brown (Sec)
Tyrone Dunn (Dir-Sls & Mktg)
Bishop David Hall (Treas)

ATYR PHARMA, INC.
10240 Sorrento Vly Rd Ste 300, San Diego, CA 92121
Tel.: (858) 731-8389   DE
Web Site:
   https://www.atyrpharma.com
Year Founded: 2005
ATYR—(NASDAQ)
Rev.: $10,386,000
Assets: $95,786,000
Liabilities: $24,502,000
Net Worth: $71,284,000
Earnings: ($45,338,000)
Emp.: 65
Fiscal Year-end: 12/31/22
Pharmaceuticals Mfr
N.A.I.C.S.: 325412
Paul R. Schimmel (Co-Founder)
Andrea Cubitt (VP-External Scientific Alliances & Intellectual Property)
Sanjay S. Shukla (Pres & CEO)
Jill M. Broadfoot (CFO)
Peter Villiger (VP-Corp Dev)
Leslie Nangle (VP-Res)
Nancy Denyes (Gen Counsel)
Robert W. Ashworth (VP)
Danielle Campbell (VP)

AUBURN BANCORP, INC.
256 Ct St, Auburn, ME 04212
Tel.: (207) 782-6871
Web Site:
   https://www.auburnsavings.com
ABBB—(OTCIQ)
Rev.: $4,447,861
Assets: $88,702,837
Liabilities: $80,881,682
Net Worth: $7,821,155
Earnings: $289,913
Emp.: 16
Fiscal Year-end: 06/30/20
Offices of Bank Holding Companies
N.A.I.C.S.: 551111
William C. Tracy (Pres & CEO)
Martha L. Adams (Co-COO & Exec VP)
J. Thomas (Vice Chm)
Heather A. Hunter (Chm)
Melissa M. Record (Officer-BSA & Compliance & VP)
David J. Krause (CFO & Exec VP)
Margaret E. Collamorecampbell (Co-COO & Sr VP)
Robert A. Michaud (Officer-Loan & VP)
Brian M. Judkins (Officer-Loan & VP)
Audrey L. Patterson (Officer-Retail Banking & Asst VP)
Brian N. Casey (Asst VP)

Subsidiaries:

Auburn Savings Bank (1)
256 Court St, Auburn, ME 04210
Tel.: (207) 782-6871
Web Site: http://www.auburnsavings.com

Sales Range: $25-49.9 Million
Emp.: 17
Banking Services
N.A.I.C.S.: 522110
William C. Tracy (Exec VP & Sr Officer-Loan)
Martha L. Adams (COO & Exec VP)

AUBURN NATIONAL BANCORPORATION, INC.
100 N Gay St, Auburn, AL 36830
Tel.: (334) 821-9200   DE
Web Site:
   https://www.auburnbank.com
Year Founded: 1907
AUBN—(NASDAQ)
Rev.: $36,051,000
Assets: $1,023,888,000
Liabilities: $955,847,000
Net Worth: $68,041,000
Earnings: $10,346,000
Emp.: 150
Fiscal Year-end: 12/31/22
Bank Holding Company
N.A.I.C.S.: 551111
C. Wayne Alderman (Sec)
David A. Hedges (Pres & CEO)
William James Walker IV (CFO, Chief Acctg Officer & Sr VP)
Marla Kickliter (Sr VP-Compliance & Auditor-Internal-AuburnBank)
Shannon S. O'Donnell (Chief Risk Officer & Sr VP-Credit Admin-AuburnBank)
Eddie C. Smith (Pres-City-Opelika & Sr VP-AuburnBank)
Scottie Arnold (VP-Admin-Deposit Products & Svcs-AuburnBank)
Suzanne Gibson (Officer-Portfolio Mgmt & Asst VP-AuburnBank)
Jerry Siegel (CTO & Sr VP-IT-AuburnBank)

Subsidiaries:

AuburnBank (1)
100 N Gay St, Auburn, AL 36830
Tel.: (334) 821-9200
Web Site: http://www.auburnbank.com
Sales Range: $100-124.9 Million
Commercial Bank
N.A.I.C.S.: 522110
C. Wayne Alderman (Sec)
David A. Hedges (Pres & CEO)
William James Walker IV (CFO, Chief Acctg Officer & Sr VP)
Terrell E. Bishop (Sr VP)
James E. Dulaney (Sr VP-Bus Dev & Mktg)
William Thomas Johnson (Sr VP)
Marla Kickliter (Sr VP-Compliance & Auditor)
Shannon S. O'Donnell (Chief Risk Officer & Sr VP-Credit Admin)
Bruce Emfinger (VP-Comml & Consumers Loans-Valley Branch)
Christy A. Fogle (Officer-CRA & VP-Credit Admin)
Cyndee Redmond (VP-Bus Sys Analysis)
David Warren (Sr VP-Comml & Consumer Loans)
Ginnie Y. Lunsford (VP-Loan Ops)
James Pack (VP-Fin Reporting)
Jeff Stanfield (VP-Comml & Consumer Loans-Opelika Branch)
Joanna Watts (Asst VP-IT & IS)
Kris W. Blackmon (Chief Investment Officer, VP & Mgr-Asset & Liability)
Laura Carrington (Officer-HR & VP)
Marcia Otwell (VP-Admin & Shareholder Rels)
Pamela Meigs Fuller (Sr VP-Ops)
Patty Allen (VP-Comml & Consumer Loans-Opelika Branch)
April Herring (VP & Mgr-Mortgage Div)
Karen Bence (Officer-OFAC & Asst VP-Bank Security & BSA)
Woody Odom (Asst VP-IT & IS)
Cindy Royster (Asst VP-Branch Admin)
Rhonda Sanders (Officer-Deposit Ops & Customer Identification Program)
Leigh Ann Thompson (Officer-Data Analytics)
Latoya Watts (Officer-Trng)

Auburn National Bancorporation, Inc.—(Continued)

Vickie Garner *(VP-Loan Ops)*
Lolly Steiner *(Dir-Community Rels & Mktg)*
Robert Lawrence Smith Jr. *(Chief Lending Officer & Sr VP)*
S. Mark Bridges Sr. *(Sr VP-Comml & Consumer Loans)*

AUDACY, INC.

2400 Market St 4th Fl, Philadelphia, PA 19103
Tel.: (610) 660-5610   **PA**
Web Site: https://www.audacyinc.com
Year Founded: 1968
AUD—(NYSE)
Rev.: $1,253,664,000
Assets: $3,284,893,000
Liabilities: $2,764,274,000
Net Worth: $520,619,000
Earnings: ($140,671,000)
Emp.: 3,539
Fiscal Year-end: 12/31/22
Holding Company; Radio Broadcasting Stations Owner & Operator
N.A.I.C.S.: 551112
Joseph M. Field *(Founder)*
David J. Field *(Chm, Pres & CEO)*
Richard J. Schmaeling *(CFO & Exec VP)*
Michael Dee *(Pres-Sports)*
Paul Suchman *(CMO)*
Elizabeth Bramowski *(Chief Acctg Officer & Controller)*
Susan Larkin *(COO)*
Idil Cakim *(Sr VP-Res & Insights)*
Ashok Sinha *(Head-Corp Comm & PR)*
Brian Benedik *(Chief Revenue Officer)*
Andrew P. Sutor IV *(Gen Counsel & Exec VP)*

Subsidiaries:

Entercom Radio, LLC (1)
2400 Market St 4th Fl, Philadelphia, PA 19103
Tel.: (610) 660-5610
Web Site: https://audacyinc.com
Radio Broadcasting Stations Operator
N.A.I.C.S.: 516210

Subsidiary (Domestic):

Entercom Boston, LLC (2)
20 Guest St 3rd Fl, Boston, MA 02135-2088
Tel.: (617) 779-5800
Web Site: http://www.entercom.com
Emp.: 300
Radio Broadcasting Stations
N.A.I.C.S.: 516110

Entercom Buffalo, LLC (2)
500 Corporate Pkwy Ste 200, Buffalo, NY 14226
Tel.: (716) 843-0600
Web Site: http://www.entercombuffalo.com
Radio Broadcasting Stations
N.A.I.C.S.: 516110
J. Timothy Holly *(Sr VP & Mgr-Market)*

Entercom Colorado, LLC (2)
4700 S Syracuse St Ste 1050, Denver, CO 80237
Tel.: (303) 967-2700
Web Site: http://alice1059.radio.com
Commercial Radio Broadcasting Services
N.A.I.C.S.: 516210

Unit (Domestic):

KQKS-FM (3)
4700 S Syracuse St Ste 1050, Denver, CO 80237
Tel.: (303) 967-2700
Web Site: http://www.ks1075.com
Sales Range: $10-24.9 Million
Emp.: 30
Radio Stations
N.A.I.C.S.: 516110

KYGO-FM (3)
7800 E Orchard Rd, Greenwood Village, CO 80111
Tel.: (303) 321-0950

Web Site: https://www.kygo.com
Sales Range: $75-99.9 Million
Radio Stations
N.A.I.C.S.: 516110

Subsidiary (Domestic):

Entercom Connecticut, LLC (2)
10 Executive Dr, Farmington, CT 06032
Tel.: (860) 522-9842
Web Site: http://wtic.radio.com
Commercial Radio Broadcasting Services
N.A.I.C.S.: 516210

Entercom Denver, LLC (2)
4700 S Syracuse St Ste 1050, Denver, CO 80237
Tel.: (303) 967-2700
Web Site: http://www.entercomdenver.com
Emp.: 100
Radio Broadcasting Stations
N.A.I.C.S.: 516110

Entercom Florida, LLC (2)
3600 NW 43rd St Ste B, Gainesville, FL 32606
Tel.: (352) 377-0985
Web Site: http://ktk985.radio.com
Commercial Radio Broadcasting Services
N.A.I.C.S.: 516210

Entercom Gainesville, LLC (2)
3600 NW 43rd St Bldg B, Gainesville, FL 32606
Tel.: (352) 377-0985
Web Site: http://www.entercom.com
Sales Range: $10-24.9 Million
Emp.: 30
Radio Broadcasting Stations
N.A.I.C.S.: 516110

Entercom Georgia, LLC (2)
1201 Peachtree St NE Ste 800, Atlanta, GA 30361
Tel.: (404) 898-8900
Web Site: http://star941atlanta.radio.com
Commercial Radio Broadcasting Services
N.A.I.C.S.: 516210

Entercom Greensboro, LLC (2)
7819 National Service Rd Ste 401, Greensboro, NC 27409
Tel.: (336) 605-5200
Web Site: http://www.entercom.com
Radio Broadcasting Stations
N.A.I.C.S.: 516110

Entercom Greenville, LLC (2)
25 Garlington Rd, Greenville, SC 29615
Tel.: (864) 271-9200
Web Site: http://entercom.com
Radio Broadcasting Stations
N.A.I.C.S.: 516110

Entercom Illinois, LLC (2)
180 N Stetson Ave Ste 1000, Chicago, IL 60601
Tel.: (312) 644-6767
Web Site: http://670thescore.radio.com
Commercial Radio Broadcasting Services
N.A.I.C.S.: 516210

Entercom Indiana, LLC (2)
9245 N Meridian St Ste 300, Indianapolis, IN 46260
Tel.: (317) 816-4000
Web Site: http://www.wfms.com
Radio Broadcasting Station Services
N.A.I.C.S.: 516110

Entercom Kansas City, LLC (2)
7000 Squibb Rd 2nd Fl, Kansas City, MO 66202
Tel.: (913) 744-3600
Web Site: http://www.entercom.com
Radio Broadcasting Stations
N.A.I.C.S.: 516110
Dave Albert *(Mng Dir)*

Entercom License, LLC (2)
401 E City Ave Ste 809, Bala Cynwyd, PA 19004
Tel.: (610) 660-5610
Radio Broadcasting Services
N.A.I.C.S.: 516210
David Field *(Pres)*

Entercom Louisiana, LLC (2)
400 Poydras St 8th Fl, New Orleans, LA 70130
Tel.: (504) 526-3000

Web Site: http://b97.radio.com
Commercial Radio Broadcasting Services
N.A.I.C.S.: 516210

Entercom Madison, LLC (2)
7601 Ganser Way, Madison, WI 53719
Tel.: (608) 826-0077
Web Site: http://www.entercom.com
Sales Range: $10-24.9 Million
Emp.: 25
Radio Broadcasting Stations
N.A.I.C.S.: 516110

Entercom Maryland, LLC (2)
1423 Clarkview Rd Ste 100, Baltimore, MD 21209
Tel.: (410) 825-1065
Web Site: http://mix1065baltimore.radio.com
Commercial Radio Broadcasting Services
N.A.I.C.S.: 516210

Entercom Media Corp. (2)
1271 Avenue of the Americas Fl 44, New York, NY 10020
Tel.: (212) 649-9600
Holding Company; Radio Broadcasting Services
N.A.I.C.S.: 551112
Kristin Kelly *(Sr Acct Exec)*

Unit (Domestic):

WLIF-FM (3)
1423 Clarkview Rd Ste 100, Baltimore, MD 21209
Tel.: (410) 825-1000
Web Site: http://www.1019litefm.com
Radio Broadcasting Services
N.A.I.C.S.: 516110
Hal Martin *(Dir-Mktg)*

WQSR-FM (3)
1 W Pennsylvania Ave Ste 200, Towson, MD 21204
Tel.: (410) 366-7600
Web Site: https://1027jackfm.iheart.com
Radio Broadcasting Services
N.A.I.C.S.: 516110

WVEE-FM (3)
1201 Peachtree St Ste 800, Atlanta, GA 30361
Tel.: (404) 898-8900
Web Site: http://www.v-103.com
Radio Broadcasting Services
N.A.I.C.S.: 516110
Reggie Rouse *(Program Dir)*

WXYT-FM (3)
26455 American Dr, Southfield, MI 48034
Tel.: (248) 327-2900
Web Site: http://971theticket.radio.com
Radio Broadcasting Stations
N.A.I.C.S.: 516110

WZLX-FM (3)
1 Cabot Rd Ste 320, Medford, MA 02155
Tel.: (781) 663-2500
Web Site: https://wzlx.iheart.com
Radio Broadcasting Services
N.A.I.C.S.: 516110

Subsidiary (Domestic):

Entercom Miami, LLC (2)
8300 NE 2nd Ave Ste 200, Miami, FL 33169
Tel.: (305) 521-5100
Radio Broadcasting Services
N.A.I.C.S.: 516110
Doug Abernethy *(VP & Gen Mgr)*

Entercom Michigan, LLC (2)
26455 American Dr, Southfield, MI 48034
Tel.: (248) 327-2900
Web Site: http://womc.radio.com
Commercial Radio Broadcasting Services
N.A.I.C.S.: 516210

Entercom Milwaukee, LLC (2)
11800 W Grange Ave, Hales Corners, WI 53130
Tel.: (414) 448-2140
Web Site: http://www.milwaukeemarketingresults.com
Emp.: 30
Radio Broadcasting Stations
N.A.I.C.S.: 516110

Entercom Minnesota, LLC (2)
625 2nd Ave S, Minneapolis, MN 55402

Tel.: (612) 370-0611
Web Site: http://1029thewolf.radio.com
Commercial Radio Broadcasting Services
N.A.I.C.S.: 516210

Entercom Nevada, LLC (2)
7255 S Tenaya Way Ste 100, Las Vegas, NV 89113
Tel.: (702) 889-5100
Web Site: http://kluc.radio.com
Commercial Radio Broadcasting Services
N.A.I.C.S.: 516210

Entercom New Orleans, LLC (2)
400 Poydras St 8th Fl, New Orleans, LA 70130
Tel.: (504) 593-6376
Web Site: http://www.entercom.com
Radio Broadcasting Stations
N.A.I.C.S.: 516110

Entercom Norfolk, LLC (2)
236 Clearfield Ave Ste 206, Virginia Beach, VA 23462
Tel.: (757) 497-2000
Web Site: http://www.entercom.com
Radio Broadcasting Stations
N.A.I.C.S.: 516110

Entercom North Carolina, LLC (2)
7819 National Service Rd Ste 401, Greensboro, NC 27409-9401
Tel.: (336) 605-5200
Radio Broadcasting Network Services
N.A.I.C.S.: 516210

Entercom Ohio, LLC (2)
1041 Huron Rd, Cleveland, OH 44115
Tel.: (216) 578-1021
Web Site: http://star102cleveland.radio.com
Commercial Radio Broadcasting Services
N.A.I.C.S.: 516210

Entercom Oregon, LLC (2)
700 SW Bancroft St, Portland, OR 97239
Tel.: (503) 250-1080
Web Site: http://1080thefan.radio.com
Commercial Radio Broadcasting Services
N.A.I.C.S.: 516210

Entercom Pennsylvania, LLC (2)
305 Hwy 315, Pittston, PA 18640
Tel.: (570) 883-9800
Web Site: http://froggy101.radio.com
Commercial Radio Broadcasting Services
N.A.I.C.S.: 516210

Entercom Portland, LLC (2)
700 SW Bancroft St, Portland, OR 97239
Tel.: (503) 535-9100
Web Site: http://www.entercomportland.com
Emp.: 125
Radio Broadcasting Services
N.A.I.C.S.: 516210

Entercom Rochester, LLC (2)
High Falls Studios 70 Commercial St, Rochester, NY 14614-1010
Tel.: (585) 423-2900
Web Site: http://www.entercomrochester.com
Radio Broadcasting Stations
N.A.I.C.S.: 516110

Entercom San Diego, LLC (2)
1615 Murray Canyon Rd Ste 710, San Diego, CA 92108
Tel.: (619) 291-9797
Radio Broadcasting Stations
N.A.I.C.S.: 516110
Karyn Cerulli *(Sr VP & Dir-Sls)*
Jeff Federman *(Pres)*

Entercom Seattle, LLC (2)
800 5th Ave Ste 1400, Seattle, WA 98104
Tel.: (206) 577-8600
Web Site: http://www.entercomseattle.com
Emp.: 150
Radio Broadcasting Stations
N.A.I.C.S.: 516110

Entercom South Carolina, LLC (2)
25 Garlington Rd, Greenville, SC 29615
Tel.: (864) 271-9200
Web Site: http://933theplanetrocks.radio.com
Commercial Radio Broadcasting Services
N.A.I.C.S.: 516210

Entercom Texas, LLC (2)

24 Greenway Plz Ste 1900, Houston, TX
77046
Tel.: (713) 881-5100
Web Site: http://mix965houston.radio.com
Commercial Radio Broadcasting Services
N.A.I.C.S.: 516210

Entercom Washington DC, LLC (2)
1015 Half St SE Ste 200, Washington, DC
20003
Tel.: (202) 479-9227
Web Site: http://elzolradio.radio.com
Commercial Radio Broadcasting Services
N.A.I.C.S.: 516210

Entercom Washington, LLC (2)
800 5th Ave Ste 1400, Seattle, WA 98104-
3176
Tel.: (206) 577-8600
Web Site: http://1077theend.radio.com
Commercial Radio Broadcasting Services
N.A.I.C.S.: 516210

Entercom Wichita, LLC (2)
9111 E Douglas Ste 130, Wichita, KS
67207
Tel.: (316) 685-2121
Web Site: http://www.entercom.com
Emp.: 55
Radio Broadcasting Stations
N.A.I.C.S.: 516110
Jackie Wise (Sr VP & Gen Mgr)

Entercom Wilkes-Barre Scranton,
LLC (2)
305 Hwy 315, Pittston, PA 18640
Tel.: (570) 883-9850
Web Site: http://www.entercom.com
Radio Broadcasting Stations
N.A.I.C.S.: 516110

Entercom Wisconsin, LLC (2)
11800 W Grange Ave, Hales Corners, WI
53130
Tel.: (414) 529-1250
Web Site: http://1037kissfm.radio.com
Commercial Radio Broadcasting Services
N.A.I.C.S.: 516210

Lincoln Financial Media Company of
Georgia (2)
210 Interstate N Cir Ste 600, Atlanta, GA
30326
Tel.: (404) 261-2970
Web Site: http://www.star94.com
Sales Range: $10-24.9 Million
Emp.: 100
Radio Broadcasting Stations
N.A.I.C.S.: 516110

AUDDIA INC.
2100 Central Ave Ste 200, Boulder,
CO 80301
Tel.: (303) 219-9771　　　DE
Web Site: https://www.auddia.com
Year Founded: 2012
AUUD—(NASDAQ)
Rev.: $1
Assets: $6,111,526
Liabilities: $2,261,443
Net Worth: $3,850,083
Earnings: ($6,897,446)
Emp.: 15
Fiscal Year-end: 12/31/22
Internet Radio Broadcasting Services
N.A.I.C.S.: 516210
John E. Mahoney (CFO)
Jeffrey Thramann (Founder & Exec
Chm)
Michael Lawless (CEO)
Theo Romeo (CMO)
Kirin Smith (Pres)

AUDIOEYE, INC.
5210 E Williams Cir Ste 750, Tucson,
AZ 85711　　　DE
Web Site: https://www.audioeye.com
Year Founded: 2003
AEYE—(NASDAQ)
Rev.: $29,913,000
Assets: $24,428,000
Liabilities: $13,839,000
Net Worth: $10,589,000
Earnings: ($10,433,000)

Emp.: 120
Fiscal Year-end: 12/31/22
Internet Content Publication & Distri-
bution Software
N.A.I.C.S.: 513210
Carr Bettis (Exec Chm)
David Moradi (CEO)
Kelly Georgevich (CFO & Principal
Acctg Officer)
Mase Graye (CTO)
Mikel Chertudi (Chief Revenue Offi-
cer)

AULT ALLIANCE, INC.
11411 Sern Highlands Pkwy Ste 240,
Las Vegas, NV 89141
Tel.: (949) 444-5464　　　DE
Web Site: https://ault.com
Year Founded: 1969
AULT—(NYSEAMEX)
Rev.: $134,334,000
Assets: $561,514,000
Liabilities: $337,526,000
Net Worth: $223,988,000
Earnings: ($181,816,000)
Emp.: 598
Fiscal Year-end: 12/31/22
Offices of Other Holding Companies
N.A.I.C.S.: 551112
Robert O. Smith (Bd of Dirs, Bd of
Dirs, Board of Directors, Chm, Pres &
CEO)
William B. Horne (CEO)
Milton C. Ault III (Exec Chm)
Douglas Gintz (CTO & Dir-Global
Tech Implementation)
Milton C. Ault III (Chm)
Henry C. W. Nisser (Pres & Gen
Counsel)
Kenneth S. Cragun (CFO)

Subsidiaries:

Gresham Worldwide, Inc. (1)
7272 E Indian School Rd Ste 540, Scotts-
dale, AZ 85251
Tel.: (925) 328-4650
Web Site: https://greshamworldwide.com
Rev.: $9,027,000
Assets: $8,055,000
Liabilities: $4,330,000
Net Worth: $3,725,000
Earnings: ($2,768,000)
Emp.: 45
Fiscal Year-end: 03/26/2022
Instrument Manufacturing for Measuring &
Testing Electricity & Electrical Signals
N.A.I.C.S.: 334515

Subsidiary (Non-US):

Enertec Systems 2001 Ltd. (2)
Hanapach 8, Instrudual Area 5, 50030,
Karmiel, Israel
Tel.: (972) 49585680
Web Site: http://www.enertec.co.il
Electronic Products Mfr
N.A.I.C.S.: 334419
Zvi Avni (CEO)
Nissim Ovadia (CFO)
Avi Saad (Head-Medical Division)
Amos Kohn (Chm)
Ran Sherman (EVP-Strategic Bus Dev)

Division (Domestic):

Giga-tronics Instruments (2)
4650 Norris Canyon Rd, San Ramon, CA
94583-1320　　　(100%)
Tel.: (925) 328-4650
Web Site: http://www.gigatronics.com
Sales Range: $10-24.9 Million
Provider of Microwave Signal Generator &
Microwave Power Meters
N.A.I.C.S.: 334515

Subsidiary (Domestic):

Gresham Holdings, Inc. (2)
7272 E Indian School Rd Ste 540, Scotts-
dale, AZ 85251
Web Site: https://greshamworldwide.com
Radar & Missile Guidance Mfr
N.A.I.C.S.: 336419

Subsidiary (Non-US):

Gresham Power Electronics
Limited (3)
Telford Road, Salisbury, SP2 7PH, Walt-
shire, United Kingdom
Tel.: (44) 1722413060
Web Site: http://www.greshampower.com
Sales Range: $10-24.9 Million
Designs & Manufactures Power Supplies
N.A.I.C.S.: 334419
Alison Smithson (Controller-Fin & Mgr-PSU
Comml Bus)
Karen Jay (Dir-Ops & Defence Bus)
Steve Willis (Dir-Sls & Mktg)

Subsidiary (Domestic):

Microphase Corporation (2)
100 Trap Falls Rd Ext, Shelton, CT 06484-
4655
Tel.: (203) 866-8000
Web Site: https://www.microphase.com
Sales Range: $1-9.9 Million
Filter & Microwave Components Designers
& Mfr
N.A.I.C.S.: 334220
Nedt F. Ergul (Founder & Pres)

Subsidiary (Non-US):

Relec Electronics Ltd. (2)
Animal House Justin Business Park Sand-
ford Lane, Wareham, BH20 4DY, Dorset,
United Kingdom
Tel.: (44) 1929555700
Web Site: http://www.relec.co.uk
Display Product Mfr
N.A.I.C.S.: 337215
Peter Lappin (Mng Dir)
Jonathan Smith (Acct Mgr)
Mathew Rehm (Acct Mgr)
John Stone (Sls Dir)
Neil Pain (Acct Mgr)

TurnOnGreen, Inc. (1)
1421 McCarthy Blvd, Milpitas, CA 95035
Tel.: (510) 657-2635
Web Site: https://turnongreen.com
Holding Company
N.A.I.C.S.: 551112
Douglas Gintz (CTO)
Amos Kohn (Chm & CEO)
Marcus Charuvastra (Pres & Chief Revenue
Officer)

Subsidiary (Domestic):

Digital Power Corporation (2)
1421 McCarthy Blvd, Milpitas, CA 95035
Tel.: (510) 657-2635
Web Site: http://www.digipwr.com
Power Circuit Equipment Mfr
N.A.I.C.S.: 335999
Amos Kohn (Pres & CEO)
Olga Chupric (Controller-Fin)

AULT DISRUPTIVE TECH-
NOLOGIES CORPORATION
11411 Sern Highlands Pkwy Ste 240,
Las Vegas, NV 89141
Tel.: (949) 444-5464　　　DE
Web Site: https://aultdisruptive.com
Year Founded: 2021
ADRT—(NYSEAMEX)
Rev.: $1,675,581
Assets: $118,829,028
Liabilities: $121,796,136
Net Worth: ($2,967,108)
Earnings: ($128,392)
Emp.: 5
Fiscal Year-end: 12/31/22
Miscellaneous Financial Investment
Activities
N.A.I.C.S.: 523999
William B. Horne (CEO)
Henry C. W. Nisser (Pres & Gen
Counsel)
Kenneth S. Cragun (CFO)
David Katzoff (VP-Finance)
Milton C. Ault III (Chm)

AURA BIOSCIENCES, INC.
80 Guest St 5th Fl, Boston, MA
02135

Tel.: (603) 315-0618
Web Site:
　　https://www.aurabiosciences.com
AURA—(NASDAQ)
Rev.: $1,864,000
Assets: $223,935,000
Liabilities: $28,352,000
Net Worth: $195,583,000
Earnings: ($58,763,000)
Emp.: 70
Fiscal Year-end: 12/31/22
Research & Development in Biotech-
nology (except Nanobiotechnology)
N.A.I.C.S.: 541714
Mark Plavsic (CTO)
Julie Feder (CFO)
Kylie Reynolds (VP-Fin)
Elisabeth de los Pinos (Bd of Dirs,
Founder, Pres & CEO)

AURA SYSTEMS, INC.
20431 N Sea Cir, Lake Forest, CA
92630
Tel.: (310) 643-5300　　　DE
Web Site:
　　https://www.aurasystems.com
Year Founded: 1987
AUSI—(OTCIQ)
Rev.: $100,406
Assets: $2,194,515
Liabilities: $23,414,050
Net Worth: ($21,219,535)
Earnings: ($3,991,863)
Emp.: 10
Fiscal Year-end: 02/28/22
Motor Vehicle Electrical & Electronic
Equipment Manufacturing
N.A.I.C.S.: 336320
Robert T. Lempert (Sec)
Cipora Lavut (Chm & Pres)

AURASOURCE, INC.
1490 S Price Rd Ste 210, Chandler,
AZ 85286
Tel.: (480) 553-1778　　　NV
Web Site:
　　https://www.aurasourceinc.com
Year Founded: 1990
ARAO—(OTCIQ)
Rev.: $120,500
Assets: $115,541
Liabilities: $6,536,266
Net Worth: ($6,420,725)
Earnings: ($1,023,680)
Emp.: 3
Fiscal Year-end: 03/31/23
Support Activities for Coal Mining
N.A.I.C.S.: 213113
Philip Liu (Chm, Pres & CEO)
Eric Stoppenhagen (CFO & Treas)

AURI, INC.
1712 Pioneer Ave Ste 500, Chey-
enne, WY 82001
Tel.: (214) 418-6940　　　WY
Web Site: https://auritoken.io
AURI—(OTCIQ)
Holding Company; Investment Ser-
vices
N.A.I.C.S.: 551112
Edward I. Vakser (Chm, CEO & Sec)

Subsidiaries:

SUTIMCo International, Inc. (1)
1712 Pioneer Ave, Cheyenne, WY 82001
Tel.: (214) 418-6940
Research & Development Services
N.A.I.C.S.: 541714
Edward I. Vakser (Pres & CEO)

AURORA INNOVATION, INC.
280 N Bernardo Ave, Mountain View,
CA 94043　　　DE
Web Site: https://www.aurora.tech
Year Founded: 2017

Aurora Innovation, Inc.—(Continued)

AUR—(NASDAQ)
Rev.: $68,000,000
Assets: $2,001,000,000
Liabilities: $217,000,000
Net Worth: $1,784,000,000
Earnings: ($1,723,000,000)
Emp.: 1,700
Fiscal Year-end: 12/31/22
Information Technology Services
N.A.I.C.S.: 541512
David Maday (CFO & Principal Acctg Officer)
Chris Urmson (Founder, Chm & CEO)
Richard Tame (CTO)
Nolan Shenai (Gen Counsel)

AURORA SPINE CORPORATION
1930 Palomar Point Way Ste 103, Carlsbad, CA 92008
Tel.: (760) 424-2004
Web Site: https://www.aurora-spine.com
Year Founded: 2012
ASG—(TSXV)
Rev.: $8,645,621
Assets: $7,155,149
Liabilities: $3,873,844
Net Worth: $3,281,305
Earnings: ($232,085)
Fiscal Year-end: 12/31/20
Medical Device Mfr
N.A.I.C.S.: 339112
Trent J. Northcutt (Co/Co-Founder, CEO & CEO)
Laszlo Garamszegi (Co-Founder & CTO)
David Meyer (Chief Legal Officer & VP)
David Aubrey Rosenkrantz (Chm)
Chad Clouse (CFO)

AURVANDIL ACQUISITION CORP.
1 Technology Dr Ste B117, Irvine, CA 92618
Tel.: (949) 473-4031   DE
Year Founded: 2021
AURVU—(NASDAQ)
Investment Services
N.A.I.C.S.: 523999
Greg Horowitt (Chief Strategy Officer)
J. Rune Sandell (CFO)
Robert A. Moody II (CEO)

AURYN MINING CORPORATION
9449 Priority Way W Dr Ste 140, Indianapolis, IN 46240
Tel.: (317) 204-2020   NV
Web Site:
https://www.aurynminingcorp.com
Year Founded: 1999
AUMC—(OTCIQ)
Gold, Silver & Copper Mining
N.A.I.C.S.: 212220
Maurizio Cordova (Chm & CEO)

AUSCRETE CORPORATION
49 John Day Dam Rd, Goldendale, WA 98620
Tel.: (509) 261-2525   WY
Web Site:
https://www.auscretehomes.com
Year Founded: 2009
ASCK—(OTCIQ)
Rev.: $89,847
Assets: $75,208
Liabilities: $1,708,608
Net Worth: ($1,633,400)
Earnings: ($257,348)
Emp.: 2
Fiscal Year-end: 12/31/22

Pre-Cast Wall, Roof & Interior Panels Mfr & Supplier
N.A.I.C.S.: 327390
A. John Sprovieri (Founder, Pres & CEO)
Michael Young (CFO & VP-Ops)

AUSTRALIS CAPITAL, INC.
8020 S Rainbow Blvd Ste 100 Box Ste 391, Las Vegas, NV 89139
Web Site: https://www.ausa-corp.com
AUSAF—(OTCEM)
Rev.: $529,771
Assets: $60,910,821
Liabilities: $11,642,111
Net Worth: $49,268,710
Earnings: ($18,807,203)
Emp.: 19
Fiscal Year-end: 12/31/21
Research & Development in Biotechnology (except Nanobiotechnology)
N.A.I.C.S.: 541714
Brent Reuter (Executives)
Jon Paul (CFO)
Terry Booth (CEO)
Leah S. Bailey (Chief Bus Officer)

AUTHENTIC EQUITY ACQUISITION CORP.
32 Elm Pl 2nd Fl, Rye, NY 10580
Tel.: (646) 374-0919   Ky
Year Founded: 2020
AEACU—(NASDAQ)
Investment Services
N.A.I.C.S.: 523999
David M. Hooper (Chm & CEO)
Thomas Flocco (Pres & COO)
Todd Khoury (CFO)

AUTHENTIC HOLDINGS, INC.
50 Division St, Somerville, NJ 08876
Tel.: (973) 390-0072   NV
Web Site:
https://authenticholdingsinc.com
Year Founded: 2005
AHRO—(OTCIQ)
Assets: $5,418,043
Liabilities: $5,623,581
Net Worth: ($205,538)
Earnings: ($1,658,455)
Emp.: 3
Fiscal Year-end: 12/31/23
Clothing Products Distr
N.A.I.C.S.: 424310
Christopher H. Giordano (Chm & Pres)
Paul Serbiak (CEO, Treas & Sec)

Subsidiaries:

Authentic Heroes, Inc.   (1)
50 Division St Ste 501, Somerville, NJ 08876
Web Site: https://authenticheroes.com
Real Estate Services
N.A.I.C.S.: 531320

AUTHID.AI,
1580 N Logan St Ste 660, Denver, CO 80203
Tel.: (516) 274-8700   DE
Web Site: https://www.authid.ai
Year Founded: 2011
AUID—(NASDAQ)
Rev.: $190,289
Assets: $15,411,913
Liabilities: $2,214,167
Net Worth: $13,197,746
Earnings: ($19,400,376)
Emp.: 22
Fiscal Year-end: 12/31/23
Biometric Handheld Identification & Mobile Payment Mfr
N.A.I.C.S.: 335999
Graham Arad (Gen Counsel)
Phillip L. Kumnick (Chm)
Tom Thimot (CEO)
Jacqueline L. White (Sr VP-Engrg)

Christine Prendamano (Dir-Strategic Partnerships)
Trevor James (Mng Dir-Cards Plus SA)
Edward Sellitto (CFO)

AUTO PARTS 4LESS GROUP, INC.
106 Mayflower Ave, North Las Vegas, NV 89030
Tel.: (702) 267-6100   NV
Web Site:
https://www.autoparts4less.com
Year Founded: 2004
FLES—(OTCIQ)
Rev.: $4,202,880
Assets: $407,768
Liabilities: $21,810,894
Net Worth: ($21,403,126)
Earnings: ($17,784,525)
Emp.: 2
Fiscal Year-end: 01/31/23
Web Search Portal Operator
N.A.I.C.S.: 441330
Christopher Davenport (CEO, CFO & Pres-AutoParts4Less, Inc)

AUTODESK, INC.
1 Market St Ste 400, San Francisco, CA 94105
Tel.: (415) 507-5000   DE
Web Site: https://www.autodesk.com
Year Founded: 1982
ADSK—(NASDAQ)
Rev.: $5,497,000,000
Assets: $9,912,000,000
Liabilities: $8,057,000,000
Net Worth: $1,855,000,000
Earnings: $906,000,000
Emp.: 14,100
Fiscal Year-end: 01/31/24
3D Design, Engineering & Entertainment Software
N.A.I.C.S.: 513210
Steven M. Blum (COO & Exec VP)
Elizabeth S. Rafael (Interim CFO)
Dara Treseder (CMO)
Amy L. Bunszel (Exec VP-Architecture, Engrg, and Construction Design Solutions)
Deborah L. Clifford (Chief Strategy Officer & Exec VP)
Stephen W. Hope (Chief Acctg Officer & VP)
Diana Colella (Sr VP-Media & Entertainment Solutions)
Raji Arasu (CTO & Exec VP)
James A. Lynch (Sr VP & Gen Mgr-Autodesk Construction Solutions)
Ruth Ann Keene (Chief Legal Officer)
Sebastian Goodwin (Chief Trust Officer)
Prakash Kota (CIO)
Ronald Zelles (Exec VP)
Andrew Anagnost (Pres & CEO)

Subsidiaries:

Autodesk (China) Software Research and Development Co., Ltd.   (1)
L2&L3 Bldg A L2&L3 Bldg B399 Pudian Road, Pudong New District, Shanghai, 200122, China
Tel.: (86) 2138653333
Web Site: http://www.autodesk.com.cn
Software Development Services
N.A.I.C.S.: 541511

Autodesk (EMEA) Sarl   (1)
Worbstrasse 223 Guemligen, 3073, Muri, Switzerland   (100%)
Tel.: (41) 319582020
Web Site: http://www.autodesk.com
Sales Range: $250-299.9 Million
Emp.: 200
Holding Company; Digital Design Software Publisher & Distr
N.A.I.C.S.: 551112

Subsidiary (Non-US):

Autodesk AB   (2)
Molndalsvagen 24, PO Box 14261, Vastra Gotaland, 412 63, Gothenburg, Sweden   (100%)
Tel.: (46) 317260000
Web Site: http://www.autodesk.se
Sales Range: $25-49.9 Million
Emp.: 50
Digital Design Software Publisher & Distr
N.A.I.C.S.: 513210

Autodesk Benelux B.V.   (2)
Taurus Ave 3, NL 2132 LS, Hoofddorp, Netherlands   (100%)
Tel.: (31) 180691000
Web Site: http://www.autodesk.nl
Sales Range: $10-24.9 Million
Emp.: 16
Digital Design Software Publisher & Distr
N.A.I.C.S.: 513210

Subsidiary (Domestic):

Autodesk Development Sarl   (2)
Rue du Puits-Godet 6, Neuchatel, 2002, Switzerland   (100%)
Tel.: (41) 327239100
Web Site: http://www.autodesk.ch
Digital Design Software Developer
N.A.I.C.S.: 541715

Subsidiary (Non-US):

Autodesk GesmbH   (2)
Schottengasse 1, 1010, Vienna, Austria   (100%)
Tel.: (43) 724268465
Web Site: http://www.autodesk.com
Sales Range: $10-24.9 Million
Emp.: 6
Digital Design Software Publisher & Distr
N.A.I.C.S.: 513210

Autodesk GmbH   (2)
Balanstrasse 71a, 81541, Munich, Germany   (100%)
Tel.: (49) 89547690
Web Site: https://www.autodesk.com
Sales Range: $50-74.9 Million
Emp.: 200
Digital Design Software Publisher & Distr
N.A.I.C.S.: 513210

Autodesk Limited   (2)
Tel.: (44) 1217665544
Web Site: https://www.autodesk.com
Sales Range: $25-49.9 Million
Emp.: 150
Digital Design Software Publisher & Distr
N.A.I.C.S.: 513210

Autodesk ApS   (1)
Havnegade 39, 1058, Copenhagen, Denmark
Tel.: (45) 80881220
Web Site: http://www.autodesk.dk
Software Distr
N.A.I.C.S.: 513210

Autodesk Asia Pte. Ltd.   (1)
3 Fusionopolis Way 10-21 Symbiosis, Singapore, 138633, Singapore   (100%)
Tel.: (65) 64618100
Web Site: http://www.autodesk.com.sg
Sales Range: $100-124.9 Million
Emp.: 600
Holding Company; Digital Design Software Publisher & Distr
N.A.I.C.S.: 551112

Subsidiary (Non-US):

Autodesk India Private Limited   (2)
4th Floor - Block A& B Sunriver Embassy Golf Links Business Park, Domlur, Bengaluru, 560071, India   (100%)
Tel.: (91) 8041199900
Web Site: https://www.autodesk.in
Digital Design Software Publisher & Distr
N.A.I.C.S.: 513210

Autodesk Software (China) Co., Ltd.   (2)
Unit 04-06 9th Floor Block A Beijing Parkview Green Plaza Office, Building No 9 Dongdaqiao Road Chaoyang District, Beijing, 100020, China   (100%)
Tel.: (86) 1085658800
Web Site: http://www.autodesk.com.cn

Sales Range: $25-49.9 Million
Emp.: 60
Digital Design Software Publisher & Distr
N.A.I.C.S.: 513210

Autodesk Asia Pte. Ltd. (1)
Autodesk Asia Pte Ltd Regional Office Axiata Tower 27 Floor, Suite 30 31 KL Sentral Jalan Stesen Sentral 5, 50470, Kuala Lumpur, Malaysia
Tel.: (60) 3 2776 6818
Web Site: http://www.autodesk.com
Digital Design Software Distr
N.A.I.C.S.: 423430

Autodesk B.V. (1)
Zuidtoren Taurusavenue 3a, 2132 LS, Hoofddorp, Netherlands
Tel.: (31) 237990890
Web Site: http://www.autodesk.com
Emp.: 20
Computer Software Development Services
N.A.I.C.S.: 541511

Autodesk Canada Co. (1)
Tel.: (416) 362-9181
Web Site: http://www.autodesk.com
Sales Range: $50-74.9 Million
Emp.: 220
Digital Design Software Publisher & Distr
N.A.I.C.S.: 513210
Carl Bass *(CEO)*

Autodesk Canada Co. (1)
10 Rue Duke, Montreal, H3C 2L7, QC, Canada
Tel.: (514) 393-1616
Digital Design Software Publisher & Distr
N.A.I.C.S.: 513210

Autodesk Ltd. Japan (1)
8F Toranomon Hills Mori Tower 1-23-1 Toranomon, Minato-ku, Osaka, 105-6308, Japan
Tel.: (81) 663505223
Web Site: https://www.autodesk.co.jp
Software Development Services
N.A.I.C.S.: 541511

Autodesk S.r.l. (1)
Via Tortona 37/41, 20144, Milan, Italy
Tel.: (39) 02575511
Web Site: http://www.autodesk.it
Prepackaged Software Solution Provider
N.A.I.C.S.: 541512

Autodesk SA (1)
Bercy Building 2/22 Place des Vins de France Hall C - 3rd floor, 75012, Paris, France
Tel.: (33) 146463800
Web Site: https://www.autodesk.com
Sales Range: $25-49.9 Million
Emp.: 80
Entertainment Software Development Services
N.A.I.C.S.: 541511

Autodesk Software, Unipessoal, Lda. (1)
Quinta da Fonte Edificio D Pedro I, Paco d'Arcos, Oeiras, 2780-730, Portugal
Tel.: (351) 210001806
Web Site: http://www.autodesk.pt
Software Development Services
N.A.I.C.S.: 541512

Autodesk de Mexico S.A. de C.V. (1)
Paseo de las Palmas 405 Oficina 801 Oficina 801, 11000, Mexico, Mexico **(100%)**
Tel.: (52) 5552496060
Web Site: http://www.autodesk.mx
Sales Range: $25-49.9 Million
Emp.: 12
Digital Design Software Distr
N.A.I.C.S.: 423430

Autodesk do Brasil Ltda (1)
Rue James Joule 65 - 4o andar, 04576-080, Sao Paulo, Brazil
Tel.: (55) 1155012500
Web Site: http://www.autodesk.com.br
Computer Software Application Services
N.A.I.C.S.: 541511

Autodesk, Inc. - UK (1)
Small Heath Business Park Talbot Way, Birmingham, B10 0HJ, United Kingdom
Tel.: (44) 121 766 5544
Web Site: http://www.autodesk.com

Computer System Design & Software Development Services
N.A.I.C.S.: 513210

Subsidiary (Non-US):

Delcam France (2)
89 Quai Panhard Et Levassor, 75013, Paris, France
Tel.: (33) 169591400
Web Site: http://www.delcam.com
Sales Range: $25-49.9 Million
Emp.: 80
Computer Software Design & Sales
N.A.I.C.S.: 541512

Delcam Italia s.r.l. (2)
Via Priv Maestri del Lavoro, Legnano, 020025, MI, Italy
Tel.: (39) 0331 742840
Web Site: http://www.delcam.com
Computer Software Design & Sales
N.A.I.C.S.: 541512

Delcam Japan Kabushiki Kaisya (2)
Sanhaitsu Kanda Kitamura Bldg 10F, 30 Kanda Higashi Konyacho, Chiyoda-ku, Tokyo, 101 0034, Japan
Tel.: (81) 3 5295 7066
Web Site: http://www.delcam.com
Computer Software & Sales
N.A.I.C.S.: 541512

Subsidiary (Domestic):

Delcam PartMaker Limited (2)
Talbot Way Small Heath Business Park, Birmingham, B10 0HJ, United Kingdom
Tel.: (44) 1217665544
Web Site: http://www.autodesk.com
Emp.: 250
Software Services
N.A.I.C.S.: 541511
Peter Bixter *(Mng Dir)*

Subsidiary (US):

PartMaker, Inc. (2)
550 Pinetown Rd Ste 470, Fort Washington, PA 19034
Tel.: (215) 643-5077
Web Site: http://www.partmaker.com
Sales Range: $25-49.9 Million
Emp.: 20
Computer Software Design & Sales
N.A.I.C.S.: 541512

BitSquid AB (1)
Roselundsg 29 C floor-1, Stockholm, 118 63, Sweden
Tel.: (46) 8205170
Web Site: http://www.bitsquid.se
Software Development Services
N.A.I.C.S.: 541511

Configure One Europe Limited (1)
Harlow Enterprise Hub Kao Hockham Building, Edinburgh Way, Harlow, CM20 2NQ, Essex, United Kingdom
Tel.: (44) 1279311420
Web Site: http://www.configureone.com
Electronic Store Operator
N.A.I.C.S.: 449210

Configure One, Inc. (1)
900 Jorie Blvd Ste 190, Oak Brook, IL 60523
Tel.: (630) 368-9950
Web Site: http://www.configureone.com
Electronic Store Operator
N.A.I.C.S.: 449210

Creative Market Labs, Inc. (1)
333 S State St Ste V 232, Lake Oswego, OR 97034
Tel.: (415) 356-3291
Web Site: http://www.colourlovers.com
Software Development Services
N.A.I.C.S.: 541511

Delcam Indonesia (1)
Jl Pahlawan Seribu Blok Q41 BSD City, Tangerang, Banten, Indonesia
Tel.: (62) 2153161465
Web Site: https://digital-mfg.co.id
Engineering Software Publishing Services
N.A.I.C.S.: 513210

Graitec GmbH (1)
Dietrich-Oppenberg-Platz 1, 45127, Essen, Germany

Tel.: (49) 20164729750
Web Site: http://www.graitec.de
Software Development Services
N.A.I.C.S.: 541511

Graitec SAS (1)
17 Burospace, Bievres, 91572, France
Tel.: (33) 169855622
Web Site: http://www.graitec.com
Software Development Services
N.A.I.C.S.: 541511

Innovyze, Inc. (1)
6720 SW Macadam Ave Ste 200, Portland, OR 97229
Tel.: (888) 554-5022
Web Site: http://www.innovyze.com
Software Development Services
N.A.I.C.S.: 541511
Colby T. Manwaring *(Pres)*
Sudesh Mudaliar *(VP-Asia Pacific & Mgr-Ops & Product Dev)*

Moldflow B.V. (1)
Taurusavenue 3, Hoofddorp, 2132 LS, Netherlands
Tel.: (31) 237990890
Computer Peripheral Distr
N.A.I.C.S.: 423430

PlanGrid, Inc. (1)
2111 Mission St Ste 400, San Francisco, CA 94110
Web Site: http://www.plangrid.com
Warehouse Construction Services
N.A.I.C.S.: 541511

Pype LLC (1)
11921 Freedom Dr Ste 920, Reston, VA 20190
Web Site: https://www.pype.io
Computer Software Services
N.A.I.C.S.: 541511
Sunil Dorairajan *(Co-Founder & CEO)*
Karuna Ammireddy *(Co-Founder & CTO)*
Alistair Potts *(VP-Sls)*
Varada Pyda *(Dir-Innovation)*

SeeControl, Inc. (1)
444 Townsend, San Francisco, CA 94107
Tel.: (614) 799-9900
Web Site: http://www.seecontrol.com
Software Designing Services
N.A.I.C.S.: 541511

Solid Angle Limited (1)
Autodesk Media and Entertainment Ingeni Building, 15-17 Broadwick Street, London, W1F 0DE, United Kingdom
Tel.: (44) 2078518000
Web Site: http://www.solidangle.com
Animation Software Provider Services
N.A.I.C.S.: 512110

Solid Angle, S.L.U. (1)
Gran Via 51 5th Floor, 28013, Madrid, Spain
Tel.: (34) 911151559
Animation Software Provider Services
N.A.I.C.S.: 512110
Marcos Fajardo *(Founder)*

TeamUp Technologies, Inc. (1)
5605 De Gaspe Suite 205, Montreal, H2T 2A4, QC, Canada
Tel.: (514) 758-2818
Web Site: http://home.lagoa.com
Software Development Services
N.A.I.C.S.: 541511

Within Technologies Limited (1)
15 Calico Row Plantation Wharf, London, SW11 3YH, United Kingdom
Tel.: (44) 2076177316
Web Site: http://www.withinlab.com
Software Development Services
N.A.I.C.S.: 541511

netfabb GmbH (1)
Steinmuhler Str 2a, 92331, Parsberg, Germany
Tel.: (49) 94926016400
Web Site: http://www.netfabb.com
Software Publisher
N.A.I.C.S.: 513210

AUTOMATIC DATA PROCESSING, INC.
1 ADP Blvd, Roseland, NJ 07068
Tel.: (973) 974-5000 DE

Web Site: https://www.adp.com
Year Founded: 1949
ADP—(NASDAQ)
Rev.: $19,202,600,000
Assets: $54,362,700,000
Liabilities: $49,815,100,000
Net Worth: $4,547,600,000
Earnings: $3,752,000,000
Emp.: 130,000
Fiscal Year-end: 06/30/24
Software Development Services
N.A.I.C.S.: 551112
Michael A. Bonarti *(Chief Admin Officer)*
Don Edward McGuire *(CFO & VP)*
Maria Black *(Pres & CEO)*
Deborah L. Dyson *(Pres-Natl Accounts Svcs)*
David Kwon *(Chief Legal Officer, Gen Counsel & VP)*
Sreeni Kutam *(Chief HR Officer)*
Laura Brown *(Pres-Major Account Svcs)*
Joe DeSilva *(Pres-Small Bus Svcs, Retirement Svcs & Insurance Svcs)*
Brian Michaud *(Pres-Smart Compliance Solutions)*
Chris D'Ambrosio *(Chief Strategy Officer)*
Alex Quevedo *(Pres-HR Outsourcing)*

Subsidiaries:

ADP Brasil Ltda (1)
Rua Joao Tibirica 1112 Vl Anastacio, Sao Paulo, 05077-000, Brazil
Tel.: (55) 1130031237
Web Site: https://br.adp.com
Information Technology Services
N.A.I.C.S.: 519290

ADP Business Services (Shanghai) Co., Ltd. (1)
Unit AB 5th & 3rd Floor Building 2 Youyou Century Plaza, No 428 Yanggao South Road Pudong New District, Shanghai, 200021, China
Tel.: (86) 4008215632
Web Site: http://www.adpchina.com
Business Process Outsourcing Services
N.A.I.C.S.: 561499

ADP Europe S.A. (1)
31 Ave Jules Quentin, 92016, Nanterre, France
Tel.: (33) 155635000
Web Site: http://www.europe.adp.com
Sales Range: $75-99.9 Million
Emp.: 900
Outsourced Employer Services
N.A.I.C.S.: 541214
Alan Brennan *(Mng Dir)*

Subsidiary (Non-US):

ADP Belgium CVA (2)
Gontrode Heirweg 192 9090, Melle, Belgium
Tel.: (32) 92161111
Information Technology Development Services
N.A.I.C.S.: 541512

ADP Dealer Services Italia s.r.l. (2)
Via Julia 39Â 35010 Vigonza, Padua, Italy
Tel.: (39) 0498284811
Web Site: http://www.adpdsi.it
Management Consulting Services
N.A.I.C.S.: 541611

ADP Employer Services GmbH (2)
Frankfurter Strasse 227, 63263, Neu-Isenburg, Germany
Tel.: (49) 6958040
Web Site: http://www.de-adp.com
Emp.: 100
Data Processing Services
N.A.I.C.S.: 518210

Subsidiary (Domestic):

ADP GSI France SAS (2)
31 avenue Jules Quentin, 92000, Nanterre, France
Tel.: (33) 806230103
Web Site: https://www.fr.adp.com

Automatic Data Processing, Inc.—(Continued)

Emp.: 2,000
Information Technology Development Services
N.A.I.C.S.: 541512
Sebastien Alburquerque *(CEO)*

Subsidiary (Non-US):

ADP GSI Italia SpA   **(2)**
Viale Giulio Richard 5/A, 20143, Milan, Italy
Tel.: (39) 02891731
Web Site: http://www.it-adp.com
Management Consulting Services
N.A.I.C.S.: 541611

ADP Nederland B.V.   **(2)**
K P v/d Mandelelaan 9-35, Rotterdam, 3062MB, Netherlands
Tel.: (31) 104598911
Web Site: http://www.adp.nl
Automatic Data Processing Services
N.A.I.C.S.: 518210

Subsidiary (Domestic):

ADP GlobalView B.V.   **(3)**
Lylantse Baan 1, 2908 LG, Capelle aan den IJssel, Netherlands
Tel.: (31) 104598644
Web Site: https://nl.adp.com
Business Process Outsourcing Services
N.A.I.C.S.: 561499

Subsidiary (Non-US):

Automatic Data Processing Limited   **(2)**
2 Causeway Park The Causeway, Staines-upon-Thames, TW18 3BF, Surrey, United Kingdom
Tel.: (44) 1784905000
Web Site: https://uk.adp.com
Emp.: 400
Payroll & HR Outsourcing Services
N.A.I.C.S.: 541214

Subsidiary (Domestic):

OneClickHR plc   **(3)**
2 Bromley Road, Beckenham, BR3 5JE, Kent, United Kingdom
Tel.: (44) 2086634500
Web Site: http://www.oneclickhrplc.com
Sales Range: $1-9.9 Million
Human Resources Outsourcing, Consulting & Training Services
N.A.I.C.S.: 541612

Subsidiary (Domestic):

Vizual Human Resources plc   **(3)**
2 Bromley Road, Beckenham, BR3 5JE, Kent, United Kingdom
Tel.: (44) 2086634500
Outsourced Human Resource Services
N.A.I.C.S.: 561499

Vizual Learning plc   **(4)**
Syward Place Pyrcroft Rd, Chertsey, KT16 9JT, Surrey, United Kingdom
Tel.: (44) 2086634500
Web Site: http://www.uk.adp.com
Emp.: 600
Human Resources Training Services
N.A.I.C.S.: 611430
Frank Beechinor-Collins *(CEO)*

ADP International Services BV   **(1)**
Lylantse Baan 1, Capelle aan den IJssel, 2908 LG, Netherlands
Tel.: (31) 104598911
Human Resource Consulting Services
N.A.I.C.S.: 541612

ADP Private Limited   **(1)**
ADP Boulevard Survey No 88/AA and 88/E Nanakramguda Village, Serilingampally Mandal Ranga Reddy District, Hyderabad, 500 008, Telengana, India
Tel.: (91) 4067571000
Web Site: https://in.adp.com
Payroll Services
N.A.I.C.S.: 541214

ADP TotalSource I, Inc.   **(1)**
10200 Sunset Dr, Miami, FL 33173
Tel.: (305) 630-1242
Human Resource Consulting Services
N.A.I.C.S.: 541612

ADP, Inc.   **(1)**
1 ADP Blvd, Roseland, NJ 07068
Tel.: (973) 974-5000
Web Site: http://www.adp.com
Computerized Transaction Processing, Record Keeping, Payroll & Information Services
N.A.I.C.S.: 518210

Subsidiary (Domestic):

ADP Atlantic, LLC   **(2)**
800 Delaware Ave, Wilmington, DE 19801-1322
Tel.: (302) 571-0820
Web Site: http://www.adp.com
Sales Range: $25-49.9 Million
Emp.: 13
Business Services
N.A.I.C.S.: 561499

Subsidiary (Non-US):

ADP Canada Co.   **(2)**
3250 Bloor Street West 16th Floor East Tower, Toronto, M8X 2X9, ON, Canada   **(100%)**
Tel.: (416) 207-2900
Web Site: https://www.adp.ca
Sales Range: $150-199.9 Million
Emp.: 1,000
Payroll Processing Services
N.A.I.C.S.: 541214
Holger Kormann *(Pres)*
Carlos Gonzalez *(VP-Implementation & Upgrades)*
Heather Haslam *(VP-Mktg)*
William J. Piggot *(VP-Intl Money Movement)*
Mohamad Chakroun *(VP-Product Dev)*
Helen Vesce *(VP-Svc Delivery)*
Andrea Wynter *(Head-HR)*
Anne Conte *(Sr VP)*
Kelly Parascandalo *(VP)*
Raul Sibaja *(CFO)*

Subsidiary (Domestic):

Broadridge Financial Solutions, Inc.   **(3)**
5970 Chetworth Way, Mississauga, L5R 4G5, ON, Canada   **(100%)**
Tel.: (905) 507-5100
Sales Range: $25-49.9 Million
Emp.: 100
Direct Mail Advertising Services
N.A.I.C.S.: 541860
Patricia Rosch *(Pres-Investor Comm Solutions-Intl)*

Corp. Consultants Performance, Inc.   **(3)**
1040 Saint Joseph Blvd Ste 5, Gatineau, Hull, J8Z 1T3, QC, Canada   **(100%)**
Tel.: (819) 776-3610
Web Site:
   http://www.performance20group.com
Sales Range: $10-24.9 Million
Emp.: 5
Automobile Dealership Consulting Services
N.A.I.C.S.: 441330

Unit (Domestic):

ADP National Account Services   **(2)**
4125 Hopyard Rd, Pleasanton, CA 94588-8534
Tel.: (925) 737-3500
Web Site: http://www.westnsc.adp.com
Sales Range: $200-249.9 Million
Emp.: 1,200
Employee Administrative Services
N.A.I.C.S.: 541214
Greg M. Stivers *(VP-SIS)*
Terry Corallo *(Dir-Pub Rels)*

ADP National Account Services   **(2)**
2835 Decker Lk Dr, Salt Lake City, UT 84119
Tel.: (801) 956-6000
Web Site: http://www.adp.com
Sales Range: $100-124.9 Million
Emp.: 400
Advisory Services Insurance
N.A.I.C.S.: 524298

ADP Screening & Selection Services   **(2)**
301 Remington St, Fort Collins, CO 80524-2806   **(100%)**
Tel.: (970) 484-7722

Web Site: http://www.azp.com
Sales Range: $25-49.9 Million
Emp.: 165
Accumulates & Provides Information Relating to Workers' Compensation Claims, Criminal History, Driving Record, Credit Rating, Education & Previous Employment
N.A.I.C.S.: 517810
Dan Ingalls *(Acct Mgr)*
Wesley Morley *(Mgr-Bus Dev)*
Cara Muth *(Mgr-Compliance)*
Chris Christian *(Mgr-Compliance & Ops)*
Bria Berger *(Mgr-Solution Center)*

ADP Securities Industry Software   **(2)**
4725 Independence St, Wheat Ridge, CO 80033-2937
Tel.: (303) 590-6000
Web Site: http://www.adp.com
Rev.: $100,000,000
Emp.: 140
Computer Software Development
N.A.I.C.S.: 541511

ADP Tax Credit Services   **(2)**
2205 Enterprise Dr Ste G, Florence, SC 29501
Tel.: (843) 667-1836
Web Site: http://www.taxcredits.adp.com
Sales Range: $75-99.9 Million
Provider of Computer-based Business Management Services
N.A.I.C.S.: 561499
Tim Norwood *(Exec VP)*

ADP TotalSource   **(2)**
10200 SW 72nd St, Miami, FL 33173-3033   **(100%)**
Tel.: (305) 630-1000
Web Site: http://www.adptotalsource.com
Sales Range: $125-149.9 Million
Emp.: 600
Employers Services & Payroll
N.A.I.C.S.: 541611

Subsidiary (Domestic):

ADP TotalSource Group, Inc.   **(2)**
10200 Sunset Dr, Miami, FL 33173-3033
Tel.: (305) 630-1000
Web Site: http://www.adptotalsource.com
Human Resource Consulting Services
N.A.I.C.S.: 541612

Branch (Domestic):

ADP, Inc. - Alpharetta (Westside) Office   **(2)**
2575 Westside Pkwy Ste 500, Alpharetta, GA 30004-3852
Tel.: (770) 619-7200
Web Site: http://www.adp.com
Sales Range: $1-9.9 Million
Emp.: 450
ADP Benefit Services
N.A.I.C.S.: 541612

ADP, Inc. - Alpharetta (Windward) Office   **(2)**
5800 Windward Pkwy, Alpharetta, GA 30005-8802
Tel.: (770) 360-2000
Web Site: http://www.adp.com
Sales Range: $500-549.9 Million
Emp.: 2,000
Custom Computer Programming Services
N.A.I.C.S.: 518210

ADP, Inc. - Camarillo Office   **(2)**
5153 Camino Ruiz, Camarillo, CA 93012-8601
Tel.: (805) 383-5630
Web Site: http://www.adp.com
Labor Resource Planning & Management Services & Application for Large Healthcare, Transportation & Manufacturing Corporations
N.A.I.C.S.: 518210

Subsidiary (Domestic):

Asparity Decision Solutions, Inc.   **(2)**
115 Market St, Durham, NC 27701
Tel.: (919) 688-1430
Web Site: http://www.asparity.com
Sales Range: $10-24.9 Million
Emp.: 25
Benefits Administration Solutions
N.A.I.C.S.: 513210

Colleen Murphy *(Pres)*

CarInk, Inc.   **(2)**
10200 SW Sunset Dr, Miami, FL 33173   **(100%)**
Tel.: (305) 630-1700
Web Site: http://www.carink.com
Sales Range: Less than $1 Million
Emp.: 50
Custom Computer Programming Services
N.A.I.C.S.: 541511

Employease, Inc.   **(2)**
34500 Euclid Ave, Willoughby, OH 44094
Tel.: (440) 918-7900
Web Site: http://www.employeaseinc.com
Information Technology Development Services
N.A.I.C.S.: 541512

Performance Incorporated   **(2)**
3855 Centerview Dr Ste 500, Chantilly, VA 20151-3285
Tel.: (703) 481-0200
Web Site:
   http://www.performance20groups.com
Rev.: $2,800,000
Emp.: 34
Management Consulting Services
N.A.I.C.S.: 541611
Joe Garafolo *(Founder)*

The Marcus Buckingham Company, LLC.   **(2)**
8350 Wilshire Blvd Ste 200, Beverly Hills, CA 90211
Tel.: (323) 302-9810
Web Site: http://www.tmbc.com
Information Technology Consulting Services
N.A.I.C.S.: 541512
David Wagner *(CTO)*
Amy Leschke-Kahle *(VP-Performance Acceleration)*
Marcus Buckingham *(Founder & CEO)*
Christian Gomez *(VP-Strategy)*
Brady Donnelly *(Dir-Fin)*
Joe Sullivan *(COO)*
Laura Martin *(VP-Product & Client Experience)*
Amy Powell *(VP-Leader Dev)*
Rachelle Steen *(VP-Client Svcs)*
Sam Herskovitz *(Product Dir)*

Workscape Inc.   **(2)**
123 Felton St, Marlborough, MA 01752-1999
Tel.: (508) 861-5500
Web Site: http://www.workscape.com
Sales Range: $100-124.9 Million
Emp.: 400
Business Oriented Computer Software
N.A.I.C.S.: 513210
Donald R. Fitch *(CFO)*

Automatic Data Processing Insurance Agency, Inc.   **(1)**
1 ADP Blvd, Roseland, NJ 07068
Web Site: https://insurance.adp.com
Payroll Services
N.A.I.C.S.: 541214

Automatic Data Processing Limited   **(1)**
Level 1 6 Nexus Ct, Mulgrave, 3170, VIC, Australia
Tel.: (61) 395665100
Web Site: http://au.adp.com
Information Technology Development Services
N.A.I.C.S.: 541512

Global Cash Card, Inc.   **(1)**
3972 Barranca Pkwy Ste J610, Irvine, CA 92606
Tel.: (949) 751-0360
Web Site: https://www.globalcashcard.com
Financial Services
N.A.I.C.S.: 523999
Joseph Purcell *(Founder & COO)*

Work Market Inc.   **(1)**
240 W 37th St 10th Fl, New York, NY 10018
Tel.: (212) 229-9675
Web Site: https://www.workmarket.com
Software Development Services
N.A.I.C.S.: 541511
Stephen Dewitt *(CEO)*

AUTONATION, INC.

200 SW 1st Ave, Fort Lauderdale, FL 33301
Tel.: (954) 769-6000   DE
Web Site:
https://www.autonation.com
Year Founded: 1991
AN—(NYSE)
Rev.: $26,948,900,000
Assets: $11,980,000,000
Liabilities: $9,768,600,000
Net Worth: $2,211,400,000
Earnings: $1,021,100,000
Emp.: 25,300
Fiscal Year-end: 12/31/23
Automotive Retail & Financing Services
N.A.I.C.S.: 441110
Jeff M. Parent *(COO)*
David L. Koehler *(COO-Non-Franchised Bus)*
C. Coleman Edmunds *(Gen Counsel, Sec & Exec VP)*
Harry Wayne Huizenga *(Founder)*
Thomas A. Szlosek *(CFO & Exec VP)*
Michael Manley *(CEO)*
Kimberly Dees *(Chief Acctg Officer & Sr VP)*
Jeffrey W. Butler *(Pres)*
Lisa Esparza *(Chief HR Officer)*

Subsidiaries:

ACER Fiduciary, Inc.   **(1)**
110 SE 6th St 20th Fl, Fort Lauderdale, FL 33301
Tel.: (954) 769-6000
Car & Truck Dealer Services
N.A.I.C.S.: 441110

AN Cadillac of WPB, LLC   **(1)**
2101 45th St, West Palm Beach, FL 33407-3296
Tel.: (561) 491-2967
Web Site:
https://www.autonationcadillacwestpalmbeach.com
Emp.: 50
Car & Commercial Vehicle Dealer
N.A.I.C.S.: 441227

AN Central Region Management, LLC   **(1)**
200 SW 1st Ave, Fort Lauderdale, FL 33301
Tel.: (954) 769-6000
Business Management Services
N.A.I.C.S.: 561110

AN Chevrolet - Arrowhead, Inc.   **(1)**
9055 W Bell Rd, Peoria, AZ 85382-3715
Tel.: (623) 748-0880
Web Site:
https://www.autonationchevroletarrowhead.com
Car & Commercial Vehicle Dealer
N.A.I.C.S.: 441227

AN Collision Center FTL South, Inc.   **(1)**
122 SW 22nd St, Fort Lauderdale, FL 33315
Tel.: (954) 440-5382
Automotive Retailer
N.A.I.C.S.: 441110

AN Collision Center of Addison, Inc.   **(1)**
4300 Lindbergh Dr, Addison, TX 75001
Tel.: (682) 214-2011
Web Site:
http://www.autonationcollisioncenters.com
Car & Commercial Vehicle Dealer
N.A.I.C.S.: 441227
Mike Jackson *(CEO)*

AN Collision Center of Las Vegas, Inc.   **(1)**
5720 W Sahara Ave, Las Vegas, NV 89146
Tel.: (725) 291-2014
Automotive Retailer
N.A.I.C.S.: 441110

AN Collision Center of North Houston, Inc.   **(1)**
325 FM 1960 E, Houston, TX 77073
Tel.: (713) 496-1833

Automotive Retailer
N.A.I.C.S.: 441110

AN Collision Center of Sarasota, Inc.   **(1)**
6828 Tamiami Trl, Sarasota, FL 34231
Tel.: (941) 363-6709
Automobile Maintenance Services
N.A.I.C.S.: 811111

AN Collision Center of Tempe, Inc.   **(1)**
7245 S Harl Ave, Tempe, AZ 85283
Tel.: (602) 892-0082
Automotive Retailer
N.A.I.C.S.: 441110

AN Corpus Christi Chevrolet, LP   **(1)**
6650 S Padre Is Dr, Corpus Christi, TX 78412-4902
Tel.: (832) 369-8263
Web Site:
http://www.autonationchevroletsouthcorpuschristi.com
Car & Commercial Vehicle Dealer
N.A.I.C.S.: 441227

AN Corpus Christi Motors, Inc.   **(1)**
6686 S Padre Island Dr, Corpus Christi, TX 78412
Tel.: (361) 541-6765
Web Site:
https://www.autonationhyundaicorpuschristi.com
Car & Commercial Vehicle Dealer
N.A.I.C.S.: 441227

AN Corpus Christi T. Imports, LP   **(1)**
6672 S Padre Island Dr, Corpus Christi, TX 78412
Tel.: (361) 827-2557
Web Site:
https://www.autonationtoyotacorpuschristi.com
Automotive Retailer
N.A.I.C.S.: 441110

AN County Line Ford, Inc.   **(1)**
850 N Burleson Blvd, Burleson, TX 76028
Tel.: (682) 307-5770
Web Site:
https://www.autonationfordburleson.com
Automotive Retailer
N.A.I.C.S.: 441110

AN Fort Myers Imports, LLC   **(1)**
2555 Colonial Blvd, Fort Myers, FL 33907
Tel.: (239) 326-9135
Web Site: https://www.autonationtoyotafortmyers.com
Automotive Retailer
N.A.I.C.S.: 441110

AN Fremont Luxury Imports, Inc.   **(1)**
5720 Cushing Pkwy, Fremont, CA 94538
Tel.: (510) 954-6447
Web Site: https://www.bmwoffremont.com
Automotive Retailer
N.A.I.C.S.: 441110

AN H. Imports of Atlanta, LLC   **(1)**
3445 Buford Dr, Buford, GA 30519
Tel.: (470) 824-3073
Web Site:
https://www.autonationhyundaimallofgeorgia.com
Automotive Retailer
N.A.I.C.S.: 441110

AN Imports of Ft. Lauderdale, Inc.   **(1)**
400 W Copans Rd, Pompano Beach, FL 33064
Tel.: (954) 869-5676
Web Site:
https://www.jaguarfortlauderdale.com
Automotive Retailer
N.A.I.C.S.: 441110

AN Imports of Spokane, Inc.   **(1)**
8201 E Sprague Ave, Spokane Valley, WA 99212
Tel.: (509) 676-4270
Web Site:
https://www.autonationhondaspokanevalley.com
Automotive Retailer
N.A.I.C.S.: 441110

AN Imports of Stevens Creek, Inc.   **(1)**

4201 Stevens Creek Blvd, Santa Clara, CA 95051
Tel.: (408) 641-4608
Web Site:
https://www.miniofstevenscreek.com
Automotive Retailer
N.A.I.C.S.: 441110

AN Imports on Weston Road, Inc.   **(1)**
4050 Weston Rd, Davie, FL 33331
Tel.: (754) 206-7999
Web Site:
https://www.autonationtoyotaweston.com
Automotive Retailer
N.A.I.C.S.: 441110

AN Luxury Imports GP, LLC   **(1)**
110 SE 6th St 20th Fl, Fort Lauderdale, FL 33301
Tel.: (954) 769-4132
Non-Durable Goods Distr
N.A.I.C.S.: 424990

AN Luxury Imports of Coconut Creek, Inc.   **(1)**
4250 N State Rd 7, Coconut Creek, FL 33073
Tel.: (954) 488-2339
Web Site:
https://www.mercedescoconutcreek.com
Automotive Retailer
N.A.I.C.S.: 441110

AN Luxury Imports of Marietta, LLC   **(1)**
810 Cobb Pkwy SE, Marietta, GA 30060
Tel.: (470) 623-1647
Web Site: https://www.mbmarietta.com
Automotive Retailer
N.A.I.C.S.: 441110

AN Luxury Imports of Palm Beach, Inc.   **(1)**
1001 Linton Blvd, Delray Beach, FL 33444
Tel.: (561) 291-6095
Web Site:
https://www.mercedesbenzofdelray.com
Automotive Retailer
N.A.I.C.S.: 441110

AN Luxury Imports of Pembroke Pines, Inc.   **(1)**
14199 Pines Blvd, Pembroke Pines, FL 33027
Tel.: (754) 755-5526
Web Site:
https://www.mercedesbenzofpembrokepines.com
Automotive Retailer
N.A.I.C.S.: 441110

AN Luxury Imports of Phoenix, Inc.   **(1)**
2322 W Van Winkle Way, Peoria, IL 61615
Web Site: https://www.audipeoria.com
Automotive Retailer
N.A.I.C.S.: 441110

AN Luxury Imports of Sanford, Inc.   **(1)**
1100 Rinehart Rd, Sanford, FL 32771-7360
Tel.: (689) 207-3698
Web Site: https://www.mercedesbenznorthorlando.com
Sales Range: $25-49.9 Million
Car & Commercial Vehicle Dealer
N.A.I.C.S.: 441227

AN Luxury Imports of Sarasota, Inc.   **(1)**
4754 Clark Rd, Sarasota, FL 34233
Tel.: (941) 300-6924
Web Site: https://www.mercedesbenzofsarasota.com
Automotive Retailer
N.A.I.C.S.: 441110

AN Luxury Imports of Spokane, Inc.   **(1)**
8325 E Sprague Ave, Spokane Valley, WA 99212
Tel.: (509) 676-3833
Web Site:
https://www.autonationacuraspokanevalley.com
Automotive Retailer
N.A.I.C.S.: 441110

AN Luxury Imports of Tucson, Inc.   **(1)**

855 W Wetmore Rd, Tucson, AZ 85705
Tel.: (520) 200-1371
Web Site: https://www.bmwoftucson.com
Automotive Retailer
N.A.I.C.S.: 441110

AN Luxury Imports, Ltd.   **(1)**
6200 Lemmon Ave, Dallas, TX 75209
Tel.: (469) 694-0633
Web Site: https://www.bmwofdallas.com
Automotive Retailer
N.A.I.C.S.: 441110

AN Motors of Brooksville, Inc.   **(1)**
7200 S Broad St, Brooksville, FL 34601
Tel.: (352) 725-8673
Web Site:
https://www.autonationfordbrooksville.com
Automotive Retailer
N.A.I.C.S.: 441110

AN Motors of Dallas, Inc.   **(1)**
4747 Lyndon B Johnson Fwy, Dallas, TX 75244-5909   **(100%)**
Tel.: (972) 763-5444
Web Site:
http://www.mygalleriachevrolet.com
Sales Range: $200-249.9 Million
Automobile Dealership
N.A.I.C.S.: 441110

AN Motors of Memphis, Inc.   **(1)**
2621 Mendenhall Rd, Memphis, TN 38115-1503
Tel.: (901) 881-0179
Web Site:
https://www.autonationgmcmemphis.com
Automotive Retailer
N.A.I.C.S.: 441110

AN Motors of Pembroke, LLC   **(1)**
8600 Pines Blvd, Pembroke Pines, FL 33024-6534
Tel.: (954) 357-0524
Web Site:
https://www.autonationchevroletpembrokepines.com
New & Used Car Dealer
N.A.I.C.S.: 441110

AN Motors of Scottsdale, LLC   **(1)**
8555 Frank Lloyd Wright Blvd, Scottsdale, AZ 85260
Tel.: (623) 473-9481
Web Site:
https://www.autonationfordscottsdale.com
Car & Commercial Vehicle Dealer
N.A.I.C.S.: 441110

AN Motors on Federal Highway, LLC   **(1)**
1400 NE 16th Ter, Fort Lauderdale, FL 33304
Tel.: (954) 390-6258
Web Site:
http://www.griecofordoffortlauderdale.com
Car Dealer Services
N.A.I.C.S.: 441110

AN Motors on South Padre, LP   **(1)**
6650 S Padre Island Dr, Corpus Christi, TX 78412-4902
Tel.: (832) 369-8303
Web Site:
http://www.autonationchevroletsouthcorpuschristi.com
New & Used Car Dealer
N.A.I.C.S.: 441110

AN North Phoenix Collision, Inc.   **(1)**
16800 N 26th Ave, Phoenix, AZ 85023
Tel.: (480) 658-0389
New & Used Car Dealer
N.A.I.C.S.: 441110
Speckmann John *(Gen Mgr)*

AN San Jose Luxury Imports, Inc.   **(1)**
4500 Stevens Creek Blvd, San Jose, CA 95129
Tel.: (650) 810-7629
Web Site:
https://www.mbofstevenscreek.com
New & Used Car Dealer
N.A.I.C.S.: 441110

AN Subaru Motors, Inc.   **(1)**
15678 N Northsight Blvd, Scottsdale, AZ 85260
Tel.: (480) 420-3440

AutoNation, Inc.—(Continued)

Web Site:
https://www.autonationsubaruscotts
dale.com
Car Dealer Services
N.A.I.C.S.: 441110

AN Subaru Motors, Inc. (1)
15678 N Northsight Blvd, Scottsdale, AZ
85260
Tel.: (602) 834-0017
Web Site:
https://www.autonationsubaruscotts
dale.com
Automotive Retailer
N.A.I.C.S.: 441110

AN T. Imports of Atlanta, LLC (1)
3505 Buford Dr, Buford, GA 30519
Web Site:
https://www.autonationtoyotamallof
georgia.com
Automotive Retailer
N.A.I.C.S.: 441110

AN/CF Acquisition Corp. (1)
8252 S Broadway, Littleton, CO 80122
Tel.: (720) 809-8340
Web Site:
https://www.autonationfordlittleton.com
Car & Commercial Vehicle Dealer
N.A.I.C.S.: 441227

AN/MNI Acquisition Corp. (1)
4140 Hacks Cross Rd, Memphis, TN 38125
Tel.: (901) 677-1643
Web Site:
https://www.autonationnissanmem
phis.com
Automotive Retailer
N.A.I.C.S.: 441110

AN/MNI Acquisition Corp. (1)
4140 Hacks Cross Rd, Memphis, TN 38125
Tel.: (901) 209-1318
Web Site:
http://www.autonationnissanmemphis.com
Financial Investment Services
N.A.I.C.S.: 523910

AN/PF Acquisition Corp. (1)
411 116th Ave NE, Bellevue, WA 98005
Tel.: (425) 272-6549
Web Site:
https://www.autonationfordbellevue.com
Automotive Retailer
N.A.I.C.S.: 441110

Abraham Chevrolet-Miami, Inc. (1)
4181 SW 8th St, Miami, FL 33134-2699
Tel.: (305) 306-0846
Web Site:
https://www.autonationchevroletcoral
gables.com
Automotive Retailer
N.A.I.C.S.: 441110

Abraham Chevrolet-Miami, Inc. (1)
4181 SW 8th St, Miami, FL 33134-2699
Tel.: (305) 306-0846
Web Site:
https://www.autonationchevroletcoral
gables.com
Car & Truck Dealer Services
N.A.I.C.S.: 441110

Albuquerque ANUSA, LLC (1)
9100 Pan American Fwy NE, Albuquerque,
NM 87113
Electric Car Mfr & Distr
N.A.I.C.S.: 336320

**Allen Samuels Chevrolet of Corpus
Christi, Inc.** (1)
2118 S Padre Island Dr at Crosstown, Cor-
pus Christi, TX 78416-1100
Tel.: (361) 356-1716
Web Site:
https://www.autonationchevroletnorthcor
puschristi.com
New & Used Car Dealer
N.A.I.C.S.: 441110

**Allen Samuels Chevrolet of Waco,
Inc.** (1)
1625 N Valley Mills Dr, Waco, TX 76710-
2592
Tel.: (254) 230-4750
Web Site:
https://www.autonationchevroletwaco.com

Automotive Retailer
N.A.I.C.S.: 441110

Allison Bavarian (1)
150 E El Camino Real, Mountain View, CA
94040
Tel.: (650) 918-5299
Web Site:
https://www.bmwofmountainview.com
Automotive Retailer
N.A.I.C.S.: 441110

Allison Bavarian (1)
150 E El Camino Real, Mountain View, CA
94040
Tel.: (650) 200-0149
Web Site:
https://www.bmwofmountainview.com
Car Dealer Services
N.A.I.C.S.: 441110

American Way Motors, Inc. (1)
4030 Hacks Cross Rd, Memphis, TN 38125
Tel.: (901) 519-4677
Web Site:
https://www.autonationhonda385.com
Automotive Retailer
N.A.I.C.S.: 441110

Appleway Chevrolet, Inc. (1)
8500 E Sprague Ave, Spokane, WA 99212-
2978
Tel.: (509) 209-9973
Web Site:
https://www.autonationchevroletspokane
valley.com
Automotive Retailer
N.A.I.C.S.: 441110

Auto Car, Inc. (1)
2512 Nolensville Pike, Nashville, TN 37211
Tel.: (615) 752-3006
Web Site: https://autocarnashville.us
Car & Commercial Vehicle Dealer
N.A.I.C.S.: 441227

Auto Company VI, Inc. (1)
5930 W Plano Pkwy, Plano, TX 75093
Tel.: (972) 249-0905
Web Site: https://www.audiplano.com
Automotive Retailer
N.A.I.C.S.: 441110

Auto Company VII, Inc. (1)
5924 W Planoa Pkwy, Plano, TX 75093
Tel.: (972) 249-0910
Web Site:
https://www.porscheplanotexas.com
Car Dealer Services
N.A.I.C.S.: 441110
Craig Sanborn (Mgr-Sls)
Aaron Woods (Mgr-Svc)
Larry Irby (Mgr-Parts)
Manny Venegas (Mgr-Svc)

Auto Company VIII, Inc. (1)
300 Central Expy, Richardson, TX 75080
Tel.: (972) 249-0907
Car Dealer Services
N.A.I.C.S.: 441110

Auto Company XI, Inc. (1)
21027 N Fwy Ste Ih-45, Spring, TX 77388-
5606
Tel.: (832) 835-6306
Web Site:
https://www.autonationchryslerdodge
jeepramspring.com
Automotive Retailer
N.A.I.C.S.: 441110

Auto Company XII, Inc. (1)
1661 Wet N Wild Way, Arlington, TX 76011
Tel.: (817) 993-9903
Car Dealer Services
N.A.I.C.S.: 441110

Auto Company XIII, Inc. (1)
1150 S Gilbert Rd, Chandler, AZ 85286
Tel.: (480) 505-5186
Web Site:
https://www.autonationhondachandler.com
Car Dealer Services
N.A.I.C.S.: 441110

Auto Company XIV, Inc. (1)
8050 S Autoplex Loop, Tempe, AZ 85284
Tel.: (480) 903-7914
Web Site:
https://www.autonationhyundaitempe.com
Automotive Retailer

N.A.I.C.S.: 441110

Auto Company XIX, Inc. (1)
14500 Scientific Way, Irvine, CA 92618
Web Site: https://www.porscheirvine.com
Automotive Retailer
N.A.I.C.S.: 441110

Auto Company XVII, Inc. (1)
3118 Government Blvd, Mobile, AL 36606-
2612
Tel.: (251) 250-1446
Web Site:
https://www.autonationchryslerdodge
jeeprammobile.com
Automotive Retailer
N.A.I.C.S.: 441110

Auto Company XXI, Inc. (1)
1533 120th Ave NE, Bellevue, WA 98005
Web Site: https://www.audibellevue.com
Automotive Retailer
N.A.I.C.S.: 441110

Auto Company XXII, Inc. (1)
3000 E Capitol Expy, San Jose, CA 95148
Tel.: (650) 810-7169
Web Site: https://www.mbsanjose.com
Automotive Retailer
N.A.I.C.S.: 441110

Auto Company XXIII, Inc. (1)
23820 Creekside Rd, Valencia, CA 91355-
1719
Tel.: (661) 490-9443
Web Site:
https://www.autonationchryslerdodge
jeepramvalencia.com
Automotive Retailer
N.A.I.C.S.: 441110

Auto Company XXV, Inc. (1)
11500 S Virginia St, Reno, NV 89511
Tel.: (775) 900-9307
Web Site: https://www.mbofreno.com
Automotive Retailer
N.A.I.C.S.: 441110

Auto Company XXVII, Inc. (1)
1311 Linton Blvd, Delray Beach, FL 33444
Tel.: (561) 880-9828
Web Site: https://www.bmwdelraybeach.com
Automotive Retailer
N.A.I.C.S.: 441110

Auto Dealership III, LLC (1)
1533 S River Rd, Des Plaines, IL 60018
Tel.: (224) 757-3488
Web Site:
https://www.autonationhondaohare.com
Automotive Retailer
N.A.I.C.S.: 441110

Auto Dealership IV, LLC (1)
1509 S River Rd, Des Plaines, IL 60018
Tel.: (224) 540-1933
Web Site:
https://www.autonationhyundaiohare.com
Automotive Retailer
N.A.I.C.S.: 441110

Auto Dealership V, LLC (1)
2383 Willow Oak Dr, Wesley Chapel, FL
33544
Tel.: (813) 279-1330
Web Site: https://www.mbwesleychapel.com
Automotive Retailer
N.A.I.C.S.: 441110

Auto Dealership VI, LLC (1)
3711 Buford Dr, Buford, GA 30519
Tel.: (470) 824-3254
Web Site:
https://www.autonationvwmallofgeor
gia.com
Automotive Retailer
N.A.I.C.S.: 441110

Auto Mission Ltd. (1)
24773 Mission Blvd, Hayward, CA 94544
Tel.: (510) 224-4854
Web Site:
https://www.autonationtoyotahayward.com
Car Dealer Services
N.A.I.C.S.: 441110

Auto Mission Ltd. (1)
24773 Mission Blvd, Hayward, CA 94544
Tel.: (510) 880-4847
Web Site:
https://www.autonationtoyotahayward.com
Automotive Retailer

Automotive Retailer
N.A.I.C.S.: 441110

Auto Motors of Englewood, LLC (1)
9980 E Arapahoe Rd, Englewood, CO
80112-3712
Tel.: (720) 807-5543
Web Site:
https://www.autonationchryslerjeeppara
pahoe.com
New & Used Car Dealer
N.A.I.C.S.: 441110

**AutoNation Chevrolet Cadillac Corpus
Christi** (1)
6650 S Padre Is Dr, Corpus Christi, TX
78412
Tel.: (361) 444-0022
Web Site:
http://www.autonationchevroletsouthcor
puschristi.com
New & Used Car Dealers
N.A.I.C.S.: 441110

**AutoNation Dodge of Pembroke
Pines, Inc.** (1)
13601 Pines Blvd, Pembroke Pines, FL
33027
Tel.: (954) 271-1606
Web Site:
http://www.maroonedodgeofpembroke
pines.com
Sales Range: $50-74.9 Million
Emp.: 250
Car & Commercial Vehicle Dealer
N.A.I.C.S.: 441227

AutoNation Fleet Services, LLC (1)
3191 Fanum Rd, White Bear Lake, MN
55110
Tel.: (651) 288-6269
Automobile Service Provider
N.A.I.C.S.: 811111

AutoNation Ford Amherst (1)
8000 Leavitt Rd, Amherst, OH 44001
Tel.: (440) 296-3021
Web Site:
https://www.autonationfordamherst.com
Retail New & Used Automobiles
N.A.I.C.S.: 441110

AutoNation Ford Burleson (1)
850 N Burleson Blvd, Burleson, TX 76028
Tel.: (682) 318-3257
Web Site:
https://www.autonationfordburleson.com
Sales Range: $25-49.9 Million
Emp.: 100
Car & Commercial Vehicle Dealer
N.A.I.C.S.: 441227

AutoNation Ford Frisco (1)
6850 Hwy 121, Frisco, TX 75034
Tel.: (972) 763-5523
Web Site:
https://www.autonationfordfrisco.com
Automobile Dealership
N.A.I.C.S.: 441110

AutoNation Ford Memphis (1)
2515 Mt Moriah Rd, Memphis, TN 38115
Tel.: (901) 602-6011
Web Site:
https://www.autonationfordmemphis.com
Emp.: 60
Car Dealer
N.A.I.C.S.: 441110

AutoNation Ford Panama City (1)
730 W 15th St, Panama City, FL 32401
Tel.: (850) 812-4701
Web Site:
https://www.autonationfordpanamacity.com
New & Used Car Dealers
N.A.I.C.S.: 441110

**AutoNation Ford South Fort
Worth** (1)
5300 Campus Dr, Fort Worth, TX 76119
Tel.: (817) 522-3225
Web Site:
https://www.autonationfordsouthfort
worth.com
Emp.: 100
Car Sales Services
N.A.I.C.S.: 441110

AutoNation Ford Tustin (1)
2 Auto Center Dr, Tustin, CA 92782-8401

Tel.: (657) 655-7801
Web Site:
http://www.autonationfordtustin.net
Rev.: $49,500,000
Emp.: 100
Car Dealership
N.A.I.C.S.: 441110

AutoNation Fort Worth Motors, Ltd. (1)
7769 Grapevine Hwy, North Richland Hills, TX 76180-7199
Tel.: (817) 500-5467
Web Site:
https://www.autonationchevroletnorthrich landhills.com
Automotive Retailer
N.A.I.C.S.: 441110

AutoNation Imports of Katy, L.P. (1)
25550 Kingsland Blvd, Katy, TX 77494
Tel.: (281) 305-8961
Web Site:
http://www.autonationnissankaty.com
Car Dealer Services
N.A.I.C.S.: 441110

AutoNation Imports of Lithia Springs, Inc. (1)
1000 Blairs Bridge Rd, Lithia Springs, GA 30122-3259
Tel.; (470) 938-4046
Web Site:
https://www.autonationtoyotathornton road.com
Sales Range: $25-49.9 Million
Car & Commercial Vehicle Dealer
N.A.I.C.S.: 441227
Mohammed Babssi (Gen Mgr)

AutoNation Imports of Longwood, Inc. (1)
1000 Rinehart Rd, Sanford, FL 32771
Tel.: (689) 444-2958
Web Site:
https://www.autonationhondasanford.com
Car & Commercial Vehicle Dealer
N.A.I.C.S.: 441227
Julie Miller (Gen Mgr)

AutoNation Imports of Palm Beach, Inc. (1)
5700 Okeechobee Blvd, West Palm Beach, FL 33417-4320
Tel.: (561) 461-4419
Web Site:
https://www.lexusofpalmbeach.com
Car & Commercial Vehicle Dealer
N.A.I.C.S.: 441227
Jason Morgan (Dir-Fin)
Alex Quinones (Mgr-Fin)
Darryl Lewis (Mgr-VIP)
Dave Matushin (Mgr-VIP)
Marianne Noya (Mgr-VIP)
Juan Mundo (Mgr-VIP)
Jackson Hughes (Mgr-VIP)
Eli Garcia (Mgr-Used Car)
Marc Cherenson (Mgr-Internet Sls)
Criag Lopata (Mgr-Internet Sls)
Rick Pomante (Mgr-Internet Sls)
Ron Speck (Mgr-Internet Sls)
Derek Postin (Mgr-Fin)
Rob Paprin (Mgr-Fin)
Tony Skulski (Dir-Internet)
Tim Downey (Asst Mgr-Parts)

AutoNation Imports of Winter Park, Inc. (1)
225 N Semoran Blvd, Winter Park, FL 32792
Tel.: (689) 444-2149
Web Site:
https://www.autonationtoyotawinter park.com
Automotive Retailer
N.A.I.C.S.: 441110

AutoNation Imports of Winter Park, Inc. (1)
225 N Semoran Blvd, Winter Park, FL 32792
Tel.: (689) 444-2311
Web Site:
https://www.autonationtoyotawinter park.com
Car Dealer Services
N.A.I.C.S.: 441110

AutoNation Nissan Orange Park (1)

7447 Blanding Blvd, Jacksonville, FL 32244
Tel.: (904) 270-9954
Web Site:
http://www.autonationnissanorange park.com
Car Dealership Services
N.A.I.C.S.: 441110

AutoNation V. Imports of Delray Beach, LLC (1)
2201 N Federal Hwy, Delray Beach, FL 33483-6013
Tel.: (561) 243-4600
Emp.: 200
Car Dealer Services
N.A.I.C.S.: 441110
Joseph Gunther (Owner)

AutoNationDirect.com, Inc. (1)
110 S E 6th St 20th Fl, Fort Lauderdale, FL 33301
Tel.: (877) 600-3011
Web Site: http://www.autonationdirect.com
Car & Commercial Vehicle Dealer
N.A.I.C.S.: 441227

Autohaus Holdings, Inc.
350 W Copans Rd, Pompano Beach, FL 33064
Tel.: (954) 644-4832
Emp.: 220
Car Dealer Services
N.A.I.C.S.: 441110
John Monteleone (Gen Mgr)

Autonation Chevrolet Fort Lauderdale (1)
1300 N Federal Hwy, Fort Lauderdale, FL 33304
Tel.: (954) 889-5451
Web Site:
http://www.autonationchevroletfortlau derdale.com
Car Sales Services
N.A.I.C.S.: 441110

Autonation Chevrolet Spokane Valley (1)
8500 E Sprague Ave, Spokane Valley, WA 99212-2978
Tel.: (509) 209-9973
Web Site:
https://www.autonationchevroletspokane valley.com
Car & Commercial Vehicle Dealer
N.A.I.C.S.: 441110

Autonation Ford East (1)
28825 Euclid Ave, Wickliffe, OH 44092
Tel.: (440) 782-8540
Web Site:
http://www.autonationfordeast.com
New & Used Car Dealers
N.A.I.C.S.: 441120

Autonation Ford Wolfcase (1)
7925 Stage Rd, Memphis, TN 38133
Tel.: (901) 686-9622
Web Site:
https://www.autonationfordwolfchase.com
New & Used Car Dealers
N.A.I.C.S.: 441110

Autonation Nissan Lewisville (1)
1601 S Stemmons Fwy, Lewisville, TX 75067
Tel.: (972) 853-9551
Web Site:
https://www.nissanoflewisville.com
Car & Commercial Vehicle Dealer
N.A.I.C.S.: 441227

Autonation Toyota Cerritos (1)
18700 Studebaker Rd, Cerritos, CA 90703
Tel.: (562) 850-2324
Web Site:
https://www.autonationtoyotacerritos.com
Emp.: 200
Auto Dealerships
N.A.I.C.S.: 441110

Autonation Toyota Corpus Christi (1)
6672 S Padre Island Dr, Corpus Christi, TX 78412
Tel.: (361) 827-2161
Web Site:
https://www.autonationtoyotacorpus christi.com
Car & Commercial Vehicle Dealer
N.A.I.C.S.: 441110

Bargain Rent-A-Car (1)
317 S Escondido Blvd, Escondido, CA 92025
Tel.: (760) 489-8550
Web Site: https://www.bargainrentacar.net
Car & Commercial Vehicle Dealer
N.A.I.C.S.: 441227

Beacon Motors, Inc. (1)
1201 NW 89th Ct, Miami, FL 33172-3015
Tel.: (786) 220-0901
Web Site:
https://www.autonationchevroletdoral.com
Automotive Retailer
N.A.I.C.S.: 441110

Beacon Motors, Inc. (1)
1201 NW 89th Ct, Miami, FL 33172-3015
Tel.: (786) 220-0901
Web Site:
https://www.autonationchevroletdoral.com
Car Repair Services
N.A.I.C.S.: 811111

Bell Dodge, L.L.C. (1)
1217 N Coast Hwy 101, Newport, OR 97365
Tel.: (541) 293-6744
Automotive Retailer
N.A.I.C.S.: 441110

Bell Motors, LLC (1)
16406 N 26th Ave, Phoenix, AZ 85023-3100
Tel.: (480) 660-9945
Automotive Retailer
N.A.I.C.S.: 441110

Bellevue Automotive, Inc. (1)
120 116th Ave NE, Bellevue, WA 98004-5215
Tel.: (425) 970-8422
Web Site:
https://www.autonationchryslerdodgejeep rambellevue.com
Automotive Retailer
N.A.I.C.S.: 441110

Bellevue Collision, Inc. (1)
1424 130th Ave NE, Bellevue, WA 98005
Tel.: (425) 504-8731
Web Site:
https://www.autonationcollisioncen ters.com
Automotive Retailer
N.A.I.C.S.: 441110

Bellevue Collision, Inc. (1)
1424 130th Ave NE, Bellevue, WA 98005
New & Used Car Dealer
N.A.I.C.S.: 441110

Bengal Motor Company, Ltd. (1)
5925 NW 167th St, Miami Lakes, FL 33015
Tel.: (305) 707-0143
Web Site:
https://www.autonationhondamiami lakes.com
Car Dealer Services
N.A.I.C.S.: 441110

Bengal Motor Company, Ltd. (1)
5925 NW 167th St, Miami Lakes, FL 33015
Web Site:
https://www.autonationhondamiami lakes.com
Automotive Retailer
N.A.I.C.S.: 441110

Bethesda Luxury Imports, LLC (1)
11617 Old Georgetown Rd, Bethesda, MD 20852
Tel.: (240) 903-9960
Web Site: https://www.jaguarbethesda.com
New & Used Car Dealer
N.A.I.C.S.: 441110

Bill Ayares Chevrolet, LLC (1)
500 Washington Blvd, Laurel, MD 20707-4697
Tel.: (240) 294-5149
Web Site:
https://www.autonationchevroletlaurel.com
Automotive Retailer
N.A.I.C.S.: 441110

Brown & Brown Chevrolet - Superstition Springs, LLC (1)
6330 E Superstition Springs Blvd, Mesa, AZ 85206-4395
Tel.: (480) 304-7640

Web Site:
https://www.autonationchevroletmesa.com
Sales Range: $25-49.9 Million
New & Used Car Dealing Services
N.A.I.C.S.: 441110

Brown & Brown Chevrolet, Inc. (1)
3215 S Auto Way, Gilbert, AZ 85297-0446
Tel.: (480) 359-2264
Web Site:
https://www.autonationchevroletgilbert.com
Sales Range: $125-149.9 Million
New & Used Automobiles Dealership
N.A.I.C.S.: 441110

Brown & Brown Nissan Mesa, LLC (1)
1350 S Gilbert Rd, Chandler, AZ 85286
Tel.: (623) 259-5735
Web Site:
https://www.autonationnissanchandler.com
Automotive Retailer
N.A.I.C.S.: 441110

Brown & Brown Nissan Mesa, LLC (1)
1350 S Gilbert Rd, Chandler, AZ 85286
Tel.: (623) 259-5832
Web Site:
https://www.autonationnissanchandler.com
New & Used Car Dealer
N.A.I.C.S.: 441110

Brown & Brown Nissan, Inc. (1)
7755 S Autoplex Loop, Tempe, AZ 85284
Tel.: (623) 432-8125
Web Site:
https://www.autonationnissantempe.com
Car Dealer Services
N.A.I.C.S.: 441110

Brown & Brown Nissan, Inc. (1)
7755 S Autoplex Loop, Tempe, AZ 85284
Tel.: (602) 691-6012
Web Site:
https://www.autonationnissantempe.com
Automotive Retailer
N.A.I.C.S.: 441110

Buena Park Luxury Imports, Inc. (1)
6750 Auto Center Dr, Buena Park, CA 90621
Tel.: (657) 660-4035
Web Site: https://www.bmwbuenapark.com
Automotive Retailer
N.A.I.C.S.: 441110

Bull Motors, LLC (1)
16800 NW 57th Ave, Miami, FL 33015
Web Site:
https://www.autonationfordmiami.com
Automotive Retailer
N.A.I.C.S.: 441110

CT Intercontinental, Ltd. (1)
17730 N Fwy, Houston, TX 77090
Tel.: (281) 271-5290
Web Site:
https://www.bmwofhoustonnorth.com
Automotive Retailer
N.A.I.C.S.: 441110

CT Motors, Inc. (1)
1125 Gulf Fwy S, League City, TX 77573
Tel.: (346) 509-6855
Web Site:
https://www.autonationacuragulffree way.com
Automotive Retailer
N.A.I.C.S.: 441110

CarCountry Motors, Inc. (1)
703 S Glenstone, Springfield, MO 65802
Tel.: (417) 865-1800
Web Site:
https://www.carcountrymotors.com
Electric Vehicle Distr
N.A.I.C.S.: 423110

Carlisle Motors, LLC (1)
4220 Ave Q, Lubbock, TX 79412
Tel.: (806) 747-3456
Web Site: https://carlislemotors.com
Automotive Retailer
N.A.I.C.S.: 441110

Carwell, LLC (1)
3311 Pacific Coast Hwy, Torrance, CA 90505
Tel.: (213) 556-3969
Web Site: https://www.sbmercedes.com

AutoNation, Inc.—(Continued)
Car Dealer Services
N.A.I.C.S.: 441110

Carwell, LLC (1)
3311 Pacific Coast Hwy, Torrance, CA 90505
Tel.: (213) 556-0663
Web Site: https://www.sbmercedes.com
Automotive Retailer
N.A.I.C.S.: 441110

Centennial Automotive, LLC (1)
10743 E Arapahoe Rd, Centennial, CO 80112-3809
Tel.: (720) 615-2791
Web Site:
https://www.autonationdodgeramarapahoe.com
Car Dealer Services
N.A.I.C.S.: 441110

Cerritos Body Works, Inc. (1)
44 Auto Ctr Dr, Irvine, CA 92618
Tel.: (949) 478-0585
Car Dealer Services
N.A.I.C.S.: 441110

Champion Chevrolet, LLC (1)
3606 Bristol Hwy, Johnson City, TN 37601
Tel.: (423) 670-7938
Web Site: https://www.championjc.com
Automotive Retailer
N.A.I.C.S.: 441110

Champion Ford, Inc. (1)
1114 W US Hwy 30, Carroll, IA 51401
Tel.: (712) 792-1505
Web Site:
https://www.championfordofcarroll.com
New Car Dealers
N.A.I.C.S.: 441110

Chandler Collision, Inc. (1)
3536 E Cherokee Ave, Sallisaw, OK 74955
Tel.: (918) 776-0606
Web Site:
https://www.chandlercollisioncenter.net
New Car & Used Car Dealing Services
N.A.I.C.S.: 441110

Charleston ANUSA, LLC (1)
2250 Savannah Hwy, Charleston, SC 29414
Electric Car Mfr & Distr
N.A.I.C.S.: 336320

Charlie Hillard, Inc. (1)
5000 Bryant Irvin Rd, Fort Worth, TX 76132
Tel.: (682) 808-6524
Web Site:
https://www.autonationfordfortworth.com
Car Dealer Services
N.A.I.C.S.: 441110

Charlie Hillard, Inc. (1)
5000 Bryant Irvin Rd, Fort Worth, TX 76132
Tel.: (682) 331-8580
Web Site:
https://www.autonationfordfortworth.com
Automotive Retailer
N.A.I.C.S.: 441110

Charlie Thomas Chevrolet, Ltd. (1)
13800 Gulf Fwy, Houston, TX 77034-5009
Tel.: (281) 914-4354
Web Site:
https://www.autonationchevroletgulffreeway.com
Automotive Retailer
N.A.I.C.S.: 441110

Charlie Thomas Courtesy Ford, Ltd. (1)
6250 S Padre Island Dr, Corpus Christi, TX 78412
Tel.: (361) 827-2912
Web Site:
https://www.autonationfordcorpuschristi.com
Automotive Retailer
N.A.I.C.S.: 441110

Charlie Thomas Ford, Ltd. (1)
12227 Gulf Fwy, Houston, TX 77034-4503
Tel.: (346) 766-0130
Web Site: https://www.autonationfordgulffreeway.com
Sales Range: $900-999.9 Million
Car Dealership Owner & Operator
N.A.I.C.S.: 441110

Charlie Thomas Ford, Ltd. (1)
12227 Gulf Fwy, Houston, TX 77034
Tel.: (346) 971-4038
Web Site: https://www.autonationfordgulffreeway.com
Car & Commercial Vehicles
N.A.I.C.S.: 441110

Chesrown Chevrolet, LLC (1)
7320 N BRdway, Denver, CO 80221-3610
Tel.: (720) 836-7087
Web Site:
https://www.autonationchevroletnorth.com
New Car Dealers
N.A.I.C.S.: 441110

Chesrown Collision Center, Inc. (1)
7420 N Washington, Denver, CO 80229
Tel.: (303) 578-6105
Web Site:
http://www.autonationcollisioncenters.com
New Car Dealers
N.A.I.C.S.: 441110

Chevrolet World, Inc. (1)
5600 Lee Vista Blvd, Orlando, FL 32812-3021
Tel.: (407) 270-1585
Web Site:
https://www.autonationchevroletairport.com
Automotive Retailer
N.A.I.C.S.: 441110

Chevrolet World, Inc. (1)
5600 Lee Vista Blvd, Orlando, FL 32812-3021
Tel.: (407) 270-1585
Web Site:
https://www.autonationchevroletairport.com
Car Dealer Services
N.A.I.C.S.: 441110

Chuck Clancy Ford of Marietta, LLC (1)
869 Cobb Pkwy S, Marietta, GA 30060
Tel.: (470) 922-9194
Web Site:
https://www.autonationfordmarietta.com
Car Dealer Services
N.A.I.C.S.: 441110

Chuck Clancy Ford of Marietta, LLC (1)
869 Cobb Pkwy SE, Marietta, GA 30060
Tel.: (470) 970-5054
Web Site:
https://www.autonationfordmarietta.com
Automotive Retailer
N.A.I.C.S.: 441110

Coastal Cadillac, Inc. (1)
8559 Ocean Hwy, Pawleys Island, SC 29585
Tel.: (843) 894-1081
Web Site:
https://www.coastalcadillacpawleys.com
New Car Dealers
N.A.I.C.S.: 441110

Colorado Springs ANUSA, LLC (1)
5120 New Car Dr, Colorado Springs, CO 80923
Tel.: (719) 715-2581
Electric Car Mfr & Distr
N.A.I.C.S.: 336320

Contemporary Cars, Inc. (1)
810 N Orlando Ave, Maitland, FL 32751
Tel.: (689) 444-2646
Web Site: https://www.mborlando.com
Automotive Retailer
N.A.I.C.S.: 441110

Cook-Whitehead Ford, Inc. (1)
730 W 15th St, Panama City, FL 32401
Tel.: (850) 904-8046
Web Site:
https://www.autonationfordpanamacity.com
Automotive Retailer
N.A.I.C.S.: 441110

Corpus Christi ANUSA, LLC (1)
3115 S Padre Island Dr, Corpus Christi, TX 78415
Tel.: (361) 208-0227
Web Site: http://www.autonationusa.com
New & Used Car Dealer

Corpus Christi Collision Center, Inc. (1)
1310 Daly, Corpus Christi, TX 78412
Tel.: (316) 400-1222
Automotive Repair Services
N.A.I.C.S.: 811111
Jerry Labrador (Gen Mgr)

Costa Mesa Cars, Inc. (1)
2888 Harbor Blvd, Costa Mesa, CA 92626
Tel.: (657) 655-3815
Web Site:
https://www.autonationhondacostamesa.com
Automotive Retailer
N.A.I.C.S.: 441110

Courtesy Chevrolet Inc. (1)
3707 W Colonial Dr, Orlando, FL 32808-7905
Tel.: (407) 295-7000
Web Site: http://www.autonation.com
Sales Range: $100-124.9 Million
Emp.: 130
Automobile Dealership
N.A.I.C.S.: 441110

Covington Pike Motors, Inc. (1)
1990 Covington Pike, Memphis, TN 38128
Tel.: (901) 587-4458
Web Site:
https://www.autonationhondacovingtonpike.com
Automotive Retailer
N.A.I.C.S.: 441110

D/L Motor Company (1)
17275 US Hwy 19 N, Clearwater, FL 33764
Tel.: (727) 977-1253
Web Site:
https://www.autonationhondaclearwater.com
Automotive Retailer
N.A.I.C.S.: 441110

D/L Motor Company (1)
17275 US Hwy 19 N, Clearwater, FL 33764
Tel.: (727) 855-3585
Web Site:
https://www.autonationhondaclearwater.com
Car Dealer Services
N.A.I.C.S.: 441110

Denver 104 ANUSA, LLC (1)
759 W 104th Ave, Denver, CO 80234
Tel.: (720) 973-8616
Electric Car Mfr & Distr
N.A.I.C.S.: 336320

Desert Buick-GMC Trucks, L.L.C. (1)
6400 W Sahara, Las Vegas, NV 89146-3033
Tel.: (702) 948-7277
Web Site:
https://www.autonationbuickgmcwestsahara.com
New Car Dealers
N.A.I.C.S.: 441110

Desert GMC, L.L.C. (1)
330 N Gibson Rd, Henderson, NV 89014-6702
Tel.: (702) 979-2044
Web Site:
https://www.autonationbuickgmchenderson.com
New & Used Car Dealer Services
N.A.I.C.S.: 441110

Dobbs Ford of Memphis, Inc. (1)
7925 Stage Rd, Memphis, TN 38133
Tel.: (901) 810-6116
Web Site:
https://www.autonationfordwolfchase.com
Automotive Retailer
N.A.I.C.S.: 441110

Dobbs Ford, Inc. (1)
2515 Mt Moriah Rd, Memphis, TN 38115
Tel.: (901) 902-5696
Web Site:
https://www.autonationfordmemphis.com
Automotive Retailer
N.A.I.C.S.: 441110

Dobbs Mobile Bay, Inc. (1)
901 E I65 Service Rd S, Mobile, AL 36606

Tel.: (251) 202-2016
Web Site:
https://www.autonationfordmobile.com
Car Dealer Services
N.A.I.C.S.: 441110

Dobbs Mobile Bay, Inc. (1)
901 E Interstate 65 Service Rd S, Mobile, AL 36606
Web Site:
https://www.autonationfordmobile.com
Automotive Retailer
N.A.I.C.S.: 441110

Dobbs Motors of Arizona, Inc. (1)
810 W Wetmore Rd, Tucson, AZ 85705
Tel.: (520) 200-8394
Web Site:
https://www.autonationdatucsonautomall.com
Automotive Retailer
N.A.I.C.S.: 441110

Dobbs Motors of Arizona, Inc. (1)
810 W Wetmore Rd, Tucson, AZ 85705
Tel.: (520) 200-8630
Web Site:
https://www.autonationdatucsonautomall.com
New & Used Car Dealer
N.A.I.C.S.: 441110

Dodge of Bellevue, Inc. (1)
120 116th Ave NE, Bellevue, WA 98004
Tel.: (425) 276-7124
Web Site:
https://www.autonationchryslerdodgejeeprambellevue.com
New Car Dealers
N.A.I.C.S.: 441110

Don Mealey Chevrolet, Inc. (1)
17185 State Rd 50, Clermont, FL 34711-8011
Tel.: (352) 432-1163
Web Site: https://www.dmchevy.com
Car Dealer Services
N.A.I.C.S.: 441110
Jon Boam (Gen Mgr-Sls)

Don Mealey Chevrolet, Inc. (1)
17185 State Rd 50, Clermont, FL 34711-8011
Tel.: (352) 432-1163
Web Site: https://www.dmchevy.com
Automotive Retailer
N.A.I.C.S.: 441110

Don Mealey Imports, Inc. (1)
1001 Rinehart Rd, Sanford, FL 32771
Tel.: (689) 444-2624
Web Site:
http://www.autonationacuranorthorlando.com
Sales Range: $10-24.9 Million
New & Used Car Dealer
N.A.I.C.S.: 441110
Robert Breedlove (Gen Mgr)

Ed Mullinax Ford, LLC (1)
8000 Leavitt Rd, Amherst, OH 44001
Tel.: (440) 652-2505
Web Site:
https://www.autonationfordamherst.com
Automotive Retailer
N.A.I.C.S.: 441110

Edgren Motor Company, Inc. (1)
5780 Cushing Pkwy, Fremont, CA 94538
Tel.: (510) 999-9570
Web Site:
https://www.autonationhondafremont.com
Automotive Retailer
N.A.I.C.S.: 441110

Edgren Motor Company, Inc. (1)
5780 Cushing Pkwy, Fremont, CA 94538
Tel.: (510) 963-4087
Web Site:
https://www.autonationhondafremont.com
Car Dealer Services
N.A.I.C.S.: 441110

Emich Subaru West, LLC (1)
16351 W Colfax Ave, Golden, CO 80401
Tel.: (720) 407-5768
Web Site:
https://www.autonationsubaruwest.com
Car Dealer Services
N.A.I.C.S.: 441110

Emich Subaru West, LLC (1)
16351 W Colfax Ave, Golden, CO 80401
Tel.: (720) 808-1779
Web Site:
https://www.autonationsubaruwest.com
Automotive Retailer
N.A.I.C.S.: 441110

First Team Ford of Manatee, Ltd. (1)
5325 14th St W, Bradenton, FL 34207
Tel.: (941) 770-5321
Web Site:
https://www.autonationfordbradenton.com
Automotive Retailer
N.A.I.C.S.: 441110

First Team Ford, Ltd (1)
4911 Wayside Dr, Sanford, FL 32771
Tel.: (689) 444-2865
Web Site:
https://www.autonationfordsanford.com
Automotive Retailer
N.A.I.C.S.: 441110

First Team Ford, Ltd. (1)
4911 Wayside Dr, Sanford, FL 32771
Tel.: (407) 794-2679
Web Site:
https://www.autonationfordsanford.com
Car Dealer Services
N.A.I.C.S.: 441110

Fit Kit, Inc. (1)
6400 Beach Blvd, Buena Park, CA 90621
Tel.: (657) 655-4818
Web Site:
https://www.autonationtoyotabuena
park.com
Car Dealer Services
N.A.I.C.S.: 441110

Fit Kit, Inc. (1)
6400 Beach Blvd, Buena Park, CA 90621
Tel.: (657) 966-7994
Web Site:
https://www.autonationtoyotabuena
park.com
Automotive Retailer
N.A.I.C.S.: 441110

Ford Lincoln of Bellevue (1)
411 116th Ave NE, Bellevue, WA 98004
Tel.: (425) 454-9585
Web Site: http://www.flmofbellevue.com
Sales Range: $10-24.9 Million
Emp.: 60
Automobiles, New & Used
N.A.I.C.S.: 441110

Ford of Kirkland, Inc. (1)
11800 124th Ave NE, Kirkland, WA 98034-
8109
Tel.: (425) 284-9514
Web Site: https://www.fordofkirkland.com
New Car Dealers
N.A.I.C.S.: 441110
Richard Ewing (Mgr-Sls)
Steve Cunnington (Mgr-Fleet)
Chris Busik (Mgr-Sls)
Noel Holler (Mgr-Customer Svc)

Fox Automotive Group (1)
501 Washington Blvd S 5, Laurel, MD
20707
Tel.: (301) 725-2700
Web Site: http://www.foxdealers.com
Sales Range: $50-74.9 Million
Emp.: 84
Automobile Sales
N.A.I.C.S.: 441110

Fox Chevrolet, LLC (1)
632 E Main St SE, Caledonia, MI 49316
Tel.: (410) 265-7777
Web Site: https://www.foxchevrolet.com
New Car Dealers
N.A.I.C.S.: 441110
Jeff Dickinson (Office Mgr)
Keegan Geldersma (Mgr-Bus)
Tim Tape (Mgr-Body Shop)
Joe Birtles (Mgr-Parts)
Jerry Moore (Dir-Div)
Brad Maslowski (Sls Mgr-New Car)
Adam Versluis (Mgr-Svc)

Fox Motors, LLC (1)
1 Randall Ave, Mine Hill, NJ 07803
Tel.: (973) 343-6585
Web Site: https://foxmotorsag.com
Emp.: 1

New Car Dealers
N.A.I.C.S.: 441110
Mark Forman (Owner)

Ft. Lauderdale Nissan, Inc. (1)
1051 S Federal Hwy, Fort Lauderdale, FL
33316
Tel.: (954) 271-0538
Web Site:
http://www.ftlauderdalenissan.com
New Car Dealers
N.A.I.C.S.: 441110

**G.B. Import Sales & Service,
LLC** (1)
3010 Pacific Coast Hwy, Torrance, CA
90505
Tel.: (424) 253-6969
Car Dealer Services
N.A.I.C.S.: 441110

GA CDJR Motors, LLC (1)
3000 N Lake Pkwy Bldg 100, Columbus,
GA 31909-2514
Tel.: (706) 408-8827
Web Site:
https://www.autonationchryslerdodgejeep
ramnorthcolumbus.com
New & Used Car Dealer
N.A.I.C.S.: 441110

GA Columbus Imports, LLC (1)
3000 N Lake Pkwy Bldg 300, Columbus,
GA 31909
Tel.: (762) 286-3599
Web Site:
https://www.autonationvolkswagenco
lumbus.com
New & Used Car Dealer
N.A.I.C.S.: 441110

GA H Imports, LLC (1)
3000 N Lake Pkwy Ste 400, Columbus, GA
31909
Tel.: (762) 286-5169
Web Site:
https://www.autonationhondacolum
bus.com
New & Used Car Dealer
N.A.I.C.S.: 441110

GA HY Imports, LLC (1)
3000 N Lake Pkwy, Columbus, GA 31909
Tel.: (762) 286-4105
Web Site:
https://www.autonationhyundaicolum
bus.com
New & Used Car Dealer
N.A.I.C.S.: 441110

GA-CC Columbus, Inc. (1)
300 N Lake Pkwy, Columbus, GA 31909
Tel.: (706) 610-0805
Automotive Engine Repair & Replacement
Services
N.A.I.C.S.: 811111

Gene Evans Ford, LLC (1)
4355 Jonesboro Rd, Union City, GA 30291
Tel.: (470) 412-6896
Web Site:
https://www.autonationfordunioncity.com
Automotive Retailer
N.A.I.C.S.: 441110

Gene Evans Ford, LLC (1)
4355 Jonesboro Rd, Union City, GA 30291
Tel.: (470) 649-0812
Web Site:
https://www.autonationfordunioncity.com
Emp.: 200
Car Dealer Services
N.A.I.C.S.: 441110
Bill Miller (Gen Mgr)

George Sutherlin Nissan, LLC (1)
925 Cobb Pkwy SE, Marietta, GA 30060
Tel.: (470) 748-2296
Web Site:
https://www.autonationnissanmarietta.com
Automotive Retailer
N.A.I.C.S.: 441110

Gilbert Body Shop, Inc. (1)
2190 S Douglas Dr, Chandler, AZ 85286
Tel.: (480) 269-1990
Automotive Engine Repair & Replacement
Services
N.A.I.C.S.: 811111
Kenneth Martin (Gen Mgr)

Go Cars and Trucks (1)
16400 W Colfax Ave, Golden, CO
80401-3850 **(100%)**
Tel.: (303) 278-4433
Web Site: http://www.gocarsandtrucks.com
Sales Range: $125-149.9 Million
Emp.: 250
Car Dealership
N.A.I.C.S.: 441110

**Government Boulevard Motors,
Inc.** (1)
1175 E I-65 Service Rd S, Mobile, AL
36606
Tel.: (251) 200-4838
Web Site:
https://www.autonationhondaatbelair
mall.com
New & Used Car Dealer
N.A.I.C.S.: 441110

Gulf Management, Inc. (1)
27547 US Hwy 19 N, Clearwater, FL 33761
Tel.: (727) 250-5159
Web Site:
https://www.lexusofclearwater.com
Automotive Retailer
N.A.I.C.S.: 441110

HH-CDJR Motors, Inc. (1)
14920 Crest Rd, Papillion, NE 68138
Tel.: (402) 339-3131
Web Site: https://www.hhjeepdodgeram.com
Electric Vehicle Services
N.A.I.C.S.: 811198

HH-Collision, Inc. (1)
2924 Cincinnati-Dayton Rd, Middletown, OH
45044
Tel.: (513) 422-1062
Web Site: https://www.hhcollision.com
Vehicle Maintenance Services
N.A.I.C.S.: 811198

HV York Road Imports, LLC (1)
183 Greenwich Ave Ste B, Goshen, NY
10924
Tel.: (845) 926-2167
Web Site: https://www.hvnyimports.com
Mini Truck Distr
N.A.I.C.S.: 423110

HVA Imports, LLC (1)
9800 York Rd, Cockeysville, MD 21030
Web Site: https://www.audihuntvalley.com
New & Used Car Dealer
N.A.I.C.S.: 441110

HVM Imports, LLC (1)
9800 York Rd, Cockeysville, MD 21030
Tel.: (667) 930-1702
Web Site:
https://www.mercedesbenzofhuntval
ley.com
New & Used Car Dealer
N.A.I.C.S.: 441110

HVS Motors, LLC (1)
9800 York Rd Ste 2, Cockeysville, MD
21030
Tel.: (667) 358-5866
Web Site:
https://www.autonationsubaruhuntval
ley.com
New & Used Car Dealer
N.A.I.C.S.: 441110

Henderson ANUSA, LLC (1)
380 N Gibson Rd, Henderson, NV 89014
Tel.: (725) 201-7650
Web Site: http://www.autonationusa.com
Used Car & Truck Retailer
N.A.I.C.S.: 441120

Henderson Collision, Inc. (1)
560 Hardee St, Dallas, GA 30132
Tel.: (770) 443-1341
Web Site:
https://www.hendersoncollision.com
Auto Body Repair Services
N.A.I.C.S.: 811121
Jimmy Henderson (Owner)

Hollywood Imports Limited, Inc. (1)
2400 N State Rd 7, Hollywood, FL 33021
Tel.: (954) 998-0945
Web Site: https://www.autonationhondaholly
wood.com
Automotive Retailer
N.A.I.C.S.: 441110

Horizon Chevrolet, Inc. (1)
1569 W Ogden Ave, Naperville, IL 60540
Tel.: (630) 537-0312
Car Dealer Services
N.A.I.C.S.: 441110
Dan Wolf (Owner)

Houston ANUSA, LLC (1)
8526 N Fwy, Houston, TX 77037
Tel.: (281) 657-9663
Used Car & Truck Retailer
N.A.I.C.S.: 441120

**Houston Auto M. Imports Greenway,
Ltd.** (1)
3900 SW Fwy, Houston, TX 77027
Tel.: (346) 396-3980
Web Site:
https://www.mercedesbenzgreenway.com
Car Dealer Services
N.A.I.C.S.: 441110

**Houston Auto M. Imports Greenway,
Ltd.** (1)
3900 Southwest Fwy, Houston, TX 77027
Tel.: (346) 646-6090
Web Site:
https://www.mercedesbenzgreenway.com
Automotive Retailer
N.A.I.C.S.: 441110

**Houston Auto M. Imports North,
Ltd.** (1)
17510 North Fwy, Houston, TX 77090
Tel.: (346) 509-7587
Web Site:
https://www.mercedesbenzhouston
north.com
Automotive Retailer
N.A.I.C.S.: 441110

Infiniti South Bay (1)
3233 Pacific Coast Hwy, Torrance, CA
90505-6613
Tel.: (424) 245-0985
Web Site: http://www.infinitiofsouthbay.com
Emp.: 50
Car Dealer Services
N.A.I.C.S.: 441110

Infiniti Tustin (1)
33 Auto Ctr Dr, Tustin, CA 92782 **(100%)**
Tel.: (714) 627-5556
Web Site: http://www.infinitioftustin.com
Sales Range: $50-74.9 Million
Emp.: 50
New & Used Car Dealers
N.A.I.C.S.: 441110

Irvine Imports, Inc. (1)
9101 Research Dr, Irvine, CA 92618-4206
Tel.: (949) 287-8766
Web Site:
https://www.autonationtoyotairvine.com
New & Used Car Dealers
N.A.I.C.S.: 441110

J-R Motors Company North (1)
2999 W 104th Ave, Westminster, CO 80234
Tel.: (720) 767-0340
Web Site:
https://www.autonationhonda104.com
Car Dealer Services
N.A.I.C.S.: 441110

JRJ Investments, Inc. (1)
6335 W Sahara Ave, Las Vegas, NV 89146
Tel.: (702) 570-0276
Web Site: https://www.audilasvegas.com
Car Dealer
N.A.I.C.S.: 441110
Todd Maul (Pres)

Jim Quinlan Chevrolet Co. (1)
15005 US Hwy 19 N, Clearwater, FL
33764-7163
Tel.: (727) 378-2758
Web Site:
https://www.autonationchevroletclear
water.com
Automotive Retailer
N.A.I.C.S.: 441110

Joe MacPherson Ford (1)
2 Auto Center Dr, Tustin, CA 92782
Tel.: (657) 600-6535
Web Site:
https://www.autonationfordtustin.com
Automotive Retailer
N.A.I.C.S.: 441110

AutoNation, Inc.—(Continued)

Joe MacPherson Ford (1)
2 Auto Ctr Dr, Tustin, CA 92782
Tel.: (657) 966-7997
Web Site:
  http://www.autonationfordtustin.com
Car Dealer
N.A.I.C.S.: 441110
Jeffrey Nicols (CEO & Sec)

Joe MacPherson Infiniti (1)
33 Auto Center Dr, Tustin, CA 92782
Tel.: (657) 660-1700
Web Site: https://www.infinitioftustin.com
Automotive Retailer
N.A.I.C.S.: 441110

John M. Lance Ford, LLC (1)
23775 Center Ridge Rd, Westlake, OH
44145
Tel.: (440) 782-8323
New Car Dealers
N.A.I.C.S.: 441110
Dean Szalai (Gen Mgr)

Katy ANUSA, LLC (1)
15625 Katy Fwy, Houston, TX 77094
Tel.: (832) 436-0599
Web Site: http://www.autonationusa.com
Used Car & Truck Retailer
N.A.I.C.S.: 441120

King's Crown Ford, Inc. (1)
10720 Phillips Hwy, Jacksonville, FL 32256
Tel.: (904) 578-7923
Web Site:
  https://www.autonationfordjacksonvil
  le.com
Car Dealer Services
N.A.I.C.S.: 441110

King's Crown Ford, Inc. (1)
10720 Phillips Hwy, Jacksonville, FL 32256
Tel.: (904) 456-0976
Web Site:
  https://www.autonationfordjacksonvil
  le.com
Automotive Retailer
N.A.I.C.S.: 441110

Kirkland Motors (1)
124 S Main St Ste 2-F, Jonesboro, GA
30236
Tel.: (404) 374-8926
Web Site: http://www.garrettkirkland.com
Car Dealer Services
N.A.I.C.S.: 441110
Garrett Kirkland (Pres)

L.P. Evans Motors WPB, Inc. (1)
1200 NW 167th St, Miami, FL 33169
Tel.: (305) 707-0147
Web Site:
  https://www.mercedesbenzofmiami.com
Car Dealer Services
N.A.I.C.S.: 441110

L.P. Evans Motors WPB, Inc. (1)
1200 NW 167th St, Miami, FL 33169
Web Site:
  https://www.mercedesbenzofmiami.com
Automotive Retailer
N.A.I.C.S.: 441110

L.P. Evans Motors, Inc. (1)
3345 SW 8th St, Miami, FL 33135
Web Site:
  https://www.autonationnissanmiami.com
Automotive Retailer
N.A.I.C.S.: 441110

L.P. Evans Motors, Inc. (1)
3345 SW 8th St, Miami, FL 33135
Tel.: (305) 707-0145
Web Site:
  https://www.autonationnissanmiami.com
Car Dealer Services
N.A.I.C.S.: 441110

Leesburg Motors, LLC (1)
1 Cardinal Park Dr SE, Leesburg, VA 20175
Tel.: (571) 899-6732
Web Site:
  https://www.autonationtoyotaleesburg.com
Automotive Retailer
N.A.I.C.S.: 441110

Lewisville Collision, Inc. (1)
170 E Country Ridge Rd, Lewisville, TX
75067

Tel.: (972) 249-0922
Automotive Engine Repair & Replacement
Services
N.A.I.C.S.: 811111
Haefs Dan (Asst Mgr)

Lewisville Imports, Ltd. (1)
601 Waters Ridge Dr, Lewisville, TX 75057
Tel.: (469) 817-7526
Web Site:
  https://www.autonationhondalewisvil
  le.com
Automotive Retailer
N.A.I.C.S.: 441110

**Lexus of Cerritos Limited
Partnership** (1)
18800 Studebaker Rd, Cerritos, CA 90703
Tel.: (562) 661-6793
Web Site: https://www.cerritoslexus.com
Car Dealer Services
N.A.I.C.S.: 441110
Walid Sarsak (Mgr-Sls)
Anthony Olmedo (Mgr)
Moon Kim (Dir-Fleet & Mgr-Lease Retention)
Sean Wyda (Asst Mgr)
Ruben Oredo (Asst Mgr)
Omar Salgado (Mgr-Sls)
Natalie Barrera (Sls Mgr)
Mario Vasquez (Mgr-)
Brian Walker (Gen Mgr)
Sonia Mendoza (Mgr)

Luxury Orlando Imports, Inc. (1)
4725 Vineland Rd, Orlando, FL 32811
Web Site:
  https://www.audisouthorlando.com
Automotive Retailer
N.A.I.C.S.: 441110

Luxury Woodlands Imports, Inc. (1)
17830 InterState 45 S, The Woodlands, TX
77384
Tel.: (936) 777-8252
Web Site:
  https://www.bmwofthewoodlands.com
New & Used Car Dealer
N.A.I.C.S.: 441110

Magic Acquisition Corp. (1)
23920 Creekside Rd, Valencia, CA 91355-
1732
Tel.: (661) 583-0138
Web Site:
  https://www.autonationfordvalencia.com
Car Dealer Services
N.A.I.C.S.: 441110
Chance Corbitt (CEO & Sec)

Magic Acquisition Corp. (1)
23920 Creekside Rd, Valencia, CA 91355-
1732
Tel.: (661) 844-8390
Web Site:
  https://www.autonationfordvalencia.com
Automotive Retailer
N.A.I.C.S.: 441110

Maitland Luxury Imports, Inc. (1)
9590 US Highway 17-92, Maitland, FL
32751
Tel.: (689) 207-0581
Web Site: https://www.porscheorlando.com
Car Dealer Services
N.A.I.C.S.: 441110
David Kennedy (Mgr-Parts)

Marks Transport, Inc. (1)
4359 Hwy 34, Junction City, WI 54443
Tel.: (715) 457-2936
Web Site: https://www.markstransportation.com
Sales Range: $100-124.9 Million
New Car Dealers
N.A.I.C.S.: 441110

Maroone Auto Plaza (1)
8600 Pines Blvd, Pembroke Pines, FL
33024
Tel.: (954) 433-3300
Web Site: http://www.maroone.com
Sales Range: $250-299.9 Million
Emp.: 500
N.A.I.C.S.: 441110

Maroone Dodge, LLC (1)
13601 Pines Blvd, Pembroke Pines, FL
33027
Tel.: (877) 215-8880
Web Site: http://www.maroone.com

Car Dealer Services
N.A.I.C.S.: 441110

Mercedes-Benz of Sarasota (1)
4754 Clark Rd, Sarasota, FL 34233
Tel.: (941) 275-1293
Web Site:
  https://www.mercedesbenzofsarasota.com
Car Dealership
N.A.I.C.S.: 441110

Mercedes-Benz of South Bay (1)
3311 Pacific Coast Hwy, Torrance, CA
90505
Tel.: (213) 556-3861
Web Site: http://www.sbmercedes.com
Rev.: $72,000,000
Emp.: 200
Auto Dealership
N.A.I.C.S.: 441110

Mesa Collision, Inc. (1)
4134 E Valley Auto Dr, Mesa, AZ 85206
Tel.: (480) 658-0386
Automotive Engine Repair & Replacement
Services
N.A.I.C.S.: 811111

Mike Hall Chevrolet, Inc. (1)
13800 Gulf Fwy 8, Houston, TX 77034-
5009
Tel.: (281) 914-4750
Sales Range: $25-49.9 Million
Emp.: 80
New & Used Car Dealer
N.A.I.C.S.: 441110

Mike Shad Ford, Inc. (1)
7700 Blanding Blvd, Jacksonville, FL 32244
Tel.: (904) 578-7987
Web Site: https://www.autonationfordorange
  park.com
New & Used Car Dealing Services
N.A.I.C.S.: 441110

Mortimer Collision, LLC (1)
4025 Mortimer Ave, Baltimore, MD 21215
Tel.: (410) 306-7126
Automotive Engine Repair & Replacement
Services
N.A.I.C.S.: 811111

Mr. Wheels Solutions, LLC (1)
1060 S State Rd 7, Hollywood, FL 33023
Tel.: (954) 963-3882
Web Site: https://mrwheels.com
Auto Wheel Repair Services
N.A.I.C.S.: 811111

Mr. Wheels, Inc (1)
1060 S State Rd 7, Hollywood, FL 33023
Tel.: (954) 963-3882
Web Site: https://mrwheels.com
Car Sales Services
N.A.I.C.S.: 441110

Mullinax East, LLC (1)
28825 Euclid Ave, Wickliffe, OH 44092-
2528
Tel.: (440) 782-8540
Web Site:
  http://www.mullinaxeast.dealerconnec
  tion.com
Car Sales Services
N.A.I.C.S.: 441110

Mullinax Ford North Canton, Inc. (1)
5900 Whipple Ave NW, North Canton, OH
44720
Tel.: (234) 286-5682
Web Site:
  https://www.autonationfordnorthcan
  ton.com
Car Sales Services
N.A.I.C.S.: 441110

Mullinax Ford South, Inc. (1)
5401 W Copans Rd, Margate, FL 33063
Tel.: (754) 755-8657
Web Site:
  https://www.autonationfordmargate.com
Automotive Retailer
N.A.I.C.S.: 441110

Mullinax Lincoln-Mercury, Inc. (1)
550 First St NW, Cleveland, TN 37311
Tel.: (423) 476-6501
Web Site:
  http://www.mullinaxlincolnonline.com
Car Sales Services
N.A.I.C.S.: 441110

Jeff Henry (Gen Mgr)
Bill Erickson (Mgr-Sls-Used Car)
Tyson Lafferty (Mgr-Svc)

NY LNR Luxury Imports, Inc. (1)
64 Nardozzi Pl, New Rochelle, NY 10805
Tel.: (914) 904-9489
Web Site:
  https://www.landrovernewrochelle.com
Used Car & Truck Retailer
N.A.I.C.S.: 441120
Kevin Hoge (Gen Mgr-Automotive)

**NY Luxury Motors of Mt. Kisco,
Inc.** (1)
299 Kisco Ave, Mount Kisco, NY 10549
Tel.: (914) 904-7998
Web Site: https://www.landrovermtkisco.com
New & Used Car Dealer
N.A.I.C.S.: 441110

**NY MT. Kisco Luxury Imports,
Inc.** (1)
250 Kisco Ave, Mount Kisco, NY 10549
Tel.: (914) 241-4444
Web Site: https://www.bmwmtkisco.com
Used & New Car Dealer
N.A.I.C.S.: 441110

**NY White Plains Luxury Imports,
Inc.** (1)
295 E Main St, Elmsford, NY 10523
Tel.: (914) 770-4694
Web Site:
  https://www.landroverwhiteplains.com
Used Car & Truck Retailer
N.A.I.C.S.: 441120
John Deangelis (Gen Mgr)

Naperville Imports, Inc. (1)
1569 W Ogden Ave, Naperville, IL 60540
Tel.: (331) 472-1778
Web Site: https://www.mbofnaperville.com
Car Sales Services
N.A.I.C.S.: 441110

Newport Beach Cars, LLC (1)
445 E Pacific Coast Hwy, Newport Beach,
CA 92660
Tel.: (949) 478-0590
Web Site:
  https://www.bentleynewportbeach.com
Car Dealer Services
N.A.I.C.S.: 441110

Nichols Ford, Ltd. (1)
5300 Campus Dr, Fort Worth, TX 76119
Tel.: (682) 802-7203
Web Site:
  https://www.autonationfordsouthfort
  worth.com
Automotive Retailer
N.A.I.C.S.: 441110

Nissan of Brandon, Inc. (1)
9920 Adamo Dr, Tampa, FL 33619
Tel.: (813) 305-7681
Web Site: http://www.nissanofbrandon.com
Car Sales Services
N.A.I.C.S.: 441110

Northpoint Chevrolet, LLC (1)
2175 Mansell Rd, Alpharetta, GA 30009
Tel.: (770) 383-1536
Web Site: http://www.teamchevyautos.com
Sales Range: $25-49.9 Million
Emp.: 90
Car Sales Services
N.A.I.C.S.: 441110

Northpoint Ford, Inc. (1)
4400 Landers Rd, North Little Rock, AR
72117-2526
Tel.: (501) 955-7710
Web Site: http://www.northpointford.com
New Car Sales Services
N.A.I.C.S.: 441110

Northwest Financial Group, Inc. (1)
11959 Northup Way, Bellevue, WA 98005
Web Site: https://www.bmwbellevue.com
Automotive Retailer
N.A.I.C.S.: 441110

Ontario Dodge, Inc. (1)
1201 Auto Center Dr, Ontario, CA 91761
Tel.: (909) 390-4191
Car Sales Services
N.A.I.C.S.: 441110

Pembroke Motors, Inc. (1)

13601 Pines Blvd, Pembroke Pines, FL
33027-1511
Tel.: (954) 440-7599
Web Site:
https://www.autonationchryslerdodgejeep
rampembrokepines.com
Automotive Retailer
N.A.I.C.S.: 441110

Peyton Cramer Automotive (1)
3010 Pacific Coast Hwy, Torrance, CA
90505
Tel.: (213) 877-4625
Web Site:
https://www.autonationacurasouthbay.com
Car Dealer Services
N.A.I.C.S.: 441110
Israel Miranda *(Mgr)*
Hasan Roberson *(Mgr-Sales)*
Hannah Felix *(Mgr)*
Lance Edmond *(Gen Mgr-Sales)*
Hani Albawab *(Dir-Finance)*
Azi Kazemi *(Dir-Finance)*
Stacey Hoerning *(Coord)*

Peyton Cramer Ford (1)
3111 Pacific Coast Hwy, Torrance, CA
90505
Tel.: (310) 912-6478
Web Site:
https://www.autonationfordtorrance.com
Automotive Retailer
N.A.I.C.S.: 441110

Peyton Cramer Infiniti (1)
3035 Pac Cst Hwy, Lomita, CA 90717
Tel.: (310) 325-5555
Car Dealer Services
N.A.I.C.S.: 441110

Phoenix ANUSA, LLC (1)
2625 W Bell Rd, Phoenix, AZ 85023
Tel.: (623) 295-0430
Web Site: http://www.autonationusa.com
Used Car & Truck Retailer
N.A.I.C.S.: 441120

Phoenix Avondale ANUSA, LLC (1)
10601 W Papago Fwy, Avondale, AZ 85323
Electric Car Mfr & Distr
N.A.I.C.S.: 336320

Pierce, LLC (1)
433 S Main St, West Hartford, CT 06110
Tel.: (860) 560-8179
Web Site: https://piercellclaw.com
Automotive Retailer
N.A.I.C.S.: 441110

Plains Chevrolet, Ltd. (1)
2200 I-40 E, Amarillo, TX 79103
Tel.: (806) 553-5676
Web Site:
http://www.autonationchevroletamaril
lo.com
Car Dealership
N.A.I.C.S.: 441110

Plano ANUSA, LLC (1)
4051 W Plano Pkwy, Plano, TX 75093
Electric Car Mfr & Distr
N.A.I.C.S.: 336320

Plano Collision, Inc. (1)
4455 Tradition Trl, Plano, TX 75093
Tel.: (972) 465-9587
Automotive Engine Repair & Replacement
Services
N.A.I.C.S.: 811111

Port City Imports, Inc. (1)
6702 S Padre Island Dr, Corpus Christi, TX
78412
Tel.: (361) 444-0127
Web Site:
https://www.autonationhondasouthcorpus
christi.com
Car Dealer Services
N.A.I.C.S.: 441110

Prime Auto Resources, Inc. (1)
777 W 190th St, Gardena, CA 90248
Tel.: (310) 380-4686
Web Site:
http://www.autonationautoauction.com
Sales Range: $25-49.9 Million
Car Dealer Services
N.A.I.C.S.: 441110

Quality Nissan, Ltd. (1)

41895 Motor Car Pkwy, Temecula, CA
92591-4652
Tel.: (909) 676-6601
Car Dealer Services
N.A.I.C.S.: 441110

Quinlan Motors, Inc. (1)
4301 Clinton Hwy, Knoxville, TN 37912
Tel.: (865) 622-7380
Web Site: https://www.reederchevy.com
Car Dealer Services
N.A.I.C.S.: 441110

RI/BB Acquisition Corp. (1)
9200 E Colonial Dr, Orlando, FL 32817
Tel.: (689) 218-0167
Web Site:
https://www.autonationcollisioncen
ters.com
Automotive Retailer
N.A.I.C.S.: 441110

**RI/Hollywood Nissan Acquisition
Corp.** (1)
8890 Pines Blvd, Pembroke Pines, FL
33024
Tel.: (954) 329-2185
Web Site:
https://www.autonationnissanpembroke
pines.com
Automotive Retailer
N.A.I.C.S.: 441110

**RI/Hollywood Nissan Acquisition
Corp.** (1)
8890 Pines Blvd, Pembroke Pines, FL
33024
Tel.: (754) 354-1185
Web Site:
https://www.autonationnissanpembroke
pines.com
Car Dealer Services
N.A.I.C.S.: 441110

RI/LLC Acquisition Corp. (1)
10030 E Arapahoe Rd, Centennial, CO
80112
Tel.: (720) 207-6454
Web Site:
http://www.autonationnissanarapahoe.com
Car Dealer Services
N.A.I.C.S.: 441110

RI/RMC Acquisition, Ltd. (1)
11400 Research Blvd, Austin, TX 78759-
4154
Tel.: (512) 540-4260
Web Site:
https://www.autonationchevroletwestaus
tin.com
Automotive Retailer
N.A.I.C.S.: 441110

RI/RMP Acquisition Corp. (1)
8710 Research Blvd, Austin, TX 78758
Tel.: (972) 630-5349
Financial Investment Services
N.A.I.C.S.: 523910

RI/RMT Acquisition, Ltd. (1)
4800 S Interstate Hwy 35, Austin, TX 78745
Tel.: (512) 518-6900
Web Site:
https://www.autonationtoyotasouthaus
tin.com
Car Dealer Services
N.A.I.C.S.: 441110

RI/RMT Acquisition, Ltd. (1)
4800 S Interstate Hwy 35, Austin, TX 78745
Web Site:
https://www.autonationtoyotasouthaus
tin.com
Automotive Retailer
N.A.I.C.S.: 441110

RKR Motors, Inc. (1)
350 W Copans Rd, Pompano Beach, FL
33064
Tel.: (754) 732-7084
Web Site:
https://www.mercedesbenzofpompa
no.com
Car Dealer Services
N.A.I.C.S.: 441110

RKR Motors, Inc. (1)
350 W Copans Rd, Pompano Beach, FL
33064
Tel.: (754) 755-4872

Web Site:
https://www.mercedesbenzofpompa
no.com
Automotive Retailer
N.A.I.C.S.: 441110

Renton H Imports, Inc. (1)
3701 E Valley Rd, Renton, WA 98057
Tel.: (425) 698-2132
Web Site:
https://www.autonationhondarenton.com
New & Used Car Dealer
N.A.I.C.S.: 441110

RepairSmith, Inc. (1)
2333 Utah Ave Ste 105, El Segundo, CA
90245
Web Site: https://www.repairsmith.com
Automotive Repair & Maintenance Services
N.A.I.C.S.: 811111
Felix-Matthias Walter *(Chief Comml Officer)*
Joel Milne *(CEO)*
Andreas Biebl *(CMO)*
Martin Rosenquist *(CFO)*

Rockville Luxury Imports, LLC (1)
1450 Rockville Pike, Rockville, MD 20852
Tel.: (240) 552-7146
Web Site: https://www.bmwrockville.com
Automobile Dealership Services
N.A.I.C.S.: 611692

Roseville Motor Corporation (1)
200 Automall Dr, Roseville, CA 95661-3001
Tel.: (916) 510-0130
Web Site:
https://www.autonationchryslerdodgejeep
ramroseville.com
Car Dealership Services
N.A.I.C.S.: 441110
Henry Khachaturian *(Pres)*

Roundtree Mobile, LLC (1)
3118 Government Blvd, Mobile, AL 36606
Tel.: (251) 202-2253
Car Whslr
N.A.I.C.S.: 441110

Sacramento Collision, Inc. (1)
5289 Auburn Blvd, Sacramento, CA 95841
Tel.: (916) 266-0860
Automotive Collision Repair Services
N.A.I.C.S.: 811111

Sahara Imports, Inc. (1)
1700 E Sahara Ave, Las Vegas, NV 89104
Tel.: (725) 677-6632
Web Site:
https://www.autonationhondaeastlas
vegas.com
Car Dealer Services
N.A.I.C.S.: 441110

Sahara Nissan, Inc. (1)
5800 W Sahara Ave, Las Vegas, NV 89146
Tel.: (702) 570-1013
Web Site:
https://www.autonationnissanlasve
gas.com
Car Dealership Services
N.A.I.C.S.: 441110

San Antonio ANUSA, LLC (1)
15423 W Interstate 10, San Antonio, TX
78249
Tel.: (726) 245-8646
Automotive Retailer
N.A.I.C.S.: 441110

Smythe European, Inc. (1)
4500 Stevens Creek Blvd, San Jose, CA
95129
Tel.: (408) 641-4610
Web Site: http://www.smythe.com
Emp.: 290
Car Dealership Services
N.A.I.C.S.: 441110
Mark Akbar *(Gen Mgr)*

South Broadway Motors, LLC (1)
5445 S Broadway, Littleton, CO 80121-
8002
Tel.: (720) 547-2888
Web Site:
https://www.autonationchryslerjeepbroad
way.com
Automotive Retailer
N.A.I.C.S.: 441110

**Southwest Motors of Denver,
LLC** (1)

7980 W Tufts Ave, Littleton, CO 80123-
2400
Tel.: (303) 872-7287
Web Site:
https://www.autonationchryslerdodgejeep
ramsouthwest.com
Car Dealer Services
N.A.I.C.S.: 441110

Star Motors, LLC (1)
6270 Atlanta Hwy, Alpharetta, GA 30004
Tel.: (678) 762-7200
Web Site: https://starmotorsga.com
Automotive Retailer
N.A.I.C.S.: 441110

Star Motors, LLC (1)
2411 S Federal Hwy, Fort Lauderdale, FL
33316
Tel.: (754) 755-5798
Web Site:
https://www.mercedesbenzfortlauder
dale.com
Car Dealer Services
N.A.I.C.S.: 441110

**Steve Moore Chevrolet Delray,
LLC** (1)
1111 Linton Blvd, Delray Beach, FL 33444
Tel.: (561) 278-3225
Web Site: http://www.autonation.com
Sales Range: $25-49.9 Million
Emp.: 100
Car Dealership Services
N.A.I.C.S.: 441110

Steve Moore Chevrolet, LLC (1)
5757 Lake Worth Rd, Greenacres City, FL
33463-3207
Tel.: (561) 491-2969
Web Site:
https://www.autonationchevroletgreena
cres.net
Car Dealership Services
N.A.I.C.S.: 441110

**Stevens Creek Luxury Imports,
Inc.** (1)
4520 Stevens Creek Blvd, San Jose, CA
95129
Tel.: (408) 549-1726
Web Site:
https://www.maseratiofstevenscreek.com
Automotive Retailer
N.A.I.C.S.: 441110

Stevens Creek Motors, Inc. (1)
4747 Stevens Creek Bl, Santa Clara, CA
95051
Tel.: (408) 758-5502
Web Site:
https://www.autonationacurastevens
creek.com
Sales Range: $25-49.9 Million
Car Dealership Owner & Operator
N.A.I.C.S.: 441110

Stuart Nissan, LLC (1)
4313 S Federal Hwy, Stuart, FL 33483
Tel.: (772) 286-8000
Web Site:
http://www.wallacenissanofstuart.com
Car Dealer Services
N.A.I.C.S.: 441110

Sutherlin H. Imports, LLC (1)
1979 Thornton Rd, Lithia Springs, GA
30122
Tel.: (470) 995-0886
Web Site:
https://www.autonationhondathornton
road.com
Car Dealer Services
N.A.I.C.S.: 441110

Sutherlin H. Imports, LLC (1)
1979 Thornton Rd, Lithia Springs, GA
30122
Tel.: (470) 995-4270
Web Site:
https://www.autonationhondathornton
road.com
Automotive Retailer
N.A.I.C.S.: 441110

Sutherlin Imports, LLC (1)
8501 US Hwy 19 N, Pinellas Park, FL
33781
Tel.: (727) 855-7353
Web Site:
https://www.autonationtoyotapinellas
park.com

AutoNation, Inc.—(Continued)

Automotive Retailer
N.A.I.C.S.: 441110

Sutherlin Nissan, LLC (1)
811 Thornton Rd, Lithia Springs, GA 30122
Tel.: (770) 674-6080
Web Site:
http://www.autonationnissanthornton
road.com
Car Dealership Services
N.A.I.C.S.: 441110

T-West Sales & Service, Inc. (1)
6300 W Sahara Ave, Las Vegas, NV 89146
Tel.: (725) 677-1425
Web Site:
https://www.autonationtoyotalasvegas.com
Automotive Retailer
N.A.I.C.S.: 441110

TN CDJR Motors, LLC (1)
3700 Bristol Hwy, Johnson City, TN 37601-
1376
Tel.: (423) 482-8458
Web Site:
https://www.autonationchryslerdodgejeep
ramjohnsoncity.com
New & Used Car Dealer
N.A.I.C.S.: 441110

TX Alliance Motors, Inc. (1)
11200 N Fwy, Fort Worth, TX 76177-6900
Tel.: (817) 983-7131
Web Site:
https://www.autonationchryslerdodge
jeepramftworth.com
New & Used Car Dealer
N.A.I.C.S.: 441110

TX Motors of North Richland Hills,
Inc. (1)
7740 NE Loop 820, North Richland Hills,
TX 76180-8303
Tel.: (817) 522-3118
Web Site:
http://www.autonationchryslerdodgejeep
ramnorthrichlandhills.com
New & Used Car Dealer
N.A.I.C.S.: 441110

TX Motors on Katy Freeway, Inc. (1)
21777 Katy Fwy, Katy, TX 77450-1800
Tel.: (832) 835-6621
Web Site:
https://www.autonationchryslerdodgejeep
ramkaty.com
New & Used Car Dealer
N.A.I.C.S.: 441110

TX West Houston Motors, Inc. (1)
1515 S Loop, Houston, TX 77054-3813
Tel.: (002) 900-0022
Web Site:
https://www.autonationchryslerdodgejeep
ramhouston.com
New & Used Car Dealer
N.A.I.C.S.: 441110

TX-CC Dallas, Inc. (1)
6700 Maple Ave, Dallas, TX 75235
Tel.: (972) 895-3044
Automotive Engine Repair & Replacement
Services
N.A.I.C.S.: 811111
Gregg W Wunneburger (Gen Mgr)

TX-CC Galleria, Inc. (1)
5251 Gulfton St, Houston, TX 77081
Tel.: (713) 714-2207
Automotive Engine Repair & Replacement
Services
N.A.I.C.S.: 811111
Joe Clopton (Mgr-Parts)

TX-CC Spring, Inc. (1)
21055 N Fwy I-45, Spring, TX 77388
Tel.: (281) 766-8208
Automotive Engine Repair & Replacement
Services
N.A.I.C.S.: 811111

Terry York Motor Cars, Ltd. (1)
22006 Erwin St, Woodland Hills, CA 91367
Tel.: (747) 307-6238
Web Site:
https://www.jaguarwoodlandhills.com
Automotive Retailer
N.A.I.C.S.: 441110

Terry York Motor Cars, Ltd. (1)
22006 Erwin St, Woodland Hills, CA 91367
Tel.: (747) 330-9784
Web Site: https://www.landroverencino.com
Car Dealership Services
N.A.I.C.S.: 441110

Texan Ford Sales, Ltd. (1)
1400 W I-20, Arlington, TX 76017
Tel.: (682) 812-7848
Web Site:
https://www.autonationfordarlington.com
New & Used Car Dealer
N.A.I.C.S.: 441110

Texan Ford Sales, Ltd. (1)
1400 W I-20, Arlington, TX 76017
Tel.: (682) 895-5397
Web Site:
https://www.autonationfordarlington.com
Automotive Retailer
N.A.I.C.S.: 441110

Texan Ford, Inc. (1)
20777 I-10 W, Katy, TX 77450
Tel.: (346) 553-2748
Web Site:
https://www.autonationfordkaty.com
Automotive Retailer
N.A.I.C.S.: 441110

The Consulting Source, Inc.1990 (1)
1403 S Addison Ct, Aurora, CO 80018-6003
Tel.: (303) 366-4800
Web Site: https://www.consultingsource.com
Consulting Services
N.A.I.C.S.: 541690

Torrance Nissan, LLC (1)
20550 Hawthorne Blvd, Torrance, CA 90503
Tel.: (310) 905-8732
Web Site: https://www.nissanoftorrance.com
Car Dealer Services
N.A.I.C.S.: 441110

Tousley Ford, Inc. (1)
1493 E County Rd E, White Bear Lake, MN
55110
Tel.: (651) 301-8386
Web Site:
https://www.autonationfordwhitebear
lake.com
New & Used Car Dealer
N.A.I.C.S.: 441110

Town & Country Chrysler Jeep,
Inc. (1)
13733 Aurora Ave N, Seattle, WA 98133
Tel.: (888) 518-9698
Web Site:
http://www.townandcountryjeep.com
Car Dealership Services
N.A.I.C.S.: 441110

Valencia B. Imports, Inc. (1)
23435 Valencia Blvd, Valencia, CA 91355
Tel.: (661) 200-9111
Web Site: https://www.valenciabmw.com
Car Dealership Services
N.A.I.C.S.: 441110

Valencia H. Imports, Inc. (1)
23551 Magic Mountain Pkwy, Valencia, CA
91355
Tel.: (661) 200-9110
Web Site:
https://www.autonationhondavalencia.com
Car Dealership Services
N.A.I.C.S.: 441110

Vanderbeek Motors, Inc. (1)
500 Automall Dr, Roseville, CA 95661
Tel.: (916) 790-1990
Web Site: https://www.bmwofroseville.com
Car Dealer
N.A.I.C.S.: 441110
Les Braner (CEO & Sec)

Vanderbeek Motors, Inc. (1)
250 Automall Dr, Roseville, CA 95661
Tel.: (279) 214-9069
Web Site:
https://www.autonationsubarurosevil
le.com
Automotive Retailer
N.A.I.C.S.: 441110

Village Motors, LLC (1)
529 1st St E, Conover, NC 28613
Tel.: (704) 325-6622
Web Site: https://www.villagemotors.com

Sales Range: $25-49.9 Million
Car Dealership Services
N.A.I.C.S.: 441110

Vince Wiese Chevrolet, Inc. (1)
23649 W Valencia Blvd, Valencia, CA
91355-1705
Tel.: (661) 877-4076
Web Site:
https://www.autonationchevroletvalen
cia.com
Car Dealership Services
N.A.I.C.S.: 441110

VistaCal Luxury Imports, Inc. (1)
1715 Hacienda Dr, Vista, CA 92081
Tel.: (760) 307-8202
Web Site: https://www.bmwofvista.com
New & Used Car Dealer
N.A.I.C.S.: 441110

WPB Collision, Inc. (1)
1030 N Congress Ave, West Palm Beach,
FL 33409
Tel.: (561) 287-6234
Automotive Engine Repair & Replacement
Services
N.A.I.C.S.: 811111

Wallace Ford, LLC (1)
1475 SW 4th Ave, Delray Beach, FL 33444
Tel.: (561) 782-4002
Automotive Retailer
N.A.I.C.S.: 441110

Wallace Ford, LLC (1)
1475 SW 4th Ave, Delray Beach, FL 33444
Tel.: (561) 491-2347
Web Site:
http://www.autonationcollisioncenters.com
Car Dealer Services
N.A.I.C.S.: 441110

Webb Automotive Group, Inc. (1)
3911 E Main St, Farmington, NM 87402
Tel.: (505) 325-1911
Web Site: https://www.webbauto.com
Car Dealership Services
N.A.I.C.S.: 441110
James Larson (Gen Mgr-Sls)

Wesley Chapel ANUSA, LLC (1)
2807 Creek Grass Way, Lutz, FL 33559
Electric Car Mfr & Distr
N.A.I.C.S.: 336320

West Colorado Motors, LLC (1)
16300 W Colfax Ave, Golden, CO 80401-
3855
Tel.: (720) 735-5907
Web Site:
https://www.autonationchryslerjeep
west.com
Car Dealer Services
N.A.I.C.S.: 441110

West Houston Luxury Imports,
Inc. (1)
20415 Katy Fwy, Katy, TX 77450
Tel.: (281) 612-9773
Web Site:
https://www.landroverwesthouston.com
Automotive Retailer
N.A.I.C.S.: 441110

West Side Motors, Inc. (1)
10117 Parkside Dr, Knoxville, TN 37922
Tel.: (865) 666-3099
Web Site:
https://www.autonationhondawestknox
ville.com
Automotive Retailer
N.A.I.C.S.: 441110

Westgate Chevrolet, Ltd. (1)
7300 I 40 W, Amarillo, TX 79106-1809
Tel.: (806) 553-5668
Web Site:
https://www.autonationchevroletcadil
lac.com
Car Dealership Services
N.A.I.C.S.: 441110

Westmont A. Imports, Inc. (1)
276 E Ogden Ave, Westmont, IL 60559
Tel.: (630) 537-0310
Web Site: https://www.audiwestmont.com
Car Dealership Services
N.A.I.C.S.: 441110

Westmont A. Imports, Inc. (1)

276 E Ogden Ave, Westmont, IL 60559
Web Site: https://www.audiwestmont.com
Automotive Retailer
N.A.I.C.S.: 441110

Westmont B. Imports, Inc. (1)
430 E Ogden Ave, Westmont, IL 60559
Tel.: (630) 537-0311
Web Site: https://www.laurelbmw.com
Car Dealership Services
N.A.I.C.S.: 441110
Rich Stoll (Mgr-Sls)
John Blaschek (Dir-Ops)
Chris Creedon (Gen Mgr)
Joe Komendadanchik (Fin Mgr)
Devon Reid (Fin Dir)

Westmont Collision, Inc. (1)
433 Plz Dr, Westmont, IL 60559
Tel.: (630) 332-0444
Automotive Engine Repair & Replacement
Services
N.A.I.C.S.: 811111

Westmont M. Imports, Inc. (1)
200 E Ogden Ave, Westmont, IL 60559
Tel.: (630) 537-0313
Web Site: https://www.mercedesbenzofwest
mont.com
Sales Range: $25-49.9 Million
New & Used Car Dealer
N.A.I.C.S.: 441110

AUTONOMIX MEDICAL, INC.
21 Waterway Ave Ste 300, The
Woodlands, TX 77380
Tel.: (713) 588-6150 DE
Web Site:
https://www.autonomix.com
Year Founded: 2014
AMIX—(NASDAQ)
Rev.: $127,000
Assets: $9,407,000
Liabilities: $1,779,000
Net Worth: $7,628,000
Earnings: ($15,426,000)
Emp.: 5
Fiscal Year-end: 03/31/24
Medical Device Mfr
N.A.I.C.S.: 339112

AUTOSCOPE TECHNOLOGIES
CORPORATION
400 Spruce Tree Centre 1600 Univer-
sity Ave W, Saint Paul, MN 55104
Tel.: (651) 603-7700 MN
Web Site:
http://www.imagesensing.com
Year Founded: 1984
AATC—(NASDAQ)
Rev.: $13,242,000
Assets: $22,367,000
Liabilities: $2,573,000
Net Worth: $19,794,000
Earnings: $2,295,000
Emp.: 36
Fiscal Year-end: 12/31/21
Developer & Marketer of Video Image
Processing Technology & Products
N.A.I.C.S.: 561621
Francis G. Hallowell (CFO, Interim
Pres & Interim CEO)
Andrew T. Berger (Exec Chm)

Subsidiaries:

Image Sensing Systems Europe
Limited (1)
Unit 4 Caxton Place Caxton Way, Steve-
nage, SG1 2UG, Herts, United Kingdom
Tel.: (44) 1438 347 555
Sales Range: $100-124.9 Million
Emp.: 7
Vehicle Detection System Distr
N.A.I.C.S.: 334511

Image Sensing Systems Germany,
GmbH (1)
Unnauer Weg 7a, 50767, Cologne, Ger-
many
Tel.: (49) 22130229141
Web Site: http://www.image-sensing.de
Electronic Product Distr
N.A.I.C.S.: 423690

Image Sensing Systems HK Limited (1)
Suite 605 6th Floor Queens Place 74 Queens Road, Central, China (Hong Kong)
Tel.: (852) 28271123
Web Site: http://www.flowtraffic.com.cn
Sales Range: $100-124.9 Million
Emp.: 2
Vehicle Detection System Distr
N.A.I.C.S.: 334511

Image Sensing Systems UK Limited (1)
Unit 4 Caxton Place, Caxton Way, Stevenage, SG1 2UG, Herts, United Kingdom
Tel.: (44) 1438 347 555
Web Site: http://www.imagesensing.com
Sales Range: $25-49.9 Million
Emp.: 15
Automatic Number Plate Recognition Software & Hardware Provider
N.A.I.C.S.: 561621

AUTOZONE, INC.
123 S Front St, Memphis, TN 38103
Tel.: (901) 495-6500   NV
Web Site: https://www.autozone.com
Year Founded: 1979
AZO—(NYSE)
Rev.: $18,490,268,000
Assets: $17,176,538,000
Liabilities: $21,926,152,000
Net Worth: ($4,749,614,000)
Earnings: $2,662,427,000
Emp.: 126,000
Fiscal Year-end: 08/31/24
Retailer of Auto Parts & Accessories
N.A.I.C.S.: 441330
William C. Rhodes III *(Exec Chm-Customer Satisfaction)*
Thomas B. Newbern *(COO)*
Eric S. Gould *(Sr VP-Supply Chain)*
William R. Hackney *(Exec VP-Mdsg, Mktg, and Supply Chain)*
Richard C. Smith *(Sr VP-HR)*
Philip B. Daniele III *(Pres/CEO-Customer Satisfaction)*
Grant E. McGee *(Sr VP-Comml)*
J. Scott Murphy *(Principal Acctg Officer, VP & Controller-Customer Satisfaction)*
Albert Saltiel *(Sr VP-Mktg & E-Commerce)*
Kristen Collier Wright *(Gen Counsel, Sec & Sr VP)*
Domingo J. Hurtado *(Sr VP-Intl)*
Seong K. Ohm *(Sr VP-Mdsg)*
Dennis W. Leriche *(Sr VP-Store Ops)*
K. Michelle Borninkhof *(CIO & Sr VP)*
Jamere Jackson *(CFO)*
Joseph Reeves Hyde III *(Founder)*
Charlie Pleas III *(Sr VP-Fin & Acctg-Customer Satisfaction)*

Subsidiaries:

ALLDATA LLC (1)
9650 W Traon Dr Ste 100, Elk Grove, CA 95757
Tel.: (916) 478-3105
Web Site: https://www.alldata.com
Sales Range: $75-99.9 Million
Emp.: 350
Provider of Automotive Diagnostic Services
N.A.I.C.S.: 513210
Satwinder Mangat *(Pres)*

AutoZone Development LLC (1)
123 S Front St, Memphis, TN 38103
Tel.: (901) 495-6500
Web Site: http://www.autozone.com
Sales Range: $25-49.9 Million
Emp.: 25
Automotive Services
N.A.I.C.S.: 441330

AutoZone Northeast, Inc. (1)
993 Central St, Stoughton, MA 02072
Tel.: (781) 341-1744
Web Site: http://www.autozone.com
Sales Range: $150-199.9 Million
Emp.: 10
Automotive Services

N.A.I.C.S.: 441330

AutoZone Parts, Inc. (1)
123 S Front St, Memphis, TN 38103
Tel.: (901) 495-6500
Web Site: http://www.autozone.com
Automotive Replacement Parts & Accessory Retailer
N.A.I.C.S.: 441330

AutoZone Stores, Inc. (1)
123 S Front St, Memphis, TN 38103
Tel.: (901) 495-6500
Sales Range: $150-199.9 Million
Automotive Services
N.A.I.C.S.: 441330

AutoZone Texas, L.P. (1)
103 Rancier E, Killeen, TX 76541
Tel.: (254) 526-7757
Web Site: http://www.autozone.com
Sales Range: $10-24.9 Million
Emp.: 8
Provider of Automotive Services
N.A.I.C.S.: 441330

AutoZone.com, Inc. (1)
123 S Front St Ste 31801, Memphis, TN 38103
Tel.: (901) 495-6500
Web Site: http://www.autozone.com
Sales Range: $125-149.9 Million
Emp.: 300
Automotive Services
N.A.I.C.S.: 441330

AVALANCHE INTERNATIONAL CORP.
5940 S Rainbow Blvd, Las Vegas, NV 89118   NV
Web Site: http://www.avalancheinternationalcorp.com
Year Founded: 2011
AVLP—(OTCIQ)
Sales Range: Less than $1 Million
Emp.: 2
Investment Services
N.A.I.C.S.: 523999
William B. Horne *(CFO)*
Milton C. Ault III *(Chm)*
Philip E. Mansour *(Pres, CEO, Treas & Sec)*

AVALO THERAPEUTICS, INC.
540 Gaither Rd Ste 400, Rockville, MD 20850
Tel.: (410) 522-8707   DE
Web Site: https://www.avalotx.com
Year Founded: 2011
AVTX—(NASDAQ)
Rev.: $1,924,000
Assets: $20,993,000
Liabilities: $13,689,000
Net Worth: $7,304,000
Earnings: ($31,544,000)
Emp.: 19
Fiscal Year-end: 12/31/23
Biopharmaceutical Mfr
N.A.I.C.S.: 325412
Paul C. Varki *(Chief Legal Officer)*
Garry A. Neil *(Pres)*
Michael F. Cola *(CEO)*
Christopher Sullivan *(CFO)*
Younok Dumortier Shin *(CTO)*
Lisa Hegg *(VP-R&D Programs & Project Mgmt)*
Colleen Matkowski *(VP-Global Regulatory Affairs)*
Mittie Doyle *(Chief Medical Officer)*

Subsidiaries:

Aevi Genomic Medicine, LLC (1)
435 Devon Park Dr Ste 715, Wayne, PA 19087
Tel.: (610) 254-4201
Web Site: http://www.cerecor.com
Biopharmaceutical Research & Development Services
N.A.I.C.S.: 541715

Subsidiary (Non-US):

Medgenics Medical (Israel) Limited (2)
Teradion Business Park, PO Box 14, Misgav, 20179, Israel   (100%)
Tel.: (972) 49028900
Therapeutic Protein Delivery Technology Developer
N.A.I.C.S.: 541715

AVALON GLOBOCARE CORP.
4400 Rte 9 S Ste 3100, Freehold, NJ 07728
Tel.: (732) 780-4400   DE
Web Site: https://www.avalon-globocare.com
Year Founded: 2014
ALBT—(NASDAQ)
Rev.: $1,202,169
Assets: $19,751,905
Liabilities: $8,592,957
Net Worth: $11,158,948
Earnings: ($11,930,847)
Emp.: 5
Fiscal Year-end: 12/31/22
Biotechnology Research & Development Services
N.A.I.C.S.: 541714
Luisa Ingargiola *(CFO)*
David Jin *(Pres & CEO)*
Meng Li *(COO & Sec)*
Wenzhao Lu *(Chm)*

AVALON HOLDINGS CORPORATION
1 American Way, Warren, OH 44484-5555
Tel.: (330) 856-8800   OH
Web Site: https://www.avalonholdings.com
Year Founded: 1986
AWX—(NYSEAMEX)
Rev.: $81,180,000
Assets: $89,750,000
Liabilities: $51,607,000
Net Worth: $38,143,000
Earnings: ($583,000)
Emp.: 796
Fiscal Year-end: 12/31/22
Holding Company for Waste Management Operations
N.A.I.C.S.: 562920
Frances R. Klingle *(Chief Admin Officer)*
Ronald E. Klingle *(Chm & CEO)*
Bryan P. Saksa *(CFO, Treas & Sec)*
Clifford P. Davis *(CTO)*

Subsidiaries:

AWMS Holdings, LLC (1)
1 American Way, Warren, OH 44484-5555
Tel.: (330) 856-8800
Holding Company
N.A.I.C.S.: 551112

American Landfill Management, Inc. (1)
1 American Way, Warren, OH 44484-5555
Tel.: (330) 856-8800
Emp.: 8
Solid Waste Management Services
N.A.I.C.S.: 562212
Steven Kilper *(Pres)*

Subsidiary (Domestic):

American Construction Supply, Inc. (2)
1 American Way, Warren, OH 44484-5555
Tel.: (330) 856-8800
Web Site: http://www.lastmat.com
Hardwood Timber Mats Mfr
N.A.I.C.S.: 321211

American Waste Management Services, Inc. (1)
1 American Way, Warren, OH 44484-5555
Tel.: (330) 856-8800
Web Site: https://www.awmsi.com

Sales Range: $75-99.9 Million
Waste Disposal Brokerage & Management Company
N.A.I.C.S.: 541990
Kenneth J. McMahon *(Pres)*
Mark B. Cawthorne *(VP)*
James E. Smith *(VP-Disposal Sls)*
Robert D. Hazen *(VP-Accounts-Natl)*
Paula Monske *(Mgr-Customer Svc)*

Avalon Country Club at Sharon, Inc. (1)
1030 Forker Blvd, Hermitage, PA 16148-1566
Tel.: (724) 981-6700
Golf & Country Clubs Operator
N.A.I.C.S.: 713910

Avalon Golf and Country Club, Inc. (1)
9519 E Market St, Warren, OH 44484-5531
Tel.: (330) 856-1900
Web Site: https://www.avalongcc.com
Golf & Country Club Operator
N.A.I.C.S.: 713910
Christine M. Bell *(Pres)*

Avalon Lakes Golf, Inc. (1)
1 American Way NE, Warren, OH 44484-5555
Tel.: (330) 856-8898
Golf Courses & Country Clubs Operator
N.A.I.C.S.: 713910
Adam Scott *(Dir-Golf)*

Subsidiary (Domestic):

Avalon Travel, Inc. (2)
1 American Way, Warren, OH 44484-5555
Tel.: (330) 856-8400
Travel & Tour Operating Agencies
N.A.I.C.S.: 561510
Robin Fauceglia *(Gen Mgr)*

Avalon Resorts, Inc. (1)
9519 E Market St, Warren, OH 44484
Tel.: (330) 856-1900
Web Site: http://www.avalongcc.com
Restaurant Services
N.A.I.C.S.: 721120

AVALONBAY COMMUNITIES, INC.
4040 Wilson Blvd Ste 1000, Arlington, VA 22203
Tel.: (703) 329-6300   MD
Web Site: https://www.avaloncommunities.com
Year Founded: 1998
AVB—(NYSE)
Rev.: $2,767,909,000
Assets: $20,678,214,000
Liabilities: $8,894,896,000
Net Worth: $11,783,318,000
Earnings: $928,825,000
Emp.: 3,039
Fiscal Year-end: 12/31/23
Real Estate Management Services
N.A.I.C.S.: 531390
Kevin P. O'Shea *(CFO)*
Kurt Conway *(Sr VP-Brand Strategy & Mktg)*
David J. Alagno *(Sr VP-Human Resources)*
Lisa Bongardt *(Sr VP-Operations)*
Jong Chung *(Sr VP-Design)*
Micah Conn *(Sr VP-Development)*
David O. Gillespie *(Sr VP-Development)*
Patrick J. Gniadek *(Sr VP-Investments)*
Martin J. Howle *(Sr VP-Development)*
Mark D. Janda *(Sr VP-Development)*
Joe Kirchofer *(Sr VP-Development)*
Sarah A. Mathewson *(Sr VP-Operations)*
Rajiv Verma *(Sr VP-Revenue Mgmt)*
Benjamin W. Schall *(Pres & CEO)*
Sean J. Breslin *(COO)*
Matthew H. Birenbaum *(Chief Investment Officer)*

AvalonBay Communities, Inc.—(Continued)

Rukevbe Esi *(Chief Digital Officer & Sr VP)*
Edward M. Schulman *(Exec VP)*
Pamela Thomas *(Exec VP-Portfolio & Asset Mgmt)*
Melissa Dulski *(Sr VP & Assoc Gen Counsel)*
Mitch Forlenza *(Sr VP-Construction)*
James L. Graves *(Sr VP-Information Technology)*
Stewart Royer *(Sr VP-Structured Investments)*
Michael Simel *(Sr VP-Capital Markets)*
Jacqueline L. Todesco *(Sr VP-Asset Mgmt)*
Eric S. Wayne *(Sr VP-Construction)*
Jennifer Wiebrand *(Sr VP-Development)*
Sean T. Willson *(Sr VP & Controller)*

Subsidiaries:

ASN Tanforan Crossing II LLC (1)
1099 Admiral Ct, San Bruno, CA 94066
Tel.: (650) 589-9100
Beauty Care Services
N.A.I.C.S.: 812112

AVA Pacific Beach Solar, LLC (1)
3883 Ingraham St, San Diego, CA 92109
Tel.: (858) 264-1825
Hotel Services
N.A.I.C.S.: 721110

AVA Pasadena Solar, LLC (1)
385 S Catalina Ave, Pasadena, CA 91106
Tel.: (626) 361-4798
Apartment Rental Services
N.A.I.C.S.: 531110

Archstone Boca Raton REIT LP (1)
9200 E Panorama Cir Ste 400, Englewood, CO 80112
Tel.: (303) 708-5959
Property Management Services
N.A.I.C.S.: 531311

Archstone Financial Services LLC (1)
403 S Main St Ste 202D, Doylestown, PA 18901
Tel.: (215) 348-5370
Management Consulting Services
N.A.I.C.S.: 541611

Avalon Acton, Inc. (1)
1000 Avalon Dr, Acton, MA 01720
Tel.: (978) 705-6105
Web Site: http://www.avalonacton.com
Emp.: 10
Property Management Services
N.A.I.C.S.: 523940

Avalon Anaheim Stadium, L.P. (1)
2100 E Katella Ave, Anaheim, CA 92806
Tel.: (714) 939-7935
Web Site:
http://www.avaloncommunities.com
Emp.: 10
Property Rental & Leasing Services
N.A.I.C.S.: 531210

Avalon Arundel Crossing, LLC (1)
820 Concorde Cir, Linthicum Heights, MD 21090
Tel.: (443) 290-6620
Web Site:
https://www.avaloncommunities.com
Real Estate Services
N.A.I.C.S.: 531390

Avalon Bonterra, LLC (1)
3545 W 98th St, Hialeah, FL 33018
Tel.: (305) 200-1424
Web Site: http://www.avalonbonterra.com
Apartment Rental Services
N.A.I.C.S.: 531110

Avalon Campbell Solar, LLC (1)
508 Railway Ave, Campbell, CA 95008
Tel.: (408) 872-8586
Apartment Rental Services
N.A.I.C.S.: 531110

Avalon Cerritos, L.P. (1)

12651 Artesia Blvd, Cerritos, CA 90703
Tel.: (562) 379-6441
Web Site:
https://www.avaloncommunities.com
Apartment Rental Services
N.A.I.C.S.: 531110

Avalon Columbia Pike, LLC (1)
1028 S Walter Reed Dr, Arlington, VA 22204
Tel.: (703) 420-3391
Web Site:
https://www.avaloncommunities.com
Real Estate Services
N.A.I.C.S.: 531390

Avalon Del Rey Apartments, LLC (1)
5535 Westlawn Ave, Los Angeles, CA 90066
Tel.: (310) 306-3900
Web Site:
http://www.avaloncommunities.com
Emp.: 20
Property Management Services
N.A.I.C.S.: 523940

Avalon Encino, L.P. (1)
16350 Ventura Blvd, Encino, CA 91436
Tel.: (747) 223-6277
Web Site:
https://www.avaloncommunities.com
Property Rental & Leasing Services
N.A.I.C.S.: 531210

Avalon Fashion Valley, L.P. (1)
7084 Friars Rd, San Diego, CA 92108
Tel.: (619) 752-3683
Property Rental & Leasing Services
N.A.I.C.S.: 531210

Avalon Hoboken, LLC (1)
800 Madison St, Hoboken, NJ 07030
Tel.: (551) 205-5455
Web Site:
https://www.avaloncommunities.com
Real Estate Services
N.A.I.C.S.: 531390

Avalon Irvine, L.P. (1)
2777 Alton Pkwy, Irvine, CA 92606
Tel.: (949) 863-9549
Web Site:
http://www.avaloncommunities.com
Property Management Services
N.A.I.C.S.: 531390

Avalon New Canaan, LLC (1)
100 Avalon Dr E, New Canaan, CT 06840
Tel.: (475) 234-3695
Real Estate Services
N.A.I.C.S.: 531390

Avalon Newport, L.P. (1)
1765 Santa Ana Ave, Costa Mesa, CA 92627
Tel.: (949) 763-4624
Web Site: http://www.avanewport.com
Emp.: 5
Property Management Services
N.A.I.C.S.: 523940

Avalon North Bergen, LLC (1)
5665 Kennedy Blvd Ste 1, North Bergen, NJ 07047
Tel.: (551) 231-1413
Web Site:
https://www.avaloncommunities.com
Sales Range: $25-49.9 Million
Emp.: 4
Property Management Services
N.A.I.C.S.: 523940

Avalon Oaks, Inc. (1)
4040 Wilson Blvd Ste 1000, Arlington, VA 22203
Tel.: (351) 666-6850
Property Management Services
N.A.I.C.S.: 523940

Avalon Ocean Avenue, L.P. (1)
1200 Ocean Ave, San Francisco, CA 94112
Tel.: (415) 993-7795
Web Site: http://www.avaloceanaven.com
Emp.: 6
Property Rental & Leasing Services
N.A.I.C.S.: 531210

Avalon Park Crest, LLC (1)
8250 Westpark Dr, Tysons Corner, VA 22102
Tel.: (703) 420-3436

Web Site:
http://www.avaloncommunities.com
Emp.: 9
Property Management Services
N.A.I.C.S.: 523940

Avalon Portico at Silver Spring Metro, LLC (1)
4040 Wilson Blvd Ste 1000, Arlington, VA 22203
Tel.: (240) 623-5326
Apartment Rental Services
N.A.I.C.S.: 531110

Avalon Riverview North, LLC (1)
4-75 48th Ave, Long Island City, NY 11109
Tel.: (917) 456-8483
Property Rental & Leasing Services
N.A.I.C.S.: 531210
Timothy J. Naughton *(Pres)*

Avalon Sharon, Inc. (1)
4040 Wilson Blvd Ste 1000, Arlington, VA 22203
Tel.: (339) 674-6037
Property Management Services
N.A.I.C.S.: 523940

Avalon Somers, LLC (1)
49 Clayton Blvd, Baldwin Place, NY 10505
Tel.: (914) 313-8506
Web Site:
https://www.avaloncommunities.com
Real Estate Services
N.A.I.C.S.: 531390

Avalon Somerville Station Urban Renewal, LLC (1)
445 Artisan Way, Somerville, MA 02145
Tel.: (617) 870-6501
Apartment Rental Services
N.A.I.C.S.: 531110
Cassandra Danielle Barci *(Sls Mgr)*

Avalon Tinton Falls, LLC (1)
Autumn Dr, Tinton Falls, NJ 07753
Tel.: (732) 643-9840
Property Management Services
N.A.I.C.S.: 523940

Avalon Towers Bellevue, LLC (1)
10349 NE 10th St, Bellevue, WA 98004
Tel.: (425) 414-7571
Web Site:
http://www.avaloncommunities.com
Property Management Services
N.A.I.C.S.: 523940

Avalon Union City, L.P. (1)
24 Union Sq, Union City, CA 94587
Tel.: (510) 369-1664
Web Site:
https://www.avaloncommunities.com
Property Management Services
N.A.I.C.S.: 523940

Avalon West Long Branch, LLC (1)
10 Avalon Ct, West Long Branch, NJ 07764
Tel.: (732) 945-4041
Web Site:
http://www.avalonwestlongbranch.com
Emp.: 5
Property Rental & Leasing Services
N.A.I.C.S.: 531210

Avalon Woodland Hills, L.P. (1)
20544 Ventura Blvd, Woodland Hills, CA 91364
Tel.: (818) 583-8681
Web Site:
http://www.avalonwoodlandhills.com
Emp.: 20
Property Rental & Leasing Services
N.A.I.C.S.: 531210

Avalon at Ballston, LLC (1)
4650 N Washington Blvd, Arlington, VA 22201
Tel.: (571) 620-6326
Web Site:
http://www.avalonbaycommunities.com
Emp.: 4
Property Rental & Leasing Services
N.A.I.C.S.: 531210

Avalon at Diamond Heights, L.P. (1)
5285 Diamond Heights Blvd, San Francisco, CA 94131
Tel.: (415) 285-1231
Web Site:
http://www.avaloncommunities.com

Property Rental & Leasing Services
N.A.I.C.S.: 531210

Avalon at Providence Park, LLC (1)
10608 Kitty Pozer Dr Ste E, Fairfax, VA 22030-4266
Tel.: (703) 691-1097
Web Site:
http://www.avaloncommunities.com
Property Rental & Leasing Services
N.A.I.C.S.: 531210

AvalonBay Assembly Row, Inc. (1)
4040 Wilson Blvd Ste 1000, Arlington, VA 22203
Tel.: (617) 658-3840
Apartment Rental Services
N.A.I.C.S.: 531110

AvalonBay Grosvenor, Inc. (1)
10306 Strathmore Hall St, Bethesda, MD 20852-6654
Tel.: (240) 839-6908
Web Site:
http://www.avaloncommunities.com
Sales Range: $25-49.9 Million
Property Rental & Leasing Services
N.A.I.C.S.: 531210

AvalonBay Shrewsbury, Inc. (1)
870-890 Hartford Turnpike, Shrewsbury, MA 01545
Tel.: (866) 639-1894
Property Management Services
N.A.I.C.S.: 523940

AvalonBay Traville, LLC (1)
14240 Alta Oaks Dr, North Potomac, MD 20850
Tel.: (301) 900-5628
Web Site: http://www.avalonattraville.com
Emp.: 62
Property Management Services
N.A.I.C.S.: 523940

Eaves Burlington, LLC (1)
1 Farms Dr, Burlington, MA 01803-3749
Tel.: (781) 996-2257
Web Site: http://www.eavesburlington.com
Emp.: 4
Property Management Services
N.A.I.C.S.: 531311

Eaves Creekside Solar, LLC (1)
151 Calderon Ave, Mountain View, CA 94041
Tel.: (650) 758-0149
Apartment Rental Services
N.A.I.C.S.: 531110

Eaves Huntington Beach (1)
6700 Warner Ave, Huntington Beach, CA 92647
Tel.: (714) 847-6047
Web Site:
http://www.avaloncommunities.com
Emp.: 3
Property Management Services
N.A.I.C.S.: 531311

Garden City Townhomes, LLC (1)
4024 Kessler Ave, Garden City, GA 31408
Tel.: (912) 480-9080
Property Management Services
N.A.I.C.S.: 523940

Gates Financing, LLC (1)
255 W 6th St, San Pedro, CA 90731-3315
Tel.: (424) 210-3080
Property Management Services
N.A.I.C.S.: 523940

Newcastle Construction Management, LLC (1)
12715 SE 74th St, Newcastle, WA 98056
Tel.: (425) 765-3275
Property Management Services
N.A.I.C.S.: 531311

Saugus Avalon Retail, LLC (1)
4040 Wilson Blvd Ste 1000, Arlington, VA 22203
Tel.: (781) 381-4877
Apartment Rental Services
N.A.I.C.S.: 531110
Sharyn Hoover *(Mgr-Community)*

Sudbury Avalon, Inc. (1)
4040 Wilson Blvd Ste 1000, Arlington, VA 22203
Tel.: (978) 307-1527

Real Estate Services
N.A.I.C.S.: 531390

AVANEA ENERGY ACQUISITION CORP.

2181 Greenwich St, San Francisco, CA 94123
Tel.: (413) 221-6627   **Ky**
Year Founded: 2021
AVEAU—(NASDAQ)
Investment Services
N.A.I.C.S.: 523999
Peter Gajdos *(Co-CEO)*
Faysal Sohail *(Co-CEO)*
Adam Wilczek *(CFO)*

AVANOS MEDICAL, INC.

5405 Windward Pkwy, Alpharetta, GA 30004   **DE**
Web Site: https://www.avanos.com
Year Founded: 2014
AVNS—(NYSE)
Rev.: $673,300,000
Assets: $1,692,400,000
Liabilities: $456,100,000
Net Worth: $1,236,300,000
Earnings: ($61,800,000)
Emp.: 3,771
Fiscal Year-end: 12/31/23
Health Care Products Mfr
N.A.I.C.S.: 423450
Joseph F. Woody *(CEO)*
Michael C. Greiner *(CFO, Chief Transformation Officer & Sr VP)*
Burnes Lee *(Sr VP-R&D-Global)*
Kerr W. Holbrook *(Chief Comml Officer & Sr VP)*
Michelle Scharfenberg *(Chief Ethics & Compliance Officer & Sr VP)*
Moji James *(Gen Counsel & Sr VP)*
John J. Hurley *(Principal Acctg Officer & Controller)*
John Cato *(VP)*
Angela Cushman *(Sr VP)*
Scott Galovan *(Sr VP)*
Katrine Kubis *(VP)*
Sudhakar Varshney *(Sr VP)*
Chip Zimliki *(Sr VP)*

Subsidiaries:

Avanos Medical Australia Pty Ltd.   **(1)**
Suite 10 04 Level 10 Tower 1 495 Victoria Avenue, Chatswood, 2067, NSW, Australia
Tel.: (61) 1800101021
Web Site: https://avanos.com.au
Health Care Products Mfr
N.A.I.C.S.: 339112

Avanos Medical Deutschland GmbH   **(1)**
c/o Pier 11 Schauenburgerstrasse 10, 20095, Hamburg, Germany
Tel.: (49) 8001802298
Web Site: https://avanos.de
Health Care Products Mfr
N.A.I.C.S.: 339112

Avanos Medical Singapore Pte. Ltd.   **(1)**
United Square 101 Thomson Rd Unit 17-03, Singapore, 307591, Singapore
Tel.: (65) 63504330
Health Care Products Mfr
N.A.I.C.S.: 339112
Aijaz Shaikh *(Bus Dir-Pain Mgmt-APAC)*

CORPAK MedSystems, Inc.   **(1)**
1001 Asbury Dr, Buffalo Grove, IL 60089
Tel.: (847) 403-3400
Web Site:
   http://www.corpakmedsystems.com
Enteral Medical Device & Surgical Protection Product Mfr
N.A.I.C.S.: 339112
Frank McCaney *(Pres & CEO)*

CoolSystems, Inc.   **(1)**
5405 Windward Pkwy, Alpharetta, GA 30004
Tel.: (510) 868-2100

Web Site: https://www.gameready.com
Therapeutic Medical Device Mfr
N.A.I.C.S.: 339112
Chris Schulken *(COO)*

Halyard Belgium BVBA   **(1)**
Greenhouse Berkenlaan 8B, 1831, Diegem, Belgium
Tel.: (32) 80089013
Medical Equipment Whslr
N.A.I.C.S.: 423450

Halyard China Co., Ltd.   **(1)**
10th Fl HuaXinHaiXin Bldg No 666 Fu Zhou Rd, Shanghai, 200001, China
Tel.: (86) 2160283400
Medical Equipment Whslr
N.A.I.C.S.: 423450

Halyard Deutschland GmbH   **(1)**
Hohnerweg 2, 69469, Weinheim, Germany
Tel.: (49) 8001802298
Medical Equipment Whslr
N.A.I.C.S.: 423450

Halyard Health India Private Limited   **(1)**
World Trade Ctr Tower 1 Unit 308 Kharadi, Pune, 411 014, Maharashtra, India
Tel.: (91) 2046845500
Medical Equipment Whslr
N.A.I.C.S.: 423450
Mangesh Damare *(Mgr-Supply Chain)*

Halyard Nederland B.V.   **(1)**
Het Rietveld 55A, 7321 CT, Apeldoorn, Netherlands
Tel.: (31) 8000231079
Medical Equipment Whslr
N.A.I.C.S.: 423450

Halyard Singapore Pte. Ltd.   **(1)**
United Sq 101 Thomson Rd Unit Ste 17-03, Singapore, SG 307591, Singapore
Tel.: (65) 63504330
Medical Equipment Whslr
N.A.I.C.S.: 423450

Maxter Catheters SAS   **(1)**
6 place de la Madeleine, 75008, Paris, France
Tel.: (33) 491467305
Medical Equipment Whslr
N.A.I.C.S.: 423450

NeoMed, Inc.   **(1)**
100 Londonderry Ct - Ste 112, Woodstock, GA 30188
Tel.: (770) 516-2225
Web Site: http://www.neomedinc.com
Medical Product Mfr & Distr
N.A.I.C.S.: 339112

AVANTOR, INC.

Radnor Corporate Ctr Bldg 1 Ste 200 100 Matsonford Rd, Radnor, PA 19087
Tel.: (610) 386-1700   **DE**
Web Site:
   https://www.avantorsciences.com
Year Founded: 2017
AVTR—(NYSE)
Rev.: $6,967,200,000
Assets: $12,972,700,000
Liabilities: $7,720,100,000
Net Worth: $5,252,600,000
Earnings: $321,100,000
Emp.: 14,500
Fiscal Year-end: 12/31/23
Holding Company; Medical Equipment & Supplies Mfr & Distr
N.A.I.C.S.: 551112
R. Brent Jones *(CFO & Exec VP)*
Michael Stubblefield *(Pres & CEO)*
James Bramwell *(Exec VP-Sls & Customer Excellence)*
Justin Miller *(Gen Counsel, Sec & Exec VP)*

Subsidiaries:

Advanced Chromatography Technologies Ltd.   **(1)**
Cirrus Building 6 International Avenue Abz Business Park Syce, Aberdeen, AB21 0AF, United Kingdom
Tel.: (44) 1224704554

Web Site: http://www.ace-hplc.com
Pharmaceuticals Product Mfr
N.A.I.C.S.: 325412

Avantor Performance Materials India Limited   **(1)**
19th Floor Building No 5 Tower CDLF Cyber City Phase-III, Gurgaon, 122002, Haryana, India
Tel.: (91) 1244656700
Laboratory Equipment Mfr & Distr
N.A.I.C.S.: 339112

Avantor Performance Materials Korea Limited   **(1)**
2nd Floor unit 201-204 ACE Gwanggyo Tower 17 Daehak 4-Ro, Youngtong-Gu, Suwon, 16226, Gyeonggi-Do, Korea (South)
Tel.: (82) 316457250
Laboratory Equipment Mfr & Distr
N.A.I.C.S.: 339112

Avantor Performance Materials Taiwan Co., Ltd.   **(1)**
No 38-1 Tai Yuen St, Tai Yuen Hi-Tech Industrial Park, Zhubei, 30265, HsinChu Hsien, Taiwan
Tel.: (886) 35600789
Laboratory Equipment Mfr & Distr
N.A.I.C.S.: 339112

Avantor Performance Materials, LLC   **(1)**
3477 Corporate Pkwy, Center Valley, PA 18034
Tel.: (908) 859-2151
High-Performance Chemicals & Materials Mfr & Marketer
N.A.I.C.S.: 325180

Subsidiary (Non-US):

Avantor Performance Materials S.A. de C.V.   **(2)**
Industrial Esfuerzo Nacional Xalostoc, 55320, Ecatepec, Mexico
Tel.: (52) 5556990250
High-Performance Chemicals & Materials Mfr & Marketer
N.A.I.C.S.: 325998

Avantor Performance Materials Sdn Bhd   **(2)**
A-1201-2 12th Floor Kelana Brem Tower 1 Jalan SS7/15, Kelana Jaya, 47301, Petaling Jaya, Selangor, Malaysia
Tel.: (60) 378030378
High-Performance Chemicals & Materials Mfr & Marketer
N.A.I.C.S.: 325998

Subsidiary (Domestic):

Puritan Products, Inc.   **(2)**
2290 Ave A, Bethlehem, PA 18017
Tel.: (610) 573-2600
Web Site: http://www.puritanproducts.com
Chemicals Mfr
N.A.I.C.S.: 325998

VWR Corporation   **(2)**
Radnor Corporate Ctr Bldg One Ste 200 100 Matsonford Rd, Radnor, PA 19087
Tel.: (610) 386-1700
Web Site: http://www.vwr.com
Rev.: $4,514,200,000
Assets: $4,962,500,000
Liabilities: $3,468,100,000
Net Worth: $1,494,400,000
Earnings: $148,200,000
Emp.: 10,200
Fiscal Year-end: 12/31/2016
Holding Company; Laboratory Supplies Mfr
N.A.I.C.S.: 551112

Subsidiary (Domestic):

Reliable Biopharmaceutical LLC   **(3)**
1945 Walton Rd, Saint Louis, MO 63114   **(100%)**
Tel.: (314) 429-7700
Web Site: http://www.reliablebiopharm.com
Pharmaceutical Ingredients Mfr & Developer
N.A.I.C.S.: 325512
Lance Kunkel *(VP-Ops)*

Therapak LLC   **(3)**
651 Wharton Dr, Claremont, CA 91711   **(100%)**
Tel.: (909) 267-2000

Web Site: https://www.therapak.com
Global Supplier of Pre-Packaged Convenience Kits & Procedure Packs for the Clinical Trial, Pharmaceutical, Diagnostics & Clinical Laboratory Markets.
N.A.I.C.S.: 423450

VWR Funding, Inc.   **(3)**
Radnor Corporate Ctr Bldg 1 Ste 200 100 Matsonford Rd, Radnor, PA 19087 **(100%)**
Tel.: (610) 386-1700
Web Site: http://www.vwr.com
Holding Company; Laboratory Supplies Distr
N.A.I.C.S.: 551112

Division (Domestic):

VWR International, LLC   **(4)**
Radnor Corporate Ctr Bldg 1 Ste 200 100 Matsonford Rd, Radnor, PA 19087-8660
Tel.: (610) 386-1700
Web Site: https://www.vwr.com
Laboratory Supplies Distr
N.A.I.C.S.: 423450

Subsidiary (Domestic):

Avantor Fluid Handling, LLC   **(5)**
29 Saratoga Blvd, Devens, MA 01434-5216
Tel.: (978) 772-6166
Web Site: https://www.avantorsciences.com
Fluid Handling Product Mfr & Distr
N.A.I.C.S.: 423840
Dwight Long *(Pres)*
Douglas Long *(VP)*
Heidi DeGrazia *(CFO)*
Scott Jennings *(Dir-Quality)*
Steve Peters *(Dir-Technical)*
Sean DeFusco *(Mng Dir)*
Donald Long *(Founder)*

Subsidiary (Non-US):

Global Science and Technology Ltd.   **(5)**
Tel.: (64) 9 443 5867
Web Site: http://www.nz.vwr.com
Pharmaceutical Product Supplier
N.A.I.C.S.: 424210
Graeme Thompson *(Gen Mgr)*

Subsidiary (Domestic):

VWR Advanced Instruments, LLC   **(5)**
Bo Cotto Norte Carr 686 Int 670, Manati, PR 00674
Tel.: (787) 621-3600
Web Site: https://pr.vwr.com
Analytical Instrument Distr
N.A.I.C.S.: 423490

Subsidiary (Non-US):

VWR International - Material de Laboratorio, Lda.   **(5)**
Edificio Ramazzotti Avenida do Forte n 6 P-1 09 and P-1 10, Carnaxide, 2790-072, Portugal
Tel.: (351) 213600770
Web Site: https://pt.vwr.com
Laboratory Testing Services
N.A.I.C.S.: 541380

VWR International AB   **(5)**
Esbogatan 16, Kista, 164 74, Stockholm, Sweden
Tel.: (46) 86213420
Web Site: https://se.vwr.com
Laboratory Testing Services
N.A.I.C.S.: 541380

VWR International B.V.   **(5)**
Orlyplein 85, 1043 DS, Amsterdam, Netherlands
Tel.: (31) 204808400
Web Site: https://nl.vwr.com
Chemical Products Distr
N.A.I.C.S.: 424690

VWR International Co.   **(5)**
2360 Argentia Road, Mississauga, L5N 5Z7, ON, Canada
Tel.: (905) 813-7377
Web Site: https://ca.vwr.com
Laboratory Supplies Distr
N.A.I.C.S.: 423450

VWR International GmbH   **(5)**
Graumanngasse 7, 1150, Vienna, Austria

Avantor, Inc.—(Continued)
Tel.: (43) 1970020
Web Site: https://at.vwr.com
Pharmaceutical Products Distr
N.A.I.C.S.: 424210

VWR International GmbH (5)
Lerzenstrasse 16/18, 8953, Dietikon, Switzerland
Tel.: (41) 44 7451313
Web Site: https://ch.vwr.com
Chemical Products Distr
N.A.I.C.S.: 424690

VWR International Kft. (5)
Simon Laszlo utca 4, 4034, Debrecen, Hungary
Tel.: (36) 52521130
Web Site: https://hu.vwr.com
Laboratory Testing Services
N.A.I.C.S.: 541380

VWR International Ltd (5)
Orion Business Campus Northwest Business Park Ballycoolin, Blanchardstown, 15, Dublin, Ireland
Tel.: (353) 18822222
Web Site: https://ie.vwr.com
Chemical Products Distr
N.A.I.C.S.: 424690

VWR International Oy (5)
Valimotie 17-19, 00380, Helsinki, Finland
Tel.: (358) 980455300
Web Site: https://fi.vwr.com
Chemical Products Distr
N.A.I.C.S.: 424690

VWR International PBI S.r.l. (5)
Via San Giusto 85, 20153, Milan, Italy
Tel.: (39) 02 3320311
Web Site: http://www.it.vwr.com
Laboratory Testing Services
N.A.I.C.S.: 541380

VWR International S. de R.L. de C.V. (5)
Km 14 5 Carretera Tlalnepantla-Cuautitlan Col Lecheria, CP 54940, Mexico, Edo, Mexico
Tel.: (52) 5550050100
Web Site: https://mx.vwr.com
Laboratory Testing Services
N.A.I.C.S.: 541380

VWR International S.A.S. (5)
Immeuble l'Estreo 1-3 rue d'Aurion, F-93114, Rosny-sous-Bois, cedex, France
Tel.: (33) 145148500
Web Site: https://fr.vwr.com
Pharmaceutical Products Distr
N.A.I.C.S.: 424210

VWR International Sp. z o.o. (5)
ul Limbowa 5, 80-175, Gdansk, Poland
Tel.: (48) 583238200
Web Site: https://pl.vwr.com
Laboratory Testing Services
N.A.I.C.S.: 541380

VWR International bvba (5)
Researchpark Haasrode 2020 Geldenaaksebaan 464, 3001, Leuven, Belgium
Tel.: (32) 16385011
Web Site: http://www.be.vwr.com
Sales Range: $50-74.9 Million
Emp.: 350
Pharmaceutical Products Distr
N.A.I.C.S.: 424210
Alex Braeckman (Dir-Sls)
Kris De Blauwe (Dir-Catalyst Svc)
Kris Nijs (Dir-Fin & Controlling)
Ann Pacques (Dir-HH)
Christine Van Weddingen (Dir-Integrated Mgmt Sys)
Ronny Kennis (Mgr-Production-Europe)

VWR International s. r. o. (5)
Prazska 442, 281 67, Stribrna Skalice, Czech Republic
Tel.: (420) 321570321
Web Site: https://cz.vwr.com
Laboratory Testing Services
N.A.I.C.S.: 541380

VWR International s.r.o. (5)
Prievozska 6, SK-82109, Bratislava, Slovakia
Tel.: (421) 23 260 3831
Web Site: https://sk.vwr.com

Chemical Products Distr
N.A.I.C.S.: 424690

Avantor VWR (Shanghai) Co., Ltd. (1)
1st-3rd floor Building No 1 No 3728 Jinke Road, Pudong New District, Shanghai, 200123, China
Tel.: (86) 2158986888
Laboratory Equipment Mfr & Distr
N.A.I.C.S.: 339112

Clemens GmbH (1)
Dachdeckerstr 5, Waldbuttelbrunn, 97297, Wurzburg, Germany
Tel.: (49) 931497010
Web Site: https://www.clemens-electronics.de
Engineering & Electrical Services
N.A.I.C.S.: 541330
Wolfgang Schoe (Head-Pur & Quality Mgmt)
Daniel Moisoni (Head-Electronics Production)
Christian Klug (Head-Device Production)
Martin Leu (Mng Dir)

EPL Archives, SAS (1)
14 eme Rue, Zone Industrielle, 06510, Carros, France
Tel.: (33) 492080183
Biotechnology Research & Development Services
N.A.I.C.S.: 541714

EPL Pathology Archives, LLC (1)
45610 Terminal Dr, 20166, Sterling, VA
Tel.: (703) 435-8780
Web Site: https://www.avantorsciences.com
Biotechnology Research & Development Services
N.A.I.C.S.: 541714

Hichrom Limited (1)
1 The Markham Centre Station Road, Theale, Reading, RG7 4PE, Berkshire, United Kingdom
Tel.: (44) 1189303660
Web Site: http://www.hichrom.com
Liquid Chromatography Product Mfr & Distr
N.A.I.C.S.: 334513

Klen International (74) Pty Ltd. (1)
36 Hemisphere Street, Neerabup, Perth, 6031, WA, Australia
Tel.: (61) 893068900
Web Site: https://www.klen.com.au
Fire Assay Flux Product Mfr
N.A.I.C.S.: 339999

MESM, LLC (1)
3150 County Line Rd Ste 9, Lakeland, FL 33811
Tel.: (863) 940-3944
Web Site: https://www.mesm.com
Medical Equipment Mfr
N.A.I.C.S.: 339112

Masterflex LLC (1)
625 E Bunker Ct, Vernon Hills, IL 60061
Tel.: (847) 381-7050
Web Site: https://www.masterflex.com
Biotechnology Research Services
N.A.I.C.S.: 541714
Bernd Brust (CEO & Chm)
Jaime Robles (Mgr)
Jon Salkin (COO)
Patrick Marschall (CFO)

Ritter d.o.o. (1)
Volcja Draga 42, Volcja Draga, 5293, Dragatus, Slovenia
Tel.: (386) 53302803
Web Site: https://ritter-online.si
Medical Equipment Mfr
N.A.I.C.S.: 339113

Seastar Chemicals ULC (1)
10005 McDonald Park Road, Sidney, V8L 5Y2, BC, Canada
Tel.: (250) 655-5880
Web Site: http://www.seastarchemicals.com
Chemicals Mfr
N.A.I.C.S.: 325998

VWR International A/S (1)
Tobaksvejen 21, 2860, Soborg, Denmark
Tel.: (45) 43868788
Web Site: https://dk.vwr.com
Laboratory Equipment Mfr & Distr
N.A.I.C.S.: 339112

VWR International AS (1)
Brynsalleen 4, 0667, Oslo, Norway
Tel.: (47) 22900000
Web Site: https://no.vwr.com
Laboratory Equipment Mfr & Distr
N.A.I.C.S.: 339112

VWR International Eurolab, S.L. (1)
c/ De la Tecnologia 5-7 A-7 Llinars Park, 08450, Llinars del Valles, Spain
Tel.: (34) 902222897
Web Site: https://es.vwr.com
Laboratory Equipment Distr
N.A.I.C.S.: 423450

VWR International Limitada (1)
Del cruce de La Valencia 400 Este Ruta 5 Zona Franca Zeta Lote G, Edificio A, 40306, Heredia, Costa Rica
Tel.: (506) 22602206
Web Site: https://us.vwr.com
Laboratory Equipment Mfr & Distr
N.A.I.C.S.: 339112

VWR International Ltd. (1)
Hunter Boulevard Magna Park, Lutterworth, LE17 4XN, Leicestershire, United Kingdom
Tel.: (44) 1455558600
Web Site: https://uk.vwr.com
Laboratory Equipment Mfr & Distr
N.A.I.C.S.: 339112
Eilidh Robertson (VP-Sls)

VWR Lab Products Private Limited (1)
2nd Floor Front Wing 135/12 Brigade Towers Brigade Road, Bangalore, India
Tel.: (91) 8041117126
Web Site: http://in.vwr.com
Laboratory Equipment Mfr & Distr
N.A.I.C.S.: 339112

VWR NA Services, Ltd. (1)
3rd Floor Trade and Marketing Center Mer Rouge, Port Louis, Mauritius
Tel.: (230) 2060123
Laboratory Equipment Mfr & Distr
N.A.I.C.S.: 339112

VWR Singapore Pte. Ltd. (1)
The Metropolis Tower 1 05-03 9 North Buona Vista Drive, Singapore, 138588, Singapore
Tel.: (65) 65050760
Web Site: http://sg.vwr.com
Laboratory Equipment Mfr & Distr
N.A.I.C.S.: 339112

AVATAR SYSTEMS, INC.
2801 Network Blvd Ste 210, Frisco, TX 75034
Tel.: (972) 720-1800   TX
Web Site:
    http://www.avatarsystems.net
Year Founded: 1996
AVSY—(OTCIQ)
Computer Applications for Oil & Gas Industry
N.A.I.C.S.: 513210

AVEANNA HEALTHCARE HOLDINGS INC.
400 Interstate N Pkwy Ste 1600, Atlanta, GA 30339
Tel.: (770) 441-1580   DE
Web Site: https://www.aveanna.com
Year Founded: 2010
AVAH—(NASDAQ)
Rev.: $1,678,618,000
Assets: $2,334,371,000
Liabilities: $1,698,555,000
Net Worth: $635,816,000
Earnings: ($117,044,000)
Emp.: 33,000
Fiscal Year-end: 01/01/22
Offices of Other Holding Companies
N.A.I.C.S.: 551110
Jeffrey S. Shaner (Pres & CEO)
Matthew Buckhalter (CFO)
Rodney D. Windley (Chm)
Ed Reisz (Chief Admin Officer)
Beth Rubio (Chief Clinical Officer)

Patrick Cunningham (Chief Compliance Officer)
Debbie Stewart (Principal Acctg Officer & Sr VP)

Subsidiaries:

Dunn & Berger, Inc. (1)
5955 De Soto Ave Ste 160, Woodland Hills, CA 91367
Tel.: (818) 986-1234
Sales Range: $1-9.9 Million
Emp.: 500
Women Healthcare Services
N.A.I.C.S.: 621610
Barry Berger (Founder & Pres)

AVENIR WELLNESS SOLUTIONS, INC.
5805 Sepulveda Blvd Ste 801, Sherman Oaks, CA 91411
Tel.: (424) 273-8675   NV
Web Site:
    https://www.avenirwellness.com
Year Founded: 2014
AVRW—(OTCQB)
Rev.: $4,347,000
Assets: $2,607,000
Liabilities: $12,493,000
Net Worth: ($9,886,000)
Earnings: ($3,444,000)
Emp.: 11
Fiscal Year-end: 12/31/23
Investment Services
N.A.I.C.S.: 523999
Robert Steven Davidson (Chief Scientist)
Nancy Duitch (CEO)
John Cammarano (Sr VP-Sls)
Tracy Jankowski (VP-Digital Mktg)
Marian McNear (VP-Brand Mktg)
Rick Petry (Sr VP & Exec Creative Dir)
Joel M. Bennett (CFO)

Subsidiaries:

Avenir Wellness Solutions of California, LLC (1)
1620 Beacon Pl, Oxnard, CA 93033
Tel.: (805) 824-0410
Web Site:
    https://www.curepharmaceutical.com
Pharmaceutical Products Distr
N.A.I.C.S.: 424210

Oak Therapeutics, Inc. (1)
2029 Becker, Lawrence, KS 66047
Tel.: (913) 346-0990
Web Site: https://www.oaktherapeutics.com
Biotechnology Research & Development Services
N.A.I.C.S.: 541714
Edward Maliski (Co-Founder, Pres & CEO)
Gerhard Apfelthaler (Co-Founder & Chm)

AVENUE THERAPEUTICS, INC.
1111 Kane Concourse Ste 301, Bay Harbor Islands, FL 33154
Tel.: (781) 652-4500   DE
Web Site: https://www.avenuetx.com
Year Founded: 2015
ATXI—(NASDAQ)
Rev.: $20,000
Assets: $6,045,000
Liabilities: $3,579,000
Net Worth: $3,266,000
Earnings: ($3,552,000)
Emp.: 2
Fiscal Year-end: 12/31/22
Biotechnology Research & Development Services
N.A.I.C.S.: 541713
Scott A. Reines (Chief Medical Officer-Interim)
Jay Kranzler (Chm)
David Jin (Interim CFO & COO)
Michael Ryan (VP-Clinical Ops & Program Mgmt)
Alexandra MacLean (CEO)

AVEPOINT, INC.
525 Washington Blvd Ste 1400, Jersey City, NJ 07310
Tel.: (201) 793-1111 DE
Web Site: https://www.avepoint.com
Year Founded: 2019
AVPT—(NASDAQ)
Rev.: $232,339,000
Assets: $415,533,000
Liabilities: $172,379,000
Net Worth: $243,154,000
Earnings: ($38,688,000)
Emp.: 2,187
Fiscal Year-end: 12/31/22
Software Publisher
N.A.I.C.S.: 513210
Xunkai Gong (Exec Chm)
Tianyi Jiang (Founder & CEO)
Brian Michael Brown (Chief Legal Officer, Chief Compliance Officer & Sec)

AVERY DENNISON CORPORATION
8080 Norton Pkwy, Mentor, OH 44060
Tel.: (440) 534-6000 DE
Web Site:
https://www.averydennison.com
Year Founded: 1935
AVY—(NYSE)
Rev.: $8,364,300,000
Assets: $8,209,800,000
Liabilities: $6,081,900,000
Net Worth: $2,127,900,000
Earnings: $503,000,000
Emp.: 35,000
Fiscal Year-end: 12/30/23
Pressure-Sensitive Adhesives & Materials, Office Products, Labels, Tags, Retail Systems & Specialty Chemicals Mfr
N.A.I.C.S.: 561910
Deon M. Stander (Pres & CEO)
Isabela Galli (VP)
Michael Barton (Sr VP)
Ryan Yost (VP)
Divina F. Santiago (Principal Acctg Officer, VP & Controller)
Mitchell R. Butier (Chm & Exec Chm)
Greg Lovins (CFO & Sr VP)
Margaret Chung (Treas & VP)
Nick Colisto (CIO & Sr VP)
Michael Colarossi (Head-Enterprise Sustainability)

Subsidiaries:

AVERY DENNISON (KENYA) PRIVATE LIMITED (1)
WH 10-11 Saku Business Park Mombasa Highway, Nairobi, Kenya
Tel.: (254) 719779624
Packaging Materials Mfr
N.A.I.C.S.: 326130

AVERY DENNISON (THAILAND) LTD. (1)
64/11 Moo 4 Route No 331, Pluak-Daeong Sub-District, Rayong, 21140, Thailand
Tel.: (66) 3 310 1813
Web Site: http://www.averydennison.com
Coated & Laminated Paper Mfr
N.A.I.C.S.: 322220

AVERY DENNISON BELGIUM MANAGEMENT SERVICES SPRL (1)
Boulevard John F Kennedy, 7060, Soignies, Belgium
Tel.: (32) 67346333
Corporate Office Services
N.A.I.C.S.: 551114

AVERY DENNISON HOLDING LIMITED (1)
5 The Switchback Gardner Road, Maidenhead, SL6 7RJ, United Kingdom
Tel.: (44) 1628764000
Printing Services
N.A.I.C.S.: 323111

AVERY DENNISON HONG KONG HOLDING I B.V. (1)
Willem Einthovenstraat 11, 2342 BH, Oegstgeest, Netherlands
Tel.: (31) 850002000
Investment Holding Services
N.A.I.C.S.: 551112

AVERY DENNISON JAPAN MATERIALS COMPANY LTD. (1)
Shiodome Building 13F 1-2-20, Kaigan Minato-ku, Tokyo, 105-0022, Japan
Tel.: (81) 35 776 1771
Web Site:
http://www.graphicsap.averydennison.com
Emp.: 40
Packaging Materials Mfr
N.A.I.C.S.: 326130

AVERY DENNISON OVERSEAS CORPORATION (1)
207 Goode, Glendale, CA 91203
Tel.: (626) 304-2000
Web Site: https://www.averydennison.com
Label & Packaging Materials Mfr
N.A.I.C.S.: 339999

AVERY DENNISON R.I.S. POLSKA SP.ZO.O (1)
Ul Marywilska 34 Budynek C1, 01-001, Warsaw, Poland
Tel.: (48) 225194600
Sales Range: $25-49.9 Million
Emp.: 3
Coated & Laminated Paper Mfr
N.A.I.C.S.: 322220

AVERY DENNISON RBIS PTY LTD (1)
61 Vore St, Silverwater, 2128, NSW, Australia
Tel.: (61) 297416900
Web Site: https://www.rbis-averydennison.com.au
Emp.: 30
Labeling Material Mfr
N.A.I.C.S.: 339940

AVERY DENNISON RETAIL INFORMATION SERVICES LLC (1)
207 Goode Ave, Glendale, CA 91203
Tel.: (626) 304-2000
Web Site: https://www.averydennison.com
Apparel Accessories Mfr
N.A.I.C.S.: 315990

AVERY DENNISON S.R.L. (1)
29 B Dul Tudor Vladimirescu Dist 5, Bucuresti Sectorul, Bucharest, 050881, Romania
Tel.: (40) 214117779
Web Site: https://www.averydennison.com
Knitting Mills
N.A.I.C.S.: 313240
Arena Constantine (Dir)

AVERY DENNISON SYSTEMES D'ETIQUETAGE FRANCE S.A.S. (1)
10 12 rue du Saule Trapu, Massy, 91300, France
Tel.: (33) 169535600
Web Site: http://www.averydennison.com
Sales Range: $25-49.9 Million
Emp.: 82
Paper Products Mfr
N.A.I.C.S.: 322299

Avery Dennison (Fuzhou) Converted Products Limited (1)
M9511 Industrial District Kuaian Avenue 5F Building D, Fuzhou, 350015, Fujian, China
Tel.: (86) 5918397739
Converted Paper Product Mfr
N.A.I.C.S.: 322299

Avery Dennison (Hong Kong) Ltd. (1)
Room 908 910 9/F Shatin Galleria, 18 24 Shan Mei St, Hong Kong, China (Hong Kong) (75%)
Tel.: (852) 26005300
Web Site: https://www.averydennison.com
Sales Range: $125-149.9 Million
Emp.: 20
Tickets, Tags, Labels & Related Equipment Mfr
N.A.I.C.S.: 333248

Avery Dennison (Nederland) B.V. (1)

Willem Einthovenstraat 11, 2342 BH, Oegstgeest, Netherlands
Tel.: (31) 1850002000
Web Site: http://www.europe.fasson.com
Sales Range: $100-124.9 Million
Emp.: 150
Paperboard Product Mfr
N.A.I.C.S.: 424130

Avery Dennison (Suzhou) Co. Limited (1)
No 56 YanPu Road, Suzhou Industrial Park, Suzhou, Jiangsu, China
Tel.: (86) 51262628888
Emp.: 1,000
Coated & Laminated Paper Mfr
N.A.I.C.S.: 322220

Avery Dennison - Industrial & Automotive Products Division (1)
15939 Industrial Pkwy, Cleveland, OH 44135
Tel.: (216) 267-8700
Sales Range: $50-74.9 Million
Emp.: 200
Custom Labels & Machinery Mfr
N.A.I.C.S.: 322220
Matthew Wilkinson (Sr Mgr-IT)

Avery Dennison - Performance Films Division, Schererville (1)
650 W 67th Ave, Schererville, IN 46375
Tel.: (219) 322-5030
Sales Range: $1-9.9 Million
Emp.: 40
Pressure Sensitive Coated Papers, Films & Foils Mfr
N.A.I.C.S.: 322220

Avery Dennison - Reflective Films Division, Niles (1)
7542 N Natchez, Niles, IL 60714
Tel.: (847) 647-7717
Web Site:
https://www.reflectives.averydennison.com
Rev.: $96,000,000
Emp.: 200
Self Adhesive Labels Mfr
N.A.I.C.S.: 322220

Avery Dennison - Specialty Tape U.S. (1)
250 Chester St Bldg 5, Painesville, OH 44077-9176
Tel.: (440) 358-3000
Web Site: http://stus.averydennison.com
Sales Range: $25-49.9 Million
Emp.: 23
Tape & Packaging Materials Mfr
N.A.I.C.S.: 322220

Avery Dennison Belgie BVBA (1)
Tieblokkenlaan 1, Antwerp, Turnhout, Belgium
Tel.: (32) 14404811
Adhesive Tape Mfr & Distr
N.A.I.C.S.: 339113

Avery Dennison Central Europe GmbH (1)
Kleinbeckstrasse 3-17, Sprockhovel, 45549, Germany
Tel.: (49) 232470020
Web Site: https://www.averydennison.com
Labelling Products Mfr
N.A.I.C.S.: 561910

Avery Dennison Chile S.A. (1)
Antillanca 560 Commune of Pudahuel Module 6 and 7 Santiago de Chile, Santiago, Chile
Tel.: (56) 28988063
Flexible Packaging Products Mfr
N.A.I.C.S.: 322220

Avery Dennison Colombia S. A. (1)
Calle 48 Sur 49-30, Envigado, Colombia
Tel.: (57) 43356000
Coated & Laminated Paper Mfr
N.A.I.C.S.: 322220

Avery Dennison Corp. - Retail Branding & Information Solutions (1)
7 Bishop St, Framingham, MA 01702
Tel.: (508) 879-0511
Web Site: http://www.ris.averydennison.com
Sales Range: $25-49.9 Million
Emp.: 130
Retail Printing, Labelling & Fastener Systems Developer & Mfr

N.A.I.C.S.: 561910
Helena Shen (Head-HR-Global)
Sanjay Agrawal (VP-IT)

Subsidiary (Non-US):

AVERY DENNISON R.I.S. FRANCE S. A. S. (2)
19 Avenue Leon Gambetta, 92120, Montrouge, France
Tel.: (33) 178160667
Marking & Labelling Machinery Mfr
N.A.I.C.S.: 339940
Grigoire Pastour (Gen Mgr)

Division (Domestic):

Avery Dennison Printer Systems Division (2)
170 Monarch Ln, Miamisburg, OH 45342
Tel.: (937) 865-2123
Web Site: http://www.averydennison.com
Emp.: 500
Product Identification Systems & Services for Retail Industries & Alternative Markets
N.A.I.C.S.: 541512

Subsidiary (Non-US):

Avery Dennison R.I.S. Italia S.R.L. (2)
Via Luraghi 2 C, Alfa Business Park, 20020, Arese, MI, Italy
Tel.: (39) 02938631
Coated & Laminated Paper Mfr
N.A.I.C.S.: 322220

Avery Dennison RIS Dominican Republic (2)
Nave 42 Parque Pisano, Santiago, Dominican Republic
Tel.: (809) 2418566
Sales Range: $50-74.9 Million
Brand Management
N.A.I.C.S.: 541613
Carlos Sanchez (Gen Mgr)

Avery Dennison RIS Korea Ltd. (2)
16 Maeheon-ro, Seocho-gu, Seoul, Korea (South)
Tel.: (82) 234977348
Web Site: http://www.averydennison.jp
Sales Range: $25-49.9 Million
Emp.: 90
Coated & Laminated Paper Mfr
N.A.I.C.S.: 322220

Avery Dennison RIS Taiwan Ltd. (2)
1-2F No 26 Wuquan 8th Road, New Taipei City, Taiwan
Tel.: (886) 426811582
Coated & Laminated Paper Mfr
N.A.I.C.S.: 322220

Unit (Domestic):

Avery Dennison Retail Branding & Information Solutions - Fair Lawn (2)
16-00 Pollitt Dr, Fair Lawn, NJ 07410
Tel.: (201) 956-6100
Web Site:
http://www.rbis.averydennison.com
Sales Range: $10-24.9 Million
Emp.: 80
Mfr of Woven Labels
N.A.I.C.S.: 339910

Avery Dennison Retail Branding & Information Solutions - Greensboro (2)
2025 16th St, Greensboro, NC 27405-5119
Tel.: (336) 621-0383
Web Site:
http://www.rbis.averydennison.com
Sales Range: $10-24.9 Million
Emp.: 30
Tags, Labels & Tickets Mfr
N.A.I.C.S.: 322220

Avery Dennison Retail Branding & Information Solutions - Lenoir (2)
950 German St, Lenoir, NC 28645-0735
Tel.: (828) 758-2338
Web Site:
http://www.rbis.averydennison.com
Sales Range: $1-9.9 Million
Mfr of Printed Labels
N.A.I.C.S.: 313210

Avery Dennison Corporation—(Continued)

Avery Dennison Retail Branding & Information Solutions - Sayre (2)
170 Monarch Ln, Miamisburg, OH 45342
Tel.: (937) 865-2123
Sales Range: $75-99.9 Million
Mfr of Electronic Bar Code & Labeling Systems, Including Printers, Software, Fabric Label Tape, Graphic Products & Inks
N.A.I.C.S.: 333248

Subsidiary (Non-US):

Avery Dennison Retail Information Services de Mexico, S.A. de C.V. (2)
Av La Montana 114 Mod 2 Parque Industrial, Queretaro, Mexico
Tel.: (52) 442 229 5600
Coated & Laminated Paper Mfr
N.A.I.C.S.: 322220

DM Label Group (2)
104 Min Chi Road Sec 1, Tai Shan Town, Taipei, Taiwan
Tel.: (886) 229092201
Web Site: http://www.dmlabel.com
Woven Label Mfr
N.A.I.C.S.: 561910

Subsidiary (Domestic):

Dah Mei Silk Weaving Fty Co., Ltd. (3)
52 Yue Sher Road Tachia, Taichung, Taiwan
Tel.: (886) 426811582
Web Site: http://www.dmlabel.com
Sales Range: $100-124.9 Million
Woven Label Mfr
N.A.I.C.S.: 561910

Subsidiary (Non-US):

P.T. Pacific Label Incorporated (3)
Diamond Techno Park BI C-1/14 Lemahabang, Bekasi, 17550, Indonesia
Tel.: (62) 218973958
Sales Range: $100-124.9 Million
Woven Label Mfr
N.A.I.C.S.: 561910

Subsidiary (Non-US):

PAXAR Corporation Pty. Ltd. (2)
61 Vore Street, Silverwater, 2128, NSW, Australia
Tel.: (61) 296471833
Web Site: http://www.rbis-averydennison.com.au
Sales Range: $10-24.9 Million
Emp.: 40
Brand Management
N.A.I.C.G.: 541010

Avery Dennison Fasson Canada, Inc. (1)
81 Dowty Rd, Ajax, L1S 2G3, ON, Canada (100%)
Tel.: (905) 686-0085
Web Site: http://www.averydennison.com
Sales Range: $25-49.9 Million
Emp.: 100
Coated & Laminated Paper Mfr
N.A.I.C.S.: 322220

Avery Dennison Group Singapore (Pte) Limited (1)
460 Alexandra Road PSA Building 28-02/03, Singapore, 119963, Singapore
Tel.: (65) 64307000
Flexible Packing Material Mfr
N.A.I.C.S.: 322220
Freda Chong (Gen Mgr)

Avery Dennison Gulf FZCO (1)
ZF07 Jebel Ali Free Zone, Dubai, United Arab Emirates
Tel.: (971) 48833970
Stationery & Office Supply Merchant Whslr
N.A.I.C.S.: 424130

Avery Dennison Ireland Ltd. (1)
Dublin Distribution Center Unit 35 Fonthill Business Park, Dublin, DUB22, Ireland
Tel.: (353) 16235544
Web Site: http://www.averydennison.com
Sales Range: $10-24.9 Million
Pressure Sensitive Adhesive Backed Paper & Film Mfr

Avery Dennison Italia S.p.A. (1)
Via per Uboldo 48, 21040, Gerenzano, Italy
Tel.: (39) 0296393203
Web Site: http://stus.averydennison.com
Sales Range: $300-349.9 Million
Pressure Sensitive Adhesive Backed Paper & Film Mfr
N.A.I.C.S.: 322220

Avery Dennison Management GmbH (1)
In der Graslake 41-49, 58332, Schwelm, Germany
Tel.: (49) 2336430
Management Consulting Services
N.A.I.C.S.: 541611

Avery Dennison Materials GmbH (1)
In Der Graslake 41-49, 58332, Schwelm, Germany (100%)
Tel.: (49) 2336430
Web Site: https://www.jac.de
Sales Range: $300-349.9 Million
Self-Adhesive Papers, Films & Labels Mfr
N.A.I.C.S.: 322220

Avery Dennison Materials Pty Ltd (1)
Hewittson Road, Elizabeth, 5113, SA, Australia (100%)
Tel.: (61) 882093201
Web Site: https://www.rbis-averydennison.com.au
Sales Range: $25-49.9 Million
Emp.: 80
Self Adhesive Labels Mfr
N.A.I.C.S.: 322220

Avery Dennison NTP A.S. (1)
Gaupnegrandane 19, 6868, Gaupne, Norway
Tel.: (47) 5 768 0500
Web Site: https://en.averydennisonntp.no
Emp.: 130
Coated & Laminated Paper Mfr
N.A.I.C.S.: 322220

Avery Dennison Performance Polymers (1)
Sonnenwiesenstrasse 18, 8280, Kreuzlingen, Switzerland (100%)
Tel.: (41) 716868100
Web Site: http://www.averydennison.com
Sales Range: $25-49.9 Million
Emp.: 80
Adhesive Mfr
N.A.I.C.S.: 325520

Avery Dennison Praha Spol. s.r.o. (1)
Ezi Uvozy 2131/2, Praha 9 Horni Pooornioo, 19300, Prague, Czech Republic
Tel.: (420) 28 102 1132
Web Site: https://label.averydennison.com
Stationery Product Mfr
N.A.I.C.S.: 322230

Avery Dennison RIS Vietnam Co. Ltd. (1)
Lot E 01 Trung Tam Road, Long Hau Industrial Park, Can Giuoc, Vietnam
Tel.: (84) 837763336
Sales Range: $150-199.9 Million
Emp.: 60
Coated & Laminated Paper Mfr
N.A.I.C.S.: 322220

Avery Dennison Scandinavia AB (1)
Gronegatan 4 B, Scania, 431 35, Lund, Sweden
Tel.: (46) 406941630
Sales Range: $25-49.9 Million
Emp.: 20
Office Supplies Distr
N.A.I.C.S.: 424120

Avery Dennison Singapore (Pte) Ltd. (1)
5B Toh Guan Road East 05-03, Singapore, 608829, Singapore
Tel.: (65) 6 349 0333
Web Site: http://www.averydennison.com
Coated & Laminated Paper Mfr
N.A.I.C.S.: 322220

Avery Dennison U.K. Ltd. (1)
6 Switchback Office Park Gardner Road,

Maidenhead, SL6 7RJ, Berkshire, United Kingdom (100%)
Tel.: (44) 800805020
Web Site: https://www.avery.co.uk
Labeling Systems & Functional Materials Mfr
N.A.I.C.S.: 322220

Avery Dennison do Brasil Ltda. (1)
Rua Francisco Foga 225 A B Distrito Industrial, Vinhedo, Sao Paulo, Brazil
Tel.: (55) 1938767759
Adhesive Mfr
N.A.I.C.S.: 322220
Fernanda Goncalves (Coord-Acctg)

Avery Dennison, S.A. de C.V. (1)
Kalos Aristoteles 123 Parque Industrial, Apodaca, Nuevo Leon, Mexico
Tel.: (52) 8188644100
Paper Products Mfr
N.A.I.C.S.: 322299

Avery Etichette Italia S.p.A. (1)
Via Honduras 15, Pomezia, 00071, Rome, Italy
Tel.: (39) 06910461
Web Site: http://www.avery.it
Sales Range: $300-349.9 Million
Emp.: 35
Self Adhesive Labels Mfr
N.A.I.C.S.: 322220

Avery Graphics and Reflective Products Division (1)
Willem Einthovenstraat 11, 2342 BH, Oegstgeest, Netherlands (100%)
Tel.: (31) 850002415
Web Site: http://www.europe.averygraphics.com
Sales Range: $300-349.9 Million
Emp.: 400
Self-Adhesive Types Mfr
N.A.I.C.S.: 322220
Carlo Kolker (Bus Dir-EMEA)

Avery Zweckform GmbH (1)
Miesbacher Str 5, Oberlaindern, 83626, Munich, Germany
Tel.: (49) 80246410
Web Site: https://www.avery-zweckform.com
Office Product Mfr
N.A.I.C.S.: 424120
Peter Sperl (Mng Dir)

FINESSE MEDICAL LTD. (1)
IDA Business Park Ballinalee Road, Longford, Ireland
Tel.: (353) 433349586
Web Site: http://www.finessemedical.com
Wound Care Product Mfr & Distr
N.A.I.C.S.: 339113

Fasson Roll North America - Fort Wayne (1)
3011 Independence Dr, Fort Wayne, IN 46808
Tel.: (260) 483-1124
Web Site: http://www.averydennison.com
Sales Range: $50-74.9 Million
Emp.: 188
Pressure Sensitive Label Mfr
N.A.I.C.S.: 322220

Fasson Roll North America - Peachtree (1)
513 Hwy 74 S, Peachtree City, GA 30269-2097
Tel.: (770) 487-3574
Web Site: http://www.na.fasson.com
Sales Range: $50-74.9 Million
Emp.: 200
Pressure Sensitive Materials Mfr
N.A.I.C.S.: 322220

HANITA COATINGS USA, INC. (1)
31 Cambridge Ln Ste 2, Newtown, PA 18940
Tel.: (215) 860-7479
Durable Goods Mfr & Distr
N.A.I.C.S.: 335210

HANITA PACIFIC PTY LTD. (1)
4/50 Rooks Road, Nunawading, 3131, VIC, Australia
Tel.: (61) 398729872
Solar Reflective Film Distr
N.A.I.C.S.: 423330
Jack Krispin (Mgr-Bus Dev)

HANITATEK, LLC (1)

4010 La Reunion Pkwy Ste 100, Dallas, TX 75212
Tel.: (214) 351-5818
Solar Reflective Film Distr
N.A.I.C.S.: 423330

HEBEI YONGLE TAPE CO., LTD. (1)
No 9 East Yanyi Road Industrial Park Zhuozho, Hebei, 72750, China
Tel.: (86) 3123975800
Web Site: https://www.yongletape.com
Adhesive Tape Mfr
N.A.I.C.S.: 339113

INK MILL CORP. (1)
6 Bay Rd, Sanbornton, NH 03269
Tel.: (603) 217-4144
Web Site: https://www.inkmillcorp.com
Printing Ink Mfr
N.A.I.C.S.: 325910

Lion Brothers Company, Inc. (1)
10246 Reisterstown Rd, Owings Mills, MD 21117
Tel.: (410) 363-1000
Web Site: http://www.lionbrothers.com
Sales Range: $10-24.9 Million
Emp.: 60
Decoration, Identification & Commemoration Products Mfr
N.A.I.C.S.: 313310
Susan J. Ganz (Chm)
Cesar Aguilar (Exec VP-Sls & Mktg)
Steven R. Walton (Exec Dir-Lion Intl)
Christopher Heyn (Pres & CEO)

Subsidiary (Non-US):

Lion Brothers Far East, LTD. (2)
5/F Po Shing Industrial Bldg 23 Tai Yau Street, San Po Kong, Kowloon, China (Hong Kong)
Tel.: (852) 23238205
Embroidery Services
N.A.I.C.S.: 313220

MACtac Europe sprl (1)
Boulevard Kennedy, 7060, Soignies, Belgium
Tel.: (32) 67346211
Web Site: http://www.mactac-europe.com
Pressure Sensitive Packaging Mfr & Distr
N.A.I.C.S.: 325520

Subsidiary (Non-US):

MACtac Deutschland GmbH (2)
Mathias-Bruggen-Strasse 140, D-50829, Cologne, Germany
Tel.: (49) 221597890
Web Site: http://www.mactac-europe.com
Pressure-Sensitive Packaging Mfr
N.A.I.C.S.: 325520

MACtac France SARL (2)
3 avenue Jeanne Garnerin Batiment Le Pelican CS 90097, 91325, Wissous, France
Tel.: (33) 164547800
Web Site: http://www.mactac.eu
Emp.: 8
Pressure-Sensitive Adhesive Pressure Stock Mfr
N.A.I.C.S.: 325520

Mactac POLSKA (2)
Ul Ozarowska 40/42, 05-850, Duchnice, Poland
Tel.: (48) 227383727
Web Site: http://www.mactacgraphics.eu
Emp.: 7
Flexible Packaging Mfr
N.A.I.C.S.: 326112

MONARCH INDUSTRIES, INC. (1)
6405 Metcalf Ave Ste 201, Shawnee Mission, KS 66202-3999
Tel.: (913) 262-4505
Stationery & Office Products Whslr
N.A.I.C.S.: 424120

MULTI-FIX BVBA (1)
Boulevard Kennedy, 7060, Soignies, Belgium
Tel.: (32) 67346211
Web Site: http://www.multi-fix.com
Adhesive Mfr
N.A.I.C.S.: 322220

PT Avery Dennison Indonesia (1)

West Java Distribution Center Jalan Ja-
babeka Block V-81 Lemah Abang, Karang
Baru, Bekasi, 17550, Indonesia
Tel.: (62) 218936033
Coated & Laminated Paper Mfr
N.A.I.C.S.: 322220

Rietveld Serigrafie B.V. (1)
Industrieweg 50, Rijndijk, 2382 NW, Zoeter-
woude, Netherlands
Tel.: (31) 172493525
Web Site: https://www.rietveld-serigrafie.nl
Textile Printing Services
N.A.I.C.S.: 541490

SMARTRAC N.V. (1)
Strawinskylaan 851, 1077 XX, Amsterdam,
Netherlands
Tel.: (31) 20 30 50 150
Web Site: http://www.smartrac-group.com
Sales Range: $300-349.9 Million
Emp.: 900
Holding Company; Radio Frequency Identi-
fication Products Mfr
N.A.I.C.S.: 551112
Christian Uhl (CEO & Member-Exec Bd)
Robert Harmzen (Member-Exec Bd)
Dinesh Dhamija (CTO & Member-Exec Bd)
Kerstin Reden (CFO)
Sanjay Agrawal (VP-Information Technol-
ogy)
Hannah Bernard (Sr Dir-Marketing Commu-
nications)
Jeremy Chura (VP-Human Resources)
Gustavo Gomez Iglesias (Sr Dir-Finance)
Roger Machado (VP-Procurement-Supply
Chain)
Erik Mols (Sr Dir-Supply Chain)
Michael Sanders (VP-Business Develop-
ment)
Jeremy Schenof (VP-Strategy)
Bill Toney (VP-Retail)
Juha Virtanen (Head-Research & Develop-
ment)
Max Winograd (VP)
Graham Wladimiroff (VP & Asst Gen Coun-
sel)
Sanjay Agrawal (VP-Information Technol-
ogy)
Hannah Bernard (Sr Dir-Marketing Commu-
nications)
Jeremy Chura (VP-Human Resources)
Gustavo Gomez Iglesias (Sr Dir-Finance)
Roger Machado (VP-Procurement-Supply
Chain)
Erik Mols (Sr Dir-Supply Chain)
Michael Sanders (VP-Business Develop-
ment)
Jeremy Schenof (VP-Strategy)
Bill Toney (VP-Retail)
Juha Virtanen (Head-Research & Develop-
ment)
Max Winograd (VP)
Graham Wladimiroff (VP & Asst Gen Coun-
sel)

Subsidiary (Non-US):

SMARTRAC Technology GmbH (2)
Tel.: (49) 7116569260
Web Site: https://www.smartrac-group.com
Sales Range: $25-49.9 Million
Radio Frequency Identification Products Mfr
N.A.I.C.S.: 334419

SMARTRAC Technology Ltd. (2)
142 Moo 1 Hi-Tech Industrial Estate Tam-
bon Ban Laean, Amphor Bang-pa-in, Phra
Nakhon Si Ayutthaya, 13160, Thailand
Tel.: (66) 35314020
Web Site: http://www.smartrac-group.com
Sales Range: $10-24.9 Million
Radio Frequency Identification Products Mfr
N.A.I.C.S.: 334419

Subsidiary (US):

SMARTRAC Technology US Inc. (2)
1546 Lake Dr W, Chanhassen, MN 55317
Tel.: (952) 442-1112
Radio Frequency Identification Products Mfr
N.A.I.C.S.: 334419

Subsidiary (Domestic):

Neology, Inc. (3)
1917 Palomar Oaks Way Ste 110, Carlsbad, CA 92008
Tel.: (858) 391-0260
Web Site: https://www.neology.net

Sales Range: $1-9.9 Million
Emp.: 150
Radio Frequency Identification Equipment
Mfr
N.A.I.C.S.: 334515
Joe Mullis (Gen Mgr)
Francisco Martinez De Velasco (Founder)
Manuel Moreno (Sr VP-Sls & Strategy)
Luke Normington (Mng Dir-EMEA & Gen
Mgr-ALPR)
John Miller (VP-Product & Technical Deliv-
ery)
Bradley H. Feldmann (Chm & CEO)

Thermopatch (Canada) Inc. (1)
25 Groff Place Unit No 5, Kitchener, N2E
2L6, ON, Canada
Tel.: (519) 748-5027
Textile Emblem & Label Designing Services
N.A.I.C.S.: 541490

Thermopatch B.V. (1)
Draaibrugweg 14, 1332 AD, Almere, Nether-
lands
Tel.: (31) 365491111
Web Site: https://www.thermopatch.com
Emp.: 60
Textile Emblem & Label Designing Services
N.A.I.C.S.: 541490

Thermopatch Deutschland Gmbh (1)
Grunteweg 33, 26127, Oldenburg, Germany
Tel.: (49) 4413802110
Textile Emblem & Label Designing Services
N.A.I.C.S.: 541490

Thermopatch Uk Ltd. (1)
Unit 3C Shap Road Industrial Estate, Ken-
dal, LA9 6NZ, Cumbria, United Kingdom
Tel.: (44) 1539722122
Textile Emblem & Label Designing Services
N.A.I.C.S.: 541490

Yongle Tape Co., Ltd. (1)
No 9 East Yanyi Road Industrial Park of
Zhouzhou Development Zone, Zhuozhou,
072750, China
Tel.: (86) 3123975918
Pressure Sensitive Adhesive & PVC Prod-
ucts & Equipment Mfr
N.A.I.C.S.: 325520

Subsidiary (Domestic):

Hebei Huaxia Enterprise Co.Ltd. (2)
No 88 Yongle Avenue, Zhuozhou, 072750,
China
Tel.: (86) 3123975877
PVC Tape Mfr
N.A.I.C.S.: 325211

AVIAT NETWORKS, INC.

200 Parker Dr Ste C100A, Austin, TX
78728
Tel.: (512) 265-3680   DE
Web Site:
   https://www.aviatnetworks.com
Year Founded: 2007
AVNW—(NASDAQ)
Rev.: $408,083,000
Assets: $535,223,000
Liabilities: $279,338,000
Net Worth: $255,885,000
Earnings: $10,760,000
Emp.: 909
Fiscal Year-end: 06/28/24
Holding Company; Wireless Telecom-
munications Network Solutions &
Services
N.A.I.C.S.: 551112
John Mutch (Chm)
Peter A. Smith (Pres & CEO)
Keith Fanneron (VP-IR & Fin-Global)
Gary Croke (VP-Mktg & Product Line
Mgmt)
Christy Cornet (VP-Supply Chain &
Ops-Global)
Erin Boase (VP-Legal Affairs)
Astrid Elbe (VP-Product Dev)
Spencer Stoakley (VP-HR)
Chi Yang Chua (VP-Svcs & Sls-
APAC)
Steve Toteda (VP-Europe, Middle
East & Africa)

Subsidiaries:

**Aviat Communications Technology
(Shenzhen) Company Ltd.** (1)
Unit A01 4th Floor Building W2-A No 25 4th
Gaoxin South Avenue, Hi-Tech Industrial
Park Nanshan District, Shenzhen, 518057,
China   **(100%)**
Tel.: (86) 3302973088
Web Site: https://www.aviatnetworks.com
Sales Range: $10-24.9 Million
Emp.: 30
Wireless Telecommunications Network So-
lutions & Services
N.A.I.C.S.: 334220

**Aviat Net Works Saudi Telecom &
Information Technology Co.** (1)
ALOula Building Office 408 King Fahad
Road, PO Box 93850, Riyadh, 11683, Saudi
Arabia
Tel.: (966) 112079775
Network Wireless Transport Product Mfr
N.A.I.C.S.: 334290

**Aviat Networks (Australia) Pty.
Ltd.** (1)
Unit 701 Building F Lane Cove Business
Park 16 Mars Road, Lane Cove, 2066,
NSW, Australia
Tel.: (61) 294207300
Emp.: 5
Electronic Equipment Whslr
N.A.I.C.S.: 423690

**Aviat Networks (India) Private
Limited** (1)
Unit No-306 307 308 3rd Floor, JMD Pacific
Square Sector-15, Gurgaon, 122 001, Hary-
ana, India
Tel.: (91) 1246798000
Wireless Telecommunication Services
N.A.I.C.S.: 517112

Aviat Networks (NZ) Limited (1)
20 Peterkin Street, Lower Hutt, 5019, New
Zealand
Tel.: (64) 45778800
Sales Range: $25-49.9 Million
Emp.: 100
Transmission Equipment Mfr
N.A.I.C.S.: 334290
Mike Pinga (CEO)

Aviat Networks (S) Pte. Ltd. (1)
51 Changi Business Park Central 2 08-03
The Signature Building, Singapore, 486066,
Singapore
Tel.: (65) 64960900
Sales Range: $25-49.9 Million
Emp.: 41
Wireless Telecommunications Service Pro-
vider
N.A.I.C.S.: 517112

Aviat Networks (Thailand) Ltd. (1)
87 M Thai Tower All Seasons Place 23Rd
Floor Wireless Road Lumpini, Phatumwan,
Bangkok, 10330, Thailand
Tel.: (66) 26279017
Sales Range: $10-24.9 Million
Emp.: 8
Communication Equipment Mfr
N.A.I.C.S.: 334290

Aviat Networks (UK) Limited (1)
77 Fulham Palace Road, London, W6 8JA,
Greater London, United Kingdom   **(100%)**
Tel.: (44) 2070022200
Web Site: https://www.aviatnetworks.com
Sales Range: $25-49.9 Million
Emp.: 80
Wireless Telecommunications Network So-
lutions & Services
N.A.I.C.S.: 334220

**Aviat Networks Brasil Servicos em
Communicacoes Ltda.** (1)
Alameda Araguaia 933 5 andar sala 57,
Alphaville - Barueri, Sao Paulo, CEP
06455-000, Brazil   **(100%)**
Tel.: (55) 1141963670
Web Site: https://www.aviatnetworks.com
Sales Range: $100-124.9 Million
Emp.: 30
Wireless Telecommunications Network So-
lutions & Services
N.A.I.C.S.: 334220

Aviat Networks Canada ULC (1)

1425 Trans-Canada Highway Suite 200,
Dorval, H9P 2V3, QC, Canada   **(100%)**
Tel.: (514) 421-8400
Sales Range: $25-49.9 Million
Emp.: 100
Wireless Telecommunications Network Solu-
tions & Services
N.A.I.C.S.: 334220

**Aviat Networks Communication Solu-
tions Limited** (1)
Plot 4/6 Ajose Adeogun Street, Victoria Is-
land, Lagos, 101242, Nigeria   **(100%)**
Tel.: (234) 12707556
Sales Range: $10-24.9 Million
Wireless Telecommunications Network So-
lutions & Services
N.A.I.C.S.: 334220

Aviat Networks Cote d'Ivoire (1)
Immeuble Sayegh Rue de Jardins 3eme
Etage, Deux Plateaux, Abidjan, Cote
d'Ivoire
Tel.: (225) 2722548775
Telecommunications Equipment Mfr
N.A.I.C.S.: 334220

Aviat Networks Ghana Limited (1)
3Rd Floor Advantage Place 7th Avenue
Mayor Road Ridge West, PO Box 2319,
Accra, Ghana
Tel.: (233) 302669740
Sales Range: $10-24.9 Million
Emp.: 9
Wireless Telecommunication Services
N.A.I.C.S.: 517112

**Aviat Networks Malaysia Sdn.
Bhd.** (1)
Unit 6 10 Level 6 Block J No 2 Jalan So-
laris, Solaris Mont Kiara, Kuala Lumpur,
50480, Malaysia
Tel.: (60) 362036678
Emp.: 8
Communication Equipment Mfr
N.A.I.C.S.: 334290
Nandha Kumar (Dir-Country)

Aviat Networks Philippines, Inc. (1)
15/F The Trade and Finance Tower 7th Av-
enue cor 32nd Street, Bonifacio Global City,
Taguig, Philippines
Tel.: (63) 28185111
Sales Range: $25-49.9 Million
Emp.: 30
Communication Equipment Mfr
N.A.I.C.S.: 334290

Aviat Networks Polska Sp. z.o.o. (1)
Regus Office North Gate building ul Boni-
fraterska 17 6th floor, 00-203, Warsaw,
Poland
Tel.: (48) 223075020
Communication Equipment Mfr
N.A.I.C.S.: 334290

Aviat Networks Saudi Arabia (1)
Al Oula Building Office #408 King Fahad
Road, PO Box 93850, Riyadh, 11683, Saudi
Arabia
Tel.: (966) 1 12079775
Sales Range: $100-124.9 Million
Wireless Telecommunications Network So-
lutions & Services
N.A.I.C.S.: 334220

**Aviat Networks de Mexico, S.A. de
C.V.** (1)
Ejercito Nacional No 926 Piso 3 Col Los
Morales, Seccion Palmas, 11540, Mexico,
Mexico   **(100%)**
Tel.: (52) 5591389700
Web Site: http://www.aviatnet.com
Sales Range: $10-24.9 Million
Emp.: 20
Wireless Telecommunications Network So-
lutions & Services
N.A.I.C.S.: 334220

Aviat U.S., Inc. (1)
5250 Prue Rd Bldg 5 Ste 535, San Antonio,
TX 78240   **(100%)**
Tel.: (210) 526-6300
Web Site: https://www.aviatnetworks.com
Sales Range: $75-99.9 Million
Emp.: 450
Wireless Telecommunications Network So-
lutions & Services
N.A.I.C.S.: 334220

Aviat Networks, Inc.—(Continued)

Unit (Domestic):

Aviat U.S., Inc. - San Antonio   (2)
5757 Farinon Dr, San Antonio, TX 78249
Tel.: (210) 561-7300
Sales Range: $25-49.9 Million
Emp.: 150
Wireless Telecommunications Network So-
lutions & Services
N.A.I.C.S.: 334220

Aviat storitveno podjetje, d.o.o.   (1)
Motnica 9, 1236, Trzin, Ljubljana, Slovenia
Tel.: (386) 15887001
Sales Range: $25-49.9 Million
Emp.: 66
Communication Equipment Mfr
N.A.I.C.S.: 334290

Harris Communication Argentina
SA   (1)
Tucuman 540 Piso 28 J, C1049AAL, Bue-
nos Aires, Argentina
Tel.: (54) 11 4325 0182
Web Site: http://www.aviatnetworks.com
Wireless Telecommunications Network So-
lutions & Services
N.A.I.C.S.: 334220

Redline Communications Group
Inc.   (1)
302 Town Centre Blvd 4th Floor, Markham,
L3R 0E8, ON, Canada
Tel.: (905) 479-8344
Web Site: http://rdlcom.com
Rev.: $18,515,390
Assets: $18,357,258
Liabilities: $7,200,632
Net Worth: $11,156,626
Earnings: ($3,899,707)
Emp.: 105
Fiscal Year-end: 12/31/2020
Broadband Wireless Product Designer, Mfr
& Sales
N.A.I.C.S.: 517112
Abdelsalam Aldwikat (VP-Ops & Tech)
Reno Moccia (Exec VP-Sls & Mktg-Global)
Brad Stimpson (VP-Engrg)
Philip Jones (CFO)

Subsidiary (Non-US):

Redline Communications Romania
Ltd.   (2)
Strada Paltinis Nr 18, 200127, Craiova,
Dolj, Romania
Tel.: (40) 351401504
Wireless Communication Device Distr
N.A.I.C.S.: 423690

AVID BIOSERVICES, INC.

14191 Myford Rd, Tustin, CA 92780
Tel.: (714) 508-6100   DE
Web Site: https://www.avidbio.com
Year Founded: 1996
CDMO—(NASDAQ)
Rev.: $139,911,000
Assets: $336,557,000
Liabilities: $275,668,000
Net Worth: $60,889,000
Earnings: ($140,753,000)
Emp.: 371
Fiscal Year-end: 04/30/24
Anti-Cancer Drug Mfr
N.A.I.C.S.: 325412
Richard A. Richieri (COO)
Mark R. Ziebell (Gen Councol, Soo &
VP)
Daniel R. Hart (CFO)
Ray Marzouk (VP-Quality)
Lorna Larson (Sr Dir-HR)
Nick Ferguson (Exec Dir-IT)
Nicholas S. Green (Pres & CEO)
Drew Brennan (Gen Mgr-Viral Vector
Technologies)
Elie G. Hanania (VP-Process Dev-
Viral Vector Technologies)
Michael Alston Jr. (VP-Ops)
Oksana Lukash (VP-People)

AVIDBANK HOLDINGS, INC.

821 Winslow St, Redwood City, CA
94063
Tel.: (650) 843-2265   CA
Web Site: https://www.avidbank.com
Year Founded: 2003
AVBH—(OTCIQ)
Rev.: $122,330,000
Assets: $2,230,836,000
Liabilities: $2,065,524,000
Net Worth: $165,312,000
Earnings: $16,801,000
Emp.: 143
Fiscal Year-end: 12/31/23
Bank Holding Company
N.A.I.C.S.: 551111
Mark D. Mordell (Chm & CEO)
Geoff Butner (Chief Credit Officer &
Exec VP)
Gina T. Peterson (COO & Exec VP)
Dori Hamilton (Chief Banking Officer
& Exec VP)
Fergal J. O'Boyle (Exec VP-
Construction Lending)
Sam Bhaumik (Exec VP-Venture
Lending)
Joe Maleti (Exec VP-Comml & Real
Estate Lending)
Mark Cameron (Exec VP/Sr VP-
Structured Fin)
Patrick Oakes (CFO & Exec VP)
Arthur Wasson (Exec VP & Treasury
Mgmt Svcs)

Subsidiaries:

Avidbank   (1)
400 Emerson St, Palo Alto, CA 94301
Tel.: (650) 843-2265
Web Site: http://www.avidbank.com
Rev.: $17,089,000
Assets: $500,653,000
Liabilities: $453,741,000
Net Worth: $46,912,000
Earnings: $2,502,000
Fiscal Year-end: 12/31/2013
Commericial Banking
N.A.I.C.S.: 522110
Steven Leen (CFO & Exec VP)
Jon Krogstad (Exec VP-Specialty Fin)
Kenneth D. Brenner (Head-Strategic Rela-
tionships)
Geoff Butner (Chief Credit Officer & Exec
VP)
Gina Thoma Peterson (COO & Exec VP)

AVIDITY BIOSCIENCES, INC.

10578 Science Ctr Dr Ste 125, San
Diego, CA 92121
Tel.: (858) 401-7900   DE
Web Site:
https://www.aviditybiosciences.com
Year Founded: 2012
RNA—(NASDAQ)
Rev.: $9,560,000
Assets: $628,555,000
Liabilities: $127,791,000
Net Worth: $500,764,000
Earnings: ($212,220,000)
Emp.: 253
Fiscal Year-end: 12/31/23
Biotechnology Research & Develop-
ment Services
N.A.I.C.S.: 541714
Eric B. Mosbrooker (Chief Strategy
Officer)
Troy Wilson (Founder & Chm)
W. Michael Flanagan (Chief Scientific
& Technical Officer)
Teresa McCarthy (Chief HR Officer)
Steve Hughes (Chief Medical Officer)
Kathleen Gallagher (Sr VP)
Sarah Boyce (Pres & CEO)
John W. Wallen III (Gen Counsel)
Michael F. MacLean (CFO & Chief
Bus Officer)

AVIDXCHANGE HOLDINGS,
INC.

1210 AvidXchange Ln, Charlotte, NC
28206   DE
Web Site:
https://www.avidxchange.com
Year Founded: 2021
AVDX—(NASDAQ)
Rev.: $316,350,000
Assets: $2,211,996,000
Liabilities: $1,554,552,000
Net Worth: $657,444,000
Earnings: ($101,284,000)
Emp.: 1,600
Fiscal Year-end: 12/31/22
Offices of Other Holding Companies
N.A.I.C.S.: 551112
Daniel Drees (Pres)
Michael Praeger (Founder & CEO)
Joel Wilhite (CFO & Sr VP)
Angelic Gibson (CIO & Sr VP)
Todd Cunningham (Chief People Offi-
cer & Sr VP)
Ryan Stahl (Gen Counsel, Sec & Sr
VP)
James Sutton (Chief Revenue Offi-
cer)

Subsidiaries:

AvidXchange, Inc.   (1)
1210 AvidXchange Ln, Charlotte, NC 28206
Tel.: (704) 971-8170
Web Site: https://www.avidxchange.com
Bill Payment Software Publisher
N.A.I.C.S.: 513210
Michael Praeger (Co-Founder & CEO)
Joel Wilhite (CFO)
Todd Cunningham (Sr VP-Human Capital &
Human Capital)
Dan Drees (Chief Growth Officer)
Angelic Gibson (CIO)

Subsidiary (Domestic):

BTS Alliance, LLC   (2)
319 Park Creek Dr, Columbus, MS 39705
Tel.: (662) 245-6622
Web Site: https://www.avidxchange.com
Emp.: 100
Software & Technology Development Ser-
vices
N.A.I.C.S.: 513210
Core Associates, LLC   (2)
172 N Tustin St Ste 101, Orange, CA
92867-7780
Tel.: (714) 997-0951
Web Site: http://www.core-assoc.com
Offices of Certified Public Accountants
N.A.I.C.S.: 541211
Frank Grenci (Co-Founder & CEO)
Bernard Ross (Co-Founder & Chief Sls Offi-
cer)
Piracle, Inc.   (2)
556 Confluence Ave, Murray, UT 84123
Tel.: (801) 322-5222
Web Site: http://www.piracle.com
Sales Range: $10-24.9 Million
Emp.: 30
Payment Processing Software Publisher
N.A.I.C.S.: 513210
Linda Ford (Owner)
John Hanousek (VP-Bus Dev)
Lynn Shimada (VP)
Kandice Lambert (Controller)
Jeremy Collins (Dir-Sls)
Dan Parker (Dir-Mktg)
Dan Dempsey (Mgr-Support & Quality As-
surance)
Strongroom Solutions, LLC   (2)
410 Pierce St Ste 209, Houston, TX 77002
Tel.: (713) 574-1111
Web Site:
http://www.strongroomsolutions.com
Software Publisher
N.A.I.C.S.: 513210
Scott Mury (Founder, CTO & VP-Software)
Tyler Gill (CEO)
Leon Davila (Dir-Sls)
Erin Rapp (Dir-Ops)

AVIENT CORPORATION

33587 Walker Rd, Avon Lake, OH
44012

Tel.: (440) 930-1000   OH
Web Site: https://www.avient.com
Year Founded: 2000
AVNT—(NYSE)
Rev.: $3,396,900,000
Assets: $6,085,000,000
Liabilities: $3,732,200,000
Net Worth: $2,352,800,000
Earnings: $703,100,000
Emp.: 9,700
Fiscal Year-end: 12/31/22
Specialty Ink, Polymer & Elastomer
Developer, Mfr & Distr
N.A.I.C.S.: 325211
Ashish K. Khandpur (Pres & CEO)
Holger Kronimus (VP/Gen Mgr-
Engineered Materials-Europe)
Jamie A. Beggs (CFO & Sr VP)
Kyle G. Rose (VP-Marketing & Com-
munications)
Kristen Gajewski (Chief HR Officer &
Sr VP)
Christopher L. Pederson (Pres-
Specialty Engineered Materials & Sr
VP)
Joel Rathbun (Sr VP-Mergers & Ac-
quisitions)
Giuseppe Di Salvo (Treas & VP-IR)
Avery Johnson (VP-Tax)
George Inglis (VP & Controller)
Say-Eng Lee (VP & Gen Mgr-Color,
Additives, and Inks Asia)
Norbert Merklein (VP & Gen Mgr-
EMEA, Color, Additives, and Inks)
Leslie Sequeira (CIO)
M. John Midea Jr. (Sr VP-Global Ops
& Process Improvement)

Subsidiaries:

Avient (Thailand) Co., Ltd.   (1)
79 Moo 11 Soi Kingthong Kingkaew Road,
Rachatewa Bangplee, Samut Prakan,
10540, Thailand
Tel.: (66) 23279100
Electronic Equipment Mfr & Distr
N.A.I.C.S.: 335311

Avient Argentina S.A.   (1)
Av Jose Garibaldi 2401, Lomas de Zamora,
01836, Buenos Aires, Argentina
Tel.: (54) 1120402320
Building & Construction Services
N.A.I.C.S.: 236220

Avient Canada ULC   (1)
5915 Airport Road Suite 520, Mississauga,
L4V 1T1, ON, Canada
Tel.: (905) 405-0003
Thermoplastic Resin Material Mfr & Distr
N.A.I.C.S.: 325211

Avient Chile S.p.A.   (1)
Camino a Melipilla No 15170, Maipu, San-
tiago, Chile
Tel.: (56) 232108550
Building & Construction Services
N.A.I.C.S.: 236220

Avient Colorants (Thailand) Ltd.   (1)
700/848 Moo 1 Amata City Chonburi Indus-
trial Estate, Tamboi Phan Thong Amphur
Phan Thong, Chon Buri, 20160, Thailand
Tel.: (66) 25061200
Chemical Product Mfr & Distr
N.A.I.C.S.: 325998

Avient Colorants Belgium SA   (1)
Fond Jean Paques 1, 1348, Louvain-la-
Neuve, Belgium
Tel.: (32) 10480511
Plastics Product Mfr
N.A.I.C.S.: 326199

Avient Colorants Italy S.R.L.   (1)
Via Bergamo 51, Merate, 23807, Lecco,
Italy
Tel.: (39) 0299184300
Thermoplastic Resin Material Mfr & Distr
N.A.I.C.S.: 325211

Avient Colorants Malaysia Sdn.
Bhd.   (1)
Lot 1232 MK 15 Kawasan Industri Kecil &
Sederhana, Simpang Ampat SPS, 14120,

Penang, Malaysia
Tel.: (60) 390784700
Chemical Product Mfr & Distr
N.A.I.C.S.: 325998

Avient Colorants Singapore Pte. Ltd. (1)
No 8 Third Chin Bee Road Jurong Industrial Estate, Jurong, 618684, Singapore
Tel.: (65) 69298400
Chemical Product Mfr & Distr
N.A.I.C.S.: 325998

Avient Colorants Switzerland AG (1)
Rothausstrasse 61, 4132, Muttenz, Switzerland
Tel.: (41) 614696296
Plastics Product Mfr
N.A.I.C.S.: 326199

Avient Finland OY (1)
Ayritie 8 D, 01510, Vantaa, Finland
Tel.: (358) 406717200
Plastics Product Mfr
N.A.I.C.S.: 326199

Avient Japan K.K. (1)
904 9F Hirakawacho Visix 1-5-15 Hirakawa-cho, Chiyoda-ku, Tokyo, 102-0093, Japan
Tel.: (81) 362613980
Web Site: https://www.avient.jp
Industrial Chemical Product Distr
N.A.I.C.S.: 424690

Avient Luxembourg S.a r.l. (1)
19 Route de Bastogne, L-9638, Luxembourg, Luxembourg
Tel.: (352) 26905035
Industrial Chemical Product Distr
N.A.I.C.S.: 424690

Avient New Zealand Limited (1)
4 Rothwell Avenue Albany Industrial Estate, Auckland, 0632, New Zealand
Tel.: (64) 99145566
Plastic Fabrication Mfr & Distr
N.A.I.C.S.: 326199

Avient Saudi Industries Co., Ltd. (1)
Jazan Road Industrial City II Street 23, PO Box 2137, Jeddah, 22758, Saudi Arabia
Tel.: (966) 125107180
Plastic Fabrication Mfr & Distr
N.A.I.C.S.: 326199

Avient Singapore Pte. Ltd. (1)
3 International Business Park Nordic European Centre 04-14/15, Singapore, 609927, Singapore
Tel.: (65) 68619325
Chemical Product Mfr & Distr
N.A.I.C.S.: 325998

Avient Th. Bergmann GmbH (1)
Adolf Dambach-Strasse 2, 76571, Gaggenau, Germany
Tel.: (49) 722568020
Polymer Material Mfr & Distr
N.A.I.C.S.: 325211

COMPTEK Kunststoffverarbeitung GmbH (1)
Heinrich-Hertz-Str 15, 65582, Diez, Germany
Tel.: (49) 643264560
Web Site: http://www.comptek.de
Rigid Plastic & Fiberglass Mfr
N.A.I.C.S.: 326199

Clariant Material Science (Guangzhou) Ltd. (1)
No 2 Nan Yun San Road Science City, Guangzhou Hi-Tech Industrial Zone, Guangzhou, 510663, China
Tel.: (86) 2028202222
Specialty Chemicals Mfr
N.A.I.C.S.: 325998

Clariant Plastics & Coatings (France) (1)
14 avenue de l'Eguillette ZA du Vert Galant, 95310, Saint-Ouen-l'Aumone, France
Tel.: (33) 134403950
Specialty Chemicals Mfr
N.A.I.C.S.: 325998

Clariant Plastics & Coatings (Italia) S.p.A. (1)
Via Manzoni 37, Palazzolo Milanese, 20030, Milan, Italy
Tel.: (39) 02363141

Specialty Chemicals Mfr
N.A.I.C.S.: 325998

Clariant Plastics & Coatings (Polska) Sp. z o.o. (1)
Ul Langiewicza 50, 95-050, Konstantynow Lodzki, Poland
Tel.: (48) 422790854
Specialty Chemicals Mfr
N.A.I.C.S.: 325998

Clariant Plastics & Coatings (Taiwan) Co., Ltd. (1)
5th Fl No 96 Chien Kuo N road Section 1, Taipei, 10489, Taiwan
Tel.: (886) 225166886
Specialty Chemicals Mfr
N.A.I.C.S.: 325998

Clariant Plastics & Coatings (Thailand) Ltd. (1)
Phase 8 700/848 Moo 1 Tambol Phan Thong, Amata Nakorn Industrial Estate Amphur Phan Thong, 20160, Phan Thong, Chonburi, Thailand
Tel.: (66) 38939599
Specialty Chemicals Mfr
N.A.I.C.S.: 325998

Clariant Plastics and Coatings (RUS) LLC (1)
Andropova Pr-t 61 Bld 6, 115432, Moscow, Russia
Tel.: (7) 4957875050
Specialty Chemicals Mfr
N.A.I.C.S.: 325998

ColorMatrix Group, Inc. (1)
680 N Rocky River Dr, Berea, OH 44017-1628
Tel.: (216) 622-0100
Web Site: http://www.polyone.com
Emp.: 8,200
Synthetic Dye & Pigment Mfr
N.A.I.C.S.: 325130

Subsidiary (Non-US):

ColorMatrix Asia Limited (2)
16/F Sun Life Tower The Gateway Harbour City, Tsim Sha Tsui, Kowloon, China (Hong Kong)
Tel.: (852) 2 369 6263
Web Site: https://www.colormatrix.com
Emp.: 30
Liquid color & Additives Mfr
N.A.I.C.S.: 325510

Subsidiary (Domestic):

ColorMatrix Corporation (2)
680 N Rocky River Dr, Berea, OH 44017-1628
Tel.: (216) 622-0100
Web Site: http://www.colormatrix.com
Sales Range: $150-199.9 Million
Emp.: 80
Liquid Colorants Mfr
N.A.I.C.S.: 325130
Bob Tatterson (CEO)

Subsidiary (Non-US):

ColorMatrix Europe Limited (2)
Unity Grove, Knowsley Business Park, Knowsley, L34 9GT, Merseyside, United Kingdom
Tel.: (44) 151 632 8800
Web Site: https://www.colormatrix.com
Emp.: 100
Holding Company; Paint, Varnish & Allied Product Mfr & Distr
N.A.I.C.S.: 551112

Subsidiary (Non-US):

ColorMatrix Europe BV (3)
Fahrenheit avenue 8, 9207 HE, Drachten, Netherlands
Tel.: (31) 402916510
Emp.: 100
Color Concentrates & Pigment Dispersions Mfr
N.A.I.C.S.: 325510

ColorMatrix Russia LLC (3)
Khimki Leningradskaya street 39 bld 6 of 8A2, Business Park Khimki, 141400, Moscow, Russia
Tel.: (7) 9296370700
Web Site: https://www.polyone.com

Liquid color & Additives Mfr
N.A.I.C.S.: 325510

Subsidiary (Domestic):

ColorMatrix UK Limited (3)
Unity Grove, Knowsley Business Park, Knowsley, L34 9GT, Merseyside, United Kingdom
Tel.: (44) 1515476636
Paint, Varnish & Allied Product Mfr & Distr
N.A.I.C.S.: 325510
Steve Tattum (Gen Mgr)

ColorMatrix South Africa (Pty) Ltd. (1)
329 Tungsten Road, Strydom Park, Randburg, 2125, South Africa
Tel.: (27) 105005130
Color & Additive Mfr & Distr
N.A.I.C.S.: 325998

Colorant Chromatics AG (1)
Gotthardstrasse 28, 6302, Zug, Switzerland
Tel.: (41) 417410101
Sales Range: $25-49.9 Million
Emp.: 4
Color Concentrates & Pigment Dispersions Mfr
N.A.I.C.S.: 325510

Subsidiary (US):

Chromatics, Inc. (2)
19 Francis J Clarke Cir, Bethel, CT 06801
Web Site: http://www.colorant-chromatics.com
Sales Range: $25-49.9 Million
Emp.: 22
Color Concentrates & Pigment Dispersions Mfr
N.A.I.C.S.: 325510

Colorant Chromatics Europe B.V. (1)
Hastelweg 269-273, 5652 CV, Eindhoven, Netherlands
Tel.: (31) 402916510
Web Site: https://www.colorant-chromatics.com
Polymer Additives Mfr
N.A.I.C.S.: 325998

Fiber-Line International B.V. (1)
Uranusweg 3, 8938 AJ, Leeuwarden, Netherlands
Tel.: (31) 582167599
Synthetic Fiber Product Mfr
N.A.I.C.S.: 325220

Fiber-Line, LLC (1)
3050 Campus Dr, Hatfield, PA 19440
Tel.: (215) 997-9181
Web Site: https://www.fiber-line.com
Synthetic Fiber Product Mfr
N.A.I.C.S.: 325220
Vern Z. Detwiler (Co-Founder & Co-Owner)
Vince J. Pappas (Co-Founder & Co-Owner)
Lou A. Vitola (Co-Founder & Co-Owner)

GLS Corporation (1)
833 Ridgeview Dr, McHenry, IL 60050
Tel.: (815) 385-8500
Thermoplastic Elastomer Compound Developer & Mfr
N.A.I.C.S.: 326199

Subsidiary (Domestic):

Composites One LLC (2)
955-10 National Pkwy, Schaumburg, IL 60173
Tel.: (847) 437-0200
Web Site: https://www.compositesone.com
Sales Range: $150-199.9 Million
Fiberglass & Composite Materials Distr
N.A.I.C.S.: 424610
Steve Dehmlow (Chm)
Leon Garoufalis (Pres & CEO)
Marcy Offner (Dir-Mktg Comm)
Don Hairhoger (VP-Ops)
Andy Flad (VP-Sales-West)
Dave Forner (VP-Strategic Initiatives)
Andy Bhojwani (CIO)
Dwight Baker (VP)
Brian Jackson (VP-Sls-East)
Sharon Hansen (VP-HR)
Cynthia Tarka (Dir-Health-Safety-Environment)
Al Dobbeck (COO & Exec VP)
Harish Gally (Chief Information & Digital Officer)

Carlie Dobbeck (VP)
Brad Wilhite (VP-Sales-Western Reg)
Harish Gally (Chief Information & Digital Officer)
Carlie Dobbeck (VP)
Brad Wilhite (VP-Sales-Western Reg)
Dave Smith III (VP-Mktg)

Subsidiary (Non-US):

GLS Hong Kong Limited (2)
2/F South Tower Cathay Pacific City 8 Scenic Road, Hong Kong International Airport Lantau, Hong Kong, China (Hong Kong)
Tel.: (852) 28331880
Web Site: https://www.glshk.com
Sales Range: $25-49.9 Million
Emp.: 50
Thermoplastic Elastomer Mfr
N.A.I.C.S.: 326199
Sang Hwan Oh (Mng Dir)

GLS Thermoplastic Alloys Suzhou Co., Ltd. (2)
77 Shenggang Street SIP, Suzhou, 215021, China
Tel.: (86) 51283982500
Web Site: https://www.glstpes.com
Sales Range: $125-149.9 Million
Emp.: 60
Thermoplastic Elastomer Mfr
N.A.I.C.S.: 326199

Glasforms, Inc. (1)
3850 Pinson Valley Pkwy, Birmingham, AL 35217
Tel.: (205) 856-0033
Web Site: http://www.avient.com
Designer & Mfr of Carbon Fiber & Fiberglass
N.A.I.C.S.: 325211

IQAP Czech, s.r.o. (1)
Prumyslova 451 Plana nad Luznici, 391 02, Sezimovo Usti, Czech Republic
Tel.: (420) 381621170
Alkalie & Chemical Mfr
N.A.I.C.S.: 325180

IQAP Masterbatch Group, S.L. (1)
Carretera de Vic a Olot C153 km 5, Masies de Roda, 08510, Barcelona, 08510, Spain
Tel.: (34) 938500066
Alkalie & Chemical Mfr
N.A.I.C.S.: 325180

Juffali-PolyOne Master Batches Company (1)
Jazan Road Industrial City II Street 23, PO Box 2137, Jeddah, 22758, Saudi Arabia
Tel.: (966) 125107180
Industrial Machinery Mfr
N.A.I.C.S.: 333310

Magenta Master Fibers Co., Ltd. (1)
Ying Gang East Dong Rd 8376 Textile Science and Technology Park, Qingpu Industrial Zone, Shanghai, 201700, China
Tel.: (86) 2169732233
Color & Additive Mfr & Distr
N.A.I.C.S.: 325998

Magenta Master Fibers S.r.l (1)
Corso Magenta 10, 20013, Milan, MI, Italy
Tel.: (39) 029721991
Web Site: http://www.magentamaster.com
Emp.: 40
Synthetic Fiber Product Mfr
N.A.I.C.S.: 325220
Andrea Lampertico (Gen Mgr)

Magna Colours Limited (1)
Dodworth Business Park Upper Cliffe Rd, Barnsley, S75 3SP, United Kingdom
Tel.: (44) 1226731751
Web Site: https://www.magnacolours.com
Printing Ink Mfr & Distr
N.A.I.C.S.: 325910

Mesa Industries, Inc. (1)
230 N 48th Ave, Phoenix, AZ 85043
Tel.: (602) 269-3199
Web Site: http://www.mesaindustries.com
Organic Color Pigments Mfr
N.A.I.C.S.: 325130

NEU Specialty Engineered Materials, LLC (1)
15 Corporate Dr, North Haven, CT 06473
Tel.: (203) 239-9629
Web Site: http://www.neuinc.com

Avient Corporation—(Continued)

Emp.: 25
Polymer Product Mfr
N.A.I.C.S.: 325211

P.T. Avient Colorants Indonesia (1)
Gatot Subroto KM 4 Jalan Kalisabi No 1
Building 37 Kel Uwung Jaya, Kec Cibodas,
Tangerang, 15138, Banten, Indonesia
Tel.: (62) 2180524800
Polymer Material Mfr & Distr
N.A.I.C.S.: 325211

PlastiComp, Inc. (1)
110 Galewski Dr, Winona, MN 55987
Tel.: (507) 454-4334
Web Site: https://www.plasticomp.com
Awning, Rigid Plastic & Fiberglass Mfr
N.A.I.C.S.: 326199
Eric J. Wollan (Gen Mgr)
Steve Ouendag (Mgr-Application Dev)

**PolyOne Corp. - Long Beach
Plant** (1)
2104 E 223rd St, Carson, CA 90810
Tel.: (310) 513-7100
Web Site: http://www.polyone.com
Sales Range: $25-49.9 Million
Emp.: 40
All Other Plastics Product Mfr
N.A.I.C.S.: 326199

PolyOne Corp. - Wichita (1)
1444 S Tyler Rd Sedgwick, Wichita, KS
67209-1849 (100%)
Tel.: (316) 722-8621
Sales Range: $25-49.9 Million
Emp.: 106
Rigid Plastic Sheet & Rollstock Mfr
N.A.I.C.S.: 326199
George Radcoiff (Plant Mgr)

**PolyOne Corporation UK Limited
Trading Company** (1)
Unity Grove Knowsley Business Park,
Knowsley, L34 9GT, Merseyside, United
Kingdom
Tel.: (44) 1515476051
Web Site: http://www.polyone.com
Polymer Additives Mfr
N.A.I.C.S.: 325998

PolyOne DSS Canada Inc. (1)
440 Rue Robinson S, Granby, J2G 9R3,
QC, Canada
Tel.: (450) 378-8433
Polymer Additives Mfr
N.A.I.C.S.: 325998

PolyOne Japan K.K. (1)
904 9F Hirakawacho Visix 1-5-15,
Hirakawa-cho Chiyoda-ku, Tokyo, 102-0093,
Japan
Tel.: (81) 36 261 3980
Web Site: https://www.avient.jp
Polymer & Elastomer Products Mfr
N.A.I.C.S.: 325211

**PolyOne Management (Shanghai)
Co. Ltd.** (1)
2F Block C 200 Jinsu Road, Pudong,
Shanghai, 201206, China
Tel.: (86) 2160284888
Polymer Additives Mfr
N.A.I.C.S.: 325998
Rob T. Bindner (VP-Asia)

PolyOne Polymers India Pvt. Ltd (1)
Plot No F-27 MIDC Ranjangaon, Taluka-
Shirur, Pune, 412 220, India
Tel.: (91) 2138613221
Sales Range: $25-49.9 Million
Emp.: 50
Polymer & Elastomer Products Mfr
N.A.I.C.S.: 325211

PolyOne Shanghai, China (1)
Zhang Jiang Hi-tech Park No 88 Guoshou-
jing Road, Pudong, Shanghai, 201203,
China
Tel.: (86) 2128981188
Polymer & Elastomer Products Mfr
N.A.I.C.S.: 325211

PolyOne Shenzhen Co. Ltd. (1)
No 1 QiHang Industrial Park HaoXiang
Road, Shajing Town Baoan District, Shen-
zhen, 518104, China
Tel.: (86) 75529692888
Polymer & Elastomer Products Mfr

N.A.I.C.S.: 325211

PolyOne Singapore, Ltd. (1)
3 International Business Park Nordic Euro-
pean Centre 04-14/15, Singapore, 609927,
Singapore
Tel.: (65) 68619325
Web Site: http://www.polyone.com
Polymer & Elastomer Products Mfr
N.A.I.C.S.: 325211

PolyOne Suzhou, China (1)
Building No 13 855 Zhujiang Road, Suzhou
New District, Suzhou, 215129, China
Tel.: (86) 51266900333
Plastic Materials Mfr
N.A.I.C.S.: 325211

**PolyOne de Mexico Distribution, S.
de R.L. de C.V.** (1)
Eje 128 No 220 Zona Industrial, 78395,
San Luis Potosi, Mexico
Tel.: (52) 8448660023
Polymer Product Distr
N.A.I.C.S.: 424610

**Prestadora de Servicios Industriales
de Personal, S.A. de R.L. de
C.V.** (1)
Calle Gama 650, 25100, Saltillo, Mexico
Tel.: (52) 8444166393
Management Consulting Services
N.A.I.C.S.: 541611

Rutland Group, Inc. (1)
10021 Rodney St, Pineville, NC 28134
Tel.: (704) 553-0046
Web Site: http://www.rutlandgroup.com
Textile Printing Ink Mfr
N.A.I.C.S.: 325910

Rutland International Limited (1)
9-15 Unity Grove Knowsley Business Park,
Prescot, L34 9GT, Kent, United Kingdom
Tel.: (44) 1892834555
Plastic & Fiberglass Mfr
N.A.I.C.S.: 326199

**Rutland Plastic Technologies,
Inc.** (1)
10021 Rodney St, Pineville, NC 28134
Tel.: (704) 553-0046
Web Site: http://www.rutlandinc.com
Specialty Inks & Plastic Coatings Mfr
N.A.I.C.S.: 325910

SilCoTec, Inc. (1)
707 Boyd Blvd, La Porte, IN 46350
Tel.: (219) 324-4411
Paint & Coating Mfr
N.A.I.C.S.: 325510

Sociedad Quimica Alemana S.A. (1)
Av Revolucion 842 Zona Industrial venta-
nilla Callao, Lima, Peru
Tel.: (51) 16134242
Art & Commercial Services
N.A.I.C.S.: 541430

AVINGER, INC.

400 Chesapeake Dr, Redwood City,
CA 94063
Tel.: (650) 363-2400   DE
Web Site: https://www.avinger.com
Year Founded: 2007
AVGR—(NASDAQ)
Rev.: $8,273,000
Assets: $24,195,000
Liabilities: $20,049,000
Net Worth: $4,146,000
Earnings: ($17,623,000)
Emp.: 67
Fiscal Year-end: 12/31/22
Surgical & Medical Instrument Mfr
N.A.I.C.S.: 339112
James G. Cullen (Chm)
Jeffrey M. Soinski (Pres & CEO)
Himanshu N. Patel (CTO)
Nabeel Subainati (Principal Fin Offi-
cer & Principal Acctg Officer)
Phil Preuss (CMO)
Elmar Horn (VP-International)

AVIS BUDGET GROUP, INC.

379 Interpace Parkway, Parsippany,
NJ 07054

Tel.: (973) 496-4700   DE
Web Site:
https://www.avisbudgetgroup.com
CAR—(NASDAQ)
Rev.: $12,008,000,000
Assets: $32,569,000,000
Liabilities: $32,912,000,000
Net Worth: ($343,000,000)
Earnings: $1,632,000,000
Emp.: 18,000
Fiscal Year-end: 12/31/23
Car & Truck Rental Services
N.A.I.C.S.: 921130
Izilda P. Martins (CFO & Exec VP)
Edward P. Linnen (Chief HR Officer &
Exec VP)
Brian J. Choi (Chief Transformation
Officer & Exec VP)
Keith Rankin (Pres-Intl)
Cathleen DeGenova (Chief Acctg Of-
ficer & VP)
Joe Ferraro (Pres)
David Calabria (Treas)

Subsidiaries:

ACE Rent A Car, Inc. (1)
8639 W Washington St, Indianapolis, IN
46241
Tel.: (317) 399-5247
Web Site: https://www.acerentacar.com
Car Rental Services
N.A.I.C.S.: 532111

Apex Rent A Car Ltd. (1)
PO Box 10233, Christchurch, New Zealand
Tel.: (64) 35952530
Web Site: http://www.apexrentals.co.nz
Car Rental Services
N.A.I.C.S.: 532111

Armadale Commercial Ltd. (1)
Avis Budget House Park Road, Bracknell,
RG12 2EW, Berkshire, United Kingdom
Tel.: (44) 1501730563
Car Rental Services
N.A.I.C.S.: 532111

Avis Autovermietung AG (1)
Hofwisenstrasse 36, 8153, Rumlang, Swit-
zerland
Tel.: (41) 448091818
Web Site: https://www.avis.ch
Car Rental Services
N.A.I.C.S.: 532111

**Avis Autovermietung Gesellschaft
m.b.H** (1)
Lehrbachgasse 2, 1120, Vienna, Austria
Tel.: (43) 1601870
Web Site: https://www.avis.al
Car Rental Services
N.A.I.C.S.: 532111

Avis Belgium SA (1)
Kouterveldstraat 14, Box 7, 1831, Diegem,
Belgium
Tel.: (32) 27306211
Web Site: https://www.avis.be
Car Rental Services
N.A.I.C.S.: 532111

Avis Budget Auto Service GmbH (1)
Zimmersmuhlenweg 21, Oberursel, 61437,
Germany
Tel.: (49) 6171680
Car Rental Services
N.A.I.C.S.: 532111

Avis Budget Autoverhuur BV (1)
Louis Armstrongweg 4, 1311 RK, Almere,
Netherlands
Tel.: (31) 882847000
Web Site: http://www.avis.nl
Car Rental Services
N.A.I.C.S.: 532111

Avis Budget Autovermietung AG (1)
Hofwisenstrasse 36, 8153, Rumlang, Swit-
zerland
Tel.: (41) 448091818
Web Site: https://www.avis.ch
Car Rental Services
N.A.I.C.S.: 532111
Martin Graber (Mng Dir)
Laurent Sculier (Mng Dir)

Avis Budget Denmark AS (1)

Roskildevej 14, 2620, Albertslund, Denmark
Tel.: (45) 33268080
Web Site: https://www.avis.dk
Car Rental Services
N.A.I.C.S.: 532111

**Avis Budget Europe International Re-
insurance Limited** (1)
1st Floor Rose House Circular Road, Douglas, IM1 1AZ, Isle of Man
Tel.: (44) 1624629852
Car Rental Services
N.A.I.C.S.: 532111

Avis Budget Services Limited (1)
Avis Budget House Park Road, Bracknell,
RG12 2EW, Berkshire, United Kingdom
Tel.: (44) 2033686982
Web Site: http://www.avis.co.uk
Car Rental Services
N.A.I.C.S.: 532111

**Avis Budget Technology Innovations
Private Limited** (1)
AVIS House Plot Number 92 Sector-44,
Gurgaon, 122003, India
Tel.: (91) 1244724888
Web Site: https://www.avis.co.in
Vehicle Rental Services
N.A.I.C.S.: 532120

Avis Car Sales UTD, LLC (1)
379 Interpace Pkwy, Parsippany, NJ 07054
Web Site: https://www.ruby-car.com
Car Retailer
N.A.I.C.S.: 441110

Avis Car Sales, LLC (1)
6363 E Colonial Dr, Orlando, FL 32807
Web Site:
http://www.orlando.aviscarsales.com
Used Car Retailer
N.A.I.C.S.: 441120

Avis Europe plc (1)
Avis Budget House Park Road, Bracknell,
RG12 2EW, Berkshire, United
Kingdom (100%)
Tel.: (44) 1344426644
Web Site: http://www.avisworld.com
Sales Range: $1-4.9 Billion
Emp.: 5,671
Car Rental Services
N.A.I.C.S.: 532111

Subsidiary (Non-US):

**Avis Autovermietung GmbH & Co
KG** (2)
Zimmersmuhlenweg 21, 61437, Oberursel,
Germany (100%)
Tel.: (49) 6171680
Web Site: https://www.avis.de
Sales Range: $100-124.9 Million
Emp.: 300
Passenger Car Rental
N.A.I.C.S.: 532111

Subsidiary (Domestic):

Avis Budget EMEA Ltd (2)
Avis Budget House Park Road, Bracknell,
RG12 2EW, Berkshire, United Kingdom
Tel.: (44) 1344426644
Web Site: http://www.avis.co.uk
Rental Car Services
N.A.I.C.S.: 532111

Avis Finance Company Plc (2)
Avis House Park Rd, Bracknell, RG12 2EW,
Berkshire, United Kingdom (100%)
Tel.: (44) 1344426644
Web Site: http://www.avis-europe.com
Sales Range: $150-199.9 Million
Emp.: 614
Nondepository Credit Intermediation
N.A.I.C.S.: 522299

Avis Rent A Car Limited (2)
Ebeneezer Street, Shalesmoor, Sheffield,
S3 8UR, United Kingdom (100%)
Tel.: (44) 3445446093
Web Site: http://www.avis.co.uk
Passenger Car Rental
N.A.I.C.S.: 532111

Avis Location de Voitures S.a r.l (1)
Aeroport de Findel, Findel, 1110, Sand-
weiler, Luxembourg
Tel.: (352) 435171
Web Site: https://www.avis.lu

Emp.: 20
Car Rental Services
N.A.I.C.S.: 532111

Avis Rent A Car System, LLC (1)
6 Sylvan Way, Parsippany, NJ
07054 (100%)
Tel.: (973) 496-3500
Web Site: https://www.avis.com
Car Rental Services
N.A.I.C.S.: 532111

Budget International, Inc. (1)
1935 NE 147th Ln, Miami, FL 33181
Tel.: (305) 945-2662
Car Rental Services
N.A.I.C.S.: 532111

Budget Rent A Car Australia Pty.
Ltd. (1)
Tower A Level 7 197-201 Coward St, Mascot, 2020, NSW, Australia
Tel.: (61) 295781000
Web Site: https://www.budget.com.au
Car Rental Services
N.A.I.C.S.: 532111

Budget Rent A Car Licensor,
LLC (1)
6 Sylvan Way, Parsippany, NJ 07054
Tel.: (973) 496-4980
Car Rental Services
N.A.I.C.S.: 532111

Budget Rent A Car System, Inc. (1)
379 Parsippany Rd, Parsippany, NJ
07054 (100%)
Tel.: (973) 240-1160
Web Site: http://www.budget.com
Sales Range: $1-4.9 Billion
Car & Truck Rental Services
N.A.I.C.S.: 532111

Subsidiary (Domestic):

Budget Truck Rental LLC (2)
6 Sylvan Way, Parsippany, NJ
07054 (100%)
Tel.: (973) 496-4700
Web Site: https://www.budgettruck.com
Truck Rental Services
N.A.I.C.S.: 532120

Carey International, Inc. (1)
4530 Wisconsin Ave NW, Washington, DC
20016 (45%)
Tel.: (202) 895-1200
Web Site: http://www.carey.com
Sales Range: $250-299.9 Million
Chauffeur Services & Ground Transportation Logistics Management Services
N.A.I.C.S.: 485320
Mitchell J. Lahr *(CFO)*
Sandy Miller *(CEO)*
Dan Miller *(COO)*

McNicoll Vehicle Hire Ltd. (1)
22 Cliftonhall Road Newbridge Industrial
Estate, Newbridge, EH28 8PJ, United Kingdom
Tel.: (44) 1316084809
Web Site:
https://www.mcnicollvehiclehire.co.uk
Automobile Service Provider
N.A.I.C.S.: 811111

McNicoll Vehicle Sales Ltd. (1)
22 Cliftonhall Road, Newbridge Midlothian,
Edinburgh, EH28 8PJ, United Kingdom
Tel.: (44) 7375553619
Web Site:
https://www.mcnicollvehiclesales.co.uk
Vehicle Rental Services
N.A.I.C.S.: 532111

Morini SpA (1)
Via Giuseppe di Vittorio 15, Peschiera Borromeo, 20068, Milan, Italy
Tel.: (39) 028478771
Web Site: https://www.morinirent.com
Commercial Vehicle Rental Services
N.A.I.C.S.: 532111

Orlin, Inc. (1)
304 Courtleigh St, Wichita, KS 67218
Tel.: (316) 612-9181
Business Support Services
N.A.I.C.S.: 561990
Orlin Phelps *(Owner)*

Payless Car Rental Canada Inc. (1)

1970 Wellington Ave, Winnipeg, R3H 0E3,
MB, Canada
Tel.: (204) 989-7545
Web Site: http://www.paylesscar.com
Car Rental Services
N.A.I.C.S.: 532111

Payless Car Rental, Inc. (1)
7135 Gilespie St, Las Vegas, NV 89119
Tel.: (702) 531-1569
Web Site: https://www.paylesscar.com
Car Rental Services
N.A.I.C.S.: 532111

Payless Parking, LLC (1)
5309 McCoy Rd, Orlando, FL 32812
Tel.: (407) 856-5539
Web Site: http://www.paylessparking.com
Vehicle Parking Services
N.A.I.C.S.: 812930

RAC Norway AS (1)
Drengsrudbekken 12, 1383, Asker, Norway
Tel.: (47) 66771010
Web Site: https://www.avis.no
Car Rental Services
N.A.I.C.S.: 532111

Runabout, LLC (1)
7955 San Fernando Rd, Sun Valley, CA
91352-4614
Tel.: (805) 541-2544
Car Rental Services
N.A.I.C.S.: 532111

Sweden Rent A Car AB (1)
Lofstroms Alle 7, PO Box 6050, Sundbyberg, 172 66, Stockholm, Sweden
Tel.: (46) 858744751
Web Site: https://www.avis.se
Car Rental Services
N.A.I.C.S.: 532111

Turiscar Rent A Car, S.A. (1)
Av Severiano Falcao no 9, 2685-379, Prior
Velho, Portugal
Tel.: (351) 21 949 2626
Web Site: https://www.turiscar.pt
Emp.: 100
Commercial Vehicle Rental Services
N.A.I.C.S.: 532111

ZIPCAR, INC. (1)
25 First St 4th Fl, Cambridge, MA 02141
Tel.: (617) 995-4231
Web Site: http://www.zipcar.com
Rev.: $278,868,000
Assets: $417,293,000
Liabilities: $169,793,000
Net Worth: $247,500,000
Earnings: $14,187,000
Emp.: 553
Fiscal Year-end: 12/31/2012
Car Sharing Services
N.A.I.C.S.: 532111

Subsidiary (Domestic):

Zipcar on Campus, Inc. (2)
25 1st St 4th Fl, Cambridge, MA 02141
Tel.: (617) 336-4400
Sales Range: $25-49.9 Million
Emp.: 20
Automobiles Rental & Leasing Services
N.A.I.C.S.: 532111

Branch (Domestic):

Zipcar, Inc. - Seattle (2)
380 Union St, Seattle, WA 98101-2206
Tel.: (206) 682-0107
Web Site: http://www.zipcar.com
Car Sharing Services
N.A.I.C.S.: 532111

Zipcar France S.A.S. (1)
99 Avenue Charles De Gaulle, 92200,
Neuilly-sur-Seine, France
Tel.: (33) 987675067
Web Site: http://www.zipcar.fr
Car Rental Services
N.A.I.C.S.: 532111

AVISTA CORPORATION
1411 E Mission Ave, Spokane, WA
99202-2600
Tel.: (509) 489-0500 **WA**
Web Site:
https://investor.avistacorp.com
Year Founded: 1889

AVA—(NYSE)
Rev.: $1,710,207,000
Assets: $7,417,350,000
Liabilities: $5,082,682,000
Net Worth: $2,334,668,000
Earnings: $155,176,000
Emp.: 1,767
Fiscal Year-end: 12/31/22
Energy Production, Transmission &
Distribution & Other Energy Related
Activities
N.A.I.C.S.: 221122
James M. Kensok *(CIO & VP)*
Dennis P. Vermillion *(CEO)*
David J. Meyer *(VP)*
Kevin J. Christie *(CFO, Treas & Sr
VP-Regulatory Affairs)*
Heather L. Rosentrater *(Pres & COO)*
Latisha D. Hill *(VP-Community &
Economic Vitality)*
Gregory C. Hesler *(Chief Ethics &
Compliance Officer, General Counsel,
Sec & Sr VP)*
Bryan A. Cox *(Chief People Officer &
Sr VP-Safety)*
Ryan L. Krasselt *(Principal Acctg Officer, VP & Controller)*
Scott Kinney *(VP-Energy Resources)*
Josh DiLuciano *(VP-Energy Delivery)*
Julie A. Bentz *(Principal)*
Jason Thackston *(Chief Strategy Officer, Officer-Clean Energy & Sr VP)*
Wayne Manuel *(CIO, Chief Security
Officer & VP)*

Subsidiaries:

Avista Capital, Inc. (1)
1411 E Mission Ave, Spokane, WA 99202-
2600
Tel.: (509) 489-0500
Energy Consulting Services
N.A.I.C.S.: 541690

Avista Utilities (1)
1411 E Mission Ave, Spokane, WA
99252-0001 (100%)
Tel.: (509) 489-0500
Web Site: https://www.myavista.com
Sales Range: $1-4.9 Billion
Emp.: 1,500
Electric & Natural Gas Operations
N.A.I.C.S.: 221118
Dennis P. Vermillion *(VP-Energy Resources)*

ENGIE Insight Services, Inc. (1)
Rockpoint E 1313 N Atlantic St Ste 5000,
Spokane, WA 99201
Tel.: (509) 329-7600
Web Site: http://www.engieimpact.com
Sales Range: $125-149.9 Million
Emp.: 1,200
Corporate Expense Management Services
N.A.I.C.S.: 541618
Vincent Manier *(CFO)*
Christine Uri *(Chief Sustainability & Legal
Officer)*
Claire Brabec-Lagrange *(Mng Dir-Key Client
office)*
Jesse Rebello *(Chief Strategy, Innovation &
Culture Officer)*

Steam Plant Square, LLC (1)
159 S Lincoln, Spokane, WA 99201
Tel.: (509) 777-3900
Web Site: https://steamplantspokane.com
Property Management Services
N.A.I.C.S.: 531311

AVITA MEDICAL, INC.
28159 Ave Stanford Ste 220, Valencia, CA 91355
Tel.: (661) 367-9170 **AU**
Web Site:
https://www.avitamedical.com
RCEL—(NASDAQ)
Rev.: $34,421,000
Assets: $98,264,000
Liabilities: $13,524,000
Net Worth: $84,740,000
Earnings: ($26,665,000)
Emp.: 126

Fiscal Year-end: 12/31/22
Research & Development in Biotechnology (except Nanobiotechnology)
N.A.I.C.S.: 541714
Erin Liberto *(Chief Comml Officer)*
James M. Corbett *(Pres & CEO)*
Nicole Linda Kelsey *(Chief Legal Officer, Chief Compliance Officer & Sec)*
Andrew Quick *(CTO)*
Kathy McGee *(COO)*
Michael Holder *(CFO)*

Subsidiaries:

Avita Medical Americas LLC (1)
28159 Ave Stanford Ste 220, Valencia, CA
91355
Tel.: (781) 995-4174
Web Site: https://avitamedical.com
Sales Range: $25-49.9 Million
Emp.: 6
Respiratory Devices Mfr & Sales
N.A.I.C.S.: 334510

Avita Medical Europe Ltd. (1)
Unit B1 Beech House Melbourn Science
Park, Cambridge Road Melbourn, Royston,
SG8 6HB, Herts, United Kingdom
Tel.: (44) 1763 269770
Web Site: http://www.avitamedical.com
Emp.: 13
Medical Equipments Mfr & Sales
N.A.I.C.S.: 334510

Visiomed Group Ltd (1)
PO Box 207, Subiaco, 6008, WA, Australia
Tel.: (61) 893890700
Web Site: http://www.visiomed.com.au
Medical Equipments Mfr & Sales
N.A.I.C.S.: 334510

AVIX TECHNOLOGIES, INC.
3773 Howard Hughes Pkwy Ste
500S, Las Vegas, NV 89169
Tel.: (702) 723-7203 **NV**
Web Site:
http://www.avixtechnologies.com
AVIX—(OTCIQ)
Information Technology Services
N.A.I.C.S.: 541519
Zhang Tao *(Pres & CEO)*

AVNET, INC.
2211 S 47th St, Phoenix, AZ 85034
Tel.: (480) 643-2000 **NY**
Web Site: https://www.avnet.com
Year Founded: 1921
AVT—(NASDAQ)
Rev.: $23,757,129,000
Assets: $12,209,147,000
Liabilities: $7,283,643,000
Net Worth: $4,925,504,000
Earnings: $498,699,000
Emp.: 15,462
Fiscal Year-end: 06/29/24
Electricity Distribution Services
N.A.I.C.S.: 551112
Rebeca Obregon-Jimenez *(Sr VP-
Strategic Bus Engagements & Supplier Mgmt)*
Ken Arnold *(Chief People Officer)*
Max Chan *(CIO)*
Michael McCoy *(Chief Legal Officer &
Gen Counsel)*
Dayna Badhorn *(Pres-Electronics
Components-Americas)*
Beth McMullen *(VP-Ops-Global)*
Kenneth A. Jacobson *(CFO)*

Subsidiaries:

AVID Technologies, Inc. (1)
315 Alexandra Road, 03-01 Sime Darby
Business Centre, Singapore, 159944, Singapore
Tel.: (65) 64767666
Software Services
N.A.I.C.S.: 541511
Chin-Soon Tan *(Fin Dir)*

Avent USI (1)
2775 W Cypress Creek Rd, Fort Lauderdale, FL 33309

Avnet, Inc.—(Continued)

Tel.: (954) 493-8111
Web Site: http://www.avnetusi.com
Sales Range: $50-74.9 Million
Emp.: 45
Electronic Parts Distr
N.A.I.C.S.: 423690

Avnet (Holdings) Ltd (1)
Avnet House Rutherford Close, Stevenage,
SG1 2EF, Hertfordshire, United Kingdom
Tel.: (44) 1438788500
Emp.: 60
Investment Management Service
N.A.I.C.S.: 551112

Avnet (NZ) (1)
17A 150 Cavendish Road Casebrook,
Christchurch, 8053, New Zealand (100%)
Tel.: (64) 39620580
Sales Range: $25-49.9 Million
Emp.: 5
Component Distr
N.A.I.C.S.: 441330
Adam Tsui (Mng Dir)

Avnet ASIC Israel Ltd (1)
Avnet building 1 Ha-Brosh st, PO Box 121,
Bnei Dror, Tel Mond, 4581500, Israel
Tel.: (972) 97780273
Web Site: https://www.avnet-asic.com
Sales Range: $10-24.9 Million
Emp.: 18
Engineering & Design Services
N.A.I.C.S.: 541330
Nadav Ben-Ezer (Mng Dir)
Eugene Lyubinsky (VP-Engrg)
Yulia Milshtein (Dir-Ops & Bus Dev)
Arie Komarnitzky (Dir-Engrg)
Pavel Vilk (Dir-Engrg)

Avnet B.V. (1)
Stadionstraat 2 6th fl, 4815 NG, Breda,
Netherlands
Tel.: (31) 765722700
Sales Range: $25-49.9 Million
Emp.: 45
Computer & Electronic Equipment Sales &
Distr
N.A.I.C.S.: 423430
Wen Henebeens (Mng Dir)

Avnet Chile S.A. (1)
Joseph Avenue Ananias 207 Macul, San-
tiago, Chile
Tel.: (56) 227564300
Computer & Computer Peripheral Device
Distr
N.A.I.C.S.: 423430

**Avnet Components Brasil Participa-
coes Ltda.** (1)
Alameda Rio Negro 1030/Cj 1701 An 17
Alphaville Industrial, Barueri, Sao Paulo,
Brazil
Tel.: (55) 1142084212
Electronic Component & Semiconductor
Distr
N.A.I.C.S.: 423690

Avnet Components Israel Limited (1)
1 Habrosh Street, Bney Dror, Tel Mond,
4581500, Israel
Tel.: (972) 97780280
Web Site: http://www.avnet-israel.co.il
Emp.: 107
Electronic Component & Semiconductor
Distr
N.A.I.C.S.: 423690

Avnet Components Ltd. (1)
Industrial Center Dror Douth Building 2, PO
Box 48, 40600, Tel Mond, Israel
Tel.: (972) 97780280
Web Site: http://www.avnet-israel.com
Sales Range: $50-74.9 Million
Emp.: 90
Computer & Electronic Equipment Sales &
Distr
N.A.I.C.S.: 423430

**Avnet Computer Service (Hong Kong)
Limited** (1)
Unit 1 20/F Tower 2 Enterprise Square Five
38 Wang Chiu Road, Kowloon Bay, Hong
Kong, China (Hong Kong)
Tel.: (852) 21972888
Web Site: http://www.ats.avnet.com.hk
Emp.: 40

Computer & Computer Peripheral Device
Distr
N.A.I.C.S.: 423430

**Avnet Computer Service (Macau)
Limited** (1)
13Fl Unit G Macau Square, Macau, China
(Macau)
Tel.: (853) 0028750628
Web Site: http://www.ats.avnet.com.hk
Emp.: 4
Computer & Computer Peripheral Device
Distr
N.A.I.C.S.: 423430

Avnet EMG AG (1)
Rossliweg 29 A, 4852, Rothrist, Switzerland
Tel.: (41) 629195555
Emp.: 18
Electronic Component & Semiconductor
Distr
N.A.I.C.S.: 423690

**Avnet EMG Elektronische Bauele-
mente GmbH** (1)
Grunbergstr 15/1 Top 4, 1120, Vienna, Aus-
tria
Tel.: (43) 186642300
Computer Product Mfr & Distr
N.A.I.C.S.: 334111

Avnet EMG France (1)
Immeuble Marie Louise Paris 12 rue Jean
Bart, 91349, Massy, Cedex, France
Tel.: (33) 164472929
Computer Product Mfr & Distr
N.A.I.C.S.: 334111

Avnet EMG Italy S.r.l. (1)
Via Manzoni 44, 20095, Cusano Milanino,
MI, Italy
Tel.: (39) 02660921
Web Site: http://www.avnet-memec.eu
Emp.: 155
Electronic Component & Semiconductor
Distr
N.A.I.C.S.: 423690

Avnet Electronics Marketing (1)
2211 S 47th St, Phoenix, AZ 85034
Tel.: (480) 643-5600
Web Site: http://www.em.avnet.com
Sales Range: $150-199.9 Million
Electronics Sales & Distr
N.A.I.C.S.: 423690

Subsidiary (Non-US):

Alpha 3 Manufacturing Limited (2)
Deltron Emcon House Hargreaves Way,
Sawcliffe Industrial Park, Scunthorpe, DN15
8RF, North Lincolnshire, United Kingdom
Tel.: (44) 1724273200
Web Site:
  http://www.alpha3manufacturing.com
Electromechanical Sub-Assembly
N.A.I.C.S.: 333242

Division (Domestic):

CCS Electronics (UK) Ltd. (3)
4 Aragon Court Manor Park, Runcorn, WA7
1SP, Cheshire, United Kingdom
Tel.: (44) 1928579797
Web Site: http://www.ccselec.com
Sales Range: $10-24.9 Million
Emp.: 60
Electric Component Whslr
N.A.I.C.S.: 449210
Clifford Friel (Mng Dir)

CTL Manufacturing (3)
Waterside House Brunel Way Stroud Water
Bus Pk, Stonehouse, GL10 3SW, Glouces-
tershire, United Kingdom
Tel.: (44) 1453794100
Web Site:
  http://www.alpha3manufacturing.com
Sales Range: $25-49.9 Million
Emp.: 250
Mfr of Cables
N.A.I.C.S.: 335929

DEM Manufacturing (3)
Deltron Emcon House Hargreaves Way,
Sawcliffe Industrial Park, Scunthorpe, DN15
8RF, North Lincolnshire, United Kingdom
Tel.: (44) 1724273200
Web Site: http://www.dem-uk.com
Electronics Mfr; Connectors, Die Cast En-
closures & Filters

N.A.I.C.S.: 334419

Subsidiary (Non-US):

Avnet EM Sp. z.o o. (2)
Targ Rybny 11/13, 80-838, Gdansk, Poland
Tel.: (48) 588814451
Global Technology Distr; Computer & Elec-
tronic Equipment Sales, Supply Chain Ser-
vices, Technical Support & Software Pub-
lisher
N.A.I.C.S.: 423430

**Avnet EMG Elektronische Bauel-
mente GmbH** (2)
Schoenbrunner Strasse 297-307, 1120, Vi-
enna, Austria
Tel.: (43) 186642300
Sales Range: $25-49.9 Million
Emp.: 10
Computer & Electronic Equipment Sales &
Distr
N.A.I.C.S.: 423430

Avnet EMG France S.A. (2)
12 rue Jean Bart Le Copernic bat B, 91349,
Massy, Cedex, France
Tel.: (33) 164472929
Web Site: http://www.avnet-memec.eu
Sales Range: $50-74.9 Million
Emp.: 150
Computer & Electronic Equipment Sales &
Distr
N.A.I.C.S.: 423430

Avnet EMG GmbH (2)
Im Technologiepark 2-8, 85586, Poing, Ger-
many
Tel.: (49) 812177702
Web Site: http://www.avnet-memec.eu
Sales Range: $250-299.9 Million
Emp.: 250
Semiconductor Distr
N.A.I.C.S.: 334413

Subsidiary (Non-US):

Avnet EM Sp. z.o o. (3)
Staromiejska No 7, 40-013, Katowice, Po-
land
Tel.: (48) 323375620
Web Site: http://www.avnet.eu
Sales Range: $150-199.9 Million
Emp.: 5
Semiconductor Sales & Distr
N.A.I.C.S.: 423690

Avnet EMG Ltd. (3)
Building 5 Waltham Park, White Waltham,
Maidenhead, SL6 3TN, Berkshire, United
Kingdom (100%)
Tel.: (44) 1628512900
Sales Range: $10-24.9 Million
Emp.: 30
Semiconductor Distr
N.A.I.C.S.: 423690

Unit (Domestic):

Avnet Electronics Marketing (2)
2021 Lakeside Blvd Fl 2, Richardson, TX
75082
Tel.: (214) 553-4300
Web Site: http://www.em.avnet.com
Sales Range: $75-99.9 Million
Emp.: 200
Electrical Components & Semiconductors
Distr
N.A.I.C.S.: 423690

Avnet Electronics Marketing (2)
135 Engineers RD, Hauppauge, NY
11788-4226 (100%)
Tel.: (631) 582-7743
Web Site: http://www.em.avnet.com
Sales Range: $25-49.9 Million
Emp.: 28
Electronic Components Distr
N.A.I.C.S.: 423610

Unit (Non-US):

Avnet Electronics Marketing (2)
6950 Creditview Rd Unit 2, Mississauga,
L5N 0A6, ON, Canada (100%)
Tel.: (905) 812-4400
Web Site: http://www.em.avnet.com
Sales Range: $25-49.9 Million
Emp.: 100
Electronic Components Distr
N.A.I.C.S.: 449210

Avnet Electronics Marketing (2)
7575 Trans Canada Hwy Ste 600, Saint
Laurent, H4T 1V6, QC, Canada (100%)
Tel.: (514) 335-1000
Sales Range: $25-49.9 Million
Emp.: 20
Electronic Parts Distr
N.A.I.C.S.: 441330

Avnet Electronics Marketing (2)
Ste 100 4299 Canada Way, Burnaby, V5G
1H3, BC, Canada (100%)
Tel.: (604) 444-3810
Web Site: http://www.em.avnet.com
Sales Range: $10-24.9 Million
Emp.: 12
Electronic Parts Distr
N.A.I.C.S.: 449210

Avnet Electronics Marketing (2)
Suite 115 1925 18th Avenue NE, Calgary,
T2E 7T8, AB, Canada
Tel.: (403) 291-5510
Web Site: http://www.em.avnet.com
Sales Range: $10-24.9 Million
Emp.: 10
Computer Products Distr
N.A.I.C.S.: 423430

Unit (Domestic):

Avnet Electronics Marketing (2)
20951 Burbank Blvd, Woodland Hills, CA
91367
Tel.: (818) 594-8370
Web Site: http://www.em.avnet.com
Sales Range: $650-699.9 Million
Emp.: 1,000
Semiconductors, Connectors, Passive Com-
ponents, Computer Subsystems & Peripher-
als, Production Supplies, Tool Kits, Instru-
mentation & Workstations Distr
N.A.I.C.S.: 423690

Subsidiary (Non-US):

Avnet Silica (2)
Gruber Strasse 60 C, 85586, Munich, Ger-
many
Tel.: (49) 812177702
Web Site: http://www.silica.com
Sales Range: $100-124.9 Million
Emp.: 300
Semiconductor Sales & Distr
N.A.I.C.S.: 334413
Mario Orlandi (Pres)
Frank Hansen (VP-Technical Resources &
Mktg)
Laurent Bizouard (VP-Assets)
Enrico De Salve (VP-Strategy & Program
Mgmt)
Gilles Beltran (VP-Sls)
Rico Dornieden (Mgr-Bus Controlling)
Marina Gualtieri (Partner-HR Bus)
Nina d'Maine (Assoc Gen Counsel)
Tom Oelschlaeger (Dir-Mktg Comm)

Division (Non-US):

Avnet Silica (3)
Hagalokkveien 7, PO Box 63, NO 1371,
Asker, Norway (100%)
Tel.: (47) 66773600
Web Site: http://www.silica.com
Sales Range: $10-24.9 Million
Emp.: 12
Electronic Products Sales
N.A.I.C.S.: 423620

Avnet Silica (3)
Luvftroms Alle 5, Sundbyberg, 17267, Swe-
den
Tel.: (46) 858746100
Web Site: http://www.silica.com
Sales Range: $25-49.9 Million
Emp.: 40
Electronic Products Sales
N.A.I.C.S.: 441330
Frank Hansen (Mng Dir)
Thomas Ludascher (Mng Dir)
Frank Stephan (Mng Dir)
Brian Wilken (Mng Dir)
Gilles Beltran (Pres)
Laurent Bizouard (VP-Assets)
Tim Willies (VP-Bus Ops, Data Analytics &
Strategy)
Laurence Dellicott (Dir-Fulfillment Sls &
Supplier Mgmt)
Thomas Foj (Dir-Vertical Markets)

An Rutten *(Partner-HR Bus)*
Lisa Rees *(Dir-Mktg & Comm)*
Rico Dornieden *(Controller-Bus)*

Avnet Silica (3)
Avnet House Rutherford Close, Meadway,
Stevenage, SG1 2EF, Herts, United Kingdom
Tel.: (44) 1438788310
Web Site: https://www.avnet.com
Semiconductor Sales & Distr
N.A.I.C.S.: 423690

Avnet Silica (3)
14 Ave Carnot, 91349, Massy,
France (100%)
Tel.: (33) 164472929
Web Site: http://www.silica.com
Sales Range: $25-49.9 Mlllion
Emp.: 120
Electronic Components Sales & Distr
N.A.I.C.S.: 449210

Subsidiary (Non-US):

Avnet Time (2)
60C Gruber Str, Poing, 85586, Munich,
Germany
Tel.: (49) 812177701
Web Site: http://www.avnettime.com
Sales Range: $150-199.9 Million
Emp.: 400
Interconnect, Passive, Electromechanical &
Power Supply Distr
N.A.I.C.S.: 423690

EBV Elektronik GmbH & Co. KG (2)
Im Technologiepark 2-8, 85586, Poing, Germany
Tel.: (49) 81217740
Web Site: https://my.avnet.com
Sales Range: $1-4.9 Billion
Emp.: 350
Semiconductor Distr
N.A.I.C.S.: 423690
Thomas Ludascher *(Mng Dir)*
Slobodan Puljarevic *(Mng Dir)*

Subsidiary (Non-US):

EBV Electrolink (PTY) Ltd (3)
1 Mediterranean Street 5th Floor MSC
House, Foreshore, ZA-8001, Cape Town,
South Africa
Tel.: (27) 214021940
Web Site: http://www.ebv.com
Semiconductor Sales & Distr
N.A.I.C.S.: 423690

EBV Elektronik KFT (3)
Budafoki ut 91-93 West Irodahaz, 1117, Budapest, Hungary
Tel.: (36) 14367229
Sales Range: $10-24.9 Million
Emp.: 6
Semiconductor Distr
N.A.I.C.S.: 423690

EBV Elektronik Ltd. (3)
Drorrim S Commercial Ctr Avnet Bldg 2, PO
Box 149, 40600, Tel Mond, Israel
Tel.: (972) 97780260
Web Site: http://www.ebv.com
Sales Range: $50-74.9 Million
Emp.: 100
Semiconductor Sales & Distr
N.A.I.C.S.: 423690

EBV Elektronik M (3)
Korovinskoye Shosse 10 Build 2 Off 28,
127486, Moscow, Russia
Tel.: (7) 4957303170
Web Site: http://www.ebv.com
Sales Range: $10-24.9 Million
Emp.: 9
Semiconductor Sales & Distr
N.A.I.C.S.: 423690

EBV Elektronik Ticaret Ltd. (3)
Tatlisu Mahallesi Pakdil Sokak 7 Umraniye,
34774, Istanbul, Turkiye
Tel.: (90) 2165288310
Web Site: http://www.ebv.com
Sales Range: $10-24.9 Million
Emp.: 13
Semiconductors Sales
N.A.I.C.S.: 423690

EBV Elektronik s.r.l. (3)
Via Alessandro Manzoni 44, 20095, Cusano
Milanino, Milan, Italy

Tel.: (39) 0266096290
Sales Range: $25-49.9 Million
Emp.: 70
Semiconductor Sales & Distr
N.A.I.C.S.: 423690

EBV Elektronik spol. S.r.o. (3)
Amazon Court Karolinska 661/4, 186 00,
Prague, Czech Republic
Tel.: (420) 234091011
Web Site: http://www.ebv.com
Sales Range: $10-24.9 Million
Emp.: 15
Semiconductor Sales & Distr
N.A.I.C.S.: 423690

Subsidiary (Non-US):

Unidux Electronics Limited (2)
18 Boon Lay Way 05-133, Tradehub 21,
609966, Singapore, Singapore
Tel.: (65) 65693611
Web Site: http://www.unidux.com.sg
Sales Range: $150-199.9 Million
Electronic Components Mfr
N.A.I.C.S.: 334511
Alex Hu Seong Toh *(Dir-Dev & Plng)*

Subsidiary (Non-US):

Unidux (Malaysia) Sdn Bhd (3)
1-7 A NB Plz 3000 Jalan Baru, 13700, Prai,
Penang, Malaysia
Tel.: (60) 43992212
Sales Range: $25-49.9 Million
Emp.: 14
Electronic Components Distr
N.A.I.C.S.: 423690
Wilson Lim *(Mgr)*

Subsidiary (Domestic):

Unidux (Singapore) Pte Ltd (3)
18 Boon Lay Way 05-133 Tradehub 21,
Singapore, 609966, Singapore
Tel.: (65) 65693611
Web Site: http://www.unidux.com.sg
Sales Range: $25-49.9 Million
Emp.: 20
Electronic Components Distr
N.A.I.C.S.: 423690
Grace Ho *(Mgr-HR)*

Subsidiary (Non-US):

Unidux (Thailand) Co., Ltd. (3)
No 1/24 12 Floor Unit A Bangna Thani
Building Bangna Trad Road, Bangna, Bangkok, 10260, Thailand
Tel.: (66) 23993007
Sales Range: $25-49.9 Million
Emp.: 10
Electronic Components Distr
N.A.I.C.S.: 423690

Avnet Electronics Technology (Shenzhen) Limited (1)
5 Floor Building 1 Wise R&D Centre 1 Liuxian Road, Boa an District, Shenzhen,
518101, Guangdong, China
Tel.: (86) 75521845666
Computer Product Mfr & Distr
N.A.I.C.S.: 334111

**Avnet Electronics Turkey ithalat ihracat Sanayi ve Ticaret Limited
Sirketi** (1)
26 Eylul 2012, Carsamba, Istanbul, Turkiye
Tel.: (90) 2164112333
Electronic Components Distr
N.A.I.C.S.: 423690

Avnet Embedded (Freiburg) GmbH (1)
Munzinger Strasse 3, 79427, Eschbach,
Germany
Tel.: (49) 76345903400
Medical Equipment Mfr
N.A.I.C.S.: 339112

Avnet Embedded GmbH (1)
Industriestrasse 16, 76297, Stutensee, Germany
Tel.: (49) 72499100
Web Site: https://embedded.avnet.com
Chip & Display Mfr & Distr
N.A.I.C.S.: 334413
Silvano Geissler *(Co-Mng Dir)*
Darrel Scott Jackson *(Co-Mng Dir)*

Avnet Embedded Industria e Comercio Ltda (1)
Suribim 504 -7o Street floor-Room, Sao
Paulo, 04571-050, Sao Paulo, Brazil
Tel.: (55) 1121077900
Web Site: http://www.em.avnet.com
Electronic Product Distr
N.A.I.C.S.: 423690

Avnet Enterprise Solutions (1)
190 Colonnade Rd, Ottawa, K2E 7J5, ON,
Canada (100%)
Tel.: (613) 727-2000
Sales Range: $25-49.9 Million
Emp.: 20
Computer Products Distr
N.A.I.C.S.: 423430

Avnet Europe BV (1)
De Kleetlan 3, 1831, Diegem, Belgium
Tel.: (32) 27099000
Computer Product Mfr & Distr
N.A.I.C.S.: 334111

Avnet Europe Executive BVBA (1)
De Kleetlan 3, 1831, Diegem, Belgium
Tel.: (32) 27099000
Management Consulting Services
N.A.I.C.S.: 541611

Avnet Finance B.V. (1)
Takkebijsters 2, Breda, 4817 BL, Noord-Brabant, Netherlands
Tel.: (31) 765784911
Custodial Services
N.A.I.C.S.: 561720

Avnet Holdings UK Limited (1)
Avnet House Rutherford Close, Stevenage,
SG1 2EF, Hertfordshire, United Kingdom
Tel.: (44) 1438788551
Investment Management Service
N.A.I.C.S.: 551112

Avnet Hong Kong Limited (1)
20/F, Tower 2, Enterprise Square Five, 38
Wang Chiu Road, Kowloon, China (Hong Kong) (100%)
Tel.: (852) 21765388
Web Site: http://www.avnet.com.cn
Sales Range: $25-49.9 Million
Emp.: 100
Electronic Components & Computer Products Distr
N.A.I.C.S.: 334419

Avnet Iberia S.A. (1)
C/Chile 10 Plta 2 Ofic 229 Edificio Madrid
92, 28290, Las Rozas, Madrid, Spain
Tel.: (34) 913727100
Sales Range: $25-49.9 Million
Emp.: 50
Electronic Component & Semiconductor
Distr
N.A.I.C.S.: 423690

Avnet Integrated Resources Reparo de Eletronicos Ltda. (1)
Av Marechal Mascarenhas de Moraes
1048, Recife, Brazil
Tel.: (55) 8130280988
Electronic Component & Semiconductor
Distr
N.A.I.C.S.: 423690

Avnet International (Canada) Ltd. (1)
6950 Creditview Rd 2, Mississauga, L5N
0A6, ON, Canada
Tel.: (905) 812-4400
Electronic Component & Semiconductor
Distr
N.A.I.C.S.: 423690

Avnet Japan (Asia) Limited (1)
18 Boon Lay Way No 05-133 Tradehub 21,
Singapore, 609966, Singapore
Tel.: (65) 65693611
Emp.: 120
Electronic Components Distr
N.A.I.C.S.: 423690
Tan Yew Teong *(Pres)*
Chan Siu Ngan *(Dir-Fin)*
Takashi Sekine *(Dir-Sls & Ops)*
Alex Toh Hu Seong *(Dir-Corp Dev Plng)*
Cheong Hock Kuen *(Controller-Fin)*

Avnet Japan (HK) Limited (1)
22/ F Tower 2 Enterprises Square Five
Kowloon Bay, Kowloon, China (Hong Kong)
Tel.: (852) 35863456

Electronic Components Distr
N.A.I.C.S.: 423690
Kimitaka Oyagi *(Branch Mgr)*

Avnet Japan (Malaysia) Sdn. Bhd. (1)
1-7-A NB Plaza 3000 Jalan Baru, 13700,
Perai, Penang, Malaysia
Tel.: (60) 43992212
Electronic Components Distr
N.A.I.C.S.: 423690

Avnet Japan (Singapore) Pte Ltd. (1)
18 Boon Lay Way Suite 05-133 Tradehub
21, Singapore, 609966, Singapore
Tel.: (65) 65693611
Web Site: http://www.avnet.co.jp
Emp.: 120
Electronic Product Distr
N.A.I.C.S.: 423690
Yew Teong Tan *(Pres)*

Avnet Kabushiki Kaisha (1)
10th Floor Yebisu Garden Place Tower 20-3
Ebisu 4-chome, Shibuya-ku, Tokyo, 150-6010, Japan
Tel.: (81) 357928210
Web Site: http://www.avnet.co.jp
Emp.: 480
Electronic Components Distr
N.A.I.C.S.: 423690

Avnet Kopp (Pty) Limited (1)
31 Commerce Crescent, Eastgate Extension 12, Sandton, 2148, South Africa
Tel.: (27) 118096100
Web Site: http://www.avnet.co.za
Sales Range: $25-49.9 Million
Emp.: 70
Computers & Electronic Equipment Sales &
Distr
N.A.I.C.S.: 423430

Avnet Logistics (1)
60 S McKemy Ave, Chandler, AZ 85226
Tel.: (480) 643-2000
Web Site: http://logistics.avnet.com
Sales Range: $650-699.9 Million
Emp.: 500
Electronic Component & Enterprise Computer Warehousing, Supply Chain & Logistics Services
N.A.I.C.S.: 541614

Subsidiary (Non-US):

Avnet Logistics GmbH (2)
Im Technologiepark 12, 85586, Poing, Germany
Tel.: (49) 812177040
Web Site: http://www.avnet-logistics.eu
Sales Range: $150-199.9 Million
Emp.: 300
Electronic Component & Enterprise Computer Warehousing, Supply Chain & Logistics Services
N.A.I.C.S.: 541614

Avnet Logistics B.V.B.A. (1)
Limesweg 4 Industriepark Oost, 3700, Tongeren, Belgium
Tel.: (32) 12242711
Web Site: http://www.avnet-logistics.eu
Electronic Components Distr
N.A.I.C.S.: 423690

Avnet Logistics PMC Stutensee GmbH (1)
Industriestr 18, 76297, Stutensee, Germany
Tel.: (49) 89608070
Logistics Consulting Servies
N.A.I.C.S.: 541614

Avnet Logistics Stutensee GmbH (1)
Industriestr 18, 76297, Stutensee, Germany
Tel.: (49) 7249910114
Logistics Consulting Servies
N.A.I.C.S.: 541614

Avnet Logistics do Brasil Ltda. (1)
Rua Portugal 59, Manaus, 69078-551,
Amazonas, Brazil
Tel.: (55) 1921077934
Logistics Management Consulting Services
N.A.I.C.S.: 541614

Avnet Malaysia Sdn Bhd (1)
First Subang mall S-06-07 Jalan SS15/4G,
47500, Subang Jaya, Selangor Darul Ehsan, Malaysia

Avnet, Inc.—(Continued)

Tel.: (60) 356227230
Web Site: http://www.avnetasia.com
Sales Range: $25-49.9 Million
Emp.: 60
Electronic Components Distr
N.A.I.C.S.: 423690

Avnet Nortec A/S (1)
Lyskrer 9, 2730, Herlev, Denmark
Tel.: (45) 43228010
Web Site: http://www.avnetsileca.com
Sales Range: $10-24.9 Million
Emp.: 10
Computer & Electronic Equipment Sales &
Distr
N.A.I.C.S.: 423430

Avnet Nortec AB (1)
Hemvarnsgatan 9, PO Box 1830, 171 54,
Solna, Sweden (100%)
Tel.: (46) 858746100
Web Site: http://www.avnet.se
Sales Range: $10-24.9 Million
Emp.: 50
Electronic Component Sales
N.A.I.C.S.: 449210

Avnet Nortec AS (1)
Solbraveien 45 2 Floor, 1383, Asker, 1383,
Norway
Tel.: (47) 66773600
Electronic Product Distr
N.A.I.C.S.: 423690

Avnet Nortec Oy (1)
Pihatorma 1B, 02240, Espoo, Finland
Tel.: (358) 207499220
Web Site: http://www.avnet-embedded.eu
Electronic Components Distr
N.A.I.C.S.: 423690

Avnet Partner Solutions, S. de R.L. de C.V. (1)
Vasco de Quiroga 1900-3rd Floor, Santa
Fe, Mexico, Mexico
Tel.: (52) 52924950
Web Site: http://www.aps.avnet.com.mx
Computer Based Information Services
N.A.I.C.S.: 519290
Jose Gomez Obregon (Dir Gen)

Avnet S.r.l. (1)
Via Manzoni 44, Cusano Milanino, 20095,
Milan, Italy
Tel.: (39) 02660921
Electronic Components Distr
N.A.I.C.S.: 423690

Avnet Solutions Pte. Ltd. (1)
50 Kallang Avenue 09-02 Noel Corporate
Building, Singapore, 339505, Singapore
Tel.: (65) 62951788
Electronic Components Distr
N.A.I.C.S.: 423690

Avnet Sp. z o.o. (1)
Ul 1 Sierpnia 6a, 02-135, Warsaw, Poland
Tel.: (48) 228787722
Emp.: 70
Electronic Components Distr
N.A.I.C.S.: 423690

Avnet Technology Electronics Marketing (Taiwan) Co., Ltd. (1)
5F No 3 YuanCyu Street NanKang Software
Park, Taipei, 115, Taiwan
Tel.: (886) 226558688
Web Site: http://www.prospect.com.tw
Electronic Components Distr
N.A.I.C.S.: 423690

Avnet Unidux (HK) Limited (1)
15F Innov Tower 1801 Hongmei Road,
Shanghai, 200023, China
Tel.: (86) 2153017536
Web Site: http://www.em.avnet.co.jp
Emp.: 300
Electronic Product Distr
N.A.I.C.S.: 423690

Avnet Unidux (Malaysia) Sdn. Bhd. (1)
1-7-A NB Plaza 3000 Jalan Baru, 13700,
Prai, Penang, Malaysia
Tel.: (60) 43992212
Web Site: http://www.em.avnet.co.jp
Electronic Product Distr
N.A.I.C.S.: 423690

Avnet Unidux (Thailand) Company Limited (1)
1/24 Bangna-Thani Building 12th Floor Unit
A Bangna-Trad Road, Bangna, Bangkok,
Thailand
Tel.: (66) 23993009
Web Site: http://www.em.avnet.co.jp
Electronic Product Distr
N.A.I.C.S.: 423690

Avnet d. o. o. (1)
Korzo 11, Rijeka, 51000, Croatia
Tel.: (385) 51320200
Emp.: 16
Computer System Design Services
N.A.I.C.S.: 541512

Avnet d.o.o., Beograd (1)
Bul Mihajla Pupina 181, Belgrade, 11070,
Serbia
Tel.: (381) 113190218
Computer System Design Services
N.A.I.C.S.: 541512

Avnet de Mexico, S.A. de C.V. (1)
Periferico Sur 7980, Colonia Santa Maria
Tequepexpan, 45601, Tlaquepaque, Jalisco,
Mexico
Tel.: (52) 3331342324
Web Site: http://www.avnet.com
Sales Range: $25-49.9 Million
Emp.: 27
Computer & Electronic Equipment Sales &
Distr
N.A.I.C.S.: 423430

Avnet de Puerto Rico, Inc. (1)
Metro Office Park 6, Guaynabo, PR 00968-
1704
Tel.: (787) 706-1888
Electronic Component & Semiconductor
Distr
N.A.I.C.S.: 423690

Avnet do Brasil LTDA (1)
Rua Surubim 504 Cj 71, Itaim Bibi, 04043-
300, Sao Paulo, Brazil
Tel.: (55) 1150792150
Sales Range: $25-49.9 Million
Emp.: 25
Computer & Electronic Equipment Sales &
Distr
N.A.I.C.S.: 423430

Avnet s.r.o. (1)
V Olsinach 75, 100 00, Prague, Czech Re-
public
Tel.: (420) 281002383
Web Site: http://www.ps.avnet.com.cz
Sales Range: $75-99.9 Million
Emp.: 70
Computer & Electronic Solutions
N.A.I.C.S.: 541519

BrightStar Partners, Inc. (1)
1701 W Golf Rd Tower III Ste 3-604, Rolling
Meadows, IL 60008
Tel.: (847) 439-0308
Web Site: http://www.brightstarpartners.com
Rev.: $5,500,000
Emp.: 27
Custom Computer Programming Services
N.A.I.C.S.: 541511

Canvas Systems B.V. (1)
Coengebouw Kabelweg 37, 1014 BA, Am-
sterdam, Netherlands
Tel.: (31) 206061060
Web Site: http://www.canvassystems.com
Sales Range: $25-49.9 Million
Emp.: 5
Electronic Components Distr
N.A.I.C.S.: 423690

Canvas Systems UK Limited (1)
Unit 6 Titan Business Centre Spartan
Close, Warwick, CV34 6RR, United King-
dom
Tel.: (44) 1926477600
Web Site: http://www.canvassystems.co.uk
Sales Range: $25-49.9 Million
Emp.: 18
Electronic Components Distr
N.A.I.C.S.: 423690
Jorjeet Singh (Acct Mgr-Global Sls)
Idris Mohamed (Sr Acct Mgr)
Nick Barlow (Acct Mgr)
Robert Doherty (Mgr-Channel Partner)
John Gladstone (Head-Technical Svcs-
European)

Chinatronic Technology Limited (1)
16/F Spectrum Tower 53 Hung To Road,
Kwun Tong, Kowloon, China (Hong Kong)
Tel.: (852) 21765388
Electronic Components Distr
N.A.I.C.S.: 423690

Combined Precision Components Limited (1)
Component House Fulwood, Preston, PR2
9PP, United Kingdom
Tel.: (44) 3447880088
Web Site: https://cpc.farnell.com
Electronic Parts & Equipment Distr
N.A.I.C.S.: 423690

DSM Computer GmbH (1)
Am Loferfeld 50-54, Gewerbepark, 81249,
Munich, Germany
Tel.: (49) 8915798250
Web Site: http://www.dsm-computer.de
Embedded Electronic Component Mfr
N.A.I.C.S.: 334419

Dragon Innovation, Inc. (1)
1 Alewife Ctr Ste 310, Cambridge, MA
02140
Tel.: (781) 290-8945
Web Site: http://www.dragoninnovation.com
Cloud Based File Online Publishing Ser-
vices
N.A.I.C.S.: 513199
Scott N. Miller (Co-Founder & CEO)
Herman Pang (Co-Founder & Pres)

Dritte TENVA Property GmbH Nettetal (1)
Lotscher Weg 66, 41334, Nettetal, Germany
Tel.: (49) 21537330
Electronic Components Distr
N.A.I.C.S.: 423690

EBV Elektronik ApS (1)
Elkjaervej 19 1 sal, Abyhoj, 8230, Arhus,
Denmark
Tel.: (45) 86250466
Web Site: http://www.ebv.com
Electronic Components Distr
N.A.I.C.S.: 423690

EBV Elektronik EOOD (1)
48 Sitnyakovo Blvd Serdika offices 10th
floor Unit 1006, 1505, Sofia, 1505, Bulgaria
Tel.: (359) 29264337
Electronic Goods Whslr
N.A.I.C.S.: 423690

EBV Elektronik France SAS (1)
3 Rue de la Renaissance, 92184, Antony,
France
Tel.: (33) 140963000
Electronic Components Distr
N.A.I.C.S.: 423690
Franck Maul (Mgr-Vertical Segment)
Etienne Lanoy (Reg Mgr-Application)

EBV Elektronik GmbH & Co. KG (1)
Im Technologiepark 2-8, 85586, Poing, Ger-
many
Tel.: (49) 81217740
Electronic Components Distr
N.A.I.C.S.: 423690

EBV Elektronik Israel (2008) Ltd. (1)
1 Habrosh St Bnei Dror, Netanya, 4581500,
Israel
Tel.: (972) 97780280
Computer Product Mfr & Distr
N.A.I.C.S.: 334111

EBV Elektronik OU (1)
Suur-Joe 63, 80042, Parnu, Estonia
Tel.: (372) 58864446
Emp.: 2
Management Consulting Services
N.A.I.C.S.: 541618

EBV Elektronik S.R.L. (1)
Building Sky Tower 246C Calea Floreasca,
District 1, 014476, Bucharest, Romania
Tel.: (40) 215281612
Electronic Components Distr
N.A.I.C.S.: 423690

EBV Elektronik SAS (1)
115 Rue Nicolas Ledoux Immeuble Hemiris
Batiment A, 13854, Aix-en-Provence,
France
Tel.: (33) 442396540
Emp.: 6
Electronic Components Distr

N.A.I.C.S.: 423690
Franck Maul (Mgr-Vertical Segment)
Etienne Lanoy (Reg Mgr-Application)
Karim Khebere (Dir-Technical)

EBV Elektronik Sp. z o.o. (1)
Rotunda Eng Edgar Cardoso 23-14 G, Uni-
pessoal Lda/Edificio Tower Plaza, 4400-
676, Vila Nova de Gaia, Portugal
Tel.: (351) 220920260
Electronic Component Mfr & Distr
N.A.I.C.S.: 334419
Nuno Lopes (Reg Sls Mgr)

EBV Elektronik Spain S.L. (1)
Centro Empresarial Euronova Ronda de
Poniente 4 Planta 2, 28760, Tres Cantos,
Madrid, Spain
Tel.: (34) 918043256
Electronic Components Distr
N.A.I.C.S.: 423690

EBV Elektronik TOV (1)
Vasilovskaya str 14 off 422-423, 03040,
Kiev, Ukraine
Tel.: (380) 444962226
Web Site: http://www.ebv.com
Sales Range: $25-49.9 Million
Emp.: 3
Electronic Components Distr
N.A.I.C.S.: 423690

EBV Elektronik TOV (1)
Grunbergstrasse 15/1 Top 4, 1120, Vienna,
Austria
Tel.: (43) 1891520
Electronic Component Mfr & Distr
N.A.I.C.S.: 334419

EBV Elektronik d.o.o. (1)
Milentija Popovica 5B, Belgrade, 11070,
Serbia
Tel.: (381) 114049901
Electronic Product Distr
N.A.I.C.S.: 423690

EBV Elektronik s.r.o. (1)
Turcianska 2 Green Point Offices, 82109,
Bratislava, Slovakia
Tel.: (421) 232242600
Electronic Components Distr
N.A.I.C.S.: 423690

EBV Elektronik sp. z o.o. (1)
Pl Solny 16, 50-062, Wroclaw, Poland
Tel.: (48) 713422944
Web Site: http://www.ebv.com
Emp.: 20
Electronic Components Distr
N.A.I.C.S.: 423690
Krzysztof Zajac (Mng Dir)

EBV Elektronik, Druzba Za Posredo-vanje D.O.O. (1)
Dunajska cesta167, 1000, Ljubljana, 1000,
Slovenia
Tel.: (386) 15609778
Web Site: http://www.ebv.com
Emp.: 11
Electronic Product Distr
N.A.I.C.S.: 423690

EBV Elektronik, Unipessoal Lda, (1)
Edificio Tower Plaza Rotunda Eng Edgar
Cardoso 23 - 14 G, 4400-676, Vila Nova de
Gaia, Portugal
Tel.: (351) 220920260
Web Site: http://www.bridgelux.com
Electronic Components Distr
N.A.I.C.S.: 423690

EBV-Elektronik GmbH (1)
Grunbergstrasse 15/1 Top 4, 1120, Vienna,
Austria
Tel.: (43) 1891520
Web Site: http://www.ebv.com
Electronic Product Distr
N.A.I.C.S.: 423690

Eastele Technology China Limited (1)
Room 402 Nan Fung Commercial Centre
19 Lam Lok Street, Kowloon Bay, Hong
Kong, China (Hong Kong)
Tel.: (852) 21806166
Web Site: http://www.rti.com.hk
Emp.: 30
Electronic Product Distr
N.A.I.C.S.: 423690
Gary Ng (Country Mgr)

Electron House (Overseas) Limited (1)
Avnet House Rutherford Close, Stevenage, SG1 2EF, Hertfordshire, United Kingdom
Tel.: (44) 1438788310
Holding Company; Financial Management Services
N.A.I.C.S.: 551112

Eluomeng Limited (1)
21st Floor Tower 2 Enterprise Square Five 38 Wang Chiu Road, Kowloon Bay, Kowloon, China (Hong Kong)
Tel.: (852) 22689888
Web Site: https://hk.element14.com
Computer Product Mfr & Distr
N.A.I.C.S.: 334111

Enlaces Computacionales, S. de R.L. de C.V. (1)
Culiacan No 123 Piso 11, Distrito Federal, Mexico, 06170, Mexico
Tel.: (52) 5580003000
Emp.: 3
Computer & Computer Peripheral Device Distr
N.A.I.C.S.: 423430

Exit Certified Ltd. (1)
40 Eglinton Avenue E Suite 305, Toronto, M4P 3A2, ON, Canada
Tel.: (416) 487-3948
Web Site: http://www.exitcertified.com
Computer Training Services
N.A.I.C.S.: 611420

ExitCertified Corp. (1)
450 Sansome St Ste 600, San Francisco, CA 94111
Tel.: (415) 975-3948
Computer Training Services
N.A.I.C.S.: 611420
Allison Stevenson (Coord-Ops)

Flint Distribution Limited (1)
Walker Road Bardon Hill, Coalville, LE67 1TU, Leicestershire, United Kingdom
Tel.: (44) 1530510333
Web Site: http://www.flint.co.uk
Sales Range: $25-49.9 Million
Emp.: 22
Electronic Components Distr
N.A.I.C.S.: 423690
David Pritchard (Mgr-Pareto)
Rachel Waby (Mgr-HR & Trng)
Tony Plunkett (Acct Mgr)
Sarah Williams (Supvr-Internal Sls)

HCGI Hartford (1)
10440 Little Patuxent Pkwy 3rd Fl, Columbia, MD 21044
Tel.: (410) 740-3020
Web Site: http://www.hcgi.com
Holding Company; Information Technology & Software Products Distr & Support Services
N.A.I.C.S.: 551112
Bill Heneghan (Founder & Pres)
Brian Stubblefield (Dir-Data Center Solutions)
Bill Hottman (Dir-A & V Design & Installation)
Fiona Gambino (Mktg Dir)

Subsidiary (Domestic):

Nexicore Services, LLC (2)
4201 Guardian St, Simi Valley, CA 93063
Tel.: (805) 306-2500
Web Site: http://www.avnetintegrated.com
Sales Range: $25-49.9 Million
Information Technology Parts Distr & Repair Services
N.A.I.C.S.: 811210
Jo Lamoreaux (CFO)

Unit (Domestic):

Nexicore Services, LLC - Call Center (3)
7916 Evolutions Way Ste 210, New Port Richey, FL 34655
Tel.: (727) 372-3711
Web Site: http://www.avnetintegrated.com
Information Technology Repair Dispatch Services
N.A.I.C.S.: 561421

J-TEQ EMS Solutions Ltd. (1)
6 Bain Square Kirkton Campus, Livingston,

EH54 7DQ, United Kingdom
Tel.: (44) 1506460555
Web Site: http://www.j-teq.co.uk
Embedded Electronic Component Mfr
N.A.I.C.S.: 334419
James Shaw (Mng Dir)

M S C - Vertriebs - SK s. r. o. (1)
Kuzmanyho 8, Zilina, 010 01, Slovakia
Tel.: (421) 415001240
Electronic Components Distr
N.A.I.C.S.: 423690

MSC (Malta) Limited (1)
UB40 San Gwann Industrial Estate, San Gwann, SGN 3000, Malta
Tel.: (356) 25706000
Emp.: 65
Electronic Components Distr
N.A.I.C.S.: 423690

MSC Investoren GmbH (1)
Industriestrasse 16, Stutensee, 76297, Germany
Tel.: (49) 72499100
Electronic Components Distr
N.A.I.C.S.: 423690
Dominic Ressing (Pres)

MSC Technologies GmbH (1)
Industriestr 16, 76297, Stutensee, Germany
Tel.: (49) 72499100
Web Site: http://www.msc-technologies.eu
Emp.: 371
Electronic Component Mfr & Distr
N.A.I.C.S.: 334419
Silvano Geissler (Mng Dir)
Darrel Scott Jackson (Mng Dir)
Dominik Ressing (Mng Dir)

MSC Technologies Systems GmbH (1)
Munzinger Strasse 3, 79111, Freiburg, Germany
Tel.: (49) 76188190
Emp.: 200
Electronic Components Distr
N.A.I.C.S.: 423690
Silvano Geissler (Mng Dir)
Darrel Scott Jackson (Mng Dir)

Magirus UK Ltd (1)
Clifton House, Berkshire, Bracknell, RG12 9BQ, United Kingdom
Tel.: (44) 1344401600
Emp.: 50
Custom Computer Programming Services
N.A.I.C.S.: 541511

Memec Group Limited (1)
Avnet House Rutherford Close, Stevenage, SG1 2EF, Hertfordshire, United Kingdom
Tel.: (44) 1438788551
Electronic Components Distr
N.A.I.C.S.: 423690

Orchestra Service GmbH (1)
Zeppelinstrasse 2, 82205, Gilching, Germany
Tel.: (49) 81053700
Web Site: http://www.orchestra.de
Data Management Services
N.A.I.C.S.: 518210
Roman Rudolf (Mng Dir)

Ormic Components Ltd. (1)
2A Habarzel St, PO Box 13180, 69710, Tel Aviv, Israel
Tel.: (972) 37657290
Web Site: http://www.ormic.co.il
Sales Range: $150-199.9 Million
Electronic Product Distr
N.A.I.C.S.: 423690
Ron Mizrahi (Mng Dir)
Nir Mizrahi (Engr-Sls)
Nurit Ginati (Ops Mgr-Sls)

PDSI B.V. (1)
De Geer 2, 4004 LT, Tiel, Netherlands
Tel.: (31) 344633370
Web Site: http://www.avnetintegrated.com
Emp.: 45
Electronic Product Distr
N.A.I.C.S.: 423690
Goost Messeur (Gen Mgr)

PDSI Singapore Pte. Ltd. (1)
50 Kallang Avenue No 09-02, Singapore, 339505, Singapore
Tel.: (65) 62951788
Web Site: http://www.avnetintegrated.com

Electronic Component Repair Service
N.A.I.C.S.: 811210

PT Tech Data Advanced Solutions Indonesia (1)
BSG Building 6th Floor Abdul Muis 40, Jakarta, 10160, Indonesia
Tel.: (62) 213448848
Web Site: http://www.avnet.co.id
IT Solution Distr
N.A.I.C.S.: 541511

Phoenics Electronics Corporation (1)
31 Nagog Park, Acton, MA 01720
Tel.: (978) 856-0111
Web Site: http://www.phoenicselectronics.com
Semiconductor Product Distr
N.A.I.C.S.: 423690

Premier Farnell Limited (1)
Farnell House Forge Lane, Leeds, LS12 2NE, United Kingdom
Tel.: (44) 8701298608
Web Site: https://www.farnell.com
Emp.: 3,500
Holding Company; Electronic Components, Industrial Maintenance & Repair Products Sales
N.A.I.C.S.: 551112
Chris Breslin (Pres)

Subsidiary (Non-US):

FARNELL COMPONENTS (IRELAND) LIMITED (2)
Riverside One Sir John Rogerson's Quay, Dublin, 2, Ireland
Tel.: (353) 1800936198
Web Site: https://ie.farnell.com
Electronic Components Distr
N.A.I.C.S.: 423690

Farnell (Belgium) NV (2)
Liege DC Rue de l'Aeropostale 11, 4460, Grace-Hollogne, Belgium
Tel.: (32) 34752810
Web Site: https://be.farnell.com
Electronic Components Distr
N.A.I.C.S.: 423690

Farnell (France) SAS (2)
314 Allee des Noisetiers ZAC des Bruyeres, 69760, Limonest, France
Tel.: (33) 472293001
Web Site: https://fr.farnell.com
Electronic Equipment Distr
N.A.I.C.S.: 423690

Farnell (Netherlands) BV (2)
Zonnebaan 9, 3542EA, Utrecht, 3542 EA, Netherlands
Tel.: (31) 302417373
Web Site: https://www.nl.farnell.com
Electronic Components Distr
N.A.I.C.S.: 423690

Farnell AG (2)
Bahnhofftrasestrasse 10, 6300, Zug, Switzerland
Tel.: (41) 442046464
Web Site: https://ch.farnell.com
Electronic Components Distr
N.A.I.C.S.: 423690

Farnell Components AB (2)
Box 1830, Box 227, 171 27, Solna, Sweden
Tel.: (46) 87305000
Web Site: https://www.se.farnell.com
Electronic Components Distr
N.A.I.C.S.: 423690

Farnell Components SL (2)
Paseo Castellana 28-Piso 2, 28046, Madrid, Spain
Tel.: (34) 934758805
Web Site: https://es.farnell.com
Electronic Components Distr
N.A.I.C.S.: 423690

Farnell Danmark AS (2)
Lyskaer 9, 2730, Herlev, Denmark
Tel.: (45) 44536644
Web Site: https://dk.farnell.com
Electronic Components Distr
N.A.I.C.S.: 423690

Group (Domestic):

Farnell Electronic Components Limited (2)

150 Armley Road, Leeds, LS12 2QQ, West Yorkshire, United Kingdom
Tel.: (44) 1132790101
Web Site: http://www.element14.com
Electronics & Industrial Products Mfr & Distr
N.A.I.C.S.: 423930

Subsidiary (Non-US):

Element 14 sp. zoo (3)
Floor 6 and 7 Building B Quattro Business Park, AL Gen Bora-Komorowskiego 25, 31-476, Krakow, Poland
Tel.: (48) 123497000
Electronic Components Distr
N.A.I.C.S.: 423690

Element14 Asia Pte. Ltd. (3)
151 Lorong Chuan New Tech Park Lobby C 05-03, Singapore, 556741, Singapore
Tel.: (65) 67880200
Web Site: https://sg.element14.com
Electronic Parts & Equipment Distr
N.A.I.C.S.: 423690

Element14 Co., Ltd. (3)
Q House Lumpini Level Q House Lumpini 27 1 South Sathorn Road, Tungmahamek Sathorn, Bangkok, Thailand
Tel.: (66) 1800658137
Web Site: http://th.element14.com
Electronic Components Distr
N.A.I.C.S.: 423690

Element14 Holding BV (3)
Zonnebaan 9, 3542 EA, Utrecht, Netherlands
Tel.: (31) 302417337
Web Site: http://nl.farnell.com
Electronic Parts & Equipment Distr
N.A.I.C.S.: 423690

Element14 India Pvt Limited (3)
D Block 11th Floor IBC Knowledge Park 4/1, Bannerghatta Main Rd Bhavani Nagar Suddagunte Palya, Bengaluru, Karnataka, India
Tel.: (91) 18001083888
Web Site: https://in.element14.com
Electronic Parts & Equipment Distr
N.A.I.C.S.: 423690

Element14 Limited (3)
300 Richmond Road, PO Box 74342, Grey Lynn, Auckland, 1021, New Zealand
Tel.: (64) 800908088
Web Site: https://nz.element14.com
Electronic Components Distr
N.A.I.C.S.: 423690

Element14 Limited (3)
21st Floor Tower 2 Enterprise Square Five 38 Wang Chui Road, Kowloon Bay, Kowloon, China (Hong Kong)
Tel.: (852) 22689888
Web Site: http://hk.element14.com
Electronic Components Distr
N.A.I.C.S.: 423690

Element14 Pte Ltd (3)
15 Tai Seng Drive #05-01, Singapore, 535220, Singapore
Tel.: (65) 67883922
Web Site: http://www.sg.element14.com
Electronic Components Distr
N.A.I.C.S.: 423690
Brian Low (Reg Mgr-Sls)

Element14 Pte. Ltd. (3)
614 10 Seonyu-ro 9-gil Munrae-dong 6-ga Munrae SK V1 Center, Yeongdeungpo-gu, Seoul, 07281, Korea (South)
Tel.: (82) 16441419
Web Site: https://kr.element14.com
Electronic Components Distr
N.A.I.C.S.: 423690

Element14 Pty Ltd (3)
72 Ferndell Street, Chester Hill, 2162, NSW, Australia
Tel.: (61) 1300361005
Web Site: https://www.au.element14.com
Electronic Components Distr
N.A.I.C.S.: 423690

Element14. S. De R.I. De C.V (3)
Av Aviacion 5051-18 Col San Juan de Ocotan, 45019, Zapopan, Mexico
Tel.: (52) 8004639275
Web Site: https://mexico.newark.com
Electronic Components Distr

Avnet, Inc.—(Continued)

N.A.I.C.S.: 423690

element14 Sdn. Bhd. (3)
Unit S-06-07 First Subang Mall, Jalan
SS15/4G, 47500, Subang Jaya, Selangor
Darul Ehsan, Malaysia
Tel.: (60) 356350686
Web Site: https://my.element14.com
Electronic Components Distr
N.A.I.C.S.: 423690

Subsidiary (Non-US):

Farnell GmbH (2)
Im Technologiepark 2-8, 85586, Poing, Germany
Tel.: (49) 8961393939
Web Site: https://www.de.farnell.com
Electronic & Electrical Component Distr
N.A.I.C.S.: 423690
Robert Rospedzihowski (Mng Dir)
Darrel Jackson (Mng Dir)
Gavin Hodgson-Silke (Mng Dir)

Farnell Italia SRL (2)
Via Manzoni 44 12, 20095, Cusano
Milanino, MI, Italy
Tel.: (39) 0293995200
Web Site: https://it.farnell.com
Electronic Components Distr
N.A.I.C.S.: 423690

Oy Farnell AB (2)
C/O Azets Insight Oy PB1, FI-0047, Helsinki, Uusimaa, Finland
Tel.: (358) 95607780
Web Site: http://fi.farnell.com
Electronic Components Distr
N.A.I.C.S.: 423690

Subsidiary (Domestic):

**Premier Farnell (Scotland)
Limited** (2)
150 Armley Road, Leeds, LS12 2QQ,
United Kingdom
Tel.: (44) 8701298608
Web Site: http://uk.farnell.com
Electronic Components Distr
N.A.I.C.S.: 423690

Subsidiary (Non-US):

Premier Farnell Canada Limited (2)
Postal Station A, PO Box 4275, Toronto,
M5W 5V8, ON, Canada
Tel.: (905) 670-4177
Web Site: http://canada.newark.com
Electronic Components Distr
N.A.I.C.S.: 423690

Subsidiary (US):

Premier Farnell Corp. (2)
300 S Riverside Plz Ste 2200, Chicago, IL
60606
Tel.: (800) 463-9275
Web Site: http://www.farnell.com
Holding Company; Regional Managing Office
N.A.I.C.S.: 551112
Chris Breslin (Pres)

Subsidiary (Domestic):

AVID Technologies, Inc. (3)
2112 Case Prkwy S, Twinsburg, OH 44087
Tel.: (330) 487-0770
Web Site: http://www.avid-tech.com
Engineering Services
N.A.I.C.S.: 541330

MCM Electronics Inc. (3)
650 Congress Pk Dr, Centerville, OH
45459-4035 (100%)
Tel.: (877) 626-3532
Web Site: http://www.mcmelectronics.com
Electronics Whslr
N.A.I.C.S.: 449210

Newark Corporation (3)
300 S Riverside Plz Ste 2200, Chicago, IL
60606 (100%)
Web Site: https://www.newark.com
Electronic Parts & Components Whslr
N.A.I.C.S.: 423690
Uma Pingali (Pres-Bus)

Subsidiary (Non-US):

**Premier Farnell Electronics de
Mexico SRL** (2)
Av Aviacion No 5051 Nave 18, Zapopan,
45019, Mexico
Tel.: (52) 3337775000
Electronic Equipment Whslr
N.A.I.C.S.: 423690

Subsidiary (Domestic):

Premier Farnell UK Ltd (2)
150 Armley Rd, Leeds, LS12 2QQ, United
Kingdom (100%)
Tel.: (44) 8701298608
Web Site: https://uk.farnell.com
Electronic & Telecommuinications Equipment Whslr
N.A.I.C.S.: 423690

Subsidiary (Domestic):

CPC PLC (3)
Component House Faraday Dr, Preston,
PR2 9PP, United Kingdom (100%)
Tel.: (44) 3447880088
Web Site: http://www.cpc.farnell.com
Electronic & Computer Components
N.A.I.C.S.: 334118

RTI Technology China Limited (1)
Room 402 Nan Fung Commercial Centre
19 Lam Lok Street, Kowloon Bay, Hong
Kong, China (Hong Kong)
Tel.: (852) 21806166
Web Site: http://www.rti.com.hk
Electric Component Whslr
N.A.I.C.S.: 423690

Rausch Netzwerktechnik GmbH (1)
Englerstrasse 26, 76275, Ettlingen, Germany
Tel.: (49) 724359290
Web Site: http://www.rnt.de
Electronic Components Distr
N.A.I.C.S.: 423690

Round2 Technologies, Inc. (1)
1340 Airport Commerce Dr Bldg 3 Ste 300,
Austin, TX 78741-6836
Tel.: (512) 342-8855
Web Site: http://www.round2.net
Sales Range: $25-49.9 Million
Emp.: 400
Holding Company; Electronics Recycling
Services
N.A.I.C.S.: 551112
Randall Weiss (Pres & CEO)

Subsidiary (Domestic):

ROUND2 Inc. (2)
1040 Airport Commerce Dr Bldg 3 Ste 300,
Austin, TX 78741-6836
Tel.: (512) 342-8855
Web Site: http://www.round2.net
Sales Range: $25-49.9 Million
Emp.: 50
Electronics Recycling Services
N.A.I.C.S.: 562920
Randall Weiss (Co-Founder, Pres & CEO)

**Shenzhen Embest Technology Co.,
Ltd.** (1)
TowerB 4/F Shanshui Building, Nanshan
Yungu Innovation Industry Park Liuxian Ave
Nanshan District, Shenzhen, China
Tel.: (86) 75533190846
Web Site: http://www.embest-tech.com
Semiconductor Product Mfr & Distr
N.A.I.C.S.: 333242

Softweb Solutions Inc. (1)
2000 W Center Dr Ste B401, Hoffman Estates, IL 60192
Tel.: (224) 699-2111
Web Site: https://www.softwebsolutions.com
Sales Range: $1-9.9 Million
Emp.: 545
Software Devolepment
N.A.I.C.S.: 513210
Ripal Vyas (Founder)

TSSLink, Inc. (1)
Ste 3102099 Gateway Pl, San Jose, CA
95110
Tel.: (408) 338-0750
Web Site: http://www.tsslink.com
Computer Related Services

N.A.I.C.S.: 541519

Tekdata Interconnections Limited (1)
Innovation House The Glades Festival Way
Etruria, Stoke-on-Trent, ST1 5SQ, Staffordshire, United Kingdom
Tel.: (44) 1782254700
Web Site: http://www.tekdata-interconnect.com
Electrical Component Mfr
N.A.I.C.S.: 335999

Telmil Electronics, Inc. (1)
290 Norwood Ave Ste 206, Deal, NJ 07723
Tel.: (732) 517-0501
Electronic Components Distr
N.A.I.C.S.: 423690

Thomas Kaubisch GmbH (1)
Im Technologiepark 2, 85586, Poing, Germany
Tel.: (49) 81217760
Web Site: http://www.kaubisch.com
Advertising Agency Services
N.A.I.C.S.: 541810

WBT Systems, Inc. (1)
38 Spring St, Nashua, NH 03060-0801
Tel.: (603) 654-3500
Web Site: http://www.wbtsystems.com
Sales Range: $25-49.9 Million
Emp.: 50
Software Development Services
N.A.I.C.S.: 541511

Witekio GmbH (1)
Industriestrasse 16, 76297, Stutensee, Germany
Tel.: (49) 60316937070
Web Site: https://witekio.com
Computer Product Mfr & Distr
N.A.I.C.S.: 334111

**YEL Electronics Hong Kong
Limited** (1)
1203-04 Hilder Centre 2 Sung Ping Street,
Hung Hom, China (Hong Kong)
Tel.: (852) 31299833
Electronic Components Distr
N.A.I.C.S.: 423690
Alex Yiu (Mgr-Field Application)

YEL Electronics Pte Ltd (1)
No 2 Kaki Bukit Avenue 1 05-07Kampong
Ubi Industrial Estate, Singapore, 417938,
Singapore
Tel.: (65) 67454248
Sales Range: $25-49.9 Million
Emp.: 15
Electronic Components Distr
N.A.I.C.S.: 423690

AVP, INC.
1187 Coast Vlg Rd Ste 319, Santa
Barbara, CA 93108
Tel.: (805) 969-7482   DE
AVPI—(OTCIQ)
Sport & Recreation Services
N.A.I.C.S.: 611620
Jeffrey Wattenberg (Pres, CEO &
Sec)
Andrew Reif (COO)

AWARE, INC.
76 Blanchard Rd, Burlington, MA
01803
Tel.: (781) 687-0300   MA
Web Site: https://www.aware.com
Year Founded: 1986
AWRE—(NASDAQ)
Rev.: $16,008,000
Assets: $51,192,000
Liabilities: $10,983,000
Net Worth: $40,209,000
Earnings: ($1,726,000)
Emp.: 82
Fiscal Year-end: 12/31/22
Digital Subscriber Lines (DSL) Technology Services
N.A.I.C.S.: 541511
David Traverse (Principal Fin Officer
& Treas)
Mohamed Lazzouni (CTO)
Heidi Hunter (Chief Product Officer)

Lindsey Savarino (Sr Dir-Human Resources)
Sarah Eckert (Corp Counsel)
Mario Cesar Santos (VP-Global Solutions)
Robert A. Eckel (Pres & CEO)

Subsidiaries:

AFIX Technologies, Inc. (1)
205 N Walnut St, Pittsburg, KS 66762
Tel.: (620) 232-6420
Web Site: http://www.afix.net
Fingerprint, Palmprint & Biometric Identification Solutions
N.A.I.C.S.: 334118
Scott Howard (Dir-Biometrics)

Aware Security Corporation (1)
40 Middlesex Tpke, Bedford, MA 01730-1404
Tel.: (781) 276-4000
Web Site: http://www.aware.com
Sales Range: $75-99.9 Million
Engineeering Services
N.A.I.C.S.: 541330

AWAYSIS CAPITAL, INC.
3400 Lakeside Dr Ste 100, Miramar,
FL 33027   DE
Web Site:
    https://www.awaysisgroup.com
Year Founded: 2008
AWCA—(OTCIQ)
Emp.: 8
Offices of Other Holding Companies
N.A.I.C.S.: 551112
Andrew E. Trumbach (Pres & CFO)
Michael Singh (CEO)

AXALTA COATING SYSTEMS
LTD.
50 Applied Bank Blvd Ste 300, Glen
Mills, PA 19342   BM
Web Site: https://www.axalta.com
Year Founded: 2012
AXTA—(NYSE)
Rev.: $5,184,100,000
Assets: $7,272,100,000
Liabilities: $5,499,300,000
Net Worth: $1,772,800,000
Earnings: $267,400,000
Emp.: 12,000
Fiscal Year-end: 12/31/23
Holding Company; Coatings Mfr
N.A.I.C.S.: 551112
Anthony Massey (Chief Acctg Officer,
VP & Controller-Global)
Barry S. Snyder (Chief Ops & Supply
Chain Officer & Sr VP)
Chrishan Villavarayan (Pres & CEO)
Troy Weaver (Sr VP-Global Refinish)
Ashish Jawadiwar (Chief Information
& Digital Officer & VP)
Shelley J. Bausch (Pres-Global Industrial Coatings)
Jacqueline Scanlan (Chief HR Officer
& Sr VP)
Jim Muse (VP-Sls-Global Refinish)
Tim Bowes (Chief Transformation Officer)
Keith Silverman (Chief Ops Officer)

Subsidiaries:

**Axalta Coating Systems Belgium
BVBA** (1)
Geerdegem-Schonenberg 248, 2800,
Mechelen, Belgium
Tel.: (32) 15478501
Web Site: https://www.axalta.com
Paint & Coating Distr
N.A.I.C.S.: 423330

**Axalta Coating Systems Canada
Company** (1)
408 Fairall Street, Ajax, L1S 1R6, ON,
Canada
Coating Mfr
N.A.I.C.S.: 325510

Axalta Coating Systems France SAS **(1)**
Allee de Chantereine, 78711, Mantes-la-Ville, France
Tel.: (33) 130928000
Web Site: https://www.axalta.com
Coating Mfr
N.A.I.C.S.: 325510

Axalta Coating Systems Mexico, S. de R.L. de C.V. **(1)**
Industria Electrica 10 Industrial Barrientos, 54015, Tlalnepantla, 54015, Mexico
Tel.: (52) 5553665300
Coating Mfr
N.A.I.C.S.: 325510

Axalta Coating Systems, LLC **(1)**
2001 Market St Two Commerce Sq Ste 3600, Philadelphia, PA 19103
Tel.: (302) 992-2261
Web Site: http://www.axalta.com
Sales Range: $125-149.9 Million
Liquid & Powder Coatings Developer, Mfr & Marketer
N.A.I.C.S.: 325510

Subsidiary (Non-US):

Axalta Coating Systems Australia Pty Ltd **(2)**
16 Darling Street, Marsden Park, Sydney, 2765, NSW, Australia
Tel.: (61) 800292582
Web Site: https://www.axalta.com
Liquid & Powder Coatings Developer, Mfr & Marketer
N.A.I.C.S.: 325510
Nancy Lane *(Mktg Mgr)*

Axalta Coating Systems UK Limited **(2)**
Wedgwood Way, Stevenage, SG1 4QN, Hertfordshire, United Kingdom
Tel.: (44) 1438 734000
Sales Range: $50-74.9 Million
Emp.: 200
Plastics Product Mfr
N.A.I.C.S.: 326199

Subsidiary (Domestic):

Axalta Powder Coating Systems USA, Inc. **(2)**
9800 Genard Rd, Houston, TX 77041-7624
Tel.: (713) 939-4000
Powder Coating Mfr
N.A.I.C.S.: 325510

Century Industrial Coatings Incorporated **(2)**
37094 Hwy 69, Jacksonville, TX 75766
Tel.: (903) 586-9197
Web Site: http://www.centurypaint.com
Paint & Coating Mfr
N.A.I.C.S.: 325510
Michael Cash *(Pres)*

Dura Coat Products, Inc. **(2)**
5361 Via Ricardo, Riverside, CA 92509
Tel.: (951) 341-6500
Web Site:
  https://www.duracoatproducts.com
Emp.: 102
Coil & Spray Coatings Mfr
N.A.I.C.S.: 325510

Subsidiary (Non-US):

Plascoat Systems Limited **(2)**
Farnham Trading Estate, Farnham, GU9 9NY, Surrey, United Kingdom **(100%)**
Tel.: (44) 1252733777
Web Site: http://www.plascoat.com
Plastic Coating Materials
N.A.I.C.S.: 325211

Dura Coat Products of Alabama, Inc. **(1)**
26655 Peoples Rd, Madison, AL 35756
Tel.: (256) 353-7800
Web Site:
  https://www.duracoatproducts.com
Coil Coating Mfr
N.A.I.C.S.: 325510

AXCELIS TECHNOLOGIES, INC.

108 Cherry Hill Dr, Beverly, MA 01915-1088
Tel.: (978) 787-4000   DE
Web Site: https://www.axcelis.com
Year Founded: 1995
ACLS—(NASDAQ)
Rev.: $919,998,000
Assets: $1,013,641,000
Liabilities: $346,385,000
Net Worth: $667,256,000
Earnings: $183,079,000
Emp.: 1,388
Fiscal Year-end: 12/31/22
Ion Implantation, Dry Strip, Thermal Processing & Curing Equipment Used in the Production of Semiconductor Chips Mfr
N.A.I.C.S.: 333242
Russell J. Low *(Pres & CEO)*
Lynnette C. Fallon *(Exec VP-HR & Legal)*
Douglas A. Lawson *(Exec VP-Corp Mktg & Strategy)*
James G. Coogan *(CFO, Principal Acctg Officer & Exec VP)*
Greg Redinbo *(Exec VP)*

Subsidiaries:

Axcelis Technologies GmbH **(1)**
Zur Wetterwarte 50/Haus 337/G, 01109, Dresden, Germany **(100%)**
Tel.: (49) 3517959200
Web Site: https://www.axcelis.com
Sales Range: $25-49.9 Million
Ion Implantation, Dry Strip, Thermal Processing & Curing Equipment Used in the Production of Semiconductor Chips Mfr
N.A.I.C.S.: 333242

Axcelis Technologies Ltd. **(1)**
109 Ichon Town 692 10 Ami Ri Bubal, Kyunggi-do, Incheon, 467 866, Korea (South)
Tel.: (82) 316363821
Web Site: https://www.axcelis.com
Sales Range: $25-49.9 Million
Emp.: 10
Ion Implantation, Dry Strip, Thermal Processing & Curing Equipment Used in the Production of Semiconductor Chips Mfr
N.A.I.C.S.: 333242

Axcelis Technologies Ltd. **(1)**
4F No 6-5 Duxing Road Hsinchu Science Park, Hsin-chu, 30078, Taiwan
Tel.: (886) 35648000
Sales Range: $25-49.9 Million
Emp.: 70
Ion Implantation, Dry Strip, Thermal Processing & Curing Equipment Used in the Production of Semiconductor Chips Mfr
N.A.I.C.S.: 333242

Axcelis Technologies Pte. Ltd. **(1)**
53 Serangoon North Avenue 4 05-01/02, Singapore, 555852, Singapore
Tel.: (65) 64196988
Ion Implantation, Dry Strip, Thermal Processing & Curing Equipment Used in the Production of Semiconductor Chips Mfr
N.A.I.C.S.: 333242

Axcelis Technologies, S.A.R.L. **(1)**
155-157 Cours Berriat, 38028, Grenoble, Cedex 1, France
Tel.: (33) 35179590
Ion Implantation, Dry Strip, Thermal Processing & Curing Equipment (Used in the Production of Semiconductor Chips) Mfr
N.A.I.C.S.: 333242

Axcelis Technologies, S.r.l. **(1)**
Centro Direzionale Colleoni Palazzo Cassiopea 1 Via Paracelso 22, Agrate Brianza, 20864, Milan, Italy
Tel.: (39) 039656151
Web Site: http://www.axcelis.com
Sales Range: $125-149.9 Million
Ion Implantation, Dry Strip, Thermal Processing & Curing Equipment Used in the Production of Semiconductor Chips Mfr
N.A.I.C.S.: 333242

Sumitomo Eaton Nova Corporation **(1)**

SBS Tower 9F, 10-1 Yoga 4chome, Setagaya-ku, Tokyo, 158 0097, Japan
Tel.: (81) 354917800
Sales Range: $200-249.9 Million
Emp.: 403
Ion Implantation Systems; Owned 50% by Sumitomo Heavy Industries, Ltd. & 50% Axcelis Technologies, Inc.
N.A.I.C.S.: 334516

AXCELLA HEALTH INC.
840 Memorial Dr, Cambridge, MA 02139
Tel.: (857) 320-2200   DE
Web Site: https://www.axcellatx.com
Year Founded: 2008
AXLA—(NASDAQ)
Rev.: $504,000
Assets: $18,927,000
Liabilities: $14,763,000
Net Worth: $4,164,000
Earnings: ($81,186,000)
Emp.: 11
Fiscal Year-end: 12/31/22
Biotechnology Research & Development Services
N.A.I.C.S.: 541714
Craig R. Jalbert *(Pres, Principal Exec Officer, Principal Fin Officer, Principal Acctg Officer, Treas & Sec)*

AXIM BIOTECHNOLOGIES, INC.
6191 Cornerstone Ct E Ste 114, San Diego, CA 92121
Tel.: (858) 923-4422   NV
Web Site:
  https://www.aximbiotech.com
Year Founded: 2010
AXIM—(OTCQB)
Rev.: $39,518
Assets: $4,121,548
Liabilities: $11,778,195
Net Worth: ($7,656,647)
Earnings: ($8,059,682)
Emp.: 6
Fiscal Year-end: 12/31/23
Cannabis-Based Medicines & Pharmaceuticals
N.A.I.C.S.: 325411
George E. Anastassov *(Founder)*
Robert Malasek *(CFO & Sec)*
Alim Seit-Nebi *(CTO-Sapphire Biotech Inc)*
Kurt Phinney *(COO)*
John W. Huemoeller II *(Pres, CEO & Chm)*

AXION POWER INTERNATIONAL, INC.
3601 Clover Ln, New Castle, PA 16105
Tel.: (724) 654-9300   DE
Web Site:
  http://www.axionpower.com
Year Founded: 1997
AXPWQ—(OTCEM)
Batteries & Energy Storage Product Developer & Mfr
N.A.I.C.S.: 335910
Richard H. Bogan *(Chm & CEO)*

AXIOS SUSTAINABLE GROWTH ACQUISITION CORPORATION
1409 Hopewell Rd Hidden Pines Farm, Alpharetta, GA 30004
Tel.: (770) 813-6500   Ky
Year Founded: 2021
AXAC—(NYSE)
Investment Services
N.A.I.C.S.: 523999
Martin Richenhagen *(Chm)*
Benedikt Fortig *(CEO)*
Anthony V. Raftopol *(COO)*

AXIS TECHNOLOGIES GROUP, INC.
11777 San Vicente Blvd, Los Angeles, CA 90049
Tel.: (626) 429-2780   DE
AXTG—(OTCIQ)
Electronic Components Mfr
N.A.I.C.S.: 334419
Richard Casinelli *(CFO)*
Doreen Sim *(VP-Operations)*
Gerard McKeon *(VP-Media)*
William Tien *(Pres & CEO)*

AXOGEN, INC.
13631 Progress Blvd Ste 400, Alachua, FL 32615
Tel.: (386) 462-6880   MN
Web Site:
  https://www.axogeninc.com
Year Founded: 1977
AXGN—(NASDAQ)
Rev.: $138,584,000
Assets: $195,387,000
Liabilities: $94,388,000
Net Worth: $100,999,000
Earnings: ($28,948,000)
Emp.: 394
Fiscal Year-end: 12/31/22
Regenerative Medical Products Developer & Mfr
N.A.I.C.S.: 551112
Michael Dale *(Pres & CEO)*
Isabelle Billet *(Chief Strategy & Bus Dev Officer)*
Maria Martinez *(Chief HR Officer)*
Ivica Ducic *(Dir-Medical)*
Nir Naor *(CFO)*
Marc Began *(Gen Counsel)*
Jens Schroeder Kemp *(CMO)*
Doris Quackenbush *(VP)*
Harold D. Tamayo *(VP-Fin & IR)*

Subsidiaries:

AxoGen Corporation **(1)**
13631 Progress Blvd Ste 400, Alachua, FL 32615
Tel.: (386) 462-6800
Web Site: https://www.axogeninc.com
Sales Range: $1-9.9 Million
Emp.: 50
Research & Development in Biotechnology
N.A.I.C.S.: 541714
Karen Zaderej *(Chm)*
Marc Began *(Exec VP)*
Nir Naor *(CFO)*
Jens Schroeder Kemp *(CMO)*
Ivica Ducic *(Chief Medical Officer)*
Todd Puckett *(VP-Operations)*
Stacy Arnold *(VP-Product Development & Clinical Res)*
Al Jacks *(VP-Quality)*
Angela Nelson *(VP-Regulatory Affairs)*
Doris Quackenbush *(VP-Sales)*

AXON ENTERPRISE, INC.
17800 N 85th St, Scottsdale, AZ 85255
Tel.: (480) 444-4000   DE
Web Site: https://www.axon.com
Year Founded: 1993
AXON—(NASDAQ)
Rev.: $1,563,391,000
Assets: $3,436,845,000
Liabilities: $1,824,811,000
Net Worth: $1,612,034,000
Earnings: $174,227,000
Emp.: 3,330
Fiscal Year-end: 12/31/23
Electronic Control Devices Mfr
N.A.I.C.S.: 334519
Brittany Bagley *(CFO & COO)*
Joshua M. Isner *(Pres)*
Josh Goldman *(Sr VP-Ops)*
Jenner Holden *(Chief Information Security Officer)*
Richard Coleman II *(Pres)*
Pat Madden *(Sr VP)*

Axon Enterprise, Inc.—(Continued)

Jim Zito (Sr VP)
Arvind Bobra (Sr VP)
Matt Morstad (Sr VP)
Hans Moritz (VP)
Mike Wagers (Sr VP)
Patrick W. Smith (Co-Founder & CEO)

Subsidiaries:

Axon Public Safety UK Limited   (1)
2c Riley Close, Daventry, NN11 8QT, Northamptonshire, United Kingdom
Tel.: (44) 132 770 9666
Web Site: https://www.uk.axon.com
Personal Safety Device Distr
N.A.I.C.S.: 423620

Familiar, Inc.   (1)
117 E Louisa St Ste 504, Seattle, WA 98102
Tel.: (415) 484-6511
Mobile Application Development Services
N.A.I.C.S.: 541511

Misfit, Inc.   (1)
839 Mitten Rd Ste 100, Burlingame, CA 94010
Web Site: http://www.misfit.com
Wearable Technology & Connected Devices Developer, Mfr & Whslr
N.A.I.C.S.: 334519

VIEVU LLC   (1)
105 W John St, Seattle, WA 98119-4201
Web Site: https://www.vievu.com
Police & Security Body-worn Cameras & Related Equipment Mfr
N.A.I.C.S.: 334310

AXONICS, INC.

26 Technology Dr, Irvine, CA 92618
Tel.: (949) 396-6320   DE
Web Site: https://www.axonics.com
Year Founded: 2012
AXNX—(NASDAQ)
Rev.: $273,702,000
Assets: $659,353,000
Liabilities: $89,214,000
Net Worth: $570,139,000
Earnings: ($59,698,000)
Emp.: 610
Fiscal Year-end: 12/31/22
Surgical Appliance & Supplies Manufacturing
N.A.I.C.S.: 339113
Raymond W. Cohen (CEO)
Michael H. Carrel (Chm)
Prabodh Mathur (Chief Product Dev Officer)
Guangqiang Jiang (CTO)
Karen Noblett (Chief Medical Officer)
Al Ford (Chief Comml Officer)
Rinda Sama (COO)
Kari Keese (Pres & CFO)

AXONPRIME INFRASTRUCTURE ACQUISITION CORP.

126 E 56th St 30th Fl, New York, NY 10022
Tel.: (212) 479-2000   DE
Year Founded: 2021
APMI—(NASDAQ)
Rev.: $2,172,759
Assets: $152,502,182
Liabilities: $159,038,482
Net Worth: ($6,536,300)
Earnings: $5,934,049
Emp.: 1
Fiscal Year-end: 12/31/22
Investment Services
N.A.I.C.S.: 523999
Dinakar Singh (Co-Founder & CEO)
Dakin Sloss (Co-Founder)

AXOS FINANCIAL, INC.

9205 W Russell Rd Ste 400, Las Vegas, NV 89148
Tel.: (858) 649-2218   DE

Web Site:
https://www.axosfinancial.com
AX—(NYSE)
Rev.: $1,878,267,000
Assets: $22,855,334,000
Liabilities: $20,564,738,000
Net Worth: $2,290,596,000
Earnings: $450,008,000
Emp.: 1,781
Fiscal Year-end: 06/30/24
Bank Holding Company
N.A.I.C.S.: 551111
Andrew J. Micheletti (Exec VP-Fin)
Paul J. Grinberg (Chm)
Gregory Garrabrants (Pres & CEO)
Nicholas A. Mosich (Vice Chm)
Derrick K. Walsh (CFO, Chief Acctg Officer & Exec VP)
Johnny Lai (Sr VP-Corp Dev & IR)
Angela Lopez (Sec)

Subsidiaries:

Axos Bank   (1)
Tel.: (858) 350-6200
Web Site: https://www.axosbank.com
Sales Range: $150-199.9 Million
Emp.: 300
Federal Savings Bank
N.A.I.C.S.: 522180
Andrew J. Micheletti (Exec VP-Fin)
Paul J. Grinberg (Chm)
Gregory Garrabrants (Pres & CEO)
Nicholas A. Mosich (Vice Chm)
Derrick K. Walsh (CFO, Chief Acctg Officer & Exec VP)
Thomas Constantine (Chief Credit Officer & Exec VP)
Eshel Bar-Adon (Chief Legal Officer & Exec VP-Strategic Partnerships)
Brian Swanson (Exec VP & Head-Consumer Bank)
David Park (Exec VP-Comml Banking & Treasury Mgmt)
John Tolla (Chief Governance, Risk & Compliance Officer & Exec VP)
Mary Ellen Ciafardini (Exec VP-HR)
Raymond D. Matsumoto (COO & Exec VP)
Greg Frost (Sr VP-Comm)

Axos Clearing LLC   (1)
15950 W Dodge Rd Ste 300, Omaha, NE 68118
Tel.: (402) 384-6100
Web Site: https://www.axosclearing.com
Investment Advisory Services
N.A.I.C.S.: 331513
Gary Wiedman (Pres & Mng Principal)
Michael Scaplen (Sr VP-Sales)
Jeremy Franzluebbers (Chief Risk Officer)
David Vaughan (CFO)
Rick Hastings (COO & Sr VP)

Axos Digital Assets LLC   (1)
9205 W Russell Rd Ste 400, Las Vegas, NV 89148
Web Site:
https://www.axosdigitalassets.com
Crypto Asset Trading Services
N.A.I.C.S.: 518210

COR Clearing LLC   (1)
1299 Farnam St Ste 800, Omaha, NE 68102-1916
Tel.: (402) 384-6100
Web Site: http://www.corclearing.com
Securities Brokerage
N.A.I.C.S.: 523150

Zentith Information Systems, Inc.   (1)
18757 Burbank Blvd Ste 315, Tarzana, CA 91356
Tel.: (818) 206-8634
Web Site: https://www.zis.com
Financial Management Services
N.A.I.C.S.: 522320

AXSOME THERAPEUTICS, INC.

1 World Trade Ctr 22nd Fl, New York, NY 10007
Tel.: (212) 332-3241
Web Site: https://www.axsome.com
AXSM—(NASDAQ)
Rev.: $270,600,000

Assets: $588,236,000
Liabilities: $397,259,000
Net Worth: $190,977,000
Earnings: ($239,238,000)
Emp.: 545
Fiscal Year-end: 12/31/23
Pharmaceutical Preparation Mfr
N.A.I.C.S.: 325412
Herriot Tabuteau (Chm & CEO)
Mark L. Jacobson (COO)
Nick Pizzie (CFO)
Hunter Murdock (Gen Counsel)
Darren Opland (Dir-Corp Comm)
Cedric O'Gorman (Sr VP-Medical Affairs)

AXT, INC.

4281 Technology Dr, Fremont, CA 94538
Tel.: (510) 438-4700   DE
Web Site: https://www.axt.com
Year Founded: 1986
AXTI—(NASDAQ)
Rev.: $141,118,000
Assets: $370,072,000
Liabilities: $125,172,000
Net Worth: $244,900,000
Earnings: $15,811,000
Emp.: 1,076
Fiscal Year-end: 12/31/22
Semiconductor Substrates & Opto-Electronic Semiconductor Devices Mfr, Designer & Distr
N.A.I.C.S.: 334413
Morris S. Young (Co-Founder, Chm & CEO)
Gary L. Fischer (CFO, Sec & VP)

Subsidiaries:

Beijing BoYu Semiconductor Vessel Craftwork Technology Co., Ltd.   (1)
No 7 Yunshan Road, Tongzhou, Beijing, 101101, China
Tel.: (86) 1081595615
Web Site: http://www.bypbn.com
Semiconductor & Related Device Mfr
N.A.I.C.S.: 334413

Beijing Tongmei Xtal Technology Co, Ltd.   (1)
4 Eastern Second Street Industrial Development Zone, Zhangjiawan Ind Development Zone Tongzhou District, Beijing, 101113, China   (100%)
Tel.: (86) 1061562241
Semiconductor Mfr & Distr
N.A.I.C.S.: 334413

Nanjing Jin Mei Gallium Co., Ltd   (1)
718 General Avenue, Jiangning Development Zone, Nanjing, 211165, Jiangsu, China
Tel.: (86) 4214160666
Web Site: https://www.jm-gallium.com
Semiconductor Material Distr
N.A.I.C.S.: 423690

AYALA PHARMACEUTICALS, INC.

9 Deer Park Dr Ste K-1, Monmouth Junction, NJ 08852
Tel.: (609) 452-9813   DE
Web Site: http://www.advaxis.com
ADXS—(OTCQX)
Rev.: $250,000
Assets: $25,930,000
Liabilities: $2,303,000
Net Worth: $23,627,000
Earnings: ($14,359,000)
Emp.: 14
Fiscal Year-end: 10/31/22
Cancer & Infectious Diseases Immunotherapies Developer
N.A.I.C.S.: 325412
David Sidransky (Chm)
James P. Patton (Vice Chm)
Kenneth A. Berlin (Pres & CEO)
Andres A. Gutierrez (Chief Medical Officer & Exec VP)

Igor Gitelman (Interim CFO, Chief Acctg Officer & VP-Fin)

Subsidiaries:

Old Ayala, Inc.   (1)
Oppenheimer 4, Rehovot, 7670104, Israel
Tel.: (972) 83731541
Web Site: http://www.ayalapharma.com
Rev.: $692,000
Assets: $7,769,000
Liabilities: $8,868,000
Net Worth: ($1,099,000)
Earnings: ($38,013,000)
Emp.: 14
Fiscal Year-end: 12/31/2022
Biotechnology Research & Development Services
N.A.I.C.S.: 541714
David Sidransky (Chm)
Roni Mamluk (Founder & CEO)
Dana Gelbaum (Chief Bus Officer)
David Caron (VP-CMC)
Irit Klipper-Avni (VP-HR)
Carmit Nadri-Shay (VP-Regulatory Affairs)

AYRO, INC.

900 E Old Settlers Blvd Ste 100, Round Rock, TX 78664
Tel.: (512) 994-4917   DE
Web Site: https://www.ayro.com
AYRO—(NASDAQ)
Rev.: $2,990,497
Assets: $54,990,084
Liabilities: $2,931,695
Net Worth: $52,058,389
Earnings: ($22,935,353)
Emp.: 44
Fiscal Year-end: 12/31/22
Infrastructure Engineering Services for Wireless Communication, Specialty Construction & Electrical Power
N.A.I.C.S.: 541330
Joshua N. Silverman (Exec Chm, Principal Exec Officer, Interim Principal Fin Officer & Interim Principal Acctg Officer)
Joshua N. Silverman (Chm)
David E. Hollingsworth (Interim Pres-AYRO Operating Company)
Christian Okonsky (Founder)

Subsidiaries:

Max Engineering LLC   (1)
804 Lebanon Dr, Saint Louis, MO 63104-3505
Tel.: (614) 264-0021
Sales Range: $1-4.9 Billion
Turnkey Engineering & Installation of Wireless Communication Infrastructure
N.A.I.C.S.: 237990

WPCS Incorporated   (1)
1 E Uwchlan Ave, Uwchland, PA 19480
Tel.: (610) 903-0400
Wireless Communication Infrastructure Engineering Services
N.A.I.C.S.: 541330

AYTU BIOPHARMA, INC.

Tel.: (720) 437-6580   DE
Web Site: https://aytubio.com
Year Founded: 2002
AYTU—(NASDAQ)
Rev.: $81,002,000
Assets: $118,095,000
Liabilities: $90,379,000
Net Worth: $27,716,000
Earnings: ($15,844,000)
Emp.: 99
Fiscal Year-end: 06/30/24
Investment Services
N.A.I.C.S.: 523999
Joshua R. Disbrow (Founder, Chm & CEO)
Richard I. Eisenstadt (CFO, Principal Acctg Officer, Treas & Sec)
Jarrett T. Disbrow (Exec-VP-Corp Ops)

Greg Pyszczymuka (Exec VP-Comml Ops)
Russ McMahen (Sr VP-R&D)
Margaret Cabano (VP-Ops)
Suzane Kennedy (VP-Regulatory Affairs & Quality Assurance)
Ryan Selhorn (Exec VP-Finance & Bus Optimization)

Subsidiaries:

Innovus Pharmaceuticals, Inc.   (1)
8845 Rehco Rd, San Diego, CA 92121
Tel.: (858) 249-7870
Web Site: http://aytuhealth.com
Pharmaceuticals Mfr
N.A.I.C.S.: 325412

Subsidiary (Domestic):

Semprae Laboratories, Inc.   (2)
160 Pehle Ave Park 80 East Ste 301, Saddle Brook, NJ 07663
Tel.: (201) 518-8200
Web Site: http://www.zestra.com
Feminine Biopharmaceuticals Developer & Mfr
N.A.I.C.S.: 325414

Supplement Hunt, Inc.   (2)
8895 Towne Ctr Dr - Ste 105 282, San Diego, CA 92122
Web Site: https://www.supplementhunt.com
Healthcare Product Distr
N.A.I.C.S.: 424210

Neos Therapeutics, Inc.   (1)
2940 N Hwy 360, Grand Prairie, TX 75050
Tel.: (972) 408-1300
Web Site: http://www.neostx.com
Rev.: $64,649,000
Assets: $90,873,000
Liabilities: $97,003,000
Net Worth: ($6,130,000)
Earnings: ($16,902,000)
Emp.: 213
Fiscal Year-end: 12/31/2019
Pharmaceuticals Mfr
N.A.I.C.S.: 325412
Russ McMahen (Sr VP-R&D)
Margaret Cabano (VP-Ops)
Carolyn Sikes (VP-Clinical Affairs)
Asif Mughal (VP-Quality Assurance)
Greg Pyszczymuka (VP-Comml Strategy & Market Access)
Darren Heath (VP-Sls)
Sarah Foster (VP-HR)

AYUJOY HERBALS LTD.

8942 Quioccasin Rd Ste 109, Henrico, VA 23229   NJ
Web Site: http://www.ayujoy.com
AJOY—(OTCIQ)
Management Consulting Services
N.A.I.C.S.: 541618
Suyogi Bianka Maria Gessner (CEO)
Jeff Palumbo (Pres)
Ron Loudoun (Sec)
William Murray (Sr VP-Retail)

AZENTA, INC.

200 Summit Dr 6th Fl, Burlington, MA 01803
Tel.: (978) 262-2626   DE
Web Site: https://www.azenta.com
Year Founded: 1978
AZTA—(NASDAQ)
Rev.: $665,072,000
Assets: $2,885,720,000
Liabilities: $351,220,000
Net Worth: $2,534,500,000
Earnings: ($14,257,000)
Emp.: 3,500
Fiscal Year-end: 09/30/23
Semiconductor Automation & Cryogenic Solutions Provider
N.A.I.C.S.: 332410
Joseph R. Martin (Chm)
William T. Montone (Sr VP-HR)
David F. Pietrantoni (Principal Acctg Officer, VP-Fin & Controller)
Jason W. Joseph (Gen Counsel, Sec & Sr VP)

David E. Jarzynka (Pres-Semiconductor Solutions Grp)
John E. O'Brien (VP-Corp Dev)
David C. Gray (Chief Strategy & New Bus Officer & Sr VP)
Robin Vacha (Sr VP & Gen Mgr-Life Sciences Products)
Kimberly Crowley (Chief HR Officer & Sr VP)
Linda De Jesus (Chief Comml Officer-Brooks Life Sciences & Sr VP)
Sara Silverman (Dir-IR)
Herman Cueto (CFO & Exec VP)
John P. Marotta (Pres & CEO)

Subsidiaries:

4titude Ltd.   (1)
The North Barn Surrey Hills Business Park Damphurst Lane, Wotton, Westcott, RH5 6QT, Surrey, United Kingdom
Tel.: (44) 1306848885
Web Site: http://www.4ti.co.uk
Life Science Product Mfr
N.A.I.C.S.: 339113
Peter Collins (Founder)

Azenta (Guangzhou) Life Science Co., Ltd.
Room 212 Guangdong Huanan New Medicine Center Building F Venture, Headquarter Base 3 Lanyue Road Kexue City Luogang Residential District, Guangzhou, 510670, China
Tel.: (86) 2083908200
Biotechnology Research & Development Services
N.A.I.C.S.: 541714

Azenta (Tianjin) Biotechnology Co., Ltd.   (1)
Floor 4-5 B06 Building Venture Headquarter Base, Wuqing Development Area, Tianjin, 301700, China
Tel.: (86) 2259096300
Biomedical Laboratory Equipment Mfr
N.A.I.C.S.: 339112

Azenta Beijing Technologies Limited   (1)
Baishan Village East, Baishan Changping District, Beijing, 102211, China
Tel.: (86) 1080181587
Biotechnology Research & Development Services
N.A.I.C.S.: 541714

Azenta Germany GmbH   (1)
Im Leuschnerpark 1b, 64347, Griesheim, Germany
Tel.: (49) 61558981011
Biotechnology Research & Development Services
N.A.I.C.S.: 541714

Azenta Life Sciences Canada, Inc.   (1)
2307 rue Guenette, Saint-Laurent, Montreal, H4R 2E9, QC, Canada
Tel.: (514) 333-4450
Semiconductor Product Mfr
N.A.I.C.S.: 334413

Azenta Singapore Pte. Ltd.   (1)
2 International Business Park 02-36 The Strategy, Singapore, 609930, Singapore
Tel.: (65) 88669752
Biomedical Laboratory Equipment Mfr
N.A.I.C.S.: 339112

B Medical Systems India Private Limited   (1)
Ground Floor Premise No 2 Girikunj Building 71 NS Road Marine Drive, Mumbai, 400020, Maharashtra, India
Tel.: (91) 8928483465
Medical Refrigeration Device Mfr & Distr
N.A.I.C.S.: 339112

B Medical Systems North America LLC   (1)
14560 Bergen Blvd Ste 200, Noblesville, IN 46060
Tel.: (317) 900-7136
Medical Refrigeration Device Mfr & Distr
N.A.I.C.S.: 339112

B Medical Systems S.a.r.l.   (1)

17 op der Hei, L-9809, Hosingen, Luxembourg
Tel.: (352) 9207311
Web Site: https://www.bmedicalsystems.com
Medical Refrigeration Device Mfr & Distr
N.A.I.C.S.: 339112

Barkey Corporation   (1)
500 W Cummings Park Ste 1900, Woburn, MA 01801
Blood Cell Thawing Device Mfr & Distr
N.A.I.C.S.: 339112

Barkey GmbH & Co. KG   (1)
Gewerbestrasse 8, 33818, Leopoldshohe, Germany
Tel.: (49) 520298010
Web Site: https://en.barkey.de
Emp.: 100
Blood Cell Thawing Device Mfr & Distr
N.A.I.C.S.: 339112

BioStorage Technologies, Inc   (1)
2910 Fortune Cir W Ste E, Indianapolis, IN 46241
Tel.: (317) 268-5500
Web Site: http://www.biostorage.com
Sales Range: $25-49.9 Million
Emp.: 34
Research & Development in Biotechnology
N.A.I.C.S.: 541714

Biostorage Technologies Asia Pacific Pte. Ltd.   (1)
1 Kaki Bukit Avenue 07-04, Singapore, 417939, Singapore
Tel.: (65) 31576199
Medical Sample Storage Product Mfr
N.A.I.C.S.: 339113
Jason Huang (Mng Dir)

Biostorage Technologies GmbH   (1)
Im Leuschnerpark 1B, 64347, Griesheim, Germany
Tel.: (49) 61558981011
Medical Sample Storage Product Mfr
N.A.I.C.S.: 339113

Brooks Automation (Germany) GmbH   (1)
Im Wiesengrund 17, 78315, Radolfzell, Germany
Tel.: (49) 773294090
Web Site: http://www.brooks.com
Mfr, Developer, Retailer & Servicer Automation Products for the Semiconductor Market
N.A.I.C.S.: 238210

Branch (Domestic):

Brooks Automation (Germany) GmbH - Mistelgau   (2)
Gartenstrasse 19, 95490, Mistelgau, Germany
Tel.: (49) 9279991550
Web Site: http://www.brooks.com
Sales Range: $125-149.9 Million
Emp.: 17
Development & Implementation of Automation Solutions for Global Customers
N.A.I.C.S.: 334112

Brooks Automation (Singapore), Pte Ltd.   (1)
Blk 5008 Ang Mo Kio Avenue 5 05-08 Techplace II, Singapore, 569874, Singapore
Tel.: (65) 68363168
Web Site: http://www.brooks.com
Sales Range: $10-24.9 Million
Emp.: 18
Retailer & Servicer of Automation Products & Solutions for the Semiconductor Market
N.A.I.C.S.: 238210

Brooks Automation France SAS   (1)
Les Jardins de Maupertuis 7 Chemin de la Dhuy, Batiment Le Juparana, 38240, Meylan, France   (100%)
Tel.: (33) 476189200
Web Site: http://www.brooks.com
Sales Range: $10-24.9 Million
Emp.: 7
Development & Implementation of Automation Solutions for Global Customers
N.A.I.C.S.: 334118

Brooks Automation Israel, Ltd.   (1)
Mevo Yerach 5, Kiryat Gat, 82000, Israel   (100%)

Tel.: (972) 86722988
Web Site: http://www.brooks.com
Sales Range: $125-149.9 Million
Emp.: 10
Automation Solutions for Computer Systems
N.A.I.C.S.: 334112

Brooks Automation Korea, Ltd.   (1)
35 Giheungdanji-Ro 121Beon-Gil, Giheung-Gu, Yongin, 17086, Gyeonggi-Do, Korea (South)   (100%)
Tel.: (82) 312882500
Web Site: http://www.brooks.com
Sales Range: $100-124.9 Million
Emp.: 70
Automation Products & Solutions for the Semiconductor Markets
N.A.I.C.S.: 334413

Brooks Automation Luxembourg SARL   (1)
Ave de la Gare 41, 1611, Luxembourg, Luxembourg
Tel.: (352) 26270963
Semiconductors & Related Devices Mfr
N.A.I.C.S.: 334413

Brooks Automation Taiwan Company Ltd.   (1)
5F-5 No 32 Tai-Yuen Street, Chu-Pei City, Hsin-chu, 302, Taiwan   (100%)
Tel.: (886) 35525258
Web Site: http://www.brooks.com
Sales Range: $25-49.9 Million
Emp.: 100
Development & Implementation of Automation Solutions for Global Customers
N.A.I.C.S.: 334112

Brooks Automation, Inc.   (1)
46702 Bayside Pkwy, Fremont, CA 94538
Tel.: (510) 661-5000
Web Site: http://www.brooks.com
Sales Range: $50-74.9 Million
Mfr of Wafer Automation Equipment & Services
N.A.I.C.S.: 334413
Joseph R. Martin (Chm)

Brooks CCS GmbH   (1)
Im Wiesengrund 17, 78315, Radolfzell, Germany
Tel.: (49) 7732 9409 0
Web Site: http://www.brooks.com
Sales Range: $25-49.9 Million
Automated Cleaner & Stocker Products for Semiconductors
N.A.I.C.S.: 334413

Brooks CCS Japan KK   (1)
Nisso Bldg No 16 9F 3-8-8 ShinYokohama, Kohoku-ku, Yokohama, 222-0033, Kanagawa, Japan
Tel.: (81) 454775570
Automation Semiconductor Machinery Mfr
N.A.I.C.S.: 333242

Brooks CCS RS AG   (1)
Lohstampfestrasse 11, Tagerwilen, 8274, Kreuzlingen, Switzerland
Tel.: (41) 716667210
Semiconductor Equipment Mfr
N.A.I.C.S.: 333242

Brooks Japan K.K.   (1)
Nisso Bldg No 16 9F 3-8-8 ShinYokohama, Kohoku-ku, Yokohama, 222-0033, Kanagawa, Japan
Tel.: (81) 454775570
Web Site: http://www.brooks.com
Semiconductor Automation Products & Services
N.A.I.C.S.: 334413

Brooks Life Science Systems   (1)
Northbank Industrial Park, Irlam, Manchester, M44 5AY, United Kingdom
Tel.: (44) 1617772000
Web Site: https://www.azenta.com
Sales Range: $25-49.9 Million
Emp.: 70
Pharmaceutical & Biotechnology Automation Products Developer & Mfr
N.A.I.C.S.: 541330

Brooks Life Science Systems   (1)
14100 Danielson St Bldg 100, Poway, CA 92064-6898
Tel.: (858) 527-7000

Azenta, Inc.—(Continued)

Sales Range: $25-49.9 Million
Emp.: 30
Automated Sample Management System Mfr
N.A.I.C.S.: 334516
Andrew Brooks *(Chief Scientific Officer)*
Robin Grimwood *(VP-Automated Solutions Grp)*
Martin Long *(VP-Svcs & Informatics)*

Subsidiary (Non-US):

Brooks Automation AG **(2)**
Bernstrasse 134, CH-3613, Steffisburg, Switzerland
Tel.: (41) 31 770 70 70
Web Site: http://www.brooks.com
Automated Sample Processing & Storage Systems Mfr
N.A.I.C.S.: 333248

NEXUS Biosystems Nihon K.K. **(2)**
C-5 Building 9F-B 1-21-5 Kanda Suda-cho, Chiyoda-ku, Tokyo, 101-0041, Japan
Tel.: (81) 3 5207 3071
Automated Sample Management System Mfr
N.A.I.C.S.: 334516

Brooks Life Sciences **(1)**
22841 Lockness Ave, Torrance, CA 90501
Web Site:
http://www.brookslifesciences.com
Logistics, Transport & Storage Biological Collections Services
N.A.I.C.S.: 541714

Brooks Technology (Shanghai) Limited **(1)**
Room 202 Building D Lane 2889 Jinke Road, Pudong New Area, Shanghai, 201203, China
Tel.: (86) 2160911760
Web Site: http://www.brooks.com
Emp.: 28
Development & Implementation of Automation Solutions
N.A.I.C.S.: 333310

CCS Japan **(1)**
Sapia Tower 19F, 1-7-12 Marunouchi Chiyoda-ku, Tokyo, 100-0005, Japan
Tel.: (81) 362687610
Web Site: http://www.japanccs.com
Health Care Srvices
N.A.I.C.S.: 621610

Cedrex **(1)**
Notgangen 3, 2690, Karlslunde, Denmark
Tel.: (45) 32575181
Web Site: http://www.cedrex.dk
Furniture Store Operator
N.A.I.C.S.: 449110

FluidX Ltd **(1)**
Monks Heath Hall, Chelford Road, Alderley Edge, SK10 4SY, Cheshire, United Kingdom
Tel.: (44) 1625861614
Web Site: http://www.fluidx.eu
Drugs & Druggist Sundries Merchant Whslr
N.A.I.C.S.: 424210

GENEWIZ, Inc. **(1)**
115 Corporate Blvd, South Plainfield, NJ 07080
Tel.: (908) 222-0711
Web Site: http://www.genewiz.com
Gene Research
N.A.I.C.S.: 541715
Amy Guojian Liao *(Pres)*

Genewiz (Guangzhou), Ltd. **(1)**
Room 212 Guangdong Huanan New Medicine Center Building F Venture, Headquarter Base 3 Lanyue Road Kexue City Luogang Residential District, Guangzhou, 510670, China
Tel.: (86) 2083908200
Biotechnology Research Services
N.A.I.C.S.: 541714

Genewiz (Suzhou), Ltd. **(1)**
Building B1 and C3 218 Xinghu Road, Suzhou Industrial Park, Suzhou, 215123, China
Tel.: (86) 51268731001
Biotechnology Research Services
N.A.I.C.S.: 541714

Genewiz France, Ltd. **(1)**
4 rue de Marivaux, 75002, Paris, France
Tel.: (33) 1279873837
Biotechnology Research Services
N.A.I.C.S.: 541714

Genewiz GmbH **(1)**
Muhlbachstrasse 20, Bodman, 78351, Ludwigshafen, Germany
Tel.: (49) 3415201220
Biotechnology Research Services
N.A.I.C.S.: 541714

Genewiz Japan **(1)**
Room 508 Office Room 553 Lab 3-12-18 Kami-Aoki, Saitama Industrial Technology Center 5F, Kawaguchi, 333-0844, Saitama, Japan
Tel.: (81) 484834980
Biotechnology Research Services
N.A.I.C.S.: 541714

Genewiz Tianjin, Ltd. **(1)**
Floor 4-5 B06 Building Venture Headquarter Base, Wuqing Development Area, Tianjin, 301700, China
Tel.: (86) 2259096300
Biotechnology Research Services
N.A.I.C.S.: 541714

Ruro Incorporated **(1)**
321 Ballenger Center Dr Ste 102, Frederick, MD 21703
Tel.: (240) 422-0814
Web Site: http://www.ruro.com
Custom Computer Programming Services
N.A.I.C.S.: 541511
Kurt Harris *(VP-Sls)*
Stephen Ferrell *(Chief Compliance Officer)*

SMIF Equipment (Tianjin) Co., Ltd **(1)**
Unit A-F 25/F 58 Xiangcheng Road Pudong New Area, Shanghai, 200122, China
Tel.: (86) 2168406060
Web Site: http://www.asyst.com
Industrial Equipment Mfr
N.A.I.C.S.: 333310

Ulvac Cryogenics Korea Inc. **(1)**
107 Hyeongoksandan-ro Cheongbuk-eup, Pyeongtaek, Gyeonggi-do, Korea (South)
Tel.: (82) 316832926
Web Site: https://www.ulvac-cryo.co.kr
Vaccum Pump Mfr
N.A.I.C.S.: 333914

Ulvac Cryogenics Ningbo Inc. **(1)**
1-2 Floor Shuguang Building No 6 Jingyuan Road, Ningbo National Hi-Tech Zone, Ningbo, 315040, China
Tel.: (86) 57487903322
Vaccum Pump Mfr
N.A.I.C.S.: 333914

Yaskawa Brooks Automation, Inc. **(1)**
Shin-Yokohama 214 SF 2-14-2, Shin-Yokohama Kohoku-ku, Yokohama, 222 0033, Kanagawa, Japan **(50%)**
Tel.: (81) 454787370
Web Site: http://www.brooks.com
Sales Range: $125-149.9 Million
Development & Implementation of Automatic Solutions
N.A.I.C.S.: 334112

Ziath B.V. **(1)**
Prins Hendriklaan 376 Unit 14, 6443 AE, Brunssum, Netherlands
Tel.: (31) 643141195
Software Development Services
N.A.I.C.S.: 541512

Ziath Ltd. **(1)**
Unit 2A Solopark Trading Estate Pampisford, Cambridge, CB22 3HB, United Kingdom
Tel.: (44) 1223855021
Web Site: https://ziath.com
Software Development Services
N.A.I.C.S.: 541512

AZITRA INC.
21 Business Park Dr, Branford, CT 06405
Tel.: (203) 646-6446 **DE**
Web Site: https://www.azitrainc.com
Year Founded: 2014

AZTR—(NYSEAMEX)
Rev.: $284,000
Assets: $7,167,443
Liabilities: $43,427,753
Net Worth: ($36,260,310)
Earnings: ($10,680,366)
Emp.: 10
Fiscal Year-end: 12/31/22
Research & Development in Biotechnology (except Nanobiotechnology)
N.A.I.C.S.: 541714
Francisco D. Saiva *(Pres)*
Travis Whitfill *(Founder)*

AZZ, INC.
1 Museum Pl 3100 W 7th St Ste 500, Fort Worth, TX 76107
Tel.: (817) 810-0095 **TX**
Web Site: https://www.azz.com
Year Founded: 1957
AZZ—(NYSE)
Rev.: $1,323,649,000
Assets: $2,221,479,000
Liabilities: $1,368,019,000
Net Worth: $853,460,000
Earnings: ($52,974,000)
Emp.: 4,956
Fiscal Year-end: 02/28/23
Plain-End Tubing, Finished Oilfield Products, Galvanized Steel Products & Electrical Products
N.A.I.C.S.: 335999
Daniel R. Feehan *(Chm)*
Bryan L. Stovall *(COO-Metal Coatings)*
Thomas E. Ferguson *(CEO)*
Matthew Varley Emery *(CIO & Chief HR Officer)*
Chris Bacius *(VP-Corp Dev)*
David Nark *(VP-Mktg, Comm, and IR)*
Kurt Russell *(Pres & COO)*
David Nark *(Sr VP-Comm, IR, and Mktg & VP-Mktg, Comm, and IR)*

Subsidiaries:

AAA Galvanizing - Chelsea, Inc. **(1)**
6022 S Industrial Rd, Chelsea, OK 74016
Tel.: (918) 789-9333
Metal Galvanizing Services
N.A.I.C.S.: 331110

AAA Galvanizing - Dixon, Inc. **(1)**
310 E Progress Dr, Dixon, IL 61021
Tel.: (815) 284-5001
Web Site: http://www.azzgalv.com
Metal Galvanizing Cervices
N.A.I.C.S.: 331110

AAA Galvanizing - Hamilton, Inc. **(1)**
7825 S Homestead Dr, Hamilton, IN 46742
Tel.: (260) 488-4477
Emp.: 100
Metal Galvanizing Services
N.A.I.C.S.: 331110
Hollie Jackson *(Office Mgr)*

AAA Galvanizing - Joliet, Inc. **(1)**
625 Mills Rd, Joliet, IL 60433
Tel.: (815) 723-5000
Metal Galvanizing Services
N.A.I.C.S.: 331110

AAA Galvanizing - Peoria, Inc. **(1)**
6718 W Plank Rd, Peoria, IL 61604
Tel.: (309) 697-4100
Metal Galvanizing Services
N.A.I.C.S.: 331110
Ryan Hix *(Sls Mgr)*

AAA Galvanizing - Winsted, Inc. **(1)**
800 6th St S, Winsted, MN 55395
Tel.: (320) 485-5001
Web Site: http://www.azzgalv.com
Emp.: 100
Metal Galvanizing Services
N.A.I.C.S.: 331110

AZZ Canada Limited **(1)**
49 Commerce Crescent, Acton, L7J 2X2, ON, Canada
Tel.: (519) 853-3540
Galvanizing Services
N.A.I.C.S.: 238160

AZZ Electrical/Industrial Products **(1)**
1 Museum Pl 3100 W 7th St Ste 500, Fort Worth, TX 76107
Tel.: (817) 810-0095
Web Site: http://www.azz.com
Sales Range: $10-24.9 Million
Emp.: 55
Electrical Product Engineering & Mfr
N.A.I.C.S.: 335132

Subsidiary (Domestic):

AZZ CGIT **(2)**
51 Alder St, Medway, MA 02053 **(100%)**
Tel.: (774) 854-0700
Web Site: http://www.cgit-westboro.com
Electrical Transmission
N.A.I.C.S.: 335313

AZZ Calvert **(2)**
120 Aztec Dr, Richland, MS 39218-9796
Tel.: (601) 939-9191
Web Site: http://www.calvertbus.com
Mfr of Plain End Tubing Finished Oilfield Products Galvanized Steel Products & Electrical Products
N.A.I.C.S.: 335313

AZZ Central Electric **(2)**
7900 US Hwy 54, Fulton, MO 65251
Tel.: (573) 642-6811
Web Site: http://www.poweraisle.com
Switchgear & Switchboard Apparatus
N.A.I.C.S.: 335313

AZZ Enclosure Systems LLC **(2)**
1801 E 27th St Ter, Pittsburg, KS 66762
Tel.: (620) 231-6900
Web Site: http://www.azz.com
Emp.: 150
Electrical Enclosure Systems Mfr
N.A.I.C.S.: 335313

AZZ R-A-L **(2)**
8500 Hansen Rd, Houston, TX, 77075-1006 **(100%)**
Tel.: (713) 943-0340
Web Site: http://www.rigalite.com
Illumination Components
N.A.I.C.S.: 335132

Aztec Tubular Products **(2)**
400 N Tarrant, Crowley, TX 76036-2527 **(100%)**
Tel.: (817) 297-0110
Web Site: http://www.aztectubing.com
Emp.: 37
Tubular Products & Services for Petrochemical & Industrial Markets
N.A.I.C.S.: 331210

AZZ Enclosure Systems - Chattanooga LLC **(1)**
1919 Polymer Dr, Chattanooga, TN 37421
Tel.: (423) 894-9268
Electrical Engineering Services
N.A.I.C.S.: 541330

AZZ Galvanizing - Big Spring, LLC **(1)**
4701 N US Hwy 87, Big Spring, TX 79720
Tel.: (432) 714-4491
Emp.: 5
Bus-Metal Galvanizing Services
N.A.I.C.S.: 332812

AZZ Galvanizing - Bristol LLC **(1)**
14781 Industrial Park Rd, Bristol, VA 24202
Tel.: (276) 466-5558
Electrical Engineering Services
N.A.I.C.S.: 541330

AZZ Galvanizing - Chattanooga LLC **(1)**
1535 Industrial Blvd, Jasper, TN 37347
Metal Plating Services
N.A.I.C.S.: 332812
Dennis Rains *(Plant Mgr)*

AZZ Galvanizing - Kennedale, LLC **(1)**
1530 Gilman Rd, Kennedale, TX 76060
Tel.: (817) 572-2280
Emp.: 7
Bus-Metal Galvanizing Services
N.A.I.C.S.: 332812

AZZ Galvanizing - Kosciusko, LLC **(1)**

2235 Attala Rd Ste 2202, Kosciusko, MS 39090
Tel.: (662) 290-1500
Bus-Metal Galvanizing Services
N.A.I.C.S.: 332812

AZZ Galvanizing - Morgan City, LLC **(1)**
1618 Hwy 182 E, Morgan City, LA 73080
Tel.: (985) 395-6188
Emp.: 8
Bus-Metal Galvanizing Services
N.A.I.C.S.: 332812

AZZ Galvanizing - Nashville **(1)**
3201 Elkins Ave, Nashville, TN 37209
Tel.: (615) 297-9581
Metal Plating Services
N.A.I.C.S.: 332812
Jessica Hayes (Plant Mgr)

AZZ Galvanizing - Nebraska, LLC **(1)**
87561 477th Ave, Atkinson, NE 68713
Tel.: (402) 925-5576
Bus-Metal Galvanizing Services
N.A.I.C.S.: 332812

AZZ Galvanizing - San Antonio, LLC **(1)**
5731 FM 1346, San Antonio, TX 78220
Tel.: (210) 661-8574
Bus-Metal Galvanizing Services
N.A.I.C.S.: 332812

AZZ Galvanizing - Virginia LLC **(1)**
14781 Industrial Park Rd, Bristol, VA 24202-3771
Tel.: (276) 466-5558
Industrial Equipment Repair Services
N.A.I.C.S.: 811310

AZZ Galvanizing Services **(1)**
3100, Fort Worth, TX 76107
Tel.: (817) 810-0095
Web Site: http://www.aztecgalvanizing.com
Sales Range: $25-49.9 Million
Emp.: 50
Hot Dip Galvanizing Services
N.A.I.C.S.: 332812
Bryan L. Stovall (Pres)

Subsidiary (Domestic):

Arizona Galvanizing Inc. **(2)**
15775 Elwood St, Goodyear, AZ 85338 **(100%)**
Tel.: (623) 925-1000
Web Site: http://www.aztecgalvanizing.com
Sales Range: $50-74.9 Million
Emp.: 70
Hot Dip Galvanizing
N.A.I.C.S.: 332812

Arkansas Galvanizing Inc. **(2)**
998 Escue Dr, Prairie Grove, AR 72753 **(100%)**
Tel.: (479) 846-4500
Web Site: http://www.aztecgalvanizing.com
Hot Dip Galvanizing
N.A.I.C.S.: 332812

Aztec Crowley **(2)**
200 N Beverly, Crowley, TX 76036-2527 **(100%)**
Tel.: (817) 297-4361
Web Site: http://www.azz.com
Sales Range: $50-74.9 Million
Hot Dip Galvanizing
N.A.I.C.S.: 332812

Gulf Coast Galvanizing Inc. **(2)**
17640 Industrial Park Dr E, Citronelle, AL 36522 **(100%)**
Tel.: (251) 866-2873
Web Site: https://www.azz.com
Sales Range: $25-49.9 Million
Emp.: 30
Hot Dip Galvanizing
N.A.I.C.S.: 332812

Hobson Galvanizing, Inc. **(2)**
2402 Engineers Rd, Belle Chasse, LA 70037 **(100%)**
Tel.: (504) 394-5700
Web Site: http://www.azz.com
Sales Range: $50-74.9 Million
Emp.: 49
Galvanizing
N.A.I.C.S.: 332812

International Galvanizers LP **(2)**
5898 Industrial Rd, Beaumont, TX 77705 **(100%)**
Tel.: (409) 842-0216
Web Site: http://www.azz.com
Sales Range: $25-49.9 Million
Emp.: 35
Galvanizing
N.A.I.C.S.: 332812

North American Galvanizing & Coatings, Inc. **(2)**
3100 W 7th St Ste 500, Fort Worth, TX 76107
Tel.: (817) 810-0095
Web Site: http://www.nagalv.com
Sales Range: $75-99.9 Million
Galvanizing & Coatings Mfr
N.A.I.C.S.: 332812

Westside Galvanizing Services, Inc. **(2)**
3520 S Riverview, Port Allen, LA 70767 **(100%)**
Tel.: (225) 344-2775
Web Site: https://www.azz.com
Sales Range: $50-74.9 Million
Emp.: 40
Galvanizing
N.A.I.C.S.: 332812

AZZ Galvanizing – Chattanooga LLC **(1)**
1535 Industrial Blvd, Jasper, TN 37347
Tel.: (423) 942-1020
Web Site: https://www.azz.com
Rev.: $8,865,000
Emp.: 45
Metal Coating, Engraving & Allied Galvanizing Services
N.A.I.C.S.: 332812
David Ware (Pres)

AZZ Holdings, Inc. **(1)**
3100 W 7th St Ste 500, Fort Worth, TX 76101-8701
Tel.: (817) 297-0110
Asset Management Services
N.A.I.C.S.: 531390

AZZ Surface Technologies - Gainesville LLC **(1)**
3333 N I-35 Frontage Rd, Gainesville, TX 76240
Tel.: (940) 665-2030
Metal Plating Services
N.A.I.C.S.: 332812

AZZ Surface Technologies - Garland South LLC **(1)**
2406 Executive Dr, Garland, TX 75041
Tel.: (972) 840-0943
Metal Plating Services
N.A.I.C.S.: 332812

AZZ Surface Technologies - Tampa LLC **(1)**
4901 Distribution Dr, Tampa, FL 33605
Tel.: (813) 390-2802
Metal Plating Services
N.A.I.C.S.: 332812

AZZ Surface Technologies - Terrell LLC **(1)**
100 FM 148, Terrell, TX 75160
Tel.: (972) 563-0883
Metal Plating Services
N.A.I.C.S.: 212290

AZZ Surface Technologies – Rowlett LLC **(1)**
3300 Enterprise Dr, Rowlett, TX 75088
Tel.: (972) 475-7077
Sales Range: $1-9.9 Million
Industrial Wet Paint Services
N.A.I.C.S.: 332812

AZZ Texas Welded Wire, LLC **(1)**
637 W Hurst Blvd, Hurst, TX 76053
Tel.: (817) 268-2414
Engineering Related Services
N.A.I.C.S.: 541330

AZZ Trading (Shanghai) Co., Ltd **(1)**
1701 W Beijing Rd Fortune Gate Building Room 2305-2306, Jingan District, Shanghai, 20040, China
Tel.: (86) 2162889116
Web Site: http://www.azz.com
Emp.: 35

Electrical Equipment & Component Mfr
N.A.I.C.S.: 335999

AZZ WSI B.V. **(1)**
Marconiweg 16, 3225 LV, Hellevoetsluis, Netherlands
Tel.: (31) 882784539
Web Site: http://www.azz.com
Emp.: 25
Industrial Machinery Maintenance Services
N.A.I.C.S.: 811310

AZZ WSI Canada, ULC **(1)**
7502 36th Street, Leduc, T9E 0Z5, AB, Canada
Tel.: (780) 440-2427
Web Site: http://www.azz.com
Industrial Machinery Maintenance Services
N.A.I.C.S.: 811310

AZZ WSI Holding B.V. **(1)**
Marconiweg 16, 3225 LV, Hellevoetsluis, Netherlands
Tel.: (31) 882784539
Holding Company
N.A.I.C.S.: 551112

AZZ WSI do Brasil Ltda. **(1)**
Alameda Caiapos 644, Barueri, 06460-110, Sao Paulo, Brazil
Tel.: (55) 1131737383
Web Site: http://www.azz.com
Emp.: 20
Industrial Machinery Maintenance Services
N.A.I.C.S.: 811310

Acme Galvanizing, Inc. **(1)**
2730 S 19th St, Milwaukee, WI 53215
Tel.: (414) 645-3250
Web Site: http://www.acmegalv.com
Sales Range: $1-9.9 Million
Emp.: 110
Plating/Polishing Service Coating/Engraving Service
N.A.I.C.S.: 332813
Edward J. Weiss (Pres)
Jim Weiss (VP)

Aquilex Specialty Repair & Overhaul Inc. **(1)**
3344 Peachtree Rd NE Ste 2100, Atlanta, GA 30326
Tel.: (404) 869-6677
Industrial Equipment Maintenance, Repair & Overhaul Services
N.A.I.C.S.: 811310

Subsidiary (Domestic):

AZZ WSI, Inc. **(2)**
560 Horizon Point Ste 100, Suwanee, GA 30024
Tel.: (678) 728-9100
Web Site: http://www.azz.com
Equipment Maintenance, Repair & Overhaul Services
N.A.I.C.S.: 811310

Division (Domestic):

Aquilex WSI Nuclear Services **(3)**
2225 Skyland Ct, Norcross, GA 30071
Tel.: (800) 868-9353
Nuclear Power Equipment Maintenance, Repair & Overhaul Services
N.A.I.C.S.: 811310
Tony Papso (Dir-Bus Dev)
Douglas JAcobs (Sr VP & Gen Mgr)

Subsidiary (Non-US):

Aquilex Welding Services Poland Sp. z o.o. **(2)**
Ul Kozienicka 97, 26-600, Radom, Poland
Tel.: (48) 483855056
Industrial Equipment Maintenance, Repair & Overhaul Services
N.A.I.C.S.: 811310

Aquilex Welding Services, B.V. **(2)**
Marconiweg 1, 3225 LV, Hellevoetsluis, Netherlands
Tel.: (31) 882 784 539
Web Site: http://www.azz.com
Emp.: 25
Industrial Equipment Maintenance, Repair & Overhaul Services
N.A.I.C.S.: 811310

Arbor-Crowley, LLC **(1)**

3100 W 7th St 1 Museum Pl Ste 500, Fort Worth, TX 76107
Tel.: (817) 810-0095
Web Site: http://www.azz.com
Electrical Equipment & Component Mfr
N.A.I.C.S.: 335999

Automatic Processing Incorporated **(1)**
PO Box 8580, Moss Point, MS 39562
Tel.: (228) 475-0342
Silverware & Holloware Mfr
N.A.I.C.S.: 332999

Aztec Industries, Inc. **(1)**
125 Aztec Dr, Richland, MS 39218 **(100%)**
Tel.: (601) 939-8522
Web Site: http://www.azz.com
Hot Dip Galvanizing
N.A.I.C.S.: 332812
Millie Skelton (Project Mgr)

Aztec Manufacturing - Waskom Partnership, Ltd. **(1)**
990 E Texas Ave Harrison, Waskom, TX 75692
Tel.: (903) 687-3920
Web Site: http://www.azzgalv.com
Emp.: 35
Metal Coating & Engraving Mfr
N.A.I.C.S.: 332812

Aztec Manufacturing Partnership, Ltd. **(1)**
1300 S University Dr Ste 200, Fort Worth, TX 76107
Tel.: (817) 297-4361
Metal Galvanizing Services
N.A.I.C.S.: 331110

CGIT Systems, Inc. **(1)**
51 Alder St, Medway, MA 02053
Tel.: (774) 854-0700
Web Site: http://www.azz.com
Transmission Bus System Mfr
N.A.I.C.S.: 333613

Central Electric Company **(1)**
430 Walker St, Watsonville, CA 95076
Tel.: (831) 724-6321
Web Site:
  https://www.centralelectriccompany.com
Electrical & Control Equipment Mfr
N.A.I.C.S.: 335313
Tony Kulich (Co-Owner, Pres & CEO)
Patty Kulich (Co-Owner & COO-Payroll Mgmt)

Central Electric Manufacturing Company **(1)**
7911 Old US Hwy 54, Fulton, MO 65251
Tel.: (573) 642-6811
Electrical & Control Equipment Mfr
N.A.I.C.S.: 335313

Enhanced Powder Coating Ltd. **(1)**
3333 N I-35 Bldg A B, Gainesville, TX 76240
Tel.: (940) 665-2035
Web Site: http://www.epcoatings.com
Powder Coating, Plating & Anodizing Services
N.A.I.C.S.: 332811
Dean Spence (Founder & Pres)

Nuzinc Enterprises, LLC **(1)**
3727 Marquis Dr Ste 139, Garland, TX 75042
Tel.: (972) 494-1376
Web Site: http://www.nuzinc.com
Sales Range: $1-9.9 Million
Emp.: 40
Plate Work Mfr
N.A.I.C.S.: 332313
Jo Ann Brumitt (CEO)

Power Electronics, Inc. **(1)**
3011 Millington Rd, Millington, MD 21651
Tel.: (410) 928-7700
Web Site: http://www.azz.com
Rev.: $2,700,000
Emp.: 35
Switchgear & Switchboard Apparatus Mfr
N.A.I.C.S.: 335313

Powergrid Solutions LLC **(1)**
3110 Progress Dr, Oshkosh, WI 54901
Tel.: (920) 232-8888
Electric Equipment Mfr
N.A.I.C.S.: 335311

AZZ, Inc.—(Continued)

Reinforcing Services, Inc. (1)
5101 Bird Creek Ave, Catoosa, OK 74015
Tel.: (918) 379-0090
Web Site: http://www.azz.com
Jewelry & Silverware Mfr
N.A.I.C.S.: 339910

Rig-A-Lite Partnership, Ltd. (1)
8500 Hansen Rd, Houston, TX 77075
Tel.: (713) 943-0340
Web Site: http://www.azz.com
Emp.: 55
Lighting Equipment Mfr
N.A.I.C.S.: 335139

Sequa Corp. - Precoat Metals Division (1)
1310 Papin St, Saint Louis, MO 63103
Tel.: (314) 436-7010
Web Site: http://www.precoat.com
Sales Range: $250-299.9 Million
Emp.: 730
Coats Aluminum & Steel Coil for Building Products, Containers & Appliances
N.A.I.C.S.: 336412

The Calvert Company (1)
120 Aztec Dr, Richland, MS 39218
Tel.: (601) 939-9191
Web Site: http://www.azz.com
Emp.: 111
Electrical Bus Duct Component Mfr
N.A.I.C.S.: 335999

Witt Galvanizing - Cincinnati, LLC (1)
4454 Steel Pl, Cincinnati, OH 45209
Tel.: (513) 871-5700
Emp.: 45
Industrial Equipment Repair Services
N.A.I.C.S.: 811310

Witt Galvanizing - Muncie, LLC (1)
2415 S Walnut St, Muncie, IN 47302-4143
Tel.: (765) 289-3427
Web Site: http://www.wittgalvanizing.com
Sales Range: $10-24.9 Million
Emp.: 55
Fabricated Metal Product & Galvanizing Mfr
N.A.I.C.S.: 331110

Witt Galvanizing - Plymouth, LLC (1)
2631 Jim Neu Dr, Plymouth, IN 46563
Tel.: (574) 935-4500
Emp.: 7
Industrial Equipment Repair Services
N.A.I.C.S.: 811310

Zalk Steel & Supply Co. (1)
446 Saint Anthony Pkwy, Minneapolis, MN 55418
Tel.: (612) 781-6801
Web Site: http://www.azzgalv.com
Metal Galvanizing Services
N.A.I.C.S.: 331110

B&G FOODS, INC.

4 Gatehall Dr, Parsippany, NJ 07054
Tel.: (973) 401-6500   DE
Web Site: https://www.bgfoods.com
Year Founded: 1996
BGS—(NYSE)
Rev.: $2,062,313,000
Assets: $3,463,290,000
Liabilities: $2,627,827,000
Net Worth: $835,463,000
Earnings: ($66,198,000)
Emp.: 2,912
Fiscal Year-end: 12/30/23
Holding Company; Branded Food & Household Products Mfr & Distr
N.A.I.C.S.: 551112
Scott E. Lerner (Chief Compliance Officer, Gen Counsel, Sec & Exec VP)
Bruce C. Wacha (CFO & Exec VP-Fin)
Eric H. Hart (Chief HR Officer & Exec VP-HR)
Kenneth Casey Keller (Pres & CEO)
Andrew D. Vogel (Pres)
Kristen Thompson (Pres)

Subsidiaries:

B&G Foods North America, Inc. (1)

4 Gatehall Dr, Parsippany, NJ 07054
Tel.: (973) 401-6500
Web Site: http://www.bgfoods.com
Branded Food & Household Products Mfr & Distr
N.A.I.C.S.: 311999

Subsidiary (Domestic):

Back to Nature Foods Company, LLC (2)
10641 Airport Pulling Rd Ste 26, Naples, FL 34109
Tel.: (239) 260-3200
Web Site: http://www.backtonaturefoods.com
Reduced-fat & Fat-free Cookies & Crackers Brand Products
N.A.I.C.S.: 311919

Clabber Girl Corporation (2)
900 Wabash Ave, Terre Haute, IN 47807-3208
Tel.: (812) 232-9446
Web Site: https://www.clabbergirl.com
Emp.: 200
Baking Soda, Corn Starch & Other Foodstuffs Mfr & Distr
N.A.I.C.S.: 311999

B&G Foods Snacks, Inc. (1)
4 Gatehall Dr Ste 110, Parsippany, NJ 07054
Tel.: (973) 401-6500
Web Site: http://www.bgfoods.com
Food Store Operator
N.A.I.C.S.: 445298

Spartan Foods of America Inc (1)
4250 Orchard Park Blvd, Spartanburg, SC 29303
Tel.: (864) 595-6262
Web Site: http://www.mamamarys.com
Specialty Food Restaurant Operator
N.A.I.C.S.: 722515

B. RILEY FINANCIAL, INC.

11100 Santa Monica Blvd Ste 800, Los Angeles, CA 90025
Tel.: (310) 966-1444   DE
Web Site: https://www.brileyfin.com
Year Founded: 2009
RILY—(NASDAQ)
Rev.: $1,080,670,000
Assets: $6,111,202,000
Liabilities: $5,605,309,000
Net Worth: $505,893,000
Earnings: ($159,829,000)
Emp.: 2,210
Fiscal Year-end: 12/31/22
Holding Company; Corporate Liquidation, Asset Disposition, Auction & Appraisal Services
N.A.I.C.S.: 551112
Bryant Richard Riley (Chm & Co-CEO)
Daniel Shribman (Pres, CFO & Chief Investment Officer)
Thomas John Kelleher (Co-CEO)
Kenneth M. Young (Pres & CEO-Principal Investments)
Phillip J. Ahn (CFO & COO)
Howard E. Weitzman (Chief Acctg Officer)
Jon Merriman (Chief Bus Officer)
Alan N. Forman (Gen Counsel & Sec)
Timothy J. Shilling (Exec VP-Retail Solutions)
Scott Carpenter (CEO-Retail Solutions)
Michael Marchlik (Co-CEO)
Ian Ratner (Co-CEO)
Jimmy Baker (Pres)
Ananth Veluppillai (COO)
Michael Jerbich (Pres)
Chuck Hastings (Co-CEO)
Michael Mullen (Co-CEO)
Nancy Feeney (Chief HR Officer)
Aaron Goodwin (Chief Information Security Officer)
Tim Wood (CIO)

Jen Arnett (CMO)
Gary Chase (Co-COO)
John DeSena (Co-COO)
Adam Cohen (VP)
Adam Fitzmaurice (VP)
Andrew Hewlett (Mng Dir)
Becky Yang O'Malley (Mng Dir)
Caroline Rowse (Officer)
Becky Popoff (Dir)
Benjamin Matz (Mng Dir)
Garret Orbach (VP)
Martin F. Bernstein (Head-Private Investments)
D. Jonathan Merriman (Chief Bus Officer)
D. Jonathan Merriman (Chief Bus Officer)

Subsidiaries:

Anderson Bauman Tourtellot Vos & Co. (1)
Parkview Building 5821 Fairview Rd Ste 110, Charlotte, NC 28209
Tel.: (336) 275-9110
Web Site: http://www.abtv.com
Rev.: $1,000,000
Emp.: 14
Industrial Building Construction
N.A.I.C.S.: 236210
Neal A. Anderson (Founder)
Linda Hayes (Office Mgr)
Edward Bauman (Founder)
Peter L. Tourtellot (Founder)
Gerardus Vos (Founder)

B. Riley & Co., LLC (1)
11100 Santa Monica Blvd Ste 800, Los Angeles, CA 90025
Tel.: (310) 966-1444
Web Site: http://www.brileyco.com
Investment Banking Services
N.A.I.C.S.: 523150
Michael Markunas (Chief Compliance Officer & Deputy Gen Counsel)
Ryan Bernath (Sr Mng Dir & Head-Investment Banking)
Salomon Kamalodine (Mng Dir)
Alan Forman (Gen Counsel, Sec & Exec VP)

B. Riley Alternatives GP, LLC (1)
119 Rowayton Ave 2nd Fl, Norwalk, CT 06853
Tel.: (212) 230-3220
Investment Management Service
N.A.I.C.S.: 523940

B. Riley Capital Management, LLC (1)
590 Madison Ave 29th Fl, New York, NY 10022
Tel.: (212) 409-2400
Investment Advisory Services
N.A.I.C.S.: 522320
John A. Fichthorn (Head-Alternative Investments)
Jonathan Mitchell (Mng Dir)

B. Riley FBR, Inc. (1)
11100 Santa Monica Blvd Ste 800, Los Angeles, CA 90025
Tel.: (310) 966-1444
Web Site: http://www.brileyfbr.com
Investment Banking & Asset Management Services
N.A.I.C.S.: 523150
Andy Moore (CEO)
Alan Forman (Gen Counsel & Exec VP)
Mike McCoy (CFO)
Jimmy Baker (Exec VP & Head-Capital Markets)
Michael Markunas (Chief Compliance Officer)
Craig A. Ellis (Dir-Res)
Mike Crawford (Head-Discovery Grp)
Perry Mandarino (Sr Mng Dir & Co-Head-Investment Banking)
Jon Merriman (Sr Mng Dir & Chief Bus Officer)
Patrice McNicoll (Sr Mng Dir & Co-Head-Investment Banking)
Eric Rajewski (Head-Institutional Sls)
Dan Ondeck (Head-East Coast Sls)
Knut Grevle (Head-Trading)

Subsidiary (Domestic):

FBR Fund Advisers, LLC (2)

1300 N 17th St Ste 1300, Arlington, VA 22209
Tel.: (703) 312-9500
Web Site: http://www.brileyfbr.com
Investment Management Service
N.A.I.C.S.: 523940

B. Riley FBR, Inc. (1)
11100 Santa Monica Blvd Ste 800, Los Angeles, CA 90025
Tel.: (310) 966-1444
Web Site: http://www.brileyfbr.com
Commercial Banking Services
N.A.I.C.S.: 522110
Alan Forman (Gen Counsel & Exec VP)
Andy Moore (Co-CEO)

B. Riley Wealth Management, Inc. (1)
40 Main St Ste 1800, Memphis, TN 38103
Tel.: (901) 251-1330
Web Site: http://www.brileywealth.com
Financial Advisory & Investment Banking Services
N.A.I.C.S.: 523940
Chuck Hastings (CEO)

Division (Domestic):

Dominick & Dominick (2)
150 E 52nd St 3rd Fl, New York, NY 10022
Tel.: (800) 221-2869
Web Site: http://www.dominickanddominick.com
Security & Commodity Services
N.A.I.C.S.: 523150

B. Riley Wealth Management, Inc. (1)
40 S Main Ste 1800, Memphis, TN 38119-3971
Tel.: (901) 251-1330
Web Site: http://www.brileywealth.com
Holding Company; Wealth Management & Investment Banking Services
N.A.I.C.S.: 551112
Philip Zanone (CEO)
Steve Bonnema (Chief Administrative Officer)
Chuck Hasting (Dir-Strategic Initiatives)
Craig Pirtle (Mng Dir-Wealth Mgmt)

Subsidiary (Domestic):

Fiduciary Financial Services Wealth Management (2)
13155 Noel Rd Ste 750, Dallas, TX 75240
Tel.: (972) 934-9070
Web Site: https://www.ffss.net
Investment Advisory & Wealth Management Services
N.A.I.C.S.: 523940
Richard A. Wright (VP & Portfolio Mgr)
Regina K. Kolkhorst (Dir-II)

Crawford Financial Consulting, LLC (1)
535 Griswold St Ste 1500, Detroit, MI 48226
Tel.: (313) 965-9700
Web Site: http://www.candwfinancial.com
Other Accounting Services
N.A.I.C.S.: 541219
Robert J. Winiarski (Mgr)

Eos Energy Enterprises, Inc. (1)
3920 Park Ave, Edison, NJ 08820
Tel.: (732) 225-8400
Web Site: https://investors.eose.com
Rev.: $17,924,000
Assets: $106,788,000
Liabilities: $239,499,000
Net Worth: ($132,711,000)
Earnings: ($229,813,000)
Emp.: 333
Fiscal Year-end: 12/31/2022
Investment Services
N.A.I.C.S.: 523999
Russell M. Stidolph (Chm)
Joe Mastrangelo (CEO)
Nathan G. Kroeker (CFO)
Jesper Helt (Chief People Officer)
Balakrishnan G. Iyer (Chief Comml Officer)
Mack Treece (Chief Strategic Alliances Officer)
Daniel Friberg (Sr VP-Engrg)
Michael W. Silberman (Chief Compliance Officer, Gen Counsel & Sec)
Sumeet Puri (Chief Acctg Officer)
Francis Richey (Dir-R&D)

Subsidiary (Domestic):

Eos Energy Storage LLC (2)
3920 Park Ave, Edison, NJ 08820
Tel.: (212) 628-7191
Web Site: http://www.eosenergystorage.com
Electric Energy Storage Solutions Services
N.A.I.C.S.: 221121
Russell M. Stidolph (Chm)
Russell Stidolph (Chm)
David A. Henry (CFO)
David A. Henry (CFO)
George Adamson (VP-R&D)
Jim Hughes (Chm)
Jeff Wiener (Sr VP-Global Sls)
Richard Hanna (VP-Mfg)
Daniel Friberg (Dir-Sys Engrg & Integration)
Keith Powers (Dir-Field Ops)
Joe Mastrangelo (CEO)

Football Club des Girondins de Bordeaux (1)
Rue Joliot Curie, 33187, Le Haillan, Cedex, France
Tel.: (33) 8 92 68 34 33
Web Site: http://www.girondins.com
Professional Soccer Club
N.A.I.C.S.: 711211

Franchise Group, Inc. (1)
109 Innovation Ct Ste J, Delaware, OH 43015
Tel.: (740) 363-2222
Web Site: https://www.franchisegrp.com
Rev.: $4,397,832,000
Assets: $3,630,412,000
Liabilities: $3,209,032,000
Net Worth: $421,380,000
Earnings: ($68,573,000)
Emp.: 8,575
Fiscal Year-end: 12/31/2022
Holding Company; Tax Preparation Services
N.A.I.C.S.: 551112
Eric F. Seeton (CFO)
Andrew Kaminsky (Chief Admin Officer & Exec VP)
Kenneth Todd Evans (Chief Franchising Officer)
Jason Mattes (VP-Franchise Dev)
Scott Harvey (VP-Franchise Ops)
Tiffany McMillan-McWaters (Gen Counsel, Dir & Deputy Gen Counsel)

Subsidiary (Domestic):

American Freight, LLC (2)
109 Innovation Ct Ste J, Delaware, OH 43015
Web Site: http://www.americanfreight.com
Freight Transportation Services
N.A.I.C.S.: 488510

Furniture Factory Outlet, LLC (2)
8819 Rogers Ave, Fort Smith, AR 72908
Tel.: (479) 452-2869
Web Site: http://www.ffohome.com
Furniture & Home Furnishings Retailer
N.A.I.C.S.: 449110
Keri Durkin (COO)
Jay Peters (Chief Merchandising Officer & Exec VP)
Hank Mullany (CEO)

JTH Financial, LLC (2)
1716 Corporate Landing Pkwy, Virginia Beach, VA 23454
Web Site: http://www.jthfinancialllc.com
Investment Advisory Services
N.A.I.C.S.: 523940

JTH Tax, Inc. (2)
1716 Corporate Landing Pkwy, Virginia Beach, VA 23454-5681
Tel.: (757) 493-8855
Web Site: http://www.libertytax.com
Sales Range: $75-99.9 Million
Tax Preparation Services
N.A.I.C.S.: 541213

Liberty Tax Service Inc. (2)
1716 Corporate Landing Pkwy, Virginia Beach, VA 23454
Tel.: (757) 493-8855
Web Site: http://www.libertytax.com
Investment Advisory Services
N.A.I.C.S.: 523940
Shaun York (COO)
Nicole Ossenfort (Pres & CEO)
John T. Hewitt (Chm)

Subsidiary (Domestic):

Vitamin Shoppe, Inc. (3)
300 Harmon Meadow Blvd, Secaucus, NJ 07094
Tel.: (201) 868-5959
Web Site: http://www.vitaminshoppe.com
Rev.: $1,114,160,000
Assets: $388,079,000
Liabilities: $199,738,000
Net Worth: $188,341,000
Earnings: ($3,752,000)
Emp.: 3,503
Fiscal Year-end: 12/29/2018
Holding Company; Vitamins & Other Health Supplements Retailer
N.A.I.C.S.: 551112
Teresa Orth (Chief People Officer & Exec VP)
Andrew Laudato (COO & Exec VP)
Neal Panza (Exec VP-Retail Sls, Ops & Svcs)
Muriel F. Gonzalez (Chief Mdsg & Mktg Officer & Exec VP)
Laura Coffey (CFO & Exec VP)
Sharon M. Leite (CEO)

Subsidiary (Domestic):

Betancourt Sports Nutrition, LLC (4)
14700 NW 60th Ave, Miami Lakes, FL 33014
Tel.: (305) 593-9296
Web Site: http://www.betancournutrition.com
Bodybuilder Food Supplement Distr
N.A.I.C.S.: 456191

FDC Vitamins, Inc. (4)
14620 NW 60 Ave, Miami, FL 33014
Tel.: (305) 468-1600
Web Site: http://www.fdcvitamins.com
Sales Range: $1-9.9 Million
Emp.: 25
Drugs, Proprietaries, And Sundries
N.A.I.C.S.: 424210
Mike Beargall (CEO)

VS Direct Inc. (4)
2100 88th St F4, North Bergen, NJ 07047
Tel.: (201) 758-0404
Web Site: http://www.vitaminshoppe.com
Online Vitamin & Health Supplement Retailer
N.A.I.C.S.: 456191

VS Hercules LLC (4)
2101 91st St, North Bergen, NJ 07047
Tel.: (201) 868-5959
Pharmaceuticals Product Mfr
N.A.I.C.S.: 325412

Vitamin Shoppe Industries, Inc. (4)
2100 88th St F4, North Bergen, NJ 07047
Tel.: (201) 758-0404
Web Site: http://www.vitaminshoppe.com
Emp.: 200
Vitamin & Health Supplement Store Operator
N.A.I.C.S.: 456191
Richard L. Markee (Chm)

Subsidiary (Domestic):

PSP Stores LLC (2)
22710 Haggerty Ste 100, Farmington Hills, MI 48335
Tel.: (248) 348-7300
Pet Supplies Store
N.A.I.C.S.: 459910
Alex Roberts (VP-Franchising)
Dave Bolen (Pres & CEO)

Subsidiary (Domestic):

PSP Group, LLC (3)
29493 7 Mile Rd, Livonia, MI 48152-1909
Tel.: (248) 615-0039
Web Site: http://www.petsuppliesplus.com
Sales Range: $10-24.9 Million
Emp.: 16
Sales of Pet Food & Related Products
N.A.I.C.S.: 459910
Dan Boose (CFO)
Heidi Char (Sr VP-HR)
Derek T. Panfil (Sr VP-Merchandising-Marketing)
Christopher Rowland (CEO)
Jeff Suttle (Sr VP-Merchandising)
Dan McNamara (CFO)

Nick Russo (Sr VP)
Stan Mac (CIO-Information Technology & Sr VP-Information Technology)
Dan McNamara (CFO)
Nick Russo (Sr VP)
Stan Mac (CIO-Information Technology & Sr VP-Information Technology)
Kenneth Miles Tedder Jr. (COO)

Subsidiary (Domestic):

SiempreTax LLC (2)
1716 Corporate Landing Pkwy, Virginia Beach, VA 23454
Tel.: (800) 790-3863
Investment Advisory Services
N.A.I.C.S.: 523940

GlassRatner Advisory & Capital Group, LLC (1)
3445 Peachtree Rd Ste 1225, Atlanta, GA 30326-1000
Tel.: (678) 904-1990
Web Site: http://www.glassratner.com
Business Management Consulting Services
N.A.I.C.S.: 541611
Alan Barbee (Principal)
Tom Buck (Principal)
Paul Dopp (Principal)
Carol L. Fox (Principal)
Ronald Glass (Principal)
Timothy G. Hannon (Mng Dir)

Great American Capital Partners, LLC (1)
11100 Santa Monica Blvd Ste 800, Los Angeles, CA 90025
Tel.: (310) 966-1446
Web Site: http://www.gacapitalpartners.com
Financial Support Services
N.A.I.C.S.: 522320
John Jongdoo Ahn (Pres)
Robert Louzan (Mng Dir)

Great American Group, LLC (1)
21860 Burbank Blvd Ste 300 S, Woodland Hills, CA 91367
Tel.: (818) 884-3737
Web Site: http://www.greatamerican.com
Sales Range: $25-49.9 Million
Emp.: 100
Corporate Liquidation, Asset Disposition, Auction & Appraisal Services
N.A.I.C.S.: 561499
Peter Wyke (Sr VP-GA Global Partners)
Alan Forman (Gen Counsel & Exec VP)
Marc Musitano (COO-Advisory & Valuation Appraisal Div)
Chad Yutka (Mng Dir & Head-CAVS)
Adam Alexander (CEO, Pres-Auction Div & Partner-Global)
Jeff Tanenbaum (Pres & Partners-Global)
Jennie Kim (Mng Dir-Western Reg)
Drew Jakubek (Mng Dir-Southwest & Mgr-Mktg-Natl)
Bill Soncini (Mng Dir-Midwest & Mgr-Mktg-Natl)
Mindy McLees (Dir-Property Tax)
Michael Petruski (Mng Dir-Global Partners)
Paul Brown (VP & Partners-Global)
Michael Presto (VP & Partners-Global)
Billy Nichols (Sr VP & Dir-Mdsg)
Ryan Mulcunry (Exec VP-Northeast)
Neil Axler (Mng Dir-Real Estate, Corp Advisory & Valuations Div)
Thomas McNulty (Mng Dir-CAVS)
Thomas Popovic (Mng Dir)
Robert Louzan (Pres-GACP)
Dan Daitchman (Dir)
Gregg Johnson (Dir)
Michael Marchlik (CEO-Advisory & Valuations)

Subsidiary (Non-US):

MS Mode Nederland B.V. (2)
Diemermere 1, 1112 TA, Diemen, Netherlands
Tel.: (31) 205809891
Web Site: https://www.msmode.nl
Sales Range: $50-74.9 Million
Emp.: 200
Women's Apparel Stores
N.A.I.C.S.: 458110

National Holdings Corporation (1)
200 Vesey St 25th Fl, New York, NY 10281 (45%)
Tel.: (212) 417-8000

Web Site: http://www.nhldcorp.com
Rev.: $229,875,000
Assets: $107,237,000
Liabilities: $60,602,000
Net Worth: $46,635,000
Earnings: ($5,938,000)
Emp.: 390
Fiscal Year-end: 09/30/2020
Holding Company
N.A.I.C.S.: 551112
Jonathan C. Rich (Exec VP)
William L. Groeneveld (Chief Risk Officer & Exec VP)
John Koenigsberg (Mng Dir-Ops)
Fred N. Knopf (Gen Counsel)
John C. DeSena (COO)
Thomas Kowalczyk (Exec VP & Head-Platform)
Henry E. Kaplan (Exec VP & Head-Products & Svcs)
David C. Levine (Exec VP & Mgr-Relationship)
Debbie Walsh (Exec VP & Head-HR)
Sagiv Shiv (Sr Mng Dir & Head-Advisory Svcs)
Kathryn Travis (Sr Mng Dir-Tax)
Dan Ortega (Mng Dir & Chief Supervisory Officer)
Harold G. Chaffee (Mng Dir & Chief Compliance Officer)
Kurosh Golchubian (Mng Dir-Tech)
Chris Ann Campana (Pres-Insurance)
Michael T. Gill (Mng Dir & Head-Recruiting)
Chelsea Nantz (Sr VP-Corp Comm)
Jamie Dorrian (Chief Admin Officer-Natl Tax & Financial Svcs)
Mahesh Sahore (CTO)
Arthur R. Hogan III (Mng Dir & Head-Equity Capital Markets)

Subsidiary (Domestic):

Gilman Ciocia, Inc. (2)
11 Raymond Ave, Poughkeepsie, NY 12603 (100%)
Tel.: (800) 552-0067
Web Site: http://www.gtax.com
Sales Range: $25-49.9 Million
Income Tax Preparation & Financial Planning Services
N.A.I.C.S.: 523940

National Asset Management, Inc. (2)
1 Union Square Ste 2900 600 University St, Seattle, WA 98101
Tel.: (206) 343-6238
Web Site: http://www.namadvisorguide.com
Investment Advisory Services
N.A.I.C.S.: 523940
Michael A. Mullen (Chm)

National Securities Corporation (2)
410 Park Ave 14th Fl, New York, NY 10022
Tel.: (212) 417-8000
Web Site: http://www.nationalsecurities.com
Securities Brokerage Services
N.A.I.C.S.: 523150
Thomas Kowalczyk (Exec VP & Head-Investment Solutions)
John A. Koenigsberg (Mng Dir-Ops)
Jonathan C. Rich (Exec VP & Head-Investment Banking)
William Groeneveld (Chief Risk Mgmt Officer & Exec VP)
David C. Levine (Exec VP & Mgr-Sls-Natl)
Chad D. Champion (Mng Dir & Head-Equity Capital Markets)
Christopher Testa (Mng Dir & Head-Res)
Chris Ann Campana (Dir-Insurance)
Marguerite O'Brien (Sr VP & Mgr-Syndicate)

Subsidiary (Non-US):

vFinance, Inc. (2)
Tel.: (561) 981-1000
Emp.: 91
Investment Banking & Securities Brokerage Services
N.A.I.C.S.: 523150

Subsidiary (Non-US):

vFinance Investments, Inc. (3)
Tel.: (561) 981-1000
Securities Brokerage Services
N.A.I.C.S.: 523150

Tidewatch Select, LLC (1)
8 Parker Ln, Bedford, NH 03110
Tel.: (603) 559-9999

B. Riley Financial, Inc.—(Continued)

Web Site: https://www.tidewatch.com
Market Research Services
N.A.I.C.S.: 541910
Ken Campel *(Co-Founder & Mng Dir)*
Michael Pinholster *(Co-Founder & Mng Dir)*

United Online, Inc. **(1)**
21255 Burbank Blvd, Woodland Hills, CA 91367
Tel.: (818) 287-3000
Web Site: https://www.unitedonline.com
Online Services
N.A.I.C.S.: 519290

bebe stores, inc. **(1)**
105E3 4th St No 137, New York, NY 10016 **(76%)**
Tel.: (415) 215-3355
Web Site: https://www.bebe.com
Rev.: $30,895,000
Assets: $74,709,000
Liabilities: $36,222,000
Net Worth: $38,487,000
Earnings: $6,934,000
Emp.: 231
Fiscal Year-end: 07/03/2021
Retail Clothing Stores Owner & Operator
N.A.I.C.S.: 458110

Joint Venture (Domestic):

Brookstone Company, Inc. **(2)**
1 Innovation Way, Merrimack, NH 03054-4873
Tel.: (603) 880-9500
Web Site: http://www.brookstone.com
Sales Range: $450-499.9 Million
Emp.: 1,214
Specialty Products Retailer
N.A.I.C.S.: 459420
Stephen A. Gould *(VP & Gen Counsel)*
Steven H. Schwartz *(Chief Mdsg Officer)*
Piau Phang Foo *(Chm)*
Valen Tong *(CFO & VP)*
Jim Ferguson *(Sr VP-Retail)*
Frank Hu *(VP-Ops)*
Scott Schultz *(VP-Ecommerce)*
Steven Goldsmith *(Pres & CEO)*
Kenneth Boremi *(VP-Retail)*

Subsidiary (Domestic):

bebe studio, inc. **(2)**
10345 W Olympic Blvd, Los Angeles, CA 90064
Tel.: (213) 362-2338
Sales Range: $25-49.9 Million
Clothing Design Services
N.A.I.C.S.: 315250

magicJack VocalTec Ltd. **(1)**
12 Haomanut Street 2nd Floor, Poleg Industrial Zone, Netanya, 425U445, Israel
Tel.: (972) 99703888
Web Site: http://www.vocaltec.com
Rev.: $87,993,000
Assets: $141,042,000
Liabilities: $104,480,000
Net Worth: $36,562,000
Earnings: ($24,963,000)
Emp.: 136
Fiscal Year-end: 12/31/2017
Voice over IP (VoIP) Cloud-based Communications
N.A.I.C.S.: 517112
Dvir Salomon *(CTO & Exec VP)*
Thomas Fuller *(CFO & Exec VP)*
Izhak Gross *(Chm)*
Kerrin Parker *(CEO-Broadsmart)*
Kristin Beischel *(Chief Mktg Officer & Exec VP)*
Don Carlos Bell III *(Pres & CEO)*

Subsidiary (US):

TigerJet Network, Inc. **(2)**
50 Airport Pkwy, San Jose, CA 95110
Tel.: (408) 437-7727
Networking Component Mfr
N.A.I.C.S.: 541519

Subsidiary (Non-US):

VocalTec Communications, LLC **(2)**
15 Prestige Cir, Allen, TX 75002
Tel.: (972) 359-6600
Wireless Communication Services
N.A.I.C.S.: 517112

BAB, INC.

500 Lake Cook Rd Ste 475, Deerfield, IL 60015
Tel.: (847) 948-7520 DE
Web Site: https://www.babcorp.com
Year Founded: 1993
BABB—(NASDAQ)
Rev.: $3,287,087
Assets: $4,294,607
Liabilities: $1,219,560
Net Worth: $3,075,047
Earnings: $431,992
Emp.: 12
Fiscal Year-end: 11/30/22
Bagel, Muffin & Coffee Retail Store Operator & Franchisor
N.A.I.C.S.: 311811
Michael W. Evans *(Pres & CEO)*
Michael K. Murtaugh *(Gen Counsel, Sec & VP)*

Subsidiaries:

BAB Systems, Inc. **(1)**
500 Lk Cook Rd Ste 475, Deerfield, IL 60015
Web Site: https://www.babcorp.com
Restaurant Services
N.A.I.C.S.: 722511
Michael W. Evans *(Pres & CEO)*

Brewster's Franchise Corporation **(1)**
500 Lake Cook Rd Ste 475, Deerfield, IL 60015
Tel.: (847) 948-7520
Sales Range: $25-49.9 Million
Coffee Shop Operator & Franchisor
N.A.I.C.S.: 311920
Michael W. Evans *(Pres)*

BABCOCK & WILCOX ENTERPRISES, INC.

1200 E Market St Ste 650, Akron, OH 44305
Tel.: (330) 753-4511 DE
Web Site: https://www.babcock.com
BW—(NYSE)
Rev.: $889,815,000
Assets: $942,655,000
Liabilities: $944,744,000
Net Worth: ($2,089,000)
Earnings: ($22,861,000)
Emp.: 2,100
Fiscal Year-end: 12/31/22
Holding Company; Power Generation Equipment Mfr
N.A.I.C.S.: 551112
Kenneth M. Young *(CEO)*
Brandy Johnson *(CTO)*
Chris Riker *(Sr VP)*
Gillianne Hetrick *(VP)*
Sarah Serafin *(VP)*
Louis Salamone Jr. *(CFO, Chief Acctg Officer & Exec VP)*

Subsidiaries:

Americon Equipment Services, Inc. **(1)**
3353 Gallimore Rd, Sabina, OH 45169
Tel.: (937) 486-3101
Web Site: http://www.aesmowers.com
Industrial Equipment & Machinery Repair Services
N.A.I.C.S.: 811310

Americon, LLC **(1)**
900 Flynn Rd, Camarillo, CA 93012-8703
Tel.: (805) 987-0412
Web Site: https://www.americon-usa.com
Emp.: 55
Audio Visual Equipment Mfr
N.A.I.C.S.: 334310

Babcock & Wilcox Beijing Co., Ltd. **(1)**
36 Shijingshan Road Shijingshan District, Beijing, 100043, China
Tel.: (86) 1068862244
Web Site: http://www.oa.bwbc.cn
Power & Heating Equipment Whslr
N.A.I.C.S.: 423720

Babcock & Wilcox ME Holdings Limited **(1)**
DIFC The Gate 15th Floor, Dubai, United Arab Emirates
Tel.: (971) 44019112
Heating Equipment Mfr
N.A.I.C.S.: 333414

Babcock & Wilcox Power Generation Group, Inc. **(1)**
20 S Van Buren Ave, Barberton, OH 44203-0351 **(100%)**
Tel.: (330) 753-4511
Web Site: http://www.babcock.com
Sales Range: $1-4.9 Billion
Emp.: 200
Fossil Power Generation & Equipment
N.A.I.C.S.: 221112

Subsidiary (Non-US):

Babcock & Wilcox Volund A/S **(2)**
Falkevej 2, 6705, Esbjerg, Denmark
Tel.: (45) 7 614 3400
Web Site: http://www.volund.dk
Sales Range: $125-149.9 Million
Emp.: 415
Thermal Energy Equipment Mfr
N.A.I.C.S.: 332410

Subsidiary (Domestic):

Delta Power Services, LLC **(2)**
363 N Sam Houston Pkwy E Ste 600, Houston, TX 77060
Tel.: (281) 405-6888
Web Site:
  http://www.deltapowerservices.com
Sales Range: $25-49.9 Million
Emp.: 6
Industrial Machinery Mfr
N.A.I.C.S.: 333248
Gary Anderson *(Pres)*

Diamond Power International, Inc. **(2)**
2600 E Main St, Lancaster, OH 43130 **(100%)**
Tel.: (740) 687-6500
Web Site: http://www.diamondpower.com
Sales Range: $75-99.9 Million
Emp.: 1,500
Industrial Machinery Mfr
N.A.I.C.S.: 333248

Division (Domestic):

Allen-Sherman-Hoff **(3)**
436 Creamery Way Ste 350, Exton, PA 19341-2508
Tel.: (484) 875-1600
Web Site: http://www.a-s-h.com
Sales Range: $25-40.0 Million
Emp.: 75
Air Purification Equipment Mfr
N.A.I.C.S.: 333413

Subsidiary (Non-US):

Diamond Power Australia Pty., Ltd. **(3)**
8 Jones Road, Morwell, 3840, VIC, Australia
Tel.: (61) 351368400
Web Site: http://www.diamondpower.com.au
Boiler Cleaning & Ash Handling Equipment Mfr
N.A.I.C.S.: 333248

Diamond Power Central & Eastern Europe s.r.o. **(3)**
Barvicova 41, 602 00, Brno, Czech Republic
Tel.: (420) 543213705
Web Site: http://www.diamondpower-cee.com
Boiler Cleaning & Ash Handling Equipment Mfr
N.A.I.C.S.: 333248

Diamond Power Finland Oy **(3)**
Hogberginhaara 5, 04360, Tuusula, Finland
Tel.: (358) 201983550
Web Site: http://www.diamondpower.fi
Emp.: 11
Turnkey Services for Installation & Commissioning of Sootblowers, Port Rodders & Diagnostic Equipment
N.A.I.C.S.: 333248

Diamond Power Germany GmbH **(3)**
Thura Mark 3, 06780, Zorbig, Germany
Tel.: (49) 3495639895
Web Site: https://www.diamondpower-deutschland.com
Emp.: 20
Boiler Cleaning & Ash Handling Equipment Mfr
N.A.I.C.S.: 333248
Jan Brummerloh *(Mng Dir)*
Jorg Illigens *(Sls Mgr)*

Diamond Power Machine (Hubei) Co., Inc. **(3)**
365 Xinyang Avenue, Economic Development Zone Jingshan, Wuhan, 431899, Jingshan Hubei, China
Tel.: (86) 2759222209
Web Site:
  https://www.diamondpower.com.cn
Emp.: 400
Boiler Cleaning & Ash Handling Equipment Mfr
N.A.I.C.S.: 333248

Diamond Power Services S.E.A. Ltd. **(3)**
51/1 Moo 4 Tambol Nadee Amphur, Muang, Samut Sakhon, Thailand
Tel.: (66) 34870978
Boiler Cleaning & Ash Handling Equipment Mfr
N.A.I.C.S.: 333248

Diamond Power Specialty (Pty) Ltd. **(3)**
4 Kobalt Street, Vanderbijlpark, 1900, South Africa
Tel.: (27) 16 981 4017
Boiler Cleaning & Ash Handling Equipment Mfr
N.A.I.C.S.: 333248

Division (Domestic):

Diamond Power Specialty Company **(3)**
2540 Mountain Industrial Blvd, Tucker, GA 30084
Tel.: (770) 939-3430
Web Site: http://www.diamondpower.com
Emp.: 4
Industrial Machinery Mfr
N.A.I.C.S.: 333248

Subsidiary (Non-US):

Diamond Power Specialty Ltd. **(3)**
Block 10, Vale of Leven Industrial Estate, Dumbarton, G82 3AD, United Kingdom
Tel.: (44) 138 972 7900
Web Site: http://www.diamondpower.co.uk
Emp.: 150
Boiler Cleaning & Ash Handling Equipment Mfr
N.A.I.C.S.: 333248

Diamond Power Sweden AB **(3)**
Djupdalsvagen 10, PO Box 506, 19251, Sollentuna, Sweden
Tel.: (46) 8290440
Web Site: http://www.diamondpower.se
Boiler Cleaning & Ash Handling Equipment Mfr
N.A.I.C.S.: 333248

Loibl Allen-Sherman-Hoff GmbH **(3)**
Arberstrasse 40, 94315, Straubing, Germany
Tel.: (49) 942192560
Web Site: http://www.loibl.biz
Emp.: 120
Material Handling Equipment Mfr
N.A.I.C.S.: 333248

Babcock & Wilcox SPIG, Inc. **(1)**
9988 Hibert St Ste 102, San Diego, CA 92131-2480
Tel.: (877) 955-7744
Boilers & Heating Equipment Mfr
N.A.I.C.S.: 333414

Babcock & Wilcox Volund Limited **(1)**
6 Bevis Marks, London, EC3A 7BA, United Kingdom
Tel.: (44) 1217671384
Web Site: http://www.volund.dk
Power Plant Construction Services
N.A.I.C.S.: 237130

Babcock & Wilcox de Monterrey, S.A. de C.V. (1)
Valle Alegre No 136, Colonia Valle Soleado, 67114, Guadalupe, Nuevo Leon, Mexico
Tel.: (52) 8181315260
Industrial Equipment & Machinery Repair Services
N.A.I.C.S.: 811310
Andres Morales Ayala *(Mgr-Ops)*

Ebensburg Power Co. (1)
2840 New Germany Rd, Ebensburg, PA 15931
Tel.: (814) 472-1140
Web Site: https://robindale.energy
Emp.: 25
Eletric Power Generation Services
N.A.I.C.S.: 221118

Gotaverken Miljo AB (1)
Anders Carlssons Gata 14, PO Box 8876, 402 72, Gothenburg, Sweden
Tel.: (46) 31501960
Web Site: http://www.gmab.se
Industrial Equipment & Machinery Mfr
N.A.I.C.S.: 333310

MTS Environmental GmbH (1)
Honeywellstrasse 18, 63477, Maintal, Germany
Tel.: (49) 618194040
Industrial Equipment & Machinery Repair Services
N.A.I.C.S.: 811310
Michael Klose *(Mgr-Process Engrg)*

Optimus Industries, LLC (1)
5727 S Lewis Ave Ste 600, Tulsa, OK 74105
Tel.: (918) 491-9191
Web Site: http://www.optimus-tulsa.com
Fabricated Structural Metal
N.A.I.C.S.: 332312
G. Scott Lewis *(Pres)*
Kevin Brown *(VP-Sls)*
Jim Scheiper *(CFO)*

Subsidiary (Domestic):

CFT, Inc. (2)
5727 S Lewis Ave Ste 600, Tulsa, OK 74105
Tel.: (918) 491-9191
Web Site: http://www.optimus-tulsa.com
Sales Range: $10-24.9 Million
Emp.: 10
Tube Fins & Stamped Metal
N.A.I.C.S.: 332119
G. Scott Lewis *(Pres)*

Chanute Manufacturing Company (2)
1700 S Washington Ave, Chanute, KS 66720
Tel.: (620) 431-3100
Web Site: http://www.chanutemfg.com
Pressure Parts Mfr
N.A.I.C.S.: 332410

Power Systems Operations, Inc. (1)
PO Box 1219, Bellevue, WA 98009
Tel.: (425) 739-9367
Web Site: http://www.powersysops.com
Software Development Services
N.A.I.C.S.: 541511
Vicki Vanderburg *(Founder & Pres)*
Mark Sundsten *(VP-Product Dev)*
Kenneth Jones *(CEO)*
Heather Frazier *(VP-Implementation)*

SPIG Cooling Towers India Private Limited (1)
608 Palmspring Link Road, Malad W, Mumbai, 400 064, India
Tel.: (91) 2240890500
Power & Heating Equipment Whslr
N.A.I.C.S.: 423720
Mahendra Daswani *(Mng Dir)*

SPIG KOREA LTD. (1)
702 7th Floor Kangnam-officetel 40 Seocho-Daero 73-Gil, Seocho-gu, Seoul, 137-857, Korea (South)
Tel.: (82) 1032486489
Power & Heating Equipment Whslr
N.A.I.C.S.: 423720

SPIG Kuhlturmtechnologien GmbH (1)
Im Lipperfeld 25, 46047, Oberhausen, Germany
Tel.: (49) 20894188428
Power & Heating Equipment Whslr
N.A.I.C.S.: 423720

SPIG S.p.A. (1)
Via Borgomanero 34, 28040, Paruzzaro, Italy
Tel.: (39) 0322245401
Power & Heating Equipment Whslr
N.A.I.C.S.: 423720

SPIG Sogutma Sistemleri Tlc Ldt (1)
Sair Esref Bulv No 22/812, 35230, Izmir, Turkiye
Tel.: (90) 2324410846
Power & Heating Equipment Whslr
N.A.I.C.S.: 423720

SPIG Torres de Resfriamento Ltda. (1)
Rua Rangel Pestana 533 - Conjunto 21 - Centro, Jundiai, 13201-903, Sao Paulo, Brazil
Tel.: (55) 1145227434
Power & Heating Equipment Whslr
N.A.I.C.S.: 423720

Thermax Babcock & Wilcox Energy Solutions Private Limited (1)
Adisa Icon Gat No 301/2/1 Mumbai Bangalore Highway, Opposite HEMRL Bavdhan Budruk, Pune, 411 021, Maharashtra, India
Tel.: (91) 2071800652
Web Site: http://www.tbwes.com
Boilers & Heating Equipment Mfr
N.A.I.C.S.: 333414

BABYLON HOLDINGS LIMITED

2500 Bee Cave Rd Bldg 1-Ste 400, Austin, TX 78746
Tel.: (512) 967-3787   JE
Web Site:
   https://www.babylonhealth.com
Year Founded: 2013
BBLN—(NYSE)
Rev.: $1,109,669,000
Assets: $246,110,000
Liabilities: $502,009,000
Net Worth: ($255,899,000)
Earnings: ($221,449,000)
Emp.: 1,895
Fiscal Year-end: 12/31/22
Holding Company
N.A.I.C.S.: 551112
Ali Parsadoust *(CEO)*
Mairi Johnson *(Chief Partnerships Officer)*
Paul-Henri Ferrand *(COO)*

BACKBLAZE, INC.

201 Baldwin Ave, San Mateo, CA 94401
Tel.: (650) 352-3738   DE
Web Site: https://www.backblaze.com
Year Founded: 2007
BLZE—(NASDAQ)
Rev.: $85,155,000
Assets: $152,458,000
Liabilities: $83,710,000
Net Worth: $68,748,000
Earnings: ($51,398,000)
Emp.: 393
Fiscal Year-end: 12/31/22
Computing Infrastructure Providers, Data Processing, Web Hosting & Related Services
N.A.I.C.S.: 518210
Gleb Budman *(Founder, Chm & CEO)*
Brian Wilson *(CTO)*
Tom MacMitchell *(Chief Compliance Officer & Gen Counsel)*
Tim Nufire *(Chief Cloud Officer)*
Jeanette Foster *(Comm Mgr)*

BADGER METER, INC.

4545 W Brown Deer Rd, Milwaukee, WI 53224
Tel.: (414) 355-0400   WI
Web Site:
   https://www.badgermeter.com
Year Founded: 1905
BMI—(NYSE)
Rev.: $703,592,000
Assets: $716,919,000
Liabilities: $200,437,000
Net Worth: $516,482,000
Earnings: $92,598,000
Emp.: 2,140
Fiscal Year-end: 12/31/23
Flow Measurement Devices & Precision Valves Mfr
N.A.I.C.S.: 334514
William R. A. Bergum *(Gen Counsel, Sec & VP)*
Fred J. Begale *(VP-Engrg)*
Karen M. Bauer *(Treas & VP-IR & Corp Strategy)*
Robert A. Wrocklage *(CFO & Sr VP)*
Daniel R. Weltzien *(VP & Controller)*
Sheryl L. Hopkins *(VP-HR)*
Richard Htwe *(VP)*
Lars Bo Kristensen *(VP)*
Matthew L. Stuyvenberg *(VP)*
Kenneth C. Bockhorst *(Chm, Pres & CEO)*

Subsidiaries:

Analytical Technology, Inc. (1)
6 Iron Bridge Dr, Collegeville, PA 19426
Tel.: (610) 917-0991
Web Site:
   http://www.analyticaltechnology.com
Rev.: $5,180,000
Emp.: 40
Totalizing Fluid Meter & Counting Device Mfr
N.A.I.C.S.: 334514

Badger Meter Europe, GmbH (1)
Nurtinger Str 76, 72639, Neuffen, Germany   (100%)
Tel.: (49) 702592080
Web Site: http://www.badgermeter.de
Sales Range: $10-24.9 Million
Emp.: 60
Mfr & Sales of Badger Meter Products
N.A.I.C.S.: 334513

Subsidiary (Non-US):

Badger Meter Slovakia (2)
Racianska 109 / B, 831 02, Bratislava, Slovakia
Tel.: (421) 905532802
Web Site: https://hydroing.sk
Sales Range: $10-24.9 Million
Emp.: 3
Fluid Meter & Measuring Device Mfr
N.A.I.C.S.: 334514

Badger Meter International, Inc. (1)
4545 W Brown Deer Rd, Milwaukee, WI 53223-2413
Tel.: (414) 355-0400
Web Site: http://www.badgermeter.com
Sales Range: $75-99.9 Million
Emp.: 300
Management Consulting Services
N.A.I.C.S.: 541611

Subsidiary (Non-US):

Badger Meter Czech Republic (2)
Marikova 26, 621 00, Brno, Czech Republic
Tel.: (420) 54 142 0411
Web Site: http://www.badgermeter.cz
Sales Range: $25-49.9 Million
Emp.: 3
Measurement Instruments & Flow Meters Mfr
N.A.I.C.S.: 334513

Badger Meter Swiss AG (2)
Mittelholzerstrasse 8, 3006, Bern, Switzerland
Tel.: (41) 31 932 0111
Web Site: http://www.badgermeter.ch
Fluid Meter & Measuring Device Mfr
N.A.I.C.S.: 334514

Badger Meter de Mexico, SA de CV (1)
Pedro Luis Ogazon No 32 Colony Guadalupe Inn, 01050, Mexico, Mexico
Tel.: (52) 5556620882
Web Site: http://www.badgermeter.com
Fluid Meter & Measuring Device Mfr
N.A.I.C.S.: 334514

Badger Meter de las Americas, S.A. de C.V. (1)
Pedro Luis Ogazon 32, Col Guadalupe Inn, Mexico, 01020, Mexico   (100%)
Tel.: (52) 5556620882
Sales Range: $1-9.9 Million
Emp.: 5
Mfr of Flow Measurement Devices
N.A.I.C.S.: 334513

Badger Meter, Inc. - Racine (1)
8635 Washington Ave, Racine, WI 53406-3738
Tel.: (262) 639-6770
Web Site: http://www.badgermeter.com
Sales Range: $25-49.9 Million
Emp.: 120
Vibrators For Concrete Construction; Flow Instruments, Industrial Process Type
N.A.I.C.S.: 334513

Division (Domestic):

Blancett (2)
8635 Washington Ave, Racine, WI 53406   (100%)
Tel.: (262) 639-6770
Web Site: http://www.badgermeter.com
Sales Range: $10-24.9 Million
Emp.: 75
Liquid Flow Measuring & Monitoring Products Mfr
N.A.I.C.S.: 334519

Subsidiary (Non-US):

Premier Control Technologies, Ltd. (2)
Office 64 Hethel Engineering Centre Chapman Way, Hethel, Norwich, NR14 8FB, United Kingdom
Tel.: (44) 1953609930
Web Site: https://www.pctflow.com
Sales Range: $25-49.9 Million
Emp.: 1
Measuring Instrument Supplier
N.A.I.C.S.: 423490
Andy Mangell *(Dir-Sls)*
James Kybird *(Mng Dir)*
Peter Hill *(Engr-Internal Sls & Svc)*
John Bannatyne *(Mgr-Bus Dev)*
Guy Beavan *(Engr-Customer Support)*

Division (Domestic):

The Wyco Tool Company (2)
8635 Washington Ave, Racine, WI 53406
Tel.: (262) 639-6770
Web Site: http://www.wycotool.com
Sales Range: $1-9.9 Million
Concrete Vibrators Mfr
N.A.I.C.S.: 333120

Cox Flow Measurement, Inc. (1)
15555 N 79th Pl, Scottsdale, AZ 85260
Tel.: (480) 922-7446
Web Site: http://www.BadgerMeter.com
Sales Range: $25-49.9 Million
Emp.: 40
Flow Measurement Instruments Mfr
N.A.I.C.S.: 334513

D-Flow Technology, AB (1)
Gammelstadsvagen 5B, 972 41, Lulea, Norrbotten County, Sweden
Tel.: (46) 920528300
Fluid Meter Controlling Equipment Distr
N.A.I.C.S.: 423830
Mats Lindgren *(Mng Dir)*

National Meter and Automation, Inc. (1)
7220 S Fraser St, Centennial, CO 80112
Tel.: (303) 339-9100
Web Site: http://www.nmaai.com
Emp.: 20
Measuring & Controlling Device Mfr
N.A.I.C.S.: 334513

Scan France SARL (1)
370 Route de Saint Canadet, 13100, Aix-en-Provence, France
Tel.: (33) 442203501

Industrial Water Monitoring System & Software Services
N.A.I.C.S.: 541840

Syrinix Limited　　　　　　　　　　**(1)**
Hethel Engineering Centre Chapman Way, Hethel, Norwich, NR14 8FB, United Kingdom
Tel.: (44) 1953859128
Web Site: https://www.syrinix.com
Network Monitoring Equipment Distr
N.A.I.C.S.: 423690

BAGGER DAVE'S BURGER TAVERN, INC.
405 Main Ave W Ste 2D, West Fargo, ND 58078
Tel.: (231) 486-0527　　　　　**NV**
Web Site:
　　https://www.baggerdaves.com
Year Founded: 2016
BDVB—(OTCIQ)
Restaurant Operators
N.A.I.C.S.: 722511
Gary Copperud *(CEO)*
Kenneth W. Brimmer *(CFO)*

BAIN CAPITAL SPECIALTY FINANCE, INC.
200 Clarendon St, Boston, MA 02116
Tel.: (617) 516-2000　　　　　**DE**
Web Site:
　　https://www.baincapitalspecialtyfi
　　nance.com
Year Founded: 2015
BCSF—(NYSE)
Rev.: $197,394,000
Assets: $2,571,193,000
Liabilities: $1,471,187,000
Net Worth: $1,100,006,000
Earnings: $87,738,000
Fiscal Year-end: 12/31/21
Financial Investment Services
N.A.I.C.S.: 523940
Amit Joshi *(CFO & CFO-Bain Capital Private Credit)*
Sally F. Dornaus *(Grp CFO-Capital Markets)*
James Goldman *(Chief Compliance Officer)*
Michael A. Ewald *(CEO)*
Michael J. Boyle *(Pres)*

BAKER BOYER BANCORP
7 W Main, Walla Walla, WA 00362
Tel.: (509) 525-2000　　　　　**WA**
Web Site:
　　https://www.bakerboyer.com
Year Founded: 1986
BBBK—(OTCIQ)
Rev.: $34,559,000
Assets: $709,377,000
Liabilities: $659,675,000
Net Worth: $49,702,000
Earnings: $3,172,000
Fiscal Year-end: 12/31/23
Bank Holding Company
N.A.I.C.S.: 551111
Mark Kajita *(Pres & CEO)*
Jolene Riggs *(CFO & Exec VP)*
John Cunnison *(Chief Investment Officer & VP)*
Subsidiaries:

Baker-Boyer National Bank Inc.　**(1)**
7 W Main St, Walla Walla, WA 99362
Tel.: (509) 525-2000
Web Site: http://www.bakerboyer.com
Sales Range: $10-24.9 Million
Emp.: 100
Commercial Banking Services
N.A.I.C.S.: 522110

BAKER HUGHES COMPANY
575 N Dairy Ashford Rd Ste 100, Houston, TX 77079-1121
Tel.: (713) 439-8600　　　　　**DE**

Web Site:
　　https://www.bakerhughes.com
BKR—(NASDAQ)
Rev.: $25,506,000,000
Assets: $36,945,000,000
Liabilities: $21,426,000,000
Net Worth: $15,519,000,000
Earnings: $1,943,000,000
Emp.: 58,000
Fiscal Year-end: 12/31/23
Holding Company; Oil & Gas Equipment Developer, Mfr, Whslr & Services
N.A.I.C.S.: 541990
Lorenzo Simonelli *(Chm, Pres & CEO)*
Jeff Fleece *(CIO)*
Jim Apostolides *(Sr VP-Enterprise Operational Excellence)*
Nancy K. Buese *(CFO)*
Amerino Gatti *(Exec VP-Oilfield Svcs & Equipment)*
Ganesh Ramaswamy *(Exec VP-Industrial & Energy Tech)*
Muzzamil Khider Ahmed *(Chief People Officer & Chief Culture Officer)*
Georgia Magno *(Chief Legal Officer)*

Subsidiaries:

Baker Hughes Digital Solutions GmbH　　　　　　　　　　　　**(1)**
Robert Bosch St 3, 50354, Hurth, Germany
Tel.: (49) 22336010
Radiographic, Ultrasonic & Eddy Current Equipment Mfr
N.A.I.C.S.: 334519

Baker Hughes Holdings LLC　　**(1)**
17021 Aldine Westfield Rd, Houston, TX 77073-5101　　　　　　**(22.82%)**
Tel.: (713) 439-8600
Web Site: https://www.bakerhughes.com
Rev.: $21,155,999,999
Assets: $34,172,000,000
Liabilities: $19,513,000,000
Net Worth: $14,659,000,000
Earnings: ($526,000,000)
Emp.: 55,000
Fiscal Year-end: 12/31/2022
Engine Equipment Mfr
N.A.I.C.S.: 333618
Lorenzo Simonelli *(Pres & CEO)*
Jeff Fleece *(CIO)*
Nancy Buese *(CFO)*
Ganesh Ramaswamy *(Exec VP)*
Deanna Jones *(Exec VP)*
Jim Apostolides *(Sr VP)*
Judson E. Bailey *(VP)*
Rebecca Charlton *(Chief Acctg Officer, Sr VP & Controller)*

Subsidiary (Domestic):

BJ Services Company　　　　　　**(2)**
2929 Allen Pkwy Ste 2100, Houston, TX 77019-2118
Tel.: (713) 439-8600
Web Site: http://www.bakerhughes.com
Pressure Pumping & Other Oilfield Services to the Petroleum Industry
N.A.I.C.S.: 211120

Division (Domestic):

BJ Process & Pipeline Services Co.　　　　　　　　　　　　　**(3)**
4101 Oates Rd, Houston, TX 77013
Tel.: (832) 519-2000
Sales Range: $10-24.9 Million
Emp.: 90
Oil Field Services
N.A.I.C.S.: 213112

Subsidiary (Non-US):

BJ Services Co. (Singapore) Pte Ltd　　　　　　　　　　　　　**(3)**
17 Tuas Avenue 3, Singapore, 639414, Singapore
Tel.: (65) 68778700
Web Site: http://www.bakerhughes.com
Sales Range: $25-49.9 Million
Emp.: 100
Pipeline & Process Services

N.A.I.C.S.: 541990

BJ Services Company Italia S.R.L.　　　　　　　　　　　　　**(3)**
Contrada Pantanelli 3, Siracusa, 96100, Italy
Tel.: (39) 0931468511
Web Site: http://www.bjservices.com
Sales Range: $25-49.9 Million
Emp.: 65
Completion Fluids
N.A.I.C.S.: 324191

BJ Tubular Services B.V.　　　**(3)**
Schrijnwerkersweg 1, Den Helder, 1786 PC, Netherlands
Tel.: (31) 223668122
Wire Line Services
N.A.I.C.S.: 486990

BJ Tubular Services Limited　　**(3)**
Yarmouth Business Park Suffolk Road, Great Yarmouth, NR31 0ER, United Kingdom
Tel.: (44) 1493653048
Web Site: http://www.bjservices.com
Sales Range: $10-24.9 Million
Emp.: 14
Wire Line Services
N.A.I.C.S.: 541990

Subsidiary (Domestic):

Baker Atlas　　　　　　　　　　**(2)**
2001 Rankin Rd, Houston, TX 77073-5100
Tel.: (713) 625-4200
Sales Range: $450-499.9 Million
Emp.: 3,000
Wireline Logging & Completion Services
N.A.I.C.S.: 532412

Branch (Domestic):

Baker Atlas - Denver　　　　　**(3)**
1675 Broadway, Denver, CO 80202
Tel.: (303) 573-2781
Sales Range: $10-24.9 Million
Emp.: 10
Wireline Logging Services for the Oil & Gas Industry
N.A.I.C.S.: 213112

Baker Atlas - Pearland　　　　**(3)**
3401 S Main St, Pearland, TX 77581
Tel.: (281) 485-8311
Web Site: http://www.bakerhughes.com
Sales Range: $50-74.9 Million
Emp.: 60
Oil & Gas Wells Services
N.A.I.C.S.: 213112

Subsidiary (Non-US):

Baker Hughes (Deutschland) Holding GmbH　　　　　　　　　　　**(2)**
Baker Hughes Str 1, 29221, Celle, Germany　　　　　　　　　　**(100%)**
Tel.: (49) 51412030
Web Site: http://www.bakerhughes.de
Sales Range: $350-399.9 Million
Emp.: 1,200
Mfr of Industrial Machinery
N.A.I.C.S.: 333248

Subsidiary (Domestic):

Baker Hughes INTEQ GmbH　　**(3)**
Baker hughes Street 1, 29221, Celle, Germany　　　　　　　　　**(100%)**
Tel.: (49) 51412030
Web Site: http://www.bakerhughes.de
Sales Range: $250-299.9 Million
Oil Field Service Industry
N.A.I.C.S.: 333132

Plant (Domestic):

Baker Hughes INTEQ GmbH　　**(4)**
Marktplatz 9, 35781, Weilburg, Germany　　　　　　　　　　**(100%)**
Tel.: (49) 6471379165
Sales Range: $25-49.9 Million
Emp.: 12
Oil, Gas & Geothermal Services
N.A.I.C.S.: 213112

Subsidiary (Domestic):

Baker Oil Tools GmbH　　　　　**(3)**
Baker-Hughes-Str 1, 29221, Celle, Germany

Tel.: (49) 514181018
Mfr of Cementing & Downhole Equipment for Oil Exploration & Production
N.A.I.C.S.: 213112

Subsidiary (Non-US):

Baker Hughes (Nederland) B.V.　**(2)**
Westblaak 89, 3012 KG, Rotterdam, Netherlands
Tel.: (31) 102711300
Oil & Gas Field Machinery Equipment Mfr
N.A.I.C.S.: 333132

Division (Domestic):

Baker Hughes - Hughes Christensen　　　　　　　　　　**(2)**
9110 Grogans Mill Rd, The Woodlands, TX 77380-3615
Tel.: (281) 363-6000
Sales Range: $200-249.9 Million
Emp.: 750
Technological Developer, Mfr & Retailer of Drilling Bits & Tool Joints for Oil & Gas Exploration; Tungsten Carbide Products
N.A.I.C.S.: 333132

Branch (Non-US):

Hughes Christensen　　　　　　**(3)**
36 Montgomery Rd, Belfast, BT6 9HQ, County Antrim, United Kingdom　**(100%)**
Tel.: (44) 2890559300
Sales Range: $75-99.9 Million
Emp.: 400
Mfr & Marketer of Oilfield Tools & Equipment
N.A.I.C.S.: 333132

Subsidiary (Non-US):

Baker Hughes Asia Pacific Limited　　　　　　　　　　**(2)**
15 Fl Guohua Plaza No 3 Dongzhimen avenue, Chaoyangmen Ave, Beijing, 100007, China　　　　　　　　　　**(100%)**
Tel.: (86) 1084007888
Web Site: http://www.bakerhughes.com
Sales Range: $10-24.9 Million
Emp.: 8
Mfr of Oil Drilling Equipment
N.A.I.C.S.: 333132

Baker Hughes Australia Pty Limited　　　　　　　　　　**(2)**
Level 7 256 St Georges Trace, Perth, 6000, WA, Australia
Tel.: (61) 892177100
Web Site: http://www.bakkerhughes.com
Rev.: $58,800,000
Emp.: 330
Construction & Mining Machinery & Equipment Merchant Whslr
N.A.I.C.S.: 423810

Division (Domestic):

Baker Hughes Australia - Canning Vale　　　　　　　　　　**(3)**
1-5 Bell St, Canning Vale, 6155, WA, Australia　　　　　　　　**(100%)**
Tel.: (61) 894550155
Sales Range: $75-99.9 Million
Emp.: 100
Oilfield Tools Sales
N.A.I.C.S.: 213112

Subsidiary (Non-US):

Baker Hughes Canada Company　**(2)**
401 9th Ave SW Ste 1000, Calgary, T2P 3C5, AB, Canada　　　　　　**(100%)**
Tel.: (403) 537-3400
Sales Range: $300-349.9 Million
Emp.: 1,100
Oil & Gas Services
N.A.I.C.S.: 213112

Baker Hughes Do Brazil Ltda.　　**(2)**
Rua 19 De Fevereiro N 30 1 2 E 3 Andar, Rio de Janeiro, 22280030, Brazil　**(100%)**
Tel.: (55) 2122668400
Sales Range: $25-49.9 Million
Emp.: 80
Mfr & Marketer of Tools & Equipment
N.A.I.C.S.: 333132
Dalva Reais *(Sec)*

N.A.I.C.S.: 213112

Baker Hughes Drilling Fluids (2)
1010 Rankin Rd, Houston, TX 77267-1888
Tel.: (713) 625-5400
Web Site: http://www.bakerhughes.com
Sales Range: $50-74.9 Million
Emp.: 50
Oil & Gas Related Services
N.A.I.C.S.: 213112

Baker Hughes INTEQ (2)
2001 Rankin Rd, Houston, TX
77073-5114   (100%)
Tel.: (713) 625-4200
Web Site: http://www.bakerhughes.com
Sales Range: $450-499.9 Million
Emp.: 1,800
Oil Field Machinery & Equipment Mfr
N.A.I.C.S.: 333132

Subsidiary (Non-US):

**Baker Hughes INTEQ (M) Sdn
Bhd** (3)
25th Floor Menara Tan And Tan 207 Jalan
Tun Razak, 50400, Kuala Lumpur,
Malaysia   (100%)
Tel.: (60) 321647888
Web Site:
     http://www.bakerhughesdirect.com
Sales Range: $50-74.9 Million
Emp.: 80
Mfr of Cementing & Downhole Equipment
for Oil Exploration & Production
N.A.I.C.S.: 333132
Norita Jocuri (Mgr-Comm)

Subsidiary (Non-US):

**Baker Hughes International Coopera-
tief U.A.** (2)
Westblaak 89, Rotterdam, 3012 KG, Neth-
erlands
Tel.: (31) 102313803
Web Site: http://www.bakerhughes.com
Emp.: 2
Oil & Gas Field Machinery Equipment Mfr
N.A.I.C.S.: 333132

Baker Hughes Italiana Srl (2)
Corso Delle Province 170, 95127, Catania,
Italy
Tel.: (39) 095434804
Sales Range: $10-24.9 Million
Emp.: 3
Chemical Delivery Services
N.A.I.C.S.: 213112

Baker Hughes SRL (2)
Av Principal De La Castellana Edificio Cen-
tro Letonia, Torre Ing Bank Piso 18 La Cast
Distrito CapitaL, Caracas,
Venezuela   (100%)
Tel.: (58) 2122772253
Sales Range: $50-74.9 Million
Emp.: 30
Support Activities for Oil & Gas Operations
N.A.I.C.S.: 213112

Baker Hughes Singapore Pvt (2)
273 Jalan Ahmad Ibrahim, Singapore,
629150, Singapore   (100%)
Tel.: (65) 68611855
Web Site: http://www.bakerhughes.com
Sales Range: $150-199.9 Million
Emp.: 200
Pipeline Management
N.A.I.C.S.: 213112

Subsidiary (Domestic):

Baker Petrolite LLC (2)
12645 W Airport Blvd, Sugar Land, TX
77478-6120
Tel.: (281) 276-5400
Web Site: http://newphase.bhge.com
Chemical Technology Solutions
N.A.I.C.S.: 325998

Subsidiary (Non-US):

Baker Petrolite (3)
Nieuwe Langeweg 145 147 Hoogvliet, 3194
DC, Rotterdam, Netherlands   (100%)
Tel.: (31) 102313800
Sales Range: $150-199.9 Million
Emp.: 2
Chemicals

N.A.I.C.S.: 213112

Baker Petrolite (3)
Level 5 191 St Georges Terrace, Perth,
6000, WA, Australia
Tel.: (61) 892177100
Web Site:
     http://www.bakerhughesdirect.com
Sales Range: $50-74.9 Million
Emp.: 80
Chemical Services & Products in the Hydro-
carbon Recovery & Processing, Pipeline
Transportation, Refining, Petrochemical,
Aquatic Herbicides & Polymers Industries
N.A.I.C.S.: 213112

**Baker Petrolite (Malaysia) Sdn.
Bhd.** (3)
25th Fl Menara Tan And Tan, Kuala Lum-
pur, Malaysia
Tel.: (60) 321647888
Web Site: http://www.bakerhughes.com
Sales Range: $10-24.9 Million
Emp.: 300
Oil, Gas & Geothermal Services
N.A.I.C.S.: 213112

Baker Petrolite Iberica, S.A. (3)
54 C/ Canarias, 28045, Madrid, Spain
Tel.: (34) 914672161
Web Site: http://www.bakerhughes.com
Sales Range: $10-24.9 Million
Emp.: 10
Oil, Gas & Geothermal Services
N.A.I.C.S.: 213112

Baker Petrolite Limited (3)
The Ark 201 Talgarth Road, Hammersmith,
London, W6 8BJ, United Kingdom
Tel.: (44) 515462855
Web Site: http://www.bakerhughes.com
Chemical Product Retailer
N.A.I.C.S.: 424690

Baker Petrolite Norge (3)
Ekofiskveien 1, 4056, Tananger,
Norway   (100%)
Tel.: (47) 51717950
Sales Range: $10-24.9 Million
Emp.: 7
Oil, Gas & Geothermal Services
N.A.I.C.S.: 213112

Baker Petrolite Saudi Arabia Ltd (3)
Ibn Al Haitham, PO Box 1940, Dammam,
31441, Saudi Arabia
Tel.: (966) 38471814
Sales Range: $25-49.9 Million
Emp.: 40
Oil, Gas & Geothermal Services
N.A.I.C.S.: 213112

P.T. Petrolite Indonesia Pratama (3)
Garden Centre 6th Floor Suite 6-7 Cilandak
Commercial Estate, PO Box 7508, Ji Cilan-
dak KKO, Jakarta, 12560,
Indonesia   (100%)
Tel.: (62) 217800737
Sales Range: $25-49.9 Million
Emp.: 15
Oil, Gas & Geothermal Services
N.A.I.C.S.: 213112

Subsidiary (Domestic):

ProductionQuest (2)
2851 Commerce St, Blacksburg, VA 24060-
6657
Tel.: (540) 961-0593
Web Site: http://www.bakerhughes.com
Sales Range: $25-49.9 Million
Emp.: 38
Well Monitoring & Chemical Injection Ser-
vices
N.A.I.C.S.: 213111

Quest Integrity Group, LLC (1)
10750 Cash Rd, Stafford, TX 77477
Tel.: (832) 500-1000
Web Site: http://www.questintegrity.com
Applications Software Programming Ser-
vices
N.A.I.C.S.: 513210

Subsidiary (Non-US):

Quest Integrity NZL Limited (2)
NZCIS Level 2 D Block 20 Somme Road,
Upper Hutt, 5018, New Zealand
Tel.: (64) 49786630
Web Site: http://www.questintegrity.com

Engineering Assessment Services
N.A.I.C.S.: 541330

Subsidiary (Non-US):

Quest Integrity MYS Sdn Bhd (3)
F-1-5 The Latitude Jalan C180/1 Dataran
C180 Batu 11, 43200, Kuala Selangor,
43200, Malaysia
Tel.: (60) 390552800
Application Software Development Services
N.A.I.C.S.: 541511

Subsidiary (Domestic):

Quest Integrity USA, LLC (2)
10750 Cash Rd, Stafford, TX 77477
Tel.: (281) 786-4700
Web Site: https://www.questintegrity.com
Sales Range: $25-49.9 Million
Emp.: 30
Pipeline Inspection Services
N.A.I.C.S.: 541990

Waygate Technologies USA, LP (1)
50 Industrial Park Rd, Lewistown, PA 17044
Tel.: (717) 242-0327
Ultrasonic Inspection, Thickness Measure-
ment; Training Courses; Ultrasonic Weld
Inspection
N.A.I.C.S.: 334419

BAKKT HOLDINGS, INC.
10000 Avalon Blvd Ste 1000, Al-
pharetta, GA 30009
Tel.: (678) 534-5849   Ky
Web Site: https://www.bakkt.com
Year Founded: 2020
BKKT—(NYSE)
Rev.: $54,567,000
Assets: $455,502,000
Liabilities: $119,428,000
Net Worth: $336,074,000
Earnings: ($578,105,000)
Emp.: 1,037
Fiscal Year-end: 12/31/22
Miscellaneous Financial Investment
Activities
N.A.I.C.S.: 523999
Andrew A. Main (Pres & CEO)

BALANCE LABS, INC.
350 Lincoln Rd 2nd Fl, Miami Beach,
FL 33139
Tel.: (305) 907-7600   DE
Web Site: https://www.balancelabs.co
Year Founded: 2014
BLNC—(OTCIQ)
Rev.: $247,500
Assets: $429,119
Liabilities: $4,590,431
Net Worth: ($4,161,312)
Earnings: ($768,351)
Fiscal Year-end: 12/31/22
Administrative Management & Gen-
eral Management Consulting Ser-
vices
N.A.I.C.S.: 541611
Carmen Villegas (Sec)
Derek Rawden-Lewis (VP-Bus Dev)
Robert M. Wolf (Co-CFO & Control-
ler)
Michael D. Farkas (Chm, Pres &
CEO)

Subsidiaries:

Balance Agrotech Co. (1)
1691 Michigan Ave Ste 601, Miami Beach,
FL 33139
Tel.: (305) 907-7600
Web Site: http://gdelaguardia.wixsite.com
Administrative Management Services
N.A.I.C.S.: 541611

BALCHEM CORPORATION
5 Paragon Dr, Montvale, NJ 07645
Tel.: (845) 326-5600   MD
Web Site: https://www.balchem.com
Year Founded: 1967
BCPC—(NASDAQ)
Rev.: $942,358,000
Assets: $1,624,512,000

Liabilities: $686,228,000
Net Worth: $938,284,000
Earnings: $105,367,000
Emp.: 1,340
Fiscal Year-end: 12/31/22
International, Secondary Market & All
Other Nondepository Credit Interme-
diation
N.A.I.C.S.: 522299
Theodore L. Harris (Chm, Pres &
CEO)
James Hyde (Sr VP/Gen Mgr-Human
Nutrition & Health)
Jonathan H. Griffin (Sr VP-Corp Dev)
Job Van Gunsteren (VP/Gen Mgr-
Specialty Products)
Hatsuki Miyata (Gen Counsel)
Martin Reid (Chief Supply Chain Offi-
cer)

Subsidiaries:

Albion Laboratories, Inc. (1)
67 S Main St Ste 200, Layton, UT 84041
Tel.: (801) 773-4631
Web Site: http://www.albionminerals.com
Manufactures & Sells Mineral Products for
Plant & Human Health
N.A.I.C.S.: 327999

Subsidiary (Domestic):

Cardinal Associates Inc. (2)
1000 W 8th St, Vancouver, WA 98660
Tel.: (360) 693-1883
Web Site: http://www.bergstromnutrition.com
Sales Range: $1-9.9 Million
Emp.: 29
Pharmaceutical Preparation Mfr
N.A.I.C.S.: 325412
Rodney Benjamin (Dir-Technical)
Tim Hammond (VP-Sls & Mktg)

BCP Ingredients, Inc. (1)
299 Extension St, Verona, MO 65769
Tel.: (417) 498-6625
Web Site: http://www.balchem.com
Emp.: 85
Chemical Products Mfr
N.A.I.C.S.: 325199

Balchem BV (1)
Herengracht 340 O, 1016 CG, Amsterdam,
Netherlands
Tel.: (31) 206231520
Basic Organic Chemical Mfr
N.A.I.C.S.: 325199

Balchem Italia, S.r.l. (1)
Via del Porto Snc, Ticino, 28040, Marano,
Italy
Tel.: (39) 03219791
Chemicals Mfr
N.A.I.C.S.: 325998

Bioscreen Technologies Srl (1)
Via Caduti di via Fani 830, 47032, Berti-
noro, FC, Italy
Tel.: (39) 0543449411
Web Site:
     http://www.bioscreentechnologies.com
Animal Feed Mfr
N.A.I.C.S.: 311119

Chemogas N.V. (1)
Westvaartdijk 85, 1850, Grimbergen, Bel-
gium
Tel.: (32) 22516087
Web Site: http://www.chemogas.com
Chemical Gases Mfr & Distr
N.A.I.C.S.: 325120
Jurgen De Smet (Mgr-Ops & Pur)
Guy De Backer (Mgr-Logistics)
Ann Van Elewyck (Mgr-Acctg)
Sebastien Verwilghen (Sls Dir)
Adamo Pia (Mgr-HR & SHEQ)
Geert Maes (Reg Sls Mgr-Intern)
Leon Deneef (Reg Sls Mgr-Intern)

Innovative Food Processors, Inc. (1)
2125 Airport Dr, Faribault, MN 55021
Tel.: (507) 334-2730
Web Site: http://www.ifpinc.biz
Food Powder Mfr
N.A.I.C.S.: 311999

Kappa Bioscience AS (1)
Silurveien 2, Oslo, 0380, Norway

Balchem Corporation—(Continued)

Tel.: (47) 2108 0680
Web Site: https://www.kappabio.com
Vitamin Product Mfr
N.A.I.C.S.: 325412

SensoryEffects, Inc. (1)
13723 Riverport Dr Ste 201, Maryland
Heights, MO 63043
Tel.: (314) 291-5444
Web Site:
    http://ingredientsolutions.balchem.com
Holding Company; Custom Food & Beverage Ingredients & Products Mfr & Distr
N.A.I.C.S.: 551112

Subsidiary (Domestic):

SensoryEffects Cereal Systems, Inc. (2)
4343 NW 38th St, Lincoln, NE 68524
Tel.: (402) 470-2021
Web Site: http://www.sensoryeffects.com
Breakfast Cereals & Cereal Ingredients Mfr & Whslr
N.A.I.C.S.: 311230

SensoryEffects Flavor Company (2)
231 Rock Industrial Park Dr, Bridgeton, MO 63044
Tel.: (314) 291-5444
Web Site: http://www.sensoryeffects.com
Food & Beverage Ingredients Mfr & Distr
N.A.I.C.S.: 311999

SensoryEffects Powder Systems, Inc. (2)
136 Fox Run Dr, Defiance, OH 43512-1394
Tel.: (419) 783-5518
Web Site: http://www.sensoryeffects.com
Sales Range: $25-49.9 Million
Emp.: 150
Custom Powder Food Ingredients & Products Mfr & Distr
N.A.I.C.S.: 311999

Stereo Sdn Bhd (1)
No 37 Lorong Sungai Puloh 1A/KU 6,
41050, Klang, Selangor, Malaysia
Tel.: (60) 332902263
Web Site: http://www.stereocorp.com
Sterilization Gas Distribution Services
N.A.I.C.S.: 221210

BALL CORPORATION
9200 W 108th Cir, Westminster, CO 80021
Tel.: (303) 469-3131   IN
Web Site: https://www.ball.com
Year Founded: 1880
DALL—(NYSE)
Rev.: $14,029,000,000
Assets: $19,303,000,000
Liabilities: $15,466,000,000
Net Worth: $3,837,000,000
Earnings: $707,000,000
Emp.: 21,000
Fiscal Year-end: 12/31/23
Holding Company; Metal & Plastic Packaging Products Mfr ; Aerospace Products Mfr
N.A.I.C.S.: 551112
Charles E. Baker (Gen Counsel, Sec & VP)
Ann T. Scott (VP-IR)
Daniel W. Fisher (Chm & CEO)
Nate C. Carey (VP & Controller)
Courtney K. Reynolds (VP-Comm & Corp Affairs)
Howard H. Yu (CFO & Exec VP)
Ronald J. Lewis (COO-Global Beverage Pkg & Sr VP)
Stacey Valy Panayiotou (Chief HR Officer & Sr VP)
Dave Kaufman (Pres)
Ramon Arratia (VP)
Brian Gabbard (CIO)
Deron Goodwin (Treas)

Subsidiaries:

BD Print Limited (1)
Marathon Place Moss Side Industrial Es-

tate, Preston, PR26 7QN, Lancashire, United Kingdom
Tel.: (44) 1772435050
Web Site: https://www.bdprints.co.uk
Packaging Can Distr
N.A.I.C.S.: 423510
Glenn Whewell (Mng Dir)
Alan Ferguson (Dir-Sls)
Michael Rawcliffe (Dir-Ops)
Jocelyn Perkins (Fin Dir)
Geoff Bibby (Mgr)
Paul Hollowood (Sr Mgr)
Louise Bowtell (Mgr)
Dave Webster (Dir-Purchasing)

Ball (UK) Holdings, Ltd. (1)
Lekside, Chester, CH4 9QT, United Kingdom
Tel.: (44) 1244681155
Sales Range: $25-49.9 Million
Emp.: 40
Baverage Cans Mfr
N.A.I.C.S.: 332431

Ball Advanced Aluminum Technologies Corp. (1)
56 Dunsmore Rd, Verona, VA 24482
Tel.: (540) 248-2703
Emp.: 80
Aluminum Material Mfr
N.A.I.C.S.: 331315
Stan Platek (Pres & CEO)

Ball Aerocan Europe S.A.S. (1)
28 Rue Des Arts, 59033, Lille, France
Tel.: (33) 320536860
Emp.: 13
Aluminum Packaging Product Mfr
N.A.I.C.S.: 331315
Federico Bisio (Dir-Sls & Mktg)

Subsidiary (Non-US):

Ball Aerocan CZ s.r.o. (2)
Palackeho 639, Velim, 281 01, Kolin, Czech Republic
Tel.: (420) 321739820
Web Site: http://www.aerocan.cz
Aluminum Packaging Product Mfr
N.A.I.C.S.: 331315
Jan Kliment (Plant Mgr)

Subsidiary (Domestic):

Ball Aerocan-France S.A.S (2)
COPAL 489 route de Marcollin, Route de la Plaine, 38270, Beaurepaire, France
Tel.: (33) 474792444
Aluminum Packaging Product Mfr
N.A.I.C.S.: 331315
Goran Milenkovic (Dir-R&D)
Christel Paret (Project Mgr-R&D)

Subsidiary (Non-US):

Ball Aerocan UK Ltd. (2)
Folly Road, Roundway, Devizes, SN10 2HT, Wiltshire, United Kingdom
Tel.: (44) 1380732400
Emp.: 140
Aluminum Packaging Product Mfr
N.A.I.C.S.: 331315
Jason Galley (Dir-R&D)

Ball Aerocan Mexico S.A. de C.V. (1)
Eje 140 950 Zona Industrial, 78395, San Luis Potosi, Mexico
Tel.: (52) 4441615074
Aluminum Packaging Product Mfr
N.A.I.C.S.: 331315

Ball Aerosol Packaging India Private Limited (1)
Plot SM-9/2 GIDC Estate Sanand II, Village BOL Taluka Sanand, Ahmedabad, 382110, Gujarat, India
Tel.: (91) 2717661800
Aerosol Packaging Services
N.A.I.C.S.: 561910

Ball Aerospace & Technologies Corp. (1)
1600 Commerce St, Boulder, CO 80301-2734 (100%)
Tel.: (303) 939-4000
Web Site: https://www.ballaerospace.com
Sales Range: $600-649.9 Million
Mfr of Electro-Optic Sensors, Electro-Mechanical Devices, Tactical Products & Stored Cryogen Systems

N.A.I.C.S.: 541330
Jeffrey B. Osterkamp (VP-Security)
Makenzie Lystrup (VP& Gen Mgr)
Dave Kaufman (Pres)
Alison Medbery (VP-Finance)
Vikki A. Schiff (VP-Human Resources)
Steven A. Smith (VP& Gen Mgr)
Mike Gazarik (VP-Engineering)
Paula Burns (VP-Operations)
Fred Doyle (VP)
Jake Sauer (VP & Gen Mgr)
Mark Healy (VP & Gen Mgr)
Alan Frohbieter (Chief Engr & VP)
Kathryn E. Haber (Sr Dir)
Michael H. Witt (Chief Security Officer & Sr Dir-Security)
Jeanne Atwell (VP)
Murali Krishnan (VP/Gen Mgr-Ground Sys & Svcs)
Donald Speranzini (VP/Gen Mgr-Ground Sys & Svcs)

Subsidiary (Domestic):

Wavefront Technologies, Inc. (2)
7090 Columbia Gateway Dr Ste 160, Columbia, MD 21046 (100%)
Tel.: (301) 490-0013
Web Site: http://www.ball.com
Communications & IT Support to U.S. Government & Commercial Industries
N.A.I.C.S.: 541512
Timothy Calais (Owner)

Ball Asia Pacific Limited (1)
Units 1610-1619 Tower 1 Grand Century Place, 193 Prince Edward Rd West Mongkok, Kowloon, China (Hong Kong) (100%)
Tel.: (852) 26856600
Web Site: http://www.ball.com
Holding Company; Food, Beverage & Other Consumer Goods Packaging Products Mfr & Distr
N.A.I.C.S.: 551112

Ball Beverage Packaging Egypt SAE (1)
Phase 3 Plot 2, 6th of October Industrial Zone, 6th of October City, Egypt
Tel.: (20) 238333514
Beverage Packaging Services
N.A.I.C.S.: 561910

Ball Chile S.A. (1)
Km 16 1/2 Ex Panamericana Norte Avenida Presidente Eduardo Frei, Montalva Camino La Montana - N 1294 - Comuna de Lampa, Santiago, Chile
Tel.: (56) 224432525
Packaging Can Distr
N.A.I.C.S.: 423510

Ball Europe GmbH (1)
Leutschenbachstrasse 52, 8050, Zurich, Switzerland (100%)
Tel.: (41) 445597100
Web Site: http://www.argaghgroup.com
Business Support Services, Including Procurement, Sales & Marketing Services
N.A.I.C.S.: 561499
Frank Weekers (Mng Dir)

Subsidiary (Non-US):

Ball Trading France S.A.S. (2)
Office La Ciotat Zone Industrielle Athelia IV, 13600, La Ciotat, France
Tel.: (33) 442088656
Metal Container Distr
N.A.I.C.S.: 423840
Yann Rodi (Dir-Sls-Southern Europe & Export)
Philippe Vanhelst (Mgr-Sls-France)

Ball Trading Germany GmbH (2)
Hauptstr 170, 56575, Weissenthurm, Germany
Tel.: (49) 2637607521
Metal Container Distr
N.A.I.C.S.: 423840
Frank Sasse (Dir-Sls-Central, Eastern Europe & Retail)
Holger Grabow (Mgr-Sls-Northern & Southern Reg)
Daniel Etchemendy (Mgr-Sls-Western)

Ball Trading Poland Sp. z o.o. (2)
ul Krasickiego 150/152, Radomsko, 97-500, Poland
Tel.: (48) 446859214 (100%)

Web Site: http://www.ball-europe.com
Metal Container Distr
N.A.I.C.S.: 423840

Ball Trading UK Ltd. (2)
Lakeside Chester Business Park, Wrexham Road, Chester, CH4 9QT, United Kingdom (100%)
Tel.: (44) 1244681155
Web Site: http://www.ball-europe.com
Metal Container Distr
N.A.I.C.S.: 423840

The Ball Trading Netherlands B.V. (2)
Parallelweg 1, 5349 AD, Oss, Netherlands (100%)
Tel.: (31) 412 665 237
Web Site: http://www.ball-europe.com
Metal Container Distr
N.A.I.C.S.: 423840

Ball Foundation-not for profit (1)
526 N Main St, Glen Ellyn, IL 60137
Tel.: (630) 469-6270
Web Site: https://www.ballfoundation.org
Packaging Can Distr
N.A.I.C.S.: 423510
Anna Ball (Pres)
Susannah Ball (VP)
Peg Hendershot (VP)
Todd Billings (VP)
Kevin Field (Dir-Res)
Victoria Harmon (Coord-Res-Assessment Sys)
Lynne Bournazos (Coord-Customer Svc)
Georgia Koch (Coord-Community Outreach)

Ball Global Business Services Europe and AMEA d.o.o. Beograd-Novi Beograd (1)
Batajnicki drum 21A, 11080, Belgrade, Serbia
Tel.: (381) 113770600
Packaging Can Distr
N.A.I.C.S.: 423510

Ball Metal Beverage Container Corp. (1)
9300 W 108th Cir, Broomfield, CO 80021-3682 (100%)
Tel.: (303) 469-5511
Sales Range: $1-4.9 Billion
Emp.: 450
Metal Beverage Containers Mfr
N.A.I.C.S.: 332431
Michael D. Herdman (Chief Comml Officer)

Plant (Domestic):

Ball Metal Beverage Container Corp. (2)
1800 Reynolds Ave, Kansas City, MO 64120
Tel.: (816) 242-9200
Web Site: http://www.ball.com
Sales Range: $100-124.9 Million
Aluminium Cans Mfr
N.A.I.C.S.: 332431

Ball Metal Beverage Container Corp. (2)
500 Crenshaw Blvd, Westminster, CA 90503-1705
Tel.: (310) 212-3600
Web Site: http://www.ball.com
Sales Range: $75-99.9 Million
Emp.: 140
Aluminium Cans Mfr
N.A.I.C.S.: 332431

Ball Metal Beverage Container Corp. (2)
6600 Will Rogers Blvd, Fort Worth, TX 76140-6006
Tel.: (817) 551-3156
Web Site: http://www.ball.com
Sales Range: $50-74.9 Million
Emp.: 180
Aluminium Cans Mfr
N.A.I.C.S.: 332431

Ball Metal Beverage Container Corp. (2)
91-320 Komohana St, Kapolei, HI 96707-1714
Tel.: (808) 682-1202
Web Site: http://www.ball.com
Sales Range: $100-124.9 Million
Aluminium Cans Mfr
N.A.I.C.S.: 332431

Ball Metal Food Container Corp. **(1)**
10 Longs Peak Dr, Broomfield, CO
80021-3682 **(100%)**
Tel.: (303) 469-5511
Web Site: http://www.ball.com
Sales Range: $800-899.9 Million
Emp.: 1,940
Plain & Lithographed All-Metal Containers
Mfr
N.A.I.C.S.: 311422

Subsidiary (Domestic):

Ball Metal Food Container (Oakdale),
LLC **(2)**
300 W Greger St, Oakdale, CA 95361
Tel.: (209) 848-6500
Metal Container Mfr
N.A.I.C.S.: 331315

Ball Packaging Corp. **(1)**
10 Longs Peak Dr, Broomfield, CO 80021
Tel.: (303) 939-4000
Web Site: http://www.ball.com
Metal Container Mfr
N.A.I.C.S.: 332431

Subsidiary (Non-US):

Ball Packaging Europe Holding
B.V. **(2)**
Parallelweg 1, Oss, 5349 AD, Netherlands
Tel.: (31) 412665911
Web Site: https://www.ballpackaging.com
Sales Range: $25-49.9 Million
Emp.: 200
Packaging Materials Mfr
N.A.I.C.S.: 332431
David Banjai (Gen Mgr)

Subsidiary (Non-US):

Ball Packaging Europe Lublin Sp. z
o.o. **(3)**
Mazowieckie Wisniowa 40, 02-520, War-
saw, Poland
Tel.: (48) 225424082
Packaging Materials Mfr
N.A.I.C.S.: 332439

Ball Packaging Europe Trading Sp. z
o.o. **(3)**
ul Wisniowa 40 Mazowieckie, Warsaw, 02-
520, Mazowieckie, Poland
Tel.: (48) 225424081
Packaging Materials Mfr
N.A.I.C.S.: 332439

Ball Packaging Europe France
S.A.S. **(1)**
Zone d Entreprises de Bergues, 59380,
Bierne, France
Tel.: (33) 328687673
Web Site: https://www.ball.com
Aluminum Container Product Mfr
N.A.I.C.S.: 331315

Ball Packaging Europe Handelsges
mbH **(1)**
Simmeringer Hauptstrasse 24, Vienna,
1110, Austria
Tel.: (43) 174040211
Web Site: http://www.ball.com
Emp.: 4
Metal Container Mfr
N.A.I.C.S.: 332439

Ball Packaging Europe Holding
GmbH & Co. KG **(1)**
(61%)
Tel.: (49) 21021300
Web Site: http://www.ball-europe.com
Sales Range: $900-999.9 Million
Emp.: 100
Holding Company; Food, Beverage & Other
Consumer Goods Metal Packaging Prod-
ucts Mfr & Distr
N.A.I.C.S.: 551112

Plant (Non-US):

Ball Packaging Europe Bierne
S.A.S. **(2)**
(100%)
Tel.: (33) 328687673
Web Site: http://www.ball-europe.com
Sales Range: $100-124.9 Million
Metal Tank Mfr
N.A.I.C.S.: 332431

Ball Packaging Europe GmbH **(2)**
(100%)
Tel.: (49) 39206640
Web Site: http://www.ball-europe.com
Sales Range: $75-99.9 Million
Emp.: 85
Packaging Products Mfr
N.A.I.C.S.: 332431

Ball Packaging Europe GmbH -
Braunschweig **(2)**
Tel.: (49) 5313940
Web Site: http://www.ball-europe.com
Sales Range: $75-99.9 Million
Emp.: 192
Metal Tank Mfr
N.A.I.C.S.: 332431

Ball Packaging Europe La Ciotat
S.A.S. **(2)**
Tel.: (33) 442088600
Web Site: http://www.ball-europe.com
Sales Range: $75-99.9 Million
Emp.: 170
Metal Tank Mfr
N.A.I.C.S.: 332431

Subsidiary (Non-US):

Ball Packaging Europe Radomsko
Sp.z o.o. **(2)**
Tel.: (48) 446821052
Packaging Materials Mfr
N.A.I.C.S.: 332439

recan d.o.o. **(2)**
Tel.: (381) 112087460
Metal Can Recycling Services
N.A.I.C.S.: 332439

Ball Packaging Products Canada
Corp. **(1)**
1506 Wentworth Street West, Whitby, L1N
7C1, ON, Canada **(100%)**
Tel.: (905) 666-3600
Web Site: https://www.ball.com
Sales Range: $350-399.9 Million
Aluminum & Steel Cans Mfr
N.A.I.C.S.: 332431

Ball Technologies Holdings Corp. **(1)**
10 Longs Peak Dr, Broomfield, CO 80021
Tel.: (303) 939-6100
Holding Company
N.A.I.C.S.: 551112

Copal S.A.S. **(1)**
489 route de Marcollin, 38270, Beaurepaire-
d'Isere, France
Tel.: (33) 474792444
Packaging Can Distr
N.A.I.C.S.: 423510
Arnaud Reymann (Mgr-Production)

Envases Universales Rexam de Cen-
troamerica SA **(1)**
Kilometro 32 Ruta al Pacifico Parque Indus-
trial Flor de Campo, Guatemala, Guatemala
Tel.: (502) 66434000
Web Site: https://www.ecaguatemala.com
Packaging Can Distr
N.A.I.C.S.: 423510

Envases del Istmo SA **(1)**
Corregimiento de Coco Solo Edificio 1148,
Colon, 500, Panama
Tel.: (507) 4305038
Packaging Can Distr
N.A.I.C.S.: 423510

Hanil Can Co Limited **(1)**
21 Yusangongdan 4-gil, Yangsan,
Gyeongsangnam-do, Korea (South)
Tel.: (82) 553706666
Web Site: http://www.hanilcan.co.kr
Packaging Can Distr
N.A.I.C.S.: 423510
Dong-Taek Jung (Pres)

Latas Industria De Embalagens De
Aluminio De Brasil Ltda. **(1)**
Rod Br 101 Km 112 S/N Sede, Alagoinhas,
48010-970, Bahia, Brazil
Tel.: (55) 1121712423
Packaging Can Distr
N.A.I.C.S.: 423510

Rexam Limited **(1)**
100 Capability Green, Luton, LU1 3LG,
United Kingdom **(100%)**

Tel.: (44) 1582408999
Holding Company; Beverage Can Mfr
N.A.I.C.S.: 551112
Nikki Rolfe (Dir-HR)

Subsidiary (Non-US):

Ball Beverage Can Americas, S.A. de
C.V. **(2)**
Avda Coahuila 7b Zona Industrial Benito
Juarez, 76120, Queretaro, Mexico
Tel.: (52) 4422963300
Baverage Cans Mfr
N.A.I.C.S.: 332431

Ball Beverage Can Egypt S.A.E. **(2)**
Phase 3 6th of October Industrial Zone Plot
2, 6th of October City, Egypt
Tel.: (20) 238333514
Packaging Can Distr
N.A.I.C.S.: 423510

Ball Beverage Can South America
SA **(2)**
3434-Condominio Mario Henrique
Simonsen-Bloco 2 6 7, Andares Barra da
Tijuca, Rio de Janeiro, 22640-102,
Brazil **(100%)**
Tel.: (55) 2121043300
Web Site: http://www.ball.com
Aluminum Beverage Can Mfr & Distr
N.A.I.C.S.: 332431

Ball Beverage Packaging (India) Pri-
vate Limited **(2)**
Taluka Panvel Maharashtra Taloja Industrial
Area District Raigad, Mumbai, 410 208,
India
Tel.: (91) 2230911300
Packaging Can Distr
N.A.I.C.S.: 423510

Subsidiary (Domestic):

Ball Beverage Packaging Europe
Limited **(2)**
100 Capability Green, Luton, LU1 3LG,
United Kingdom **(100%)**
Tel.: (44) 1582408999
Beverage Metal Cans Mfr
N.A.I.C.S.: 332431
Jason Ramskill (VP-Ops)

Subsidiary (Non-US):

Ball Beverage Packaging Czech Re-
public sro **(3)**
Dysina 292, 330 02, Dysina, Czech
Republic **(100%)**
Tel.: (420) 378011511
Aluminium Cans Mfr
N.A.I.C.S.: 332431

Ball Beverage Packaging Fosie
AB **(3)**
Stenaeldersgatan 4, 200 39, Malmo,
Sweden **(100%)**
Tel.: (46) 40209300
Aluminium Cans Mfr
N.A.I.C.S.: 332431

Ball Beverage Packaging France
SAS **(3)**
BP 17 Usine de Mont, 64170, Mont,
France **(100%)**
Tel.: (33) 559387777
Aluminium Cans Mfr
N.A.I.C.S.: 332431

Ball Beverage Packaging Fredericia
A/S **(3)**
Vejlbyvej 29, Fredericia, 700, Denmark
Tel.: (45) 76200208
Packaging Can Distr
N.A.I.C.S.: 423510

Ball Beverage Packaging Gelsen-
kirchen GmbH **(3)**
Emscherstrasse 46 Buer, 45891, Gelsen-
kirchen, Germany
Tel.: (49) 20970020
Packaging Can Distr
N.A.I.C.S.: 423510

Ball Beverage Packaging Iberica
SL **(3)**
Poligono Industrial Silva, La Selva Del
Camp, 43470, Tarragona, Spain **(100%)**
Tel.: (34) 977758700
Aluminium Cans Mfr

N.A.I.C.S.: 332431

Ball Beverage Packaging Ireland
Limited **(3)**
Cork Road Industrial Park, Waterford,
Ireland **(100%)**
Tel.: (353) 51359100
Aluminium Cans Mfr
N.A.I.C.S.: 332431

Ball Beverage Packaging Italia
SRL **(3)**
Via Molino Di Sopra 64, Nogara, 37054,
Verona, Italy **(100%)**
Tel.: (39) 0442537555
Web Site: http://www.ball.com
Aluminium Cans Mfr
N.A.I.C.S.: 332431

Plant (Domestic):

Ball Beverage Packaging Italia SRL -
San Martino **(4)**
Localita Campotrino Zona Inustriale, San
Martino, 66010, Sulla Marrucina, Italy
Tel.: (39) 087180391
Aluminium Cans Mfr
N.A.I.C.S.: 332431

Subsidiary (Non-US):

Ball Beverage Packaging Ludesch
GmbH **(3)**
Neugut 1 Ludesch, 6713, Bludenz, Austria
Tel.: (43) 5550214290
Packaging Can Distr
N.A.I.C.S.: 423510

Ball Beverage Packaging Mantsala
Oy **(3)**
Mattilantie 60 Numminen, 04660, Helsinki,
Finland
Tel.: (358) 505977232
Packaging Can Distr
N.A.I.C.S.: 423510

Ball Beverage Packaging Oss
BV **(3)**
IJsselstraat 30, 5347 KG, Oss, Netherlands
Tel.: (31) 412660800
Packaging Can Distr
N.A.I.C.S.: 423510

Ball Beverage Packaging Widnau
GmbH **(3)**
Espenstrasse 125 Widnau, 9443, Saint Gal-
len, Switzerland
Tel.: (41) 717279600
Packaging Can Distr
N.A.I.C.S.: 423510

Subsidiary (Non-US):

Ball Beverage Packaging Naro-
Fominsk LLC **(2)**
Novaya Olkhovka 1 Zavodskaya Str Naro-
Fominsk, Moscow, 143325, Russia
Tel.: (7) 4957974455
Packaging Can Distr
N.A.I.C.S.: 423510

Subsidiary (Domestic):

Ball Beverage Packaging UK
Ltd. **(2)**
Northfields Drive Northfields, Milton Keynes,
MK15 0DA, Bucks, United
Kingdom **(100%)**
Tel.: (44) 1908240505
Aluminium Cans Mfr
N.A.I.C.S.: 332431

Subsidiary (Non-US):

Ball Beverage Packaging Vsevo-
lozhsk LLC **(2)**
Quarter 5 Industrial Zone Kirpichny Zavod,
Vsevolozhsk Leningrad, Saint Petersburg,
188640, Russia
Tel.: (7) 81233608600
Packaging Can Distr
N.A.I.C.S.: 423510

Ball Beverage Turkey Paketleme
Sanayi ve Ticaret AS **(2)**
Organise Sanayi Bolgesi 50 YIL Caddesi,
Manisa, 45030, Turkiye **(100%)**
Tel.: (90) 2362262900
Aluminium Cans Mfr
N.A.I.C.S.: 332431

Ball Corporation—(Continued)

Bahadir Seymen *(Mgr-Procurement)*

Subsidiary (Domestic):

Rexam Pension Trustees Limited (2)
Weald Court 101-103 Tonbridge Road,
Hildenborough, Tonbridge, TN11 9BF, Kent,
United Kingdom
Tel.: (44) 1732835100
Web Site:
https://www.rexampensionplan.co.uk
Packaging Can Distr
N.A.I.C.S.: 423510

Sario Grundstucks-
Vermietungsgesellschaft mbH & CO.
Objekt Elfi (1)
Konigsallee 106, 40215, Dusseldorf, Germany
Tel.: (49) 21199460
Metal Container Mfr
N.A.I.C.S.: 331315

Sekopac d.o.o. (1)
Bulevar Mihajla Pupina 10 B ulaz 2 3 sprat,
11070, Novi Beograd, Serbia
Tel.: (381) 113130153
Web Site: http://www.sekopak.com
Waste Management Services
N.A.I.C.S.: 562111
Violeta Belanovic Kokir *(Gen Mgr)*

Slopak (1)
Vodovodna cesta 100, 1000, Ljubljana, Slovenia
Tel.: (386) 15600250
Web Site: https://www.slopak.si
Packaging Can Distr
N.A.I.C.S.: 423510

Thai Beverage Can Ltd. (1)
99 Moo 9 SIL Industrial Land Nongplakradi
Road, Nongpling, Nongkhae, 18140, Saraburi, Thailand
Tel.: (66) 36373600
Web Site: https://thaibeveragecan.com
Emp.: 500
Packaging Can Distr
N.A.I.C.S.: 423510
Saovaluck Chayavivatkul *(Exec VP-Admin)*

recan Organizacja Odzysku S.A. (1)
Ul Mariensztat 8, Warsaw, 00-302, Poland
Tel.: (48) 225389172
Industrial Product Recycling Services
N.A.I.C.S.: 325991

BALLISTIC RECOVERY SYS-
TEMS, INC.
41383 US Hwy 1, Pinebluff, NC
28373-8330
Tel.: (651) 457-7491   MN
Web Site: https://brsaerospace.com
Year Founded: 1980
BRSI—(OTCQB)
Whole-Aircraft Parachute Recovery
Systems for General Aviation Mfr
N.A.I.C.S.: 541715
Enrique Dillon *(CEO)*

BALLSTON SPA BANCORP
INC.
990 State Route 67, Ballston Spa,
NY 12020
Tel.: (518) 363-8199
Web Site: https://www.bsnb.com
Year Founded: 1838
BSPA—(OTCQB)
Sales Range: Less than $1 Million
Emp.: 114
Banking Services
N.A.I.C.S.: 522110
Timothy J. Provost *(Vice Chm)*
Robert E. Van Vranken *(Chm)*
Christopher R. Dowd *(Pres & CEO)*
Ervin M. Murray *(CIO & Sr VP)*
Timothy E. Blow *(CFO, Sec & Exec
VP)*
Margaret K. de Koning *(Chief Banking Officer & Exec VP)*
Tammy L. Zaiko *(Sr VP-Trust & Investments)*

Donna D. Avery *(VP-Retail Sls)*
John B. Chandler *(VP-Trust & Investments)*
Timothy J. Collins *(VP-Comml Lending)*
Leslie S. Dorsey *(VP-HR-Ballston
Spa National Bank)*
Margaret G. Gavin *(VP-Fin)*
William F. MacDuff *(VP-Deposit Ops)*
Deborah A. Poulin *(VP-Credit Admin)*
Susan M. Slovic *(VP-Mktg)*
Thomas M. White *(VP-Trust & Investments)*
Patricia Fogg *(Mgr-Relationship)*

BALLY'S CORPORATION
100 Westminster St, Providence, RI
02903
Tel.: (401) 475-8474   DE
Web Site: https://www.ballys.com
BALY—(NYSE)
Rev.: $2,449,073,000
Assets: $6,861,103,000
Liabilities: $6,225,249,000
Net Worth: $635,854,000
Earnings: ($187,500,000)
Emp.: 10,500
Fiscal Year-end: 12/31/23
Holding Company; Casino, Casino
Hotel & Racetrack Owner & Operator
N.A.I.C.S.: 551112
Robeson M. Reeves *(CEO)*
Jaymin B. Patel *(Vice Chm)*
Marcus Glover *(CFO & Exec VP)*
H. C. Charles Diao *(Treas & Sr VP-
Fin)*
George T. Papanier *(Pres)*
Kim Barker Lee *(Chief Legal Officer)*

Subsidiaries:

Bally's Atlantic City LLC (1)
1900 Pacific Ave, Atlantic City, NJ 08401
Tel.: (609) 340-2000
Web Site: http://www.ballysac.com
Sales Range: $200-249.9 Million
Emp.: 5,000
Hotel & Casino
N.A.I.C.S.: 721120

Dover Downs Gaming & Entertain-
ment, Inc. (1)
1131 N DuPont Hwy, Dover, DE 19901
Tel.: (302) 674-4600
Hotel, Casino & Harness Horse Racing
Track Operator
N.A.I.C.S.: 713290

Subsidiary (Domestic):

Dover Downs, Inc (2)
1131 N Dupont Hwy, Dover, DE 19901
Tel.: (302) 674-4600
Sales Range: $75-99.9 Million
Casino Hotel Services
N.A.I.C.S.: 721120
Denis L. McGlynn *(Pres & CEO)*
Timothy R. Horne *(CFO, Treas & Sr VP-Fin)*

Fantasy Sports Shark, LLC (1)
1165 Lincoln Ave Ste 8401, San Jose, CA
95125
Web Site: https://www.monkeyknifefight.com
Fantasy Sports Services
N.A.I.C.S.: 711219

Gamesys Group plc (1)
Tel.: (44) 2074788100
Web Site: https://www.gamesysgroup.com
Software Development Services
N.A.I.C.S.: 541511
Keith Laslop *(CFO)*

Subsidiary (Non-US):

Simplicity V8 Hong Kong Ltd. (2)
Units 602-8 6/F Dah Sing Financial Centre
248 Queen's Road East, Wan Chai, Hong
Kong, China (Hong Kong)
Tel.: (852) 34605562
Web Site: https://www.sv8hk.com
Software Development Services
N.A.I.C.S.: 541511

Golden Mardi Gras Casino (1)

300 Main St, Black Hawk, CO 80422
Tel.: (303) 582-2629
Web Site:
http://www.thegoldengatescasino.com
Casinos Services
N.A.I.C.S.: 713210

Isle of Capri Casinos, Inc. (1)
1800 E Frnt St, Kansas City, MO 64120
Tel.: (816) 855-7777
Web Site:
http://www.isleofcaprikansascity.com
Lodging & Entertainment Facilities Operator
N.A.I.C.S.: 713990
Malia Jackson *(Dir-HR)*

Subsidiary (Domestic):

IOC-Kansas City, Inc. (2)
1800 E Frnt St, Kansas City, MO 64120
Tel.: (816) 855-4165
Web Site:
http://www.isleofcaprikansascity.com
Casino Hotel Operator
N.A.I.C.S.: 721120

Isle of Capri Bettendorf, L.C. (2)
1777 Isle Pkwy, Bettendorf, IA 52722
Tel.: (563) 441-7000
Web Site: http://www.islebettendorf.com
Casino Hotel Operator
N.A.I.C.S.: 721120

Isle of Capri Black Hawk, LLC (2)
401 Main St, Black Hawk, CO 80422
Tel.: (303) 998-7777
Web Site: http://www.isleblackhawk.com
Casino Hotel Operator
N.A.I.C.S.: 721120

PPI, Inc. (2)
1 Caesars Palace Dr, Las Vegas, NV 89109
Tel.: (954) 972-2000
Web Site: http://www.islepompanopark.com
Casino Operator
N.A.I.C.S.: 721120

Rainbow Casino-Vicksburg Partner-
ship, L.P. (2)
1380 Warrenton Rd, Vicksburg, MS 39180
Tel.: (601) 636-7575
Web Site: http://www.ladyluckvicksburg.com
Casino Operator
N.A.I.C.S.: 721120

Riverboat Corporation of
Mississippi (2)
151 Beach Blvd, Biloxi, MS 39530
Tel.: (228) 435-5400
Web Site: https://www.goldennugget.com
Casino Hotel Operator
N.A.I.C.S.: 713990
Leslie Barfield *(Dir-Sls)*
Scott King *(VP-Mktg)*

Premier Entertainment Biloxi,
LLC (1)
777 Beach Blvd, Biloxi, MS 39530
Tel.: (228) 374-7625
Web Site: http://www.hrhcbiloxi.com
Casino
N.A.I.C.S.: 721120

Telescope UK Ltd. (1)
Tel.: (44) 1132383066
Web Site: https://telescopegroup.co.uk
Advertising & Marketing Services
N.A.I.C.S.: 541810
Tracy Haunch *(Acct Dir & Head)*
Nicola Lawless *(Head-Commercial)*
Stuart Black *(Head-Sales)*
Ian Leach *(Mng Dir)*
Carl Garnett *(CEO)*

Twin River - Tiverton, LLC (1)
777 Tiverton Casino Blvd, Tiverton, RI
02878-2497
Tel.: (401) 816-6000
Web Site: http://www.twinrivertiverton.com
Casino Hotel Services
N.A.I.C.S.: 721120

UTGR, Inc. (1)
100 Twin River Rd, Lincoln, RI 02865
Casino Hotel Services
N.A.I.C.S.: 721120

BALTIC INTERNATIONAL USA,
INC.

6002 Rogerdale Rd Ste 500, Houston, TX 77072
Tel.: (713) 961-9299   TX
Web Site: https://www.baltic-intl.com
Year Founded: 1991
BISA—(OTCIQ)
Administrative Management & General Management Consulting Services
N.A.I.C.S.: 541611
David A. Grossman *(CEO, CFO &
Sec)*

BANC OF CALIFORNIA, INC.
3 MacArthur Pl, Santa Ana, CA
92707   MD
Web Site: https://www.bancofcal.com
Year Founded: 2002
BANC—(NYSE)
Rev.: $390,122,000
Assets: $9,197,016,000
Liabilities: $8,237,398,000
Net Worth: $959,618,000
Earnings: $120,939,000
Emp.: 685
Fiscal Year-end: 12/31/22
Bank Holding Company
N.A.I.C.S.: 551111
Jared M. Wolff *(Vice Chm, Pres &
CEO)*
Diana C. Hanson *(Sr VP & Controller)*
John K. Sotoodeh *(COO)*
Raymond J. Rindone *(Chief Acctg
Officer, Deputy CFO & Exec VP)*
Olivia Lindsay *(Chief Risk Officer &
Exec VP)*
Joseph Kauder *(CFO & Exec VP)*
Robert G. Dyck *(Exec VP)*

Subsidiaries:

Banc of California, N.A. (1)
3 MacArthur Pl, Santa Ana, CA
92707   (100%)
Web Site: https://www.bancofcal.com
Emp.: 1,600
Federal Savings Bank
N.A.I.C.S.: 522180
Jared M. Wolff *(Chm, Pres & CEO)*
Robert G. Dyck *(Chief Credit Officer & Exec
VP)*
Diana C. Hanson *(Sr VP & Controller)*
Ido Dotan *(Chief Admin Officer, Gen Counsel & Exec VP)*
John K. Sotoodeh *(COO)*
Raymond J. Rindone *(Chief Acctg Officer,
Deputy CFO & Exec VP)*
Olivia Lindsay *(Chief Risk Officer)*
Joseph Kauder *(Exec VP)*

PacWest Bancorp (1)
9701 Wilshire Blvd Ste 700, Beverly Hills,
CA 90212
Tel.: (310) 887-8500
Web Site: https://www.pacwestbancorp.com
Rev.: $1,631,316,000
Assets: $41,228,936,000
Liabilities: $37,278,405,000
Net Worth: $3,950,531,000
Earnings: $423,613,000
Emp.: 2,438
Fiscal Year-end: 12/31/2022
Bank Holding Company
N.A.I.C.S.: 551111
Monica L. Sparks *(Chief Acctg Officer &
Exec VP)*
Bryan M. Corsini *(Chief Credit Officer &
Exec VP)*
Christopher D. Blake *(Pres/CEO-
Community Bank Grp & Exec VP)*
Bart R. Olson *(Exec VP-Fin)*
Mark T. Yung *(COO & Exec VP)*
Stanley R. Ivie *(Chief Risk Officer & Exec
VP)*
Rebecca H. Cordes *(Exec VP-HR)*
Angela M. W. Kelley *(Gen Counsel)*
William J. Black Jr. *(Exec VP)*

Subsidiary (Domestic):

Civic Financial Services, LLC (2)
2015 Manhattan Beach Blvd Ste 106, Redondo Beach, CA 90278

Web Site: https://civicfs.com
Mortgage Broker & Real Estate Services
N.A.I.C.S.: 522310

Pacific Western Bank **(2)**
9320 Wilshire BlvdSte 105, Beverly Hills,
CA 90212
Tel.: (310) 278-7200
Web Site: https://www.pacwest.com
Commericial Banking
N.A.I.C.S.: 522110
Paul W. Taylor *(Pres & CEO)*
Monica L. Sparks *(Chief Acctg Officer &
Exec VP)*
Matthew P. Wagner *(Chm)*
Michael J. Perdue *(Pres-San Diego & Des-
ert Reg)*
Christopher D. Blake *(Pres/CEO-
Community Banking Grp & Exec VP)*
Bart R. Olson *(Exec VP-Fin)*
Mark T. Yung *(COO & Exec VP)*
Bryan M. Corsini *(Chief Credit Officer &
Exec VP)*
William J. Black *(Exec VP-Strategy & Corp
Dev)*
Rebecca H. Cordes *(Exec VP-HR)*
Stanley R. Ivie *(Chief Risk Officer & Exec
VP)*
Sean Lynden *(Pres-Venture Banking)*
Bart R. Olson *(CFO & Exec VP)*
Christopher Baron *(Pres-Los Angeles Reg)*
Michael W. Schrim *(Pres-Eastern Reg)*
Thomas R. Strait *(Pres-Central Coast Reg)*
Angela Kelley *(Gen Counsel & Exec VP)*

Division (Domestic):

CapitalSource **(3)**
5404 Wisconsin Ave 2nd Fl, Chevy Chase,
MD 20815
Tel.: (301) 841-2700
Web Site: http://www.capitalsource.com
Commercial Lending Services
N.A.I.C.S.: 522292

Subsidiary (Domestic):

Celtic Capital Corporation **(3)**
23622 Calabasas Rd Ste 323, Calabasas,
CA 91302
Tel.: (310) 314-7333
Web Site: https://www.celticcapital.com
Sales Range: $1-9.9 Million
Emp.: 26
Corporate Financial Services
N.A.I.C.S.: 522299
Alexander P. Falo *(Chief Credit Officer &
Exec VP)*

Subsidiary (Domestic):

Square 1 Asset Management,
Inc. **(2)**
501 Second St Ste 212, San Francisco, CA
94107
Tel.: (415) 757-2644
Unique Liquidity Management Services
N.A.I.C.S.: 522320
Michael Nguyen *(Mng Dir)*
Patrick J. Rusnak *(CFO)*
Sook Kuan Loh *(VP & Dir-Credit Risk & Re-
search)*
Michelle Tran *(Dir-Client Rels)*

Pacific Mercantile Bancorp **(1)**
949 S Coast Dr Ste 300, Costa Mesa, CA
92626
Tel.: (714) 438-2500
Web Site: http://www.pmbank.com
Rev.: $66,935,000
Assets: $1,587,590,000
Liabilities: $1,428,841,000
Net Worth: $158,749,000
Earnings: $8,334,000
Emp.: 146
Fiscal Year-end: 12/31/2020
Bank Holding Company
N.A.I.C.S.: 551111
Nancy A. Gray *(Chief Acctg Officer)*
Curt A. Christianssen *(CFO & Exec VP)*
Robert Anderson *(Chief Credit Officer &
Exec VP-Pacific Mercantile Bank)*
Maxwell G. Sinclair *(Chief Compliance Offi-
cer & Exec VP-Pacific Mercantile Bank)*

Subsidiary (Domestic):

Pacific Mercantile Bank **(2)**
949 S Coast Dr 3rd Fl, Costa Mesa, CA
92626

Tel.: (714) 438-2500
Web Site: http://www.pmbank.com
Sales Range: $100-124.9 Million
Emp.: 200
Banking Services
N.A.I.C.S.: 522110
Edward J. Carpenter *(Chm)*
Robert Anderson *(Chief Credit Officer &
Exec VP)*

BANCFIRST CORPORATION
100 N Broadway Ave, Oklahoma City,
OK 73102
Tel.: (405) 270-1086 **OK**
Web Site: https://www.bancfirst.bank
Year Founded: 1984
BANF—(NASDAQ)
Rev.: $603,567,000
Assets: $12,387,863,000
Liabilities: $11,137,027,000
Net Worth: $1,250,836,000
Earnings: $193,100,000
Emp.: 2,051
Fiscal Year-end: 12/31/22
Bank Holding Company
N.A.I.C.S.: 551111
William O. Johnstone *(Vice Chm)*
David E. Rainbolt *(Exec Chm)*
David R. Harlow *(Pres & CEO)*
Randy P. Foraker *(Chief Risk Officer
& Exec VP)*
Kevin Lawrence *(Exec VP)*

Subsidiaries:

BancFirst **(1)**
101 N Broadway Ste 200, Oklahoma City,
OK 73102
Tel.: (405) 270-1000
Web Site: http://www.bancfirst.com
Sales Range: $25-49.9 Million
Emp.: 5,000
Commericial Banking
N.A.I.C.S.: 522110
David E. Rainbolt *(Exec Chm)*
Darryl W. Schmidt *(CEO)*
Michael K. Wallace *(Executives)*

Subsidiary (Domestic):

BancFirst Insurance Services,
Inc. **(2)**
3300 E Shawnee Rd, Muskogee, OK 74403
Tel.: (918) 683-0893
Web Site: http://www.bfins.com
Emp.: 82
General Insurance Services
N.A.I.C.S.: 524113

First Bank & Trust Company **(2)**
111 S Casaver Ave, Wagoner, OK 74667
Tel.: (918) 485-2173
Web Site: https://www.fbtwagoner.com
Commericial Banking
N.A.I.C.S.: 522110
Gary Roy *(Pres-Luther)*

First Bank of Chandler **(2)**
902 Manvel Ave, Chandler, OK 74834
Tel.: (405) 258-1210
Web Site: http://www.firstbankchandler.com
Sales Range: $1-9.9 Million
Emp.: 18
Commericial Banking
N.A.I.C.S.: 522110

Council Oak Partners, LLC **(1)**
101 N Broadway Ste 400, Oklahoma City,
OK 73102
Tel.: (405) 218-4696
Web Site: http://www.council-oak.com
Sales Range: $25-49.9 Million
Commercial Banking Services
N.A.I.C.S.: 522110

Pegasus Bank **(1)**
4515 W Mockingbird Ln, Dallas, TX 75209
Tel.: (214) 353-3000
Web Site:
https://www.pegasusbankdallas.com
Sales Range: $10-24.9 Million
Commericial Banking
N.A.I.C.S.: 522110
Joe R. Goyne *(Chm)*
Harry Smith *(Pres)*

Worthington National Bank **(1)**

200 W Main St, Arlington, TX 76010
Tel.: (817) 303-5900
Web Site: http://www.worthingtonbank.com
Sales Range: $1-9.9 Million
Emp.: 16
Commercial Banking Services
N.A.I.C.S.: 522110
Sammie Slocum *(Sr VP-Ops)*
Maureen Higham *(Sr VP-Compliance)*
Jared Treesh *(Sr VP-Comml Lending)*
Cee Yager *(Pres)*
Barbara Kelley *(Asst VP-Fin Svcs)*
Brooke Falkenbach *(Asst VP-Acctg)*
Chuck Sheridan *(Sr VP-Mortgage Lending)*
Dan Mocio *(Chief Lending Officer & Exec
VP)*
Greg Morse *(CEO)*
Justin Coon *(VP-Comml & Banking)*
Les Shuler *(CFO & Exec VP)*
Lucas Sawyer *(VP-Comml & Banking)*
Scott Brandt *(VP-Comml & Banking)*
Aaron Loose *(Pres-Edwards Ranch)*
Jason Ellis *(Pres-Downtown Fort Worth)*

BANCORP 34, INC.
500 E 10th St Ste 100, Alamogordo,
NM 88310
Tel.: (575) 437-9334 **MD**
Web Site: http://www.bank34.com
Year Founded: 2016
BCTF—(OTCQB)
Rev.: $22,174,875
Assets: $527,652,160
Liabilities: $486,910,164
Net Worth: $40,741,996
Earnings: $3,399,530
Emp.: 66
Fiscal Year-end: 12/31/21
Bank Holding Company
N.A.I.C.S.: 551111
Ciaran McMullan *(Chm, CEO &
Chm/CEO-Southwest Heritage Bank)*
William F. Burt *(Vice Chm)*
Jan R. Thiry *(CFO, Treas & Exec VP)*
Angelica Marquez *(VP & Dir-HR-Bank
34)*
Henry Martinez *(VP & Mgr-IT-Bank
34)*
Laura Pannell *(VP-Comml Lender-
Bank 34)*
Judie Ruiz *(VP & Dir-Mortgage Port-
folio Lending-Bank 34)*
Lee Ann Bain *(Asst VP-Mortgage
Loan Originator)*
Theresa Murray *(Asst VP-Mortgage
Loan Originator)*
Merna Reed *(Asst VP & Mgr-Loan
Ops)*
Dorothy Valdez *(Asst VP)*

Subsidiaries:

BANK 34 **(1)**
500 E 10th St, Alamogordo, NM 88310
Tel.: (575) 437-9334
Web Site: http://www.bank34.com
Emp.: 29
Federal Savings Bank
N.A.I.C.S.: 522180
Ray J. Russell *(Chief Credit Officer & Exec
VP)*
William P. Kauper *(Dir-Corp Dev)*
Jan R. Thiry *(CFO & Exec VP)*

Division (Domestic):

BANK 34 - Arizona Division **(2)**
14850 N Scottsdale Rd Ste 100, Phoenix,
AZ 85054
Tel.: (623) 463-1440
Web Site: http://www.bank34.com
Emp.: 300
Regional Managing Office; Banking Ser-
vices
N.A.I.C.S.: 551114
William Kauper *(Pres)*

BANCORP OF SOUTHERN IN-
DIANA
125 S Chestnut St, Seymour, IN
47274
Tel.: (812) 522-3607 **IN**

Web Site: http://www.jcbank.com
Year Founded: 1982
BCSO—(OTCIQ)
Rev.: $35,626,000
Assets: $706,613,000
Liabilities: $641,739,000
Net Worth: $64,874,000
Earnings: $6,955,000
Emp.: 136
Fiscal Year-end: 12/31/20
Bank Holding Company
N.A.I.C.S.: 551111
Marvin S. Veatch *(Pres & CEO)*
Melodie K. Yarnell *(Sec & VP)*
Peymon Torabi *(Treas & VP)*

Subsidiaries:

Jackson County Bank **(1)**
125 S Chestnut St, Seymour, IN 47274
Tel.: (812) 522-3607
Web Site: http://www.jcbank.com
Retail & Commercial Banking
N.A.I.C.S.: 522110
Marvin Veatch *(Pres & CEO)*
Mark J. Maloney *(VP-Retail Lending)*
Jeffrey B. Nolting *(Chief Lending Officer &
Sr VP)*
Andy Applewhite *(Chief Mortgage & Con-
sumer Lending Officer & Sr VP)*
Dave Richardson *(VP-Comml Banking)*

BANDWIDTH INC.
2230 Bandmate Way, Raleigh, NC
27607 **DE**
Web Site:
https://www.bandwidth.com
Year Founded: 2000
BAND—(NASDAQ)
Rev.: $573,152,000
Assets: $929,318,000
Liabilities: $657,141,000
Net Worth: $272,177,000
Earnings: ($11,604,000)
Emp.: 1,200
Fiscal Year-end: 12/31/22
All Other Telecommunications
N.A.I.C.S.: 517810
David A. Morken *(Co-Founder &
CEO)*
Rebecca G. Bottorff *(Chief People
Officer)*
Amaya Lantero *(Sr VP)*
Scott Mullen *(CTO)*

BANG HOLDINGS CORP.
1400 NE Miami Gardens Dr Ste 208,
North Miami Beach, FL 33179
Tel.: (305) 600-2417 **CO**
Web Site:
http://www.bangdigitalmedia.com
Year Founded: 2014
BXNG—(OTCEM)
Sales Range: Less than $1 Million
Emp.: 4
Holding Company; Vaporizer Pens &
E-Liquids
N.A.I.C.S.: 551112
William Berke *(Chief Medical Officer)*
Steve Berke *(Chm, Pres, CEO &
Sec)*
Adam Mutchler *(CFO, COO & Treas)*
Lee Molloy *(CMO & Chief Mktg Offi-
cer)*

BANK FIRST CORPORATION
Tel.: (920) 652-3100 **WI**
Web Site: https://www.bankfirst.com
BFC—(NASDAQ)
Rev.: $136,381,000
Assets: $3,660,432,000
Liabilities: $3,207,329,000
Net Worth: $453,103,000
Earnings: $45,214,000
Emp.: 382
Fiscal Year-end: 12/31/22
Bank Holding Company
N.A.I.C.S.: 551111

Bank First Corporation—(Continued)

Timothy J. McFarlane (Pres)
Michael B. Molepske (Chm & CEO)
Kevin M. LeMahieu (CFO & Exec VP)
Jason V. Krepline (Chief Lending Officer & Exec VP)
Debbie Weyker (VP-Marketing)

Subsidiaries:

Bank First, N.A.　　　　　　　　(1)
402 N 8th St, Manitowoc, WI 54220-4010
Tel.: (920) 652-3100
Web Site: https://bankfirst.com
Sales Range: $100-124.9 Million
Emp.: 200
Savings Bank
N.A.I.C.S.: 522180

DENMARK BANCSHARES, INC. (1)
103 E Main St, Denmark, WI 54208-0130
Tel.: (920) 863-2161
Web Site: http://www.denmarkstate.com
Bank Holding Company
N.A.I.C.S.: 551111
Scot G. Thompson (Pres & CEO)

BANK OF AMERICA CORPORATION

100 N Tryon St, Charlotte, NC 28255　　　　　　　　　　　　　　DE
Web Site:
https://www.bankofamerica.com
Year Founded: 1904
BAC—(NYSE)
Rev.: $98,581,000,000
Assets: $3,180,151,000,000
Liabilities: $2,888,505,000,000
Net Worth: $291,646,000,000
Earnings: $24,866,000,000
Emp.: 213,000
Fiscal Year-end: 12/31/23
Bank Holding Company; Commercial, Investment & Wealth Management Banking Services
N.A.I.C.S.: 551111
Alastair Borthwick (Vice Chm-Global Diversity & Inclusion Council & CFO)
D. Steve Boland (Chief Admin Officer)
Wendy Stewart (Pres-Comml Banking-Global)
Paul Donofrio (Vice Chm)
Lauren Mogensen (Gen Counsel)
Eric Schimpf (Pres)
Brian T. Moynihan (Chm, Pres & CEO)
Bernard A. Mensah (CEO & Pres-Intl)
Bruce R. Thompson (Vice Chm & Head-Institutional Credit Exposure Mgmt)
Thong M. Nguyen (Vice Chm & Head-Global Strategy & Enterprise Platforms)
Lindsay Hans (Co-Pres & Head Merrill Wealth Mgmt)
Geoffrey S. Greener (Chief Risk Officer)
Sheri B. Bronstein (Chief HR Officer)
Matthew M. Koder (Pres-Investment Banking & Corp-Global)
Raul A. Anaya (Pres-Bus Banking)
Aditya Bhasin (CIO & Co-CTO)
James P. DeMare (Pres-Global Markets)
Faiz A. Ahmad (Head-Global Capital Markets)
Michael C. Ankrom (Head-Global Compliance & Operational Risk)
Alexandre Bettamio (Head-Global Investment Banking)
Lawrence T. Di Rita (Head-Public Policy)
Craig Froelich (Co-CTO)
April L. Francois (Head-Global Strategic Plng)
Karen Fang (Head-Sustainable Fin)
Sarang R. Gadkari (Head-Global Capital Markets)

Debbie U. Helvig (Head-Global Corp Comm)
Shannon Lilly (Treas)
E. Lee McEntire (Head-Investor Relations & Local Markets Organization)
Mark Monaco (Head-Global Payments Solutions)
Jessica A. Oppenheim (Head-External Comm)
Lorna R. Sabbia (Head-Retirement & Personal Wealth Solutions)
Purna R. Saggurti (Vice Chm)
Thomas J. Sheehan (Head-Global Investment Banking)
David C. Tyrie (CMO & Chief Digital Officer)
Elif Bilgi Zapparoli (Head-Intl Client Strategy)

Subsidiaries:

Aswan Village Associates, LLC (1)
2888 NW 132nd St, Opa Locka, FL 33054-4871
Tel.: (305) 688-5566
Web Site: http://www.aswanvillage.com
Emp.: 6
Real Estate Agents & Brokerage Services
N.A.I.C.S.: 531210

Audubon Urban Investments, LLC　　　　　　　　　　(1)
10631 Nacogdoches Rd, San Antonio, TX 78217-2900
Tel.: (210) 656-3388
Real Estate Services
N.A.I.C.S.: 531110
Randall Martinez (Mgr)

BA Leasing BSC, LLC　　　　(1)
555 California St Ste 4, San Francisco, CA 94104
Tel.: (415) 765-7451
Equipment Rental & Leasing Services
N.A.I.C.S.: 532490

BA Properties, Inc.　　　　　(1)
1915 E Walnut St, Stockton, CA 95205
Tel.: (209) 986-7861
Real Estate Management Services
N.A.I.C.S.: 531390

BAL Global Finance (Deutschland) GmbH　　　　　　　　　(1)
Oststrasse 10, Dusseldorf, 40211, Germany
Tel.: (49) 2111792500
Commercial Banking Services
N.A.I.C.S.: 522110

BJCC, Inc.　　　　　　　　　(1)
14546 Jefferson Davis Hwy, Woodbridge, VA 22191
Tel.: (703) 491-0641
Commercial Banking Services
N.A.I.C.S.: 522110

Banc of America Community Development Corporation　　　　(1)
214 N Tryon St NC1 027 20 05, Charlotte, NC 28255-0001
Tel.: (980) 388-3731
Real Estate Property Services
N.A.I.C.S.: 531190

Banc of America Credit Products, Inc.　　　　　　　　　　(1)
1 Bryant Park 115 W 42nd St, New York, NY 10036
Tel.: (212) 764-0694
Financial Management Services
N.A.I.C.S.: 541611

Banc of America FSC Holdings, Inc.　　　　　　　　　　(1)
555 California St 4th Fl, San Francisco, CA 94104
Tel.: (415) 765-7349
Holding Company
N.A.I.C.S.: 551112

Banc of America Leasing & Capital, LLC　　　　　　　　　　(1)
555 California St Fl 4, San Francisco, CA 94104-1506
Tel.: (415) 765-7349
Sales Financing Services
N.A.I.C.S.: 522220

Richard Fleischer (Pres)

Banc of America Preferred Funding Corporation　　　　　　　(1)
214 N Tryon, Charlotte, NC 28255
Tel.: (980) 386-4161
Investment Management Service
N.A.I.C.S.: 523940
Jason Strand (Controller)

Bank of America Custodial Services (Ireland) Limited　　　　(1)
Two Park Place Hatch Street, Dublin, Ireland
Tel.: (353) 16196100
Web Site: http://www.bankofamerica.com
Emp.: 30
Banking Services
N.A.I.C.S.: 522110

Bank of America Merrill Lynch Banco Multiplo S.A.　　　　　(1)
Avenida Brigadeiro Faria Lima 3400 - 12 Andar, Sao Paulo, 04538-132, SP, Brazil
Tel.: (55) 112 188 4000
Web Site: https://www.bofabrasil.com.br
Banking Services
N.A.I.C.S.: 522110

Bank of America Merrill Lynch International Limited　　　　(1)
2 King Edward Street, London, EC1A 1HQ, United Kingdom
Tel.: (44) 2071744000
Financial Management Services
N.A.I.C.S.: 541611

Division (Domestic):

Bank of America Merrill Lynch (2)
5 Canada Square Canary Wharf, London, E14 5AQ, United Kingdom　(100%)
Tel.: (44) 2071744000
Sales Range: $350-399.9 Million
Emp.: 6,500
Commercial Bank
N.A.I.C.S.: 522110
Anya Weaving (Mng Dir-Natural Resources Unit-Global)
Robert Gidlow (Sr VP-Global Liquidity Product)
Luca Ferrari (Head-Mergers & Acq Bus-EMEA)
Jack MacDonald (Head-Global Merger & Acq)
Adrian Mee (Head-Global Merger & Acq)
Patrick Ramsey (Head-Global Merger & Acq)
Luigi Rizzo (Head-Investment Banking-EMEA)
Philippe Chryssicopoulos (Head-Infrastructure Investment Banking & Power & Utilities-EMEA)
Ray Wood (Head-Global Power Investment Banking)
Anya Weaving (Mng Dir-Natural Resources Unit-Global)
Mark C. Perry (Vice Chm-Comml Bank-Global)
Sanaz Zaimi (Head-BofA Securities Europe & Global Fixed Income, Currencies &)
Jason Feuerstein (Head-Entertainment Indus Grp-Los Angeles)
Shannon Lilly (Deputy CEO-BofA Securities Europe)
Tom Montag (COO)
Dong Qu (Mng Dir-Global Risk Analytics)
Justin Jantz (VP/Mgr-Customer Rels-Idaho & Montana)

Bank of America Mexico, S.A., Institucion de Banca Multiple　(1)
Pedregal No 24 piso 22 Torre Virreyes Col Molino del Rey Alcaldia, 11040, Acuamanala de Miguel Hidalgo, Mexico
Tel.: (52) 5552013200
Web Site:
https://www.bankofamerica.com.mx
Banking Services
N.A.I.C.S.: 522110

Bank of America, N.A.　　　　(1)
Bank of America Corporate Ctr 100 N Tryon St, Charlotte, NC 28255　(100%)
Tel.: (704) 386-5681
Web Site: http://www.bankofamerica.com
Sales Range: $1-9.9 Million
Commercial, Investment & Wealth Management Banking Services

N.A.I.C.S.: 522110

Representative Office (Non-US):

Bank of America (France)　　(2)
51 Rue La Boetie, 75008, Paris, France　　　　　　　　　　(100%)
Tel.: (33) 187700364
Emp.: 600
International Business Banking
N.A.I.C.S.: 522299

Unit (Domestic):

Bank of America Business Capital　　　　　　　　　　(2)
200 Glastonbury Blvd, Glastonbury, CT 06033-4418
Tel.: (860) 659-3200
Web Site: http://www.fleetcapital.com
Rev.: $217,000,000
Emp.: 233
Commercial Financing
N.A.I.C.S.: 522299
Karen Sessions (Pres)
Seth Benefield (Mgr-Marketing-Natl)

Branch (Domestic):

Bank of America Business Capital　　　　　　　　　　(3)
55 S Lk Ave Ste 900, Pasadena, CA 91101
Tel.: (626) 397-1200
Sales Range: $10-24.9 Million
Emp.: 70
Business Credit Services
N.A.I.C.S.: 541618
Ira Kreft (Mgr-Mktg-Central)
Bobby Bans (Mktg Mgr-West)
Peter Langburd (Mktg Mgr-East)
Steve Pomerantz (Mktg Mgr-Central)
Christopher Tran (Sr VP-Midwest)

Unit (Domestic):

Bank of America Business Credit (2)
114 W 47th St Ste C-1, New York, NY 10036-1592　　　　　　　(100%)
Tel.: (212) 503-7405
Web Site: http://locators.bankofamerica.com
Sales Range: $25-49.9 Million
Emp.: 8
Security Transfer & Trust Company
N.A.I.C.S.: 522299

Subsidiary (Domestic):

Bank of America Capital Management Company　　　　　　　(2)
300 S Grand Ave Ste 2500, Los Angeles, CA 90071-3131
Tel.: (213) 312-9000
Sales Range: $75-99.9 Million
Investment Advice
N.A.I.C.S.: 561990

Subsidiary (Domestic):

Bank of America Leasing　　(3)
135 S LaSalle St Ste LL18, Chicago, IL 60603
Tel.: (312) 443-2000
Web Site: http://www.bankofamerica.com
Direct Working Capital Financing
N.A.I.C.S.: 522299

Subsidiary (Non-US):

Bank of America Leasing Canada　　　　　　　　　(3)
200 Front St, Toronto, M9B 6B7, ON, Canada
Tel.: (416) 236-2120
Sales Range: $1-9.9 Million
Emp.: 5
Short Term Business Credit Institution Except Agriculture
N.A.I.C.S.: 522299

Division (Domestic):

Bank of America Global Consumer & Small Business Banking　(2)
100 N Tryon St Ste 170, Charlotte, NC 28202
Tel.: (980) 335-3561
Web Site: http://www.bankofamerica.com
Sales Range: $10-24.9 Million
Emp.: 50
Banking
N.A.I.C.S.: 522110

Subsidiary (Domestic):

BA Merchant Services, LLC (3)
1231 Durrett Ln, Louisville, KY 40213
Tel.: (502) 315-2000
Web Site: http://www.bankofamerica.com
Sales Range: $450-499.9 Million
Emp.: 1,700
Computer Processing & Data Preparation
N.A.I.C.S.: 518210

Bank of America Mortgage (3)
100 N Tryon St Ste 170, Charlotte, NC
28202
Tel.: (980) 335-3561
Web Site: http://www.bankofamerica.com
Sales Range: $150-199.9 Million
Emp.: 1,130
Mortgage Bankers & Loan Correspondents
N.A.I.C.S.: 522110

Subsidiary (Domestic):

Bank of America Home Loans (4)
10825 Financial Ctr Pkwy, Little Rock, AR
72211-3554 (100%)
Tel.: (501) 224-4063
Web Site:
    http://mortgage.bankofamerica.com
Sales Range: $25-49.9 Million
Emp.: 30
Mortgage Loans & Services
N.A.I.C.S.: 522310

Subsidiary (Non-US):

BofA Canada Bank (4)
1600 James Naismith Dr, Ottawa, K1B 5N8,
ON, Canada
Tel.: (613) 907-4955
Sales Range: $500-549.9 Million
Emp.: 1,700
Banking Services
N.A.I.C.S.: 522110

MBNA Limited (4)
Cawley House Chester Business Park, PO
Box 1004, Chester, CH4 9FB, United King-
dom
Tel.: (44) 1244659005
Web Site: https://www.mbna.co.uk
Sales Range: $1-4.9 Billion
Emp.: 6,000
Credit Cards, Banking & Insurance Services
N.A.I.C.S.: 522210

Subsidiary (Domestic):

MBNA Marketing Systems, Inc. (4)
16001 Dallas Pkwy, Addison, TX 75001
Tel.: (972) 233-7101
Sales Range: $75-99.9 Million
Sales & Telemarketing Services
N.A.I.C.S.: 561422

Division (Domestic):

**Bank of America Global Corporate &
Investment Banking** (2)
100 N Tryon St Ste 170, Charlotte, NC
28255
Tel.: (980) 335-3561
Web Site: http://corp.bankofamerica.com
Sales Range: $5-14.9 Billion
Emp.: 200,000
Banking
N.A.I.C.S.: 522110

**Bank of America Global Wealth &
Investment Management** (2)
100 Federal St, Boston, MA 02110-1802
Tel.: (866) 828-8989
Web Site: http://www.bankofamerica.com
Investment & Wealth Management Services
N.A.I.C.S.: 523940

Subsidiary (Domestic):

**Columbia Management Group,
LLC** (3)
1 Financial Ctr, Boston, MA 02111-2621
Tel.: (617) 341-2200
Sales Range: $250-299.9 Million
Security & Funds
N.A.I.C.S.: 525910
Greg A. Shell Sr. *(Executives)*

**U.S. Trust, Bank of America Private
Wealth Management** (3)
114 W 47th St 7th Fl, New York, NY 10036

Tel.: (212) 852-1000
Web Site: http://www.bankofamerica.com
Sales Range: $800-899.9 Million
Emp.: 2,100
Holding Company; Wealth & Investment
Management Services
N.A.I.C.S.: 551112
Erica Tyree *(Sr VP & Mgr-Private Client)*

Subsidiary (Domestic):

U.S. Trust Company, N.A. (4)
114 W 47th St, New York, NY 10036-1510
Tel.: (212) 852-3739
Web Site: http://www.bankofamerica.com
Sales Range: $1-4.9 Billion
Emp.: 400
Investment & Asset Management Services
N.A.I.C.S.: 523940

Branch (Domestic):

U.S. Trust Company (5)
121 SW Morrison 12th Fl, Portland, OR
97204
Tel.: (503) 795-6300
Web Site: http://www.bankofamerica.com
Sales Range: $100-124.9 Million
Emp.: 50
Investment & Asset Management Services
N.A.I.C.S.: 523940

U.S. Trust Company (5)
1800 K St NW, Washington, DC 20006
Tel.: (202) 442-7441
Web Site: http://www.bankofamerica.com
Sales Range: $100-124.9 Million
Emp.: 30
Investment & Asset Management Services
N.A.I.C.S.: 523940

U.S. Trust Company (5)
845 Alexander Rd, Princeton, NJ 08540-
6313
Tel.: (609) 734-7700
Web Site: http://www.ustrust.com
Sales Range: $100-124.9 Million
Emp.: 40
Investment & Asset Management Services
N.A.I.C.S.: 523940

U.S. Trust Company (5)
280 E Palmetto Park Rd, Boca Raton, FL
33432
Tel.: (561) 338-3510
Web Site: http://www.uscrop.com
Sales Range: $75-99.9 Million
Emp.: 20
Investment & Asset Management Services
N.A.I.C.S.: 523940

U.S. Trust Company (5)
515 S Flower St Ste 2700, Los Angeles, CA
90071-2291
Tel.: (213) 861-5000
Web Site: http://locations.ustrust.com
Investment & Asset Management Services
N.A.I.C.S.: 523940

U.S. Trust Company (5)
500 Newport Ctr Dr Ste 333, Newport
Beach, CA 92660
Tel.: (949) 760-4570
Web Site: http://www.bankofamerica.com
Sales Range: $100-124.9 Million
Emp.: 50
Investment & Asset Management Services
N.A.I.C.S.: 523940

U.S. Trust Company (5)
555 California St 7th Fl, San Francisco, CA
94104
Tel.: (415) 913-3438
Web Site: http://www.bankofamerica.com
Sales Range: $150-199.9 Million
Emp.: 100
Investment & Asset Management Services
N.A.I.C.S.: 523940

U.S. Trust Company (5)
114 W 47th St, New York, NY
10036 (100%)
Web Site: http://www.bankofamerica.com
Investment & Asset Management Services
N.A.I.C.S.: 523940

U.S. Trust Company (5)
1581 Franklin Ave, Garden City, NY 11530
Tel.: (516) 877-8800
Web Site: http://www.bankofamerica.com

Sales Range: $75-99.9 Million
Emp.: 26
Investment & Asset Management Services
N.A.I.C.S.: 523940

U.S. Trust Company (5)
6 Landmark Sq 4th Fl, Stamford, CT 06091-
2704
Tel.: (203) 352-4400
Web Site: http://www.bankofamerica.com
Sales Range: $50-74.9 Million
Emp.: 50
Investment & Asset Management Services
N.A.I.C.S.: 523940

U.S. Trust Company (5)
29 S Main St, West Hartford, CT 06107
Tel.: (860) 313-7000
Web Site: http://www.bankofamerica.com
Sales Range: $75-99.9 Million
Emp.: 18
Investment & Asset Management Services
N.A.I.C.S.: 523940

U.S. Trust Company (5)
132 Royal Palm Way, Palm Beach, FL
33480
Tel.: (561) 659-1550
Web Site: http://www.bankofamerica.com
Sales Range: $125-149.9 Million
Emp.: 65
Investment & Asset Management Services
N.A.I.C.S.: 523940

U.S. Trust Company (5)
765 Seagate Dr, Naples, FL 34103
Tel.: (239) 254-3200
Web Site: http://www.bankofamerica.com
Sales Range: $75-99.9 Million
Emp.: 17
Investment & Asset Management Services
N.A.I.C.S.: 523940

U.S. Trust Company (5)
660 Beachland Blvd Ste 209, Vero Beach,
FL 32963
Tel.: (772) 234-1090
Web Site: http://www.ustrust.com
Sales Range: $75-99.9 Million
Emp.: 12
Investment & Asset Management Services
N.A.I.C.S.: 523940

U.S. Trust Company (5)
901 Main St 19th Fl, Dallas, TX 75202
Tel.: (214) 754-1200
Web Site: http://www.locations.ustrust.com
Sales Range: $100-124.9 Million
Emp.: 31
Investment & Asset Management Services
N.A.I.C.S.: 523940

U.S. Trust Company (5)
700 Louisiana St 6th Fl, Houston, TX 77002
Tel.: (713) 247-7723
Web Site: http://www.bankofamerica.com
Sales Range: $75-99.9 Million
Emp.: 18
Investment & Asset Management Services
N.A.I.C.S.: 523940
Silvia Salle *(Sr VP)*

U.S. Trust Company (5)
55 Railroad Ave, Greenwich, CT 06830
Tel.: (203) 422-5200
Web Site: http://www.bankofamerica.com
Sales Range: $50-74.9 Million
Emp.: 14
Investment & Asset Management Services
N.A.I.C.S.: 523940

U.S. Trust Company (5)
3075 B Hansen Way, Palo Alto, CA 94304
Tel.: (650) 473-2047
Web Site: http://www.bankofamerica.com
Sales Range: $50-74.9 Million
Emp.: 50
Investment & Asset Management Services
N.A.I.C.S.: 523940

U.S. Trust Company (5)
1100 N King St Bracebridge 1, Wilmington,
DE 19884
Tel.: (302) 416-3370
Web Site: http://www.ustrust.com
Investment & Asset Management Services
N.A.I.C.S.: 523940

U.S. Trust Company (5)
800 Green Valley Rd Ste 502, Greensboro,
NC 27408

Tel.: (336) 272-5100
Web Site: http://www.ustrust.com
Sales Range: $100-124.9 Million
Emp.: 40
Investment & Asset Management Services
N.A.I.C.S.: 523940

U.S. Trust Company (5)
4242 6 Forks Rd 17th Fl, Raleigh, NC
27609
Tel.: (919) 829-6769
Web Site: http://www.ustrust.com
Sales Range: $100-124.9 Million
Emp.: 20
Investment & Asset Management Services
N.A.I.C.S.: 523991

Representative Office (Non-US):

**Bank of America Singapore
Limited** (2)
OUE Bayfront 14-01 50 Collyer Quay, Sin-
gapore, 049321, Singapore (100%)
Tel.: (65) 66780000
Web Site: http://www.bankofamerica.com
Sales Range: $150-199.9 Million
Banking
N.A.I.C.S.: 522110

Bank of America, N.A. - Canada (2)
200 Front St W Ste 2700, Toronto, M5V
3K2, ON, Canada
Tel.: (416) 349-4100
Web Site: http://www.bankamerica.com
Sales Range: $50-74.9 Million
Emp.: 350
National Commercial Banks
N.A.I.C.S.: 522110

Subsidiary (Domestic):

**HealthLogic Systems
Corporation** (2)
2059 Northlake Pkwy, Tucker, GA 30084
Web Site:
    http://www.external.healthlogic.com
Health Care Clearing House
N.A.I.C.S.: 621999

Recon Trust Company, N.A. (2)
400 Countrywide Way, Simi Valley, CA
93065-6298
Tel.: (805) 520-5100
Web Site: http://www.recontrustco.com
Sales Range: $50-74.9 Million
Emp.: 1,000
Holding Company Financial & Insurance
Services
N.A.I.C.S.: 531210

BofA Securities India Limited (1)
Ground 16th 17th 18th Floor A Wing One
BKC G Block, Bandra Kurla Complex Ban-
dra East, Mumbai, 400 051, India
Tel.: (91) 2266323000
Web Site: https://ml-india.com
Financial Services
N.A.I.C.S.: 522320

BofA Securities Japan Co., Ltd. (1)
Nihonbashi 1-chome Mitsui Building 1-4-1,
Nihonbashi Chuo-ku, Tokyo, 103-8230, Ja-
pan
Tel.: (81) 362257000
Web Site: https://www.bofaml.com
Security Brokerage Services
N.A.I.C.S.: 523150

C-Zone S.p.A. (1)
154 Corso Vittorio Emanuele II, 00186,
Rome, Italy
Tel.: (39) 0668445288
Banking Services
N.A.I.C.S.: 522110

Card Processing Reseller, Inc. (1)
16001 Dallas Pkwy, Addison, TX 75001-
3311
Tel.: (972) 233-7101
Information Technology Services
N.A.I.C.S.: 541512

**Countrywide Financial
Corporation** (1)
4500 Park Granada, Calabasas, CA 91302
Tel.: (818) 225-3000
Emp.: 50,386
Mortgage Brokerage Services
N.A.I.C.S.: 522310

Bank of America Corporation—(Continued)

Dresdner Kleinwort Pfandbriefe Investments, Inc. (1)
103 Foulk Rd, Wilmington, DE 19803-3742
Tel.: (302) 691-6228
Commercial Banking Services
N.A.I.C.S.: 522110

Equity Analytics, LLC (1)
14614 N Keirland Blvd, Scottsdale, AZ 85254
Tel.: (480) 998-3515
Software Development Services
N.A.I.C.S.: 541511

FSC Corp. (1)
2300 Windy Rdg Pkwy SE Ste 1100, Atlanta, GA 30339
Tel.: (770) 916-6636
Web Site: http://www.joinfsc.com
Commercial Banking Services
N.A.I.C.S.: 522110

Incapital Holdings, LLC (1)
200 S Wacker Dr Ste 3700, Chicago, IL 60606
Tel.: (312) 379-3700
Commercial Banking Services
N.A.I.C.S.: 522110

JCCA, Inc. (1)
5005 Pacific Hwy E Ste 10, Fife, WA 98424-2245
Tel.: (253) 397-9115
Commercial Banking Services
N.A.I.C.S.: 522110
Maria Acosta (CFO)

KBA Mortgage, LLC (1)
7105 Corporate Dr, Plano, TX 75024
Tel.: (206) 358-1460
Mortgage Banking Services
N.A.I.C.S.: 522292

LandSafe, Inc. (1)
6400 Legacy Dr, Plano, TX 75024-3609
Tel.: (972) 608-6000
Sales Range: $700-749.9 Million
Holding Company; Financial & Insurance Services
N.A.I.C.S.: 524127

Subsidiary (Domestic):

LandSafe Flood Determination, Inc. (2)
6400 Legacy Dr, Plano, TX 75024
Tel.: (972) 608-6000
Flood Determination Products
N.A.I.C.S.: 531390

LandSafe Title Agency, Inc. (2)
101 S Marengo Ave # 4, Pasadena, CA 91101-2420
Tel.: (626) 229-5600
Sales Range: $50-74.9 Million
Emp.: 100
Real Estate Title Business
N.A.I.C.S.: 541191

Merrill Lynch & Co., Inc. (1)
Bank of America Corp Ctr 100 N Tryon St, Charlotte, NC 28255 (100%)
Tel.: (704) 386-5681
Web Site: http://www.ml.com
Rev.: $27,321,000,000
Assets: $602,928,000,000
Liabilities: $538,528,000,000
Net Worth: $64,400,000,000
Earnings: $290,000,000
Emp.: 64,200
Fiscal Year-end: 12/31/2012
Financial Holding Company, Securities Brokerage, Investment Banking, Wealth Management & Investment Advisory Services
N.A.I.C.S.: 551111
Brian T. Moynihan (Chm)
Reid Searles (First VP)

Subsidiary (Domestic):

Business Lenders, LLC (2)
Goodwin Sq 16th Fl 225 Asylum St, Hartford, CT 06103
Tel.: (860) 244-9202
Web Site: https://www.businesslenders.com
Sales Range: $25-49.9 Million
Emp.: 25
Loan Brokerage Services
N.A.I.C.S.: 522310

Ken Ritter (Pres)

Equity Methods, LLC (2)
17800 N Perimeter Dr Ste 200, Scottsdale, AZ 85255
Tel.: (480) 428-1200
Web Site: https://www.equitymethods.com
Sales Range: Less than $1 Million
Emp.: 50
Employee Stock Option Consulting Services
N.A.I.C.S.: 541618
Takis Makridis (Pres & CEO)
James Lecher (Sr Mgr-Valuation Svcs)
Nathan O'Connor (Mng Dir)
Qi Ding (Mgr)
Yudian Tang (Mgr)
Xiao Yu (Mgr)
Paul Brunoforte (Controller)
Yuxi Chen (Mgr)
Benjamin Clow (Mgr)
Nick Faris (Mgr)
Matt Gabrielson (Mgr)
Kiel Greenfield (Mgr)
Cristina Ramsey (Sr Coord-Marketing)
Nicholas Reitter (Sr Mgr)
Siddharth Thaker (Mgr)
Yang Wang (Supvr)
Dan Wood (Mgr-Information Technology)
Paul Brunoforte (Controller)
Yuxi Chen (Mgr)
Benjamin Clow (Mgr)
Nick Faris (Mgr)
Matt Gabrielson (Mgr)
Kiel Greenfield (Mgr)
Cristina Ramsey (Sr Coord-Marketing)
Nicholas Reitter (Sr Mgr)
Siddharth Thaker (Mgr)
Yang Wang (Supvr)
Dan Wood (Mgr-Information Technology)

Subsidiary (Non-US):

Merrill Lynch Canada Inc. (2)
Bce Place Wellington Tower 181 Bay Street 4th and 5th Floors, Toronto, M5J 2V8, ON, Canada
Tel.: (416) 369-7400
Web Site: https://www.ml.com
Investment Banking Services
N.A.I.C.S.: 523150

Merrill Lynch Derivative Products AG (2)
Stockerstrasse 23, 8002, Zurich, Switzerland
Tel.: (41) 442977400
Investment Banking Services
N.A.I.C.S.: 523150

Merrill Lynch Japan Securities Co., Ltd. (2)
Nihonbashi 1-chome Mitsui Building 1-4-1 Nihonbashi, Tokyo, 103-8230, Japan
Tel.: (81) 362257000
Web Site: http://www.japan.ml.com
Investment Banking Services
N.A.I.C.S.: 523150

Merrill Lynch Mexico, S.A. de C.V., Casa de Bolsa (2)
Pedregal No 24 piso 22 Torre Virreyes Col Molino del Rey, 11040, Acuamanala de Miguel Hidalgo, Mexico
Tel.: (52) 5552013200
Web Site: http://www.bankofamerica.com.mx
Investment Brokerage Services
N.A.I.C.S.: 523150

Subsidiary (Domestic):

Merrill Lynch Professional Clearing Corp. (2)
1 Bryant Park 6th Fl, New York, NY 10036
Tel.: (646) 743-1277
Security & Commodity Transaction Clearing Services
N.A.I.C.S.: 522320
S. Faruque Alam (CFO)

Subsidiary (Non-US):

Merrill Lynch S.A. Corretora de Titulos e Valores Mobiliarios (2)
Avenida Brigadeiro Faria Lima 3400 12 Andar, Sao Paulo, 04538-132, SP, Brazil
Tel.: (55) 1121884000
Web Site: https://www.merrilllynch-brasil.com.br
Investment Banking Services

N.A.I.C.S.: 523150

Merrill Lynch Yatirim Bank A.S. (2)
Kanyon Ofis Kat 11 Buyukdere Cad No 185, Levent, Istanbul, 34394, Turkiye
Tel.: (90) 2123199500
Web Site: http://www.ml.com.tr
Financial Services
N.A.I.C.S.: 522320

Merrill Lynch, Kingdom of Saudi Arabia Company (2)
Kingdom Tower Floor 22 2239 Orouba Road - Olaya Unit No 50 9597, Riyadh, 12214, Saudi Arabia
Tel.: (966) 112993700
Web Site: https://www.ml-ksa.com
Financial Services
N.A.I.C.S.: 523940

OOO Merrill Lynch Securities (2)
7 Petrovka Street, 107031, Moscow, Russia
Tel.: (7) 4956626000
Web Site: http://www.mlsecurities.ru
Banking Services
N.A.I.C.S.: 522110

Mortgages plc (1)
Merrill Lynch Financial Centre 2 King Edward Street, London, EC1A 1HQ, United Kingdom
Tel.: (44) 3448922872
Web Site: https://www.mortgagesplc.com
Mortgage Banking Services
N.A.I.C.S.: 522292

One Bryant Park LLC (1)
1 Bryant Park, New York, NY 10036
Tel.: (212) 278-8312
Banking Services
N.A.I.C.S.: 522110

Oshkosh/McNeilus Financial Services Partnership (1)
524 E Hwy St 14, Dodge Center, MN 55927
Tel.: (507) 374-6321
Recreational Vehicle Rental & Leasing Services
N.A.I.C.S.: 532120

Quality Properties Asset Management Company (1)
135 S Lasalle St Ste 2430, Chicago, IL 60603-4149
Tel.: (213) 621-7553
International Trade Financing Services
N.A.I.C.S.: 522299

Resort Funding LLC (1)
1 Dupli Park Dr, Syracuse, NY 13204
Tel.: (315) 422-9088
Web Site: http://www.resortfunding.com
Financial Management Services
N.A.I.C.S.: 541611

The Bank of America Charitable Foundation, Inc. (1)
401 N Tryon St, Charlotte, NC 28202
Tel.: (980) 388-5138
Charity Foundation
N.A.I.C.S.: 813211

Villages Urban Investments, LLC (1)
4130 S Mill Ave, Tempe, AZ 85282
Tel.: (480) 829-0999
Commercial Banking Services
N.A.I.C.S.: 522110

Washington Mill Lofts LLC (1)
270 Canal St, Lawrence, MA 01840
Tel.: (978) 685-3333
Web Site: http://www.wmlofts.com
Commercial Banking Services
N.A.I.C.S.: 522110

clearXchange, LLC (1)
333 Market St 26th Fl, San Francisco, CA 94105
Tel.: (415) 371-4111
Financial Management Services
N.A.I.C.S.: 541611
Michael Kennedy (CEO)
Michael J. Kennedy (Co-Founder)

BANK OF BOTETOURT INC.
19747 Main St, Buchanan, VA 24066
Tel.: (540) 254-1721   VA
Web Site:
  https://www.bankofbotetourt.com
Year Founded: 1901

BORT—(OTCIQ)
Rev.: $26,448,853
Assets: $596,595,221
Liabilities: $542,778,926
Net Worth: $53,816,295
Earnings: $4,630,609
Emp.: 123
Fiscal Year-end: 12/31/20
Banking Services
N.A.I.C.S.: 522110
Lyn G. Hayth III (Vice Chm & CEO)
Michelle R. Austin (Pres & COO)
George E. Honts IV (Chief Lending Officer & Exec VP)
Andrew T. Shotwell (CIO & Sr VP)
Barbara G. Anderson (Chief Compliance Officer, Chief Risk Officer & Sr VP)
Laurie C. Hart (Chief Strategy Officer & Sr VP)
Dustin Bays (CFO & Sr VP)

BANK OF COMMERCE HOLDINGS
555 Capitol Mall Ste 1255, Sacramento, CA 95814   CA
Web Site:
  http://www.bankofcommerceholdings.com
Year Founded: 1982
BOCH—(NASDAQ)
Rev.: $64,131,000
Assets: $1,763,954,000
Liabilities: $1,586,252,000
Net Worth: $177,702,000
Earnings: $14,164,000
Emp.: 206
Fiscal Year-end: 12/31/20
Bank Holding Company
N.A.I.C.S.: 551111
Carl W. Rood (COO & Exec VP)
Lyle L. Tullis (Chm)
Randall S. Eslick (Pres & CEO)
Robert H. Muttera (Chief Credit Officer & Exec VP)
James A. Sundquist (CFO & Exec VP)
Jon W. Halfhide (Vice Chm)
Bonnie A. Smith (Chief HR Officer & Sr VP)
John-David Phelps (CIO & Sr VP)
Andrea M. Newburn (VP)
Desiree E. Fosnaugh (Chief Risk Officer & Exec VP)

Subsidiaries:

Merchants Bank of Commerce (1)
1901 Churn Creek Rd, Redding, CA 96002
Web Site: http://www.mboc.com
Commercial Banking Services
N.A.I.C.S.: 522110
Lyle L. Tullis (Chm)
Randall S. Eslick (Pres & CEO)
Jon W. Halfhide (Vice Chm)
James A. Sundquist (CFO & Exec VP)
Andrea M. Newburn (VP)

Redding Bank of Commerce (1)
1951 Churn Creek Rd, Redding, CA 96002   (100%)
Tel.: (530) 224-3333
Web Site:
  http://www.reddingbankofcommerce.com
Sales Range: $25-49.9 Million
Commercial Banking
N.A.I.C.S.: 522110
Lyle L. Tullis (Chm)
Randall S. Eslick (Pres & CEO)
Jon W. Halfhide (Vice Chm)

BANK OF HAWAII CORPORATION
130 Merchant St, Honolulu, HI 96813
Tel.: (808) 643-3888   DE
Web Site: https://www.boh.com
Year Founded: 1971
BOH—(NYSE)
Rev.: $986,634,000

Assets: $23,733,296,000
Liabilities: $22,319,054,000
Net Worth: $1,414,242,000
Earnings: $163,325,000
Emp.: 1,899
Fiscal Year-end: 12/31/23
Bank Holding Company; Commercial Banking & Financial Services
N.A.I.C.S.: 551111
Peter S. Ho (Chm, Pres & CEO)
S. Bradley Shairson (Vice Chm & Chief Risk Officer)
Patrick McGuirk (Gen Counsel, Sec & Sr Exec VP)
Taryn L. Salmon (Vice Chm, CIO & Chief Operations Officer)
Sharlene Ginoza-Lee (Exec VP)
Marco A. Abbruzzese (Vice Chm & Sr Exec Dir-Wealth Mgmt)
Susan L. Ing (CMO & Sr Exec VP)
Kristine R. Stebbins (Exec VP & Deputy CMO)
Edward Kim (Sr Exec VP & Sr Exec Dir-Consumer Lending)

Subsidiaries:

Bank of Hawaii   (1)
111 S King St, Honolulu, HI 96813 **(99.7%)**
Tel.: (808) 694-4773
Web Site: https://www.boh.com
Sales Range: $100-124.9 Million
Retail, Commercial & Investment Banking
N.A.I.C.S.: 522110
Dean Y. Shigemura (Vice Chm, CFO & Principal Acctg Officer)
Ken Niimura (Mgr-Intl Client Grp)
Peter S. Ho (Pres)

Subsidiary (Domestic):

Bankoh Investment Services, Inc.   (2)
130 Merchant St Ste 850, Honolulu, HI 96813   **(100%)**
Tel.: (808) 694-8500
Securities Brokerage Services
N.A.I.C.S.: 523940
Chris Otto (Pres & CEO)

Banque de Tahiti S.A.   (1)
38 rue Francois Cardella, BP 1602, 98713, Papeete, Tahiti, French Polynesia **(92.4%)**
Tel.: (689) 40417000
Web Site: https://www.banque-tahiti.pf
Sales Range: $75-99.9 Million
Emp.: 275
Provider of Banking Services
N.A.I.C.S.: 522299

Hawaii Diversified Innovation Fund, LLC   (1)
820 Mililani St, Honolulu, HI 96813
Tel.: (808) 237-5388
Financial Services
N.A.I.C.S.: 523910

BANK OF IDAHO HOLDING COMPANY
399 N Capital Ave, Idaho Falls, ID 83402
Tel.: (208) 715-9445   ID
Web Site:
   https://www.bankofidaho.com
BOID—(OTCIQ)
Rev.: $17,431,044
Assets: $405,251,915
Liabilities: $354,553,115
Net Worth: $50,698,800
Earnings: $2,714,057
Fiscal Year-end: 12/31/19
Bank Holding Company
N.A.I.C.S.: 551111
Jeffrey K. Newgard (Pres & CEO)

Subsidiaries:

Bank of Idaho   (1)
1230 Yellowstone Ave, Pocatello, ID 83201
Tel.: (208) 232-1700
Web Site: http://www.bankofidaho.com
Sales Range: $1-9.9 Million
Emp.: 10
Miscellaneous Business Credit Institution

N.A.I.C.S.: 522299
Thomas O. Jedd (Principal)

BANK OF MARIN BANCORP
504 Redwood Blvd Ste 100, Novato, CA 94947
Tel.: (415) 763-4520   CA
Web Site:
   https://www.bankofmarin.com
BMRC—(NASDAQ)
Rev.: $140,946,000
Assets: $4,147,464,000
Liabilities: $3,735,372,000
Net Worth: $412,092,000
Earnings: $46,586,000
Emp.: 313
Fiscal Year-end: 12/31/22
Bank Holding Company
N.A.I.C.S.: 551111
David Bloom (Exec VP & Head-Comml Banking)
Tani Girton (CFO, Principal Acctg Officer & Exec VP)
Timothy D. Myers (Pres & CEO)
Misako Stewart (Chief Credit Officer & Exec VP)
Robert Gotelli (Exec VP & Dir-HR)
Nikki Sloan (Head-Growth & Strategy)
Sathis Arasadi (CIO)

Subsidiaries:

American River Bankshares   (1)
3100 Zinfandel Dr, Rancho Cordova, CA 95670
Tel.: (916) 851-0123
Web Site:
   http://www.americanriverbank.com
Rev.: $29,426,000
Assets: $868,991,000
Liabilities: $775,896,000
Net Worth: $93,095,000
Earnings: $7,055,000
Emp.: 100
Fiscal Year-end: 12/31/2020
Bank Holding Company
N.A.I.C.S.: 551111

Bank of Marin   (1)
504 Redwood Blvd Ste 100, Novato, CA 94947
Tel.: (415) 763-4520
Web Site: https://www.bankofmarin.com
Sales Range: $100-124.9 Million
Emp.: 200
Personal & Commercial Banking Services
N.A.I.C.S.: 522110
Brian M. Sobel (Chm)
William H. McDevitt Jr. (Vice Chm)
David Bloom (Exec VP & Head-Comml Banking)
Tani Girton (CFO, Principal Acctg Officer & Exec VP)
Timothy D. Myers (Pres & CEO)
Joel Sklar (Executives, Bd of Dirs)
Misako Stewart (Chief Credit Officer & Exec VP)
Wim-Kees van Hout (Reg Mgr-Comml Banking)

BANK OF SAN FRANCISCO
345 California St Ste 1600, San Francisco, CA 94104
Tel.: (415) 744-6700   CA
Web Site: https://www.bankbsf.com
Year Founded: 2005
BSFO—(OTCQX)
Rev.: $16,728,908
Assets: $397,345,997
Liabilities: $356,364,663
Net Worth: $40,981,334
Earnings: $4,057,760
Fiscal Year-end: 12/31/19
Commercial Banking Services
N.A.I.C.S.: 522110
Samuel Clonmell (Sr VP)
John Dzida (Sr VP)
Neal Tandowsky (Sr VP)
John Verdoia (Sr VP)
Lia Economopoulos (Sr VP)
Victor Vazquez (Sr VP)

Alec Saucedo (Mgr-Relationship)
Grace Datuin (VP & Mgr-Client Services)
Jessica Curry (VP & Mgr-Private Banking Svc)
Geannie Lam (Officer-Client Services)
Joseph P. Cristiano (Chm)
Roberta Achtenberg (Vice Chm)
Ed Obuchowski (Co-Founder & CEO)
Jeffrey Cheung (Co-Pres)
Wendy A. Ross (Co-Founder & Co-Pres)
David B. Lichtman (Chief Banking Officer & Exec VP)
Margaret Mak (Exec VP & Head-Private Banking)
Jennifer Corr (CFO & Exec VP)
Juanna Collin (COO & Exec VP)
Michael De Vivo (Chief Credit Officer & Exec VP)

BANK OF SOUTH CAROLINA CORPORATION
256 Meeting St, Charleston, SC 29401
Tel.: (843) 724-1500   SC
Web Site: https://www.banksc.com
Year Founded: 1986
BKSC—(NASDAQ)
Rev.: $19,198,483
Assets: $653,345,609
Liabilities: $614,534,222
Net Worth: $38,811,387
Earnings: $6,655,140
Emp.: 80
Fiscal Year-end: 12/31/22
Bank Holding Company
N.A.I.C.S.: 551111
Fleetwood S. Hassell (Pres & CEO)
Richard W. Hutson Jr. (Sec)
Douglas Hutson Sass (Exec VP)
Susanne K. Boyd (COO & Exec VP)
Eugene H. Walpole IV (CFO & Exec VP)
Hugh C. Lane Jr. (Chm)

Subsidiaries:

The Bank of South Carolina   (1)
256 Meeting St, Charleston, SC 29401
Tel.: (843) 724-1500
Web Site: https://www.banksc.com
Sales Range: $25-49.9 Million
Emp.: 100
Commercial Banking Services
N.A.I.C.S.: 522110
Fleetwood S. Hassell (Pres & CEO)
Douglas Hutson Sass (Exec VP)
Susanne K. Boyd (COO & Exec VP)
Eugene H. Walpole IV (CFO & Exec VP)
Hugh C. Lane Jr. (Chm)

BANK OF THE JAMES FINANCIAL GROUP, INC.
828 Main St, Lynchburg, VA 24504
Tel.: (434) 846-2000   VA
Web Site:
   https://www.bankofthejames.bank
Year Founded: 2003
BOJF—(NASDAQ)
Rev.: $39,362,000
Assets: $969,371,000
Liabilities: $909,332,000
Net Worth: $60,039,000
Earnings: $8,704,000
Emp.: 163
Fiscal Year-end: 12/31/23
Bank Holding Company
N.A.I.C.S.: 551111
Robert R. Chapman III (Pres)
John Todd Scruggs (Treas & Sec)
Augustus A. Petticolas Jr. (Vice Chm)
Brian E. Cash (Pres-Mortgage Div)

Subsidiaries:

BOTJ Investment Group, Inc.   (1)
615 Church St Ste 1, Lynchburg, VA 24504
Tel.: (434) 846-2279

Invested Management Services
N.A.I.C.S.: 523940

Bank of the James   (1)
828 Main St, Lynchburg, VA 24504 **(100%)**
Tel.: (434) 846-2000
Web Site: https://www.bankofthejames.bank
Sales Range: $50-74.9 Million
Emp.: 150
Commercial Banking Services
N.A.I.C.S.: 522110
Robert R. Chapman III (Founder & CEO)
John Todd Scruggs (CFO, Sec & Exec VP)
Michael A. Syrek (Pres)
Brian E. Cash (Pres-Mortgage)
Scott Brown (Officer-Mortgage Loan)
Rich Edwards (Officer-Mortgage Loan & VP)
Debbie Grishaw (Officer-Mortgage Loan & VP)
Brad Harris (Officer-Mortgage Loan)
Jennifer Holdaway (Officer-Mortgage Loan)
Heather Nipper (Officer-Mortgage Loan)
Kirstin McHenry (Exec VP)
Patrick Richardson (Exec VP)
Thomas D. Rea (Exec VP)
J. Todd Scruggs (Sec)
Rick Sorenson (Exec VP)
Rayetta M. Webb (Officer-Reverse Mortgage Loan)
Paula Ironmonger (Officer-Mortgage Loan)
Jamie Yowell (Officer-Mortgage Loan)
Mitch Scott (Officer-Mortgage Loan)
Trevania F. Cottrill (Pres-Market Buena Vista Lexington and Rockbridge County)
Jared R. Feury (Pres-Market Bank of the James-Charlottesville)
Bradford K. Harris (Pres-Market Roanoke/Roanoke Valley)

BANK OF UTICA
222 Genesee St, Utica, NY 13502
Tel.: (315) 797-2700   NY
Web Site:
   https://www.bankofutica.com
Year Founded: 1927
BKUT—(OTCIQ)
Sales Range: $25-49.9 Million
Emp.: 38
Banking Services
N.A.I.C.S.: 522110
Tom E. Sinnott (Pres & CEO)
Brian Loughlin (Exec VP-Bus Banking Ops)
Marie Bord (Sr VP)
Claire Murphy (Asst VP)
Debra Schantz (Asst VP)
Leon DeBernardis Jr. (Sec & VP)

BANK OZK
18000 Cantrell Rd, Little Rock, AR 72223
Tel.: (501) 978-2265   AR
Web Site: https://www.ozk.com
Year Founded: 1903
OZK—(NASDAQ)
Rev.: $2,128,173,000
Assets: $34,237,457,000
Liabilities: $29,097,481,000
Net Worth: $5,139,976,000
Earnings: $690,839,000
Emp.: 2,744
Fiscal Year-end: 12/31/23
Bank Holding Company
N.A.I.C.S.: 551111
Greg L. McKinney (CFO & Chief Acctg Officer)
Tyler A. Vance (COO)
Edward J. Wydock (Chief Risk Officer)
Jennifer Junker (Mng Dir-Trust & Wealth Div)
George G. Gleason (Chm & CEO)
Dennis James (Exec VP & Dir-Regulatory and Government Rels)
Tim Hicks (Chief Admin Officer & Exec Dir-IR)

Bank OZK—(Continued)

Alan Jessup *(Dir-Community Banking)*
Brannon Hamblen *(Pres & COO-RESG)*
Jake Shapiro *(Mng Dir-Digital Banking)*
Carmen McClennon *(Chief Retail Banking Officer)*
John Carter *(Chief Credit Officer)*

Subsidiaries:

Bank of the Ozarks   (1)
17901 Chenal Pkwy, Little Rock, AR
72231-8811   **(100%)**
Tel.: (501) 978-2265
Web Site: http://www.bankozarks.com
Sales Range: $250-299.9 Million
Commercial & Investment Banking
N.A.I.C.S.: 522110
Greg L. McKinney *(CFO & Chief Acctg Officer)*
Scott Hastings *(Pres-Leasing Div)*
Gene Holman *(Pres-Mortgage Div)*
R. Darrel Russell *(Chief Credit Officer)*
Dan Thomas *(Vice Chm, Chief Lending Officer & Pres-Real Estate Specialty Grp)*
Tyler A. Vance *(COO & Chief Banking Officer)*
Edward J. Wydock *(Chief Risk Officer)*
Jennifer Junker *(Mng Dir-Trust & Wealth Mgmt Div)*
George G. Gleason *(Chm & CEO)*
Dennis James *(Exec VP & Dir-Mergers & Acq)*
Tim Hicks *(Exec VP & Chief of Staff)*
John Carter *(Dir-Community Banking)*
Matt Buchanan *(Sr VP)*

Division (Domestic):

Bank of the Ozarks - Mortgage
Division   (2)
17901 Chenal Pkwy, Little Rock, AR 72223
Tel.: (501) 978-2265
Web Site: http://www.bankozarks.com
Emp.: 20
Mortgage Services
N.A.I.C.S.: 522310
Gene Holman *(Pres-Mortgage)*

BANK7 CORP.

1039 N W 63rd St, Oklahoma City,
OK 73116
Tel.: (405) 810-8600   **OK**
Web Site: https://www.bank7.com
Year Founded: 2004
BSVN—(NASDAQ)
Rev.: $81,688,000
Assets: $1,584,169,000
Liabilities: $1,440,069,000
Net Worth: $144,100,000
Earnings: $29,638,000
Emp.: 123
Fiscal Year-end: 12/31/22
Holding Company
N.A.I.C.S.: 551111
Thomas L. Travis *(Pres, CEO & Vice Chm/CEO-Bank)*
Kelly J. Harris *(CFO & Exec VP)*
William Brad Haines *(Founder)*
John T. Phillips *(COO, COO/Sr Exec VP-Bank, Sec & Sr Exec VP)*
Jason Estes *(Chief Credit Officer, Exec VP & Mgr-Comml Loan)*
Lisa Haines *(CMO & Exec VP)*
Doug Haines *(Reg Pres-Western Oklahoma & Kansas)*
Andy Levinson *(Pres-Tulsa)*
Darrell Mathews *(Officer-IT & Sr VP-Ops)*
Sri Gunaratnam *(Sr VP-Dallas)*

Subsidiaries:

Watonga Bancshares, Inc.   (1)
115 W A St, Watonga, OK 73772
Tel.: (580) 623-8551
Sales Range: $1-9.9 Million
Emp.: 27
Commercial Bank
N.A.I.C.S.: 522110

David Ennen *(Pres)*

BANKFINANCIAL CORPORATION

48 Orland Square Dr, Orland Park, IL
60462   **MD**
Web Site:
https://www.bankfinancial.com
BFIN—(NASDAQ)
Rev.: $61,272,000
Assets: $1,575,137,000
Liabilities: $1,423,466,000
Net Worth: $151,671,000
Earnings: $10,494,000
Emp.: 180
Fiscal Year-end: 12/31/22
Offices of Bank Holding Companies
N.A.I.C.S.: 551111
F. Morgan Gasior *(Chm, Pres & CEO)*
Elizabeth A. Doolan *(Sr VP & Controller)*

Subsidiaries:

BankFinancial, F.S.B.   (1)
15 W 060 N Frontage Rd, Burr Ridge, IL
60527
Tel.: (708) 747-2000
Web Site: http://www.bankfinancial.com
Sales Range: $100-124.9 Million
Emp.: 113
Federal Savings Bank
N.A.I.C.S.: 522180
F. Morgan Gasior *(Chm, Pres & CEO)*

BANKFIRST CAPITAL CORPORATION

900 Main St, Columbus, MS 39701
Tel.: (662) 328-2345
Web Site:
https://www.bankfirstfs.com
Year Founded: 1987
BFCC—(OTCIQ)
Sales Range: $25-49.9 Million
Bank Holding Company
N.A.I.C.S.: 551111
Moak Griffin *(Pres & CEO)*
Luke Yeatman *(CFO & Sr VP)*
Jim McAlexander *(Chief Retail & Ops Officer & Exec VP)*

Subsidiaries:

BankFirst Financial Services   (1)
900 Main St, Columbus, MS 39701
Tel.: (662) 328-2345
Web Site: http://www.bankfirstfs.com
Sales Range: $25-49.9 Million
Emp.: 198
Commericial Banking
N.A.I.C.S.: 522110
William Corder *(Pres-Columbus)*
Luke Yeatman *(CFO)*
Leon Manning *(First VP & Dir-Mktg)*
Moak Griffin *(Pres & CEO)*
Renee Rice *(Pres-Community Banking-Madison County)*

FNB Bancshares of Central Alabama,
Inc.   (1)
2323 Paul W Bryant Dr, Tuscaloosa, AL
35401
Tel.: (205) 469-1700
Web Site: http://www.fnbca.com
Bank Holding Company
N.A.I.C.S.: 551111
Jim Fleming *(Pres & CEO)*

Subsidiary (Domestic):

FNB of Central Alabama   (2)
2323 Paul W Bryant Dr, Tuscaloosa, AL
35401
Tel.: (205) 469-1700
Web Site: http://www.fnbca.com
Sales Range: $50-74.9 Million
Emp.: 75
Provider of Banking Services
N.A.I.C.S.: 522110
Heyward Gould *(Pres & CEO)*

BANKGUAM HOLDING COMPANY

111 W Chalan Santo Papa, Hagatna,
GU 96910
Tel.: (671) 472-5300
Web Site:
https://www.bankofguam.com
Year Founded: 1972
BKGM—(OTCIQ)
Rev.: $110,429,000
Assets: $2,791,588,000
Liabilities: $2,610,839,000
Net Worth: $180,749,000
Earnings: $19,981,000
Emp.: 529
Fiscal Year-end: 12/31/21
Commercial Banking Services
N.A.I.C.S.: 522110
Joaquin Phillip Leon Guerrero Cook *(Vice Chm, Pres & CEO)*
Symon A. Madrazo *(CFO & Sr VP)*
Maria Eugenia H. Leon Guerrero *(COO & Exec VP)*
William David Leon Guerrero *(Chm)*
Roger Powell Crouthamel *(Sec)*
Martin Dela Rosa Leon Guerrero *(Treas & Asst Sec)*

Subsidiaries:

BG Investment Services, Inc.   (1)
11 Chalan Santo Papa Juan Pablo Dos,
Hagatna, GU 96910
Tel.: (671) 472-5490
Web Site: http://www.bankofguam.com
Investment Advisory Services
N.A.I.C.S.: 523940

Bank of Guam   (1)
111 W Chalan Santo Papa, Hagatna, GU
96910
Tel.: (671) 472-5300
Web Site: http://www.bankofguam.com
Commercial Banking Services
N.A.I.C.S.: 522110
Joaquin Phillip Leon Guerrero-Cook *(Pres & CEO)*
Symon A. Madrazo *(VP & Controller)*

BankGuam Insurance Underwriters
Ltd.   (1)
111 West Chalan Santo Papa, Hagatna, GU
96910
Tel.: (671) 479-2265
Web Site: http://www.bankofguam.com
Commercial Insurance Provider
N.A.I.C.S.: 524298

BANKPROV

5 Market St, Amesbury, MA 01913
Tel.: (978) 834-8555   **MA**
Web Site: https://bankprov.com
PVBC—(NASDAQ)
Rev.: $85,476,000
Assets: $1,636,381,000
Liabilities: $1,428,839,000
Net Worth: $207,542,000
Earnings: ($21,468,000)
Emp.: 198
Fiscal Year-end: 12/31/22
Bank Holding Company
N.A.I.C.S.: 551111
Laurie H. Knapp *(Chm)*
Joseph B. Reilly *(Pres, CEO & Pres/CEO-BankProv)*
Kenneth R. Fisher *(Acting CFO)*
Joe Kenney *(Exec VP & Dir-Comml Lending)*
Joseph Mancini *(COO & Exec VP)*

Subsidiaries:

The Provident Bank   (1)
5 Market St, Amesbury, MA 01913
Tel.: (978) 388-0050
Web Site: https://bankprov.com
Emp.: 50
Banking Services
N.A.I.C.S.: 522110
Joe Reilly *(Pres)*
Joe Kenney *(Exec VP)*
Joe Mancini *(Exec VP)*
Ken Fisher *(Exec VP)*
Janine Jakubauskas *(Exec VP)*
Leanne Corning *(Sr VP-Client Experience)*
Amber Barbere *(Sr VP-Human Resources)*

BANKUNITED, INC.

14817 Oak Ln, Miami Lakes, FL
33016   **DE**
Tel.: (305) 569-2000
Web Site:
https://www.bankunited.com
BKU—(NYSE)
Rev.: $1,944,419,000
Assets: $35,761,607,000
Liabilities: $33,183,686,000
Net Worth: $2,577,921,000
Earnings: $178,671,000
Emp.: 1,588
Fiscal Year-end: 12/31/23
Federal Savings Bank
N.A.I.C.S.: 522180
Rajinder P. Singh *(Founder, Chm, Pres & CEO)*
Leslie N. Lunak *(CFO)*
Thomas M. Cornish *(COO)*
Matthew Gallo *(Exec VP & Mng Dir-Corp Banking)*
Daniel Mills *(Sr VP & Mgr-Relationship-Corp Banking)*
Laura Ackerman *(VP & Mgr-Relationship-Corp Banking)*

Subsidiaries:

BankUnited, N.A.   (1)
808 SE 17th St, Fort Lauderdale, FL 33316
Tel.: (954) 848-0100
Web Site: https://www.bankunited.com
Commercial Banking Services
N.A.I.C.S.: 522110
Jay D. Richards *(Chief Risk Officer)*
Jaclyn Coffin *(Sr VP & Mgr-Treasury Mgmt Sls)*
Carly Berfas *(Sr VP)*
Lisa Anderson *(Sr VP)*

Bridge Funding Group, Inc.   (1)
215 Sheling Cir Ste 100, Hunt Valley, MD
21031
Tel.: (410) 771-9600
Web Site:
https://www.bridgefundinggroupinc.com
Equipment Finance & Leasing
N.A.I.C.S.: 532490
Dan McKew *(Pres)*

Herald National Bank   (1)
623 Fifth Avenue 11th Floor, New York, NY
10022
Tel.: (212) 409-1200
Web Site: http://www.heritagebankny.com
Sales Range: $10-24.9 Million
Emp.: 60
Banking Services
N.A.I.C.S.: 522110
David S. Bagatelle *(Founder)*

Pinnacle Public Finance, Inc.   (1)
8377 E Hartford Dr Ste 115, Scottsdale, AZ
85255
Tel.: (480) 419-4800
Web Site:
https://www.pinnaclepublicfinance.com
Sales Range: $25-49.9 Million
Municipal Lending Services
N.A.I.C.S.: 522310

BANKWELL FINANCIAL GROUP, INC.

1065 Post Rd, Darien, CT 06820
Tel.: (203) 652-2690   **CT**
Web Site:
https://www.mybankwell.com
Year Founded: 2007
BWFG—(NASDAQ)
Rev.: $120,985,000
Assets: $3,252,449,000
Liabilities: $3,013,980,000
Net Worth: $238,469,000
Earnings: $37,429,000
Emp.: 136
Fiscal Year-end: 12/31/22
Bank Holding Company
N.A.I.C.S.: 551111
Christopher R. Gruseke *(Pres & CEO)*
Courtney E. Sacchetti *(CFO & Exec VP)*

Eric J. Dale *(Vice Chm)*
Todd H. Lampert *(Executives, Bd of Dirs)*
Christine Chivily *(Chief Credit Officer, Chief Risk Officer & Exec VP)*
Laura J. Waitz *(COO & Exec VP)*
Matthew J. McNeill *(Chief Banking Officer)*

Subsidiaries:

Bankwell Bank   (1)
156 Cherry St, New Canaan, CT 06840
Tel.: (203) 966-7080
Web Site: https://www.mybankwell.com
Sales Range: $50-74.9 Million
Emp.: 71
Commericial Banking
N.A.I.C.S.: 522110
Blake S. Drexler *(Chm)*
Christopher R. Gruseke *(Pres & CEO)*
Courtney E. Sacchetti *(CFO & Exec VP)*
Christine Chivily *(Chief Credit Officer, Chief Risk Officer & Exec VP)*
Matthew J. McNeill *(Chief Banking Officer & Exec VP)*

BANNER ACQUISITION CORP.
300 S 1350 E 2nd Fl, Lehi, UT 84043
Tel.: (801) 447-1534   DE
Web Site:
   https://www.banneracquisition.com
Year Founded: 2021
BNNR—(NASDAQ)
Assets: $161,243,995
Liabilities: $166,648,624
Net Worth: ($5,404,629)
Earnings: ($145,576)
Emp.: 3
Fiscal Year-end: 12/31/22
Investment Services
N.A.I.C.S.: 523999
Christopher R. Christensen *(Chm)*
Tanner Ainge *(CEO)*
Tyler Price *(Principal-Ventures)*
Cooper Ainge *(VP-Ventures)*
Josh Cowdin *(CFO & Mng Dir-IR)*

BANNER CORPORATION
10 S 1st Ave, Walla Walla, WA 99362
Tel.: (509) 527-3636   WA
Web Site:
   https://www.bannerbank.com
Year Founded: 1995
BANR—(NASDAQ)
Rev.: $647,824,000
Assets: $15,833,431,000
Liabilities: $14,376,999,000
Net Worth: $1,456,432,000
Earnings: $195,378,000
Emp.: 1,931
Fiscal Year-end: 12/31/22
Bank Holding Company
N.A.I.C.S.: 551111
Jill M. Rice *(Chief Credit Officer & Exec VP)*
Mark J. Grescovich *(Pres & CEO)*
M. Kirk Quillin *(Exec VP)*
James T. Reed Jr. *(Exec VP-Comml Banking)*
Kayleen R. Kohler *(Exec VP-HR)*
Kenneth A. Larsen *(Exec VP & Dir-Mortgage Banking)*
James P.G. McLean *(Exec VP-Real Estate Lending Ops)*
Janet Brown *(CIO & Exec VP)*
Sherrey Luetjen *(Gen Counsel & Exec VP)*

Subsidiaries:

AltaPacific Bancorp   (1)
4845 Old Redwood Hwy, Santa Rosa, CA 95403
Tel.: (707) 236-1500
Web Site: http://www.apbconnect.com
Sales Range: $10-24.9 Million
Emp.: 39
Bank Holding Company
N.A.I.C.S.: 551111

Charles O. Hall *(CEO)*
Allen R. Christenson *(CFO & Exec VP)*
Sheila Thomas Moran *(Officer-Compliance & Sr VP)*
Sean K. Olhan *(Officer-Risk & Sr VP)*
Jeanne Marie Reade *(Exec VP)*
Shirley Law *(Chief Credit Officer & Exec VP)*

Banner Bank   (1)
10 S 1st Ave, Walla Walla, WA 99362-0265   (100%)
Tel.: (509) 527-3636
Web Site: https://www.bannerbank.com
Sales Range: $400-449.9 Million
Emp.: 750
Personal & Commercial Banking Services
N.A.I.C.S.: 522110

Subsidiary (Domestic):

Community Financial Corporation   (2)
412 A Ave Ste 150, Lake Oswego, OR 97034
Tel.: (503) 636-4800
Web Site: https://www.communityfc.com
Emp.: 15
Commercial Lending
N.A.I.C.S.: 522310
John Satterberg *(Pres)*
David Baker *(Treas)*
Bernadette Phillips *(VP & Mgr-RE Loan Admin & Closing)*
Michael Gault *(VP)*

Nickerson Street Associates, LLC   (2)
520 Pike St Ste 1200, Seattle, WA 98101
Tel.: (206) 332-0270
Web Site:
   http://www.nickersonassociates.com
Business Consulting Services
N.A.I.C.S.: 541330

Springer Development LLC   (2)
10 S 1st Ave, Walla Walla, WA 99362-1942
Tel.: (509) 527-3636
Office Administrative Services
N.A.I.C.S.: 561110
Mark J. Gerscovich *(Gen Mgr)*

Blue Star Properties, Inc.   (1)
12176 Industrial Blvd Ste 1, Victorville, CA 92395
Tel.: (760) 241-5995
Web Site: https://www.bluestarsocal.com
Property Management Services
N.A.I.C.S.: 531210
Benton Lamson *(Partner)*

Islanders Bank   (1)
225 Blair Ave, Friday Harbor, WA 98250
Tel.: (360) 378-2265
Web Site: http://www.islandersbank.com
Sales Range: $10-24.9 Million
Commericial Banking
N.A.I.C.S.: 522110
Brian Brown *(Chm)*

BANNIX ACQUISITION CORP.
8265 W Sunset Blvd Ste 107, West Hollywood, CA 90046
Tel.: (302) 305-4790   DE
Year Founded: 2021
BNIX—(NASDAQ)
Rev.: $1,271,333
Assets: $71,466,678
Liabilities: $72,709,290
Net Worth: ($1,242,612)
Earnings: $47,107
Emp.: 1
Fiscal Year-end: 12/31/22
Investment Services
N.A.I.C.S.: 523999
Erik Klinger *(CFO)*
Douglas L. Davis *(Co-Chm, CEO, Principal & Sec)*

BANTEC, INC.
37 Main St, Sparta, NJ 07871
Tel.: (203) 220-2296   DE
Web Site: https://www.bantecinc.com
Year Founded: 1972
BANT—(OTCIQ)
Rev.: $2,324,307

Assets: $495,926
Liabilities: $17,288,398
Net Worth: ($16,792,472)
Earnings: ($2,371,317)
Emp.: 7
Fiscal Year-end: 09/30/23
Aerospace Component Mfr
N.A.I.C.S.: 334511
Michael Bannon *(Pres)*
Rodrigo Kuntz Rangel *(CTO)*

Subsidiaries:

Drone USA, LLC   (1)
195 Paterson Ave, Little Falls, NJ 07426
Tel.: (203) 410-8924
Web Site: https://www.droneusainc.com
Unmanned Aerial Vehicle Mfr & Distr
N.A.I.C.S.: 336390

Howco Distributing Co.   (1)
6025 E 18th St, Vancouver, WA 98661
Tel.: (360) 693-9092
Web Site:
   https://www.howcodistributing.com
Motor Vehicle Parts Mfr & Distr
N.A.I.C.S.: 336390

BANYAN ACQUISITION CORPORATION
400 Skokie Blvd Ste 820, Northbrook, IL 60062
Tel.: (847) 757-3812   DE
Year Founded: 2021
BYN—(NYSE)
Rev.: $18,301,195
Assets: $251,106,671
Liabilities: $261,808,659
Net Worth: ($10,701,988)
Earnings: $15,763,981
Fiscal Year-end: 12/31/22
Investment Holding Company
N.A.I.C.S.: 551112
Jerry Hyman *(Chm)*
Keith Jaffee *(CEO)*
George Courtot *(CFO)*

BAR HARBOR BANKSHARES
Tel.: (207) 288-3314   ME
Web Site:
   https://www.barharbor.bank
Year Founded: 1984
BHB—(NYSEAMEX)
Rev.: $146,098,000
Assets: $3,909,803,000
Liabilities: $3,516,353,000
Net Worth: $393,450,000
Earnings: $43,557,000
Emp.: 486
Fiscal Year-end: 12/31/22
Bank Holding Company
N.A.I.C.S.: 551111
Curtis C. Simard *(Pres & CEO)*
Josephine Iannelli *(CFO, Treas & Exec VP)*
John M. Mercier *(Chief Lending Officer & Exec VP)*
Marion Colombo *(Exec VP-Retail Delivery)*
Joseph Scully *(CIO, Sr VP & Dir-Ops)*
John Williams *(Chief Risk Officer & Sr VP)*
Jason Edgar *(Pres)*
Alison DiPaola *(Chief HR Officer)*
Joseph Schmitt *(CMO)*

Subsidiaries:

Bar Harbor Bank & Trust   (1)
82 Main St, Bar Harbor, ME 04609 **(100%)**
Tel.: (207) 288-3314
Web Site: http://www.bhbt.com
Sales Range: $50-74.9 Million
Commercial Banking & Trust Services
N.A.I.C.S.: 522110
Joseph M. Pratt *(Sr VP & Sr Mgr-Wealth)*
David B. Woodside *(Chm)*
Curtis C. Simard *(Pres & CEO)*
Josephine Iannelli *(CFO, Treas & Exec VP)*
Richard B. Maltz *(COO, Chief Risk Officer & Exec VP)*

Joseph Schmitt *(CMO & Sr VP)*
Marion Colombo *(Exec VP & Dir-Retail Delivery)*
Holly Archer *(VP)*
Luke Cote *(Asst VP)*
Joe Delano *(Sr VP & Mgr-Customer Rels-Southern Maine)*
Tom Dorrity *(Asst VP & Mgr-Customer Rels-Central Maine Reg)*
Rebecca Emerson *(Officer-Bus Dev-Reg & VP)*
Steve Gurin *(Sr VP & Dir-Community Banking)*
Jamie Haining *(Officer-Treasury Sls & VP)*
Krystal Jordan *(VP-Community Banking & Mgr-Customer Rels)*
Colleen Maynard *(VP & Reg Mgr-Customer Rels)*
Jennifer Seekins *(Sr VP-Treasury Svcs Sls)*
Daryl Wentworth *(Sr VP & Dir-Middle Market Banking)*
Melanie Bowden *(VP & Sr Mgr-Wealth)*

Subsidiary (Domestic):

Bar Harbor Trust Services   (2)
135 High St, Ellsworth, ME 04605
Tel.: (207) 667-3883
Web Site: http://www.bhbt.com
Sales Range: $25-49.9 Million
Emp.: 20
Trust & Fiduciary Services
N.A.I.C.S.: 523991
Joshua A. Radel *(Chief Investment Officer & VP)*
Melanie J. Bowden *(VP & Sr Mgr-Wealth)*
Joseph M. Pratt *(VP & Sr Mgr-Wealth)*
John Testa *(Officer-Trust Investment & VP)*
Kenneth Huitt *(VP & Mgr-Wealth)*
Ruth Dunbar *(VP & Sr Mgr-Wealth)*
Jason Edgar *(Pres)*
James Cox *(VP & Mgr-Wealth)*
Ellen Ziobron *(Asst VP)*
Susan Kenney *(Asst VP)*

Charter Trust Company   (2)
90 N Main St, Concord, NH 03301-4915   (100%)
Tel.: (603) 224-1350
Web Site: http://www.chartertrust.com
Trust, Estate Planning, Retirement Planning & Investment Management Services
N.A.I.C.S.: 523991
Bryan W. Sanford *(Officer-Investment & VP)*
Krista McCarthy *(Officer-Tax & VP)*
Mark W. Ungewitter *(Officer-Investment & Sr VP)*
Deanna C. Wilson *(Sr VP & Sr Mgr-Wealth-New London Office)*
Maureen Kimball *(Sr VP & Sr Mgr-Wealth)*
Jason Edgar *(Pres)*
Lara K. Horner *(Sr VP & Dir-Trust Ops)*
Lynne M. J. Ford *(VP & Mgr-Wealth)*
Timothy Allen *(VP & Mgr-Wealth)*
Halie Alosky *(Asst VP & Mgr-Wealth)*
Amy Tardiff *(Asst VP & Mgr-Wealth)*
Marcie MacKenzie *(Asst VP & Mgr-Wealth)*
Jessica Pope *(Asst VP & Mgr-Wealth)*
Marianne D. Loew *(Officer-Investment & Sr VP)*
Janna Michael *(Officer-Investment & VP)*
Devin Cowette *(Officer-Investment & VP)*
Arleen Gosselin *(VP & Ops Mgr-Trust)*

BARABOO BANCORPORATION, INC.
Tel.: (608) 356-7703
Web Site:
   https://www.baraboobank.com
BAOB—(OTCIQ)
Offices of Bank Holding Companies
N.A.I.C.S.: 551111
Merlin Zitzner *(CEO)*

Subsidiaries:

The Baraboo National Bank   (1)
101 3rd Ave, Baraboo, WI 53913
Tel.: (608) 356-7703
Web Site:
   http://www.baraboonationalbank.com
Banking Services
N.A.I.C.S.: 522110
Merlin Zitzner *(CEO)*

BARFRESH FOOD GROUP INC.

Barfresh Food Group Inc.—(Continued)

3600 Wilshire Blvd Ste 1720, Los Angeles, CA 90010
Tel.: (310) 598-7113   **DE**
Web Site: https://www.barfresh.com
Year Founded: 2010
BRFH—(NASDAQ)
Rev.: $9,162,000
Assets: $5,093,000
Liabilities: $2,572,000
Net Worth: $2,521,000
Earnings: ($6,219,000)
Emp.: 13
Fiscal Year-end: 12/31/22
Soft Drink Manufacturing
N.A.I.C.S.: 312111
Arnold Tinter *(Sec)*
Riccardo Delle Coste *(Founder, Chm, Pres & CEO)*
Lisa Roger *(CFO)*
Joseph M. Cugine *(Executives, Bd of Dirs)*

BARINGS BDC, INC.
300 S Tryon St Ste 2500, Charlotte, NC 28202
Tel.: (704) 805-7200   **MD**
Web Site: https://www.barings.com
Year Founded: 2006
BBDC—(NYSE)
Rev.: $161,488,000
Assets: $2,709,957,000
Liabilities: $1,517,628,000
Net Worth: $1,192,329,000
Earnings: $115,656,000
Emp.: 2
Fiscal Year-end: 12/31/22
Financial Management Services
N.A.I.C.S.: 541618
Christopher A. DeFrancis *(Interim Chief Compliance Officer)*
Elizabeth A. Murray *(CFO, COO & Chief Acctg Officer)*
Eric J. Lloyd *(Exec Chm & CEO)*
Sheldon Francis *(Chief Admin Officer)*
Patrick Hoefling *(CFO)*
Jawad Malik *(CIO)*
Caroline Mandeville *(Chief HR Officer)*
Duncan Robertson *(Head)*

Subsidiaries:

Energy Hardware Holdings, Inc.   **(1)**
2730 E Phillips Rd, Greer, SC 29650
Tel.: (864) 213-9499
Web Site: http://www.energyhardware.com
Holding Company
N.A.I.C.S.: 551112

MVC Capital, Inc.   **(1)**
287 Bowman Ave, Purchase, NY 10577
Tel.: (914) 701-0310
Web Site: http://www.mvccapital.com
Rev.: $30,549,564
Assets: $362,162,640
Liabilities: $134,203,956
Net Worth: $227,958,684
Earnings: $11,580,328
Emp.: 28
Fiscal Year-end: 10/31/2019
Closed-End Investment Fund
N.A.I.C.S.: 525990
Michael Theodore Tokarz *(Chm, CEO & Portfolio Mgr-Fund)*
Scott J. Schuenke *(CFO)*
Jaclyn Shapiro-Rothchild *(Sec & VP)*
Warren E. Holtsberg *(Head-Portfolio Mgmt-TTG Advisers)*
Patrick Mullins *(Controller)*
Kevin M. Byrne *(Chief Compliance Officer)*
David J. Williams *(Sr Mng Dir)*

Subsidiary (Domestic):

MVC Financial Services, Inc.   **(2)**
287 Bowman Ave 2nd Fl, Purchase, NY 10577
Tel.: (914) 701-0310
Sales Range: $25-49.9 Million
Emp.: 12

Investment Sourcing, Execution & Monitoring Services
N.A.I.C.S.: 523999
Shivani Khurana *(Mng Dir)*
Puneet Sanan *(Mng Dir)*

Holding (Domestic):

Ohio Medical Corp.   **(2)**
1111 Lakeside Dr, Gurnee, IL 60031-2489
Tel.: (847) 855-0500
Web Site: http://www.ohiomedical.com
Sales Range: $25-49.9 Million
Suction & Oxygen Therapy & Medical Gas Equipment Mfr
N.A.I.C.S.: 339112

Sierra Income Corporation   **(1)**
280 Park Ave 6th Fl E, New York, NY 10017
Tel.: (212) 759-0777
Web Site: http://www.sierraincomecorp.com
Rev.: $47,893,107
Assets: $677,708,042
Liabilities: $151,967,103
Net Worth: $525,740,939
Earnings: ($2,473,081)
Fiscal Year-end: 12/31/2020
Investment Management Service
N.A.I.C.S.: 523910
John Fredericks *(Chief Compliance Officer)*

BARISTAS COFFEE COMPANY, INC.
19930 68th Ave NE, Kenmore, WA 98028
Tel.: (206) 579-0222   **NV**
Web Site: https://www.baristas.tv
Year Founded: 1996
BCCI—(OTCIQ)
Coffee Mfr & Distr
N.A.I.C.S.: 311920
Troy Scott Steciw *(Pres)*
Barry Henthorn *(CEO & CTO)*

BARK, INC.
221 Canal St Fl 2, New York, NY 10013
Tel.: (212) 818-8800   **DE**
Web Site: https://www.bark.co
Year Founded: 2020
BARK—(NYSE)
Rev.: $507,406,000
Assets: $434,061,000
Liabilities: $217,000,000
Net Worth: $217,061,000
Earnings: ($68,299,000)
Emp.: 643
Fiscal Year-end: 03/31/22
Investment Services
N.A.I.C.S.: 523999
Matt Meeker *(Co-Founder, Exec Chm & CEO)*
Zahir Ibrahim *(CFO)*
Jonathan J. Ledecky *(Pres & COO)*
Henrik Werdelin *(Co-Founder)*
Carly Strife *(Co-Founder)*
Allison Koehler *(Gen Counsel)*

Subsidiaries:

Barkbox, Inc.   **(1)**
120 Broadway Fl 12, New York, NY 10271
Tel.: (855) 520-2275
Web Site: https://www.barkbox.com
Sales Range: $25-49.9 Million
Pet Product Distr
N.A.I.C.S.: 459910
Matt Meeker *(Founder)*

BARNES & NOBLE EDUCATION, INC.
120 Mountain View Blvd, Basking Ridge, NJ 07920
Tel.: (908) 991-2665   **DE**
Web Site: https://www.bned.com
BNED—(NYSE)
Rev.: $1,567,135,000
Assets: $905,084,000
Liabilities: $834,505,000
Net Worth: $70,579,000
Earnings: ($63,211,000)
Emp.: 2,520

Fiscal Year-end: 04/27/24
Higher Education Book Retailer
N.A.I.C.S.: 459210
Kevin F. Watson *(CFO & Exec VP)*
Jonathan Shar *(CEO)*
Seema C. Paul *(Chief Acctg Officer & Sr VP)*
Carolyn J. Brown *(Chief Comm Officer & Sr VP)*
Stephen Culver *(CIO & Sr VP)*
Philip O'Reilly *(Sr VP-Retail Fin-Tax)*
Jonathan Shar *(Exec VP-Retail)*
David G. Henderson *(Exec VP-Strategic Svcs)*
Andy Milevoj *(VP-Corporate Finance-Investor Relations)*
Hunter Blankenbaker *(VP-IR)*
Jonathan Shar *(Exec VP-Retail)*

Subsidiaries:

Barnes & Noble College Booksellers, LLC   **(1)**
120 Mountain View Blvd, Basking Ridge, NJ 07920
Tel.: (908) 991-2665
Web Site: https://www.bncollege.com
Sales Range: $1-4.9 Billion
Emp.: 14,400
College Bookstore Operator
N.A.I.C.S.: 459210
Jonathan Shar *(Pres)*
Stephen Culver *(CIO & Sr VP)*
Joann Magill *(Sr VP-HR)*
Lisa Malat *(Pres)*

LoudCloud Systems, Inc.   **(1)**
5720 Lyndon B Johnson Freeway Ste 550, Dallas, TX 75240
Tel.: (855) 568-3256
Web Site: http://www.loudcloudsystems.com
Teaching & Learning Software Publishers
N.A.I.C.S.: 513210

MBS Direct, LLC   **(1)**
2711 W Ash St, Columbia, MO 65203
Tel.: (573) 441-9179
Online Book Store Operator
N.A.I.C.S.: 459210
Andy Gingrich *(CFO)*
Bill Dampier *(Exec VP)*
David Henderson *(Pres)*
Josh Wheatley *(VP-Retail Ops)*
Dave Easton *(VP-Tech)*
Sarah Shiflett *(VP-Tech)*
Michael Tolly *(VP-Inventory Control)*
Pat Sullivan *(VP-Publr Rels)*
Mark Pulliam *(VP-Distr)*
Jerome Rader *(VP-HR)*
Bradley J. Hood *(VP-Fin Reporting & Taxation)*

MBS Textbook Exchange, LLC   **(1)**
2711 W Ash St, Columbia, MO 65203
Tel.: (573) 441-9179
Web Site: https://www.mbsbooks.com
College Textbook Bookstore Operations Software & E-Commerce Solutions Provider
N.A.I.C.S.: 424920
Andy Gingrich *(CFO)*
David Henderson *(Pres)*
Bill Dampier *(Exec VP)*
Sarah Shiflett *(VP-MBS Tech)*
Dave Easton *(VP-MBS Tech)*
Pat Sullivan *(VP-Publisher Rels)*
Mark Pulliam *(VP-Logistics)*
Jerome Rader *(VP-HR)*
Bradley J. Hood *(VP-Fin Reporting & Taxation)*
Chris Bovi *(Sls Mgr-Store Tech Solutions)*
Josh Wheatley *(VP-Retail Ops)*
Michael Tolly *(VP-Inventory Control)*
Todd Biggs *(Mgr-Field Mktg Territory)*
Paul Breun *(Mgr-Field Mktg Territory)*
Heidi Ellingboe *(Mgr-Field Mktg Territory)*
Beth Gallagher *(Mgr-Field Mktg Territory)*
Heather Gillespie *(Mgr-Field Mktg Territory)*
Jeremy Hawkins *(Mgr-Field Mktg Territory)*
Dustin Lindeman *(Mgr-Field Mktg Territory)*
Jerry Lynch *(Dir-Field Mktg)*
Kerry McCorkle *(Mgr-Field Mktg Territory)*
Liz Morris *(Mgr-Field Mktg Territory)*
David Mulberger *(Reg Mgr)*
Miranda Nelp *(Mgr-Field Mktg Territory)*
David Ritz *(Mgr-Field Mktg Territory)*
Cathy Slane *(Mgr-Field Mktg Territory)*

Elizabeth Taylor *(Assoc Dir-Field Mktg)*
Bonnie Washburn *(Mgr-Field Mktg Territory)*
Julie Wood *(Mgr-Field Mktg Territory)*

Promoversity LLC   **(1)**
6213 Factory Rd, Crystal Lake, IL 60014
Tel.: (877) 737-7137
Education Book Distr
N.A.I.C.S.: 459210

TXTB.com LLC   **(1)**
125 Lincoln St Fl 2, Boston, MA 02111
Tel.: (573) 445-2243
Education Book Distr
N.A.I.C.S.: 459210

BARNES GROUP INC.
123 Main St, Bristol, CT 06010
Tel.: (860) 583-7070   **DE**
Web Site:
  https://www.onebarnes.com
Year Founded: 1857
B—(NYSE)
Rev.: $1,261,868,000
Assets: $2,413,730,000
Liabilities: $1,067,403,000
Net Worth: $1,346,327,000
Earnings: $13,479,000
Emp.: 5,200
Fiscal Year-end: 12/31/22
Holding Company; Aerospace & Industrial Products Mfr & Distr
N.A.I.C.S.: 551112
Dawn N. Edwards *(Sr VP-HR)*
Lukas Hovorka *(Sr VP-Corp Dev)*
William E. Pitts *(VP-IR)*
Thomas J. Hook *(Pres & CEO)*
Julie K. Streich *(CFO & Sr VP-Fin)*
Ian Reason *(Pres)*
Jay B. Knoll *(Gen Counsel)*

Subsidiaries:

Associated Spring Raymond GmbH   **(1)**
Heimrodtr 10, 64625, Bensheim, Germany
Tel.: (49) 62519 332 5204
Web Site: https://www.asraymond.de
Hardware Mfr & Distr
N.A.I.C.S.: 332510

Barnes Aerospace   **(1)**
169 Kennedy Rd, Windsor, CT 06095-2043
Tel.: (860) 298-7740
Web Site: http://www.barnesaero.com
Sales Range: $25-49.9 Million
Emp.: 200
Complex Precision Machine Parts for Aircraft, Airline & Aerospace Markets Mfr
N.A.I.C.S.: 336412
Michael Beck *(Pres)*

Plant (Domestic):

Barnes Aerospace - East Granby   **(2)**
7 Connecticut S Dr, East Granby, CT 06026-9738
Tel.: (860) 653-5531
Web Site: http://www.barnesaero.com
Sales Range: $75-99.9 Million
Emp.: 120
Repair & Overhaul of Jet Engine Parts
N.A.I.C.S.: 811310

Barnes Aerospace - Lansing   **(2)**
5300 Aurelius Rd, Lansing, MI 48911-4116
Tel.: (517) 393-5110
Web Site: http://www.barnesaero.com
Rev.: $13,000,000
Emp.: 110
Titanium Jet Engine Parts Mfr
N.A.I.C.S.: 336412

Subsidiary (Non-US):

Windsor Airmotive Asia Pte. Ltd.   **(2)**
No 21 Loyang Lane, Singapore, 508921, Singapore   **(100%)**
Tel.: (65) 11656 542 4885
Web Site: http://www.windsorasia.com.sg

Sales Range: $25-49.9 Million
Repair & Overhaul of Jet Engine Parts
N.A.I.C.S.: 811310

Barnes Group (U.K.) Limited (1)
Unit 4 Grosvenor Business Centre, Evesham, WR11 1GS, Worcestershire, United Kingdom
Tel.: (44) 1386443366
Web Site: https://www.assocspring.co.uk
Sales Range: $75-99.9 Million
Industrial Maintenance & Automotive Repair Products Distr
N.A.I.C.S.: 441330

Barnes Group Spain SRL (1)
La Pena 6 - Pab 5, 01013, Vitoria-Gasteiz, Spain
Tel.: (34) 94 514 7542
Web Site: https://www.bgespana.com
Emp.: 4
Investment Management Service
N.A.I.C.S.: 333611

Barnes Korea Ltd. (1)
1110 Sungjee Starwith 954-6 Gwanyang-Dong, Dongan-Ku, Anyang, 014-059, Gyeonggi-do, Korea (South)
Tel.: (82) 31 422 4591
Web Site: http://www.kaller.com
Nitrogen Gas Products Distr
N.A.I.C.S.: 221210

FOBOHA (Germany) Gmbh (1)
Im Muhlegrun 8, 77716, Haslach im Kinzigtal, Germany
Tel.: (49) 7 832 7980
Web Site: https://www.foboha.com
Injection Molding Machine Mfr
N.A.I.C.S.: 333248

GF Controls GmbH (1)
Peter - Sander - Strasse 41A, Mainz Kastel, 55252, Wiesbaden, Germany
Tel.: (49) 6134948900
Web Site: https://gammaflux.com
Temperature Controller Whslr
N.A.I.C.S.: 423830
Daniel Vesper *(Mng Dir)*
Andreas Muller *(Mng Dir)*

Gammaflux Inc. (1)
113 Executive Dr Dock 106, Sterling, VA 20166
Tel.: (703) 471-5050
Web Site: http://www.gammaflux.com
Hazardous Waste Treatment & Disposal
N.A.I.C.S.: 562211

Gimatic Automation Engineering (Changshu) Co., Ltd. (1)
Room 902 N 333 Southeast Avenue, New & High-Tech Industrial Development Zone, Changshu, 215500, China
Tel.: (86) 51252977396
Controlling Device Mfr
N.A.I.C.S.: 334519

Gimatic Automation Technology (Shanghai) Co., Ltd. (1)
Room 707-709 Combo Branch Building No 955 Jianchuan Rd, Minghang District, Shanghai, 200241, China
Tel.: (86) 2154735580
Automotive Controlling Equipment Distr
N.A.I.C.S.: 423840

Gimatic Balkan d.o.o. Beograd - Savski Venac (1)
Belgrade 54 Veljka Dugosevica Street Building B5, 11000, Belgrade, Serbia
Tel.: (381) 117839615
Automotive Controlling Equipment Distr
N.A.I.C.S.: 423840

Gimatic Bulgaria Ltd. (1)
Pozitano street 9, 1000, Sofia, Bulgaria
Tel.: (359) 899157609
Industrial Tool & Gripper Product Mfr
N.A.I.C.S.: 333248

Gimatic France S.a.r.l. (1)
265 Rue Denis Papin, 38090, Villefontaine, France
Tel.: (33) 768380865
Automotive Controlling Equipment Distr
N.A.I.C.S.: 423840

Gimatic Iberia S.L. (1)
Carrer Del Oficis N5, 08860, Gava, Spain
Tel.: (34) 984493897

Industrial Tool & Gripper Product Mfr
N.A.I.C.S.: 333248

Gimatic Japan Limited (1)
11F Room41 TOC Building 7-22-17, Nishi-Gotanda Shinagawa-City, Tokyo, 141-0031, Japan
Tel.: (81) 362064235
Automotive Controlling Equipment Distr
N.A.I.C.S.: 423840

Gimatic Korea Limited (1)
719-2 Ll Center 50 Hogupo-ro, Namdong-Gu, Incheon, 15080, Gyeonggi, Korea (South)
Tel.: (82) 315048771
Automotive Controlling Equipment Distr
N.A.I.C.S.: 423840

Gimatic Nordic A.B. (1)
Levgrensvagen 27, Morarp, 685 30, Torsby, Sweden
Tel.: (46) 812144500
Automotive Controlling Equipment Distr
N.A.I.C.S.: 423840

Gimatic Otomasyon Ticaret Anonim Sirketi (1)
Perpa Tic Merk A Blok Kat 11 No 1472, Okmeydani, 34384, Istanbul, Türkiye
Tel.: (90) 2122108391
Automotive Controlling Equipment Distr
N.A.I.C.S.: 423840

Gimatic Polska Sp. z o.o (1)
Ul Okulickiego 23B/58, 42-200, Czestochowa, Poland
Tel.: (48) 343873052
Automotive Controlling Equipment Distr
N.A.I.C.S.: 423840

Gimatic S.r.l. (1)
Via Enzo Ferrari 2/4, 25030, Roncadelle, BS, Italy
Tel.: (39) 0302584655
Web Site: http://www.gimatic.com
Automotive Controlling Equipment Mfr
N.A.I.C.S.: 334519

Gimatic Sistemi industrijska avtomatizacija, d.o.o. (1)
Sternadova Ulica 5, 1000, Ljubljana, Slovenia
Tel.: (386) 40883456
Automotive Controlling Equipment Distr
N.A.I.C.S.: 423840

Gimatic UK Limited (1)
Unit 28 Graphite Way, Hadfield, Manchester, SK13 1QH, United Kingdom
Tel.: (44) 7568517497
Robotic & Automatic Machine Tool Component Mfr
N.A.I.C.S.: 336411

Gimatrade S.r.l. (1)
Via Piola 84/H, Gattico, 28013, Novara, Italy
Tel.: (39) 0322830624
Automotive Controlling Equipment Distr
N.A.I.C.S.: 423840

HPE S.p.A. (1)
Via Carlo Viola 74, 11026, Pont San Martin, Aosta Valle d'Aosta, Italy
Tel.: (39) 0125800311
Vehicle Components Mfr
N.A.I.C.S.: 336412

Industrial Gas Springs Inc. (1)
162 S Pinnacle Dr, Romeoville, IL 60446
Gas Spring Mfr & Distr
N.A.I.C.S.: 332613

Industrial Gas Springs Limited (1)
22 Wates Way, Mitcham, CR4 4HR, Surrey, United Kingdom
Tel.: (44) 2086466595
Web Site:
    http://www.industrialgassprings.com
Gas Spring Mfr & Distr
N.A.I.C.S.: 332613

MB Aerospace Holdings Inc. (1)
39 Bradley Park Rd, East Granby, CT 06026
Tel.: (806) 653-5041
Web Site: http://www.mbaerospace.com
Holding Company; Aerospace Engineering, Repair Services & Engine Component Mfr
N.A.I.C.S.: 551112

Craig Gallagher *(CEO)*
Ed Coates *(Head-Corp Fin & Dev)*
Gregor Goodwin *(CFO)*
Brian Selfors *(Exec VP-Sls & Comml)*
Kate Collins *(Gen Counsel)*
Matthew Scagnelli *(Chief HR Officer)*
Tom Tanner *(VP-CoE Product Strategy)*
John Kozma *(VP-Procurement)*
Dave Farmery *(VP-OE Component Mfg Sls)*
Ian Taylor *(VP-Repair Sls)*
George Adams *(COO)*
Howard Coffin *(CIO)*
Gary Coghill *(VP-Grp Engrg)*
Nathan Fowler *(VP-Quality)*
Jacob Ness *(VP-Materials)*
Michael Greenwald *(Gen Mgr)*

Subsidiary (Non-US):

MB Aerospace Limited (2)
Logans Road, PO Box 4, Motherwell, ML1 3NP, Lanarkshire, United Kingdom
Tel.: (44) 1698 242 400
Web Site: http://www.mbaerospace.co.uk
Aerospace Engine Components Mfr
N.A.I.C.S.: 336412

Subsidiary (Domestic):

MB Aerospace Sterling Heights, Inc. (2)
38111 Commerce Dr, Sterling Heights, MI 48312
Tel.: (586) 977-9200
Web Site: http://www.mbaerospace.com
Machine Shop, Jobbing & Repair
N.A.I.C.S.: 332710

MB Aerospace Warren, LLC (2)
25250 Easy St, Warren, MI 48089
Tel.: (586) 772-2500
Web Site: http://www.mbaerospace.com
Emp.: 1,600
Aerospace Engine Components Mfr & Repair Services
N.A.I.C.S.: 336412

Manner Hong Kong Limited (1)
Suite No 8B on 11/F Tower 1 China Hong Kong City 33 Canton Road, Tsim Sha Tsui, Kowloon, China (Hong Kong)
Tel.: (852) 23451281
Plastic Product Molding Mfr
N.A.I.C.S.: 333248

Manner USA, Inc. (1)
1105 Progress Industrial Blvd, Lawrenceville, GA 30043
Tel.: (770) 449-1820
Web Site: https://www.maenner-group.com
Emp.: 37
Industrial Molding Machinery Mfr
N.A.I.C.S.: 333248

OOO Gimatic Rus (1)
Kirova Str 4 Office 606, 394018, Voronezh, Russia
Tel.: (7) 9162178848
Robotic & Automatic Machine Tool Component Mfr
N.A.I.C.S.: 336411

Otto Manner GmbH (1)
Unter Gereuth 9-11, 79353, Bahlingen am Kaiserstuhl, Germany
Tel.: (49) 7 663 6090
Web Site: https://www.maenner-group.com
Emp.: 550
Industrial Molding Machinery Mfr
N.A.I.C.S.: 333248
Hans-Peter Manner *(Pres)*

Otto Manner Prazisionsformenbau AG, Schweiz (1)
Feldstrasse 11, 9434, Au, Switzerland
Tel.: (41) 717479955
Web Site: http://www.mannergroup.com
Emp.: 44
Hardware Mfr & Distr
N.A.I.C.S.: 332510

Priamus System Technologies AG (1)
Rheinweg 4, 8200, Schaffhausen, Switzerland
Tel.: (41) 526322626
Web Site: http://www.priamus.com
Vehicle Components Mfr
N.A.I.C.S.: 336412

Marcel Fenner *(Mgr & Pres)*
Max Muller *(Sls Mgr & Project Mgr)*

Priamus System Technologies GmbH (1)
Donzdorfer Strasse 20, Sussen, 73079, Goppingen, Germany
Tel.: (49) 7162267480
Web Site: http://www.priamus.com
Vehicle Components Mfr
N.A.I.C.S.: 336412
Erwin Konig *(Mng Dir & Head-Sales)*

Resortes Argentina S.A. (1)
Av Velez Sarsfield 3150-5016, 3150-5016, Cordoba, Argentina
Tel.: (54) 3514610458
Web Site: https://www.resortesar.com
Spring Mfr & Distr
N.A.I.C.S.: 332613

Ressorts SPEC, SAS (1)
Batiment Hermes 2 ZA de Pissaloup 4 rue Edouard Branly, 78190, Trappes, France (100%)
Tel.: (33) 1 3068 6363
Web Site: http://www.ressortsspec.com
Sales Range: $10-24.9 Million
Aerospace & Industrial Components Distr
N.A.I.C.S.: 423830

Seeger-Orbis GmbH & Co. OHG (1)
Wiesbadener Str 243, 61462, Konigstein, Germany
Tel.: (49) 61742050
Web Site: http://www.seeger-orbis.com
Emp.: 250
Investment Management Service
N.A.I.C.S.: 333611
Frank Dupre *(Mng Dir)*
Birgit Chorianopoulos *(Mng Dir)*
Robert Maas *(Mng Dir)*
Marco Schneider *(Mng Dir)*

Stromsholmen AB (1)
Verkstadsgatan 16, 573 41, Tranas, Sweden
Tel.: (46) 1 405 7100
Web Site: https://www.stromsholmen.com
Emp.: 700
Investment Management Service
N.A.I.C.S.: 333611
Johan Runesson *(Pres & CEO)*

Synventive Molding Solutions (Suzhou) Co., Ltd. (1)
12B Gang Tian Industrial Square, Suzhou Industrial Park, Suzhou, 215021, China
Tel.: (86) 5126 283 8870
Web Site: http://www.synventive.com
Industrial Molding Machinery Mfr
N.A.I.C.S.: 333248

Synventive Molding Solutions BV (1)
Windmolen 5, 4751 VM, Oud Gastel, Netherlands
Tel.: (31) 62 519 3320
Web Site: http://www.synventive.com
Emp.: 4
Hardware Spare Parts Distr
N.A.I.C.S.: 423710

Synventive Molding Solutions JBJ Private Limited (1)
Unit no 4 KAT Industries Center Indo German Technology Park, S No 297 298 Urawade Industrial Area Pirangut Lavasa Road, Pune, 412 115, India
Tel.: (91) 2067780000
Industrial Molding Machinery Mfr
N.A.I.C.S.: 333248

Synventive Molding Solutions K.K. (1)
6F of Masuni No 1 Building 2-4-6 Shin-Yokohama, Kouhoku-ku, Yokohama, 222-0033, Kanagawa, Japan
Tel.: (81) 45 472 1239
Web Site: http://www.synventive.com
Industrial Molding Machinery Mfr
N.A.I.C.S.: 333248

Synventive Molding Solutions LDA (1)
Rua Dr Manuel Ribeiro De Oliveira R/C Esq, 2400-178, Leiria, Portugal
Tel.: (351) 24 482 9790
Web Site: http://www.synventive.com
Emp.: 10

Barnes Group Inc.—(Continued)

Hardware Spare Parts Distr
N.A.I.C.S.: 423710

Synventive Molding Solutions Limited (1)
The Pinnacle 160 Midsummer Buld, Milton Keynes, MK9 1FF, United Kingdom
Tel.: (44) 32979683
Web Site: http://www.synventive.com
Hardware Spare Parts Distr
N.A.I.C.S.: 423710

Synventive Molding Solutions Ltda (1)
Rua Wallace Barnes 301, Distrito Industrial, 13054-701, Campinas, 13054-701, Sao Paulo, Brazil
Tel.: (55) 1937251092
Industrial Molding Plastic Parts Mfr
N.A.I.C.S.: 326199

Synventive Molding Solutions Pte Ltd. (1)
Block 5008 Techplace II 04-09 M14 Ang Mo Kio Ave 5, Singapore, 569874, Singapore
Tel.: (65) 9 186 2680
Web Site: http://www.synventive.com
Emp.: 10
Industrial Molding Machinery Mfr
N.A.I.C.S.: 333248

Synventive Molding Solutions S.R.L. (1)
Via Carlo Viola 74, 11026, Pont San Martin, AO, Italy
Tel.: (39) 01251931110
Hardware Spare Parts Distr
N.A.I.C.S.: 423710
Alessandro Del Maschio (Mgr-Mediterranean)

Synventive Molding Solutions SAS (1)
265 Rue Denis Papin, 38090, Villefontaine, France
Tel.: (33) 474991600
Hardware Spare Parts Distr
N.A.I.C.S.: 423710

Synventive Molding Solutions SL (1)
Rua Dr Manuel Ribeiro De Oliveira R/C Esq, 2400-178, Leiria, Portugal
Tel.: (351) 244829790
Web Site: http://www.synventive.com
Industrial Molding Machinery Mfr
N.A.I.C.S.: 333248

Synventive Molding Solutions s.r.o. (1)
Sezemicka 2757/2, 193 00, Prague, Czech Republic
Tel.: (420) 22 620 3000
Web Site: http://www.synventive.com
Emp.: 20
Hardware Spare Parts Distr
N.A.I.C.S.: 423710

Synventive Molding Solutions, Inc. (1)
10 Centennial Dr, Peabody, MA 01960
Tel.: (978) 750-8065
Web Site: https://www.synventive.com
Sales Range: $200-249.9 Million
Hot Runner Systems & Components Mfr & Distr
N.A.I.C.S.: 333248

Subsidiary (Non-US):

Synventive Molding Solutions GmbH (2)
Heimrodstrasse 10, 64625, Bensheim, Germany
Tel.: (49) 62 519 3320
Web Site: http://www.synventive.com
Emp.: 200
Hot Runner Systems & Components Mfr & Distr
N.A.I.C.S.: 333248

Thermoplay Brasil Sistemas de Injecao Ltda (1)
Rua Santo Antonio 721 Jardim Mexico, Itatiba, 13253-400, Brazil
Tel.: (55) 1145942116
Plastic Fabrication Machinery Mfr
N.A.I.C.S.: 333511

Thermoplay Deutschland GmbH (1)
Hoffmeister 15, 58511, Ludenscheid, Germany
Tel.: (49) 2351661180
Web Site: http://www.thermoplay.it
Plastic Fabrication Machinery Mfr
N.A.I.C.S.: 333511

Thermoplay Hot Runner Systems (Beijing) Co. Ltd (1)
Rui Jing Industrial Park C-02S-28 No 1 Da Huan Zhuang West Road, Jiu Xian Qiao North Chao Yang, Beijing, China
Tel.: (86) 1051077406
Plastic Fabrication Machinery Mfr
N.A.I.C.S.: 333511
Roberto Tavernese (Gen Mgr)

Thermoplay India Private Limited (1)
Lee Ann 10 Flat No 1 Ground Floor Lake View Colony, Miramar, Panaji, 403 001, Goa, India
Tel.: (91) 8322461155
Web Site: http://www.thermoplay.it
Plastic Fabrication Machinery Mfr
N.A.I.C.S.: 333511
Noella De Melo (Sec)

Thermoplay Portugal Unipessoal Lda (1)
Estr Nazare Nr 200 R/c Esq Letra A Amieirinha, 2430-024, Marinha Grande, Portugal
Tel.: (351) 244577247
Plastic Fabrication Machinery Mfr
N.A.I.C.S.: 333511
Mario Fernandes (Mgr-Engrg)

Thermoplay S.p.A. (1)
Via Carlo Viola 74, 11026, Pont San Martin, AO, Italy
Tel.: (39) 0125800311
Web Site: https://www.thermoplay.it
Emp.: 179
Plastic Fabrication Machinery Mfr
N.A.I.C.S.: 333511
Roberto Bertone (CEO)

Thermoplay U.K. Ltd. (1)
Business Centre 8 Madeira Avenue, Leigh-on-Sea, SS9 3EB, Essex, United Kingdom
Tel.: (44) 1702473876
Web Site: http://www.thermoplay.it
Plastic Fabrication Machinery Mfr
N.A.I.C.S.: 333511

manner Japan Co. Ltd. (1)
30-8 Sumiyoshi-cho, Mito, 310-0844, Ibaraki, Japan
Tel.: (81) 292123341
Plastic Product Molding Mfr
N.A.I.C.S.: 333248

BARNWELL INDUSTRIES, INC.
1100 Alakea St Ste 500, Honolulu, HI 96813-2840
Tel.: (808) 531-8400   DE
Web Site: https://www.brninc.com
Year Founded: 1956
BRN—(NYSEAMEX)
Rev.: $21,724,000
Assets: $30,669,000
Liabilities: $17,607,000
Net Worth: $13,062,000
Earnings: ($5,331,000)
Emp.: 27
Fiscal Year-end: 09/30/24
Crude Petroleum Extraction Services
N.A.I.C.S.: 211120
Alexander C. Kinzler (Exec Chm, Gen Counsel & Sec)
Russell M. Gifford (CFO, Treas, Sec & Exec VP)
Sheryl A. L. Villanueva (Asst VP & Asst Controller)
Heidi M. Uratsuka (Asst VP)
Kenneth S. Grossman (Vice Chm)
Denise L. Miyasato (Asst Sec)
Kenneth S. Grossman (Chm)
Joy Matsukawa (Asst VP & Asst Controller)

Subsidiaries:

Barnwell Geothermal Corporation (1)

1100 Alakea St Ste 2900, Honolulu, HI 96813-2840
Tel.: (808) 531-8422
Sales Range: $50-74.9 Million
Well Drilling Services & Water Pumping System Installation & Repairs
N.A.I.C.S.: 213111
Morton H. Kinzler (Chm & CEO)

Barnwell Hawaiian Properties, Inc. (1)
1100 Alakea St Ste 2900, Honolulu, HI 96813
Tel.: (808) 531-8422
Web Site: http://www.brninc.com
Sales Range: Less than $1 Million
Emp.: 12
Residential Real Estate & Investments
N.A.I.C.S.: 237210

Barnwell Kona Corporation (1)
1100 Alakea St Ste 2900, Honolulu, HI 96813-2840
Tel.: (808) 531-8400
Oil & Gas Exploration Services
N.A.I.C.S.: 211120

Barnwell Management Co., Inc. (1)
1100 Alakea St Ste 2900, Honolulu, HI 96813-2840
Tel.: (808) 531-8400
Web Site: http://www.brninc.com
Sales Range: Less than $1 Million
Emp.: 10
Land Investment
N.A.I.C.S.: 237210

Barnwell Overseas, Inc. (1)
1100 Alakea St Ste 2900, Honolulu, HI 96813-2840
Tel.: (808) 882-7207
Web Site: http://www.brninc.com
Sales Range: $10-24.9 Million
Emp.: 10
Well Drilling Services
N.A.I.C.S.: 213111

Barnwell Shallow Oil, Inc. (1)
1100 Alakea St Ste 2900, Honolulu, HI 96813-2840
Tel.: (808) 531-8400
Web Site: http://www.brninc.com
Sales Range: $25-49.9 Million
Emp.: 27
Natural Gas Drilling Operations
N.A.I.C.S.: 213111

Barnwell of Canada Limited (1)
639 5th Avenue Southwest Suite 900, Calgary, T2P 0M9, AB, Canada   (100%)
Tel.: (403) 531-1560
Web Site: http://www.brninc.com
Sales Range: $25-49.9 Million
Emp.: 15
Oil & Gas Exploration & Development
N.A.I.C.S.: 211120
Nancy M. Lee (Controller)

Geothermal Exploration Co., Inc. (1)
1100 Alakea St Ste 2900, Honolulu, HI 96813-2840
Tel.: (808) 531-8400
Web Site: http://www.brninc.com
Sales Range: $150-199.9 Million
Petroleum & Natural Gas Extraction
N.A.I.C.S.: 211120

Kaupulehu Developments (1)
1100 Alakea St Ste 2900, Honolulu, HI 96813
Tel.: (808) 531-8400
Web Site: http://www.brninc.com
Emp.: 10
Real Estate Brokerage Services
N.A.I.C.S.: 531210

Water Resources International, Inc. (1)
PO Box 44520, Kamuela, HI 96743-4301   (100%)
Tel.: (808) 882-7207
Sales Range: $1-9.9 Million
Emp.: 18
Water Well Drilling Services
N.A.I.C.S.: 237110
Russell M. Gifford (Pres)

BARON ENERGY, INC.

300 S C M Allen Pkwy Ste 218, San Marcos, TX 78666
Tel.: (512) 392-5775   NV
Web Site:
https://www.baronenergy.com
Year Founded: 2007
BROE—(OTCEM)
Sales Range: Less than $1 Million
Oil & Gas Exploration Services
N.A.I.C.S.: 211120
Lisa P. Hamilton (CFO & Exec VP)
Ronnie L. Steinocher (Chm, Pres & CEO)

BARREL ENERGY, INC.
4005 W Reno Ave Ste F, Las Vegas, NV 89118
Tel.: (702) 595-2247   NV
Web Site:
http://www.barrelenergyinc.com
Year Founded: 2014
BRLL—(OTCIQ)
Assets: $3,796,290
Liabilities: $5,515,914
Net Worth: ($1,719,624)
Earnings: ($2,745,564)
Emp.: 2
Fiscal Year-end: 09/30/20
Oil & Gas Exploration
N.A.I.C.S.: 211120
Craig Alford (Pres)
Syed Rahman (Ops Mgr)
S. A. Gaffoor (CEO)
Lowell Thomas Holden (CFO)
Harpreet Singh Sangha (Chm)

BARRETT BUSINESS SERVICES, INC.
8100 NE Pkwy Dr Ste 200, Vancouver, WA 98662
Tel.: (360) 828-0700   MD
Web Site: https://www.bbsi.com
Year Founded: 1965
BBSI—(NASDAQ)
Rev.: $1,054,326,000
Assets: $686,938,000
Liabilities: $509,096,000
Net Worth: $177,842,000
Earnings: $47,268,000
Emp.: 127,141
Fiscal Year-end: 12/31/22
Human Resource Management Services
N.A.I.C.S.: 561320
Anthony J. Harris (CFO, Treas & Exec VP)
James R. Potts (Gen Counsel)
Gary E. Kramer (Pres & CEO)

Subsidiaries:

BBS I, LLC (1)
2 CenterPointe Dr Ste 120, Lake Oswego, OR 97035
Tel.: (503) 403-1355
Web Site: http://www.bbsi.com
Business Management Services
N.A.I.C.S.: 561110

Barrett Business Services (1)
1910 3rd St, Tillamook, OR 97141 (100%)
Tel.: (503) 842-1145
Web Site: http://www.barrettbusiness.com
Sales Range: $1-9.9 Million
Emp.: 2
Employment Services
N.A.I.C.S.: 561320

BASANITE, INC.
2660 NW 15th Ct, Pompano Beach, FL 33069
Tel.: (954) 532-4653   NV
Web Site:
https://www.basaniteindustries.com
Year Founded: 2006
BASA—(OTCIQ)
Rev.: $7,161
Assets: $2,848,467
Liabilities: $3,552,528

Net Worth: ($704,061)
Earnings: ($4,199,331)
Emp.: 23
Fiscal Year-end: 12/31/20
Mobile Marketing Services & Offers
N.A.I.C.S.: 541810
Ronald J. LoRicco Sr. *(Chm & Interim CEO)*
Vesna Stanic *(Dir-Quality)*
Jacqueline Placeres *(CFO, Treas & Sec)*
Frederick H. Tingberg Jr. *(CTO)*

Subsidiaries:

Basanite Industries, LLC   **(1)**
2041 NW 15th Ave, Pompano Beach, FL 33069
Tel.: (954) 532-4653
Web Site:
    http://www.ir.basaniteindustries.com
Rev.: $193,194
Assets: $5,211,286
Liabilities: $5,029,528
Net Worth: $181,758
Earnings: ($16,477,823)
Emp.: 23
Fiscal Year-end: 12/31/2021
Building Materials Mfr
N.A.I.C.S.: 327120
Dave Anderson *(COO & Exec VP)*
Isabella Barbera *(CFO)*
Simon R. Kay *(Pres)*

BASIC ENERGY SERVICES INC.
801 Cherry St Ste 2100, Fort Worth, TX 76102
Tel.: (817) 334-4100   DE
Web Site: https://www.basices.com
Year Founded: 1992
BASX—(OTCIQ)
Rev.: $411,375,000
Assets: $349,073,000
Liabilities: $529,705,000
Net Worth: ($180,632,000)
Earnings: ($268,175,000)
Emp.: 2,800
Fiscal Year-end: 12/31/20
Building, Repairing & Dismantling Oil & Gas Wells
N.A.I.C.S.: 237120
Keith L. Schilling *(Pres & CEO)*
James F. Newman *(Exec VP-Ops)*
Brandon McGuire *(Sr VP-Central Reg)*
Eric Lannen *(Chief HR Officer)*
Trey Stolz *(VP-IR)*
Adam L. Hurley *(CFO, Treas, Sec & Exec VP)*
Pedro R. Buhicas *(Chief IT Officer)*
Jack Renshaw *(Sr VP-Western Reg)*
Michael S. Henry *(Chief Acctg Officer & VP)*
Spencer Davis Armour III *(Co-Founder)*
Robert J. Reeb III *(Gen Counsel & VP)*

Subsidiaries:

Acid Services, LLC   **(1)**
100 S Main St Ste 607, Wichita, KS 67202
Tel.: (316) 262-3699
Energy Consulting Services
N.A.I.C.S.: 541690
Kevin Gordley *(Mgr)*

Agua Libre Midstream LLC   **(1)**
801 Cherry St Ste 2100, Fort Worth, TX 76102
Tel.: (817) 334-4162
Web Site: http://www.agualibre.com
Oilfield Management Services
N.A.I.C.S.: 213111
Joey Pineda *(Acct Mgr)*

Basic Energy Services, L.P.   **(1)**
3503 Industrial Dr, Hobbs, NM 88240
Tel.: (575) 392-6498
Oil & Gas Pipeline Construction Services
N.A.I.C.S.: 237120

C&J Well Services, Inc.   **(1)**
515 W Greens Rd Ste 1200, Houston, TX 77067-4536
Tel.: (281) 874-0035
Emp.: 8
Oil Field Contractors & Services
N.A.I.C.S.: 213111
Billy Rumbaugh *(Sr Mgr)*

Platinum Pressure Services, Inc.   **(1)**
2618 S US 287, Decatur, TX 76234
Tel.: (940) 626-8297
Web Site: http://www.platinumpressure.com
Oil & Gas Field Drilling Services
N.A.I.C.S.: 213111

Taylor Industries, LLC   **(1)**
6015 N Xanthus Ave, Tulsa, OK 74130
Tel.: (918) 266-7301
Web Site: http://www.taylorindustries.net
Emp.: 40
Oil & Gas Field Machinery Mfr
N.A.I.C.S.: 333132
Oscar Taylor *(Founder)*

BASSETT FURNITURE INDUSTRIES, INCORPORATED
3525 Fairystone Park Hwy, Bassett, VA 24055
Tel.: (276) 629-6000   VA
Web Site:
    https://www.bassettfurniture.com
Year Founded: 1902
BSET—(NASDAQ)
Rev.: $485,601,000
Assets: $406,273,000
Liabilities: $210,664,000
Net Worth: $195,609,000
Earnings: $65,345,000
Emp.: 1,561
Fiscal Year-end: 11/26/22
Furniture Mfr & Retailer
N.A.I.C.S.: 337122
Jay R. Hervey *(Gen Counsel, Sec & VP)*
J. Michael Daniel *(Chief Financial & Admin Officer & Sr VP)*
Robert H. Spilman Jr. *(Chm, Pres & CEO)*
Bruce R. Cohenour *(Chief Sls Officer & Sr VP)*
Kara Kelchner-Strong *(Officer-Customer Experience & Sr VP)*
John E. Bassett III *(COO & Sr VP)*

Subsidiaries:

BDU NY, LLC   **(1)**
1600 Lexington Ave, Rochester, NY 14606
Tel.: (585) 427-0608
Nonupholstered Wood Household Furniture Mfr
N.A.I.C.S.: 337122

Bassett Direct NC, LLC   **(1)**
3525 Fairystone Park Hwy, Bassett, VA 24055
Tel.: (276) 629-6000
Sales Range: $300-349.9 Million
Emp.: 1,500
Furniture Stores
N.A.I.C.S.: 449121
Eddie White *(VP-HR)*

Bassett Direct SC, LLC   **(1)**
3525 Fairystone Hwy, Bassett, VA 24055
Tel.: (276) 629-6000
Web Site: http://www.bassfurniture.com
Sales Range: $100-124.9 Million
Emp.: 100
Furniture Stores
N.A.I.C.S.: 449121

Bassett Furniture Co.   **(1)**
3525 Fairystone Park Hwy, Bassett, VA 24055
Tel.: (276) 629-6000
Web Site: http://www.bassettfurniture.com
Sales Range: $10-24.9 Million
Emp.: 200
Mfr of Furniture
N.A.I.C.S.: 337121

Bassett Upholstery Division   **(1)**
1111 E 20th St, Newton, NC 28658
Tel.: (828) 465-7700

Web Site: http://www.bassettfurniture.com
Sales Range: $300-349.9 Million
Emp.: 104
Mfg Upholstered Furniture
N.A.I.C.S.: 337121

Zenith Freight Lines Inc.   **(1)**
PO Box 969, Conover, NC 28613
Tel.: (828) 465-7036
Web Site: http://www.zenithfreight.com
Furniture Transport Services
N.A.I.C.S.: 484230

BATH & BODY WORKS, INC.
3 Limited Pkwy, Columbus, OH 43230
Tel.: (614) 415-7000   DE
Web Site:
    https://www.bathandbodyworks.com
Year Founded: 1990
BBWI—(NYSE)
Rev.: $7,429,000,000
Assets: $5,463,000,000
Liabilities: $7,089,000,000
Net Worth: ($1,626,000,000)
Earnings: $878,000,000
Emp.: 8,981
Fiscal Year-end: 02/03/24
Personal Care Product Distr
N.A.I.C.S.: 458110
Gina R. Boswell *(CEO)*
Bruce A. Soll *(Vice Chm-Intl)*
Eva C. Boratto *(CFO)*
Gina Boswell *(CEO)*
Amber L. Williams *(Sr VP & Deputy Gen Counsel)*

Subsidiaries:

Bath & Body Works, LLC   **(1)**
7 Limited Pkwy E, Reynoldsburg, OH 43068-5300
Tel.: (614) 856-6000
Web Site:
    http://www.bathandbodyworks.com
Sales Range: $1-4.9 Billion
Emp.: 2,000
Cosmetics & Personal Care Products Sales
N.A.I.C.S.: 456120
Andrew M. Meslow *(CEO)*

Subsidiary (Domestic):

Bath & Body Works Brand Management, Inc.   **(2)**
7 Limited Pkwy, Reynoldsburg, OH 43068
Tel.: (614) 415-7000
Apparel Distr
N.A.I.C.S.: 459999

The White Barn Candle Co.   **(2)**
7 Limited Pkwy E, Reynoldsburg, OH 43068
Tel.: (614) 856-6000
Web Site: http://www.lbrands.com
Sales Range: $650-699.9 Million
Emp.: 1,000
Candle Sales
N.A.I.C.S.: 459999

Limited Brand & Creative Services   **(1)**
3 Limited Pkwy, Columbus, OH 43230
Tel.: (614) 415-6200
Web Site: http://www.lb.com
Sales Range: $25-49.9 Million
Emp.: 100
Marketing Services
N.A.I.C.S.: 561499

Limited Real Estate   **(1)**
3 Limited Pkwy, Columbus, OH 43230-1467   **(100%)**
Tel.: (614) 415-7000
Web Site: http://www.lbrands.com
Sales Range: $50-74.9 Million
Emp.: 102
Real Estate Services
N.A.I.C.S.: 531390

Mast Logistics Services, Inc.   **(1)**
2 Limited Pkwy, Columbus, OH 43230-1445   **(100%)**
Tel.: (614) 415-7500
Sales Range: $300-349.9 Million
Emp.: 700
Distribution Services

N.A.I.C.S.: 488210

Mast Technology Services, Inc.   **(1)**
3 Limited Pkwy, Columbus, OH 43230-1467
Tel.: (614) 415-7000
Web Site: http://www.lbrands.com
Sales Range: $200-249.9 Million
Emp.: 800
Data Processing & Preparation Services
N.A.I.C.S.: 561499

Retail Store Operations, Inc.   **(1)**
3 Limited Pkwy, Columbus, OH 43230-1467
Tel.: (614) 479-2000
Cosmetics Retailer
N.A.I.C.S.: 456120

Victoria's Secret UK Limited   **(1)**
16 Garrick Street, London, WC2E 9BA, United Kingdom
Tel.: (44) 2073181740
Web Site: http://www.victoriassecret.co.uk
Fashion Product Retailer
N.A.I.C.S.: 456120

BATTALION OIL CORP.
820 Gessner Rd Ste 1100, Houston, TX 77024
Tel.: (832) 538-0300   DE
Web Site:
    https://www.battalionoil.com
Year Founded: 2004
BATL—(NYSEAMEX)
Rev.: $359,064,000
Assets: $485,358,000
Liabilities: $400,730,000
Net Worth: $84,628,000
Earnings: $18,589,000
Emp.: 63
Fiscal Year-end: 12/31/22
Oil & Gas Exploration Services
N.A.I.C.S.: 211120
Leah R. Kasparek *(Sr VP-HR & Admin)*
Matthew B. Steele *(CEO)*
Daniel P. Rohling *(COO & Exec VP)*
Jonathan Barrett *(Chm)*
Walter Mayer *(VP-Legal)*
Grant R. Evans *(VP-Exploration & Geoscience)*
Chris Lang *(Dir-Fin & IR)*

Subsidiaries:

HK Resources, LLC   **(1)**
5791 Pelican Shores Ct, Longmont, CO 80504
Tel.: (303) 772-2037
Administrative & General Management Consulting Services
N.A.I.C.S.: 541611

HRC Energy Resources (WV), Inc.   **(1)**
1000 Louisiana St Ste 6700, Houston, TX 77002
Tel.: (832) 538-0300
Oil & Gas Field Services
N.A.I.C.S.: 213112

Halcon Energy Properties, Inc.   **(1)**
1000 La St Ste 6700, Houston, TX 77002
Tel.: (832) 649-4015
Natural Gas Extraction Services
N.A.I.C.S.: 211130

Halcon Field Services, LLC   **(1)**
2894 Kirila Blvd, Hermitage, PA 16148
Tel.: (724) 342-3793
Oil & Gas Field Services
N.A.I.C.S.: 213112
Rich DiMichele *(Pres)*

BATTERY FUTURE ACQUISITION CORP.
8 The Green Ste 18195, Dover, DE 19901
Tel.: (929) 465-9707   Ky
Web Site:
    https://www.futureacquisition.com
Year Founded: 2021
BFAC—(NYSE)
Rev.: $22,819,453
Assets: $357,665,227

Battery Future Acquisition Corp.—(Continued)

Liabilities: $359,821,431
Net Worth: ($2,156,204)
Earnings: $21,252,998
Emp.: 4
Fiscal Year-end: 12/31/22
Investment Services
N.A.I.C.S.: 523999
Josh Payne (COO)
Nick O'Loughlin (Chief Dev Officer)
Fanghan Sui (Chm & CEO)

BAUDAX BIO, INC.
490 Lapp Rd, Malvern, PA 19355
Tel.: (484) 395-2440   **PA**
Web Site:
https://www.baudaxbio.com
Year Founded: 2019
BXRXQ—(OTCIQ)
Rev.: $1,269,000
Assets: $10,032,000
Liabilities: $34,274,000
Net Worth: ($24,242,000)
Earnings: ($58,795,000)
Emp.: 9
Fiscal Year-end: 12/31/22
Pharmaceuticals Mfr
N.A.I.C.S.: 325412
Gerri Henwood (Pres & CEO)
Wayne B. Weisman (Chm)
Yong Chan Kim (Chief Scientific Officer)

BAXTER INTERNATIONAL INC.
1 Baxter Pkwy, Deerfield, IL 60015
Tel.: (224) 948-2000   **DE**
Web Site: https://www.baxter.com
Year Founded: 1931
BAX—(NYSE)
Rev.: $14,813,000,000
Assets: $28,276,000,000
Liabilities: $19,808,000,000
Net Worth: $8,468,000,000
Earnings: $2,656,000,000
Emp.: 60,000
Fiscal Year-end: 12/31/23
Biopharmaceutical Fluid & Drug Delivery Products Mfr for Treatment of Hemophilia, Immune Deficiencies & Other Life-Threatening Disorders
N.A.I.C.S.: 325414
Jose E. Almeida (Chm, Pres, CEO & Exec Officer)
Jeanne Mason (Sr VP-HR)
Reaz Rasul (Gen Mgr-Acute Therapies)
James Borzi (Chief Supply Chain Officer & Sr VP)
David S. Rosenbloom (Gen Counsel & Sr VP)
Alok Sonig (Pres, Grp Pres-Pharmaceuticals & Exec VP)
Chris Toth (Grp Pres-Kidney Care & Exec VP)
Gerard Greco (Chief Quality Officer & Sr VP)
Charles Patel (CIO & Sr VP)
Daniel Wolf (Chief Strategy Officer, Chief M&A Officer & Sr VP)
Heather Knight (Pres-Medical Products, Therapies, and Grp & Exec VP)
Joel T. Grade (CFO, Interim Chief Acctg Officer & Exec VP)

Subsidiaries:

Baxter (India) Private Limited   **(1)**
5th Floor Tower A Building No 9 DLF Cyber City DLF Phase - 3, Gurgaon, 122002, Haryana, India
Tel.: (91) 124 450 0200
Web Site: https://www.baxter.in
Pharmaceuticals Product Mfr
N.A.I.C.S.: 325412
Shikha Arora (Sr Mgr-Corporate Communications)

Baxter AG   **(1)**

Thurgauerstrasse 130, Glattpark, 8152, Opfikon, Switzerland
Tel.: (41) 449085050
Web Site: http://www.baxter.ch
Sales Range: $25-49.9 Million
Medical Supplies Whslr
N.A.I.C.S.: 423450
Paul Van de Velde (Mng Dir)

Baxter AS   **(1)**
Nydalsveien 33, Nydalen, 0484, Norway
Tel.: (47) 22584800
Web Site: http://www.baxter.no
Pharmaceutical Preparation Mfr
N.A.I.C.S.: 325412

Baxter Argentina S.A.   **(1)**
Av Olivos 4140, Buenos Aires, Argentina
Tel.: (54) 1147114100
Pharmaceutical Product Whslr
N.A.I.C.S.: 424210

Baxter B.V.   **(1)**
Kobaltweg 49, 3542 CE, Utrecht, Netherlands
Tel.: (31) 302488911
Web Site: http://www.baxter.nl
Emp.: 150
Health Care Srvices
N.A.I.C.S.: 621111

Baxter Belgium SPRL   **(1)**
Boulevard d'Angleterre 2-4, Braine-l'Alleud, 1420, Brussels, Belgium
Tel.: (32) 23868000
Web Site: https://www.baxter.be
Healthcare Equipment Distr
N.A.I.C.S.: 423450

Baxter Deutschland GmbH   **(1)**
Edisonstrasse 4, 85716, Unterschleissheim, Germany
Tel.: (49) 89317010
Web Site: http://www.baxter.de
Emp.: 950
Pharmaceutical Product Whslr
N.A.I.C.S.: 424210

Baxter Distribution Center Europe SA   **(1)**
Boulevard Rena Branquart 80, 7860, Lessines, Belgium
Tel.: (32) 68272211
Web Site: http://www.baxter.be
Medical Equipment Distr
N.A.I.C.S.: 423450

Baxter Healthcare (Holdings) Limited   **(1)**
Caxton Way, Thetford, IP24 3SE, Norfolk, United Kingdom
Tel.: (44) 1842767000
Web Site: http://www.braxter.com
Emp.: 500
Holding Company
N.A.I.C.S.: 551112

Baxter Healthcare (Thailand) Company Limited   **(1)**
1550 Thanaphum Building 11th Floor New Petchburi Road, Makkasan Sub-district Ratchathewi, Bangkok, 10400, Thailand
Tel.: (66) 26670505
Web Site: http://www.baxter.co.th
Health Care Srvices
N.A.I.C.S.: 621111

Baxter Healthcare Corporation   **(1)**
1 Baxter Pkwy, Deerfield, IL 60015-4625   **(100%)**
Tel.: (224) 948-1812
Web Site: http://www.baxter.com
Sales Range: $10-24.9 Million
Distribution of Medical Products & Supplies
N.A.I.C.S.: 339112

Subsidiary (Non-US):

ApaTech Limited   **(2)**
360 Centennial Avenue Centennial Park, Elstree, WD6 3TJ, Herdfordshire, United Kingdom
Tel.: (44) 2087314640
Pharmaceutical Preparation Mfr
N.A.I.C.S.: 325412
Andrew Neil Goldney (Dir)

Subsidiary (Domestic):

Baxa Corporation   **(2)**

14445 Grasslands Dr, Englewood, CO 80112
Tel.: (303) 690-4204
Web Site: http://www.baxa.com
Emp.: 400
Pharmacy & Nursing Product Mfr
N.A.I.C.S.: 339113

Subsidiary (Non-US):

Baxter (Hellas) EPE   **(2)**
Mar Antypa 47 and Anafis, 141 21, Iraklion, Greece
Tel.: (30) 210 288 0000
Web Site: https://www.baxter.com.gr
Pharmaceutical Preparation Mfr
N.A.I.C.S.: 325412

Baxter BioScience Manufacturing Sarl   **(2)**
Route De Pierre A Bot 111, 2000, Neuchatel, Switzerland
Tel.: (41) 327297297
Pharmaceutical Preparation Mfr
N.A.I.C.S.: 325412

Division (Domestic):

Baxter Bioscience Division   **(2)**
4501 Colorado Blvd, Los Angeles, CA 90039-1103   **(100%)**
Tel.: (818) 240-5600
Sales Range: $10-24.9 Million
Emp.: 50
Develops, Manufactures & Markets Proprietary Surgical Hemostatic Sealant Products
N.A.I.C.S.: 325411
Chester Zelaya (Gen Mgr)
John J. Orloff (VP)

Subsidiary (Domestic):

Baxter Caribe, Inc.   **(2)**
Rd 3 Km 144 2, Guayama, PR 00784
Tel.: (787) 864-5050
Web Site: http://www.baxter.com
Emp.: 500
Mfr of Pharmaceutical Preparations
N.A.I.C.S.: 325412

Subsidiary (Non-US):

Baxter Deutschland Holding GmbH   **(2)**
Edisonstrasse 4, 85716, Unterschleissheim, Germany
Tel.: (49) 89317010
Web Site: http://www.baxter.de
Healthcare Providers & Services
N.A.I.C.S.: 621491

Baxter Healthcare (Guangzhou) Company Ltd   **(2)**
No 6 Jiaoyuan Road Dongji Industrial, Guangzhou, 510730, Guangdong, China
Tel.: (86) 2032121000
Pharmaceutical Preparation Mfr
N.A.I.C.S.: 325412

Subsidiary (Domestic):

Baxter Healthcare Corporation of Puerto Rico   **(2)**
Rte 3 km 142 5, Guayama, PR 00785
Tel.: (787) 864-5050
Web Site: http://www.baxter.com
Medical Supplies Whslr
N.A.I.C.S.: 423450

Subsidiary (Non-US):

Baxter Healthcare Limited   **(2)**
Wallingford Road, Compton, Newbury, RG20 7QW, Berkshire, United Kingdom   **(100%)**
Tel.: (44) 1635206000
Web Site: http://www.baxterhealthcare.co.uk
Clinical & Technical Medical Information
N.A.I.C.S.: 325412

Baxter Healthcare Limited   **(2)**
Caxton Way, Thetford, IP24 3SE, Norfolk, United Kingdom   **(100%)**
Tel.: (44) 1842767000
Web Site:
https://www.baxterhealthcare.co.uk
Sales Range: $1-9.9 Million.
Emp.: 400
Pharmaceutical Manufacturing & Health Administration Services
N.A.I.C.S.: 325412

Baxter Healthcare Limited   **(2)**
Leningrad highway 16A Bld 1, Moscow, 125171, Russia   **(100%)**
Tel.: (7) 495 956 38 39
Web Site: http://www.baxter.ru
Sales Range: $10-24.9 Million
Healtcare Services
N.A.I.C.S.: 325412

Baxter Healthcare Limited   **(2)**
32 Bolshooj Samsonievs Kij Ave, Ste 2a-301, Saint Petersburg, 194044, Russia   **(100%)**
Tel.: (7) 8123248668
Web Site: http://www.baxter.ru
Sales Range: $1-9.9 Million
Emp.: 7
Healthcare & Pharmaceutical Preparations
N.A.I.C.S.: 325412

Baxter Healthcare Limited   **(2)**
Bereznyakovskaya St Buiding 29 office A, Kiev, 02098, Ukraine
Tel.: (380) 445948050
Web Site: http://www.baxter.ru
Health Services
N.A.I.C.S.: 325412

Baxter Healthcare Pty Ltd   **(2)**
1 Baxter Dve, Old Toongabbie, Sydney, 2146, NSW, Australia
Tel.: (61) 29 848 1111
Web Site: http://www.baxter.com
Pharmaceutical Preparation Mfr
N.A.I.C.S.: 325412

Baxter Healthcare SA   **(2)**
Thurgauerstrasse 130, Glattpark, 8152, Opfikon, Switzerland
Tel.: (41) 449085050
Web Site: http://www.baxter.ch
Healthcare providers & services
N.A.I.C.S.: 621491

Baxter Hospitalar Ltda.   **(2)**
Avenida Alfredo e de Souza Aranha 100, Sao Paulo, 04726-908, Brazil
Tel.: (55) 1156948500
Pharmaceutical Preparation Mfr
N.A.I.C.S.: 325412

Baxter Medical AB   **(2)**
Torshamnsgatan 48, Box 63, 164 94, Kista, Sweden
Tel.: (46) 20788115
Healthcare Providers & Services
N.A.I.C.S.: 621491
Magnus Lindholm (Pres)

Division (Domestic):

Baxter Medication Delivery   **(2)**
1 Baxter Pkwy, Deerfield, IL 60015-4625
Tel.: (847) 546-6311
Web Site: http://www.baxter.com
Intravenous Solutions, Premixed Drugs in IV Solutions, Administrative Sets, Catheters & Flow Control Devices, Parenteral & Enteral Nutrition Products, Irrigating Solutions
N.A.I.C.S.: 339112

Subsidiary (Domestic):

Baxter Pharmaceutical Solutions LLC   **(2)**
927 S Curry Pike, Bloomington, IN 47403
Tel.: (812) 333-0887
Pharmaceutical Preparation Mfr
N.A.I.C.S.: 325412

Division (Domestic):

Baxter Renal Division   **(2)**
1620 Waukegan Rd, Waukegan, IL 60085
Tel.: (847) 473-6840
Web Site: http://www.baxterhealthcare.ie
Mfr of Hemodialysis & Peritoneal Dialysis Equipment
N.A.I.C.S.: 561110

Subsidiary (Non-US):

Bieffe Medital S.p.A.   **(2)**
Via Nuova Provinciale, Grosotto, 23034, Sondrio, Italy
Tel.: (39) 034 284 1000
Web Site: https://www.baxteritalia.it
Pharmaceutical Preparation Mfr
N.A.I.C.S.: 325412

Subsidiary (Domestic):

Synovis Life Technologies, Inc. (2)
2575 University Ave W, Saint Paul, MN
55114-1024
Tel.: (651) 796-7300
Medical & Surgical Instrument Developer,
Mfr & Marketer
N.A.I.C.S.: 339113

Subsidiary (Domestic):

Synovis Micro Companies Alliance,
Inc. (3)
439 Industrial Ln, Birmingham, AL 35211
Tel.: (205) 941-0111
Web Site: http://www.synovismicro.com
Sales Range: $10-24.9 Million
Medical Equipment Components Mfr
N.A.I.C.S.: 339112
Michael K. Campbell (Asst VP-Biosurgery)
Terry Harrell (Dir-Sls)
Lauren Pollock Mott (Sr Mgr-Mktg)
Massimiliano Ciniglio (Mgr-Dermaclose
Clinical)
Peggy Trueb (Sr Mgr-Ops)
Kyle Karson (Mgr-Fin & Microsurgery Fin
Team)
Jurg Pfeiffer (Mgr-Sls-Microsurgical Prod-
ucts)

Baxter Healthcare GmbH (1)
Stella-Klein-Low-Weg 15, 1020, Vienna,
Austria
Tel.: (43) 1711200
Web Site: http://www.baxter.at
Emp.: 80
Healthcare Equipment Distr
N.A.I.C.S.: 423450

Baxter Healthcare Holding
GmbH (1)
Thurcauer strasse 130, Zurich, 8152, Swit-
zerland
Tel.: (41) 448786000
Web Site: http://www.baxter.ch
Holding Company
N.A.I.C.S.: 551112

Baxter Healthcare Limited (1)
Suites 2701-3 27/F Oxford House Taikoo
Place, 979 Kings Road Island East, Hong
Kong, China (Hong Kong)
Tel.: (852) 28078500
Web Site: http://www.baxter.com.hk
Health Care Srvices
N.A.I.C.S.: 622110

Baxter Holding B.V. (1)
Kobaltweg 49, 3542 CE, Utrecht, Nether-
lands
Tel.: (31) 302488897
Web Site: http://www.baxter.nl
Pharmaceutical Preparation Mfr
N.A.I.C.S.: 325412

Baxter Holding Mexico, S. de R.L. de
C.V. (1)
Av De Los 50 Metros 2, Jiutepec, 62578,
Mexico
Tel.: (52) 7773296000
Pharmaceutical Preparation Mfr
N.A.I.C.S.: 325412

Baxter Innovations GmbH (1)
Stella-Klein-Low-Weg 15, 1020, Vienna,
Austria
Tel.: (43) 1711200
Web Site: http://www.baxter.at
Pharmaceuticals Product Mfr
N.A.I.C.S.: 325412

Baxter Limited (1)
1-8-10 Harumi Triton Square Tower X9F,
Harumi Chuo, Tokyo, 104-0053, Japan
Tel.: (81) 120506871
Medical Supplies Whslr
N.A.I.C.S.: 423450

Baxter Manufacturing (Thailand) Co.,
Ltd. (1)
No 1550 Thanapoom Tower 11th Floor New
Petchburi Road, Makkasan, Bangkok,
10400, Thailand
Tel.: (66) 26670505
Web Site: http://www.baxter.co.th
Health Care Srvices
N.A.I.C.S.: 621111

Baxter Manufacturing Sp z o.o. (1)

ul Wojciechowska 42B, 20-704, Lublin, Po-
land
Tel.: (48) 815246694
Health Care Equipment Mfr
N.A.I.C.S.: 339112

Baxter Medico Famaceutica,
Lda. (1)
Sintra Business Park Edificio 10, 2710-089,
Sintra, Portugal
Tel.: (351) 219252500
Web Site: http://www.baxter.pt
Emp.: 100
Pharmaceutical Products Distr
N.A.I.C.S.: 424210

Baxter Oncology GmbH (1)
Kantstrasse 2, 33790, Halle,
Germany (100%)
Tel.: (49) 52017110
Web Site: https://www.baxter-oncology.de
Health Care Products Mfr
N.A.I.C.S.: 334510

Baxter Pharmaceuticals India Pvt.
Ltd. (1)
2nd Floor Tower-C Building No 8, DLF Cy-
ber City DLF Phase-II, Gurgaon, 122 022,
Haryana, India
Tel.: (91) 1244500200
Web Site: http://www.baxter.in
Health Care Srvices
N.A.I.C.S.: 622110
Amish Vyas (Sr Dir-OUS Portfolio Mgmt-
Pharmaceuticals)
Ravinder Dang (Gen Mgr)
Nagaraj Bhat (Dir-Global Delivery Centers)
Shalini Naagar (Dir-HR)
Satish Chandra Je (Sr Dir-R&D)
Rishikesh Jaiwant (Dir-Mfg & Ops)

Baxter Polska Sp. z o.o. (1)
ul Kruczkowskiego 8, 00-380, Warsaw, Po-
land
Tel.: (48) 22 488 3777
Web Site: https://www.baxter.com.pl
Healthcare Equipment Mfr & Distr
N.A.I.C.S.: 339112

Baxter R and D Europe S.C.R.L. (1)
Boulevard d'Anglais 2-4, 1420, Braine-
l'Alleud, Belgium
Tel.: (32) 23868000
Web Site: https://www.baxter.be
Healthcare Equipment Distr
N.A.I.C.S.: 423450

Baxter S.A. (1)
Boulevard Rene Branquart 80, 7860, Less-
ines, Belgium
Tel.: (32) 6 827 2211
Web Site: https://www.baxter.be
Pharmaceutical Preparation Mfr
N.A.I.C.S.: 339112

Baxter S.A. de C.V. (1)
Presidente Masarik 111-4 Piso Del Miguel
Hidalgo, Mexico, 11570, Mexico
Tel.: (52) 5591265000
Web Site:
     http://www.latinoamerica.baxter.com
Pharmaceuticals Product Mfr
N.A.I.C.S.: 325412

Baxter S.A.S. (1)
4 bis Rue de la Redoute, 78280, Guyan-
court, France
Tel.: (33) 13 461 5050
Web Site: https://www.baxter.fr
Emp.: 1,100
Medical Equipment Distr
N.A.I.C.S.: 423450

Baxter S.L. (1)
Poligono Industrial Sector 14 Calle Pouet
de Camilo 2, Ribarroja del Turia, 46394,
Valencia, Spain
Tel.: (34) 96 272 2800
Web Site: https://www.baxter.es
Pharmaceutical Mfr & Distr
N.A.I.C.S.: 325412

Baxter S.p.A. (1)
Piazzale dell'Industria 20, 00144, Rome,
Italy
Tel.: (39) 06324911
Web Site: http://www.baxteritalia.it
Pharmaceuticals Product Mfr
N.A.I.C.S.: 325412

Bieffe Medital Nederland N.V. (1)

Kobaltweg 49, 3542 CE, Utrecht, Nether-
lands
Tel.: (31) 302488911
Industrial Chemical Distr
N.A.I.C.S.: 424690

Cheetah Medical (Israel), Ltd. (1)
2A Hashlosha St F-32, Tel Aviv, 6706055,
Israel
Tel.: (972) 36440288
Medical Device & Equipment Mfr
N.A.I.C.S.: 339112
Eliezer Schusman (Dir-Hardware)

Cheetah Medical (UK) Limited (1)
Unit 2 Maidenhead Enterprise CenterCord-
wallis St, Maidenhead, SL6 7EP, Berkshire,
United Kingdom
Tel.: (44) 1628636806
Medical Device & Equipment Mfr
N.A.I.C.S.: 339112

Cheetah Medical, Inc. (1)
1320 Centre St Ste 401, Newton Center,
MA 02459
Tel.: (617) 964-0613
Web Site: http://www.cheetah-medical.com
Fluid Control Equipment & Instrument Distr
N.A.I.C.S.: 423830

Eczacibasi-Baxter Hastane Urunleri
Sanayi ve Ticaret A.S. (1)
Cendere Yolu Pinal Kexeli Bahcesi,
Ayazaga, 34396, Istanbul, Turkiye
Tel.: (90) 2123296200
Web Site: http://www.eczacibasi-
     baxter.com.tr
Industrial Chemicals Mfr
N.A.I.C.S.: 325998

Gambro AB (1)
Magistratsvagen 16, 22643, Lund, Sweden
Tel.: (46) 86136500
Web Site: http://www.baxter.com
Sales Range: $1-4.9 Billion
Emp.: 800
Dialysis Technologies & Other Renal Care
Products Developer, Mfr, Sales & Services
N.A.I.C.S.: 334510

Subsidiary (Non-US):

Bioprod Biomedicinski Produkti
d.o.o. (2)
Stegene 25, 1521, Ljubljana, Slovenia
Tel.: (386) 15133770
Web Site: http://www.bioprod.si
Dialysis Technologies & Other Renal Care
Products Mfr
N.A.I.C.S.: 334510

Diaverum Hungary (2)
Furj utca 2, 1124, Budapest, Hungary
Tel.: (36) 15500237
Web Site: http://www.diaverum.com
Rev.: $11,730,000
Emp.: 260
Dialysis Technologies & Other Renal Care
Products Sales & Services
N.A.I.C.S.: 423450
Eleonora Zajko (Dir-Nursing & Quality)
Marietta Torok (Dir-Medical)
Oliver Schonek (Dir-Fin)
Antal Szilard (Dir-Ops & IT)
Tamas Kohler (Mng Dir)
Kovacs Renata (Deputy Dir-Nursing)

Gambro A/S (2)
Jydekrogen 8, 2625, Vallensbaek, Denmark
Tel.: (45) 43620500
Web Site: http://www.gambro.dk
Sales Range: $25-49.9 Million
Emp.: 20
Dialysis Technologies & Other Renal Care
Products Sales & Services
N.A.I.C.S.: 423450

Gambro China Ltd. (2)
Room 3206-8 32/F New York Life Tower
Windsor House, 311 Gloucester Rd, Cause-
way Bay, China (Hong Kong)
Tel.: (852) 25762688
Web Site: http://www.gambro.com
Dialysis Technologies & Other Renal Care
Products Developer, Mfr, Sales & Services
N.A.I.C.S.: 334510

Subsidiary (Non-US):

Gambro Medical Products (Shanghai)
Co. Ltd. (3)

170 Yuanyang Road Minhang District, Tech-
nological Develop Zone, Shanghai, 200245,
China
Tel.: (86) 2164620700
Sales Range: $75-99.9 Million
Emp.: 300
Dialysis Technologies & Other Renal Care
Products Mfr
N.A.I.C.S.: 334510
Zhu Jing (Gen Mgr)

Subsidiary (Non-US):

Gambro Dasco S.p.A. (2)
Via Modenese 66, 43136, Medolla, MO,
Italy
Tel.: (39) 05 355 0111
Web Site: http://www.gambro.com
Sales Range: $200-249.9 Million
Dialysis Technologies & Other Renal Care
Products Mfr
N.A.I.C.S.: 334510

Unit (Domestic):

Gambro Export (2)
Scheelevagen 34, 220 10, Lund, Sweden
Tel.: (46) 169000
Web Site: http://www.gambro.dk
Dialysis Technologies & Other Renal Care
Products Sales & Services
N.A.I.C.S.: 423450

Subsidiary (Non-US):

Gambro GmbH (2)
Danziger Strasse 23, 82194, Grobenzell,
Germany
Tel.: (49) 814596190
Medical Equipment Distr
N.A.I.C.S.: 423450

Gambro Hospal S.p.A. (2)
Via Ferrarese 219, 40128, Bologna, BO,
Italy
Tel.: (39) 051638267
Web Site: http://www.hospal.com
Sales Range: $10-24.9 Million
Emp.: 55
Dialysis Technologies & Other Renal Care
Products Marketing & Sales
N.A.I.C.S.: 622110

Plant (Domestic):

Gambro S.p.A. (3)
Via Camurana 2, 41037, Mirandola, MO,
Italy
Tel.: (39) 07736691
Web Site: http://www.gambro.it
Dialysis Technologies & Other Renal Care
Products Mfr
N.A.I.C.S.: 334510

Gambro S.p.A. (3)
Via Modenese 66, PO Box 62, 41036,
Medolla, MO, Italy
Tel.: (39) 053550111
Web Site: http://www.gambro.dk
Dialysis Solutions Mfr
N.A.I.C.S.: 334510

Subsidiary (Non-US):

Gambro Inc. (2)
2 East Beaver Creek Rd Building 4, Rich-
mond Hill, Toronto, L4B 2N3, ON, Canada
Tel.: (905) 762-0690
Web Site: http://www.gambro.com
Sales Range: $25-49.9 Million
Emp.: 100
Dialysis Technologies & Other Renal Care
Products Developer, Mfr, Sales & Services
N.A.I.C.S.: 334510

Subsidiary (US):

Gambro Inc. (2)
14143 Denver W Pkwy Ste 400, Lakewood,
CO 80401
Tel.: (303) 222-6500
Web Site: http://www.gambro.com
Sales Range: $50-74.9 Million
Emp.: 200
Mfr & Marketer of Medical Technology Prod-
ucts Specializing in Renal Care, Blood
Component Technology & Health Patient
Service
N.A.I.C.S.: 339112

Baxter International Inc.—(Continued)

Subsidiary (Non-US):

Gambro Industries SAS (2)
7 Avenue Lionel Terray, 69883, Meyzieu,
Cedex, France
Tel.: (33) 472452525
Web Site: http://www.baxter.com
Pharmaceutical Product Whslr
N.A.I.C.S.: 424210

Gambro Korea Ltd. (2)
1st Fl KLC Bldg 145-9 Samseong-Dong,
Gangnam Gu, Seoul, 135 090, Korea
(South)
Tel.: (82) 222400500
Web Site: http://www.gambro.com
Sales Range: $25-49.9 Million
Emp.: 125
Dialysis Technologies & Other Renal Care
Products Developer, Mfr, Sales & Services
N.A.I.C.S.: 334510

Gambro Meopta S.R.O. (2)
Kabelikova 1, 750 02, Prerov, Czech Re-
public
Tel.: (420) 581241111
Web Site: http://www.meopta.com
Sales Range: $150-199.9 Million
Emp.: 660
Dialysis Technologies & Other Renal Care
Products Mfr
N.A.I.C.S.: 334510

Gambro Norge NUF (2)
Bjellandveien 24, 3172, Vear, Norway
Tel.: (47) 33301420
Web Site: http://www.gambro.com
Dialysis Technologies & Other Renal Care
Products Sales & Services
N.A.I.C.S.: 423450

Gambro Poland Sp. z o.o. (2)
Ul Cylichowska 13 15, PL-04 769, Warsaw,
Poland
Tel.: (48) 225160700
Web Site: http://www.gambro.com
Sales Range: $25-49.9 Million
Emp.: 10
Dialysis Technologies & Other Renal Care
Products Sales & Services
N.A.I.C.S.: 423450

Gambro Pty. Ltd. (Sydney) (2)
62 Norwest Boulevard Suite 2 Level 4, PO
Box 6604, Baulkham Hills, 2153, NSW,
Australia
Tel.: (61) 296802711
Web Site: http://www.gambro.com
Sales Range: $25-49.9 Million
Emp.: 100
Dialysis Technologies & Other Renal Care
Products Designer, Mfr, Sales & Services
N.A.I.C.S.: 334510

Branch (Domestic):

Gambro Pty. Ltd. (Brisbane) (3)
Unit 16 56 Lavarack Avenue, PO Box 1164,
Eagle Farm, 4009, QLD, Australia
Tel.: (61) 732167544
Web Site: http://www.gambro.com
Sales Range: $25-49.9 Million
Emp.: 70
Dialysis Technologies & Other Renal Care
Products Sales & Services
N.A.I.C.S.: 423450

Unit (Domestic):

Gambro Research (2)
Magistratsvagen 16, 222 41, Lund, Sweden
Tel.: (46) 46169000
Web Site: http://www.gambro.com
Sales Range: $200-249.9 Million
Emp.: 900
Dialysis Technologies & Other Renal Care
Products Developer
N.A.I.C.S.: 334510
Niclas Jonasson (Mng Dir)

Plant (Domestic):

Gambro BiCart (3)
Gambro Svenska Forsaljning, PO Box 101
01, SE-22010, Lund, Sweden
Tel.: (46) 46169000
Web Site: http://www.gambro.com
Sales Range: $150-199.9 Million
Emp.: 850

Dialysis Technologies & Other Renal Care
Products Mfr
N.A.I.C.S.: 334510

Subsidiary (Non-US):

Gambro S.A. (2)
Avenida de la Industria 16, Coslada, 28823,
Madrid, Spain
Tel.: (34) 914852540
Web Site: http://www.gambro.com
Sales Range: $25-49.9 Million
Emp.: 40
Dialysis Technologies & Other Renal Care
Products Warehousing
N.A.I.C.S.: 493190

Gambro Taiwan Ltd. (2)
7F No 305 Sector-3 Nan King E Road, Tai-
pei, 104, Taiwan
Tel.: (886) 22766600
Sales Range: $25-49.9 Million
Emp.: 30
Dialysis Technologies & Other Renal Care
Products Developer, Mfr, Sales & Services
N.A.I.C.S.: 423450

Gambro de Mexico, S.A. de C.V. (2)
patricio sanz 1249 Benito Juarez, 03100,
Mexico, DF, Mexico
Tel.: (52) 55 5335 2100
Web Site: http://www.caridianbct.com
Sales Range: $25-49.9 Million
Emp.: 50
Automated Blood Collection, Therapeutic
Apheresis, Cell Therapy, Blood Component
Separation & Purification Technologies
Whslr
N.A.I.C.S.: 423450

Gambro/Hospal Austria GmbH (2)
Stella-Klein-Low-Weg 15, Vienna, 1020,
Austria
Tel.: (43) 1711202456666
Web Site: http://www.gambro.at
Sales Range: $25-49.9 Million
Emp.: 25
Dialysis Technologies & Other Renal Care
Products Sales & Services
N.A.I.C.S.: 423450

Gambro/Hospal GmbH (2)
Danziger Strasse 23, 82194, Grobenzell,
Germany
Tel.: (49) 814265190
Web Site: http://www.gambro.com
Sales Range: $25-49.9 Million
Emp.: 40
Dialysis Technologies & Other Renal Care
Products Developer, Mfr, Sales & Services
N.A.I.C.S.: 334510

Subsidiary (Domestic):

Gambro Dialysatoren GmbH (3)
Holger-Crafoord-Strasse 26, 72379, Hechin-
gen, Germany
Tel.: (49) 7471170
Web Site: http://www.gambro.com
Surgical & Medical Instrument Manufactur-
ing
N.A.I.C.S.: 339112

Subsidiary (Non-US):

Gambro/Hospal Industrie S.A. (2)
7 Avenue Lionel Terray, PO Box 126,
69883, Meyzieu, Cedex, France
Tel.: (33) 472452525
Web Site: http://www.gambro.com
Sales Range: $150-199.9 Million
Emp.: 700
Dialysis Technologies & Other Renal Care
Products Mfr
N.A.I.C.S.: 334510

Subsidiary (Domestic):

Gambro S.A.S. (3)
1-3 Boulevard Charles De Gaulle, FR-
92707, Colombes, Cedex, France
Tel.: (33) 141193100
Web Site: http://www.gambro.fr
Sales Range: $25-49.9 Million
Emp.: 60
Dialysis Technologies & Other Renal Care
Products Sales & Services
N.A.I.C.S.: 423450

Hospal S.A. (3)
7 Avenue Lionel Terray, PO Box 7315, FR-

69881, Meyzieu, Cedex, France
Tel.: (33) 437281111
Web Site: http://www.gambro.com
Sales Range: $50-74.9 Million
Emp.: 700
Dialysis Technologies & Other Renal Care
Products
N.A.I.C.S.: 423450

Subsidiary (Non-US):

Gambro/Hospal Ltd. (2)
Unit 3 the Forum Minerva Business Park,
Peterborough, PE2 6FT, United Kingdom
Tel.: (44) 1480444000
Web Site: http://www.gambro.co.uk
Sales Range: $25-49.9 Million
Emp.: 100
Dialysis Technologies & Other Renal Care
Products Developer, Mfr, Sales & Services
N.A.I.C.S.: 334510

Gambro/Hospal Schweiz AG (2)
Sagereistrasse 24, CH-8152, Glattbrugg,
Switzerland
Tel.: (41) 1828 8200
Web Site: http://www.gambro.dk
Sales Range: $25-49.9 Million
Emp.: 25
Dialysis Technologies & Other Renal Care
Products Sales & Services
N.A.I.C.S.: 423450

Oy Gambro (2)
Sahaajankatu 24 Pl 30, 00811, Helsinki,
Finland
Tel.: (358) 97594120
Web Site: http://www.gambro.com
Sales Range: $25-49.9 Million
Emp.: 15
Dialysis Technologies & Other Renal Care
Products Marketing & Sales
N.A.I.C.S.: 423450

**Gambro Dialisis de Mexico, SA. De
R.L.** (1)
Calle Insurgentes 8 Benito Juarez, Distrito
Federal, 03100, Mexico, Mexico
Tel.: (52) 5553006116
Management Consulting Services
N.A.I.C.S.: 541611

Gambro Holding AB (1)
Magistratsvgen 16, PO Box 7373, 22643,
Lund, Sweden (51%)
Tel.: (46) 86136500
Web Site: http://www.gambro.com
Sales Range: $250-299.9 Million
Emp.: 800
Holding Company
N.A.I.C.S.: 551112

Gambro UF Solutions, Inc. (1)
7601 Northland Dr N Ste 170, Brooklyn
Park, MN 55428
Tel.: (763) 463-4600
Health Care Products Mfr.
N.A.I.C.S.: 334510

Hill-Rom Holdings, Inc. (1)
130 E Randolph St Ste 1000, Chicago, IL
60601
Tel.: (312) 819-7200
Web Site: http://www.hill-rom.com
Rev.: $3,018,700,000
Assets: $4,999,100,000
Liabilities: $3,119,400,000
Net Worth: $1,879,700,000
Earnings: $248,500,000
Emp.: 10,000
Fiscal Year-end: 09/30/2021
Holding Company; Medical Technologies
Mfr & Distr
N.A.I.C.S.: 551112
Andreas G. Frank (Pres-Front Line Care &
Sr VP)
Deborah M. Rasin (Chief Legal Officer, Sec
& Sr VP)
Ilana Shulman (Chief Compliance Officer)
Paul D. Johnson (Pres-Patient Support Sys
& Sr VP)
Francisco Canal (Pres-Europe, Middle East
& Africa)
Tim Lawrence (Sr VP-Ops)
Richard Marritt (CMO)
Mark Wallwork (Pres-Asia Pacific)
Cheryl James (Chief HR Officer)
Jessica Smith (VP-Regulatory Affairs)
Janet Stevens (VP-Quality Assurance)

Subsidiary (Non-US):

**Hill-Rom Sociedade Unipessoal,
LDA** (2)
Rua da Bela Vista a Graca 130, 1170-059,
Lisbon, Portugal
Tel.: (351) 213224900
Surgical & Medical Apparatus Mfr
N.A.I.C.S.: 334510

Subsidiary (Domestic):

Hill-Rom, Inc. (2)
1069 State Route 46 E, Batesville, IN
47006-7502
Tel.: (812) 934-7777
Web Site: https://www.hillrom.com
Medical Technologies Developer, Mfr &
Distr
N.A.I.C.S.: 339112

Subsidiary (Domestic):

Allen Medical Systems, Inc. (3)
100 Discovery Way, Acton, MA 01720
Tel.: (978) 266-4200
Web Site: http://www.allenmedical.com
Emp.: 123
Surgical & Medical Equipments Mfr
N.A.I.C.S.: 339112

Subsidiary (Domestic):

AMATECH Corporation (4)
1 Post Office Sq, Acton, MA 01720
Tel.: (978) 263-5401
Medical Device Equipment Mfr
N.A.I.C.S.: 339112

Subsidiary (Domestic):

Anodyne Medical Device, Inc. (3)
4200 NW 120th Ave, Coral Springs, FL
33065
Web Site: http://www.tridien.com
Medical Device Developer & Mfr
N.A.I.C.S.: 339112
Bernie Laurel (Pres & CEO)
Ian West (VP-Engrg)

Subsidiary (Non-US):

Hill-Rom AB (3)
Nedre Vagen 100, 975 92, Lulea, Norrbot-
ten, Sweden
Tel.: (46) 920474700
Web Site: http://www2.hill-rom.com
Medical Device Equipment Mfr
N.A.I.C.S.: 339112

Subsidiary (Domestic):

Liko AB (4)
Nedre Vagen 100, 975 92, Lulea, Sweden
Tel.: (46) 920474700
Web Site: http://www.liko.se
Emp.: 120
Medical Device Equipment Mfr
N.A.I.C.S.: 339112
Anna Rasmuson (Mng Dir)

Subsidiary (Non-US):

Hill-Rom Austria GmbH (3)
Inkustrasse 1-7 Buropark Donau Haus 6,
3400, Klosterneuburg, Austria
Tel.: (43) 224328550
Web Site: https://www.hillrom.at
Medical Device Equipment Mfr
N.A.I.C.S.: 339112

Subsidiary (Domestic):

**Trumpf Medizinsystems Osterreich
GmbH** (4)
Klosterneuburg Buropark Donau Haus 8
Inkustrabe 1-7, 3400, Klosterneuburg, Aus-
tria
Tel.: (43) 224328550
Medical Instrument Mfr
N.A.I.C.S.: 339112

**Trumpf Medizinsystems Osterreich
GmbH** (4)
Industriepark 24, Pasching, 4601, Austria
Tel.: (43) 722160342150
Surgical Supplies Mfr
N.A.I.C.S.: 339113

Subsidiary (Non-US):

Hill-Rom B.V. (3)
Hagenweg 1-A, 4131 LX, Vianen, Netherlands
Tel.: (31) 347323532
Web Site: http://www.hill-rom.nl
Hospital Equipment Whslr
N.A.I.C.S.: 423450

Hill-Rom Canada, Ltd. (3)
6950 Creditview Rd Unit 4, Mississauga, L5N 0A6, ON, Canada
Tel.: (905) 206-1355
Web Site: http://www.hill-rom.ca
Sales Range: $25-49.9 Million
Emp.: 25
Hospital Equipment Whslr
N.A.I.C.S.: 423450

Hill-Rom Comercializador a de Mexico S de RL de CV (3)
Berna No 6 Septimo Piso, Colonia Juarez, Mexico, 06600, Mexico
Tel.: (52) 5555259888
Web Site: http://www.hillrom.com
Emp.: 3
Medical Device Equipment Mfr
N.A.I.C.S.: 339112

Subsidiary (Domestic):

Hill-Rom Company, Inc. (3)
1069 State Rte 46 E, Batesville, IN 47006-7520   (100%)
Tel.: (812) 934-7777
Web Site: http://www.hill-rom.com
Sales Range: $100-124.9 Million
Emp.: 2,000
Mfr of Patient Care Products & Specialized Rental Therapy Products
N.A.I.C.S.: 339113

Unit (Domestic):

Hill-Rom - Charleston (4)
7236 Cross Park Dr, Charleston, SC 29418
Tel.: (843) 740-8000
Web Site: http://www.hill-rom.com
Sales Range: Less than $1 Million
Emp.: 250
Medical Equipment Rental
N.A.I.C.S.: 339113

Subsidiary (Domestic):

Hill-Rom Logistics, LLC (4)
1069 State Rte 46 E, Batesville, IN 47006
Tel.: (812) 934-7427
Medical Device Equipment Mfr
N.A.I.C.S.: 339112
John Vogelsang *(Mgr)*

MEDIQ/PRN Life Support Systems, LLC (4)
4531 Ayers St, Corpus Christi, TX 78415
Tel.: (361) 225-2962
Hospital Equipments Mfr
N.A.I.C.S.: 339113

Subsidiary (Domestic):

Hill-Rom DTC, Inc. (3)
1069 State Route 46 E, Batesville, IN 47006-7520
Tel.: (812) 934-7777
Web Site: http://www.hill-rom.com
Emp.: 3,000
Medical Device Equipment Mfr
N.A.I.C.S.: 339112

Subsidiary (Non-US):

Hill-Rom GmbH (3)
Wullener Feld 79, 58454, Witten, Germany
Tel.: (49) 8008635537
Web Site: http://www.hill-rom.com
Medical Device Equipment Mfr
N.A.I.C.S.: 339112

Hill-Rom Iberia S.L. (3)
Plaza Europa 9-11 Planta 17 Hospialet de, 08908, Llobregat, Barcelona, Spain
Tel.: (34) 936856000
Web Site: http://www.hill-rom.es
Emp.: 25
Hospital Equipment Whslr
N.A.I.C.S.: 423450

Hill-Rom Industries SA (3)
188 rue du Caducee, Parc Euromedecine,

34195, Montpellier, Cedex 5, France
Tel.: (33) 467046404
Web Site: http://www.hill-rom.fr
Hospital Equipment Whslr
N.A.I.C.S.: 423450

Hill-Rom Japan KK (3)
Metro City Kamiyacho 5F 5-1-5, Toranomon Minato-ku, Tokyo, 105-0001, Japan
Tel.: (81) 45201700
Medical Device Equipment Mfr
N.A.I.C.S.: 339112

Hill-Rom Ltd. (3)
Clinitron House Excelsior Road, Ashby de la Zouch, Leicester, LE65 1JG, United Kingdom
Tel.: (44) 1530411000
Web Site: http://www.hill-rom.co.uk
Emp.: 6
Hospital Equipment Whslr
N.A.I.C.S.: 423450
Miguel Antonanzas *(Mng Dir)*

Subsidiary (Domestic):

Hill-Rom Manufacturing, Inc. (3)
1225 Crescent Green Ste 300, Cary, NC 27518
Tel.: (919) 854-3600
Web Site: http://www.hill-rom.com
Emp.: 350
Medical Device Equipment Mfr
N.A.I.C.S.: 339112

Subsidiary (Non-US):

Hill-Rom Pty, Ltd (3)
79 79 99 St. Hilliers Road, Auburn, 2144, NSW, Australia
Tel.: (61) 295620900
Emp.: 30
Medical Device Equipment Mfr
N.A.I.C.S.: 339112
Paul Eisen *(Gen Mgr)*

Hill-Rom S.A.S. (3)
ZI du Talhouet, BP 14, 56330, Pluvigner, France   (100%)
Tel.: (33) 297509212
Web Site: https://www.hillrom.fr
Sales Range: $50-74.9 Million
Emp.: 400
Mfr of Patient Care Systems
N.A.I.C.S.: 334510

Hill-Rom SARL (3)
ZI du Talhouet, BP 14, 56330, Pluvigner, France
Tel.: (33) 297509212
Web Site: http://www.hill-rom.fr
Medical Device Equipment Mfr
N.A.I.C.S.: 339112

Hill-Rom SPRL (3)
Luchthavenlaan 25B, 1800, Vilvoorde, Belgium
Tel.: (32) 27619640
Web Site: http://www.hill-rom.com
Emp.: 9
Medical Device Equipment Mfr
N.A.I.C.S.: 339112

Hill-Rom Services Pte, Ltd. (3)
1 Yishun Avenue 7, Singapore, 768923, Singapore
Tel.: (65) 64997350
Web Site: http://www.hill-rom.com
Emp.: 90
Medical Device Equipment Mfr
N.A.I.C.S.: 339112

Subsidiary (Non-US):

Hill-Rom Canada Respiratory, Ltd. (4)
1705 Tech Ave Unit 3, Mississauga, L4W 0A2, ON, Canada
Tel.: (905) 206-1355
Web Site: http://www.hill-rom.ca
Women Healthcare Services
N.A.I.C.S.: 621610

Subsidiary (Non-US):

Hill-Rom Servicios S de RL de CV (3)
Telefono No 200, Apodaca, 66634, Nuevo Leon, Mexico
Tel.: (52) 8182624491
Emp.: 220

Furniture Mfr
N.A.I.C.S.: 337127
Javier Ayala *(Gen Mgr)*

Hill-Rom Shanghai Ltd. (3)
No 398 Jiangsu Road 16F Sunyoung Center Building A, Shanghai, 200050, China
Tel.: (86) 2153301500
Web Site: https://www.hillrom.cn
Medical Instrument Mfr
N.A.I.C.S.: 339112

Hill-Rom Sociedade Unipessoal, LDA (3)
Rua Dos Tractores 506 Armazem Ar Alto Estanqueiro-Jardia, Montijo, 2870-607, Portugal
Tel.: (351) 210991891
Medical Device Equipment Mfr
N.A.I.C.S.: 339112

Hill-Rom Sociedade Unipessoal, LDA a Portuguese corporation (3)
c/o Sano-Tecnica Medical Rua da Bela Vista a Graca 130, 1170-059, Lisbon, Portugal
Tel.: (351) 213224900
Medical Instrument Mfr
N.A.I.C.S.: 339112

Hill-Rom Turkey Medikal Urunler Dagitim ve Ticaret Limited Sirketi (3)
No 8 Floor 14, Zeytinburnu, Istanbul, Turkiye
Tel.: (90) 2165105409
Web Site: http://www.hill-rom.com
Medical Device Equipment Mfr
N.A.I.C.S.: 339112

Hill-Rom UK (Holdings) Ltd. (3)
Clinitron House Excelsior Road, Ashby de la Zouch, LE651JG, Leicestershire, United Kingdom
Tel.: (44) 1530411000
Web Site: http://www.hill-rom.co.uk
Emp.: 60
Medical Device Equipment Mfr
N.A.I.C.S.: 339112

Subsidiary (Domestic):

Aspen Medical Europe Limited (4)
Thornhill Road North Moon's Moat, Redditch, B98 9NL, Worcestershire, United Kingdom
Tel.: (44) 1527587700
Web Site:
   http://www.aspenmedicaleurope.com
Medical Instrument Mfr
N.A.I.C.S.: 339112

Aspen Medical Europe Limited (UK) (4)
Thornhill Road North Moon's Moat, Redditch, B98 9NL, Worcestershire, United Kingdom
Tel.: (44) 1527587700
Web Site:
   http://www.aspenmedicaleurope.com
Emp.: 150
Medical Device Equipment Mfr
N.A.I.C.S.: 339112

Subsidiary (Non-US):

Hill-Rom, S.p.A (3)
Via Ambrosoli 6, 20053, Rodano, MI, Italy
Tel.: (39) 02950541
Web Site: http://www.hill-rom.it
Hospital Equipment Whslr
N.A.I.C.S.: 423450

Subsidiary (Domestic):

Mortara Instrument, Inc. (3)
7865 N 86th St, Milwaukee, WI 53224
Tel.: (414) 354-1600
Web Site: http://www.mortara.com
Electromedical & Electrotherapeutic Apparatus Mfr
N.A.I.C.S.: 334510
David W. Mortara *(Founder)*

Trumpf Medical Systems, Inc. (3)
1046 LeGrand Blvd, Charleston, SC 29492
Tel.: (843) 388-8011
Web Site: http://www.us.trumpf.med.com
Emp.: 75
Medical Equipment Mfr
N.A.I.C.S.: 334510

Subsidiary (Non-US):

Trumpf Medizin Systeme GmbH & Co. KG (3)
Carl-Zeiss-Strasse 7-9, 07318, Saalfeld, Germany
Tel.: (49) 36715860
Web Site: http://www.trumpfmedical.com
Sales Range: $250-299.9 Million
Emp.: 400
Medical Equipment Mfr
N.A.I.C.S.: 334510

Subsidiary (Non-US):

OOO Trumpf Med (4)
Yaroslavskaya Str bld 2 office 13A, 129366, Moscow, Russia
Tel.: (7) 4957821961
Web Site: http://www.trumpf.ru
Medical Equipment Whslr
N.A.I.C.S.: 423450

Trumpf Med (Aust) Pty. Limited (4)
Level 2 52 Gibbes St, Chatswood, Sydney, 2067, NSW, Australia
Medical Equipment Mfr
N.A.I.C.S.: 334510
Santosh Revadekar *(Project Mgr & Mgr-Svc)*

Trumpf Med Italia S.r.l. (4)
Via Cesare Battisti 31/C, 35010, Limena, PD, Italy
Tel.: (39) 0498843800
Medical Equipment Whslr
N.A.I.C.S.: 423450

Trumpf Medical Systems (Taicang) Co., Ltd. (4)
No 68 East Nanjing Road, Jiangsu, 215400, Taicang, China
Tel.: (86) 51253287700
Medical Equipment Mfr
N.A.I.C.S.: 334510

Trumpf Medical Systems Ltd. (4)
Clinitron House Excelsior Road, Ashby de la Zouch, LE65 1JG, Leicestershire, United Kingdom
Tel.: (44) 1530411000
Medical Instrument Mfr
N.A.I.C.S.: 339112

Subsidiary (Non-US):

Hillrom Belgium B.V. (2)
Luchthavenlaan 25B, 1800, Vilvoorde, Belgium
Tel.: (32) 27619640
Healtcare Services
N.A.I.C.S.: 621999

Trumpf Medizin Systeme Beteiligungs GmbH (2)
Benzstrasse 26, 82178, Puchheim, Germany
Tel.: (49) 89809070
Web Site: http://www.trumpfmedical.com
Surgical & Medical Apparatus Mfr
N.A.I.C.S.: 334510

Videomed S.r.l. (2)
Via Cesare Battisti 31, 35010, Limena, Padua, Italy
Tel.: (39) 0499819113
Emp.: 654
Medical Instrument Mfr
N.A.I.C.S.: 339112

Subsidiary (Domestic):

Voalte, Inc. (2)
5101 Fruitville Rd Ste 200, Sarasota, FL 34232
Tel.: (941) 312-2830
Web Site: http://www.voalte.com
Sales Range: $1-9.9 Million
Emp.: 50
Hospital & Healthcare Related Mobile Software Developer
N.A.I.C.S.: 513210
Trey Lauderdale *(Co-Founder)*
Oscar Callejas *(Co-Founder)*
Philip Fibiger *(VP-Engineering)*
Eric Brill *(Gen Mgr)*
Keith DeYoung *(VP-Sales)*
Naila Maroon *(Dir-Marketing Communications)*

Baxter International Inc.—(Continued)

Subsidiary (Non-US):

Welch Allyn Malaysia SDN, Bhd (2)
Suite GF 101-2 Ground Floor Tower 2
Kelana Brem Towers, Jln SS7/15 Kelana
Jaya, 47301, Petaling Jaya, Selangor, Malaysia
Tel.: (60) 378843341
Diagnostic Equipment Distr
N.A.I.C.S.: 423450
A. Chandrasegaran (Gen Mgr)
Diana Daniel (Mgr-Sls)
Gan Soon Siong (Controller-Fin)

Welch Allyn Productos Medicos S. de R.L. de C.V.
Av Ejercito Nacional 253 A Mezanine Col
Anahuac Miguel Hidalgo DF, Mexico,
11320, Mexico
Tel.: (52) 5552832470
Medical & Hospital Equipment Distr
N.A.I.C.S.: 423450

Welch Allyn South Africa Pty, Ltd. (2)
Building 21 Ground Floor Woodlands Office
Park 20 Woodlands Drive, Woodmead, Johannesburg, 1619, South Africa
Tel.: (27) 100017788
Web Site: http://www.welchallyn.co.za
Diagnostic Equipment Distr
N.A.I.C.S.: 423450

Welch Allyn de Mexico s. de R.L. de C.V. (2)
Av Ejercito Nacional 253-A Mezanine Col
Anahuac Miguel Hidalgo DF, 11320,
Mexico, Mexico
Tel.: (52) 5552832470
Medical Product Whslr
N.A.I.C.S.: 423450
Gabriela Hernandez (Supvr-HR)

Welch Allyn do Brasil Comercia de Equipmentos Medicos, Ltda (2)
Alameda Andromeda 885-1 andar, Edificio
Brascan Century Plaza-sala 106 Green Valley, Barueri, 06473-000, Brazil
Tel.: (55) 1141330800
Medical Equipment Mfr
N.A.I.C.S.: 334510

Subsidiary (Domestic):

Welch Allyn, Inc. (2)
4341 State St Rd, Skaneateles Falls, NY
13153
Tel.: (315) 685-4100
Web Site: http://www.welchallyn.com
Medical Diagnostic Tools Mfr
N.A.I.C.S.: 339112

Subsidiary (Non-US):

Welch Allyn (U.K.) Ltd. (3)
Clinitron House Excelsior Road, Ashby de
la Zouch, LE65 1JG, Leicestershire, United
Kingdom
Tel.: (44) 2073656780
Web Site: http://www.welchallyn.co.uk
Medical Diagnostic Tools Mfr
N.A.I.C.S.: 339112
Claire Buchan (Reg Sls Mgr-Scotland)

Welch Allyn Australia (Pty) Limited (3)
Suite 4 01 2-4 Lyonpark Road, Macquarie
Park, 2113, NSW, Australia
Tel.: (61) 2 9562 0900
Web Site: http://www.welchallyn.com.au
Medical Diagnostic Tools Mfr
N.A.I.C.S.: 339112

Welch Allyn B.V. (3)
Amerika Building - 7th Floor Hoogoorddreef
15, 1101 BA, Amsterdam, Netherlands
Tel.: (31) 202061360
Web Site: http://www.welchallyn.nl
Medical Diagnostic Tools Mfr
N.A.I.C.S.: 339112

Subsidiary (Domestic):

Welch Allyn Beaverton Development and Technology Center (3)
9525 SW Gemini Dr, Beaverton, OR 97008
Tel.: (503) 530-7500
Web Site: http://www.welchallyn.com

Medical Instrumentation Systems Mfr
N.A.I.C.S.: 339112

Subsidiary (Non-US):

Welch Allyn Canada Ltd. (3)
160 Matheson Blvd E Suite 2, Mississauga,
L4Z 1V4, ON, Canada
Tel.: (905) 890-0004
Web Site: http://www.welchallyn.ca
Medical Diagnostic Tools Whslr
N.A.I.C.S.: 423450

Welch Allyn Japan K.K. (3)
6F Kinseisha Bldg 3-15 Kanda-nishikicho,
Chiyoda-ku, Tokyo, 101-0054, Japan
Tel.: (81) 3 3219 0071
Web Site: http://www.welchallyn.jp
Medical Diagnostic Tools Mfr
N.A.I.C.S.: 339112

Welch Allyn Ltd. (3)
IDA Business Park, Johnstown, Navan,
Meath, Ireland
Tel.: (353) 46 906 7700
Web Site: http://www.welchallyn.de
Medical Diagnostic Tools Mfr
N.A.I.C.S.: 339112

Subsidiary (Non-US):

Welch Allyn Sverige (4)
Svardvagen 21, 182 33, Danderyd, Sweden
Tel.: (46) 705230396
Web Site: http://www.emeai.welchallyn.com
Diagnostic Equipment Distr
N.A.I.C.S.: 423450

Subsidiary (Non-US):

Welch Allyn Service GmbH (3)
Hofgartenstrasse 16, 72379, Hechingen,
Germany
Tel.: (49) 74719841140
Web Site: https://www.hillrom.de
Emp.: 16
Medical Diagnostic Tools Mfr
N.A.I.C.S.: 339112

Welch Allyn Singapore Pte. Ltd. (3)
1 Yishun Avenue 7, Singapore, 768923,
Singapore
Tel.: (65) 68709164
Web Site: http://www.welchallyn.com
Emp.: 30
Medical Diagnostic Tools Mfr
N.A.I.C.S.: 339112

Medicina Corporativa de Dialisis SA (1)
3 Escuintla 15 Calle 2-48, Guatemala, Guatemala
Tel.: (502) 78841793
Healthcare Equipment Distr
N.A.I.C.S.: 423450

Sapa Prodotti Plastici Sagl (1)
Zona Niscio, San Vittore, Switzerland
Tel.: (41) 918273355
Plastic & Chemical Product Distr
N.A.I.C.S.: 424690

True Process, Inc. (1)
Washington Bldg 2 S 4650 N Port Washington Rd, Glendale, WI 53212
Tel.: (414) 935-4030
Web Site: http://www.trueprocess.com
Sales Range: $1-9.9 Million
Emp.: 38
IT Consulting Services
N.A.I.C.S.: 519290

BAYCOM CORP

500 Ygnacio Valley Rd Ste 130, Walnut Creek, CA 94596
Tel.: (925) 476-1800   CA
Web Site:
http://www.unitedbusinessbank.com
Year Founded: 2016
BCML—(NASDAQ)
Rev.: $117,738,000
Assets: $2,513,334,000
Liabilities: $2,196,185,000
Net Worth: $317,149,000
Earnings: $26,987,000
Emp.: 374
Fiscal Year-end: 12/31/22
Bank Holding Company

N.A.I.C.S.: 551111
Keary L. Colwell (CFO, Sec & Sr Exec VP)
David M. Spatz (Founder)
Izabella L. Zhu (Chief Risk Officer & Exec VP-United Business Bank)
George J. Guarini (Founder, Pres & CEO)
Janet L. King (COO & Sr Exec VP)
Robert G. Laverne (Founder)
David J. Funkhouser (Chief Credit Officer & Exec VP-United Business Bank)
Mary Therese Curley (Exec VP & Dir-Labor Svc Div-United Business Bank)

Subsidiaries:

United Business Bank (1)
500 Ygnacio Valley Rd Ste 130, Walnut
Creek, CA 94596
Tel.: (925) 476-1880
Web Site:
https://www.unitedbusinessbank.com
Sales Range: $50-74.9 Million
Commercial Banking
N.A.I.C.S.: 522110
Keary L. Colwell (CFO, Chief Admin Officer & Sec)
Izabella L. Zhu (Chief Risk Officer & Exec VP)
Lloyd W. Kendall Jr. (Chm)
George J. Guarini (Pres & CEO)
Janet L. King (COO & Sr Exec VP)
Rick Pak (Chief Lending Officer & Exec VP)
Terry Curley (Chief Credit Officer, Exec VP, Exec VP, Dir-Labor Svc Division & Dir-Labor Svc Div)

BAYFIRST FINANCIAL CORP.

700 Central Ave, Saint Petersburg,
FL 33701
Tel.: (727) 394-2265   FL
Web Site:
https://ir.bayfirstfinancial.com
Year Founded: 2000
BAFN—(NASDAQ)
Rev.: $118,272,000
Assets: $1,117,766,000
Liabilities: $1,017,059,000
Net Worth: $100,707,000
Earnings: $5,702,000
Emp.: 304
Fiscal Year-end: 12/31/23
Bank Holding Company
N.A.I.C.S.: 551111
Anthony N. Leo (CEO)
Denise Unley (Sr VP)
Anthony Saravanos (Chm)
Matthew A. McDonald (COO)
Jeffrey Tanner (Sr VP-Govt Guaranteed Lending)

Subsidiaries:

BayFirst National Bank (1)
700 Central Ave, Saint Petersburg, FL
33701
Tel.: (727) 440-6848
Web Site: https://bayfirstfinancial.com
Rev.: $3,081,000
Assets: $75,494,000
Liabilities: $71,486,000
Net Worth: $4,008,000
Earnings: $90,000
Emp.: 23
Fiscal Year-end: 12/31/2013
Commercial Banking
N.A.I.C.S.: 522110
Anthony Leo (Pres)

BAYING ECOLOGICAL HOLDING GROUP, INC.

850 Stephenson Hwy Ste 310, Troy,
MI 90265
Tel.: (310) 887-6391   NV
Year Founded: 2005
BYIN—(OTCIQ)
Liabilities: $255,143
Net Worth: ($255,143)
Earnings: ($40,941)
Emp.: 30

Fiscal Year-end: 06/30/19
Walnut & Related Products Production
N.A.I.C.S.: 111336
Parashar Patel (Pres, CEO, CFO, Chief Acctg Officer & Treas)
Jiao Zhouping (Chm)
Yan Yuehong (Sec)

BAYPORT INTERNATIONAL HOLDINGS, INC.

550 Federal Hwy, Fort Lauderdale,
FL 33301
Tel.: (954) 609-2554   NV
Web Site:
http://www.bayportinternational.com
BAYP—(OTCIQ)
Sales Range: Less than $1 Million
Oil & Gas Exploration; Metal Ore
Mining
N.A.I.C.S.: 211120
Jerrold R. Krystoff (CEO)

BAYSIDE CORP.

1500 Won Rd Ste 200, Weston, FL
33326
Tel.: (954) 905-1299
Web Site:
https://www.baysidecorp.com
Year Founded: 1984
BYSD—(OTCIQ)
Sales Range: Less than $1 Million
Offices of Other Holding Companies
N.A.I.C.S.: 551112
Steven Hoffman (Interim CEO)

BBHC, INC.

24980 N 83rd Ave Ste 100, Peoria,
AZ 85383   DE
Year Founded: 2005
TRNX—(OTCIQ)
Hydrogen Based Fuel Distr
N.A.I.C.S.: 324199

Subsidiaries:

MagneGas Arc Applied Solutions (1)
Rue Aux Fleurs 1, Brussels, 1000, Belgium
Tel.: (32) 7279461484
Web Site: http://www.magnegas.eu
Oil & Gas Field Services
N.A.I.C.S.: 213112
Ermanno P. Santilli (Pres)
Ruggero Maria Santilli (Exec Dir)

Paris Oxygen Company (1)
3320 NE Loop 286, Paris, TX 75460
Tel.: (903) 739-8000
Hardware Stores
N.A.I.C.S.: 444140

Trico Welding Supplies, Inc. (1)
1590 E Kentucky Ave, Woodland, CA
95776   (100%)
Tel.: (530) 666-7997
Web Site: http://www.tricowelding.com
Industrial Supplies Merchant Whslr
N.A.I.C.S.: 423840

BBX CAPITAL, INC.

201 E Las Olas Blvd Ste 1900, Fort
Lauderdale, FL 33301
Tel.: (954) 940-4000   FL
Web Site: https://bbxcapital.com
Year Founded: 2020
BBXIB—(OTC)
Investment Management Service
N.A.I.C.S.: 523999
Brett Sheppard (CFO)
Terry Frank (Dir-Marketing & Strategic Projects)
David Friedman (Mng Dir)
Lois A. Marino (Dir)
Andy Meran (Mng Dir)
Anna Tovbin (Sr Dir-Human Resources)
Seth M. Wise (Exec VP)
Jarett S. Levan (Pres & CEO)
John E. Abdo (Vice Chm)

Jarett S. Levan *(Pres & CEO)*
Seth M. Wise *(Exec VP)*
John E. Abdo *(Vice Chm)*

BCB BANCORP, INC.
104-110 Ave C, Bayonne, NJ 07002
Tel.: (201) 823-0700   NJ
Web Site: https://www.bcb.bank
BCBP—(NASDAQ)
Rev.: $133,036,000
Assets: $3,546,193,000
Liabilities: $3,254,939,000
Net Worth: $291,254,000
Earnings: $45,579,000
Emp.: 301
Fiscal Year-end: 12/31/22
Bank Holding Company
N.A.I.C.S.: 551111
Michael A. Shriner *(Pres & CEO)*
Ryan Blake *(Bd of Dirs, COO, Sec & Exec VP)*
Robert Ballance *(Bd of Dirs & Founder)*
Jawad Chaudhry *(CFO)*
Kenneth G. Emerson *(Chief Strategy Officer)*
Karen M. Duran *(Chief Acctg Officer)*
Wing Su *(Chief IT Officer)*

Subsidiaries:

BCB Community Bank   (1)
104-110 Ave C, Bayonne, NJ 07002
Tel.: (201) 823-0700
Web Site: http://www.bcb.bank
Sales Range: $75-99.9 Million
Emp.: 350
Commericial Banking
N.A.I.C.S.: 522110
Michael A. Shriner *(Pres & CEO)*
James E. Collins *(Co-Founder)*
Sandra L. Sievewright *(Chief Compliance Officer & Co-Chief Risk Officer)*
Ryan Blake *(COO, Sec & Exec VP)*
Jawad Chaudhry *(CFO)*
Thomas M. Coughlin *(Executives, Bd of Dirs)*
Thomas P. Keating *(CFO & Sr VP)*
Kenneth G. Emerson *(Chief Strategy Officer, Co-Chief Risk Officer & Sr VP)*
Wing Siu *(Chief IT & Information Security Officer & Sr VP)*
David Garcia *(Chief Lending Officer & Sr VP)*
Vince Davis *(VP & Mgr-Bus Dev)*
Terrance R. Howard *(Chief Retail & C&I Lending Officer & VP)*

BCII ENTERPRISES, INC.
53 Calle Las Palmeras 6th Fl, San Juan, PR 00901
Tel.: (925) 292-6226   DE
Web Site: https://bciienterprises.com
Year Founded: 2009
BCII—(OTCIQ)
Investment Holding Company
N.A.I.C.S.: 551112
Andreas Typaldos *(Chm & CEO)*

BCLS ACQUISITION CORP.
200 Clarendon St, Boston, MA 02116
Tel.: (617) 516-2000   Ky
Year Founded: 2020
BLSA—(NASDAQ)
Assets: $144,595,871
Liabilities: $149,198,349
Net Worth: ($4,602,478)
Earnings: ($847,038)
Emp.: 2
Fiscal Year-end: 12/31/21
Investment Services
N.A.I.C.S.: 523999
Adam Koppel *(Chm)*
Jeffrey Schwartz *(CEO)*
Andrew Hack *(CFO)*

BEACH COMMUNITY BANCSHARES, INC.
17 SE Eglin Pkwy, Fort Walton Beach, FL 32548

Tel.: (850) 244-9900   FL
Web Site:
  http://www.beachcommunity
  bank.com
Year Founded: 2004
BCBF—(OTCIQ)
Bank Holding Company
N.A.I.C.S.: 551111
Suzanne B. Kelly *(Sr VP)*
A. Anthony Hughes *(Pres & CEO)*
Gary E. Johns *(CFO & Exec VP)*
Caroline A. Hartnett *(Chief Credit Officer & Sr VP)*
Judith L. Winter *(Sr VP)*
Matthew S. Hamilton *(Sr VP)*
Pamela G. Woodall *(Pres-Beach Community Mortgage & Sr VP)*
Joseph W. Henderson *(Chm)*
Allison M. Cochran *(VP)*
Anthony Del Gallo *(Asst VP)*
Robert W. Massey *(Sr VP)*
Cecilia McAdams *(Asst VP)*
Cherie L. Johnson *(Sr VP)*
Courtney Falasca *(VP)*
Cynthia Stephens *(Asst VP)*
Deborah Patzig *(Asst VP)*
Elayne Jones *(VP)*
Gwen Stephenson *(Asst VP)*
Jessica Rybarczyk *(VP)*
Karen Bennett *(VP)*
Karen Helms *(Asst VP)*
Kelly J. Fish *(Sr VP)*
Lisa Branson *(Officer-Banking)*
Malinda E. Ritter *(Asst VP)*
Michelle L. Williams *(Asst VP)*
Qian Wang *(Officer-Banking)*
Renee Frizzle *(Officer-Banking)*
Scott McCormick *(Sr VP)*
Sharmon V. Morris *(Asst VP)*
Sharon Hines *(Asst VP)*
Tina Brock *(Officer-Banking)*
Tommy Files *(VP)*
Tonya Reid *(Officer-Banking)*

Subsidiaries:

Beach Community Bank   (1)
17 SE Eglin Pkwy, Fort Walton Beach, FL 32548
Tel.: (850) 244-9900
Web Site:
  http://www.beachcommunitybank.com
Sales Range: $10-24.9 Million
Emp.: 40
Commericial Banking
N.A.I.C.S.: 522110
Carl J. Chaney *(Chm)*
Suzanne B. Kelly *(Sr VP)*
Gary E. Johns *(CFO & Exec VP)*
Caroline A. Hartnett *(Chief Credit Officer & Sr VP)*
Judith L. Winter *(Sr VP)*
Matthew S. Hamilton *(Sr VP)*
Pamela G. Woodall *(Pres-Beach Community Mortgage & Sr VP)*
Kimberly A. Cox *(Exec VP-Branch Admin)*
W. Scott McCormick *(Sr VP)*
Keith D. Parks *(Officer-Lending & Exec VP)*
Karen J. Bennett *(VP)*
Allison M. Cochran *(VP)*
Elayne E. Jones-Yon *(VP)*
Karen J. Helms *(Asst VP)*
Cecilia M. McAdams *(Asst VP)*
Carl Chaney *(Chm)*
Charles Reeves *(Pres & CEO)*

BEACON REDEVELOPMENT INDUSTRIAL CORP.
1440 W Taylor St Suite 607, chicago, IL 60607
Tel.: (847) 481-0304   DE
Web Site:
  http://www.beaconredevelop
  ment.com
BCND—(OTCIQ)
Bricks Mfr
N.A.I.C.S.: 327331
Al Gonzalez *(Pres, CEO & CFO)*

Subsidiaries:

Beacon Recycling Inc.   (1)

1241 E Keating Ave, Muskegon, MI 49442
Tel.: (231) 727-0722
Web Site: http://www.beaconrecycling.com
Recyclable Material Distr
N.A.I.C.S.: 423930
Aaron Gowell *(Mgr-Non Ferrous)*

BEACON ROOFING SUPPLY, INC.
505 Huntmar Park Dr Ste 300, Herndon, VA 20170
Tel.: (571) 323-3939   DE
Web Site: https://www.becn.com
Year Founded: 1928
BECN—(NASDAQ)
Rev.: $8,429,700,000
Assets: $6,003,500,000
Liabilities: $4,099,400,000
Net Worth: $1,904,100,000
Earnings: $434,400,000
Emp.: 7,478
Fiscal Year-end: 12/31/22
Residential & Non-Residential Building & Roofing Materials Distr
N.A.I.C.S.: 423330
David J. Wrabel *(Chief Credit Officer & VP)*
Christopher C. Nelson *(CIO & Exec VP)*
J. Jake Gosa *(Pres-North Div)*
Jason L. Taylor *(Pres-West Div)*
Stephen O. Balogun *(VP-Internal Audit)*
Julian G. Francis *(Pres & CEO)*
Prithvi Gandhi *(CFO & Exec VP)*
Jonathan S. Bennett *(Chief Comml Officer & Exec VP)*
Binit Sanghvi *(Treas & VP-Capital Markets)*
Sean M. McDevitt *(Chief HR Officer & Exec VP)*
Christine S. Reddy *(Gen Counsel, Sec & Exec VP)*
Birte von Schwarzenfeld *(Sr VP-Comml Solutions)*
Dan Worley *(VP-Environment, Health & Safety)*
Jennifer N. Lewis *(VP)*
Martin S. Harrell *(Pres)*
Jamie Samide *(VP)*
C. Munroe Best III *(Pres-South Div)*
Samuel M. Guzman Jr. *(Chief Acctg Officer & VP)*

Subsidiaries:

Al's Roofing Supply, Inc.   (1)
23305 Bernhardt St, Hayward, CA 94545
Tel.: (510) 782-0780
Web Site: https://www.alsroofingsupply.net
Roofing Supply Distr
N.A.I.C.S.: 423330
Kevin Lewis *(Gen Mgr)*

Allied Building Products Corporation   (1)
15 E Union Ave, East Rutherford, NJ 07073-2127
Tel.: (201) 507-8400
Web Site: http://www.alliedbuilding.com
Emp.: 3,100
Roofing, Siding, Insulation, Sheet Metal & Waterproofing
N.A.I.C.S.: 423310
Bob Feury *(CEO)*

Branch (Domestic):

Allied Building Products Corp. - Ferndale   (2)
1700 E 9 Mile Rd, Ferndale, MI 48220
Tel.: (248) 398-5005
Web Site: http://www.alliedbuilding.com
Lumber, Plywood, Millwork & Wood Panel Merchant Whslr
N.A.I.C.S.: 423310
Bernett Dockery *(Ops Mgr)*
Robert Robertson *(Branch Mgr)*

Allied Building Products Corp. - Hickory Hills - Tri-State Wholesale   (2)

9630 S 76th Ave, Hickory Hills, IL 60457
Tel.: (708) 599-9770
Web Site: http://www.alliedbuilding.com
Roofing, Siding & Sheet Metal Sales
N.A.I.C.S.: 423330
Sean Garza *(Branch Mgr)*
Blaise Sylvester *(Ops Mgr)*

Allied Building Products Corp. - Rockville (2)
128 Derwood Cir, Rockville, MD 20850
Tel.: (301) 294-4611
Web Site: http://www.alliedbuilding.com
Residential & Commercial Roofing, Waterproofing & Siding Materials Whslr
N.A.I.C.S.: 423330
Yovaniy Ramos *(Ops Mgr)*

Subsidiary (Domestic):

Builders Gypsum Supply   (2)
2015 Pasket Ln, Houston, TX 77092-8409
Tel.: (713) 681-2201
Lumber, Plywood & Millwork Distr
N.A.I.C.S.: 423310

United Products Corp.   (2)
165 W Sycamore St, Saint Paul, MN 55117
Tel.: (651) 227-8731
Residential & Commercial Roofing & Siding Distr
N.A.I.C.S.: 423330
Brad Holden *(Branch Mgr)*
Guillermo Noren *(Ops Mgr)*

American Building & Roofing   (1)
5 W Washington Ave, Yakima, WA 98903
Tel.: (425) 355-7300
Web Site:
  http://www.americanbuildingandroofing.com
Roofing, Siding & Insulation Material Merchant Whslr
N.A.I.C.S.: 423330

Atlas Supply, Inc.   (1)
611 S Charlestown St, Seattle, WA 98108
Tel.: (206) 623-4697
Web Site: https://www.atlassupply.com
Industrial Supplies Whslr
N.A.I.C.S.: 423840
Todd Bennett *(VP-Sls)*

Beacon Roofing Supply Canada Company   (1)
13145 Rue Prince Arthur, Montreal, H1A 1A9, QC, Canada
Tel.: (514) 642-8998
Web Site: https://beacon-canada.com
Sales Range: $25-49.9 Million
Emp.: 40
Roofing Supplies
N.A.I.C.S.: 423330

Beacon Roofing Supply, Inc. - Pittsburgh   (1)
2295 Preble Ave, Pittsburgh, PA 15233
Tel.: (412) 321-8987
Web Site: http://www.brsbecn.com
Roofing, Siding & Insulation Products Distr
N.A.I.C.S.: 423330

Coastal Construction Products, LLC   (1)
3401 Philips Hwy, Jacksonville, FL 32207
Tel.: (239) 690-9797
Web Site: https://www.coastalone.com
Sealants, Waterproofing & Fire Protection Products Distr
N.A.I.C.S.: 423390
Ron Mans *(Mgr)*

Complete Supply, Inc.   (1)
835 79th St, Willowbrook, IL 60527
Tel.: (630) 325-9044
Web Site: http://www.completesupply.com
Exterior Building Products Whslr
N.A.I.C.S.: 423830
Lee Horowitz *(Pres)*

Construction Materials Supply, Inc.   (1)
7275 National Dr Ste D, Livermore, CA 94550
Tel.: (925) 606-4400
Web Site: http://www.cmssupply.com
Sales Range: $10-24.9 Million
Roofing Supplies Whslr
N.A.I.C.S.: 423330

Crabtree Siding & Supply   (1)

Beacon Roofing Supply, Inc.—(Continued)

149 Old Gainesboro Hwy, Cookeville, TN
38501-8940
Tel.: (931) 268-2098
Web Site: http://www.crabtreesiding.com
Roofing, Siding & Insulation Material Merchant Whslr
N.A.I.C.S.: 423330

Crossroads Roofing & Supply, Inc. (1)
2800 N Santa Fe Ave, Oklahoma City, OK
73103
Tel.: (405) 528-7663
Web Site:
http://www.crossroadsroofingsupply.com
Sales Range: $1-9.9 Million
Emp.: 19
Ret Lumber/Building Materials
N.A.I.C.S.: 423310
Lisa Curtis (Owner)

Dallas-Fort Worth Roofing Supply, LLC (1)
1100 Placid Ave, Plano, TX 75074-8622
Tel.: (972) 641-5000
Durable Goods Merchant Whslr
N.A.I.C.S.: 423990

Ford Wholesale Co., Inc. of San Jose (1)
200 San Jose Ave, San Jose, CA 95125
Tel.: (408) 293-5947
Web Site: http://www.fordwholesale.com
Sales Range: $10-24.9 Million
Roofing, Siding & Insulation Whslr
N.A.I.C.S.: 423330

Fort Worth Roofing Supply, LLC (1)
5328 E Lancaster Ave, Fort Worth, TX
76112
Tel.: (817) 446-7504
Emp.: 25
Roofing, Siding & Insulation Material Merchant Whslr
N.A.I.C.S.: 423330

Fox Brothers Company (1)
4615 W Grand River Ave, Lansing, MI
48906
Tel.: (517) 323-2323
Web Site: http://www.foxbrothersco.com
Emp.: 30
Building Materials Distr
N.A.I.C.S.: 423330

Garvin Construction Products, Inc. (1)
8 Bunker Hill Industrial Park, Charlestown,
MA 02129
Tel.: (617) 242-2525
Web Site: http://www.garvinproducts.com
Sales Range: $1 0.0 Million
Emp.: 27
Lumber, Plywood, Millwork & Wood Panel
Whslr
N.A.I.C.S.: 423310
Brendan Garvin (CEO)

H & H Roofing Supply, LLC (1)
2900 Gateway Ave, Bakersfield, CA 93307
Tel.: (661) 377-7663
Web Site:
http://www.handhroofingsupply.com
Roofing Products & Materials Distr
N.A.I.C.S.: 423330
Scott Hill (Co-Founder)
Gary Hackney (Co-Founder)

JGA Beacon (1)
1841 Massaro Blvd, Tampa, FL 33619
Tel.: (010) 006 4444
Web Site: http://www.jgabeacon.com
Sales Range: $25-49.9 Million
Emp.: 42
Roofing & Siding Distr
N.A.I.C.S.: 423330

LYF-TYM Building Products Co., Inc. (1)
3820 N Davidson St, Charlotte, NC 28205
Tel.: (704) 372-3480
Web Site: http://www.lyftym.com
Vinyl Siding, Windows, Gutter Supplies,
Gutter Machines, Home Accessories, Vinyl
Decking & Railing & Other Siding Products
Whslr & Distr
N.A.I.C.S.: 423310
Curt Corder (Pres)

Las Vegas Roofing Supply, LLC (1)
3860 W Naples Dr, Las Vegas, NV 89103
Tel.: (702) 227-6655
Roofing, Siding & Insulation Material Merchant Whslr
N.A.I.C.S.: 423330

Lowry's Inc. (1)
8501 Telfair Ave, Sun Valley, CA 91352
Web Site: https://www.halowry.com
Sealants & Waterproofing Products Distr
N.A.I.C.S.: 423840
David Erney (Sls Mgr)
Misti Williams (District Mgr)

Branch (Domestic):

Lowry's (2)
8840 Complex Dr, San Diego, CA 92123
Tel.: (858) 430-1260
Web Site: http://www.halowry.com
Sealants & Waterproofing Products Whslr
N.A.I.C.S.: 423840

North Coast Commercial Roofing Systems (1)
2440 Edison Blvd, Twinsburg, OH 44087
Tel.: (330) 425-3359
Web Site: http://www.nccrs.com
Sales Range: $250-299.9 Million
Emp.: 197
Roofing & Siding Materials
N.A.I.C.S.: 423330

Roofers Mart of Southern California, Inc. (1)
358 Paseo Tesoro, Walnut, CA 91789
Tel.: (909) 598-8408
Web Site: http://www.roofers-mart.com
Sales Range: $1-9.9 Million
Emp.: 32
Roofing & Insulation Material Whslr
N.A.I.C.S.: 423330
Greg Robles (Pres & CEO)
Cecile Robles (CFO)
Flabio Alcaraz (Gen Mgr)

Roofers' Supply of Greenville, Inc. (1)
834 Piedmont Hwy, Piedmont, SC 29673
Tel.: (864) 299-0055
Web Site: http://www.rooferssupplyinc.com
Sales Range: $1-9.9 Million
Emp.: 22
Roofing, Siding & Insulation Material Merchant Whslr
N.A.I.C.S.: 423330
Michael Wingo (Pres)
Chris Causey (Pres)
Glenn Holland (VP-RSG-BS)
Joanne Hornkohl (Mgr-Ops)
Justin White (Mgr-Sls-Charlotte)
Kenny Gaut (Mgr Charlotte Branch)
David Hartis (Coord-Architectural Sls-
Charlotte)
Gloria Karabin (VP-Ops-Greenville)
Patrick Lawrence (Mgr-Garner Branch)
Mike Thornsbury (Mgr-Warehouse-
Charlotte)

Roofing & Insulation Supply Inc. (1)
12221 Merit Dr Ste 1015, Dallas, TX 75251-
3100
Tel.: (972) 239-8309
Web Site: http://www.risris.com
Roofing & Insulation Materials Distr
N.A.I.C.S.: 423330
Sprague Mullikin (Founder)

Roofing Supply Group - Alabama, LLC (1)
521 31st St N, Birmingham, AL 35203
Tel.: (205) 994-3003
Roofing, Siding & Insulation Material Merchant Whslr
N.A.I.C.S.: 423330

Roofing Supply Group - Bay Area, LLC (1)
1809 N 43rd St, Tampa, FL 33605
Tel.: (813) 716-6253
Roofing, Siding & Insulation Material Merchant Whslr
N.A.I.C.S.: 423330

Roofing Supply Group - Kentucky, LLC (1)
809 Enterprise Dr, Lexington, KY 40510
Tel.: (859) 559-0177

Roofing, Siding & Insulation Material Merchant Whslr
N.A.I.C.S.: 423330

Roofing Supply Group - Polk County, LLC (1)
3595 Recker Hwy, Winter Haven, FL 33880
Tel.: (863) 293-1555
Roofing, Siding & Insulation Material Merchant Whslr
N.A.I.C.S.: 423330

Roofing Supply Group - Raleigh, LCC (1)
1424 S Bloodworth, Raleigh, NC 27610
Tel.: (919) 779-6210
Roofing, Siding & Insulation Material Merchant Whslr
N.A.I.C.S.: 423330

Roofing Supply Group - Tampa, LLC (1)
8501 Sabal Industrial Blvd, Tampa, FL
33619
Tel.: (813) 740-8790
Roofing, Siding & Insulation Material Merchant Whslr
N.A.I.C.S.: 423330

Roofing Supply Group - Tuscaloosa, LLC (1)
2705 Southside Dr, Tuscaloosa, AL 35401
Tel.: (205) 345-7003
Roofing, Siding & Insulation Material Merchant Whslr
N.A.I.C.S.: 423330

Roofing Supply Group Orlando, LLC (1)
1600 W New Hampshire St, Orlando, FL
32804
Tel.: (407) 859-9997
Roofing, Siding & Insulation Material Merchant Whslr
N.A.I.C.S.: 423330

Roofing Supply Group San Diego, LLC (1)
5660 Kearny Villa Rd, San Diego, CA
92123
Tel.: (858) 715-0808
Roofing, Siding & Insulation Material Merchant Whslr
N.A.I.C.S.: 423330

Roofing Supply Group Utah, LLC (1)
1631 W 2550 S, Ogden, UT 84401
Tel.: (801) 394-7663
Roofing, Siding & Insulation Material Merchant Whslr
N.A.I.C.S.: 423330

Roofing Supply Group of Columbus, LLC (1)
3203 E 11th Ave, Columbus, OH 43219
Tel.: (614) 239-1111
Roofing, Siding & Insulation Material Merchant Whslr
N.A.I.C.S.: 423330

Roofing Supply Group of Oklahoma, LLC (1)
5120 NW 5th St, Oklahoma City, OK 73127
Tel.: (405) 605-7807
Roofing, Siding & Insulation Material Merchant Whslr
N.A.I.C.S.: 423330

Roofing Supply Group of Virginia, LLC (1)
10991 Richardson Rd, Ashland, VA 23005
Tel.: (804) 585-3069
Roofing, Siding & Insulation Material Merchant Whslr
N.A.I.C.S.: 423330

Roofing Supply Group, LLC (1)
3890 W NW Hwy Ste 400, Dallas, TX
75220
Tel.: (214) 956-5100
Web Site:
http://www.roofingsupplygroup.com
Holding Company; Roofing Supplies & Construction Materials Whslr
N.A.I.C.S.: 551112
Vin Perella (Founder)

Subsidiary (Domestic):

RSG Columbia (2)

1240 Atlas Rd, Columbia, SC 29209
Tel.: (803) 799-7055
Web Site: http://www.rsgroof.com
Roofing Supplies & Construction Materials
Whslr
N.A.I.C.S.: 423330

RSG Spokane Intermountain Supply (2)
7011 E Mission Ave, Spokane Valley, WA
99212
Tel.: (509) 891-8802
Web Site: http://rsgroof.com
Roofing Supplies & Construction Materials
Whslr
N.A.I.C.S.: 423330

Roofing Supply Group - Austin (2)
8319 N Lamar Blvd, Austin, TX 78753
Tel.: (512) 834-4347
Web Site: http://www.rsgroof.com
Roofing Supplies & Construction Materials
Whslr
N.A.I.C.S.: 423330

Branch (Domestic):

Roofing Supply Group - Corpus Christi (3)
5608 Old Brownsville Rd, Corpus Christi,
TX 78417
Tel.: (361) 299-7663
Web Site: http://www.rsgroof.com
Emp.: 50
Roofing Supplies & Construction Materials
Whslr
N.A.I.C.S.: 423330

Subsidiary (Domestic):

Roofing Supply Group - Kansas City (2)
1800 E 103rd St, Kansas City, MO 64131
Tel.: (816) 412-9990
Web Site: http://rsgroof.com
Roofing Supplies & Construction Materials
Whslr
N.A.I.C.S.: 423330

Roofing Supply Group-Cincinnati (2)
227 Circle Fwy Dr, Cincinnati, OH 45246
Tel.: (513) 782-5800
Web Site: http://rsgroof.com
Emp.: 18
Roofing Supplies & Construction Materials
Whslr
N.A.I.C.S.: 423330

Roofing Supply Group-Omaha (2)
15001 W Ctr Rd, Omaha, NE 68144
Tel.: (402) 734-2322
Web Site: http://www.rsgroof.com
Roofing Supplies & Construction Materials
Whslr
N.A.I.C.S.: 423330

Roofing Supply of Arizona-East Valley (2)
235 S Hibbert, Mesa, AZ 85210
Tel.: (480) 557-6309
Web Site: http://www.rsgroof.com
Roofing Supplies & Construction Materials
Whslr
N.A.I.C.S.: 423330

Branch (Domestic):

Roofing Supply, LLC - Houston (2)
2600 W Mt Houston Rd, Houston, TX
77038
Tel.: (281) 447-7759
Web Site: http://www.rsgroof.com
Roofing Supplies & Construction Materials
Whslr
N.A.I.C.S.: 423330

Subsidiary (Domestic):

Supreme Building Products, Inc. (2)
2705 Southside Dr, Tuscaloosa, AL 35401
Tel.: (205) 345-7003
Web Site:
https://www.suprememetalproducts.com
Metal Roofing Mfr
N.A.I.C.S.: 332332

Roofing Supply Transportation, LLC (1)
3890 W NW Hwy 400, Dallas, TX 75220
Tel.: (214) 956-5176

Roofing, Siding & Insulation Material Merchant Whslr
N.A.I.C.S.: 423330

Roofing Supply of Arizona - Tucson, LLC (1)
3655 E Refinery Way, Tucson, AZ 85713
Tel.: (520) 790-5750
Roofing, Siding & Insulation Material Merchant Whslr
N.A.I.C.S.: 423330

Roofing Supply of Arizona, LLC (1)
5307 W Missouri Ave, Glendale, AZ 85301
Tel.: (623) 931-0054
Roofing, Siding & Insulation Material Merchant Whslr
N.A.I.C.S.: 423330

Roofing Supply of Atlanta, LLC (1)
6835 Southlake Pkwy, Morrow, GA 30260
Tel.: (770) 961-1995
Roofing, Siding & Insulation Material Merchant Whslr
N.A.I.C.S.: 423330

Roofing Supply of Charlotte, LLC (1)
1600 Westinghouse Blvd, Charlotte, NC 28273
Tel.: (704) 332-8440
Roofing, Siding & Insulation Material Merchant Whslr
N.A.I.C.S.: 423330

Roofing Supply of Nashville, LLC (1)
1707 River Hills Dr, Nashville, TN 37210
Tel.: (615) 242-7663
Roofing, Siding & Insulation Material Merchant Whslr
N.A.I.C.S.: 423330

Roofing Supply of New Mexico, LLC (1)
2222 4th St NW, Albuquerque, NM 87102
Tel.: (505) 343-8000
Roofing, Siding & Insulation Material Merchant Whslr
N.A.I.C.S.: 423330

Roofing Supply of Tennessee, LLC (1)
1810 Getwell, Memphis, TN 38111
Tel.: (901) 866-7663
Roofing, Siding & Insulation Material Merchant Whslr
N.A.I.C.S.: 423330

S & H Building Material Corp. (1)
3177 Route 112, Medford, NY 11763
Tel.: (631) 732-8000
Web Site:
     http://www.shbuildingmaterials.com
Sales Range: $1-9.9 Million
Emp.: 12
Roofing, Siding & Insulation Material Merchant Whslr
N.A.I.C.S.: 423330
Brian Rosenstein (Exec VP)

Statewide Wholesale, Inc. (1)
1205 S Platte River Dr Ste 104, Denver, CO 80223
Tel.: (303) 744-7111
Sales Range: $1-9.9 Million
Emp.: 43
Roofing Materials & Supplies Distr
N.A.I.C.S.: 423330

Structural Materials Co., Inc. (1)
1201 E McFadden Ave, Santa Ana, CA 92705
Tel.: (714) 567-0198
Web Site:
     http://www.structuralmaterials.com
Sales Range: $75-99.9 Million
Emp.: 100
Roofing, Siding & Insulation Materials Whslr
N.A.I.C.S.: 423330

West End Roofing, Siding & Windows (1)
2902 W 12th St, Houston, TX 77008
Tel.: (713) 688-9726
Web Site: http://www.westendroofing.com
Sales Range: $75-99.9 Million
Emp.: 230
Building Materials Distr
N.A.I.C.S.: 423330

BEAM GLOBAL

Tel.: (858) 799-4583   NV
Web Site: http://beamforall.com
BEEM—(NASDAQ)
Rev.: $67,353,000
Assets: $77,643,000
Liabilities: $28,101,000
Net Worth: $49,542,000
Earnings: ($16,060,000)
Emp.: 323
Fiscal Year-end: 12/31/23
Renewable Energy Device Mfr
N.A.I.C.S.: 333242
Desmond Wheatley (Chm, Pres & CEO)
Sandra Peterson (VP-Sls & Mktg)
Lisa A. Potok (CFO)

BEAM THERAPEUTICS INC.
238 Main St, Cambridge, MA 02142
Tel.: (857) 327-8775   DE
Web Site: https://www.beamtx.com
Year Founded: 2017
BEAM—(NASDAQ)
Rev.: $60,920,000
Assets: $1,341,714,000
Liabilities: $608,240,000
Net Worth: $733,474,000
Earnings: ($289,088,000)
Emp.: 507
Fiscal Year-end: 12/31/22
Biotechnology Research & Development Services
N.A.I.C.S.: 541714
John Evans (CEO, Principal Acctg Officer & Principal Fin Officer)
Giuseppe Ciaramella (Pres & Chief Scientific Officer)
Christine Bellon (Chief Legal Officer & Sr VP)
Suzanne Fleming (Sr VP-Fin)
Francine Gregoire (Sr VP & Head-Vivo Programs)
Susan O'Connor (Chief HR Officer)
Brian Riley (Sr VP-Technical Ops)
Manmohan Singh (Sr VP-Pharmaceutical Sciences & Delivery Tech)
Courtney Wallace (Chief Bus Officer)
Christine Swenson (Sr VP-Regulatory Affairs)
David R. Liu (Co-Founder)
J. Keith Joung (Co-Founder)
Feng Zhang (Co-Founder)
Amy Simon (Chief Medical Officer)

BEAMZ INTERACTIVE, INC.
15354 N 83rd Way Ste 101, Scottsdale, AZ 85260
Tel.: (480) 424-2053   DE
Web Site: https://www.thebeamz.com
Year Founded: 2001
BZIC—(OTCIQ)
Sales Range: Less than $1 Million
Emp.: 2
Interactive Music Systems
N.A.I.C.S.: 334310
Joan Brubacher (CFO)
Albert J. Ingallinera Jr. (VP-Business Development)

BEARD ENERGY TRANSITION ACQUISITION CORP.
595 Madison Ave 28th Fl, New York, NY 10022
Tel.: (713) 446-6259   DE
Web Site: https://www.beardacq.com
Year Founded: 2021
BRD—(NYSE)
Rev.: $3,320,716
Assets: $239,351,513
Liabilities: $247,432,355
Net Worth: ($8,080,842)
Earnings: $1,207,275
Emp.: 2
Fiscal Year-end: 12/31/22
Investment Services

N.A.I.C.S.: 523999
Gregory A. Beard (Chm & CEO)
Sarah James (CFO & Chief Acctg Officer)

BEASLEY BROADCAST GROUP, INC.
3033 Riviera Dr Ste 200, Naples, FL 34103
Tel.: (239) 263-5000   DE
Web Site: https://www.bbgi.com
Year Founded: 1961
BBGI—(NASDAQ)
Rev.: $247,109,258
Assets: $574,267,938
Liabilities: $425,289,303
Net Worth: $148,978,635
Earnings: ($75,120,138)
Emp.: 755
Fiscal Year-end: 12/31/23
Holding Company; Radio Broadcasting Stations Owner & Operator
N.A.I.C.S.: 551112
Bruce G. Beasley (Pres)
B. Caroline Beasley (CEO)
Brian E. Beasley (COO & Exec VP)
Marie Tedesco (CFO)
Michael Cooney (CTO & VP-Engrg)
Justin Chase (Chief Content Officer)
Heidi Raphael (Chief Communications Officer)
Dan Frisbie (VP-Digital Sls)
Lori Burgess (COO-Beasley XP)
Brad Beasley (VP-Ops)
Erika Beasley (VP-Digital Content)
Tina Murley (VP-Sls)
Jennifer Williams (VP-Digital Mktg)

Subsidiaries:

Beasley Mezzanine Holdings, LLC (1)
3033 Riviera Dr Ste 200, Naples, FL 34103
Tel.: (239) 263-5000
Web Site: https://www.bbgi.com
Emp.: 30
Holding Company
N.A.I.C.S.: 551112

Subsidiary (Domestic):

Beasley Media Group, Inc. (2)
3033 Riviera Dr Ste 200, Naples, FL 34103
Tel.: (239) 263-5000
Web Site: https://bbgi.com
Radio Broadcasting Stations Operator
N.A.I.C.S.: 516210
Bruce G. Beasley (Pres)
B. Caroline Beasley (CEO)
Brian E. Beasley (COO & Exec VP)
Bob McCurdy (VP-Sls)
Heather Monahan (Chief Revenue Officer)
Justin Chase (Chief Content Officer)
Michael Cooney (CTO & VP)
Kimberly R. Sonneborn (VP-Digital Product Dev)
Janice McDuff (VP-Fin)
Marie Tedesco (CFO)
Brian Kalinowski (Exec VP-Digital-Charlotte)
Heidi Raphael (VP-Corp Comm)
Steve Meyers (Grp Exec VP)
Dan Frisbie (VP-Digital Sls)
Peter W. Burton (VP & Mgr-Las Vegas)
Erika Beasley (Corp Dir-Digital Content-Local Markets)
Kent Dunn (VP-Radio Clusters-Augusta & Fayetteville)
Todd Handy (Chief Digital Officer)
Scott Jameson (Dir-Programming-Detroit)
Mac Edwards (VP & Mgr-Market)
Brad Beasley (VP-Ops)
AJ Lurie (VP & Mgr-Cluster-Southwest Florida)

Unit (Domestic):

Beasley Broadcast Group, Inc. - Boston (3)
552 Massachusetts Ave Ste 201, Cambridge, MA 02139-4088
Tel.: (617) 492-3300
Web Site: http://www.1330wrca.com
Radio Broadcasting Stations
N.A.I.C.S.: 516110

Beasley Broadcast Group, Inc. - Greenville (3)
2929 Radio Station Rd, Greenville, NC 27834
Tel.: (252) 757-0011
Web Site: http://www.1079wnct.com
Emp.: 8
Radio Broadcasting Stations
N.A.I.C.S.: 516110

Jersey Shore Broadcasting Corporation (1)
610 Main St, Belmar, NJ 07719
Tel.: (732) 681-9591
Web Site: https://www.wjrz.com
Radio Broadcasting Services
N.A.I.C.S.: 516110
Matt Knight (Program Dir)
Marge Guglielmo (Sls Dir & Sls Mgr)
Christina Corrado (Dir-Promo & Program)

BEAZER HOMES USA, INC.
2002 Summit Blvd NE 15th Fl, Atlanta, GA 30319
Tel.: (770) 829-3700   DE
Web Site: https://www.beazer.com
Year Founded: 1985
BZH—(NYSE)
Rev.: $2,330,197,000
Assets: $2,591,527,000
Liabilities: $1,359,416,000
Net Worth: $1,232,111,000
Earnings: $140,175,000
Emp.: 1,158
Fiscal Year-end: 09/30/24
Residential Construction
N.A.I.C.S.: 236115
Allan P. Merrill (Chm, Pres & CEO)
David I. Goldberg (CFO & Sr VP)

Subsidiaries:

Arden Park Ventures, LLC (1)
1000 Abernathy Rd Ste 1200, Atlanta, GA 30328
Tel.: (770) 829-3700
Residential Construction Services
N.A.I.C.S.: 236117

Beazer Homes Corp. (1)
1018 Elm Hill Pike, Nashville, TN 37210-3619
Tel.: (615) 244-9600
Web Site: http://www.Beazer.net
Sales Range: $50-74.9 Million
Emp.: 40
New Housing Operative Builders
N.A.I.C.S.: 236117
Geoff Hart (Pres)

Beazer Homes Indiana Holdings Corp. (1)
9202 N Meridian St 300, Indianapolis, IN 46260-1800
Tel.: (317) 843-9514
Buliding Construction & Installation Services
N.A.I.C.S.: 236210
Bruce Craig (VP)

Beazer Homes Indiana, LLP (1)
9202 N Meridian St Ste 300, Indianapolis, IN 46260-1833   (100%)
Tel.: (317) 843-9514
Web Site: http://www.beazer.com
Sales Range: $300-349.9 Million
Emp.: 150
New Housing Operative Builders
N.A.I.C.S.: 236117

Beazer Homes Investments, LLC (1)
1000 Abernathy Rd Ste 1200, Atlanta, GA 30328
Tel.: (770) 829-3737
Residential Construction Services
N.A.I.C.S.: 236117

Beazer Homes Sales, Inc. (1)
1621 W Riosalado Pkwy Ste 103, Tempe, AZ 85281-6944   (100%)
Tel.: (480) 921-4600
Web Site: http://www.beazer.com
Sales Range: $150-199.9 Million
Emp.: 110
New Housing Sales & Construction Services
N.A.I.C.S.: 531210

Beazer Homes USA, Inc.—(Continued)

Beazer Homes Texas, LP (1)
10110 W Sam Houston Pkwy N Ste A100,
Houston, TX 77064
Tel.: (281) 897-2100
Sales Range: $25-49.9 Million
Emp.: 82
New Housing Operative Builders
N.A.I.C.S.: 236117

Beazer Mortgage Corporation (1)
1000 Abernathy Rd Ste 260, Atlanta, GA
30328
Tel.: (770) 829-3700
Web Site: http://www.beazer.com
Sales Range: $125-149.9 Million
Mortgage Lending Services
N.A.I.C.S.: 522310
Allan P. Merrill (Pres & CEO)

Beazer Realty Los Angeles, Inc. (1)
1000 Abernathy Rd Ste 260, Atlanta, GA
30328
Tel.: (770) 829-3700
Real Estate Manangement Services
N.A.I.C.S.: 531390

Beazer Realty Services, LLC (1)
8778 S Maryland Pkwy, Las Vegas, NV
89123
Tel.: (702) 478-7020
Real Estate Manangement Services
N.A.I.C.S.: 531390

Beazer SPE, LLC (1)
1000 Abernathy Rd Ste 260, Atlanta, GA
30328
Tel.: (770) 829-3700
Housing
N.A.I.C.S.: 236117

Beazer-Inspirada LLC (1)
1000 Abernathy Rd Ste 260, Atlanta, GA
30328
Tel.: (770) 829-3700
Residential Building Construction Services
N.A.I.C.S.: 236116

United Home Insurance Company, A Risk Retention Group (1)
100 Bank St Ste 610, Burlington, VT 05401-4699
Tel.: (802) 864-5599
Insurance Management Services
N.A.I.C.S.: 524298

BEBOP CHANNEL CORPORATION
Tel.: (202) 302-6703
Web Site: https://www.beboptv.com
Year Founded: 2019
BBOP—(OTCIQ)
Media Entertainment
N.A.I.C.S.: 512199
Sue Veres Royal (COO)

Subsidiaries:

Madavor Media, LLC (1)
25 Braintree Hill Office Park Ste 404, Braintree, MA 02184
Tel.: (617) 706-9110
Web Site: http://www.madavor.com
Emp.: 20
Publisher Company
N.A.I.C.S.: 513120
Susan Fitzgerald (Publr)
Jeffrey C. Wolk (Chm & CEO)

Subsidiary (Domestic):

Teddy Bear and Friends Magazines (2)
N7528 Aanstad Rd, Iola, WI 54945
Tel.: (715) 445-5000
Web Site:
http://www.teddybearandfriends.com
Sales Range: $10-24.9 Million
Periodicals
N.A.I.C.S.: 513120
Terrence Lynch (Editor-in-Chief)

BECTON, DICKINSON & COMPANY
1 Becton Dr, Franklin Lakes, NJ
07417-1880
Tel.: (201) 847-6800   NJ

Web Site: https://www.bd.com
Year Founded: 1897
BDX—(NYSE)
Rev.: $20,178,000,000
Assets: $57,286,000,000
Liabilities: $31,396,000,000
Net Worth: $25,890,000,000
Earnings: $1,705,000,000
Emp.: 74,000
Fiscal Year-end: 09/30/24
Medical Supplies, Devices & Diagnostic Systems Mfr & Sales
N.A.I.C.S.: 339112
Devdatt Kurdikar (Pres & CEO)
Thomas E. Polen (Chm, Pres & CEO)
Gary M. DeFazio (Sec, Sr VP & Assoc Gen Counsel)
Roland Goette (Pres-EMEA & Exec VP)
Thomas J. Spoerel (Chief Acctg Officer, Sr VP & Controller)
Michelle Quinn (Gen Counsel & Exec VP)
Ami E. Simunovich (Chief Regulatory Officer-Pub Affairs, Interim Chief Quality Officer & Exec VP)
Antoine C. Ezell (CMO & Exec VP-North America)
David Shan (Chief Integrated Supply Chain Officer & Exec VP)
Michael Garrison (Pres-Medical Segment & Exec VP)
Elizabeth McCombs (CTO & Exec VP)
Christopher J. DelOrefice (CFO & Exec VP)
Troy Kirkpatrick (VP-PR)
Francesca DeMartino (Sr VP-IR)
Richard Byrd (Pres-Interventional Segment & Exec VP)
Denise Russell Fleming (CIO & Exec VP-Tech & Global Svcs)
Vishy Kanda (Chief Strategy Officer & Sr VP)
Pavan Mocherla (Pres-Greater Asia & Exec VP)
Shana Neal (Chief People Officer & Exec VP)
Rima Alameddine (Pres--Worldwide)
Eric Borin (Pres--Worldwide)
Laura Boros (Pres--Worldwide)
Carla Burigatto (Chief Comm Officer & Sr VP)
Steve Conly (Pres--Worldwide)
Claudia Curtis (Chief Ethics & Compliance Officer & Sr VP)
James Deng (Sr VP & Gen Mgr-Greater China)
Ebonee Lewis (VP)
Rodrigo Luiz Hanna (Sr VP & Gen Mgr-Latin America)
Padraic O'Brien (Pres--Worldwide)
Stephen Richard (Chief Risk Officer & Sr VP)
Gregory Rodetis (Treas, Sr VP & Head-IR)
Puneet Sarin (Pres--Worldwide)
Brooke Story (Pres--Worldwide)
Elizabeth Woody (Sr VP-Pub Affairs)
Ronald Silverman (Chief Medical Officer & Exec VP)
Christopher DelOrefice (CFO & Exec VP)

Subsidiaries:

ARX Automatizacion de Farmacias, S.L.U. (1)
Camino de Casabermeja 118 Bajo, Malaga,
29014, Spain
Tel.: (34) 902011237
Pharmacies & Drug Mfr & Distr
N.A.I.C.S.: 456110
Dirk vom Hovel (Mgr-Sls North Spain & Majorca)

ARX BVBA (1)

Henri Jasparlaan 99, 1060, Saint Gillis-Waas, Belgium
Tel.: (32) 25392539
Medical Equipment Mfr
N.A.I.C.S.: 334510

ARX Limited (1)
Unit 6 Beaumont Works Hedley Road, Saint
Albans, AL1 5LU, United Kingdom
Tel.: (44) 1727893360
Pharmaceutical Hardware Mfr
N.A.I.C.S.: 332510
Tom Simcox (CEO)

ARX SA (1)
Rue Thalberg 2, Case Postale 1507, 1211,
Geneva, Switzerland
Tel.: (41) 227389541
Housing Construction Services
N.A.I.C.S.: 236116

ARX SAS (1)
La Pette Periche-Route des Navrans,
72200, Bazouges-sur-le-Loir, France
Tel.: (33) 243480050
Housing Construction Services
N.A.I.C.S.: 236116
Sandrine Katz (Office Mgr)

Accuri Cytometers, Inc. (1)
173 Parkland Plz, Ann Arbor, MI 48103-6299
Tel.: (734) 994-8000
Web Site: http://www.bdbiosciences.com
Sales Range: $25-49.9 Million
Emp.: 60
Laboratory Apparatus Mfr
N.A.I.C.S.: 334516
Jennifer A. Baird (Co-Founder)

Subsidiary (Non-US):

Accuri Cytometers (Europe) Ltd. (2)
56 Edison Road, Saint Ives, PE27 3LF,
United Kingdom
Tel.: (44) 1480308380
Laboratory Apparatus Mfr
N.A.I.C.S.: 333248

BD Diagnostic Systems (1)
7 Loveton Cir, Sparks, MD 21152-9212
Tel.: (410) 316-4000
Web Site: http://www.bd.com
Sales Range: $1-4.9 Billion
Emp.: 1,650
Medical & Diagnostic Instruments Mfr & Distr
N.A.I.C.S.: 339112

Division (Domestic):

BD Diagnostic Systems-Informatics (2)
515 S Capital of Texas Highway Ste 240,
Austin, TX 78746
Tel.: (512) 892-4594
Web Site: http://www.bd.com
Sales Range: $10-24.9 Million
Emp.: 17
Healthcare Software Developer
N.A.I.C.S.: 513210

TriPath Imaging, Inc. (2)
780 Plantation Dr, Burlington, NC 27215
Tel.: (336) 222-9707
Web Site: http://www.bd.com
Sales Range: $75-99.9 Million
Emp.: 300
Cervical Cancer Screening Products Mfr
N.A.I.C.S.: 339112

Subsidiary (Domestic):

TriPath Oncology, Inc. (3)
4025 Stirrup Creek Dr Ste 400, Durham,
NC 27703
Tel.: (919) 206-7132
Research & Development in Genomics & Proteomics for Detection of Cancer
N.A.I.C.S.: 541715
Bonnie Rib (Gen Mgr)

BD Holding S. de R.L. de C.V. (1)
Monte Pelvoux No 111 Col Lomas de
Chapultepec Fl 89, Mexico, 11000, Mexico
Tel.: (52) 5559998200
Surgical & Medical Equipment Mfr
N.A.I.C.S.: 333249
Adelaida Gomez (Gen Mgr)

BD Kiestra BV (1)

Marconilaan 6, 9207 JC, Drachten, Netherlands
Tel.: (31) 512510710
Web Site: http://www.bd.com
Emp.: 325
Surgical & Medical Equipment Mfr
N.A.I.C.S.: 339113

BD Norge AS (1)
Medisinsk Teknisk Senter Olav Kyrres Gt 9,
Trondheim, 7489, Norway
Tel.: (47) 73591200
Healthcare Equipment Distr
N.A.I.C.S.: 423450

BD Preanalytical (1)
1 Becton Dr, Franklin Lakes, NJ
07417-1815   (100%)
Tel.: (201) 847-6800
Web Site: http://www.bd.com
Sales Range: $500-549.9 Million
Emp.: 1,400
Blood Collection Systems, Urine & Sputum Specimen Collection Devices & Microcollection Products Mfr
N.A.I.C.S.: 339112

Joint Venture (Non-US):

PreAnalytiX GmbH (2)
Feldbachstrasse, 8634, Hombrechtikon,
Switzerland   (50%)
Tel.: (41) 614852222
Web Site: http://www.preanalytix.com
Sales Range: $75-99.9 Million
Nucleic Acids Molecular Diagnostic Testing Services
N.A.I.C.S.: 541380

BD Rx Inc. (1)
1 Becton Dr, Franklin Lakes, NJ 07417
Tel.: (201) 847-6800
Web Site: http://www.bdrxinc.com
Pharmaceuticals Product Mfr
N.A.I.C.S.: 325412

BD Technologies (1)
21 Davis Dr, Research Triangle Park, NC
27709   (100%)
Tel.: (919) 549-8641
Web Site: http://www.bd.com
Sales Range: $75-99.9 Million
Emp.: 220
Pharmacological, Toxicological, Biochemical & Other Biomedical Tests
N.A.I.C.S.: 541720

BD Ventures LLC (1)
1 Becton Dr, Franklin Lakes, NJ
07417-1880   (100%)
Tel.: (201) 847-6800
Web Site: http://www.bd.com
Sales Range: $450-499.9 Million
Emp.: 1,600
Venture Capital Services
N.A.I.C.S.: 523999
Peter A. Origenes (Pres & Gen Mgr)

Becton Dickinson (Pty) Ltd. (1)
20 Woodlands Drive The Woodlands Office
Park Building 31 2nd Floor, Accra, Woodmead, 2199, South Africa   (100%)
Tel.: (27) 116032620
Web Site: http://www.bd.com
Sales Range: $25-49.9 Million
Emp.: 15
Medical Products Sales
N.A.I.C.S.: 423450

Becton Dickinson (Royston) Limited (1)
1030 Eskdale Road Winnersh Triangle,
Wokingham, RG41 5TS, Berkshire, United
Kingdom
Tel.: (44) 1865748844
Web Site: http://www.bectondickinson.co.uk
Surgical & Medical Equipment Mfr
N.A.I.C.S.: 339113

Becton Dickinson (Thailand) Limited (1)
24th Fl The offices at Central World 999/9
Rama 1 Road, Pathumwan, Bangkok,
10330, Thailand
Tel.: (66) 26461800
Web Site: http://www.bd.com
Sales Range: $25-49.9 Million
Emp.: 40
Surgical & Medical Instrument Mfr & Distr
N.A.I.C.S.: 423450

Becton Dickinson A/S (1)
Firskovvej 25B, 2800, Lyngby,
Denmark (100%)
Tel.: (45) 43434566
Web Site: http://www.bd.com
Sales Range: $25-49.9 Million
Emp.: 24
Medical Products Sales
N.A.I.C.S.: 423450

Becton Dickinson AG (1)
Binningerstr 94, 4123, Allschwil,
Switzerland (100%)
Tel.: (41) 614852222
Web Site: http://www.bd.com
Sales Range: $25-49.9 Million
Emp.: 30
Medical Products Sales
N.A.I.C.S.: 423450
Matthias Borst *(Mng Dir)*

Subsidiary (Domestic):

**Becton Dickinson Advanced Pen In-
jection Systems GmbH** (2)
Binningerstrasse 94, 4123, Allschwil,
Switzerland (100%)
Tel.: (41) 614852222
Medical Injection Products Sales
N.A.I.C.S.: 423450

Subsidiary (Non-US):

Becton Dickinson Austria GmbH (2)
Rinnbockstr 3, 1030, Vienna,
Austria (100%)
Tel.: (43) 170636600
Web Site: http://www.bd.com
Sales Range: $25-49.9 Million
Emp.: 21
Medical Products Sales
N.A.I.C.S.: 423450
Roland P. Seger *(Mng Dir)*

Becton Dickinson Aktiebolag (1)
Marieviksgatan 25, Box 472 04, 117 43,
Stockholm, Sweden (100%)
Tel.: (46) 87755100
Web Site: http://www.bd.com
Emp.: 120
Medical Products & Systems Mfr
N.A.I.C.S.: 339112

Subsidiary (Domestic):

**Becton Dickinson Infusion Therapy
AB** (2)
PO Box 47204, 10074, Stockholm,
Sweden (100%)
Tel.: (46) 87755100
Web Site: http://www.bd.com
Emp.: 50
Medicinal Product Mfr
N.A.I.C.S.: 339112

Subsidiary (Non-US):

Becton Dickinson Oy (2)
Ayritie 18, PO Box 47204, 01510, Vantaa,
Finland (100%)
Tel.: (358) 98870780
Web Site: http://www.bd.com
Sales Range: $1-9.9 Million
Emp.: 16
Medical Products & Systems Mfr
N.A.I.C.S.: 339112
Hilena Bragd *(Pres)*

**Becton Dickinson Argentina
S.R.L.** (1)
Av Del Libertador 110 2 Piso, C1638BEN,
Vicente Lopez, Buenos Aires,
Argentina (100%)
Tel.: (54) 1151944900
Web Site: http://www.bd.com
Sales Range: $25-49.9 Million
Emp.: 50
Medical Products Distr & Sales
N.A.I.C.S.: 423450

Becton Dickinson Asia Limited (1)
Unit 1908 10 19 F Chevalier Commerce
Centre 8 Wang Hoi Road, Kowloon Bay,
Kowloon, China (Hong Kong)
Tel.: (852) 25758668
Surgical & Medical Equipment Mfr
N.A.I.C.S.: 339113

**Becton Dickinson Austria Holdings
GmbH** (1)

Am Concorde Park E 1/7, 2320,
Schwechat, Austria
Tel.: (43) 170636600
Emp.: 20
Holding Company
N.A.I.C.S.: 551112
Roland Pflagar *(Gen Mgr)*

Becton Dickinson Benelux N.V. (1)
Dorp 86, 9320, Erembodegem,
Belgium (100%)
Tel.: (32) 53720211
Web Site: http://www.europe.bd.com
Sales Range: $200-249.9 Million
Emp.: 400
Medical & Pharmaceutical Products & Sys-
tems Mfr
N.A.I.C.S.: 325412

Subsidiary (Domestic):

**Becton Dickinson Distribution Center
N.V.** (2)
Laagstraat St House no 57, 9140, Temse,
Belgium (100%)
Tel.: (32) 53720211
Web Site: http://www.bd.com
Sales Range: $200-249.9 Million
Emp.: 250
Medical Product Distr
N.A.I.C.S.: 423450
Yem Degonghi *(Mng Dir)*

Subsidiary (Non-US):

Becton, Dickinson B.V. (2)
Claudius Prinsenlaan 128b, PO Box 2130,
4800 CC, Breda, Netherlands (100%)
Tel.: (31) 206545225
Web Site: http://www.bd.com
Sales Range: $50-74.9 Million
Emp.: 250
Medical Products & Systems
N.A.I.C.S.: 339112
Etienne Borms *(Mng Dir)*

**Becton Dickinson Biosciences, Sys-
tems and Reagents Inc.** (1)
2350 Qume Dr, San Jose, CA
95131-1812 (100%)
Tel.: (408) 432-9475
Web Site: http://www.bdbiosciences.com
Sales Range: $700-749.9 Million
Emp.: 1,300
Bioscience Products Mfr & Sales
N.A.I.C.S.: 339112
Vincent A. Forlenza *(Executives)*

Unit (Domestic):

**BD Biosciences Discovery
Labware** (2)
2 Oak Park, Bedford, MA 01730-9902
Tel.: (781) 275-0004
Web Site: http://www.bdbiosciences.com
Sales Range: $100-124.9 Million
Mfr of Surgical & Medical Instrments & Sup-
plies
N.A.I.C.S.: 339112

BD Biosciences PharMingen (2)
10975 Torreyana Rd, San Diego, CA
92121 (100%)
Tel.: (858) 812-8800
Web Site: http://www.bdbiosciences.com
Sales Range: $50-74.9 Million
Emp.: 400
Medicinal Product Mfr
N.A.I.C.S.: 339112
Vincent A. Forlenza *(Chm, Pres & CEO)*

Subsidiary (Domestic):

Cytopeia, Inc. (2)
12730 28th Ave NE, Seattle, WA 98125
Tel.: (206) 364-3400
Sales Range: $25-49.9 Million
Emp.: 25
Analytical Instrument Mfr
N.A.I.C.S.: 334516
Ger Vandenengh *(VP)*

Becton Dickinson Canada Inc. (1)
2100 Derry Rd W Ste 100, Mississauga,
L5N 0B3, ON, Canada (100%)
Tel.: (905) 855-4820
Web Site: http://www.bd.com
Sales Range: $25-49.9 Million
Emp.: 150
Medical Supplies Mfr

N.A.I.C.S.: 339113

**Becton Dickinson Dispensing France
SAS** (1)
11 rue Aristide Berges, 38800, Le Pont-de-
Claix, France
Tel.: (33) 476043888
Surgical & Medical Instrument Mfr
N.A.I.C.S.: 339112

**Becton Dickinson Dispensing Spain
S.L.U.** (1)
Camino de Valdeoliva s/n San Agustin de
Guadalix, 28750, Madrid, Spain
Tel.: (34) 900747213
Surgical & Medical Instrument Mfr
N.A.I.C.S.: 339112

**Becton Dickinson Dispensing UK
Ltd.** (1)
1030 Winnersh Triangle Eskdale Road,
Winnersh, RG41 5TS, United Kingdom
Tel.: (44) 8009178776
Surgical & Medical Instrument Mfr
N.A.I.C.S.: 339112

Becton Dickinson Finance B.V. (1)
Bredaseweg 185, Etten-Leur, 4872 LA,
Noord-Brabant, Netherlands
Tel.: (31) 765083526
Web Site: http://www.bd.com
Emp.: 50
Financial Management Services
N.A.I.C.S.: 523999

Becton Dickinson France S.A.S. (1)
11 rue Aristide Berges, PO Box 4, 38801,
Le Pont-de-Claix, France (100%)
Tel.: (33) 476683636
Web Site: http://www.bd.com
Sales Range: $400-449.9 Million
Emp.: 1,700
Medical Treatment Systems
N.A.I.C.S.: 339112
Dominique Henry *(Mng Dir)*

Becton Dickinson GmbH (1)
Tullastr 8-12, 69126, Heidelberg,
Germany (100%)
Tel.: (49) 62213050
Web Site: http://www.bd.com
Sales Range: $50-74.9 Million
Emp.: 400
Medical Products Mfr & Sales
N.A.I.C.S.: 339112

Subsidiary (Domestic):

**Becton Dickinson Infusion Therapy
GmbH** (2)
Tullastrasse 8-12, 69126, Heidelberg,
Germany (100%)
Tel.: (49) 62213050
Web Site: http://www.becton.com
Sales Range: $75-99.9 Million
Emp.: 450
Medical Products Mfr & Sales
N.A.I.C.S.: 339112

Becton Dickinson Hellas S.A. (1)
Amfitheas Avenue 5, Nea Smyrni, 171 22,
Athens, Greece (100%)
Tel.: (30) 2109407741
Sales Range: $25-49.9 Million
Emp.: 31
Medical Products Sales
N.A.I.C.S.: 423450

Becton Dickinson Hungary Kft. (1)
Szerena Ut 60/C I/3, Budapest, 1025, Hun-
gary
Tel.: (36) 3457090
Surgical & Medical Instrument Mfr
N.A.I.C.S.: 339112

**Becton Dickinson India Private
Limited** (1)
6th Floor Signature Tower - B South City I
NH 8, Gurgaon, 122 001, Haryana, India
Tel.: (91) 1243949390
Web Site: http://www.bd.com
Emp.: 100
Surgical & Medical Instrument Mfr
N.A.I.C.S.: 339113
Pavan Mocherla *(Mng Dir-India & South
Asia)*

**Becton Dickinson Infusion Therapy
A/S** (1)
Herstedostervej 27 29 Bygning A 2 tv,

2620, Albertslund, Denmark
Tel.: (45) 43434566
Web Site: http://www.bd.com
Emp.: 30
Surgical & Medical Equipment Mfr
N.A.I.C.S.: 339113

**Becton Dickinson Infusion Therapy
AB** (1)
Florettgatan 29 C, 254 67, Helsingborg,
Sweden
Tel.: (46) 87755100
Surgical & Medical Instrument Mfr
N.A.I.C.S.: 339112

**Becton Dickinson Infusion Therapy
B.V.** (1)
Bredaseweg 185, Etten-Leur, 4872 LA,
Noord-Brabant, Netherlands
Tel.: (31) 765083526
Web Site: http://www.bd.com
Sales Range: $10-24.9 Million
Emp.: 10
Surgical & Medical Instrument Mfr
N.A.I.C.S.: 339113

**Becton Dickinson Infusion Therapy
Holdings AB** (1)
Box 47204 Se-100 74, Box 32054, 126 11,
Stockholm, Sweden
Tel.: (46) 87755100
Web Site: http://wwwbd.com
Investment Management Service
N.A.I.C.S.: 523999

**Becton Dickinson Infusion Therapy
Holdings UK Limited** (1)
21 Between Towns Road, Oxford, OX4 3LX,
Oxfordshire, United Kingdom
Tel.: (44) 1865781597
Surgical & Medical Equipment Mfr
N.A.I.C.S.: 339113

**Becton Dickinson Infusion Therapy
Systems Inc., S.A. de C.V.** (1)
Periferico Luis Donaldo Colosio Murrieta No
579, Nogales, 84048, Sonora, Mexico
Tel.: (52) 6313114000
Surgical & Medical Equipment Mfr
N.A.I.C.S.: 339113

**Becton Dickinson Insulin Syringe,
Ltd.** (1)
Pottery Rd Kill O The Grange, Dun
Laoghaire, Co Dublin, Ireland
Tel.: (353) 12854800
Surgical & Medical Instrument Mfr
N.A.I.C.S.: 339112
Cormay Reynolds *(Gen Mgr)*

Becton Dickinson Korea Ltd. (1)
Gangnam Teheran Road 142 16th Floor
Place Ark Wu, Yoksam-dong Kangnam-ku,
Seoul, 06236, Korea (South)
Tel.: (82) 234043700
Web Site: http://www.bd.com
Surgical & Medical Instrument Mfr
N.A.I.C.S.: 339113

Becton Dickinson Ltd. (1)
14b George Bourke Drive, Mt Wellington,
Auckland, 1060, New Zealand
Tel.: (64) 95742468
Web Site: http://www.bd.com
Surgical & Medical Instruments Mfr
N.A.I.C.S.: 339113

Becton Dickinson Ltd. (1)
14b George Bourke Drive, Mt Wellington,
Auckland, 1060, New Zealand
Tel.: (64) 95742468
Web Site: http://www.bd.com
Drug Distr
N.A.I.C.S.: 424210

**Becton Dickinson Management
GmbH & Co. KG** (1)
Tullastr 8-12, 69126, Heidelberg, Germany
Tel.: (49) 62213050
Web Site: http://www.bd.com
Surgical & Medical Equipment Mfr
N.A.I.C.S.: 339113

Becton Dickinson Medical (1)
9450 S State St, Sandy, UT
84070-3213 (100%)
Tel.: (801) 565-2300
Web Site: http://www.bd.com
Sales Range: $1-4.9 Billion
Emp.: 1,200
Medical Device Mfr & Marketer

Becton, Dickinson & Company—(Continued)

N.A.I.C.S.: 339112

Unit (Domestic):

Becton Dickinson Medical (2)
411 Waverley Oaks Rd, Waltham, MA
02452-8448 **(100%)**
Tel.: (781) 906-7900
Web Site: http://www.bd.com
Sales Range: $50-74.9 Million
Emp.: 200
Disposable Surgical Blades, Stainless Steel
Handles, Disposable Knives & Sapphire
Knives & Blades Mfr
N.A.I.C.S.: 339112

**Becton, Dickinson Medical
Surgical** (2)
1852 10th Ave, Columbus, NE 68601
Tel.: (402) 564-3181
Web Site: http://www.bd.com
Sales Range: $250-299.9 Million
Emp.: 950
Medical Devices & Supplies Mfr
N.A.I.C.S.: 339112

**Becton Dickinson Medical (S) Pte
Ltd.** (1)
30 Tuas Ave 2, Singapore, 639461,
Singapore **(100%)**
Tel.: (65) 68610633
Web Site: http://www.bd.com
Sales Range: $150-199.9 Million
Emp.: 700
Medical Supplies, Devices & Systems Mfr &
Sales
N.A.I.C.S.: 339112

**Becton Dickinson Medical Devices
Co. Ltd., Suzhou** (1)
No 5 Baiyu Road Suzhou Industry Park,
Suzhou, 215021, Jiangsu, China
Tel.: (86) 51267616787
Web Site: http://www.bd.com
Healthcare Equipment Distr
N.A.I.C.S.: 423450

**Becton Dickinson Medical Devices
Co. Shanghai Ltd.** (1)
9-10 Floor Tower 3 Kerry Center, Shanghai,
1228, China
Tel.: (86) 2132104610
Surgical & Medical Instrument Mfr
N.A.I.C.S.: 339112

**Becton Dickinson Medical Products
Pte. Ltd.** (1)
30 Tuas Avenue 2, Singapore, 639461,
Singapore
Tel.: (65) 68610633
Surgical & Medical Instrument Mfr
N.A.I.C.S.: 339112

Becton Dickinson Norway AS (1)
Gjerdrums vei 8, 0484, Oslo, Norway
Tel.: (47) 64009900
Web Site: http://www.bd.com
Medical Device & Diagnostic System Mfr
N.A.I.C.S.: 339112

**Becton Dickinson Pakistan (Pvt)
Ltd.** (1)
19/D 1 Gulberg III, Lahore, 54660, Pakistan
Tel.: (92) 42357180514
Medical Device & Diagnostic System Mfr
N.A.I.C.S.: 339112

**Becton Dickinson Philippines,
Inc.** (1)
11th Floor Trade and Financial Tower 7th
Avenue Corner 32nd Street, Bonifacio
Global City, 1634, Taguig, Philippines
Tel.: (63) 24788881
Web Site: http://www.bd.com
Healthcare Equipment Distr
N.A.I.C.S.: 423450

**Becton Dickinson Polska
Sp.z.o.o.** (1)
ul Osmanska 14, 02-823, Warsaw, Poland
Tel.: (48) 223771100
Web Site: http://www.bd.com
Surgical & Medical Instrument Mfr
N.A.I.C.S.: 339112

Becton Dickinson Pty. Ltd. (1)
4 Research Park Drive Macquarie University Research Park, Heidelberg, North

Ryde, 2113, NSW, Australia **(100%)**
Tel.: (61) 288757000
Web Site: http://www.bd.com
Sales Range: $50-74.9 Million
Emp.: 150
Medical & Pharmaceutical Products
N.A.I.C.S.: 325412

**Becton Dickinson Rowa Germany
GmbH** (1)
Rowastrasse 1-3, 53539, Kelberg, Germany
Tel.: (49) 269292060
Web Site: http://www.rowa.de
Medical Device & Diagnostic System Mfr
N.A.I.C.S.: 339112

Becton Dickinson Rowa Italy Srl (1)
Via Enrico Cialdini 16, Cornaredo, 20161,
Milan, Italy
Tel.: (39) 0299990120
Medical Device & Diagnostic System Mfr
N.A.I.C.S.: 339112

Becton Dickinson Sdn. Bhd. (1)
Suite 8-7 & 8-8 Level 8 Wisma UOA Da-
mansara II No 6 Changkat Semantan, Da-
mansara Heights, 50490, Kuala Lumpur,
Wilayah Persekutuan, Malaysia
Tel.: (60) 320938788
Surgical & Medical Instrument Mfr
N.A.I.C.S.: 339112

**Becton Dickinson Sweden Holdings
AB** (1)
Marieviksgatan 25, PO Box 47204, 117 43,
Stockholm, Sweden
Tel.: (46) 87755100
Web Site: http://www.bd.com
Emp.: 60
Surgical & Medical Equipment Mfr
N.A.I.C.S.: 339113

**Becton Dickinson Switzerland Global
Holdings Sarl** (1)
Business Park Terre-Bonne Bldg A4, Route
de Crassier 17, 1262, Eysins, Switzerland
Tel.: (41) 21 556 30 00
Holding Company
N.A.I.C.S.: 551112
Roland Gotte (Mng Dir)

Subsidiary (Domestic):

BD Switzerland Sarl (2)
Terre Bonne Park - A4 Route de Crassier
17, 1262, Eysins, Switzerland **(100%)**
Tel.: (41) 215563000
Web Site: http://www.bd.com
Emp.: 10
Surgical & Medical Instrument Mfr
N.A.I.C.S.: 339112
Bradley Payne (Sr VP)

Becton Dickinson U.K. Limited (1)
The Dandy Building Edmund Halley Road,
Oxford Science Park, Oxford, OX4 4DQ,
United Kingdom **(100%)**
Tel.: (44) 1865748844
Web Site: http://www.bd.com
Medical Products & Systems Mfr
N.A.I.C.S.: 339112

Subsidiary (Domestic):

**Becton Dickinson Infusion Therapy
UK** (2)
Dandy Building Edmund Halley Road Ox-
ford Science Park, Oxford, OX4 4DQ,
United Kingdom **(100%)**
Tel.: (44) 01865748844
Web Site: http://www.bd.com
Sales Range: $75-99.9 Million
Emp.: 100
Infusion Therapy Products Sales & Mar-
keter
N.A.I.C.S.: 423450

**Becton Dickinson Verwaltungs
GmbH** (1)
Tullastrasse 8-12, 69126, Heidelberg, Ger-
many
Tel.: (49) 62213050
Surgical & Medical Instrument Mfr
N.A.I.C.S.: 339112
Mathias Borst (Mgr)

**Becton Dickinson de Colombia
Ltda.** (1)
Parque Industrial CLIS Vereda Vuelta la
Grande a 150 Mts de la, Glorieta de Siberia

via a Cota, Cundinamarca,
Colombia **(100%)**
Tel.: (57) 17566060
Web Site: http://www.bd.com
Sales Range: $25-49.9 Million
Emp.: 60
Medical Products Sales
N.A.I.C.S.: 423450

Becton Dickinson, S.A. (1)
Camino de Valdeoliva s/n, San Agustin de
Guadalix, 28750, Madrid, Spain **(100%)**
Tel.: (34) 918488100
Web Site: http://www.bd.com
Sales Range: $400-449.9 Million
Emp.: 1,000
Medical Products Mfr & Sales
N.A.I.C.S.: 339112
Carmelo Sanz (Mng Dir)

**Becton, Dickinson & Company -
Puerto Rico** (1)
Rd 916 KM 08 98 Cerro Gordo Industrial
Park, San Lorenzo, PR 00754
Tel.: (787) 736-0363
Web Site: http://www.bd.com
Sales Range: $10-24.9 Million
Emp.: 75
Medical Devices
N.A.I.C.S.: 339112

**Becton, Dickinson & Company,
Ltd.** (1)
Pottery Road, Dun Laoghaire, Co Dublin,
Ireland **(100%)**
Tel.: (353) 12025222
Web Site: http://www.bt.com
Sales Range: $50-74.9 Million
Emp.: 350
Medical Supplies & Instruments Mfr
N.A.I.C.S.: 339113

**Becton, Dickinson Industrias Cirurgi-
cas, Ltda.** (1)
Rua Alexandre Dumas 1976, Chacara
Santo Antonio, Sao Paulo, 04717-004, SP,
Brazil **(100%)**
Tel.: (55) 1151859833
Web Site: http://www.bd.com
Sales Range: $125-149.9 Million
Emp.: 1,900
Medical Device Mfr
N.A.I.C.S.: 339112

Becton, Dickinson Italia S.p.A. (1)
Via Enrico Cialdini 16, 20161, Milan,
Italy **(100%)**
Tel.: (39) 02482401
Web Site: http://www.bd.com
Sales Range: $25-49.9 Million
Emp.: 150
Medicinal Product Mfr
N.A.I.C.S.: 339112

**Becton, Dickinson de Mexico, S.A. de
C.V.** (1)
Monte Pelvoux No 111 pisos 8 9 y PH Col
Lomas de Chapultepec, 11000, Mexico,
Mexico **(100%)**
Tel.: (52) 5559998200
Web Site: http://www.bd.com
Sales Range: $400-449.9 Million
Emp.: 1,100
Medical Products & Systems
N.A.I.C.S.: 339112

Benex Ltd. (1)
Pottery Rd Dun Laoghaire, Dublin,
Ireland **(100%)**
Tel.: (353) 61472920
Web Site: http://www.bd.com
Sales Range: $25-49.9 Million
Emp.: 15
Medical Products Sales & Financial Ser-
vices
N.A.I.C.S.: 423450

BioVenture Centre Pte. Ltd. (1)
11 Biopolis Way 04-08 Helios Building, Sin-
gapore, 138667, Singapore
Tel.: (65) 68740168
Sales Range: $1-9.9 Million
Emp.: 5
Life Science Incubation Services; Owned
92% by Becton Dickinson & Company &
8% by Johns Hopkins University
N.A.I.C.S.: 541715

C.R. Bard, Inc. (1)

730 Central Ave, New Providence, NJ
07974
Tel.: (908) 277-8000
Web Site: http://www.bd.com
Medical, Surgical, Diagnostic & Patient
Care Devices & Products Mfr
N.A.I.C.S.: 339112
Sherri Haggard (Mgr-Corp Credit & Collec-
tions)

Subsidiary (Domestic):

Bard Access Systems, Inc. (2)
605 N 5600 W, Salt Lake City, UT 84116
Tel.: (801) 522-5000
Web Site: http://www.bardaccess.com
Surgical Supplies
N.A.I.C.S.: 339112

Subsidiary (Non-US):

Bard Benelux N.V. (2)
Hagelberg 2, 2250, Olen, Belgium
Tel.: (32) 14286950
Web Site: http://www.bd.com
Surgical & Medical Instrument & Supplies
Mfr
N.A.I.C.S.: 339112

Bard Canada Inc. (2)
2715 Bristol Cir Unit 1, Oakville, L6H 6X5,
ON, Canada
Tel.: (289) 291-8000
Web Site: http://www.bd.com
Surgical & Medical Instrument & Supplies
Mfr
N.A.I.C.S.: 339112

Bard Colombia S.A.S. (2)
Calle 95 No 14 - 45 Piso 8, Bogota, Colom-
bia
Tel.: (57) 6517363
Web Site: http://www.bd.com
Medical Device Mfr
N.A.I.C.S.: 339112

Bard Czech Republic s.r.o. (2)
Na Hrebenech II 1718/8, Prague, 140 00,
Czech Republic
Tel.: (420) 242408630
Web Site: http://www.bd.com
Surgical & Medical Instrument & Supplies
Mfr
N.A.I.C.S.: 339112

Subsidiary (Domestic):

Bard Devices, Inc. (2)
730 Central Ave, New Providence, NJ
07974-1139
Tel.: (908) 277-8000
Web Site: http://www.bd.com
Surgical Appliance & Supplies Mfr
N.A.I.C.S.: 339113

Subsidiary (Non-US):

Bard France S.A.S. (2)
164-166 Avenue Joseph Kessel Parkile P
14, 78960, Voisins-le-Bretonneux, France
Tel.: (33) 139305858
Web Site: http://www.bardfrance.fr
Surgical & Medical Instrument Mfr
N.A.I.C.S.: 339112

Bard Hellas S.A. (2)
Philellinon 1 and Alexandros, Argyroupolis,
164 52, Greece
Tel.: (30) 2109690770
Web Site: http://www.bd.com
Surgical & Medical Instrument & Supplies
Mfr
N.A.I.C.S.: 339112

Bard Holdings Netherlands BV (2)
Herikerbergweg 238, 1101CM, Amsterdam,
Netherlands
Tel.: (31) 306869300
Web Site: http://www.bd.com
Holding Company
N.A.I.C.S.: 551112

Subsidiary (Domestic):

**C. R. Bard Netherlands Sales
BV** (3)
Herikerbergweg 238, 1101 CM, Amsterdam,
Netherlands
Tel.: (31) 880122500
Web Site: https://www.bd.com
Medical Device Distr

N.A.I.C.S.: 423450

Subsidiary (Non-US):

Bard India Healthcare Pvt. Ltd. (2)
501 Hubtown Solaris Prof N S Phadke
Marg Andheri East, Mumbai, 400 069, Maharashtra, India
Tel.: (91) 2226111234
Web Site: http://www.crbard.in
Health Care Srvices
N.A.I.C.S.: 621111

Bard Korea Limited (2)
16th Floor Arc Place 142 Teheran-ro,
Gangnam-Gu, Seoul, Korea (South)
Tel.: (82) 234043700
Web Site: http://www.bd.com
Medical Device Mfr & Distr
N.A.I.C.S.: 339112

Bard Limited (2)
Forest House Tilgate Forest Business Park
Brighton Road, Crawley, RH11 9BP, West
Sussex, United Kingdom
Tel.: (44) 1293529555
Surgical & Medical Instrument Mfr
N.A.I.C.S.: 339112

Bard Medica S.A. (2)
Rinnbockstrasse 3, Modecenterstrabe 22,
1030, Vienna, Austria
Tel.: (43) 14949130
Web Site: http://www.bd.com
Surgical & Medical Instrument Mfr
N.A.I.C.S.: 339112

Division (Domestic):

Bard Medical Division (2)
8195 Industrial Blvd NE, Covington, GA
30014-1497 (100%)
Tel.: (770) 784-6100
Web Site: http://www.bd.com
Urological Products Mfr
N.A.I.C.S.: 339113

Subsidiary (Domestic):

Medivance, Inc. (3)
321 S Taylor Ave, Louisville, CO 80027
Tel.: (303) 926-1917
Web Site: http://www.medivance.com
Surgical & Medical Instrument Mfr
N.A.I.C.S.: 339112
Gary A. Carson (VP-Engrg)
Gene R. McGrevin (Chm)

Subsidiary (Non-US):

**Bard Pacific Health Care Company
Ltd.** (2)
10F No 26 Section 3 Nanjing East Road,
Zhongshan District, Taipei, Taiwan
Tel.: (886) 225031900
Web Site: http://www.bd.com
Surgical & Medical Instrument Mfr
N.A.I.C.S.: 339112

Subsidiary (Domestic):

Bard Peripheral Vascular, Inc. (2)
1625 W 3rd St, Tempe, AZ 85281
Tel.: (480) 894-9515
Web Site: http://www.bd.com
Health Care Products Mfr
N.A.I.C.S.: 339112

Subsidiary (Domestic):

FlowCardia, Inc. (3)
745 N Pastoria Ave, Sunnyvale, CA 94085
Tel.: (408) 617-0352
Polystyrene Foam Product Mfr
N.A.I.C.S.: 326140
Wick Goodspeed (CEO)
Deborah DeFilippo (CFO)

Loma Vista Medical, Inc. (3)
863A Mitten Rd Ste 100A, Burlingame, CA
94010-1303
Tel.: (650) 490-4747
Medical Device Mfr
N.A.I.C.S.: 339112

Subsidiary (Non-US):

Bard Poland Sp. z.o.o. (2)
ul Osmanska 14, 02-823, Warsaw, Poland
Tel.: (48) 223771100
Web Site: https://www.bd.com
Surgical & Medical Instrument Mfr

N.A.I.C.S.: 339112

Bard Singapore Private Limited (2)
1 Harbourfront Avenue 04-11/13 Keppel
Bay Tower, Singapore, 098632, Singapore
Tel.: (65) 65805988
Web Site: http://www.bd.com
Surgical & Medical Instrument & Supplies
Mfr
N.A.I.C.S.: 339112

Bard Sweden AB (2)
Scania County, PO Box 22210, Helsingborg, 250 24, Sweden
Tel.: (46) 42386000
Web Site: http://www.bd.com
Surgical & Medical Instrument Mfr
N.A.I.C.S.: 339112

C. R. Bard GmbH (2)
Wachhausstrasse 6, 76227, Karlsruhe, Germany
Tel.: (49) 7219445800
Web Site: https://www.bardcare.de
Surgical & Medical Instrument Mfr
N.A.I.C.S.: 339112

Plant (Domestic):

C.R. Bard, Inc. (2)
289 Bay Rd, Queensbury, NY 12804
Tel.: (518) 793-2531
Web Site: http://www.crbard.com
Medical Device Mfr
N.A.I.C.S.: 339112

Subsidiary (Non-US):

**Clearstream Technologies Group
Limited** (2)
Moyne Upper, Enniscorthy, Co Wexford,
Ireland
Tel.: (353) 539237111
Web Site: http://www.clearstream.ie
Catheters & Stents Mfr
N.A.I.C.S.: 339112

Subsidiary (Domestic):

**ClearStream Technologies
Limited** (3)
Moyne Upper, Enniscorthy, Y21 K6Y8, Co
Wexford, Ireland
Tel.: (353) 539237111
Web Site: http://www.clearstream.ie
Medical Device Mfr
N.A.I.C.S.: 339112

Subsidiary (Domestic):

Davol Inc. (2)
100 Crossrings Blvd, Warwick, RI
02886 (100%)
Tel.: (401) 463-7000
Web Site: http://www.bd.com
Surgical Prosthetics & Irrigation Systems
Mfr
N.A.I.C.S.: 339113

Subsidiary (Domestic):

Bridger Biomed, Inc. (3)
2430 N 7th Ave, Bozeman, MT 59715
Tel.: (406) 586-7666
Surgical & Medical Instrument & Health
Care Products Mfr
N.A.I.C.S.: 339112

Neomend, Inc. (3)
60 Technology Dr, Irvine, CA 92618
Tel.: (949) 916-1630
Medical Device Mfr
N.A.I.C.S.: 339112
David Renzi (Pres & CEO)

Subsidiary (Domestic):

Liberator Medical Holdings, Inc. (2)
2979 SE Gran Pkwy, Stuart, FL 34997
Tel.: (772) 324-3285
Web Site: http://www.liberatormedical.com
Holding Company; Direct-to-Consumer
Medical Supplies Retailer
N.A.I.C.S.: 551112
Timothy M. Moore (Officer-Privacy)

Subsidiary (Domestic):

Liberator Health & Wellness, Inc. (3)
2979 SE Gran Pkwy, Stuart, FL 34997
Tel.: (772) 287-2414
Web Site: http://www.liberatormedical.com

Medical & Surgical Equipment Distr
N.A.I.C.S.: 423450

Liberator Medical Supply, Inc. (3)
2979 SE Gran Pkwy, Stuart, FL 34997
Tel.: (772) 324-3285
Web Site: http://www.liberatormedical.com
Direct-To Consumer Medical Supplies
N.A.I.C.S.: 423450

Tri-County Medical & Ostomy Supplies, Inc. (3)
1904 Knob Creek Rd, Johnson City, TN
37604
Tel.: (423) 282-6933
Web Site: http://www.tri-countymedical.com
Medical & Surgical Equipment Distr
N.A.I.C.S.: 423450

Subsidiary (Domestic):

Lutonix, Inc. (2)
9409 Science Ctr Dr, New Hope, MN 55428
Tel.: (763) 445-2352
Web Site: http://www.lutonixdcb.com
Surgical & Medical Instrument Mfr
N.A.I.C.S.: 339112

Medafor, Inc. (2)
2700 Freeway Blvd Ste 800, Minneapolis,
MN 55430
Tel.: (763) 571-6300
Web Site: http://www.medafor.com
Medical Device Mfr
N.A.I.C.S.: 325412

Subsidiary (Non-US):

**Productos Bard de Mexico S.A. de
C.V.** (2)
Paseo de la Reforma 505 Piso 15 Col,
Cuauhtemoc, 06500, Mexico, Mexico
Tel.: (52) 5520002501
Surgical & Medical Instrument Mfr
N.A.I.C.S.: 339112

CME America LLC (1)
14998 W 6th Ave Ste 830, Golden, CO
80401
Tel.: (303) 936-4945
Web Site: http://www.cmeamerica.com
Surgical & Medical Instrument Mfr
N.A.I.C.S.: 339112

CME Medical (UK) Limited (1)
Unit 1 Kincraig Business Park Kincraig
Road, Blackpool, FY2 0PJ, Lancashire,
United Kingdom
Tel.: (44) 1253206700
Web Site: http://www.cmemedical.co.uk
Medical Technology Product & Services
N.A.I.C.S.: 621498

CRISI Medical Systems, Inc. (1)
4225 Executive Sq Ste 420, San Diego, CA
92037
Tel.: (858) 754-8640
Pharmaceutical Product & Drug Mfr
N.A.I.C.S.: 325412
Joe Calabro (VP-Ops)

CareFusion Corporation (1)
3750 Torrey View Ct, San Diego, CA
92130-2622 (100%)
Tel.: (858) 617-2000
Web Site: http://www.bd.com
Sales Range: $1-4.9 Billion
Emp.: 16,000
Medical Instrument Mfr
N.A.I.C.S.: 339112

Subsidiary (Non-US):

CareFusion Asia (HK) Limited (2)
1605B Sino Plaza, 255-257 Gloucester
Road, Causeway Bay, China (Hong Kong)
Tel.: (852) 28348066
Medical Equipment Mfr
N.A.I.C.S.: 334510

CareFusion Denmark 329 A/S (2)
Firskovvej 25 B, 2800, Lyngby,
Denmark (100%)
Tel.: (45) 70203074
Sales Range: $10-24.9 Million
Emp.: 5
Surgical & Medical Instrument Mfr
N.A.I.C.S.: 339112
Beoit Holst (Bus Mgr)

CareFusion France 309 S.A.S. (2)

2 rue Rene Caudron, 78960, Voisins-le-
Bretonneux, France (100%)
Tel.: (33) 1 30 02 81 41
Web Site: http://www.carefusion.com
Sales Range: $10-24.9 Million
Emp.: 25
Medical Products Mfr & Distr
N.A.I.C.S.: 339112

CareFusion Germany 318 GmbH (2)
Tullastrasse 8-12, 69126, Heidelberg,
Germany (100%)
Tel.: (49) 931 4972 838
Web Site: http://www.carefusion.de
Sales Range: $25-49.9 Million
Emp.: 70
Mfr & Developer of Drug Infusion Systems
N.A.I.C.S.: 339112

CareFusion Germany 326 GmbH (2)
Rowastrasse, 53539, Kelberg, Germany
Tel.: (49) 269292060
Medical Instrument Mfr
N.A.I.C.S.: 339112

CareFusion Hong Kong Limited (2)
1605B Sino Plaza, 255-257 Gloucester
Road, Causeway Bay, China (Hong Kong)
Tel.: (852) 2834 8066
Web Site: http://www.carefusion.com
Ventilators & Respiratory Devices Distr
N.A.I.C.S.: 423450

CareFusion Israel 330 Ltd. (2)
Rehov Menachem Begin 11, 52681, Ramat
Gan, Israel
Tel.: (972) 46271737
Medical Instrument Mfr
N.A.I.C.S.: 339112

CareFusion Italy 311 S.r.l. (2)
Via Ticino 4, Sesto Fiorentino, 50019, Florence, Italy (100%)
Tel.: (39) 055 303391
Web Site: http://www.carefusion.it
Emp.: 20
Mfr & Developer of Drug Infusion Systems
N.A.I.C.S.: 339112

CareFusion Italy 327 S.r.l. (2)
Via Brera 28, 20010, Cornaredo, MI, Italy
Tel.: (39) 0299990120
Medical Instrument Mfr
N.A.I.C.S.: 339112

**CareFusion Mexico 215 SA de
CV** (2)
Boulevard Insurgentes 20351, 22114, Tijuana, Baja California, Mexico
Tel.: (52) 6646278257
Medical Instrument Mfr
N.A.I.C.S.: 339112

**CareFusion New Zealand 313
Limited** (2)
Unit 14B George Bourke Drive, Mt Wellington, Auckland, 1060, New Zealand (100%)
Tel.: (64) 92733901
Web Site: http://www.carefusion.com
Emp.: 10
Drug Infusion Systems Distr
N.A.I.C.S.: 423450

CareFusion Norway 315 A/S (2)
Fjordveien 3, 1363, Hovik, Norway
Tel.: (47) 66987600
Web Site: http://www.carefusion.com
Emp.: 5
Medical Product Distr
N.A.I.C.S.: 423450

**CareFusion S.A. 319 (Proprietary)
Limited** (2)
Unit 2 Oude Molen Business Park Oude
Molen Road, Ndabeni, Cape Town, 7405,
South Africa (100%)
Tel.: (27) 21 510 7562
Web Site: http://www.carefusion.co.za
Emp.: 25
Drug Infusion Systems Distr
N.A.I.C.S.: 423450

Subsidiary (Domestic):

CareFusion Solutions, LLC (2)
12120 Sunset Hills Rd 3rd Flr, Reston, VA
20190
Tel.: (571) 521-8900
Sales Range: $25-49.9 Million
Emp.: 80

Becton, Dickinson & Company—(Continued)

Developer of Portable Barcode-Scanning Systems for Hospital Patient Identification & Treatment Management
N.A.I.C.S.: 339112
Nancy Smith *(Mgr-Product Mgmt & Mktg)*

Subsidiary (Non-US):

CareFusion U.K. 306 Limited **(2)**
The Crescent Jays Close, Basingstoke, RG22 4BS, Hamps, United Kingdom **(100%)**
Tel.: (44) 1256 388 284
Web Site: http://www.carefusion.co.uk
Sales Range: $50-74.9 Million
Emp.: 150
Mfr & Developer of Drug Infusion Systems
N.A.I.C.S.: 339112

Cato Software Solutions GmbH **(1)**
Millennium Tower Handelskai 94-96, 1200, Vienna, Austria
Tel.: (43) 17895117
Web Site: http://www.cato.eu
Emp.: 50
Software Development Services
N.A.I.C.S.: 541511

Cellular Research, Inc. **(1)**
4040 Campbell Ave Ste 110, Menlo Park, CA 94025
Tel.: (650) 665-2400
Web Site: http://www.cellular-research.com
Research & Development In Biotechnology
N.A.I.C.S.: 541713
Ari A. Chaney *(CFO)*

Chemocato LLC **(1)**
35 E 7th St, New York, NY 10003
Tel.: (212) 473-2362
Web Site: http://www.chemocato.com
Software Development Services
N.A.I.C.S.: 541511

Cytognos Spain S.L.U. **(1)**
Pol La Serna Nave 9, Santa Marta de Tormes, 37900, Salamanca, Spain
Tel.: (34) 923125067
Web Site: https://www.cytognos.com
Emp.: 65
Medical Device Mfr & Distr
N.A.I.C.S.: 339112

Difco Laboratories Incorporated **(1)**
920 Henry St, Detroit, MI 48201-2532
Tel.: (313) 442-8800
Surgical & Medical Instrument Mfr
N.A.I.C.S.: 339112

FlowJo LLC **(1)**
385 Williamson Way, Ashland, OR 97520
Tel.: (541) 201-0022
Web Site: http://www.flowjo.com
Scientific Workflow Data Management Services
N.A.I.C.S.: 541513

GSL Solutions, Inc. **(1)**
4018 NE 112th Ave Ste D9, Vancouver, WA 98682
Tel.: (360) 896-5354
Web Site: http://www.gslcorp.com
Food Service Contractors
N.A.I.C.S.: 722310
Kristen Laurino *(Mgr)*
Shelton Shelton Louie *(Co-Founder & CEO)*

Galatea Surgical, Inc. **(1)**
99 Hayden Ave Ste 360, Lexington, MA 02421
Tel.: (727) 220-7566
Web Site: https://www.galateasurgical.com
Medical Equipment Mfr & Distr
N.A.I.C.S.: 339112

GenCell Biosystems Ltd. **(1)**
Ballycummin Avenue Raheen Business Park, Limerick, Ireland
Tel.: (353) 35361307734
Web Site: http://www.cliclp.com
Research & Development In Genetics
N.A.I.C.S.: 541713

GeneOhm Sciences Canada Inc. **(1)**
2555 Boul Du Parc Technologique, Quebec, G1P 4S5, QC, Canada
Tel.: (418) 780-5800
Sales Range: $50-74.9 Million
Emp.: 30
Surgical & Medical Instrument Mfr

N.A.I.C.S.: 621493
Jean Cote *(CEO)*

Goetech LLC **(1)**
9191 Sheridan Blvd Ste 103, Westminster, CO 80031
Tel.: (720) 250-0100
Web Site: http://www.medkeeper.com
Sales Range: $1-9.9 Million
Emp.: 30
Custom Computer Programming Services
N.A.I.C.S.: 541511
Jason Kilgour *(Pres)*
Kaveh Arabfakhry *(Exec VP & Chief Architect)*

Intermed Equipamento Medico Hospitalar Ltda. **(1)**
R Santa Monica 980-Pq Industrial San Jose Cotia, Sao Paulo, 06715-865, SP, Brazil
Tel.: (55) 1146159300
Medical Equipment Mfr
N.A.I.C.S.: 334510

Nippon Becton Dickinson Company, Ltd. **(1)**
Akasaka Garden City 4-15-1 Akasaka, Minato-ku, Tokyo, 107-0052, Japan
Tel.: (81) 120855590
Web Site: http://www.bdj.co.jp
Emp.: 670
Pharmaceuticals Product Mfr
N.A.I.C.S.: 325412
Tatsuo Achiba *(Pres)*

PT Becton Dickinson Indonesia **(1)**
Sampoerna Strategic Square South Tower 24th Floor, Jl Jenderal Sudirman Kav 45-46, Jakarta, 12930, Indonesia
Tel.: (62) 215771920
Web Site: http://www.bd.com
Healthcare Equipment Distr
N.A.I.C.S.: 423450

Parata Systems, LLC **(1)**
106 Roche Dr, Durham, NC 27703
Tel.: (888) 989-7822
Web Site: http://www.parata.com
Pharmaceutical Machine Mfr
N.A.I.C.S.: 325412
Karen Thomas-Smith *(Sr VP-Sls & Mktg)*
Jason Buchwald *(VP & Gen Mgr)*
Dan Sullivan *(Sr VP-Customer Success)*
Chet Coates *(COO)*

Puls Medical Devices AS LC **(1)**
Fjordveien 3, 1363, Hovik, Norway
Tel.: (47) 64009900
Medical Device & Diagnostic System Mfr
N.A.I.C.S.: 339112

PureWick Corporation **(1)**
2030 Gillespie Way Ste 109, El Cajon, CA 92020
Tel.: (619) 660-0734
Web Site: http://www.purewick.com
Medical Device & Diagnostic System Mfr
N.A.I.C.S.: 339112

Safety Syringes Inc. **(1)**
2875 Loker Ave E, Carlsbad, CA 92010
Tel.: (760) 918-9908
Web Site: http://www.safetysyringes.com
Sales Range: $10-24.9 Million
Emp.: 20
Surgical & Medical Instrument Mfr
N.A.I.C.S.: 339112

Sirigen Limited **(1)**
Brightwater House Market Place, Ringwood, BH24 1AP, United Kingdom
Tel.: (44) 2031760444
Healthcare Technology Services
N.A.I.C.S.: 541715

Sirigen, Inc. **(1)**
11085 N Torrey Pines Rd Ste 300, La Jolla, CA 92037
Tel.: (858) 401-1260
Web Site: http://www.sirigen.com
Emp.: 19
Biotechnology Research & Development Services
N.A.I.C.S.: 541714

Surgical Site Solutions, Inc. **(1)**
4539 S Taylor Dr, Sheboygan, WI 53081
Tel.: (920) 694-1816
Healthcare Product Distr
N.A.I.C.S.: 424210
Larry Panzer *(VP-Tech)*

Synergy Medical BRG Inc. **(1)**
2600 Jacques-Cartier Blvd East, Longueuil, J4N 1P8, QC, Canada
Tel.: (450) 500-7385
Web Site: https://synmedrx.com
Medical Device Mfr & Distr
N.A.I.C.S.: 339112

Synergy Medical Europe Ltd. **(1)**
400 Pavilion Drive, Northampton, NN4 7PA, United Kingdom
Tel.: (44) 2039036318
Web Site: https://synmedrx.co.uk
Medical Device Mfr & Distr
N.A.I.C.S.: 339112

TVA Medical, Inc. **(1)**
7000 Bee Caves Rd Ste 250, Austin, TX 78746
Tel.: (512) 582-2460
Web Site: http://www.tvamedical.com
Surgical Appliance & Supply Mfr
N.A.I.C.S.: 339113
Adam L. Berman *(Founder & CEO)*

U.K. Medical Limited **(1)**
Albreda House Lydgate Lane, Sheffield, S10 5FH, United Kingdom
Tel.: (44) 1142688800
Holding Company
N.A.I.C.S.: 551112

U.K. Medical, Ltd. **(1)**
Albreda House Lydgate Lane, Sheffield, S10 5FH, United Kingdom
Tel.: (44) 1142688800
Medical Equipment Mfr
N.A.I.C.S.: 334510

Venclose, Inc. **(1)**
2570 N 1st 2nd Fl Ste 221, San Jose, CA 95131
Web Site: https://venclose.com
Medical Equipment Mfr & Distr
N.A.I.C.S.: 339112

Vyaire Medical, Inc. **(1)**
26125 N Riverwoods Blvd, Mettawa, IL 60045 **(49.9%)**
Tel.: (833) 327-3284
Web Site: http://www.vyaire.com
Respiratory Products Mfr & Distr
N.A.I.C.S.: 339112
Steven Dyson *(Chm)*
John T. Bibb *(Grp CEO)*
Gaurav Agarwal *(CEO)*

Branch (Domestic):

Vyaire Medical **(2)**
22745 Savi Ranch Pkwy, Yorba Linda, CA 92887
Tel.: (714) 283-2228
Web Site: http://www.vyaire.com
Respiratory Diagnostics, Ventilation & Anesthesia Delivery & Patient Monitoring Services
N.A.I.C.S.: 339112

Plant (Non-US):

Vyaire Medical **(2)**
Cda Via De La Produccion No 85, Mexicali, B C 21397, Mexico
Tel.: (52) 6865615500
Surgical & Medical Instrument Mfr
N.A.I.C.S.: 339112

BEL FUSE INC.

300 Executive Dr Ste 300, West Orange, NJ 07052
Tel.: (201) 432-0463 **NJ**
Web Site: https://www.belfuse.com
Year Founded: 1949
BELFA—(NASDAQ)
Rev.: $639,813,000
Assets: $571,631,000
Liabilities: $231,073,000
Net Worth: $340,558,000
Earnings: $73,831,000
Emp.: 5,260
Fiscal Year-end: 12/31/23
Capacitor, Resistor, Coil, Transformer & Other Inductor Manufacturing
N.A.I.C.S.: 334416
Daniel Bernstein *(Pres & CEO)*
Kenneth Lai *(VP-Ops-Asia)*

Suzanne Kozlovsky *(Head)*
Joe Berry *(VP)*
Peter G. Bittner III *(Pres-Bel Connectivity Solutions & VP)*

Subsidiaries:

BCMZ Precision Engineering Limited **(1)**
Unit 7-9 Bull Lane Industrial Estate, Acton, Sudbury, Suffolk, United Kingdom
Tel.: (44) 1787880699
Web Site: http://www.bcmz.co.uk
Automobile Component Distr
N.A.I.C.S.: 441330

BPS Cooperatief U.A. **(1)**
Teleportboulevard 140, 1043EJ, Amsterdam, North Holland, Netherlands
Tel.: (31) 205405800
Electronic Components Mfr
N.A.I.C.S.: 334419

Bel Connector Inc. **(1)**
11118 Susquehanna Trl S, Glen Rock, PA 17327-9199
Tel.: (717) 235-7512
Web Site: http://www.belfuse.com
Emp.: 80
Electronic Connector Mfr
N.A.I.C.S.: 334417

Bel Fuse (Macao Commerical Offshore) Limited **(1)**
Rua De Xangai No 175 Edificio Da Associacao Commercial De Macau 13, Andar H-J, Macau, China (Macau) **(100%)**
Tel.: (853) 2870 6137
Web Site: http://www.belfuse.com
Sales Range: $25-49.9 Million
Emp.: 21
Electronic Components Mfr
N.A.I.C.S.: 334419

Bel Fuse America, Inc. **(1)**
206 Van Vorst St, Jersey City, NJ 07302-4421 **(100%)**
Tel.: (201) 432-0463
Web Site: http://www.belfuse.com
Sales Range: $10-24.9 Million
Emp.: 40
Marketer of Telecommunication Apparatus Components
N.A.I.C.S.: 334419

Bel Fuse Europe Ltd. **(1)**
28 Turkey Court Turkey Mill, Ashford Road, Maidstone, ME14 5PP, United Kingdom
Tel.: (44) 1622 757395
Web Site: http://www.belfuse.com
Emp.: 7
Network Electronic Components Mfr & Distr
N.A.I.C.S.: 334416

Bel Fuse Ltd. **(1)**
8/F Luk Hop Industrial Bldg 8 Luk Hop Street, San Po Kong, Kowloon, China (Hong Kong) **(100%)**
Tel.: (852) 2 328 5515
Web Site: http://www.belfuse.com
Sales Range: $50-74.9 Million
Emp.: 200
Mfr of Electronic Components
N.A.I.C.S.: 334419

Bel Power (Hangzhou) Co. Ltd. **(1)**
66 Dongxin Avenue 2nd Floor Building E, Eastcom City, Hangzhou, 310053, Zhejiang, China
Tel.: (86) 57186696947
Network Electronic Components Mfr & Distr
N.A.I.C.S.: 334416

Bel Power Europe S.r.l. **(1)**
Via Resegone 28, 20857, Camparada, MB, Italy
Tel.: (39) 0396013849
Web Site: http://www.belpowersolutions.com
Electrical Equipment Mfr & Distr
N.A.I.C.S.: 334419

Bel Power Inc. **(1)**
2400 Computer Dr, Westborough, MA 01581
Tel.: (508) 870-9775
Web Site: http://www.belpowersolutions.com
Power Management & Conversion Products Mfr
N.A.I.C.S.: 335999

Bel Power Products Inc. (1)
180 Turnpike Rd Ste B, Westborough, MA
01581-2829
Tel.: (508) 393-7698
Sales Range: $10-24.9 Million
Emp.: 5
Developer of Power Conversion Products
N.A.I.C.S.: 423830

Bel Power Solutions Co. Ltd. (1)
Hong Fa Hi-Tech Industrial Park Guang-
ming Road, Guangming, Shenzhen,
518132, China
Tel.: (86) 75529885888
Electrical Equipment Mfr & Distr
N.A.I.C.S.: 334419

Bel Power Solutions GmbH (1)
Ackerstrasse 56, 8610, Uster, Switzerland
Tel.: (41) 449448044
Electrical Equipment & Component Mfr
N.A.I.C.S.: 335999

Bel Power Solutions Inc. (1)
2390 Walsh Ave, Santa Clara, CA 95051
Tel.: (408) 785-5200
Web Site: http://www.belpowersolutions.com
Electrical Equipment Mfr & Distr
N.A.I.C.S.: 334419

**Bel Power Solutions Ireland
Limited** (1)
2nd Floor Citygate House Ballycummin Av-
enue, Raheen Business Park, Limerick, V94
H9YE, Ireland
Tel.: (353) 61302912
Emp.: 20
Electrical Equipment & Component Mfr
N.A.I.C.S.: 335999

Bel Power Solutions Limited (1)
9th Floor 107 Cheapside, London, EC2V
6DN, United Kingdom
Tel.: (44) 13285224792
Web Site: http://www.belpowersolutions.com
Emp.: 8
Electrical Apparatus & Equipment Whslr
N.A.I.C.S.: 423610

Bel Power Solutions Ltd. (1)
Units 2101-03 & 11-12 21 F Tower 2 Ever
Gain Plaza 88, Container Port Road, Kwai
Chung, New Territories, China (Hong Kong)
Tel.: (852) 25784412
Electrical Equipment Mfr & Distr
N.A.I.C.S.: 334419
Gordon Hu *(Sr Mgr-Engrg)*

Bel Power Solutions s.r.o. (1)
Tel.: (421) 423919999
Web Site: http://www.belpowersolutions.com
Electrical Equipment & Component Mfr
N.A.I.C.S.: 335999

**Bel Stewart Connector Systems,
Inc.** (1)
11118 Susquehanna Trl S, Glen Rock, PA
17327
Tel.: (717) 235-7512
Web Site: http://www.belfuse.com
Sales Range: $25-49.9 Million
Emp.: 100
Mfr of Printed Circuit Board Connectors &
Modular Plugs & Connectors
N.A.I.C.S.: 334417

Bel Stewart s.r.o. (1)
On the Battlefield 2, 120 00, Prague, Czech
Republic
Tel.: (420) 2961800001
Web Site: http://www.belstewart.cz
Sales Range: $10-24.9 Million
Emp.: 10
Network Electronic Components Mfr & Distr
N.A.I.C.S.: 334416
Catherine Deswarte *(Mng Dir)*

Bel Transformer Inc. (1)
128 Atlantic Ave, Lynbrook, NY 11563
Tel.: (516) 239-5777
Web Site: http://www.signaltransformer.com
Electronic Coil & Transformer Mfr
N.A.I.C.S.: 334416

Bel Ventures Inc. (1)
206 Van Vorst St, Jersey City, NJ 07302
Tel.: (201) 432-0463
Web Site: http://www.belfuse.com
Sales Range: $600-649.9 Million
Emp.: 25
Investment Services

N.A.I.C.S.: 523999

Cinch Connectors Inc. (1)
1700 Finley Rd, Lombard, IL 60148
Tel.: (630) 705-6000
Web Site: http://www.cinch.com
Sales Range: $50-74.9 Million
Emp.: 65
Interconnect Products Mfr
N.A.I.C.S.: 334417

Subsidiary (Non-US):

**Cinch Connectivity Solutions (Shang-
hai) Co., Ltd.** (2)
Building 1 No 800 ShenFu Road XinZhuang
Industry Park, Shanghai, China
Tel.: (86) 2154427668
Electrical Equipment Mfr & Distr
N.A.I.C.S.: 334419
Roger Cao *(Engr-Sls)*

**Cinch Connectivity Solutions
LTD** (2)
11 Bilton Road, Chelmsford, CM1 2UP, Es-
sex, United Kingdom
Tel.: (44) 1245342060
Web Site: http://www.connectivity.com
Emp.: 100
Electronic Connector Mfr
N.A.I.C.S.: 335313

Cinch Connectors Ltd. (2)
Shireoaks Road, Worksop, S80 3HA, Not-
tinghamshire, United Kingdom **(100%)**
Tel.: (44) 190 947 4131
Web Site: http://www.cinchuk.com
Sales Range: $25-49.9 Million
Emp.: 85
Electronic Connector Mfr
N.A.I.C.S.: 334417

**Cinch Connectors de Mexico, S.A. de
C.V.** (2)
Parque Industrial Maquilpark, 88614, Rey-
nosa, Tamaulipas, Mexico
Tel.: (52) 8999240520
Web Site: http://www.cinch.com
Sales Range: $125-149.9 Million
Electronic Connector Mfr
N.A.I.C.S.: 334417

Subsidiary (Domestic):

Connectivity Solutions (2)
3000 Lakeside Dr Ste 308N, Bannockburn,
IL 60015
Tel.: (847) 739-0300
Web Site: http://www.cinch.com
Electronic Connector Mfr
N.A.I.C.S.: 423690

Branch (Domestic):

**Cinch Connectivity Solutions -
Waseca** (3)
299 Johnson Ave SW Ste 100, Waseca,
MN 56093
Tel.: (507) 833-8822
Web Site: http://www.cinch.com
Sales Range: $50-74.9 Million
Emp.: 250
Electronic Connector Mfr
N.A.I.C.S.: 334417

Signal Transformer Co., Inc. (1)
500 Bayview Ave, Inwood, NY 11096-1702
Tel.: (516) 239-5777
Web Site: http://www.signaltransformer.com
Sales Range: $25-49.9 Million
Emp.: 90
Transformers for Hi-Tech Industries
N.A.I.C.S.: 334416

TRP Connector B.V. (1)
Evert van de Beekstraat 310, 1118 CX,
Schiphol, Netherlands
Tel.: (31) 205214777
Electronic Connector Mfr
N.A.I.C.S.: 335313

TRP Connector Limited (1)
Rua de Xangai No 175 Edificio da Associa-
cao Comercial de Macau, 13 Andar K, Ma-
cau, China (Macau)
Tel.: (853) 28783747
Web Site: http://www.trpconnector.com
Electronic Connector Mfr
N.A.I.C.S.: 335313

BELDEN, INC.
1 N Brentwood Blvd 15th Fl, Saint
Louis, MO 63105
Tel.: (314) 854-8000   DE
Web Site: https://www.belden.com
Year Founded: 1902
BDC—(NYSE)
Rev.: $2,606,485,000
Assets: $3,161,675,000
Liabilities: $2,017,725,000
Net Worth: $1,143,950,000
Earnings: $254,663,000
Emp.: 8,000
Fiscal Year-end: 12/31/22
Wire & Cable Products; Insulated
Copper Wires, Cables & Cords; Fiber
Optics Mfr
N.A.I.C.S.: 331491
Brian E. Anderson *(Gen Counsel,
Sec & Sr VP-Legal)*
Ashish Chand *(Pres & CEO)*
Jeremy Parks *(CFO & Sr VP-Fin)*
Leah Tate *(Sr VP-HR)*
Brian Lieser *(Exec VP-Industrial Au-
tomation Solutions)*
Aaron Reddington *(VP-IR)*
Jay Wirts *(Exec VP-Enterprise Solu-
tions)*
Hiran Bhadra *(Sr VP)*
Anshu Mehrotra *(Exec VP)*

Subsidiaries:

Belden & Hirschmann - France (1)
Batiment Y Park Mail 24b avenue de la
Demi Lune, CS19012 Roissy-en-France
Roissy Ch De Gaulle, 95722, Domont,
France
Tel.: (33) 139350100
Web Site: http://www.hirschmann.com
Sales Range: $25-49.9 Million
Emp.: 20
Electric & Electronic Components Whslr
N.A.I.C.S.: 449210

Belden & Hirschmann - Spain (1)
Anabel Segura 10 Edificio Fiteni IX, 28108,
Alcobendas, 28108, Spain
Tel.: (34) 917461730
Web Site: http://www.belden.com
Emp.: 10
Electric & Electronic Components Whslr
N.A.I.C.S.: 423690

Belden AB (1)
PO Box 9014, 200 39, Malmo, Sweden
Tel.: (46) 406998860
Web Site: http://www.beldensolutions.com
Wire & Cable Mfr
N.A.I.C.S.: 335929

Belden CDT (Canada) Inc. (1)
2310 Alfred-Nobel Blvd, Saint Laurent, H4S
2B4, QC, Canada **(100%)**
Tel.: (514) 822-2345
Web Site: http://www.belden.com
Rev.: $50,000,000
Emp.: 75
Mfr, Designer & Developer of Structured
Cabling Systems
N.A.I.C.S.: 331318

**Belden CDT European Shared Ser-
vices B.V.** (1)
Edisonstraat 9, 5928 PG, Venlo, 5928 PG,
Netherlands
Tel.: (31) 773878555
Sales Range: $75-99.9 Million
Emp.: 10
Wire & Cable Mfr
N.A.I.C.S.: 335929
Beth Serreira *(Pres)*

Belden Cekan A/S (1)
Videhoejvej 4, Gjern, 8883, Denmark
Tel.: (45) 86875299
Web Site: http://www.belden.com
Sales Range: $25-49.9 Million
Electrical Equipment & Plastic Products Mfr
N.A.I.C.S.: 326199
Beth Serreira *(Pres)*

**Belden Commercial Services
B.V.** (1)

9 Edison Street, 5928 PG, Venlo, Nether-
lands
Tel.: (31) 773878555
Electronic Equipment Distr
N.A.I.C.S.: 423690

Belden Deutschland GmbH (1)
Im Gewerbepark 2, 58579, Schalksmuhle,
Germany
Tel.: (49) 23555044000
Web Site: http://www.beldensolutions.com
Wire & Cable Mfr
N.A.I.C.S.: 335929

**Belden Electronics Americas
Division** (1)
2200 US Hwy 27 S, Richmond, IN 47374-
7279
Tel.: (765) 983-5200
Web Site: http://www.belden.com
Wire & Cable Products; Insulated Copper
Wires, Cables & Cords; Fiber Optics Mfr
N.A.I.C.S.: 332618

Subsidiary (Domestic):

Alpha Wire Company (2)
711 Lidgerwood Ave, Elizabeth, NJ 07207
Tel.: (908) 925-8000
Web Site: https://www.alphawire.com
Sales Range: $50-74.9 Million
Emp.: 125
Mfr of Wire, Cable, Tubing & Interconnect
Products
N.A.I.C.S.: 331420

Subsidiary (Domestic):

Coast Wire & Plastic Tech, LLC (3)
1048 E Burgrove St, Carson, CA 90746-
3514
Tel.: (310) 639-9473
Web Site: http://www.coastwire.com
Fabricated Wire Product Mfr
N.A.I.C.S.: 332618
David Ibanez *(COO)*

Belden Electronics GmbH (1)
Stuttgarter Strasse 45-51, Neckartenzlin-
gen, 72654, Esslingen, Germany
Tel.: (49) 7127140
Cable Product Distr
N.A.I.C.S.: 423510
Martina Maier *(Mgr-Vertical Sls Programme)*

Belden Europe B.V. (1)
Edisonstraat 9, 5928 PG, Venlo, Nether-
lands
Tel.: (31) 773878555
Web Site: http://www.belden.com
Wire & Cable Mfr
N.A.I.C.S.: 335929

Belden Grass Valley Asia Limited (1)
7/F Harbour View 2 16 Science Park East
Avenue, Sha tin, Hong Kong, China (Hong
Kong)
Tel.: (852) 29553260
Television Production & Broadcasting
Equipment Mfr
N.A.I.C.S.: 334220

**Belden Grass Valley Industria E Co-
mercio E Servicos Ltda.** (1)
Rua Surubim 577-Andar Cidade Moncoes,
Sao Paulo, 04571-050, Brazil
Tel.: (55) 1140581513
Television Production & Broadcasting
Equipment Mfr
N.A.I.C.S.: 334220

**Belden Hirschmann Networking Sys-
tem Trading (Shanghai) Co. Ltd.** (1)
Unit 301 No 19 Building 1515 Gu Mei Road
, Shanghai, 200233, China
Tel.: (86) 2134182688
Web Site: http://www.belden.com
Electronic & Telecommunications Equip-
ment & Parts Whslr
N.A.I.C.S.: 423690

**Belden Hirschmann Solutions
(Shanghai) Company Limited** (1)
24/F Block C No 900 Yishan Road, Shang-
hai, 200233, China
Tel.: (86) 2134182688
Electrical Equipment & Component Mfr
N.A.I.C.S.: 335999

Belden Holdings, Inc. (1)

Belden, Inc.—(Continued)

401 Pennsylvania Pkwy Ste 200, Indianapolis, IN 46280
Tel.: (317) 818-6300
Web Site: http://www.belden.com
Holding Company
N.A.I.C.S.: 551112

Belden International Inc. - Hong Kong Office (1)
7/F Harbour View 2 16 Science Park East Avenue, Hong Kong Science Park, Sha Tin, China (Hong Kong)
Tel.: (852) 29550128
Communications Equipment Sales
N.A.I.C.S.: 423610
S.K. Tam (Mgr-Sls)

Belden Poliron Industria E Comercio De Cabos Especiais Ltda. (1)
Avenida Maria Leonor 1222 Parque Reid, Diadema, 09920-080, Brazil
Tel.: (55) 1140929000
Web Site: http://www.poliron.com.br
Electrical & Electronic Product Mfr
N.A.I.C.S.: 335999

Belden Solutions Asia Limited (1)
Unit 3801-04 09 38/F AIA Tower 183 Electric Road, North Point, Hong Kong, China (Hong Kong)
Tel.: (852) 29550128
Electrical Equipment & Component Mfr
N.A.I.C.S.: 335999

Belden Venlo Holding B.V. (1)
Edisonstraat 9, 5928 PG, Venlo, Netherlands
Tel.: (31) 773878555
Holding Company
N.A.I.C.S.: 551112

Belden Wire & Cable Company LLC (1)
1200 Columbia Ave Ste 311, Monticello, KY 42633
Tel.: (606) 348-8433
Sales Range: $50-74.9 Million
Emp.: 300
Fiber Optic Cable Mfr
N.A.I.C.S.: 335921
John S. Stroup (CEO)

Belden, Inc. - Kentucky Plant (1)
1200 W Columbia Ave, Monticello, KY 42633
Tel.: (606) 348-8433
Web Site: http://www.belden.com
Sales Range: $75-99.9 Million
Emp.: 270
Mfr of Wire & Cable Products; Insulated Copper Wires, Cables & Cords; Fiber Optics
N.A.I.C.S.: 335921

Belden, Inc. - Pennsylvania Plant (1)
2001 N Main St, Washington, PA 15301
Tel.: (724) 228-7373
Web Site: https://www.belden.com
Sales Range: $50-74.9 Million
Emp.: 80
Mfr of Specialized Metal Enclosures & Wiring Panels for Use in Computer & Network Systems
N.A.I.C.S.: 332322

Belden-Duna Kabel Kft (1)
Hengermalom Ut 43, 1116, Budapest, Hungary
Tel.: (36) 12061987
Web Site: http://www.belden.com
Wire & Telephone Cable Mfr
N.A.I.C.S.: 335999

Cekan/CDT A/S (1)
Videhojvej 4, 8883, Gjern, Denmark (100%)
Tel.: (45) 86875299
Sales Range: $10-24.9 Million
Emp.: 30
Mfr of High-Performance Telecommunications Connectors
N.A.I.C.S.: 517111
Frank Andersen (Mng Dir)

Communication Associates (1)
1750 Coleman Road, Anniston, AL 36207
Tel.: (256) 835-0900
Web Site: http://www.caisolutions.com
Rev.: $8,000,000

Emp.: 20
Other Electronic Component Mfr
N.A.I.C.S.: 334419

GarrettCom Europe Ltd. (1)
1 The Technology Centre Station Road, Framlingham, Suffolk, IP13 9EZ, United Kingdom
Tel.: (44) 1614983748
Sales Range: $10-24.9 Million
Emp.: 5
Industrial Ethernet Products Supplier
N.A.I.C.S.: 517810

GarrettCom India Pvt. Ltd. (1)
F/45 Omaxe Square Jasola Commercial Centre, New Delhi, 110044, India
Tel.: (91) 1146601398
Sales Range: $10-24.9 Million
Emp.: 2
Wire & Cable Mfr
N.A.I.C.S.: 335929

Hirschmann Automation & Control GmbH (1)
Stuttgarter Strasse 45-51, 72654, Neckartenzlingen, Germany
Tel.: (49) 7127140
Web Site: http://www.hirschmann.de
Sales Range: $25-49.9 Million
CATV Antenna Systems, Electric & Electronic Components, Network Systems, Car Aerials & Connectors & Mobile & Stationary Transmitting & Receiving Systems Mfr
N.A.I.C.S.: 334419

Unit (US):

Hirschmann & Lumberg Automation USA (2)
1540 Orchard Dr, Chambersburg, PA 17201
Tel.: (717) 217-2200
Web Site: http://www.hirschmann.com
Sales Range: $25-49.9 Million
Emp.: 75
Electric & Electronic Components, Optical Transmission Systems, Car Aerials & Electronic Connectors Mfr
N.A.I.C.S.: 423120

Joint Venture (Non-US):

Xuzhou Hirschmann Electronics Co., Ltd. (2)
No 11 Baoliansi Road, Xuzhou Economic Dev Zone, Xuzhou, 221001, Jiangsu, China (50%)
Tel.: (86) 516 8788 5799
Web Site: http://www.hirschmann-js.com
Emp.: 300
Electronic Components Mfr
N.A.I.C.S.: 334419

LLC Belden RUS (1)
9 Zemlyanoy val Suites 4037 and 4038 4th Floor, Regus Business Centre Citydel, 105064, Moscow, Russia
Tel.: (7) 4952871391
Electrical Equipment & Component Mfr
N.A.I.C.S.: 335999

Miranda Asia K.K. (1)
2-13-9 Nihonbashi Hamacho Hamacho House, Chuo-ku, Tokyo, 103-0007, Japan
Tel.: (81) 356447533
Web Site: http://www.miranda.com
Sales Range: $10-24.9 Million
Hardware & Software Developer, Mfr & Marketer
N.A.I.C.S.: 332510

Miranda Technologies Asia Ltd. (1)
Unit 3602 Citicorp Centre 18 Whitfield Road, Causeway Bay, China (Hong Kong)
Tel.: (852) 25396987
Web Site: http://www.miranda.com
Sales Range: $10-24.9 Million
Emp.: 10
Hardware & Software Developer, Mfr & Marketer
N.A.I.C.S.: 332510

Miranda Technologies France SAS (1)
105 rue des Moines, 75017, Paris, France
Tel.: (33) 155868788
Web Site: http://www.miranda.com
Sales Range: $25-49.9 Million
Emp.: 8

Hardware & Software Developer, Mfr & Marketer
N.A.I.C.S.: 332510

OTN Systems NV (1)
Industrielaan 17b, 2250, Olen, Belgium
Tel.: (32) 1 425 2847
Web Site: https://www.otnsystems.com
Emp.: 86
Communication Equipment Distr
N.A.I.C.S.: 423690
Dirk Van den Berghen (CEO)
Jurgen Michielsen (Chief Product Officer)
Jan Luyckx (CFO)
Stefaan Verhoeven (VP-Sales)
Bart Sprengers (VP-Research & Development)
Tom Geysen (VP-Operations)

Opterna Am, Inc. (1)
44901 Falcon Pl Ste 116, Sterling, VA 20166
Tel.: (703) 653-1100
Web Site: http://www.opterna.com
Fiber Optic Cable & Product Mfr
N.A.I.C.S.: 335921

Opterna Europe Limited (1)
Artemis House 4a Bramley Road, Bletchley, Milton Keynes, MK1 1PT, Bucks, United Kingdom
Tel.: (44) 2031301717
Fiber Optic Cable & Product Mfr
N.A.I.C.S.: 335921
Icy Varghese (Dir-Engr)

Opterna Technology Limited (1)
National Technology Park, Limerick, Ireland
Tel.: (353) 61334466
Fiber Optic Cable & Product Mfr & Distr
N.A.I.C.S.: 335921

Opterna Trading (1)
1010 Jiangnan Huafu 1 Donghuan Er Road Longhua Street, Baoan District, Shenzhen, China
Tel.: (86) 75589954293
Fiber Optic Cable & Product Mfr & Distr
N.A.I.C.S.: 335921

PPC Broadband, Inc. (1)
6176 E Molloy Rd, East Syracuse, NY 13057-0278
Tel.: (315) 431-7200
Web Site: https://www.ppc-online.com
Fiber Optic Cable Mfr
N.A.I.C.S.: 335921

Port GmbH (1)
Regensburger Strasse 7B, 06132, Halle, Germany
Tel.: (49) 345777550
Web Site: https://www.port.de
Sales Range: $10-24.9 Million
Emp.: 22
Software & Hardware Development Services
N.A.I.C.S.: 335929

Precision Optical Technologies, Inc. (1)
2245 Brighton-Henrietta Townline Rd, Rochester, NY 14623
Tel.: (585) 500-4090
Web Site: https://www.precisionot.com
Emp.: 100
Communications Equipment Mfr & Whslr
N.A.I.C.S.: 334220
David Halladay (Pres & CEO)

Subsidiary (Domestic):

Opticonx, Inc. (2)
36 Town Forest Rd, Oxford, MA 01540
Tel.: (508) 987-9288
Web Site: http://www.opticonx.com
Rev.: $3,220,000
Emp.: 20
Data Processing, Hosting & Related Services
N.A.I.C.S.: 518210
Brian Keane (VP-Mktg)
Paul Doherty (VP-Sls)
Paul Shultz (VP-Product Engrg & Mgmt)
Paul Langlois (VP-Mfg Ops & Mgmt)

ProSoft Technology (Asia Pacific) SDN BHD (1)
Suite 03-02 Level 3 Tower A Vertical Business Suite, Bangsar South City No 8 Jalan Kerinchi, 59200, Kuala Lumpur, Malaysia

Tel.: (60) 322422020
Web Site: http://www.prosoft-technology.com
Cable Product Distr
N.A.I.C.S.: 423510

ProSoft Technology SAS (1)
17 rue des Briquetiers, 31700, Blagnac, France
Tel.: (33) 534368720
Web Site: http://www.prosoft-technology.com
Cable Product Distr
N.A.I.C.S.: 423510

Prosoft Technology, Inc. (1)
9201 Camino Media Ste 200, Bakersfield, CA 93311
Tel.: (661) 716-5100
Web Site: https://www.prosoft-technology.com
Cable Product Distr
N.A.I.C.S.: 423510

Red Hawk Network Essentials, Inc. (1)
1405 S Milpitas Blvd, Milpitas, CA 95035-6828
Tel.: (408) 945-1800
Web Site: http://www.red-hawk.com
Sales Range: $10-24.9 Million
Emp.: 19
Supplier Of Fiber Optic Assemblies To The OEM Market For Voice Video & Data Equipment
N.A.I.C.S.: 334419

Softel Ltd. (1)
12 Queen Eleanor House, Kingsclere Park Kingsclere, Hampshire, RG20 4SW, United Kingdom
Tel.: (44) 1189842151
Web Site: http://www.softelgroup.com
Broadcasting & Content Production Software Developer
N.A.I.C.S.: 513210

Thinklogical, LLC (1)
100 Washington St, Milford, CT 06460
Tel.: (203) 647-8700
Emp.: 48
Electric Equipment Mfr
N.A.I.C.S.: 334220
Larry Wachter (VP-Engrg)
Richard Cooper (VP)

West Penn Wire (1)
2833 W Chestnut St, Washington, PA 15301
Web Site: https://www.westpennwire.com
Sales Range: $100-124.9 Million
Insulated Wire for Coaxial, Communication, Telephone, Control, Alarm, Hook-Up & Business Machine Cable Mfr
N.A.I.C.S.: 332618

BELITE BIO, INC.
12750 High Bluff Dr Ste 475, San Diego, CA 92121
Tel.: (858) 246-6240 Ky
Web Site: https://www.belitebio.com
Year Founded: 2018
BLTE—(NASDAQ)
Rev.: $74,000
Assets: $94,642,000
Liabilities: $4,211,000
Net Worth: $90,431,000
Earnings: ($31,632,000)
Emp.: 20
Fiscal Year-end: 12/31/23
Biotechnology Research & Development Services
N.A.I.C.S.: 541714
Yu-Hsin Lin (CEO, Founder & Chm)
Hao-Yuan Chuang (CFO)
Nathan L. Mata (Chief Scientific Officer)

BELL BUCKLE HOLDINGS, INC.
8903 Glades Rd Ste A14 2021, Boca Raton, FL 33434
Tel.: (313) 475-3516 FL
Year Founded: 2000
BLLB—(OTCIQ)

Canned Fresh Products Mfr
N.A.I.C.S.: 327910
Roger Stevenson Hood *(CEO)*

BELL INDUSTRIES, INC.
4400 W 96th St, Indianapolis, IN
46268
Tel.: (317) 333-7777   CA
Web Site: http://www.bellind.com
Year Founded: 1952
BLLI—(OTCIQ)
Sales Range: $100-124.9 Million
Emp.: 615
Holding Company for Operating Business, Bell Techlogix
N.A.I.C.S.: 551112
Mark E. Schwarz *(Chm)*

Subsidiaries:

Bell Techlogix   (1)
4400 W 96th St, Indianapolis, IN
46268   (100%)
Tel.: (317) 333-7777
Web Site: http://www.belltechlogix.com
Distr of Computer & Computer Peripheral Equipment; Whslr of Software
N.A.I.C.S.: 541519
Mark Begle *(Controller)*
Anthony D'Ambrosi *(Pres)*
Don Imaizumi *(Sr VP-Client Svcs)*
Douglas Cramer *(VP-Svc Design)*
Elizabeth K. Kubycheck *(Sr VP-Mktg & Comm)*
Kathleen Gilmore *(VP-Admin & HR)*
Scott Allen *(VP-Enterprise Svcs)*
Steven Bass *(Sr VP-Sls & Svc Mgmt)*
Jack Mansfield *(VP-End User & Infrastructure Svcs)*
Ron S. Frankenfield *(CEO)*
Mark Schwarz *(Chm)*
Dale Dye *(Sr VP-Digital Workplace Svcs)*
Marc Othersen *(Chief Info Security Officer)*
Shawn Moore *(Dir-Global Field Svcs)*
Kellie Wilson *(Mgr-Svc Desk Ops)*
Wes Hopkins *(Mgr-Svc Desk)*
Hollie Doyle *(VP-Svc Ops)*
Kevin Miller *(Sr VP-Workplace Svcs-Global)*

Recreational Products Div.   (1)
11425 Brown Deer Rd, Milwaukee, WI
53224   (100%)
Tel.: (414) 354-5734
Web Site: http://www.bellrpg.com
Sales Range: $25-49.9 Million
Emp.: 60
After-Market Products for the Recreational Vehicle, Mobile Home, Motorcycle, Snowmobile & Marine Vehicles Distr
N.A.I.C.S.: 423690
Jim Schulteis *(Branch Mgr)*

Recreational Products Div.   (1)
580 Yankee Doodle Rd, Eagan, MN
55121   (100%)
Tel.: (651) 450-9020
Web Site: http://www.bellindustries.com
Sales Range: $50-74.9 Million
Emp.: 50
Distr of After-Market Products For The Recreational Vehicle, Mobile Home & Motorcycle
N.A.I.C.S.: 423910

Recreational Products Div.   (1)
4674 Clay Ave SW, Grand Rapids, MI
49548-3000   (100%)
Tel.: (616) 531-5415
Web Site: http://www.bellrpg.com
Sales Range: $50-74.9 Million
Emp.: 20
Distr of After Market Products Recreational Vehicles, Mobile Homes & Motorcycles
N.A.I.C.S.: 441222
Doug Larson *(Gen Mgr)*

BELL ROSE CAPITAL, INC.
30 Wall St 8th Fl, New York, NY
10005
Tel.: (954) 837-6833   WY
Web Site:
   http://www.bellrosecapital.net
Year Founded: 2005
BELR—(OTCIQ)
Real Estate Investment Services

N.A.I.C.S.: 531390
Carlos Zacarias Salgado *(CEO)*
Irina Veselinovic *(Sec)*
Ahyende Sandy *(Dir-Business Development)*

BELLEROPHON THERAPEUTICS, INC.
184 Liberty Corner Rd Ste 302, Warren, NJ 07059
Tel.: (908) 574-4770   DE
Web Site:
   http://www.bellerophon.com
Year Founded: 2013
BLPH—(NASDAQ)
Rev.: $135,000
Assets: $7,935,000
Liabilities: $5,401,000
Net Worth: $2,534,000
Earnings: ($19,831,000)
Emp.: 18
Fiscal Year-end: 12/31/22
Pharmaceutical & Medical Device Mfr
N.A.I.C.S.: 325412
Amy Edmonds *(VP-Clinical Ops & Admin)*
Edwin L. Parsley *(Chief Medical Officer-Acting)*

BELLEVUE LIFE SCIENCES ACQUISITION CORP.
10900 NE 4th St Ste 2300, Bellevue, WA 98004
Tel.: (425) 635-7700   DE
Web Site:
   https://www.bellevuespac.com
Year Founded: 2020
BLAC—(NASDAQ)
Investment Holding Company
N.A.I.C.S.: 551112
Kuk Hyoun Hwang *(CEO)*
David J. Yoo *(CFO)*
Steven Reed *(Chm)*

BELLICUM PHARMACEUTICALS, INC.
3730 Kirby Dr Ste 1200, Houston, TX
77098
Tel.: (832) 384-1100   DE
Web Site: http://www.bellicum.com
Year Founded: 2004
BLCM—(NASDAQ)
Rev.: $1,500,000
Assets: $23,823,000
Liabilities: $21,808,000
Net Worth: $2,015,000
Earnings: ($24,973,000)
Emp.: 13
Fiscal Year-end: 12/31/22
Biopharmaceutical Mfr
N.A.I.C.S.: 325412
David M. Spencer *(Founder)*
Joseph Senesac *(Sr VP-Technical Ops)*
James F. Brown *(Chm)*

BELONG ACQUISITION CORP.
2 Commerce Sq 2001 Market St Ste
3400, Philadelphia, PA 19103
Tel.: (215) 731-9450   DE
Year Founded: 2020
BLNG—(NASDAQ)
Rev.: $5,046,485
Assets: $52,318,630
Liabilities: $58,497,507
Net Worth: ($6,178,877)
Earnings: $2,986,976
Emp.: 2
Fiscal Year-end: 12/31/22
Investment Services
N.A.I.C.S.: 523999
Jennifer Deason *(Chm)*
Peter Saldarriaga *(CEO & CFO)*
Joel Washington *(Pres & Chief Investment Officer)*

BELPOINTE PREP, LLC
255 Glenville Rd, Greenwich, CT
06831
Tel.: (203) 883-1944   DE
Web Site: https://belpointeoz.com
Year Founded: 2018
OZ—(NYSEAMEX)
Rev.: $1,391,000
Assets: $353,995,000
Liabilities: $21,343,000
Net Worth: $332,652,000
Earnings: ($7,683,000)
Fiscal Year-end: 12/31/22
Real Estate Investment Services
N.A.I.C.S.: 531210
Brandon E. Lacoff *(Chm & CEO)*
Martin Lacoff *(Chief Strategic Officer)*
Lori Wortz *(COO)*
Cody Laidlaw *(Chief Bus Dev Officer)*
Adam Snitkoff *(VP-Finance)*
Eric Fenton *(VP-Development)*
Ela Cole *(VP-Property Ops)*

BELPOINTE REIT, INC.
125 Greenwich Ave 3rd Fl, Greenwich, CT 06830
Tel.: (203) 883-1944   MD
Web Site:
   http://www.belpointereit.com
Year Founded: 2011
BELP—(OTCIQ)
Rev.: $70,000
Assets: $54,880,000
Liabilities: $15,016,000
Net Worth: $39,864,000
Earnings: ($544,000)
Fiscal Year-end: 12/31/19
Real Estate Manangement Services
N.A.I.C.S.: 531900
Brandon Lacof *(Co-Founder, Pres & CEO)*
Martin Lacoff *(Co-Founder & Chief Strategic Officer)*
Lori Wortz *(VP-Dev)*
Paxton Kinol *(Chief Investment Officer)*

BEN-TAM, INC.
1 Tampa City Ctr Ste 3200, Tampa,
FL 33602
Tel.: (813) 221-2626   DE
BTAM—(OTCIQ)
Nonwoven Fabric Product Mfr
N.A.I.C.S.: 313230
Debra Romano *(Pres)*

BENCHMARK BANKSHARES INC.
100 S Broad St, Kenbridge, VA
23944
Tel.: (434) 676-9054   VA
Web Site: http://www.bcbonline.com
BMBN—(OTCIQ)
Rev.: $32,789,842
Assets: $711,895,139
Liabilities: $643,184,353
Net Worth: $68,710,786
Earnings: $9,452,659
Emp.: 105
Fiscal Year-end: 12/31/19
Bank Holding Company
N.A.I.C.S.: 551111
E. Neil Burke *(Pres, CEO, CFO, Exec VP & Exec Dir)*

BENCHMARK ELECTRONICS, INC.
56 S Rockford Dr, Tempe, AZ 85288
Tel.: (623) 300-7000   TX
Web Site: https://www.bench.com
Year Founded: 1979
BHE—(NYSE)
Rev.: $2,886,331,000
Assets: $2,227,331,000
Liabilities: $1,200,915,000
Net Worth: $1,026,416,000

Earnings: $68,229,000
Emp.: 11,873
Fiscal Year-end: 12/31/22
Printed Circuit Board Mfr
N.A.I.C.S.: 334412
Cary T. Fu *(Co-Founder)*
Stephen J. Beaver *(Chief Legal Officer, Gen Counsel & Sr VP)*
Jeffrey W. Benck *(Pres & CEO)*
Jan Janick *(CTO & Sr VP)*
Scott Hicar *(CIO & Sr VP)*
Rhonda Turner *(Chief HR Officer & Sr VP)*

Subsidiaries:

Benchmark Electronics Inc.   (1)
4807 Bradford Dr NW, Huntsville, AL
35805-1948   (100%)
Tel.: (256) 722-6000
Web Site: http://www.bench.com
Sales Range: $100-124.9 Million
Emp.: 330
Mfr of Contract Electronic Products
N.A.I.C.S.: 334419

Benchmark Electronics Inc.   (1)
4065 Theurer Blvd, Winona, MN
55987   (100%)
Tel.: (507) 452-8932
Web Site: http://www.bench.com
Sales Range: $400-449.9 Million
Emp.: 1,000
Mfr & Designer of Contract Electronics
N.A.I.C.S.: 334419
Eric Derbyshire *(Principal & Engr-Supplier Dev)*

Benchmark Electronics Inc.   (1)
3535 Technology Dr NW, Rochester, MN
55901
Tel.: (507) 535-4000
Web Site: http://www.bench.com
Sales Range: $100-124.9 Million
Printed Circuit Board Mfr
N.A.I.C.S.: 334412

Benchmark Electronics Inc. - New
Hampshire Division   (1)
100 Innovative Way, Nashua, NH 03062
Tel.: (603) 879-7000
Web Site: http://www.bench.com
Emp.: 500
Printed Circuit Assemblies & Fully Integrated Products Mfr
N.A.I.C.S.: 334418

Benchmark Electronics Manufacturing
Solutions (Moorpark), Inc.   (1)
200 Science Dr, Moorpark, CA 93021
Tel.: (805) 532-2800
Electronic Equipment Distr
N.A.I.C.S.: 423620

Benchmark Electronics Netherlands
Holding B.V.   (1)
Lelyweg 10 7602 EA, Almelo, Netherlands
Tel.: (31) 546535111
Electronic Product Mfr & Services
N.A.I.C.S.: 335999

CTS Electronics Manufacturing
Solutions   (1)
200 Science Dr, Moorpark, CA 93021-2003
Tel.: (805) 532-2800
Sales Range: $150-199.9 Million
Emp.: 1,000
Electronics Manufacturing Services
N.A.I.C.S.: 334412

Subsidiary (Non-US):

CTS Electro de Matamoros S.A. de
C.V.   (2)
Norte 7 SN KM 7.5 Poniente 2 y Lauro Villar Ciudad Industrial, 87499, Matamoros,
Tamaulipas, Mexico   (100%)
Tel.: (52) 8688128235
Web Site: http://www.ctscorp.com
Sales Range: $10-24.9 Million
Emp.: 150
Selector Switches, Loudspeakers & Electromechanical Subsystem Assemblies Mfr
N.A.I.C.S.: 441330

Subsidiary (Domestic):

CTS Electronics Manufacturing
Solutions   (2)

Benchmark Electronics, Inc.—(Continued)

5550 Hellyer Ave, San Jose, CA 95138
Tel.: (408) 988-6404
Emp.: 75
Electronics Manufacturing Services
N.A.I.C.S.: 813910

Subsidiary (Non-US):

CTS Electronics Manufacturing
Solutions   (2)
Bang Pa In Industrial Estate, 592 Moo 2
Udom Sorayuth Rd, Ayutthaya, 13160,
Thailand   (100%)
Tel.: (66) 35221570
Sales Range: $10-24.9 Million
Emp.: 400
Electronics Manufacturing Services
N.A.I.C.S.: 336320

Subsidiary (Domestic):

Electronics Manufacturing
Solutions   (2)
34 Londonderry Rd A 1, Londonderry, NH
03053-3338   (100%)
Tel.: (603) 421-2546
Emp.: 185
Interconnect Products Mfr
N.A.I.C.S.: 334111

EFTC Operating Corporation   (1)
2501 W Grandview Rd, Phoenix, AZ 85023
Tel.: (602) 789-6600
Emp.: 1,863
Electronic Equipment Distr
N.A.I.C.S.: 423620

RodniC LLC   (1)
1400 Gillingham Ln, Sugar Land, TX
77478-2896
Tel.: (281) 240-9319
Electronic Equipment Distr
N.A.I.C.S.: 423620

BENESSERE CAPITAL ACQUISITION CORP.

777 SW 37th Ave Ste 510, Miami, FL
33135-3250
Tel.: (561) 467-5200   DE
Year Founded: 2020
BENEU—(NASDAQ)
Investment Services
N.A.I.C.S.: 523999
Patrick Orlando (Chm & CEO)
Francisco O. Flores (CFO & Sec)

BENSON HILLS, INC.

1001 N Warson Rd, Saint Louis, MO
63132
Tel.: (314) 222-8218   DE
Web Site: https://www.bensonhill.com
BHIL—(NYSE)
Rev.: $381,233,000
Assets: $500,920,000
Liabilities: $307,018,000
Net Worth: $193,902,000
Earnings: ($127,905,000)
Emp.: 440
Fiscal Year-end: 12/31/22
Crop Improvement Services
N.A.I.C.S.: 926140
Susan Keefe (CFO)
Adrienne D. Elsner (CEO)

Subsidiaries:

Benson Hill Holdings, Inc.   (1)
1001 N Warson Rd, Saint Louis, MO
63132-2900
Tel.: (314) 222-8218
Web Site: https://bensonhill.com
Crop Improvement Services
N.A.I.C.S.: 926140

Subsidiary (Domestic):

Dakota Dry Bean Inc.   (2)
2534 17th Ave S Ste D2, Grand Forks, ND
58201-5215
Tel.: (701) 746-7493
Web Site: http://www.dakotadrybean.com
Food Manufacturing
N.A.I.C.S.: 311999
David Polries (Pres)

BENTLEY SYSTEMS, INC.

685 Stockton Dr, Exton, PA 19341
Tel.: (610) 458-5000   DE
Web Site: https://www.bentley.com
Year Founded: 1984
BSY—(NASDAQ)
Rev.: $1,228,413,000
Assets: $3,319,850,000
Liabilities: $2,435,868,000
Net Worth: $883,982,000
Earnings: $326,787,000
Emp.: 5,200
Fiscal Year-end: 12/31/23
Software Products Mfr
N.A.I.C.S.: 513210
Gregory S. Bentley (Exec Chm & Pres)
Keith A. Bentley (Co-Founder)
Barry J. Bentley (Co-Founder)
Nicholas H. Cumins (CEO)
Michael M. Campbell (Chief Product Officer)
Nicholas Cumins (COO)
Katriona Lord-Levins (Chief Success Officer)
Chris Bradshaw (CMO)
Werner Andre (CFO)
David R. Shaman (Chief Legal Officer & Sec)
James Lawton (Chief Digital Officer)
Julien Moutte (CTO)
Eric Boyer (Head-IR)
Brock Ballard (Chief Revenue Officer)

Subsidiaries:

AarhusGeosoftware ApS   (1)
Skolegade 21 1, 8000, Aarhus, Denmark
Tel.: (45) 61656570
Web Site:
    https://www.aarhusgeosoftware.dk
Emp.: 10
Software Development Services
N.A.I.C.S.: 541511
Toke Hojbjerg Soltoft (CEO)
Stinne Host (CTO)

BLUERIDGE Analytics Inc.   (1)
325 Arlington Ave Ste 630, Charlotte, NC
28203-4491
Tel.: (704) 373-1884
Web Site: http://www.siteops.com
Emp.: 10
Computer Systems Optimization Software
Solutions
N.A.I.C.S.: 513210
Michael W. Detwiler (Pres & CEO)

Bentley Canada, Inc   (1)
510-5th Street SW Suite 700 7th Fl, Calgary, T2P3S2, AB, Canada
Tel.: (403) 221-9370
Software Development Services
N.A.I.C.S.: 541511

Bentley Systems (Beijing) Co.,
Ltd.   (1)
Unit 1403 05-06 Tower 1 No 81 Jianguo
Road, China Central Place, Beijing, 100025,
China
Tel.: (86) 1059297110
Web Site: http://www.bentley.com
Software Development Services
N.A.I.C.S.: 541511

Bentley Systems (UK) Ltd.   (1)
20 Gracechurch Street 9th Floor, London,
EC3V 0BG, United Kingdom
Tel.: (44) 8081019247
Sales Range: $10-24.9 Million
Emp.: 60
Software Development Services
N.A.I.C.S.: 541511

Bentley Systems Austria GmbH   (1)
Am Eisernen Tor 1, 8010, Graz, Austria
Tel.: (43) 800601159
Sales Range: $10-24.9 Million
Emp.: 15
Software Publisher
N.A.I.C.S.: 513210
Vanja Samec (Dir-Bus Product)

Bentley Systems CR s.r.o.   (1)
Mosnova 4/1306, 15000, Prague, Czech
Republic
Tel.: (420) 257314131
Web Site: http://www.bentley.com
Software Development Services
N.A.I.C.S.: 541511

Bentley Systems Co., Ltd.   (1)
8F Ikebukuro YS Bldg 1-13-23 Minami Ike-
bukuro, Toshima-ku, Tokyo, 171-0022, Ja-
pan
Tel.: (81) 6633812905
Web Site: http://www.bentley.com
Sales Range: $10-24.9 Million
Emp.: 20
Software Development Services
N.A.I.C.S.: 541511

Bentley Systems Europe B.V.   (1)
Aquarius Siriusdreef 16, PO Box 2045,
2132 WT, Hoofddorp, Netherlands
Tel.: (31) 8002737842
Sales Range: $25-49.9 Million
Emp.: 150
Software Development Services
N.A.I.C.S.: 513210

Bentley Systems Finland Oy   (1)
Eerikinkatu 6 b, 20100, Turku, Finland
Tel.: (358) 108301200
Software Development Services
N.A.I.C.S.: 541511

Bentley Systems France Sarl   (1)
12 Avenue De l Arche Immeuble, Le Coli-
see Batiment B, 92419, Courbevoie, France
Tel.: (33) 1 55 23 84 00
Software Development Services
N.A.I.C.S.: 513210

Bentley Systems Germany
GmbH   (1)
Birketweg 21, 80639, Munich, Germany
Tel.: (49) 8001818565
Software Development Services
N.A.I.C.S.: 541511

Bentley Systems Hong Kong Ltd. (1)
16/F Tower 5 The Gateway Harbour City,
Tsim Sha Tsui, Kowloon, China (Hong
Kong)
Tel.: (852) 28021030
Web Site: https://www.bentley.com
Sales Range: $10-24.9 Million
Emp.: 10
Software Development Services
N.A.I.C.S.: 541511

Bentley Systems Iberica, S.A.   (1)
Parque Empresarial La Finca Paseo del
Club Deportivo, 1 Edificio 4 Pozuelo de
Alarcon, 28224, Madrid, Spain
Tel.: (34) 900947894
Software Development Services
N.A.I.C.S.: 541511

Bentley Systems India Pvt. Ltd.   (1)
WorkWell Suites Max House Level 10 1 Dr
Jha Marg Okhla Phase III, New Delhi,
110020, India
Tel.: (91) 8001008434
Emp.: 500
Software Development Services
N.A.I.C.S.: 541511
Nitin Choudharic (Dir-Indus Sls)

Bentley Systems International
Ltd.   (1)
Charlemont Exchange 5th Floor Charlemont
Street, D02 VN88, Dublin, 2, Ireland
Tel.: (353) 14364600
Software Development Services
N.A.I.C.S.: 541511

Bentley Systems Italia Srl   (1)
Strada 1-Palazzo Centro Congressi-
Milanofiori, 20090, Assago, Milan, Italy
Tel.: (39) 02 82276411
Web Site: http://www.bentley.com
Sales Range: $10-24.9 Million
Emp.: 18
Software Development Services
N.A.I.C.S.: 541511

Bentley Systems Korea, Inc.   (1)
5F Anje Tower 718-2 Yeoksam-Dong,
Gangnam-Gu, Seoul, 135080, Korea
(South)
Tel.: (82) 2 5570555
Web Site: http://www.bentleysystems.com
Emp.: 17
Software Publisher
N.A.I.C.S.: 513210

Bentley Systems Pakistan (Pvt.)
Limited   (1)
Evacuee Trust Complex Suite 204 2nd
Floor Agha Khan Road F-5/1, Islamabad,
44000, Pakistan
Tel.: (92) 518842358
Software Development Services
N.A.I.C.S.: 541511

Bentley Systems Polska sp. z
o.o.   (1)
ul Nowogrodzka 68, 02-014, Warsaw, Po-
land
Tel.: (48) 8001242559
Software Development Services
N.A.I.C.S.: 541511

Bentley Systems Pty. Ltd.   (1)
Level 10 2 Southbank Boulevard, South-
bank, Melbourne, 3006, VIC, Australia
Tel.: (61) 1800500227
Software Publisher
N.A.I.C.S.: 513210

Bentley Systems Russia (OOO)   (1)
Dubininskaya St Buil 53-5, 115054, Mos-
cow, Russia
Tel.: (7) 4999182622
Software Development Services
N.A.I.C.S.: 541511

Bentley Systems Scandinavia
A/S   (1)
Skolegade 21 1, 8000, Aarhus, Denmark
Tel.: (45) 80887424
Software Development Services
N.A.I.C.S.: 541511

Bentley Systems Scandinavia
NUF   (1)
Fjordveien 1, 1363, Hovik, Norway
Tel.: (47) 80013542
Software Development Services
N.A.I.C.S.: 541511

Bentley Systems Sdn. Bhd.   (1)
Equatorial Plaza 18F Jalan Sultan Ismail,
Changkat Raja Chulan, 50250, Kuala Lum-
pur, Malaysia
Tel.: (60) 327834396
Software Development Services
N.A.I.C.S.: 541511

Bentley Systems Singapore Pte.
Ltd.   (1)
3 HarbourFront Place 05-01 HarbourFront
Tower 2, Singapore, 099254, Singapore
Tel.: (65) 66926592
Software Development Services
N.A.I.C.S.: 541511

Bentley Systems South Africa (Pty)
Ltd.   (1)
First Floor Building B Westend Office Park
254 Hall Street, Rivonia, Centurion, 0157,
South Africa
Tel.: (27) 800980615
Software Development Services
N.A.I.C.S.: 541511

Bentley Systems Sweden AB   (1)
Birger Jarlsgatan 55, 111 45, Stockholm,
Sweden
Tel.: (46) 20794616
Software Development Services
N.A.I.C.S.: 541511

Bentley Systems Switzerland AG (1)
Theodorshofweg 31/33, 4310, Rheinfelden,
Switzerland
Tel.: (41) 800000263
Software Development Services
N.A.I.C.S.: 513210

Bentley Systems Yazilim Cozumleri
Ltd.   (1)
Mustafa Kemal Mah Dumlupinar Bulv No
266/C-63 Tepe Prime, Cankaya, 06800, An-
kara, Turkiye
Tel.: (90) 3122101650
Web Site: http://www.bentley.com
Software Development Services
N.A.I.C.S.: 541511

Bentley Systems de Mexico SA de
CV   (1)
Corporativo del Parque Insurgentes Sur No
1106 Piso 7, Col Noche Buena, 03720,
Mexico, Mexico
Tel.: (52) 18554340914

Sales Range: $10-24.9 Million
Emp.: 30
Software Development Services
N.A.I.C.S.: 541511

Bentley Systems, Inc. - Carlsbad (1)
2744 Loker Ave W Ste 103, Carlsbad, CA 92010
Tel.: (760) 431-3610
Sales Range: $25-49.9 Million
Emp.: 20
Software Developer
N.A.I.C.S.: 513210

Bentley Systems, Incorporated (1)
Room 1551 15th floor No 168 Sec 3 Nanjing E Rd, Taipei, 104, Taiwan
Tel.: (886) 277426346
Software Development Services
N.A.I.C.S.: 541511
Brock Ballard (Chief Revenue Officer)
Nicholas Cumins (COO)
Eric Boyer (Officer-IR)
Greg Bentley (CEO)
Allen Li (Gen Mgr-China)
Kristin Fallon (CMO)
Chris Bradshaw (Chief Sustainability Officer)
Colin Ellam (CEO-Cohesive)
Oliver Conze (Sr VP-Bentley Infrastructure Cloud)

Blyncsy, Inc. (1)
650 S 500 W Ste 360, Salt Lake City, UT 84401
Tel.: (385) 216-0590
Web Site: https://www.blyncsy.com
Roadway Management & Maintenance Services
N.A.I.C.S.: 237310

Citilabs, Inc. (1)
685 Stockton Dr, Exton, PA 19341
Computer System Design Services
N.A.I.C.S.: 541512

E-ON Software SARL (1)
15 Rue Traversiere, 75012, Paris, France
Tel.: (33) 188463921
Web Site: http://www.info.e-onsoftware.com
Software Development Services
N.A.I.C.S.: 541511

E7 Pty Ltd (1)
PO Box 2203, Graceville, Brisbane, 4075, QLD, Australia
Tel.: (61) 733690038
Web Site: https://e7.site
Information Technology Services
N.A.I.C.S.: 541511
Hugh Hofmeister (CEO & Co-Founder)
Adrian Smith (Co-Founder & CTO)
Nate Kane (Head-Engineering)
Kirk Kulbe (Mgr)
Trevor Mogg (Mgr)

Exor Corporation (1)
Clifton Heights Clifton, Bristol, BS8 1EJ, United Kingdom
Tel.: (44) 1179 006 200
Software Development Services
N.A.I.C.S.: 541511

Infrasoft Corporation (1)
685 Stockton Dr, Exton, PA 19341
Tel.: (640) 458-5000
Web Site: http://www.infrasoft-civil.com
Rev.: $11,000,000
Emp.: 8
Software, Business & Non-Game
N.A.I.C.S.: 449210

InspectTech Systems, Inc. (1)
810 River Ave Ste 300, Pittsburgh, PA 15212
Tel.: (412) 681-1521
Web Site: http://www.inspecttech.com
Sales Range: $10-24.9 Million
Emp.: 10
Infrastructure Inspection Software Developer
N.A.I.C.S.: 513210

Ivara Corporation (1)
5046 Mainway, Burlington, L7L 5Z1, ON, Canada
Tel.: (877) 746-3787
Web Site: http://www.ivara.com
Software Development Services
N.A.I.C.S.: 541511

Nadhi Information Technologies Private Limited (1)
4 Aswathi 2nd Crescent Park Street Gandhi Nagar, Adyar, Chennai, 600 020, Tamil Nadu, India
Tel.: (91) 444 354 6224
Web Site: https://www.nadhi.in
Software Development Services
N.A.I.C.S.: 541511
Kalyan Vaidyanathan (CEO & Co-Founder)
Ravi Mundoli (Co-Founder)

NoteVault, Inc. (1)
6305 Lusk Blvd, San Diego, CA 92121
Tel.: (858) 755-9800
Web Site: http://www.notevault.com
Software Publisher
N.A.I.C.S.: 513210
John Roshala (Pres)

Ontracks EAM Consulting Ltd. (1)
202 14127 23 Ave NW, Edmonton, T6R 0G4, AB, Canada
Tel.: (780) 637-4130
Web Site: https://ontracks.com
Software Development Services
N.A.I.C.S.: 541511

Oxplus B.V. (1)
Eisenhowerweg 14E, 5466 AC, Veghel, Netherlands
Tel.: (31) 850401111
Web Site: https://oxplus.com
Asset Management Services
N.A.I.C.S.: 531390

Professional Construction Strategies Group Limited (1)
10th Floor Corinthian House 17 Lansdowne Road, Croydon, CR0 2BX, United Kingdom
Tel.: (44) 2086804120
Web Site: http://www.pcsg.co.uk
Construction Services
N.A.I.C.S.: 236220
Mark Bew (Chm)
Katherine Bew (Mng Dir)
Adrian Burgess (Dir-Tech)
Tina Burgess (Assoc Dir)
Olly Thomas (Bus Dir)

Research Engineers International (1)
22700 Savi Ranch Pkwy, Yorba Linda, CA 92887-4608
Tel.: (714) 974-2500
Web Site: http://www.reiworld.com
Sales Range: $25-49.9 Million
Emp.: 35
Mfr of Document Review & Collaboration Software
N.A.I.C.S.: 541330

SRO Solutions Limited (1)
4th Floor Phoenix House 47 Cross St, Manchester, M2 4JF, United Kingdom
Tel.: (44) 8454084250
Web Site: https://www.srosolutions.net
Information Technology Services
N.A.I.C.S.: 541511

Seequent Australia Pty Limited (1)
Level 2 11 Mounts Bay Road, Perth, 6000, WA, Australia
Tel.: (61) 893367397
Software Development Services
N.A.I.C.S.: 541511

Seequent Chile SpA (1)
Calle Cerro el Plomo Oficina 1007-1008, Las Condes, 5855, Santiago, Chile
Tel.: (56) 232026533
Software Development Services
N.A.I.C.S.: 541511

Seequent Limited (1)
20 Moorhouse Ave, Addington, Christchurch, 8011, New Zealand
Tel.: (64) 3 961 10 31
Web Site: http://www.seequent.com
Geological Modeling Solutions
N.A.I.C.S.: 334610
Graham Grant (CEO)
Daniel Wallace (Chief Revenue Officer)
James Lawton (CTO)
Jo Knight (Chief Customer Officer)
Anthony Stephens (Gen Counsel)
Lisa Wall (Chief People Officer)

Subsidiary (Non-US):

Geosoft Inc. (2)

Tel.: (416) 369-0111
Software Solutions Services
N.A.I.C.S.: 513210

Seequent Peru S.A.C (1)
Tel.: (51) 16409175
Software Development Services
N.A.I.C.S.: 541511

Seequent South Africa Pty Limited (1)
2nd Floor 18 Melrose Boulevard Melrose Arch, Melrose North, Johannesburg, 2196, South Africa
Tel.: (27) 448743270
Software Development Services
N.A.I.C.S.: 541511

Seequent UK Limited (1)
Morris House 20-26 Spittal Street, Marlow, SL7 1DB, Buckinghamshire, United Kingdom
Tel.: (44) 207 438 2082
Software Development Services
N.A.I.C.S.: 541511

Seequent USA Inc. (1)
8181 Arista Pl St 100, Broomfield, CO 80021
Tel.: (416) 369-0111
Software Development Services
N.A.I.C.S.: 541511

Sensemetrics, Inc. (1)
750 B St Ste 1630, San Diego, CA 92101
Tel.: (619) 485-0575
Web Site: https://www.sensemetrics.com
Software Development Services
N.A.I.C.S.: 541511

SignCAD Systems, Inc. (1)
9800 Shelard Pkwy Ste 120, Plymouth, MN 55441
Tel.: (952) 544-9559
Traffic Sign Mfr
N.A.I.C.S.: 339999

Spidaweb LLC (1)
781 Science Blvd Ste 225, Gahanna, OH 43230
Tel.: (614) 470-9882
Web Site: https://www.spidasoftware.com
Software Development Services
N.A.I.C.S.: 541511
Amber Schmiesing (Mgr-Customer Care)
Beth Carmean (Mgr)
Brad Johnson (Dir-Business Development-Strategy)
Brett Willitt (Pres)
Courteney Miller (Mktg Mgr)

gINT Software, Inc. (1)
1160 N Dutton Ave Ste 140, Santa Rosa, CA 95401
Tel.: (707) 284-2200
Web Site: http://www.gintsoftware.com
Sales Range: $10-24.9 Million
Emp.: 15
Geotechnical & Geoenvironmental Software Developer
N.A.I.C.S.: 513210

BENTON FINANCIAL CORP.
300 E 5th St, Fowler, IN 47944-0511
Tel.: (765) 884-1200   IN
BTOF—(OTCIQ)
Rev.: $7,784,931
Assets: $167,420,324
Liabilities: $142,324,180
Net Worth: $25,096,144
Earnings: $2,381,312
Fiscal Year-end: 12/31/19
Banking Holding Company
N.A.I.C.S.: 551111
Steven T. Pettet (Pres & CEO)

BEO BANCORP
279 N Main St, Heppner, OR 97836
Tel.: (541) 676-9125   OR
Web Site: https://www.beobank.com
Year Founded: 1997
BEOB—(OTCIQ)
Rev.: $30,932,910
Assets: $666,698,664
Liabilities: $624,763,504
Net Worth: $41,935,160

Earnings: $5,523,488
Emp.: 103
Fiscal Year-end: 12/31/20
Bank Holding Company
N.A.I.C.S.: 551111
Jeffery L. Bailey (Pres & CEO)
Mark D. Lemmon (CFO & Exec VP-Bank of Eastern Oregon)
Gary L. Propheter (Co-COO & Exec VP-BEO Bank)
Bradley B. Anderson (Vice Chm)
Joe Gonzalez (Chm)
Ed Rollins (Chief Credit Officer & Exec VP-Bank of Eastern Oregon)
Jim Bleth (VP & Mgr-IT-Bank of Eastern Oregon)
Becky Kindle (Co-COO & Exec VP-BEO Bank)
Tricia Rollins (VP & Mgr-Loan Ops-Bank of Eastern Oregon)
Anita Orem (Project Mgr-Foundation Div)
John Qualls (Chief Lending Officer & Exec VP-Bank of Eastern Oregon)

Subsidiaries:

Bank of Eastern Oregon (1)
279 N Main St, Heppner, OR 97836
Tel.: (541) 676-9125
Web Site: http://www.beobank.com
Sales Range: $10-24.9 Million
Commericial Banking
N.A.I.C.S.: 522110
Mark D. Lemmon (CFO & Exec VP)
Gary L. Propheter (COO & Exec VP)
Jeff L. Bailey (Pres & CEO)
John Qualls (Sr VP & Sr Loan Officer)
Becky Kindle (Sr VP-Branch Admin)
Ed Rollins (Sr VP-Credit Admin)

BERGIO INTERNATIONAL, INC.
41 S Shore Rd, Marmora, NJ 08223
Tel.: (973) 227-3230   DE
Web Site: https://www.bergio.com
Year Founded: 2007
BRGO—(OTCIQ)
Rev.: $9,817,426
Assets: $9,472,312
Liabilities: $4,520,025
Net Worth: $4,952,287
Earnings: ($2,269,691)
Emp.: 17
Fiscal Year-end: 12/31/22
Offices of Other Holding Companies
N.A.I.C.S.: 551112
Berge Abajian (Chm, Pres, CEO & Designer)

BERKSHIRE HATHAWAY INC.
3555 Farnam St, Omaha, NE 68131
Tel.: (402) 346-1400   DE
Web Site:
https://www.berkshirehathaway.com
Year Founded: 1839
BRKL—(NYSE)
Rev.: $364,482,000,000
Assets: $1,069,978,000,000
Liabilities: $502,469,000,000
Net Worth: $567,509,000,000
Earnings: $96,223,000,000
Emp.: 396,500
Fiscal Year-end: 12/31/23
Financial Investment Services
N.A.I.C.S.: 551112
Marc D. Hamburg (CFO & Sr VP)
Daniel J. Jaksich (Chief Acctg Officer & VP)
Todd Anthony Combs (Executives, Bd of Dirs)
Ajit Jain (Vice Chm-Insurance Ops)
Warren Edward Buffett (Chm & CEO)
Gregory E. Abel (Vice Chm-Non-Insurance Ops)

Subsidiaries:

Acme Brick Company (1)

Berkshire Hathaway Inc.—(Continued)

3024 Acme Brick Plz, Fort Worth, TX
76109-4104
Tel.: (817) 332-4101
Web Site: http://www.brick.com
Sales Range: $550-599.9 Million
Emp.: 150
Face Brick & Concrete Building Products
Mfr & Ceramic & Marble Floor & Wall Tile
Distr
N.A.I.C.S.: 327120
Dennis Knautz (Pres & CEO)

Subsidiary (Domestic):

**Acme-Ochs Brick and Stone,
Inc.**   **(2)**
7175 Cahill Rd, Edina, MN 55439-2037
Tel.: (952) 903-0300
Web Site: http://www.brick.com
Sales Range: $10-24.9 Million
Emp.: 10
Brick Mfr & Whslr
N.A.I.C.S.: 327120

Featherlite Building Products   **(2)**
508 McNeil Rd, Round Rock, TX
78681   **(100%)**
Tel.: (512) 255-2573
Web Site: http://www.featherlitetexas.com
Sales Range: $25-49.9 Million
Emp.: 4
Concrete Block
N.A.I.C.S.: 327331

**Jenkins Brick Company, Inc.
-Attalla**
532 Gilbert Ferry Rd SE, Attalla, AL 35954-
3331
Tel.: (256) 538-2212
Sales Range: $1-9.9 Million
Emp.: 9
Building Material Dealers
N.A.I.C.S.: 444180
Ladue Fossett (Mgr-Div)
Jeff Cornutt (Mgr-Customer Svc)

Albecca Inc.   **(1)**
3900 Steve Reynolds Blvd, Norcross, GA
30093   **(100%)**
Tel.: (770) 279-5200
Custom Frame Designer, Mfr & Distr
N.A.I.C.S.: 339999

Subsidiary (Domestic):

Larson-Juhl US LLC   **(2)**
990 Peachtree Industrial Blvd Ste 3829,
Suwanee, GA 30024
Web Site: https://www.larsonjuhl.com
Financial Investment Services
N.A.I.C.S.: 523999

Alleghany Corporation   **(1)**
1411 Broadway 34th Fl, New York, NY
10018   **(100%)**
Tel.: (212) 752-1356
Web Site: https://www.alleghany.com
Rev.: $12,004,105,000
Assets: $32,268,675,000
Liabilities: $23,081,793,000
Net Worth: $9,186,882,000
Earnings: $1,034,892,000
Emp.: 13,313
Fiscal Year-end: 12/31/2021
Holding Company; Property & Casualty In-
surance, Reinsurance & Other Related
Products & Services
N.A.I.C.S.: 551112
Jerry G. Borrelli (Chief Acctg Officer & VP-
Fin)
Peter R. Sismondo (Treas, VP, Controller &
Asst Sec)
Christopher K. Dalrymple (Gen Counsel,
Sec & Sr VP)
Susan E. Giarrusso (VP)
Jefferson W. Kirby (Chm)
John Carr (VP & Dir-Tax)
Joseph Patrick Brandon (Pres)
Stela Burghart (Chief Compliance Officer &
VP)
Kerry Josephine Jacobs (CFO & Exec VP)
John F. Shannon (Chief Investment Officer
& Sr VP)
Antonio Celii (VP & Assoc Gen Counsel)
Rebekah Edwards (VP & Head-Internal Au-
dit)
Dale James (Chief Risk Officer & VP-Corp
Fin)

Subsidiary (Domestic):

Alleghany Capital Corporation   **(2)**
1411 Broadway 34th Fl, New York, NY
10018
Tel.: (212) 752-1356
Holding Company
N.A.I.C.S.: 523999
Udi Yehuda Toledano (Chm)
Udi Toledano (Chm)

Subsidiary (Domestic):

**Piedmont Manufacturing Group
LLC**   **(3)**
100 N Main St, Belmont, NC 28012
Tel.: (866) 273-1810
Plastic Component Mfr
N.A.I.C.S.: 326199

Subsidiary (Domestic):

Wilbert Inc.   **(4)**
2001 Oaks Pkwy, Belmont, NC 28012
Tel.: (708) 865-1600
Web Site: http://www.wilbertinc.com
Sales Range: $150-199.9 Million
Holding Company; Industrial Plastics & Fu-
neral Vaults Mfr
N.A.I.C.S.: 551112
Robert Gray (VP-Sales-Marketing)

Plant (Domestic):

Wilbert Inc. - Bellevue Facility   **(5)**
635 Southwest St, Bellevue, OH 44811
Tel.: (419) 483-2300
Emp.: 148
Plastics Product Mfr
N.A.I.C.S.: 326199

Wilbert Inc. - Belmont Facility   **(5)**
1000 Oaks Pkwy, Belmont, NC 28012
Tel.: (704) 822-1423
Emp.: 81
Plastics Product Mfr
N.A.I.C.S.: 326199

Wilbert Inc. - Easley Facility   **(5)**
2930 Greenville Hwy, Easley, SC 29640
Tel.: (864) 859-7548
Emp.: 215
Plastics Product Mfr
N.A.I.C.S.: 326199

Wilbert Inc. - Forest City Facility   **(5)**
486 Vance St, Forest City, NC 28043
Tel.: (828) 247-4900
Emp.: 105
Plastics Product Mfr
N.A.I.C.S.: 326199

Wilbert Inc. - Harrisburg Facility   **(5)**
7301 Caldwell Rd, Harrisburg, NC 28075
Tel.: (704) 455-5191
Emp.: 90
Plastics Product Mfr
N.A.I.C.S.: 326199

Wilbert Inc. - Lebanon Facility   **(5)**
655 Industrial Dr, Lebanon, KY 40033
Tel.: (270) 692-0901
Emp.: 124
Plastics Product Mfr
N.A.I.C.S.: 326199

**Wilbert Inc. - White Bear Lake
Facility**   **(5)**
4221 Otter Lake Rd, White Bear Lake, MN
55110
Tel.: (651) 426-7319
Emp.: 145
Plastics Product Mfr
N.A.I.C.S.: 326199

Subsidiary (Domestic):

Wilbert Plastic Services, Inc.   **(5)**
100 N Main St, Belmont, NC
28012   **(100%)**
Tel.: (704) 247-3850
Web Site: https://wilbertplastics.com
Sales Range: $100-124.9 Million
Plastics Product Mfr
N.A.I.C.S.: 326199
Bob Gray (VP-Sales-Marketing)

Subsidiary (Domestic):

Wilbert Funeral Services, Inc.   **(3)**

2913 Gardner Rd, Broadview, IL 60155-
4402
Tel.: (708) 865-1600
Web Site: http://www.wilbert.com
Supplier of Burial Vaults
N.A.I.C.S.: 327390
Dennis Welzenbach (Pres & CEO)

Subsidiary (Domestic):

Knauer's Wilbert Vault Inc.   **(4)**
19505 NE Frntage Rd, Joliet, IL 60431-
1567
Tel.: (815) 725-0246
Web Site: http://www.wilbertonline.com
Mfr of Concrete Burial Vaults
N.A.I.C.S.: 327390

Subsidiary (Domestic):

**Alleghany Insurance Holdings
LLC**   **(2)**
375 Park Ave Ste 3201, New York, NY
10152-0002
Tel.: (212) 752-1356
Direct Property Insurance Carrier Services
N.A.I.C.S.: 524126

Alleghany Properties LLC   **(2)**
300 University Ave Ste 210, Sacramento,
CA 95825
Tel.: (916) 648-7700
Web Site: https://www.natomascrossing.com
Sales Range: $300-349.9 Million
Real Estate Services
N.A.I.C.S.: 531390
David J. Bugatto (Pres & CEO)

Bourn & Koch, Inc.   **(2)**
2500 Kishwaukee St, Rockford, IL 61104
Tel.: (815) 965-4013
Web Site: http://www.bourn-koch.com
Sales Range: $25-49.9 Million
Emp.: 60
Machine Tools Mfr
N.A.I.C.S.: 333517

Group (Domestic):

**Bourn & Koch Fellows Services
Group**   **(3)**
7 Everett Ln, Windsor, VT 05089
Tel.: (802) 674-6500
Sales Range: $10-24.9 Million
Emp.: 10
Mfr of Gear Cutting & Finishing Machines;
Optical Comparators
N.A.I.C.S.: 333517

Division (Domestic):

**Bourn & Koch, Inc.-Replacement
Parts Division**   **(3)**
2500 Kishwaukee St, Rockford, IL 61104
Tel.: (815) 965-4013
Web Site: http://www.bourn-koch.com
Sales Range: $25-49.9 Million
Original & Replacement Tooling Products
Used in Industrial Machine Tools Mfr
N.A.I.C.S.: 423830

Subsidiary (Domestic):

CAC LLC   **(2)**
4350 La Jolla Village Dr, San Diego, CA
92122
Tel.: (858) 452-4302
Investment Management Service
N.A.I.C.S.: 523940
Rod Dammeyer (Owner)

CapSpecialty   **(2)**
1600 Aspen Commons Ste 300, Middleton,
WI 53562-4718
Tel.: (608) 829-4200
Web Site: https://www.capspecialty.com
Sales Range: $100-124.9 Million
Emp.: 200
Specialty Insurance Services
N.A.I.C.S.: 524126
Adam Sills (Head-Specialty Underwriting)
Lynne Fletcher (Head-Mktg & Distr)
Andrew Diaz-Matos (Gen Counsel)
Dan McGinnis (COO & Chief Underwriting
Officer)
Jack Sennott (Chm, Pres & CEO)
Melanie Wilhelm (Chief Compliance Officer)
Julianne Splain (Chief Claims Officer)
Ryan Byrnes (CFO)

Todd Burrick (Chief Underwriting & Risk Of-
ficer)
Alona Croteau (Chief Claims Officer)
Mary Haefer (Chief Claims Officer)

Subsidiary (Domestic):

Capitol Indemnity Corporation   **(3)**
1600 Aspen Commons Ste 300, Middleton,
WI 53562
Tel.: (608) 829-4200
Web Site: http://www.capitolindemnity.com
Sales Range: $100-124.9 Million
Emp.: 200
Specialty Insurance Services
N.A.I.C.S.: 524126

Subsidiary (Domestic):

CapSpecialty, Inc.   **(2)**
1600 Aspen Cmns Ste 300, Middleton, WI
53562
Tel.: (608) 829-4200
Web Site: https://www.capspecialty.com
Insurance Services
N.A.I.C.S.: 524298

Hirschfeld Industries, Inc.   **(2)**
112 W 29th St, San Angelo, TX 76903
Tel.: (972) 518-2173
Web Site:
     http://www.hirschfeld.wwafcosteel.com
Structural Steel Mfr
N.A.I.C.S.: 332312

Jazwares, Inc.   **(2)**
963 Shotgun Rd, Sunrise, FL 33326-1906
Tel.: (954) 845-0800
Web Site: http://www.jazwares.com
Sales Range: $1-9.9 Million
Emp.: 17
Toy & Electronic Products Mfr
N.A.I.C.S.: 339930
Laura Zebersky (Co-Founder, Pres & Chief
Comml Officer)
David Neustein (COO)
Matt Siesel (CFO)
Judd Karofsky (Exec VP-Jazwares)
Sam Ferguson (Sr VP-Global Licensing)

Subsidiary (Domestic):

First Act Inc.   **(3)**
745 Boylston St 3rd Fl, Boston, MA 02116
Tel.: (617) 226-7888
Web Site: http://www.firstact.com
Rev.: $2,100,000
Emp.: 25
Musical Instrument Supplier
N.A.I.C.S.: 459140
Bernard Chiu (Chm & CEO)

Kelly Toys Holdings, LLC   **(3)**
4811 S Alameda St, Los Angeles, CA 90058
Tel.: (323) 588-8697
Web Site: http://www.kellytoy.com
Toy & Hobby Supplies Merchant Whslr
N.A.I.C.S.: 423920
Jonathan Kelly (Pres)

Subsidiary (Domestic):

**Las Serenas Senior Apartments
LP**   **(2)**
2090 Yosemite Ave, Simi Valley, CA 93063
Tel.: (805) 520-9542
Web Site:
     https://lasserenassenior.usamfm.com
Insurance Services
N.A.I.C.S.: 524298

Platte River Insurance Company   **(2)**
1600 Aspen Commons, Middleton, WI
53562-4719
Tel.: (608) 829-4200
Direct Property Insurance Carrier Services
N.A.I.C.S.: 524126

R. C. Tway Company, LLC   **(2)**
3400 Robards Ct, Louisville, KY 40218
Tel.: (502) 638-6080
Web Site: http://www.kytrailer.com
Specialty Trailers, Truck Bodies & Custom
Transport Vehicles Mfr
N.A.I.C.S.: 336212

Gary Smith (Co-Pres & CEO)
Bob Bachman (Sr VP-Medical Solutions-AMST-University Park)
Dan Murphy (Sr VP & Gen Mgr-Reconditioning & Aftermarket Parts)
Jake Lambroza (VP-Sls-Moving & Storage)
Charles Ducas (CMO & Chief Sls Officer)
Greg Larkin (CFO & Sr VP)
Gary Parker (Co-Pres)
Randy Doering (Sr VP-Sls, Mktg & Bus Dev)
Tom Harper (VP-Sls, Mktg & Bus Dev)
Robert Headrick (VP-Supply Chain & Strategic Sourcing)
Scott Stewart (Sr Dir-Engrg)
Don Hobbs (Dir-Sls)
Gregg Lutes (Dir-Customer Svc)
Dianna Raisor (Sr Dir-Strategic Plng & Mktg)
Brian Clark (Mgr-Svc)
Larry Scott (Mgr-Sls-Truck Body)
Bill Schlaupitz (Coord-Quality & Warranty)
David Smith (Mgr-Sls & Mktg)
Jeff Hamilton (VP & Gen Mgr)
Jacob Law (Engr-Sls)
Tracy Walker (Gen Counsel & Sec)

Subsidiary (Domestic):

CEI Equipment Company LLC   (3)
5555 16th Ave SW, Cedar Rapids, IA 52404-2404
Tel.: (319) 396-7336
Web Site: https://ktpacer.com
Aluminum Feed Trailer & Feed Body Transportation Equipment Design & Mfr
N.A.I.C.S.: 336999

Division (Domestic):

Kentucky Trailer Technologies   (3)
1240 N Pontiac Trl, Walled Lake, MI 48390
Tel.: (248) 960-9700
Truck Trailer Mfr
N.A.I.C.S.: 336212
Tom Harper (VP-Sls, Mktg & Bus Dev)

Subsidiary (Non-US):

Smit Mobile Equipment B.V.   (3)
Buys Ballotstraat 6, 3261 LA, Oud-Beijerland, Netherlands
Tel.: (31) 186614322
Web Site: http://www.smit.one
Emp.: 30
Mobile Medical Equipment Mfr
N.A.I.C.S.: 339112

Subsidiary (Domestic):

RSUI Group, Inc.   (2)
945 E Paces Ferry Rd NE Ste 1800, Atlanta, GA 30326-1125
Tel.: (404) 231-2366
Web Site: http://www.rsui.com
Underwriting Services (Wholesale Specialty Insurance)
N.A.I.C.S.: 524298
Phillip McCrorie (CEO)
John Gerdts (Mgr & Sr VP)
Kym Hadzick (Mgr & Sr VP)
Phil Coletti (Mgr & Sr VP)
Clint Nokes (Mgr & Sr VP)
Andrew J. Whittington (Pres & Chief Underwriting Officer)
Lee Sjostrom (COO)
David E. Leonard (Chm)

Subsidiary (Domestic):

RSUI Indemnity Company   (3)
945 E Paces Ferry Rd Ste 1800, Atlanta, GA 30326-1160
Tel.: (404) 231-2366
Investment Management Service
N.A.I.C.S.: 523940

Resurgens Specialty Underwriting, Inc.   (3)
945 E Paces Ferry Rd NE Ste 1800, Atlanta, GA 30326-1125
Tel.: (404) 231-2366
Web Site: http://www.rsui.com
Emp.: 300
Investment Management Service
N.A.I.C.S.: 523940

Subsidiary (Domestic):

Roundwood Asset Management LLC   (2)

1411 Bdwy Fl 34, New York, NY 10018
Tel.: (212) 752-1356
Web Site: http://www.roundwoodasset.com
Asset Management Services
N.A.I.C.S.: 523940

Subsidiary (Non-US):

TransRe Europe S.A.   (2)
1 Avenue du Bois, 1251, Luxembourg, Luxembourg
Tel.: (352) 27300500
Insurance Services
N.A.I.C.S.: 524210
Louise Rose (Pres)

Subsidiary (Domestic):

Transatlantic Holdings, Inc.   (2)
80 Pine St, New York, NY 10005
Tel.: (212) 770-2000
Web Site: http://www.transre.com
Emp.: 248
Direct Property Insurance Carrier Services
N.A.I.C.S.: 524126
Kenneth Apfel (Chief Actuary)
Paul A. Bonny (Vice Chm)
Michael C. Sapnar (Co-Pres & Co-CEO)
Donna Byron (Exec VP-Human Resources)
Kenneth Brandt (Co-Pres & Co-CEO)
James Whitelaw (CMO)
George Di Martino (CIO)
Greg Richardson (Chief Strategy Officer & Chief Risk Officer)
Beth Levene (Chief Claims Officer)
Matt Mahoney (CFO)
Ken Yapp (Gen Counsel)

Subsidiary (Non-US):

Calpe Insurance Company Limited   (3)
First Floor Grand Ocean Plaza Ocean Village, PO Box 1338, Gibraltar, Gibraltar
Tel.: (350) 20074570
Reinsurance Services
N.A.I.C.S.: 524130

Subsidiary (Domestic):

Professional Risk Management Services, Inc.   (3)
4300 Wilson Blvd Ste 700, Arlington, VA 22203   (100%)
Tel.: (703) 907-3800
Web Site: https://www.prms.com
Sales Range: $1-9.9 Million
Risk Managemeng Srvices
N.A.I.C.S.: 524298
Melanie Smith (Sr VP)
Donna Vanderpool (Dir-Risk Mgmt)
Charles David Cash (Assoc Dir-Risk Mgmt)
Danielle Bolger (Mktg Dir)
Justin A. Pope (Mgr-Risk)
Ann McNary (Sr Mgr-Risk)

Transatlantic Reinsurance Company   (3)
1 Liberty Plz 165 Broadway, New York, NY 10006
Tel.: (212) 365-2200
Web Site: https://www.transre.com
Sales Range: $75-99.9 Million
Treaty & Facultative Reinsurance Services
N.A.I.C.S.: 524113
Beth A. Levene (Chief Claims Officer)
Michael C. Sapnar (Co-Pres & Co-CEO)
George Di Martino (CIO)
Matthew Mahoney (CFO)
Kenneth Apfel (Chief Actuary)
Greg Richardson (Chief Strategy Officer & Chief Risk Officer)
James Whitelaw (CMO)
Paul Bonny (Chm)
Kenneth Brandt (Co-Pres & Co-CEO)
Donna Byron (Sr VP & Head-HR)

Subsidiary (Domestic):

Fair American Insurance & Reinsurance Company   (4)
1 Liberty Plz 165 Broadway, New York, NY 10006
Tel.: (212) 770-2000
Web Site: https://www.fairco.com
Sales Range: $75-99.9 Million
Reinsurance Services
N.A.I.C.S.: 524130

Subsidiary (Domestic):

Fair American Select Insurance Company   (5)
1 Liberty Plz 165 Broadway, New York, NY 10006
Tel.: (212) 365-2200
Web Site: https://www.fairco.com
Emp.: 400
Casualty Insurance Services
N.A.I.C.S.: 524210
Michael Sapnar (Pres)

Subsidiary (Non-US):

Trans Re Zurich Reinsurance Company Ltd   (4)
Nuschelerstrasse 32, PO Box 1475, Zurich, 8021, Switzerland   (100%)
Tel.: (41) 442276100
Web Site: http://www.transre.com
Sales Range: $25-49.9 Million
Emp.: 40
Casualty, Property, Life & Health Reinsurance Products
N.A.I.C.S.: 524130
Alain D. Manfre (CEO & Gen Mgr)

TransRe London Limited   (4)
Corn Exchange 55 Mark Lane, London, EC3R 7NE, United Kingdom
Tel.: (44) 2072048600
Casualty Insurance Services
N.A.I.C.S.: 524210
Jonathan Bowers (Mgr-Accident & Health)

TransRe S.A.   (4)
Torre de Panama Piso 26 Boulevard Costa del Este y, Avenida de La Rotonda, Panama, Panama
Tel.: (507) 2826900
Reinsurance Services
N.A.I.C.S.: 524130

TransRe Zurich Ltd.   (4)
Sihlstrasse 38, PO Box 1475, 8021, Zurich, Switzerland
Tel.: (41) 442276100
Web Site: http://www.transre.com
Reinsurance Services
N.A.I.C.S.: 524130

Transatlantic Re (Argentina) S.A.   (4)
Juana Manso 555 - 2 F, C1107CBK, Buenos Aires, Argentina
Tel.: (54) 1152963500
Web Site: http://www.transre.com
Emp.: 5
Reinsurance Services
N.A.I.C.S.: 524130

AltaLink Investments, L.P.   (1)
2611 3 Ave SE, Calgary, T2A 7W7, AB, Canada
Tel.: (403) 267-3400
Web Site: http://www.altalink.ca
Emp.: 4
Electricity Transmission System Operator
N.A.I.C.S.: 221121

BH Shoe Holdings, Inc.   (1)
3555 Farnam St Ste 1440, Omaha, NE 68131
Tel.: (402) 346-1400
Web Site:
   http://www.berkshirehathaway.com
Sales Range: $25-49.9 Million
Emp.: 24
Holding Company & Footwear Mfr
N.A.I.C.S.: 551112

Subsidiary (Domestic):

H.H. Brown Shoe Company, Inc.   (2)
124 W Putnam Ave, Greenwich, CT 06830
Tel.: (203) 661-2424
Web Site: https://www.hhbrown.com
Footwear Mfr
N.A.I.C.S.: 316210

Subsidiary (Domestic):

Cove Shoe Company   (3)
107 Highland St, Martinsburg, PA 16662-1424
Tel.: (814) 793-7007
Web Site: http://www.coveshoe.com
Sales Range: $100-124.9 Million
Emp.: 301
Men's Shoes

N.A.I.C.S.: 316210
Victor Sanders (CFO & COO)

Dexter Shoe Company   (3)
71 Railroad Ave, Dexter, ME 04930   (100%)
Tel.: (207) 924-7341
Web Site: http://www.dextershoe.com
Sales Range: $500-549.9 Million
Shoe Mfr
N.A.I.C.S.: 316210

Subsidiary (Domestic):

Dexter Shoe Company   (4)
71 Railroad Ave, Dexter, ME 04930
Tel.: (207) 924-7341
Sales Range: $450-499.9 Million
Footwear Retailer
N.A.I.C.S.: 424340

Subsidiary (Domestic):

Double H Boot Company   (3)
107 Highland St, Martinsburg, PA 16662
Tel.: (814) 793-3786
Web Site: http://www.doublehboots.com
Sales Range: $75-99.9 Million
Emp.: 350
Footwear Mfr
N.A.I.C.S.: 316210

Sofft Shoe Company, Inc.   (3)
100 Brickstone Sq Ste 502, Andover, MA 01810
Tel.: (978) 933-4300
Web Site: http://www.sofftshoe.com
Sales Range: $100-124.9 Million
Emp.: 250
Women's Service & Casual Shoes Mfr
N.A.I.C.S.: 316210

BHH Affiliates, LLC   (1)
18500 Von Karman Ave Ste 400, Irvine, CA 92612
Tel.: (812) 478-1979
Real Estate Services
N.A.I.C.S.: 531210

BHSF, Inc.   (1)
1440 Kiewit Plz, Omaha, NE 68131
Tel.: (402) 346-1400
Holding Company
N.A.I.C.S.: 524113

Subsidiary (Domestic):

Scott Fetzer Company   (2)
28800 Clemens Rd, Westlake, OH 44145-1134   (100%)
Tel.: (440) 892-3000
Web Site: https://www.scottfetzer.com
Consumer & Commercial Appliances Mfr
N.A.I.C.S.: 333912
George Scott (Co-Founder)
Carl Fetzer (Co-Founder)

Division (Domestic):

Adalet   (3)
4801 W 150th St, Cleveland, OH 44135
Tel.: (216) 267-9000
Web Site: http://www.adalet.com
Sales Range: $10-24.9 Million
Emp.: 60
Conduit Fittings, Explosion Proof Fittings & Junction Boxes Mfr
N.A.I.C.S.: 334419

Arbortech   (3)
3203 W Old Lincoln Way, Wooster, OH 44691
Tel.: (330) 264-7441
Web Site:
   http://www.arbortechchipbodies.com
Sales Range: $100-124.9 Million
Emp.: 150
Chip Body Mfr
N.A.I.C.S.: 333310

Campbell Hausfeld   (3)
225 Pictoria Dr Ste 210, Cincinnati, OH 45246
Tel.: (513) 367-4811
Web Site: http://www.campbellhausfeld.com
Sales Range: $300-349.9 Million
Emp.: 100

Berkshire Hathaway Inc.—(Continued)

Portable Air Compressor, Painting Systems, Air Tools, Generators, Pressure Washers & Welders
N.A.I.C.S.: 333912

Carefree of Colorado (3)
2145 W 6th Ave, Broomfield, CO 80020-1656
Tel.: (303) 469-3324
Web Site:
http://www.carefreeofcolorado.com
Sales Range: $100-124.9 Million
Emp.: 200
Accessories for RV's & Motor Homes, Awnings & Canopies Mfr, Marine Accessories & Residential Sun & Shade Accessories
N.A.I.C.S.: 314910
Scott Thompson (Pres)

Douglas/Quikut (3)
118 E Douglas Rd, Walnut Ridge, AR 72476 (100%)
Tel.: (870) 886-6774
Web Site: http://www.ginsubrands.com
Sales Range: $25-49.9 Million
Emp.: 250
Soaps & Specialty Cleaners; Electric & Manual Fillet Knives, Cutlery & Cutting Boards; Camping Products & Sporting Goods Mfr
N.A.I.C.S.: 332215

Halex (3)
23901 Aurora Rd, Cleveland, OH 44146
Tel.: (440) 439-1616
Web Site: http://www.halexco.com
Sales Range: $25-49.9 Million
Emp.: 25
Electrical Products Whslr & Distr
N.A.I.C.S.: 423610

Kirby World Headquarters (3)
1920 W 114th St, Cleveland, OH 44102-2322 (100%)
Tel.: (216) 228-2400
Web Site: http://www.kirby.com
Sales Range: $125-149.9 Million
Emp.: 300
Vacuum Cleaner Mfr
N.A.I.C.S.: 335210

Meriam Instrument (3)
28800 Clemens Rd, Westlake, OH 44145-1134
Tel.: (440) 892-3000
Web Site: http://www.meriam.com
Industrial Instrument Mfr
N.A.I.C.S.: 334513

STAHL/Scott Fetzer Company (3)
3201 W Old Lincoln Way, Wooster, OH 44691-3258
Tel.: (330) 264-7441
Web Site: http://www.stahltruckbodies.com
Sales Range: $50-74.9 Million
Emp.: 100
Custom Steel Service Bodies & Tool Boxes for Trucks Mfr
N.A.I.C.S.: 336212

Scot Laboratories (3)
16841 Park Cir Dr, Chagrin Falls, OH 44023 (100%)
Tel.: (440) 543-3033
Web Site: http://www.scotlabs.com
Sales Range: $10-24.9 Million
Emp.: 25
Specialty Cleaning Product Mfr
N.A.I.C.S.: 325612

The ScottCare Corporation (3)
4791 W 150th St, Cleveland, OH 44135
Tel.: (216) 362-0550
Web Site: http://www.scottcare.com
Sales Range: $25-49.9 Million
Emp.: 100
Telemetry & Telemedicine Patient Monitoring Systems
N.A.I.C.S.: 334510

Subsidiary (Domestic):

Rozinn Electronics, Inc. (4)
10 Kodiak Dr, Woodbury, NY 11797-2705
Tel.: (718) 386-5526
Web Site: http://www.rozinn.com
Sales Range: $25-49.9 Million
Emp.: 30
Medical Equipment Mfr

N.A.I.C.S.: 423450

Subsidiary (Domestic):

United Consumer Financial Services Company (3)
865 Bassett Rd, Westlake, OH 44145
Tel.: (440) 835-6643
Web Site: http://www.ucfs.net
Sales Range: $125-149.9 Million
Emp.: 230
Consumer Financing
N.A.I.C.S.: 522210
Nick Codispoti (Pres)
Eric Cyr (VP-Kiby North America)
Candace Carter (VP-Legal & Compliance)
John Simon (VP-Sls & Mktg-North America)
Michele Liebenauer (Controller)
David Girt (Dir-Acct Svcs)
Christopher Georgas (Dir-Underwriting & Client Svcs)
Eric Saint Cyr (VP)
Scott Borthwick (Reg VP)

Division (Domestic):

Wayne Water Systems (3)
101 Production Dr, Harrison, OH 45030
Tel.: (513) 367-9979
Web Site: https://www.waynepumps.com
Sales Range: $100-124.9 Million
Pumps & Water Accessories Mfr
N.A.I.C.S.: 333914

Western Enterprises Division (3)
875 Bassett Rd, Westlake, OH 44145-1196
Tel.: (440) 871-2160
Web Site:
http://www.westernenterprises.com
Sales Range: $75-99.9 Million
Emp.: 200
Compressed Gas Fittings & Regulators Mfr
N.A.I.C.S.: 333992
Drew Theshire (Pres)

Western Plastics (3)
105 Western Dr, Portland, TN 37148
Tel.: (615) 325-7331
Web Site: http://www.westernplasticstn.com
Sales Range: $50-74.9 Million
Emp.: 150
Injection Molding Plastics Mfr
N.A.I.C.S.: 333248
Gene Ketter (CFO)

Subsidiary (Domestic):

World Book/Scott Fetzer Company, Inc. (3)
180 N LaSalle St Ste 900, Chicago, IL 60601-5519
Tel.: (312) 729-5800
Web Site: https://www.worldbook.com
Sales Range: $50-74.9 Million
Emp.: 180
Book Publishers
N.A.I.C.S.: 513130

Benjamin Moore & Co. (1)
101 Paragon Dr, Montvale, NJ 07645
Tel.: (201) 573-9600
Web Site: http://www2.benjaminmoore.com
Sales Range: $900-999.9 Million
Emp.: 2,951
Paints, Stains & Enamels Mfr
N.A.I.C.S.: 325510
Dan Calkins (Chm & CEO)

Unit (Domestic):

Benjamin Moore & Co. (2)
109 Bamberg Dr, Pell City, AL 35125
Tel.: (205) 338-4440
Web Site: http://www.benjaminmoore.com
Paint & Coating Mfr & Whslr
N.A.I.C.S.: 325510

Subsidiary (Domestic):

Insl-X Products Corp. (2)
101 Paragon Dr, Montvale, NJ 07645
Tel.: (201) 573-9600
Web Site: http://www.insl-x.com
Sales Range: $25-49.9 Million
Emp.: 360
Paint, Stain & Finish Mfr
N.A.I.C.S.: 325510

Janovic-Plaza Inc. (2)
3035 Thomson Ave, Long Island City, NY 11101

Tel.: (718) 392-3999
Web Site: http://www.janovic.com
Sales Range: $50-74.9 Million
Emp.: 60
Paint Retailer
N.A.I.C.S.: 424950

Berkshire Hathaway Automotive Inc. (1)
8333 Royal Ridge Pkwy Ste 100, Irving, TX 75063
Tel.: (972) 607-9295
Web Site:
https://www.berkshirehathawayautomotive.com
Emp.: 125
Holding Company; Automobile Dealerships
N.A.I.C.S.: 551112
Larry Van Tuyl (Chm)
Jeffrey C. Rachor (CEO)

Subsidiary (Domestic):

Van Tuyl Group, LLC (2)
1550 E Missouri Ave Ste 300, Phoenix, AZ 85014-6460
Tel.: (602) 230-1051
Web Site: http://www.vantuylgroup.com
Sales Range: $5-14.9 Billion
Holding Company; New & Used Car Dealerships
N.A.I.C.S.: 551112
Jeffrey C. Rachor (CEO)

Berkshire Hathaway Credit Corporation (1)
1440 Kiewit Plz, Omaha, NE 68131
Tel.: (402) 346-1400
Web Site:
http://www.berkshirehathaway.com
Emp.: 25
Real Estate Financial Services
N.A.I.C.S.: 531390
Charles Thomas Munger (Vice Chm)

Berkshire Hathaway Energy Company (1)
666 Grand Ave, Des Moines, IA 50306-0657 (88.2%)
Tel.: (515) 242-3022
Web Site: https://www.brkenergy.com
Rev.: $26,337,000,000
Assets: $133,840,000,000
Liabilities: $83,201,000,000
Net Worth: $50,639,000,000
Earnings: $2,721,000,000
Emp.: 24,000
Fiscal Year-end: 12/31/2022
Holding Company; Electric & Gas Distribution & Generation Services
N.A.I.C.S.: 551112
William J. Fehrman (Pres & CEO)
R. Patrick Reiten (Sr VP-Pub Policy)
Cathy S. Woollums (Chief Sustainability Officer & Sr VP)
Calvin D. Haack (CFO & Sr VP)
Scott W. Thon (Pres)

Subsidiary (Non-US):

AltaLink L.P. (2)
2611-3rd Avenue SE, Calgary, T2A 7W7, AB, Canada
Tel.: (403) 267-3400
Web Site: http://www.altalink.ca
Rev.: $713,336,832
Assets: $7,320,422,053
Liabilities: $4,756,170,154
Net Worth: $2,564,251,899
Earnings: $194,594,410
Emp.: 745
Fiscal Year-end: 12/31/2019
Electricity Transmission Facilities Owner & Operator
N.A.I.C.S.: 221122
Scott Thon (CEO)
Zora Lazic (Gen Counsel & Sr VP-Law & Regulatory)
David A. Tuer (Chm)
Scott Schreiner (VP-External Engagement)
David Koch (CFO & Exec VP)
Johanne Picard-Thompson (Exec VP-Customer & Corp Svcs)
Chris Lomore (Treas & VP)
Gary Hart (Pres & COO)
Cayla Saby (Dir-Customer Svc)
Sheri Allen (Sr VP-HR)
Mike Bartel (VP-Ops)
Paul Lee (VP-Projects)

Subsidiary (Domestic):

BHE Renewables, LLC (2)
666 Grand Ave Ste 500, Des Moines, IA 50309-2580
Tel.: (515) 242-3033
Web Site: https://www.bherenewables.com
Eletric Power Generation Services
N.A.I.C.S.: 221118
Alicia R. Knapp (Pres & CEO)
William J. Fehrman (Pres & CEO)

Kern River Gas Transmission Company (2)
2755 E Cottonwood Pkwy Ste 300, Salt Lake City, UT 84121 (100%)
Tel.: (801) 937-6000
Web Site: http://www.kernrivergas.com
Sales Range: $25-49.9 Million
Emp.: 100
Natural Gas Transmission Services
N.A.I.C.S.: 486210
Robert S. Checketts (VP-Ops & Engrg)
John T. Dushinske (VP-Customer Svc & Bus Dev)
Kirk L. Lavengood (Gen Counsel & VP-Regulatory Affairs)
Mark A. Hewett (Pres & CEO)

MidAmerican Funding, LLC (2)
666 Grand Ave, Des Moines, IA 50309-2580
Tel.: (515) 242-4300
Rev.: $4,025,000,000
Assets: $25,254,000,000
Liabilities: $14,575,000,000
Net Worth: $10,679,000,000
Earnings: $947,000,000
Emp.: 3,400
Fiscal Year-end: 12/31/2022
Holding Company; Electric Power & Natural Gas Distr & Regional Business & Economic Development Services
N.A.I.C.S.: 551112
Thomas B. Specketer (VP & Controller)
Natalie L. Hocken (Mgr)
Daniel S. Fick (Mgr)
Kelcey A. Brown (Pres)
Calvin D. Haack (Mgr)

Subsidiary (Domestic):

MidAmerican Energy Company (3)
666 Grand Ave, Des Moines, IA 50309-2580
Tel.: (515) 242-4300
Web Site:
https://www.midamericanenergy.com
Rev.: $4,025,000,000
Assets: $23,978,000,000
Liabilities: $14,333,000,000
Net Worth: $9,645,000,000
Earnings: $961,000,000
Emp.: 3,400
Fiscal Year-end: 12/31/2022
Electric Power & Natural Gas Distr
N.A.I.C.S.: 221122
Kathryn M. Kunert (VP-Economic Connections & Integration)
Michael A. Gehringer (VP-Customer Ops)
John A. Guy (VP-Electric Delivery)
Tina L. Hoffman (VP-Corp Comm & Pub Affairs)
Ryan M. Sawyer (VP-HR)
Chelsea C. McCracken (VP)
Damian M. Vallas (VP)
Mark D. Lowe (VP)
Nick J. Nation (VP)
Peggi S. Allenback (VP)
Scott L. DeRosier (VP)
Arick R. Sears (VP)

Subsidiary (Domestic):

NV Energy, Inc. (2)
6226 W Sahara Ave, Las Vegas, NV 89146
Tel.: (702) 402-5000
Web Site: http://www.nvenergy.com
Holding Company; Electric Power & Gas Distr
N.A.I.C.S.: 551112
Doug Cannon (Pres & CEO)
Michael Cole (CFO & VP)
Dave Ulozas (Sr VP-Renewable Energy & Origination)
Jennifer Oswald (Sr VP-HR & Corp Svcs)
Tony F. Sanchez III (Exec VP-Bus Dev & Extension Rels)

Subsidiary (Domestic):

Nevada Power Company (3)

6226 W Sahara Ave, Las Vegas, NV
89146   **(100%)**
Tel.: (702) 402-5000
Web Site: https://www.nvenergy.com
Rev.: $3,088,000,000
Assets: $10,727,000,000
Liabilities: $6,763,000,000
Net Worth: $3,964,000,000
Earnings: $260,000,000
Emp.: 1,500
Fiscal Year-end: 12/31/2023
Electricity, Natural Gas & Renewable En-
ergy Services
N.A.I.C.S.: 221122
Douglas A. Cannon *(Chm)*
Michael E. Cole *(CFO, Treas & VP)*
Michael R. Niggli Jr. *(Pres & CEO)*
Michael J. Behrens *(CTO)*
Dave Ulozas *(Sr VP)*

Sierra Pacific Power Company   **(3)**
6100 Neil Rd, Reno, NV 89511
Tel.: (775) 834-4011
Web Site: https://www.nvenergy.com
Rev.: $1,431,000,000
Assets: $4,772,000,000
Liabilities: $2,707,000,000
Net Worth: $2,065,000,000
Earnings: $117,000,000
Emp.: 1,000
Fiscal Year-end: 12/31/2023
Electric & Gas Utility Services
N.A.I.C.S.: 221118
Michael J. Behrens *(Interim CFO)*

Subsidiary (Domestic):

Northern Natural Gas Company   **(2)**
1111 S 103rd St, Omaha, NE
68124-1072   **(100%)**
Tel.: (402) 398-7200
Web Site:
    http://www.northernnaturalgas.com
Sales Range: $1-4.9 Billion
Emp.: 1,000
Natural Gas Transportation
N.A.I.C.S.: 486210

PacifiCorp   **(2)**
825 NE Multnomah St, Portland, OR 97232
Tel.: (503) 813-6666
Web Site: https://www.pacificorp.com
Rev.: $5,679,000,000
Assets: $29,405,000,000
Liabilities: $18,664,000,000
Net Worth: $10,741,000,000
Earnings: $920,000,000
Emp.: 4,800
Fiscal Year-end: 12/31/2022
Electric Power Transmission & Distribution
Services
N.A.I.C.S.: 221111
William J. Fehrman *(Chm & CEO)*
Stefan A. Bird *(Pres & CEO-Pacific Power)*
Gary Hoogeveen *(CFO)*

Subsidiary (Domestic):

Rocky Mountain Power   **(3)**
1407 W North Temple, Salt Lake City, UT
84116
Tel.: (503) 813-6666
Web Site:
    https://www.rockymountainpower.net
Sales Range: $200-249.9 Million
Electric Utility
N.A.I.C.S.: 221118

**Berkshire Hathaway Life Insurance
Company of Nebraska**   **(1)**
3024 Harney St, Omaha, NE 68131-3580
Tel.: (402) 916-3000
Web Site: http://www.bhln.com
Sales Range: $150-199.9 Million
Insurance Services
N.A.I.C.S.: 524113

Subsidiary (Non-US):

**Berkshire Hathaway International In-
surance Limited**   **(2)**
4th Floor 8 Fenchurch Place, London,
EC3M 4AJ, United Kingdom
Tel.: (44) 207 342 2000
Web Site: https://www.bhiil.com
Insurance Agency Services
N.A.I.C.S.: 524210

Subsidiary (Domestic):

**Central States Indemnity Co. of
Omaha**   **(2)**

1212 N 96th St, Omaha, NE 68114
Tel.: (402) 997-8000
Web Site: http://www.csi-omaha.com
Sales Range: $75-99.9 Million
Insurance Services
N.A.I.C.S.: 524210
John E. Keiser *(Pres)*

**General Reinsurance
Corporation**   **(2)**
120 Long Ridge Rd, Stamford, CT
06902-1843   **(100%)**
Tel.: (203) 328-5000
Web Site: http://www.genre.com
Reinsurance Carriers
N.A.I.C.S.: 524126

Subsidiary (Non-US):

Gen RE Corporation   **(3)**
Theoval Block 3 Balls Bridge, Dublin, D4,
Ireland   **(100%)**
Tel.: (353) 16738500
Web Site: http://www.genre.com
Sales Range: Less than $1 Million
Emp.: 10
Insurance Related Services
N.A.I.C.S.: 524298

Gen Re Mexico, S.A   **(3)**
Paseo De La Reforma 350 6 Fl, Torre del
Angel Col Juarez, 06600, Mexico,
Mexico   **(51%)**
Tel.: (52) 5591719200
Web Site: http://www.genre.com
Sales Range: $1-9.9 Million
Emp.: 28
Insurance & Related Services
N.A.I.C.S.: 524298
Horst Agata *(Branch Mgr)*
Paola Messina *(Branch Mgr)*
Carmelo Galante *(Mng Dir & Dir-Life &
Health Reg)*
Luis Rayes *(Reg Mgr)*

**General & Cologne RE (Sur) Compa-
nia de Reaseguros S.A.**   **(3)**
Compania de Reaseguros S.A., Manuela
Saenz 323/343, piso 7, 1061, Buenos Aires,
Argentina   **(100%)**
Tel.: (54) 1141147000
Web Site: http://www.genre.com
Sales Range: $1-9.9 Million
Emp.: 10
Insurance & Related Services
N.A.I.C.S.: 524298

General Life Re UK Limited   **(3)**
55 Mark Lane Corn Exchange, London,
EC3R 7NE, United Kingdom   **(100%)**
Tel.: (44) 2074261846
Web Site: http://www.de.genre.com
Sales Range: $100-124.9 Million
Emp.: 200
Reinsurance Carriers
N.A.I.C.S.: 524130

General Re Beirut s.a.l.   **(3)**
Societe Centre Ville 1341 S A L Bldg 2F
Patriarch Howeik Street, PO Box 11 7742,
Riad El Solh, Beirut, 2014-5401,
Lebanon   **(100%)**
Tel.: (961) 1999888
Web Site: http://www.genre.com
Sales Range: Less than $1 Million
Emp.: 18
Insurance Related Services
N.A.I.C.S.: 524298

Subsidiary (Domestic):

General Re Corporation   **(3)**
120 Long Ridge Rd, Stamford, CT 06902
Tel.: (203) 352-3000
Web Site: http://www.genre.com
Sales Range: $25-49.9 Million
Emp.: 100
Reinsurance Carriers
N.A.I.C.S.: 524130

Subsidiary (Domestic):

**Berkshire Hathaway Homestate In-
surance Company**   **(4)**
9290 W Dodge Rd, Omaha, NE
68114   **(100%)**
Tel.: (402) 393-7255
Web Site: http://www.bhhc.com
Insurance Carrier
N.A.I.C.S.: 524128

David Speights *(VP-Analytics)*
Danny Engell *(Chief Underwriting & Data
Analytics Officer & Sr VP)*
Rob Darby *(Pres & CEO)*

**Continental Divide Insurance
Company**   **(4)**
7730 E Belleview Ave Ste 300, Greenwood
Village, CO 80111   **(100%)**
Web Site: http://www.bhhc.com
General Insurance Services
N.A.I.C.S.: 524126

Subsidiary (Non-US):

Faraday Holdings Limited   **(4)**
Corn Exchange 5th Floor 55 Mark Lane
Corn Exchange, London, EC3R 7NE,
United Kingdom
Tel.: (44) 2077023333
Web Site: http://www.faraday.com
Sales Range: $75-99.9 Million
Emp.: 200
Insurance Holding Company
N.A.I.C.S.: 551112

Subsidiary (Domestic):

**Faraday Reinsurance Company
Ltd.**   **(5)**
Corn Exchange 55 Mark Ln, London, EC3R
7NE, United Kingdom
Tel.: (44) 2077023333
Web Site: http://www.faraday.com
Sales Range: $50-74.9 Million
Emp.: 100
Insurance Services
N.A.I.C.S.: 524128

Faraday Underwriting Limited   **(5)**
5th Floor 55 Mark Lane, London, EC3R
7NE, United Kingdom
Tel.: (44) 2077023333
Web Site: http://www.faraday.com
Emp.: 200
Insurance Services
N.A.I.C.S.: 524128
Tom Shelley *(CEO)*
Chris Thorne *(Chief Underwriting Officer)*
Kevin Harker *(Dir-Fin)*
Jason Bond *(COO)*
Charles Glaisher *(Head-Claims)*
Liz Richardson *(Sec)*

Subsidiary (Domestic):

**Gen Re Intermediaries
Corporation**   **(4)**
695 Main St Ste 600, Stamford, CT
06901   **(100%)**
Tel.: (203) 357-8883
Web Site: http://www.genre.com
Sales Range: $75-99.9 Million
Emp.: 25
Reinsurance Intermediary
N.A.I.C.S.: 523160

Gen Re Securities Holdings LLC **(4)**
125 Broad St Suite 500, New York, NY
10004
Tel.: (212) 341-8000
Web Site: http://www.genre.com
Sales Range: $75-99.9 Million
Emp.: 40
Financial Services
N.A.I.C.S.: 523150

**General Star Indemnity
Company**   **(4)**
120 Long Ridge Rd, Stamford, CT
06902   **(100%)**
Tel.: (203) 328-5700
Web Site: http://www.generalstar.com
Insurance Services
N.A.I.C.S.: 524114

**General Star National Insurance
Company**   **(4)**
120 Long Ridge Rd, Stamford, CT 06902-
2354
Tel.: (203) 328-5700
Web Site: https://www.generalstar.com
Sales Range: $75-99.9 Million
Insurance Services
N.A.I.C.S.: 524210

GeneralCologne Re   **(4)**
120 Long Ridge Rd, Stamford, CT
06902   **(100%)**

Tel.: (203) 328-5000
Web Site: http://www.genre.com
Emp.: 100
Reinsurance Services
N.A.I.C.S.: 524130

Subsidiary (Domestic):

**Genesis Underwriting Management
Company**   **(5)**
120 Long Ridge Rd, Stamford, CT
06902-2352   **(100%)**
Tel.: (203) 328-6660
Web Site: http://www.gumc.com
Sales Range: $1-9.9 Million
Emp.: 30
Underwrites Brokered Business from Non-
Traditional or Alternative Risk Markets
N.A.I.C.S.: 524210

Subsidiary (Domestic):

**Genesis Indemnity Insurance
Company**   **(4)**
120 Long Rdg Rd, Stamford, CT 06902
Tel.: (203) 328-5000
Web Site: http://www.gumc.com
Sales Range: $10-24.9 Million
Insurance Services
N.A.I.C.S.: 524210

Genesis Insurance Company   **(4)**
120 Long Ridge Rd, Stamford, CT 06902-
1839
Tel.: (203) 328-6660
Web Site:
    https://www.genesisinsurance.com
Sales Range: $75-99.9 Million
Insurance Services
N.A.I.C.S.: 524210

Division (Non-US):

General Reinsurance AG   **(3)**
Theodor-Heuss-Ring 11, 50668, Cologne,
Germany
Tel.: (49) 2 219 7380
Web Site: http://www.genre.com
Sales Range: $500-549.9 Million
Emp.: 800
Reinsurance Services
N.A.I.C.S.: 524130

Subsidiary (Non-US):

General Re Riga SIA   **(4)**
Elizabetes iela 11-4, Riga, 1010,
Latvia   **(100%)**
Tel.: (371) 67830107
Web Site: http://www.genre.com
Sales Range: Less than $1 Million
Emp.: 2
Insurance Related Services
N.A.I.C.S.: 524298

**General Reinsurance Scandinavia
A/S**   **(4)**
Weidekampsgade 14A 2nd floor, Copenha-
gen, 2300, Denmark
Tel.: (45) 33337878
Web Site: http://www.genre.com
Sales Range: Less than $1 Million
Emp.: 14
Insurance Related Services
N.A.I.C.S.: 524298
Elizabeth A. Bos *(Accountant-Client)*

**GeneralCologne Re Iberica Corres-
dores de Reaseguros, S.A**   **(4)**
Fortuny Numero 6 2 Izquierda, Planta 6,
28010, Madrid, Spain   **(100%)**
Tel.: (34) 913195750
Web Site: http://www.genre.com
Sales Range: $1-9.9 Million
Emp.: 28
Insurance Related Services
N.A.I.C.S.: 524298

Subsidiary (Non-US):

General Reinsurance Africa Ltd. **(3)**
2nd Floor South Wing Granger Bay Court
Granger Bay V&A Waterfront, PO Box 444,
Cape Town, 8002, South Africa
Tel.: (27) 214127700
Web Site: http://www.genre.com

Berkshire Hathaway Inc.—(Continued)

Sales Range: $1-9.9 Million
Emp.: 30
Insurance & Related Services
N.A.I.C.S.: 524298

General Reinsurance Australia Ltd. (3)
Level 20 1 O'Connell Street, Sydney, 2000, NSW, Australia
Tel.: (61) 28 236 6100
Web Site: https://www.genre.com
Sales Range: $10-24.9 Million
Emp.: 78
Insurance & Related Services
N.A.I.C.S.: 524298
Rob Frank (Mgr-Claims)
James Louw (Deputy Gen Mgr)
Scott Unterrheiner (Chief Risk Officer)
Robert Kerr (Sr Acct Mgr)
Viviane Murphy (Sr Acct Mgr)

Branch (Domestic):

General Re Australia Ltd. (4)
Level 5 520 Collins St, Melbourne, 3000, VIC, Australia (100%)
Tel.: (61) 396284000
Web Site: http://www.genre.com
Sales Range: $10-24.9 Million
Emp.: 7
Insurance & Related Services
N.A.I.C.S.: 524298

Branch (Non-US):

General Reinsurance Australia Ltd. (4)
Level 15 Forsyth Barr Tower 55 Shortland Street, Auckland, 1010, New Zealand
Tel.: (64) 93093638
Web Site: http://www.genre.com
Sales Range: $10-24.9 Million
Emp.: 3
Reinsurance Services
N.A.I.C.S.: 524130

Subsidiary (Non-US):

General Reinsurance Corporation (3)
1 First Canadian Place Suite 5705, PO Box 471, Toronto, M5X 1E4, ON, Canada (100%)
Tel.: (416) 869-0490
Web Site: http://www.genre.com
Sales Range: Less than $1 Million
Emp.: 21
Insurance-Related Services to Companies of the General Re Group
N.A.I.C.S.: 524298
Tracey Foreman (Mgr-Field Ops-Toronto)
Valerie J. Sheehy (Branch Mgr-Montreal)
Murray McCutcheon (Branch Mgr-Montreal)

Branch (Domestic):

General Reinsurance Corporation (3)
1890 World Trade Ctr, Saint Paul, MN 55102 (100%)
Tel.: (651) 293-0075
Web Site: http://www.genre.com
Sales Range: $10-24.9 Million
Emp.: 11
Insurance-Related Services to Companies of the General Re Group
N.A.I.C.S.: 524130

General Reinsurance Corporation (3)
1 California St Ste 600, San Francisco, CA 94111
Tel.: (415) 781-1700
Web Site: http://www.genre.com
Sales Range: $25-49.9 Million
Emp.: 40
Insurance-Related Services to Companies of the General Re Group
N.A.I.C.S.: 524130

General Reinsurance Corporation (3)
Two Commerce Sqr 2001 Market St Ste 500, Philadelphia, PA 19103
Tel.: (215) 988-7100
Web Site: http://www.genre.com

Sales Range: $10-24.9 Million
Emp.: 26
Reinsurance Carriers
N.A.I.C.S.: 524130

General Reinsurance Corporation (3)
550 S Hope St Ste 600, Los Angeles, CA 90071-2849
Tel.: (213) 630-1900
Web Site: http://www.genre.com
Insurance Related Services
N.A.I.C.S.: 524130

General Reinsurance Corporation (3)
32 Corporate Woods 9225 Indian Creek Pkwy Ste 1000, Overland Park, KS 66210-2008 (100%)
Tel.: (913) 345-2011
Web Site: http://www.genre.com
Sales Range: $10-24.9 Million
Emp.: 10
Insurance-Related Services to Companies of the General Re Group
N.A.I.C.S.: 524130
Steven J. Moran (Branch Mgr-Kansas City)
Duane C. Soper (Specialist-Program-Kansas City)

General Reinsurance Corporation (3)
One Financial Plz Fl 9 755 Main St Ste 1650, Hartford, CT 06103-2670
Tel.: (860) 547-0200
Web Site: http://www.genre.com
Sales Range: $25-49.9 Million
Emp.: 60
Insurance-Related Services to Companies of the General Re Group
N.A.I.C.S.: 524130
Mark G. Schmitz (Mgr-Standards)

General Reinsurance Corporation (3)
The Colonnade II 15303 N Dallas Pkwy Ste 500, Addison, TX 75001
Tel.: (214) 691-3000
Web Site: http://www.genre.com
Sales Range: $10-24.9 Million
Emp.: 16
Reinsurance Carriers
N.A.I.C.S.: 524130

General Reinsurance Corporation (3)
471 E Broad St Ste 2001, Columbus, OH 43215-3891
Tel.: (614) 221-7111
Web Site: http://www.gcr.com
Sales Range: $10-24.9 Million
Emp.: 20
Provides Insurance-Related Services to Companies of the General Re Group
N.A.I.C.S.: 524126
Charlie Shamieh (Chm)
Kara Raiguel (Pres & CEO)
Mike O'Dea (CFO)
Sandra Bell (Chief HR Officer)
Sabine Denne (Head-Global Mktg & Client Comm)

General Reinsurance Corporation (3)
1 N Wacker Dr Ste 800, Chicago, IL 60606
Tel.: (312) 207-5300
Web Site: http://www.genre.com
Sales Range: $1-9.9 Million
Emp.: 65
Insurance Related Services
N.A.I.C.S.: 524210

General Reinsurance Corporation (3)
125 High St Oliver St Tower Ste 1932, Boston, MA 02110-1817
Tel.: (617) 728-3800
Web Site: http://www.genre.com
Sales Range: $10-24.9 Million
Emp.: 15
Reinsurance Carriers
N.A.I.C.S.: 524130
Michael E. Brennan (Mgr-Program-Boston)
Richard R. Richter (Branch Mgr-Boston)
Thomas P. Welch (Mgr-Program-Boston)
Michael Brennan (Mgr)
Richard Richter (Branch Mgr)
Thomas Welch (Mgr)

General Reinsurance Corporation (3)

3575 Piedmont Rd NE Bldg 15 Ste 1400, Atlanta, GA 30305-1533
Tel.: (404) 237-2555
Web Site: http://www.genre.com
Sales Range: $50-74.9 Million
Emp.: 50
Reinsurance Carriers
N.A.I.C.S.: 524130
Charlie Shamieh (Chm)
Kara Raiguel (Pres & CEO)
Mike O'Dea (CFO)
Sandra Bell (Chief HR Officer)
Sabine Denne (Head-Mktg & Client Comm-Global)
Frank Schmid (CTO)

Subsidiary (Non-US):

General Reinsurance Life Australia Ltd. (3)
Level 20 1 O'Connell Street, Sydney, 2000, NSW, Australia
Tel.: (61) 28 236 6100
Web Site: https://www.genre.com
Insurance Services
N.A.I.C.S.: 524130

General Reinsurance UK Limited (3)
55 Mark Lane Corn Exchange, London, EC3R 7NE, United Kingdom (100%)
Tel.: (44) 2074266000
Web Site: http://www.genre.com
Sales Range: $100-124.9 Million
Emp.: 300
Insurance Related Services
N.A.I.C.S.: 524298

Subsidiary (Domestic):

Government Employees Insurance Company (3)
1 Geico Plz, Washington, DC 20076
Tel.: (301) 986-3000
Web Site: https://www.geico.com
Emp.: 43,000
Insurance Services
N.A.I.C.S.: 524298

United States Aircraft Insurance Group (3)
125 Broad St, New York, NY 10004
Tel.: (212) 952-0100
Web Site: http://www.usau.com
Sales Range: $150-199.9 Million
Emp.: 300
Aviation Insurance
N.A.I.C.S.: 524126

Subsidiary (Domestic):

National Indemnity Company (2)
1314 Douglas St Ste 1400, Omaha, NE 68102-1944 (100%)
Tel.: (402) 916-3000
Web Site: https://www.nationalindemnity.com
Emp.: 100
Property/Casualty Insurance Services
N.A.I.C.S.: 524126
Ajit Jain (Exec VP)

Subsidiary (Domestic):

Columbia Insurance Co. (3)
10820 Harney St, Omaha, NE 68154
Tel.: (402) 330-5600
Insurance Services
N.A.I.C.S.: 524126

Subsidiary (Domestic):

The Medical Protective Company (4)
5814 Reed Rd, Fort Wayne, IN 46835-3568
Tel.: (260) 485-9622
Web Site: http://www.medpro.com
Sales Range: $200-249.9 Million
Emp.: 350
Medical Professional Liability Coverage & Risk Services
N.A.I.C.S.: 524126

Subsidiary (Domestic):

Princeton Insurance Company (5)
21 Roszel Rd, Princeton, NJ 08543
Tel.: (609) 452-9404
Web Site: https://www.princetoninsurance.com
Emp.: 100
Healthcare Liability Insurance

N.A.I.C.S.: 524114

Subsidiary (Domestic):

Princeton Risk Protection, Inc. (6)
746 Alexander Rd, Princeton, NJ 08540-6305 (100%)
Tel.: (609) 452-0749
Web Site: http://www.princetonriskprotection.com
Sales Range: $25-49.9 Million
Emp.: 15
Review & Evaluation of Healthcare Facilities Equipment Management Programs & Environments
N.A.I.C.S.: 524298

Subsidiary (Domestic):

GUARD Insurance Group, Inc. (3)
16 S River St, Wilkes Barre, PA 18702-2406
Tel.: (570) 825-9900
Web Site: http://www.guard.com
Sales Range: $400-449.9 Million
Emp.: 274
Holding Company; Commercial Insurance Products & Services
N.A.I.C.S.: 551112
Sy Foguel (Pres & CEO)
Carl J. Witkowski (COO & Exec VP)
Daniel Brennan (Sr VP-Claims)
Eitan Ajchenbaum (CFO & Treas)
Sean Reaser (Sr VP-Underwriting)
Dave Simmons (Sr VP-Sls)
Jim Thomas (Sr VP-Strategy & Bus Analytics)
Melinda Thompson (Controller)

Subsidiary (Domestic):

InterGUARD, Ltd. (4)
16 S River St, Wilkes Barre, PA 18702-2406
Tel.: (570) 825-9900
Web Site: http://www.guard.com
Insurance Program Management Services
N.A.I.C.S.: 524298

NorGUARD Insurance Company (4)
16 S River St, Wilkes Barre, PA 18702
Tel.: (570) 825-9900
Web Site: http://www.guard.com
Emp.: 116
Commercial Property & Casualty Insurance, Pension & Reinsurance Products
N.A.I.C.S.: 524126

Subsidiary (Domestic):

National Fire & Marine Insurance Company (3)
1314 Douglas St Ste 1400, Omaha, NE 68102-1944
Tel.: (402) 536-3000
Web Site: http://www.nationalindemnity.com
Sales Range: $250-299.9 Million
Emp.: 1,000
Fire & Marine Insurance
N.A.I.C.S.: 524126

Subsidiary (Domestic):

NFM of Kansas Inc (4)
1601 Village W Pkwy, Kansas City, KS 66111-1878
Tel.: (913) 288-6261
Web Site: http://www.nfm.com
Emp.: 3
Furniture Retailer
N.A.I.C.S.: 449110

Subsidiary (Domestic):

National Indemnity Company of Mid-America (3)
1314 Douglas St, Omaha, NE 68102-1944
Tel.: (402) 916-3000
Web Site: http://www.nationalindemnity.com
Insurance Services
N.A.I.C.S.: 524298

National Indemnity Company of the South (3)
3024 Harney St, Omaha, NE 68131
Tel.: (402) 536-3000
Web Site: http://www.nationalindemnity.com
Sales Range: $300-349.9 Million
Emp.: 500
Fire & Casualty Insurance

N.A.I.C.S.: 524126

National Liability and Fire Insurance Company (3)
1314 Douglas St Ste 1400, Omaha, NE 68102
Tel.: (402) 536-3000
Web Site: http://www.nationalindemnity.com
Sales Range: $75-99.9 Million
Emp.: 500
Insurance Services
N.A.I.C.S.: 524210

Boat America Corporation (1)
880 S Pickett St, Alexandria, VA 22304
Tel.: (703) 823-9550
Marine Equipment Whslr
N.A.I.C.S.: 423690

Borsheim Jewelry Company, Inc. (1)
120 Regency Pkwy, Omaha, NE 68114
Tel.: (402) 391-0400
Web Site: https://www.borsheims.com
Jewelry Retailer
N.A.I.C.S.: 458310
Adrienne Perry (Chief Revenue Officer)
Sean Moore (VP-Luxury Sls)
Julie McAlpine (VP-Mdse)
Andy Brabec (VP-Mktg & E-commerce)
Jaci Stuifbergen (Mktg Dir)

Bryan-College Station Communications, Inc. (1)
1729 Briarcrest Dr, Bryan, TX 77802
Tel.: (979) 776-4444
Web Site: http://www.theeagle.com
Sales Range: $10-24.9 Million
Emp.: 100
Newspaper Publishers
N.A.I.C.S.: 513110

Burlington Northern Santa Fe, LLC (1)
2650 Lou Menk Dr, Fort Worth, TX 76131-2830
Tel.: (817) 352-1000
Web Site: https://www.bnsf.com
Rev.: $25,888,000,000
Assets: $92,611,000,000
Liabilities: $45,375,000,000
Net Worth: $47,236,000,000
Earnings: $5,946,000,000
Emp.: 36,250
Fiscal Year-end: 12/31/2022
Holding Company; Coal, Grain, Intermodal Containers, Trailers & Various Industrial, Consumer, Automotive & Forest Products Rail Transportation Services
N.A.I.C.S.: 551112
Roger Nober (Chief Legal Officer & Exec VP-Law & Corp Affairs)
Stevan B. Bobb (CMO & Exec VP)
Paul W. Bischler (Chief Acctg Officer & VP)
Kathryn M. Farmer (Pres & CEO)
Julie A. Piggott (CFO & Exec VP)
Matthew J. Igoe (COO & Exec VP)
Candace I. Palmarozzi (VP)

Subsidiary (Domestic):

BNSF Railway Company (2)
2650 Lou Menk Dr, Fort Worth, TX 76131-2830
Web Site: http://www.bnsf.com
Sales Range: $15-24.9 Billion
Emp.: 41,000
Railroad Services
N.A.I.C.S.: 482111
Roger Nober (Exec VP-Law & Corp Affairs)
Steven B. Bobb (CMO & Exec VP)
Beth Miller (Treas & Asst VP-Treasury & Risk Mgmt)
Keith Solomons (VP-Mechanical)

Subsidiary (Non-US):

Burlington Northern (Manitoba) Limited (3)
963 Lindsay Street, Winnipeg, R3N 1X6, MB, Canada
Tel.: (204) 453-4415
Sales Range: $400-449.9 Million
Emp.: 7
Railroad Operator
N.A.I.C.S.: 482111

Affiliate (Domestic):

Central California Traction Company (3)

2572 Prt Rd A, Stockton, CA 95023
Tel.: (209) 466-6927
Web Site: http://www.cctrailroad.com
Sales Range: $1-9.9 Million
Emp.: 28
Railroad Services
N.A.I.C.S.: 488210
Richard Grigsbay (Mgr-Ops & Admin)
Jerry Martinez (Mgr-Track & Equipment)
Randy Egusquiza (Gen Mgr)
Joshua Garrison (Sr Supvr-Ops)

Subsidiary (Domestic):

Los Angeles Junction Railway Company (3)
4433 Exchange Ave, Vernon, CA 90058-2622
Tel.: (323) 277-2004
Sales Range: $10-24.9 Million
Emp.: 38
Railroad Services
N.A.I.C.S.: 482111

The Belt Railway Company of Chicago (3)
6900 S Central Ave, Bedford Park, IL 60638
Tel.: (708) 496-4000
Web Site: http://www.beltrailway.com
Sales Range: $50-74.9 Million
Emp.: 520
Railroad Services
N.A.I.C.S.: 482112
Chris Steinway (Gen Counsel & Dir-HR)
Christopher Steinway (Corp Counsel)
Percy Fields III (Pres)

Subsidiary (Domestic):

FreightWise, Inc. (2)
2500 Lou Menk Dr, Fort Worth, TX 76131-2828
Tel.: (817) 333-2000
Sales Range: $100-124.9 Million
Logistic Services
N.A.I.C.S.: 488510

Subsidiary (Domestic):

BNSF Logistics, LLC (3)
2710 S 48th St, Springdale, AR 72762
Web Site: http://www.bnsflogistics.com
Sales Range: $25-49.9 Million
Emp.: 150
Logistics Consulting Servies
N.A.I.C.S.: 541614
Tom Madzy (CIO)
Brant Nieminski (Exec VP)
Cami Misch (Pres)
Ron Edmundson (Chief Acct Officer)

Division (Domestic):

BNSF Logistics International (4)
1600 Lakeside Pkwy Ste 100, Flower Mound, TX 75028
Tel.: (817) 481-8521
Web Site: http://www.bnsflogistics.com
Sales Range: $25-49.9 Million
Emp.: 65
Freight Transportation & Logistics Services
N.A.I.C.S.: 488510

BNSF Logistics, LLC (4)
611 Marker Rd, Versailles, OH 45380
Tel.: (937) 526-3141
Web Site: http://www.bnsflogistics.com
Sales Range: $10-24.9 Million
Emp.: 35
Logistic Services
N.A.I.C.S.: 541614

Subsidiary (Domestic):

Transportation Technology Services, Inc. (4)
175 Westwood Dr, Southlake, TX 76092-7908
Tel.: (817) 421-3535
Web Site: http://www.railengineer.com
Engineering & Logistics Services for Rail Shipping
N.A.I.C.S.: 488210

Subsidiary (Domestic):

Meteor Communications Corporation, Inc. (2)
22614 66th Ave S, Kent, WA 98032
Tel.: (253) 872-2521

Web Site: http://www.meteorcomm.com
Sales Range: $10-24.9 Million
Emp.: 40
Wireless Telecommunication Services
N.A.I.C.S.: 334220

Business Wire, Inc. (1)
101 California St 20th Fl, San Francisco, CA 94111 (100%)
Tel.: (415) 986-4422
Web Site: https://www.businesswire.com
Sales Range: $75-99.9 Million
Emp.: 170
Business News Services
N.A.I.C.S.: 516210
Stuart Dean (VP-Sls)

CMH Capital, Inc. (1)
1105 N Market Ste Ste 1300, Wilmington, DE 19801-1241
Tel.: (302) 651-7947
Financial Investment Services
N.A.I.C.S.: 523999

CORT Business Services Corporation (1)
11250 Waples Mill Rd Ste 500, Fairfax, VA 22030 (100%)
Tel.: (703) 968-8500
Web Site: http://www.cort.com
Sales Range: $350-399.9 Million
Emp.: 2,450
Relocation Services & Home & Office Furniture Rental & Leasing
N.A.I.C.S.: 532289
Jeff Pederson (Chm & CEO)
Deborah Lansford (CFO)
Mike Davis (Pres & COO)
Jeff Seidman (VP)
Mark Koepsell (Exec VP)
Paula Newell (Exec VP)
Bill Swets (Exec VP)
Tim Deagan (Exec VP)
Damon Ross (Grp VP)
Mike Connors (Sr VP)
Lisa Woodworth (Sr VP-Mktg)
Ann Sennewald (VP-Mdsg)

Subsidiary (Domestic):

CORT Furniture Rental (2)
7817 N Dale Mabry, Tampa, FL 33614
Tel.: (813) 933-1731
Web Site: http://www.cort.com
Sales Range: $25-49.9 Million
Emp.: 30
Office Furniture Dealer
N.A.I.C.S.: 423210

CORT Furniture Rentals & Clearance Center (2)
7400 Squire Ct, West Chester, OH 45069-2313
Tel.: (513) 777-6104
Web Site: http://stores.cort.com
Furniture Rental & Retail
N.A.I.C.S.: 459510

CTB International Corp. (1)
611 N Higbee St, Milford, IN 46542-2000
Tel.: (574) 658-4191
Web Site: https://www.ctbinc.com
Sales Range: $1-4.9 Billion
Emp.: 3,000
Automated Feeding, Watering & Ventilation Systems Mfr
N.A.I.C.S.: 333111

Subsidiary (Domestic):

CTB, Inc. (2)
611 North Higbee St, Milford, IN 46542
Tel.: (574) 658-4191
Web Site: http://www.ctbinc.com
Sales Range: $1-4.9 Billion
Emp.: 2,400
Automated Feeding, Watering & Ventilation Systems Mfr
N.A.I.C.S.: 333111
Victor A. Mancinelli (Chm & CEO)
Randy Eveler (CFO & VP)
Jack Stambaugh (CMO)
Michael J. Kissane (Chief Admin Officer & Exec VP)
Robert Janek (CIO & VP)
Jeff Miller (VP & Gen Mgr)
Will Mabee (VP-Credit-Global & Risk Mgmt)
Elizabeth Beck (VP)
John V. Stambaugh (Chief Mktg Officer)
Nicole LaFollette (VP)
Ryan DeSmith (VP)

Subsidiary (Domestic):

Ironwood Plastics, Inc. (3)
1235 Wall St, Ironwood, MI 49938
Tel.: (906) 932-5025
Web Site: http://www.ironwood.com
Sales Range: $25-49.9 Million
Emp.: 150
Injection Molded Finished Plastics Product Mfr
N.A.I.C.S.: 326199
Dave Zielinski (Mgr-Bus Dev)
Julie Sexton (Mgr-Acct)

Subsidiary (Non-US):

Meyn Food Processing Technology B.V. (3)
Westeinde 6, 1511 MA, Oostzaan, Netherlands
Tel.: (31) 20 2045 000
Web Site: http://www.meyn.com
Sales Range: $250-299.9 Million
Emp.: 900
Poultry Processing Equipment Mfr
N.A.I.C.S.: 333241
Robbert Birkhoff (Dir-Sls & Projects)
Joost Weel (Mng Dir)
Karel van Nielen (CFO)
Anita Bonder (Dir-HR)

Subsidiary (US):

Meyn America, LLC (4)
1000 Evenflo Dr, Ball Ground, GA 30107
Tel.: (770) 967-0532
Web Site: http://www.meyn.com
Sales Range: $10-24.9 Million
Emp.: 150
Poultry Equipment Mfr
N.A.I.C.S.: 333241

Division (Domestic):

Shore Measuring Systems (3)
103 N Perry St, Attica, IN 47918
Tel.: (765) 769-3000
Web Site: http://www.moisturetesters.com
Sales Range: $1-9.9 Million
Emp.: 10
Agricultural Testing Equipment Mfr
N.A.I.C.S.: 333111

Division (Domestic):

Chore-Time Cage Systems (2)
410 N Higbee St, Milford, IN 46542-2000 (100%)
Tel.: (574) 658-4101
Web Site: http://www.choretime.com
Sales Range: $25-49.9 Million
Emp.: 100
Poultry Cage Rearing Systems, Egg Collection Systems, Feeding, Ventilation, Watering & Storage Equipment Mfr
N.A.I.C.S.: 333111

Chore-Time Equipment (2)
410 N Higbee St, Milford, IN 46542-2000 (100%)
Tel.: (574) 658-4101
Web Site: http://www.choretime.com
Sales Range: $250-299.9 Million
Emp.: 800
Feeding, Ventilation, Watering & Storage Equipment Mfr
N.A.I.C.S.: 333111

Chore-Time/Brock International (2)
611 N Higbee St, Milford, IN 46542-2000 (100%)
Tel.: (574) 658-4191
Web Site: http://www.ctbworld.com
Sales Range: $300-349.9 Million
Emp.: 1,000
Farm Equipment Mfr
N.A.I.C.S.: 333111

Subsidiary (Non-US):

Fancom B.V. (2)
Industrieterrein 34, 5981 NK, Panningen, Netherlands (100%)
Tel.: (31) 773069600
Web Site: http://www.fancom.com
Sales Range: $25-49.9 Million
Emp.: 100
Agricultural Climate, Feeding & Weighing Systems
N.A.I.C.S.: 333111

Berkshire Hathaway Inc.—(Continued)

Subsidiary (Non-US):

Fancom E.u.r.l. (3)
113 Rue De Fougeres, 35500, Vitre,
France (100%)
Tel.: (33) 299753057
Web Site: http://www.fancom.fr
Sales Range: $10-24.9 Million
Emp.: 13
Agricultural Climate, Feeding & Weighing
Systems
N.A.I.C.S.: 333111

California Insurance Company (1)
950 Tower Ln Fl 14, Foster City, CA 94404-
2121
Tel.: (415) 656-5066
Web Site: http://www.auw.com
Insurance Services
N.A.I.C.S.: 524298

**Central States of Omaha Companies,
Inc.** (1)
1212 N 96th St, Omaha, NE 68114
Tel.: (402) 397-1111
Web Site: http://www.cso.com
Emp.: 140
Insurance Management Services
N.A.I.C.S.: 524298

Charter Brokerage LLC (1)
383 Main Ave Ste 400, Norwalk, CT 06851
Tel.: (203) 840-7500
Web Site: http://www.charterbrokerage.net
Insurance Brokerage Services
N.A.I.C.S.: 524210
C. Bobby Waid (CEO)
Matthew D. Anderson (Pres & COO)
Andrew K. Chaglasian (CFO)
Michael V. Cerny (Chief Legal Officer)
Jason Doscamps (CIO)
Brian E. London (VP)
Lisa Carpontor (VP)
Michael Ong (VP)
Wes Horndon (VP)
Dan Sanders (VP)
Emilia Sattari (VP)
Duane Welch (VP)

Clayton Homes, Inc. (1)
5000 Clayton Rd, Maryville, TN 37804-5550
Tel.: (865) 380-3000
Web Site: https://www.claytonhomes.com
Manufactured Homes Mfr & Developer
N.A.I.C.S.: 321991

Subsidiary (Domestic):

CMH Homes, Inc. (2)
5000 Clayton Rd, Maryville, TN 37804
Tel.: (865) 380-3000
Web Site: https://www.claytonhomes.com
Sales Range: $1-4.9 Billion
Emp.: 1,400
Retailer of Mobile Homes
N.A.I.C.S.: 459930

CMH Manufacturing, Inc. (2)
5000 Clayton Rd, Maryville, TN 37804
Web Site: https://www.claytonhomes.com
Sales Range: $1-4.9 Billion
Emp.: 1,400
Mobile Home Mfr
N.A.I.C.S.: 459930

CMH Parks, Inc. (2)
5000 Clayton Rd, Maryville, TN 37804
Tel.: (865) 380-3000
Web Site: http://www.clayton.net
Sales Range: $1-4.9 Billion
Mobile Home Community Developer
N.A.I.C.S.: 459930

Division (Domestic):

Clayton Properties Group, Inc. (2)
5000 Clayton Rd, Maryville, TN 37804
Tel.: (800) 822-0633
Web Site:
http://www.claytonpropertiesgroup.com
Housing Construction Services
N.A.I.C.S.: 321991
Keith Holdbrooks (Pres)

Subsidiary (Domestic):

Arbor Homes, LLC (3)
9225 Harrison Park Ct, Indianapolis, IN
46216
Tel.: (317) 842-1875

Web Site: http://www.yourarborhome.com
New Single-Family Housing Construction
N.A.I.C.S.: 236115

Subsidiary (Domestic):

Elite Homes (4)
16218 Shelbyville Rd, Louisville, KY 40245-
4248
Tel.: (502) 245-6159
Web Site: http://www.elitebuilthomes.com
Single-Family Housing Construction
N.A.I.C.S.: 236115
Joe Pusateri (Founder)
Rocky Pusateri (Mgr-Land Dev)
Michael Metzkes (Pres)
Geoff Scholl (Mgr-Pur)
Gretchen Fraze (Sls Mgr)
Ray Deddens (Coord-Field Warranty)
Keri Mallory (Coord-Customer Care)
Bryan Owens (Project Mgr)
Bill Murphy (Project Mgr)
Craig Brockman (VP-Ops)

Subsidiary (Domestic):

Highland Holdings, Inc. (3)
3020 S Florida Ave Ste 101, Lakeland, FL
33803
Tel.: (863) 619-7103
Web Site: https://www.highlandhomes.org
New Home Construction
N.A.I.C.S.: 236115
Robert J. Adams (Co-Founder)
Joel Adams (Co-Founder)

Oakwood Homes LLC (3)
4908 Twr Rd, Denver, CO 80249-4810
Tel.: (303) 486-8500
Web Site:
https://www.oakwoodhomesco.com
Single-Family Housing Construction
N.A.I.C.S.: 236117
Pat Hamill (Founder & CEO)

The Mungo Company, Inc. (3)
441 Western Ln, Irmo, SC 29063-9071
Tel.: (803) 749-9000
Web Site: http://www.mungo.com
Sales Range: $75-99.9 Million
Emp.: 130
Provider of Home Building Services
N.A.I.C.S.: 236115

Subsidiary (Domestic):

Mungo Homes (4)
441 Western Ln, Irmo, SC 29063
Tel.: (803) 749-9000
Housing Construction Services
N.A.I.C.S.: 236115
Mary Lou Lee (Mgr-Closing)

**Mungo Homes Of North Carolina,
Inc.** (4)
2521 Schieffelin Rd Ste 116, Apex, NC
27502
Tel.: (919) 303-8525
Housing Construction Services
N.A.I.C.S.: 236115

Mungo Homes of Georgia LLC (4)
138 Canal St Ste 203, Pooler, GA 31322
Tel.: (912) 748-3225
Housing Construction Services
N.A.I.C.S.: 236115

**Palmetto Residential Rentals,
LLC** (4)
441 Western Ln, Irmo, SC 29063
Tel.: (803) 227-8441
Web Site:
http://www.palmettoresidential.com
Residential Building Rental Services
N.A.I.C.S.: 531110

Sovereign Homes, LLC (4)
PO Box 175, Fair Lawn, NJ 07410
Tel.: (201) 566-2093
Web Site: https://www.sovhomes.com
Housing Construction Services
N.A.I.C.S.: 236115

Subsidiary (Domestic):

Doyle Mobile Homes Parts, Inc. (2)
1160 W Water St, Flemingsburg, KY 41041-
8173
Tel.: (606) 845-8601
Web Site:
http://www.claytonflemingsburg.com

Manufactured Home Dealers
N.A.I.C.S.: 459930

G&I Homes, Inc. (2)
2605 Rte 5 Herkimer Rd, Frankfort, NY
13340
Tel.: (315) 732-6136
Web Site: http://www.gihomesutica.com
Manufactured & Modular Homes Builder
N.A.I.C.S.: 459930

Goodall Homes & Communities (2)
393 Maple St Ste 100, Gallatin, TN 37066
Tel.: (615) 451-5029
Web Site: http://www.goodallhomes.com
Sales Range: $1-9.9 Million
Emp.: 100
Housing Construction Services
N.A.I.C.S.: 236117

Homesmart Construction (2)
5000 Clayton Rd, Maryville, TN 37804
Tel.: (865) 380-3000
RealStae Homes Builder Services
N.A.I.C.S.: 321991
Danny Warrick (Pres-Homes Retail)
Chuck Morgan (VP)

River Birch Homes Inc. (2)
400 River Birch Dr, Hackleburg, AL 35564-
4650
Tel.: (205) 935-1997
Web Site: http://www.riverbirchhomes.com
Manufactured Home Dealers
N.A.I.C.S.: 459930

Southern Energy Homes, Inc. (2)
144 Corporate Way, Addison, AL 35540
Tel.: (256) 747-8589
Web Site: http://www.sehomes.com
Sales Range: $125-149.9 Million
Emp.: 1,191
Manufactured Homes & Mortgage Financing
N.A.I.C.S.: 321991

Subsidiary (Domestic):

Cavalier Homes, Inc. (3)
32 Wilson Blvd 100, Addison, AL
35540 (100%)
Tel.: (256) 747-1575
Web Site: http://www.cavalieralabama.com
Sales Range: $150-199.9 Million
Emp.: 1,012
Housing Design, Construction & Sales
N.A.I.C.S.: 321991

Subsidiary (Domestic):

Cavalier Home Builders, LLC (4)
PO Box 300, Addison, AL 35540 (100%)
Tel.: (256) 747-1575
Web Site:
http://www.cavalierhomebuilders.com
Sales Range: $75-99.9 Million
Emp.: 600
Prefabricated Home Construction
N.A.I.C.S.: 321991

Subsidiary (Domestic):

Southern Energy Homes (3)
8701 Harmon Rd, Fort Worth, TX 76177
Tel.: (817) 847-1355
Web Site: http://sehomestexas.com
Mobile Homes
N.A.I.C.S.: 321991

Subsidiary (Domestic):

The Brohn Group LLC (2)
6720 Vaught Ranch Rd Ste 200, Austin, TX
78730
Tel.: (512) 320-8833
Web Site: https://www.brohnhomes.com
Home Building & Land Development
N.A.I.C.S.: 236115
Evan v (Asst Mgr-Construction)

**Vanderbilt Mortgage & Finance,
Inc.** (2)
500 Alcoa Trl, Maryville, TN 37804
Web Site: https://www.vmf.com
Sales Range: $400-449.9 Million
Emp.: 1,300
Real Estate Credit Services
N.A.I.C.S.: 522292

Subsidiary (Domestic):

Crest Homes Corporation (3)

437 N Main St, Middlebury, IN 46540
Tel.: (574) 825-7500
Web Site: http://www.cresthomes.com
Sales Range: $75-99.9 Million
Emp.: 200
Mobile & Modular Homes Mfr
N.A.I.C.S.: 459930

Plant (Domestic):

Crest Homes Corporation (4)
201 N Industrial Park Rd, Milton, PA 17847-
9221
Tel.: (570) 742-8521
Web Site: http://www.cresthomes.com
Sales Range: $50-74.9 Million
Emp.: 150
Mobile & Modular Homes Mfr
N.A.I.C.S.: 236115

Subsidiary (Domestic):

Marlette Homes, Inc. (3)
30 Industrial Park Rd, Lewistown, PA 17044
Tel.: (717) 248-3947
Web Site: http://www.marlettehomes.com
Sales Range: $150-199.9 Million
Emp.: 300
Mobile & Modular Homes Mfr
N.A.I.C.S.: 321991

**Commonwealth Realty Group,
LLC** (1)
12 Huron Dr Natick, Natick, MA 01760
Tel.: (833) 915-1608
Full-service Real Estate Brokerage
N.A.I.C.S.: 531390

Subsidiary (Domestic):

Robert Paul Properties, Inc. (2)
867 Main St, Osterville, MA 02655
Tel.: (508) 420-1414
Web Site: http://www.robertpaul.com
Real Estate Development Services
N.A.I.C.S.: 531390
Paul Grover (Co-Founder)
Robert Kinlin (Co-Founder)
Emily Clark (Pres)

Cypress Insurance Company (1)
PO Box 7027, San Francisco, CA 94120
Tel.: (415) 734-4400
Web Site: http://www.bhhc.com
Sales Range: $150-199.9 Million
Direct Property & Casualty Insurance Carri-
ers
N.A.I.C.S.: 524126

Delta Wholesale Liquors, Inc. (1)
802 Rozelle St, Memphis, TN 38104
Tel.: (901) 272-0276
Web Site: http://www.deltawholesale.com
Alcoholic Beverages Whslr
N.A.I.C.S.: 424810

**Empire Distributors of Tennessee,
Inc.** (1)
3794 Tag Rd, Chattanooga, TN 37416
Tel.: (423) 899-3962
Web Site: http://www.empiredist.com
Wine Distr & Whslr
N.A.I.C.S.: 424820

FlightSafety International, Inc. (1)
Marine Air Terminal LaGuardia Airport,
Flushing, NY 11371-1061 (100%)
Tel.: (718) 565-4170
Web Site: http://www.flightsafety.com
Sales Range: $650-699.9 Million
Emp.: 3,300
Aviation & Marine Training Consulting Ser-
vices
N.A.I.C.S.: 611699
Steve Gross (Sr VP-Sls & Mktg)
Kelly Allender (Mgr-Learning Center-Dallas-
North)
Andy Johnson (Reg Mgr-Ops & Mgr-
Learning Center-Savannah)
Danny Robayo (VP-Procurement)
Jamie Hopkins (Mgr-Learning Center-
Atlanta)
Suren Meras (Mgr-Learning Center-
Houston)
Diana Wheeler (Sr VP-Teammate Re-
sources)
David D. Dyche (Mgr-Center)
Chad Raney (Mgr-San Antonio Center)
Brad Thress (Pres & CEO)
Patricia Arundell-Lampe (CFO & Sr VP)

Glenn Hausmann *(Mgr-Learning Center)*
Alex Curtis *(Reg Sls Mgr)*
Keith McGann *(Dir-Reg MX Sls)*
Mindy Drummond *(Chief Admin Officer)*
Nathan Speiser *(Exec VP-Sls & Mktg)*
D. Richard Meikle *(Exec VP-Safety)*
Marie Bentz Martin *(Gen Counsel, Sec & Exec VP)*
Kelly Reich *(Sr VP-Strategic Ops)*
Daniel Davis *(Pres-FSI Defense)*
Michael Vercio *(Sr VP-Simulation Sys)*

Unit (Domestic):

FlightSafety International   (2)
5695 Campus Pkwy, Hazelwood, MO
63042-2338   **(100%)**
Tel.: (314) 551-8400
Web Site: http://www.flightsafety.com
Sales Range: $50-74.9 Million
Emp.: 160
Designs & Produces Visual Systems for
Simulators
N.A.I.C.S.: 611699
Brad Thress *(Pres & CEO)*
Steve Gross *(Sr VP-Sls & Mktg)*
Brian Moore *(Sr VP-Ops)*
D. Richard Meikle *(Exec VP)*
Daniel Davis *(Pres)*
Doug May *(Exec VP)*
Michael Vercio *(Sr VP)*
Mindy Drummond *(Chief Admin Officer)*
Nathan Speiser *(Exec VP)*
Suzanne West *(CFO)*

Division (Domestic):

**FlightSafety International Courseware
Support**   (2)
8972 Trinity Blvd, Hurst, TX 76053 **(100%)**
Tel.: (817) 276-7500
Web Site: http://www.flightsafety.com
Sales Range: $25-49.9 Million
Emp.: 100
Courseware Design & Production
N.A.I.C.S.: 611710

**FlightSafety International Simulation
Systems**   (2)
700 N 9th St, Broken Arrow, OK
74012   **(100%)**
Tel.: (918) 259-5532
Web Site: http://www.flightsafety.com
Sales Range: $125-149.9 Million
Emp.: 730
Simulation & Learning Systems Mfr
N.A.I.C.S.: 611699

Subsidiary (Domestic):

**FlightSafety Services
Corporation**   (2)
6755 N Yampa St, Denver, CO
80249   **(100%)**
Web Site: http://www.flightsafety.com
Sales Range: $75-99.9 Million
Military Aircraft Crew Training
N.A.I.C.S.: 611699
Mike King *(Pres)*

Forest River, Inc.   (1)
55470 County Rd 1, Elkhart, IN 46514
Tel.: (574) 389-4600
Web Site: http://www.forestriverinc.com
Sales Range: $1-4.9 Billion
Emp.: 5,800
RVs, Cargo Trailers, Buses, Boats & Manu-
factured Buildings Mfr
N.A.I.C.S.: 336214
Peter J. Liegl *(Founder)*

Division (Domestic):

**Coachmen Recreational Vehicle
Company**   (2)
423 N Main St, Middlebury, IN 46540-0030
Tel.: (574) 825-5821
Web Site: http://www.coachmenrv.com
Sales Range: $350-399.9 Million
Emp.: 1,015
Recreational Vehicles
N.A.I.C.S.: 336213
Michael R. Terlep *(Pres)*

Subsidiary (Domestic):

**Coachmen Recreational Vehicle
Company of Georgia**   (3)
Northside Industrial Park 142 Benjamin Hills
Dr, Fitzgerald, GA 31750

Tel.: (229) 423-5471
Web Site: http://www.coachmenrv.com
Rev.: $29,000,000
Emp.: 150
Travel Trailers & Campers
N.A.I.C.S.: 336214

Pro Designs   (3)
3400 Reedy Dr, Elkhart, IN 46514-7667
Tel.: (574) 262-9250
Web Site:
   http://www.prodesignproducts.com
Rev.: $8,000,000
Emp.: 200
Van Tops & Fiberglass RV Parts
N.A.I.C.S.: 326199

Viking Recreational Vehicles LLC   (3)
580 W Burr Oak St, Centreville, MI 49032-
9592
Tel.: (269) 467-6321
Web Site: http://www.vikingrv.com
Sales Range: $1-9.9 Million
Emp.: 105
Sales Of Recreational Vehicles
N.A.I.C.S.: 336214

Subsidiary (Domestic):

Forest River Bus, LLC   (2)
2367 Century Dr., Goshen, IN 46528
Tel.: (800) 348-7440
Web Site: https://forestriverbus.com
Emp.: 650
Vehicle Transportation & Mfg.
N.A.I.C.S.: 336999

Subsidiary (Domestic):

Collins Bus Corporation   (3)
415 W 6th St, South Hutchinson, KS 67505
Tel.: (620) 662-9000
Web Site: http://www.collinsbuscorp.com
Sales Range: $25-49.9 Million
Emp.: 180
Small School & Transit Bus Mfr
N.A.I.C.S.: 336211
Matt Scheuler *(Pres)*
Cody Stefek *(Engr-Design)*

Division (Domestic):

Forest River Inc.   (2)
3010 College Ave, Goshen, IN 46528-5002
Tel.: (574) 533-5934
Web Site: http://www.forestriverinc.com
Sales Range: $50-74.9 Million
Emp.: 200
RV & Cargo Trailer Mfr
N.A.I.C.S.: 811121

Freo Group Pty Ltd   (1)
91 Investigator Drive, Hope Valley, Kwi-
nana, 6165, WA, Australia
Tel.: (61) 894999600
Web Site: https://freogroup.com.au
Insurance Services
N.A.I.C.S.: 524298

Fruit of the Loom, Inc.   (1)
1 Fruit of the Loom Dr, Bowling Green, KY
42103   **(100%)**
Tel.: (270) 781-6400
Web Site: https://www.fotlinc.com
Sales Range: $5-14.9 Billion
Emp.: 33,000
Apparels Mfr
N.A.I.C.S.: 315120

Subsidiary (Non-US):

Fruit of the Loom Limited   (2)
Halefield 10 G, Telford, TF7 4QP, Shrop-
shire, United Kingdom
Tel.: (44) 1952587123
Web Site: http://www.fruitoftheloom.com
Sales Range: $75-99.9 Million
Emp.: 22,400
Mfr of Apparel
N.A.I.C.S.: 315990
John Griffith *(Chief Acctg Officer & VP)*

Division (Domestic):

**Fruit of the Loom Sports &
Licensing**   (2)
1 Fruit of the Loom Dr, Bowling Green, KY
42102
Tel.: (270) 781-6400
Web Site: http://www.fruit.com

Sales Range: $350-399.9 Million
Emp.: 900
Apparels Mfr
N.A.I.C.S.: 315210
Rick Midland *(Pres & CEO)*

Subsidiary (Domestic):

Russell Corporation   (2)
1 Fruit Of the Loom Dr, Bowling Green, KY
42103
Tel.: (270) 781-6400
Sales Range: $1-4.9 Billion
Emp.: 15,500
Active Wear & Other Apparel Mfr, Designer
& Marketer; Uniform Supplier
N.A.I.C.S.: 313310

Subsidiary (Domestic):

American Athletic Inc.   (3)
200 American Ave, Jefferson, IA 50129
Tel.: (515) 386-3125
Web Site: http://www.americanathletic.com
Rev.: $18,000,000
Emp.: 140
Gym Equipment Mfr
N.A.I.C.S.: 339920

Brooks Sports Inc.   (3)
3400 Stone Way N Ste 500, Seattle, WA
98103
Tel.: (206) 858-5700
Web Site: https://www.brooksrunning.com
Sales Range: $50-74.9 Million
Emp.: 140
Athletic Shoes, Apparel & Accessories Mfr
N.A.I.C.S.: 316210
James M. Weber *(CEO)*

DeSoto Mills, Inc.   (3)
1 Fruit Of The Loom Dr, Bowling Green, KY
42103-7932
Tel.: (256) 845-6700
Sales Range: $75-99.9 Million
Emp.: 200
Athletic Socks Mfr
N.A.I.C.S.: 315120

Division (Domestic):

Jerzees   (3)
3330 Cumberland Blvd Ste 800, Atlanta,
GA 30339
Tel.: (678) 742-8000
Web Site: http://www.jerzees.com
Sales Range: $100-124.9 Million
Emp.: 200
Activewear Mfr
N.A.I.C.S.: 315120

Russell Athletic   (3)
3330 Cumberland Blvd Ste 700, Atlanta,
GA 30339
Tel.: (678) 742-8000
Web Site: http://www.russellathletic.com
Sales Range: $50-74.9 Million
Emp.: 100
Athletic Team Uniforms & Leisure Wear Mfr
& Marketer
N.A.I.C.S.: 315120

Subsidiary (Domestic):

Russell Brands, LLC   (3)
1 Fruit of the Loom Dr, Bowling Green, KY
42102
Tel.: (270) 781-6400
Web Site: http://www.russell-brands.com
Sporting & Athletic Goods Mfr
N.A.I.C.S.: 339920

Branch (Domestic):

Russell Corp. Alexander City   (3)
901A Lee St, Alexander City, AL 35010-
2607
Tel.: (256) 500-4000
Web Site: http://www.russellathletic.com
Sales Range: $350-399.9 Million
Emp.: 1,000
Cotton, Cotton Blend & Man-Made Fabric
Mfr
N.A.I.C.S.: 315120
Rick Medlin *(CEO)*

Subsidiary (Non-US):

Russell Europe Limited   (3)
1 Bain Square Kirkton Campus, Livingston,
EH54 7DQ, West Lothian, United Kingdom

Tel.: (44) 1506502000
Web Site: http://www.russelleurope.com
Sales Range: $75-99.9 Million
Emp.: 100
Leisure Apparel Marketer & Sales
N.A.I.C.S.: 423910

Division (Domestic):

Spalding   (3)
150 Brookdale Dr, Springfield, MA 01104
Tel.: (413) 735-1400
Web Site: http://www.spalding.com
Sales Range: $10-24.9 Million
Emp.: 57
Basketballs, Footballs, Volleyballs, Soccer
Balls & Other Inflatable Sports Related
Products Mfr
N.A.I.C.S.: 339920

Subsidiary (Domestic):

Union Underwear Company, Inc.   (2)
1 Fruit Of The Loom Dr, Bowling Green, KY
42103-7932   **(100%)**
Tel.: (270) 781-6400
Web Site: http://www.fruit.com
Sales Range: $1-9.9 Million
Emp.: 600
Underwear, Activewear, Family Hosiery,
Fleecewear & Screen Print T-Shirts Mfr
N.A.I.C.S.: 315120
Rick Netlin *(CEO)*

GEICO Corporation   (1)
One Geico Plz, Washington, DC 20076-
0001
Tel.: (301) 986-2500
Web Site: http://www.geico.com
Sales Range: $5-14.9 Billion
Emp.: 7,561
Insurance Holding Company
N.A.I.C.S.: 551112
Todd Anthony Combs *(Chm, Pres & CEO)*
Damon Burrell *(CMO)*

Subsidiary (Domestic):

**GEICO Choice Insurance
Company**   (2)
144 Kiewit Plz, Omaha, NE 68131
Tel.: (301) 986-3000
Insurance Management Services
N.A.I.C.S.: 524298

**GEICO General Insurance
Company**   (2)
5260 Western Ave, Chevy Chase, MD
20815   **(100%)**
Tel.: (301) 986-3000
Web Site: http://www.geico.com
Sales Range: $1-4.9 Billion
Emp.: 24,000
Automobile Insurance
N.A.I.C.S.: 524126

GEICO Indemnity Company   (2)
1 Geico Plz, Washington, DC
20076   **(100%)**
Tel.: (301) 986-3000
Web Site: http://www.geico.com
Sales Range: $10-24.9 Million
Emp.: 10
Standard Risk Private Passenger Auto &
Motorcycle Insurance Services
N.A.I.C.S.: 524126

Resolute Reinsurance Company   (2)
100 Stamford Pl 203, Stamford, CT
06902   **(100%)**
Tel.: (203) 391-5230
Sales Range: $10-24.9 Million
Emp.: 25
Property & Casualty Reinsurance
N.A.I.C.S.: 524126

Garan, Incorporated   (1)
200 Madison Ave, New York, NY 10016
Tel.: (212) 563-2000
Web Site: http://www.garanimals.com
Sales Range: $750-799.9 Million
Emp.: 5,100
Children's Clothing Mfr
N.A.I.C.S.: 315250

Subsidiary (Domestic):

Garan Manufacturing Corp.   (2)
601 Hwy 12 E, Starkville, MS
39759   **(100%)**
Tel.: (662) 324-2400

Berkshire Hathaway Inc.—(Continued)

Web Site: http://www.garaninala.com
Sales Range: $100-124.9 Million
Emp.: 124
Apparels Mfr
N.A.I.C.S.: 315210
Lillian McNalley (Dir-HR)

General Re Life Corporation (1)
120 Long Ridge Rd, Stamford, CT 06902
Tel.: (203) 352-3000
Web Site: https://www.genre.com
Insurance Management Services
N.A.I.C.S.: 524298

General Reinsurance AG (1)
Theodor-Heuss-Ring 11, 50668, Cologne,
Germany
Tel.: (49) 22197380
Insurance Services
N.A.I.C.S.: 524298

Global Cranes Pty Ltd (1)
U 3 57 Hayward St, Stafford, 4053, QLD,
Australia
Tel.: (61) 733565888
Web Site: http://www.globalcranes.com.au
Crane Rental Services
N.A.I.C.S.: 238990

Helzberg's Diamond Shops, Inc. (1)
7210 NW 86th Pl Ste 184, Kansas City, MO
64153
Tel.: (816) 741-7333
Web Site: http://www.helzberg.com
Sales Range: $450-499.9 Million
Emp.: 2,500
Retail Jewelry Store
N.A.I.C.S.: 458310

HomeServices of America, Inc. (1)
333 S 7th St 27th Fl, Minneapolis, MN
55402
Tel.: (949) 794-7900
Web Site: https://www.homeservices.com
Real Estate Brokerage Services
N.A.I.C.S.: 531210
Ronald J. Peltier (Chm)
Jim Lamphere (VP-Title)
Gino Blefari (Pres & CEO)
Marian Padgett (Natl Dir-Bus Dev-
HomeSvcs Relocation)
Alon Chaver (CIO)
Jaime Besser (VP-Fin Ops)
Mike Browne (Gen Counsel & VP)
Stuart Lyle (VP-HR)
Alex Seavall (CFO & VP-Bus Dev & Acqui-
sitions)
Patty Smejkal (CTO)
Dana Strandmo (Chief Admin Officer & Sr
VP)
Jon Coile (VP-MLS & Indus Rels)
Chris Stuart (Sr VP-Tech & Client Solutions)
Joe Sweeney (VP & Controller)
Mary Lee Blaylock (Sr VP)
Teresa Palacios Smith (Chief Diversity, Eq-
uity & Inclusion Officer)
Brent Grooms (Co-CIO)
Chris Sears (VP-Bus Dev)
Steven John (Pres & CEO-Home Svcs Re-
location)
Gary Conerly (Dir-Client Dev-Home Svcs
Relocation)

Subsidiary (Domestic):

Beach Properties of Florida (2)
2063 S Co Hwy 395, Santa Rosa Beach,
FL 32459
Tel.: (850) 534-3006
Web Site:
http://www.beachpropertiesofflorida.com
Offices of Real Estate Agents & Brokers
N.A.I.C.S.: 531210

**Berkshire Hathaway HomeServices
Fox & Roach, REALTORS** (2)
431 W Lancaster Ave, Devon, PA 19333
Tel.: (610) 651-2700
Web Site: http://www.foxroach.com
Real Estate Brokers & Agents
N.A.I.C.S.: 531210
Debbie McCabe (Reg Sls Mgr)
Joan Docktor (Pres)
Ron Slizofski (CFO & Exec VP)
Scott Crowley (CIO & VP)
Brad Patt (Reg Sls Mgr)
Rajeev Sajja (Sr VP-Digital Mktg & Innova-
tion)

Gina Verdi (VP-HR)
Scott Waldman (Chief Legal Officer)
Melissa Wilks-Cunningham (VP-Mktg &
Brand)
Alan Reburn (Reg Sls Mgr)
Lisa DeWolf (Pres)
Larry Flick V (CEO)

**Berkshire Hathaway HomeServices
New England Properties** (2)
860 N Main St Ext, Wallingford, CT 06492
Tel.: (860) 571-7000
Web Site:
http://www.berkshirehathawayhs.com
Real Estate Brokers & Agents
N.A.I.C.S.: 531210

CBSHOME Real Estate (2)
15950 W Dodge Rd Ste 200, Omaha, NE
68118
Tel.: (402) 934-1590
Web Site: http://www.cbshome.com
Sales Range: $50-74.9 Million
Emp.: 100
Real Estate
N.A.I.C.S.: 531210

Champion Realty Inc. (2)
541B Baltimore Annapolis Blvd, Severna
Park, MD 21146-3934
Tel.: (410) 975-3000
Web Site: http://www.championrealty.com
Sales Range: $10-24.9 Million
Emp.: 50
Real Estate Agents & Managers
N.A.I.C.S.: 531210
Jonathan R. M. Coile (Pres & CEO)
Constance Giddings (Mgr-Property)

Dauphin Realty Corporation (2)
2569 Dauphin St, Mobile, AL 36606
Tel.: (251) 479-1314
Web Site: http://www.dauphinrealty.com
Sales Range: $25-49.9 Million
Emp.: 80
Holding Company; Residential Real Estate
Agencies
N.A.I.C.S.: 551112

Subsidiary (Domestic):

Dauphin Realty of Mobile, Inc. (3)
2569 Dauphin St, Mobile, AL 36606
Tel.: (251) 479-1314
Web Site: http://www.dauphinrealty.com
Sales Range: $1-9.9 Million
Emp.: 50
Residential Real Estate Agency
N.A.I.C.S.: 531210

Subsidiary (Domestic):

Ebby Halliday Real Estate, Inc. (2)
5560 Tennyson Pkwy Ste 100, Plano, TX
75244
Tel.: (972) 980-6600
Web Site: http://www.ebby.com
Real Estate Agent/Manager
N.A.I.C.S.: 531210
Chris Kelly (Pres & CEO)
Betsy Cameron (VP)
Catherine Sims (VP)
Sherry Adams (VP)
Steve Smith (VP)
Travis Mathews (COO)

Subsidiary (Domestic):

**Williams Trew Real Estate Services,
LLC** (3)
3707 Camp Bowie Ste 300, Fort Worth, TX
76107
Tel.: (817) 732-8400
Web Site: http://www.williamstrew.com
Other Activities Related to Real Estate
N.A.I.C.S.: 531390

Subsidiary (Domestic):

Edina Realty, Inc. (2)
6800 France Ave S Ste 230, Edina, MN
55435
Tel.: (952) 927-1100
Web Site: http://www.edinarealty.com
Sales Range: $150-199.9 Million
Emp.: 118
Real Estate Sales & Management Services
N.A.I.C.S.: 531210
Greg Mason (Pres & CEO-Home Svcs)
Sharry Schmid (Pres)

C. J. Deike (VP)
Marge Kane (Sr VP & Reg Mgr)
Mark Christopherson (Gen Counsel & Sr
VP)
Michele Cici (CFO)
Denise Crosley (VP)
Amy Dunkelberger (VP-HR)
Nick Kozel (CMO)
Terry McDonough (Pres-ERRN)
Jay Olson (VP-Facilities & Pur)
Nancy Ostrom (VP & Mgr-Title Production)
David Schmid (VP-Product Dev)
Jim Young (Sr VP & Reg Mgr)
Brad Fisher (Pres-Title)
Joe Brown (Pres-Mortgage)
Doug Koch (CIO)
Travis Peltier (Sr VP & Reg Mgr)
Nicole Suchy (Sr VP & Reg Mgr)
Scott Teece (VP-Sls-Edina Realty Insur-
ance)

Subsidiary (Domestic):

Edina Realty (3)
15354 Delwood Dr Ste 100, Baxter, MN
56425-7744
Tel.: (218) 828-7000
Web Site: http://www.edinarealty.com
Sales Range: $50-74.9 Million
Emp.: 50
Real Estate Sales & Management Services
N.A.I.C.S.: 531210
Jim Eisler (Mgr)
Sharry Schmid (Pres)

Edina Realty Title (3)
6800 France Ave S Ste 230, Edina, MN
55435-2009
Tel.: (952) 928-5181
Web Site: http://www.edinarealty.com
Sales Range: $150-199.9 Million
Title Abstract Services
N.A.I.C.S.: 541191

Subsidiary (Domestic):

**Esslinger-Wooten-Maxwell Realtors,
Inc.** (2)
1360 S Dixie Hwy, Coral Gables, FL 33146-
2904
Tel.: (305) 667-8871
Web Site: http://www.ewm.com
Real Estate Services
N.A.I.C.S.: 531210
Hena M. Aguirre (CFO)
Aniella Gonzalez (Gen Counsel & VP)
Sherrie Porter (Gen Sls Mgr)
Patrick M. O'Connell (Sr VP-New Bus Dev)
Casey Lee (VP-Mktg)
Brian Williams (VP-Professional Dev)
Anita Duran Cachaldora (VP)
Christian Basick (VP)
Sean Poroon (VP)

First Realty/GMAC Real Estate (2)
3501 Westown Pkwy, West Des Moines, IA
50266
Tel.: (515) 222-4600
Web Site: http://www.firstrealtyhomes.com
Sales Range: $10-24.9 Million
Emp.: 50
Real Estate Services
N.A.I.C.S.: 531210

Harry Norman Realtors (2)
532 E Paces Ferry Rd NE Ste 200, Atlanta,
GA 30305
Tel.: (404) 233-4142
Web Site: http://www.harrynorman.com
Sales Range: $1-9.9 Million
Emp.: 35
Real Estate Services
N.A.I.C.S.: 531210
Scott Bennett (VP-IT)
David Allsteadt (CFO)
Jenni Bonura (Pres & CEO)
Tamra Asbury (Mgr-HR)
B. J. Baskin (Mgr-Corp Accounts)
Heather Ferguson (Mgr-Mktg Ops)
Todd Emerson (Gen Mgr)
Melissa Gailey (Art Dir)
Shelle Kreger (Coord-Commission Process-
ing)
Susan Jones (Coord-Commission Process-
ing)
Christine Schardt (Coord-Commission Pro-
cessing)
Brendan Pagano (Sls Mgr-Area)
Emily Norris (VP-Ops & Culture)

Mary Short (Coord-Acctg)
Shea Zimmerman (Sr VP-Buckhead)
BJ Baskin (Mgr)

Home Real Estate Inc. (2)
3355 Orwell Ste 102, Lincoln, NE 68516
Tel.: (402) 436-3310
Web Site: http://www.homerealestate.com
Sales Range: $1-9.9 Million
Emp.: 35
Real Estate Services
N.A.I.C.S.: 531210

Houlihan Lawrence Inc. (2)
800 Westchester Ave Ste N 505, Rye
Brook, NY 10573
Tel.: (914) 220-7000
Web Site:
https://www.houlihanlawrence.com
Real Estate Brokers & Agents
N.A.I.C.S.: 531210
Stephen Meyers (Chm)
Liz Nunan (Pres & CEO)

Intero Real Estate Services, Inc. (2)
496 First St Ste 200, Los Altos, CA 94022
Tel.: (650) 947-4700
Web Site: http://www.interorealestate.com
Emp.: 2,000
Offices of Real Estate Agents & Brokers
N.A.I.C.S.: 531210
Robert T. Moles (Chm)
Stuart Blomgren (CFO)
Brian Crane (Co-Founder & CEO)
Renee Kunz (Mng Officer & Sr VP-Strategic
Partnerships)
Christopher Moles (Mng Officer, Gen Coun-
sel & VP)
Heather Victoria (Controller)
Scott Chase (COO)
Terry Meyer (Co-Founder)

Iowa Realty Co., Inc. (2)
3501 Westown Pkwy, West Des Moines, IA
50266
Tel.: (515) 224-6222
Web Site: http://www.iowarealty.com
Sales Range: $300-349.9 Million
Emp.: 200
Real Estate Services
N.A.I.C.S.: 531210
Kim Bakey (CEO)
Lori Hodges (Dir-HR)
Beth Ann Mahaffey (Dir-Bus Dev)
Deb Partee (Mgr-Midland Title & Escrow)
Jason Froehlich (Reg Mgr-HomeServices
Lending)
Randee Slings (Pres)

**Kentwood Real Estate Services
LLC** (2)
5690 DTC Blvd Ste 600W, Greenwood Vil-　(100%)
lage, CO 80111
Tel.: (303) 773-3399
Web Site: http://www.denverrealestate.com
Emp.: 200
Real Estate Agents & Brokers
N.A.I.C.S.: 531210
Dierk Herbermann (COO)
Karen Pearce (CFO)

**Koenig & Strey GMAC Real
Estate** (2)
4709 W Golf Rd Ste 1100, Skokie, IL
60076-1261
Tel.: (847) 853-5000
Web Site: http://www.koenigstrey.com
Sales Range: $250-299.9 Million
Emp.: 900
Real Estate Brokers & Agents
N.A.I.C.S.: 522310

Lattey International Realty, LLC (2)
45 Glen Cove Rd, Greenvale, NY 11548
Tel.: (516) 200-5700
Web Site: http://www.bhhslaffey.com
Real Estate Services
N.A.I.C.S.: 531210

Long Realty Company (2)
900 E River Rd, Tucson, AZ 85718
Tel.: (520) 888-8844
Web Site: http://www.longrealty.com
Sales Range: $50-74.9 Million
Emp.: 90
Real Estate Company
N.A.I.C.S.: 531210
Rosey Koberlein (CEO-Long Companies
Home Office)
Chris Patterson (Branch Mgr)

Megan Miller *(Gen Counsel & VP)*
Lisa Gaare *(Branch Mgr)*
Ralph Roehrich *(Branch Mgr-Tanque Verde)*
Melvin Edwards *(Dir-Network Svcs)*
K. C. Woods Gri *(Branch Mgr)*
Chip Morgan *(Branch Mgr)*
Erin Fitzgerald *(Pres)*

New Star Realty & Investment (2)
2284 Griffin Way Ste 104, Corona, CA
92882 **(100%)**
Tel.: (951) 279-8989
Web Site: http://www.newstarrealty.com
Emp.: 2,000
Real Estate Investment Services
N.A.I.C.S.: 531210

Prudential California Realty (2)
2365 Northside Dr Ste 200, San Diego, CA
92108
Tel.: (619) 972-8798
Web Site: http://www.prudentialcal.com
Sales Range: $50-74.9 Million
Emp.: 100
Real Estate Services
N.A.I.C.S.: 531210
David M. Cabot *(Pres & CEO)*

**Prudential Northwest Realty Associ-
ates, LLC** (2)
4700 42nd Ave SW Ste 470, Seattle, WA
98116
Tel.: (206) 932-4500
Web Site: http://www.pnwrealty.com
Rev.: $14,000,000
Emp.: 30
Real Estate Brokers & Agents
N.A.I.C.S.: 531210

RealtySouth (2)
2501 20th Pl S Ste 400, Birmingham, AL
35223-1744
Tel.: (205) 322-7500
Web Site: http://www.realtysouth.com
Sales Range: $25-49.9 Million
Emp.: 80
Real Estate Agency
N.A.I.C.S.: 531210
Richard Grimes *(Pres & CEO)*

Rector-Hayden Realtors (2)
1099 Duval St Ste 250, Lexington, KY
40515
Tel.: (859) 644-9383
Web Site: http://www.rhr.com
Sales Range: $125-149.9 Million
Emp.: 220
Real Estate Services
N.A.I.C.S.: 531210

Reece & Nichols Realtors (2)
11601 Granada Ln, Leawood, KS 66211
Tel.: (913) 491-1001
Web Site: http://www.reecenichols.com
Sales Range: $75-99.9 Million
Emp.: 110
Real Estate Services
N.A.I.C.S.: 531210
Mike Frazier *(Pres & CEO)*
Chad Dumas *(Sr VP-Brokerage)*
Krista Wilson *(Sr VP-Brokerage)*
Marissa Easter *(Mktg Dir)*
Missy Greene *(VP-Bus & Lead Dev)*
Debbie Hood *(Mgr-HR)*
Glenda Jones *(Sr VP-Fin & Admin)*
Connie Kruetzkamp *(Dir-Career Dev)*
Paula Rieckman *(Dir-Relocation)*
Rosemary Vitale *(VP-New Homes Dev)*
Samantha Burrell *(Mgr-Corp Relocation &
Property)*
Sandy Fogel *(Sr Mgr-Relocation)*
Cameron Hoorfar *(VP)*
David Gubin *(Sr VP)*

Semonin Realtors (2)
600 N Hurstbourne Pkwy Ste 200, Louis-
ville, KY 40222
Tel.: (502) 420-5000
Web Site: http://www.semonin.com
Emp.: 50
Real Estate Services
N.A.I.C.S.: 531210
Stacy Durbin *(Gen Mgr-Sls)*

Tomie Raines, Inc. (2)
1400 Abbot Rd Ste 200, East Lansing, MI
48823
Tel.: (517) 351-3617
Web Site: http://www.tomieraines.com
Sales Range: $1-9.9 Million
Emp.: 85
Real Estate Brokerage Services

N.A.I.C.S.: 531210

Woods Bros Realty, Inc. (2)
4501 S 86th St, Lincoln, NE 68526
Tel.: (402) 434-3700
Web Site: http://www.woodsbros.com
Sales Range: $350-399.9 Million
Emp.: 280
Real Estate Services
N.A.I.C.S.: 531210
Matt Hardesty *(Mgr-Sls)*

**Horizon Wine & Spirits - Nashville,
Inc.** (1)
3851 Industrial Pkwy, Nashville, TN 37218
Tel.: (615) 320-7292
Alcoholic Beverages Whslr
N.A.I.C.S.: 424810

**IMC International Metalworking Com-
panies B.V.** (1)
Zwolleweg 6, 2803 PS, Gouda,
Netherlands **(80%)**
Tel.: (31) 182 559 992
Web Site: http://www.imc-companies.com
Holding Company; Metalworking & Cutting
Tools Mfr
N.A.I.C.S.: 551112
Jacob Harpaz *(Chm & Pres)*
Stef Wertheimer *(Chm & CEO)*

Subsidiary (US):

IMC Group USA Holdings, Inc. (2)
300 Westway Pl, Arlington, TX 76018-1021
Tel.: (817) 258-3200
Web Site: http://www.imc-companies.com
Holding Company; Metalworking & Cutting
Tools Mfr
N.A.I.C.S.: 551112

Subsidiary (Domestic):

Ingersoll Cutting Tool Company (3)
845 S Lyford Rd, Rockford, IL 61108
Tel.: (815) 387-6600
Web Site: https://www.ingersoll-imc.com
Emp.: 600
Cutting Tool Mfr
N.A.I.C.S.: 333515

Subsidiary (Non-US):

Ingersoll Werkzeuge GmbH (4)
Kalteiche-Ring 21-25, 35708, Haiger, Ger-
many
Tel.: (49) 2 773 7420
Web Site: https://www.ingersoll-imc.de
Metal Cutting Tool Mfr
N.A.I.C.S.: 333515

Subsidiary (Non-US):

IMC Holdings GmbH (2)
Florianstr 17, 71665, Vaihingen, Germany
Tel.: (49) 704283160
Investment Management Service
N.A.I.C.S.: 523940

Subsidiary (Domestic):

IMC (Germany) Holdings GmbH (3)
Florianstr 17, 71665, Vaihingen, Baden-
Wurttemberg, Germany
Tel.: (49) 704283160
Holding Company
N.A.I.C.S.: 551112

Subsidiary (Non-US):

Iscar Ltd. (2)
4 Derech Hashalom, Tel Aviv, Israel
Tel.: (972) 35680068
Web Site: http://www.iscar.com
Sales Range: $300-349.9 Million
Emp.: 1,000
Tungsten & Titanium Carbide Powder, Metal
Machining & Wood Working Tool Mfr
N.A.I.C.S.: 333517
Baruch Vita *(Mgr-Mktg & Sls)*

Subsidiary (Non-US):

ISCAR Austria GmbH (3)
Im Stadtgut C 2 Gleink, 4407, Steyr, Austria
Tel.: (43) 7252 71200 0
Web Site: http://www.iscor.at
Emp.: 17
Tungsten & Titanium Carbide Powder, Metal
Machining & Wood Working Tool Mfr
N.A.I.C.S.: 333517

ISCAR Benelux s.a. (3)
Roekhout 13, 1702, Dilbeek, Belgium
Tel.: (32) 2 464 20 20
Web Site: http://www.iscar.be
Emp.: 40
Tungsten & Titanium Carbide Powder, Metal
Machining & Wood Working Tool Mfr
N.A.I.C.S.: 333517
Stefaan Deprez *(Mgr)*

ISCAR Bulgaria Ltd (3)
Starozagorska 1 Str, Floor 1 Office G, 6100,
Kazanlak, Bulgaria
Tel.: (359) 431 62557
Web Site: http://www.iscar.com
Emp.: 16
Tungsten & Titanium Carbide Powder, Metal
Machining & Wood Working Tool Mfr
N.A.I.C.S.: 333517

ISCAR CR s.r.o. (3)
Manesova 73, 301 00, Plzen, Czech Re-
public
Tel.: (420) 37 74 20 625
Web Site: http://www.iscar.cz
Tungsten & Titanium Carbide Powder, Metal
Machining & Wood Working Tool Mfr
N.A.I.C.S.: 333517

ISCAR FINLAND OY (3)
Ahertajantie 6, 02100, Espoo, Finland
Tel.: (358) 9 439 1420
Web Site: http://www.iscar.fi
Emp.: 2
Tungsten & Titanium Carbide Powder, Metal
Machining & Wood Working Tool Mfr
N.A.I.C.S.: 327910

ISCAR FRANCE SAS (3)
8 Rue Georges Guynemer, 78280, Guyan-
court, France
Tel.: (33) 130129292
Emp.: 80
Tungsten & Titanium Carbide Powder, Metal
Machining & Wood Working Tool Mfr
N.A.I.C.S.: 333517

ISCAR Germany GmbH (3)
Eisenstockstrasse 14, 76275, Ettlingen,
Germany
Tel.: (49) 724399080
Tungsten & Titanium Carbide Powder, Metal
Machining & Wood Working Tool Mfr
N.A.I.C.S.: 333517

ISCAR HARTMETALL AG (3)
Wespenstrasse 14, 8500, Frauenfeld, Swit-
zerland
Tel.: (41) 52 728 0850
Web Site: http://www.iscar.ch
Emp.: 15
Tungsten & Titanium Carbide Powder, Metal
Machining & Wood Working Tool Mfr
N.A.I.C.S.: 333517
Hans-jurgen Buechner *(Gen Mgr)*

ISCAR Hungary KFT. (3)
Kassai u 151, H 1142, Budapest, Hungary
Tel.: (36) 2515688
Web Site: http://www.iscar.hu
Tungsten & Titanium Carbide Powder, Metal
Machining & Wood Working Tool Mfr
N.A.I.C.S.: 333517

ISCAR Iberica AS (3)
Parc Tecnologic Del Valles Avda Univ Au-
tonoma 19-21, Cerdanyola, Barcelona,
08290, Spain
Tel.: (34) 93 594 6484
Web Site: http://www.iscarib.es
Emp.: 50
Tungsten & Titanium Carbide Powder, Metal
Machining & Wood Working Tool Mfr
N.A.I.C.S.: 333517
Toni Vineyards *(Mng Dir)*

ISCAR Italia srl (3)
via Varese 43, 20020, Lainate, MI, Italy
Tel.: (39) 02935281
Tungsten & Titanium Carbide Powder, Metal
Machining & Wood Working Tool Mfr
N.A.I.C.S.: 333517

ISCAR Netherlands BV (3)
Zwolleweg 6, PO Box 704, 2803 PS,
Gouda, Netherlands
Tel.: (31) 182 535 523
Web Site: http://www.iscar.com.nl
Emp.: 20
Tungsten & Titanium Carbide Powder, Metal
Machining & Wood Working Tool Mfr

N.A.I.C.S.: 333517

ISCAR Poland Sp. z o.o. (3)
Ul Gospodarcza 14, 40432, Katowice, Po-
land
Tel.: (48) 32 735 77 00
Web Site: http://www.iscar.pl
Emp.: 50
Tungsten & Titanium Carbide Powder, Metal
Machining & Wood Working Tool Mfr
N.A.I.C.S.: 333517
Slawomir Marianski *(Gen Mgr)*

ISCAR Portugal SA (3)
Avd Dr Domingos Caetano De Sousa,
Santa Maria da Feira, Porto, 4520-176,
Portugal
Tel.: (351) 256579950
Web Site: http://www.iscar.com
Tungsten & Titanium Carbide Powder, Metal
Machining & Wood Working Tool Mfr
N.A.I.C.S.: 333517

ISCAR RUSSIA LLC (3)
BC Kvadrum st Centralnaya 20B, Mytishchi,
141014, Russia
Tel.: (7) 4956609125
Web Site: http://www.iscar.ru
Emp.: 50
Tungsten & Titanium Carbide Powder, Metal
Machining & Wood Working Tool Mfr
N.A.I.C.S.: 333517
Valery Litvak *(Pres)*

ISCAR SR, s.r.o. (3)
K Museu 3, 010 03, Zilina, Slovakia
Tel.: (421) 415074301
Tungsten & Titanium Carbide Powder, Metal
Machining & Wood Working Tool Mfr
N.A.I.C.S.: 333517

ISCAR SVERIGE AB (3)
Kungsangsvagen 17B, PO Box 845, 751
08, Uppsala, Sweden
Tel.: (46) 18 66 90 60
Web Site: http://www.iscar.se
Emp.: 30
Tungsten & Titanium Carbide Powder, Metal
Machining & Wood Working Tool Mfr
N.A.I.C.S.: 333517

ISCAR Slovenija d.o.o. (3)
IOC Motnica 14, 1236, Trzin, Slovenia
Tel.: (386) 1 580 9230
Web Site: http://www.iscar.si
Emp.: 30
Tungsten & Titanium Carbide Powder, Metal
Machining & Wood Working Tool Mfr
N.A.I.C.S.: 333517

ISCAR Tools Ltd. (3)
Woodgate Business Park, Bartley Green,
Birmingham, B32 3DE, United Kingdom
Tel.: (44) 1214228585
Emp.: 50
Tungsten & Titanium Carbide Powder, Metal
Machining & Wood Working Tool Mfr
N.A.I.C.S.: 333517
Gorton Taylor *(Mng Dir)*

ISCAR Tools SRL (3)
Str Maramures nr 38 Corp 2, Otopeni,
075100, Romania
Tel.: (40) 312 286 614
Web Site: http://www.iscar.com
Emp.: 12
Tungsten & Titanium Carbide Powder, Metal
Machining & Wood Working Tool Mfr
N.A.I.C.S.: 333517

ISCAR alati d.o.o (3)
J Jelacicaa 134, 10430, Samobor, Croatia
Tel.: (385) 1 332 3301
Web Site: http://www.iscar.hr
Emp.: 13
Tungsten & Titanium Carbide Powder, Metal
Machining & Wood Working Tool Mfr
N.A.I.C.S.: 333517

Serbia ISCAR TOOLS d.o.o. (3)
Autoput 22, RS 11080, Zemun, Serbia
Tel.: (381) 1 1 314 90
Web Site: http://www.iscar.com
Tungsten & Titanium Carbide Powder, Metal
Machining & Wood Working Tool Mfr
N.A.I.C.S.: 333517

Berkshire Hathaway Inc.—(Continued)

Subsidiary (Non-US):

TaeguTec Ltd **(2)**
1040 Gachang-ro Gachang-myeon,
Dalseong-gun, Daegu, 42936, Korea
(South)
Tel.: (82) 53 760 7640
Web Site: https://www.taegutec.com
Cutting Tool Mfr
N.A.I.C.S.: 333515

Tungaloy Corp. **(2)**
11-1 Yoshima-Kogyodanchi, Fukushima,
Iwaki, 970-1144, Fukushima, Japan
Tel.: (81) 24 636 8501
Web Site: https://www.tungaloy.com
Sales Range: Less than $1 Million
Emp.: 950
Super Hard Alloys, Grinding Tools, Friction-
Resistant Tools, Mine Engineering Tools &
Friction Material Parts Mfr
N.A.I.C.S.: 333517
Satoshi Kinoshita *(Pres & CEO)*
Jacob Harpaz *(Chm)*

International Dairy Queen, Inc. **(1)**
8000 Tower Ste 700 8331 Norman Ctr Dr,
Bloomington, MN 55437
Tel.: (952) 830-0200
Web Site: http://www.dairyqueen.com
Holding Company; Limited Service Restau-
rant Franchisor
N.A.I.C.S.: 551112
Troy Bader *(Pres & CEO)*
Dan Kropp *(COO)*
Mark Vinton *(CFO)*
Jean Champagne *(COO-Intl)*

Subsidiary (Domestic):

**American Dairy Queen
Corporation** **(2)**
7505 Metro Blvd, Minneapolis, MN
55439-0286 **(100%)**
Tel.: (952) 830-0200
Web Site: http://www.dairyqueen.com
Sales Range: $100-124.9 Million
Emp.: 250
Hard Ice Cream, Soft Serve Treats, Hot
Foods, Novelties, Frozen Cakes & Logs
N.A.I.C.S.: 311520
Mark Vinton *(CFO)*
Dan Kropp *(COO)*
Jean Champagne *(COO-Intl)*

Subsidiary (Non-US):

Dairy Queen Canada, Inc. **(2)**
1111 International Blvd, PO Box 430, Burl-
ington, L7R 3Y3, ON, Canada **(100%)**
Tel.: (905) 639-1492
Web Site: http://www.dairyqueen.com
Sales Range: $25-49.9 Million
Emp.: 40
Confections Promoter
N.A.I.C.S.: 311514

I.D.Q. Canada, Inc. **(2)**
5045 Selfservice Rd Ste 3000, Burlington,
L7L 5Y7, ON, Canada **(100%)**
Tel.: (905) 639-1492
Web Site: http://www.dairyqueen.com
Sales Range: $25-49.9 Million
Emp.: 64
Confections Promoter
N.A.I.C.S.: 311514

Subsidiary (Domestic):

Orange Julius of America **(2)**
7505 Metro Blvd, Minneapolis, MN
55439-0286 **(100%)**
Tel.: (952) 830-0200
Web Site: http://www.orangejulius.com
Sales Range: $25-49.9 Million
Emp.: 50
Fast Food Services
N.A.I.C.S.: 722513

Johns Manville Corporation **(1)**
PO Box 5108, Denver, CO 80217-5108
Tel.: (303) 978-2000
Web Site: http://www.jm.com
Sales Range: $1-4.9 Billion
Emp.: 350
Holding Company; Premium-Quality Build-
ing & Specialty Products Mfr & Marketer
N.A.I.C.S.: 551112

Robert Wamboldt *(Pres & CEO)*
Eric Brown *(Dir-Corp Comm)*
Katherine Albery *(Gen Counsel & VP)*

Affiliate (Domestic):

Industrial Insulation Group, LLC **(2)**
2100 Line St, Brunswick, GA
31520 **(50%)**
Tel.: (912) 264-6372
Web Site: http://www.iig-llc.com
Insulation: Rock Wool, Slag & Silica Miner-
als
N.A.I.C.S.: 327993

Subsidiary (Domestic):

Johns Manville **(2)**
717 17th St, Denver, CO 80202 **(100%)**
Tel.: (303) 978-2000
Web Site: http://www.jm.com
Sales Range: $75-99.9 Million
Emp.: 400
Marketing & Sales of Building Products
N.A.I.C.S.: 561499
Mary K. Rhinehart *(Chm)*

Subsidiary (Non-US):

Johns Manville Canada Inc. **(2)**
4704 58th St, Innisfail, T4G 1A2, AB,
Canada **(100%)**
Tel.: (403) 227-7100
Web Site: http://www.jm.com
Sales Range: $10-24.9 Million
Emp.: 37
Phenolic Insulation Products, Roofing Mem-
brane Mfr
N.A.I.C.S.: 325211

**Johns Manville Canada Inc. -
Innisfail** **(2)**
4704 58th St, Innisfail, T4G 1A2, AB,
Canada
Tel.: (403) 227-7100
Web Site: http://www.johnsmanville.com
Sales Range: $50-74.9 Million
Emp.: 150
Construction Materials Whslr
N.A.I.C.S.: 423390

Plant (Domestic):

**Johns Manville Corp. - Engineered
Products, Waterville** **(2)**
7500 Dutch Rd, Waterville, OH 43566
Tel.: (419) 878-8111
Web Site: http://www.jm.com
Sales Range: $250-299.9 Million
Emp.: 800
Insulation Mfr
N.A.I.C.S.: 327993

Subsidiary (Non-US):

Johns Manville Slovakia, a.s. **(2)**
Strojarenska 1, 917 99, Trnava, Slovakia
Tel.: (421) 33 591 8249
Web Site: https://www.jm.com
Sales Range: $350-399.9 Million
Production & Treatment of Glass Fibres &
Rovings
N.A.I.C.S.: 327212

Johns Manville Europe GmbH **(1)**
Max-Fischer-Strasse 11, 86399, Bobingen,
Germany
Tel.: (49) 82349670551
Insurance Services
N.A.I.C.S.: 524210

Johns Manville GmbH **(1)**
Werner-Schuller-Str 1, 97877, Wertheim,
Germany
Tel.: (49) 9342801261
Insurance Services
N.A.I.C.S.: 524210

Jordan's Furniture, Inc. **(1)**
100 Stockwell Dr, Avon, MA 02322
Tel.: (508) 580-4900
Web Site: https://www.jordans.com
Sales Range: $100-124.9 Million
Emp.: 300
Furniture Retailer
N.A.I.C.S.: 449110

Justin Brands, Inc. **(1)**
610 W Daggett Ave, Fort Worth, TX
76104-1103 **(100%)**
Tel.: (817) 332-4385

Web Site: http://www.justinbrands.com
Sales Range: $300-349.9 Million
Emp.: 900
Footwear Mfr
N.A.I.C.S.: 316210

Plant (Domestic):

Justin Boot Company **(2)**
1100 Presley Dr, Cassville, MO
65625 **(100%)**
Tel.: (417) 847-4191
Web Site: http://www.justinbrands.com
Sales Range: $100-124.9 Million
Emp.: 250
Footwear Mfr
N.A.I.C.S.: 316210

Kahn Ventures, Inc. **(1)**
3755 Atlanta Industrial Pkwy, Atlanta, GA
30331-1027
Tel.: (404) 572-4100
Financial Investment Services
N.A.I.C.S.: 523999
Bill MacPhail *(CIO)*

Kovack Realtors **(1)**
1392 High St Ste 105, Wadsworth, OH
44281
Tel.: (330) 722-3302
Offices of Real Estate Agents & Brokers
N.A.I.C.S.: 531210

Lipotec, S.A. **(1)**
Isaac Peral 17 Pol Ind Cami Ral, 08850,
Barcelona, Spain
Tel.: (34) 936388000
Web Site: http://www.lipotec.com
Emp.: 130
Cosmetics Mfr
N.A.I.C.S.: 325620

**LiquidPower Specialty Products
Inc.** **(1)**
1 BriarLake Plz 2000 W Sam Houston
Pkwy S Fourth Fl Ste 400, Houston, TX
77042
Tel.: (713) 339-8703
Web Site: http://www.liquidpower.com
Financial Investment Services
N.A.I.C.S.: 523999
Mike Robles *(Chief HR Officer)*

Subsidiary (Non-US):

Conoco Specialty Products Ltd. **(2)**
Medialaan 50, Vilvoorde, 1800, Belgium
Tel.: (32) 22630520
Web Site: http://www.liquidpower.com
Petroleum Related Products
N.A.I.C.S.: 424720

MLMIC Insurance Company **(1)**
2 Park Ave, New York, NY 10016
Tel.: (212) 576-9800
Web Site: http://www.mlmic.com
Insurance Services
N.A.I.C.S.: 524210

Marmon Holdings, Inc. **(1)**
181 W Madison St Ste 3900, Chicago, IL
60602-4510
Tel.: (312) 372-9500
Web Site: https://www.marmon.com
Emp.: 20,000
Holding Company
N.A.I.C.S.: 551112
Angelo V. Pantaleo *(CEO)*

Subsidiary (Domestic):

Aoumod LLC **(2)**
5885 NW Cornelius Pass Rd, Hillsboro, OR
97124
Tel.: (503) 627-9957
Web Site: http://www.acumed.net
Sales Range: $25-49.9 Million
Emp.: 250
Orthopaedic Trauma & Reconstruction
Products
N.A.I.C.S.: 339113
Craig Starkey *(VP-HR)*
Bengie Burgos *(VP)*
Diego Palacios *(Mng Dir)*
Hjalmar Pompe van Meerdervoort *(Pres)*
Jeff Wyman *(VP)*
Lee Brown *(VP)*
Marko Huterer *(VP)*
Seth Brusseau *(VP)*

Subsidiary (Non-US):

Acumed Iberica S.L. **(3)**
C/ Alvaro Caballero 14, 28023, Madrid,
Spain
Tel.: (34) 913516357
Surgical Instrument Mfr
N.A.I.C.S.: 339112
Marian Porcel *(Acct Mgr-Key)*

Acumed Ltd. **(3)**
Huebner House Weyhill The Fairground,
Andover, SP11 0QN, Hants, United King-
dom
Tel.: (44) 1264774450
Web Site: http://www.acumed.net
Sales Range: $10-24.9 Million
Emp.: 10
Orthopaedic Trauma & Reconstruction
Product Mfr
N.A.I.C.S.: 339113

Subsidiary (Non-US):

Apex Tools & Orthopedics Co. **(2)**
25#,Yonghua Road, Yonghe, GETDD,
Guangzhou, China
Tel.: (86) 2082986918
Web Site: http://www.apextooltool.com
Tool Design & Manufacturing
N.A.I.C.S.: 332999

Subsidiary (Domestic):

**MicroAire Surgical Instruments
Inc.** **(2)**
3590 Grand Forks Blvd, Charlottesville, VA
22911
Tel.: (434) 975-8000
Web Site: http://www.microaire.com
Sales Range: $25-49.9 Million
Emp.: 150
Surgical & Medical Instruments Mfr
N.A.I.C.S.: 339112

Osteomed Corporation **(2)**
3885 Arapaho Rd, Addison, TX 75001
Tel.: (972) 677-4600
Web Site: http://www.osteomed.com
Sales Range: $10-24.9 Million
Emp.: 125
Surgical Instruments & Apparatus Mfr
N.A.I.C.S.: 339112

**Precision Edge Surgical Products
Company Inc.** **(2)**
415 W 12th Ave, Sault Sainte Marie, MI
49783-2607
Tel.: (906) 632-4800
Web Site: http://www.precisionedge.com
Sales Range: $25-49.9 Million
Emp.: 190
Surgical & Medical Instruments
N.A.I.C.S.: 339112
John Truckey *(Pres)*

Skeletal Kinetics LLC **(2)**
3885 Arapaho Rd, Addison, TX 75001
Tel.: (972) 677-4600
Web Site: http://www.skeletalkinetics.com
Sales Range: $10-24.9 Million
Emp.: 25
Surgical & Medical Instrument Mfr
N.A.I.C.S.: 339112

The Marmon Group LLC **(2)**
181 W Madison St 26th Fl, Chicago, IL
60602-4504 **(60%)**
Tel.: (312) 372-9500
Web Site: http://www.marmon.com
Sales Range: $5-14.9 Billion
Emp.: 18,000
Holding Company
N.A.I.C.S.: 551112

Subsidiary (Domestic):

3Wire Group Inc. **(3)**
201 BRdway St W, Osseo, MN 55369
Tel.: (763) 488-3000
Web Site: http://www.3wire.com
Foodservice & Beverage Dispensing Parts
Management Services
N.A.I.C.S.: 423850

Cornelius, Inc. **(3)**
101 Broadway St W, Osseo, MN 55369
Tel.: (763) 488-8200
Web Site: http://www.cornelius.com

Beverage & Food Dispensing Equipment
Mfr
N.A.I.C.S.: 333914

Subsidiary (Non-US):

Cornelius (Pacific) Ltd.   (4)
15/F Hale Weal Industrial Bldg 22-28 Tai
Chung Road, Tsuen Wan, New Territories,
China (Hong Kong)
Tel.: (852) 2789 9882
Web Site: http://www.cornelius.com.cn
Holding Company; Regional Managing Office
N.A.I.C.S.: 551112

Subsidiary (Non-US):

Cornelius (Singapore) Pte. Ltd.   (5)
1A International Business Park Unit 06-02,
Singapore, 609933, Singapore
Tel.: (65) 6 862 5542
Web Site: http://www.cornelius.com
Emp.: 20
Beverage Processing Machinery Mfr
N.A.I.C.S.: 333241

Cornelius (Tianjin) Co., Ltd.   (5)
12 Xingtai Road Teda, Tianjin, 300457,
China
Tel.: (86) 22 252 90858
Web Site: http://www.cornelius.com.cn
Beverage Machinery Mfr & Distr
N.A.I.C.S.: 333241

Cornelius Australia Pty. Ltd.   (5)
10 Marigold Place, Milperra, 2214, NSW,
Australia
Tel.: (61) 2 9774 4533
Web Site: http://www.cornelius.com
Emp.: 16
Beverage Processing Machinery Distr
N.A.I.C.S.: 423830

Subsidiary (Non-US):

Cornelius Europe SA   (4)
Antwerpsesteenweg 144, 2950, Kapellen,
Belgium
Tel.: (32) 3 660 1020
Web Site: http://www.cornelius-emea.com
Holding Company; Regional Managing Office; Beverage Processing Machinery Mfr &
Distr
N.A.I.C.S.: 551112

Subsidiary (Non-US):

Cornelius Beverage Technologies
Limited   (5)
Russell Way Bradford Road, Brighouse,
HD6 4LX, W Yorkshire, United Kingdom
Tel.: (44) 1484714584
Web Site: http://www.cornelius-emea.com
Beverage Processing Machinery Mfr & Distr
N.A.I.C.S.: 333241

Cornelius Deutschland GmbH   (5)
Carl Leverkus Strasse 15, 40764, Langenfeld, Germany
Tel.: (49) 2173 793 0
Web Site: http://www.corneliusemea.com
Emp.: 200
Beverage Processing Machinery Mfr & Distr
N.A.I.C.S.: 333241
Brian Watson (Mng Dir)

Cornelius Espana S.A.   (5)
C/Energia 2 Pol Ind La Post, 8850, Gava,
Spain
Tel.: (34) 93 6335800
Beverage Processed Machinery Mfr
N.A.I.C.S.: 333241

Cornelius Italia s.r.l.   (5)
Via 2 Torri Bianche 1, 20871, Vimercate,
MB, Italy
Tel.: (39) 039 661 1958
Web Site: http://www.cornelius-emea.com
Beverage Processing Machinery Mfr & Distr
N.A.I.C.S.: 333241

Cornelius Osterreich Ges.m.b.H.   (5)
Percostrasse 31 / A5, 1220, Vienna, Austria
Tel.: (43) 1 7344022 0
Web Site: http://www.cornelius-emea.com
Beverage Processing Machinery Mfr
N.A.I.C.S.: 333241

Cornelius Ukraine LLC   (5)

Grekovskaya Str 102, Kharkiv, 61010,
Ukraine
Tel.: (380) 57 733 2036
Web Site: http://www.cornelius-emea.com
Beverage Processing Machinery Mfr
N.A.I.C.S.: 333241

IMI Cornelius Hellas S.A.   (5)
55 Theomitoros Street, Alimos, 174 55, Athens, Greece
Tel.: (30) 2109856000
Beverage Processing Machinery Mfr
N.A.I.C.S.: 333241

Plant (Domestic):

Cornelius Inc. - Glendale Heights   (4)
101 Regency Dr, Glendale Heights, IL
60139
Tel.: (630) 539-6850
Web Site: http://www.cornelius-usa.com
Mfr of Refrigeration Products, Icemakers,
Ice Dispensers, Refrigerated Liquid Chillers
& Temperature Control Units
N.A.I.C.S.: 333415
Ben Miller (VP-Mfg & Tech)
Nancy Stark (Dir-Pur)

Subsidiary (Non-US):

Cornelius de Mexico SA de CV   (4)
Manuel Dublan No 35 Col Tacubaya,
11870, Mexico, Mexico
Tel.: (52) 55 5278 1904
Beverage Processing Machinery Mfr
N.A.I.C.S.: 333310

Subsidiary (Domestic):

Display Technologies, LLC   (3)
1111 Marcus Ave Ste M68, Lake Success,
NY 11042
Tel.: (718) 321-3100
Web Site: http://www.display-
    technologies.com
Sales Range: $25-49.9 Million
Emp.: 55
Point of Purchase Displays & Shelving
Products Mfr
N.A.I.C.S.: 337215
Dick Jay (Pres)
Laura Umana (Controller)
Diogo Pereira (VP & Gen Mgr-Global)
Jon Noce (VP-Innovation & Bus Dev)
Christopher Curcio (CIO)
Ulf Hansson (VP-Global Supply Chain)
Dan Gatto (Dir-Innovation & NPD)
Michael Noxon (Dir-Key Acct Mgmt & Coca-
Cola Bus Unit)
Jose Salinas (Dir-Strategic Accounts-Sls)

Division (Domestic):

Marmon Building Wire   (3)
181 W Madison St 26th Fl, Chicago, IL
60602
Tel.: (312) 372-9500
Web Site: http://www.marmon.com
Sales Range: $150-199.9 Million
Copper Electrical Wire
N.A.I.C.S.: 331420

Subsidiary (Domestic):

Cerro Wire LLC   (4)
1099 Thompson Rd SE, Hartselle, AL
35640-8471
Tel.: (256) 773-2522
Web Site: https://www.cerrowire.com
Sales Range: $75-99.9 Million
Emp.: 300
Copper Wires Mfr
N.A.I.C.S.: 331420
Robert A. Pritzker (Chm)

Division (Domestic):

Marmon Crane Services, Inc.   (3)
181 W Madison, Chicago, IL 60602
Tel.: (303) 422-0434
Web Site: http://www.marmoncranes.com
Sales Range: $125-149.9 Million
Crane Services
N.A.I.C.S.: 333923
Timothy Benjamin (Grp Pres)

Subsidiary (Domestic):

Joyce Steel Erection, LLC   (4)
31 Frj Dr, Longview, TX 75602
Tel.: (903) 757-3061

Web Site: http://www.joycecrane.com
Sales Range: $1-9.9 Million
Heavy Construction Equipment Rental, Nsk
N.A.I.C.S.: 532412
Joe Bob Joyce (Founder)

Subsidiary (Non-US):

Sterling Crane   (4)
2440 - 76 Avenue, PO Box 8610, Edmonton, T6E 6R2, AB, Canada
Tel.: (780) 440-4434
Web Site: http://www.sterlingcrane.ca
Crane Rentals
N.A.I.C.S.: 532412

Subsidiary (Domestic):

ENTREC Cranes & Heavy Haul
(Western) Ltd.   (5)
3545 Highway 16 East, Terrace, V8G 5J3,
BC, Canada
Tel.: (250) 635-6802
Web Site: http://www.entrec.com
Gas Natural Liquid Extraction Services
N.A.I.C.S.: 211130

Division (Domestic):

Procrane Engineering   (5)
2440-76th Avenue Stn South, PO Box
8610, Edmonton, T6E 6R2, AB, Canada
Tel.: (780) 440-4434
Web Site: http://www.sterlingcrane.com
Sales Range: $75-99.9 Million
Emp.: 40
Engineeering Services
N.A.I.C.S.: 541330

Procrane Sales Inc.   (5)
2440 76th Avenue Stn South, PO Box
8610, Edmonton, T6E 6R2, AB, Canada
Tel.: (780) 466-8440
Web Site: http://www.procranesales.com
Sales Range: $1-9.9 Million
New & Used Crane Sales
N.A.I.C.S.: 532412

Sterling Crane - Contract Lifting
Division   (5)
2440 - 76 Ave, PO Box 8610, Edmonton,
T6T 1J5, AB, Canada
Tel.: (780) 440-4434
Web Site: http://www.sterlingcrane.com
Sales Range: $75-99.9 Million
Emp.: 100
Crane Equipment Hauling & Project Management
N.A.I.C.S.: 532412
Robin Bailey (Pres)

Sterling Crane - Rentals Division   (5)
Stn South 2440 - 76 Avenue, PO Box 8610,
Edmonton, T6E 6R2, AB, Canada
Tel.: (780) 440-4434
Web Site: http://www.sterlingcrane.com
Emp.: 600
Crane Rental & Service
N.A.I.C.S.: 532412
Robin Bailey (Pres)

Division (Domestic):

Marmon Distribution Services   (3)
181 W Madison St Ste 2600, Chicago, IL
60602-4510
Tel.: (312) 372-9500
Distribution Services
N.A.I.C.S.: 541614

Subsidiary (Domestic):

Bushwick Metals, LLC   (4)
560 N Washington Ave, Bridgeport, CT
06604
Tel.: (203) 576-1800
Web Site: http://www.bushwickmetals.com
Carbon Steel Distr
N.A.I.C.S.: 423510

Division (Domestic):

AZCO Steel Company   (5)
1641 New Market Ave, South Plainfield, NJ
07080
Tel.: (908) 754-8700
Web Site: http://www.azcosteel.com
Sales Range: $25-49.9 Million
Emp.: 75
Structural Steel, Plate, Sheet & Bar Products

N.A.I.C.S.: 331221

Bushwick Metals LLC - Binghamton
Division   (5)
13 Spud Ln, Binghamton, NY 13904
Tel.: (607) 775-1500
Web Site: http://www.bushwickmetals.com
Steel Service Center
N.A.I.C.S.: 423510

Subsidiary (Domestic):

Future Metals, Inc.   (4)
10401 State St, Tamarac, FL 33321
Tel.: (954) 724-1400
Web Site: http://www.futuremetals.com
Aerospace Tubing & Specialty Metal Products Distribution
N.A.I.C.S.: 423510

Marmon/Keystone LLC   (4)
225 E Cunningham St, Butler, PA 16001
Tel.: (724) 283-3000
Web Site:
    https://www.marmonkeystone.com
Pipe & Tubing Products Distr
N.A.I.C.S.: 423440

Subsidiary (Domestic):

Marmon/Keystone Corporation   (5)
225 E Cunningham St, Butler, PA 16001-
6018
Tel.: (724) 283-3000
Web Site:
    https://www.marmonkeystone.com
Pipe & Tubing Steel Whslr
N.A.I.C.S.: 423510

Subsidiary (Non-US):

Marmon/Keystone Canada, Inc.   (6)
1220 Heritage Road, Burlington, L7L 4X9,
ON, Canada
Tel.: (905) 319-4646
Web Site: http://www.mkcanada.com
Sales Range: $50-74.9 Million
Emp.: 1,300
Steel Tube Mfr
N.A.I.C.S.: 331210
David Rombough (Pres)

Plant (Domestic):

Marmon/Keystone Corporation   (6)
4521 Willow Pkwy, Cleveland, OH 44125
Tel.: (216) 641-9339
Web Site: http://www.marmonkeystone.com
Rev.: $25,000,000
Emp.: 46
Pipe & Tubing, Steel Mfr
N.A.I.C.S.: 423510

Division (Domestic):

Marmon Engineered Wire &
Cable   (3)
181 W Madison St 26th Fl, Chicago, IL
60602-4510
Tel.: (312) 372-9500
Web Site: http://www.marmon.com
Sales Range: $100-124.9 Million
Emp.: 80
Wire & Cable Products & Services
N.A.I.C.S.: 332618

Subsidiary (Domestic):

Dekoron Unitherm, Inc.   (4)
1531 Commerce Creek Blvd, Cape Coral,
FL 33909
Tel.: (239) 995-8111
Web Site: http://www.unithermcc.com
Sales Range: $25-49.9 Million
Emp.: 50
Heated Hose Bundles, Steam & Electrical
Traced Tubing Bundles & Preinsulated Tubing Mfr
N.A.I.C.S.: 332618
Mike Goddard (VP-Sls & Mktg)

Dekoron Wire & Cable, Inc.   (4)
1300 Industrial Rd, Mount Pleasant, TX
75455
Tel.: (903) 572-3475
Web Site: http://www.dekoroncable.com
Sales Range: $50-74.9 Million
Emp.: 70
Thermoplastic Wire Mfr
N.A.I.C.S.: 332618

Berkshire Hathaway Inc.—(Continued)

Subsidiary (Non-US):

Dekoron Wire & Cable Asia Pte Ltd **(5)**
Pantech Industrial Complex 192 Pandan Loop 01-10, Singapore, 128381, Singapore
Tel.: (65) 67791904
Web Site: http://www.dekoroncable.com
Sales Range: $100-124.9 Million
Emp.: 1
Thermoplastic Wire Mfr
N.A.I.C.S.: 332618

Subsidiary (Domestic):

Harbour Industries, Inc. **(4)**
4744 Shelburne Rd, Shelburne, VT 05482
Tel.: (802) 985-3311
Web Site: http://www.harbourind.com
Sales Range: $100-124.9 Million
Wire & Cable Mfr
N.A.I.C.S.: 332618

Subsidiary (Non-US):

Harbour Industries Canada Ltd. **(5)**
1365 Industrial Blvd, Farnham, J2N 2X3, QC, Canada
Tel.: (450) 293-5304
Web Site: http://www.harbourind.com
Sales Range: $10-24.9 Million
Emp.: 55
Wires & Cables Mfr
N.A.I.C.S.: 332618

Subsidiary (Domestic):

Hendrix Marmon Utility LLC **(4)**
53 Old Wilton Rd, Milford, NH 03055
Tel.: (603) 673-2040
Web Site: http://www.hendrix-wc.com
Sales Range: $50-74.9 Million
Underground & Overhead Electrical Distribution Cable, Cable Systems & Accessories Mfr
N.A.I.C.S.: 335921

RSCC Wire & Cable LLC **(4)**
20 Bradley Park Rd, East Granby, CT 06026
Tel.: (860) 653-8300
Web Site: http://www.r-scc.com
Sales Range: $100-124.9 Million
Engineered Wire & Cable Products
N.A.I.C.S.: 332618

Subsidiary (Domestic):

Rockbestos-Surprenant Cable Corp. **(5)**
20 Bradley Park Rd, East Granby, CT 06026
Tel.: (860) 653-8300
Web Site: http://www.r-scc.com
Sales Range: $75-99.9 Million
Wire & Cable Product Mfr
N.A.I.C.S.: 332618
Dennis Chalk (Pres)

Subsidiary (Domestic):

RSCC Aerospace & Defense **(6)**
680 Hayward St, Manchester, NH 03103
Tel.: (603) 622-3500
Web Site: https://www.marmon-ad.com
Sales Range: $50-74.9 Million
Emp.: 100
Engineered Wire & Cable Products
N.A.I.C.S.: 332618

Division (Domestic):

Rockbestos-Surprenant Cable Corp. Oil/Petrochemical Division **(6)**
20 Bradley Park Rd, East Granby, CT 06026
Tel.: (860) 653-8390
Web Site: http://www.r-scc.com
Sales Range: $125-149.9 Million
Emp.: 300
Engineered Wire & Cable Products
N.A.I.C.S.: 332618

Rockbestos-Surprenant Cable Corp. Transportation Market Division **(6)**
20 Bradley Park Rd, East Granby, CT 06026
Tel.: (860) 653-8365
Web Site: http://www.r-scc.com

Sales Range: $125-149.9 Million
Emp.: 300
Engineered Wire & Cable Products
N.A.I.C.S.: 332618

Rockbestos-Surprenant Cable Corp. Utility/Industrial Market Division **(6)**
20 Bradley Park Rd, East Granby, CT 06026
Tel.: (860) 653-8300
Sales Range: $100-124.9 Million
Engineered Wire & Cable Products
N.A.I.C.S.: 332618
Mike Mennone (VP & Gen Mgr)
Jim Notarfrancesco (Dir-Sls & Mktg)
Doug Soulliere (Mgr-Contract Admin)

Subsidiary (Domestic):

TE Wire & Cable LLC **(6)**
107 N 5th St, Saddle Brook, NJ 07663-6167
Tel.: (201) 845-9400
Web Site: https://tewire.com
Sales Range: $50-74.9 Million
Emp.: 70
Industrial Thermocouple Wire & Cable
N.A.I.C.S.: 332618
Robert M. Canny (Pres)
Todd Waters (Controller)
Joanne Ward (Mgr-Inside Sls)
Vlad Fedorchak (VP)

Subsidiary (Domestic):

The Kerite Company **(4)**
49 Day St, Seymour, CT 06483
Tel.: (203) 888-2591
Web Site: http://www.marmonutility.com
Sales Range: $50-74.9 Million
Rubber Insulated Power Cable
N.A.I.C.S.: 332618

Division (Domestic):

Marmon Flow Products **(3)**
181 W Madison St 26th Fl, Chicago, IL 60602
Tel.: (312) 372-9500
Web Site: http://www.marmon.com
Sales Range: $25-49.9 Million
Emp.: 100
Copper Tubing, Aluminum Shapes, Valves & Fittings
N.A.I.C.S.: 331210

Subsidiary (Domestic):

Cerro Flow Products, Inc. **(4)**
3000 Mississippi Ave, Sauget, IL 62206-1057
Tel.: (618) 337-6000
Web Site: http://www.cerroflow.com
Copper Tube Plumbing Products
N.A.I.C.S.: 331420

Plant (Domestic):

Cerro Flow Products, Inc. **(5)**
101 S Douglas St, Shelbina, MO 63468
Tel.: (618) 337-6000
Web Site: http://www.cerroflow.com
Sales Range: $50-74.9 Million
Emp.: 150
Copper Tube Plumbing Products
N.A.I.C.S.: 331420

Division (Domestic):

Marmon Food Service Equipment **(3)**
181 W Madison St 26th Fl, Chicago, IL 60602
Tel.: (312) 372-9500
Web Site: http://www.marmon.com
Sales Range: $50-74.9 Million
Emp.: 100
Food Service Equipment Products & Services
N.A.I.C.S.: 333241

Subsidiary (Non-US):

Catequip S.A. **(4)**
19 Rue De La Paix, 10320, Bouilly, France
Tel.: (33) 325402910
Web Site: http://www.catequip.com
Emp.: 20
Retail Equipment Distr
N.A.I.C.S.: 423850

Subsidiary (Domestic):

Prince Castle, Inc. **(4)**
355 E Kehoe Blvd, Carol Stream, IL 60188
Tel.: (630) 462-8800
Web Site: https://www.princecastle.com
Sales Range: $100-124.9 Million
Specialty Restaurant Equipment Mfr
N.A.I.C.S.: 333310

Silver King Refrigeration, Inc **(4)**
1600 Xenium Ln N, Plymouth, MN 55441-3706
Tel.: (763) 553-1881
Web Site: http://www.silverking.com
Sales Range: $50-74.9 Million
Milk Dispensers & Refrigerated Food Service Equipment Mfr
N.A.I.C.S.: 333415

Unarco Industries LLC **(4)**
400 SE 15th St, Wagoner, OK 74467
Tel.: (918) 485-9531
Web Site: http://www.unarco.com
Sales Range: $100-124.9 Million
Emp.: 50
Wire & Plastic Shopping Carts Mfr
N.A.I.C.S.: 332618

Division (Domestic):

Marmon Highway Technologies **(3)**
3110 Industrial Pkwy, Jasper, AL 35501
Tel.: (205) 208-2001
Web Site: http://www.marmonhitech.com
Sales Range: $25-49.9 Million
Emp.: 7
Truck Parts & Accessories
N.A.I.C.S.: 423120

Subsidiary (Domestic):

Fleetline Products **(4)**
784 Bill Jones Industrial Dr, Springfield, TN 37172
Tel.: (615) 332-6653
Web Site: http://www.fleetlineproducts.com
Spray Suppression Systems
N.A.I.C.S.: 336390

Fontaine Fifth Wheel Company **(4)**
3520 Industrial Prkwy, Jasper, AL 35501
Tel.: (205) 847-3250
Web Site: http://www.fontaineintl.com
Fifth Wheel Mfr
N.A.I.C.S.: 333924

Fontaine Modification Company **(4)**
9827 Mount Holly Rd, Charlotte, NC 28214-9214
Tel.: (704) 392-8502
Web Site: http://www.fontainemod.com
Sales Range: $25-49.9 Million
Traditional Truck Equipment & Modifications
N.A.I.C.S.: 333924
Jamil Young (Pres-Medium & Heavy Truck Ops)
Tim Vitt (Sls Mgr--Central)
Carlos Francisco (Sls Mgr--West)
Kevin Campbell (Sls Mgr--East)

Fontaine Trailer Company **(4)**
430 Letson Rd, Haleyville, AL 35565
Tel.: (205) 486-5251
Web Site: http://www.fontainetrailer.com
Emp.: 200
Flatbed Trailer Mfr
N.A.I.C.S.: 336212

Hogebuilt, Inc. **(4)**
784 Bill Jones Industrial Dr, Springfield, TN 37172
Tel.: (626) 330-2356
Web Site: http://www.hogebuilt.com
Truck & Trailer Spray Suppression Systems
N.A.I.C.S.: 336330

Marmon-Herrington **(4)**
13001 Magisterial Dr, Louisville, KY 40223
Tel.: (502) 253-0277
Web Site: http://www.marmon-herrington.com
Sales Range: $25-49.9 Million
Automotive Engineering
N.A.I.C.S.: 336211

Perfection Clutch **(4)**
100 Perfection Way, Timmonsville, SC 29161
Tel.: (843) 326-5544
Web Site: http://www.perfectionclutch.com

Sales Range: $10-24.9 Million
Automotive Clutches, Clutch Facings, Lined & Unlined clutch Discs & Clutch Hydraulics
N.A.I.C.S.: 336350

Triangle Suspension Systems, Inc. **(4)**
200 E Maloney Rd, Du Bois, PA 15801
Tel.: (814) 375-7211
Web Site: http://www.triangleusa.com
Sales Range: $75-99.9 Million
Vehicle Undercarriage Parts
N.A.I.C.S.: 336390
Vince Roth (VP-Sls & Mktg)

Division (Domestic):

Marmon Industrial Products **(3)**
181 W Madison St, Chicago, IL 60602
Tel.: (312) 372-9500
Web Site: http://www.marmon.com
Sales Range: $25-49.9 Million
Emp.: 65
Railway Motor Cars Mfr
N.A.I.C.S.: 336510

Subsidiary (Domestic):

Atlas Bolt & Screw Company **(4)**
1628 Troy Rd, Ashland, OH 44805
Tel.: (419) 289-6171
Web Site: https://www.atlasfasteners.com
Sales Range: $50-74.9 Million
Emp.: 100
Steel Fasteners Mfr
N.A.I.C.S.: 332722

Cerro Fabricated Products, Inc. **(4)**
300 Triangle Dr, Weyers Cave, VA 24486
Tel.: (540) 234-9252
Web Site: http://www.cerrofabricated.com
Sales Range: $75-99.9 Million
Emp.: 150
Aluminum, Brass, Copper, Bronze & Other Specialized Non-Ferrous Alloys Custom Mfr
N.A.I.C.S.: 332112

Deerwood Fasteners International **(4)**
638 Reese Dr, Conover, NC 28613
Tel.: (828) 469-1075
Web Site: http://www.deerwood.com
Rev: $3,700,000
Emp.: 43
Industrial Supplies Whslr
N.A.I.C.S.: 423840
Thil Lail (Pres)

IMPulse NC, LLC **(4)**
100 IMPulse Way, Mount Olive, NC 28365-8691
Tel.: (919) 658-2200
Web Site: http://www.impulsenc.com
Sales Range: $10-24.9 Million
Emp.: 17
Overhead Contact System Hardware Designer & Mfr
N.A.I.C.S.: 332510
Jeff Wharton (Pres)

Koehler-Bright Star, Inc. **(4)**
380 Stewart Rd, Hanover, PA 18706
Tel.: (570) 825-1900
Web Site: http://www.koehlerlighting.com
Sales Range: $10-24.9 Million
Emp.: 30
Portable Industrial Lighting Mfr
N.A.I.C.S.: 335139

Unit (Domestic):

Bright Star, Inc. **(5)**
380 Stewart Rd, Hanover, PA 18706
Tel.: (570) 825-1900
Web Site: http://www.flashlight.com
Carbon-Zinc Batteries
N.A.I.C.S.: 335910

Koehler Lighting Products **(5)**
380 Stewart Rd, Wilkes Barre, PA 18706
Tel.: (570) 825-1900
Web Site: http://www.koehlerlighting.com
Lighting Products
N.A.I.C.S.: 335132

Subsidiary (Domestic):

Penn Aluminum International, Inc. **(4)**
1117 N 2nd St, Murphysboro, IL 62966
Tel.: (618) 684-2146

Web Site: http://www.pennaluminum.com
Sales Range: $50-74.9 Million
Aluminum Extruded Product Mfr
N.A.I.C.S.: 331318

Subsidiary (Non-US):

Robertson Inc.   (4)
1185 Corporate Drive Unit 1, Burlington,
L7L 5V5, ON, Canada
Tel.: (905) 332-7776
Web Site: http://www.robertsonscrew.com
Sales Range: $25-49.9 Million
Emp.: 20
Standard & Specialty Fasteners
N.A.I.C.S.: 332722

Division (Domestic):

Marmon Retail Store Fixtures   (3)
225 W Washington St, Chicago, IL 60606
Tel.: (312) 332-0317
Sales Range: $50-74.9 Million
Retail Consulting Services
N.A.I.C.S.: 541614

Subsidiary (Non-US):

Ecodyne Limited   (4)
4475 Corporate Drive, Burlington, L7L 5T9,
ON, Canada
Tel.: (905) 332-1404
Web Site: http://www.ecodyne.com
Sales Range: $1-9.9 Million
Emp.: 70
Water Treatment Equipment & Systems
N.A.I.C.S.: 237110

Eden Industries (UK) Limited   (4)
2-20 Booth Drive, Park Farm Estate,
Wellingborough, NN8 6GR, Northants,
United Kingdom
Tel.: (44) 1933401555
Web Site: http://www.eden-industries.co.uk
Sales Range: $50-74.9 Million
Emp.: 180
Retail Shelving Systems & Metal Store Fix-
tures
N.A.I.C.S.: 337215

Subsidiary (Domestic):

L.A. Darling Company   (4)
1401 Hwy 49 B, Paragould, AR 72450-3139
Tel.: (870) 239-9564
Web Site: http://www.ladarling.com
Metal, Wood & Wire Retail Display Systems
N.A.I.C.S.: 332618
John Harguess (Dir-Ops)

Subsidiary (Non-US):

Leader Metal Industry Co., Ltd.   (4)
Longshi District Wuguishan, Zhongshan,
528458, China
Tel.: (86) 760 2818 8168
Web Site: http://www.leader-marmon.com
Emp.: 1,200
Retail Shelving Systems & Metal Store Fix-
tures Mfr
N.A.I.C.S.: 337215

Subsidiary (Domestic):

Store Opening Solutions, Inc.   (4)
800 Middle Tennessee Blvd, Murfreesboro,
TN 37129
Tel.: (615) 867-0858
Web Site: http://www.store-solutions.com
Sales Range: $100-124.9 Million
Emp.: 55
New Store Openings, Remodels/Resets &
Rollouts
N.A.I.C.S.: 541410

Streater, Inc.   (4)
411 S 1st Ave, Albert Lea, MN 56007-1779
Tel.: (507) 373-0611
Web Site: http://www.streater.com
Sales Range: $25-49.9 Million
Emp.: 250
Store Fixture Mfr
N.A.I.C.S.: 332618

Division (Domestic):

Marmon Transportation Services &
Engineered Products   (3)
181 W Madison St 26th Fl, Chicago, IL
60602
Tel.: (312) 372-9500

Web Site: http://www.marmon.com
Sales Range: $300-349.9 Million
Emp.: 100
Transportation & Engineered Products
N.A.I.C.S.: 336999

Subsidiary (Domestic):

EXSIF Worldwide, Inc.   (4)
2700 Westchester Ave Ste 400, Purchase,
NY 10577
Tel.: (914) 848-4200
Sales Range: $25-49.9 Million
Emp.: 27
Intermodal Tank Container Leasing
N.A.I.C.S.: 213112

Subsidiary (Non-US):

Enersul Inc.   (4)
7210 Blackfoot Trl SE, Calgary, T2H 1M5,
AB, Canada
Tel.: (403) 253-5969
Web Site: http://www.enersul.com
Sales Range: $75-99.9 Million
Emp.: 250
Sulfur Handling & Processing
N.A.I.C.S.: 325180

Division (Domestic):

Enersul Operations   (5)
7210 Blackfoot Trail SE, Calgary, T2H 1M5,
AB, Canada
Tel.: (403) 253-5969
Web Site: http://www.enersul.com
Sales Range: $25-49.9 Million
Emp.: 70
Sulphur Forming, Processing & Transport-
ing
N.A.I.C.S.: 325180

Enersul Technologies   (5)
7210 Blackfoot Trail SE, Calgary, T2H 1M5,
AB, Canada
Tel.: (403) 253-5969
Web Site: http://www.enersul.com
Sales Range: $50-74.9 Million
Emp.: 50
Sulfur Technology Sales, Project Manage-
ment & After-Sales Service
N.A.I.C.S.: 424690

Subsidiary (Domestic):

Penn Machine Company   (4)
106 Station St, Johnstown, PA 15905-3995
Tel.: (814) 288-1547
Web Site: https://www.pennmach.com
Sales Range: $75-99.9 Million
Light Rail Transit Wheel, Axle & Gear Sets
N.A.I.C.S.: 333612
Kevin Frich (VP-Ops)

Division (Domestic):

Penn Locomotive Gear   (5)
310 Innovation Dr, Blairsville, PA 15717
Tel.: (724) 459-0302
Web Site:
         http://www.pennlocomotivegear.com
Sales Range: $10-24.9 Million
Emp.: 8
Locomotive Gears Mfr
N.A.I.C.S.: 333612

Subsidiary (Non-US):

Procor Limited   (4)
585 Michigan Drive Unit 2, Oakville, L6L
0G1, ON, Canada
Tel.: (613) 996-6666
Web Site: https://www.procor.com
Sales Range: $25-49.9 Million
Tank & Freight Car Leasing
N.A.I.C.S.: 532411

Subsidiary (Domestic):

Railserve Inc.   (4)
1691 Phoenix Blvd Ste 250, Atlanta, GA
30349-5565
Tel.: (770) 996-6838
Web Site: http://www.railserve.biz
Sales Range: $250-299.9 Million
Switching & Terminal Services
N.A.I.C.S.: 488210
Tami S. Kopish (VP-Fin)
Charles E. Crosby (VP & Gen Mgr-
Switching Ops)

Christopher Rogers (VP & Gen Mgr-Material
Handling & Logistics)
Laurie Stiles (VP)
Margaret Paauwe (VP)

Trackmobile, Inc.   (4)
1602 Executive Dr, Lagrange, GA 30240-
5746
Tel.: (706) 884-6651
Web Site: http://www.trackmobile.com
Sales Range: $10-24.9 Million
Emp.: 100
Railroad Equipment Mfr
N.A.I.C.S.: 336510

Uni-Form Components Co.   (4)
10703 Sheldon Rd, Houston, TX 77044
Tel.: (281) 456-9310
Web Site:
     http://www.uniformcomponents.com
Sales Range: $10-24.9 Million
Emp.: 77
Carbon, Stainless Steel & Aluminum Tank
Head Mfr
N.A.I.C.S.: 332911

Union Tank Car Company   (4)
175 W Jackson Blvd Ste 2100, Chicago, IL
60604
Tel.: (312) 431-3111
Web Site: https://www.utlx.com
Emp.: 3,000
Railroad Tank Cars Mfr
N.A.I.C.S.: 336510

Division (Domestic):

Marmon Water Treatment   (3)
181 W Madison St 26th Fl, Chicago, IL
60602
Tel.: (312) 372-9500
Web Site: http://www.marmon.com
Sales Range: $200-249.9 Million
Water Treatment Products & Services
N.A.I.C.S.: 562219

Subsidiary (Domestic):

Amarillo Gear Company Inc.   (4)
2401 Sundown Ln, Amarillo, TX 79118-6004
Tel.: (806) 622-1273
Web Site: http://www.amarillogear.com
Sales Range: $75-99.9 Million
Emp.: 150
Speed Changers, Drives & Gears Mfr
N.A.I.C.S.: 333612
Tera Davis (Coord-Admin)
Bob Neely (Sls Mgr-Cooling Products)
Tony Sample (Sls Mgr-Pump Products)
Monty Williams (Mgr-Inside Sls-Cooling &
Pump Products)

Subsidiary (Domestic):

Amarillo Wind Machine Company
Inc.   (5)
20513 Ave 256, Exeter, CA 93221
Tel.: (559) 592-4256
Web Site: http://www.amarillowind.com
Sales Range: $1-9.9 Million
Emp.: 20
Wind Machine Systems Mfr
N.A.I.C.S.: 333111

Subsidiary (Non-US):

Reductores de Mexico S.A.   (5)
Callejon Los Arredondo 183, Col Ex Haci-
enda De Arredondos, 66362, Santa Cata-
rina, Mexico
Tel.: (52) 8115222780
Web Site: http://www.amarillogear.com
Sales Range: $125-149.9 Million
Emp.: 30
Gear Drive Mfr
N.A.I.C.S.: 333612

Subsidiary (Domestic):

EcoWater Systems LLC   (4)
1890 Woodlane Dr, Woodbury, MN 55125
Tel.: (651) 739-5330
Web Site: https://www.ecowater.com
Sales Range: $700-749.9 Million
Emp.: 575
Water Conditioning Equipment Mfr
N.A.I.C.S.: 221310

Subsidiary (Non-US):

Ecowater Canada Ltd.   (5)

5240 Bradco Blvd, Mississauga, L4W 1G7,
ON, Canada
Tel.: (905) 629-0190
Web Site: http://www.watercanada.net
Sales Range: $10-24.9 Million
Emp.: 13
Water Treatment Equipment
N.A.I.C.S.: 221310

Subsidiary (Domestic):

Ecodyne Heat Exchangers, Inc.   (4)
4847 Homestead Rd, Houston, TX 77028
Tel.: (713) 675-3511
Web Site: http://www.ecodyne-
heatexchangers.com
Sales Range: $50-74.9 Million
Emp.: 100
Aircooler Equipment & Tubing Mfr
N.A.I.C.S.: 333415

Graver Technologies LLC   (4)
200 Lake Dr, Glasgow, DE 19702-3319
Tel.: (302) 731-1700
Web Site: http://www.gravertech.com
Sales Range: $75-99.9 Million
Emp.: 165
Industrial Filtration, Separation & Purifica-
tion Products
N.A.I.C.S.: 333248
Bill Cummings (Pres)
Stephanie O'Brien (VP-Fin)
Kartik Potukuchi (VP & Gen Mgr-Filtration &
Separation)
Anand Harohalli (VP & Gen Mgr-Ion Ex-
change & Utilities)
Bill Wallace (VP)
Rick Williams (VP)

Graver Water Systems LLC   (4)
30 Technology Dr Ste 2F, Warren, NJ
07059
Tel.: (908) 516-1400
Web Site: https://graver.com
Rev.: $4,000,000
Emp.: 50
Industrial & Municipal Water Treatment Sys-
tems
N.A.I.C.S.: 333310

Subsidiary (Domestic):

PRISM Plastics, Inc.   (3)
52111 Sierra Dr, Chesterfield, MI 48047
Tel.: (810) 292-6300
Web Site: https://www.prismplastics.com
Automotive Plastic Components Mfr
N.A.I.C.S.: 326199

Plant (Domestic):

PRISM Plastics, Inc. - Harlingen
Plant   (4)
2901 N Expy 77, Harlingen, TX 78552
Tel.: (956) 425-3300
Web Site: http://www.prismplastics.com
Automotive Plastic Components Mfr
N.A.I.C.S.: 326199

PRISM Plastics, Inc. - Meadville
Plant   (4)
1045 French St, Meadville, PA 16335
Tel.: (810) 292-6300
Web Site: http://www.prismplastics.com
Molded Plastic Product Mfr
N.A.I.C.S.: 333511

Subsidiary (Domestic):

Wells Lamont LLC   (3)
5215 Old Orchard Rd Ste 725, Skokie, IL
60077
Tel.: (847) 647-8200
Web Site: http://www.wellslamont.com
Sales Range: $200-249.9 Million
Emp.: 450
Glove & Hand Protection Product Mfr
N.A.I.C.S.: 315990

Division (Non-US):

Jomac Canada   (4)
10 Rue Bachelder, Stanstead, J0B 3E2,
QC, Canada
Tel.: (819) 876-7531
Web Site: http://www.jomaccanada.com
Sales Range: $50-74.9 Million
Emp.: 100
Glove Mfr
N.A.I.C.S.: 315990

Berkshire Hathaway Inc.—(Continued)

Subsidiary (Domestic):

**Wells Lamont Industry Group
LLC** (4)
5215 Old Orchard Rd Ste 725, Skokie, IL
60077
Tel.: (847) 647-8200
Web Site: http://wellslamontindustrial.com
Sales Range: $25-49.9 Million
Emp.: 25
Protective Glove Mfr
N.A.I.C.S.: 315990

Unit (Domestic):

Wells Lamont Retail Group (4)
5215 Old Orchard Rd Ste 725l, Skokie, IL
60077
Tel.: (847) 647-8200
Web Site: http://www.wellslamont.com
Sales Range: $50-74.9 Million
Emp.: 100
Fabric Dress & Work Gloves Mfr
N.A.I.C.S.: 315990

Subsidiary (Domestic):

Transco Railway Products Inc. (2)
2310 S Ctr St, Newton Falls, OH
44444 (100%)
Tel.: (330) 872-0394
Web Site: http://www.transcorailway.com
Railcar Modification
N.A.I.C.S.: 333924
Bob Nelson (Pres)

McLane Company, Inc. (1)
4747 McLane Pkwy, Temple, TX 76504
Tel.: (254) 771-7500
Web Site: https://www.mclaneco.com
Emp.: 20,000
Food & Beverage Distr
N.A.I.C.S.: 424410
Tony Frankenberger (CEO)
James Barnes (Dir-Comm & PR)
Chris Smith (Pres-Grocery)

Subsidiary (Domestic):

Empire Distributors, Inc. (2)
685 Hartman Rd, Austell, GA 30168
Tel.: (404) 572-4100
Web Site: https://www.empiredist.com
Sales Range: $250-299.9 Million
Emp.: 700
Alcoholic Beverage Distr
N.A.I.C.S.: 424820

Subsidiary (Domestic):

Empire Distributors Inc-Charlotte (3)
13833 Carowinds Blvd, Charlotte, NC
28273
Tel.: (704) 588-9463
Web Site: http://www.empiredist.com
Emp.: 80
Alcoholic Beverage Distr
N.A.I.C.S.: 424820

Branch (Domestic):

**Empire Distributors of North Carolina
Inc. - Raleigh** (4)
1757 TW Alexander Dr, Durham, NC 27703
Tel.: (919) 424-4200
Web Site: http://www.empiredist.com
Emp.: 500
Alcoholic Beverage Distr
N.A.I.C.S.: 424820
Nelson Wixson (Gen Mgr)

**Empire Distributors of North Carolina,
Inc. - Wilmington** (4)
4805 Las Tortugas Dr, Castle Hayne, NC
28429
Tel.: (910) 675-3280
Web Site: http://www.empiredist.com
Alcoholic Beverage Distr
N.A.I.C.S.: 424820
Jay McGrady (Gen Mgr-Wilmington)

Branch (Domestic):

**Empire Distributors, Inc. -
Augusta** (3)
312 UN Ct, Grovetown, GA 30813-8131
Tel.: (706) 869-0232
Web Site: http://www.empiredist.com
Alcoholic Beverage Distr

N.A.I.C.S.: 424820

**Empire Distributors, Inc. -
Savannah** (3)
9 Aviation Ct, Garden City, GA 31408
Tel.: (912) 965-0611
Web Site: http://www.empiredist.com
Alcoholic Beverage Distr
N.A.I.C.S.: 424820

Empire Distributors, Inc. - Tifton (3)
41 Union Industrial Way, Tifton, GA 31793
Tel.: (229) 396-5601
Web Site: http://www.empiredist.com
Emp.: 15
Alcoholic Beverage Distr
N.A.I.C.S.: 424820
Lee Pollock (Gen Mgr)

Subsidiary (Domestic):

Horizon Wine & Spirits, Inc. (3)
3851 Industrial Park Way, Nashville, TN
37218
Tel.: (615) 320-7292
Web Site:
http://www.horizonwineandspirits.com
Sales Range: $50-74.9 Million
Emp.: 100
Wine & Beverage Distr
N.A.I.C.S.: 424820

Subsidiary (Domestic):

McLane Foodservice, Inc. (2)
2085 Midway Rd, Carrollton, TX 75006-
5063
Tel.: (972) 364-2000
Web Site: https://www.mclaneco.com
Sales Range: $100-124.9 Million
Emp.: 200
Wholesale Food Distr
N.A.I.C.S.: 424420
Susan Adzick (COO & Exec VP)

**Meadowbrook Meat Company,
Inc.** (2)
2641 Meadowbrook Rd, Rocky Mount, NC
27801
Tel.: (252) 985-7200
Web Site: http://www.mclaneco.com
Food Products Distr
N.A.I.C.S.: 445290

MedPro Group Inc (1)
5814 Reed Rd, Fort Wayne, IN 46835
Tel.: (260) 485-9622
Web Site: https://www.medpro.com
Health Care Srvices
N.A.I.C.S.: 622110
Timothy Kenesey (Pres & CEO)

**Medical Liability Mutual Insurance
Company** (1)
2 Park Ave 25th Fl, New York, NY 10016-
9301
Tel.: (212) 576-9800
Web Site: http://www.mlmic.com
Sales Range: $50-74.9 Million
Emp.: 200
Medical Malpractice Insurance Services
N.A.I.C.S.: 524126

Branch (Domestic):

**Medical Liability Mutual Insurance
Co. - Latham** (2)
8 British American Blvd, Latham, NY 12110
Tel.: (518) 786-2700
Web Site: http://www.mlmic.com
Emp.: 100
Provider of Liability Insurance
N.A.I.C.S.: 524126

Subsidiary (Domestic):

**Professional Liability Insurance Com-
pany of America** (100%)
2 Park Ave Fl 25, New York, NY
10016-9301
Tel.: (212) 576-9800
Web Site: http://www.mlmic.com
Sales Range: $50-74.9 Million
Emp.: 100
Insurance & Medical Services
N.A.I.C.S.: 524126

Medical Protective Corporation (1)
5814 Reed Rd, Fort Wayne, IN 46835-3500
Tel.: (260) 485-9622

Medical Insurance Services
N.A.I.C.S.: 524114

MiTek Industries, Inc. (1)
16023 Swingley Ridge Rd, Chesterfield, MO
63017
Tel.: (314) 434-1200
Web Site: http://www.mitek-us.com
Sales Range: $150-199.9 Million
Emp.: 200
Holding Company; Steel Building Compo-
nents, Hydraulic & Pneumatic Presses &
Construction Products Mfr
N.A.I.C.S.: 551112
Mark Thom (Chm & CEO)
David Sell (Chief Innovation Officer & Sr
VP)
Bryan Bohme (VP)
Faith Tang (CIO)
Robert Stubbs (Mng Dir)

Subsidiary (Domestic):

Aegis Metal Framing, LLC (2)
16023 Swingley Rdg Rd, Chesterfield, MO
63017
Tel.: (314) 851-2200
Web Site:
http://www.aegismetalframing.com
Light Gauge Steel Framing Systems Mfr
N.A.I.C.S.: 332312

Benson Industries, LLC (2)
1650 NW Naito Pkwy Ste 250, Portland,
OR 97209
Tel.: (503) 226-7611
Web Site: http://www.bensonglobal.com
Sales Range: $50-74.9 Million
Emp.: 89
Design, Engineering, Assembly & Installa-
tion of Curtain Wall Windows
N.A.I.C.S.: 238150

Subsidiary (Non-US):

Benson Ltd. (3)
Room Suite 1408 Namwoon Plaza 299-10
Mugeo 1 Nam, Nam-Ku, Ulsan, Korea
(South)
Tel.: (82) 522496060
Web Site: http://www.bensonglobal.com
Engineering Consulting Services
N.A.I.C.S.: 541330

Subsidiary (Domestic):

BuilderMT, Inc. (2)
1746 Cole Blvd Ste 225, Lakewood, CO
80401-3210
Tel.: (303) 914-1144
Web Site: http://www.buildermt.com
Workflow Process Management Software
Developer & Publisher
N.A.I.C.S.: 513210
Alicia Perri (Dir-Ops)

Subsidiary (Domestic):

Sales Simplicity Software, Inc. (3)
325 E Elliot Rd Ste 24, Chandler, AZ 85225
Tel.: (480) 892-2500
Web Site: http://www.salessimplicity.com
Sales Management Software Developer &
Publisher
N.A.I.C.S.: 513210

Subsidiary (Domestic):

Cubic Designs, Inc. (2)
5487 S Westridge Dr, New Berlin, WI
53151
Tel.: (262) 789-1966
Web Site: http://www.cubicdesigns.com
Sales Range: $1-9.9 Million
Emp.: 41
Mfr of Mezzanines for Industry, Equipment
Platforms, Custom Fabrication Facility &
Industrial Safety Products
N.A.I.C.S.: 238120
Mike Stearns (Mgr-East Coast)

**Ellis & Watts Global Industries,
LLC** (2)
4400 Glen Willow Lake Ln, Batavia, OH
45103
Tel.: (513) 752-9000
Web Site: http://www.elliswatts.com
Sales Range: $75-99.9 Million
Emp.: 80

Nuclear HVAC Systems, ASME Code Vessels, Military Shelters, Environmental Control Units & Blast Resistant Doors Mfr
N.A.I.C.S.: 339999

Heat Pipe Technology, Inc. (2)
6904 Parke E Blvd, Tampa, FL 33610
Tel.: (813) 470-4250
Web Site: http://www.heatpipe.com
Sales Range: $1-9.9 Million
Emp.: 24
Metal Valve & Pipe Fitting Mfr
N.A.I.C.S.: 332919

Hohmann & Barnard, Inc. (2)
30 Rasons Ct, Hauppauge, NY 11788-4206
Tel.: (631) 234-0600
Web Site: http://www.h-b.com
Sales Range: $50-74.9 Million
Emp.: 100
Concrete & Stone Anchor System, Rein-
forcement & Tie Mfr
N.A.I.C.S.: 423320

Subsidiary (Domestic):

Foamtastic Products, Inc. (3)
1985 Ticonderoga Blvd Ste 15, Chester
Springs, PA 19425
Tel.: (610) 873-0070
Web Site: http://www.foamfiller.com
Sales Range: $75-99.9 Million
Emp.: 30
Foam Flashing & Filler Material Developer
& Mfr
N.A.I.C.S.: 326140

Division (Domestic):

**R.K.L. Building Specialties Co.,
Inc.** (3)
15-30 131st St, College Point, NY 11356
Tel.: (718) 728-7788
Web Site: https://www.rklbuilding.com
Sales Range: $1-9.9 Million
Custom Stone & Masonry Anchors & Acces-
sories Mfr
N.A.I.C.S.: 332510

Subsidiary (Domestic):

Kova Solutions, Inc. (2)
400 Trade Ctr Ste 5900, Woburn, MA
01801
Tel.: (781) 569-0090
Web Site: http://www.kovasolutions.com
Sales Range: $1-9.9 Million
Homebuilding Financial & Operational Man-
agement Software Publisher
N.A.I.C.S.: 513210

M&M Manufacturing, LLC (2)
4001 Mark IV Pkwy, Fort Worth, TX 76106
Tel.: (017) 000-2011
Web Site: http://www.mmmfg.com
Sales Range: $200-249.9 Million
Sheet Metal Products Mfr
N.A.I.C.S.: 332322
Chris Van Rite (VP-Sls)

Plant (Domestic):

**M&M Manufacturing, LLC - Dallas
Plant** (3)
360 S Shiloh Rd, Garland, TX 75042-6616
Tel.: (972) 485-1504
Web Site: http://www.mmmfg.com
Emp.: 120
Sheet Metal Products Mfr
N.A.I.C.S.: 332322
Rodney McCormac (Asst Mgr-Plant)

**M&M Manufacturing, LLC - Fort
Worth (Adolph Street) Plant** (3)
200 Adolph St, Fort Worth, TX 76107
Tel.: (817) 334-0034
Web Site: http://www.mmmfg.com
Emp.: 75
Sheet Metal Products Mfr
N.A.I.C.S.: 332322
Chris Van Rite (VP-Sls)

**M&M Manufacturing, LLC - Houston
Plant** (3)
5555 Guhn Rd, Houston, TX 77040-6125
Tel.: (713) 690-0585
Web Site: http://www.mmmfg.com
Emp.: 75
Sheet Metal Products Mfr
N.A.I.C.S.: 332322

Kevin Stephenson (Mgr-Inside Sls)

Subsidiary (Non-US):

MiTek Canada, Inc. (2)
100 Industrial Road, Bradford, L3Z 3G7, ON, Canada
Tel.: (800) 268-3434
Web Site: http://www.mitek.ca
Emp.: 80
Industrial Machinery Whslr
N.A.I.C.S.: 423830

Subsidiary (Domestic):

MiTek USA, Inc. (2)
16023 Swingley Ridge Rd, Chesterfield, MO 63017
Tel.: (314) 434-1200
Web Site: https://www.mitek-us.com
Emp.: 200
Construction Structural Connector Products & Assembly Machinery Mfr
N.A.I.C.S.: 332999

National Liability & Fire Insurance Company (1)
PO Box 113247, Stamford, CT 06911-3247
Web Site: http://www.nlf-info.com
Insurance Services
N.A.I.C.S.: 524210

Nebraska Furniture Mart, Inc. (1)
700 S 72nd St, Omaha, NE 68114-4614
Tel.: (402) 392-3202
Web Site: https://www.nfm.com
Sales Range: $450-499.9 Million
Emp.: 1,500
Home Furnishings Retailer
N.A.I.C.S.: 449110
Ron Blumkin (Co-Chm & Co-CEO)
Tony Boldt (Pres & COO)
Irv Blumkin (Co-Chm & CEO)
Shane Pohlman (Dir-Furniture)
Nora Gomez (Chief Mdsg Officer)
Elizabeth Barton (Dir-Customer Rels)
Megan Berry Barlow (Dir-HR)
Dave Chambers (Dir-Flooring)
Jeff Douglas (Dir-E-commerce)
Doug Hamlin (CFO)
Marc Harris (Dir-Supply Chain)
Robyn Messerly (Dir-IT)
Jody Rusnak (Dir-Appliances & Electronics)
Scott Baker (Dir-Store-Omaha)
Ed Lipsett (Dir-Store-Colony)
Ethan Stover (Dir-Store-Kansas)
Amy Myers (CMO)

Subsidiary (Domestic):

Homemakers Plaza, Inc. (2)
10215 Douglas Ave, Urbandale, IA 50322
Tel.: (515) 276-2772
Web Site: https://www.homemakers.com
Sales Range: $100-124.9 Million
Emp.: 200
Furniture Retailer
N.A.I.C.S.: 449110

NetJets Inc. (1)
4151 Bridgeway Ave, Columbus, OH 43219
Tel.: (614) 239-5500
Web Site: https://www.netjets.com
Sales Range: $500-549.9 Million
Emp.: 1,000
Business Jet Charters, Management, Maintenance, Pilot Training, Avionics Service & Installation, Aircraft Brokerage, Sales & Leasing
N.A.I.C.S.: 481219
Adam M. Johnson (Chm & CEO)

Subsidiary (Domestic):

Marquis Jet Partners Inc. (2)
230 Park Ave Ste 840, New York, NY 10169
Tel.: (866) 538-0707
Private Jet Leasing Services
N.A.I.C.S.: 481219
Kenneth Dichter (Founder)

North American Casualty Co. (1)
One Applied Pkwy, Omaha, NE 68144
Web Site: https://www.nacasualty.com
Insurance Services
N.A.I.C.S.: 524298

Northern Powergrid Limited (1)
Manor House Station Road, Penshaw, Houghton le Spring, DH4 7LA, Tyne &

Wear, United Kingdom
Tel.: (44) 8001692996
Web Site:
    http://www.northernpowergrid.com
Electric Power Distr
N.A.I.C.S.: 221122

Subsidiary (Domestic):

Northern Electric plc (2)
Lloyds Court 78 Grey Street, Newcastle upon Tyne, NE1 6AF, Tyne And Wear, United Kingdom
Tel.: (44) 1912235151
Web Site: http://www.ce-electricuk.com
Rev.: $672,339,855
Assets: $4,452,096,990
Liabilities: $2,768,205,990
Net Worth: $1,683,891,000
Earnings: $127,002,480
Emp.: 1,669
Fiscal Year-end: 12/31/2022
Electric Power Distribution Services
N.A.I.C.S.: 221122
Thomas E. Fielden (Gen Counsel)

Northern Powergrid U.K. Holdings (2)
Network Connections Cargo Fleet Lane, Middlesbrough, TS3 8DG, United Kingdom
Tel.: (44) 8450702703
Electric Power Distr
N.A.I.C.S.: 221122

Subsidiary (Domestic):

Oak River Insurance Company (1)
1314 Douglas St, Omaha, NE 68102
Tel.: (402) 393-7255
Web Site: http://www.bhhc.com
Sales Range: $150-199.9 Million
Emp.: 100
Direct Life Insurance Carriers
N.A.I.C.S.: 524113

Old United Casualty Company (1)
8500 Shawnee Mission Pkwy Ste 200, Merriam, KS 66202
Tel.: (913) 895-0200
Web Site: http://www.oldunited.com
Insurance Services
N.A.I.C.S.: 524113

Oriental Trading Company, Inc. (1)
4206 S 108th St, Omaha, NE 68137-1215
Tel.: (402) 331-6800
Web Site: https://www.orientaltrading.com
Emp.: 2,000
Party Supplies, Arts & Crafts Products, Toys & Novelty Items Catalog Retailer
N.A.I.C.S.: 423920
Sandra J. Horbach (Chm)

Subsidiary (Domestic):

MindWare, Inc. (2)
2100 County Rd C W, Saint Paul, MN 55113-2501
Tel.: (651) 268-2850
Web Site: http://www.mindware.com
Toy Mfr & Distr
N.A.I.C.S.: 339930
Jonathan Staruck (Pres)

OTC Brands, Inc. (2)
4206 S 108th St, Omaha, NE 68137
Tel.: (800) 228-0038
Insurance Agency Services
N.A.I.C.S.: 524210

SmileMakers, Inc. (2)
PO Box 2543, Spartanburg, SC 29304
Tel.: (864) 583-2405
Web Site: https://www.smilemakers.com
Sales Range: $75-99.9 Million
Emp.: 150
Toys & Novelties Distr
N.A.I.C.S.: 423920

Subsidiary (Non-US):

SmileMakers for Children Co. (3)
91 Station St Unit 4, Ajax, L1S 3H2, ON, Canada
Tel.: (888) 456-7645
Web Site:
    http://www.smilemakerscanada.com
Toys & Novelties Distr
N.A.I.C.S.: 423920

PCG Agencies, Inc. (1)
119 14th St NW Ste 300, Saint Paul, MN 55112

Tel.: (651) 605-2777
Web Site: http://www.pcgagencies.com
Sales Range: $25-49.9 Million
Personal & Home Insurance Services
N.A.I.C.S.: 524126

PLICO, Inc. (1)
126 Harrison Ave, Oklahoma City, OK 73104
Tel.: (405) 815-4800
Web Site: https://www.plico.com
Health Care Srvices
N.A.I.C.S.: 622110
Carl T. Hook (Chm)
Sherry Haworth (Pres)
Becky Meares (VP-IT)
Matthew J. Moore (VP-Bus Dev)
Shari Moore (VP-Risk Mgmt)
Dale Neikirk (COO)
Jeff Weigl (VP-Underwriting)

Pilot Travel Centers LLC (1)
5508 Lonas Dr, Knoxville, TN 37909   (100%)
Web Site: http://www.pilotflyingj.com
Sales Range: $1-4.9 Billion
Emp.: 28,000
Travel Centers & Gasoline Stations
N.A.I.C.S.: 457110
Shannon Johnson (VP-Food Innovation)
Whitney Haslam-Johnson (Chief Experience Officer)
Brad Jenkins (Sr VP-Petroleum Supply & Distr)
David Hughes (Sr VP-Sls)
Michael Rodgers (CIO & Co-Chief Strategy Officer)
Paul Shore (Chief People Officer)
Shameek Konar (Co-Chief Strategy Officer)

Subsidiary (Domestic):

Maxum Petroleum, Inc. (2)
20 Horseneck Ln, Greenwich, CT 06830
Tel.: (203) 861-1200
Web Site: https://www.maxumpetroleum.com
Refined Petroleum Products Marketer & Logistics Services
N.A.I.C.S.: 424720
Patrick C. Graney III (Sr VP)

Subsidiary (Domestic):

Paulson Oil Company Inc. (3)
950 Wabash Ave, Chesterton, IN 46304-2252
Tel.: (219) 926-4379
Web Site: http://www.pocooil.com
Sales Range: $25-49.9 Million
Emp.: 45
Fuels & Lubricants Distr
N.A.I.C.S.: 424720
Glenn Pumpelly (Exec VP & Reg Mgr-South)
Larry J. Stoddard (Pres & CEO)

Simons Petroleum Inc. (3)
210 Park Ave Ste 1800, Oklahoma City, OK 73102
Tel.: (405) 848-3500
Web Site: http://www.simonspetroleum.com
Sales Range: $25-49.9 Million
Emp.: 200
Petroleum & Petroleum Products Distr
N.A.I.C.S.: 424720

Western Petroleum LLC (3)
1521 S 1500 E, Vernal, UT 84078
Tel.: (435) 789-1832
Web Site:
    http://www.pilotlogisticsservices.com
Sales Range: $300-349.9 Million
Emp.: 500
Holding Company; Petroleum & Petroleum Products Wholesale Distr
N.A.I.C.S.: 551112
Russ Labrum (Mgr-Ops)

Subsidiary (Domestic):

RBJ & Associates LLC (2)
30137 County Rd 5, Warroad, MN 56763
Tel.: (218) 242-1783
Web Site: http://www.rbjassoc.com
Professional, Scientific & Technical Services
N.A.I.C.S.: 541990

TransMontaigne Product Services, LLC (2)

3773 Cherry Creek N Dr Ste 1000, Denver, CO 80209
Tel.: (303) 815-1010
Web Site: http://tpsl.nglep.com
Refined Petroleum Product Mfr & Distr
N.A.I.C.S.: 424720

Precision Castparts Corp. (1)
4650 SW Macadam Ave Ste 400, Portland, OR 97239
Tel.: (503) 946-4800
Web Site: http://www.precast.com
Metal Components, Investment Castings, Fasteners, Airfoils, Specialty Alloys, Sewer Systems & Precision Tools Mfr
N.A.I.C.S.: 331513

Subsidiary (Non-US):

AF Aerospace Limited (2)
2 Chariot Way Glebe Farm Industrial Estate, Rugby, CV21 1DA, Warks, United Kingdom
Tel.: (44) 1788578431
Web Site: http://www.afaerospace.co.uk
Steel Investment Foundries
N.A.I.C.S.: 331512

Subsidiary (Domestic):

Aerocraft Heat Treating Co., Inc. (2)
15701 Minnesota Ave, Paramount, CA 90723
Tel.: (562) 674-2400
Web Site: https://www.aerocraft-ht.com
Metal Heat Treating Services
N.A.I.C.S.: 332811

Aerospace Dynamics International Inc. (2)
25540 Rye Canyon Rd, Valencia, CA 91355-1109
Tel.: (661) 257-3535
Web Site: http://www.pccaero.com
Aerospace Parts & Assemblies Mfr
N.A.I.C.S.: 336413

Airdrome Precision Components (2)
14800 S Figueroa St, Gardena, CA 90247
Tel.: (562) 426-9411
Web Site: http://www.airdrome.com
Hydraulic & Pneumatic Tube Fittings Mfr
N.A.I.C.S.: 332919

AlloyWorks, LLC (2)
814 W Innes St, Salisbury, NC 28144
Tel.: (704) 645-0511
Nonferrous Metal Smelting, Refining & Alloying
N.A.I.C.S.: 331410

Alu-Forge, Inc. (2)
165 S Spruce Ave, Rialto, CA 92376
Tel.: (909) 546-1900
Web Site: https://www.handforge.com
Aluminum & Titanium Mfr & Stainless Steel Open Die Forgings
N.A.I.C.S.: 331313

Atlantic Precision, Inc. (2)
1461 NW Commerce Ctr Pkwy, Port Saint Lucie, FL 34986
Tel.: (772) 466-1011
Web Site: http://www.atlanticprecision.com
Aircraft Machining Services
N.A.I.C.S.: 336412

Avibank Services, LLC (2)
100 Washington St Ste 304, Reno, NV 89503
Tel.: (775) 786-1991
Airline Sales, Product & Technical Repair Support & Services
N.A.I.C.S.: 561990

Brittain Machine, Inc. (2)
2520 S Sheridan Ave, Wichita, KS 67217-1340
Tel.: (316) 942-8223
Web Site: http://www.pccaero.com
Aircraft Part Mfr & Distr
N.A.I.C.S.: 336413

Subsidiary (Non-US):

Caledonian Alloys Group Limited (2)
Wyman Gordon Complex Houston Road, Livingston, EH54 5BZ, United Kingdom
Tel.: (44) 1506446543
Web Site:
    http://www.pccforgedproducts.com

Berkshire Hathaway Inc.—(Continued)

Steel Investment Foundries
N.A.I.C.S.: 331512

Subsidiary (Domestic):

Caledonian Alloys Limited (3)
Houstoun Rd, Livingston, EH54 5BZ, United
Kingdom
Tel.: (44) 1506446543
Web Site:
   http://www.pccforgedproducts.com
Steel Investment Foundry Services
N.A.I.C.S.: 331512

Subsidiary (Domestic):

Carlton Forge Works (2)
7743 E Adams St, Paramount, CA 90723
Tel.: (562) 633-1131
Web Site:
   https://www.carltonforgeworks.com
Seamless Rolled Rings & Open & Closed
Die Forgings
N.A.I.C.S.: 332112

Subsidiary (Non-US):

Centra Industries Inc. (2)
24 Cherry Blossom Rd, Cambridge, N3H
4R7, ON, Canada
Tel.: (519) 650-2828
Web Site: https://www.pccaero.com
Aircraft Components Mfr
N.A.I.C.S.: 336411

Subsidiary (Domestic):

Dickson Testing Company, Inc. (2)
11126 Palmer Ave, South Gate, CA 90280
Tel.: (562) 862-8378
Web Site: https://www.dicksontesting.com
Destructive Testing Services
N.A.I.C.S.: 541380

Environment-One Corporation (2)
2773 Balltown Rd, Niskayuna, NY
12309-1090   **(100%)**
Tel.: (518) 346-6161
Web Site: https://www.eone.com
Disposal & Residential Sanitary Waste
Products Mfr & Services
N.A.I.C.S.: 562119

Exacta Aerospace, Inc. (2)
4200 W Harry St, Wichita, KS 67209
Tel.: (316) 941-4200
Web Site: http://www.pccaero.com
Aerospace Component Distr
N.A.I.C.S.: 336413

GSC Foundries, Inc. (2)
2738 Commerce Way, Ogden, UT 84401
Tel.: (801) 627-1660
Aluminum & Steel Manufacturing
N.A.I.C.S.: 331315

Helicomb International, Inc. (2)
1402 S 69th E Ave, Tulsa, OK 74112
Tel.: (918) 835-3999
Aircraft Part Mfr
N.A.I.C.S.: 336413

Subsidiary (Non-US):

KALISTRUT Aerospace S.A.S. (2)
1 av Marc Seguin Cs 14189, 26241, Saint
Vallier, Cedex, France
Tel.: (33) 475034040
Web Site: https://kalistrut-aerospace.com
Insurance Services
N.A.I.C.S.: 524298

KG Coating Limited (2)
Unit 5 Whitegate Industrial Estate, White-
gate Road, Wrexham, LL13 8UG, United
Kingdom
Tel.: (44) 1978356917
Web Site: https://www.kgcoating.co.uk
Aircraft Metal Coating Services
N.A.I.C.S.: 332812

Subsidiary (Domestic):

**KLAD Manufacturing Company,
Ltd.** (2)
403 South Loop W, Houston, TX 77054
Tel.: (888) 433-5523
Web Site:
   http://www.pccforgedproducts.com
Steel Pipe & Tubes Mfr & Distr

N.A.I.C.S.: 331210

NSS Technologies, Inc. (2)
8680 N Haggerty Rd, Canton, MI 48187
Tel.: (734) 459-9500
Web Site: https://www.netshaped.com
Engineered Fasteners Mfr
N.A.I.C.S.: 332722

Subsidiary (Non-US):

Noranco Inc. (2)
710 Rowntree Dairy Rd, Woodbridge, L4L
5T7, ON, Canada
Tel.: (905) 264-2050
Web Site: http://pccaero.com
Aircraft Components Mfr
N.A.I.C.S.: 336413

Division (US):

**Noranco Inc. - Deer Valley
Division** (3)
1620 W Knudsen Dr, Phoenix, AZ 85027
Tel.: (623) 582-2261
Web Site: http://pccaero.com
Aircraft Components Mfr
N.A.I.C.S.: 336413

Subsidiary (Non-US):

Overall Forge Nominees Pty Ltd (2)
70 RW Henry Drive, Albury, 2640, NSW,
Australia
Tel.: (61) 260256777
Web Site: http://www.overallforge.com.au
Ball & Roller Bearing Mfr
N.A.I.C.S.: 332991

Overall Forge Pty Ltd (2)
70 RW Henry Drive Ettamogah, Albury,
2640, NSW, Australia
Tel.: (61) 260256777
Web Site: https://www.overallforge.com.au
Ball & Roller Bearing Mfr
N.A.I.C.S.: 332991

Subsidiary (Domestic):

PCC Aerostructures Auburn (2)
701 Milwaukee Ave N, Kent, WA 98001
Tel.: (253) 876-1500
Web Site: http://www.pccaero.com
Aircraft Part Mfr
N.A.I.C.S.: 336413

Subsidiary (Domestic):

Accra Manufacturing, Inc. (3)
17703 15th Ave SE, Bothell, WA 98012
Tel.: (425) 424-1000
Web Site: http://www.pccaero.com
Machine Part Mfr
N.A.I.C.S.: 332999

Walden's Machine LLC (3)
3030 N Erie Ave, Tulsa, OK 74115
Tel.: (918) 836-6317
Web Site: http://www.pccaero.com
Aircraft Part Mfr
N.A.I.C.S.: 336413

Subsidiary (Non-US):

PCC Aerostructures Dorval Inc. (2)
123 Avro Street, Dorval, H9P 2Y9, QC,
Canada
Tel.: (514) 421-0344
Web Site: http://www.pccaero.com
Aerospace Component Mfr
N.A.I.C.S.: 336413

Subsidiary (Domestic):

PCC Airfoils LLC (2)
3401 Enterprise Pkwy Ste 200, Beachwood,
OH 44122
Tel.: (216) 831-3590
Web Site: https://www.pccairfoils.com
Insurance Services
N.A.I.C.S.: 524298

Subsidiary (Non-US):

PCC Airfoils S.A. de C.V. (2)
Tablaje Catastral 18464 Fraccionamiento
Ampliacion-Cd Industrial, Periferico por Ter-
moelectrica, 97288, Merida, Yucatan,
Mexico
Tel.: (52) 9999302700
Web Site: http://www.pccairfoils.com
Aluminum Casting Mfr

N.A.I.C.S.: 331318

Subsidiary (Domestic):

PCC Airfoils, LLC (2)
3401 Enterprise Pkwy Ste 200, Beachwood,
OH 44122   **(100%)**
Tel.: (216) 831-3590
Web Site: https://www.pccairfoils.com
Cast Airfoils Mfr
N.A.I.C.S.: 331529
Dean Wheeler (Pres)

Subsidiary (Non-US):

AETC Limited (3)
Victoria Avenue Yeadon, Leeds, LS19 7AW,
United Kingdom
Tel.: (44) 8700666060
Web Site: https://www.pccairfoils.com
Cast Airfoils Mfr
N.A.I.C.S.: 331529

Subsidiary (Domestic):

PCC Energy Group (2)
10825 Telge Rd, Houston, TX 77095
Tel.: (281) 856-9900
Web Site: http://www.pccenergy.com
Metal Components & Products, Forgings &
Fastener Systems Mfr
N.A.I.C.S.: 331420

Subsidiary (Domestic):

PCC Rollmet, Inc. (3)
1822 Deere Ave, Irvine, CA 92606
Tel.: (949) 221-5333
Web Site: https://www.rollmetusa.com
Internal & External Roll Mfr
N.A.I.C.S.: 333517

Texas Honing, Inc. (3)
1710 Mykawa Rd, Pearland, TX 77581
Tel.: (281) 485-8339
Web Site: http://www.pccenergy.com
Pipe Processing Services, Including Honing,
Boring, Straightening & Turning
N.A.I.C.S.: 332111

Subsidiary (Domestic):

PCC Structurals, Inc. (2)
9200 SE Sunnybrook Blvd Ste 240, Clacka-
mas, OR 97015
Tel.: (503) 777-3881
Web Site: http://www.pccstructurals.com
Aerospace & Industrial Gas Turbine Cast-
ings Mfr
N.A.I.C.S.: 336413

Subsidiary (Non-US):

PCC Structurals (France) (3)
Zone Industrielle, PO Box 11, 64680, Ogeu-
les-Bains, France
Tel.: (33) 559349455
Web Site: https://www.pccstructurals.com
Nickel-based Superalloy, Titanium, Stainless
Steel & Aluminum Cast Components
N.A.I.C.S.: 331221

Subsidiary (Non-US):

PT. Flo-Bend Indonesia (2)
Executive Industrial Park Block A3 No 8
Batam Center, Batam, Indonesia
Tel.: (62) 7784806888
Web Site: https://www.ptflobend.com
Insurance Services
N.A.I.C.S.: 524298

Subsidiary (Domestic):

Permaswage Holdings, Inc. (2)
14800 S Figueroa St, Gardena, CA
90248   **(100%)**
Tel.: (661) 256-7166
Web Site: http://www.permaswage.com
Holding Company; Tube, Pipe & Cable Fit-
tings Systems Mfr
N.A.I.C.S.: 551112

Subsidiary (Domestic):

**Designed Metal Connections,
Inc.** (3)
14800 S Figueroa St, Gardena, CA 90248-
1795
Tel.: (310) 323-6200
Web Site: http://www.permaswage.com
Tube, Pipe & Cable Fittings Systems Mfr

N.A.I.C.S.: 332919

Subsidiary (Non-US):

Permaswage S.A. (3)
5 rue des Dames, BP 60025, 78344, Les
Clayes-sous-Bois, Cedex, France
Tel.: (33) 130791720
Web Site: http://www.permaswage.com
Tube, Pipe & Cable Fittings Systems Mfr
N.A.I.C.S.: 332919

Subsidiary (Domestic):

Progressive Incorporated (2)
1030 Commercial Blvd N, Arlington, TX
76001
Tel.: (817) 465-3221
Web Site: http://www.pccaero.com
Aerostructure Components Mfr
N.A.I.C.S.: 336413

Protective Coatings Inc. (2)
4321 Webster St, Dayton, OH 45414
Tel.: (937) 275-7711
Web Site: http://www.pci-corp.biz
Aircraft Metal Coating Services
N.A.I.C.S.: 332812
Kevin Conley (Pres)
Kaylee Lebo (Ops Mgr)

RathGibson Janesville LLC (2)
2505 Foster Ave, Janesville, WI 53547-
0389
Tel.: (608) 754-2222
Web Site:
   http://www.pccforgedproducts.com
Precision Welded Tubing & Pipe Mfr
N.A.I.C.S.: 332919

Subsidiary (Domestic):

Greenville Tube Company, LLC (3)
S Montgomery St, Clarksville, AR 72830
Tel.: (608) 531-3140
Web Site: http://www.pccenergy.com
Stainless Steel Tubing Mfr
N.A.I.C.S.: 331210
Rick Bresnan (Sls Dir)

RathGibson North Branch LLC (3)
100 Aspen Hill Rd, North Branch, NJ 08876
Tel.: (908) 526-3665
Web Site:
   http://www.pccforgedproducts.com
Iron & Steel Pipe Mfr
N.A.I.C.S.: 331210

Subsidiary (Domestic):

SOS Metals, Inc. (2)
201 E Gardena Blvd, Gardena, CA 90248
Tel.: (310) 217-8848
Recyclable Material Whslr
N.A.I.C.S.: 423930

SPS Technologies, LLC (2)
301 Highland Ave, Jenkintown, PA 19046
Tel.: (215) 572-3000
Web Site: http://www.spstech.com
Fasteners, Rivets, Washers & Precision
Components Mfr
N.A.I.C.S.: 332722

Subsidiary (Domestic):

Air Industries Company (3)
12570 Knott St, Garden Grove, CA 92841
Tel.: (714) 892-5571
Web Site: http://www.air-industries.com
Precision Fasteners, Bolts, Rivets, Screws,
Special Tools, Screwdriver Bits & Punches
Mfr & Distr
N.A.I.C.S.: 332722

Avibank Mfg., Inc. (3)
11500 Sherman Way, North Hollywood, CA
91605
Tel.: (818) 392-2100
Web Site: https://www.avibank.com
Fasteners, Ball Lock Quick Release Pin;
Self Retaining Bolts & Electronic Latching
Devices Mfr
N.A.I.C.S.: 332722

Cannon-Muskegon Corporation (3)
2875 Lincoln St, Muskegon, MI 49441
Tel.: (231) 755-1681
Web Site:
   https://www.cannonmuskegon.com
Super Alloys Mfr
N.A.I.C.S.: 331314

Erik Gentzkow *(Gen Mgr)*
Michael King *(Dir-Sls & Mktg)*
Ken Harris *(Dir-Tech)*
Andy Smith *(Plant Mgr)*
Myles Lemin *(Mgr-HR)*
Dan Carroll *(Mgr-Quality)*
Matthew Werksma *(Controller)*
Nick Huston *(Mgr-Inside Sls)*

Subsidiary (Domestic):

Greenville Metals, Inc. **(4)**
99 Crestview Dr Ext, Transfer, PA 16154
Tel.: (724) 509-1861
Web Site:
   http://www.pccforgedproducts.com
Metal Products Mfr
N.A.I.C.S.: 332919

Subsidiary (Domestic):

Cherry Aerospace LLC **(3)**
1224 E Warner Ave, Santa Ana, CA 92705
Tel.: (714) 545-5511
Web Site: http://www.cherryaerospace.com
Aerospace Fastening Systems Mfr
N.A.I.C.S.: 332722

Fatigue Technology Inc. **(3)**
401 Andover Park E, Seattle, WA 98188
Tel.: (206) 246-2010
Web Site: http://www.fatiguetech.com
Cold Expansion, Nut Plates, Fasteners &
Fittings
N.A.I.C.S.: 332722

Subsidiary (Non-US):

Hi-Life Tools **(3)**
Bays 122-125 Shannon Industrial Estate,
County Clare, Shannon, Ireland
Tel.: (353) 61239503
Web Site: http://www.ptgtools.com
Tool & Special Formed Parts Mfr
N.A.I.C.S.: 333515

Subsidiary (Domestic):

Klune Industries, Inc. **(3)**
7323 Coldwater Canyon Ave, North Holly-
wood, CA 91605
Tel.: (818) 503-8100
Web Site: http://www.pccaero.com
Metal Aerostructures Mfr
N.A.I.C.S.: 336413

Subsidiary (Non-US):

**Metalac SPS Industria e Comercio
Ltda.** **(3)**
Av Itavuvu 4690, Sorocaba, 18078-005,
Sao Paolo, Brazil
Tel.: (55) 1533343500
Web Site: http://www.metalac.com.br
Meallic Fasteners & Bolts Mfr
N.A.I.C.S.: 332722

PCC Distribution Japan K. K. **(3)**
2-25-4 Ogawa, Machida, Tokyo, 194-0003,
Japan
Tel.: (81) 427995991
Web Site:
   https://www.pccdistributionjapan.com
Industrial Fasteners & Screws Mfr
N.A.I.C.S.: 339993

Subsidiary (Domestic):

Paul R. Briles Inc. **(3)**
1700 W 132nd St, Gardena, CA 90249
Tel.: (310) 323-6222
Web Site: http://www.pccfasteners.com
Aircraft Fastener Mfr
N.A.I.C.S.: 332722

Subsidiary (Non-US):

SPS Aerostructures Limited **(3)**
Willow Dr Sherwood Business Park, Annes-
ley, NG15 0DP, Nottinghamshire, United
Kingdom
Tel.: (44) 1159880000
Web Site: http://www.pccaero.com
Fabricated Assemblies & Sheetmetal Com-
ponents Mfr
N.A.I.C.S.: 332999

Subsidiary (Domestic):

**SPS Technologies - Greer Stop
Nut** **(3)**

481 McNally Dr, Nashville, TN 37211
Tel.: (615) 832-8375
Web Site: http://www.pccfasteners.com
Fastener, Bolt, Nut & Screw Mfr
N.A.I.C.S.: 332722

Subsidiary (Non-US):

SPS Technologies Limited **(3)**
191 Barkby Rd Troon Industrial Area, Leicester, LE4 9HX, United Kingdom
Tel.: (44) 1162768261
High Strength Bolts, Nuts, Studs & Precision Components Mfr
N.A.I.C.S.: 332722

Subsidiary (Domestic):

Shur-Lok Company **(3)**
2541 White Rd, Irvine, CA 92614-6235
Tel.: (949) 474-6000
Web Site: https://www.shur-lok.com
Fasteners, Nuts, Mounts, Hooks, Clamps &
Hydraulic Fittings Mfr
N.A.I.C.S.: 332722

Affiliate (Non-US):

Shur-Lok International S.A. **(4)**
Parc Industriel de et, 4800, Petit-Rechain,
Belgium
Tel.: (32) 87320711
Web Site: http://www.shur-lok.com
Precision Fasteners Designer & Mfr
N.A.I.C.S.: 332722

Subsidiary (Domestic):

Southwest United Industries, Inc. **(2)**
422 S Saint Louis Ave, Tulsa, OK 74120
Tel.: (918) 587-4161
Web Site: http://www.pccaero.com
Metal Coating & Finishing Services
N.A.I.C.S.: 332812

Subsidiary (Non-US):

Southwest United Canada, Inc. **(3)**
85 Stafford Dr, Brampton, L6W 1L3, ON,
Canada
Tel.: (905) 456-3245
Web Site: https://www.pccaero.com
Metal Plating Services
N.A.I.C.S.: 332812

**Southwest United de Mexico, S.A. de
C.V.** **(3)**
Ave De la Luz No 24 Int 16, Queretaro,
76120, QRO, Mexico
Tel.: (52) 4222095184
Web Site: http://www.pccaero.com
Metal Plating Services
N.A.I.C.S.: 332812

Subsidiary (Domestic):

Special Metals Corporation **(2)**
3200 Riverside Dr, Huntington, WV 25705
Tel.: (304) 526-5100
Web Site: https://www.specialmetals.com
Super Alloys & Special Alloys Mfr
N.A.I.C.S.: 331491

Division (Non-US):

Special Metals Wiggin Ltd. **(3)**
Holmer Road, Hereford, HR4 9SL, United
Kingdom
Tel.: (44) 1432 352230
Web Site: http://www.incotest.co.uk
Metal Processing Services
N.A.I.C.S.: 423510

Subsidiary (Non-US):

**Special Metals Wiggin Trustees
Limited** **(2)**
Holmer Road, Hereford, HR4 9SL, United
Kingdom
Tel.: (44) 1432382200
Web Site: https://www.specialmetals.com
Investment Castings Products Mfr
N.A.I.C.S.: 331523

Subsidiary (Domestic):

Specialized Pipe Services, Inc. **(2)**
11971 Fm 529 Rd, Houston, TX 77041
Tel.: (832) 379-2892
Oil & Gas Pipeline Construction Services
N.A.I.C.S.: 237120
Joe Jenkins *(VP)*

Summit Machine, LLC **(2)**
2880 E Philadelphia St, Ontario, CA 91761
Tel.: (909) 923-2744
Web Site:
   https://www.summitmachining.com
Emp.: 130
Aerospace Component Mfr
N.A.I.C.S.: 334511

Subsidiary (Non-US):

The Caley Group Limited **(2)**
250 Seaward St, Glasgow, G41 1NG,
United Kingdom
Tel.: (44) 1419511500
Web Site: https://www.caleygroup.com
Insurance Services
N.A.I.C.S.: 524298

Subsidiary (Domestic):

Titanium Metals Corporation **(2)**
4832 Richmond Rd Ste 100, Warrensville
Heights, OH 44128 **(100%)**
Tel.: (216) 910-0770
Web Site: https://www.timet.com
Titanium Metal Products Mfr
N.A.I.C.S.: 331491

Subsidiary (Non-US):

TIMET UK Limited **(3)**
The Hub Holford Road off Witton Road,
Witton, Birmingham, B6 7BJ, United King-
dom
Tel.: (44) 121 356 1155
Web Site: http://www.timet.com
Titanium Product Mfr
N.A.I.C.S.: 331491

Subsidiary (Non-US):

TIMET Germany, GmbH **(4)**
Hans-Bockler-Strasse 1, Dusseldorf, 40476,
Germany
Tel.: (49) 211 23088 0
Web Site: http://www.timet.com
Titanium Product Sales
N.A.I.C.S.: 423510

TIMET Savoie, SA **(4)**
62 Avenue Paul Girod, 73400, Ugine,
France
Tel.: (33) 479897303
Web Site: https://www.timet.com
Titanium Product Sales
N.A.I.C.S.: 331491

Subsidiary (Domestic):

University Swaging Corporation **(2)**
6525 240th St SE Bldg A, Woodinville, WA
98072
Tel.: (425) 318-4500
Web Site: http://www.pccaero.com
Aircraft Components Mfr
N.A.I.C.S.: 336411

Subsidiary (Non-US):

Wyman-Gordon (Lincoln) Limited **(2)**
Waterside North, PO Box 590, Lincoln, LN2
5XY, United Kingdom
Tel.: (44) 1522525492
Web Site:
   http://www.pccforgedproducts.com
Forged Products Mfr
N.A.I.C.S.: 331513

Subsidiary (Domestic):

Wyman-Gordon Company **(2)**
244 Worcester St, North Grafton, MA
01536-8001
Tel.: (508) 839-4441
Web Site:
   http://www.pccforgedproducts.com
Highly-engineered, Closed & Open-die Titanium, Steel & Nickel-based Forgings Mfr
N.A.I.C.S.: 332112

Subsidiary (Non-US):

Precision Castparts CZ s.r.o. **(3)**
Univerzitni 36, 30100, Plzen, Czech Repub-
lic
Tel.: (420) 377680511
Web Site: http://www.precast.cz
Steel, Nickel & Titanium Alloys Processing
N.A.I.C.S.: 332111

**Western Australian Specialty Alloys,
Pty. Ltd.** **(3)**
2-4 Hopewell St, Canning Vale, 6155, WA,
Australia
Tel.: (61) 894554111
Web Site: http://www.wasa.com.au
Melting & Forging Facilities
N.A.I.C.S.: 332111

Subsidiary (Domestic):

**Wyman Gordon Forgings (Cleveland),
Inc.** **(3)**
3097 E 61st St, Cleveland, OH 44127
Tel.: (216) 341-0085
Web Site:
   http://www.pccforgedproducts.com
Iron Forging
N.A.I.C.S.: 332111

Plant (Domestic):

Wyman-Gordon Co. - Brighton **(3)**
7250 Whitmore Lake Rd, Brighton, MI
48116
Tel.: (810) 229-9550
Web Site:
   http://www.pccforgedproducts.com
Steel Investment Foundries
N.A.I.C.S.: 331512

Subsidiary (Domestic):

Wyman-Gordon Forgings, Inc. **(3)**
10825 Telge Rd, Houston, TX 77095
Tel.: (281) 856-9900
Web Site:
   http://www.pccforgedproducts.com
Metal Products Mfr
N.A.I.C.S.: 332111

Subsidiary (Non-US):

Wyman-Gordon Limited **(3)**
Waterside N, PO Box 590, Lincoln, LN2
5XY, United Kingdom
Tel.: (44) 1522525492
Web Site:
   http://www.pccforgedproducts.com
Forgings
N.A.I.C.S.: 332111

**Wyman-Gordon de Monterrey S. de
R.L. de C.V.** **(3)**
Avenida Lasnorias 1050, Col Sierra
Morena, Guadalupe, CP 67190, Nuevo
Leon, Mexico
Tel.: (52) 8182159301
Web Site:
   http://www.pccforgedproducts.com
Metal Forging
N.A.I.C.S.: 332111

Subsidiary (Domestic):

Precision Steel Warehouse, Inc. **(1)**
3500 Wolf Rd, Franklin Park, IL
60131-1395 **(100%)**
Tel.: (847) 737-7099
Web Site: http://www.precisionsteel.com
Sales Range: $50-74.9 Million
Emp.: 197
Specialty Metals Processor & Steel Ware-
housing
N.A.I.C.S.: 423510
Terry A. Piper *(Chm, Pres & CEO)*

Primal Nutrition, LLC **(1)**
1641 S Rose Ave, Oxnard, CA 93033
Tel.: (888) 774-6259
Web Site: http://www.primalblueprint.com
Food & Health Supplement Stores
N.A.I.C.S.: 456191
Farhad Mostaedi *(Dir-Ops)*

Prudential California Realty **(1)**
22800 Savi Ranch Pkwy Ste 110a, Yorba
Linda, CA 92887
Tel.: (714) 624-5659
Management Consulting Services
N.A.I.C.S.: 541618

R.C. Willey Home Furnishings **(1)**
2301 S 300 W, Salt Lake City, UT 84115-
2516
Tel.: (801) 461-3900
Web Site: http://www.rcwilley.com
Sales Range: $50-74.9 Million
Emp.: 200
Furniture Stores; Electric Household Appli-
ances; High Fidelity Stereo Equipment
N.A.I.C.S.: 449110

Berkshire Hathaway Inc.—(Continued)

Branch (Domestic):

R. C. Willey Home Furnishings (2)
900 Cottage Grove Rd, Bloomfield, CT
06002
Tel.: (801) 461-3800
Insurance Agency Services
N.A.I.C.S.: 524210

Subsidiary (Domestic):

Richline Group, Inc. (1)
6701 Nob Hill Rd, Tamarac, FL
33321 (100%)
Web Site: https://www.richlinegroup.com
Sales Range: $1-4.9 Billion
Jewelry Mfr & Distr
N.A.I.C.S.: 339910

Subsidiary (Domestic):

Aurafin LLC (2)
6701 Nob Hill Rd, Tamarac, FL 33321
Tel.: (954) 718-3200
Web Site: http://www.richlinegroup.com
Sales Range: $50-74.9 Million
Emp.: 300
Gold Jewelry Mfr
N.A.I.C.S.: 339910

Subsidiary (Domestic):

Aurafin OroAmerica (3)
443 N Varney St, Burbank, CA 91502-1733
Tel.: (818) 848-5555
Web Site: http://www.richlinegroup.com
Sales Range: $10-24.9 Million
Emp.: 19
Precious Metal Jewelry Mfr
N.A.I.C.S.: 339910

Subsidiary (Domestic):

Bel-Oro International, Inc. (2)
115 S Macquesten Pkwy, Mount Vernon,
NY 10550-1724
Tel.: (212) 398-3456
Sales Range: $650-699.9 Million
Emp.: 1,000
Jewelry Mfr & Distr
N.A.I.C.S.: 423940

Subsidiary (Domestic):

Michael Anthony Jewelers, Inc. (3)
115 S MacQuesten Pkwy, Mount Vernon,
NY 10550
Web Site: http://www.richlinegroup.com
Sales Range: $100-124.9 Million
Emp.: 730
Handcrafted Jewelry Mfr & Retailer
N.A.I.C.S.: 339910

Subsidiary (Domestic):

Gemvara, Inc. (2)
155 Federal St Ste 700, Boston, MA 02110
Tel.: (800) 436-8803
Web Site: http://www.gemvara.com
Online Retailer of Jewelry
N.A.I.C.S.: 339910

Inverness Corporation (2)
49 Pearl St, Attleboro, MA 02703
Tel.: (774) 203-1130
Web Site: http://www.invernesscorp.com
Sales Range: $25-49.9 Million
Emp.: 70
Ear-Piercing Systems Mfr & Distr
N.A.I.C.S.: 333310

Branch (Non-US):

Inverness UK (3)
Blue River Inverness 10 Waterloo Park,
Bidford-on-Avon, B50 4JG, United
Kingdom (100%)
Tel.: (44) 1 789 491935
Web Site: http://www.invernesscorp.com
Sales Range: $1-9.9 Million
Emp.: 2
Ear-Piercing Systems Mfr & Distr
N.A.I.C.S.: 333310

Subsidiary (Domestic):

John C. Nordt Co., Inc. (2)
1420 Coulter Dr NW, Roanoke, VA 24012
Tel.: (540) 362-9717
Web Site: http://www.jcnordt.com
Rev.: $8,100,000
Emp.: 130

Jewelry, except Costume, Mfr
N.A.I.C.S.: 339910

LeachGarner (2)
49 Pearl St, Attleboro, MA 02703
Tel.: (508) 222-7400
Web Site: https://www.leachgarner.com
Sales Range: $200-249.9 Million
Emp.: 500
Holding Company; Jewelry & Precious
Metal Fabricator & Distr
N.A.I.C.S.: 551112

Subsidiary (Domestic):

Findings Inc. (3)
160 Water St, Keene, NH 03431
Tel.: (603) 352-3717
Web Site: http://www.findingsinc.net
Rev.: $12,100,000
Emp.: 100
Jewelers' Materials & Lapidary Work
N.A.I.C.S.: 339910

Stern Metals, Inc. (3)
49 Pearl St, Attleboro, MA 02703
Tel.: (508) 222-7400
Web Site: http://www.leachgarner.com
Sales Range: $100-124.9 Million
Precious Metal Mill Products & Findings for
Jewelry & Industrial Applications
N.A.I.C.S.: 331491

Subsidiary (Domestic):

Rio Grande Inc. (2)
7500 Bluewater Rd NW, Albuquerque, NM
87121-1962
Tel.: (505) 839-3011
Web Site: https://www.riogrande.com
Sales Range: $200-249.9 Million
Emp.: 320
Jewelry & Jewelry Product Mail Order
Wholesaler
N.A.I.C.S.: 423940
Alan Bell (Dir)
Eddie Bell (Founder)

Silpada Designs LLC (2)
11550 Renner Blvd, Lenexa, KS 66219-
9600
Tel.: (844) 278-1878
Web Site: http://www.silpada.com
Sterling Silver Jewelry Distr
N.A.I.C.S.: 458310

Schuller GmbH (1)
Bertha-Benz-Str 16, 74343, Sachsenheim,
Germany
Tel.: (49) 7147923672
Web Site: https://www.schullergmbh.de
Lighting Fixture Mfr & Distr
N.A.I.C.S.: 335132

See's Candies, Inc. (1)
210 El Camino Real, South San Francisco,
CA 94080-5968 (100%)
Tel.: (415) 349-5894
Web Site: http://www.sees.com
Sales Range: $1-4.9 Billion
Emp.: 1,500
Candy Mfr & Sales
N.A.I.C.S.: 445292

Subsidiary (Domestic):

See's Candy Shops, Inc. (2)
20600 S Alameda St, Carson, CA 90810
Tel.: (310) 604-6200
Web Site: https://www.sees.com
Food Product Preparation Services
N.A.I.C.S.: 311352

Shaw Industries Group, Inc. (1)
616 E Walnut Ave, Dalton, GA 30720
Tel.: (706) 555-5555
Web Site: http://www.shawinc.com
Sales Range: $5-14.9 Billion
Emp.: 28,974
Carpets, Rugs & Flooring Mfr
N.A.I.C.S.: 314110
Tommie Mack (Dir-IT Sys & Automation)
Russell Headrick (Dir-Fin Svcs)
Annie Cowart (VP-Mktg)
Jeff Wright (Dir-Technical Dev)
Melissa Pateritsas (Mgr-IT Project Mgmt
Office)
Laruthie Mason (Mgr-Industrial Maintenance
Trng)
Jim Andrews (VP-Mfg Divisional)
Joanna Cantrell (Reg Mgr-Claims)

Robert Davidson (Mgr-Project Admin)
Desiree Perkins (VP-Strategic Accounts)
Jay Henry (Dir-Innovation & Ops Support)
Amanda James (Mgr-Fabrication-Hard Sur-
face)
Bea Brahmbhatt (Mgr-Reclamation-Comml
Div)
Troy Virgo (Dir-Sustainability & Product
Stewardship)
Scott Sandlin (Exec VP-Residential Bus)
Matt Morrison (Comm Mgr)
Amanda Edwards (VP)
John Stephens (VP)
Teresa Tran (VP)
Torrance Ford (VP)
Winston Massengale (VP)

Plant (Domestic):

Shaw Industries Group (2)
185 S Industrial Blvd, Calhoun, GA 30701-
3031
Tel.: (706) 629-9234
Sales Range: $400-449.9 Million
Emp.: 1,100
Carpet Mfr
N.A.I.C.S.: 314110

Subsidiary (Domestic):

Shaw Industries Inc. (2)
10901 Texland Blvd, Charlotte, NC
28273 (100%)
Web Site: http://www.shawinc.com
Hardwood Flooring Mfr
N.A.I.C.S.: 321918

Joint Venture (Non-US):

Terza, S.A. de C.V. (2)
Carretera a Monclova Km 11 5, 66550, El
Carmen, Mexico
Tel.: (52) 8187484900
Web Site: http://www.terza.com
Sales Range: $25-49.9 Million
Emp.: 200
Carpet Mfr; Owned by Alfa, S.A.B. de C.V.
& Shaw Industries
N.A.I.C.S.: 314110

Subsidiary (Domestic):

Tricycle, Inc. (2)
1293 Riverfront Pkwy Ste 1293-B, Chatta-
nooga, TN 37402
Tel.: (800) 808-4809
Web Site: http://www.tricycleinc.com
Software Publisher
N.A.I.C.S.: 513210

Star Furniture Company (1)
16666 Barker Springs Rd, Houston, TX
77084-5032
Tel.: (281) 492-5494
Web Site: http://www.starfurniture.com
Sales Range: $250-299.9 Million
Emp.: 875
Furniture Retailer
N.A.I.C.S.: 449110
Jodi FitzGerald (Chief Comml Officer)

TTI, Inc. (1)
2441 Northeast Pkwy, Fort Worth, TX
76106-1816
Tel.: (817) 740-9000
Web Site: http://www.ttiinc.com
Sales Range: $800-899.9 Million
Emp.: 600
Passive Components & Interconnects Distr
N.A.I.C.S.: 423690
Mike Morton (COO)

Subsidiary (Domestic):

Astrex Electronics Inc. (2)
205 Express St, Plainview, NY 11803-2420
Tel.: (516) 433-1700
Web Site: http://www.astrex.net
Sales Range: $10-24.9 Million
Emp.: 60
Electronic Parts & Components Distr
N.A.I.C.S.: 423690

Mouser Electronics Inc. (2)
1000 N Main St, Mansfield, TX 76063
Tel.: (817) 804-3888
Web Site: https://www.mouser.com
Sales Range: $200-249.9 Million
Emp.: 500
Electronic Parts & Equipment Distr
N.A.I.C.S.: 423690

Glenn Smith (Pres & CEO)
Kevin Hess (Sr VP-Mktg)
Jeff Newell (Sr VP-Products)
Mark Burr-Lonnon (Sr VP-Svc & Bus-APAC
& EMEA-Global)
Raju Shah (Sr VP-Information Svcs)
Pete Shopp (Sr VP-Bus Ops)
Todd McAtee (VP-Bus Dev)
Hayne Shumate (Sr VP-Internet Bus)
Lori Hartman (VP-Customer Experience)

Subsidiary (Non-US):

Mouser Electronics Pte. Ltd. (3)
3 Changi North Street 2 LogisTech Building
03-01 B, Singapore, 498827, Singapore
Tel.: (65) 67889233
Web Site: http://www.mouser.com
Sales Range: $150-199.9 Million
Emp.: 8
Electronic Parts Distr
N.A.I.C.S.: 423690
Daphne Tien (VP-Mktg & Bus Dev-APAC)

Subsidiary (Domestic):

Sager Electrical Supply Co (2)
19 Leona Dr, Middleboro, MA 02346
Tel.: (508) 947-8888
Web Site: http://www.sager.com
Sales Range: $350-399.9 Million
Emp.: 230
Electronic Parts & Equipment Distribution
N.A.I.C.S.: 423690
Frank Flynn (Pres)
Bruce Kellar (Sr VP-Sls)
Craig Sanderson (VP-Product Mktg)
Faris Aruri (Sr VP-Mktg)
Brian Flynn (VP-Sls)
Karen Renzi (Dir-HR)
Monica Otis (Controller)
Derek Ollerhead (Dir-Bus Analytics)

Symmetry Electronics Corp. (2)
5400 W Rosecrans Ave, Hawthorne, CA
90250
Tel.: (310) 536-6190
Web Site:
http://www.semiconductorstore.com
Electronic Parts & Equipment
N.A.I.C.S.: 423690

The Ben Bridge Corporation (1)
2901 3rd Ave Ste 200, Seattle, WA 98121-
3013
Tel.: (206) 448-8800
Web Site: http://www.benbridge.com
Sales Range: $100-124.9 Million
Emp.: 200
Jewelry Stores
N.A.I.C.S.: 458310
Robert Bridge (Chm)

Subsidiary (Domestic):

Ben Bridge Jeweler, Inc. (2)
Dept 791 2901 3rd Ave Ste 200, Seattle,
WA 98121-3013
Tel.: (206) 448-8800
Web Site: https://www.benbridge.com
Sales Range: $75-99.9 Million
Emp.: 135
Jewelry Stores
N.A.I.C.S.: 458310

The Duracell Company (1)
14 Research Dr Berkshire Corporate Park,
Bethel, CT 06801
Tel.: (203) 796-4000
Web Site: http://www.duracell.com
Holding Company; Primary Battery Mfr &
Distr
N.A.I.C.S.: 551112
Roberto Mendez (Pres-North America)

**The Fechheimer Brothers
Company** (1)
4545 Malsbary Rd, Cincinnati, OH
45242-5624 (100%)
Tel.: (513) 793-5400
Web Site: https://www.fechheimer.com
Sales Range: $300-349.9 Million
Emp.: 700
Public Safety Uniforms Mfr
N.A.I.C.S.: 315250

**The Kansas Bankers Surety
Company** (1)
1220 SW Executive Dr, Topeka, KS
66615 (100%)

Tel.: (785) 228-0000
Web Site:
    http://www.berkshirehathaway.com
Sales Range: $10-24.9 Million
Emp.: 18
Bank Reinsurance Services
N.A.I.C.S.: 524130

The Kraft Heinz Company   **(1)**
200 E Randolph St, Chicago, IL
60601   **(27%)**
Tel.: (412) 456-5700
Web Site: https://www.kraftheinz.com
Rev.: $26,640,000,000
Assets: $90,339,000,000
Liabilities: $40,813,000,000
Net Worth: $49,526,000,000
Earnings: $2,855,000,000
Emp.: 36,000
Fiscal Year-end: 12/30/2023
Holding Company; Food Products Mfr &
Whslr
N.A.I.C.S.: 551112
John Tobin Cahill *(Vice Chm)*
Carlos Abrams-Rivera *(CEO)*
Vince Garlati *(Chief Acctg Officer, VP &
Controller-Global)*
Carlos Abrams-Rivera *(Pres/Exec VP-North
America)*
Marcos Eloi Lima *(Chief Procurement Offi-
cer & Exec VP)*
Sam Greenwood *(CMO/Comml Dir-Northern
Europe)*
Alex Abraham *(VP-Corp Comm & Reputa-
tion Mgmt-Global)*
Yang Xu *(Treas-Global, Sr VP & Head-Corp
Dev-Global)*
Diana Frost *(Chief Growth Officer-North
America)*
Janelle Orozco *(Chief Procurement Officer-
North America)*
Andre Maciel *(CFO-Global & Exec VP)*

Subsidiary (Domestic):

Kraft Heinz Foods Company   **(2)**
1 PPG Pl Ste 34, Pittsburgh, PA 15222
Tel.: (412) 456-5700
Web Site:
    http://www.kraftheinzcompany.com
Sales Range: $5-14.9 Billion
Emp.: 31,900
Ketchup, Condiments & Sauces, Frozen
Foods, Baby Foods, Beans & Pasta Meals,
Soups & Other Processed Foods Mfr
N.A.I.C.S.: 311941
Michael Mullen *(Sr VP-Corp & Govt Affairs)*
Emin Mammadov *(Pres-Russia, Turkey,
Middle East & Africa)*
Eduardo Machado de Carvalho Pelleissone
(Exec VP-Ops)
Andy Keatings *(Chief Quality Officer)*
Lisa West *(Mgr-Reward-UK & Ireland)*
Shirley Weinstein *(Head-Rewards-Global)*
Leandro Balbinot *(CIO & Sr VP-IT-Global)*
Jose Parolin *(CIO-North America)*

Subsidiary (Non-US):

Delimex de Mexico S.A. de C.V.   **(3)**
Av Periferico Sur No 7980, Jalisco, 45600,
Mexico
Tel.: (52) 33 3001 3800
Specialty Foods Mfr
N.A.I.C.S.: 311999

Subsidiary (Domestic):

H.J. Heinz Company, L.P.   **(3)**
357 6th Ave, Pittsburgh, PA 15222-2530
Tel.: (412) 237-5757
Web Site:
    http://www.kraftheinzcompany.com
Convenience Foods Mfr
N.A.I.C.S.: 311999
Priyank Jasani *(Mgr)*

Subsidiary (Non-US):

Alimentos Heinz C.A.   **(4)**
Calle Orinoco Torre 1 Piso 1, Las Mer-
cedes, Caracas, 1060, Venezuela
Tel.: (58) 2129091999
Emp.: 200
Canned Fruits & Vegetables, Pickles,
Sauces & Dressings; Grocery Store Opera-
tions
N.A.I.C.S.: 311422
Ana Urquia *(Dir-HR)*
William Gonzalez *(Mgr-Acctg)*

Alimentos Heinz de Costa Rica
S.A.   **(4)**
1km al Este y 200m, San Jose, Costa Rica
Tel.: (506) 2549 9800
Condiments Mfr
N.A.I.C.S.: 311999

Cairo Foods Industries SAE   **(4)**
6 October City 2nd Ind Zone Location No
36, Cairo, 12581, Egypt
Tel.: (20) 238330474
Web Site: http://www.heinz-ame.com
Sales Range: $100-124.9 Million
Emp.: 400
Ketchup, Condiments & Sauces Mfr
N.A.I.C.S.: 311941
Osman Serag Eldin *(Mng Dir)*

H.J. Heinz CR/SR a.s.   **(4)**
Pocernicka 272/96, 108 00, Prague, Czech
Republic
Tel.: (420) 267 021 333
Specialty Foods Mfr
N.A.I.C.S.: 311999

H.J. Heinz Company Australia
Ltd.   **(4)**
Locked Bag 2, South Melbourne, 3205,
VIC, Australia
Tel.: (61) 398615757
Web Site: http://www.heinz.com.au
Sales Range: $250-299.9 Million
Emp.: 600
Food Products Mfr & Distr
N.A.I.C.S.: 311423
Rafael Oliveira *(CEO-Australia, New Zea-
land, and Papua New Guinea)*
Sarah Bryant *(Mgr-Outsourcing Procure-
ment)*

Unit (Non-US):

Heinz Wattie's Limited   **(5)**
513 King Street North, Hastings, 4122, New
Zealand
Tel.: (64) 68731600
Web Site: http://www.watties.co.nz
Sales Range: $450-499.9 Million
Soups, Frozen & Packaged Fruit & Veg-
etables, Sauces & Other Foods Mfr
N.A.I.C.S.: 311421
Mike Pretty *(Mng Dir)*
Mike Butcher *(Mgr-Trade Fin)*

Subsidiary (Non-US):

H.J. Heinz Company of Canada
Ltd.   **(4)**
90 Sheppard Avenue East Suite 400, North
York, M2N 7K5, ON, Canada
Tel.: (416) 226-5757
Web Site:
    http://www.kraftheinzcompany.com
Sales Range: $600-649.9 Million
Emp.: 255
Convenience Meals, Pet Foods & Treats,
Infant Feeding Products & Specialty Condi-
ments Mfr
N.A.I.C.S.: 311421
Don Holdsworth *(Head-Condiments 7
Spreads)*
Amanda Dingman *(Head-Talent Mgmt)*
Shawn Jones *(Dir-Fin)*

Subsidiary (Domestic):

Renee's Gourmet Foods, Inc.   **(5)**
90 Sheppard Ave E Ste 400, North York,
M2N 7K5, ON, Canada
Web Site: http://www.kraftcanada.com
Sales Range: $25-49.9 Million
Emp.: 100
Salad Dressings, Sauces, Dips, Marinades
& Mayonnaise Mfr & Distr
N.A.I.C.S.: 311941

Subsidiary (Non-US):

Heinz European Holding B.V.   **(4)**
Arnhemse Bovenweg 160-178, Zeist, 3708
AH, Utrecht, Netherlands
Tel.: (31) 306973700
Web Site: http://www.heinz.nl
Emp.: 400
Holding Company
N.A.I.C.S.: 551112
Matt Hill *(Pres)*

Subsidiary (Domestic):

H.J. Heinz B.V.   **(5)**

Kantorenpark de Breul Arnhemse
Bovenweg 160-178, Zeist, 3708 AH, Neth-
erlands
Tel.: (31) 306973700
Web Site: http://www.heinz.nl
Sales Range: $75-99.9 Million
Emp.: 400
Processed Food Products Mfr & Distr
N.A.I.C.S.: 311999
Micha Medendorp *(Dir-Mktg-Belgium, Neth-
erlands & Luxembourg)*

Unit (Domestic):

Honig Merkartikelen   **(6)**
Arnhemse Bovenweg 160-178, 3708 AH,
Zeist, Netherlands
Tel.: (31) 30 697 3700
Web Site: http://www.honig.nl
Emp.: 300
Packaged & Dried Foods, Pasta, Sauce
Mixes, Cereals, Cake, Pudding & Pancake
Mixes, Dehydrated Soups
N.A.I.C.S.: 311999
Peter Boterman *(Dir-Mktg Ops-Europe)*

Subsidiary (Domestic):

Koninklijke De Ruijter BV   **(6)**
Postbus 397, 3700 AJ, Zeist, Netherlands
Tel.: (31) 306973700
Web Site: http://www.deruijter.nl
Emp.: 75
Confectionery Sprinkles Mfr
N.A.I.C.S.: 311352

Subsidiary (Non-US):

H.J. Heinz Belgium N.V.   **(5)**
Bleukenlaan 12, 2300, Turnhout, Belgium
Tel.: (32) 14 42 16 01
Web Site: http://www.heinz.be
Emp.: 135
Sauces & Sandwich Spreads Mfr & Distr
N.A.I.C.S.: 311941
Vets Luc *(Mgr)*

H.J. Heinz Company (Ireland)
Limited   **(5)**
Stradbrook House Stradbrook Road, Black-
rock, Dublin, Ireland
Tel.: (353) 12805757
Web Site: http://www.heinz.ie
Sales Range: $10-24.9 Million
Emp.: 14
Distribution of Groceries & Canned Foods
N.A.I.C.S.: 424490
Anne Sewell *(Dir-HR-Europe)*
Jan Kruise *(Mng Dir-UK & Ireland)*

H.J. Heinz Company Limited   **(5)**
Shard 32 London Bridge Street, London,
SE1 9SG, Mddx, United Kingdom
Tel.: (44) 2085737757
Web Site: http://www.heinz.co.uk
Sales Range: $150-199.9 Million
Emp.: 300
Canned Food Products; Fresh & Processed
Dairy Products Mfr
N.A.I.C.S.: 311421
Matt Hill *(Pres-Europe)*
Ross Longton *(Mgr-Sauces Mktg)*

Unit (Domestic):

H.J. Heinz Foodservice   **(6)**
London Bridge Street, SE19SG, London,
Middlesex, United Kingdom
Tel.: (44) 2085737757
Web Site: http://www.heinz.co.uk
Sales Range: $150-199.9 Million
Emp.: 350
Food Products Distr
N.A.I.C.S.: 722310
Jane Hyde *(Brand Mgr)*

Subsidiary (Domestic):

H.J. Heinz Frozen & Chilled Foods
Limited   **(6)**
The Shard, London Bridge Street, London,
SE1 9SJ, Middlesex, United Kingdom
Tel.: (44) 2085737757
Emp.: 75
Frozen Food Mfr
N.A.I.C.S.: 311412

Subsidiary (Non-US):

H.J. Heinz France S.A.S.   **(5)**
1 Place de la Pyramide Tour Atlantique,

92911, Paris, Cedex, La Defense, France
Tel.: (33) 1 41 96 70 01
Web Site: http://www.heinz.fr
Sales Range: $25-49.9 Million
Emp.: 50
Condiments Mfr
N.A.I.C.S.: 311941
Pradels Jacques *(Mng Dir)*

H.J. Heinz GmbH   **(5)**
Erkrather Strasse 228b, 40233, Dusseldorf,
Germany
Tel.: (49) 211 960766 00
Web Site: http://www.hjheinz.de
Sales Range: $25-49.9 Million
Emp.: 75
Sales & Administration of Food & Condi-
ments
N.A.I.C.S.: 424410
Heiko Gerling *(Mng Dir-Central, North &
East Europe)*

HJ Heinz Polska Sp. z o.o.   **(5)**
Budynek Orion ul Postepu 18B, Warsaw, 02
676, Poland
Tel.: (48) 22 567 21 11
Web Site: http://www.heinz.pl
Emp.: 75
Canned Foods, Pickles, Sauces & Ready
Meals Mfr
N.A.I.C.S.: 311421
Emilia Zlotnicka *(Head-HR-Central, North &
Eastern Europe)*
Dorota Marciniak-Lewandowska *(Head-Fin)*
Robert Krzyzewski *(Dir-Sls)*
Grzegorz Lis *(Head-Mktg-Central, North &
East Europe)*

Heinz Iberica, S.A.   **(5)**
Plaza glai corpes, Madrid, 28014, Spain
Tel.: (34) 902 94 51 84
Web Site: http://www.heinz.es
Sales Range: $25-49.9 Million
Emp.: 75
Canned Foods Mfr
N.A.I.C.S.: 311421
Ilari Gaztelumendi *(Dir-Fin)*

Heinz Italia S.p.A.   **(5)**
Via Cascina Belcasule 7, Milan, 20141, Italy
Tel.: (39) 0252561
Web Site: http://www.heinz.it
Emp.: 750
Convenience Foods Mfr & Distr
N.A.I.C.S.: 311999
Marco Bozzini *(Mgr-Fin Statements)*

Division (Domestic):

Heinz North America   **(4)**
1 PPG Pl # 3200, Pittsburgh, PA 15222-
2500
Tel.: (412) 237-5757
Web Site:
    http://www.kraftheinzcompany.com
Sales Range: $550-599.9 Million
Emp.: 2,500
Canned Tuna & Pet Food Products Mfr
N.A.I.C.S.: 311111
Eduardo Luz *(Pres)*

Unit (Domestic):

Boca Foods Company   **(5)**
910 Mayer Ave, Madison, WI 53708
Tel.: (608) 285-6950
Web Site: http://www.bocaburger.com
Sales Range: $250-299.9 Million
Meat Alternative Food Products
N.A.I.C.S.: 311412

Churny Company Inc.   **(5)**
3 Lakes Dr, Glenview, IL 60025
Tel.: (847) 646-5500
Web Site: http://www.churny.com
Sales Range: $150-199.9 Million
Specialty Cheeses Mfr & Distr
N.A.I.C.S.: 424430
Howard Friedman *(Pres-Cheese & Dairy &
Exec VP)*

Claussen Pickle Co.   **(5)**
1300 Claussen Dr, Woodstock, IL 60098-
2155
Tel.: (815) 338-7000
Web Site: http://www.kraftbrands.com
Sales Range: $150-199.9 Million
Emp.: 400
Pickle, Sauerkraut & Relish Mfr
N.A.I.C.S.: 311421

Berkshire Hathaway Inc.—(Continued)

Escalon Premier Brands (5)
1905 McHenry Ave, Escalon, CA 95320
Tel.: (209) 838-7341
Web Site: http://www.escalon.net
Sales Range: $25-49.9 Million
Emp.: 75
Tomato Sauce Mfr
N.A.I.C.S.: 311421
Scott Adrian (Plant Mgr)
Dan Milazzo (Sr Mgr-Sls & Mktg)

Portion Pac (5)
7325 Snider Rd, Mason, OH 45040-9601
Tel.: (513) 398-0400
Sales Range: $200-249.9 Million
Emp.: 400
Carry-Out & Fast-Food Condiments,
Sauces & Dressings Mfr
N.A.I.C.S.: 311941
Jacque Pelfrey (Coord-Sanitation)

Quality Chef Foods (5)
5005 C St SW, Cedar Rapids, IA 52404
Tel.: (319) 362-9633
Sales Range: $125-149.9 Million
Emp.: 275
Frozen Food Mfr
N.A.I.C.S.: 311412
Steve Maddocks (Plant Mgr)

Todds (5)
2450 White Rd, Irvine, CA 92614-6250
Tel.: (949) 930-2062
Emp.: 300
Salad Dressings, Sauces & Soups Mfr for
Restaurants
N.A.I.C.S.: 311422
Dan Milazzo (Sr Mgr-Sls & Mktg)

Plant (Domestic):

Todds Foods (6)
610 S 56th Ave, Phoenix, AZ 85043-4622
Tel.: (602) 282-6101
Emp.: 200
Soups & Salad Dressings Mfr
N.A.I.C.S.: 311422
Dan Milazzo (Sr Mgr-Sls & Mktg)

Subsidiary (Non-US):

Heinz-UFE Ltd. (4)
Yan Tang Sha He, Guangzhou, 510507,
Guangdong, China
Tel.: (86) 87706218
Web Site: http://www.heinz.com.cn
Emp.: 200
Instant Baby Food Mfr & Distr
N.A.I.C.S.: 311421
Alice Wang (VP-Corp Affairs)

Subsidiary (Non-US):

H.J. Heinz Finance UK PLC (3)
The Shard 32 London Bridge Street, Lon-
don, SE1 9SG, United Kingdom
Tel.: (44) 7723549818
Web Site: https://heinz-finance.com
Insurance Services
N.A.I.C.S.: 524298

Kraft Canada Inc. (3)
95 Moatfield Drive, Toronto, M3B 3L6, ON,
Canada
Tel.: (416) 441-5000
Web Site:
    http://www.kraftsciencecompany.com
Sales Range: $1-4.9 Billion
Emp.: 4,500
Food Products Mfr & Distr
N.A.I.C.S.: 311513
Tony Matta (Chief Mktg Officer)
Bernardo Heez (CEO)

Plant (Domestic):

Kraft Canada, Inc.-Ingleside (4)
70 Dickinson Dr, Ingleside, K0C 1M0, ON,
Canada
Tel.: (613) 537-2226
Web Site: http://www.kraftcanada.com
Sales Range: $150-199.9 Million
Emp.: 400
Natural & Processed Cheese Mfr
N.A.I.C.S.: 311513

Kraft Canada, Inc.-Mount-Royal (4)
8600 Devonshire Rd, Mount-Royal, H4P
2K9, QC, Canada

Tel.: (514) 343-3300
Web Site: http://www.kraftcanada.com
Sales Range: $550-599.9 Million
Emp.: 1,300
Natural & Processed Cheese Mfr
N.A.I.C.S.: 311513

Affiliate (Domestic):

Kraft Food Ingredients Corp. (3)
8000 Horizon Ctr Blvd, Memphis, TN 38133
Tel.: (901) 381-6500
Web Site:
    http://www.kraftfoodingredients.com
Sales Range: $25-49.9 Million
Emp.: 100
Food Products, Seasonings & Flavorings
Mfr
N.A.I.C.S.: 424430
Peter Losee (Dir-Mktg)
Stephen Williams (Dir-Tech)
Jill Thrasher (Assoc Dir-Ops)
Erica Lamar (Sr Mgr-Quality)
Jennifer Davidson (Reg Sls Mgr)

Subsidiary (Domestic):

**Kraft Foods Group Puerto Rico,
LLC** (3)
9615 Ave Los Romeros, Guaynabo, PR
00968-8033
Tel.: (787) 620-2525
Web Site: http://www.kraftpr.com
Food & Beverage Products Mfr
N.A.I.C.S.: 722330

Plant (Domestic):

Kraft Heinz Company - Addison (3)
2250 W Pinehurst Blvd Ste 150, Addison, IL
60101-6103
Tel.: (630) 547-6000
Sales Range: $100-124.9 Million
Food Product Whslr
N.A.I.C.S.: 424490

Kraft Heinz Company - Charlotte (3)
1338 Hunter Oaks Ln Ste A, Charlotte, NC
28217-3995
Tel.: (704) 565-5500
Sales Range: $75-99.9 Million
Food Products Mfr
N.A.I.C.S.: 311999

Kraft Heinz Company - Columbia (3)
4600 Waco Rd, Columbia, MO 65202-9335
Tel.: (573) 474-9477
Web Site: http://www.kraftfoods.com
Sales Range: $250-299.9 Million
Food Production Services
N.A.I.C.S.: 311999

**Kraft Heinz Company -
Coshocton** (3)
1660 S 2nd St, Coshocton, OH 43812-1950
Tel.: (740) 622-6433
Sales Range: $200-249.9 Million
Bacon Mfr
N.A.I.C.S.: 311999

Kraft Heinz Company - Dover (3)
1250 W N St, Dover, DE 19904
Tel.: (302) 734-6100
Sales Range: $400-449.9 Million
Food Products Mfr
N.A.I.C.S.: 311999

Kraft Heinz Company - Fullerton (3)
1500 E Walnut Ave, Fullerton, CA 92831-
4731
Tel.: (714) 870-8235
Sales Range: $200-249.9 Million
Food Products Mfr
N.A.I.C.S.: 311999

Kraft Heinz Company - Garland (3)
2340 Forest Ln, Garland, TX 75042-7924
Tel.: (972) 272-7511
Sales Range: $250-299.9 Million
Food Products Mfr
N.A.I.C.S.: 311421

**Kraft Heinz Company - Granite
City** (3)
200 E Randolph St, Chicago, IL 60601
Tel.: (618) 451-4820
Web Site: http://www.kraftrecipes.com
Sales Range: $350-399.9 Million
Fruit Drink Mfr
N.A.I.C.S.: 311411

Kraft Heinz Company - Irvine (3)
185 Technology Dr, Irvine, CA 92618
Tel.: (949) 453-3500
Web Site:
    http://www.kraftfoodscompany.com
Sales Range: $75-99.9 Million
Food Products Mfr
N.A.I.C.S.: 311999

**Kraft Heinz Company - Lehigh
Valley** (3)
7352 Industrial Blvd, Allentown, PA 18106-
9344
Tel.: (610) 997-6200
Sales Range: $500-549.9 Million
Emp.: 100
Natural & Processed Cheese Mfr
N.A.I.C.S.: 311513

**Kraft Heinz Company -
Livermore** (3)
477 N Canyon Pkwy Ste D, Livermore, CA
94550-9490
Tel.: (925) 454-4500
Sales Range: $75-99.9 Million
Food Products Mfr
N.A.I.C.S.: 311999

Unit (Domestic):

**Kraft Heinz Company - Louis
Rich** (3)
3704 Louis Rich Rd, Newberry, SC 29108-
1413
Tel.: (803) 276-5015
Web Site: http://www.kraftfoods.com
Sales Range: $500-549.9 Million
Emp.: 2,400
Poultry Processing
N.A.I.C.S.: 311615
Paul Wright (Plant Mgr)

Plant (Domestic):

Kraft Heinz Company - Lowville (3)
7388 Utica Blvd, Lowville, NY 13367-9503
Tel.: (315) 376-6575
Web Site: http://www.kraftfoods.com
Sales Range: $150-199.9 Million
Emp.: 300
Food Products Mfr
N.A.I.C.S.: 311999
Marc Page (Plant Mgr)

**Kraft Heinz Company - Mason
City** (3)
1022 12th St NW, Mason City, IA 50401-
1802
Tel.: (641) 421-2900
Web Site: http://www.kraftfoods.com
Emp.: 274
Food Products Mfr
N.A.I.C.S.: 311999

Unit (Domestic):

**Kraft Heinz Company - Maxwell
House Coffee** (3)
735 E Bay St, Jacksonville, FL 32202-2303
Tel.: (904) 632-3400
Web Site:
    http://www.maxwellhousecoffee.com
Sales Range: $200-249.9 Million
Emp.: 425
Coffee Mfr
N.A.I.C.S.: 311920
Joe Waryold (Plant Mgr)

Plant (Domestic):

Kraft Heinz Company - New Ulm (3)
2525 S Bridge St, New Ulm, MN 56073-
3955
Tel.: (507) 354-4131
Web Site: http://www.kraftfoods.com
Sales Range: $250-299.9 Million
Emp.: 600
Food Production Services
N.A.I.C.S.: 311999

Unit (Domestic):

**Kraft Heinz Company - Oscar
Mayer** (3)
910 Mayer Ave, Madison, WI 53704-4256
Tel.: (608) 241-3311
Web Site: http://www.oscarmayer.com
Sales Range: $300-349.9 Million
Emp.: 1,250
Lunch Meat, Hot Dog & Bacon Mfr

N.A.I.C.S.: 311612

Kraft Heinz Company - Planters (3)
4020 Planters Rd, Fort Smith, AR 72908-
8438
Tel.: (479) 648-0100
Web Site: http://www.planters.com
Sales Range: $150-199.9 Million
Emp.: 300
Salted & Roasted Nuts & Seeds Producer
N.A.I.C.S.: 311423

Plant (Domestic):

**Kraft Heinz Company -
Richmond** (3)
6002 S Laburnum Ave, Richmond, VA
23231-5002
Tel.: (804) 222-8802
Sales Range: $300-349.9 Million
Emp.: 750
Crackers, Cookies & Bakery Products Mfr
N.A.I.C.S.: 311812

**Kraft Heinz Company - San
Leandro** (3)
100 Halcyon Dr, San Leandro, CA 94578
Tel.: (510) 639-5000
Sales Range: $150-199.9 Million
Food Products Mfr
N.A.I.C.S.: 311999

**Kraft Heinz Company -
Springfield** (3)
2035 E Bennett St, Springfield, MO 65804-
1731
Tel.: (417) 881-2701
Sales Range: $50-74.9 Million
Food Products Mfr
N.A.I.C.S.: 311999

Kraft Heinz Company - Tulare (3)
10800 Avenue 184, Tulare, CA 93274-9514
Tel.: (559) 685-0790
Sales Range: $50-74.9 Million
Food Products Mfr
N.A.I.C.S.: 311999

Kraft Heinz Company - Wausau (3)
1077 Town Line Rd, Wausau, WI 54403-
6561
Tel.: (715) 842-2077
Sales Range: $50-74.9 Million
Food Products Mfr
N.A.I.C.S.: 311999

**Kraft Heinz Company - Wilkes
Barre** (3)
50 New Commerce Blvd, Wilkes Barre, PA
18762
Tel.: (570) 820-1200
Sales Range: $100-124.9 Million
Food Mfr
N.A.I.C.S.: 311999

The Lubrizol Corporation (1)
29400 Lakeland Blvd, Wickliffe, OH 44092
Tel.: (440) 943-4200
Web Site: http://www.lubrizol.com
Sales Range: $5-14.9 Billion
Emp.: 8,700
Lubricant & Fuel Additive Mfr
N.A.I.C.S.: 325998
Suzanne F. Day (Chief Legal & Ethics Offi-
cer & Sr VP)
Julie Edgar (CTO & Sr VP)
Rebecca B. Liebert (Pres & CEO)
Tom Curtis (Sr VP)
LG Tackett (Sr VP-Ops)
Mary Rhinehart (Chm)
Shuja Ishrat (CIO & Sr VP)
James J. T. Jones (Chief Procurement Offi-
cer & Sr VP-Procurement & High-Growth
Regions)
Flavio Kliger (Pres-Lubrizol Additives & Sr
VP)
Trina Nally (Chief HR Officer & Sr VP)
Arnau Pano (Pres-Lubrizol Advanced Mate-
rials & Sr VP)
Eduardo Pedreira (VP-Supply Chain)
Davies Walker (CFO, Treas & Sr VP)
Jeff Lauderdale (Interim Chief Legal Officer)
Jose Gonzalez-Magaz (Chief Legal Officer
& Sr VP)

Subsidiary (Domestic):

Chemtool, Inc. (2)
801 W Rockton Rd, Rockton, IL 61072
Tel.: (815) 957-4140

Web Site: http://chemtool.com
Sales Range: $25-49.9 Million
Emp.: 100
Lubricants, Cleaners & Metalworking Fluids
Mfr
N.A.I.C.S.: 324191
Tim Little *(Dir-Sls-Process Fluids)*
Chuck Kleeberger *(VP-Fin)*
Joseph Flies *(Sls Dir-Grease)*
Steven de Waard *(Dir-Strategic Mktg & Product Mgmt)*
Mike Costello *(Dir-Strategic Res & Innovation)*
David Sharp *(Partner-HR Bus-Global)*

Lubrizol Advanced Materials, Inc. (2)
9911 Brecksville Rd, Cleveland, OH 44141-3247
Tel.: (216) 447-5000
Web Site: http://www.lubrizol.com
Sales Range: $1-4.9 Billion
Emp.: 2,500
Mfr of Specialty Polymers, Polymer-Based Additives & Chemical Additives for Consumer & Industrial Applications
N.A.I.C.S.: 325998
Rick Tolin *(Pres)*

Subsidiary (Domestic):

Lipotec USA, Inc. (3)
1097 Yates St, Lewisville, TX 75057
Tel.: (972) 221-7500
Web Site: http://na.lipotec.com
Botanical Extracts & Natural Performance & Specialty Cosmetic Ingredients Mfr
N.A.I.C.S.: 325620

Lubrizol Advanced Materials International, Inc. (3)
9911 Brecksville Rd, Cleveland, OH 44141
Tel.: (216) 447-5000
Emp.: 600
Chemical Product Mfr & Distr
N.A.I.C.S.: 325199

Subsidiary (Non-US):

Lubrizol Advanced Materials Asia Pacific Limited (4)
Rm 1107-1110 11/f Shui On Ctr 6 - 8 Harbour Rd, Wanchai, China (Hong Kong) **(100%)**
Tel.: (852) 25081021
Sales Range: $50-74.9 Million
Emp.: 30
Sales of Industrial & Specialty Chemicals
N.A.I.C.S.: 424690

Lubrizol Advanced Materials Europe BVBA (4)
Chaussee de Wavre 1945, 1160, Brussels, Belgium **(100%)**
Tel.: (32) 26781911
Web Site: https://www.lubrizol.com
Sales Range: $25-49.9 Million
Emp.: 80
Industrial Chemical Distr
N.A.I.C.S.: 424690
Arnau Pano *(Sr VP)*
Rebecca Liebert *(Pres)*
Trina Nally *(Chief HR Officer)*
Lg Tackett *(Sr VP)*
Davies Walker *(CFO)*
Julie Edgar *(CTO)*
Jose Gonzalez-Magaz *(Chief Legal Officer)*
Shuja Ishrat *(CIO)*
James Jones *(Sr VP)*
Eduardo Pedreira *(VP)*
Flavio Kliger *(Sr VP)*

Plant (Domestic):

Lubrizol Advanced Materials, Inc. - Paso Robles (3)
3115 Propeller Dr, Paso Robles, CA 93447
Tel.: (805) 239-1550
Web Site: http://www.lubrizol.com
Sales Range: $10-24.9 Million
Emp.: 60
Surface Active Agent Mfr
N.A.I.C.S.: 325613

Branch (Non-US):

Lubrizol Australia (2)
126 Bertie Street, Port Melbourne, 3207, VIC, Australia
Tel.: (61) 386453555
Web Site: https://www.lubrizol.com

Sales Range: $10-24.9 Million
Emp.: 25
Chemicals & Additives Whslr
N.A.I.C.S.: 424690

Subsidiary (Non-US):

Lubrizol Canada Ltd. (2)
3700 Steeles Ave W Suite 201, Vaughan, L4L 8K8, ON, Canada **(100%)**
Tel.: (905) 264-4646
Web Site: https://www.lubrizol.com
Marketer & Retailer of Chemicals
N.A.I.C.S.: 424690

Lubrizol Deutschland GmbH (2)
Billbrookdeich 157, 22113, Hamburg, Germany **(100%)**
Tel.: (49) 403232820
Sales Range: $25-49.9 Million
Emp.: 15
Sales of Chemicals
N.A.I.C.S.: 424690

Lubrizol Espanola, S.A. (2)
Bravo Murillo 29 1 C, Madrid, 28015, Spain **(100%)**
Tel.: (34) 914445480
Web Site: http://www.lubrizol.com
Sales Range: $50-74.9 Million
Emp.: 5
Sales of Chemicals
N.A.I.C.S.: 424690

Lubrizol France SAS (2)
Tour Pacific 11 cours Valmy, La Defense, 92977, Paris, France **(100%)**
Tel.: (33) 14 125 1300
Web Site: https://france.lubrizol.com
Sales Range: $150-199.9 Million
Emp.: 20
Sales of Chemicals
N.A.I.C.S.: 424690

Lubrizol GmbH (2)
Mariahilferstrasse 103/3/55 56A, 1060, Vienna, Austria **(100%)**
Tel.: (43) 15973570
Sales Range: $50-74.9 Million
Emp.: 10
Sales of Chemicals
N.A.I.C.S.: 424690
Gotfried Pollack *(Gen Mgr)*

Lubrizol Group, LLP (2)
The Knowle Nether Lane Hazelwood, Derby, DE56 4AN, Derbyshire, United Kingdom
Tel.: (44) 1332842211
Web Site: http://www.lubrizol.com
Financial Investment Services
N.A.I.C.S.: 523999

Affiliate (Non-US):

Lubrizol India Pvt. Ltd. (2)
9/3 Thane Belapur Road, Turbhe, Navi Mumbai, 400705, India **(74%)**
Tel.: (91) 2267759000
Emp.: 322
Chemical Additives Mfr & Distr
N.A.I.C.S.: 325998
V. N. Garg *(Head-Fin)*

Subsidiary (Non-US):

Lubrizol Italiana, S.p.A. (2)
Centro Direzionale Milano Oltre Palazzo Cimabue, Via Cassenese 224, 20090, Milan, Italy **(100%)**
Tel.: (39) 02269761
Sales Range: $50-74.9 Million
Emp.: 5
Sales of Chemicals
N.A.I.C.S.: 424690

Lubrizol Japan Limited (2)
1 1 Aza 5 Gochi Taketoyo Cho, Chita, 470-2341, Aichi, Japan **(100%)**
Tel.: (81) 569721321
Sales Range: $25-49.9 Million
Emp.: 100
Sales of Chemicals
N.A.I.C.S.: 424690

Lubrizol Limited (2)
3000 Hillswood Drive, Hillswood Business Park, Chertsey, KT16 ORS, Surrey, United Kingdom **(100%)**
Tel.: (44) 1932454280
Web Site: http://www.lubrizol.com

Sales Range: $50-74.9 Million
Emp.: 4
Sales of Oil Additives
N.A.I.C.S.: 424690

Lubrizol Luxembourg S.a.r.l. (2)
12 Rue Eugene Ruppert, Luxembourg, 2453, Luxembourg
Tel.: (352) 33235581483
Cosmetics Mfr
N.A.I.C.S.: 325620

Subsidiary (Domestic):

Lubrizol Oilfield Solutions, Inc. (2)
4420 S Flores Rd, Elmendorf, TX 78112
Tel.: (210) 621-2156
Insurance Agency Services
N.A.I.C.S.: 524210

Lubrizol Overseas Trading Corporation (2)
29400 Lakeland Blvd, Wickliffe, OH 44092
Tel.: (440) 943-4200
Web Site: http://www.lubrizol.com
Chemical Products Mfr
N.A.I.C.S.: 325199

Subsidiary (Non-US):

Lubrizol Southeast Asia (Pte.) Ltd. (2)
44 Tanjong Penjuru, Singapore, 609032, Singapore **(100%)**
Tel.: (65) 6 264 1644
Web Site: https://www.lubrizol.com
Sales Range: $25-49.9 Million
Emp.: 70
Chemical Additives Sales & Customer Service
N.A.I.C.S.: 424690

Subsidiary (Domestic):

Lubrizol Specialty Products LLC (2)
1 Briar Lk Plz 2000 W Sam Houston Pkwy S 4th Fl Ste 400, Houston, TX 77042
Tel.: (713) 339-8703
Web Site: http://www.liquidpower.com
Emp.: 300
Pipeline Engineering Services
N.A.I.C.S.: 541330

Subsidiary (Non-US):

Lubrizol do Brasil Aditivos Ltda. (2)
Estrada Belford Roxo 1375, Belford Roxo, Rio de Janeiro, 26110-260, Brazil
Tel.: (55) 21 2762 5864
Web Site: http://www.lubrizol.com
Sales Range: $25-49.9 Million
Emp.: 123
Chemical Additives Mfr & Distr
N.A.I.C.S.: 325998

Warwick International Group Limited (2)
The Knowle Nether Lane Hazelwood, Derby, DE56 4AN, United Kingdom
Tel.: (44) 1745560651
Web Site: http://www.warwickchem.com
Specialty Chemicals Mfr
N.A.I.C.S.: 325998
Steve Williams *(Mng Dir)*

The Pampered Chef, Ltd. (1)
1 Pampered Chef Ln, Addison, IL 60101-5630
Tel.: (630) 261-8900
Web Site: https://www.pamperedchef.com
Sales Range: $550-599.9 Million
Emp.: 500
Direct-Seller of High-Quality Kitchen Tools
N.A.I.C.S.: 332215
Tracy Britt Cool *(CEO)*
Doris Christopher *(Founder & Chm)*
Andrew Treanor *(CEO)*

U.S. Investment Corporation (1)
190 S Warner Rd, Wayne, PA 19087
Tel.: (215) 877-3917
Insurance Services
N.A.I.C.S.: 524126

Subsidiary (Domestic):

U.S. Underwriters Insurance Company (2)
1190 Devon Park Dr, Wayne, PA 19087
Tel.: (610) 688-2535
Web Site: http://www.usli.com

Insurance Services
N.A.I.C.S.: 524126

UTLX Company (1)
175 W Jackson Blvd Ste 2100, Chicago, IL 60604
Tel.: (312) 431-3111
Web Site: http://www.utlx.com
Emp.: 3,000
Transportation & Crane Services
N.A.I.C.S.: 488999

United States Liability Insurance Company (1)
1190 Devon Park Dr, Wayne, PA 19087-2191
Tel.: (610) 688-2535
Web Site: https://www.usli.com
Sales Range: $250-299.9 Million
Emp.: 500
Insurance Services
N.A.I.C.S.: 524126
Thomas P. Nerney *(Chm, Co-Pres & CEO)*
Jack Carballo *(Chief Admin Officer & Exec VP)*
Thomas C. Snyder *(Pres-Customer Distr)*
Lisa Kuesel Traynor *(COO & Exec VP)*
Drew Mitala *(Co-Pres & Chief Underwriting Officer)*
Sasha Moul *(Exec VP-Admin)*
Lauren Reiley *(Chief Compliance Officer, Gen Counsel & Sr VP)*
Mark Addiego *(Chief Actuarial Officer & Sr VP)*
James Scalise *(Chief Claims Officer & Exec VP)*
Aaron Miller *(CTO & Sr VP)*

Subsidiary (Domestic):

Mount Vernon Fire Insurance Company (2)
1190 Devon Park Dr, Wayne, PA 19087
Tel.: (610) 688-2535
Web Site: http://www.usli.com
Sales Range: $250-299.9 Million
Fire Insurance Services
N.A.I.C.S.: 524126

Vanity Fair Brands, LP (1)
1 Fruit of the Loom Dr, Bowling Green, KY 42102
Tel.: (270) 781-6400
Web Site: http://www.vanityfairlingerie.com
Women Apparel & Clothing Distr
N.A.I.C.S.: 458110

WPLG, Inc. (1)
3401 W Hallandale Beach Blvd, Pembroke Park, FL 33023
Tel.: (954) 364-2500
Web Site: https://www.local10.com
Sales Range: $50-74.9 Million
Emp.: 200
Television Broadcasting
N.A.I.C.S.: 516120

XTRA Corporation (1)
7911 Forsyth Blvd, Saint Louis, MO 63105-3860
Tel.: (314) 719-0400
Web Site: http://www.xtralease.com
Holding Company; Leasing Trailers & Containers
N.A.I.C.S.: 532120
Michael Dreller *(CFO)*

Subsidiary (Domestic):

XTRA LLC (2)
1632 Park 370 Ct Hazelwood, Saint Louis, MO 63042-4418
Tel.: (314) 209-0504
Web Site: http://www.xtralease.com
Transportation Equipment Leasing Services
N.A.I.C.S.: 532411

Subsidiary (Domestic):

XTRA Lease LLC (3)
1632 Park 370 Ct, Hazelwood, MO 63042-4418 **(100%)**
Tel.: (314) 209-0504
Web Site: http://www.xtralease.com
Leasing Trailer & Container Services
N.A.I.C.S.: 532120

BERKSHIRE HILLS BANCORP, INC.

Berkshire Hills Bancorp, Inc.—(Continued)

60 State St, Boston, MA 02109
Tel.: (617) 641-9206　　　DE
Web Site:
　https://www.berkshirebank.com
Year Founded: 1846
BHLB—(NYSE)
Rev.: $456,194,000
Assets: $11,662,864,000
Liabilities: $10,708,802,000
Net Worth: $954,062,000
Earnings: $92,533,000
Emp.: 1,310
Fiscal Year-end: 12/31/22
Bank Holding Company
N.A.I.C.S.: 551111
Sean A. Gray (Sr Exec VP)
Nitin J. Mhatre (Pres & CEO)
Brett Brbovic (CFO, Chief Acctg Officer & Exec VP)
Greg Lindenmuth (Chief Credit Officer)
Jason White (CIO & Sr Exec VP)
Philip Jurgeleit (Chief Credit Officer, Chief Creative Officer & Exec VP)
Ashlee Flores (Chief Compliance Officer & Exec VP)
Jacqueline Courtwright (Chief HR Officer, Chief Culture Officer & Sr Exec VP)
Andrew R. Plumridge (Chief Internal Audit Officer & Exec VP)
Sumant Pustake (CMO, Chief Strategy Officer, Chief Transformation Officer & Exec VP)
Gordon Prescott (Gen Counsel, Sec & Sr Exec VP)
James C. Brown (Sr Exec VP-Commercial Banking & Head-Comml Banking)
Ellen Steinfeld (Sr Exec VP & Head-Consumer Lending & Payments)
Kevin Conn (Sr VP-IR & Corp Dev)

Subsidiaries:

Berkshire Bank　　　　　　　　(1)
24 N St, Pittsfield, MA 01201
Tel.: (413) 443-5601
Web Site: https://www.berkshirebank.com
Retail, Commercial & Investment Banking
N.A.I.C.S.: 522110
Sean A. Gray (Pres & COO)
George F. Bacigalupo (Dir-Comml & Enterprise Sls Mgmt)
David M. Brunelle (Chm)
Nitin J. Mhatre (CEO)
Brett Brbovic (CFO, Chief Acctg Officer & Exec VP)
Tami M. Gunsch (Sr Exec VP & Head-Consumer Banking)

Division (Domestic):

44 Business Capital　　　　　　(2)
1787 Sentry Pkwy W Bldg 16 Ste 200, Blue Bell, PA 19422
Tel.: (215) 985-4400
Web Site:
　https://www.44businesscapital.com
Commercial Lending Services
N.A.I.C.S.: 522291
Greg Poehlmann (Co-Founder & Sr VP-Bus Banking)
Phil Rapone (Co-Founder)
Joe Dreyer (Sr VP-Natl Sls)
Jeff Sherry (Co-Founder & Sr VP-Bus Banking)
Phil Martin (First VP-SBA Lending)
Michael Hahn (First VP-SBA Lending)
Scott Stevens (First VP-SBA Lending)
Debbie Godt (First VP-SBA Lending)
Michael DeVito (First VP-SBA Lending)
Dwight E. Williams (First VP-SBA Lending)
David Nayor (First VP-SBA Lending)
Frank Coppola (First VP-SBA Lending)
Dee Kuestner (VP)
Dana Neas (VP)
Deborah Thomas (VP)
Roxanne Selwyn (VP & Mgr-SBA Construction Loan)
Joan Whiteley (VP-SBA Loan Servicing)

Trish Dade (Asst VP)
Deborah C. Hudson (First VP)
Lynne Singletary (First VP-SBA Lending)
Marissa Ames (First VP-SBA Lending)
James Stolt (First VP-SBA Lending)
Margaret Pugh (VP)
Michael E. Pillitteri (Officer-Comml Credit & VP)
Wendy Fleischmann McNatt (VP)

Subsidiary (Domestic):

Hampden Investment Corporation II　　　　　　　　　　　　(2)
24 N St, Pittsfield, MA 01201
Tel.: (413) 567-3796
Commercial Banking Investment Services
N.A.I.C.S.: 522110

RNL & Associates　　　　　　(2)
86 N Main St, Rutland, VT 05701
Tel.: (802) 773-4115
Web Site: https://www.rnlpc.com
Tax Preparation Services
N.A.I.C.S.: 541213
Katherine B. Brady (Office Mgr-Ops)

Berkshire Insurance Group, Inc.　(1)
31 Court St, Westfield, MA 10850
Tel.: (413) 562-3659
Web Site:
　http://www.berkshireinsurancegroup.com
Insurance Services
N.A.I.C.S.: 524210
Norma LaForest (Asst VP-Comml Lines)

Firestone Financial, LLC　　　(1)
1 Van de Graaf Dr Ste 502, Burlington, MA 01803　　　　　　　　　(100%)
Web Site: https://www.firestonefinancial.com
Commercial Equipment Sales Financing
N.A.I.C.S.: 522220

SI Financial Group, Inc.　　　(1)
803 Main St, Willimantic, CT 06226
Tel.: (860) 423-4581
Web Site: http://www.mysifi.com
Rev.: $58,171,000
Assets: $1,649,827,000
Liabilities: $1,477,699,000
Net Worth: $172,128,000
Earnings: $9,565,000
Emp.: 274
Fiscal Year-end: 12/31/2018
Bank Holding Company
N.A.I.C.S.: 551111

BERRY CORPORATION (BRY)
16000 N Dallas Pkwy Ste 500, Dallas, TX 75248
Tel.: (661) 616-3900　　　DE
Web Site: https://www.bry.com
Year Founded: 1909
BRY—(NASDAQ)
Rev.: $918,341,000
Assets: $1,631,030,000
Liabilities: $830,545,000
Net Worth: $800,485,000
Earnings: $250,168,000
Emp.: 1,372
Fiscal Year-end: 12/31/22
Crude Petroleum Extraction Services
N.A.I.C.S.: 211120
Fernando Araujo (CEO)
Kurt Neher (Exec VP-Bus Dev)
Mike S. Helm (CFO, Chief Acctg Officer & VP)
Danielle E. Hunter (Pres-Fin, HR, Legal, and HSE)

Subsidiaries:

Berry Petroleum Company, LLC　(1)
5201 Truxtun Ave Ste 100, Bakersfield, CA 93309
Tel.: (661) 616-3900
Web Site: http://berrypetroleum.com
Petroleum & Natural Gas Extraction
N.A.I.C.S.: 211120
Kenneth A. Olson (Dir-HR & Asst Sec)
A. T. Smith (CEO)
Cary Baetz (CFO & Exec VP)
Gary Grove (COO & Exec VP)
Kurt Neher (Exec VP-Bus Dev)
Kendrick Royer (Gen Counsel, Sec & Exec VP)

Subsidiary (Domestic):

Macpherson Energy Corp.　　　(2)
2716 Ocean Park Blvd, Santa Monica, CA 90405
Tel.: (310) 452-3880
Web Site: http://www.macphersonoil.com
Sales Range: $1-9.9 Million
Emp.: 30
Support Activities for Oil & Gas Operations
N.A.I.C.S.: 213112
Donald MacPherson (Pres & CEO)

BERRY GLOBAL GROUP, INC
101 Oakley St, Evansville, IN 47710
Tel.: (812) 424-2904　　　DE
Web Site:
　https://www.berryglobal.com
Year Founded: 2005
BERY—(NYSE)
Rev.: $12,258,000,000
Assets: $16,613,000,000
Liabilities: $13,005,000,000
Net Worth: $3,608,000,000
Earnings: $516,000,000
Emp.: 42,000
Fiscal Year-end: 09/28/24
Holding Company; Plastic Consumer Packaging & Engineered Materials Mfr
N.A.I.C.S.: 551112
Mark W. Miles (CFO)
Kevin J. Kwilinski (CEO)
Jason K. Greene (Chief Legal Officer, Sec & Exec VP)
Stephen E. Sterrett (Chm)
Debbie Garrison (CIO & Exec VP)
Michael E. Hill (Pres-Engineered Materials Div)
James M. Till (Exec VP & Controller)
Tarun Manroa (Chief Strategy Officer & Exec VP)
Anastasia Matthews (VP-Global Diversity & Inclusion/Corp HR)
Jeff Bennett (Chief HR Officer & Exec VP)
Wiliam J. Norman (Pres & CFO)
Rodgers K. Greenawalt (Pres, CFO & Exec VP)

Subsidiaries:

AEP Industries Finance Inc.　　(1)
125 Phillips Ave, South Hackensack, NJ 07606
Tel.: (201) 641-6600
Web Site: http://www.aepinc.com
Financial Services
N.A.I.C.S.: 525990

AT Films Inc.　　　　　　　　(1)
4605 101 Avenue, Edmonton, T5J 2L4, AB, Canada
Tel.: (780) 450-7760
Web Site: http://www.atfilmsinc.com
Polyethylene Film Product Mfr & Distr
N.A.I.C.S.: 326113

Ace Corporation Holdings Limited　　　　　　　　　　(1)
Unit 510 5/F Vanta Industrial Centre 21-23 Tai Lin Pai Road, Kwai Chung, New Territories, China (Hong Kong)
Tel.: (852) 24876282
Web Site: http://www.acecorpholdings.com
Plastic Injection Mold Mfr
N.A.I.C.S.: 333511

Ace Mold (HeFei) Company Limited　　　　　　　　　　(1)
No 1929 Tian Du Road, Economic and Technological Development Area, Hefei, 230601, Anhui, China
Tel.: (86) 55168103088
Plastic Injection Mold Mfr
N.A.I.C.S.: 333511

Ace Mold (Shanghai) Company Limited　　　　　　　　　　(1)
888 North Round-the-city Road, Nanqiao Shanghai Industrial Comprehensive Development Zone Fengxian, Shanghai, 201401, China
Tel.: (86) 2157436636

Plastic Injection Mold Mfr
N.A.I.C.S.: 333511

Ace Mold Industrial (Shenzhen) Company Limited　　　　　　　(1)
10 Min Fu Road Shatou Community, Shajing Jiedao Baoan District, Shenzhen, 518104, China
Tel.: (86) 75527266898
Plastic Injection Mold Mfr
N.A.I.C.S.: 333511

Ace Plastics (Shenzhen) Company Limited　　　　　　　　　　(1)
Section H 3rd Industrial Zone, Gonghe Community Shajing Jiedao Baoan District, Shenzhen, 518100, China
Tel.: (86) 75527685268
Plastic Injection Mold Mfr
N.A.I.C.S.: 333511

Ace Plastics (Zhuhai) Company Limited　　　　　　　　　　(1)
8 Dingwan 7 Road, Dingjiawan Industrial Park Sanzao Town Jinwan District, Zhuhai, 519040, China
Tel.: (86) 7567517668
Plastic Injection Mold Mfr
N.A.I.C.S.: 333511

Adchem Corporation　　　　　(1)
1852 Old Country Rd, Riverhead, NY 11901
Tel.: (631) 208-4400
Web Site: http://www.adchem.com
Adhesive Tape Systems Including Double-Coated Papers, Films, Tissues, Foams & Fabrics, Transfer Tapes, Single-Coated Products & Other Custom-Coated Specialty Products Mfr
N.A.I.C.S.: 322220
John Pufahl (Bus Dev Mgr)

Amber Plastics Pty. Limited　　(1)
45 Colemans Road, Carrum Downs, 3201, VIC, Australia
Tel.: (61) 397082143
Web Site: http://www.amberplastics.com.au
Plastic Packaging Product Mfr & Distr
N.A.I.C.S.: 326199

BPRex Brazil Holding Inc.　　(1)
101 Oakley St, Evansville, IN 47710
Tel.: (812) 306-2764
Holding Company
N.A.I.C.S.: 551112

Berry Ace Packaging (Jiaxing) Company Limited　　　　　　　(1)
No 688 Fenghua Road Chengnan Street Economic Development Zone, Jiaxing, 233200, Zhejiang, China
Tel.: (86) 57382851688
Molding Product Mfr & Distr
N.A.I.C.S.: 333511

Berry Global India Private Limited　　　　　　　　　　(1)
485 13th Cross Peenya 4th Phase, Peenya Industrial Area, Bengaluru, Karnataka, India
Tel.: (91) 9008065972
Plastic Product Mfr & Distr
N.A.I.C.S.: 326199

Berry Plastics Corporation　　(1)
101 Oakley St, Evansville, IN 47710
Tel.: (812) 424-2904
Injection-Molded Plastic Packaging & Houseware Products Mfr
N.A.I.C.S.: 326121

Subsidiary (Domestic):

AVINTIV Inc.　　　　　　　　(2)
9335 Harris Corners Pkwy Ste 300, Charlotte, NC 28269
Tel.: (704) 697-5100
Web Site: http://www.avintiv.com
Holding Company; Specialty Nonwoven Materials Developer, Mfr & Marketer
N.A.I.C.S.: 551112
David Wang (Pres-Asia)

Subsidiary (Domestic):

AVINTIV Specialty Materials Inc.　(3)
9335 Harris Corners Pkwy Ste 300, Charlotte, NC 28269-3817
Tel.: (704) 697-5100
Emp.: 100

Nonwoven Fabric & Oriented Polymer Materials Mfr
N.A.I.C.S.: 313210
Daniel Guerrero (Sr VP-Global Strategic Plng & Bus Dev)
Bob Dale (Sr VP-Special Projects)

Subsidiary (Domestic):

Chicopee Inc. (4)
9335 Harris Corners Pkwy Ste 300, Charlotte, NC 28269
Tel.: (888) 835-2442
Web Site: http://chicopee.com
Towel & Wiping Products Mfr
N.A.I.C.S.: 313230
Mike Roth (Mgr-Central Reg)

Division (Non-US):

Chicopee Europe (5)
PO Box 15, 5430 AA, Cuijk, Netherlands
Tel.: (31) 485 398 426
Web Site: http://chicopee.com
Wipes & Cleaning Materials Mfr
N.A.I.C.S.: 313230

Subsidiary (Non-US):

Fiberweb Geosynthetics Ltd (4)
Blackwater Trading Estate The Causeway, Maldon, CM9 4GG, Essex, United Kingdom
Tel.: (44) 1621874200
Web Site: http://www.terram.com
Thermoplastic Films Mfr
N.A.I.C.S.: 325211

Subsidiary (Domestic):

Terram Limited (5)
Blackwater Trading Estate The Causeway, Maldon, CM9 4GG, Essex, United Kingdom
Tel.: (44) 1621874200
Web Site: http://www.terram.com
Geosynthetic Materials Mfr
N.A.I.C.S.: 314999
Stephen Hancock (Sls Dir-Europe)

Subsidiary (Domestic):

Aerocon, LLC (2)
101 Oakley St, Evansville, IN 47710-1237
Tel.: (812) 424-2904
Consumer Plastic Packaging Product Mfr
N.A.I.C.S.: 326199

BPRex Closures, LLC (2)
3245 Kansas Rd, Evansville, IN 47725-9757
Tel.: (812) 867-6671
Consumer Plastic Packaging Product Mfr
N.A.I.C.S.: 326199

BPRex Delta, Inc. (2)
106 Delta Pl, Hot Springs, AR 71913
Tel.: (501) 760-3000
Consumer Plastic Packaging Product Mfr
N.A.I.C.S.: 326199

Plant (Domestic):

Berry Global, Inc (2)
4611 Central Ave, Monroe, LA 71203
Tel.: (318) 388-2200
Sales Range: $25-49.9 Million
Emp.: 85
Polyethylene Film
N.A.I.C.S.: 326113

Plant (Non-US):

Berry Global, Inc. (2)
Tel.: (812) 386-1525
Web Site: https://www.berryglobal.com
Sales Range: $25-49.9 Million
Emp.: 100
Mfr of Child Resistant & Screw Closures
N.A.I.C.S.: 326199

Plant (Domestic):

Berry Global, Inc. (2)
7447 Candlewood Rd, Hanover, MD 21076
Tel.: (410) 850-4242
Sales Range: $10-24.9 Million
Emp.: 120
Plastics Product Mfr
N.A.I.C.S.: 326199

Subsidiary (Domestic):

Berry Iowa, LLC (2)

1036 Industrial Park Rd, Iowa Falls, IA 50126-8021
Tel.: (641) 648-5047
Consumer Plastic Packaging Product Mfr
N.A.I.C.S.: 326199

Plant (Domestic):

Berry Plastics Corp. - Anaheim (2)
4875 E Hunter Ave, Anaheim, CA 92807
Tel.: (714) 777-5200
Sales Range: Less than $1 Million
Emp.: 467
Plastic Containers & Closures Mfr
N.A.I.C.S.: 326160

Berry Plastics Corp. - Baltimore (2)
1810 Portal St, Baltimore, MD 21224-6512
Tel.: (410) 633-1990
Web Site: http://www.berryplastics.com
Sales Range: Less than $1 Million
Emp.: 350
Plastic Closures, Fitments, Applicators & Droppers Mfr
N.A.I.C.S.: 326199

Berry Plastics Corp. - Chicago (2)
5750 W 118th St, Chicago, IL 60803
Tel.: (708) 396-1470
Rev.: $226,400,000
Emp.: 1,300
Plastic Containers/Lids Mfr
N.A.I.C.S.: 326199

Berry Plastics Corp. - Cranbury (2)
34 Engelhard Dr, Monroe Township, NJ 08831
Tel.: (609) 655-4600
Sales Range: $25-49.9 Million
Emp.: 270
Plastics Product Mfr
N.A.I.C.S.: 326199

Berry Plastics Corp. - Evansville (2)
3245 Kansas Rd, Evansville, IN 47725-9757
Tel.: (812) 867-6671
Web Site: http://www.berryplastics.com
Sales Range: $125-149.9 Million
Emp.: 350
Child Resistant & Screw Closures Mfr
N.A.I.C.S.: 326199

Berry Plastics Corp. - Flexible Packaging, Schaumburg Plant (2)
1228 E Tower Rd, Schaumburg, IL 60173
Tel.: (847) 884-1200
Web Site: http://www.berryplastics.com
Sales Range: $50-74.9 Million
Emp.: 120
Plastic Bags & Packaging Film Mfr
N.A.I.C.S.: 326112

Berry Plastics Corp. - Henderson (2)
800 E Horizon Dr, Henderson, NV 89015
Tel.: (702) 564-7770
Web Site: http://www.berryplastics.com
Emp.: 170
Consumer Plastic Packaging Product Mfr
N.A.I.C.S.: 326199
Don Abney (CEO)

Berry Plastics Corp. - Lancaster (2)
1846 Charter Ln, Lancaster, PA 17601-6706
Tel.: (717) 390-8460
Sales Range: $25-49.9 Million
Emp.: 50
Plastic Closure Mfr
N.A.I.C.S.: 326199

Berry Plastics Corp. - Sarasota (2)
7350 26th Ct E, Sarasota, FL 34243
Tel.: (941) 355-7166
Web Site: http://www.berryplastics.com
Sales Range: $200-249.9 Million
Emp.: 150
Plastic Mfr
N.A.I.C.S.: 326199

Berry Plastics Corp. - Suffolk (2)
1401 Progress Rd, Suffolk, VA 23434-2147
Tel.: (757) 538-2000
Emp.: 25
Consumer Plastic Packaging Product Mfr
N.A.I.C.S.: 326199

Unit (Domestic):

Berry Plastics Corp. - Tubed Products Division (2)
44 O'Neil St, Easthampton, MA 01027-1179

Tel.: (413) 527-1250
Web Site: http://www.superfos.com
Sales Range: $200-249.9 Million
Emp.: 202
Plastic Squeeze Tubes Mfr
N.A.I.C.S.: 326199

Subsidiary (Domestic):

Berry Plastics Filmco, Inc. (2)
1450 S Chillicothe Rd, Aurora, OH 44202
Tel.: (330) 562-6111
Consumer Plastic Packaging Product Mfr
N.A.I.C.S.: 326199

Berry Plastics SP, Inc. (2)
11301 Superfos Dr SE, Cumberland, MD 21502-8772
Tel.: (301) 759-3145
Web Site: http://www.berryplastics.com
Emp.: 200
Injection Molded Rigid Open Top Container Mfr
N.A.I.C.S.: 326199

Captive Plastics, Inc. (2)
251 Circle Dr N, Piscataway, NJ 08854-3701
Tel.: (732) 469-7900
Web Site: http://www.berryplastics.com
Sales Range: $25-49.9 Million
Emp.: 20
Plastic Packaging Mfr
N.A.I.C.S.: 326199

Plant (Domestic):

Captive Plastics, Inc. (3)
2635 E Magnolia St, Phoenix, AZ 85034-6909
Tel.: (602) 629-2700
Sales Range: $25-49.9 Million
Plastic Packaging Mfr
N.A.I.C.S.: 326199

Subsidiary (Domestic):

Covalence Specialty Adhesives LLC (2)
25 Forge Pkwy, Franklin, MA 02038
Tel.: (508) 918-1600
Adhesive & Corrosion Protection Product Mfr
N.A.I.C.S.: 325520

Grafco Industries Limited Partnership (2)
7447 Candlewood Rd, Hanover, MD 21076-3102
Tel.: (410) 850-4242
Consumer Plastic Packaging Product Mfr
N.A.I.C.S.: 326199

Knight Plastics, LLC (2)
1008 Courtaulds Dr, Woodstock, IL 60098
Tel.: (815) 334-1240
Dispensing Plastic Closure Mfr
N.A.I.C.S.: 326199

Packerware, LLC (2)
2330 Packer Rd, Lawrence, KS 66049
Tel.: (785) 842-3000
Web Site: http://www.berryplastics.com
Emp.: 800
Plastic Container Mfr
N.A.I.C.S.: 326199
Jonathan D. Rich (CEO)

Rollpak Corporation (2)
1413 Eisenhower Dr S, Goshen, IN 46526
Tel.: (574) 533-0541
Polyethylene & Trash Bag Mfr
N.A.I.C.S.: 326111

Setco, LLC (2)
34 Engelhard Dr, Monroe Township, NJ 08831-3796
Tel.: (610) 321-9760
Consumer Plastic Packaging Product Mfr
N.A.I.C.S.: 326199

Sun Coast Industries, LLC (2)
2700 S Westmoreland Ave, Dallas, TX 75233
Tel.: (214) 373-7864
Plastic Closure Mfr & Whslr
N.A.I.C.S.: 326199

Berry Superfos Besancon SAS (1)
Spotorno Alle 8 2630, Taastrup, Denmark
Tel.: (45) 59111110

Web Site: https://superfos.com
Plastic Material & Resin Mfr
N.A.I.C.S.: 325211

Berry Superfos Deventer B.V. (1)
Bergweidedijk 1, 7418 AB, Deventer, Netherlands
Tel.: (31) 570682312
Plastic Packaging Equipment Mfr & Distr
N.A.I.C.S.: 326112

Berry Superfos Pamplona SA (1)
Calle L 14-16, Poligono Industrial Comarca N1 Orcoyen, 31160, Navarra, Spain
Tel.: (34) 948368054
Plastic Container Mfr & Distr
N.A.I.C.S.: 326199

Clopay Plastic Products Company (1)
463 Harding Industrial Dr, Nashville, TN 37211-3100
Tel.: (513) 770-4800
Specialty Plastic Films & Laminates Developer & Mfr
N.A.I.C.S.: 322220

Subsidiary (Non-US):

Clopay Aschersleben GmbH (2)
Daimlerstrasse 10, D-06449, Aschersleben, Germany
Tel.: (49) 34738892000
Specialty Plastic Films Mfr
N.A.I.C.S.: 326113

Clopay do Brasil Ltda. (2)
Rua Gustavo Henrique Meerson N70, Distrito Industrial FazGran, Jundiai, 13213-086, Sao Paulo, Brazil
Tel.: (55) 1121365000
Specialty Plastic Films & Composites Mfr
N.A.I.C.S.: 326113
Fabio Fujimura (Dir-Sls & Mktg)
Rubia Raddi (Coord-HR)

Dominion Textile (USA), LLC (1)
9335 Harris Corners Pkwy Ste 300, Charlotte, NC 28269
Tel.: (704) 697-5100
Textile Products Mfr
N.A.I.C.S.: 314999

Dounor SAS (1)
Z I 30/32 Rue Du Vertuquet, Cedex, 59535, Neuville-en-Ferrain, France
Tel.: (33) 320375205
Textile Products Mfr
N.A.I.C.S.: 314999

ESE BV (1)
De Pinckart 37-39, 5674 CB, Nuenen, Netherlands
Tel.: (31) 402838485
Waste & Recycling Container Mfr
N.A.I.C.S.: 326199

ESE France SA (1)
42 rue Paul Sabatier, BP 40329, 71108, Chalon-sur-Saone, Cedex, France
Tel.: (33) 385472700
Waste & Recycling Container Mfr
N.A.I.C.S.: 326199

ESE GmbH (1)
Friedrich-Buckling-Strasse 8, 16816, Neuruppin, Germany
Tel.: (49) 3391516505
Waste & Recycling Container Mfr
N.A.I.C.S.: 326199

ESE Kft (1)
Vaci Ut 144-150, 1138, Budapest, Hungary
Tel.: (36) 13758414
Waste & Recycling Container Mfr
N.A.I.C.S.: 326199

ESE NV (1)
Diamantstraat 8/341, 2200, Herentals, Belgium
Tel.: (32) 14321531
Waste & Recycling Container Mfr
N.A.I.C.S.: 326199

ESE Sp. z o.o. (1)
ul Postepu 21, 02-676, Warsaw, Poland
Tel.: (48) 224300471
Waste & Recycling Container Mfr
N.A.I.C.S.: 326199

ESE World BV (1)

Berry Global Group, Inc—(Continued)

Luxemburglaan 35, 6199 AM, Maastricht, Netherlands
Tel.: (31) 433517000
Web Site: http://www.ese.com
Waste & Recycling Container Mfr
N.A.I.C.S.: 326199

F & S Tool, Inc. (1)
2300 Powell Ave, Erie, PA 16506
Tel.: (814) 838-7991
Web Site: http://www.fs-tool.com
Rev.: $7,500,000
Emp.: 50
Industrial Mold Mfr
N.A.I.C.S.: 333511
Erin Zambroski (Office Mgr)

Fiberweb Italia SpA (1)
Via Bologna 7, 20060, Trezzano Rosa, Italy
Tel.: (39) 02909991
Textile Products Mfr
N.A.I.C.S.: 314999

Galion SA (1)
Fouchana Chebedda Street, Naassen, 1135, Tunis, Tunisia
Tel.: (216) 71308500
Web Site: http://www.galion.com
Plastic Container Mfr
N.A.I.C.S.: 326199

ITUB ehf (1)
Gunnarsbraut 12, 620, Dalvik, Iceland
Tel.: (354) 4605044
Plastic Tub Rental Services
N.A.I.C.S.: 532490

J P Plast S R O (1)
Svatoborska 988, 697 01, Kyjov, Czech Republic
Tel.: (420) 518698110
Web Site: http://www.jpplast.eu
Plastic Container Mfr
N.A.I.C.S.: 326199
Koller Lukas (Bus Mgr)

J P Plast Slovakia spol S R O (1)
Hasicska 4, 971 01, Prievidza, Slovakia
Tel.: (421) 465423372
Plastic Container Mfr
N.A.I.C.S.: 326199
Letavayova Martina (Bus Mgr)

Jordan Plastics Limited (1)
109 Summerisland Road, Portadown, Armagh, BT62 1SJ, United Kingdom
Tel.: (44) 2838853111
Web Site: http://www.jordanplastics.com
Plastic Container Mfr
N.A.I.C.S.: 326199

LLC ESE South America S.R.L. (1)
Av Camino Real 348, San Isidro, 1502, Lima, Peru
Tel.: (51) 958455118
Waste & Recycling Container Mfr
N.A.I.C.S.: 326199

Laddawn Inc. (1)
2 Northeast Blvd, Sterling, MA 01564
Tel.: (978) 422-3371
Web Site: http://www.laddawn.com
Sales Range: $125-149.9 Million
Emp.: 380
Plastic Bags
N.A.I.C.S.: 326111

Letica Resources Inc. (1)
52585 Dequindre, Rochester Hills, MI 48307
Web Site: http://www.leticafreightlines.com
General Freight Trucking Services
N.A.I.C.S.: 488510

Nordfolien GmbH (1)
Am Tannenkamp 21, Steinfeld, 49439, Vechta, Germany
Tel.: (49) 5492880
Web Site: http://www.nordfolien.com
Emp.: 320
Plastic Packaging Products Mfr
N.A.I.C.S.: 326199

Nordfolien Polska Sp. z o.o. (1)
ul Rozwadzka 4, Zdzieszowice, 47-330, Krapkowice, Poland
Tel.: (48) 774726670
Emp.: 78
Plastic Packaging Product Distr
N.A.I.C.S.: 424610

PET Power BV (1)
Hermelijnweg 2, 4877 AE, Etten-Leur, Netherlands
Tel.: (31) 765038283
Web Site: http://www.petpower.eu
Plastic Packaging Products Mfr
N.A.I.C.S.: 326199

PET Power Handels GmbH (1)
Brunnergasse 1-9 Top 3, 2380, Perchtoldsdorf, Austria
Tel.: (43) 18695616
Plastic Packaging Product Distr
N.A.I.C.S.: 424610

PET-Power Deutschland GmbH (1)
Dr-Herbert-Kittel-Strasse 1, 87600, Kaufbeuren, Germany
Tel.: (49) 834199569
Plastic Packaging Product Distr
N.A.I.C.S.: 424610

PGI Acquisition Limited (1)
161 Bay St Ste 3700, Toronto, M5J 2S1, ON, Canada
Tel.: (416) 861-9911
Metal Mining Services
N.A.I.C.S.: 213114

PGI Columbia LTDA (1)
Zona Franca del Pacifico Km 6 Via Yumbo Aeropuerto, Cali, Colombia
Tel.: (57) 22801242
Metal Mining Services
N.A.I.C.S.: 213114

PGI Nonwovens B.V. (1)
Lange Oijen 16, 5433 NG, Katwijk, Netherlands
Tel.: (31) 485398111
Metal Mining Services
N.A.I.C.S.: 213114

PWS Danmark A/S (1)
Skejby Nordlandsvej 305, 8200, Aarhus, Denmark
Tel.: (45) 70701173
Web Site: https://www.pwsas.dk
Emp.: 25
Plastic Packaging Product Distr
N.A.I.C.S.: 424610
Lotte Engemann (Mgr-Internal Sls & Mktg)

PWS Finland OY (1)
Teknobulevardi 3-5, 01530, Vantaa, Finland
Tel.: (358) 405268850
Plastic Packaging Product Distr
N.A.I.C.S.: 424610

PWS Nordic AB (1)
Hassleholmsvagen 10, Box 47, 284 21, Perstorp, Sweden
Tel.: (46) 43536930
Web Site: http://www.pwsab.se
Plastic Packaging Products Mfr.
N.A.I.C.S.: 326199
Dan Hakansson (CEO)
Annette Nilsson (Controller)

PWS Norge AS (1)
Ringtunveien 2, 1712, Gralum, Norway
Tel.: (47) 43536930
Plastic Packaging Product Distr
N.A.I.C.S.: 424610

Plasgran Limited (1)
Manea Road, Wimblington, PE15 0PE, Cambridgeshire, United Kingdom
Tel.: (44) 1354740005
Web Site: http://www.plasgranltd.co.uk
Plastic Recycling Product Mfr
N.A.I.C.S.: 325991
Mark Roberts (Mng Dir)

Plasti-ape S.p.A. (1)
Via Primo Maggio 8, 23875, Osnago, LC, Italy
Tel.: (39) 039952981
Web Site: http://www.plastiape.it
Emp.: 300
Plastic Packaging Products Mfr
N.A.I.C.S.: 326199

Plastiape Sp. z o.o. (1)
U L II Armi W Polskiego 1, 08-400, Garwolin, PL, Poland
Tel.: (48) 257861123
Plastic Packaging Product Distr
N.A.I.C.S.: 424610

Pro-Western Plastics Ltd. (1)

30 Riel Drive, Saint Albert, T8N 3Z7, AB, Canada
Tel.: (780) 459-4491
Web Site: https://www.pro-westernplastics.com
Plastic Injection Moulding Machine Mfr & Distr
N.A.I.C.S.: 333511

RPC Astrapak Proprietary Limited (1)
25A Old Main Road Clifton Park, Gillitts, Durban, 3610, KwaZulu-Natal, South Africa
Tel.: (27) 877420710
Web Site: http://www.rpc-astrapak.com
Plastic Packaging Mfr
N.A.I.C.S.: 326112
Craig Matthews (Mng Dir)
Douglas Slogrove (Mgr-Bus Dev)

RPC Bebo Food Packaging GmbH (1)
Konigstr 2 a, Kaltenkirchen, 24568, Hamburg, Germany
Tel.: (49) 41919567161
Web Site: http://www.rpc-group.com
Plastic Packaging Mfr
N.A.I.C.S.: 326112

RPC Bramlage Division GmbH & Co., KG (1)
Braegeler Str 70, 49393, Lohne, Germany
Tel.: (49) 44428810
Web Site: http://www.rpc-bramlage.com
Plastics Bottle Mfr
N.A.I.C.S.: 326160

RPC Group Plc (1)
Sapphire House Crown Way, Rushden, NN10 6FB, Northamptonshire, United Kingdom
Tel.: (44) 1933416528
Web Site: http://www.rpc-group.com
Rev.: $5,056,097,024
Assets: $6,453,380,608
Liabilities: $3,862,935,296
Net Worth: $2,590,445,312
Earnings: $342,406,656
Emp.: 24,868
Fiscal Year-end: 03/31/2018
Plastic Packaging Mfr
N.A.I.C.S.: 326199
Jamie Pike (Chm)
Nick Giles (Sec)

Subsidiary (Domestic):

Barplas Limited (2)
Barplas Industrial Park Raymond Street, Bradford, BD58DG, West Yorkshire, United Kingdom (100%)
Tel.: (44) 1274727111
Web Site: http://www.barplas.com
Sales Range: $25-49.9 Million
Emp.: 42
Plastics Product Mfr
N.A.I.C.S.: 326199
David Scott (Gen Mgr)

British Polythene Industries Limited (2)
Sapphire House Crown Way, Rushden, NN10 6FB, Northamptonshire, United Kingdom (100%)
Tel.: (44) 1475501000
Polythene Product Mfr
N.A.I.C.S.: 326112

Subsidiary (Non-US):

BPI Europe B V (3)
Bruchterweg 88 W A3, 7772 BJ, Hardenberg, Netherlands (100%)
Tel.: (31) 523288888
Web Site: http://www.indupac.com
Sales Range: $25-49.9 Million
Emp.: 6
Religious Organizations
N.A.I.C.S.: 813110

Subsidiary (Domestic):

BPI plc (3)
The Moor Road, Sevenoaks, TN14 5EQ, Kent, United Kingdom
Tel.: (44) 1732450001
Web Site: http://www.bpifilms.com
Sales Range: $25-49.9 Million
Emp.: 80
Plastics Product Mfr

N.A.I.C.S.: 326199

British Polythene Limited (3)
96 Port Glasgow Road, Greenock, PA15 2UL, Herefordshire, United Kingdom
Tel.: (44) 1475501100
Web Site: http://www.redbooklive.com
Sales Range: $50-74.9 Million
Emp.: 250
Polythene Products Mfr
N.A.I.C.S.: 326113

Subsidiary (Non-US):

RPC BPI Agriculture (3)
4605-101 Ave, Edmonton, T6B 3R4, AB, Canada
Tel.: (780) 450-7760
Web Site: http://www.atfilmsinc.com
Polythene Film Products Mfr
N.A.I.C.S.: 326113
Calvin Mazurenko (Mng Dir)

Subsidiary (Non-US):

Global Closure Systems France 1 SAS (2)
220 Bureaux de la Colline, 92213, Saint-Cloud, Cedex, France
Tel.: (33) 1 78 76 44 38
Web Site: http://www.gcs.com
Specialty & Beverage Closure Systems Mfr
N.A.I.C.S.: 326160

Subsidiary (Non-US):

Bender GmbH (3)
Frankenstrasse 14, Postfach 1245, Frankenthal, 67227, Pfalz, Germany (100%)
Tel.: (49) 62334410
Web Site: http://www.gcs.com
Sales Range: $50-74.9 Million
Plastic Closure Mfr
N.A.I.C.S.: 339991

Subsidiary (US):

Letica Corporation (2)
52585 Dequindre, Rochester Hills, MI 48307
Tel.: (248) 652-0557
Web Site: http://www.letica.com
Miscellaneous Plastics Products, Pails & Cups Mfr
N.A.I.C.S.: 326199

Plant (Domestic):

Letica Corporation - Letica of Alabama Facility (3)
3715 S Phillips Rd, Lanett, AL 36863
Tel.: (800) 544-1736
Web Site: http://www.letica.com
Food Packaging Container Mfr
N.A.I.C.S.: 326199

Letica Corporation - Letica of Delaware Facility (3)
801 Industrial Rd, Middletown, DE 19709
Tel.: (800) 347-0187
Web Site: http://www.letica.com
Food Packaging Container Mfr
N.A.I.C.S.: 326199

Letica Corporation - Letica of Georgia Facility (3)
2020 Steeda Way, Valdosta, GA 31601
Tel.: (866) 892-0303
Web Site: http://www.letica.com
Food Packaging Container Mfr
N.A.I.C.S.: 326199

Letica Corporation - Letica of Indiana Facility (3)
701 E Depot St, Fremont, IN 46737
Tel.: (800) 347-8985
Web Site: http://www.letica.com
Food Packaging Container Mfr
N.A.I.C.S.: 326199

Letica Corporation - Letica of Iowa Facility (3)
5710 49th St S, Muscatine, IA 52761
Tel.: (800) 347-8505
Web Site: http://www.letica.com
Food Packaging Container Mfr
N.A.I.C.S.: 326199

Letica Corporation - Letica of Kentucky Facility (3)
191 Industrial Park Rd, Fulton, KY 42041

Tel.: (800) 423-3579
Web Site: http://www.letica.com
Food Packaging Container Mfr
N.A.I.C.S.: 326199

Letica Corporation - Letica of Nevada Facility (3)
1 Letica Rd, Jean, NV 89019
Tel.: (800) 347-1403
Web Site: http://www.letica.com
Food Packaging Container Mfr
N.A.I.C.S.: 326199

Letica Corporation - Letica of Oklahoma Facility (3)
7428 SW 29th St, Oklahoma City, OK 73179
Tel.: (800) 347-0486
Web Site: http://www.letica.com
Food Packaging Container Mfr
N.A.I.C.S.: 326199

Letica Corporation - Letica of Oregon Facility (3)
58231 Old Portland Rd, Saint Helens, OR 97053
Tel.: (503) 397-5611
Web Site: http://www.letica.com
Food Packaging Container Mfr
N.A.I.C.S.: 326199

Subsidiary (Non-US):

Mipac AB (2)
Industrivagen 13, Mullsjo, 565 22, Sweden
Tel.: (46) 39 23 85 00
Web Site: http://www.supersos.com
Sales Range: $25-49.9 Million
Emp.: 200
Injection Molded Packaging Material Mfr
N.A.I.C.S.: 326112
Josef Bjoerck *(Gen Mgr)*

Promens AS (2)
Priluky 38, 760 01, Zlin, Czech Republic (100%)
Tel.: (420) 577 051 101
Web Site: http://www.rpc-group.com
Sales Range: $50-74.9 Million
Emp.: 200
Plastics Product Mfr
N.A.I.C.S.: 326199

Promens AS (2)
Tehase 4, 61001, Rongu, Estonia
Tel.: (372) 7 307 230
Web Site: http://rpc-promens.ee
Sales Range: $50-74.9 Million
Emp.: 270
Plastics Product Mfr
N.A.I.C.S.: 326199

Promens Deventer B.V. (2)
Zweedsestraat 10, 7418 BG, Deventer, Netherlands
Tel.: (31) 570660711
Web Site: https://www.varibox-ibc.com
Sales Range: $25-49.9 Million
Emp.: 100
Plastic Material Handling Products Mfr
N.A.I.C.S.: 326160

Promens Firenze S.R.L. (2)
Via delle Bertesche 11/M, 50058, San Mauro a Signa, FI, Italy (100%)
Tel.: (39) 055894261
Plastic Bottle & Container Mfr
N.A.I.C.S.: 326160

Promens Hockenheim GmbH (2)
4 Industriestrasse 18, 68766, Hockenheim, Germany
Tel.: (49) 620520990
Web Site: http://rpc-promens-roto.de
Sales Range: $50-74.9 Million
Emp.: 120
Thermoplastic Molded Parts Mfr
N.A.I.C.S.: 326199
Maik Altendorf *(Mng Dir-Vehicles Bus Unit & VP)*

Promens Monastir SARL (2)
Route Mazdour Jemmel, BP No 6, Bembla, 5021, Monastir, Tunisia
Tel.: (216) 70 016 114
Sales Range: $25-49.9 Million
Emp.: 80
Moulded Plastic Components Mfr
N.A.I.C.S.: 326199

Anis Ben Abdelhafidh *(Sls Mgr)*
Saief Eddine Boudhalaa *(Project Mgr)*
Amir Essahli *(Mgr-Plant Quality)*
Mohamed Amine Jradi *(Plant Mgr)*

Promens Munchen GmbH (2)
Klausnerring 8, D-85551, Kirchheim, Germany
Tel.: (49) 899919320
Sales Range: $25-49.9 Million
Emp.: 40
Plastic Component Mfr
N.A.I.C.S.: 326199

Promens Nitra s.r.o. (2)
Prazska 33, 949 01, Nitra, Slovakia (100%)
Tel.: (421) 918940370
Sales Range: $25-49.9 Million
Emp.: 1
Plastic Component Parts Mfr
N.A.I.C.S.: 326199
Boris Pevny *(Mgr-Fin)*

Promens Oy (2)
Vanha Tampereentie 260, 20380, Turku, Finland (100%)
Tel.: (358) 2 489 555
Web Site: http://www.rpc-promens.com
Sales Range: $25-49.9 Million
Emp.: 100
Plastic Packaging & Containers Mfr
N.A.I.C.S.: 326160

Promens Packaging GmbH (2)
Gewerbestr 5, Theessen, 39291, Mockern, Germany
Tel.: (49) 724358660
Web Site: http://politainer.de
Plastic Bottles & Containers Mfr
N.A.I.C.S.: 326199
Dragan Stjepanovic *(Mng Dir)*

Plant (Domestic):

Promens Packaging GmbH - Ettlingen (3)
Hertzstrasse 22, 76275, Ettlingen, Germany
Tel.: (49) 7243 5866 0
Web Site: http://www.rpc-promens.com
Emp.: 82
Plastic Container Mfr
N.A.I.C.S.: 326199
Herr Bernd Bsonek *(Officer-Data Protection & Controller)*
Dragan Stjepanovic *(Mng Dir)*
Pim Vervaat *(Mng Dir)*
Simon Kesterton *(Mng Dir)*

Promens Packaging GmbH - Neumunster (3)
Gadelander Strasse 137, 24539, Neumunster, Germany
Tel.: (49) 4321 9878 0
Web Site: http://www.rpc-promens.com
Sales Range: $100-124.9 Million
Emp.: 300
Plastics Bottle Mfr
N.A.I.C.S.: 326160
Alexandra Erdmann *(Mgr-Sls)*

Subsidiary (Domestic):

Promens Packaging Ltd. (2)
Engineer Park, Sandycroft, Deeside, CH5 2QD, Flintshire, United Kingdom
Tel.: (44) 1244537555
Web Site: http://www.rpc-promens.com
Industrial Plastic Packaging Mfr
N.A.I.C.S.: 326199
Bruno Mousset *(Mng Dir-UK & Southern & Eastern Europe)*

Subsidiary (Non-US):

Promens Packaging SAU (2)
Pol Ind Can Roca, Barcelona, 8292, Spain
Tel.: (34) 937772448
Sales Range: $25-49.9 Million
Emp.: 100
Plastics Product Mfr
N.A.I.C.S.: 326199

Promens Rijen B.V. (2)
Provincienbaan 21, 5121 DK, Rijen, Netherlands
Tel.: (31) 161222330
Web Site: http://www.rpc-promens.com

Sales Range: $50-74.9 Million
Emp.: 110
Plastics Product Mfr
N.A.I.C.S.: 326199

Promens SA (2)
5 rue Castellion, Bellignat, 01117, Oyonnax, cedex, France
Tel.: (33) 474817481
Web Site: http://www.rpc-bramlage.de
Sales Range: $25-49.9 Million
Emp.: 200
Plastic Packaging Mfr
N.A.I.C.S.: 326199

Branch (Domestic):

Promens SA - Geovreisset (3)
Route d'oyonnax, 01104, Oyonnax, cedex, France
Tel.: (33) 474817481
Web Site: http://www.rpc-bramlage.de
Sales Range: $25-49.9 Million
Emp.: 63
Plastic Packaging Mfr
N.A.I.C.S.: 326199

Subsidiary (Non-US):

Promens SARL (2)
ZI de la Balme 481 rue des Voirons, BP 145, 74805, La Roche-sur-Foron, France
Tel.: (33) 450251700
Web Site: http://www.rpc-bramlage.de
Sales Range: $25-49.9 Million
Emp.: 60
Plastic Packaging Mfr
N.A.I.C.S.: 326199

Promens Zevenaar B.V. (2)
Einsteinstraat 22, 6902 PB, Zevenaar, Netherlands (100%)
Tel.: (31) 316586100
Web Site: http://rpc-promens-roto.de
Sales Range: $50-74.9 Million
Emp.: 200
Industrial Plastic Component Parts Mfr
N.A.I.C.S.: 326199

RPC Astrapak (2)
25A Old Man Road Gillittes, Durban, 3610, South Africa
Tel.: (27) 87 742 0710
Web Site: http://www.rpc-astrapak.com
Packaging Services
N.A.I.C.S.: 561910
Craig Matthews *(Mng Dir)*
Douglas Slogrove *(Mgr-Bus Dev)*
Helmien Raath *(Mgr-SHEQ)*

Subsidiary (Domestic):

Astraflex (Pty) Ltd (3)
6 Mahogany Road Mahogany Ridge, Pinetown, 3610, South Africa
Tel.: (27) 31 792 8350
Web Site: http://www.astrapak.co.za
Commercial Packaging Services
N.A.I.C.S.: 561910

Astrapak Gauteng (Pty) Ltd (3)
87 Uraium Road Volcania, Brakpan, 1540, Gauteng, South Africa (100%)
Tel.: (27) 118179000
Web Site: http://www.astrapak.co.za
Sales Range: $125-149.9 Million
Emp.: 426
Plastics Product Mfr
N.A.I.C.S.: 326199

Subsidiary (Domestic):

Coralline Investments (Pty) Ltd (4)
13 Bussing Road, Randfontein, 1759, Gauteng, South Africa
Tel.: (27) 114123954
Sales Range: $25-49.9 Million
Emp.: 2
Packaging Plastic Products Mfr
N.A.I.C.S.: 322220
Piet Buitendag *(Gen Mgr)*

Subsidiary (Domestic):

Astrapak KwaZulu-Natal (Pty) Ltd (3)
Riverhouse Walley Estate, 1 Imvumbu Park Close, Durban, South Africa (100%)
Tel.: (27) 315696100
Web Site: http://www.astrapak.co.za

Sales Range: $50-74.9 Million
Emp.: 230
Plastics Material & Resin Mfr
N.A.I.C.S.: 325211

Division (Domestic):

Astrapak Limited - Cinqplast Plastop Denver Division (3)
5 Kruger Street Denver, Johannesburg, 2094, South Africa
Tel.: (27) 11 417 6300
Sales Range: $50-74.9 Million
Emp.: 20
Packaging Plastic Products Mfr
N.A.I.C.S.: 322220
Grant Matthews *(Gen Mgr)*
Raymond Moussa *(Mgr-Sls)*
Thomas Gersbach *(Acct Mgr)*
Nils Osberg *(Acct Mgr-Kwazulu Natal)*
Adeel Moosa *(Mgr-Fin)*

Astrapak Limited - City Packaging Division (3)
Corner Hilston Tanjovan Roads, Kya Sands, Randburg, South Africa
Tel.: (27) 11 708 1110
Web Site: http://www.astrapak.co.za
Shrink Film Packaging Products Mfr
N.A.I.C.S.: 322220

Astrapak Limited - Packaging Consultants Division (3)
1 Imvumbu Park Close Riverhorse Valley, Durban, South Africa
Tel.: (27) 31 569 6100
Sales Range: $125-149.9 Million
Emp.: 300
Plastic Packaging Products Mfr
N.A.I.C.S.: 322220

Astrapak Limited - Peninsula Packaging Division (3)
Proton Crescent Stikland, Bellville, 7530, South Africa
Tel.: (27) 21 948 0717
Packaging Plastic Products Mfr
N.A.I.C.S.: 322220
Paul Dewrance *(Mgr-Sls & Mktg)*
Pieter Walters *(Mgr-Fin)*
Lotter Visser *(Mgr-Sls-Fresh Produce)*

Astrapak Limited - Plastform Division (3)
Flamindo Crescent Lansdowne, 7780, Cape Town, South Africa
Tel.: (27) 21 763 0400
Web Site: http://www.astrapak.co.za
Sales Range: $50-74.9 Million
Emp.: 190
Packaging Plastic Products Mfr
N.A.I.C.S.: 322220

Astrapak Limited - Plastop Bronkhorstspruit Division (3)
197/1 Manganese Street, Ekandustria, Bronkhorstspruit, South Africa
Tel.: (27) 13 933 3205
Sales Range: $125-149.9 Million
Emp.: 400
Plastic Packaging Products Mfr
N.A.I.C.S.: 322220

Astrapak Limited - Tristar Plastics Division (3)
104 Adcock Ingram Avenue Aeroton, Johannesburg, 2013, South Africa
Tel.: (27) 11 494 2103
Web Site: http://www.astrapak.co.za
Plastic Packaging Products Mfr
N.A.I.C.S.: 322220

Astrapak Limited - Ultrapak Division (3)
Dick King Place Wilsonia, East London, South Africa
Tel.: (27) 43 745 2233
Web Site: http://www.astrapak.co.za
Sales Range: $50-74.9 Million
Emp.: 150
Plastic Packaging Products Mfr
N.A.I.C.S.: 322220

Subsidiary (Domestic):

Astrapak Manufacturing Holdings (Pty) Ltd (3)
5 Kruger Street, Johannesburg, 2094, Gauteng, South Africa

Berry Global Group, Inc—(Continued)

Tel.: (27) 116158011
Web Site: http://www.astrapak.co.za
Emp.: 20
Plastic Packaging Products Mfr
N.A.I.C.S.: 326199
Manley Eiedloff (Mng Dir)

Consupaq (Pty) Ltd (3)
40 Marseilles Crescent, Briardene Industrial Park, Durban, 4051, kwazulu-natal, South Africa (100%)
Tel.: (27) 315711050
Web Site: http://www.consupaq.co.za
Sales Range: $25-49.9 Million
Emp.: 150
Packaging & Labeling Services
N.A.I.C.S.: 561910
Robin Rigney (Mng Dir)

Diverse Labelling Consultants (Pty) Ltd (3)
29 Gillitz Road, Westmead, Durban, 4001, South Africa
Tel.: (27) 31 702 0521
Flexible Packaging Services
N.A.I.C.S.: 561910
Greg Petzer (Gen Mgr)

Hilfort Plastics (Pty) Ltd (3)
3 Electron Street, Stikland, Cape Town, 7530, South Africa
Tel.: (27) 21 941 5060
Web Site: http://www.hilfort.co.za
Sales Range: $125-149.9 Million
Emp.: 30
Plastic Container Mfr
N.A.I.C.S.: 326199
Ivana Ruzickova (Gen Mgr)

International Tube Technology (Pty) Ltd (3)
19 Jellicoe avenue Epping 1, Cape Town, 7460, South Africa
Tel.: (27) 215344779
Web Site: https://ittsa.co.za
Industrial Cores & Tubes Mfr & Distr
N.A.I.C.S.: 322219
Peter Jooste (Mng Dir)

Knilam Packaging (Pty) Ltd (3)
63 Bell Cresent, Westlake Business Park, 7945, Cape Town, South Africa (70%)
Tel.: (27) 217021822
Web Site: http://www.knilam.co.za
Sales Range: $25-49.9 Million
Emp.: 30
Packing & Crating
N.A.I.C.S.: 488991

Marcom Plastics (Pty) Ltd (3)
100 Pepler Street Rosslyn, Pretoria, 0200, South Africa (50%)
Tel.: (27) 125412784
Web Site: http://www.marcomplastics.co.za
Sales Range: $50-74.9 Million
Emp.: 110
Plastics Material & Resin Mfr
N.A.I.C.S.: 325211

PAK 2000 (Pty) Ltd (3)
20 Mahogany Road, Mahogany Ridge, Pinetown, 3610, kwazulu-natal, South Africa (100%)
Tel.: (27) 317009771
Web Site: http://www.astrapak.co.za
Packing & Crating
N.A.I.C.S.: 488991

Pack-Line Holdings (Pty) Ltd (3)
5 Belfast Road Gately, East London, South Africa (100%)
Tel.: (27) 437311696
Sales Range: $25-49.9 Million
Emp.: 80
Packing & Crating
N.A.I.C.S.: 488991

Plas-Top (Pty) Ltd (3)
197/1 Manganese Street, Ekandustria, Bronkhorstspruit, 1028, South Africa
Tel.: (27) 13 933 3205
Web Site: http://www.astrapak.co.za
Sales Range: $125-149.9 Million
Emp.: 400
Rigid Plastic Packaging Component Mfr
N.A.I.C.S.: 326199

Plastech Moulders (Pty) Ltd (3)
2 Osmond Street, East London, 5247, East-

ern Cape, South Africa
Tel.: (27) 437452207
Web Site: http://www.astrapak.co.za
Emp.: 15
Plastic Packaging Products Mfr
N.A.I.C.S.: 326199

Plastop KwaZulu-Natal (Pty) Ltd (3)
3 Mack Rd, Prospecton, Durban, 4001, kwazulu-natal, South Africa
Tel.: (27) 319121270
Web Site: http://www.astrapak.com
Plastics Product Mfr
N.A.I.C.S.: 326199

Saflite Packaging (Pty) Ltd (3)
Unit 17 River Park, 77 De Waal Road Diep River, Cape Town, 7800, South Africa (75%)
Tel.: (27) 217055882
Web Site: http://www.astrapak.co.za
Sales Range: $25-49.9 Million
Emp.: 13
Packing & Crating
N.A.I.C.S.: 488991

Thermopac (Pty) Ltd (3)
6th Avenue, Elsies River, Cape Town, 7490, South Africa (100%)
Tel.: (27) 215921100
Web Site: http://www.thermopac.co.za
Sales Range: $75-99.9 Million
Emp.: 400
Packaging & Labeling Services
N.A.I.C.S.: 561910

Subsidiary (Non-US):

RPC Bebo Food Packaging - Kristiansand (2)
Stadionveien 15, PO Box 1514, Lundsiden, 4688, Kristiansand, Norway
Tel.: (47) 38 14 40 20
Web Site: http://www.rpc-bebo.com
Plastic Food Packaging Mfr
N.A.I.C.S.: 326199

RPC Bebo Nederland BV (2)
Zilverwerf 14, PO Box 169, 6641 TD, Beuningen, Netherlands
Tel.: (31) 547281111
Web Site: http://www.rpc-bebo.nl
Sales Range: $25-49.9 Million
Emp.: 100
Unsupported Plastics Packaging Film & Sheet Mfr
N.A.I.C.S.: 326112

RPC Bebo Plastik GmbH (2)
Lloydstrasse 6, 27432, Bremervorde, Germany (100%)
Tel.: (49) 4761860132
Web Site: http://www.rpc-beboplastik.de
Sales Range: $250-299.9 Million
Emp.: 625
Plastics Materials & Basic Forms & Shapes Whslr
N.A.I.C.S.: 424610

RPC Bebo Polska Sp. z o.o. (2)
ul Ledochowskiej 33/55, 60-462, Poznan, Poland
Tel.: (48) 618496406
Web Site: http://www.rpc-bebo.com
Plastics Material & Resin Mfr
N.A.I.C.S.: 325211

RPC Bebo Print Patent GmbH (2)
Lloydstr 6, Bremervorde, 27432, Germany
Tel.: (49) 47618600
Web Site: http://www.rpc-group.com
Sales Range: $125-149.9 Million
Emp.: 30
Commercial Printing Services
N.A.I.C.S.: 323111

RPC Bramlage GmbH (2)
Brageler Strasse 70, 49393, Lohne, Germany (100%)
Tel.: (49) 4442 881 0
Web Site: http://www.rpc-bramlage.de
Sales Range: $200-249.9 Million
Emp.: 600
Plastics Product Mfr
N.A.I.C.S.: 326199

Subsidiary (Non-US):

LLC RPC Bramlage Yekaterinburg (3)
Federation al Bazovyi 21, Mailbox 171,

620089, Yekaterinburg, Russia (100%)
Tel.: (7) 3433510032
Web Site: http://www.rpc-group.com
Plastics Product Mfr
N.A.I.C.S.: 326199

Maynard & Harris Plastics (3)
London Road, Beccles, NR34 8TS, Suffolk, United Kingdom
Tel.: (44) 1502715518
Web Site: https://www.mhplastics.com
Sales Range: $50-74.9 Million
Emp.: 220
Rigid Plastic Packaging Container Mfr
N.A.I.C.S.: 326199

Subsidiary (US):

M&H Plastics Inc. (4)
485 Brooke Rd, Winchester, VA 22603-5764
Tel.: (540) 504-0030
Web Site: http://www.mhplastics.com
Rigid Plastic Packaging Products Mfr
N.A.I.C.S.: 326199
Steve Thigpen (CEO)

Subsidiary (Non-US):

RPC Beaute Marolles SAS (3)
ZI La Touche, 72260, Marolles-les-Braults, France
Tel.: (33) 243315610
Web Site: http://www.rpc-beaute.com
Sales Range: $50-74.9 Million
Emp.: 200
Plastics Product Mfr
N.A.I.C.S.: 326199
Jean Philippe Caspar (Mng Dir)

Branch (Non-US):

RPC Bramlage - Lainate (3)
Via Ramazzotti 12, 20020, Lainate, MI, Italy
Tel.: (39) 029370669
Web Site: http://www.rpc-group.com
Sales Range: $25-49.9 Million
Emp.: 32
Plastic Packaging Product Distr
N.A.I.C.S.: 424610

Subsidiary (Non-US):

RPC Bramlage Antwerpen NV (3)
Terbekehofdreef 29, 2610, Wilrijk, Belgium
Tel.: (32) 38704280
Web Site: http://www.rpc-bramlage-antwerpen.be
Sales Range: $25-49.9 Million
Emp.: 50
Plastics Product Mfr
N.A.I.C.S.: 326199
Chris Cooreman (Mng Dir)

Subsidiary (Domestic):

RPC Bramlage Food GmbH (3)
Bremer Weg 205, 29223, Celle, Germany
Tel.: (49) 51415920
Web Site: http://www.rpc-group.com
Sales Range: $75-99.9 Million
Emp.: 125
Regulation & Administration of Communications Electric Gas
N.A.I.C.S.: 926130

Subsidiary (Non-US):

RPC Bramlage Velky Meder S.r.o. (3)
Okocska 74, 932 01, Velky Meder, Slovakia
Tel.: (421) 315912300
Web Site: http://www.rpc-bramlage.sk
Real Estate Property Lessors
N.A.I.C.S.: 531190

RPC Bramlage Warszawa Sp. z.o.o. (3)
Batorego 6, 05-400, Otwock, Poland
Tel.: (48) 22 7199900
Web Site: http://www.rpc-bramlage.de
Sales Range: $50-74.9 Million
Emp.: 200
Industrial Plastic Container Packaging Mfr
N.A.I.C.S.: 326199

RPC Envases SA (3)
Poligono Industrial Borondo Avenida de la Industria 4, Campo Real, 28510, Madrid, Spain
Tel.: (34) 918714602

Web Site: http://www.rpc-bramlage.de
Unsupported Plastics Profile Shape Mfr
N.A.I.C.S.: 326121

Subsidiary (Domestic):

RPC Formatec GmbH (3)
Stockheimer Str 30, 97638, Mellrichstadt, Germany (100%)
Tel.: (49) 977660911
Web Site: http://www.rpc-formatec.de
Sales Range: $25-49.9 Million
Emp.: 9
Plastics Product Mfr
N.A.I.C.S.: 326199

RPC Wiko GmbH (3)
Donatusstrasse 102, 50259, Pulheim, Germany
Tel.: (49) 2234 9858 0
Web Site: http://www.rpc-bramlage.de
Sales Range: $125-149.9 Million
Emp.: 300
Plastics Product Mfr
N.A.I.C.S.: 326199

Subsidiary (US):

Wiko-USA Inc. (4)
1075 Hemlock Rd, Morgantown, PA 19543
Tel.: (610) 286-0805
Web Site: http://www.wiko-usa.com
Sales Range: $25-49.9 Million
Emp.: 50
Plastic Packaging Products Whslr
N.A.I.C.S.: 424610
Harald Hoika (Pres)
Mary Ann Kimes (Sec)

Subsidiary (Domestic):

RPC Containers Ltd. (2)
Haslingden Road Guide, Blackburn, BB1 2PX, Lancashire, United Kingdom
Tel.: (44) 1254682298
Web Site: http://www.rpc-group.com
Sales Range: $25-49.9 Million
Emp.: 290
Plastic Packaging Mfr
N.A.I.C.S.: 325211

Subsidiary (Non-US):

RPC Emballages Montpont SA (2)
Les Touppes, Montpont-en-Bresse Saone-et-Loire, Bourgogne, 71470, France (100%)
Tel.: (33) 385763395
Web Site: http://www.rpc-montpont.fr
Sales Range: $25-49.9 Million
Emp.: 37
Unsupported Plastics Film & Sheet Mfr
N.A.I.C.S.: 326113

RPC Neutraubling GmbH (2)
Pommernstrasse 12, 93073, Nuremberg, Germany
Tel.: (49) 94018870
Web Site: http://www.rpc-neutraubling.de
Sales Range: $25-49.9 Million
Emp.: 20
Unsupported Plastics Film & Sheet Mfr
N.A.I.C.S.: 326113

RPC Packaging Gent NV (2)
Singel 18-20 Havennr 0955 B, Gent, 9000, Belgium
Tel.: (32) 92500611
Web Site: http://www.rpc-gent.be
Sales Range: $50-74.9 Million
Emp.: 160
Plastics Product Mfr
N.A.I.C.S.: 326199

RPC Packaging Holdings BV (2)
Bergweidedijk 1, Deventer, 7418 AB, Netherlands
Tel.: (31) 570682351
Investment Management Service
N.A.I.C.S.: 523999

RPC Packaging Kerkrade BV (2)
Spekhofstraat 16, 6466 LZ, Kerkrade, 6466 LZ, Netherlands
Tel.: (31) 455436643
Web Site: http://www.rpc-kerkrade.nl
Sales Range: $25-49.9 Million
Emp.: 100
Plastics Material & Resin Mfr
N.A.I.C.S.: 325211

RPC Promens A/S (2)
Gl Donsvej 12, 6000, Kolding,
Denmark (100%)
Tel.: (45) 76322400
Web Site: http://www.rpc-promens.com
Sales Range: $25-49.9 Million
Emp.: 90
Plastic Product Whslr
N.A.I.C.S.: 424610

RPC Promens Bjaeverskov A/S (2)
Industrivej 3, 4632, Bjaeverskov, Denmark
Tel.: (45) 70266810
Web Site: http://www.rpc-promens.com
Sales Range: $25-49.9 Million
Emp.: 50
Plastic Product Whslr
N.A.I.C.S.: 424610

RPC Promens EKE NV (2)
Begoniastraat 44, B-9810, Eke,
Belgium (100%)
Tel.: (32) 9 250 06 54
Web Site: http://www.rpc-promens.com
Plastic Packaging Container Mfr
N.A.I.C.S.: 326199
Kristien Van der Borght (Coord-Sls)

RPC Promens Group AS (2)
Brevikveien 535, 1539, Moss,
Norway (100%)
Tel.: (47) 69279500
Web Site: http://www.rpc-promens.com
Sales Range: $50-74.9 Million
Emp.: 110
Plastic Packaging Product Distr
N.A.I.C.S.: 424610

RPC Superfos a/s (2)
Spotorno Alle 8, 2630, Taastrup, Hovedsta-
den, Denmark
Tel.: (45) 59111110
Web Site: http://www.superfos.com
Sales Range: $450-499.9 Million
Emp.: 20
Injection Molded Plastic Packaging Mfr
N.A.I.C.S.: 326199
Benny Nielsen (Dir-Tech)

Branch (Non-US):

RPC Superfos - Hamburg (3)
Hugh-Greene-Weg 2, 22529, Hamburg,
Germany
Tel.: (49) 408539010
Web Site: http://www.superfos.com
Sales Range: $25-49.9 Million
Emp.: 20
Plastic Container Mfr
N.A.I.C.S.: 326199
Soren Rohleder (Reg Dir-Central Reg)
Uwe Zinnert (Mgr-Sls & Mktg)
Karl-Heinz Dahl (Area Mgr-Sls-Food)
Matthias Scheller (Area Mgr-Sls-Non-Food)
Christian Luidl (Area Mgr-Sls-Non-Food)
Marco Diepens (Area Mgr-Sls-Food)
Jens Michaelis (Mgr-Sls-Food)
Michael Janke (Acct Mgr-Food)
Peter Marbach (Mgr-Sls-Spreads-Central)
Uwe Lutzke (Mgr-Sls-Food)

Subsidiary (Non-US):

RPC Superfos Besancon SAS (3)
11 rue La Fayette, CS 99401, 25071, Be-
sancon, Cedex 9, France (100%)
Tel.: (33) 381211700
Web Site: http://www.superfos.com
Sales Range: $25-49.9 Million
Emp.: 110
Plastic Container Mfr
N.A.I.C.S.: 326199
Jean Scandella (Dir-French & South East)
Laurent Morel (Dir-Sls-French & South
East)
Beno Boris Silec (Dir-Sls-Balkans)
Sebastien Morey (Mgr-Factory-French &
South East)
Stephane Navoret (Dir-Technical-French &
South East)
Clarisse Guerin (Mgr-Sls-French & South
East)
Christine Decayeux (Mgr-Sls-French &
South East)
Isabelle Rival (Mgr-Sls-French & South
East)
Nicolas Le Saux (Mgr-Sls-French & South
East)
Jean Verne (Mgr-Sls-French & South East)

RPC Superfos Lidkoping AB (3)
Skogvaktarevagen 2, 531 17, Lidkoping,
Sweden
Tel.: (46) 510310000
Web Site: http://www.promens.com
Sales Range: $25-49.9 Million
Emp.: 122
Plastic Packaging Mfr
N.A.I.C.S.: 326199
Johan Bratt (Mgr-Site)
Soren Marcussen (Reg Dir)
Roland Lingman (Dir-Sls & Mktg)
Stefan Rosenqvist (Mgr-Sls)

RPC Superfos Mullsjo AB (3)
Industrivagen 13, 565 91, Mullsjo, Sweden
Tel.: (46) 392 61 61 00
Web Site: http://www.superfos.com
Sales Range: $25-49.9 Million
Emp.: 180
Plastic Packaging Mfr
N.A.I.C.S.: 326199
Per Sollenby (Sls Dir-Nordic Food)
Johan Rosell (Mgr-Site)

Subsidiary (Domestic):

RPC Superfos Stilling A/S (3)
Industrivej 12, Stilling, 8660, Skanderborg,
Mid Jutland, Denmark (100%)
Tel.: (45) 87935300
Web Site: http://www.rpc-superfos.com
Sales Range: $25-49.9 Million
Emp.: 100
Plastic Container Mfr
N.A.I.C.S.: 326199
Lars Smidt (Mgr-Factory)

Subsidiary (Non-US):

RPC Superfos Wetteren NV (3)
Biezeweg 19, 9230, Wetteren, Belgium
Tel.: (32) 92523101
Web Site: http://www.superfos.com
Sales Range: $25-49.9 Million
Emp.: 80
Plastic Container Mfr
N.A.I.C.S.: 326199
Flemming Madsen (Mgr-Factory-Central)
Soren Rohleder (Reg Dir-Central Reg)

Subsidiary (Domestic):

RPC Tedeco-Gizeh (UK) Limited (2)
Kenfig Ind Estate Water Street, Margam,
Port Talbot, SA13 2PG, West Glamorgan,
United Kingdom
Tel.: (44) 1656749183
Web Site: http://www.rpc-tedeco-gizeh.com
Sales Range: $25-49.9 Million
Emp.: 75
Plastics Product Mfr
N.A.I.C.S.: 326199

Subsidiary (Non-US):

RPC Tedeco-Gizeh GmbH (2)
Robert-Bosch-Str 16, 77656, Offenburg,
Germany
Tel.: (49) 7816040
Web Site: http://www.rpc-tedeco-gizeh.com
Sales Range: $25-49.9 Million
Emp.: 30
Industrial & Personal Service Paper Whslr
N.A.I.C.S.: 424130

RPC Tedeco-Gizeh Kft (2)
Ipartelep 1771, Kajarpec, 9123, Gyor, Hun-
gary
Tel.: (36) 96378286
Web Site: http://www.rpc-tedeco-gizeh.com
Sales Range: $25-49.9 Million
Emp.: 32
Plastics Product Mfr
N.A.I.C.S.: 326199

RPC Tedeco-Gizeh SAS (2)
Zone Industrielle, 67330, Bouxwiller, France
Tel.: (33) 388717800
Web Site: http://www.rpc-tedeco-gizeh.com
Sales Range: $50-74.9 Million
Emp.: 200
Plastics Product Mfr
N.A.I.C.S.: 326199

**RPC Tedeco-Gizeh Troyes
SASU** (2)
199 Avenue Pierre Brossolette, BP 2,
10001, Troyes, France
Tel.: (33) 325713535

Plastic Packaging Materials Mfr
N.A.I.C.S.: 326112

**RPC Verpackungen Kutenholz
GmbH** (2)
Industriestrasse 3, Kutenholz, 27449,
Stade, Germany
Tel.: (49) 4762890
Web Site: http://www.rpc-kutenholz.de
Sales Range: $50-74.9 Million
Emp.: 190
Unsupported Plastics Profile Shape Mfr
N.A.I.C.S.: 326121
Andreas Klein (Mng Dir)

Saeplast Iceland ehf (2)
Gunnarsbraut 12, 620, Dalvik,
Iceland (100%)
Tel.: (354) 4605000
Web Site: http://europe.saeplast.com
Sales Range: $50-74.9 Million
Emp.: 250
Plastic Molded Tubs Mfr
N.A.I.C.S.: 326199
Holmar Svansson (Mng Dir)

Subsidiary (Non-US):

Saeplast Americas Inc. (3)
100 Industrial Drive, Saint John, E2R 1A5,
NB, Canada (100%)
Tel.: (506) 633-0101
Web Site: http://americas.saeplast.com
Sales Range: $25-49.9 Million
Plastics Product Mfr
N.A.I.C.S.: 326199
Mike Kilpatrick (Mgr-Bus Dev)
Brian Gooding (Mng Dir)
Loriann Dickeson (Coord-Sls-East)
Chris French (Sls Dir-North America)

Saeplast Norway AS (3)
Tverrvegen 37, 6020, Alesund,
Norway (100%)
Tel.: (47) 71401900
Web Site: http://europe.saeplast.com
Plastic Product Distr
N.A.I.C.S.: 424610

Saeplast Spain SAU (3)
Poligono Industrial 15, 36880, La Caniza,
Spain (100%)
Tel.: (34) 986 663 091
Web Site: http://europe.saeplast.com
Sales Range: $25-49.9 Million
Emp.: 28
Plastic Container Mfr
N.A.I.C.S.: 326199
Holmar Svansson (Mng Dir-Europe)

Subsidiary (Non-US):

Seaplast (India) Private Limited (2)
B 212 Ratnaakar Nine Square Opp Kes-
havbaug Party Plot Mansi Road, Prahladna-
gar Road, Ahmedabad, 380 015, Gujarat,
India
Tel.: (91) 7940073880
Web Site: https://seaplastindia.com
Emp.: 15
Plastics Product Mfr
N.A.I.C.S.: 326199

Tempra ehf. (2)
Ishella 8, 221, Hafnarfjordur,
Iceland (100%)
Tel.: (354) 520 5400
Web Site: http://www.tempra.is
Sales Range: $25-49.9 Million
Emp.: 15
Extruded Polystyrene Housing Insulation &
Food Packaging Products Mfr
N.A.I.C.S.: 326199
Steinunn Gudmundsdottir (CFO)

RPC Kolding A/S (1)
Gl Donsvej 12, 6000, Kolding, Denmark
Tel.: (45) 76322400
Web Site: http://www.rpc-kolding.com
Plastic Packaging Products Mfr
N.A.I.C.S.: 326199

**RPC Promens Industrial Jagtenberg
B.V** (1)
Hogewaard 12, Heerewaarden, 6624 KP,
Maasdriel, Netherlands
Tel.: (31) 418662289
Web Site: http://www.rpc-promens.com
Plastic Packaging Products Mfr
N.A.I.C.S.: 326199

Coen Pullens (Mgr-Supply Chain)

RPC Superfos Balkan d.o.o. (1)
Branilaca grada bb, 75320, Gracanica, Bos-
nia & Herzegovina
Tel.: (387) 35701111
Plastic Packaging Product Distr
N.A.I.C.S.: 424610
Mejra Husakovic (Sls Mgr-Bosnia)

RPC Superfos Italy S.R.L. (1)
Via S Carlo 10 Int 20/22, 40023, Castel
Guelfo di Bologna, BO, Italy
Tel.: (39) 0542670480
Plastic Packaging Product Distr
N.A.I.C.S.: 424610
Antonio Fallanca (Acct Mgr & Sls Mgr-Italy)
Laurent Morel (Sls Dir-Italy)

RPC Superfos La Genete SAS (1)
1B Route Departementale 975 CS 30011,
La Genete, 71290, Bourgogne, France
Tel.: (33) 385322755
Plastic Packaging Product Distr
N.A.I.C.S.: 424610
Jean Scandella (Reg Dir-La Genete)
Sebastien Morey (Mgr-Factory-La Genete)
Laurent Morel (Sls Dir-France)
Stephane Navoret (Dir-Reg Technical)
Clarisse Guerin (Sls Mgr-France)

RPC Superfos Pamplona SA (1)
Poligono Industrial Comarca n1 Calle L 14-
16, Orcoyen, 31160, Pamplona, Navarra,
Spain
Tel.: (34) 948368054
Plastic Packaging Product Distr
N.A.I.C.S.: 424610
Patxi Buldain (Reg Dir-Pamplona)
Ignacio Igea (Reg Dir-Sls)
Mikel Iragui (Sls Mgr-Spain)
Daniel Barrero (Sls Mgr-Spain)
Antonio Alcaide (Sls Mgr-Spain)

RPC Superfos Poland Sp. z o.o. (1)
Kaliska 140, Lubien Kujawski, 87-840, Wlo-
clawek, Poland
Tel.: (48) 544291000
Plastic Packaging Product Distr
N.A.I.C.S.: 424610
Tomasz Przygodzki (Mgr-Factory-Poland)
Zbigniew Hryniewicz (Sls Dir-Poland)
Wieslawa Lusztak (Sls Mgr-Poland)

RPC Superfos Pori Oy (1)
Valtakatu 6, 28100, Pori, Finland
Tel.: (358) 26307500
Plastic Packaging Product Distr
N.A.I.C.S.: 424610
Rauno Eskelinen (Sls Dir-Finland)

RPC Superfos US Inc. (1)
411 Brooke Rd, Winchester, VA 22603
Tel.: (540) 504-7176
Plastic Packaging Products Mfr
N.A.I.C.S.: 326199
Sam DeBarr (Mgr-Plant & Ops)

**RPC Zeller Plastik Libertyville
Inc.** (1)
1515 Franklin Blvd, Libertyville, IL 60048-
4459
Tel.: (847) 247-7900
Plastic Packaging Products Mfr
N.A.I.C.S.: 326199

SPA Galion Algerie (1)
Section 06 Property block No 284, Hamadi,
Boumerdes, 35000, Algeria
Tel.: (213) 770991982
Plastic Packaging Product Distr
N.A.I.C.S.: 424610
Bouzid Issam (Gen Mgr)

Stopaq B.V. (1)
Gasselterstraat 20, PO Box 285, Stadska-
naal, 9503 JB, Groningen, Netherlands
Tel.: (31) 599696170
Web Site: http://www.stopaq.com
Plastics Product Mfr
N.A.I.C.S.:

Synergy Packaging Pty. Limited (1)
10 International Square, Tullamarine, 3043,
VIC, Australia
Tel.: (61) 393382626
Web Site: http://www.synergypack.com.au
Plastic Packaging Product Mfr & Distr
N.A.I.C.S.: 326199

**Terram Geosynthetics Private
Limited** (1)

Berry Global Group, Inc—(Continued)

A 704 Safal Pegasus, Anandnagar Road,
Ahmedabad, 380 015, Gujarat, India
Tel.: (91) 7940064529
Web Site:
http://www.terramgeosynthetics.com
Construction Related Services
N.A.I.C.S.: 237990

Tubex Limited (1)
12-14 Aberaman Park, Aberdare, CF44
6DA, United Kingdom
Tel.: (44) 1621874201
Chemical Products Mfr
N.A.I.C.S.: 325998

UK Polyfilm Limited (1)
7 Brunel Close, Drayton Fields Industrial
Estate, Daventry, NN11 8RB, Northampton-
shire, United Kingdom
Tel.: (44) 1327876071
Polyethylene Film Product Mfr & Distr
N.A.I.C.S.: 326113

UK Polythene Limited (1)
31c Avenue One Station Lane, Witney,
OX28 4XZ, Oxfordshire, United Kingdom
Tel.: (44) 8456431601
Web Site: http://www.polytheneuk.co.uk
Polyethylene Film Product Mfr & Distr
N.A.I.C.S.: 326113
James Woollard (Mng Dir)

Zeller Engineering GmbH (1)
Hallenbergstrasse 23, 78166, Donaueschin-
gen, Germany
Tel.: (49) 7705919111
Web Site: http://www.zellerengineering.de
Industrial Machinery Mfr
N.A.I.C.S.: 333248

Zeller Plastik Shanghai Limited (1)
No 89 Lane 1985 Chun Shen Road, Min-
hang District, Shanghai, 200237, China
Tel.: (86) 2154296938
Plastic Packaging Product Distr
N.A.I.C.S.: 424610

iTUB AS (1)
Tverrveien 37, 6020, Alesund, Norway
Tel.: (47) 71401900
Web Site: http://www.itub-rental.com
Plastic Tub Rental Services
N.A.I.C.S.: 532490
Christian Caspersen (Sls Mgr)

iTUB Danmark ApS (1)
Auktionsgade 2, 6700, Esbjerg, Denmark
Tel.: (45) 76131358
Plastic Tub Rental Services
N.A.I.C.S.: 532490

BESPOKE EXTRACTS, INC.
12001 E 33rd Ave Unit O, Aurora, CO
80010   NV
Web Site:
https://www.bespokeextracts.com
BSPK—(OTCQB)
Rev.: $3,407
Assets: $409,591
Liabilities: $1,081,687
Net Worth: ($672,096)
Earnings: ($4,116,227)
Emp.: 5
Fiscal Year-end: 12/31/22
Miscellaneous Financial Investment
Activities
N.A.I.C.S.: 523999
Hunter Garth (Chief Strategy Officer)
Michael Feinsod (Chm & CEO)
Hunter Garth (Chief Strategy Officer
& Chief Strategy Officer)

BEST BUY CO., INC.
7601 Penn Ave S, Richfield, MN
55423
Tel.: (612) 291-1000   MN
Web Site: https://www.bestbuy.com
Year Founded: 1966
BBY—(NYSE)
Rev.: $43,452,000,000
Assets: $14,967,000,000
Liabilities: $11,914,000,000
Net Worth: $3,053,000,000
Earnings: $1,241,000,000

Emp.: 85,000
Fiscal Year-end: 02/03/24
Electronics Appliance Mfr
N.A.I.C.S.: 449210
Matthew Furman (Chief Comm & Pub
Affairs Officer)
Mathew R. Watson (Chief Acctg Offi-
cer, Sr VP & Controller)
Damien Harmon (Sr Exec VP-
Customer, Channel Experiences, and
Enterprise Svcs)
Brian Tilzer (CTO & Chief Digital Offi-
cer)
Corie Sue Barry (CEO)
Ron Wilson (Pres-Intl)
Rob Bass (Chief Supply Chain &
Global Properties Officer)
Melanie Cornell (Chief Learning Offi-
cer)
Keri Grafing (Chief Compliance Offi-
cer)
Damien Harmon (Sr Exec VP-
Customer, Channel Experiences, and
Enterprise Svcs)
Howard Rankin (Chief Employee Rels
Officer)
Mark A. Irvin (Chief Supply Chain Of-
ficer & Exec VP)

Subsidiaries:

BBC Insurance Agency, Inc. (1)
1831 S Main St, Jacksonville, IL 62650
Tel.: (217) 243-1616
Web Site: http://www.bbcinsurance.com
Emp.: 2
Insurance & Financial Services
N.A.I.C.S.: 524210
Rose Drake (Co-Founder & Owner)

Best Buy Canada Ltd. (1)
8800 Glenlyon Parkway, Burnaby, V5J 5K3,
BC, Canada (100%)
Tel.: (604) 435-8223
Web Site: http://www.bestbuy.ca
Sales Range: $150-199.9 Million
Emp.: 1,500
Retailer of Consumer Goods
N.A.I.C.S.: 423620
Ron Wilson (Pres-Intl)
Thierry Hay-Sabourin (Sr VP-eCommerce,
Marketplace & Tech)
Mat Povse (Sr VP-Retail & Geek Squad
Svcs)
Angela Scardillo (Sr VP-Mktg & Store De-
sign)
Chris Taylor (Chief HR Officer)
Jason Abrams (Sr VP-Mdsg)
Polly Tracey (VP-Comm)
Bryan Kooistra (CFO)

Division (Domestic):

Future Shop Ltd. (2)
8800 Glenlyon Parkway, Burnaby, V5J 5K3,
BC, Canada (100%)
Tel.: (604) 435-8223
Web Site: http://www.futureshop.ca
Sales Range: $700-749.9 Million
Emp.: 7,100
Computer & Electronic Products
N.A.I.C.S.: 423620

**Best Buy Enterprises, S. de R.L. de
C.V.** (1)
Avenida Santa Fe No 440 Floor 2 Office
202 & 203, Colonia Santa Fe Cuajimalpa,
05348, Mexico, Mexico
Tel.: (52) 5552378289
Web Site: http://www.bestbuy.com.mx
Home Office Products, Electronic Equip-
ment & Appliances Retailer
N.A.I.C.S.: 449210

Best Buy Stores L.P. (1)
7601 Penn Ave S, Richfield, MN
55423 (100%)
Tel.: (612) 291-1000
Web Site: http://www.bestbuy.com
Sales Range: $1-4.9 Billion
Emp.: 6,000
Electronics Retailer
N.A.I.C.S.: 449210

Subsidiary (Domestic):

BestBuy.com, LLC (2)

1541 Carl D Silver Pkwy, Fredericksburg,
VA 22401
Tel.: (540) 785-2200
Web Site: http://www.bestbuy.com
Electronic Appliance Distr
N.A.I.C.S.: 423620

Magnolia Hi-Fi, LLC (2)
330 NE Northgate Way, Seattle, WA 98125
Tel.: (206) 306-7663
Emp.: 100
Audio Equipment Retailer
N.A.I.C.S.: 449210
Darrell Harris (Branch Mgr)

**Best Buy Stores, S. de R.L. de
C.V.** (1)
Avenida Santa Fe No 440 Floor 2 Office
202 and 203, Colonia Santa Fe Cuajimalpa
Delegation Cuajimalpa, Mexico, Mexico
Tel.: (52) 5552378289
Web Site: http://www.bestbuy.com.mx
Audio Equipment Retailer
N.A.I.C.S.: 449210

Greatcall, Inc. (1)
2200 Faraday Ave Ste 100, Carlsbad, CA
92008
Tel.: (858) 720-7500
Web Site: https://www.lively.com
Wireless Telecommunications Carriers
N.A.I.C.S.: 517112
Brian Berning (CFO)
David Inns (CEO)
Lynn Herrick (Chief Legal Officer & Chief
HR Officer)
Bill Yates (CMO)

Magnolia Audio Video (1)
6305 S 231st St, Kent, WA
98032-1872 (100%)
Tel.: (253) 372-4434
Web Site: http://www.magnoliaav.com
Sales Range: $50-74.9 Million
Emp.: 250
Retail Stereophonic Video Equipment; Car
Stereos & Computers
N.A.I.C.S.: 449210

**Ningbo Xingpu Five Star Appliance
Co., Ltd** (1)
No 146 Yaoxing Street, Haishu District,
Ningbo, China
Tel.: (86) 57483891388
Electronic Appliance Distr
N.A.I.C.S.: 423620

**Pacific Sales Kitchen and Bath Cen-
ters, LLC** (1)
24120 Garnier St, Torrance, CA 90505
Tel.: (310) 784-6100
Home Building & Remodeling Services
N.A.I.C.S.: 236118

Redline Entertainment, Inc. (1)
30 Music Sq W, Nashville, TN 37203-3267
Tel.: (615) 340-0056
Web Site:
http://www.redlineentertaininc.com
Electronic Equipment Store
N.A.I.C.S.: 449210
Wes Mayers (Founder & Pres)

**BETTER CHOICE COMPANY,
INC.**
12400 Race Track Rd, Tampa, FL
33626
Tel.: (212) 896-1254   DE
Web Site:
https://www.betterchoicecompa
ny.com
Year Founded: 2001
BTTR—(NYSEAMEX)
Rev.: $54,660,000
Assets: $38,676,000
Liabilities: $17,148,000
Net Worth: $21,528,000
Earnings: ($39,316,000)
Emp.: 46
Fiscal Year-end: 12/31/22
Nutritional & Dietary Supplement
Sales
N.A.I.C.S.: 424210
Michael Young (Chm)
Ryan Wilson (VP-Mktg)

Jennifer Condon (Exec VP-Digital
Sls)
Carolina Martinez (CFO, Treas &
Sec)
Kent Cunningham (CEO)

Subsidiaries:

Bona Vida, Inc. (1)
442 Broadway 2nd Fl, New York, NY 10013
Web Site: https://www.bonavida.com
Natural Ingredient Product Mfr
N.A.I.C.S.: 325199

Halo, Purely for Pets, Inc. (1)
12400 Race Track Rd, Tampa, FL 33626
Web Site: https://www.halopets.com
Pet Food Mfr
N.A.I.C.S.: 311111

TruPet LLC (1)
164 Douglas Rd E, Oldsmar, FL 34677
Web Site: http://www.trudog.com
Pet Food Distr
N.A.I.C.S.: 459910
Lori R. Taylor (Founder)

**BETTER ENVIRONMENT CON-
CEPTS, INC.**
910 8th Ave Ste 1118, Seattle, WA
98104
Tel.: (206) 214-6038
Web Site:
http://www.betterenvironmentcon
cepts.com
BEEN—(OTCIQ)
Waste Treatment Services
N.A.I.C.S.: 237110
Cloyce Brent Riddle (CEO)

**BETTER FOR YOU WELL-
NESS, INC.**
1349 E Broad St, Columbus, OH
43205
Tel.: (614) 368-9898   NV
Web Site: https://www.bfyw.com
Year Founded: 2020
BFYW—(OTCIQ)
Rev.: $10,321
Assets: $221,266
Liabilities: $2,215,313
Net Worth: ($1,994,047)
Earnings: ($2,453,934)
Emp.: 4
Fiscal Year-end: 02/28/24
Personal Care Product Mfr & Distr
N.A.I.C.S.: 325620
Ian James (Chm & CEO)
Pratibha Chaurasia (CFO)
Stephen Letourneau (COO & Chief
Branding Officer)
Jacob Ellman (Chief Bus Dev Officer)
Mark Jared Hamlin (Principal Acctg
Officer)

Subsidiaries:

Sauer Energy, Inc. (1)
1620 Emerson Ave, Oxnard, CA 93033
Web Site: http://www.sauerenergy.com
Wind Turbine Development & Marketing
N.A.I.C.S.: 221115
Dan Woods (CTO)
Ana Rosa (Exec Ops Officer)
Dieter R. Sauer Jr. (Pres & CEO)

Subsidiary (Domestic):

Helix Wind, Corp. (2)
13125 Danielson St Ste 101, Poway, CA
92064
Tel.: (619) 501-3932
Web Site: http://www.helixwind.com
Sales Range: Less than $1 Million
Emp.: 3
Wind Turbine Mfr
N.A.I.C.S.: 333611

**BETTER HOME & FINANCE
HOLDING COMPANY**
3 World Trade Center 175 Greenwich
St 57th Fl, New York, NY 10007
Tel.: (415) 523-8837   DE
Web Site: https://www.better.com

BETR—(NASDAQ)
Rev.: $4,262,222
Assets: $282,703,802
Liabilities: $262,125,384
Net Worth: $20,578,418
Earnings: $8,735,542
Emp.: 3
Fiscal Year-end: 12/31/22
Financial Investment Services
N.A.I.C.S.: 523999
Vishal Garg *(Dir)*
Chad Smith *(Pres & COO)*
Vishal Garg *(CEO)*
Kevin Ryan *(CFO)*

Subsidiaries:

Better Mortgage Corporation. **(1)**
2529 Norwood Ave, Bellmore, NY 11710-1747
Web Site:
http://www.iwantabettermortgage.com
Real Estate Credit
N.A.I.C.S.: 522292
Vishal Garg *(Founder & CEO)*
Chad Smith *(Pres & COO)*
Vishal Garg *(Founder & CEO)*
Denise Creichton *(VP)*
Jeff Corbett *(Dir-Bus Dev)*
Sean Hundtofte *(Head-Credit Risk)*
Sushil Sharma *(Chief Growth Officer)*
Steve Riddell *(Head-Sls)*
Ryan Jewison *(Head-Cover)*
Nick Taylor *(Head-Real Estate)*
Josh Durodola *(Head-Svcs)*
Brian Ro *(VP-People)*
Jennifer Malin *(VP-Enterprise Risk)*
Nitin Bhutani *(VP-Mktg)*

BETTER THERAPEUTICS, INC.
548 Market St Ste 49404, San Francisco, CA 94101
Tel.: (415) 887-2311   DE
Web Site: https://www.bettertx.com
Year Founded: 2020
BTTX—(NASDAQ)
Holding Company; Health Condition Therapeutical Products Developer
N.A.I.C.S.: 551112
David P. Perry *(Chm)*
Frank Karbe *(Pres & CEO)*
Mark Berman *(Chief Medical Officer)*
Kristin Wynholds *(Chief Product Officer)*
Mark Heinen *(Head-Finance)*

BETTWORK INDUSTRIES, INC.
704 N 39th St Ste 130, Fort Pierce, FL 34947
Web Site: https://www.betw-ind.com
BETW—(OTCIQ)
Telecommunication Support Services
N.A.I.C.S.: 517112
Ashvin Mascarenhas *(Pres)*

BEXIL CORPORATION
Tel.: (212) 785-0900   MD
Web Site: https://www.bexil.com
BXLC—(OTCIQ)
Rev.: $1,595,839
Assets: $23,010,594
Liabilities: $294,686
Net Worth: $22,715,908
Earnings: $968,428
Emp.: 11
Fiscal Year-end: 12/31/20
Holding Company
N.A.I.C.S.: 551112
Thomas O'Malley *(CFO, Chief Acctg Officer & Treas)*
Heidi Keating *(VP)*
Anne M. Chi *(Coord-Acctg)*
Russell Kamerman *(Chief Compliance Officer, Gen Counsel & Sec)*
Donald Klimoski II *(Asst Sec & Asst Gen Counsel)*

BEYOND AIR, INC.

900 Stewart Ave Ste 301, Garden City, NY 11530
Tel.: (516) 665-8200   DE
Web Site: https://www.beyondair.net
Year Founded: 2015
XAIR—(NASDAQ)
Rev.: $1,159,000
Assets: $56,961,000
Liabilities: $29,775,000
Net Worth: $27,186,000
Earnings: ($64,295,000)
Emp.: 107
Fiscal Year-end: 03/31/24
Biopharmaceutical Research Services
N.A.I.C.S.: 325412
Steven A. Lisi *(Chm & CEO)*
Amir Avniel *(Co-Founder, Pres & Chief Bus Officer)*
Frederick Montgomery *(VP-Medical Sys)*
Duncan Fatkin *(Chief Comml Officer)*
Michael Gaul *(COO)*
Maria Yonkoski *(Head-IR)*
Jedidiah Monson *(Chief Medical Officer-Beyond Cancer)*
Susan Howell Jones *(CFO-Beyond Cancer)*
Jeff Myers *(Chief Medical Officer)*
Edward Barger *(Head-IR)*
Kori-Ann Taylor *(Head-Mktg)*
Andrew Colin *(Sr Dir-Medical-Global Clinical Leadership)*
Douglas Larson *(CFO & Principal Acctg Officer)*

BEYOND COMMERCE, INC.
3773 Howard Hughes Pkwy, Las Vegas, NV 89169
Tel.: (702) 675-8022   NV
Web Site:
https://www.beyondcommerce
inc.com
BYOC—(OTCIQ)
Rev.: $4,046,071
Assets: $4,664,586
Liabilities: $10,075,218
Net Worth: ($5,410,632)
Earnings: ($2,398,607)
Emp.: 21
Fiscal Year-end: 12/31/22
E-commerce & Social Networking Services
N.A.I.C.S.: 541890
Geordan G. Pursglove *(Chm, Pres, CEO, Treas & Sec)*
Peter M. Stazzone *(CFO)*
Remo Weber *(COO)*

Subsidiaries:

Issues & Answers Network, Inc. **(1)**
5151 Bonney Rd Ste 100, Virginia Beach, VA 23462
Tel.: (757) 456-1100
Web Site: http://www.issans.net
Market Research Services
N.A.I.C.S.: 541910
Peter McGuinness *(Pres)*

BEYOND MEAT, INC.
888 N Douglas St Ste 100, El Segundo, CA 90245   DE
Web Site:
https://www.beyondmeat.com
Year Founded: 2011
BYND—(NASDAQ)
Rev.: $418,933,000
Assets: $1,062,224,000
Liabilities: $1,265,772,000
Net Worth: ($203,548,000)
Earnings: ($366,137,000)
Emp.: 787
Fiscal Year-end: 12/31/22
Poultry Processing
N.A.I.C.S.: 311615
Teri L. Witteman *(Chief Legal Officer, Gen Counsel & Sec)*
Ethan Brown *(Founder, Pres & CEO)*

Dariush Ajami *(Chief Innovation Officer)*
Beth Moskowitz *(Chief Creative Officer)*
Gary A. Schultz *(VP & Controller)*
Lubi Kutua *(CFO & Treas)*

BEYOND, INC.,
799 W Coliseum Way, Midvale, UT 84047
Tel.: (801) 947-3100   DE
Web Site: https://beyond.com
Year Founded: 1999
BYON—(NYSE)
Rev.: $1,561,122,000
Assets: $635,818,000
Liabilities: $276,686,000
Net Worth: $359,132,000
Earnings: ($307,842,000)
Emp.: 830
Fiscal Year-end: 12/31/23
Surplus & Close-Out Merchandise Wholesaler
N.A.I.C.S.: 423220
Marcus A. Lemonis *(Exec Chm)*
Adrianne B. Lee *(CFO, Chief Admin Officer & Principal Acctg Officer)*
E. Glen Nickle *(Chief Legal Officer & Sec)*
Carlisha Robinson *(Chief Product Officer)*
Guncha Mehta *(CIO-Chief Digital)*
Jennifer Evans *(CMO-Brand & Creative)*
David J. Nielsen *(Pres & CEO)*

Subsidiaries:

Blue Ocean Technologies, LLC **(1)**
215 Park Ave S 11th Fl, New York, NY 10003
Tel.: (917) 338-1195
Web Site: https://www.blueoceantech.us
Web Development Services
N.A.I.C.S.: 541511

Cirrus Services LLC **(1)**
3929 20th St N, Fargo, ND 58104
Tel.: (701) 793-2444
Web Site: https://learntoflyfar.com
Industrial Machinery Whslr
N.A.I.C.S.: 423830

Overstock.com Real Estate LLC **(1)**
6350 S 3000 E, Salt Lake City, UT 84121-5952
Tel.: (801) 947-3100
Web Site: http://www.overstock.com
Property Management Services
N.A.I.C.S.: 531390

Pro Securities, LLC **(1)**
29 Broadway, New York, NY 10006
Tel.: (917) 359-9168
Securities Brokerage Services
N.A.I.C.S.: 523150

T0.com, Inc. **(1)**
799 W Coliseum Way, Midvale, UT 84047-4867
Tel.: (855) 773-3310
Web Site: http://www.tzero.com
Programming Services
N.A.I.C.S.: 522291
Patrick Byrne *(Chm)*

tZERO ATS, LLC **(1)**
1 World Trade Center 285 Fulton St 58th Fl, New York, NY 10007
Web Site: http://www.ats.tzero.com
Financial Investment Services
N.A.I.C.S.: 523999
Alex Vlastakis *(Pres)*
Brian Capuano *(COO & Chief Compliance Officer)*
Joel Quall *(CFO)*

BEYONDSPRING INC.
100 Campus Dr, Florham Park, NJ 07932
Tel.: (646) 305-6387   DE
Web Site:
https://www.beyondspringphar
ma.com

Year Founded: 2010
BYSI—(NASDAQ)
Rev.: $1,351,000
Assets: $46,222,000
Liabilities: $60,303,000
Net Worth: ($14,081,000)
Earnings: ($33,279,000)
Emp.: 67
Fiscal Year-end: 12/31/22
Biopharmaceutical Product Research & Development Services
N.A.I.C.S.: 541715
Lan Huang *(CEO, Founder & Chm)*
Ramon W. Mohanlal *(Chief Medical Officer & Exec VP-Research & Development)*
Gordon L. Schooley *(Chief Regulatory Officer)*

Subsidiaries:

SEED Technology Limited **(1)**
Ballymountain, Waterford, X91 V6YR, Ireland
Tel.: (353) 51832814
Web Site: https://www.seedtech.ie
Seed Whslr
N.A.I.C.S.: 424510
Tim O. Donovan *(Dir-Technical)*
Daniel Norris *(Production Mgr)*
Tony Byrne *(Mgr-Logistics)*

BG MEDICINE, INC.
303 Wyman St Ste 300, Waltham, MA 02451
Tel.: (781) 890-1199   DE
Web Site: http://www.bg-medicine.com
Year Founded: 2000
BGMD—(OTCIQ)
Sales Range: $1-9.9 Million
Emp.: 5
Biopharmaceutical Developer, Mfr & Marketer
N.A.I.C.S.: 325412
Stephen P. Hall *(CFO & Exec VP)*
Paul R. Sohmer *(Pres & CEO)*
Aram Adourian *(Chief Scientific Officer)*
Harry W. Wilcox III *(Chm)*

BGC GROUP, INC.
499 Park Ave, New York, NY 10022
Tel.: (646) 346-7000   DE
Web Site: https://www.bgcg.com
Year Founded: 1999
BGC—(NASDAQ)
Rev.: $1,795,302,000
Assets: $3,074,971,000
Liabilities: $2,341,763,000
Net Worth: $733,208,000
Earnings: $48,712,000
Emp.: 3,818
Fiscal Year-end: 12/31/22
Financial Trading Execution, Brokerage, Clearing & Processing Services
N.A.I.C.S.: 523150
Shaun D. Lynn *(Vice Chm)*
Daniel M. Lavecchia *(Exec Mng Dir-North America & Head-FX Products-Global)*
Jean-Pierre Aubin *(Co-Head-Global Brokerage)*
Lori Pennay *(Sr Mng Dir & Head-HR & Partnership-Global)*
Karen Laureano-Rikardsen *(CMO)*
Steven Sadoff *(CIO)*
Jason W. Hauf *(CFO)*
John Abularrage *(Co-Head)*
Howard W. Lutnick *(Chm & CEO)*
Jason Chryssicas *(Head-IR)*

Subsidiaries:

APARTMENT REALTY ADVISORS OF ARIZONA, LLLP **(1)**
2555 E Camelback Rd Ste 600, Phoenix, AZ 85016
Tel.: (602) 952-3800

BGC Group, Inc.—(Continued)

Real Estate Services
N.A.I.C.S.: 531210

APARTMENT REALTY ADVISORS OF FLORIDA, INC. (1)
750 Park Of Commerce Blvd Ste 230, Boca Raton, FL 33487
Tel.: (561) 988-8800
Real Estate Services
N.A.I.C.S.: 531210

ARA NATIONAL LAND SERVICES, LLC (1)
8405 Greensboro Dr Ste 200, McLean, VA 22102
Tel.: (214) 415-0756
Emp.: 6
Real Estate Services
N.A.I.C.S.: 531210
John Giebel (Principal)

Aqua Securities, L.P. (1)
199 Water St, New York, NY 10038 (49%)
Tel.: (212) 821-1100
Web Site: https://www.aquaequities.com
Emp.: 20
Securities Trading Services
N.A.I.C.S.: 523150
Kevin Foley (Founder, Pres & CEO)

BGC Capital Markets & Foreign Exchange Broker (Korea) Ltd. (1)
10/F Seoul Finance Centre 84 Taepyungro 1-ka 136 Sejongtaero Chung-ku, Seoul, 04-520, Korea (South)
Tel.: (82) 220218300
Web Site: http://www.bgcpartners.com
Sales Range: $50-74.9 Million
Emp.: 24
Foreign Exchange Brokerage & Financial Services
N.A.I.C.S.: 523160

BGC Capital Markets (Hong Kong) Ltd. (1)
Suite 6402-08 64/F Two International Finance Centre, 8 Finance Street, Central, China (Hong Kong)
Tel.: (852) 34777888
Web Site: http://www.bgcpartners.com
Sales Range: $125-149.9 Million
Emp.: 110
Monetary & Foreign Exchange Trading & Brokerage Services
N.A.I.C.S.: 425120

BGC Capital Markets (Japan), LLC (1)
Akasaka Biz Tower 38F 5-3-1, Akasaka Minato-ku, Tokyo, 107-6338, Japan
Tel.: (81) 345899100
Web Site: http://www.bgcpartners.com
Monetary & Foreign Exchange Trading & Brokerage Services
N.A.I.C.S.: 425120

BGC Environmental Brokerage Services, L.P. (1)
1 Seaport Plz 199 Water St 19th Fl, New York, NY 10038
Tel.: (646) 346-6899
Web Site: https://www.bgcebs.com
Sales Range: $50-74.9 Million
Emp.: 10
Financial Transaction Processing & Advisory Services
N.A.I.C.S.: 522320
Craig Slinn (Mng Dir)

BGC Financial Group, Inc. (1)
Seaport Plz / 199 Water St 19th Fl, New York, NY 10038
Tel.: (646) 346-7000
Web Site: http://www.bgcpartners.com
Emp.: 500
Bond Brokerage Services
N.A.I.C.S.: 523150
Steven R. Vigliotti (CFO)

BGC International, L.P. (1)
5 Churchill Place, Canary Wharf, London, E14 5RD, United Kingdom (100%)
Tel.: (44) 2078947700
Web Site: http://www.bgcpartners.com
Sales Range: $150-199.9 Million
Emp.: 600

Holding Company; Voice, Hybrid & Fully Electronic Financial Trading Execution & Brokerage Services
N.A.I.C.S.: 551112

Subsidiary (Non-US):

Aurel BGC (2)
15-17 Rue Vivienne, 75002, Paris, France
Tel.: (33) 153895389
Web Site: https://www.aurel-bgc.com
Emp.: 187
Inter-Dealer Brokerage Services
N.A.I.C.S.: 425120

Subsidiary (Domestic):

BGC Brokers L.P. (2)
5 Churchill Place, Canary Wharf, London, E14 5RD, United Kingdom
Tel.: (44) 2078947700
Web Site: http://www.bgcpartners.com
Emp.: 600
Securities & Commodity Contracts Brokerage Services
N.A.I.C.S.: 523150
Shaun D. Lynn (Pres)

Subsidiary (Non-US):

BGC Capital Markets (Switzerland) LLC (2)
Alfred Cortot 4, 1260, Nyon, Switzerland
Tel.: (41) 229948001
Web Site: http://www.bgcpartners.com
Monetary & Foreign Exchange Trading & Brokerage Services
N.A.I.C.S.: 425120

Subsidiary (Domestic):

BGC International (2)
5 Churchill Place, Canary Wharf, London, E14 5RD, United Kingdom
Tel.: (44) 2078947000
Web Site: http://www.bgcpartners.com
Financial Intermediation Services
N.A.I.C.S.: 523150

Subsidiary (Non-US):

BGC Securities SARL (2)
Alfred Cortot 4, 1260, Nyon, Switzerland
Tel.: (41) 229948001
Web Site: http://www.bgcpartners.com
Financial Brokerage Services
N.A.I.C.S.: 523150

BGC LIQUIDEZ DISTRIBUIDORA DE TITULOS E VALORES MOBILIARIOS LTDA. (1)
Av Brigadeiro Faria Lima 3144 - 7 andar, Jardim Paulistano, Sao Paulo, 01451-000, Brazil
Tel.: (55) 1145022300
Electronic Brokerage Services
N.A.I.C.S.: 523160
Laureano Mule (Controller-Fin)

BGC Market Data, L.P. (1)
199 Water St 1 Seaport Plz, New York, NY 10038
Tel.: (212) 829-4840
Web Site: http://www.bgcmarketdata.com
Sales Range: $50-74.9 Million
Emp.: 20
Electronic Financial Transaction Services
N.A.I.C.S.: 522320

BGC Partners (Australia) Pty. Ltd. (1)
Level 56 Suite 56 01 25 Martin Place, Sydney, 2000, NSW, Australia
Tel.: (61) 282228888
Web Site: http://www.bgcpartners.com
Sales Range: $75-99.9 Million
Emp.: 55
Voice, Hybrid & Fully Electronic Brokerage Services
N.A.I.C.S.: 425120

BGC Partners (Singapore) Limited (1)
1 Temasek Avenue 22-01 Millenia Tower, Singapore, 039192, Singapore
Tel.: (65) 65123000
Security Brokerage Services
N.A.I.C.S.: 523150

BGC Partners CIS LLC (1)
Office 502 4th Lesnoy lane 4, Moscow,

125047, Russia
Tel.: (7) 4956604520
Web Site: http://www.bgcpartners.com
Sales Range: $50-74.9 Million
Emp.: 7
Electronic Brokerage Services
N.A.I.C.S.: 523150

BGC Partners Menkul Degerler A.S. (1)
Maslak Mah Eski Buyukdere Caddesi Iz Plaza Blok No 9 Ic Kapi No 39, Sariyer, Istanbul, Turkiye
Tel.: (90) 2123651096
Web Site: https://www.vestamenkul.com.tr
Sales Range: $50-74.9 Million
Emp.: 32
Electronic Brokerage Services
N.A.I.C.S.: 523150

BGC SA Financial Brokers (Pty) Limited (1)
Cube WS Building 9 The Straights Cnr Straight & Forest Roads, Pineslopes Fourways, Johannesburg, 2191, South Africa
Tel.: (27) 101410288
Web Site: http://www.bgcpartners.com
Financial Management Services
N.A.I.C.S.: 523999

BGC Securities (Hong Kong) LLC (1)
Suite 6402-08 64/F Two International Finance Centre, 8 Finance Street, Central, China (Hong Kong)
Tel.: (852) 34777888
Web Site: http://www.bgcpartners.com
Emp.: 150
Securities & Other Financial Products Trading & Brokerage Services
N.A.I.C.S.: 425120

BGC Shoken Kaisha Limited (1)
Akasaka Biz Tower 38F 5-3-1, Akasaka Minato-ku, Tokyo, 107-6338, Japan
Tel.: (81) 345899100
Web Site: http://www.bgcpartners.com
Inter-Dealer Brokerage Services
N.A.I.C.S.: 425120

BGC USA, L.P. (1)
1 Seaport Plz 199 Water St 19th Fl, New York, NY 10038 (100%)
Tel.: (646) 346-7000
Web Site: http://www.bgcpartners.com
Sales Range: $450-499.9 Million
Emp.: 500
Voice, Hybrid & Fully Electronic Financial Trading Execution & Brokerage Services
N.A.I.C.S.: 522320

Besso Grimme Insurance Brokersgmhh (1)
Alstertor 17, 20095, Hamburg, Germany
Tel.: (49) 4085599810
Web Site: http://www.bgib.com
Emp.: 250
Insurance Services
N.A.I.C.S.: 524210
Christian Grimme (Mng Dir)

Besso Insurance Group Limited (1)
2 Minster Court, London, EC3R 7PD, United Kingdom
Tel.: (44) 2074801000
Web Site: https://www.besso.co.uk
Emp.: 200
Insurance Services
N.A.I.C.S.: 524210
Sam Hovey (CFO)

Besso Re Brasil Corrotora Do Reseguros Ltda. (1)
Rua Sao Jose N 90-Sala 2107 Centro, Rio de Janeiro, 20010-020, Brazil
Tel.: (55) 21999616951
Web Site: https://www.besso.co.uk
Insurance Services
N.A.I.C.S.: 524210
Marco Antonio Santos (Mgr-Fin Admin)

Besso Sigorta Ve Reasurans Brokerligi Ltd. (1)
Kanyon Ofis Binasi Buyukdere cad No 185 Kat 13 Levent, 34394, Istanbul, Turkiye
Tel.: (90) 2123530710
Web Site: https://www.besso.co.uk
Insurance Services
N.A.I.C.S.: 524210

Candan Ozcan (Mng Dir)

Converge Towers, LLC (1)
770 Broadway Ste 212, New York, NY 10003-9522
Tel.: (646) 415-7715
Financial Management Services
N.A.I.C.S.: 523999

ED Broking Miami Inc. (1)
800 Brickell Ave Ste 1115, Miami, FL 33131
Tel.: (305) 537-4000
Insurance Brokerage Services
N.A.I.C.S.: 524210
Eugenio Chinchilla (Head-Bus Dev-Latin America)

Epsilon Insurance Broking Services Pty. Ltd. (1)
Suite 1503 Level 15 1 Market Street, Sydney, 2000, NSW, Australia
Tel.: (61) 292993466
Web Site: https://www.epsiloninsurance.com
Disability Insurance Services
N.A.I.C.S.: 524126
Morgan Long (CEO)
Paul O'Leary (Chief Underwriting Officer)
Amanda Gabriel (CFO)
Lesa Tedesco (Mgr-Liability)
Lester Scott (Portfolio Mgr-Construction)

Euro Brokers Mexico S.A. de C.V. (1)
Montes Urales 470-PH Col Lomas de Chapultepec, Mexico, 11000, Mexico
Tel.: (52) 5552023925
Security Brokerage Services
N.A.I.C.S.: 327910
Guillermo R. Somerville (Mng Dir)

Fenics FX, LLC (1)
199 Water St, New York, NY 10038
Tel.: (646) 344-6090
Web Site: https://www.fenicsfx.com
Software Development Services
N.A.I.C.S.: 513210
Howard Silverman (Sr Mng Dir & Mgr-Product)

Fenics Markets Xchange, LLC (1)
199 Water St 19th Fl, New York, NY 10038
Tel.: (646) 346-7099
Web Site: https://www.fmx.com
Financial Security Exchange Services
N.A.I.C.S.: 523210

Fintan Partners, LLC (1)
203 Redwood Shores Pkwy Ste 230, Redwood City, CA 94065
Tel.: (650) 687-3450
Web Site: http://www.fintanpartners.com
Investment Management Service
N.A.I.C.S.: 523940
Alexander Klikoff (Sr Mng Dir)

Freedom International Brokerage Company (1)
181 University Ave Ste 1500, Toronto, M5H 3M7, ON, Canada
Tel.: (416) 367-2588
Web Site: https://www.freedom.ca
Sales Range: $50-74.9 Million
Emp.: 50
Electronic Brokerage Services
N.A.I.C.S.: 523150
Kevin Kirby (Pres & CEO)
Mark Bradshaw (VP, VP-Provincial, Corp, Maple, and Strip Desk & Mgr)
Al Galvez (Mgr-IT & Comm)
Keith Hardy (VP, VP-Inter-Bank,Money Markets & Mgr)
Tim Anastakis (VP-Derivatives)
Arbi Shahnazarian (VP)

GFI Group Inc. (1)
55 Water St, New York, NY 10041
Tel.: (212) 968-4100
Web Site: https://www.gfigroup.com
Sales Range: $800-899.9 Million
Emp.: 2,000
Derivatives Trading & Brokerage Services
N.A.I.C.S.: 523150
Colin Heffron (CEO)
Julian Swain (Sr Mng Dir-EMEA)
Richard Giles (Mng Dir & Head-Americas Broking)
James Martin (Mng Dir-London-EMEA)
Herve Alfon (Mng Dir-Paris-EMEA)
Stephane Chouffan (Mng Dir-Paris-EMEA)
Francesco Cicero (Head-E-Trading)

Darryl Denyssen *(Dir-Fin-EMEA)*
Gautam Kapur *(Head-E-Commerce & Hybrid Execution-Asia Pacific)*
Prash Naik *(COO-Americas, EMEA & Asia-Pac)*
Marc Souffir *(Mng Dir-EMEA)*
Matt Woodhams *(Head-E-Commerce-EMEA)*

Subsidiary (Domestic):

Amerex Brokers LLC (2)
1 Sugar Creek Ctr Blvd Ste 700, Sugar Land, TX 77478
Tel.: (281) 340-5200
Web Site: https://www.amerexenergy.com
Energy Consulting & Brokerage Services
N.A.I.C.S.: 541690

Unit (Domestic):

Amerex Energy Services (3)
1 Sugar Creek Ctr Blvd Ste 700, Sugar Land, TX 77478
Tel.: (281) 340-5200
Web Site:
    https://www.amerexenergyservices.com
Energy Consulting & Brokerage Services
N.A.I.C.S.: 541690
Phyllis Anzalone *(VP-Energy Consulting)*
Vince Martinez *(VP-Energy Consulting)*
Rob McKim *(VP-Pricing & Structured Products)*
Steve Willett *(VP-Energy Consulting)*
Francisco Gonzalez de Cosio *(Sr Dir-Portfolio Mgmt & Pricing & Structured Products)*
Chris Elliott *(VP-Energy Consulting)*
Chris Wiederspahn *(VP-Bus Dev)*

Subsidiary (Non-US):

GFI Group Pte. Ltd. (2)
16 Collyer Quay 31-00 Income at Raffles, Singapore, 049318, Singapore
Tel.: (65) 66323888
Web Site: http://www.gfigroup.com
Brokerage & Trade Execution Services
N.A.I.C.S.: 523150

GFI Group Services Lux Ltd (2)
1 Snowden Street, London, EC2A 2DQ, United Kingdom
Tel.: (44) 2074221000
Web Site: http://www.gfigroup.com
Brokerage & Trade Execution Services
N.A.I.C.S.: 523150

GFI Securities Ltd. (2)
1 Snowden Street, London, EC2A 2DQ, United Kingdom
Tel.: (44) 2074221000
Web Site: http://www.gfigroup.com
Emp.: 1,100
Brokerage & Trade Execution Services
N.A.I.C.S.: 523150

GUNTHER LUBSEN GMBH (1)
Hohe Bleichen 11, 20354, Hamburg, Germany
Tel.: (49) 40350030
Web Site: https://www.luebsen.de
Insurance Agency Services
N.A.I.C.S.: 524210

Ginalfi Finance (1)
15-17 Rue Vivienne, Paris, 75002, France
Tel.: (33) 142618000
Web Site: http://www.ginalfi.fr
Sales Range: $50-74.9 Million
Emp.: 13
Investment Intermediation Services
N.A.I.C.S.: 523150

Ginga Petroleum (Singapore) Pte Ltd (1)
83 Clemenceau Avenue 15-08 UE Square, Singapore, 239920, Singapore
Tel.: (65) 62928484
Petroleum Product Distr
N.A.I.C.S.: 424720

Globe Underwriting Limited (1)
2 Minster Court, London, EC3R 7PD, United Kingdom
Tel.: (44) 1473276136
Web Site: https://www.globeuw.com
Insurance Brokerage Services
N.A.I.C.S.: 524210
David Dymond *(Head-Div)*
Marcus Meredith *(CEO)*

Kalahari Limited (1)
5 Churchill Place, Canary Wharf, London, E14 5RD, Surrey, United Kingdom
Tel.: (44) 2078776699
Web Site: https://www.kacefinancial.com
Customer Care Services
N.A.I.C.S.: 517810

Lucera Financial Infrastructures, LLC (1)
199 Water St, New York, NY 10038
Web Site: https://www.lucera.com
Administrative Management Consulting Services
N.A.I.C.S.: 541611
Kothavade Durkan *(CEO)*
Praneet Kothavade *(CIO)*
Michael Badrov *(CTO)*

Merlin Advisors, LLC (1)
5847 San Felipe Ste 800, Houston, TX 77057
Tel.: (713) 344-2370
Web Site: https://www.merlinadvisors.com
Technology & Engineering Services
N.A.I.C.S.: 541330
Ilmars Kerbers *(Mgr)*

Newmark & Company Real Estate, Inc. (1)
125 Park Ave, New York, NY 10017
Tel.: (212) 372-2000
Web Site: http://www.ngkf.com
Real Estate Consulting Service
N.A.I.C.S.: 531390
James D. Kuhn *(Pres & Head-Investor Svcs)*
Jim McGrath *(Exec Mng Dir-Denver)*
Alex W. Bergeson *(Mng Dir-Los Angeles)*
Maura Carland *(Mgr-Transaction-Minneapolis)*
John A. Ennis *(Sr VP-Whippany-Valuation & Advisory)*
Brett S. Lake *(Sr VP-Whippany-Valuation & Advisory)*
Issa Abbassi *(Dir)*
Harrison Abramowitz *(Mng Dir)*
Gary Alterman *(Exec Mng Dir)*
Matthew Augarten *(Assoc Dir)*
Anthony Barra *(Mgr-Fin Ops)*
David Behin *(Exec Mng Dir)*
Karen Bellantoni *(Vice Chm)*
Nick Berger *(Mng Dir)*
David Berke *(Sr Mng Dir)*
Ross Berkowitz *(Sr Mng Dir)*
Corey Borg *(Mng Dir)*
Scott M. Brown *(Mng Dir)*
Eric Cagner *(Exec Mng Dir)*
John Michael Cilmi *(Assoc Dir)*
Michael Rispoli *(CFO)*
John D. Busi *(Pres-Valuation & Advisory)*
Anthony Orso *(Pres-Capital Markets Strategies)*
Roger Anscher *(Chief Admin Officer)*
Maggie Argyros *(Sr Mng Dir)*
Richard Bertasi *(CEO)*
Benjamin S. Birnbaum *(Vice Chm)*
Josh Bullock *(Sr VP)*
Ted Calaman *(Mng Dir)*
Brian Cohen *(Sr Mng Dir)*
J. D. Cohen *(Mng Dir)*
William G. Cohen *(Vice Chm)*
Michael Collins *(Mng Dir)*
E. N. Cutler *(Mng Dir)*
Paul Davidson *(Sr Mng Dir)*
Joshua Davis *(Gen Counsel)*
Justin DiMare *(Exec VP)*
Auston Dimitry *(Mng Dir)*
Thomas Dobrowski *(Vice Chm)*
Adam Doneger *(Vice Chm)*
Matt Duthie *(Sr VP)*
Brandon Eisenman *(Sr Mng Dir)*
Scott Ellard *(Mng Dir)*
David L. Emden *(Sr Mng Dir)*
Robert B. Emden *(Exec Mng Dir)*
Adam Etra *(Vice Chm)*
Jeremy Ezra *(Vice Chm)*
David A. Falk *(Pres-New York Tri-State Reg)*

Subsidiary (Non-US):

Grubb & Ellis Company (2)
Tel.: (714) 667-8252
Web Site: http://www.grubb-ellis.com
Sales Range: $550-599.9 Million
Holding Company; Real Estate Brokerage, Property Management & Consulting Services

N.A.I.C.S.: 551112

Subsidiary (Non-US):

Computerized Facility Integration, L.L.C. (3)
Tel.: (248) 557-4234
Web Site: http://www.gocfi.com
Consulting & IT Services to Public & Private Clients
N.A.I.C.S.: 541513

Grubb & Ellis Management Services, Inc. (3)
Tel.: (714) 667-8252
Property, Asset, Construction, Business & Engineering Management Services
N.A.I.C.S.: 531390

Grubb & Ellis New York, Inc. (3)
Tel.: (212) 759-9700
Web Site: http://www.newmarkkf.com
Sales Range: $50-74.9 Million
Emp.: 70
Real Estate Services
N.A.I.C.S.: 531120

Affiliate (Non-US):

Levy Beffort, LLC (3)
Tel.: (405) 840-1500
Web Site: https://newmarkrp.com
Sales Range: $1-9.9 Million
Emp.: 40
Real Estate Brokerage Services
N.A.I.C.S.: 531210

Branch (Non-US):

Newmark Grubb Knight Frank - Atlanta (3)
Tel.: (770) 552-2400
Sales Range: $75-99.9 Million
Emp.: 90
Real Estate Brokerage Services
N.A.I.C.S.: 531210

Newmark Grubb Knight Frank - Chicago (3)
Tel.: (312) 698-6700
Web Site: http://www.ngkf.com
Sales Range: $100-124.9 Million
Emp.: 172
Real Estate Brokerage Services
N.A.I.C.S.: 531210

Newmark Grubb Knight Frank - Detroit (3)
Tel.: (248) 350-9500
Web Site: https://www.nmrk.com
Sales Range: $75-99.9 Million
Emp.: 50
Real Estate Services
N.A.I.C.S.: 531210

Affiliate (Non-US):

Newmark Grubb Phoenix Realty Group, Inc. (3)
Tel.: (904) 399-5222
Web Site: https://www.phoenixrealty.net
Real Estate Brokerage Services
N.A.I.C.S.: 531210

Subsidiary (Non-US):

Ross Real Estate Ltd. (3)
Tel.: (303) 892-1111
Web Site: https://www.nmrk.com
Sales Range: $10-24.9 Million
Real Estate Brokers & Agents
N.A.I.C.S.: 531210

Subsidiary (Domestic):

Jackson & Cooksey Inc. (2)
12770 Merit Dr Ste 760, Dallas, TX 75251-1294
Tel.: (972) 934-9757
Real Estate Agents & Brokers
N.A.I.C.S.: 531210
Jim Cooksey *(Partner)*

Newmark Construction Services, LLC (2)
67 Wall St Ste 2502, New York, NY 10005-3103
Tel.: (212) 528-4090
Construction Engineering Services
N.A.I.C.S.: 541330

Newmark Cornish & Carey (2)
2804 Mission College Blvd Ste 120, Santa Clara, CA 95054-1803
Tel.: (408) 727-9600
Web Site: http://www.newmarkccarey.com
Real Estate Agency Services
N.A.I.C.S.: 531210
Mark C. Davis *(Exec Mng Dir)*
Philip A. Mahoney *(Vice Chm)*
Thomas P. Sweeney *(Sr Mng Dir)*
Michael Saign *(Vice Chm)*
Chris Brown *(Sr Mng Dir)*
Todd Shaffer *(Exec VP)*

Newmark Real Estate of Dallas, LLC (2)
2400 Dallas Pkwy Ste 300, Plano, TX 75093
Tel.: (469) 467-2000
Real Estate Brokerage Services
N.A.I.C.S.: 531210

Newmark Real Estate of Houston, LLC (2)
5847 San Felipe St, Houston, TX 77057
Tel.: (713) 490-9990
Real Estate Brokerage Services
N.A.I.C.S.: 531210

Newmark Real Estate of New Jersey, LLC (2)
201 State Rt 17, Rutherford, NJ 07070
Tel.: (201) 842-6700
Web Site: https://www.nmrk.com
Real Estate Brokerage Services
N.A.I.C.S.: 531210

Newmark of Long Island LLC (2)
290 Broadhollow Rd Ste 103E, Melville, NY 11747
Tel.: (631) 424-4800
Web Site: https://www.nmrk.com
Sales Range: $50-74.9 Million
Emp.: 25
Electronic Brokerage Services
N.A.I.C.S.: 523150
Charles V. Tabone *(Mng Dir & Exec VP)*
Daniel T. Gazzola *(Mng Dir)*
Brian D. Lee *(Exec Mng Dir)*
Jeffrey Uvezian *(Mng Dir)*
Kyle Burkhardt *(Exec Mng Dir)*
Joshua Cohen *(Mng Dir)*

Newmark of Washington D.C. LLC (2)
1899 Pennsylvania Ave NW, Washington, DC 20005
Tel.: (202) 331-7000
Web Site: http://www.ngkf.com
Emp.: 230
Security Brokerage Services
N.A.I.C.S.: 523150
Karen Gaydos *(Sr Mgr-Bus Ops)*
Mathew Adler *(Mng Dir)*
Lisa Benjamin *(Sr Mng Dir)*
John Boland *(Vice Chm)*
Marcus Bourn *(Sr Mng Dir-Retail Occupier Svcs)*
Todd Canterbury *(Exec VP)*
Rob Cantizano *(Exec Mng Dir)*
James P. Cassidy *(Exec Mng Dir)*
Doug Damron *(Sr Mng Dir)*
David R. Decamp *(Mng Dir)*
Brett R. Diamond *(Exec Mng Dir)*
Joseph Donato *(Vice Chm)*
Bart Drummond *(Exec Mng Dir)*
Todd Grinspoon *(Mng Dir)*
Allison DiGiovanni *(Exec VP)*
William L. Hill *(Vice Chm)*
Brian Johnson *(Exec VP)*
Tim Lenahan *(Exec Mng Dir)*
Andrea McGowan *(Sr VP)*
Douglas L. Nickel *(Sr Mng Dir)*
Miles Spencer *(Vice Chm)*
Edwin M. Clark III *(Exec Mng Dir)*

The CRE Group, Inc. (2)
465 California St Ste 435, San Francisco, CA 94104
Tel.: (925) 934-4822
Web Site: http://www.thecregroup.com
Sales Range: $1-9.9 Million
Emp.: 29
Real Estate Project Management & Construction Management Services
N.A.I.C.S.: 541330

O'BOYLE PROPERTIES, INC. (1)
14114 Dallas Pkwy Ste 520, Dallas, TX 75254-4349

BGC Group, Inc.—(Continued)

Tel.: (972) 934-3400
Real Estate Services
N.A.I.C.S.: 531210

O.S.T.C LIMITED (1)
21-25 North Street, Bromley, BR1 1SD, Kent, United Kingdom
Tel.: (44) 2033269050
Web Site: https://www.ostc.com
Investment Management Service
N.A.I.C.S.: 523940
Jonny Aucamp *(Chm)*
Mark Slade *(Vice Chm)*
Michael Shirley *(Head-Trading)*
Justina Naik *(Sec)*
Surya Fletcher *(Chief Risk Officer)*
Kenny Su *(CFO-Interim)*
Peter Lenardos *(CFO)*

Poten & Partners (Australia) Pty. Ltd. (1)
Suite 1 6 9 Havelock Street, West Perth, 6005, WA, Australia
Tel.: (61) 864687943
Oil & Gas Shipping Market Services
N.A.I.C.S.: 213112

Poten & Partners (Hellas) Ltd. (1)
5 Grypari Street Gr-Neo Psychico, 15451, Athens, 15451, Greece
Tel.: (30) 2106777603
Oil & Gas Shipping Market Services
N.A.I.C.S.: 213112
Athina Lavranou *(Mgr-Ops)*

Poten & Partners (UK) Ltd. (1)
101 Wigmore Street, London, W1U 1QU, United Kingdom
Tel.: (44) 2037474800
Oil & Gas Shipping Market Services
N.A.I.C.S.: 213112

Poten & Partners Pte. Ltd. (1)
16 Collyer Quay 31-00 Collyer Quay Centre, Singapore, 049318, Singapore
Tel.: (65) 64319050
Oil & Gas Shipping Market Services
N.A.I.C.S.: 213112
Ashrafe Hanifar *(Mgr-Comml)*

Poten & Partners, Inc. (1)
666 3rd Ave 27th Fl, New York, NY 10017
Tel.: (212) 230-2000
Web Site: http://www.poten.com
N.A.I.C.S.: 488510
Steven M. Garten *(CEO)*
Jason Feer *(Mgr-Global)*
Erik Broekhuizen *(Mgr-Tanker Res & Consulting-Global)*
Robert Rexer *(Mgr-Period Charter, Sale, and Purchase Brokerage-Global)*

QUBED DERIVATIVES LLP (1)
Business Design Centre 52 Unit 227 Upper Street, London, N1 0QH, United Kingdom
Tel.: (44) 2030346600
Web Site: https://www.qubed-derivatives.com
Investment Management Service
N.A.I.C.S.: 523940
Simon Cosgrave *(Partner)*

REMATE LINCE, S.A.P.I. de C.V. (1)
Av Vasco de Quiroga 2121, 1er Piso Col Santa Fe, 01210, Mexico, Mexico
Tel.: (52) 5552598070
Web Site: https://www.remate.com
Investment Management Service
N.A.I.C.S.: 523940

Remate USA Inc. (1)
55 Water St 10th Fl, New York, NY 10041
Tel.: (646) 346-6871
Web Site: https://www.remate.com
Investment Management Service
N.A.I.C.S.: 523940

Rexx Index, LLC (1)
257 Weaver St, Greenwich, CT 06831
Tel.: (203) 542-5475
Web Site: http://www.rexxindex.com
Real Estate Brokerage Services
N.A.I.C.S.: 531210

SOUTHWEST RESIDENTIAL PARTNERS, INC.
1220 Augusta Dr Ste 150, Houston, TX 77057
Tel.: (713) 599-1800

Real Estate Services
N.A.I.C.S.: 531210

STEFFNER COMMERCIAL REAL ESTATE, LLC (1)
555 Perkins Extended Ste 410, Memphis, TN 38117
Tel.: (901) 761-1717
Real Estate Services
N.A.I.C.S.: 531210

Smith Mack & Co., Inc. (1)
880 E Swedesford Rd Ste 100, Wayne, PA 19087-2129
Tel.: (610) 265-0600
Real Estate Brokerage Services
N.A.I.C.S.: 531210

Sunrise Brokers (Hong Kong) Ltd. (1)
Suite 6402-08 Two International Finance Centre 8 Finance Street, Central, China (Hong Kong)
Tel.: (852) 31809000
Over-The-Counter & Interdealer Broker Services
N.A.I.C.S.: 425120
Xavier Laurens *(Mng Dir)*

Sunrise Brokers LLP (1)
6th Floor 20 Triton Street, London, NW1 3BF, United Kingdom
Tel.: (44) 2070349800
Web Site: https://www.sunrisebrokers.com
Over-The-Counter & Interdealer Broker Services
N.A.I.C.S.: 425120

Sunrise Brokers, LLC (1)
135 E 57th St, New York, NY 10022
Tel.: (212) 403-6900
Marketing Brokerage Services
N.A.I.C.S.: 523160

TEUCRIUM TRADING, LLC (1)
3 Main St Ste 215, Burlington, VT 05401
Tel.: (802) 257-1617
Web Site: https://www.teucrium.com
Investment Management Service
N.A.I.C.S.: 523940

BGSF, INC.
5850 Granite Pkwy Ste 730, Plano, TX 75024
Tel.: (972) 692-2400 DE
Web Site: https://www.bgsf.com
Year Founded: 2007
BGSF—(NYSE)
Rev.: $298,421,828
Assets: $194,673,165
Liabilities: $93,936,632
Net Worth: $100,736,533
Earnings: $25,360,873
Emp.: 540
Fiscal Year-end: 01/01/23
Employment Placement Agencies; Temporary Staffing Services
N.A.I.C.S.: 561311
John Barnett *(CFO & Sec)*
Beth A. Garvey *(Chm, Pres & CEO)*
Eric Peters *(Pres-Professional Div)*
Janel Hunt *(VP-People)*
Chris Loope *(Chief Strategy Officer)*
John R. Barnett *(CFO & Sec)*
Eric Samargedlis *(Sr VP-Professional Resources)*
Stuart Sides *(Sr VP-Strategic Sls)*
Dennis Waggoner *(VP-Bus Dev)*
Steven Howard Smith *(VP-Professional Div)*
Jenn Rhoder *(VP-Real Estate)*
Andra Padgett *(Mng Dir-Multifamily)*
Amy Bush *(Mng Dir-Multifamily)*
Katie Pearson *(Reg Mng Dir-Talent)*
Melissa Phillips *(Chief Digital Officer)*
Nycole Rosen *(CIO)*
Matt Murray *(VP)*
Betsy Kirkpatrick *(Mng Dir & Mng Dir-Strategic Programs)*
Kelly Brown *(Pres-Real Estate)*
Emily Burroughs *(VP-Mktg & Mktg)*
Gilbert Hernando *(VP-Real Estate & Real Estate)*

Kay Steelman *(VP-Professional Svcs)*
Sarah Fox *(VP-Real Estate)*
Andrew Hill *(Sr VP-Property Mgmt)*
Tim Gibbons *(Sr VP-Professional Div)*

Subsidiaries:

EdgeRock Technologies, LLC (1)
10 Post Office Sq, Boston, MA 02109
Tel.: (617) 412-4300
Web Site: http://www.edgerock.com
Information Technology Consulting Services
N.A.I.C.S.: 541690
Stephen Sorrentino *(CFO)*
Matt Murray *(VP-Sls)*
Tim Gibbons *(VP-Delivery)*
Alex Breitmaier *(Gen Mgr)*

L.J. Kushner & Associates, L.L.C. (1)
36 W Main St, Freehold, NJ 07728
Tel.: (732) 577-8100
Executive Search Service
N.A.I.C.S.: 561312
Lee Kushner *(Pres)*

Momentum Solutionz, LLC (1)
288 Sleepy Hollow, Roanoke, VA 24018
Tel.: (804) 306-2155
Web Site: http://www.momentumsolutionz.com
Information Technology Consulting Services
N.A.I.C.S.: 541512
Jeff Servidio *(Mng Partner)*

Vision Technology Services, LLC (1)
230 Schilling Cir Ste 200, Hunt Valley, MD 21031
Tel.: (410) 560-1444
Web Site: http://www.vistechs.com
Information Technology Staffing Services
N.A.I.C.S.: 561330

Zycron Inc. (1)
100 Westwood Place Ste 110 Bldg 4, Brentwood, TN 37027
Tel.: (615) 251-9588
Web Site: http://www.bgstaffing.com
Customer-focused Information Technology Solutions Services
N.A.I.C.S.: 518210
Darrell S. Freeman Sr. *(Exec Mng Dir)*

BHPA, INC.
3 Bethesda Metro Ctr Ste 700, Bethesda, MD 20814
Tel.: (202) 536-5191 NV
Year Founded: 2005
BHPA—(OTCIQ)
Data Processing Services
N.A.I.C.S.: 518210
Kevin Tseng *(CEO)*
David E. Price *(Gen Counsel & Sec)*

BIG 5 SPORTING GOODS CORPORATION
2525 El Segundo Blvd, El Segundo, CA 90245
Tel.: (310) 536-0611 DE
Web Site: https://www.big5sportinggoods.com
Year Founded: 1955
BGFV—(NASDAQ)
Rev.: $1,161,820,000
Assets: $753,953,000
Liabilities: $486,644,000
Net Worth: $267,309,000
Earnings: $102,386,000
Emp.: 420
Fiscal Year-end: 01/02/22
Sporting Goods Retailer
N.A.I.C.S.: 459110
Barry D. Emerson *(CFO, Treas, Exec VP & Asst Sec)*
Shane O. Starr *(Sr VP-Ops)*
Michael J. Shinagawa *(CIO & Sr VP-IT)*
Peter C. Mulvaney *(Sr VP-Adv & Mktg)*
John L. Lucero *(Sr VP, Controller & Asst Treas)*
Steven G. Miller *(Chm, Pres & CEO)*

Subsidiaries:

Big 5 Corporation Distribution Center (1)
6125 Sycamore Canyon Blvd, Riverside, CA 92507 (100%)
Tel.: (951) 774-1600
Web Site: https://www.big5sportinggoods.com
Sales Range: $50-74.9 Million
Emp.: 50
Distribution Center for Big 5 Stores
N.A.I.C.S.: 459999

BIG LOTS, INC.
4900 E Dublin-Granville Rd, Columbus, OH 43081-7651
Tel.: (614) 278-7165 OH
Web Site: https://www.biglots.com
Year Founded: 1967
BIG—(NYSE)
Rev.: $5,468,329,000
Assets: $3,690,931,000
Liabilities: $2,927,024,000
Net Worth: $763,907,000
Earnings: ($210,708,000)
Emp.: 10,200
Fiscal Year-end: 01/28/23
Holding Company; Specialty Retail Stores, Wholesale Housewares, Electronics, Hardware, Automotive Equipment, Accessories, Food Items, Health & Beauty Aids, Sports Goods, Toys & Jewelry
N.A.I.C.S.: 455219
Jonathan E. Ramsden *(CFO, Chief Admin Officer & Exec VP)*
Ronald A. Robins Jr. *(Chief Legal & Governance Officer, Gen Counsel, Sec & Exec VP)*
Michael Allen Schlonsky *(Exec VP-HR)*
Bruce K. Thorn *(Pres & CEO)*
Kristen Cox *(Chief Stores Officer & Sr VP)*
Seth Marks *(Sr VP-Extreme Value Sourcing)*
Juan Guerrero *(Chief Supply Chain Officer & Sr VP)*
John Alpaugh *(CMO & Sr VP)*

Subsidiaries:

Big Lots Stores, Inc. (1)
Tel.: (380) 215-0121
Web Site: https://www.biglots.com
Sales Range: $250-299.9 Million
Emp.: 1,000
Retail Department Stores
N.A.I.C.S.: 455219

CSC Distribution, Inc. (1)
300 Phillipi Rd, Columbus, OH 43228
Tel.: (614) 278-6800
Web Site: http://www.biglots.com
Sales Range: $10-24.9 Million
Emp.: 50
Business Management Services
N.A.I.C.S.: 541611

Closeout Distribution, Inc. (1)
300 Phillipi Rd, Columbus, OH 43228
Tel.: (614) 278-6800
Web Site: http://www.biglotscorporate.com
Sales Range: $75-99.9 Million
Business Management Services
N.A.I.C.S.: 541611

North American Solutions Inc. (1)
2880 S Jones Blvd Ste 2, Las Vegas, NV 89146
Tel.: (702) 262-7922
Web Site: https://www.nasco-nw.com
Emp.: 3
Nutritional Supplement Distr
N.A.I.C.S.: 456191
Amir Ghalanbor *(CEO)*

PNS Stores, Inc. (1)
1410 E Plz Blvd, National City, CA 91950
Tel.: (619) 477-4225
Home Furnishing Merchant Whslr
N.A.I.C.S.: 423220

Sonoran LLC (1)
5104 N 32nd St Ste 226, Phoenix, AZ
85018
Tel.: (602) 692-5888
Iron & Steel Products Mfr
N.A.I.C.S.: 331110

West Coast Liquidators, Inc. (1)
12434 4th St, Rancho Cucamonga, CA
91730
Tel.: (909) 899-2511
Web Site: http://www.biglots.com
General Store Services
N.A.I.C.S.: 455219

BIG SCREEN ENTERTAINMENT GROUP, INC.
8306 Wilshire Blvd Ste 514, Beverly
Hills, CA 90211
Tel.: (323) 654-3400   NV
Web Site:
   https://www.bigscreenentgroup.com
Year Founded: 2005
BSEG—(OTCIQ)
Motion Picture, Television, Music &
Computer Game Developer, Producer
& Distr
N.A.I.C.S.: 512110
Jimmy Jiang (CEO-BSEG Capital,
Treas-Big Screen)
Kimberley Kates (Founder & CEO)
Stephen Eckelberry (Chm)
Michael Gardiner (Pres-Bus Affairs)
Robert Laskowski (Gen Counsel)
Catherine Taylor (Pres-Dev)

BIG TIME HOLDINGS, INC.
30 Wall St Level 8, New York, NY
10005
Tel.: (212) 709-8206   DE
Web Site: http://www.bigtimehi.us
BTH—(OTCIQ)
Holding Company
N.A.I.C.S.: 551112
Brian Kistler (Pres, CEO, CFO, Treas
& Sec)

BIGCOMMERCE HOLDINGS, INC.
11305 4 Points Dr Bldg II 1st Fl, Austin, TX 78726
Tel.: (512) 865-4500   DE
Web Site:
   https://www.bigcommerce.com
Year Founded: 2013
BIGC—(NASDAQ)
Rev.: $279,075,000
Assets: $474,056,000
Liabilities: $428,384,000
Net Worth: $45,672,000
Earnings: ($139,919,000)
Emp.: 1,500
Fiscal Year-end: 12/31/22
Holding Company
N.A.I.C.S.: 551112
Brent Bellm (Chm, Interim Pres &
CEO)
Daniel Lentz (CFO)
Lisa Eggerton (CMO)
Brian Dhatt (CTO)
Jeff Mengoli (Chief Legal Officer)
Russell Klein (Chief Comml Officer)
Sherri Manning (Chief People Officer)
Hubert Ban (Chief Acctg Officer)
Travis Hess (Pres)
Rosie Rivel (CIO)
Chuck Cassidy (Gen Counsel)
Troy Cox (Chief Product Officer)
Dan Holden (Chief Information Security Officer)
Becky Logan (Sr VP-People)

BIGLARI HOLDINGS INC.
19100 Ridgewood Pkwy Ste 1200,
San Antonio, TX 78259
Tel.: (210) 344-3400   IN

Web Site:
   https://www.biglariholdings.com
Year Founded: 1934
BH—(NYSE)
Rev.: $368,231,000
Assets: $828,474,000
Liabilities: $272,906,000
Net Worth: $555,568,000
Earnings: ($32,018,000)
Emp.: 2,559
Fiscal Year-end: 12/31/22
Restaurant Owner, Operator & Franchiser
N.A.I.C.S.: 722511
Sardar Biglari (Chm & CEO)
Philip L. Cooley (Vice Chm)
Bruce W. Lewis (Controller)

Subsidiaries:

1st Guard Corporation (1)
240 Nokomis Ave S, Venice, FL 34285
Web Site: https://www.1stguard.com
Insurance Management Services
N.A.I.C.S.: 524298

Maxim Inc. (1)
415 Madison Ave 48th St, New York, NY
10017
Tel.: (212) 308-6140
Web Site: http://www.maxim.com
Magazine Publisher
N.A.I.C.S.: 513120

SNS Investment Company (1)
36 S Pennsylvania St, Indianapolis, IN
46204-3634   (100%)
Tel.: (317) 633-4100
Web Site: http://www.steaknshake.com
Sales Range: $10-24.9 Million
Emp.: 48
Investment Holding Company
N.A.I.C.S.: 561499

Southern Pioneer Property & Casualty Insurance Company (1)
2816 Longview Dr, Jonesboro, AR 72401
Tel.: (870) 336-3100
Web Site: https://www.southernpioneer.com
Insurance Services
N.A.I.C.S.: 524210
Ben Hyneman (Chm)
Hal Hyneman (Pres)
Brian Hyneman (Treas & Sec)
Hunter Hyneman (VP)
Rob Shaughnessy (VP-Claims)

Steak n Shake Alamo Ranch,
LLC (1)
5619 W Loop 1604 N, San Antonio, TX
78253-5793
Tel.: (210) 688-9692
Web Site: http://www.steaknshake.com
Emp.: 30
Restaurant Management Services
N.A.I.C.S.: 722511

Steak n Shake Enterprises, Inc. (1)
36 S Pennsylvania St, Indianapolis, IN
46204-3634
Tel.: (317) 633-4100
Restaurant Operating Services
N.A.I.C.S.: 722511
David Parker (Mgr-IT Infrastructure)

Steak n Shake Operations, Inc. (1)
107 S Pennsylvania St Ste 400, Indianapolis, IN 46204
Tel.: (317) 633-4100
Web Site: http://www.steaknshake.com
Full-Service Restaurants
N.A.I.C.S.: 722511

Steak n Shake, LLC (1)
520 N Town Center Rd, Mooresville, IN
46158
Tel.: (317) 831-1600
Web Site: http://www.steaknshake.com
Restaurant Management Services
N.A.I.C.S.: 722511

Western Properties, Inc. (1)
304 Cleveland, Sundance, WY 82729
Tel.: (888) 283-1901
Web Site:
   http://www.westernpropertiesonline.com
Real Estate Brokerage Services
N.A.I.C.S.: 531390

Western Sizzlin Corporation (1)
PO Box 12167, Roanoke, VA 24023
Tel.: (540) 345-3195
Web Site: http://www.western-sizzlin.com
Restaurant Operator & Franchisor
N.A.I.C.S.: 722511

BIGSUPERSEARCH.COM, INC.
746 North Dr Ste A, Melbourne, FL
32934
Year Founded: 2005
BSPR—(OTCIQ)
Internet Search Engine Services
N.A.I.C.S.: 519290
Robert Clark (CEO)

BIGTINCAN HOLDINGS LIMITED
260 Charles St - Ste 200, Waltham,
MA 02453
Tel.: (617) 981-7557   AU
Web Site: https://www.bigtincan.com
Year Founded: 2011
BTH—(ASX)
Rev.: $797,023,538
Assets: $208,749,429
Liabilities: $60,795,462
Net Worth: $147,953,968
Earnings: ($17,852,253)
Fiscal Year-end: 06/30/23
Holding Company; Mobile Software
Development Services
N.A.I.C.S.: 551112
David Keane (Founder & CEO)
Mark Ohlsson (Sec)
Tom Amos (Chm)

Subsidiaries:

Brainshark, Inc. (1)
130 Turner St, Waltham, MA 02453
Tel.: (781) 370-8000
Web Site: http://www.brainshark.com
Emp.: 201
Software Development Services
N.A.I.C.S.: 541511
Greg Flynn (Founder & CEO)
Mike McEachern (CFO & Exec VP)
Chris Caruso (CTO)
Diane Gordon (Chief Customer Officer)
Chet Barnard (Chief Revenue Officer & Sr
VP-Bus Dev)
Robin Saitz (CMO)
Mike Kunkle (Sr Dir-Sls Enablement)
Jim Ninivaggi (Sr VP-Strategic Prtnerships)
Colleen Honan (Chief Sls Officer)

ClearSlide, Inc. (1)
995 Market St 12th Fl, San Francisco, CA
94105
Tel.: (877) 360-3366
Web Site: http://www.clearslide.com
Business Software Developer
N.A.I.C.S.: 513210
Al Lieb (Co-Founder)
Jim Benton (Co-Founder)
Grant Wilson (Co-Founder & Mng Partner)
Chris Carsen (Gen Counsel)
Jason Wesbecher (Exec VP-Sls & Mktg)
Gerard Metrailler (Exec VP-Global Products)
Rob Charlebois (Exec VP-Global ECommerce & Digital Mktg)
Prasannaa Ganesan (COO)
Brad Jewett (CFO)
Patrick Nichols (CEO)

Xinnovation, Inc. (1)
51 Melcher St Fl 1, Boston, MA 02210
Tel.: (781) 272-3300
Computer Software Solutions, Document
Solutions & Publishing Services
N.A.I.C.S.: 541511

BILANDER ACQUISITION CORP.
4 Embarcadero Ctr Ste 2100, San
Francisco, CA 94111
Tel.: (415) 780-9975   DE
Year Founded: 2021
TWCB—(NASDAQ)
Rev.: $7,943,119
Assets: $170,676,292

Liabilities: $182,363,887
Net Worth: ($11,687,595)
Earnings: $2,490,917
Emp.: 3
Fiscal Year-end: 12/31/22
Investment Services
N.A.I.C.S.: 523999
Scott W. Wagner (CEO)
Rufina A. Adams (CFO & Sec)
James H. Greene Jr. (Chm)

BILL HOLDINGS, INC.
6220 America Center Dr Ste 100,
San Jose, CA 95022
Tel.: (650) 621-7700   DE
Web Site: https://www.bill.com
Year Founded: 2006
BILL—(NYSE)
Rev.: $1,290,172,000
Assets: $9,178,813,000
Liabilities: $5,044,612,000
Net Worth: $4,134,201,000
Earnings: ($28,878,000)
Emp.: 2,187
Fiscal Year-end: 06/30/24
Holding Company
N.A.I.C.S.: 551112
Germaine Cota (Principal Acctg Officer & Sr VP-Fin & Acctg)
Rene Lacerte (Chm & CEO)
John Rettig (CFO & Exec VP-Fin &
Ops)
Sofya Pogreb (COO)
Sarah Acton (CMO)
Irana Wasti (Chief Product Officer)
Michelle Hughes Benfer (Sr VP-Sls)
Yael Zheng (CMO)

Subsidiaries:

DivvyPay, LLC (1)
13707 S 200 W Ste 100, Draper, UT 84020
Web Site: http://www.getdivvy.com
Financial Services
N.A.I.C.S.: 523999

Invoice2Go, LLC (1)
6220 America Center Dr Ste 100, San Jose,
CA 95002
Tel.: (916) 445-1254
Web Site: https://invoice.2go.com
Online Payment Services
N.A.I.C.S.: 522320

BILOXI MARSH LANDS CORP.
1 Galleria Blvd Ste 902, Metairie, LA
70001
Tel.: (504) 837-4337   DE
Web Site:
   https://www.biloximarshlands
   corp.com
Year Founded: 1936
BLMC—(OTCEM)
Rev.: $683,560
Assets: $8,136,766
Liabilities: $1,022,615
Net Worth: $7,114,151
Earnings: $31,156
Fiscal Year-end: 12/31/23
Oil & Gas Exploration Services
N.A.I.C.S.: 213112
William A. Rudolf (Pres & CEO)

BIMINI CAPITAL MANAGEMENT, INC.
3305 Flamingo Dr, Vero Beach, FL
32963
Tel.: (772) 231-1400   MD
Web Site:
   https://www.biminicapital.com
Year Founded: 2003
BMNM—(OTCQB)
Rev.: $16,150,685
Assets: $86,316,951
Liabilities: $74,192,872
Net Worth: $12,124,079
Earnings: ($19,823,105)
Emp.: 8
Fiscal Year-end: 12/31/22

Bimini Capital Management, Inc.—(Continued)

Real Estate Investment Trust
N.A.I.C.S.: 525990
Jerry M. Sintes (VP & Controller)
Robert E. Cauley (Chm, CEO & Sec)
George Hunter Haas IV (Pres, CFO, Chief Investment Officer & Treas)

Subsidiaries:

Royal Palm Capital, LLC (1)
655 Deep Valley Dr Ste 260, Rolling Hills Estates, CA 90274
Tel.: (310) 265-5939
Web Site:
https://www.royalpalmscapital.com
Financial Services
N.A.I.C.S.: 523940

BIO ESSENCE CORP.
8 Studebaker Dr, Irvine, CA 92618 CA
Tel.: (949) 706-9966
Web Site:
https://www.bioessencecorp.com
Year Founded: 2000
BIOE—(OTCIQ)
Rev.: $985,757
Assets: $1,547,725
Liabilities: $4,786,140
Net Worth: ($3,238,415)
Earnings: ($809,679)
Emp.: 11
Fiscal Year-end: 12/31/22
Food & Health Supplement Stores
N.A.I.C.S.: 456191
Yin Yan (Chm, CEO & Chief Acctg Officer)
William E. Sluss (CFO)

BIO-BRIDGE SCIENCE, INC.
PO Box 168081, Chicago, IL 60616
Tel.: (630) 613-9687 DE
BGES—(OTCIQ)
Biopharmaceutical Mfr
N.A.I.C.S.: 325412
Liang Qiao (Chm & CEO)

BIO-CLEAN INTERNATIONAL, INC.
22431 Antonio Pkwy B160-649, Rancho Santa Margarita, CA 92688
Tel.: (949) 269-8333 NV
BCLE—(OTCIQ)
Environmentally Safe Product Mfr & Distr
N.A.I.C.S.: 325612
Mike Roth (Pres)

BIO-EN HOLDINGS CORP.
1 County Rd Unit B6, Secaucus, NJ 07094
Tel.: (845) 364-7151 DE
Year Founded: 2011
BENH—(OTCIQ)
Assets: $15,633
Liabilities: $500,249
Net Worth: ($484,616)
Earnings: ($41,838)
Fiscal Year-end: 12/31/21
Recycled Ethanol & Butanol Production & Sales
N.A.I.C.S.: 213112
Alon Shany (Exec VP)

BIO-KEY INTERNATIONAL, INC.
101 Crawfords Corner Rd Ste 4116, Holmdel, NJ 07733
Tel.: (732) 359-1100 DE
Web Site: https://www.bio-key.com
Year Founded: 2004
BKYI—(NASDAQ)
Rev.: $7,754,905
Assets: $4,517,035
Liabilities: $3,453,470
Net Worth: $1,063,565
Earnings: ($8,521,837)

Emp.: 43
Fiscal Year-end: 12/31/23
Software Publisher
N.A.I.C.S.: 513210
Cecilia C. Welch (CFO)
Michael W. DePasquale (Chm & CEO)
Mira K. LaCous (CTO)
Scott Mahnken (VP-Channel Mktg)
Jim Sullivan (Chief Legal Officer & VP-Strategy & Compliance)
Mark Cochran (Pres-PortalGuard)

Subsidiaries:

BIO-key Hong Kong Limited (1)
1806 18th Floor Tower 2 Lippo Centre 89 Queensway, Hong Kong, China (Hong Kong)
Tel.: (852) 90300848
Biometric Software Development Services
N.A.I.C.S.: 541511

PistolStar, Inc. (1)
800 Poor Farm Rd, Francestown, NH 03043
Tel.: (603) 546-2300
Web Site: http://www.pistolstar.com
Custom Computer Programming Services
N.A.I.C.S.: 541511

BIO-MATRIX SCIENTIFIC GROUP, INC.
4700 Spring St Ste 304, La Mesa, CA 91942
Tel.: (619) 702-1404 DE
Web Site: http://www.bmsn.us
BMSN—(OTCIQ)
Sales Range: Less than $1 Million
Emp.: 3
Biotechnology Research & Development
N.A.I.C.S.: 541714
David R. Koos (Chm, Pres, CEO, Acting CFO & Sec)

Subsidiaries:

Regen Biopharma, Inc. (1)
4700 Spring St Ste 304, La Mesa, CA 91942
Tel.: (619) 722-5505
Web Site:
https://www.regenbiopharmainc.com
Rev.: $236,560
Assets: $353,617
Liabilities: $5,457,617
Net Worth: ($5,104,000)
Earnings: $1,023,508
Emp.: 1
Fiscal Year-end: 09/30/2023
Pharmaceuticals Mfr
N.A.I.C.S.: 325412
David R. Koos (Chm, Pres, CEO, Treas & Sec)

BIO-PATH HOLDINGS, INC.
4710 Bellaire Blvd Ste 210, Bellaire, TX 77401
Tel.: (832) 742-1357 UT
Web Site:
https://www.biopathholdings.com
Year Founded: 2007
BPTH—(NASDAQ)
Rev.: $33,000
Assets: $15,971,000
Liabilities: $1,797,000
Net Worth: $14,174,000
Earnings: ($13,868,000)
Emp.: 10
Fiscal Year-end: 12/31/22
Pharmaceutical Developer & Mfr
N.A.I.C.S.: 325412
Peter H. Nielsen (Pres, CEO, CFO, Chm & Treas)
Douglas P. Morris (Dir-Investment Rels & Sec)
Ana Tari Ashizawa (Co-Founder & Sr VP-R&D & Clinical Design)
Anthony Price (Sr VP-Fin, Acctg & Admin)

Michael Roberts (Dir-Mfg Plng & En-grg)
Michael Hickey (Dir-Clinical Program Mgmt)

BIO-RAD LABORATORIES, INC.
1000 Alfred Nobel Dr, Hercules, CA 94547
Tel.: (510) 724-7000 DE
Web Site: https://www.bio-rad.com
Year Founded: 1952
BIO—(NYSE)
Rev.: $2,671,262,000
Assets: $12,299,070,000
Liabilities: $3,557,937,000
Net Worth: $8,741,133,000
Earnings: ($637,324,000)
Emp.: 8,030
Fiscal Year-end: 12/31/23
Laboratory Instrument Mfr
N.A.I.C.S.: 334516
Roop K. Lakkaraju (CFO & Exec VP)
Alice Norman Schwartz (Co-Founder)
Timothy S. Ernst (Gen Counsel, Sec & Exec VP)
Michael Crowley (Exec VP-Global Comml Ops)
Diane Dahowski (Exec VP)
Tania DeVilliers (Interim Principal Acctg Officer & Controller)
Jonathan P. DiVincenzo (Pres & COO)
Norman D. Schwartz (Chm & CEO)

Subsidiaries:

Bio Rad S.A. (1)
Eugenia 197 Piso 10-A Colonia Narvarte, Delegacion Benito Juarez, 03020, Mexico, Mexico (100%)
Tel.: (52) 5554887670
Web Site: http://www.bio-rad.com
Sales Range: $75-99.9 Million
Medical Laboratory Instrument Mfr
N.A.I.C.S.: 334516

Bio-Metrics, Limited (1)
PO Box 340, Gladys, VA 22501
Tel.: (804) 448-2520
Web Site: http://www.biometricsltd.com
Medical Instrument Mfr
N.A.I.C.S.: 339112

Bio-Rad AbD Serotec GmbH (1)
Campus Neuried Anna-Sigmund-Str 5, 82061, Neuried, Germany
Tel.: (40) 000000050
Web Site: http://www.bionity.com
Emp.: 100
Medical Laboratory Instrument Mfr
N.A.I.C.S.: 334516

Bio-Rad AbD Serotec Ltd (1)
Endeavour House Langford Business Park Langford Lane, Kidlington, OX5 1GE, Oxfordshire, United Kingdom
Tel.: (44) 1865852700
Web Site: http://www.abdserotec.com
Emp.: 90
Medical Laboratory Instrument Mfr
N.A.I.C.S.: 334516

Bio-Rad Denmark ApS (1)
Symbion Science Park Fruebjergvej 3, 2100, Copenhagen, Denmark
Tel.: (45) 44521000
Laboratory Instruments Distr
N.A.I.C.S.: 423490

Bio-Rad Finland Oy (1)
Kutomotie 16, 00380, Helsinki, Finland
Tel.: (358) 98042200
Life Science Research Services
N.A.I.C.S.: 541715

Bio-Rad France (1)
3 Bld Raymond Poincare, 92430, Marnes-la-Coquette, France
Tel.: (33) 147959300
Analytical Laboratory Instrument Distr
N.A.I.C.S.: 424210

Bio-Rad France Holding (1)
3 Blvd Raymond Poincare, Paris, 92430,

Marnes-la-Coquette, France (100%)
Tel.: (33) 147956000
Web Site: http://www.biorad.com
Sales Range: $150-199.9 Million
Holding Company
N.A.I.C.S.: 424690

Subsidiary (Domestic):

Bio-Rad Laboratories S.A.S. (2)
3 bld Raymond Poincare, 92430, Marnes-la-Coquette, France (100%)
Tel.: (33) 147959300
Web Site: http://www.biorad.fr
Sales Range: $10-24.9 Million
Emp.: 24
Research & Clinical Diagnostic Services
N.A.I.C.S.: 541714

Unit (Domestic):

Bio-Rad (3)
3 bld Raymond Poincare, 92430, Marnes-la-Coquette, France (100%)
Tel.: (33) 147959300
Web Site: http://www.bio-rad.com
Sales Range: $10-24.9 Million
Pharmaceutical Preparation Services
N.A.I.C.S.: 325412

Bio-Rad Verdot (3)
1 Rue Andre Messager, 63200, Riom, France (100%)
Tel.: (33) 473337070
Web Site: http://www.bio-rad.com
Laboratory Instrument Mfr
N.A.I.C.S.: 334516

Bio-Rad Haifa Ltd. (1)
Guthwirth Park Technion Campus, PO Box 16, Haifa, 32000, Israel
Tel.: (972) 48123103
Web Site: http://www.bio-rad.com
Sales Range: $10-24.9 Million
Emp.: 25
Medical Laboratory Instrument Mfr
N.A.I.C.S.: 334516

Bio-Rad Hungary Trading Ltd. (1)
Futo utca 47-53, 1082, Budapest, Hungary (100%)
Tel.: (36) 14596190
Web Site: http://www.biorad.com
Sales Range: $50-74.9 Million
Distr of Diagnostic Chemicals & Kits
N.A.I.C.S.: 424210

Bio-Rad Korea Limited (1)
10th Floor Hyunjuk Building, Gangnam-Gu, Seoul, 135-080, Korea (South)
Tel.: (82) 234734460
Sales Range: $25-49.9 Million
Emp.: 35
Medical Laboratory Instrument Mfr
N.A.I.C.S.: 334516
Michael Cho (Mgr-Div)

Bio-Rad Laboratories (1)
Nizhny Susalny pereulok 5 building 5A, 105064, Moscow, Russia (100%)
Tel.: (7) 4957211404
Web Site: http://www.bio-rad.com
Sales Range: $150-199.9 Million
Emp.: 100
Life Science & Clinical Diagnostic Services
N.A.I.C.S.: 325412

Bio-Rad Laboratories (Canada) Ltd. (1)
1329 Meyerside Drive, Mississauga, L5T 1C9, ON, Canada (100%)
Tel.: (905) 364-3435
Web Site: http://www.bio-rad.com
Sales Range: $25-49.9 Million
Medical Laboratory Instrument Mfr
N.A.I.C.S.: 334516

Bio-Rad Laboratories (India) Pvt. Ltd. (1)
Emaar Digital Greens 9th Floor Tower A-Sector 61, Gurgaon, 122 102, Haryana, India
Tel.: (91) 1244029300
Web Site: http://www.bio-rad.com
Medical Laboratory Instrument Mfr
N.A.I.C.S.: 334516

Bio-Rad Laboratories (Shanghai) Co., Ltd. (1)
Room 601 Anlian Building No 168 Jingzhou

Road, Yangpu District, Shanghai, 200082, China
Tel.: (86) 216 169 8500
Web Site: http://www.bio-rad.com
Medical Laboratory Instrument Mfr
N.A.I.C.S.: 334516

Bio-Rad Laboratories (Singapore) Pte. Limited (1)
3A International Business Park Road 11-10/16 ICON IBP Tower B, Singapore, 609935, Singapore
Tel.: (65) 64153170
Web Site: http://www.bio-rad.com
Medical Laboratory Instrument Mfr
N.A.I.C.S.: 334516

Bio-Rad Laboratories AB (1)
Vretenvagen 13, PO Box 1097, Solna, 171 54, Sundbyberg, Sweden **(100%)**
Tel.: (46) 84498053
Web Site: http://www.bio-rad.com
Sales Range: $50-74.9 Million
Medical Laboratory Instrument Mfr
N.A.I.C.S.: 334516
Henrik Skoglund (Mng Dir)

Bio-Rad Laboratories AG (1)
Pra Rond 23, 1785, Cressier, Switzerland
Tel.: (41) 617179555
Laboratory Instruments Distr
N.A.I.C.S.: 423490

Bio-Rad Laboratories B.V. (1)
PO Box 222, 3905 AE, Veenendaal, Netherlands
Tel.: (31) 318540666
Laboratory Instruments Distr
N.A.I.C.S.: 423490

Bio-Rad Laboratories E.P.E. (1)
2-4 Mesogion Ave Athens Tower, 11527, Athens, Greece
Tel.: (30) 21077744396
Web Site: http://www.bio-rad.com
Sales Range: $50-74.9 Million
Diagnostic Chemical & Kit Distr
N.A.I.C.S.: 424210
Demetre Cyritsis (Mng Dir)

Bio-Rad Laboratories Europe Limited (1)
3 Riverview Business Park, Perth, PH2 8DF, Perthshire, United Kingdom
Tel.: (44) 1738444102
Sales Range: $10-24.9 Million
Emp.: 4
Analytical & Biomedical Laboratory Instrument Mfr
N.A.I.C.S.: 334516

Bio-Rad Laboratories GmbH (1)
Kapellenstrasse 12, 85622, Feldkirchen, Germany **(100%)**
Tel.: (49) 8931884393
Web Site: http://www.bio-rad.com
Medical Laboratory Instrument Mfr
N.A.I.C.S.: 334516

Subsidiary (Non-US):

Bio-Rad Laboratories, Ges.m.b.H. (2)
Euro Plaza Business Center Am Euro Platz 2, 1120, Vienna, Austria **(100%)**
Tel.: (43) 187789019
Web Site: http://www.bio-rad.com
Sales Range: $10-24.9 Million
Medical Laboratory Instrument Mfr
N.A.I.C.S.: 334516

Bio-Rad Laboratories Israel (1996) Ltd. (1)
14 Hahoma Street, New Industrial Area, Rishon le Zion, 7565513, Israel **(100%)**
Tel.: (972) 39636000
Web Site: http://www.biorad.com
Sales Range: $150-199.9 Million
Emp.: 55
Diagnostic Chemical & Kit Distr
N.A.I.C.S.: 424210

Bio-Rad Laboratories K.K. (1)
2-2-24 Higashi-shinagawa, Shinagawa-ku, Tokyo, 140-0002, Japan
Tel.: (81) 36 361 7070
Web Site: https://www.bio-rad.com
Medical Laboratory Instrument Mfr
N.A.I.C.S.: 334516

Bio-Rad Laboratories Limited (1)
1st and 2nd Floor Lumpini -1 Building 239/2 Rajbamri Road, Lumpini Pathumwan, Bangkok, 10330, Thailand
Tel.: (66) 26518311
Web Site: http://www.bio-rad.com
Sales Range: $25-49.9 Million
Analytical & Biomedical Instrument Mfr & Marketer
N.A.I.C.S.: 334516

Bio-Rad Laboratories Ltd. (1)
The Junction Station Road, Watford, WD17 1ET, Herdfordshire, United Kingdom **(100%)**
Tel.: (44) 1923471301
Web Site: http://www.bio-rad.com
Sales Range: $50-74.9 Million
Medical Laboratory Instrument Mfr
N.A.I.C.S.: 334516

Bio-Rad Laboratories M E.P.E. (1)
2-4 Mesogion Ave Athens Tower, Ampelokipi, 11527, Athens, Greece
Tel.: (30) 210 777 4396
Web Site: http://www.bio-rad.com
Medical Laboratory Instrument Mfr
N.A.I.C.S.: 334516

Bio-Rad Laboratories Pty. Limited (1)
Unit 1A 62 Ferndell Street, Gladesville, 2142, NSW, Australia **(100%)**
Tel.: (61) 299142800
Web Site: http://www.bio-rad.com
Sales Range: $25-49.9 Million
Medical Laboratory Instrument Mfr
N.A.I.C.S.: 334516

Bio-Rad Laboratories S.A. (1)
Garrotxa 10-12 Parc de Negocis Mas Blau, El Prat de Llobregat, 08820, Barcelona, Spain **(100%)**
Tel.: (34) 914906580
Web Site: http://www.bio-rad.com
Sales Range: $50-74.9 Million
Emp.: 15
Medical Laboratory Instrument Mfr
N.A.I.C.S.: 334516

Bio-Rad Laboratories S.A. (1)
Edificio Gorbea 4 pl 1 Avenida Bruselas 20, El Soto de la Moraleja, 28108, Alcobendas, Spain **(100%)**
Tel.: (34) 914906580
Web Site: http://www.bio-rad.com
Sales Range: $350-399.9 Million
Distr of Diagnostic Chemicals & Kits
N.A.I.C.S.: 424210

Bio-Rad Laboratories S.r.L. (1)
Via Cellini 18/A, 20090, Segrate, MI, Italy **(100%)**
Tel.: (39) 0249486600
Web Site: http://www.bio-rad.com
Sales Range: $50-74.9 Million
Medical Laboratory Instrument Mfr
N.A.I.C.S.: 334516

Bio-Rad Laboratories, Inc. (1)
6565 185th Ave NE, Redmond, WA 98052-5039 **(100%)**
Tel.: (425) 881-8300
Web Site: http://www.bio-rad.com
Sales Range: $50-74.9 Million
Emp.: 210
Diagnostic & Therapeutic Product Mfr
N.A.I.C.S.: 334516

Bio-Rad Laboratories, Inc. - Clinical Diagnostics (1)
1000 Alfred Nobel Dr, Hercules, CA 94547-1803
Tel.: (510) 724-7000
Web Site: http://www.bio-rad.com
Sales Range: $10-24.9 Million
Emp.: 500
Clinical Diagnostic Product & Test Kit Mfr
N.A.I.C.S.: 339112

Bio-Rad Laboratories, Inc. - Life Science Group (1)
1000 Alfred Nobel Dr, Hercules, CA 94547-1801
Tel.: (510) 741-1000
Web Site: http://www.bio-rad.com
Sales Range: $700-749.9 Million
Emp.: 1,400
Instrument & Chemical System Component Mfr

Bio-Rad Laboratories, Inc. - Spectroscopy Products (1)
2000 Market St, Philadelphia, PA 19103
Tel.: (267) 322-6931
Web Site: http://www.bio-rad.com
Sales Range: $10-24.9 Million
Emp.: 25
Retail Data & Software Product Mfr
N.A.I.C.S.: 334610

Bio-Rad Laboratories-Aparelhos e Reagentes para Laboratorios, LDA (1)
Torre Monsanto Rua Afonso Praca 30 7 andar, 1495-061, Alges, Portugal
Tel.: (351) 21 472 7700
Web Site: http://www.bio-rad.com
Medical Laboratory Instrument Mfr
N.A.I.C.S.: 334516

Bio-Rad Laboratorii LLC (1)
Nizhny Susalny lane building 5 building 5A, Moscow, 105064, Russia
Tel.: (7) 4957211404
Diagnostic Products Mfr
N.A.I.C.S.: 325413

Bio-Rad Laboratorii OOO (1)
Nizhniy Susalny lane 5 Building 5A, 105064, Moscow, Russia
Tel.: (7) 4957211404
Web Site: http://www.diamed.com
Medical Laboratory Instrument Mfr
N.A.I.C.S.: 334516

Bio-Rad Laboratorios Brasil Ltda. (1)
Avenida Doutor Chucri Zaidan 1240 cj 1902 e 1904 Morumbi Corporate, Santo Amaro, Sao Paulo, 04711-130, SP, Brazil **(100%)**
Tel.: (55) 1130657550
Web Site: http://www.biorad.com
Sales Range: $50-74.9 Million
Emp.: 30
Medical Laboratory Instrument Mfr
N.A.I.C.S.: 334516

Bio-Rad Laboratorios Brasil Ltda. (1)
Avenida Doutor Chucri Zaidan 1 240 cj 1902 e 1904 Morumbi Corporate, Santo Amaro, Sao Paulo, 04711-130, Brazil
Tel.: (55) 113 065 7550
Web Site: http://www.bio-rad.com
Diagnostic Chemical & Kit Distr
N.A.I.C.S.: 424210

Bio-Rad Ltd. (1)
Bio-Rad House Maylands Avenue, Bio-Rad House Maxted Road, Hemel Hempstead, HP2 7TD, Hertfordshire, United Kingdom
Tel.: (44) 1442232552
Analytical & Biomedical Instrument Mfr & Distr
N.A.I.C.S.: 334516

Bio-Rad New Zealand (1)
189 Bush Road, Rosedale, Auckland, 0632, New Zealand
Tel.: (64) 94152280
Life Science Research Services
N.A.I.C.S.: 541715

Bio-Rad Pacific Ltd. (1)
Unit 1101 11/Fl DCH Commercial Centre 25 Westlands Rd, 25 Westlands Rd, Quarry Bay, China (Hong Kong) **(100%)**
Tel.: (852) 27893300
Web Site: http://www.bio-rad.com
Sales Range: $25-49.9 Million
Emp.: 30
Medical & Hospital Equipment Retailer
N.A.I.C.S.: 423450

Bio-Rad Polska Sp. z o.o. (1)
Przyokopowa 33 Level 4 building A, 01-208, Warsaw, Poland
Tel.: (48) 223319981
Web Site: http://www.bio-rad.com
Medical Laboratory Instrument Mfr
N.A.I.C.S.: 334516

Bio-Rad QSD Division (1)
9500 Jeronimo Rd, Irvine, CA 92618-2017
Tel.: (949) 598-1200
Web Site: http://www.biorad.com
Sales Range: $200-249.9 Million
Emp.: 500
Control Sera & Solution Mfr

N.A.I.C.S.: 325411
Norman D. Schwartz (Chm, Pres & CEO)

Bio-Rad SNC (1)
3 bld Raymond Poincare, Marnes-la-Coquette, 92430, Paris, France
Tel.: (33) 147956000
Web Site: http://www.bio-rad.com
Laboratory Equipment Distr
N.A.I.C.S.: 423450

Bio-Rad Services UK Limited (1)
The Junction 4th Floor Station Road, Watford, WD17 1ET, Herdfordshire, United Kingdom
Tel.: (44) 1923471301
Laboratory Instruments Distr
N.A.I.C.S.: 423490

Bio-Rad spol. sr.o (1)
Pikrtova 1737/1a, 140 00, Prague, Czech Republic
Tel.: (420) 241431660
Web Site: http://www.bio-rad.com
Sales Range: $50-74.9 Million
Medical Laboratory Instrument Mfr
N.A.I.C.S.: 334516

BioMetrics Ltd (1)
PO Box 340 Ladysmith, Ruther Glen, VA 22501
Tel.: (804) 448-2520
Web Site: https://www.biometricsltd.com
Analytical & Biomedical Instrument Mfr
N.A.I.C.S.: 334516

Central Labo Europe SAS (1)
3 Boulevard Raymond Poincare, Marnes La Coquette, Boulogne-Billancourt, 92430, France
Tel.: (33) 147956000
Blood & Plasma Handling Tool & Component Mfr
N.A.I.C.S.: 334516

DiaMed (G.B.) Limited (1)
Unit 2 Whitehill Business Centre, Dalkeith, EH22 2QB, Midlothian, United Kingdom
Tel.: (44) 1316540876
Web Site: http://www.diamed.com
Clinical Diagnostic Device Mfr
N.A.I.C.S.: 334516

DiaMed (Schweiz) G.m.b.H. (1)
Route du Pra Rond 23, 1785, Cressier, Switzerland
Tel.: (41) 26 674 5111
Web Site: https://ih-area.bio-rad.com
Clinical Diagnostic Device Mfr
N.A.I.C.S.: 334516

DiaMed Benelux, N.V. (1)
Winninglaan 3, 9140, Temse, Belgium
Tel.: (32) 37105300
Web Site: http://www.diamed.com
Clinical Diagnostic Device Mfr
N.A.I.C.S.: 334516

DiaMed Diagnostika Deutschland G.m.b.H. (1)
Heidemannstrasse 164, 80939, Munich, Germany
Tel.: (49) 89 318 84 0
Web Site: http://www.diamed.com
Clinical Diagnostic Device Mfr
N.A.I.C.S.: 334516

DiaMed Fennica Oy (1)
Valimotie 1 B, 00380, Helsinki, Finland
Tel.: (358) 97597500
Web Site: http://www.diamed.com
Sales Range: $10-24.9 Million
Emp.: 12
Clinical Diagnostic Device Mfr
N.A.I.C.S.: 334516

DiaMed G.m.b.H. (1)
Route du Pra Rond 23, 1785, Cressier, FR, Switzerland
Tel.: (41) 266745111
Web Site: http://www.diamed.com
Laboratory Equipment Mfr
N.A.I.C.S.: 334515
Bruno Spycher (Partner-HR-Bus)

DiaMed Holding AG (1)
A Division Of Bio-Rad Route Du Pra-Rond 23, Cressier, 1785, Switzerland **(77.7%)**
Tel.: (41) 266745111
Sales Range: $200-249.9 Million
Emp.: 400
Laboratory Diagnostic Product Distr

N.A.I.C.S.: 423490
Norman D. Schwartz (Chm, Pres & CEO)

Bio-Rad Laboratories, Inc.—(Continued)

N.A.I.C.S.: 621511

Subsidiary (Domestic):

DiaMed AG **(2)**
Rte du Pra Rond 23, 1785, Cressier, Switzerland
Tel.: (41) 266745111
Web Site: http://www.diamed.com
Sales Range: $100-124.9 Million
Emp.: 250
Research & Development Production Services
N.A.I.C.S.: 334516

Subsidiary (Non-US):

DiaMed Deutschland GmbH **(2)**
Heidemannstrasse 164, 80939, Munich, Germany
Tel.: (49) 89318840
Sales Range: $150-199.9 Million
Emp.: 300
Laboratory Diagnostic Products Whslr
N.A.I.C.S.: 423450

DiaMed France S.A. **(2)**
3 Boulevard Raymond Poincare, 92430, Marnes-la-Coquette, France
Tel.: (33) 147959300
Web Site: http://www.bio-rad.com
Laboratory Diagnostic Products Mfr
N.A.I.C.S.: 334516

DiaMed Latino America S.A. **(2)**
Rua Alfredo Albano Costa 100, Distrito Industrial Genesco A de Oliveira, Lagoa Santa, 33240-095, MG, Brazil
Tel.: (55) 3136896600
Web Site: https://diamed.com.br
Sales Range: $50-74.9 Million
Emp.: 100
Clinical Diagnostic Device Mfr
N.A.I.C.S.: 334516

DiaMed Osterreich GmbH **(2)**
Hummelgasse 88 3-6, 1130, Vienna, Austria
Tel.: (43) 1877890133
Web Site: http://www.diamed.com
Sales Range: $150-199.9 Million
Emp.: 6
Clinical Diagnostic Device Mfr
N.A.I.C.S.: 334516
Anita Glombik (Mng Dir)

IMV Medical Information Division, Inc. **(1)**
1400 E Touhy Ave Ste 250, Des Plaines, IL 60018-3339
Tel.: (847) 297-1404
Web Site: http://www.imvinfo.com
Health Care Consulting Services
N.A.I.C.S.: 621610

International Marketing Ventures, Limited **(1)**
671 North Glebe Rd Ste 1610, Arlington, VA 22203
Tel.: (703) 778-3080
Web Site: http://www.imvinfo.com
Healthcare Consulting Firm Services
N.A.I.C.S.: 621610

RSL N.V. **(1)**
Begoniastraat 5, Nazareth, 9810, Belgium **(100%)**
Tel.: (32) 93855511
Web Site: http://www.bio-rad.com
Sales Range: $150-199.9 Million
Emp.: 40
Warehouse Distr
N.A.I.C.S.: 493190

RainDance Technologies, Inc. **(1)**
749 Middlesex Tpke, Billerica, MA 01821
Tel.: (978) 495-3300
Web Site: http://www.raindancetech.com
Laboratory Instruments & Chemicals Mfr
N.A.I.C.S.: 334516
Jonathan M. Rothberg (Founder)

BIO-TECHNE CORPORATION
614 McKinley Pl NE, Minneapolis, MN 55413
Tel.: (612) 379-8854 **MN**
Web Site: https://www.bio-techne.com

Year Founded: 1981
TECH—(NASDAQ)
Rev.: $1,159,060,000
Assets: $2,703,867,000
Liabilities: $635,017,000
Net Worth: $2,068,850,000
Earnings: $168,105,000
Emp.: 3,100
Fiscal Year-end: 06/30/24
Holding Company; Biotechnology Products; Genes, Cytokines & Polyclonal & Monoclonal Antibodies, Clinical Research Diagnostics Kits & Hematology Controls Developer & Producer
N.A.I.C.S.: 551112
Matthew F. McManus (Pres-Diagnostics & Genomics Segment)
Robert V. Baumgartner (Chm)
James T. Hippel (CFO & Exec VP)
Robert Gavin (Sr VP-Analytical Solutions Div)
Kim Kelderman (COO)
Peter Breloer (VP-APAC)
Michael Deines (VP-Reagent Solutions Div)
Steven M. Silverman (VP-Exosome Diagnostics)
Kevin Smyth (Chief Digital Officer & Sr VP)
Gary Stapleton (VP-EMEA)
William Alexander Geist (Pres-Protein Sciences Segment)
Steve Crouse (VP-Analytical Solutions Div)
Shane Bohnen (Gen Counsel, Sec & Sr VP)

Subsidiaries:

Advanced Cell Diagnostics, Inc. **(1)**
7707 Gateway Blvd, Newark, CA 94560 **(100%)**
Tel.: (510) 576-8800
Web Site: https://www.acdbio.com
Sales Range: $25-49.9 Million
Emp.: 100
Develops Cell & Tissue Based Diagnostic Testing
N.A.I.C.S.: 541380
Christopher Bunker (VP-Bus Dev)

Asuragen, Inc. **(1)**
2150 Woodward St Ste 100, Austin, TX 78744-1837
Tel.: (512) 681-5200
Web Site: http://www2.asuragen.com
Oncology Testing Kits Development, Mfr & Commercialization
N.A.I.C.S.: 541714
Matthew Winkler (Chm)
Tom Copa (VP-Comml)
Bernard F. Andruss (COO)
Gary J. Latham (Chief Scientific Officer)

B-MoGen Biotechnologies Inc. **(1)**
1621 E Hennepin Ave Ste B-15, Minneapolis, MN 55414
Tel.: (612) 353-5562
Web Site: http://www.bmogen.com
Emp.: 1,500
Biotechnology Research & Development Services
N.A.I.C.S.: 541714
Jeff S. Liter (Pres & CEO)

Bio-Techne Ltd. **(1)**
19 Barton Lane Abingdon Science Park, Abingdon, OX14 3NB, United Kingdom
Tel.: (44) 1235529449
Biotechnology Research & Development Services
N.A.I.C.S.: 541714

Cliniqa Corporation **(1)**
495 Enterprise St, San Marcos, CA 92078
Tel.: (760) 744-1900
Web Site: http://www.cliniqa.com
Clinical Diagnostic & Biological Material Products Mfr
N.A.I.C.S.: 325414
Shing Kwan (VP-Dev)
Bruce Thompson (Sr Dir-Sls)

Exosome Diagnostics, Inc. **(1)**

266 2nd Ave Ste 200, Waltham, MA 02451
Tel.: (617) 588-0500
Web Site: https://www.exosomedx.com
Research & Development Services
N.A.I.C.S.: 541714

Novus Biologicals, LLC **(1)**
10771 E Easter Ave, Centennial, CO 80112
Tel.: (303) 730-1950
Web Site: https://www.novusbio.com
Sales Range: $1-9.9 Million
Emp.: 75
Biological Products Research & Development
N.A.I.C.S.: 325414
Karen Padgett (Founder)

ProteinSimple **(1)**
3001 Orchard Pkwy, San Jose, CA 95134
Tel.: (408) 510-5500
Web Site: http://www.proteinsimple.com
Sales Range: $50-74.9 Million
Emp.: 170
Instrumentation Systems, Software & Assay Product Mfr
N.A.I.C.S.: 334516

Subsidiary (Non-US):

ProteinSimple Ltd. **(2)**
21 Canmotor Ave, Etobicoke, Toronto, M8Z 4E6, ON, Canada
Tel.: (613) 591-7715
Web Site: http://www.proteinsimple.com
Instrumentation Systems, Software & Assay Product Mfr
N.A.I.C.S.: 334516

Research and Diagnostic Systems, Inc. **(1)**
614 McKinley Pl NE, Minneapolis, MN 55413-2610 **(100%)**
Tel.: (612) 379-2956
Web Site: https://www.rndsystems.com
Sales Range: $200-249.9 Million
Emp.: 630
Biotechnology Products Mfr; Genes, Cytokines & Polyclonal & Monoclonal Antibodies, Clinical Research Diagnostics Kits & Clinical Diagnostics
N.A.I.C.S.: 541714

Subsidiary (Domestic):

Bionostics Inc. **(2)**
7 Jackson Rd, Devens, MA 01434 **(100%)**
Tel.: (978) 772-7070
Web Site: http://www.bionostics.com
Sales Range: $25-49.9 Million
Emp.: 97
Developer & Mfr of Calibrators & Quality Control Products for Critical Care/Point-of-Care & Diabetes Diagnostics Test Systems
N.A.I.C.S.: 330112
Matthew Rice (Mng Dir)

BiosPacific, Inc. **(2)**
5980 Horton St Ste 360, Emeryville, CA 94608
Tel.: (510) 652-6155
Web Site: http://www.biospacific.com
Develops, Manufactures & Sells Biotechnology Research & Diagnostic Products
N.A.I.C.S.: 541714
Patricia Facchini (Mng Dir)

Boston Biochem, Inc. **(2)**
840 Memorial Dr, Cambridge, MA 02139
Tel.: (617) 576-2210
Web Site: http://www.bostonbiochem.com
Production of Ubiquitin-Related Research Products
N.A.I.C.S.: 541715
Francesco Melandri (Founder)

Subsidiary (Non-US):

R&D Systems China Co., Ltd. **(2)**
15 k Hua Min Empire Plaza, 726 West Yan An Road, Shanghai, 200050, China
Tel.: (86) 21 52380373
Web Site:
http://www.rndsystemschina.com.cn
Biotechnology Products Distr
N.A.I.C.S.: 423450

Subsidiary (Domestic):

Shanghai PrimeGene Bio-Tech Co., Ltd. **(3)**
Unit 1901 Tower 3 Raffles City Changning

Office 1193 Changning Road, Shanghai, 200051, China
Tel.: (86) 2160276091
Web Site: http://www.primegene.com
Emp.: 50
Biological Products Research & Development
N.A.I.C.S.: 325414
Huisheng Wang (CEO)

Subsidiary (Non-US):

R&D Systems Europe, Ltd. **(2)**
19 Barton Lane Abingdon Science Park, Abingdon, OX14 3NB, Oxfordshire, United Kingdom **(100%)**
Tel.: (44) 1235 529449
Web Site: http://www.bio-techne.com
Sales Range: $10-24.9 Million
Emp.: 55
Biotechnology Products Distr
N.A.I.C.S.: 541714
Ruth Bright (Mng Dir)

Subsidiary (Non-US):

R&D Systems GmbH **(3)**
Borιig Strasse 7, Wiesbaden, 65205, Germany **(100%)**
Tel.: (49) 612290980
Web Site: http://www.rndsystems.com
Sales Range: $10-24.9 Million
Emp.: 15
Seller of Biotechnology Products; Cytokines & Polyclonal & Monoclonal Antibodies, Clinical Research & Diagnostics Kits
N.A.I.C.S.: 541714

Subsidiary (Domestic):

Tocris Cookson Limited **(3)**
Tocris House IO Centre, Moorend Farm Avenue, Bristol, BS11 0QL, United Kingdom
Tel.: (44) 177 916 3333
Web Site: http://www.tocris.com
Reagents Mfr & Supplier
N.A.I.C.S.: 325414

Trevigen, Inc. **(1)**
8405 Helgerman Ct, Gaithersburg, MD 20877
Tel.: (301) 216-2800
Web Site: http://www.trevigen.com
Sales Range: $1-9.9 Million
Emp.: 12
Biotechnology Research & Development
N.A.I.C.S.: 541714
Michael Elliott (Pres)

BIOADAPTIVES, INC.
2620 Regatta Dr Ste 102, Las Vegas, NV 89128
Tel.: (702) 659-8829 **DE**
Web Site: https://bioadaptives.com
Year Founded: 2013
BDPT—(OTCIQ)
Rev.: $17,176
Assets: $37,314
Liabilities: $1,488,815
Net Worth: ($1,451,501)
Earnings: ($895,570)
Emp.: 3
Fiscal Year-end: 12/31/22
Dietary Supplements & Specialty Food Items
N.A.I.C.S.: 325411
J. Tim Pruban (Chief Restructuring Officer)

BIOAFFINITY TECHNOLOGIES, INC.
22211 W Interstate 10 Ste 1206, San Antonio, TX 78257
Tel.: (210) 698-5334 **DE**
Web Site:
https://www.bioaffinitytech.com
Year Founded: 2014
BIAF—(NASDAQ)
Rev.: $4,803
Assets: $12,182,125
Liabilities: $1,138,682
Net Worth: $11,043,443
Earnings: ($8,154,113)
Emp.: 14

Fiscal Year-end: 12/31/22
Research & Development in Biotech-
nology (except Nanobiotechnology)
N.A.I.C.S.: 541714
Maria Zannes (Founder, Pres & CEO)
Steven Girgenti (Chm)
Julie Anne Overton (Dir-Comm)
J. Michael Edwards (Interim CFO &
Principal Acctg Officer)

BIOASIS TECHNOLOGIES INC.

157 Church St 19 th Fl, New Haven,
CT 06510
Tel.: (203) 533-7082   BC
Web Site: http://www.bioasis.us
Year Founded: 2006
BTI—(TSXV)
Rev.: $3,190,239
Assets: $2,563,032
Liabilities: $2,244,490
Net Worth: $318,541
Earnings: $546,352
Fiscal Year-end: 02/28/21
Neurological Disease Therapeutics &
Diagnostics Researcher, Developer &
Mfr
N.A.I.C.S.: 541715
Deborah A. Rathjen (Chm, Pres &
CEO)
Dave Jenkins (CFO)
Mei Mei Tian (VP & Head-External
Res)
Michael Discepolo (Controller)
David M. Wurzer (Dir-Lead)

BIOATLA, INC

11085 Torreyana Rd, San Diego, CA
92121-2719
Tel.: (858) 558-0708
Web Site: https://www.bioatla.com
Year Founded: 2007
BCAB—(NASDAQ)
Emp.: 65
Electronic Shopping
N.A.I.C.S.: 325411
Jay Short (Mgr)
Richard Waldron (CFO)
Eric Sievers (Chief Medical Officer)
Sheri Lydick (Chief Comml Officer)
Cathy Chang (Sr VP-Res & Develop-
ment)
Gerhard Frey (Sr VP-Tech Dev)
Susie Melody (Sr VP-Human Re-
sources)
Monica Sullivan (Sr VP-Intellectual
Property & Contracts)
Chris Vasquez (Sr VP-Finance)
Michael Melnick (VP-CMC)
Scott A. Smith (Exec Dir)

BIOCARDIA, INC.

320 Soquel Way, Sunnyvale, CA
94085
Tel.: (650) 226-0120   DE
Web Site: https://www.biocardia.com
Year Founded: 2002
BCDA—(NASDAQ)
Rev.: $477,000
Assets: $2,987,000
Liabilities: $4,590,000
Net Worth: ($1,603,000)
Earnings: ($11,571,000)
Emp.: 16
Fiscal Year-end: 12/31/23
Holding Company; Biopharmaceutical
Developer & Mfr
N.A.I.C.S.: 551112
Ian McNiece (Chief Scientific Officer)
Peter A. Altman (Pres & CEO)
David McClung (CFO)
Sujith Shetty (Chief Medical Officer &
VP-Clinical & Regulatory)
Edward Gillis (Sr VP-Devices)

Subsidiaries:

BioCardia Lifesciences, Inc.   (1)

125 Shoreway Rd Ste B, San Carlos, CA
94070-2718
Tel.: (650) 226-0120
Web Site: http://www.biocardia.com
Sales Range: $1-9.9 Million
Emp.: 30
Biopharmaceutical Developer & Mfr
N.A.I.C.S.: 325412

BIOCENTRIC ENERGY HOLD-INGS, INC.

7030 Gelding, Scottsdale, AZ 85260
Tel.: (714) 914-3686   FL
Year Founded: 1996
BEHL—(OTCIQ)
Renewable Energy Consulting Ser-
vices
N.A.I.C.S.: 541690
Michael Burton (Pres, Treas & Sec)

BIOCEPT, INC.

9955 Mesa Rim Rd, San Diego, CA
92121
Tel.: (858) 320-8200   DE
Web Site: https://www.biocept.com
Year Founded: 1997
BIOC—(NASDAQ)
Rev.: $25,858,000
Assets: $30,873,000
Liabilities: $22,013,000
Net Worth: $8,860,000
Earnings: ($32,087,000)
Emp.: 50
Fiscal Year-end: 12/31/22
Cancer Research & Testing Laborato-
ries
N.A.I.C.S.: 621511

BIOCORRX INC.

2390 E Orangewood Ave Ste 500,
Anaheim, CA 92806
Tel.: (714) 462-4880   NV
Web Site: https://www.biocorrx.com
Year Founded: 2008
BICX—(OTCQB)
Rev.: $213,841
Assets: $766,594
Liabilities: $8,968,325
Net Worth: ($8,201,731)
Earnings: ($4,369,413)
Fiscal Year-end: 12/31/22
Alcoholism Treatment Services
N.A.I.C.S.: 621420
Lourdes Felix (Founder, CEO & CFO)
George Fallieras (Dir-Medical)
Louis Charles Lucido (Pres)

BIOCRYST PHARMACEUTI-CALS, INC.

4505 Emperor Blvd Ste 200, Durham,
NC 27703
Tel.: (919) 859-1302   DE
Web Site: https://www.biocryst.com
Year Founded: 1986
BCRX—(NASDAQ)
Rev.: $270,827,000
Assets: $550,000,000
Liabilities: $844,597,000
Net Worth: ($294,597,000)
Earnings: ($247,116,000)
Emp.: 531
Fiscal Year-end: 12/31/22
Small Molecule Pharmaceutical Re-
search & Development Services
N.A.I.C.S.: 325414
Helen M. Thackray (Chief R&D Offi-
cer)
William P. Sheridan (Chief Dev Offi-
cer)
Jon P. Stonehouse (Pres & CEO)
Anthony J. Doyle (CFO, Interim Prin-
cipal Acctg Officer & Sr VP)
Ryan Arnold (Chief Medical Officer)
Yarlagadda S. Babu (Chief Discovery
Officer)
Alane P. Barnes (Chief Legal Officer)
Michael L. Jones (Exec Dir-Fin)

Charlie Gayer (Chief Comml Officer)
John Bluth (Chief Comm Officer)
Stephanie Angelini (Chief People Offi-
cer)
Anthony J. Doyle (CFO)
Clayton Fletcher (Chief Bus Dev Offi-
cer)
Philip George (Chief Strategy Officer)
Jinky Rosselli (Chief Data Officer)

Subsidiaries:

MDCP, LLC   (1)
5120 Woodway Dr Ste 6022, Houston, TX
77056
Tel.: (928) 634-9536
Pharmaceuticals Product Mfr
N.A.I.C.S.: 325412

BIODESIX, INC.

919 W Dillon Rd, Louisville, CO
80027
Tel.: (303) 417-0500   DE
Web Site: https://www.biodesix.com
Year Founded: 2005
BDSX—(NASDAQ)
Rev.: $38,212,000
Assets: $92,906,000
Liabilities: $72,300,000
Net Worth: $20,606,000
Earnings: ($65,447,000)
Emp.: 245
Fiscal Year-end: 12/31/22
Biotechnology Research & Develop-
ment Services
N.A.I.C.S.: 541714
James R. Jett (Co-Chief Medical Offi-
cer)
Kieran O'Kane (Chief Comml Officer)
John Patience (Chm)
Robin Harper Cowie (CFO, Treas &
Sec)
Gary Pestano (Chief Dev Officer)
Steven Springmeyer (Co-Chief Medi-
cal Officer)
Christopher Vazquez (Chief Acctg
Officer)
Matthew Pink (Sr Dir)
Brianna Phillips (VP)
Molli Halvorson (Dir)
Robbie Lunt (Sr Dir)
Mark DeBlock (VP)
Scott Hutton (Pres & CEO)

BIOELECTRONICS CORP.

4539 Metropolitan Ct, Frederick, MD
21704
Tel.: (301) 874-4890
Web Site: https://www.bielcorp.com
BIEL—(OTCIQ)
Electromedical Equipment Mfr
N.A.I.C.S.: 334510
Kelly Whelan (Pres & CEO)
Keith Nalepka (VP-Sales & Market-
ing)
John M. Martinez (VP-Engineering)

BIOELIFE CORP.

12340 Seal Beach Blvd Ste B 190,
Seal Beach, CA 90740
Tel.: (702) 866-2500   NV
Web Site:
  http://www.uslithiumcorp.com
Year Founded: 2006
LITH—(OTCIQ)
Sales Range: Less than $1 Million
Metal Mining & Exploration Services
N.A.I.C.S.: 212290
Gregory C. Rotelli (Pres, CEO, CFO,
Treas & Sec)

BIOETHICS, LTD.

1661 Lakeview Cir, Ogden, UT 84403
Tel.: (801) 399-3632   NV
Year Founded: 1990
BOTH—(OTCIQ)
Assets: $138

Liabilities: $776,403
Net Worth: ($776,265)
Earnings: ($97,149)
Fiscal Year-end: 12/31/23
Investment Services
N.A.I.C.S.: 523999
Mark A. Scharmann (CEO & Treas)

BIOFORCE NANOSCIENCES HOLDINGS, INC.

2020 General Booth Blvd Ste 230,
Virginia Beach, VA 23454
Tel.: (757) 306-6090   NV
Web Site:
  https://www.bioforceeclipse.com
Year Founded: 1999
BFNH—(OTCIQ)
Assets: $638
Liabilities: $1,819,868
Net Worth: ($1,819,230)
Earnings: ($471,953)
Emp.: 3
Fiscal Year-end: 12/31/23
Nutritional Supplement Distr
N.A.I.C.S.: 456191
Merle Ferguson (Chm)
Steven Gagnon (Co-CEO)
John LaViolette (Co-CEO)
Sasha Shapiro (Pres)
Richard Kaiser (CFO, Principal Acctg
Officer & Sec)

BIOFRONTERA INC.

120 Presidential Way Ste 330, Wo-
burn, MA 01801
Tel.: (781) 245-1325   DE
Web Site: https://www.biofrontera-
us.com
Year Founded: 2015
BFRI—(NASDAQ)
Rev.: $28,674,000
Assets: $50,884,000
Liabilities: $27,006,000
Net Worth: $23,878,000
Earnings: ($640,000)
Emp.: 81
Fiscal Year-end: 12/31/22
Research & Development in Biotech-
nology (except Nanobiotechnology)
N.A.I.C.S.: 541714
Hermann Luebbert (Chm & CEO)
Mark Baldyga (Sls Dir-Natl)
Dan Walker (Dir-Comml Ops)
Jeff Holm (Head-Professional &
Comml Dev)
Christopher Almeida (Head-Market
Access & Trade)
Daniel Hakansson (Gen Counsel &
Head-Compliance)
Erica Gates (Controller)
Montserrat Foguet (Sr VP-Regulatory
Affairs & Technical Ops)
Wiebke Meyer-Wendt (VP-Quality
Mgmt)
Armin Ollig (VP-IT)
Leslie Hopkins (Assoc Dir-Mktg)
Fred Leffler (CFO)

BIOGEN INC.

225 Binney St, Cambridge, MA 02142
Tel.: (781) 464-2000   DE
Web Site: https://www.biogen.com
Year Founded: 2003
BIIB—(NASDAQ)
Rev.: $9,835,600,000
Assets: $26,844,800,000
Liabilities: $12,045,400,000
Net Worth: $14,799,400,000
Earnings: $1,161,100,000
Emp.: 7,570
Fiscal Year-end: 12/31/23
Pharmaceuticals Mfr
N.A.I.C.S.: 325414
Phillip A. Sharp (Founder)
Robin C. Kramer (Chief Acctg Officer,
Sr VP & Head-Global Bus Svcs &
Treasury)

Biogen Inc.—(Continued)

Christopher A. Viehbacher (Pres & CEO)
Alphonse Galdes (Exec VP- Technology)
Michael R. McDonnell (CFO & Exec VP)
Jane Grogan (Exec VP & Head-Res)
Priya Singhal (Exec VP & Head-Dev)
Maha Radhakrishnan (Chief Medical Officer & Sr VP)
Wolfram Schmidt (Partner, Pres, Europe & Canada)
Kendra Thomas (Chief Legal Officer, Corp Counsel, Sec & Sr VP)
Caroline D. Dorsa (Chm)
Ginger Gregory (Chief HR Officer & Exec VP)

Subsidiaries:

Biogen (Argentina) SRL (1)
Av del Libertador 350-7 piso, Vicente Lopez, Buenos Aires, Argentina
Tel.: (54) 1155508150
Web Site: https://ar.biogen.com
Pharmaceutical Product Whslr
N.A.I.C.S.: 424210

Biogen (Czech Republic) s.r.o. (1)
Na Pankraci 1683/127, Praha 4, 140 00, Prague, Czech Republic
Tel.: (420) 255706200
Web Site: https://www.biogen.com.cz
Pharmaceuticals Product Mfr
N.A.I.C.S.: 325412

Biogen (Denmark) A/S (1)
Stationsparken 37 3, 2600, Glostrup, Denmark
Tel.: (45) 77415757
Web Site: http://www.biogen.dk
Pharmaceutical Preparation Mfr
N.A.I.C.S.: 325412

Subsidiary (Domestic):

Biogen Idec (Denmark) Manufacturing ApS (2)
Biotek Alle 1, 3400, Hillerod, Denmark (100%)
Tel.: (45) 77416000
Web Site: http://www.biogenidec.dk
Emp.: 200
Pharmaceuticals Mfr
N.A.I.C.S.: 325412

Biogen (Denmark) A/S (1)
Stationsparken 37 3, Glostrup, 2600, Denmark
Tel.: (45) 77415757
Web Site: http://www.biogen.dk
Biological Product Mfr
N.A.I.C.S.: 325414

Biogen Australia PTY Ltd (1)
Level 4 2 Banfield Road, Macquarie Park, 2113, NSW, Australia
Tel.: (61) 288753900
Web Site: https://www.biogen.com.au
Pharmaceutical Product Whslr
N.A.I.C.S.: 424210

Biogen Belgium N.V./S.A. (1)
Parklane-Culliganlaan 2G, 1831, Diegem, Belgium
Tel.: (32) 22191218
Web Site: http://www.biogen.be
Pharmaceuticals Product Mfr
N.A.I.C.S.: 325412
Kris Schellens (Mng Dir)

Biogen Brasil Produtos Farmaceuticos LTDA (1)
Condominio E-Tower Rua Funchal 418 - 7th floor, Vila Olimpia, Sao Paulo, 04551-060, SP, Brazil
Tel.: (55) 1135683400
Web Site: http://br.biogen.com
Pharmaceuticals Product Mfr
N.A.I.C.S.: 325412

Biogen Canada Inc. (1)
3250 Bloor Street West East Tower Suite 1200, Toronto, M8X 2X9, ON, Canada
Tel.: (416) 234-7999
Web Site: http://www.biogen.ca

Therapy Preparation Mfr & Distr
N.A.I.C.S.: 325414
Marina Vasiliou (Dir Gen & VP)

Biogen Estonia OU (1)
Kesklinna linnaosa Hobujaama tn 4, 10151, Tallinn, Estonia
Tel.: (372) 6189551
Web Site: https://www.biogen.ee
Biotechnology Development Services
N.A.I.C.S.: 541714

Biogen Finland OY (1)
Bertel Jungin aukio 5c, 02600, Espoo, Finland
Tel.: (358) 207401200
Web Site: https://www.biogen.fi
Pharmaceuticals Product Mfr
N.A.I.C.S.: 325412
Dennis Baars (Sr Mgr-Fin)

Biogen France S.A.S. (1)
1 Passerelle des Reflets Tour CBX, La Defense, 92913, Paris, Cedex, France
Tel.: (33) 141379595
Web Site: https://www.biogen.fr
Pharmaceuticals Product Mfr
N.A.I.C.S.: 325412
David Setboun (Mng Dir & VP)

Biogen GmbH (1)
Riedenburger Strasse 7, 81677, Munich, Germany
Tel.: (49) 89996170
Web Site: http://www.biogen.de
Pharmaceuticals Product Mfr
N.A.I.C.S.: 325412

Biogen Hemophilia Inc. (1)
225 Binney St, Cambridge, MA 02142
Tel.: (781) 464-3260
Web Site: http://www.biogenhemophilia.com
Biological Product Mfr
N.A.I.C.S.: 325414
David Spotts (Sr Mgr-Product)

Biogen Hong Kong Limited (1)
Level 46 Lee Garden One 33 Hysan Avenue, Causeway Bay, China (Hong Kong)
Tel.: (852) 25883483
Biotechnology Development Services
N.A.I.C.S.: 541714

Biogen Hungary KFT (1)
Dorottya Udvar C epulet 1 emelet Bocskai ut 134-146 1113 Budapest, 1113, Budapest, Hungary
Tel.: (36) 18999880
Web Site: https://www.biogen.hu
Pharmaceutical Product Mfr
N.A.I.C.S.: 325412

Biogen Idec (Ireland) Ltd. (1)
United Drug House Magna Business Park Magna Drive, Dublin, D24 XKE5, Ireland
Tel.: (353) 14637725
Web Site: https://www.biogen-uk-ie.com
Biological Product Mfr
N.A.I.C.S.: 325414

Biogen Idec (Singapore) Pte Ltd (1)
460 Alexandra Rd Unit No 15-01 PSA Building, Singapore, 119963, Singapore
Tel.: (65) 68764588
Sales Range: $25-49.9 Million
Emp.: 7
Biological Product Mfr
N.A.I.C.S.: 325414
Fred McMahon (Mng Dir)

Biogen Idec Belgium S.A./N.V. (1)
Parklane - Culliganlaan 2G, PO Box 1831, 1831, Diegem, Belgium
Tel.: (32) 22191218
Web Site: http://www.biogenidec.be
Sales Range: $10-24.9 Million
Emp.: 27
Provider of Pharmaceutical Preparations
N.A.I.C.S.: 325412

Biogen Idec France (1)
1 passerelle des Reflets Tour CBX, 92913, Paris, France (100%)
Tel.: (33) 141379595
Web Site: https://www.biogen.fr
Sales Range: $10-24.9 Million
Emp.: 50
Pharmaceuticals Mfr
N.A.I.C.S.: 325412
David Setboun (Chm)

Biogen Idec GmbH (1)
Riedenburger Strsse 7, 81677, Munich, Germany (100%)
Tel.: (49) 89996170
Web Site: http://www.biogen.de
Sales Range: $10-24.9 Million
Emp.: 400
Provider of Pharmaceutical Preparations
N.A.I.C.S.: 325412

Biogen Idec GmbH (1)
Stella-Klein-Low-Weg 15/3, 1020, Vienna, Austria (100%)
Tel.: (43) 14844613
Web Site: https://www.biogen.at
Sales Range: $10-24.9 Million
Emp.: 20
Provider of Pharmaceutical Preparations
N.A.I.C.S.: 325412

Biogen Idec Iberia (1)
Paseo De La Castellana 41 1st Fl, 28046, Madrid, Spain
Tel.: (34) 913107110
Web Site: http://www.biogen.com.es
Sales Range: $150-199.9 Million
Emp.: 40
Developer, Manufacturer & Marketer of Pharmaceuticals
N.A.I.C.S.: 325412

Biogen Idec International B.V. (1)
Prins Mauritslaan 13-19, 1171 LP, Badhoevedorp, Netherlands (100%)
Tel.: (31) 205422000
Web Site: https://www.biogen.nl
Sales Range: $25-49.9 Million
Emp.: 40
Pharmaceuticals Mfr
N.A.I.C.S.: 325412

Biogen Idec International GmbH (1)
Landis Gyr Strasse 3, Zug, 6300, Switzerland
Tel.: (41) 413921700
Web Site: http://www.biogen.com
Pharmaceuticals Product Mfr
N.A.I.C.S.: 325412

Biogen Idec Japan Ltd. (1)
Nihonbashi 1-chome Mitsui Building 14F 4-1, Chuo-ku, Tokyo, 103-0027, Japan
Tel.: (81) 332751900
Web Site: http://www.biogenidec.co.jp
Sales Range: $10-24.9 Million
Emp.: 50
Provider of Pharmaceutical Preparations
N.A.I.C.S.: 325412

Biogen Idec Limited (1)
Innovation House 70 Norden Road, Maidenhead, SL6 4AY, Berkshire, United Kingdom (100%)
Tel.: (44) 1628501000
Web Site: https://www.biogen.uk.com
Sales Range: $50-74.9 Million
Provider of Pharmaceutical Preparations
N.A.I.C.S.: 325412

Biogen Idec MA Inc. (1)
14 Cambridge Ctr, Cambridge, MA 02142
Tel.: (617) 679-2000
Biotechnology Research & Development Services
N.A.I.C.S.: 541714

Biogen Idec Portugal Sociedade Farmaceutica, Unipessoal, Lda. (1)
Avenida Duque D'Avila 141 - 7 Andar, 1050-081, Lisbon, Portugal
Tel.: (351) 213188450
Web Site: http://www.biogen.pt
Sales Range: $25-49.9 Million
Emp.: 27
Pharmaceuticals Product Mfr
N.A.I.C.S.: 325412
Anabela Fernandes (CEO)

Biogen Idec Research & Corporate Campus (1)
5000 Davis Dr, Research Triangle Park, NC 27709-4627 (100%)
Tel.: (919) 941-1100
Web Site: http://www.biogen.com
Sales Range: $150-199.9 Million
N.A.I.C.S.: 325412

Biogen Idec Sweden AB (1)
Kanalvagen 12 plan 5, 194 61, Upplands Vasby, Sweden

Tel.: (46) 859411360
Web Site: http://www.biogen.se
Pharmaceutical Preparation Mfr
N.A.I.C.S.: 325412

Biogen International GmbH (1)
Neuhofstrasse 30, 6340, Baar, Switzerland
Tel.: (41) 413921700
Web Site: https://www.biogen-international.com
Pharmaceuticals Product Mfr
N.A.I.C.S.: 325412

Biogen Italia SRL (1)
Centro Leoni Via Spadolini 5, 20141, Milan, Italy
Tel.: (39) 025849901
Web Site: https://www.biogenitalia.it
Biological Product Mfr
N.A.I.C.S.: 325414

Biogen Japan Ltd. (1)
14th floor Nihonbashi 1-chome Mitsui Building 1-4-1, Nihonbashi Chuo-Ku, Tokyo, 103-0027, Japan
Tel.: (81) 332751900
Web Site: http://www.biogen.co.jp
Biological Product Mfr
N.A.I.C.S.: 325414

Biogen Korea (1)
Sindeok-ri Seongnam-myeon, Cheonan, 330-893, Chungcheongnam-do, Korea (South)
Tel.: (82) 415236201
Web Site: http://biogen.koreasme.com
Food Additive Mfr & Distr
N.A.I.C.S.: 311999

Biogen Latvia SIA (1)
Audeju iela 15-4, Riga, 1050, Latvia
Tel.: (371) 68688158
Web Site: https://www.biogen.lv
Biotechnology Development Services
N.A.I.C.S.: 541714

Biogen Lithuania UAB (1)
Gedimino pr 20, Vilnius, Lithuania
Tel.: (370) 52596176
Web Site: https://www.biogen.lt
Biotechnology Development Services
N.A.I.C.S.: 541714

Biogen NZ Biopharma Ltd. (1)
188 Quay Street, Auckland, 1010, New Zealand
Tel.: (64) 800852289
Web Site: https://www.biogen.co.nz
Biological Product Mfr
N.A.I.C.S.: 325414

Biogen Netherlands B.V. (1)
Prins Mauritslaan 13-19, 1171 LP, Badhoevedorp, Netherlands
Tel.: (31) 205422000
Pharmaceuticals Product Mfr
N.A.I.C.S.: 325412

Biogen New Ventures Inc. (1)
5200 Research Pl, San Diego, CA 92122
Tel.: (858) 401-8000
Hospital & Medical Service Provider
N.A.I.C.S.: 525190

Biogen Norway AS (1)
Vitaminveien 1 a, 0485, Oslo, Norway
Tel.: (47) 23400100
Web Site: https://www.biogen.no
Biological Product Mfr
N.A.I.C.S.: 325414

Biogen Pharma d.o.o. (1)
Savska cesta 32, 10000, Zagreb, Croatia
Tel.: (385) 17757322
Biotechnology Development Services
N.A.I.C.S.: 541714

Biogen Pharma, farmacevtska in biotehnoloska druzba d.o.o (1)
Ameriska ulica 8, 1000, Ljubljana, Slovenia
Tel.: (386) 15110290
Web Site: http://www.biogen-pharma.si
Biomedical Product Mfr
N.A.I.C.S.: 325414

Biogen Poland Sp. z.o.o (1)
Ul Salsy 2, 02-823, Warsaw, Poland
Tel.: (48) 223515100
Web Site: https://www.biogen-poland.pl
Biological Product Mfr

N.A.I.C.S.: 325414

Biogen Portugal Sociedade Farmaceutica, Unipessoal, Lda. (1)
Av Duque de Avila 141 - 7 andar, 1050-081, Lisbon, Portugal
Tel.: (351) 213188450
Web Site: http://www.biogen.pt
Pharmaceuticals Product Mfr
N.A.I.C.S.: 325412

Biogen Slovakia s.r.o. (1)
Aupark Tower Einsteinova 24, 851 01, Bratislava, Slovakia
Tel.: (421) 232334008
Web Site: https://www.biogen.sk
Biomedical Product Mfr
N.A.I.C.S.: 325414

Biogen Spain, S.L. (1)
Paseo De La Castellana 41, 28046, Madrid, Spain
Tel.: (34) 913107110
Web Site: https://www.biogen.com.es
Pharmaceuticals Product Mfr
N.A.I.C.S.: 325412

Biogen Sweden AB (1)
Kanalvagen 10A 7tr, 194 61, Upplands Vasby, Sweden
Tel.: (46) 859411360
Pharmaceutical Medicine Distr
N.A.I.C.S.: 424210

Biogen Switzerland AG (1)
Neuhofstrasse 30, 6340, Baar, Switzerland
Tel.: (41) 417287444
Web Site: https://www.biogen.ch
Pharmaceuticals Product Mfr
N.A.I.C.S.: 325412
Ronald Alder (Head-Comml)

Biogen U.S. Corporation (1)
225 Binney St, Cambridge, MA 02142-1026
Tel.: (781) 464-2000
Web Site: https://www.biogen.com
Pharmaceutical Product Whslr
N.A.I.C.S.: 424210

Convergence Pharmaceuticals Ltd. (1)
Maia Building Babraham Research Campus, Cambridge, CB22 3AT, United Kingdom
Tel.: (44) 1223755501
Web Site: http://www.convergencepharma.com
Biomedical Product Mfr
N.A.I.C.S.: 325414
Brenda Reynolds (COO)

Fundacion Biogen (1)
Av San Martin 224, Salta, Argentina
Tel.: (54) 3874212257
Web Site: http://biogen.org.ar
Pharmaceuticals Product Mfr
N.A.I.C.S.: 325412

Nightstar Therapeutics plc (1)
10 Midford Place 2nd Floor, London, W1T 5BJ, United Kingdom
Tel.: (44) 20 7062 2777
Web Site: http://www.nightstartx.com
Biotechnology Research & Development Services
N.A.I.C.S.: 541714

Reata Pharmaceuticals, Inc. (1)
5320 Legacy Dr, Plano, TX 75024
Tel.: (972) 865-2213
Web Site: http://www.reatapharma.com
Rev.: $2,700,000
Emp.: 35
Fiscal Year-end: 12/31/2006
Pharmaceutical Developer
N.A.I.C.S.: 325412

BIOHAVEN LTD.
215 Church St, New Haven, CT 06510
Tel.: (203) 404-0410   VG
Web Site: https://www.biohaven.com
Year Founded: 2022
BHVN—(NYSE)
Rev.: $26,500,000
Assets: $513,212,000
Liabilities: $85,237,000
Net Worth: $427,975,000
Earnings: ($408,168,000)

Emp.: 239
Fiscal Year-end: 12/31/23
Biotechnology Research & Development Services
N.A.I.C.S.: 541714

BIOLARGO, INC.
14921 Chestnut St, Westminster, CA 92683
Tel.: (949) 643-9540   DE
Web Site: https://www.biolargo.com
BLGO—(OTCQB)
Rev.: $5,884,000
Assets: $4,858,000
Liabilities: $2,847,000
Net Worth: $2,011,000
Earnings: ($4,473,000)
Emp.: 32
Fiscal Year-end: 12/31/22
Chemical Products Mfr
N.A.I.C.S.: 325998
Dennis P. Calvert (Chm, Pres & CEO)
Kenneth Reay Code (Chief Science Officer)
Joseph L. Provenzano (Sec & Exec VP-Ops)
Tonya Chandler (Dir-Strategic Mktg & Bus Dev)
Charles K. Dargan II (CFO)
A. J. Sexton V (Dir-Bus Dev)

Subsidiaries:

BioLargo Engineering, Science & Technologies, LLC (1)
105 Fordham Rd, Oak Ridge, TN 37830
Tel.: (865) 813-6455
Web Site: https://www.biolargoengineering.com
Chemical Products Mfr
N.A.I.C.S.: 325998
Dan Jarvis (Dir-Ops)
Russell Bryson (Principal, VP, VP & Engr)
Kevin Jackson (VP & Dir-Technical)
Randall Moore (Pres)
Wes Larsen (VP-West Coast Ops)

BioLargo Water, Inc. (1)
6020-118 St NW, Edmonton, T6G 2E1, AB, Canada
Tel.: (780) 492-6994
Web Site: http://www.biolargowater.com
Water Decontamination Services
N.A.I.C.S.: 562910
Richard Smith (Pres & CEO)
Laura Patterson-Fortin (Chief Science Officer)

ONM Environmental, Inc. (1)
14921 Chestnut St, Westminster, CA 92683
Web Site: https://onmenvironmental.com
Engineering Services
N.A.I.C.S.: 541330
Joseph Provenzano (Pres & CEO)
Kenneth R. Code (Chief Science Officer)
Mitch Noto (Dir-Bus Dev)
Bonnie Guthrie (Acct Mgr)
Levi Rodriguez (Mgr-Warehouse)

BIOLASE, INC.
27042 Towne Centre Dr Ste 270, Foothill Ranch, CA 92610-2811
Tel.: (949) 361-1200   DE
Web Site: https://www.biolase.com
Year Founded: 1994
BIOL—(NASDAQ)
Rev.: $48,462,000
Assets: $38,186,000
Liabilities: $33,297,000
Net Worth: $4,889,000
Earnings: ($28,634,000)
Emp.: 188
Fiscal Year-end: 12/31/22
Dental Equipment & Supplies Manufacturing
N.A.I.C.S.: 339114
Jennifer Bright (CFO)
Richard R. Whipp (VP-Ops)
Samuel B. Low (Chief Dental Officer & VP-Dental & Clinical Affairs)
Matthew Wilson (VP-HR)

John R. Beaver (Pres & CEO)
Stephen I. Jang (VP-APAC, EMEA & Latin America)
David L. Rodriguez (VP-Dental Education & Professional Rels)
Steven Sandor (COO)

Subsidiaries:

Biolase Europe GmbH (1)
Paintweg 10a, 92685, Floss, Germany
Tel.: (49) 960 380 8202
Web Site: https://www.biolase.de
Sales Range: $1-9.9 Million
Emp.: 10
Medical & Dental Laser Mfr
N.A.I.C.S.: 339112

BIOLIFE SOLUTIONS, INC.
3303 Monte Villa Pkwy Ste 310, Bothell, WA 98021
Tel.: (425) 402-1400   DE
Web Site:
   https://www.biolifesolutions.com
Year Founded: 1998
BLFS—(NASDAQ)
Rev.: $161,759,000
Assets: $450,229,000
Liabilities: $86,041,000
Net Worth: $364,188,000
Earnings: ($139,805,000)
Emp.: 466
Fiscal Year-end: 12/31/22
Biological Product Mfr
N.A.I.C.S.: 325414
Geraint Phillips (Sr VP-Global Ops)
Roderick de Greef (Chm, Pres & CEO)
Aby J. Mathew (Chief Scientific Officer & Exec VP)
Todd Berard (CMO)
Karen A. Foster (Chief Quality Officer)
Sarah Aebersold (VP-HR-Global)
Troy Wichterman (CFO)
Garrie Richardson (Chief Revenue Officer)

BIOMAGNETICS DIAGNOSTICS CORP.
8864 Greenback Ln Ste E, Orangevale, CA 95662
Tel.: (916) 987-7078   NV
BMGP—(OTCIQ)
Diagnostic Equipment Mfr
N.A.I.C.S.: 334510
Clayton A. Hardman (Pres & CEO)

BIOMARIN PHARMACEUTICAL INC.
770 Lindaro St, San Rafael, CA 94901
Tel.: (415) 506-6700   DE
Web Site: https://www.bmrn.com
Year Founded: 1997
BMRN—(NASDAQ)
Rev.: $2,419,226,000
Assets: $6,841,603,000
Liabilities: $1,890,054,000
Net Worth: $4,951,549,000
Earnings: $167,645,000
Emp.: 3,401
Fiscal Year-end: 12/31/23
Biotechnology Research & Development Services
N.A.I.C.S.: 541714
Richard A. Meier (Chm)
Alexander Hardy (Pres & CEO)
Henry J. Fuchs (Pres-Worldwide & R&D)
Brinda Balakrishnan (VP-Corp & Bus Dev-Grp)
Harold S Bernstein (Chief Medical Officer, Sr VP & Head-Clinical Dev)

Subsidiaries:

BioMarin Brasil Farmaceutica Ltda. (1)

Rua James Joule 92 - 4 andar, Moncoes, Sao Paulo, 04576-080, Brazil
Tel.: (55) 8007220350
Web Site: http://www.biomarin.com
Sales Range: $25-49.9 Million
Emp.: 30
Biopharmaceutical Product Mfr
N.A.I.C.S.: 541715

BioMarin International Ltd (1)
Shanbally, Cork, Ringaskiddy, P43 R298, Ireland
Tel.: (353) 215007990
Pharmaceuticals Product Mfr
N.A.I.C.S.: 325412
Siobhan O'Sullivan (Coord-HR)

BioMarin Leiden Holding BV (1)
Barbara Strozzilaan 201, 1083 HN, Amsterdam, Netherlands
Tel.: (31) 713322100
Pharmaceutical Preparation Mfr & Distr
N.A.I.C.S.: 325412

BIOMEA FUSION, INC.
900 Middlefield Rd 4th Fl, Redwood City, CA 94063
Tel.: (650) 980-9099   DE
Web Site:
   https://www.biomeafusion.com
Year Founded: 2017
BMEA—(NASDAQ)
Rev.: $1,806,000
Assets: $129,307,000
Liabilities: $20,768,000
Net Worth: $108,539,000
Earnings: ($81,828,000)
Emp.: 83
Fiscal Year-end: 12/31/22
Biotechnology Research & Development Services
N.A.I.C.S.: 541714
Franco Valle (CFO & Principal Acctg Officer)
Rainer M. Erdtmann (Co-Founder, Pres & COO)
Heow Tan (Chief Technical & Quality Officer)
Naomi Cretcher (Chief People Officer)
Anthony Souza (Head-IT)
Thorsten Kirschberg (Exec VP-Chemistry)
Taisei Kinoshita (VP-Biology)
John Paul Frias (Chief Medical Officer)
Steve Morris (Chief Dev Officer)
Thomas Butler (Co-Founder, Chm & CEO)

BIOMERICA, INC.
17571 Von Karman Ave, Irvine, CA 92614
Tel.: (949) 645-2111   DE
Web Site: https://www.biomerica.com
Year Founded: 1971
BMRA—(NASDAQ)
Rev.: $5,415,000
Assets: $9,254,000
Liabilities: $2,663,000
Net Worth: $6,591,000
Earnings: ($5,978,000)
Emp.: 63
Fiscal Year-end: 05/31/24
Medical Diagnostic Product Mfr & Distr
N.A.I.C.S.: 334510
Zack Irani-Cohen (Chm & CEO)
Susan Luka (Mgr-HR)
Connie Trahan (Mgr-Sls Promo & Corp Librarian)
Joe Rink (Mgr-Quality Control)
Allen C. Barbieri (Vice Chm & Sec)
Patrick Garcia (Mgr-MIS)
Gary Lu (CFO & Principal Acctg Officer)

Subsidiaries:

BioEurope GmbH   (1)

Biomerica, Inc.—(Continued)

Europaplatz 1, 88131, Lindau, Germany
Tel.: (49) 83829479790
Web Site: https://www.bioeuropegmbh.com
Medical Equipment Mfr
N.A.I.C.S.: 339112

BIOMIMIX, INC.
44081 Pipeline Plz Ste 320, Ashburn,
VA 20147
Tel.: (703) 889-8332　　　　DE
Year Founded: 1986
BMMX—(OTCIQ)
Medical Equipment & Device Mfr
N.A.I.C.S.: 339112
Robert Lyles (Chm & CEO)

**BION ENVIRONMENTAL TECH-
NOLOGIES, INC.**
Tel.: (516) 249-5682　　　　CO
Web Site: https://www.biontech.com
Year Founded: 1987
BNET—(OTCQB)
Rev.: $652
Assets: $112,252
Liabilities: $5,883,180
Net Worth: ($5,770,928)
Earnings: ($11,691,115)
Emp.: 5
Fiscal Year-end: 06/30/24
Waste Management Solutions for Ag-
ricultural & Farming Industries
N.A.I.C.S.: 562111
Dominic Bassani (CEO)
Jon Northrop (Sec)
Edward Thomas Schafer (Vice Chm)

BIONANO GENOMICS, INC.
9540 Towne Ctr Dr Ste 100, San Di-
ego, CA 92121
Tel.: (858) 888-7600　　　　DE
Web Site: https://bionano.com
Year Founded: 2003
BNGO—(NASDAQ)
Rev.: $36,116,000
Assets: $214,404,000
Liabilities: $118,247,000
Net Worth: $96,157,000
Earnings: ($232,493,000)
Emp.: 344
Fiscal Year-end: 12/31/23
Analytical Laboratory Instrument Mfr
& Distr
N.A.I.C.S.: 334516
R. Erik Holmlin (Pres, CEO & Princi-
pal Fin Officer)
David L. Barker (Chm)
Alka Chaubey (Chief Medical Officer)
Mark Oldakowski (COO)
Stanislas Marin (VP-Global Sls)
Donna Polizio (Head-Market Access)
Alex Hastie (VP-Clinical & Scientific
Affairs)
Patrick Lynch (VP-Platform Dev)
Viren Wasnikar (VP-Software Engrg)
Mike Stringfellow (VP-Global Cus-
tomer Solutions)
Jonathan Dixon (Gen Counsel)
Cory Kreeck (Head-Global People
Ops)
Todd Woodring (VP-Operations)
Klint Rose (Head-Research & Devel-
opment)
Albert Luderer (Chm)

Subsidiaries:

BioDiscovery, Inc.　　　　　　　(1)
715 N Douglas St, El Segundo, CA 90245
Tel.: (310) 414-8100
Web Site: https://www.biodiscovery.com
Analysis, Interpretation & Genomics Data
Reporting Services
N.A.I.C.S.: 518210
Mindy Lee-Olsen (VP-Mktg Svcs)

Lineagen, Inc.　　　　　　　　　(1)

423 Wakara Way Ste 200, Salt Lake City,
UT 84108
Tel.: (801) 931-6200
Web Site: http://www.lineagen.com
Medical Laboratories
N.A.I.C.S.: 621511

**BIONITROGEN HOLDINGS
CORP.**
8300 NW 53 St Ste 350, Doral, FL
33166
Tel.: (561) 600-9550　　　　NJ
Web Site: http://www.bionitrogen.com
Year Founded: 1990
BIONQ—(OTCIQ)
Fertilizer Mfr
N.A.I.C.S.: 325311
Graham Lyndhurst Copley (CEO)
Francis X. Gramlich (Compliance Of-
ficer)
Ernesto Iznaga (VP-Ops)
Carla Wolin (Head-HR & Dir-Human
Resources & Labor Relations)
James Calvijo (VP-Corporate Fi-
nance)
Jessie Lozada Jr. (Co-Founder)
Lesley Hollenbeck (Office Mgr & Ac-
countant)
Carlos A. Contreras Sr. (Chm)

**BIOPHAN TECHNOLOGIES,
INC.**
15 Schoen Pl, Pittsford, NY 14534
Tel.: (585) 214-2441
Web Site: http://www.biophan.com
Year Founded: 1968
ACAI—(OTCIQ)
Liabilities: $9
Net Worth: ($9)
Earnings: ($47,000)
Emp.: 1
Fiscal Year-end: 02/29/20
Mfr of Medical Devices
N.A.I.C.S.: 339112

BIOPLUS ACQUISITION CORP.
260 Madison Ave Ste 800, New York,
NY 10016
Tel.: (212) 287-4092　　　　Ky
Year Founded: 2021
BIOS—(NASDAQ)
Rev.: $3,167,128
Assets: $238,324,586
Liabilities: $253,102,698
Net Worth: ($14,778,112)
Earnings: $1,995,932
Emp.: 2
Fiscal Year-end: 12/31/22
Investment Services
N.A.I.C.S.: 523999
Alan C. Mendelson (Chm)
Ross Haghighat (Co-CEO & CFO)
J. Leighton Read (Co-CEO)

BIOQUAL INC.
9600 Medical Center Dr Ste 101,
Rockville, MD 20850-3336
Tel.: (240) 404-7654
Web Site: https://www.bioqual.com
Year Founded: 1981
BIOQ—(OTCIQ)
Rev.: $12,256,453
Emp.: 65
Biological Research
N.A.I.C.S.: 541720
Chander P. Sarma (VP-Facility Ops &
Dir-IT)
Mark G. Lewis (Pres & CEO)
Hanne Andersen (Dir-Res)
Nancy A. Madden (VP-Admin Ops &
Officer-Biosafety)
Mitch Franklin (VP-Ops)
Charles C. Kirk Jr. (CFO)

BIOQUEST CORP.

4570 Campus Dr, Newport Beach,
CA 92660
Tel.: (714) 978-4425　　　　NV
Web Site:
　http://www.bioquestcorp.com
Year Founded: 2011
BQST—(OTCIQ)
Assets: $33,540
Liabilities: $466,530
Net Worth: ($432,990)
Earnings: ($821,022)
Emp.: 7
Fiscal Year-end: 04/30/22
Internet Protocol Television Solutions
N.A.I.C.S.: 334220

BIORA THERAPEUTICS, INC.
4330 La Jolla Vlg Dr Ste 300, San
Diego, CA 92122　　　　DE
Web Site:
　https://www.bioratherapeutics.com
Year Founded: 2012
BIOR—(NASDAQ)
Rev.: $305,000
Assets: $53,525,000
Liabilities: $155,812,000
Net Worth: ($102,287,000)
Earnings: ($38,157,000)
Emp.: 54
Fiscal Year-end: 12/31/22
Medical Testing Services
N.A.I.C.S.: 621511
Aditya P. Mohanty (CEO)
Clarke Neumann (Gen Counsel, Sec
& Sr VP)
Eric d'Esparbes (CFO & Exec VP)
Robyn Hatton (VP-HR & Head-
Human Resources)
Ariella Kelman (Chief Medical Officer)
James Knight (Head-Business Devel-
opment)
Paul Shabram (Head-Technical Ops)
Sharat Singh (Head-Res)
Maria Villanueva (VP-Product Dev
Ops & Program Mgmt)

BIOREGENX, INC.
7407 Ziegler Rd, Chattanooga, TN
37421　　　　NV
Web Site: https://bioregenx.com
BRGX—(OTCIQ)
Rev.: $22,243
Assets: $31,640
Liabilities: $253,612
Net Worth: $221,972
Earnings: ($571,171)
Emp.: 10
Fiscal Year-end: 12/31/23
Research & Development in Biotech-
nology (except Nanobiotechnology)
N.A.I.C.S.: 541714
William R. Resides (CEO)
Sherri Adams (COO)
Dan Cortes (CFO)
Bob Doran (Founder)

**BIORESTORATIVE THERA-
PIES, INC.**
40 Marcus Dr Ste 1, Melville, NY
11747
Tel.: (631) 760-8100　　　　NV
Web Site:
　https://www.biorestorative.com
Year Founded: 1997
BRTX—(NASDAQ)
Rev.: $145,800
Assets: $12,611,720
Liabilities: $1,063,392
Net Worth: $11,548,328
Earnings: ($14,415,484)
Emp.: 11
Fiscal Year-end: 12/31/23
Cellular-Based Treatment Developer
N.A.I.C.S.: 325414
Lance Alstodt (Chm, Pres & CEO)
Mandy D. Clyde (Sec & VP-Ops)

Robert E. Kristal (CFO)
Edward L. Field (Pres-Disc/Spine Div)
Francisco Silva (Sec & VP-R&D)
Robert Paccasassi (VP-Quality &
Compliance)
Robert Kristal (CFO)

**BIOSCIENCE NEUTRACEUTI-
CALS, INC.**
500 N Michigan Ave Ste 600, Chi-
cago, IL 60611
Tel.: (773) 236-8132　　　　NV
Year Founded: 2010
DEVV—(OTCIQ)
Liabilities: $244,142
Net Worth: ($244,142)
Earnings: ($626,046)
Emp.: 2
Fiscal Year-end: 12/31/19
High End Pure Organic Oil Products
Mfr
N.A.I.C.S.: 325998
Liang Chen (CEO & CFO)

**BIOSHAFT WATER TECHNOL-
OGY, INC.**
222 W 6th St #400, San Pedro, CA
90731
Tel.: (310) 707-2553　　　　NV
Web Site: http://www.bioshaft.com
Year Founded: 2006
BSHF—(OTCIQ)
Sales Range: Less than $1 Million
Wastewater Treatment
N.A.I.C.S.: 562219
Imad Kamel Yassine (Co-Founder &
COO)
Bashar Amin (CEO)
Nelson Galan (Mgr-Engrg)
Hisham Younis (VP-Bus Dev)
Zeid Amin (Mgr-Project)

BIOSIG TECHNOLOGIES, INC.
12424 Wilshire Blvd Ste 745, Los An-
geles, CA 90025
Tel.: (203) 409-5444　　　　DE
Web Site: https://www.biosig.com
Year Founded: 2009
BSGM—(NASDAQ)
Rev.: $18,000
Assets: $1,798,000
Liabilities: $4,790,000
Net Worth: ($2,992,000)
Earnings: ($28,690,000)
Emp.: 4
Fiscal Year-end: 12/31/23
Electromedical Device Mfr
N.A.I.C.S.: 334510
Kenneth L. Londoner (Founder)
Kenneth L. Londoner (Chm & CEO)
Anthony Amato (Pres & CEO)
Julie Stephenson (VP-Clinical Affairs)
Andrew Ballou (VP-IR)

**BIOSTEM TECHNOLOGIES,
INC.**
2836 Ctr Port Cir, Pompano Beach,
FL 33064
Tel.: (954) 380-8342
Web Site:
　https://www.biostemtechnology.com
BSEM—(OTCIQ)
Sales Range: Less than $1 Million
Research & Development in the
Physical, Engineering & Life Sciences
(except Nanotechnology & Biotech-
nology)
N.A.I.C.S.: 541715
Thomas J. Dugan (Chm)
Jason Matuszewski (Co-Founder &
CFO)
Andrew Van Vurst (COO & Co-
Founder)
Larry Jones (Chief Revenue Officer)
Chip Van Vurst (CEO & Founder)

BIOTE CORP.

1875 W Walnut Hill Ln Ste100, Irving, TX 75038   DE
Web Site: https://www.biote.com
Year Founded: 2012
BTMD—(NASDAQ)
Rev.: $164,957,000
Assets: $111,645,000
Liabilities: $169,919,000
Net Worth: ($58,274,000)
Earnings: ($969,000)
Emp.: 186
Fiscal Year-end: 12/31/22
Biotechnology Research & Development Services
N.A.I.C.S.: 541714
Robert Peterson (CFO & Principal Acctg Officer)
Marc D. Beer (Exec Chm)
Ross McQuivey (Chief Medical Officer)
Teresa S. Weber (CEO)
James Gibbs (Chief People Officer)
Kevin Key (Chief Digital Officer)
Marybeth Conlon (Gen Counsel & VP-Business Development)
John Olsen (CIO)

BIOTECH ACQUISITION COMPANY

545 W 25th St 20th Fl, New York, NY 10001
Tel.: (212) 227-1905   Ky
Year Founded: 2020
BIOTU—(NASDAQ)
Rev.: $21,259
Assets: $230,320,701
Liabilities: $257,490,450
Net Worth: ($27,169,749)
Earnings: ($6,864,581)
Emp.: 4
Fiscal Year-end: 12/31/21
Investment Services
N.A.I.C.S.: 523999
Michael Shleifer (Chm & CEO)
Ivan Jarry (COO)
Albert F. Hummel (Chief Investment Officer)
Thomas Fratacci (CFO & Treas)

BIOTECH GROUP ACQUISITION CORPORATION

2400 Barranca Pkwy Ste 300, Irvine, CA 92606
Tel.: (949) 468-7078   DE
Year Founded: 2022
BIOT—(NASDAQ)
Investment Services
N.A.I.C.S.: 523999
Yiru Shi (CEO & Chm)
Manu Ohri (CFO)

BIOTECH MEDICS, INC.

5850 Canoga Ave Ste 400, Woodland Hills, CA 91367
Tel.: (727) 789-1848   WY
Year Founded: 2004
BMCS—(OTCIQ)
Health Care Srvices
N.A.I.C.S.: 621112
Natasha Mercer (VP)

BIOTRICITY INC.

203 Redwood Shores Pkwy Ste 600, Redwood City, CA 94065
Tel.: (650) 832-1626   NV
Web Site: https://www.biotricity.com
Year Founded: 2012
BTCY—(NASDAQ)
Rev.: $12,063,345
Assets: $5,942,625
Liabilities: $37,408,362
Net Worth: ($31,465,737)
Earnings: ($14,928,960)
Emp.: 55
Fiscal Year-end: 03/31/24

Energy Software Developer
N.A.I.C.S.: 513210
Waqaas Al-Siddiq (Founder, Chm, Pres & CEO)
John Ayanoglou (CFO)
Amir Ali (Chief Dev Officer)
Spencer LaDow (VP-Engineering)
Ronald McClurg (Executives, Bd of Dirs)

BIOVENTUS INC.

4721 Emperor Blvd Ste 100, Durham, NC 27703
Tel.: (919) 474-6700   DE
Web Site: https://www.bioventus.com
Year Founded: 2015
BVS—(NASDAQ)
Rev.: $512,117,000
Assets: $1,372,649,000
Liabilities: $1,032,317,000
Net Worth: $340,332,000
Earnings: ($158,704,000)
Emp.: 1,120
Fiscal Year-end: 12/31/22
Holding Company
N.A.I.C.S.: 551112
Mark Singleton (CFO, Principal Acctg Officer & Sr VP)
Katrina Church (Chief Compliance Officer & Sr VP)
Anthony D. D'Adamio (Gen Counsel & Sr VP)
Helen Leupold (Chief HR Officer & Sr VP)
Kellie Stefaniak (VP-Global Regulatory & Quality)
Mike Crow (Sr VP-Operations)
Andrew Hosmer (Gen Mgr-Surgical Solutions)
Robert E. Claypoole (Pres & CEO)

Subsidiaries:

Bioness, Inc.   **(1)**
25134 Rye Canyon Loop, Santa Clarita, CA 91355
Tel.: (661) 362-4850
Web Site: https://www.bioness.com
Sales Range: $1-9.9 Million
Emp.: 65
Electromedical & Electrotherapeutic Apparatus Mfr
N.A.I.C.S.: 334510
Todd Cushman (CEO)
Eric Grigsby (Chief Medical Officer)

Bioventus Cooperatief U.A.   **(1)**
Taurusavenue 31, 2132 LS, Hoofddorp, Netherlands
Tel.: (31) 235548888
Medical Device Mfr
N.A.I.C.S.: 339112

Misonix, Inc.   **(1)**
1938 New Hwy, Farmingdale, NY 11735
Tel.: (631) 694-9555
Web Site: http://www.misonix.com
Rev.: $74,024,073
Assets: $198,860,218
Liabilities: $63,660,589
Net Worth: $135,199,629
Earnings: ($14,473,325)
Emp.: 281
Fiscal Year-end: 06/30/2021
Ultrasonic Equipment & Medical Devices Mfr
N.A.I.C.S.: 339112

Subsidiary (Domestic):

Fibra-Sonics (NY) Inc.   **(2)**
1938 New Hwy, Farmingdale, NY 11735
Tel.: (631) 694-9555
Medical & Hospital Equipment Whslr
N.A.I.C.S.: 423450

Solsys Medical, LLC   **(2)**
11830 Canon Blvd Ste A, Newport News, VA 23606
Tel.: (757) 877-8899
Surgical & Medical Equipment Supplier
N.A.I.C.S.: 423490

BIOVIE, INC.

680 W Nye Ln Ste 201, Carson City, NV 89703
Tel.: (775) 888-3162   NV
Web Site: https://bioviepharma.com
Year Founded: 2013
BIVI—(NASDAQ)
Rev.: $1,136,703
Assets: $25,208,345
Liabilities: $9,702,130
Net Worth: $15,506,215
Earnings: ($32,120,533)
Emp.: 14
Fiscal Year-end: 06/30/24
Pharmaceuticals Mfr
N.A.I.C.S.: 325412
James Lang (Chm)
Cuong Do (Pres & CEO)
Joanne Wendy Kim (CFO & Sec)
Joseph M. Palumbo (Chief Medical Officer, Exec VP-Research & Development, Head, Head & Head)
Penelope Markham (Exec VP-Liver Disease & R&D & Sr VP-Liver Disease & Long COVID Programs)
Chris Reading (Exec VP-Neuroscience & R&D & Sr VP-Alzheimer, ', and s Disease Program)
Clarence Ahlem (Exec VP-Neuroscience Product Dev & Sr VP-Operations)

BIOXCEL THERAPEUTICS, INC.

555 Long Wharf Dr 12th Fl, New Haven, CT 06511
Tel.: (475) 238-6837   DE
Web Site:
   https://www.bioxceltherapeutics.com
Year Founded: 2017
BTAI—(NASDAQ)
Rev.: $375,000
Assets: $205,853,000
Liabilities: $129,078,000
Net Worth: $76,775,000
Earnings: ($165,757,000)
Emp.: 183
Fiscal Year-end: 12/31/22
Drug Research & Development Services
N.A.I.C.S.: 541714
Richard I. Steinhart (CFO & Sr VP)
Peter R. Mueller (Chm)
Vincent J. O'Neill (Chief Product Dev & Medical Officer & Exec VP)
Vimal D. Mehta (Pres & CEO)
Frank D. Yocca (Chief Scientific Officer)
Javier Rodriguez (Chief Legal Officer, Sec & Sr VP)
Robert Risinger (Chief Medical Officer)
Rajiv Patni (CEO)

BIOXYTRAN, INC.

233 Needham St Ste 300, Newton, MA 02464
Tel.: (617) 454-1199   NV
Web Site:
   http://www.bioxytraninc.com
Year Founded: 2008
BIXT—(OTCQB)
Assets: $370,936
Liabilities: $3,663,482
Net Worth: ($3,292,546)
Earnings: ($2,463,932)
Fiscal Year-end: 12/31/22
Mineral Distr
N.A.I.C.S.: 423520
David Platt (Founder, Chm, Pres & CEO)
Ola Soderquist (CFO, Treas & Sec)
Mike Sheikh (VP-Bus Dev)

BIRD GLOBAL, INC.

392 NE 191st St 20388, Miami, FL 33179   DE

Web Site: https://ir.bird.co
Year Founded: 2017
BRDS—(NYSE)
Rev.: $244,660,000
Assets: $225,656,000
Liabilities: $200,546,000
Net Worth: $25,110,000
Earnings: ($358,741,000)
Emp.: 425
Fiscal Year-end: 12/31/22
Transportation Services
N.A.I.C.S.: 484220
John Bitove (Founder & Chm)
Stewart Lyons (Pres)
Travis VanderZanden (Founder)
H. Joseph Prodan (CFO)
Hunter Gray (CTO)

BISHOP CAPITAL CORP/WYOMING

222 N Broadway, Riverton, WY 82501
Tel.: (307) 856-3800   WY
BPCP—(OTCIQ)
Real Estate Manangement Services
N.A.I.C.S.: 531210
Robert E. Thraikill (Pres & CEO)
Sherry A. Moore (CFO & Sec)

BIT DIGITAL, INC.

31 Hudson Yards Fl 11, New York, NY 10001
Tel.: (212) 463-5121   Ky
Web Site: https://www.bit-digital.com
Year Founded: 2015
BTBT—(NASDAQ)
Rev.: $44,916,131
Assets: $189,328,382
Liabilities: $36,624,526
Net Worth: $152,703,856
Earnings: ($13,893,281)
Emp.: 24
Fiscal Year-end: 12/31/23
Online Financial Services
N.A.I.C.S.: 522291
Erke Huang (CFO)
Bryan Bullett (CEO)
Sam V. Tabar (Chief Strategy Officer)
Zhaohui Deng (Chm)

BITCOIN DEPOT INC.

2870 Peachtree Rd Ste 327, Atlanta, GA 30305
Tel.: (678) 435-9604
Web Site:
   https://www.bitcoindepot.com
BTM—(NASDAQ)
Financial Investment Services
N.A.I.C.S.: 523999
Glen S. Leibowitz (CFO)
Brandon Mintz (Chm, Pres & CEO)
Scott Buchanan (COO)
Mark Smalley (Chief Compliance Officer)

BITCOIN SERVICES, INC.

3616 Kirkwood Hwy, Wilmington, DE 19808
Year Founded: 2004
BTSC—(OTCIQ)
Escrow Services
N.A.I.C.S.: 523991
Richard T. Fasanella (CEO)

BITECH TECHNOLOGIES CORPORATION

895 Dove St Ste 300, Newport Beach, CA 92660   DE
Web Site: https://bitech.tech
Year Founded: 1998
BTTC—(OTCQB)
Rev.: $308
Assets: $163,417
Liabilities: $35,229
Net Worth: $128,188

Bitech Technologies Corporation—(Continued)

Earnings: ($811,693)
Emp.: 8
Fiscal Year-end: 12/31/23
Holding Company
N.A.I.C.S.: 551112
Robert J. Brilon (CFO)
Benjamin B. Tran (Chm, Pres & CEO)
Paul Vuljanic (Exec VP)
Bradley Kayton (CMO)
Roy Bao (CTO)
Sid Sung (CIO)
Charlie Rosenberry (VP-Sales)
Clay Johnson (VP-Business Development)
Jimmy Harter (VP-Finance)
Julien Tan (Dir-Corporate Communications)

BJ'S RESTAURANTS, INC.

7755 Center Ave Ste 300, Huntington Beach, CA 92647
Tel.: (714) 500-2400   CA
Web Site:
   https://www.bjsrestaurants.com
Year Founded: 1978
BJRI—(NASDAQ)
Rev.: $1,283,926,000
Assets: $1,045,922,000
Liabilities: $700,407,000
Net Worth: $345,515,000
Earnings: $4,076,000
Emp.: 22,000
Fiscal Year-end: 01/03/23
Family Restaurant & Brewhouse Owner & Operator
N.A.I.C.S.: 722511
Alexander M. Puchner (Sr VP-Brewing Ops)
Gregory S. Lynds (Chief Dev Officer & Exec VP)
Thomas A. Houdek (CFO & Sr VP)
Jacob J. Guild (Chief Acctg Officer & Sr VP)
Amy B. Krallman (Chief People Officer, Exec VP & & &)
Putnam K. Shin (Chief Growth Officer, Chief Innovation Officer & Exec VP)
C. Bradford Richmond (Interim CEO)
Lyle D. Tick (Pres & Chief Concept Officer)

Subsidiaries:

BJ's Restaurant Operations Company   (1)
2421 W Osceola Pkwy, Kissimmee, FL 34741
Tel.: (407) 932-5245
Web Site: http://www.bjsrestaurants.com
Emp.: 100
Restaurant Operating Services
N.A.I.C.S.: 722511

Chicago Pizza & Brewery, LP   (1)
2609 S Stemmons Fwy, Lewisville, TX 75067
Tel.: (972) 459-9700
Web Site: https://www.bjsrestaurants.com
Restaurant Operating Services
N.A.I.C.S.: 722511
Fred Greenleaf (Gen Mgr)

Chicago Pizza Hospitality Holding, Inc.   (1)
1106 Town E Mall, Mesquite, TX 75150-4117
Tel.: (972) 682-5800
Investment Management Service
N.A.I.C.S.: 551112

BJ'S WHOLESALE CLUB HOLDINGS, INC.

350 Campus Dr, Marlborough, MA 01752
Tel.: (774) 512-7400   DE
Web Site: https://www.bjs.com

Year Founded: 2011
BJ—(NYSE)
Rev.: $19,968,689,000
Assets: $6,677,622,000
Liabilities: $5,218,771,000
Net Worth: $1,458,851,000
Earnings: $523,741,000
Emp.: 34,000
Fiscal Year-end: 02/03/24
Holding Company
N.A.I.C.S.: 551112
Anjana Harve (CIO & Exec VP)
Robert W. Eddy (Chm, Pres & CEO)
Laura L. Felice (CFO & Exec VP)
Christopher J. Baldwin (Chm)
Paul Cichocki (Chief Comml Officer & Exec VP)
Monica Schwartz (Chief Digital Officer & Exec VP)
William Werner (Exec VP-Strategy & Dev)
Rachel Vegas (Chief Mdsg Officer & Exec VP)
Tim Morningstar (Chief Membership Officer & Exec VP)
Catherine Park (VP-IR)
Peter Frangie (VP-Corp Comm)
Kirk Saville (Head-Corp Comm)

BK TECHNOLOGIES CORPORATION

7100 Technology Dr, West Melbourne, FL 32904
Tel.: (321) 984-1414   NV
Web Site:
   https://www.bktechnologies.com
Year Founded: 1968
BKTI—(NYSEAMEX)
Rev.: $50,951,000
Assets: $48,832,000
Liabilities: $28,697,000
Net Worth: $20,135,000
Earnings: ($11,633,000)
Emp.: 148
Fiscal Year-end: 12/31/22
Mobile Radio Products Mfr
N.A.I.C.S.: 334220
John M. Suzuki (Pres & CEO)

BKF CAPITAL GROUP, INC.

31248 Oak Crest Dr Ste 110, Westlake Village, CA 91361
Tel.: (805) 623-4184   DE
Web Site: http://www.bkfcapital.com
Year Founded: 1954
BKFGD—(OTCIQ)
Sales Range: Less than $1 Million
Emp.: 1
Investment Services
N.A.I.C.S.: 523999
Eugene Vlad Robin (VP)
Steven N. Bronson (Chm & CEO)

BLACK BIRD BIOTECH, INC.

11961 Hilltop Rd Ste 22, Argyle, TX 76226
Tel.: (626) 581-3335   NV
Web Site:
   http://www.digitaldevelopmentpartners.com
Year Founded: 2006
BBBT—(OTCIQ)
Rev.: $82,563
Assets: $218,508
Liabilities: $868,678
Net Worth: ($650,170)
Earnings: ($1,658,766)
Emp.: 4
Fiscal Year-end: 12/31/22
Digital-Related Services
N.A.I.C.S.: 541519
Nelson W. Grist (CEO)
Eric Newlan (Sec & VP)
Fabian G. Deneault (Co-Founder)
Eric Newlan (Co-Founder, Sec & VP)
William A. Sluss (CFO & VP-Finance)

BLACK DIAMOND THERAPEUTICS, INC.

1 Main St PH 14th Fl, Cambridge, MA 02142
Tel.: (617) 401-8444   DE
Web Site:
   https://www.blackdiamondtherapeutics.com
Year Founded: 2014
BDTX—(NASDAQ)
Rev.: $2,031,000
Assets: $156,255,000
Liabilities: $40,560,000
Net Worth: $115,695,000
Earnings: ($91,169,000)
Emp.: 65
Fiscal Year-end: 12/31/22
Biotechnology Research & Development Services
N.A.I.C.S.: 541714
Elizabeth Buck (Chief Scientific Officer)
David M. Epstein (Co-Founder, Pres & CEO)
Brent Hatzis-Schoch (COO & Gen Counsel)
Fang Ni (Interim CFO & Chief Bus Officer)
Sergey Yurasov (Chief Medical Officer)
Erika Jones (Principal Acctg Officer, VP-Fin & Controller)
Mark A. Velleca (Chm, Pres & CEO)
David M. Epstein (Co-Founder)

BLACK DRAGON RESOURCE COMPANIES, INC.

16350 Ventura Blvd Ste D565, Encino, CA 91436
Tel.: (214) 418-6940   WY
Year Founded: 1998
BDGR—(OTCIQ)
Oil & Gas Exploration Services
N.A.I.C.S.: 213112
Edward I. Vakser (CEO)

BLACK HAWK ACQUISITION CORPORATION

4125 Blackhawk Plz Cir Ste 166, Danville, CA 94506
Tel.: (925) 217-4482   Ky
Web Site: https://www.bhspac.com
Year Founded: 2023
BKHA—(NASDAQ)
Investment Management Service
N.A.I.C.S.: 523999

BLACK HILLS CORPORATION

7001 Mount Rushmore Rd, Rapid City, SD 57702
Tel.: (605) 721-1700   SD
Web Site: https://ir.blackhillscorp.com
Year Founded: 1941
BKH—(NYSE)
Rev.: $2,551,816,000
Assets: $9,618,230,000
Liabilities: $6,528,335,000
Net Worth: $3,089,895,000
Earnings: $270,758,000
Emp.: 2,982
Fiscal Year-end: 12/31/22
Electric Power & Natural Gas Distr & Marketer
N.A.I.C.S.: 221122
Todd Jacobs (Sr VP-Growth & Strategy)
Linden R. Evans (Pres & CEO)
Jerome E. Nichols (Dir-IR)
Marne M. Jones (Sr VP-Utilities)
Kimberly Nooney (CFO & Sr VP)
Erik D. Keller (CIO & Sr VP)

Subsidiaries:

Black Hills Electric Generation, LLC   (1)
625 9th St, Rapid City, SD 57701

Tel.: (605) 721-1700
Web Site: http://www.blackhillspower.com
Emp.: 23
Electric Power Distr
N.A.I.C.S.: 221122

Black Hills Energy Services Company   (1)
4510 Airport Rd, Kearney, NE 68847
Web Site:
   https://www.blackhillsenergyservices.com
Natural Gas Distribution Services
N.A.I.C.S.: 221210

Black Hills Exploration & Production, Inc.   (1)
1515 Wynkoop St Ste 500, Denver, CO 80202-2062   (100%)
Tel.: (720) 210-1358
Web Site: http://www.bhep.com
Sales Range: $10-24.9 Million
Emp.: 150
Oil & Gas Production
N.A.I.C.S.: 213112

Black Hills Gas, LLC   (1)
1515 Wynkoop St 5th Fl, Denver, CO 80202
Tel.: (888) 890-5554
Web Site: http://www.blackhillsenergy.com
Natural Gas Distr
N.A.I.C.S.: 221210
Carly Dollar West (Mgr)

Subsidiary (Domestic):

Rocky Mountain Natural Gas LLC   (2)
1515 Arapahoe St Tower 1 Ste 1200, Denver, CO 80202
Tel.: (303) 243-3400
Natural Gas Transmission
N.A.I.C.S.: 221210

Black Hills Power, Inc.   (1)
7001 Mt Rushmore Rd, Rapid City, SD 57702   (100%)
Tel.: (605) 721-1700
Web Site: http://www.blackhillspower.com
Rev.: $291,219,000
Assets: $1,260,357,000
Liabilities: $809,434,000
Net Worth: $450,923,000
Earnings: $46,902,000
Emp.: 217
Fiscal Year-end: 12/31/2019
Electricity Generation, Transmission, Sales & Distr
N.A.I.C.S.: 221118
Linden R. Evans (Chm, Pres & CEO)
Richard W. Kinzley (CFO, Chief Acctg Officer & Sr VP)

Black Hills/Colorado Electric Utility Company, LP   (1)
105 S Victoria Ave, Pueblo, CO 81003
Tel.: (719) 546-6594
Electric Power Distr
N.A.I.C.S.: 221122

Black Hills/Colorado Utility Company, LLC   (1)
PO Box 6006, Rapid City, SD 57709-6006
Tel.: (719) 546-6468
Web Site: http://www.blackhillscorp.com
Sales Range: $125-149.9 Million
Emp.: 198
Electric Power Distr
N.A.I.C.S.: 221210

Black Hills/Iowa Gas Utility Company, LLC   (1)
1701 48th St Ste 260, West Des Moines, IA 50266
Tel.: (515) 224-1404
Sales Range: $75-99.9 Million
Emp.: 205
Natural Gas Distr
N.A.I.C.S.: 221210

Black Hills/Kansas Gas Utility Company, LLC   (1)
3845 W Harry, Wichita, KS 67213
Tel.: (316) 941-1656

Sales Range: $50-74.9 Million
Emp.: 155
Natural Gas Distr
N.A.I.C.S.: 221210
Ivan Vancas (VP-Ops)
Jerry Watkins (Gen Mgr)

Black Hills/Nebraska Gas Utility Company, LLC **(1)**
1601 Windhoek Dr, Lincoln, NE 68512-1272
Tel.: (402) 437-1772
Web Site: http://www.blackhillscorp.com
Sales Range: $75-99.9 Million
Emp.: 242
Natural Gas Distr
N.A.I.C.S.: 221210

Cheyenne Light, Fuel & Power Co. **(1)**
1301 W 24th St, Cheyenne, WY 82001
Tel.: (307) 630-4454
Web Site: http://www.cheyennelight.com
Sales Range: $75-99.9 Million
Emp.: 110
Electric & Gas Utility
N.A.I.C.S.: 221122

Generation Development Company, LLC **(1)**
5932 Tarleton Dr, Oak Ridge, NC 27310
Tel.: (336) 643-0856
Oil & gas field services
N.A.I.C.S.: 213112

Wyodak Resources Development Corp. **(1)**
3338 Garner Lake Rd, Gillette, WY 82716 **(100%)**
Tel.: (605) 348-1700
Web Site: https://www.blackhillscorp.com
Coal Mine
N.A.I.C.S.: 531210

BLACK MOUNTAIN ACQUISITION CORP.

425 Houston St Ste 400, Fort Worth, TX 76102
Tel.: (817) 698-9901 DE
Web Site:
http://www.blackmountainaq.com
Year Founded: 2021
BMAC—(NYSE)
Rev.: $4,121,363
Assets: $285,272,023
Liabilities: $294,942,081
Net Worth: ($9,670,058)
Earnings: $2,199,522
Emp.: 2
Fiscal Year-end: 12/31/22
Investment Services
N.A.I.C.S.: 523999
Rhett Bennett (Chm & CEO)
Jacob Smith (CFO, Chief Acctg Officer & Sec)

BLACK STALLION OIL AND GAS, INC.

633 W 5th St 26th Fl, Los Angeles, CA 90071
Tel.: (213) 223-2071 DE
Web Site:
http://www.blackstallionoil.com
Year Founded: 2011
BLKG—(OTCIQ)
Emp.: 1
Oil & Gas Exploration
N.A.I.C.S.: 211120
Michael L. Pinnell (VP-Exploration)
Ira Morris (Pres)

BLACK STONE MINERALS, L.P.

1001 Fannin Ste 2020, Houston, TX 77002
Tel.: (713) 445-3200
Web Site:
https://www.blackstoneminerals.com
Year Founded: 2014
BSM—(NYSE)
Rev.: $592,216,000
Assets: $1,266,884,000

Liabilities: $49,539,000
Net Worth: $1,217,345,000
Earnings: $400,773,000
Emp.: 108
Fiscal Year-end: 12/31/23
Oil & Natural Gas Operations
N.A.I.C.S.: 213112
Thomas L. Carter Jr. (Chm & CEO)
Steve Putman (Gen Counsel, Sec & Sr VP)
Garrett Gremillion (VP)
John Gearing (VP)
Thad Montgomery (VP)
Kristin Wiggs (VP)

Subsidiaries:

Black Stone Energy Company, LLC **(1)**
1001 Fannin St Ste 2020, Houston, TX 77002
Tel.: (713) 658-0647
Emp.: 100
Oil & Gas Field Exploration Services
N.A.I.C.S.: 211120
Thomas L. Carter Jr. (CEO)

Black Stone Minerals Company, L.P. **(1)**
1001 Fannin Ste 2020, Houston, TX 77002
Tel.: (713) 445-3200
Web Site:
https://www.blackstoneminerals.com
Natural Gas Distr
N.A.I.C.S.: 221210

BLACKBAUD, INC.

65 Fairchild St, Charleston, SC 29492
Tel.: (843) 216-6200 DE
Web Site:
https://www.blackbaud.com
Year Founded: 1981
BLKB—(NASDAQ)
Rev.: $1,105,432,000
Assets: $2,912,279,000
Liabilities: $2,103,574,000
Net Worth: $808,705,000
Earnings: $1,820,000
Emp.: 3,000
Fiscal Year-end: 12/31/23
Software Publisher
N.A.I.C.S.: 513210
Kevin W. Mooney (Exec VP-Strategy & Bus Dev)
Jon W. Olson (Gen Counsel & Sr VP)
Stephen Halleck (Sr VP-Bus Ops)
Kevin McDearis (CTO & Exec VP)
Catherine Cook LaCour (CMO)
Kevin P. Gregoire (COO & Exec VP)
Margaret Driscoll (Chief People Officer & Chief Culture Officer)
David Benjamin (Chief Comml Officer & Exec VP)
Tom Davidson (Exec VP)
Anthony Boor (CFO & Exec VP-Finance & Administration)
Chad Anderson (Chief Acctg Officer)
Sudip Datta (Chief Product Officer)
Dale Strange (Sr VP & Head-Corp Impact)
Michael P. Gianoni (Vice Chm, Pres & CEO)

Subsidiaries:

AcademicWorks, LLC **(1)**
3800 N Lamar Blvd Ste 320, Austin, TX 78756
Web Site: http://www.academicworks.com
Computer Software Development Services
N.A.I.C.S.: 541511

AngelPoints, LLC **(1)**
30 Liberty Ship Way Ste 3150, Sausalito, CA 94965
Tel.: (415) 331-4881
Software Programming Services
N.A.I.C.S.: 541511

Blackbaud Canada, Inc. **(1)**
150 King Street West IQ Offices Suite 706,

Toronto, M5H 1J9, ON, Canada
Web Site: https://www.blackbaud.ca
Software Development Services
N.A.I.C.S.: 541511

Blackbaud Europe Ltd. **(1)**
Canterbury Court Studio 1 19 1-3 Brixton Rd, Kennington Business Park, London, SW9 6DE, United Kingdom
Tel.: (44) 2039321600
Web Site: https://www.blackbaud.co.uk
Software Development Services
N.A.I.C.S.: 541511

Blackbaud Pacific Pty. Ltd. **(1)**
Level 2 65 Berry Street, North Sydney, 2060, NSW, Australia
Tel.: (61) 289181200
IT Consulting Services
N.A.I.C.S.: 541618
Sam Dickenson (Mgr-Bus Dev)

Everyday Hero Pty. Ltd. **(1)**
Level 8 333 Ann Street, Brisbane, 4000, QLD, Australia
Tel.: (61) 732267800
Web Site: https://www.everydayhero.com.au
Emp.: 55
Online Fundraising Services
N.A.I.C.S.: 561499

Subsidiary (Non-US):

Everyday Hero Ltd. **(2)**
Shackleton House 5th Floor 4 Battle Bridge Lane, London, SE1 2HP, United Kingdom
Tel.: (44) 845 680 9719
Web Site: http://www.everydayhero.co.uk
Online Fundraising Services
N.A.I.C.S.: 561499

Good + Geek, LLC **(1)**
718 7th St NW, Washington, DC 20001
Tel.: (202) 988-3549
Web Site: http://www.attentive.ly
Computer Software Development Services
N.A.I.C.S.: 541511

MicroEdge, LLC **(1)**
619 W 54th St 10 Fl, New York, NY 10019-3545
Tel.: (212) 757-1522
Web Site: http://www.microedge.com
Sales Range: $50-74.9 Million
Emp.: 100
Software Publisher
N.A.I.C.S.: 513210

MyCharity, Ltd. **(1)**
Office 512 8 Dawson St, Dublin, 2, Ireland
Tel.: (353) 14372200
Web Site: https://www.mycharity.ie
Charitable Service Provider
N.A.I.C.S.: 813211

Public Interest Data, LLC **(1)**
1800 Diagonal Rd Ste 400, Alexandria, VA 22314
Tel.: (703) 683-9500
Web Site: http://www.pidi.com
Database Management Services
N.A.I.C.S.: 541611

Reeher LLC **(1)**
370 Wabasha St N Ste 1200, Saint Paul, MN 55102
Tel.: (651) 313-6000
Web Site: http://www.reeher.com
Information Technology Support Services
N.A.I.C.S.: 541512
Andy Reeher (Pres & CEO)

Seraphim Software, LLC **(1)**
3770 Rdg Pike - Lowr Ste, Collegeville, PA 19426
Web Site: http://www.seraphimsoftware.com
Software Development Services
N.A.I.C.S.: 513210
Sam Batterman (Co-Founder & CTO)
Chris Caldwell (Co-Founder & CFO)
Mike Weisman (Mgr-Customer Support)
Luke Stitzinger (Mgr-Customer Relationship)
Taylor Thompson (Mgr-Customer Relationship)

Smart, LLC **(1)**
70680 County Rd 23, New Paris, IN 46553
Tel.: (574) 831-5010
Web Site: https://www.smartcabinetry.com
Kitchen & Bathroom Cabinet Mfr & Distr

N.A.I.C.S.: 337110

Whipplehill Communications, Inc. **(1)**
5 Eastpoint Dr Building C, Bedford, NH 03110
Tel.: (603) 669-5975
Web Site: http://whipplehill.com
Sales Range: $10-24.9 Million
Emp.: 50
Data Processing, Hosting & Related Services
N.A.I.C.S.: 518210

YourCause, LLC **(1)**
6111 W Plano Pkwy Ste 1000YC, Plano, TX 75093
Tel.: (972) 755-3950
Web Site: https://solutions.yourcause.com
Social Networking Software Developer
N.A.I.C.S.: 513210

BLACKBOXSTOCKS INC.

5430 LBJ Fwy Ste 1485, Dallas, TX 75240
Tel.: (972) 726-9203 NV
Web Site:
https://www.blackboxstocks.com
Year Founded: 2011
BLBX—(NASDAQ)
Rev.: $4,959,109
Assets: $4,335,781
Liabilities: $2,158,128
Net Worth: $2,177,653
Earnings: ($5,019,882)
Emp.: 14
Fiscal Year-end: 12/31/22
Analytical Platform Tool Software Publisher & Distr
N.A.I.C.S.: 513210
Brandon Smith (CTO)
David Kyle (Co-Founder)
Robert L. Winspear (CFO, Sec & Dir)
Ray Balestri (Dir)
Dalya Sulaiman (Dir)
Keller Reid (Dir)
Gust Kepler (Co-Founder & CEO)

BLACKLINE, INC.

21300 Victory Blvd 12th Fl, Woodland Hills, CA 91367
Tel.: (818) 223-9008 DE
Web Site: https://www.blackline.com
Year Founded: 2001
BL—(NASDAQ)
Rev.: $522,938,000
Assets: $1,943,656,000
Liabilities: $1,831,788,000
Net Worth: $111,868,000
Earnings: ($29,391,000)
Emp.: 1,814
Fiscal Year-end: 12/31/22
Software Development Services
N.A.I.C.S.: 541511
Therese Tucker (Founder & Co-CEO)
Mark W. Partin (CFO)
Mark Woodhams (Chief Revenue Officer)
Owen M. Ryan (Chm & Co-CEO)
Patrick Villanova (Chief Acctg Officer)
Tammy F. Coley (Chief Transformation Officer)
Lisa Schreiber (Chief Customer Officer)
Jill Knesek (Chief Information Security Officer)
Karole Morgan-Prager (Chief Admin Officer & Chief Legal Officer)

Subsidiaries:

BlackLine Systems Germany Gmb H **(1)**
The Squaire 12 Am Flughafen, 60549, Frankfurt, Germany
Tel.: (49) 6920457820
Web Site: http://www.blackline.com
Software Development Services
N.A.I.C.S.: 541511

BlackLine, Inc.—(Continued)

BlackLine Systems Limited (1)
33 Charlotte Street, London, W1T 1RR,
United Kingdom
Tel.: (44) 2033185941
Software Development Services
N.A.I.C.S.: 541511

BlackLine Systems Pte. Ltd. (1)
101 Telok Ayer Street 03-02, Singapore,
068574, Singapore
Tel.: (65) 68185714
Software Development Services
N.A.I.C.S.: 541511

BlackLine Systems S.a r.l. (1)
127 avenue Charles de Gaulle, 92200,
Neuilly-sur-Seine, France
Tel.: (33) 184880229
Software Development Services
N.A.I.C.S.: 541511

BlackLine Systems, Ltd. (1)
2794 Fenton Road, Ottawa, K1T 8T7, ON,
Canada
Tel.: (613) 822-9933
Web Site: https://www.blackline.ca
Software Development Services
N.A.I.C.S.: 541511

Data Interconnect Ltd. (1)
Units 45-50 Shrivenham Hundred Business
Park Majors Road, Watchfield, Swindon,
SN6 8TZ, United Kingdom
Tel.: (44) 1367245777
Web Site: https://www.datainterconnect.com
Software Development Services
N.A.I.C.S.: 541511

Rimilia Canada Ltd. (1)
1055 W Hastings St 18th Floor, Vancouver,
V6E 2E9, BC, Canada
Computer Software Services
N.A.I.C.S.: 541511

Rimilia Europe Ltd. (1)
198 High Holborn West, London, WC1V
7BD, United Kingdom
Tel.: (44) 2033185941
Computer Software Services
N.A.I.C.S.: 541511

BLACKROCK 2022 GLOBAL INCOME OPPORTUNITY TRUST
100 Bellevue Pkwy, Wilmington, DE
19809
BGIO—(NYSE)
Management Investment Services
N.A.I.C.S.: 525910
Jacob Caplain *(VP)*

BLACKROCK CAPITAL INVESTMENT CORPORATION
50 Hudson Yards, New York, NY
10001
Tel.: (212) 810-5800   DE
Web Site:
https://www.blackrockbkcc.com
Year Founded: 2005
BKCC—(NASDAQ)
Rev.: $57,935,794
Assets: $589,060,146
Liabilities: $270,537,793
Net Worth: $318,522,353
Earnings: $29,371,122
Fiscal Year-end: 12/31/22
Investment Services
N.A.I.C.S.: 523940
Laurence D. Paredes *(Gen Counsel & Sec)*
James E. Keenan *(Chm, Interim CEO, Mng Dir & Head-Credit-Global)*
Nik Singhal *(Pres)*
Sean Berry *(Mng Dir)*
Rob DiPaolo *(Mng Dir)*
Christian Donohue *(Mng Dir)*
Carolyn Glick *(Mng Dir)*
Phil Tseng *(Mng Dir)*
Raj Vig *(Mng Dir)*
Patrick Wolfe *(Mng Dir)*
Dan Worrell *(Mng Dir)*
Eric Yuan *(Mng Dir)*

Chip Holladay *(Interim CFO & Treas)*
John Doyle *(Mng Dir)*
Jeffrey Gordon *(Mng Dir)*
Oliver Hammond *(Mng Dir)*
Jon Hugo *(Mng Dir)*
Alan Tom *(Mng Dir)*
Shan Arunachalam *(VP)*
Brian Bulger *(VP)*
Connor Lockhart *(VP)*
Yogesh Mavilla *(VP)*
Andrew D. Norman *(VP)*
Alexa Oyague *(VP)*
Kelly Punjabi *(VP)*
Lucy Qu *(VP)*

BLACKROCK CORE BOND TRUST
100 Bellevue Pkwy Mutual Fund
Dept, Wilmington, DE 19809   DE
BHK—(NYSE)
Investment Services
N.A.I.C.S.: 523999

BLACKROCK CORPORATE HIGH YIELD FUND, INC.
100 Bellevue Pkwy, Wilmington, DE
19809
HYT—(NYSE)
Rev.: $128,558,891
Assets: $2,091,847,313
Liabilities: $639,979,548
Net Worth: $1,451,867,765
Earnings: $97,471,136
Fiscal Year-end: 08/31/19
Investment Management Service
N.A.I.C.S.: 525990

BLACKROCK CREDIT ALLOCATION INCOME TRUST
100 Bellevue Pkwy, Wilmington, DE
95014
BTZ—(NYSE)
Investment Management Service
N.A.I.C.S.: 525910

BLACKROCK DEBT STRATEGIES FUND, INC.
100 Bellevue Pkwy, Wilmington, DE
19809   MD
DSU—(NYSE)
Rev.: $43,468,425
Assets: $893,334,584
Liabilities: $288,094,430
Net Worth: $605,240,154
Earnings: $32,028,542
Fiscal Year-end: 12/31/19
Investment Management Service
N.A.I.C.S.: 525990

BLACKROCK ENHANCED CAPITAL & INCOME FUND, INC.
100 Bellevue Pkwy, Wilmington, DE
19809
CII—(NYSE)
Rev.: $14,786,735
Assets: $805,687,310
Liabilities: $13,048,914
Net Worth: $792,638,396
Earnings: $8,012,154
Fiscal Year-end: 12/31/19
Investment Management Service
N.A.I.C.S.: 525990

BLACKROCK ENHANCED EQUITY DIVIDEND TRUST
100 Bellevue Pkwy, Wilmington, DE
19809   DE
BDJ—(NYSE)
Rev.: $51,074,171
Assets: $1,913,156,861
Liabilities: $31,481,571
Net Worth: $1,881,675,290
Earnings: $35,572,226
Fiscal Year-end: 12/31/19

Investment Management Service
N.A.I.C.S.: 525990

BLACKROCK ENHANCED GLOBAL DIVIDEND TRUST
100 Bellevue Pkwy, Wilmington, DE
19809   DE
BOE—(NYSE)
Rev.: $28,104,792
Assets: $817,635,083
Liabilities: $9,923,301
Net Worth: $807,711,782
Earnings: $20,684,957
Fiscal Year-end: 12/31/19
Investment Management Service
N.A.I.C.S.: 525990

BLACKROCK ENHANCED GOVERNMENT FUND, INC.
100 Bellevue Pkwy, Wilmington, DE
19809   MD
EGF—(NYSE)
Rev.: $2,798,625
Assets: $80,849,143
Liabilities: $16,845,425
Net Worth: $64,003,718
Earnings: $1,724,287
Fiscal Year-end: 12/31/19
Investment Management Service
N.A.I.C.S.: 525990

BLACKROCK ENHANCED INTERNATIONAL DIVIDEND TRUST
100 Bellevue Pkwy, Wilmington, DE
19809   DE
BGY—(NYSE)
Rev.: $23,704,684
Assets: $691,816,474
Liabilities: $8,569,347
Net Worth: $683,247,127
Earnings: $16,918,169
Fiscal Year-end: 12/31/19
Investment Management Service
N.A.I.C.S.: 525990

BLACKROCK FLOATING RATE INCOME STRATEGIES FUND, INC.
100 Bellevue Pkwy, Wilmington, DE
19809
FRA—(NYSE)
Rev.: $43,923,422
Assets: $755,085,041
Liabilities: $233,440,332
Net Worth: $522,544,709
Earnings: $30,775,188
Fiscal Year-end: 08/31/19
Investment Management Service
N.A.I.C.S.: 525990

BLACKROCK FLOATING RATE INCOME TRUST
100 Bellevue Pkwy, Wilmington, DE
19809-3700
BGT—(NYSE)
Rev.: $26,435,440
Assets: $465,883,918
Liabilities: $142,175,520
Net Worth: $323,708,398
Earnings: $18,566,145
Fiscal Year-end: 10/31/19
Investment Management Service
N.A.I.C.S.: 525990

BLACKROCK INCOME TRUST, INC.
100 Bellevue Pkwy Mutual Fund
Dept, Wilmington, DE 19809   MD
BKT—(NYSE)
Investment Trust Management Services
N.A.I.C.S.: 523940
John M. Perlowski *(Pres & CEO)*
Richard E. Cavanagh *(Co-Chm)*

BLACKROCK INVESTMENT QUALITY MUNI TR
100 Bellevue Pkwy Mutual Fund
Dept, Wilmington, DE 19809   MD
BKN—(NYSE)
Rev.: $18,808,994
Assets: $450,356,146
Liabilities: $179,649,336
Net Worth: $270,706,810
Earnings: $12,176,372
Fiscal Year-end: 04/30/19
Investment Management Service
N.A.I.C.S.: 525990

BLACKROCK LIMITED DURATION INCOME TRUST
100 Bellevue Pkwy Mutual Fund
Dept, Wilmington, DE 19809   DE
BLW—(NYSE)
Investment Trust Management Services
N.A.I.C.S.: 523940

BLACKROCK LONG-TERM MUNICIPAL ADTGTRUST
100 Bellevue Pkwy, Wilmington, DE
19809
BTA—(NYSE)
Rev.: $12,740,739
Assets: $280,099,426
Liabilities: $112,668,309
Net Worth: $167,431,117
Earnings: $8,367,102
Fiscal Year-end: 04/30/19
Investment Management Service
N.A.I.C.S.: 525990

BLACKROCK MARYLAND MUNICIPAL BOND TRUST
100 Bellevue Pkwy, Wilmington, DE
19809
BZM—(NYSEAMEX)
Rev.: $1,925,809
Assets: $51,653,311
Liabilities: $19,152,547
Net Worth: $32,500,764
Earnings: $992,587
Fiscal Year-end: 08/31/19
Investment Management Service
N.A.I.C.S.: 525990
Ted Jaeckel *(Mgr-Fund)*

BLACKROCK MASSACHUSETTS TAX-EXEMPT TRUST
100 Bellevue Pkwy, Wilmington, DE
19809
MHE—(NYSEAMEX)
Rev.: $2,101,215
Assets: $55,215,219
Liabilities: $21,714,064
Net Worth: $33,501,155
Earnings: $1,185,123
Fiscal Year-end: 08/31/19
Investment Management Service
N.A.I.C.S.: 525990
Bob Sneeden *(Mgr-Fund)*

BLACKROCK MUNI NEW YORK INTERMEDIATE DURATION FUND, INC.
100 Bellevue Pkwy, Wilmington, DE
19809
MNE—(NYSE)
Investment Management Service
N.A.I.C.S.: 525990
Michael Kalinoski *(Mgr-Fund)*

BLACKROCK MUNIASSETS FUND, INC.
100 Bellevue Pkwy, Wilmington, DE
19809   MD
MUA—(NYSE)
Rev.: $29,090,397
Assets: $586,179,924
Liabilities: $76,535,299

Net Worth: $509,644,625
Earnings: $24,002,582
Fiscal Year-end: 04/30/19
Investment Management Service
N.A.I.C.S.: 525990

BLACKROCK MUNICIPAL 2030 TARGET TERM TRUST

100 Bellevue Pkwy, Wilmington, DE 19809
Tel.: (302) 797-2000   DE
Web Site: http://www.blackrock.com
Year Founded: 2011
BTT—(NYSE)
Rev.: $93,377,974
Assets: $2,872,499,644
Liabilities: $1,017,627,044
Net Worth: $1,854,872,600
Earnings: $65,164,868
Fiscal Year-end: 07/31/20
Investment Services
N.A.I.C.S.: 523999
John M. Perlowski (Pres & CEO)
Richard E. Cavanagh (Chm)
Charles Choon Sik Park (Chief Compliance Officer)
Theodore R. Jaeckel (Portfolio Mgr)
Phillip Soccio (Dir & Portfolio Mgr-Municipal Mutual Funds)
Walter O'Connor (Mng Dir, Co-Head-Municipal Funds & Portfolio Mgr)
Kevin Maloney (Co-Head-Municipal Funds, Dir & Portfolio Mgr)
Kristi Manidis (Dir & Portfolio Mgr)
Christian Romaglino (Dir & Portfolio Mgr)

BLACKROCK MUNICIPAL INCOME FUND, INC.

100 Bellevue Pkwy, Wilmington, DE 19809
MUI—(NYSE)
Rev.: $36,537,366
Assets: $973,655,481
Liabilities: $383,768,798
Net Worth: $589,886,683
Earnings: $21,439,587
Fiscal Year-end: 04/30/19
Investment Management Service
N.A.I.C.S.: 525990

BLACKROCK MUNICIPAL INCOME INVESTMENT QUALITY TRUST

100 Bellevue Pkwy, Wilmington, DE 19809
BAF—(NYSE)
Rev.: $9,383,277
Assets: $234,331,124
Liabilities: $97,105,612
Net Worth: $137,225,512
Earnings: $5,709,453
Fiscal Year-end: 08/31/19
Investment Management Service
N.A.I.C.S.: 525990
Bob Sneeden (Mgr-Fund)

BLACKROCK MUNICIPAL INCOME INVESTMENT TRUST

100 Bellevue Pkwy, Wilmington, DE 19809
BBF—(NYSE)
Rev.: $10,921,712
Assets: $255,337,062
Liabilities: $110,672,017
Net Worth: $144,665,045
Earnings: $7,037,901
Fiscal Year-end: 07/31/19
Investment Management Service
N.A.I.C.S.: 525990
Bob Sneeden (Mgr-Fund)

BLACKROCK MUNICIPAL INCOME QUALITY TRUST

100 Bellevue Pkwy, Wilmington, DE 19809

BYM—(NYSE)
Rev.: $26,069,256
Assets: $673,368,608
Liabilities: $258,241,131
Net Worth: $415,127,477
Earnings: $16,163,564
Fiscal Year-end: 08/31/19
Investment Management Service
N.A.I.C.S.: 525990

BLACKROCK MUNICIPAL INCOME TRUST

100 Bellevue Pkwy Mutual Fund Dept, Wilmington, DE 19809   DE
BFK—(NYSE)
Rev.: $46,242,126
Assets: $1,029,850,770
Liabilities: $394,775,242
Net Worth: $635,075,528
Earnings: $30,368,713
Fiscal Year-end: 04/30/19
Financial Consulting Services
N.A.I.C.S.: 541611

BLACKROCK MUNICIPAL INCOME TRUST II

100 Bellevue Pkwy, Wilmington, DE 19809   DE
BLE—(NYSEAMEX)
Rev.: $25,373,039
Assets: $569,580,023
Liabilities: $212,931,280
Net Worth: $356,648,743
Earnings: $16,652,798
Fiscal Year-end: 08/31/19
Investment Management Service
N.A.I.C.S.: 525990

BLACKROCK MUNIENHANCED FUND, INC.

100 Bellevue Pkwy, Wilmington, DE 19809
MEN—(NYSE)
Rev.: $24,443,524
Assets: $585,786,976
Liabilities: $236,592,566
Net Worth: $349,194,410
Earnings: $15,890,070
Fiscal Year-end: 04/30/19
Investment Management Service
N.A.I.C.S.: 525990
Michael Kalinoski (Mgr-Fund)

BLACKROCK MUNIHOLDINGS CALIFORNIA QUALITY FUND, INC.

100 Bellevue Pkwy, Wilmington, DE 19809   MD
MUC—(NYSE)
Rev.: $38,775,775
Assets: $1,066,370,105
Liabilities: $428,548,122
Net Worth: $637,821,983
Earnings: $23,450,577
Fiscal Year-end: 07/31/19
Investment Management Service
N.A.I.C.S.: 525990

BLACKROCK MUNIHOLDINGS FUND II, INC.

100 Bellevue Pkwy, Wilmington, DE 19809
MUH—(NYSE)
Rev.: $12,968,409
Assets: $283,303,250
Liabilities: $109,675,692
Net Worth: $173,627,558
Earnings: $8,585,611
Fiscal Year-end: 04/30/19
Investment Management Service
N.A.I.C.S.: 525990
Walter C. O'connor (Mgr-Fund)

BLACKROCK MUNIHOLDINGS FUND, INC.

100 Bellevue Pkwy, Wilmington, DE 19809
MHD—(NYSE)
Rev.: $17,233,858
Assets: $372,994,327
Liabilities: $137,965,517
Net Worth: $235,028,810
Earnings: $11,524,910
Fiscal Year-end: 04/30/19
Investment Management Service
N.A.I.C.S.: 525990

BLACKROCK MUNIHOLDINGS INVESTMENT QUALITY FUND

100 Bellevue Pkwy, Wilmington, DE 19809
MFL—(NYSE)
Investment Management Service
N.A.I.C.S.: 525990
Bob Sneeden (Mgr-Fund)

BLACKROCK MUNIHOLDINGS NEW JERSEY QUALITY FUND, INC.

100 Bellevue Pkwy, Wilmington, DE 19809   MD
MUJ—(NYSE)
Rev.: $28,980,924
Assets: $795,136,932
Liabilities: $305,033,714
Net Worth: $490,103,218
Earnings: $22,057,671
Fiscal Year-end: 07/31/21
Investment Management Service
N.A.I.C.S.: 525990

BLACKROCK MUNIHOLDINGS QUALITY FUND II, INC.

100 Bellevue Pkwy, Wilmington, DE 19809
MUE—(NYSE)
Rev.: $20,252,747
Assets: $508,636,796
Liabilities: $195,230,669
Net Worth: $313,406,127
Earnings: $12,835,636
Fiscal Year-end: 07/31/19
Investment Management Service
N.A.I.C.S.: 525990

BLACKROCK MUNIHOLDINGS QUALITY FUND, INC.

100 Bellevue Pkwy, Wilmington, DE 19809
MUS—(NYSE)
Rev.: $29,090,397
Assets: $289,544,716
Liabilities: $113,634,421
Net Worth: $175,910,295
Earnings: $24,002,582
Fiscal Year-end: 04/30/19
Investment Management Service
N.A.I.C.S.: 525990
Bob Sneeden (Mgr-Fund)

BLACKROCK MUNIVEST FUND II, INC.

100 Bellevue Pkwy, Wilmington, DE 19809   MD
MVT—(NYSE)
Rev.: $23,493,434
Assets: $507,127,123
Liabilities: $189,952,564
Net Worth: $317,174,559
Earnings: $15,853,019
Fiscal Year-end: 04/30/19
Investment Management Service
N.A.I.C.S.: 525990

BLACKROCK MUNIYIELD ARIZONA FUND, INC.

100 Bellevue Pkwy, Wilmington, DE 19809
MZA—(NYSEAMEX)
Rev.: $4,302,420
Assets: $111,251,999

Liabilities: $42,806,034
Net Worth: $68,445,965
Earnings: $2,586,685
Fiscal Year-end: 07/31/19
Investment Management Service
N.A.I.C.S.: 525990
Michael Kalinoski (Mgr-Fund)

BLACKROCK MUNIYIELD CALIFORNIA FUND, INC.

100 Bellevue Pkwy, Wilmington, DE 19809
MYC—(NYSE)
Rev.: $20,367,329
Assets: $574,937,708
Liabilities: $240,285,738
Net Worth: $334,651,970
Earnings: $11,922,364
Fiscal Year-end: 07/31/19
Investment Management Service
N.A.I.C.S.: 525990
Ted Jaeckel (Mgr-Fund)

BLACKROCK MUNIYIELD CALIFORNIA QUALITY FUND, INC.

100 Bellevue Pkwy, Wilmington, DE 19809
MCA—(NYSE)
Rev.: $34,323,492
Assets: $942,183,864
Liabilities: $398,997,907
Net Worth: $543,185,957
Earnings: $20,674,671
Fiscal Year-end: 07/31/19
Investment Management Service
N.A.I.C.S.: 525990
Ted Jaeckel (Mgr-Fund)

BLACKROCK MUNIYIELD FUND, INC.

100 Bellevue Pkwy, Wilmington, DE 19809   NJ
MYD—(NYSE)
Rev.: $49,427,348
Assets: $1,075,508,140
Liabilities: $392,675,987
Net Worth: $682,832,153
Earnings: $34,206,699
Fiscal Year-end: 04/30/19
Investment Management Service
N.A.I.C.S.: 525990

BLACKROCK MUNIYIELD INVESTMENT QUALITY FUND

100 Bellevue Pkwy, Wilmington, DE 19809
MFT—(NYSE)
Rev.: $8,778,007
Assets: $214,617,939
Liabilities: $93,723,384
Net Worth: $120,894,555
Earnings: $5,476,513
Fiscal Year-end: 07/31/19
Investment Management Service
N.A.I.C.S.: 525990
Bob Sneeden (Mgr-Fund)

BLACKROCK MUNIYIELD INVSTMT FD

100 Bellevue Pkwy, Wilmington, DE 19809
MYF—(NYSE)
Rev.: $14,976,103
Assets: $330,104,849
Liabilities: $131,459,667
Net Worth: $198,645,182
Earnings: $10,029,486
Fiscal Year-end: 07/31/19
Investment Management Service
N.A.I.C.S.: 525990
Bob Sneeden (Mgr-Fund)

BLACKROCK MUNIYIELD MICHIGAN QUALITY FUND, INC.

Blackrock Muniyield Michigan Quality Fund,
Inc.—(Continued)

100 Bellevue Pkwy, Wilmington, DE
19809-3700   **NJ**
MIY—(NYSE)
Rev.: $29,280,621
Assets: $763,054,213
Liabilities: $298,688,578
Net Worth: $464,365,635
Earnings: $18,330,527
Fiscal Year-end: 07/31/19
Investment Management Service
N.A.I.C.S.: 525990

BLACKROCK MUNIYIELD NEW JERSEY FUND, INC.

100 Bellevue Pkwy, Wilmington, DE
19809
MYJ—(NYSE)
Rev.: $26,727,761
Assets: $632,640,750
Liabilities: $244,241,633
Net Worth: $388,399,117
Earnings: $17,449,927
Fiscal Year-end: 07/31/19
Investment Management Service
N.A.I.C.S.: 525990
Ted Jaeckel (Mgr-Fund)

BLACKROCK MUNIYIELD PENNSYLVANIA QUALITY FUND

100 Bellevue Pkwy, Wilmington, DE
19809   **NJ**
MPA—(NYSE)
Rev.: $13,640,382
Assets: $352,584,076
Liabilities: $138,225,139
Net Worth: $214,358,937
Earnings: $8,422,880
Fiscal Year-end: 07/31/19
Investment Management Service
N.A.I.C.S.: 525990

BLACKROCK MUNIYIELD QUALITY FUND II

100 Bellevue Pkwy, Wilmington, DE
19809   **NJ**
MQT—(NYSE)
Rev.: $21,263,490
Assets: $520,179,397
Liabilities: $209,568,385
Net Worth: $310,611,012
Earnings: $13,470,302
Fiscal Year-end: 04/30/19
Investment Management Service
N.A.I.C.S.: 525990

BLACKROCK MUNIYIELD QUALITY FUND, INC.

100 Bellevue Pkwy, Wilmington, DE
19809   **NJ**
MQY—(NYSE)
Rev.: $32,826,207
Assets: $795,935,887
Liabilities: $314,724,079
Net Worth: $481,211,808
Earnings: $21,247,583
Fiscal Year-end: 04/30/19
Investment Management Service
N.A.I.C.S.: 525000

BLACKROCK NEW YORK MUNICIPAL BOND TRUST

100 Bellevue Pkwy, Wilmington, DE
19809
BQH—(NYSE)
Rev.: $2,886,852
Assets: $76,929,467
Liabilities: $30,755,966
Net Worth: $46,173,501
Earnings: $1,499,702
Fiscal Year-end: 08/31/19
Investment Management Service
N.A.I.C.S.: 525990
Walter C. O'connor (Mgr-Fund)

BLACKROCK NEW YORK MUNICIPAL INCOME QUALITY TRUST

100 Bellevue Pkwy, Wilmington, DE
19809
BSE—(NYSE)
Rev.: $5,873,163
Assets: $164,279,534
Liabilities: $64,274,389
Net Worth: $100,005,145
Earnings: $3,274,648
Fiscal Year-end: 08/31/19
Investment Management Service
N.A.I.C.S.: 525990
Walter C. O'connor (Mgr-Fund)

BLACKROCK RESOURCES & COMMODITIES STRATEGY TRUST

100 Bellevue Pkwy, Wilmington, DE
19809
Tel.: (302) 797-2000   **DE**
Year Founded: 2010
BCX—(NYSE)
Investment Trust
N.A.I.C.S.: 525920

BLACKROCK SCIENCE & TECHNOLOGY TRUST

100 Bellevue Pkwy, Wilmington, DE
19809
Tel.: (302) 797-2000   **DE**
BST—(NYSE)
Rev.: $2,847,452
Assets: $754,298,347
Liabilities: $11,626,829
Net Worth: $742,671,518
Earnings: ($3,710,069)
Fiscal Year-end: 12/31/19
Investment Management Service
N.A.I.C.S.: 525990

BLACKROCK STRATEGIC MUNICIPAL TRUST

100 Bellevue Pkwy, Wilmington, DE
19809
BSD—(NYSE)
Rev.: $7,837,142
Assets: $173,951,801
Liabilities: $70,522,265
Net Worth: $103,429,536
Earnings: $4,989,987
Fiscal Year-end: 04/30/19
Investment Management Service
N.A.I.C.S.: 525990
Ted Jaeckel (Mgr-Fund)

BLACKROCK TAXABLE MUNICIPAL BOND TRUST

100 Bellevue Pkwy, Wilmington, DE
19809
Tel.: (212) 810-5300   **DE**
BBN—(NYSE)
Sales Range: $100-124.9 Million
Investment Trust
N.A.I.C.S.: 525920

BLACKROCK TCP CAPITAL CORP.

2951 28th St Ste 1000, Santa
Monica, CA 90405
Tel.: (310) 566-1094   **DE**
Web Site: https://www.tcpcapital.com
Year Founded: 2006
TCPC—(NASDAQ)
Rev.: $181,002,459
Assets: $1,719,349,849
Liabilities: $972,596,059
Net Worth: $746,753,790
Earnings: $88,438,173
Fiscal Year-end: 12/31/22
Investment Services
N.A.I.C.S.: 523999

Jason A. Mehring (COO)
Philip M. Tseng (Pres)
Rajneesh Vig (Chm & CEO)
Laurence D. Paredes (Gen Counsel)

BLACKROCK UTILITIES, INFRASTRUCTURE & POWER OPPORTUNITIES TRUST

100 Bellevue Pkwy, Wilmington, DE
19809
Tel.: (302) 797-2000   **MD**
Web Site: http://blackrock.com
BUI—(NYSE)
Sales Range: $1-9.9 Million
Investment Trust
N.A.I.C.S.: 525920
Kyle McClements (Portfolio Mgr)
Christopher Accettella (Portfolio Mgr)
Alastair Bishop (Portfolio Mgr)

BLACKROCK VIRGINIA MUNICIPAL BOND TRUST

100 Bellevue Pkwy Mutual Fund
Dept, Wilmington, DE 19809   **DE**
BHV—(NYSEAMEX)
Rev.: $2,886,852
Assets: $76,929,467
Liabilities: $30,755,966
Net Worth: $46,173,501
Earnings: $1,499,702
Fiscal Year-end: 08/31/19
Investment Management Service
N.A.I.C.S.: 525990

BLACKROCK, INC.

50 Hudson Yards, New York, NY
10001
Tel.: (212) 810-5300   **DE**
Web Site: https://www.blackrock.com
Year Founded: 1998
BLK—(NYSE)
Rev.: $17,859,000,000
Assets: $123,211,000,000
Liabilities: $83,711,000,000
Net Worth: $39,500,000,000
Earnings: $5,502,000,000
Emp.: 19,800
Fiscal Year-end: 12/31/23
Financial Investment Services
N.A.I.C.S.: 523999
Barbara G. Novick (Co-Founder)
Robert Steven Kapito (Co-Founder &
Pres)
Philip M. Tseng (Mng Dir)
Philipp M. Hildebrand (Vice Chm)
Robert L. Goldstein (COO & Head-
Solutions-Global)
Susan L. Wagner (Co-Founder)
Samara Cohen (Chief Investment
Officer-ETF & Index Investments)
Laurence Douglas Fink (Chm & CEO)
Lance Braunstein (Head-Aladdin En-
grg)
Charles Hatami (Head-Global Fin &
Strategic Investors Grp)
John Kelly (Head-Global Corp Affairs)
Rich Kushel (Head-Portfolio Mgmt
Grp)
Christopher Meade (Chief Legal Offi-
cer)
Raj Rao (Pres & COO-Global Infra-
structure Partners)
Mark Wiedman (Head-Global Client
Bus)
Ed Fishwick (Chief Risk Officer &
Head-Risk & Quantitative Analysis)

Subsidiaries:

Aperio Group LLC   **(1)**
3 Harbor Dr Ste 204, Sausalito, CA 94965
Tel.: (415) 339-4300
Web Site: https://www.aperiogroup.com
Investment Management Firm
N.A.I.C.S.: 523940
Patrick Geddes (CEO)
Ran Leshem (Chief Investment Officer)

Lisa Goldberg (Dir-Res)
Pete Hand (Dir-Quantitative Strategies)
Robert Tymoczko (Dir-Portfolio Mgmt)

BlackRock (Channel Islands)
Limited   **(1)**
4th Floor One Waverley Place, Saint Helier,
JE10BR, Jersey
Tel.: (44) 153 460 0800
Sales Range: $25-49.9 Million
Emp.: 6
International Trade Financing Services
N.A.I.C.S.: 522299
Frank Le Feuvri (Mng Dir)

BlackRock (Luxembourg) S.A.   **(1)**
35a Avenue JF Kennedy, 1855, Luxem-
bourg, Luxembourg
Tel.: (352) 3420104201
Web Site: https://www.blackrock.com
Emp.: 83
Investment Management & Financial Ser-
vices
N.A.I.C.S.: 523940

BlackRock (Netherlands) B.V.   **(1)**
Amstelplein 1 Rembrandt Tower, 1096 HA,
Amsterdam, Netherlands
Tel.: (31) 20 549 5200
Web Site: http://www.blackrock.com
Emp.: 40
Investment Management Service
N.A.I.C.S.: 541618

BlackRock (Shanghai) Co., Ltd.   **(1)**
Azia Center 1233 Lujiazui Ring Road, Pu-
dong, Shanghai, China
Tel.: (86) 2180225188
Investment Management Service
N.A.I.C.S.: 523940
Jim Zhang (COO)

BlackRock (Singapore Holdco) Pte.
Limited   **(1)**
Twenty Anson 18-01 20 Anson Road, Sin-
gapore, 079912, Singapore
Tel.: (65) 6 411 3000
Web Site: https://www.blackrock.com
Emp.: 400
Investment Management Service
N.A.I.C.S.: 541618

BlackRock (Singapore) Limited   **(1)**
Twenty Anson 18-01 20 Anson Road, Sin-
gapore, 079912, Singapore
Tel.: (65) 64113000
Web Site: https://www.blackrock.com
Investment Management & Financial Ser-
vices
N.A.I.C.S.: 523940

BlackRock Argentina Asesorias
Ltda.   **(1)**
Calle Malpu, 1210, Buenos Aires, Argentina
Tel.: (54) 1148728100
Investment Management Service
N.A.I.C.S.: 525910

BlackRock Asset Management
(Schweiz) AG   **(1)**
Bahnhofstrasse 39, 8001, Zurich, Switzer-
land
Tel.: (41) 2077433300
Web Site: https://www.blackrock.com
Emp.: 110
Investment Management & Financial Ser-
vices
N.A.I.C.S.: 523940

BlackRock Asset Management
Canada Limited   **(1)**
161 Bay Street, Toronto, M5J 2S1, ON,
Canada
Tel.: (416) 643-4000
Web Site: http://www.blackrock.com
Sales Range: $25-49.9 Million
Financial Planning Consultants Services
N.A.I.C.S.: 541618
Pat Chiefalo (Dir)

BlackRock Asset Management North
Asia Limited   **(1)**
15/F 16/F 17/F Champion Tower 17/F ICBC
Tower Three Garden Road, Central, China
(Hong Kong)
Tel.: (852) 39032688
Web Site: https://www.blackrock.com
Investment Management & Financial Ser-
vices
N.A.I.C.S.: 523940

BlackRock Capital Management, Inc. (1)
251 Little Falls Dr, Wilmington, DE 19808
Asset Management Services
N.A.I.C.S.: 523999

BlackRock Colombia Infraestructura S.A.S. (1)
Savile 10 Avenida Calle 82 No 9-65, Bogota, 110231, Colombia
Tel.: (57) 13192598
Investment Management Service
N.A.I.C.S.: 523940

BlackRock Colombia SAS (1)
Avenida Calle 82 No 9 - 65 Office 501
Savile Building, Bogota, Colombia
Tel.: (57) 17432106
Web Site: https://www.blackrock.com
Investment Management & Financial Services
N.A.I.C.S.: 523940

BlackRock Energy & Resources (1)
100 Bellevue Pkwy, Wilmington, DE 19809
Rev.: $14,462,925
Assets: $379,850,347
Liabilities: $4,954,524
Net Worth: $374,895,823
Earnings: $10,075,651
Fiscal Year-end: 12/31/2019
Financial Consulting Services
N.A.I.C.S.: 541611

BlackRock Finance Europe Limited (1)
12 Throgmorton Ave, London, EC2N 2DL, United Kingdom
Tel.: (44) 2077433000
Investment Management Service
N.A.I.C.S.: 523999

BlackRock Financial Management, Inc. (1)
60 State St, Boston, MA 02109
Tel.: (617) 357-1200
Web Site: http://www.blackrock.com
Sales Range: $250-299.9 Million
Investment Adviser & Management Services
N.A.I.C.S.: 523940

BlackRock Hungary Kft (1)
White House 47 Vaci Ut District XIII, Budapest, Hungary
Tel.: (36) 16860000
Investment Management Service
N.A.I.C.S.: 523940
Orsolya Kelemen (VP)

BlackRock International Limited (1)
Exchange Place One 1 Semple Street, Edinburgh, EH3 8BL, United Kingdom
Tel.: (44) 131 472 7200
Web Site: http://www.blackrock.com
Emp.: 30
Fund Management Services
N.A.I.C.S.: 523940

BlackRock Investment Management (Australia) Limited (1)
Grosvenor Place, PO Box N43, Sydney, 1220, NSW, Australia
Tel.: (61) 1300366100
Investment Management & Financial Services
N.A.I.C.S.: 523940

BlackRock Investment Management (Taiwan) Limited (1)
28F No 100 Songren Rd, Xinyi, Taipei, 110, Taiwan
Tel.: (886) 223261600
Investment Management & Financial Services
N.A.I.C.S.: 523940

BlackRock Investment Management (UK) Limited (1)
12 Throgmorton Avenue, London, EC2N 2DL, United Kingdom (100%)
Tel.: (44) 207 743 3000
Web Site: https://www.blackrock.com
Sales Range: $1-4.9 Billion
Equity, Fixed Income, Asset Management & Alternative Investment Products & Services
N.A.I.C.S.: 523940

BlackRock Investment Management International Limited (1)

33 King William Street, London, EC4R 9AS, United Kingdom
Tel.: (44) 2077435334
Investment Management Service
N.A.I.C.S.: 541611

BlackRock Investment Management, LLC (1)
100 Bellevue Pkwy, Wilmington, DE 19809-3700
Tel.: (302) 797-2000
Web Site: http://www.bfm.com
Sales Range: $10-24.9 Million
Emp.: 700
Investment Advisory Services
N.A.I.C.S.: 812990

BlackRock Investments Canada, Inc. (1)
161 Bay Street, PO Box 2541, Toronto, M5J 2S1, ON, Canada (100%)
Tel.: (416) 643-4000
Web Site: http://ca.ishares.com
Rev.: $6,000,000,000
Emp.: 80
Exchange Traded Funds Management
N.A.I.C.S.: 525910

BlackRock Japan Co., Ltd. (1)
Marunouchi Trust Tower Main Building 1-8-3 Marunouchi, Chiyoda-ku, Tokyo, 100-8217, Japan (100%)
Tel.: (81) 36 703 4100
Web Site: https://www.blackrock.com
Emp.: 383
Investment Services
N.A.I.C.S.: 523999
Arita Hiroyuki (Pres)
Helen Zhu (Portfolio Mgr)

BlackRock Peru Asesorias S.A. (1)
Edificio Fibra Calle Las Orquideas 585 San Isidro, Lima, Peru
Tel.: (51) 17123938
Investment Management Service
N.A.I.C.S.: 523940

BlackRock Saudi Arabia (1)
Olaya Towers - Tower B 3074 Prince Mohammed bin Abdulaziz St, Olaya District, Riyadh, 12213-8022, Saudi Arabia
Tel.: (966) 118383602
Web Site: https://www.blackrock.com
Investment Management & Financial Services
N.A.I.C.S.: 523940

BlackRock Services India Private Limited (1)
14th 15th Floor Tower C D DLF Building No 14 DLF, Cyber City Phase-III Gurgaon, Gurgaon, 122 002, Haryana, India
Tel.: (91) 1244950000
Investment Management Service
N.A.I.C.S.: 541611

BlackRock UK Holdco Limited (1)
12 Throgmorton Avenue, London, EC2N 2DL, United Kingdom
Tel.: (44) 2077433000
Investment Management Service
N.A.I.C.S.: 523940

Cachematrix Holdings, LLC (1)
44 Cook St 8 Fl, Denver, CO 80206
Tel.: (303) 468-5500
Web Site: https://www.cachematrix.com
Investment Management Service
N.A.I.C.S.: 523940
George Hagerman (Founder & Chm)
Dave Agostine (CEO)
Cindy Bernhardt (COO)
Matt Crooks (CIO)
Kevin Sun (CTO)
Kevin Ancell (Head-Ops-Global)
Arlene Chua (Dir-Project Delivery & Data Svcs)

DSP BlackRock Investment Managers Private Limited (1)
302 Natraj, Plot no 194, MB Rd Junction, Western Express Highway, Andheri east, Mumbai, 400069, India (40%)
Tel.: (91) 2267178000
Web Site: http://www.dspblackrock.com
Investment Management Service
N.A.I.C.S.: 541611
Kalpen Parekh (Pres)

FutureAdvisor, Inc. (1)

400 Howard St, San Francisco, CA 94105
Web Site: http://www.futureadvisor.com
Financial Advisory Services
N.A.I.C.S.: 523940

Global Infrastructure Management, LLC (1)
1345 Ave of the Americas 30th Fl, New York, NY 10105
Tel.: (212) 315-8100
Web Site: http://www.global-infra.com
Sales Range: $25-49.9 Billion
Emp.: 58,000
Equity Investment Services
N.A.I.C.S.: 523999
Adebayo O. Ogunlesi (Bd of Dirs, Executives)
Jonathan Bram (Partner)
Joseph Blum (Chief Compliance Officer, Gen Counsel & Partner)
William A. Woodburn (Partner)
Matthew C. Harris (Partner)
Mark L. Levitt (Mng Dir & COO)
James P. Jenkins (Mng Dir)
Salim Samaha (Partner)
William J. Brilliant (Partner)
Gregg Myers (Dir-Fin & Acctg)
Jack Cowell (Dir-Mktg & Comm)
Andrew Froberg (Dir-Tax)
James Cleary (Mng Dir)
Lori Gish (Mng Dir & Chief Admin Officer)
Rob Stewart (Mng Partner)
Jason Baer (Principal-Fin)
Ronnie S. Hawkins (Partner & Mng Dir)
Deepak Agrawal (Partner)
Andrew Gillespie-Smith (Partner)
Michael McGhee (Partner)
Jennifer Powers (Partner)
Raj Rao (Partner)
Robert O'Brien (Mng Dir)
Annabel Wiscarson (Mng Dir & Head-IR)
Di Xu (Mng Dir-IR Focus)
Tufan Erginbilgic (Partner)
Scott E. Telesz (Operating Partner)

Joint Venture (Non-US):

Asciano Limited (2)
Level 4 476 St Kilda Road, Melbourne, 3004, VIC, Australia
Tel.: (61) 3 92487000
Web Site: http://www.asciano.com.au
Sales Range: $1-4.9 Billion
Ports & Rail Assets Management
N.A.I.C.S.: 485112
Roger Burrows (CFO)
Lyndall Stoyles (Gen Counsel & Sec)

Joint Venture (Non-US):

C3 Limited (3)
58 Cross Road Sulphur Point, Tauranga, 3110, New Zealand
Tel.: (64) 75728972
Web Site: https://www.c3.co.nz
Emp.: 800
Marine Cargo Handling Services
N.A.I.C.S.: 488320
Chris Sutherland (Gen Mgr-Logistics-New Zealand)
Walter Naera (Gen Mgr-Employee Rels-New Zealand)

Holding (Domestic):

Clearway Energy, Inc. (2)
300 Carnegie Ctr Ste 300, Princeton, NJ 08540 (55.1%)
Tel.: (609) 608-1525
Rev.: $1,314,000,000
Assets: $14,701,000,000
Liabilities: $9,707,000,000
Net Worth: $4,994,000,000
Earnings: $79,000,000
Emp.: 61
Fiscal Year-end: 12/31/2023
Electric Power Generation
N.A.I.C.S.: 221118
Jonathan Bram (Chm)
Craig Cornelius (Pres & CEO)
Michael Murphy (Chief Investment Officer)
Sarah Rubenstein (CFO, Chief Acctg Officer & Exec VP)

Subsidiary (Domestic):

Avenal Park LLC (3)
33039 Ave 36, Avenal, CA 93204
Tel.: (858) 638-7115
Solar Heating Contracting Services

N.A.I.C.S.: 238220

Energy Center Harrisburg LLC (3)
100 N 10th St Fl 3, Harrisburg, PA 17101-2440
Steam Heating Distr
N.A.I.C.S.: 221330

Energy Center Minneapolis LLC (3)
80 S 8th St Ste 2850, Minneapolis, MN 55402-2103
Power Generation Services
N.A.I.C.S.: 221118

Energy Center Paxton LLC (3)
100 N 10th St, Harrisburg, PA 17101
Tel.: (717) 234-4600
Water Supply
N.A.I.C.S.: 221330

Energy Center Phoenix LL (3)
1 E Washington St Ste 280, Phoenix, AZ 85004-2492
Tel.: (602) 281-9848
Combined Heat & Power Plant Mfr
N.A.I.C.S.: 221118

Energy Center Pittsburgh LLC (3)
111 S Commons, Pittsburgh, PA 15212
Electric & Other Services Combined
N.A.I.C.S.: 221118
Mauricio Gutierrez (Pres & CEO)
Donna Benefield (Sr VP-Program Office)
Michael Bramnick (Chief Compliance Officer, Administration Officer & Sr VP)

Energy Systems Co. (3)
2152 Howard St, Omaha, NE 68102
Tel.: (402) 346-9066
Sales Range: $1-9.9 Million
Emp.: 35
Heating & Air Conditioning Services
N.A.I.C.S.: 238220
Truch Stevens (Gen Mgr)

Laredo Ridge Wind, LLC (3)
701 Winslow Way E Ste B, Bainbridge Island, WA 98110
Tel.: (206) 780-3551
Energy Conservation Services
N.A.I.C.S.: 444110

NRG Energy Center Dover LLC (3)
1280 W N St, Dover, DE 19904
Tel.: (302) 678-4666
Rev.: $4,000,000
Emp.: 18
Electric Power Generation
N.A.I.C.S.: 221118
Michael Carrol (Pres)

NRG Energy Center San Francisco LLC (3)
14 Mint St Ste 200, San Francisco, CA 94103
Tel.: (415) 777-3415
Electric Power Distribution Services
N.A.I.C.S.: 221122
Gordon Judd (Gen Mgr)
Peggy Avery (Controller-Acctg)
Lisa Smethurst (Acct Mgr & Mgr-Customer Svc)
Mike Eurkus (Mgr-Svc & Distr)
Wendy Gallegos (Office Mgr)

NRG Thermal LLC (3)
80 S 8th St Ste 2850, Minneapolis, MN 55402-2200
Tel.: (612) 436-4108
Electrical Energy Distr
N.A.I.C.S.: 221118

Pikes Peak Solar Garden I LLC (3)
218 E Cache La Poudre St, Colorado Springs, CO 80903
Tel.: (210) 275-2381
Electric Energy Services
N.A.I.C.S.: 221118

Holding (Domestic):

Competitive Power Ventures Holdings, LLC (2)
8403 Colesville Rd Ste 915, Silver Spring, MD 20910
Tel.: (240) 723-2300
Web Site: http://www.cpv.com
Electric Power Generation Development & Asset Management Services
N.A.I.C.S.: 221115

BlackRock, Inc.—(Continued)

Dave Magill *(Sr VP-Asset Mgmt Grp)*
Peter Podurgiel *(Sr VP-Thermal Dev)*

Holding (Domestic):

Optim Energy Altura CoGen LLC **(3)**
2330 Sheldon Rd, Channelview, TX 77530
Tel.: (281) 457-1404
Electric Power
N.A.I.C.S.: 221121

Joint Venture (Domestic):

CyrusOne Inc. **(2)**
2850 N Harwood St Ste 2200, Dallas, TX 75201
Tel.: (972) 350-0060
Web Site: http://www.cyrusone.com
Rev.: $1,205,700,000
Assets: $7,452,000,000
Liabilities: $4,528,300,000
Net Worth: $2,923,700,000
Earnings: $25,300,000
Emp.: 456
Fiscal Year-end: 12/31/2021
Real Estate Investment Trust; Information Technology Networks Designer & Operator
N.A.I.C.S.: 525990
John Hatem *(COO & Exec VP)*
David H. Ferdman *(Founder)*
Lynn A. Wentworth *(Chm)*
Mark E. Skomal *(Chief Acctg Officer & Sr VP)*
Matt Pullen *(Mng Dir-Europe & Exec VP)*
Michael Nudelman *(Sr VP-Project Dev)*
Eric Schwartz *(Pres & CEO)*
Michael Schafer *(Interim CFO & Sr VP-Fin)*

Subsidiary (Domestic):

CyrusOne LLC **(3)**
1649 W Frankford Rd, Carrollton, TX 75007
Tel.: (972) 350-0060
Web Site: http://www.cyrusone.com
Information Technology Networks Designer & Operator
N.A.I.C.S.: 541513

Holding (Non-US):

Edinburgh Airport Limited **(2)**
Edinburgh Airport, Edinburgh, EH12 9DN, Scotland, United Kingdom
Tel.: (44) 844 448 8833
Web Site: http://www.edinburghairport.com
Rev.: $258,768,406
Assets: $1,424,125,970
Liabilities: $1,294,967,652
Net Worth: $129,158,318
Earnings: $77,603,111
Emp.: 661
Fiscal Year-end: 12/31/2018
Airport
N.A.I.C.S.: 488119
Gordon Dewar *(CEO)*
John Elvidge *(Chm)*
John Watson *(Chief Comml Officer)*
Alastair Couper *(CFO)*
Gillian Pollock *(Dir-HR)*
Gordon Robertson *(Dir-Comm)*
David Gammie *(Dir-IT)*
Stephen Swan *(Sec & Dir-Legal)*
Adrian Witherow *(COO)*
David Feltham *(Head-Organisational Change)*
Kate Sherry *(Dir-Aviation)*

International Port Holdings Ltd. **(2)**
The Peak 6th Floor 5 Wilton Road, London, SW1V 1AN, United Kingdom
Tel.: (44) 7941 028130
Sales Range: $50-74.9 Million
Emp.: 25
Holding Company; Port Operations
N.A.I.C.S.: 551112
Alistair Baillie *(Chm)*
Eliza O'Toole *(Vice Chm)*

Joint Venture (Non-US):

Signature Aviation Limited **(2)**
Percival Way, Luton, London, LU2 9PA, United Kingdom
Tel.: (44) 3300271281
Web Site: https://www.signatureaviation.com
Rev.: $1,413,900,000
Assets: $4,587,400,000
Liabilities: $2,997,300,000
Net Worth: $1,590,100,000

Earnings: $9,500,000
Emp.: 6,469
Fiscal Year-end: 12/31/2020
Holding Company; Aircraft Parts Mfr, Repair, Maintenance & Flight Support Services
N.A.I.C.S.: 551112
Tristan Dorian *(Gen Mgr)*

Group (US):

BBA Aviation Engine Repair & Overhaul Group **(3)**
900 Nolen Dr Ste 100, Grapevine, TX 76051-8641
Tel.: (214) 956-3000
Web Site: http://www.bbaaviationero.com
Sales Range: $75-99.9 Million
Emp.: 220
Subsidiary Managing Office; Aircraft Engine Repair & Overhaul Services
N.A.I.C.S.: 551114
Hugh E. McElroy Jr. *(Pres)*
Nandakumar Madireddi *(Sr VP-Bus Ops)*
Dennis DiMarco *(VP-Sls & Mktg-North America)*
Doris Hastings *(VP-HR)*
Gerardo Gomez *(Mgr-Sls-Mexico)*

Subsidiary (Domestic):

Dallas Airmotive, Inc. **(4)**
900 Nolen Dr Ste 100, Grapevine, TX 76051-8641
Tel.: (214) 956-3001
Web Site: http://www.bbaaviationero.com
Rev.: $42,750,769
Emp.: 80
Aircraft Engine Repair & Overhaul Services
N.A.I.C.S.: 336412

Unit (Domestic):

Dallas Airmotive, Inc. - Dallas Facility **(5)**
2988 W Walnut Hill Ln DFW Airport, Dallas, TX 75261
Tel.: (214) 956-3001
Web Site: http://www.dallasairmotive.com
Sales Range: $25-49.9 Million
Aircraft Engine Repair & Overhaul Services
N.A.I.C.S.: 336412
Thomas Kennedy *(Mgr-Engine-Danvers Reg)*

Subsidiary (Non-US):

H+S Aviation Limited **(4)**
Airport Service Road, Portsmouth, PO3 5PJ, Hampshire, United Kingdom
Tel.: (44) 2392304000
Web Site: https://www.hsaviation.co.uk
Emp.: 320
Aircraft Engine Repair & Overhaul Services
N.A.I.C.S.: 000412
Ann New *(Dir-HR)*

Group (US):

BBA Aviation Legacy Support Group **(3)**
20400 Plummer St, Chatsworth, CA 91311
Tel.: (818) 678-6555
Web Site: http://www.bbaaviation.com
Subsidiary Managing Office; Legacy Aircraft Parts Mfr & Whslr
N.A.I.C.S.: 551114

Subsidiary (Domestic):

International Governor Services, LLC **(4)**
7290 W 118th Pl, Broomfield, CO 80020
Tel.: (303) 464-0043
Web Site: http://www.internationalgovernor.com
Emp.: 17
Small Aircraft Turbine Engine Controls Repair & Overhaul Services
N.A.I.C.S.: 335314

Subsidiary (Domestic):

Balderton Aviation Holdings Limited **(3)**
20 Balderton Street, London, W1K 6TL, United Kingdom
Tel.: (44) 20 7016 6800
Web Site: http://www.baldertoncapital.com
Emp.: 23
Investment Management Service

N.A.I.C.S.: 523999

Subsidiary (US):

Barrett Turbine Engine Company **(3)**
1626 Tobacco Rd, Augusta, GA 30906
Tel.: (706) 790-1977
Web Site: http://www.barrettturbineengine.com
Aircraft Engine Mfr
N.A.I.C.S.: 336412
Russell Cathey *(VP & Gen Mgr)*
Albert Poor *(VP-Sls)*

Subsidiary (Non-US):

Dallas Airmotive South Africa Pty Limited **(3)**
Hanger 201 Lanseria International Airport Airport Road, Lanseria, 1748, South Africa
Tel.: (27) 117012611
Aircraft Leasing & Rental Services
N.A.I.C.S.: 532411

Subsidiary (US):

EPIC Aviation, LLC **(3)**
222 W Las Colinas Blvd Ste 1425 N, Irving, TX 75039
Tel.: (503) 362-3633
Web Site: https://www.epicfuels.com
Petroleum & Bulk Fuels
N.A.I.C.S.: 424720

General Aviation Flying Services, Inc. **(3)**
485 Industrial Ave, Teterboro, NJ 07608
Tel.: (201) 288-5040
Sales Range: $1-9.9 Million
Emp.: 100
Air Courier Services
N.A.I.C.S.: 492110
Ken C. Forester *(CEO)*

Subsidiary (Non-US):

SFS Munich GmbH & Co. KG **(3)**
PO Box 241431, 85336, Munich, Germany
Tel.: (49) 8997597730
Aircraft Maintenance Services
N.A.I.C.S.: 488190
Oliver Trono *(Gen Mgr)*

Group (US):

Signature Flight Support Corp. **(3)**
13485 Veterans Way Ste 600, Orlando, FL 32827
Tel.: (407) 648-7200
Web Site: http://www.signatureflight.com
Sales Range: $550-599.9 Million
Emp.: 1,300
Private Aircraft Ground Support Services
N.A.I.C.S.: 488119
Tony Lefebvre *(CEO)*
Amy Alexy *(Chief People Officer)*
Derek DeCross *(Sr VP)*
Rick Elieson *(Sr VP)*
Mike Eshoo *(CFO)*
Maria Garton *(Gen Counsel)*
Anurag Gupta *(CIO)*
Marty Kretchman *(Sr VP)*

Unit (Domestic):

Signature Flight Support - BED **(4)**
180 Hanscom Dr, Bedford, MA 01730
Tel.: (781) 274-0010
Web Site: https://www.signatureaviation.com
Emp.: 25
Air Transportation Support Services
N.A.I.C.S.: 488190

Signature Flight Support - MKE **(4)**
923 E Layton Ave, Milwaukee, WI 53207
Tel.: (414) 747-5100
Web Site: http://www.signatureflight.com
Sales Range: $25-49.9 Million
Emp.: 33
Private Aircraft Ground Support Services
N.A.I.C.S.: 488119

Signature Flight Support - MMU **(4)**
1 Airport Rd, Morristown, NJ 07960
Tel.: (973) 292-1300
Web Site: http://www.signatureflight.com
Emp.: 44
Private Aircraft Ground Support Services
N.A.I.C.S.: 488119
Pasquale Raguseo *(Dir-Art-MQS & KMQS)*

Signature Flight Support - PIE **(4)**
14525 Airport Pkwy, Clearwater, FL 33762
Tel.: (727) 531-1441
Web Site: http://www.signatureflight.com
Sales Range: $50-74.9 Million
Emp.: 120
Private Aircraft Ground Support Services
N.A.I.C.S.: 488119

Signature Flight Support - PWK **(4)**
1100 S Milwaukee Ave, Wheeling, IL 60090-6309
Tel.: (847) 537-1200
Web Site: http://www.signatureflight.com
Sales Range: $25-49.9 Million
Emp.: 13
Private Aircraft Ground Support Services
N.A.I.C.S.: 488119
Mark Costa *(Gen Mgr)*

Signature Flight Support - STL **(4)**
5995 James S McDonnell Blvd, Saint Louis, MO 63134
Tel.: (314) 731-7111
Web Site: http://www.signatureflight.com
Sales Range: $25-49.9 Million
Emp.: 30
Private Aircraft Ground Support Services
N.A.I.C.S.: 488119

Subsidiary (Non-US):

Signature Flight Support Paris SA **(4)**
45 Avenue de l'Europe Zone Aviation d'Affaires, 93350, Le Bourget, France
Tel.: (33) 149927581
Web Site: http://www.signatureflight.com
Sales Range: $25-49.9 Million
Emp.: 25
Oil Transportation Services
N.A.I.C.S.: 488190
Andriot Nathalie *(Gen Mgr)*

Subsidiary (US):

Signature Flight Support Washington National, Inc. **(3)**
1 General Aviation Terminal Hangar 7, Washington, DC 20001
Tel.: (703) 417-3500
Aircraft Maintenance Services
N.A.I.C.S.: 488190
Pablo Espitia *(Gen Mgr)*

Portland Natural Gas Transmission System **(1)**
1 Harbour Pl, Portsmouth, NH 03801
Tel.: (603) 559-5500
Web Site: http://www.pngts.com
Natural Gas Transmission & Power Services; Owned 62% by TransCanada Corporation & 38% by Northern New England Energy Corporation
N.A.I.C.S.: 486210

SFP Holding, Inc. **(1)**
3414 M-32 W, Alpena, MI 49707
Tel.: (231) 947-6035
Web Site: http://www.summitcompanies.com
Sales Range: $1-9.9 Million
Emp.: 5,000
Business Management Services
N.A.I.C.S.: 561499
Jeff Evrard *(CEO)*
Ryan Bierwerth *(Exec VP)*
Jeff Evrard *(CEO)*

Subsidiary (Domestic):

Summit Fire Protection Co. **(2)**
575 Minnehaha Ave W, Saint Paul, MN 55103
Tel.: (888) 220-7866
Web Site: https://www.summitfire.com
Fire Sprinkler System Installation
N.A.I.C.S.: 238220
Chris Gillen *(Pres)*

Subsidiary (Domestic):

ABC Fire Extinguisher Co. Inc. **(3)**
2910 Brookspark Dr, North, Las Vegas, NV 89030
Tel.: (702) 432-8558
Fire Prevention Products & Services
N.A.I.C.S.: 922160

Summit Fire & Security **(3)**
1025 Telegraph Street, Reno, NV 89502

Tel.: (888) 229-4146
Web Site: https://summitfiresecurity.com
Support Services
N.A.I.C.S.: 561990
Nic Brown *(Pres)*

Tennenbaum Capital Partners, LLC (1)
2951 28th St Ste 1000, Santa Monica, CA 90405
Tel.: (310) 566-1000
Web Site:
   http://www.tennenbaumcapital.com
Sales Range: $25-49.9 Million
Emp.: 65
Privater Equity Firm
N.A.I.C.S.: 523999

Tower General Partner Limited (1)
Kirsh Family Office York Gate 100 Marylebone Road, London, NW1 5DX, United Kingdom
Tel.: (44) 2073791000
Emp.: 1
Investment Management Service
N.A.I.C.S.: 523999
Norman Brown *(Sec)*

Transaction Data Systems Inc. (1)
6021 Rio Grande Ave S Suite 3E, 32809, Orlando, FL
Tel.: (407) 614-0050
Web Site: http://www.rx30.com
Custom Computer Programming Services
N.A.I.C.S.: 541511
Al Farrell *(CFO)*
Tycene Fritcher *(CMO)*
Jude Dieterman *(CEO)*
Maureen Brennan *(Chief People Officer)*
Alex Miguel *(COO)*
Grant Chapin *(Sr VP-Merger & Acq)*
Tom Mullin *(Chief Commercialization Officer)*
Matt Pokress *(CTO)*

Subsidiary (Domestic):

Pharm Assess, Inc. (2)
10540 Marty St #110, 66212, Overland Park, KS
Tel.: (913) 897-4343
Drugs & Druggists' Sundries Merchant Whslr
N.A.I.C.S.: 424210

PrescribeWellness (2)
49 Discovery Ste 200, Irvine, CA 92618
Web Site: http://www.prescribewellness.com
Sales Range: $1-9.9 Million
Emp.: 41
Healthcare Software Development Services
N.A.I.C.S.: 541511
Al Babbington *(Co-Founder & CEO)*
Jay Williams *(VP-Mktg)*
Mindy Smith *(VP-Pharmacy Practice Innovation)*
Sean Power *(Co-Founder & Vice Chm)*
Susan Lewis *(Co-Founder)*
Kelly Keegan *(Chief Growth Officer)*
Rob Gerger *(CFO)*
Todd Plesco *(Chief Info Security Officer)*
Yesi Orihuela *(CTO)*
Patty Kumbera *(COO)*

Warkentine, Inc. (2)
11825 S Portland Ave, Oklahoma City, OK 73170
Tel.: (405) 799-5282
Web Site: http://www.winrx.net
Computer & Computer Peripheral Equipment & Software Merchant Whslr
N.A.I.C.S.: 423430
Jude Dieterman *(CEO)*
Michael Johnson *(Chief Revenue Officer)*
Kevin Lathrop *(COO)*

eFront (Jersey) Limited (1)
Fifth Floor 37 Esplanade, Saint Helier, JE1 2TR, Jersey
Tel.: (44) 1534610969
Software Development Services
N.A.I.C.S.: 541511

eFront GmbH (1)
Worringer Str 30, 50668, Cologne, Germany
Tel.: (49) 22167788721
Software Development Services
N.A.I.C.S.: 541511

eFront Hong Kong Limited (1)
16/F Champion Tower Three Garden Road, Central, China (Hong Kong)
Tel.: (852) 39032800
Software Development Services
N.A.I.C.S.: 541511

eFront Kabushiki Kaisha (1)
1-8-3 Marunouchi Marunouchi Trust Main Tower, Chiyoda-ku, Tokyo, 100-8217, Japan
Tel.: (81) 367034100
Software Development Services
N.A.I.C.S.: 541511

eFront Ltd. (1)
12 Throgmorton Avenue, London, EC2N 2DL, United Kingdom
Tel.: (44) 2077433000
Software Development Services
N.A.I.C.S.: 541511
Stuart Tait *(Sls Dir)*

eFront SASU (1)
2-4 rue Louis David, 75116, Paris, France
Tel.: (33) 1 4996 4060
Web Site: http://www.efront.com
Alternative Assets Management Software Publisher & Whslr
N.A.I.C.S.: 513210

Subsidiary (US):

eFront Financial Solutions Inc. (2)
40 E 52nd St, New York, NY 10022
Tel.: (212) 810-5300
Web Site: http://www.efront.com
Alternative Assets Management Software Publisher & Whslr
N.A.I.C.S.: 513210

eFront Singapore Pte. Ltd. (1)
Twenty Anson 20 Anson Road, Singapore, 079912, Singapore
Tel.: (65) 64113000
Software Development Services
N.A.I.C.S.: 541511

eFront Software Luxembourg S.a r.l. (1)
26b Boulevard Royal, 2449, Luxembourg, Luxembourg
Tel.: (352) 28290400
Software Development Services
N.A.I.C.S.: 541511

eFront Solutions Financeieres Inc. (1)
1010 Sherbrooke St W, Montreal, H3A 2R7, QC, Canada
Tel.: (514) 843-5069
Software Development Services
N.A.I.C.S.: 541511

eFront d.o.o. (1)
Kneza Mihaila 1 - 3, 11000, Belgrade, Serbia
Tel.: (381) 114439000
Software Development Services
N.A.I.C.S.: 541511

BLACKSKY TECHNOLOGY INC.
13241 Woodland Park Rd Ste 300, Herndon, VA 20171
Tel.: (571) 267-1571 DE
SFTW—(NYSE)
Rev.: $65,350,000
Assets: $234,090,000
Liabilities: $112,216,000
Net Worth: $121,874,000
Earnings: ($74,172,000)
Emp.: 259
Fiscal Year-end: 12/31/22
Geospatial Intelligence Solutions
N.A.I.C.S.: 541511
Jonathan Z. Cohen *(Co-Founder)*
Johan Broekhuysen *(CFO)*
Brian E. O'Toole *(Pres & CEO)*

BLACKSTAR ENTERPRISE GROUP, INC
4450 Arapahoe Ave Ste 100, Boulder, CO 80303
Tel.: (303) 500-3210 DE
Web Site:
   https://www.blackstareg.com

Year Founded: 2007
BEGI—(OTCIQ)
Assets: $303,770
Liabilities: $1,033,380
Net Worth: ($729,610)
Earnings: ($1,225,207)
Fiscal Year-end: 12/31/22
Merchant Banking & Financial Services
N.A.I.C.S.: 522110
Joseph E. Kurczodyna *(Acting CEO & CFO)*

BLACKSTONE INC.
345 Park Ave, New York, NY 10154
Tel.: (212) 583-5000 DE
Web Site:
   https://www.blackstone.com
Year Founded: 1985
BX—(NYSE)
Rev.: $8,022,841,000
Assets: $40,287,530,000
Liabilities: $23,391,389,000
Net Worth: $16,896,141,000
Earnings: $2,444,253,000
Emp.: 4,735
Fiscal Year-end: 12/31/23
Private Equity & Real Estate Investment Firm
N.A.I.C.S.: 523999
Gregory R. Blank *(Sr Mng Dir)*
Harish Manwani *(Sr Partner-Operating)*
Nicholas L. Kuhar *(Mng Dir)*
Ari Brettman *(Mng Dir-Life Science Grp)*
David Payne *(Chief Acctg Officer)*
Joseph Baratta *(Head)*
David Blitzer *(Head)*
Martin Brand *(Head)*
Gilles Dellaert *(Head)*
Joe Dowling *(Head)*
Michael Addeo *(Mng Dir)*
A. J. Agarwal *(Sr Mng Dir)*
Akin Akinrinade *(Mng Dir)*
Farez Alibay *(Mng Dir)*
Matt Anderson *(Mng Dir)*
Martin Brand *(Head)*
Stephen Allen Schwarzman *(Co-Founder, Chm & CEO)*
Jonathan D. Gray *(Pres & COO)*

Subsidiaries:

Alinamin Pharmaceutical Co., Ltd. (1)
1-8-2 Marunouchi 23rd floor Tekko Buildin, Chiyoda-ku, Tokyo, 100-0005, Japan
Tel.: (81) 362128501
Web Site: https://alinamin-pharma.co.jp
Pharmaceuticals Products & Medical Devices Mfr & Sales
N.A.I.C.S.: 325412

American Campus Communities, Inc. (1)
12700 Hill Country Blvd Ste T-200, Austin, TX 78738
Tel.: (512) 732-1000
Web Site: http://www.americancampus.com
Rev.: $942,409,000
Assets: $7,574,586,000
Liabilities: $4,305,159,000
Net Worth: $3,269,427,000
Earnings: $35,489,000
Emp.: 3,006
Fiscal Year-end: 12/31/2021
Real Estate Investment Trust
N.A.I.C.S.: 525990
William C. Bayless Jr. *(Founder & Vice Chm)*
Brian Winger *(Gen Counsel)*
Jason R. Wills *(CMO)*
Jorge De Cardenas *(CTO & Exec VP)*
William W. Talbot *(Chief Investment Officer & Exec VP)*
Kim K. Voss *(CFO)*
Jennifer Beese *(Pres & COO)*
Rob Palleschi *(CEO)*
Steve Beinke *(Sr VP-Tax)*
Noel Brinkman *(Sr VP-Pub & Private Partnerships)*

Emily Ellis *(Sr VP-Reg)*
Daniel Crownover *(Sr VP-Portfolio Mgmt)*
Ryan Dennison *(Sr VP-Capital Markets & IR)*
Larry Greenberg *(Sr VP-Ops)*
Stacey Heller *(Sr VP-Internal Audit & Enterprise Risk Mgmt)*
James Henson *(Sr VP-Reg)*
Kimberly Kelley *(Sr VP-Leasing & Mktg)*
Kris Kelley *(Sr VP-Acquisitions)*
Heather Laney *(Sr VP-Dev & Property Integration)*
Jeff Langen *(Sr VP-Reg)*
Lonnie Ledbetter *(Sr VP-HR, Organizational Dev & Culture)*
Laura Mack *(Sr VP & Controller-Property)*
Angela Testa *(Sr VP)*
James E. Wilhelm III *(Exec VP-Pub Private Transactions)*

Subsidiary (Domestic):

American Campus Communities Operating Partnership, LP (2)
12700 Hill Country Blvd Ste T-200, Austin, TX 78738
Tel.: (512) 732-1000
Web Site: http://www.americancampus.com
Rev.: $870,583,999
Assets: $7,531,159,999
Liabilities: $4,350,055,999
Net Worth: $3,181,103,999
Earnings: $73,107,000
Emp.: 2,987
Fiscal Year-end: 12/31/2020
Property Management Services
N.A.I.C.S.: 531210
Jorge de Cardenas *(CTO & Exec VP)*
William W. Talbot *(Chief Investment Officer & Exec VP)*
Steve Beinke *(Sr VP-Tax)*
Ryan Dennison *(Sr VP-Capital Markets & IR)*
Emily Ellis *(Sr VP-Reg)*
Larry Greenberg *(Sr VP-Ops)*
James Henson *(Sr VP-Reg)*
Jennifer Jones *(Sr VP-Transactions)*
Kimberly Kelley *(Sr VP-Leasing & Mktg)*
Kris Kelley *(Sr VP-Acquisitions)*
Heather Laney *(Sr VP-Dev & Property Integration)*
Jeff Langen *(Sr VP-Reg)*
Jake Newman *(Sr VP-Dev)*
Rob Palleschi *(CEO)*
Tosha Bowles *(Sr VP)*
Clint Braun *(Sr VP)*
Noel Brinkman *(Sr VP)*
Steve Crawford *(Sr VP)*
Bill Bayless *(Co-Founder)*
James E. Wilhelm III *(Exec VP-Pub Private Transactions)*

American Campus Communities Services, Inc. (2)
408 Campus View Dr, Towson, MD 21204
Tel.: (410) 583-0500
Real Estate Services
N.A.I.C.S.: 531390

GMH Communities, LP (2)
10 Campus Blvd, Newtown Square, PA 19073
Tel.: (610) 355-8000
Web Site: https://www.gmhcommunities.com
Emp.: 1,574
Real Estate Services
N.A.I.C.S.: 531390

Ancestry.com LLC (1)
360 W 4800 N, Provo, UT 84604
Tel.: (801) 705-7000
Web Site: http://www.ancestry.com
Rev.: $683,105,000
Assets: $1,621,760,000
Liabilities: $1,340,842,000
Net Worth: $280,918,000
Earnings: $29,418,000
Emp.: 1,176
Fiscal Year-end: 12/31/2015
Electronic Equipment Distr
N.A.I.C.S.: 423690
Deborah Liu *(Pres & CEO)*
Evan Wittenberg *(Chief People Officer & Exec VP)*
Sriram Thiagarajan *(CIO & Exec VP)*
Carla S. Newell *(Chief Legal Officer & Chief Risk Officer)*
Cathy Ball *(Chief Scientific Officer)*
Mike Linton *(Chief Revenue Officer)*

Blackstone Inc.—(Continued)

Deborah Liu (CEO)
Mark Thompson (Chm)
David Graham (Sr VP-Family History Product)
Julie Miller (COO & Sr VP)
Todd Godfrey (VP-Global Content)
Jennifer Utley (Dir-Family History Res)
Azadeh Moghtaderi (VP-Data Science & Analytics)
Howard Hochhauser (CFO & COO)

Subsidiary (Domestic):

AdPay, Inc. (2)
391 Inverness Pkwy Ste 100, Englewood, CO 80112
Tel.: (303) 268-1527
Web Site: http://www.adpay.com
Software & Technology Development Services
N.A.I.C.S.: 513210
Mike Galusha (Sr Mgr-Sys Dev)
Spencer Heintz (Sr Product Mgr)
Mike Mullen (Mgr-Software Dev)
Devin Parkes (Mgr-Customer Support Ops)

Subsidiary (Non-US):

Ancestry.com Europe S.a r.l. (2)
15 rue Edward Steichen, L 2540, Luxembourg, Luxembourg
Tel.: (352) 27 112 7144
Genealogy Information Publishing & Research Services
N.A.I.C.S.: 513140

Apria Healthcare Group Inc. (1)
26220 Enterprise Ct, Lake Forest, CA 92630
Tel.: (949) 639-2000
Web Site: https://www.apria.com
Home Healthcare Products & Services
N.A.I.C.S.: 621610

Subsidiary (Domestic):

Coram Specialty Infusion Services (2)
555 17th St Ste 1500, Denver, CO 80202
Tel.: (303) 292-4973
Web Site: http://www.coramhc.com
Sales Range: $500-549.9 Million
Emp.: 60
Home Infusion Therapies & Ambulatory Suites Services
N.A.I.C.S.: 621610
John G. Figueroa (Chm & CEO)

Aqua Finance, Inc.
1 Corporate Dr Ste 300, Wausau, WI 54401
Tel.: (715) 848-5425
Web Site: http://www.aquafinance.com
Consumer Lending
N.A.I.C.S.: 522291
Scott Treu (Sr VP-Credit)
Robert Chadwell (Founder & Chm)
Richard Morrin (Pres & CEO)
Bian Sabatke (CFO & Exec VP)
Mark Vander Sanden (CIO & Exec VP)
Scott Chittum (Sr VP-Acct Servicing)
Robert L. Heyman (Sr VP-HR)

Ascend Learning, LLC (1)
25 Mall Rd 6th Fl, Burlington, MA 01803
Tel.: (855) 856-7705
Web Site: https://www.ascendlearning.com
Holding Company; Education & Professional Assessment, Training & Certification Products & Services
N.A.I.C.S.: 551112
Greg DeLasky (CEO)
Larry Gold (Gen Counsel & Sr VP)
Mandeep Johar (CFO)
Laurie McCartney (Pres-Fitness & Wellness)
Jeff Langenbach (Exec VP)
Sean Burke (Pres-Healthcare)
Mehul Patel (Pres-Safety, Security & Intl)
Cheryl Kennedy (Chief HR Officer)
Ash Siebecker (CTO)
Jeff Langenbach (Exec VP-Corp Dev & Strategy)

Subsidiary (Domestic):

Assessment Technologies Institute, LLC (2)
11161 Overbrook Rd, Leawood, KS 66211
Tel.: (913) 685-2740

Web Site: https://www.atitesting.com
Nursing Professional Testing Preparation & Education Support Services
N.A.I.C.S.: 611430
Ada Woo (VP)

Subsidiary (Domestic):

MedHub, LLC (3)
510 Marquette Ave S 3rd Fl, Minneapolis, MN 55402
Tel.: (612) 253-0130
Web Site: https://www.medhub.com
Healthcare Education Program Management Software Publisher
N.A.I.C.S.: 513210

Subsidiary (Domestic):

ClickSafety.com, Inc. (2)
25 Mall Rd, Burlington, MA 01803
Tel.: (800) 971-1080
Web Site: https://www.clicksafety.com
Online Compliance Course Interactive Training Services
N.A.I.C.S.: 611430

Jones & Bartlett Learning, LLC (2)
25 Mall Rd, Burlington, MA 01803
Tel.: (978) 443-5000
Web Site: https://www.jblearning.com
Instructional, Assessment & Educational Books Publisher
N.A.I.C.S.: 513130

Audio Visual Services Corporation (1)
111 W Ocean Blvd Ste 1110, Long Beach, CA 90802
Tel.: (562) 366-0620
Web Site: http://www.psav.com
Emp.: 4,750
Holding Company; Live Meeting Audio Visual Equipment Support Services
N.A.I.C.S.: 551112
Michael McIlwain (CEO)
Whitney J. Markowitz (Chief Legal Officer)
Greg Van Dyke (Sr VP-Sls & Mktg-Global)
Sky Cunningham (COO)
Annette Moody (Sr VP-Product Mgmt)
Brian Lagestee (Sr VP-Revenue Mgmt)
Susan DeVito (Sr VP-Hotel Sls-Global)
Ali Vafa (Sr VP-Ops-Central Reg & Intl)
John Rissi (Sr VP-Ops-Western Reg)
Stephen Lipa (Sr VP-Eastern Reg Ops-Hotel Svcs Div)
Mike Stengel (Sr VP)
Craig Hill (Sr VP-Ops)
Steve Oliver (Sr VP-Ops-Southern Reg)
Todd Schorr (Sr VP-HR)
Ken Russell (Sr VP-Premier Global Events)
Arthur A. Clyne Jr. (Sr VP & Gen Mgr)

Subsidiary (Domestic):

Audio Visual Services Group, LLC (2)
5100 N River Rd Ste 300, Schiller Park, IL 60176
Tel.: (866) 719-8271
Web Site: http://www.psav.com
Live Meeting Audio Visual Equipment Support Services
N.A.I.C.S.: 541990
Michael McIlwain (CEO)

Averys SA (1)
94 Boulevard du Montparnasse, 75014, Paris, France
Tel.: (33) 1 42 08 82 90
Web Site: http://www.averys.fr
Sales Range: $500-549.9 Million
Emp.: 1,300
Design, Production & Installation of Storage Systems
N.A.I.C.S.: 337215
O. Dentan (CFO)
Jean-Domique Perraux (Pres & CEO)
J. Berthoux (Dir-Indus)

Subsidiary (Domestic):

Acial SAS (2)
14 Avenue du Blanc, 41110, Saint-Aignan sur Cher, France
Tel.: (33) 254711414
Web Site: https://www.stow-group.com
Emp.: 175
Shelving, Lockers, Storage & Filing Systems Mfr

N.A.I.C.S.: 337215

Feralco (2)
Route de Troyes, BP 91, 51122, Sezanne, Cedex, France
Tel.: (33) 3 26 80 76 76
Web Site: http://www.feralco.fr
Emp.: 100
Storage Equipment Installation
N.A.I.C.S.: 238990
S. Bossard (Plant Mgr)
Y. Boiteux (Sls Mgr)
S. Hugot (Mgr-Fin)

Lapouyade (2)
98 boulevard Fayol, BP 210, ZI des Prairies, 42704, Firminy, Cedex, France
Tel.: (33) 4 77 40 27 27
Web Site: http://www.lapouyade.com
Metal Shelving Mfr
N.A.I.C.S.: 332999
A. Chagneux (Mng Dir)
H. Cros (Mgr-Fin)
C. Barrellon (Plant Mgr)

Subsidiary (Non-US):

Saar-Lager-und Profiltechnik GmbH (2)
Hausenstrasse 67, 66333, Volklingen, Germany
Tel.: (49) 68983020
Web Site: http://www.slp-regaltechnik.com
Metal Shelving Mfr
N.A.I.C.S.: 337215
Armin Quirin (Head-Ops & Mgr-Production)

Standard Depo Ve Raf Sistemleri A.S. (2)
Mahmutpasa Mevkii, Kullar Koyu, 41270, Izmit, Türkiye
Tel.: (90) 262 349 30 16
Web Site: http://www.averys-group.com
Metal Shelving Mfr
N.A.I.C.S.: 337215

Stow International NV (2)
Industriepark 6 B, 8587, Spiere, West-Vlaanderen, Belgium
Tel.: (32) 56481111
Web Site: https://www.stow-group.com
Sales Range: $200-249.9 Million
Emp.: 620
Static Storage Systems Mfr
N.A.I.C.S.: 337215
Stefan Pieters (CEO)
Stijn Vanneste (COO)
Machteld Leybaert (Chief HR Officer)
Tom Gysens (CFO)
Detlef Ganz (CTO)

Subsidiary (Non-US):

Shanghai Stow Storage Equipment Co. Ltd. (3)
No 1680 Shengli Road, QingPu Industrial Zone, Shanghai, 201700, China
Tel.: (86) 21 6922 5600
Web Site: http://www.stow.com.cn
Storage Racks Mfr
N.A.I.C.S.: 337215

Stow (UK) Limited (3)
Unit 7 Copse Farm Lancaster Place, South Marston Ind Est, Swindon, SN3 4UQ, Wiltshire, United Kingdom
Tel.: (44) 845 201 35 40
Web Site: http://www.stow.co.uk
Static Storage Systems Distr
N.A.I.C.S.: 423990

Stow Austria GmbH (3)
Heinrich Schneidmadl Strasse 15 BIZ TOP 0 06 EG, 3100, Saint Polten, Austria
Tel.: (43) 274249144
Web Site: https://www.stow-group.com
Sales Range: $25-49.9 Million
Emp.: 10
Racking Systems Mfr
N.A.I.C.S.: 337215
Michael Tessun (Mgr-Sls)

Stow Ceska Republika s.r.o (3)
Modletice 141, 251 01, Ricany, Czech Republic
Tel.: (420) 311344300
Web Site: https://www.stow-group.com
Sales Range: $25-49.9 Million
Emp.: 25
Racking Systems Mfr

N.A.I.C.S.: 337215
Petr Svejnoha (Mng Dir)

Stow Deutschland GmbH (3)
Kreuzberger Ring 66, 65205, Wiesbaden, Germany
Tel.: (49) 611267690
Web Site: https://www.stow-group.com
Static Storage Systems Mfr
N.A.I.C.S.: 337215
Michael Tessun (Mng Dir)

Stow France S.A.S. (3)
Avenue de la Tour-Maury, PO Box 46, ZAC du Fresne, 91280, Saint-Pierre-du-Perray, France
Tel.: (33) 169895050
Web Site: https://www.stow-group.com
Sales Range: $25-49.9 Million
Emp.: 23
Racking Systems Mfr
N.A.I.C.S.: 337215

Stow Nederland bv (3)
Minervum 7208, 4817 ZJ, Breda, Netherlands
Tel.: (31) 765798181
Web Site: https://www.stow-group.com
Static Storage Systems Distr
N.A.I.C.S.: 337215

Stow Polska Sp. z o.o. (3)
ulica Rzymowskiego 31, 02-697, Warsaw, Poland
Tel.: (48) 226470651
Web Site: http://www.stow-group.com
Sales Range: $25-49.9 Million
Emp.: 29
Racking Systems Mfr
N.A.I.C.S.: 337215
Marek Sosniak (Mng Dir)

Subsidiary (Domestic):

Tixit (2)
4 rue Ettore Bugatti, BP 50075, 67502, Haguenau, France
Tel.: (33) 3 88 63 86 20
Web Site: http://www.tixit.com
Metal Shelving Mfr
N.A.I.C.S.: 332999
Francis Blumenau (Mng Dir)
R. Sorrentino (Mgr-Fin & HR)

Blackstone / GSO Strategic Credit Fund (1)
345 Park Ave 31st Fl, New York, NY 10154
Tel.: (212) 503-2100
Web Site: http://www.blackstone.com
Sales Range: $75-99.9 Million
Closed-End Investment Fund
N.A.I.C.S.: 525990
Daniel H. Smith Jr. (Chm, Pres & CEO)

Blackstone Advisory Partners L.P. (1)
345 Park Ave, New York, NY 10154-0191
Tel.: (212) 583-5000
Web Site: http://www.blackstone.com
Emp.: 1,000
Investment Advisory Services
N.A.I.C.S.: 523940

Blackstone Alternative Asset Management L.P. (1)
345 Park Ave, New York, NY 10154
Tel.: (212) 583-5000
Sales Range: $450-499.9 Million
Emp.: 1,700
Asset Management Services
N.A.I.C.S.: 523940
Brian F. Gavin (COO)
Gideon Berger (Sr Mng Dir & CIO)
Anthony Maniscalco (Mng Dir-Investment)
Limin Wang (Mng Dir-Quantitative Res)
Yan Gu (Mng Dir & Head-Quantitative Res)
Jamey Thompson (Mng Dir & Head-Systematic Investing)
John McCormick (Pres & CEO)
Raymond Chan (Mng Dir-Portfolio Mgmt & Investment Res Team)
Brett Condron (Sr Mng Dir & Head-Global Individual & Investor Solutions)
Scott Bommer (Chief Investment Officer-Blackstone Horizon)

Blackstone Alternative Credit Advisors LP (1)
345 Park Ave, New York, NY 10154
Tel.: (212) 503-2100

Alternative Investment Asset Management
Services
N.A.I.C.S.: 523940
Daniel H. Smith Jr. *(Sr Mng Dir)*
Michael Addeo *(Mng Dir)*
Amira Artis *(Mng Dir)*
John Beberus *(Mng Dir)*
Jared Becker *(Mng Dir)*
Jonathan Bock *(Sr Mng Dir)*
Bradley Boggess *(Mng Dir)*
Bonnie Brookshaw *(Mng Dir)*
Tao Bu *(Mng Dir)*
Jimmy Byun *(Mng Dir)*
Bob Carroll *(Mng Dir)*
Beth Chartoff Spector *(Mng Dir)*
Jonathan Cohen *(Mng Dir)*
Brad Colman *(Sr Mng Dir)*
Sean Cort *(Sr Mng Dir)*
John DePalma *(Mng Dir)*
Teddy Desloge *(Mng Dir)*
Michael Zawadzki *(Sr Mng Dir)*
Alexander Zarzhevsky *(Mng Dir)*
Robert Zable *(Sr Mng Dir)*
Eric Yuen *(Mng Dir)*
John Wrafter *(Sr Mng Dir)*
Rob Walsh *(Mng Dir)*
Philip Volpicelli *(Mng Dir)*
Brian Towers *(Mng Dir)*
Alice Taormina *(Mng Dir)*
Michael Sobol *(Mng Dir)*
Joseph Soares *(Mng Dir)*
Dan Smith *(Sr Mng Dir)*
Will Sirignano *(Mng Dir)*
Carter Simpson *(Mng Dir)*
Erich Schram *(Sr Mng Dir)*
John Schmidt *(Mng Dir)*
Lou Salvatore *(Sr Mng Dir)*
Marwan Salem *(Mng Dir)*
Mark Rutledge *(Mng Dir)*
Zachary Rubenstein *(Mng Dir)*
Kate Rubenstein *(Mng Dir)*
Robert Post *(Mng Dir)*
Angelina Perkovic *(Mng Dir)*
Viral Patel *(Sr Mng Dir)*
Daniel Oneglia *(Sr Mng Dir)*
Shannon O'Grady *(Mng Dir)*
Eric Nadan *(Mng Dir)*
Zaheen Mir *(Mng Dir)*
Alan Milstein *(Mng Dir)*
Daniel McMullen *(Sr Mng Dir)*
Joseph McKnight *(Mng Dir)*
Gordon McKemie *(Mng Dir)*
Rita Mangalick *(Mng Dir)*
Charlotte MacKenzie *(Mng Dir)*
Lisa Lew *(Mng Dir)*
Eugene Lee *(Mng Dir)*
Joshua Lafer *(Mng Dir)*
Kevin Kresge *(Mng Dir)*
Laura Keenan *(Mng Dir)*
Chris Joseph *(Mng Dir)*
Graham Jones *(Mng Dir)*
Sarah Jiang *(Mng Dir)*
Thomas Iannarone *(Sr Mng Dir)*
Heather von Zuben *(Sr Mng Dir)*
Adam Hermida *(Mng Dir)*
Craig Harris *(Sr Mng Dir)*
Justin Hall *(Sr Mng Dir)*
Benji Guilford *(Mng Dir)*
Christine Harrington Gallaudet *(Mng Dir)*
Marc Dietrich *(Mng Dir)*

Joint Venture (Domestic):

EMI Music Publishing   **(2)**
75 9th Ave, New York, NY 10011
Tel.: (212) 492-1200
Music Publisher & Distr
N.A.I.C.S.: 512230

Subsidiary (Non-US):

**EMI Music Publishing (Belgium) SA
NV**   **(3)**
E Plaskylaan 179, 1030, Brussels, Belgium
Tel.: (32) 22450320
Sales Range: $10-24.9 Million
Emp.: 4
Music Publisher & Distr
N.A.I.C.S.: 512250

**EMI Music Publishing (Greece)
LLC**   **(3)**
259 Messoghion Avenue, N Psychiko, 154
51, Athens, Greece
Tel.: (30) 2106714626
Sales Range: $10-24.9 Million
Emp.: 2
Music Publisher & Distr
N.A.I.C.S.: 512230

**EMI Music Publishing (Holland)
B.V.**   **(3)**
Groest 91 93, 1211 EB, Hilversum, Nether-
lands
Tel.: (31) 356462000
Sales Range: $25-49.9 Million
Emp.: 15
Music Publisher & Distr
N.A.I.C.S.: 512250

EMI Music Publishing Canada   **(3)**
109 Atlantic Ave Ste 301, Toronto, M6K
1X4, ON, Canada
Tel.: (416) 583-5481
Web Site: http://www.emimusicpub.com
Music Publisher & Distr
N.A.I.C.S.: 512230

**EMI Music Publishing Ceska Repub-
lika, a.s.**   **(3)**
Kovarova 39, Stodulky, 155 00, Prague,
Czech Republic
Tel.: (420) 296397115
Web Site: http://www.emi.com
Sales Range: $10-24.9 Million
Emp.: 2
Music Publisher & Distr
N.A.I.C.S.: 512230

EMI Music Publishing Chile   **(3)**
Alfredo Barros Errazuriz, Providencia, 1954,
Santiago, Chile
Tel.: (56) 22091009
Sales Range: $10-24.9 Million
Emp.: 5
Music Publisher & Distr
N.A.I.C.S.: 512250

**EMI Music Publishing Denmark
A/S**   **(3)**
Bjorns Tradgardsgrand 1, SE 116-21,
Stockholm, Sweden
Tel.: (46) 8 441 19 60
Web Site: http://www.sonyatv.com
Emp.: 19
Music Publisher & Distr
N.A.I.C.S.: 512230
Patrik Sventelius *(Mng Dir)*

**EMI Music Publishing Hong
Kong**   **(3)**
Unit 207 Prosterhui Millenni Plz, 6-8 Har-
bour Road, North Point, China (Hong Kong)
Tel.: (852) 29565400
Web Site: http://www.sonyatv.com
Sales Range: $25-49.9 Million
Emp.: 13
Music Publisher & Distr
N.A.I.C.S.: 512250

EMI Music Publishing Italia SRL   **(3)**
Via Moremendo 2 27, 20149, Milan, Italy
Tel.: (39) 0248010216
Sales Range: $25-49.9 Million
Emp.: 23
Music Publisher & Distr
N.A.I.C.S.: 512250

EMI Music Publishing Ltd.   **(3)**
30 Golden Sq, London, W1F 9LD, United
Kingdom
Tel.: (44) 2030593059
Music Publisher & Distr
N.A.I.C.S.: 512230

**EMI Music Publishing Malaysia SDN
BHD**   **(3)**
Suite 21 7 The Boulevard Lingakaran Syed
Putra, Mid Valley City, 59200, Kuala Lum-
pur, Malaysia
Tel.: (60) 22016888
Music Publishing & Distr
N.A.I.C.S.: 512250

EMI Music Publishing Mexico   **(3)**
Blvd Manuel Avila Camacho 76 Piso 5, Col
Lomas de Chapultepec Miguel Hidalgo,
Mexico, 11000, Mexico
Tel.: (52) 5555407930
Sales Range: $10-24.9 Million
Emp.: 25
Music Publishing & Distr
N.A.I.C.S.: 512250

EMI Music Publishing Portugal   **(3)**
Praca Nuno Rodriguez dos Santos, Urban
Das Laranjeiras 7, 1600 171, Lisbon, Portu-
gal
Tel.: (351) 217217400

Sales Range: $10-24.9 Million
Emp.: 5
Music Publisher & Distributor
N.A.I.C.S.: 512250

**EMI Music Publishing Scandinavia
AB**   **(3)**
Sveavagen 24 26, 103 63, Stockholm, Swe-
den
Tel.: (46) 858795500
Sales Range: $10-24.9 Million
Emp.: 14
Music Publisher & Distr
N.A.I.C.S.: 512250
Johnny Tennander *(Mng Dir)*

EMI Music Publishing Spain   **(3)**
Calle Gran Via 39 7a Planta, Madrid,
28013, Spain
Tel.: (34) 915239940
Sales Range: $10-24.9 Million
Emp.: 20
Music Publisher & Distr
N.A.I.C.S.: 512250
Juan Ignacio *(Mng Dir)*

Subsidiary (Domestic):

**GSO Capital Partners (Texas)
LP**   **(2)**
1111 Bagby St Ste 2050, Houston, TX
77002
Tel.: (713) 358-1400
Financial Advisory Services
N.A.I.C.S.: 523940

**GSO European Senior Debt Associ-
ates LLC**   **(2)**
345 Park Ave, New York, NY 10154
Tel.: (212) 503-2100
Investment Advisory Services
N.A.I.C.S.: 523940

Joint Venture (Domestic):

TERM Holdings, LLC   **(2)**
8847 W Sam Houston Pkwy N, Houston,
TX 77040   **(50%)**
Tel.: (713) 341-7300
Web Site: http://www.twineagle.com
Emp.: 500
Holding Company
N.A.I.C.S.: 551112
Griff Jones *(Pres/CEO-Twin Eagle Re-
source Mgmt)*
Chuck Watson *(Chm)*

Subsidiary (Domestic):

**Twin Eagle Resource Management,
LLC**   **(3)**
1700 City Plaza Dr Ste 500, Spring, TX
77389
Tel.: (713) 341-7300
Web Site: http://www.twineagle.com
Petroleum & Natural Gas Transportation &
Distribution Services
N.A.I.C.S.: 213112
Griff Jones *(Pres & CEO)*
Charles L. Watson *(Chm)*
Larry B. Leverett *(Exec VP)*
James F. Thomas *(Exec VP-Midstream
Ops)*
Tom Godbold *(Gen Counsel & Exec VP)*
Larry Leverett *(CFO)*
Jimmy Thomas *(Chief Admin Officer)*
Jeremy Davis *(Chief Comml Officer)*

**Blackstone Assessoria em Investi-
mentos Ltda**   **(1)**
Edificio Plaza Iguatemi Avenida Brigadeiro
Faria Lima 2277 Suite 1201, Suite 1201
and 1202, Sao Paulo, 01452-000, Brazil
Tel.: (55) 1120504700
Financial Investment Services
N.A.I.C.S.: 523999

Blackstone Capital Partners   **(1)**
1228 E Katella Ave 205, Orange, CA 92867
Tel.: (949) 250-8789
Web Site: http://www.blackstone.com
Rev.: $2,772,000
Emp.: 7
Consumer Lending
N.A.I.C.S.: 522291
Hamilton Evans James *(Pres & COO)*
Andrew Dowler *(Mng Dir)*

Blackstone Debt Advisors L.P.   **(1)**
345 Park Ave, New York, NY 10154

Tel.: (212) 583-5000
Web Site: http://www.blackstone.com
Investment Advisory Services
N.A.I.C.S.: 523940

Blackstone Ireland Limited   **(1)**
30 Herbert Street 2nd Floor, Dublin, 2, Ire-
land
Tel.: (353) 14360100
Aircraft Leasing & Rental Services
N.A.I.C.S.: 532411

Blackstone Mortgage Trust, Inc.   **(1)**
345 Park Ave 24th Fl, New York, NY 10154
Tel.: (212) 655-0220
Web Site:
    https://www.blackstonemortgagetrust.com
Rev.: $2,037,621,000
Assets: $24,036,178,000
Liabilities: $19,648,674,000
Net Worth: $4,387,504,000
Earnings: $246,555,000
Fiscal Year-end: 12/31/2023
Real Estate Investment Trust
N.A.I.C.S.: 525990
Weston Tucker *(Sr Mng Dir & Head-IR)*
Timothy S. Johnson *(Sr Mng Dir)*
Jimmy Yung *(Mng Dir-The Blackstone
Group Inc)*
Robert Sitman *(Mng Dir & Head-Loan Asset
Mgmt)*
Anthony F. Marone Jr. *(Pres, CEO, Mng Dir
& Sr VP)*
Kenneth Caplan *(Sr Mng Dir)*
Kathleen McCarthy *(Sr Mng Dir)*
Stephen Plavin *(Sr Mng Dir)*
Tim Johnson *(Sr Mng Dir)*
Rob Harper *(Sr Mng Dir)*
Will Skinner *(Sr Mng Dir)*
Michael Wiebolt *(Sr Mng Dir)*
Austin Pena *(Mng Dir)*
J. T. Sizemore *(Mng Dir)*
Clarke Hitch *(Mng Dir)*
Paul Kolodziej *(Head)*
Tony LaBarbera *(Mng Dir)*
Courtney Cheng *(VP)*
Michael Nagelberg *(Mng Dir)*
Katharine A. Keenan *(Pres & CEO)*
Anthony F. Marone Jr. *(CFO & Treas)*

Blackstone Private Credit Fund   **(1)**
345 Park Ave 31st Fl, New York, NY 10154
Tel.: (212) 503-2100
Web Site: https://www.bcred.com
Closed-End Investment Trust
N.A.I.C.S.: 525990

Blackstone Real Estate Advisors   **(1)**
345 Park Ave, New York, NY 10154
Tel.: (212) 583-5000
Web Site: http://www.blackstone.com
Real Estate Investment Firm
N.A.I.C.S.: 531390
Michael B. Nash *(Sr Mng Dir)*
Frank Cohen *(Sr Mng Dir)*
William J. Stein *(Sr Mng Dir & Global Head-
Asset Mgmt)*

Holding (Domestic):

Apartment Income REIT LLC   **(2)**
4582 S Ulster St Ste 1700, Denver, CO
80237
Tel.: (303) 757-8101
Web Site: https://www.aircommunities.com
Rev.: $820,036,000
Assets: $6,134,752,000
Liabilities: $3,584,378,000
Net Worth: $2,550,374,000
Earnings: $634,444,000
Emp.: 760
Fiscal Year-end: 12/31/2023
Real Estate Investment Trust
N.A.I.C.S.: 525990
Molly H. N. Syke *(Chief Acctg Officer & VP)*
Lisa R. Cohn *(Pres & Gen Counsel)*
Paul Beldin *(CFO & Exec VP)*
Terry Considine *(CEO)*

Subsidiary (Domestic):

Apartment Income REIT, L.P.   **(3)**
4582 S Ulster St Ste 1700, Denver, CO
80237
Tel.: (303) 757-8101
Web Site: https://www.aircommunities.com
Rev.: $820,035,999
Assets: $6,134,751,999
Liabilities: $3,584,377,999
Net Worth: $2,550,373,999

Blackstone Inc.—(Continued)
Earnings: $677,165,000
Emp.: 759
Fiscal Year-end: 12/31/2023
Residential Real Estate Acquisition, Development & Property Management Services
N.A.I.C.S.: 531311
Terry Considine (CEO)
Molly H. N. Syke (Chief Acctg Officer & VP)

Subsidiary (Domestic):

AIMCO 21 FITZSIMONS, LLC (4)
2100 N Ursula St, Aurora, CO 80045
Tel.: (720) 575-0567
Web Site: http://www.21fitzsimons.com
Apartment Community Management Services
N.A.I.C.S.: 531311

AIMCO BROADWAY LOFTS, L.P. (4)
1007 5th Ave, San Diego, CA 92101-5129
Tel.: (619) 234-0322
Web Site: http://www.broadwaylofts.com
Apartment Community Management Services
N.A.I.C.S.: 531311

AIMCO MONTEREY GROVE APARTMENTS, LLC (4)
6100 Monterey Hwy, San Jose, CA 95138-1701
Tel.: (562) 386-0668
Web Site: http://www.montereygrove.com
Property Rental & Leasing Services
N.A.I.C.S.: 531110

AIMCO/NASHUA, L.L.C. (4)
Clubhouse Royal Crest Dr, Nashua, NH 03060
Tel.: (603) 888-1234
Web Site: http://www.aimco.com
Emp.: 14
Property Rental & Leasing Services
N.A.I.C.S.: 531110

Aimco 777 South Broad, LLC (4)
777 S Broad St, Philadelphia, PA 19147
Tel.: (267) 214-4927
Web Site: https://www.777southbroad.com
Real Estate Services
N.A.I.C.S.: 531390

Aimco Bent Tree, LLC (4)
13630 Bent Tree Cir, Centreville, VA 20121
Tel.: (703) 584-7436
Real Estate Services
N.A.I.C.S.: 531390

Aimco Locust On The Park, LLC (4)
201 S 25th St, Philadelphia, PA 19103
Tel.: (267) 385-8283
Real Estate Services
N.A.I.C.S.: 531390

BAY PARC PLAZA APARTMENTS, L.P. (4)
4582 S Ulster St Ste 1700, Denver, CO 80237
Tel.: (305) 702-0248
Web Site: http://www.livebayparc.com
Apartment Community Management Services
N.A.I.C.S.: 531311

Springhill Lake Investors Limited Partnership Co. (4)
55 Beattie Pl Ste 300, Greenville, SC 29601-2127 (86%)
Tel.: (617) 330-8600
Web Site: http://www.aimco.com
Sales Range: $25-49.9 Million
Emp.: 2
Real Estate Operations
N.A.I.C.S.: 531210

Holding (Domestic):

BRE Diamond Hotel LLC (2)
345 Park Ave, New York, NY 10154
Tel.: (212) 583-5000
Real Estate Investment Trust
N.A.I.C.S.: 525990
William J. Stein (CEO & Sr Mng Dir)

BRE Retail Centers Corp (2)
345 Park Ave, New York, NY 10154
Tel.: (212) 583-5000
Emp.: 40

Real Estate Investment Trust
N.A.I.C.S.: 525990
James Y. Nakagawa (CFO)

Subsidiary (Domestic):

Excel Trust, L.P. (3)
17140 Bernardo Ctr Dr Ste 300, San Diego, CA 92128
Tel.: (858) 613-1800
Web Site: http://www.exceltrust.com
Emp.: 81
Real Estate Investment Services
N.A.I.C.S.: 525990

Holding (Domestic):

BioMed Realty, L.P. (2)
4570 Executive Dr Ste 400, San Diego, CA 92121
Tel.: (858) 485-9840
Web Site: http://www.biomedrealty.com
Real Estate Investment Management Services
N.A.I.C.S.: 531390
Timothy M. Schoen (CEO)
Ankit Patel (CFO & Exec VP)
Jonathan M. Bergschneider (Pres-West Coast Markets)
William F. X. Kane (Exec VP-East Coast & Markets-UK)
Kevin Simonsen (Gen Counsel, Sec & Exec VP)
Ryan Anderson (CIO & Sr VP)
Janice Kameir (Sr VP-HR)
Stephen Willey (Chief Acctg Officer & Sr VP)
Kevin Slein (Sr VP-Facilities)
Tracy Perrelle (Sr VP-Property Mgmt)
Maria Huntalas (VP-Corp Comm & Mktg)
Allyn Aguirre (Sr VP-Acctg & Treasury)
Emily Yu (VP-Legal)
Lan Nguyen (VP-Risk Mgmt)
David Hsiao (CIO)
Salvatore Zinno (Sr VP)
Carlye Murphy (Sr VP)
Salil Payappilly (Sr VP)
Kevin Tremblay (Sr VP)

Subsidiary (Non-US):

Blackstone Real Estate Asia Pte. Ltd. (2)
Level 32 Marina Bay Financial Centre Tower 1, 8 Marina Boulevard, Singapore, 018981, Singapore
Tel.: (65) 68507500
Emp.: 30
Real Estate Investment Firm
N.A.I.C.S.: 531390
Harish Manwani (Sr Mng Dir)
Vikram Garg (Sr Mng Dir)
Ambika Goel (Mng Dir)
Lukas Lambach (Mng Dir)
Eugene Min (COO)
Alan Miyasaki (Sr Mng Dir)
Melissa Skidell (Mng Dir)
Peng Wei Tan (Mng Dir)
Roger Zhang (Mng Dir)
Herbert Suen (Sr Mng Dir)
Gautam Banerjee (Sr Mng Dir)
Charmaine Chin (Mng Dir)
Harish Manwani (Sr Mng Dir)
Melanie Ng (Mng Dir)
Catherine Ow (Mng Dir)
Manali Parekh (Mng Dir)
Geoff Stockwell (Sr Mng Dir)

Holding (Non-US):

Dream Global Real Estate Investment Trust (2)
30 Adelaide Street East Suite 301, Toronto, M5C 3H1, ON, Canada
Tel.: (416) 365-3535
Web Site: http://www.dream.ca
Sales Range: $300-349.9 Million
Emp.: 65
Real Estate Investment Trust
N.A.I.C.S.: 525990
P. Jane Gavan (Pres & CEO)
Alexander Sannikov (COO)
Bruce Traversy (Sr VP-Investments)
R. Sacha Bhatia (Chm)
Rajeev Viswanathan (CFO)

Subsidiary (Non-US):

Embassy Property Developments Pvt. Ltd. (2)

Embassy Point 1st Floor 150 Infantry Road, Bengaluru, 560 001, India
Tel.: (91) 8041799999
Web Site: https://www.embassyindia.com
Real Estate Developers
N.A.I.C.S.: 531390
Jitu Virwani (Chm & Mng Dir)

Subsidiary (Domestic):

Mac Charles (India) Limited (3)
72/4 1st Floor Cunningham Road, Bengaluru, 560 052, Karnataka, India (98.1%)
Tel.: (91) 8049030000
Web Site: https://www.maccharlesindia.com
Rev.: $11,590,432
Assets: $94,557,640
Liabilities: $65,647,143
Net Worth: $28,910,497
Earnings: $5,102,812
Emp.: 6
Fiscal Year-end: 03/31/2023
Luxury Hotel & Resort Management Services
N.A.I.C.S.: 721110
M. S. Reddy (Officer-Compliance, Sec & Exec Dir)
C. B. Pardhanani (Chm)
Suresh K. Badlaney (VP-Ops & Mgr)
Pranesha K. Rao (CFO)

Holding (Domestic):

Equity Office Management, LLC (2)
233 S Wacker Dr Ste 5430, Chicago, IL 60606 (100%)
Tel.: (312) 466-3300
Web Site: http://www.eqoffice.com
Sales Range: $75-99.9 Million
Emp.: 140
Real Estate Portfolio Management Services
N.A.I.C.S.: 531312
Lauren Sozio (Sr VP-Strategic Mktg)
Brendan McCracken (Sr VP & Portfolio Dir)
Paul Gordon (Sr VP-Ops)
David Marks (Dir-Leasing-Seattle)
Josh Hatfield (COO)
Amanda Bates (VP)
Kimberly Chan (Sr VP)
Eva Mondazzi (Sr VP)
Sara Parker-Wallace (Sr VP)
Zach Zaborowski (Sr VP)

Joint Venture (Domestic):

Extended Stay America, Inc. (2)
11525 N Community House Rd Ste 100, Charlotte, NC 28277 (50%)
Tel.: (980) 345-1600
Web Site: http://www.esa.com
Rev.: $1,042,316,000
Assets: $4,089,149,000
Liabilities: $2,951,706,000
Net Worth: $1,137,443,000
Earnings: $23,267,000
Emp.: 4,200
Fiscal Year-end: 12/31/2020
Home Management Services
N.A.I.C.S.: 721110
Howard J. Weissman (Chief Acctg Officer & Controller)

Subsidiary (Domestic):

ESH Hospitality, Inc. (3)
11525 N Community House Rd Ste 100, Charlotte, NC 28277
Tel.: (980) 345-1600
Web Site: http://www.esa.com
Rev.: $562,809,000
Assets: $3,951,117,000
Liabilities: $2,855,835,000
Net Worth: $1,095,282,000
Earnings: $175,868,000
Emp.: 4,199
Fiscal Year-end: 12/31/2020
Real Estate Investment Services
N.A.I.C.S.: 523999
Howard J. Weissman (Chief Acctg Officer & Controller)
Douglas G. Geoga (Chm)
David A. Clarkson (CFO)
Bruce N. Haase (Pres & CEO)
Christopher N. Dekle (Gen Counsel & Sec)
Judi Bikulege (Chief Investment Officer)

Subsidiary (Domestic):

Gramercy Property Trust (2)
90 Park Ave 32nd Fl, New York, NY 10016

Tel.: (212) 297-1000
Web Site: http://www.linklogistics.com
Real Estate Investment Trust
N.A.I.C.S.: 525990
Nicholas L. Pell (Pres & Chief Investment Officer)
Anna Marie Yang (CFO)
Sonya A. Huffman (COO)
Britton T. Winterer (Mng Dir & Head-Dev)
Clifton H. Coffey (Mng Dir-Southeast)
Nicholas F. Brady (VP-Southeast)
Andrew G. Houston (Dir-Northwest Reg)
J. Taylor Malfitano (VP-Natl Accounts)
Benjamin P. Harris (CEO)
Edward J. Matey Jr. (Gen Counsel)

Subsidiary (Domestic):

GPT Operating Partnership LP (3)
521 5th Ave Fl 30, New York, NY 10175
Tel.: (215) 887-2280
Commercial Real Estate Services
N.A.I.C.S.: 531312
Gordon F. DuGan (CEO)

Holding (Non-US):

Hansteen Holdings PLC (2)
1st Floor Pegasus House 37-43 Sackville Street, London, W1S 3DL, United Kingdom
Tel.: (44) 2074087000
Web Site: http://www.hansteen.co.uk
Sales Range: $125-149.9 Million
Emp.: 104
Investment Management
N.A.I.C.S.: 523940

Holding (Domestic):

International Market Centers, Inc. (2)
475 S Grand Central Pkwy, Las Vegas, NV 89106
Tel.: (702) 599-9621
Web Site: http://www.imcenters.com
Real Estate Investment Trust
N.A.I.C.S.: 525990
Robert J. Maricich (Chm & CEO)
Greg Avitabile (Exec VP-Ops)
Bill Lacey (CFO & Exec VP)
Shannon Knox (CTO & Exec VP)

Subsidiary (Domestic):

AMC, Inc. (3)
240 Peachtree St NW, Atlanta, GA 30303-1327
Tel.: (404) 220-3000
Web Site: http://www.americasmart.com
Trade Show Center Manager
N.A.I.C.S.: 531120
Jeffrey L. Portman Sr. (Chm, Pres, CEO & COO)

Holding (Domestic):

Park Hill Real Estate Group L.L.C. (2)
280 Park Ave, New York, NY 10017
Tel.: (212) 364-7800
Web Site: https://pjtpartners.com
Financial Advisory Services
N.A.I.C.S.: 523940

Holding (Non-US):

Pure Industrial Real Estate Trust (2)
1055 W Hastings Street Suite 2050, Vancouver, V6E 2E9, BC, Canada (62%)
Tel.: (604) 398-2836
Web Site: https://pureindustrial.ca
Sales Range: $300-349.9 Million
Real Estate Investment Trust
N.A.I.C.S.: 525990
Charlie Deeks (Chief Investment Officer)
Jonathan Rovira (VP-Leasing)
Deanna Ramoul (VP-Property Mgmt)

Sponda Oyj (2)
Korkeavuorenkatu 45, PO Box 940, 00101, Helsinki, Finland
Tel.: (358) 2043131
Web Site: http://www.sponda.fi
Rev.: $273,805,770
Assets: $4,152,552,866
Liabilities: $3,050,498,640
Net Worth: $1,102,054,226
Earnings: $83,877,514
Emp.: 136

Fiscal Year-end: 12/31/2019
Real Estate Investment Services
N.A.I.C.S.: 531390
Timo Pantsari *(CTO & Member-Exec Bd)*
Ari Kakela *(Chief Legal Officer & Member-Exec Bd)*
Kari Autio *(Mgr-Dev-Office Leasing)*
Tuuli Auvinen *(Acct Mgr)*
Ari-Pekka Lehtonen *(Reg Mgr)*

Subsidiary (Domestic):

Helsingin Itamerenkatu 21 Koy   **(3)**
Itamerenkatu 21, Helsinki, 00180, Finland
Tel.: (358) 931580387
Real Estate Manangement Services
N.A.I.C.S.: 531390

KOy Nimismiehenniitty   **(3)**
Realia Management Oy Puutarhurinkuja 2, 00300, Helsinki, Finland
Tel.: (358) 102286328
Real Estate Development Services
N.A.I.C.S.: 531390

Kiinteisto Oy Vantaan Tahtainkuja 3   **(3)**
Korkeavuorenkatu 45, 00130, Helsinki, Finland
Tel.: (358) 20 43 131
Real Estate Manangement Services
N.A.I.C.S.: 531390

Koy Helsingin Itakatu 11   **(3)**
Korkeavuorenkatu 45, 00130, Helsinki, Finland
Tel.: (358) 400 472272
Real Estate Manangement Services
N.A.I.C.S.: 531390

Koy Kuninkaankaari   **(3)**
Korkeavuorenkatu 45, 00310, Helsinki, Finland
Tel.: (358) 400472270
Real Estate Development Services
N.A.I.C.S.: 531390

Koy Zeppelinin City Keskus   **(3)**
C/o Oulun Toimitila Oy Isokatu 21 C 38 B, 90100, Oulu, Finland
Tel.: (358) 8 570 0570
Real Estate Manangement Services
N.A.I.C.S.: 531390

Subsidiary (Non-US):

OOO Inform Future   **(3)**
ul Tambovskaya 12, Saint Petersburg, 192007, Russia
Tel.: (7) 812 766 46 34
Web Site: http://www.inform-future.ru
Property Leasing & Rental Services
N.A.I.C.S.: 531120

Subsidiary (Domestic):

Sponda Kiinteistot Oy   **(3)**
Pieni Korkeiuorenkatu 45, Helsinki, 001001, Finland
Tel.: (358) 2035 56677
Web Site: http://www.kapiteeli.fi
Property Management Services
N.A.I.C.S.: 531312

Vepema Oy   **(3)**
Tehtaankatu 21, 11710, Riihimaki, Finland
Tel.: (358) 19724000
Web Site: https://en.vepro.fi
Property Development Services
N.A.I.C.S.: 531312

Holding (Non-US):

Tysan Holdings Limited   **(2)**
20/F One Island South 2 Heung Yip Road, Wong Chuk Hang, Hong Kong, China (Hong Kong)   **(86.28%)**
Tel.: (852) 28823632
Web Site: https://www.tysan.com
Building Construction Services
N.A.I.C.S.: 236210
Kay Wong *(Gen Mgr-Shenyang Property Dev Div)*
Chin Hung Chiu *(Dir-Bus Dev & Mgmt-Foundation Bus)*
Chiu Chak Victor Fung *(Vice Chm, CEO & Mng Dir)*
Kin Fai Lau *(Dir-Tianjin Property Dev Div-PRC)*

Kitty Suk Han Wong *(Sec & Dir-Corp Affairs)*
Xiaoqiong Wang *(Co-Controller)*
Kok Wai Lai *(Dir-Tysan Foundation Holdings)*

Subsidiary (Domestic):

Tysan Foundation Limited   **(3)**
20/F One Island South 2 Heung Yip Road, Wanchai, China (Hong Kong)   **(100%)**
Tel.: (852) 28823632
Web Site: http://www.tysan.com
Foundation Piling Contract Services
N.A.I.C.S.: 238910
Kok Wai Lai *(Dir)*

Tysan Machinery Hire Limited   **(3)**
11 F Harbour Ctr 25 Harbour Rd, Wanchai, China (Hong Kong)   **(100%)**
Tel.: (852) 28823632
Machinery Hiring Services
N.A.I.C.S.: 532490

Holding (Domestic):

WHM LLC   **(2)**
501 E Camino Real, Boca Raton, FL 33432
Tel.: (561) 447-5300
Web Site: http://www.luxuryresorts.com
Sales Range: $600-649.9 Million
Emp.: 770
Hotel & Motel Real Estate Investment Trust
N.A.I.C.S.: 525990

Unit (Domestic):

Boulders Resort & Golden Door Spa   **(3)**
34631 N Tom Darlington Dr, Scottsdale, AZ 85262
Tel.: (480) 488-9009
Web Site: http://www.bouldersresort.com
Sales Range: $25-49.9 Million
Emp.: 600
Resort & Hospitality Services
N.A.I.C.S.: 721110

Buena Vista Palace   **(3)**
1900 N Buena Vista Dr, Lake Buena Vista, FL 32830
Tel.: (407) 827-2727
Web Site: http://www.buenavistapalace.com
Sales Range: $75-99.9 Million
Emp.: 500
Hotel & Spa Services
N.A.I.C.S.: 721110

El Conquistador Resort   **(3)**
1000 El Conquistador Ave, Fajardo, PR 00738
Tel.: (787) 863-1000
Web Site:
   https://www.conquistadorresort.com
Emp.: 1,000
Hotel Services
N.A.I.C.S.: 721110
Dermot Conolly *(Mng Dir)*

The London West Hollywood Hotel   **(3)**
1020 N San Vicente Blvd, West Hollywood, CA 90069   **(100%)**
Tel.: (310) 854-1111
Web Site:
   http://www.thelondonwesthollywood.com
Sales Range: $10-24.9 Million
Emp.: 250
Hotel Services
N.A.I.C.S.: 721110

Blackstone Real Estate Income Trust, Inc.   **(1)**
345 Park Ave, New York, NY 10154
Tel.: (212) 583-5000
Web Site: https://www.breit.com
Rev.: $7,646,378,000
Assets: $142,687,424,000
Liabilities: $92,486,673,000
Net Worth: $50,200,751,000
Earnings: ($883,519,000)
Emp.: 217
Fiscal Year-end: 12/31/2022
Real Estate Investment Services
N.A.I.C.S.: 531210
Robert G. Harper *(Pres)*
Anthony F. Marone Jr. *(CFO & Treas)*
Robert G. Harper *(Head-Asset Mgmt)*
Karen Sprogis *(Head-IR)*
Leon Volchyok *(Chief Legal Officer & Sec)*

Paul Kolodziej *(Chief Acctg Officer)*
Brian Kim *(Head-Acquisitions & Capital Markets)*
Wesley LePatner *(CEO & COO)*

Holding (Domestic):

Preferred Apartment Communities, Inc.   **(2)**
3284 Northside Pkwy NW Ste 150, Atlanta, GA 30327
Tel.: (770) 818-4100
Web Site: http://www.pacapts.com
Rev.: $502,197,000
Assets: $4,281,079,000
Liabilities: $2,842,631,000
Net Worth: $1,438,448,000
Earnings: ($177,788,000)
Emp.: 402
Fiscal Year-end: 12/31/2020
Real Estate Investment Services
N.A.I.C.S.: 525990
Leonard A. Silverstein *(Founder)*
Michael Joseph Cronin *(Chief Acctg Officer, Treas & Exec VP)*
Jeffrey R. Sprain *(Gen Counsel, Sec & Exec VP)*
John A. Isakson *(CFO)*
Paul Cullen *(Exec VP-IR)*
Kimberly Barkwell Hodge *(Chief Property Mgmt Officer-Multifamily & Exec VP)*
Randy Forth *(Chief Asset Mgmt Officer & Exec VP)*
Jeffrey D. Sherman *(Pres-Multifamily)*
Michael C. Aide *(Pres-Grocery & Anchored Retail)*
Jared A. Seff *(Sr VP, Asst Sec & Deputy Gen Counsel)*
Stephanie Hart *(COO-Grocery & Anchored Retail & Exec VP)*
Boone Dupree *(Pres-Office)*
Ginger L. Park *(Chief Acctg Officer-Grocery & Anchored Retail & VP)*
Cary Y. Dickson *(Exec VP-Asset Mgmt Office)*

Subsidiary (Domestic):

Neapolitan Way Shopping Center, LLC   **(3)**
4625 Tamiami Trl N, Naples, FL 34103
Tel.: (239) 435-1862
Web Site:
   https://www.naplessmokeshop.com
Cigar Distr
N.A.I.C.S.: 459991

PAC Parkside at the Beach, LLC   **(3)**
17225 Panama City Beach Pkwy, Panama City Beach, FL 32413
Tel.: (850) 730-1482
Web Site: http://www.parksidepcb.com
Apartment Rental Services
N.A.I.C.S.: 531110

Preferred Apartment Communities Operating Partnership, L.P.   **(3)**
3284 Northside Parkway Suite 150, Atlanta, GA 30327
Tel.: (770) 818-4100
Real Estate Investment Services
N.A.I.C.S.: 525990

Sandstone Creek, LLC   **(3)**
3851 Newt Fulford Rd, Bloomington, IN 47404
Tel.: (812) 320-3747
Web Site:
   https://www.sandstonecreekllc.com
Residential Building & Dwelling Leasing Services
N.A.I.C.S.: 531110

Stoneridge Farms Hunt Club, LLC   **(3)**
2325 Nashville Pike, Gallatin, TN 37066
Tel.: (615) 451-7057
Web Site: http://stoneridgehuntclubapts.com
Residential Building & Dwelling Leasing Services
N.A.I.C.S.: 531110

Holding (Domestic):

QTS Realty Trust, Inc.   **(2)**
12851 Foster St, Overland Park, KS 66213
Tel.: (913) 312-5503
Web Site: http://www.qtsdatacenters.com
Rev.: $539,368,000
Assets: $3,898,572,000

Liabilities: $2,313,874,000
Net Worth: $1,584,698,000
Earnings: $15,906,000
Emp.: 634
Fiscal Year-end: 12/31/2020
Real Estate Investment Trust
N.A.I.C.S.: 525990
Jeffrey H. Berson *(CFO)*
Jon D. Greaves *(Exec VP-Quality Special Ops)*
David Robey *(COO)*
Brent Bentsen *(CTO)*
Shelagh Montgomery *(Chief People Officer)*
Matt N. Thomson Jr. *(Gen Counsel)*

Subsidiary (Domestic):

QTS Finance Corporation   **(3)**
12851 Foster St, Overland Park, KS 66213
Tel.: (913) 814-9988
Software Development Services
N.A.I.C.S.: 541511

Quality Investment Properties Miami, LLC   **(3)**
6815 Biscayne Blvd #103, Miami, FL 33138
Tel.: (786) 322-6550
Real Estate Investment Services
N.A.I.C.S.: 531210

Quality Investment Properties Richmond, LLC   **(3)**
6000 Technology Blvd, Sandston, VA 23150
Tel.: (804) 328-5107
Software Development Services
N.A.I.C.S.: 541511

QualityTech, LP   **(3)**
12851 Foster St, Overland Park, KS 66213   **(79.6%)**
Tel.: (913) 814-9988
Web Site: http://www.qtsdatacenters.com
Sales Range: $450-499.9 Million
Emp.: 611
Real Estate Investment Trust; Data Service Centers
N.A.I.C.S.: 525990
Jon D. Greaves *(Exec VP-Quality Special Ops)*
Chad L. Williams *(Chm & CEO)*

Holding (Domestic):

Resource REIT, Inc.   **(2)**
1845 Walnut St 17th Fl, Philadelphia, PA 19103
Tel.: (215) 231-7050
Web Site: http://www.resourcereit.com
Rev.: $242,089,000
Assets: $2,317,276,000
Liabilities: $1,449,681,000
Net Worth: $867,595,000
Earnings: $52,254,000
Emp.: 44
Fiscal Year-end: 12/31/2021
Real Estate Investment Trust
N.A.I.C.S.: 525990
Steven R. Saltzman *(Chief Acctg Officer & VP)*
Shelle Weisbaum *(Chief Legal Officer, Sec & Sr VP)*
Alan F. Feldman *(CEO, Pres & Chm)*
Thomas C. Elliott *(CFO, Treas & Exec VP)*
Marshall P. Hayes *(Chief Investment Officer & Sr VP)*
Peggy L. Gold *(VP)*

Holding (Non-US):

Tricon Residential Inc.   **(2)**
7 St Thomas Street Suite 801, Toronto, M5S 2B7, ON, Canada
Tel.: (416) 925-7228
Web Site: https://triconresidential.com
Rev.: $505,028,234
Assets: $9,740,126,037
Liabilities: $6,769,789,320
Net Worth: $2,970,336,717
Earnings: $637,151,414
Emp.: 1,010
Fiscal Year-end: 12/31/2022
Real Estate Investment & Management Services
N.A.I.C.S.: 531390
Wissam Francis *(CFO & Exec VP)*
Sandra Pereira *(Sr VP & Head-Tax Svcs)*
Wojtek Nowak *(Mng Dir-Capital Markets)*
David Mark *(Mng Dir-Fin)*
Evelyne Dube *(Mng Dir-Private Funds)*
John English *(Head-Dev)*

Blackstone Inc.—(Continued)

Kerry Steer (Sr VP-Construction)
Kent Ahlering (Sr VP)
Steve Best (VP)
Reshma Block (Head)
Sue Brodecky (VP)
Kim Ciabattoni (VP)
Dawn Dalton (Sr VP)
David Dan (VP)
Connor Doss (Sr VP)
Brian Edge (Sr VP)
Thomas Fichman (Sr VP)
Sarah Hicks (VP)
Minh Hoang (VP)
Matthew Holz (VP)
Austin Joynes (VP)
Larry Kiradziev (VP)
Gregg Knutson (Sr VP)
Tina McClelland (VP)
Drew McGray (VP)
Ali Merali (Head)
Marc Munoz (VP)
Josh Nogowski (VP)
Alan O'Brien (Chief Resident Experience Officer)
Tobias Oriwol (VP)

Subsidiary (Domestic):

Starlight U.S. Multi-Family (No. 5) Core Fund (3)
3280 Bloor Street West Suite 1400 Centre Tower, Toronto, M8X 2X3, ON, Canada
Tel.: (416) 234-8444
Web Site: https://www.starlightus.com
Real Estate Investment Trust
N.A.I.C.S.: 525990

Subsidiary (US):

Tricon American Homes LLC (3)
1508 Brookhollow Dr, Santa Ana, CA 92705
Web Site:
    http://www.triconamericanhomes.com
Residential Real Estate Investment, Property Management & Rental Services
N.A.I.C.S.: 531390
Kevin Baldridge (Pres)
Alan O'Brien (Exec VP-Ops)
Sherrie Suski (Sr VP-HR)
Bill Richard (Exec VP-Investments & Asset Mgmt)
Gregg Knutson (Sr VP-IT)
Kristine Blasko (Dir-Property Mgmt)
Connor Doss (Dir-Maintenance)
Kent Crandall (Exec VP-Acctg)
Thomas Walsh (Gen Counsel)

Holding (Non-US):

WPT Industrial Real Estate Investment Trust (2)
199 Bay Street Suite 4000, Toronto, M5J 1A9, ON, Canada
Tel.: (612) 800-8530
Web Site: http://www.wptreit.com
Real Estate Investment Trust
N.A.I.C.S.: 525990
Scott T. Frederiksen (Chm & CEO)
Matthew J. Cimino (COO & Gen Counsel)
Judd K. Gilats (CFO)
Pat Qualley (VP-Construction & Dev)
Scott Haugen (Sr VP-Asset Mgmt)
Spencer Gerberding (Sr VP-Asset Mgmt)
Jennifer R. Widener (Head-West Reg)
Ryan Doyle (Head-Investments-Central Reg)

Blackstone Senfina Advisors LLC (1)
601 Lexington Ave, New York, NY 10022
Tel.: (212) 893-8800
Investment Advisory Services
N.A.I.C.S.: 523940

Blackstone Singapore Pte. Ltd. (1)
Level 32 Marina Bay Financial Centre Tower 18 Marina Boulevard, Singapore, 018981, Singapore
Tel.: (65) 68507500
Aircraft Leasing & Rental Services
N.A.I.C.S.: 532411

Bluewater Thermal Procession, LLC (1)
126 Millport Cir, Greenville, SC 29607
Tel.: (864) 990-0050
Web Site: http://www.bluewaterthermal.com
Sales Range: $10-24.9 Million
Emp.: 3
Metal Heat Treating Services

N.A.I.C.S.: 332811
Jeffrey D. Hemmer (Pres, CEO & COO)
Craig B. Zimmerman (Dir-Technical)
Eric C. Mannix (CFO)
Clint Ooten (Dir-Comml & HR)
Clifton Higdon (Dir-Quality)

Subsidiary (Domestic):

Benton Harbor LLC (2)
1256 Milton St, Benton Harbor, MI 49022
Tel.: (269) 926-1161
Web Site:
    http://www.bentonmetalrecycling.com
Metal Treating Services
N.A.I.C.S.: 332811

Boca Resorts, Inc. (1)
501 E Camino Real, Boca Raton, FL 33432-6127
Tel.: (561) 447-5300
Web Site: http://www.bocaresort.com
Sales Range: $300-349.9 Million
Emp.: 1,000
Holding Company; Operator of Leisure, Recreation, Entertainment & Sports Businesses
N.A.I.C.S.: 721110
Victoria Jones (Gen Mgr-Mktg & Sls)

Subsidiary (Domestic):

Naples Grande Resort and Club (2)
475 Seagate Dr, Naples, FL 34103
Tel.: (239) 597-3232
Web Site: https://www.naplesgrande.com
Sales Range: $125-149.9 Million
Resort
N.A.I.C.S.: 721110

Bourne Leisure Group Ltd. (1)
1 Park Lane, Hemel Hempstead, HP2 4YL, Herts, United Kingdom
Tel.: (44) 1442234067
Sales Range: $300-349.9 Million
Emp.: 5,000
Package Holiday Provider
N.A.I.C.S.: 721199
John Kirk (Mng Dir)
Mickdermont King (Controller)
Louise Tansey (Natl Sls Mgr)
Erman Housein (Head-Trade Sls & Mktg)
Krishna Thakore (Mktg Mgr-Trade)

Subsidiary (Domestic):

Butlin's Limited (2)
1 Park Ln, Hemel Hempstead, HP2 4YL, Herts, United Kingdom
Tel.: (44) 1442230300
Web Site: http://www.butlinsonline.co.uk
Sales Range: $25-49.9 Million
Emp.: 200
Holiday Centers & Holiday Hotels Operator
N.A.I.C.S.: 721110
Richard Bages (Mng Dir)
Jacky Martin (Dir-Sls & Mktg)

Haven Leisure Ltd. (2)
1 Park Ln, Hemel Hempstead, HP2 4YL, Hertfordshire, United Kingdom (100%)
Tel.: (44) 3332002520
Web Site: https://www.haven.com
Sales Range: $100-124.9 Million
Emp.: 750
Operation of Caravan Parks in the United Kingdom, France & Spain
N.A.I.C.S.: 721211
Peter Harris (Mng Dir)

Warner Leisure Ltd. (2)
1 Park Ln, Hemel Hempstead, HP2 4YL, Hertfordshire, United Kingdom (100%)
Tel.: (44) 1442230300
Web Site: http://www.warnerholidays.co.uk
Sales Range: $100-124.9 Million
Adult Only Holidays in the United Kingdom
N.A.I.C.S.: 721199

Brixmor Property Group Inc. (1)
450 Lexington Ave, New York, NY 10017 (70%)
Tel.: (212) 869-3000
Web Site: https://www.brixmor.com
Rev.: $1,245,036,000
Assets: $8,332,716,000
Liabilities: $5,482,415,000
Net Worth: $2,850,301,000
Earnings: $305,087,000
Emp.: 510
Fiscal Year-end: 12/31/2023

Real Estate Investment Trust; Commercial Retail Shopping Centers Owner & Developer
N.A.I.C.S.: 523999
Steven F. Siegel (Gen Counsel, Sec & Exec VP)
Brian T. Finnegan (COO & Sr Exec VP)
James M. Taylor Jr. (Pres & CEO)
Mark T. Horgan (Chief Investment Officer & Exec VP)
Steven T. Gallagher (CFO, Chief Acctg Officer & Sr VP)
William Lawrence Brown (Exec VP-Dev & Redevelopment)
Haig B. Buchakjian (Exec VP-Ops)
Matthew Ryan (Pres-South Reg & Exec VP)
John M. Hendrickson (Pres-Midwest Reg & Exec VP)
David Vender (Pres-North Reg & Exec VP)
Angela Aman (CFO & Exec VP)

Division (Domestic):

Brixmor LLC- Southwest (2)
3901 Bellaire Blvd, Houston, TX 77025
Tel.: (713) 660-4300
Web Site: http://www.brixmor.com
Sales Range: $75-99.9 Million
Emp.: 180
Nonresidential Building Operators
N.A.I.C.S.: 531120

Subsidiary (Domestic):

Brixmor Operating Partnership LP (2)
450 Lexington Ave, New York, NY 10017
Tel.: (212) 869-3000
Rev.: $1,245,035,999
Assets: $8,332,715,999
Liabilities: $5,482,435,999
Net Worth: $2,850,280,000
Earnings: $305,086,999
Emp.: 509
Fiscal Year-end: 12/31/2023
Financial Management Services
N.A.I.C.S.: 551112

Division (Domestic):

Brixmor Property Group Inc. - Conshohocken (2)
2 Tower Bridge 1 Fayette St Ste 150, Conshohocken, PA 19428
Tel.: (610) 825-7100
Web Site: http://www.brixmor.com
Sales Range: $550-599.9 Million
Emp.: 152
Real Estate Investment Services
N.A.I.C.S.: 525990
Mark Wilson (COO)

Centro Properties Group - Northeast (2)
111 Middlesex Tpke 2nd Fl, Burlington, MA 01803 (100%)
Tel.: (781) 313-2000
Web Site: http://www.brixmor.com
Sales Range: $350-399.9 Million
Emp.: 55
Commercial Real Estate Management
N.A.I.C.S.: 531312

Center for Autism and Related Disorders, LLC (1)
5850 Granite Pkwy Ste 600, Plano, TX 75024
Tel.: (469) 694-1754
Web Site: http://www.centerforautism.com
Outpatient Mental Health & Substance Abuse Centers
N.A.I.C.S.: 621420
Jennifer Webster (CEO)
Dennis Dixon (Chief Clinical Officer)
Jodi Taylor (Chief HR Officer)
Chris Boult (CIO)
Jeffrey Hulburt (Chief Revenue Officer)
Frank Keim (CFO)
Michelle Rapoport (Gen Counsel)

Civica Group Limited (1)
8th Floor South Bank Central 30 Stamford Street, London, SE1 9LQ, United Kingdom
Tel.: (44) 2077602800
Web Site: http://www.civica.co.uk
Software Publisher; IT Consulting & Management Services
N.A.I.C.S.: 513210
Simon Downing (Chm)
John Hood (Chief Infrastructure Officer)

Phil Rowland (CFO)
Wayne Story (CEO)
Julie Chell (Chief People Officer)

Subsidiary (Non-US):

Civica Pty. Ltd. (2)
Level 10 163-175 O Riordan St, Mascot, 2020, NSW, Australia
Tel.: (61) 283243000
Web Site: http://www.civica.com
Software & Information Technology Services
N.A.I.C.S.: 513210

Subsidiary (Domestic):

Civica Education Pty Limited (3)
Level 6 140 St George's Terrace, Perth, 6000, WA, Australia
Tel.: (61) 8.6466 2999
Web Site:
    http://www.civicaeducation.com.au
Educational Books & CD-Rom Publisher
N.A.I.C.S.: 513210

Branch (Domestic):

Civica Education Pty Limited - Melbourne (4)
Level 7 565 Bourke St, Melbourne, 3000, VIC, Australia
Tel.: (61) 3 8676 4400
Web Site:
    http://www.civicaeducation.com.au
Educational Book & CD-Rom Publisher
N.A.I.C.S.: 513210

Clarus Ventures LLC (1)
101 Main St Ste 1210, Cambridge, MA 02142
Tel.: (617) 949-2200
Web Site: http://www.clarusventures.com
Privater Equity Firm
N.A.I.C.S.: 523999
Nicholas Simon (Mng Dir)
Kurt C. Wheeler (Mng Dir)

Subsidiary (Domestic):

Clarus Ventures LLC (2)
601 Gateway Blvd Ste 1270, South San Francisco, CA 94080
Tel.: (650) 238-5000
Web Site: http://www.clarusventures.com
Privater Equity Firm
N.A.I.C.S.: 523999

Crown Resorts Limited (1)
Level 3 Crown Towers 8 Whiteman Street, Southbank, 3006, VIC, Australia
Tel.: (61) 392928824
Web Site: http://www.crownresorts.com.au
Rev.: $1,336,695,074
Assets: $5,440,255,476
Liabilities: $2,018,604,174
Net Worth: $3,421,651,302
Earnings: ($200,205,447)
Emp.: 12,489
Fiscal Year-end: 06/30/2021
Casino Hotels & Gaming Establishments
N.A.I.C.S.: 721120

Subsidiary (Domestic):

Crown Melbourne Limited (2)
8 Whiteman Street, Southbank, 3006, VIC, Australia
Tel.: (61) 392928888
Web Site:
    http://www.crownmelbourne.com.au
Sales Range: $1-4.9 Billion
Emp.: 8,000
Casino Hotels
N.A.I.C.S.: 721120

Crown Perth (2)
Great Eastern Highway, Burswood, 6100, WA, Australia
Tel.: (61) 893627777
Web Site: https://www.crownperth.com.au
Emp.: 5,800
Resort Hotel & Casino
N.A.I.C.S.: 721120
Barry J. Felstead (CEO-Australian Resorts)

Crown Sydney Pty Ltd (2)
1 Barangaroo Avenue, Barangaroo, Sydney, 2000, NSW, Australia
Tel.: (61) 288717188
Web Site: https://www.crownsydney.com.au

Resort Services
N.A.I.C.S.: 721110

Melbourne Golf Academy Pty Ltd (2)
385 Centre Dandenong Road, Heatherton,
3202, VIC, Australia
Tel.: (61) 392926690
Web Site: https://www.mgagolf.com.au
Golf Training Services
N.A.I.C.S.: 713910

Cvent Holding Corp. (1)
1765 Greensboro Station Pl 7th Fl, Tysons,
VA 22102
Tel.: (703) 226-3500
Web Site: https://www.cvent.com
Rev.: $630,558,000
Assets: $2,265,933,000
Liabilities: $655,068,000
Net Worth: $1,610,865,000
Earnings: ($100,270,000)
Emp.: 4,900
Fiscal Year-end: 12/31/2022
Meetings, Events & Hospitality Technology
Provider
N.A.I.C.S.: 541511
Reggie Aggarwal *(Founder & CEO)*
Chuck Ghoorah *(President of Worldwide
Sales and Marketing & Co-founder)*
David Quattrone *(Co-founder-Chief Technol-
ogy Officer)*
Grace Lee *(Global Head of Human RE-
sources)*
Patrick Smith *(Sr VP-Chief Marketing Offi-
cer)*
Jeannette Koonce *(Gen Counsel & Corpo-
rate Secretary)*
Jeannette Koonce *(Corporate Secretary)*
Stacey Fontenot *(Sr VP-Marketing)*
Bharet Malhotra *(Sr VP-Sls)*
Brian Ludwig *(Sr VP-Sls)*
Anil Punyapu *(Sr VP-Enterprise Sales)*
Pradeep Mannakkara *(Sr VP-Chief Informa-
tion Officer)*
Billy Newman *(Sr VP-Chief Financial Offi-
cer)*
David Johnson *(Sr VP-Engrg)*
Nitin Malhotra *(Sr VP-Corp Dev)*

Subsidiary (Domestic):

Cvent, Inc. (2)
1765 Greensboro Station Pl 7th Fl, Tysons
Corner, VA 22102
Tel.: (703) 226-3500
Web Site: http://www.cvent.com
Event Management Software Solutions
N.A.I.C.S.: 518210
Reggie Aggarwal *(Co-Founder, Chm &
CEO)*
Brian Ludwig *(Sr VP-Sls)*
Charles V. Ghoorah *(Co-Founder & Pres-
Worldwide Sls & Mktg)*
David Quattrone *(Co-Founder & CTO)*
Anil Punyapu *(Sr VP-Enterprise Sls)*
Dane Risley *(Sr VP-Sls)*
Patrick Smith *(CMO & Sr VP)*
Pradeep Mannakkara *(CIO & Sr VP)*

Subsidiary (Domestic):

CrowdCompass, L.L.C. (3)
308 SW 2nd Ave Ste 200, Portland, OR
97204
Tel.: (503) 501-2425
Web Site: http://www.crowdcompass.com
Software Publisher
N.A.I.C.S.: 513210

Subsidiary (Non-US):

Cvent Europe Ltd. (3)
40 Eastbourne Terrace, London, W2 6LG,
United Kingdom
Tel.: (44) 8082344540
Web Site: http://www.cvent.com
Event Management Services
N.A.I.C.S.: 711320
David Abelman *(Sr Mgr-Sls Dev & Ops)*
Graham Pope *(Head-European Sls-
Hospitality Cloud Platform)*

Cvent India Private Limited (3)
19th Floor Building No 14C DLF Cyber City
DLF Phase 2, Gurgaon, 122002, Haryana,
India
Tel.: (91) 1243305875
Web Site: http://www.cvent.com
Event Management Services
N.A.I.C.S.: 711320

Ashish Arora *(Assoc VP)*

Subsidiary (Domestic):

Elite Meetings International, LLC (3)
925 De La Vina St Ste 300, Santa Barbara,
CA 93101
Tel.: (805) 730-1000
Web Site: http://www.elitemeetings.com
Hospitality Marketing Services
N.A.I.C.S.: 541613
Shameka Alford *(Area Sls Dir)*

Lanyon, Inc. (3)
717 N Harwood, Dallas, TX 75201
Tel.: (817) 226-5656
Web Site: http://www.lanyon.com
Holding Company; Event & Hotel Manage-
ment Software Application Developer &
Cloud Services
N.A.I.C.S.: 551112

Subsidiary (Domestic):

Lanyon Solutions, Inc. (4)
717 N Harwood St Ste 2200, Dallas, TX
75201-6515
Web Site: https://www.lanyon.com
Sales Range: $10-24.9 Million
Emp.: 80
Event & Hotel Management Software Appli-
cation Developer & Cloud Services
N.A.I.C.S.: 541511

EPL Ltd. (1)
Top Floor Times Tower Kamala City, Sena-
pati Bapat Marg Lower Parel, Mumbai, 400
013, India **(57.03%)**
Tel.: (91) 2224819000
Web Site: https://www.eplglobal.com
Rev.: $423,982,650
Assets: $411,056,100
Liabilities: $174,720,000
Net Worth: $236,336,100
Earnings: $33,346,950
Emp.: 1,154
Fiscal Year-end: 03/31/2021
Specialty Packaging Products Mfr
N.A.I.C.S.: 322220
Ashok Kumar Goel *(Chm)*
M. R. Ramasamy *(COO)*
Vinay Mokashi *(CFO)*
Dileep Joshi *(Dir-Human Capital)*
Alan Conner *(Reg VP-Europe)*
Prakash Dharmani *(CIO-Global)*
Suresh Savaliya *(Officer-Compliance, Sec &
Head-Legal)*
Kelvin Wang *(Reg VP-EAP)*
Hariharan K. *(VP-C & I)*
Rajesh Bhogavalli *(Head-Supply Chain
Global)*
Mauro Catopodis *(Reg VP-Americas)*
Deepak Ganjoo *(Reg VP-AMESA)*
Sudhanshu Vats *(CEO & Mng Dir)*

Ellucian Company L.P. (1)
2003 Edmund Halley Dr, Reston, VA 20191
Tel.: (703) 968-9000
Web Site: http://www.ellucian.com
Business Solution Software Developer
N.A.I.C.S.: 513210
Toby Williams *(Chief Product Officer, Chief
Strategy Officer & Sr VP)*
Pete Sinisgalli *(Chm)*
Laura K. Ipsen *(Pres & CEO)*
Martin Banjo *(Pres)*
Harshan Bhangdia *(CFO)*
Greg Giangrande *(Chief People Officer)*
Melissa King *(Chief Transformation Officer)*
Susan Morrow *(Chief Mktg Officer)*
Martin Mrugal *(COO)*
Toby J. Williams *(Chief Strategy Officer,
Chief Product Officer & Sr VP)*

Subsidiary (Domestic):

WriterAccess (2)
205 Portland St Ste 500, Boston, MA 02114
Tel.: (617) 227-8800
Web Site: http://www.writeraccess.com
Sales Range: $1-9.9 Million
Emp.: 10
Document Preparation Services
N.A.I.C.S.: 561410

Exeter Finance LLC (1)
PO Box 166008, Irving, TX 75016
Tel.: (214) 572-8276
Web Site: http://www.exeterfinance.com
Emp.: 78

Art Finance Services
N.A.I.C.S.: 522220
Jason Grubb *(CEO)*
Jason A. Kulas *(Vice Chm & CFO)*

First Eagle Holdings, Inc. (1)
1345 Ave of the Americas, New York, NY
10105-4300
Tel.: (212) 698-3300
Holding Company; Asset Management Advi-
sory Services
N.A.I.C.S.: 551112
Mehdi A. Mahmud *(Pres & CEO)*
Mehdi Mahmud *(Pres & CEO)*
Katherine Lynn Perkins *(CFO & Treas)*

Subsidiary (Domestic):

**First Eagle Investment Management,
LLC** (2)
1345 Avenue of the Americas, New York,
NY 10105-4300 **(100%)**
Tel.: (212) 698-3300
Web Site: https://www.firsteagle.com
Rev.: $102,000,000,000
Asset Management Advisory Services
N.A.I.C.S.: 523940
Mehdi A. Mahmud *(Pres & CEO)*
Mehdi Mahmud *(Pres & CEO)*
Melanie Dow *(Chief Admin Officer)*
Jon Dorfman *(CIO)*
Brian Margulies *(CFO)*
Kimball Brooker Jr. *(Deputy Head-Global
Value Team & Portfolio Mgr)*

Subsidiary (Domestic):

First Eagle Private Credit, LLC (3)
500 Boylston St Ste 1250, Boston, MA
02116
Tel.: (617) 848-2500
Web Site: http://www.feim.com
Commercial Lending & Equipment Financ-
ing Services
N.A.I.C.S.: 522299
Timothy J. Conway *(Pres & Head-Private
Credit)*
Robert K. Brown *(Mng Dir & Head-Corp
Dev)*
Daniel D. McCready *(Mng Dir & Head-
Credit Risk Mgmt)*
Jeffrey R. Greene *(Portfolio Mgr)*
Walter J. Marullo *(Portfolio Mgr)*
Patrick F. McAuliffe *(Mng Dir & Head-Direct
Origination)*
Robert F. Milordi *(Sr Portfolio Mgr)*
Brian A. Senatore *(Portfolio Mgr)*
E. Scott Trefry *(Portfolio Mgr)*
Paul Horton *(Mng Dir-Middle Market Direct
Lending)*
Jason A. Wendorf *(Mng Dir-Middle Market
Direct Lending)*
Kevin T. Mulcahy *(Portfolio Mgr)*
Joseph E. Sileo *(Mng Dir & Head-Capital
Markets)*
Matthew R. Colucci *(Mng Dir-Middle Market
Direct Lending)*
Matthew R. Colucci *(Mng Dir-Middle Market
Direct Lending)*

THL Credit Advisors LLC (3)
100 Federal St, Boston, MA 02110
Tel.: (212) 829-3100
Web Site: http://www.thlcredit.com
Trust, Fiduciary & Custody Activities
N.A.I.C.S.: 523991
Christopher J. Flynn *(CEO)*
Brian Murphy *(Head-Capital Markets)*
Christopher Todisco *(Dir-Bus Dev-New
York)*
Michael Herzig *(Mng Dir & Head-Bus Dev)*

G6 Hospitality LLC (1)
4001 International Pkwy, Carrollton, TX
75007
Tel.: (972) 360-9000
Web Site: http://www.g6hospitality.com
Emp.: 10,000
Holding Company; Motel & Extended-Stay
Hotel Operator & Franchisor
N.A.I.C.S.: 551112
Julie Arrowsmith *(Pres & Interim CEO)*

Subsidiary (Domestic):

Motel 6 Operating L.P. (2)
4001 International Pkwy, Carrollton, TX
75007
Tel.: (972) 360-9000
Web Site: https://www.motel6.com

Sales Range: $50-74.9 Million
Motel Chain Operator
N.A.I.C.S.: 721110

Gates Industrial Corporation plc (1)
1144 15th St, Denver, CO 80202
Tel.: (303) 744-1911
Web Site: https://www.gates.com
Rev.: $3,570,200,000
Assets: $7,254,500,000
Liabilities: $3,710,600,000
Net Worth: $3,543,900,000
Earnings: $232,900,000
Emp.: 14,700
Fiscal Year-end: 09/30/2023
Electricit Power Transmission Equipment
Mfr
N.A.I.C.S.: 327910
Ivo Jurek *(CEO)*
Grant L. Gawronski *(Chief Comml Officer &
Exec VP)*
Roger C. Gaston *(Exec VP-Human Re-
sources)*
Thomas G. Pitstick *(CMO & Sr VP-Strategic
Plng)*
Wei Shen *(VP & Gen Mgr-Gates Greater
China)*
Cristin Bracken *(Chief Legal Officer)*
Josef Parzhuber *(Pres-EMEA)*
Diego Silva *(CIO)*
Gwen Montgomery *(Sr VP)*
Chris Cooney *(Sr VP)*
Andy Low *(VP)*
John S. Patouhas *(Chief Acctg Officer & Sr
VP)*
L. Brooks Mallard *(CFO & Exec VP)*

Subsidiary (Domestic):

Gates Corporation (2)
1144 15th St, Denver, CO 80202
Tel.: (303) 744-5651
Web Site: http://www.gates.com
Automotive Belts, Hoses & Other Rubber
Related Products Mfr
N.A.I.C.S.: 326220
Ivo Jurek *(CEO)*
Wei Shen *(VP & Gen Mgr-Gates Greater
China)*
Cristin C. Bracken *(Chief Legal Officer)*
Chris Cooney *(Sr VP)*
Gwen Montgomery *(Sr VP)*
Josef Parzhuber *(Pres)*
Andy Low *(VP)*
Lou Rosen *(Pres)*
Diego Silva *(CIO)*

Plant (Non-US):

Gates Argentina S.A. (3)
Bartolome Cruz 1810 5th Floor, B1638BHR,
Buenos Aires, Argentina
Tel.: (54) 1140185050
Web Site: http://www.gates-
argentina.com.ar
Sales Range: $75-99.9 Million
Emp.: 25
Belts & Hoses Mfr
N.A.I.C.S.: 326220

Gates Australia Pty. Ltd. (3)
1-15 Hydrive Close, Dandenong, 3175, VIC,
Australia
Tel.: (61) 397979688
Web Site: http://www.gatesaustralia.com.au
Hardware & Tools Distr
N.A.I.C.S.: 423710
Ivo Jurek *(CEO)*
Walt Lifsey *(COO)*
Tom Pitstick *(CMO & Sr VP)*
Roger Gaston *(Sr VP-HR)*
Michael Rhymes *(CIO)*
Ts Khoo *(VP-East Asia)*

Gates Canada Inc. (3)
225 Henry Street, Brantford, N3S7P2, ON,
Canada
Tel.: (519) 759-4141
Web Site: http://www.gates.com
Belts & Hoses Mfr
N.A.I.C.S.: 326220

Subsidiary (Domestic):

Gates Corp (3)
1144 15th St, Denver, CO 80202
Tel.: (303) 744-1911
Web Site: http://www.gates.com
Emp.: 800

Blackstone Inc.—(Continued)

Belts & Hoses Mfr
N.A.I.C.S.: 445132

Plant (Domestic):

Gates Corp   **(3)**
3040 Cravens Rd, Poplar Bluff, MO 63901-
8649
Tel.: (573) 727-9650
Web Site: http://www.gates.com
Emp.: 485
Belts & Hoses Mfr
N.A.I.C.S.: 326220

Plant (Non-US):

Gates Europe B.V.B.A   **(3)**
Korte Keppestraat 21/51, 9320, Aalst, Bel-
gium
Tel.: (32) 53762711
Web Site: http://ww2.gates.com
Belting & Hoses Mfr
N.A.I.C.S.: 326220

Subsidiary (Non-US):

Gates GmbH   **(4)**
Eisenbahnweg 50, 52068, Aachen, Ger-
many
Tel.: (49) 241 5108 0
Web Site: http://ww2.gates.com
Belts & Hoses Whslr
N.A.I.C.S.: 424990

Gates Hydraulics Ltd.   **(4)**
5 Alpha Drive, Eaton Socon, PE19 8JJ,
Cambs, United Kingdom   **(100%)**
Tel.: (44) 1480402300
Web Site: http://ww2.gates.com
Belts & Hoses Mfr
N.A.I.C.S.: 326220

Gates PT Spain S.A.   **(4)**
P I Les Mallotes S/N, Barcelona, 08660,
Balsareny, Spain
Tel.: (34) 938777000
Web Site: http://ww2.gates.com
Emp.: 240
Belts & Hoses Mfr
N.A.I.C.S.: 326220

Subsidiary (Domestic):

Gates Rubber Co. Inc.   **(3)**
1144 15th St Ste 1400, Denver, CO 80202
Tel.: (303) 744-5651
Web Site: http://www.gates.com
Emp.: 150
Belting & Hoses Mfr
N.A.I.C.S.: 326220

Plant (Non-US):

Gates de México S.A. de C.V.   **(3)**
Cerrada de Galeana No 5 Col Fracciona-
miento Industrial la Loma, 54060, Tlal-
nepantla, Mexico
Tel.: (52) 5520002700
Web Site: http://www.gates.com.mx
Belts & Hoses Mfr
N.A.I.C.S.: 326220

Gates do Brasil Industria e Comerico
Limited
Rua Doutor Renato Paes de Barros 1017,
Itaim Bibi, Sao Paulo, 04530-001, Brazil
Tel.: (55) 11 3848 8122
Web Site: http://www.gatesbrasil.com.br
Sales Range: $75-99.9 Million
Emp.: 75
Belts & Hoses Mfr
N.A.I.C.S.: 326220

Subsidiary (Domestic):

The Gates Rubber Company   **(3)**
1551 WeWatta St, Denver, CO 80202
Tel.: (303) 744-1911
Web Site: http://www.gates.com
Rev.: $1,390,000,000
Emp.: 1,000
Automotive Belts, Hoses & Other Rubber
Related Products Mfr
N.A.I.C.S.: 326220

Harvest Fund Advisors, LLC   **(1)**
100 W Lancaster Ave Ste 200, Wayne, PA
19087
Tel.: (610) 293-7800
Web Site: http://www.harvestmlp.com

Investment Advisory Services
N.A.I.C.S.: 523940
Eric Conklin (Mng Partner & Sr Mng Dir)
David Thayer (Sr Mng Dir & CFO)
Anthony Merhige (Sr Mng Dir & COO)
John Simkiss (Sr Mng Dir)
Nicholas Gaspari (Mng Dir-Investments)
Brandon Adams (VP-Investments)
Judge Hug (Asst VP-Ops)

HealthEdge Software, Inc.   **(1)**
30 Corporate Dr, Burlington, MA 01803
Tel.: (781) 285-1300
Web Site: http://www.healthedge.com
Emp.: 130
Healthcare Software Mfr
N.A.I.C.S.: 513210
Matthew Kuntz (CTO)
Chris Conte (Chief Revenue Officer & Exec
VP)
Alan Stein (Chief Comml Officer)
Steve Krupa (CEO)
Craig Wilson (Gen Counsel & Exec VP)
Rick Jelinek (Chm)
Matthew McLaughlin (CFO)
John Lopez-Ona (Chief Strategy & Mktg
Officer)
Heather Bender (Chief People Officer)
Matt Kuntz (CTO)
Alex Saltzman (Sr VP)
Ken Hayes (Sr VP)
Michele Oliveto-Hill (Gen Counsel)
Dan Vnuk (CTO)
Jacob Sattelmair (Exec VP)
Ryan Mooney (Exec VP)
Sagnik Bhattacharya (Exec VP)
Jerry Sto. Tomas (Chief Information Secu-
rity Officer)
Sandhya Gardner (Chief Medical Officer)

Subsidiary (Domestic):

Altruista Health, Inc.   **(2)**
11800 Sunrise Valley D Ste 1100, Reston,
VA 20191
Tel.: (703) 707-8890
Web Site: http://www.altruistahealth.com
Women Healthcare Services
N.A.I.C.S.: 621610
Munish Khaneja (Chief Medical Officer)
Ashish Kachru (CEO)
Thomas R. Joyer (Chief Comml Officer)
Robert Kalchthaler (CFO)
Jenifer Brown (Chief Admin Officer & Gen
Counsel)
Craig Wigginton (CTO)
Carol Sims (Officer-Customer Success)
Mike McKitterick (Exec VP-Clinical Svcs)
Vijay Kalle (Sr VP-Product Dev)
Hemant Lanjewar (VP-Data Sciences &
Clinical Quality)
Prashantha Gawhney (VP-Engrg)
Subramaniam Shanmugavelu (VP-Plng &
Delivery)
Sandra Lukic-Dapoigny (Sr Dir-
Implementation Svcs)
Kishore Babu Kancharla (Mgr-Engrg)
Nisha Kurup (Mgr-Bus Analysis)
Harish Avula (Sr Project Mgr)

The Burgess Group, LLC   **(2)**
1940 Duke St, Alexandria, VA 22314
Tel.: (703) 894-1800
Web Site: http://www.burgessgroup.com
Custom Computer Programming Services
N.A.I.C.S.: 541511
Tariq Abu-Jaber (VP-Client Solutions)
Josko Silobrcic (Chief Strategy & Bus Dev
Officer)

HealthMarkets, Inc.   **(1)**
9151 Blvd 26, North Richland Hills, TX
76180
Tel.: (817) 255-3100
Web Site: http://www.healthmarketsinc.com
Rev.: $568,277,000
Assets: $1,258,117,000
Liabilities: $988,190,000
Net Worth: $269,927,000
Earnings: ($6,934,000)
Emp.: 640
Fiscal Year-end: 12/31/2012
Holding Company; Health & Life Insurance
Products & Services; Owned 54% by The
Blackstone Group L.P., 22% by The Gold-
man Sachs Group, Inc. & 11% by DLJ Mer-
chant Banking Partners
N.A.I.C.S.: 551112

Subsidiary (Domestic):

Insphere Insurance Solutions,
Inc.   **(2)**
9151 Blvd 26 Ste B-1B, North Richland
Hills, TX 76180-5798
Web Site: https://www.healthmarketsinc.com
Sales Range: $650-699.9 Million
Insurance Brokers
N.A.I.C.S.: 524210

Mid-West National Life Insurance
Company of Tennessee   **(2)**
9151 Blvd 26, North Richland Hills, TX
76180
Tel.: (817) 255-3100
Web Site: http://www.midwestlife.com
Sales Range: $1-4.9 Billion
Life & Health Insurance Products & Ser-
vices
N.A.I.C.S.: 524113

The Chesapeake Life Insurance
Co.   **(2)**
9151 Blvd 26, North Richland Hills, TX
76180
Tel.: (817) 255-3100
Web Site: http://www.chesapeakeins.com
Sales Range: $125-149.9 Million
Emp.: 150
Life & Health Insurance Products & Ser-
vices
N.A.I.C.S.: 524113

The Mega Life and Health Insurance
Company   **(2)**
9151 Blvd 26, North Richland Hills, TX
76180
Tel.: (817) 255-5394
Web Site: http://www.megainsurance.com
Sales Range: $25-49.9 Million
Emp.: 200
Life & Health Insurance Products & Ser-
vices
N.A.I.C.S.: 524113

Hispania Activos Inmobiliarios SO-
CIMI, S.A.   **(1)**
Gran Capita, Sant Joan Despi, 28001, Bar-
celona, Spain
Tel.: (34) 913106370
Web Site: http://www.reigjofre.com
Rev.: $224,203,811
Assets: $351,204,894
Liabilities: $151,716,393
Net Worth: $199,488,501
Earnings: $5,530,989
Emp.: 1,000
Fiscal Year-end: 12/31/2019
Real Estate Investment Trust
N.A.I.C.S.: 525990
Alvaro Hernandez (Sec)

ITW Chemtronics   **(1)**
8125 Cobb Ctr Dr, Kennesaw, GA 30152
Tel.: (678) 928-6162
Web Site: http://www.chemtronics.com
Sales Range: $25-49.9 Million
Emp.: 100
Electronic Maintenance & Repair
N.A.I.C.S.: 325998

Industrials REIT Limited   **(1)**
3rd floor 180 Great Portland St, London,
W1W 5QZ, United Kingdom
Tel.: (44) 2039186600
Web Site: http://www.stenprop.com
Rev.: $57,838,937
Assets: $816,406,732
Liabilities: $303,130,434
Net Worth: $513,276,298
Earnings: $19,882,544
Emp.: 28
Fiscal Year-end: 03/31/2020
Real Estate Investment Services
N.A.I.C.S.: 531390
Paul Arenson (CEO)
James Beaumont (CFO)
Julian Carey (Exec Dir-Property)

Interplex Holdings Pte. Ltd.   **(1)**
298 Tiong Bahru Road, #17-01 Central
Plaza, Singapore, 168730, Singapore
Tel.: (65) 62640033
Web Site: http://www.interplex.com
Holding Company; Mechanical & Electro-
Mechanical Components Mfr
N.A.I.C.S.: 551112
Adrian Guan How Teo (COO-Ops-
Southeast Asia & India)

Alessandro Perrotta (CEO)
Nantha Kumar Chandran (Chief Sustainabil-
ity Officer)
Alex Perrotta (CEO)

Subsidiary (Non-US):

AE Rubber Sdn. Bhd.   **(2)**
No 12 Jalan Istimewa 1 Taman Perindus-
trian Cemerlang, Ulu Tiram, 81800, Johor,
Malaysia
Tel.: (60) 78616608
Web Site: https://www.aerubber.com
Emp.: 200
All Other Rubber Product Mfr
N.A.I.C.S.: 326299
Tai Nan Ching (Mng Dir)

Subsidiary (Domestic):

Amlab Services Pte. Ltd.   **(2)**
7 Soon Lee Street 03-10/11 /13 iSpace,
Singapore, 627608, Singapore
Tel.: (65) 66639882
Web Site: http://www.amlab.com.sg
Technical Testing & Analysis Services
N.A.I.C.S.: 541380
William Pang (Mgr)

Subsidiary (Non-US):

Amtek Precision Engineering (Shang-
hai) Co., Ltd.   **(2)**
No 819 Xuanhuang Highway Nanhui Indus-
trial Park, Pudong, Shanghai, 201399,
China
Tel.: (86) 2138286688
Metal Stamping Services
N.A.I.C.S.: 332119

Cheval Electronic Enclosure Co.
Ltd.   **(2)**
145 Bangplee Industrial Estate Soi 4 Moo
17, Bangsaotong, Samut Prakan, 10570,
Thailand
Tel.: (66) 23151504
Web Site: https://chevalgrp.com
Emp.: 82
Electronic Products Mfr
N.A.I.C.S.: 334419

Cheval Technology Co. Ltd.   **(2)**
121/4 Moo 10 Chae Chang, San Kamp-
hang, Chiang Mai, 50130, Thailand
Tel.: (66) 531291257
Emp.: 150
Mechanical Assemblies Mfr
N.A.I.C.S.: 811114

Huizhou Interplex Technology,
Ltd.   **(2)**
No 484 Xiaojin Section of Jinlong Road Lu-
oyang Street, Boluo County, Huizhou,
516171, Guangdong, China
Tel.: (86) 7522612449
Web Site: http://www.interplex.com
Emp.: 224
Prototyping & Precision Cold Forged Metal
Stamping Services
N.A.I.C.S.: 332119

Interplex (Huizhou) Industries
Ltd.   **(2)**
No 484 Xiaojin Section of Jinlong Road Lu-
oyang Street, Boluo County, Huizhou,
516171, Guangdong, China
Tel.: (86) 7522612449
Emp.: 596
Metal Stamping Components Mfr
N.A.I.C.S.: 332119

Interplex (Suzhou) Precision Engi-
neering Ltd.   **(2)**
No 36 Xing Ming Street CSS Industrial
Park, Suzhou, 215021, Jiangsu, China
Tel.: (86) 51267630088
Emp.: 1,000
Metal Stamping Components Mfr
N.A.I.C.S.: 332119

Interplex Electronic (Dalian) Co.,
Ltd.   **(2)**
No 6 Ave Digital 2 Street DD Port, Dalian,
116620, Liaoning, China
Tel.: (86) 41139966988
Web Site: http://www.interplex.com
Emp.: 153
Metal Stamping & Tool Equipment Mfr
N.A.I.C.S.: 333517
Roland Wang (Mgr-Sls)

Interplex Electronic Hangzhou Co., Ltd. (2)
No 280 Ave 10 HEDA, Hangzhou, 310018, Zhejiang, China
Tel.: (86) 57186735599
Industrial Supplies Whslr
N.A.I.C.S.: 423840

Interplex Electronics India Pvt Limited (2)
89A Electronics City Hosur Road, Bengaluru, 560 100, India
Tel.: (91) 8066445300
Web Site: http://www.interplex.com
Emp.: 290
Precision Metal Stamping, Electroplating & Molding Services
N.A.I.C.S.: 332119
B. R. Nagaraj (Project Engr)

Interplex Electronics Malaysia Sdn. Bhd. (2)
Lot 72 & 73 Jalan Bunga Raya Parit Buntar Industrial Estate, 34200, Parit Buntar, Perak Darul Ridzuan, Malaysia
Tel.: (60) 57169550
Web Site: http://www.interplex.com
Emp.: 48
Industrial Supplies Whslr
N.A.I.C.S.: 423840
Thava Thavamuni (Mgr-Quality & Matls)

Interplex Huizhou (HK) Industries Ltd. (2)
Rm 1608 16/F Grand Central Plz TWR 11, 138 Shatin Rural Committee Rd Sha Tin, Hong Kong, New Territories, China (Hong Kong)
Tel.: (852) 2753 6886
Metal Stamping Components Mfr
N.A.I.C.S.: 332119

Interplex Hungary, Kft. (2)
Ipari Park 07/28, 5440, Kunszentmarton, Hungary
Tel.: (36) 56560283
Web Site: http://www.interplex.com
Emp.: 120
Industrial Supplies Whslr
N.A.I.C.S.: 423840
Pierre Bonpontet (Plant Mgr)

Subsidiary (US):

Interplex Industries Inc. (2)
14 34 110th St #301, College Point, NY 11356
Tel.: (718) 961-6212
Product Design & Application Development Services
N.A.I.C.S.: 332813
Jack Seidler (Pres & CEO)
Steven Feinstein (Exec VP)

Subsidiary (Domestic):

Interplex Automation, Inc. (3)
54 Venus Way, Attleboro, MA 02703
Tel.: (508) 399-6810
Web Site: http://www.interplex.com
Industrial Supplies Whslr
N.A.I.C.S.: 423840

Interplex Daystar, Inc. (3)
11130 King St, Franklin Park, IL 60131
Tel.: (847) 455-2424
Web Site: http://www.interplex.com
Emp.: 115
Metal Stamping Services
N.A.I.C.S.: 332119

Interplex Engineered Products, Inc. (3)
231 Ferris Ave, East Providence, RI 02916
Tel.: (401) 434-6543
Web Site: http://www.interplex.com
Thermoplastic Semi-Conductor & Electronic Packages Supplier & Mfr
N.A.I.C.S.: 333242
Danney Crane (Mgr-Quality)

Interplex Medical, LLC (3)
25 Whitney Dr, Milford, OH 45150
Tel.: (513) 248-5120
Web Site: http://www.interplexmedical.com
Emp.: 28
Medical Device Mfr
N.A.I.C.S.: 339112
Craig Berky (Gen Mgr)

Interplex NAS Inc. (3)
232 Pegasus Ave, Northvale, NJ 07647
Tel.: (201) 367-1300
Web Site: http://interplex.com
Emp.: 100
Precision Metal Stampings Mfr
N.A.I.C.S.: 332119

Interplex Nascal, Inc. (3)
15777 Gateway Cir, Tustin, CA 92780
Tel.: (714) 505-2900
Web Site: http://www.interplex.com
Emp.: 60
Metal Stamping Services
N.A.I.C.S.: 332119
John Fili (Gen Mgr)

Interplex Sunbelt, Inc. (3)
6690 Hiatus Rd, Tamarac, FL 33321
Tel.: (954) 718-1700
Web Site: http://www.interplex.com
Emp.: 180
Metal Stamping Mfr
N.A.I.C.S.: 332119
Robert Koppel (Pres)

Teka Interconnection Systems, Inc. (3)
231 Ferris Ave, Rumford, RI 02916
Tel.: (401) 785-4110
Web Site: https://www.tekais.com
Electronic Connector Mfr
N.A.I.C.S.: 334417
Stephen Cabana (Supvr-Molding & Tool Room)

Subsidiary (Non-US):

Interplex Metalforming (Shanghai) Ltd. (2)
No 819 Xuanhuang Highway Nanhui Industrial Park, Pudong, Shanghai, 201399, China
Tel.: (86) 2138286688
Emp.: 1,400
Metal Stamping Components Mfr
N.A.I.C.S.: 332119

Interplex NAS Electronics GmbH (2)
Otto-Hahn-Strasse 8, 74078, Heilbronn, Germany
Tel.: (49) 7066941410
Web Site: http://www.interplexnas.de
Emp.: 15
Industrial Electronics Mfr
N.A.I.C.S.: 333511

Interplex PMP Limited (2)
Elliot Industrial Estate, Arbroath, DD11 2NN, United Kingdom
Tel.: (44) 1241873867
Web Site: http://www.interplex.com
Precision Component Mfr
N.A.I.C.S.: 332119
Steven Barlo (Gen Mgr)

Interplex Precision Engineering Czech Republic s.r.o (2)
Za Pazdernou 1531, 397 01, Pisek, Czech Republic
Tel.: (420) 382734411
Emp.: 550
Precision Metal Stamping Components Mfr
N.A.I.C.S.: 332119

Interplex Precision Technology (Hanoi) Co., Ltd. (2)
Lot VI-1 1 D3 Road Que Vo II Industrial Zone, Ngoc Xa Commune Que Vo District, Bac Ninh, Vietnam
Tel.: (84) 2223634465
Emp.: 630
Metal Stamping Components Mfr
N.A.I.C.S.: 332119

Subsidiary (Domestic):

Interplex Precision Technology (Singapore) Pte. Ltd. (2)
298 Tiong Bahru Road, 17-01 Central Plaza, Singapore, 168730, Singapore
Tel.: (65) 62640033
Metal Stamping Services
N.A.I.C.S.: 332119

Interplex Singapore Pte. Ltd. (2)
298 Tiong Bahru Road 17-01 Central Plaza, Singapore, 168730, Singapore
Tel.: (65) 62640033

Precision Metal Stamping, Electrolytic Plating & Molding Services
N.A.I.C.S.: 332119

Subsidiary (Non-US):

Interplex Soprec SAS (2)
6 Rue Thales ZI La Maltiere, 25410, Dannemarie-sur-Crete, France
Tel.: (33) 381483400
Web Site: http://www.interplex.com
Emp.: 85
Precision Metal Stamping, Electrolytic Plating & Molding Services
N.A.I.C.S.: 332119
Christian Millet (Gen Mgr)

Interplex Technology (H.K.) Limited (2)
Rm 1608 16/F Grand Central Plz TWR 11, 138 Shatin Rural Committee Rd Sha Tin, Hong Kong, New Territories, China (Hong Kong)
Tel.: (852) 2753 6886
Metal Parts & Tools Whslr
N.A.I.C.S.: 423510

Subsidiary (Domestic):

Interplex Technology Pte. Ltd. (2)
298 Tiong Bahru Road, 17-01 Central Plaza, Singapore, 168730, Singapore
Tel.: (65) 62640033
Semiconductor Equipment Mfr
N.A.I.C.S.: 334413

Subsidiary (Non-US):

Interplexico Manufacturing Company, S.A. de C.V. (2)
Calle Paseo del Norte No 4690, Parque Industrial Guadalajara Technology Park, 45134, Zapopan, Jalisco, Mexico
Tel.: (52) 3330006000
Web Site: http://www.interplex.com
Emp.: 320
Precision Metal Stamping, Electrolytic Plating & Molding Services
N.A.I.C.S.: 332119

Subsidiary (US):

OCP Group, Inc. (2)
7130 Engineer Rd, San Diego, CA 92111
Tel.: (858) 279-7400
Web Site: http://www.ocp.com
Computer Terminals, Nsk
N.A.I.C.S.: 334118
Jeff Savell (Acct Mgr-Sls)

Subsidiary (Non-US):

PT Amtek Engineering Batam (2)
Block E No 1 Jl Letjen Soeprapto Cammo Industrial Park, Batam Centre, Batam, 29432, Indonesia
Tel.: (62) 778464698
Emp.: 1,483
Metal Stamping Components Mfr
N.A.I.C.S.: 332119

PT Amtek Plastic Batam (2)
Lot 11 Citra Buana Industrial Park III Jalan Engku Putri, Batam Centre, Batam, 29461, Indonesia
Tel.: (62) 778471694
Emp.: 400
Plastics Product Mfr
N.A.I.C.S.: 326199

PT Amtek Precision Components Batam (2)
Lot 1 Citra Buana Industrial Park III Jalan Engku Putri, Batam Centre, Batam, 29461, Indonesia
Tel.: (62) 778471988
Emp.: 500
Precision Machining Services
N.A.I.C.S.: 811210

Irth Solutions LLC (1)
5009 Horizons Dr, Columbus, OH 43220
Tel.: (614) 784-8000
Web Site: https://www.irthsolutions.com
Software Development Services
N.A.I.C.S.: 513210
Brad Gammons (CEO)

Subsidiary (Non-US):

OneSoft Solutions Inc. (2)

4227 10230 Jasper Avenue, Edmonton, T5J 4P6, AB, Canada
Tel.: (800) 270-5024
Web Site: https://www.onesoft.ca
Rev: $3,474,850
Assets: $5,398,737
Liabilities: $1,581,843
Net Worth: $3,816,894
Earnings: ($3,042,224)
Emp.: 31
Fiscal Year-end: 12/31/2021
Holding Company; Cloud Data Solutions
N.A.I.C.S.: 551112

Subsidiary (Domestic):

OneBridge Solutions Inc. (3)
4227 10230 Jasper Avenue, Edmonton, T5J 4P6, AB, Canada
Web Site:
https://www.onebridgesolutions.com
Information Technology Services
N.A.I.C.S.: 541511

Subsidiary (US):

OneBridge Solutions, Inc. (3)
1775 W State St Ste 141, Boise, ID 83702
Web Site:
http://www.onebridgesolutions.com
Information Technology Services
N.A.I.C.S.: 541511
Tim Edward (Pres)
Jordan Dubuc (CTO)
Wendy Aucoin (Product Mgr-Integrity Mgmt)
Dan Tipton (VP-Sls)

Legence Holdings LLC (1)
1601 Las Plumas Ave, San Jose, CA 95133
Tel.: (408) 347-3500
Web Site: https://www.wearelegence.com
Environmental Services
N.A.I.C.S.: 541620
Jeff Sprau (CEO)

Subsidiary (Domestic):

A.O. Reed & Co. (2)
4777 Ruffner St, San Diego, CA 92111
Tel.: (858) 565-4131
Web Site: http://www.aoreed.com
Plumbing, Heating & Air-Conditioning Contractors
N.A.I.C.S.: 238220
Steve Andrade (CEO)
David Clarkin (Pres)

LORD Green Real Estate Strategies, Inc. (2)
6440 N Central Expwy Ste 703, Dallas, TX 75206
Tel.: (214) 369-3990
Web Site:
http://www.lordgreenstrategies.com
General Management Consulting Services
N.A.I.C.S.: 541611
Mychele R. Lord (Pres)

OCI Associates, Inc. (2)
600 S Orlando Ave, Maitland, FL 32751
Tel.: (407) 332-5110
Web Site: http://www.ociassociates.com
Sales Range: $1-9.9 Million
Emp.: 21
Engineering Services, Nsk
N.A.I.C.S.: 541330
Jason Smith (Dir-Mechanical Engrg)
Amir Kazeminia (Pres)
Jason Diehl (Engr-Mechanical)
Keith Liatsos (Dir-Electrical Engrg)
Sudharma Wijegunawardana (Engr-Electrical)
Valmiki Rasul (Engr-Mechanical)
Warren Reid (Engr-Electrical)

P2S Inc. (2)
5000 E Spring St Ste 800, Long Beach, CA 90815
Tel.: (562) 497-2999
Web Site: https://www.p2sinc.com
Sales Range: $1-9.9 Million
Emp.: 250
Engineeering Services
N.A.I.C.S.: 541330
Kevin L. Peterson (Pres & CEO)
Jagjit Singh (Principal)

Lexington National Land Services, LLC (1)
39 W 37th St Fl 12A, New York, NY 10018

Blackstone Inc.—(Continued)

Tel.: (646) 237-0822
Web Site: http://www.lexnls.com
Real Estate Services
N.A.I.C.S.: 531390
Harry Hayes *(Gen Counsel)*
Andrea London *(Sr VP-Bus Dev)*
Eric Seal *(COO)*

Marco's Auto Body, Inc. **(1)**
600 E Las Tunas Dr, San Gabriel, CA
91776
Tel.: (626) 309-9100
Web Site: http://www.marcosautobody.com
Sales Range: $1-9.9 Million
Emp.: 30
Auto Body Repair/Painting Automotive Repair
N.A.I.C.S.: 811121

Mphasis Limited **(1)**
Bagmane World Technology Center
Marathahalli Outer Ring Road, Doddanakundi Village Mahadevapura, Bengaluru,
560 048, Karnataka, India **(55.97%)**
Tel.: (91) 8067501000
Web Site: https://www.mphasis.com
Rev.: $1,345,242,444
Assets: $1,282,956,402
Liabilities: $392,060,487
Net Worth: $890,895,915
Earnings: $166,093,883
Emp.: 15,110
Fiscal Year-end: 03/31/2021
Infrastructure Technology, Applications &
Business Process Outsourcing Services
N.A.I.C.S.: 541519
Davinder Singh Brar *(Chm)*
Dinesh Venugopal *(Pres-Direct & Digital)*
Nitin Rakesh *(CEO)*
Srikanth Karra *(Chief HR Officer)*
Eric Winston *(Chief Ethics & Compliance
Officer, Gen Counsel & Exec VP)*
Sundar Subramanian *(Pres-Global Delivery)*
Subramanian Narayan *(Sec & VP)*
Andres Ricaurte *(Sr VP & Head-Payments-
Global)*
Ravi Vasantraj *(Sr VP & Head-Bus Process
Svcs-Global)*
Manish Dugar *(CFO)*

Subsidiary (US):

Blink Interactive, Inc. **(2)**
1011 Western Ave Ste 810, Seattle, WA
98104
Tel.: (206) 447-9551
Web Site: http://www.blinkux.com
Sales Range: $1-9.9 Million
Emp.: 31
Website Design Services
N.A.I.C.S.: 541511
Jason Murphy *(COO)*
Linda Wagener *(Chief Culture Officer)*

Digital Risk, LLC **(2)**
2301 Maitland Center Pkwy Ste 165, Maitland, FL 32751 **(100%)**
Tel.: (212) 704-7385
Web Site: https://digitalrisk.mphasis.com
Mortgage Risk Management Solutions
N.A.I.C.S.: 522310
Joseph Chacko *(Head-Delivery-Global)*
Ravi Vasantraj *(Sr VP & Head-Bus Process
Svcs-Global)*

Holding (Non-US):

Mphasis Consulting Limited **(2)**
4th Floor 15 Bishopsgate, Bishopsgate WeWork, London, EC2N 3AR, United Kingdom
Tel.: (44) 2078467653
Web Site: https://www.mphasis.com
Infrastructure Technology & Business Process Outsourcing Services
N.A.I.C.S.: 541690

Subsidiary (Domestic):

eBECS Limited **(3)**
Manor Offices Old Rd, Chesterfield, S40
3QT, Derbyshire, United Kingdom
Tel.: (44) 8455441441
Web Site: http://www.ebecs.com
Information Technology Services
N.A.I.C.S.: 541512
Kevin Hall *(Dir)*

Subsidiary (US):

Wyde Corporation **(2)**

3600 American Blvd W Ste 110, Bloomington, MN 55431
Tel.: (651) 882-2400
Web Site: http://www.wyde.com
Computer System Design Services
N.A.I.C.S.: 541512

NIBC Holding N.V. **(1)**
Carnegieplein 4, 2517, Hague,
Netherlands
Tel.: (31) 703425425 **(97.68%)**
Web Site: http://www.nibc.com
Rev.: $664,076,980
Assets: $25,056,867,500
Liabilities: $22,763,394,220
Net Worth: $2,293,473,280
Earnings: $230,691,160
Emp.: 711
Fiscal Year-end: 12/31/2019
Bank Holding Company
N.A.I.C.S.: 551111
Herman Dijkhulzen *(Vice Chm-Mgmt Bd &
CFO)*
Paulus de Wilt *(Chm-Mgmt Bd & CEO)*
D. M. Sluimers *(Chm-Supervisory Bd)*
Reinout van Riel *(Chief Risk Officer &
Member-Mgmt Bd)*
Angelien G. Z. Kemna *(Vice Chm-
Supervisory Bd)*

Subsidiary (Domestic):

NIBC Bank N.V. **(2)**
Carnegieplein 4, 2517 KJ, Hague, Netherlands
Tel.: (31) 703425425
Web Site: https://www.nibc.com
Rev.: $655,118,100
Assets: $25,092,703,020
Liabilities: $22,780,192,120
Net Worth: $2,312,510,900
Earnings: $226,211,720
Emp.: 667
Fiscal Year-end: 12/31/2019
Commercial Banking Services
N.A.I.C.S.: 522110
Paulus de Wilt *(Chm-Mgmt Bd & CEO)*
Herman Dijkhuizen *(Vice Chm-Mgmt Bd &
CFO)*
D. M. Sluimers *(Chm-Supervisory Bd)*
Reinout van Riel *(Chief Risk Officer &
Member-Mgmt Bd)*
Angelien G. Z. Kemna *(Vice Chm-
Supervisory Bd)*

Holding (Domestic):

N.V. Deli Maatschappij **(3)**
Wijnhaven 65, NL-3011 WJ, Rotterdam,
Netherlands
Tel.: (31) 104021700
Web Site: http://www.deli-maatschappij.nl
Sales Range: $50-74.9 Million
Holding Company; Timber & Building Products, Agri Products & Tobacco; Owned by
NPM Capital N.V. & by NIBC Bank N.V.
N.A.I.C.S.: 551112
Ron H. J. Bosch *(Member-Exec Bd)*

Subsidiary (Domestic):

Astrimex B.V. **(4)**
Kalkoven 4, 9351 NP, Leek, Netherlands
Tel.: (31) 594552323
Web Site: https://www.astrimex.nl
Sales Range: $1-9.9 Million
Whslr of Construction Materials
N.A.I.C.S.: 444180

Branch (Domestic):

Astrimex Utrecht **(5)**
Cartesiusweg 127a, 3534 BC, Utrecht,
Netherlands
Tel.: (31) 302635888
Web Site: http://www.astrimex.nl
Wholesale Construction Materials
N.A.I.C.S.: 423390

Subsidiary (Domestic):

**B.V. Deli-HTL Tabak
Maatschappij** **(4)**
Kanaaldijk Noord 123, 5642 JA, Eindhoven,
Netherlands
Tel.: (31) 402810275
Web Site: http://www.deli-htl.nl
Sales Range: $1-9.9 Million
Mfr of Tobacco
N.A.I.C.S.: 111910

Subsidiary (Non-US):

Deutsch-Hollandische Tabakgesellschaft mbH & Co. KG **(5)**
2 Industriestrasse 6, 68766, Hockenheim,
Germany
Tel.: (49) 6205379100
Web Site: http://www.htl-dht.com
Emp.: 50
Tobacco Company
N.A.I.C.S.: 459991

Subsidiary (Domestic):

Jongeneel B.V. **(4)**
Atoomweg 300, PO Box 49, 3542 AB,
Utrecht, Netherlands
Tel.: (31) 302346347
Web Site: https://www.jongeneel.nl
Sales Range: $1-9.9 Million
Insulation Products
N.A.I.C.S.: 423330
Michiel De Haan *(CEO)*

Van Rees Group **(4)**
Blaak 16, PO Box 914, 3011 TA, Rotterdam, Netherlands
Tel.: (31) 104021750
Web Site: https://www.vanrees.com
Sales Range: $10-24.9 Million
Emp.: 20
International Suppliers & Processors of Tea
N.A.I.C.S.: 311920

Representative Office (Non-US):

**NIBC Bank N.V. - Brussells
Office** **(3)**
Rue Royale 71, 1000, Brussels, Belgium
Tel.: (32) 22358803
Web Site: https://www.nibc.com
Commercial Banking
N.A.I.C.S.: 522110

NIBC Bank N.V. - London Office **(3)**
Tel.: (44) 2073757777
Web Site: http://www.nibc.com
Commericial Banking
N.A.I.C.S.: 522110
Annemiek Hofland *(Chief Country Officer)*

Holding (Domestic):

NIBC Markets N.V. **(3)**
Nieuwezijds Voorburgwal 162, 1012 SJ,
Amsterdam, Netherlands **(100%)**
Tel.: (31) 205508500
Web Site: http://www.nibcmarkets.com
Investment Banking & Securities Services
N.A.I.C.S.: 523150

PS Business Parks, Inc. **(1)**
701 Western Ave, Glendale, CA 91201-
2340
Tel.: (818) 244-8080
Web Site: http://www.psbusinessparks.com
Rev.: $415,623,000
Assets: $2,057,705,000
Liabilities: $82,065,000
Net Worth: $1,975,640,000
Earnings: $206,705,000
Emp.: 155
Fiscal Year-end: 12/31/2020
Real Estate Investment Trust; Commercial
Properties Owner & Lessor
N.A.I.C.S.: 525990
Coby Holley *(VP-Real Estate)*
Eddie F. Ruiz *(VP & Dir-Facilities)*
David Vicars *(VP-Texas)*
Stuart Hutchison *(VP-Southern California &
Seattle)*
Eugene Uhlman *(VP-Construction Mgmt)*
Trenton A. Groves *(Chief Acctg Officer & Sr
VP)*
Jeff Paschal *(VP-Texas)*
Mark Antrobius *(VP-Southern California &
Seattle)*
Christopher M. Auth *(VP-Northern Virginia &
Maryland)*
Amy Heritage *(VP-Austin)*
Dan Ashworth *(VP & Controller-Property
Ops)*
Tom Driscoll *(VP-Northern Virginia & Maryland)*
Ngoc Vu Rossi *(VP-Northern California)*
Ed Zaptin *(VP-Northern Virginia & Maryland)*
Stephen W. Wilson *(Pres & CEO)*
Craig Morrow *(VP-Southern California &
Seattle)*

Rich Guertin *(VP-Florida)*
Dick Scott *(VP-Northern California)*
Adeel Khan *(CFO & Exec VP)*

Subsidiary (Domestic):

Metro Park I, L.L.C. **(2)**
7529 Standish Pl Ste 250, Rockville, MD
20855-2792
Tel.: (703) 278-2325
Web Site: http://www.psbusinessparks.com
Real Estate Investment Services
N.A.I.C.S.: 531110

Metro Park V, LLC **(2)**
7361 Calhoun Pl, Rockville, MD 20855
Tel.: (301) 340-0901
Financial Investment Services
N.A.I.C.S.: 525990

**Miami International Commerce
Center** **(2)**
8216 NW 14th St, Doral, FL 33126
Tel.: (305) 590-1515
Web Site: http://www.psbusinessparks.com
Sales Range: $50-74.9 Million
Emp.: 20
Real Estate Investment Services
N.A.I.C.S.: 531110

Park Hill Group LLC **(1)**
280 Park Ave, New York, NY 10017
Tel.: (212) 364-6099
Web Site: http://www.parkhillgroup.com
Sales Range: $50-74.9 Million
Emp.: 100
Alternative Asset Placement Services
N.A.I.C.S.: 523999
Brian Levine *(Founder & Partner)*
Joseph M. Herman *(Partner)*

**Philadelphia Financial Group,
Inc.** **(1)**
1650 Market St One Liberty Pl 54th Fl,
Philadelphia, PA 19103
Tel.: (484) 530-4820
Web Site:
　　http://www.lombardinternational.com
Emp.: 500
Holding Company; High Net Worth Insurance Products & Services
N.A.I.C.S.: 551112

Subsidiary (Domestic):

**Lombard International Administration
Services Company, LLC** **(2)**
1 Liberty Pl 1650 Market St 54th Fl, Philadelphia, PA 19103
Tel.: (484) 530-4800
Web Site:
　　http://www.lombardinternational.com
Private Placement Insurance Administration
Services
N.A.I.C.S.: 524292

**Lombard International Life Assurance
Company** **(2)**
1 Liberty Pl 1650 Market St 54th Fl, Philadelphia, PA 19103
Tel.: (484) 530-4800
Web Site:
　　http://www.lombardinternational.com
High Net Worth Insurance Products & Services
N.A.I.C.S.: 525190

Phoenix Tower International LLC **(1)**
999 Yamato Rd Ste 100, Boca Raton, FL
33431
Tel.: (561) 257-0557
Web Site: http://www.phoenixintnl.com
Telecommunication Servicesb
N.A.I.C.S.: 517810
Dagan T. Kasavana *(Founder & CEO)*
Michael Bremer *(CFO)*
Marcella Barry *(Chief People Officer)*
Rajiv Datta *(COO)*
Miguel Garrido *(Gen Counsel)*
Shylesh Moras *(Sr VP)*
Carlos Travaglia *(Chief Acctg Officer)*
Charles Duntze *(VP)*
Scott Lewis *(VP)*
Josh Wade *(Gen Counsel)*
Michelle Brea *(Gen Counsel)*

Subsidiary (Domestic):

Tower Ventures Holdings LLC **(2)**

495 Tennessee St Ste 152, Memphis, TN
38118-6106
Tel.: (901) 794-9494
Web Site: http://www.towerventures.com
Power & Communication Line Construction
N.A.I.C.S.: 237130
William Orgel *(Pres, CEO & Principal)*
Jay Lindy *(COO, Principal & Gen Counsel)*
Craig Weiss *(Principal & Exec VP-Carrier Leasing)*
Michael McLaughlin *(CFO)*
Craig Royal *(Principal & VP-Construction & Ops)*
Benjamin Orgel *(Principal)*
David Goldstein *(Principal)*

**Posadas De San Juan
Associates** (1)
6063 Isla Verde Ave, Carolina, PR 00979
Tel.: (787) 791-1000
Sales Range: $75-99.9 Million
Emp.: 600
Hotel & Casino Services
N.A.I.C.S.: 721120
Jorge Garcia *(Gen Mgr)*

R Systems International Limited (1)
C 40 Sector 59, Noida, 201 307, UP,
India (52%)
Tel.: (91) 1204303500
Web Site: https://www.rsystems.com
Rev.: $163,463,528
Assets: $94,503,318
Liabilities: $31,672,914
Net Worth: $62,830,404
Earnings: $19,306,014
Emp.: 2,936
Fiscal Year-end: 12/31/2021
Software Product Development & Business
Process Outsourcing Services
N.A.I.C.S.: 541512
Satinder Singh Rekhi *(Founder & Mng Dir)*
Nand Sardana *(CFO)*
Mandeep Singh Sodhi *(COO-R Systems-USA)*
Sartaj Rekhi *(Exec Dir)*
Chan Kum Ming *(CEO-ECnet & R Systems-Singapore)*
Sidhartha Dubey *(VP-Analytics & Knowledge Svcs)*
Ramneet Rekhi *(Mng Dir-Digital)*
Raj Gupta *(Pres-Digital Svcs)*
Avirag Jain *(CTO)*
Raluca Rusu *(CEO-R Systems Europe)*

Subsidiary (Non-US):

Computaris International Limited (2)
Swan House 9 Queens Road, Brentwood,
CM14 4HE, Essex, United Kingdom
Tel.: (44) 2071939189
Web Site: http://www.computaris.com
Sales Range: $25-49.9 Million
Emp.: 2
Information Technology Management Services
N.A.I.C.S.: 541611
Raluca Rusu *(CEO)*
Bogdan Tudan *(COO)*

ECnet (Hong Kong) Limited (2)
Room 1903 World Wide house 19-DES
Voeux Rd, Central, China (Hong Kong)
Tel.: (852) 26206078
Web Site: http://www.ecnet.com
Information Technology Management Services
N.A.I.C.S.: 541611
Kum Ming Chan *(Pres)*

ECnet (M) Sdn. Bhd. (2)
Lot No 5F-1 5th Floor Puchong Financial
Corporate Centre, Jalan Puteri 1/2 Bandar
Puteri, 47100, Puchong, Selangor, Malaysia
Tel.: (60) 380666160
Web Site: http://www.ecnet.com
Sales Range: $25-49.9 Million
Emp.: 30
Supply Chain Management Services
N.A.I.C.S.: 541611

ECnet Limited (2)
16 Jelan Kelang Unit No 04-01 Hoi Hup
Building, Singapore, 159416, Singapore
Tel.: (65) 67855266
Web Site: http://www.ecnet.com
Sales Range: $25-49.9 Million
Emp.: 40
Supply Chain Management Services
N.A.I.C.S.: 541611

Chen Shao Zhong *(Sr VP-Enterprise Solutions)*
Joydeep Sen Chaudhuri *(Sr VP-Sls)*
K. C. Chen *(CEO)*

Subsidiary (Non-US):

ECnet (Shanghai) Co. Ltd. (3)
Room H 20 Floor Foresight Mansion No
768 Xie Tu Road, Shanghai, 200 023,
China
Tel.: (86) 2153025032
Business Process Outsourcing Services
N.A.I.C.S.: 541511
Chan Kun Ming *(Mng Dir)*

ECnet Kabushiki Kaisha (3)
Godo Building 6F Kaji-cho 1-6-17, Chiyoda-
Ku, Tokyo, Japan
Tel.: (81) 335263611
Supply Chain Management Services
N.A.I.C.S.: 541611

**ECnet Systems (Thailand) Company
Limited** (3)
2/3 Moo 14 Bangna Tower A 2nd Floor
Room No 205, Bangna-Trad Km 6 5 Bang-
kaew, Bang Phli, 10540, Samut Prakan,
Thailand
Tel.: (66) 27519663
Web Site: http://www.ecnet.com
Sales Range: $25-49.9 Million
Emp.: 5
Supply Chain Management Services
N.A.I.C.S.: 541611
Patcharanan Limpornchaicharoen *(Country Mgr-Sls)*

Subsidiary (Domestic):

**IBIZ Consultancy Services India Pvt.
Ltd.** (2)
Plot NP 1 and 2, Industrial Estate Sidco
Industrial Estate Guindy, Chennai, 600032,
India
Tel.: (91) 4442615235
Information Technology Services
N.A.I.C.S.: 541511

Subsidiary (Non-US):

**IBIZ Consulting Services (Shanghai)
Co., Ltd.** (2)
1721 17F Building A CCIG International
Plaza 331 North Caoxi Rd, Xuhui District,
Shanghai, 200030, China
Tel.: (86) 2164399027
Information Technology Services
N.A.I.C.S.: 541511

Subsidiary (US):

Innovizant, LLC (2)
1431 Opus Pl Ste 630, Downers Grove, IL
60515
Tel.: (630) 885-9200
Information Technology Services
N.A.I.C.S.: 541511

Subsidiary (Non-US):

**PT. R Systems IBIZCS
International** (2)
Setiabudi Bldg -2 2nd Floor Suite 203 Jl H
R Rasuna Said Kav 62, Jakarta Selatan,
Indonesia
Tel.: (62) 2152921365
Information Technology Services
N.A.I.C.S.: 541511

**R Systems Computaris Europe
SRL** (2)
5 Gheorghe Manu St Gr Floor 1st Floor and
6th Floor 2 Sector-1, 010442, Bucharest,
Romania
Tel.: (40) 212045200
Information Technology Services
N.A.I.C.S.: 541511

**R Systems Computaris Malaysia Sdn.
Bhd.** (2)
Suite 5F-1 5th Floor Tower 5 Puchong Fi-
nancial Corporate Center, Jalan Puteri 1/2
Bandar Puteri, 47100, Puchong, Selangor,
Malaysia
Tel.: (60) 380522009
Information Technology Services
N.A.I.C.S.: 541511

**R Systems Computaris Philippines
Pte. Ltd. Inc.** (2)
21B Rufino Pacific Tower 6784 Ayala Ave
Corner V A Rufino St, Legaspi Village,
Makati, Philippines
Tel.: (63) 22241833
Information Technology Services
N.A.I.C.S.: 541511

**R Systems Computaris Poland Sp z
o.o.** (2)
Al Jana Pawla II 80, 00-175, Warsaw, Po-
land
Tel.: (48) 228695040
Information Technology Services
N.A.I.C.S.: 541511

R Systems Computaris S.R.L. (2)
Vlaicu Pircalab St 63 Et 8 Oficiu B Sky
Tower Business Center, MD2012, Chisinau,
Moldova
Tel.: (373) 22240225
Information Technology Services
N.A.I.C.S.: 541511

**R Systems Consulting Services
(Shanghai) Co., Ltd.** (2)
Rm H 20th Floor Foresight Mansion No 768
Xie Tu Rd, Shanghai, China
Tel.: (86) 2153025032
Information Technology Services
N.A.I.C.S.: 541511

R Systems Europe B.V. (2)
Brammelerstraat 8, PO Box 447, Enschede,
7511 JG, Netherlands
Tel.: (31) 534860000
Web Site: http://www.rsystems.eu
Sales Range: $10-24.9 Million
Emp.: 120
Computer Softwares Mfr
N.A.I.C.S.: 513210

Subsidiary (Non-US):

R Systems S.A.S. (3)
9 Rue Thomas Edison, PO Box 85001,
57071, Metz, Cedex 3, France
Tel.: (33) 387170000
Web Site: http://www.rsystems.com
Computer Related Services
N.A.I.C.S.: 541512

Subsidiary (Non-US):

R Systems IBIZCS Sdn. Bhd. (2)
Suite 5F-1 5th Floor Tower 5 Puchong Fi-
nancial Corporate Center, Jalan Puteri 1/2
Bandar Puteri, 47100, Puchong, Selangor,
Malaysia
Tel.: (60) 380669665
Information Technology Services
N.A.I.C.S.: 541511

Subsidiary (US):

R Systems Inc. (2)
5000 Windplay Dr Ste 5, El Dorado Hills,
CA 95762
Tel.: (916) 939-9696
Web Site: https://www.rsystems.com
Sales Range: $25-49.9 Million
Emp.: 400
Software Product Development & Business
Process Outsourcing Services
N.A.I.C.S.: 541512

Subsidiary (Non-US):

R Systems Singapore Ltd. (2)
15 Changi Business Park Central 1, Unit
02-01 Invensys Bldg, Singapore, 486057,
Singapore
Tel.: (65) 67855266
Web Site: http://www.rsystems.com
Sales Range: $25-49.9 Million
Emp.: 50
Software Product Development & Business
Process Outsourcing Services
N.A.I.C.S.: 541512
Chan Kum Ming *(Pres)*

Subsidiary (US):

R Systems Solutions, Inc. (2)
5000 Windplay Dr Ste 5, El Dorado Hills,
CA 95762
Information Technology Management Services
N.A.I.C.S.: 541511

Subsidiary (Non-US):

RSYS Technologies Ltd. (2)
2425 Matheson Blvd East Unit 778, Missis-
sauga, L4W 5K4, ON, Canada
Tel.: (905) 361-6484
Information Technology Services
N.A.I.C.S.: 541511

RGIS (1)
2000 Taylor Rd, Auburn Hills, MI 48326
Tel.: (248) 221-4000
Web Site: http://www.rgis.com
Sales Range: $1-4.9 Billion
Emp.: 300
Inventory Services
N.A.I.C.S.: 561499

Subsidiary (Non-US):

Orridge & Co Ltd. (2)
Suite A Equity House 4-6 Market Street,
Harlow, CM17 0AH, Essex, United Kingdom
Tel.: (44) 1279775600
Web Site: http://www.orridge.co.uk
Sales Range: $25-49.9 Million
Emp.: 12
Stocktaking Solutions
N.A.I.C.S.: 561990
Paul Harding *(Mng Dir)*

Orridge SA (2)
Avenue Du Port 100, 1000, Brussels, Bel-
gium
Tel.: (32) 26462547
Web Site: http://www.orridge.eu
Sales Range: $25-49.9 Million
Emp.: 3
Stocktake & Inventory Management Ser-
vices
N.A.I.C.S.: 541618

SESAC Performing Rights, Inc. (1)
35 Music Sq E, Nashville, TN 37027
Tel.: (615) 320-0055
Web Site: http://www.sesac.com
Performance Rights Organization
N.A.I.C.S.: 813920
Scott Jungmichel *(Pres & COO)*
John Josephson *(Chm & CEO)*
Christos P. Badavas *(Gen Counsel & Exec VP)*
Alexander Wolf *(Pres-Intl)*
J. D. Connell *(Sr VP-Media Licensing)*
Rose Cook *(Sr VP-Licensing Ops)*
Michael Deighan *(CFO & Exec VP)*
Jonathan Farmer *(Sr VP-Licensing Ops)*
Susan King *(VP & Controller)*
Nadia Lightwala *(VP-Fin & Acctg)*
Muhammad Qasim *(CTO & Sr VP-Data)*
Reid Alan Waltz *(VP)*
John Sweeney *(VP)*
Eric Lense *(VP)*
Erin Collins *(VP)*

Subsidiary (Domestic):

The Harry Fox Agency, Inc. (2)
40 Wall St 6th Fl, New York, NY 10005-
1344
Tel.: (212) 843-0100
Web Site: http://www.harryfox.com
Music Publishing Services
N.A.I.C.S.: 512230
Michael S. Simon *(Pres & CEO)*
John Raso *(Sr VP-Client Svcs)*
Stephen Block *(Sr VP-Bus & Legal Affairs)*
Lauren Apolito *(Sr VP-Strategy & Bus Dev)*

Service King Paint & Body, LLC (1)
2375 N Glenville Dr Bldg A Ste 500, Rich-
ardson, TX 75082
Tel.: (972) 960-7595
Web Site: http://www.serviceking.com
Sales Range: $300-349.9 Million
Automotive Body & Paint Repair Centers
Operator
N.A.I.C.S.: 811121
Jaime Jaramillo *(CIO)*

Servpro Industries, LLC (1)
801 Industrial Blvd, Gallatin, TN 37066
Tel.: (615) 451-0200
Web Site: http://www.servpro.com
Cleaning & Restoration Services
N.A.I.C.S.: 624230
Randall Isaacson *(Pres)*
Richard Isaacson *(Exec VP)*
Rich Isaacson *(CEO)*
John Sooker *(COO)*

Blackstone Inc.—(Continued)

Jeff Fields *(CIO)*
Matt Preston *(Chief Legal Officer)*
Mike Stahl *(Chief Mktg Officer)*
Todd Lindsey *(CFO)*
Brian Voss *(Chief Franchise Operating Officer)*
Maribeth Bearfield *(Chief HR Officer)*

Division (Domestic):

SERVPRO of The Quad Cities, LLC   **(2)**
3470 Gnat Pond Rd, Muscle Shoals, AL 35661
Tel.: (256) 383-4470
Web Site:
   http://www.servprothequadcities.com
Residential & Commercial Restoration & Cleaning Services
N.A.I.C.S.: 561720

Signature Aviation Limited   **(1)**
Percival Way, Luton, London, LU2 9PA, United Kingdom
Tel.: (44) 3300271281
Web Site: https://www.signatureaviation.com
Rev.: $1,413,900,000
Assets: $4,587,400,000
Liabilities: $2,997,300,000
Net Worth: $1,590,100,000
Earnings: $9,500,000
Emp.: 6,469
Fiscal Year-end: 12/31/2020
Holding Company; Aircraft Parts Mfr, Repair, Maintenance & Flight Support Services
N.A.I.C.S.: 551112
Tristan Dorian *(Gen Mgr)*

Group (US):

BBA Aviation Engine Repair & Overhaul Group   **(2)**
900 Nolen Dr Ste 100, Grapevine, TX 76051-8641
Tel.: (214) 956-3000
Web Site: http://www.bbaaviationero.com
Sales Range: $75-99.9 Million
Emp.: 220
Subsidiary Managing Office; Aircraft Engine Repair & Overhaul Services
N.A.I.C.S.: 551114
Hugh E. McElroy Jr. *(Pres)*
Nandakumar Madireddi *(Sr VP-Bus Ops)*
Dennis DiMarco *(VP-Sls & Mktg-North America)*
Doris Hastings *(VP-HR)*
Gerardo Gomez *(Mgr-Sls-Mexico)*

Subsidiary (Domestic):

Dallas Airmotive, Inc.   **(3)**
900 Nolen Dr Ste 100, Grapevine, TX 76051-8641
Tel.: (214) 956-3001
Web Site: http://www.bbaaviationero.com
Rev.: $42,750,769
Emp.: 80
Aircraft Engine Repair & Overhaul Services
N.A.I.C.S.: 336412

Unit (Domestic):

Dallas Airmotive, Inc. - Dallas Facility   **(4)**
2988 W Walnut Hill Ln DFW Airport, Dallas, TX 75261
Tel.: (214) 956-3001
Web Site: http://www.dallasairmotive.com
Sales Range: $25-49.9 Million
Aircraft Engine Repair & Overhaul Services
N.A.I.C.S.: 336412
Thomas Kennedy *(Mgr-Engine-Danvers Reg)*

Subsidiary (Non-US):

H+S Aviation Limited   **(3)**
Airport Service Road, Portsmouth, PO3 5PJ, Hampshire, United Kingdom
Tel.: (44) 2392304000
Web Site: https://www.hsaviation.co.uk
Emp.: 320
Aircraft Engine Repair & Overhaul Services
N.A.I.C.S.: 336412
Ann New *(Dir-HR)*

Group (US):

BBA Aviation Legacy Support Group   **(2)**

20400 Plummer St, Chatsworth, CA 91311
Tel.: (818) 678-6555
Web Site: http://www.bbaaviation.com
Subsidiary Managing Office; Legacy Aircraft Parts Mfr & Whslr
N.A.I.C.S.: 551114

Subsidiary (Domestic):

International Governor Services, LLC   **(3)**
7290 W 118th Pl, Broomfield, CO 80020
Tel.: (303) 464-0043
Web Site:
   http://www.internationalgovernor.com
Emp.: 17
Small Aircraft Turbine Engine Controls Repair & Overhaul Services
N.A.I.C.S.: 335314

Subsidiary (Domestic):

Balderton Aviation Holdings Limited   **(2)**
20 Balderton Street, London, W1K 6TL, United Kingdom
Tel.: (44) 20 7016 6800
Web Site: http://www.baldertoncapital.com
Emp.: 23
Investment Management Service
N.A.I.C.S.: 523999

Subsidiary (US):

Barrett Turbine Engine Company   **(2)**
1626 Tobacco Rd, Augusta, GA 30906
Tel.: (706) 790-1977
Web Site:
   http://www.barrettturbineengine.com
Aircraft Engine Mfr
N.A.I.C.S.: 336412
Russell Cathey *(VP & Gen Mgr)*
Albert Poor *(VP-Sls)*

Subsidiary (Non-US):

Dallas Airmotive South Africa Pty Limited   **(2)**
Hanger 201 Lanseria International Airport, Airport Road, Lanseria, 1748, South Africa
Tel.: (27) 117012611
Aircraft Leasing & Rental Services
N.A.I.C.S.: 532411

Subsidiary (US):

EPIC Aviation, LLC   **(2)**
222 W Las Colinas Blvd Ste 1425 N, Irving, TX 75039
Tel.: (503) 362-3633
Web Site: https://www.epicfuels.com
Petroleum & Bulk Fuels
N.A.I.C.S.: 424720

General Aviation Flying Services, Inc.   **(2)**
485 Industrial Ave, Teterboro, NJ 07608
Tel.: (201) 288-5040
Sales Range: $1-9.9 Million
Emp.: 100
Air Courier Services
N.A.I.C.S.: 492110
Ken C. Forester *(CEO)*

Subsidiary (Non-US):

SFS Munich GmbH & Co. KG   **(2)**
PO Box 241431, 85336, Munich, Germany
Tel.: (49) 8997597730
Aircraft Maintenance Services
N.A.I.C.S.: 488190
Oliver Trono *(Gen Mgr)*

Group (US):

Signature Flight Support Corp.   **(2)**
13485 Veterans Way Ste 600, Orlando, FL 32827
Tel.: (407) 648-7200
Web Site: http://www.signatureflight.com
Sales Range: $550-599.9 Million
Emp.: 1,300
Private Aircraft Ground Support Services
N.A.I.C.S.: 488119
Tony Lefebvre *(CEO)*
Amy Alexy *(Chief People Officer)*
Derek DeCross *(Sr VP)*
Rick Elieson *(Sr VP)*
Mike Eshoo *(CFO)*

Maria Garton *(Gen Counsel)*
Anurag Gupta *(CIO)*
Marty Kretchman *(Sr VP)*

Unit (Domestic):

Signature Flight Support - BED   **(3)**
180 Hanscom Dr, Bedford, MA 01730
Tel.: (781) 274-0010
Web Site: https://www.signatureaviation.com
Emp.: 25
Air Transportation Support Services
N.A.I.C.S.: 488190

Signature Flight Support - MKE   **(3)**
923 E Layton Ave, Milwaukee, WI 53207
Tel.: (414) 747-5100
Web Site: http://www.signatureflight.com
Sales Range: $25-49.9 Million
Emp.: 33
Private Aircraft Ground Support Services
N.A.I.C.S.: 488119

Signature Flight Support - MMU   **(3)**
1 Airport Rd, Morristown, NJ 07960
Tel.: (973) 292-1300
Web Site: http://www.signatureflight.com
Emp.: 44
Private Aircraft Ground Support Services
N.A.I.C.S.: 488119
Pasquale Raguseo *(Dir-Art-MQS & KMQS)*

Signature Flight Support - PIE   **(3)**
14525 Airport Pkwy, Clearwater, FL 33762
Tel.: (727) 531-1441
Web Site: http://www.signatureflight.com
Sales Range: $50-74.9 Million
Emp.: 120
Private Aircraft Ground Support Services
N.A.I.C.S.: 488119

Signature Flight Support - PWK   **(3)**
1100 S Milwaukee Ave, Wheeling, IL 60090-6309
Tel.: (847) 537-1200
Web Site: http://www.signatureflight.com
Sales Range: $25-49.9 Million
Emp.: 13
Private Aircraft Ground Support Services
N.A.I.C.S.: 488119
Mark Costa *(Gen Mgr)*

Signature Flight Support - STL   **(3)**
5995 James S McDonnell Blvd, Saint Louis, MO 63134
Tel.: (314) 731-7111
Web Site: http://www.signatureflight.com
Sales Range: $25-49.9 Million
Emp.: 30
Private Aircraft Ground Support Services
N.A.I.C.S.: 488119

Subsidiary (Non-US):

Signature Flight Support Paris SA   **(3)**
45 Avenue de l'Europe Zone Aviation d'Affaires, 93350, Le Bourget, France
Tel.: (33) 149927581
Web Site: http://www.signatureflight.com
Sales Range: $25-49.9 Million
Emp.: 25
Oil Transportation Services
N.A.I.C.S.: 488190
Andriot Nathalie *(Gen Mgr)*

Subsidiary (US):

Signature Flight Support Washington National, Inc.   **(2)**
1 General Aviation Terminal Hangar 7, Washington, DC 20001
Tel.: (703) 417-3500
Aircraft Maintenance Services
N.A.I.C.S.: 488190
Pablo Espitia *(Gen Mgr)*

St. Modwen Properties PLC   **(1)**
Two Devon Way, Longbridge, Birmingham, B31 2TS, United Kingdom
Tel.: (44) 1212229400
Web Site: https://www.stmodwen.co.uk
Commercial Property Redevelopment Services
N.A.I.C.S.: 531390
Dave Smith *(Mng Dir-St Modwen Homes)*
Jane Saint *(Grp Dir-HR)*
Sarwjit Sambhi *(CEO)*
Polly Troughton *(Mng Dir-St. Modwen Logistics)*
Lisa Minns *(Gen Counsel & Sec)*
Tom Olsen *(CFO)*

Affiliate (Domestic):

Barton Business Park Limited   **(2)**
58-62 Hagley Rd, Birmingham, United Kingdom   **(50%)**
Tel.: (44) 1214562800
Real Estate Agents & Brokers
N.A.I.C.S.: 531210

Subsidiary (Domestic):

Leisure Living Limited   **(2)**
180 Great Portland Street, London, W1W 5QZ, United Kingdom   **(100%)**
Tel.: (44) 1217425561
Web Site: http://www.stmodwen.co.uk
Property Management Services
N.A.I.C.S.: 531390

Norton & Proffitt Developments Limited   **(2)**
Lyndon Ho 58 62 Hagley Rd, Birmingham, United Kingdom   **(75%)**
Tel.: (44) 1214562800
Web Site: http://www.stmodwen.com
Real Estate Agents & Brokers
N.A.I.C.S.: 531210

Redman Heenan Properties Limited   **(2)**
Park Point 17 High St Longbridge, Birmingham, B31 2UQ, United Kingdom   **(100%)**
Tel.: (44) 1212229400
Web Site: http://www.stmodwen.co.uk
Sales Range: $150-199.9 Million
Emp.: 50
Real Estate Property Lessors
N.A.I.C.S.: 531190

St. Modwen Developments Limited   **(2)**
Lyndon Ho 58-62 Hagley Rd, Birmingham, United Kingdom   **(100%)**
Tel.: (44) 1214562800
Land Subdivision
N.A.I.C.S.: 237210

St. Modwen Ventures Limited   **(2)**
Park Point 17 High Street Longbridge, Birmingham, B31 2UQ, United Kingdom   **(100%)**
Tel.: (44) 1212229400
Web Site: http://www.stmodwen.co.uk
Sales Range: $10-24.9 Million
Emp.: 180
Business Services
N.A.I.C.S.: 561499

Stoke-on-Trent Regeneration Limited   **(2)**
Lyndon Ho 58-62 Hagley Rd, Birmingham, United Kingdom   **(81%)**
Tel.: (44) 1214562800
Land Subdivision
N.A.I.C.S.: 237210

Trentham Leisure Limited   **(2)**
Stone Road, Stoke-On-Trent, Stafford, ST4 8JG, United Kingdom   **(80%)**
Tel.: (44) 1782657341
Web Site: https://trentham.co.uk
Sales Range: $50-74.9 Million
Emp.: 70
Amusement & Recreation
N.A.I.C.S.: 713990

Uttoxeter Estates Limited   **(2)**
Lyndon Ho 58-62 Hagley Rd, Birmingham, United Kingdom   **(81%)**
Tel.: (44) 1214562800
Nonresidential Buildings Lessors
N.A.I.C.S.: 531120

Widnes Regeneration Limited   **(2)**
Lyndon Ho 58-62 Hagley Rd, Birmingham, United Kingdom   **(81%)**
Tel.: (44) 1214562800
Real Estate Agents & Brokers
N.A.I.C.S.: 531210

Stearns Holdings, LLC   **(1)**
401 E Corporate Dr Ste 150, Lewisville, TX 75057
Tel.: (855) 839-6487
Web Site: http://www.stearns.com
Mortgage Lending Services
N.A.I.C.S.: 522310
David Schneider *(CEO)*

Subsidiary (Domestic):

Stearns Lending, LLC   **(2)**

350 10th Ave Ste 1000 Office 1086, San Diego, CA 92101
Tel.: (619) 723-6118
Web Site:
   https://mortgagesbyladdgraham.com
Emp.: 2,000
Mortgage Bankers & Loan Brokerage Services
N.A.I.C.S.: 522310
Glenn Stearns *(Founder)*
Steve Smith *(Pres & CFO)*
David C. Schneider *(CEO)*
Terry McCoy *(Chief Investment Officer)*
Radha Thompson *(CIO)*
Tammy Jetton *(Chief HR Officer)*
Todd Bergwall *(Gen Counsel)*
Allyson Knudsen *(Chief Risk Officer)*
Jim Linnane *(Pres-Retail Lending)*
Steven Stein *(Pres-Joint Venture Partnerships)*
Nick Pabarcus *(Pres-Wholesale Lending)*
Andrew Pohlmann *(CMO)*
Jim Clapp *(Pres-Certainty Home Loans)*
Teresa Whitehead *(Pres-Citywide Home Loans)*

Subsidiary (Domestic):

Gibraltar Mortgage Services, LLC **(3)**
5120 Woodway Dr Ste 5016, Houston, TX 77056
Tel.: (713) 935-1100
Web Site: http://www.gibraltarlending.com
Sales Range: $25-49.9 Million
Emp.: 20
Mortgage Services
N.A.I.C.S.: 522110

Tallgrass Energy, LP **(1)**
4200 W 115th St Ste 350, Leawood, KS 66211
Tel.: (913) 928-6060
Web Site: http://www.tallgrassenergy.com
Rev.: $868,548,000
Assets: $6,214,086,000
Liabilities: $4,021,208,000
Net Worth: $2,192,878,000
Earnings: $248,809,000
Emp.: 800
Fiscal Year-end: 12/31/2019
Oil & Gas Investments
N.A.I.C.S.: 213112
Gary D. Watkins *(Chief Acctg Officer & Exec VP)*
Christopher R. Jones *(Gen Counsel, Sec & Exec VP)*

Subsidiary (Domestic):

Stanchion Energy, LLC **(2)**
4200 W 115th St Ste 350, Leawood, KS 66211
Tel.: (913) 312-3267
Web Site: https://www.stanchionenergy.com
Natural Gas Transportation Services
N.A.I.C.S.: 486210
Mike Purmort *(VP & Gen Mgr)*
Ryan Hoshor *(Dir)*

Tallgrass Energy Partners, LP **(2)**
4200 W 115th St Ste 350, Leawood, KS 66211 **(100%)**
Tel.: (913) 928-6060
Web Site: http://www.tallgrassenergylp.com
Holding Company; Midstream Oil & Gas Operations
N.A.I.C.S.: 551112

Subsidiary (Domestic):

Buckhorn Energy Services, LLC **(3)**
5690 DTC Blvd 530W, Greenwood Village, CO 80111
Tel.: (720) 242-9853
Crude Petroleum & Natural Gas Extraction
N.A.I.C.S.: 211120

Tallgrass MLP Operations, LLC **(3)**
6640 W 143rd St Ste 200, Overland Park, KS 66223
Tel.: (913) 928-6060
Natural Gas Transportation Services
N.A.I.C.S.: 486990

Tallgrass Midstream, LLC **(3)**
370 Van Gordon St, Lakewood, CO 80228
Tel.: (303) 763-2950
Web Site: http://www.tallgrassenergylp.com
Natural Gas Transportation Services

N.A.I.C.S.: 486990

Team Health Holdings, Inc. **(1)**
265 Brookview Ctr Way Ste 400, Knoxville, TN 37919
Tel.: (865) 693-1000
Web Site: http://www.teamhealth.com
Holding Company; Outsourced Healthcare Professional Staffing & Administrative Services
N.A.I.C.S.: 551112
David Jones *(CFO)*
Lynn Massingale *(Founder & Chm)*
Leif M. Murphy *(Pres & CEO)*
Khadeja Haye *(Dir-Medical-Natl-Obstetrics & Gynecology)*

Subsidiary (Domestic):

Anesthesia Special Operations, LLC **(2)**
7111 Fairway Dr Ste 450, Palm Beach Gardens, FL 33418
Tel.: (561) 799-3552
Pain Management Services
N.A.I.C.S.: 621111
Jeffrey Weiss *(Pres)*

Clinic Management Services, Inc. **(2)**
265 Brookview Ctr Way Ste 400, Knoxville, TN 37919
Tel.: (800) 342-2898
Web Site: http://www.teamhealth.com
Nursing Care Facilities
N.A.I.C.S.: 623110

Daniel & Yeager, LLC **(2)**
6767 Old Madison Pike, Huntsville, AL 35806
Web Site: https://www.dystaffing.com
Healthcare Staffing Services
N.A.I.C.S.: 561311

Emergency Coverage Corporation **(2)**
265 Brookview Ctr Way Ste 400, Knoxville, TN 37919
Tel.: (865) 690-7868
Web Site: http://www.teamhealth.com
Healthcare Staffing Services
N.A.I.C.S.: 561311

Emergency Medicine Consultants, Ltd. **(2)**
6451 Brentwood Stair Rd Ste 200, Fort Worth, TX 76112
Tel.: (817) 496-9700
Web Site: http://www.emdocs.com
Medical Practitioner Staffing, Office Administrative & Business Support Services
N.A.I.C.S.: 561330
Heather Owen *(Chief Clinical Officer-Emergency Medicine)*

Florida Gulf-to-Bay Anesthesiology Associates, LLC **(2)**
400 N Ashley Dr Ste 1625, Tampa, FL 33602-4395
Tel.: (813) 868-7499
Web Site: http://www.fgtba.com
Anesthesiology Services
N.A.I.C.S.: 621111

Florida Hospital Medicine Services, LLC **(2)**
14050 NW 14th St Ste 190, Fort Lauderdale, FL 33323
Tel.: (954) 835-0750
Web Site: http://www.flacs.net
Nursing Care Facilities
N.A.I.C.S.: 623110

HCFS Health Care Financial Services, LLC **(2)**
265 Brookview Ctr Way Ste 400, Knoxville, TN 37919
Tel.: (800) 443-3672
Web Site: http://www.hcfin.com
Billing Management Services
N.A.I.C.S.: 561110

Healthcare Revenue Recovery Group, LLC **(2)**
1643 N Harrison Pkwy Bldg H Ste 100, Sunrise, FL 33323
Tel.: (954) 792-5227
Web Site:
   http://www.healthcarerevenuerecovery
group.com

Mortgage Brokerage Services
N.A.I.C.S.: 522310

IPC Healthcare, Inc. **(2)**
4605 Lankershim Blvd Ste 617, North Hollywood, CA 91602
Tel.: (818) 766-3502
Web Site: http://www.hospitalist.com
Holding Company; Hospital Management Services
N.A.I.C.S.: 551112

Medical Management Resources, Inc. **(2)**
9485 Regency Sq Blvd Ste 200, Jacksonville, FL 32225
Tel.: (904) 725-4591
Emergency Care Services
N.A.I.C.S.: 621493

Premier Health Care Services, LLC **(2)**
110 N Main St Ste 1200, Dayton, OH 45402
Tel.: (937) 499-7441
Web Site: http://www.premierhealth.com
Health Care Srvices
N.A.I.C.S.: 621610
Diane Ewing *(VP-Govt Affairs)*
Ben Sutherly *(Dir-Sys Comm)*
Mary H. Boosalis *(Pres & CEO)*
Barbara A. Johnson *(COO & Exec VP)*
Marc Belcastro *(Chief Medical Officer-Sys)*
Kathy Harper *(CMO & Chief Comm Officer)*
Peggy Mark *(Chief Nursing Officer & Sr VP)*
K. Duane Martin *(Sr VP-Corp Compliance & Enterprise Risk Mgmt)*
Scott Shelton *(CFO & Sr VP)*
Geoff Walker *(Chief Legal Officer)*
Renee Roberts *(Mgr-Site-Community & PR)*

Premier Physician Services, Inc. **(2)**
332 Congress Park Dr, Dayton, OH 45459
Tel.: (937) 312-3627
Health Care Srvices
N.A.I.C.S.: 621610

Sharp HealthCare **(2)**
8695 Spectrum Ctr Blvd, San Diego, CA 92123
Tel.: (858) 499-4000
Web Site: https://www.sharp.com
Emp.: 19,000
Hospital Owner & Operator
N.A.I.C.S.: 622110
Dede Alpert *(Vice Chm)*
Lori Moore *(Chm)*
Regina A. Petty *(Sec)*
Alison J. Fleury *(Sr VP-Bus Dev)*
Trisha Khaleghi *(CEO-Sharp Mary Birch Hospital & Sr VP)*
Bill Littlejohn *(CEO-Sharp HealthCare Foundation & Sr VP)*
Jim Nuckols *(CMO & Sr VP-Mktg & Comm)*
Tim Smith *(CEO-Sharp Memorial Hospital & Sr VP)*
Pablo Velez *(CEO-Sharp Chula Vista Medical Center & Sr VP)*
Staci Dickerson *(CFO & Sr VP-Fin)*
Amy A. Adome *(Sr VP-Clinical Effectiveness)*
John R. LeMoine *(Chief Medical Information Officer)*
Susan Stone *(CEO-Sharp Coronado Hospital & Sr VP)*
Stacey Hrountas *(CEO-Sharp Rees-Stealy Medical Centers)*
Melissa Hayden Cook *(Pres & CEO-Sharp Health Plan)*
Christopher D. Howard *(Pres & CEO)*
Jennifer Chatfield *(Mgr-PR & Comm)*
John Cihomsky *(VP-PR & Comm)*
Pam Hardy *(Mgr-Internal Comm & Editorial Strategy)*
Rick L. Grossman *(Gen Counsel & Sr VP)*
Lisa Allen *(Sr VP-HR & Talent Mgmt)*
Brett McClain *(COO & Exec VP)*
Michael Reagin *(Chief Information & Innovation Officer & Sr VP)*

Southeastern Physician Associates, LLC **(2)**
265 Brookview Centre Way Ste 400, Knoxville, TN 37919
Tel.: (800) 342-2898
Web Site: http://www.teamhealth.com
Emergency Care Services
N.A.I.C.S.: 621493

Southwest Florida Emergency Management, LLC **(2)**

14050 NW 14th St #190, Sunrise, FL 33323
Tel.: (954) 475-1300
Emergency Care Services
N.A.I.C.S.: 621493

Spectrum Healthcare Services, Inc. **(2)**
9850 Von Allmen Ct Ste 201, Louisville, KY 40241
Tel.: (502) 454-5250
Web Site: https://www.spectrumhcs.com
Medical Staffing Services
N.A.I.C.S.: 561311
Linda Greer *(Pres & CEO)*

Spectrum Primary Care, Inc. **(2)**
12647 Olive Blvd Ste 600, Saint Louis, MO 63141
Tel.: (314) 744-4100
Web Site: https://www.spectrumhealth.com
Healthcare Staffing Services
N.A.I.C.S.: 561311

Team Health, LLC **(2)**
265 Brookview Ctr Way Ste 400, Knoxville, TN 37919
Tel.: (865) 693-1000
Web Site: http://www.teamhealth.com
Health Care Staffing & Management Services
N.A.I.C.S.: 541611

Subsidiary (Domestic):

After Hours Pediatrics, Inc. **(3)**
3294 Cove Bend Dr, Tampa, FL 33613
Tel.: (813) 910-8888
Web Site:
   http://www.afterhourspediatrics.com
Medical Emergency Services
N.A.I.C.S.: 621999
Kim Kirsch *(Mgr-HR)*
Lou Romig *(Dir-Medical)*
Gregory Levy *(Dir-Ops-After Hours Pediatrics Urgent Care)*

The Blackstone Group Denmark ApS **(1)**
Tuborg Boulevard 12 3rd Floor, Hellerup, 2900, Copenhagen, Denmark
Tel.: (45) 36944057
Financial Investment Services
N.A.I.C.S.: 523999

The Blackstone Group International Limited **(1)**
40 Berkeley Square, London, W1J 5AL, United Kingdom
Tel.: (44) 2074514000
Web Site: http://www.blackstone.com
Privater Equity Firm
N.A.I.C.S.: 523999

Holding (Domestic):

Alliance Automotive Holding Limited **(2)**
Roydsdale House Roydsdale Way, Euroway Trading Estate, Bradford, BD4 6SE, United Kingdom
Tel.: (44) 1274 654 600
Web Site:
   http://www.allianceautomotivegroup.eu
Holding Company; Automotive Parts Distr
N.A.I.C.S.: 551112
Alistair Brown *(Co-Founder)*
Angelo Arnone *(Gen Mgr)*
Steve Richardson *(Gen Mgr)*
Jean-Jacques Lafont *(Co-Founder & Exec Chm)*
Franck Baduel *(CEO)*
Thomas Tabiasco *(CFO)*
Christian Schmolke *(CIO)*
Sylvain Lemercier *(Chief Pur Officer)*
Peter Meyer *(Dir-Supply Chain)*
Asireh Moradkhani *(Mgr-HR)*

Subsidiary (Domestic):

Apec Limited **(3)**
Unit G2 Titan Road, Bristol, BS34 6FD, United Kingdom **(100%)**
Tel.: (44) 1174288100
Web Site: https://apecautomotive.co.uk
Braking Components Distr
N.A.I.C.S.: 336340

BTN Turbocharger Service Limited **(3)**

Blackstone Inc.—(Continued)

Bridge House 3 Timothys Bridge Rd,
Stratford-upon-Avon, CV37 9NQ, Warwick-
shire, United Kingdom **(100%)**
Tel.: (44) 1895466666
Web Site: http://www.btnturbo.com
Turbochargers Distr
N.A.I.C.S.: 423730
Jamie Hall *(Gen Mgr)*
Rachel Birch *(Mgr-Comml)*

Ferraris Piston Service Ltd. **(3)**
Bridge House 3 Timothys Bridge Road
Stratford Enterprise Park, Stratford-upon-
Avon, CV37 9NQ, Warwickshire, United
Kingdom
Tel.: (44) 1789 413 000
Web Site: http://www.fpsdistribution.com
Automotive Parts Wholesale Distr
N.A.I.C.S.: 423120
Steve Richardson *(Mng Dir)*
Angelo Arnone *(Mng Dir)*

Subsidiary (Domestic):

FPS Distribution Limited **(4)**
5 Parkway Rise, Sheffield, S9 4WQ, War-
wickshire, United Kingdom
Tel.: (44) 3300021161
Web Site: http://fpsdistribution.com
Holding Company;Automotive Parts Distr
N.A.I.C.S.: 423120
Garry Parkinson *(Dir-Sls)*

Subsidiary (Domestic):

GROUPAUTO UK & Ireland Ltd. **(3)**
Roydsdale House Roydsdale Way, Euroway
Trading Estate, Bradford, BD4 6SE, United
Kingdom
Tel.: (44) 1274654600
Web Site: http://www.groupauto.co.uk
Automobile Parts Distr
N.A.I.C.S.: 423120
Gill Miles *(Office Mgr)*
Maria McCullough *(Mgr-Network)*
Caroline Hoy *(Coord-Garage Network)*
Jackie Saville *(Coord-Garage Network Trng)*
Michelle McGowan *(Mgr-Bureau)*
Cade Galvin *(Head-Fin)*
Karen Martin *(Sls Dir)*
Carol Coulthard *(Coord-Garage Network)*
James Hutchings *(Mgr-Bus Dev-South West
& South Wales)*
Mark Johnson *(Mgr-Bus Dev-South & South
East)*
Neil Clark *(Mgr-Bus Dev-North West &
Northern Ireland)*
Neil Rayner *(Controller-Fin)*

Joint Venture (Non-US):

AlphaVille Urbanismo S.A. **(2)**
United Nations Avenue 8501, Pinheiros,
Sao Paulo, 05425-070, Brazil
Tel.: (55) 1130305100
Web Site:
http://www.alphavilleurbanismo.com.br
Urban Residential Development & Building
N.A.I.C.S.: 925120

Holding (Non-US):

**Antipca Restaurant Group
Limited** **(2)**
6 Antares Place, Rosedale, Auckland, 0632,
New Zealand
Tel.: (64) 800425464
Web Site: http://www.burgerking.co.nz
Holding Company; Fast Food Restaurants
Franchisor & Operator
N.A.I.C.S.: 551112
Michelle Alexander *(CEO)*

Anticipa Real Estate, SLU **(2)**
Polig Ind Mas Mateu C/ Roure 6-8 4,
08820, El Prat de Llobregat, Spain
Tel.: (34) 900102748
Web Site: http://www.anticipa.com
Emp.: 400
Real Estate Manangement Services
N.A.I.C.S.: 531210
Eduard Mendiluce *(CEO)*

Joint Venture (Non-US):

Armacell GmbH **(2)**
Robert-Bosch-Strasse 10, 48153, Munster,
Germany
Tel.: (49) 25176030

Web Site: https://www.local.armacell.com
Emp.: 715
Engineered Foam Rubber & Technical Insu-
lation Product Mfr
N.A.I.C.S.: 326150

Subsidiary (Non-US):

**Blackstone Advisors India Private
Limited** **(2)**
Express Towers Nariman Point, Mumbai,
400 021, Maharashtra, India
Tel.: (91) 226 752 8500
Web Site: http://www.blackstone.com
Sales Range: $25-49.9 Million
Emp.: 35
Investment Advisory Services
N.A.I.C.S.: 523940

Subsidiary (Domestic):

**Blackstone Property Management
Limited** **(2)**
40 Berkeley Square, London, W1J 5AL,
United Kingdom
Tel.: (44) 207 451 4000
Web Site: http://www.blackstone.com
Emp.: 50
Financial Advisory Services
N.A.I.C.S.: 523940

Holding (Domestic):

Clarion Events Ltd. **(2)**
Fulham Green 69-79 Fulham High Street,
London, SW6 3JW, United Kingdom
Tel.: (44) 2073847700
Web Site: http://www.clarionevents.com
Exhibition Shows & Trade Fair Organizers
N.A.I.C.S.: 561920
Simon Kimble *(Chm)*
Richard Johnson *(CFO)*
Adam Ford *(COO)*
Chris Gallon *(CEO)*

Subsidiary (Domestic):

IGaming Business Limited **(3)**
Fulham Green Bedford House 69 - 79 Ful-
ham High Street, London, SW6 3JW,
United Kingdom
Tel.: (44) 2073848269
Web Site: http://www.igamingbusiness.com
Emp.: 160
Information Publishing Services
N.A.I.C.S.: 513199
Richard Linn *(Dir-Publ)*
Stephen Carter *(Dir-Editorial)*
Guy Parsons *(Editor-Production)*

Holding (Non-US):

**Comstar Automotive Technologies Pvt
Ltd** **(2)**
Keelakaranai Village Malrosapuram Post
Maraimalai Nagar, Chengalpattu, 603 204,
India
Tel.: (91) 44 37473700
Web Site: http://www.comstarauto.com
Alternators & Starter Motors Mfr
N.A.I.C.S.: 336390

Plant (US):

Comstar Automotive LLC USA **(3)**
900 Industrial Dr, Tecumseh, MI 49286
Tel.: (517) 266-2445
Web Site: http://www.comstarauto.com
Automobile Parts Distr
N.A.I.C.S.: 423120

Subsidiary (Domestic):

**GSO Capital Partners International
LLP** **(2)**
40 Berkeley Square, London, W1J 5AL,
United Kingdom
Tel.: (44) 2077589000
Web Site: http://www.gso.com
Sales Range: $25-49.9 Million
Emp.: 25
Financial Advisory Services
N.A.I.C.S.: 523940

Holding (Non-US):

Global Sources Ltd. **(2)**
22/F Vita Tower, 29 Wong Chuk Hang
Road, Hong Kong, China (Hong Kong)
Tel.: (852) 81212000

Web Site: http://www.globalsources.com
Rev.: $157,667,000
Assets: $271,452,000
Liabilities: $105,475,000
Net Worth: $165,977,000
Earnings: $18,369,000
Emp.: 1,095
Fiscal Year-end: 12/31/2016
Online Business-to-Business Marketplace
for Import Export Trade
N.A.I.C.S.: 425120
Hu Wei *(CEO)*
Connie Lai *(CFO)*
Carol Lau *(Sr VP-Client Svc, Sls Support &
Analytics)*
John Kao *(VP-Hong Kong Show & Over-
seas Show)*
Wendy Lai *(VP-Global Sources Exhibitions)*
Coral Deng *(Head-HR)*

Joint Venture (Non-US):

Leica Camera AG **(2)**
Am Leitz-Park 5, 35578, Wetzlar,
Germany **(45%)**
Tel.: (49) 644120800
Web Site: https://leica-camera.com
Sales Range: $350-399.9 Million
Photography Equipment Hunting Lense
Projector Laser Rangefinder Binocular &
Telescope Mfr
N.A.I.C.S.: 333310
Andreas Kaufmann *(Chm-Supervisory Bd)*
Matthias Harsch *(Chm-Exec Bd & CEO)*

Subsidiary (US):

Leica Camera, Inc. **(3)**
1 Pearl Ct Unit A, Allendale, NJ 07401-1610
Tel.: (201) 995-0051
Web Site: http://www.leica-camera.com
Sales Range: $25-49.9 Million
Emp.: 30
Distr of Cameras, Binoculars & Accessories
N.A.I.C.S.: 333310
Matthias Harsch *(Chm-Exec Bd)*
Marita Paasch *(Member-Exec Bd)*
Ronald Marcel Peters *(Member-Exec Bd)*

Holding (Non-US):

**Lombard International Assurance
SA** **(2)**
4 Rue Lou Hemmer, 1748, Luxembourg,
Luxembourg
Tel.: (352) 3461911
Web Site:
http://www.lombardinternational.com
Emp.: 500
Financial Management Consulting Services
N.A.I.C.S.: 541611

One Five One Property Pty Ltd. **(2)**
Level 6 151 Castlereagh St, Sydney, 2000,
NSW, Australia
Tel.: (61) 282576600
Web Site: https://151property.com.au
Real Estate Investment & Management
Services
N.A.I.C.S.: 525990
Ramsey Fodda *(Gen Mgr-Leasing & Retail)*
Justin Mitchell *(CFO)*

Subsidiary (Non-US):

**Valad Property Holdings (UK)
Limited** **(3)**
Europa House 20 Esplanade, Scarborough,
YO11 2AQ, N Yorkshire, United Kingdom
Tel.: (44) 1723500208
Web Site: http://www.valad.eu
Real Estate Investment Trust
N.A.I.C.S.: 525990

Holding (Non-US):

Schenck Process Holding GmbH **(2)**
Pallaswiesenstrasse 100, 64293, Darm-
stadt, Germany
Tel.: (49) 615115310
Web Site: https://www.schenckprocess.com
Industrial Weighing, Feeding, Screening &
Automation Measuring Technologies
N.A.I.C.S.: 334513
Thomas Spitzenpfeil *(CFO)*

Subsidiary (Non-US):

Baker Perkins Holdings Limited **(3)**
Manor Drive Paston Parkway, Peterbor-

ough, PE4 7AP, United Kingdom
Tel.: (44) 1733283000
Web Site: https://www.bakerperkins.com
Sales Range: $75-99.9 Million
Emp.: 350
Food Machinery Mfr
N.A.I.C.S.: 333241

Subsidiary (US):

Baker Perkins Inc. **(4)**
3223 Kraft Ave SE, Grand Rapids, MI
49512-2027
Tel.: (616) 784-3111
Web Site: http://www.apvbaker.com
Sales Range: $10-24.9 Million
Emp.: 50
Food Industry Machinery Mfr
N.A.I.C.S.: 333241

Subsidiary (Non-US):

**Bracker GmbH Innovativer
Maschinenbau** **(4)**
St Quentin Fallavier Str 1, 63579, Freiger-
icht, Germany
Tel.: (49) 6055934510
Web Site: https://www.bracker-imb.de
Industrial Machinery & Equipment Distr
N.A.I.C.S.: 423830

Subsidiary (Non-US):

Clyde Process Ltd. **(3)**
Unit 6-9 Railway Court Off Ten Pound Walk,
Lakeside, Doncaster, DN4 5FB, South York-
shire, United Kingdom **(100%)**
Tel.: (44) 1302321313
Web Site: http://www.clydeprocess.com
Pneumatic & Vacuum Materials Conveyanc-
ing Systems Mfr
N.A.I.C.S.: 333922
Andy Johnson *(Engr-Commissioning)*
Martin Chisholm *(Dir-Technical)*

Subsidiary (US):

Schenck Process LLC **(3)**
7901 NW 107th Ter, Kansas City, MO
64153
Tel.: (816) 891-9300
Web Site: http://www.schenckprocess.com
Bulk Solids Handling Products, Systems &
Controls Mfr
N.A.I.C.S.: 333248

Stock Equipment Company Inc. **(3)**
16940 Chillicothe Rd, Chagrin Falls, OH
44023-4326
Tel.: (440) 543-6000
Web Site: http://www.schenckprocess.com
Materials Handling Equipment
N.A.I.C.S.: 333922

Subsidiary (Domestic):

Stock Fairfield Corporation **(4)**
1213 Cheney Ave, Marion, OH 43302
Tel.: (740) 387-3327
Web Site:
http://www.fairfieldengineering.com
Sales Range: $50-74.9 Million
Emp.: 1,700
Material Handling & Conveying Systems Mfr
N.A.I.C.S.: 423610

Subsidiary (Non-US):

Stock Redler Limited **(4)**
Unit 3 Alpha Court Capitol Park, Thorne,
Doncaster, DN8 5TZ, United Kingdom
Tel.: (44) 1302321313
Web Site: http://www.schenckprocess.com
Materials Handling Equipment
N.A.I.C.S.: 333922
Nicholas Jones *(Sec)*

Subsidiary (Non-US):

**The Blackstone Group (HK)
Limited** **(2)**
Two International Finance Centre Suite 901
8 Finance Street, Central, Hong Kong,
China (Hong Kong)
Tel.: (852) 36568600
Financial Advisory Services
N.A.I.C.S.: 523940
Liping Zhang *(Sr Mng Dir & Chm-Greater
China)*

The Blackstone Group Germany GmbH (2)
Bockenheimer Anlage 46, 60322, Frankfurt am Main, Germany
Tel.: (49) 2118628400
Financial Advisory Services
N.A.I.C.S.: 523940

The Blackstone Group International Partners LLP (2)
278 Boulevard, Saint-Germain, 75007, Paris, France
Tel.: (33) 170982330
Investment Advisory Services
N.A.I.C.S.: 523940

The Blackstone Group Japan K.K. (2)
10F Marunouchi Building 2-4-1, Marunouchi Chiyoda-ku, Tokyo, 100-6310, Japan
Tel.: (81) 345778400
Emp.: 30
Investment Advisory Services
N.A.I.C.S.: 523940

Holding (Domestic):

The Office Group Limited (2)
179 Great Portland Street, Marylebone, London, W1W 5PL, United Kingdom
Tel.: (44) 2033558543
Web Site: http://www.theofficegroup.com
Commercial Office Space, Meeting Room & Event Venue Developer, Operator & Lessor
N.A.I.C.S.: 531120

Therma Corporation (1)
1601 Las Plumas Ave, San Jose, CA 95133
Tel.: (408) 347-3400
Web Site: http://www.therma.com
Plumbing Contractor
N.A.I.C.S.: 238220
Greg Conn (Dir-Ops)
Mike Fisher (Pres)
Joseph C. Parisi Jr. (Chm)

Subsidiary (Domestic):

Gilbert Mechanical Contractors, LLC (2)
5251 W 74th St, Edina, MN 55439
Tel.: (952) 835-3810
Web Site: http://www.gilbertmech.com
Sales Range: $50-74.9 Million
Emp.: 150
Electronic Services
N.A.I.C.S.: 238210
P. Dan Gilbert (Pres)
John Gorman (VP)
Ed Dahlgren (VP)

VarcoMac LLC (2)
1360 Blair Dr Ste A, Odenton, MD 21113
Tel.: (301) 317-7900
Web Site: http://www.varcomac.com
Sales Range: $25-49.9 Million
Emp.: 150
Electrical Contracting Services
N.A.I.C.S.: 238210
Gregory Wisor (Mgr-Pur)
Shane Wilemon (Pres)

Tradesmen International, LLC (1)
9760 Shepard Rd, Macedonia, OH 44056
Tel.: (440) 276-0826
Web Site: https://www.tradesmeninternational.com
Employment Agencies
N.A.I.C.S.: 561311
Matt McClone (VP-Workforce Dev)
Marty Wick (CEO)
Patrick Flynn (Gen Counsel & VP)
Jesse Klebba (CIO)
Chad Arnold (VP-Strategic Accounts)

Vungle, Inc. (1)
1255 Battery St Ste 500, San Francisco, CA 94111
Tel.: (415) 800-1400
Web Site: http://www.vungle.com
Emp.: 263
Media Representatives
N.A.I.C.S.: 541840
Hammond Guerin (Head-Data Science)

Subsidiary (Domestic):

TreSensa Inc. (2)
443 Park Ave S Ste 601, New York, NY 10016

Tel.: (646) 481-9571
Web Site: http://www.tresensa.com
Software Publisher
N.A.I.C.S.: 513210
Rakesh Raju (Co-Founder & CTO)

BLACKSTONE LONG-SHORT CREDIT INCOME FUND
C/O Gso Capital Partners Lp 345 Park Ave, New York, NY 10154
Tel.: (212) 503-2100
BGX—(NYSE)
Investment Management Service
N.A.I.C.S.: 525990
Daniel H. Smith Jr. (Chm, Pres & CEO)

BLACKSTONE SENIOR FLOATING RATE 2027 TERM FUND
C/O Gso Capital Partners Lp 345 Park Ave, New York, NY 10154
Tel.: (212) 503-2100
BSL—(NYSE)
Investment Management Service
N.A.I.C.S.: 525990
Daniel H. Smith Jr. (Chm, Pres & CEO)

BLACKWELL 3D CONSTRUCTION CORP
701 S Carson Str Ste 200, Carson City, NV 89701
Tel.: (702) 718-0807
BDCC—(OTCIQ)
Power Generation Services
N.A.I.C.S.: 221112

BLADE AIR MOBILITY, INC.
31 Hudson Yards 14th Fl, New York, NY 10001
Tel.: (212) 967-1009   DE
Web Site: https://www.blade.com
Year Founded: 2014
BLDE—(NASDAQ)
Rev.: $146,120,000
Assets: $325,025,000
Liabilities: $50,536,000
Net Worth: $274,489,000
Earnings: $27,260,000
Emp.: 246
Fiscal Year-end: 12/31/22
Schedules Passenger Air Transportation
N.A.I.C.S.: 481111
Robert S. Wiesenthal (CEO)
Amir M. Cohen (Chief Acctg Officer)
William A. Heyburn (CFO & Head-Corporate Development)
Eric L. Affeldt (Chm)
Melissa Tomkiel (Pres & Gen Counsel)

Subsidiaries:

BLADE Urban Air Mobility, Inc. (1)
55 Hudson Yards 14th Fl, New York, NY 10001
Web Site: https://www.blade.com
Air Mobility Platform
N.A.I.C.S.: 513199
Eric Affeldt (Chm)

Subsidiary (Domestic):

Trinity Air Medical, Inc. (2)
1437 W Auto Dr, Tempe, AZ 85284
Web Site: http://www.trinityairmedical.com
Transportation Services
N.A.I.C.S.: 541614
Seth Bacon (Founder, CEO & Mng Partner)
Scott Wunsch (COO)
Ted Becerra (CFO)
Andrew Marreel (Dir-Bus Dev)
Jessica Morgan (Mgr-Payroll)

BLEND LABS, INC.
415 Kearny St, San Francisco, CA 94108
Tel.: (650) 550-4810   DE

Web Site: https://blend.com
BLND—(NYSE)
Rev.: $235,201,000
Assets: $432,764,000
Liabilities: $309,592,000
Net Worth: $123,172,000
Earnings: ($768,610,000)
Emp.: 1,546
Fiscal Year-end: 12/31/22
Software Publr
N.A.I.C.S.: 513210
Amir Jafari (Principal Fin Officer & Head-Admin & Fin)
Nima Ghamsari (Co-Founder & Chm)
Timothy J. Mayopoulos (Pres)
Erin James Collard (Co-Founder)
Jonathan Chan (Controller)
Dean Klinger (Head-Revenue)
Oxana Tkach (Principal Acctg Officer & Controller)

BLEUACACIA LTD.
500 5th Ave, New York, NY 10110
Tel.: (212) 935-5599   Ky
Web Site: https://www.acacia.blue
Year Founded: 2021
BLEU—(NASDAQ)
Assets: $279,704,543
Liabilities: $289,475,957
Net Worth: ($9,771,414)
Earnings: $2,505,451
Emp.: 4
Fiscal Year-end: 12/31/22
Investment Services
N.A.I.C.S.: 523999
Jide Zeitlin (Co-Chm & Co-CEO)
Lew Frankfort (Co-Chm & Co-CEO)
Charles McGuigan (Pres & COO)
Thomas Northover (Exec Dir)
Kat Peeler (Dir)

BLINK CHARGING CO.
605 Lincoln Rd 5th Fl, Miami Beach, FL 33139
Tel.: (305) 521-0200   NV
Web Site: https://www.blinkcharging.com
BLNK—(NASDAQ)
Rev.: $61,139,000
Assets: $362,542,000
Liabilities: $101,585,000
Net Worth: $260,957,000
Earnings: ($91,560,000)
Emp.: 564
Fiscal Year-end: 12/31/22
Electric Car Charging Stations
N.A.I.C.S.: 334419
Michael P. Rama (CFO)
Harjinder Bhade (CTO)
Rebecca Gutierrez (VP-Mktg & PR)
Vitale Stelea (VP-IR)
Tony Sargent (Sr VP)
Amy Dobrikova (VP)
Michael Uribe (Gen Mgr)
Alex Calnan (Mng Dir)
Yogi Rajpal (Sr VP)
Michael C. Battaglia (Pres & CEO)
Michael D. Farkas (Chm)

Subsidiaries:

Blink Mobility, LLC (1)
555 West 5th St, Los Angeles, CA 90013
Tel.: (888) 998-2546
Web Site: https://blinkmobility.com
Electric Car Charging Stations
N.A.I.C.S.: 334419

Subsidiary (Domestic):

Envoy Technologies, Inc. (2)
8575 Washington Blvd, Culver City, CA 90323
Tel.: (732) 636-4700
Web Site: https://www.envoythere.com
Custom Computer Programming Services
N.A.I.C.S.: 541511
Aric Ohana (Co/Co-Founder, Co-Pres & CEO)
Drew Hopkins (COO)

Joe Prospero (Dir-Community)
Anna Hanley (Dir-Fleet Ops)
Sky Hirschkron (Dir-Customer Service)
Rod Bertone (Dir-Sales)
Marilyn Mota (Mgr-Marketing)

CCGI / Mall of America, LLC (1)
60 E Broadway, Bloomington, MN 55425
Tel.: (952) 883-8800
Web Site: http://www.mallofamerica.com
Emp.: 11,000
Shopping Mall Operator
N.A.I.C.S.: 531120

U-Go Stations Inc. (1)
1818 Market St - 13th Fl, Philadelphia, PA 19103
Web Site: https://www.ugostations.com
Electric Vehicle Charging Services
N.A.I.C.S.: 811111

BLOCK CAPITAL CORP
3637 4th St N Ste 330, Saint Petersburg, FL 33704
Tel.: (727) 498-8514   NV
Year Founded: 2004
IFXY—(OTCIQ)
Emp.: 4
Smart Grid Technology
N.A.I.C.S.: 541519
Sam Talari (Chm)

BLOCK, INC.
1955 Broadway Ste 600, Oakland, CA 94612
Tel.: (415) 375-3176   DE
Web Site: https://www.squareup.com
Year Founded: 2009
SQ—(NYSE)
Rev.: $21,915,623,000
Assets: $34,069,893,000
Liabilities: $15,377,057,000
Net Worth: $18,692,836,000
Earnings: $9,772,000
Emp.: 12,985
Fiscal Year-end: 12/31/23
Electronic Payment Processing Services
N.A.I.C.S.: 522320
Ajmere Dale (Chief Acctg Officer)
Chrysty Esperanza (Interim Chief Legal Officer, Gen Counsel & Sec)
Jim M. McKelvey (Co-Founder)
Jack Dorsey (Co-Founder & Chm)

Subsidiaries:

Afterpay Limited (1)
406 Collin St, Melbourne, 3000, VIC, Australia
Tel.: (61) 1300100729
Rev.: $363,120,000
Assets: $1,124,986,999
Liabilities: $463,118,573
Net Worth: $661,868,426
Earnings: ($15,985,957)
Emp.: 650
Fiscal Year-end: 06/30/2020
Holding Company
N.A.I.C.S.: 551112

Subsidiary (Domestic):

Afterpay Holdings Limited (2)
Level 5 406 Collins Street, Melbourne, 3000, VIC, Australia   (100%)
Tel.: (61) 1800286824
Web Site: https://www.afterpaytouch.com
Online Payment Solutions
N.A.I.C.S.: 522320

Touchcorp Limited (2)
Level 5 406 Collins Street, Melbourne, 3000, VIC, Australia   (100%)
Tel.: (61) 1800286824
Web Site: http://www.afterpaytouch.com
Mobile Payment Applications, Electronic Point-of-Sale Systems, Automated Teller Machines & Self-Service Kiosks Network Operator
N.A.I.C.S.: 518210

Subsidiary (Domestic):

Touch Holdings Pty. Limited (3)

Block, Inc.—(Continued)

Level 16 380 La Trobe Street, Melbourne, 3000, VIC, Australia **(100%)**
Tel.: (61) 800286824
Web Site: http://www.afterpaytouch.com
Holding Company
N.A.I.C.S.: 551112

Subsidiary (Domestic):

Touch Networks Pty. Ltd. **(4)**
Level 16 380 La Trobe Street, Melbourne, 3000, VIC, Australia **(100%)**
Tel.: (61) 390186800
Web Site: http://afterpaytouch.com
Mobile Payment Applications, Electronic Point-of-Sale Systems, Automated Teller Machines & Self-Service Kiosks Network Operator
N.A.I.C.S.: 518210

Aspiro AB **(1)**
Stora Varvsgatan 6 A, SE-211 19, Malmo, Sweden
Tel.: (46) 406300300
Holding Company; Hosted TV & Music Streaming Services
N.A.I.C.S.: 551112
Chris Hart *(CFO)*

Square Canada, Inc. **(1)**
5000 Yonge Street Suite 1501, Toronto, M2G 7E9, ON, Canada
Tel.: (416) 204-0032
Digital Payment Services
N.A.I.C.S.: 522320

Stitch Labs, Inc. **(1)**
461 2nd St Unit T251, San Francisco, CA 94107
Tel.: (700) 002-9114
Web Site: http://www.stitchlabs.com
Business Support Services
N.A.I.C.S.: 561499

Verse Payments Lithuania UAB **(1)**
Workland G9 Gedimino pr 9 4th floor, 01105, Vilnius, Lithuania
Tel.: (370) 932204859
Web Site: https://verse.me
Financial Services
N.A.I.C.S.: 522320

Weebly, Inc. **(1)**
1455 Market St Ste 600, San Francisco, CA 94103
Tel.: (844) 493-3259
Web Site: http://www.weebly.com
Software Publisher
N.A.I.C.S.: 513210

BLOCKCHAIN MOON ACQUISITION CORP.
4651 Salisbury Rd Ste 400, Jacksonville, FL 32256
Tel.: (424) 262-6097 DE
Year Founded: 2021
BMAQ—(NASDAQ)
Rev.: $1,316,544
Assets: $18,754,214
Liabilities: $27,446,530
Net Worth: ($8,692,316)
Earnings: ($4,287,805)
Emp.: 2
Fiscal Year-end: 12/31/22
Investment Services
N.A.I.C.S.: 523999
Enzo A. Villani *(Chm & CEO)*
Wes Levitt *(CFO)*

BLOCKHOLD CAPITAL CORPORATION
9350 Wilshire Blvd Ste 203, Beverly Hills, CA 90212
Tel.: (310) 819-4637 NV
Web Site: http://www.momscorner.com
Year Founded: 2010
BHLD—(OTCIQ)
Emp.: 2
Mom Oriented Community Website
N.A.I.C.S.: 513199

BLONDER TONGUE LABORATORIES, INC.
1 Jake Brown Rd, Old Bridge, NJ 08857
Tel.: (732) 679-4000 DE
Web Site: https://www.blondertongue.com
Year Founded: 1950
BDRL—(OTCQB)
Rev.: $18,115,000
Assets: $15,005,000
Liabilities: $13,931,000
Net Worth: $1,074,000
Earnings: ($2,920,000)
Emp.: 67
Fiscal Year-end: 12/31/22
Electronics & Systems Equipment Mfr, Designer & Supplier for the Cable Television Industry
N.A.I.C.S.: 334220
Steven Latus Shea *(Chm)*
Robert J. Palle Jr. *(Pres & CEO)*

Subsidiaries:

Blonder Tongue International Inc. **(1)**
1 Jake Brown Rd, Old Bridge, NJ 08857
Tel.: (732) 679-4000
Web Site: http://www.blondertongue.com
Sales Range: $25-49.9 Million
Emp.: 120
TV Signal Distribution Equipment
N.A.I.C.S.: 423610

R. L. Drake Holdings, LLC **(1)**
710 Pleasant Valley Dr, Springboro, OH 45066
Tel.: (937) 746-4556
Web Site: http://www.rldrake.com
Sales Range: $10-24.9 Million
Emp.: 12
Cable Television Transmission & Receiving Equipment Mfr
N.A.I.C.S.: 334220

R. L. Drake, LLC **(1)**
710 Pleasant Vly Dr, Springboro, OH 45066
Tel.: (937) 746-4556
Web Site: http://www.rldrake.com
Sales Range: $10-24.9 Million
Emp.: 12
Electronic Communications Equipment Developer & Mfr
N.A.I.C.S.: 334220

BLOOM ENERGY CORPORATION
4353 N 1st St, San Jose, CA 95134
Tel.: (408) 543-1500 DE
Web Site: https://www.bloomenergy.com
Year Founded: 2001
BE—(NYSE)
Rev.: $1,199,125,000
Assets: $1,946,627,000
Liabilities: $1,567,811,000
Net Worth: $378,816,000
Earnings: $315,086,000
Emp.: 2,530
Fiscal Year-end: 12/31/22
Power Generation Equipment Mfr & Distr
N.A.I.C.S.: 334413
K. R. Sridhar *(Founder, Chm & CEO)*
Shawn Soderberg *(Gen Counsel, Sec & Exec VP)*
Sonja M. Wilkerson *(Chief People Officer & Exec VP)*
Daniel Berenbaum *(CFO)*
Carl Cottuli *(Sr VP)*
Ravi Prasher *(CTO)*

Subsidiaries:

Bloom Energy (India) Put. Ltd. **(1)**
North Block III Floor IT/BT Park Rajajinagar Industrial Estate, Bengaluru, 560 044, India
Tel.: (91) 7203040225
Electric Power Distribution Services
N.A.I.C.S.: 221122

Bloom Energy (India) Pvt. Ltd. **(1)**
247 B-block 7th Floor LBS Marg Gandhina-

gar, Vikhroli West, Mumbai, 400083, India
Tel.: (91) 7203040225
Semiconductor & Related Device Mfr
N.A.I.C.S.: 334413
M. K. Premkumar *(Gen Mgr)*

BLOOMIN' BRANDS, INC.
2202 NW Shore Blvd Ste 500, Tampa, FL 33607
Tel.: (813) 282-1225 DE
Web Site: https://www.bloominbrands.com
Year Founded: 2006
BLMN—(NASDAQ)
Rev.: $4,671,470,000
Assets: $3,424,081,000
Liabilities: $3,012,078,000
Net Worth: $412,003,000
Earnings: $247,386,000
Emp.: 87,000
Fiscal Year-end: 12/31/23
Holding Company; Restaurants
N.A.I.C.S.: 551112
Christopher Meyer *(CFO & Exec VP)*
Cathie Koch *(Grp VP-Corp Affairs)*
William Michael Healy *(CFO & Exec VP-Global Bus Dev)*
Annette Rodriguez *(Sr VP-Development & Franchising)*
Elizabeth Daly *(Dir)*
Astrid Isaacs *(CTO & Sr VP)*
Philip Pace *(Chief Acctg Officer & Sr VP)*
Suzann Trevisan *(Chief HR Officer & Sr VP)*
Suk Singh *(Pres-Aussie Grill)*
Beth Scott *(Pres-Fleming, ', s Prime Steakhouse, and Wine Bar & Sr VP)*
Lissette Gonzalez *(Chief Supply Chain Officer & Chief Ops Excellence Officer & Sr VP)*
Mark Graff *(Pres-Bonefish Grill & Fine Dining, Exec VP & Sr VP)*
Pierre Berenstein *(Chief Customer Officer & Exec VP)*
Pat Hafner *(Pres-Carrabba, ', s Italian Grill, and Aussie Grill)*
Gregg Scarlett *(COO & Exec VP)*

Subsidiaries:

Annapolis Outback, Inc. **(1)**
2207 Forest Dr, Annapolis, MD 21401-3884
Tel.: (410) 266-7229
Web Site: http://www.outback.com
Emp.: 83
Restaurant Operating Services
N.A.I.C.S.: 722511

Bel Air Outback, Inc. **(1)**
607 Bel Air, Bel Air, MD 21014-4325
Tel.: (410) 893-0110
Web Site: http://www.outback.com
Emp.: 84
Restaurant Operating Services
N.A.I.C.S.: 722511

Bloom No.2 Limited **(1)**
Shop 3A Ground Floor Site 4 Whampo Garden Hung Hom, Kowloon, Hong Kong, China (Hong Kong)
Tel.: (852) 27662823
Restaurant Operating Services
N.A.I.C.S.: 722511

Bonefish Grill of Florida, LLC **(1)**
2202 N W Shore Blvd, Tampa, FL 33607-5761
Tel.: (813) 282-1225
Web Site: http://www.bonefishgrill.com
Restaurant Operating Services
N.A.I.C.S.: 722511

Bonefish Grill, LLC **(1)**
3665 Henderson Blvd, Tampa, FL 33609
Tel.: (813) 876-3535
Web Site: https://www.bonefishgrill.com
Restaurant Operators
N.A.I.C.S.: 722511

Bonefish Holdings, LLC **(1)**
726 Kames Hill Rd, Columbia, PA 17512-8424
Tel.: (717) 856-4517

Investment Management Service
N.A.I.C.S.: 523940

Bonefish of Bel Air, LLC **(1)**
696 J Bel Air Rd, Bel Air, MD 21014-4288
Tel.: (410) 420-9113
Web Site: https://www.bonefishgrill.com
Emp.: 50
Restaurant Operating Services
N.A.I.C.S.: 722511

Bonefish of Gaithersburg, Inc. **(1)**
82 Market St, Gaithersburg, MD 20878-6532
Tel.: (240) 631-2401
Web Site: http://www.bonefishgrill.com
Emp.: 30
Restaurant Operating Services
N.A.I.C.S.: 722511
Jacob Vinal *(Mng Partner)*

Bonefish/Centreville, Limited Partnership **(1)**
6315 Multiplex Dr, Centreville, VA 20121-5327
Tel.: (703) 815-7427
Web Site: http://www.bonefishgrill.com
Emp.: 25
Restaurant Operating Services
N.A.I.C.S.: 722511
David Amnathvong *(Mng Partner-Arlington)*

Bonefish/Crescent Springs, Limited Partnership **(1)**
588 Buttermilk Pike, Crescent Springs, KY 41017-1635
Tel.: (859) 426-8666
Web Site: http://www.bonefishgrill.com
Restaurant Operating Services
N.A.I.C.S.: 722511
Nathan Aders *(Mng Partner)*

Bonefish/Fredericksburg, Limited Partnership **(1)**
1779 Carl D Silver Pkwy, Fredericksburg, VA 22401-4964
Tel.: (540) 548-1984
Web Site: http://www.bonefishgrill.com
Restaurant Operating Services
N.A.I.C.S.: 722511
Patrick Fountain *(Mng Partner)*

Bonefish/Greensboro, Limited Partnership **(1)**
2100 Koury Blvd, Greensboro, NC 27407-4959
Tel.: (336) 851-8900
Web Site: http://www.bonefishgrill.com
Emp.: 60
Restaurant Operating Services
N.A.I.C.S.: 722511

Bonefish/Hyde Park, Limited Partnership **(1)**
2737 Madison Rd, Cincinnati, OH 45209-2208
Tel.: (513) 321-5222
Web Site: http://www.bonefishgrill.com
Restaurant Operating Services
N.A.I.C.S.: 722511

Bonefish/Newport News, Limited Partnership **(1)**
340 Oyster Point Rd, Newport News, VA 23602-7174
Tel.: (757) 269-0002
Web Site: http://www.bonefishgrill.com
Restaurant Operating Services
N.A.I.C.S.: 722511

Bonefish/Richmond, Limited Partnership **(1)**
6081 Harbour Park Dr, Midlothian, VA 23112-2160
Tel.: (804) 639-2747
Web Site: http://www.bonefishgrill.com
Emp.: 60
Restaurant Operating Services
N.A.I.C.S.: 722511

Bonefish/Tallahassee, Limited Partnership **(1)**
3491 Thomasville Rd, Tallahassee, FL 32308
Tel.: (850) 297-0460
Web Site: http://www.bonefishgrill.com
Emp.: 60
Fiscal Year-end: 12/31/2014
Restaurant Operating Services

N.A.I.C.S.: 722511

Bonefish/Virginia, Limited Partnership (1)
3333 Virginia Beach Blvd, Virginia Beach, VA 23452-5616
Tel.: (757) 306-3323
Web Site: http://www.bonefishgrill.com
Restaurant Operating Services
N.A.I.C.S.: 722511

CIGI Beverages of Texas, LLC (1)
9100 SW Freeway Ste 220, Houston, TX 77074
Tel.: (813) 282-1225
Restaurant Operating Services
N.A.I.C.S.: 722511

Carrabba's Italian Grill of Howard County, Inc. (1)
4430 Long Gate Pkwy, Ellicott City, MD 21043-5005
Tel.: (410) 461-5200
Web Site: http://www.carrabbas.com
Restaurant Operating Services
N.A.I.C.S.: 722511

Carrabba's Italian Grill of Overlea, Inc. (1)
7600 Belair Rd, Baltimore, MD 21236-4088
Tel.: (410) 661-5444
Web Site: http://www.carrabbas.com
Restaurant Operating Services
N.A.I.C.S.: 722511

Carrabba's Italian Grill, LLC (1)
2202 N W Shore Blvd Fl 5, Tampa, FL 33607
Tel.: (813) 282-1225
Web Site: http://www.carrabbas.com
Sales Range: $25-49.9 Million
Emp.: 700
Casual Dining Italian Restaurants
N.A.I.C.S.: 722511

Carrabba's of Germantown, Inc. (1)
19935 Century Blvd, Germantown, MD 20874-7120
Tel.: (240) 686-1100
Web Site: http://www.carrabbas.com
Restaurant Operating Services
N.A.I.C.S.: 722511

Carrabba's of Ocean City, Inc. (1)
12728 Ocean Gateway, Ocean City, MD 21842-9823
Tel.: (410) 213-0037
Web Site: http://www.carrabbas.com
Restaurant Operating Services
N.A.I.C.S.: 722511

Carrabba's of Pasadena, Inc. (1)
8030 Ritchie Hwy, Pasadena, MD 21122-1084
Tel.: (410) 863-5960
Web Site: http://www.carrabbas.com
Emp.: 40
Restaurant Operating Services
N.A.I.C.S.: 722511

Carrabba's of Waldorf, Inc. (1)
3754 Crain Hwy, Waldorf, MD 20602
Tel.: (301) 645-0094
Web Site: http://www.carrabbas.com
Restaurant Operating Services
N.A.I.C.S.: 722511

Carrabba's/Cool Springs, Limited Partnership (1)
553 Cool Springs Blvd, Franklin, TN 37067-7253
Tel.: (615) 778-9111
Web Site: http://www.carrabbas.com
Restaurant Operating Services
N.A.I.C.S.: 722511

Carrabba's/Deerfield Township, Limited Partnership (1)
5152 Merten Dr, Mason, OH 45040
Tel.: (513) 339-0900
Web Site: http://www.carrabbas.com
Emp.: 78
Restaurant Operating Services
N.A.I.C.S.: 722511

Carrabba's/Green Hills, Limited Partnership (1)
2110 Green Hills Vlg Dr, Nashville, TN 37215-2601
Tel.: (615) 463-3000

Web Site: http://www.carrabbas.com
Emp.: 45
Restaurant Operating Services
N.A.I.C.S.: 722511

Carrabba's/Lexington, Limited Partnership (1)
1881 Plaudit Pl, Lexington, KY 40509
Tel.: (859) 264-8395
Web Site: http://www.carrabbas.com
Restaurant Operating Services
N.A.I.C.S.: 722511

Carrabba's/Miami Beach, Limited Partnership (1)
9231 W Flagler St, Miami, FL 33172
Tel.: (305) 226-9430
Web Site: http://www.carrabbas.com
Restaurant Operating Services
N.A.I.C.S.: 722511

Fleming's Prime Steakhouse & Wine Bar
4322 W Boy Scout Blvd, Tampa, FL 33607
Tel.: (813) 874-9463
Web Site:
http://www.flemingssteakhouse.com
Restaurant Operators
N.A.I.C.S.: 722511
Beth Scott (Pres)

Fleming's of Baltimore, LLC (1)
720 Aliceanna St, Baltimore, MD 21202
Tel.: (410) 332-1666
Web Site:
http://www.flemingssteakhouse.com
Sales Range: $10-24.9 Million
Emp.: 70
Restaurant Operating Services
N.A.I.C.S.: 722511

Frederick Outback, Inc. (1)
1007 W Patrick St, Frederick, MD 21702-3903
Tel.: (301) 662-9584
Web Site: http://www.outback.com
Emp.: 93
Restaurant Operating Services
N.A.I.C.S.: 722511

Hagerstown Outback, Inc. (1)
240 Railway Ln, Hagerstown, MD 21740-6936
Tel.: (240) 420-6868
Web Site: http://www.outback.com
Sales Range: $10-24.9 Million
Restaurant Operating Services
N.A.I.C.S.: 722511

OSI/Fleming's, LLC (1)
9200 Stony Point Pkwy Ste 131, Richmond, VA 23235-1971
Tel.: (804) 272-7755
Web Site:
http://www.flemingssteakhouse.com
Restaurant Operating Services
N.A.I.C.S.: 722511

Ocean City Outback, Inc. (1)
12741 Ocean Gateway Ste 920, Ocean City, MD 21842-9554
Tel.: (410) 213-2595
Web Site: http://www.outback.com
Emp.: 67
Restaurant Operating Services
N.A.I.C.S.: 722511

Outback Catering, Inc. (1)
14731 Keswick St, Van Nuys, CA 91405
Tel.: (818) 909-9449
Web Site: https://www.outbackcatering.com
Emp.: 30
Catering Services
N.A.I.C.S.: 722320

Outback Kansas LLC (1)
7006 NW Barry Rd, Kansas City, MO 64153-1718
Tel.: (816) 741-8900
Web Site: http://www.outback.com
Emp.: 63
Restaurant Operating Services
N.A.I.C.S.: 722511

Outback Steakhouse International, LLC (1)
11308 N 56th St, Temple Terrace, FL 33617-2235
Tel.: (813) 980-0755
Web Site: http://www.outback.com

Emp.: 73
Restaurant Operating Services
N.A.I.C.S.: 722511

Outback Steakhouse Japan Co., Ltd. (1)
Keikyu EX Inn B1F 4-10-8 Takanawa, Minato-ku, Tokyo, 108-0074, Japan
Tel.: (81) 357983501
Web Site:
http://www.outbacksteakhouse.co.jp
Restaurant Operating Services
N.A.I.C.S.: 722511

Outback Steakhouse Korea, Ltd. (1)
672-1 Deungchon-Dong Kangseo-gu, Kangseo-gu, Seoul, 157-040, Korea (South)
Tel.: (82) 236611101
Web Site: http://www.outback.com
Sales Range: $10-24.9 Million
Emp.: 55
Restaurant Operating Services
N.A.I.C.S.: 722511

Outback Steakhouse West Virginia, Inc. (1)
311 Greasy Ridge Rd, Princeton, WV 24740
Tel.: (304) 487-1971
Web Site: http://www.outback.com
Emp.: 67
Restaurant Operating Services
N.A.I.C.S.: 722511

Outback Steakhouse of Bowie, Inc. (1)
6800 Race Track Rd, Bowie, MD 20715
Tel.: (301) 464-5800
Web Site: http://www.outback.com
Restaurant Operating Services
N.A.I.C.S.: 722511

Outback Steakhouse of Canton, Inc. (1)
2400 Boston St, Baltimore, MD 21224-4723
Tel.: (410) 522-7757
Web Site: http://www.outback.com
Emp.: 49
Restaurant Operating Services
N.A.I.C.S.: 722511

Outback Steakhouse of Howard County, Inc. (1)
4420 Long Gate Pkwy, Ellicott City, MD 21043-5005
Tel.: (410) 480-0472
Web Site: http://www.outback.com
Emp.: 98
Restaurant Operating Services
N.A.I.C.S.: 722511

Outback Steakhouse of Jonesboro, Inc. (1)
906 C SW Dr, Jonesboro, AR 72401-7081
Tel.: (870) 910-5600
Web Site: http://www.outback.com
Emp.: 65
Restaurant Management Services
N.A.I.C.S.: 722511

Outback Steakhouse of St. Mary's County, Inc. (1)
23415 Three Notch Rd, California, MD 20619-4017
Tel.: (301) 863-5530
Web Site: http://www.outback.com
Emp.: 79
Restaurant Operating Services
N.A.I.C.S.: 722511

Outback of Aspen Hill, Inc. (1)
13703 Georgia Ave, Silver Spring, MD 20906-5216
Tel.: (301) 933-4385
Web Site: http://www.outback.com
Emp.: 34
Restaurant Operating Services
N.A.I.C.S.: 722511

Outback of Germantown, Inc. (1)
12609 Wisteria Dr, Germantown, MD 20874-5390
Tel.: (301) 353-9499
Emp.: 53
Restaurant Operating Services
N.A.I.C.S.: 722511

Outback of La Plata, Inc. (1)
6649 Crain Hwy, La Plata, MD 20646-4287

Tel.: (301) 934-9599
Web Site: http://www.outback.com
Emp.: 58
Restaurant Operating Services
N.A.I.C.S.: 722511

Outback of Waldorf, Inc. (1)
3020 Crain Hwy, Waldorf, MD 20601-2800
Tel.: (301) 645-4120
Web Site: http://www.outback.com
Emp.: 62
Restaurant Operating Services
N.A.I.C.S.: 722511

Outback/Southfield, Limited Partnership (1)
23501 Greenfield Rd, Southfield, MI 48075-3762
Tel.: (248) 424-9696
Web Site: http://www.outback.com
Restaurant Operating Services
N.A.I.C.S.: 722511

PRP Holdings, LLC (1)
3168 Theodore Dr, Arnold, MO 63010
Tel.: (636) 282-3893
Emp.: 2
Investment Management Service
N.A.I.C.S.: 551112

Perry Hall Outback, Inc. (1)
4215 Ebenezer Rd, Baltimore, MD 21236-2168
Tel.: (410) 529-7200
Web Site: http://www.outback.com
Emp.: 90
Restaurant Operating Services
N.A.I.C.S.: 722511

BLOOMIOS, INC.
701 Anacapa St Ste C, Santa Barbara, CA 93101
Tel.: (805) 222-6330   NV
Year Founded: 2001
BLMS—(OTCQB)
Rev.: $6,077,080
Assets: $26,010,888
Liabilities: $27,331,835
Net Worth: ($1,320,947)
Earnings: ($13,774,165)
Fiscal Year-end: 12/31/22
Healtcare Services
N.A.I.C.S.: 621999
Michael Hill (CEO)
John Bennett (CFO)
Barrett Evans (Pres & Chief Strategy Officer)

BLOX, INC.
5th Fl 1177 Ave of Americas, New York, NY 10036
Tel.: (604) 314-9293
Web Site: http://www.bloxinc.com
Year Founded: 2005
BLXX—(OTCIQ)
Assets: $165,369
Liabilities: $810,779
Net Worth: ($645,410)
Earnings: ($12,858,000)
Fiscal Year-end: 03/31/20
Mineral Exploration Services
N.A.I.C.S.: 213114
Ronald Renee (Chm, CEO & Interim CFO)

BLUBUZZARD, INC.
1800D Mineral Spring Ave Ste 164, North Providence, RI 02904
Tel.: (508) 443-1859   DE
Web Site: http://www.blubuzzard.com
Year Founded: 2018
BZRD—(OTCIQ)
Liabilities: $121,211
Net Worth: ($121,211)
Earnings: ($33,474)
Emp.: 1
Fiscal Year-end: 12/31/22
Holding Company
N.A.I.C.S.: 551112
Thomas DeNunzio (CEO & CFO)

BLUE BIOFUELS, INC.—(Continued)

BLUE BIOFUELS, INC.
3710 Buckeye St Ste 120, Palm
Beach Gardens, FL 33410
Tel.: (561) 359-8222　　　　　NV
Web Site: https://bluebiofuels.com
Year Founded: 2012
BIOF—(OTCQB)
Assets: $1,105,919
Liabilities: $3,462,836
Net Worth: ($2,356,917)
Earnings: ($3,960,183)
Emp.: 7
Fiscal Year-end: 12/31/22
Renewable Energy & Bio-Fuels
N.A.I.C.S.: 324199
George D. Bolton (Sec)
Benjamin Slager (Chm & CEO)
Kevin Hissem (Dir-Engineering)
Eric Libra (VP-Technology)
Anthony E. Santelli II (CFO & COO)

BLUE CALYPSO, INC.
101 W Renner Rd Ste200, Richard-
son, TX 75082
Tel.: (800) 378-2297　　　　　DE
Web Site:
　　http://www.bluecalypso.com
Year Founded: 2007
BCYP—(OTCIQ)
Sales Range: $1-9.9 Million
Emp.: 17
Mobile Social Marketing & Advertising
N.A.I.C.S.: 541890
Andrew E. Levi (Founder, Chm, CEO
& CTO)
Chris Fameree (CFO)
Brad Bauer (Dir-Innovation)
Jeff Spock (Dir-Sls)
Brad Rushing (Creative Dir)
Vivian Pham (Dir-Mktg & Client Svcs)
William Mould Jr. (VP-Sls)

BLUE DIAMOND VENTURES, INC.
535 N Michigan Ave Ste 3001, Chi-
cago, IL 60611
Tel.: (312) 296-8910　　　　　CO
Web Site: https://www.bldv.us
BLDV—(OTCIQ)
Grocery Product Distr
N.A.I.C.S.: 424490
Joshua B. Alper (COO)
Yale Peebles (CEO)
Sebastian Nassau (Dir)
Todd Scattini (Chm)

BLUE DOLPHIN ENERGY COMPANY
801 Travis St Ste 2100, Houston, TX
77002
Tel.: (713) 568-4725　　　　　DE
Web Site: https://www.blue-dolphin-
　energy.com
Year Founded: 1986
BDCO—(OTCQX)
Rev.: $487,504,000
Assets: $83,904,000
Liabilities: $73,316,000
Net Worth: $10,588,000
Earnings: $32,892,000
Emp.: 116
Fiscal Year-end: 12/31/22
Oil & Gas Pipeline Transportation; Oil
& Gas Exploration Services
N.A.I.C.S.: 211120
Jonathan P. Carroll (Chm, Pres,
CEO, Sec & Asst Treas)

Subsidiaries:

Blue Dolphin Exploration
Company　　　　　　　　　　　(1)
801 Travis St Ste 2100, Houston, TX
77002-5705
Tel.: (713) 568-4725
Web Site: http://www.blue-dolphin.com

Sales Range: $10-24.9 Million
Gas & Oil Exploration
N.A.I.C.S.: 213111

Blue Dolphin Petroleum
Company　　　　　　　　　　　(1)
801 Travis St Ste 2100, Houston, TX
77002-5705
Tel.: (713) 568-4725
Web Site: http://www.blue-dolphin.com
Oil & Gas Exploration & Production
N.A.I.C.S.: 211120

Blue Dolphin Services Co.　　　(1)
801 Travis St, Houston, TX 77002
Tel.: (713) 568-4725
Sales Range: $10-24.9 Million
Oil & Gas Support Services
N.A.I.C.S.: 213112

Lazarus Refining & Marketing,
LLC　　　　　　　　　　　　　(1)
11372 US Hwy 87 E, Nixon, TX 78140-
4021
Tel.: (830) 582-3202
Oil & Gas Exploration Services
N.A.I.C.S.: 211120

BLUE FOUNDRY BANCORP
19 Park Ave, Rutherford, NJ 07070
Tel.: (201) 939-5000　　　　　DE
Web Site:
　　https://www.bluefoundrybank.com
Year Founded: 1939
BLFY—(NASDAQ)
Rev.: $65,077,000
Assets: $2,043,338,000
Liabilities: $1,649,620,000
Net Worth: $393,718,000
Earnings: $2,396,000
Emp.: 198
Fiscal Year-end: 12/31/22
Bank Holding Company
N.A.I.C.S.: 551111
Kelly Pecoraro (CFO & Exec VP)
James D. Nesci (Pres & CEO)
J. Christopher Ely (Vice Chm)
Alex Agnoletto (VP & Controller)

BLUE LINE PROTECTION GROUP, INC.
5765 Logan St, Denver, CO
80216　　　　　　　　　　　　NV
Web Site:
　　https://www.bluelineprotection
　　group.com
BLPG—(OTCIQ)
Rev.: $3,876,227
Assets: $1,382,346
Liabilities: $3,273,744
Net Worth: ($1,891,398)
Earnings: ($294,528)
Emp.: 32
Fiscal Year-end: 12/31/22
Armed Protection, Financial Solu-
tions, Logistics & Compliance Ser-
vices for the Cannabis Industry
N.A.I.C.S.: 561612
Daniel L. Allen (CEO)
Christopher E. Galvin (Chm)

BLUE OCEAN ACQUISITION CORP.
2 Wisconsin Cir, Chevy Chase, MD
20815
Tel.: (240) 235-5049　　　　　Ky
Web Site:
　　https://www.boacquisition.com
Year Founded: 2021
BOCN—(NASDAQ)
Rev.: $854,167
Assets: $197,089,953
Liabilities: $205,764,521
Net Worth: ($8,674,568)
Earnings: $12,658,706
Emp.: 4
Fiscal Year-end: 12/31/22
Miscellaneous Financial Investment
Activities
N.A.I.C.S.: 523999

Marcus Brauchli (Co-Founder & Chm)
Richard Leggett (CEO)
Marcus Brauchli (Co-Founder & Chm)
Sean Glodek (VP)
Matt Lasov (CFO)

BLUE OWL CAPITAL INC.
399 Park Ave, New York, NY 10022
Tel.: (212) 419-3000　　　　　DE
Web Site: https://www.blueowl.com
Year Founded: 2020
OWL—(NYSE)
Rev.: $1,731,608,000
Assets: $8,817,621,000
Liabilities: $3,539,690,000
Net Worth: $5,277,931,000
Earnings: $54,343,000
Emp.: 685
Fiscal Year-end: 12/31/23
Investment Services
N.A.I.C.S.: 523999
Douglas I. Ostrover (Co-Founder,
Chm & Co-CEO)
Craig W. Packer (Co-Pres)
Ivan Q. Zinn (Head-Alternative Credit)
Marc S. Lipschultz (Co-CEO)
Michael D. Rees (Co-Founder & Co-
Pres)
Alan Kirshenbaum (CFO)
Andrew R. Polland (COO)
Neena A. Reddy (Chief Legal Officer,
Corp Counsel & Sec)
Andrew Laurino (Sr Mng Dir)
Sean Ward (Sr Mng Dir)
Marc Zahr (Co-Pres)

Subsidiaries:

Atalaya Capital Management LP　(1)
780 3rd Ave 27th Fl, New York, NY 10017
Tel.: (212) 201-1910
Web Site: https://www.atalayacap.com
Emp.: 24
Investment Advisory Services
N.A.I.C.S.: 523940
Josh Ufberg (Partner)
Raymond S. Chan (Partner & Co-Head-
Specialty Fin)
Robert M. Flowers (Partner)
Bharath Subramanian (Mng Dir-Specialty
Fin Practice)
Young Kwon (Mng Dir)
Jerry V. Cammarata (Mng Dir)
Adam D. Nadborny (Chief Compliance Offi-
cer & Gen Counsel)
Justin Burns (Principal)
James Intermont (Principal)
Roland Jeon (Principal)
Daniel Rosato (Principal)
Rebecca Chia (Head-Bus Dev & IR)
David Aidi (Partner & Co-Head-Specialty
Fin)
David Coons (Head-Sls-Atalaya Leasing)
Rana Mitra (Mng Dir & Head-Atalaya Leas-
ing)

Subsidiary (Domestic):

Consultants Group Commercial
Finance　　　　　　　　　　　(2)
2211 Michelson Dr Ste 1110, Irvine, CA
92612　　　　　　　　　　　(100%)
Tel.: (800) 303-4006
Web Site: http://www.cgcommercial.com
Financial & Debt Financing, Software Leas-
ing & Structured Project Solutions
N.A.I.C.S.: 525990
Jill Miller (Dir-Mktg)
Jonathan Albin (COO)
Scott McCullum (Pres)
Sharon Curreri (VP-Acctg)
Tobin Junowich (Exec VP)
Robert Davis (Chief Credit Officer)
William Dalton (VP-Capital Markets)
Kevin Adkins (VP-Credit)

Blue Owl Capital Corporation　　(1)
399 Park Ave 38th Fl, New York, NY 10022
Tel.: (212) 419-3000
Web Site:
　https://www.blueowlcapitalcorporation.com
Rev.: $1,582,094,000
Assets: $13,511,396,000
Liabilities: $7,490,003,000

Net Worth: $6,021,393,000
Earnings: $753,611,000
Fiscal Year-end: 12/31/2023
Consumer Lending Services
N.A.I.C.S.: 522291
Douglas I. Ostrover (Co-Founder)
Craig W. Packer (Co-Founder, Pres & CEO)
Marc S. Lipschultz (Co-Founder)
Alan Kirshenbaum (Exec VP)
Jonathan Lamm (CFO & COO)

Blue Owl Capital Corporation II　(1)
399 Park Ave, New York, NY 10022
Tel.: (212) 419-3000
Closed-End Investment Fund
N.A.I.C.S.: 525990
Craig W. Packer (Pres & CEO)

Blue Owl Capital Corporation III　(1)
399 Park Ave, New York, NY 10022
Tel.: (212) 419-3000
Closed-End Investment Fund
N.A.I.C.S.: 525990

Dyal Capital Partners　　　　　(1)
1290 Ave of the Americas, New York, NY
10104
Tel.: (800) 223-6448
Investment Services
N.A.I.C.S.: 523999

Oak Street Real Estate Capital,
LLC　　　　　　　　　　　　　(1)
30 N. LaSalle St, Ste 4140, Chicago, IL
60602
Tel.: (312) 448-7831
Web Site: https://www.blueowl.com
Private Equity Real Estate
N.A.I.C.S.: 523999
Marc Zahr (CEO & Mng Partner)

Joint Venture (Domestic):

STORE Capital Corporation　　(2)
8377 E Hartford Dr Ste 100, Scottsdale, AZ
85255
Tel.: (480) 256-1100
Web Site: http://www.storecapital.com
Rev.: $782,664,000
Assets: $9,773,082,000
Liabilities: $4,628,953,000
Net Worth: $5,144,129,000
Earnings: $268,348,000
Emp.: 117
Fiscal Year-end: 12/31/2021
Real Estate Investment Services
N.A.I.C.S.: 525990
Mary B. Fedewa (Pres & CEO)
Chad A. Freed (Exec VP)
Tyler Maertz (Exec VP-Acquisitions)
Catherine Long (Co-Founder)

Subsidiary (Domestic):

STORE Master Funding I, LLC　(3)
8501 E Princess Dr 190, Scottsdale, AZ
85255
Tel.: (480) 256-1100
Mortgage Banking Services
N.A.I.C.S.: 522292

BLUE RIDGE BANKSHARES, INC.
1807 Seminole Trl, Charlottesville, VA
22901
Tel.: (540) 743-6521　　　　　VA
Web Site: https://www.blueridgebank
　shares.com
BRBS—(NYSEAMEX)
Rev.: $175,508,000
Assets: $3,141,045,000
Liabilities: $2,881,672,000
Net Worth: $259,373,000
Earnings: $27,913,000
Emp.: 496
Fiscal Year-end: 12/31/22
Bank Holding Company
N.A.I.C.S.: 551111
G. William Beale (Pres & CEO)
Larry Dees (Chm)
Judy C. Gavant (CFO & Exec VP)
Mensel D. Dean Jr. (Vice Chm)

Subsidiaries:

Bay Banks of Virginia, Inc.　　　(1)

1801 Bayberry Ct Ste 101, Richmond, VA
23226
Tel.: (804) 325-3775
Web Site: http://www.baybanks.com
Rev.: $55,376,000
Assets: $1,131,923,000
Liabilities: $1,005,738,000
Net Worth: $126,185,000
Earnings: $7,058,000
Emp.: 170
Fiscal Year-end: 12/31/2019
Bank Holding Company
N.A.I.C.S.: 551111
Eric F. Nost (Exec VP)
Michael H. Troutman (Exec VP)
Pamela A. Varnier (Sec)
Peggy G. George (VP)

Subsidiary (Domestic):

VCB Financial Group, Inc.   (2)
5706 Grove Ave Ste 202, Richmond, VA
23226
Tel.: (804) 548-4020
Web Site: http://www.vcb.financial
Financial Planning Services
N.A.I.C.S.: 523940
Judy C. Gavant (CFO, Treas & Exec VP)
Eric F. Nost (Vice Chm, Pres & CEO)
C. Frank Scott III (Chm)
Ed Pittman (Sr VP-Wealth Mgmt-Northern
Neck Reg)
Thomas M. Baker (VP-Trust Svcs-Northern
Neck Reg)
Russell Carter (VP-Trust Svcs)
Bruce McCook (VP-Wealth Mgmt)

Virginia Commonwealth Bank   (2)
1801 Bayberry Ct, Richmond, VA 23226
Tel.: (844) 404-9668
Web Site: http://www.vacommbank.com
Commericial Banking
N.A.I.C.S.: 522110
Michael H. Troutman (Chief Revenue Offi-
cer & Exec VP)

Blue Ridge Bank   (1)
17 W Main St, Luray, VA 22835
Tel.: (540) 743-6521
Commericial Banking
N.A.I.C.S.: 522110
Judy C. Gavant (Pres & CFO)
Brett E. Raynor (Chief Acctg Officer)
G. William Beale (CEO)
Amanda G. Story (Sec)

Money Wise Payroll Solutions   (1)
102 S 1st St Ste 301, Charlottesville, VA
22902
Tel.: (434) 817-8788
Web Site:
   https://www.moneywisepayroll.com
Payroll Services
N.A.I.C.S.: 541214

Virginia Community Bankshares,
Inc.   (1)
408 E Main St, Louisa, VA 23093
Tel.: (540) 967-2111
Web Site:
   http://www.virginiacommunitybank.com
Bank Holding Company
N.A.I.C.S.: 551111
A. Pierce Stone (Chm)
A. Preston Moore Jr. (Pres & CEO)

Subsidiary (Domestic):

Virginia Community Bank   (2)
408 E Main St, Louisa, VA 23093
Tel.: (540) 967-2111
Web Site:
   http://www.virginiacommunitybank.com
Sales Range: $10-24.9 Million
Emp.: 14
Commericial Banking
N.A.I.C.S.: 522110
A. Preston Moore Jr. (Pres & CEO)

BLUE RIDGE REAL ESTATE
COMPANY
5 Blue Rdg Ct, Blakeslee, PA 18610
Tel.: (570) 443-8433   PA
Web Site: https://www.brreco.com
BRRE—(OTCIQ)
Rev.: $5,228,518
Assets: $17,875,383
Liabilities: $2,910,150

Net Worth: $14,965,233
Earnings: ($1,578,143)
Emp.: 9
Fiscal Year-end: 10/31/20
Ski Lodge Owner & Operator
N.A.I.C.S.: 713990
Cynthia A. Van Horn (CFO & Treas)
Christine A. Liebold (Sec)
Bruce F. Beaty (Chm, Pres & CEO)
Kristen Warner (Asst Sec)

BLUE SPHERE CORPORA-
TION
301 McCullough Dr 4th Fl, Charlotte,
NC 28262
Tel.: (704) 909-2806   NV
Web Site:
   http://www.bluespherecorpo
      rate.com
Year Founded: 2007
BLSP—(OTCQB)
Rev.: $10,901,000
Assets: $42,713,000
Liabilities: $51,924,000
Net Worth: ($9,211,000)
Earnings: ($10,443,000)
Emp.: 9
Fiscal Year-end: 12/31/18
Project Integrator for Greenhouse
Gas Emission & Renewable Energy
Production
N.A.I.C.S.: 213112
Shlomi Palas (CEO)
Joshua Shoham (Chm)
Roy Amitzur (Exec VP)
Efim Monosov (CTO)

BLUE STAR FOODS CORP.
3000 NW 109th Ave, Miami, FL
33172
Tel.: (305) 836-6858   DE
Web Site:
   https://www.bluestarfoods.com
Year Founded: 2017
BSFC—(NASDAQ)
Rev.: $12,767,145
Assets: $8,678,477
Liabilities: $9,924,200
Net Worth: ($1,245,723)
Earnings: ($13,194,969)
Emp.: 35
Fiscal Year-end: 12/31/22
Frozen Seafood Distr
N.A.I.C.S.: 424460
John Keeler (CEO, Chm, Treas &
Sec)
Silvia Alana (CFO)
Miozotis Ponce (COO)

Subsidiaries:

John Keeler & Co., Inc.   (1)
3000 NW 109th Ave, Miami, FL 33172
Tel.: (305) 836-6858
Seafood Canning Services
N.A.I.C.S.: 311710
John Keeler (CEO)

Subsidiary (Domestic):

Coastal Pride Co Inc.   (2)
2201 Boundary St Ste 306, Beaufort, SC
29902
Web Site: http://www.coastalpride.com
Crabmeat Distr & Importer
N.A.I.C.S.: 445250
Tracy Greco (CFO)
Frank Lubkin (VP)

BLUE STAR OPPORTUNITIES
CORP.
50 W Liberty Plz Ste 880, Reno, NV
89501
Tel.: (438) 501-6500   NV
Web Site: http://www.bstocorp.com
Year Founded: 1986
BSTO—(OTCIQ)
Rev.: $2,248,658
Assets: $6,534,285

Liabilities: $818,717
Net Worth: $5,715,568
Earnings: $52,643
Emp.: 15
Fiscal Year-end: 12/31/20
Environmentally Friendly Construction
Materials Mfr & Supplier
N.A.I.C.S.: 321999
Joseph Hozer (Chm)
Laurel Harris (Pres)

BLUE WATER VACCINES, INC.
201 E 5th St Ste 1900, Cincinnati,
OH 45202
Tel.: (513) 620-4101   DE
Year Founded: 2018
BWV—(NASDAQ)
Assets: $26,310,447
Liabilities: $3,922,445
Net Worth: $22,388,002
Earnings: ($13,419,830)
Emp.: 12
Fiscal Year-end: 12/31/22
Biotechnology Research & Develop-
ment Services
N.A.I.C.S.: 541714
Joseph Hernandez (Founder, Chm &
CEO)
Erin Henderson (Chief Bus Officer)
Jon Garfield (CFO)
Ronald R. Cobb (Head)
Andrew Skibo (Head)

BLUE WORLD ACQUISITION
CORPORATION
244 5th Ave Ste B-88, New York, NY
10001
Tel.: (212) 726-2880   Ky
Year Founded: 2021
BWAQ—(NASDAQ)
Rev.: $3,169,676
Assets: $70,723,169
Liabilities: $75,572,083
Net Worth: ($4,848,914)
Earnings: $2,181,905
Emp.: 3
Fiscal Year-end: 06/30/23
Investment Services
N.A.I.C.S.: 523999
Liang Shi (Chm, CEO, Chief Admin
Officer, Chief Legal Officer & Sec)
Tianyong Yan (CFO)
Weixiong Cheong (COO)

BLUEBIRD BIO, INC.
455 Grand Union Blvd, Somerville,
MA 02145
Tel.: (339) 499-9300   DE
Web Site:
   https://www.bluebirdbio.com
Year Founded: 1992
BLUE—(NASDAQ)
Rev.: $29,497,000
Assets: $619,161,000
Liabilities: $424,624,000
Net Worth: $194,537,000
Earnings: ($211,913,000)
Emp.: 375
Fiscal Year-end: 12/31/23
Research & Development in Biotech-
nology (except Nanobiotechnology)
N.A.I.C.S.: 541714
Andrew Obenshain (Head-Europe)
O. James Sterling (CFO & Principal
Acctg Officer)
Joseph Vittiglio (Chief Bus & Legal
Officer)
Thomas J. Klima (Chief Comml &
Operating Officer)
Katherine Breedis (Interim CFO)
Andrew Obenshain (CEO)

Subsidiaries:

Bluebird Bio Greece Single Member,
L.L.C.   (1)
166A Kifissias Avenue and 2 Sofokleous

Str, Maroussi, 151 26, Athens, Greece
Tel.: (30) 2107264118
Biotechnology Development Services
N.A.I.C.S.: 541714

BLUEFIRE RENEWABLES,
INC.
25108 Marguerite Pkwy Ste A-321,
Mission Viejo, CA 92692
Tel.: (949) 588-3767   NV
Web Site:
   http://www.bluefireethanol.com
BFRE—(OTCIQ)
Emp.: 1
Carbohydrate-Based Transportation
Fuel Plants Developer, Owner & Op-
erator
N.A.I.C.S.: 221112
Arnold R. Klann (Chm, Pres & CEO)
John E. Cuzens (CTO & Sr VP)
Soo Kwan Shin (Exec VP-Ops)

BLUEHARBOR BANK
Tel.: (704) 662-7700
Web Site:
   https://www.blueharborbank.com
Year Founded: 2008
BLHK—(OTCQX)
Banking Services
N.A.I.C.S.: 522110
Don Flowe (Chief Credit Officer & Sr
VP)
Kelley Earnhardt Miller (Chm)
William P. Pope (Vice Chm)
Carl Larson (CFO, Sr VP, VP & Con-
troller)
Lindsey Huffman (CFO & Sr VP)
Gerald Huffman (Sr VP & Sr Comml
Lender)
Chris Nichols (Sr VP & Sr Comml
Lender)
Cliff Hunnicutt (VP-Bus Banker)
Heather Troutman (VP-Mortgage &
Consumer Lender Covering)
Kim Atwell (VP-Comml Lender)
Thom Kincaid (VP-Comml Lender)
Beth Mills (VP-Loan Ops)
Karen Patterson (VP-Mortgage &
Consumer Lending)

BLUEJAY DIAGNOSTICS, INC.
360 Massachusetts Ave Ste 203, Ac-
ton, MA 01720
Tel.: (978) 631-4884   DE
Web Site: https://www.bluejaydx.com
Year Founded: 2015
BJDX—(NASDAQ)
Rev.: $249,040
Assets: $13,521,265
Liabilities: $1,979,992
Net Worth: $11,541,273
Earnings: ($9,296,948)
Emp.: 16
Fiscal Year-end: 12/31/22
Pharmaceutical Preparation Manufac-
turing
N.A.I.C.S.: 325412
Douglas C. Wurth (Chm)
Les DeLuca (VP)
Indranil Dey (Co-Founder, Pres &
CEO)

BLUEONE CARD, INC.
4695 MacArthur Ct, Newport Beach,
CA 92260   NV
Web Site:
   https://www.blueonecard.com
Year Founded: 2007
BCRD—(OTCQX)
Rev.: $4,000
Assets: $986,032
Liabilities: $741,230
Net Worth: $244,802
Earnings: ($1,613,140)
Emp.: 1
Fiscal Year-end: 03/31/24

BlueOne Card, Inc.—(Continued)

Holding Company; Services
N.A.I.C.S.: 551112
James Koh *(Pres, CEO, CFO & Sec)*
James Koh *(Chm)*

**BLUEPRINT MEDICINES COR-
PORATION**
45 Sidney St, Cambridge, MA 02139
Tel.: (617) 374-7580   DE
Web Site:
    https://www.blueprintmedicines.com
Year Founded: 2008
BPMC—(NASDAQ)
Rev.: $204,036,000
Assets: $1,349,902,000
Liabilities: $835,225,000
Net Worth: $514,677,000
Earnings: ($557,517,000)
Emp.: 641
Fiscal Year-end: 12/31/22
Pharmaceuticals Mfr
N.A.I.C.S.: 325412
Christopher K. Murray *(Sr VP-
Technical Ops)*
Debbie Durso-Bumpus *(Chief People
Officer)*
Michael Landsittel *(CFO)*
Becker Hewes *(Chief Medical Officer)*
Percy H. Carter *(Chief Scientific Offi-
cer)*
Helen Ho *(Chief Bus Officer)*
Sherwin Sattarzadeh *(Sr VP)*
Tracey L. McCain *(Chief Compliance
& Legal Officer & Exec VP)*
Fouad Namouni *(Pres-R&D)*
Christina Rossi *(COO)*
Alexis A. Borisy *(Co-Founder)*
Kathryn Haviland *(Pres & CEO)*

**BLUEPRINT TECHNOLOGIES,
INC.**
15500 Roosevelt Blvd Ste 101, Clear-
water, FL 33760
Tel.: (727) 535-2151   FL
Web Site: http://www.bptech-inc.com
Year Founded: 2005
BKSD—(OTCEM)
Sales Range: $10-24.9 Million
Holding Company; Voice & Data Con-
vergent Communications, Video &
Web Conferencing, Access Control,
Security & Surveillance Products &
Services
N.A.I.C.S.: 551111
Ben Rizzo *(VP-Mktg)*
Daniel Nole *(VP-Fin & Admin)*
Ellen Wood *(Coord-Mktg & Comm)*

Subsidiaries:

Cortel Business Solutions, Inc.   (1)
470 7th Ave 8th Fl, New York, NY 10018
Tel.: (212) 627-4200
Web Site: http://www.bptech-inc.com
Emp.: 40
Communication Service
N.A.I.C.S.: 517112
Dennis Larkin *(Dir-Maintenance Svcs)*

Standard Tel Networks, Inc.   (1)
15155 Springdale Ave, Huntington Beach,
CA 92649
Tel.: (562) 308-5200
Web Site: http://www.stn1.com
Communication Service
N.A.I.C.S.: 517112
Michael Promotico *(CEO)*
Michael Ferry *(Pres-Western Reg)*

**BLUERIVER ACQUISITION
CORP.**
250 W Nottingham Dr Ste 400, San
Antonio, TX 78209
Tel.: (210) 832-3305   Ky
Web Site:
    https://www.blueriverspac.com
Year Founded: 2020

BLUA—(NYSEAMEX)
Rev.: $4,004,716
Assets: $291,566,253
Liabilities: $303,120,314
Net Worth: ($11,554,061)
Earnings: $8,485,910
Emp.: 3
Fiscal Year-end: 12/31/22
Investment Services
N.A.I.C.S.: 523999
John Gregg *(Co-Chm & Co-CEO)*
Randall Mays *(Co-Chm, Co-CEO &
CFO)*
Eric Medina *(Mng Dir & Head-Fin &
Corp Dev)*

**BLUEROCK RESIDENTIAL
GROWTH REIT, INC.**
1345 Ave of the Americas 32nd Fl,
New York, NY 10105
Tel.: (212) 843-1601   MD
Web Site:
    http://www.bluerockresidential.com
Year Founded: 2008
BRG—(NYSEAMEX)
Rev.: $220,651,000
Assets: $2,599,333,000
Liabilities: $2,469,940,000
Net Worth: $129,393,000
Earnings: $3,473,000
Fiscal Year-end: 12/31/21
Real Estate Investment tRUST
N.A.I.C.S.: 525990
R. Ramin Kamfar *(Chm & CEO)*
Michael L. Konig *(Chief Legal Officer
& Sec)*
Christopher J. Vohs *(CFO & Treas)*
Ryan S. MacDonald *(Chief Invest-
ment Officer)*
Michael DiFranco *(Exec VP-Ops)*
James G. Babb III *(Chief Strategy
Officer)*

Subsidiaries:

Belmont Crossing, LLC   (1)
4201 7th St SE, Washington, DC 20032
Tel.: (202) 561-1301
Residential Building Services
N.A.I.C.S.: 531110

Thornton Flats JV, LLC   (1)
2501 Thornton Rd, Austin, TX 78704
Tel.: (512) 298-4327
Residential Construction Services
N.A.I.C.S.: 236118

**BLUESCAPE OPPORTUNITIES
ACQUISITION CORP.**
200 Crescent Ct 19th Fl, Dallas, TX
75201
Tel.: (469) 398-2200   Ky
Year Founded: 2020
BOAC—(NYSE)
Rev.: $33,537,977
Assets: $75,166,727
Liabilities: $103,201,677
Net Worth: ($28,034,950)
Earnings: $32,492,215
Emp.: 3
Fiscal Year-end: 12/31/22
Investment Services
N.A.I.C.S.: 523000
Jonathan Siegler *(Pres & COO)*
Lillian Meyer *(CFO)*
Charles John Wilder Jr. *(Chm &
CEO)*

BLUESTEM GROUP INC.
7075 Flying Cloud Dr, Eden Prairie,
MN 55344
Tel.: (952) 656-3700   NV
Web Site: http://www.bluestem.com
BGRP—(OTCIQ)
Sales Range: $1-4.9 Billion
Emp.: 1,900
Holding Company
N.A.I.C.S.: 551112

Peter Michielutti *(CFO)*
Neil Ayotte *(Gen Counsel)*

BM TECHNOLOGIES, INC.
Tel.: (212) 235-0430   DE
Web Site: https://bmtx.com
Year Founded: 2017
BMTX—(NYSEAMEX)
Rev.: $83,597,000
Assets: $71,036,000
Liabilities: $22,178,000
Net Worth: $48,858,000
Earnings: ($779,000)
Emp.: 275
Fiscal Year-end: 12/31/22
Investment Services
N.A.I.C.S.: 523999
Ajay Asija *(CFO)*
Luvleen Sidhu *(Founder, Chm &
CEO)*
Warren Taylor *(Chief Customer Offi-
cer)*

BNCCORP, INC.
322 E Main, Bismarck, ND 58502-
4050
Tel.: (701) 250-3040   DE
Web Site: https://www.bnccorp.com
Year Founded: 1987
BNCC—(OTCIQ)
Rev.: $122,500,000
Assets: $1,074,131,000
Liabilities: $955,902,000
Net Worth: $118,229,000
Earnings: $44,614,000
Emp.: 275
Fiscal Year-end: 12/31/20
Bank Holding Company
N.A.I.C.S.: 551111
Michael M. Vekich *(Chm)*

Subsidiaries:

BNC National Bank   (1)
322 E Main Ave, Bismarck, ND
58501-4008   (100%)
Tel.: (701) 250-3000
Web Site: http://www.bncbank.com
Banking Services
N.A.I.C.S.: 522110
Jan Nelson *(Dir-Mktg)*
Timothy J. Franz *(Pres & CEO)*

BNET MEDIA GROUP, INC.
352 S 200 W Ste 3, Farmington, UT
84025
Tel.: (801) 928-8266   NV
Year Founded: 2008
BNTT—(OTCIQ)
Sales Range: Less than $1 Million
Book Publishers
N.A.I.C.S.: 513130
Gerald E. Sklar *(Chm, CEO & Sec)*

BNK PETROLEUM INC.
760 Paseo Camarillo Ste 350, Cama-
rillo, CA 93010
Tel.: (805) 484-3613   BC
Web Site:
    http://www.bnkpetroleum.com
Year Founded: 2008
BKX—(TSX)
Rev.: $17,411,000
Assets: $161,208,000
Liabilities: $35,173,000
Net Worth: $126,035,000
Earnings: ($177,000)
Emp.: 10
Fiscal Year-end: 12/31/19
Oil & Gas Exploration Services
N.A.I.C.S.: 211120
Wolf E. Regener *(Pres & CEO)*
Ford Nicholson *(Chm)*
Steve Raunsbak *(Controller)*
Gary W. Johnson *(CFO & VP)*
Derrick Schneider *(Sr Engr)*

BNY MELLON HIGH YIELD

STRATEGIES FUND
240 Greenwich St, New York, NY
10286
Tel.: (212) 922-6400   MA
DHF—(NYSE)
Fund Management Services
N.A.I.C.S.: 523940
Joseph S. DiMartino *(Chm)*

**BNY MELLON MUNICIPAL IN-
COME, INC.**
240 Greenwich St, New York, NY
10286
Tel.: (212) 922-6400
Web Site: http://www.bnymellon.com
Year Founded: 1784
DMF—(NYSEAMEX)
Investment Management Service
N.A.I.C.S.: 523940
Joseph S. DiMartino *(Chm)*
Thomas P. Gibbons *(CEO)*
Robert Salviolo *(Treas)*
Robert Svagna *(Asst Treas)*
Daniel A. Rabasco *(Portfolio Mgr)*
Jeffrey B. Burger *(Portfolio Mgr)*

**BNY MELLON STRATEGIC
MUNICIPAL BOND FUND, INC.**
240 Greenwich St, New York, NY
10286
Tel.: (212) 922-6400   MD
DSM—(NYSE)
Fund Management Services
N.A.I.C.S.: 523940

**BNY MELLON STRATEGIC
MUNICIPALS, INC.**
240 Greenwich St, New York, NY
10286
Tel.: (212) 922-6400   MD
LEO—(NYSE)
Financial Securities Services
N.A.I.C.S.: 523999

**BOARDWALKTECH SOFT-
WARE CORP.**
10050 N Wolfe Rd Ste SW1-276, Cu-
pertino, CA 95014
Tel.: (650) 618-6118   BC
Year Founded: 1996
BWLK—(TSXV)
Investment Services
N.A.I.C.S.: 523999

Subsidiaries:

Boardwalktech, Inc.   (1)
10050 N Wolfe Rd Ste SW1-276, Cuper-
tino, CA 95014
Tel.: (650) 618-6200
Web Site: http://www.boardwalktech.com
Software Publisher
N.A.I.C.S.: 513210
Glenn Cordingley *(Sr VP)*
Andrew Duncan *(Chm & CEO)*
Ravi Krishnan *(CTO)*
Dharmesh Dadbhawala *(Sr VP-Products)*
Charlie Glavin *(CFO & Sec)*
JB Kuppe *(Sr VP-Sls & Mktg)*

BOATIM, INC.
7950 NW 53rd St Ste 337, Miami, FL
33166
Tel.: (305) 239-9993   NV
Web Site: http://www.boatim.com
Year Founded: 2014
BTIM—(OTCIQ)
Rev.: $900
Assets: $685,387
Liabilities: $2,489,789
Net Worth: ($1,804,402)
Earnings: ($3,116,169)
Emp.: 7
Fiscal Year-end: 08/31/21
Motor Boat Distr
N.A.I.C.S.: 441222

Veng Kun Lun *(COO)*
Patrick Burkert *(CMO)*
Matthew Grady *(Head-Sales)*
Joseph Johnson *(CEO)*
Artem Loginov *(Head)*

BOGEN COMMUNICATIONS INTERNATIONAL INC.
50 Spring St, Ramsey, NJ 07446
Tel.: (201) 934-8500   DE
Web Site:
  http://www.bogencommunications
  internationalinc.com
Year Founded: 1932
BOGN—(OTCIQ)
Sales Range: $1-9.9 Million
Emp.: 125
Audio & Communications Equipment
Mfr, Designer & Marketer
N.A.I.C.S.: 334210
Maureen A. Flotard *(CFO & VP-Fin)*
Michael P. Fleischer *(Pres)*
Jonathan G. Guss *(CEO)*
Jeffrey E. Schwarz *(Co-Chm)*
Cyndi Ashey *(CFO & VP-Fin)*
Yoav Stern *(Co-Chm)*

Subsidiaries:

Bogen Corporation   (1)
1200 MacArthur Blvd Ste 304, Mahwah, NJ
07430   (100%)
Tel.: (201) 934-8500
Sales Range: $25-49.9 Million
Emp.: 50
Holding Company
N.A.I.C.S.: 334310
Michael Sleischer *(Pres)*

Subsidiary (Domestic):

Bogen Communications, Inc.   (2)
1200 MacArthur Blvd Ste304, Mahwah, NJ
07430   (100%)
Tel.: (201) 934-8500
Web Site: http://www.bogen.com
Sales Range: $25-49.9 Million
Emp.: 100
Designer, Manufacturer & Marketer of Audio
& Communications Equipment
N.A.I.C.S.: 334210
Micheal Fleischer *(CEO)*

Subsidiary (Domestic):

Apogee Sound International,
LLC   (3)
1200 MacArthur Blvd, Mahwah, NJ
07430   (100%)
Tel.: (201) 995-2001
Web Site: http://www.apogee-sound.com
Sales Range: $10-24.9 Million
Emp.: 65
Mfr of Audio Equipment
N.A.I.C.S.: 334310
Michael Fleischer *(Pres)*

Subsidiary (Non-US):

Speech Design GmbH   (3)
Gasstrasse 18 Building 3, 22761, Hamburg,
Germany   (100%)
Tel.: (49) 403199210
Web Site: http://www.speech-design.de
Electronic Components Mfr
N.A.I.C.S.: 334419
Kasimar Arciszewski *(Mng Dir)*

Subsidiary (Non-US):

Satelco AG   (4)
Seestrasse 241, CH-8804, Wadenswil,
Switzerland
Tel.: (41) 447870607
Web Site: http://www.satelco.ch
Mfr & Sale of Electronic Parts & Equipment
N.A.I.C.S.: 423690

Subsidiary (Domestic):

Speech Design Carrier Systems
GmbH   (4)
Industriestrasse 25A, 22880, Wedel,
Germany   (100%)
Tel.: (49) 410391420
Web Site: http://www.speech-design.de

Sales Range: $10-24.9 Million
Emp.: 30
Mfr of Telecommunication Equipment
N.A.I.O.S.: 532490

BOGOTA FINANCIAL CORP.
819 Teaneck Rd, Teaneck, NJ 07666
Tel.: (201) 862-0660   MD
Web Site:
  https://www.bogotasavingsbank.com
Year Founded: 2019
BSBK—(NASDAQ)
Rev.: $31,470,147
Assets: $951,099,003
Liabilities: $811,439,880
Net Worth: $139,659,123
Earnings: $6,876,861
Emp.: 61
Fiscal Year-end: 12/31/22
Bank Holding Company
N.A.I.C.S.: 551111
Kevin Pace *(Pres & CEO)*
Brian McCourt *(CFO & Exec VP)*

BOK FINANCIAL CORPORATION
Bank of Oklahoma Tower Boston Ave
at 2nd St, Tulsa, OK 74172
Tel.: (918) 588-6000   OK
Web Site: https://www.bokf.com
Year Founded: 1910
BOKF—(NASDAQ)
Rev.: $2,342,464,000
Assets: $49,824,830,000
Liabilities: $44,679,411,000
Net Worth: $5,145,419,000
Earnings: $530,746,000
Emp.: 4,966
Fiscal Year-end: 12/31/23
Financial Holding Company
N.A.I.C.S.: 551111
Stanley A. Lybarger *(Vice Chm)*
Stacy C. Kymes *(Pres & CEO)*
Scott B. Grauer *(Exec VP-Wealth
Mgmt)*
Rebecca D. Keesling *(Exec VP)*
Mike Rogers *(Chief Acctg Officer)*
Mindy Mahaney *(Chief Risk Officer)*
Michael J. Rogers *(Chief Acctg Offi-
cer)*
Jim Dietz *(Chief Credit Officer)*
Brad A. Vincent *(Exec VP)*

Subsidiaries:

BOK Financial Private Wealth,
Inc.   (1)
1600 Broadway 4th Fl, Denver, CO 80202
Tel.: (303) 539-0100
Web Site:
  https://www.bokfinancialprivatewealth.com
Financial Services
N.A.I.C.S.: 523940

BOK Financial Securities, Inc.   (1)
PO Box 2300, Tulsa, OK 74172
Tel.: (918) 588-8283
Web Site:
  https://www.securities.bokfinancial.com
Security Brokers & Investment Services
N.A.I.C.S.: 523150

BOKF, National Association   (1)
Bank of Oklahoma Tower One Williams Ctr,
Tulsa, OK 74172   (100%)
Tel.: (918) 588-6437
Web Site: http://www.bankofoklahoma.com
Federal Savings Bank
N.A.I.C.S.: 522180
Stanley A. Lybarger *(Vice Chm)*
George B. Kaiser *(Chm)*

Subsidiary (Domestic):

BOK Financial Asset Management,
Inc.   (2)
440 Louisiana St Ste 2500, Houston, TX
77002
Tel.: (713) 228-6444
Web Site:
  http://www.assetmanagement.bokfinan
  cial.com

Personal & Commercial Finance Services
N.A.I.C.S.: 524126

BOK Financial Equipment Finance,
Inc.   (2)
5956 Sherry Ln Ste 600, Dallas, TX 75225
Tel.: (214) 987-8818
Web Site: https://www.bokf.com
Equipment Rental & Leasing Services
N.A.I.C.S.: 532490
Zane Burgess *(Pres)*

Division (Domestic):

BOKF, N.A. - Bank of
Albuquerque   (2)
5915 Wyoming Blvd NE, Albuquerque, NM
87109
Tel.: (505) 855-0690
Web Site:
  http://www.bankofalbuquerque.com
Sales Range: $50-74.9 Million
Emp.: 218
Retail, Commercial & Investment Banking;
Regional Managing Office
N.A.I.C.S.: 522110

BOKF, N.A. - Bank of Arizona   (2)
16767 N Perimeter Dr Ste 200, Scottsdale,
AZ 85260
Tel.: (480) 459-2821
Web Site: http://www.bankofarizona.com
Sales Range: $800-899.9 Million
Retail, Commercial & Investment Banking;
Regional Managing Office
N.A.I.C.S.: 522110

BOKF, N.A. - Bank of Arkansas   (2)
3500 N College, Fayetteville, AR 72703
Tel.: (479) 973-2660
Web Site: http://www.bankofarkansas.com
Sales Range: $1-9.9 Million
Emp.: 4,700
Retail, Commercial & Investment Banking;
Regional Managing Office
N.A.I.C.S.: 522110
Jett C. Cato *(Pres & CEO)*

BOKF, N.A. - Bank of Texas   (2)
6701 Preston Rd, Dallas, TX 75205
Tel.: (214) 525-7665
Web Site: http://www.bankoftexas.com
Sales Range: $125-149.9 Million
Emp.: 500
Retail, Commercial & Investment Banking;
Regional Managing Office
N.A.I.C.S.: 522110
Norman P. Bagwell *(CEO)*

Branch (Domestic):

BOKF, N.A. - Bank of Texas, Houston
Regional Office   (3)
500 Chimney Rock Rd, Houston, TX 77056-
1220
Tel.: (713) 706-1410
Web Site: http://www.bankoftexas.com
Sales Range: $1-9.9 Million
Emp.: 15
Retail, Commercial & Investment Banking;
Regional Managing Office
N.A.I.C.S.: 522110

Division (Domestic):

BOKF, N.A. - Colorado State Bank &
Trust   (2)
1600 Broadway, Denver, CO 80202
Tel.: (303) 863-4400
Web Site: http://www.csbt.com
Sales Range: $800-899.9 Million
Emp.: 250
Retail, Commercial & Investment Banking;
Regional Managing Office
N.A.I.C.S.: 522110
William J. Sullivan *(CEO)*

BOKF, N.A. - Mobank   (2)
1044 Main St, Kansas City, MO 64105
Tel.: (816) 881-8200
Web Site: http://www.mobank.com
Commericial Banking
N.A.I.C.S.: 522110
Daniel Weintraub *(Sr VP & Mgr-Market-Bus
Banking Team)*

Subsidiary (Domestic):

BOSC Agency, Inc.   (2)

3900 Vassar Dr NE, Albuquerque, NM
87107
Tel.: (505) 855-0855
Commercial Banking Services
N.A.I.C.S.: 522110

BOSC Agency, Inc.   (2)
1 Williams Ctr Plz SE, Tulsa, OK 74172
Tel.: (918) 588-6000
Securities Brokerage Services
N.A.I.C.S.: 523150

BancOklahoma Mortgage
Corporation   (2)
7060 S Yale Ste 100, Tulsa, OK 74136
Tel.: (918) 488-7140
Web Site: http://www.bankofoklahoma.com
Sales Range: $25-49.9 Million
Emp.: 10
Mortgage Banker
N.A.I.C.S.: 522310

Callicotte Ranch HOA, LLC   (2)
0290 Hwy 133, Carbondale, CO 81623
Tel.: (970) 704-3211
Homeowner Association Management Ser-
vices
N.A.I.C.S.: 813990
Leann Katchuk *(Chm)*
John McMahon *(Vice Chm)*
Deb Lenahan *(Sec)*
Kevin Strom *(Treas)*

MBM Advisors, Inc.   (2)
440 Louisiana St Ste 2500, Houston, TX
77002
Tel.: (713) 228-6444
Web Site: http://www.mbm-inc.com
Sales Range: $25-49.9 Million
Emp.: 28
Investment Advisory Services
N.A.I.C.S.: 523940

Heartland Food Products, LLC   (1)
1900 W 47th Pl, Westwood, KS 66205
Tel.: (913) 831-4446
Web Site: http://www.heartlandwaffles.com
Food Products Distr
N.A.I.C.S.: 424420
Mark Truitt *(Pres)*
Mary Steeb *(Founder)*

Quality Aircraft Accessories, Inc.   (1)
5746 E Apache St, Tulsa, OK 74115
Tel.: (918) 835-6948
Web Site: http://www.qaa.com
Aircraft Accessory Distr
N.A.I.C.S.: 423860
Brett Benton *(Pres)*
Kevin Fiske *(CFO)*
Justin Phillips *(Mgr-Customer Svc)*
Joseph Ellis *(Mgr-Quality)*
Victor Algarin *(Ops Mgr)*
Brandon Stewart *(Gen Mgr-)*

Switchgrass Holdings, LLC   (1)
611 S Elm Pl, Broken Arrow, OK 74012
Tel.: (918) 251-7060
Web Site:
  https://www.switchgrassmgmt.com
Restaurant Operators
N.A.I.C.S.: 722513
Rick Verity *(CEO)*
Eric Weissman *(Mng Partner)*
Wayne Roberts *(Pres-Ops)*

BOL BANCSHARES, INC.
300 St Charles Ave, New Orleans, LA
22314
Tel.: (504) 592-0600   LA
Web Site:
  http://www.bankoflouisiana.com
BOLB—(OTCEM)
Bank Holding Services
N.A.I.C.S.: 551111
Peggy L. Schaefer *(CFO)*

BOLLINGER INDUSTRIES, INC.
3025 N Great Southwest Pkwy,
Grand Prairie, TX 75050
Tel.: (972) 343-1000   DE
Year Founded: 1993
BOLL—(OTCIQ)
Sporting Goods Product Distr
N.A.I.C.S.: 423910
Glenn A. Bollinger *(CEO)*
Matt Bramlett *(CFO)*

Bollinger Industries, Inc.—(Continued)

BOLT BIOTHERAPEUTICS, INC.

900 Chesapeake Dr, Redwood City, CA 94063
Tel.: (650) 665-9295   DE
Web Site: https://www.boltbio.com
Year Founded: 2015
BOLT—(NASDAQ)
Rev.: $5,729,000
Assets: $227,807,000
Liabilities: $56,301,000
Net Worth: $171,506,000
Earnings: ($88,098,000)
Emp.: 94
Fiscal Year-end: 12/31/22
Biotechnology Research & Development Services
N.A.I.C.S.: 541714
Grant Yonehiro (COO & Chief Bus Officer)
William P. Quinn (CFO)
Grant Yonehiro (Chief Bus Officer)
Michael N. Alonso (VP-Immunology & Pharmacology)
Liang Fang (VP-Biometrics & Bioinformatics)
Amreen Husain (VP-Clinical Dev & Translational Medicine)
Nathan Ihle (VP-CMC & Quality)
Marcin Kowanetz (VP-Target Validation & Translational Sciences)
Triona O'Hanlon (VP-Project Mgmt)
Brian Safina (VP-Medicinal Chemistry & Bioconjugation)
Edgar G. Engleman (Founder)
Karen L. Bergman (VP-Comm & IR)
William P. Quinn (Pres, CEO & CFO)

BONAL INTERNATIONAL, INC.

1300 N Campbell Rd, Royal Oak, MI 48067
Tel.: (248) 582-0900   DE
Web Site: https://www.bonal.com
BONL—(OTCIQ)
Rev.: $1,777,283
Assets: $1,965,113
Liabilities: $334,295
Net Worth: $1,630,818
Earnings: $51,321
Emp.: 12
Fiscal Year-end: 03/31/23
Rolling Mill & Other Metalworking Machinery Manufacturing
N.A.I.C.S.: 333519
Thomas E. Hebel (Pres & CEO)

Subsidiaries:

Bonal Technologies, Inc.   (1)
1300 N Campbell Rd, Royal Oak, MI 48067
Tel.: (248) 582-0900
Web Site: http://www.bonal.com
Vibration Stress Relief Metal Mfr
N.A.I.C.S.: 332999
Daniel Kazmierski (Acct Mgr)

BONE BIOLOGICS, CORP.

2 Burlington Woods Dr Ste 100, Burlington, MA 01803
Tel.: (781) 552-4452   DE
Web Site:
  https://www.bonebiologics.com
Year Founded: 2004
BBLG—(NASDAQ)
Rev.: $479,572
Assets: $3,737,763
Liabilities: $831,402
Net Worth: $2,906,361
Earnings: ($8,948,731)
Emp.: 2
Fiscal Year-end: 12/31/23
Bone Regeneration Research & Development Services
N.A.I.C.S.: 541715
Deina H. Walsh (CFO)
Don R. Hankey (Chm)
Jeffrey Frelick (Pres & CEO)

BONTEX, INC.

1207 Hunakai St, Honolulu, HI 96816-4614
Tel.: (540) 261-2181   VA
Web Site: http://www.bontex.com
Year Founded: 1946
BOTX—(OTCIQ)
Sales Range: Less than $1 Million
Emp.: 90
Specialty Papers & Vinyl Coated Fabrics Mfr for Luggage, Footwear, Gaskets & Automotive Applications
N.A.I.C.S.: 325220
Larry E. Morris (CFO)
Steve Lane (Dir-Global Mktg & Sls)
Lester Lin (Sr Mgr)

Subsidiaries:

Bontex (Asia) Holding Company Limited   (1)
Rm 908-909 Baohua Tower, 1211 Changde Road, Shanghai, China   (100%)
Tel.: (86) 2152567999
Web Site: http://www.bontex-asia.com
Specialty Materials Mfr
N.A.I.C.S.: 313230
Larry Morris (Gen Mgr)
Steve Lane (Dir-Sls & Mktg)
Lester Lin (Sr Mgr)

Bontex De Mexico, S.A. De C.V.   (1)
Blvd Mariano Escobedo 801, Interior 4 Colonia Andrade, Leon, CP 37370, Guanajuato, Mexico   (100%)
Tel.: (52) 47707162
Web Site: http://www.bontex.com
Sales Range: $1-9.9 Million
Emp.: 6
N.A.I.C.S.: 322220

Bontex Korea   (1)
Songnam Bldg Room 603 76-1 4-GA, PO Box 581, Chungang Dong Chung Gu, Busan, 600-014, Korea (South)
Tel.: (82) 514627778
Web Site: http://www.bontex.com
Sales Range: $1-9.9 Million
Emp.: 3
Paper Manufacturer
N.A.I.C.S.: 322220
Jae Soo Choo (Gen Mgr)

BOOKING HOLDINGS, INC.

800 Connecticut Ave, Norwalk, CT 06854
Tel.: (203) 299-8000   DE
Web Site:
  https://www.bookingholdings.com
Year Founded: 1997
BKNG—(NASDAQ)
Rev.: $21,365,000,000
Assets: $24,342,000,000
Liabilities: $27,086,000,000
Net Worth: ($2,744,000,000)
Earnings: $11,867,000,000
Emp.: 23,600
Fiscal Year-end: 12/31/23
Travel Arrangement & Reservation Services
N.A.I.C.S.: 561599
Glenn D. Fogel (Pres & CEO)
Ewout L. Steenbergen (CFO & Exec VP)
Paulo Pisano (Chief HR Officer)
Peter J. Millones Jr. (Gen Counsel & Exec VP)

Subsidiaries:

Booking.com B.V.   (1)
Weteringschans 28-3 1017 SG, Amsterdam, Netherlands
Tel.: (31) 207125600
Web Site: http://www.booking.com
Sales Range: $125-149.9 Million
Hotel Reservation Services
N.A.I.C.S.: 721110
Susana D'Emic (Interim CFO)
Glenn D. Fogel (CEO)
Santosh Kumar (Country Mgr-India, Sri Lanka, Maldives & Indonesia)
Nuno Guerreiro (Reg Dir-South Asia-Pacific & Chains)

Booking.com Brasil Servicos de Reserva de Hoteis Ltda   (1)
Alameda Santos 960 - 8th and 9th Floor, Cerqueira Cesar, Sao Paulo, 01418-100, Brazil
Tel.: (55) 1139564000
Online Travel & Related Services
N.A.I.C.S.: 561599

Consumer Club Inc.   (1)
3010 LBJ Fwy Ste 1550, Dallas, TX 75234
Tel.: (800) 468-3578
Web Site: http://www.consumerclub.com
Travel Arrangement & Reservation Services
N.A.I.C.S.: 561599

KAYAK Software Corporation   (1)
7 Market St, Stamford, CT 06902
Tel.: (203) 899-3100
Web Site: http://www.kayak.com
Rev.: $292,723,000
Assets: $427,045,000
Liabilities: $42,610,000
Net Worth: $384,435,000
Earnings: $18,810,000
Emp.: 205
Fiscal Year-end: 12/31/2012
Online Travel Arrangement Services
N.A.I.C.S.: 561599

Subsidiary (Non-US):

Momondo Group Limited   (2)
100 New Bridge Street, London, EC4V 6JA, United Kingdom
Tel.: (44) 2032197616
Web Site: http://www.cheapflights.co.uk
Airfare Comparison Website
N.A.I.C.S.: 513140

Subsidiary (Non-US):

Momondo A/S   (3)
Farvergade 10 1, 1463, Copenhagen, K, Denmark
Tel.: (45) 33378080
Web Site: https://www.momondo.dk
Online Information Services
N.A.I.C.S.: 513199
Pia Vemmelund (Mng Dir)

OpenTable, Inc.   (1)
1 Montgomery St Ste 500, San Francisco, CA 94104
Tel.: (415) 344-4200
Web Site: https://www.opentable.com
Reservation, Table Management & Guest Management Software
N.A.I.C.S.: 513210
Joseph Essas (CTO)

TravelJigsaw Holdings Limited   (1)
100 New Bridge Street, London, EC4V 6JA, United Kingdom
Tel.: (44) 8000151451
Holding Company
N.A.I.C.S.: 551112

Subsidiary (Domestic):

TravelJigsaw Ltd.   (2)
Floors 9-12 Sunlight House, Quay Street, Manchester, M3 3JZ, United Kingdom
Tel.: (44) 1618305704
Web Site: http://www.rentalcars.com
Emp.: 1,000
Motor Vehicle Rental Services
N.A.I.C.S.: 532111

BOOT BARN HOLDINGS, INC.

15345 Barranca Pkwy, Irvine, CA 92618
Tel.: (949) 453-4400   DE
Web Site: https://www.bootbarn.com
Year Founded: 1978
BOOT—(NYSE)
Rev.: $1,667,009,000
Assets: $1,705,592,000
Liabilities: $761,949,000
Net Worth: $943,643,000
Earnings: $146,996,000
Emp.: 3,100
Fiscal Year-end: 03/30/24
Holding Company; Western Clothing Stores
N.A.I.C.S.: 551112

James M. Watkins (CFO, Principal Acctg Officer & Sec)
Laurie Grijalva (Chief Mdsg Officer)
Jim Watkins (Sr VP-Fin & IR)
John Hazen (Chief Digital Officer)
Michael A. Love (Sr VP-Stores)
James G. Conroy (Pres & CEO)

Subsidiaries:

Boot Barn, Inc.   (1)
15345 Barranca Pkwy, Irvine, CA 92618-3111
Web Site: https://www.bootbarn.com
Sales Range: $1-9.9 Million
Clothing Store Operator
N.A.I.C.S.: 458110

Subsidiary (Domestic):

RCC Western Stores, Inc.   (2)
1180 Creek Dr, Rapid City, SD 57703
Tel.: (605) 342-5223
Web Site: http://rccwesternstores.com
Sales Range: $10-24.9 Million
Emp.: 220
Western Apparel
N.A.I.C.S.: 458110

Sheplers, Inc.   (2)
6501 W Kellogg Dr, Wichita, KS 67209-2211
Tel.: (316) 946-3786
Web Site: https://www.sheplers.com
Department Store & Mail Order Sales
N.A.I.C.S.: 458110

Drysdales Inc.   (1)
3220 S Memorial Dr, Tulsa, OK 74145
Tel.: (918) 664-6481
Web Site: https://www.drysdales.com
Western Apparel Retailer
N.A.I.C.S.: 458110
Jim McClure (Pres)

G. & L. Clothing, Inc.   (1)
1801 Ingersoll Ave, Des Moines, IA 50309-3333
Tel.: (515) 243-7431
Web Site: http://www.gandlclothing.com
Sales Range: $1-9.9 Million
Emp.: 45
Clothing, Apparel & Accessories Stores
N.A.I.C.S.: 458110
Jim Conroy (CEO)

Wood's Boots   (1)
891 E Interstate 20, Colorado City, TX 79512-3101
Tel.: (325) 728-3722
Web Site: https://www.woodsboots.com
Western Boot & Associated Apparel Mfr & Dist
N.A.I.C.S.: 316210
Don Wood (Pres & CEO)
Billy Joe Wood (Founder)

BOOZ ALLEN HAMILTON HOLDING CORPORATION

8283 Greensboro Dr, McLean, VA 22102
Tel.: (703) 902-5000   VA
Web Site: https://www.boozallen.com
Year Founded: 2008
BAH—(NYSE)
Rev.: $10,661,896,000
Assets: $6,563,688,000
Liabilities: $5,517,126,000
Net Worth: $1,046,562,000
Earnings: $605,706,000
Emp.: 34,200
Fiscal Year-end: 03/31/24
Holding Company; Management & Technology Consulting Services
N.A.I.C.S.: 551112
Ralph W. Shrader (Chm)
Elizabeth M. Thompson (Chief People Officer & Exec VP)
Susan L. Penfield (Chief Innovation Officer & Exec VP)
Nancy J. Laben (Chief Legal Officer & Exec VP)
Kristine Martin Anderson (Exec VP)
Judith Dotson (Pres-Global Defense)

Matthew A. Calderone (CFO & Exec VP)
Horacio D. Rozanski (Chm, Pres & CEO)

Subsidiaries:

Booz Allen Hamilton Inc. (1)
8283 Greensboro Dr Hamilton Bldg,
McLean, VA 22102
Tel.: (703) 902-5000
Web Site: https://www.boozallen.com
Sales Range: $50-74.9 Million
Emp.: 200
Management & Technology Consulting Services
N.A.I.C.S.: 541611
Lloyd W. Howell Jr. (Exec VP)
Stephen Labaton (Exec VP-Corp Affairs)
Raymond J. Lane (Executives)

EverWatch Corp. (1)
11180 Sunrise Valley Dr Ste 220, Reston, VA 20191
Tel.: (703) 682-4575
Web Site: https://everwatchsolutions.com
Intelligence & Mission Support Services
N.A.I.C.S.: 541715

PAR Government Systems Corporation (1)
421 Ridge St, Rome, NY 13440
Tel.: (315) 339-0491
Web Site: https://www.pargovernment.com
Sales Range: $75-99.9 Million
Emp.: 300
Designer of High Technology Information Processing Systems for the Department of Defense & Other Governmental Agencies; Provider of Site Management & Engineering Services for Government Operations
N.A.I.C.S.: 334513
Michael Nelson (Pres)

BORGWARNER INC.

3850 Hamlin Rd, Auburn Hills, MI 48326
Tel.: (248) 754-9200   DE
Web Site:
https://www.borgwarner.com
Year Founded: 1928
BWA—(NYSE)
Rev.: $14,198,000,000
Assets: $14,453,000,000
Liabilities: $8,387,000,000
Net Worth: $6,066,000,000
Earnings: $625,000,000
Emp.: 39,900
Fiscal Year-end: 12/31/23
Holding Company; Automotive Components & Systems Mfr
N.A.I.C.S.: 551112
Joseph F. Fadool (COO & Exec VP)
Stefan Demmerle (VP)
Frederic B. Lissalde (Pres & CEO)
Volker Weng (VP)
Craig D. Aaron (CFO & Exec VP)
Isabelle McKenzie (VP)
Tonit M. Calaway (Chief Admin Officer, Gen Counsel, Sec & Exec VP)
Henk Vanthournout (VP)
Alexis P. Michas (Chm)

Subsidiaries:

Akasol AG (1)
Landwehrstrasse 55, 64293, Darmstadt, Germany   (92.94%)
Tel.: (49) 6151800500
Web Site: http://www.akasol.com
Rev.: $53,359,089
Assets: $167,860,295
Liabilities: $61,417,602
Net Worth: $106,442,693
Earnings: ($7,204,059)
Emp.: 284
Fiscal Year-end: 12/31/2019
Motor Vehicle Battery Mfr & Distr
N.A.I.C.S.: 336390
Sven Schulz (CEO, Founder & Mng Dir)
Carsten Bovenschen (CFO & Member-Exec Bd)
Christoph Reimnitz (Chm-Supervisory Bd)
Henk Vanthournout (CEO & Member-Exec Bd)

Jorg Reinhardt (Member-Exec Bd)
Robert Boyle (Member-Exec Bd)
Henk Vanthournout (CEO & Member-Exec Bd)
Jorg Reinhardt (Member-Exec Bd)
Robert Boyle (Member-Exec Bd)

Bassi S.r.l. (1)
Via Mensa 3/2 S Maria in Fabriago, Ravenna, 48022, Lugo, Italy
Tel.: (39) 0545995008
Web Site: http://www.bassi-srl.eu
Battery Charger Mfr & Distr
N.A.I.C.S.: 335999
Riccardo Morici (Mgr-R&D)

BorgWarner (Thailand) Limited (1)
989/18 Moo 6 Phraeksa, Muang Samut Prakan, Samut Prakan, 10280, Thailand
Tel.: (66) 2 324 3956
Web Site: http://www.borgwarner.com
Automobile Parts Mfr
N.A.I.C.S.: 336350

BorgWarner Aftermarket Europe GmbH (1)
Alte B40 Nr 1, 67292, Kirchheimbolanden, Germany
Tel.: (49) 63524032300
Web Site: http://www.turbos.bwauto.com
Automobile Parts Distr
N.A.I.C.S.: 423120

BorgWarner Arden LLC (1)
1849 Brevard Rd, Arden, NC 28704
Tel.: (828) 684-4000
Motor Vehicle Parts Mfr
N.A.I.C.S.: 336390

BorgWarner Automotive Components (Ningbo) Co., Ltd. (1)
No 188 Jingu Zhong Rd West, Yinzhou District, Ningbo, 315104, China
Tel.: (86) 57488209088
Production & Sales of Turbochargers for Automobiles
N.A.I.C.S.: 336390

BorgWarner BERU Systems GmbH (1)
Moerikestrasse 155, 71636, Ludwigsburg, Germany   (100%)
Tel.: (49) 71411320
Web Site: http://www.beru.com
Sales Range: $550-599.9 Million
Emp.: 1,953
Automotive Ignition, Electronics & Sensor Technology
N.A.I.C.S.: 336390

Subsidiary (Domestic):

BERU Eichenauer GmbH (2)
Jahnstrasse 2, 76870, Kandel, Rhineland-Palatinate, Germany   (100%)
Tel.: (49) 72757070
Web Site: http://www.beru.com
Automotive Ignition, Electronics & Sensor Technology
N.A.I.C.S.: 336390

Subsidiary (Non-US):

BERU Italia S.r.l. (2)
Via Roma 108 Cassina Plaza, Cassina de' Pecchi, 20060, MI, Italy
Tel.: (39) 0295139000
Web Site: http://www.beruparts.it
Automotive Ignition, Electronics & Sensors Distr
N.A.I.C.S.: 423120

BERU Mexico S.A. de C.V. (2)
Av Centenario Esq 21 Este SN Civac, Civac, 62500, Jiutepec, Mexico   (100%)
Tel.: (52) 73197925
Web Site: http://www.beru.com
Automotive Ignition, Electronics & Sensors Distr
N.A.I.C.S.: 423120

Subsidiary (Domestic):

BorgWarner BERU Systems Kandel GmbH (2)
Morike 155, Ludwigsburg, 71636, Germany
Tel.: (49) 71411320
Web Site: http://www.beru.com
Motor Vehicle Electronic Parts Mfr
N.A.I.C.S.: 336320

Subsidiary (Non-US):

BorgWarner Chungju Ltd. (2)
131 Gieopdosi 2-ro, Daesowon-myeon, Chungju, 27465, Chungcheongbuk-do, Korea (South)
Tel.: (82) 438529946
Web Site: http://www.beru.com
Sales Range: $25-49.9 Million
Automotive Ignition, Electronics & Sensor Technology
N.A.I.C.S.: 336390

BorgWarner Brasil, Ltda. (1)
Rua Blumenau 91, PO Box 6540, Brusque, 88355-000, Santa Catarina, Brazil
Tel.: (55) 4732113500
Sales Range: $75-99.9 Million
Emp.: 340
Sales & Production of Turbochargers, Fans & Viscous Fan Drives
N.A.I.C.S.: 336390

BorgWarner Canada Inc. (1)
430-137 Glasgow St, PO Box 520, Kitchener, N2G 4X8, ON, Canada
Tel.: (226) 476-1253
Sales Range: $25-49.9 Million
Emp.: 53
Timing Chains & Transmission Chains Mfr
N.A.I.C.S.: 336350

BorgWarner Drivetrain Management Services de Mexico S.A. de C.V. (1)
Blvd Kappa No 1125, Parque Industrial Santa Maria, Ramos Arizpe, 25903, Coahuila, Mexico
Tel.: (52) 8448660200
Transmission Parts Mfr
N.A.I.C.S.: 336350

BorgWarner Emissions Systems Ltda. (1)
Avenida Comendador Leopoldo Dedini 310, Piracicaba, 13422-210, Brazil
Tel.: (55) 1934299000
Automotive Components Mfr
N.A.I.C.S.: 336320

BorgWarner Emissions Systems Portugal Unipessoal Lda. (1)
Zona Industrial de Gandra Lote 5, 4930-310, Valenca, Portugal
Tel.: (351) 251000100
Web Site: http://www.borgwarner.com
Sales Range: $100-124.9 Million
Emp.: 600
Motor Vehicle Electronic Equipment Mfr
N.A.I.C.S.: 336320

BorgWarner Emissions Systems Spain S.L. (1)
Ctra Zamans 20, 36315, Vigo, Spain
Tel.: (34) 98 646 8302
Web Site: http://www.borgwarner.com
Sales Range: $75-99.9 Million
Motor Vehicle Parts Mfr
N.A.I.C.S.: 336390

BorgWarner Emissions Systems of Michigan Inc. (1)
3800 Automation Ave, Auburn Hills, MI 48326-1781
Tel.: (248) 754-9600
Motor Vehicle Transmission Parts Mfr
N.A.I.C.S.: 336350

BorgWarner Emissions Talegaon Private Limited (1)
Navlakh Umbre Tal Maval Plot No A-13/2 Opp General Motors, Pune, 410 507, India
Tel.: (91) 2114306789
Automotive Components Mfr
N.A.I.C.S.: 336320
Vilas Dhaygude (Mgr-Mfg)

BorgWarner Engineering Services Switzerland AG (1)
Industriestrasse 37 2nd and 3rd Floors, Berne, 2555, Brugg, Switzerland
Tel.: (41) 323327932
Electronic Engineering Services
N.A.I.C.S.: 541330

BorgWarner Esslingen GmbH (1)
Hindenburgstrasse 146, 73730, Esslingen am Neckar, Germany
Tel.: (49) 71131520
Automobile Parts Distr
N.A.I.C.S.: 423120

BorgWarner Europe GmbH (1)
Drivetrain Competence Center Hockenheimer Str 165-167, 68755, Ketsch, Germany
Tel.: (49) 62026010
Holding Company
N.A.I.C.S.: 551112

Subsidiary (Domestic):

BorgWarner Germany GmbH (2)
Im Fuchsloch 16, Heidelberg, 69123, Germany
Tel.: (49) 62217080
Web Site: http://www.borgwarner.com
Financial & Insurance Activities
N.A.I.C.S.: 561499

BorgWarner IT Services Group GmbH (2)
Morikestrasse 155, 71636, Ludwigsburg, Germany
Tel.: (49) 71411320
Web Site: http://www.borgwarner.com
Information Technology Services
N.A.I.C.S.: 541519

BorgWarner France S.A.S. (1)
54 route de Sartrouville, 78230, Le Pecq, France
Tel.: (33) 130159444
Web Site: http://www.turbodriven.com
Sales Range: $25-49.9 Million
Emp.: 10
Sales of Motor Vehicle Parts
N.A.I.C.S.: 423120

BorgWarner Heidelberg II RE GmbH & Co. KG (1)
Hockenheimer Str 165 - 167, 68775, Ketsch, Germany
Tel.: (49) 62026010
Automobile Parts Distr
N.A.I.C.S.: 423120

BorgWarner IT Services Europe GmbH (1)
Marnheimer Strasse 85/87, 67292, Kirchheimbolanden, Germany
Tel.: (49) 63524030
Web Site: http://www.borgwarner.com
Automobile Parts Distr
N.A.I.C.S.: 423120

BorgWarner Kft. (1)
Tancsics Mihaly ut 111, Komarom-Esztergom, 2840, Oroszlany, Hungary
Tel.: (36) 34562300
Automobile Parts Mfr
N.A.I.C.S.: 336390
Attila Mato (Mgr-Interim-Plant)

BorgWarner Ludwigsburg GmbH (1)
Morikestrasse 155, 71636, Ludwigsburg, Germany
Tel.: (49) 71411320
Web Site: http://www.borgwarner.com
Automobile Parts Distr
N.A.I.C.S.: 423120

BorgWarner Massachusetts Inc. (1)
155 Northboro Rd Ste 1, Southborough, MA 01772   (100%)
Tel.: (508) 281-5500
Mfr, Designer & Marketer of Solid-State Controls for Electric Vehicles; Metallized Film Capacitors for Electronics Applications
N.A.I.C.S.: 444180

Subsidiary (Non-US):

BorgWarner Gateshead Limited (2)
Princesway Team Valley Trading Estate, NE11 0QA, Gateshead, United Kingdom - England
Tel.: (44) 1914979000
Web Site: http://www.borgwarner.com
Designer, Manufacturer & Marketer of Microprocessor Based Electric Motor Control Systems for Battery Powered Vehicles
N.A.I.C.S.: 335314

Subsidiary (Domestic):

Industrial Capacitors (Wrexham) Limited (3)
Miners Rd, Llay Industrial Estate, Wrexham, LL12 0PJ, United Kingdom
Tel.: (44) 1591610408
Web Site: https://www.icwltd.co.uk

BorgWarner Inc.—(Continued)

Mfr of Metallized Film Capacitors
N.A.I.C.S.: 335999

Subsidiary (Domestic):

BorgWarner Southborough Inc. (2)
155 Northboro Rd Ste 1, Southborough, MA
01772
Tel.: (508) 281-5500
Automotive Electronic Component Mfr
N.A.I.C.S.: 336320

Subsidiary (Non-US):

Sevcon Japan KK (2)
720-5 Kasuga, Saku, Nagano, 384-2205,
Japan
Tel.: (81) 267777343
Web Site: http://www.sevcon.com
Electric Vehicle Mfr
N.A.I.C.S.: 336320

Sevcon SAS (2)
Parc d Activite du Vert Galant, 95041,
Cergy-Pontoise, France
Tel.: (33) 134303500
Web Site: http://www.sevcon.com
Designer, Manufacturer & Marketer of Mi-
croprocessor Based Electric Motor Control
Systems for Battery Powered Vehicles
N.A.I.C.S.: 335314

**BorgWarner Morse Systems India
Private Limited** (1)
No 79 Sidco Industrial Estate Kakkalur,
Tiruvallur, 602 003, India
Tel.: (91) 4433621200
Automotive Components Mfr
N.A.I.C.S.: 336320
T. Kannan (Sr Mgr-Engrg)

**BorgWarner Morse Systems Italy
S.r.l.** (1)
Via Cesare Battisti 122, 20862, Arcore,
Monza & Brianza, Italy
Tel.: (39) 03962711
Automotive Components Mfr
N.A.I.C.S.: 336320
Barbara Radice (Engr-Supplier Quality)

**BorgWarner Morse Systems Japan
K.K.** (1)
1300-50 Yabata, Nabari, 518-0495, Mie
Prefecture, Japan
Tel.: (81) 595644111
Web Site: http://www.borgwarner.co.jp
Automotive Parts Mfr & Distr
N.A.I.C.S.: 336350

**BorgWarner New Energy (Xiangyang)
Co., Ltd.** (1)
No 59 Guanyu Road, Xiangyang, 441000,
Hubei, China
Tel.: (86) 7102309484
Automotive Parts Mfr & Distr
N.A.I.C.S.: 336390

BorgWarner Noblesville LLC (1)
13975 BorgWarner Dr, Noblesville, IN
46060
Tel.: (765) 778-6696
Automotive Parts Mfr & Distr
N.A.I.C.S.: 336390

BorgWarner Ochang Inc. (1)
653-1 Gak-Ri, Ochang-Eup, Cheongwon,
Choongbuk-Do, Korea (South)
Tel.: (82) 432100302
Automotive Components & Systems Mfr
N.A.I.C.S.: 336390

BorgWarner Oroszlany Kft. (1)
Tancsics Mihaly Ut 111, 2840, Oroszlany,
Komarom-Esztergom, Hungary
Tel.: (36) 34562300
Automobile Parts Distr
N.A.I.C.S.: 423120
Attila Mato (Mgr-Product Line)

**BorgWarner PDS (Changnyeong)
Inc.** (1)
78 Myeongri-gil Gyeseong-myeon,
Changnyeong-Gun, Changnyeong,
Gyeongsangnam-Do, Korea (South)
Tel.: (82) 555202000
Automotive Components Mfr
N.A.I.C.S.: 336320

BorgWarner PDS (Ochang) Inc. (1)

653-1 Gak-Ri Chungwon-Gun, Ochang,
28125, Choongbuk, Korea (South)
Tel.: (82) 432100302
Automotive Components Mfr
N.A.I.C.S.: 336320

BorgWarner PDS (USA) Inc. (1)
3850 Hamlin Rd, Auburn Hills, MI 48326
Tel.: (248) 754-9200
Web Site: http://www.borgwarner.com
Sales Range: $300-349.9 Million
Automotive Drivetrain Components Mfr
N.A.I.C.S.: 336390

Subsidiary (Non-US):

**BorgWarner PDS Beijing Co.
Ltd.** (2)
No 5 Lucheng Middle Rd Lucheng Town,
Tongzhou District, Beijing, 101107,
China (80%)
Tel.: (86) 1069561515
Web Site: http://www.borgwarner.com
Motor Vehicle Parts Mfr
N.A.I.C.S.: 336390

Affiliate (Non-US):

Divgi TorqTransfer Systems (2)
75 General Block MIDC, Bhosari, Pune, 411
026, India
Tel.: (91) 2027302000
Web Site: https://www.divgi-tts.com
Torque Transfer Applications for Motor Ve-
hicles
N.A.I.C.S.: 336390
Jitendra B. Divgi (Mng Dir)
Prasanna B. Deshpande (Head-
Engineering-Product Development)
Suresh V. Deshmukh (Head)
Hirendra B. Divgi (Exec Dir)
Sudhir M. Mirjankar (Head-Fin & Company
Affairs)
Deepak A. Vani (Head)
Gopal K. Dalvi (Head-HR & OD)
Yogesh P. Katyarmal (Head-Mgmt Sys)
Sadashiv Manjari (Mgr-Sales-Customer
Support)
Balaji Veerabhadram (Head-Sls, Mktg &
Advance Bus Dev)
Balu N. Patil (Head-Ops-Grp)
Rakesh R. Sharma (Head-Growth & Launch
Mgmt)
Praveen Kadle (Chm)
Mark John (VP)

**BorgWarner PDS Brasil Produtos Au-
tomotivos Ltda.** (1)
Rua Blumenau 91 Santa Catarina, Brusque,
Brazil
Tel.: (55) 4732113500
Automotive Components Mfr
N.A.I.C.S.: 336320

**BorgWarner PDS Technologies,
L.L.C.** (1)
600 Corporation Dr, Pendleton, IN 46064
Tel.: (765) 778-6408
Machinery Part Mfr
N.A.I.C.S.: 333519

**BorgWarner Powdered Metals
Inc.** (1)
32059 Schoolcraft, Livonia, MI 48150
Tel.: (734) 261-5322
Motor Vehicle Parts Mfr
N.A.I.C.S.: 336390

BorgWarner Pyongtaek LLC (1)
47-18 Cheongbuksandanro Cheongbuk-
Eup, Pyeongtaek, 17792, Gyonggi-do, Ko-
rea (South)
Tel.: (82) 316800000
Automobile Parts Mfr
N.A.I.C.S.: 336390

**BorgWarner Reynosa S de R.L. de
C.VI** (1)
Av de los Encinos 1050 Parque Industrial
Villa Florida, 88718, Reynosa, Tamaulipas,
Mexico
Tel.: (52) 8996893024
Automotive Parts Mfr & Distr
N.A.I.C.S.: 336390

**BorgWarner SLP S. de R.L. de
C.V.** (1)
Circuito Mexico 105 Parque Industrial Tres
Naciones Fase 1, 78395, San Luis Potosi,
Mexico

Tel.: (52) 4445007953
Automotive Parts Mfr & Distr
N.A.I.C.S.: 336390

**BorgWarner Saltillo S. de R.L. de
C.V.** (1)
Blvd Isidro Lopez Zertuche 4248 Colonia
Virreyes Obrera, 25220, Saltillo, Coahuila,
Mexico
Tel.: (52) 8444389060
Automotive Parts Mfr & Distr
N.A.I.C.S.: 336390

**BorgWarner Shenglong (Ningbo) Co.
Ltd.** (1)
No 888 East Songjiang Road, Technology
Incubator Center, Ningbo, 315192, Zheji-
ang, China (70%)
Tel.: (86) 57488209922
Sales Range: $25-49.9 Million
Motor Vehicle Fans & Fan Drives Mfr;
Owned 70% by BorgWarner Inc. & 30% by
Ningbo Shenglong Group Co., Ltd.
N.A.I.C.S.: 336390

BorgWarner Stuttgart GmbH (1)
Morikestrasse 155, 71636, Ludwigsburg,
Germany
Tel.: (49) 71411320
Automotive Parts Mfr & Distr
N.A.I.C.S.: 336320

BorgWarner Sweden AB (1)
Instrumentgatan 15, Box 505, 261 51,
Landskrona, Sweden
Tel.: (46) 418476500
Motor Vehicle Parts Distr
N.A.I.C.S.: 423120

BorgWarner Systems Lugo S.r.l. (1)
Via Mensa 3/2, S Maria in Fabriago, 48022,
Lugo, RA, Italy
Tel.: (39) 054 599 5008
Web Site: http://www.bassi-srl.eu
Emp.: 2,017
Motor Vehicle Electrical Equipment Mfr
N.A.I.C.S.: 336320

**BorgWarner TTS, S. de R.L. de
C.V.** (1)
Rio Danubio 303 Parque T Industrial Castro
Del Rio, Irapuato, 36810, Mexico
Tel.: (52) 4626067500
Automobile Parts Distr
N.A.I.C.S.: 423120

**BorgWarner Thermal Systems
Inc.** (1)
3800 Automation Ave, Auburn Hills, MI
48326
Tel.: (248) 754-9600
Web Site: http://www.borgwarner.com
Sales Range: $25-49.9 Million
Emp.: 1,300
Cooling Systems Designer & Mfr
N.A.I.C.S.: 335314

Subsidiary (Non-US):

**BorgWarner Cooling Systems (India)
Private Limited** (2)
Plot No E14 Sipcot Industrial Park, Mam-
bakkam Sriperumbudur, Chennai, 602105,
India
Tel.: (91) 4467183000
Web Site: http://www.borgwarner.com
Automotive Engine Cooling Systems Mfr
N.A.I.C.S.: 336390

**BorgWarner Cooling Systems
GmbH** (2)
Planckstr 4 6, 88677, Markdorf, Germany
Tel.: (49) 754 496 9219
Web Site: http://www.borgwarner.com
Sales Range: $50-74.9 Million
Emp.: 300
Automotive Engine Cooling Systems Mfr
N.A.I.C.S.: 336390

**BorgWarner Cooling Systems Korea,
Inc.** (2)
4-5 Standard Factory 36 Palyong-Dong,
Changwon, 641 315, Korea (South)
Tel.: (82) 552376771
Sales Range: $25-49.9 Million
Emp.: 30
Engine Cooling Systems Parts Mfr & Sales
N.A.I.C.S.: 336390

**BorgWarner TorqTransfer Systems
AB** (1)

Instrumentgatan 15, Box 505, 261 51,
Landskrona, Sweden
Tel.: (46) 418476500
Automobile Parts Distr
N.A.I.C.S.: 423120

BorgWarner Tralee Ltd. (1)
Monavalley Industrial Estate, Tralee, Ireland
Tel.: (353) 667121472
Automobile Parts Distr
N.A.I.C.S.: 423120

**BorgWarner Transmission Systems
Inc.** (1)
3800 Automation Ave 500, Auburn Hills, MI
48326
Tel.: (248) 754-9200
Sales Range: $300-349.9 Million
Emp.: 4,000
Transmission Product Development, Sales
& Marketing
N.A.I.C.S.: 336350

Subsidiary (Non-US):

**BorgWarner Drivetrain de Mexico
S.A. de C.V.** (2)
C Aerojuarez 1 7940 Aerojuarez Industrial
Park, Chihuahua, 32696, Ciudad Juarez,
Mexico
Tel.: (52) 6568435075
Web Site: http://www.bwauto.com
Sales Range: $25-49.9 Million
Motor Vehicle Transmission Systems Parts
Mfr
N.A.I.C.S.: 336350

**BorgWarner Transmission Systems
GmbH** (2)
Kurpfalzring, 69123, Heidelberg, Germany
Tel.: (49) 62217080
Web Site: http://www.borgwarner.com
Sales Range: $50-74.9 Million
Motor Vehicle Transmission Systems Parts
Mfr
N.A.I.C.S.: 336350

Subsidiary (Domestic):

**BorgWarner Drivetrain Engineering
GmbH** (3)
Hockenheimer Str 165-167, 68755, Ketsch,
Germany
Tel.: (49) 6 202 6010
Web Site: http://www.borgwarner.com
Sales Range: $75-99.9 Million
Motor Vehicle Transmission Systems Parts
Mfr
N.A.I.C.S.: 336350

**BorgWarner Transmission Systems
Arnstadt GmbH** (3)
August-Broemel-Strasse 4, 99310, Arnstadt,
Germany
Tel.: (49) 3 628 5830
Web Site: http://www.bwauto.com
Sales Range: $25-49.9 Million
Motor Vehicle Transmission Systems Parts
Mfr
N.A.I.C.S.: 336350

**BorgWarner Vertriebs und Verwal-
tungs GmbH** (3)
Drivetrain Competence Center Hocken-
heimer Str 165-167, 68755, Ketsch, Ger-
many
Tel.: (49) 62026010
Web Site: http://www.borgwarner.com
Sales Range: $50-74.9 Million
Emp.: 260
Motor Vehicle Transmission Systems Parts
Mfr & Distr
N.A.I.C.S.: 336350

Subsidiary (Non-US):

**BorgWarner Transmission Systems
Korea Ltd.** (2)
19 Hansam-ro 251beon-gil Daeso-myeon,
Eumsung-kun, Eumseong, 027-676,
Chungcheongbuk-do, Korea (South)
Tel.: (82) 43 879 1004
Web Site: http://www.borgwarner.com
Sales Range: $50-74.9 Million
Motor Vehicle Transmission Systems Parts
Mfr
N.A.I.C.S.: 336350

**BorgWarner Transmission Systems
Monaco S.A.M.** (2)

17 Avenue Albert Ii, Monaco, 98000, Monaco **(100%)**
Tel.: (377) 93100500
Sales Range: $50-74.9 Million
Emp.: 200
Electromechanical & Electronic Control Components; Relays & Industrial Controls
N.A.I.C.S.: 336350
Philippe Willmann *(Gen Mgr)*

BorgWarner Transmission Systems Tulle S.A.S. **(2)**
ZAC De La Montane Est 1 Impasse Albert Cochery, Eyrein, 19800, Tulle, France
Tel.: (33) 555274100
Web Site: http://www.bwauto.com
Sales Range: $50-74.9 Million
Motor Vehicle Transmission Systems Parts Mfr
N.A.I.C.S.: 336350

Joint Venture (Non-US):

NSK-Warner (Shanghai) Co., Ltd. **(2)**
No 2518 Huancheng Road West, Fengxian District, Shanghai, 201401, China
Tel.: (86) 2133655757
Web Site: http://www.nsk-warner.com
Motor Vehicle Transmission Systems Parts Mfr
N.A.I.C.S.: 336350

NSK-Warner Kabushiki Kaisha **(2)**
2345 Aino, Fukuroi, 437-8545, Shizuoka, Japan
Tel.: (81) 538431121
Web Site: http://www.nsk-warner.com
Sales Range: $200-249.9 Million
Emp.: 988
Motor Vehicle Transmission Systems Parts Mfr; Joint Venture Owned 50% by BorgWarner Inc. & 50% by NSK Limited
N.A.I.C.S.: 336350

Joint Venture (Domestic):

NSK-Warner U.S.A., Inc. **(2)**
3001 W Big Beaver Rd, Troy, MI 48084-3101
Tel.: (248) 822-8888
Sales Range: $25-49.9 Million
Emp.: 40
Sales of Automotive Components; Joint Venture Owned 50% by BorgWarner Inc. & 50% by NSK Ltd.
N.A.I.C.S.: 423120
Michael Madley *(Dir-Sls)*

BorgWarner Turbo & Emissions Systems France S.A.S. **(1)**
23 Bis Avenue de I, 78400, Chatou, France
Tel.: (33) 130159444
Turbocharger System Mfr
N.A.I.C.S.: 336390

BorgWarner Turbo Systems Worldwide Headquarters GmbH **(1)**
KaiserStrasse 1, 67292, Kirchheimbolanden, Germany
Tel.: (49) 63524035800
Web Site: http://www.turbos.bwauto.com
Headquarters of BorgWarner Turbo Systems
N.A.I.C.S.: 551114
Martin Fischer *(Gen Mgr)*

Subsidiary (Non-US):

BorgWarner Holdings Limited **(2)**
Euroway Industrial Estate, Roydsdale Way, Bradford, BD4 6SE, United Kingdom
Tel.: (44) 1274470801
Web Site: http://www.borgwarner.com
Holding Company
N.A.I.C.S.: 551112

Subsidiary (Domestic):

BorgWarner Limited **(3)**
Roydsdale Way, Euroway Industrial Estate, Bradford, BD4 6SE, West Yorkshire, United Kingdom
Tel.: (44) 127 447 0801
Web Site: http://www.borgwarner.com
Motor Vehicle Parts Mfr & Sales
N.A.I.C.S.: 336390

Subsidiary (Non-US):

BorgWarner Turbo Systems Alkatreszgyarto Kft. **(2)**

Tancsics Mihaly ut 111, H 2840, Oroszlany, Hungary
Tel.: (36) 34562300
Web Site: http://www.turbodriven.com
Passenger Car Turbochargers Mfr
N.A.I.C.S.: 336350

Subsidiary (Domestic):

BorgWarner Turbo Systems Engineering GmbH **(2)**
Marnheimer Strasse 85/87, 67292, Kirchheimbolanden, Germany
Tel.: (49) 6352 403 0
Web Site: http://www.turbos.bwauto.com
Motor Vehicle Parts Engineering Services
N.A.I.C.S.: 336390

BorgWarner Turbo Systems GmbH **(2)**
Kaiserstrasse 1, 67292, Kirchheimbolanden, Germany
Tel.: (49) 6352 403 5800
Web Site: http://www.turbos.bwauto.com
Sales Range: $350-399.9 Million
Production & Sales of Turbochargers for Automobiles
N.A.I.C.S.: 336390

Branch (US):

BorgWarner Turbo Systems Inc. **(3)**
1849 Brevard Rd, Arden, NC 28704
Tel.: (828) 684-4000
Web Site: http://www.turbos.borgwarner.com
Sales Range: $100-124.9 Million
Motor Vehicle Turbo Systems Sales & Production
N.A.I.C.S.: 336390

Subsidiary (Non-US):

BorgWarner Turbo Systems Poland Sp.z.o.o **(2)**
Jasionka 950 Building B, Rzeszow District, Jasionka, 36-002, Poland
Tel.: (48) 178508800
Web Site: http://www.borgwarner.com
Emp.: 500
Production & Sales of Turbochargers
N.A.I.C.S.: 423120

SeohanWarner Turbo Systems, Ltd. **(2)**
63 Hansan-gil, Cheongbuk-eup, Pyeongtaek, 17792, Gyeonggi-do, Korea (South) **(71%)**
Tel.: (82) 316803000
Web Site: http://www.turbos.bwauto.com
Sales Range: $25-49.9 Million
Production & Sales of Turbochargers for Automobiles; Owned 71% by BorgWarner Inc. & 29% by Korea Flange Company
N.A.I.C.S.: 336390

BorgWarner Wrexham Limited **(1)**
Princesway Team Valley Trading Estate, Gateshead, NE11 0QA, United Kingdom
Tel.: (44) 1914979000
Web Site: http://www.icwltd.co.uk
Automobile Component Distr
N.A.I.C.S.: 423120

BorgWarner eMobility Poland Sp. z o.o. **(1)**
Stefana Batorego 8, Pass, 05 870, Blonie, Poland
Tel.: (48) 227311600
Automotive Parts Mfr & Distr
N.A.I.C.S.: 336390

Cascadia Motion, LLC **(1)**
7929 SW Burns Way Ste F, Wilsonville, OR 97070-7678
Tel.: (503) 344-5085
Web Site: https://www.cascadiamotion.com
Electric & Hybrid Propulsion Solutions
N.A.I.C.S.: 333618
Brock Fraser *(Gen Mgr)*

Subsidiary (Domestic):

Rinehart Motion Systems LLC **(2)**
7929 SW Burns Way Ste B, Wilsonville, OR 97070-7678
Tel.: (503) 344-5085
Web Site: https://www.cascadiamotion.com
Propulsion Inverters & Ancillary Power Electronics Mfr
N.A.I.C.S.: 336320

Todd Rydman *(Dir-Ops)*

Kuhlman LLC **(1)**
704 S Broadway Unit L, Redondo Beach, CA 90277
Tel.: (206) 226-6433
Web Site: http://www.kuhlmanusa.com
Automobile Parts Distr
N.A.I.C.S.: 423120

NSK-Warner Mexico, S.A. de C.V **(1)**
Tel.: (52) 4724783601
Motor Vehicle Parts Distr
N.A.I.C.S.: 423120

PolyCharge America, Inc. **(1)**
10960 N Stallard Pl, Tucson, AZ 85737
Tel.: (520) 441-9909
Web Site: http://www.polycharge.com
Motor Vehicle Parts Mfr
N.A.I.C.S.: 336390

Rhombus Energy Solutions, Inc. **(1)**
10915 Technology Place, San Diego, CA 92127
Tel.: (858) 391-0127
Web Site: http://www.rhombusenergysolutions.com
Power Conversion & Energy Management Systems Mfr
N.A.I.C.S.: 335311
Richard J. Sander *(CEO)*
Joseph Gottlieb *(CTO)*

Subsidiary (Domestic):

Rhombus Energy Solutions, Inc. - High Power Energy Group **(2)**
15201 Century Dr Ste 607 608, Dearborn, MI 48120-1232
Tel.: (313) 406-3292
Power Conversion Equipment Mfr
N.A.I.C.S.: 335999
Anil Tuladhar *(CTO)*
Kent Harmon *(Pres)*
Deanne Davidson *(VP & Gen Mgr)*

Sevcon GmbH **(1)**
Carl Benz Strasse 6, 73235, Weilheim, Germany
Tel.: (49) 70239438969
Web Site: http://www.sevcon.com
Automotive Electrical Component Distr
N.A.I.C.S.: 423120

Sevcon New Energy Technology (Hubei) Company Limited **(1)**
1001-b Donghe Centre Dongfeng Third Road, Wuhan Economic & Technological Development Zone, Wuhan, 430056, China
Tel.: (86) 2784705277
Automotive Electrical Component Distr
N.A.I.C.S.: 423120

Shanghai BorgWarner Automotive (Group) Co., Ltd. **(1)**
No 1188 Zi Xing Road, Minhang District, Shanghai, China
Tel.: (86) 2160833000
Automotive Parts Mfr & Distr
N.A.I.C.S.: 336390

Turbo Energy Private Ltd. **(1)**
67 Chamiers road, Chennai, 600028, India
Tel.: (91) 4427425706
Web Site: http://www.turboenergy.co.in
Motor Vehicle Parts Mfr
N.A.I.C.S.: 336390

BORN INC.
50 West Liberty St Ste 880, Reno, NV 89501
Tel.: (646) 768-8417   NV
Web Site: https://www.borninc.com
Year Founded: 2011
BRRN—(OTCEM)
Liabilities: $8,896
Net Worth: ($8,896)
Earnings: ($4,752)
Fiscal Year-end: 12/31/22
Healthcare Software Solution Services
N.A.I.C.S.: 541511
Sidney Born Jr. *(CEO)*

BORROWMONEY.COM, INC.

512 Bayshore Dr, Fort Lauderdale, FL 33304
Tel.: (212) 265-2525   FL
Web Site:
https://www.borrowmoney.com
Year Founded: 2000
BWMY—(OTCIQ)
Rev.: $10,936
Assets: $55,798
Liabilities: $828,175
Net Worth: ($772,377)
Earnings: ($94,459)
Fiscal Year-end: 08/31/23
Mortgage Lending Services
N.A.I.C.S.: 522292
Aldo Piscitello *(Founder, Chm, Pres, CEO, Treas & Sec)*
Houston Reid *(COO)*

BOSS HOLDINGS, INC.
1221 Page St, Kewanee, IL 61443-2101
Tel.: (309) 852-2131   DE
Web Site:
https://bossholdingsinc.com
Year Founded: 1893
BSHI—(OTCIQ)
Sales Range: $50-74.9 Million
Emp.: 203
Holding Company; Work Gloves, Boots & Rain Gear, Pet Products & Balloons Mfr & Distr
N.A.I.C.S.: 551112
Richard F. Bern *(COO)*
Diana DeSmit *(Treas & VP-Finance)*
Dianna Ogorzalek *(Asst Sec)*

Subsidiaries:

Boss Manufacturing Company **(1)**
1221 Page St, Kewanee, IL 61443-2101 **(100%)**
Tel.: (309) 852-2131
Web Site: http://www.bossgloves.com
Sales Range: $75-99.9 Million
Emp.: 100
Protective Products, Gloves, Rainwear, Boots & Job-Related Safety Products Importer & Distr
N.A.I.C.S.: 424350
Brian Wise *(VP-Sls)*
Josh Miskinif *(Dir-Art)*

Division (Domestic):

Boss Balloon Company **(2)**
1221 Page St, Kewanee, IL 61443
Tel.: (309) 852-2131
Sales Range: $25-49.9 Million
Emp.: 60
Latex Balloons & Custom Products Distr
N.A.I.C.S.: 326299

Subsidiary (Non-US):

Boss Canada, Inc. **(2)**
20 A Courtland Ave, Concord, L4K 5B3, ON, Canada
Tel.: (905) 738-5855
Web Site: http://www.bossgloves.com
Sales Range: $10-24.9 Million
Emp.: 10
Mfr of Working Gloves, Footwear & Plastic Products
N.A.I.C.S.: 326199
Joanne Michele *(Mgr-Ops)*

Boss Pet Products, Inc. **(1)**
16485 Rockside Rd, Maple Heights, OH 44137 **(100%)**
Tel.: (216) 332-0832
Web Site: http://www.bosspet.com
Sales Range: $450-499.9 Million
Emp.: 15
Pet Care Products Mfr & Distr
N.A.I.C.S.: 459910

BOSTON OMAHA CORPORATION
1601 Dodge St Ste 3300, Omaha, NE 68102
Tel.: (857) 256-0079   DE

Boston Omaha Corporation—(Continued)

Web Site:
https://www.bostonomaha.com
Year Founded: 2009
BOC—(NYSE)
Rev.: $81,234,194
Assets: $683,717,859
Liabilities: $172,781,501
Net Worth: $510,936,358
Earnings: $7,139,548
Emp.: 420
Fiscal Year-end: 12/31/22
Holding Company; Real Estate, Advertising & Insurance Services
N.A.I.C.S.: 551112
Adam K. Peterson (Chm, Pres & CEO)
Joshua P. Weisenburger (CFO, Treas & Sec)
J. Max Meisinger (Chief Acctg Officer)

Subsidiaries:

General Indemnity Group, LLC　　(1)
303 Congress St Ste 502, Boston, MA 02210
Tel.: (857) 256-0079
Web Site: https://www.gi.insure
Insurance Services
N.A.I.C.S.: 524210
David Herman (Pres & COO)
Liz McEwan (VP-Bus Sys & Operations)
Kyle Fowler (CFO)
Kelly Specht (VP-Compliance and Special Projects)
Branda Peebles (Dir-Human Resources)
Kevin Gergely (Sr Dir-Information Technology)
Lyndon Dmello (Mgr-Lead Product)
Kellie Faulkner (Dir-Marketing)
Delaney Cooney (Mgr-Marketing)
Jennifer Adler (Mgr-Brand)

Subsidiary (Domestic):

South Coast Surety Insurance Services, LLC　　(2)
781 Neeb Rd, Cincinnati, OH 45233
Tel.: (949) 361-1692
Web Site: https://www.southcoastsurety.com
Direct Property & Casualty Insurance Carriers
N.A.I.C.S.: 524126
Kelly Specht (VP-Info Mgmt & Ops)
Phyllis Draughon (Mgr-Customer Svcs)

Surety Support Services, LLC　　(2)
781 Neeb Rd, Cincinnati, OH 45233
Web Site: https://www.bosshonds.com
Direct Property & Casualty Insurance Carriers
N.A.I.C.S.: 524126
Gary E. Bradley (Founder)
Zach Bradley (Pres)
Chrissy Flavin (Office Mgr)

Link Media Georgia, LLC　　(1)
200 Mansell Ct E Bldg 200 Ste 360, Roswell, GA 30076
Web Site: https://linkmediaoutdoor.com
Media Company
N.A.I.C.S.: 541840

Subsidiary (Domestic):

Key Outdoor Inc.　　(2)
1873 Armour Rd, Bourbonnais, IL 60914
Tel.: (815) 937-4579
Outdoor (Billboard) Advertising
N.A.I.C.S.: 541850

Tammy Lynn Outdoor, LLC　　(1)
US RT 460 Professional Plz Ste 7A, Bluefield, WV 24701
Tel.: (304) 324-7610
Web Site: http://tammylynnoutdoor.com
Outdoor Advertising Services
N.A.I.C.S.: 541850
Tammy Acken (Owner)
Bud Acken (Owner)
John Mayo (Acct Exec)
Maura Harvey (Acct Exec)
Laura Acken Cole (Acct Exec)

The Warnock Agency, Inc.　　(1)
781 Neeb Rd, Cincinnati, OH 45233

Tel.: (678) 971-4195
Web Site: https://www.bossbonds.com
Surety Insurance Agency
N.A.I.C.S.: 524210
Delanie Davis-McCrossan (Acct Mgr)
Madeline Brown (Acct Mgr)
Jo Ann Smith (Head-Client Services)
Cynthia Richter (Mgr-Client Services)
Jessica Doll (Mgr-Client Services)
Tony Balzano (Head-Contract)
Richard Bredow (Head-Business Development)
John Williams (Mgr-Comml Surety)

United Casualty & Surety Insurance Company　　(1)
233 Needham St Ste 440, Newton, MA 02464
Tel.: (617) 471-1112
Web Site: https://www.unitedcasualty.com
Surety Bond Services
N.A.I.C.S.: 524126

Utah Broadband, LLC　　(1)
14015 Minuteman Dr, Draper, UT 84020
Web Site: http://www.utahbroadband.com
Wired Telecommunications Carriers
N.A.I.C.S.: 517111
Steven McGhie (Founder & CEO)

BOSTON PRIVATE FINANCIAL HOLDINGS, INC.

10 Post Office Sq, Boston, MA 02109
Tel.: (617) 912-1900　　　　MA
Web Site:
http://www.bostonprivate.com
Year Founded: 1988
BPFH—(NASDAQ)
Rev.: $273,705,000
Assets: $10,048,733,000
Liabilities: $9,180,725,000
Net Worth: $868,008,000
Earnings: $45,153,000
Emp.: 804
Fiscal Year-end: 12/31/20
Bank Holding Company
N.A.I.C.S.: 551111
Timothy Macdonald (Chief Risk Officer & Exec VP)
Anthony DeChellis (Pres & CEO)
Paul M. Simons (Pres-Private Banking, Wealth & Trust)
James C. Brown (Pres-Comml Banking)
Stephen M. Waters (Chm)
Charles Nilsen (Natl Dir-Residential Lending)
Steven M. Gaven (CFO & Exec VP)
Joy McCune (Chief HH Officer-New England)
Joseph D. Regan (Sr VP & Controller)
Maura S. Almy (Chief Operating & Platform Officer & Exec VP)
Allison Bird (CMO)
Colleen Graham (Gen Counsel & Exec VP)
Andrew Plumridge (Sr VP)
Karen Roses (Mng Dir & Head-Private Lending)

Subsidiaries:

Boston Private Bank & Trust Company　　(1)
10 Post Office Sq, Boston, MA 02109　　(100%)
Tel.: (617) 912-1900
Web Site:
http://www.bostonprivatebank.com
Sales Range: $100-124.9 Million
Emp.: 227
Federal Savings & Loan & Investment Products
N.A.I.C.S.: 522110
Jacqueline S. Shoback (CMO & Exec VP)
Anthony DeChellis (Pres & CEO)
Paul M. Simons (Pres-Private Banking, Wealth & Trust)
Gisela A. LoPiano (Chief Lending Officer-Specialty & Comml Lending)
Robert J. Nentwig (Chief Lending Officer-Comml & Industrial)

Torrance Childs (Head-Private Banking-Private & Comml Banking)
Thomas K. Anderson (Exec VP)
Lidy Mata (Mgr-Private Banking Relationship)
Britt Hultgren (Sr VP-Comml Lending)
Emily Boynton Rush (Exec VP-Comml Real Estate & Private Equity Sponsors)
John Longley (Pres-Western Reg-Northern California)
Patrick Dwyer (Head-Strategic Bus Dev)
Allison Baird (CMO)
Colleen Graham (Gen Counsel & Exec VP)
Eunice Miyaji (Chief Experience Officer)
Andrew Plumridge (Sr VP)
Bill Woodson (Exec VP & Head-Wealth Advisory & Family Office Svcs)
Gerald Baker (Exec Mng Dir & Chief Fiduciary Officer)
Stephen Mergler (Exec Mng Dir)
Shannon Saccocia (Chief Investment Officer)
Esther Schlorholtz (Sr VP & Dir-Community Investment)
Karen Roses (Mng Dir & Head-Private Lending)
Kristen Hess (Chief Admin Officer & Sr VP)
Denise Piper (Sr VP)

Division (Domestic):

Boston Private Bank & Trust Co. - San Francisco Bay Area Division　　(2)
160 Bovet Rd, San Mateo, CA 94402
Tel.: (650) 378-3700
Web Site:
http://www.bostonprivatebank.com
Sales Range: $25-49.9 Million
Emp.: 90
Banking Services
N.A.I.C.S.: 522110

Boston Private Bank & Trust Co. - Southern California Division　　(2)
16000 Ventura Blvd, Encino, CA 91436
Tel.: (818) 501-1700
Web Site: http://www.bostonprivate.com
Sales Range: $25-49.9 Million
Emp.: 30
Commercial Banking & Trust Services
N.A.I.C.S.: 522110

Dalton, Greiner, Hartman & Maher & Co. LLC　　(1)
565 5th Ave Ste 2101, New York, NY 10017-2413
Tel.: (212) 557-2445
Web Site: http://www.dghm.com
Emp.: 24
Investment Management Service
N.A.I.C.S.: 523940
Bruce H. Geller (CEO)
Jeffrey C. Baker (Chief Investment Officer)
Joshua A. Waltuch (Sr VP)
Michael S. Dunn (Sr VP & Dir-Sls & Mktg)
Peter A. Gulli (Sr VP)
Randall F. Watsek (Sr VP)
Dolores A. Casaletto (Sr VP)
Douglas A. Chudy (Sr VP)
Edward W. Turville (Mng Dir-Real Estate Mgmt Svcs Grp)
Kate B. O'Brien (Sr VP)
Kenneth J. Greiner (Co-Founder & Vice Chm)
Lisa E. Hurst (Sr VP)
Audrey E. Niesen (CFO & Chief Compliance Officer)
Gene Vladimirov (VP)
Timothy G. Dalton Jr. (Co-Founder & Chm)

KLS Professional Advisors Group, LLC　　(1)
1325 Ave of the Americas 14th Fl, New York, NY 10019
Tel.: (212) 355-0346
Web Site: http://www.klsadvisors.com
Emp.: 55
Financial Services
N.A.I.C.S.: 523940
Arthur N. Langhaus (Sr Mng Dir)
Alan J. Brod (Sr Mng Dir)
Gary P. Sica (Sr Mng Dir)
Georgia Pangle (Sr Mng Dir)
Wade Canter (Mng Dir)
Susan Matlow (Mng Dir)
Michael T. McCarville (Mng Dir)
David A. Paley (Mng Dir)
Amanda D. Dekki (Mng Dir)

Mark Bricker (Mng Dir)
Tara Carley (Dir-Client Svcs)
Tara D. Vagnone (Dir)
Andrew Hoercher (Dir)
Robert Sherman (Assoc Dir)
Jason Cain (Mng Dir)
Richard Perez (Mng Dir)
Joan Young (Dir & Mgr-Relationship)
Meghan van Dusen Spear (Dir-Bus Dev)
Raja Raza (Assoc Dir)

BOSTON PROPERTIES, INC.

Prudential Ctr 800 Boylston St, Boston, MA 02199-8103
Tel.: (617) 236-3300　　　　DE
Web Site: https://www.bxp.com
Year Founded: 1970
BXP—(NYSE)
Rev.: $3,273,569,000
Assets: $26,026,149,000
Liabilities: $17,842,168,000
Net Worth: $8,183,981,000
Earnings: $190,215,000
Emp.: 836
Fiscal Year-end: 12/31/23
Real Estate Investment Trust
N.A.I.C.S.: 525990
Douglas T. Linde (Pres)
Michael E. LaBelle (CFO, Treas & Exec VP)
Raymond A. Ritchey (Sr Exec VP)
Bryan J. Koop (Exec VP-Boston Reg)
Robert E. Pester (Exec VP-San Francisco Reg)
Michael R. Walsh (Chief Acctg Officer & Sr VP)
James Whalen (Chief IT Officer & Sr VP)
Laura M. Sesody (Sr VP-Corp Mktg & Comm)
Helen Han (VP-IR)
Hilary Spann (Exec VP)
Pete Otteni (Exec VP)
Jake Stroman (Exec VP)
Eric G. Kevorkian (Chief Legal Officer)
James Magaldi (Sr VP)
Ben Myers (Sr VP)
Owen D. Thomas (Chm & CEO)

Subsidiaries:

100 Federal Subsidiary REIT LLC　　(1)
Prudential Ctr 800 Boylston St Ste 1900, Boston, MA 02199
Tel.: (617) 236-3300
Real Estate Investment Services
N.A.I.C.S.: 531390

Annapolis Junction NFM LLC　　(1)
800 Boylston St Ste 1900, Boston, MA 02199
Tel.: (617) 236-3300
Real Estate Property Services
N.A.I.C.S.: 531190
Jammie Rheaune (Office Mgr)

BP Kingstowne Office Building T LLC　　(1)
2200 Pennsylvania Ave NW, Washington, DC 20037-1701
Tel.: (202) 585-0800
Web Site: http://www.bostonproperties.com
Real Estate Property Services
N.A.I.C.S.: 531190

BP Management, L.P.　　(1)
800 Boylston St at The Prudential Ctr, Boston, MA 02199-8103
Tel.: (617) 236-3300
Web Site: http://www.bostonproperties.com
Real Estate Property Services
N.A.I.C.S.: 531190

BXP 601 & 651 Gateway Center LP　　(1)
800 Boylston St Ste 1900, Boston, MA 02199-8101
Tel.: (617) 236-3455
Real Estate Investment Services
N.A.I.C.S.: 531390

Boston Properties Limited Partnership　　(1)

Prudential Ctr 800 Boylston St Ste 1900,
Boston, MA 02199-8103
Tel.: (617) 236-3300
Web Site: https://www.bxp.com
Rev.: $3,273,568,999
Assets: $25,783,251,000
Liabilities: $19,189,743,000
Net Worth: $6,593,508,000
Earnings: $219,771,000
Emp.: 835
Fiscal Year-end: 12/31/2023
Real Estate Property Services
N.A.I.C.S.: 531190
Michael E. LaBelle *(CFO)*

Subsidiary (Domestic):

Atlantic Wharf JV LLC   (2)
280 Congress St, Boston, MA 02210
Tel.: (617) 603-7195
Web Site:
   https://www.atlanticwharfboston.com
Events Services
N.A.I.C.S.: 711310

Boston Properties Services, LLC   (1)
1570 Tremont St, Boston, MA 02120
Tel.: (617) 274-8655
Web Site:
   https://www.bostonpropertyservices.com
Real Estate Agency & Brokerage Services
N.A.I.C.S.: 531210

Cambridge Center North Trust   (1)
800 Boylston St, Boston, MA 02199-8001
Tel.: (617) 236-3300
Real Estate Investment Services
N.A.I.C.S.: 531110

Embarcadero Center Associates (1)
4 Embarcadero Ctr, San Francisco, CA
94111-5994
Tel.: (415) 772-0700
Real Estate Investment Services
N.A.I.C.S.: 531110
Sofia Bautista *(Office Mgr)*

**One Embarcadero Center
Venture**   (1)
4 Embarcadero Center Ste 1, San Fran-
cisco, CA 94111
Tel.: (415) 772-0700
Real Estate Investment Services
N.A.I.C.S.: 531390

One Freedom Square, L.L.C.   (1)
4701 Cox Rd Ste 285, Glen Allen, VA
23060-6808
Tel.: (571) 203-0601
Real Estate Services
N.A.I.C.S.: 525990

**School Street Associates Limited
Partnership**   (1)
67 School St, Hillsborough, NH 03244
Tel.: (603) 464-5561
Real Estate Investment Services
N.A.I.C.S.: 531110

The Double B Partnership   (1)
125 Trolley Rd, York Springs, PA 17372-
9582
Tel.: (717) 528-8676
Real Estate Investment Services
N.A.I.C.S.: 531110

Two Freedom Square, L.L.C.   (1)
800 Boylston St Ste 1900, Boston, MA
02199-8101
Tel.: (571) 203-2700
Real Estate Investment Services
N.A.I.C.S.: 531110

BOSTON SAND & GRAVEL COMPANY
100 N Washington St, Boston, MA
02114
Tel.: (617) 227-9000   **MA**
Web Site:
   https://www.bostonsand.com
Year Founded: 1914
BSND—(OTCEM)
Sales Range: $25-49.9 Million
Emp.: 510
Mfr of Central-Mixed Concrete
N.A.I.C.S.: 327320
John J. Mahoney Jr. *(Chm)*

Subsidiaries:

**Lawrence Ready Mixed Concrete
Co.**   (1)
181 Kiahs Way, Sandwich, MA 02563
Tel.: (508) 888-8002
Web Site: http://www.bostonsand.com
Sales Range: $10-24.9 Million
Emp.: 12
Mfr of Central-Mixed Concrete
N.A.I.C.S.: 423320

**Manchester Sand, Gravel & Cement
Co. Inc.**   (1)
1355 Hooksett Rd, Hooksett, NH
03106-1849   **(100%)**
Tel.: (603) 668-4000
Sales Range: $10-24.9 Million
Emp.: 30
Sand, Gravel, Cement & Other Building
Materials
N.A.I.C.S.: 444180

**New Hampshire Northcoast
Corp.**   (1)
Rt 16, Ossipee, NH 03864
Tel.: (603) 539-2789
Web Site: http://www.nhnorthcoast.com
Sales Range: $10-24.9 Million
Emp.: 8
Transportation Services
N.A.I.C.S.: 488210
Kevin Verrill *(Supvr-Ops)*

Ossipee Aggregates Corp   (1)
368 Route 16, Ossipee, NH 03864
Tel.: (603) 539-6820
Web Site:
   http://www.ossipeeaggregates.com
Sand & Gravel Mining Services
N.A.I.C.S.: 212319

**Outdoor World of New England,
Inc.**   (1)
1367 Hooksett Rd DW Hwy, Hooksett, NH
03106
Tel.: (603) 625-2400
Web Site: http://www.outdoorworldne.com
Building Materials Distr
N.A.I.C.S.: 423390

Rosenfeld Concrete Corp.   (1)
75 Plain St, Hopedale, MA 01747-2107
Tel.: (508) 473-7200
Web Site: http://www.bostonsand.com
Sales Range: $10-24.9 Million
Emp.: 75
Mfr of Central-Mixed Concrete
N.A.I.C.S.: 327320
Anthony Cordella *(Mgr-Quality Control)*

Weymouth Concrete Inc.   (1)
611 Pleasant St, Weymouth, MA 02189-
3201
Tel.: (781) 848-9390
Sales Range: $10-24.9 Million
Emp.: 9
Lumber & Other Building Materials
N.A.I.C.S.: 444180

BOSTON SCIENTIFIC CORPO-RATION
300 Boston Scientific Way, Marlbor-
ough, MA 01752-1234
Tel.: (508) 683-4000   **DE**
Web Site:
   https://www.bostonscientific.com
Year Founded: 1979
BSX—(NYSE)
Rev.: $14,240,000,000
Assets: $35,136,000,000
Liabilities: $15,606,000,000
Net Worth: $19,530,000,000
Earnings: $1,570,000,000
Emp.: 48,000
Fiscal Year-end: 12/31/23
Medical Device Mfr
N.A.I.C.S.: 339112
Joseph M. Fitzgerald *(Grp Pres-
Cardiology & Exec VP)*
Wendy Carruthers *(Exec VP-HR)*
Jeffrey B. Mirviss *(Pres-Peripheral
Interventions & Exec VP)*
Maulik Nanavaty *(Pres-
Neuromodulation & Sr VP)*

Brad Sorenson *(Exec VP-Ops-Global)*
Eric Thepaut *(Pres-Europe, Middle
East & Africa & Exec VP)*
Ian T. Meredith *(Chief Medical
Officer-Global & Exec VP)*
Jodi E. Eddy *(CIO, Chief Digital Offi-
cer, Sr VP & Head-Shared Services-
Global)*
Jonathan Monson *(Sr VP-IR)*
Meghan M. Scanlon *(Pres-Urology &
Pelvic Health & Sr VP)*
Michael Jones *(Pres-Endoscopy & Sr
VP)*
Charlie Attlan *(Sr VP)*
Lance Bates *(Sr VP)*
Vance R. Brown *(Gen Counsel)*
Rosaleen Burke *(Sr VP)*
Stephen Morse *(Pres)*
Arthur C. Butcher *(Grp Pres-MedSurg
& Exec VP)*
Daniel J. Brennan *(CFO & Exec VP)*
Michael F. Mahoney *(Chm, Pres &
CEO)*

Subsidiaries:

Apollo Endosurgery, Inc.   (1)
1120 S Capital of Texas Hwy Bldg 1 Ste
300, Austin, TX 78746
Tel.: (512) 279-5100
Web Site: https://www.apolloendo.com
Rev.: $76,856,000
Assets: $110,231,000
Liabilities: $77,637,000
Net Worth: $32,594,000
Earnings: ($39,839,000)
Emp.: 281
Fiscal Year-end: 12/31/2022
Holding Company; Biological Products De-
veloper
N.A.I.C.S.: 551112
Stefanie Cavanaugh *(Treas & Sec)*
Christopher J. Gostout *(Chief Medical Offi-
cer)*
Mary League *(VP-HR)*
Boris Fischer *(VP-Bus Process & Sys)*
Mike Gutteridge *(VP-Sls & Mktg-Intl)*
Brian Szymczak *(VP-Legal & Compliance)*
Felix L. Nieves *(VP-Mfg Ops)*
David Hooper *(VP-Quality & Regulatory Af-
fairs)*
Tiffanie Gilbreth *(VP-Clinical & Medical Af-
fairs)*
Chrissy Citzler-Carr *(Controller)*
Kirk Ellis *(VP-Sls-US)*
Steve Bosrock *(VP-Mktg & Medical Educa-
tion)*

Subsidiary (Non-US):

**Apollo Endosurgery Costa Rica
S.R.L.**   (2)
Zona Franca Coyol Edificio B13 3, Alajuela,
Costa Rica
Tel.: (506) 40554000
Medical Equipment Mfr
N.A.I.C.S.: 339114

Apollo Endosurgery UK Ltd.   (2)
St James Business Park 10 Grimbald Crag
Cl, Knaresborough, HG5 8QB, United King-
dom
Tel.: (44) 3332200483
Medical Equipment Mfr
N.A.I.C.S.: 339112

Subsidiary (Domestic):

Apollo Endosurgery US, Inc.   (2)
1120 S Capital of Texas Hwy Bldg 1 Ste
300, Austin, TX 78746
Tel.: (512) 279-5100
Web Site: https://www.apolloendo.com
Medical Instrument Mfr
N.A.I.C.S.: 339112

Asthmatx, Inc.   (1)
888 Ross Dr Ste 100, Sunnyvale, CA
94089   **(100%)**
Tel.: (408) 419-0100
Web Site: http://www.asthmatx.com
Sales Range: $25-49.9 Million
Emp.: 32
Medical Device Research & Development
N.A.I.C.S.: 339112
Glendon E. French *(Founder)*

Atritech, Inc.   (1)
3750 Annapolis Ln N Ste105, Minneapolis,
MN 55447
Tel.: (763) 258-0250
Web Site: http://www.atritech.net
Sales Range: $10-24.9 Million
Emp.: 22
Medical Device Mfr
N.A.I.C.S.: 339112

BTG plc   (1)
5 Fleet Place, London, EC4M 7RD, United
Kingdom   **(100%)**
Tel.: (44) 2075750000
Web Site: http://www.btgplc.com
Rev.: $837,128,960
Assets: $1,568,621,824
Liabilities: $337,145,088
Net Worth: $1,231,476,736
Earnings: $17,133,824
Emp.: 1,631
Fiscal Year-end: 03/31/2018
Healthcare Company; Interventional Medi-
cine Mfr
N.A.I.C.S.: 325412
John R. Sylvester *(Chief Comml Officer)*

Subsidiary (Non-US):

BTG Australasia Pty Limited   (2)
RSD Turretfield RC 129 Holland Road,
Rosedale, 5350, SA, Australia
Tel.: (61) 885249700
Pharmaceuticals Product Mfr
N.A.I.C.S.: 325412

Subsidiary (Domestic):

BTG International (Holdings) Ltd (2)
5 Fleet Place, London, EC4M 7RD, United
Kingdom
Tel.: (44) 2075750000
Web Site: https://www.btgplc.com
Sales Range: $25-49.9 Million
Emp.: 65
Health Care Srvices
N.A.I.C.S.: 456199

Subsidiary (US):

BTG International Inc.   (2)
5 Tower Bridge Ste 800 300 Barr Harbor
Dr, West Conshohocken, PA 19428
Tel.: (610) 278-1660
Web Site: http://www.btgplc.com
Sales Range: $25-49.9 Million
Emp.: 20
Database & Directory Publishers
N.A.I.C.S.: 513140
Louise Makin *(CEO)*

Subsidiary (Domestic):

BTG International Ltd.   (2)
5 Fleet Place, London, EC4M 7RD, United
Kingdom
Tel.: (44) 2075750000
Sales Range: $25-49.9 Million
Emp.: 60
Drug & Technology Development Services
N.A.I.C.S.: 541715
Louise Makin *(CEO)*

Subsidiary (US):

Biocompatibles Inc.   (2)
115 Hurley Rd Bldg 3C, Oxford, CT 06478
Tel.: (314) 239-1714
Web Site: https://www.bostonscientific.com
Pharmaceutical Products Distr
N.A.I.C.S.: 424210

Subsidiary (Domestic):

Biocompatibles UK Limited   (2)
Chapman House Farnham Business Park,
Farnham, GU9 8QL, Surrey, United King-
dom
Tel.: (44) 1252732732
Oncology Products Distr
N.A.I.C.S.: 423450

Subsidiary (US):

Galil Medical Inc.   (2)
4364 Round Lake Rd, Arden Hills, MN
55112
Tel.: (651) 287-5000
Web Site: https://www.galilmedical.com

Boston Scientific Corporation—(Continued)

Sales Range: $1-9.9 Million
Emp.: 82
Health & Personal Care Stores
N.A.I.C.S.: 456199
Martin J. Emerson *(Pres & CEO)*

Subsidiary (Domestic):

Protherics UK Limited (2)
Blaenwaun Ffostrasol, Llandysul, SA44 5JT,
Ceredigion, United Kingdom
Tel.: (44) 1239 851 122
Web Site: http://www.btgplc.com
Sales Range: $50-74.9 Million
Emp.: 120
Health Care Pharmaceutical Products Mfr
N.A.I.C.S.: 325412

Subsidiary (US):

Protherics Utah Inc. (2)
615 Arapeen Dr, Salt Lake City, UT 84108-1267
Tel.: (801) 583-8077
Pharmaceuticals Product Mfr
N.A.I.C.S.: 325412

Roxwood Medical, Inc. (2)
400 Seaport Ct Ste 103, Redwood City, CA
94063-2799
Tel.: (408) 373-4751
Advanced Cardiovascular Specialty Catheters Mfr
N.A.I.C.S.: 339112
Traci Kiss Gray *(Dir-Sls)*

Baylis Medical Co. Inc. (1)
5959 Trans Canada Highway, Montreal,
H4T 1A1, QC, Canada
Tel.: (514) 488-9801
Web Site: http://www.baylismedical.com
Sales Range: $25-49.9 Million
Emp.: 130
Cardiology, Pain Management & Radiology
Products Mfr & Distr
N.A.I.C.S.: 339113
Kris Shah *(Pres)*
Howard Andrews *(VP-Fin & Acctg)*
Thomas Chavez *(VP-Sls-Cardiology-Global)*
Gloria Yee *(VP-Mktg)*

Subsidiary (US):

Baylis Medical Company Inc. (2)
78 Blanchard Rd Ste 204, Burlington, MA
01083
Tel.: (781) 229-9801
Web Site: http://www.baylismedical.com
Medical Equipment Distr
N.A.I.C.S.: 423450

Subsidiary (Domestic):

Fralex Therapeutics Inc. (2)
190 Attwell Drive Suite 580, Toronto, M9W
6H8, ON, Canada
Tel.: (416) 213-8118
Web Site: http://www.fralex.com
Pharmaceuticals Mfr
N.A.I.C.S.: 325412
Alex Thomas *(VP-Res)*

Boston Scientific (South Africa) Proprietary Limited (1)
8 Anslow Crescent Anslow Office Park, PO
Box 69975, Bryanston, 2021, South Africa
Tel.: (27) 11 840 8600
Web Site: https://www.bostonscientific.com
Surgical Instrument Mfr
N.A.I.C.S.: 339112

Boston Scientific (Thailand) Ltd. (1)
98 Sathorn Square Office Tower 29th Floor
Unit 2907-2911, North Sathorn Road Silom
Bangrak, Bangkok, 10500, Thailand
Tel.: (66) 20321888
Web Site: http://www.bostonscientific.com
Medical Equipment Mfr
N.A.I.C.S.: 339112

Boston Scientific - Arden Hills/Saint Paul (1)
4100 Hamline Ave N, Saint Paul, MN
55112-5798
Tel.: (651) 582-4000
Web Site: http://www.bostonscientific.com
Sales Range: $1-4.9 Billion
Emp.: 2,335

Mfr of Pacemakers, Implantable Cardioverter Defibrillators & Cardiac Resynchronization Therapy Devices
N.A.I.C.S.: 334510

Boston Scientific - Electrophysiology - Lowell (1)
55 Technology Dr, Lowell, MA 01851
Tel.: (908) 277-8000
Web Site: http://www.epresourcecenter.com
Sales Range: $100-124.9 Million
Emp.: 150
Mfr & Marketer of Medical Equipment, Catheters & Accessories Used in Cardiac Electrophysiology Procedures
N.A.I.C.S.: 334510

Boston Scientific - Fremont (1)
47215 Lakeview Blvd, Fremont, CA 94538-6530
Tel.: (510) 440-7700
Web Site: http://www.bostonscientific.com
Sales Range: $25-49.9 Million
Emp.: 750
Mfr of Minimally Invasive Peripheral Vascular Surgical Devices
N.A.I.C.S.: 339112

Boston Scientific - Maple Grove (1)
1 Scimed Pl, Maple Grove, MN
55311-1566 **(100%)**
Tel.: (763) 494-1700
Web Site: http://www.bostonscientific.com
Mfr of Cardiac & Cardiovascular Devices for
Minimally Invasive Treatments
N.A.I.C.S.: 339112

Boston Scientific - Plymouth Technology Center (1)
5905 Nathan Ln N, Plymouth, MN 55442
Tel.: (763) 694-5500
Web Site: http://www.bostonscientific.com
Sales Range: $100-124.9 Million
Emp.: 2,000
Mfr of Angioplasty Devices & Stents
N.A.I.C.S.: 339112

Boston Scientific - San Jose (1)
150 Baytech Dr, San Jose, CA 95134-2012
Tel.: (408) 935-3400
Web Site: http://www.bostonscientific.com
Sales Range: $75-99.9 Million
Emp.: 500
Mfr of Minimally Invasive Peripheral Vascular Surgical Devices
N.A.I.C.S.: 339112

Boston Scientific - Spencer (1)
780 Brookside Dr, Spencer, IN
47460-1080 **(100%)**
Tel.: (812) 829-4877
Web Site: http://www.bsci.com
Sales Range: $400-449.9 Million
Emp.: 1,008
Mfr of Minimally Invasive Peripheral Vascular Surgical Devices
N.A.I.C.S.: 339112

Boston Scientific Asia Pacific Pte. Ltd. (1)
9 North Buona Vista Drive 20-01 The Metropolis Tower One, Singapore, 138588,
Singapore
Tel.: (65) 64188888
Medical Equipment Whslr
N.A.I.C.S.: 423450
Meghan M. Scanlon *(Pres)*
Arthur C. Butcher *(Grp Pres)*
Charlie Attlan *(Sr VP)*
Lance Bates *(Pres)*
Daniel J. Brennan *(CFO)*
Vance R. Brown *(Gen Counsel)*
Rosaleen Burke *(Sr VP)*
Arthur Butcher *(Exec VP)*
Wendy Carruthers *(Exec VP)*
Jodi Eddy *(Chief Information Officer)*
Joseph M. Fitzgerald *(Exec VP)*
Michael Jones *(Pres)*
Ian Meredith *(Chief Medical Officer)*
Jeff Mirviss *(Pres)*
Stephen Morse *(Pres)*
Mary Beth Moynihan *(CMO)*
Maulik Nanavaty *(Pres)*
Scott Olson *(Pres)*
Meghan Scanlon *(Pres)*
Brad Sorenson *(Exec VP)*
Kenneth Stein *(Chief Medical Officer)*
Eric Thepaut *(Pres)*

Boston Scientific Cardiac Diagnostics, Inc. (1)

1717 N Sam Houston Pkwy W Ste 100,
Houston, TX 77038
Tel.: (281) 760-0357
Web Site:
https://www.cdx.bostonscientific.com
Health Care Equipment Mfr
N.A.I.C.S.: 339112

Boston Scientific Colombia Limitada (1)
Calle 113 No 7- 45 Torre B - Oficina 713,
Bogota, Colombia
Tel.: (57) 16295045
Medical Equipment Whslr
N.A.I.C.S.: 423450

Boston Scientific Cork Limited (1)
Business Technology Park Model Farm
Road, Cork, Ireland
Tel.: (353) 214531000
Web Site: http://www.bostonscientific.com
Emp.: 500
Medical Equipment Whslr
N.A.I.C.S.: 423450

Boston Scientific Gesellschaft m.b.H. (1)
Vienna Twin Tower Turm A/ 19 OG Wienerbergstrasse 11, 1100, Vienna, Austria
Tel.: (43) 160810
Medical Equipment Whslr
N.A.I.C.S.: 423450

Boston Scientific Group plc (1)
6th floor Haarlerbergweg 23-G, Amsterdam,
6468 EX, Netherlands
Tel.: (31) 433568220
Emp.: 150
Medical Equipment Distr
N.A.I.C.S.: 423450

Boston Scientific Hellas S.A. (1)
336 Vouliagmenis Ave and 1 Griva Digeni,
Agios Dimitrios, 17342, Athens, Greece
Tel.: (30) 210 954 2400
Web Site: http://www.baci.com
Medical Equipment Whslr
N.A.I.C.S.: 622110

Boston Scientific Hong Kong Limited (1)
12/F W Square 318 Hennessy Road, Wanchai, 135 984, China (Hong Kong)
Tel.: (852) 29607100
Medical Equipment Whslr
N.A.I.C.S.: 423450

Boston Scientific International B.V. (1)
Vestastraat 6, 6468 EX, Kerkrade, Netherlands
Tel.: (31) 455467700
Web Site: https://www.bsce.com
Emp.: 3
Medical Equipment Mfr & Whslr
N.A.I.C.S.: 334510

Boston Scientific International S.A. (1)
Parc d'Affaires Le Val Saint-Quentin-
Batiment H 2 Rue Rene Caudron, 78960,
Voisins-le-Bretonneux, France **(100%)**
Tel.: (33) 3 930 4900
Web Site: http://www.bostonscientific.com
Cardiology & Electrophysiology Medical Devices & Therapies
N.A.I.C.S.: 334510

Group (Non-US):

Guidant Europe SA/NV (2)
Green Square Lambroekstraat 5D, 1831,
Diegem, Belgium
Tel.: (32) 2 416 7011
Web Site: https://www.bostonscientific.com
Sales Range: $350-399.9 Million
Emp.: 100
Cardiovascular Therapeutic Devices & Related Products Developer & Distr
N.A.I.C.S.: 339112

Branch (Non-US):

Boston Scientific - Vienna (3)
Vienna Twin Tower Turm A/19 OG, Wienerbergstrasse 11, 1100, Vienna, Austria
Tel.: (43) 160810
Web Site: http://www.bostonscientific.com
Sales Range: $50-74.9 Million
Emp.: 100

Cardiovascular Therapeutic Devices & Related Products
N.A.I.C.S.: 423450

Subsidiary (Non-US):

Boston Scientific Clonmel (CRM) (3)
Cashel Rd, Clonmel, Co Tipperary, Ireland
Tel.: (353) 526181000
Web Site: http://www.bostonscientific.com
Sales Range: $500-549.9 Million
Emp.: 830
Mfr of Cardiovascular Therapeutic Devices
& Related Products
N.A.I.C.S.: 339112

Boston Scientific Japan K.K. (1)
Nakano Central Park South 15th Floor
4-10-2, Nakano-ku, Tokyo, 164-0001,
Japan **(100%)**
Tel.: (81) 36 853 1000
Web Site: https://www.bostonscientific.com
Cardiac & Cardiovascular Devices Mfr
N.A.I.C.S.: 334510
Tomoyuki Morikawa *(CEO)*

Boston Scientific Latin America B.V. (1)
Gaetano Martinolaan 50, Maastricht, 6229
GS, Netherlands
Tel.: (31) 433568220
Medical Equipment Whslr
N.A.I.C.S.: 423450

Boston Scientific Lebanon SAL (1)
Rashid Karame St Ibiza Bldg 5th Fl, PO
Box 13-6045, Beirut, Lebanon
Tel.: (961) 1 805 282
Medical Equipment Whslr
N.A.I.C.S.: 423450

Boston Scientific Limited (1)
5060 Spectrum Way Suite 500A, Mississauga, L4W 5N5, ON, Canada **(100%)**
Tel.: (905) 219-6900
Web Site: https://www.bostonscientific.ca
Sales Range: $10-24.9 Million
Emp.: 40
Cardiac & Cardiovascular Devices Mfr
N.A.I.C.S.: 334510

Boston Scientific Medizintechnik GmbH (1)
Klaus-Bungert-Strasse 8, 40468, Dusseldorf, Germany
Tel.: (49) 2118 823 9000
Web Site: https://www.bostonscientific.com
Medical Equipment Whslr
N.A.I.C.S.: 423450
Emily Marie Woodworth *(Mng Dir)*

Boston Scientific Nederland B.V. (1)
Vestastraat 6, 6468 EX, Kerkrade, Netherlands
Tel.: (31) 455467700
Sales Range: $900-999.9 Million
Emp.: 35
Distr of Cardiovascular Therapeutic Devices
& Related Products
N.A.I.C.S.: 339112

Boston Scientific Neuromodulation Corporation (1)
25155 Rye Canyon Loop, Valencia, CA
91355
Tel.: (661) 949-4000
Web Site: https://www.controlyourpain.com
Sales Range: $300-349.9 Million
Developer of Implantable Neuromodulation
Devices
N.A.I.C.S.: 339112

Subsidiary (Domestic):

Cosman Medical, LLC (2)
22 Terry Ave, Burlington, MA
01803 **(100%)**
Tel.: (781) 272-6561
Develops & Distributes Radiofrequency
Pain Management & Neurosurgery Products
N.A.I.C.S.: 334510

Boston Scientific New Zealand Limited (1)
3 Diamond Street, Eden Terrace, Auckland,
1021, New Zealand
Tel.: (64) 800742678
Sales Range: $25-49.9 Million
Emp.: 4
Medical Equipment Whslr

N.A.I.C.S.: 423450

Boston Scientific Nordic AB **(1)**
Jarnvagsgatan 45, 252 25, Helsingborg,
Sweden
Tel.: (46) 42256900
Medical Equipment Distr
N.A.I.C.S.: 423450

Boston Scientific Philippines, Inc. **(1)**
Unit 2503 Antel Global Corporate Centre
Julia Vargas Avenue, Ortigas Center, Pasig,
1605, Philippines
Tel.: (63) 26876994
Web Site: https://www.bostonscientific.com
Sales Range: $25-49.9 Million
Emp.: 12
Medical Equipment Mfr & Whslr
N.A.I.C.S.: 423450

Boston Scientific Polska Sp. Z
o.o. **(1)**
Al Jana Pawla II 22 pietro 7, 00-133, War-
saw, Poland
Tel.: (48) 224351414
Medical Equipment Whslr
N.A.I.C.S.: 423450

Boston Scientific Pty. Ltd. **(1)**
Building 1 Level 6 Connect Corporate Cen-
tre 191 ORiordan Street, Mascot, 2020,
NSW, Australia
Tel.: (61) 800676133
Web Site:
    https://www.bostonscientific.com.au
Hospital Equipment Whslr
N.A.I.C.S.: 423450

Boston Scientific S.A.S. **(1)**
Parc d'Affaires Le Val Saint-Quentin - Bati-
ment H 2 Rue Rene Caudron, 78960,
Voisins-le-Bretonneux, France
Tel.: (33) 139309700
Web Site: https://www.bostonscientific.com
Medical Equipment Whslr
N.A.I.C.S.: 423450

Boston Scientific Scimed, Inc. **(1)**
1 Scimed Pl, Maple Grove, MN 55311-1566
Tel.: (763) 494-1700
Medical Equipment Whslr
N.A.I.C.S.: 423450

Boston Scientific SpA **(1)**
Viale Enrico Forlanini 23, 20134, Milan, Italy
Tel.: (39) 02269831
Web Site: http://www.bostonscientific-
    international.com
Sales Range: $50-74.9 Million
Emp.: 100
Cardiovascular Therapeutic Devices & Re-
lated Products
N.A.I.C.S.: 423450

Boston Scientific Sverige AB **(1)**
Berga Alle 1, Helsingborg, 254 52, Sweden
Tel.: (46) 42256900
Medical Equipment
N.A.I.C.S.: 423450

Boston Scientific de Mexico, S.A. de
C.V. **(1)**
Insurgentes Sur 1602 Piso 2 Colonia Credit
Builder Benito Juarez, Del Valle, 03940,
Mexico, Mexico
Tel.: (52) 5559924100
Sales Range: $25-49.9 Million
Emp.: 50
Medical Equipment Whslr
N.A.I.C.S.: 423450

Boston Scientific del Carribe,
Inc. **(1)**
350 Chardon Ave Torre Chardon Ste 820,
San Juan, PR 00918
Tel.: (787) 620-9240
Web Site: http://www.bostonscientific.com
Sales Range: $100-124.9 Million
Emp.: 200
Pacemakers, Implantable Cardioverter Defi-
brillators, Cardiac Resynchronization
Therapy Devices & Minimally Invasive Car-
diac Surgery Devices
N.A.I.C.S.: 339112

Claret Medical, Inc. **(1)**
1745 Copperhill Pkwy Ste 1, Santa Rosa,
CA 95403
Tel.: (707) 528-7253
Web Site: http://www.claretmedical.com

Medical Equipment Mfr
N.A.I.C.S.: 339112

EndoChoice Holdings, Inc. **(1)**
11810 Wills Rd, Alpharetta, GA 30009
Tel.: (888) 682-3636
Web Site: http://www.endochoice.com
Holding Company; Medical Device Mfr
N.A.I.C.S.: 551112

Subsidiary (Domestic):

EndoChoice, Inc. **(2)**
11810 Wills Rd, Alpharetta, GA 30009
Tel.: (888) 682-3636
Web Site: https://www.endochoice.com
Medical Diagnostic Device Mfr
N.A.I.C.S.: 334510

Lumenis Ltd. **(1)**
Yokneam Industrial Park Hakidma 6, Yok-
neam, 2069204, Israel
Tel.: (972) 4 959 9000
Web Site: https://www.lumenis.com
Sales Range: $250-299.9 Million
Medical Equipment & Supplies Mfr & Distr
N.A.I.C.S.: 339112
Qiying Zhai *(Reg Pres-APAC & Japan & Sr*
VP)
Noa Greenshpon *(Dir-Human Resources-*
Israel,EMEA)
Doug Stante *(Dir)*
Roy Ramati *(Reg-Business Development)*
Hadas Padan *(VP)*
Ezi Hayon *(VP-Operations)*
Ayelet Peled *(VP-Human Resources)*
Amir Lichter *(VP-Research & Development-*
Global)
Eran Cohen *(VP-Operations-Global)*
Shlomi Cohen *(CFO)*
Osnat Philipp *(VP & Gen Mgr)*
Brad Oliver *(Reg & Reg)*
Ido Warshavski *(Gen Counsel, Sec & VP)*
Tzipi Ozer-Armon *(CEO)*
Rani Hagag *(VP)*
Karen Smith *(VP-Regulatory Affairs-Quality)*

Subsidiary (US):

Lumenis **(2)**
2033 Gateway Pl Ste 200, San Jose, CA
95110
Tel.: (408) 764-3000
Web Site: http://www.lumenis.com
Sales Range: $50-74.9 Million
Emp.: 150
Ophthalmic & Surgical Laser Mfr
N.A.I.C.S.: 334516
George Rodriguez *(Coord-Medical Demo)*
Dana Rivinius *(Mgr-Customer Support)*
Audrey Szutu *(VP-Fin)*

Subsidiary (Non-US):

Lumenis (France) SARL **(2)**
Plateau Technologique de Saclay Batiment
Le Diamant, 4 rue Rene Razel, 91400, Or-
say, France
Tel.: (33) 169331420
Drugs & Druggists Sundries Whslr
N.A.I.C.S.: 424210

Lumenis (Germany) GmbH **(2)**
Hanauer Landstrasse 291A, 60314, Frank-
furt am Main, Germany
Tel.: (49) 610383350
Sales Range: $25-49.9 Million
Emp.: 40
Electromedical & Electrotherapeutic Appa-
ratE Mfr
N.A.I.C.S.: 334510

Lumenis (HK) Limited **(2)**
16/F The Cameron 33 Cameron Road,
Tsimshatsui, Kowloon, China (Hong Kong)
Tel.: (852) 21742800
Web Site: https://www.lumenis.com
Sales Range: $25-49.9 Million
Emp.: 18
Medical Industrial & Scientific Laser Mfr
N.A.I.C.S.: 334517

Lumenis (Italy) SRL **(2)**
Via Delle Macere 20, 00060, Formello,
Rome, Italy
Tel.: (39) 069075230
Web Site: https://www.lumenis.com
Electromedical Device Mfr
N.A.I.C.S.: 334510

Lumenis (UK), Ltd. **(2)**

2nd Floor Merit House, The Hyde, London,
NW9 5AB, United Kingdom
Tel.: (44) 2083244200
Sales Range: $25-49.9 Million
Emp.: 10
Surgical & Medical Instrument Mfr
N.A.I.C.S.: 339112

Lumenis Holdings (Holland) B.V. **(2)**
Regus Gebouw Herengracht 574, 1017CJ,
Amsterdam, Netherlands
Tel.: (31) 203475060
Medical Dental & Hospital Equipment &
Supplies Whslr
N.A.I.C.S.: 423450

Lumenis India Private Ltd **(2)**
Unit 308 309 3rd Floor Suncity Business
Tower, Sector-54 Golf Course Road, Gur-
gaon, 122002, Haryana, India
Tel.: (91) 124 4210795
Web Site: http://www.lumenis.com
Sales Range: $25-49.9 Million
Emp.: 50
Medical Device Mfr
N.A.I.C.S.: 334510
Paritosh Arora *(Country Mgr)*

Lumenis Japan Co. Ltd. **(2)**
No 31 Kowa Bldg, 3-19-1 Shirokanedai
Minato-ku, 108-0071, Tokyo, Japan
Tel.: (81) 357898300
Medical Dental & Hospital Equipment &
Supplies Whslr
N.A.I.C.S.: 423450

PT Boston Scientific Indonesia **(1)**
Prudential Tower 28th Floor, Jl Jenderal
Sudirman Kav 79 Setiabudi, Jakarta,
12920, Indonesia
Tel.: (62) 80869000
Web Site: https://amcham.or.id
Medical Equipment Distr
N.A.I.C.S.: 423450

Precision Vascular Systems, Inc. **(1)**
2405 W Orton Cir, West Valley City, UT
84119
Tel.: (801) 974-1700
Sales Range: $50-74.9 Million
Emp.: 300
Surgical & Medical Instrument Mfr
N.A.I.C.S.: 339112

Relievant Medsystems Inc. **(1)**
2688 Middlefield Rd Ste A, Redwood City,
CA 94063-3483
Tel.: (650) 298-9205
Web Site: http://www.relievant.com
Surgical & Medical Instrument Mfr
N.A.I.C.S.: 339112
Richard W. Mott *(Chm)*
Alex Di Nello *(COO)*
Ray M. Baker *(Chief Medical Officer)*
Tyler Binney *(Pres & CEO)*

Rhythmia Medical, Inc. **(1)**
111 S Bedford St Ste 205, Burlington, MA
01803
Tel.: (617) 591-9191
Medical Equipment Distr
N.A.I.C.S.: 423450

Sadra Medical, Inc. **(1)**
160 Knowles Dr, Los Gatos, CA
95032 **(100%)**
Tel.: (408) 370-1550
Web Site: http://www.sadramedical.com
Sales Range: $25-49.9 Million
Emp.: 100
Medical Device Mfr
N.A.I.C.S.: 339112
Micheal McConnohie *(Pres)*

Silk Road Medical, Inc. **(1)**
1213 Innsbruck Dr, Sunnyvale, CA 94089
Tel.: (408) 720-9002
Web Site: https://www.silkroadmed.com
Rev.: $138,638,000
Assets: $269,685,000
Liabilities: $105,810,000
Net Worth: $163,875,000
Earnings: ($55,010,000)
Emp.: 414
Fiscal Year-end: 12/31/2022
Medical Device Mfr & Distr
N.A.I.C.S.: 339113
Daniel J. Brennan *(Officer)*
Michael F. Mahoney *(Officer)*
Emily M. Woodworth *(Officer)*

StarMedTec GmbH **(1)**
Kreuzstrasse 22, Starnberg, 82319, Ger-
many
Tel.: (49) 8151268610
Medical Equipment Distr
N.A.I.C.S.: 423450

Symetis SA **(1)**
Chemin de la Venoge 11, 1024, Ecublens,
Switzerland
Tel.: (41) 216510160
Web Site: http://www.bostonscientific.com
Heart Valve Replacement Devices Devel-
oper & Mfr
N.A.I.C.S.: 339112

Veniti, Inc. **(1)**
4025 Clipper Ct, Fremont, CA
94538 **(100%)**
Tel.: (314) 888-9225
Medical Device Company
N.A.I.C.S.: 339112
Daniel Recinella *(VP-R&D)*

BOTS INC.
1064 Ave Ponce De Leon Ste 200,
San Juan, PR 00907
Tel.: (939) 212-9068   NV
Web Site: https://www.bots.bz
Year Founded: 2010
BTZI—(OTCIQ)
Rev.: $115
Assets: $915,934
Liabilities: $727,946
Net Worth: $187,988
Earnings: ($3,883,988)
Emp.: 3
Fiscal Year-end: 04/30/20
Cannabis Technology, Products &
Services Distr
N.A.I.C.S.: 424210
Simon Rubin *(Chm & Interim CEO)*
Yuri Abramov *(Dir)*

BOULDER GROWTH & IN-
COME FUND INC.
2344 Spruce St Ste A, Boulder, CO
80302
Tel.: (303) 449-0426
BIF—(NYSE)
Rev.: $22,447,483
Assets: $1,394,163,574
Liabilities: $1,610,406
Net Worth: $1,392,553,168
Earnings: $7,319,011
Fiscal Year-end: 11/30/19
Investment Management Service
N.A.I.C.S.: 525990
Stewart Ralph Horejsi *(Mgr-Fund)*
Joel W. Looney *(Chm & Pres)*

BOULEVARD ACQUISITION
CORP. II
399 Park Ave 6th Fl, New York, NY
10022
Tel.: (212) 878-3500   DE
Year Founded: 2015
BLVDU—(NASDAQ)
Sales Range: Less than $1 Million
Emp.: 3
Investment Services
N.A.I.C.S.: 523999
Thomas More Larkin *(CFO)*
Marc Lasry *(Chm)*
Randolph Scott Takian *(VP-Acq)*
Stephen S. Trevor *(Pres, CEO &*
Sec)

BOURQUE INDUSTRIES, INC.
8700 E Tanque Verde Rd Ste 134,
Tucson, AZ 85749
Tel.: (520) 390-6099   AZ
Web Site:
http://www.bourqueindustriesinc.com
Year Founded: 1978
BORK—(OTCIQ)
Sales Range: Less than $1 Million

Bourque Industries, Inc.—(Continued)

Metal Alloy Mfr
N.A.I.C.S.: 331110
Carol J. Condon *(Interim CEO)*
John M. Bourque *(Chief Science Officer)*
Juan C. Mendoza *(Chief Security Officer)*

BOWEN ACQUISITION CORP.
420 Lexington Ave Ste 2446, New York, NY 10170
Tel.: (203) 998-5540 Ky
Web Site:
https://www.bowenspac.com
Year Founded: 2023
BOWN—(NASDAQ)
Investment Management Service
N.A.I.C.S.: 523999

BOWLERO CORP
222 W 44th St, New York, NY 10036
Tel.: (212) 680-0012
Web Site:
http://www.bowlerocorp.com
BOWL—(NYSE)
Rev.: $1,154,614,000
Assets: $3,114,035,000
Liabilities: $3,163,887,000
Net Worth: ($49,852,000)
Earnings: ($83,581,000)
Emp.: 3,419
Fiscal Year-end: 06/30/24
Bowling Center Operator
N.A.I.C.S.: 713950
Robert Lavan *(CFO)*
Thomas F. Shannon *(Founder & CEO)*
Brett I. Parker *(Vice Chm)*
Bobby Lavan *(CFO)*

Subsidiaries:

Bowl America Incorporated (1)
6446 Edsall Rd, Alexandria, VA 22312
Tel.: (703) 941-6300
Web Site: http://www.bowl-america.com
Rev.: $17,780,942
Assets: $28,613,309
Liabilities: $6,096,292
Net Worth: $22,517,017
Earnings: $403,192
Emp.: 250
Fiscal Year-end: 06/28/2020
Bowling Centers Operator; Food & Beverage Services, Game Rooms, Rental Lockers & Playroom Facilities
N.A.I.C.S.: 713950

Subsidiary (Domestic):

Bowl America Shirley Inc. (2)
6450 Edsall Rd, Alexandria, VA 22312
Tel.: (703) 354-3300
Bowling Centers
N.A.I.C.S.: 713950

Falls Church Bowl Inc. (2)
140 S Maple Ave, Falls Church, VA 22046
Tel.: (703) 534-1370
Bowling Centers
N.A.I.C.S.: 713950
Leslie H. Goldberg *(Pres)*

Double Decker Lanes (1)
300 Golf Course Dr, Rohnert Park, CA 94928-1799
Tel.: (707) 585-0226
Web Site:
http://www.doubledeckerlanes.com
Bowling Centers
N.A.I.C.S.: 713950
Jim Decker III *(Owner)*

Manatee Lanes (1)
7715 W Gulf To Lk Hwy, Crystal River, FL 34429-7929
Tel.: (352) 795-4546
Web Site: http://www.manatee-lanes.com
Bowling Centers
N.A.I.C.S.: 713950

Strike Holdings LLC (1)
222 W 44th St, New York, NY 10036

Tel.: (212) 777-2214
Web Site: http://www.bowlmor-amf.com
Sales Range: $450-499.9 Million
Emp.: 7,500
Bowling Alley Operator
N.A.I.C.S.: 713990
Thomas Shannon *(Founder, Chm, Pres & CEO)*
Brett Parker *(Vice Chm, CFO & Exec VP)*

Subsidiary (Domestic):

AMF Bowling Worldwide, Inc. (2)
7313 Bell Creek Rd, Mechanicsville, VA 23111
Tel.: (804) 730-4000
Web Site: http://www.amf.com
Sales Range: $500-549.9 Million
Bowling Equipment & Supplies Mfr; Bowling Lanes & Bowling Centers Operator
N.A.I.C.S.: 713950
Tom Shannon *(CEO)*

Subsidiary (Domestic):

AMF Bowling Centers, Inc. (3)
7313 Bell Creek Rd, Mechanicsville, VA 23111
Tel.: (804) 730-4000
Web Site: http://www.amf.com
Sales Range: $25-49.9 Million
Emp.: 200
Bowling Lanes & Bowling Centers Operator
N.A.I.C.S.: 713950
Kelly Clifton *(Coord-Mktg-Food & Beverage)*
Shelby Hale *(Mgr-Benefits)*

QubicaAMF Worldwide, LLC (3)
8100 AMF Dr, Mechanicsville, VA 23111 (50%)
Tel.: (804) 569-1000
Web Site: http://www.qubicaamf.com
Sales Range: $25-49.9 Million
Emp.: 300
Bowling Equipment & Supplies Mfr & Marketer
N.A.I.C.S.: 339920
Stephanie Darby *(Dir-Mktg)*
Mark Kilpatrick *(Sr VP-Ops)*
Jay Buhl *(Sr VP & Gen Mgr)*
Roger Creamer *(Dir-Intl Rels & Sports Dev & Reg Mgr)*
Pat Ciniello *(Chm)*
Luca Drusiani *(Exec VP-Ops & Intl Svcs)*
Alberto Elli *(Pres & COO)*
Chris Caesar *(CFO & Sr VP-HR)*
Massimo Baraldi *(CTO)*
Wayne White *(Sr VP & Gen Mgr-Pins)*

Sheridan Lanes, Inc. (3)
3121 S Sheridan Rd, Tulsa, OK 74145
Tel.: (918) 627-2728
Web Site: http://www.amf.com
Sales Range: $1-9.9 Million
Emp.: 150
Bowling Centers
N.A.I.C.S.: 713950

Strikes Unlimited, Inc. (1)
5681 Lonetree Blvd, Rocklin, CA 95765-3735
Tel.: (916) 626-3600
Web Site: http://www.strikesrocklin.com
Bowling Centers
N.A.I.C.S.: 713950
Stacy Aldred *(Gen Mgr)*

BOWLIN TRAVEL CENTERS, INC.
150 Louisiana Blvd NE, Albuquerque, NM 87108
Tel.: (505) 266-5985 NV
Web Site: https://www.bowlintc.com
BWTL—(OTCIQ)
Rev.: $29,748,650
Assets: $27,576,052
Liabilities: $13,765,723
Net Worth: $13,810,329
Earnings: $790,870
Fiscal Year-end: 01/31/21
Gasoline Stations with Convenience Stores
N.A.I.C.S.: 457110

BOWMAN CONSULTING GROUP LTD.

12355 Sunrise Valley Dr Ste 520, Reston, VA 20191
Tel.: (703) 464-1000
Web Site: https://www.bowman.com
Year Founded: 1995
BWMN—(NASDAQ)
Rev.: $261,714,000
Assets: $255,757,000
Liabilities: $132,898,000
Net Worth: $122,859,000
Earnings: $4,222,000
Emp.: 1,600
Fiscal Year-end: 12/31/22
Engineering Consulting Services
N.A.I.C.S.: 541330
Gary Bowman *(Founder, Chm & Pres)*
Michael Bruen *(CEO)*
Bruce Labovitz *(CFO)*
Daniel Swayze *(COO)*
Matt Mullenix *(CIO & Exec VP)*

Subsidiaries:

Advanced Applied Engineering, Inc. (1)
601 Valencia Ave Ste 250, Brea, CA 92823
Tel.: (714) 940-0100
Web Site: https://www.infrastructure-engineers.com
Sales Range: $1-9.9 Million
Emp.: 22
Engineering Services
N.A.I.C.S.: 541330

BTM Engineering Inc. (1)
3001 Taylor Springs Dr, Louisville, KY 40220
Tel.: (502) 459-8402
Web Site: http://www.btmeng.com
Rev.: $3,000,000
Emp.: 40
Engineering Services
N.A.I.C.S.: 541330
John M. Addington *(Mgr-Plng)*
Michael J. Smith *(Pres)*

Blankinship & Associates, Inc. (1)
1590 Drew Ave Ste 120, Davis, CA 95618-7849
Tel.: (530) 757-0941
Web Site: http://www.h2osci.com
Environmental Consulting Services
N.A.I.C.S.: 541620
Mike Blankinship *(Founder & Pres)*

Cfa, Inc. (1)
1150 Corporate Blvd, Reno, NV 89502
Tel.: (775) 856-1150
Web Site: http://www.cfareno.com
Sales Range: $1-9.9 Million
Emp.: 37
Engineering Services
N.A.I.C.S.: 541330
Angela Fuss *(Dir-Plng)*
Robert O. LaRiviere *(Pres)*
Ashley Elson *(Designer-Civil)*
Brenda Hermes *(Designer-Civil)*
Jonathon D. Lau *(Designer-Civil)*
Kevin German *(Principal & Dir-Surveying)*
Lonnie Johnson *(Principal & Dir-Engrg)*
Russell Applegate *(Project Mgr)*

Dennis Corporation (1)
1800 Huger St, Columbia, SC 29201
Tel.: (803) 252-0991
Web Site:
https://www.denniscorporation.com
Sales Range: $10-24.9 Million
Emp.: 72
Construction Management Services
N.A.I.C.S.: 237990
Dan Dennis *(Pres)*
Roger Burriss *(Mgr-ITS)*
Frank Hribar *(VP)*
Mark Johnston *(VP-Ops)*
Travis Miller *(Mgr-West Virginia)*
Andrew Nichols *(Mgr-Traffic Engrg)*
Kyle Titus *(Mgr-Civil Infrastructure)*
Charles Arndt *(Mgr-ITS)*
Matt Hines *(Mgr-Transportation Design)*
Ricky Craps *(VP & Mgr-Special Inspections)*

Excellence Engineering, LLC (1)
8760 S Peoria Ave, Tulsa, OK 74132
Tel.: (918) 298-5500
Web Site: http://www.eeinco.com

Electrical Contractor
N.A.I.C.S.: 238210
Dee Hays *(CEO)*

Fabre Engineering, Inc. (1)
119 Gregory Sq, Pensacola, FL 32502
Tel.: (850) 433-6438
Web Site: http://www.fabreinc.com
Sales Range: $1-9.9 Million
Emp.: 24
Engineering Services
N.A.I.C.S.: 541330
Frank J. Fabre *(Founder & Pres)*

Hess Rountree Inc (1)
9831 S 51st St, Phoenix, AZ 85044
Tel.: (480) 496-0244
Web Site: http://www.hessrountree.com
Rev.: $2,300,000
Emp.: 20
Engineering Services
N.A.I.C.S.: 541330

Hole Montes, Inc. (1)
950 Encore Way, Naples, FL 34110
Tel.: (239) 254-2000
Web Site: https://www.holemontes.com
Sales Range: $10-24.9 Million
Emp.: 110
Engineering Services
N.A.I.C.S.: 541330
George Hermanson *(Sr VP)*
Terry Cole *(VP)*
Bob Mulhere *(CEO)*

KTA Group Inc. (1)
13755 Sunrise Valley Dr Ste 500, Herndon, VA 20171
Tel.: (703) 713-0300
Web Site: http://www.ktagroup.com
Rev.: $10,000,000
Emp.: 100
Engineering Services
N.A.I.C.S.: 541330
Robert Grimes *(Sr VP)*
Enrique H. Rodriguez *(Dir-Electrical Engrg)*
Randolph Thompson *(Pres)*

McFarland-Dyer & Associates Inc. (1)
4174 Silver Peak Pkwy, Suwanee, GA 30024
Tel.: (770) 932-6550
Web Site: http://www.gomda.net
Rev.: $2,000,000
Emp.: 21
Engineering Services
N.A.I.C.S.: 541330
Phyllis Lamme *(Pres)*
Chris Whitley *(Principal)*

Omland Engineering Associates, Inc. (1)
51 Horsehill Rd, Cedar Knolls, NJ 07027
Tel.: (973) 359-8400
Web Site: http://www.omland.com
Engineering Services
N.A.I.C.S.: 541330
Stanley T. Omland *(Pres)*
Dave Dixon *(Dir-Surveying)*
Eric L. Keller *(Pres)*
Geoffrey R. Lanza *(VP)*
William H. Hamilton *(VP)*
James Woods *(Chief Engr)*
Charles Thomas Jr. *(VP)*

PCD Engineering Services, Inc. (1)
323 3rd Ave Ste 3, Longmont, CO 80501-1970
Tel.: (303) 678-1108
Web Site: http://www.pcdengineering.com
Engineering Services
N.A.I.C.S.: 541330
Peter D'Antonio *(Pres)*

Richter & Associates Inc. (1)
15865 Crabbs Branch Way, Derwood, MD 20855-2635
Tel.: (301) 154-7475
Web Site: http://richter-associates.com
Power & Communication Line Construction
N.A.I.C.S.: 237130
Stephen Richter *(Founder & CEO)*

Speece Lewis Engineers, Inc. (1)
3534 S 48th St Ste 4, Lincoln, NE 68506
Tel.: (402) 483-5466
Web Site: http://www.speecelewis.com
Sales Range: $1-9.9 Million
Emp.: 24
Engineering Services

N.A.I.C.S.: 541330
Chris Lane *(VP)*

Surdex Corp. **(1)**
520 Spirit Of Saint Louis Blvd, Chesterfield, MO 63005
Tel.: (636) 532-3427
Web Site: http://www.surdex.com
Rev.: $5,530,000
Emp.: 70
Geophysical Surveying & Mapping Services
N.A.I.C.S.: 541360
Ron Hoffmann *(Pres)*
Ed Turner *(VP-Sls)*

Trudell Consulting Engineers, Inc. **(1)**
478 Blair Park Rd, Williston, VT 05495
Tel.: (802) 879-6331
Web Site: https://tcevt.com
Rev.: $1,896,000
Emp.: 12
Engineeering Services
N.A.I.C.S.: 541330
Jeremy Matosky *(Pres)*

BOWMO, INC.
99 Wall St Ste 891, New York, NY 10005
Tel.: (212) 398-0002   OK
Web Site: https://bowmo.com
Year Founded: 1999
BOMO—(OTCIQ)
Rev.: $243,434
Assets: $26,318
Liabilities: $4,664,862
Net Worth: ($4,638,544)
Earnings: ($3,748,952)
Fiscal Year-end: 12/31/23
Franchise Development Services
N.A.I.C.S.: 533110
Michael Neece *(Chief Product Officer)*
Jay Curry *(Chief People Officer)*
Keith Carlson *(CIO)*
Eddie Aizman *(Founder & CEO)*
Michael E. Lakshin *(Chm & Pres)*

BOWX ACQUISITION CORP.
2400 Sand Hill Rd Ste 200, Menlo Park, CA 94025
Tel.: (650) 352-4877   DE
Year Founded: 2020
BOWXU—(NASDAQ)
Investment Services
N.A.I.C.S.: 523999
Vivek Ranadive *(Chm & Co-CEO)*
Murray Rode *(Co-CEO, CFO, Treas & Sec)*

BOX, INC.
900 Jefferson Ave, Redwood City, CA 94063   DE
Web Site: https://www.box.com
Year Founded: 2005
BOX—(NYSE)
Rev.: $990,874,000
Assets: $1,207,165,000
Liabilities: $1,731,016,000
Net Worth: ($523,851,000)
Earnings: $8,567,000
Emp.: 2,487
Fiscal Year-end: 01/31/23
Content Sharing Software
N.A.I.C.S.: 513210
Arnold Goldberg *(Executives)*
Mark Wayland *(Chief Revenue Officer)*
Jessica Swank *(Chief People Officer & Sr VP)*
Thierry Chassaing *(Sr VP-Engrg)*
Diego Dugatkin *(Chief Product Officer & Sr VP)*
Ravi Malick *(CIO-Global)*
Julien Soriano *(Chief Information Security Officer)*
Katsunori Furuichi *(Pres & Mng Dir-Japan)*
Sebastien Marotte *(Pres & Pres-Europe, The Middle East, and Africa)*

Aaron Levie *(Co-Founder, CEO & CEO)*
Dylan Smith *(CFO)*
Olivia Nottebohm *(COO)*
David Leeb *(Chief Legal Officer & Sec)*
Jon Herstein *(Chief Customer Officer & Sr VP-Customer Success)*

Subsidiaries:

Box.com (UK) Ltd **(1)**
14-15th Floors White Collar Factory 1 Old Street Yard, London, EC1Y 8AF, United Kingdom
Tel.: (44) 8081890504
Software Development Services
N.A.I.C.S.: 541511

BOXLIGHT CORPORATION
2750 Premier Pkwy Ste 900, Duluth, GA 30097
Tel.: (678) 367-0809   NV
Web Site: https://www.boxlight.com
Year Founded: 2014
BOXL—(NASDAQ)
Rev.: $221,781,000
Assets: $195,395,000
Liabilities: $143,502,000
Net Worth: $51,893,000
Earnings: ($5,012,000)
Emp.: 187
Fiscal Year-end: 12/31/22
Interactive Educational Product Distr
N.A.I.C.S.: 423430
Dale W. Strang *(Interim CEO)*
Shaun Marklew *(CTO)*
Greg Wiggins *(CFO)*
Sunshine Nance *(VP-Global Mktg & Comm)*
Dale W. Strang *(CEO)*
James Mark Elliott *(Chief Comml Officer)*

Subsidiaries:

Modern Robotics Inc. **(1)**
13335 SW 124th St Ste 115, Miami, FL 33186
Tel.: (786) 393-6886
Web Site: http://www.modernroboticsinc.com
Electrical & Electronic Equipment Mfr
N.A.I.C.S.: 336320

Qwizdom **(1)**
12617 Meridian E, Puyallup, WA 98373
Web Site: http://www.qwizdom.com
Educational Software Development Services
N.A.I.C.S.: 513210

Sahara Presentation Systems Limited **(1)**
Europa House Littlebrook DC1 Shield Road, Dartford, DA1 5PZ, United Kingdom
Tel.: (44) 2083197777
Web Site: https://www.saharaav.com
Electronic Equipment Distr
N.A.I.C.S.: 423690

Sedao Limited **(1)**
Europa House Littlebrook Shield Road, Dartford, DA1 5PZ, United Kingdom
Tel.: (44) 1271440400
Web Site: http://www.sedaosignage.com
Information Technology Services
N.A.I.C.S.: 541519

BOYD GAMING CORPORATION
6465 S Rainbow Blvd, Las Vegas, NV 89118
Tel.: (702) 792-7200   NV
Web Site: https://www.boydgaming.com
Year Founded: 1974
BYD—(NYSE)
Rev.: $3,738,492,000
Assets: $6,273,126,000
Liabilities: $4,529,024,000
Net Worth: $1,744,102,000
Earnings: $620,023,000

Emp.: 16,129
Fiscal Year-end: 12/31/23
Holding Company; Casino Hotels Owner & Operator
N.A.I.C.S.: 551112
William R. Boyd *(VP)*
Keith E. Smith *(Pres & CEO)*
William S. Boyd *(Co-Founder)*
Stephen S. Thompson *(Chief Admin Officer)*
Josh Hirsberg *(CFO, Treas & Exec VP)*
Theodore A. Bogich *(COO)*
Lori M. Nelson *(Chief Acctg Officer)*
Uri Clinton *(Gen Counsel)*
Marianne Boyd Johnson *(Exec Chm)*

Subsidiaries:

ALST Casino Holdco, LLC **(1)**
7300 Aliante Pkwy, North Las Vegas, NV 89084
Tel.: (702) 692-7777
Web Site: http://www.aliantegaming.com
Sales Range: $75-99.9 Million
Holding Company; Casino Hotel Operator
N.A.I.C.S.: 551112

Subsidiary (Domestic):

Aliante Gaming, LLC **(2)**
7300 Aliante Pkwy, North Las Vegas, NV 89084
Tel.: (702) 692-7777
Web Site: https://aliante.boydgaming.com
Casino Hotel Operator
N.A.I.C.S.: 721120

Ameristar Casino Kansas City, LLC **(1)**
3200 N Ameristar Dr, Kansas City, MO 64161   **(100%)**
Tel.: (816) 414-7000
Web Site: https://ameristarkansascity.boydgaming.com
Sales Range: $200-249.9 Million
Emp.: 2,000
Hotel & Casino Operations
N.A.I.C.S.: 721120

Ameristar Casino St. Charles, LLC **(1)**
1 Ameristar Blvd, Saint Charles, MO 63301   **(100%)**
Tel.: (636) 949-7777
Web Site: https://ameristarstcharles.boydgaming.com
Sales Range: $75-99.9 Million
Emp.: 2,400
Hotel & Casino Operations
N.A.I.C.S.: 721120

Belle of Orleans, LLC **(1)**
500 Lake Palourde Rd, Amelia, LA 70340
Tel.: (985) 631-1777
Web Site: https://www.ameliabellecasino.com
Sales Range: $100-124.9 Million
Emp.: 300
Riverboat Casino Operator
N.A.I.C.S.: 713210

Belterra Resort Indiana, LLC **(1)**
777 Belterra Dr, Florence, IN 47020
Tel.: (812) 427-7777
Web Site: http://www.belterracasino.com
Emp.: 950
Casino Hotels
N.A.I.C.S.: 721120

Blue Chip Casino, LLC **(1)**
777 Blue Chip Dr, Michigan City, IN 46360
Tel.: (219) 879-7711
Web Site: https://bluechip.boydgaming.com
Hotel Operating Services
N.A.I.C.S.: 721120

Boyd Biloxi, LLC **(1)**
850 Bayview Ave, Biloxi, MS 39530-1701
Tel.: (228) 436-3000
Hotel Operating Services
N.A.I.C.S.: 721120
Vincent Schwartz *(Sr VP)*

Boyd Racing, L.L.C. **(1)**
2717 Delta Downs Dr, Vinton, LA 70668

Tel.: (702) 792-7200
Web Site: https://deltadowns.boydgaming.com
Hotel Operating Services
N.A.I.C.S.: 721120

Boyd Shared Services Inc. **(1)**
2200 Moser Dr, Henderson, NV 89011
Tel.: (702) 692-8754
Casino & Gaming Services
N.A.I.C.S.: 721120

Boyd Tunica, Inc. **(1)**
1477 Casino Strip Resort Blvd, Robinsonville, MS 38664
Tel.: (662) 363-0711
Web Site: https://samstowntunica.boydgaming.com
Hotel & Casino
N.A.I.C.S.: 721120

California Hotel & Casino **(1)**
12 E Ogden Ave, Las Vegas, NV 89101-2943
Tel.: (702) 385-1222
Web Site: https://thecal.boydgaming.com
Hotel Operating Services
N.A.I.C.S.: 721120

Subsidiary (Domestic):

Eldorado, Inc. **(2)**
510 Avenida Cesar E Chavez, Kansas City, MO 64108
Tel.: (816) 474-3838
Web Site: https://www.eldo.us
Sales Range: $10-24.9 Million
Emp.: 25
Hotel Operating Services
N.A.I.C.S.: 721120

Coast Casinos, Inc. **(1)**
4000 W Flamingo Rd, Las Vegas, NV 89103
Tel.: (702) 367-7111
Web Site: http://www.goldcoastcasino.com
Sales Range: $25-49.9 Million
Emp.: 400
Hotel & Motel Services
N.A.I.C.S.: 721120

Subsidiary (Domestic):

Coast Hotels & Casinos, Inc. **(2)**
4000 W Flamingo Rd, Las Vegas, NV 89103
Tel.: (702) 367-7111
Web Site: https://goldcoast.boydgaming.com
Emp.: 7,742
Casino & Gaming Services
N.A.I.C.S.: 721120

Diamond Jo Worth, LLC **(1)**
777 Diamond Jo Ln, Northwood, IA 50459
Tel.: (641) 323-7777
Web Site: https://diamondjoworth.boydgaming.com
Casino
N.A.I.C.S.: 713210

Diamond Jo, LLC **(1)**
301 Bell St, Dubuque, IA 52001
Tel.: (563) 690-4800
Web Site: https://diamondjodubuque.boydgaming.com
Emp.: 450
Casino Operator
N.A.I.C.S.: 713210

Kansas Star Casino, LLC **(1)**
777 Kansas Star Dr, Mulvane, KS 67110
Tel.: (316) 719-5000
Web Site: https://kansasstar.boydgaming.com
Casino
N.A.I.C.S.: 713210

Lattner Entertainment Group Illinois, LLC **(1)**
4003 Tyler Dr, Ottawa, IL 61350
Tel.: (815) 313-0060
Web Site: https://www.lattnergaming.com
Gambling Industry Services
N.A.I.C.S.: 713290
Bobby Walsh *(Pres)*
Rick Hayne *(Acct Mgr)*
Nicholas Lanclos *(Dir-Ops)*
Gregg Maggio *(Acct Mgr)*
Phil Harth *(Mgr-Compliance)*
Maeckenzie Perino *(Mktg Mgr)*

Boyd Gaming Corporation—(Continued)

Subsidiary (Domestic):

Rock Solid Amusements, LLC   (2)
4003 Tyler Dr, Ottawa, IL 61350
Tel.: (815) 313-9562
Web Site:
    http://www.rocksolidamusements.com
Entertainment Services
N.A.I.C.S.: 713120

Nevada Palace, LLC   (1)
5255 Boulder Hwy, Las Vegas, NV 89122
Tel.: (702) 856-5300
Casino Hotel Owner & Operator
N.A.I.C.S.: 721120

Par-A-Dice Gaming Corporation   (1)
21 Blackjack Blvd, East Peoria, IL 61611
Tel.: (309) 699-7711
Web Site: https://paradice.boydgaming.com
Emp.: 700
Hotel Operating Services
N.A.I.C.S.: 721120

Red River Entertainment of Shreveport, LLC   (1)
315 Clyde Fant Pkwy, Shreveport, LA 71101
Tel.: (318) 424-7777
Web Site:
    https://www.samstownshreveport.com
Hotel Operating Services
N.A.I.C.S.: 721120

The Cannery Hotel & Casino, LLC   (1)
2121 E Craig Rd, North Las Vegas, NV 89030
Tel.: (702) 507-5700
Web Site: https://www.cannerycasino.com
Hotel & Casino Operator
N.A.I.C.S.: 721120

The Old Evangeline Downs, LLC   (1)
2235 Creswell Ln Ext, Opelousas, LA 70570
Tel.: (337) 594-3000
Web Site: http://www.evangelinedowns.com
Sales Range: $25-49.9 Million
Emp.: 500
Horse Race Track & Casino Operations
N.A.I.C.S.: 711212

Treasure Chest Casino, L.L.C.   (1)
4540 Williams Blvd, Kenner, LA 70065
Tel.: (504) 443-8000
Web Site:
    https://treasurechest.boydgaming.com
Casino & Gaming Services
N.A.I.C.S.: 721120

Treasure Chest, LLC   (1)
5050 Williams Blvd, Kenner, LA 70065
Tel.: (504) 443-8000
Web Site:
    https://treasurechest.boydgaming.com
Hotel Operating Services
N.A.I.C.S.: 721120

Tunica Golf Course, LLC   (1)
1205 Nine Lakes Dr, Robinsonville, MS 38664
Tel.: (662) 363-1005
Emp.: 28
Casino & Gaming Services
N.A.I.C.S.: 721120

Subsidiary (Domestic):

The Aragon Group   (2)
301 E Dania Beach Blvd, Dania Beach, FL 33004
Tel.: (954) 920-1511
Casino & Gaming Services
N.A.I.C.S.: 721120

Valley Forge Convention Center Partners, LLC   (1)
1160 1st Ave, King of Prussia, PA 19406-1355
Tel.: (610) 354-8118
Web Site: https://www.vfcasino.com
Casino Hotel Operator
N.A.I.C.S.: 721120

BOYLE BANCORP INC.
304 W Main St, Danville, KY 40422
Tel.: (859) 236-2926

Web Site: https://www.fnbky.com
BYLB—(OTCIQ)
Offices of Bank Holding Companies
N.A.I.C.S.: 551111

Subsidiaries:

The Farmers National Bank of Danville   (1)
304 W Main St, Danville, KY 40422
Tel.: (859) 236-2926
Web Site: http://www.fnbky.com
Sales Range: $25-49.9 Million
Emp.: 160
National Commercial Banks
N.A.I.C.S.: 522110
Marty Gibson (Pres)
David Simpson (Pres-WealthSouth)
Greg W. Caudill (CEO)
Blake Shewmaker (VP & Mgr-Mercer County)
Linda Dunn (VP & Mgr-Loan Ops)
Chris Sparrow (VP & Controller)
Kevin Arnold (Sr VP)
Rusty Clark (Head-Lending)
Beth Pike (Asst VP)

BP MIDSTREAM PARTNERS LP
501 Westlake Park Blvd, Houston, TX 77079
Tel.: (281) 366-2000   DE
Web Site:
    http://www.bpmidstreampartners.com
Year Founded: 2017
BPMP—(NYSE)
Rev.: $172,400,000
Assets: $738,900,000
Liabilities: $484,900,000
Net Worth: $254,000,000
Earnings: $168,400,000
Fiscal Year-end: 12/31/20
Oil & Gas Pipeline Services
N.A.I.C.S.: 486990
J. Douglas Sparkman (Chm)

BP PRUDHOE BAY ROYALTY TRUST
601 Travis St 16th Fl, Houston, TX 77002
Tel.: (713) 483-6020   DE
Web Site:
    https://www.bpt.q4web.com
Year Founded: 1989
BPT—(NYSE)
Rev.: $82,283,000
Assets: $6,067,000
Liabilities: $280,000
Net Worth: $5,787,000
Earnings: $80,888,000
Emp.: 22,106
Fiscal Year-end: 12/31/22
Trust Management Services
N.A.I.C.S.: 523940
Elaina C. Rodgers (VP)

BRADY CORPORATION
6555 W Good Hope Rd, Milwaukee, WI 53223
Tel.: (414) 358-6600   WI
Web Site: https://www.bradyid.com
Year Founded: 1914
BRC—(NYSE)
Rev.: $1,341,393,000
Assets: $1,515,569,000
Liabilities: $448,911,000
Net Worth: $1,066,658,000
Earnings: $197,215,000
Emp.: 5,700
Fiscal Year-end: 07/31/24
Informational & Safety Signs, Identification Products, Specialty Tapes & Traffic Control Products Mfr
N.A.I.C.S.: 339950
Bradley C. Richardson (Chm)
Bentley N. Curran (CIO & VP-Digital Bus)
Russell R. Shaller (Pres & CEO)

Ann E. Thornton (CFO, Chief Acctg Officer & Controller)
Andrew T. Gorman (Gen Counsel & Sec)
Olivier P. Bojarski (Pres-Identification Solutions)
Brett Wilms (Pres-EMEA & Australia)

Subsidiaries:

Brady (Beijing) Co. Ltd.   (1)
Building 8 Unit 8401 - 8402 No 3 Yongchang North Road, Beijing Economic and Technological Development Zone, Beijing, 100176, China   (100%)
Tel.: (86) 1067887799
Web Site: http://www.brady.com.cn
Signs, Identification Products & Specialty Tapes Mfr
N.A.I.C.S.: 339950

Brady A/S   (1)
Egelundsvej 16, 5260, Odense, Denmark
Tel.: (45) 66144400
Web Site: https://www.bradydenmark.dk
Emp.: 8
Industrial Machinery & Equipment Whslr
N.A.I.C.S.: 532490
Laszlo Felfoldi (Pres & CEO)

Brady AB   (1)
(100%)
Tel.: (46) 856642538
Web Site: https://www.brady.se
Sales Range: $10-24.9 Million
Emp.: 11
Signs, Identification Products & Specialty Tapes Mfr
N.A.I.C.S.: 339950

Brady Australia Pty. Ltd.   (1)
2 Bellevue Circuit, Greystanes, 2145, NSW, Australia   (100%)
Tel.: (61) 1800620816
Web Site: https://www.bradyid.com.au
Sales Range: $75-99.9 Million
Emp.: 130
Safety & Identification Signs, Tapes & Other Products
N.A.I.C.S.: 339950
Kerry Birchall (Mng Dir)

Subsidiary (Domestic):

Seton Australia Pty. Ltd.   (2)
2 Bellevue Circuit, 391 Park Rd Greystanes, Sydney, 2143, NSW, Australia   (100%)
Tel.: (61) 287176300
Web Site: http://www.seton.com.au
Sales Range: $75-99.9 Million
Emp.: 150
Safety & Identification Signs, Tapes & Other Products
N.A.I.C.S.: 339950
Bill Pike (Mng Dir)

Brady B.V.   (1)
Keyserswey 4A, 2201 CW, Noordwijk, Netherlands
Tel.: (31) 703236298
Industrial Machinery & Equipment Whslr
N.A.I.C.S.: 532490

Brady Company India Private Limited   (1)
No 26P Survey No 41 Konappana Agrahara Begur Hobli, Electronic City Phase II, Bengaluru, 560 100, Karnataka, India   (100%)
Tel.: (91) 8066582900
Web Site: https://www.bradyindia.co.in
Emp.: 120
Mfr of Precision Die Cut Parts, Printed Labels & Silk Screen Printed Substrates
N.A.I.C.S.: 323120

Brady Corporation Asia Pacific Pte. Ltd.   (1)
1 Kaki Bukit Crescent, Singapore, 416236, Singapore
Tel.: (65) 64777261
Industrial Machinery & Equipment Whslr
N.A.I.C.S.: 532490

Brady Corporation Asia Pte. Ltd.   (1)
1 Kaki Bukit Crescent, Singapore, 416236, Singapore   (100%)
Tel.: (65) 64777261
Web Site: https://www.bradyid.com.sg

Sales Range: $25-49.9 Million
Emp.: 100
Signs, Identification Products & Specialty Tapes Mfr
N.A.I.C.S.: 339950

Brady Corporation Hong Kong Limited   (1)
Unit A 28/F EGL Tower 83 Hung To Road, Kwun Tong, Kowloon, China (Hong Kong)   (100%)
Tel.: (852) 22169283
Web Site: https://www.bradyid.com.hk
Emp.: 20
Identification Accessory Products Mfr & Distr
N.A.I.C.S.: 323113

Brady Corporation Ltd.   (1)
Wildmere Industrial Estate, Banbury, OX16 3JU, Oxon, United Kingdom   (100%)
Tel.: (44) 1295228288
Web Site: http://www.brady.co.uk
Sales Range: $75-99.9 Million
Emp.: 75
Signs, Identification Products & Specialty Tapes Mfr
N.A.I.C.S.: 339950

Branch (Domestic):

Brady Corporation Ltd.   (2)
Dencora Business Ctr, 36 Whitehouse Road, Ipswich, IP1 5NX, Suffolk, United Kingdom   (100%)
Tel.: (44) 2086148832
Web Site: http://www.big.co.uk
Sales Range: $10-24.9 Million
Emp.: 35
Signs, Identification Products & Specialty Tapes Mfr
N.A.I.C.S.: 339950

Brady Etiket ve Isaretleme Ticaret Ltd. Sirketi   (1)
Orta Mah Cengizhan Street No 3, Tuzla, 34956, Istanbul, Turkiye   (100%)
Tel.: (90) 2122640220
Web Site: https://www.brady.com.tr
Emp.: 6
Identification Wristbands & Armbands Mfr & Sales
N.A.I.C.S.: 339999

Brady GmbH   (1)
Brady-Strasse 1, 63329, Egelsbach, Germany
Tel.: (49) 61037598660
Web Site: https://www.brady.de
Security Systems & Products Mfr & Distr
N.A.I.C.S.: 334290

Brady Groupe S.A.S   (1)
2 rue de la 3eme Revolution Industrielle, Pierre Mauroy business park, 59223, Roncq, Cedex, France
Tel.: (33) 320769448
Web Site: https://www.brady.fr
Sales Range: $50-74.9 Million
Emp.: 100
Industrial Machinery & Equipment Whslr
N.A.I.C.S.: 532490

Brady Identificacion S.L.U.   (1)
C/ Foronda 6 3 Dcha, 28034, Madrid, Spain   (100%)
Tel.: (34) 900902993
Web Site: https://www.brady.es
Identification Products Sales
N.A.I.C.S.: 423990

Brady Italia, S.r.l.   (1)
Via Degli Abeti 44, 20064, Gorgonzola, MI, Italy   (100%)
Tel.: (39) 0226000022
Web Site: https://www.bradycorp.it
Sales Range: $10-24.9 Million
Emp.: 17
Signs, Identification Products & Specialty Tapes Mfr
N.A.I.C.S.: 339950

Brady Korea LLP   (1)
838 Yeoksam-dong, Gangnam-gu, Seoul, Korea (South)   (100%)
Tel.: (82) 2 2192 0700
Web Site: http://www.brady.co.kr
Identification Products Mfr & Distr
N.A.I.C.S.: 339999

Brady LLC (1)
ul Kalanchevskaya House 16 Building 2 Office 107, Moscow, 129090, Russia
Tel.: (7) 4952694787
Printer Merchant Whslr
N.A.I.C.S.: 423430

Brady Mexico, S. de R.L. de C.V. (1)
Avenida Guerrero Negro 2 Bis 1, Parque Industrial Nordika, Tijuana, Baja California, Mexico
Tel.: (52) 6646821711
Emp.: 1,000
Plastics Product Mfr
N.A.I.C.S.: 325211

Brady Polska Sp. Z.o.o. (1)
ul Pulawska 405, 02-801, Warsaw, Poland
Tel.: (48) 221046262
Web Site: https://www.brady.pl
Barcode Printer & Reader Mfr & Distr
N.A.I.C.S.: 334118

Brady Technologies (Thailand) Co. Ltd. (1)
Olympia Thai Plaza Building 6th Floor 444 Ratchadapisek Road, Samsennok Huay Kwang, Bangkok, 10310, Thailand
Tel.: (66) 2 515 2400
Web Site: http://www.brady.co.th
Die-Cut Solutions & Identification Products Mfr & Distr
N.A.I.C.S.: 339999
Nichakoi Yawanops (Gen Mgr)

Brady Technology Sdn. Bhd. (1)
Plot 6 Hilir Sungai Keluang 4 Phase IV Bayan Lepas, Bayan Lepas Free Industrial Zone, 11900, Penang, Malaysia (100%)
Tel.: (60) 48101688
Sales Range: $25-49.9 Million
Emp.: 150
Signs, Identification Products & Specialty Tapes Mfr
N.A.I.C.S.: 339950

Brady Vietnam Company Limited (1)
Unit 1502B 15th Floor Centre Point Tower 106 Nguyen Van Troi Street, Ward 08 Phu Nhuan District, Ho Chi Minh City, Vietnam
Tel.: (84) 2836368992
Web Site: https://bradyvietnam.com
Barcode Printer & Reader Mfr & Distr
N.A.I.C.S.: 334118

Brady Worldwide, Inc. (1)
6555 W Good Hope Rd, Milwaukee, WI 53223 (100%)
Tel.: (414) 358-6600
Web Site: https://www.bradyid.com
Sales Range: $150-199.9 Million
Emp.: 500
Signs, Identification Products & Specialty Tapes Mfr
N.A.I.C.S.: 332216

Brady s.r.o. (1)
Na Pantoch 18, 831 06, Bratislava, Slovakia
Tel.: (421) 902939406
Web Site: https://www.brady.sk
Sales Range: $25-49.9 Million
Emp.: 12
Identification Solutions Mfr
N.A.I.C.S.: 532490

Brady/TISCOR, Inc. (1)
10815 Rancho Bernardo Rd Ste 205, San Diego, CA 92127 (100%)
Tel.: (858) 524-7700
Web Site: http://www.tiscor.com
Sales Range: $10-24.9 Million
Emp.: 50
Wireless & Internet-Enabled Mobile Workforce Automation Solutions
N.A.I.C.S.: 541512

Clement Communications Inc. (1)
2491 Wehrle Dr, Williamsville, NY 14221 (100%)
Tel.: (610) 459-4200
Web Site: http://www.clement.com
Sales Range: $10-24.9 Million
Emp.: 85
Business Information Materials Publisher
N.A.I.C.S.: 513199

Emedco Inc. (1)
2491 Wehrle Dr, Williamsville, NY 14221
Tel.: (716) 626-1616

Web Site: http://www.emedco.com
Sales Range: $50-74.9 Million
Emp.: 190
Signs & Advertising Specialties
N.A.I.C.S.: 339950
Pascal Deman (Pres)

Grafo Wiremarkers Pty. Ltd. (1)
361 Olympic Duel Northlands Business Park Newmarket Road, Randburg, 2153, South Africa
Tel.: (27) 117043295
Web Site: http://www.grafo.co.za
Plastics Product Mfr
N.A.I.C.S.: 325211

Holland Mounting Systems B.V. (1)
Wattstraat 7a, Sassenheim, 2171 TP, Netherlands
Tel.: (31) 252241381
Web Site: http://www.hmf.com
Emp.: 25
Industrial Machinery & Equipment Whslr
N.A.I.C.S.: 532490

IDenticard Systems, Inc. (1)
148 E Stiegel St, Manheim, PA 17545
Tel.: (717) 569-5797
Web Site: http://www.identicard.com
Sales Range: $50-74.9 Million
Emp.: 50
Security Identification Systems & Access Control Systems; Custom Identification Cards & Supplies
N.A.I.C.S.: 326199
Aaron Henderson (Dir-Product & Support)

Subsidiary (Non-US):

IDenticard Systems Canada Ltd. (2)
50 Vogell road unit 3-4, Richmond Hill, L4B3K6, ON, Canada
Tel.: (905) 513-0373
Web Site: http://identicard.ca
Security Identification Systems, Custom Identification Cards & Supplies
N.A.I.C.S.: 561621

Magicard Ltd. (1)
Waverley House Hampshire Road Granby Industrial Estate, Weymouth, DT4 9XD, Dorset, United Kingdom
Tel.: (44) 1305470000
Web Site: https://magicard.com
ID Card Printer Mfr & Distr
N.A.I.C.S.: 323111

Maquila Products del Noroeste S.de R.L. de C.V. (1)
Calle Heroes De La Independencia 10351 parque, Industrial/Zona Industrial El, Tijuana, 22244, Mexico
Tel.: (52) 6649013088
Plastics Product Mfr
N.A.I.C.S.: 325211

Nippon Brady K.K. (1)
Akatsuki-cho 1-31-16, Hachioji, Tokyo, 1920043, Japan (100%)
Tel.: (81) 426552531
Web Site: https://www.brady.co.jp
Sales Range: $75-99.9 Million
Emp.: 43
Signs, Identification Products & Specialty Tapes Mfr
N.A.I.C.S.: 339950
Yasushi Arai (Pres & CEO)

Precision Dynamics Corporation (1)
25124 Springfield Ct Ste 200, Valencia, CA 91355 (100%)
Tel.: (661) 257-0233
Web Site: https://www.pdcorp.com
Sales Range: $50-74.9 Million
Emp.: 180
Patient Identification Wristbands & Radio Frequency Identification Products Mfr
N.A.I.C.S.: 339112
Eric Banks (Dir-Ops-Global)
Karen Bender (Dir-HR)
Sean Souffie (VP-SIs)

Subsidiary (Non-US):

PDC Brazeletes y Productos S. de R.L. de C.V. (2)
lvd La Encantada Industrial No Ext 24050 Int A, Parque Industrial El Florido II, Tijuana, 22244, Baja California, Mexico (100%)

Web Site: http://www.brazaletes-pdc.mx
Emp.: 600
Identification Wristbands, Armboards & Infant Footprinters Mfr
N.A.I.C.S.: 339999
Daniel Gonzalez (Plant Mgr)

PDC Europe Sprl (2)
Rue de l'Industrie 17, 1400, Nivelles, Belgium (100%)
Tel.: (32) 67895656
Web Site: http://www.pdc-europe.com
Sales Range: $10-24.9 Million
Emp.: 5
Patient Identification Wristbands & Radio Frequency Identification Products Distr
N.A.I.C.S.: 339112

Subsidiary (Domestic):

Precision Dynamics (2)
144 Tower Dr, Burr Ridge, IL 60527
Tel.: (630) 986-1800
Sales Range: $50-74.9 Million
Emp.: 200
Pressure-Sensitive Tapes & Labels Mfr
N.A.I.C.S.: 322220
Mark Bouchard (Dir-Corp Accts)
Robert Case (CEO)

Runelandhs Forsaljnings AB (1)
Flygplatsvagen 22, PO Box 842 391 28, 392 41, Kalmar, Sweden
Tel.: (46) 48015940
Web Site: http://www.runelandhs.se
Emp.: 20
Plastics Product Mfr
N.A.I.C.S.: 325211

Transposafe Systems Holland B.V. (1)
Wattstraat 7, 2171 TP, Sassenheim, Netherlands
Tel.: (31) 252241231
Web Site: http://www.transposafe.com
Emp.: 35
Industrial Machinery & Equipment Whslr
N.A.I.C.S.: 532490

Transposafe Systems Polska Sp. Z.o.o. (1)
Tel.: (48) 713526133
Sales Range: $25-49.9 Million
Emp.: 12
Industrial Machinery & Equipment Whslr
N.A.I.C.S.: 532490

Tricor Direct Inc. (1)
PO Box 458, Buffalo, NY 14240-0458 (100%)
Tel.: (203) 488-8059
Web Site: https://www.seton.com
Sales Range: $75-99.9 Million
Emp.: 40
Holding Company
N.A.I.C.S.: 332812

Tricor Groupe S.A. (1)
45 Ave De l Europe, 59436, Roncq, France
Tel.: (33) 320010606
Web Site: http://www.seton.fr
Sales Range: $50-74.9 Million
Emp.: 150
Signs, Identification Products & Specialty Tapes Mfr
N.A.I.C.S.: 339950
Joe Wan (CEO-Hong Kong)

W.H. Brady S. de R.L. de C.V. (1)
Autopista Tijuana-Tecate No 20370 Int 12-B, Colonia Ciudad Industrial Tijuana Baja California, 22444, Mexico, Mexico (100%)
Tel.: (52) 6646249475
Web Site: https://www.bradylatinamerica.com
Signs, Identification Products & Specialty Tapes Mfr
N.A.I.C.S.: 339950

W.H. Brady, NV (1)
Poldergotestraat 9, 9240, Zele, Belgium (100%)
Tel.: (32) 52457811
Web Site: https://www.nl.brady.be
Sales Range: $25-49.9 Million
Emp.: 210
Signs, Identification Products & Specialty Tapes Mfr
N.A.I.C.S.: 339950

W.H.B. Identification Solutions, Inc. (1)
710 Cochrane Drive, Markham, L3R 5N7, ON, Canada (100%)
Tel.: (905) 764-1717
Web Site: https://www.bradycanada.ca
Sales Range: $25-49.9 Million
Emp.: 100
Identification Solutions
N.A.I.C.S.: 561621

W.H.B. do Brasil Ltda. (1)
Ceci Avenue 238, Osasco, Barueri, 06460-120, SP, Brazil (100%)
Tel.: (55) 1141661500
Web Site: https://www.brady.com.br
Sales Range: $75-99.9 Million
Signs, Identification Products & Specialty Tapes Mfr
N.A.I.C.S.: 339950

BRAEMAR HOTELS & RESORTS, INC.
14185 Dallas Pkwy Ste 1200, Dallas, TX 75254
Tel.: (972) 490-9600 MD
Web Site: https://www.bhrreit.com
BHR—(NYSE)
Rev.: $669,585,000
Assets: $2,397,714,000
Liabilities: $2,003,951,000
Net Worth: $393,763,000
Earnings: $17,761,000
Emp.: 102
Fiscal Year-end: 12/31/22
Real Estate Investment Trust
N.A.I.C.S.: 525990
Montgomery J. Bennett IV (Founder)
Deric S. Eubanks (CFO)
Richard J. Stockton (Pres & CEO)
Alex Rose (Gen Counsel)

Subsidiaries:

Ashford TRS Pier House LLC (1)
1 Duval St, Key West, FL 33040
Tel.: (305) 296-4600
Web Site: https://www.pierhouse.com
Sales Range: $25-49.9 Million
Emp.: 100
Resort Hotel & Spa
N.A.I.C.S.: 721110

Four Seasons Resort Scottsdale at Troon North (1)
10600 E Crescent Moon Dr, Scottsdale, AZ 85262-8342
Tel.: (480) 515-5700
Web Site: http://www.fourseasons.com
Hotel Operator
N.A.I.C.S.: 721110
Robby Delaney (Dir-Room)

Hotel Yountville (1)
6462 Washington St, Yountville, CA 94599
Tel.: (707) 967-7900
Web Site: https://www.hotelyountville.com
Luxury Hotel & Resort Operator
N.A.I.C.S.: 721110

BRAINSTORM CELL THERAPEUTICS INC.
1325 Ave of Americas 28th Fl, New York, NY 10019
Tel.: (201) 488-0460 DE
Web Site: https://www.brainstorm-cell.com
BCLI—(NASDAQ)
Rev.: $545,000
Assets: $8,451,000
Liabilities: $11,466,000
Net Worth: ($3,015,000)
Earnings: ($24,277,000)
Emp.: 43
Fiscal Year-end: 12/31/22
Stem Cell Research & Development Services
N.A.I.C.S.: 541715
Jacob A. Frenkel (Chm)
Chaim Lebovits (Pres & CEO)
Irit Arbel (Founder & Vice Chm)

BrainStorm Cell Therapeutics Inc.—(Continued)

Uri Yablonka *(Chief Bus Officer, Sec & Exec VP)*
Yael Gothelf *(VP-Scientific & Regulatory Affairs)*
Yossef Levy *(VP-Cell Production)*
Revital Geffen-Aricha *(VP-R&D)*
Mary Kay Turner *(VP-Patient Advocacy & Govt Affairs)*
Anthony P. Waclawski *(Exec VP & Head-Regulatory Affairs-Global)*
William K. White *(Sr VP & Head-Market Access & Pricing)*
Sidney A. Spector *(Sr VP-Global Strategy & Medical Affairs)*
Kim Thacker *(Sr VP-Medical Affairs & Clinical Innovation)*
Ibrahim B. Dagher *(Chief Medical Officer & Exec VP)*
Hartoun Hartounian *(COO & Exec VP)*

Subsidiaries:

BrainStorm Cell Therapeutics Ltd.   **(1)**
12 Bazel Street, PO Box 10019, Kiryat Aryeh, Petah Tiqwa, 4900101, Israel
Tel.: (972) 39236384
Web Site: http://www.brainstorm-cell.com
Sales Range: $75-99.9 Million
Emp.: 12
Stem Cell Therapeutic Products Research & Developer
N.A.I.C.S.: 541715

BRANCHOUT FOOD INC.

20724 Carmen Loop Ste 110, Bend, OR 97702   NV
Web Site:
https://www.branchoutfood.com
Year Founded: 2017
BOF—(NASDAQ)
Rev.: $752,178
Assets: $3,264,305
Liabilities: $8,404,033
Net Worth: ($5,139,728)
Earnings: ($4,643,352)
Emp.: 4
Fiscal Year-end: 12/31/22
Other Snack Food Manufacturing
N.A.I.C.S.: 311919
John Dalfonsi *(CFO)*
Christopher Coulter *(Pres)*

BRAND ENGAGEMENT NETWORK, INC.

Tel.: (312) 810-7422   Ky
Web Site: https://beninc.ai
Year Founded: 2020
BNAI—(NASDAQ)
Rev.: ($4,070,029)
Assets: $22,101,750
Liabilities: $8,782,145
Net Worth: ($8,737,310)
Earnings: ($6,879,994)
Fiscal Year-end: 12/31/23
Software Publisher
N.A.I.C.S.: 513210
Bill Williams *(CFO)*
Paul Chang *(CEO)*
Ruy Carrasco *(Chief Informatics Medical Officer)*
James D. Henderson *(Gen Counsel & Sec)*
James Richard Howard *(Chief Information & Data Officer)*
Tyler J. Luck *(Chief Product Officer)*
Patrick O. Nunally *(CTO & Chief Scientist Officer)*
Venkata Ramana Pinnam *(Sr VP-Engineering)*

BRANDYWINE REALTY TRUST

2929 Arch St Ste 1800, Philadelphia, PA 19104
Tel.: (610) 325-5600   MD

Web Site:
https://www.brandywinerealty.com
Year Founded: 1986
BDN—(NYSE)
Rev.: $506,100,000
Assets: $3,874,505,000
Liabilities: $2,241,171,000
Net Worth: $1,633,334,000
Earnings: $53,824,000
Emp.: 328
Fiscal Year-end: 12/31/22
Real Estate Investment Trust
N.A.I.C.S.: 525990
Gerard H. Sweeney *(Pres & CEO)*
H. Jeffrey DeVuono *(Sr Mng Dir & Exec VP-Life Science)*
George D. Johnstone *(Exec VP-Ops)*
Regina Sitler *(VP-Portfolio Mgmt)*
K. Suzanne Stumpf *(Sr VP-Asset Mgmt-Austin)*
Paul J. Commito *(Sr VP-Dev)*
Laura Krebs Miller *(VP-Mktg, Media, and Brand Mgmt)*
Shawn Neuman *(Gen Counsel & Sr VP)*
Ronald J. Becker *(Sr VP-Ops & Sustainability)*
Jim Kurek *(Chief Tech & Innovation Officer & VP)*
Ann Lisa Braun *(Gen Counsel)*
Joey Caperton *(VP)*
Matthew Croce *(VP)*
Christopher Franklin *(VP)*
Stephen Harris *(VP)*
John Hill *(VP)*
Jerry Kilkenny *(VP)*
Barry Lohr *(VP)*
Kyle Mcdonald *(VP)*
Brian Orr *(VP)*
Keith Oldt *(VP)*
Leon Shadowen *(Sr VP)*
Natalie Shieh *(VP)*
Jennifer Unterberger *(VP)*
Thomas E. Wirth *(CFO)*

Subsidiaries:

BOI Carlsbad LLC   **(1)**
5963 La Place Ct Ste 206, Carlsbad, CA 92008-8823
Tel.: (760) 438-4242
Emp.: 5
Property Rental & Leasing Services
N.A.I.C.S.: 531110

Brandywine Operating Partnership, LP   **(1)**
2929 Arch St Ste 1800, Philadelphia, PA 19104   **(95.7%)**
Tel.: (610) 325-5600
Web Site: https://www.brandywinerealty.com
Rev.: $514,650,999
Assets: $3,732,446,999
Liabilities: $2,411,074,999
Net Worth: $1,321,371,999
Earnings: ($197,948,000)
Emp.: 322
Fiscal Year-end: 12/31/2023
Real Estate Services
N.A.I.C.S.: 531390
Gerard H. Sweeney *(Pres & CEO)*

Subsidiary (Domestic):

Brandywine Realty Services Corporation   **(2)**
555 E Lancaster Ave Ste 110, Radnor, PA 19087   **(100%)**
Tel.: (610) 325-5600
Web Site: https://www.brandywinerealty.com
Sales Range: $150-199.9 Million
Emp.: 100
Owns, Manages, Leases, Acquiresi & Develops Office & Industrial Properties
N.A.I.C.S.: 531190
Gerard H. Sweeney *(Pres & CEO)*

BRANDYWINEGLOBAL - GLOBAL INCOME OPPORTUNITIES FUND INC.

620 8th Ave, New York, NY 10018   MD

Year Founded: 2010
BWG—(NYSE)
Rev.: $21,599,922
Assets: $352,359,523
Liabilities: $128,271,578
Net Worth: $224,087,945
Earnings: $13,437,425
Fiscal Year-end: 10/31/20
Investment Services
N.A.I.C.S.: 523999
Thomas C. Mandia *(Sr VP & Asst Sec)*
Jeanne Marie Kelly *(Sr VP)*
Christopher Berarducci *(Officer-Fin & Treas)*
Fred Jensen *(Chief Compliance Officer)*
Jane E. Trust *(Chm, Pres & CEO)*
David F. Hoffman *(Portfolio Mgr)*
Jack P. McIntyre *(Portfolio Mgr)*
Anujeet Sareen *(Portfolio Mgr)*
Brian Kloss *(Portfolio Mgr)*
Tracy Chen *(Portfolio Mgr)*
Marc A. De Oliveira *(Chief Legal Officer & Sec)*

BRAVADA INTERNATIONAL, LTD.

1458 San Pedro St Unit L31, Los Angeles, CA 90015
Tel.: (323) 936-0569   DE
Web Site:
http://www.worldofleggings.com
Year Founded: 1997
BRAV—(OTCIQ)
Sales Range: Less than $1 Million
Emp.: 20
Women's Clothing Retailer
N.A.I.C.S.: 458110
Daniel Alex *(Pres & CEO)*

BRAVATEK SOLUTIONS, INC.

2028 E Ben White Blvd Ste #240 2835, Austin, TX 78741   CO
Web Site: https://www.bravatek.com
Year Founded: 2007
BVTK—(OTCIQ)
Sales Range: Less than $1 Million
Software Publisher
N.A.I.C.S.: 513210
Thomas A. Cellucci *(Chm & CEO)*
Debbie King *(CFO)*
Ian Treleaven *(VP-Software)*

BRAVO MULTINATIONAL INCORPORATED

2020 General Booth Blvd Unit 230, Virginia Beach, VA 23454
Tel.: (757) 306-6090   WY
Year Founded: 1989
BRVO—(OTCIQ)
Assets: $1,180
Liabilities: $409,883
Net Worth: ($408,703)
Earnings: $4,847,145
Fiscal Year-end: 12/31/23
Holding Company; Entertainment Streaming Services
N.A.I.C.S.: 551112
Richard Kaiser *(CFO-Acting, Officer-Corp Governance & Sec)*
Grant Cramer *(CEO)*
Frank Hagan *(Pres)*

BRAZE, INC.

63 Madison Bldg 28 E 28th St Fl 12, New York, NY 10016
Tel.: (609) 964-0585   DE
Web Site: https://www.braze.com
Year Founded: 2011
BRZE—(NASDAQ)
Rev.: $355,426,000
Assets: $705,406,000
Liabilities: $260,103,000
Net Worth: $445,303,000
Earnings: ($138,966,000)

Emp.: 1,501
Fiscal Year-end: 01/31/23
Software Development Services
N.A.I.C.S.: 541511
Bill Magnuson *(Co-Founder, Chm & CEO)*
Jon Hyman *(Co-Founder & CTO)*
Isabelle Winkles *(CFO)*
Myles Kleeger *(Pres & Chief Comml Officer)*
Astha Malik *(Chief Bus Officer)*
Pankaj Malik *(Chief Acctg Officer)*
Susan Wiseman *(Gen Counsel)*
Kevin Wang *(Chief Product Officer)*
Brian Wheeler *(Sr VP-Engineering)*
Priyanka Singh *(Chief People Officer)*

BRC INC.

1144 S 500 W, Salt Lake City, UT 84101
Tel.: (801) 874-1189   DE
Web Site:
https://www.blackriflecoffee.com
Year Founded: 2021
BRCC—(NYSE)
Holding Company; Coffee Mfr, Distr & Retailer
N.A.I.C.S.: 551112
Chris Mondzelewski *(Pres & CEO)*
Evan Hafer *(Co-Founder & Exec Chm)*
Stephen M. Kadenacy *(CFO)*
Scott Bollinger *(Chief Admin Officer)*
Andrew McCormick *(Gen Counsel & Sec)*
Mat Best *(Co-Founder & Chief Creative Officer)*
Jarred Taylor *(Co-Founder)*

Subsidiaries:

Black Rifle Coffee Company LLC   **(1)**
1144 S 500 W, Salt Lake City, UT 84101
Tel.: (385) 262-7184
Web Site: https://www.blackriflecoffee.com
Coffee Mfr, Distr & Related Merchandise Retailer
N.A.I.C.S.: 311920
Chris Mondzelewski *(Pres & CMO)*
Evan Hafer *(Founder & Co-CEO)*
Thomas E. Davin *(Co-CEO)*

BREAD FINANCIAL HOLDINGS INC.

3075 Loyalty Cir, Columbus, OH 43219
Tel.: (614) 729-4000   DE
Web Site:
http://www.alliancedata.com
Year Founded: 1996
BFH—(NYSE)
Rev.: $5,145,000,000
Assets: $23,141,000,000
Liabilities: $20,223,000,000
Net Worth: $2,918,000,000
Earnings: $718,000,000
Emp.: 7,000
Fiscal Year-end: 12/31/23
Network Services, Payment Systems & Database Services
N.A.I.C.S.: 513140
Ralph J. Andretta *(Pres & CEO)*
Perry S. Beberman *(CFO & Exec VP)*
Joseph L. Motes III *(Chief Admin Officer, Gen Counsel, Sec & Exec VP)*

Subsidiaries:

ADI, LLC   **(1)**
21 Goodway Dr, Rochester, NY 14623
Tel.: (585) 239-6057
Web Site: https://www.adillc.net
Computer System Design Services
N.A.I.C.S.: 541512

ADS Alliance Data Systems, Inc.   **(1)**
7500 Dallas Pkwy Ste 700, Plano, TX 75024-4006
Tel.: (214) 494-3000
Web Site: http://www.alliancedata.com

Sales Range: $100-124.9 Million
Data Processing Services
N.A.I.C.S.: 518210

Acorn Direct Marketing Limited (1)
Lower Ground Floor 6 Ontario Terrace,
Dublin, Ireland
Tel.: (353) 14126222
General Marketing Services
N.A.I.C.S.: 541613

Brand Loyalty BV (1)
Koningsweg 101, 5211 BH, 's-
Hertogenbosch, Netherlands
Tel.: (31) 736444343
Web Site: http://www.brandloyalty.com
General Marketing Services
N.A.I.C.S.: 541613

Brand Loyalty France Sarl (1)
29 Avenue Aristide Briand, 94110, Arcueil,
France
Tel.: (33) 140929232
General Marketing Services
N.A.I.C.S.: 541613
Michele Ketcha *(Mgr-Fin)*

Brand Loyalty Japan KK (1)
Shin Meguro Toky building 13F 2-25-2 Ka-
miosaki, Shinagawa-Ku, Tokyo, 141-0021,
Japan
Tel.: (81) 357405377
General Marketing Services
N.A.I.C.S.: 541613

Brand Loyalty Limited (1)
Admiralty Centre 18 Harcourt Road Room
2104 Tower 1, Hong Kong, China (Hong
Kong)
Tel.: (852) 28613106
Emp.: 60
General Marketing Services
N.A.I.C.S.: 541613
May Fong *(Mgr-Fin)*

Comenity Capital Bank (1)
12921 S Vista Station Blvd Ste 400, Draper,
UT 84020
Tel.: (801) 527-2277
General Marketing Services
N.A.I.C.S.: 541613

**Equifax Direct Marketing Solutions,
Inc.** (1)
999 Yamato Rd, Boca Raton, FL 33431
Tel.: (404) 885-8000
Emp.: 200
Consumer Data Base Marketing Information
& Direct Marketing Services
N.A.I.C.S.: 541810

Subsidiary (Domestic):

INTEGRATEC (2)
3003 Chamblee Tucker Rd, Atlanta, GA
30341-4112
Tel.: (408) 765-8080
Emp.: 850
Financial Service Company
N.A.I.C.S.: 561440

**ICOM Information & Communications
L.P.** (1)
111 Gordon Baker Road Suite 300, Toronto,
M2H 3R1, ON, Canada
Web Site: http://www.shoppersvoice.ca
Data Communication Solutions & Research
Provider
N.A.I.C.S.: 541910

IceMobile Agency BV (1)
Mensinge 2, 1083 HA, Amsterdam, Nether-
lands
Tel.: (31) 203680645
Web Site: https://www.icemobile.com
Emp.: 140
General Marketing Services
N.A.I.C.S.: 541613
Julien Rappy *(Mng Dir)*

Lon Operations LLC (1)
PO Box 1264, New York, NY 10276
Web Site: https://www.breadpayments.com
Online Payment Services
N.A.I.C.S.: 522320

LoyaltyOne US, Inc. (1)
4445 Lake Forest Dr Ste 200, Cincinnati,
OH 45242-3743
Tel.: (513) 977-2291
Web Site: http://www.colloquy.com

Sales Range: $100-124.9 Million
Loyalty Marketing Services
N.A.I.C.S.: 561499
Blair Cameron *(Pres-AIR MILES Reward
Program)*
Todd Gulbransen *(Sr VP-Client Svcs &
Strategic Partnerships)*
Rachel MacQueen *(Sr VP-Collector Experi-
ence & Mktg)*
Bruno Scalzitti *(VP-Fin Plng & Analysis)*
Dimitri Benak *(VP-Talent & Experience)*
Hussein Dharsi *(VP-IT)*

LoyaltyOne, Inc. (1)
438 University Ave, Toronto, M5G 2L1, ON,
Canada
Tel.: (416) 228-6500
Computer System Design Services
N.A.I.C.S.: 541512

Mediaplex Systems, Inc. (1)
5111 Commerce Crossings Dr Ste 200,
Louisville, KY 40229
Tel.: (502) 810-5000
General Marketing Services
N.A.I.C.S.: 541613

Merison (Australia) Pty. Ltd. (1)
Level 3 188 Coventry Street, PO Box 5096,
South Melbourne, 3205, VIC, Australia
Tel.: (61) 396906830
Food Related Product Distr
N.A.I.C.S.: 424490

Merison Retail (HK) Ltd. (1)
12/Floor Comweb Plaza No 12 Cheung Yue
Street, Kowloon, China (Hong Kong)
Tel.: (852) 31051113
Food Products Distr
N.A.I.C.S.: 424490

Merison Retail B.V. (1)
Joop Geesinkweg 224, Duivendrecht, 1114
AB, Amsterdam, Netherlands
Tel.: (31) 202103250
Web Site: https://www.merison.com
Emp.: 25
Food Products Distr
N.A.I.C.S.: 424490

WFN Credit Company, LLC (1)
1 Righter Pkwy Ste 100, Wilmington, DE
19803
Tel.: (302) 529-6140
Investment Services
N.A.I.C.S.: 523999
Timothy King *(Pres)*

World Financial Capital Bank (1)
2795 E Cottonwood Pkwy, Salt Lake City,
UT 84121
Tel.: (801) 527-2276
Sales Range: $150-199.9 Million
Emp.: 20
Financial Services
N.A.I.C.S.: 525990
Ron Ostler *(Chm)*

BREEZE HOLDINGS ACQUISI-
TION CORP.
955 W John Carpenter Fwy Ste 100-
929, Irving, TX 75039
Tel.: (619) 500-7747   DE
Year Founded: 2020
BREZ—(NASDAQ)
Rev.: $6,113,466
Assets: $17,933,674
Liabilities: $24,465,436
Net Worth: ($6,531,762)
Earnings: $3,788,224
Emp.: 4
Fiscal Year-end: 12/31/22
Investment Services
N.A.I.C.S.: 523999
J. Douglas Ramsey *(Chm, CEO &
CFO)*
Russell D. Griffin *(Pres)*
Charles C. Ross *(COO)*

BRESLER & REINER, INC.
11200 Rockville Pike Ste 502, Rockville, MD 20852-7105
Tel.: (301) 945-4300   DE
Web Site:
http://www.breslerandreiner.com
BRER—(OTCIQ)

Operators of Apartment Buildings,
Office Buildings, Shopping Centers,
Real Estate Development Manage-
ment
N.A.I.C.S.: 531110
Sidney M. Bresler *(Pres & CEO)*
Darryl Edelstein *(CFO)*

BREWBILT BREWING COM-
PANY
110 Spring Hill Dr Ste 17, Grass Val-
ley, CA 95945
Tel.: (530) 206-0420   FL
Web Site:
https://www.brewbiltbrewing.com
Year Founded: 2021
BRBL—(OTCIQ)
Rev.: $307,171
Assets: $847,836
Liabilities: $16,098,630
Net Worth: $16,946,466
Earnings: ($6,858,992)
Emp.: 10
Fiscal Year-end: 12/31/21
Beer Brewery
N.A.I.C.S.: 312120
Bennett Buchanan *(CEO, Treas &
Sec)*
Richard Hylen *(Chm & Sec)*
Jeffrey Lewis *(Pres, CEO & Treas)*

BREWBILT MANUFACTURING,
INC.
110 Spring Hill Dr Ste 10, Grass Val-
ley, CA 95945
Tel.: (530) 802-5023   FL
Web Site: https://www.brewbilt.com
Year Founded: 2014
BBRWD—(OTCIQ)
Rev.: $348,610
Assets: $2,067,316
Liabilities: $19,634,353
Net Worth: ($17,567,037)
Earnings: ($7,485,886)
Emp.: 15
Fiscal Year-end: 12/31/22
Online Shopping Services
N.A.I.C.S.: 459999
Jeffrey Lewis *(Founder, Chm, Pres,
CEO, CFO, Treas & Sec)*
Devin Van Sant *(Head-Sls)*

BRIDGE INVESTMENT GROUP
HOLDINGS INC.
111 E Sego Lily Dr Ste 400, Salt
Lake City, UT 84070
Tel.: (801) 716-4500   DE
Web Site: https://www.bridgeig.com
Year Founded: 2021
BRDG—(NYSE)
Rev.: $409,049,000
Assets: $1,154,835,000
Liabilities: $508,516,000
Net Worth: $646,319,000
Earnings: $184,229,000
Emp.: 2,250
Fiscal Year-end: 12/31/22
Offices of Other Holding Companies
N.A.I.C.S.: 551112
Robert R. Morse *(Exec Chm)*
Jonathan Slager *(CEO)*
Adam O'Farrell *(COO)*
Dean Allara *(Vice Chm & Head-Client
Solutions Grp)*
Katherine Elsnab *(CFO & Controller)*
Adam Haughton *(Chief Investment
Officer-Bridge Renewable Energy)*
Garrett Behling *(Mng Dir, Chief Acctg
Officer & Controller)*

Subsidiaries:

**Bridge Commercial Real Estate
LLC** (1)
1277 Lenox Park Blvd Ste 200, Atlanta, GA
30319
Tel.: (404) 907-3100

Web Site: https://www.bridgecre-office.com
Commercial Real Estate Leasing Services
N.A.I.C.S.: 531120
Jeff Shaw *(CEO & Sr Mng Dir)*
Mark Ferris *(Mng Dir & COO)*
Brian Siebert *(CFO)*
John Ward *(Sr Mng Dir, Sr Mng Dir & Chief
Investment Officer)*
Brenden Welch *(Dir)*
Rachel Williams *(Dir)*
Tamala Herd *(Sr Mgr-Design)*
Keith Everett *(Dir-Construction Mgmt)*
Greg Walters *(Dir-Engineering)*
Jennifer Oats *(Dir-Property Mgmt)*
Steven Greenhut *(Deputy Gen Counsel)*

Newbury Partners LLC (1)
100 1st Stamford Pl, Stamford, CT 06902
Tel.: (203) 428-3600
Web Site: http://www.newbury-partners.com
Privater Equity Firm
N.A.I.C.S.: 523999
Richard Lichter *(Founder & Vice Chm)*
Gerald Esposito *(Mng Dir, CFO & Chief
Compliance Officer)*
David Stallone *(Dir-Fin)*
Chris Jaroch *(Mng Dir)*
Andrew Levy *(Mng Dir)*
Warren Symon *(Mng Dir)*

BRIDGEBIO PHARMA, INC.
3160 Porter Dr Ste 250, Palo Alto,
CA 94304
Tel.: (650) 391-9740   DE
Web Site: https://www.bridgebio.com
Year Founded: 2019
BBIO—(NASDAQ)
Rev.: $9,303,000
Assets: $546,380,000
Liabilities: $1,889,393,000
Net Worth: ($1,343,013,000)
Earnings: ($643,202,000)
Emp.: 550
Fiscal Year-end: 12/31/23
Biotechnology Research & Develop-
ment Services
N.A.I.C.S.: 541714
Uma Sinha *(Chief Scientific Officer)*
Cameron Turtle *(Sr VP-Portfolio
Mgmt & Corp Dev)*
Neil Kumar *(Co-Founder & CEO)*
Damian W. Wilmot *(Chief Legal Offi-
cer & Sec)*
Brian C. Stephenson *(CFO & Princi-
pal Acctg Officer)*
Frank McCormick *(Chm-Oncology)*
Michael Henderson *(Chief Bus Offi-
cer)*
Cameron Turtle *(Sr VP-Portfolio
Mgmt & Corp Dev)*
Jonathan C. Fox *(CMO)*
Charles J. Homcy *(Chm-
Pharmaceuticals)*
Andrew W. Lo *(Co-Founder)*
Frank P McCormick *(Chm-Oncology)*
Michael Henderson *(Chief Bus Offi-
cer)*
Richard H. Scheller *(Chm-R&D)*

Subsidiaries:

Eidos Therapeutics, Inc. (1)
1800 Owens St, San Francisco, CA
94158   (100%)
Tel.: (415) 887-1471
Web Site: https://www.eidostx.com
Rev.: $26,691,000
Assets: $203,820,000
Liabilities: $32,393,000
Net Worth: $171,427,000
Earnings: ($37,835,000)
Emp.: 34
Fiscal Year-end: 12/31/2019
Biopharmaceutical Research & Develop-
ment Services
N.A.I.C.S.: 541714
Uma Sinha *(Chief Scientific Officer)*
Neil Kumar *(CEO)*
Jonathan C. Fox *(Pres & Chief Medical Offi-
cer)*
Isabella Graef *(Co-Founder)*
Mamoun Alhamadsheh *(Co-Founder)*
Matt Outten *(Chief Comml Officer)*

BridgeBio Pharma, Inc.—(Continued)

Origin Biosciences, Inc.   **(1)**
75 Federal St, San Francisco, CA 94107
Tel.: (650) 391-9740
Web Site: https://www.origintx.com
Research & Development In Biotechnology
Services
N.A.I.C.S.: 541713
Eric B. Mosbrooker (COO)
Neil Kumar (Chm & Pres)
Eric B. Mosbrooker (COO)

Phoenix Tissue Repair, Inc.   **(1)**
75 Park Plz Ste 2, Boston, MA 02116-3934
Tel.: (650) 391-9740
Web Site:
https://www.phoenixtissuerepair.com
Pharmaceutical Tissue Product Mfr
N.A.I.C.S.: 325412
Ramsey Johnson (VP-Ops)
Hal Landy (Chief Medical Officer)
Sanuj K. Ravindran (Chm)
Kelly Neelon (VP-Technical Ops)
Deborah Ramsdell (COO)

QED Therapeutics, Inc.   **(1)**
75 Federal St, San Francisco, CA 94107
Web Site: https://www.qedtx.com
Research & Development In Biotechnology
Services
N.A.I.C.S.: 541713
Michael Henderson (CEO)
Matt Outten (Chief Comml Officer)
Rick Panicucci (Sr VP-CMC)
Gary Li (Sr VP)

BRIDGEGATE PICTURES CORPORATION
200 S Main St Ste 305, Corona, CA
92882
Tel.: (714) 906-6843   **NV**
Web Site:
http://bridgegatepictures.com
Year Founded: 1997
BBGP—(OTCIQ)
Sales Range: $1-9.9 Million
Investment Services
N.A.I.C.S.: 523999
Lee Caplin (CEO)
Guy Griffithe (Pres)

BRIDGELINE DIGITAL, INC.
100 Sylvan Rd Ste G700, Woburn,
MA 01801
Tel.: (781) 376-5555   **DE**
Web Site: https://www.bridgeline.com
BLIN—(NASDAQ)
Rev.: $15,885,000
Assets: $17,631,000
Liabilities: $6,171,000
Net Worth: $11,460,000
Earnings: ($9,435,000)
Emp.: 55
Fiscal Year-end: 09/30/23
Web Software Tools & Applications
N.A.I.C.S.: 513210
Joni Kahn (Chm)
Roger E. Kahn (Pres & CEO)
Thomas Windhausen (CFO & Treas)
John Murcott (Exec VP)
Erin McCue (Exec VP)
Danielle Erwin (Sr VP)
Filippo Impennato (VP)
Scott Gillenwater (Sr VP)

Subsidiaries:

Bridgeline Digital, Inc. - Tampa   **(1)**
5321 Primrose Lake Circle, Tampa, FL
33647
Tel.: (877) 932-7526
Web Site: http://www.bridgelinedigital.com
Software Application Publisher
N.A.I.C.S.: 513210

Hawk Search, Inc.   **(1)**
2700 S River Rd Ste 400, Des Plaines, IL
60018
Tel.: (312) 784-5720
Web Site: https://www.hawksearch.com
Sales Range: $1-9.9 Million
Emp.: 16
Online Shopping Services

N.A.I.C.S.: 541511
Nicholas Svanascini (Ops Mgr)
Michael Benedict (Gen Mgr)

Indigio Group, Inc.   **(1)**
410 17th St 6th Fl, Denver, CO 80202
Tel.: (303) 785-3800
Web Site: http://www.indigio.com
Rev.: $6,000,000
Custom Computer Programming Services
N.A.I.C.S.: 541511

MarketNet, Inc.   **(1)**
5360 Legacy Dr Ste 175, Plano, TX 75024
Tel.: (972) 941-3200
Web Site: http://www.marketnet.com
Sales Range: $1-9.9 Million
Web Design, Application Development &
Content Services
N.A.I.C.S.: 541511
Alan Bach (Principal & VP)

BRIDGER AEROSPACE GROUP HOLDINGS, INC.
90 Aviation Ln, Belgrade, MT 59714
Tel.: (406) 813-0079   **DE**
Web Site:
https://www.bridgeraerospace.com
Year Founded: 2022
BAER—(NASDAQ)
Rev.: $46,387,963
Assets: $305,978,901
Liabilities: $228,393,011
Net Worth: $77,585,890
Earnings: ($42,121,959)
Emp.: 166
Fiscal Year-end: 12/31/22
Offices of Other Holding Companies
N.A.I.C.S.: 551112
Darren Wilkins (Pres)
Eric Gerratt (CFO)
James Muchmore (Chief Legal Officer)
Timothy Sheehy (Founder)

Subsidiaries:

Bridger Aerospace Group Holdings,
LLC   **(1)**
90 Aviation Ln, Belgrade, MT 59714
Tel.: (406) 813-0079
Holding Company
N.A.I.C.S.: 551112

Subsidiary (Domestic):

Bridger Aerospace, LLC   **(2)**
90 Aviation Ln, Belgrade, MT 59714
Tel.: (406) 813-0079
Web Site: https://bridgeraerospace.com
Aerial Fire Suppression Systems & Services
N.A.I.C.S.: 336413

Jack Creek Investment Corp.   **(1)**
386 Park Ave S Fl 20, New York, NY 10016
Tel.: (212) 710-5060
Rev.: $17,182,200
Assets: $345,585,366
Liabilities: $372,215,431
Net Worth: ($26,630,065)
Earnings: $15,113,643
Emp.: 68
Fiscal Year-end: 12/31/2021
Investment Holding Company
N.A.I.C.S.: 551112
Jeffrey E. Kelter (Chm)
Robert F. Savage (CEO)
Thomas Jermoluk (Pres)
James H. Clark (CTO)
Lauren D. Ores (CFO)

BRIDGEWATER BANCSHARES, INC.
4450 Excelsior Blvd Ste 100, Saint
Louis Park, MN 55416
Tel.: (952) 893-6868   **MN**
Web Site:
https://www.bridgewaterbank.com
Year Founded: 2005
BWB—(NASDAQ)
Rev.: $170,027,000
Assets: $4,345,662,000
Liabilities: $3,951,598,000
Net Worth: $394,064,000

Earnings: $49,338,000
Emp.: 246
Fiscal Year-end: 12/31/22
Bank Holding Company
N.A.I.C.S.: 551111
Mary Jayne Crocker (Chief Strategy
Officer & Exec VP)
Jerry J. Baack (Co-Founder, Chm &
CEO)
Jeffrey D. Shellberg (Co-Founder,
Chief Credit Officer, Sec & Exec VP)
Laura Espeseth (Chief Acctg Officer)
Mary Jayne Crocker (COO & Exec
VP)
Joseph M. Chybowski (Pres, CFO &
Principal Operating Officer)
Lisa M. Salazar (Chief Deposit Officer)
Mark Hokanson (CTO)
Nick Place (Chief Lending Officer)

Subsidiaries:

Bridgewater Bank   **(1)**
3800 American Blvd W Ste 100, Bloomington, MN 55431
Tel.: (952) 893-6868
Web Site:
http://www.bridgewaterbankmn.com
Sales Range: $25-49.9 Million
Emp.: 71
Commericial Banking
N.A.I.C.S.: 522110
Mary Jayne Crocker (COO & Exec VP)
Jerry J. Baack (Founder, Chm, Pres &
CEO)
Jeffrey D. Shellberg (Co-Founder, Chief
Credit Officer, Sec & Exec VP)
Nick Chou (VP-Bus Svcs)
John Uremovich (Sr VP-Professional Svcs)
Andrew Bates (Sr VP)
Dan Koch (VP)
Eric Gundersen (Sr VP)
Erik Schwegler (Sr VP)
Gayle Larson (VP)
Joe Chybowski (CFO)
Jon Tollefson (Mng Dir)
Kevin Westerhaus (VP)
Liz Pomplun (VP)
Mark Hokanson (CTO)
Mike Morris (VP)
Nick Bellestri (Sr VP)
Patrick Craig (VP)
Ross Wieser (Sr VP)
Ryan Meier (Sr VP)
Seth Vogelsang (VP)
Shaundra Lex (VP)
Tom Grotbo (Sr VP)
Tony Ferraro (Mng Dir)
Tyler Manning (Sr VP)

BRIDGEWAY NATIONAL CORP.
1015 15th St NW Ste 1030, Washington, DC 20005
Tel.: (202) 846-7869   **DE**
Web Site:
http://www.bridgewaynational.com
Year Founded: 2012
BDGY—(OTCIQ)
Assets: $803,276
Liabilities: $4,442,381
Net Worth: ($3,639,105)
Earnings: ($4,167,837)
Emp.: 6
Fiscal Year-end: 12/31/20
Holding Company
N.A.I.C.S.: 551112
Eric C. Blue (Chm, CEO, CFO &
Chief Investment Officer)
Eon Washington (COO & Dir-Ops)

BRIDGFORD FOODS CORPORATION
1707 S Good Latimer Expy, Dallas,
TX 75226
Tel.: (214) 428-1535   **CA**
Web Site: https://www.bridgford.com
Year Founded: 1931
BRID—(NASDAQ)
Rev.: $265,898,000
Assets: $176,348,000

Liabilities: $50,023,000
Net Worth: $126,325,000
Earnings: $45,066,000
Emp.: 695
Fiscal Year-end: 10/28/22
Ready-to-Bake Frozen Bread, Rolls,
Luncheon Meats, Biscuits & Dry Sausage
N.A.I.C.S.: 311412
William L. Bridgford (VP)
John V. Simmons (VP)
Chris Cole (Sr VP)
Cindy Matthews-Morales (Sec & Controller)
Bob Delong (VP-Information Technologies)
Monty Griffith (VP-North Carolina)
Michael W. Bridgford (Chm)
Baron R. H. Bridgford II (Pres)
Blaine K. Bridgford (Pres-Superior
Foods Div-Dallas)
Jeffrey D. Robinson (Mgr-Bakery-
Bread Div-Anaheim)
Brandon Bridgford (Mgr-Bakery-
Frozen-Rite Div-Dallas)
William deAlcuaz (Mgr-Frozen,Rite
Div,Dallas)
Christian Quigley (VP)

Subsidiaries:

Bridgford Food Processing
Corporation   **(1)**
170 N Green St, Chicago, IL
60607-2313   **(100%)**
Tel.: (312) 733-0300
Web Site: http://www.bridgfordfoods.com
Sales Range: $100-124.9 Million
Emp.: 200
Processed Meat Product Mfr
N.A.I.C.S.: 311612

Bridgford Food Processing of Texas,
L.P.   **(1)**
1601 S Good-Latimer Expwy, Dallas, TX
75226
Tel.: (214) 428-1535
Refrigerated & Snack Food Products Mfr &
Distr
N.A.I.C.S.: 311412

Bridgford Marketing Company   **(1)**
1308 N Patt St, Anaheim, CA 92801
Tel.: (714) 526-5533
Baked Food Supplier & Mfr
N.A.I.C.S.: 311991
Chris Cole (Sr VP)

BRIGHT GREEN CORPORATION
1033 George Hanosh Blvd, Grants,
NM 87020
Tel.: (201) 370-1140   **DE**
Web Site: https://brightgreen.us
Year Founded: 2019
BGXX—(NASDAQ)
Assets: $22,788,293
Liabilities: $11,209,457
Net Worth: $11,578,836
Earnings: ($27,662,077)
Emp.: 23
Fiscal Year-end: 12/31/22
Cannabis Product Distr
N.A.I.C.S.: 424210
Lynn Stockwell (Founder & Chm)
Saleem Elmasri (CFO)
Gurvinder Singh (CEO)

BRIGHT LIGHTS ACQUISITION CORP.
12100 Wilshire Blvd Ste 1150, Los
Angeles, CA 90025
Tel.: (310) 421-1472   **DE**
Year Founded: 2020
BLTS—(NASDAQ)
Rev.: $5,835,798
Assets: $230,701,499

Liabilities: $258,025,185
Net Worth: ($27,323,686)
Earnings: ($1,341,378)
Emp.: 2
Fiscal Year-end: 12/31/21
Investment Services
N.A.I.C.S.: 523999
Michael Mahan *(CEO)*
Hahn Lee *(CFO & Sec)*

BRIGHT MINDS BIOSCIENCES INC.

Tel.: (647) 407-2515   BC
Web Site:
   https://www.brightmindsbio.com
Year Founded: 2019
DRUG—(NASDAQ)
Assets: $5,131,788
Liabilities: $209,519
Net Worth: $4,922,269
Earnings: ($5,499,680)
Emp.: 1
Fiscal Year-end: 09/30/23
Biotechnology Research & Development Services
N.A.I.C.S.: 541714
Ryan Cheung *(CFO)*
Ian McDonald *(Pres)*
Mark A. Smith *(Chief Medical Officer)*

BRIGHT MOUNTAIN MEDIA, INC.

6400 Congress Ave, Boca Raton, FL 33487
Tel.: (561) 807-6350   FL
Web Site:
   https://www.brightmountainme
   dia.com
Year Founded: 2010
BMTM—(OTCQB)
Rev.: $19,580,000
Assets: $29,200,000
Liabilities: $43,271,000
Net Worth: ($14,071,000)
Earnings: ($8,130,000)
Emp.: 52
Fiscal Year-end: 12/31/22
Offices of Other Holding Companies
N.A.I.C.S.: 551112
Miriam Martinez *(CFO)*
Todd F. Speyer *(COO-Bright Mountain LLC)*
Matthew Drinkwater *(CEO)*

BRIGHTCOVE, INC.

281 Summer St, Boston, MA 02210
Tel.: (617) 500-4947   DE
Web Site:
   https://www.brightcove.com
Year Founded: 2004
BCOV—(NASDAQ)
Rev.: $201,187,000
Assets: $216,107,000
Liabilities: $122,194,000
Net Worth: $93,913,000
Earnings: ($22,886,000)
Emp.: 671
Fiscal Year-end: 12/31/23
Internet Television Services
N.A.I.C.S.: 517121
John Wagner *(CFO, Principal Acctg Officer & Treas)*
Trisha Stiles *(Chief People Officer)*
Marc DeBevoise *(CEO)*
David Beck *(COO & Chief Strategy & Corp Dev Officer)*
Marc DeBevoise *(CEO)*
Dan Freund *(Chief Revenue Officer)*
Deb Richards *(Exec VP-Global Customer Success)*
Jim Norton *(Chief Revenue Officer)*
Kathy Klingler *(CMO)*
David Plotkin *(Chief Legal Officer)*

Subsidiaries:

Brightcove FZ-LLC   (1)

Executive Office No 02, Ground Floor Building 16 - Dubai Internet City, Dubai, United Arab Emirates
Tel.: (971) 43604550
Data Processing, Hosting & Related Services
N.A.I.C.S.: 518210

Brightcove India Pte. Ltd.   (1)
WorkEZ Centre S No 278/3A & 278/9A Rajiv Gandhi Salai OMR VOC Street, Kottivakam, Chennai, 600119, Tamil Nadu, India
Tel.: (91) 2266879308
Internet Publishing & Broadcasting Services
N.A.I.C.S.: 516210
Janvi Morzaria *(Dir-Sls)*

Brightcove Korea   (1)
16F 83 Uisadang-daero, Yeongdeungpo-gu, Seoul, 07325, Korea (South)
Tel.: (82) 269336747
Data Processing, Hosting & Related Services
N.A.I.C.S.: 518210

Brightcove Singapore Pte. Ltd.   (1)
38 Beach Road 04-14 South Beach Tower, Singapore, 189767, Singapore
Tel.: (65) 31635555
Data Processing, Hosting & Related Services
N.A.I.C.S.: 518210
Antoine Bouchacourt *(Mgr-Sls-Asia)*

Brightcove UK Ltd   (1)
55 Strand 2nd Floor, London, WC2R 0LQ, United Kingdom
Tel.: (44) 2071486450
Web Site: http://www.brightcove.com
Data Processing, Hosting & Related Services
N.A.I.C.S.: 518210

Zencoder Inc.   (1)
149 9th St Ste 300, San Francisco, CA 94103
Tel.: (415) 795-1565
Web Site: https://ww.brightcove.com
Internet Publishing & Broadcasting Services
N.A.I.C.S.: 516210

BRIGHTHOUSE FINANCIAL, INC.

11225 N Community House Rd, Charlotte, NC 28277
Tel.: (980) 365-7100   DE
Web Site:
   https://www.brighthousefinan
   cial.com
Year Founded: 2016
BHF—(NASDAQ)
Rev.: $4,117,000,000
Assets: $236,340,000,000
Liabilities: $231,332,000,000
Net Worth: $5,008,000,000
Earnings: ($1,214,000,000)
Emp.: 1,500
Fiscal Year-end: 12/31/23
Fire Insurance Services
N.A.I.C.S.: 524113
Myles J. Lambert *(Chief Distr & Mktg Officer & Exec VP)*
John L. Rosenthal *(Chief Investment Officer & Exec VP)*
Edward A. Spehar *(CFO & Exec VP)*
Eric T. Steigerwalt *(Pres & CEO)*

BRIGHTSPARK CAPITOL CORP.

1300 17th St N Ste 820, Arlington, VA 22209
Tel.: (202) 654-7060   DE
Year Founded: 2021
BRYTU—(NASDAQ)
Investment Services
N.A.I.C.S.: 523999
Helena B. Foulkes *(Co-Chm & Co-CEO)*
Marla Beck *(Co-Chm & Co-CEO)*
Alfheidur H. Saemundsson *(CFO, Sec & Treas)*

BRIGHTSPHERE INVESTMENT GROUP INC.

---

200 State St 13th Fl, Boston, MA 02109
Tel.: (617) 369-7300
Web Site: https://www.bsig.com
Year Founded: 2014
BSIG—(NYSE)
Rev.: $426,600,000
Assets: $611,400,000
Liabilities: $561,900,000
Net Worth: $49,500,000
Earnings: $65,800,000
Emp.: 387
Fiscal Year-end: 12/31/23
Asset Management
N.A.I.C.S.: 523999
Richard Hart *(Chief Legal Officer)*
Suren Rana *(Bd of Dirs, Executives)*

Subsidiaries:

BrightSphere International, Ltd.   (1)
Millennium Bridge House 2 Lambeth Hill, London, EC4V 4GG, United Kingdom
Tel.: (44) 2036087441
Financial Investment Services
N.A.I.C.S.: 523999

Campbell Global, LLC   (1)
1300 SW 5th Ave Ste 3200, Portland, OR 97201
Tel.: (503) 275-9675
Web Site: https://www.campbellglobal.com
Management Services
N.A.I.C.S.: 561110
Stephen Levesque *(Mng Dir-Ops)*
Stan Renecker *(Mng Dir-Acquisitions)*
Mark Simmons *(Mng Dir & CFO)*
John Gilleland *(Chm & CEO)*
Angie Davis *(Pres)*
Dave Rumker *(Mng Dir & Chief Investment Officer)*
Neil Radzins *(Dir-Acctg)*
Rhonda Stephens *(Dir-HR)*
Kyle Stinchfield *(Gen Counsel)*
Carrie Wheeler *(Mgr-Log Acctg)*

Copper Rock Capital Partners
LLC   (1)
John Hancock Tower 200 Clarendon St, Boston, MA 02116
Tel.: (617) 369-7140
Web Site: http://www.copperrockcapital.com
Management Services
N.A.I.C.S.: 561110
Stephen Dexter *(Chm & Chief Investment Officer)*

OMAM Inc.   (1)
200 State St 13th Fl, Boston, MA 02109
Tel.: (617) 369-7300
Web Site: http://www.omam.com
Holding Company; Investment Advisory & Asset Management Services
N.A.I.C.S.: 551112
Stephen H. Belgrad *(CFO & Exec VP)*
Linda Tilton Gibson *(Exec VP & Head-Global Distr)*

Subsidiary (Domestic):

Acadian Asset Management LLC   (2)
260 Franklin St, Boston, MA 02110 **(100%)**
Tel.: (617) 850-3500
Web Site: https://www.acadian-asset.com
Emp.: 200
Asset Management
N.A.I.C.S.: 523940
Brendan O. Bradley *(Chief Investment Officer & Exec VP)*
Kelly Young *(CMO & Exec VP)*
Jean-christophe De Beaulieu *(Sr VP & Head-Investments-Australia)*
Scott Dias *(Chief Compliance Officer, Gen Counsel & Sr VP)*
Ted Noon *(Sr VP)*
Marlene Shaw *(Sr VP)*
Alexandre Voitenok *(Sr VP & Dir-Implementation)*
Charmaine Catania *(CFO, CFO & Sr VP)*
James Crumlish *(CIO, CTO & Sr VP)*
Michael Brewer *(Sr VP)*

Subsidiary (Non-US):

Acadian Asset Management (Singapore) Pte. Ltd.   (3)
8 Marina View 40-01 Asia Square Tower 1, Singapore, 018960, Singapore **(100%)**

Tel.: (65) 65082200
Web Site: https://www.acadian-asset.com
Sales Range: $50-74.9 Million
Emp.: 10
Asset Management
N.A.I.C.S.: 531390

BRIGHTSPIRE CAPITAL, INC.

590 Madison Ave 33rd Fl, New York, NY 10022
Tel.: (212) 547-2631   MD
Web Site:
   https://www.brightspire.com
Year Founded: 2017
BRSP—(NYSE)
Rev.: $298,702,000
Assets: $4,198,254,000
Liabilities: $2,919,788,000
Net Worth: $1,278,466,000
Earnings: ($15,549,000)
Emp.: 54
Fiscal Year-end: 12/31/23
Real Estate Investment Trust Services
N.A.I.C.S.: 531210
Frank V. Saracino *(CFO, Chief Acctg Officer & Treas)*
Michael J. Mazzei *(Pres & CEO)*
George H. Kok *(Chief Credit Officer)*
Matthew Heslin *(Mng Dir)*
Gary Newman *(Mng Dir)*
Brad Nichol *(Mng Dir)*
Tyler H. Ferrer *(Mng Dir)*

BRIGHTVIEW HOLDINGS, INC.

980 Jolly Rd Ste 300, Blue Bell, PA 19422
Tel.: (484) 567-7204   DE
Web Site: https://www.brightview.com
Year Founded: 2013
BV—(NYSE)
Rev.: $2,767,100,000
Assets: $3,391,800,000
Liabilities: $1,609,400,000
Net Worth: $1,782,400,000
Earnings: $66,400,000
Emp.: 19,100
Fiscal Year-end: 09/30/24
Holding Company
N.A.I.C.S.: 551112
Dale A. Asplund *(Pres & CEO)*
Paul E. Raether *(Chm)*
Michael Dozier *(Pres-Evergreen East Maintenance Svcs)*
Brian Bruce *(CIO & Exec VP)*
Todd Chambers *(CMO & Exec VP)*
Jonathan M. Gottsegen *(Chief Legal Officer, Sec & Exec VP)*
Amanda Orders *(Chief HR Officer & Exec VP)*
Brett Urban *(CFO & Exec VP)*
Fred Freund *(Pres-Evergreen West)*
Brian Jackson *(Chief Acctg Officer)*
David Freireich *(VP-Comm & Pub Affairs)*

Subsidiaries:

Benchmark Landscapes, LLC   (1)
1814 W Howard Ln, Austin, TX 78728
Tel.: (512) 266-3167
Web Site:
   http://www.benchmarklandscapes.com
Landscape Architectural Services
N.A.I.C.S.: 541320

Clean Cut Lawns, LLC   (1)
4125 E Presidio St, Mesa, AZ 85215
Tel.: (480) 813-8964
Web Site: http://www.cleancutlm.com
Landscaping Services
N.A.I.C.S.: 561730

Commercial Tree Care, Inc.   (1)
PO Box 549, Santa Clara, CA 95052
Tel.: (408) 985-8733
Web Site: http://www.commercialtree.com
Landscaping Services
N.A.I.C.S.: 561730

BrightView Holdings, Inc.—(Continued)

Cutting Edge Property Maintenance, Inc. (1)
2730 Fernbrook Ln, Plymouth, MN 55447
Tel.: (757) 335-6440
Web Site: http://www.cuttingedgepm.com
Commercial & Institutional Building Construction
N.A.I.C.S.: 236220

Emerald Landscape Company, Inc. (1)
2265 Research Dr, Livermore, CA 94550-3847
Tel.: (925) 449-4743
Web Site: http://www.emeraldlandscapeco.com
Proactive Landscape Management
N.A.I.C.S.: 561730

Heaviland Enterprises, Inc. (1)
2180 La Mirada Dr, Vista, CA 92081
Tel.: (760) 598-7065
Web Site: http://www.heaviland.net
Lawn & Garden Construction Services
N.A.I.C.S.: 561730
Thomas Heaviland (Founder)

Intermountain Plantings Inc. (1)
579 W 14600 S, Bluffdale, UT 84065
Tel.: (801) 523-6100
Web Site: http://www.intermountainplantings.com
Sales Range: $1-9.9 Million
Emp.: 80
Landscape Architectural Services
N.A.I.C.S.: 541320

Island Plant Company, LLC (1)
1500 Lower Kula Rd, Makawao, HI 96768
Tel.: (808) 572-5094
Sales Range: $1-9.9 Million
Emp.: 80
Landscaping Services
N.A.I.C.S.: 561730
Aaron Beel (Accountant)

West Bay Landscape, Inc. (1)
6009 15th St E, Bradenton, FL 34203
Tel.: (941) 753-8225
Web Site: http://wblcompany.com
Landscaping Services
N.A.I.C.S.: 561730
Ron Sikkema (Pres)

BRILLIANT EARTH GROUP, INC.
300 Grant Ave 3rd Fl, San Francisco, CA 94108
Tel.: (415) 354-4623   DE
Web Site: https://www.brilliantearth.com
Year Founded: 2021
BRLT—(NASDAQ)
Rev.: $439,882,000
Assets: $262,574,000
Liabilities: $169,433,000
Net Worth: $93,141,000
Earnings: $19,025,000
Emp.: 591
Fiscal Year-end: 12/31/22
Holding Company
N.A.I.C.S.: 551112
Eric Grossberg (Co-Founder & Chm)
Beth Gerstein (Co-Founder & CEO)
Jeffrey Kuo (CFO)

BRINKER INTERNATIONAL, INC.
3000 Olympus Blvd, Dallas, TX 75019
Tel.: (972) 980-9917   DE
Web Site: https://www.brinker.com
Year Founded: 1975
EAT—(NYSE)
Rev.: $4,415,100,000
Assets: $2,593,100,000
Liabilities: $2,553,700,000
Net Worth: $39,400,000
Earnings: $155,300,000
Emp.: 68,852
Fiscal Year-end: 06/26/24
Restaurant Operator & Franchisor

N.A.I.C.S.: 722511
Joseph Michael DePinto (Chm)
Chris Caldwell (CIO & Sr VP)
Dan Fuller (Gen Counsel, Sec & Sr VP)
David Weston (VP-Dev & Bus Fin-Global)
Kim Sanders (Treas & VP-Fin & Risk Mgmt)
Kevin Hochman (Pres & CEO)
Aaron White (Chief People Officer, Chief People & Admin Officer & Exec VP)
Kyle Lindelof (VP-Food & Beverage)
Dominique Bertolone (Sr VP)
James Butler (Chief Supply Chain Officer & Sr VP)
Julie Feldman (VP & Asst Gen Counsel)
Melissa Richardson (VP-Internal Audit)
Nathan Huber (VP-Information Technology)
Jason Landry (VP-Compensation, Benefits, and Restaurant Support Center PeopleWorks)
Sarah Coco (VP-Accounting)
Jared Miller (Treas & VP-Corporate Financial Planning & Analysis)
Margaret Suarez (VP-Enterprise Project Mgmt)

Subsidiaries:

BRINKER LOUISIANA, INC. (1)
6820 Lbj Freeway, Dallas, TX 75240-6511
Tel.: (972) 980-9917
Sales Range: $75-99.9 Million
Emp.: 700
Restaurant Operating Services
N.A.I.C.S.: 561599

Brinker Restaurant Corporation (1)
6820 LBJ Freeway, Dallas, TX 75240
Tel.: (972) 980-9917
Web Site: http://www.brinker.com
Sales Range: $200-249.9 Million
Emp.: 1,300
Restaurant Owner & Operator
N.A.I.C.S.: 722511

CHILI'S OF MARYLAND, INC. (1)
9615 Deereco Rd, Timonium, MD 21093-6903
Tel.: (410) 308-8740
Restaurant Operating Services
N.A.I.C.S.: 561599

Chili's of Salisbury, LLC (1)
2750 N Salisbury Blvd, Salisbury, MD 21801
Tel.: (410) 860-4700
Restaurant Operators
N.A.I.C.S.: 722511

Chili's, Inc. (1)
6820 LBJ Freeway, Dallas, TX 75240
Tel.: (972) 980-9917
Web Site: https://chilis.com
Sales Range: $50-74.9 Million
Restaurant Operators
N.A.I.C.S.: 722511
Wyman T. Roberts (Pres)

Chilis of Kanasa, Inc. (1)
1710 Village W Pkwy, Kansas City, KS 66111
Tel.: (913) 334-9728
Food Retailer
N.A.I.C.S.: 445110

MAGGIANO'S BEVERAGE COMPANY (1)
10910 Domain Dr Ste 100, Austin, TX 78758
Tel.: (512) 501-7870
Restaurant Operating Services
N.A.I.C.S.: 561599

MAGGIANO'S, INC. (1)
6820 LBJ Fwy, Dallas, TX 75240
Tel.: (972) 980-9917
Web Site: http://www.brinker.com
Sales Range: $50-74.9 Million
Italian Restaurant Operator
N.A.I.C.S.: 722513

Pepper Dining Inc. (1)
11600 N Community House Rd Ste 200, Charlotte, NC 28277-1812
Tel.: (704) 943-5276
Restaurants Owner & Operator
N.A.I.C.S.: 722511
Kelli Valade (Pres)
Doug Comings (COO & Sr VP)

BRISTOL-MYERS SQUIBB COMPANY
Rte 206 & Province Line Rd, Princeton, NJ 08543
Tel.: (609) 252-4621   DE
Web Site: https://www.bms.com
Year Founded: 1933
BMY—(NYSE)
Rev.: $45,006,000,000
Assets: $95,159,000,000
Liabilities: $65,674,000,000
Net Worth: $29,485,000,000
Earnings: $8,025,000,000
Emp.: 34,100
Fiscal Year-end: 12/31/23
Beauty, Health, Nutritional, Pharmaceutical, Household Products & Medical Devices Mfr & Whslr
N.A.I.C.S.: 325412
Sandra Leung (Gen Counsel & Exec VP)
David V. Elkins (CFO & Exec VP)
Louis S. Schmukler (Pres-Product Dev & Supply-Global & Exec VP)
Paul von Autenried (CIO & Exec VP)
Ann Powell Judge (Head-Human Resources-Global)
Laura Hortas (Head)
Tim Power (VP-Investor Relations)
Christopher S. Boerner (Chm & CEO)
Adam Dubow (Chief Compliance & Ethics Officer & Chief Compliance & Ethics Officer)
Rupert Vessey (Pres-Res & Early Dev & Exec VP)
David V. Elkins (CFO & Exec VP)
Joseph E. Eid (Sr VP & Head-Medical Affairs-Global)
Samit Hirawat (Chief Medical Officer-Drug Dev-Global & Exec VP)
Nina Goworek (Exec Dir-Investor Relations)
Beatrice Anduze-Faris (VP-Central New Jersey)
Michaela Bowden (Dir)
Cynthia Brogdon (Head-Oncology Portfolio Strategy-Oncology Medical)
Binodh DeSilva (VP-Discovery & Optimization-Central New Jersey)
Evan Janovitz (Dir-Pathology-Discovery Toxicology-Central New Jersey)
Elizabeth A. Mily (Exec VP-Strategy & Bus Dev)
Karen Wheeler (Dir-Investor Relations)
Pamela Fisher (Chief Diversity Officer, Chief Inclusion Officer & VP)
Estelle Vester-Blokland (Sr VP-Medical Affairs-Global)
Sharon Greenlees (Sr VP & Controller)
Teresa Foy (Sr VP-Immuno-Oncology & Cell Therapy)
Karin Shanahan (Exec VP-Global Product Dev & Supply)
Christopher S. Boerner (Chm & CEO)
Ann M. Powell (Chief HR Officer-Global & Exec VP)

Subsidiaries:

Adnexus, a Bristol-Myers Squibb R&D Company (1)
100 Beaver St, Waltham, MA 02453
Tel.: (781) 209-2301
Pharmaceutical Product Mfr & Distr
N.A.I.C.S.: 325412

Apothecon, Inc. (1)

Dieselweg 25, Bunschoten, 3752 LB, Netherlands
Tel.: (31) 342426120
Pharmaceuticals Product Mfr
N.A.I.C.S.: 325412

BMS Holdings Spain, S.L. (1)
C/ Quintanaduenas 6, 28050, Madrid, Spain
Tel.: (34) 914565300
Web Site: http://www.bms.com
Pharmaceutical Preparation Mfr
N.A.I.C.S.: 325412

BMS Pharmaceutical Korea Limited (1)
12th Floor Haesung 1 Building 504
Teheran-ro, Gangnam-gu, Seoul, 06178, Korea (South)
Tel.: (82) 23 404 1300
Web Site: https://www.bms.com
Pharmaceutical Preparation Mfr
N.A.I.C.S.: 325412

Bristol-Myers De Venezuela, S.A. (1)
Calle Bernardet Edificio BMS, Los Cortijos, 1060 A, Caracas, Venezuela (100%)
Tel.: (58) 2123005311
Sales Range: $150-199.9 Million
Emp.: 300
Medicine Whlsr
N.A.I.C.S.: 424210

Bristol-Myers K.K. (1)
Shinjuku i-Land Tower 6-5-1 Nishi-Shinjuku 6-chome, Shinjuku, Tokyo, 163-1328, Japan
Tel.: (81) 353238302
Pharmaceutical Products Distr
N.A.I.C.S.: 424210

Bristol-Myers Pharmaceutical (1)
Columbusgasse 4, 1011, Vienna, Austria (100%)
Tel.: (43) 1601430
Web Site: http://www.b-ms.at
Sales Range: $25-49.9 Million
Emp.: 80
Pharmaceuticals Mfr
N.A.I.C.S.: 325412

Bristol-Myers Squibb (Hong Kong) Limited (1)
34 Windsor House, Causeway Bay, China (Hong Kong) (100%)
Tel.: (852) 25106105
Sales Range: $200-249.9 Million
Cosmetics Mfr
N.A.I.C.S.: 325620

Bristol-Myers Squibb (Israel) Ltd (1)
18 Aharon Bart St, Kiryat Arye, Petah Tikva, 4951448, Israel
Tel.: (972) 235231021
Web Site: https://www.bms.com
Pharmaceuticals Mfr
N.A.I.C.S.: 325412

Bristol-Myers Squibb (NZ) Limited (1)
Simpson Grierson 88 Shortland Street, Auckland, New Zealand
Tel.: (64) 800167567
Web Site: https://www.bms.com
Health Care Product Development Services
N.A.I.C.S.: 541714

Bristol-Myers Squibb (Singapore) Pte. Limited (1)
80 Marine Parade Road 20-01 Parkway Parade, Singapore, 449269, Singapore
Tel.: (65) 63450822
Pharmaceuticals Product Mfr
N.A.I.C.S.: 325412

Bristol-Myers Squibb (Taiwan) Ltd. (1)
5th Fl No 156 Jiankang Road, Taipei, Taiwan
Tel.: (886) 227561234
Web Site: https://www.bms.com
Pharmaceuticals Mfr
N.A.I.C.S.: 325412

Bristol-Myers Squibb AB (1)
Hemvarnsgatan 9, PO Box 152 00, 171 54, Solna, 167 15, Sweden (100%)
Tel.: (46) 87047100
Web Site: http://www.bms.com
Sales Range: $50-74.9 Million
Emp.: 206
Pharmaceuticals Mfr

N.A.I.C.S.: 325412

Branch (Non-US):

Bristol-Myers Squibb Denmark (2)
Hummeltoftevej 49, 2830, Virum, Denmark
Tel.: (45) 45930506
Web Site: https://www.bms.com.dk
Sales Range: $10-24.9 Million
Emp.: 37
Pharmaceuticals Mfr
N.A.I.C.S.: 325412

Bristol-Myers Squibb AG (1)
Hinterbergstrasse 16, 6312, Steinhausen,
Switzerland
Tel.: (41) 7677255
Web Site: https://www.bms.com
Sales Range: $75-99.9 Million
Emp.: 130
Pharmaceuticals Distr
N.A.I.C.S.: 424210

Bristol-Myers Squibb Aktiebolag (1)
Hemvarnsgatan 9, 171 54, Solna, Sweden
Tel.: (46) 87047100
Web Site: https://www.bms.com
Health Care Product Development Services
N.A.I.C.S.: 541714

**Bristol-Myers Squibb Argentina
S.R.L.** (1)
Av del Libertador 101 6th floor, Vicente Lo-
pez, Buenos Aires, Argentina
Tel.: (54) 8006661179
Web Site: https://www.bms.com
Sales Range: $25-49.9 Million
Emp.: 120
Pharmaceuticals Mfr
N.A.I.C.S.: 325412

**Bristol-Myers Squibb Australia Pty.
Ltd.** (1)
Level 2 4 Nexus Court, Mulgrave, 3170,
VIC, Australia
Tel.: (61) 385234200
Web Site: https://www.bms.com
Sales Range: $150-199.9 Million
Pharmaceutical Products Whslr & Mfr
N.A.I.C.S.: 325412

Bristol-Myers Squibb B.V. (1)
Orteliuslaan 1000, Post Office Box 4058,
3528 BD, Utrecht, Netherlands (100%)
Tel.: (31) 303002222
Web Site: https://www.bms.com
Sales Range: $100-124.9 Million
Wholesale Distributor of Drugs
N.A.I.C.S.: 424210

**Bristol-Myers Squibb Belgium
S.A.** (1)
Parc de l'Alliance Avenue de Finlande 4,
1420, Braine-l'Alleud, Belgium (100%)
Tel.: (32) 23527611
Web Site: https://www.bms.com
Sales Range: $75-99.9 Million
Pharmaceuticals & Cosmetics Mfr
N.A.I.C.S.: 325412

**Bristol-Myers Squibb Business Ser-
vices Limited** (1)
Lakewood Heronsway Chester Business
Park Wrexham Road, Chester, CH4 9QW,
United Kingdom
Tel.: (44) 1244586100
Sales Range: $25-49.9 Million
Emp.: 250
Financial Services
N.A.I.C.S.: 921130

**Bristol-Myers Squibb Canada
Co.** (1)
2344 Alfred-Nobel Boulevard Suite 300,
Saint Laurent, H4S 0A4, QC,
Canada (100%)
Tel.: (514) 333-3200
Web Site: http://www.bmscanada.ca
Sales Range: $250-299.9 Million
Pharmaceutical Product Whslr
N.A.I.C.S.: 424210

**Bristol-Myers Squibb Canada Interna-
tional Limited** (1)
535 Legget Dr Ste 900, Kanata, K2K 3B8,
ON, Canada
Tel.: (613) 595-4700
Sales Range: $50-74.9 Million
Emp.: 20
Pharmaceuticals Product Mfr

**Bristol-Myers Squibb Company -
Lawrenceville R&D Facility** (1)
Rte 206 Province Line Rd, Princeton, NJ
08540
Tel.: (609) 252-4000
Web Site: http://www.bms.com
Sales Range: $150-199.9 Million
Clinical Development
N.A.I.C.S.: 325412

**Bristol-Myers Squibb Company -
Wallingford R&D Facility** (1)
5 Research Pkwy, Wallingford, CT 06492-
1951
Tel.: (203) 677-6000
Web Site: http://www.bms.com
Sales Range: Less than $1 Million
Pharmaceutical Research
N.A.I.C.S.: 541715

**Bristol-Myers Squibb Denmark Filial
of Bristol-Myers Squibb AB** (1)
Hummeltoftevej 49, 2830, Virum, Denmark
Tel.: (45) 45930506
Pharmaceutical Product Mfr & Distr
N.A.I.C.S.: 325412

**Bristol-Myers Squibb Farmaceutica
Ltda** (1)
Av Portugal 1100 Unidade 4 Modulo 2,
Itapevi, 06696-060, SP, Brazil
Tel.: (55) 1133822446
Pharmaceutical Product Whslr
N.A.I.C.S.: 424210

**Bristol-Myers Squibb Farmaceutica
Portuguesa S.A.** (1)
National Road No 9 KM17, Terrugem, 2709-
504, Sintra, Portugal
Tel.: (351) 214407000
Web Site: https://www.bms.com
Pharmaceuticals Product Mfr
N.A.I.C.S.: 325412

**Bristol-Myers Squibb Ges.
m.b.H.** (1)
Rivergate / Gate 1 / 5 OG Handelskai 92,
1200, Vienna, Austria
Tel.: (43) 1601430
Web Site: https://www.bms.com
Pharmaceutical Preparation Mfr
N.A.I.C.S.: 325412

Bristol-Myers Squibb GesmbH. (1)
Rivergate/Gate 1/5 OG Handelskai 92,
1200, Vienna, Austria
Tel.: (43) 1601430
Web Site: https://www.bms.com
Health Care Product Development Services
N.A.I.C.S.: 541714

Bristol-Myers Squibb GmbH (1)
Arnulfstr 29, 80636, Munich,
Germany (100%)
Tel.: (49) 8007242410
Web Site: http://www.b-ms.de
Sales Range: $150-199.9 Million
Emp.: 350
Pharmaceuticals Mfr
N.A.I.C.S.: 325412

**Bristol-Myers Squibb Holdings Ger-
many Verwaltungs Gmbh** (1)
Arnulfstr 29, 80636, Munich, 80636, Ger-
many
Tel.: (49) 8007242410
Pharmaceutical Preparation Mfr
N.A.I.C.S.: 325412

Bristol-Myers Squibb Ilaclari, Inc. (1)
Maslak Mah Dereboyu Cad Science Sk Sun
Plaza No 5 Floor 17, Sariyer, 34485, Istan-
bul, Turkiye
Tel.: (90) 2123358900
Pharmaceuticals Product Mfr
N.A.I.C.S.: 325412

**Bristol-Myers Squibb India Pvt.
Ltd.** (1)
One International Center 6th Floor Tower 1
Senapati Bapat Marg, Elphinstone, Mumbai,
400013, Maharashtra, India
Tel.: (91) 8004401165
Web Site: http://www.bmsi.co.in
Sales Range: $25-49.9 Million
Emp.: 15
Pharmaceuticals Product Mfr
N.A.I.C.S.: 325412

Pheroze Khan *(Mng Dir)*

Bristol-Myers Squibb K.K. (1)
16-13 28 Shinjuku Island Tower 5-1, Nishi
Shinjuku Shinjuku-kuTokyo, Tokyo, 163-
1328, Japan
Tel.: (81) 367057000
Pharmaceuticals Product Mfr
N.A.I.C.S.: 325412

**Bristol-Myers Squibb Limited Liability
Company** (1)
Zemlyanoy Val 9, 105064, Moscow, Russia
Tel.: (7) 4957559267
Pharmaceuticals Product Mfr
N.A.I.C.S.: 325412

**Bristol-Myers Squibb Marketing Ser-
vices S.R.L.** (1)
Europe House Bd Lascar Catargiu 47-53 et
5 sector 1, 010665, Bucharest, Romania
Tel.: (40) 212721619
Web Site: https://www.bms.com
Health Care Product Development Services
N.A.I.C.S.: 541714

**Bristol-Myers Squibb Marketing Ser-
vices S.R.L.** (1)
Piazzale dell Industria 40-46, 00144, Rome,
Italy
Tel.: (39) 06503961
Web Site: https://www.bms.com
Pharmaceutical Product Whslr
N.A.I.C.S.: 424210

**Bristol-Myers Squibb Middle East &
Africa FZ-LLC** (1)
Dubai Science Park HQ Towers North 18th
floor, Barsha South, Dubai, United Arab
Emirates
Tel.: (971) 44502100
Web Site: https://www.bms.com
Health Care Product Development Services
N.A.I.C.S.: 541714

**Bristol-Myers Squibb Norway
Ltd.** (1)
Lysaker Torg 35, 1366, Lysaker, Norway
Tel.: (47) 67555350
Web Site: http://www.bms.com
Pharmaceuticals Product Mfr
N.A.I.C.S.: 325412

Bristol-Myers Squibb Peru S.A. (1)
Ave Canaval y Moreyra 380, Lima, 27, Peru
Tel.: (51) 14116200
Sales Range: $200-249.9 Million
Emp.: 400
Pharmaceuticals Mfr
N.A.I.C.S.: 325412

**Bristol-Myers Squibb Pharma (Thai-
land) Co. Ltd.** (1)
388 Sukhumvit Rd Khlong Toei, Bangkok,
10110, Thailand
Tel.: (66) 27251400
Pharmaceutical & Medicinal Products Mfr
N.A.I.C.S.: 325412

**Bristol-Myers Squibb Pharmaceuticals
Limited** (1)
ARC UxbridgeSanderson Road, New Den-
ham, Uxbridge, UB8 1DH, Buckingham-
shire, United Kingdom
Tel.: (44) 1895523000
Web Site: http://www.b-ms.co.uk
Sales Range: $200-249.9 Million
Pharmaceuticals Mfr
N.A.I.C.S.: 325412

**Bristol-Myers Squibb Pharmaceuticals
Unlimited Company** (1)
Plaza 254 Blanchardstown Corporate Park
2, Dublin, D15 T867, Ireland
Tel.: (353) 14833625
Web Site: http://www.bms.com
Pharmaceuticals Product Mfr
N.A.I.C.S.: 325412

**Bristol-Myers Squibb Polska
Sp.z.o.o.** (1)
Armii Ludowej 26, 00-609, Warsaw, Poland
Tel.: (48) 222606400
Web Site: http://www.b-ms.pl
Pharmaceutical Preparation Mfr
N.A.I.C.S.: 325412

**Bristol-Myers Squibb Puerto Rico,
Inc. - Humacao Plant** (1)
Rd 3 KM 77.5, Humacao, PR 00792

Tel.: (787) 852-1255
Web Site: http://www.bms.com
Sales Range: $400-449.9 Million
Emp.: 300
Pharmaceuticals Mfr
N.A.I.C.S.: 424210

**Bristol-Myers Squibb Puerto Rico,
Inc. - Manati Plant** (1)
Km 2/3 Hm 3 Rr 686, Manati, PR 00674
Tel.: (787) 815-1000
Web Site: http://www.bms.com
Emp.: 450
Pharmaceutical Preparation Mfr
N.A.I.C.S.: 325412

Bristol-Myers Squibb S.A. (1)
Quimpa Vibes 15, 28050, Madrid, Spain
Tel.: (34) 914565300
Web Site: http://www.bms.es
Sales Range: $100-124.9 Million
Emp.: 312
Pharmaceuticals Mfr
N.A.I.C.S.: 325412

Bristol-Myers Squibb S.r.l. (1)
Piazzale dell Industria 40-46, 00144, Rome,
Italy
Tel.: (39) 06503961
Web Site: http://www.bms.com
Pharmaceuticals Mfr
N.A.I.C.S.: 325412

Bristol-Myers Squibb SA (1)
Hinterbergstrasse 16, 6312, Steinhausen,
Switzerland
Tel.: (41) 417677255
Web Site: https://www.bms.com
Health Care Product Development Services
N.A.I.C.S.: 541714

Bristol-Myers Squibb Sarl (1)
3 rue Joseph Monier, 92500, Rueil-
Malmaison, France
Tel.: (33) 158838496
Web Site: https://www.bms.com
Health Care Product Development Services
N.A.I.C.S.: 541714

**Bristol-Myers Squibb Services Sp. z
o.o.** (1)
Armii Ludowej 26, 00-609, Warsaw, Poland
Tel.: (48) 22 260 6400
Pharmaceuticals Product Mfr
N.A.I.C.S.: 325412

**Bristol-Myers Squibb Trustees
Ltd.** (1)
BMS House Uxbridge Business Park Sand-
erson Road, Uxbridge, UB8 1DH, Middle-
sex, United Kingdom
Tel.: (44) 1895523000
Web Site: http://www.b-ms.co.uk
Biopharma Consulting Services
N.A.I.C.S.: 541690

**Bristol-Myers Squibb de Guatemala,
S.A.** (1)
Cl 77 B 57-141 Of 418Â , Barranquilla, Co-
lombia
Tel.: (57) 53531353
Pharmaceutical Product Whslr
N.A.I.C.S.: 424210

Bristol-Myers Squibb spol. s r.o. (1)
Budejovicka 778/3, 140 00, Prague, 4,
Czech Republic
Tel.: (420) 221016111
Web Site: https://www.bms.com
Pharmaceuticals Product Mfr
N.A.I.C.S.: 325412

Bristol-Myers Squibb, S.A.U. (1)
C/ Quintanaduenas 6, 28050, Madrid, Spain
Tel.: (34) 914565300
Web Site: https://www.bms.com
Pharmaceutical Product Whslr
N.A.I.C.S.: 424210

Cardioxyl Pharmaceuticals, Inc. (1)
1450 Raleigh Rd Ste 212, Chapel Hill, NC
27517
Pharmaceuticals Product Mfr
N.A.I.C.S.: 325199

Celgene Corporation (1)
86 Morris Ave, Summit, NJ 07901
Tel.: (908) 673-9000
Web Site: http://www.celgene.com

Bristol-Myers Squibb Company—(Continued)

Sales Range: $15-24.9 Billion
Pharmaceutical Developer & Mfr
N.A.I.C.S.: 325412
Aijaz Tobaccowalla *(Chief Info & Digital Officer & Sr VP)*

Subsidiary (Domestic):

Avila Therapeutics, Inc. (2)
45 Wiggins Ave, Bedford, MA 01730
Tel.: (781) 541-3700
Web Site: http://www.avilatx.com
Biotechnological Drug Developer
N.A.I.C.S.: 541714

Subsidiary (Non-US):

Celgene AB (2)
Torshamnsgatan 44, 164 40, Kista, Sweden
Tel.: (46) 8 704 7100
Cancer Treatment Drug Mfr
N.A.I.C.S.: 325412

Celgene Ab (2)
Ayritie 18, 01510, Vantaa, Finland
Tel.: (358) 925108400
Web Site: http://www.celgene.fi
Cancer Treatment Drug Mfr
N.A.I.C.S.: 325412

Celgene ApS (2)
Hummeltoftevej 49, Virum, 2830, Denmark
Tel.: (45) 45930506
Web Site: https://www.celgene.dk
Cancer Treatment Drug Mfr
N.A.I.C.S.: 325412

Subsidiary (Domestic):

Celgene Avilomics Research, Inc. (2)
45 Wiggins Ave, Bedford, MA 01730-2314
Tel.: (781) 541-3700
Web Site: http://www.celgene.com
Pharmaceuticals Mfr
N.A.I.C.S.: 325412

Subsidiary (Non-US):

Celgene B.V. (2)
Winthontlaan 2, PO Box 2507, 3500 GM, Utrecht, Netherlands
Tel.: (31) 303002222
Web Site: http://www.celgene.nl
Sales Range: $10-24.9 Million
Pharmaceutical Developer & Mfr
N.A.I.C.S.: 325412

Celgene BVBA (2)
Building D-E Bloc E1 Place du Luxembourg 1, 1420, Braine-l'Alleud, Belgium
Tel.: (32) 27934811
Web Site: https://www.celgene.com
Pharmaceuticals Mfr
N.A.I.C.S.: 325412

Celgene Chemicals Sarl (2)
Untere Bruhlstrasse 4, 4800, Zofingen, Switzerland
Tel.: (41) 627467270
Cancer Treatment Drug Mfr
N.A.I.C.S.: 325412

Celgene Co. (2)
11th floor 504 Teheran-ro, Gangnam-gu, Seoul, Korea (South)
Tel.: (82) 23 404 1300
Web Site: https://www.celgene.kr
Cancer Treatment Drug Mfr
N.A.I.C.S.: 325412

Celgene Distribution BV (2)
Winthontlaan 6 N, 3526 KV, Utrecht, Netherlands
Tel.: (31) 302844500
Pharmaceuticals Distr
N.A.I.C.S.: 424210

Celgene Europe, Limited (2)
1 Longwalk Road Stockley Park, Uxbridge, UB11 1DB, United Kingdom
Tel.: (44) 2088318300
Web Site: http://www.celgene.co.uk
Sales Range: $50-74.9 Million
Cancer Treatment Drug Mfr
N.A.I.C.S.: 325412

Celgene GmbH (2)

Rudolf-Wissell-Str 28a, 37079, Gottingen, Germany
Tel.: (49) 89451519010
Web Site: https://www.celgene.de
Sales Range: $150-199.9 Million
Pharmaceutical Development & Mfr
N.A.I.C.S.: 325412

Celgene GmbH (2)
Euro Plaza Gebaude E Technologiestrasse 10, 1120, Vienna, Austria
Tel.: (43) 181144
Web Site: http://www.celgene.at
Sales Range: $150-199.9 Million
Pharmaceutical Developer & Mfr
N.A.I.C.S.: 325412

Celgene GmbH (2)
Bandliweg 20, 8048, Zurich, Switzerland
Tel.: (41) 444378800
Web Site: http://www.celgene.ch
Cancer Treatment Drug Mfr
N.A.I.C.S.: 325412

Celgene Ilac Pazarlama ve Tic. Ltd. (2)
Levazim Mahallesi Koru Sokak No 2, Zorlu Center D Blok T-3 Kati D344 Besiktas, 34340, Istanbul, Turkiye
Tel.: (90) 2163859333
Web Site: http://www.celgene.com.tr
Biotechnology Research & Development Services
N.A.I.C.S.: 541714

Celgene Inc. (2)
6755 Mississauga Road Suite 600, Mississauga, L5N 7Y2, ON, Canada (100%)
Web Site: http://www.celgene.ca
Pharmaceuticals Mfr
N.A.I.C.S.: 325412

Celgene International Sarl (2)
Route de Perreux 1, 2017, Boudry, Switzerland
Tel.: (41) 327298500
Web Site: http://www.celgene.com
Sales Range: $150-199.9 Million
Pharmaceutical Developer & Mfr
N.A.I.C.S.: 325412

Celgene Limited (2)
1 Longwalk Road Stockley Park, Uxbridge, UB11 1DB, United Kingdom
Tel.: (44) 2088318300
Web Site: http://www.celgene.co.uk
Sales Range: $150-199.9 Million
Pharmaceutical Developer & Mfr
N.A.I.C.S.: 325412

Celgene Limited (2)
9th Floor No 11073 Chung Yan Road, Xinyi District, Taipei, 11073, Taiwan
Tel.: (886) 287298888
Web Site: http://www.celgene.com
Emp.: 15
Cancer Treatment Drug Mfr
N.A.I.C.S.: 325412

Celgene Limited (2)
PO Box 3035, Wellington, 6011, New Zealand
Tel.: (64) 93639586
Pharmaceutical Products Distr
N.A.I.C.S.: 424210

Celgene Logistics Sarl (2)
Route de Perreux 1, 2017, Boudry, Switzerland
Tel.: (41) 327298500
Sales Range: $150-199.9 Million
Emp.: 500
Cancer Treatment Drug Mfr
N.A.I.C.S.: 325412

Celgene Netherlands BV (2)
PO Box 2507, 3500 GM, Utrecht, Netherlands
Tel.: (31) 303002222
Web Site: http://www.celgene.nl
Sales Range: $25-49.9 Million
Cancer Treatment Drug Mfr
N.A.I.C.S.: 424210

Celgene PTE Ltd (2)
200 Newton Road 04-01 Newton 200, Singapore, 307983, Singapore
Tel.: (65) 65725100
Web Site: http://www.celgene.com
Sales Range: $25-49.9 Million
Cancer Treatment Drug Mfr
N.A.I.C.S.: 325412

Celgene Pharmaceutical (Shanghai) Company Limited (2)
Unit 2207 233 Taichang Road Platinum Tower, Huang Pu District, Shanghai, 200020, China
Tel.: (86) 2160626003
Pharmaceutical Products Distr
N.A.I.C.S.: 424210

Celgene Pty Limited (2)
Level 15 60 City Road, Southbank, 3006, VIC, Australia
Tel.: (61) 3 9539 5500
Web Site: http://www.celgene.com.au
Emp.: 60
Pharmaceuticals Mfr
N.A.I.C.S.: 325412

Subsidiary (Domestic):

Celgene Quanticel Research, Inc. (2)
1500 Owens St Ste 500, San Francisco, CA 94158
Tel.: (415) 358-7609
Web Site: http://www.quanticel.com
Pharmaceutical Developer & Mfr
N.A.I.C.S.: 325412

Subsidiary (Non-US):

Celgene Sarl (2)
16/18 Rue du Quatre Septembre, 75002, Paris, France
Tel.: (33) 153424300
Web Site: http://www.celgene.fr
Cancer Treatment Drug Mfr
N.A.I.C.S.: 325412

Celgene Sociedade Unipessoal Lda (2)
Lagoas Park Edificio 7 - Piso 1 Sul, 2740-244, Porto Salvo, Portugal
Tel.: (351) 210044300
Web Site: http://www.celgene.pt
Sales Range: $25-49.9 Million
Cancer Treatment Drug Mfr
N.A.I.C.S.: 325412

Celgene Srl (2)
Piazzale del Industria 40-46, 00144, Rome, Italy
Tel.: (39) 06503961
Web Site: http://www.celgene.com
Sales Range: $10-24.9 Million
Pharmaceutical Developer & Mfr
N.A.I.C.S.: 325412

Celgene Ilac Pazarlama ve Tic.Ltd. Sti. (2)
Buyukdere Cad N 103 Sarl Business Centre Block B Apartment 3, Mecidiyekoy, Istanbul, Turkiye
Tel.: (90) 2123541806
Cancer Treatment Drug Mfr
N.A.I.C.S.: 325412
Marco Caligiuri *(Exec Dir)*

Celgene s.r.o (2)
Novodvorska 994 5th floor, Praha 4, 142 21, Prague, 4 142 21, Czech Republic
Tel.: (420) 241097500
Biotechnology Research & Development Services
N.A.I.C.S.: 541714

Celgene s.r.o. (2)
Prievozska 4B, Bratislava, 821 09, Slovakia
Tel.: (421) 232638000
Biotechnology Research & Development Services
N.A.I.C.S.: 541714

Celgene sp. zoo (2)
Armii Ludowej 26, 00-609, Warsaw, Poland
Tel.: (48) 222606400
Web Site: http://www.celgene.com
Sales Range: $25-49.9 Million
Cancer Treatment Drug Mfr
N.A.I.C.S.: 325412

Celgene, S. de R.I. de C.V. (2)
Juan Salvador Agraz 65 piso 17 Col Lomas de Santa Fe, 05300, Mexico, Mexico
Tel.: (52) 5541236700
Web Site: https://www.celgene.mx
Pharmaceuticals Product Mfr
N.A.I.C.S.: 325412

Celgene, SL (2)

Paseo De Recoletos 37-39 4th Floor, Madrid, 28004, Spain
Tel.: (34) 914229000
Web Site: http://www.celgene.com
Sales Range: $10-24.9 Million
Emp.: 70
Pharmaceutical Developer & Mfr
N.A.I.C.S.: 325412
Tom Cavanagh *(Mng Dir)*

EngMab Sarl (2)
Etzelstrasse 27 Pfaffikon, 8808, Schwyz, Switzerland
Tel.: (41) 434338128
Web Site: http://www.engmab.com
Biotechnology Research & Development Services
N.A.I.C.S.: 541714

Subsidiary (Domestic):

Juno Therapeutics, Inc. (2)
400 Dexter Ave N Ste 1200, Seattle, WA 98109
Tel.: (206) 582-1600
Web Site: http://www.junotherapeutics.com
Biopharmaceutical Mfr
N.A.I.C.S.: 325412

Receptos Services LLC (2)
3033 Science Park Rd Ste 300, San Diego, CA 92121 (100%)
Tel.: (858) 652-5700
Web Site: http://www.receptos.com
Biopharmaceutical Mfr
N.A.I.C.S.: 325412
Marcus F. Boehm *(Founder & CTO)*

E. R. Squibb & Sons Limited (1)
BMS House Uxbridge Business Park Sanderson Road, Uxbridge, UB8 1DH, Middlesex, United Kingdom
Tel.: (44) 1895523000
Pharmaceuticals Product Mfr
N.A.I.C.S.: 325412

EWI Corporation (1)
7506 S Blue Creek Rd, Evergreen, CO 80439
Tel.: (303) 674-7362
Web Site: http://ewi-corp.com
Pharmaceutical Product Whslr
N.A.I.C.S.: 424210

Inhibitex, L.L.C. (1)
1165 Sanctuary Pkwy Ste 400, Alpharetta, GA 30009
Tel.: (678) 746-1100
Sales Range: $1-9.9 Million
Emp.: 33
Pharmaceutical Services for the Treatment & Prevention of Infections
N.A.I.C.S.: 325414

Karuna Therapeutics, Inc. (1)
99 High St 26th Fl, Boston, MA 02110
Tel.: (857) 449-2244
Web Site: https://www.karunatx.com
Rev.: $10,637,000
Assets: $1,163,334,000
Liabilities: $37,096,000
Net Worth: $1,126,238,000
Earnings: ($276,336,000)
Emp.: 210
Fiscal Year-end: 12/31/2022
Biotechnology Research & Development Services
N.A.I.C.S.: 541714
Kimberly M. Jablonski *(Sec & VP)*
Sandra Ramos-Alves *(Pres & Treas)*
Sophia Park *(VP)*
Scott Matarese *(VP)*
Stephen Brannan *(Chief Medical Officer)*
Andrew Miller *(Founder & Pres-R&D)*
Mia Kelley *(Gen Counsel & Sec)*
Stephanie Moore *(VP-HR)*
Will Kane *(Chief Comml Officer)*
Lisa A. Atkins *(Asst Sec)*
Elisabeth Bradley *(Asst Sec)*
Jonathan Rosin *(Chief HR Officer)*

Mead Johnson Jamaica Ltd. (1)
3 Carifta Ave, Kingston, 11, Jamaica
Tel.: (876) 7572724
Pharmaceutical Product Whslr
N.A.I.C.S.: 424210

Mirati Therapeutics, Inc. (1)
3545 Cray Ct, San Diego, CA 92121
Tel.: (858) 332-3410

Web Site: https://www.mirati.com
Rev.: $12,436,000
Assets: $1,202,647,000
Liabilities: $206,131,000
Net Worth: $996,516,000
Earnings: ($740,867,000)
Emp.: 593
Fiscal Year-end: 12/31/2022
Biopharmaceutical Developer & Mfr
N.A.I.C.S.: 325414
Benjamin J. Hickey (Chief Comml Officer)
James Christensen (Chief Scientific Officer)
Reena Desai (Gen Counsel & Sec)
John Moriarty (Chief Legal Officer)
Mike Paolucci (Chief People Officer)
Alan Sandler (Chief Medical Officer)

MyoKardia, Inc. (1)
1000 Sierra Pt Pkwy, Brisbane, CA 94080
Tel.: (650) 741-0900
Web Site: http://www.myokardia.com
Rev.: $11,621,000
Assets: $456,094,000
Liabilities: $49,820,000
Net Worth: $406,274,000
Earnings: ($276,213,000)
Emp.: 235
Fiscal Year-end: 12/31/2019
Research & Development in Biotechnology
N.A.I.C.S.: 541714
Marc Semigran (Sr VP-Medical Sciences)
Ingrid Boyes (Sr VP-HR)
Joseph Lambing (Sr VP-Nonclinical & Pharmaceutical Dev)
Jay Edelberg (Chief Medical Officer)
Willem van Weperen (Sr VP)
Barbara Troupin (Sr VP-Medical Affairs)
Elizabeth Mily (Pres)
Jeffrey Galik (Treas & VP)
Sophia Park (VP)
Lisa Goldey (VP)
Katherine R. Kelly (Sec & VP)
Elisabeth Bradley (Asst Sec)
Jake B. Bauer (Chief Bus Officer)
Robert S. McDowell (Chief Scientific Officer)

Oy Bristol-Myers Squibb (Finland) AB (1)
Tammasaarenkatu 3, PO Box 59, 00180, Helsinki, Finland
Tel.: (358) 925121230
Web Site: https://www.bms.com
Sales Range: $10-24.9 Million
Pharmaceuticals Mfr
N.A.I.C.S.: 325412

RayzeBio, Inc. (1)
5505 Morehouse Dr Ste 300, San Diego, CA 92121
Tel.: (619) 937-2754
Web Site: https://www.rayzebio.com
Rev.: $3,520,000
Assets: $324,776,000
Liabilities: $436,070,000
Net Worth: ($111,294,000)
Earnings: ($73,150,000)
Emp.: 88
Fiscal Year-end: 12/31/2022
Biotechnology Research & Development Services
N.A.I.C.S.: 541714
Benjamin J. Hickey (Pres)
Kimberly M. Jablonski (Sec & VP)
Sandra Ramos-Alves (Treas & VP)
Sophia Park (VP)
Scott Matarese (VP)
Benjamin Hickey (Pres)

Sino-American Shanghai Squibb Pharmaceuticals Ltd. (1)
No 1315 Jianchuan Road, Minhang District, Shanghai, China
Tel.: (86) 2164302740
Sales Range: $450-499.9 Million
Emp.: 983
Pharmaceuticals Mfr
N.A.I.C.S.: 325412

Turning Point Therapeutics, Inc. (1)
10628 Science Center Dr Ste 200, San Diego, CA 92121
Tel.: (858) 926-5251
Web Site: http://www.tptherapeutics.com
Rev.: $30,829,000
Assets: $1,003,463,000
Liabilities: $49,038,000
Net Worth: $954,425,000
Earnings: ($236,551,000)
Emp.: 250

Fiscal Year-end: 12/31/2021
Biotechnology Research & Development Services
N.A.I.C.S.: 541714
Paolo Tombesi (CFO, Principal Acctg Officer & Exec VP)
Adam D. Levy (Sr VP-IR & Corp Comm)
Kyri K. Van Hoose (VP-Acctg)

Von Heyden Pharma GmbH (1)
Sapporobogen 6-8, 80809, Munich, Germany
Tel.: (49) 89121420
Sales Range: $1-9.9 Million
Emp.: 2
Pharmaceuticals Mfr
N.A.I.C.S.: 325412

Westwood-Intrafin, S.A. (1)
Hinterbergstrasse 16, 6312, Steinhausen, Switzerland
Tel.: (41) 417677255
Web Site: http://www.bms.com
Sales Range: $75-99.9 Million
Emp.: 160
Pharmaceuticals Whslr
N.A.I.C.S.: 456191

BRISTOW GROUP, INC.
945 Bunker Hill Rd Ste 650, Houston, TX 77024
Tel.: (713) 369-4700   DE
Web Site:
http://www.erahelicopters.com
VTOL—(NYSE)
Rev.: $1,297,429,000
Assets: $1,937,278,000
Liabilities: $1,114,099,000
Net Worth: $823,179,000
Earnings: ($6,780,000)
Emp.: 3,298
Fiscal Year-end: 12/31/23
Holding Company; Chartered Helicopter Passenger Transportation Services
N.A.I.C.S.: 551112
Jennifer Dawn Whalen (CFO & Sr VP)
Stuart Stavley (COO-Offshore Energy Svcs)
Paul White (Sr VP-Comml)
David Zaworski (Dir-Safety & Compliance)
Michael May (CTO)
Grant Newman (Sr VP-Strategy & Corp Dev)
David F. Stepanek (Chief Transformation Officer & Exec VP-Sls)
G. Mark Mickelson (Chm)
Christopher S. Bradshaw (Pres & Acting CEO)

Subsidiaries:

Apical Industries (1)
2608 Temple Heights Dr, Oceanside, CA 92056-3512
Tel.: (760) 724-5300
Helicopter Transport Operator
N.A.I.C.S.: 487990
Lisa Mansfield (Project Mgr-Tech Support)
Pablo Bravo (Dir-Engrg)
Jesus Vargas (Mgr-Inventory Control)
Daniela De La Rosa (Office Mgr)

Bristow Holdings U.S. Inc. (1)
3151 Briarpark Dr Ste 700 7th Fl, Houston, TX 77042
Tel.: (713) 267-7600
Web Site: https://www.bristowgroup.com
Rev.: $1,178,062,000
Assets: $1,992,270,000
Liabilities: $1,095,199,000
Net Worth: $897,071,000
Earnings: ($56,094,000)
Emp.: 3,167
Fiscal Year-end: 03/31/2021
Nonscheduled Chartered Passenger Air Transportation
N.A.I.C.S.: 481211
Jennifer Dawn Whalen (CFO & Sr VP)
G. Mark Mickelson (Chm)
Mary Wersebe (VP-HR)
Alan Corbett (COO-Govt Svcs)
Robert A. Phillips (Sr VP-Americas)

Victoria Lazar (Gen Counsel, Sec & Sr VP)
Hooman Yazhari (Vice Chm)
Donna Anderson (Chief Acctg Officer & VP)
L. Don Miller (Pres & CEO)

Subsidiary (Non-US):

Air Kilroe Limited (2)
Schiphol House Humberside Airport, Kirmington, DN39 6YH, United Kingdom
Tel.: (44) 8703669199
Web Site: http://www.easternairways.com
Oil Transportation Services
N.A.I.C.S.: 532411

Aircraft Logistics Pty. Ltd. (2)
4 Lancaster Road Marrara, PO Box 39548, Darwin, 0812, NT, Australia
Tel.: (61) 889204000
Web Site: https://www.airnorth.com.au
Emp.: 225
Oil Transportation Services
N.A.I.C.S.: 532411

BGI Aviation Technical Services (Overseas) Limited. (2)
Terminal Building Redhill Aerodrome Kingsmill Lane, Redhill, RH1 5YP, Surrey, United Kingdom
Tel.: (44) 1737822353
Emp.: 80
Oil Transportation Services
N.A.I.C.S.: 532411

Subsidiary (Domestic):

BHNA Holdings Inc. (2)
2103 City W Blvd 4th Fl, Houston, TX 77042
Tel.: (713) 267-7600
Oil Transportation Services
N.A.I.C.S.: 532411

Division (Domestic):

Bristow Academy, Inc. (2)
365 Golden Knights Blvd, Titusville, FL 32780
Tel.: (321) 385-2919
Web Site: http://www.heli.com
Sales Range: $25-49.9 Million
Emp.: 110
Helicopter Training Services
N.A.I.C.S.: 611699
Todd Smith (Dir-School)

Subsidiary (Non-US):

Bristow Caribbean Ltd. (2)
Hangar 4 Piarco International Airport, Piarco, Trinidad & Tobago
Tel.: (868) 6698101
Web Site: http://www.bristowgroup.com
Emp.: 20
Automotive & Aviation Services
N.A.I.C.S.: 336411

Bristow Helicopter Group Limited (2)
Redhill Aerodrome, Redhill, RH1 5JZ, United Kingdom
Tel.: (44) 1737822353
Emp.: 95
Airlines Technical Support Services
N.A.I.C.S.: 561990

Bristow Helicopters (Australia Pty.) Ltd (2)
130 Fauntleroy Ave, Redcliffe, 6104, WA, Australia
Tel.: (61) 894783388
Web Site: http://www.bristowgroup.com
Emp.: 291
Oil Transportation Services
N.A.I.C.S.: 481111

Bristow Management Services Pty Limited (2)
130 Fauntleroy Ave, Redcliffe, 6104, WA, Australia
Tel.: (61) 746914463
Aircraft Training & Educational Services
N.A.I.C.S.: 611519

Bristow Norway AS (2)
Tel.: (47) 51646600
Emp.: 300
Oil Transportation Services
N.A.I.C.S.: 481211

Bristow Travel Proprietary Limited (2)

130 Fauntleroy Avenue, Redcliffe, 6104, WA, Australia
Tel.: (61) 894783388
Oil Transportation Services
N.A.I.C.S.: 532411

Division (Domestic):

Bristow U.S. LLC (2)
4605 Industrial Dr Acadiana Regional Airport, New Iberia, LA 70560
Tel.: (337) 365-6771
Web Site: http://www.bristowgroup.com
Sales Range: $250-299.9 Million
Emp.: 600
Helicopter Transportation Services
N.A.I.C.S.: 481219

Subsidiary (Non-US):

Capiteq Limited (2)
4 Lancaster Road, Marrara, Darwin, 0821, NT, Australia
Tel.: (61) 889204000
Web Site: http://www.airnorth.com.au
Oil Transportation Services
N.A.I.C.S.: 532411

Eastern Airways (UK) Limited (2)
Schiphol House Humberside Airport, Kirmington, DN39 6YH, United Kingdom
Tel.: (44) 8703669100
Web Site: http://www.easternairways.com
Emp.: 500
Oil Transportation Services
N.A.I.C.S.: 532411

Pan African Airlines (Nigeria) Limited (2)
Old Domestic Wing Murtala Muhammed Airport, PO Box 21054, Ikeja, Lagos, Nigeria
Tel.: (234) 127167324
Web Site: http://www.pan-africanairlines.com
Airline Transportation Services
N.A.I.C.S.: 541614

Dart Holding Company Ltd. (1)
1270 Aberdeen Street, Hawkesbury, K6A 1K7, ON, Canada   (50%)
Tel.: (613) 632-3336
Web Site: http://www.dartaero.com
Emp.: 80
Holding Company
N.A.I.C.S.: 551112
Mike O'Reilly (Owner)

Subsidiary (Domestic):

Dart Helicopter Services Canada, Inc. (2)
1270 Aberdeen Street, Hawkesbury, K6A 1K7, ON, Canada
Tel.: (613) 632-3336
Emp.: 80
Markets & Sells Helicopters & Aftermarket Helicopter Accessories
N.A.I.C.S.: 336411
Bill Beckett (CEO)

Era Flightseeing LLC (1)
6160 Carl Brady Dr, Anchorage, AK 99502
Web Site: http://www.eraflightseeing.com
Helicopter Charter Services
N.A.I.C.S.: 487990

Era Helicopters, LLC (1)
600 Airport Service Rd, Lake Charles, LA 70605
Tel.: (337) 478-6131
Web Site: http://www.erahelicopters.com
Sales Range: $600-649.9 Million
Emp.: 200
Freight Air Transportation Services
N.A.I.C.S.: 551112

Era Leasing LLC (1)
600 Airport Service Rd, Lake Charles, LA 70605
Tel.: (337) 478-6131
Web Site: http://www.erahelicopters.com
Freight Air Transportation Services
N.A.I.C.S.: 551112

Era Med LLC (1)
1 Earhart Dr 11, Coatesville, PA 19320
Tel.: (484) 288-2800

Bristow Group, Inc.—(Continued)

Emp.: 32
Freight Air Transportation Services
N.A.I.C.S.: 551112

Era Training Center, LLC   **(1)**
960 W Lincoln Rd, Lake Charles, LA
70607   **(50%)**
Tel.: (337) 656-4200
Web Site: http://www.eratrainingcenter.com
Helicopter Pilot Training
N.A.I.C.S.: 611512

Heli-Tech, Inc.   **(1)**
190 S Danebo Ave, Eugene, OR 97402
Tel.: (541) 344-2304
Web Site: http://www.helitech.com
Aircraft Mfr
N.A.I.C.S.: 336411

Offshore Helicopter Support Services, Inc.   **(1)**
200 Burgess Dr, Broussard, LA 70518
Tel.: (337) 839-0700
Freight Air Transportation Services
N.A.I.C.S.: 551112
Melissa Thibodeaux *(Office Mgr)*

BRITANNIA MINING INC.
1001 Ave of the Americas Ste 1204,
New York, NY 10018
Tel.: (646) 580-1153   **NV**
Web Site:
    http://www.britanniamining.com
Year Founded: 2013
BMIN—(OTCIQ)
Sales Range: Less than $1 Million
Iron Ore Mining
N.A.I.C.S.: 212210
Kenneth Roberts *(Chm & CEO)*
Nicola Newmarch *(COO & Sec)*
Bradley Rudman *(VP-North America)*
Conrad Williams *(VP-Asia)*
Lloyd Thomson *(Exec Dir-Malawi)*
Alan Reeves *(Project Mgr & Engr)*
Noel Marshall *(Country Mgr & Engr)*
Mike Spratley *(Gen Mgr-Bastillion Resources)*
Paul Webb *(Engr)*

BRITE-STRIKE TACTICAL IL-LUMINATION PRODUCTS, INC.
1145 Franklin St, Duxbury, MA 02332
Tel.: (781) 585-3525   **DE**
Year Founded: 2006
BSTK—(OTCIQ)
Semiconductor Devices Mfr
N.A.I.C.S.: 334413
Glenn Bushee *(Pres)*
Sarah Bushee *(Sec & VP)*

BROAD CAPITAL ACQUISI-TION CORP.
6208 Sandpebble Ct, Dallas, TX
75254
Tel.: (469) 951-3088   **DE**
Year Founded: 2020
BRAC—(NASDAQ)
Assets: $104,553,953
Liabilities: $108,847,416
Net Worth: ($4,293,463)
Earnings: ($433,615)
Emp.: 2
Fiscal Year-end: 12/31/22
Investment Services
N.A.I.C.S.: 523999
Johann Tse *(CEO)*
Rongrong Jiang *(CFO)*

BROADCAST MARKETING GROUP, INC.
4741 Central St Ste 900, Kansas
City, MO 64112
Tel.: (816) 753-3277   **FL**
Year Founded: 1980
BDCM—(OTCIQ)
Radio Broadcasting Services
N.A.I.C.S.: 334220
Aubrey E. Potter *(Founder & Pres)*

BROADCOM INC.
3421 Hillview Ave, Palo Alto, CA
94304
Tel.: (650) 427-6000   **CA**
Web Site: https://www.broadcom.com
Year Founded: 2018
AVGO—(NASDAQ)
Rev.: $51,574,000,000
Assets: $165,645,000,000
Liabilities: $97,967,000,000
Net Worth: $67,678,000,000
Earnings: $5,895,000,000
Emp.: 37,000
Fiscal Year-end: 11/03/24
Semiconductor Product Mfr
N.A.I.C.S.: 551112
Hock E. Tan *(Pres & CEO)*
Hock E. Tan *(Pres & CEO)*
Kirsten M. Spears *(CFO)*
Mark Brazeal *(Chief Legal Officer)*
Charlie B. Kawwas *(COO)*
Youngwoo Kwon *(Sr VP & Gen Mgr-Wireless Semiconductor Div)*
Andy Nallappan *(CIO-Global IT & VP)*
Ivy Pong *(VP-Taxation-Global)*
Yuan Xing Lee *(VP-Central Engrg)*
Debbie Streeter *(VP-HR)*
Greg Fischer *(Sr VP & Gen Mgr-Broadband Carrier Access Products Div)*
Mark Gonikberg *(Sr VP & Gen Mgr-Wireless Comm & Connectivity)*
Art Gilliland *(Sr VP & Gen Mgr-Symantec Enterprise Div)*
Lorenzo Longo *(Sr VP & Gen Mgr-Physical Layer Products Div)*
Greg Lotko *(Sr VP & Gen Mgr-Mainframe Software Div)*
Rich Nelson *(Sr VP & Gen Mgr-Set-Top Box & Cable Modem Products Div)*
Frank Ostojic *(Sr VP & Gen Mgr-ASIC Products Div)*
Ed Redmond *(Sr VP & Gen Mgr-Compute & Connectivity Div)*
Jack Rondoni *(Sr VP & Gen Mgr-Brocade Storage Networking Div)*
Ram Velaga *(Sr VP & Gen Mgr-Switch Products Div)*
Matt Cooke *(VP & Gen Mgr-Payment Security Div)*
Sally Doherty *(VP & Gen Mgr-PreAmp Components Div)*
Patrick Henderson *(VP & Gen Mgr-Mixed Signal ASICs Products)*
Jeff Hoogenboom *(VP & Gen Mgr-Emulex Connectivity Div)*
Hassan Hussain *(VP & Gen Mgr-Motion Control Products Div)*
Francis Khor *(VP & Gen Mgr-Optoelectronic Products Div)*
Gary Tay *(VP & Gen Mgr-Isolation Products Div)*
Mark Terrano *(VP & Gen Mgr-Intellectual Property & Licensing Div)*
Jas Tremblay *(VP & Gen Mgr-Data Center Solutions Grp)*
Myles Wakayama *(VP & Gen Mgr-Mixed Signal ASICs Products Div)*
Martin Weigert *(VP & Gen Mgr-Industrial Fiber Products Div)*
Alexis Black Bjorlin *(Sr VP & Gen Mgr-Optical Sys Div)*
Rebecca Boyden *(VP-Corp Fin)*
Alan Davidson *(CIO-Global Tech Organization)*
Adam Bromwich *(VP & Gen Mgr-Symantec Endpoint Security)*
Clayton Donley *(VP & Gen Mgr-Identity Mgmt Security Div)*
Rob Greer *(VP & Gen Mgr-Network Information Security Div)*
Vijay Janapaty *(VP & Gen Mgr-Physical Layer Products)*
Serge Lucio *(VP & Gen Mgr-Enterprise Software Div)*

Jill Turner *(VP)*
Near Margalit *(VP)*
Thomas H. Krause Jr. *(Pres-Infrastructure Software Grp)*

Subsidiaries:

Broadcom Corporation   **(1)**
1320 Ridder Park Dr, San Jose, CA 95131
Tel.: (408) 433-8000
Web Site: http://www.broadcom.com
Wired & Wireless Broadband Communications Semiconductor Designer & Mfr
N.A.I.C.S.: 334413
Henry Samueli *(Co-Founder)*

Subsidiary (Domestic):

Avago Technologies U.S. Inc.   **(2)**
350 W Trimble Rd Bldg 90, San Jose, CA 95131
Tel.: (408) 435-7400
Web Site: http://www.avagotech.com
Semiconductor Devices Mfr
N.A.I.C.S.: 334413

Subsidiary (Domestic):

Avago Technologies Wireless (U.S.A.) Manufacturing Inc.   **(3)**
4380 Ziegler Rd, Fort Collins, CO 80525-9631
Tel.: (970) 288-2575
Semiconductor Devices Mfr
N.A.I.C.S.: 334413
Brian Ingram *(Pres)*

CyOptics, Inc.   **(3)**
9999 Hamilton Blvd, Breinigsville, PA 18031
Tel.: (484) 397-2000
Web Site: http://www.cyoptics.com
Sales Range: $200-249.9 Million
Emp.: 550
Optical Chips & Components Mfr
N.A.I.C.S.: 334413

East Texas Integrated Circuits, Inc.   **(3)**
275 W Campbell Rd Ste 310, Richardson, TX 75080
Tel.: (972) 234-5656
Web Site: http://www.easttexasic.com
Emp.: 2
Integrated Circuits Mfr
N.A.I.C.S.: 334413
Eryce Edmonds *(Mgr)*

Subsidiary (Non-US):

Broadcom Singapore Pte. Ltd.   **(2)**
1 Yishun Avenue 7, Singapore, 768923, Singapore
Tel.: (65) 6 755 7888
Web Site: https://www.broadcom.com
Wired & Wireless Broadband Communications Semiconductors Mfr
N.A.I.C.S.: 334413

Broadcom UK Ltd.   **(2)**
Unit 406 Science Park, Milton Park, Cambridge, CB4 0WW, United Kingdom
Tel.: (44) 1223381300
Sales Range: $25-49.9 Million
Emp.: 150
Wired & Wireless Broadband Communications Semiconductors Mfr
N.A.I.C.S.: 334413
July Snow *(Mgr-Corp Svcs)*

CA, Inc.   **(1)**
520 Madison Ave, New York, NY 10022
Tel.: (800) 225-5224
Web Site: http://www.ca.com
Rev.: $4,235,000,000
Assets: $13,060,000,000
Liabilities: $7,165,000,000
Net Worth: $5,895,000,000
Earnings: $476,000,000
Emp.: 11,800
Fiscal Year-end: 03/31/2018
Information Technology Management Software Publisher
N.A.I.C.S.: 513210
Thomas H. Krause *(CFO & Treas)*

Subsidiary (Domestic):

Arcot Systems Inc.   **(2)**
455 W Maude Ave Ste 210, Sunnyvale, CA 94085

Tel.: (408) 969-6100
Web Site: http://www.arcot.com
Sales Range: $50-74.9 Million
Emp.: 165
Custom Computer Programming Services
N.A.I.C.S.: 541511

Subsidiary (Non-US):

Arcot Deutschland GmbH   **(3)**
Schulweg 7, D 82334, Pocking, Germany
Tel.: (49) 8157997793
Web Site: http://www.arcot.com
Sales Range: $25-49.9 Million
Emp.: 10
Authentication & Digital Signing Solutions for Businesses & Consumers
N.A.I.C.S.: 541519

Arcot R&D Software Private Ltd.   **(3)**
3rd Floor Oxford Towers, #139 Airport Road, Bengaluru, 560 008, Karnataka, India
Tel.: (91) 8066602745
Web Site: http://www.arcot.com
Computer Software Research & Development
N.A.I.C.S.: 513210

Subsidiary (Non-US):

Automic Software GmbH   **(2)**
Am Ruroplatz 5, 1120, Vienna, Austria
Tel.: (43) 5 7080 0
Web Site: http://www.automic.com
Sales Range: $75-99.9 Million
Emp.: 110
Process Automation Software & Services
N.A.I.C.S.: 513210
Todd DeLaughter *(CEO)*

Co-Headquarters (US):

Automic Software, Inc.   **(3)**
14475 NE 24th St Ste 210, Bellevue, WA 98007-3739
Tel.: (425) 644-2121
Web Site: http://www.automic.com
Process Automation Software & Services
N.A.I.C.S.: 513210
Todd DeLaughter *(CEO)*

Subsidiary (Non-US):

CA (Hong Kong) Limited   **(2)**
Suite 2301-06 23/F Dah Sing Financial Centre 108 Gloucester Road, Wanchai, China (Hong Kong)
Tel.: (852) 34207800
Web Site: http://www.ca.com
Enterprise Information Technology Management Software Solution Provider
N.A.I.C.S.: 513210

CA (India) Technologies Private Limited   **(2)**
Ground Floor Vibgyor Tower Plot C- 62 G-Block Bandra-Kurla Complex, Bandra East, Mumbai, 400 051, India
Tel.: (91) 2266413800
Web Site: http://www.ca.com
Sales Range: $25-49.9 Million
Emp.: 60
Enterprise Information Technology Management Software Solution Provider
N.A.I.C.S.: 513210

CA (Singapore) Pte Ltd   **(2)**
16 Collyer Quay Suite 12-00, Singapore, 049218, Singapore
Tel.: (65) 63372822
Web Site: http://www.ca.com
Emp.: 100
Government Entities & Educational Institutions Management Software Tools Provider
N.A.I.C.S.: 541511

CA Arabia FZ-LLC   **(2)**
202 Canon Bldg Dubai Internet City, Dubai, 500402, United Arab Emirates
Tel.: (971) 44462904
Enterprise Information Technology Management Software Solution Provider
N.A.I.C.S.: 513210

CA Belgium BVBA   **(2)**
Leonardo Da Vincilaan 11 Bus F2, 1935, Zaventem, Belgium
Tel.: (32) 27732811
Web Site: http://www.ca.com
Software Services
N.A.I.C.S.: 541511

CA Belgium SA (2)
The Corporate Village Leonardo Da Vinci-
laan 11 Bus F2, 1935, Zaventem, Belgium
Tel.: (32) 27732811
Emp.: 50
Enterprise Information Technology Manage-
ment Software Solution Provider
N.A.I.C.S.: 513210

CA Deutschland GmbH (2)
Marienburgstrasse 35, 64297, Darmstadt,
Germany (100%)
Tel.: (49) 61519490
Web Site: http://www.ca.com
Sales Range: $50-74.9 Million
Emp.: 250
Provides Software Services
N.A.I.C.S.: 541511

Subsidiary (Domestic):

CA Investment Holding, Inc. (2)
1 CA Plz, Islandia, NY 11749
Tel.: (800) 225-5224
Web Site: http://www.ca.com
Holding Company
N.A.I.C.S.: 513210

Subsidiary (Non-US):

CA Japan, Ltd. (2)
Aobadai Hills 4-7-7 Aobadai, Meguro-ku,
Tokyo, Japan
Tel.: (81) 1530042
Semiconductor & Electronic Component Mfr
N.A.I.C.S.: 334413

CA Korea Inc. (2)
22nd Floor City Air Tower Bldg 159-9
Samsung-dong Kangnam-ku, Seoul, 135-
973, Korea (South)
Tel.: (82) 25594100
Web Site: http://www.ca.com
Sales Range: $25-49.9 Million
Emp.: 46
Enterprise Information Technology Manage-
ment Software Solution Provider
N.A.I.C.S.: 513210

Subsidiary (Domestic):

CA Marketing Corporation (2)
490 W Wrightwood Ave, Elmhurst, IL 60126
Tel.: (630) 279-3100
Enterprise Information Technology Manage-
ment Software Solution Provider
N.A.I.C.S.: 513210

CA Montessori Children's Center,
Inc. (2)
1 CA Plz, Islandia, NY 11749
Tel.: (631) 342-6072
Child Care Services
N.A.I.C.S.: 623990

CA Montessori Children's Center,
Inc. (2)
5465 Legacy Dr, Plano, TX 75024
Tel.: (214) 473-1151
Child Care Services
N.A.I.C.S.: 623990

CA Montessori Children's Center,
Inc. (2)
2291 Wood Oak Dr, Herndon, VA 20171
Tel.: (703) 708-3699
Emp.: 7
Child Care Services
N.A.I.C.S.: 623990
Danielle Stoeseo (Gen Mgr)

CA Montessori Children's Center,
Inc. (2)
100 Staples Dr, Framingham, MA 01702
Tel.: (508) 628-8429
Web Site: http://www.cdc.com
Child Care Services
N.A.I.C.S.: 623990

Subsidiary (Non-US):

CA Programas de Computador Par-
ticipacoas Servicos Ltda. (2)
Av das Nacoes Unidas 12901 Torre Norte 6
Andar Brooklin Novo, Sao Paulo, 04578-
903, Brazil
Tel.: (55) 1155036000
Web Site: http://www.ca.com
Enterprise Information Technology Manage-
ment Software Solution Provider

N.A.I.C.S.: 513210

Subsidiary (Domestic):

CA Research, Inc. (2)
1 Computer Associates Plz, Islandia, NY
11749
Tel.: (631) 342-5224
Web Site: http://www.ca.com
Research Services
N.A.I.C.S.: 541720

Subsidiary (Non-US):

CA Sales (Thailand) Co., Ltd (2)
87/2 Lumphini, Bangkok, 10330, Thailand
Tel.: (66) 26253023
Computer Hardware & Software Provider
N.A.I.C.S.: 449210

Subsidiary (Domestic):

CA Services, LLC (2)
340 Bagley St, Pontiac, MI 48341-2400
Tel.: (248) 338-5990
Enterprise Information Technology Manage-
ment Software Solution Provider
N.A.I.C.S.: 513210

Subsidiary (Non-US):

CA Software Finland OY (2)
Keilaranta 5, 2150, Espoo, Finland
Tel.: (358) 207411680
Enterprise Information Technology Manage-
ment Software Solution Provider
N.A.I.C.S.: 513210

CA Software Finland Oy (2)
Keilaranta 1, 2150, Espoo, Finland (100%)
Tel.: (358) 207411680
Web Site: http://www.ca.com
Software Services
N.A.I.C.S.: 541511

CA Software Israel Ltd. (2)
16 Shenkar St, PO BOX 2207, Herzliyya,
46120, Israel
Tel.: (972) 99626000
Web Site: http://www.ca.com
Enterprise Information Technology Manage-
ment Software Solution Provider
N.A.I.C.S.: 513210

CA Software Norway A/S (2)
Lysaker torg 5, Lysaker, 1366, Akershus,
Norway
Tel.: (47) 67524000
Web Site: http://www.ca.com
Enterprise Information Technology Manage-
ment Software Solution Provider
N.A.I.C.S.: 513210

CA Software Osterreich GmbH (2)
Euro Plaza Haus E Wienerbergstrasse 41,
1120, Vienna, Austria
Tel.: (43) 1917790
Web Site: http://www.ca.com
Emp.: 25
Enterprise Information Technology Manage-
ment Software Solution Provider
N.A.I.C.S.: 513210

CA Software Sweden AB (2)
Sveavagen 159, Stockholm, 113 46, Swe-
den
Tel.: (46) 86222200
Web Site: http://www.ca.com
Enterprise Information Technology Manage-
ment Software Solution Provider
N.A.I.C.S.: 513210

CA Software de Colombia S.A. (2)
Carrera 7 No 99-53 Tower 2-401 Office
Building Grupo Santander Centra, Bogota,
Colombia
Tel.: (57) 16326000
Sales Range: $10-24.9 Million
Emp.: 30
Enterprise Information Technology Manage-
ment Software Solution Provider
N.A.I.C.S.: 513210
Claudia Vasquev (Gen Mgr)

CA Software de Peru S.A. (2)
Paseo de la Republica 3211-11th Floor, San
Isidro, Lima, Peru
Tel.: (51) 14417888
Web Site: http://www.ca.com
Emp.: 15

Enterprise Information Technology Management Software Solution Provider
N.A.I.C.S.: 513210

CA Sp. z.o.o. (2)
Ul Emilii Plater 53, 001 13, Warsaw,
Poland (100%)
Tel.: (48) 225286681
Sales Range: $10-24.9 Million
Emp.: 14
Software Services
N.A.I.C.S.: 541511
Michael Foremann (Reg Mgr)

Branch (Domestic):

CA Technologies (2)
2002 Summit Blvd Ste 1500, Atlanta, GA
30319
Web Site: http://www.ca.com
Sales Range: $10-24.9 Million
Emp.: 12
Develops, Markets & Supports a Family of
Turnkey, Automated, Scaleable, Software-
Based Performance A
N.A.I.C.S.: 513210
Martin Mackay (Pres & Gen Mgr-Asia Pa-
cific & Japan)

CA Technologies (2)
5001 Plaza on the Lake Ste 200, Austin, TX
78746
Tel.: (512) 407-9443
Web Site: http://www.netqos.com
Sales Range: $25-49.9 Million
Emp.: 214
Network Monitoring Software Mfr
N.A.I.C.S.: 513210

Subsidiary (Domestic):

CA Technologies (2)
3333 Walnut St, Boulder, CO 80301
Tel.: (303) 565-2800
Web Site: http://www.ca.com
Software Developer
N.A.I.C.S.: 513210

Subsidiary (Non-US):

CA Technologies Private Ltd. (2)
Ground Floor Vibgyor Tower Plot C 62, G
Block Bandra Kurla Complex, Mumbai, 400
051, Bandra East, India
Tel.: (91) 2266413800
Web Site: http://www.ca.com
Sales Range: $10-24.9 Million
Emp.: 38
Computer Systems Design
N.A.I.C.S.: 334610

CA s.r.l. (2)
Via Francesco Sforza 3 Milano 3 City,
20080, Basiglio, Milan, Italy
Tel.: (39) 02904641
Web Site: http://www.ca.com
Enterprise Information Technology Manage-
ment Software Solution Provider
N.A.I.C.S.: 513210

CA software B.V. (2)
Orteliuslaan 1000 5th floor, Utrecht, 3528
BD, Netherlands
Tel.: (31) 306048345
Web Site: http://www.ca.com
Enterprise Information Technology Manage-
ment Software Services
N.A.I.C.S.: 513210

Computer Associates (CAI) de Ven-
ezuela, C.A. (2)
Av Francisco de Miranda Centro Lido Torre
D Piso 4 Ofic 41D El Rosal, 1060, Caracas,
Venezuela (100%)
Tel.: (58) 212 9056336
Web Site: http://www.ca.com
Sales Range: $10-24.9 Million
Emp.: 26
Custom Computer Programming Services
N.A.I.C.S.: 541511

Computer Associates AG (2)
Oberdorfstrasse 14, CH 8302, Kloten,
Switzerland (100%)
Tel.: (41) 18047878
Sales Range: $10-24.9 Million
Emp.: 70
Custom Computer Programing
N.A.I.C.S.: 541511

Enterprise Information Technology Management Software Solution Provider
N.A.I.C.S.: 513210

Computer Associates Africa (Pty.)
Ltd. (2)
Gilloolys Office park BLK F 1 Ospornene
Bedfordview, PO Box 59, Bedfordview,
2026, South Africa (100%)
Tel.: (27) 0114178699
Web Site: http://www.ca.com
Sales Range: $10-24.9 Million
Emp.: 80
Software Services
N.A.I.C.S.: 541511

Computer Associates De Argentina
S.A. (2)
Av Alicia Moreau De Justo 400 2 F, 1107,
Buenos Aires, Argentina (99%)
Tel.: (54) 1143171500
Web Site: http://www.ca.com
Sales Range: $1-9.9 Million
Emp.: 40
Custom Computer Programing
N.A.I.C.S.: 541511

Computer Associates Hungary (2)
Zahony utca 7 Graphisoft Park Building C,
H 1031, Budapest, Hungary (100%)
Tel.: (36) 14303500
Web Site: http://www.ca.com
Sales Range: $1-9.9 Million
Emp.: 10
Software Services
N.A.I.C.S.: 541511

Computer Associates International
GmbH (2)
Wienerberg strasse 41, 1120, Vienna, Aus-
tria
Tel.: (43) 1917790
Web Site: http://www.ca.com
Sales Range: $10-24.9 Million
Emp.: 40
Custom Computer Programing
N.A.I.C.S.: 334610

Computer Associates International
Limited (2)
2301 206 25th Fl Tahsing Financial Ctr 108
Gloucester Rd, 1 Wanchai, Hong Kong,
China (Hong Kong) (100%)
Tel.: (852) 25871388
Web Site: http://www.ca.com
Sales Range: $10-24.9 Million
Emp.: 80
N.A.I.C.S.: 334610

Computer Associates International,
Inc. (2)
555 Dr Frederik-Philips Blvd Ste 240, Saint
Laurent, H4M2X4, QC, Canada (100%)
Tel.: (514) 747-8100
Web Site: http://www.ca.com
Sales Range: $25-49.9 Million
Emp.: 120
Custom Computer Programming Services
N.A.I.C.S.: 541511

Computer Associates Japan, Ltd. (2)
Shinjuku Mitsui Bldg 2 1 1 Nishi Shinjuku,
Shinjuku Ku, Tokyo, 163-0439,
Japan (100%)
Tel.: (81) 353203805
Web Site: http://www.ca.com
Sales Range: $100-124.9 Million
Software Reproducing
N.A.I.C.S.: 334610

Computer Associates Korea Ltd. (2)
22nd Fl City Air Tower 159 9 San Sung
Dong, Kanan Ku, Seoul, 135 973, Korea
(South) (100%)
Tel.: (82) 25594100
Web Site: http://www.cai.co.kr
Sales Range: $10-24.9 Million
Emp.: 40
Software Reproducing
N.A.I.C.S.: 334610

Computer Associates Middle
East (2)
Office 124 1st Floor Akarya Plaza Olaya St,
PO Box 2392, Riyadh, 12244, Saudi Arabia
Tel.: (966) 114649548
Web Site: http://www.ca.com
Software Services
N.A.I.C.S.: 334610

Computer Associates Middle
East (2)
Dubai Internet City, PO Box 62632, Bldg 17

Broadcom Inc.—(Continued)

Ste 358, Dubai, United Arab Emirates **(100%)**
Tel.: (971) 43616710
Web Site: http://www.ca.com
Custom Computer Programming Services
N.A.I.C.S.: 334610

Computer Associates Netherlands **(2)**
Orteliuslaan 1001, 5328 BE, Utrecht, Holland, Netherlands **(100%)**
Tel.: (31) 306048345
Web Site: http://www.ca.com.nl
Sales Range: $25-49.9 Million
Emp.: 100
Custom Computer Programing
N.A.I.C.S.: 541511

Computer Associates Norway A/S **(2)**
Lysaker Torg 5 3 etg, PO Box 450, 1327, Lysaker, Norway **(100%)**
Tel.: (47) 67524000
Web Site: http://www.ca.com
Sales Range: $10-24.9 Million
Emp.: 37
Provides Software Services
N.A.I.C.S.: 541511

Computer Associates Plc **(2)**
Ditton Park Riding Court Rd, Slough, SL3 9LL, Berks, United Kingdom **(100%)**
Tel.: (44) 1753577733
Web Site: http://www.ca.com
Sales Range: $200-249.9 Million
Emp.: 800
Software Services
N.A.I.C.S.: 541511

Computer Associates Pte. Ltd. **(2)**
16 Collyer Quay Unit 12-00, 10 01 03 Suntec Tower 2, Singapore, 49318, Singapore **(100%)**
Tel.: (65) 63372822
Web Site: http://www.ca.com
Sales Range: $25-49.9 Million
Emp.: 100
Provider of Computer Services
N.A.I.C.S.: 541511

Computer Associates Pty. Ltd. **(2)**
6 Eden Park Drive, North Ryde, 2113, NSW, Australia
Tel.: (61) 1800023386
Web Site: http://www.ca.com.au
Software Reproducing
N.A.I.C.S.: 334610

Computer Associates S.A. **(2)**
Tower Opus 12 4 Place Des Pyramides La Defense No 9, 92914, Paris, 92914, France **(100%)**
Tel.: (33) 149025000
Web Site: http://www.ca.com
Sales Range: $75-99.9 Million
Emp.: 250
Custom Computer Programming
N.A.I.C.S.: 541511

Computer Associates S.p.A. **(2)**
Palazzo Leonardo Via Francesco Sforza 3, 20080, Milan, Italy
Tel.: (39) 02904641
Web Site: http://www.ca.com
Sales Range: $75-99.9 Million
Emp.: 200
Software Services
N.A.I.C.S.: 541511

Computer Associates Scandinavia A/S **(2)**
Porutvang 5 B, 2750, Ballerup, Denmark
Tel.: (45) 45474141
Web Site: http://www.ca.com
Sales Range: $10-24.9 Million
Emp.: 50
Provides Software Services
N.A.I.C.S.: 541511

Computer Associates Sweden AB **(2)**
Sveavagen 159, 11346, Stockholm, Sweden **(100%)**
Tel.: (46) 86222200
Web Site: http://www.ca.com
Sales Range: $10-24.9 Million
Emp.: 50
Custom Computer Programing

N.A.I.C.S.: 541511

Computer Associates Taiwan Ltd. **(2)**
6th Fl 105 Sec 2 Tun Hwa S Rd, 106, Taipei, ROC, Taiwan **(100%)**
Tel.: (886) 227009218
Web Site: http://www.ca.com.tw
Sales Range: $10-24.9 Million
Emp.: 10
Provider of Computer Services
N.A.I.C.S.: 541511

Computer Associates de Chile S.A. **(2)**
Providencia 1760 Oficina 1501, Edificio Palladio, Santiago, Chile
Tel.: (56) 24316200
Sales Range: $10-24.9 Million
Emp.: 20
Provides Software Services
N.A.I.C.S.: 541511

Computer Associates de Colombia S.A. **(2)**
Edificio Grupo Santander Central Hispano Carrera 7, Bogota, DC, Colombia **(100%)**
Tel.: (57) 16326000
Web Site: http://www.ca.com
Sales Range: $10-24.9 Million
Emp.: 29
Custom Computer Programming Services
N.A.I.C.S.: 541511

Computer Associates del Peru **(2)**
Paseo de la Republica 3211 Piso 11, San Isidro, Lima, Peru **(100%)**
Tel.: (51) 14417888
Web Site: http://www.ca.com
Sales Range: $10-24.9 Million
Emp.: 18
Software Services
N.A.I.C.S.: 541511

Computer Associates do Brasil Ltda. **(2)**
Centro Empresarial Nacoes Unidas Torre Norte, Av Das Nacoes Unidas 12901, Sao Paulo, 04578 903, SP, Brazil
Tel.: (55) 1155036000
Web Site: http://www.ca.com
Sales Range: $75-99.9 Million
Emp.: 350
Custom Computer Programing
N.A.I.C.S.: 541511

Philippine Computer Associates International, Inc. **(2)**
30/F Philamlife Tower 8767, Paseo De Roxas St, 1227, Makati, Philippines **(100%)**
Tel.: (63) 28850441
Web Site: http://www.philippinecompanies.com
Sales Range: $1-9.9 Million
Emp.: 32
Software Reproducing
N.A.I.C.S.: 334610

Subsidiary (Domestic):

Realia, Inc. **(2)**
9619 Lawndale Dr, Silver Spring, MD 20901-3022
Tel.: (301) 578-1927
Enterprise Information Technology Management Software Solution Provider
N.A.I.C.S.: 513210

Subsidiary (Non-US):

SE-Consulting GmbH **(2)**
Im Dorfle 11, 79400, Kandern, Germany
Tel.: (49) 76266844
Web Site: https://se-consulting.de
Semiconductor Distr
N.A.I.C.S.: 423690

Sterling Software (Netherlands) IV B.V. **(2)**
Orteliuslaan 1001, Utrecht, 3528 BE, Netherlands
Tel.: (31) 306048345
Software Development Services
N.A.I.C.S.: 541511

Nemicon Corporation **(1)**
Shimbashi Enter Bldg 6F 5-8-11 Shimbashi, Minato-ku, Tokyo, 105-0004, Japan
Tel.: (81) 357761711

Web Site: http://www.nemicon.co.jp
Emp.: 24
Semiconductor Devices Mfr
N.A.I.C.S.: 334413
Tetsuo Ogishima *(Pres)*

VMware LLC **(1)**
3401 Hillview Ave, Palo Alto, CA 94304
Tel.: (650) 427-5000
Web Site: https://www.vmware.com
Rev.: $13,350,000,000
Assets: $31,237,000,000
Liabilities: $29,703,000,000
Net Worth: $1,534,000,000
Earnings: $1,314,000,000
Emp.: 38,300
Fiscal Year-end: 02/03/2023
Software Development Services
N.A.I.C.S.: 541511
Betsy Sutter *(Chief People Officer & Exec VP)*
Luigi Freguia *(Sr VP & Gen Mgr-Europe, Middle East, and Africa)*
Mike Hayes *(Chief Digital Transformation Officer & Sr VP)*

Subsidiary (Domestic):

AetherPal Inc. **(2)**
377 Hoes Ln Ste 101, Piscataway, NJ 08854
Tel.: (908) 205-0102
Web Site: http://www.aetherpal.com
Software Development Services
N.A.I.C.S.: 513210
Tom Flaherty *(CFO)*

Subsidiary (Non-US):

AetherPal (INDIA) Private Limited **(3)**
6/2 Willingdon Crescent First Floor Pycrofts Garden Road, Thousand Lights, Chennai, India
Tel.: (91) 4442300379
Software Development Services
N.A.I.C.S.: 513210

Subsidiary (Domestic):

Cloudhealth Technologies Inc. **(2)**
100 Summer St 20th Fl, Boston, MA 02210
Tel.: (617) 986-3900
Web Site: http://www.cloudhealthtech.com
Cloud Service Management
N.A.I.C.S.: 513210
Tom Axbey *(CEO)*

Nicira, Inc. **(2)**
3401 Hillview Ave, Palo Alto, CA 94304
Tel.: (650) 473-9777
Web Site: http://www.vmware.com
Software Networking Services
N.A.I.C.S.: 541511

Pivotal Software, Inc. **(2)**
875 Howard St Fifth Fl, San Francisco, CA 94103
Tel.: (415) 777-4868
Web Site: http://www.pivotal.io
Rev.: $657,494,000
Assets: $1,850,468,000
Liabilities: $584,990,000
Net Worth: $1,265,478,000
Earnings: ($141,903,000)
Emp.: 2,949
Fiscal Year-end: 02/01/2019
Cloud Platform Software Developer
N.A.I.C.S.: 541511
Paul A. Maritz *(Chm)*
James Watters *(Sr VP-Strategy)*
Bill Cook *(Pres)*
Robert Mee *(CEO)*
Scott Yara *(Sr VP-Products)*
Andrew M. Cohen *(Gen Counsel)*
Edward Hieatt *(Sr VP-Customer Svcs)*
Elisabeth Hendrickson *(VP-R&D-Data)*
Ian Andrews *(Sr VP-Products & Mktg)*
Joe Militello *(Chief People Officer)*
Onsi Fakhouri *(Sr VP-R&D-Cloud)*
Lawrence Crowther *(Head--Asia Pacific,Japan)*

Subsidiary (Non-US):

Taiwan VMware Information Technology LLC **(2)**
7 Xinyi Road Section 5, 110, Taipei, Taiwan
Tel.: (886) 287582804
Web Site: http://www.vmware.com

Information Technology Equipment Services
N.A.I.C.S.: 541511

VMware Australia Pty Ltd **(2)**
Level 8 175 Pitt Street, Sydney, 2000, NSW, Australia
Tel.: (61) 292935600
Web Site: http://www.vmware.com
Virtualization Solutions
N.A.I.C.S.: 513210
Sean Kopelke *(Sr Dir-Tech-Australia & New Zealand)*
Brad Anderson *(Mng Dir/VP-Australia & New Zealand)*

VMware Belgium **(2)**
Cullinganlaan 5/004, MeetDistrict Diegem, 1831, Diegem, Belgium
Tel.: (32) 207039500
Web Site: http://www.vmware.com
Cloud Services
N.A.I.C.S.: 541519

VMware Bulgaria EOOD **(2)**
16A G M Dimitrov Blvd, 1797, Sofia, Bulgaria
Tel.: (359) 28041344
Web Site: http://www.vmware.com
Cloud Software Services
N.A.I.C.S.: 541511

VMware Canada Inc. **(2)**
1122 International Blvd Suite 300, Burlington, L7L 6Z8, ON, Canada
Tel.: (905) 315-6000
Web Site: http://www.vmware.com
Emp.: 20
Cloud Software Services
N.A.I.C.S.: 541511

VMware Denmark ApS. **(2)**
Linde Alle 9b, 2850, Naerum, Denmark
Tel.: (45) 70106888
Web Site: http://www.vmware.com
Cloud Software Services
N.A.I.C.S.: 541511
Henri van der Vaeren *(VP-Southern Europe, Middle East & Africa)*

VMware Eastern Europe **(2)**
Forum Business Center 48/3 Mamikonyants str, Yerevan, 0014, Armenia
Tel.: (374) 60612900
Web Site: http://www.vmware.com
Cloud Software Services
N.A.I.C.S.: 541511

VMware France SAS. **(2)**
100-101 Terrasse Boieldieu La Defense 8, 92042, Paris, Cedex, France
Tel.: (33) 171230874
Web Site: http://www.vmware.com
Virtualization Solutions
N.A.I.C.S.: 513210

Subsidiary (Domestic):

VMware Global, Inc. **(2)**
3401 Hillview Ave, Palo Alto, CA 94304
Tel.: (650) 427-1000
Web Site: http://www.vmware.com
Virtualization Solutions
N.A.I.C.S.: 513210

Subsidiary (Non-US):

VMware Hong Kong Limited **(2)**
Suites 401-02 & 12-14 4th Floor Cityplaza Four, 12 Taikoo Wan Road Taikoo Shing Island East, Hong Kong, China (Hong Kong)
Tel.: (852) 236966110
Web Site: http://www.vmware.com
Virtualization Solutions
N.A.I.C.S.: 513210

VMware Information Technology(China) Co. Ltd **(2)**
01F 08F 09F 10F 17F 18F South Wing Building C Raycom InfoTech Park, No 2 Kexueyuan South Road Haidian District, Beijing, 100190, China
Tel.: (86) 1059934201
Web Site: http://www.vmware.com
Virtualization Solutions
N.A.I.C.S.: 513210

VMware International Limited **(2)**
Behan House Barrack Square, Ballincollig, Cork, Ireland
Tel.: (353) 214660000

Web Site: http://www.vmware.com
Cloud Software Services
N.A.I.C.S.: 541511

VMware Israel Ltd. (2)
Ampa Building 5 Sapir St Ground Floor, PO
Box 12093, Herzliya Pituach, 4685209,
Israel
Tel.: (972) 747170700
Web Site: https://www.vmware.com
Software Development Services
N.A.I.C.S.: 541511

VMware Italy S.r.l. (2)
Via Melchiorre Gioia 26 7th floor, 20124,
Milan, Italy
Tel.: (39) 0269430373
Web Site: http://www.vmware.com
Information Technology Equipment Services
N.A.I.C.S.: 541511

VMware Korea Co., Ltd. (2)
13th Floor ASEM Tower 517 Yeongdong-
daero, Gangnam-gu, Seoul, 06164, Korea
(South)
Tel.: (82) 230166500
Web Site: https://www.vmware.com
Cloud Services
N.A.I.C.S.: 541519

**VMware Marketing Austria
GmbH** (2)
The Icon Tower Gertrude Frohlich-Sandner
Strasse 2, 1040, Vienna, Austria
Tel.: (43) 800201241
Web Site: http://www.vmware.com
Virtualization Solutions
N.A.I.C.S.: 513210

VMware Netherlands B.V. (2)
Millennium Tower Radarweg 29 7th floor
wing A, 1043 NX, Amsterdam, Netherlands
Tel.: (31) 207039500
Web Site: http://www.vmware.com
Virtualization Solutions
N.A.I.C.S.: 513210

VMware Singapore Pte. Ltd. (2)
6 Temasek Blvd 6th Floor Suntec Tower 4,
Singapore, 038986, Singapore
Tel.: (65) 65012002
Web Site: https://www.vmware.com
Virtualization Solutions
N.A.I.C.S.: 513210
Sanjay Mirchandani (Sr VP & Gen Mgr-Asia
Pacific & Japan)
Pradeepto Dey (Dir-Distr-Asia Pacific & Ja-
pan)
Gabriel Breeman (Sr Dir-Partner Bus Sls-
Asia Pacific & Japan)
Uma Thana Balasingam (VP-Asia Pacific &
Japan)

VMware Software India Pvt. Ltd (2)
Kalyani Vista 2 Sy No 164/4 164/5 and
165/1 P, Bilekahalli Village Begur Hobli
Bengaluru South Taluk, Bengaluru, 560076,
India
Tel.: (91) 8042486800
Web Site: https://www.vmware.com
Virtualization Solutions
N.A.I.C.S.: 513210

VMware Spain, S.L. (2)
Calle Rafael Boti 26 2nd floor, 28023, Ma-
drid, Spain
Tel.: (34) 914125000
Web Site: http://www.vmware.com
Virtualization Solutions
N.A.I.C.S.: 513210

VMware Sweden AB (2)
Gustav III s Boulevard 54, 169 74, Solna,
Sweden
Tel.: (46) 86350300
Web Site: http://www.vmware.com
Virtualization Solutions
N.A.I.C.S.: 513210

VMware Switzerland S.a.r.l. (2)
Baslerstrasse 60, 8048, Zurich, Switzerland
Tel.: (41) 33147627900
Web Site: http://www.vmware.com
Cloud Software Services
N.A.I.C.S.: 541511

VMware UK Limited (2)
Flow 1 2 River Park Avenue, Staines-upon-
Thames, TW18 3FA, United Kingdom
Tel.: (44) 1276414300
Web Site: https://www.vmware.com

Virtualization Solutions
N.A.I.C.S.: 513210

VMware, K.K. (2)
18F msb Tamachi Station Tower N 3
Chome-1-1 Shibaura, Minato City, Tokyo,
108-0023, Japan
Tel.: (81) 343345600
Web Site: https://www.vmware.com
Virtualization Solutions
N.A.I.C.S.: 513210
Guru Venkatachalam (CTO)

BROADRIDGE FINANCIAL SO-
LUTIONS, INC.
5 Dakota Dr Ste 300, Lake Success,
NY 11042
Tel.: (516) 472-5400   DE
Web Site:
  https://www.broadridge.com
Year Founded: 1965
BR—(NYSE)
Rev.: $6,506,800,000
Assets: $8,242,400,000
Liabilities: $6,074,200,000
Net Worth: $2,168,200,000
Earnings: $698,100,000
Emp.: 14,600
Fiscal Year-end: 06/30/24
Holding Company; Financial Market
Investor Communications & Support
Services
N.A.I.C.S.: 551112
John D. Hogan (Sr Mng Dir)
Robert Schifellite (Pres/Sr VP-
Investor Comm Solutions)
Douglas R. DeSchutter (Pres-
Customer Comm & VP)
Robert F. Kalenka (VP-Investor
Comm Solutions Ops)
Robert Schifellite (Pres/Sr VP-
Investor Comm Solutions)
Thomas Carey (Pres-Ops & Tech-
Global & VP)
Michael Dignam (Pres-Canada)
Michael Liberatore (Chief Transforma-
tion Officer-Logistics & VP)
Vijay Mayadas (Pres/VP-Capital Mar-
kets)
Yupeng Zhang (VP-Software Engi-
neering)
Christopher J. Perry (Pres)
Laura Matlin (Chief Compliance Offi-
cer, Chief Governance Officer, VP &
Deputy Gen Counsel)
Michael S. Tae (Pres-Mutual Fund &
Retirement & VP)
Bob Santangelo (Pres-Sls-Intl)
Tyler Derr (CTO)
Vincent G. Roux (Sr VP & Head-Corp
Dev-Global)
Mike Sleightholme (Pres-Intl)
Scott Turley (VP-Product Evolution)
Michael Alexander (Pres-Wealth
Mgmt)
Dorothy J. Flynn (Pres-Corporate Is-
suer Solutions)
Martin Koopman (Pres-Investor
Comm Solutions & Bank Broker-
Dealer)
John Oliveri (CTO-Investor Comm
Solutions)
Samir Pandiri (Pres-Intl)
Jeremy Hintze (VP & Head-Global
Operations)
Naadia Y. Burrows (Chief Diversity
Officer)
Keir D. Gumbs (Chief Legal Officer &
VP)
Kate O'Connor (VP-Digital Center of
Excellence)
German Soto Sanchez (Sr VP-Corp
Strategy)
Rich Stingi (Chief HR Officer)
Dipti Kachru (CMO-Global)
Leslie Wims Morris (Sr VP-Bus Dev
& Strategy)

Timothy C. Gokey (CEO)
Richard J. Daly (Exec Chm)

Subsidiaries:

605 Studios, LLC (1)
8604 Sagamore Rd, Leawood, KS 66206
Tel.: (512) 423-9340
Web Site: https://www.studio605.com
Construction & Interior Design Services
N.A.I.C.S.: 541410

Access Data Corp. (1)
2 Chatham Ctr Ste 200 240 & 1150, Pitts-
burgh, PA 15219
Tel.: (412) 201-6000
Web Site: http://www.accessdc.com
Process & Logistics Consulting Services
N.A.I.C.S.: 541614

ActivePath Solutions Ltd. (1)
Kiryat Atidim Building 7, Tel Aviv, 6158001,
Israel
Tel.: (972) 733201241
Software Development Services
N.A.I.C.S.: 518210

ActivePath Solutions, Inc. (1)
3422 SW 15 St Ste 8898, Deerfield Beach,
FL 33442
Tel.: (646) 475-2212
Software Development Services
N.A.I.C.S.: 518210

AdvisorStream Ltd. (1)
2300-120 Bremner Blvd, Toronto, M5J 0A8,
ON, Canada
Web Site: https://www.advisorstream.com
Financial Advisory Services
N.A.I.C.S.: 523940

Bonaire Software Solutions, LLC (1)
125 High St Fl 3, Boston, MA 02110
Tel.: (617) 338-0107
Web Site: http://www.broadridge.com
Emp.: 60
Financial Services
N.A.I.C.S.: 522299
Christopher John (CEO)

Broadridge (Japan) Ltd. (1)
7F S-GATE Akasaka Sanno 2-5-1 Akasaka,
Minato-ku, Tokyo, 107-0052, Japan
Tel.: (81) 357978300
Data Processing Services
N.A.I.C.S.: 518210

**Broadridge (Singapore) Private
Limited** (1)
30 Raffles Pl Ste 30-01, Singapore,
048622, Singapore
Tel.: (65) 64381144
Data Processing Services
N.A.I.C.S.: 518210

**Broadridge Business Process Out-
sourcing, LLC** (1)
5 Dakota Dr Ste 300, Lake Success, NY
11042
Tel.: (516) 472-5008
Web Site: http://www.broadridgebpo.com
Financial Services
N.A.I.C.S.: 522299
James Port (Chief Compliance Officer)

**Broadridge Corporate Issuer Solu-
tions, Inc.** (1)
1155 Long Island Ave, Edgewood, NY
11717-8309
Tel.: (720) 414-6858
Web Site:
  https://www.shareholder.broadridge.com
Investment Management Service
N.A.I.C.S.: 523940

**Broadridge FX & Liquidity Solutions,
LLC** (1)
10 Bank St Ste 880, White Plains, NY
10606
Tel.: (914) 220-8800
Web Site: http://www.twofour.com
Sales Range: $10-24.9 Million
Emp.: 55
Financial Transaction Software Publisher &
Services
N.A.I.C.S.: 513210

**Broadridge Financial Solutions
Limited** (1)

193 Marsh Wall, London, E14 9SG, United
Kingdom
Tel.: (44) 2075513000
Web Site: https://www.broadridge.com
Financial Market Investor Communications
& Support Services
N.A.I.C.S.: 561499
Mike Thrower (Head-Sls-EMEA)
Bob Santangelo (Pres-Sls-Intl)

**Broadridge Financial Solutions, Inc. -
Jersey City** (1)
2 Journal Sq Plz, Jersey City, NJ 07306
Tel.: (800) 353-0103
Web Site: http://www.broadridge.com
Financial Market Investor Communications
& Support Services
N.A.I.C.S.: 561499

**Broadridge Investor Communications
Corporation** (1)
5970 Chedworth Way, Mississauga, L5R
4G5, ON, Canada   (100%)
Tel.: (905) 507-5100
Emp.: 130
Direct Mail Advertising Services
N.A.I.C.S.: 541860
Patricia Rosch (Pres)

**Broadridge Managed Solutions,
Inc.** (1)
605 3Rd Ave Fl 41, New York, NY 10158
Tel.: (646) 214-3700
Web Site: http://www.paladyne.com
Investment Management Software & Sup-
port Services
N.A.I.C.S.: 513210

**ClearStructure Financial Technology,
LLC** (1)
83 Wooster Heights Rd, Danbury, CT
06810
Tel.: (203) 205-2700
Portfolio Management Systems
N.A.I.C.S.: 513210
John Partenza (Product Mgr)

Direxxis LLC (1)
250 First Ave Ste 201, Needham, MA
02494
Tel.: (781) 444-7900
Web Site: http://www.direxxismarketing.com
Financial Services
N.A.I.C.S.: 522299

Fi360, Inc. (1)
3 Penn Ctr W Ste 400, Pittsburgh, PA
15276
Tel.: (412) 569-3301
Web Site: https://www.fi360.com
Financial Investment Activities
N.A.I.C.S.: 523999
Blaine Aikin (Chm)
John Faustino (Head-Strategy & Ops)
Tyler Kirkland (Dir-Bus Dev & Client En-
gagement)
Michael Muirhead (Sr Dir-Learning & Dev)
David Palascak (Product Mgr-Software)
Sara Houk (VP)
Nicholas Goossen (Head-Software Dev &
Architecture)

FundAssist Limited (1)
5 Dundrum Business Park, Dundrum, Dub-
lin, D14 DD89, Ireland
Tel.: (353) 12079700
Financial Services
N.A.I.C.S.: 518210

Itiviti Group AB (1)
Kungsgatan 36 5th Floor, PO Box 7742,
Stockholm, SE-103 95, Sweden
Tel.: (46) 8 506 477 00
Software Publisher
N.A.I.C.S.: 513210
Per E Larsson (Chm)
Ray Tierney (Pres)

Subsidiary (Non-US):

Itiviti Limited (2)
23 Camomile Street 3Rd Floor Camomile
Court, London, EC3A 7LL, United Kingdom
Tel.: (44) 20 7942 0950
Web Site: http://www.itiviti.com
Multi-Asset Trading Technologies & Infra-
structure Sales, Data Hosting & Technical
Support Services
N.A.I.C.S.: 518210

Broadridge Financial Solutions, Inc.—(Continued)

Subsidiary (Domestic):

Orc Group AB (2)
Kungsgatan 36 5th Floor, PO Box 7742,
103 95, Stockholm, Sweden
Tel.: (46) 850647700
Web Site: http://www.orc-group.com
Emp.: 380
Electronic Trading Software Developer
N.A.I.C.S.: 513210
Fredrik Skogby (VP-Bus Dev)
Joakim Dahlstedt (CTO)
Jesper Alfredsson (Pres-Americas)
Bertil Lundell (VP-Engrg)
Troels Philip Jensen (COO)
Torben Munch (CEO)
Tony Falck (CFO)
Oscar Jonsson (VP-Sls-Americas)

Subsidiary (Domestic):

Dancharia Research & Trade East AB (3)
PO Box 7742, 103 95, Stockholm, Sweden
Tel.: (46) 8 21 17 50
Computer Software Development Services
N.A.I.C.S.: 541511

Subsidiary (Non-US):

Orc Australia Pty Ltd. (3)
Level 18 56 Pitt St, Sydney, 2000, NSW,
Australia
Tel.: (61) 292402400
Sales Range: $25-49.9 Million
Emp.: 20
Electronic Trading Software Developer
N.A.I.C.S.: 513210
Greg Chambers (Pres-Asia Pacific)

Subsidiary (Domestic):

Orc Education AB (3)
Kungsgatan 33, 111 56, Stockholm, Sweden
Tel.: (46) 8 545 122 50
Education Software Developer
N.A.I.C.S.: 513210

Orc ExNet Transaction Services AB (3)
Kungsgatan 36, Stockholm, 111 35, Sweden
Tel.: (46) 84073800
Web Site: http://www.orc-group.com
Sales Range: $50-74.9 Million
Emp.: 110
Electronic Trading Software Developer
N.A.I.C.S.: 513210
Torben Munch (CEO)

Subsidiary (Non-US):

Orc Italy S.r.l. (3)
Corso Vittorio Emanuele II 13, 20122, Milan, Italy
Tel.: (39) 028058071
Sales Range: $25-49.9 Million
Emp.: 15
Electronic Trading Software Developer
N.A.I.C.S.: 513210

Orc Netherlands B.V. (3)
Strawinskylaan 1061 Tower D Level 10,
World Trade Center, 1077 XX, Amsterdam,
Netherlands
Tel.: (31) 208813085
Sales Range: $25-49.9 Million
Emp.: 5
Electronic Trading Software Developer
N.A.I.C.S.: 513210

Orc Software GmbH (3)
Grobe Eschenheimer St 45, 60313, Frankfurt am Main, Germany
Tel.: (49) 697167390
Electronic Trading Software Developer
N.A.I.C.S.: 513210

Orc Software GmbH (3)
Singerstrasse 6 7, 1010, Vienna, Austria
Tel.: (43) 1 512 69 93
Sales Range: $25-49.9 Million
Emp.: 4
Electronic Trading Software Developer
N.A.I.C.S.: 513210

Orc Software HK Ltd. (3)

18 F 100 Queens Rd, Central, China (Hong Kong)
Tel.: (852) 21671950
Web Site: http://www.orc-group.com
Sales Range: $25-49.9 Million
Emp.: 20
Electronic Trading Software Developer
N.A.I.C.S.: 513210
Greg Chambers (Pres)

Orc Software Ltd. (3)
23 Camomile St, London, EC3A 7LL, United Kingdom
Tel.: (44) 2079420950
Web Site: http://www.orc-group.com
Sales Range: $25-49.9 Million
Emp.: 40
Electronic Trading Software Developer
N.A.I.C.S.: 513210
Lee Griggs (Pres-EMEA)
Jon Freebody (VP-Sls)

Subsidiary (Domestic):

Orc Software Stockholm AB (3)
Kungsgatan 36 5th Fl, Stockholm, 11135,
Sweden
Tel.: (46) 850647700
Web Site: http://www.orc-group.com
Sales Range: $50-74.9 Million
Emp.: 100
Electronic Trading Software Developer
N.A.I.C.S.: 513210
Preben Munch (CEO)

Subsidiary (US):

Orc USA Inc. (3)
111 Broadway Ste 602, New York, NY
10006
Tel.: (212) 351-7600
Web Site: http://www.orcsoftware.com
Electronic Trading Software Developer
N.A.I.C.S.: 513210

Subsidiary (Non-US):

Ullink Global SAS (2)
21 Boulevard Haussmann, 75009, Paris,
France
Tel.: (33) 1 4995 3000
Holding Company; Multi-Asset Trading
Technologies & Infrastructure Developer,
Publisher, Sales, Data Hosting & Technical
Support Services
N.A.I.C.S.: 551112

Subsidiary (US):

Ullink Inc. (3)
11 Times Sq 31st Fl, New York, NY 10036
Tel.: (646) 565-6681
Multi-Asset Trading Technologies & Infrastructure Sales, Data Hosting & Technical
Support Services
N.A.I.C.S.: 518210

Subsidiary (Non-US):

Ullink Limited (3)
Room 4201-05 Hopwell Centre 183 Queens
Road East, Hong Kong, China (Hong Kong)
Tel.: (852) 2167 1950
Multi-Asset Trading Technologies & Infrastructure Sales, Data Hosting & Technical
Support Services
N.A.I.C.S.: 518210

LiquidX, Inc. (1)
285 Madison Ave Ste 1402, New York, NY
10017
Tel.: (212) 612-3394
Web Site: https://www.liquidx.com
Trade Financing Services
N.A.I.C.S.: 522299
Jim Toffey (CEO)
Andy Phillips (Gen Counsel)
Abhishek Khandelwal (CFO)
Frank DiMarco (COO)

Matrix Trust Company (1)
717 17th St Ste 1300, Denver, CO 80202
Tel.: (888) 947-3472
Data Processing Services
N.A.I.C.S.: 518210

Rockall Technologies Limited (1)
Block 1 West Pier Business Campus, Dun
Laoghaire, Dublin, A96 F8C0, Ireland
Tel.: (353) 14873700
Web Site: http://www.rockall.com

Emp.: 90
Business Support Services
N.A.I.C.S.: 561499
Luke Nestor (Founder)

BROADSCALE ACQUISITION CORP.

1845 Walnut St Ste 1111, Philadelphia, PA 19103
Tel.: (646) 849-9975   DE
Year Founded: 2020
SCLE—(NASDAQ)
Rev.: $10,976,077
Assets: $345,831,765
Liabilities: $28,441,363
Net Worth: $317,390,402
Earnings: $6,339,281
Fiscal Year-end: 12/31/21
Investment Services
N.A.I.C.S.: 523999
Andrew L. Shapiro (Chm & CEO)
Edward E. Cohen (Vice Chm)
John P. Hanna (CFO & Head-Acquisitions)
Jeffrey F. Brotman (Chief Legal Officer & Sec)

BROADSTONE NET LEASE, INC.

207 High Point Dr Ste 300, Victor,
NY 14564
Tel.: (585) 287-6500   MD
Web Site:
https://www.broadstone.com
Year Founded: 2007
BNL—(NYSE)
Rev.: $442,888,000
Assets: $5,268,735,000
Liabilities: $2,074,394,000
Net Worth: $3,194,341,000
Earnings: $155,478,000
Emp.: 74
Fiscal Year-end: 12/31/23
Offices of Real Estate Agents & Brokers
N.A.I.C.S.: 531210
Ryan M. Albano (Pres & COO)
John D. Moragne (CEO)
John D. Callan (Gen Counsel, Sr VP & Asst Sec)
Kevin M. Fennell (CFO & Exec VP)
Andrea T. Wright (Sr VP-Property Mgmt)
Laurier James Lessard Jr. (Sr VP-Asset Mgmt)
Jennie O'Brien (Chief Acctg Officer & Sr VP)

BROADWAY FINANCIAL CORPORATION

4601 Wilshire Blvd, Los Angeles, CA
90010-3865
Tel.: (202) 243-7100   DE
Web Site:
https://www.cityfirstbank.com
Year Founded: 1995
BYFC—(NASDAQ)
Rev.: $37,464,000
Assets: $1,184,293,000
Liabilities: $904,641,000
Net Worth: $279,652,000
Earnings: $5,636,000
Emp.: 83
Fiscal Year-end: 12/31/22
Bank Holding Company
N.A.I.C.S.: 522180
Wayne-Kent A. Bradshaw (Chm)
Brenda J. Battey (CFO)
Brian E. Argrett (Vice Chm, Pres & CEO)

Subsidiaries:

Broadway Federal Bank, f.s.b. (1)
4800 Wilshire Blvd, Los Angeles, CA 90010
Tel.: (323) 634-1700
Web Site:
http://www.broadwayfederalbank.com

Sales Range: $25-49.9 Million
Federal Savings & Loan
N.A.I.C.S.: 522180
Virgil P. Roberts (Chm)
Wayne-Kent A. Bradshaw (Pres & CEO)
Brenda J. Battey (CFO & Exec VP)
Norman E. Bellefeuille (Chief Loan Officer & Exec VP)
Ruth McCloud (Chief Retail Banking Officer & Exec VP)
James Samkhem (Exec VP & Controller)

BROADWIND, INC.

3240 S Central Ave, Cicero, IL 60804
Tel.: (708) 780-4800   DE
Web Site: https://www.bwen.com
BWEN—(NASDAQ)
Rev.: $176,759,000
Assets: $144,540,000
Liabilities: $98,267,000
Net Worth: $46,273,000
Earnings: ($9,730,000)
Emp.: 499
Fiscal Year-end: 12/31/22
Wind Towers, Oil, Gas, Mining & Other Industrial Products & Equipment Mfr
N.A.I.C.S.: 332311
Eric B. Blashford (Pres & CEO)
Thomas A. Ciccone (CFO & VP)
Hayes Kennedy (Chief HR Officer)

Subsidiaries:

Brad Foote Gear Works, Inc. (1)
1309 S Cicero Ave, Cicero, IL 60804
Tel.: (708) 298-1100
Web Site: http://www.bwen.com
Custom Gear & Gearbox Mfr
N.A.I.C.S.: 333612

Broadwind Heavy Fabrications, Inc. (1)
101 S 16th St, Manitowoc, WI 54220
Tel.: (920) 482-3582
Wind Turbine Tower & Fabrication Mfr
N.A.I.C.S.: 333611
Dennis Janda (VP-Engrg)

Broadwind Services, LLC (1)
300 Wall St, Abilene, TX 79603
Tel.: (325) 690-1622
Industrial Machinery & Equipment Whslr
N.A.I.C.S.: 423830

Red Wolf Company, LLC (1)
1826 Boone Trl Rd, Sanford, NC 27330
Tel.: (919) 777-2907
Web Site: http://www.redwolfllc.com
Fabricated Metal Product Manufacturing
N.A.I.C.S.: 332999

BROOKDALE SENIOR LIVING INC.

111 Westwood Pl Ste 400, Brentwood, TN 37027
Tel.: (615) 221-2250   DE
Web Site: https://www.brookdale.com
Year Founded: 1978
BKD—(NYSE)
Rev.: $2,825,379,000
Assets: $5,937,062,000
Liabilities: $5,352,909,000
Net Worth: $584,153,000
Earnings: ($238,427,000)
Emp.: 36,000
Fiscal Year-end: 12/31/22
Senior Living Facilities Operator
N.A.I.C.S.: 020011
H. Todd Kaestner (Pres-Entry Fee & Exec VP-Asset Mgmt)
George T. Hicks (Treas & Exec VP-Fin)
Lucinda M. Baier (Pres & CEO)
Dawn L. Kussow (CFO & Exec VP)
Chad C. White (Gen Counsel, Sec & Exec VP)
David Cygan (CMO)
Kim Elliott (Chief Nursing Officer)
Laura Fischer (VP)
Jaclyn Pritchett (Exec VP)
Tara Jones (CIO)
Rick Wigginton (Chief Sls Officer)
Ben Ricci (VP)

Subsidiaries:

AHC Southland-Melbourne, LLC (1)
111 Westwood Pl Ste 400, Brentwood, TN 37027
Tel.: (321) 255-5443
Senior Living Community Operator
N.A.I.C.S.: 623311

AHC Southland-Ormond Beach, LLC (1)
111 Westwood Pl Ste 400, Brentwood, TN 37027
Tel.: (386) 677-0782
Senior Living Community Operator
N.A.I.C.S.: 623311

ALS Leasing, Inc. (1)
10050 Old Saint Augustine Rd, Jacksonville, FL 32257-6018
Tel.: (904) 385-9582
Web Site: https://www.brookdale.co
Health Care Srvices
N.A.I.C.S.: 621999
Mark Ohlendorf (Pres)

ARC Bay Pines Inc (1)
9797 Bay Pines Blvd, Saint Petersburg, FL 33708-3775
Tel.: (727) 222-4623
Web Site: http://www.brookdale.com
Emp.: 50
Health Care Srvices
N.A.I.C.S.: 621999
Mark Ohlendorf (Pres)

ARC Boynton Beach LLC (1)
2400 S Congress Ave, Boynton Beach, FL 33426-7439
Tel.: (561) 268-0219
Health Care Srvices
N.A.I.C.S.: 621999
Mark Ohlendorf (Pres)

ARC Bradenton HC, Inc. (1)
6406 21st Ave W, Bradenton, FL 34209
Tel.: (941) 210-6153
Health Care Srvices
N.A.I.C.S.: 621999

ARC Brandywine, LP (1)
15 Freedom Blvd, Coatesville, PA 19320-1549
Tel.: (610) 383-5100
Health Care Srvices
N.A.I.C.S.: 621999

ARC Coconut Creek LLC (1)
4175 W Sample Rd, Coconut Creek, FL 33073-4456
Tel.: (954) 417-4846
Health Care Srvices
N.A.I.C.S.: 621999

ARC Countryside LLC (1)
3260 N Mcmullen Booth Rd, Clearwater, FL 33761
Tel.: (727) 222-4634
Web Site: http://www.brookdaleliving.com
Health Care Srvices
N.A.I.C.S.: 621999

ARC Freedom Square LLC (1)
7800 Liberty Ln, Seminole, FL 33772-4746
Tel.: (727) 547-3315
Health Care Srvices
N.A.I.C.S.: 621999

ARC Galleria Woods Inc (1)
3850 Galleria Woods Dr, Birmingham, AL 35244-1098
Tel.: (205) 985-7537
Health Care Srvices
N.A.I.C.S.: 621999

ARC Greenwood Village Inc (1)
6450 S Boston St, Greenwood Village, CO 80111-5336
Tel.: (303) 224-9455
Web Site: https://www.brookdale.com
Health Care Srvices
N.A.I.C.S.: 621999

ARC Parklane Inc (1)
2 Towers Park Ln, San Antonio, TX 78209-6410
Tel.: (210) 829-1400
Web Site:
 https://www.parklanewesthealthcare.com
Health Care Srvices
N.A.I.C.S.: 621999

ARC Richmond Heights LLC (1)
562 Richmond Rd, Richmond Heights, OH 44143
Tel.: (216) 291-8585
Nursing & Custodial Care Facilities Services
N.A.I.C.S.: 623110
Elizabeth Ribar (Gen Mgr)

ARC Richmond Place Inc (1)
2770 Palumbo Dr, Lexington, KY 40508
Tel.: (859) 269-6308
Web Site: http://www.brookdaleliving.com
Health Care Srvices
N.A.I.C.S.: 621999

ARC Santa Catalina Inc (1)
7500 N Calle Sin Envidia, Tucson, AZ 85718-7300
Tel.: (520) 742-6242
Nursing & Custodial Care Facilities Services
N.A.I.C.S.: 623110

Alternative Living Services Home Care, Inc. (1)
101 Bundy Rd, Ithaca, NY 14850-9052
Tel.: (607) 269-4221
Web Site: https://www.brookdale.com
Health Care Srvices
N.A.I.C.S.: 621999

American Retirement Corporation (1)
111 Westwood Pl Ste 200, Brentwood, TN 37027
Tel.: (615) 221-2250
Health Care Srvices
N.A.I.C.S.: 621610
Bryan D. Richardson (CFO)

Arvada Meridian, LLC (1)
9555 W 59th Ave Apt 211, Arvada, CO 80004
Tel.: (303) 425-1900
Living Facilities Operator
N.A.I.C.S.: 623311

Assisted Living Properties Inc (1)
240 Interchange Blvd, Ormond Beach, FL 32174-1835
Tel.: (386) 243-9819
Web Site: https://www.brookdale.com
Nursing & Custodial Care Facilities Services
N.A.I.C.S.: 623110

BKD Belle Meade, LLC (1)
6767 Brookmont Ter, Nashville, TN 37205
Tel.: (615) 353-1990
Web Site: https://www.brookdale.com
Senior Health Care Services
N.A.I.C.S.: 623312

BKD College Place, LLC (1)
550 E Whitman, College Place, WA 99324
Tel.: (509) 526-7007
Web Site: https://www.brookdale.com
Senior Health Care Services
N.A.I.C.S.: 623312

BKD Jones Farm, LLC (1)
2815 Carl T Jones Dr SE, Huntsville, AL 35802
Tel.: (256) 881-6111
Web Site: https://www.brookdale.com
Senior Health Care Services
N.A.I.C.S.: 623312

BKD Lawrenceville, LLC (1)
1000 River Centre Pl, Lawrenceville, GA 30043
Tel.: (770) 963-9934
Web Site: https://www.brookdale.com
Senior Health Care Services
N.A.I.C.S.: 623312

BKD Lodi, LLC (1)
2220 W Kettleman Ln, Lodi, CA 95242
Tel.: (209) 367-8870
Web Site: https://www.brookdale.com
Senior Health Care Services
N.A.I.C.S.: 623312

BKD Murray, LLC (1)
905 Glendale Rd, Murray, KY 42071
Tel.: (270) 917-8578
Web Site: https://www.brookdale.com
Senior Health Care Services
N.A.I.C.S.: 623312

BKD Newnan, LLC (1)
355 Millard Farmer Industrial Blvd, Newnan, GA 30263

BKD North Gilbert, LLC (1)
Tel.: (770) 252-9007
Web Site: https://www.brookdale.com
Senior Health Care Services
N.A.I.C.S.: 623312

BKD North Gilbert, LLC (1)
845 N El Dorado Dr, Gilbert, AZ 85233
Tel.: (480) 539-0801
Web Site: https://www.brookdale.com
Senior Health Care Services
N.A.I.C.S.: 623312

BKD North Glendale, LLC (1)
6735 W Hillcrest Blvd, Glendale, AZ 85310
Tel.: (623) 572-7400
Web Site: https://www.brookdale.com
Senior Health Care Services
N.A.I.C.S.: 623312

BKD Oak Park, LLC (1)
1111 Ontario St, Oak Park, IL 60302
Tel.: (708) 383-1111
Web Site: https://www.brookdale.com
Senior Health Care Services
N.A.I.C.S.: 623312

BKD Parkplace, LLC (1)
111 Emerson St, Denver, CO 80218
Tel.: (303) 744-0400
Web Site: https://www.brookdale.com
Senior Health Care Services
N.A.I.C.S.: 623312

BKD South Bay, LLC (1)
1959 Kingstown Rd, South Kingstown, RI 02879
Tel.: (401) 789-4880
Web Site: https://www.brookdale.com
Senior Health Care Services
N.A.I.C.S.: 623312

BKD Tanque Verde, LLC (1)
9050 E Tanque Verde Rd, Tucson, AZ 85749
Tel.: (520) 749-9200
Web Site: https://www.brookdale.com
Senior Health Care Services
N.A.I.C.S.: 623312

BKD Tullahoma, LLC (1)
801 Wilson Ave, Tullahoma, TN 37388
Tel.: (931) 455-2000
Web Site: https://www.brookdale.com
Senior Health Care Services
N.A.I.C.S.: 623312

BKD Wekiwa Springs, LLC (1)
203 S Wekiwa Springs Rd, Apopka, FL 32703
Tel.: (407) 889-7704
Web Site: https://www.brookdale.com
Senior Health Care Services
N.A.I.C.S.: 623312

BKD Wilsonville,LLC (1)
8170 Vlahos Dr, Wilsonville, OR 97070
Tel.: (503) 682-0653
Web Site: https://www.brookdale.com
Senior Health Care Services
N.A.I.C.S.: 623312

BLC Atrium-Jacksonville, LLC (1)
9960 Atrium Way, Jacksonville, FL 32225
Tel.: (904) 724-4726
Web Site: https://www.brookdale.com
Nursing & Custodial Care Facilities Services
N.A.I.C.S.: 623110

BLC Foxwood Springs LLC (1)
1500 W Foxwood Dr, Raymore, MO 64083-9347
Tel.: (816) 331-3111
Web Site: https://foxwoodseniorliving.org
Emp.: 300
Nursing & Custodial Care Facilities Services
N.A.I.C.S.: 623110

BLC Gables Monrovia LP (1)
201 E Foothill Blvd, Monrovia, CA 91016
Tel.: (626) 385-4952
Web Site: https://www.brookdale.com
Custodial Care Facilities Services
N.A.I.C.S.: 621999

BLC Ramsey LLC (1)
1611 27th St, Des Moines, IA 50310-5400
Tel.: (660) 530-2339
Web Site:
 https://www.crmscommunities.com
Nursing & Custodial Care Facilities Services
N.A.I.C.S.: 623110

BLC Tampa GC LLC (1)
4902 Bayshore Blvd, Tampa, FL 33611
Tel.: (813) 358-4964
Web Site: https://www.brookdale.com
Emp.: 80
Nursing & Custodial Care Facilities Services
N.A.I.C.S.: 623110

BREA Atlanta Court LLC (1)
1262 Hightower Trl, Atlanta, GA 30350-2913
Tel.: (770) 650-8200
Web Site: http://www.emeritus.com
Sales Range: $10-24.9 Million
Emp.: 57
Nursing Care Facilities Services
N.A.I.C.S.: 623110

BREA Boynton Beach LLC (1)
1935 S Federal Hwy, Boynton Beach, FL 33435
Tel.: (561) 736-2424
Web Site: http://www.emeritus.com
Assisted Living Facilities Services
N.A.I.C.S.: 623311

BREA Denver LLC (1)
3790 W Quincy Ave, Denver, CO 80236-3644
Tel.: (303) 578-4790
Web Site: https://www.brookdale.com
Sales Range: $10-24.9 Million
Emp.: 60
Continuing Care Senior Living Community
N.A.I.C.S.: 623311

BREA East Mesa LLC (1)
6145 E Arbor Ave, Mesa, AZ 85206
Tel.: (480) 389-1930
Web Site: https://www.brookdale.com
Assisted Living Facilities Services
N.A.I.C.S.: 623311

BREA Peoria LLC (1)
9296 W Union Hills Dr, Peoria, AZ 85382
Tel.: (480) 618-6923
Web Site: https://www.emeritus.com
Sales Range: $10-24.9 Million
Emp.: 30
Assisted Living Facilities Services
N.A.I.C.S.: 623311

BREA Reno LLC (1)
3105 Plumas St, Reno, NV 89509
Tel.: (775) 234-2321
Web Site: https://www.emeritus.com
Emp.: 60
Assisted Living Facilities Services
N.A.I.C.S.: 623311

BREA Roanoke LLC (1)
1127 Persinger Rd SW, Roanoke, VA 24015
Tel.: (540) 218-1092
Web Site: https://www.brookdale.com
Nursing Care Facilities Services
N.A.I.C.S.: 623110

BREA Sarasota LLC (1)
5501 Swift Rd, Sarasota, FL 34231
Tel.: (941) 922-8778
Nursing Care Facilities Services
N.A.I.C.S.: 623110

BREA West Orange LLC (1)
520 Prospect Ave, West Orange, NJ 07052
Tel.: (973) 221-3364
Web Site: https://www.brookdale.com
Assisted Living Facilities
N.A.I.C.S.: 623312

Brookdale Bend OR, LLC (1)
1099 NE Watt Way, Bend, OR 97701
Tel.: (541) 585-6775
Home & Healthcare Services
N.A.I.C.S.: 621498

Brookdale Castle Hills, LLC (1)
1207 Jackson Keller Rd, San Antonio, TX 78213
Tel.: (210) 570-3352
Residential Building Leasing Services
N.A.I.C.S.: 531110

Brookdale Eau Gallie (1)
2680 Croton Rd, Melbourne, FL 32935
Tel.: (321) 238-8419
Web Site: http://www.brookdale.com
Health Care & Center Services
N.A.I.C.S.: 621999

Brookdale Senior Living Inc.—(Continued)

Brookdale Gardens Inc (1)
935 Broad St Ste 1, Bloomfield, NJ 07003
Tel.: (973) 743-0666
Health Care Srvices
N.A.I.C.S.: 621999

Brookdale Home Health (1)
300 Valencia Dr SE, Albuquerque, NM
87108-3058
Tel.: (505) 209-3850
Web Site: http://www.brookdale.com
Emp.: 40
Healtcare Services
N.A.I.C.S.: 621999

Brookdale Leawood (1)
4400 W 115th St, Leawood, KS 66211-2684
Tel.: (913) 871-6797
Web Site: http://www.brookdale.com
Emp.: 150
Nursing & Custodial Care Facilities Services
N.A.I.C.S.: 623110

**Brookdale Living Communities of
North Carolina, Inc.** (1)
1200 Carlos Dr, Raleigh, NC 27609-4766
Tel.: (919) 338-5394
Emp.: 32
Retirement Home & Assisted Living Center
Service
N.A.I.C.S.: 623312

**Brookdale McMinnville Westside,
LLC** (1)
300 NW Hillside Park Way, McMinnville,
OR 97128
Tel.: (503) 389-5934
Emp.: 30
Senior Living Services
N.A.I.C.S.: 623312
Joeda Simonson (Gen Mgr)

**Brookdale Place at Fall Creek,
LLC** (1)
5011 Kessler Blvd E, Indianapolis, IN 46220
Tel.: (317) 251-1300
Senior Living Services
N.A.I.C.S.: 623312

**Brookdale Place at Kenwood,
LLC** (1)
9090 Montgomery, Cincinnati, OH 45242-
7712
Tel.: (513) 745-9292
Web Site: https://www.brookdale.com
Senior Living Services
N.A.I.C.S.: 623312

**Brookdale Place at Oakwood,
LLC** (1)
1701 Far Hills Ave, Dayton, OH 45419
Tel.: (937) 294-1772
Web Site: https://www.brookdale.com
Senior Living Services
N.A.I.C.S.: 623312
Ellen Rice (Exec Dir)

**Brookdale Place at Willow Lake,
LLC** (1)
2725 Lk Cir Dr, Indianapolis, IN 46268
Tel.: (317) 268-8188
Senior Living Services
N.A.I.C.S.: 623312

**Brookdale Place of Ann Arbor,
LLC** (1)
2190 Ann Arbor Saline Rd, Ann Arbor, MI
48103
Tel.: (734) 327-1350
Web Site: https://www.brookdale.com
Nursing & Custodial Care Facilities Services
N.A.I.C.S.: 623110

Brookdale Place of Augusta, LLC (1)
326 Boy Scout Rd, Augusta, GA 30909
Tel.: (706) 738-6003
Web Site: https://www.brookdale.com
Senior Living Services
N.A.I.C.S.: 623312

Brookdale Place of Bath, LLC (1)
101 N Cleveland/Massillon Rd, Akron, OH
44333
Tel.: (330) 590-6023
Nursing & Custodial Care Facilities Services
N.A.I.C.S.: 623110

**Brookdale Place of Englewood,
LLC** (1)

95 W Wenger Rd, Englewood, OH 45322
Tel.: (937) 832-8500
Web Site: https://www.brookdale.com
Senior Living Services
N.A.I.C.S.: 623312
Charlie Thomson (Exec Dir)

**Brookdale Place of West Hartford,
LLC** (1)
22 Simsbury Rd, West Hartford, CT 06117
Tel.: (959) 666-9361
Web Site: https://www.brookdale.com
Senior Living Services
N.A.I.C.S.: 623312

Brookdale Place of Wilton, LLC (1)
96 Danbury Rd, Wilton, CT 06897
Tel.: (203) 761-8999
Web Site: https://www.brookdale.com
Residential Building Leasing Services
N.A.I.C.S.: 531110

**Brookdale Place of Wooster,
LLC** (1)
1615 Cleveland Rd, Wooster, OH 44691
Tel.: (330) 262-1615
Web Site: https://www.brookdale.com
Senior Living Services
N.A.I.C.S.: 623312

**Brookdale Senior Living Inc. -
Jacksonville** (1)
9601 Southbrook Dr, Jacksonville, FL
32256
Tel.: (904) 413-0876
Health Care Srvices
N.A.I.C.S.: 621999

Brookdale Senior Living, Inc. (1)
6737 W Washington St Ste 2300, Milwau-
kee, WI 53214
Tel.: (414) 918-5000
Web Site: https://www.brookdale.com
Sales Range: $400-449.9 Million
Emp.: 7,900
Operator of Assisted Living Residences
N.A.I.C.S.: 623311
D. Lee Field (Pres-ALS Canada & Sr VP)

Brookdale St. Augustine LLC (1)
150 Mariner Health Way, Saint Augustine,
FL 32086-3215
Tel.: (904) 794-9988
Web Site: https://www.brookdale.com
Emp.: 50
Assisted Living Facilities Services
N.A.I.C.S.: 623311
Katrina Williams (Exec Dir)

Brookdale Wellington, Inc. (1)
500 N Plum St, Wellington, KS 67152-3574
Tel.: (620) 326-3031
Senior Living Services
N.A.I.C.S.: 623312

Brookdale Yorktowne (1)
1675 Dunlawton Ave, Port Orange, FL
32127
Tel.: (386) 243-9812
Web Site: http://www.brookdale.com
Assisted Living Facilities Services
N.A.I.C.S.: 623311

Burlington Manor, LLC (1)
3615 S Mebane St, Burlington, NC 27215
Tel.: (336) 584-9066
Web Site: https://www.brookdale.com
Senior Living Services
N.A.I.C.S.: 623312

**CCRC - Freedom Pointe at the Vil-
lages, LLC** (1)
4600 S Syracuse St Ste 500, Denver, CO
80237
Tel.: (352) 750-1355
Senior Living Services
N.A.I.C.S.: 623312

CCRC - Regency Oaks, LLC (1)
2751 Regency Oaks Blvd, Clearwater, FL
33759
Tel.: (727) 330-2142
Senior Living Services
N.A.I.C.S.: 623312

CMCP Montrose LLC (1)
100 Brookmont Rd, Akron, OH 44333
Tel.: (330) 666-4545
Web Site: https://www.brookdale.com
Emp.: 100
Nursing & Custodial Care Facilities Services

N.A.I.C.S.: 623110

CSH Lake Orienta LLC (1)
4600 S Syracuse St Ste 500, Denver, CO
80237
Tel.: (407) 260-2345
Assisted Living Services
N.A.I.C.S.: 623312
Mark Pulasky (Gen Mgr)

CSH North Richland Hills LLC (1)
8500 Emerald Hills Way, Richland Hills, TX
76180-5662
Tel.: (817) 577-3337
Living Facilities Operator
N.A.I.C.S.: 623311
Jeanee Shore (Mgr)

CSH Port St. Lucie LLC (1)
4600 S Syracuse St Ste 500, Denver, CO
80237
Tel.: (772) 337-0084
Assisted Living Services
N.A.I.C.S.: 623312
Wendy Smith (Gen Mgr)

CSH Round Rock LLC (1)
8005 Cornerwood Dr, Austin, TX 78717
Tel.: (512) 238-7200
Living Facilities Operator
N.A.I.C.S.: 623311

CSH San Marcos LLC (1)
1720 Old Ranch Rd 12, San Marcos, TX
78666
Tel.: (512) 392-7200
Living Facilities Operator
N.A.I.C.S.: 623311
Clay King (Mng Dir)

**Carolina House of Chapel Hill,
LLC** (1)
100 Lanark Rd, Chapel Hill, NC 27517
Tel.: (919) 263-0495
Senior Living Services
N.A.I.C.S.: 623312

Carolina House of Durham, LLC (1)
176 Lassiter Homestead Rd, Durham, NC
27713
Tel.: (919) 263-0493
Web Site:
  https://www.carolinaeatingdisorders.com
Senior Living Services
N.A.I.C.S.: 623312
Jessica Hendricks (CEO)

**Carolina House of Forest City,
LLC** (1)
493 Piney Ridge Rd, Forest City, NC 28043
Tel.: (949) 287-4600
Senior Living Services
N.A.I.C.S.: 623312

**Carolina House of Lexington,
LLC** (1)
161 Young Dr, Lexington, NC 27292
Tel.: (336) 238-1700
Senior Living Services
N.A.I.C.S.: 623312

**Carolina House of Morehead City,
LLC** (1)
107 Bryan St, Morehead City, NC 28557
Tel.: (949) 287-4600
Senior Living Services
N.A.I.C.S.: 623312

**Carolina House of Smithfield,
LLC** (1)
830 Berkshire Rd, Smithfield, NC 27577
Tel.: (919) 989-3100
Senior Living Services
N.A.I.C.S.: 623312

Emeri-Sky SC LLC (1)
3131 Elliott Ave Ste 500, Seattle, WA
98121-1032
Tel.: (206) 298-2909
Nursing Care Services
N.A.I.C.S.: 623110

EmeriCare Skylyn Place LLC (1)
1705 Skylyn Dr, Spartanburg, SC 29307-
1077
Tel.: (864) 582-6838
Assisted Living Facilities Services
N.A.I.C.S.: 623311
Britney Cobb (Exec Dir)

Emeritol Grand Terrace LLC (1)

22325 Barton Rd, Grand Terrace, CA 92313
Tel.: (909) 254-4106
Residential Care Facilities Services
N.A.I.C.S.: 623210

Emeritus Corporation (1)
3131 Elliott Ave Ste 500, Seattle, WA
98121-1032
Tel.: (206) 298-2909
Rev.: $1,960,618,000
Assets: $4,594,648,000
Liabilities: $4,480,629,000
Net Worth: $114,019,000
Earnings: ($152,970,000)
Emp.: 21,675
Fiscal Year-end: 12/31/2013
Senior Citizen Assisted Living & Retirement
Communities Owner & Operator
N.A.I.C.S.: 623311
Kellie Murray (VP-Hospital Rels & Transi-
tional Care Mgmt)
Eugenia Liu (Sr Dir-Legal)

EmeritusMerced Inc. (1)
3420 R St, Merced, CA 95348-2376
Tel.: (209) 384-9700
Emp.: 30
Nursing Care Facilities Services
N.A.I.C.S.: 623110

Emeriweg Deerfield LLC (1)
5535 Irwin Simpson Rd, Mason, OH 45040
Tel.: (513) 770-0512
Web Site: http://www.brookdale.com
Senior Living Services
N.A.I.C.S.: 623312

Englewood Meridian LLC (1)
3455 S Corona St, Englewood, CO 80113
Tel.: (720) 588-3914
Assisted Living Services
N.A.I.C.S.: 623312
Lindsey Jo Caudill (Coord-Mktg)

**Freedom Village of Bradenton,
LLC** (1)
6406 21st Ave W, Bradenton, FL 34209
Tel.: (941) 219-5294
Retirement Community Care Services
N.A.I.C.S.: 623311

**Freedom Village of Holland
Michigan** (1)
145 Columbia Ave, Holland, MI 49423
Tel.: (616) 200-7271
Web Site: https://fvhollandseniorliving.com
Senior Living Services
N.A.I.C.S.: 623312

**Freedom Village of Sun City Center,
Ltd.** (1)
1010 American Eagle Blvd, Sun City Cen-
ter, FL 33573
Tel.: (813) 280-5009
Real Estate Property Management Services
N.A.I.C.S.: 531312

Greensboro Manor, LP (1)
5809 Old Oak Ridge Rd, Greensboro, NC
27410
Tel.: (336) 297-9900
Senior Living Services
N.A.I.C.S.: 623312

High Point Manor, LP (1)
201 W Hartley Dr, High Point, NC 27265
Tel.: (336) 885-8600
Senior Living Services
N.A.I.C.S.: 623312

**Homewood at Brookmont Terrace,
LLC** (1)
111 Westwood Pl Ste 400, Brentwood, TN
37027-5057
Tel.: (615) 353-1990
Senior Living Services
N.A.I.C.S.: 623312

**Innovative Senior Care Home Health
of Nashville LLC** (1)
1000 Health Park Dr Ste 500, Brentwood,
TN 37027
Tel.: (615) 333-2152
Nursing & Custodial Care Facilities Services
N.A.I.C.S.: 623110

LH Assisted Living, LLC (1)
376 Goshen Rd, Torrington, CT 06790
Tel.: (860) 489-8022
Web Site: http://www.brookdale.com
Assisted Living Facilities

N.A.I.C.S.: 623312

Lake Seminole Square, LLC   (1)
8333 Seminole Blvd, Seminole, FL 33772
Tel.: (727) 914-5982
Web Site:
    https://lakeseminoleseniorliving.com
Senior Living Services
N.A.I.C.S.: 623312

Lakewood Meridian LLC   (1)
1805 S Balsam St, Lakewood, CO 80232
Tel.: (303) 980-5500
Assisted Living Services
N.A.I.C.S.: 623312
Susan Johnson *(Exec Dir)*

Nurse on Call, Inc.   (1)
6702-A Plantation Rd, Pensacola, FL 32504
Tel.: (850) 474-9803
Web Site: https://www.nursesoncallinc.com
Nursing Care Services
N.A.I.C.S.: 623110

**Nurse-on-Call of South Florida,
Inc.**   (1)
1926 10th Ave N Ste 205, Lake Worth, FL
33461-3368
Tel.: (561) 282-6014
Web Site: http://www.nurseoncallfl.com
Women Healthcare Services
N.A.I.C.S.: 621610

PHNTUS Creekside LLC   (1)
2000 W Spring Creek Pkwy, Plano, TX
75023
Tel.: (972) 479-5933
Web Site: http://www.brookdale.com
Emp.: 21
Senior Citizen Care Service
N.A.I.C.S.: 623312

PHNTUS Pinehurst LLC   (1)
5403 Plantation Dr, Tyler, TX 75703
Tel.: (903) 534-4955
Emp.: 5
Nursing Care Services
N.A.I.C.S.: 623110

PHNTUS Quail Ridge LLC   (1)
5204 Elgin Ave, Lubbock, TX 79413
Tel.: (806) 788-1919
Web Site: https://www.brookdale.com
Emp.: 10
Senior Citizen Care Service
N.A.I.C.S.: 623312

S-H OpCo Carlsbad, LLC   (1)
3140 El Camino Real, Carlsbad, CA 92008-
2108
Tel.: (760) 720-9898
Health Care Srvices
N.A.I.C.S.: 621610

S-H OpCo Cliff View, LLC   (1)
1910 Fairview Ave E Ste 200, Seattle, WA
98102
Tel.: (435) 628-1117
Health Care Srvices
N.A.I.C.S.: 621610

S-H OpCo Cottage Village, LLC   (1)
110 Frankford Ave, Lubbock, TX 79416-
1426
Tel.: (806) 799-4225
Health Care Srvices
N.A.I.C.S.: 621610

**S-H OpCo Dartmouth Village,
LLC**   (1)
1910 Fairview Ave E Ste 200, Seattle, WA
98102
Tel.: (508) 999-0404
Health Care Srvices
N.A.I.C.S.: 621610

S-H OpCo East Bay Manor, LLC   (1)
1440 Wampanoag Trl, Riverside, RI 02915
Tel.: (401) 433-5000
Assisted Living Services
N.A.I.C.S.: 623312
Jean Pears *(Gen Mgr)*

S-H OpCo Fox River, LLC   (1)
2800 E Enterprise Ave Ste 333, Appleton,
WI 54913
Tel.: (920) 997-0725
Health Care Srvices
N.A.I.C.S.: 621610

**S-H OpCo Greenwich Bay Manor,
LLC**   (1)

945 Main St, East Greenwich, RI 02818-
3150
Tel.: (401) 885-3334
Assisted Living Services
N.A.I.C.S.: 623312
Dawn Lindelow *(Exec Dir)*

S-H OpCo Lincoln Heights, LLC   (1)
855 E Basse Rd, San Antonio, TX 78209
Tel.: (210) 930-1040
Web Site: http://www.brookdale.com
Emp.: 120
Health Care Srvices
N.A.I.C.S.: 621610

S-H OpCo Northpark Place, LLC   (1)
2562 Pierce St, Sioux City, IA 51104
Tel.: (712) 255-1200
Web Site: http://www.brookdale.com
Health Care Srvices
N.A.I.C.S.: 621610

S-H OpCo Prosperity Oaks, LLC   (1)
4600 S Syracuse St Ste 500, Denver, CO
80237
Tel.: (561) 694-9709
Assisted Living Services
N.A.I.C.S.: 623312
Suzanne Baron *(Exec Dir)*

**S-H OpCo Spicewood Springs,
LLC**   (1)
4401 Spicewood Springs Rd, Austin, TX
78759
Tel.: (512) 418-8822
Web Site: http://www.brookdale.com
Health Care Srvices
N.A.I.C.S.: 621610

**S-H OpCo Spring Creek Gardens,
LLC**   (1)
6410 Old Orchard Dr, Plano, TX 53214-
5647
Tel.: (972) 208-9865
Health Care Srvices
N.A.I.C.S.: 621610

S-H OpCo Spring Pointe, LLC   (1)
1400 Redwood Cir, Grants Pass, OR 97527
Tel.: (541) 474-2838
Health Care Srvices
N.A.I.C.S.: 621610

S-H OpCo Spring Village, LLC   (1)
1420 Redwood Cir, Grants Pass, OR 97527
Tel.: (541) 474-0200
Health Care Srvices
N.A.I.C.S.: 621610

S-H OpCo Wilson Mountain, LLC (1)
391 Common St, Dedham, MA 02026
Tel.: (781) 407-7711
Health Care Srvices
N.A.I.C.S.: 621610

**S-H Thirty-Five OpCo - Pocasset,
LLC**   (1)
12 Old Pocasset Ln, Johnston, RI 02919
Tel.: (401) 421-6610
Assisted Living Services
N.A.I.C.S.: 623312
Kelly Lafazia *(Exec Dir)*

**S-H Thirty-Five OpCo - Willowwood,
LLC**   (1)
2855 W Commercial Blvd, Fort Lauderdale,
FL 33309
Tel.: (954) 739-4200
Assisted Living Services
N.A.I.C.S.: 623312

Silver Lake Assisted Living, LLC (1)
12806 Bothell-Everett Hwy, Everett, WA
98208
Tel.: (425) 948-2654
Web Site: https://www.brookdale.com
Sales Range: $10-24.9 Million
Emp.: 50
Assisted Living Facilities
N.A.I.C.S.: 623312

Southern Assisted Living, LLC   (1)
2441 E Broad St, Statesville, NC 28625
Tel.: (704) 452-7506
Emp.: 35
Nursing & Custodial Care Facilities Services
N.A.I.C.S.: 623110
Dedra Shumaker *(Mgr)*

Summerville at North Hills LLC (1)
1575 Bowers Ln, Zanesville, OH 43701

Tel.: (740) 206-8268
Web Site: https://www.brookdale.com
Emp.: 100
Assisted Living Facilities Services
N.A.I.C.S.: 623311

**Summerville at Outlook Manor
LLC**   (1)
690 Cooper Rd, Westerville, OH 43081-
8919
Tel.: (614) 794-2499
Senior Living Community Operator
N.A.I.C.S.: 623311
Melissa Watson *(Exec Dir)*

**Summerville at Prince William,
Inc.**   (1)
3940 Prince William Pkwy, Woodbridge, VA
22192
Tel.: (703) 680-0600
Web Site: http://www.brookdale.com
Nursing Care Facilities Services
N.A.I.C.S.: 623110

**Summerville at Ridgewood Gardens
LLC**   (1)
3131 Elliott Ave Ste 500, Seattle, WA
98121-1032
Tel.: (540) 218-1153
Emp.: 50
Assisted Living Facilities Services
N.A.I.C.S.: 623311
Jennifar McGarry *(Exec Dir)*

**Summerville at Roseville Gardens
LLC**   (1)
1 Somer Rdg Dr, Roseville, CA 95661
Tel.: (916) 773-5955
Sales Range: $10-24.9 Million
Emp.: 30
Assisted Living Facilities Services
N.A.I.C.S.: 623311
Mayra Vote *(Exec Dir)*

Summerville at Stafford, LLC   (1)
1275 Rte 72 W, Manahawkin, NJ 08050-
2473
Tel.: (609) 225-4182
Web Site: https://www.brookdale.com
Assisted Living Facilities
N.A.I.C.S.: 623312

Summerville at Voorhees, LLC   (1)
1301 Laurel Oak Rd Ste 209, Voorhees, NJ
08043
Tel.: (856) 783-8383
Senior Living Community Operator
N.A.I.C.S.: 623311
Lisa Williams *(Exec Dir)*

**Summerville at Wekiwa Springs
LLC**   (1)
203 S Wekiwa Springs Rd, Apopka, FL
32703
Tel.: (689) 910-5226
Web Site: https://www.emeritus.com
Emp.: 54
Assisted Living Services
N.A.I.C.S.: 623110

**Summerville at Westminster,
LLC**   (1)
45 Washington Rd, Westminster, MD 21157
Tel.: (410) 751-2300
Web Site: http://www.brookdale.com
Assisted Living Facilities Services
N.A.I.C.S.: 623311

**Trinity Towers Limited
Partnership**   (1)
101 N Upper Broadway, Corpus Christi, TX
78401
Tel.: (361) 444-1128
Sales Range: $25-49.9 Million
Emp.: 200
Nursing & Custodial Care Facilities Services
N.A.I.C.S.: 623110

BROOKFIELD DTLA FUND OF-
FICE TRUST INVESTOR, INC.
250 Vesey St 15th Fl, New York, NY
10281-0221
Tel.: (212) 417-7000
Web Site: https://www.brookfield.com
Year Founded: 2013
DTLA.P—(NYSE)
Rev.: $295,900,000
Assets: $2,544,169,000

Liabilities: $2,359,060,000
Net Worth: $185,109,000
Earnings: ($282,794,000)
Fiscal Year-end: 12/31/22
Investment Management Service
N.A.I.C.S.: 525990
Michelle L. Campbell *(Sec & Sr VP)*
Ian Parker *(COO)*
G. Mark Brown *(Chm & CEO)*
Bryan D. Smith *(CFO)*

BROOKFIELD RENEWABLE
CORPORATION
250 Vesey St 15th Fl, New York, NY
10281-1023
Tel.: (416) 649-8172
Web Site: https://bep.brookfield.com
BEPC—(NYSE)
Rev.: $3,967,000,000
Assets: $49,421,000,000
Liabilities: $32,292,000,000
Net Worth: $17,129,000,000
Earnings: $308,000,000
Emp.: 1,376
Fiscal Year-end: 12/31/23
Real Estate Asset Management Ser-
vices
N.A.I.C.S.: 531390
Connor Teskey *(Mng Partner & CEO-
Renewable Power)*
Mitch Davidson *(Mng Partner-
Renewable Power)*
Wyatt Hartley *(Mng Partner-
Renewable Power & CFO)*
Ruth Kent *(Mng Partner-Renewable
Power)*
Jennifer Mazin *(Mng Partner-
Renewable Power)*

Subsidiaries:

Brookfideld Renewable Power Pre-
ferred Equality Inc.   (1)
Brookfield Place Suite 100 181 Bay Street,
Toronto, M5J 2T3, ON, Canada
Tel.: (416) 363-9491
Renewable Energy Services
N.A.I.C.S.: 221118

BROOKLINE BANCORP, INC.
131 Clarendon St, Boston, MA 02116
Tel.: (617) 425-4600   DE
Web Site:
    https://www.brooklinebancorp.com
Year Founded: 1998
BRKL—(NASDAQ)
Rev.: $373,533,000
Assets: $9,185,836,000
Liabilities: $8,193,711,000
Net Worth: $992,125,000
Earnings: $109,744,000
Emp.: 813
Fiscal Year-end: 12/31/22
Bank Holding Company
N.A.I.C.S.: 551111
Mark J. Meiklejohn *(Chief Credit Offi-
cer)*
Paul A. Perrault *(Chm & CEO)*
Michael W. McCurdy *(Pres & COO)*
Janytra M. Brooks *(Chief HR Officer)*
Marissa Martin *(Gen Counsel)*

Subsidiaries:

Bank Rhode Island   (1)
1 Turks Head Pl, Providence, RI
02903   (100%)
Tel.: (401) 456-5000
Web Site: https://www.bankri.com
Sales Range: $75-99.9 Million
Emp.: 250
Retail & Commercial Banking
N.A.I.C.S.: 522110
Scott Lajoie *(VP-Comml Banking)*
Alisa Loiselle *(VP-Comml Banking)*
Keb Brackenbury *(Sr VP-Comml Real Es-
tate)*
Dan Hartnett *(VP-Cash Mgmt Svcs)*

Brookline Bancorp, Inc.—(Continued)

William C. Tsonos (Pres & CEO)
Steven M. Parente (Exec VP & Dir-Retail Banking)
Tom Fitzgerald (Sr VP-Comml Banking & Head-Franchise Financing Div)
Nancy Dufresne (VP-Bus Banking)
Jane Long (Asst VP-Comml Real Estate & Mgr-Customer Rels)
Russell W. Hahn (Sr VP-Comml Banking)
Kasey Vivenzio (Mgr-North Kingstown)
Andrew Deluski (Sr VP-Comml Real Estate)
Robin Erban-Moses (Sr VP-Comml Banking)
Kevin Hazebrouck (Mgr-Relationship-Bus Banking)
Melissa L. Trapp (Sr VP & Mgr-Investment)
Alan J. Testa (Asst VP)
Meredith A. Curren (Vice Chm)
Joseph Brito (VP-Bus Banking)
Mary Ettinger (Sr VP-Comml Real Estate)
Matthew McCann (Officer-Loan-Comml Real Estate)
Dana A. Sherman (Compliance Officer & VP)
William Lucey III (VP-Comml Banking)

Subsidiary (Domestic):

Macrolease Corporation (2)
185 Exp St Ste 100, Plainview, NY 11803-2328
Tel.: (516) 576-9000
Web Site: https://www.macrolease.com
Emp.: 15
Equipment Finance Leasing Services
N.A.I.C.S.: 522220
Salvatore Venuto (Exec VP-Sls)
Paul Vecker (Pres & CEO)

Brookline Bank (1)
2 Harvard St, Brookline, MA 02445
Tel.: (617) 730-3500
Sales Range: $75-99.9 Million
Emp.: 100
Federal Savings Bank
N.A.I.C.S.: 522180
Paul A. Perrault (Chm)
Paul A. Perrault (Chm)
Robert E. Brown (Exec VP)
Peter Lennon (Sr VP)
Zepur Kahwajian (Mgr-Waltham)
Yury Afenheim (Mgr-Washington Square)
Darryl J. Fess (Pres & CEO)
David Paikin (Sr VP-Wakefield)
Leslie Joannides-Burgos (Exec VP)
Sean McGrath (VP-Wakefield)
Tricia Dandrow (Sr VP)
Mark Miller (Sr VP)
Henri A. Soucy (Sr VP)
David Yesue (Sr VP)
Tom Smith (VP)
Ali Abdullah (Sr VP)
Ryan Abbott (VP)
Marcelo Dutra (VP)
Dianne Lopes (VP)
David Scherer (VP)

First Ipswich Bank (1)
31 Market St, Ipswich, MA 01938 (100%)
Tel.: (978) 356-6100
Web Site: http://www.firstipswich.com
Full-service Financial Institution
N.A.I.C.S.: 522110

PCSB Financial Corporation (1)
2651 Strang Blvd Ste 100, Yorktown Heights, NY 10598
Tel.: (914) 248-7272
Web Site: https://www.pcsb.com
Rev.: $62,499,000
Assets: $1,989,132,000
Liabilities: $1,711,970,000
Net Worth: $277,162,000
Earnings: $14,879,000
Emp.: 154
Fiscal Year-end: 06/30/2022
Holding Company
N.A.I.C.S.: 551111
Carol Bray (CIO & Sr VP)
Michael P. Goldrick (Chief Lending Officer & Exec VP)
Ruth A. Leser (Sr VP & Dir-HR)
David McNamara (Officer-CRA & Sr VP-Compliance)
Scott D. Nogles (COO/Treas/Exec VP-PCSB Bank)
Richard J. Petrone (Chief Credit Officer & Sr VP)

Clifford S. Weber (Chief Risk Officer, Gen Counsel & Sr VP)
Jeffrey M. Helf (CFO & Sr VP)

Subsidiary (Domestic):

PCSB Bank (2)
2651 Strang Blvd, Yorktown Heights, NY 10598
Tel.: (914) 248-7272
Web Site: https://www.pcsb.com
Commercial Banking Services
N.A.I.C.S.: 522110
Joseph D. Roberto (Pres, CEO & Chm)
Scott D. Nogles (COO, Exec VP & Treasurer)
Michael P. Goldrick (Chief Lending Officer & Exec VP)
Carol F. Bray (CIO & Sr VP)
Jeffrey M. Helf (CFO & Sr VP)

**BROTHERHOOD
BANCSHARES INC.**
8325 Lenexa Dr Ste 300, Lenexa, KS 66214
Tel.: (913) 321-4242   **KS**
Web Site:
    http://www.brotherhoodbank.com
BHDB—(OTCIQ)
Bank Holding Company
N.A.I.C.S.: 551111
William J. Miller (CEO)
Robert McCall (Pres)
Aaron Bowman (CFO)
Zach Sheridan (Controller)
Kandi Kinsella (Sec)
Warren Fairley (Chm)

Subsidiaries:

Brotherhood Bank & Trust Co (1)
756 Minnesota Ave, Kansas City, KS 66101
Tel.: (913) 321-4242
Web Site: http://www.brotherhoodbank.com
Rev.: $24,721,000
Emp.: 200
State Commercial Banks
N.A.I.C.S.: 522110
David M. Duggins (Sr VP)
Thomas W. Johnson (Sr VP)
David Moll (VP)
Bob McCall (Pres & CEO)

BROWN & BROWN, INC.
300 N Beach St, Daytona Beach, FL 32114
Tel.: (386) 252-9601   **FL**
Web Site:
    https://www.bbinsurance.com
Year Founded: 1939
BRO—(NYSE)
Rev.: $4,357,600,000
Assets: $14,883,400,000
Liabilities: $9,304,600,000
Net Worth: $5,578,800,000
Earnings: $890,500,000
Emp.: 16,152
Fiscal Year-end: 12/31/23
Holding Company; Insurance Brokerage & Support Services
N.A.I.C.S.: 551112
J. Scott Penny (Chief Acquisitions Officer & Exec VP)
Barry R. Hensley (Chief Security Officer)
H. Vaughn Stoll (Sr VP & Dir-Acquisitions)
P. Barrett Brown (Pres-Retail Segment & Exec VP)
R. Andrew Watts (CFO, Treas & Exec VP)
Stephen M. Boyd (Pres-Wholesale Brokerage Segment & Exec VP)
Chris L. Walker (Pres-Natl Programs Seg & Exec VP)
Kathy H. Colangelo (Sr VP)
Jenny Goco (Dir-Comm)
Julie Turpin (Chief People Officer & Sr VP)
Michael Vaughan (Chief Data Officer)
Gray Nester (CIO)

Pattysue Rauh (Chief Audit Officer)
R. Andrew Watts (CFO)
Rob Burch (Chief Info Security Officer)
Julie L. Turpin (Exec VP)
Mike Bruce (Pres)
J. Powell Brown (Pres & CEO)

Subsidiaries:

Acorn International Network Pte. Ltd. (1)
167 Geylang Road 04-01, Singapore, 389242, Singapore
Tel.: (65) 67979231
Web Site: https://www.acornint.com
Insurance Brokerage Services
N.A.I.C.S.: 524210

Acumen Re Management Corporation (1)
302 Fellowship Rd Ste 130, Mount Laurel, NJ 08054-1233
Tel.: (856) 722-5200
Reinsurance & Workers Compensation Underwriter
N.A.I.C.S.: 524130

Advocate Insurance Services Corp. (1)
6475 E Pacific Coast Hwy Ste 333, Long Beach, CA 90803
Web Site: https://www.advocate-insurance.com
Insurance Services
N.A.I.C.S.: 524210
Chris Cockey (Principal)
Wanda Cookey (Principal)

Alan & Thomas Insurance Brokers Limited (1)
314-316 Bournemouth Road, Poole, BH14 9AP, United Kingdom
Tel.: (44) 1202754900
Web Site: https://www.alan-thomas.co.uk
Insurance Brokerage Services
N.A.I.C.S.: 524210

Alford Burton and Company Limited (1)
4 St Kenelm Court Steel Park Road, Halesowen, B62 8HD, West Midlands, United Kingdom
Tel.: (44) 1214494901
Insurance Brokerage Services
N.A.I.C.S.: 524210

Allocation Services, Inc. (1)
280 Wekiva Springs Rd Ste 3050, Longwood, FL 32779
Tel.: (407) 389-1303
Web Site: http://www.mynuquest.com
Insurance Agencies & Brokerage Services
N.A.I.C.S.: 524210
Tracey Lazzopina (CEO)
Lisa Rainey (COO)
Robert Sagrillo (Pres-Natl Accounts & Settlement Consulting)
Jennifer Shymanski (Dir-Implementation & Strategy)
Patrick Czuprynski (Dir-Lien Resolution)
Bridget Smith (VP-Compliance & Customer Rels)
Carla Roberts (Sr VP)
Barbara J. Fairchild (CEO)

American Claims Management - Atlantic Region, LLC (1)
PO Box 1620, Alpharetta, GA 30009-1620
Tel.: (678) 942-2300
Insurance Service Provider
N.A.I.C.S.: 524210

American Specialty Insurance & Risk Services, Inc. (1)
7609 W Jefferson Blvd Ste 100, Fort Wayne, IN 46804
Tel.: (260) 969-5203
Web Site:
    https://www.americanspecialty.com
Sales Range: $10-24.9 Million
Emp.: 60
Insurance Agents & Brokers
N.A.I.C.S.: 524210
Drew Smith (Pres)

Amicus Insurance Solutions Limited (1)

Bourne House 475 Godstone Road, Whyteleafe, CR3 0BL, United Kingdom
Tel.: (44) 2086690991
Web Site: https://www.amicus-insurance.co.uk
Insurance Brokerage Services
N.A.I.C.S.: 524210

Anderson Ashcroft Limited (1)
Unit 6a Edward VII Quay Navigation Way, Preston, PR2 2YF, United Kingdom
Tel.: (44) 1772204707
Web Site:
    https://www.andersonashcroft.co.uk
Insurance Brokerage Services
N.A.I.C.S.: 524210

Anglo Hibernian Bloodstock Insurance Services Limited (1)
7th Floor Corn Exchange 55 Mark Lane, London, EC3R 7NE, United Kingdom
Tel.: (44) 7749837594
Web Site: https://www.anglo-hibernian.co.uk
Insurance Brokerage Services
N.A.I.C.S.: 524210

Apex Insurance Agency, Inc. (1)
201 Concourse Blvd Ste 260, Glen Allen, VA 23059
Tel.: (804) 967-0198
Web Site: https://www.apexinsurance.com
Sales Range: Less than $1 Million
Emp.: 17
Insurance Underwriting & Brokerage Services
N.A.I.C.S.: 524210

Aquilla Insurance Brokers Limited (1)
7th Floor Corn Market Exchange 55 Mark Lane, London, EC3R 7NE, United Kingdom
Tel.: (44) 2039002950
Web Site: https://www.aquillainsurance.co.uk
Insurance Brokerage Services
N.A.I.C.S.: 524210

Archenfield Insurance Management Limited (1)
17 Church Street, Monmouth, NP25 3BX, Monmouthshire, United Kingdom
Tel.: (44) 1600719999
Web Site: https://archenfield.co.uk
Insurance Brokerage Services
N.A.I.C.S.: 524210

Arrowhead General Insurance Agency Holding Corp. (1)
701 B St Ste 2100, San Diego, CA 92101
Tel.: (619) 881-8600
Insurance Agencies & Brokerage Services
N.A.I.C.S.: 524210

Subsidiary (Domestic):

ARROWHEAD General Insurance Agency, Inc. (2)
701 B St Ste 2100, San Diego, CA 92101
Tel.: (619) 881-8600
Web Site: https://www.arrowheadgrp.com
Sales Range: $100-124.9 Million
Emp.: 300
Personal & Commercial Property & Casualty Insurance
N.A.I.C.S.: 524126
Mark Corey (Pres-Personal Property)
Joseph Shomphe (CTO)
Adam Nordost (CIO)
David Putz (Exec VP)
Tom Kussurelis (COO & Exec VP)
Steve Bouker (Exec VP)
Jimmy Saldana (Dir-Strategic Initiative)
Wendy Castelo (VP-Mktg Svcs)
Chip Craze (Pres-Personal Auto)
Matt Hetrick (VP-Corp Dev)
Becky Holt (Dir-Clear Risk Solutions & Bus Dev)
Adam Johnson (Pres-Automotive Aftermarket)
Angie Keus (VP-Residential Earthquake)
Becky Pinto (Pres-Workers Compensation)
Michael Powell (Pres-Bellingham Underwriters)
Niels Seebeck (Chief Underwriting Officer & Mgr-Arrowhead Risk)
Brian Turnbull (Officer-Underwriting & Pres-Clear & Arrowhead Programs)
Duane Williams (VP-Mktg)
Lew Defuria (Pres-Commercial-Earthquake)

Arrowhead Insurance Risk Managers, LLC (1)

3655 N Point Pkwy Ste 675, Alpharetta, GA 30005
Tel.: (678) 353-2400
Insurance Services
N.A.I.C.S.: 524210

Subsidiary (Domestic):

American Claims Management, Inc. (2)
701 B St Ste 2100, San Diego, CA 92101
Tel.: (760) 827-4800
Insurance Agencies & Brokerage Services
N.A.I.C.S.: 524210
Dhara Patel (Pres)
Viviane Ruiz (CIO)
Fred Tucker (Sr VP- &)
Kevin Pendergast (Sr VP- &)
Steven Bucey (Sr VP-Operations)
Cheryl Gulasa (VP)
Lorna Gillespie (VP-)

Arrowhead Wholesale Insurance Services, LLC (2)
5675 Ruffin Rd Ste 100, San Diego, CA 92123
Tel.: (619) 876-4118
Web Site: https://www.arrowheadwholesale.com
Sales Range: $125-149.9 Million
Emp.: 30
Insurance Agents, Brokers & Services
N.A.I.C.S.: 524126
Kevin Kilkenny (CEO)
Mike Kuhn (Pres)
Kathy Bleasdale (Asst VP-Property & Casualty & Workers Compensation)
Glenn Bautista (VP-Information Technology-Ops)
Robert Olson (Asst VP-Property & Casualty)
Julie Dorschel (Asst VP-Property & Casualty)
Edith Bond (Acct Mgr-Property & Casualty)
Ana Cardenas (Asst VP-Professional Liability)
Tiffany Blair (Acct Mgr-Property & Casualty)
Chris Hedrick (Acct Mgr)
Rachel Schneider (Controller)
Chris Hedrick (Acct Mgr)
Rachel Schneider (Controller)

Subsidiary (Domestic):

First Capital-AWIS LLC (3)
5675 Ruffin Rd Ste 100, San Diego, CA 92123
Tel.: (516) 466-1313
Web Site: https://www.fcawis.com
Sales Range: $25-49.9 Million
Emp.: 5
Insurance Services
N.A.I.C.S.: 524210
Kevin Kilkenny (CEO)
Rachel Schneider (Controller)
Glenn Bautista (VP-Information Technology)
Christine Wong (VP)

B & B Protector Plans, Inc. (1)
655 N Franklin St Ste 1800, Tampa, FL 33602
Tel.: (813) 222-4100
Web Site: http://www.bbprotectorplans.com
Insurance Agencies & Brokerage Services
N.A.I.C.S.: 524210

Subsidiary (Domestic):

Harold Diers & Co. (2)
11635 Arbor, Suite 230, Omaha, NE 68144
Tel.: (402) 391-1300
Web Site: http://www.hdiers.com
Insurance Agencies & Brokerages
N.A.I.C.S.: 524210

BDB (UK) Limited (1)
52-54 Leadenhall Street, London, EC3A 2BJ, United Kingdom
Tel.: (44) 2039066202
Insurance Brokerage Services
N.A.I.C.S.: 524210

BDB Limited (1)
52-54 Leadenhall Street, London, EC3A 2BJ, United Kingdom
Tel.: (44) 2039066200
Insurance & Reinsurance Services
N.A.I.C.S.: 524130

BHK Insurance Services Limited (1)

Suite 11 Hadleigh Business Centre 351 London Rd, Hadleigh, Benfleet, SS7 2BT, Essex, United Kingdom
Tel.: (44) 1702719016
Web Site: https://www.bhkinsurance.com
Business Insurance Services
N.A.I.C.S.: 524210

BIG Insurance Limited (1)
Athena House 612-616 Wimborne Road, Winton, Bournemouth, BH9 2EN, Dorset, United Kingdom
Tel.: (44) 1202512161
Web Site: https://www.big-insurance.co.uk
Business Insurance Services
N.A.I.C.S.: 524210

BPW Insurance Services Limited (1)
Cathedral Chambers 107 Stow Hill, Newport, NP20 4ED, United Kingdom
Tel.: (44) 1633213116
Web Site: https://www.bpw-insurance.co.uk
Insurance Brokerage Services
N.A.I.C.S.: 524210

Barpax Associates Limited (1)
1 St Marys Street, Worcester, WR1 1HA, United Kingdom
Tel.: (44) 190526400
Insurance Brokerage Services
N.A.I.C.S.: 524210

Bayliss & Cooke Limited (1)
St Johns House Weston Road, Stafford, ST16 3RZ, United Kingdom
Tel.: (44) 1785212424
Web Site: https://www.baylissandcooke.co.uk
Commercial Insurance Brokerage Services
N.A.I.C.S.: 524210

Beech Underwriting Agencies Limited (1)
Room 30 Maidstone Innovation Centre Gidds Pond Way, Maidstone, ME14 5FY, Kent, United Kingdom
Tel.: (44) 1622755218
Web Site: https://beechunderwriting.co.uk
Insurance Underwriting Services
N.A.I.C.S.: 524113

Beecher Carlson Holdings, Inc. (1)
6 Concourse Pkwy Ste 2300, Atlanta, GA 30328
Tel.: (404) 460-1400
Web Site: http://www.beechercarlson.com
Sales Range: $100-124.9 Million
Emp.: 200
Insurance Brokerage & Risk Management Consulting Services
N.A.I.C.S.: 524210
Marci Steiding (VP-Marketing-Communications)
Joe Siech (CEO)
Kimberly Jenis (CFO)
Berni Bussell (Exec Mng Dir-Healthcare)
Jason Flaxbeard (Exec Mng Dir)
John Kerns (Exec Mng Dir-Northeast)
Bob Lane (Mng Dir-Real Estate)
Jeffrey Lattmann (Exec Mng Dir-Exec Liability)
Erin Lynch (Pres-Energy)
Greg Myers (Exec Mng Dir-Mfg)
Mary T. Pipino (Pres-Real Estate & Exec VP)
Jay Sampson (Exec Mng Dir-Risk Optimization)
Cliff Simpson (Exec Mng Dir-Property)
Bill Daly (COO)
Andrew Golub (Mng Dir & Chief Analytics Officer)
Raven James (VP-Team Resources & Dir-Diversity & Inclusion)

Beecher Carlson Management, Ltd. (1)
Maxwell Roberts Building 7th Floor 1 Church Street, PO Box 2461, Hamilton, HM 11, Bermuda
Tel.: (441) 4412950519
Web Site: http://www.beechercarlson.com
Emp.: 12
Insurance Service Provider
N.A.I.C.S.: 524210

Bellingham Underwriters, Inc. (1)
1417 N State St, Bellingham, WA 98225
Tel.: (360) 671-0500
Web Site: https://www.bell-uw.com

Sales Range: $1-9.9 Million
Emp.: 21
Insurance Underwriting Services
N.A.I.C.S.: 524298
Kenneth A. Robinette (Principal)

Berkeley Insurance Group Limited (1)
78 Pall Mall, London, SW1Y 5ES, United Kingdom
Tel.: (44) 2031707333
Insurance Brokerage Services
N.A.I.C.S.: 524210

Berkeley Insurance Group UK Limited (1)
2 Colton Square, Leicester, LE1 1QH, United Kingdom
Web Site: https://www.berkeleyinsurancegroup.co.uk
Insurance Brokerage Services
N.A.I.C.S.: 524210

Braishfield Associates, Inc. (1)
5750 Major Blvd Ste 200, Orlando, FL 32819
Tel.: (407) 825-9911
Web Site: http://www.braishfield.com
Sales Range: $50-74.9 Million
Emp.: 58
Insurance Program Management Services
N.A.I.C.S.: 524292
Donna Mooney (Controller)
John Barfield (Exec VP)
Philip Cooper (VP)
Jeanette Lumbert (Supvr-Acctg)
Elizabeth Mekchand (Acct Mgr)
Maribel Ayala (Acct Mgr)
Omar Martinez (Acct Mgr)
Yun Duong (Acct Mgr)
Felicia Berry (Acct Mgr)
Kassandra Colon (Acct Mgr)
Alyssa Lewis (Acct Mgr)
Diana Watson (Acct Mgr)
Ken Rambo (Acct Mgr)
Melinda Vargas (Acct Mgr)
Shelby-rebecca Warren (Acct Mgr)
Robert Mason (Asst VP)
Cynthia Davis (Acct Mgr)
Cristina Meza (Acct Mgr)
Gianna Gaither (Acct Mgr)
Betty Lau Tang (Acct Mgr)
James Shannon (Acct Mgr)
Rachel Moore (Acct Mgr)
Cristhian Labra (Acct Mgr)
Francis X. McCahill III (Founder)

Bright & Associates, Inc. (1)
10 The Pines Ct, Saint Louis, MO 63141
Tel.: (314) 878-6778
Web Site: http://www.brightassoc.com
Sales Range: $1-9.9 Million
Emp.: 14
Insurance Agents, Brokers, And Service, N
N.A.I.C.S.: 524210
James Bright (Pres)

Brown & Brown (Europe) Limited (1)
7th Floor 55 Mark Lane,, London, EC3R 7NE, United Kingdom
Tel.: (44) 2038136900
Insurance Agencies
N.A.I.C.S.: 524210

Subsidiary (Domestic):

BBPS Limited (2)
7th Floor Corn Exchange 55 Mark Lane, London, EC3R 7NE, United Kingdom
Tel.: (44) 3301756455
Web Site: https://www.hedronnetwork.co.uk
Reinsurance Services
N.A.I.C.S.: 524130

The Purple Partnership Limited (2)
7th Floor Corn Exchange, 55 Mark Lane,, London, EC3R 7NE, United Kingdom
Tel.: (44) 1173171853
Insurance Agency & Brokerage Services
N.A.I.C.S.: 524210

Brown & Brown Absence Services Group, LLC (1)
701 Edgewater Dr Ste 150, Wakefield, MA 01880
Tel.: (781) 246-8975
Web Site: http://www.bbabsence.com
Insurance Agencies & Brokerage Services
N.A.I.C.S.: 524210

Mike Shunney (CEO)

Subsidiary (Domestic):

Medval, LLC (2)
9256 Bendix Rd Ste 304, Columbia, MD 21045
Tel.: (410) 740-3084
Web Site: http://www.medval.com
Insurance Services
N.A.I.C.S.: 541611
Jon Gunter (Pres)
Jessica Wingenroth (VP-Ops)
Jennifer Alvarez (Dir-Risk Assessment & Compliance Programs)
Laura Johnson (Dir-HR)
Charlotte Chovanec (Dir-Clinical)
Julie Woloszyn-Pratts (Natl Dir-Accounts & Bus Dev)

Professional Disability Associates, PA (2)
Monument Sq, Portland, ME 04101
Web Site: http://www.professionaldisabilityassociates.com
Disability Services Company: Specialty Risk Resources Provider including Medical, Vocational & Claim Management Services
N.A.I.C.S.: 541618
Kevin Riley (Sr VP)
George Falcon (VP-Client Svcs)
Michael Cleveland (Pres)
Courtney Scott (Sr VP-Business Development-Marketing)
Sean Sullivan (Sr VP-Operations)
Megan Reid (VP-)
Melissa Prudente (Dir-Administrative Services)

Brown & Brown Agency of Insurance Professionals, Inc. (1)
208 N Mill, Pryor, OK 74361
Tel.: (918) 825-3295
Web Site: http://www.bb-ok.com
Sales Range: $1-9.9 Million
Emp.: 30
Insurance Services
N.A.I.C.S.: 524210
Bill Evans (Exec VP)

Brown & Brown Benefit Advisors, Inc. (1)
56 Livingston Ave Ste 220, Roseland, NJ 07068
Tel.: (973) 549-1900
Web Site: https://www.advisorsbb.com
Sales Range: $25-49.9 Million
Emp.: 38
Employee Benefit Administration Services
N.A.I.C.S.: 524292

Brown & Brown Disaster Relief Foundation, Inc. (1)
300 N Beach St, Daytona Beach, FL 32174
Tel.: (386) 239-5786
Web Site: https://www.bbdisasterrelief.org
Insurance Agencies & Brokerage Services
N.A.I.C.S.: 524210

Brown & Brown Insurance Agency of Virginia, Inc. (1)
11220 Asset Loop Ste 304, Manasas, VA 20109
Tel.: (703) 361-3191
Web Site: http://www.bbdcmetro.com
Sales Range: $10-24.9 Million
Emp.: 20
Insurance Services
N.A.I.C.S.: 524210

Subsidiary (Domestic):

Lambert, Riddle, Schimmel & Company, LLLP (2)
3931 University Dr, Fairfax, VA 22030
Tel.: (703) 691-1300
Insurance Agents
N.A.I.C.S.: 524210

Brown & Brown Insurance Brokers of Sacramento, Inc. (1)
5750 W Oaks Blvd Ste 140, Rocklin, CA 95765
Tel.: (916) 630-8643
Web Site: http://www.bbsacramento.com
Emp.: 50
Insurance Agencies & Brokerage Services
N.A.I.C.S.: 524210

Brown & Brown, Inc.—(Continued)

Brown & Brown Insurance Services of California, Inc. (1)
504 Redwood Blvd Ste 330, Novato, CA 94947
Tel.: (510) 452-0458
Web Site: http://www.bbnca.com
Insurance Agencies & Brokerage Services
N.A.I.C.S.: 524210

Brown & Brown Insurance Services of Texas, Inc. (1)
1717 N Sam Houston Pkwy Ste 115, Houston, TX 77038
Tel.: (281) 260-2000
Web Site: http://www.bbtexas.com
Sales Range: $1-9.9 Million
Emp.: 37
Insurance Agents
N.A.I.C.S.: 524210
Ryan Beavers *(Exec VP)*

Subsidiary (Domestic):

Brown & Brown Insurance Services of San Antonio, Inc. (2)
100 NE Loop 410 Ste 650, San Antonio, TX 78216-4713
Tel.: (201) 340-8985
Web Site: http://www.apexinsurance.com
Insurance Services
N.A.I.C.S.: 524210

Brown & Brown Insurance of Arizona, Inc. (1)
2800 N Central Ave Ste 1100, Phoenix, AZ 85004 (100%)
Tel.: (602) 277-6672
Web Site: http://www.bbphoenix.com
Sales Range: $10-24.9 Million
Emp.: 120
Insurance
N.A.I.C.S.: 524210

Branch (Domestic):

Brown & Brown Insurance of Arizona, Inc. - Prescott (2)
1055 Iron Springs Rd, Prescott, AZ 86305
Tel.: (928) 445-3540
Web Site: http://www.bbprescott.com
Sales Range: $1-9.9 Million
Emp.: 12
Insurance Agency; Health, Life, Casualty, Property & Surety Insurance
N.A.I.C.S.: 524298

Brown & Brown Insurance of Georgia, Inc. (1)
900 N Point Pkwy Ste 300, Alpharetta, GA 30005
Tel.: (770) 512-5001
Web Site: http://www.bbatlanta.com
Sales Range: $1-9.9 Million
Emp.: 39
Insurance Agents
N.A.I.C.S.: 524210

Brown & Brown Insurance of Nevada, Inc. (1)
975 Kelly Johnson Dr Ste 100, Las Vegas, NV 89119
Tel.: (702) 457-2268
Web Site: http://www.bbnevada.com
Sales Range: $1-9.9 Million
Emp.: 20
Insurance Brokerage & Consultancy Services
N.A.I.C.S.: 524210

Brown & Brown Lone Star Insurance Services, Inc. (1)
8000 Center Park Dr Ste 370, Austin, TX 78754
Tel.: (512) 343-0000
Web Site: https://www.bbtexas.com
Insurance Agencies & Brokerage Services
N.A.I.C.S.: 524210

Subsidiary (Domestic):

Verhagen Glendenning & Walker LLP (2)
192 S Main, Van Alstyne, TX 75495
Tel.: (972) 727-8949
Web Site: http://www.insurewithwalker.com
Insurance Related Activities
N.A.I.C.S.: 524298

Brown & Brown Metro, Inc. (1)
56 Livingston Ave 2nd Fl, Roseland, NJ 07068
Tel.: (973) 549-1900
Web Site: http://www.bbmetro.com
Sales Range: $75-99.9 Million
Emp.: 150
Insurance Agency & Insurance Services
N.A.I.C.S.: 524210

Branch (Domestic):

Brown & Brown Metro, Inc. - Mount Laurel (2)
1000 Bishops Gate Blvd Ste 100, Mount Laurel, NJ 08054
Tel.: (856) 552-6330
Web Site: http://www.bbinsurance.com
Insurance Agencies & Brokerage Services
N.A.I.C.S.: 524210

Brown & Brown Pacific Insurance Services, Inc. (1)
700 Bishop St Ste 1400, Honolulu, HI 96813-4116
Tel.: (808) 540-3333
Web Site: http://www.bbpacific.com
Emp.: 51
General Insurance Agency
N.A.I.C.S.: 524210
Malcolm Tajiri *(Pres-Employee Benefits Div)*
Dean Hirahara *(Pres-Property & Casualty Div)*

Brown & Brown of Arkansas, Inc. (1)
2120 Riverfront Dr Ste 200, Little Rock, AR 72202-2063
Tel.: (501) 372-2232
Web Site: https://www.bbarkansas.com
Sales Range: $1-9.9 Million
Emp.: 15
Insurance Services
N.A.I.C.S.: 524210

Brown & Brown of Bartlesville, Inc. (1)
501 SE Frank Phillips Blvd, Bartlesville, OK 74005
Tel.: (800) 456-8123
Holding Company; Insurance Agencies & Brokerage Services
N.A.I.C.S.: 551112

Subsidiary (Domestic):

Graham-Rogers, Inc. (2)
501 SE Frank Phillips Blvd Ste 300, Bartlesville, OK 74003
Tel.: (918) 336-2800
Web Site: https://www.graham-rogers.com
Sales Range: $1-9.9 Million
Emp.: 50
Insurance Whslr
N.A.I.C.S.: 524210
Adam Hibdon *(VP)*
Rika May *(Coord-Marketing)*

Brown & Brown of Central Michigan, Inc. (1)
1605 Concentric Blvd 1, Saginaw, MI 48604
Tel.: (989) 249-5960
Insurance Agencies & Brokerage Services
N.A.I.C.S.: 524210
Angela Garner *(Exec VP)*

Brown & Brown of Central Oklahoma, Inc. (1)
13901 Technology Dr, Oklahoma City, OK 73134
Tel.: (405) 607-6314
Web Site: http://www.bb-ok.com
Sales Range: Less than $1 Million
Emp.: 20
Insurance Services
N.A.I.C.S.: 524210

Brown & Brown of Colorado, Inc. (1)
101 N Cascade Ave Ste 410, Colorado Springs, CO 80903
Tel.: (719) 471-0262
Web Site: http://www.bbcolorado.com
Sales Range: Less than $1 Million
Emp.: 5
Insurance Services
N.A.I.C.S.: 524210
Karen E. Siwek *(VP)*
Heather Barbera *(Acct Exec-Employee Benefits)*
Matthew Laine *(Acct Exec-Comml Insurance)*

Tyler B. Allen *(Dir-Claims)*
Jody Harris *(Acct Mgr-Comml Lines)*
Patrick O'Farrell *(Exec VP)*
Danaka Freyling *(Acct Mgr-Comml Lines)*
Mari Ellen Addington *(Acct Mgr-Comml Lines)*
Kerri Carpenter *(Acct Mgr-Personal Lines)*

Brown & Brown of Connecticut, Inc. (1)
55 Capital Blvd Ste 102, Rocky Hill, CT 06067
Tel.: (860) 667-9000
Web Site: https://www.bbconnecticut.com
Sales Range: $1-9.9 Million
Emp.: 100
Insurance Services
N.A.I.C.S.: 524210
Paul Cutler *(VP-Sales)*
Jennifer Miller *(VP-Marketing)*

Brown & Brown of Delaware, Inc. (1)
750 Prides Crossing Ste 301, Newark, DE 19713
Insurance Agencies & Brokerage Services
N.A.I.C.S.: 524210

Brown & Brown of Detroit, Inc. (1)
35735 Mound Rd, Sterling Heights, MI 48310
Tel.: (586) 977-6300
Web Site: https://www.bbdetroit.com
Insurance Agencies & Brokerage Services
N.A.I.C.S.: 524210

Brown & Brown of Florida, Inc. (1)
300 N Beach St, Daytona Beach, FL 32114
Tel.: (386) 252-6176
Web Site: http://www.bbinsurance.com
Sales Range: $75-99.9 Million
Emp.: 200
Insurance Agencies & Underwriting Services
N.A.I.C.S.: 524210

Unit (Domestic):

Brown & Brown Insurance (2)
1421 Pine Ridge Rd Ste 200 & 228, Naples, FL 34109
Tel.: (239) 261-3000
Web Site: http://www.bbswfla.com
Emp.: 35
Insurance Provider
N.A.I.C.S.: 524210

Branch (Domestic):

Brown & Brown of Florida, Inc. - Brevard (2)
100 Rialto Pl Ste 900, Melbourne, FL 32901
Tel.: (321) 757-8686
Web Site: http://www.bbinsurance.com
Sales Range: $1-9.9 Million
Emp.: 28
Insurance Agents
N.A.I.C.S.: 524210
Paul Corbley *(Exec VP)*

Brown & Brown of Florida, Inc. - Brooksville (2)
273 N Broad St, Brooksville, FL 34601-2907
Tel.: (352) 796-8200
Web Site: http://www.bbinsurance.com
Rev.: $1,300,000
Emp.: 9
Insurance Agents
N.A.I.C.S.: 524210

Brown & Brown of Florida, Inc. - Ft. Lauderdale (2)
1201 W Cypress Creek Rd Ste 130, Fort Lauderdale, FL 33309
Tel.: (954) 776-2222
Web Site: http://www.brownandbrownmarine.com
Sales Range: $25-49.9 Million
Emp.: 125
Insurance Agents
N.A.I.C.S.: 524210
Michael L. Keeby *(Pres-Retail Div & Sr VP)*

Brown & Brown of Florida, Inc. - Ft. Myers (2)
6611 Orion Dr Ste 200, Fort Myers, FL 33912
Tel.: (239) 278-0278
Web Site: http://www.bbinsurance.com

Sales Range: $1-9.9 Million
Emp.: 36
Insurance Agents
N.A.I.C.S.: 524210

Brown & Brown of Florida, Inc. - Jacksonville (2)
10151 Deerwood Park Blvd Bldg 100 Ste 100, Jacksonville, FL 32256
Tel.: (904) 565-1952
Web Site: http://www.bbjax.com
Insurance Agents
N.A.I.C.S.: 524210

Brown & Brown of Florida, Inc. - Leesburg (2)
1300 Citizens Blvd 100, Leesburg, FL 34748-6309
Tel.: (352) 787-2431
Web Site: http://www.bbleesburg.com
Rev.: $4,000,000
Emp.: 28
Insurance Agents
N.A.I.C.S.: 524210

Brown & Brown of Florida, Inc. - Miami (2)
14900 NW 79th Ct Ste 200, Miami Lakes, FL 33016
Tel.: (305) 714-4400
Web Site: http://www.bbmia.com
Insurance Agents
N.A.I.C.S.: 524210
Broderick Ureel *(Sr VP)*
Darlene Merino *(VP)*
Dolly Cardona *(VP)*
Anya Penate *(VP)*
Markey Almarales *(VP)*
Elsie Martin *(VP)*
Eric Woodling *(VP)*
Fausto Alvarez Jr. *(Exec VP)*

Brown & Brown of Florida, Inc. - Monticello (2)
1020 W Washington St, Monticello, FL 32344
Tel.: (850) 997-2533
Web Site: http://www.bbinsurance.com
Sales Range: $1-9.9 Million
Emp.: 10
Insurance Agents
N.A.I.C.S.: 524210

Brown & Brown of Florida, Inc. - Naples (2)
1421 Pine Ridge Rd Ste 200 228, Naples, FL 34109
Tel.: (239) 261-3000
Web Site: http://www.bbinsurance.com
Insurance Agents
N.A.I.C.S.: 524210
Tom Ellis *(Sr VP)*

Brown & Brown of Florida, Inc. - Orlando (2)
2290 Lucien Way Ste 400, Maitland, FL 32751
Tel.: (407) 660-8282
Web Site: http://www.bborlando.com
Sales Range: $1-9.9 Million
Emp.: 80
Insurance Agents
N.A.I.C.S.: 524210

Brown & Brown of Florida, Inc. - Sarasota (2)
240 S Pineapple Ave Ste 301, Sarasota, FL 34236
Tel.: (941) 893-2200
Web Site: http://www.bbinsurance.com
Sales Range: $1-9.9 Million
Emp.: 32
Insurance Agents
N.A.I.C.S.: 524210

Brown & Brown of Florida, Inc. - Tampa (2)
655 N Franklin St 1900, Tampa, FL 33602
Tel.: (813) 226-1300
Web Site: http://www.bbtampa.com
Sales Range: $50-74.9 Million
Emp.: 180
Insurance Agents
N.A.I.C.S.: 524210

Brown & Brown of Florida, Inc. - West Palm Beach (2)
1661 Worthington Rd Ste 175, West Palm Beach, FL 33409

Tel.: (561) 688-5046
Web Site: http://bb-wpb.com
Sales Range: $1-9.9 Million
Emp.: 33
Insurance Agents
N.A.I.C.S.: 524210

Brown & Brown of Garden City, Inc. (1)
595 Stewart Ave, Garden City, NY 11530
Tel.: (516) 745-1111
Web Site: https://www.bbinsgc.com
Emp.: 70
Insurance Agencies & Brokerage Services
N.A.I.C.S.: 524210
Alan Labadorf *(Mng Dir)*
Gigi Cabasso *(Sr VP)*

Brown & Brown of Illinois, Inc. (1)
263 Shuman Blvd Ste 110, Naperville, IL 60563
Tel.: (630) 245-4646
Web Site: http://www.bbofillinois.com
Emp.: 10
Insurance Agencies & Brokerage Services
N.A.I.C.S.: 524210

Brown & Brown of Indiana, Inc. (1)
11595 N Meridian St Ste 250, Carmel, IN 46032 **(100%)**
Tel.: (317) 574-5000
Web Site:
    http://www.brownandbrownindiana.com
Sales Range: $1-9.9 Million
Emp.: 20
Commercial & Personal Insurance
N.A.I.C.S.: 524210

Brown & Brown of Kentucky, Inc. (1)
13101 Magisterial Dr Ste 200, Louisville, KY 40223
Tel.: (502) 241-7072
Web Site: https://www.bbkentucky.com
Insurance Agencies & Brokerage Services
N.A.I.C.S.: 524210

Subsidiary (Domestic):

Dealer Associates, Inc. (2)
2425 W Pioneer Pkwy Ste 100, Arlington, TX 76013-6044
Tel.: (817) 299-8338
Web Site: http://www.dealerassociates.com
Sales Range: $1-9.9 Million
Finance & Insurance Consulting Services
N.A.I.C.S.: 541618
Tony Fincannon *(Pres)*

United Development Systems, Inc. (2)
17755 US Hwy 19 N Ste 100, Clearwater, FL 33764
Tel.: (727) 507-8200
Web Site: http://www.udsdealerservices.com
Administrative Management & General Management Consulting Service
N.A.I.C.S.: 541611

Brown & Brown of Lehigh Valley, Inc. (1)
3001 Emrick Blvd Ste 120, Bethlehem, PA 18020
Tel.: (610) 974-9490
Web Site: http://www.bbinslv.com
Sales Range: $1-9.9 Million
Emp.: 24
Insurance Agency; Health, Life, Casualty, Property & Surety Insurance
N.A.I.C.S.: 524210

Brown & Brown of Louisiana, Inc. (1)
102 Asma Blvd Ste 300, Lafayette, LA 70508
Tel.: (337) 234-5111
Web Site: http://www.bbgulfstates.com
Sales Range: $1-9.9 Million
Emp.: 32
Insurance Services
N.A.I.C.S.: 524210

Brown & Brown of Massachusetts, LLC (1)
333 Elm St 3rd Fl, Dedham, MA 02026
Tel.: (781) 455-6664
Web Site: http://www.bbdedham.com
Insurance Agencies & Brokerage Services
N.A.I.C.S.: 524210
Mike Ross *(Pres)*
Kathi Ferragamo *(Mgr)*
Sandy McQuade *(Sr VP)*
Daniel M. Fiscus *(Mgr)*

Subsidiary (Domestic):

Amity Insurance Agency, Inc. (2)
500 Victory Rd Marina Bay, North Quincy, MA 02171
Tel.: (617) 471-1220
Web Site: http://www.amityins.com
Rev.: $4,100,000
Emp.: 36
Insurance Agencies & Brokerages
N.A.I.C.S.: 524210
Jonathan Lanza *(Sec, VP & Dir-Risk Mgmt)*
Bob Abraham *(Acct Mgr-Comml)*
Kathy Duchaney *(Acct Mgr)*
Frank Griffin *(Acct Mgr)*
Paul Shanley *(Dir-Professional Liability)*
Matt Fager *(VP-Legal Professional Liability Div)*

Claim Technologies Inc. (2)
100 Court Ave Ste 306, Des Moines, IA 50309
Tel.: (515) 244-7322
Web Site: http://www.claimtechnologies.com
Rev.: $2,000,000
Emp.: 20
Other Management Consulting Services
N.A.I.C.S.: 541618
Patricia Gagne *(VP)*
Daniel Montgomery *(VP)*
Rob Rater *(VP)*

Poole Professional Ltd. (2)
107 Audubon Rd Ste 305, Wakefield, MA 01880-6230
Tel.: (781) 245-5400
Web Site: http://www.poolepl.com
Insurance Services
N.A.I.C.S.: 524210
Christopher Poole *(Principal)*
Tom Mullard *(Principal)*
Mary-Beth Rumble *(Principal)*

Rodman Insurance Agency, Inc. (2)
980 Washington St. Ste 325 N, Dedham, MA 02026
Tel.: (781) 247-7800
Web Site: http://www.rodmanins.com
Insurance Services
N.A.I.C.S.: 524210
James Stoller *(VP)*
Jeffrey Grosser *(VP)*
Evan Tobasky *(VP)*
James Rodman *(VP)*
Andrew Altman *(Pres)*
Becky Deperry *(Mgr-Mktg)*

Brown & Brown of Michigan, Inc. (1)
1150 Torrey Rd, Fenton, MI 48430
Tel.: (810) 629-1566
Web Site: http://www.bbmich.com
Insurance Agencies & Brokerage Services
N.A.I.C.S.: 524210

Subsidiary (Domestic):

Buiten & Associates, LLC (2)
5738 Foremost Dr SE, Grand Rapids, MI 49546
Tel.: (616) 949-0490
Web Site: http://www.buiteninsurance.com
Sales Range: $1-9.9 Million
Emp.: 32
Insurance Agencies & Brokerages
N.A.I.C.S.: 524210
Jon Lunderberg *(Partner)*
Amy Devries *(Acct Mgr-Benefits)*
Kori Ammon *(Acct Mgr-Benefits)*
Sarah Anderson *(Acct Mgr-Bus Insurance)*
Char Blondin *(Acct Mgr-Bus Insurance)*
Paul S. Buiten *(Partner-Bonds & Bus Insurance)*
Kevin Cumings *(Partner-Benefits & VP-Grp Benefits)*
Brenda Chase *(Acct Mgr-Bus Insurance)*
Lisa B. Deboer *(Acct Mgr-Benefits)*
Lori Fisher *(Acct Mgr-Bonds & Bus Insurance)*
Rod W. Hathaway *(Partner-Benefits & Bus Insurance)*
Ally Flinski *(Acct Mgr-Benefits)*
Ruth Hume *(Acct Mgr-Personal Insurance)*
Kimberly Humphrey *(Acct Mgr-Personal Insurance)*
Benjamin J. Knoester *(Partner-Bus Insurance)*
Laura S. Jensen *(Acct Mgr-Bus Insurance)*
Shelley Lehmann *(Acct Mgr-Personal Insurance)*
Darryl Mulder *(Partner-Bus Insurance)*

V. Jean Nolf *(Acct Mgr-Bonds, Bus Insurance & Personal Insurance)*
Laura J. Northouse *(Acct Mgr-Bonds)*
Linda Paulsen *(Acct Mgr-Bus Insurance)*
Darcy Plummer *(Acct Mgr-Personal Insurance)*
Ana Potroanchenu *(Acct Mgr-Bus Insurance)*
Ryan T. Pylman *(Partner-Benefits)*
Daniel B. Rink *(Partner-Bus Insurance)*

Brown & Brown of Minnesota, Inc. (1)
1120 S Ave, Mankato, MN 56003
Tel.: (507) 388-2010
Web Site: https://www.brownmn.com
Sales Range: Less than $1 Million
Emp.: 10
Insurance Services
N.A.I.C.S.: 524210

Branch (Domestic):

Brown & Brown of Minnesota, Inc. - Retail Division (2)
7301 Ohms Ln Ste 210, Minneapolis, MN 55439
Tel.: (952) 698-4432
Insurance Agencies & Brokerage Services
N.A.I.C.S.: 524210
Tim Schwartz *(Gen Mgr)*

Brown & Brown of Mississippi, LLC (1)
1105 30th Ave Ste 300, Gulfport, MS 39501
Tel.: (228) 864-1550
Web Site: https://www.bbgulfstates.com
Insurance Service Provider
N.A.I.C.S.: 524210

Brown & Brown of Missouri, Inc. (1)
9666 Olive Blvd Ste 200, Saint Louis, MO 63132-3012
Tel.: (314) 692-0300
Web Site: http://www.pipinsure.com
Sales Range: Less than $1 Million
Emp.: 13
Insurance Services
N.A.I.C.S.: 524210

Brown & Brown of New Jersey, LLC (1)
1314 S Shore Rd, Marmora, NJ 08223
Tel.: (609) 390-3360
Web Site: http://www.bbinj.com
Insurance Agency; Health, Life, Casualty, Property & Surety Insurance
N.A.I.C.S.: 524298

Brown & Brown of New Mexico, Inc. (1)
627 Paseo Del Pueblo Sur, Taos, NM 87571 **(100%)**
Tel.: (575) 758-2244
Sales Range: Less than $1 Million
Emp.: 13
Insurance
N.A.I.C.S.: 524210

Branch (Domestic):

Brown & Brown of New Mexico, Inc. - Albuquerque (2)
8100 Lang Ave NE Ste 101, Albuquerque, NM 87109
Tel.: (505) 821-5888
Web Site: http://www.bbnm.com
Sales Range: Less than $1 Million
Emp.: 80
Insurance Agents
N.A.I.C.S.: 524210

Brown & Brown of New York, Inc. (1)
45 E Ave, Rochester, NY 14604
Tel.: (585) 232-2424
Web Site: https://www.bbnyinsurance.com
Sales Range: $25-49.9 Million
Emp.: 540
Insurance Agents, Brokers & Service
N.A.I.C.S.: 524210

Branch (Domestic):

Brown & Brown of New York, Inc. - Syracuse (2)
500 Plum St 200, Syracuse, NY 13204-1480
Tel.: (315) 474-3374
Web Site: http://www.bbempirestate.com

Sales Range: $10-24.9 Million
Emp.: 92
Insurance Agents
N.A.I.C.S.: 524210
Nicholas J. Dereszynski *(Pres)*

Subsidiary (Domestic):

The Rollins Agency, Inc. (2)
800 Westchester Ave Ste N311, Rye Brook, NY 10573
Tel.: (914) 337-1833
Web Site: http://www.rollinsinsurance.com
Sales Range: $50-74.9 Million
Emp.: 30
Insurance Agents
N.A.I.C.S.: 524210

Brown & Brown of Northern California, Inc. (1)
504 Redwood Blvd, Novato, CA 94947
Tel.: (510) 452-0458
Web Site: http://www.bbnca.com
Sales Range: $1-9.9 Million
Emp.: 10
Provider of Insurance Services
N.A.I.C.S.: 524210

Subsidiary (Domestic):

Sitzmann, Morris & Lavis Insurance Agency, Inc. (2)
3697 Mt Diablo Blvd Ste 100, Lafayette, CA 94549
Tel.: (510) 452-0458
Web Site: http://www.smlinc.com
Insurance Agencies & Brokerages
N.A.I.C.S.: 524210
Gary R. Sitzmann *(Co-Founder)*
Daphne A. Boyle *(Co-Founder & Owner)*
Donald E. Morris Jr. *(Partner)*

Brown & Brown of Northern Illinois, Inc. (1)
220 N Larkin Ave, Joliet, IL 60435-6648
Tel.: (815) 729-4650
Web Site: http://www.bbinsurance.com
Sales Range: Less than $1 Million
Emp.: 10
Insurance Brokerage Services Specializing in Employee Benefits
N.A.I.C.S.: 524210

Brown & Brown of Ohio, Inc. (1)
360 3 Meadows Dr, Perrysburg, OH 43551-3138 **(100%)**
Tel.: (419) 874-1974
Web Site: http://www.bbtoledo.com
Sales Range: $25-49.9 Million
Emp.: 20
N.A.I.C.S.: 524298

Brown & Brown of Oklahoma, Inc. (1)
13901 Technology Dr Ste AB, Oklahoma City, OK 73134
Tel.: (405) 607-6314
Web Site: http://www.bb-ok.com
Insurance Services
N.A.I.C.S.: 524210
Joe Stanton *(CFO-Retail)*
Ignus Bezuidenhout *(CIO-Retail)*

Brown & Brown of Oregon, LLC (1)
601 SW 2nd Ave Ste 1200, Portland, OR 97204
Tel.: (503) 274-6511
Web Site: https://www.bbnw.com
Emp.: 100
Insurance Service Provider
N.A.I.C.S.: 524210

Brown & Brown of Pennsylvania, Inc. (1)
125 E Elm St Ste 210, Conshohocken, PA 19428
Tel.: (215) 829-1776
Web Site: https://www.bbofpa.com
Emp.: 85
Insurance Agencies & Brokerage Services
N.A.I.C.S.: 524210

Brown & Brown of South Carolina, Inc. (1)
10 Falcon Crest Dr Ste 100, Greenville, SC 29607 **(100%)**
Tel.: (864) 234-8889
Web Site: https://www.cbbins.com
Sales Range: Less than $1 Million
Emp.: 15

Brown & Brown, Inc.—(Continued)

Provider of Property & Casualty Insurance Services
N.A.I.C.S.: 524210

Brown & Brown of Southwest Indiana, Inc. (1)
8788 Ruffian Ln, Newburgh, IN 47630
Tel.: (812) 858-3544
Insurance Agencies & Brokerage Services
N.A.I.C.S.: 524210

Brown & Brown of Tennessee, Inc. (1)
6 Cadillac Dr Ste 200, Brentwood, TN 37027
Tel.: (615) 277-9840
Web Site: http://www.bbtennessee.com
Emp.: 70
Insurance Agents
N.A.I.C.S.: 524210
Ryan P. Rothrock (Exec VP)
Courtney Nelson (VP)
Donna Thompson (Mgr-Select Benefits Dept)
Cara Arnold (Mgr-Svc)
David Massey (Sr VP-Employee Benefits)
Al Phillips (Sr VP)
Paul Roussel (VP-Employee Benefits)
Randall Ritter (Sr VP)
Kevin Mathis (VP-Employee Benefits)
Bob McClintock (Sr VP)
Sam Cook III (Sr VP)

Subsidiary (Domestic):

Frank E. Neal & Co., Inc. (2)
2223 8th Ave S, Nashville, TN 37204-2205
Tel.: (615) 383-8874
Web Site: http://www.feneal.com
Sales Range: $1-9.9 Million
Emp.: 23
Insurance Brokerage Services
N.A.I.C.S.: 524210

Brown & Brown of Washington, Inc. (1)
2106 Pacific Ave Ste 501, Tacoma, WA 98402-3530
Tel.: (253) 396-5500
Web Site: https://www.bbtacoma.com
Sales Range: $1-9.9 Million
Emp.: 43
Insurance Services
N.A.I.C.S.: 524210

Branch (Domestic):

Brown & Brown of Washington, Inc. - Lynden-SSK (2)
501 Frnt St, Lynden, WA 98264
Tel.: (360) 354-4488
Web Site: http://www.sskinsurance.com
Sales Range: $1-9.9 Million
Emp.: 25
Insurance Agencies & Brokerages
N.A.I.C.S.: 524210

Brown & Brown of Washington, Inc. - Seattle (2)
Columbia Ctr 701 5th Ave Ste 550, Seattle, WA 98104
Tel.: (206) 956-1600
Web Site: http://www.bnbseattle.com
Sales Range: $1-9.9 Million
Emp.: 20
Insurance Brokerage Services
N.A.I.C.S.: 524210
Alex Bogaard (Pres)

Brown & Brown of Wisconsin, Inc. (1)
1062 Oak Forest Dr 120, Onalaska, WI 54650
Tel.: (608) 784-7676
Sales Range: Less than $1 Million
Emp.: 16
Insurance Services
N.A.I.C.S.: 524210

Brown & Brown, Inc. - Tampa Corporate Office (1)
655 N Franklin St Ste 1900, Tampa, FL 33602
Tel.: (813) 226-1300
Web Site: http://www.bbtampa.com
Sales Range: $50-74.9 Million
Emp.: 170

Marketing of Malpractice & Surety Insurance
N.A.I.C.S.: 561110

Subsidiary (Domestic):

Smith Insurance Associates, Inc. (2)
1120 Bethlehem Pike, Spring House, PA 19477
Tel.: (215) 542-5959
Web Site: https://www.smithinsurance.com
Insurance Agencies & Brokerages
N.A.I.C.S.: 524210
Stephen R. Smith Sr. (Founder)

Brownlee Agency, Inc. (1)
PO Box 710, Tifton, GA 31793
Tel.: (229) 382-3396
Web Site: http://www.brownleeagency.com
Insurance Agencies & Brokerages
N.A.I.C.S.: 524210
Dara Sutton (Mgr-Comml Lines)

CKP Insurance, LLC (1)
21845 Powerline Rd Ste 205, Boca Raton, FL 33433
Tel.: (561) 807-0900
Web Site: http://www.ckpinsurance.com
Insurance Related Activities
N.A.I.C.S.: 524298
Jennifer Kohnken (Dir-HR & Ops)

Capstone Insurance Brokers Limited (1)
Unit 601-604 6th Floor 41 Heung Yip Road, Wong Chuk Hang, Hong Kong, China (Hong Kong)
Tel.: (852) 36118375
Web Site: https://www.capstonebrokers.asia
Insurance Brokerage Services
N.A.I.C.S.: 524210

Castle Insurance Services (North East) Limited (1)
15 Marshall Terrace, Gilesgate, Durham, DH1 2HX, United Kingdom
Tel.: (44) 1913830401
Web Site: https://www.castleinsuranceservices.co.uk
Property Insurance Services
N.A.I.C.S.: 524126

Cavendish Munro Professional Risks Limited (1)
International House 1 St Katherines Way, London, E1W 1UN, United Kingdom
Tel.: (44) 2072640545
Web Site: https://www.cavendishmunro.com
Insurance Brokerage Services
N.A.I.C.S.: 524210

Christopher Trigg Limited (1)
1 Norfolk Court Norfolk Road, Rickmansworth, WD3 1LA, Hertfordshire, United Kingdom
Tel.: (44) 1923712434
Web Site: https://www.christophertrigg.co.uk
Business & Property Insurance Services
N.A.I.C.S.: 524126

Claims Management Of Missouri, LLC (1)
15450 S Outer 40 Rd Ste 200, Chesterfield, MO 63017
Tel.: (636) 537-1360
Web Site: https://mmm-a.com
Emp.: 15,000
Insurance Claims Management Services
N.A.I.C.S.: 524292

Combined Group Insurance Services, Inc. (1)
14785 Preston Rd Ste 350, Dallas, TX 75254
Tel.: (214) 295-1600
Web Site: http://www.combinedgroup.com
Insurance Agencies & Brokerage Services
N.A.I.C.S.: 524210
Blake Y. Stock (CEO)
Mark Van Horn (Pres-Quantum Integrated Sys)
Ken Dahl (Mgr-Nonsubscription)
Rob MacLean (CFO)
Bobby Jacobs (Controller)
Sallie Sills (Mgr-Mktg)

Country & Commercial Insurance Brokers Limited (1)
Office 4 Fairfield Business Park Longsight

Road, Clayton-le-Dale, Blackburn, BB2 7JA, United Kingdom
Tel.: (44) 1772780600
Web Site: https://www.cciblltd.net
Commercial Insurance Brokerage Services
N.A.I.C.S.: 524210

County Insurance Consultants Limited (1)
One Millennium Gate Westmere Drive Crewe Business Park, Crewe, CW1 6AY, United Kingdom
Tel.: (44) 3334002316
Web Site: https://www.countyins.com
Insurance Brokerage Services
N.A.I.C.S.: 524210

Crendon Insurance Brokers Limited (1)
4 St Kenelm Court Steel Park Road, Halesowen, B62 8HD, West Midlands, United Kingdom
Tel.: (44) 1214545100
Web Site: https://www.crendoninsurance.co.uk
Insurance Brokerage Services
N.A.I.C.S.: 524210

Crotty Insurance Brokers Limited (1)
Getcover House Unit 6 Leopardstown Office Park, Sandyford, Dublin, 18, Ireland
Tel.: (353) 12908800
Web Site: https://www.crottyinsurance.ie
Insurance Brokerage Services
N.A.I.C.S.: 524210

Davison & Associates (NI) Limited (1)
Ladas House 285 Castlereagh Road, Belfast, BT5 5FL, United Kingdom
Tel.: (44) 2890706900
Web Site: https://www.davisonandassociates.co.uk
Insurance Brokerage Services
N.A.I.C.S.: 524210

Digney Grant Limited (1)
6 Sugar Island, County Down, Newry, BT35 6HT, United Kingdom
Tel.: (44) 2830267017
Web Site: https://www.digneygrant.co.uk
Insurance Brokerage Services
N.A.I.C.S.: 524210

Douglas Insurance Brokers Limited (1)
2nd Floor Frigate House Quay Parade, Swansea, SA1 1SR, United Kingdom
Tel.: (44) 1792446202
Web Site: https://www.douglas-insurance.co.uk
Insurance Brokerage Services
N.A.I.C.S.: 524210

ECC Insurance Brokers, Inc. (1)
1 Tower Ln Ste 2850, Oakbrook Terrace, IL 60181
Tel.: (630) 954-1414
Web Site: https://www.eccins.com
Emp.: 30
Insurance Agencies & Brokerage Services
N.A.I.C.S.: 524210
Dan Real (Founder)
Scott Brumberg (Exec VP)
Chris Green (Pres)
Jeff Roth (Asst VP)
John Goolsby (VP)
Josie Ramirez (Asst VP)

Edmondsons Limited (1)
1st Floor Premier House Elstree Way, Borehamwood, WD6 1JH, United Kingdom
Tel.: (44) 2072514544
Web Site: https://www.edmondsons.net
Commercial Insurance Brokerage Services
N.A.I.C.S.: 524210

Energy & Marine Underwriters, Inc. (1)
100 James Dr E Ste 130, Saint Rose, LA 70087
Tel.: (504) 464-4545
Sales Range: Less than $1 Million
Emp.: 12
Wholesale Brokers of Insurance Services
N.A.I.C.S.: 524210

Eric Rawlins & Co., Ltd. (1)
Suite 6 Landmark Business Centre Parkhouse Industrial Estate East, Newcastle-

under-Lyme, ST5 7RG, United Kingdom
Tel.: (44) 1782498693
Web Site: https://www.rawlinsinsurance.co.uk
Business Insurance Services
N.A.I.C.S.: 524210

Evolve Cyber Insurance Services LLC (1)
50 San Francisco St, San Francisco, CA 94133
Tel.: (415) 257-2170
Web Site: https://evolvemga.com
Insurance Brokerage Services
N.A.I.C.S.: 524210

Fitness Insurance, LLC (1)
1125 17th St Ste 1450, Denver, CO 80202
Web Site: https://www.fitnessinsurance.com
Fitness Insurance Services
N.A.I.C.S.: 524210

Five Insurance Brokers Limited (1)
53 Barrack Square Martlesham Heath Business Park, Martlesham Heath, Ipswich, IP5 3RF, United Kingdom
Tel.: (44) 1473610057
Web Site: https://fiveinsurancebrokers.co.uk
Insurance Brokerage Services
N.A.I.C.S.: 524210

Florida Intracoastal Underwriters, Limited Company (1)
1600 Sawgrass Corp Pkwy Ste 200, Sunrise, FL 33323
Tel.: (954) 332-9050
Sales Range: $1-9.9 Million
Emp.: 30
N.A.I.C.S.: 524298

Gauntlet Insurance Services Limited (1)
Corn Exchange 55 Mark Lane, London, EC3R 7NE, United Kingdom
Tel.: (44) 2073942400
Web Site: https://www.gauntlet.uk.com
Insurance Brokerage Services
N.A.I.C.S.: 524210

Gower House Limited (1)
3 Myrtle Grove, Sketty, Swansea, SA2 0SH, United Kingdom
Tel.: (44) 1792416080
Web Site: https://www.gowerhouse.co.uk
Financial Advisory Services
N.A.I.C.S.: 523940

Gremesco of New Jersey, LLC (1)
1711 Ginesi Dr, Freehold, NJ 07728-8592
Tel.: (732) 761-9904
Web Site: http://www.gremesconj.com
Insurance Agencies & Brokerages
N.A.I.C.S.: 524210
Joe Certo (Pres)

Guardian IB Limited (1)
Worthington Way, Wigan, WN3 6XE, Greater Manchester, United Kingdom
Tel.: (44) 1942665788
Web Site: https://guardianib.co.uk
Insurance Brokerage Services
N.A.I.C.S.: 524210

Halcyon Underwriters, Inc. (1)
555 Winderley Pl Ste 420, Maitland, FL 32751-7233
Tel.: (407) 660-1881
Web Site: http://www.halcyonuw.com
Sales Range: $1-9.9 Million
Emp.: 40
Underwriting Insurance Services
N.A.I.C.S.: 524298
Paul Lyons (Exec VP)
Jason Mata (Mgr-Bus Dev & Compliance)
Augusta Godinho (VP)
Sarah Cadle (VP)
Brian Polino (VP)

Hays Companies Inc. (1)
80 S 8th St Ste 700, Minneapolis, MN 55402
Tel.: (612) 333-3323
Web Site: http://www.hayscompanies.com
Sales Range: $10-24.9 Million
Emp.: 200
Insurance Agents & Brokers
N.A.I.C.S.: 524210
James Charles Hays (Co-Founder, Pres & CEO)
William L. Mershon (Mng Partner)
Mike Egan (Pres & COO)
Mary Raveling (Pres)

Subsidiary (Domestic):

Hays Companies of New Jersey, Inc. (2)
190 Headquarters Plz E Tower 6th Fl, Morristown, NJ 07960
Tel.: (973) 359-3600
General Insurance Services
N.A.I.C.S.: 524210

Hays Group of Wisconsin LLC (2)
1200 N Mayfair Rd Ste 100, Milwaukee, WI 53226
Tel.: (414) 443-0000
Emp.: 100
Insurance Agents, Brokers & Service
N.A.I.C.S.: 524210
Daniel Shapiro (Pres)

Hays Insurance Brokerage of New England, LLC (2)
20 Trafalgar Sq 2nd Fl, Nashua, NH 03063
Tel.: (603) 589-4065
General Insurance Services
N.A.I.C.S.: 524210

Hays of Utah Insurance Services Inc (2)
201 Main St 2100, Salt Lake City, UT 84111
Tel.: (801) 505-6500
Web Site: http://www.hayscompanies.com
Emp.: 19
General Insurance Services
N.A.I.C.S.: 524210
Dave Knoop (Sr VP)

Health Special Risk, Inc. (1)
880 Sibley Memorial Hwy, Saint Paul, MN 55118
Tel.: (651) 455-8889
Web Site: http://www.healthspecialrisk.com
Insurance Agents, Brokers & Service
N.A.I.C.S.: 524210

Healthcare Insurance Professionals, Inc. (1)
800 Gessner Rd Ste 325, Houston, TX 77024-4529
Tel.: (713) 255-8450
Insurance Agencies & Brokerage Services
N.A.I.C.S.: 524210

Home Counties Insurance Services Limited (1)
10 Queensbridge, Northampton, NN4 7BF, Northamptonshire, United Kingdom
Tel.: (44) 1525719955
Insurance Brokerage Services
N.A.I.C.S.: 524210

Hull & Company, LLC (1)
2 Oakwood Blvd Ste 100, Hollywood, FL 33020 **(100%)**
Tel.: (954) 527-4855
Web Site: http://www.hullco.com
Sales Range: $200-249.9 Million
Emp.: 650
Wholesale Insurance Intermediary
N.A.I.C.S.: 524210
Richard F. Hull (Founder)

Branch (Domestic):

Hull & Company, Inc. - Tampa (2)
970 Lake Carillon Dr Ste 200, Saint Petersburg, FL 33716
Tel.: (727) 561-4855
Web Site: http://hulltampabay.com
Sales Range: $50-74.9 Million
Emp.: 25
Insurance Services
N.A.I.C.S.: 524298

Subsidiary (Domestic):

Izzo Insurance Services, Inc. (2)
150 S Bloomingdale Rd, Bloomingdale, IL 60108
Tel.: (630) 582-2800
Web Site: http://www.izzoinsurance.com
Insurance Agency & Wholesale Brokerage
N.A.I.C.S.: 524210
Karen J. Izzo (Founder)

South & Western General Agency, Inc. (2)
15835 Quorum Dr, Addison, TX 75001
Tel.: (972) 855-2900
Web Site: http://www.southandwestern.com

Sales Range: $1-9.9 Million
Emp.: 58
Insurance Agencies & Brokerages
N.A.I.C.S.: 524210
John Horan (Pres)
Ruth Peck (Mgr-Personal Lines)

Texas All Risk General Agency, Inc. (2)
9696 Skillman St, Dallas, TX 75243-8253
Tel.: (972) 669-1188
Web Site: http://www.allriskga.com
Insurance Agencies & Brokerages
N.A.I.C.S.: 524210
Kelly Davis (Pres & CEO)

Subsidiary (Domestic):

Select General Agency, LLC (3)
9696 Skillman St Ste 170, Dallas, TX 75243-8253
Web Site: https://www.selectgeneral.com
Insurance Agencies & Brokerages
N.A.I.C.S.: 524210

Subsidiary (Domestic):

The Colonial Group, Inc. (2)
5506 W Friendly Ave Ste 200, Greensboro, NC 27410
Tel.: (336) 855-1300
Web Site: http://www.thecolonialgroup.com
Insurance Agents
N.A.I.C.S.: 524210
Robert W. Burke (Pres & CEO)

Industry Consulting Group, Inc. (1)
2777 N Stemmons Fwy Ste 940, Dallas, TX 75207
Tel.: (972) 991-0391
Insurance Services
N.A.I.C.S.: 524210

Insync Insurance Solutions Limited (1)
Albany Park Cabot Lane, Poole, BH17 7BX, Dorset, United Kingdom
Tel.: (44) 1200309516
Web Site: https://insyncinsurance.co.uk
Insurance Brokerage Services
N.A.I.C.S.: 524210

Irving Weber Associates, Inc. (1)
6900 College Blvd Ste 1000, Overland Park, KS 66211
Tel.: (631) 366-3900
Web Site: https://www.iwains.com
Sales Range: $25-49.9 Million
Emp.: 15
Insurance Agencies & Brokerages
N.A.I.C.S.: 524210
Anne Marie Castelli (Dir-Underwriting)
Christine Brazier (VP-Bus Dev)
Adam Johnson (Pres)

John Henshall Limited (1)
Gower House 14-16 High St, Telford, Newport, TF10 7AN, Shropshire, United Kingdom
Tel.: (44) 1952820358
Web Site: https://henshalls.com
Insurance Brokerage Services
N.A.I.C.S.: 524210

KPTI Limited (1)
235-241 Kingsbury Road, London, NW9 8UG, United Kingdom
Tel.: (44) 2082053000
Web Site: https://isgroupuk.com
Insurance Brokerage Services
N.A.I.C.S.: 524210

Kingsway Insurance Services Limited (1)
12 St Johns Business Park, Lutterworth, LE17 4HB, Leicestershire, United Kingdom
Tel.: (44) 1455554884
Web Site: https://kingswayinsurance.co.uk
Commercial Insurance Services
N.A.I.C.S.: 524298

Kronholm Insurance Services (1)
155 Oak St, Glastonbury, CT 06033-2317
Tel.: (860) 633-1440
Web Site: http://www.kronholminsurance.com
Insurance Agencies & Brokerages
N.A.I.C.S.: 524210

Lancer Claims Services, Inc. (1)
681 S Parker St 300, Orange, CA 92868

Web Site: https://www.lancerclaims.com
Insurance Agencies & Brokerage Services
N.A.I.C.S.: 524210
Tom A. Hext (Pres)
Robert Steedman (VP)

Lawrence Fraser Brokers Limited (1)
40 Park Square North, Leeds, LS1 2NP, United Kingdom
Tel.: (44) 1133220166
Web Site: https://www.lfbrokers.co.uk
Insurance Brokerage Services
N.A.I.C.S.: 524210

Lonmar Global Risks Limited (1)
Corn Exchange 55 Mark Lane, London, EC3R 7NE, United Kingdom
Tel.: (44) 2072043600
Web Site: https://www.lonmar.com
Insurance Brokerage Services
N.A.I.C.S.: 524210

MacDuff Underwriters, Inc. (1)
1717 N Clyde Morris Blvd Ste 120, Daytona Beach, FL 32117
Tel.: (386) 366-6300
Web Site: https://www.macduff-fla.com
Sales Range: $1-9.9 Million
Emp.: 30
Insurance Underwriting Services
N.A.I.C.S.: 524298

Marquee Managed Care Solutions, Inc. (1)
PO Box 85251, San Diego, CA 92189-5251
Tel.: (619) 881-5510
Web Site: https://www.marqueemcs.com
Insurance Service Provider
N.A.I.C.S.: 524210

Marshall Wooldridge Limited (1)
Rawdon Court 20 Leeds Road Rawdon, Leeds, LS19 6AX, United Kingdom
Tel.: (44) 1132506614
Web Site:
https://www.marshallwooldridge.com
Insurance Brokerage Services
N.A.I.C.S.: 524210

McGrady Limited (1)
52 St Patricks Avenue, Co Down, Downpatrick, BT30 6DS, United Kingdom
Tel.: (44) 2844615933
Web Site:
https://www.mcgradyinsurance.com
Insurance Brokerage Services
N.A.I.C.S.: 524210

Mcnamara, Co. (1)
1330 Highway 96 E, Saint Paul, MN 55110-3651
Tel.: (651) 426-0607
Web Site:
http://www.mcnamaracompany.com
Rev.: $1,300,000
Emp.: 14
Insurance Agencies & Brokerages
N.A.I.C.S.: 524210

Millstream Underwriting Limited (1)
52-56 Leadenhall St, London, EC3A 2EB, United Kingdom
Tel.: (44) 3306600561
Web Site: https://www.millstreamonline.com
Insurance Brokerage Services
N.A.I.C.S.: 524210

Mithras Underwriting Europe S.R.L. (1)
Broekstraat/Rue du Marais 49-53 b6, 1000, Brussels, Belgium
Tel.: (32) 24455320
Insurance Brokerage Services
N.A.I.C.S.: 524210

Mithras Underwriting Italia S.R.L. (1)
Via Caradosso 6, 20123, Milan, Italy
Tel.: (39) 027220201
Insurance Brokerage Services
N.A.I.C.S.: 524210

Mithras Underwriting Ltd. (1)
52-54 Leadenhall Street, London, EC3A 2BJ, United Kingdom
Tel.: (44) 2039066200
Insurance Underwriting Services
N.A.I.C.S.: 524113

Moten Associates (1)
2108 Dekalb Pike, Norristown, PA 19401
Tel.: (610) 941-1252

Web Site: http://www.motenassociates.com
Sales Range: $25-49.9 Million
Emp.: 14
Insurance Agencies & Brokerages
N.A.I.C.S.: 524210

Newstead Insurance Brokers Limited (1)
4 St Kenelm Court Steel Park Road, Halesowen, B62 8HD, United Kingdom
Tel.: (44) 1214102400
Web Site: https://www.newstead.co.uk
Insurance Brokerage Services
N.A.I.C.S.: 524210

Nucleus Underwriting Limited (1)
21 Archer Drive, Aylesbury, HP20 1EP, Buckinghamshire, United Kingdom
Tel.: (44) 2039580586
Web Site:
https://www.nucleusunderwriting.com
Insurance Underwriting Services
N.A.I.C.S.: 524113

O'Leary Insurances Galway Limited (1)
13 Liosban Business Park Tuam Rd, Galway, H91 DW01, Ireland
Tel.: (353) 91778677
Web Site: https://www.olearyinsurances.ie
Insurance Services
N.A.I.C.S.: 524210
Michael Tarpey (Mng Dir)

O'Leary Insurances Waterford Limited (1)
96 Meaghers Quay, Waterford, X91 E094, Ireland
Tel.: (353) 51309130
Web Site: https://www.olearyinsurances.ie
Insurance Services
N.A.I.C.S.: 524210

Occam Underwriting Limited (1)
155 Fenchurch Street, London, EC3M 6AL, United Kingdom
Tel.: (44) 7823449014
Web Site:
https://www.occamunderwriting.com
Insurance Underwriting Services
N.A.I.C.S.: 524113

OnPoint Underwriting, Inc. (1)
8390 E Crescent Pkwy Ste 200, Greenwood Village, CO 80111
Tel.: (303) 694-6466
Web Site:
https://www.onpointunderwriting.com
Insurance Service Provider
N.A.I.C.S.: 524210

Orchid Underwriters Agency, LLC (1)
1201 19th Pl Ste A110, Vero Beach, FL 32960
Tel.: (772) 226-5546
Web Site: https://orchidinsurance.com
Property Insurance Services
N.A.I.C.S.: 524126

Pacific Resources Benefits Advisors, LLC (1)
321 N Clark St Ste 940, Chicago, IL 60654-5015
Tel.: (312) 922-7850
Web Site: http://www.pacresbenefits.com
Emp.: 15
Insurance Service Provider
N.A.I.C.S.: 524210
Chris Judd (CEO)
Patricia Purdy (Mng Dir)
Ken Vaughan (Pres)
Jen Hartman (Dir-HR, Learning & Dev)
Mike Scire (VP-Finance-Operations)
Tony Herron (Mng Dir)
Connie S. Moore (Asst VP-Ops)
Brandon Brickweg (VP-Distr)
Chris Kenney (Asst VP-Fin & Absence Solutions)
Melissa Manthey (Controller)
Rob Glueck (Asst VP-Products & Mktg)
Joe Shortal (Sr Mng Dir)
Greg Cronin (Mng Dir)
Chris Tillotson (Mng Dir)
Geoff Widlak (Mng Dir)

Peachtree Special Risk Brokers, LLC (1)
3525 Piedmont Rd NE Bldg 5 Ste 700, Atlanta, GA 30305

Brown & Brown, Inc.—(Continued)

Tel.: (404) 467-6428
Web Site: https://www.psrllc.com
Sales Range: $10-24.9 Million
Emp.: 76
Commercial Insurance Broker
N.A.I.C.S.: 524210
Liz White (Pres-Inland Marine & Property)
John Vedder (Exec VP)
Eric Johnston (Exec VP)
Amie Meschi (Exec VP)
Michael Blackmon (VP)
Jake Brodhead (Asst VP)

Petherwick Insurance Brokers Limited (1)
3 Gordon Mews Gordon Close, Portslade, BN41 1HU, East Sussex, United Kingdom
Tel.: (44) 1273822222
Insurance Brokerage Services
N.A.I.C.S.: 524210

Piper Jordan, LLC (1)
11622 El Camino Real Ste 100, San Diego, CA 92130
Tel.: (858) 350-1774
Web Site: http://www.piperjordan.com
Insurance Agencies & Brokerage Services
N.A.I.C.S.: 524210
Jay Jordan (Principal)
Robyn Piper (Principal)

Plum Underwriting Limited (1)
Phoenix House Christopher Martin Road, Basildon, SS14 3EZ, Essex, United Kingdom
Tel.: (44) 3451300802
Web Site: https://www.plum-underwriting.com
Insurance Underwriting Services
N.A.I.C.S.: 524113

Preferred Governmental Claim Solutions, Inc. (1)
615 Crescent Executive Ct, Lake Mary, FL 32795-8456
Web Site: https://pgcsclaims.com
Insurance Agencies & Brokerage Services
N.A.I.C.S.: 524210

Premier Choice Healthcare Limited (1)
Plum Park Estate, Paulerspury, NN12 6LQ, Northants, United Kingdom
Tel.: (44) 8009701618
Web Site: https://www.premierchoicegroup.co.uk
Insurance Brokerage Services
N.A.I.C.S.: 524210

Prescott Jones Limited (1)
Caswell House 53 Walter Road, Swansea, SA1 5PW, United Kingdom
Tel.: (44) 1792459898
Web Site: https://prescott-jones.co.uk
Insurance Brokerage Services
N.A.I.C.S.: 524210

Proctor Financial, Inc. (1)
5225 Crooks Rd, Troy, MI 48098
Tel.: (248) 824-1464
Insurance Agencies & Brokerage Services
N.A.I.C.S.: 524210

Professional & Medical Insurance Solutions Limited (1)
Lake Meadows Business Park 13 Woodbrook Crescent, Billericay, CM12 0EQ, Essex, United Kingdom
Tel.: (44) 1277288237
Web Site: https://www.promedinsurance.co.uk
Insurance Brokerage Services
N.A.I.C.S.: 524210

Public Risk Underwriters Insurance Services of Texas, LLC (1)
101 W Renner Rd Ste 300, Richardson, TX 75082-4437
Tel.: (469) 449-1516
Web Site: https://www.pru-tx.com
Emp.: 7
Insurance Agencies & Brokerage Services
N.A.I.C.S.: 524210
Chris Fuller (VP)
Dale E. Powell III (VP)
Jan Skovbjerg (VP)

Public Risk Underwriters of Florida, Inc. (1)

615 Crescent Executive Ct Ste 60, Lake Mary, FL 32746
Tel.: (321) 832-1450
Emp.: 25
Insurance Agencies & Brokerage Services
N.A.I.C.S.: 524210

Public Risk Underwriters of Indiana, LLC (1)
1320 City Center Dr Ste 325, Carmel, IN 46032
Tel.: (765) 457-9161
Web Site: https://www.ipep.com
Insurance Agencies & Brokerages
N.A.I.C.S.: 524210
Timothy Downey (Pres)

Public Risk Underwriters of the Northwest, Inc. (1)
451 Diamond Dr, Ephrata, WA 98823
Tel.: (509) 754-2027
Insurance Agencies & Brokerage Services
N.A.I.C.S.: 524210

RIB Group Limited (1)
Silicon House Farfield Park Manvers Way, Wath Upon Dearne, Rotherham, S63 5DB, United Kingdom
Tel.: (44) 1709875548
Web Site: https://rib-group.co.uk
Insurance Brokerage Services
N.A.I.C.S.: 524210

Rowlands & Barranca Agency, Inc. (1)
6 Tower Pl, Albany, NY 12203
Tel.: (518) 482-5192
Web Site: http://www.rowbarinc.com
Sales Range: $1-9.9 Million
Emp.: 10
Employee Benefit & Insurance Services
N.A.I.C.S.: 923130

Shearwater Insurance Services Limited (1)
11 Regent Gate High Street, Waltham Cross, EN8 7AF, Hertfordshire, United Kingdom
Tel.: (44) 1992718666
Web Site: https://www.shearwater-insurance.co.uk
General Insurance Services
N.A.I.C.S.: 524210

Social Security Advocates for the Disabled, LLC (1)
136 Longwater Dr Ste 100, Norwell, MA 02061
Tel.: (800) 825-7734
Web Site: http://www.ssadreps.com
Specialized Advocacy Organization Operator
N.A.I.C.S.: 813319
Megan Reid (Sr VP-Operations)
Nelson Acosta (VP-Information Technology)
Seth Matthews (Dir)

Special Risk Insurance Managers Ltd. (1)
2-242 Goulet Street, Winnipeg, R2H 0S2, MB, Canada
Tel.: (204) 257-6670
Web Site: https://www.srim.ca
Disability Insurance Services
N.A.I.C.S.: 524126
Taryn Vaughan (Pres & COO)
Neville Harriman (VP)
Jessica Fryer (Chief Underwriting Officer)
Brita Lorenz (VP-Marketing)
Brooke Speirs (Dir-Human Resources)
Chantal Biech (Dir)
Sarah Norfield (Dir)
Ashley Burt (Dir-Special Projects)
Neville Harriman (VP)
Brita Lorenz (VP-Marketing)
Brooke Speirs (Dir-Human Resources)
Sarah Norfield (Dir)
Ashley Burt (Dir-Special Projects)

Spectrum Risk Management and Reinsurance DMCC (1)
10th Floor Swiss Tower 1001-17 Jumeriah Lakes, Dubai, United Arab Emirates
Tel.: (971) 45613768
Insurance Brokerage Services
N.A.I.C.S.: 524210

Square Circle Brokers Limited (1)
Oakmare Belmont Business Park, Durham,

DH1 1TW, United Kingdom
Tel.: (44) 1913830112
Web Site: https://www.squarecircleinsurance.co.uk
Insurance Agencies & Brokerage Services
N.A.I.C.S.: 524210

TSG Premium Finance, LLC (1)
18545 Sigma Rd, San Antonio, TX 78258-4268
Tel.: (210) 764-1233
Insurance Service Provider
N.A.I.C.S.: 524210

Texas Security General Insurance Agency, Inc. (1)
18545 Sigma Rd, San Antonio, TX 78258
Tel.: (210) 764-1233
Web Site: https://www.texassecuritygeneral.com
Insurance Service Provider
N.A.I.C.S.: 524210
Tom Contreras (Pres & CEO)
Larry Thompson (Mktg Dir-)
Sheila Wilkins (Mgr-Compliance & Claims)
Carolyn Fey (VP-Personal Lines)
Alicia Dale (Accountant)
Robert Salinas (Sr Mgr-)
Anne Watkins (Sr Mgr-)
Hector Collazo (Sr VP- &)

The Flagship Group, Ltd. (1)
500 E Main St Ste 600, Norfolk, VA 23510
Tel.: (757) 625-0938
Sales Range: $1-9.9 Million
Emp.: 25
Insurance Agents
N.A.I.C.S.: 524210
Rich Freebourn (Gen Mgr)

The Wright Insurance Group LLC (1)
333 Earle Ovington Blvd 505, Uniondale, NY 11553-3624
Tel.: (516) 227-2300
Insurance Service Provider
N.A.I.C.S.: 524210

Subsidiary (Domestic):

Wright National Flood Insurance Company (2)
801 94th Ave N Ste 110, Saint Petersburg, FL 33702
Tel.: (727) 803-2040
Web Site: https://www.wrightflood.com
Emp.: 300
Flood Insurance Services
N.A.I.C.S.: 524126
G. Michael Stone (CMO & Exec VP)
Patty Templeton-Jones (Pres)

Wright Program Management, LLC (2)
20 Soundview Market Pl, Port Washington, NY 11050
Tel.: (516) 767-6041
Insurance Service Provider
N.A.I.C.S.: 524210

Wright Risk Consulting, LLC (2)
333 Earle Ovington Blvd Ste 505, Uniondale, NY 11553-3622
Tel.: (516) 227-2300
Web Site: https://www.wrightrisk.com
Emp.: 150
Insurance Service Provider
N.A.I.C.S.: 524210

Wright Risk Management Company, LLC (2)
333 Earle Ovington Blvd Ste 505, Uniondale, NY 11553-3624
Tel.: (516) 750-9391
Insurance Service Provider
N.A.I.C.S.: 524210

Wright Specialty Insurance Agency, LLC (2)
900 Stewart Ave Ste 600, Garden City, NY 11530-4869
Tel.: (516) 750-3902
Web Site: http://www.wrightspecialty.com
Emp.: 200
Insurance Service Provider
N.A.I.C.S.: 524210
Kevin C. Beer (Pres)
Jonathan D. Hirt (VP-Underwriting)
Ellen Dividock (VP-Bus Dev)

Andrew L. Graham (Mng Dir-Risk Mgmt Svcs)
Debra Perlowin (Mgr-Client Svcs)
Chuck Smith (VP-Team Resource & Admin)

Thomas Sagar Insurances Limited (1)
Group First House 12a Mead Way Shuttleworth Mead, Padiham, BB12 7NG, Lancashire, United Kingdom
Tel.: (44) 1282858250
Web Site: https://www.sagarinsurances.co.uk
Insurance Brokerage Services
N.A.I.C.S.: 524210

Thompson Brothers Insurance Consultants Limited (1)
111 Wellington Road South, Stockport, SK1 3TH, Cheshire, United Kingdom
Tel.: (44) 1614806444
Web Site: https://thompsonbrothers.net
Insurance Brokerage Services
N.A.I.C.S.: 524210

Three Sixty Insure Limited (1)
Unit A7 Ashworth House Rear Deakins Business Park, Egerton, Bolton, BL7 9RP, United Kingdom
Tel.: (44) 1204301423
Web Site: https://threesixtyinsure.com
Insurance Brokerage Services
N.A.I.C.S.: 524210

U-Sure Insurance Services Limited (1)
Raglan House 6-8 William Brown Close Llantarnam Industrial Park, Cwmbran, NP44 3AB, United Kingdom
Tel.: (44) 1633838976
Web Site: https://www.u-sure.com
Insurance Brokerage Services
N.A.I.C.S.: 524210

USIS, Inc. (1)
5728 Major Blvd, Orlando, FL 32819
Tel.: (407) 352-0374
Web Site: https://www.usisinet.com
Third Party Insurance Company for Workers Compensation Claims
N.A.I.C.S.: 524298

Vehicle Administrative Services, Ltd. (1)
14135 Midway Rd, Addison, TX 75001
Tel.: (972) 455-1900
Web Site: http://vehicleadminservices.com
Sales Range: $1-9.9 Million
Emp.: 16
Emergency Roadside Assistance & Related Consumer Auto Protection Services
N.A.I.C.S.: 524298
William Breindel (Pres & CEO)

WM Brokers Limited (1)
Friars House 2 Falcon Street, Ipswich, IP1 1SL, Suffolk, United Kingdom
Tel.: (44) 1473408408
Web Site: https://wmbrokers.co.uk
Insurance Brokerage Services
N.A.I.C.S.: 524210

Web Shaw Limited (1)
1 Alverton Street, Penzance, TR18 4ET, Cornwall, United Kingdom
Tel.: (44) 1736364336
Web Site: https://www.jacksonsgroup.co.uk
Insurance Brokerage Services
N.A.I.C.S.: 524210

Xenia Broking Group Limited (1)
52-56 Leadenhall Street, London, EC3A 2EB, United Kingdom
Tel.: (44) 3330155005
Web Site: https://xeniabroking.com
Credit Insurance Brokerage Services
N.A.I.C.S.: 524210

Xenia Broking Limited (1)
52-56 Leadenhall Street, London, EC3A 2EB, United Kingdom
Tel.: (44) 3330155005
Web Site: https://xeniabroking.com
Insurance Brokerage Services
N.A.I.C.S.: 524210

YouZoom Insurance Services, Inc. (1)
701 B St Ste 2100, San Diego, CA 92101
Web Site: https://www.youzoom.com

Insurance Service Provider
N.A.I.C.S.: 524210

BROWN-FORMAN CORPORATION

850 Dixie Hwy, Louisville, KY 40210
Tel.: (502) 774-7690   DE
Web Site: https://www.brown-forman.com
Year Founded: 1870
BF.B—(NYSE)
Rev.: $5,328,000,000
Assets: $8,166,000,000
Liabilities: $4,649,000,000
Net Worth: $3,517,000,000
Earnings: $1,024,000,000
Emp.: 5,700
Fiscal Year-end: 04/30/24
Holding Company; Alcoholic Beverage Distr
N.A.I.C.S.: 551112
Marshall B. Farrer (Chief Strategic Growth Officer & Exec VP)
Lawson E. Whiting (Pres & CEO)
Ralph E. de Chabert (Chief Diversity Inclusion & Global Community Rels Officer & Sr VP)
Campbell P. Brown (Chm)
John V. Hayes (Pres-Canada & Sr VP)
Michael A. Masick (Pres-Emerging Intl & Mng Dir-Latin America, Africa, Ukraine, and CIS markets)
Matias Bentel (Chief Brands Officer)
Heather V. Howell (Executives)
Elizabeth Conway (Dir-External Comm)
Larry Combs (CIO & Dir-Supply Chain Integration & Strategy)
Tim Nall (Chief Global Supply Chain & Tech Officer & Sr VP)
Leanne Cunningham (CFO)

Subsidiaries:

Brown-Forman Australia Pty. Ltd. (1)
Level 6 280 Elizabeth Street Surry Hills, Sydney, 2010, NSW, Australia
Tel.: (61) 297648777
Web Site: https://www.brownforman.com.au
Sales Range: $50-74.9 Million
Emp.: 157
Wine & Distilled Alcoholic Beverages Whslr
N.A.I.C.S.: 424820

Brown-Forman Beverages (1)
850 Dixie Hwy, Louisville, KY 40210-1038
Tel.: (502) 585-1100
Web Site: http://www.brown-forman.com
Sales Range: $750-799.9 Million
Emp.: 3,000
Distilled Spirits & Wines
N.A.I.C.S.: 312140
James L. Bareuther (COO & Exec VP)

Subsidiary (Domestic):

The Woodford Reserve Distillery (2)
7855 McCracken Pike, Versailles, KY 40383-9781
Tel.: (859) 879-1812
Web Site: http://www.woodfordreserve.com
Sales Range: $25-49.9 Million
Emp.: 40
Bourbon Whiskey Producer
N.A.I.C.S.: 312130

Brown-Forman Beverages Australia Pty Ltd. (1)
5 Harbourview Cres Level 5, Crescent, Milsons Point, 2060, NSW, Australia
Tel.: (61) 89230700
Web Site: http://www.brown-forman.com
Sales Range: $150-199.9 Million
Beverages Mfr & Marketer
N.A.I.C.S.: 424810

Brown-Forman Beverages Europe, Ltd. (1)
Part Fourth Floor W 45 Mortimer St, London, W1W 8HJ, United Kingdom (100%)
Tel.: (44) 2074781300

Sales Range: $75-99.9 Million
Emp.: 70
Beverages Mfr & Marketer
N.A.I.C.S.: 424810

Subsidiary (Non-US):

Brown-Forman Deutschland GmbH (2)
Dammtorwall 7, 20354, Hamburg, Germany (100%)
Tel.: (49) 404503320
Web Site: http://www.brown-forman.de
Emp.: 100
Alcoholic Beverage Distr
N.A.I.C.S.: 424820
Yiannis Pafilis (Mng Dir)
Jens-Peter Janiak (Mng Dir)

Brown-Forman Beverages North Asia, LLC (1)
850 Dixie Hwy, Louisville, KY 40210
Tel.: (502) 585-1100
Web Site: http://www.brown-forman.com
Sales Range: $1-4.9 Billion
Emp.: 3,000
Beverages Mfr & Marketer
N.A.I.C.S.: 424810

Subsidiary (Non-US):

Brown-Forman Worldwide (Shanghai) Co., Ltd. (2)
Suite E 19/F Jiu Shi Renaissance Mansion, 918 Huai Hai Road Middle, Shanghai, 200020, China
Tel.: (86) 21 6415 9379
Sales Range: $150-199.9 Million
Beverages Mfr & Marketer
N.A.I.C.S.: 424820

Brown-Forman Cooperage (1)
PO Box 37210, Louisville, KY 40233
Tel.: (502) 364-4564
Web Site: http://www.brownformancooperages.com
Sales Range: $50-74.9 Million
Emp.: 50
Wooden Barrel Mfr
N.A.I.C.S.: 321912

Brown-Forman Corp. - Louisville Distillery (1)
2921 Dixie Hwy, Louisville, KY 40210-1037
Tel.: (502) 774-2960
Web Site: http://www.brown-forman.com
Sales Range: $50-74.9 Million
Emp.: 30
Distilled & Blended Liquors
N.A.I.C.S.: 424820

Brown-Forman Finland Oy (1)
Porkkalankatu 24 4 Krs, 180, Helsinki, Finland
Tel.: (358) 207200500
Emp.: 20
Alcoholic Beverages Mfr
N.A.I.C.S.: 312120
Minna Vaisasvaara (Mgr-Logistics)

Brown-Forman Korea Ltd. (1)
4/f Namhangang Bldg 85 - 3 Chongdam2-dong Kangnam-gu, Seoul, 135-954, Korea (South) (100%)
Tel.: (82) 25187700
Web Site: http://www.jackdaniels.com
Sales Range: $25-49.9 Million
Emp.: 30
Wine Mfr
N.A.I.C.S.: 312140

Brown-Forman Ljubljana Marketing, d.o.o (1)
Tehnoloski park 19, 1000, Ljubljana, Slovenia
Tel.: (386) 18100304
Web Site: http://spirits.si
Alcoholic Beverage Distr
N.A.I.C.S.: 424820

Brown-Forman Media Services (1)
3310 W End Ave Ste 600, Nashville, TN 37203-1058
Tel.: (615) 279-4169
Advetising Agency
N.A.I.C.S.: 541810
Julia Hall (Media Dir)

Brown-Forman Ro S.R.L. (1)

Str Dr Robert Koch 6, 050528, Bucharest, Romania
Tel.: (40) 725826735
Alcoholic Beverages Mfr
N.A.I.C.S.: 312120
Dan Crisan (Mgr-East Balkan)

Brown-Forman Rus L.L.C. (1)
Maly Ivanovsky Lane 9, Moscow, 109028, Russia
Tel.: (7) 4957834195
Web Site: http://www.brown-forman.com
Alcoholic Beverages Mfr
N.A.I.C.S.: 312120

Brown-Forman Spain, S.L. (1)
Avenida Diagonal 618 - P 9, 08021, Barcelona, Spain
Tel.: (34) 932093634
Web Site: http://www.b-f.com
Alcoholic Beverages Mfr
N.A.I.C.S.: 312120

Canadian Mist Distillers Limited (1)
202 MacDonald Rd, Collingwood, L9Y 4J2, ON, Canada (100%)
Tel.: (705) 445-4690
Web Site: http://www.canadianmist.com
Sales Range: $25-49.9 Million
Emp.: 40
Distillery
N.A.I.C.S.: 312140

Early Times Distillers Company (1)
850 Dixie Hwy, Louisville, KY 40210 (100%)
Tel.: (502) 585-1100
Web Site: http://www.earlytimes.com
Sales Range: $25-49.9 Million
Emp.: 60
Whiskey & Bourbon Producer
N.A.I.C.S.: 312140

Jack Daniel's Properties, Inc. (1)
4040 Civic Ctr Dr Ste 528, San Rafael, CA 94903 (100%)
Tel.: (317) 921-0021
Web Site: http://www.jackdaniels.com
Sales Range: $10-24.9 Million
Emp.: 8
Whiskey Mfr & Marketer
N.A.I.C.S.: 312140
Melvin Keebler (Gen Mgr-Supply Chain)

Subsidiary (Domestic):

Jack Daniel Distillery, Lem Motlow, Prop., Inc. (2)
182 Lynchburg Hwy, Lynchburg, TN 37352 (100%)
Tel.: (931) 759-6180
Web Site: http://www.jackdaniels.com
Whiskey Distiller & Marketer
N.A.I.C.S.: 312140

Longnorth Limited (1)
Robin Hood Rd, Clondalkin, Ireland (100%)
Tel.: (353) 14508633
Web Site: http://www.brown-forman.com
Sales Range: $25-49.9 Million
Emp.: 40
Liquor Mfr
N.A.I.C.S.: 312140

The BenRiach Distillery Co. Ltd. (1)
Queen Anne Drive, Lochend Industrial Estate, Newbridge, EH28 8PL, United Kingdom
Tel.: (44) 1314562681
Web Site: https://www.benriachdistillery.com
Whiskey Distillery
N.A.I.C.S.: 312120
Alan McConnochie (Mgr-Distillery)
Ewan George (Mgr-Warehouse)

Subsidiary (Domestic):

Glenglassaugh Distillery Ltd. (2)
Glenglassaugh Distillery, Portsoy, AB45 2SQ, Aberdeenshire, United Kingdom
Tel.: (44) 1313355135
Web Site: http://www.glenglassaugh.com
Distilled & Blended Liquors
N.A.I.C.S.: 312140

BROWNIE'S MARINE GROUP, INC.

3001 NW 25 th Ave, Pompano Beach, FL 33069
Tel.: (954) 462-5570   NV
Web Site: https://www.browniesmarinegroup.com
BWMG—(OTCQB)
Rev.: $8,577,372
Assets: $5,665,484
Liabilities: $3,143,111
Net Worth: $2,522,373
Earnings: ($1,892,891)
Emp.: 36
Fiscal Year-end: 12/31/22
Recreational Hookah Diving, Yacht Based Scuba Air Compressor Mfr & Distr
N.A.I.C.S.: 339920
Robert M. Carmichael (Chm, Pres, CEO & CFO)

Subsidiaries:

BLU3, Inc. (1)
3001 NW 25th Ave, Pompano Beach, FL 33069-1028
Tel.: (954) 388-5650
Web Site: https://www.diveblu3.com
Underwater Diving Equipment Mfr
N.A.I.C.S.: 339920

BRT APARTMENTS CORP.

60 Cutter Mill Rd Ste 303, Great Neck, NY 11021
Tel.: (516) 466-3100   MA
Web Site: https://www.brtapartments.com
Year Founded: 1972
BRT—(NYSE)
Rev.: $70,527,000
Assets: $732,118,000
Liabilities: $482,048,000
Net Worth: $250,070,000
Earnings: $49,955,000
Emp.: 10
Fiscal Year-end: 12/31/22
Other Financial Vehicles
N.A.I.C.S.: 525990
Mitchell K. Gould (Exec VP)
George E. Zweier (CFO & VP)
Mark H. Lundy (Gen Counsel & Sr VP)
Alon Rosenzweig (VP)
Christine Grippo (VP)
Brenda E. Maldonado (Asst Controller)
Jeffrey A. Gould (CEO)
Matthew J. Gould (Sr VP)

Subsidiaries:

TRB Apopka LLC (1)
500 Jordan Stuart Cir, Apopka, FL 32703
Tel.: (407) 339-7200
Real Estate Management Services
N.A.I.C.S.: 531390

TRB Arlington LLC (1)
3102 Maple Ave Ste 450, Dallas, TX 75201
Tel.: (214) 953-9385
Real Estate Management Services
N.A.I.C.S.: 531390

TRB No. 1 Corp. (1)
60 Cutter Mill Rd Ste 303, Great Neck, NY 11021
Tel.: (516) 466-3100
Web Site: http://www.gouldlp.com
Emp.: 20
Real Estate Management Services
N.A.I.C.S.: 531390
Israel Rosenzweig (Chm-BRT Realty Trust)

BRUKER CORPORATION

40 Manning Rd, Billerica, MA 01821
Tel.: (978) 663-3660   DE
Web Site: https://www.bruker.com
Year Founded: 1960
BRKR—(NASDAQ)
Rev.: $2,964,500,000
Assets: $4,249,900,000
Liabilities: $2,855,300,000
Net Worth: $1,394,600,000

Bruker Corporation—(Continued)

Earnings: $427,200,000
Emp.: 9,707
Fiscal Year-end: 12/31/23
Life Science & Advanced Materials
Research Tools Developer
N.A.I.C.S.: 334516
Frank H. Laukien *(Chm, Pres & CEO)*
Gerald N. Herman *(VP)*
Falko Busse *(Pres-BioSpin-Grp)*
Juergen Srega *(Pres-CALID Grp &
Bruker Daltonics Div)*

Subsidiaries:

Acuity Spatial Genomics, Inc. (1)
112 Robin Hill Rd, Santa Barbara, CA
93117
Web Site: https://acuityspatialgenomics.com
Pharmaceutical Research & Development
Services
N.A.I.C.S.: 541714

Alicona Corporation (1)
150 Pierce Rd Ste 130, Itasca, IL 60143
Tel.: (630) 372-9900
Measuring Instrument Mfr & Distr
N.A.I.C.S.: 334513

Alicona GmbH (1)
Rathausplatz 16 1/2, 83471, Ber-
chtesgaden, Germany
Tel.: (49) 86526553901
Measuring Instrument Mfr & Distr
N.A.I.C.S.: 334513

Alicona Imaging GmbH (1)
Dr Auner Strasse 19, Raaba, 8074, Graz,
Austria
Tel.: (43) 316403010700
Web Site: https://www.alicona.com
Emp.: 120
Measuring Instrument Mfr & Distr
N.A.I.C.S.: 334513

Alicona Korea Pcific Ltd. (1)
Daeryung Post Tower 1 Cha 288 Suite 207
Digital-ro, Guro-gu, 152-790, Seoul, Korea
(South)
Tel.: (82) 1090376854
Measuring Instrument Mfr & Distr
N.A.I.C.S.: 334513

Alicona SARL (1)
4 rue Marguerite Syamour, 25000, Besan-
con, France
Tel.: (33) 381588630
Measuring Instrument Mfr & Distr
N.A.I.C.S.: 334513

Alicona UK Limited (1)
Michael Francis House 3 Trimbush Way,
Market Harborough, LE16 7XY, Leicester-
shire, United Kingdom
Tel.: (44) 1858462799
Measuring Instrument Mfr & Distr
N.A.I.C.S.: 334513

Alicona s.r.l. (1)
Via Leonardo da Vinci 12, 39100, Bolzano,
Italy
Tel.: (39) 03408419670
Measuring Instrument Mfr & Distr
N.A.I.C.S.: 334513

Anasys Instruments Corp. (1)
325 Chapala St, Santa Barbara, CA 93101
Tel.: (805) 730-3310
Web Site:
http://www.anasysinstruments.com
Nanoscale Material Properties Measuring
Device Mfr
N.A.I.C.S.: 334516

Bruker AXS, Inc. (1)
5465 E Cheryl Pkwy, Madison, WI 53711-
5373
Tel.: (608) 276-3000
Web Site: http://www.bruker.com
Sales Range: $150-199.9 Million
Emp.: 80
Mfrof X-Ray Apparatus & Tubes
N.A.I.C.S.: 334517

Subsidiary (Non-US):

Bruker AXS GmbH (2)
Oestliche Rheinbrueckenstr 49, 76187,
Karlsruhe, Germany

Tel.: (49) 721509970
Web Site: http://www.bruker.com
Laboratory Instrument Mfr
N.A.I.C.S.: 334516

Subsidiary (Non-US):

**Bruker AXS Analytical Instruments
Pvt. Ltd.** (3)
914 International Trade Tower Nehru Place,
New Delhi, 110019, India
Tel.: (91) 1146518588
Web Site: http://www.bruker.com
Sales Range: $10-24.9 Million
Emp.: 15
Analytical Laboratory Instrument Mfr
N.A.I.C.S.: 334516

Bruker AXS Nordic AB (3)
Vallgatan 5, 170 67, Solna, Stockholm,
Sweden
Tel.: (46) 0086552560
Sales Range: $10-24.9 Million
Emp.: 10
Spectrometer Product Mfr
N.A.I.C.S.: 334516

Bruker AXS Pte Ltd (3)
11 Biopolis Way No 10-10 The Helios, Sin-
gapore, 138667, Singapore
Tel.: (65) 65007288
Web Site: http://www.bruker.sg
Scientific Instrument Mfr
N.A.I.C.S.: 334516

Bruker Austria GmbH (3)
Lembockgasse 47b / 10, 1230, Vienna,
Austria
Tel.: (43) 180478810
Scientific Instrument Mfr
N.A.I.C.S.: 334516

Subsidiary (Domestic):

Bruker Elemental GmbH (3)
Kastellstrasse 31-35, 47546, Kalkar, Ger-
many
Tel.: (49) 2824976500
Web Site: http://www.bruker.com
Spectrometer Product Mfr
N.A.I.C.S.: 334516

Subsidiary (Domestic):

Bruker Nano GmbH (4)
Am Studio 2D, 12489, Berlin, Germany
Tel.: (49) 306709900
Web Site: http://www.bruker.com
Sales Range: $25-49.9 Million
Emp.: 176
Xray System & Component Mfr
N.A.I.C.S.: 334516

Subsidiary (Non-US):

Bruker Mexicana, S.A. de C.V. (3)
Damas 130 Oficina 501 San Jose Insur-
gents Ciudad de, 03900, Mexico, Mexico
Tel.: (52) 5556012599
Web Site: http://www.bruker.com
Emp.: 20
Sales & Service of Analytical Instruments
N.A.I.C.S.: 334516

Bruker Polska Sp. Z o.o. (3)
ul Budziszynska 69, 60-178, Poznan, Po-
land
Tel.: (48) 618689008
Web Site: http://bruker.poznan.pl
Analytical Laboratory Instrument Mfr
N.A.I.C.S.: 334516

Bruker South Africa Pty Ltd. (3)
Unit A-A001-G Ground floor Lincolnwood
Office Park Woodlands Drive, Woodmead,
Johannesburg, 2191, South Africa
Tel.: (27) 114636040
Web Site: http://www.bruker.com
Sales Range: $1-9.9 Million
Emp.: 18
Sales & Service of Analytical Instruments
N.A.I.C.S.: 334516
Pari Antalis *(Mng Dir)*

Bruker do Brasil Ltda. (3)
Condominio BBP - Barao de Maua Rod D
Pedro I km 87 5, Maua, Atibaia, 12954-260,
Sao Paulo, Brazil
Tel.: (55) 1121191750
Web Site: http://www.bruker.com.br

Sales Range: $25-49.9 Million
Emp.: 45
Analytical Laboratory Instrument Mfr
N.A.I.C.S.: 334516
Alexandre Schefer *(Exec Dir)*

Subsidiary (Domestic):

InCoaTec GmbH (3)
Max-Planck-Str 2, 21502, Geesthacht, Ger-
many
Tel.: (49) 4152889381
Web Site: https://www.incoatec.de
Sales Range: $25-49.9 Million
Emp.: 50
Xray System & Component Mfr
N.A.I.C.S.: 334516
Carsten Michaelsen *(Mng Dir)*
Jorg Wiesmann *(Mng Dir)*

Subsidiary (Domestic):

Bruker AXS Handheld Inc. (2)
415 N Quay St, Kennewick, WA 99336
Tel.: (509) 783-9850
Analytical Laboratory Instrument Mfr
N.A.I.C.S.: 334516
Terry Brown *(Mgr-Production)*

Subsidiary (Non-US):

Bruker AXS K.K. (3)
3-9 Moriya-cho, Kanagawa-ku, Yokohama,
221-0022, Japan
Tel.: (81) 454531960
Web Site: http://www.bruker.jp
Emp.: 100
Analytical Laboratory Instrument Mfr
N.A.I.C.S.: 334516

Subsidiary (Domestic):

Bruker Nano, Inc. (2)
3400 E Britannia Dr Ste 150, Tucson, AZ
85706
Tel.: (520) 741-1044
Web Site: http://www.bruker.com
Emp.: 80
Analytical Laboratory Instrument Mfr
N.A.I.C.S.: 334516

Division (Domestic):

Bruker Nano, Inc. (3)
8825 N 23rd Ave Ste 100, Phoenix, AZ
85021
Tel.: (408) 376-4040
Web Site: http://www.bruker.com
Sales Range: $25-49.9 Million
Emp.: 30
Test Equipment Mfr
N.A.I.C.S.: 334516

Subsidiary (Domestic):

Inscopix, Inc. (3)
2462 Embarcadero Way, Palo Alto, CA
94025-5204
Tel.: (650) 600-3886
Web Site: http://www.inscopix.com
Research & Development in Biotechnology
N.A.I.C.S.: 541714
Scott Norviel *(Product Dir-Mktg)*

**Bruker BioSciences Korea Co.,
Ltd.** (1)
KINS Tower 15F 25-1 Jeongja-dong
Bundang-gu, Seocho-Gu, Seongnam, 463-
844, Gyeonggi-do, Korea (South)
Tel.: (82) 25963232
Sales Range: $25-49.9 Million
Emp.: 25
Analytical Laboratory Instrument Mfr
N.A.I.C.S.: 334516
Sang-Hyuk Im *(Gen Mgr)*

Bruker BioSpin Corporation (1)
15 Fortune Dr, Billerica, MA 01821-3991
Tel.: (978) 667-9580
Web Site: http://www.bruker-biospin.com
Sales Range: $200-249.9 Million
Emp.: 155
Mfr & Provider of Life Science Tools Based
on Magnetic Resonance
N.A.I.C.S.: 334516

Subsidiary (Non-US):

Bruker Belgium SA/NV (2)
Kartuizersweg 3B, 2550, Kontich, Belgium
Tel.: (32) 27267626

Web Site: http://www.bruker.com
Sales Range: $1-9.9 Million
Emp.: 20
Sales & Service of Analytical Instruments
N.A.I.C.S.: 334516

Bruker BioSpin AG (2)
Industriestrasse 26, 8117, Fallanden, Swit-
zerland
Tel.: (41) 448259111
Magnetic Resonance Imaging Product Mfr
N.A.I.C.S.: 334516
Renejker Cher *(CEO)*

Subsidiary (Non-US):

Mestrelab Research S.L. (3)
Feliciano Barrera 9B - Bajo, 15706, San-
tiago de Compostela, Spain
Tel.: (34) 881976775
Web Site: https://mestrelab.com
Software Development Services
N.A.I.C.S.: 541511
Carlos Cobas *(Co-Founder & Pres)*
Santiago Dominguez *(Co-Founder & CEO)*
Javier Sardina *(Co-Founder)*
Izabella Krol *(Mgr-Consulting)*
Enrique Sanchez *(Editor-Contents)*
Esther Vaz *(Mgr-Quality)*
Cristina Geada *(Mgr-Office & Sls)*
Guy Desmarquets *(Sr VP-Global Sls &
Strategic Partnership)*
Gary Sharman *(Sr Dir-Scientific)*
Vanessa Castro *(Mgr-Regulatory & Pub
Funding)*
Alejandro Garcia *(Accountant)*
Miguel A. Garcia *(Mgr-Compliance)*

Subsidiary (Non-US):

Bruker BioSpin International AG (2)
Aegeristrasse 52, Zug, 6301, Switzerland
Tel.: (41) 447104433
Financial Investment Services
N.A.I.C.S.: 523999

Subsidiary (Non-US):

Bruker (Malaysia) SDN BHD (3)
Suite 03-12-13 and Suite 03-12-13A Level
12 Tower 3 Suite 03-12-13A, No 1 Jalan
Pengaturcara U1/51a Kawasan Perindus-
trian Temasya, 40150, Shah Alam, Selan-
gor, Malaysia
Tel.: (60) 358701388
Web Site: http://www.bruker.com
Scientific Instrument Mfr
N.A.I.C.S.: 334516

Representative Office (Non-US):

**Bruker BioSpin International AG -
Thailand Office** (3)
No 175 10th Floor Sathorn City Tower
South Sathorn Road, Kwaeng Thungma-
hamek Khet Sathorn, Bangkok, 10120,
Thailand
Tel.: (66) 20328999
Web Site: http://www.bruker.com
Sales Range: $1-9.9 Million
Emp.: 20
Sales & Service of Analytical Instruments
N.A.I.C.S.: 334516

Subsidiary (Non-US):

Bruker BioSpin Pte. Ltd. (3)
30 Biopolis Street Matrix 09-01, Singapore,
138671, Singapore
Tel.: (65) 65404388
Web Site: http://www.bruker.com
Sales Range: $25-49.9 Million
Emp.: 50
Magnetic Resonance Imaging Product Mfr
N.A.I.C.S.: 334516

Bruker Singapore Pte. Ltd. (3)
30 Biopolis Street Matrix 09-01, Singapore,
138671, Singapore
Tel.: (65) 65404388
Web Site: http://www.bruker.com
Analytical Equipment Distr
N.A.I.C.S.: 423490

Subsidiary (Non-US):

Bruker BioSpin K.K. (2)
8-29 Nishimiyahara 1-chome, Yodogawa-ku,
Osaka, 532-0004, Japan
Tel.: (81) 663948989
Magnetic Resonance Imaging Product Mfr

N.A.I.C.S.: 334516

Bruker BioSpin Korea Co. Ltd. (2)
14F KINS Tower 25-1 Jeongja-dong,
Bundang-gu, Seongnam, 463-847,
Gyeonggi-do, Korea (South)
Tel.: (82) 317267171
Magnetic Resonance Imaging Product Mfr
N.A.I.C.S.: 334516

Bruker BioSpin MRI GmbH (2)
Rudolf-Plank-Str 23, 76275, Ettlingen, Germany
Tel.: (49) 72437695155
Web Site: http://www.bruker.com
Emp.: 50
Magnetic Resonance Imaging Product Mfr
N.A.I.C.S.: 334516
Thorsten Thiel (VP-Mktg-Grp)

Subsidiary (Domestic):

Bruker BioSpin MRI Inc. (2)
15 Fortune Dr, Billerica, MA 01821-3991
Tel.: (978) 667-9580
Web Site: http://www.bruker-biospin.com
Emp.: 200
Magnetic Resonance Imaging Product Mfr
N.A.I.C.S.: 334516

Subsidiary (Non-US):

Bruker BioSpin S.A. (2)
34 rue de l industrie, 67166, Wissembourg,
France
Tel.: (33) 388736800
Web Site: http://www.bruker.com
Sales Range: $75-99.9 Million
Emp.: 340
Magnetic Resonance Imaging Product Mfr
N.A.I.C.S.: 334516
Alain Belguise (Pres)

Bruker BioSpin S.A. / N.V. (2)
Rue Colonel Bourg 122/ Bte 6, 1140, Brussels, Belgium
Tel.: (32) 27267626
Magnetic Resonance Imaging Product Mfr
N.A.I.C.S.: 334516

Bruker BioSpin Scandinavia AB (2)
Vallgatan 5, 170 67, Solna, Sweden
Tel.: (46) 86552510
Web Site: http://www.bruker.com
Sales Range: $10-24.9 Million
Emp.: 20
Magnetic Resonance Imaging Product Mfr
N.A.I.C.S.: 334516
Larus Einarsson (CEO)

Bruker Espanola S.A. (2)
Parque Empresarial Rivas Futura Edificio
Alfa Planta Baja, Rivas-Vaciamadrid, 28521,
Madrid, Spain
Tel.: (34) 914994080
Web Site: https://www.bruker.com
Sales Range: $10-24.9 Million
Emp.: 50
Sales & Service of Analytical Instruments
N.A.I.C.S.: 334516
Victor Darcia Pidal (Mng Dir)

Bruker India Scientific Pvt. Ltd. (2)
4th Floor Arliga North Star Building Bangalore Bellary Road, Yelahanka Post - Yelahanka Bangalore District, Bengaluru, 560
064, Karnataka, India
Tel.: (91) 8049278000
Life Science & Advanced Materials Research Tools Developer
N.A.I.C.S.: 334516

Bruker Nederland B.V. (2)
Elisabethhof 15, 2353 EW, Leiderdorp,
Netherlands
Tel.: (31) 881122700
Web Site: http://www.bruker.com
Sales Range: $25-49.9 Million
Emp.: 38
Magnetic Resonance Imaging Product Mfr
N.A.I.C.S.: 334516

Bruker Physik GmbH (2)
Rudolf-Plank-Strasse 23, 76275, Ettlingen,
Germany (50.5%)
Tel.: (49) 72151616500
Web Site: http://www.bruker.com
Analytical Laboratory Instrument Mfr
N.A.I.C.S.: 334516

Bruker Pty. Ltd. (2)

1A/28 Albert Street, Preston, 3072, VIC,
Australia
Tel.: (61) 295506422
Web Site: http://www.bruker.com
Magnetic Resonance Imaging Product Mfr
N.A.I.C.S.: 334516

Bruker Cellular Analysis, Inc. (1)
5858 Horton St Ste 320, Emeryville, CA
94608
Tel.: (510) 858-2855
Web Site: http://www.berkeleylights.com
Rev.: $78,595,000
Assets: $226,094,000
Liabilities: $84,039,000
Net Worth: $142,055,000
Earnings: ($98,040,000)
Emp.: 285
Fiscal Year-end: 12/31/2022
Biotechnology Research & Development
Services
N.A.I.C.S.: 541714
Siddhartha Kadia (CEO)
Scott Chaplin (Chief Legal Officer)
Gregory T. Lucier (Bd of Dirs, Executives)

Subsidiary (Domestic):

IsoPlexis Corporation (2)
35 NE Industrial Rd, Branford, CT 06405
Tel.: (203) 208-4111
Web Site: http://www.isoplexis.com
Rev.: $16,761,000
Assets: $109,068,000
Liabilities: $67,801,000
Net Worth: $41,267,000
Earnings: ($105,997,000)
Emp.: 290
Fiscal Year-end: 12/31/2022
Biotechnology Research & Development
Services
N.A.I.C.S.: 541714
Sean Mackay (Co-Founder)
Richard W. Rew II (Gen Counsel, Sec & Sr
VP)

Bruker Daltonics Inc. (1)
40 Manning Rd, Billerica, MA 01821
Tel.: (978) 663-3660
Web Site: http://www.bdal.com
Sales Range: $50-74.9 Million
Emp.: 200
Sales & Service of Analytical Instruments
N.A.I.C.S.: 334516

Division (Domestic):

**Bruker Chemical & Applied
Markets** (2)
3500 W Warren Ave, Fremont, CA 94538
Tel.: (510) 683-4300
Web Site: http://www.bruker.com
Laboratory Instrument Mfr
N.A.I.C.S.: 334516

Subsidiary (Non-US):

Bruker Daltonics K.K. (2)
9-A-6F Moriya-cho 3-chome, Kanagawa-ku,
Yokohama, 221-0022, Kanagawa, Japan
Tel.: (81) 454400471
Web Site: http://www.bruker.co.jp
Sales Range: $10-24.9 Million
Emp.: 18
Sales & Service of Analytical Instruments
N.A.I.C.S.: 334516

Bruker Daltonics Ltd. (2)
Banner Lane, Coventry, CV4 9GH, United
Kingdom
Tel.: (44) 2476855200
Web Site: http://www.bruker.com
Sales Range: $25-49.9 Million
Emp.: 100
Sale & Service of Analytical Instruments
N.A.I.C.S.: 334516

Bruker Daltonics Ltd. (2)
2800 Highpoint Dr Suite 206, Milton, L9T
6P4, ON, Canada
Tel.: (905) 876-4641
Web Site: https://www.bruker.com
Sales Range: $1-9.9 Million
Emp.: 40
Sales & Serivce of Analytical Instruments
N.A.I.C.S.: 334516

Bruker Daltonics Pte. Ltd. (2)
11 Biopolis Way 10 10 Helios, Singapore,
138667, Singapore
Tel.: (65) 65007288

Web Site: http://www.bruker.sg
Sales Range: $1-9.9 Million
Emp.: 6
Sales & Service of Analytical Instruments
N.A.I.C.S.: 334516

Bruker Daltonics Pty Ltd. (2)
PO Box 1091, Cramerview, 2060, South
Africa
Tel.: (27) 114636040
Analytical Laboratory Instrument Mfr
N.A.I.C.S.: 334516

Bruker Daltonics S.r.l. (2)
Via Cluentina 26/R, 62010, Macerata, Italy
Tel.: (39) 0733283141
Sales Range: $10-24.9 Million
Emp.: 11
Analytical Laboratory Instrument Mfr
N.A.I.C.S.: 334516
Simone Rubini (Mng Dir)

Bruker Daltonics SPRL/BVBA (2)
Kolonel Bourgstraat 122/Bus 6, 1140, Brussels, Belgium
Tel.: (32) 27267626
Web Site: http://www.bruker.com
Analytical Laboratory Instrument Mfr
N.A.I.C.S.: 334516

Bruker Daltonics Scandinavia AB (2)
Vallgatan 5, 170 67, Solna, Sweden
Tel.: (46) 86552540
Web Site: http://www.bruker.com
Sales Range: $25-49.9 Million
Emp.: 25
Sales & Service of Analytical Instruments
N.A.I.C.S.: 334516

Branch (Non-US):

Bruker Daltonics Scandinavia AB (3)
Kocksvej 22, 3600, Frederiksberg, Denmark
Tel.: (45) 20215444
Web Site: http://www.btal.com
Sales Range: $10-24.9 Million
Emp.: 25
Sales & Service of Analytical Instruments
N.A.I.C.S.: 334516

Subsidiary (Non-US):

Bruker Daltonics s.r.o. (2)
Prazakova 1000/60, 619 00, Brno, Czech
Republic
Tel.: (420) 544526988
Web Site: http://www.bruker.com
Sales Range: $10-24.9 Million
Emp.: 10
Spectrometer Product Mfr
N.A.I.C.S.: 334516
Michal Bohac (Mng Dir)

Bruker Daltonics, Inc. (2)
5 FL 3 No 1 Sec 1 Chung Yang Rd, Taipei,
Taiwan
Tel.: (886) 289823710
Web Site: http://www.bruker.com
Sales Range: $100-124.9 Million
Emp.: 10
Sales & Service of Analytical Instruments
N.A.I.C.S.: 334516

Bruker Daltonik GmbH (2)
Fahrenheitstr 4, 28359, Bremen, Germany
Tel.: (49) 4212205350
Sales Range: $75-99.9 Million
Emp.: 10
Sales & Service of Analytical Instruments
N.A.I.C.S.: 334516

Plant (Domestic):

Bruker Daltonik GmbH (3)
Permoserstr 15, 04318, Leipzig, Germany
Tel.: (49) 341243130
Web Site: http://www.bruker-daltonik.de
Sales Range: $50-74.9 Million
Emp.: 120
Sales & Service of Analytical Instruments
N.A.I.C.S.: 334516

Subsidiary (Domestic):

InVivo Biotech Svs GmbH. (3)
Neuendorfstr 24a, 16761, Hennigsdorf Berlin, Germany
Tel.: (49) 33028669321
Web Site: https://www.invivo.de
Pharma Research Application Tool Development Services
N.A.I.C.S.: 541512

Merlin Diagnostika GmbH (3)
Kleinstr 14, 53332, Bornheim, Germany
Tel.: (49) 222296310
Web Site: http://www.merlin-diagnostika.de
Pharma Research Application Tool Development Services
N.A.I.C.S.: 541512

Subsidiary (Non-US):

Bruker France S.A.S (2)
34 Rue de l'Industrie, Marne la Vallee,
67160, Wissembourg, Cedex,
France (100%)
Tel.: (33) 160954750
Web Site: http://www.bruker.com
Analytical Instruments Mfr & Services
N.A.I.C.S.: 334516

Bruker Finance B.V. (1)
Elisabeth court 15, 2353 EW, Leiderdorp,
Netherlands
Tel.: (31) 102711300
Analytical Equipment Distr
N.A.I.C.S.: 423490

Bruker France S.A.S. (1)
34 rue de l'industrie, 67166, Wissembourg,
Cedex, France
Tel.: (33) 388736800
Pharma Research Application Tool Development Services
N.A.I.C.S.: 541512

Bruker Italia S.r.l. (1)
Viale V Lancetti 43, 20158, Milan, Italy
Tel.: (39) 0270636370
Analytical Laboratory Instrument Mfr
N.A.I.C.S.: 334516
Silvia Di Stefano (Mgr-Mktg & Comm)

Bruker JV Israel Ltd. (1)
Zone 6 Ramat Gavriel Industrial Zone,
Migdal Ha'Emeq, 23100, Israel
Tel.: (972) 46543666
Scientific Instrument Mfr
N.A.I.C.S.: 334517

Subsidiary (Non-US):

Bruker JV UK Ltd. (2)
Belmont Business Park Belmont, Durham,
DH1 1TW, United Kingdom
Tel.: (44) 1913324700
Scientific Instrument Mfr
N.A.I.C.S.: 334517

Bruker Korea Co. Ltd. (1)
4F KTNET Building 338 Pangyo-ro,
Bundang-gu, Seongnam, 13493, Gyeonggi-do, Korea (South)
Tel.: (82) 317190123
Web Site: http://www.bruker.com
Emp.: 70
Analytical Equipment Distr
N.A.I.C.S.: 423490

Bruker Ltd. (1)
50/2-1 Pyatnitskaya Str, 119017, Moscow,
Russia
Tel.: (7) 4955179284
Scientific Instrument Mfr
N.A.I.C.S.: 334517

Bruker MicroCT N.V. (1)
Kartuizersweg 3B, 2550, Kontich, Belgium
Tel.: (32) 28805005
Analytical Equipment Distr
N.A.I.C.S.: 423490
Alexander Sasov (CEO & Mng Dir)

Bruker Optics Inc. (1)
19 Fortune Dr Manning Park, Billerica, MA
01821-3991
Tel.: (978) 439-9899
Web Site: http://www.bruker.com
Sales Range: $25-49.9 Million
Emp.: 30
Spectrometer Product Mfr
N.A.I.C.S.: 334516

Subsidiary (Non-US):

Bruker Optics AB (2)
Vallgatan 5, 170 67, Solna, Sweden
Tel.: (46) 86552530
Web Site: http://www.bruker.com
Spectrometer Product Mfr
N.A.I.C.S.: 334516

Bruker Optics GmbH (2)

Bruker Corporation—(Continued)

Industriestrasse 26, 8117, Fallanden, Switzerland
Tel.: (41) 448259111
Web Site: http://www.bruker.com
Spectrometer Product Mfr
N.A.I.C.S.: 334516

Bruker Optics K.K. (2)
3-9 Moriya-cho, Kanagawa-ku, Yokohama, 221-0022, Kanagawa, Japan (100%)
Tel.: (81) 454501601
Web Site: http://www.bruker.com
Spectrometer Product Mfr
N.A.I.C.S.: 334516

Bruker Optics LTD (2)
555 Steeles Ave East, Milton, L9T 1Y6, ON, Canada
Tel.: (905) 876-4641
Web Site: http://www.bruker.com
Analytical Laboratory Instrument Mfr
N.A.I.C.S.: 334516

Bruker Optics Ukraine
Kudryavskij spusk 5-B of 505, 04655, Kiev, Ukraine
Tel.: (380) 4427212581258
Web Site: https://brukeroptics.all.biz
Emp.: 2
Spectrometer Product Mfr
N.A.I.C.S.: 334516

Bruker Optik Asia Pacific Limited (2)
Unit 608 6/F Tower 1 Enterprise Sq No 9 Sheung Yuet Rd, Kowloon Bay, Hong Kong, China (Hong Kong)
Tel.: (852) 27966100
Web Site: http://www.bruker.com
Emp.: 10
Spectrometer Product Mfr
N.A.I.C.S.: 334516

Subsidiary (Non-US):

Bruker Korea Co., Ltd. (3)
4F KtNet Building 338 Pangyoro, Bundang-gu, Seongnam, 13493, Gyeonggi-do, Korea (South)
Tel.: (82) 317192100
Spectrometer Product Mfr
N.A.I.C.S.: 334516
Joo-Kang Park (Country Mgr)

Bruker Optics Taiwan Ltd. (3)
7F-12 No 16 Lane 609 Sec 5 Chung Hsien Rd, 24159, San Chung, Taipei, Taiwan
Tel.: (886) 222787358
Spectrometer Product Mfr
N.A.I.C.S.: 334516

Subsidiary (Non-US):

Bruker Optik GmbH (2)
Rudolf-Plank-Str 27, 76275, Ettlingen, Germany
Tel.: (49) 72435042000
Analytical Laboratory Instrument Mfr
N.A.I.C.S.: 334516

Subsidiary (Non-US):

Bruker Optics Scandinavia AB (3)
Vallgatan 5, 170 67, Solna, Sweden
Tel.: (46) 86552530
Analytical Equipment Distr
N.A.I.C.S.: 423490
Conny Holm (Bus Mgr)

Subsidiary (Non-US):

Bruker Optique SA (2)
4 Allee Hendrik Lorentz Parc de la Haute Maison - Bat A5, Champs-sur-Marne, Cedex, France
Tel.: (33) 164618110
Web Site: http://www.bruker.com
Emp.: 16
Analytical Laboratory Instrument Mfr
N.A.I.C.S.: 334516

Bruker Portugal Unipessoal LDA (1)
Rua da Quinta da Quinta 5 Quinta de Fonte, Edificio Plaza II RC - Fracao B, 2770-203, Paco d'Arcos, Portugal
Tel.: (351) 218257150
Analytical Laboratory Instrument Mfr
N.A.I.C.S.: 334516

Bruker Pty. Ltd. (1)
1A/28 Albert Street, Preston, 3072, VIC, Australia
Tel.: (61) 394747000
Web Site: http://www.bruker.com
Laboratory Equipment Distr
N.A.I.C.S.: 423490

Bruker Scientific Instruments Hong Kong Co., Ltd. (1)
Unit 608 6/F Tower 1 Enterprise Square 9 Sheung Yuet Road, Kowloon Bay, China (Hong Kong)
Tel.: (852) 27966100
Web Site: http://www.bruker.com
Analytical Equipment Distr
N.A.I.C.S.: 423490

Bruker Scientific Israel Ltd. (1)
5 Golda Me'ir st Science Park, PO Box 2445, Rehovot, 76123, Israel
Tel.: (972) 89477705
Emp.: 7
Spectrometer Product Mfr
N.A.I.C.S.: 334516
Itzhak Cohen (Gen Mgr)

Subsidiary (Domestic):

Jordan Valley Semiconductors, Ltd. (2)
Zone 6 Ramat Gavriel Industrial Zone, Migdal Ha'Emeq, 23100, Israel
Tel.: (972) 46543666
Web Site: http://www.jvsemi.com
Semiconductor Metrology Products & Services
N.A.I.C.S.: 333242
Isaac Mazor (Founder & CEO)
Avi Lifshitz (CFO)
Amos Gvirtzman (COO)
Matthew Wormington (CTO)
Kenneth Levy (Chm)

Subsidiary (Non-US):

Jordan Valley Semiconductor Co Ltd. (3)
10F - 2 No 120 Sec 2 Gongdao 5th Rd, Hsin-chu, 300, Taiwan
Tel.: (886) 3 5733180
Web Site: http://www.jvsemi.com
Semiconductor Metrology Products & Services
N.A.I.C.S.: 333242

Jordan Valley Semiconductors Korea Ltd. (3)
3F Poongsan Bldg 12-2 Hanil-ro, Gongse-dong Giheung-gu, Yongin, 446-902, Gyeonggi-do, Korea (South)
Tel.: (82) 31 275 3690
Web Site: http://www.jvsemi.com
Emp.: 15
Semiconductor Metrology Products & Services
N.A.I.C.S.: 333242

Jordan Valley Semiconductors UK, Ltd. (3)
Belmont Business Park, Belmont, Durham, DH1 1TW, United Kingdom
Tel.: (44) 1913324700
Web Site: http://www.jvsemi.com
X-Ray Metrology
N.A.I.C.S.: 334517

Subsidiary (US):

Jordan Valley Semiconductors, Inc. (3)
3913 Todd Ln Ste 106, Austin, TX 78744
Tel.: (512) 832-8470
Web Site: http://www.jvsemi.com
Semiconductor Metrology Products & Services
N.A.I.C.S.: 333242
Isaac Mazor (CEO)

Bruker Scientific LLC (1)
40 Manning Rd Manning Park, Billerica, MA 01821
Tel.: (978) 663-3660
Scientific Instrument Mfr
N.A.I.C.S.: 334517

Subsidiary (Domestic):

Bruker Detection Corporation (2)
40 Manning Rd, Billerica, MA 01821
Tel.: (978) 663-3660

Web Site: http://www.bruker.com
Radiation Detection Equipment Mfr
N.A.I.C.S.: 334519

Bruker Switzerland AG (1)
Industriestr 26, Faellanden, 8117, Zurich, Switzerland
Tel.: (41) 448259111
Laboratory Instrument Mfr
N.A.I.C.S.: 334516

Bruker Taiwan Co. Ltd. (1)
3F-3 No 6 Taiyuan 1st St, Hsinchu County, Zhubei, 30288, Taiwan
Tel.: (886) 35601212
Web Site: http://www.bruker.com
Analytical Laboratory Instrument Mfr
N.A.I.C.S.: 334516

ELITech Group SAS (1)
13-15 bis rue Jean Jaures, 92800, Puteaux, France
Tel.: (33) 141450710
Web Site: http://www.elitechgroup.com
Diagnostic Products Distr & Mfr
N.A.I.C.S.: 424210

Subsidiary (Domestic):

ELITech France SAS (2)
13-15 rue jean Jaures, 92800, Puteaux, France
Tel.: (33) 4 83 36 10 82
Web Site: http://www.elitechgroup.com
Medical Equipment Distr
N.A.I.C.S.: 423450

Subsidiary (Non-US):

ELITech Ltda. (2)
R Jose Vivacqua 35, Jabour, Vitoria, Espirito Santo, Brazil
Tel.: (55) 27 3025 1415
Web Site: http://www.elitechgroup.com
Medical Equipment Distr
N.A.I.C.S.: 423450

Subsidiary (Domestic):

ELITech Microbio SAS (2)
Parc d'Activites 19 Allee d'Athenes, 83870, Signes, France
Tel.: (33) 4 94 88 55 00
Web Site: http://www.elitechgroup.com
Medical Equipment Distr
N.A.I.C.S.: 423450

Subsidiary (Non-US):

ELITech SA/NV (2)
Trapstraat 16, 9620, Zottegem, Belgium
Tel.: (32) 9 2820 531
Web Site: http://www.elitechgroup.com
Medical Equipment Distr
N.A.I.C.S.: 423450

ELITech SR d.o.o. (2)
Boze Jankovica br 42, Belgrade, Serbia
Tel.: (381) 11 2467119
Web Site: http://www.elitechgroup.com
Medical Equipment Distr
N.A.I.C.S.: 423450

ELITech UK Limited (2)
Unit 6 River Park Industrial Estate Billet Lane, Berkhamsted, HP4 IHL, Herts, United Kingdom
Tel.: (44) 1442 869320,
Web Site: http://www.elitechgroup.com
Medical Equipment Distr
N.A.I.C.S.: 423450

ELITechGroup Australia Pty. Ltd. (2)
65 Mills Road, Braeside, 3195, VIC, Australia (100%)
Tel.: (61) 2 9894 6988
Web Site: http://www.elitechgroup.com
Laboratory Diagnostics & Instrumentation Distr
N.A.I.C.S.: 423450

Subsidiary (Non-US):

ELITechGroup (NZ) Limited (3)
PO Box 128-016, Remuera, Auckland, New Zealand
Tel.: (64) 800555611
Web Site: http://www.elitechgroup.com
Laboratory Diagnostics & Instrumentation Distr
N.A.I.C.S.: 423450

Subsidiary (Non-US):

ELITechGroup B.V. (2)
Van Rensselaerweg 4, Spankeren, 6956 AV, Dieren, Netherlands
Tel.: (31) 313 430 500
Web Site: http://www.elitechgroup.com
Medical Equipment Distr
N.A.I.C.S.: 423450

Subsidiary (Domestic):

ELITechGroup Clinical Systems SAS (2)
Zone Industrielle 4 rue Auguste Mottin, 61500, Sees, France
Tel.: (33) 2 33 81 21 00
Web Site: http://www.elitechgroup.com
Pharmaceuticals Product Mfr
N.A.I.C.S.: 325412

Subsidiary (US):

ELITechGroup Inc. (2)
370 W 1700 S, Logan, UT 84321
Tel.: (435) 752-6011
Web Site: http://www.elitechgroup.com
Clinical Chemistry, Molecular Diagnostics, Microbiology, Cystic Fibrosis & Transplant Monitoring
N.A.I.C.S.: 339112
Chris Larsen (Sr Dir-Sls-North America)
Amanda Warren (Dir-Mktg)
Diana Mejia (Sls Mgr-Latin America)
Bryce McEuen (VP-Biomedical Sys)

Division (Domestic):

ELITechGroup Molecular Diagnostics (3)
21720 23rd Dr SE Ste 150, Bothell, WA 98021
Tel.: (425) 482-5555
Web Site: http://www.elitechgroup.com
Diagnostic Products Mfr
N.A.I.C.S.: 334516

Subsidiary (Non-US):

ELITechGroup S.p.A. (2)
C so Svizzera 185, 10149, Turin, Italy
Tel.: (39) 011976191
Web Site: http://www.elitechgroup.com
Diagnostic Systems & Products Mfr & Distr
N.A.I.C.S.: 423450

Flextra Lab KFT. (1)
Jokai u 26/c, 1195, Budapest, Hungary (100%)
Tel.: (36) 12827800
Web Site: http://www.bruker.hu
Rev.: $503,237
Emp.: 7
Fiscal Year-end: 12/31/2014
Sales & Service of Analytical Instruments
N.A.I.C.S.: 334516

Hain LifeScience UK Ltd. (1)
Unit 3-4 Byfleet Technical Centre Canada Road, Byfleet, KT14 7JX, Surrey, United Kingdom
Tel.: (44) 1932344550
Scientific Instrument Mfr & Distr
N.A.I.C.S.: 334517

Hain LifeSciences S.A. Pty. Ltd. (1)
Building A Lincolnwood Office Park Woodlands Drive, Woodmead, 2191, South Africa
Tel.: (27) 126651000
Web Site: http://www.hain-lifescience.co.za
Scientific Instrument Distr
N.A.I.C.S.: 423490
Shanil Govindpershad (Gen Mgr)

Hydrostatic Extrusions Ltd. (1)
Banner Lane, Coventry, CV4 9GH, Warks, United Kingdom
Tel.: (44) 1738494500
Web Site: http://www.bruker-est.com
Electrical Conductor Distr
N.A.I.C.S.: 423690

Hysitron, Inc. (1)
9625 W 76th St, Minneapolis, MN 55344
Tel.: (952) 835-6366
Web Site: http://www.hysitron.com
Sales Range: $10-24.9 Million
Emp.: 57
Nanomechanical Test Instruments Mfr & Distr
N.A.I.C.S.: 334413

InVivo Biotech Svx GmbH (1)
Neuendorfstr 24a, 16761, Hennigsdorf Berlin, Germany
Tel.: (49) 3302866930
Web Site: https://www.invivo.de
Pharmaceutical Research & Development Services
N.A.I.C.S.: 541714

Ionsense, Inc. (1)
999 Broadway Ste 404, Saugus, MA 01906-4510
Tel.: (781) 484-1043
Web Site: http://www.ionsense.com
Analytical Laboratory Instrument Mfr
N.A.I.C.S.: 334516

Luxendo GmbH (1)
Kurfursten-Anlage 58, 69115, Heidelberg, Germany
Tel.: (49) 62211873150
Web Site: http://luxendo.eu
Pharma Research Application Tool Development Services
N.A.I.C.S.: 541512

NanoString Technologies, Inc. (1)
530 Fairview Ave N, Seattle, WA 98109
Tel.: (206) 378-6266
Web Site: https://www.nanostring.com
Rev.: $127,262,000
Assets: $353,412,000
Liabilities: $307,598,000
Net Worth: $45,814,000
Earnings: ($159,543,000)
Emp.: 703
Fiscal Year-end: 12/31/2022
Research & Development in Biotechnology (except Nanobiotechnology)
N.A.I.C.S.: 541714
Kathryn Surace-Smith (Sr VP-HR & Legal Affairs)
David W. Ghesquiere (Sr VP-Corp & Bus Dev)
Mark A. Winham (Sr VP-Ops)
Todd Garland (Chief Comml Officer)

Nion, Co. (1)
1102 8th St, Kirkland, WA 98033
Tel.: (425) 576-9060
Web Site: http://www.nion.com
Sales Range: $1-9.9 Million
Emp.: 13
Professional Equipment & Supplies Merchant Whslr
N.A.I.C.S.: 423490
Niklas Dellby (VP-Res)

PMOD Technologies LLC (1)
Industriestrasse 26, 8117, Fallanden, Switzerland
Tel.: (41) 443504600
Web Site: https://www.pmod.com
Software Development Services
N.A.I.C.S.: 541511
Cyrill Burger (CEO)

Perch Solutions OY (1)
Hyrrakatu 3A1, 70500, Kuopio, Finland
Tel.: (358) 174418582
Web Site: http://perch-solutions-oy.ohjeistaa.fi
Software Development Services
N.A.I.C.S.: 541511

Prairie Technologies, Inc. (1)
3030 Laura Ln Ste 140, Middleton, WI 53562
Tel.: (608) 662-0022
Web Site: http://www.prairie-technologies.com
Sales Range: $10-24.9 Million
Emp.: 30
Microscopy Photon Systems Mfr
N.A.I.C.S.: 334419

Precision Diagnostics, Inc. (1)
4215 Sorrento Valley Blvd, San Diego, CA 92121
Web Site: https://www.precisiondxlab.com
Laboratory Testing Services
N.A.I.C.S.: 541380
Miguel Gallego (Pres & CEO)
Cortney Hergenroeder (VP-Sls)
Colm Driscoll (CFO)
Richard Thomas (Chief Scientific Officer)

RAVE LLC (1)
430 S Congress Ave Ste 7, Delray Beach, FL 33445

Tel.: (561) 330-0411
Web Site: http://www.ravenano.com
Process Solutions to Semiconductor & Photomask Industries Provider
N.A.I.C.S.: 423690

SmartTip BV (1)
High Tech Factory Veldmaat 17, 7522 NB, Enschede, Netherlands
Tel.: (31) 537112700
Web Site: http://www.smarttip.nl
Laboratory Testing Services
N.A.I.C.S.: 541380

BRUNSWICK CORPORATION
26125 N Riverwoods Blvd Ste 500, Mettawa, IL 60045-3420
Tel.: (847) 735-4700   DE
Web Site: https://www.brunswick.com
Year Founded: 1845
BC—(NYSE)
Rev.: $6,401,400,000
Assets: $6,230,500,000
Liabilities: $4,143,100,000
Net Worth: $2,087,400,000
Earnings: $420,400,000
Emp.: 17,300
Fiscal Year-end: 12/31/23
Boats, Marine Parts & Accessories, Engines & Recreational Products Marketer & Mfr
N.A.I.C.S.: 336612
Christopher F. Dekker (Chief Compliance Officer, Gen Counsel, Sec & Exec VP)
David M. Foulkes (CEO)
Randall S. Altman (Sr VP & Controller)
Brenna D. Preisser (Pres-Bus Acceleration & Exec VP-Strategy)
Jeffry K. Behan (VP-Corp Strategy)
Ryan M. Gwillim (CFO & Exec VP)
Neha J. Clark (Sr VP-Enterprise Fin)
Brett A. Dibkey (Pres-Navico Grp & Exec VP)
Aine L. Denari (Pres-Brunswick Boat Grp & Exec VP)
Lee B. Gordon (VP-Corp Comm, Pub Affairs, and Global PR)
Michael D. Adams (CIO & VP)
Jill M. Wrobel (Chief HR Officer & Exec VP)
John G. Buelow (Pres-Mercury Marine & Exec VP)
Aine L. Denari (Pres-Brunswick Boat Grp & Exec VP)
Lauren E. Beckstedt (CMO & VP)
Alexandra Cattelan (CTO)
Neha J. Clark (Sr VP-Enterprise Fin)
Gordon B. Lee (VP)

Subsidiaries:

Aus Holdco Pty. Limited (1)
131 Rivergate Pl Murarrie, Brisbane, 4172, QLD, Australia
Tel.: (61) 130 025 2725
Web Site: https://www.bla.com.au
Emp.: 140
Sporting & Athletic Goods Distr
N.A.I.C.S.: 423910

Brunswick Boat Group (1)
1st Tennessee Plz Bldg Ste 1200 800 S Gay St, Knoxville, TN 37929
Tel.: (865) 582-2200
Web Site: http://www.brunswick.com
Sales Range: $1-4.9 Billion
Boats, Marine Parts & Accessories Mfr & Distr
N.A.I.C.S.: 336612
Huw S. Bower (Pres & VP)
Aine L. Denari (CEO, Exec VP & VP)

Subsidiary (Domestic):

Attwood Corporation (2)
1016 N Monroe St, Lowell, MI 49331
Tel.: (616) 897-2301
Web Site: https://new.attwoodmarine.com
Sales Range: $75-99.9 Million
Marine Accessories & Hardware Mfr
N.A.I.C.S.: 332510

Boston Whaler, Inc. (2)
100 Whaler Way, Edgewater, FL 32141
Tel.: (386) 428-0057
Web Site: https://www.bostonwhaler.com
Sales Range: $200-249.9 Million
Fiberglass Power Boats Mfr
N.A.I.C.S.: 336612

Affiliate (Domestic):

Brunswick Commercial & Government Products, Inc. (3)
100 Whaler Way, Edgewater, FL 32141
Tel.: (386) 423-2900
Web Site: https://www.brunswickcgp.com
Sales Range: $25-49.9 Million
Emp.: 100
Commercial & Government Boats Mfr
N.A.I.C.S.: 336612

Subsidiary (Domestic):

Brunswick Leisure Boat Company, LLC (2)
2801 W State Blvd, Fort Wayne, IN 46808-1801
Tel.: (260) 432-4555
Web Site: http://www.brunswick.com
Sales Range: $25-49.9 Million
Emp.: 200
Boat Mfr
N.A.I.C.S.: 336612

Crestliner, Inc. (2)
1301 Crestview Dr, Little Falls, MN 56345-2207
Tel.: (320) 632-6686
Web Site: http://www.crestliner.com
Sales Range: $125-149.9 Million
Emp.: 20
Aluminum Boats Mfr
N.A.I.C.S.: 336612

Freedom Boat Club LLC (2)
990 Laguna Dr, Venice, FL 34285
Tel.: (941) 451-8756
Web Site: http://www.freedomboatclub.com
Sales Range: $1-9.9 Million
Emp.: 100
Boat Club Owner & Franchisor
N.A.I.C.S.: 713910
Barry Slade (VP-Business Development)
Louis Chemi (VP)
Lindsay Sheffield (Dir-Administration-Member Service)
Bill Edinger (Dir-Jacksonville Beach)
Martha Wagley (Mgr-Trng)
Stephen Jacobs (Dir)
Nick Gosselin (Dir-Mktg)
Mike Pratt (Dir)
John Combes (Dir-South)
Nicholas Thomas (Sr Dir-Operations)
Jim Cull (Coord-Business Development)
Joe Bettley (CFO)
Ryan Brunette (Dir-Operations-Jacksonville,St. Augustine)
George Biastre Jr. (Dir)
Randy Underwood II (Mgr)

Hatteras Yachts (2)
110 N Glenburnie Rd, New Bern, NC 28560   (100%)
Tel.: (252) 633-3101
Web Site: https://www.hatterasyachts.com
Sales Range: $75-99.9 Million
Emp.: 200
Yacht Mfr
N.A.I.C.S.: 336612
Gregory Segall (Chm)

Land 'N' Sea Distributing, Inc. (2)
3131 N Andrews Ave Ext, Pompano Beach, FL 33064
Tel.: (954) 792-9971
Web Site: https://www.landnsea.com
Sales Range: $50-74.9 Million
Marine Parts & Accessories Distr
N.A.I.C.S.: 423860

Lowe Boats (2)
2900 Industrial Dr, Lebanon, MO 65536
Tel.: (417) 532-9101
Web Site: https://www.loweboats.com
Sales Range: $125-149.9 Million
Emp.: 325
Boat Mfr
N.A.I.C.S.: 336612
Greg Falkner (Gen Mgr)

Lund Boat Company (2)

19 E Centennial 84 Dr, New York Mills, MN 56567
Tel.: (218) 385-2855
Web Site: http://vaughnautomarine.com
Sales Range: $200-249.9 Million
Aluminum & Fiberglass Boats Mfr
N.A.I.C.S.: 336612

Subsidiary (Non-US):

Princecraft Boats, Inc. (2)
725 Saint-Henri, Princeville, G6L 5C2, QC, Canada   (100%)
Tel.: (819) 364-5581
Web Site: https://www.princecraft.com
Sales Range: $125-149.9 Million
Aluminum Fishing Boats Mfr
N.A.I.C.S.: 336612

Subsidiary (Domestic):

Sea Ray Boats, Inc. (2)
800 S Gay St Ste 1200, Knoxville, TN 37929
Tel.: (865) 582-2200
Web Site: http://www.searay.com
Sales Range: $250-299.9 Million
Emp.: 2,385
Fiberglass Boat Mfr
N.A.I.C.S.: 336612
Terry McNew (Sr VP-Product Dev & Engrg)

Brunswick Indoor Recreation Group (1)
1 N Field Ct, Lake Forest, IL 60045
Tel.: (847) 735-4700
Web Site: http://www.brunswickbowling.com
Sales Range: $10-24.9 Million
Emp.: 35
Bowling Centers Owner & Operator
N.A.I.C.S.: 713950

Subsidiary (Domestic):

Brunswick Bowling & Billiards Corporation (2)
1 N Field Ct, Lake Forest, IL 60045-4811
Tel.: (847) 735-4700
Web Site: http://www.brunswickbowling.com
Bowling Equipment Mfr
N.A.I.C.S.: 339920

Brunswick International Limited (1)
1 N Field Ct, Lake Forest, IL 60045-4810
Tel.: (847) 735-4765
Holding Company
N.A.I.C.S.: 551112

Subsidiary (Non-US):

Brunswick GmbH (2)
Prater Hauptallee 124, Vienna, 1020, Austria
Tel.: (43) 172807090
Web Site: http://www.us_play.com
Printed Circuit Board Assemblies Mfr & Testing & Assembly of Electronics Systems & Sub Systems
N.A.I.C.S.: 334412

Brunswick Hungary Manufacturing and Trading Limited Liability Company (2)
Sosto St 4, Szekesfehervar, 8000, Hungary
Tel.: (36) 22512900
Web Site: http://www.bruneowl.com
Emp.: 60
Marine Parts & Accessories, Engines & Recreational Products Marketer & Mfr
N.A.I.C.S.: 423860
Jozsef Toth (Mng Dir)

Brunswick International GmbH (2)
Ginnheimer Strasse 6, Eschborn, 65760, Germany
Tel.: (49) 619647270
Bowling Ball Mfr
N.A.I.C.S.: 339920

Brunswick Netherlands B.V. (2)
Oude Haagseweg 47, 1066 BV, Amsterdam, 1066, Netherlands
Tel.: (31) 205110011
Printed Circuit Board Assemblies Mfr & Testing & Assembly of Electronics Systems & Sub Systems
N.A.I.C.S.: 334412
Marcel Rijnbeek (Mng Dir)

Cy-Tech GmbH (1)

Brunswick Corporation—(Continued)

Happurger Str 84-88, 90482, Nuremberg, Germany
Tel.: (49) 911544450
Web Site: http://www.indoorcycling.com
Sporting & Athletic Goods Distr
N.A.I.C.S.: 423910

Fanautic Club, S.L. (1)
Gremi Cirurgians I Barbers 48, Baleares, 07009, Palma de Mallorca, Spain
Tel.: (34) 971571344
Web Site: https://www.fanauticclub.com
Sailing Club Services
N.A.I.C.S.: 713930

Fliteboard Europe B.V. (1)
Tt Vasumweg 114, 1033 SH, Amsterdam, Netherlands
Tel.: (31) 648013732
Web Site: https://eu.fliteboard.com
Sports Goods Mfr & Distr
N.A.I.C.S.: 339920

Fliteboard Pty Limited (1)
156 Jonson Street, Byron Bay, 2481, NSW, Australia
Tel.: (61) 251189888
Web Site: https://fliteboard.com
Emp.: 50
Electrical Product Mfr & Distr
N.A.I.C.S.: 335999

Indoor Cycling Group GmbH (1)
Happurger Str 86, 90482, Nuremberg, Germany
Tel.: (49) 911544450
Web Site: http://www.teamicg.com
Sporting & Athletic Goods Distr
N.A.I.C.S.: 423910

Lankhorst Taselaar B.V. (1)
Komeet 13, 8448 CG, Heerenveen, Netherlands
Tel.: (31) 32 027 4611
Web Site: http://www.lankhorst-taselaar.nl
Marine Products Distr
N.A.I.C.S.: 423860

Lenco Marine Solutions, LLC (1)
4700 SE Municipal Ct, Stuart, FL 34997
Tel.: (772) 288-2662
Web Site: https://www.lencomarine.com
Marine Transportation Equipment Distr
N.A.I.C.S.: 423860

Mercury Marine Group (1)
6250 W Pioneer Rd, Fond Du Lac, WI 54935-1939
Tel.: (920) 929-5000
Web Site: https://www.mercurymarine.com
Sales Range: $1-4.9 Billion
Emp.: 6,200
Marine Propulsion Systems Mfr
N.A.I.C.S.: 333618
Jeff Etapa (Engr-Sound)
Patti Trapp (Dir-Quality)
Mike Butler (Mgr-Svc)
Kevin Muth (Mgr-Trng)
William Robertson (Engr-Emissions)
Todd Dannenberg (Dir-Design)
Matt Jaeger (Engr-Mechanical)
Steve Miller (Mgr-Category)

Subsidiary (Non-US):

Brunswick Marine in EMEA, Inc. (2)
Parc Industriel de Petit-Rechain, 4800, Verviers, Belgium
Tel.: (32) 87323211
Web Site: http://www.mercury-marine.eu
Sales Range: $150-199.9 Million
Boat & Marine Equipment & Accessories Wholr
N.A.I.C.S.: 423860
Martin Bass (Gen Mgr)

Marine Power International Pty. Ltd. (2)
41-71 Bessemer Dr, Dandenong, 3175, VIC, Australia
Tel.: (61) 397915822
Web Site: http://www.mercurymarine.com.au
Sales Range: $25-49.9 Million
Emp.: 80
Outboard Motors Mfr
N.A.I.C.S.: 333618

Division (Domestic):

Mercury Electronics & Plastics Manufacturing (2)

1000 Robinson Ave, Saint Cloud, FL 34769-4026
Tel.: (407) 892-2121
Web Site: https://www.mercepm.com
Sales Range: $10-24.9 Million
Emp.: 65
Electronics & Plastics Mfr
N.A.I.C.S.: 334419

Subsidiary (Non-US):

Mercury Marine Ltd. (2)
8698 Escartment way, Milton, L9T0M1, ON, Canada
Tel.: (905) 567-6372
Web Site: http://www.mercurymarine.com
Sales Range: $25-49.9 Million
Emp.: 45
Marine Propulsion Systems Mfr
N.A.I.C.S.: 333618
Jeff Etapa (Engr-Sound)
Patti Trapp (Dir-Quality)
William Robertson (Engr-Emissions)
Kevin Muth (Mgr-Trng)
Mike Butler (Mgr-Svc)
Matt Jaeger (Engr-Mechanical)
Todd Dannenberg (Dir-Design)
Steve Miller (Mgr-Category)

Mercury Marine Singapore Pte Ltd (2)
11 Changi South Street 3 01-02, Singapore, 486122, Singapore
Tel.: (65) 6 805 8100
Web Site: http://www.mercurymarine.com
Marine Engine Products Mfr
N.A.I.C.S.: 333618

Productos Marine de Mexico, S.A. de C.V. (2)
Calle Ohm 8451, 32470, Ciudad Juarez, Chihuahua, Mexico
Tel.: (52) 6566250770
Web Site: http://www.mercurymarine.com
Sales Range: $200-249.9 Million
Emp.: 700
Marine Equipment Mfr
N.A.I.C.S.: 333618

Munster Simms Engineering Limited (1)
1 and 2 Enterprise Road, Bangor, BT19 7TA, Down, United Kingdom
Tel.: (44) 2891270531
Web Site: https://www.whalepumps.com
Heating System Mfr & Distr
N.A.I.C.S.: 333414
Patrick Roberts (Mng Dir)

Navico Australia Pty Limited (1)
Level 8 15 Orion Rd, Lane Cove, 2066, NSW, Australia
Tel.: (61) 29 936 1000
Marine Parts Mfr
N.A.I.C.S.: 333618

Navico Holding AS (1)
Elganeveien 1, 4373, Egersund, Norway
Tel.: (47) 51463230
Web Site: https://www.navico.com
Sales Range: $300-349.9 Million
Emp.: 1,500
Holding Company; Marine Electronics Equipment Mfr & Distr
N.A.I.C.S.: 551112
Gordon Sprouse (Dir-Marketing-Americas)
Marc Jourlait (Deputy CEO)
Steve Rae (Mgr)
Tara Norton (Chief Sustainability Officer)
Knut Frostad (Pres & CEO)
Jarred Clayton (CTO)
Chris Davies (Gen Counsel)
Patricia Gyorey (Chief Supply Chain Officer)
Simon Little (Chief HR Officer)
Jordi Neves (CMO)
Alain Pakiry (Chief Comml Officer)
Jeroen van de Polder (Chief Acctg Officer)
Jarred Clayton (CTO)
Chris Davies (Gen Counsel)
Patricia Gyorey (Chief Supply Chain Officer)
Simon Little (Chief HR Officer)
Jordi Neves (CMO)
Alain Pakiry (Chief Comml Officer)
Jeroen van de Polder (Chief Acctg Officer)

Division (US):

Blue Sea Systems (2)
4600 Ryzex Way, Bellingham, WA 98226
Tel.: (360) 738-8230

Web Site: http://www.bluesea.com
Marine & Specialty Vehicle Electrical Systems Mfr
N.A.I.C.S.: 335931

Subsidiary (Non-US):

Brookes & Gatehouse, Ltd. (2)
Premier Way Abbey Pk, Romsey, SO51 9DH, Hampshire, United Kingdom
Tel.: (44) 1794510010
Web Site: http://www.bandg.com
Sales Range: $25-49.9 Million
Emp.: 30
Mfr of Marine Navigation Products
N.A.I.C.S.: 334511

Subsidiary (US):

Navico, Inc. (2)
4500 S 129th East Ave Ste 200, Tulsa, OK 74134
Tel.: (918) 437-6881
Web Site: http://www.lowrance.com
Sonar & Navigational Equipment & Accessories Mfr & Distr
N.A.I.C.S.: 334511
Tracy Brown (Engr-Software-II)
Kent Jopling (Sr VP-R&D)

Power Products, LLC (1)
N85 W12545 Westbrook Crossing, Menomonee Falls, WI 53051
Tel.: (262) 293-0600
Web Site: https://www.powerprodllc.com
Holding Company; Electric Technological Products Mfr & Distr
N.A.I.C.S.: 551112

SCIFIT Systems, Inc. (1)
5151 S 110th E Ave, Tulsa, OK 74146-5840
Tel.: (918) 359-2000
Web Site: http://www.scifit.com
Sporting & Athletic Goods Mfr
N.A.I.C.S.: 339920

Thunder Jet Boats, Inc. (1)
1401 Bridge St, Clarkston, WA 99403
Tel.: (509) 769-2142
Web Site: https://www.thunderjet.com
Boat Whslr
N.A.I.C.S.: 441222

BRYN MAWR BANK CORPORATION
801 Lancaster Ave, Bryn Mawr, PA 19010
Tel.: (610) 525-1700 PA
Web Site: http://www.bmtc.com
Year Founded: 1889
BMTC—(NASDAQ)
Rev.: $249,652,000
Assets: $5,432,022,000
Liabilities: $4,809,700,000
Net Worth: $622,322,000
Earnings: $32,573,000
Emp.: 603
Fiscal Year-end: 12/31/20
Bank Holding Company
N.A.I.C.S.: 551111
Britton H. Murdoch (Chm)
F. Kevin Tylus (Pres-BMT Banking)
Lori A. Buchanan Goldman (Gen Counsel, Sec & Sr VP)
Patrick M. Killeen (Chief Risk Officer & Exec VP)
Jennifer Dempsey Fox (Pres-Wealth Mgmt)
Liam Brickloy (Chief Credit Officer & Sr VP)
Adam D. Bonanno (CTO & Exec VP)
Linda A. Sanchez (Chief HR Officer & Exec VP)
Emanuel Ball (Sr VP & Dir-Facilities)

Subsidiaries:

Bryn Mawr Brokerage Co., Inc. (1)
801 W Lancaster Ave, Bryn Mawr, PA 19010
Tel.: (610) 525-1700
Web Site: http://www.bmtc.com
Insurance Agency & Brokerage Services
N.A.I.C.S.: 524210

The Bryn Mawr Trust Company (1)

801 Lancaster Ave, Bryn Mawr, PA 19010
Tel.: (610) 581-4839
Web Site: http://www.bmt.com
Commercial Banking
N.A.I.C.S.: 522110
F. Kevin Tylus (Pres-Banking)
Patrick M. Killeen (Chief Risk Officer & Exec VP)
Jennifer Dempsey Fox (Pres-Wealth Mgmt)
Tina S. McDonald (Sr VP-Mktg)
Christopher McGill (Pres-Philadelphia & Southern New Jersey)
Michael Thompson (CFO-Banking Div & Sr VP)
Mark E. Bradford (Sr VP & Dir-Wealth Banking)
Jim Donovan (Sr VP-Comml & Industrial Banking)
Jim Egan (Sr VP-Comml & R/E Lending)
Lindsay Saling (Sr VP & Dir-Retail Banking)
Neil Orechiwsky (Sr VP & Mng Dir-Capital Markets)
Thomas Forker (Sr VP & Area Mgr-Mortgage)
Todd Ferrara (Sr VP-Corp Sls)
Steven R. Klammer (Sr VP & Dir-Wealth Advisory Svcs)
Philip C. Wagner (Sr VP & Dir-Investment Advisory Svcs)
Dick Boothby (Sr VP)
William Higgins (Dir-Comml Lines)
James R. Domenick (Sr VP)
Rachel Lindeman (Sr VP & Mgr-Comml Real Estate Relationship & Construction Loan)
George Robostello (Sr VP & Mng Dir-Comml Banking-New Jersey South)
Jerry Cary (Chief Diversity Officer & VP)
Lori Buchanan Goldman (Gen Counsel & Exec VP)

Subsidiary (Domestic):

BMT Insurance Advisors Inc. (2)
Daylesford Plz 1436 Lancaster Ave, Berwyn, PA 19312
Tel.: (610) 527-1881
Web Site: http://www.bmtc.com
Insurance Brokerage & Risk Management Consulting Services
N.A.I.C.S.: 524210
Colleen K. Crenny (VP-Comml Insurance)
Nancy K. Albanese (VP-Personal Insurance)
Dennis B. LeVasseur (Sr VP & Sls Mgr-Comml Insurance)
Kimberly Trubiano (Pres)

Division (Domestic):

Domenick & Associates (3)
325 Chestnut St Ste 916, Philadelphia, PA 19106
Tel.: (215) 629-5701
Insurance Brokerage
N.A.I.C.S.: 524210
Jim Domenick (Pres)

The Bryn Mawr Trust Company of Delaware (1)
20 Montchanin Rd Ste 100, Greenville, DE 19807
Tel.: (302) 798-1790
Web Site: http://www.bmtcwealth.com
Emp.: 10
Investment Banking, Trust & Wealth Management Services
N.A.I.C.S.: 523150
Robert W. Eaddy (Pres)

Subsidiary (Domestic):

Lau Associates LLC (2)
20 Montchanin Rd Ste 110, Greenville, DE 19807
Tel.: (302) 792-5955
Web Site: http://www.lauassociates.net
Sales Range: $25-49.9 Million
Emp.: 13
Investment Advisory Services
N.A.I.C.S.: 523940

BRYN RESOURCES, INC.
635 16th St, Niagara Falls, NY 14301
Tel.: (716) 371-0184 CO
BRYN—(OTCIQ)
Communications Infrastructure Services
N.A.I.C.S.: 517810

Kimberly L. Moore *(CEO)*

BSR REAL ESTATE INVESTMENT TRUST
1400 W Markham Ste 202, Little Rock, AR 72201
Tel.: (501) 374-5050
Web Site: http://www.bsrreit.com
Year Founded: 2018
HOM—(TSX)
Rev.: $111,664,000
Assets: $1,122,701,000
Liabilities: $837,697,000
Net Worth: $285,004,000
Earnings: ($53,207,000)
Fiscal Year-end: 12/31/19
Real Estate Investment Services
N.A.I.C.S.: 531210
John S. Bailey *(CEO)*
Susan R. Koehn *(CFO)*
F. Blake Brazeal *(Pres & COO)*
Daniel M. Oberste *(Chief Investment Officer & Exec VP)*
Davi Miesner *(VP-Ops)*

BT BRANDS, INC.
405 Main Ave W Ste 2D, West Fargo, ND 58078
Tel.: (701) 277-0080   WY
Year Founded: 2016
BTBD—(NASDAQ)
Rev.: $12,601,169
Assets: $16,769,697
Liabilities: $6,617,075
Net Worth: $10,152,622
Earnings: ($562,285)
Emp.: 54
Fiscal Year-end: 01/01/23
Food Products Mfr
N.A.I.C.S.: 311919
Gary Copperud *(CEO)*
Kenneth Brimmer *(Chm, CFO, COO & Principal Acctg Officer)*
Allan Anderson *(Dir)*

BTCS INC.
9466 Georgia Ave Ste 124, Silver Spring, MD 20910
Tel.: (202) 987-8368   NV
Web Site: https://www.btcs.com
BTCS—(NASDAQ)
Rev.: $1,692,454
Assets: $9,917,575
Liabilities: $586,412
Net Worth: $9,331,163
Earnings: ($15,892,738)
Emp.: 5
Fiscal Year-end: 12/31/22
Electronic Shopping Services
N.A.I.C.S.: 459999
Charles W. Allen *(Chm & CEO)*
Michal Handerhan *(Sec)*
Michael Prevoznik *(CFO)*
Manish Paranjape *(CTO)*

BUCK HILL FALLS CO.
270 Golf Dr, Buck Hill Falls, PA 18323
Tel.: (570) 595-7511   PA
Web Site:
   https://www.buckhillfalls.com
Year Founded: 1901
BUHF—(OTCIQ)
Recreational Activity Services
N.A.I.C.S.: 713990
Joseph Munson *(CEO)*
Michael A. O'Shea *(Pres)*
Paul Mandry *(Sec)*
David Toomey *(Chm)*

BUILD ACQUISITION CORP.
3500 Jefferson St Ste 303, Austin, TX 78731
Tel.: (512) 994-2983   DE
Web Site: http://www.buildspac.com
Year Founded: 2021

BGSX—(NYSE)
Rev.: $358,138
Assets: $200,988,952
Liabilities: $214,987,046
Net Worth: ($13,998,094)
Earnings: ($854,585)
Emp.: 3
Fiscal Year-end: 12/31/21
Investment Services
N.A.I.C.S.: 523999
A. Lanham Napier *(Chm & Co-CEO)*
Zeynep Young *(Co-CEO)*
Christina Fok *(CFO & Officer-Compliance)*

BUILD-A-BEAR WORKSHOP, INC.
415 S 18th St Ste 200, Saint Louis, MO 63103
Tel.: (314) 423-8000   DE
Web Site:
   https://www.buildabear.com
Year Founded: 1997
BBW—(NYSE)
Rev.: $467,937,000
Assets: $280,794,000
Liabilities: $161,677,000
Net Worth: $119,117,000
Earnings: $47,985,000
Emp.: 1,000
Fiscal Year-end: 01/28/23
Mfr & Retailer of Make-Your-Own Stuffed Animals
N.A.I.C.S.: 459120
Eric Fencl *(Chief Admin Officer)*
Sharon Price John *(Pres & CEO)*
J. Christopher Hurt *(COO)*
Voin Todorovic *(CFO)*
Craig A. Leavitt *(Chm)*

Subsidiaries:

Build-A-Bear Retail Management, Inc.   **(1)**
1954 Innerbelt Business Ctr Dr, Saint Louis, MO 63114
Tel.: (314) 423-8000
Professional & Management Development Services
N.A.I.C.S.: 611430

Build-A-Bear Workshop Denmark ApS   **(1)**
Vesterbrogade 3, 1702, Copenhagen, Denmark
Tel.: (45) 33138030
Web Site: http://www.buildabear.co.uk
Stuffed Toys & Hobby Goods Merchant Whslr
N.A.I.C.S.: 423920

Build-A-Bear Workshop UK Holdings Ltd.   **(1)**
St Stephens House Arthur Road, Windsor, SL4 1RU, Berks, United Kingdom
Tel.: (44) 8702245130
Web Site: http://www.buildabear.co.uk
Sales Range: $25-49.9 Million
Emp.: 25
Holding Company
N.A.I.C.S.: 551112

BUILDERS FIRSTSOURCE, INC.
6031 Connection Dr Ste 400, Irving, TX 75039
Tel.: (214) 880-3500   DE
Web Site: https://www.bldr.com
Year Founded: 1998
BLDR—(NYSE)
Rev.: $17,097,330,000
Assets: $10,499,452,000
Liabilities: $5,767,101,000
Net Worth: $4,732,351,000
Earnings: $1,540,555,000
Emp.: 29,000
Fiscal Year-end: 12/31/23
Holding Company; Lumber, Plywood, Millwork & Structural Building Products Mfr & Whslr

N.A.I.C.S.: 551112
Amy Bass Messersmith *(Chief People Officer)*
Mike Farmer *(Pres-Comml Ops)*
David E. Rush *(CEO)*
Peter M. Jackson *(Pres & CEO)*

Subsidiaries:

ACR Family Construction, Inc   **(1)**
19900 Independence Blvd, Groveland, FL 34736
Tel.: (352) 429-0304
Residential Remodeler
N.A.I.C.S.: 236118

BMC Stock Holdings, Inc.   **(1)**
4800 Falls of Neuse Rd Ste 400, Raleigh, NC 27609
Tel.: (919) 431-1000
Web Site: http://www.buildwithbmc.com
Holding Company; Building Materials Distr & Construction Support Services
N.A.I.C.S.: 551112

Subsidiary (Domestic):

A-1 Roof Trusses, LLC   **(2)**
4451 St Luci Blvd, Fort Pierce, FL 34946
Tel.: (772) 409-1010
Web Site: http://www.a1truss.com
Rev.: $13,000,000
Emp.: 200
Structural Building Truss Mfr
N.A.I.C.S.: 321215
John R. Herring *(Founder, Pres & CEO)*
Michael Ruede *(COO & Exec VP)*
Jan S. Beck *(CFO & Exec VP)*
Bobby Henry *(Dir-Ops)*
Travis White *(Mgr-Design)*
Frances Ortiz *(Dir-HR)*
Tom Sennott *(Controller)*
Keith Buelta *(Dir-IT)*

BMC East, LLC   **(2)**
8020 Arco Corporate Dr Ste 400, Raleigh, NC 27617
Tel.: (919) 431-1000
Web Site: http://www.buildwithbmc.com
Marketing & Distribution of Building Supplies
N.A.I.C.S.: 423310

Subsidiary (Domestic):

SBS/Bison Building Materials, LLC   **(3)**
1445 W Sam Houston Pkwy N, Houston, TX 77043
Tel.: (713) 467-6700
Building Materials Distr
N.A.I.C.S.: 444180
Dozier Taylor *(Supvr-Fleet)*

Subsidiary (Domestic):

Bison Building Materials Ltd.   **(4)**
1445 W Sam Houston Pkwy N, Houston, TX 77043-3110
Tel.: (713) 467-6700
Web Site: http://www.bisonbuilding.com
Sales Range: $100-124.9 Million
Emp.: 600
Lumber & Plywood Mfr
N.A.I.C.S.: 423310

Branch (Domestic):

Stock Building Supply   **(3)**
200 Flintlake Rd, Columbia, SC 29223
Tel.: (803) 788-8950
Sales Range: $25-49.9 Million
Emp.: 80
Wholesale & Retail Lumber & Building Materials; Manufacture Architectural Woodwork & Pressure-Treated Lumber
N.A.I.C.S.: 423310

Stock Building Supply   **(3)**
3382 Lincoln Hwy E, Paradise, PA 17562-9611
Tel.: (717) 442-4304
Sales Range: $25-49.9 Million
Emp.: 50
Retail Lumber; Millwork; Roofing; Roof & Floor Trusses; Pre-Fabricated Wall Sections
N.A.I.C.S.: 423310

Stock Building Supply   **(3)**
3263 All American Blvd, Orlando, FL 32810

Tel.: (386) 668-7294
Web Site: http://www.stocksupply.com
Sales Range: $25-49.9 Million
Emp.: 25
Lumber, Plywood & Millwork Whslr
N.A.I.C.S.: 423310

Stock Building Supply   **(3)**
3386 Lawrenceville Hwy, Tucker, GA 30084
Tel.: (770) 934-1400
Lumber & Building Materials Distr
N.A.I.C.S.: 423310

Stock Building Supply   **(3)**
23126 Drayton St Saugus, Santa Clarita, CA 91350
Tel.: (661) 254-3113
Web Site: http://www.buildwithbmc.com
Lumber & Building Materials Distr
N.A.I.C.S.: 423310

Subsidiary (Domestic):

Stock Building Supply of Arkansas, LLC   **(3)**
Hwy 265 N, Springdale, AR 72764-0789
Tel.: (479) 756-1700
Sales Range: $100-124.9 Million
Emp.: 500
Lumber & Other Building Materials Dealers
N.A.I.C.S.: 444110

TBSG, LLC   **(3)**
1000 Loudermilk Dr Ste 300, Marietta, GA 30060
Tel.: (770) 499-8382
Building Materials Distr
N.A.I.C.S.: 444180

Plant (Domestic):

BMC Select - ABILENE TRUSS PLANT   **(2)**
2241 Industrial Blvd, Abilene, TX 79602
Tel.: (325) 692-8450
Truss Mfr
N.A.I.C.S.: 321215
Carla Mcnoaly *(Mgr)*

BMC Select - EVERETT TRUSS PLANT   **(2)**
3200 35th Ave NE, Everett, WA 98201
Tel.: (425) 303-0661
Truss Mfr
N.A.I.C.S.: 321215
Steve Cottengim *(Plant Mgr-Truss)*
Glen Sterley *(Mgr-Sls)*

BMC Select - HELENA TRUSS PLANT   **(2)**
790 Nicole St, Helena, MT 59601
Tel.: (406) 449-5553
Truss Mfr
N.A.I.C.S.: 321215

BMC Select - IDAHO FALLS TRUSS PLANT   **(2)**
3715 Bombardier Ave, Idaho Falls, ID 83402
Tel.: (208) 523-6691
Web Site: http://www.buildwithbmc.com
Emp.: 30
Truss Mfr
N.A.I.C.S.: 321215

BMC Select - INDIO TRUSS AND PANEL PLANT   **(2)**
45-491 Golf Ctr Pkwy, Indio, CA 92203
Tel.: (760) 347-3332
Web Site: http://www.bmc.com
Truss Mfr
N.A.I.C.S.: 321215

BMC Select - KALISPELL TRUSS PLANT   **(2)**
448 Ash Rd, Kalispell, MT 59901
Tel.: (406) 752-8393
Web Site: http://www.bmc.com
Emp.: 10
Truss Mfr
N.A.I.C.S.: 321215

BMC Select - MISSOULA TRUSS PLANT   **(2)**
7320 Expressway, Missoula, MT 59808
Tel.: (406) 728-4750
Truss Mfr
N.A.I.C.S.: 321215

BMC Select - NEW BRAUNFELS TRUSS AND PANEL PLANT   **(2)**

Builders FirstSource, Inc.—(Continued)

3620 FM 482, New Braunfels, TX 78132
Tel.: (830) 606-7020
Truss Mfr
N.A.I.C.S.: 321215
Brad Shepherd (Gen Mgr)

BMC Select - WEST JORDAN TRUSS PLANT (2)
7902 S 1410 W, West Jordan, UT 84088
Tel.: (801) 565-3500
Truss Mfr
N.A.I.C.S.: 321215

Subsidiary (Domestic):

BMC West Corporation (2)
720 Park Blvd Ste 200, Boise, ID 83712-7764
Tel.: (208) 331-4300
Web Site: http://www.bmcwest.com
Emp.: 150
Building Materials Distr
N.A.I.C.S.: 444180

Barefoot & Company, LLC (2)
3980 Mthews Indian Trl Rd, Indian Trail, NC 28079
Tel.: (704) 821-7688
Web Site:
   http://www.barefootandcompany.com
Commercial & Institutional Building Construction Products Distr
N.A.I.C.S.: 236220
Lynn Najaka (VP)
Chris Childers (Mgr-South)
Michael Najaka (Partner)
Bill Green (Dir-Ops)
Tom Schellin (Gen Mgr)
Derrick Manning (Mgr-Blinds, Shades & Shutters)
Laura Barefoot (Mgr-Mktg & Quality Assurance)
Mandy Braswell (Office Mgr)
Chad Hughes (Mgr-South Window)
Tommy Morrison (Mgr-Production)
David Piddock (Mgr-North Window)
Mark Tyson (Area Mgr-Sls & Custom)

Deford Lumber Company Inc. (2)
1018 N Duncanville Rd, Duncanville, TX 75116
Tel.: (972) 298-7121
Web Site: http://www.defords.com
Sales Range: $10-24.9 Million
Emp.: 150
Lumber
N.A.I.C.S.: 423310

Locust Lumber Company, Inc. (2)
312 E Main St, Locust, NC 28097
Tel.: (704) 488-4411
Building & Construction Supply Distr
N.A.I.C.S.: 423390

Subsidiary (Non-US):

SelectBuild Construction, Inc. (2)
Tel.: (415) 627-9100
Contract Construction Services for Homebuilders
N.A.I.C.S.: 236115

Branch (Non-US):

SelectBuild of Nevada (3)
Tel.: (702) 636-5588
Web Site: http://www.bmcwest.com
Sales Range: $150-199.9 Million
Emp.: 30
Plastering, Drywall & Insulation Services
N.A.I.C.S.: 238310

Builders FirstSource - Florida, LLC (1)
6550 Roosevelt Blvd, Jacksonville, FL 32244
Tel.: (904) 772-6100
Web Site: https://www.bldr.com
Building Materials Distr
N.A.I.C.S.: 423310
Frank Ayala (Gen Mgr)

Builders FirstSource - MBS, LLC (1)
3403 E Abram St, Arlington, TX 76010
Tel.: (817) 640-1234
Web Site:
   http://www.buildersfirstsource.com
Wood Doors & Trim, Windows & Lumber Distr

N.A.I.C.S.: 423310

Builders FirstSource - Southeast Group, LLC (1)
2451 Hwy 501 E, Conway, SC 29526
Tel.: (843) 347-4235
Holding Company; Regional Managing Office
N.A.I.C.S.: 551112

Builders FirstSource of Greenville (1)
801 S Washington Ave, Greenville, SC 29611
Tel.: (864) 269-8110
Web Site: http://www.bldr.com
Lumber & Millwork Whslr
N.A.I.C.S.: 423310

Builders FirstSource of High Point (1)
7601 Boeing Dr, Greensboro, NC 27409
Tel.: (336) 884-5454
Web Site: http://www.bldr.com
Emp.: 80
Lumber & Millwork Whslr
N.A.I.C.S.: 423310
Sean Hines (Gen Mgr)

Builders FirstSource of Southport (1)
1609 Howe St SE, Southport, NC 28461
Tel.: (910) 457-6455
Web Site:
   http://www.buildersfirstsource.com
Lumber & Millwork Whslr
N.A.I.C.S.: 423310

Builders FirstSource of Sumter (1)
114 Myrtle Beach Hwy, Sumter, SC 29153
Tel.: (803) 778-1921
Web Site:
   http://www.buildersfirstsource.com
Steel & Wood Trusses & Engineered Wood Products Mfr & Supplier
N.A.I.C.S.: 321215

California Trusframe, LLC (1)
23665 Cajalco Rd, Perris, CA 92570-8181
Tel.: (951) 657-7491
Web Site: http://www.caltrusframe.com
Sales Range: $1-9.9 Million
Emp.: 202
Truss Mfr
N.A.I.C.S.: 321215
Jason Walsh (VP-Sls)
Phillip David (Dir-Builder Dev)
Steven L. Stroder (Pres & CEO)
Susan Engquist (CFO)
James Davis (Sr VP-Ops)
Jason Ward (VP-HR)
Bryan Sylvester (VP-IT)

Dixieline Lumber & Home Centers (1)
3250 Sports Arena Blvd, San Diego, CA 92110
Tel.: (619) 224-4120
Web Site: https://www.dixieline.com
Emp.: 1,000
Hardware & Lumber Retailer
N.A.I.C.S.: 444140

Subsidiary (Domestic):

Dixieline Builders Fund Control, Inc. (2)
3250 Sports Arena Blvd, San Diego, CA 92110
Tel.: (619) 224-4120
Web Site: https://www.dixieline.com
Escrow Services
N.A.I.C.S.: 522320

Douglas Lumber Corporation (1)
125 Douglas Pike, Smithfield, RI 02917
Tel.: (401) 231-6800
Web Site: https://www.douglaslumber.com
Sales Range: $25-49.9 Million
Emp.: 50
Home Improvement Supplies Retailer
N.A.I.C.S.: 444140
Steven Carlino (Pres)
Jay Pires (Coord-Sls)

John's Lumber & Hardware Co. (1)
34151 S Gratiot Ave, Clinton Township, MI 48035
Tel.: (586) 791-1200
Web Site: http://www.johnslumber.com

Sales Range: $25-49.9 Million
Emp.: 55
Distr of Lumber & Other Building Materials
N.A.I.C.S.: 423310
Paul Aggeler (Pres)

Kleet Lumber Company, Inc. (1)
777 Park Ave, Huntington, NY 11743
Tel.: (631) 427-7060
Web Site: http://www.kleet.com
Sales Range: $10-24.9 Million
Emp.: 70
Building Materials Whslr
N.A.I.C.S.: 444180
Jon Bieselin (VP)
David Kleet (Office Mgr)
Howard Kleet (Co-Owner)
Warren Kleet (Co-Owner)
Robin Kohl (Mgr-Credit)
Michael Kremen (Mgr-Window & Millwork)
Linda Nussbaum (VP)
William Schultz (Mgr-Facilities)
Elaine Wikins (Asst Mgr-Credit)
Gene Wolff (Mgr-Pur)
Ray Nurnberger (Mgr-Store)
Teresa Abbatepaolo (Sec)

National Lumber Company (1)
71 Maple St, Mansfield, MA 02048
Tel.: (508) 339-8020
Web Site: http://www.national-lumber.com
Millwork & Lumber
N.A.I.C.S.: 444110

Spenard Builders Supply LLC (1)
300 E 54th Ave Ste 201, Anchorage, AK 99518
Tel.: (907) 563-3141
Web Site: https://www.sbsalaska.com
Building Material Mfr & Distr
N.A.I.C.S.: 321992

Valley Truss Company (1)
4100 S Eagleson Rd, Boise, ID 83705
Tel.: (208) 362-1089
Web Site: http://www.valleytruss.com
Rev.: $4,900,000
Emp.: 40
Engineered Wood Member, except Truss, Mfr
N.A.I.C.S.: 321215
Jason Moodie (Pres)

WTS Paradigm LLC (1)
1600 Aspen Commons Ste 500, Middleton, WI 53562
Tel.: (608) 664-9292
Web Site: http://www.wtsparadigm.com
Software Development Services
N.A.I.C.S.: 541511
Dave Flynn (Dir-Catalog Svcs)
Diane Rivers (Dir-HR)
Joel Fields (CFO)
Lyn Hartl (Founder)
Nathan Herbst (CEO)
Mike Benson (VP-Sls)
Tadd Smejkal (Sr Mgr-Software Dev)

Wyoming Millwork Co. (1)
140 Vepco Blvd, Camden Wyoming, DE 19934
Tel.: (302) 697-8650
Web Site: http://www.wyomingmillwork.com
Sales Range: $10-24.9 Million
Emp.: 45
Lumber & Building Material Distr
N.A.I.C.S.: 423310

BULLFROG AI HOLDINGS, INC.
325 Ellington Blvd Ste 317, Gaithersburg, MD 20878
Tel.: (240) 658-6710
Web Site: https://www.bullfrogai.com
Year Founded: 2020
BFRG—(NASDAQ)
Rev.: $10,000
Assets: $80,369
Liabilities: $3,137,721
Net Worth: ($3,057,352)
Earnings: ($2,802,487)
Emp.: 4
Fiscal Year-end: 12/31/22
Offices of Other Holding Companies
N.A.I.C.S.: 551112
Toby Sayre (VP-Bus Dev)
Vin Singh (Founder & CEO)

Enrique Garcia-Rivera (VP-Artificial Intelligence)
Dane Saglio (CFO)
David Recker (Chief Medical Officer)

BULLPEN PARLAY ACQUISITION COMPANY
38 Keyes Ave Ste 100, San Francisco, CA 94129
Tel.: (415) 649-6923
Web Site:
   https://bullpenparlayacquisitioncom
   pany.gcs-web.com
Year Founded: 2021
BPAC—(NASDAQ)
Assets: $237,713,295
Liabilities: $246,463,715
Net Worth: ($8,750,420)
Earnings: $15,306,093
Emp.: 4
Fiscal Year-end: 12/31/22
Investment Services
N.A.I.C.S.: 523999
Paul Martino (Chm)
David Van Egmond (CEO)
Eric Wiesen (Pres)
Duncan Davidson (Exec VP)

BUMBLE, INC.
1105 W 41st St, Austin, TX 78756
Tel.: (512) 696-1409
Web Site: https://www.bumble.com
Year Founded: 2020
BMBL—(NASDAQ)
Rev.: $903,503,000
Assets: $3,692,621,000
Liabilities: $1,239,042,000
Net Worth: $2,453,579,000
Earnings: ($79,746,000)
Emp.: 950
Fiscal Year-end: 12/31/22
Application Development Services
N.A.I.C.S.: 541511
Anuradha B. Subramanian (CFO)
David Ard (Chief People Officer)
Selby Drummond (CMO)
Antoine Leblond (CTO)
Elizabeth Monteleone (Chief Legal Officer)
Ali Rayl (Chief Product Officer)
Whitney Wolfe Herd (Founder & Exec Chm)
Lidiane S. Jones (CEO)

BUNGE LIMITED
1391 Timberlake Manor Pkwy, Chesterfield, MO 63017
Tel.: (314) 292-2000
Web Site: https://www.bunge.com
Year Founded: 1818
BG—(NYSE)
Rev.: $67,232,000,000
Assets: $24,580,000,000
Liabilities: $14,624,000,000
Net Worth: $9,956,000,000
Earnings: $1,610,000,000
Emp.: 23,000
Fiscal Year-end: 12/31/22
Holding Company; Agribusiness
N.A.I.C.S.: 493130
Pierre Mauger (Chief Transformation Officer)
Sheila Colleen Bair (Deputy Chm)
Mark N. Zenuk (Chm)
Joseph A. Podwika (Chief Legal Officer)
Robert Wagner (Chief Risk Officer)
Ruth Ann Wisener (VP-IR)
Robert Coviello (Chief Sustainability Officer)
Kellie Sears (Chief HR Officer)
Debra King (Chief Tech Officer)
J. Matt Simmons Jr. (Principal Acctg Officer)

Subsidiaries:

BLA Servicios, S.A. (1)

Diagonal 6 12-42 Edificio Design Center,
Torre Ciudad, 1003, Guatemala, Guatemala
Tel.: (502) 23153200
Farm Product Warehousing & Storage Services
N.A.I.C.S.: 493120

Bunge (Nanjing) Grain and Oils Co.,Ltd. (1)
No 99 Xingang Road Economic and Technological Development Zone, Nanjing, 210038, Jiangsu, China
Tel.: (86) 2585802866
Web Site: http://www.bunge.com.cn
Food Products Mfr
N.A.I.C.S.: 311225

Bunge (Thailand) Ltd. (1)
17th Floor Unit 1706 Millennia Tower 62 Langsuan Road, Lumphini Pathum Wan, 10330, Bangkok, Thailand
Tel.: (66) 2265055258
Web Site: http://www.bunge.com
Emp.: 5
Food Products Mfr
N.A.I.C.S.: 424510

Bunge Agribusiness Australia Pty. Ltd. (1)
Level 1 99 Coventry St, South Melbourne, 3205, VIC, Australia
Tel.: (61) 39 275 6555
Web Site: https://www.bunge.com
Sales Range: $25-49.9 Million
Emp.: 8
Food Products Mfr
N.A.I.C.S.: 424510

Bunge Agribusiness Singapore Pte. Ltd. (1)
77 Robinson Road 28-00 Sia Building, Singapore, 068896, Singapore
Tel.: (65) 62270090
Sales Range: $50-74.9 Million
Emp.: 100
Food Products Mfr
N.A.I.C.S.: 424510

Bunge Agritrade S.A. (1)
Brigadier General Juan Antonio Lavalleja Ruta 8 9065 Edificio Arroba2, Local 110 Zonamerica, Montevideo, 91600, Uruguay
Tel.: (598) 25182181
Food Products Mfr
N.A.I.C.S.: 424510

Bunge Argentina S.A. (1)
25 de mayo 501, Buenos Aires, C1002ABK, Argentina (100%)
Tel.: (54) 115 169 3200
Web Site: https://www.bungeargentina.com
Sales Range: $250-299.9 Million
Holding Company: Agribusiness Operations
N.A.I.C.S.: 551112

Subsidiary (Domestic):

Bunge Argentina (2)
25 de Mayo 1119, Tancacha, Cordoba, 5933, Argentina
Tel.: (54) 3571460125
Web Site: www.bungeargentina.com
Vegetable Oil Mills
N.A.I.C.S.: 311224

Bunge Asia Pte. Ltd. (1)
1 Wallich Street 08-01 Guoco Tower, Singapore, 078881, Singapore
Tel.: (65) 62270090
Agricultural Marketing Services
N.A.I.C.S.: 484220
Cheryl Koh (Mgr-Treasury)

Bunge Canada (1)
2190 South Service Road West, Oakville, L6L 5N1, ON, Canada (100%)
Tel.: (905) 825-7900
Web Site: http://www.bungecanada.com
Sales Range: $50-74.9 Million
Emp.: 150
Oilseed Crushing & Refining; Manufacturing, Packaging & Distributing of Edible Oil Products
N.A.I.C.S.: 311224

Bunge Colombia S.A.S. (1)
Calle 93 B 12 18 Of 303, Bogota, 10001, Colombia
Tel.: (57) 16369814
Food Products Mfr

N.A.I.C.S.: 424510

Bunge Comercializadora de Energia Ltda. (1)
Av Maria Coelho Aguiar 215 Bloco A-5 Andar, Sao Paulo, 05804-900, Brazil
Tel.: (55) 1137418519
Food Products Mfr
N.A.I.C.S.: 424510
Osmar Pereira (Gen Mgr)

Bunge Corporation (1)
50 Main St Fl 6, White Plains, NY 10606-1901 (100%)
Tel.: (914) 684-2800
Sales Range: $75-99.9 Million
Emp.: 100
Food Processing; Grain & Soybean Processing & Milling
N.A.I.C.S.: 424510

Bunge Corporation Ltd. (1)
65 London Wall Room 113, London, EC2M 5TU, United Kingdom (100%)
Tel.: (44) 2073740863
Sales Range: $10-24.9 Million
Emp.: 4
Provider of Soybean Processing & Grain Export
N.A.I.C.S.: 311224

Bunge Deutschland G.m.b.H. (1)
Bonadiesstr 3-5, 68169, Mannheim, Germany
Tel.: (49) 6 213 7040
Web Site: https://www.bunge-deutschland.de
Food Products Mfr
N.A.I.C.S.: 424510

Bunge ETGO L.P. (1)
2190 S Service Rd W, Oakville, L6L 5N1, ON, Canada
Tel.: (905) 825-7900
Web Site: http://www.bungecanada.com
Food Products Mfr
N.A.I.C.S.: 424510

Bunge Fertilizantes S.A. (1)
Av Maria Coelho Aguiar 215 bloco D, 3 and 5 andares, Sao Paulo, 05804-900, Brazil
Tel.: (55) 1137415550
Farm Product Warehousing & Storage Services
N.A.I.C.S.: 493120

Bunge Finance B.V. (1)
Weena 320, 3012 NJ, Rotterdam, Netherlands
Tel.: (31) 102176666
Sales Range: $25-49.9 Million
Emp.: 15
Food Products Mfr
N.A.I.C.S.: 424510

Bunge Global Markets, Inc. (1)
50 Main St, White Plains, NY 10606-1901
Tel.: (914) 684-3300
Web Site: http://www.bunge.com
Food Products Mfr
N.A.I.C.S.: 424510

Bunge Holdings France S.A.S. (1)
Arts 28 t Rue De La Paix Et Des, 44600, Saint Nazaire, France
Tel.: (33) 251164400
Food Products Mfr
N.A.I.C.S.: 424510

Bunge Iberica Portugal, S.A. (1)
Rua de Palenca Palenca de Baixo, Apartado 551, 2801-601, Almada, Portugal
Tel.: (351) 212949100
Web Site: https://www.bungeportugal.com
Sales Range: $25-49.9 Million
Emp.: 8
Food Products Mfr
N.A.I.C.S.: 424510

Bunge Investment Iberica S.L.U. (1)
Constitucion 1 Edif B Pta 1, 08960, Sant Just Desvern, Spain
Tel.: (34) 934705320
Web Site: http://www.bunge.com
Sales Range: $25-49.9 Million
Emp.: 80
Food Products Mfr
N.A.I.C.S.: 424510

Bunge Italia S.p.A. (1)
Via Baiona 203, 48123, Ravenna, Italy

Tel.: (39) 054 453 7711
Web Site: https://bunge.com
Sales Range: $50-74.9 Million
Emp.: 10
Food Products Mfr
N.A.I.C.S.: 424510

Bunge Loders (Xiamen) Oils Technology, Co. Ltd. (1)
No 101 Cang Jiang Road, Xiamen Area Pilot Free Trade Zone, Xiamen, 361026, China
Tel.: (86) 5923201888
Vegetable Oil & Fat Product Mfr
N.A.I.C.S.: 311225

Bunge Loders Croklaan (Ghana) Ltd. (1)
Evergreen House Com 4, Tema, Greater Accra, Ghana
Tel.: (233) 303200088
Web Site: http://www.africa.bungeloders.com
Cooking Oil Mfr
N.A.I.C.S.: 311225
Antoine Turpin (Gen Mgr)

Bunge Loders Croklaan (Shanghai) Trading Co. Ltd. (1)
50F Maxdo Centre No 8 Xing Yi Road, Shanghai, 20336, China
Tel.: (86) 2180252000
Vegetable Oil & Fat Product Mfr
N.A.I.C.S.: 311225
Cheerine Zhang (Asst Mgr-Mktg)

Bunge Loders Croklaan Group B.V. (1)
Hogeweg 1, 1521 AZ, Wormerveer, 1521 AZ, Netherlands (70%)
Tel.: (31) 756292911
Web Site: http://europe.bungeloders.com
Holding Company; Palm Oil & Other Specialty Lipids Mfr
N.A.I.C.S.: 551112
Aaron Buettner (Pres)

Subsidiary (Domestic):

Bung Loders Croklaan B.V. (2)
Antarcticaweg 191, 3199 KA, Rotterdam, Netherlands
Tel.: (31) 756292911
Web Site: http://europe.bungeloders.com
Specialty & Nutritional Lipids Mfr
N.A.I.C.S.: 311224

Subsidiary (Non-US):

Loders Croklaan Canada Inc. (3)
195 Belfield Road, Rexdale, Toronto, M9W 1G8, ON, Canada
Web Site: http://northamerica.bungeloders.com
Fats & Oil Refining Services
N.A.I.C.S.: 324110

Subsidiary (US):

Loders Croklaan USA, LLC (3)
24708 W Durkee Rd, Channahon, IL 60410-5249
Tel.: (815) 730-5200
Web Site: https://amea.bungeloders.com
Specialty & Nutritional Lipids Producer
N.A.I.C.S.: 311225

Subsidiary (Domestic):

Bunge Loders Croklaan Oils B.V. (2)
Antarcticaweg 191, 3199 KA, Rotterdam, Netherlands
Tel.: (31) 756292911
Vegetable Oil & Palm Oil Mfr
N.A.I.C.S.: 311224

Bunge Loders Croklaan Oils Sdn Bhd (1)
Plo 8 9 Jalan Timah Pasir Gudang Industrial Estate, 81700, Pasir Gudang, Johor, Malaysia
Tel.: (60) 73818888
Web Site: http://www.asiapacific.bungeloders.com
Cooking Oil Mfr
N.A.I.C.S.: 311224
Manuel Laborde (VP-Asia)
Eugenia Zorila (VP-Ops)

Bunge Mexico Holdings, Inc. (1)

Alfonso Napoles Gandara no 50 Piso 3 Col Santa Fe Pena Blanca, Alvaro Obregon, 01210, Mexico, Mexico
Tel.: (52) 5552733388
Web Site: http://www.bungenorthamerica.com
Holding Company
N.A.I.C.S.: 551112

Bunge Milling, Inc. (1)
11720 Borman Dr, Saint Louis, MO 63146
Tel.: (314) 292-2000
Web Site: http://www.bungemilling.com
Food Products Mfr
N.A.I.C.S.: 424510

Bunge Milling, LLC (1)
321 E North St, Danville, IL 61834
Tel.: (217) 442-1800
Web Site: http://www.bunge.com
Emp.: 114
Farm Product Warehousing & Storage Services
N.A.I.C.S.: 493120

Bunge N.A. Finance L.P. (1)
50 Main St, White Plains, NY 10606
Tel.: (914) 684-2800
Web Site: http://www.bunge.com
Investment Management Service
N.A.I.C.S.: 541611

Bunge North America, Inc. (1)
1391 Timberlake Manor Pkwy, Chesterfield, MO 63017-6058 (100%)
Tel.: (314) 292-2000
Web Site: http://www.bungenorthamerica.com
Sales Range: $300-349.9 Million
Emp.: 500
Food Processing; Grain & Soybean Processing & Milling
N.A.I.C.S.: 424510

Division (Domestic):

Bunge - Morristown Grain Company (2)
120 E Broadway, Morristown, IN 46161
Tel.: (765) 763-1215
Grains & Oilseeds Production
N.A.I.C.S.: 424510

Subsidiary (Domestic):

Bunge Milling (Southwest), Inc. (2)
2049 Fernwood Ave, Red Oak, IA 51566
Tel.: (712) 623-5255
Web Site: http://www.minsa.com
Flour Milling
N.A.I.C.S.: 311211

Division (Domestic):

Bunge North America East (2)
38 Colfax St, Pawtucket, RI 02860-3422
Tel.: (401) 724-3800
Web Site: http://www.bungenorthamerica.com
Sales Range: $250-299.9 Million
Mfr of Vegetable Oil Mills, Vegetable Shortenings, Animal & Marine Fats & Oils
N.A.I.C.S.: 311225

Bunge S.A. (1)
13 Route De Florissant Geneva 12 case 518, Geneva, 1211, Switzerland
Tel.: (41) 225929100
Web Site: http://www.bunge.com
Emp.: 250
Food Products Mfr
N.A.I.C.S.: 424510

Bunge-SCF Grain, LLC (1)
651 N Frnt St, Fairmount, IL 62201
Tel.: (618) 271-2202
Emp.: 25
Farm Product Warehousing & Storage Services
N.A.I.C.S.: 493120
Rick Bauwens (Mgr)

Fertimport S.A. (1)
25 de Mayo 501 5th floor, 1002 ABK, Buenos Aires, Argentina
Tel.: (54) 1143242050
Web Site: https://www.fertimport.com.ar
Emp.: 3
Food Products Mfr
N.A.I.C.S.: 424510

Bunge Limited—(Continued)

Fertimport S.A. (1)
Rua Frei Graspar 22 8th & 9th Floor Santos, Sao Paulo, 11010-090, Brazil
Tel.: (55) 1332019114
Web Site: http://www.fertimport.com.br
Emp.: 40
Freight Transportation Services
N.A.I.C.S.: 488510

G3 Canada Limited (1)
200 Portage Avenue 3rd Floor, Winnipeg, R3C 3X2, MB, Canada
Tel.: (204) 983-0239
Web Site: http://www.g3.ca
Oilseed Merchant Mfr
N.A.I.C.S.: 311224
Janice Watson (VP-HR)
Don Chapman (CEO)
Don MacDonald (VP-Ops)
Jeff Losch (Gen Counsel, Sec & VP)
Maureen Kinnear (VP)
Jon Bray (VP)

Industria Molinera Montserrat, S.A. de C.V. (1)
Mariano Arisa No 1625, Veracruz, VERA 91700, Mexico
Tel.: (52) 2299348833
Flour Mill Services
N.A.I.C.S.: 311211

International Produce Ltd. (1)
Unit 1 Foxbridge Way, Normanton, WF6 1TN, West Yorkshire, United Kingdom
Tel.: (44) 1924124444
Web Site: https://www.ipl-ltd.com
Fruit & Vegetable Distr
N.A.I.C.S.: 424480

Loders Croklaan for Oils S.A.E. (1)
6 El Sad El Aly Street, Maadi, 11431, Cairo, Egypt
Tel.: (20) 23596767
Vegetable Oil Mfr
N.A.I.C.S.: 311224

Moinho Pacifico Ltda. (1)
Praca Guilherme Aralhe 20 Estuario, Santos, Brazil
Tel.: (55) 1332787910
Web Site: http://www.moinhopacifico.com.br
Wheat Processing Services
N.A.I.C.S.: 311211

Novaol Austria G.m.b.H. (1)
Industriegelande West 3, Bruck an der Leitha, 2460, Austria
Tel.: (43) 216260633
Farm Product Warehousing & Storage Services
N.A.I.C.S.: 493120

Prio Biocombustibil SRL (1)
Strada Lisabona Nr 3, Lehliu-Gara, 915300, Calarasi, Romania
Tel.: (40) 213053230
Farm Product Warehousing & Storage Services
N.A.I.C.S.: 493120

Terminal Bahia Blanca S.A. (1)
Carrega 3900 - Engineer White, Buenos Aires, Argentina
Tel.: (54) 291 457 3035
Web Site: https://www.terminalbb.com.ar
Emp.: 99
Food Products Mfr
N.A.I.C.S.: 424510

Terminal de Fertilizantes Argentinos CA (1)
Hipolito Irigoyen s/n, Puerto San Martin, Santa Fe, Argentina
Tel.: (54) 347 644 0600
Web Site: https://www.tfasa.com.ar
Farm Product Warehousing & Storage Services
N.A.I.C.S.: 493120

Universal Financial Services, L.P. (1)
1321 S Winchester Blvd S-352, San Jose, CA 95128-4320
Tel.: (408) 505-7385
Web Site: http://www.ufs-sfday.com
Emp.: 6
Farm Product Warehousing & Storage Services

N.A.I.C.S.: 493120
David Mowbray (Pres)

Walter Rau Neusser Ol und Fett AG (1)
Industriestrasse 36-40, 41460, Neuss, Germany
Tel.: (49) 2 131 2080
Web Site: https://www.walterrauag.com
Oil Mfr & Distr
N.A.I.C.S.: 311224

Westfalische Lebensmittel werke Lindemann GmbH & Co. KG (1)
Herforder Strasse 173-179, 32257, Bunde, Germany
Tel.: (49) 52 238 2030
Web Site: https://www.lindemann.info
Margarine Mfr
N.A.I.C.S.: 311221
Carsten-Dirc Hoffmann (Mng Dir)

Whole Harvest Foods, LLC (1)
376 W Park Dr, Warsaw, NC 28398
Tel.: (910) 293-7917
Web Site: http://www.wholeharvest.com
Packaged Oil Distr
N.A.I.C.S.: 424490

Z.T. Kruszwica S.A. (1)
ul Niepodleglosci 42, 88-150, Kruszwica, Poland
Tel.: (48) 523535202
Web Site: http://www.ztkruszwica.pl
Food Products Mfr
N.A.I.C.S.: 424510

BURGERFI INTERNATIONAL, INC.
200 W Cypress Creek Rd Ste 220, Fort Lauderdale, FL 33309
Tel.: (954) 618-2000   DE
Web Site: https://www.burgerfi.com
Year Founded: 2017
BFI—(NASDAQ)
Rev.: $178,720,000
Assets: $276,780,000
Liabilities: $197,833,000
Net Worth: $78,947,000
Earnings: ($103,432,000)
Emp.: 808
Fiscal Year-end: 01/02/23
Investment Services
N.A.I.C.S.: 523999
Carl J. Bachmann (CEO)
Christopher E. Jones (CFO)
Tad Nash (CTO)
Michelle Zavolta (Chief People Officer)
Cindy Syracuse (CMO)

Subsidiaries:

Anthony's Coal Fired Pizza of Aventura, LLC (1)
17901 Biscayne Blvd, Aventura, FL 33160-2502
Tel.: (305) 830-2625
Food Meal Mfr
N.A.I.C.S.: 311991

Anthony's Coal Fired Pizza of Boca Raton, LLC (1)
1835 NE 123rd Ste, North Miami Beach, FL 33181
Tel.: (305) 899-8887
Food Meal Mfr
N.A.I.C.S.: 311991

Anthony's Coal Fired Pizza of Edison, LLC (1)
80 Parsonage Rd, Edison, NJ 08837
Tel.: (732) 744-1500
Food Meal Mfr
N.A.I.C.S.: 311991

Anthony's Coal Fired Pizza of Littleton, LLC (1)
Tel.: (781) 944-8454
Food Meal Mfr
N.A.I.C.S.: 311991

Anthony's Coal Fired Pizza of Monroeville, LLC (1)
2740 Stroschein Rd, Monroeville, PA 15146
Tel.: (412) 373-0700

Food Meal Mfr
N.A.I.C.S.: 311991

Anthony's Coal Fired Pizza of Plantation, LLC (1)
512 N Pine Island Rd, Plantation, FL 33324
Tel.: (954) 474-3311
Food Meal Mfr
N.A.I.C.S.: 311991

Anthony's Coal Fired Pizza of Reading, LLC (1)
48 Walkers Brook Dr, Reading, MA 01867
Tel.: (781) 944-8454
Food Meal Mfr
N.A.I.C.S.: 311991

Anthony's Coal Fired Pizza of South Tampa, LLC (1)
1901 S Dale Mabry Hwy, Tampa, FL 33629
Tel.: (813) 258-2625
Food Meal Mfr
N.A.I.C.S.: 311991

Anthony's Coal Fired Pizza of Stony Brook, LLC (1)
137 Old Country Rd, Carle Place, NY 11514
Tel.: (516) 877-7750
Food Meal Mfr
N.A.I.C.S.: 311991

Anthony's Coal Fired Pizza of Trexlertown LLC (1)
750 N Krocks Rd Ste 208, Allentown, PA 18106
Tel.: (610) 366-9701
Food Meal Mfr
N.A.I.C.S.: 311991

Anthony's Coal Fired Pizza of Wynnewood, LLC (1)
50 E Wynnewood Rd, Wynnewood, PA 19096
Tel.: (610) 645-5453
Food Meal Mfr
N.A.I.C.S.: 311991

BURNED MEDIA LTD.
631 N Stephanie St Ste 548, Henderson, NV 89014
Tel.: (416) 855-2061
Web Site:
http://www.burnedmusic.com
Year Founded: 2005
BUNM—(OTCIQ)
Online Entertainment Services
N.A.I.C.S.: 516210
Michael Devellano (Pres & CEO)

BURNHAM HOLDINGS, INC.
1241 Harrisburg Pike, Lancaster, PA 17604
Tel.: (717) 390-7800   NY
Web Site:
https://www.burnhamholdings.com
Year Founded: 1856
BURCA—(OTCIQ)
Rev.: $187,461,000
Assets: $154,375,000
Liabilities: $63,160,000
Net Worth: $91,215,000
Earnings: $6,547,000
Emp.: 780
Fiscal Year-end: 12/31/20
Holding Company; Heating Boilers, Radiation & Gray-Iron Castings
N.A.I.C.S.: 551112
Dale R. Bowman (CFO, VP & Asst Sec)
John W. Lyman (Chm)
Bradley C. Ehlert (Controller & Dir-IT)
Douglas S. Brossman (Vice Chm)
Christopher R. Drew (Pres & COO)
John A. Roda (Gen Counsel, Sec & VP)

Subsidiaries:

Bryan Steam LLC (1)
783 N Chile Ave, Peru, IN 46970
Tel.: (765) 473-6651
Web Site: http://www.bryanboilers.com

Sales Range: $250-299.9 Million
Emp.: 150
Mfr of Hot Water & Steam Boilers
N.A.I.C.S.: 332410
Bryan O'Toole (Pres)

Subsidiary (Domestic):

Wendland Manufacturing Corporation (2)
601 W 11th St, San Angelo, TX 76903   (100%)
Tel.: (325) 655-6778
Web Site: http://www.wendlandmfg.com
Sales Range: $75-99.9 Million
Emp.: 40
Heating Boilers, Radiation & Gray-Iron Castings
N.A.I.C.S.: 332313

Casting Solutions, LLC (1)
2345 Licking Rd, Zanesville, OH 43701
Tel.: (740) 452-9371
Web Site: http://www.castingsolutions.com
Sales Range: $50-74.9 Million
Emp.: 125
Gray Iron Foundry
N.A.I.C.S.: 331511
Art Boehme (Mgr-Mfg Svc)

Governale Co., Inc. (1)
788 Williams Ave, Brooklyn, NY 11207-7619   (100%)
Tel.: (718) 272-2300
Web Site: http://www.goverle.com
Sales Range: $150-199.9 Million
Mfr of Cast Iron Radiators & Convectors
N.A.I.C.S.: 423720

New Yorker Boiler Co. Inc. (1)
1241 Harrisburg Pike, Lancaster, PA 17604   (100%)
Tel.: (717) 390-7800
Sales Range: $25-49.9 Million
Emp.: 6
Mfr of Low Pressure Heating Boilers, Water Heaters & Residential Steel & Cast Iron Boilers
N.A.I.C.S.: 333414

Thermo Products, LLC (1)
5235 W State Hwy 10, North Judson, IN 46366   (100%)
Tel.: (574) 896-2133
Web Site: http://www.thermopride.com
Sales Range: $25-49.9 Million
Emp.: 9
N.A.I.C.S.: 333414

BURTECH ACQUISITION CORP.
7770 Norfolk Ave, Bethesda, MD 20814
Tel.: (202) 790-8050   DE
Year Founded: 2021
BRKH—(NASDAQ)
Rev.: $3,989,294
Assets: $296,011,458
Liabilities: $306,156,128
Net Worth: ($10,144,670)
Earnings: $1,673,607
Emp.: 5
Fiscal Year-end: 12/31/22
Investment Services
N.A.I.C.S.: 523999
Isaac Chetrit (Pres)
Shahal Khan (Chm & CEO)
Roman Livson (CFO)
Payel Farasat (Chief Investment Officer)
Christopher Schroeder (CMO)

BURZYNSKI RESEARCH INSTITUTE, INC.
9432 Katy Fwy, Houston, TX 77055
Tel.: (713) 335-5664   DE
Web Site: https://propcitweb.ddns.net
Year Founded: 1984
BZYR—(OTCIQ)
Assets: $4,661
Liabilities: $3,455
Net Worth: $1,206
Earnings: ($976,656)
Fiscal Year-end: 02/28/22

Medical Chemical Compounds Researcher & Mfr
N.A.I.C.S.: 325998
Stanislaw R. Burzynski (Chm & Pres)
Patryk P. Goscianski (Treas & Sec)
Tomasz Janicki (VP-Clinical Trials)

BUSCAR CO.
9663 Santa Monica Blvd Ste 688, Beverly Hills, CA 90210
Tel.: (661) 418-7842   NV
Year Founded: 2010
CGLD—(OTCIQ)
Emp.: 1
Investment Services
N.A.I.C.S.: 523999
Jose Kreidler (Pres)
Andrew Osichnuk (CFO)
Alexander Dekhtyar (Chm & CEO)

BUSINESS FIRST BANCSHARES, INC.
500 Laurel St Ste 101, Baton Rouge, LA 70801
Tel.: (225) 248-7600   LA
Web Site: https://www.b1bank.com
Year Founded: 2006
BFST—(NASDAQ)
Rev.: $353,327,000
Assets: $6,584,550,000
Liabilities: $5,940,291,000
Net Worth: $644,259,000
Earnings: $71,043,000
Emp.: 751
Fiscal Year-end: 12/31/23
Bank Holding Company
N.A.I.C.S.: 551111
David R. Melville III (Acting Chm, Pres & CEO)
Gregory Robertson (CFO)
Jerome Vascocu Jr. (Chief Admin Officer)

Subsidiaries:

Pedestal Bancshares, Inc.   (1)
1300 W Tunnel Blvd, Houma, LA 70360
Tel.: (985) 580-2265
Web Site: http://www.pedestal.bank
Bank Holding Company
N.A.I.C.S.: 551111

Subsidiary (Domestic):

Pedestal Bank   (2)
1300 W Tunnel Blvd, Houma, LA 70360
Tel.: (985) 580-2265
Web Site: http://www.pedestal.bank
Rev.: $5,492,200
Emp.: 31
Banking Services
N.A.I.C.S.: 522110

Texas Citizens Bancorp, Inc.   (1)
4949 Fairmont Pkwy Ste 100, Pasadena, TX 77505-3757
Tel.: (713) 948-5700
Web Site: http://www.texascitizensbank.com
Bank Holding Company
N.A.I.C.S.: 551111
Duncan W. Stewart (Chm & CEO)

Subsidiary (Domestic):

Texas Citizens Bank, N.A.   (2)
4949 Fairmont Pkwy, Pasadena, TX 77505-3757
Tel.: (713) 948-5700
Web Site: http://www.texascitizensbank.com
Savings Bank
N.A.I.C.S.: 522180
Duncan W. Stewart (Chm & CEO)
Michael L. Cornett (Pres)

b1BANK   (1)
500 Laurel St, Baton Rouge, LA 70801-1811
Tel.: (225) 248-7600
Web Site: https://www.b1bank.com
Sales Range: $25-49.9 Million
Commericial Banking
N.A.I.C.S.: 522110

David R. Melville III (Acting Chm, Pres & CEO)
Jude Melville (Chm)

BUTLER NATIONAL CORPORATION
1 Aero Plz, New Century, KS 66031
Tel.: (913) 780-9595   DE
Web Site:
   https://www.butlernational.com
BUKS—(OTCQX)
Rev.: $78,376,000
Assets: $113,975,000
Liabilities: $59,534,000
Net Worth: $54,441,000
Earnings: $12,512,000
Emp.: 327
Fiscal Year-end: 04/30/24
Aerospace, Environmental & Management Services
N.A.I.C.S.: 336411
Clark D. Stewart (Pres & CEO)
R. Warren Wagoner (Chm)
Christopher J. Reedy (Pres & CEO)
Tad M. McMahon (CFO & Sec)

Subsidiaries:

Avcon Industries, Inc.   (1)
714 N Oliver Rd, Newton, KS 67114
Tel.: (316) 284-2842
Web Site: https://www.avconindustries.com
Airport Operation Services
N.A.I.C.S.: 488119
Aric Peters (Dir-Sls)

BCS Design, Inc.   (1)
19920 W 161st St, Olathe, KS 66062
Tel.: (913) 780-4820
Web Site: http://www.bcsarchitects.com
Emp.: 10
Architectural Services
N.A.I.C.S.: 541310
Jeffrey H. Shinkle (Founder & Pres)

BHCMC, LLC   (1)
4000 W Comanche Ave, Dodge City, KS 67801
Tel.: (620) 682-7777
Web Site: https://www.boothillcasino.com
Casino Operator
N.A.I.C.S.: 721120

Butler Avionics, Inc.   (1)
1 Aero Plz, New Century, KS 66031-1104
Tel.: (913) 829-4606
Web Site: https://www.butleravionics.com
Electric Equipment Mfr
N.A.I.C.S.: 334419

BUTTERFLY NETWORK, INC.
530 Old Whitfield St, Guilford, CT 06437
Tel.: (781) 557-4800   DE
Web Site:
   https://www.butterflynetwork.com
Year Founded: 2011
BFLY—(NYSE)
Rev.: $73,390,000
Assets: $417,570,000
Liabilities: $92,210,000
Net Worth: $325,360,000
Earnings: ($168,723,000)
Emp.: 330
Fiscal Year-end: 12/31/22
Ultrasound Operating Systems
N.A.I.C.S.: 621512
Jonathan M. Rothberg (Founder)
Heather C. Getz (CFO, COO & Exec VP)
Joseph M. DeVivo (Chm, Pres & CEO)

BUZZFEED, INC.
229 W 43rd St 10th Fl, New York, NY 10036
Tel.: (646) 589-8592   DE
Web Site:
   https://www.buzzfeednews.com
Year Founded: 2020
BZFD—(NASDAQ)
Rev.: $436,674,000

Assets: $529,972,000
Liabilities: $335,418,000
Net Worth: $194,554,000
Earnings: ($200,957,000)
Emp.: 1,368
Fiscal Year-end: 12/31/22
Investment Services
N.A.I.C.S.: 523999
David Arroyo (Chief Legal & Compliance Officer & Sec)
Matthew Omer (CFO)
Jonah Peretti (Founder, Chm & CEO)

Subsidiaries:

BuzzFeed, Inc.   (1)
200 5th Ave 8th Fl, New York, NY 10010
Tel.: (212) 431-7464
Web Site: http://www.buzzfeed.com
Sales Range: $75-99.9 Million
Emp.: 550
Online Social News & Entertainment Publisher
N.A.I.C.S.: 516210
Marcela Martin (Pres)
Jonah Peretti (Co-Founder & CEO)
John Johnson (Co-Founder)
Mark Wilkie (CTO)
Mark Frackt (CFO)
Allison Lucas (Gen Counsel)
Chris Johanesen (Mgr-Principal Product)
Dao Nguyen (Publr)
Weesie Vieira (Dir-Editorial Comm)
Lenke Taylor (Chief People Officer)
Laura Henderson (Sr VP-Mktg)
Carole Robinson (Chief Comm Officer)
Mark Jafar (VP-Corp Comm)
Jinen Kamdar (VP-Product)
Eric Karp (Head-Licensing)
Cindy Vanegas-Gesuale (Head-Programming)
Shani Hilton (VP-News & Programming)
Lauren Dolgen (Head-Studios-Los Angeles)
Mark Schoofs (Editor-in-Chief)
Amita Tomkoria (Sr VP-IR)
Christian Baesler (COO)

TheHuffingtonPost.com, Inc.   (1)
229 W 43RD St, 10TH Fl, New York, NY 10036
Tel.: (800) 827-6364
Web Site: http://www.huffingtonpost.com
Online Source of News & Opinion
N.A.I.C.S.: 513199
Christy Havranek (Head-Visuals)
Paige Lavender (Dir-News)
Marta Rodriguez (Head-Ops)
Buck Wolf (Dir-Trends)
Kristen Aiken (Head-Life & Commerce)
Noah Michelson (Head-Personal)
Rajul Punjabi (Dir-Voices)
Abigail Williams (Head-Audience)
Benjamin Currie (Art Dir-Art)
Jianan Liu (Art Dir)
Jorn Rose (Head-Strategic Growth & Insight)
Kelly Hanshaw (Sr Product Mgr)
Andrea Handevidt (Dir-Engrg)
Cristina Fuser (Dir-Product)
Francesca Syrett (Sr Mgr-Bus Ops)
Arianna Huffington (Founder)

BWX TECHNOLOGIES, INC.
800 Main St 4th Fl, Lynchburg, VA 24504
Tel.: (980) 365-4300   DE
Web Site: https://www.bwxt.com
Year Founded: 1867
BWXT—(NYSE)
Rev.: $2,496,309,000
Assets: $2,747,065,000
Liabilities: $1,813,764,000
Net Worth: $933,301,000
Earnings: $245,849,000
Emp.: 7,800
Fiscal Year-end: 12/31/23
Holding Company; Nuclear Power Generation Equipment Mfr, Whslr & Support Services
N.A.I.C.S.: 551112
John R. MacQuarrie (Pres-Nuclear Power Grp-BWXT Canada Ltd)
Robb A. LeMasters (CFO & Sr VP)
Jud Simmons (Dir-Media & PR)

Rex D. Geveden (Pres & CEO)
Mark A. Kratz (VP-IR)
Robert Duffy (Chief Admin Officer & Sr VP)
Michael Fitzgerald (Chief Acctg Officer & VP-Fin)
Kevin Gorman (Controller)
Ronald O. Whitford Jr. (Chief Compliance Officer, Gen Counsel, Sec & Sr VP)
Omar F. Meguid (Chief Digital Officer)
Kevin M. McCoy (Pres-Govt Ops)
Chase A. Jacobson (VP)
Kurt Bender (Dir-IT)

Subsidiaries:

BWXT Canada Ltd.   (1)
581 Coronation Boulevard, Cambridge, N1R 3E9, ON, Canada   (100%)
Tel.: (519) 621-2130
Web Site: http://www.bwxt.com
Power Generating Equipment Mfr
N.A.I.C.S.: 332410
John R. MacQuarrie (Pres)

BWXT Government Group, Inc.   (1)
1570 Mount Athos Rd, Lynchburg, VA 24504-5447
Tel.: (434) 522-6000
Web Site: http://www.bwxt.com
Nuclear Materials, Facilities & Technologies Management Services
N.A.I.C.S.: 562920

Subsidiary (Domestic):

BWXT Y-12, LLC   (2)
Y-12 Natl Security Complex Bear Creek Rd 765 Perimeter Rd K-1065D, Oak Ridge, TN 37830-2009
Tel.: (865) 574-1500
Web Site: https://www.y12.doe.gov
Sales Range: $450-499.9 Million
Emp.: 4,300
Security Complex Manager for Department of Energy & National Nuclear Security Administration
N.A.I.C.S.: 561210

BWXT Nuclear Energy Canada Inc.   (1)
1160 Monaghan Road, Peterborough, K9J 0A8, ON, Canada
Web Site: https://www.nec.bwxt.com
Nuclear Product Mfr
N.A.I.C.S.: 332410

BWXT Technical Services Group, Inc.   (1)
109 Ramsey Pl, Lynchburg, VA 24501
Tel.: (434) 316-7500
Web Site: http://www.bwxt.com
Nuclear Operations & Management Services
N.A.I.C.S.: 523940

Babcock & Wilcox Investment Company   (1)
13024 Ballantyne Corporate Pl Ste 700, Charlotte, NC 28277
Tel.: (704) 625-4900
Eletric Power Generation Services
N.A.I.C.S.: 221113

Intech International Inc.   (1)
20 Innovation Dr, Dundas, L9H 7P3, ON, Canada
Tel.: (905) 689-7300
Web Site:
   http://www.intechinternational.com
Emp.: 15
Nuclear Facility Testing, Maintenance & Engineering Services
N.A.I.C.S.: 541330

BYLINE BANCORP, INC.
180 N LaSalle St Ste 300, Chicago, IL 60601
Tel.: (773) 244-7000   IL
Web Site:
   https://www.bylinebank.com
Year Founded: 1978
BY—(NYSE)
Rev.: $358,873,000
Assets: $7,362,941,000

Byline Bancorp, Inc.—(Continued)

Liabilities: $6,597,125,000
Net Worth: $765,816,000
Earnings: $87,954,000
Emp.: 948
Fiscal Year-end: 12/31/22
Offices of Bank Holding Companies
N.A.I.C.S.: 551111
Mark Fucinato *(Chief Credit Officer & Exec VP)*
Thomas J. Bell III *(CFO, Treas & Exec VP)*
Maria Sherylle A. Olano *(Chief Acctg Officer & Sr VP)*
Roberto R. Herencia *(Exec Chm & CEO)*
Alberto J. Paracchini *(Pres)*
Megan Biggam *(Exec VP)*
Brogan Ptacin *(Exec VP)*
John M. Barkidjija *(Exec VP)*
Angela Hart *(Exec VP)*
Dana Rose *(Chief HR Officer)*
Thomas Abraham *(Pres)*
Michelle Johnson *(Chief Risk Officer)*
Nicolas Mando *(CTO)*
Ana Casanueva *(Sr VP)*

Subsidiaries:

Byline Bank   **(1)**
180 N La Salle St Ste 300, Chicago, IL 60601-3110
Tel.: (773) 244-7000
Web Site: https://www.bylinebank.com
Commericial Banking
N.A.I.C.S.: 522110
Thomas J. Bell III *(CFO, Treas & Exec VP)*
Maria Sherylle A. Olano *(Chief Acctg Officer & Sr VP)*
Alberto J. Paracchini *(Pres & CEO)*
Megan Biggam *(Exec VP & Head-Retail Banking)*
Thomas Abraham *(Pres-Small Bus Capital)*
John Barkidjija *(Exec VP & Head-Comml Real Estate & Specialty Fin)*
Dana Traci *(Chief HR Officer & Exec VP)*
Brogan Ptacin *(Exec VP & Head-Comml Banking)*
Ana Casanueva *(Sr VP)*
Angela Hart *(Exec VP)*
Nicolas Mando *(Sr VP)*
Sherylle Olano *(Chief Acctg Officer)*
Thomas J. Bell III *(Treas & Sr VP)*

Inland Bancorp, Inc.   **(1)**
2805 Butterfield Rd, Oak Brook, IL 60523-1159
Web Site: http://www.inlandbank.com
Sales Range: $50-74.9 Million
Emp.: 285
Bank Holding Company
N.A.I.C.S.: 551111
Howard A. Jaffe *(Pres & COO)*
Daniel L. Goodwin *(Chm & CEO)*
Peter Stickler *(Pres/CEO-Inland Bank & Trust)*

Subsidiary (Domestic):

Inland Bank & Trust   **(2)**
2805 Butterfield Rd, Oak Brook, IL 60523
Web Site: http://www.inlandbank.com
Wireless Telecommunication Services
N.A.I.C.S.: 522110
David Horkey *(Dir-Mktg)*
Peter Stickler *(Pres & CEO)*
Thomas Marvinac *(Chief Credit Officer & Exec VP)*
William Chioros *(Sr VP-Comml Real Estate Lending)*
Christopher Metcalf *(VP-Comml Real Estate)*
Dan Healy *(Exec VP-Comml Banking)*
Michael Corr *(Sr VP & Mgr-Bus Banking)*

BYRNA TECHNOLOGIES INC.
100 Burtt Rd Ste 115, Andover, MA 01810
Tel.: (978) 868-5011   **DE**
Web Site: https://www.byrna.com
Year Founded: 2005
BYRN—(NASDAQ)
Rev.: $42,644,000

Assets: $52,314,000
Liabilities: $9,995,000
Net Worth: $42,319,000
Earnings: ($8,192,000)
Emp.: 106
Fiscal Year-end: 11/30/23
Ammunition Mfr
N.A.I.C.S.: 332993
Bryan Scott Ganz *(Pres & CEO)*
Andre J. Buys *(CTO)*
Herbert Hughes *(Chm)*
Etienne Roux *(Exec VP-Intl Sls & Mktg)*
Luan Pham *(CMO & Chief Revenue Officer)*
Sandra Driscoll *(Chief People Officer)*
Michael Wager *(Chief Strategy Officer)*
Laurilee Kearnes *(CFO & Principal Acctg Officer)*

C&F FINANCIAL CORPORATION
3600 La Grange Pkwy, Toano, VA 23168
Tel.: (804) 843-2360   **VA**
Web Site: https://www.cffc.com
Year Founded: 1994
CFFI—(NASDAQ)
Rev.: $129,836,000
Assets: $2,332,317,000
Liabilities: $2,136,084,000
Net Worth: $196,233,000
Earnings: $29,159,000
Emp.: 613
Fiscal Year-end: 12/31/22
Offices of Bank Holding Companies
N.A.I.C.S.: 551111
Larry G. Dillon *(Chm)*
Thomas F. Cherry *(Pres & CEO)*
Jason E. Long *(CFO, Sec & Sr VP)*

Subsidiaries:

Citizens & Farmers Bank   **(1)**
415-14th St, West Point, VA 23181 **(100%)**
Tel.: (804) 843-2360
Web Site: http://www.cffc.com
Sales Range: $10-24.9 Million
Emp.: 35
State Commercial Banks
N.A.I.C.S.: 522110
Larry G. Dillon *(Chm)*
Thomas F. Cherry *(Pres)*

Subsidiary (Domestic):

C&F Finance Company   **(2)**
5500 Audubon Dr, Henrico, VA 23231
Tel.: (804) 236-9601
Web Site: https://www.cffc.com
Sales Range: $125-149.9 Million
Finance Services Specializing in Indirect, New & Used Automobile Lending
N.A.I.C.S.: 522220

C&F Mortgage Corporation   **(2)**
1400 Alverser Dr, Midlothian, VA 23113   **(100%)**
Tel.: (804) 858-8300
Web Site: https://www.cfmortgagecorp.com
Sales Range: $50-74.9 Million
Emp.: 45
Mortgage Banker
N.A.I.C.S.: 522292

Subsidiary (Domestic):

Certified Appraisals LLC   **(3)**
1400 Alverser Dr, Midlothian, VA 23113-2610
Tel.: (804) 920-3839
Web Site: https://www.certifiedappraisalsllc.com
Real Estate Appraisal Services
N.A.I.C.S.: 531320

Subsidiary (Domestic):

C&F Wealth Management Corporation   **(2)**
415 14th St, West Point, VA 23181 **(100%)**
Tel.: (757) 741-2253
Web Site: http://www.cffc.com

Sales Range: $50-74.9 Million
Emp.: 6
Investment Services; Security Broker
N.A.I.C.S.: 523150
Douglas L. Cash *(First VP)*
Douglas L. Hartz *(First VP)*
William C. Morrison *(Pres)*

C-BOND SYSTEMS, INC.
6035 S Loop E, Houston, TX 77033
Tel.: (210) 455-9414   **CO**
Web Site:
https://www.cbondsystems.com
Year Founded: 2007
CBNT—(OTCQB)
Rev.: $2,488,493
Assets: $2,283,113
Liabilities: $6,607,648
Net Worth: ($4,324,535)
Earnings: $1,886,807
Emp.: 20
Fiscal Year-end: 12/31/23
Nanotechnology Application & Process Services
N.A.I.C.S.: 541690
Scott R. Silverman *(Chm, CEO, Interim CFO & Treas)*
Allison F. Tomek *(Pres)*

C.H. ROBINSON WORLDWIDE, INC.
14701 Charlson Rd, Eden Prairie, MN 55347-5076
Tel.: (952) 683-2800   **DE**
Web Site:
https://www.chrobinson.com
Year Founded: 1905
CHRW—(NASDAQ)
Rev.: $17,596,443,000
Assets: $5,225,380,000
Liabilities: $3,806,583,000
Net Worth: $1,418,697,000
Earnings: $325,129,000
Emp.: 15,246
Fiscal Year-end: 12/31/23
Holding Company; Freight Transportation & Logistics Services
N.A.I.C.S.: 551112
Angela K. Freeman *(Chief Human Resources & ESG Officer)*
Christopher J. O'Brien *(Chief Comml Officer)*
David P. Bozeman *(Pres & CEO)*
Ben G. Campbell *(Chief Legal Officer & Sec)*
Michael J. Short *(Pres-Freight Forwarding-Global)*
Jordan T. Kass *(Pres-Managed Svcs)*
Michael W. Neill *(CTO)*
Michael Castagnetto *(Pres-North American Surface Transportation)*
Chuck Ives *(Dir-IR)*
Duncan Burns *(Mgr-Comm)*
Arun Rajan *(COO, Chief Strategy Officer & Chief Innovation Officer)*

Subsidiaries:

C.H Robinson Worldwide (Shanghai) Co. Ltd.   **(1)**
Rm A 8 F Tower W 618 Yanan Rd E, Huangpu, Shanghai, 200001, China
Tel.: (86) 2123226068
Sales Range: $25-49.9 Million
Emp.: 15
Logistic Services
N.A.I.C.S.: 541614
Jack Chang *(VP-Global Forwarding-Asia)*
John Chen *(VP-Global Forwarding-Asia)*

C.H. Robinson Austria GmbH   **(1)**
Soho 2 Grabenweg 68, 6020, Innsbruck, Austria
Tel.: (43) 5129022100
Logistics Consulting Servies
N.A.I.C.S.: 541614
Chucko Beslic *(Mgr)*

C.H. Robinson Company   **(1)**
14701 Charlson Rd Ste 900, Eden Prairie, MN 55347

Tel.: (952) 937-6713
Web Site: http://www.chrobinson.com
Freight Transportation & Logistics Services
N.A.I.C.S.: 488510

Subsidiary (Domestic):

C.H. Robinson Freight Services, Ltd.   **(2)**
1501 N Mittel Blvd Ste B, Wood Dale, IL 60191-1055
Tel.: (630) 766-4445
Emp.: 2,000
Fiscal Year-end: 06/30/2012
Freight Forwarding Services
N.A.I.C.S.: 488510
Stephane D. Rambaud *(CEO)*
Emil Sanchez *(CFO)*
Andy Wang *(Pres)*
Lori Buckley *(Gen Counsel & VP-HR)*
Andy Polley *(Mng Dir)*

freightquote.com   **(2)**
901 W Carondelet Dr, Kansas City, MO 64114
Web Site: https://www.freightquote.com
Emp.: 1,000
Freight & Shipping Services
N.A.I.C.S.: 488510

C.H. Robinson Company (Canada) Ltd.   **(1)**
2875 Laurier Blvd 220, Quebec, G1V 2M2, QC, Canada
Tel.: (418) 650-1203
Sales Range: $25-49.9 Million
Emp.: 6
Transportation Services
N.A.I.C.S.: 488999

C.H. Robinson Czech Republic s.r.o.   **(1)**
Logistics Consulting Servies
N.A.I.C.S.: 541614
Bart Burgmans *(Mgr)*

C.H. Robinson Europe B.V.   **(1)**
Teleportboulevard 120, 1043 EJ, Amsterdam, Netherlands
Tel.: (31) 20 517 0221
Web Site: https://www.chrobinson.com
Sales Range: $25-49.9 Million
Holding Company; Regional Managing Office
N.A.I.C.S.: 551112

Subsidiary (Non-US):

C.H. Robinson Hungaria Kft.   **(2)**
Tel.: (36) 13827230
Web Site: http://www.chreurope.com
Sales Range: $10-24.9 Million
Emp.: 12
Freight Transportation Services
N.A.I.C.S.: 488510

C.H. Robinson International Italy, SRL   **(2)**
Viale del Mulino n 1 Edificio U10 - Livello 2, Assago, 20090, Milan, Italy
Tel.: (39) 028 250 7201
Web Site: https://www.chrobinson.com
Freight Transportation Services
N.A.I.C.S.: 488510

C.H. Robinson Worldwide (Ireland) Ltd.   **(2)**
  (100%)
Tel.: (353) 18091515
Web Site: http://www.chrobinson.com
Sales Range: $100-124.9 Million
Emp.: 20
Freight Transportation Services
N.A.I.C.S.: 488510
Mark O'Shaughnessy *(Mng Dir)*

C.H. Robinson Worldwide (UK) Ltd.   **(2)**
Building 5 Suite 13 Exchange Quay Salford Quays, Manchester, M5 3EJ, United Kingdom
Tel.: (44) 1618682988
Emp.: 20
All Other Transportation Services
N.A.I.C.S.: 481112
Dan Oderkirk *(Gen Mgr)*

Subsidiary (Domestic):

C.H. Robinson (UK) Ltd.   **(3)**

Bldg 8 Ste 2 2 Exchange Quays, Salford Quays, Manchester, M5 3EF, United Kingdom
Tel.: (44) 1618743500
Web Site: http://www.chrobinson.com
Sales Range: $10-24.9 Million
Emp.: 7
Freight Transportation & Logistics Services
N.A.I.C.S.: 488510

Subsidiary (Non-US):

C.H. Robinson Worldwide GmbH (2)
Caffamacherreihe 5, 20355, Hamburg, Germany
Tel.: (49) 402 808 8023
Web Site: https://www.chrobinson.com
Sales Range: $10-24.9 Million
Freight Transportation Services
N.A.I.C.S.: 488510

C.H. Robinson-Shannon International (2)
Kilsheelan House Shannon Town Centre, Shannon, County Clare, Ireland (100%)
Tel.: (353) 61 362122
Web Site: http://www.chrobinson.com
Freight Forwarding Operations
N.A.I.C.S.: 488510

C.H. Robinson France SAS (1)
165 Avenue du bois de la Pie Parc de reflets BAT 1 ZAC Paris Nord II, BP 58321, 95700, Roissy-en-France, CDG Cedex, France
Tel.: (33) 176739261
Web Site: http://www.chrobinson.com
Global Freight Forwarding
N.A.I.C.S.: 488510

C.H. Robinson Freight Services (China) Ltd. (1)
Room 1702 Tower 18 No 5 Shuguang Xili, Beijing, 100028, China
Tel.: (86) 85685588
Freight & Logistic Services
N.A.I.C.S.: 541614

C.H. Robinson Freight Services (Singapore) Pte. Ltd. (1)
No 164 Kallang Way 06-07/08/09 Solaris Kallang 164, Singapore, 349248, Singapore
Tel.: (65) 6 488 4188
Web Site: https://www.chrobinson.com
Logistics Consulting Servies
N.A.I.C.S.: 541614

C.H. Robinson Freight Services (Taiwan) Ltd. (1)
Tel.: (886) 225080777
Emp.: 40
Freight Forwarding Services
N.A.I.C.S.: 541614
Ching Wen Wang (Pres)

C.H. Robinson Freight Services (Thailand) Ltd. (1)
52 Thaniya Plaza Building 21st Floor Silom Road, Suriyawong Subdistrict Suriyawong Bangrak, Bangkok, 10500, Thailand
Tel.: (66) 2666353536
Freight Forwarding Services
N.A.I.C.S.: 484121

C.H. Robinson Freight Services (Vietnam) Company Limited (1)
11/F 12/F Golden Tower No 6 Nguyen Thi Minh Khai St, Da Kao Ward District 1, Ho Chi Minh City, Vietnam
Tel.: (84) 2839330723
Freight Transportation Services
N.A.I.C.S.: 484110
Roy Chau (Mgr)

C.H. Robinson Freight Services Middle East DMCC (1)
Unit 706 Palladium Tower Cluster C JLT, Dubai, United Arab Emirates
Tel.: (971) 45763971
Freight Forwarding & Transportation Services
N.A.I.C.S.: 532411

C.H. Robinson International (India) Private Ltd. (1)
Excom House 7 Saki Vihar Road Saki Naka, Andheri, Mumbai, 400 072, Maharashtra, India
Tel.: (91) 2266916644
Logistics Consulting Servies

N.A.I.C.S.: 541614
Anil Nair (Branch Mgr)

C.H. Robinson International Columbia SAS (1)
Logistic Services
N.A.I.C.S.: 488510
Kevin Scola (Mgr-Capacity Acct)

C.H. Robinson International, Inc. (1)
14701 Charlson Rd, Eden Prairie, MN 55347-5076
Emp.: 400
Transport Management Services
N.A.I.C.S.: 541614

C.H. Robinson Luxembourg Finance S.a r.l. (1)
33 rue de Gasperich Building H20 Second floor, Hesperange, 5826, Luxembourg
Tel.: (352) 2664471
Logistic Services
N.A.I.C.S.: 541614

C.H. Robinson Polska S.A. (1)
Al Jana Pawla II 29, 00-867, Warsaw, Poland
Tel.: (48) 22 653 6530
Web Site: https://www.chrobinson.com
Logistics Consulting Servies
N.A.I.C.S.: 541614

C.H. Robinson Project Logistics Ltd. (1)
Suite 102 6715 - 8th Street N E, Calgary, T2E 7H7, AB, Canada
Tel.: (403) 295-9716
Logistics Consulting Servies
N.A.I.C.S.: 541614

C.H. Robinson Project Logistics Pte. Ltd. (1)
150 Kampong Ampat KA Centre No 06-06, Singapore, 368324, Singapore
Tel.: (65) 65434847
Logistics Consulting Servies
N.A.I.C.S.: 541614

C.H. Robinson Project Logistics, Inc. (1)
842 West Sam Houston Pkwy N Ste 325, Houston, TX 77024
Tel.: (281) 313-6000
Web Site: https://www.chrobinson.com
Logistics Consulting Servies
N.A.I.C.S.: 541614

C.H. Robinson Shanghai Trading Co. (1)
13th Floor No 1258 Yu Yuan Road, Chang Ning District, Shanghai, 200050, China
Tel.: (86) 216 102 0303
Transportation Services
N.A.I.C.S.: 485999

C.H. Robinson Slovakia, s.r.o. (1)
Karadzicova 16, Bratislava, 821 08, Slovakia
Tel.: (421) 232784550
Logistic Services
N.A.I.C.S.: 541614

C.H. Robinson Switzerland GmbH (1)
Stanzlergasse 4, 4051, Basel, Switzerland
Tel.: (41) 612259100
Logistics Consulting Servies
N.A.I.C.S.: 541614
Michel Datz (Mgr)

C.H. Robinson Technology LLC (1)
14701 Charlson Rd, Eden Prairie, MN 55347
Tel.: (952) 683-2800
Transportation Services
N.A.I.C.S.: 485999

C.H. Robinson Worldwide (Australia) Pty. Ltd. (1)
460 Bay Street, Port Melbourne, 3207, VIC, Australia
Tel.: (61) 396447222
Web Site: https://www.chrobinson.com
Freight Transportation & Logistics Services
N.A.I.C.S.: 541614

C.H. Robinson Worldwide (NZ) Ltd. (1)
63b Richard Pearse Drive Airport Oaks Mangere, Auckland, 2022, New Zealand

Tel.: (64) 92753493
Logistic Services
N.A.I.C.S.: 541614
Mark White (Mgr-Intl Dev & Sls)

C.H. Robinson Worldwide Argentina, S.A. (1)
Maipu 1252 11th Floor, Buenos Aires, 1006, Argentina
Tel.: (54) 115 555 6300
Web Site: https://www.chrobinson.com
Transportation Services
N.A.I.C.S.: 488999

C.H. Robinson Worldwide Freight India Private Limited (1)
A-303 Navratna Corporate Park Bopal Ambli Road, H L College Road Navrangpura, Ahmedabad, 380058, Gujarat, India
Tel.: (91) 792 991 5301
Web Site: https://www.chrobinson.com
Sales Range: $25-49.9 Million
Freight Transportation Services
N.A.I.C.S.: 488510

C.H. Robinson Worldwide Freight Lanka (Private) Limited (1)
No 347/1 Dr Colvin R De Silva Mawatha, Colombo, 00200, Sri Lanka
Tel.: (94) 11 454 1422
Transportation Services
N.A.I.C.S.: 485999

C.H. Robinson Worldwide Singapore Pte. Ltd (1)
No 164 Kallang Way 06-07/08/09 Solaris Kallang 164, Singapore, 349248, Singapore
Tel.: (65) 64884188
Sales Range: $25-49.9 Million
Emp.: 15
Transportation Services
N.A.I.C.S.: 488999

C.H. Robinson de Mexico, S.A. de C.V. (1)
Ave Patria 2085 Piso 4, Colonia Puerta de Hierro, 45116, Guadalajara, Jalisco, Mexico
Tel.: (52) 333 818 0230
Web Site: https://www.chrobinson.com
All Other Transportation Services
N.A.I.C.S.: 488999

CH Robinson Freight Services (Malaysia) Sdn. Bhd. (1)
6th and 7th Floor Menara Amverton No 3 Jalan Istana, Garden Business Centre, 41000, Klang, Selangor, Malaysia
Tel.: (60) 33 373 8828
Web Site: https://www.chrobinson.com
Freight Forwarding Services
N.A.I.C.S.: 484121

CH Robinson Project Logistics Sdn. Bhd. (1)
6th Floor Menara A&M Garden Business Centre No 3 Jalan Istana, 41000, Klang, Selangor, Malaysia
Tel.: (60) 333738828
Web Site: http://www.chrobinson.com
Emp.: 50
Logistics Consulting Servies
N.A.I.C.S.: 541614

DEMA SERVICE S.p.A. (1)
Via Pietro Nenni 300, 66020, San Giovanni Teatino, CH, Italy
Web Site: http://www.chrobinson.com
Logistics Consultancy Services
N.A.I.C.S.: 541614
Mauro De Lellis (Founder)

Enterprise TMS LLC (1)
901 W Carondelet Dr, Kansas City, MO 64114
Tel.: (913) 982-2010
Web Site: https://www.enterprisetms.com
Freight Transportation Arrangement Services
N.A.I.C.S.: 488510

Freighquote.com, Inc. (1)
901 W Carondelet Dr, Kansas City, MO 64114
Tel.: (913) 642-4700
Web Site: http://www.freightquote.com
Freight Transportation Arrangement Services
N.A.I.C.S.: 488510
Chris Kolquist (Pres)
Tracy Kenison (VP-Sls)

Mike Collins (VP-Bus Strategy)
Doug Grojean (VP-Ops)
Mark Fennewald (Dir-IT)

Freightview, Inc. (1)
7900 Conser Ste 20, Overland Park, KS 66204
Tel.: (913) 353-6188
Web Site: http://www.freightview.com
Transportation & Logistics Consulting Services
N.A.I.C.S.: 541614

M.O.T. Intermodal Shipping Inc. (1)
400-645 Wellington St, Montreal, H3C 0L1, QC, Canada
Tel.: (514) 849-6144
Logistic Services
N.A.I.C.S.: 541614
Mia Ginter (Gen Mgr)

M.O.T. Intermodal Shipping USA Inc. (1)
1200-A Scottsville Rd, Rochester, NY 14624
Tel.: (585) 758-5800
Web Site: http://www.milgram.com
Freight Transportation Services
N.A.I.C.S.: 488510
Ole Enderslev (Pres)

Prime Distribution Services, Inc. (1)
9955 AllPoints Pkwy, Plainfield, IN 46168
Tel.: (317) 837-0088
Web Site: http://www.chrobinson.com
Distribution & Logistic Consulting Services
N.A.I.C.S.: 541614
William Vechiarella (Pres)

Robinson Fresh BV (1)
Teleportboulevard 120, 1043 EJ, Amsterdam, Netherlands
Tel.: (31) 205170221
Web Site: http://www.robinsonfresh.com
Food & Nutrition Services
N.A.I.C.S.: 311421

Space Cargo Services S.A. (1)
Calle Artic 132-134 Zal, 08040, Barcelona, Spain
Tel.: (34) 932625656
Web Site: http://www.space-cargo.com
Cargo Freight Transportation Services
N.A.I.C.S.: 481112
Alfonso Valenzuela Rodriguez (CFO)

C2 BLOCKCHAIN, INC.
123 SE 3rd Ave Ste 130, Miami, FL 33131   NV
Web Site:
https://www.c2blockchain.com
Year Founded: 2021
CBLO—(OTCIQ)
Assets: $30
Liabilities: $61,214
Net Worth: ($61,184)
Earnings: ($30,020)
Emp.: 1
Fiscal Year-end: 06/30/24
Digital Cinema Equipment Installation Services
N.A.I.C.S.: 238210
Levi Jacobson (CFO)

C2E ENERGY, INC.
1801 Century Park E 2400, Los Angeles, CA 90067
Tel.: (424) 354-0990   FL
Year Founded: 2001
OOGI—(OTCIQ)
Liabilities: $675,534
Net Worth: ($675,534)
Earnings: ($404,819)
Fiscal Year-end: 12/31/22
Fuel Power Generation Services
N.A.I.C.S.: 221112
Shee Fu Mak (Chm)

C3.AI, INC.
1400 Seaport Blvd, Redwood City, CA 94063
Tel.: (650) 503-2200   DE
Web Site: https://c3.ai
Year Founded: 2009

C3.ai, Inc.—(Continued)

AI—(NYSE)
Rev.: $266,795,000
Assets: $1,103,028,000
Liabilities: $173,363,000
Net Worth: $929,665,000
Earnings: ($268,839,000)
Emp.: 914
Fiscal Year-end: 04/30/23
Software Development Services
N.A.I.C.S.: 541511
Edward Y. Abbo *(CTO & Exec VP)*
Thomas M. Siebel *(Founder, Chm & CEO)*

C4 THERAPEUTICS, INC.

490 Arsenal Way Ste 120, Watertown, MA 02472
Tel.: (617) 231-0700   DE
Web Site:
  https://www.c4therapeutics.com
Year Founded: 2015
CCCC—(NASDAQ)
Rev.: $20,756,000
Assets: $376,451,000
Liabilities: $130,337,000
Net Worth: $246,114,000
Earnings: ($132,493,000)
Emp.: 145
Fiscal Year-end: 12/31/23
Biotechnology Research & Development Services
N.A.I.C.S.: 541714
Andrew J. Hirsch *(Pres & CEO)*
Andrew Hirsch *(Pres & CEO)*
Leonard M. J. Reyno *(Chief Medical Officer)*
Kendra Adams *(CFO & Treas)*
Marc A. Cohen *(Founder)*
Stewart Fisher *(Chief Scientific Officer)*
Jolie M. Siegel *(Chief Legal Officer)*
Kelly Schick *(Chief People Officer)*
Kendra Adams *(Sr VP-Comm & IR)*
Scott Boyle *(Chief Bus Officer)*
Hagop Youssoufian *(Interim Chief Medical Officer)*
Courtney Solberg *(Sr Mgr-IR)*
Loraine Spreen *(Sr Dir-Corp Comm & Patient Advocacy)*

C5 ACQUISITION CORPORATION

1701 Pennsylvania Ave NW Ste 460, Washington, DC 20006
Tel.: (202) 452-9133   DE
Web Site:
  https://www.c5acquisitions.com
Year Founded: 2021
CXAC—(NYSE)
Rev.: $4,183,071
Assets: $298,948,558
Liabilities: $307,726,374
Net Worth: ($8,777,816)
Earnings: $1,516,291
Emp.: 2
Fiscal Year-end: 12/31/22
Investment Services
N.A.I.C.S.: 523999
Robert Meyerson *(CEO)*
David Glickman *(CFO & Chief Bus Dev Officer)*

CA HEALTHCARE ACQUISITION CORP.

99 Summer St Ste 200, Boston, MA 02110
Tel.: (617) 314-3901   DE
Web Site: http://www.cahcspac.com
Year Founded: 2020
CAHCU—(NASDAQ)
Investment Services
N.A.I.C.S.: 523999
Larry J. Neiterman *(Chm & CEO)*
Jeffrey H. Barnes *(Pres & CFO)*

CABALETTA BIO, INC.

2929 Arch St Ste 600, Philadelphia, PA 19104
Tel.: (267) 759-3100   DE
Web Site:
  https://www.cabalettabio.com
Year Founded: 2017
CABA—(NASDAQ)
Rev.: $1,164,000
Assets: $116,968,000
Liabilities: $12,448,000
Net Worth: $104,520,000
Earnings: ($52,975,000)
Emp.: 58
Fiscal Year-end: 12/31/22
Biotechnology Research & Development Services
N.A.I.C.S.: 541714
Gwendolyn Binder *(Exec VP-Science & Tech)*
David J. Chang *(Chief Medical Officer)*
J. Brian Stalter *(Gen Counsel)*
Arun Das *(Sr Dir-New Product Plng & Bus Dev)*
Anup Marda *(CFO)*
Martha O'Connor *(Chief HR Officer)*
Gwendolyn Binder *(Executives)*
Steven A. Nichtberger *(Founder, Chm, Pres & CEO)*

CABLE ONE, INC.

210 E Earll Dr, Phoenix, AZ 85012
Tel.: (602) 364-6000   DE
Web Site: https://ir.cableone.net
CABO—(NYSE)
Rev.: $1,678,081,000
Assets: $6,846,933,000
Liabilities: $4,973,788,000
Net Worth: $1,873,145,000
Earnings: $267,436,000
Emp.: 2,993
Fiscal Year-end: 12/31/23
Cable TV Services
N.A.I.C.S.: 516210
Julia M. Laulis *(Chm, Pres & CEO)*
Michael E. Bowker *(Chief Growth Officer)*
Trish Niemann *(VP-Comm Strategy)*
Eric M. Lardy *(Sr VP-Ops & Integration)*
Christopher D. Boone *(Sr VP-Bus Svcs & Emerging Markets)*
Kenneth E. Johnson *(COO)*
Peter N. Witty *(Gen Counsel, Sec & Sr VP)*
James A. Obermeyer *(Sr VP-Mktg & Sls)*
Todd M. Koetje *(CFO)*
Megan M. Detz *(Sr VP)*

Subsidiaries:

Delta Communications, LLC   **(1)**
2 N Vine St, Harrisburg, IL 62946
Tel.: (618) 294-8000
Web Site: http://clearwave.com
Telecommunication Servicesb
N.A.I.C.S.: 517112

Fidelity Communications Co.   **(1)**
64 N Clark St, Sullivan, MO 63080
Tel.: (573) 468-8081
Web Site:
  http://www.fidelitycommunications.com
Local Telephone Communications
N.A.I.C.S.: 517121

Subsidiary (Domestic):

Fidelity Cable Vision Inc.   **(2)**
64 N Clark St, Sullivan, MO 63080
Tel.: (573) 468-8081
Cable Television Services
N.A.I.C.S.: 516210

Fidelity Systems Plus Inc.   **(2)**
64 N Clark St, Sullivan, MO 63080
Tel.: (573) 468-8081
Telephone Equipment & Systems
N.A.I.C.S.: 517111

Hargray Communications Group, Inc.   **(1)**
856 William Hilton Pkwy, Hilton Head Island, SC 29928
Tel.: (843) 341-1501
Web Site: https://www.hargray.com
Telephone, Internet & Television Services
N.A.I.C.S.: 517111

Telecommunications Management, LLC   **(1)**
1 Montgomery Plz 3rd Fl, Sikeston, MO 63801
Tel.: (844) 546-3278
Web Site: http://www.newwavecom.com
Broadband Company
N.A.I.C.S.: 517112

CABLECLIX USA, INC.

50 W Liberty St Ste 880, Reno, NV 89501   NV
Year Founded: 2013
CCLX—(OTCIQ)
Network Broadcasting Services
N.A.I.C.S.: 516210
Roland J. Vetter *(Accountant)*
Kris Domich *(Pres & CEO)*
Gregory Steinke *(Sec & Dir)*

CABOT CORPORATION   DE

Web Site: https://www.cabotcorp.com
Year Founded: 1882
CBT—(NYSE)
Rev.: $3,931,000,000
Assets: $3,604,000,000
Liabilities: $2,197,000,000
Net Worth: $1,407,000,000
Earnings: $445,000,000
Emp.: 4,300
Fiscal Year-end: 09/30/23
Carbon Black, Fumed Metal Oxides, Inkjet Colorants, Tantalum & Related Products Mfr
N.A.I.C.S.: 325180
Sean D. Keohane *(Pres & CEO)*
Lisa M. Dumont *(Principal Acctg Officer, VP & Controller)*
Steven Delahunt *(Treas & VP-IR)*
Patricia A. Hubbard *(CTO & Sr VP)*
Aled Rees *(Pres-Global Bus Svcs-EMEA & Sr VP)*
Arthur T. Wood *(Chief HR Officer & Sr VP)*
Karen A. Kalita *(Gen Counsel & Sr VP)*
Aaron Johnson *(Pres-Purification Solutions Segment & Sr VP)*
Erica J. McLaughlin *(CFO & Sr VP)*

Subsidiaries:

Anglo Dutch Water Carbons Ltd.   **(1)**
Riddle Street, Berkeley, GL13 9HN, Gloucestershire, United Kingdom
Tel.: (44) 1942275400
Carbon Black Mfr
N.A.I.C.S.: 325180

CS Cabot spol, s.r.o.   **(1)**
Masarykova 753, Krasno Nad Becvou, 757 01, Valasske Mezirici, Czech Republic
Tel.: (420) 571681111
Web Site: http://www.cabotcorp.com
Chemical Products Mfr
N.A.I.C.S.: 424690

Cabot (China) Limited   **(1)**
558 Shuangbai Road, Minhang District, Shanghai, 201108, China
Tel.: (86) 2151758800
Emp.: 300
Carbon Black Mfr
N.A.I.C.S.: 325180
Jeff Zhu *(Sr VP)*

Cabot Activated Carbon B.V.   **(1)**
Botlekstraat 2c, Botlek Rotterdam, Rotterdam, 3197 KA, Zuid-Holland, Netherlands
Tel.: (31) 181291888
Web Site: http://www.cabotcorporation.com
Emp.: 100
Carbon Black Mfr
N.A.I.C.S.: 325180

Cabot Advanced Battery Materials (Tianjin) Co., Ltd.   **(1)**
No 45 Xixia Rd Chemical Industrial Park, Hangu District, Tianjin, 300480, China
Tel.: (86) 2259911000
Electric Vehicle Mfr
N.A.I.C.S.: 336320

Cabot Aerogel GmbH   **(1)**
Industriepark Hochst Bldg D 660, 65926, Frankfurt am Main, Germany
Tel.: (49) 6930580878
Chemical Products Mfr
N.A.I.C.S.: 424690

Cabot Argentina S.A.I.C.   **(1)**
Av Larrabure 203 Casilla de Correo 15, Campana, B2804ERC, Argentina
Tel.: (54) 3489434000
Emp.: 100
Refined Petroleum Product Mfr
N.A.I.C.S.: 324199

Cabot B.V.   **(1)**
Botlekstraat 2, PO Box 1009, 3197 KA, Rotterdam, Netherlands
Tel.: (31) 181291888
Web Site: http://www.cabotcorp.com
Sales Range: $50-74.9 Million
Emp.: 100
Chemical Products Mfr
N.A.I.C.S.: 424690
Harold Corstjens *(Mng Dir)*

Cabot Brasil Industria e Comercio Ltda.   **(1)**
Rua do Paraiso 148 - 5 andar, Sao Paulo, 04103-000, Brazil
Tel.: (55) 1121446429
Web Site: http://www.cabotcorp.com.br
Chemical Products Mfr
N.A.I.C.S.: 424690

Cabot Canada Ltd.   **(1)**
800 Tashmoo Ave, Sarnia, N7T 7N4, ON, Canada   **(100%)**
Tel.: (519) 336-2261
Web Site: http://www.cabot.com
Sales Range: $25-49.9 Million
Emp.: 100
Carbon Black Manufacturing
N.A.I.C.S.: 325180

Cabot Carbon Limited   **(1)**
Sully Moors Road, Sully, CF64 5RP, Vale of Glamorgan, United Kingdom
Tel.: (44) 1446736999
Web Site: http://www.cabotcarbon.com
Emp.: 90
Carbon Black Mfr
N.A.I.C.S.: 325180
Stephen Knight *(Gen Mgr)*

Cabot Colombiana S.A.   **(1)**
Carretera Mamonal km 12 Apartado Aereo 2903, Cartagena, Bolivar, Colombia
Tel.: (57) 56688511
Web Site: http://www.cabotcorp.com
Emp.: 75
Chemical Products Mfr
N.A.I.C.S.: 424690

Cabot Corporation - Business & Technology Center   **(1)**
157 Concord Rd, Billerica, MA 01821-7001
Tel.: (978) 663-3455
Web Site: http://www.cabotcorp.com
Emp.: 300
Product Research & Development Sevices
N.A.I.C.S.: 541715

Cabot Corporation Carbon Black Division   **(1)**
2 Sea Port Ln, Boston, MA 02210
Tel.: (978) 663-3455
Web Site: http://www.cabot-corp.com
Sales Range: $50-74.9 Million
Emp.: 130
Mfr of Carbon Black
N.A.I.C.S.: 325180

Cabot GmbH   **(1)**
Kronenstrasse 2, 79618, Rheinfelden, Germany
Tel.: (49) 76237070
Chemical Products Mfr
N.A.I.C.S.: 325998

Cabot India Limited   **(1)**
Kesar Solitaire 12th Floor Plot No 5 Sector

No 19 Palm Beach Road, Sanpada, Navi Mumbai, 400 705, Maharashtra, India
Tel.: (91) 2261791101
Emp.: 30
Chemical Products Distr
N.A.I.C.S.: 423830
P. Ganesh *(Controller-Fin)*

Cabot International GmbH (1)
Baarerstrasse 78, Zug, Switzerland
Tel.: (41) 7295943
Sales Range: $25-49.9 Million
Emp.: 2
Chemical Products Mfr
N.A.I.C.S.: 424690

Cabot Malaysia Sdn. Bhd. (1)
Batu 2 Jalan Pantai, PO Box 30, Port Dickson, Negeri Sembilan, Malaysia
Tel.: (60) 6 6482222
Chemical Products Mfr
N.A.I.C.S.: 325998

Cabot Norit Americas, Inc. (1)
3200 University Ave, Marshall, TX 75670
Tel.: (903) 923-1000
Web Site: http://www.cabotcorp.com
Sales Range: $50-74.9 Million
Emp.: 265
Activated Carbon Mfr
N.A.I.C.S.: 335991

Subsidiary (Non-US):

Cabot Norit Nederland B.V. (2)
Astronaut 34, Amersfoort, 3824 MJ, Netherlands
Tel.: (31) 334648911
Web Site: http://www.cabotcorp.com
Emp.: 60
Activated Carbon Mfr
N.A.I.C.S.: 335991

Cabot Norit Italia S.p.A. (1)
Via Negrini 9 ZI Bassette, 48123, Ravenna, Italy
Tel.: (39) 0544451514
Carbon Black Mfr
N.A.I.C.S.: 325180

Cabot Norit Japan Co. Ltd. (1)
95 Anesaki-Kaigan, Ichihara, 299-0107, Chiba, Japan
Tel.: (81) 334346551
Unlaminated Plastic Film & Sheet Mfr
N.A.I.C.S.: 326113

Cabot Norit Singapore Pte. Ltd. (1)
101 Thomson Road United Square 16-04, Singapore, 307591, Singapore
Tel.: (65) 66319392
Emp.: 5
Carbon Black Mfr
N.A.I.C.S.: 325180
Raymond Chua *(Mng Dir)*

Cabot Performance Materials (Zhuhai) Co., Ltd. (1)
1084 Gaolan Port Blvd, Gaolan Port Economic Zone, Zhuhai, 519050, Guangdong, China
Tel.: (86) 7566832866
Emp.: 200
Chemical Products Mfr
N.A.I.C.S.: 325998

Cabot Performance Materials Netherlands B.V. (1)
Botlekstraat 2, Botlek, Rotterdam, 3197KA, Netherlands
Tel.: (31) 181291888
Web Site: http://www.cabotcorp.com
Chemical Products Distr
N.A.I.C.S.: 424690

Cabot Plastics Belgium S.A. (1)
Rue Prevochamps 78, 4860, Pepinster, Belgium (100%)
Tel.: (32) 87392711
Web Site: http://www.cabot.com
Sales Range: $100-124.9 Million
Emp.: 128
Mf. of Carbon Black
N.A.I.C.S.: 325180

Cabot Plastics Canada LP (1)
707 Pierre Tremblay Boulevard, Saint-Jean-sur-Richelieu, J2X 5G5, QC, Canada
Tel.: (450) 347-4371
Basic Inorganic Chemical Mfr
N.A.I.C.S.: 325180

Cabot Plastics Hong Kong Limited (1)
18 Dai Kwai Street, Tai Po Industrial Estate, Hong Kong, China (Hong Kong)
Tel.: (852) 26662666
Chemical Products Mfr
N.A.I.C.S.: 424690

Cabot Rheinfelden GmbH & Co. KG (1)
Kronenstrasse 2, Rheinfelden, 79618, Baden, Germany
Tel.: (49) 76237070
Web Site: http://www.cabot-corp.com
Sales Range: $25-49.9 Million
Emp.: 70
Mfr of Silica Aerogels
N.A.I.C.S.: 325180
George Sutter *(Mng Dir)*

Cabot Sanmar Ltd. (1)
9 Cathedral Road, Chennai, 600 086, India
Tel.: (91) 4428128500
Web Site: http://www.sanmargroups.com
Emp.: 50
Fumed Silica Mfr; Owned By Sanmar Holdings Ltd. & by Cabot Corporation
N.A.I.C.S.: 325998

Cabot Singapore Pte. Ltd. (1)
101 Thomson Road United Square 16-04, Singapore, 307591, Singapore
Tel.: (65) 66319392
Unlaminated Plastic Film & Sheet Mfr
N.A.I.C.S.: 326113

Cabot Specialty Chemicals Coordination Center (1)
Interleuvenlaan 15i, B-3001, Leuven, Belgium (100%)
Tel.: (32) 16392400
Web Site: http://www.cabot.com
Rev.: $6,919,512
Emp.: 110
Mfr of Chemicals & Plastics
N.A.I.C.S.: 326199

Cabot Specialty Chemicals Mexico S.A.P.I. de C.V. (1)
Carretera Tampico-Mante Km 13 5 Col Laguna de La Puerta, 89603, Altamira, Tamaulipas, Mexico
Tel.: (52) 8332290500
Emp.: 140
Chemical Products Mfr
N.A.I.C.S.: 325998

Cabot Specialty Chemicals, Inc. (1)
Sumitomo Shiba-Daimon Bldg 3F 2-5-5 Shiba Daimon, Minato-ku, Tokyo, 105-0012, Japan (100%)
Tel.: (81) 334311721
Web Site: http://www.cabotcorp.cn
Emp.: 50
Chemical Preparations Mfr
N.A.I.C.S.: 325998

Cabot Supermetals K.K. (1)
11th Fl Sumitomo Shiba Daimon Bldg 5-5 Shiba Daimon 2, Minato-ku, Tokyo, Japan
Tel.: (81) 334343711
Electric Equipment Mfr
N.A.I.C.S.: 334419

Cabot Switzerland GmbH (1)
Durachpark Muhlentalstrasse 36, 8200, Schaffhausen, Switzerland
Tel.: (41) 526303800
Sales Range: $25-49.9 Million
Emp.: 4
Chemical Products Mfr
N.A.I.C.S.: 424690
Jaume Campana *(Gen Mgr)*

HDF Investments Limited (1)
6600 Lost Horizon Dr, Austin, TX 78759-6175
Tel.: (512) 794-0207
Investment Management Service
N.A.I.C.S.: 523910

Nhumo, S.A.P.I. de C.V. (1)
Carretera Tampico-Mante Km 13 5 Col Laguna de La Puerta, 89603, Altamira, Tamaulipas, Mexico
Tel.: (52) 8332290500
Web Site: http://www.nhumo.com.mx
Emp.: 140
Carbon Black Mfr
N.A.I.C.S.: 325180

Norit (UK) Holding Limited (1)
Clydesmill Place Cambuslang Industrial Estate, Glasgow, G32 8RF, United Kingdom
Tel.: (44) 1416417671
Holding Company
N.A.I.C.S.: 551112

Norit Real Estate B.V. (1)
Nijverheidsweg-Noord 105, Amersfoort, Utrecht, 3800 RZ, Netherlands
Tel.: (31) 334648911
Real Estate Development Services
N.A.I.C.S.: 531390

SIA Cabot Latvia (1)
101 Mukusalas Street, Riga, LV-1004, Latvia
Tel.: (371) 67050700
Chemical Products Distr
N.A.I.C.S.: 424690

Tokai Carbon (Tianjin) Co., Ltd. (1)
No 45 Xixia Road TEDA Hangu Modern Industry Park, Tianjin, 300480, China
Tel.: (86) 2259911000
Web Site: http://www.ttctj.com
Carbon Black Mfr
N.A.I.C.S.: 325180

CACI INTERNATIONAL INC.

12021 Sunset Hills Rd, Reston, VA 20190
Tel.: (703) 841-7800   DE
Web Site: https://www.caci.com
Year Founded: 1962
CACI—(NYSE)
Rev.: $7,659,832,000
Assets: $6,796,101,000
Liabilities: $3,277,894,000
Net Worth: $3,518,207,000
Earnings: $419,924,000
Emp.: 24,000
Fiscal Year-end: 06/30/24
Computer System Design Services
N.A.I.C.S.: 541512
John S. Mengucci *(Pres & CEO)*
Jeffrey D. MacLauchlan *(CFO, Treas & Exec VP)*
Michael A. Daniels *(Chm)*
Mike Gaffney *(Chief Growth Officer & Exec VP)*
Daniel Leckburg *(Sr VP-IR)*
Glenn Kurowski *(CTO & Sr VP)*
Peter Gallagher *(Sr VP)*
Meisha Lutsey *(Pres-Ops Support & Svcs)*
Joe Mazur *(VP-Bus Dev)*
Lorraine Corcoran *(Exec VP-Corp Comm)*
Bob Busey *(Sr VP-Supply Chain Mgmt & Pur)*
DeEtte Gray *(Pres-Ops-U.S.)*
J. William Koegel Jr. *(Gen Counsel, Sec & Exec VP)*

Subsidiaries:

Applied Insight, LLC (1)
11180 Sunrise Vly Dr Ste 300, Reston, VA 20191
Tel.: (703) 215-8100
Web Site: http://www.applied-insight.com
Emp.: 650
Cloud Data Services
N.A.I.C.S.: 518210
John Hynes *(Chm)*
Stacey Page *(Pres & Chief Growth Officer)*
Steve Radanovic *(CFO)*
Adam Gruber *(CTO)*
April Swain *(Chief Admin Officer)*
Andie Borcz *(Chief People Officer)*

Subsidiary (Domestic):

Bridges Consulting, Inc. (2)
7880 Milestone Parkway, Suite 450, Hanover, MD 21076
Tel.: (301) 974-6200
Web Site: http://www.bridges-inc.com
Management Consulting Services
N.A.I.C.S.: 541611
Chuck Faughnan *(CEO)*
Chuck Faughnan III *(CFO & COO)*
Brian Dahlheimer *(Chief Visionary Officer)*

Zavda Technologies, LLC (2)
9250 Bendix Rd Ste 540, Columbia, MD 21045-1832
Web Site: http://www.zavda.com
Computer System Design Services
N.A.I.C.S.: 541512
Stacy Trammell *(Pres & CEO)*

Azure Summit Technology, Inc. (1)
3050 Chain Bridge Rd Ste 600, Fairfax, VA 22030-2834
Tel.: (321) 215-2070
Web Site: http://www.azuresummit.com
Research & Development in the Physical, Engineering & Life Sciences
N.A.I.C.S.: 541715
Mark Sullivan *(Treas)*
Thomas Green *(CEO)*

CACI Dynamic Systems, Inc. (1)
2120 Washington Blvd Ste 300, Arlington, VA 22204-5708
Tel.: (703) 486-3266
Web Site: http://www.caci.com
Sales Range: $10-24.9 Million
Emp.: 27
Information Technology & Communication Solutions
N.A.I.C.S.: 541512

CACI Limited (1)
Avonmore Road, Kensington Village, London, W14 8TS, United Kingdom
Tel.: (44) 2076026000
Web Site: https://www.caci.co.uk
Sales Range: $50-74.9 Million
Emp.: 200
Information Technology & Communication Solutions
N.A.I.C.S.: 541511
Paul Winters *(Mng Dir & Exec VP)*

CACI N.V. (1)
De Ruijterkade 7, 1013 AA, Amsterdam, Netherlands
Tel.: (31) 886543500
Web Site: https://www.caci.nl
Emp.: 75
Information Technology Services
N.A.I.C.S.: 541519

CACI Premier Technology, Inc. (1)
14370 Newbrook Dr, Chantilly, VA 20151
Tel.: (703) 679-4177
Computer System Design Services
N.A.I.C.S.: 541512

CACI Technologies, Inc (1)
14151 Park Meadow Dr, Herndon, VA 20151
Tel.: (703) 679-3851
Web Site: http://www.caci.com
Sales Range: $10-24.9 Million
Emp.: 15
Media Production Services
N.A.I.C.S.: 541512

CACI, Inc.-Federal (1)
14370 New Brook Dr, Chantilly, VA 20151
Tel.: (703) 679-3100
Web Site: http://www.caci.com
Sales Range: $100-124.9 Million
Information Technology & Communication Solutions
N.A.I.C.S.: 541512

CACI-ISS, Inc. (1)
14360 Newbrook Dr, Chantilly, VA 20151-4206
Tel.: (703) 679-4221
Web Site: http://www.caci.com
Emp.: 1,000
Custom Computer Programming Services
N.A.I.C.S.: 541511

CACI-WGI, Inc. (1)
8618 Westwood Ctr Dr Ste 200, Vienna, VA 22182 (100%)
Tel.: (703) 852-5400
Web Site: http://www.caci.com
Administrative Management Services
N.A.I.C.S.: 541611

Emergint Technologies, Inc. (1)
455 S 4th St Ste 1250, Louisville, KY 40202
Tel.: (502) 896-6210
Web Site: http://www.emergint.com
Sales Range: $25-49.9 Million
Emp.: 200
Computer System Design Services

CACI International Inc.—(Continued)
N.A.I.C.S.: 541512

IDL Solutions, Inc. (1)
N16 W 18627 Morse Dr, Germantown, WI 53022
Tel.: (262) 432-0555
Web Site: http://www.idl.com
Sales Range: $10-24.9 Million
Emp.: 35
IT Professional Services
N.A.I.C.S.: 541512
Baly Ambegaoker (Pres)

LGS Innovations LLC (1)
13665 Dulles Technology Dr Ste 150, Herndon, VA 20171
Tel.: (336) 638-2967
Web Site: http://www.lgsinnovations.com
Sales Range: $150-199.9 Million
Emp.: 125
Network Designing Services
N.A.I.C.S.: 541512
Linda Braun (Sr VP)

LTC Engineering Associates, Inc. (1)
6851 Professional Pkwy W, Lakewood Ranch, FL 34240
Tel.: (941) 921-9046
Web Site: http://www.ltceng.com
Sales Range: $10-24.9 Million
Emp.: 50
Engineeering Services
N.A.I.C.S.: 541330

Mastodon Design LLC (1)
55 Science Parkway, Rochester, NY 14620
Tel.: (585) 752-3255
Web Site: http://www.mastodondesign.com
Radio, Television Broadcasting & Wireless Communications Equipment Mfr
N.A.I.C.S.: 334220

Six3 Systems, Inc. (1)
1430 Spring Hill Rd Ste 525, McLean, VA 22102
Tel.: (703) 442-6650
Web Site: http://www.six3systems.com
Sales Range: $450-499.9 Million
Emp.: 1,600
ISR, Cyber & Intelligence Products & Services
N.A.I.C.S.: 519290
Robert Coleman (Founder, Pres & CEO)
Chris Holmes (VP-Enterprise Solutions)

Subsidiary (Domestic):

BIT Systems, Inc. (2)
45200 Business Ct, Dulles, VA 20166
Tel.: (703) 742-7660
Web Site: http://www.bit-sys.com
Sales Range: $25-10.0 Million
Emp.: 500
Intelligence, Surveillance & Reconnaissance Systems Engineering Services
N.A.I.C.S.: 541330
Tom Ladd (Pres)

Ticom Geomatics, Inc. (2)
9130 Jollyville Rd Ste 100, Austin, TX 78759
Tel.: (512) 345-5006
Web Site: http://www.ticom-geo.com
Sales Range: $50-74.9 Million
Emp.: 180
Geolocation & ISR Services
N.A.I.C.S.: 519290
Mark P. Leach (Pres & CEO)

Technigraphics, Inc (1)
2000 Nuble Dr, Wooster, OH 44691
Tel.: (330) 263-6222
Web Site: http://www.tgstech.com
Sales Range: $25-49.9 Million
Emp.: 450
Visual Information Systems
N.A.I.C.S.: 541519
Dee Vaidya (Pres & CEO)

The Wexford Group International (1)
8618 Westwood Ctr Dr Ste 200, Vienna, VA 22182
Tel.: (703) 852-5400
Sales Range: $50-74.9 Million
Emp.: 190
Management & Technical Consulting Services
N.A.I.C.S.: 541618

CACTUS, INC.
920 Memorial City Way Ste 300, Houston, TX 77024
Tel.: (713) 626-8800   DE
Web Site:
  https://www.cactuswhd.com
Year Founded: 2017
WHD—(NYSE)
Rev.: $688,369,000
Assets: $1,118,896,000
Liabilities: $408,451,000
Net Worth: $710,445,000
Earnings: $110,174,000
Emp.: 1,550
Fiscal Year-end: 12/31/22
Oil & Gas Field Machinery & Equipment Manufacturing
N.A.I.C.S.: 333132
William D. Marsh (Gen Counsel, Sec & VP-Admin)
Scott Bender (Chm & CEO)
Jay A. Nutt (CFO, Principal Acctg Officer, Treas & Exec VP)
Scott Bender (Pres & CEO)
Joel Bender (Pres)
Steven Bender (COO)
Stephen D. Tadlock (CEO-Spoolable Technologies, Treas & Exec VP)
John Fitzgerald (Dir-Dev & IR)

CADENCE DESIGN SYSTEMS, INC.
2655 Seely Ave, San Jose, CA 95134
Tel.: (408) 943-1234   DE
Web Site: https://www.cadence.com
Year Founded: 1988
CDNS—(NASDAQ)
Rev.: $4,089,986,000
Assets: $5,669,491,000
Liabilities: $2,265,220,000
Net Worth: $3,404,271,000
Earnings: $1,041,144,000
Emp.: 11,200
Fiscal Year-end: 12/31/23
Electronic Design Automation Software & Hardware Products Developer & Mfr
N.A.I.C.S.: 513210
Tina Jones (Sr VP-HR-Global)
John M. Wall (CFO & Sr VP)
Anirudh Devgan (Pres & CEO)
Paul Cunningham (Sr VP)
Karna Nisewaner (Corp Counsel)

Subsidiaries:

AWR Corporation (1)
1960 E Grand Ave Ste 430, El Segundo, CA 90245
Tel.: (310) 726-3000
Web Site: http://www.awrcorp.com
Sales Range: $25-49.9 Million
Emp.: 50
Software Developer
N.A.I.C.S.: 513210

Subsidiary (Non-US):

AWR-APLAC Corporation (2)
Lars Sonckin kaari 10, 02600, Espoo, Finland
Tel.: (358) 108345900
Web Site: http://www.awrcorp.com
Communications Analysis & Simulation Software
N.A.I.C.S.: 513210

C2 Design Automation (1)
100 Century Ctr Ct Ste 302, San Jose, CA 95112
Tel.: (408) 487-9340
Web Site: http://www.forteds.com
Sales Range: $1-9.9 Million
Emp.: 75
Software Publisher
N.A.I.C.S.: 513210

Cadence AMS Design India Private Limited (1)
2nd Floor Block 11B Pritech Park SEZ Survey No 51-64/4, Bellandur Village, Bengaluru, 560103, Karnataka, India

Tel.: (91) 8041841111
Web Site: http://www.cadence.com
Emp.: 700
Electronic Automation Software & Hardware Designing Services
N.A.I.C.S.: 541512

Cadence Design (Israel) II Ltd. (1)
18 Aharon Barth St, PO Box 3941, Petah Tikva, 4951448, Israel
Tel.: (972) 39004000
Emp.: 100
Electronic Design Automation Software Publisher
N.A.I.C.S.: 513210

Cadence Design Services TYK (1)
2-100-45 Shin, Kohoku-ku, Yokohama, 222-0033, Japan
Tel.: (81) 45 475 2221
Web Site: http://www.cadence.co.jp
Sales Range: $100-124.9 Million
Emp.: 230
Computer Design Services
N.A.I.C.S.: 541512

Cadence Design Systems (India) Private Ltd. (1)
Plot Nos 57 A B C 11 10, Noida Special Economic Zone PO NSEZ, Noida, 201305, India
Tel.: (91) 1204308300
Sales Range: $100-124.9 Million
Emp.: 1,000
Computer Design Services
N.A.I.C.S.: 541512
Jaswinder Ahuja (Mng Dir)

Cadence Design Systems (Ireland) Limited (1)
Block S Eastpoint Business Park, Fairview, Dublin, 3, Ireland
Tel.: (353) 18054300
Emp.: 80
Electronic Design Automation Software Publisher
N.A.I.C.S.: 513210

Cadence Design Systems (Israel) Limited (1)
18 Aharon Barth St, PO Box 3941, Life Plaza building C, Petach Tikva, 4951448, Israel
Tel.: (972) 39004000
Emp.: 50
Electronic Design Automation Software Publisher
N.A.I.C.S.: 513210

Cadence Design Systems (Japan) B.V. (1)
2-100-45 Shin-Yokohama, Kohoku-ku, Yokohama, 222-0033, Japan
Tel.: (81) 454752221
Web Site: https://www.cadence.com
Electronic Design Automation Software Publisher
N.A.I.C.S.: 513210

Cadence Design Systems (S) Pte Ltd. (1)
2 International Business Park Units 09-10/11 The Strategy Tower 1, Singapore, 609930, Singapore
Tel.: (65) 65678600
Sales Range: $10-24.9 Million
Emp.: 25
Electronic Design Automation Software Publisher
N.A.I.C.S.: 513210

Cadence Design Systems AB (1)
Isafjordsgatan 30C, Kista, 164 40, Kista, 164 40, Sweden
Tel.: (46) 856612300
Electronic Design Automation Software Publisher
N.A.I.C.S.: 513210

Cadence Design Systems GmbH (1)
Mozartstrasse 2, D-85622, Feldkirchen, Germany
Tel.: (49) 8945630
Sales Range: $25-49.9 Million
Emp.: 120
Electronic Design Automation Software Publisher
N.A.I.C.S.: 513210

Cadence Design Systems Kft. (1)

Kalman Imre U 1, 1054, Budapest, Hungary
Tel.: (36) 14751332
Web Site: http://www.cadence.com
Electronic Design Automation Software & Hardware Designing Services
N.A.I.C.S.: 541512

Cadence Design Systems Limited (1)
Maxis 1 Western Road, Bracknell, RG12 1RT, Berkshire, United Kingdom
Tel.: (44) 134 436 0333
Web Site: https://www.cadence.com
Sales Range: $25-49.9 Million
Emp.: 100
Computer Design Services
N.A.I.C.S.: 541512

Cadence Design Systems Management (Shanghai) Co., Ltd. (1)
New Bund World Trade Center Phase III 5F-10F Building A No 1 Lane 221, Dongyu Road Pudong District, Shanghai, 200126, China
Tel.: (86) 2138798000
Web Site: http://www.cadence.com
Sales Range: $100-124.9 Million
Emp.: 450
Computer Design Services
N.A.I.C.S.: 541512

Cadence Design Systems S.A.S. (1)
18 Rue Grange Dame Rose, 78148, Velizy-Villacoublay, France
Tel.: (33) 13 488 5300
Web Site: https://www.cadence.com
Emp.: 50
Electronic Design Automation Software Publisher
N.A.I.C.S.: 513210

Cadence Design Systems do Brasil Microeletronica Ltda. (1)
Rua Desembargador Jorge Fontana 50 12 &ar Belvedere, Belo Horizonte, 30320-670, MG, Brazil
Tel.: (55) 1130535566
Web Site:
  http://www.atlastecnologicodemg.com.br
Computer System Design Services
N.A.I.C.S.: 541512

Cadence Korea Ltd. (1)
M Tower 5F 8 Gumi-ro, Bundang-gu, Seongnam, Gyeonggi-do, Korea (South)
Tel.: (82) 31 728 3114
Web Site: http://www.cadence.com
Sales Range: $25-49.9 Million
Emp.: 54
Electronic Design Automation Software Publisher
N.A.I.C.S.: 513210

Forte Design Systems, K.K. (1)
Kaede Dai2 Building 3F 2 5 10 Shin, Kouhoku, Yokohama, 222-0033, Kanagawa, Japan
Tel.: (81) 454782268
Web Site: http://www.edsfair.com
Electronic Automation Software & Hardware Designing Services
N.A.I.C.S.: 541512

Jasper Design Automation - Israel, Ltd. (1)
Matam Hi-Tech Industrial Park Saharov St Matam Tower 3 7th floor, PO Box 15115, Haifa, 31905, Israel
Tel.: (972) 49118044
Electronic Automation Software & Hardware Designing Services
N.A.I.C.S.: 541512
Ziyad Hanna (Gen Mgr)

Jasper Design Automation do Brasil Informatica e Microelectronica Ltda. (1)
Rua Desembargador Jorge Fontana 50-12th floor, Belvedere, 30320-670, Belo Horizonte, Minas Gerais, Brazil
Tel.: (55) 3132863903
Electronic Automation Software & Hardware Designing Services
N.A.I.C.S.: 541512

Jasper Design Automation, A.B. (1)
Kvarnbergsgatan 2, Gothenburg, 411 05, Sweden
Tel.: (46) 317451909

Electronic Automation Software & Hardware Designing Services
N.A.I.C.S.: 541512
Lars Lundgren (Engr-R&D)

Jasper Design Automation, Inc. (1)
707 California St, Mountain View, CA 94041
Tel.: (650) 966-0200
Web Site: http://www.jasper-da.com
Sales Range: $1-9.9 Million
Emp.: 45
Electronic Design Automation Services
N.A.I.C.S.: 541512

Numeca India Software Private Limited (1)
208 2nd Floor Richmond Towers 12 Richmond Road, Bengaluru, India
Tel.: (91) 806 555 5673
Web Site: https://www.numeca.be
Automobile Mfr
N.A.I.C.S.: 336390

Numflo SA (1)
Boulevard Initialis 7/2, Mons, Belgium
Tel.: (32) 65709200
Web Site: https://www.numflo.eu
Engineering Support Services
N.A.I.C.S.: 541330

Openeye Scientific Software, Inc. (1)
3600 Cerrillos Rd # 1107, Santa Fe, NM 87507
Tel.: (505) 473-7385
Web Site: http://www.eyesopen.com
Sales Range: $1-9.9 Million
Emp.: 13
Computer & Computer Peripheral Equipment & Software Merchant Whslr
N.A.I.C.S.: 423430

Pointwise, Inc. (1)
213 S Jennings Ave, Fort Worth, TX 76104
Tel.: (817) 377-2807
Web Site: https://www.pointwise.com
Custom Computer Programming Services, Nsk
N.A.I.C.S.: 541511
Heather McCoy (Mgr-Sls & Mktg)
Carolyn Woeber (Mgr-Technical Support Team)
John Chawner (Co-Founder & Pres)
Claudio Pita (Sr Engr)
Daniel LaCroix (Sr Engr)
David Garlisch (Sr Engr)
Jim Colby (Sr Engr)
John Dreese (Sr Engr)
John P. Steinbrenner (VP-R&D)
Nick Wyman (Dir-Applied Res Team)
Pat Baker (Mgr-Product Dev Team)
Richard J. Matus (VP-Sls & Mktg)
Rose Mary Crager (Mgr-Bus & Admin Svcs Team)

Rocketick Technologies Ltd. (1)
11 Tuval St 4th Floor, Ramat Gan, 52522, Israel
Tel.: (972) 35757996
Web Site: http://www.rocketick.com
Electronic Chip Mfr
N.A.I.C.S.: 334413

Rocketick, Inc. (1)
1735 N 1st St Ste 312, San Jose, CA 95112
Tel.: (408) 459-7600
Web Site: http://www.rocketick.com
Electronic Chip Mfr
N.A.I.C.S.: 334413
Avraam Fried (Chm)

SFM Technology, Inc. (1)
110 S Race St Ste 201, Urbana, IL 61801
Tel.: (217) 383-0150
Web Site: http://www.sfmtech.com
Software Development Services
N.A.I.C.S.: 513210
James A. Stori (Founder)

Spin Technologies Pvt. Ltd. (1)
2971 2nd Floor Esturi Towers K R Road BSK 2nd Stage, opp BDA Complex, Bengaluru, 560 070, Karnataka, India
Tel.: (91) 8040805000
Web Site: http://www.spintech.in
Location Intelligence & Telematics Software Publisher
N.A.I.C.S.: 513210
Srinivasa Datta (CEO)

Tundra Holdings, Inc. (1)

1634 N Stevens St, Rhinelander, WI 54501
Tel.: (715) 362-7031
Holding Company
N.A.I.C.S.: 551114

CADIZ INC.
550 S Hope St Ste 2850, Los Angeles, CA 90071
Tel.: (213) 271-1600   DE
Web Site: https://www.cadizinc.com
Year Founded: 1983
CDZI—(NASDAQ)
Rev.: $1,501,000
Assets: $110,787,000
Liabilities: $76,564,000
Net Worth: $34,223,000
Earnings: ($24,792,000)
Emp.: 9
Fiscal Year-end: 12/31/22
Land & Water Resource Management Services & Underground Water Storage
N.A.I.C.S.: 221310
Keith Brackpool (Founder)
Timothy J. Shaheen (Dir-Dev)
Courtney Degener (VP-Comm & External Rels)
Teffiny Bagnara (Controller)
Lesley Thornburg (Ops Mgr)
Miya Smith (Office Mgr)
Susan P. Kennedy (Chm & CEO)

Subsidiaries:

ATEC Systems, Inc. (1)
1690 Lana Way Ste A, Hollister, CA 95023-2569
Tel.: (831) 637-9264
Business Support Services
N.A.I.C.S.: 561499
Lee Odell (COO)

Rancho Cadiz Mutual Water Company (1)
550 S Hope St Ste 2850, Los Angeles, CA 90071
Tel.: (213) 271-1600
Water Supply & Distribution Services
N.A.I.C.S.: 221310

CADRE HOLDINGS, INC.
45 Broadway Ste 1150, New York, NY 10006
Tel.: (904) 741-5400   DE
Web Site: https://www.cadre-holdings.com
Year Founded: 2012
CDRE—(NYSE)
Rev.: $457,837,000
Assets: $391,952,000
Liabilities: $226,062,000
Net Worth: $165,890,000
Earnings: $5,820,000
Emp.: 2,274
Fiscal Year-end: 12/31/22
Holding Company
N.A.I.C.S.: 551112
Warren B. Kanders (CEO)
Brad Williams (Pres)
Blaine Browers (CFO)

Subsidiaries:

Cyalume Technologies, Inc. (1)
96 Windsor St, West Springfield, MA 01089
Tel.: (888) 858-7881
Web Site: http://www.cyalume.com
Chemical & Electronic Light Systems Mfr
N.A.I.C.S.: 335139
Earl Cranor (VP-Tech)
Karen McFetridge (VP-HR)
Robert Nobile (CFO)
Donald Schmidt (Sr VP-Product, Program Mgmt & Sls)

Subsidiary (Non-US):

Cyalume Technologies S.A.S. (2)
295 rue Mayor de Montricher - ZI Les Milles, CS 40435, 13591, Aix-en-Provence, Cedex 3, France
Tel.: (33) 442371780
Web Site: https://www.cyalume.eu

Lighting Equipment Mfr
N.A.I.C.S.: 335139
Tony Slaney (Dir-Bus Dev-EMEA)
Geraldine Bello (Mgr-Mktg & Bus Dev)

CADRENAL THERAPEUTICS, INC.
822 A1A N Ste 320, Ponte Vedra Beach, FL 32082
Tel.: (904) 300-0701   DE
Web Site: https://www.cadrenal.com
Year Founded: 2022
CVKD—(NASDAQ)
Emp.: 1
Research & Development in Biotechnology (except Nanobiotechnology)
N.A.I.C.S.: 541714
Jeffrey Cole (COO)
Quang Pham (CEO & Chm)
Matthew Szot (CFO)

CAESARS ENTERTAINMENT, INC.
100 W Liberty St 12th Fl, Reno, NV 89501
Tel.: (775) 328-0100   NV
Web Site: https://www.caesars.com
Year Founded: 1937
CZR—(NASDAQ)
Rev.: $11,528,000,000
Assets: $33,366,000,000
Liabilities: $28,646,000,000
Net Worth: $4,720,000,000
Earnings: $786,000,000
Emp.: 51,000
Fiscal Year-end: 12/31/23
Holding Company; Casino Hotels & Resorts Owner & Operator
N.A.I.C.S.: 551112
Gary L. Carano (Chm)
Anthony L. Carano (Pres & COO)
Stephanie D. Lepori (Chief Admin Officer & Chief Acctg Officer)
Bret Yunker (CFO)
Josh Jones (CMO)
Edmund L. Quatmann (Chief Legal Officer)
Rajendran Anbalagan (CIO & Chief Product Transformation Officer)
Thomas R. Reeg (CEO)

Subsidiaries:

CC-Reno, LLC (1)
500 N Sierra St, Reno, NV 89503-4717
Tel.: (775) 329-0711
Web Site: http://www.circusreno.com
Sales Range: $200-249.9 Million
Emp.: 2,000
Hotel & Casino
N.A.I.C.S.: 721120

Caesars Holdings, Inc. (1)
1 Caesars Palace Dr, Las Vegas, NV 89109
Tel.: (702) 407-6000
Web Site: http://www.caesars.com
Rev.: $8,742,000,000
Assets: $25,345,000,000
Liabilities: $23,134,000,000
Net Worth: $2,211,000,000
Earnings: ($1,195,000,000)
Emp.: 64,000
Fiscal Year-end: 12/31/2019
Holding Company; Casinos & Casino Hotels Owner & Operator
N.A.I.C.S.: 551112
Eric Hession (CFO & Exec VP)
Christian D. Stuart (Exec VP-Gaming & Interactive Entertainment)
Chris Holdren (Chief Mktg Officer & Exec VP)
Anthony P. Rodio (CEO)
Salil Kulkarni (CIO & Exec VP-Interim)
Richard D. Broome (Exec VP-Comm & Govt Rels)
Richard D. Broome (Exec VP-Comm & Govt Rels)

Subsidiary (Domestic):

Caesars Entertainment Operating Company, Inc. (2)
801 Boardwalk, Atlantic City, NJ 08401

1 Caesars Palace Dr, Las Vegas, NV 89109
Tel.: (702) 407-6000
Web Site: http://www.caesars.com
Hotels & Casinos Operator
N.A.I.C.S.: 551114

Subsidiary (Domestic):

Caesars New Jersey, Inc. (3)
2100 Pacific Ave, Atlantic City, NJ 08401
Tel.: (609) 348-4411
Web Site: http://www.caesars.com
Sales Range: $200-249.9 Million
Emp.: 4,291
Hotel & Casino Services
N.A.I.C.S.: 721120

Caesars Palace Corporation (3)
3570 Las Vegas Blvd S, Las Vegas, NV 89109
Tel.: (702) 731-7110
Web Site: http://www.caesars.com
Sales Range: $200-249.9 Million
Emp.: 5,000
Hotels & Casinos
N.A.I.C.S.: 721120

Caesars Riverboat Casino, LLC (3)
11999 Casino Ctr Dr SE, Elizabeth, IN 47117
Tel.: (812) 969-6000
Web Site: http://www.horseshoe-indiana.com
Sales Range: $300-349.9 Million
Emp.: 2,000
Riverboat Casino Hotel
N.A.I.C.S.: 713210

Grand Casinos of Biloxi, LLC (3)
280 Beach Blvd, Biloxi, MS 39530
Tel.: (228) 436-2946
Web Site: https://www.grandbiloxi.com
Sales Range: $100-124.9 Million
Emp.: 900
Hotel & Casino
N.A.I.C.S.: 721120

Harrah's Arizona Corporation (3)
15406 N Maricopa Rd, Maricopa, AZ 85139-2819
Tel.: (480) 802-5000
Sales Range: $75-99.9 Million
Emp.: 700
Casino Hotels
N.A.I.C.S.: 721120

Harrah's Bossier City Management Company, LLC (3)
8000 E Texas St, Bossier City, LA 71111
Tel.: (318) 742-5555
Web Site: http://www.harrahslouisianadowns.com
Sales Range: $150-199.9 Million
Emp.: 1,000
Horse Racetrack, Casino, Hotel, Bar & Restaurant Operator
N.A.I.C.S.: 711212

Harrah's Illinois Corporation (3)
151 N Joliet St, Joliet, IL 60432
Tel.: (815) 740-7800
Web Site: https://www.caesars.com
Sales Range: $75-99.9 Million
Emp.: 1,100
Casino Hotels
N.A.I.C.S.: 721120

Unit (Domestic):

Harrah's Reno (3)
219 N Center St, Reno, NV 89501-1500
Tel.: (775) 786-3232
Web Site: http://www.harrahsreno.com
Rev.: $32,000,000
Emp.: 2,000
Hotel & Casino
N.A.I.C.S.: 721120

Subsidiary (Domestic):

Harveys Tahoe Management Company, Inc. (3)
18 US-Hwy 50, Stateline, NV 89449
Tel.: (775) 588-6611
Web Site: https://www.harveystahoe.com
Hotel & Resort Services
N.A.I.C.S.: 721120

Showboat Atlantic City Operating Company, LLC (3)
801 Boardwalk, Atlantic City, NJ 08401

Caesars Entertainment, Inc.—(Continued)

Tel.: (609) 487-4600
Web Site: https://www.showboathotelac.com
Sales Range: $150-199.9 Million.
Emp.: 4,000
Casino Hotels
N.A.I.C.S.: 721120
Kevin Ortzman *(Gen Mgr)*

Southern Illinois Riverboat/Casino Cruises, Inc. (3)
100 E Front St, Metropolis, IL 62960-2021
Tel.: (618) 524-2628
Web Site: http://www.caesars.com
Sales Range: $50-74.9 Million
Emp.: 300
Hotel & Casino Services
N.A.I.C.S.: 721120

ThistleDown Racetrack, LLC (3)
21501 Emery Rd, Cleveland, OH 44128
Tel.: (216) 662-8600
Web Site:
  https://www.jackentertainment.com
Sales Range: $10-24.9 Million
Horse Race Track & Casino Operator
N.A.I.C.S.: 711212

Subsidiary (Non-US):

Caesars Entertainment UK Ltd. (2)
55 Baker Street, London, W1U 8EW, United Kingdom
Tel.: (44) 2075180000
Web Site: http://www.caesars.co.uk
Emp.: 65
Casino Owner & Operator
N.A.I.C.S.: 713210
William Timmins *(CEO)*

Subsidiary (Domestic):

London Clubs (Overseas) Limited (3)
55 Baker Street, London, W1U 8EW, United Kingdom
Tel.: (44) 2075180000
Web Site: http://www.caesars.co.uk
Emp.: 60
Holding Company; Casino Operator
N.A.I.C.S.: 551112

London Clubs Management Limited (3)
55 Baker Street, London, W1U 8EW, United Kingdom
Tel.: (44) 2075180000
Web Site: http://www.caesars.co.uk
Sales Range: $25-49.9 Million
Emp.: 60
Holding Company; Casino Operator
N.A.I.C.S.: 551112

Holding (Domestic):

London Clubs LSQ Limited (4)
55 Baker Street, London, W1U 8EW, United Kingdom
Tel.: (44) 2036278407
Web Site: http://www.thecasinolsq.com
Casino, Bar & Restaurant
N.A.I.C.S.: 713210

London Clubs Southend Limited (4)
55 Baker Street, London, W1U 8EW, Essex, United Kingdom
Tel.: (44) 1702616000
Web Site: http://www.rendezvouscasino.com
Casino, Bar & Restaurant
N.A.I.C.S.: 713210
Johanna Johnstone *(CEO)*

The Sportsman Club Limited (4)
55 Baker Street, London, W1U 8EW, United Kingdom
Tel.: (44) 2039444586
Web Site:
  http://www.thesportsmancasino.com
Casino, Bar & Restaurant
N.A.I.C.S.: 713210

Subsidiary (Non-US):

Caesars Entertainment Windsor Holding Inc. (2)
377 Riverside Drive East, Windsor, N9A 7H7, ON, Canada
Tel.: (519) 258-7878
Web Site: http://www.caesarswindsor.com

Sales Range: $25-49.9 Million
Emp.: 3,000
Holding Company; Casino Hotel
N.A.I.C.S.: 551112

Affiliate (Domestic):

Windsor Casino Limited (3)
377 Riverside Drive East, Windsor, N9A 7H7, ON, Canada
Tel.: (519) 258-7878
Web Site: https://www.casinowindsor.com
Emp.: 3,000
Casino Hotels
N.A.I.C.S.: 721120

Subsidiary (Domestic):

Caesars Growth Partners, LLC (2)
1 Caesars Palace Dr, Las Vegas, NV 89109
Tel.: (702) 407-6000
Web Site: http://www.caesars.com
Investment Holding Company; Casino Hotels & Interactive Gambling Media Services
N.A.I.C.S.: 551112

Subsidiary (Domestic):

Caesars Growth Bally's LV, LLC (2)
1 Caesars Palace Dr, Las Vegas, NV 89109
Tel.: (702) 407-6000
Web Site: http://www.caesars.com
Casino & Gaming Services
N.A.I.C.S.: 721120

Unit (Domestic):

Bally's Las Vegas (4)
3645 Las Vegas Blvd S, Las Vegas, NV 89109
Tel.: (702) 739-4111
Web Site: http://www.ballyslasvegas.com
Hotel & Casino Operator
N.A.I.C.S.: 721120

Subsidiary (Domestic):

Caesars Interactive Entertainment, LLC (3)
1 Caesars Palace Dr, Las Vegas, NV 89109
Tel.: (702) 407-6000
Web Site: http://www.caesarsinteractive.com
Online, Mobile & Social Gaming Media Publisher
N.A.I.C.S.: 513199
Marco Ceccarelli *(CIO & Sr VP)*

Jazz Casino Company, LLC (3)
228 Poydras St, New Orleans, LA 70130
Tel.: (504) 533-6000
Web Site:
  http://www.harrahsneworleans.com
Hotel & Casino Operator
N.A.I.C.S.: 721120

PHW Las Vegas, LLC (3)
3667 Las Vegas Blvd S, Las Vegas, NV 89109
Tel.: (702) 785-5555
Web Site:
  http://www.planethollywoodresort.com
Hotel & Casino Operator
N.A.I.C.S.: 721120

Unit (Domestic):

The Cromwell (Las Vegas) Hotel & Casino (3)
3595 Las Vegas Blvd S, Las Vegas, NV 89109
Tel.: (702) 777-3777
Web Site: http://www.thecromwell.com
Hotel & Casino Operator
N.A.I.C.S.: 721120

The LINQ Hotel & Casino (3)
3535 Las Vegas Blvd S, Las Vegas, NV 89109
Tel.: (702) 794-3366
Web Site: http://www.caesars.com
Hotel & Casino Operator
N.A.I.C.S.: 721120

Subsidiary (Domestic):

Corner Investment Company, LLC (2)
1 Caesars Palace Dr, Las Vegas, NV 89109
Tel.: (702) 407-6000
Web Site: http://www.caesars.com
Casino & Gaming Services

N.A.I.C.S.: 721120

Flamingo Las Vegas Operating Company, LLC (2)
3555 Las Vegas Blvd S, Las Vegas, NV 89109
Tel.: (702) 733-3111
Web Site: https://www.caesars.com
Sales Range: $200-249.9 Million
Emp.: 5,000
Hotel & Casino Services
N.A.I.C.S.: 721120

Harrah's Atlantic City Operating Company, LLC (2)
777 Harrah's Blvd, Atlantic City, NJ 08401
Tel.: (609) 441-5000
Web Site: http://www.harrahsresort.com
Sales Range: $350-399.9 Million
Emp.: 3,200
Hotel & Casino
N.A.I.C.S.: 721120

Harrah's Las Vegas, LLC (2)
3475 Las Vegas Blvd S, Las Vegas, NV 89109
Tel.: (702) 369-5000
Sales Range: $200-249.9 Million
Emp.: 5,000
Hotel & Casino
N.A.I.C.S.: 721120

Harrah's Laughlin, LLC (2)
2900 S Casino Dr, Laughlin, NV 89029-1521
Tel.: (702) 298-4600
Web Site: http://www.harrahslaughlin.com
Sales Range: $75-99.9 Million
Emp.: 1,500
Hotel Casino
N.A.I.C.S.: 721120

New Centaur, LLC (2)
111 Monument Cir Ste 777, Indianapolis, IN 46204
Tel.: (317) 656-8787
Holding Company; Casino Hotel, Racetrack & Entertainment Venue Operator
N.A.I.C.S.: 551112
Roderick J. Ratcliff *(Chm & CEO)*
Jahnae Erpenbach *(VP & Gen Mgr-Gaming-Indiana Grand Racing & Casino)*
Michael Facenda *(VP & Gen Mgr-Gaming-Hoosier Park Racing & Casino)*
Richard B. Moore *(VP & Gen Mgr-Racing-Hoosier Park Racing & Casino)*
Jonathan B. Schuster *(VP & Gen Mgr-Racing-Indiana Grand Racing & Casino)*

Subsidiary (Domestic):

Centaur Acquisition, LLC (3)
4300 N Michigan Rd, Shelbyville, IN 46176
Web Site: https://www.caesars.com
Casino Hotel, Racetrack & Entertainment Venue Operator
N.A.I.C.S.: 721120

Hoosier Park, LLC (3)
4500 Dan Patch Cir, Anderson, IN 46013-3165
Tel.: (765) 642-7223
Web Site: https://www.caesars.com
Horse Racetrack
N.A.I.C.S.: 711212

Subsidiary (Domestic):

Paris Las Vegas Operating Company, LLC (2)
3655 Las Vegas Blvd S, Las Vegas, NV 89109
Tel.: (702) 946-7000
Web Site: http://www.parislasvegas.com
Sales Range: $150-199.9 Million
Emp.: 4,000
Hotel & Casino
N.A.I.C.S.: 721120

Rio Properties, Inc. (2)
3700 W Flamingo Rd, Las Vegas, NV 89103
Tel.: (702) 777-7777
Web Site: http://www.caesars.com
Sales Range: $25-49.9 Million
Holding Company; Casino Hotel
N.A.I.C.S.: 551112

Circus & Eldorado Joint Venture, LLC (1)

407 N Virginia St, Reno, NV 89501 **(100%)**
Tel.: (775) 329-4777
Web Site: https://www.silverlegacyreno.com
Casino Hotel Operator
N.A.I.C.S.: 721120

Eldorado Resorts LLC (1)
345 N Virginia St, Reno, NV 89501-1136
Tel.: (775) 786-5700
Web Site: http://www.eldoradoreno.com
Casino Hotel Operator
N.A.I.C.S.: 721120

Elgin Riverboat Resort (1)
250 S Grove Ave, Elgin, IL 60120
Tel.: (847) 468-7000
Web Site:
  http://www.grandvictoriacasino.com
Sales Range: $150-199.9 Million
Emp.: 800
Operator of Resort & Casino
N.A.I.C.S.: 721120

Emerald Safari Resort (Pty) Limited (1)
777 Frikkie Meyer Boulevard, Vanderbijlpark, 1911, South Africa
Tel.: (27) 169828000
Web Site: http://www.emeraldcasino.co.za
Hotel Operator
N.A.I.C.S.: 721120

Horseshoe Entertainment, Inc. (1)
711 Horseshoe Blvd, Bossier City, LA 71111
Casino & Hotel Operator
N.A.I.C.S.: 721120

Scioto Downs, Inc. (1)
6000 S High St, Columbus, OH 43207
Tel.: (614) 295-4700
Web Site: https://www.sciotodowns.com
Race Track Services
N.A.I.C.S.: 711212

Tropicana Entertainment Inc. (1)
8345 W Sunset Rd, Las Vegas, NV 89113
Tel.: (702) 739-3629
Riverboat Casinos & Casino Hotel Resorts Owner & Operator
N.A.I.C.S.: 721120

Subsidiary (Domestic):

Aztar Riverboat Holding Company, LLC (2)
207 Grandview Dr, Fort Mitchell, KY 41017
Tel.: (859) 578-1100
Financial Investment Services
N.A.I.C.S.: 523999

Subsidiary (Domestic):

Aztar Indiana Gaming Company, LLC (3)
421 NW Riverside Dr, Evansville, IN 47708
Tel.: (812) 433-4444
Financial Investment Services
N.A.I.C.S.: 523999

Unit (Domestic):

Bally's Lake Tahoe (2)
55 Hwy 50, Stateline, NV 89449
Tel.: (775) 586-3515
Web Site: https://casinos.ballys.com
Emp.: 600
Casino Hotels
N.A.I.C.S.: 721120

Subsidiary (Domestic):

CP Laughlin Realty, LLC (2)
740 Ctr View Blvd, Crestview Hills, KY 41017
Tel.: (859) 669-1500
Hotel & Resort Management Services
N.A.I.C.S.: 721110

Casino One Corporation (2)
999 N 2nd St, Saint Louis, MO 63102
Tel.: (314) 881-7777
Web Site: http://www.lumiereplace.com
Casino Hotel & Resort Operator
N.A.I.C.S.: 721120

Catfish Queen Partnership in Commendam (2)
103 France St, Baton Rouge, LA 70802
Tel.: (225) 242-2600

Web Site:
https://www.belleofbatonrouge.com
Sales Range: $75-99.9 Million
Emp.: 729
Financial Investment Services
N.A.I.C.S.: 523999

Columbia Properties Laughlin, LLC (2)
2700 S Casino Dr, Laughlin, NV 89029
Tel.: (702) 298-2242
Web Site: http://www.laughlinriverlodge.com
Emp.: 3
Hotel & Resort Management Services
N.A.I.C.S.: 721110

Columbia Properties Tahoe, LLC (2)
55 Hwy 50, Stateline, NV 89449
Tel.: (775) 588-3515
Emp.: 700
Financial Investment Services
N.A.I.C.S.: 523999

Lighthouse Point, LLC (2)
199 N Lakefront Rd, Greenville, MS 38701
Tel.: (662) 332-6900
Web Site: https://www.tropgreenville.com
Financial Investment Services
N.A.I.C.S.: 523999

Tropicana Laughlin, LLC (2)
2121 S Casino Dr, Laughlin, NV 89029
Tel.: (702) 298-4200
Web Site: http://www.troplaughlin.com
Financial Investment Services
N.A.I.C.S.: 523999

CAI INTERNATIONAL, INC.
Steuart Tower 1 Market Plz Ste 2400, San Francisco, CA 94105
Tel.: (415) 788-0100   DE
Web Site: http://www.capps.com
Year Founded: 1989
CAI—(NYSE)
Rev.: $294,013,000
Assets: $2,612,632,000
Liabilities: $1,910,392,000
Net Worth: $702,240,000
Earnings: $18,904,000
Emp.: 99
Fiscal Year-end: 12/31/20
Container Leasing & Management Services
N.A.I.C.S.: 488510
Camille G. Cutino *(Officer-HR & Sr VP-Ops)*
David G. Remington *(Chm)*
Timothy B. Page *(Pres & CEO)*
Daniel James Hallahan *(Sr VP-Mktg-Global)*
Matthew Easton *(CTO & VP-IT)*
Steven Garcia *(Chief Legal Officer, Sec & VP)*
David Morris *(Chief Acctg Officer & VP)*

Subsidiaries:

CAI Chile S.p.A (1)
Julio Fossa Calderon N 190, Vina del Mar, Chile
Tel.: (56) 993370752
Freight Transportation Services
N.A.I.C.S.: 488510

CAI International GmbH (1)
Lahusenstrasse 1, 27749, Delmenhorst, Germany
Tel.: (49) 4221685870
Web Site: http://www.capps.com
Sales Range: $25-49.9 Million
Emp.: 4
Container Rental & Leasing Services
N.A.I.C.S.: 532289

CAI Logistics Inc. (1)
Steuart Tower 1 Market Plz Ste 2400, San Francisco, CA 94105
Tel.: (415) 788-0100
Web Site: http://www.capps.com
Logistics Consulting Servies
N.A.I.C.S.: 541614

Subsidiary (Domestic):

Hybrid Logistics, Inc. (2)

10255 SW Park Way, Portland, OR 97225   **(100%)**
Web Site: http://www.hybridl.com
Sales Range: $10-24.9 Million
Emp.: 30
Freight Transportation & Logistics & Supply Chain Services
N.A.I.C.S.: 488510
Robert Thompson *(Pres)*

CAI-Charleston (1)
1180 Sam Rittenberg Blvd Ste 205, Charleston, SC 29407
Tel.: (843) 763-6868
Web Site: http://www.capps.com
Sales Range: $100-124.9 Million
Emp.: 6
Freight Container Leasing & Management Services
N.A.I.C.S.: 488510

Challenger Overseas LLC (1)
7 Christopher Way, Eatontown, NJ 07724
Tel.: (732) 460-1100
Web Site:
http://www.challengeroverseas.com
Freight Transportation Services
N.A.I.C.S.: 488510
George Meyer *(Partner)*

Container Applications International (Australia) Pty Ltd. (1)
Suite 408 4th Floor 460 Pacific Highway, Saint Leonards, 2065, NSW, Australia
Tel.: (61) 294370999
Web Site: http://wwwcapps.com
Logistics Consulting Servies
N.A.I.C.S.: 541614

Container Applications International (U.K.) Limited (1)
Kingsgate 1 King Edward Road, Brentwood, CM14 4HG, Essex, United Kingdom
Tel.: (44) 1277223666
Web Site: http://www.capps.com
Sales Range: $25-49.9 Million
Emp.: 11
Transportation Equipment Rental & Leasing Services
N.A.I.C.S.: 532411

Oceania Leasing Agencies (1)
Suite 8 1st Floor 75 Pacific Highway Waitara, Sydney, 2077, NSW, Australia
Tel.: (61) 294895375
Sales Range: $100-124.9 Million
Emp.: 3
Freight & Logistics
N.A.I.C.S.: 488510

CAL-BAY INTERNATIONAL, INC.
1887 Whitney Mesa Dr Ste 2127, Henderson, NY 89014
Tel.: (303) 260-6480   NV
Year Founded: 2001
CBYI—(OTCIQ)
Electrical Instrument Mfr
N.A.I.C.S.: 334516
Luke A. Joseph *(CEO)*

CAL-MAINE FOODS, INC.
1052 Highland Colony Pkwy Ste 200, Ridgeland, MS 39157
Tel.: (601) 948-6813   DE
Web Site:
https://www.calmainefoods.com
Year Founded: 1969
CALM—(NASDAQ)
Rev.: $2,326,443,000
Assets: $2,184,761,000
Liabilities: $387,718,000
Net Worth: $1,797,043,000
Earnings: $276,282,000
Emp.: 3,067
Fiscal Year-end: 06/01/24
Fresh Shell Egg Production, Grading, Packing & Sales
N.A.I.C.S.: 112310
Adolphus B. Baker *(Chm)*
Sherman L. Miller *(Pres & CEO)*
Todd Walters *(COO & VP)*
Robert Holladay *(Gen Counsel & VP)*
Kevin Lastowski *(VP-Ops)*

Christopher Myers *(VP-Ops)*
Matthew Arrowsmith *(VP-Egg Sls)*
Wil Webb *(VP-Ops)*
Timothy Thompson *(VP-Ops)*
Michael Ermon *(VP-Ops)*
Max P. Bowman *(CFO & VP)*
Josh Moore *(VP-Ops)*
Scott Hull *(Sr VP-Sls)*
Matthew S. Glover *(Principal Acctg Officer & VP-Acctg)*
Jia Scott *(VP-Treasury)*
Rhonda Whiteman *(VP-Operational Acctg)*
Matt Whiteman *(VP-Ops)*

Subsidiaries:

American Egg Products, Inc. (1)
375 Pierce Industrial Blvd, Blackshear, GA 31516   **(99.5%)**
Tel.: (912) 449-5700
Web Site: http://www.calmainefoods.com
Sales Range: $25-49.9 Million
Emp.: 60
Processed Egg Products Mfr
N.A.I.C.S.: 424440

Cal-Maine Foods (1)
234 Pickens Rd, Green Forest, AR 72638
Tel.: (870) 438-5233
Sales Range: $75-99.9 Million
Emp.: 60
Chicken Egg Production
N.A.I.C.S.: 424440

Delta Egg Farm, LLC (1)
9246 N 4000 W, Delta, UT 84624
Tel.: (435) 864-4991
Egg Production & Distr
N.A.I.C.S.: 112310

Fassio Egg Farms, Inc. (1)
5763 Droubay Rd, Tooele, UT 84074-9741
Tel.: (801) 969-9831
Sales Range: $1-9.9 Million
Emp.: 20
Chicken Egg Production Services
N.A.I.C.S.: 112310
Dick Fassio *(Principal)*

Featherland Egg Farms, Inc. (1)
1255 Stolte Rd, Marion, TX 78124-6031
Tel.: (830) 914-4949
Egg Farm
N.A.I.C.S.: 112310

Mahard Egg Farm, Inc. (1)
PO Box 248, Prosper, TX 75078
Tel.: (972) 347-2421
Web Site: http://www.mahard.com
Chicken Egg Production Services
N.A.I.C.S.: 112310
Andy Mahard *(Pres)*

South Texas Applicators, Inc. (1)
1680 County Rd 431, Waelder, TX 78959
Tel.: (830) 540-4105
Processed Egg Products Whslr
N.A.I.C.S.: 424440

Southern Equipment Distributors, Inc. (1)
335 Hwy 72, Collierville, TN 38017
Tel.: (901) 861-0110
Web Site:
https://www.southernequipmentdist.com
Sales Range: $25-49.9 Million
Emp.: 5
Advertising Material Distr
N.A.I.C.S.: 541870

Texas Egg Products, LLC (1)
1808 E US Hwy 90, Waelder, TX 78959
Tel.: (830) 788-7792
Grocery Product Distr
N.A.I.C.S.: 424410

Wharton County Foods, LLC (1)
4429 FM 442, Boling, TX 77420
Tel.: (979) 657-2891
Grocery Product Distr
N.A.I.C.S.: 424410
Scott Telhiard *(Mgr-Admin)*

CALAMOS CONVERTIBLE & HIGH INCOME FUND
2020 Calamos Ct, Naperville, IL 60563-1463

Tel.: (630) 245-1046
CHY—(NASDAQ)
Rev.: $63,061,916
Assets: $1,247,633,775
Liabilities: $429,222,143
Net Worth: $818,411,632
Earnings: $39,415,297
Fiscal Year-end: 10/31/19
Investment Management Service
N.A.I.C.S.: 525990
John Peter Calamos Sr. *(Pres & Mgr-Fund)*

CALAMOS CONVERTIBLE OP-PRTNTY & INCOME
2020 Calamos Ct, Naperville, IL 60563-1463
Tel.: (630) 245-1046
CHI—(NASDAQ)
Rev.: $57,184,826
Assets: $1,146,482,586
Liabilities: $392,172,557
Net Worth: $754,310,029
Earnings: $35,624,207
Fiscal Year-end: 10/31/19
Investment Services
N.A.I.C.S.: 523999
John Peter Calamos Sr. *(Mgr-Fund)*

CALAMOS DYNAMIC CONVERTIBLE AND INCOME FUND
2020 Calamos Ct, Naperville, IL 60563-2787
Tel.: (630) 245-7200   DE
Web Site: http://www.calamos.com
CCD—(NASDAQ)
Rev.: $33,377,365
Assets: $744,260,311
Liabilities: $256,551,561
Net Worth: $487,708,750
Earnings: $17,860,913
Fiscal Year-end: 10/31/19
Investment Services
N.A.I.C.S.: 523999
John Peter Calamos Sr. *(Pres)*
Mark J. Mickey *(Chief Compliance Officer)*
John S. Koudounis *(Pres, CEO & VP)*
Robert F. Behan *(Chief Distribution Officer, Exec VP & VP)*

CALAMOS GLOBAL DYNAMIC INCOME FUND
2020 Calamos Ct, Naperville, IL 60563-1463
Tel.: (630) 245-1046   DE
CHW—(NASDAQ)
Rev.: $25,946,097
Assets: $759,226,219
Liabilities: $291,040,530
Net Worth: $468,185,689
Earnings: $9,949,469
Fiscal Year-end: 10/31/19
Investment Management Service
N.A.I.C.S.: 525990
John Peter Calamos Sr. *(Pres & Mgr-Fund)*

CALAMOS GLOBAL TOTAL RETURN FUND
2020 Calamos Ct, Naperville, IL 60563-1463
Tel.: (630) 245-1046   DE
CGO—(NASDAQ)
Investment Management Service
N.A.I.C.S.: 525990

CALAMOS STRATEGIC TOTAL RETURN FUND
2020 Calamos Ct, Naperville, IL 60653
Tel.: (630) 245-1046   DE
Web Site: http://www.calamos.com
CSQ—(NASDAQ)
Rev.: $86,185,998
Assets: $2,929,409,352

Calamos Strategic Total Return Fund—(Continued)

Liabilities: $928,700,473
Net Worth: $2,000,708,879
Earnings: $27,261,995
Fiscal Year-end: 10/31/19
Investment Management Service
N.A.I.C.S.: 525990
John Peter Calamos Sr. *(Pres)*

CALAMP CORP.

2200 Faraday Ave Ste 220, Carlsbad,
CA 92008
Tel.: (949) 600-5600　　　　　DE
Web Site: https://www.calamp.com
Year Founded: 1981
CAMP—(NASDAQ)
Rev.: $294,949,000
Assets: $380,120,000
Liabilities: $365,813,000
Net Worth: $14,307,000
Earnings: ($32,490,000)
Emp.: 644
Fiscal Year-end: 02/28/23
Radio & Television Broadcasting &
Wireless Communications Equipment
Manufacturing
N.A.I.C.S.: 334220
Henry J. Maier *(Chm)*
Jikun Kim *(CFO, Principal Acctg Offi-
cer & Sr VP)*
Monica Van Berkel *(Sr VP-HR)*
Jeff Clark *(Sr VP-Product Mgmt)*
Nathan Lowstuter *(Sr VP-Global Sup-
ply Chain & Ops)*
Maurizio Iperti *(Interim Chief Rev-
enue Officer & Pres-Europe, Middle
East & Africa)*
Cindy Zhang *(Sr VP-Fin Plng &
Analysis)*
Xiaolian Zhang *(Sr VP-Fin Plng &
Analysis)*
Mark Gaydos *(Chief Mktg & Product
Officer)*
Christopher R. Adams *(Pres & CEO)*

Subsidiaries:

California Amplifier S.A.R.L　　　　(1)
1 Rue de la Haye, Roissy CDG, 9573,
Paris, Cedex, France　　　　　(100%)
Tel.: (33) 149192262
Web Site: http://www.calamp.com
Sales Range: $1-9.9 Million
Emp.: 1
Mfr & Designer of Microwave Reception
Equipment Used Primarily in the Delivery of
Multichannel Pay Television Via Satellite &
Wireless Cable
N.A.I.C.S.: 334220

LoJack Corporation　　　　　　(1)
40 Pequot Way, Canton, MA
02021　　　　　　　　　　(100%)
Tel.: (781) 302-4200
Web Site: https://www.lojack.com
Sales Range: $125-149.9 Million
Stolen Vehicle & Personal Property Loca-
tion & Recovery Devices Mfr
N.A.I.C.S.: 334290

Subsidiary (Non-US):

Car Mart Comunicaciones, S.A. de
C.V.　　　　　　　　　　　(2)
Alejandro Dumas No 304 Col Polanco,
Deleg Miguel Hidalgo, 11550, Mexico,
Mexico
Tel.: (52) 5525811060
Web Site: http://www.lojack.com.mx
Vehicle Security System Distr
N.A.I.C.S.: 561621

LJ Network Holding BV　　　　(2)
Ketelweg 33A, 3356 LD, Papendrecht,
Netherlands
Tel.: (31) 880005525
Web Site: http://www.lojack.nl
Security Device Mfr
N.A.I.C.S.: 334290
Guus Wesselink *(Chm-Supervisory Bd)*
Scott Nilson *(VP-Intl)*

LoJack Equipment Ireland
Limited　　　　　　　　　　(2)
5 Lamps Place Amiens Street, D01 A7V2,
Dublin, Ireland
Tel.: (353) 17040102
Web Site: http://www.lojack.ie
Automotive Tracking Device Mfr
N.A.I.C.S.: 334290

LoJack de Mexico, S. de R.L. de
CV　　　　　　　　　　　　(1)
Lago Victoria 74 piso 2 Colonia Granada,
Alcaldia Miguel Hidalgo, 11520, Mexico,
Mexico
Tel.: (52) 5525811060
Web Site: https://www.lojack.com.mx
Tracking System Operation Services
N.A.I.C.S.: 517810

Smart Driver Club Ltd.　　　　(1)
Timsons Business Centre Bath Rd, Ketter-
ing, NN16 8NQ, Northamptonshire, United
Kingdom
Tel.: (44) 3337720489
Web Site: https://www.viewpoint.smartdriver
club.co.uk
Driver Insurance Services
N.A.I.C.S.: 524210

Synovia Solutions LLC　　　　(1)
9330 Priority Way W Dr, Indianapolis, IN
46240
Tel.: (317) 208-1700
Web Site: http://www.synoviasolutions.com
Emp.: 50
Fleet Management Solutions
N.A.I.C.S.: 513210

CALAVO GROWERS, INC.

1141-A Cummings Rd, Santa Paula,
CA 93060
Tel.: (805) 525-1245　　　　　CA
Web Site: https://www.calavo.com
Year Founded: 1924
CVGW—(NASDAQ)
Rev.: $971,948,000
Assets: $386,854,000
Liabilities: $176,625,000
Net Worth: $210,229,000
Earnings: ($8,344,000)
Emp.: 3,064
Fiscal Year-end: 10/31/23
Avocado Marketing & Packaging Ser-
vices
N.A.I.C.S.: 926140
Steven Hayworth *(Sls Mgr-Intl)*
Shawn C. Munsell *(CFO)*
Kyla Maxfield *(Sr Acct Mgr)*
Gabriel Soltero *(Mgr-Diversified Dept)*
Teri Morrison *(Acct Mgr)*
Juan Magdaleno *(Acct Mgr)*
Carlos Duarte *(Acct Mgr)*
LeighAnne Thomsen *(Acct Mgr)*
Lindsay Martinez *(Mktg Mgr-Fresh &
Foods Div)*
Lisa Mueller *(Sr VP-Financial Profiles
Inc)*
Raina Nelson *(Exec VP-Bus Dev)*
Melissa Brucker *(Acct Mgr-
Foodservice)*
Tim Vallejo *(Acct Mgr)*
Megan Stallings *(Acct Mgr-Tomato
Sls)*
Angela Tallant *(Acct Mgr-Canada)*
Thomas Federl *(VP-Comm, Mktg &
ESG)*
Tommy Padilla *(Sr Dir-Intl Sls)*
Danny Dumas *(Sr VP-Grown Div &
Gen Mgr-Grown Div)*
Andy Foster *(VP-Sls & Natl Ac-
counts)*
Kate Brooks *(Sr VP-Sls)*
Eloy Hintz *(VP)*

Subsidiaries:

Calavo Foods, Inc.　　　　　　(1)
1141A Cummings Rd, Santa Paula, CA
93060-9118
Tel.: (805) 525-1245
Fruit Farming Services
N.A.I.C.S.: 111339

Renaissance Food Group, LLC.　(1)
11020 White Rock Rd Ste 100, Rancho
Cordova, CA 95670
Tel.: (916) 638-8825
Web Site: http://www.rfgfoods.com
Sales Range: $25-49.9 Million
Emp.: 50
Grocery Stores
N.A.I.C.S.: 445110
Jim Gibson *(Pres)*
Mark Lodge *(COO)*
Lee Cole *(Chm & CEO)*

CALCIMEDICA, INC.

505 Coast Blvd S Ste 307, La Jolla,
CA 92037
Tel.: (858) 952-5500　　　　　DE
Web Site: https://calcimedica.com
Year Founded: 2015
CALC—(NASDAQ)
Rev.: $575,000
Assets: $39,670,000
Liabilities: $3,699,000
Net Worth: $35,971,000
Earnings: ($35,605,000)
Emp.: 8
Fiscal Year-end: 12/31/22
Biotechnology Research & Develop-
ment Services
N.A.I.C.S.: 541714
Raven Jaeger *(Chief Regulatory Offi-
cer)*
Andrew Cunningham *(Sr VP-Clinical
Dev)*
Rachel Leheny *(CEO)*
John M. Dunn *(Gen Counsel)*
Sudarshan Hebbar *(Chief Medical
Officer)*
Kenneth A. Stauderman *(Chief Scien-
tific Officer)*
Daniel Geffken *(Interim CFO)*
Sean P. Lawler *(VP-Finance)*
Eric W. Roberts *(Vice Chm & Chief
Bus Officer)*
Michael J. Dunn *(Pres & COO)*

Subsidiaries:

CalciMedica Subsidiary, Inc.　　(1)
505 Coast Blvd S Ste 209, La Jolla, CA
92037
Tel.: (858) 952-5500
Web Site: https://www.calcimedica.com
Drug Discovery & Development Services
N.A.I.C.S.: 541715
Peter McWilliams *(Chm)*
Rachel Leheny *(CEO)*

CALERES, INC.

8300 Maryland Ave, Saint Louis, MO
63105
Tel.: (314) 854-4000　　　　　NY
Web Site: https://www.caleres.com
Year Founded: 1878
CAL—(NYSE)
Rev.: $2,817,294,000
Assets: $1,804,746,000
Liabilities: $1,237,176,000
Net Worth: $567,570,000
Earnings: $171,391,000
Emp.: 5,100
Fiscal Year-end: 02/03/24
Shoe Importing, Wholesale & Retail
N.A.I.C.S.: 316210
Daniel R. Friedman *(Chief Sourcing
Officer)*
John W. Schmidt *(Pres & CEO)*
Natelle Baddeley *(Chief Design &
Product Officer)*
Jack P. Calandra *(CFO & Sr VP)*
Liz Dunn *(Sr VP-Corporate Develop-
ment & Strategic Comm)*
Willis D. Hill *(CIO & Sr VP)*
Todd E. Hasty *(Chief Acctg Officer &
Sr VP)*
Michael R. Edwards *(Pres-Famous
Footwear)*
Sam Edelman *(Pres-Div)*

Thomas C. Burke *(Gen Counsel, Sec
& VP)*
Erica Mackoul *(Sr VP-Intl)*
Diane M. Sullivan *(Exec Chm)*

Subsidiaries:

Allen Edmonds LLC　　　　　　(1)
201 E Seven Hills Rd, Port Washington, WI
53074-2504
Tel.: (262) 235-6000
Web Site: http://www.allenedmonds.com
Men's Shoe Mfr
N.A.I.C.S.: 316210
Jay Schauer *(CFO)*

Unit (Domestic):

Woodlore　　　　　　　　　　(2)
3820 Hwy KW, Port Washington, WI 53074
Tel.: (262) 235-6343
Web Site: http://www.woodlore.com
Cedar Products Mfr
N.A.I.C.S.: 321999

American Sporting Goods
Corporation　　　　　　　　(1)
101 Enterprise Ste 100, Aliso Viejo, CA
92656
Tel.: (949) 267-2800
Web Site: http://www.avia.com
Sales Range: $200-249.9 Million
Emp.: 325
Athletic Footwear Mfr & Marketer
N.A.I.C.S.: 424340

Caleres Canada, Inc.　　　　　(1)
1857 Rogers Road, Perth, K7H 1P7, ON,
Canada　　　　　　　　　　(100%)
Tel.: (613) 267-2000
Web Site: http://www.brownshoe.com
Sales Range: $25-49.9 Million
Emp.: 30
Men's Clothing Mfr
N.A.I.C.S.: 315250

Caleres Italy S.r.l.　　　　　　(1)
Via Francesco Berni 1, Empoli, 50053, Flor-
ence, Italy
Tel.: (39) 0571533726
Emp.: 8
Footwear Whslr
N.A.I.C.S.: 458210
Roberto Giovannoni *(VP)*

DongGuan Leeway Footwear Com-
pany Limited　　　　　　　　(1)
Baima Section of Hongtu Road, Nancheng
District, Dongguan, 523080, Guangdong,
China
Tel.: (86) 76922009999
Footwear Whslr
N.A.I.C.S.: 424340

Famous Footwear　　　　　　(1)
8300 Maryland Ave, Saint Louis, MO
63105　　　　　　　　　　(100%)
Tel.: (314) 854-4000
Web Site: http://www.famousfootwear.com
Sales Range: $1-4.9 Billion
Emp.: 10,000
Shoe Retailer
N.A.I.C.S.: 458210
Michael R. Edwards *(Pres)*

Pagoda International Footwear
Limited　　　　　　　　　　(1)
Room 1701-5 17/F Stelux House 698
Prince Edward Road East, San Po Kong,
Kowloon, China (Hong Kong)
Tel.: (852) 26215151
Footwear Mfr
N.A.I.C.S.: 316210

Sidney Rich Associates Inc.　　(1)
8300 Maryland Ave, Saint Louis, MO
63105-3645　　　　　　　　(100%)
Tel.: (314) 854-4142
Web Site: http://www.brownshoes.com
Sales Range: $150-199.9 Million
Wholesale Distribution of Footwear
N.A.I.C.S.: 424340

Vionic Group LLC　　　　　　(1)
4040 Civic Ctr Dr Ste 430, San Rafael, CA
94903
Web Site: https://www.vionicshoes.com
Footwear Whslr
N.A.I.C.S.: 424340

CALETHOS, INC.
11753 Willard Ave, Tustin, CA 92782
Tel.: (714) 352-5315   NV
Web Site: https://www.calethos.com
Year Founded: 2002
BUUZ—(OTCIQ)
Rev.: $3,918,000
Assets: $2,071,000
Liabilities: $5,214,000
Net Worth: ($3,143,000)
Earnings: $2,181,000
Emp.: 1
Fiscal Year-end: 12/31/22
Real Estate Brokerage & Management
N.A.I.C.S.: 531210
Michael Campbell (Chm & CEO)
Joel Stone (Pres & COO)
Brian Mattson (Chief Strategy Officer & Chief Dev Officer)
Timothy Coe (VP-Data Center Dev)

CALIBERCOS, INC.
8901 E Mountain View Rd Ste 150, Scottsdale, AZ 85258
Tel.: (480) 295-7600   DE
Web Site: https://www.caliberco.com
Year Founded: 2009
CWD—(NASDAQ)
Rev.: $56,033,000
Assets: $245,648,000
Liabilities: $195,955,000
Net Worth: $49,693,000
Earnings: ($698,000)
Emp.: 73
Fiscal Year-end: 12/31/21
Miscellaneous Financial Investment Activities
N.A.I.C.S.: 523999
Ignacio Martinez (COO)
Jade Leung (Sec)
Jennifer Schrader (Co-Founder & Pres)

CALIDI BIOTHERAPEUTICS, INC.
4475 Executive Dr Ste 200, San Diego, CA 92121
Tel.: (858) 794-9600   DE
Web Site: https://www.calidibio.com
Year Founded: 2021
CLDI—(NYSEAMEX)
Rev.: $8,546,701
Assets: $42,854,778
Liabilities: $48,060,254
Net Worth: ($5,205,476)
Earnings: $3,530,190
Emp.: 2
Fiscal Year-end: 12/31/22
Offices of Other Holding Companies
N.A.I.C.S.: 551112
Allan J. Camaisa (Chm & CEO)
Boris Radoslavov Minev (Pres-Medical & Scientific Affairs)
Andrew Jackson (CFO)
Thomas Vecchiolla (Operating Partner)

Subsidiaries:

Calidi Biotherapeutics (Nevada), Inc.   (1)
4475 Executive Dr Ste 200, San Diego, CA 92121
Tel.: (858) 794-9600
Biopharmaceutical Developer & Mfr
N.A.I.C.S.: 325414
Allan J. Camaisa (Chm & CEO)
Boris Radoslavov Minev (Pres-Medical & Scientific Affairs)

CALIFORNIA BANCORP
12265 El Camino Real Ste 100, San Diego, CA 92130
Tel.: (844) 265-7622   CA
Web Site: http://www.banksocal.com
BCAL—(NASDAQ)
Rev.: $97,250,000

Assets: $2,283,927,000
Liabilities: $2,023,572,000
Net Worth: $260,355,000
Earnings: $16,113,000
Fiscal Year-end: 12/31/22
Bank Holding Company
N.A.I.C.S.: 551111
David I. Rainer (Chm & CEO)
Michele M. Wirfel (COO, Chief Admin Officer & Exec VP)

Subsidiaries:

Bank of Santa Clarita   (1)
23780 Magic Mountain Pkwy, Santa Clarita, CA 91355
Tel.: (661) 362-6000
Web Site:
    http://www.bankofsantaclarita.com
Rev.: $12,322,000
Assets: $307,409,000
Liabilities: $274,326,000
Net Worth: $33,083,000
Earnings: $3,184,000
Emp.: 33
Fiscal Year-end: 12/31/2018
Commericial Banking
N.A.I.C.S.: 551111
Barbara Andriuzzo (First VP & Mgr-Consumer Loan)
Brenda Neilson (Branch Mgr-Client Svcs)
Carol Morrissey (Mgr-Central Ops)
Craig S. Conner (Mgr-SBA)
Elizabeth Hopp (Exec VP)
Eric R. Jensen (Mgr-Info Svcs)
Gregory A. Weinberg (Exec VP)
John S. Carlson (Officer-Comml Loan & First VP)
John M. Vescovo (Exec VP)
Mary Hernandez (Mgr-Note Dept)
Stephanie M. Stephens (Sr VP & Controller)
Walt N. Purdy (Exec VP)
William McCloskey (First VP & Mgr-Real Estate)
Donna Reller (Officer-Comml Loan & Asst VP)
Robert A. Kaplan (Sr VP)
Will Saylor. (VP)

California Bank of Commerce, N.A.   (1)
3142 Tiger Run Ct Ste 107, Carlsbad, CA 92010
Tel.: (760) 599-7044
Web Site: http://www.banksocal.com
Sales Range: $25-49.9 Million
Emp.: 73
Federal Savings Bank
N.A.I.C.S.: 522180
David I. Rainer (Chm & CEO)
Anne Williams (Chief Credit Officer & Exec VP)
Michele M. Wirfel (COO & Exec VP)
Nathan L. Rogge (Pres)
James H. Burgess (Deputy CFO)
Pamela C. Isaacson (Chief Admin Officer & Exec VP)
Michael Helmuth (Grp Mng Dir & Sr VP)
Mariam Siryani (Sr Mng Dir)
Sandy Apodaca (Branch Mgr-Svc)
David I. Rainer (Chm)
Martin Liska (Chief Risk Officer & Exec VP)
Thomas G. Dolan (CFO & Exec VP)
Danni Remington Smithson (Exec VP & Reg Mgr-Orange)
Stephanie Johnson (Asst VP)
Christopher D. Maggio (Sr VP)
Bill Sloan (Exec VP & Mgr-Comml Banking)
Elizabeth Swift (Sr VP-Comml Real Estate Lender)
Ross Macdonald (Sr VP & Reg Mgr-Comml Lending)
Lily Dastur (VP & Sr Mgr-Relationship Banking)

CALIFORNIA BUSINESS BANK
3200 El Camino Real Ste 220, Irvine, CA 92602
Tel.: (714) 389-9970   CA
Web Site:
    https://www.californiabusiness
    bank.com
Year Founded: 2005
CABB—(OTCIQ)
Commericial Banking
N.A.I.C.S.: 522110

Richard Li Pin Tan (Chm)

CALIFORNIA INTERNATIONAL BANK
15606 Brookhurst St Ste C-D, Westminster, CA 92683
Tel.: (714) 338-8700   CA
Web Site: https://www.cali.bank
Year Founded: 2006
CAIB—(OTCIQ)
Commercial Banking Services
N.A.I.C.S.: 522110
Thanh Pham (Pres)

CALIFORNIA ORCHARDS CO.
PO Box 25010, Ventura, CA 93002
Tel.: (831) 385-3858   CA
Year Founded: 1919
CAOX—(OTCIQ)
Fruit & Vegetable Retailer
N.A.I.C.S.: 445230
Gregory Daniel Joseph Smith (Sec)

CALIFORNIA RESOURCES CORPORATION
1 World Trade Ctr Ste 1500, Long Beach, CA 90831   DE
Web Site: https://www.crc.com
Year Founded: 2014
CRC—(NYSE)
Rev.: $2,707,000,000
Assets: $3,967,000,000
Liabilities: $2,103,000,000
Net Worth: $1,864,000,000
Earnings: $524,000,000
Emp.: 1,060
Fiscal Year-end: 12/31/22
Oil & Natural Gas Exploration Services
N.A.I.C.S.: 211120
Manuela Molina Peralta (CFO & Exec VP)
Francisco J. Leon (Pres & CEO)
Chris Gould (Chief Sustainability Officer & Exec VP)
Omar Hyat (Exec VP)
Jay A. Bys (Chief Comml Officer & Exec VP)
Sergio De Castro (Sr VP-Transformation Office)
Alana Sotiri (Sr VP-People Ops)

Subsidiaries:

CRC Services, LLC   (1)
813 Williams St Ste 212, Longmeadow, MA 01106
Tel.: (413) 437-5100
Web Site: https://www.crcservicesllc.com
Vocational Rehabilitation Services
N.A.I.C.S.: 624310
David M. Soja (Founder & Owner)
Kerry A. Skillin (Mgr)

California Resources Elk Hills, LLC   (1)
11109 River Run Blvd, Bakersfield, CA 93311
Tel.: (661) 412-5000
Petroleum Refining Services
N.A.I.C.S.: 324110

California Resources Long Beach, Inc.   (1)
111 W Ocean Blvd Ste 800, Long Beach, CA 90802
Tel.: (562) 624-3400
Gas Exploration Services
N.A.I.C.S.: 211130
Carlos Contreras (VP)

California Resources Production Corporation   (1)
855 Harter Pkwy Ste 200, Yuba City, CA 95993
Tel.: (530) 671-8201
Gas Exploration Services
N.A.I.C.S.: 211130

CALIFORNIA STYLE PALMS, INC.

349 N Renee St, Orange, CA 92869-3122
Tel.: (714) 814-8525   DE
Web Site:
    http://www.californiastylepalms
    inc.com
CFPI—(OTCIQ)
Agriculture Product Distr
N.A.I.C.S.: 424910
Burl Gregory (CEO)

CALIFORNIA WATER SERVICE GROUP
1720 N 1st St, San Jose, CA 95112
Tel.: (408) 367-8200   DE
Web Site:
    https://www.calwatergroup.com
Year Founded: 1926
CWT—(NYSE)
Rev.: $846,431,000
Assets: $3,850,752,000
Liabilities: $1,475,871,000
Net Worth: $2,374,881,000
Earnings: $96,011,000
Emp.: 1,225
Fiscal Year-end: 12/31/22
Offices of Other Holding Companies
N.A.I.C.S.: 551112
Martin A. Kropelnicki (Chm, Pres & CEO)
Shannon C. Dean (Chief Citizenship Officer & VP-Customer Svc)
James P. Lynch (CFO, Treas & Sr VP)
David B. Healey (Interim Principal Fin Officer)
Michael B. Luu (Chief Risk Officer & Sr VP-Corp Svcs)
Elissa Y. Ouyang (Chief Procurement & Lead CI Officer)
Gerald A. Simon (Chief Safety, Security & Emergency Preparedness Officer & VP)
Michelle R. Mortensen (Sec & VP)
Michael S. Mares (VP-Ops)
Todd K. Peters (Chief Engrg Officer)
Sophie M. James (Chief Water Quality Officer)
Kenneth G. Jenkins (Chief Water Resource Sustainability Officer)
Thomas A. Scanlon (Principal Acctg Officer & Controller)
Justin B. Skarb (VP-Govt & Community Affairs)
Shawn C. Bunting (Gen Counsel)
Daryl L. Osby (VP)

Subsidiaries:

California Water Service
Company   (1)
2632 W 237 St, Torrance, CA
90505   (100%)
Tel.: (408) 367-8200
Water Supply & Distribution
N.A.I.C.S.: 221310
Martin A. Kropelnicki (Chm, Pres & CEO)

California Water Service
Company   (1)
2632 W 237 St, Torrance, CA
90505   (100%)
Tel.: (408) 367-8200
Water Supply & Distribution
N.A.I.C.S.: 221310
Martin A. Kropelnicki (Chm, Pres & CEO)

California Water Service
Company   (1)
2632 W 237 St, Torrance, CA
90505   (100%)
Tel.: (408) 367-8200
Water Supply & Distribution
N.A.I.C.S.: 221310
Martin A. Kropelnicki (Chm, Pres & CEO)

California Water Service
Company   (1)
2632 W 237 St, Torrance, CA
90505   (100%)
Tel.: (408) 367-8200
Water Supply & Distribution

California Water Service Group—(Continued)

N.A.I.C.S.: 221310
Martin A. Kropelnicki *(Chm, Pres & CEO)*

California Water Service Company (1)
2632 W 237 St, Torrance, CA 90505 **(100%)**
Tel.: (408) 367-8200
Water Supply & Distribution
N.A.I.C.S.: 221310
Martin A. Kropelnicki *(Chm, Pres & CEO)*

California Water Service Company (1)
2632 W 237 St, Torrance, CA 90505 **(100%)**
Tel.: (408) 367-8200
Water Supply & Distribution
N.A.I.C.S.: 221310
Martin A. Kropelnicki *(Chm, Pres & CEO)*

California Water Service Company (1)
2632 W 237 St, Torrance, CA 90505 **(100%)**
Tel.: (408) 367-8200
Water Supply & Distribution
N.A.I.C.S.: 221310
Martin A. Kropelnicki *(Chm, Pres & CEO)*

California Water Service Company (1)
2632 W 237 St, Torrance, CA 90505 **(100%)**
Tel.: (408) 367-8200
Water Supply & Distribution
N.A.I.C.S.: 221310
Martin A. Kropelnicki *(Chm, Pres & CEO)*

California Water Service Company (1)
2632 W 237 St, Torrance, CA 90505 **(100%)**
Tel.: (408) 367-8200
Water Supply & Distribution
N.A.I.C.S.: 221310
Martin A. Kropelnicki *(Chm, Pres & CEO)*

California Water Service Company (1)
2632 W 237 St, Torrance, CA 90505 **(100%)**
Tel.: (408) 367-8200
Water Supply & Distribution
N.A.I.C.S.: 221310
Martin A. Kropelnicki *(Chm, Pres & CEO)*

Hawaii Water Service Company (1)
68-1845 Waikoloa Rd Unit 216, Waikoloa, HI 96738
Tel.: (808) 883-2046
Web Site: https://www.hawaiiwaterservice.com
Sales Range: Less than $1 Million
Emp.: 45
Water Supply Services
N.A.I.C.S.: 221310

New Mexico Water Service Company (1)
401 Horner St, Rio Communities, NM 87002
Tel.: (505) 864-2218
Web Site: https://www.newmexicowater.com
Water Supply Services
N.A.I.C.S.: 221310

Washington Water Service Company (1)
14519 Peacock Hill Ave, Gig Harbor, WA 98332 **(100%)**
Tel.: (253) 857-5414
Web Site: https://www.wawater.com
Sales Range: $25-49.9 Million
Emp.: 50
Water Supply Services
N.A.I.C.S.: 221310

Subsidiary (Domestic):

Rainier View Water Co, Inc. (2)
5410 189th ST E, Puyallup, WA 98375
Tel.: (253) 537-6634
Web Site: http://www.rainierviewwater.com
Sales Range: $1-9.9 Million
Emp.: 32
Private Water Supply System
N.A.I.C.S.: 221310
Neil Richardson *(Pres)*

CALIFORNIA-ENGELS MINING CO
4276 Napa Loop, Roseville, CA 95747
Tel.: (530) 394-7045   **CA**

Year Founded: 1922
CAEN—(OTCIQ)
Mineral Mining Services
N.A.I.C.S.: 212390
Norman A. Lamb *(Pres)*
M. Blair Ogden *(Sec)*
Katherine A. Lamb *(Treas & VP)*

CALISSIO RESOURCES GROUP INC.
4742 N 24th St, Phoenix, AZ 85016
Tel.: (480) 525-7722   **NV**
Web Site: https://www.calissioresources.com
Year Founded: 2000
CRGP—(OTCIQ)
Sales Range: $10-24.9 Million
Copper, Gold & Silver Mining
N.A.I.C.S.: 212230
Alberto Navarro *(Treas)*
Clement Lockwood *(Pres & CEO)*

CALITHERA BIOSCIENCES, INC.
343 Oyster Point Blvd Ste 200, South San Francisco, CA 94080
Tel.: (650) 870-1000   **DE**
Web Site: http://www.calithera.com
Year Founded: 2010
CALA—(NASDAQ)
Rev.: $9,750,000
Assets: $64,756,000
Liabilities: $56,374,000
Net Worth: $8,382,000
Earnings: ($115,088,000)
Emp.: 63
Fiscal Year-end: 12/31/21
Pharmaceuticals Product Mfr
N.A.I.C.S.: 325412
Emil T. Kuriakose *(Chief Medical Officer)*
Stephanie Wong *(CFO & Sec)*
Susan M. Molineaux *(Co-Founder, Pres & CEO)*

CALIX INC.
2777 Orchard Pkwy, San Jose, CA 95134
Tel.: (408) 514-3000   **DE**
Web Site: https://www.calix.com
Year Founded: 1999
CALX—(NYSE)
Rev.: $867,827,000
Assets: $884,835,000
Liabilities: $205,268,000
Net Worth: $679,567,000
Earnings: $41,010,000
Emp.: 1,426
Fiscal Year-end: 12/31/22
Telecommunications Equipment Mfr & Supplier
N.A.I.C.S.: 334220
Michel Langlois *(Chief Development Officer-Intelligent Access EDGE Products)*
Michael Weening *(Pres & CEO)*
Shane Eleniak *(Chief Product Officer)*
Cory Sindelar *(CFO)*
John Durocher *(Chief Customer Officer)*
Parul Kapoor *(Sr VP)*
Doug McNitt *(Gen Counsel)*
Jerry Cederlund *(Sr VP)*

Subsidiaries:

Calix (1)
6868 Cortona Dr, Santa Barbara, CA 93117
Tel.: (805) 692-2900
Web Site: http://www.calix.com
Sales Range: $75-99.9 Million
Emp.: 50
Telecommunications Transmission Equipment Mfr
N.A.I.C.S.: 334210

Calix Inc. - Development Center (1)
16305 36th Ave N Ste 300, Minneapolis, MN 55446

Tel.: (763) 268-3300
Fiber Optics Communications Equipment
N.A.I.C.S.: 334210
Carl E. Russo *(Pres & CEO)*

CALLODINE ACQUISITION CORPORATION
2 International Pl Ste 1830, Boston, MA 02110
Tel.: (617) 880-7480   **DE**
Year Founded: 2021
CALQU—(NASDAQ)
Emp.: 4
Investment Services
N.A.I.C.S.: 523999
James S. Morrow *(Founder, Chm & CEO)*
Tyler Bak *(Head-Bus Dev)*
Marc Irizarry *(Pres)*

Subsidiaries:

Callodine Group, LLC (1)
2 International Pl Ste 1830, Boston, MA 02110
Tel.: (617) 880-7484
Web Site: https://www.callodine.com
Asset Management Services
N.A.I.C.S.: 523999
James S. Morrow *(Founder & CEO)*

Subsidiary (Domestic):

Manning & Napier, Inc. (2)
290 Woodcliff Dr, Fairport, NY 14450
Tel.: (585) 325-6880
Web Site: http://www.manning-napier.com
Rev.: $145,581,000
Assets: $171,423,000
Liabilities: $79,022,000
Net Worth: $92,401,000
Earnings: $25,105,000
Emp.: 270
Fiscal Year-end: 12/31/2021
Investment Management Service
N.A.I.C.S.: 523150
Ebrahim Busheri *(Dir-Investments)*
Sarah Turner *(Gen Counsel & Sec)*
Nicole Kingsley Brunner *(CMO)*
Aaron McGreevy *(Mng Dir-Institutional & Intermediary Sls)*
Chris Briley *(CTO)*
Greg Woodard *(Mng Dir-Wealth Mgmt)*
Stacey Green *(Head-HR)*
Scott Morabito *(Mng Dir-Client Svc & Bus Ops)*
Paul J. Battaglia Jr. *(CFO)*

Subsidiary (Domestic):

2100 Xenon Group LLC (3)
430 W Erie St Ste 300, Chicago, IL 60654
Tel.: (312) 337-9411
Web Site: http://www.2100xenon.com
Investment Management Service
N.A.I.C.S.: 523940

Exeter Trust Company (3)
155 Fleet St, Portsmouth, NH 03801
Tel.: (603) 778-0020
Financial Support Services
N.A.I.C.S.: 522320
Paul Peltier *(Pres)*

Manning & Napier Advisors, LLC (3)
290 Woodcliff Dr, Fairport, NY 14450-4217
Tel.: (585) 325-6880
Web Site: http://www.manning-napier.com
Sales Range: $150-199.9 Million
Emp.: 150
Investment Advisory Services
N.A.I.C.S.: 523940

Subsidiary (Domestic):

Rainier Investment Management, Inc. (4)
601 Union St Ste 2801, Seattle, WA 98101
Web Site: http://www.rainierfunds.com
Sales Range: $1-9.9 Million
Emp.: 37
Investment Advice
N.A.I.C.S.: 523940

Subsidiary (Domestic):

Manning & Napier Benefits, LLC (3)
295 Woodcliff Dr, Fairport, NY 14450-4212

Tel.: (585) 598-7171
Web Site: http://www.manning-napier-benefits.com
Benefits Planning & Consulting Services
N.A.I.C.S.: 561499
John Mann Jr. *(Mng Dir)*

Perspective Partners, LLC (3)
290 Woodcliff Dr, Fairport, NY 14450
Tel.: (585) 325-3925
Web Site: http://www.perspectivepartners.com
Financial Planning Services
N.A.I.C.S.: 525990

CALLON PETROLEUM COMPANY
1 Briarlake Plz 2000 W Sam Houston Pkwy S Ste 2000, Houston, TX 77042
Tel.: (281) 589-5200   **DE**
Web Site: https://www.callon.com
Year Founded: 1950
CPE—(NYSE)
Rev.: $2,342,984,000
Assets: $6,711,476,000
Liabilities: $2,720,115,000
Net Worth: $3,991,361,000
Earnings: $401,201,000
Emp.: 281
Fiscal Year-end: 12/31/23
Exploration & Drilling of Natural Gas & Petroleum
N.A.I.C.S.: 211120

Subsidiaries:

Callon Offshore Production (1)
200 N Canal St, Natchez, MS 39120-3212 **(100%)**
Tel.: (601) 442-1601
Web Site: http://www.callon.com
Sales Range: $75-99.9 Million
Emp.: 60
Production of Oil & Gas
N.A.I.C.S.: 211120

Callon Petroleum Operating Company (1)
200 N Canal St, Natchez, MS 39120
Tel.: (601) 442-1601
Sales Range: $50-74.9 Million
Emp.: 35
Oil & Gas Operation Services
N.A.I.C.S.: 213112
Fred L. Callon *(Chm, Pres & CEO)*
Bobby F. Weatherly Jr. *(Chief Admin Officer, Sec & Exec VP)*

Carrizo Oil & Gas, Inc. (1)
500 Dallas St Ste 2300, Houston, TX 77002
Tel.: (713) 328-1000
Web Site: http://www.carrizo.com
Rev.: $1,065,942,000
Assets: $3,185,310,000
Liabilities: $2,204,196,000
Net Worth: $980,904,000
Earnings: $376,076,000
Emp.: 239
Fiscal Year-end: 12/31/2018
Oil & Natural Gas Explorer, Developer & Producer
N.A.I.C.S.: 211120
J. Bradley Fisher *(COO & VP)*
David L. Pitts *(CFO & VP)*
Jim Pritts *(VP-Tech & New Bus Dev)*
Gerald A. Morton *(Gen Counsel & VP-Bus Dev)*
Andrew R. Agosto *(VP-Bus Dev)*
Gregory F. Conaway *(Chief Acctg Officer & VP)*
Jeff Hayden *(VP-Fin Plng & Analysis)*
Gregory E. Percival *(CIO & VP)*
Richard H. Smith *(VP-Land)*
Scott Hudson *(VP-Drilling & Completions)*
Doug Reid *(VP-Exploration)*
Shaleen Patel *(VP-Corp Dev & Fin)*
Laura Kinningham *(VP-HR)*
Kim Pinyopusarerk *(Mgr-IR)*
Rex Bigler *(VP-Production Ops)*

Subsidiary (Domestic):

Bandelier Pipeline Holding, LLC (2)
500 Dallas St, Houston, TX 77002
Tel.: (713) 328-1000
Web Site: http://www.carrizo.com

Emp.: 200
Oil & Gas Exploration Services
N.A.I.C.S.: 211120
Chip Johnson *(CEO)*

CALMARE THERAPEUTICS INCORPORATED

1375 Kings Hwy E Ste 400, Fairfield, CT 06824
Tel.: (203) 368-6044   DE
Web Site:
  http://calmaretherapeutics.com
Year Founded: 1968
CTTC—(OTCIQ)
Sales Range: $1-9.9 Million
Emp.: 7
Invention Commercialization & Patent Application Services
N.A.I.C.S.: 561499
Peter Joseph Brennan *(Chm)*
Conrad F. Mir *(Pres & CEO)*
William Lipford *(Head-Product Sls Div-US)*
Christine Chansky *(Chief Regulatory Officer)*
Thomas P. Richtarich *(CFO)*

CALUMET, INC.

1060 N Capitol Ave Ste 6-401, Indianapolis, IN 46204
Tel.: (317) 328-5660   DE
Web Site: https://calumet.com
Year Founded: 2024
CLMT—(NASDAQ)
Holding Company; Petroleum Refining & Specialty Products Mfr
N.A.I.C.S.: 551112
Todd Borgmann *(Pres & CEO)*
Scott Obermeier *(Exec VP-Specialties)*

Subsidiaries:

Calumet Specialty Products Partners, L.P.   (1)
1060 N Capitol Ave Ste 6 401, Indianapolis, IN 46204-1044
Tel.: (317) 328-5660
Web Site: https://calumet.com
Rev.: $4,686,700,000
Assets: $2,741,800,000
Liabilities: $3,279,500,000
Net Worth: ($537,700,000)
Earnings: ($165,100,000)
Emp.: 1,530
Fiscal Year-end: 12/31/2022
Crude Oil Processor
N.A.I.C.S.: 325110

Subsidiary (Domestic):

Bel-Ray Company, LLC   (2)
2780 Waterfront Pkwy E Dr, Indianapolis, IN 46214
Tel.: (317) 328-5660
Web Site: https://www.belray.com
Sales Range: $75-99.9 Million
Emp.: 120
Synthetic Lubricants Mfr
N.A.I.C.S.: 324191

Calumet Branded Products, LLC   (2)
1 Royal Purple Ln, Porter, TX 77365
Tel.: (281) 354-8600
Web Site: https://www.royalpurple.com
Hydrocarbon Product Mfr
N.A.I.C.S.: 324199

Calumet Cotton Valley Refining, LLC   (2)
1756 Old Hwy 7, Cotton Valley, LA 71018
Tel.: (318) 832-4236
Aliphatic Solvent Mfr
N.A.I.C.S.: 325194

Calumet Dickinson Refining, LLC   (2)
4401 Park Ave, Dickinson, TX 77539
Tel.: (281) 337-1534
White Mineral Oil Mfr
N.A.I.C.S.: 324110

Calumet Karns City Refining, LLC   (2)
138 Petrolia St, Karns City, PA 16041

Tel.: (724) 756-0110
White Mineral Oil Mfr
N.A.I.C.S.: 324110

Calumet Missouri, LLC   (2)
11089 Highway D, Louisiana, MO 63353
Tel.: (573) 754-6211
Web Site: http://www.calumetspeciality.com
Emp.: 120
Synthetic Lubricants Products Mfr
N.A.I.C.S.: 324191

Calumet Operating, LLC   (2)
2780 Waterfront Pkwy E Dr Ste 200, Indianapolis, IN 46214
Tel.: (317) 328-5660
Lubricants & Related Products Mfr
N.A.I.C.S.: 324191

Calumet Packaging, LLC   (2)
10411 Hwy 1, Shreveport, LA 71115
Tel.: (318) 795-3800
Web Site: http://www.calumetpackaging.com
Petrochemical Mfr
N.A.I.C.S.: 325110

Calumet Paralogics, Inc.   (2)
301 S Butterfield Rd, Muncie, IN 47303
Tel.: (765) 587-4618
Web Site: http://www.paralogicsolutions.com
Consumer Product Mfr
N.A.I.C.S.: 325998

Calumet Princeton Refining, LLC (2)
10234 Hwy 157, Princeton, LA 71067-9172
Tel.: (318) 949-2421
Lubricating Oil Mfr
N.A.I.C.S.: 324191

Calumet Refining, LLC   (2)
2780 Waterfront Pkwy E Dr Ste 200, Indianapolis, IN 46214
Tel.: (317) 328-5660
Web Site: http://www.calumetspecialty.com
Hydrocarbon Product Mfr
N.A.I.C.S.: 324199

Calumet San Antonio Refining, LLC   (2)
2780 Waterfront Pkwy E Dr Ste 200, Indianapolis, IN 46214-2030
Tel.: (317) 328-5660
Petrochemical Mfr
N.A.I.C.S.: 325110

Calumet Shreveport Refining, LLC   (2)
3333 Midway St, Shreveport, LA 71109-5719
Tel.: (318) 632-4100
Lubricating Oil & Wax Mfr
N.A.I.C.S.: 324191

Montana Refining Company Inc. (2)
1900 10th St NE, Great Falls, MT 59404-1955   (100%)
Tel.: (406) 761-4100
Web Site: http://www.montanarefining.com
Sales Range: $25-49.9 Million
Emp.: 100
Petroleum Refineries
N.A.I.C.S.: 324110

Unit (Domestic):

Penreco   (2)
138 Petrolia St, Karns City, PA 16041
Tel.: (724) 756-0110
Web Site: http://www.penreco.com
Sales Range: $50-74.9 Million
Emp.: 170
Specialty Chemical & Petroleum Mfr
N.A.I.C.S.: 325998

CALVIN B. TAYLOR BANKSHARES, INC.

24 N Main St, Berlin, MD 21811
Tel.: (410) 641-1700   MD
Web Site:
  https://www.taylorbank.com
Year Founded: 1995
TYCB—(OTCIQ)
Rev.: $23,364,334
Assets: $711,795,304
Liabilities: $617,010,174
Net Worth: $94,785,130
Earnings: $7,268,014
Emp.: 109

Fiscal Year-end: 12/31/20
Bank Holding Company
N.A.I.C.S.: 522110
Raymond M. Thompson *(Pres & CEO)*
M. Dean Lewis *(CFO & VP)*
Douglass M. Cook *(Chief Lending Officer & Exec VP)*
Atif S. Gaddis *(Officer-BSA)*
Donna E. Weaver *(Compliance Officer & VP)*

CAMBER ENERGY, INC.

12 Greenway Plz Ste 1100, Houston, TX 77046
Tel.: (281) 404-4387   NV
Web Site: https://www.camber.energy
Year Founded: 2003
CEI—(NYSEAMEX)
Rev.: $597,255
Assets: $34,696,714
Liabilities: $51,820,347
Net Worth: ($17,123,633)
Earnings: ($107,741,965)
Emp.: 9
Fiscal Year-end: 12/31/22
Crude Petroleum Extraction Services
N.A.I.C.S.: 211120
John McVicar *(CFO)*

Subsidiaries:

Viking Energy Group, Inc.   (1)
15915 Katy Fwy Ste 450, Houston, TX 77094   (100%)
Tel.: (281) 404-4387
Web Site:
  http://www.vikingenergygroup.com
Rev.: $24,038,160
Assets: $49,912,689
Liabilities: $34,547,374
Net Worth: $15,365,315
Earnings: ($15,427,329)
Emp.: 2
Fiscal Year-end: 12/31/2022
Holding Company; Financial Advisory & Investment Services
N.A.I.C.S.: 551112
John McVicar *(CFO)*
James A. Doris *(Pres & CEO)*

Subsidiary (Domestic):

Viking Investments Group, LLC   (2)
15915 Katy Fwy Ste 450, Houston, TX 77094
Tel.: (281) 404-4387
Web Site:
  https://www.vikingenergygroup.com
Financial Advisory & Investment Services
N.A.I.C.S.: 523940

CAMBEX CORPORATION

337 Turnpike Rd, Southborough, MA 01772
Tel.: (508) 281-0209   MA
Web Site: https://www.cambex.com
Year Founded: 1968
CBEX—(OTCIQ)
Sales Range: $1-9.9 Million
Emp.: 14
Computer Enhancement & Data Storage Products & Solutions Designer, Developer, Mfr & Retailer
N.A.I.C.S.: 334112
Joseph A. Kruy *(Pres)*
Peter A. Kruy *(CFO)*

CAMBIUM NETWORKS CORPORATION

2000 Center Dr Ste E A401, Hoffman Estates, IL 60192
Tel.: (345) 814-7600   Ky
Web Site:
  https://www.cambiumnetworks.com
Year Founded: 2011
CMBM—(NASDAQ)
Rev.: $296,899,000
Assets: $269,462,000
Liabilities: $124,089,000
Net Worth: $145,373,000

Earnings: $20,200,000
Emp.: 650
Fiscal Year-end: 12/31/22
Offices of Other Holding Companies
N.A.I.C.S.: 551112
Jacob A. Sayer *(CFO)*
Mary Peterson *(CMO & Sr VP)*
Nigel King *(CTO)*
Sally Rau *(Gen Counsel)*
Vibhu Vivek *(Sr VP-Products)*
Peter Strong *(Chief Architect)*
Raymond de Graaf *(Sr VP-Ops)*
Scott Imhoff *(Sr VP-Product Mgmt)*
Ron Ryan *(Sr VP-Channels-Global)*
Himanshu Motial *(VP-Sls-APAC)*
Daniel Dominguez *(VP-Sls-CALA)*
Martin de la Serna *(VP-Sls-EMEA)*
Derek Underwood *(VP-Sls-North America)*
Aarti Sharma *(Sr Dir-HR-Global)*
Morgan C. S. Kurk *(Pres & CEO)*

Subsidiaries:

Xirrus, LLC   (1)
2101 Corporate Ctr Dr, Thousand Oaks, CA 91320
Tel.: (805) 262-1600
Cloud-enabled Wi-Fi Networks Provider
N.A.I.C.S.: 517112
Dirk I. Gates *(Founder, Chm & CTO)*
George Frie *(Chief Revenue Officer)*

CAMBRIDGE BANCORP

1336 Massachusetts Ave, Cambridge, MA 02138
Tel.: (617) 876-5500   MA
Web Site:
  https://www.cambridgetrust.com
Year Founded: 1982
CATC—(NASDAQ)
Rev.: $203,002,000
Assets: $5,559,737,000
Liabilities: $5,042,185,000
Net Worth: $517,552,000
Earnings: $52,909,000
Emp.: 440
Fiscal Year-end: 12/31/22
Bank Holding Company
N.A.I.C.S.: 551111
Denis K. Sheahan *(Chm, Pres & CEO)*
Steven J. Mead *(Chief Comml Banking Officer)*
Peter Halberstadt *(Chief Credit Officer)*
Joseph P. Sapienza *(Interim CFO, Principal Acctg Officer & Sr VP)*
Michael F. Carotenuto *(CFO & Sr VP)*
Pilar Pueyo *(Sr VP & Dir-HR)*
Jennifer A. Pline *(Exec VP & Head-Wealth Mgmt)*
Kerri A. Mooney *(Sr VP & Dir-Private Banking Offices)*
Puneet Nevatia *(CIO & Sr VP)*
John J. Sullivan *(Sr VP & Dir-Consumer Lending)*

Subsidiaries:

Cambridge Trust Company   (1)
1336 Massachusetts Ave, Cambridge, MA 02138-3842
Tel.: (617) 876-5500
Web Site: https://www.cambridgetrust.com
Retail & Commercial Banking
N.A.I.C.S.: 522110
Denis K. Sheahan *(Chm & CEO)*
Steven J. Mead *(Sr VP)*
Peter Halberstadt *(Sr VP)*
Puneet Nevatia *(CIO & Sr VP)*
Kerri A. Mooney *(Sr VP & Dir-Private Banking Offices)*
Pilar Pueyo *(Sr VP & Dir-HR)*
Laura C. McGregor *(Sr VP)*
Telma C. Salvador *(VP)*
Phillips Ruben *(First VP)*
Grace Rondon *(Assoc Mgr-Office)*
John E. Riggs IV *(VP)*
Fernando Rico *(VP)*
Jason Rich *(VP)*

Cambridge Bancorp—(Continued)

Danielle Remis Hackel (CMO)
Stacie Plourde (Asst VP)
Scott Piccolo (VP)
Mary Beth Parker (Sr VP-C & I Lending)
Siobhan O'Hara (VP)
William T. Oberlies (Sr VP)
Judith K. Noel (Sr VP)
Boris Nikitin (VP)
Debbie Moore (VP)
Susan Martore-Baker (Pres-Cambridge Trust-New Hampshire)
Ryan M. Hanna (Deputy Chief Investment Officer)
Kelly Broderick (Chief Fiduciary Officer)

Subsidiary (Domestic):

Cambridge Trust Company of New Hampshire, Inc.　　　　　(2)
49 S Main St Ste 203, Concord, NH 03301
Tel.: (603) 226-1212
Commercial Banking Services
N.A.I.C.S.: 522110

Northmark Bank　　　　　　　　(2)
89 Tpke St, North Andover, MA 01845-5045
Tel.: (978) 686-9100
Web Site: http://www.northmarkbank.com
Banking Services
N.A.I.C.S.: 522110

Wellesley Investment Partners, LLC　　　　　　　　　　(2)
75 Central St, Wellesley, MA 02482
Tel.: (781) 431-1325
Web Site:
　http://www.wellesleyinvestmentpartners.com
Wealth Management Services
N.A.I.C.S.: 523940
Louis P. Crosier (Pres)
Jeremy S. Glenn (COO & Chief Compliance Officer)
Mary Beth S. Mahoney (Sr Mng Dir)
Michael Y. Fung (Chief Investment Officer)
Susan Black (Chief Plng Officer)
Phillips Ruben (Mng Dir-Fin Plng)
Susan Covo (Project Mgr)

CAMBRIDGE CAPITAL HOLDINGS, INC.

8275 S Eastern Ave Ste 200, Las Vegas, NV 89123
Tel.: (615) 255-3199　　　　　UT
Year Founded: 1987
CCHI—(OTCIQ)
Gold Ore Mining Services
N.A.I.C.S.: 212220
Christopher Jarratt (Pres & CEO)
Michael Chiodo (CFO, Treas & Sec)

CAMDEN NATIONAL CORPORATION

Tel.: (207) 236-8821　　　　　ME
Web Site:
　https://www.camdennational.com
Year Founded: 1984
CAC—(NASDAQ)
Rev.: $213,490,000
Assets: $5,671,850,000
Liabilities: $5,220,572,000
Net Worth: $451,278,000
Earnings: $61,439,000
Emp.: 630
Fiscal Year-end: 12/31/22
Bank Holding Company
N.A.I.C.S.: 551111
Simon R. Griffiths (Pres & CEO)
Renee D. Smyth (Chief Mktg & Experience Officer & Exec VP)
Michael Archer (CFO, Principal Acctg Officer, Exec VP & Controller)
Ryan A. Smith (Exec VP-Comml Banking)
Jennifer L. Mirabile (Mng Dir)
Heather D. Robinson (Chief HR Officer)

Subsidiaries:

Acadia Trust, N.A.　　　　　　(1)
5 Milk St 1st Fl, Portland, ME 04101

Tel.: (207) 774-3333
Web Site: http://www.acadiatrust.com
Sales Range: $1-4.9 Billion
Emp.: 20
Trust & Investment Services
N.A.I.C.S.: 523991

The Camden National Bank　　(1)
2 Elm St, Camden, ME
04843-1903　　　　　　　　(100%)
Tel.: (207) 230-5958
Web Site: https://www.camdennational.bank
Sales Range: $100-124.9 Million
Emp.: 610
Commericial Banking
N.A.I.C.S.: 522110
Simon R. Griffiths (Pres & CEO)
Michael Archer (CFO, Exec VP & Controller)
Elliott Barry (Officer-Comml Banking & Sr VP-Cumberland County)
David C. Peterson (Officer-Comml Banking & Sr VP)
Donna M. Ehrler (Sr VP & Dir-Comml Banking-Manchester)
Paul Doody (Officer-Comml Banking & VP)
John C. Everett (Sr VP & Dir-Comml Banking-Southern Maine)
William H. Martel (Exec VP-Tech & Support Svcs)
Michael Archer (CFO, Principal Acctg Officer & Exec VP)
James Dell'Anno (Sr VP & Dir-Mortgage Banking & Consumer Lending)
James Dell'Anno (Sr VP & Dir-Mortgage Banking & Consumer Lending)

CAMDEN PROPERTY TRUST

11 Greenway Plz Ste 2400, Houston, TX 77046
Tel.: (713) 354-2500　　　　TX
Web Site:
　https://www.camdenliving.com
Year Founded: 1993
CPT—(NYSE)
Rev.: $1,542,027,000
Assets: $9,383,737,000
Liabilities: $4,331,966,000
Net Worth: $5,051,771,000
Earnings: $410,553,000
Emp.: 1,640
Fiscal Year-end: 12/31/23
Real Estate Investment Trust
N.A.I.C.S.: 525990
Stanley Jones (VP-Real Estate Investments)
D. Keith Oden (Co-Founder & Vice Chm)
Kimberly Callahan (Sr VP-IR)
Cynthia B. Scharringhausen (Sr VP-HR)
Mark Bucci (VP-Construction)
Kristy Simonette (CIO & Sr VP-Strategic Svcs)
Alexander J. K. Jessett (Pres & CFO)
David Joyce (VP-Construction)
Robert Herr (VP-Acctg)
Stephen R. Hefner (Sr VP-Construction)
Laurie A. Baker (COO & Exec VP)
Dawn Mathwig (VP-Special Projects)
Jean Harding (VP-Real Estate Investments)
Todd Triggs (VP-Real Estate Investments)
Amy Funk (VP-Real Estate Investments)
Sarah Barletta (VP-Employee Benefits)
Ashley Anderson (VP-Internal Audit)
Jimmy Whorton (VP-IT)
Ben Fraker (Treas & VP-Fin)
Richard Key (Reg VP)
Ben Mills (VP-Facilities & Construction)
Chad Weaver (VP-Real Estate Investments)
Joshua L. Lebar (Gen Counsel, Sec & Sr VP)
Alison Hall (VP-Contact Center Ops)

Julie Keel (VP-Mktg)
Carter Powell (Reg VP)
Mike Eilertsen (VP)
James Flick (VP)
Jennifer Killen (VP)
Leticia Serrano (VP)
Will Smith (VP)
Richard Whatcott (VP)
Ben Wickert (VP)
Linda Linda (VP)
Richard J. Campo (Co-Founder, Chm & CEO)

Subsidiaries:

Camden Operating, L.P.　　　(1)
11 Greenway Plz Ste 2400, Houston, TX 77046
Tel.: (713) 354-2500
Web Site: https://www.camdenliving.com
Property Management Services
N.A.I.C.S.: 531110

Camden Summit, Inc.　　　　(1)
309 E Morehead St, Charlotte, NC 28202-2326
Tel.: (704) 334-3000
Web Site: http://www.camdenliving.com
Sales Range: $200-249.9 Million
Emp.: 450
Real Estate Investment Trust
N.A.I.C.S.: 525990

CAMPBELL SOUP COMPANY

1 Campbell Pl, Camden, NJ 08103-1701
Tel.: (856) 342-4800　　　　　NJ
Web Site:
　https://www.campbellsoupcompany.com
Year Founded: 1869
CPB—(NASDAQ)
Rev.: $9,636,000,000
Assets: $15,235,000,000
Liabilities: $11,439,000,000
Net Worth: $3,796,000,000
Earnings: $567,000,000
Emp.: 14,400
Fiscal Year-end: 07/28/24
Food Products Mfr
N.A.I.C.S.: 311422
Mark A. Clouse (Pres & CEO)
Keith R. McLoughlin (Chm)
Mindy Mackenzie (Executives)
Stanley Polomski (VP & Controller)
Craig S. Slavtcheff (Chief R&D & Innovation Officer & Exec VP)
Carrie L. Anderson (CFO & Exec VP)
Mick J. Beekhuizen (Pres-Meals & Beverages & Exec VP)
Christopher D. Foley (Pres-Snacks & Exec VP)
Carlos Abrams-Rivera (Exec VP)
Rebecca Gardy (VP-IR)
Camille Pierce (Chief Culture Officer & Sr VP)
Anthony J. Sanzio (Sr VP-Comm & Pub Affairs)
Diane Johnson May (Chief HR Officer & Exec VP)
Archbold D. van Beuren (Executives)
Charles A. Brawley III (Gen Counsel, Sec & Exec VP)

Subsidiaries:

BF Bolthouse Holdco LLC　　(1)
7200 E Brundage Ln, Bakersfield, CA 93307
Tel.: (661) 366-7205
Web Site: http://www.bolthouse.com
Holding Company
N.A.I.C.S.: 551112

Bolthouse Farms Japan YK　　(1)
Landmark Tower 39th Floor 2 2 1, Minatomirai Nishi Ku, Yokohama, 220 8139, Kanagawa, Japan
Tel.: (81) 452243005
Vegetable Farming Services
N.A.I.C.S.: 111219

Bolthouse Investment Company　(1)
7200 E Brundage Ln, Bakersfield, CA 93307-3016
Tel.: (661) 366-7209
Investment Management Service
N.A.I.C.S.: 523940

Bolthouse Juice Products, LLC　(1)
7200 E Brundage Ln, Bakersfield, CA 93307-3099
Tel.: (661) 366-7270
Juice Product Mfr
N.A.I.C.S.: 311421

Campbell Arnotts Limited　　(1)
24 George St N Stratfield, Sydney, 2137, NSW, Australia　　　　　(100%)
Tel.: (61) 293943555
Web Site: http://www.arnotts.com
Sales Range: $200-249.9 Million
Emp.: 500
Cookies, Crackers, Food Preparations, Candy, Bread & Cake Mfr
N.A.I.C.S.: 311821
Helge Gruettke (Chief Client Officer-Asia Pacific)

Subsidiary (Domestic):

Arnott's Biscuits Ltd.　　　　(2)
24 George St, North Strathfield, Sydney, 2137, NSW, Australia
Tel.: (61) 287677000
Web Site: http://www.arnotts.com
Biscuits, Snack Food & Nuts Mfr & Distr
N.A.I.C.S.: 311919
George Zoghbi (CEO)
Jenni Dill (CMO)

Subsidiary (Non-US):

Arnott's New Zealand Limited　(3)
Level 1, 61-73 Davis Crescent, Auckland, 1023, New Zealand
Tel.: (64) 95208040
Biscuits & Snacks Mfr
N.A.I.C.S.: 311919

Campbell Cheong Chan Malaysia Sdn Bhd　　　　　　　　(1)
36 Jalan Penchala, Petaling Jaya, 46700, Selangor, Malaysia
Tel.: (60) 377876288
Canned Soup Mfr
N.A.I.C.S.: 311999

Campbell Company of Canada Ltd　　　　　　　　　　(1)
2845 Matheson Blvd East, Mississauga, L4W 5J8, ON, Canada　　(100%)
Tel.: (416) 251-1131
Web Site: http://www.campbellsoup.ca
Sales Range: $400-449.9 Million
Emp.: 300
Mfr, Distr & Retailer of Soup
N.A.I.C.S.: 311422

Campbell Foods Belgium n.v./s.a.　　　　　　　　　(1)
Rijksweg 16, Puurs, 2870, Belgium
Tel.: (32) 38908711
Web Site: http://www.continentalfoods.com
Sales Range: $75-99.9 Million
Emp.: 30
Canned Soup Mfr
N.A.I.C.S.: 311999

Campbell Japan Incorporated　(1)
558-14 Tokyo eaeemono Hiroo, Tokyo, 150 0012, Shibuya Ku, Japan　(100%)
Tel.: (81) 354476500
Web Site: http://www.campbellsoup.co.jp
Sales Range: $10-24.9 Million
Emp.: 20
Distribution of Canned Foods
N.A.I.C.S.: 445298
Lim Mooi Cheng (Pres & CEO)

Campbell North America　　(1)
1 Campbell Pl, Camden, NJ 08103-1701
Tel.: (856) 342-4800
Web Site:
　http://www.campbellsoupcompany.com
Sales Range: $75-99.9 Million
Regional Managing Office
N.A.I.C.S.: 551114

Subsidiary (Domestic):

Campbell Foodservice Company　(2)
1 Campbell Pl, Camden, NJ 08103-1701
Tel.: (856) 342-4800

Web Site:
https://www.campbellfoodservice.com
Prepared Convenience Foods Distr
N.A.I.C.S.: 424490

Campbell Sales Company (2)
1 Campbell Pl, Camden, NJ
08103-1701 **(100%)**
Tel.: (856) 342-4800
Web Site: http://www.campbellsoup.com
Canned Soup Whslr
N.A.I.C.S.: 424490

**Campbell Soup Supply Company
L.L.C.** (2)
500 W Edgerton Ave, Milwaukee, WI
53207-6029
Tel.: (414) 482-1730
Sales Range: $25-49.9 Million
Emp.: 43
Food Processing Services
N.A.I.C.S.: 311422
Tom Dopps (Gen Mgr)

Campbell Soup Asia Limited (1)
Rm 702 7/F Caroline Centre Lee Gardens
Two 28 Yun Ping Road, Causeway Bay,
China (Hong Kong)
Tel.: (852) 28113806
Web Site: http://www.campbellsoup.com.hk
Canned Food Processor & Sales
N.A.I.C.S.: 311999
Umit Subasi (Pres-Asia Pacific)

Campbell Soup Co. - Paris Plant (1)
NW Loop 286, Paris, TX 75461-9016
Tel.: (903) 784-3341
Web Site: http://www.campbellsoup.com
Mfr of Food Products
N.A.I.C.S.: 311422

Campbell Soup Finland Oy (1)
Valimotie 5, PL 241, 01531, Vantaa, Finland
Tel.: (358) 207 681 400.
Web Site: http://www.campbellsoup.fi
Soup & Sauce Distr
N.A.I.C.S.: 424490

Campbell Soup Sweden AB (1)
Karpalundsvagen 39, 291 92, Kristianstad,
Sweden
Tel.: (46) 44 10 80 00
Web Site: http://www.campbellsoup.se
Sales Range: $50-74.9 Million
Emp.: 14
Canned Soup Mfr
N.A.I.C.S.: 311999

**Campbell Soup Trading (Shanghai)
Company Limited** (1)
Rm 3801 38/F Hongkong New World Plaza
No 300 Huaihai M Rd, Shanghai, China
Tel.: (86) 2123302670
Canned Soup Mfr
N.A.I.C.S.: 311999

**Campbell Southeast Asia Sdn
Bhd** (1)
No 3 Lrg Kilang A Off Jalan Kilang, 46050,
Petaling Jaya, Selangor, Malaysia
Tel.: (60) 377876288
Web Site: http://www.campbellsoup.com.my
Sales Range: $75-99.9 Million
Emp.: 250
Canned Soup Mfr
N.A.I.C.S.: 311999

Campbell Swire (HK) Ltd (1)
Units 1210-1211 12/F Two ICC Shanghai
ICC 288 South Shaanxi Road, Xuhui Dis-
trict, Shanghai, 200031, China
Tel.: (86) 2123302600
Soup Product Mfr & Distr
N.A.I.C.S.: 311999
Leo Meng (Gen Mgr)

Fresh Logistics, LLC (1)
7200 E Brundage Ln, Bakersfield, CA
93307
Tel.: (708) 491-1501
Web Site: http://www.freshlogistics.net
Logistics Consulting Servies
N.A.I.C.S.: 541614

Kjeldsens Limited (1)
Room 2903 25/F, Cambridge House, PO
Box 6454, Taikoo Place 979 King's Road,
Hong Kong, China (Hong Kong)
Tel.: (852) 25233009
Web Site: http://www.kjeldsens.com

Snack Food Mfr
N.A.I.C.S.: 311919

Natural Food Works, LLC (1)
4969 Colorado Blvd, Denver, CO 80216
Tel.: (303) 639-9090
Web Site: http://www.nfworks.com
Food Mfr & Distr
N.A.I.C.S.: 311919
Bill Tennant (CEO)
Dustin Richardson (Dir-Fin & Ops)
Andrea Blau (Dir-Ops & New Bus)
Richard Lappen (Founder & Partner)

Pacific Foods of Oregon, Inc. (1)
19480 SW 97th Ave, Tualatin, OR 97062
Tel.: (503) 692-9666
Web Site: https://www.pacificfoods.com
Organically Produced Soups, Beverages &
Special Diet Foods
N.A.I.C.S.: 111998
David Pimentel (Sr Mgr-IT & Information
Sys)
Erin Carlson (Dir-HR, Corp & Comml Func-
tions)
Brendan Washington (Sr Dir-Mfg & Supply
Chain)
Tim Goldsmid (VP-Mktg)
Casey Young (Dir-R&D)
Deb Kaminski (Dir-Foodservice Mktg & Sls)

Pepperidge Farm, Inc. (1)
595 Westport Ave, Norwalk, CT
06851-4413 **(100%)**
Tel.: (203) 846-7000
Web Site: https://www.pepperidgefarm.com
Sales Range: $150-199.9 Million
Emp.: 325
Fresh & Frozen Bakery Products Mfr
N.A.I.C.S.: 311812
Maureen Linder (Sr VP-Fresh & Frozen
Bakery)

Plum, PBC (1)
1485 Park Ave Ste 200, Emeryville, CA
94608
Tel.: (510) 225-4018
Web Site: http://www.plumorganics.com
Sales Range: $75-99,9 Million
Emp.: 60
Organic Baby Food Mfr
N.A.I.C.S.: 311999
Neil Grimmer (Founder)

Snyder's-Lance, Inc. (1)
PO Box 32368, Charlotte, NC 28232
Tel.: (704) 554-1421
Web Site: https://www.lance.com
Sales Range: $1-4.9 Billion
Snack Food Mfr
N.A.I.C.S.: 311821

Subsidiary (Domestic):

5C Investments, LLC (2)
4904 E Greenhurst Rd, Nampa, ID 83686
Tel.: (208) 468-9110
Web Site:
http://www.garagedoor911idaho.com
Garage Door Whslr
N.A.I.C.S.: 444180

Baptista's Bakery, Inc. (2)
4625 W Oakwood Park Dr, Franklin, WI
53132
Tel.: (414) 409-2000
Web Site: http://www.baptistas.com
Snack Food Mfr
N.A.I.C.S.: 311821

**Cape Cod Potato Chip Company
Inc.** (2)
100 Breeds Hill Rd, Hyannis, MA 02601-
1860
Tel.: (508) 775-3358
Web Site: http://www.capecodchips.com
Snack Food Mfr
N.A.I.C.S.: 311919

Diamond Foods, LLC (2)
1050 S Diamond St, Stockton, CA 95205
Tel.: (209) 467-6000
Web Site: http://www.diamondnuts.com
Assorted Snack Foods, Nuts & Fruits Mfr &
Distr
N.A.I.C.S.: 311911
Craig Hope (CEO)

Subsidiary (Domestic):

Kettle Foods, Inc. (3)

3125 Kettle Ct SE, Salem, OR 97301
Tel.: (503) 364-0399
Web Site: http://www.kettlebrand.com
Snack Food Mfr
N.A.I.C.S.: 311919

Subsidiary (Domestic):

S-L Snacks Logistics, LLC (2)
8600 South Blvd, Charlotte, NC 28273
Tel.: (704) 554-5541
Snack Food Mfr
N.A.I.C.S.: 311821

Snack Factory, LLC (2)
11 Tamarack Cir, Skillman, NJ 08558
Web Site: http://www.pretzelcrisps.com
Snack Products Mfr & Distr
N.A.I.C.S.: 311919

Sovos Brands, Inc. (1)
168 Centennial Pkwy Ste 200, Louisville,
CO 80027
Tel.: (720) 316-1225
Web Site: https://www.sovosbrands.com
Rev.: $878,371,000
Assets: $1,158,799,000
Liabilities: $682,776,000
Net Worth: $476,023,000
Earnings: ($53,451,000)
Emp.: 690
Fiscal Year-end: 12/31/2022
Food & Beverage Product Mfr
N.A.I.C.S.: 333241
Christopher W. Hall (CFO)
Lisa Y. O'Driscoll (Chief Admin Officer)
Risa Cretella (Chief Sls Officer)
Todd R. Lachman (Pres)
William R. Johnson (Chm)

StockPot Inc. (1)
1200 Merrill Creek Pkwy, Everett, WA
98203-7152 **(100%)**
Tel.: (425) 407-6400
Web Site:
http://www.campbellfoodservice.com
Sales Range: $250-299.9 Million
Emp.: 290
Fresh-Refrigerated Products Mfr
N.A.I.C.S.: 311999

Yellow Chips BV (1)
Fabrieksweg 6, 8304 AT, Emmeloord, Neth-
erlands
Tel.: (31) 858771160
Web Site: http://www.yellowchips.nl
Prepared Convenience Food Mfr
N.A.I.C.S.: 311991

CAMPING WORLD HOLDINGS,
INC.
2 Marriott Dr, Lincolnshire, IL 60069
Tel.: (847) 808-3000 DE
Web Site:
https://www.campingworld.com
Year Founded: 2016
CWH–(NYSE)
Rev.: $6,967,013,000
Assets: $4,800,147,000
Liabilities: $4,552,461,000
Net Worth: $247,686,000
Earnings: $136,947,000
Emp.: 12,942
Fiscal Year-end: 12/31/22
Holding Company; Recreational Ve-
hicle Dealerships Operator; Publish-
ing Services
N.A.I.C.S.: 551112
Marcus A. Lemonis (Chm & CEO)
Lindsey J. Christen (Chief Admin Offi-
cer, Chief Legal Officer & Sec)
Thomas E. Kirn (CFO & Principal
Acctg Officer)
Brett Andress (Sr VP-Corp Dev & IR)
Matthew D. Wagner (Pres)

Subsidiaries:

Active Sports, Inc. (1)
200 S Owasso Blvd, Saint Paul, MN 55117
Tel.: (651) 482-9995
Web Site: https://www.the-house.com
Recreational Vehicle Parts Whslr
N.A.I.C.S.: 423110
Logan Robbins (VP-Mktg & Strategy)

All Seasons RV & Marine (1)
63195 Jamison St, Bend, OR 97701-0000
Tel.: (360) 355-6067
Web Site: http://www.asrvm.com
Recreational Vehicle Dealers
N.A.I.C.S.: 441210

America Choice RV (1)
3040 NW Gainesville Rd, Ocala, FL 34475
Tel.: (352) 368-2451
Web Site: http://www.americachoicerv.com
Sales Range: $25-49.9 Million
Emp.: 98
Recreational Vehicle Dealers
N.A.I.C.S.: 441210
Cody Loughlin (Pres)

Arizona RV Centers, LLC (1)
3800 N Central Ave Ste 460, Phoenix, AZ
85012
Tel.: (480) 964-6616
Recreational Vehicle Parts Whslr
N.A.I.C.S.: 423110

B&B RV, Inc. (1)
8101 E 40th Ave, Denver, CO 80207
Tel.: (303) 322-6013
Web Site: https://bb-rv.com
Commercial Vehicle Rental Services
N.A.I.C.S.: 532111

Blaine Jensen RV Centers, LLC (1)
780 N Kays Dr, Kaysville, UT 84037
Tel.: (801) 544-4298
Emp.: 100
Recreational Vehicle Parts Whslr
N.A.I.C.S.: 423110

Bodily RV, Inc. (1)
1580 W Overland Rd, Meridian, ID 83642
Tel.: (208) 888-4241
Recreational Vehicle Parts Whslr
N.A.I.C.S.: 423110

Burnside RV Centers, LLC (1)
2735 W Houghton Lake Dr, Houghton Lake,
MI 48629
Tel.: (989) 366-8988
Recreational Vehicle Parts Whslr
N.A.I.C.S.: 423110

Camping World RV Sales, LLC (1)
8877 Interstate 70 Dr Ne, Columbia, MO
65202
Tel.: (573) 303-3490
Recreational Vehicle Parts Whslr
N.A.I.C.S.: 423110

Camping World of Davenport (1)
14040 110th Ave, Davenport, IA 52804-
9515
Web Site: https://rv.campingworld.com
Recreational Vehicle Dealers
N.A.I.C.S.: 441210

Camping World, Inc. (1)
650 Three Springs Rd, Bowling Green, KY
42104
Tel.: (270) 781-2718
Recreational Vehicle Parts Distr
N.A.I.C.S.: 423110
Marcus A. Lemonis (Pres & CEO)
Stephen Adams (Chm)

**Cullum & Maxey Camping Center,
Inc.** (1)
250 Pkwy Dr Ste 270, Lincolnshire, IL
60069-4346
Tel.: (615) 889-1600
Recreational Facilities & Services
N.A.I.C.S.: 721214

Dar-Kim, Inc. (1)
3300 Colusa Hwy, Yuba City, CA 95993
Tel.: (530) 671-9070
Web Site:
http://www.allseasonsrvcenter.com
Sales Range: $10-24.9 Million
Emp.: 30
Recreational Vehicle Dealers
N.A.I.C.S.: 441210
Ernie Friesen (Pres)
Darrel Friesen (Pres)

Dustys Camper World, LLC (1)
7400 State Rd 60 E, Bartow, FL 33830
Tel.: (866) 906-9517
Recreational Vehicle Parts Whslr
N.A.I.C.S.: 423110

Foley RV Center, LLC (1)

Camping World Holdings, Inc.—(Continued)

11063 Hwy 49, Gulfport, MS 39503
Tel.: (228) 832-7544
Web Site: https://www.foleyrvcenter.com
Recreational Vehicle Parts Whslr
N.A.I.C.S.: 423110

FreedomRoads, LLC (1)
250 Prkwy Dr Ste 270, Lincolnshire, IL
60069
Tel.: (847) 808-3000
Web Site: http://www.campingworld.com
Sales Range: $10-24.9 Million
Emp.: 350
Holding Company; Recreational Vehicle
Dealer
N.A.I.C.S.: 551112
Marcus A. Lemonis (Chm, Pres & CEO)

Golf Card International, LLC (1)
5735 Highway 85 N, Crestview, FL 32536
Web Site: https://www.golfcard.com
Golf Training Services
N.A.I.C.S.: 713910

Good Sam Enterprises, LLC (1)
250 Parkway Dr Ste 270, Lincolnshire, IL
60069-4346 (100%)
Tel.: (847) 229-6720
Web Site: https://www.goodsam.com
Traveler Discount Services
N.A.I.C.S.: 551112
Marcus A. Lemonis (Chm & CEO)
Stephen Adams (Chm)

Subsidiary (Domestic):

CWI, Inc. (2)
650 Three Springs Rd, Bowling Green, KY
42101
Tel.: (847) 808-3000
Web Site: http://www.campingworld.com
Sales Range: $75-99.9 Million
Emp.: 600
Recreational Vehicle Dealer & Accessories
Retailer
N.A.I.C.S.: 441210
Marcus A. Lemonis (Chm & CEO)

Nelson's RV'S, Inc. (1)
5309 Chinden Blvd, Boise, ID 83714
Tel.: (208) 287-3234
Web Site: http://www.nelsonsrvs.com
Truck Shop, On-site Hitch & Accessories
Installations
N.A.I.C.S.: 441210

RV World of Georgia, LLC (1)
2289 E Rock Quarry Rd, Buford, GA 30519-
4291
Tel.: (770) 945-2112
Web Site: http://www.rvworldofgeorgia.com
Recreational Vehicle Whslr
N.A.I.C.S.: 441210

RV World, LLC (1)
925 Lone Tree Ln, Nunn, CO 80648
Tel.: (970) 897-2770
Web Site: https://rvworldllc.net
Recreational Vehicle Rental Services
N.A.I.C.S.: 532120

Roy Robinson, Inc. (1)
15855 Smokey Point Blvd, Marysville, WA
98271
Tel.: (360) 659-6236
Web Site: http://www.royrobinson.com
Rev.: $75,000,000
Emp.: 120
Owner & Operator of Car Dealerships
N.A.I.C.S.: 441110
Debbie Christensen (Office Mgr)
Gordon E. Bjorg Sr. (Pres)

Southwest RV Centers, LLC (1)
27905 Katy Fwy, Katy, TX 77494
Tel.: (281) 693-2800
Emp.: 7
Recreational Vehicle Parts Whslr
N.A.I.C.S.: 423110

**Tom Johnson Camping Center Char-
lotte, Inc.** (1)
6700 Bruton Smith Blvd, Concord, NC
28027
Tel.: (704) 455-1440
Recreational Vehicle Parts Whslr
N.A.I.C.S.: 423110

W82, LLC (1)

3317 N Clark St, Chicago, IL 60657
Tel.: (888) 706-0090
Web Site: http://www.w82.com
Online Shopping Services
N.A.I.C.S.: 541512

Wheeler RV Las Vegas, LLC (1)
13175 Las Vegas Blvd S, Las Vegas, NV
89044
Tel.: (702) 896-9000
Recreational Vehicle Parts Whslr
N.A.I.C.S.: 423110

CAN B CORP.
960 S Broadway Ste 118, Hicksville,
NY 11801
Tel.: (516) 205-4751 FL
Web Site: https://www.canbcorp.com
Year Founded: 2005
CANB—(NASDAQ)
Rev.: $6,685,519
Assets: $15,559,791
Liabilities: $12,861,866
Net Worth: $2,697,925
Earnings: ($14,924,175)
Emp.: 20
Fiscal Year-end: 12/31/22
Hemp Products Mfr
N.A.I.C.S.: 621511
Marco Alfonsi (CEO & Chm)
Stanley L. Teeple (CFO & Sec)

Subsidiaries:

Duramed, LLC (1)
1015 24th St, Kenner, LA 70062
Tel.: (504) 467-4057
Web Site: https://www.duramedinc.org
Medical Equipment Distr
N.A.I.C.S.: 423450

Pure Health Products, LLC (1)
960 S Broadway Ste 120, Hicksville, NY
11801
Web Site:
https://www.purehealthproductsllc.com
Medical Equipment Mfr
N.A.I.C.S.: 339112

CANANDAIGUA NATIONAL
CORPORATION
72 S Main St, Canandaigua, NY
14424
Tel.: (585) 394-4260 NY
Web Site: https://www.cnbank.com
Year Founded: 1984
CNND—(OTCIQ)
Rev.: $184,969,000
Assets: $3,635,357,000
Liabilities: $3,339,610,000
Net Worth: $295,747,000
Earnings: $42,265,000
Emp.: 549
Fiscal Year-end: 12/31/20
Bank Holding Company
N.A.I.C.S.: 551111
Michael C. Goonan (Chm)
Frank H. Hamlin III (Pres & CEO)
Daniel P. Fuller (Vice Chm)
Karen C. Serinis (Exec VP-Retail
Banking & Mktg)
Sam Guerrieri (Exec VP-Wealth
Brands)
Annette Joyce (Exec VP-IT & Project
Mgmt)
Brian Pasley (Officer-CRA, Exec VP
& Mgr-Consumer Lending)
A. Rosamond Zatyko (Chief Admin
Officer & Exec VP)
Charles J. Vita (Chief Lending Officer
& Exec VP)
Vincent K. Yacuzzo (CFO, Treas &
Exec VP)
Jennifer N. Weidner (Gen Counsel,
Sec & Sr VP)

Subsidiaries:

Home Town Funding, Inc. (1)
72 S Main St, Canandaigua, NY 14424-
1905
Tel.: (585) 394-9100

Web Site: http://www.cnbank.com
Rev.: $407,177
Emp.: 5
Mortgage Bankers & Correspondents
N.A.I.C.S.: 522310

**The Canandaigua National Bank &
Trust Company** (1)
72 S Main St, Canandaigua, NY 14424-
1905
Tel.: (585) 394-4260
Web Site: http://www.cnbank.com
Sales Range: $50-74.9 Million
Emp.: 250
Savings, Loans, Commercial & Investment
Banking Services
N.A.I.C.S.: 522110
Michael C. Goonan (Chm)
Frank H. Hamlin III (Pres & CEO)
Linda Thompson (VP)
Dan Linehan (VP & Mgr-Banking Ops)
John Richardson (VP)
Steven Benz (VP & Mgr-Community Office)
Eric Koehler (VP/Mgr-Customer Rels-
Comml Svcs Team)
Brendon Crossing (Mgr-Customer Rels)
Greig Holman (Program Mgr-Vendor & Bus
Continuity)
Deborah Cragg (Chief Info Security Officer
& Sr VP)
Alex Broccuto (VP & Mgr-Customer Rels-
Comml Svcs)
Greg Helmer (VP & Mgr-Customer Rels-
Comml Svcs)
Brett Rawlings (VP & Mgr-Customer Rels-
Comml Svcs)
Andrew Murray (VP-Wealth Adviser)
Melissa DeSain (Asst VP)
Amy Force (Asst VP)
Harry Gibbs (Asst VP)
Laurie Haelen (Sr VP & Mgr-Investments &
Fin Plng Solutions)

CANCER CAPITAL CORP.
2157 S Lincoln St Ste 200, Salt Lake
City, UT 84106
Tel.: (801) 323-2395 WY
Year Founded: 1997
CNCL—(OTCIQ)
Assets: $16,157
Liabilities: $465,549
Net Worth: ($449,392)
Earnings: ($37,792)
Fiscal Year-end: 12/31/23
Investment Services
N.A.I.C.S.: 523999

CANCER TREATMENT HOLD-
INGS, INC.
202 N Curry St Ste 100, Carson City,
NV 89703
Tel.: (775) 885-9393 NV
CTHZ—(OTCIQ)
Healthcare Services
N.A.I.C.S.: 621610
Ullrich Klamm (Pres & CEO)

CANDEL THERAPEUTICS, INC.
117 Kendrick St Ste 450, Needham,
MA 02494
Tel.: (617) 916-5445 DE
Web Site: https://www.candeltx.com
Year Founded: 2003
CADL—(NASDAQ)
Rev.: $125,000
Assets: $77,601,000
Liabilities: $29,977,000
Net Worth: $47,714,000
Earnings: ($18,794,000)
Emp.: 76
Fiscal Year-end: 12/31/22
Research & Development in Biotech-
nology (except Nanobiotechnology)
N.A.I.C.S.: 541714
William Garrett Nichols (Chief Medi-
cal Officer)
Paul Peter Tak (Pres & CEO)
Estuardo Aguilar-Cordova (Founder)
Nathan Caffo (Chief Bus Officer)
Susan Stewart (Chief Regulatory Offi-
cer)

Chris Matheny (VP-Dev Leader)
Ileen Winick (Chief People Officer)
Francesca Barone (VP & Head Re-
search)
Paul B. Manning (Chm)

CANDLEWOOD HOTEL COM-
PANY, INC.
8621 E 21st St N Ste 200, Wichita,
KS 67206
Tel.: (316) 631-1300 DE
CNDL—(OTCIQ)
Hotel & Motel Services
N.A.I.C.S.: 721110
Jack A. DeBoer (Pres & CEO)
Warren A. Fix (CFO & Sec)

CANN AMERICAN CORP
75 Union Ave, Rutherford, NJ 07070
Tel.: (551) 285-4350 WY
Year Founded: 2004
CNNA—(OTCEM)
Assets: $1,191,191
Liabilities: $243,555
Net Worth: $947,636
Earnings: ($264,581)
Emp.: 40
Fiscal Year-end: 02/29/12
Holding Company
N.A.I.C.S.: 551112

CANNA-GLOBAL ACQUISI-
TION CORP.
4640 Admiralty Way Ste 500, Marina
Del Rey, CA 90292
Tel.: (310) 496-5700 DE
Year Founded: 2021
CNGL—(NASDAQ)
Rev.: $2,772,773
Assets: $24,685,529
Liabilities: $32,379,430
Net Worth: ($7,693,901)
Earnings: $1,159,838
Emp.: 2
Fiscal Year-end: 12/31/22
Investment Services
N.A.I.C.S.: 523999
Sharwin Sinnan (CFO)
Christine Cho (Chm-Audit Committee)
J. Gerald Combs (CEO)

CANNABIS BIOSCIENCE IN-
TERNATIONAL HOLDINGS,
INC.
6201 Bonhomme Rd Ste 466-S,
Houston, TX 77036
Tel.: (214) 733-0868 CO
Year Founded: 2003
CBIH—(OTC)
Rev.: $248,841
Assets: $57,162
Liabilities: $1,136,175
Net Worth: ($1,079,013)
Earnings: ($651,345)
Emp.: 2
Fiscal Year-end: 05/31/24
Biotechnology Research & Develop-
ment Services
N.A.I.C.S.: 541714

CANNABIS SATIVA, INC.
355 W Mesquite Blvd Ste C70, Mes-
quite, NV 89027
Tel.: (702) 762-3123 NV
Web Site: https://www.cbds.com
Year Founded: 2004
CBDS—(OTCQB)
Rev.: $1,173,830
Assets: $2,020,554
Liabilities: $1,263,163
Net Worth: $757,391
Earnings: ($1,322,917)
Fiscal Year-end: 12/31/23
Herbal Skin Care Products

N.A.I.C.S.: 325620
David M. Tobias *(Chm, Pres, CEO & Sec)*
Catherine J. Carroll *(Treas)*

CANNABIST CO HOLDINGS INC.

680 5th Ave Fl 24, New York, NY 10019
Tel.: (212) 271-0915   BC
Year Founded: 2013
CBSTF—(OTC)
N.A.I.C.S.: 551112
Jesse Channon *(Pres)*
David Hart *(CEO)*
Derek Watson *(CFO)*
Lee Ann Evans *(Sr VP)*
Bryan Olson *(Chief HR Officer)*
David Sirolly *(Chief Legal Officer)*
Michael Abbott *(Chm)*

CANNAE HOLDINGS, INC.

1701 Village Center Cir, Las Vegas, NV 89134
Tel.: (702) 323-7330   DE
Web Site:
https://www.cannaeholdings.com
Year Founded: 2014
CNNE—(NYSE)
Rev.: $570,000,000
Assets: $2,686,700,000
Liabilities: $377,500,000
Net Worth: $2,309,200,000
Earnings: ($313,400,000)
Emp.: 7,741
Fiscal Year-end: 12/31/23
Holding Company
N.A.I.C.S.: 551112
Michael L. Gravelle *(Gen Counsel, Sec & Exec VP)*
Ryan R. Caswell *(Pres & Principal Exec Officer)*
Charles R. Curley *(Gen Counsel)*
Bryan D. Coy *(CFO, Principal Acctg Officer & Exec VP)*
Peter Sadowski *(Chief Legal Officer & Exec VP)*
Richard N. Massey *(Vice Chm)*
William P. Foley II *(Chm, CEO & Chief Investment Officer)*

Subsidiaries:

ABRH, LLC   (1)
3038 Sidco Dr, Nashville, TN 37204
Tel.: (615) 256-8500
Web Site:
https://www.restaurantgrowthservices.com
Gaming Lodging & Restaurant Services
N.A.I.C.S.: 721120
W. Craig Barber *(CEO)*
Robert Langford *(Chief Concept Officer)*
Ashley Berland *(Sr VP)*
Kara Jacobs *(CFO)*
Clint Lautenschleger *(Chief People Officer)*

The Dun & Bradstreet Corporation   (1)
103 JFK Pkwy, Short Hills, NJ 07078
Tel.: (973) 921-5500
Web Site: http://www.dnb.com
Business Information, Publishing & Marketing Services
N.A.I.C.S.: 519290
Tim Solms *(Gen Mgr-Govt Segment)*
Gary Kotovets *(Chief Data Officer)*
Brian Hipsher *(CFO & Treas)*
Colleen Haley *(Sec)*
Virginia Green Gomez *(Chief Product Officer)*
Michael Manos *(CTO)*
Anthony M. Jabbour *(CEO)*
Anthony Pietrontone Jr. *(Principal Acctg Officer & Controller)*

Subsidiary (Domestic):

AllBusiness.com, Inc.   (2)
650 Townsend St Ste 450, San Francisco, CA 94103
Tel.: (415) 694-5000
Web Site: http://www.allbusiness.com

Sales Range: $25-49.9 Million
Emp.: 40
Business Resource Website Operator
N.A.I.C.S.: 513199

Corinthian Leasing Corporation   (2)
103 John F Kennedy Pkwy, Short Hills, NJ 07078-2708
Tel.: (973) 921-5500
Office Machinery Rental & Leasing Services
N.A.I.C.S.: 532420

D&B Acquisition Corp.   (2)
12194 Monaco Dr, Brighton, CO 80602
Tel.: (303) 909-4502
Financial Investment Services
N.A.I.C.S.: 523999

Subsidiary (Non-US):

D&B Europe Limited   (2)
The Point 37 North Wharf Road, London, W2 1AF, Buckinghamshire, United Kingdom
Tel.: (44) 1628492109
Web Site: http://www.db.com
Management Consulting Services
N.A.I.C.S.: 541618
Janets Storle *(Mgr-IT & HR)*

D&B Group Holdings (UK)   (2)
The Point 37 North Wharf Road, London, W2 1AF, Buckinghamshire, United Kingdom
Tel.: (44) 1628492342
Investment Management Service
N.A.I.C.S.: 551112

D&B Holdings Australia Limited   (2)
The Point 37 North Wharf Road, London, W2 1AF, United Kingdom
Tel.: (44) 1628492000
Web Site: http://www.dnb.co.uk
Emp.: 400
Investment Management Service
N.A.I.C.S.: 551112

Subsidiary (Domestic):

D&B Management Services Co.   (2)
103 JFK Pkwy, Short Hills, NJ 07078-2708
Tel.: (973) 921-5500
Web Site: http://www.schooldata.com
Holding Company
N.A.I.C.S.: 551112

D&B Sales & Marketing Solutions   (2)
460 Totten Pond Rd, Waltham, MA 02451
Tel.: (781) 672-9200
Sales Range: $10-24.9 Million
Emp.: 30
Computer Software Development
N.A.I.C.S.: 541511

Subsidiary (Non-US):

DBXB Netherlands B.V.   (2)
Stationsplein 45 4th floor C, 3013 AK, Rotterdam, Netherlands
Tel.: (31) 107109400
Web Site: http://www.dnb-nederland.nl
Emp.: 25
Management Consulting Services
N.A.I.C.S.: 541618

DBXB S.r.l.   (2)
48 Via Valtorta, 20127, Milan, Italy
Tel.: (39) 022814941
Management Consulting Services
N.A.I.C.S.: 541618

Dun & Bradstreet (HK) Ltd.   (2)
13/F BEA Tower Millennium City 5, 418 Kwun Tong Rd, Kwun Tong, Kowloon, China (Hong Kong)
Tel.: (852) 25161111
Web Site: https://www.dnb.com.hk
Sales Range: $25-49.9 Million
Emp.: 100
Credit Services
N.A.I.C.S.: 561450
Thomas Tam *(Controller)*

Dun & Bradstreet (Israel) Ltd.   (2)
53 Derech Hashalom St, Givatayim, 5345433, Israel
Tel.: (972) 37330330
Web Site: https://www.dbisrael.co.il
Sales Range: $25-49.9 Million
Emp.: 150
Credit Services

N.A.I.C.S.: 561450

Dun & Bradstreet (Singapore) Pte. Ltd.   (2)
6 Shenton Way OUE Downtown 2 17-10, Singapore, 068809, Singapore
Tel.: (65) 65656161
Web Site: https://www.dnb.com.sg
Sales Range: $100-124.9 Million
Business Information Services
N.A.I.C.S.: 519290

Dun & Bradstreet (Vietnam) LLC   (2)
Unit 2104 Floor 21 Saigon Trade Center, 37 Ton Duc Thang District 1, Ho Chi Minh City, Vietnam
Tel.: (84) 839117288
Web Site: http://www.dnb.com
Management Consulting Services
N.A.I.C.S.: 541611
Nhi Le Thi Phuong *(Dir-Bus Dev)*

Dun & Bradstreet B.V.   (2)
Otto Reuchlinweg 1032, 3072 MD, Rotterdam, Netherlands
Tel.: (31) 107109400
Web Site: http://www.dnb-nederland.nl
Sales Range: $25-49.9 Million
Emp.: 100
Business Information Services
N.A.I.C.S.: 519290
D. Tebbitt *(Mgr-Site)*

Dun & Bradstreet Belgium N.V.   (2)
Inter Access Park Pontbeekstraat 4, Dilbeek, 1702, Brussels, Belgium
Tel.: (32) 24818300
Web Site: http://www.dnb.com
Sales Range: $10-24.9 Million
Emp.: 40
Business Information Services
N.A.I.C.S.: 519290
Coraline van Hoeymissen *(Dir-HR)*

Dun & Bradstreet CIS   (2)
3rd Khoroshevsky Proyezd 1 corpus 1, 123007, Moscow, Russia
Tel.: (7) 959401816
Web Site: http://www.dnb.ru
Sales Range: $10-24.9 Million
Emp.: 15
N.A.I.C.S.: 561450

Dun & Bradstreet Canada BV   (2)
Otto Reuchlinweg 1032, Rotterdam, 3072 MD, Netherlands
Tel.: (31) 107109400
Web Site: http://www.dnb-netherlands.com
Emp.: 120
Management Consulting Services
N.A.I.C.S.: 541611
Darren Tebbitt *(Gen Mgr)*

Dun & Bradstreet Canada Ltd.   (2)
B1-5770 Hurontario St, Mississauga, L5R 3G5, ON, Canada
Tel.: (800) 668-3033
Web Site: http://www.dnb.ca
Information Services
N.A.I.C.S.: 519290
Jenal Embry *(VP-Supply Chain Solutions)*
Brian Alster *(Global Head-of Supply & Compliance Product)*
Nipa Basu *(Chief Analytics Officer)*
Ilio Krumins-Beens *(Global Head-PMO)*
Daniel Sherman *(Dir-Vulnerability Mgmt)*

Subsidiary (Domestic):

Dun & Bradstreet Credibility Corp.   (2)
22761 Pacific Coast Hwy Ste 226, Malibu, CA 90265
Tel.: (424) 644-0601
Web Site: http://www.dandb.com
Emp.: 575
Credit Monitoring Services
N.A.I.C.S.: 522390

Dun & Bradstreet Europe, Ltd.   (2)
103 JFK Pkwy, Short Hills, NJ 07078
Tel.: (973) 921-5500
Web Site: http://www.dunandbradstreet.com
Management Consulting Services
N.A.I.C.S.: 541611

Subsidiary (Non-US):

Dun & Bradstreet Information Services India Pvt Ltd.   (2)

iSprout Business Center 5th Floor Kochar Jade PLOT NO SP 22, T-S No 25 SIDCO Industrial Estate Guindy, Chennai, 600032, India
Tel.: (91) 2228574190
Web Site: http://www.dnb.com
Sales Range: $75-99.9 Million
Emp.: 350
Information Services
N.A.I.C.S.: 519290

Dun & Bradstreet International Consultant (Shanghai) Ltd.   (2)
9th Floor Building 6 Hongqiao Vanke Center No 988 Shenchang Road, 318 Fu Zhou Road, Shanghai, 200001, China
Tel.: (86) 2123213636
Web Site: https://www.dnbchina.com
Sales Range: $50-74.9 Million
Emp.: 200
Credit Bureau Services
N.A.I.C.S.: 561450

Dun & Bradstreet Investments Limited   (2)
The Point 37 North Wharf Road, London, W2 1AF, Buckinghamshire, United Kingdom
Tel.: (44) 1628492319
Web Site: http://www.dnb.co.uk
Investment Management Service
N.A.I.C.S.: 523999

Dun & Bradstreet Ltd.   (2)
The Point 37 North Wharf Road, London, W2 1AF, Buckinghamshire, United Kingdom
Tel.: (44) 1628492000
Web Site: https://www.dnb.co.uk
Sales Range: $75-99.9 Million
Emp.: 400
Business Information Services
N.A.I.C.S.: 519290

Subsidiary (Domestic):

Dun & Bradstreet NetProspex   (2)
300 3rd Ave, Waltham, MA 02451
Tel.: (888) 826-4877
Web Site: http://www.netprospex.com
B2B Business & Marketing Services
N.A.I.C.S.: 561499

Subsidiary (Non-US):

Dun & Bradstreet SpA   (2)
Via Dei Valtorta 48, 20127, Milan, Italy
Tel.: (39) 02284551
Web Site: http://www.dnb.it
Sales Range: $75-99.9 Million
Emp.: 300
Credit Services
N.A.I.C.S.: 561450

Dun & Bradstreet Technologies & Data Services Private Limited   (2)
Level 9 Prince Info City Phase 1 286/1, Kandanchavadi Rajiv Gandhi Salai OMR, Chennai, 600 096, India
Tel.: (91) 4466779999
Internet Service Provider
N.A.I.C.S.: 517121

Subsidiary (Domestic):

Dun & Bradstreet, Inc. - Credit Services   (2)
400 Penn Ctr Blvd, Pittsburgh, PA 15235
Tel.: (412) 829-3731
Sales Range: $125-149.9 Million
Business Credit Management
N.A.I.C.S.: 522390

Duns Investing Corporation   (2)
801 N West St Fl 2, Wilmington, DE 19801-1525
Tel.: (302) 656-8981
Investment Management Service
N.A.I.C.S.: 523940

Dunsnet, LLC   (2)
189 S Orange Ave Ste 1500 S, Orlando, FL 32801
Tel.: (407) 476-9854
Web Site: https://www.dunsnet.com
Financial Transaction Services
N.A.I.C.S.: 522320

First Research, Inc.   (2)
7700 W Parmer Ln Bldg A, Austin, TX 78729
Tel.: (512) 380-4808

Cannae Holdings, Inc.—(Continued)

Web Site: https://www.firstresearch.com
Sales Range: $1-9.9 Million
Emp.: 14
Industry Analysis & Marketing Products & Services
N.A.I.C.S.: 513199

Hoover's, Inc.   (2)
5800 Airport Blvd, Austin, TX 78752-4204
Tel.: (512) 374-4500
Web Site: http://www.hoovers.com
Sales Range: $50-74.9 Million
Emp.: 231
Publisher of Business Information
N.A.I.C.S.: 541990

Subsidiary (Domestic):

Visible Path Corp.   (3)
181 Metro Dr Ste 290, San Jose, CA
95110-1344
Tel.: (650) 356-2254
Sales Range: $10-24.9 Million
Emp.: 30
Online Business Networking Solutions
N.A.I.C.S.: 513210
Stephen Charles Pusey (CMO)

Subsidiary (Domestic):

Lattice Engines, Inc.   (2)
1825 S Grant Ave Ste 510, San Mateo, CA
94402
Tel.: (877) 460-0010
Web Site: http://www.lattice-engines.com
Sales Range: $1-9.9 Million
Emp.: 40
Predictive Analytics to Sales & Marketing Consumers
N.A.I.C.S.: 513210
Shashi Upadhyay (CEO)
Kent McCormick (CTO)
Ian J. Scott (VP-Pro Svcs)
Scott Harralson (VP-Pro Svcs)
Jean-Paul Gomes (VP-Bus Dev)

Market Data Retrieval   (2)
5335 Gate Pkwy, Jacksonville, FL 32256
Tel.: (973) 921-5500
Web Site: https://www.mdreducation.com
Sales Range: $25-49.9 Million
Emp.: 166
School Marketing Information & Services
N.A.I.C.S.: 541910

Purisma, Inc.   (2)
2211 Bridgepointe Pkwy Ste 300, San Mateo, CA 94404
Tel.: (650) 350-3500
Web Site: http://www.purisma.com
Sales Range: $25-49.9 Million
Emp.: 15
Data Management Services
N.A.I.C.S.: 541511

Subsidiary (Non-US):

Shanghai Huaxia Dun & Bradstreet
Business Information Consulting Co.,
Limited   (2)
Unit 907-910 Cross Tower 318 Fu Zhou
Road, Shanghai, 200001, China
Tel.: (86) 2123213636
Web Site: http://www.huaxiadnb.com
Commercial Information Consulting Services
N.A.I.C.S.: 541611

The D&B Companies of Canada
Ltd.   (2)
6750 Century Ave Suite 305, Mississauga,
L5N 0B7, ON, Canada
Tel.: (800) 668-3033
Web Site: http://www.dnb.com
Management Consulting Services
N.A.I.C.S.: 541611

Subsidiary (Domestic):

coAction.com LLC   (2)
300 Carnegie Dr, Princeton, NJ 08540
Web Site: http://www.coaction.com
Sales Range: $1-9.9 Million
Business Collaboration Software
N.A.I.C.S.: 513210
Jagdish Talreja (CEO)

CANNAGISTICS, INC.

1200 Veterans Hwy Memorial Ste
310, Hauppauge, NY 11788
Tel.: (631) 676-7230   NV
Web Site: https://www.cannagistics.io
Year Founded: 2004
CNGT—(OTCIQ)
Rev.: $87,036
Assets: $45,007
Liabilities: $5,691,710
Net Worth: ($5,646,703)
Earnings: ($2,390,353)
Fiscal Year-end: 07/31/21
Colored Diamonds Purchaser & Distr
N.A.I.C.S.: 423940

CANNAGROW HOLDINGS, INC.

8101 E Prentice Ave Ste 500, Greenwood Village, CO 80111
Tel.: (720) 486-5309
Web Site:
    http://cannagrowholdings.com
CGRW—(OTCIQ)
Rev.: $1,011,000
Assets: $3,417,000
Liabilities: $6,391,000
Net Worth: ($2,974,000)
Earnings: ($136,000)
Fiscal Year-end: 12/31/19
Cannabis Mfr.
N.A.I.C.S.: 325411
Delmar A. Janovec (CEO)
John P. Janovec (COO)
Brent Edward Crouch (CFO)
Jason Wells (Mgr-Production)

CANNAPOWDER, INC.

2170 Century Park E 210, Los Angeles, CA 90067
Tel.: (212) 400-7198   NV
Web Site: http://www.cannapowder.com
Year Founded: 1999
CAPD—(OTCIQ)
Assets: $281,775
Liabilities: $665,528
Net Worth: ($383,753)
Earnings: ($2,768,008)
Emp.: 2
Fiscal Year-end: 12/31/19
Drug Mfr & Distr
N.A.I.C.S.: 325412
Oded Gilboa (CFO)
Shai Cohen (Chm & CEO)

CANNONAU CORP.

937 Old Senecca Tpke Rd, Skaneateles, NY 13252-9318
Tel.: (315) 740-8013   NV
Web Site: https://pbec.biz
Year Founded: 2007
CNNC—(OTCIQ)
Rev.: $227
Assets: $9,025
Liabilities: $347,261
Net Worth: ($338,236)
Earnings: ($85,950)
Emp.: 4
Fiscal Year-end: 12/31/22
Clean & Renewable Power
N.A.I.C.S.: 221118

CANO HEALTH, INC.

9725 NW 117 Ave, Miami, FL 33178
Tel.: (203) 422-7718   Ky
Web Site:
    https://www.canohealth.com
Year Founded: 2019
CANO—(NYSE)
Rev.: $2,738,916,000
Assets: $1,928,927,000
Liabilities: $1,434,652,000
Net Worth: $494,275,000
Earnings: ($428,389,000)
Emp.: 4,365
Fiscal Year-end: 12/31/22

Miscellaneous Financial Investment
Activities
N.A.I.C.S.: 523999
Mark deMarquette Kent (CEO)
Michael Racich (CFO)
Marlow Hernandez (Founder)
Richard Aguilar (Chief Clinical Officer)
David Armstrong (Chief Compliance
Officer & Gen Counsel)
Pedro Cordero (Chief Population
Health Officer)
Jennifer Hevia (Chief People Officer)
Robert Camerlinck (COO)
Joel Lago (Sr VP-Acq)
Barbara Ferreiro (Chief Brand Officer)
Amy Charley (Chief Admin Officer)
Mark Kent (Chief Strategy Officer)

Subsidiaries:

Cano Health, LLC   (1)
9725 NW 117 Ave, Miami, FL 33178
Web Site: http://www.canohealth.com
Health Care Srvices
N.A.I.C.S.: 621610
Richard B. Aguilar (Chief Clinical Officer)
John McGoohan (Chief Strategy Officer)
Jennifer Fernandez (Chief People Officer)
Barbara Ferreiro (CMO)

CANOO INC.

19951 Mariner Ave, Torrance, CA
90503
Tel.: (424) 271-2144   DE
Web Site: https://www.canoo.com
GOEV—(NASDAQ)
Assets: $496,472,000
Liabilities: $259,899,000
Net Worth: $236,573,000
Earnings: ($487,694,000)
Emp.: 812
Fiscal Year-end: 12/31/22
Electric Lifestyle, Sport & Working
Vehicles
N.A.I.C.S.: 336110
Ken Manget (Pres)
Greg Ethridge (CFO)
Tony Aquila (Chm & CEO)
Ramesh Murthy (Chief Acctg Officer
& Sr VP-Fin)
Sohel Merchant (CTO)
Hector Ruiz (Gen Counsel & Sec)
Kunal Bhalla (Sr VP-Corp Dev, Corp.
Dev, and Corp Dev)
Jonathan Wolff (VP-Capital Markets
& Investor Relations)

CANSORTIUM INC.

82 NE 26th St, Miami, FL 33137
Tel.: (305) 902-2720
TIUM.U—(CNSX)
Medical Product Mfr & Distr
N.A.I.C.S.: 325411
Neal A. Hochberg (Chm)
Jeffrey Batliner (CFO)
Robert Beasley (CEO)

Subsidiaries:

RIV Capital Inc   (1)
40 King Street West Suite 3303, Toronto,
M5H 3Y2, ON, Canada
Tel.: (416) 583-5945
Web Site: https://www.rivcapital.com
Rev.: $7,250,000
Assets: $261,818,000
Liabilities: $152,971,000
Net Worth: $108,847,000
Earnings: ($179,259,000)
Emp.: 96
Fiscal Year-end: 03/31/2023
Venture Capital Funding Services
N.A.I.C.S.: 523910
Asha Daniere (Chm)
Eddie Lucarelli (CFO)
Mike Totzke (CEO)
Amanda Rico (Chief HR Officer)

CANTALOUPE, INC.

100 Deerfield Ln Ste 300, Malvern,
PA 19355

Tel.: (610) 989-0340   PA
Web Site:
    https://www.cantaloupe.com
Year Founded: 1992
CTLP—(NASDAQ)
Rev.: $268,596,000
Assets: $335,568,000
Liabilities: $151,102,000
Net Worth: $184,466,000
Earnings: $11,993,000
Emp.: 359
Fiscal Year-end: 06/30/24
Wireless, Cashless, Micro-
Transactions & Networking Services
N.A.I.C.S.: 522320
Davina Furnish (Gen Counsel)
Scott Stewart (CFO)
Ravi Venkatesan (CEO)
Jeff Dumbrell (Chief Revenue Officer)
Gaurav Singal (CTO)
Anna Novoseletsky (Chief Legal &
Compliance Officer, Gen Counsel &
Sec)
Jared Grachek (Chief Acctg Officer)

Subsidiaries:

Cantaloupe Systems Inc.   (1)
612 Howard St Ste 600, San Francisco, CA
94105
Tel.: (415) 525-8100
Vending Machine Sales Tracking
N.A.I.C.S.: 541618
Mandeep Arora (Founder)

Three Square Market Limited   (1)
Units 58/59 Coleshill Industrial Estates Station Road, West Midlands, Coleshill, B46
1JP, United Kingdom
Tel.: (44) 1156972008
Micro Market Vending Services
N.A.I.C.S.: 445132

Three Square Market, Inc.   (1)
3329 Casey St, River Falls, WI 54022
Tel.: (715) 386-2233
Web Site: https://www.32market-home.com
Micro Market Vending Services
N.A.I.C.S.: 445132

CANTERBURY PARK HOLDING CORPORATION

1100 Canterbury Rd, Shakopee, MN
55379
Tel.: (952) 445-7223   MN
Web Site:
    https://www.canterburypark.com
Year Founded: 2015
CPHC—(NASDAQ)
Rev.: $66,823,881
Assets: $92,276,179
Liabilities: $21,091,136
Net Worth: $71,185,043
Earnings: $7,512,946
Emp.: 241
Fiscal Year-end: 12/31/22
Holding Company; Racetrack Operator & Betting Services
N.A.I.C.S.: 551112
Michael D. Hochman (VP-Casino
Ops)
Jeff Maday (Mgr-Media Rels)
Mary B. Fleming (VP-HR)
Randy J. Dehmer (CFO & Sr VP)
Randall D. Sampson (Chm, Pres &
CEO)

Subsidiaries:

Canterbury Park Entertainment
LLC   (1)
1100 Canterbury Rd, Shakopee, MN 55379
Tel.: (952) 445-7223
Racetrack & Casino Operator
N.A.I.C.S.: 711212

Subsidiary (Domestic):

Canterbury Park Concessions,
Inc.   (2)
1100 Canterbury Rd S, Shakopee, MN
55379-1867
Tel.: (952) 445-7223

Food & Beverage Concession Stand Operating Services
N.A.I.C.S.: 722310

CANYON SILVER MINES, INC.
5595 Elder Rd, Ferndale, WA 98248
Tel.: (360) 303-7934
Year Founded: 1965
CANY—(OTCIQ)
Lead & Zinc Mining Services
N.A.I.C.S.: 212230
Stephen A. Morrow *(Pres)*

CAPITAL BANCORP, INC.
2275 Research Blvd Ste 600, Rockville, MA 20850
Tel.: (301) 468-8848   MD
Web Site: https://capitalbankmd.com
Year Founded: 1998
CBNK—(NASDAQ)
Bank Holding Company
N.A.I.C.S.: 551111

Subsidiaries:

Integrated Financial Holdings,
Inc.   (1)
8450 Falls of Neuse Rd Ste 204, Raleigh,
NC 27615
Tel.: (919) 948-1978
Web Site: https://www.westtownbank.com
Offices of Bank Holding Companies
N.A.I.C.S.: 551111
Eric John Bergevin *(Pres & CEO)*
Melissa Dawn Marsal *(COO & Exec VP)*
Kimberly B. Snyder *(CFO & Exec VP)*
Raymond J. Wengel *(Chief Risk Officer & Exec VP)*
James J. Kemp Jr. *(Gen Counsel)*

Subsidiary (Domestic):

Sound Bank   (2)
5039 Executive Dr, Morehead City, NC
28557
Tel.: (252) 727-5558
Web Site: http://www.soundbanking.com
Sales Range: $1-9.9 Million
Emp.: 30
Commericial Banking
N.A.I.C.S.: 522110
S. Phillip Collins *(Pres & CEO)*
Malcolm C. Garland *(Sr VP & Appraisal & Inspection Officer)*
Richard T. McIntyre *(Chief Banking Officer & Exec VP)*
Al Nelson *(CFO & Exec VP)*
Andrea Benton *(Chief Credit Officer & Exec VP)*
John Aldredge *(Sr VP & Controller)*
Christy Flynt *(Sr VP & Compliance Officer)*
Andrew Wheeler *(VP)*
Mark Gatlin *(VP-Craven County Market)*
Michael Carpenter *(VP-Onslow County Market)*
Bill Weinhold *(VP & Branch Mgr-Morehead City)*
Jody Smith *(VP & Branch Mgr-Beaufort)*
Shea Byrd *(Asst VP)*
DeAnna Bousman *(Asst VP & Mktg Mgr)*
Traci Ellingsworth *(Mgr-Loan Ops)*
Scott Eckholdt *(VP-Carteret County Market)*
Mark S. Johnson *(VP-New Hanover County Market)*
Janna Jackson *(Specialist-HR)*

West Town Bank & Trust   (2)
7820 W 26th St, North Riverside, IL 60546
Tel.: (708) 447-3330
Web Site: http://www.westtownbank.com
Emp.: 10
Commericial Banking
N.A.I.C.S.: 522110
Eric John Bergevin *(Pres & CEO)*
Melissa Dawn Marsal *(COO & Exec VP)*
Kimberly B. Snyder *(CFO & Exec VP)*
Raymond J. Wengel *(Chief Risk Officer & Exec VP)*
James J. Kemp Jr. *(Gen Counsel)*
A. Riddick Skinner *(Exec VP-Govt Lending)*
Kathryn Cuthrell *(Exec VP-Credit Dept)*
Aurora Castro *(Branch Mgr)*

CAPITAL CITY BANK GROUP, INC.

217 N Monroe St, Tallahassee, FL
32302
Tel.: (850) 402-7500   FL
Web Site: https://www.ccbg.com
Year Founded: 1982
CCBG—(NASDAQ)
Rev.: $225,975,000
Assets: $4,525,958,000
Liabilities: $4,131,942,000
Net Worth: $394,016,000
Earnings: $40,147,000
Emp.: 763
Fiscal Year-end: 12/31/22
Bank Holding Company
N.A.I.C.S.: 551111
William G. Smith Jr. *(Chm, Pres & CEO)*
Thomas A. Barron *(Treas)*
Jep Larkin *(CFO & Exec VP)*
Tom Allen *(Exec VP)*
Sharon Bradley *(Chief Diversity Officer)*
Marsha S. Crowle *(Exec VP)*
Randy Lashua *(Chief Retail Officer)*
Bill Moor *(Pres)*
Greg Shumate *(CEO)*
Ramsay Sims *(Chief Lending Officer)*
LeAnne Staalenburg *(Chief Information Security Officer)*
Cheryl Thompson *(Exec VP)*
Dale Thompson *(Chief Credit Officer)*

Subsidiaries:

Capital City Bank   (1)
217 N Monroe St, Tallahassee, FL 32302
Tel.: (850) 402-8490
Web Site: https://www.ccbg.com
Commercial Banking Services
N.A.I.C.S.: 522110
William G. Smith Jr. *(Chm)*
Thomas A. Barron *(Pres)*
Greg Shumate *(CEO-Home Loans)*
Bill Moor *(Pres-Investments)*
Dale Thompson *(Chief Credit Officer)*
LeAnne Staalenburg *(Chief Information Security Officer)*
Ramsay Sims *(Chief Lending Officer)*
Sharon Bradley *(Chief Diversity Officer)*
Pamela Gay *(Chief HR Officer)*

Subsidiary (Domestic):

Capital City Banc Investments,
Inc.   (2)
304 E Tennessee St Fl 2, Tallahassee, FL
32301
Tel.: (850) 402-7542
Web Site:
   https://www.capitalcityinvestments.com
Financial Investment Services
N.A.I.C.S.: 523999

Capital City Home Loans, LLC   (2)
1255 Lakes Pkwy Ste 300, Lawrenceville,
GA 30043   (51%)
Tel.: (770) 963-3044
Web Site: https://www.cchl.com
Emp.: 200
Real Estate Credit
N.A.I.C.S.: 522292
Greg Shumate *(CEO & Mng Dir)*
Alex Koutouzis *(Pres & Mng Partner)*

Capital City Trust Company   (2)
304 E Tennessee St, Tallahassee, FL
32301   (100%)
Web Site: https://www.ccbg.com
Emp.: 12
Fiduciary & Trust Services
N.A.I.C.S.: 523991
Bill Moor *(Pres)*
Anesta P. Boice *(Officer/Officer-Trust, Sr VP & VP)*
Seth Clark *(Sr VP & Portfolio Mgr)*
Dwayne Maddron *(Asst VP & Portfolio Mgr)*
Allie VanLandingham *(Officer-Trust & Asst VP)*
Shannon Weiler *(Officer-Trust & Asst VP)*
Lee Ebanks *(Officer-Trust)*
Rebeca Sayers *(Officer-Trust)*
Jennifer Anamoo *(Officer-Trust)*
Jeremy King *(VP)*
Mike O'Connor *(Sr VP)*
Dave Johnston *(Mng Dir-Trust Admin & Private Banking)*

CAPITAL DIRECTIONS, INC.
400 Northridge Rd Ste 350, Atlanta,
GA 30350
Tel.: (404) 237-8881   MI
Web Site: http://www.capdir.com
Year Founded: 1985
CTDN—(OTCIQ)
Financial Advisory Services
N.A.I.C.S.: 523940
John McMillen *(Chief Investment Officer)*
Dennis Covington *(CEO & Mng Dir-Advisor Svcs)*
Terry Hartigan *(Mng Dir-Private Wealth)*
Kate Pishnak *(Dir-HR)*
Katie Conroy *(Mgr-Client Svcs)*

CAPITAL FINANCIAL GLOBAL, INC.
5251 Green St Ste 250, Murray, UT
84123
Tel.: (801) 747-2000   NV
Web Site:
   https://www.capfiglobal.com
CFGX—(OTCIQ)
Other Financial Vehicles
N.A.I.C.S.: 525990
Paul Edward Norat *(Chm, Pres & CEO)*

CAPITAL FINANCIAL HOLD-INGS, INC.
1821 Burdick Expwy W, Minot, ND
58701
Tel.: (701) 837-9600   ND
Web Site:
   http://www.capitalfinancialhold
   ings.com
Year Founded: 1987
CPFH—(OTCIQ)
Sales Range: $10-24.9 Million
Emp.: 14
Financial Holding Company; Investment Advisory, Asset Management, Insurance Brokerage, Securities Brokerage & Dealing Services
N.A.I.C.S.: 551112
Gordon D. Dihle *(Chm & CEO)*

Subsidiaries:

Capital Financial Services, Inc.   (1)
1821 Burdick Expressway W, Minot, ND
58701   (100%)
Tel.: (701) 837-9600
Web Site: http://www.capfin.com
Sales Range: $50-74.9 Million
Emp.: 18
Investment Advisory, Asset Management, Insurance Brokerage, Securities Brokerage & Dealing Services
N.A.I.C.S.: 523940
Brandyn Hendrickson *(Mgr-Sls-Natl)*

CAPITAL GROUP HOLDINGS, INC.
16624 N 90th St Ste 200, Scottsdale,
AZ 85260
Tel.: (480) 998-2100
Web Site:
   http://www.capitalgrouphold
   ings.com
Year Founded: 1980
CGHC—(OTCIQ)
Sales Range: Less than $1 Million
Financial Services
N.A.I.C.S.: 523999

CAPITAL ONE FINANCIAL CORPORATION
1680 Capital One Dr, McLean, VA
22102
Tel.: (703) 720-1000   DE
Web Site:
   https://www.capitalone.com
Year Founded: 1994

COF—(NYSE)
Rev.: $38,373,000,000
Assets: $455,249,000,000
Liabilities: $402,667,000,000
Net Worth: $52,582,000,000
Earnings: $7,360,000,000
Emp.: 55,943
Fiscal Year-end: 12/31/22
Asset Management Services
N.A.I.C.S.: 551111
Sanjiv Yajnik *(Pres-Fin Svcs)*
Richard D. Fairbank *(Founder, Chm & CEO)*
Andrew Young *(CFO)*
Daniela Jorge *(Chief Design Officer & Sr VP)*

Subsidiaries:

Capital One Bank (USA), National
Association   (1)
4851 Cox Rd, Glen Allen, VA 23060
Tel.: (804) 934-2001
Web Site: http://www.capitalone.com
Credit Card & Credit Intermediation Services
N.A.I.C.S.: 522210
Richard D. Fairbank *(Chm)*

Subsidiary (Non-US):

Capital One Holdings Limited   (2)
Tel.: (44) 1159938002
Web Site: http://www.capitalone.co.uk
Sales Range: $125-149.9 Million
Financial Holding Company; Regional Managing Office
N.A.I.C.S.: 551111

Subsidiary (Non-US):

Capital One (Europe) plc   (3)
Tel.: (44) 1159938002
Web Site: https://www.capitalone.co.uk
Credit Card & Credit Intermediation Services
N.A.I.C.S.: 522210

Subsidiary (Non-US):

Capital One Services (Canada)
Inc.   (2)
5140 Yonge St 19th Fl, North York, M2N
6L7, ON, Canada
Tel.: (416) 549-2500
Web Site: http://www.capitalone.ca
Sales Range: $25-49.9 Million
Emp.: 68
Financial & Banking Services
N.A.I.C.S.: 525990

Capital One Multifamily Finance   (1)
7600 Wisconsin Ave Ste 800, Bethesda,
MD 20814
Tel.: (240) 507-1901
Web Site:
   http://www.capitalonemultifamily.com
Sales Range: $25-49.9 Million
Emp.: 150
Commercial Real Estate Lender
N.A.I.C.S.: 522310

Capital One, N.A.   (1)
15000 Capital One Dr, Richmond, VA
23238
Tel.: (703) 720-1000
Web Site: http://www.capitalonebank.com
Retail & Commercial Banking
N.A.I.C.S.: 522110
Sanjiv Yajnik *(Pres)*
Richard D. Fairbank *(Chm)*

Joint Venture (Domestic):

clearXchange, LLC   (2)
333 Market St 26th Fl, San Francisco, CA
94105
Tel.: (415) 371-4111
Financial Management Services
N.A.I.C.S.: 541611
Michael Kennedy *(CEO)*
Michael J. Kennedy *(Co-Founder)*

Monsoon Company   (1)
350 Frank H Ogawa Plz Ste 100, Oakland,
CA 94612-2015
Tel.: (510) 991-7425
Web Site: http://www.monsoonco.com
Custom Computer Programming Services
N.A.I.C.S.: 541511

Capital Properties, Inc.—(Continued)

CAPITAL PROPERTIES, INC.
5 Steeple St Unit 303, Providence, RI 02903
Tel.: (401) 435-7171   RI
Web Site:
https://www.capitalpropertiesinc.com
CPTP—(OTCQX)
Rev.: $5,525,000
Assets: $8,947,000
Liabilities: $1,356,000
Net Worth: $7,591,000
Earnings: $2,327,000
Emp.: 2
Fiscal Year-end: 12/31/23
Real Estate Development Services;
Petroleum Storage
N.A.I.C.S.: 531190
Robert H. Eder *(Chm, Pres & CEO)*
Susan R. Johnson *(CFO, Principal Acctg Officer & Treas)*

Subsidiaries:

Capital Terminal Company   (1)
100 Dexter Rd, East Providence, RI
02914-2005   (100%)
Tel.: (401) 435-3734
Web Site: http://www.capitalterminal.com
Sales Range: $25-49.9 Million
Emp.: 6
Petroleum Storage Facility
N.A.I.C.S.: 493190

Tri-State Displays Inc.   (1)
100 Dexter Rd, East Providence, RI
02914-2005   (100%)
Tel.: (401) 435-7171
Lessor of Roadside Billboards
N.A.I.C.S.: 531210

CAPITAL SOUTHWEST CORPORATION
8333 Douglas Ave Ste 1100, Dallas, TX 75225
Tel.: (214) 238-5700   TX
Web Site:
https://www.capitalsouthwest.com
Year Founded: 1961
CSWC—(NASDAQ)
Rev.: $178,135,000
Assets: $1,556,758,000
Liabilities: $801,082,000
Net Worth: $755,676,000
Earnings: $110,005,000
Emp.: 27
Fiscal Year-end: 03/31/24
Venture Capital Investment Services
N.A.I.C.S.: 523999
Bowen S. Diehl *(Pres & CEO)*
Douglas M. Kelley *(Mng Dir)*
Michael S. Sarner *(CFO)*
Joshua S. Weinstein *(Sr Mng Dir)*
Rayn Kelly *(Principal)*
Chris Rehberger *(Treas & VP-Fin)*
Amy Baker *(Controller)*
Ally Benson *(Asst Controller)*
Grant Eason *(VP)*
Rachel Bazan *(VP)*
Spencer Klein *(VP)*

Subsidiaries:

Capital Southwest Venture
Corporation   (1)
12900 Preston Rd Ste 700, Dallas, TX
75230
Tel.: (972) 233-8242
Web Site: http://www.capitalsouthwest.com
Sales Range: $100-124.9 Million
Closed-End Investment Company
N.A.I.C.S.: 523999
Joseph Brooks Armes *(Chm, Pres & CEO)*

Discovery Alliance, LLC   (1)
333 King Arthur Ct, Austin, TX
78746   (100%)
Tel.: (512) 306-8661
Web Site: http://www.discovery-ip.com
Buys & Licenses Intellectual Property
N.A.I.C.S.: 561499

Media Recovery, Inc.   (1)
510 Corporate Dr PO Box 1407, Graham,
TX 76450-3069
Tel.: (940) 549-5462
Web Site: http://www.mediarecovery.com
Sales Range: $50-74.9 Million
Data Center & Computer Supplies
N.A.I.C.S.: 518210

TitanLiner, Inc.   (1)
4100 International Plz Ste 538, Fort Worth,
TX 76109
Tel.: (817) 369-5949
Web Site: https://www.titanliner.com
Oil Containment Mfr
N.A.I.C.S.: 332420

CAPITALWORKS EMERGING MARKETS ACQUISITION CORPORATION
1345 Avenue of the Americas 11th Fl,
New York, NY 10105
Tel.: (202) 320-4822   Ky
Web Site: https://www.cemac.online
Year Founded: 2021
CMCA—(NASDAQ)
Rev.: $7,491,486
Assets: $240,684,165
Liabilities: $252,703,096
Net Worth: ($12,018,931)
Earnings: $4,970,671
Emp.: 2
Fiscal Year-end: 03/31/23
Investment Services
N.A.I.C.S.: 523999
Suresh Guduru *(Chm)*
C. Brian Coad *(CFO)*
Roberta Brzezinski *(CEO)*
Herman G. Kotze *(CTO)*
Whitney Baker *(Vice Chm)*

CAPITOL FEDERAL FINANCIAL, INC.
700 S Kansas Ave, Topeka, KS 66603
Tel.: (785) 231-6213   KS
Web Site: https://www.capfed.com
Year Founded: 1999
CFFN—(NASDAQ)
Rev.: $382,087,000
Assets: $9,527,608,000
Liabilities: $8,495,338,000
Net Worth: $1,032,270,000
Earnings: $38,010,000
Emp.: 636
Fiscal Year-end: 09/30/24
Bank Holding Company
N.A.I.C.S.: 551111
Rick C. Jackson *(Chief Lending Officer, Exec VP & Dir-Community Dev)*
John B. Dicus *(Chm, Pres & CEO)*
Kent G. Townsend *(CFO, Treas & Exec VP)*
Natalie G. Haag *(Gen Counsel & Exec VP)*
Anthony S. Barry *(Chief Corp Svcs Officer & Exec VP)*
Billy J. Skrobacz *(Chief Retail Ops Officer & Exec VP)*

Subsidiaries:

Capitol Federal Savings Bank   (1)
700 S Kansas Ave, Topeka, KS
66603-3894   (100%)
Tel.: (785) 235-1341
Web Site: https://www.capfed.com
Sales Range: $300-349.9 Million
Federal Savings Bank
N.A.I.C.S.: 522180
John B. Dicus *(Chm, Pres & CEO)*
Kent G. Townsend *(CFO, Treas & Exec VP)*
Rick C. Jackson *(Chief Lending Officer, Exec VP & Dir-Community Dev)*
Anthony S. Barry *(Exec VP-Corp Svcs)*
Billy J. Skrobacz Jr. *(Chief Retail Ops Officer)*

CAPRICOR THERAPEUTICS, INC.
10865 Rd to the Cure Ste 150, San
Diego, CA 92121
Tel.: (858) 727-1755   DE
Web Site: https://www.capricor.com
Year Founded: 2005
CAPR—(NASDAQ)
Rev.: $2,551,469
Assets: $50,094,910
Liabilities: $38,308,816
Net Worth: $11,786,094
Earnings: ($29,019,532)
Emp.: 74
Fiscal Year-end: 12/31/22
Clinical-Stage Biopharmaceutical Mfr
N.A.I.C.S.: 325412
Frank Litvack *(Exec Chm)*
Linda Marban *(Co-Founder, Pres & CEO)*
Kristi A. H. Elliott *(Chief Science Officer)*
Mark Awadalla *(VP-Clinical Ops)*
Minghao Sun *(VP-Res & Product Development)*
Yushi Feng *(VP-Regulatory Affairs)*
Anthony J. Bergmann *(CFO)*
Karen G. Krasney *(Gen Counsel, Sec & Exec VP)*
Jonathan Tayco *(VP-Program Mgmt & Bus Ops)*

CAPSTONE COMPANIES, INC.
431 Fairway Dr Ste 200, Deerfield
Beach, FL 33441
Tel.: (954) 252-3440   FL
Web Site:
https://www.capstonecompanies inc.com
Year Founded: 1989
CAPC—(OTCQB)
Rev.: $346,471
Assets: $1,889,202
Liabilities: $2,434,583
Net Worth: ($545,381)
Earnings: ($2,663,751)
Emp.: 7
Fiscal Year-end: 12/31/22
Electric Lamp Bulb & Other Lighting
Equipment Manufacturing
N.A.I.C.S.: 335139
Stewart Wallach *(Pres & CEO)*
Aimee C. Brown *(Sec & Dir-Admin)*
Dana Perez *(Interim CFO)*

Subsidiaries:

Capstone Industries, Inc.   (1)
431 Fairway Dr Ste 200, Deerfield Beach,
FL 33441
Tel.: (954) 570-8889
Web Site:
https://www.capstoneindustries.com
Home Emergency & Security Lighting Mfr
N.A.I.C.S.: 335131
Dana Perez *(Interim CFO)*

CAPSTONE THERAPEUTICS CORP.
5141 W 122nd St, Alsip, IL 60803
Tel.: (708) 371-0660   DE
Web Site:
https://www.capstonethx.com
Year Founded: 1987
CAPS—(OTCIQ)
Rev.: $45,642,000
Assets: $54,874,000
Liabilities: $49,066,000
Net Worth: $5,808,000
Earnings: $8,530,000
Emp.: 52
Fiscal Year-end: 12/31/20
Biopharmaceutical Researcher, Developer & Mfr
N.A.I.C.S.: 325412
Omar Rabbani *(CFO, Treas & VP)*
Michael Toporek *(Chm, Pres & CEO)*

CARA THERAPEUTICS, INC.
400 Atlantic St Ste 500, Stamford, CT
06901
Tel.: (203) 406-3700   DE
Web Site:
https://www.caratherapeutics.com
Year Founded: 2004
CARA—(NASDAQ)
Rev.: $41,867,000
Assets: $182,237,000
Liabilities: $23,458,000
Net Worth: $158,779,000
Earnings: ($85,474,000)
Emp.: 106
Fiscal Year-end: 12/31/22
Biopharmaceutical Mfr
N.A.I.C.S.: 325412
Derek T. Chalmers *(Co-Founder)*
Frederique Menzaghi *(Co-Founder, Chief Scientific Officer & Sr VP-R&D)*
Ryan D. Maynard *(CFO & Principal Acctg Officer)*
Eric Vandal *(Sr VP-Comml Ops)*
Michael E. Lewis *(Co-Founder)*
Iris Francesconi *(Chief Strategy Officer)*
Beth Weinberg *(Sr VP)*
Christopher A. Posner *(Pres & CEO)*

CARBON ENERGY CORPORATION
200 Union Blvd Ste 200, Lakewood,
CO 80228
Tel.: (720) 407-7030   DE
Web Site:
https://www.carbonenergycorp.com
CRBO—(OTCIQ)
Rev.: $116,625,000
Assets: $298,254,000
Liabilities: $222,033,000
Net Worth: $76,221,000
Earnings: $797,000
Emp.: 215
Fiscal Year-end: 12/31/19
Natural Gas Transportation Services
N.A.I.C.S.: 486210
Mark D. Pierce *(Pres)*
Patrick R. McDonald *(CEO)*
Kevin D. Struzeski *(CFO, Treas & Sec)*
James H. Brandi *(Chm)*
Erich William Kirsch *(Principal Fin Officer, Principal Acctg Officer & Sr VP-Fin)*

Subsidiaries:

Carbon California Operating Company, LLC   (1)
270 Quail Ct Ste B, Santa Paula, CA 93060
Tel.: (805) 933-1901
Natural Gas Transportation Services
N.A.I.C.S.: 486210

Nytis Exploration (USA) Inc.   (1)
1700 Broadway Ste 1170, Denver, CO
80290
Tel.: (720) 407-7030
Web Site: http://www.carbonenergycorp.com
Natural Gas Exploration & Production Services
N.A.I.C.S.: 211130

Subsidiary (Domestic):

Nytis Exploration Company LLC   (2)
2501 Broadway St, Catlettsburg, KY 41129-1231
Tel.: (606) 739-8864
Natural Gas Exploration & Production Services
N.A.I.C.S.: 211130

CARBONMETA TECHNOLOGIES, INC.
13110 NE 177th Pl Ste 145, Woodinville, WA 98072
Tel.: (425) 620-2366
Web Site:
https://www.carbonmetatech.com
Year Founded: 2003

COWI—(OTCIQ)
Rev.: $76,276
Assets: $191,224
Liabilities: $24,810,798
Net Worth: ($24,619,574)
Earnings: $400,432
Emp.: 36
Fiscal Year-end: 12/31/22
Software Developer
N.A.I.C.S.: 513210
Lloyd T. Spencer (CEO)

Subsidiaries:

CarbonMeta Research Ltd. (1)
3rd Floor 207 Regent Street, London, W1B
3HH, United Kingdom
Tel.: (44) 1865257222
Web Site:
https://www.carbonmetaresearch.co.uk
Waste Disposal Services
N.A.I.C.S.: 562219

**CARDIFF LEXINGTON CORPO-
RATION**
3753 Howard Hughes Pkwy Ste 200,
Las Vegas, NV 89169
Tel.: (203) 972-9200   FL
Web Site:
https://www.cardifflexington.com
Year Founded: 1987
CDIX—(OTCIQ)
Rev.: $11,998,273
Assets: $13,353,357
Liabilities: $14,823,165
Net Worth: ($1,469,808)
Earnings: ($5,429,521)
Emp.: 17
Fiscal Year-end: 12/31/22
Investment Holding Company
N.A.I.C.S.: 551112
Daniel R. Thompson (Chm)
Patrick Lambert (CFO)
Alex H. Cunningham (Pres & CEO)
Matthew T. Shafer (CTO, Treas & Sr
VP)
Rollan Roberts II (COO & Sr VP)

Subsidiaries:

JM Enterprises 1, Inc. (1)
3390 Kori Rd Ste 3, Jacksonville, FL 32257
Tel.: (904) 634-5622
Web Site: https://www.mytaxlawyer.org
Tax Attorney Services
N.A.I.C.S.: 541110

Mission Tuition, Inc. (1)
16255 Ventura Blvd Ste 525, Encino, CA
91436   (100%)
Tel.: (818) 783-2100
Web Site: http://www.missiontuition.com
Education Savings Merchant Program Op-
erator
N.A.I.C.S.: 518210

Platinum Tax Defenders, LLC (1)
2280 -B Ward Ave, Simi Valley, CA 93065
Web Site:
https://www.platinumtaxdefenders.com
Financial Services
N.A.I.C.S.: 523999
Sherri Gastellum (CEO)

Repicci's Franchise Group, LLC (1)
1032 Linkside Dr, Birmingham, AL
35242   (100%)
Tel.: (888) 732-5423
Web Site: http://www.italianice.com
Italian Ice & Gelato Mfr & Retail Franchisor
N.A.I.C.S.: 311520

CARDIFF ONCOLOGY, INC.
11055 Flintkote Ave, San Diego, CA
92121
Tel.: (858) 952-7570   DE
Web Site:
https://www.cardiffoncology.com
CRDF—(NASDAQ)
Rev.: $386,000
Assets: $116,191,000
Liabilities: $9,848,000
Net Worth: $106,343,000

Earnings: ($38,728,000)
Emp.: 25
Fiscal Year-end: 12/31/22
In-Vitro Diagnostic Substance Manu-
facturing
N.A.I.C.S.: 325413
James E. Levine (CFO & Principal
Acctg Officer)
Fairooz Kabbinavar (Chief Medical
Officer)
Tod Smeal (Chief Scientific Officer)
Charles Monahan (Sr VP)
Nancy Sherman (VP)
Mark Erlander (CEO)

CARDINAL HEALTH, INC.
7000 Cardinal Pl, Dublin, OH 43017
Tel.: (614) 757-5000   OH
Web Site:
https://www.cardinalhealth.com
Year Founded: 1971
CAH—(NYSE)
Rev.: $226,827,000,000
Assets: $45,121,000,000
Liabilities: $48,333,000,000
Net Worth: ($3,212,000,000)
Earnings: $853,000,000
Emp.: 48,900
Fiscal Year-end: 06/30/24
Holding Company; Medical & Phar-
maceutical Products Distribution &
Supply Chain Services
N.A.I.C.S.: 551112
Rajiv Mathur (VP-Skin Care)
Craig Cowman (Exec VP-Sourcing-
Global)
Jessica L. Mayer (Chief Compliance
Officer & Chief Legal Officer)
Robert Rajalingam (Pres-Medical
Products & Distr)
Ola M. Snow (Chief HR Officer)
Jason M. Hollar (CEO)
Suzanne Foster (Pres-Cardinal
Health at-Home Solutions)
Sarah Wills (Chief Corp Affairs Officer
& Exec VP)
Aaron E. Alt (CFO)
Ben Brinker (Pres-Intl-Medical Seg-
ment)
Steve C. de Baca (Exec VP-Quality &
Regulatory Affairs)
Mike Pintek (Pres-Nuclear & Preci-
sion Health Solutions)
Michelle D. Greene (CIO/Exec VP-
Global Tech & Bus Svcs)
Michelle Greene (CIO)
Mary C. Scherer (Chief Acctg Officer
& Sr VP)
Talvis Love (Executives)
Debbie Weitzman (CEO-
Pharmaceutical & Specialty Solutions
Segment)
Steve Mason (CEO-Medical Seg-
ment)
John Marotta (VP)
John P. Marotta (VP)

Subsidiaries:

A+ Secure Packaging, LLC (1)
339 Mason Rd, La Vergne, TN 37086-3606
Tel.: (615) 213-8280
Web Site: http://www.apluspak.com
Packaging Services
N.A.I.C.S.: 561910
John Thomas (Sr VP)

Abilene Nuclear, LLC (1)
3402 S 14th St, Abilene, TX 79605
Tel.: (325) 695-0491
Pharmaceuticals Product Mfr
N.A.I.C.S.: 325412

Access Closure, Inc. (1)
5452 Betsy Ross Dr, Santa Clara, CA
95054
Tel.: (408) 610-6500
Web Site: http://www.accessclosure.com
Sales Range: $75-99.9 Million
Medical Device Mfr
N.A.I.C.S.: 339112

John J. Buckley (CFO)

AssuraMed, Inc. (1)
1810 Summit Commerce Park, Twinsburg,
OH 44087
Tel.: (330) 963-6996
Web Site: http://www.assuramed.com
Holding Company; Medical Supplies Distr
N.A.I.C.S.: 551112

Subsidiary (Domestic):

RGH Enterprises, Inc. (2)
1810 Summit Commerce Park, Twinsburg,
OH 44087
Tel.: (330) 963-6998
Web Site: http://www.edgepark.com
Medical Apparatus & Supplies Distr
N.A.I.C.S.: 423450

Cardinal Health 102, Inc. (1)
1330 Enclave Pkwy, Houston, TX 77077
Tel.: (281) 749-4000
Web Site: http://www.cardinalhealth.com
Sales Range: $75-99.9 Million
Emp.: 300
Pharmacy Staffing Services
N.A.I.C.S.: 561320
Tom Burke (CEO)

Cardinal Health 104 LP (1)
2512 Westcott Blvd, Knoxville, TN 37931-
3100
Tel.: (865) 692-4500
Pharmaceuticals Product Mfr
N.A.I.C.S.: 325412

Cardinal Health 107, LLC (1)
3540 E Pike, Zanesville, OH 43701
Tel.: (740) 455-2462
Web Site: http://www.cardinalhealth.com
Emp.: 120
Drug Product Distr
N.A.I.C.S.: 424210

Cardinal Health 127, Inc. (1)
7400 W 110th St Ste 300, Overland Park,
KS 66210
Tel.: (913) 451-3955
Health Care Srvices
N.A.I.C.S.: 524114

Cardinal Health 222 (Thailand)
Ltd. (1)
7/111 Moo 4 Highway 331 Mabyangporn,
Pluakdaeng, Rayong, 21140, Thailand
Tel.: (66) 38640100
Pharmaceutical Preparation Mfr
N.A.I.C.S.: 325412

Cardinal Health 414, LLC (1)
7000 Cardinal Pl, Dublin, OH 43017
Tel.: (614) 757-5000
Health Care Srvices
N.A.I.C.S.: 621610
Tiffany P. Olson (Pres-Nuclear Pharmacy
Svcs)
Carole Watkins (Chief HR Officer)
Donald Casey Jr (CEO-Medical Segment)
Shelley Bird (Exec VP-Pub Affairs)
Mike Kaufmann (CEO)

Cardinal Health 418, Inc. (1)
16401 E 33rd Dr Ste 60, Aurora, CO 80011-
3335
Tel.: (303) 343-6800
Sales Range: $25-49.9 Million
Emp.: 20
Pharmaceutical Preparation Mfr
N.A.I.C.S.: 325412

Cardinal Health Canada 437,
Inc. (1)
1000 Tesma Way, Vaughan, L4K 5R8, ON,
Canada
Tel.: (905) 417-2900
Web Site:
http://www.cardinalhealthcanada.com
Surgical & Medical Product Mfr
N.A.I.C.S.: 339112
Martha Huston (Pres)
Jay Shoemaker (CFO & VP-France)
Frank Fortino (VP-Tech & Customer Care)
Don Cere (VP-Natl Mktg & Project Mgmt)

Cardinal Health Canada, Inc. (1)
1000 Tesma Way, Vaughan, L4K 5R8, ON,
Canada
Tel.: (905) 417-2900
Web Site: https://www.cardinalhealth.ca
Emp.: 1,400

Drugs, Medical Supplies & Equipment Services
N.A.I.C.S.: 339112

Cardinal Health Capital
Corporation (1)
7000 Cardinal Pl, Dublin, OH 43017-1091
Tel.: (614) 757-5000
Investment & Capital Raising Activities
N.A.I.C.S.: 523999

Cardinal Health Equipment Management Services (1)
1430 Waukegan Rd, McGaw Park, IL 60085
Tel.: (847) 689-8410
N.A.I.C.S.: 456191

Cardinal Health Korea Limited (1)
4F AIA Tower 16 Tongil-ro 2gil, Jung-gu,
Seoul, 04511, Korea (South)
Tel.: (82) 261908960
Web Site: https://www.cardinalhealth.kr
Medical & Laboratory Product Mfr & Distr
N.A.I.C.S.: 339112

Cardinal Health Malaysia 211 Sdn.
Bhd. (1)
Plot 74-A Bayan Lepas Industrial Zone
Phase IV, Mk 12 Lintang Bayan Lepas 3,
11900, Bayan Lepas, Pulau Pinang, Malay-
sia
Tel.: (60) 46430727
Sales Range: $25-49.9 Million
Emp.: 59
Pharmaceuticals Product Mfr
N.A.I.C.S.: 339113

Cardinal Health Malta 212
Limited (1)
A 51 Industrial Estate, HMR 15, Marsa,
Malta
Tel.: (356) 22984000
Pharmaceuticals Product Mfr
N.A.I.C.S.: 325412
David Schembri (Gen Mgr)

Cardinal Health P.R. 120, Inc. (1)
Building Ste 10 Local A Rd 165 Km 2 4,
Guaynabo, PR 00965-6211
Tel.: (787) 625-4100
Web Site: https://www.cardinalhealth.pr
Emp.: 600
Pharmaceutical Products Distr
N.A.I.C.S.: 424210
Debbie Weitzman (Sr VP)
Carla Fernandez (Sr VP)
Lesbia Martinez (VP)
Michele Montalvo (VP)
Francisco Negron (VP)
Rafael Janer (VP)

Cardinal Health Radiation Manage-
ment Services (1)
7000 Cardinal Pl, Dublin, OH
43017   (100%)
Tel.: (614) 757-4250
Web Site: http://www.cardinal.com
Sales Range: $10-24.9 Million
Emp.: 17
Develops & Supplies Quality Control & Ra-
diation Protection Products for Medical &
Industrial Imaging & Radiation Therapy
N.A.I.C.S.: 339112

Cardinal Health Singapore 225 Pte.
Ltd. (1)
10 Kallang Avenue Aperia 10-10/18, Aperia
Tower 2, Singapore, 339510, Singapore
Tel.: (65) 62302388
Sales Range: $25-49.9 Million
Emp.: 40
Pharmaceutical Preparation Manufacturing
N.A.I.C.S.: 325412
Enrique Rios (VP)

Cardinal Health Spain 219 S.L. (1)
Avenita de lavega 1 San Fernando de
Henares, 28108, Madrid, Spain (100%)
Tel.: (34) 902300550
Web Site: http://www.Cardinal.com
Sales Range: $25-49.9 Million
Emp.: 15
Mfr of Health Care Products & Provider of
Management Services
N.A.I.C.S.: 456199

Cardinal Health Specialty Pharmaceutical Services (1)
15 Ingram Ste 100, La Vergne, TN
37086   (100%)

Cardinal Health, Inc.—(Continued)

Tel.: (615) 793-4400
Web Site: http://www.cardinalhealth.com
Sales Range: $50-74.9 Million
Emp.: 200
Full-Service, Third Party Logistics & Operation Support Services
N.A.I.C.S.: 541618

Cardinal Health Systems, Inc. (1)
5532 Spellmire Dr, Cincinnati, OH 45246-4856
Tel.: (513) 874-5940
Pharmaceuticals Product Mfr
N.A.I.C.S.: 325412

Cardinal Health, Inc. - Chicago (1)
1430 Waukegan Rd, McGaw Park, IL 60085
Tel.: (847) 689-8410
Web Site: http://www.cardinalhealth.com
Distr of Health Care Products
N.A.I.C.S.: 423450

Cardinal Health, Inc. - Denver (1)
16401 E 33rd Dr, Aurora, CO 80011-3335
Tel.: (303) 343-6800
Web Site: http://www.cardinalhealth.com
Sales Range: $10-24.9 Million
Emp.: 30
Nuclear Pharmacy Service Centers
N.A.I.C.S.: 325412

Cardinal Health, Inc. - Greensboro (1)
309 S Westgate Dr Ste G, Greensboro, NC 27407-1634
Tel.: (336) 299-9891
Web Site: http://www.cardinalhealth.com
Sales Range: $50-74.9 Million
Emp.: 15
Drugs & Sundries
N.A.I.C.S.: 424210

Cardinal Health, Inc. - Houston (1)
1330 Enclave Pkwy, Houston, TX 77077-2025
Tel.: (281) 749-4000
Sales Range: $75-99.9 Million
Emp.: 285
Health Care Management Services Provider
N.A.I.C.S.: 561320

Cardinal Health, Inc. - Wayne (1)
1800 Valley Rd, Wayne, NJ 07470-2047
Tel.: (973) 709-3000
Sales Range: $200-249.9 Million
Emp.: 225
Outsourced Promotional, Marketing & Educational Services to the Pharmaceutical Industry
N.A.I.C.S.: 541618

Cardinal Health, Inc. - Zanesville (1)
3540 E Pike, Zanesville, OH 43701-9526
Tel.: (740) 455-2462
Sales Range: $75-99.9 Million
Emp.: 120
Pre Packaging Services For The Pharmaceutical Industry
N.A.I.C.S.: 424210

Cirpro de Delicias S.A. de C.V. (1)
Parque Ind Las Virgenes S/N, Ciudad Delicias, CHIH 33019, Mexico
Tel.: (52) 6394700400
Medical Disposable Product Mfr
N.A.I.C.S.: 325412

Convertors de Mexico S.A. de C.V. (1)
Calle Arcadia 1580 Colonia Salvarcar, 33019, Ciudad Juarez, Mexico
Tel.: (52) 6566498900
Pharmaceutical Preparation Mfr
N.A.I.C.S.: 325412
Ed Andrade *(Office Mgr)*

Desert PET, LLC (1)
57272 29 Palms Hwy, Yucca Valley, CA 92284-2903
Tel.: (760) 365-1990
Drug Development Services
N.A.I.C.S.: 424210

Fluke Biomedical (1)
6045 Cochran Rd, Cleveland, OH 44139-3303
Tel.: (440) 248-9300
Web Site: http://www.fluke.com

Sales Range: $50-74.9 Million
Emp.: 200
Test & Measurement Equipment & Services
N.A.I.C.S.: 335931

Healthcare Solutions Management Group, Inc. (1)
3 School St Ste 303, Glen Cove, NY 11542
Web Site: http://www.hshmedical.com
National Healthcare Consulting Firm
N.A.I.C.S.: 923120
Justin Smith *(CFO, CEO & Interim & CFO)*
Jonathan Loutzenhiser *(Exec VP)*
Douglas Millar *(Exec VP-Int Affairs)*
Richard Muckerman *(VP-Strategy & Bus)*
Blake Moorman *(VP-Ops)*

Subsidiary (Domestic):

Healthcare Solutions Holding, LLC (2)
6031 University Blvd Ste 235, Ellicott City, MD 21043-6097
Tel.: (443) 364-5220
Health Care Srvices
N.A.I.C.S.: 621610

Instant Diagnostic Systems, Inc. (1)
1740 4th Ave SE Ste A, Decatur, AL 35601
Web Site: http://www.instantdiagnostic.com
Pharmaceutical Products Distr
N.A.I.C.S.: 424210

Kinray, Inc. (1)
152-35 10th Ave, Whitestone, NY 11357-1233
Tel.: (718) 767-1234
Web Site: http://www.kinray.com
Sales Range: $1-4.9 Billion
Emp.: 1,000
Wholesale Pharmaceutical, Medical Supply & Health & Beauty Care Product Distr
N.A.I.C.S.: 424210
Howard Hirsch *(CFO)*

Medicine Shoppe International, Inc. (1)
1 Rider Trail Plz Dr Ste 300, Earth City, MO 63045 **(100%)**
Tel.: (314) 993-6000
Sales Range: $75-99.9 Million
Emp.: 250
Pharmaceutical Services
N.A.I.C.S.: 325412

Mirixa Corporation (1)
505 Market St Ste 200, West Des Moines, IA 50266
Web Site: http://www.mirixa.com
Pharmaceutical Preparation Mfr
N.A.I.C.S.: 325412
Frank Harvey *(CEO)*
Karen Litsinger *(Gen Counsel & Sr VP-Ops)*
Eric Hoessel *(VP-Sls)*

Nuclear Pharmacy Services (1)
7000 Cardinal Pl, Dublin, OH 43017
Tel.: (614) 757-5000
Web Site: http://www.cardinalhealth.com
Sales Range: $75-99.9 Million
Radiopharmacy Services Solutions
N.A.I.C.S.: 456110

Oncology Therapeutic Network (1)
305 Tech Park Ste 113, La Vergne, TN 37086 **(100%)**
Tel.: (615) 287-8999
Sales Range: $125-149.9 Million
Emp.: 200
Whslr of Drugs & Over-the-Counter Products
N.A.I.C.S.: 424210

Outcomes Incorporated (1)
505 Market St Ste 200, West Des Moines, IA 50266
Tel.: (515) 237-0001
Web Site: http://www.outcomesmtm.com
Medical Program Organizing Services
N.A.I.C.S.: 923130
Tom Halterman *(Founder & CEO)*

P4 Healthcare, LLC (1)
7172 Columbia Gateway Dr Ste 300, Columbia, MD 21046
Tel.: (443) 518-7000
Health Care Srvices
N.A.I.C.S.: 621610

Parmed Pharmaceuticals, Inc. (1)

4220 Hyde Park Blvd, Niagara Falls, NY 14305-1798
Tel.: (716) 284-5666
Web Site: http://www.parmed.com
Pharmaceutical Preparation Manufacturing
N.A.I.C.S.: 325412
Daniel H. Movens *(Sr VP)*

Sierra Radiopharmacy, LLC (1)
601 Mill St, Reno, NV 89502-1029
Tel.: (775) 786-9585
Web Site: http://www.sierraradiopharmacy.com
Pharmaceutical Preparation Manufacturing
N.A.I.C.S.: 325412
Dennis J. Latino *(CEO)*

TelePharm, LLC (1)
123 N Linn St Ste 2F, Iowa City, IA 52245
Tel.: (319) 535-0571
Web Site: https://www.telepharm.com
Software Development Services
N.A.I.C.S.: 513210

The F. Dohmen Company (1)
1101 Lund Blvd, Anoka, MN 55303-1091
Tel.: (763) 656-2300
Sales Range: $1-9.9 Million
Emp.: 72
Whslr of Pharmaceuticals & Over the Counter Merchandise
N.A.I.C.S.: 325412

The Harvard Drug Group, LLC (1)
17177 N Laurel Pk Ste 233, Livonia, MI 48152
Tel.: (734) 525-8700
Web Site: http://www.theharvarddruggroup.com
Pharmaceuticals Whslr
N.A.I.C.S.: 424210
Larry Kramer *(Sr Exec VP-Major Pharmaceuticals & Gen Mgr)*

Wavemark, Inc. (1)
300 Baker Ave, Concord, MA 01742
Tel.: (978) 431-1600
Web Site: http://www.wavemark.net
Health Care Srvices
N.A.I.C.S.: 524114

mscripts, LLC (1)
445 Bush St Ste 200, San Francisco, CA 94108
Tel.: (415) 296-8600
Web Site: https://mscripts.com
Software Publisher
N.A.I.C.S.: 513210
Peter Towle *(CEO)*
Steve Brickman *(VP-Engrg)*
Martin Schwartz *(VP-Product)*
Lara Loveman *(VP-Bus Strategy)*
Brian Davis *(VP-Sls)*

naviHealth, Inc. (1)
210 Westwood Place Ste 400, Brentwood, TN 37027
Tel.: (615) 577-1900
Web Site: http://www.navihealth.us
Post-Acute Care Services
N.A.I.C.S.: 624190
Greg Baumer *(Chief Growth Officer)*
LeToia Crozier *(Chief Compliance & Privacy Officer)*
Cathy Fackovec *(Sr VP)*
Greg Hamrick *(CIO)*
William H. Frist Jr. *(CEO & COO)*

CARDIO DIAGNOSTICS HOLDINGS, INC.
311 W Superior St Ste 444, Chicago, IL 60654
Tel.: (302) 281-2147 DE
Web Site:
https://cardiodiagnosticsinc.com
Year Founded: 2021
CDIO—(NASDAQ)
Rev.: $950
Assets: $6,249,478
Liabilities: $1,947,770
Net Worth: $4,301,708
Earnings: ($4,660,985)
Emp.: 7
Fiscal Year-end: 12/31/22
Biotechnology Research Services
N.A.I.C.S.: 541714

Tim Dogan *(CTO)*
Elisa Luqman *(CFO)*
Meesha Dogan *(Co-Founder & CEO)*
Rob Philibert *(Co-Founder & Chief Medical Officer)*
Khullani Abdullahi *(VP-Revenue & Strategy)*
Warren Hosseinion *(Chm)*

CARDLYTICS, INC
675 Ponce de Leon Ave NE Ste 4100, Atlanta, GA 30308 DE
Web Site: https://www.cardlytics.com
Year Founded: 2008
CDLX—(NASDAQ)
Rev.: $298,542,000
Assets: $691,236,000
Liabilities: $479,631,000
Net Worth: $211,605,000
Earnings: ($465,264,000)
Emp.: 501
Fiscal Year-end: 12/31/22
Advertising Software Developer
N.A.I.C.S.: 513210
Amit Gupta *(CEO & COO)*
Alexis DeSieno *(CFO & Principal Acctg Officer)*
Carson Napps *(Head-People)*
Jose Singer *(Chief Product Officer)*
Peter Chan *(CTO)*
Nick Lynton *(Chief Legal Officer & Chief Privacy Officer)*
Ian Carrington *(Gen Mgr-International)*
Evelyne Forester *(Chief Bus Officer)*

CARDXX, INC.
50 W Liberty Ste 880, Reno, NV 89501
Tel.: (303) 762-8570 NV
Year Founded: 1998
CXCQ—(OTCIQ)
Integrated Circuits Mfr
N.A.I.C.S.: 334413
Jungang Lin *(CFO)*
Wan Jia Lin *(CEO & Sec)*

CARECLOUD, INC.
7 Clyde Rd, Somerset, NJ 08873
Tel.: (732) 873-5133 DE
Web Site: https://www.carecloud.com
Year Founded: 1999
CCLD—(NASDAQ)
Rev.: $138,826,000
Assets: $136,174,000
Liabilities: $34,485,000
Net Worth: $101,689,000
Earnings: ($10,085,000)
Emp.: 4,150
Fiscal Year-end: 12/31/22
Medical Practice & Revenue Cycle Management Solutions
N.A.I.C.S.: 513210
Stephen A. Snyder *(Pres)*
Loraine Goetsch *(Pres-Div & Sr VP-Integrations)*
A. Hadi Chaudhry *(CEO)*
Norman Roth *(Interim CFO, Principal Acctg Officer & Controller)*
Alfonso Nardi *(Sr VP-Strategy)*
Kimberly Blanche *(Gen Counsel & VP-Compliance)*
Elizabeth Ferrer *(VP-HR)*
Adeel Sarwar *(CTO)*
Iram Fatima *(COO)*
Brian Zelenka *(VP)*
Ali Shaukat *(Gen Mgr)*
Mahmud U. Haq *(Founder & Exec Chm)*

Subsidiaries:

CareCloud Corporation (1)
5200 Blue Lagoon Dr Ste 900, Miami, FL 33126
Tel.: (305) 265-4200
Web Site: http://www.carecloud.com

Sales Range: $10-24.9 Million
Emp.: 130
Web-Based Healthcare Software
N.A.I.C.S.: 513210
Albert Santalo (Founder)
Mike Cuesta (CMO)
Greg Shorten (Chief Revenue Officer)
Juan Molina (Pres-Div)
Elizabeth Ferrer (VP-HR)
Daniel Masvidal (VP-Client Success)
Steve Link (VP-Client Ops)

Gulf Coast Billing (1)
15010 FM 2100 Ste 203, Crosby, TX
77532 (100%)
Tel.: (281) 462-1285
Web Site: https://www.gulfcoastbilling.com
Rev.: $1,800,000
Emp.: 20
Revenue Cycle Management Services
N.A.I.C.S.: 522320

MedMatica Consulting Associates,
Inc. (1)
18 Barrington Ln, Chester Springs, PA
19425
Tel.: (610) 827-1356
Web Site: http://www.medmatica.com
Rev.: $4,500,000
Emp.: 20
Health Services
N.A.I.C.S.: 541511
Jerry Howell (CEO)

MediGain, Inc. (1)
5501 Lyndon B Johnson Fwy Ste 250, Dal-
las, TX 75240
Tel.: (972) 212-5858
Web Site: https://www.medigain.com
Medical Billing Solutions
N.A.I.C.S.: 513210
Cindy Ranson (Sr Dlr)

Washington Medical Billing (1)
7 Clyde Rd, Somerset, NJ 08873
Tel.: (253) 833-3255
Web Site: https://www.wmb-llc.com
Medical Billing & Healthcare IT Company
N.A.I.C.S.: 522320

CAREDX, INC.
8000 Marina Blvd, Brisbane, CA
94005
Tel.: (415) 287-2300 DE
Web Site: https://www.caredx.com
Year Founded: 1998
CDNA—(NASDAQ)
Rev.: $321,793,000
Assets: $542,991,000
Liabilities: $112,080,000
Net Worth: $430,911,000
Earnings: ($76,613,000)
Emp.: 738
Fiscal Year-end: 12/31/22
Surgical & Medical Instrument Manu-
facturing
N.A.I.C.S.: 339112
Michael D. Goldberg (Chm)
John W. Hanna (Pres & CEO)
Robert N. Woodward (Sr VP-R&D)
Abhishek Jain (CFO)
Stacey Follon (Sr VP)
Marica Grskovic (Chief Ops Officer)
Mickey Kim (Sr VP)
Srini Srinivas (Chief Medical Officer)
Jarrod Borkat (Sr VP)
Pauline Callinan (VP)
Kim Clark-Langone (VP)
Hal Gibson (Sr VP)
Julian Husbands (VP)
Ashish Kothari (VP)
Marco Scheller (Sr VP)
Keith Kennedy (COO)
Jessica Meng (Chief Comml Officer)

Subsidiaries:

CareDx International AB (1)
Franzengatan 5, 112 51, Stockholm, Swe-
den
Tel.: (46) 850893900
Web Site: http://www.allabolag.se
Drug Development Services
N.A.I.C.S.: 424210

CareDx Pty Ltd. (1)
20 Collie Street, Fremantle, 6160, WA, Aus-
tralia
Tel.: (61) 893364212
Transplant Diagnostics Merchant Whslr
N.A.I.C.S.: 424210

OTTR, Inc. (1)
10202 F St, Omaha, NE
68127-1006 (100%)
Tel.: (402) 836-0000
Web Site: http://www.ottr.com
Medical Software & Complete Transplant
Management
N.A.I.C.S.: 513210

Olerup GmbH (1)
Loewengasse 47/6, 1030, Vienna, Austria
Tel.: (43) 1710150000
Transplant Diagnostics Merchant Whslr
N.A.I.C.S.: 424210
Roswitha Keller (CEO)

Olerup SSP AB (1)
Franzengatan 5, 112 51, Stockholm, Swe-
den
Tel.: (46) 850893900
Transplant Diagnostics Merchant Whslr
N.A.I.C.S.: 424210
Anna Hedlund (Head-R&D)

XynManagament, Inc. (1)
234 W Bandera Rd Ste 131, Boerne, TX
78006
Web Site: http://www.xynmanagement.com
Facing Transplant Services
N.A.I.C.S.: 812199
Mark Schnitzler (Co-Founder)
David Axelrod (Co-Founder)
Krista Lentine (Co-Founder)
Jennifer Milton (Co-Founder)

CAREMAX, INC.
1000 NW 57th Ct, Miami, FL 33126
Tel.: (305) 425-9999 DE
Web Site: https://www.caremax.com
Year Founded: 2020
CMAX—(NASDAQ)
Rev.: $631,132,000
Assets: $1,170,743,000
Liabilities: $551,196,000
Net Worth: $619,547,000
Earnings: ($37,796,000)
Emp.: 1,500
Fiscal Year-end: 12/31/22
Investment Services
N.A.I.C.S.: 523999
Steven I. Hochberg (Pres & CEO)
Richard A. Barasch (Chm)
Paul Rundell (Chief Restructuring Of-
ficer)

CARETRUST REIT, INC.
905 Calle Amanecer Ste 300, San
Clemente, CA 92673
Tel.: (949) 542-3130 MD
Web Site:
    https://www.caretrustreit.com
CTRE—(NYSE)
Rev.: $217,770,000
Assets: $2,084,838,000
Liabilities: $666,121,000
Net Worth: $1,418,717,000
Earnings: $53,735,000
Emp.: 17
Fiscal Year-end: 12/31/23
Real Estate Investment Services
N.A.I.C.S.: 523999
Gregory K. Stapley (Founder)
David M. Sedgwick (Pres & CEO)
William M. Wagner (CFO, Principal
Acctg Officer & Treas)

Subsidiaries:

18th Place Health Holdings LLC (1)
27101 Puerta Real Ste 400, Mission Viejo,
CA 92691
Tel.: (949) 540-2000
Holding Company
N.A.I.C.S.: 551112

4th Street Holdings LLC (1)

175 2nd St S Ph 13, Saint Petersburg, FL
33701
Tel.: (727) 423-8650
Web Site: http://www.4thstreetholdings.com
Holding Company
N.A.I.C.S.: 551112

CAREVIEW COMMUNICA-
TIONS, INC.
405 State Hwy 121 Bypass Ste
B-240, Lewisville, TX 75067
Tel.: (972) 943-6050 NV
Web Site: https://www.care-view.com
Year Founded: 1997
CRVW—(OTCQB)
Rev.: $7,802,226
Assets: $5,081,167
Liabilities: $117,779,465
Net Worth: ($112,698,298)
Earnings: ($10,080,363)
Emp.: 55
Fiscal Year-end: 12/31/21
Healthcare High-Speed Data Network
System Mfr
N.A.I.C.S.: 334220
Steven G. Johnson (Pres, CEO,
Treas & Sec)
L. Allen Wheeler (Founder & Chm)
Kyle B. Johnson (Dir-Engrg)
Jason T. Thompson (CFO & Chief
Acctg Officer)
Matthew E. Jackson (Gen Counsel)
Derek del Carpio (VP-Product Dev)
Sandra K. McRee (COO)
Teddy Berdan (VP-Bus Dev)
Chase Soong (Controller)

CARGO THERAPEUTICS, INC.
835 Industrial Rd Ste 400, San Car-
los, CA 94070
Tel.: (650) 499-8950 DE
Web Site: https://www.cargo-tx.com
Year Founded: 2019
CRGX—(NASDAQ)
Assets: $10,243,000
Liabilities: $45,479,000
Net Worth: ($35,236,000)
Earnings: ($40,951,000)
Emp.: 74
Fiscal Year-end: 12/31/22
Biotechnology Research & Develop-
ment Services
N.A.I.C.S.: 541714
Gina Chapman (Pres & CEO)

CARGURUS, INC.
55 Cambridge Pkwy 6th Fl, Cam-
bridge, MA 02142
Tel.: (617) 354-0068 DE
Web Site: https://www.cargurus.com
Year Founded: 2006
CARG—(NASDAQ)
Rev.: $1,655,035,000
Assets: $927,102,000
Liabilities: $192,493,000
Net Worth: $734,609,000
Earnings: $84,387,000
Emp.: 1,403
Fiscal Year-end: 12/31/22
Online Car Shopping Services
N.A.I.C.S.: 423110
E. Langley Steinert (Chm)
Jason M. Trevisan (CEO)
Dafna Sarnoff (CMO)
Kirndeep Singh (VP-IR)
Matt Quin (CTO)
Maggie Meluzio (Dir-PR)

Subsidiaries:

CarGurus Ireland Limited, an Irish
Private Company Limited by
Shares (1)
1st Floor Styne House Upper Hatch Street,
D02DY27, Dublin, Ireland
Tel.: (353) 32211122150
Web Site: http://www.cargurus.de
Car Dealer Services

N.A.I.C.S.: 441120

CarOffer, LLC (1)
15601 Dallas Pkwy Ste 600, Addison, TX
75001 (100%)
Web Site: https://www.caroffer.com
New Car Dealer Services
N.A.I.C.S.: 441110
Sherif Jitan (CIO)
Zach Hallowell (CEO)
Mike DeForest (Sr Dir-Arbitration)
Ziad Chartouni (CTO)
Blake Harvey (Head-Strategy & Operations)
Paneer Shekar (VP-Software Engrg)
Chris Beyer (VP-Finance & Accounting)
Connie Le (Sr Dir-IT Program Mgmt)
Jeff Bittancourt (Sr Dir-Sls Enablement)
Brady Townsend (Sr Dir-Customer Success)
James Sa (Dir-IT Dev)
Chris Adams (Sr Dir-Revenue Ops)
Taryn Bzdick-Kowalczyk (Dir-Creative)
Kimberlee Pinkney (Dir-Operations)
Nicole Kane (Dir-Logistics)
Erin Andersen (Head-Marketing)
Michael Schrob (Dir-Operations)
Veronica Maldonado (Controller-Operations)
Roger Knowles (Treas)

CARISMA THERAPEUTICS
INC.
3675 Market St Ste 401, Philadel-
phia, PA 19104
Tel.: (267) 491-6422 DE
Web Site: https://carismatx.com
Year Founded: 2008
CARM—(NASDAQ)
Rev.: $14,919,000
Assets: $89,554,000
Liabilities: $63,022,000
Net Worth: $26,532,000
Earnings: ($86,879,000)
Emp.: 107
Fiscal Year-end: 12/31/23
Pharmaceuticals Mfr
N.A.I.C.S.: 325412
Sanford S. Zweifach (Chm)
Steven Kelly (Pres & CEO)
Michael Klichinsky (Co-Founder &
Chief Scientific Officer)
Sascha Abramson (VP-Scientific Ops)
Thomas Condamine (VP-Discovery &
Translational Sciences)
Kenneth Locke (VP-Mfg & Supply
Chain)
Richard Morris (CFO)
Terry Shields (Sr VP-HR)
Eric Siegel (Gen Counsel & Sec)
Tom Wilton (Chief Bus Officer)
Sanford Zweifach (Chm)
Saar Gill (Co-Founder)
Eugene Kennedy (Chief Medical Offi-
cer)

CARLISLE COMPANIES IN-
CORPORATED
16430 N Scottsdale Rd Ste 400,
Scottsdale, AZ 85254
Tel.: (480) 781-5000 DE
Web Site: https://www.carlisle.com
Year Founded: 1917
CSL—(NYSE)
Rev.: $4,586,900,000
Assets: $6,620,000,000
Liabilities: $3,791,000,000
Net Worth: $2,829,000,000
Earnings: $767,400,000
Emp.: 11,000
Fiscal Year-end: 12/31/23
Holding Company; Commercial Roof-
ing Products, Specialty Tires & Food-
Service Products Mfr
N.A.I.C.S.: 551112
Scott C. Selbach (Gen Counsel, Sec
& VP)
Kevin P. Zdimal (CFO & VP)
Frank J. Ready (Pres-Carlisle Weath-
erproofing Technologies)
D. Christian Koch (Chm, Pres &
CEO)

Carlisle Companies Incorporated—(Continued)

Jim Giannakouros *(VP-IR)*
Lori A. Snyder *(VP-HR)*
Kelly P. Kamienski *(VP-Fin-Carlisle Weatherproofing Technologies)*
Mehul Patel *(VP-IR)*
Stephen F. Schwar *(Pres)*

Subsidiaries:

Carlisle Brake Products (UK) Limited   **(1)**
Omega 500 Mamhilad Technology Park, Pontypool, NP4 0JJ, United Kingdom
Tel.: (44) 1495767300
Web Site: http://www.carlisle-brake.co.uk
Sales Range: $25-49.9 Million
Emp.: 7
Construction Machinery Mfr
N.A.I.C.S.: 333120

Carlisle Canada   **(1)**
645 McMurray Road, Waterloo, N2V 2B7, ON, Canada
Tel.: (519) 885-0630
Tiles Mfr
N.A.I.C.S.: 326211

Carlisle Construction Materials, LLC   **(1)**
1285 Ritner Hwy, Carlisle, PA 17013
Web Site: https://carlisleconstructionmaterials.com
Insulation, Roofing, Waterproof Coating & Construction Materials Mfr
N.A.I.C.S.: 444180

Subsidiary (Domestic):

Accella Polyurethane Systems, LLC   **(2)**
2500 Adie Rd, Maryland Heights, MO 63043
Tel.: (314) 432-3200
Web Site: http://www.accellacorp.com
Spray Polyurethane Mfr
N.A.I.C.S.: 325211

Subsidiary (Domestic):

R-B Recycling Inc.   **(3)**
9945 N Burgard Way, Portland, OR 97203
Tel.: (503) 283-2261
Recycling, Waste Materials
N.A.I.C.S.: 562920

Ultimate RB, Inc.   **(3)**
904 NE 10th Ave, McMinnville, OR 97128
Tel.: (503) 472-4691
Web Site: https://www.ultimaterb.com
Recycled Rubber Products Mfr
N.A.I.C.S.: 326299

Subsidiary (Non-US):

Carlisle Construction Materials BV   **(2)**
Industrieweg 16, 8263 AD, Kampen, Netherlands
Tel.: (31) 383393333
Web Site: https://www.hardcast.nl
Construction Materials Distr
N.A.I.C.S.: 423320
Bart Smit *(Mgr-Technical Product)*

Carlisle Construction Materials GmbH   **(2)**
Schellerdamm 16, 21079, Hamburg, Germany
Tel.: (49) 407889330
Web Site: https://www.ccm-europe.com
Construction Material Mfr & Distr
N.A.I.C.S.: 212321

Carlisle Construction Materials UK   **(2)**
Lancaster House, Millenium Business Park, Mansfield, NG19 7DW, Notts, United Kingdom
Tel.: (44) 1623627285
Web Site: https://www.ccm-europe.com
Construction Materials Distr
N.A.I.C.S.: 423320
Paul Simms *(Mgr-Technical Svcs)*

Subsidiary (Domestic):

Carlisle SynTec Inc.   **(2)**
1285 Ritner Hwy, Carlisle, PA 17013

Tel.: (717) 245-7000
Web Site: http://www.carlislesyntec.com
Sales Range: $1-4.9 Billion
Emp.: 600
Providing Single-Ply Rubber Roofing Systems Services
N.A.I.C.S.: 324122

Subsidiary (Domestic):

Carlisle Coatings & Waterproofing Inc.   **(3)**
900 Hensley Ln, Wylie, TX 75098
Tel.: (972) 442-6545
Web Site: https://www.carlisleccw.com
Sales Range: $10-24.9 Million
Emp.: 35
Waterproof Coating Mfr
N.A.I.C.S.: 325510

Subsidiary (Domestic):

Carlisle Hardcast Inc.   **(4)**
900 Hensley Ln, Wylie, TX 75098
Tel.: (972) 442-6545
Web Site: https://www.carlislehvac.com
Heating & Air Conditioning Duct Insulation, Sealing & Connecting Products Mfr
N.A.I.C.S.: 333415

Subsidiary (Non-US):

Carlisle Hardcast Europe B.V.   **(5)**
Bloemendalerweg 25 33, Industrieterrein Noord, 1382 KB, Weesp, Netherlands
Tel.: (31) 294492188
Web Site: http://www.hardcast.nl
Sales Range: $25-49.9 Million
Emp.: 40
Heating & Air Conditioning Duct Sealant, Connecting & Insulation Products Mfr
N.A.I.C.S.: 333415
Rob Reeve *(Mng Dir)*

Subsidiary (Non-US):

DynAir Inc.   **(4)**
2100 Rememberance Rue, Lachine, H8S 1X3, QC, Canada
Tel.: (514) 639-1616
Web Site: http://www.dynair.ca
Sales Range: $10-24.9 Million
Emp.: 18
Heating & Air Conditioning Duct Connector, Sealant & Insulation Product Mfr
N.A.I.C.S.: 333415

Subsidiary (Domestic):

Hunter Panels, LLC   **(4)**
15 Franklin St, Portland, ME 04101
Tel.: (207) 761-5678
Web Site: https://www.hunterpanels.com
Roof Insulation Panel Mfr
N.A.I.C.S.: 423330
Steve Pavey *(Mgr-Sls-South Central Reg)*
Ed Krusec *(Dir-Private Label OEM)*
Matt Peterson *(Gen Mgr)*
Grant Stahl *(Mgr-Natl Sls-Xci)*
Jason Greenleaf *(Mgr-Technical & Tapered Design Svcs)*
Kyle Ryerson *(Mgr-Production)*
Illya Spiecker *(Mgr-Polyiso Production Plng)*
Joe Petty *(Mgr-Sls-Xci-East & South)*
Jeff Beckstead *(Mgr-Sls-Western)*
Andrew Myers *(Mgr-Sls-Mid-Central)*
Dimo Valtas *(Mgr-Sls-Midwest)*
Tom Rhoads *(Sls Mgr-West Reg)*
Justin Andrews *(Sls Mgr-Southeast Reg)*
Michael Strohecker *(Sls Mgr)*
Jennifer Holsinger *(Sls Mgr-Natl)*
Ryan Glaser *(Sls Mgr-Midwest Reg)*
Michelle Pelkey *(Mgr-Customer Svc)*
Luke Gower *(Mgr-Tapered Dept)*
Nicole Levesque *(Mgr-Pricing & Analytics)*
MacGregor Pierce *(Product Mgr)*
Brandon Reynolds *(Product Mgr)*
Natalie Tobey *(Mktg Mgr)*
Dee Toulouse *(Coord)*
Kevin McSweeney *(Sls Mgr)*
Brian Knight *(Sls Mgr-Mid,Central)*
Nichole Boynton *(Supvr-Customer Service)*
Sara Diaz *(Supvr-Customer Service)*
Carolyn Teeter *(Acct Mgr)*
Richard Blake *(Acct Mgr)*
Rich Pierson *(Acct Mgr)*
Brandon Reynolds *(Product Mgr)*
Natalie Tobey *(Mktg Mgr)*
Dee Toulouse *(Coord)*
Kevin McSweeney *(Sls Mgr)*

Brian Knight *(Sls Mgr-Mid,Central)*
Nichole Boynton *(Supvr-Customer Service)*
Sara Diaz *(Supvr-Customer Service)*
Carolyn Teeter *(Acct Mgr)*
Richard Blake *(Acct Mgr)*
Rich Pierson *(Acct Mgr)*
Brandon Reynolds *(Product Mgr)*
Natalie Tobey *(Mktg Mgr)*
Dee Toulouse *(Coord)*
Kevin McSweeney *(Sls Mgr)*
Brian Knight *(Sls Mgr-Mid,Central)*
Nichole Boynton *(Supvr-Customer Service)*
Sara Diaz *(Supvr-Customer Service)*
Carolyn Teeter *(Acct Mgr)*
Richard Blake *(Acct Mgr)*
Rich Pierson *(Acct Mgr)*

Subsidiary (Domestic):

Versico, LLC   **(3)**
1285 Ritner Hwy, Carlisle, PA 17013
Tel.: (717) 960-4025
Web Site: https://www.versico.com
Sales Range: $150-199.9 Million
Thermoplastic Roof Panel Mfr
N.A.I.C.S.: 423330

Subsidiary (Domestic):

Insulfoam, LLC   **(2)**
6004 NW Gate Blvd, Tacoma, WA 98406-4483
Tel.: (253) 572-5111
Web Site: http://www.insulfoam.com
Sales Range: $700-749.9 Million
Construction Polystyrene Products & Structural Insulation Panels Mfr & Whslr
N.A.I.C.S.: 326140

Division (Domestic):

Premier Building Systems   **(3)**
4609 70th Ave E, Fife, WA 98424   **(100%)**
Tel.: (253) 926-2020
Web Site: http://www.pbssips.com
Sales Range: $125-149.9 Million
Emp.: 100
Structural Insulation Panels Mfr & Whslr
N.A.I.C.S.: 321215

Carlisle Corporation   **(1)**
1 Dr ML King Jr Ave Ste 130, Memphis, TN 38103
Tel.: (901) 526-5000
Web Site: https://www.carlislecorp.com
Consumer Product Mfr & Distr
N.A.I.C.S.: 337126

Carlisle Energy Services, Inc.   **(1)**
1275 Ritner Hwy, Carlisle, PA 17013
Tel.: (877) 269-7183
Lighting Equipment Mfr
N.A.I.C.S.: 335139

Carlisle Fluid Technologies, Inc.   **(1)**
16430 N Scottsdale Rd Ste 450, Scottsdale, AZ 85254
Tel.: (480) 781-5250
Web Site: https://www.carlisleft.com
Sales Range: $75-99.9 Million
Liquid Finishing Systems & Products
N.A.I.C.S.: 325510
Andres Lacassie *(VP-Mktg & Sls-Americas)*
Caius McNaughton *(Mgr-Customer Svc)*

Subsidiary (Domestic):

Finishing Brands Holdings Inc.   **(2)**
320 Phillips Ave, Toledo, OH 43612-1467
Tel.: (419) 470-2000
Web Site: https://www.finishingbrands.com
Holding Company; Fluid Control Systems & Air Compressors Mfr
N.A.I.C.S.: 551112
Barry Holt *(Pres)*

Holding (Domestic):

BGK Finishing Systems   **(3)**
4131 Pheasant Rdg Dr NE, Minneapolis, MN 55449-7102
Tel.: (763) 784-0466
Web Site: http://www.bgk.com
Electric Infrared Equipment Mfr
N.A.I.C.S.: 334513

DeVilbiss Automotive Refinishing   **(3)**
11360 S Airfield Rd, Swanton, OH 43558
Tel.: (800) 445-3988
Web Site: http://www.autorefinishdevilbiss.com

Spray Guns & Related Equipment Mfr
N.A.I.C.S.: 333248

Holding (Non-US):

DeVilbiss Ransburg de Mexico, S. de R.L. de C.V.   **(3)**
Via Dr Gustavo Baz 3990, Col Barrientos, CP 54110, Tlalnepantla, Mexico
Tel.: (52) 55 5321 2300
Web Site: http://www.carlisleft.com.mx
Emp.: 80
Electrostatic Spray Painting Equipment Mfr & Sales
N.A.I.C.S.: 423830
Gerardo Perez *(Gen Mgr)*

Finishing Brands - International   **(3)**
Ringwood Road, Bournemouth, Dorset, BH11 9LH, United Kingdom
Tel.: (44) 1202571111
Web Site: http://www.carlisle.com
Industrial Spray Finishing Equipment Mfr
N.A.I.C.S.: 333248

Ransburg Industrial Finishing K.K.   **(3)**
15-5 Fukuura 1-Chome, Kanazawa-Ku, Yokohama, 236-0004, Japan   **(100%)**
Tel.: (81) 457856421
Web Site: http://www.ransburg.co.jp
Sales Range: $150-199.9 Million
Emp.: 100
Electrostatic Finishing Equipment
N.A.I.C.S.: 423830
Mike Kinoshita *(Pres)*

Subsidiary (Domestic):

Hosco Fittings LLC   **(2)**
28026 Oakland Oaks Ct, Wixom, MI 48393
Tel.: (248) 912-1750
Web Site: https://carlisleft.com
Precision Steel & Fluid Handling Components Mfr
N.A.I.C.S.: 332721

Subsidiary (Domestic):

Classic Precision, LLC   **(3)**
28016 Oakland Oaks Ct, Wixom, MI 48393
Tel.: (248) 349-8811
Web Site: http://www.classicprecision.net
Precision Machining Services
N.A.I.C.S.: 332710

Subsidiary (Domestic):

Integrated Dispense Solutions, LLC   **(2)**
14310 Industrial Ctr Dr, Shelby, MI 48315
Tel.: (586) 554-7404
Web Site: http://www.i-dispense.com
Dispensing Equipment Designer & Mfr
N.A.I.C.S.: 333914
Dave Ritchie *(Gen Mgr)*

Carlisle Medical Technologies (Dongguan) Co., Ltd   **(1)**
No 2 Qiaolong Rd Xinhu Industrial Park Dengwu Qiaotou Town, Dongguan, 523533, China
Tel.: (86) 76982556339
Medical Device Mfr
N.A.I.C.S.: 334510

Carlisle Mexico, S.A. de C.V.   **(1)**
Avenida Victor Hugo No 330 Fraccionamiento Complejo, Industrial Chihuahua, Chihuahua, 31109, Mexico
Tel.: (52) 14422000
Web Site: http://www.carlisle.com
Sales Range: $100-124.9 Million
Cable & Wire Mfr
N.A.I.C.S.: 335931

Carlisle Specialty Products Group   **(1)**
13925 Ballantyne Corporate Pl Ste 400, Charlotte, NC 28277
Tel.: (704) 501-1100
Sales Range: $250-299.9 Million
Automotive Transmission, Brake & Body Mfr
N.A.I.C.S.: 336350

Subsidiary (Domestic):

Carlisle Industrial Brake & Friction   **(2)**
1031 Hillside Dr, Bloomington, IN 47401

Tel.: (812) 336-3811
Web Site: http://www.carlislebrake.com
Sales Range: $300-349.9 Million
Automotive Brake System & Hydraulic
Component Developer & Mfr
N.A.I.C.S.: 336340

Motion Control Industries, Inc. (2)
1031 E Hillside Dr, Bloomington, IN 47401-6586
Tel.: (812) 336-3811
Sales Range: $75-99.9 Million
Emp.: 150
Mfr of Brakes
N.A.I.C.S.: 327910

Carlisle, LLC (1)
16430 N Scottsdale Rd Ste 400, Scottsdale, AZ 85254
Tel.: (480) 781-5000
Roofing & Coating Product Mfr
N.A.I.C.S.: 324122

Henry Company LLC (1)
999 N Pacific Coast Hwy Ste 800, El Segundo, CA 90245
Tel.: (310) 955-9200
Web Site: http://us.henry.com
Roof Sealants & Coatings Mfr
N.A.I.C.S.: 324122
Frank J. Ready (Pres & CEO)
John Dobson (Sr VP-Research & Development)
Kirk R. Kandler (Sr VP)
Kurt Leibel (Sr VP-Operations)
Christian Nolte (CMO)
Miguel Hernandez (Chief Legal Officer)
Marc Tropper (Sr VP)
Jim Wueste (Sr VP)
Mark Longfellow (Sr VP)
Rusty Kennington (CIO)

Plant (Domestic):

**Henry Company LLC -
Kimberton** (2)
336 Coldstream Rd, Kimberton, PA 19460
Tel.: (610) 933-8888
Web Site: https://www.henry.com
Protective Roof Coatings & Sealers Mfr
N.A.I.C.S.: 324122

Japan Power Brakes (1)
2453 9 Aza Dainooka, Atsugi, 243-0213, Japan
Tel.: (81) 462477564
Web Site: http://www.i-jpb.co.jp
Emp.: 25
Power Distribution & Specialty Transformer Mfr
N.A.I.C.S.: 335311
Colm Gallagher (VP)

LHI Technology Shenzen Co. (1)
172 Xinghua Community Area Guanlan Str.
Longhua New Dist, Shenzhen, 518110, China
Tel.: (86) 75529830005
Medical Cable Mfr
N.A.I.C.S.: 332618

Petersen Aluminum Corporation (1)
1008 Tonne Rd, Elk Grove Village, IL 60007
Tel.: (800) 723-2523
Web Site: http://www.pac-clad.com
Warehousing; Fabrication of Aluminum &
Steel Architectural Metals, Roll Formed
Building Panels & Architectural Signage
N.A.I.C.S.: 331315

Subsidiary (Domestic):

Charleston Industries Inc (2)
101 Industrial Dr, Charleston, MS 38921
Tel.: (662) 647-5525
Web Site: http://www.cisigns.com
Sales Range: $10-24.9 Million
Emp.: 20
Sign Company
N.A.I.C.S.: 339950

**Tri-Star Electronics International,
Inc.** (1)
2201 Rosecrans Ave, El Segundo, CA 90245
Tel.: (310) 536-0444
Electron Tube Mfr
N.A.I.C.S.: 334419
Sherri Young (Acct Mgr)
Ben Damon (Mgr-IT)

TriStar Electronics SA (1)
Centro nord-sud stabile 3a, Bioggio, 6934, Switzerland
Tel.: (41) 916115161
Web Site: http://www.tristarelectronics.com
Emp.: 80
Fabricated Metal Products Mfr
N.A.I.C.S.: 332311
Paolo Conti (Gen Mgr)

CARLYLE SECURED LENDING, INC.
1 Vanderbilt Ave Ste 3400, New York, NY 10017
Tel.: (212) 813-4900   MD
Web Site:
https://www.carlylesecuredlending.com
Year Founded: 2012
CGBD—(NASDAQ)
Rev.: $207,256,000
Assets: $2,041,697,000
Liabilities: $1,124,274,000
Net Worth: $917,423,000
Earnings: $104,042,000
Fiscal Year-end: 12/31/22
Banking & Investment Services
N.A.I.C.S.: 523150
Thomas M. Hennigan (CFO & Chief Risk Officer)
Joshua Lefkowitz (Chief Compliance Officer & Sec)
Michael Hadley (Chief Investment Officer, VP & Head-Underwriting)
Justin V. Plouffe (Pres & CEO)

CARMAX, INC.
12800 Tuckahoe Creek Pkwy, Richmond, VA 23238
Tel.: (804) 747-0422   VA
Web Site: https://www.carmax.com
Year Founded: 1996
KMX—(NYSE)
Rev.: $26,536,040,000
Assets: $27,196,797,000
Liabilities: $21,123,057,000
Net Worth: $6,073,740,000
Earnings: $479,204,000
Emp.: 29,836
Fiscal Year-end: 02/29/24
Automotive Distr
N.A.I.C.S.: 441110
Charles Joseph Wilson (COO & Exec VP)
Diane Long Cafritz (Chief HR Officer & Sr VP-Legal)
Sarah Lane (VP-Marketing)
Shamim Mohammad (CIO, CTO & Exec VP)
Jon G. Daniels (Sr VP-CarMax Auto Finance)
Tyrone Payton (Reg VP-Svc Ops)
Jill A. Livesay (Chief Acctg Officer & VP)
Darren C. Newberry (Sr VP-Store Ops)
Enrique N. Mayor-Mora (CFO & Sr VP)
David Lowenstein (Asst VP-Investor Relations)
James R. Lyski (CMO & Exec VP)
William D. Nash (Pres & CEO)

Subsidiaries:

**CarMax Auto Superstores Services,
Inc.** (1)
12800 Tuckahoe Creek Pkwy, Richmond, VA 23238-1115
Tel.: (804) 747-0422
Web Site: http://www.carmax.com
Auto Repair Services
N.A.I.C.S.: 811111

**CarMax Auto Superstores West
Coast, Inc.** (1)
1131 Central Ave, Duarte, CA 91010-2425
Tel.: (626) 357-9972

Sales Range: $125-149.9 Million
Emp.: 500
Used Car Stores
N.A.I.C.S.: 441120

CarMax Auto Superstores, Inc. (1)
12800 Tuckahoe Creek Pkwy, Richmond, VA 23238
Tel.: (804) 747-0422
Web Site: http://www.carmax.com
Used Car Stores
N.A.I.C.S.: 441120

Branch (Domestic):

CarMax Auto (2)
1121 E Memorial Rd, Oklahoma City, OK 73131   (100%)
Tel.: (405) 529-5924
Web Site: http://www.carmax.com
Sales Range: $10-24.9 Million
Emp.: 150
Used Cars
N.A.I.C.S.: 441120

CarMax Business Services, LLC (1)
225 Chastain Meadows Ct, Kennesaw, GA 30144
Tel.: (678) 594-4800
Web Site: http://www.carmax.com
Financial Services
N.A.I.C.S.: 522320

Subsidiary (Domestic):

CarMax Auto Finance (2)
225 Chastain Meadows Court Ste 210, Kennesaw, GA 30160
Tel.: (678) 594-4800
Web Site: http://www.carmax.com
Auto Financing Services
N.A.I.C.S.: 522310
Mike Callahan (CFO & VP)

**CarMax Enterprise Services,
LLC** (1)
12800 Tuckahoe Creek Pkwy, Richmond, VA 23238-1115
Web Site: https://www.carmax.com
Motor Vehicle Financial Leasing Services
N.A.I.C.S.: 525990

CARMELL CORPORATION
2403 Sidney St Ste 300, Pittsburgh, PA 15203
Tel.: (412) 894-8248   DE
Web Site:
https://www.carmellcosmetics.com
Year Founded: 2008
CTCX—(NASDAQ)
Rev.: $68,772
Assets: $63,948,803
Liabilities: $39,199,793
Net Worth: $24,749,010
Earnings: ($15,445,087)
Emp.: 7
Fiscal Year-end: 12/31/23
Biotechnology Research & Development Services
N.A.I.C.S.: 541714

CARNEGIE DEVELOPMENT, INC.
3495 Lakeside Dr Ste 1087, Reno, NV 89509   NV
Year Founded: 1988
CDJM—(NASDAQ)
Liabilities: $120,000
Net Worth: ($120,000)
Earnings: ($60,000)
Fiscal Year-end: 12/31/18
Automation Engineering Services
N.A.I.C.S.: 541330

CARNIVAL CORPORATION
3655 NW 87th Ave, Miami, FL 33178-2428
Tel.: (305) 599-2600   Pa
Web Site:
https://www.carnivalcorp.com
Year Founded: 1972
CCL—(NYSE)
Rev.: $21,593,000,000

Assets: $49,120,000,000
Liabilities: $42,238,000,000
Net Worth: $6,882,000,000
Earnings: ($74,000,000)
Emp.: 104,000
Fiscal Year-end: 11/30/23
Holding Company; Cruise Line Owner & Operator
N.A.I.C.S.: 551112
David Bernstein (CFO & Chief Acctg Officer)
Arnaldo Perez (Sec & Sr VP)
Lars Ljoen (Chief Maritime Officer)
Josh Weinstein (Pres, CEO & Chief Climate Officer)
Jerry Montgomery (Chief HR Officer)
Josh Leibowitz (Pres-Seabourn)
Felix Eichhorn (Pres-Aida Cruises)
Jan G. Swartz (Exec VP-Strategic Operations)
Peter C. Anderson (Chief Ethics & Compliance Officer)
Gregory A. Sullivan (CIO)
Simon Palethorpe (Pres)
Enrique Miguez (Gen Counsel)
Vice Admira William (Chief Maritime Officer)
Bettina Deynes (Chief HR Officer)
Renata Ribeiro (Sr VP)
Jody Venturoni (Chief Comm Officer)
Marguerite Fitzgerald (Pres)
Paul Ludlow (Pres)
Gustavo Antorcha (Pres)
John Padgett (Pres)
Ann Sherry (Chm-Australia)
Roger Frizzell (Chief Comm Officer & Sr VP)

Subsidiaries:

Carnival plc (1)
Carnival House 100 Harbour Parade, Southampton, SO15 1ST, United Kingdom
Tel.: (44) 2380655000
Web Site: http://www.carnivalplc.com
Rev.: $12,167,999,999
Assets: $51,702,999,999
Liabilities: $44,637,999,999
Net Worth: $7,064,999,999
Earnings: ($6,092,999,999)
Emp.: 84,999
Fiscal Year-end: 11/30/2022
Holding Company; Cruise Line Owner & Operator
N.A.I.C.S.: 551112
David Bernstein (CFO & Chief Acctg Officer)
Arnaldo Perez (Gen Counsel & Sec)
Josh Weinstein (Pres, CEO & Chief Climate Officer)
Randall J. Weisenburger (Chm)
Joshua Chad Leibowitz (Pres-Seabourn)
William R. Burke (Chief Maritime Officer)
Josh Weinstein (COO)
Peter C. Anderson (Chief Ethics & Compliance Officer)
Gregory A. Sullivan (CIO)
Bettina Deynes (Pres, CEO, Chief HR Officer, Sec & Sr VP)
Enrique Miguez (Pres, CEO, Chief HR Officer, Corp Counsel, Sec & Sr VP)
Renata Ribeiro (Pres, CEO, Chief HR Officer, Corp Counsel, Sec, Sr VP & Sr VP)
Jody Venturoni (Pres, CEO, Chief Comm Officer, Chief HR Officer, Corp Counsel, Sec, Sr VP & Sr VP)
Marguerite Fitzgerald (Pres)
Sture Myrmell (Pres)
Paul Ludlow (Pres)

Subsidiary (Non-US):

AIDAradio GmbH (2)
Simon-von-Utrecht-Strasse 1, 20359, Hamburg, Germany
Tel.: (49) 4030239023
Web Site: https://www.aidaradio.de
Radio Broadcasting Services
N.A.I.C.S.: 516110

Subsidiary (Domestic):

Carnival (UK) Limited (2)
Carnival House 100 Harbour Parade,

Carnival Corporation—(Continued)

Southampton, SO15 1ST, United Kingdom
Tel.: (44) 2380656653
Cruise Ship Operator
N.A.I.C.S.: 483112
Sture Myrmell (Pres)

Subsidiary (Non-US):

Carnival Corporation Hong King Limited (2)
Unit 1207 the Gateway Tower 1 Harbour City, Tsim Sha Tsui, Kowloon, China (Hong Kong)
Tel.: (852) 29528088
Emp.: 20
Cruise Terminal Services
N.A.I.C.S.: 561520
Nancy Chung (Gen Mgr)

Carnival Corporation Korea Ltd. (2)
6F The Exchange Seoul 21 Mugyo-ro, Jung-gu, Seoul, 045-20, Korea (South)
Tel.: (82) 23181918
Web Site: http://www.princess.com
Travel Tour Operator
N.A.I.C.S.: 561520

Subsidiary (US):

Carnival Cruise Lines (2)
Carnival Pl 3655 NW 87th Ave, Miami, FL 33178-2428
Tel.: (305) 599-2600
Web Site: http://www.carnival.com
Sales Range: $1-4.9 Billion
Emp.: 20,000
Cruise Line Services
N.A.I.C.S.: 483112
Christine Duffy (Pres)
Lars Ljoen (Chief Operations Officer)
Adolfo Perez (Sr VP-Global Sls & Trade Mktg)
Ken Tate (Chief Comml Officer)
Emeril Lagasse (Chief Culinary Officer)

Subsidiary (Non-US):

Carnival Maritime GmbH (2)
Grosser Grasbrook 9, 20457, Hamburg, Germany
Tel.: (49) 40302 393 1100
Web Site: https://www.carnival-maritime.com
Emp.: 250
Telecommunication Servicesb
N.A.I.C.S.: 517810
Hermann J. Klein (Mng Dir & Exec VP)

Carnival Support Services India Private Limited (2)
Kohinoor City Tower 2 Floor 5 Kirol Road Off LBS Marg Kurla West, Mumbai, 400 070, India
Tel.: (91) 7942529292
Web Site: https://www.cruisecareers.in
Recruiting Services
N.A.I.C.S.: 561311

Chantier Naval de Marseille SAS (2)
Terre Plein de Mourepiane - Porte 4 CS 40034, 13344, Marseille, Cedex, France
Tel.: (33) 491580982
Web Site: https://cndm.fr
Emp.: 110
Shipyard Services
N.A.I.C.S.: 336611

Costa Crociere S.p.A. (2)
Piazza Piccapietra 48, 16121, Genoa, Italy
Tel.: (39) 0109997988
Web Site: https://www.costacrociere.it
Sales Range: $100-124.9 Million
Emp.: 1,000
Cruise Line
N.A.I.C.S.: 483114

Subsidiary (US):

Costa Cruise Lines Inc. (3)
880 SW 145th Ave Ste 102, Pembroke Pines, FL 33027
Tel.: (954) 266-5600
Web Site: http://www.costacruises.com
Sales Range: $25-49.9 Million
Cruise Line Operator
N.A.I.C.S.: 483112

Subsidiary (Non-US):

Costa Cruceros S.A. (2)

Av Corrientes 327 10th floor, C1043AAD, Buenos Aires, Argentina
Tel.: (54) 1145907788
Web Site: https://www.costacruceros.com
Travel Tour Operator
N.A.I.C.S.: 561520

Costa Cruzeiros Agencia Maritima e Turismo Ltda. (2)
Av Paulista 460 - 9 andar, Bela Vista, 01310-100, Sao Paulo, Brazil
Tel.: (55) 1121233677
Web Site: https://www.costacruzeiros.com
Passenger Transportation Services
N.A.I.C.S.: 483112

Cozumel Cruise Terminal S.A. de C.V. (2)
Costera Sur, 77600, Cozumel, Quintana Roo, Mexico
Tel.: (52) 9878691984
Web Site: http://www.puertamaya.com
Cruise Terminal Services
N.A.I.C.S.: 561520

Subsidiary (US):

Cunard Line Ltd. (2)
24305 Town Ctr Dr Ste 200, Valencia, CA 91355   (70%)
Tel.: (661) 753-1000
Web Site: http://www.cunard.com
Sales Range: $400-449.9 Million
Cruise Line Operator
N.A.I.C.S.: 483112
Nicole Knox (Dir-Mktg)
Simon Palethorpe (Pres)
Jamie Paiko (VP-Sls)
Jeriel Lubaton (Dir-Pricing & Demand)

Branch (Non-US):

Cunard Line Ltd. - UK Office (3)
Carnival House 100 Harbour Parade, Southampton, SO15 1ST, United Kingdom
Tel.: (44) 3443388641
Web Site: http://www.cunard.com
Sales Range: $100-124.9 Million
Luxury Hotels, Luxury Passenger Shipping
N.A.I.C.S.: 483114

Subsidiary (Non-US):

Ecospray Technologies S.r.L. (2)
Via Ricotti 5, 27058, Voghera, PV, Italy
Tel.: (39) 0131854611
Web Site: https://www.ecospray.eu
Gas Cooling Services
N.A.I.C.S.: 213112

Grand Bahama Ship Yard Limited (2)
The Fishing Hole Road Grand Bahama, PO Box F-42623, Freeport, Bahamas
Tel.: (242) 2423504000
Web Site: http://www.grandbahamashipyard.com
Ship Building & Repair Services
N.A.I.C.S.: 336611
David Skentelbery (CEO)
Linda M. Turnquest (CFO)
Robert Couser (VP-Sls & Mktg)
Shannon Cooper (Project Mgr)
Valerie Barry (VP-HR)
Martin Currie (Project Mgr)
Gerard Douglas (Project Mgr)
Andrzej Joskowiak (Project Mgr)
Andrew Kemp (Project Mgr)
Ashley Burnett (Project Mgr)
Michael Butler (Mgr-Welding)
Brisco Rolle (Mgr-Steel Shop)
Elchico Godfrey (Mgr-Ship)
James Sands (Mgr-Ship)
Ricardo Saville (Mgr-Ship)
Philip Duncombe (Mgr-Quality Assurance)
Michael Mikolay (Mgr-Production)
Mark Wilson (Mgr-Plng & Resource)
Anthony Mannon (Mgr-Pipe)
Wellington Smith (Mgr-Mechanical)
Virgil Stuart (Mgr-Logistics)
David Lloyd (Mgr-Hull Treatment & Scaffolding)
Tyrone Farquharson (Mgr-HSSE)
Ekeila Sands (Mgr-HR)
Cleo Charlton (Mgr-Fin)
Martin Brent (Mgr-Estimating)
Craig Stark (Mgr-Cruise Svc)
Sam Miller (Mgr-Brokerage)
Adrian Baboi (Dir-Cruise Project Dev)
Donald Kierce Jr. (VP-Ops)

Holland America Line N.V. (2)
Otto Reuchlinweg 1110, 3072 MD, Rotterdam, Netherlands
Tel.: (31) 102976600
Web Site: http://www.hollandamerica.com
Water Transportation Services
N.A.I.C.S.: 483112
Stein Kruse (Grp CEO-Holland America Grp)

Subsidiary (US):

Holland America Line Inc. (3)
450 3rd Ave W, Seattle, WA 98119-4198   (100%)
Tel.: (206) 281-3535
Web Site: http://www.hollandamerica.com
Cruise Line Operators
N.A.I.C.S.: 561520
Beth Bodensteiner (Chief Comml Officer)
Michelle Sutter (VP-Sls-North America)
Gus Antorcha (Pres)
Jenny Verna (Mgr-Bus Dev-South Florida)
Bill Zucker (VP-PR & Comm)
Kacy Cole (VP-Mktg & ECommerce)

Division (Domestic):

Gray Line of Alaska (4)
450 3rd Ave W, Seattle, WA 98119 (100%)
Tel.: (206) 281-3535
Web Site: http://www.graylinealaska.com
Sales Range: $350-399.9 Million
Bus Tour Operation
N.A.I.C.S.: 485510

Gray Line of Seattle (4)
4500 W Marginal Way SW, Seattle, WA 98106-1511
Tel.: (206) 624-5077
Web Site: http://www.graylineofseattle.com
Sales Range: $10-24.9 Million
Emp.: 25
Bus Tour Operation
N.A.I.C.S.: 485510

Westmark Hotels, Alaska (4)
450 3rd Ave W, Seattle, WA 98119-4198
Tel.: (206) 281-3535
Web Site: http://www.westmarkhotels.com
Sales Range: $10-24.9 Million
Bus Tour Operation
N.A.I.C.S.: 721110

Subsidiary (Domestic):

P&O Cruises Limited (2)
Carnival House 100 Harbour Parade, Southampton, SO15 1ST, Hampshire, United Kingdom   (100%)
Tel.: (44) 3443388003
Web Site: http://www.pocruises.com
Sales Range: $450-499.9 Million
Emp.: 1,000
Operator of Cruise Holidays Worldwide
N.A.I.C.S.: 561599

P&O Princess Cruises International Limited (2)
Carnival House 100 Harbour Parade, Southampton, SO15 1ST, United Kingdom
Tel.: (44) 8456780014
Web Site: http://www.pocruises.com
Passenger Transportation Services
N.A.I.C.S.: 483112

Subsidiary (US):

Princess Cruises (2)
24305 Town Center Dr, Santa Clarita, CA 91355   (100%)
Tel.: (661) 753-1530
Web Site: http://www.princess.com
Sales Range: $350-399.9 Million
Emp.: 1,500
Cruise Operator
N.A.I.C.S.: 483112
Gordon Ho (CMO)
Marshall Lancaster (CIO)
John Padgett (Pres)

Division (Domestic):

Princess Tours (3)
800 5th Ave Ste 2600, Seattle, WA 98104
Tel.: (206) 336-6000
Web Site: http://www.princesslodges.com
Sales Range: $1-9.9 Million
Emp.: 322
Cruise & Tour Operator

N.A.I.C.S.: 487110

Subsidiary (US):

Royal Hyway Tours, Inc. (2)
450 3rd Ave W, Seattle, WA 98119-4002
Tel.: (206) 336-5960
Emp.: 30
Passenger Transportation Services
N.A.I.C.S.: 483112
Dave McGlothlin (VP)

Subsidiary (Non-US):

Stazioni Maritime S.p.A. (2)
Ponte Dei Mille, Genoa, 16126, Italy
Tel.: (39) 0100898300
Web Site: http://www.smge.it
Passenger Transportation Services
N.A.I.C.S.: 483112

Terminal Napoli S.p.A. (2)
Molo Angioino Stazione Marittima, 80133, Naples, Italy
Tel.: (39) 0815514448
Web Site: http://www.terminalnapoli.it
Passenger Transportation Services
N.A.I.C.S.: 483112
Tomaso Cognolato (CEO)

Venezia Terminal Passeggeri S.p.A. (2)
Fabbricato 248, 30135, Venice, Marittima, Italy
Tel.: (39) 0412403000
Web Site: http://www.vtp.it
Marine Terminal Operator
N.A.I.C.S.: 488310
Galliano Di Marco (Mng Dir)
Fabrizio Spagna (Chm)

Welcome Travel Group S.p.A. (2)
7 Via Sebenico, 20124, Milan, Italy
Tel.: (39) 0244405699
Web Site: http://www.vacanzewelcometravel.it
Travel Tour Operator
N.A.I.C.S.: 561520

Westmark Hotels of Canada, Ltd. (2)
201 Wood Street, Whitehorse, Y1A 1C8, YT, Canada
Tel.: (867) 393-9700
Web Site: http://www.westmarkhotels.com
Hotel & Motel Operator
N.A.I.C.S.: 721110
Cindy Decarlo (Mgr-Tour & Travel)
Wendy Reid (Reg Mgr-Sls)
Taryn Hemmings (Mgr-Catering)
Oscar Pacheco (Gen Mgr)

Subsidiary (US):

Westours Motor Coaches, LLC (2)
450 3rd Ave W, Seattle, WA 98119
Web Site: http://www.graylinealaska.com
Tour & Sightseeing Operator

White Pass & Yukon Route (2)
201 2nd Ave, Skagway, AK 99840-0435
Tel.: (907) 983-2217
Web Site: https://wpyr.com
Line-Haul Railroads
N.A.I.C.S.: 482111
Tyler H. Rose (Exec Dir-HR & Strategic Plng)
Bob Berto (Pres)
Vickey Moy (Exec Dir-Passenger Ops)
Jaime Bricker (Dir-PR)
Jacqueline Taylor-Rose (Mgr-Mktg & Product Dev)

Navitrans S.H.L. (1)
Via Alcide De Gasperi 45, 80133, Naples, Italy
Tel.: (39) 08119807100
Web Site: https://www.navitransnapoli.com
Marine Shipping Services
N.A.I.C.S.: 517111

CARPARTS.COM, INC.
1301 Ave T, Grand Prairie, TX 75050
Tel.: (424) 702-1455   DE
Web Site: https://www.carparts.com
Year Founded: 1995
PRTS—(NASDAQ)
Rev.: $582,440,000
Assets: $235,336,000

Liabilities: $139,768,000
Net Worth: $95,568,000
Earnings: ($10,339,000)
Emp.: 1,529
Fiscal Year-end: 01/01/22
Auto Parts Internet Sales
N.A.I.C.S.: 423120
Alfredo Gomez (Gen Counsel & VP)
Ryan Lockwood (CFO)
Michael Huffaker (COO)
Stephanie Urbach (Chief HR Officer)
Christina Thelin (CMO)
Kals Subramanian (CTO)
David Meniane (CEO)

Subsidiaries:

Whitney Automotive Group, Inc. (1)
225 N Michigan Ave Ste 1000, Chicago, IL 60601
Tel.: (312) 431-6000
Automotive Parts & Accessories Retailer
N.A.I.C.S.: 441330

CARPENTER TECHNOLOGY CORPORATION
1735 Market St 15th Fl, Philadelphia, PA 19103
Tel.: (610) 208-2000   DE
Web Site:
https://www.carpentertechnolo
gy.com
Year Founded: 1889
CRS—(NYSE)
Rev.: $2,759,700,000
Assets: $3,291,700,000
Liabilities: $1,662,900,000
Net Worth: $1,628,800,000
Earnings: $186,500,000
Emp.: 4,600
Fiscal Year-end: 06/30/24
Specialty Metals & Engineered Products Mfr, Fabricator & Distr
N.A.I.C.S.: 331513
I. Martin Inglis (Chm)
Timothy F. Lain (Sr VP)
James D. Dee (Sec, Sr VP & Gen Counsel)
Joseph E. Haniford (Sr VP-Ops)
Brian J. Malloy (COO & Sr VP)
Elizabeth A. Socci (Chief Acctg Officer, VP & Controller)
Tony R. Thene (Pres & CEO)
Rachelle H. Thompson (Chief HR Officer & VP)
Shakthimani Logasundaram (Chief Digital Officer)
Suniti Moudgil (CTO)

Subsidiaries:

Aceros Fortuna, S.A. de C.V. (1)
Av Lic Juan Fernandez Albarran 21, Fracc Industrial San Pablo Xalpa, 54090, Tlalnepantla, Mexico
Tel.: (52) 5550104820
Web Site: http://www.acerosfortuna.com.mx
Steel Distr
N.A.I.C.S.: 331513

Carpenter Additive U.S., LLC (1)
110 S Campus Dr, Imperial, PA 15126
Tel.: (412) 788-2856
Metal Additive Mfr
N.A.I.C.S.: 332119

Carpenter Powder Products AB (1)
Nybyvagen, PO Box 45, 644 21, Torshalla, Sweden
Tel.: (46) 16150100
Web Site: http://www.carpenterpowder.com
Sales Range: $25-49.9 Million
Emp.: 75
Powder Products Mfr
N.A.I.C.S.: 325510

Carpenter Powder Products GmbH (1)
Dusselthaler Strasse 9, 40211, Dusseldorf, Germany
Tel.: (49) 21117520830
Web Site: http://www.carpenterpowder.com

Sales Range: $25-49.9 Million
Emp.: 2
Powder Products
N.A.I.C.S.: 325998

Carpenter Specialty Wire Products (1)
144 Old Elloree Rd, Orangeburg, SC 29115   (100%)
Tel.: (803) 534-6910
Web Site: http://www.cartech.com
Sales Range: $25-49.9 Million
Emp.: 110
Specialty Wire Mfr
N.A.I.C.S.: 331110

Carpenter Technology (Canada) Ltd. (1)
6114 Edwards Boulevard, Mississauga, L5T 2V7, ON, Canada   (100%)
Tel.: (905) 564-5255
Web Site: http://www.cartech.com
Sales Range: $10-24.9 Million
Emp.: 7
Alloy Sales
N.A.I.C.S.: 423510

Carpenter Technology (Europe) S.A. (1)
Rue Edouard Belin 11 Mont-Saint-Guibert, 1435, Brussels, Haren, Belgium   (100%)
Tel.: (32) 10686010
Web Site: http://www.cartech.com
Sales Range: $25-49.9 Million
Emp.: 25
Alloy Sales
N.A.I.C.S.: 423510

Carpenter Technology (UK) Ltd. (1)
Unit 3 Adams Way Arden Industrial Est, Alcester, B49 6PU, Worcestershire, United Kingdom   (100%)
Tel.: (44) 1789767340
Web Site: http://www.cartech.com
Sales Range: $10-24.9 Million
Emp.: 6
Alloy Sales
N.A.I.C.S.: 423510

Carpenter Technology Asia Pacific Pte. Ltd. (1)
No 1 Grange Road 05-05 Orchard Building, Singapore, 239693, Singapore   (100%)
Tel.: (65) 67382401
Web Site: http://www.cartech.com
Sales Range: $1-9.9 Million
Emp.: 10
Metal Products Sales
N.A.I.C.S.: 541330

Latrobe Specialty Metals Company, LLC (1)
2626 Ligonier St, Latrobe, PA 15650-3246
Tel.: (724) 537-7711
Specialty Steel Products Mfr
N.A.I.C.S.: 331110

Division (Domestic):

Latrobe Specialty Steel Company Distribution (2)
1551 Vienna Pkwy, Vienna, OH 44473
Tel.: (330) 609-5137
Web Site: http://www.latrobesteel.com
Sales Range: $50-74.9 Million
Emp.: 100
Steel Product Distr
N.A.I.C.S.: 423510

Shalmet Corporation (1)
116 Pinedale Industrial Rd, Orwigsburg, PA 17961   (100%)
Tel.: (570) 366-1414
Sales Range: $75-99.9 Million
Emp.: 100
Stainless Steel, Superalloys, Titanium, Carbon Steel Bar & Coil Products Conversion Services
N.A.I.C.S.: 332813
Kurt Krammes (Gen Mgr)

Talley Metals Technology, Inc. (1)
205 Talley Metals Ln, McBee, SC 29101   (100%)
Tel.: (843) 335-7540
Sales Range: $75-99.9 Million
Emp.: 300
Stainless Steel Mfr
N.A.I.C.S.: 331110

Peter Bergman (Gen Mgr)
Ken Norris (VP)

CARRIAGE HOUSE EVENT CENTER INC.
558 Castle Pines Pkwy B-4, Castle Pines, CO 80108
Tel.: (303) 517-8845   CO
Web Site:
https://www.carriagehouseone
onta.com
Year Founded: 2010
CRGH—(OTCIQ)
Assets: $29,006
Liabilities: $154,800
Net Worth: ($125,794)
Earnings: ($15,434)
Emp.: 1
Fiscal Year-end: 12/31/23
Event Management Services
N.A.I.C.S.: 711310
Janel Ray (Sec)
A. Terry Ray (Pres, CEO & CFO)

CARRIAGE SERVICES, INC.
3040 Post Oak Blvd Ste 300, Houston, TX 77056
Tel.: (713) 332-8424   DE
Web Site:
https://www.carriageservices.com
Year Founded: 1991
CSV—(NYSE)
Rev.: $370,174,000
Assets: $1,192,950,000
Liabilities: $1,055,816,000
Net Worth: $137,134,000
Earnings: $41,381,000
Emp.: 1,174
Fiscal Year-end: 12/31/22
Funeral Homes & Funeral Services
N.A.I.C.S.: 812210
Melvin C. Payne (Founder)
Adeola Olaniyan (Controller)
Paul D. Elliott (Partner-Regional & Sr VP)
Steven D. Metzger (Pres & Sec)
Shawn R. Phillips (Partner-Regional & Sr VP)
Carlos R. Quezada (Vice Chm & CEO)
Robbie Pape (Partner-)
Shane T. Pudenz (Sr VP)
Rob Franch (CIO)

Subsidiaries:

Barnett, Demrow & Ernst, Inc (1)
545 Waynesburg Rd, Waynesburg, KY 40489
Tel.: (606) 379-2011
Funeral Support Services
N.A.I.C.S.: 812210
John Friend (Office Mgr)

CSI Funeral Services of Massachusetts, Inc. (1)
3040 Post Oak Blvd Ste 300, Houston, TX 77056
Tel.: (713) 332-8400
Sales Range: $25-49.9 Million
Emp.: 150
Funeral Support Services
N.A.I.C.S.: 812210

Carriage Funeral Holdings Inc. (1)
3040 Post Oak Blvd Ste 300, Houston, TX 77056-3028
Tel.: (713) 332-8400
Web Site: http://www.carriageservices.com
Sales Range: Less than $1 Million
Emp.: 2,000
Funeral Service & Crematories
N.A.I.C.S.: 812210
Melvin C. Payne (Chm & CEO)

Cataudella Funeral Home, Inc. (1)
126 Pleasant Valley St, Methuen, MA 01844
Tel.: (978) 685-5379
Web Site: https://www.cataudellafh.com
Funeral Support Services
N.A.I.C.S.: 812210

Christopher P. Chetsas (Co-Owner & Mng Partner)
Joseph J. Cataudella (Co-Owner & Pres)
Yesenia Torres (Dir-Licensed Funeral)
Doug Sears (Dir-Licensed Funeral)

Cloverdale Park, Inc. (1)
1200 N Cloverdale Rd, Boise, ID 83713
Tel.: (208) 375-2212
Web Site:
http://www.cloverdalefuneralhome.com
Funeral Support Services
N.A.I.C.S.: 812210
Dave Salove (Mng Partner)

Cochrane (1)
103 Lincoln St, Roseville, CA 95678
Tel.: (916) 783-7171
Emp.: 4
Funeral Support Services
N.A.I.C.S.: 812210
Doug Wagemann (Mgr)

Cochrane's Chapel of the Roses, Inc. (1)
1900 St James Pl 4th Fl, Houston, TX 77056
Tel.: (713) 332-8400
Funeral Home Operator
N.A.I.C.S.: 812210

Cypress Fairbanks Funeral Home (1)
9926 Jones Rd, Houston, TX 77065
Tel.: (281) 897-9823
Web Site: https://www.cyfairfunerals.com
Funeral Homes & Funeral Services
N.A.I.C.S.: 812210
Lois Keller (Mng Partner & Dir-Licensed Funeral)
Anastasius Avist (Mng Partner)

Fairfax Memorial Funeral Home, LLC (1)
9902 Braddock Rd, Fairfax, VA 22032
Tel.: (703) 425-9702
Web Site:
https://www.fairfaxmemorialfuneral
home.com
Funeral Home Cremation Services
N.A.I.C.S.: 812210
Archer Harmon (Gen Mgr)
Diana Downey (Ops Mgr)
Erin Sherman (Office Mgr)
Steffany Sisco (Dir-Funeral)
Victor Holland (Mng Partner)

Forastiere Family Funeral Services, Inc. (1)
45 Locust St, Springfield, MA 01108
Tel.: (413) 733-5311
Web Site:
http://www.forastierefuneralhome.com
Sales Range: $10-24.9 Million
Emp.: 20
Funeral Support Services
N.A.I.C.S.: 812210
Frank A. Forastiere (Pres)

Greenlawn Funeral Homes, Inc. (1)
3506 N National Ave, Springfield, MO 65803
Tel.: (417) 833-1111
Web Site:
http://www.greenlawnfuneralhome.com
Sales Range: $1-9.9 Million
Emp.: 65
Funeral Homes & Funeral Services
N.A.I.C.S.: 812210
Frank Burke (CEO)

Lombardo Funeral Home (1)
899 Niagara Falls Blvd, Amherst, NY 14228-4228
Tel.: (716) 837-7100
Web Site:
http://www.lombardofuneralhome.com
Funeral Homes & Funeral Services
N.A.I.C.S.: 812210
Joseph P. Lombardo (Pres)

Oakmont Memorial Park & Mortuary (1)
2099 Reliez Valley Rd, Lafayette, CA 94549
Tel.: (925) 935-3311
Web Site: http://www.oakmontmortuary.com
Sales Range: $1-9.9 Million
Emp.: 32
Funeral Homes & Funeral Services
N.A.I.C.S.: 812210

Carriage Services, Inc.—(Continued)

Salvador M. Orozco *(Mng Partner)*
Tom Richards *(Mgr-Crematory)*
Michael Trolan *(Dir-Funeral)*

Rest Haven Funeral Home, Inc. **(1)**
3701 Rowlett Rd, Rowlett, TX 75088
Tel.: (972) 412-5195
Web Site: http://www.resthavenfuneral.com
Funeral Homes & Funeral Services
N.A.I.C.S.: 812210
Dewayne Cain *(Founder)*

Rolling Hills Memorial Park **(1)**
4100 Hilltop Dr, Richmond, CA 94803
Tel.: (510) 223-6161
Web Site:
    https://www.rollinghillsmemorialpark.com
Funeral Support Services
N.A.I.C.S.: 812210

Wilson & Kratzer Mortuaries Inc. **(1)**
455 24th St, Richmond, CA 94804
Tel.: (510) 232-4383
Web Site:
    https://www.civiccenterchapel.com
Sales Range: $1-9.9 Million
Emp.: 15
Funeral Service & Crematories
N.A.I.C.S.: 812210
Jordan Baldwin *(Dir-Funeral)*

CARRIER GLOBAL CORPORA-TION

13995 Pasteur Blvd, Palm Beach Gardens, FL 33418
Tel.: (561) 365-2000 DE
Web Site:
    https://www.corporate.carrier.com
Year Founded: 2019
CARR—(NYSE)
Rev.: $20,421,000,000
Assets: $26,086,000,000
Liabilities: $18,010,000,000
Net Worth: $8,076,000,000
Earnings: $3,534,000,000
Emp.: 52,000
Fiscal Year-end: 12/31/22
Holding Company; Heating, Ventilation & Air Conditioning Products Mfr & Whslr
N.A.I.C.S.: 551112
Kevin J. O'Connor *(Chief Legal Officer & Sr VP)*
Patrick P. Goris *(CFO & Sr VP)*
Kevin O'Connor *(Chief Legal Officer & Sr VP)*
Nadia Villeneuve *(Chief HR Officer & Sr VP)*
Christopher Nelson *(Pres-HVAC)*
Ajay Agrawal *(Sr VP-Strategy & Svcs)*
Kyle Crockett *(VP & Controller)*
Mary Milmoe *(VP-Communications-Marketing)*
Jennifer Anderson *(Sr VP-Strategy-Business Development)*
Eva Azoulay *(Sr VP)*
Chris Kmetz *(Sr VP-Engineering)*
Bobby George *(Sr VP)*
Adrian Button *(Sr VP)*
Hakan Yilmaz *(CTO)*
Timothy N. White *(Chief Product Officer & Sr VP)*
David L. Gitlin *(Chm, Pres & CEO)*

Subsidiaries:

AHI Carrier FZC **(1)**
B1 21-24 SAIF Zone, PO Box 122341, Sharjah, United Arab Emirates
Tel.: (971) 6 504 5700
Web Site: https://www.ahi-carrier.com
Air Conditioning Equipment Mfr & Distr
N.A.I.C.S.: 333415

Access Solutions Belgium B.V. **(1)**
Gentsesteenweg 141 A, 2800, Mechelen, Belgium
Tel.: (32) 15649526
Web Site: https://access-solutions.be
Information Technology Services

N.A.I.C.S.: 541511

Automated Logic Australia Pty. Limited **(1)**
Unit 15 19-23 Clarinda Road, Oakleigh, 3167, VIC, Australia
Tel.: (61) 395445411
Web Site: https://automatedlogic.com.au
Software Development Services
N.A.I.C.S.: 541511

B. Grimm Carrier (Thailand) Limited **(1)**
1858/77-78 Interlink Tower Bangna Building 16th Floor, Debaratana Road Km 4 5 Bangna Tai Subdistrict Bangna District, Bangkok, 10260, Thailand
Tel.: (66) 20909992
Web Site: https://carrierthailand.com
Air Conditioning Equipment Distr
N.A.I.C.S.: 423730

Beijing Chubb Fire Security Systems Co., Limited **(1)**
18F Jingtai Tower No 24 Jianguomenwai Avenue, Chaoyang District, Beijing, 100022, China
Tel.: (86) 400 842 8534
Web Site: https://www.carrier.com
Security System Mfr & Distr
N.A.I.C.S.: 423610

Brokerbay Inc. **(1)**
90 Sumach St - Suite 408, Toronto, M5A 4R4, ON, Canada
Tel.: (416) 885-3140
Web Site: https://www.brokerbay.com
HVACR Product Mfr & Distr
N.A.I.C.S.: 333415

Carrier (Malaysia) Sdn. Bhd. **(1)**
Lot 10F-1 10th Floor Tower 5 PFCC Jalan Puteri 1/2 Bandar Puteri, 47100, Puchong, Selangor, Malaysia
Tel.: (60) 38 065 6228
Web Site: https://www.carrier.com
Air Conditioning Equipment Distr
N.A.I.C.S.: 423730

Carrier Aircon Lanka Private Limited **(1)**
3510 Level 35 West Tower WTC, Colombo, Sri Lanka
Tel.: (94) 117494107
Air Conditioning Equipment Mfr & Distr
N.A.I.C.S.: 333415

Carrier Aktiebolag **(1)**
Arods Industrivag 32 Hisings Backa, 422 43, Gothenburg, Sweden
Tel.: (46) 31655544
Air Conditioning Equipment Mfr & Distr
N.A.I.C.S.: 333415

Carrier Australia Pty Ltd **(1)**
314 Boundary Road, Dingley, Melbourne, 3172, VIC, Australia
Tel.: (61) 385510331
Web Site: https://www.carrier.com
Air Conditioning Equipment Mfr & Distr
N.A.I.C.S.: 333415

Carrier Chladiaca Technika Slovakia s.r.o. **(1)**
Dlha 91, 949 07, Nitra, Slovakia
Tel.: (421) 377764011
Air Conditioning Equipment Mfr & Distr
N.A.I.C.S.: 333415

Carrier Commercial Refrigeration (Thailand) Ltd. **(1)**
1858/63-74 Floor 14-15 Debaratana Road Km 4 5, Bangna Tai Subdistrict Bangna District, Bangkok, 10260, Thailand
Tel.: (66) 20909999
Web Site: https://www.carrier.co.th
Refrigeration Food Mfr & Distr
N.A.I.C.S.: 333241

Carrier Corporation **(1)**
13995 Pasteur Blvd, Palm Beach Gardens, FL 33418
Tel.: (561) 365-2000
Web Site: http://www.carrier.com
Sales Range: $5-14.9 Billion
Emp.: 53,000
Holding Company; Heating, Ventilation, Air Conditioning & Refrigeration Products Mfr & Whslr
N.A.I.C.S.: 551112

Chris Kmetz *(Sr VP-Engrg)*

Subsidiary (Domestic):

Automated Logic Corporation **(2)**
1150 Roberts Blvd, Kennesaw, GA 30144
Tel.: (770) 429-3000
Web Site:
    http://www.branches.automatedlogic.com
Sales Range: $50-74.9 Million
Emp.: 270
Temperature Controls, Automatic
N.A.I.C.S.: 334512

Subsidiary (Domestic):

Nlyte Software Limited **(3)**
275 Raritan Ctr Pkwy, Edison, NJ 08837
Tel.: (732) 395-6920
Web Site: http://www.nlyte.com
Software Publisher
N.A.I.C.S.: 513210
Douglas A. Sabella *(Pres & CEO)*

Subsidiary (Non-US):

Carrier (Thailand) Limited **(2)**
1858/63-74 Floor 14-15 Debaratana Road Km 4 5, Bangna Tai Subdistrict Bangna District, Bangkok, 10260, Thailand **(49%)**
Tel.: (66) 20909999
Web Site: https://www.carrier.co.th
Sales Range: $100-124.9 Million
Emp.: 270
Air-Conditioning Units Distr
N.A.I.C.S.: 423730

Carrier Air Conditioning Sales & Service (Shanghai) Co Ltd **(2)**
6/F Sheng Building No 266 Hankou Road, Shanghai, 200001, China
Tel.: (86) 2123063486
Air Conditioning Machinery Distr
N.A.I.C.S.: 333415

Carrier Airconditioning & Refrigeration Limited **(2)**
Kherki Daula Post, Narsingpur, Gurgaon, 122 001, Haryana, India
Tel.: (91) 1244825500
Web Site: https://www.carrier.com
Emp.: 1,000
Airconditioning & Refrigeration Equipment Mfr
N.A.I.C.S.: 333415

Subsidiary (Domestic):

Carrier Bryant Midsouth **(2)**
915 Murfreesboro Pke, Nashville, TN 37217-1501
Tel.: (615) 399-1776
Web Site: http://www.carrierenterprise.com
Sales Range: $50-74.9 Million
Emp.: 100
Heating & Air Conditioning Services
N.A.I.C.S.: 423730

Subsidiary (Non-US):

Carrier Enterprise Canada Ltd. **(2)**
1515 Drew Road, Mississauga, L5S 1Y8, ON, Canada **(100%)**
Tel.: (905) 672-0606
Web Site: http://www.carrier.ca
Sales Range: $75-99.9 Million
Emp.: 500
Air Conditioner Distr
N.A.I.C.S.: 423620

Division (Domestic):

Carrier Fire & Security **(2)**
13995 Pasteur Blvd, Palm Beach Gardens, FL 33418
Tel.: (561) 365-2000
Web Site: http://www.corporate.carrier.com
Fire & Security Products & Services
N.A.I.C.S.: 334419
Jurgen Timperman *(Pres)*

Subsidiary (Domestic):

UTC Fire & Security Corporation **(3)**
9 Farm Springs Rd, Farmington, CT 06037
Tel.: (860) 284-3000
Fire Safety & Security Products & Services
N.A.I.C.S.: 561621

Subsidiary (Non-US):

Angus Fire (S.A.) Limited **(4)**

260 Boeing Rd E Bedfordview, Johannesburg, 2109, South Africa
Tel.: (27) 116530400
Web Site: http://www.angusfire.co.uk
Sales Range: $75-99.9 Million
Emp.: 100
Fire Suppression Foam Concentrates Mfr
N.A.I.C.S.: 922160

Autronica Fire and Security AS **(4)**
Bromstadveien 59, 7047, Trondheim, Norway
Tel.: (47) 90905500
Web Site: https://www.autronicafire.com
Sales Range: $125-149.9 Million
Emp.: 200
Fire Safety Equipment Mfr
N.A.I.C.S.: 334512

CHUBB FIRE & SECURITY LIMITED **(4)**
PO Box 16, Manchester, M24 4JY, United Kingdom **(100%)**
Tel.: (44) 5611231
Web Site: http://www.chubb.co.uk
Installation, Rental & Maintenance of Intruder & Fire Detection Systems
N.A.I.C.S.: 561621
Robert John Sloss *(Sec)*

Subsidiary (Domestic):

Carrier Fire & Security Americas Corporation **(4)**
8985 Town Center Pkwy, Bradenton, FL 34202-5129
Tel.: (941) 739-4200
Web Site:
    http://www.utcfssecurityproducts.com
Sales Range: $1-4.9 Billion
Emp.: 4,700
Security Systems Products & Services
N.A.I.C.S.: 561621
Dean Seavers *(CEO)*

Subsidiary (Domestic):

Detector Electronics Corporation **(5)**
6901 W 110th St, Minneapolis, MN 55438
Tel.: (952) 941-5665
Web Site: https://www.det-tronics.com
Sales Range: $75-99.9 Million
Emp.: 240
Electronic Equipment for Detection of Fires & Explosions
N.A.I.C.S.: 561621

Fireye, Inc. **(5)**
3 Manchester Rd, Derry, NH 03038
Tel.: (603) 432-4100
Web Site: https://www.fireye.com
Sales Range: $50-74.9 Million
Emp.: 120
Flame Safeguard & Combustion Controls Equipment Mfr
N.A.I.C.S.: 335314

Division (Domestic):

Kidde Fire Safety **(5)**
1016 Corporate Park Dr, Mebane, NC 27302
Tel.: (919) 563-5911
Web Site: http://www.kidde.com
Sales Range: Less than $1 Million
Fire & Safety Products Mfr
N.A.I.C.S.: 922160

Subsidiary (Domestic):

Badger Fire Protection Inc. **(6)**
1016 Corporate Park Dr, Mebane, NC 27302
Tel.: (434) 973-4361
Web Site: http://www.badgerfire.com
Fire Extinguishers & Automatic Fire Suppression Systems Mfr
N.A.I.C.S.: 333414

Subsidiary (Domestic):

Kidde Fire Trainers, Inc. **(5)**
5 Pearl Court Unit D, Allendale, NJ 07401
Tel.: (201) 300-8100
Web Site: https://kft.firetrainer.com
Sales Range: $10-24.9 Million
Emp.: 63
Mfr of Specialized Firefighter Training Installations for Domestic & International Markets
N.A.I.C.S.: 811210

Kidde-Fenwal, Inc. (5)
400 Main St, Ashland, MA 01721-2150
Tel.: (508) 881-2000
Web Site: http://www.kidde-fenwal.com
Sales Range: $75-99.9 Million
Emp.: 500
Temperature Controls & Fire & Explosion
Protection Systems & Repair Kits Mfr
N.A.I.C.S.: 922160

Lenel Systems International Inc. (5)
1212 Pittsford-Victor Rd, Pittsford, NY
14534
Tel.: (585) 248-9720
Web Site: http://www.lenel.com
Sales Range: $10-24.9 Million
Emp.: 200
Integrated Systems & Security Software
Services
N.A.I.C.S.: 541511

Onity, Inc. (5)
4001 Fairview Industrial Dr SE, Salem, OR
97302
Tel.: (770) 497-3949
Web Site: https://www.onity.com
Electronic Locking Mechanisms Designer,
Mfr & Whslr
N.A.I.C.S.: 333310

**Walter Kidde Portable Equipment
Inc.** (5)
1394 S Third St, Mebane, NC 27302-8315
Tel.: (919) 563-5911
Web Site: http://www.kidde.com
Emp.: 450
Fire Extinguisher Mfr
N.A.I.C.S.: 334290
Jim Ward (Pres)

Subsidiary (Non-US):

Chubb Fire & Security Limited (4)
Littleton Road, Ashford, TW15 1TZ, Middle-
sex, United Kingdom
Tel.: (44) 1784424100
Web Site: http://www.chubbfiresecurity.com
Security & Fire Protection Services
N.A.I.C.S.: 561990

Chubb Fire & Security Pty Ltd (4)
33 Talavera Road, Macquarie Park, 2113,
NSW, Australia
Tel.: (61) 1800654435
Web Site: http://www.quell.com.au
Security & Fire Protection Services
N.A.I.C.S.: 561990

Chubb France (4)
10 avenue de l'entreprise Parc Saint Chris-
tophe - Pole Magellan 1, 95855, Cergy-
Pontoise, Cedex, France
Tel.: (33) 13 017 3737
Web Site: https://www.chubbfiresecurity.com
Fire & Rescue Services
N.A.I.C.S.: 922160
Francoise Ramirez (Officer-Comm)

Chubb Group Security Limited (4)
Pentagon House Sir Frank Whittle Road,
Derby, DE21 4XA, United Kingdom
Tel.: (44) 1332202020
Investment Management Service
N.A.I.C.S.: 523940

Chubb Hong Kong Ltd. (4)
10/F 8 Lam Chak Street, Kowloon Bay,
Kowloon, China (Hong Kong)
Tel.: (852) 27058800
Web Site: https://www.chubb.com.hk
Sales Range: $500-549.9 Million
Emp.: 2,000
Security Equipment
N.A.I.C.S.: 561621

Chubb Nederland B.V. (4)
Hettenheuvelweg 51, Amsterdam, 1101 BM,
Netherlands
Tel.: (31) 206516171
Web Site: http://www.chubbfs.nl
Financial Trust Services
N.A.I.C.S.: 523991

**Chubb Security Holdings Australia
Pty Ltd** (4)
149-155 Milton St, Ashfield, 2131, NSW,
Australia
Tel.: (61) 299304222
Holding Company
N.A.I.C.S.: 551112

Chubb Singapore Private Limited (4)
60 Macpherson Road 05-01/07, Singapore,
348615, Singapore (100%)
Tel.: (65) 60225848
Web Site: https://chubbfs.com
Sales Range: $10-24.9 Million
Emp.: 200
Security & Fire Protection Products & Ser-
vices
N.A.I.C.S.: 922160

Chubb Systems Limited (4)
Shadsworth Road, Blackburn, BB1 2PR,
United Kingdom
Tel.: (44) 1254688583
Web Site: http://www.chubbsystems.co.uk
Electronic Security & Safety System Ser-
vices
N.A.I.C.S.: 561621

Eau et Feu (4)
Zone industrielle Sud Est Rue Aloys, PO
Box 1008, Senefelder, 51683, Reims,
France
Tel.: (33) 326506410
Web Site: http://www.eauetfeu.fr
Sales Range: $25-49.9 Million
Emp.: 19
Fire Hose & Fire Suppression Foam Mfr
N.A.I.C.S.: 922160

Fyrnetics (Hong Kong) Limited (4)
Rm 308 3/F & 1/F Guardforce Ctr 3 Hok
Yuen St E, Hung Hom, Hong Kong, China
(Hong Kong)
Tel.: (852) 25534534
Smoke Alarm Mfr
N.A.I.C.S.: 922160

G.W. Sprinkler A/S (4)
Kastanievej 15, 5620, Glamsbjerg, Denmark
Tel.: (45) 64722055
Web Site: http://www.gwsprinkler.com
Sales Range: $25-49.9 Million
Emp.: 20
Water Sprinkler Systems & Equipment Mfr
N.A.I.C.S.: 333998
Richard Alber (Gen Mgr)
Brian Kjeldsen Jensen (Mgr-Ops & Supply
Chain)

**Gulf Security Technology Co.,
Ltd.** (4)
Floor 7 Block A Beijing Marriott Hotel 7th
Jianguomen South Street, Dongcheng Dis-
trict, Beijing, 100102, China
Tel.: (86) 1065540785
Web Site: https://www.gst.com.cn
Fire Detection Systems Designer, Mfr &
Distr
N.A.I.C.S.: 334290

Kidde Australia Pty Ltd. (4)
Ground Floor 10 Ferntree Place, Notting
Hill, 3168, VIC, Australia
Tel.: (61) 1800672171
Web Site: http://www.kidde.com.au
Sales Range: $10-24.9 Million
Emp.: 35
Fire Detection & Suppression Systems &
Products Mfr
N.A.I.C.S.: 922160

Kidde International Limited (4)
Windsor House, Slough, SL3 0HB, Berk-
shire, United Kingdom
Tel.: (44) 1753683245
Emp.: 60
Holding Company
N.A.I.C.S.: 551112
Peter Mcardle (Mng Dir)

Kidde Products Limited (4)
Stokenchurch House Oxford Road, Stoken-
church, HP14 3SX, Buckinghamshire,
United Kingdom
Tel.: (44) 1494480410
Emp.: 30
Fire Protection Equipment Mfr
N.A.I.C.S.: 334290
John Simpson (Gen Mgr)

Marioff Corporation Oy (4)
Plaza Business Park Halo Ayritie 24, PO
Box 1002, 01511, Vantaa, Finland
Tel.: (358) 10 688 0000
Web Site: https://www.marioff.com
Emp.: 150
Commercial Water Sprinkler & Other Fire
Protection Products Mfr & Distr

N.A.I.C.S.: 333998

Pyrene Corporation (4)
340 4 Valley Dr, Vaughan, L4K 5Z1, ON,
Canada
Tel.: (905) 695-6060
Web Site: http://www.kiddecanada.com
Sales Range: $10-24.9 Million
Emp.: 30
Fire Detection & Suppression Systems Distr
N.A.I.C.S.: 922160

SFS Fire Services Limited (4)
871/872 Plymouth Road, Slough, SL1 4LP,
Berkshire, United Kingdom
Tel.: (44) 2038414626
Web Site: http://www.sfs-fire.com
Emp.: 300
Fire Safety Systems Design, Installation &
Maintenance Services
N.A.I.C.S.: 238210

Division (Domestic):

Hall & Kay Fire Engineering (5)
Sterling Park Clapgate Lane, Woodgate
Valley, Birmingham, B32 3BU, United King-
dom
Tel.: (44) 1214213311
Web Site: http://www.hkfire.co.uk
Sales Range: $25-49.9 Million
Emp.: 40
Designer of All Forms of Fixed Fire Protec-
tion Systems
N.A.I.C.S.: 922160
Tony Pierson (CEO)

Subsidiary (Non-US):

UTC Fire & Security Canada (4)
5201 Explorer Drive, Mississauga, L4W
4H1, ON, Canada
Tel.: (905) 629-2600
Fire & Safety Equipment Mfr
N.A.I.C.S.: 339113

Subsidiary (Domestic):

**United Technologies Electronic Con-
trols, Inc.** (3)
3650 W 200 N, Huntington, IN 46750-9002
Tel.: (260) 359-3514
Web Site: http://www.uteccontrols.com
Microprocessor-Based Controls Mfr
N.A.I.C.S.: 334513
Trent Karshner (Mgr-Sls-Natl)

Subsidiary (Non-US):

**Carrier Kaltetechnik Deutschland
GmbH** (2)
Surther Hauptstrasse 173, 50999, Cologne,
Germany
Tel.: (49) 22 366 0101
Web Site: http://www.carrier.com
Sales Range: $50-74.9 Million
Emp.: 125
Refrigerated & Non-Refrigerated Display
Equipment Mfr
N.A.I.C.S.: 333415
Udo Laeis (Member-Mgmt Bd)

Subsidiary (Non-US):

AS Sisustaja (3)
Kalda 7b, Tallinn, 11625, Estonia
Tel.: (372) 6502300
Web Site: http://www.sisustaja.ee
Sales Range: $10-24.9 Million
Emp.: 17
Refrigerated & Non-Refrigerated Display
Equipment Mfr
N.A.I.C.S.: 333415

**Ahmet Yar Refrigerating Industry
Co.** (3)
Kemalpasa OSB Mahallesi 9 Sokak No 9,
Kemalpasa, Izmir, Turkiye
Tel.: (90) 2328771750
Web Site: http://www.ahmetyar.com.tr
Sales Range: $100-124.9 Million
Emp.: 350
Refrigerated & Non-Refrigerated Display
Equipment Mfr
N.A.I.C.S.: 333415

Baltic Master (3)
Dariaus ir Giereno str 175, 2189, Vilnius,
Lithuania
Tel.: (370) 52306520
Web Site: http://www.balticmaster.com

Sales Range: $125-149.9 Million
Refrigerated & Non-Refrigerated Display
Equipment Mfr
N.A.I.C.S.: 333415

**Carrier Chladici Technika Spol.
s.r.o.** (3)
Ve Zlibku 2402, 193 00, Prague, Czech
Republic
Tel.: (420) 281095111
Web Site: http://www.carrier-cht.cz
Sales Range: $25-49.9 Million
Emp.: 68
Refrigerated & Non-Refrigerated Display
Equipment Mfr
N.A.I.C.S.: 333415
Kartel Fort (Mng Dir)

**Carrier Chlodnictwo Polska Sp. z
o.o.** (3)
ul Konstruktorska 13 budynek KBC, 02-676,
Warsaw, Poland
Tel.: (48) 22 544 0100
Web Site: https://www.carrier.com
Sales Range: $25-49.9 Million
Emp.: 40
Mfr Refrigerated & Non-Refrigerated Dis-
play Equipment
N.A.I.C.S.: 333415

**Carrier Hutestechnika Forgalmazo
Magyarorszag Kft** (3)
Vaci ut 99, 1139, Budapest, Hungary
Tel.: (36) 14370510
Web Site: http://www.carrier-
refrigeration.com
Sales Range: $25-49.9 Million
Emp.: 45
Mfr Refrigerated & Non-Refrigerated Dis-
play Equipment
N.A.I.C.S.: 333415

**Carrier Kaltetechnik Austria
Ges.m.b.** (3)
Altwirthgasse 6 -10, 1232, Vienna, Austria
Tel.: (43) 810955033
Web Site: http://www.carrier-kt.at
Sales Range: $75-99.9 Million
Mfr Refrigerated & Non-Refrigerated Dis-
play Equipment
N.A.I.C.S.: 333415

Carrier Kaltetechnik Schweiz AG (3)
Netzibodenstrasse 32, CH 4133, Pratteln,
Switzerland
Tel.: (41) 618166666
Web Site: http://www.carrier.com
Sales Range: $25-49.9 Million
Emp.: 70
Mfr Refrigerated & Non-Refrigerated Dis-
play Equipment
N.A.I.C.S.: 333415

Carrier Refrigeracion Iberica SA (3)
Avenida Real de Pinto 91 Ed C Esc 2,
28021, Madrid, Spain
Tel.: (34) 934527184
Web Site: https://www.carrier.com
Sales Range: $25-49.9 Million
Emp.: 50
Sales & Refrigerated & Non-Refrigerated
Display Equipment.
N.A.I.C.S.: 423740

Carrier Refrigeration Ireland (3)
Electrolux Hse Longmile Rd, Cookstown,
Dublin, Ireland
Tel.: (353) 14568216
Sales Range: $10-24.9 Million
Emp.: 6
Mfr Refrigerated & Non-Refrigerated Dis-
play Equipment
N.A.I.C.S.: 333415

**Carrier Refrigeration Operation Italy
SpA** (3)
Via Montegrotto 125, Torreglia, 35038, Pa-
dova, Italy
Tel.: (39) 049 9998666
Web Site: http://www.carrier-
refrigeration.com
Refrigerated & Non-Refrigerated Display
Equipment Mfr
N.A.I.C.S.: 333415

Linde Refrigeration Systems Ltd. (3)
Flat B 8/F Milos Industrial Building 2-10 Tai
Yuen Street, Kwai Chung, Hong Kong, NT,
China (Hong Kong)
Tel.: (852) 26762600

Carrier Global Corporation—(Continued)

Web Site: http://www.linde.com.hk
Sales Range: $25-49.9 Million
Emp.: 26
Mfr Refrigerated & Non-Refrigerated Display Equipment
N.A.I.C.S.: 333415

Smeva B.V. (3)
J F Kennedylaan 27, PO Box 30, 5550 AA, Valkenswaard, Netherlands
Tel.: (31) 402073200
Web Site: https://www.smeva.com
Sales Range: $100-124.9 Million
Emp.: 150
Mfr Refrigerated & Non-Refrigerated Display Equipment
N.A.I.C.S.: 333415
C. Smith *(Mng Dir)*

United Refrigerator SDN BHD (3)
PTD 124299 Jalan Kempas Lama, Kampung Seelong Jaya, 81300, Skudai, Johor, Malaysia
Tel.: (60) 75951588
Web Site: https://www.ur.com.my
Sales Range: $25-49.9 Million
Emp.: 100
Mfr Refrigerated & Non-Refrigerated Display Equipment
N.A.I.C.S.: 333415

Subsidiary (Non-US):

Carrier Mexico S.A. de C.V. (2)
Carretera Villa de Garcia Km 1 3 Parque Industrial Stiva, Santa Catarina, 66376, Nuevo Leon, Mexico
Tel.: (52) 8181247600
Heating, Ventilation & Airconditioning Equipment Mfr
N.A.I.C.S.: 333415

Subsidiary (Domestic):

Carrier Northeast (2)
241 Clinton Rd, Caldwell, NJ 07006
Tel.: (973) 227-1199
Web Site: http://www.carrier.com
Rev.: $170,000,000
Emp.: 75
Air Conditioning & Ventilation Equipment & Supplies
N.A.I.C.S.: 425120

Carrier Oklahoma (2)
6101 W Reno Ave Ste 550A, Oklahoma City, OK 73127
Tel.: (405) 792-7174
Web Site: http://www.carrier.com
Rev.: $31,000,000
Emp.: 6
Warm Air Heating Equipment & Supplies
N.A.I.C.S.: 423730

Carrier Puerto Rico (2)
Amelia Distribution Center Diana St Ste 47 Lot P-1, Guaynabo, PR 00908-0357 (100%)
Tel.: (787) 788-9350
Web Site: http://www.carrier.com
Sales Range: $25-49.9 Million
Emp.: 59
Aircraft Engines & Engine Parts
N.A.I.C.S.: 423730

Carrier Rental Systems (2)
100 Southbelt Industrial Dr, Houston, TX 77047
Tel.: (713) 413-4200
Web Site: https://www.carrier.com
Sales Range: $25-49.9 Million
Emp.: 75
N.A.I.C.S.: 532412
Chris Opie *(VP-Product Mktg & Platform Strategy)*

Subsidiary (Non-US):

Carrier Singapore (Pte.) Ltd. (2)
28 Teban Gardens Crescent, Singapore, 608926, Singapore (100%)
Tel.: (65) 65675522
Web Site: http://www.carrier.com.sg
Sales Range: $50-74.9 Million
Emp.: 150
Marketing & Sales of Air Conditioning Units
N.A.I.C.S.: 423730
Oonwee Chin *(Mng Dir)*

Carrier Transicold Europe (2)
3 rue Joseph Monier Le Cristalia, 92500, Rueil-Malmaison, France
Tel.: (33) 141422800
Refrigeration Equipment Distr
N.A.I.C.S.: 423740

Subsidiary (Domestic):

International Comfort Products Corporation (2)
650 Heil Quaker Ave, Lewisburg, TN 37091-2135
Tel.: (931) 359-3511
Web Site: http://www.icpusa.com
Rev.: $600,000,000
Emp.: 200
Electric, Oil & Gas Furnaces; Central Air Conditioning; Heating & Cooling Products
N.A.I.C.S.: 333414

Subsidiary (Non-US):

International Comfort Products Corporation (Canada) (3)
1 First Canadian Pl Ste 6600, Toronto, M5X 1B8, ON, Canada (100%)
Tel.: (615) 771-0200
Emp.: 3,000
Air Conditioning, Heating Equipment & Related Products
N.A.I.C.S.: 333415

Subsidiary (Domestic):

NORESCO, LLC (2)
1 Research Dr Ste 400 C, Westborough, MA 01581
Tel.: (508) 614-1000
Web Site: http://www.noresco.com
Sales Range: $10-24.9 Million
Emp.: 60
Energy Management & Efficiency Services
N.A.I.C.S.: 541330
Neil Petchers *(Pres & CEO)*
David G. Mannherz *(CFO & Exec VP)*
Randall Clark *(Sr VP & Gen Mgr)*
Michael S. Beccaria *(Sr VP & Gen Mgr-Performance Contracting)*
Natasha Shah *(VP-Federal Bus Dev)*
Bill Z. Foster *(VP-Bus Dev)*
Wade Carleton *(Sr VP-Construction)*
Jerry Reilley *(VP-Facilities, Ops & Maintenance)*
Pablo Hernandez *(VP-Fin)*
Troy Walters *(VP & Gen Mgr-Sustainability Svcs)*
Nick Gagas *(VP-Engrg)*
Adam Nee *(Gen Counsel & VP)*

Subsidiary (Domestic):

NORESCO (3)
2540 Frontier Ave Ste 100, Boulder, CO 80301
Tel.: (303) 444-4149
Web Site: http://www.noresco.com
Sales Range: $25-49.9 Million
Emp.: 88
Engineeering Services
N.A.I.C.S.: 541330

Branch (Domestic):

NORESCO (3)
510 Thornall St Ste 170, Edison, NJ 08837
Tel.: (732) 590-0122
Web Site: http://www.noresco.com
Emp.: 50
Engineeering Services
N.A.I.C.S.: 541330

NORESCO, LLC (3)
2750 Prosperity Ave Ste 130, Fairfax, VA 22031
Tel.: (703) 846-9700
Web Site: https://www.noresco.com
Emp.: 20
Energy Management & Efficiency Services
N.A.I.C.S.: 541330

Subsidiary (Domestic):

Sensitech Inc. (2)
800 Cummings Ctr Ste 258X, Beverly, MA 01915-6197
Tel.: (978) 927-7033
Web Site: https://www.sensitech.com

Sales Range: $25-49.9 Million
Cold Chain Logistics Temperature Monitoring & Management Equipment Mfr
N.A.I.C.S.: 334513

Subsidiary (Domestic):

FreightWatch International (USA), Inc. (3)
7501 N Capital of Texas Hwy Ste A200, Austin, TX 78731
Tel.: (512) 225-6490
Web Site: http://www.freightsecurity.net
Freight Global Positioning System Technologies & Software Developer, Mfr, Distr & Support Services
N.A.I.C.S.: 334220

Plant (Domestic):

Sensitech Inc. - Redmond Plant (3)
8801 148th Ave NE, Redmond, WA 98052
Tel.: (425) 883-7926
Web Site: http://www.sensitech.com
Sales Range: $10-24.9 Million
Cold Chain Logistics Temperature Monitoring & Management Equipment Mfr
N.A.I.C.S.: 334513

Subsidiary (Domestic):

StrionAir, Inc. (2)
410 S Arthur Ave, Louisville, CO 80027
Tel.: (303) 664-1140
Web Site: http://www.strionair.com
Sales Range: $25-49.9 Million
Emp.: 50
Air Purification Equipment Mfr
N.A.I.C.S.: 333413
Douglas Powell *(Gen Mgr)*

United Electric Company, L.P. (2)
501 Galveston St, Wichita Falls, TX 76301
Tel.: (940) 397-2100
Web Site: http://www.magicaire.com
Sales Range: $125-149.9 Million
Air Conditioning & Heating Components Mfr
N.A.I.C.S.: 333415

Carrier Fire & Security Australia Pty Ltd (1)
10 Ferntree Place, Notting Hill, 3168, VIC, Australia
Tel.: (61) 395629537
Web Site:
https://www.firesecurityproducts.com.au
Security System Mfr & Distr
N.A.I.C.S.: 423610

Carrier Fire & Security B.V. (1)
Kelvinstraat 7, 6003 DH, Weert, Netherlands
Tel.: (31) 495579579
Web Site: https://nl.firesecurityproducts.com
Security System Mfr & Distr
N.A.I.C.S.: 423610

Carrier Fire & Security Danmark A/S (1)
Ellekaer 9A 2 floor, 2730, Herlev, Denmark
Tel.: (45) 43529005
Web Site:
https://dk.firesecurityproducts.com
Security System Mfr & Distr
N.A.I.C.S.: 423610

Carrier Fire & Security Deutschland GmbH (1)
Hammfelddamm 6, 41460, Neuss, Germany
Tel.: (49) 213136630
Web Site:
https://de.firesecurityproducts.com
Security System Mfr & Distr
N.A.I.C.S.: 423610

Carrier Fire & Security EMEA BV (1)
Pegasus Park - De Kleetlaan 3, 1831, Diegem, Brussels, Belgium
Tel.: (32) 27158930
Web Site:
https://be.firesecurityproducts.com
Security System Mfr & Distr
N.A.I.C.S.: 423610

Carrier Fire & Security Espana SL (1)
Verge de Guadalupe 3, Esplugues de Llobregat, 08950, Barcelona, Spain
Tel.: (34) 934809070
Security System Mfr & Distr

N.A.I.C.S.: 423610

Carrier Fire & Security France S.A.S. (1)
4 rue Edmond Michelet ZA Fontaine du vaisseau, 93360, Neuilly-Plaisance, France
Tel.: (33) 149448900
Web Site: https://fr.firesecurityproducts.com
Security System Mfr & Distr
N.A.I.C.S.: 423610

Carrier Fire & Security Ireland Limited (1)
Units 1 and 2 2004 Orchard Avenue City West Business Campus Naas Road, Dublin, D24 XR15, Ireland
Tel.: (353) 14699760
Web Site: https://ie.firesecurityproducts.com
Security System Mfr & Distr
N.A.I.C.S.: 423610

Carrier Fire & Security Italia S.r.l. (1)
Via Sempione 247 c/d, 20016, Pero, MI, Italy
Tel.: (39) 023 206 0610
Web Site: https://it.firesecurityproducts.com
Security System Mfr & Distr
N.A.I.C.S.: 423610

Carrier Fire & Security Ltd. (1)
15F No 156 Sec 1 Zhongshan Rd, Banqiao Dist, New Taipei City, 220, Taiwan
Tel.: (886) 289643777
Automation Technology Services
N.A.I.C.S.: 518210

Carrier Fire & Security Norge AS (1)
Nils Hansens Vei 10C, 0667, Oslo, Norway
Tel.: (47) 22641100
Web Site:
https://no.firesecurityproducts.com
Security System Mfr & Distr
N.A.I.C.S.: 423610

Carrier Fire & Security Polska Sp. z o.o. (1)
ul Heweliusza 18, 80-890, Gdansk, Poland
Tel.: (48) 587606512
Web Site: https://pl.firesecurityproducts.com
Security System Mfr & Distr
N.A.I.C.S.: 423610

Carrier Fire & Security South Africa Pty Ltd (1)
29 Angus Crescent Longmeadow Business Park, East Edenvale, Johannesburg, 1609, South Africa
Tel.: (27) 115797300
Web Site:
https://za.firesecurityproducts.com
Security System Mfr & Distr
N.A.I.C.S.: 423610

Carrier Fire & Security Svorige AB (1)
Norgegatan 2, 164 32, Kista, Sweden
Tel.: (46) 854443350
Web Site:
https://se.firesecurityproducts.com
Security System Mfr & Distr
N.A.I.C.S.: 423610

Carrier Fire & Security UK Limited (1)
8 Newmarket Court Chippenham Drive, Milton Keynes, MK10 0AQ, United Kingdom
Tel.: (44) 1908281981
Web Site:
https://uk.firesecurityproducts.com
Security System Mfr & Distr
N.A.I.C.S.: 423610

Carrier Guam, Inc. (1)
PO Box 23847, Barrigada, GU 96921-3847
Tel.: (671) 647-9276
HVACR Product Mfr & Distr
N.A.I.C.S.: 333415

Carrier Kuwait Airconditioning K.S.C. (1)
PO Box 21326, Safat, 13063, Kuwait, Kuwait
Tel.: (965) 22066300
Web Site: https://www.carrier.com.kw
Air Conditioning Equipment Distr
N.A.I.C.S.: 423730

Carrier Midea India Private Limited (1)
1st Floor Pearl Tower Plot No - 51 Sector -

32, Gurgaon, 122 001, Haryana, India
Tel.: (91) 1246144300
Web Site: https://carriermideaindia.com
HVACR Product Mfr & Distr
N.A.I.C.S.: 333415

Carrier Oy (1)
Uutistie 3, 01770, Vantaa, Finland
Tel.: (358) 961 3131
Web Site: https://www.carrier.com
Air Conditioning Equipment Distr
N.A.I.C.S.: 423730

Carrier Refrigeration Denmark A/S (1)
Industrivej 21, Viby, Denmark
Tel.: (45) 86550255
HVACR Product Mfr & Distr
N.A.I.C.S.: 333415

Carrier Refrigeration Distribution France SAS (1)
259 Avenue du General Leclerc, 94703, Maisons-Alfort, Cedex, France
Tel.: (33) 14 397 6100
Web Site: https://www.carrier.com
Refrigeration Equipment Distr
N.A.I.C.S.: 423740

Carrier Refrigeration Norway AS (1)
Nils Hansens vei 10 C, 0667, Oslo, Norway
Tel.: (47) 23375840
HVACR Product Mfr & Distr
N.A.I.C.S.: 333415

Carrier Refrigeration Operations France SAS (1)
Z I Saint Marc Rue Saint Marc F, 41200, Romorantin-Lanthenay, France
Tel.: (33) 254954040
Refrigeration Equipment Distr
N.A.I.C.S.: 423740

Carrier Refrigeration Sweden AB (1)
Arods Industrivag 32 Hisings Backa, 422 43, Gothenburg, Sweden
Tel.: (46) 77 133 0099
Web Site: https://www.carrier.com
Refrigeration Equipment Distr
N.A.I.C.S.: 423740

Carrier Refrigeration UK Ltd. (1)
Meridian House Peters Way, East Point Business Park Sandy Lane West, Oxford, OX4 6LB, United Kingdom
Tel.: (44) 1865337700
HVACR Product Mfr & Distr
N.A.I.C.S.: 333415

Carrier Rental Systems (UK) Limited (1)
Unit 1 Maxx House Western Road, Bracknell, RG12 1QP, United Kingdom
Tel.: (44) 8701820859
Web Site:
  https://www.carrierrentalsystems.co.uk
HVACR Product Mfr & Distr
N.A.I.C.S.: 333415

Carrier Rental Systems Asia Pte Ltd (1)
28 Teban Gardens Crescent, Singapore, 608926, Singapore
Tel.: (65) 62610800
Web Site:
  https://www.carrierrentalsystems.sg
HVACR Product Mfr & Distr
N.A.I.C.S.: 333415

Carrier S.C.S. (1)
178 Rue du Fauge - Z I Les Paluds, 13400, Aubagne, Cedex, France
Tel.: (33) 44 218 0500
Refrigeration Equipment Distr
N.A.I.C.S.: 423740

Carrier Saudi Service Company (1)
Zahran Center 11th Floor Sultan Road, Jeddah, Saudi Arabia
Tel.: (966) 122375000
Refrigeration Equipment Distr
N.A.I.C.S.: 423740

Carrier Srl (1)
Via Anagnina 584, 00118, Rome, Italy
Tel.: (39) 06 723 4972
Web Site: https://carrieritalia.com
Telecommunication Servicesb
N.A.I.C.S.: 517810

Carrier Transicold (UK) Limited (1)

260 Cygnet Court - Centre Park, Warrington, WA1 1RR, United Kingdom
Tel.: (44) 1925401200
HVACR Product Mfr & Distr
N.A.I.C.S.: 333415

Carrier Transicold Austria GmbH (1)
Tagerbachstrasse 4 and 6, 4490, Sankt Florian, Austria
Tel.: (43) 722 467 4050
Web Site: https://www.carrier.com
Transportation Services
N.A.I.C.S.: 493120

Carrier Transicold Belgium BVBA (1)
Akkerhage 8, 9000, Gent, Belgium
Tel.: (32) 9 243 4747
Web Site: https://www.carrier.com
Transportation Services
N.A.I.C.S.: 493120

Carrier Transicold Espana, S.A. (1)
Avda de Italia n 12-Transport Center, Coslada, 28820, Madrid, Spain
Tel.: (34) 91 670 7410
Web Site: https://www.carrier.com
Transportation Services
N.A.I.C.S.: 493120

Carrier Transicold France (1)
Min de Rouen - Avenue du Commandant Bicheray, 76108, Rouen, Cedex, France
Tel.: (33) 232761700
Refrigerated Product Trucking Services
N.A.I.C.S.: 484230

Carrier Transicold Hong Kong Limited (1)
Unit 8 - 9 4F Vanta Industrial Centre 21-33 Tai Lin Pai Road, Kwai Chung, New Territories, China (Hong Kong)
Tel.: (852) 6562135896
HVACR Product Mfr & Distr
N.A.I.C.S.: 333415

Carrier Transicold Italia S.r.l. (1)
Viale Industria 14 -Zona Ind D3, 15121, Alessandria, Italy
Tel.: (39) 013 124 1711
Web Site: https://www.carrier.com
Transportation Services
N.A.I.C.S.: 493120

Carrier Transicold Netherlands B.V. (1)
Pittsburghstraat 21, 3047 BL, Rotterdam, Netherlands
Tel.: (31) 10 238 0100
Web Site: https://www.carrier.com
Transportation Services
N.A.I.C.S.: 493120

Carrier Transicold Polska Sp. z o.o. (1)
Ul Bobrowiecka 1, 00-728, Warsaw, Poland
Tel.: (48) 22 257 7355
Web Site: https://www.carrier.com
Transportation Services
N.A.I.C.S.: 493120

Carrier Transicold Scandinavia A/S (1)
Industrivej 30, 6330, Padborg, Denmark
Tel.: (45) 74670015
HVACR Product Mfr & Distr
N.A.I.C.S.: 333415

Carrier Transicold Sweden AB (1)
Torbornavagen 22, 253 68, Helsingborg, Sweden
Tel.: (46) 4 238 5580
Web Site: https://www.carrier.com
Transportation Services
N.A.I.C.S.: 493120

Carrier Vietnam Air Conditioning Company Limited (1)
6th Floor Intan Building 97 Nguyen Van Troi Street, Ward 11 Phu Nhuan District, Ho Chi Minh City, Vietnam
Tel.: (84) 283 999 1670
Web Site: https://www.carrier.com
Air Conditioning Equipment Distr
N.A.I.C.S.: 423730

Chubb Delta Telesurveillance (1)
Dardilly Business Park Chemin du Chateau d'eau, BP 70, 69543, Champagne-au-Mont-d'Or, Cedex, France
Tel.: (33) 47 252 7252

Web Site: https://www.chubbdelta.fr
Security Solution Services
N.A.I.C.S.: 561621

Chubb Deutschland GmbH (1)
Langenhorner Chaussee 623 - 625, 22419, Hamburg, Germany
Tel.: (49) 406116110
Web Site: https://chubbfs.com
HVACR Product Mfr & Distr
N.A.I.C.S.: 333415

Chubb Fire & Security B.V. (1)
Papendorpseweg 83, 3528 BJ, Utrecht, Netherlands
Tel.: (31) 88 112 4000
Web Site: https://www.chubbfiresecurity.com
Security Solution Services
N.A.I.C.S.: 561621

Chubb Ireland Limited (1)
Unit 2 Stillorgan Industrial Park, Dublin, A94 A2C4, Ireland
Tel.: (353) 1 295 3333
Security Solution Services
N.A.I.C.S.: 561621

Chubb New Zealand (1)
3 Fisher Crescent Mount Wellington, Auckland, 1060, New Zealand
Tel.: (64) 9 270 7441
Web Site: https://www.chubbfiresecurity.com
Security Solution Services
N.A.I.C.S.: 561621

Chubb Osterreich GmbH (1)
Campus 21 - Businesspark Wien Sud Liebermannstrasse F02/102, 2345, Brunn am Gebirge, Austria
Tel.: (43) 223 637 7300
Web Site: https://www.chubbfiresecurity.com
Security Solution Services
N.A.I.C.S.: 561621

Chubb Security Systems B.V.B.A. (1)
Alfons Gossetlaan 28a, 1702, Dilbeek, Belgium
Tel.: (32) 27170123
Web Site: http://www.chubbfiresecurity.com
Security Solution Services
N.A.I.C.S.: 561621

Climate & Controls Benelux B.V. (1)
Papendorpseweg 83, 3528 BJ, Utrecht, Netherlands
Tel.: (31) 885676700
HVACR Product Mfr & Distr
N.A.I.C.S.: 333415

Comercial Sensitech South America Limitada (1)
Avenida del Valle 961 Norte Oficina N 1706 Edificio Patio Mayor, Ciudad Empresarial Huechuraba, 8580678, Santiago, Chile
Tel.: (56) 229416600
Web Site: https://www.sensitech.com
Logistic Services
N.A.I.C.S.: 541614

EcoEnergy Insights Limited (1)
RGA Tech Park Block-2 2nd Floor Survey No 31/1 Sarjapura Main Road, Bengaluru, 560035, Karnataka, India
Tel.: (91) 8049045454
Information Technology Services
N.A.I.C.S.: 541511

Electronic Modular Services Limited (1)
Technology House Sea Street, Herne Bay, CT6 8JZ, Kent, United Kingdom
Tel.: (44) 1227369570
Web Site: https://www.emsgroup.co.uk
HVACR Product Mfr & Distr
N.A.I.C.S.: 333415

FIT Service S.P.A. (1)
Via Ing Pilade Riello 7, Legnago, 37045, Verona, Italy
Tel.: (39) 0442630111
Web Site: https://www.fitservice.it
Measuring Instrument Distr
N.A.I.C.S.: 423830

GLORIA GmbH (1)
Diestedder Str 39, Wadersloh, 59329, Warendorf, Germany
Tel.: (49) 252379349900
Web Site: https://www.gloria.de
Security & Investigation Services

N.A.I.C.S.: 561611

Kidde Brasil Ltda (1)
Av Dr Cardoso de Melo 1955 - 8, Andar Vila Olimpia, Sao Paulo, 04548-005, Brazil
Tel.: (55) 1921018400
Web Site: https://www.kidde.com
HVACR Product Mfr & Distr
N.A.I.C.S.: 333415

Marioff GmbH (1)
Hammfelddamm 6, 41460, Neuss, Germany
Tel.: (49) 30166 375 9910
Web Site: https://www.marioff.com
Fire Protection System Mfr
N.A.I.C.S.: 334290

Marioff Hi-Fog S.L.U. (1)
Avenida Real de Pinto 91 Edificio A-17, 28021, Madrid, Spain
Tel.: (34) 916418400
Fire Protection System Mfr
N.A.I.C.S.: 334290

Marioff Ltd. (1)
25 Earl Haig Road Hillington Park, Glasgow, G52 4JU, United Kingdom
Tel.: (44) 8453880880
Fire Protection System Mfr
N.A.I.C.S.: 334290

Marioff SAS (1)
Parc Kleber - Batiment Davis - Entree 403 165-167 boulevard de Valmy, 92700, Colombes, France
Tel.: (33) 188547988
Fire Protection System Mfr
N.A.I.C.S.: 334290

Marioff SRL (1)
Via Matteotti 24, 20016, Pero, Italy
Tel.: (39) 023 391 5300
Fire Protection System Mfr
N.A.I.C.S.: 334290

Marioff Skandinavien AB (1)
Norgegatan 2, 164 32, Kista, Sweden
Tel.: (46) 87477400
Fire Protection System Mfr
N.A.I.C.S.: 334290

Mentor Business Systems Limited (1)
Pennine Business Park Longbow Close, Huddersfield, HD2 1GQ, United Kingdom
Tel.: (44) 3031231113
Web Site: https://mentorbs.com
HVACR Product Mfr & Distr
N.A.I.C.S.: 333415

Misr Refrigeration & Air Conditioning Manufacturing Company S.A.E. (1)
KM 28 Cairo-Alex Desert Road, Abou-Rawash Industrial Area, Giza, Egypt
Tel.: (20) 235366888
Web Site: https://www.miraco.com.eg
Emp.: 250
HVACR Product Mfr & Distr
N.A.I.C.S.: 333415

Nihon Sensitech Corporation (1)
Suite-201 Central Square 2-16-11 Nihonbashi, Chuo-ku, Tokyo, 103-0027, Japan
Tel.: (81) 356568900
Logistic Services
N.A.I.C.S.: 541614

Onity Co., Limited (1)
1858/63-74 14th Floor Interlink Tower Bangna-Trad Rd, Bangna, Bangkok, 10260, Thailand
Tel.: (66) 24958877
Electronic Lock Device Mfr
N.A.I.C.S.: 332510

Onity LTDA (1)
Av Dr Cardoso de Melo 1955 8 planta, Vila Olimpia, Sao Paulo, 03181-080, Brazil
Tel.: (55) 1136702555
Web Site: https://latam.onity.com
Electronic Lock Device Mfr
N.A.I.C.S.: 332510

Onity Limited (1)
8 Newmarket Court Chippenham Drive, Kingston, Milton Keynes, MK10 0AQ, United Kingdom
Tel.: (44) 1908286419
Electronic Lock Device Mfr
N.A.I.C.S.: 332510

Carrier Global Corporation—(Continued)

Onity Pty Ltd (1)
Building F Unit 1 3 - 29 Birnie Avenue, Lidcombe, 2141, NSW, Australia
Tel.: (61) 295816555
Electronic Lock Device Mfr
N.A.I.C.S.: 332510

Onity SAS (1)
4 rue Edmond Michelet ZA Fontaine du Vaisseau, 93360, Neuilly-Plaisance, France
Tel.: (33) 149448999
Electronic Lock Device Mfr
Web Site:
N.A.I.C.S.: 332510

Onity, S.L.U. (1)
Pol Ind Lanbarren c/ Aranaburu 4D, 20180, Oiartzun, Spain
Tel.: (34) 943448300
Electronic Lock Device Mfr
N.A.I.C.S.: 332510

PT Berca Carrier Indonesia (1)
Gedung Pusat Niaga 4th Floor, Arena PRJ Kemayoran, Jakarta, 10610, Indonesia
Tel.: (62) 2126645888
Web Site: https://www.bercacarrier.co.id
HVACR Product Mfr & Distr
N.A.I.C.S.: 333415

Q-Carrier (B) Sendirian Berhad (1)
Unit 7 8 9 First Floor Beribi The Walk Kg Beribi, Mukim Gadong, BE1118, Bandar Seri Begawan, Brunei Darussalam
Tel.: (673) 2653586
Web Site: https://www.carrier.com
HVACR Product Mfr & Distr
N.A.I.C.S.: 333415

Qingdao Haier-Carrier Refrigeration Equipment Company Limited (1)
No 3734 Tuanjie Road, Huangdao, Qingdao, 266500, China
Tel.: (86) 4006781888
Web Site: https://en.haiercarrier.com
Refrigeration Equipment Mfr & Distr
N.A.I.C.S.: 333415

ReefCo, LLC (1)
Sansone Plz 319 Rt 22 E, Green Brook, NJ 08812
Tel.: (908) 642-1966
Web Site: https://reefcoaquariums.com
Security Guard Services
N.A.I.C.S.: 561612

Riello Canada Inc. (1)
2165 Meadowpine Boulevard, Mississauga, L5N 6H6, ON, Canada
Tel.: (905) 542-0303
Heating Equipment Mfr
N.A.I.C.S.: 333414

Riello Hungary Kereskedelmi Zartkoruen Mukodo Reszvenytarsasag (1)
Lomb Utca 37-39, 1139, Budapest, Hungary
Tel.: (36) 1 339 9069
Web Site: https://www.riello.com
Heating Equipment Mfr
N.A.I.C.S.: 333414

Riello Ltd. (1)
The Ermine Centre Ermine Business Park, Huntingdon, PE29 6WX, Cambridgeshire, United Kingdom
Tel.: (44) 1480432144
Web Site: https://www.rielloburners.co.uk
Heating Equipment Mfr
N.A.I.C.S.: 333414

Riello RO S.r.l. (1)
Str Copilului nr 20 Parter Sector 1, 012178, Bucharest, Romania
Tel.: (40) 21 224 6648
Web Site: https://www.riello.com
Heating Equipment Mfr
N.A.I.C.S.: 333414

Riello S.A. (1)
Via Brusighell 14, CH-6807, Taverne, Switzerland
Tel.: (41) 916045022
Web Site: https://www.riello.com
Air Conditioner Mfr & Distr
N.A.I.C.S.: 333415

Rug Riello Urzadzenia Grzewcze SA (1)
Ul Konstruktorska 13, 02-673, Warsaw, Poland

Tel.: (48) 5665 716 5859
Web Site: https://www.riello.com
Heating Equipment Mfr
N.A.I.C.S.: 333414

Safety Solutions U.K. Limited (1)
61-63 Rixon Road Finedon Road Ind Est, Northants, Wellingborough, NN8 4BA, United Kingdom
Tel.: (44) 1933442220
Web Site: https://safetysolutionsuk.net
Personal Protective Equipment Mfr & Distr
N.A.I.C.S.: 339113

Security Monitoring Centre B.V. (1)
PO Box 6183, 4000 HD, Tiel, Netherlands
Tel.: (31) 34 467 8911
Web Site: https://www.smc-alarmcentrale.nl
Security System Services
N.A.I.C.S.: 561621

Security Monitoring Centre B.V.B.A./S.P.R.L. (1)
Keizer Karellaan - Av Charles Quint 345, 1083, Brussels, Belgium
Tel.: (32) 2 646 0842
Web Site:
  https://securitymonitoringcentre.be
Security Training Services
N.A.I.C.S.: 561621

Sensitech Brasil Ltda. (1)
Rua Alfredo Achcar 970 A - Bairro Nova Vinhedo Condominio Viva, Vinhedo, 13284-072, Sao Paulo, Brazil
Tel.: (55) 193 399 8650
Logistic Services
N.A.I.C.S.: 541614

Sensitech Canada Inc. (1)
1 Valleywood Drive Unit 6, Markham, L3R 5L9, ON, Canada
Tel.: (905) 479-7222
Logistic Services
N.A.I.C.S.: 541614

Sensitech EMEA B.V. (1)
Warmonderweg 11, 2171 AH, Sassenheim, Netherlands
Tel.: (31) 252211108
Logistic Services
N.A.I.C.S.: 541614

Sensitech Pty Limited (1)
96 Derby Street, Pascoe Vale, 3044, VIC, Australia
Tel.: (61) 396865622
Logistic Services
N.A.I.C.S.: 541614

Systemax Pty Ltd (1)
Unit 2 16 Natasha Street, Capalaba, 4157, QLD, Australia
Tel.: (61) 73 823 4110
Web Site: https://systemax.com.au
Construction Services
N.A.I.C.S.: 236220
Steve Green (Mng Dir)

Temperature Equipment Corporation (1)
17725 Volbrecht Rd, Lansing, IL 60438-4542 (20%)
Tel.: (708) 418-3062
Web Site: https://www.tecmungo.com
Sales Range: $10-24.9 Million
Emp.: 200
Air Conditioning Equipment Distr
N.A.I.C.S.: 423730
Skip F. Mungo (Pres & CEO)
Mike Smid (VP-Comml Sls)

Subsidiary (Domestic):

National Excelsior Company (2)
17725 Volbrecht Rd, Lansing, IL 60438
Tel.: (708) 418-6601
Web Site: http://www.excelsiorhvac.com
Sales Range: $10-24.9 Million
Emp.: 100
Heating, Ventilation & Air Conditioning Equipment & Supplies Distr
N.A.I.C.S.: 423730
Raymond Mungo (Pres)
Ernie Pudliner (Mgr-Credit)

Subsidiary (Domestic):

Excelsior Manufacturing & Supply Corp. (3)
1999 N Ruby St, Melrose Park, IL 60160

Tel.: (708) 344-1802
Metal Products Mfr
N.A.I.C.S.: 423730

Subsidiary (Domestic):

Temperature Equipment Corporation - Melrose Park (2)
2055 N Ruby St, Melrose Park, IL 60160
Tel.: (708) 681-6220
Web Site: http://www.tecmungo.com
Warm Air Heating Equipment & Air Conditioning Equipment Distr
N.A.I.C.S.: 423730

The Harry Alter Company (2)
17725 Volbrecht Rd, Lansing, IL 60438-4542
Tel.: (708) 418-0900
Web Site: http://www.harryalter.com
Sales Range: $1-9.9 Million
Emp.: 50
Refrigeration, Air Conditioning & Heating Supplies Distr
N.A.I.C.S.: 423730
Raymond Mungo (Pres)

Toshiba Carrier (Thailand) Co., Ltd. (1)
144/9 Moo 5 Bangkadi Industrial Park Tivanon Road, Muang District, Pathumthani, 12000, Thailand
Tel.: (66) 2 021 3100
Web Site: https://www.toshiba-carrier.co.th
Air Conditioning Equipment Mfr
N.A.I.C.S.: 333415

Toshiba Carrier Air Conditioning (China) Co., Ltd. (1)
Building 1 No 60 21st Avenue Baiyang Street, Hangzhou Economic and Technological Development Area, Hangzhou, 310018, Zhejiang, China
Tel.: (86) 57126892333
HVACR Product Mfr & Distr
N.A.I.C.S.: 333415

Toshiba Carrier AirConditioning Sales (Shanghai) Co., Ltd. (1)
501 5F Raffles City Office Tower 268 Xizang Zhong Road, Shanghai, 200001, China
Tel.: (86) 2163611111
HVACR Product Mfr & Distr
N.A.I.C.S.: 333415

Toshiba Carrier Corporation (1)
336 Tadewara, Fuji, 416 8521, Shizuoka, Japan (55%)
Tel.: (81) 545625521
Web Site: http://www.toshiba-carrier.co.jp
Sales Range: $800-899.9 Million
Emp.: 3,000
Mfr of Air-Conditioners
N.A.I.C.S.: 333415

Toshiba Carrier Europe S.A.S. (1)
Route de Thil, BP 49, 01120, Montluel, France
Tel.: (33) 472252555
Heating & Cooling Product Mfr & Distr
N.A.I.C.S.: 333415

Toshiba Carrier North America, Inc. (1)
3300 Riverwood Pkwy SE Ste 900, Atlanta, GA 30339
Tel.: (678) 981-4993
Heating & Cooling Product Mfr & Distr
N.A.I.C.S.: 333415

Toshiba Carrier UK Limited (1)
Elite House Guildford Road, Leatherhead, KT22 9UT, Surrey, United Kingdom
Tel.: (44) 1372220240
Web Site: https://www.toshiba-aircon.co.uk
Air Conditioning Equipment Distr
N.A.I.C.S.: 423730

UHS Pty Ltd (1)
Heritage Business Centre Level 1 Unit 2 5-9 Ricketty Street, Mascot, 2020, NSW, Australia
Tel.: (61) 29 663 2299
Web Site: https://www.uhssystems.com
Telecommunication Equipment Distr
N.A.I.C.S.: 423690

UTEC Inc. (1)
35 Warren St, Lowell, MA 01852

Tel.: (978) 856-3902
Web Site: http://www.utecinc.org
Tutoring Services
N.A.I.C.S.: 611699
Gregg Croteau (CEO)
Anita Moeller (Chief Program Officer)
Terri Steingrebe (CFO)
Dahianara Liranzo (Dir-Talent)
Will Vilas-Novas (Dir-Workforce Dev)

Watkins Hire Limited (1)
Ward Industrial Estate Church Road, Lydney, GL15 5EL, Gloucestershire, United Kingdom
Tel.: (44) 159 484 0025
Web Site: https://www.watkinshire.co.uk
Boiler Spare Distr
N.A.I.C.S.: 423720

CARS.COM INC.
300 S Riverside Plz Ste 1000, Chicago, IL 60606
Tel.: (312) 601-5000   DE
Web Site: https://www.cars.com
Year Founded: 1998
CARS—(NYSE)
Rev.: $653,876,000
Assets: $1,024,870,000
Liabilities: $640,440,000
Net Worth: $384,430,000
Earnings: $17,206,000
Emp.: 1,700
Fiscal Year-end: 12/31/22
Holding Company; Online Automobile Marketplace Operator & Services
N.A.I.C.S.: 551112
T. Alex Vetter (Pres & CEO)
Jandy Tomy (Treas & Exec VP-Fin)
Doug Miller (Pres & Chief Comml Officer)
Sonia Jain (CFO)
Greg Heidorn (CTO)
Julien Schneider (Chief Strategy Officer)
Jennifer Vianello (CMO)
Marita Hudson Thomas (Chief Comm Officer)
Angelique Strong Marks (Chief Legal Officer & Sec)
Matthew Crawford (Chief Product Officer & Chief Innovation Officer)
Sarah Archibong (Chief People Officer)

Subsidiaries:

Cars.com, LLC (1)
300 S Riverside Plz Ste 1000, Chicago, Il 60606
Tel.: (312) 601-5000
Web Site: https://www.cars.com
Online Automobile Marketplace Operator & Services
N.A.I.C.S.: 518210

D2C Media Inc. (1)
1215 Smith, Montreal, H3C 0M4, QC, Canada
Tel.: (514) 303-1310
Web Site: https://www.d2cmedia.ca
Digital Advertising Services
N.A.I.C.S.: 541850

Dealer Inspire Inc. (1)
1864 High Grove Ln Ste 124, Naperville, IL 60540
Web Site: https://www.dealerinspire.com
Software Development Services
N.A.I.C.S.: 541511
Joe Chura (Co-Founder & CEO)

Launch Digital Marketing LLC (1)
1864 High Grove Ln Ste 124, Naperville, IL 60540
Tel.: (630) 614-1823
Web Site:
  https://www.launchdigitalmarketing.com
Digital Marketing & Consulting Services
N.A.I.C.S.: 541613

CARSMARTT
2828 Coral Way Ste 412, Coral Gables, FL 33145
Tel.: (786) 409-7439   NV

Web Site: http://www.carsmartt.com
CRSM—(OTCIQ)
Rev.: $36,000
Assets: $35,000
Liabilities: $1
Net Worth: $34,999
Earnings: ($168,000)
Fiscal Year-end: 12/31/19
Car Rental Services
N.A.I.C.S.: 532111

CARTER BANKSHARES, INC.
1300 Kings Mt Rd, Martinsville, VA 24112
Tel.: (276) 656-1776   VA
Web Site: https://www.cbtcares.com
Year Founded: 2020
CARE—(NASDAQ)
Rev.: $181,900,000
Assets: $4,204,519,000
Liabilities: $3,875,892,000
Net Worth: $328,627,000
Earnings: $50,118,000
Emp.: 667
Fiscal Year-end: 12/31/22
Bank Holding Company
N.A.I.C.S.: 551111
Litz H. Van Dyke *(CEO)*
Wendy S. Bell *(CFO & Sr Exec VP)*
James W. Haskins *(Chm)*
Phyllis Q. Karavatakis *(Vice Chm)*
Joyce A. Parker *(Sec)*

Subsidiaries:

Carter Bank & Trust   (1)
1300 Kings Mountain Rd, Martinsville, VA 24112
Tel.: (276) 656-1776
Web Site: http://www.cbtcares.com
Rev.: $175,990,000
Assets: $4,006,108,000
Liabilities: $3,532,997,000
Net Worth: $473,111,000
Earnings: $26,575,000
Emp.: 977
Fiscal Year-end: 12/31/2019
Retail & Commercial Banking
N.A.I.C.S.: 522110
Jane Ann Davis *(Chief Admin Officer & Exec VP)*
Phyllis Q. Karavatakis *(Sr VP-Special Projects)*
Litz H. Van Dyke *(CEO)*
Bradford N. Langs *(Pres & Chief Strategy Officer)*
Mathew M. Speare *(CIO & Exec VP)*
Wendy S. Bell *(CFO & Sr Exec VP)*
A. Loran Adams *(Exec VP & Dir-Regulatory Risk Mgmt)*
Tami M. Buttrey *(Chief Retail Banking Officer, Exec VP & Dir-Delivery Channel)*

CARTER'S, INC.
Phipps Tower 3438 Peachtree Rd NE Ste 1800, Atlanta, GA 30326
Tel.: (678) 791-1000   DE
Web Site: https://www.carters.com
Year Founded: 2003
CRI—(NYSE)
Rev.: $2,945,594,000
Assets: $2,378,613,000
Liabilities: $1,533,363,000
Net Worth: $845,250,000
Earnings: $232,500,000
Emp.: 15,230
Fiscal Year-end: 12/30/23
Holding Company; Children's Apparel Mfr & Marketer
N.A.I.C.S.: 551112
Michael D. Casey *(Chm, Pres & CEO)*
Jill A. Wilson *(Sr VP-HR & Talent Dev)*
Karen G. Smith *(Exec VP)*
Jeffrey M. Jenkins *(Exec VP-Mktg-Global)*
Julie A. D'Emilio *(Exec VP-Sls)*
Kendra D. Krugman *(Chief Creative & Growth Officer & Sr Exec VP)*

Richard F. Westenberger *(CFO, COO & Sr Exec VP)*
Allison Peterson *(Chief Retail Officer, Chief Digital Officer & Exec VP)*
Antonio D. Robinson *(Chief Compliance Officer, Gen Counsel, Sec-Corporate Social Responsibility & Sr VP)*
Raghu Sagi *(CIO, CTO & Exec VP)*

Subsidiaries:

OshKosh B'Gosh, Inc.   (1)
3001 S Washburn Ste A60, Oshkosh, WI 54904
Tel.: (920) 426-5817
Web Site: http://www.oshkosh.com
Infants' & Children's Wear & Accessories; Workwear & Men's Sportswear
N.A.I.C.S.: 458110

Skip Hop, Inc.   (1)
50 W 23rd St, New York, NY 10010
Tel.: (212) 868-9850
Web Site: https://www.skiphop.com
Childrens Toy & Clothing Designer & Mfr
N.A.I.C.S.: 315250

The Genuine Canadian Corp   (1)
65 Struck Ct, Cambridge, N1R 8L2, ON, Canada
Tel.: (519) 624-6574
Emp.: 80
Women's Clothing Store
N.A.I.C.S.: 458110
Eric Agius *(Office Mgr)*

CARTESIAN THERAPEUTICS, INC.
704 Quince Orchard Rd Ste 210, Gaithersburg, MD 20878
Tel.: (617) 923-1400   DE
Web Site:
    https://www.cartesiantherapeu
    tics.com
Year Founded: 2007
RNAC—(NASDAQ)
Rev.: $26,004,000
Assets: $305,050,000
Liabilities: $444,680,000
Net Worth: $444,184,000
Earnings: $219,710,000
Emp.: 38
Fiscal Year-end: 12/31/23
Pharmaceutical Product Mfr & Distr
N.A.I.C.S.: 325412
Blaine T. Davis *(CFO)*
Carrie Smith Cox *(Chm)*
Matthew Bartholomae *(Gen Counsel)*

CARTICA ACQUISITION CORP.
1345 Ave of the Americas, New York, NY 10105
Tel.: (202) 741-3677   Ky
Web Site: https://carticaspac.com
Year Founded: 2021
CITE—(NASDAQ)
Rev.: $14,732,288
Assets: $241,533,221
Liabilities: $250,343,662
Net Worth: ($8,810,441)
Earnings: $12,537,322
Emp.: 2
Fiscal Year-end: 12/31/22
Investment Services
N.A.I.C.S.: 523999
Suresh Guduru *(Chm & CEO)*
Suresh Singamsetty *(Chief Investment Officer)*
C. Brian Coad *(CFO & COO)*

CARVANA CO.
300 E Rio Salado Pkwy, Tempe, AZ 85281
Tel.: (602) 852-6604   DE
Web Site: https://www.carvana.com
Year Founded: 2016
CVNA—(NYSE)
Rev.: $10,771,000,000
Assets: $7,071,000,000

Liabilities: $7,455,000,000
Net Worth: ($384,000,000)
Earnings: $450,000,000
Emp.: 13,700
Fiscal Year-end: 12/31/23
Used Car Dealers
N.A.I.C.S.: 441120
Ernest Garcia III *(Chm, Pres & CEO)*
Mark Jenkins *(CFO)*
Stephen Palmer *(VP-Acctg & Fin)*
Ernest Garcia III *(Co-Founder, Chm, Pres & CEO)*

Subsidiaries:

Adesa US Auction, LLC   (1)
804 Sollie Dr, Moody, AL 35004
Tel.: (205) 640-1010
Web Site: https://www.adesa.com
Vehicle Mfr & Distr
N.A.I.C.S.: 336320

Car360, Inc.   (1)
3495 Piedmont Rd NE Bldg 12-400, Atlanta, GA 30305
Tel.: (404) 400-2259
Web Site: http://www.car360.com
Mobile Application Development Services
N.A.I.C.S.: 513210
John Hanger *(CEO)*

CARVER BANCORP INC.
75 W 125th St, New York, NY 10027-4512
Tel.: (718) 230-2900   DE
Web Site:
    https://www.carverbank.com
Year Founded: 1996
CARV—(NASDAQ)
Rev.: $40,742,000
Assets: $756,796,000
Liabilities: $714,487,000
Net Worth: $42,309,000
Earnings: ($2,977,000)
Emp.: 113
Fiscal Year-end: 03/31/24
Bank Holding Company
N.A.I.C.S.: 522180
Christina L. Maier *(CFO)*
Craig C. MacKay *(Interim Pres & Interim CEO)*
Lewis P. Jones III *(Chm)*
Isaac Torres *(Gen Counsel, Sec & Sr VP)*

Subsidiaries:

Carver Federal Savings Bank   (1)
75 W 125th St At Lenox Ave, New York, NY 10027-4512
Tel.: (718) 230-2900
Web Site: https://www.carverbank.com
Sales Range: $25-49.9 Million
Emp.: 110
Full Banking Services
N.A.I.C.S.: 522180
Christina L. Maier *(CFO)*
Craig C. MacKay *(Interim Pres & Interim CEO)*
Lewis P. Jones III *(Chm)*
Isaac Torres *(Gen Counsel)*

CASCADE ACQUISITION CORP.
1900 Sunset Harbour Dr Ste 2102, Miami Beach, FL 33139
Tel.: (203) 856-3033   DE
Year Founded: 2020
CAS—(NYSE)
Rev.: $17,047,467
Assets: $232,897,089
Liabilities: $250,055,082
Net Worth: ($17,157,993)
Earnings: $15,040,564
Emp.: 2
Fiscal Year-end: 12/31/21
Investment Services
N.A.I.C.S.: 523999
Jay Levine *(Chm & CEO)*
Daniel Hirsch *(CFO & COO)*

CASCADIA ACQUISITION CORP.
1000 2nd Ave Ste 1200, Seattle, WA 98104
Tel.: (206) 436-2500   DE
Year Founded: 2021
CCAI—(NASDAQ)
Rev.: $8,461,774
Assets: $152,392,570
Liabilities: $157,772,368
Net Worth: ($5,379,798)
Earnings: $6,886,061
Fiscal Year-end: 12/31/22
Investment Services
N.A.I.C.S.: 523999
Michael Butler *(Chm)*
Jamie Boyd *(CEO)*

CASELLA WASTE SYSTEMS, INC.
25 Greens Hill Ln, Rutland, VT 05701
Tel.: (802) 775-0325   DE
Web Site: https://www.casella.com
Year Founded: 1975
CWST—(NASDAQ)
Rev.: $1,264,542,000
Assets: $2,535,470,000
Liabilities: $1,513,679,000
Net Worth: $1,021,791,000
Earnings: $25,399,000
Emp.: 4,200
Fiscal Year-end: 12/31/23
Regional, Integrated, Non-Hazardous Solid Waste Services; Collection, Transfer, Disposal & Recycling Services
N.A.I.C.S.: 562211
Bradford J. Helgeson *(CFO & Exec VP)*
Edmond R. Coletta *(Pres)*
Shelley E. Sayward *(Gen Counsel & Sr VP)*
Sean M. Steves *(COO-Solid Waste Ops & Sr VP)*
Paul J. Ligon *(Chief Revenue Officer & Sr VP)*
Kevin J. Drohan *(Chief Acctg Officer & VP)*
Jason M. Mead *(Treas)*
Kelley J. Robinson *(Sr VP)*
Robert J. Cappadona *(VP)*
Michael T. Stehman *(VP)*
Douglas R. Casella *(Vice Chm)*
John W. Casella *(Chm, CEO & Sec)*

Subsidiaries:

All Cycle Waste, Inc.   (1)
28 Ave B PO Box 976, Williston, VT 05495   (100%)
Tel.: (802) 864-6767
Web Site: http://www.casella.com
Sales Range: $200-249.9 Million
Collection, Transfer, Processing & Disposal of Non-Hazardous Waste
N.A.I.C.S.: 562219

Atlantic Coast Fibers, Inc.   (1)
101 7th St, Passaic, NJ 07755   (100%)
Tel.: (973) 614-9600
Sales Range: $200-249.9 Million
Emp.: 76
Waste Paper Collection & Recycling Services
N.A.I.C.S.: 562998

Blow Bros.   (1)
1 Vallee Ln, Old Orchard Beach, ME 04064
Tel.: (207) 934-2525
Web Site: http://blowbros.com
Sales Range: $10-24.9 Million
Solid Waste Collection Services
N.A.I.C.S.: 562111

C.V. Landfill, Inc.   (1)
418 US Route 2, East Montpelier, VT 05651
Tel.: (802) 479-2450
Sales Range: $25-49.9 Million
Emp.: 3
Non Hazardous Solid Waste Disposal Services
N.A.I.C.S.: 562219

Casella Waste Systems, Inc.—(Continued)

Brian Delphoia (Mgr)
James Bohlig (Principal)

Casella Organics (1)
135 Presumpscot St Unit #1, Portland, ME
04103
Tel.: (207) 781-5011
Web Site: http://www.casellaorganics.com
Sales Range: $10-24.9 Million
Emp.: 45
Removal, Transportation, Recycling, Pro-
cessing & Marketing of Organic Resources
N.A.I.C.S.: 325199

Casella Recycling, LLC (1)
13 Gibson Rd, Scarborough, ME 04074
Tel.: (207) 883-9777
Sales Range: $25-49.9 Million
Emp.: 40
Waste Management & Recycling Services
N.A.I.C.S.: 924110

Casella Transportation, Inc. (1)
25 Greens Hill Ln, Rutland, VT 05702
Tel.: (802) 775-0325
Web Site: http://www.casella.com
Non Hazardous Solid Waste Disposal Ser-
vices
N.A.I.C.S.: 562219

**Casella Waste Management of N.Y.,
Inc. - Dunkirk** (1)
2142 Lodestro Ln Jamestown, Dunkirk, NY
14701
Tel.: (716) 366-4060
Web Site: http://www.casella.com
Sales Range: $10-24.9 Million
Emp.: 25
Non-Hazardous Solid Waste Collection Ser-
vices
N.A.I.C.S.: 562111

**Casella Waste Management of Penn-
sylvania, Inc.** (1)
19 Ness Ln, Kane, PA 16735
Tel.: (814) 778-9931
Non Hazardous Waste Management Services
N.A.I.C.S.: 562998

Casella Waste Management, Inc. (1)
25 Greens Hill Ln, Rutland, VT 05701
Tel.: (802) 862-1900
Garbage Collection Services
N.A.I.C.S.: 562111

GreenerU, Inc. (1)
307 Waverley Oaks Rd Ste 202, Waltham,
MA 02452
Tel.: (781) 209-5760
Web Site: https://www.greeneru.com
Emp.: 21
Campus Sustainability & Energy Solution
Provider
N.A.I.C.S.: 541350
Rob Pratt (Co-Founder & Chm)
Matt Karp (Sr Mgr-Construction)
Rob Durning (Dir-Ops)

**Hiram Hollow Regeneration
Corp.** (1)
25 Greens Hill Ln, Rutland, VT 05701
Tel.: (518) 793-1098
Sales Range: $25-49.9 Million
Emp.: 5
Solid Waste Collection Service Provider
N.A.I.C.S.: 562211
Joe Gerard (Mgr)

KTI Bio-Fuels, Inc. (1)
32 Alfred A Plourde Pkwy, Lewiston, ME
04240 (100%)
Tel.: (207) 783-2941
Sales Range: $200-249.9 Million
Emp.: 12
Waste Management Services
N.A.I.C.S.: 562219

LMR Disposal LLC (1)
1557 Springtown Rd, Phillipsburg, NJ
08865
Tel.: (610) 737-9525
Waste Collection
N.A.I.C.S.: 562119

NEWS of Worcester LLC (1)
30 Nippnapp Trl, Worcester, MA 01607-
1783
Tel.: (508) 755-4604

Non Hazardous Solid Waste Disposal Services
N.A.I.C.S.: 562219

**New England Waste Services of Ver-
mont, Inc.** (1)
21 Landfill Ln, Coventry, VT 05855
Tel.: (802) 334-8300
Web Site: http://www.casella.com
Sales Range: $25-49.9 Million
Non Hazardous Solid Waste Disposal Ser-
vices
N.A.I.C.S.: 562219

Northern Sanitation, Inc. (1)
67 Carbide Rd, Plattsburgh, NY
12901 (100%)
Tel.: (518) 561-7021
Sales Range: $25-49.9 Million
Emp.: 40
Non-Hazardous Waste Solutions
N.A.I.C.S.: 562219
William Meyers (Mgr-Ops)

Northstar Pulp and Paper Co. (1)
89 Guion St, Springfield, MA 01104
Tel.: (413) 263-6000
Web Site:
http://www.northstarpulpandpaper.com
Recyclable Material Merchant Whslr
N.A.I.C.S.: 423930
Barry Sanborn (Gen Mgr)

Oxford Transfer Station, LLC (1)
200 Leicester Rd, Oxford, MA 01537
Tel.: (508) 892-1219
Waste Disposal Services
N.A.I.C.S.: 562111

Pine Tree Waste, Inc. (1)
87 Pleasant Hill Rd, Scarborough, ME
04074 (100%)
Tel.: (207) 773-1122
Sales Range: $200-249.9 Million
Emp.: 175
Reclamation & Non-Hazardous Waste Re-
moval
N.A.I.C.S.: 562219

Power of Three LLC (1)
PO Box 171, Palmyra, IN 47164
Tel.: (812) 472-3440
Web Site: http://www.powerofthree.biz
Management Consulting Services
N.A.I.C.S.: 541618

TAM Inc. (1)
639 N Rd, Shaftsbury, VT 05262-9501
Tel.: (802) 455-9118
Web Site: https://www.casella.com
Waste Collection
N.A.I.C.S.: 562119

Taylor Garbage Service, Inc. (1)
3051 Old Vestal Rd, Vestal, NY 13850
Tel.: (607) 797-5277
Web Site: http://www.taylorgarbage.com
Sales Range: $1-9.9 Million
Emp.: 45
Waste Collection Services
N.A.I.C.S.: 562111
Brian Taylor (VP)

U.S. Fiber, LLC (1)
Trenton Plant 30 Pinehouse Rd, Trenton,
SC 29847
Tel.: (803) 275-5023
Web Site: https://www.usfibers.com
Fiber Mfr
N.A.I.C.S.: 313110

Waste-Stream, Inc. (1)
472 W Parishville Rd, Potsdam, NY 13676
Tel.: (802) 438-2151
Web Site: http://www.casella.com
Integrated Waste Management & Solid
Waste Solutions
N.A.I.C.S.: 562219

**Willimantic Waste Paper Co.,
Inc.** (1)
1590 Main St, Willimantic, CT 06226
Tel.: (860) 423-4527
Web Site: http://www.williwaste.com
Nonhazardous Waste Treatment & Disposal
N.A.I.C.S.: 562219
Thomas E. Devivo (VP)

Winters Brothers, Inc. (1)
1198 Prospect Ave, Westbury, NY
11590 (100%)

Tel.: (631) 234-2345
Web Site: http://www.wintersbros.com
Sales Range: $200-249.9 Million
Hauling & Collection Services
N.A.I.C.S.: 562219

CASEY'S GENERAL STORES, INC.
1 SE Convenience Blvd, Ankeny, IA
50021
Tel.: (515) 965-6100 IA
Web Site: https://www.caseys.com
Year Founded: 1967
CASY—(NASDAQ)
Rev.: $14,862,913,000
Assets: $6,347,433,000
Liabilities: $3,332,052,000
Net Worth: $3,015,381,000
Earnings: $501,972,000
Emp.: 20,935
Fiscal Year-end: 04/30/24
Retailer of Gasoline, Prepared Foods
& Fountain Items, Groceries & Other
Merchandise
N.A.I.C.S.: 445131
Brian J. Johnson (Sr VP-IR & Bus
Dev)
H. Lynn Horak (Chm)
Jay Soupene (Sr VP-Operational Ex-
cellence)
Chris Boling (VP-Store Ops)
Ena Williams (COO)
Darren M. Rebelez (Pres & CEO)
Sam James (VP-Fin)
Art Sebastian (VP-Digital Experience)
Tom Brennan (Chief Mdsg officer)
Chad Frazell (Chief HR Officer)
Nathaniel Doddridge (VP-Fuels)
Brad Haga (VP-Mdsg)
Paul Suarez (Chief Information Secu-
rity Officer)
Katie Petru (Dir-Comm)
Sherri Hart (VP-Total Rewards)
Jon Hostasa (VP-Construction, Main-
tenance & Facilities)
Kendra Meyer (VP-Real Estate)
Jaime Robles (VP-Procurement)
Carrie Stojack (VP-Guest Insights)
Nan Thomae (VP-HR)
Stephen P. Bramlage Jr. (CFO)

Subsidiaries:

Casey's Marketing Company (1)
2601 SE Creekview Dr, Ankeny, IA 50021-
9437
Tel.: (515) 963-8066
Web Site: http://www.caseys.com
Sales Range: $25-49.9 Million
Emp.: 20
In House Marketing Services
N.A.I.C.S.: 541613

Casey's Retail Company (1)
1 SE Convenience Blvd, Ankeny, IA 50021-
9672
Tel.: (515) 965-6100
Convenience Store Operator
N.A.I.C.S.: 445131
Kristin Howe (Mgr-Mktg)

Casey's Services Company (1)
1 SE Covenience Blvd, Ankeny, IA 50021
Tel.: (515) 965-6100
Web Site: http://www.caseys.com
Sales Range: $50-74.9 Million
Emp.: 550
Administrative & Operational Support Ser-
vices
N.A.I.C.S.: 541611

Fikes Wholesale Inc. (1)
6261 Central Pointe Pkwy, Temple, TX
76504
Tel.: (254) 791-0009
Web Site: http://www.cefco.com
Sales Range: $10-24.9 Million
Emp.: 100
Petroleum Bulk Stations
N.A.I.C.S.: 424710
James R. Fikes (Owner)
Wyatt Cramer (Dir-Construction)
Amanda Kilgore (Partner-HR Bus)

CASHMERE VALLEY BANK
Tel.: (509) 782-1501
Web Site:
https://www.cashmerevalley
bank.com
Year Founded: 1932
CSHX—(OTCQX)
Sales Range: $25-49.9 Million
Emp.: 287
Commercial Banking Services
N.A.I.C.S.: 522110
Connie Fritz (Chief Retail Banking
Officer & Exec VP)
Shawna Alexander (Officer-Retail Ops
& VP-Leavenworth Branch)
Gregory A. Oakes (Pres & CEO)
Steve Vradenburg (Chief Lending Of-
ficer)
Sue Ozburn (CIO)
Connie Fritz (Chief Retail Banking
Officer)
Steve Vradenburg (Chief Lending Of-
ficer)
Nicole Ivarsen (Mgr-Bank Card)
Lyman Boyd (Chm)
John Doyle (Vice Chm)
Mike Lundstrom (CFO)

Subsidiaries:

**Mitchell, Reed & Schmitten Insur-
ance, Inc.** (1)
124 E Penny Rd Ste 101, Wenatchee, WA
98801
Tel.: (509) 665-0500
Web Site:
https://www.mrandsinsurance.com
Insurance Agents
N.A.I.C.S.: 524210
Brent Schmitten (Pres)

CASPER SLEEP INC.
3 World Trade Center 175 Greenwich
St Fl 39, New York, NY 10007
Tel.: (347) 941-1871 DE
Web Site: http://www.casper.com
Year Founded: 2013
CSPR—(NYSE)
Rev.: $497,000,000
Assets: $234,201,000
Liabilities: $208,734,000
Net Worth: $25,467,000
Earnings: ($89,555,000)
Emp.: 442
Fiscal Year-end: 12/31/20
Mattress, Bedding & Associated
Products Mfr & Distr
N.A.I.C.S.: 337910
Philip Krim (Co-Founder, Chm &
CEO)
Emilie Arel (Pres & CEO)
Jeffrey Chapin (Co-Founder & Chief
Product Officer)
Jonathan Truppman (Gen Counsel &
Sec)
Elizabeth Wolfson (Chief People Offi-
cer)

CASPIAN SERVICES, INC.
3959 Foothill Blvd Ste 204, La Cres-
centa, CA 91214
Tel.: (818) 957-4488 NV
Web Site:
https://www.caspianservices.net
Year Founded: 1998
CSSV—(OTCEM)
Oil Field Services
N.A.I.C.S.: 213112
Mirgali Kunayev (Chm)
Alexey Kotov (Pres & CEO)
Indira Kaliyeva (CFO)

Subsidiaries:

Tat-Arka LLP (1)
ul Azerbaev 134 md Koktobe, Almaty,
050010, Kazakhstan
Tel.: (7) 272613141
Web Site: http://www.tat-arka.kz

Seismic Survey Services
N.A.I.C.S.: 541360
Andrey Bryzgalov (Dir-Survey Dept)

CASS INFORMATION SYSTEMS, INC.
12444 Powerscourt Dr Ste 550, Saint Louis, MO 63131
Tel.: (314) 506-5500   MO
Web Site: https://www.cassinfo.com
Year Founded: 1982
CASS—(NASDAQ)
Rev.: $182,476,000
Assets: $2,573,023,000
Liabilities: $2,366,698,000
Net Worth: $206,325,000
Earnings: $34,904,000
Emp.: 940
Fiscal Year-end: 12/31/22
Freight Payment & Information Processing Services for Manufacturing, Distributing & Retail Firms
N.A.I.C.S.: 561499
Eric H. Brunngraber (Exec Chm)
Dwight D. Erdbruegger (Pres-Cass Comml Bank)
Martin H. Resch (Pres & CEO)
Michael J. Normile (CFO & Exec VP)
Teresa D. Meares (VP/Gen Mgr-Waste & Sustainability Mgmt)
Todd Wills (Sr VP-Utilities Bus & Gen Mgr-Utilities Bus)
Carl N. Friedholm (Pres)
Nicole M. Jennings (VP)
Ross M. Miller (Pres)
Sean M. Mullins (Chief Information Security Officer)
Christi A. Reiter (Sr VP)
Jeanne M. Scannell (Chief Credit Officer)
Anthony G. Urban (Pres)
James M. Cavellier (CIO & Exec VP)
Matthew S. Schuckman (Gen Counsel, Sec & Exec VP)

Subsidiaries:

Cass Commercial Bank   (1)
Ste 175 12412 Powerscourt Dr, Des Peres, MO 63131   (100%)
Tel.: (314) 506-5544
Web Site: https://www.cassbank.com
Sales Range: $10-24.9 Million
Emp.: 50
Corporate & Institutional Banking Services
N.A.I.C.S.: 522180
Lawrence A. Collett (CEO)
Douglas J. Hoffman (Treas & Exec VP)
Dwight D. Erdbruegger (Pres)
Jeanne Scannell (Chief Credit Officer & Exec VP)
Mark Benten (Exec VP-Sls & Mktg)
Michelle Gottlieb (Sr VP-Credit Admin)
Chris Dimond (Exec VP-Faith-Based)
George Hoeffner (Sr VP-Equipment Leases)
Marva Halbert (VP-Comml Banking)
Megan Zust (VP-Comml Banking)
Brad Martin (VP-Faith-Based & Non-Profit Banking)
Rod Randol (VP-Faith-Based & Non-Profit Banking)
Steve Hron (VP-Faith-Based & Non-Profit Banking)
Lincoln VerMeer (Sr VP-Faith-Based & Non-Profit Banking)
David Schoch (Asst VP-Faith-Based & Non-Profit Banking)
Dorothy Smith (Sr VP-Branch Banking Svcs)
Amy Norris (VP-Loan Svcs)
Marybeth Lee (VP-Ops)
Brigitte Clemons (Asst VP & Mgr-Client Support)
Cassie Boyer (Officer-Treasury Mgmt)
Eric Giering (Exec VP-Comml)
Jaime Jankowski (VP-Comml Banking)
Mark Wolz (VP-Comml Banking)
Todd Turner (VP-Comml Banking)
Julie Krapf (VP-Comml Banking)
Dan Mikes (Sr Mgr-Customer Rels)

James Downing (Sr VP-Franchise & Restaurant)
Michael Porter (Asst VP-Faith-Based & Non-Profit Banking)

Cass International LLC   (1)
13001 Hollenberg Dr, Bridgeton, MO 63044
Tel.: (314) 506-5500
Sales Range: $50-74.9 Million
Emp.: 300
Data Processing & Related Services
N.A.I.C.S.: 518210
Bob Mathias (Pres)

CASSAVA SCIENCES, INC.
6801 N Capital of Texas Hwy Bldg, Austin, TX 78731
Tel.: (512) 501-2444   DE
Web Site:
    https://www.cassavasciences.com
SAVA—(NASDAQ)
Rev.: $2,777,000
Assets: $234,834,000
Liabilities: $7,295,000
Net Worth: $227,539,000
Earnings: ($76,246,000)
Emp.: 26
Fiscal Year-end: 12/31/22
Pain Management Drug Mfr
N.A.I.C.S.: 325412
Nadav Friedmann (Chief Medical Officer)
Eric J. Schoen (CFO)
R. Christopher Cook (Gen Counsel & Sr VP)
George Thornton (Sr VP)
Richard Jon Barry (Pres & CEO)

CASTELLUM, INC.
3 Bethesda Metro Ctr Ste 700, Bethesda, MD 20814
Tel.: (301) 961-4895
Web Site:
    https://www.castellumus.com
CTM—(NYSEAMEX)
Rev.: $42,190,643
Assets: $33,043,008
Liabilities: $15,511,092
Net Worth: $17,531,916
Earnings: ($14,908,038)
Emp.: 207
Fiscal Year-end: 12/31/22
Biological Solutions
N.A.I.C.S.: 325414
Mark C. Fuller (Co-Founder)
Jay O. Wright (Co-Founder, Vice Chm, Gen Counsel, Treas & Sec)
Glen R. Ives (COO)
David T. Bell (CFO)

Subsidiaries:

Mainnerve Federal Services, Inc. (1)
822 A1A Ste 310, Ponte Vedra Beach, FL 32082
Tel.: (206) 679-0454
Web Site: https://www.mfsigovgroup.com
Software Development Services
N.A.I.C.S.: 541511

Specialty Systems, Inc.   (1)
1451 Rte 37 W, Toms River, NJ 08755
Tel.: (732) 341-1011
Web Site: http://www.specialtysystems.com
Sales Range: $1-9.9 Million
Emp.: 39
Custom Computer Programming Services
N.A.I.C.S.: 541511
Emil A. Kaunitz (Pres)
Amanda Douglas (Controller & Dir-Contracts Admin)
William Cabey (VP & Gen Mgr)

CASTLE BIOSCIENCES, INC.
505 S Friendswood Dr Ste 401, Friendswood, TX 77546
Tel.: (412) 820-3050   DE
Web Site:
    https://www.castlebiosciences.com
Year Founded: 2007

CSTL—(NASDAQ)
Rev.: $137,039,000
Assets: $447,329,000
Liabilities: $48,179,000
Net Worth: $399,150,000
Earnings: ($67,138,000)
Emp.: 542
Fiscal Year-end: 12/31/22
Biotechnology Research & Development Services
N.A.I.C.S.: 541714
Toby Juvenal (Chief Comml Officer)
Derek J. Maetzold (Founder, Pres & CEO)
Frank Stokes (CFO)
Kristen M. Oelschlager (COO)
Robert W. Cook (Sr VP-R&D)
Michael Maltby (Exec Dir-Managed Care)
Matthew Goldberg (Dir-Medical)
John Abbott (VP)
Greg Acosta (VP)
Sherri Borman (Exec Dir)
Jay Braxton (VP)
John Cheneval (Exec Dir)
Kevin Doman (VP)
Vicki Fish-Sidlow (VP)
Keli Greenberg (VP)
Clare Johnson (VP)
Chris Otte (VP)
Trisha Poteet (VP)
Camilla Zuckero (VP)

Subsidiaries:

AltheaDx, Inc.   (1)
3550 Dunhill St, San Diego, CA 92121
Tel.: (858) 224-7200
Web Site: http://www.altheadx.com
Rev.: $7,346,000
Assets: $8,372,000
Liabilities: $21,224,000
Net Worth: ($12,852,000)
Earnings: ($4,058,000)
Emp.: 81
Fiscal Year-end: 12/31/2013
Diagnostic Testing Laboratory Services
N.A.I.C.S.: 621511
Jorge Garces (Pres & CEO)
Shannon Blalock (Chief Comml Officer)
Juan-Sebastian Saldivar (Chief Medical Officer)
Francois Ferre (Founder & Chm)
Joel Centeno (Sr VP-Regulatory Affairs & Quality Assurance)

CASTLE CREEK PHARMACEUTICALS HOLDINGS, INC.
405 Eagleview Blvd, Exton, PA 19341
Tel.: (484) 713-6000
Web Site:
    http://www.castlecreekbio.com
CCBS—(NASDAQ)
Rev.: $149,000
Assets: $27,926,000
Liabilities: $220,135,000
Net Worth: ($192,209,000)
Earnings: ($28,619,000)
Emp.: 53
Fiscal Year-end: 12/31/20
Pharmaceutical Services & Mfr
N.A.I.C.S.: 325412
W. Bradford Middlekauff (Chief Legal Officer)
Jeffrey S. Aronin (Founder & Chm)
Michael L. Derby (Co-Founder)
Jeffrey S. Aronin (Founder & Chm)
Matthew Gantz (Pres & CEO)
Mary Spellman (Chief Medical Officer & Sr VP-R&D)
W. Bradford Middlekauff (Chief Legal Officer)
Babar Ghias (COO)
Katherine Reedy (Sr VP-Comml)
Michael J. Maurer (VP-Mfg)
Andrea Kistner (VP-Fin)
Fatima Ahmad (VP-Medical Affairs)
Jeff Hesselberg (VP-Regulatory & Quality Affairs)

January McKee (Asst VP-Process Sciences)
Anthonius Kley (Sr Dir-Facilities)
Edward Russell (Sr Dir-HR)
Jeremy Cress (Sr Dir-Mfg Ops)
Robin Blumenthal (Sr Dir-Clinical Ops)
Tracy Rarick (Sr Dir-Technical Ops Program Strategy & Mgmt)
Tymissha Jackson (Sr Dir-Regulatory Affairs)

Subsidiaries:

Fibrocell Science, Inc.   (1)
405 Eagleview Blvd, Exton, PA 19341
Tel.: (484) 713-6000
Web Site: http://www.fibrocell.com
Rev.: $921,000
Assets: $15,758,000
Liabilities: $6,201,000
Net Worth: $9,557,000
Earnings: ($10,277,000)
Emp.: 19
Fiscal Year-end: 12/31/2018
Reconstructive Cosmetic Procedures Developer
N.A.I.C.S.: 325414
Sean D. Buckley (CFO, Principal Acctg Officer & Sec)
Anna Malyala (VP-R&D)

Subsidiary (Non-US):

Isolagen Europe Ltd.   (2)
59/61 Park Royal Road, London, NW10 7JJ, United Kingdom
Tel.: (44) 2088341080
Sales Range: $150-199.9 Million
Biotechnology Product Mfr & Developer
N.A.I.C.S.: 325414

CASTLE HOSPITALITY GROUP
3 Waterfront Plz 500 Ala Moana Blvd Ste 555, Honolulu, HI 96813
Tel.: (808) 524-0900   UT
Web Site:
    https://www.castleresorts.com
Year Founded: 1981
CAGU—(OTCEM)
Sales Range: $25-49.9 Million
Home Management Services
N.A.I.C.S.: 721110
Alan R. Mattson (Pres, CEO & COO)

Subsidiaries:

Castle Resorts & Hotels, Inc.   (1)
500 Ala Moana Blvd 3 Waterfront Plz Ste 555, Honolulu, HI 96813
Tel.: (808) 524-0900
Web Site: http://www.castleresorts.com
Emp.: 600
Hotel & Resort Management Services
N.A.I.C.S.: 721110.
Alan Mattson (Pres & COO)

CASTLIGHT HEALTH, INC.
150 Spear St Ste 400, San Francisco, CA 94105
Tel.: (415) 829-1400   DE
Web Site:
    http://www.castlighthealth.com
Year Founded: 2008
CSLT—(NYSE)
Rev.: $146,709,000
Assets: $166,773,000
Liabilities: $42,907,000
Net Worth: $123,866,000
Earnings: ($62,183,000)
Emp.: 440
Fiscal Year-end: 12/31/20
Healthcare Related Software Development Services
N.A.I.C.S.: 513210
Bryan E. Roberts (Co-Founder & Chm)
Giovanni M. Colella (Co-Founder)
Maeve O'Meara (CEO)
Eric Chan (Chief Acctg Officer)
Will Bondurant (CFO & Sr VP)
Matt Moran (Sr VP-Corp Dev)

Castlight Health, Inc.—(Continued)

Alex Shvartsman *(Gen Counsel & Sr VP)*
Vijay Anand *(Exec VP-Engrg)*
Angel Rosa *(Sr VP-Customer Experience)*
Caroline Kawashima *(Dir-Corp Mktg)*
Tamar Rudnick *(Sr VP-Mktg)*
Jayesh Patel *(Sr VP-Products)*
Scott Tweedy *(Sr VP-Support & Tech)*
Heather Hagg *(VP-Analytics & Ops)*
Todd Fruchey *(VP-Enterprise Sls)*

Subsidiaries:

Engage Technologies, Inc.   **(1)**
7041 Boone Ave N, Brooklyn Park, MN 55428
Tel.: (763) 795-8856
Web Site:
  http://www.engagetechnologies.net
Packaging Equipment Mfr
N.A.I.C.S.: 333993

CATALENT, INC.

14 Schoolhouse Rd, Somerset, NJ 08873
Tel.: (732) 537-6200   **DE**
Web Site: https://www.catalent.com
Year Founded: 2007
CTLT—(NYSE)
Rev.: $4,381,000,000
Assets: $9,753,000,000
Liabilities: $6,149,000,000
Net Worth: $3,604,000,000
Earnings: ($1,043,000,000)
Emp.: 16,100
Fiscal Year-end: 06/30/24
Pharmaceutical, Biotechnology & Consumer Health Product Packaging, Manufacturing & Development Services
N.A.I.C.S.: 325412
Karen Murphy Santiago *(Officer-Bus Transformation & Integration & VP)*
Mario Gargiulo *(Pres-Biologics-Europe)*
John R. Chiminski *(Chm)*
Aristippos Gennadios *(Pres-Softgel & Oral Technologies)*
John J. Greisch *(Exec Chm)*
Ricardo Zayas *(Sr VP-Ops & Biologics-North America)*
Jonathan Arnold *(Pres-Oral & Specialty Delivery)*
Steven L. Fasman *(Chief Admin Officer & Exec VP)*
Julien Meissonnier *(Chief Scientific Officer & VP)*
Alessandro Maselli *(Pres & CEO)*
Scott Gunther *(Sr VP-Quality & Regulatory Affairs)*
Michael J. Hatzfeld Jr. *(Chief Acctg Officer & VP)*
Kay Schmidt *(Sr VP-Technical Ops)*
Ricardo Pravda *(Sr VP-HR)*
Mike Grippo *(Sr VP-Strategy & Corp Dev)*
Matti M. Masanovich *(CFO & Sr VP)*
Paul Surdez *(VP-IR)*
Wai Lam Ling *(VP)*
Karen Santiago *(Chief Acctg Officer & VP)*
Sridhar Krishnan *(VP)*
Harold A. Jenkins III *(Gen Mgr-Philadelphia Facility)*

Subsidiaries:

Accucaps Industries Limited   **(1)**
2125 Ambassador Drive, Windsor, N9C 3R5, ON, Canada
Tel.: (519) 969-5404
Web Site: http://www.accucaps.com
Emp.: 500
Pharmaceuticals Product Mfr
N.A.I.C.S.: 325412

Catalent Anagni S.r.l.   **(1)**

Localita Fontana del CerasoS P Casilina 12 n 41, 03012, Anagni, FR, Italy
Tel.: (39) 07757621
Pharmaceuticals Product Mfr
N.A.I.C.S.: 325412

Catalent Brasil Ltda   **(1)**
Avenida Jerome Case 1277, Sorocaba, Sao Paulo, Brazil
Tel.: (55) 1532353513
Web Site: http://www.brasil.catalent.com
Pharmaceuticals Product Mfr
N.A.I.C.S.: 325412

Catalent CTS (Edinburgh) Limited   **(1)**
1 Inchwood Park, Bathgate, EH48 2FY, United Kingdom
Tel.: (44) 1506813000
Pharmaceutical Product Whslr
N.A.I.C.S.: 424210

Catalent CTS (Singapore) Pvt Ltd   **(1)**
No 1 Jalan Kilang 03-01, Singapore, 159402, Singapore
Tel.: (65) 62711891
Pharmaceutical Product Whslr
N.A.I.C.S.: 424210

Catalent Dusseldorf Gmbh   **(1)**
Berghausener Strasse 98, Rheinland, 40764, Langenfeld, Germany
Tel.: (49) 217332820
Pharmaceutical Product Mfr & Distr
N.A.I.C.S.: 325412

Catalent Germany Eberbach GmbH   **(1)**
Gammelsbacher Strasse 2, 69412, Eberbach, Germany
Tel.: (49) 62719450
Pharmaceuticals Product Mfr
N.A.I.C.S.: 325412
Marcus Spohn *(Dir-Quality Unit)*

Catalent Germany Schorndorf GmbH   **(1)**
Steinbeisstrasse 1-2, 73614, Schorndorf, Germany
Tel.: (49) 718170000
Web Site: http://www.catalent-germany.com
Sales Range: $250-299.9 Million
Emp.: 600
Provides Pharmaceutical Printed Components, Analytical & Clinical Services
N.A.I.C.S.: 325412

Catalent Harmans Road, LLC   **(1)**
7555 Harmans Rd, Harmans, MD 21077
Pharmaceuticals Product Mfr
N.A.I.C.S.: 325412

Catalent Houston, LLC   **(1)**
253 W Medical Center Blvd, Webster, TX 77598
Tel.: (832) 295-3578
Pharmaceutical Product Mfr & Distr
N.A.I.C.S.: 325412

Catalent Italy Holding Srl   **(1)**
20 100 Via Nettunense, 04011, Aprilia, Latina, Italy
Tel.: (39) 06927141
Holding Company
N.A.I.C.S.: 551112

Catalent Japan K.K.   **(1)**
4-9-17 Akasaka, Minato-Ku, Tokyo, 107-0052, Japan
Tel.: (81) 334702311
Web Site: http://www.japan.catalent.com
Emp.: 250
Pharmaceuticals Product Mfr
N.A.I.C.S.: 325412

Catalent Micron Technologies Limited   **(1)**
Charles Park Crossways Boulevard, Dartford, DA2 6QY, United Kingdom
Tel.: (44) 1322425200
Pharmaceutical Products Distr
N.A.I.C.S.: 424210

Catalent Micron Technologies, Inc.   **(1)**
333 Phoenixville Pike, Malvern, PA 19355
Tel.: (610) 251-7400
Pharmaceutical Product Mfr & Distr
N.A.I.C.S.: 325412

Catalent Nottingham Limited   **(1)**
8 Orchard Place Nottingham Business Park, Nottingham, NG8 6PX, United Kingdom
Tel.: (44) 1158718888
Biopharmaceutical Product Mfr & Distr
N.A.I.C.S.: 325412

Catalent Ontario Limited   **(1)**
2125 Ambassador Drive, Windsor, N9C 3R5, ON, Canada
Tel.: (800) 665-7210
Pharmaceutical Products Distr
N.A.I.C.S.: 424210

Catalent Oxford Limited   **(1)**
Thomson Avenue, Harwell, Oxford, OX11 0GD, United Kingdom
Tel.: (44) 1235639600
Pharmaceutical Product Mfr & Distr
N.A.I.C.S.: 325412

Catalent Pharma Solutions Limited   **(1)**
Frankland Road, Blagrove, Swindon, SN5 8RU, Wiltshire, United Kingdom
Tel.: (44) 1793864000
Sales Range: $350-399.9 Million
Emp.: 600
Holding Company; Pharmaceutical Packaging Services
N.A.I.C.S.: 551112

Plant (Domestic):

Catalent Pharma Solutions Ltd. - Bolton   **(2)**
Lancaster Way Wingates Industrial Park, Westhoughton, Bolton, BL5 3XX, Lancs, United Kingdom
Tel.: (44) 1942790000
Web Site: http://www.pciservices.com
Sales Range: $100-124.9 Million
Emp.: 300
Clinical Trial Supply Encapsulation, Packaging, Printing & Distribution Services
N.A.I.C.S.: 325412

Catalent Pharma Solutions, LLC - Raleigh   **(1)**
160 Pharma Dr, Morrisville, NC 27560
Tel.: (919) 481-4855
Web Site: http://www.catalent.com
Sales Range: $75-99.9 Million
Emp.: 260
Testing Laboratories
N.A.I.C.S.: 325412

Catalent Princeton, LLC   **(1)**
104 Campus Dr, Princeton, NJ 08540
Tel.: (908) 986-3386
Pharmaceutical Product Mfr & Distr
N.A.I.C.S.: 325412

Catalent San Diego, LLC   **(1)**
7330 Carroll Rd, San Diego, CA 92121
Tel.: (858) 805-6383
Pharmaceutical Product Mfr & Distr
N.A.I.C.S.: 325412

Catalent San Diego, Inc.   **(1)**
7330 Carroll Rd, San Diego, CA 92121
Tel.: (858) 805-6383
Web Site: http://www.catalent.com
Pharmaceuticals Product Mfr
N.A.I.C.S.: 325412
Lisa Caralli *(Dir-Science & Tech)*

Catalent Shiga K.K.   **(1)**
35 Hinokigaoka Minakuchi-cho, Koka, 528-0068, Shiga, Japan
Tel.: (81) 748633300
Primary Packaging Services
N.A.I.C.S.: 561910

Catalent U.K. Packaging Limited   **(1)**
Unit A10 Hastingwood Trading Estate 35 Harbet Road, London, N18 3HT, United Kingdom
Tel.: (44) 2088841010
Web Site: http://www.unipackworldwide.com
Packaging Services
N.A.I.C.S.: 561910

Catalent USA Woodstock, Inc.   **(1)**
2010 Lake Shore Dr, Woodstock, IL 60098
Tel.: (815) 338-9500
Web Site: http://www.catalent.com
Sales Range: $200-249.9 Million
Emp.: 650

Contract Manufacturer of Pharmaceutical Products; Private Label Manufacturing; Packaging Machinery
N.A.I.C.S.: 561910

Catalent Uruguay S.A.   **(1)**
Dr Luis Bonavita 1294 WTC Free Zone - Office 407, 11300, Montevideo, Uruguay
Tel.: (598) 26262044
Pharmaceutical Product Whslr
N.A.I.C.S.: 424210
Alejandra Violates Marzovillo *(Mgr-Pur & Logistics)*

Cook Pharmica LLC   **(1)**
1300 S Patterson Dr, Bloomington, IN 47403
Tel.: (877) 312-2665
Web Site: http://www.cookpharmica.com
Pharmaceutical & Biopharmaceutical Contract Development & Manufacturing Services
N.A.I.C.S.: 541714

Juniper Pharmaceuticals, Inc.   **(1)**
33 Arch St 31st Fl Ste 3110, Boston, MA 02110
Tel.: (617) 639-1500
Web Site: http://www.juniperpharma.com
Rev.: $49,979,000
Assets: $61,220,000
Liabilities: $19,708,000
Net Worth: $41,512,000
Earnings: ($2,060,000)
Emp.: 155
Fiscal Year-end: 12/31/2017
Women's Healthcare Pharmaceutical Products Developer & Retailer
N.A.I.C.S.: 325412

Subsidiary (Non-US):

Juniper Pharma Services Limited   **(2)**
8 Orchard Place Nottingham Business Park, Nottingham Business Park, Nottingham, NG8 6PX, United Kingdom
Tel.: (44) 115 871 8888
Web Site: http://www.juniperpharma.com
Sales Range: $1-9.9 Million
Emp.: 120
Pharmaceuticals Mfr
N.A.I.C.S.: 325412

Juniper Pharmaceuticals (France) SA   **(2)**
20 Rue lavoisier Pontoise, Paris, 95300, France
Tel.: (33) 134223010
Web Site: http://www.juniperpharma.com
Emp.: 1
Women's Healthcare Pharmaceutical Products
N.A.I.C.S.: 325412

MTI Pharma Solutions, Inc.   **(1)**
333 Phoenixville Pike, Malvern, PA 19355
Tel.: (610) 251-7400
Medical Products Mfr
N.A.I.C.S.: 325411

MaSTherCell Global, Inc.   **(1)**
253 W. Medical Ctr Blvd, Webster, TX 77598
Tel.: (832) 295-3578
Cell Therapy Mfr And Medical Service Solutions
N.A.I.C.S.: 325413
Darren Head *(CEO)*

Subsidiary (Non-US):

MaSTherCell, S.A.   **(2)**
48 Rue Auguste Piccard, 6041, Gosselies, Belgium
Tel.: (32) 71347629
Web Site: http://www.masthercell.com
Cell Therapy Mfr
N.A.I.C.S.: 325413
Denis Bedoret *(Pres)*
Eric Mathieu *(COO)*
Gisele Deblandre *(Chief Scientific Officer)*
Elodie Noel *(Mgr-HR)*
Jean-Francois Chaubard *(CTO)*
Charles Jacques *(Fin Dir)*
Francois Pons *(Officer-Legal & Compliance)*

Subsidiary (Domestic):

Masthercell U.S., LLC   **(2)**
253 W Medical Ctr Blvd, Webster, TX 77598

Tel.: (832) 295-3578
Chemical & Biological Substance Mfr
N.A.I.C.S.: 325413

Micron Technologies Limited (1)
Charles Park Crossways Boulevard, Dartford, DA2 6QY, United Kingdom
Tel.: (44) 1322425200
Pharmaceuticals Product Mfr
N.A.I.C.S.: 325412
Peter Line *(Mgr-Facilities & Capital Projects)*

Paragon Bioservices, Inc. (1)
801 W Baltimore St Ste 302, Baltimore, MD 21201
Web Site:
http://www.paragonbioservices.com
Biopharmaceutical Product Mfr & Distr
N.A.I.C.S.: 325412

Redwood Bioscience Inc. (1)
5959 Horton St Ste 400, Emeryville, CA 94608
Tel.: (510) 343-6031
Web Site: http://www.biologics.catalent.com
Pharmaceutical Product Mfr & Distr
N.A.I.C.S.: 325412

CATALYST BANCORP, INC.
235 N Court St, Opelousas, LA 70570
Tel.: (337) 948-3033   LA
Web Site:
https://catalystbank.investor
room.com
Year Founded: 2021
CLST—(NASDAQ)
Rev.: $9,187,000
Assets: $263,324,000
Liabilities: $174,850,000
Net Worth: $88,474,000
Earnings: $180,000
Emp.: 50
Fiscal Year-end: 12/31/22
Bank Holding Company
N.A.I.C.S.: 551111
Joseph B. Zanco *(Pres & CEO)*
Jacques L. J. Bourque *(CFO)*
Don P. Ledet *(Chief Risk Officer & Sr VP)*
Todd A. Kidder *(Chm)*

CATALYST PHARMACEUTI-CALS, INC.
355 Alhambra Cir Ste 801, Coral Gables, FL 33134
Tel.: (305) 420-3200   DE
Web Site:
https://www.catalystpharma.com
Year Founded: 2002
CPRX—(NASDAQ)
Rev.: $214,203,000
Assets: $375,630,000
Liabilities: $75,209,000
Net Worth: $300,421,000
Earnings: $83,079,000
Emp.: 82
Fiscal Year-end: 12/31/22
Pharmaceutical Developer & Mfr
N.A.I.C.S.: 325412
Patrick J. McEnany *(Founder)*
Steven R. Miller *(COO, Chief Scientific Officer & Exec VP)*
Richard J. Daly *(Pres & CEO)*
Michael W. Kalb *(CFO & Exec VP)*
Brian Elsbernd *(Chief Legal & Compliance Officer)*
Jeffrey Del Carmen *(Chief Comml Officer & Exec VP)*
Preethi Sundaram *(Chief Strategy Officer)*
Gary Ingenito *(Chief Medical & Regulatory Officer)*

CATERPILLAR, INC.
501 SW Jefferson St, Peoria, IL 61629
Tel.: (309) 675-2337   DE
Web Site: https://www.caterpillar.com

Year Founded: 1925
CAT—(NYSE)
Rev.: $67,060,000,000
Assets: $87,476,000,000
Liabilities: $67,973,000,000
Net Worth: $19,503,000,000
Earnings: $10,335,000,000
Emp.: 113,200
Fiscal Year-end: 12/31/23
Construction & Mining Equipment, Diesel & Natural Gas Engines, Industrial Gas Turbines & Diesel-Electric Locomotives Mfr
N.A.I.C.S.: 333120
Andrew R. J. Bonfield *(CFO)*
D. James Umpleby III *(Chm & CEO)*
Cheryl H. Johnson *(Chief HR Officer)*
Bob De Lange *(Grp Pres-Mktg, Svcs, Distr, and Digital)*
Cheryl H. Johnson *(Chief HR Officer)*
Joseph E. Creed *(COO)*
Chad J. Withers *(Asst Treas)*
Marc R. Cameron *(VP-Resource Industries Sls, Svcs & Tech)*
Nicole M. Puza *(Sec)*
Andrew R. J. Bonfield *(CFO)*
Patrick T. McCartan *(Treas)*
Courtney W. Dean *(Chief Compliance Officer)*
Derek Owens *(Chief Legal Officer & Gen Counsel)*
John Newman *(Pres, CEO-Progress Rail & Sr VP)*

Subsidiaries:

10G LLC (1)
100 Eddie Jungemann Dr, Savannah, GA 31408
Tel.: (910) 448-0089
Web Site: https://www.10gllc.com
Construction Machinery Mfr
N.A.I.C.S.: 333120

Adex Zonex Pte. Ltd. (1)
13 Kwong Min Road, Singapore, 628717, Singapore
Tel.: (65) 65587789
Engine Protection Services
N.A.I.C.S.: 811310
Mark Jackson *(Gen Mgr)*

Advanced Filtration Systems, Inc. (1)
3206 Farber Dr, Champaign, IL 61822
Tel.: (217) 351-3073
Web Site: https://www.afsifilters.com
Sales Range: $75-99.9 Million
Emp.: 180
Manufactures & Markets Diesel Engine Filters; Joint Venture of Caterpillar, Inc. (50%) & Donaldson Company, Inc. (50%)
N.A.I.C.S.: 336390

Subsidiary (Non-US):

AFSI Europe s.r.o. (2)
Industrial zone Joseph 139, Havran, 434 01, Most, 1, Czech Republic
Tel.: (420) 476456411
Web Site: https://www.afsifilters.cz
Sales Range: $25-49.9 Million
Emp.: 150
Filters
N.A.I.C.S.: 333618
Michael Svitak *(Mng Dir)*

Anchor Coupling, Inc. (1)
5520 13th St, Menominee, MI 49858-1014   (100%)
Tel.: (906) 863-2671
Web Site: https://anchorcoupling.com
Sales Range: $350-399.9 Million
Emp.: 800
Construction Machinery Mfr
N.A.I.C.S.: 333120

AsiaTrak (Tianjin) Ltd. (1)
No169 Haibin Jiu Road, Tianjin Port Free Trade Zone, Tianjin, 300461, China
Tel.: (86) 2258167225
Web Site: https://www.asiatrak-cat.com
Construction Machinery Mfr
N.A.I.C.S.: 333120

Atlas Heavy Engineering Pty Ltd (1)

546-550 Old Gympie Road, Narangba, 4504, QLD, Australia
Tel.: (61) 738883157
Web Site: https://ahe1.com.au
Construction Machinery Mfr
N.A.I.C.S.: 333120

Banco Caterpillar S.A. (1)
Av Dr Chucri Zaidan 1240 Golden Tower 17 andar, Sao Paulo, 04711-130, Brazil
Tel.: (55) 1121092213
Web Site: http://www.catfinancial.com
Financial & Leasing Services
N.A.I.C.S.: 541611

Black Horse LLC (1)
9950 W Gulf Bank Rd, Houston, TX 77040
Tel.: (281) 598-8100
Web Site: http://www.blackhorsepumps.com
Pumping Mfr
N.A.I.C.S.: 333914

Broadland Radiators and Heat Exchangers Limited (1)
Broadland House Norwich Road, Lenwade, Norfolk, NR9 5SG, United Kingdom
Tel.: (44) 1603413050
Web Site:
https://www.broadlandradiators.co.uk
Oil & Gas Exploration Services
N.A.I.C.S.: 213112
Chris Goodson *(Mgr-Production)*

Bucyrus Equipment LLC (1)
209 Main St, Hillsdale, KS 66036
Tel.: (913) 783-4600
Web Site: https://www.magnumenp.com
Emp.: 22
Farm Machinery & Equipment Whslr
N.A.I.C.S.: 532289

Bucyrus Mining Australia Pty. Ltd. (1)
L 8 369 Ann St, Brisbane, 4000, QLD, Australia
Tel.: (61) 730093600
Emp.: 200
Construction & Mining Equipment Distr
N.A.I.C.S.: 423810

Caterpillar (Langfang) Mining Equipment Co., Ltd. (1)
No 22 Jinyuandongdao, Economic Development Zone, Langfang, 065001, Hebei, China
Tel.: (86) 3166086840
Emp.: 200
Mining Equipment Distr
N.A.I.C.S.: 423830

Caterpillar (Luxembourg) Investment Co. S.a.r.l. (1)
Rue Henri M Schnadt 4 A, 2530, Luxembourg, Luxembourg
Tel.: (352) 2689154100
Investment Management Service
N.A.I.C.S.: 523940

Caterpillar (NI) Limited (1)
Springvale Business Park 1 Millennium Way, Belfast, BT12 7AL, Antrim, United Kingdom
Tel.: (44) 2890495000
Web Site: http://www.caterpillar.com
Emp.: 300
Power Generation System Mfr
N.A.I.C.S.: 335312

Caterpillar (Newberry) LLC (1)
284 Mawsons Way, Newberry, SC 29108
Tel.: (803) 405-8400
Power Generator Mfr
N.A.I.C.S.: 335312

Caterpillar (Zhengzhou) Ltd. (1)
7 Jinsuo Rd Gaoxin Technology Zone, Zhengzhou, 450001, China
Tel.: (86) 37156912677
Mining Equipment Mfr & Distr
N.A.I.C.S.: 333131

Caterpillar Americas Mexico, S. de R.L. de C.V. (1)
Carretera A Villa De Garcia Km 4 5 Cruce Libramiento, Santa Catarina, 66350, Nuevo Leon, Mexico
Tel.: (52) 8183193300
Web Site: http://www.caterpillar.com
Construction Machinery Equipment Mfr
N.A.I.C.S.: 333120

Caterpillar Asia Pacific Holding, Inc. (1)
100 NE Adams St, Peoria, IL 61629-0001   (100%)
Tel.: (309) 675-1000
Web Site: http://www.cat.com
Sales Range: $900-999.9 Million
Construction Machinery Mfr
N.A.I.C.S.: 333120

Caterpillar Canada (1)
3700 Steeles Avenue W Suite 902, Woodbridge, L4L 8K8, ON, Canada   (100%)
Tel.: (905) 850-3655
Web Site: http://www.cat.com
Sales Range: $900-999.9 Million
Commercial Services
N.A.I.C.S.: 333120

Caterpillar Castings Kiel GmbH (1)
Falckensteiner Strasse 2, 24159, Kiel, 24159, Germany
Tel.: (49) 43190892910
Engine Blocks & Cylinder Heads Mfr
N.A.I.C.S.: 333120

Caterpillar Centro de Formacion, S.L. (1)
Camino de Caterpillar 2 Santa Rosalia-Maqueda, 29591, Malaga, Spain
Tel.: (34) 952418800
Sales Range: $25-49.9 Million
Emp.: 62
Information Demonstration Services
N.A.I.C.S.: 333120
Jim Stettner *(Dir)*

Caterpillar CleanAIR Systems, Inc. (1)
2600 Camino Entrada, Santa Fe, NM 87507
Tel.: (505) 474-4120
Web Site: http://www.caterpillar.com
Sales Range: $10-24.9 Million
Emp.: 65
Emissions Control Systems Mfr
N.A.I.C.S.: 333618

Caterpillar Commercial Holding S.A.R.L. (1)
Route De Frontenex 76, Geneva, 1207, Switzerland
Tel.: (41) 228494444
Web Site: http://www.cat.com
Sales Range: $50-74.9 Million
Emp.: 450
Office Administrative Services
N.A.I.C.S.: 561110

Caterpillar Commercial S.A. (1)
Avenue Des Etats-Unis 1, Charleroi, 6041, Belgium
Tel.: (32) 71252111
Construction Machinery Mfr
N.A.I.C.S.: 333120
Nicolas Polutnik *(Mgr)*

Caterpillar Distribution Services Europe B.V.B.A. (1)
Humbeeksesteenweg 98, 1850, Grimbergen, 1850, Belgium
Tel.: (32) 22544211
Web Site: http://www.caterpillar.com
Sales Range: $125-149.9 Million
Emp.: 700
Construction Machinery Mfr
N.A.I.C.S.: 333120

Caterpillar East Japan Ltd. (1)
777 Shimokuzawa, Sagamihara, 229-1134, Japan
Tel.: (81) 427752610
Construction Machinery Mfr
N.A.I.C.S.: 333120

Caterpillar Elkader LLC (1)
1003 Miller St, Elkader, IA 52043-9080
Tel.: (309) 675-6300
Web Site: http://www.caterpillar.com
Emp.: 100
Construction Machinery Mfr
N.A.I.C.S.: 333120

Caterpillar Energy Solutions Asia Pacific Pte. Ltd. (1)
11 Kian Teck Road, Singapore, 628768, Singapore
Tel.: (65) 62685311
Industrial Machinery Distr
N.A.I.C.S.: 423830

Caterpillar, Inc.—(Continued)

Caterpillar Energy Solutions GmbH (1)
Carl-Benz-Strasse 1, 68167, Mannheim, Germany
Tel.: (49) 6213840
Web Site: https://caterpillar-energy-solutions.de
Construction Machinery Mfr
N.A.I.C.S.: 333120

Caterpillar Energy Solutions Inc. (1)
1750 Breckinridge Pkwy Ste 500, Duluth, GA 30096
Tel.: (770) 279-6720
Emp.: 8
Power Generator Mfr
N.A.I.C.S.: 335312

Caterpillar Eurasia LLC (1)
82 Sadovnicheskaya Str, Moscow, 113035, Russia
Tel.: (7) 4952133340
Web Site: http://www.caterpillar.com
Forestry Machinery & Equipment Mfr
N.A.I.C.S.: 333111

Caterpillar Finance Corporation (1)
4-10-1 Yoga Sbs Tower Bldg 14f Setagaya-Ku, Tokyo, 158-0097, Japan
Tel.: (81) 357974510
Web Site: http://www.nipponcat.co.jp
Emp.: 50
Construction Machinery Mfr
N.A.I.C.S.: 333120
Farrar Christopher *(Mng Dir)*

Caterpillar Financial New Zealand Limited (1)
24 Anys Road, Hornby, Christchurch, 8441, New Zealand
Tel.: (64) 800811344
Construction Machinery Mfr
N.A.I.C.S.: 333120

Caterpillar Financial Services Asia Pte. Ltd. (1)
14 Tractor Road, Singapore, 627973, Singapore
Tel.: (65) 68287580
Construction Machinery Mfr
N.A.I.C.S.: 333120

Caterpillar Financial Services Corporation (1)
2120 W End Ave, Nashville, TN 37203-0001 **(100%)**
Tel.: (615) 341-1000
Web Site: https://www.caterpillar.com
Rev.: $3,248,000,000
Assets: $33,112,000,000
Liabilities: $29,942,000,000
Net Worth: $0,170,000,000
Earnings: $563,000,000
Emp.: 2,300
Fiscal Year-end: 12/31/2023
Finance & Leasing of Industrial Equipment & Machinery
N.A.I.C.S.: 522210

Subsidiary (Non-US):

Caterpillar Finance France S.A. (2)
84 Rue Charles Michels, 93284, Saint Denis, Cedex, France **(100%)**
Tel.: (33) 148133600
Sales Range: $50-74.9 Million
Emp.: 55
Financial Services
N.A.I.C.S.: 333120

Caterpillar Financial Australia Limited (2)
1 Caterpillar Drive, Tullamarine, 3043, VIC, Australia **(100%)**
Tel.: (61) 80 001 0808
Web Site: http://www.catfinancial.com
Industrial Equipment & Machinery Rental & Leasing; Financing Services
N.A.I.C.S.: 532412

Subsidiary (Domestic):

Caterpillar Financial Commercial Account Corporation (2)
2120 W End Ave, Nashville, TN 37203
Tel.: (615) 341-1000
Web Site: http://www.cat.com
Financial Services

N.A.I.C.S.: 541611

Subsidiary (Non-US):

Caterpillar Financial Leasing, S.A. (2)
Via de las Dos Castillas 33 Edificio 6 Planta 4, 28224, Pozuelo de Alarcon, Spain **(100%)**
Tel.: (34) 917994440
Sales Range: $75-99.9 Million
Emp.: 70
Financial Services
N.A.I.C.S.: 333120

Caterpillar Financial Nordic Services A.B. (2)
Svardvagen 3B 194 22, PO Box 115, 660 57, Upplands Vasby, Sweden **(100%)**
Tel.: (46) 854498600
Web Site: http://www.fpd.cat.com
Sales Range: $25-49.9 Million
Emp.: 1
Construction Machinery Mfr
N.A.I.C.S.: 333120

Subsidiary (US):

Caterpillar Financial Receivables, Inc. (3)
2120 W End Ave, Nashville, TN 37203 **(100%)**
Tel.: (615) 341-1000
Web Site: http://www.caterpillar.com
Construction Machinery Mfr
N.A.I.C.S.: 333120

Subsidiary (Non-US):

Caterpillar Financial Services Norway A/S (3)
Vollebekk Brobekkveien 62B, PB 144, 0520, Oslo, Norway **(100%)**
Tel.: (47) 2 263 6875
Web Site: http://www.caterpillar.com
Sales Range: $25-49.9 Million
Emp.: 1
Financial Services
N.A.I.C.S.: 333120

Subsidiary (Non-US):

Caterpillar Financial Services (U.K.) Limited (2)
Friars Gate 1011 Stratford Road, Solihull, Shirley, B90 4BN, West Midlands, United Kingdom
Tel.: (44) 156 478 6400
Web Site: http://www.catfinancial.com
Financial Services
N.A.I.C.S.: 523999

Caterpillar Financial Services GmbH (2)
Lise-Meitner-Strasse 3, 85737, Ismaning, Germany **(88%)**
Tel.: (49) 89996120
Web Site: http://www.caterpillar.com
Sales Range: $75-99.9 Million
Emp.: 75
Financial Services
N.A.I.C.S.: 333120

Subsidiary (Domestic):

Caterpillar Leasing GmbH (Leipzig) (3)
Bruhl 6, 04552, Borna, Germany **(100%)**
Tel.: (49) 3433260280
Leasing Services
N.A.I.C.S.: 532412

EDC European Excavator Design Center Verwaltungs GmbH (3)
Karl Rapp Strasse 1, Amberg, 92432, Germany **(40%)**
Tel.: (49) 9431739232
Web Site: http://www.caterpillar.com
Sales Range: $25-49.9 Million
Tires Developer
N.A.I.C.S.: 326211

Caterpillar Financial Services Korea, Ltd. (1)
2 Floor Haein Building 392-6 Yangjai 2-dong Seocho-gu, Seoul, 137-899, Korea (South)
Tel.: (82) 234840400
Construction Machinery Mfr
N.A.I.C.S.: 333120

Caterpillar Financial Services N.V. (1)
Rondebeltweg 41, 1329 BP, Almere, Netherlands **(100%)**
Tel.: (31) 887377250
Web Site: http://www.nlfinance.cat.com
Sales Range: $25-49.9 Million
Emp.: 2
Financial Services
N.A.I.C.S.: 333120
Ferdinand Van Noort *(Mgr-Sls)*

Caterpillar Financial Services Netherlands B.V. (1)
Rondebeltweg 41, 1329 BP, Almere, Netherlands
Tel.: (31) 88 737 7250
Web Site: http://www.catfinancial.com
Financial Services
N.A.I.C.S.: 523999

Caterpillar Financial Services Philippines Inc. (1)
13 Economia Street 1110, Bagumbayan, Quezon City, 1100, Metro Manila, Philippines
Tel.: (63) 26381479
Sales Range: $25-49.9 Million
Emp.: 2
Finance Services
N.A.I.C.S.: 523999

Caterpillar Financial Services Poland Sp. z o.o. (1)
ul Prosta 51, 00-838, Warsaw, Poland
Tel.: (48) 22 448 8700
Web Site: http://www.catfinancial.com
Emp.: 25
Construction Machinery Mfr
N.A.I.C.S.: 333120

Caterpillar Financial Ukraine LLC (1)
34 Vasilkovskaya of 326B, Kiev, 03022, Ukraine
Tel.: (380) 444956033
Construction Machinery Mfr
N.A.I.C.S.: 333120

Caterpillar Fluid Systems S.r.l. (1)
Via Gobetti 2a - Palazzo C, 20063, Cernusco sul Naviglio, Milan, Italy
Tel.: (39) 029 239 2611
Web Site:
https://www.anchorfluidsystems.com
Fluid Power Valve & Hose Fitting Mfr
N.A.I.C.S.: 332912

Caterpillar Global Mining Colombia S.A.S. (1)
Calle 72 10 07 Of 401, Bogota, 208, Colombia
Tel.: (57) 17461000
Mining Equipment Mfr & Distr
N.A.I.C.S.: 333131

Caterpillar Global Mining Czech Republic, a.s. (1)
Lihovarska 11/1378, Radvanice, Ostrava, 716 10, Czech Republic
Tel.: (420) 596906510
Industrial Machinery Mfr & Distr
N.A.I.C.S.: 333310
Ivo Kuncicky *(Mgr-Supply Chain)*

Caterpillar Global Mining Equipamentos De Mineracao do Brasil Ltda. (1)
Avenue Das Nacoes 4069 Distrito Industrial, Vespasiano, 33200-000, Minas Gerais, Brazil
Tel.: (55) 3121221100
Mining Equipment Mfr & Distr
N.A.I.C.S.: 333131

Caterpillar Global Mining Equipment LLC (1)
3501 S FM Hwy 1417, Denison, TX 75020
Tel.: (918) 446-3311
Web Site: http://www.hypacparts.com
Construction & Mining Equipment Distr
N.A.I.C.S.: 423810

Caterpillar Global Mining Europe GmbH (1)
Industriestrasse 1, 44534, Lunen, Germany
Tel.: (49) 23067090
Emp.: 500
Mining Equipment Mfr & Distr
N.A.I.C.S.: 333131

Caterpillar Global Mining HMS GmbH (1)

Karl-Funke-Strasse 36, 44149, Dortmund, Germany
Tel.: (49) 2319220
Mining Machinery & Equipment Mfr
N.A.I.C.S.: 333131

Caterpillar Global Mining Pty. Ltd. (1)
1 Caterpillar Dr, Tullamarine, 3043, VIC, Australia
Tel.: (61) 399539333
Web Site: http://www.australia.cat.com
Emp.: 20
Construction Machinery Mfr
N.A.I.C.S.: 333120

Caterpillar Global Mining SARL (1)
Route de Frontenex 76, 1208, Geneva, Switzerland
Tel.: (41) 228494444
Mining Equipment Distr
N.A.I.C.S.: 423830

Caterpillar Global Mining, LLC (1)
875 W Cushing St, Tucson, AZ 85745
Tel.: (414) 768-4000
Web Site: http://mining.cat.com
Sales Range: $1-4.9 Billion
Emp.: 9,800
Surface Mining Machinery & Equipment Mfr
N.A.I.C.S.: 333131

Subsidiary (Domestic):

Bucyrus International, Inc. (2)
1100 Milwaukee Ave, South Milwaukee, WI 53172
Tel.: (414) 768-4000
Web Site: http://mining.cat.com
Sales Range: $1-4.9 Billion
Emp.: 9,800
Holding Company; Mining Equipment Designer, Mfr & Marketer
N.A.I.C.S.: 551112

Subsidiary (Non-US):

Bucyrus (Langfang) Mining Machinery Co. Ltd. (3)
22 Jinyuan Rd E, Langfang, 065001, Hebei Province, China
Tel.: (86) 3166086840
Web Site: http://www.bucyrus.com
Sales Range: $10-24.9 Million
Emp.: 40
Mfr of Coal
N.A.I.C.S.: 324199

Subsidiary (Domestic):

Bucyrus America, Inc. (3)
2045 W Pike St, Houston, PA 15342-1010
Tel.: (724) 743-1200
Web Site: http://www.bucyrus.com
Sales Range: $25-49.9 Million
Emp.: 150
Mining Machinery & Equipment Mfr
N.A.I.C.S.: 333131

Subsidiary (Non-US):

Bucyrus Europe GmbH (3)
Industriestrasse 1, D 44534, Lunen, Germany
Tel.: (49) 23067090
Sales Range: $750-799.9 Million
Emp.: 3,200
Mining Technology Services
N.A.I.C.S.: 333131
Dirk Straeter *(Dir-Mktg)*
Jurgen Krekeler *(Exec VP)*
Ulrech Noll *(Gen Mgr)*
Ulrach Pastchedag *(Chief HR Officer)*

Caterpillar Holding Germany GmbH (1)
LiseMeitnerStrasse 3, 85737, Ismaning, Germany
Tel.: (49) 89996120
Construction Machinery Mfr
N.A.I.C.S.: 333120

Caterpillar Hydraulics Italia S.r.l. (1)
Via Roncaglia 69, Jesi, Ancona, 60035, Italy
Tel.: (39) 07312351
Web Site: http://www.cat.com
Sales Range: $50-74.9 Million
Emp.: 230
Construction Machinery Mfr
N.A.I.C.S.: 333120

Caterpillar India Private Limited (1)
Poonapalli Village Mathagondapalli Post,
Hosur, 635114, Tamil Nadu, India
Tel.: (91) 4344406777
Web Site: http://www.caterpillar.com
Construction Machinery Mfr
N.A.I.C.S.: 333120

**Caterpillar Insurance Holdings,
Inc.** (1)
2120 W End Ave, Nashville, TN
37203
Tel.: (615) 341-8149 **(100%)**
Web Site: http://www.caterpillar.com
Sales Range: $1-9.9 Million
Emp.: 70
Insurance Services
N.A.I.C.S.: 524210

Subsidiary (Domestic):

**Caterpillar Insurance Services
Corporation** (2)
2120 W End Ave, Nashville, TN
37203-1031 **(100%)**
Tel.: (615) 341-1000
Web Site: http://www.caterpillarfinancial.com
Emp.: 2,000
Construction Machinery Mfr
N.A.I.C.S.: 333120
Kent M. Adams (Pres & CEO)

**Caterpillar Investment Management
Ltd.** (1)
100 NE Adams St, Peoria, IL
61629-0001 **(100%)**
Tel.: (309) 675-1000
Web Site: http://www.caterpillar.com
Sales Range: $1-4.9 Billion
Emp.: 5,000
Investment Managment Company
N.A.I.C.S.: 333120

**Caterpillar Latin America Commercial
Division** (1)
701 Waterford Way, Miami, FL
33126 **(100%)**
Tel.: (305) 476-6800
Web Site: http://www.caterpillar.com
Sales Range: $100-124.9 Million
Emp.: 300
Industrial Machinery Mfr
N.A.I.C.S.: 425120

**Caterpillar Life Insurance
Company** (1)
2120 W End Ave, Nashville, TN 37203-
0001
Tel.: (615) 341-8147
Insurance Services
N.A.I.C.S.: 524114

**Caterpillar Logistics Services India
Private Limited** (1)
RMZ NXT Campus 1A - 5th Floor Whitefield
Rd Sonnenhalli Village, Bengaluru, 560066,
India
Tel.: (91) 8040638000
Construction Machinery Logistics Services
N.A.I.C.S.: 541614

Caterpillar Luxembourg LLC (1)
4a rue Henri Schnadt, Luxembourg, 2530,
Luxembourg
Tel.: (352) 2689154100
Financial Services
N.A.I.C.S.: 541611

**Caterpillar Marine Asia Pacific Pte.
Ltd.** (1)
7 Tractor Road, Singapore, 627968, Singapore
Tel.: (65) 68287600
Construction Machinery Mfr
N.A.I.C.S.: 333120

**Caterpillar Marine Asset Intelligence
LLC** (1)
5032 Rouse Dr Ste 100, Virginia Beach, VA
23462
Tel.: (757) 965-5963
Software Development Services
N.A.I.C.S.: 541512

**Caterpillar Marine Power UK
Limited** (1)
Wimbourne Marine Power Centre 22 Cobham Rd, Wimborne Minster, BH21 7PW,
United Kingdom

Tel.: (44) 1202796000
Web Site: http://www.perkins.com
Sales Range: $25-49.9 Million
Emp.: 10
Construction Machinery Mfr
N.A.I.C.S.: 333120

Caterpillar Mexico S.A. de C.V. (1)
Carr a Villa de Garcia km 4 5 Zona Industrial, 66350, Santa Catarina,
Mexico **(100%)**
Tel.: (52) 8183193300
Web Site: http://www.cat.com
Sales Range: $1-4.9 Billion
Emp.: 3,000
Tractor Sales & Service
N.A.I.C.S.: 423830

**Caterpillar Motoren (Guangdong) Co.
Ltd.** (1)
Shizhou Industrial Estate Chencun Town,
Shunde District, Foshan, 528314, Guangdong, China
Tel.: (86) 75723305100
Marine Diesel Engine & Generator Mfr
N.A.I.C.S.: 335312

**Caterpillar Motoren GmbH & Co.
KG** (1)
Falckensteiner Str 2, 24159, Kiel, Germany
Tel.: (49) 43139952528
Web Site: http://www.marine.cat.com
Diesel Engine Mfr
N.A.I.C.S.: 333618

**Caterpillar Motoren
Verwaltungs-GmbH** (1)
Falckensteiner Str 2, Kiel, 24159, Germany
Tel.: (49) 431399501
Web Site: http://www.mak-global.com
Sales Range: $250-299.9 Million
Emp.: 1,500
Construction Machinery Mfr
N.A.I.C.S.: 333120

Caterpillar OEM Solutions Group (1)
100 NE Adams St, Peoria, IL
61629-9310 **(100%)**
Tel.: (309) 636-1100
Sales Range: $100-124.9 Million
Emp.: 125
Industrial Machinery
N.A.I.C.S.: 333120
Bud David (Gen Mgr-Component Mfg & Mkt
Svcs)

Caterpillar Overseas Credit Corporation S.A. (1)
76 Rte De Frontenex, PO Box 6000, Geneva, 6, Switzerland **(100%)**
Tel.: (41) 228494444
Web Site: http://www.caterpillar.com.ch
Sales Range: $200-249.9 Million
Emp.: 500
Credit Services
N.A.I.C.S.: 333120

Caterpillar Overseas SARL (1)
Route De Frontenex 76, Geneva, 1207,
Switzerland
Tel.: (41) 228494444
Web Site: http://www.cat.com
Construction Machinery Mfr
N.A.I.C.S.: 333120

Caterpillar Partnership Ltd. (1)
Rte D G Front Ene X 76, 6, Geneva,
Switzerland **(100%)**
Tel.: (41) 0228494544
Web Site: http://www.caterpillar.com
Sales Range: $125-149.9 Million
Emp.: 500
Construction Equipment Mfr
N.A.I.C.S.: 333120

Subsidiary (Non-US):

Caterpillar (U.K.) Limited (2)
Peckleton Lane, Desford, LE9 9JT, Leicestershire, United Kingdom **(56.5%)**
Tel.: (44) 1455826826
Web Site: http://www.caterpillar.com
Emp.: 10,000
Construction Machinery Mfr
N.A.I.C.S.: 423810

Caterpillar Belgium S.A. (2)
1 Ave Des Etats Unis Boite Postal 1, 6041,
Gosselies, Belgium **(100%)**
Tel.: (32) 71252111

Web Site: http://www.caterpillar.com
Emp.: 3,000
Construction Equipment & Diesel Engines
Mfr
N.A.I.C.S.: 333120

Subsidiary (Non-US):

Caterpillar China Limited (3)
Room 36 032 06 36 Flr Windsoo House
311 Gloucester Rd, Causeway Bay, China
(Hong Kong) **(100%)**
Tel.: (852) 28480333
Sales Range: $75-99.9 Million
Emp.: 60
Construction Machinery Mfr
N.A.I.C.S.: 333120

**Caterpillar China investment Co.,
Ltd.** (3)
Rm 1601 Caterpillar Tower No 8 Wangjing
Street, No 16 Chaoyangmenwai Ave, Beijing, 100102, China
Tel.: (86) 1059210088
Turbine Engines, Turbine Powered Natural-Gas Compressor Sets, Generator Sets &
Mechanical-Drive Packages Mfr
N.A.I.C.S.: 333611

Subsidiary (Non-US):

Caterpillar France S A S (2)
40 Ave Leon Blum Boite Postal 55 Ctr De
Tri, 38041, Grenoble, Cedex 9,
France **(100%)**
Tel.: (33) 476237000
Web Site: http://www.caterpillar.com
Construction Equipment & Earthmoving Machinery Mfr
N.A.I.C.S.: 333120

Joint Venture (Non-US):

Caterpillar Japan Ltd. (2)
1106-4 Shimizu Uozumi-cho Akashi-city,
Hyogo, 674-8686, Japan
Tel.: (81) 357171121
Web Site: http://www.cat.com
Sales Range: $100-124.9 Million
Emp.: 350
Mfr, Sales & Marketing of Construction
Equipment & Engines; Joint Venture of Caterpillar Inc. & Mitsubishi Heavy Industries,
Ltd.
N.A.I.C.S.: 333120

Subsidiary (Domestic):

Caterpillar Operator Training Ltd. (3)
3700 Tana, Sagamihara, 252-5292, Kanagawa, Japan
Tel.: (81) 427637130
Web Site: http://cot.jpncat.com
Industrial Machinery Operating Training
Services
N.A.I.C.S.: 611513

Subsidiary (Non-US):

Mec-Track S.r.L. (2)
Via Muzza Spadetta 30, Bazzano, 40053,
Bologna, Italy **(100%)**
Tel.: (39) 051836111
Sales Range: $100-124.9 Million
Emp.: 300
Farm Machinery Mfr
N.A.I.C.S.: 333111

P.T. Natra Raya (2)
Jl Raya Naragong KM 19, Cileungsi, Bogor,
16820, West Java, Indonesia **(80%)**
Tel.: (62) 218239800
Web Site: http://www.caterpillar-indonesia.com
Construction Machinery Mfr
N.A.I.C.S.: 333120

Caterpillar Paving Products, Inc. (1)
9401 85th Ave N, Minneapolis, MN
55445-2154 **(100%)**
Tel.: (763) 425-4100
Web Site: http://www.cat.com
Sales Range: $50-74.9 Million
Emp.: 700
Earth & Asphalt Vibratory Compaction
Equipment, Asphalt Pavers, Soil Front End
Loaders Mfr
N.A.I.C.S.: 333120

Subsidiary (Non-US):

Caterpillar Materiels Routiers (2)

21 Avenue Jean Jaures, PO Box 2, Rantigny, 60290, France **(100%)**
Tel.: (33) 344691010
Web Site: http://www.india.cat.com
Sales Range: $75-99.9 Million
Emp.: 200
Paving Equipment Mfr
N.A.I.C.S.: 333120

Caterpillar Precision Seals Korea (1)
538-5 Segyo-dong, Pyeongtaek, 450-818,
Gyeonggi-do, Korea (South)
Tel.: (82) 316580101
Construction Machinery Mfr
N.A.I.C.S.: 333120

**Caterpillar Product Development
SARL** (1)
Route De Frontenex 76, 1208, Geneva,
1207, Switzerland
Tel.: (41) 228494444
Construction Machinery Mfr
N.A.I.C.S.: 333120

Caterpillar Propulsion AB (1)
Tarnvagen 15, Hono, 475 40, Gothenburg,
Sweden
Tel.: (46) 31976500
Web Site: http://www.catpropulsion.com
Industrial Machinery Mfr
N.A.I.C.S.: 333310

**Caterpillar Propulsion International
Trading (Shanghai) Co. Ltd.** (1)
6F Lei Shing International Plaza No 1319
West Yanan Road, 200050, Shanghai,
200050, China
Tel.: (86) 2152374800
Industrial Machinery Distr
N.A.I.C.S.: 423830

**Caterpillar Propulsion Istanbul Makina
Ticaret Limited Sirketi** (1)
Fatih Sultan Mehmet Cad Yayabey Sokak
no 12 Kat 2, Kavacik, 34810, Istanbul, Turkiye
Tel.: (90) 2166804810
Emp.: 30
Industrial Machinery Distr
N.A.I.C.S.: 423830
Roberta Tombeni (Coord-Office)

Caterpillar Propulsion Italy S.R.L. (1)
Torre WTC - 19 Piano Via De Marini 1,
16149, Genoa, Italy
Tel.: (39) 0108595452
Industrial Machinery Distr
N.A.I.C.S.: 423830

Caterpillar Propulsion Namibia (Proprietary) Limited (1)
2nd Street East & John Newman, PO Box
4407, Walvis Bay, Namibia
Tel.: (264) 64276400
Industrial Machinery Maintenance Services
N.A.I.C.S.: 811210

**Caterpillar Propulsion Production
AB** (1)
Langesand 1, Box 1005, Ockero, 475 22,
Gothenburg, Sweden
Tel.: (46) 31976500
Web Site:
http://www.caterpillarpropulsion.com
Emp.: 200
Industrial Machinery Mfr
N.A.I.C.S.: 333310

**Caterpillar Propulsion Production Pte.
Ltd.** (1)
85 Tuas South Avenue 1, Singapore,
637419, Singapore
Tel.: (65) 63775251
Industrial Machinery Mfr
N.A.I.C.S.: 333310

Caterpillar Propulsion Pte. Ltd. (1)
No 5 Tukang Innovation Grove, Singapore,
618304, Singapore
Tel.: (65) 63775251
Industrial Machinery Distr
N.A.I.C.S.: 423830
Jonas Nyberg (Reg Mgr-Sls)

**Caterpillar Propulsion Singapore Pte.
Ltd.** (1)
85 Tuas South Avenue 1, Singapore,
637419, Singapore
Tel.: (65) 63775251
Industrial Machinery Distr

Caterpillar, Inc.—(Continued)

N.A.I.C.S.: 423830
Syaiful Akmar *(Engr-Svcs)*

Caterpillar Propulsion Spain, S.L. (1)
Avda de Zumalakarregui 1 Entr A, 20008,
San Sebastian, Spain
Tel.: (34) 943116099
Industrial Machinery Distr
N.A.I.C.S.: 423830

**Caterpillar Propulsion Sweden
AB** (1)
Tarnvagen 15, 475 40, Gothenburg, Swe-
den
Tel.: (46) 31976500
Emp.: 200
Industrial Machinery Mfr
N.A.I.C.S.: 333310
Marit Borjesson *(Gen Mgr)*

**Caterpillar Ramos Arizpe, S. de R.L.
de C.V.** (1)
Blvd Industria De La Transformacion No
3135, Ramos Arizpe, 25900, Coahuila,
Mexico
Tel.: (52) 8444383058
Industrial Machinery Mfr
N.A.I.C.S.: 333310
Gustavo Cepeda *(Gen Mgr)*

**Caterpillar Remanufacture
Franklin** (1)
751 International Dr, Franklin, IN 46131-
9501
Tel.: (317) 738-9202
Sales Range: $25-49.9 Million
Emp.: 80
Motor Vehicle Component Mfr
N.A.I.C.S.: 336310

**Caterpillar Remanufacturing
Limited** (1)
Lancaster Road, Shrewsbury, SY1 3NX,
United Kingdom
Tel.: (44) 1743212000
Sales Range: $75-99.9 Million
Emp.: 350
Construction Machinery Mfr
N.A.I.C.S.: 333120
Matthew Bully *(Gen Mgr)*

**Caterpillar Remanufacturing Services
Radom Poland** (1)
ul Kozienicka 97, 26-600, Radom, Poland
Tel.: (48) 483855090
Industrial Machinery Mfr
N.A.I.C.S.: 333310
Cezary Gawor *(Plant Mgr)*

**Caterpillar Risk Management Ser-
vices Ltd.** (1)
100 NE Adams Ct, Peoria, IL
61629-5320 **(100%)**
Tel.: (309) 675-4944
Sales Range: $900-999.9 Million
Risk Management Srvices
N.A.I.C.S.: 333120

**Caterpillar Services Germany
GmbH** (1)
Falckensteiner Str 2, 24159, Kiel, Germany
Tel.: (49) 431399501
Emp.: 300
Industrial Machinery Mfr
N.A.I.C.S.: 333310

Caterpillar Servizi Italia Srl (1)
Via IV Novembre 2, 40061, Minerbio, Italy
Tel.: (39) 0516607111
Construction Machinery Mfr
N.A.I.C.S.: 333120

**Caterpillar Solution Engineering
Ltd.** (1)
3700 Tana Chuo-Ku Caterpillar Japan
Sagami Jigyoshonai, Sagamihara, 252-
0244, Kanagawa, Japan
Tel.: (81) 427637167
Construction Machinery Mfr
N.A.I.C.S.: 333120

**Caterpillar Southern Africa (Pty)
Ltd.** (1)
Gallagher Convention Centre 19 Richards
Road, PO Box 197, Halfway House, Mid-
rand, 1685, South Africa
Tel.: (27) 119615000
Construction & Mining Equipment Distr

N.A.I.C.S.: 423810

**Caterpillar Switchgear Americas
LLC** (1)
4955 Marconi Dr, Alpharetta, GA 30005
Tel.: (770) 442-9442
Web Site: http://www.cat.com
Switchgear Mfr & Tester
N.A.I.C.S.: 335313

Caterpillar Tohuku Ltd. (1)
Kakyoin Square 13F 1-1-20 Kakyoin, Aoba-
ku, Sendai, 980-0011, Miyagi, Japan
Tel.: (81) 223986659
Web Site: https://www.kmsh.co.jp
Construction & Mining Equipment Distr
N.A.I.C.S.: 423810

**Caterpillar Torreon S. de R.L. de
C.V.** (1)
Carretera Torreon Mieleras Km 6 5 S/N,
Torreon, 27400, Coahuila, Mexico
Tel.: (52) 8717294400
Construction & Mining Machinery Mfr
N.A.I.C.S.: 333120

**Caterpillar Transmissions France
S.A.R.L.** (1)
Artoipole 445 Boulevard De L Europe,
62118, Monchy-le-Preux, France
Tel.: (33) 321213950
Construction Machinery Mfr
N.A.I.C.S.: 333120

Caterpillar UK Holdings Limited (1)
Frank Perkins Way Irlam, Manchester, M44
5EW, United Kingdom
Tel.: (44) 1617765210
Web Site: http://www.neovialogistics.com
Emp.: 200
Parts Wearhouse Services
N.A.I.C.S.: 493190

**Caterpillar Underground Mining Pty.
Ltd.** (1)
2-8 Hopkinson St, Burnie, 7320, TAS, Aus-
tralia
Tel.: (61) 364329000
Mining Machinery & Equipment Mfr
N.A.I.C.S.: 333131

**Caterpillar Used Equipment Services
International SARL** (1)
Route De Frontenex 76, 1207, Geneva,
Switzerland
Tel.: (41) 228494444
Construction Machinery Mfr
N.A.I.C.S.: 333120

Caterpillar West Japan Ltd. (1)
1-23 Shimoicho, Ibaraki, 567-0066, Osaka,
Japan
Tel.: (81) 726411135
Construction Machinery Mfr
N.A.I.C.S.: 333120

Caterpillar Work Tools B.V. (1)
Sigarenmakerstraat 9, 's-Hertogenbosch,
5232 BJ, Netherlands
Tel.: (31) 736399600
Web Site: http://www.cat.com
Sales Range: $50-74.9 Million
Emp.: 250
Construction Machinery Mfr
N.A.I.C.S.: 333120

Caterpillar Work Tools, Inc. (1)
400 Work Tool Dr, Wamego, KS
66547-1299 **(100%)**
Tel.: (785) 456-2224
Sales Range: $150-199.9 Million
Emp.: 356
Snow Plows, U-Blades, Buckets & Quick
Couplers, Forestry & Landclearing Attach-
ments Mfr
N.A.I.C.S.: 333120

Caterpillar Xuzhou Ltd. (1)
Jinshanqiao Development Zone, 221004,
Xuzhou, 221004, Jiangsu, China
Tel.: (86) 51687736688
Mining Machinery & Equipment Mfr
N.A.I.C.S.: 333131

Caterpillar of Australia Ltd. (1)
1 Caterpillar Drive, Private Mail Bag 4, Tul-
lamarine, 3043, VIC, Australia **(100%)**
Tel.: (61) 399539333
Web Site: http://www.caterpillar.com.au
Sales Range: $75-99.9 Million
Emp.: 100

Construction Equipment, Earthmoving Machinery, Engines & Paving Products Mfr
N.A.I.C.S.: 333120

Caterpillar of Australia Pty. Ltd. (1)
1 Caterpillar Dr, Tullamarine, 3043, VIC,
Australia
Tel.: (61) 61399539333
Construction Machinery Mfr
N.A.I.C.S.: 333120

Caterpillar of Canada (1)
3700 Steeles Ave W, Woodbridge, L4L 8K8,
ON, Canada **(100%)**
Tel.: (905) 850-3655
Web Site: http://www.cat.com
Sales Range: $50-74.9 Million
Emp.: 20
Construction Machinery Services
N.A.I.C.S.: 333120

Caterpillar, East Peoria Plant (1)
100 NE Adams St, Peoria, IL
61629-0001 **(100%)**
Tel.: (309) 675-1000
Web Site: http://www.cate.com
Sales Range: $50-74.9 Million
Emp.: 50
Construction Machinery Mfr
N.A.I.C.S.: 333120
Douglas R. Oberhelman *(Chm & CEO)*

**EDC European Excavator Design
Center Beteiligungs-GmbH** (1)
Karl-Rapp-Str 1, Freistaat Bayern, 92442,
Wackersdorf, Germany
Tel.: (49) 94317390
Emp.: 100
Industrial Machinery Mfr
N.A.I.C.S.: 333310
Stefan Ortloff *(Gen Mgr)*

**EMD INTERNATIONAL HOLDINGS,
INC.** (1)
9301 W 55th St, La Grange, IL 60525-3214
Tel.: (708) 387-6000
New & Used Car Dealers
N.A.I.C.S.: 441110

**EMD Locomotive Company de
Mexico, S.A. de C.V.** (1)
Washington S/N, Guadalajara, 44440,
Jalisco, Mexico
Tel.: (52) 3336191488
Locomotive & Railroad Equipment Mfr
N.A.I.C.S.: 336320
Jorge J. Negrete *(Engr-Indus & Electrical)*

ESRG, LLC (1)
5032 Rouse Dr Ste100, Virginia Beach, VA
23462
Tel.: (757) 965-5963
Web Site: http://www.esrgtech.com
Emp.: 25
Engineeering Services
N.A.I.C.S.: 541330

**Electro-Motive Technical Consulting
Co. (Beijing) Ltd.** (1)
Room 1601 Caterpillar Tower No 8
Wangjing Street, Chaoyang, Beijing,
100102, China
Tel.: (86) 1065900826
Industrial Machinery Mfr
N.A.I.C.S.: 333310

**Energy Technologies Institute
LLP** (1)
Holywell Building Holywell Way, Loughbor-
ough, LE11 3UZ, Leics, United Kingdom
Tel.: (44) 1509202020
Web Site: http://www.eti.co.uk
Emp.: 70
Construction Machinery Mfr
N.A.I.C.S.: 333120

Energyst B.V. (1)
Hallenstraat 16, 5531-AB, Bladel, Nether-
lands
Tel.: (31) 497532500
Web Site: http://www.energyst.com
Emp.: 250
Power Generation Services
N.A.I.C.S.: 221118
Gary Smith *(CEO)*

Evercompounds S.p.a. (1)
Via S Barbara 192, Fusignano, 48010,
Ravenna, Italy
Tel.: (39) 0545955841

Web Site: https://www.evercompounds.com
Construction Machinery Mfr
N.A.I.C.S.: 333120

GTUIT, LLC (1)
2924 Millennium Cir Ste A, Billings, MT
59102
Tel.: (406) 867-6700
Web Site: http://www.gtuit.com
Sales Range: $10-24.9 Million
Oil & Gas Operation Services
N.A.I.C.S.: 213112
Brian Cebull *(Pres & CEO)*
Mark C. Peterson *(COO & Engr-Pro)*
James L. Haider *(CTO & Engr-Pro)*
Christian G. Orms *(CFO)*
George L. Chedsey *(VP-Bus Dev & Engr-
Pro)*

Haynes Corporation (1)
3581 Mercantile Ave, Naples, FL 34104
Tel.: (239) 643-3013
Web Site: http://www.haynesco.com
Emp.: 72
Construction Machinery Mfr
N.A.I.C.S.: 333120
Greg Schultz *(Dir-Mktg)*

Kemper Valve & Fittings Corp. (1)
3001 Darrell Rd, Island Lake, IL 60042
Tel.: (847) 526-2166
Web Site: https://www.kempervalve.com
Pressure Pipe Union & Fluid Control Prod-
uct Mfr
N.A.I.C.S.: 332919

M2M Data Corp. (1)
345 Inverness Dr S Ste C320, Englewood,
CO 80112
Tel.: (303) 768-0064
Web Site: http://www.m2mdatacorp.com
Sales Range: $1-9.9 Million
Emp.: 19
Remote Monitoring, Operation & Mainte-
nance Applications
N.A.I.C.S.: 541519

**MGE Equipamentos e Servicos Fer-
roviarios Ltda.** (1)
Georg Rexroth 609 Bloco D - Conjuntos 1
E 2, Diadema, 09951--270, Sao Paulo, Bra-
zil
Tel.: (55) 1140711234
Web Site:
    http://www.mgetransportes.com.br
Train Industrial Machinery Mfr
N.A.I.C.S.: 423830

MWM (Beijing) Co., Ltd. (1)
Room 2-02 CITIC Building Tower A No 19
Jianguomen Wai Dajie, Chaoyang, Beijing,
100004, China
Tel.: (86) 1065285116
Web Site: http://www.mwm.net
Emp.: 24
Industrial Machinery Distr
N.A.I.C.S.: 423830

MWM Austria GmbH (1)
Munchner Strabe 22, 6130, Schwaz, Austria
Tel.: (43) 524221300
Gas Engine & Machinery Mfr
N.A.I.C.S.: 336310

MWM Benelux B.V. (1)
Soerweg 13, 3088 GR, Rotterdam, Nether-
lands
Tel.: (31) 10 299 2666
Web Site: https://www.mwm.net
Emp.: 75
Power Generator Mfr
N.A.I.C.S.: 335312

MWM Energy Australia Pty Ltd (1)
1 Caterpillar Drive, Tullamarine, 3043, VIC,
Australia
Tel.: (61) 392623000
Electrical Equipment Distr
N.A.I.C.S.: 423610

MWM France S.A.S. (1)
Peripark Gennevilliers 99/101 Avenue Louis
Roche Bat E5, 92230, Gennevilliers, France
Tel.: (33) 147907780
Emp.: 35
Engine System Distr
N.A.I.C.S.: 423120

MWM GmbH (1)
Carl Benz Strasse 1, 68167, Mannheim,
Germany

Tel.: (49) 6213840
Web Site: https://www.mwm.net
Sales Range: $400-449.9 Million
Emp.: 1,000
Energy Production Systems Mfr
N.A.I.C.S.: 333618

MWM Latin America Solucoes Energeticas Ltda. (1)
Av Dr Jose Bonifacio C Nogueira 214 sala 418, 13091-611, Campinas, Sao Paulo, Brazil
Tel.: (55) 1933965777
Power Generator Distr
N.A.I.C.S.: 423120

MWM Real Estate GmbH (1)
Brauhausstieg 51, 22041, Hamburg, Germany
Tel.: (49) 15252374048
Web Site: https://www.mwm-realestate.de
Construction Machinery Mfr
N.A.I.C.S.: 333120

MaK Beteiligungs GmbH (1)
Falckensteiner Strabe 2, 24159, Kiel, Germany
Tel.: (49) 431399501
Web Site: http://www.marine.cat.com
Construction Machinery Mfr
N.A.I.C.S.: 333120

Motoren Steffens GmbH (1)
Geefacker 63, 47533, Kleve, Germany
Tel.: (49) 282 171 1370
Web Site: https://www.motoren-steffens.de
Diesel Engine Distr
N.A.I.C.S.: 423120
Ulrich Berns (Mng Dir)

Nihon Kenki Lease Co., Ltd. (1)
1-1-9 Nanatsujima, Kagoshima, 891-0132, Japan
Tel.: (81) 992622621
Construction Machinery Mfr
N.A.I.C.S.: 333120

OEM Solutions Group (1)
100 NE Adams St, Peoria, IL 61628 (100%)
Tel.: (309) 636-1081
Sales Range: $100-124.9 Million
Emp.: 125
Construction Machinery Services
N.A.I.C.S.: 333120

P.T. Caterpillar Finance Indonesia (1)
Beltway Office Park Building C Tingkat 3 Unit 301-303, Jl TB Simatupang No 41, Jakarta, 12560, Indonesia
Tel.: (62) 212 939 2999
Web Site: http://www.catfinancial.com
Emp.: 30
Construction Machinery Mfr
N.A.I.C.S.: 333120

PEPR Inc. (1)
Suite 700 521 3rd Avenue SW, Calgary, T2P 3T3, AB, Canada
Tel.: (403) 879-1693
Web Site: http://www.peprinc.com
Software Development Services
N.A.I.C.S.: 541511

PT. Caterpillar Indonesia (1)
Jl Raya Naragong KM 19 Cileungsi, Bogor, 16820, West Java, Indonesia
Tel.: (62) 218239800
Construction Machinery Mfr
N.A.I.C.S.: 333120

Peck Tech Consulting Ltd. (1)
447 Rue St Claude, Montreal, H2Y 3B6, QC, Canada
Tel.: (514) 933-1633
Web Site: http://www.pecktech.ca
Mining & Metal Services
N.A.I.C.S.: 213114

Perkins Engines Company Ltd. (1)
Frank Perkins Way, Eastfield, Peterborough, PE1 5FQ, Cambridgeshire, United Kingdom (100%)
Tel.: (44) 1733583000
Web Site: http://www.perkins.com
Sales Range: $200-249.9 Million
Diesel Engine Mfr
N.A.I.C.S.: 333618

Perkins Engines Inc (1)

1600 W Kingsbury St, Seguin, TX 78155
Tel.: (309) 578-7364
Web Site: http://www.perkins.com
Diesel Engine Equipment Mfr
N.A.I.C.S.: 333618

Perkins France (S.A.S.) (1)
Paris Nord II - Parc des Reflets 165 Avenue du Bois de la Pie, 95913, Roissy-en-France, France
Tel.: (33) 149907171
Web Site: http://www.perkins.com
Sales Range: $10-24.9 Million
Emp.: 1
Construction Machinery Mfr
N.A.I.C.S.: 333120

Perkins India Private Limited (1)
7th Floor International Tech Park Teramani Road, Teramani, Chennai, 600113, India
Tel.: (91) 2406002556
Diesel & Gas Engine Mfr & Distr
N.A.I.C.S.: 333618

Perkins International Inc. (1)
672 Delaware Ave, Buffalo, NY 14209
Tel.: (309) 675-1000
Combustion Engine Mfr
N.A.I.C.S.: 333618

Perkins Motoren GmbH (1)
Saalaeckerstrasse 4, Kleinostheim, 63801, Germany
Tel.: (49) 60275010
Construction Machinery Mfr
N.A.I.C.S.: 333120

Polyhose India (Rubber) Private Limited (1)
186/187 P H Road Alsa Towers Kilpauk, Chennai, 600 010, Tamil Nadu, India
Tel.: (91) 4426412830
Web Site: http://www.polyhose.com
Hydraulic Pneumatic Hose Mfr
N.A.I.C.S.: 332912

Progress Metal Reclamation Company (1)
1900 Frnt St, Ashland, KY 41101-7707
Tel.: (606) 329-9600
Construction Machinery Mfr
N.A.I.C.S.: 333120

Progress Rail Canada Corporation (1)
125H Saint-Joseph Boulevard, Lachine, H8S 2K9, QC, Canada
Tel.: (514) 639-1785
Web Site: http://www.progressrail.com
Emp.: 25
Fabricated Metal Product Distr
N.A.I.C.S.: 423510

Progress Rail Manufacturing Corporation (1)
3500 S Cowan Rd, Muncie, IN 47302
Tel.: (765) 281-2695
Railroad Maintenance & Repair Services
N.A.I.C.S.: 811310

Progress Rail Raceland Corporation (1)
1600 Progress Dr, Albertville, AL 35950
Tel.: (606) 834-0024
Construction Machinery Mfr
N.A.I.C.S.: 333120

Progress Rail Services Corporation (1)
1600 Progress Dr, Albertville, AL 35950 (100%)
Tel.: (256) 593-1260
Web Site: https://www.progressrail.com
Products & Services to the Railroad Industry
N.A.I.C.S.: 488210
Leah Green (Gen Counsel)
Jack Zhang (Exec VP-)
Hyung Kim (Exec VP-)
Kelly Roney (Chief Compliance Officer)
Mark Russell (Sr VP- &)
Ryan Cunningham (CFO)

Subsidiary (Domestic):

Electro-Motive Diesel, Inc. (2)
9301 W 55th St, La Grange, IL 60525-3211, (100%)
Tel.: (708) 387-6000
Web Site: http://www.emdiesels.com

Diesel-Electric Locomotives & Diesel Engines Mfr
N.A.I.C.S.: 333618

Subsidiary (Non-US):

Electro-Motive Canada Co. (3)
2021 Oxford Street East, PO Box 5160, London, N6A 4N5, ON, Canada
Tel.: (519) 452-5000
Web Site: http://www.emdiesels.com
Sales Range: $125-149.9 Million
Emp.: 700
Diesel-Electric Locomotives Design, Manufacture & Sale
N.A.I.C.S.: 333618

Plant (Domestic):

Progress Rail - Bearing Plant (2)
1415 Greg St Ste 103, Sparks, NV 89431-5939 (100%)
Tel.: (775) 331-3633
Web Site: http://www.progressrail.com
Sales Range: $25-49.9 Million
Emp.: 40
Reconditioning of Tapered Roller Bearings
N.A.I.C.S.: 332991

Progress Rail - Bearing Plant (2)
4301 Pratt Remmel Rd, Little Rock, AR 72206-3890 (100%)
Tel.: (501) 490-4230
Web Site: http://www.progressrail.com
Sales Range: $25-49.9 Million
Emp.: 85
Reconditioning of Tapered Roller Bearings
N.A.I.C.S.: 332991

Progress Rail Services UK Limited (1)
Osmaston Street, Sandiacre, Nottingham, NG10 5AN, United Kingdom
Tel.: (44) 1159218218
Web Site: https://www.progressrail.com
Emp.: 300
Railway Equipment Mfr
N.A.I.C.S.: 331110
George Law (Head-Human Resources)
David May (Dir-Sales)
John Newman (Pres)
Keri Cole (CFO)

Progress Rail Services de Mexico S.A. de C.V. (1)
20 De Noviembre No 1200, San Luis Potosi, 78030, Mexico
Tel.: (52) 4448145340
Automotive Repair & Maintenance Services
N.A.I.C.S.: 811111

Progress Rail Signaling S.p.A. (1)
Via IV Novembre 29, Serravalle Pistoiese, 51034, Pistoia, Italy
Tel.: (39) 05731916301
Railroad Infrastructure Product Services
N.A.I.C.S.: 551112

Progress Rail Switching Services LLC (1)
411 Dines Way, Rock Springs, WY 82901
Tel.: (307) 382-3839
Railroad Switching Services
N.A.I.C.S.: 488210

Pyroban (Suzhou) Safety Systems Co., Ltd. (1)
Workshop B2 North Lou Zhong Lu Suzhou Industrial Park, 215122, Suzhou, Jiang Su, China
Tel.: (86) 51262756800
Web Site: http://www.pyroban.com
Explosion Protection Product Whslr
N.A.I.C.S.: 423690

Pyroban Benelux B.V. (1)
Grotenoord 24-26, PO Box 229, 3341 LT, Hendrik-Ido-Ambacht, Netherlands
Tel.: (31) 786845570
Explosion Protection Product Mfr & Whslr
N.A.I.C.S.: 334511

Pyroban Envirosafe Limited (1)
Unit 4 Littleton Business Park, Staffordshire, Cannock, WS12 4TR, United Kingdom
Tel.: (44) 1543570048
Exhaust Emission Solution Services
N.A.I.C.S.: 811198

Pyroban Group Limited (1)
3rd floor Afon House Worthing Road, Hor-

sham, RH12 1TL, United Kingdom
Tel.: (44) 1273466200
Explosion Protection Product Mfr & Whslr
N.A.I.C.S.: 334511

Pyropress Engineering Company Limited (The) (1)
Bell Close Plympton, Devon, Plymouth, PL7 4JH, United Kingdom
Tel.: (44) 1752333939
Web Site: http://www.pyropress.com
Switch & Control Panel Mfr
N.A.I.C.S.: 334419

Pyrrha Investments B.V. (1)
Soerweg 13, 3088 GR, Rotterdam, Netherlands
Tel.: (31) 102992666
Web Site: http://www.mvmnet.hu
Holding Company
N.A.I.C.S.: 551112

Rail Product Solutions LLC (1)
8400 W 110th St Ste 300, Overland Park, KS 66210
Tel.: (913) 345-4807
Rail Machinery Mfr
N.A.I.C.S.: 332722

Rapidparts, Inc. (1)
2950 Walkent Ct NW, Grand Rapids, MI 49544
Tel.: (616) 647-2500
Web Site: http://www.rpionline.com
Sales Range: $75-99.9 Million
Emp.: 83
Construction Machinery Mfr
N.A.I.C.S.: 333120

SCM Singapore Holdings Pte. Ltd. (1)
7 Tractor Road, Singapore, 048620, Singapore
Tel.: (65) 68287333
Holding Company
N.A.I.C.S.: 551112

SPL Software Alliance LLC (1)
500 N Morton Ave, Morton, IL 61550
Tel.: (309) 266-0304
Software Development Services
N.A.I.C.S.: 541511

SPM Oil & Gas Inc. (1)
601 Herbert Dr, Fort Worth, TX 76108
Tel.: (817) 935-7500
Web Site: https://www.spmoilandgas.com
Construction Machinery Mfr
N.A.I.C.S.: 333120

Servicios Ejecutivos Progress S. de R.L. de C.V. (1)
Priv Pino Suarez No 300 Piso 7 La Finca, Monterrey, 64000, Nuevo Leon, Mexico
Tel.: (52) 8183425677
Management Consulting Services
N.A.I.C.S.: 541611
Arel Rieao Couoh (Gen Mgr)

Solar Turbines Incorporated (1)
2200 Pacific Hwy, San Diego, CA 92186-5376 (100%)
Tel.: (619) 544-5352
Web Site: https://www.solarturbines.com
Emp.: 8,000
Turbine Engines, Turbine Powered Natural-Gas Compressor Sets, Generator Sets & Mechanical-Drive Packages Mfr
N.A.I.C.S.: 333611

Subsidiary (Non-US):

Divisao Turbinas Solar S.A. de C.V. (2)
Rua Lauro Mullar 116 Room 2606, Rio de Janeiro, 22290-160, Brazil
Tel.: (55) 21 3873 8574
Turbine Engines, Turbine Powered Natural-Gas Compressor Sets, Generator Sets & Mechanical-Drive Packages Mfr
N.A.I.C.S.: 333611

P.T. Solar Services Indonesia (2)
10th Floor Landmark Center 1, Jl Jend Sudirman No 1, Jakarta, 12910, Indonesia
Tel.: (62) 215223407
Web Site: http://mysolar.cat.com
Turbine Engines, Turbine Powered Natural-Gas Compressor Sets, Generator Sets & Mechanical-Drive Packages Mfr

Caterpillar, Inc.—(Continued)
N.A.I.C.S.: 333611

Solar Turbines Canada Ltd. (2)
2510 84th Avenue, Edmonton, T6P 1K3,
AB, Canada (100%)
Tel.: (780) 464-8900
Web Site: http://www.solarturbines.com
Sales Range: $10-24.9 Million
Emp.: 20
Steam Gas Hydraulic Turbine Mfr
N.A.I.C.S.: 333611

Solar Turbines Europe S.A. (2)
Rua 21 De Janeiro, Bairro Morro Bento,
Luanda, Angola
Tel.: (244) 222338070
Web Site: http://www.mysolar.cat.com
Turbine Engines, Turbine Powered Natural-
Gas Compressor Sets, Generator Sets &
Mechanical-Drive Packages Mfr
N.A.I.C.S.: 333611

**Solar Turbines International
Company** (2)
14 Tractor Rd, Singapore, 627973, Singa-
pore
Tel.: (65) 68287000
Web Site: http://www.solarturbines.com
Turbine Engines, Turbine Powered Natural-
Gas Compressor Sets, Generator Sets &
Mechanical-Drive Packages Mfr
N.A.I.C.S.: 333611

**Solar Turbines Services Nigeria
Ltd.** (2)
Plot 133 Trans Amadi Industrial Estate Re-
deem Road, PO Box 3783, Port Harcourt,
Nigeria
Tel.: (234) 84933000
Web Site: http://www.mysolar.cat.com
Turbine Engines, Turbine Powered Natural-
Gas Compressor Sets, Generator Sets &
Mechanical-Drive Packages Mfr
N.A.I.C.S.: 333611

**Solar Turbines Services of Argentina
S.R.L.** (2)
Tucuari 202 9th Fl, Buenos Aires, C107
CAAF, Argentina
Tel.: (54) 1152358200
Web Site: http://www.solarturbines.com
Sales Range: $10-24.9 Million
Emp.: 10
Turbine Engines, Turbine Powered Natural-
Gas Compressor Sets, Generator Sets &
Mechanical-Drive Packages Mfr
N.A.I.C.S.: 333611

**Turbinas Solar de Venevuela
C.A.** (2)
Avenida Jorge Rodriquez Sector las
Garzas, Torre DVO Piso 0 Officina 0R, An-
zoategui, Venezuela
Tel.: (58) 2812869996
Web Site: http://www.solarturbines.com
Turbine Engines, Turbine Powered Natural-
Gas Compressor Sets, Generator Sets &
Mechanical-Drive Packages Mfr
N.A.I.C.S.: 333611

Turbinas Solar, S.A. de C.V. (2)
Av Framboyanes MZ 6 Lotes 1-15 Cd Ind
Bruno Pagliai, Centro, 91697, Veracruz,
Mexico
Tel.: (52) 2299897900
Web Site: http://www.solarturbines.com
Turbine Engines, Turbine Powered Natural-
Gas Compressor Sets, Generator Sets &
Mechanical-Drive Packages Mfr
N.A.I.C.S.: 333611

Turbomach S.A. (2)
Via Campagna 15, CH 6595, Riazzino,
Switzerland
Tel.: (41) 918511511
Web Site: http://www.turbomach.com
Emp.: 250
Turbine Engines, Turbine Powered Natural-
Gas Compressor Sets, Generator Sets &
Mechanical-Drive Packages Mfr
N.A.I.C.S.: 333611
Gabriella Solaini (Project Mgr-Industrial Co-
operation)
Aris Melas (COO)

**Solar Turbines India Private
Limited** (1)
417 4th Floor Time Tower Sector 28 M G

Road, Gurgaon, 122022, Haryana, India
Tel.: (91) 1244986550
Web Site: http://www.solarturbines.com
Industrial Gas Turbine Mfr
N.A.I.C.S.: 333611

**Southern California Matrial Handling
Inc.** (1)
12393 Slauson Ave, Whittier, CA 90606
Tel.: (562) 949-1000
Web Site: https://eqdepot.com
Construction Machinery Mfr
N.A.I.C.S.: 333120

Tangent Energy Solutions, Inc. (1)
206 Gale Ln Ste C, Kennett Square, PA
19348
Tel.: (610) 444-2800
Web Site: http://www.tangentenergy.com
Engineeering Services
N.A.I.C.S.: 541330

**Tangshan DBT Machinery Co.,
Ltd.** (1)
No 2 Gangyao Road, Lubei District, Tang-
shan, 063027, Hebei, China
Tel.: (86) 3153203117
Conveyor & Conveying Equipment Mfr
N.A.I.C.S.: 333922

**Tecnologia Modificada, S.A. de
C.V.** (1)
Nueva York No 204 Villas Del Oradel,
Nuevo Laredo, 88285, Tamaulipas, Mexico
Tel.: (52) 8677110000
Web Site:
http://www.catnuevolaredo.cat.com
Emp.: 1,000
Motor Vehicle Parts & Accessories Mfr
N.A.I.C.S.: 336390

Turbomach France S.A.R.L. (1)
11 rue de la Mare a Tissier, 91280, Saint-
Pierre-du-Perray, France
Tel.: (33) 169890000
Construction Machinery Mfr
N.A.I.C.S.: 333120

Turbomach GmbH (1)
Wiesenstr 10-12, Griesheim, 64347, Ger-
many
Tel.: (49) 615587490
Web Site: http://www.turbomach.cat.com
Sales Range: $25-49.9 Million
Emp.: 75
Construction Machinery Mfr
N.A.I.C.S.: 333120

Turbomach Netherlands B.V. (1)
Rijksstraatweg 22g, Sassenheim, 2171 AL,
Netherlands
Tel.: (31) 714080919
Web Site: http://www.turbomach.com
Sales Range: $10-24.9 Million
Emp.: 21
Gas Turbine Generator Mfr
N.A.I.C.S.: 335312

**Turbomach Pakistan (Private)
Limited** (1)
32-K/B-1 Gulberg 2, Lahore, 52000, Paki-
stan
Tel.: (92) 4235877760
Web Site: http://www.turbomach.com.pk
Sales Range: $10-24.9 Million
Emp.: 14
Gas Turbine Generator Mfr
N.A.I.C.S.: 333611

**Turner Powertrain Systems
Limited** (1)
Hexagon House First Floor 3 Trinity Court,
Wolverhampton Business Park, Wolver-
hampton, WV10 6UH, United Kingdom
Tel.: (44) 190 262 5627
Web Site: https://www.truner-
powertrain.co.uk
Sales Range: $25-49.9 Million
Emp.: 200
Construction Machinery Mfr
N.A.I.C.S.: 333120

**Underground Imaging Technologies
LLC** (1)
308 Wolf Rd, Latham, NY 12110-6405
Tel.: (518) 783-9848
Web Site: http://www.uit-systems.com
Sales Range: $25-49.9 Million
Emp.: 22
Engineering Consulting Services

N.A.I.C.S.: 541330
Gary Young (Gen Mgr)

XPART Limited (1)
Unit 14 Erdington Industrial Park Chester
Road, Birmingham, B24 0RD, West Mid-
lands, United Kingdom
Tel.: (44) 1162967888
Web Site: https://xpart.com
Construction Machinery Mfr
N.A.I.C.S.: 333120

CATHAY GENERAL BANCORP
777 N Broadway, Los Angeles, CA
90012
Tel.: (213) 625-4700   DE
Web Site:
   https://www.cathaybank.com
Year Founded: 1990
CATY—(NASDAQ)
Rev.: $908,095,000
Assets: $21,947,976,000
Liabilities: $19,473,936,000
Net Worth: $2,474,040,000
Earnings: $360,642,000
Emp.: 1,178
Fiscal Year-end: 12/31/22
Bank Holding Company
N.A.I.C.S.: 551111
Dunson K. Cheng (Exec Chm)
Anthony M. Tang (Co-Vice Chm)
Peter Wu (Co-Vice Chm)
Kim R. Bingham (Chief Risk Officer-
Cathay Bank & Exec VP)
Chang Ming Liu (Pres & CEO)
Heng W. Chen (CFO, Treas & Exec
VP)
Mark H. Lee (Chief Credit Officer-
Cathay Bank & Exec VP)
May K. Chan (Gen Counsel)

Subsidiaries:

Cathay Bank (1)
777 N Broadway, Los Angeles, CA 90012-
2819
Tel.: (213) 625-4791
Web Site: https://www.cathaybank.com
Sales Range: $600-649.9 Million
Emp.: 1,236
Commericial Banking
N.A.I.C.S.: 522110
Dunson K. Cheng (Exec Chm)
Anthony M. Tang (Co-Vice Chm)
Peter Wu (Co-Vice Chm)
Kim R. Bingham (Chief Risk Officer & Exec
VP)
Chang Ming Liu (Pres & CEO)
Albert Sun (Chief Credit Officer)
Thomas M. Lo (Chief Admin Officer)
May K. Chan (Exec VP)

**Cathay New Asia Community Devel-
opment Corporation** (1)
222 W Cermak Rd, Chicago, IL 60616
Tel.: (312) 225-5991
Commercial Bank Operator
N.A.I.C.S.: 522110

CATHETER PRECISION, INC.
1670 Hwy 160 W Ste 205, Fort Mill,
SC 29708
Tel.: (973) 691-2000   DE
Web Site:
   https://www.catheterprecision.com
Year Founded: 2002
VTAK—(NYSEAMEX)
Rev.: $442,000
Assets: $30,736,000
Liabilities: $9,543,000
Net Worth: $21,193,000
Earnings: ($70,572,000)
Emp.: 14
Fiscal Year-end: 12/31/23
Surgical Appliance & Supplies Manu-
facturing
N.A.I.C.S.: 339113
David A. Jenkins (Exec Chm & CEO)

CATSKILL HUDSON BAN-
CORP, INC.

95 Schwenk Dr, Kingston, NY 12401
Web Site: https://www.chbny.com
Year Founded: 1993
CSKL—(OTCIQ)
Rev.: $24,380,000
Assets: $572,575,000
Liabilities: $547,289,000
Net Worth: $25,286,000
Earnings: ($152,000)
Emp.: 85
Fiscal Year-end: 12/31/23
Bank Holding Company
N.A.I.C.S.: 551111
Mario L. Martinez (Chm & CEO)
Kevin S. McLaren (Pres)
Kevin T. Cannon (Chief Admin Officer
& Exec VP)
Robert A. Pettine (CFO & Exec VP)
Dawn M. Martinez (Mgr-Mktg)
Richard C. Murphy (Officer-Loan)
Brian V. Garis (VP & Sls Mgr)
Stephanie Zocco (Sr VP & Mgr-
Residential)
Henri D. Langevin (Officer-Loan-
Capital Reg & Sr VP)
Bryan M. Smith (Officer-Loan-Mid-
Hudson Reg & Ulster County & VP)
Fil Nieves (Officer-Loan-Mid-Hudson
Reg & Sullivan & Orange Counties &
VP)
Markland Shaw (Sr VP & Mgr-Credit)
Theodore Tomita III (CTO, Chief In-
formation Security Officer & Exec VP)

Subsidiaries:

Catskill Hudson Bank (1)
95 Schwenk Dr, Kingston, NY 12401
Tel.: (845) 943-4118
Web Site: http://www.chbny.com
Emp.: 90
Commericial Banking
N.A.I.C.S.: 522110
Mario L. Martinez (Chm & CEO)
Kevin S. McLaren (Pres)

CAVA GROUP, INC.
14 Ridge Sq NW Ste 500, Washing-
ton, DC 20016
Tel.: (202) 400-2920
Web Site: http://www.cava.com
Year Founded: 2010
CAVA—(NYSE)
Rev.: $728,700,000
Assets: $983,757,000
Liabilities: $412,955,000
Net Worth: $570,802,000
Earnings: $13,280,000
Emp.: 8,460
Fiscal Year-end: 12/31/23
Food Products Mfr
N.A.I.C.S.: 311999
Dan Jones (COO)

Subsidiaries:

Zoe's Kitchen, Inc. (1)
5760 State Hwy 121 Ste 250, Plano, TX
75024
Tel.: (214) 436-8765
Web Site: http://www.zoeskitchen.com
Rev.: $314,101,000
Assets: $240,522,000
Liabilities: $109,443,000
Net Worth: $131,079,000
Earnings: ($1,991,000)
Emp.: 5,473
Fiscal Year-end: 12/25/2017
Casual Dining Restaurants
N.A.I.C.S.: 722511
Allyn Taylor (Chief Dev Officer)
James Besch (Chief Acctg Officer & VP-
Acctg)
Gregory G. Dollarhyde (Chm)
Casey Shilling (CMO)

CAVCO INDUSTRIES, INC.
3636 N Central Ave Ste 1200, Phoenix, AZ 85012-1998
Tel.: (602) 256-6263   DE

Web Site:
https://www.cavcoindustries.com
Year Founded: 1998
CVCO—(NASDAQ)
Rev.: $1,627,158,000
Assets: $1,154,972,000
Liabilities: $324,517,000
Net Worth: $830,455,000
Earnings: $197,199,000
Emp.: 6,300
Fiscal Year-end: 04/02/22
Manufactured Home (Mobile Home)
Manufacturing
N.A.I.C.S.: 321991
Steven G. Bunger *(Chm)*
William C. Boor *(Pres & CEO)*
Steven K. Like *(Sr VP)*
Mickey R. Dragash *(Chief Compliance Officer, Gen Counsel, Sec & Exec VP)*
Matthew A. Nino *(Pres-Retail)*
Lyle D. Zeller *(Pres-CountryPlace Mortgage)*
Paul Bigbee *(Chief Acctg Officer)*

Subsidiaries:

CRG Holdings LLC   (1)
1001 N Central Ave Fl 8, Phoenix, AZ 85004
Tel.: (602) 256-6263
Web Site: http://www.cavco.com
Sales Range: $75-99.9 Million
Emp.: 190
Dealer & Retailer of Mobile Homes
N.A.I.C.S.: 459930

Catskill-Valley Homes, LLC   (1)
268 Service Rd, Parksville, NY 12768
Tel.: (845) 295-0803
Web Site:
https://www.catskillvalleyhomes.com
Modular House Building Services
N.A.I.C.S.: 236117

Chariot Eagle, LLC   (1)
931 NW 37th Ave, Ocala, FL 34470
Tel.: (352) 877-3506
Web Site: http://www.charioteagle.com
Sales Range: $10-24.9 Million
RV Park Models Producer
N.A.I.C.S.: 336214

CountryPlace Mortgage, Ltd.   (1)
15301 Spectrum Dr Ste 550, Addison, TX 75001
Tel.: (972) 763-5100
Web Site:
https://www.countryplaceloans.com
Sales Range: $25-49.9 Million
Emp.: 60
Home Loan Mortgage Services
N.A.I.C.S.: 522292
Lyle Zeller *(Pres)*
Damion St. Aubin *(Officer-Loan)*

Fairmont Homes, Inc.   (1)
2181 E Market St, Nappanee, IN 46550
Tel.: (574) 773-7941
Web Site: https://www.fairmonthomes.com
Mobile Homes & Modular Homes Mfr
N.A.I.C.S.: 321991

Fleetwood Homes, Inc.   (1)
7007 Jurupa Ave, Riverside, CA 92504-1015
Tel.: (951) 688-5353
Sales Range: $125-149.9 Million
Emp.: 200
Mobile Home Mfr
N.A.I.C.S.: 321991

Division (Domestic):

Fleetwood Homes - Douglas   (2)
1515 Kellogg Dr, Douglas, GA 31533
Tel.: (912) 384-1818
Web Site: https://www.fleetwoodhomes.com
Sales Range: $25-49.9 Million
Emp.: 200
Mobile Home Mfr
N.A.I.C.S.: 321991

Fleetwood Homes - Waco, TX   (2)
2801 Gholson Rd, Waco, TX 76705
Tel.: (254) 412-7400
Web Site: https://www.fleetwoodhomes.com

Emp.: 300
Mfr of Manufactured & Mobile Homes
N.A.I.C.S.: 321991

Fleetwood Homes of Oregon,
Inc.-Woodburn/North   (2)
2655 Progress Way, Woodburn, OR 97071
Tel.: (503) 981-3136
Web Site: https://www.fleetwoodhomes.com
Sales Range: $100-124.9 Million
Emp.: 159
Mfr of Mobile Homes
N.A.I.C.S.: 321991

Fleetwood Homes of Texas, Inc.-
Waco/Gholson Rd.   (2)
2801 Gholson Rd, Waco, TX 76705
Tel.: (254) 799-6206
Sales Range: $25-49.9 Million
Emp.: 200
Mfr of Mobile Homes
N.A.I.C.S.: 321991
Ray Parma *(Gen Mgr)*

Fleetwood Homes of Virginia,
Inc.   (2)
740 State St, Rocky Mount, VA 24151
Tel.: (540) 334-2143
Web Site: http://www.fleetwoodhomes.com
Sales Range: $125-149.9 Million
Mfr of Mobile Homes
N.A.I.C.S.: 321991

Fleetwood Homes, Inc.   (2)
2611 E Comstock Ave, Nampa, ID 83687-6806
Tel.: (208) 466-2438
Sales Range: $100-124.9 Million
Emp.: 140
Mobile Home Mfr
N.A.I.C.S.: 321991

Lexington Homes, Inc.   (1)
3636 N Central Ave StE 1200, Phoenix, AZ 85012
Tel.: (662) 834-0292
Web Site: https://www.lexington-homes.com
Mobile Home Mfr
N.A.I.C.S.: 321991

Palm Harbor Homes, Inc.   (1)
15301 Spectrum Dr Ste 500, Addison, TX 75001-4600
Tel.: (972) 991-2422
Web Site: http://www.palmharbor.com
Sales Range: $250-299.9 Million
Emp.: 1,700
Mobile & Manufactured Construction Homes & Services
N.A.I.C.S.: 321992

Subsidiary (Domestic):

Nationwide Homes, Inc.   (2)
1100 Rives Rd, Martinsville, VA 24112
Tel.: (276) 790-3966
Web Site: https://www.nationwide-homes.com
Sales Range: $25-49.9 Million
Emp.: 350
Modular Housing Mfr
N.A.I.C.S.: 321992

Palm Harbor Villages Real Estate,
LLC   (1)
15301 Spectrum Dr, Addison, TX 75001
Tel.: (972) 763-5090
Real Estate Services
N.A.I.C.S.: 531210

Standard Casualty Company   (1)
100 Northwoods Dr, New Braunfels, TX 78132
Tel.: (830) 629-6111
Web Site: https://www.stdins.com
Insurance Agents
N.A.I.C.S.: 524210

Standard Insurance Agency, Inc.   (1)
8190 Precinct Line Rd Ste 101, Colleyville, TX 76034
Tel.: (817) 285-1800
Web Site:
https://www.standardinsurance.net
Property & Casualty Insurance Services
N.A.I.C.S.: 524126

The Commodore Corporation   (1)
1423 Lincolnway E, Goshen, IN 46526-4657

Tel.: (574) 533-7100
Web Site:
http://www.commodorehomes.com
Sales Range: $125-149.9 Million
Emp.: 900
Mobile Home Mfr
N.A.I.C.S.: 321991
Erv Bontrager *(Sr VP-Mktg)*
Jeff Towns *(Supvr-Production Drafting)*

Division (Domestic):

Colony Factory Crafted Homes   (2)
20510 Paint Blvd, Shippenville, PA 16254
Tel.: (814) 226-9590
Web Site: https://www.colony-homes.com
Sales Range: $25-49.9 Million
Emp.: 200
Modular Home Designer & Mfr
N.A.I.C.S.: 321991

CAVITATION TECHNOLOGIES, INC.
10019 Canoga Ave, Chatsworth, CA 91311
Tel.: (818) 718-0905   NV
Web Site:
https://www.ctinanotech.com
CVAT—(OTCQB)
Rev.: $1,363,000
Assets: $248,000
Liabilities: $728,000
Net Worth: ($480,000)
Earnings: $439,000
Emp.: 2
Fiscal Year-end: 06/30/24
Biodiesel Nanotechnology
N.A.I.C.S.: 541713
Igor Gorodnitsky *(Founder)*
Neil D. Voloshin *(CEO)*
Maxim Promtov *(Dir-R&D)*

CAVU TECHNOLOGY ACQUISITION CORP.
4830 W Kennedy Blvd Ste 600, Tampa, FL 33609
Tel.: (813) 666-8876   DE
Year Founded: 2021
CAVUU—(NASDAQ)
Investment Services
N.A.I.C.S.: 523999
Barry Shevlin *(Chm & CEO)*
Nicole Speltz *(CFO)*
Michael Johnson *(COO)*

CB FINANCIAL SERVICES, INC.
100 N Market St, Carmichaels, PA 15320
Tel.: (724) 966-5041   PA
Web Site:
https://www.communitybank.tv
Year Founded: 2005
CBFV—(NASDAQ)
Rev.: $57,536,000
Assets: $1,408,938,000
Liabilities: $1,298,783,000
Net Worth: $110,155,000
Earnings: $11,247,000
Emp.: 184
Fiscal Year-end: 12/31/22
Bank Holding Company
N.A.I.C.S.: 551111
Charles R. Guthrie *(Vice Chm)*
Jamie L. Prah *(CFO & Exec VP)*
John H. Montgomery *(Pres & CEO)*

Subsidiaries:

Community Bank   (1)
100 N Market St, Carmichaels, PA 15320   (100%)
Tel.: (724) 966-5041
Web Site: https://www.communitybank.tv
Sales Range: $10-24.9 Million
Emp.: 133
Commericial Banking
N.A.I.C.S.: 522110
John H. Montgomery *(Pres & CEO)*
Andrew Corfont *(Sr VP-Mktg)*
John H. Montgomery *(Pres & CEO)*

CB SCIENTIFIC, INC.
10845 Griffith Peak Dr Ste 200, Las Vegas, NV 89135
Tel.: (720) 370-3554   OR
Web Site: https://cbscientificinc.com
CBSC—(OTCIQ)
Business Support Services
N.A.I.C.S.: 561499
Paul K. Danner *(Chm)*
Charles Martin *(CEO & Dir)*
Brooke Martellaro *(CFO)*
James E. Ott *(Dir)*
Zbigniew Lambo *(Dir)*

CBB BANCORP, INC.
3435 Wilshire Blvd, Ste 700, Los Angeles, CA 90010
Tel.: (323) 988-3000
Web Site: https://www.cbb-bank.com
CBBI—(OTCIQ)
Bank Holding Company
N.A.I.C.S.: 551111

Subsidiaries:

Commonwealth Business Bank   (1)
3435 Wilshire Blvd Ste 700, Los Angeles, CA 90010
Tel.: (323) 988-3000
Web Site: https://www.cbb-bank.com
Rev.: $76,366,201
Assets: $1,162,688,473
Liabilities: $1,014,604,159
Net Worth: $148,084,314
Earnings: $13,344,116
Emp.: 190
Fiscal Year-end: 12/31/2019
Commericial Banking
N.A.I.C.S.: 522110
Joanne Kim *(Pres & CEO)*
Long T. Huynh *(CFO & Exec VP)*
Alex Choi *(Chief Credit Officer & Exec VP)*

CBC HOLDING COMPANY
102 W Roanoke Dr, Fitzgerald, GA 31750
Tel.: (229) 423-4321   GA
CBHC—(OTCIQ)
Banking Holding Company
N.A.I.C.S.: 551111
George Ray *(Pres & CEO)*

CBD GLOBAL SCIENCES, INC.
225 Union Blvd Ste 350, Lakewood, CO 80228
Tel.: (303) 919-2913   Ca
Web Site:
http://www.cbdglobalsciences.com
CBDNF—(OTCIQ)
Hemp Product Distr
N.A.I.C.S.: 456191
Brad Wyatt *(Co-Founder, Pres & CEO)*
Glenn Dooley *(Co-Founder, Interim CFO & COO)*

Subsidiaries:

Global Sciences Holdings, Inc.   (1)
225 Union Boulevard Ste 350, Lakewood, CO 80228
Tel.: (720) 881-2541
Beverage & Snack Distr
N.A.I.C.S.: 722515

Subsidiary (Domestic):

Go Fast Sports & Beverage Co.   (2)
2600 W 8th Ave, Denver, CO 80204-3706
Tel.: (303) 893-1222
Web Site: http://www.gofastsports.com
Soft Drinks Mfr
N.A.I.C.S.: 312111
Troy Widgery *(Owner)*

CBD LIFE SCIENCES, INC.
10953 N Frank Lloyd Blvd Ste 108, Scottsdale, AZ 85259
Tel.: (480) 209-1720   NV
Web Site: https://thecbdvault.com
Year Founded: 2016

CBD Life Sciences, Inc.—(Continued)

CBDL—(OTCIQ)
Rev.: $79,000
Assets: $1,491,000
Liabilities: $460,000
Net Worth: $1,031,000
Earnings: ($861,000)
Emp.: 5
Fiscal Year-end: 12/31/19
Consumer Micro Lending Services
N.A.I.C.S.: 522291
Lisa M. Nelson (Founder, Pres, CEO & CFO)
Jennifer Simmons (Gen Mgr)
Koko Zaarur (Mgr-Social Media)

CBD OF DENVER, INC.
1901 Avenue of the Stars 2nd Fl, Los Angeles, CA 90067
Tel.: (310) 954-9160
Web Site:
http://www.cbdofdenver.com
CBDD—(OTCIQ)
Media Production Services
N.A.I.C.S.: 512110
William F. Veve (Pres & CEO)

CBDMD, INC.
2101 Westinghouse Blvd Ste A, Charlotte, NC 28273
Tel.: (704) 445-3060   **NC**
Web Site: https://www.cbdmd.com
Year Founded: 2015
YCBD—(NYSEAMEX)
Rev.: $19,482,167
Assets: $10,581,457
Liabilities: $8,618,040
Net Worth: $1,963,417
Earnings: ($3,700,126)
Emp.: 42
Fiscal Year-end: 09/30/24
Lifestyle Brand Products Mfr & Distr
N.A.I.C.S.: 333310
Raymond Scott Coffman (Vice Chm)
T. Ronan Kennedy (Co-CEO & CFO)
Sibyl Swift (Chief Science Officer & VP-Regulatory Affairs)
John Weston (Dir-IR)
Lance Blundell (Gen Counsel)
Shannon Charles (CMO)
Martin A. Sumichrast (Chm & Co-CEO)

CBIZ, INC.
5959 Rockside Woods Blvd N Ste 600, Cleveland, OH 44131
Tel.: (216) 447-9000   **DE**
Web Site: https://www.cbiz.com
Year Founded: 1996
CBZ—(NYSE)
Rev.: $1,411,979,000
Assets: $1,879,124,000
Liabilities: $1,165,672,000
Net Worth: $713,452,000
Earnings: $105,354,000
Emp.: 6,500
Fiscal Year-end: 12/31/22
Accounting, Tax & Employee Benefit Consulting Services
N.A.I.C.S.: 541219
Jerome P. Grisko Jr. (Pres & CEO)
Rick L. Burdick (Chm)
Mark M. Waxman (CMO & Sr VP)
Chris Spurio (Pres-Fin Svcs)
John A. Fleischer (CIO & Sr VP)
Elizabeth Newman (Chief Admin Officer)
Amy McGahan (Dir-Corp & Strategic Comm)
Jaileah Huddleston (Chief Legal Officer & Sec)
Ware H. Grove (CFO & Sr VP)

Subsidiaries:
ARC Consulting LLC   (1)

275 Battery St Ste 420, San Francisco, CA 94111
Tel.: (415) 264-3731
Web Site: http://www.arcconsultingllc.com
Accounting, Internal & External Reporting, Audit & Advisory Services
N.A.I.C.S.: 541219
Michele Bordalo (Sr Mgr)
Gary Klintworth (Co-Founder & Mng Dir)
Jim Loughmiller (Co-Founder & Mng Dir)
Claire Clemente (Ops Mgr)
Nicole Garcia (Coord-Admin)
Drew Wolski (Sr Mgr)
Andrew Wong (Sr Mgr)
Christopher Green (Sr Mgr)
Jason Spires (Sr Mgr)
Ada Kong (Sr Mgr)
Corrie Johnson (Sr Mgr)
Lillian Toy (Sr Mgr)
Jamie Singer (Sr Mgr)
Elise Parker (Sr Mgr)
Mohsin Bashir (Sr Mgr)

Actuarial Consultants, Inc.   (1)
2377 Crenshaw Blvd Ste 350, Torrance, CA 90501   (100%)
Tel.: (310) 212-2600
Web Site: http://www.acibenefits.com
Sales Range: $1-9.9 Million
Emp.: 39
Designer & Administrator of Retirement Plans
N.A.I.C.S.: 923130
Justin Bonestroo (Sr VP)

Associated Insurance Agents, Inc.   (1)
2800 Freeway Blvd Ste 100, Minneapolis, MN 55430-1751
Tel.: (763) 549-2200
Insurance Agents
N.A.I.C.S.: 524210

BeyondPay Inc.   (1)
6 State Route 173 W Ste 201, Clinton, NJ 08809
Tel.: (908) 730-0932
Web Site: http://www.beyondpay.com
Web Application Development Services
N.A.I.C.S.: 541511
Christopher Tanis (Co-Founder & COO)
Jonathan Tanis (Dir-Product Dev)
Jason Zaun (Dir-HR Svcs)
Michael Lynch (Dir-Tax & Compliance)
Jacob Tanis (Co-Founder & CEO)
Graham Watts (Dir-Ops)

Borden Perlman Insurance Agency, Inc.   (1)
2000 Lenox Dr Ste 202, Trenton, NJ 08648
Tel.: (609) 896-3434
Web Site: http://www.bordenperlman.com
Sales Range: $10-24.9 Million
Emp.: 65
Insurance Agents, Brokers, And Service, N
N.A.I.C.S.: 524210
Doug Borden (Co-Founder & Mng Dir)
Jeffrey Perlman (Co-Founder & Mng Dir)
Richard Perlman (Co-Founder)
Jeremy Perlman (VP)
Chris Borden (VP)
Douglas Coleman (Exec VP)
Kelly Myers (VP-Sports)
Arley Daniels (Dir-Mktg & Comm)
Andrew Miller (Gen Counsel)
Felipe Rodriguez (Dir-Loss Control)
Jeanne Oronzio Wermuth (Dir-Quality Assurance)
Kate Melnick (Sr Dir-Ops)
Meg Errickson (Sr Dir-Claims)
Eileen Stanton (Mgr-Sports)
Heather Vogel (Mgr-Personal Lines)
Abbie Douglas (Acct Mgr)
Andrea Guy (Acct Mgr)
Bernadette Marek (Acct Mgr)
David Yost (Mktg Mgr)
Colette Meheski (Acct Mgr)
Gianluca Milea (Acct Mgr)
Kristina Landolfi (Acct Mgr)
Kelly Matthews (Acct Mgr)
Melissa Mercer (Acct Mgr)
Nikki Kruchinsky (Acct Mgr)
Jenna Profilca (Acct Mgr)
Jerlonda Ramseur (Acct Mgr)
Rachel Leszega (Acct Mgr)

CBIZ Accounting, Tax & Advisory of Florida, LLC   (1)
5959 Rockside Woods Blvd N, Cleveland, OH 44131

Tel.: (561) 392-7929
Web Site: http://www.cbizsouthflorida.com
Emp.: 100
Financial Services
N.A.I.C.S.: 561990

CBIZ Accounting, Tax & Advisory of Ohio, LLC   (1)
4040 Embassy Pkwy Ste 100, Akron, OH 44333
Tel.: (330) 668-6500
Web Site: https://www.cbiz.com
Sales Range: $25-49.9 Million
Emp.: 45
Certified Public Accounting Services
N.A.I.C.S.: 541211

CBIZ Accounting, Tax & Advisory of Southwest Florida, LLC   (1)
13577 Feather Sound Dr Ste 400, Clearwater, FL 33762
Tel.: (305) 377-8667
Accounting & Auditing Services
N.A.I.C.S.: 541219

CBIZ Accounting, Tax & Advisory of Topeka, LLC   (1)
4601 E Douglas Ave Ste 700, Wichita, KS 67218
Tel.: (785) 272-3176
Web Site: http://www.cbiz.com
Financial & Accounting Services
N.A.I.C.S.: 541219

CBIZ Beatty Satchell, LLC   (1)
28614 Marlboro Ave Ste 103, Easton, MD 21601
Tel.: (410) 822-6950
Accounting & Consultation Services
N.A.I.C.S.: 541219
Danna Faulkner (Office Mgr)

CBIZ Benefits & Insurance Services, Inc.   (1)
4650 S National Ave Ste D 4, Springfield, MO 65810-2891
Tel.: (417) 890-5755
Financial & Insurance Services
N.A.I.C.S.: 524298
Rusty Besancenez (Sr Acct Exec)

CBIZ CMF, LLC   (1)
325 Chestnut St Ste 410, Philadelphia, PA 19106
Tel.: (215) 531-7500
Financial Investment Services
N.A.I.C.S.: 541611
Thomas Bonney (Sr Mng Dir)

CBIZ Financial Solutions, Inc.   (1)
12 N Liberty St, Cumberland, MD 21502-3026
Tel.: (301) 777-7550
Financial Services
N.A.I.C.S.: 523150

CBIZ Gibraltar Real Estate Services, LLC   (1)
225 W Wacker Dr Ste 2500, Chicago, IL 60606
Tel.: (312) 602-6900
Web Site: https://www.cbizgibraltar.com
Emp.: 15
Real Estate Solution Services
N.A.I.C.S.: 531390
Eric A. Galanti (Sr VP)
Noah A. Turner (Sr VP)
Steven L. Joseph (Pres & CEO)
William D. Main (Exec VP)
Benjamin L. Cooper (Sr VP)
Natalia Kurinna (VP-Client Svcs)
Seamus Byrne (Sr VP-Program Mgmt)
Ruth Villanueva (Controller)
Jim Javorcic (Dir-Attest Svcs)
Larry Feder (Dir-IT)
Brandon Janda (VP)
Sam Johnson (Asst VP)

CBIZ Insurance Services, Inc.   (1)
1001 Conshohocken State Rd 2-600, West Conshohocken, PA 19428   (100%)
Tel.: (610) 862-2249
Web Site: http://www.cbiz.com
Sales Range: $150-199.9 Million
Property & Casualty Insurance Services & Employee Benefits
N.A.I.C.S.: 524126
Michael A. Garguilo (Pres-Northeast & Mid-Atlantic)

Bruce Walsh (VP)
Michael Colonnello (VP)
Raul Socha (VP-Risk Mgmt & Insurance)
Kate Houlihan (VP)

CBIZ Life Insurance Solutions, Inc.   (1)
13500 Evening Creek Dr N 450, San Diego, CA 92128
Tel.: (858) 444-3100
Web Site:
https://www.lifeinsurance.cbiz.com
Insurance Agencies & Brokerage Services
N.A.I.C.S.: 524210
Don Kim (Dir-Product & Carrier Intelligence)
Steve Sublett (CEO)
Eugene Robles (Sr Mgr-Customer Rels)
Leah Fisher (Mgr-Natl Strategic Svcs)
John Louis-Barrow (Dir-Strategic Bus Ops)
Duwayne Kilbo (Principal)

CBIZ Life Insurance Solutions, Inc.   (1)
10616 Scripps Summit Ct Ste 210, San Diego, CA 92131
Tel.: (858) 444-3100
Web Site: http://www.lifeinsurance.cbiz.com
Management Consulting Services
N.A.I.C.S.: 541611

CBIZ MHM, LLC   (1)
6801 Brecksville Rd Dr N, Independence, OH 44131
Tel.: (216) 447-9000
Accounting, Tax & Financial Advisory Services
N.A.I.C.S.: 541211
Naomi D. Ganoe (Mng Dir)
David J. Giannetti (Mng Dir)
Jennifer Hura-Boehlke (Sr Mgr)
Michael Sovacool (Mgr)
Carla Spears (Mgr)
Jeffery A. Walters (Mng Dir)
Fred W. Hinkle (Mng Dir)
William M. Ganger Jr. (Sr Mgr)

Branch (Domestic):

CBIZ MHM, LLC - Bakersfield   (2)
5060 California Ave, Bakersfield, CA 93309
Tel.: (661) 325-7500
Web Site: http://www.cbiz.com
Accounting, Tax & Financial Services
N.A.I.C.S.: 541211
Kimberly Alvarado (Mng Dir)

CBIZ MHM, LLC - Kansas City   (2)
700 W 47th St Ste 1100, Kansas City, MO 64112
Tel.: (816) 945-5500
Web Site: http://www.cbiz.com
Accounting Auditing & Bookkeeping Services
N.A.I.C.S.: 541219
Jeff Carlstedt (Sr Mng Dir)
Mitchell Plattman (Mng Dir)
Ben Anderson (Mng Dir)
Christopher Baltimore (Mng Dir)
Tom Barzee (Dir-Tax)
Lindsay Beets (Sr Mgr)
Michelle Brown (Mng Dir)
Michael Borgerding (Sr Mgr)
Kerri Church (Sr Mgr)
Anthony M. Coble (Mng Dir)
Nathan B. Daniels (Mng Dir)
Robert Dowling (Mng Dir)
Cindy J. Dwyer (Mng Dir)
Joyce Farris (Mng Dir)
Jeffrey M. Fox (Mng Dir)
Daniel G. Friederich (Mng Dir)
Sean Haggerty (Dir-Tax)
Hal Hunt (Mng Dir)
Lance P. Henry (Dir)
Eileen Johnson (Sr Mgr)
Daniel F. Kjergaard (Mng Dir)
Kyle Konopasek (Mng Dir)
Pamela K. Kroll (Dir-Fin Svcs)
Seth Leibson (Mng Dir)
Michael Loritz (Mng Dir)
Rachel Martens (Dir)
Sabine Mehrer (Mgr)
Richard Mills (COO)
Jillian Mott (Mng Dir)
Boyd O'Rourke (Dir-Quality Control-Natl)
Adam Pfautsch (Dir)
Jay Power (Mng Dir)
Kathryn L. Rhodes (Mng Dir)
Laura Rodgers (Dir)
Brent A. Wilson (Mng Dir)

Heather L. Winiarski *(Dir)*
Kevin L. Winters *(Mng Dir)*
Phil Zaman *(Dir)*
Luke Crowther *(Mgr-Tax)*
Katie Daniels *(Mgr-Tax)*
Danielle Hemme *(Sr Mgr)*
Melissa Roeger *(Sr Mgr)*
Daniel Rosenthal *(Natl Dir-Mktg)*
Missi Ryherd *(Sr Mgr)*
Christian Schechinger *(Mgr-Bus Dev)*
John Shoemaker *(Mng Dir)*
Angie Snider *(Dir-Natl)*
Kevin Walker *(Mng Dir)*
Lauren Wilk *(Sr Mgr-Tax)*

CBIZ MHM, LLC - Tampa Bay   (2)
140 Fountain Pkwy N Ste 410, Saint Petersburg, FL 33716
Tel.: (727) 572-1400
Web Site: http://www.cbiz.com
Emp.: 150
Certified Public Accountants
N.A.I.C.S.: 541211
Douglas R. Birch *(Mng Dir)*
Craig A. Gilman *(Mng Dir)*
Tracey L. McDonald *(Mng Dir)*
Wendy Hawn *(Dir-HR)*
Melissa Albano *(Sr Mgr)*
Denise R. Baker *(Sr Mgr)*
Ryan Bontrager *(Mgr)*
Dana K. Burton *(Mng Dir)*
Leighton Castle *(Sr Mgr)*
Christine McAlarney *(Mng Dir)*
Steven W. Grove *(Mng Dir)*
Eric Hausman *(Mgr)*
Shaun D. McClung *(Mng Dir)*
Melissa Henry *(Dir)*
Jessica O. Janota *(Sr Mgr)*
Shay Janssen *(Sr Mgr)*
Daniel J. Johnson *(Mng Dir)*
Catherine Wilhelm *(Mgr-Audit)*
Bruce H. Murphy *(Mng Dir)*
Paul C. Dunham *(Mng Dir)*
Cindy Alvear Mull *(Mng Dir)*
Dennis J. Milam *(Sr Mgr)*
Chris Smith *(Sr Mgr)*
David C. Janosek *(Mng Dir)*
Mariem E. Talavera *(Mgr-Advisory Svcs)*
Aimee Varnum *(Sr Mgr)*
Randall Cathell *(Mng Dir-Intl Tax)*
Henry Ngo *(Mgr-Assurance)*
Chris Norton *(Mgr-Audit)*
James Pope *(Mgr-Tax)*
John S. Maceovsky III *(Mng Dir)*
W. Thomas Steiner III *(Mng Dir)*

CBIZ Private Equity Advisory, LLC   (1)
520 Walnut St Ste 1475, Philadelphia, PA 19106
Tel.: (215) 531-7500
Management Consulting Services
N.A.I.C.S.: 541618

CBIZ Risk & Advisory Services, LLC   (1)
5959 Rockside Woods Blvd N Ste 600, Cleveland, OH 44131-6951
Web Site: https://www.cbiz.com
Anti Fraud Services
N.A.I.C.S.: 561990
Frank Campagna *(Mng Dir)*

CBIZ Slaton Insurance   (1)
5713 Corporate Way Ste 200, West Palm Beach, FL 33407
Tel.: (561) 683-8383
Web Site: http://www.cbiz.com
Sales Range: $1-9.9 Million
Insurance Agencies & Brokerages
N.A.I.C.S.: 524210

CBIZ Southern California, L.L.C.   (1)
10474 Santa Monica Blvd Ste 200, Los Angeles, CA 90025-6930   **(100%)**
Tel.: (310) 268-2000
Web Site: http://www.cbiz.com
Sales Range: $75-99.9 Million
Emp.: 70
Accounting & Financial Services
N.A.I.C.S.: 541211

CBIZ Technologies, LLC   (1)
6050 Oak Tree Blvd Ste 500, Independence, OH 44131-6951   **(100%)**
Tel.: (216) 447-9000
Web Site: http://www.cbiztechnologies.com
Sales Range: $10-24.9 Million
Emp.: 25

Business Applications & Custom Developed Technological Solutions
N.A.I.C.S.: 513210

CBIZ Valuation Group, LLC   (1)
3625 Cumberland Blvd SE Ste 1100, Atlanta, GA 30339   **(100%)**
Tel.: (770) 858-4500
Web Site: http://www.cbizvaluation.com
Sales Range: $125-149.9 Million
Emp.: 54
Valuation, Financial Advisory & Litigation Support Services
N.A.I.C.S.: 523999
John Rimar *(Mng Dir-Real Estate Practice-St Louis)*
Tony Kancijanic *(Mng Dir-Central Reg)*
Deepa Menon *(Mng Dir-Dallas)*
Jeffrey L. Sumpter *(Mng Dir-Valuation, Litigation, and Forensic Svcs Practice-Phoenix)*
David Werch *(Mng Dir-Tangible Asset Practice-Dallas)*

Laurus Transaction Advisors L.L.C.   (1)
4600 S Ulster St Ste 900, Denver, CO 80237
Tel.: (720) 200-7000
Web Site: https://www.cbiz.com
Certified Public Accountants Firm & Services
N.A.I.C.S.: 541211
Patrick Martin *(Mng Dir)*
Mark Coleman *(Mng Dir)*
Tripp Mcleod *(Mng Dir)*

Marcum LLP   (1)
730 3rd Ave 11th Fl, New York, NY 10017
Tel.: (212) 485-5500
Web Site: http://www.marcumllp.com
Accounting & Consulting Services
N.A.I.C.S.: 541211
Scott G. Toothaker *(Mng Partner)*
Jeffrey Weiner *(Chm & CEO)*
Philip Weiner *(Partner-Assurance-New York)*
Mitchell Watt *(Partner-Assurance-New York)*
Paul Sherman *(Mng Partner-Firm-Wide Admin-Los Angeles)*
Dennis Schall *(Partner-Alternative Investments-Assurance-New York)*
Jeffrey Saltzer *(Partner-Tax & Bus-New York)*
John Rushford *(Partner-Assurance-New York)*
Bruce Roff *(Partner-Assurance-New York)*
Robert Pesce *(Partner)*
Alan Markowitz *(Partner-Assurance-New York)*
Stephen Lassar *(Partner-Tax & Bus-New York)*
Edward Hackert *(Partner-Assurance-New York)*
Rorrie Gregorio *(Partner)*
David First *(Partner-Tax & Bus-New York)*
Stephen Feldman *(Partner-Assurance-New York)*
Maury Cartine *(Partner-Alternative Investments-Tax & Bus-New York)*
Michael Balter *(Mng Partner-Assurance-Fort Lauderdale)*
Adam Firestein *(Partner-Assurance-Miami)*
Ann Arpino *(Dir-Tax & Bus-New Haven)*
Anthony Delfiner *(Partner-Tax & Bus-Philadelphia)*
Ari Maunula *(Partner-Tax & Bus-Greenwich)*
Eliezer Hildeshaim *(Principal-Tax & Bus-Deerfield)*
Gary Smith *(Dir-Assurance-New Haven, CT)*
Joseph Molloy *(Dir-Tax & Bus Svcs)*
Susan N. Dupuis *(Principal-Tax & Bus-Boston)*
Ronald Storch *(COO & Partner-Melville)*
Mark Harrison *(Partner & Head-Valuation & Litigation Svcs-New England Reg)*
David Appel *(Sr Partner)*
Peter Scavuzzo *(Partner-Melville)*
Carla Glass *(Mng Dir)*
Kathy A. Raffa *(Executives)*
Anael Francillon *(Sr Mgr-Assurance Practice)*
Karen O'Connor *(Partner-Melville)*
Cathy Werthan *(Mng Partner-Nashville)*
John C. Guttilla *(Partner-Fin Svcs-Saddle Brook)*
Kenneth J. Pia Jr. *(Partner & Head-Bus Valuation Svcs)*

Subsidiary (Domestic):

CWBJ, PLLC   (2)
109 Kenner Ave Ste 100, Nashville, TN 37205
Tel.: (615) 322-1225
Accounting & Bookkeeping Services
N.A.I.C.S.: 541219

Federman, Lally & Remis LLC   (2)
231 Farmington Ave., Farmington, CT 06034
Tel.: (860) 760-0850
Web Site: https://www.flrcpa.com
Emp.: 100
Accounting Services
N.A.I.C.S.: 541219

Powers & Sullivan, LLC   (2)
100 Quannapowitt Pkwy Ste 101, Wakefield, MA 01880
Tel.: (781) 914-1700
Web Site: http://www.powersandsullivan.com
Offices of Certified Public Accountants
N.A.I.C.S.: 541211
Richard L. Sullivan *(Mgr)*

Savitz Organization, Incorporated   (1)
470 Conshohocken State Rd, Bala Cynwyd, PA 19004   **(100%)**
Tel.: (215) 563-9943
Web Site: http://www.savitz.com
Sales Range: $25-49.9 Million
Emp.: 110
Employee Benefit Consultants, Actuaries & Administrators
N.A.I.C.S.: 541612

Weekes & Callaway, Inc.   (1)
3945 W Atlantic Ave, Delray Beach, FL 33445
Tel.: (561) 278-0448
Web Site: https://www.cbiz.com
Financial Investment Services
N.A.I.C.S.: 541611
Joseph Grillo *(Sr VP)*
Dennis Hoffman *(Sr VP)*
Mike Callaway *(Pres)*
Jamie Stampar *(VP)*

Weekes & Callaway   (1)
3945 W Atlantic Ave, Delray Beach, FL 33445-3902
Tel.: (561) 278-0448
Web Site: https://www.cbiz.com
Emp.: 70
Management Consulting Services
N.A.I.C.S.: 541611

CBL & ASSOCIATES PROPERTIES, INC.

2030 Hamilton Pl Blvd, Chattanooga, TN 37421
Tel.: (423) 855-0001   DE
Web Site:
https://www.cblproperties.com
Year Founded: 1978
CBL—(NYSE)
Rev.: $563,011,000
Assets: $2,678,243,000
Liabilities: $2,311,114,000
Net Worth: $367,129,000
Earnings: ($93,482,000)
Emp.: 395
Fiscal Year-end: 12/31/22
Shopping Center Development, Owner & Management Firm with Enclosed Malls, Power Centers & Community Centers
N.A.I.C.S.: 525990
Stephen D. Lebovitz *(CEO)*
Michael I. Lebovitz *(Pres)*
Alan L. Lebovitz *(Exec VP-Mgmt)*
Kathryn A. Reinsmidt *(COO & Exec VP)*
Jeffery V. Curry *(Sec)*
Justice Wade *(Sr VP-Dev & Mixed-Use)*
Jennifer Cope *(Exec VP-Risk Mgmt)*
Joseph Khalili *(Exec VP-Fin Plng & Analysis)*
Stacey Keating *(VP-Corp Comm)*

Benjamin W. Jaenicke *(CFO & Exec VP)*
Benjamin Staples *(Sr VP-People)*
Lisa harper *(VP)*
Brad Hendrix *(VP)*
Sandra Heymann *(VP)*
Lewis Hilton *(VP)*
Matt Holligan *(VP)*
Allison Houghton *(VP)*
Jason Shelton *(VP)*
Robert Snetman *(VP)*
Karen Walker *(VP)*
Tripp Wingo *(VP)*

Subsidiaries:

Alamance Crossing, LLC   (1)
1080 Piper Ln, Burlington, NC 27215
Tel.: (336) 584-8157
Web Site:
https://www.alamancecrossing.com
Sales Range: $25-49.9 Million
Emp.: 12
Property Rental & Leasing Services
N.A.I.C.S.: 531120

Asheville Mall CMBS, LLC   (1)
3 S Tunnel Rd, Asheville, NC 28805
Tel.: (828) 298-0012
Web Site: https://www.asheville-mall.com
Sales Range: $25-49.9 Million
Emp.: 6
Real Estate Investment & Management Services
N.A.I.C.S.: 525990

Atlanta Outlet Shoppes, LLC   (1)
915 Ridgewalk Pkwy, Woodstock, GA 30188
Tel.: (678) 540-7040
Web Site:
https://www.theoutletshoppesatatlanta.com
Real Estate Investment Services
N.A.I.C.S.: 531210

Bonita Lakes Mall Limited Partnership   (1)
1210 Bonita Lk Cir, Meridian, MS 39301
Tel.: (601) 693-3433
Web Site: http://www.bonitalakesmall.com
Real Estate Investment & Management Services
N.A.I.C.S.: 525990

Brookfield Square Parcel, LLC   (1)
2030 Hamiton Pl Blvd Cbl Ctr Ste 500, Chattanooga, TN 37421-6000
Tel.: (262) 797-7245
Web Site: http://www.cblproperties.com
Emp.: 9
Real Estate Investment & Management Services
N.A.I.C.S.: 525990

CBL & Associates Limited Partnership   (1)
2030 Hamilton Pl Blvd, Chattanooga, TN 37421
Tel.: (423) 855-0001
Real Estate Investment Services
N.A.I.C.S.: 531210
Stephen D. Lebovitz *(CEO)*

CBL & Associates Properties   (1)
Watermill Ctr 800 S St Ste 395, Waltham, MA 02453-1439   **(100%)**
Tel.: (781) 647-3330
Web Site: http://www.cblproperties.com
Sales Range: Less than $1 Million
Emp.: 8
Shopping Center Developer
N.A.I.C.S.: 531190

CBL Brookfield Square OP PropCo, LLC   (1)
95 N Moorland Rd, Brookfield, WI 53005
Tel.: (262) 797-7245
Web Site:
https://www.shopbrookfieldsquaremall.com
Real Estate Investment Services
N.A.I.C.S.: 812990

CBL Dakota Square Mall OP PropCo, LLC   (1)
2400 10th St SW, Minot, ND 58701
Tel.: (701) 839-7500
Web Site:
https://www.shopdakotasquare.com

CBL & Associates Properties, Inc.—(Continued)
Real Estate Investment Services
N.A.I.C.S.: 812990

CBL Fayette Hotel Member, LLC (1)
3401 Nicholasville Rd, Lexington, KY 40503
Tel.: (859) 272-3493
Web Site: http://www.shopfayette-mall.com
Cloth Retailer
N.A.I.C.S.: 458110

CBL Fayette Mall OP PropCo, LLC (1)
3401 Nicholasville Rd, Lexington, KY 40503
Tel.: (859) 272-3493
Web Site: https://www.shopfayette-mall.com
Real Estate Investment Services
N.A.I.C.S.: 812990

CBL Frontier Square PropCo, LLC (1)
1400 Dell Range Blvd, Cheyenne, WY 82009
Tel.: (307) 638-2290
Web Site: https://www.frontiermall.com
Real Estate Investment Services
N.A.I.C.S.: 812990

CBL Hamilton Place Sears OP PropCo, LLC (1)
2100 Hamilton Place Blvd, Chattanooga, TN 37421
Tel.: (423) 855-5282
Web Site: https://www.hamiltonplace.com
Real Estate Investment Services
N.A.I.C.S.: 812990

CBL Jefferson Mall Self Dev PropCo, LLC (1)
4801 Outer Loop, Louisville, KY 40219
Tel.: (502) 968-4103
Web Site: https://www.shopjefferson-mall.com
Real Estate Investment Services
N.A.I.C.S.: 812990

CBL Kirkwood Mall OP PropCo, LLC (1)
706 Kirkwood Mall, Bismarck, ND 58504
Tel.: (701) 223-3500
Web Site: https://www.shopkirkwoodmall.com
Real Estate Investment Services
N.A.I.C.S.: 812990

CBL Landing at Arbor Place OP PropCo, LLC (1)
6700 Douglas Blvd, Douglasville, GA 30135
Tel.: (770) 947-4244
Web Site: https://www.arborplace.com
Real Estate Investment Services
N.A.I.C.S.: 812990

CBL Mid Rivers Mall OP PropCo, LLC (1)
1600 Mid Rivers Mall, Saint Peters, MO 63376
Tel.: (636) 970-2610
Web Site: https://www.shopmidriversmall.com
Real Estate Investment Services
N.A.I.C.S.: 812990

CBL Monroeville Mall OP PropCo, LLC (1)
200 Mall Cir Dr, Monroeville, PA 15146
Tel.: (412) 243-4800
Web Site: https://www.monroevillemall.com
Real Estate Investment Services
N.A.I.C.S.: 812990

CBL Northpark Mall OP PropCo, LLC (1)
101 N Rangeline Rd, Joplin, MO 64801
Tel.: (417) 781-2121
Web Site: https://www.visitnorthparkmall.com
Real Estate Investment Services
N.A.I.C.S.: 812990

CBL Post Oak Mall OP PropCo, LLC (1)
1500 Harvey Rd, College Station, TX 77840
Tel.: (979) 764-0060
Web Site: https://www.postoakmall.com
Real Estate Investment Services
N.A.I.C.S.: 812990

CBL South County Center OP PropCo, LLC (1)

18 S County Ctr Way, Saint Louis, MO 63129
Tel.: (314) 892-8954
Web Site: https://www.shopsouthcountycenter.com
Real Estate Investment Services
N.A.I.C.S.: 812990

CBL Valley View Mall OP PropCo, LLC (1)
4802 Valley View Blvd NW, Roanoke, VA 24012
Tel.: (540) 563-4440
Web Site: https://www.valleyviewmall.com
Real Estate Investment Services
N.A.I.C.S.: 812990

CBL West Towne Crossing OP PropCo, LLC (1)
66 W Towne Mall, Madison, WI 53719
Tel.: (608) 833-6330
Web Site: https://www.shopwesttowne-mall.com
Real Estate Investment Services
N.A.I.C.S.: 812990

CBL York Galleria OP PropCo, LLC (1)
2899 Whiteford Rd, York, PA 17402
Tel.: (717) 840-1322
Web Site: https://www.yorkgalleria.com
Real Estate Investment Services
N.A.I.C.S.: 812990

CBL-Friendly Center, LLC (1)
3110 Kathleen Ave, Greensboro, NC 27408
Tel.: (336) 299-9802
Web Site: https://www.friendlycenter.com
Real Estate Investment & Management Services
N.A.I.C.S.: 525990

CBL/Foothills Plaza Partnership (1)
US Hwy 129 Bypass Foothills Dr, Maryville, TN 37801
Tel.: (423) 490-8644
Real Estate Investment & Management Services
N.A.I.C.S.: 525990

CBL/Monroeville, L.P. (1)
200 Mall Circle Dr, Monroeville, PA 15146
Tel.: (412) 243-4800
Web Site: https://www.monroevillemall.com
Emp.: 3
Property Rental & Leasing Services
N.A.I.C.S.: 531120

CBL/Park Plaza Mall, LLC (1)
6000 W Markham St, Little Rock, AR 72205
Tel.: (501) 664-4956
Web Site: https://www.parkplazamall.com
Emp.: 5
Property Rental & Leasing Services
N.A.I.C.S.: 531120

CBL/Stroud, Inc. (1)
344 Stroud Mall Rd, Stroudsburg, PA 18360
Tel.: (570) 424-2770
Web Site: https://www.stroud-mall.com
Sales Range: $25-49.9 Million
Emp.: 3
Property Rental & Leasing Services
N.A.I.C.S.: 531120

CBL/York, Inc. (1)
2899 Whiteford Rd, York, PA 17402
Tel.: (717) 840-1322
Web Site: http://www.yorkgalleriamall.com
Sales Range: $25-49.9 Million
Emp.: 4
Real Estate Investment & Management Services
N.A.I.C.S.: 525990

Cherryvale Mall, LLC (1)
7200 Harrison Ave Ste 5, Rockford, IL 61112
Tel.: (815) 332-2440
Web Site: https://www.shopcherryvalemall.com
Emp.: 55
Real Estate Investment & Management Services
N.A.I.C.S.: 525990

Coastal Grand, LLC (1)
2000 Coastal Grand Cir, Myrtle Beach, SC 29577
Tel.: (843) 839-9110

Web Site: https://www.coastalgrand.com
Real Estate Investment & Management Services
N.A.I.C.S.: 525990

College Station Partners, Ltd. (1)
1306 University Blvd Ste F, Tuscaloosa, AL 35401
Tel.: (205) 759-2444
Web Site: https://www.collegestationproperties.com
Emp.: 10
Real Estate Investment & Management Services
N.A.I.C.S.: 525990

Cross Creek Mall, LLC (1)
419 Cross Creek Mall, Fayetteville, NC 28303
Tel.: (910) 868-7668
Web Site: https://www.crosscreekmall.com
Property Rental & Leasing Services
N.A.I.C.S.: 531120

Dakota Square Mall CMBS, LLC (1)
2030 Hamilton Place Blvd Ste 500, Chattanooga, TN 37421
Tel.: (423) 855-0001
Real Estate Investment Services
N.A.I.C.S.: 531210

Eastgate Storage, LLC (1)
15325 W Baker Rd, Manhattan, IL 60442
Tel.: (815) 478-4472
Web Site: https://www.eastgatestorage.com
Vehicle Storage Services
N.A.I.C.S.: 721211

Eastland Mall, LLC (1)
1615 E Empire St, Bloomington, IL 61701
Tel.: (309) 663-5361
Web Site: https://www.ishopeastlandmall.com
Emp.: 30
Property Rental & Leasing Services
N.A.I.C.S.: 531120

Fashion Square Mall CMBS, LLC (1)
3410 Belle Chase Way Ste 600, Lansing, MI 48911
Tel.: (989) 793-6423
Real Estate Investment Services
N.A.I.C.S.: 531210

Foothills Mall, Inc. (1)
197 Foothills Mall, Maryville, TN 37801
Tel.: (865) 982-3613
Web Site: https://www.foothillsmall.com
Sales Range: $25-49.9 Million
Emp.: 4
Property Rental & Leasing Services
N.A.I.C.S.: 531120

Greenbrier Mall, LLC (1)
1401 Greenbrier Pkwy S, Chesapeake, VA 23320
Tel.: (757) 424-7100
Web Site: https://www.greenbriermall.com
Sales Range: $25-49.9 Million
Emp.: 10
Property Rental & Leasing Services
N.A.I.C.S.: 531120

Gulf Coast Town Center CMBS, LLC (1)
CBL Ctr Ste 500 2030 Hamilton Plc Blvd, Chattanooga, TN 37421-6000
Tel.: (239) 267-5107
Web Site: http://www.gulfcoasttowncenter.com
Property Rental & Leasing Services
N.A.I.C.S.: 531120

Hamilton Place Mall General Partnership (1)
2100 Hamilton Plc Blvd, Chattanooga, TN 37421
Tel.: (423) 894-7177
Web Site: https://www.hamiltonplace.com
Property Rental & Leasing Services
N.A.I.C.S.: 531120
Taylor Bostwick (Dir-Mktg)

Hammock Landing/West Melbourne, LLC (1)
CBL Ctr Ste 500 2030 Hamilton Plc Blvd, Chattanooga, TN 37421-6000
Tel.: (321) 674-2349
Property Rental & Leasing Services

N.A.I.C.S.: 531120
Melynda Cox (District Mgr)

Honey Creek Mall, LLC (1)
3401 S US Hwy 41, Terre Haute, IN 47802
Tel.: (812) 232-4500
Web Site: http://www.honeycreekmall.com
Property Rental & Leasing Services
N.A.I.C.S.: 531120

Imperial Valley Mall, L.P. (1)
3451 S Dogwood Ave, El Centro, CA 92243
Tel.: (760) 352-0800
Web Site: https://www.imperialvalleymall.com
Emp.: 3
Property Rental & Leasing Services
N.A.I.C.S.: 531120

Janesville Mall Limited Partnership (1)
2500 Milton Ave, Janesville, WI 53545
Tel.: (608) 752-7845
Web Site: http://www.janesvillemall.com
Emp.: 3
Property Rental & Leasing Services
N.A.I.C.S.: 531120
Julie Cubbage (Gen Mgr)

Jefferson Mall CMBS, LLC (1)
4801 Outer Loop Ste 302, Louisville, KY 40219
Tel.: (502) 968-4103
Emp.: 5
Real Estate Investment Services
N.A.I.C.S.: 531210

Laredo Outlet Shoppes, LLC (1)
1600 Water St Ste A155, Laredo, TX 78040
Tel.: (956) 625-5353
Web Site: https://www.theoutletshoppesatlaredo.com
Retail Store Services
N.A.I.C.S.: 459999

Madison/East Towne, LLC (1)
89 E Towne Mall, Madison, WI 53704-3744
Tel.: (608) 244-1387
Web Site: https://www.shopeasttowne-mall.com
Property Rental & Leasing Services
N.A.I.C.S.: 531120

Mall Del Norte, LLC (1)
5300 San Dario Ave, Laredo, TX 78041
Tel.: (956) 724-8191
Web Site: https://www.malldelnorte.com
Property Rental & Leasing Services
N.A.I.C.S.: 531120

Mayfaire Town Center, LP (1)
6835 Conservation Way, Wilmington, NC 28405
Tel.: (910) 256-5131
Web Site: https://www.mayfaire.com
Shopping Mall Operator
N.A.I.C.S.: 531120

Meridian Mall Company, Inc. (1)
1982 W Grand River Ave, Okemos, MI 48864
Tel.: (517) 349-2031
Web Site: https://www.meridianmall.com
Emp.: 4
Property Rental & Leasing Services
N.A.I.C.S.: 531120

Milford Marketplace, LLC (1)
1650 Boston Post Rd, Milford, CT 06461
Tel.: (203) 878-7630
Web Site: https://www.milfordmarketplace.com
Food Market Retailer
N.A.I.C.S.: 445110

POM-College Station, LLC (1)
1500 Harvey Rd, College Station, TX 77840-3713
Tel.: (979) 764-0060
Web Site: https://www.postoakmall.com
Property Rental & Leasing Services
N.A.I.C.S.: 531120

Parkdale Mall, LLC (1)
6155 Eastex Fwy Ste 200, Beaumont, TX 77706
Tel.: (409) 898-2222
Web Site: https://www.parkdalemalltx.com
Property Rental & Leasing Services
N.A.I.C.S.: 531120

Pearland Town Center Hotel/Residential Condominium Association, Inc. (1)
11200 Broadway St Ste 2751, Pearland, TX 77584
Tel.: (713) 340-0704
Web Site: http://www.cblproperties.com
Property Rental & Leasing Services
N.A.I.C.S.: 531120

Rivergate Mall Limited Partnership (1)
1000 Rivergate Pkwy, Goodlettsville, TN 37072
Tel.: (615) 859-3458
Web Site: https://www.rivergate-mall.com
Property Rental & Leasing Services
N.A.I.C.S.: 531120
Randall Vickers (Dir-Ops)

St. Clair Square Limited Partnership (1)
134 Saint Clair Sq, Fairview Heights, IL 62208
Tel.: (618) 632-7567
Web Site: https://www.stclairsquare.com
Property Rental & Leasing Services
N.A.I.C.S.: 531120

Stroud Mall LLC (1)
344 Stroud Mall Rd, Stroudsburg, PA 18360
Tel.: (570) 424-2770
Web Site: https://www.stroud-mall.com
Property Rental & Leasing Services
N.A.I.C.S.: 531120

The Promenade D'Iberville, LLC (1)
I-10 and I-110, Diberville, MS 39540
Tel.: (601) 261-3032
Web Site: https://www.cblproperties.com
Property Rental & Leasing Services
N.A.I.C.S.: 531120

Triangle Town Center, LLC (1)
5959 Triangle Town Blvd, Raleigh, NC 27616
Tel.: (919) 792-2020
Web Site: https://www.triangletowncenter.com
Property Rental & Leasing Services
N.A.I.C.S.: 531120

Volusia Mall SAC, LLC (1)
1700 W International Speedway Blvd, Daytona Beach, FL 32114
Tel.: (386) 253-6783
Web Site: http://www.volusiamall.net
Shopping Mall Operator
N.A.I.C.S.: 531120

Volusia Mall, LLC (1)
1700 W International Speedway Blvd, Daytona Beach, FL 32114
Tel.: (386) 253-6783
Web Site: https://www.volusiamall.net
Property Rental & Leasing Services
N.A.I.C.S.: 531120

CBM BANCORP, INC.

2001 E Joppa Rd, Baltimore, MD 21234
Tel.: (410) 665-7600   MD
Web Site: http://www.chesapeakebank.com
CBMB—(NASDAQ)
Rev.: $10,340,123
Assets: $234,803,603
Liabilities: $181,240,888
Net Worth: $53,562,715
Earnings: $942,557
Emp.: 37
Fiscal Year-end: 12/31/20
Bank Holding Company
N.A.I.C.S.: 551111
Joseph M. Solomon (Pres & CEO)
Jodi L. Beal (CFO, Chief Acctg Officer & Exec VP)
William J. Bocek Jr. (Chm)

CBOE GLOBAL MARKETS, INC.

433 W Van Buren St, Chicago, IL 60607
Tel.: (312) 786-5600   DE
Web Site: https://www.cboe.com

Year Founded: 1973
CBOE—(BZX)
Rev.: $3,773,500,000
Assets: $7,487,500,000
Liabilities: $3,502,500,000
Net Worth: $3,985,000,000
Earnings: $757,500,000
Emp.: 1,647
Fiscal Year-end: 12/31/23
Holding Company; Options Exchange Board Operations
N.A.I.C.S.: 551112
Jill M. Griebenow (CFO, Treas & Exec VP)
Christopher Andrew Isaacson (COO & Exec VP)
John F. Deters (Chief Strategy Officer & Exec VP)
Fredric J. Tomczyk (CEO)
Patrick Sexton (Gen Counsel, Sec & Exec VP)
Jill M. Griebenow (CFO, Chief Acctg Officer, Treas & Exec VP)
Fredric J. Tomczyk (CEO)
Stacie Fleming (Chief Mktg & Comm Officer)
Catherine Clay (Exec VP)
Greg Hoogasian (Chief Regulatory Officer)

Subsidiaries:

BATS Global Markets, Inc. (1)
8050 Marshall Dr, Lenexa, KS 66214
Tel.: (913) 815-7000
Web Site: http://markets.cboe.com
Holding Company
N.A.I.C.S.: 551112

Subsidiary (Domestic):

BATS Global Markets Holdings, Inc. (2)
8050 Marshall Dr Ste 120, Lenexa, KS 66214
Tel.: (913) 815-7000
Stock Exchange Services
N.A.I.C.S.: 523210

Subsidiary (Non-US):

BATS Trading Limited (3)
11 Monument Street, London, EC3R 8AF, United Kingdom
Tel.: (44) 2070128900
Web Site: https://www.batstrading.co.uk
Equity Markets Trading Services
N.A.I.C.S.: 523150
Guy Simpkin (Head-Bus Dev)

C2 Options Exchange, Incorporated (1)
400 S LaSalle St, Chicago, IL 60605
Tel.: (312) 786-5600
Web Site: http://www.c2exchange.com
Investment Management Service
N.A.I.C.S.: 523940

Cboe Clear Europe N.V. (1)
Gustav Mahlerplein 77, 1082 MS, Amsterdam, Netherlands
Tel.: (31) 205703300
Web Site: https://clear.cboe.com
Financial Services
N.A.I.C.S.: 523999

Cboe Europe Limited (1)
11 Monument Street, London, EC3R 8AF, United Kingdom
Tel.: (44) 2070128900
Web Site: https://www.cboe.com
Trade Exchange Services
N.A.I.C.S.: 523210

Chicago Board Options Exchange, Incorporated (1)
433 W Van Buren St, Chicago, IL 60607
Tel.: (312) 786-5600
Web Site: http://www.cboe.com
Emp.: 500
Securities & Commodities Exchange
N.A.I.C.S.: 523210
Terry L. Savage (Founder)

European Central Counterparty N.V. (1)

World Trade Center Tower I Level 3 Strawinskylaan 1847, 1077 XX, Amsterdam, Netherlands
Tel.: (31) 20 570 3300
Web Site: https://www.euroccp.com
Financial Transaction Services
N.A.I.C.S.: 522320
Cecile Nagel (CEO)
Arnoud Siegmann (Chief Risk Officer)
Tom Zydenbos (CFO)
Tim Beckwith (Head-Comml Dev)

Hanweck Associates, LLC (1)
30 Broad St Fl 42, New York, NY 10004-2304
Tel.: (646) 414-7330
Web Site: http://www.hanweckassoc.com
Other Health & Personal Care Stores
N.A.I.C.S.: 456199

Livevol, LLC (1)
400 S LaSalle St Ste 1302 H, Chicago, IL 60605
Tel.: (312) 786-7400
Web Site: http://www.livevol.com
Data & Custom Analytics Services
N.A.I.C.S.: 518210

Trade Alert, LLC (1)
200 Park Ave S Ste 1314, New York, NY 10003
Tel.: (212) 372-8020
Web Site: http://www.trade-alert.com
Financial Software Development Services
N.A.I.C.S.: 541511

TriAct Canada Marketplace LP (1)
222 Bay Street Suite 2605, Toronto, M5X 1B7, ON, Canada
Tel.: (416) 861-1010
Web Site: http://www.matchnow.ca
Investment Banking & Securities Dealing Services
N.A.I.C.S.: 523150

CBRE ACQUISITION HOLD-INGS, INC.

2100 McKinney Ave 12th Fl, Dallas, TX 75201
Tel.: (214) 979-6100   DE
Year Founded: 2020
CBAHU—(NASDAQ)
Investment Services
N.A.I.C.S.: 523999
William F. Concannon (CEO)
Cash J. Smith (Pres, CFO & Sec)

CBRE GROUP, INC.

2121 N Pearl St, Dallas, TX 75201
Tel.: (214) 979-6100   DE
Web Site: https://www.cbre.com
Year Founded: 1906
CBRE—(NYSE)
Rev.: $31,949,000,000
Assets: $22,548,000,000
Liabilities: $13,481,000,000
Net Worth: $9,067,000,000
Earnings: $986,000,000
Emp.: 130,000
Fiscal Year-end: 12/31/23
Commercial Real Estate Investment, Development & Property Management Services
N.A.I.C.S.: 531210
Robert E. Sulentic (Chm, Pres & CEO)
Gualberto Medina (Executives)
Jeff Lyons (Exec VP-Columbus)
E. M. Blake Hutcheson (Executives)
Emma Giamartino (CFO & Pres-Global Group)
Lindsey Caplan (Chief Acctg Officer)
Robert C. Bernard (Chief Sustainability Officer & Sr VP)
Banke Odunaike (Chief Culture Officer)
Alison Caplan (Chief Admin Officer)
Deepak Dewani (Chief Strategy Officer)
Croft Young (Chief Investment Officer)

Chad Doellinger (Gen Counsel & Sec)
Daniel G. Queenan (CEO-Real Estate Investments-Global)
Thomas Edwards (Pres-Valuation & Advisory Svcs)

Subsidiaries:

Beezley Management, LLC (1)
23632 Calabasas Rd Ste 105, Calabasas, CA 91302
Tel.: (818) 591-8555
Web Site: http://www.beezleymanagement.com
Construction Management Consulting Services
N.A.I.C.S.: 541611
Karl Bendixen (Coord-Project Controls)
Eric Brooks (Project Mgr)
Jazmin Ceballos (Project Mgr)
Larry Isrow (VP)
Bruce Johnson (Sr Project Mgr & Mgr-Construction)

Building Information Systems LLC (1)
800 Bellevue Way NE Ste 500, Bellevue, WA 98004
Tel.: (206) 388-2280
Web Site: http://www.buildingi.com
Business Products & Services
N.A.I.C.S.: 561499
Bill Nolan (Pres & CEO)
Christine Hughes (CFO)
John Coates (Dir-Sls & Mktg)
Don Barnes (Dir-Ops)

CB Richard Ellis Services, Inc. (1)
400 S Hope St 25th Fl, Los Angeles, CA 90071
Tel.: (213) 613-3333
Sales Range: $25-49.9 Million
Emp.: 200
Commercial Real Estate
N.A.I.C.S.: 531210

CB Richard Ellis, Inc. (1)
2121 Ave of the Stars Ste 1630, Los Angeles, CA 90067
Tel.: (310) 550-2500
Commercial Real Estate Brokerage Services
N.A.I.C.S.: 531210
Robert E. Sulentic (Pres & CEO)
Lewis Horne (Pres)

Affiliate (Domestic):

CB Richard Ellis - N.E. Partners, LP (2)
600 Atlantic Ave 22nd Fl, Boston, MA 02110
Tel.: (617) 912-7000
Web Site: http://www.cbre.us
Commercial Real Estate Brokerage Services
N.A.I.C.S.: 531210
Andrew Hoar (Pres & Mng Partner)
Jodie Poirier (Mng Dir)

Branch (Domestic):

CB Richard Ellis, Inc. - Chicago (2)
321 N Clark St Ste 3400, Chicago, IL 60654
Tel.: (312) 935-1400
Commercial Real Estate Brokerage Services
N.A.I.C.S.: 531210
Nancy Pacher (Vice Chm)
John A. Latessa Jr. (Pres)
Kevin Collins (Mng Dir)

CB Richard Ellis, Inc. - Los Angeles, Downtown (2)
400 S Hope St Fl 25, Los Angeles, CA 90071
Tel.: (213) 613-3333
Commercial Real Estate Brokerage Services
N.A.I.C.S.: 531210

CB Richard Ellis, Inc. - New York City (2)
200 Park Ave, New York, NY 10166
Tel.: (212) 984-8000
Emp.: 2,500

CBRE Group, Inc.—(Continued)

Commercial Real Estate Brokerage Services
N.A.I.C.S.: 531210
Mary Ann Tighe (*CEO-New York Tri-State Reg*)
Stephen Siegel (*Chm-Brokerage-Global*)
Darcy Stacom (*Chm & Head-Capital Markets*)

CBRE, Inc. - Houston   (2)
2800 Post Oak Blvd Ste 500, Houston, TX 77056
Tel.: (713) 577-1600
Web Site: https://www.cbre.com
Commercial Real Estate Brokerage Services
N.A.I.C.S.: 531210
John T. Fenoglio (*Exec VP-Debt & Structured Fin*)
James R. Kirkpatrick (*Sr VP-Debt & Structured Fin*)
Samuel Yee (*VP-Debt & Structured Fin*)
Peter Mainguy (*Sr Mng Dir*)
Michael Thompson (*Vice Chm & Co-Head-Debt & Structured Fin*)
Henry Joseph (*Mng Dir*)

CB/TCC Global Holdings Limited   (1)
St Martin's Court 10 Paternoster Row, London, EC4M 7HP, United Kingdom
Tel.: (44) 2071822000
Commercial Real Estate Services
N.A.I.C.S.: 531210

CBRE Capital Markets, Inc.   (1)
2800 Post Oak Blvd Ste 500, Houston, TX 77056
Tel.: (713) 787-1600
Real Estate Credit Services
N.A.I.C.S.: 522292
Mike Bryant (*Vice Chm-Dallas*)

CBRE Heery, Inc.   (1)
999 Peachtree St NE Ste 300, Atlanta, GA 30309-3953   (100%)
Tel.: (404) 504-7900
Web Site: https://www.heery.com
Construction Management & Design Services
N.A.I.C.S.: 541310

CBRE Investment Management, LLC   (1)
601 S Figueroa St Ste 49 Fl, Los Angeles, CA 90017
Tel.: (213) 683-4200
Web Site: https://www.cbreim.com
Sales Range: $75-99.9 Million
Emp.: 150
Real Estate Investment Management Services
N.A.I.C.S.: 531300
Gill Roantree (*COO-Real Estate-Global*)

Subsidiary (Domestic):

CBRE Clarion Securities LLC   (2)
555 E Lancaster Ave Ste 120, Radnor, PA 19087
Tel.: (610) 995-2500
Web Site: http://www.cbreclarion.com
Sales Range: $50-74.9 Million
Emp.: 70
Real Estate Investment Advisory Services
N.A.I.C.S.: 523940

Division (Non-US):

CBRE Global Investors (Asia Pacific) Limited   (2)
Level 27 One Pacifica Palace 88 Queensway, Admiralty, China (Hong Kong)
Tel.: (852) 28463002
Web Site:
    http://www.cbreglobalinvestors.com
Holding Company; Regional Managing Office
N.A.I.C.S.: 551112

Subsidiary (Domestic):

CBRE Global Investors (Asia) Limited   (3)
3501 Two Exchange Square 8 Connaught Place, Central, China (Hong Kong)
Tel.: (852) 2846 3000
Web Site:
    http://www.cbreglobalinvestors.com

Real Estate Investment Management
N.A.I.C.S.: 531390

Division (Non-US):

CBRE Global Investors Europe B.V.   (2)
Schiphol Boulevard 281, 1118 BH, Schiphol, Netherlands
Tel.: (31) 703419394
Web Site: http://www.globalinvestors.com
Emp.: 150
Holding Company; Regional Managing Office
N.A.I.C.S.: 551112
Paul Hawtin (*Head-HR-Europe, Middle East & Africa*)
Eric Decouvelaere (*Head-Retail-Europe, Middle East & Africa*)

Subsidiary (Domestic):

CBRE Global Investors (NL) B.V.   (3)
Schiphol Boulevard 281 G-tower 7th floor, Amsterdam, 1118 BH, Schiphol, Netherlands
Tel.: (31) 202022200
Emp.: 200
Real Estate Investment Management
N.A.I.C.S.: 531390

Subsidiary (Non-US):

CBRE Global Investors (UK) Ltd.   (3)
Third Floor One New Change, London, EC4M 9AF, United Kingdom
Tel.: (44) 2078099000
Web Site:
    http://www.cbreglobalinvestors.com
Sales Range: $650-699.9 Million
Emp.: 3,000
Real Estate Investment Management
N.A.I.C.S.: 531390

CBRE Global Investors Belgium   (3)
40 Rue Belliard Bte 6, PO Box 6, Etterbeek, 1040, Brussels, Belgium
Tel.: (32) 25500260
Web Site:
    http://www.cbreglobalinvestors.com
Real Estate Investment Management
N.A.I.C.S.: 531390

Branch (Domestic):

CBRE Global Investors, LLC - Boston   (2)
800 Boylston St Ste 2800, Boston, MA 02199
Tel.: (617) 425-2800
Web Site: http://www.cbreinvestors.com
Sales Range: $1-9.9 Million
Emp.: 15
Real Estate Trust Company
N.A.I.C.S.: 531120
Vance G. Maddocks (*CEO & CIO*)

CBRE Loan Services, Inc.   (1)
929 Gessner Rd Ste 1700, Houston, TX 77024-2317
Tel.: (713) 458-7200
Web Site: http://www.cbre.com
Loan Administration Services
N.A.I.C.S.: 522390
Chris Shamaly (*Sr Mng Dir-Americas*)

CBRE ServiceInsight Group   (1)
8848 Commons Blvd Ste 103, Twinsburg, OH 44087
Tel.: (330) 963-0103
Web Site:
    http://www.serviceinsight.cbre.com
Software Solutions
N.A.I.C.S.: 513210

CBRE UK   (1)
Third Floor One New Change, London, EC4M 9AF, United Kingdom
Tel.: (44) 2078099000
Web Site: http://www.cbre.co.uk
Commercial Building Technical Engineering Services
N.A.I.C.S.: 541330
Ian Entwisle (*CEO-Global Workplace Solutions-EMEA*)

Cold River Land, LLC   (1)
6445 Shiloh Rd Ste D, Alpharetta, GA 30005
Tel.: (770) 844-0782
Web Site: http://www.coldriverdev.com

Real Estate Asset Management Services
N.A.I.C.S.: 531390
John Pearson (*Mng Partner*)

FacilitySource, LLC   (1)
200 E Campus View Blvd Ste 120, Columbus, OH 43235
Tel.: (614) 318-1700
Web Site: http://www.facilitysource.com
Emp.: 800
Facility Support Services
N.A.I.C.S.: 561210
Bill Hayden (*Pres*)
Jordan Wagner (*Mng Dir-Strategy & Performance Optimization*)
Lisa Barnhart (*VP-People Team*)
Kristen Rhodes (*VP-Digital & Tech*)
Erin Plivelich (*Dir-Acct Mgmt Div*)
Odette de Lusignan (*Sr Dir-Fin*)
Ken Schwieterman (*Dir-Acct Mgmt Div*)
Mike McAlister (*VP-Sls & Mktg*)

Full Spectrum Group, LLC   (1)
23332 Mill Creek Dr., Ste 205, Laguna Hills, CA 92653
Tel.: (866) 772-3572
Web Site: http://www.fsaservice.com
Professional Equipment & Supplies Merchant Whslr
N.A.I.C.S.: 423490
Tom Fider (*Pres*)
Robert McLeese (*CEO*)

Subsidiary (Domestic):

Analytical Maintenance Services, Inc.   (2)
1120 Holland Dr Ste 18, Boca Raton, FL 33487
Tel.: (954) 791-5321
Web Site: http://www.amsinc-intl.com
Sales Range: $1-9.9 Million
Emp.: 19
Electronic & Precision Equipment Repair & Maintenance
N.A.I.C.S.: 811210
Michael Barbera (*Pres*)

Furman Co., Inc.   (1)
355 S Main St Ste 903, Greenville, SC 29601
Tel.: (864) 242-5151
Web Site: https://www.furmanco.com
Sales Range: $1-9.9 Million
Emp.: 50
Commerciall Real Estate Agents & Brokers
N.A.I.C.S.: 531210
Robert Poppleton (*VP*)

J&J Maintenance Inc.   (1)
7710 Rialto Blvd Ste 200, Austin, TX 78704-7973
Tel.: (512) 444-7271
Sales Range: $10-24.9 Million
Emp.: 3,200
Airports, Flying Fields & Services
N.A.I.C.S.: 488190
Robbie Browning (*Mgr-Payroll*)

PKF Consulting, Inc.   (1)
800 W Pender St Ste 1120, Vancouver, V6C 2V6, BC, Canada
Tel.: (604) 689-3833
Web Site: http://www.pkfcanada.com
Sales Range: $1-9.9 Million
Emp.: 100
Management Consulting Services
N.A.I.C.S.: 541618

Preuss GmbH   (1)
Podbielskistr 370, 30659, Hannover, Germany
Tel.: (49) 51142060
Web Site: http://www.preuss-pm.de
Emp.: 100
Project Management Services for Construction & Real Estate Industries
N.A.I.C.S.: 541618

Trammell Crow Company, LLC   (1)
2100 McKinney Ave Ste 800, Dallas, TX 75201-2966
Tel.: (214) 863-4101
Web Site: http://www.trammellcrow.com
Sales Range: $500-549.9 Million
Emp.: 6,200
Commercial Real Estate Development, Property Management, Brokerage & Retail Services
N.A.I.C.S.: 237210

Ann Sperling (*Sr Dir*)
Matthew S. Khourie (*CEO*)
Adam Saphier (*Pres-Eastern Ops*)
Kevin Schmok (*Exec VP*)
Rich McPhillips (*Sr VP-Washington DC*)
Robert Brandt (*Principal*)
Jeff DeBruin (*Principal*)
Brent Ball (*Sr VP*)
Kevin Hickman (*Sr VP*)
Raymond Kieffer (*VP*)
Sally Ra (*VP*)
Cliff Wood (*VP*)

Subsidiary (Non-US):

Telford Homes Plc   (2)
Telford House Queensgate Britannia Road, Waltham Cross, EN8 7TF, Herts, United Kingdom
Tel.: (44) 1992809800
Web Site: http://www.telfordhomes-ir.london
Rev.: $426,647,058
Assets: $577,002,435
Liabilities: $265,232,945
Net Worth: $311,769,490
Earnings: $50,477,325
Emp.: 265
Fiscal Year-end: 03/31/2018
Real Estate Developers
N.A.I.C.S.: 531210
Jonathan Di-Stefano (*CEO*)
Charlie Weatherill (*Dir-Capital Markets*)

Subsidiary (Domestic):

Trammell Crow Services, Inc.   (2)
3550 Lenox Rd Ste 2200, Atlanta, GA 30326
Tel.: (404) 812-5175
Web Site: http://www.tcresidential.com
Sales Range: $10-24.9 Million
Emp.: 40
Developer & Manager of Residential Real Estate
N.A.I.C.S.: 531110
Brandon Houston (*Mng Dir*)
Mark Dishaw (*Mng Dir*)
Drew Fredrick (*Exec VP*)
Harri Jarvenpaa (*VP*)
Scott Kirchhoff (*Sr VP*)
Will Lombard (*Sr VP*)
Chris Eagen (*Sr VP*)
Katherine Lynch (*Principal*)
Nicholas Frank (*VP*)

Turner & Townsend Ltd.   (1)
Low Hall Calverley Lane Horsforth, Leeds, LS18 4GH, United Kingdom   (60%)
Tel.: (44) 1132 584 400
Web Site:
    http://www.turnerandtownsend.com
Emp.: 7,000
Management Consulting Services
N.A.I.C.S.: 541611
Vincent Clancy (*Chm & CEO*)
Jon White (*Mng Dir-Ireland*)
Jeremy Lathom-Sharp (*Dir-Fin*)
Patricia Moore (*Mng Dir*)
Stephen McCartney (*Mgr-Qatar*)
Ian Donaldson (*Mng Dir-South Africa*)
Gerard McCabe (*Mng Dir*)
James Dand (*COO*)
Paul Connolly (*Mng Dir*)

Subsidiary (Non-US):

Mentor Management Limited   (2)
The Courtyard 2nd Floor General Mathenge Drive, PO Box 62899, Westlands, 200, Nairobi, Kenya   (79.5%)
Tel.: (254) 20 3744903
Web Site:
    http://www.turnerandtownsend.com
Real Estate Manangement Services
N.A.I.C.S.: 531210
Vincent Clancy (*Chm & CEO*)

CCA INDUSTRIES, INC.
PO Box 735, Little Ferry, NJ 07643
Tel.: (201) 935-3232   DE
Web Site:
    https://www.ccaindustries.com
Year Founded: 1983
CAWW—(OTCIQ)
Rev.: $14,124,251
Assets: $14,085,891
Liabilities: $3,996,118
Net Worth: $10,089,773

Earnings: ($127,477)
Emp.: 12
Fiscal Year-end: 11/30/20
Health & Beauty Aids Mfr & Distr
N.A.I.C.S.: 325620
Lance T. Funston (Chm)
Douglas J. Haas (Pres & COO)
Brent T. Funston (Vice Chm)
Christopher Dominello (CTO)
Stephen A. Heit (CFO)

CCC INTELLIGENT SOLU-TIONS HOLDINGS INC.
167 N Green St 9th Fl, Chicago, IL
60607   DE
Web Site: https://www.cccis.com
Year Founded: 2020
CCCS—(NASDAQ)
Rev.: $866,378,000
Assets: $3,051,040,000
Liabilities: $1,268,763,000
Net Worth: $1,782,277,000
Earnings: ($92,476,000)
Emp.: 2,325
Fiscal Year-end: 12/31/23
Investment Services
N.A.I.C.S.: 523999

CCF HOLDINGS LLC
5165 Emerald Pkwy Ste 100, Dublin,
OH 43017   OH
Year Founded: 2018
CCFLU—(NASDAQ)
Rev.: $334,861,000
Assets: $246,825,000
Liabilities: $273,055,000
Net Worth: ($26,230,000)
Earnings: ($52,844,000)
Emp.: 2,736
Fiscal Year-end: 12/31/19
Holding Company
N.A.I.C.S.: 551112
William E. Saunders Jr. (Chm &
CEO)

CCSB FINANCIAL CORP.
1178 W Kansas St, Liberty, MO
64068
Tel.: (816) 781-4500   DE
Web Site:
    https://www.claycountysavings.com
Year Founded: 2002
CCFC—(OTCIQ)
Rev.: $5,959,568
Assets: $155,277,061
Liabilities: $146,460,893
Net Worth: $8,816,168
Earnings: ($185,240)
Fiscal Year-end: 09/30/23
Bank Holding Company
N.A.I.C.S.: 551111
Mario Usera (Pres, CEO & CFO)
Mary D. Gray (Treas & Sr VP)
Kathryn E. Varnon (Sr VP)
Deborah A. Jones (Sec & Exec VP)
Jackie Murtha (VP)
Pamela Crow (VP)

Subsidiaries:

Clay County Savings Bank   (1)
1178 W Kansas St, Liberty, MO 64068
Tel.: (816) 781-4500
Web Site:
    http://www.claycountysavings.com
Emp.: 23
Banking Services
N.A.I.C.S.: 522110
Mario Usera (Pres & CEO)
Mary D. Gray (Treas & VP)
Kathryn E. Varnon (Sr VP)
Deborah A. Jones (Sec & Sr VP)
Alice Crowley (VP & Sr Credit Officer)

CCUR HOLDINGS INC.
3800 N Lamar Blvd Ste 200, Austin,
TX 78756
Tel.: (770) 305-6434   DE

Web Site:
    https://www.ccurholdings.com
Year Founded: 1985
CCUR—(OTCIQ)
Rev.: $12,877,000
Assets: $69,850,000
Liabilities: $8,561,000
Net Worth: $61,289,000
Earnings: $12,230,000
Emp.: 6
Fiscal Year-end: 06/30/20
Computer & Software Systems for
the Real-Time Operating
Systems/Productivity Tools Market &
The Video-On-Demand Market
N.A.I.C.S.: 334111
Steven G. Singer (Chm)
Igor Volshteyn (Pres, COO, Principal
Exec Officer, Principal Fin Officer)
Jonathan Tegge (Principal Acctg Offi-
cer)

Subsidiaries:

Concurrent Computer Corp. Pty.
Ltd   (1)
20 Br St Ste 2 Level 2 Bldg 2, Pymble,
2073, NSW, Australia
Tel.: (61) 284679800
Web Site: http://www.ccur.com.au
Sales Range: $100-124.9 Million
Mfr, Developer & Marketer of High Perfor-
mance, Real-Time Computer Systems &
Software & Video On Demand
N.A.I.C.S.: 541511

Concurrent Computer France
S.A.   (1)
1 Parc Ariane, 78284, Guyancourt, Cedex,
France
Tel.: (33) 0139305200
Web Site: http://www.concurrent.com
Sales Range: $1-9.9 Million
Emp.: 8
Mfr, Developer & Marketer of High Perfor-
mance, Real-Time Computer Systems &
Software & Video On Demand
N.A.I.C.S.: 541511
Birgit Groffmann (Mng Dir)

Branch (Domestic):

Concurrent Computer France
S.A.   (2)
Agence Sud Est ZAC Le Triganc, 138000,
Istres, France
Tel.: (33) 442569393
Web Site: http://www.ccur.com
Sales Range: $100-124.9 Million
Mfr, Developer & Marketer of High Perfor-
mance, Real-Time Computer Systems &
Software & Video On Demand
N.A.I.C.S.: 541511

Concurrent Computer Hong Kong
Limited   (1)
Unit 4204 Level 42 Tower 2 Metroplaza,
233 Hing Fong Road, Kwai Chung, NT,
China (Hong Kong)
Tel.: (852) 2880 0802
Web Site: http://www.ccur.com.hk
Sales Range: $100-124.9 Million
Emp.: 4
Computer Systems Developer
N.A.I.C.S.: 541511
K. K. Tay (Mng Dir)

Concurrent Federal Systems,
Inc.   (1)
4375 Rivergreen Pkwy Ste 100, Duluth, GA
30096
Tel.: (678) 258-4000
Web Site: http://www.ccur.com
Sales Range: $25-49.9 Million
Emp.: 100
Mfr, Developer & Marketer of High Perfor-
mance, Real-Time Computer Systems &
Software & Video On Demand
N.A.I.C.S.: 541512
Dan Mondor (CEO)

Concurrent Nippon Corporation   (1)
Yanagibashi First Building 4F 2-19-6 Yanag-
ibashi, Taito-ku, Tokyo, 111-0052, Japan
Tel.: (81) 338645711
Web Site: https://www.concurrent-rt.co.jp

Sales Range: $10-24.9 Million
Emp.: 17
Mfr, Developer & Marketer of High Perfor-
mance, Real-Time Computer Systems &
Software & Video On Demand
N.A.I.C.S.: 334111

Symbolic Logic, Inc.   (1)
3800 N Lamar Blvd Ste 200, Austin, TX
78756   (65%)
Tel.: (770) 305-6434
Web Site: https://www.symbl.com
Rev.: $26,352,000
Assets: $19,076,000
Liabilities: $9,386,000
Net Worth: $9,690,000
Earnings: $643,000
Emp.: 277
Fiscal Year-end: 12/31/2020
Software & Services to Fixed-Line, Wireless
& IP Customers
N.A.I.C.S.: 513210
Mark P. Szynkowski (VP-Fin)
Igor Volshteyn (CEO)

Subsidiary (Non-US):

Evolving Systems Limited   (2)
E-21-03 Menara Suezcap II Gateway No 2
Jalan KerinchiKL, 59200, Kuala Lumpur,
Malaysia   (100%)
Tel.: (60) 379321166
Web Site: http://www.evolving.com
Sales Range: $100-124.9 Million
Emp.: 3
Wireless & IP Software Services
N.A.I.C.S.: 513210

Evolving Systems Limited   (2)
91 Wimpole Street, London, W1G 0EF,
United Kingdom   (100%)
Tel.: (44) 2038712764
Web Site: http://www.evolving.com
Sales Range: $10-24.9 Million
Emp.: 30
Software Development Services
N.A.I.C.S.: 513210

Subsidiary (Domestic):

Lumata UK Limited   (3)
3rd Floor Henry Wood House 2 Riding
House Street, Marylebone, London, W1W
7FA, United Kingdom
Tel.: (44) 20 3770 7645
Mobile Marketing & Advertising Services
N.A.I.C.S.: 541613

Subsidiary (Domestic):

Evolving Systems NC, Inc.   (2)
4220 Apex Hwy, Durham, NC 27713
Tel.: (919) 484-2442
Telecommunication Servicesb
N.A.I.C.S.: 517810

Subsidiary (Non-US):

Evolving Systems Networks India Pvt.
Ltd.   (2)
Gurudas Heritage 3rd Floor 59/2 100 Ft
Ring Road Banashankari Stage II, Benga-
luru, 560070, India   (100%)
Tel.: (91) 8067227400
Web Site: http://www.evolving.com
Sales Range: $25-49.9 Million
Emp.: 100
Software Services
N.A.I.C.S.: 541512

Subsidiary (Domestic):

Telespree Communications   (2)
185 Berry St Ste 3600, San Francisco, CA
94107
Tel.: (415) 817-0800
Web Site: http://www.telespree.com
Sales Range: $1-9.9 Million
Emp.: 40
Wireless Cloud Data Services
N.A.I.C.S.: 423430

CD INTERNATIONAL ENTER-PRISES, INC.
431 Fairway Dr Ste 200, Deerfield
Beach, FL 33441
Tel.: (954) 363-7333   FL
Web Site: http://www.cdii.net
Year Founded: 1999

CDII—(OTCIQ)
Sales Range: Less than $1 Million
Emp.: 8
Management & Consulting Services
N.A.I.C.S.: 541618
Yuejian Wang (Founder, Chm, Pres &
CEO)

Subsidiaries:

CDI China, Inc.   (1)
431 Fairway Dr Ste 200, Deerfield Beach,
FL 33441-1823
Tel.: (561) 989-9171
Web Site: http://www.cdii.net
Management & Financial Advisory Services
N.A.I.C.S.: 541611
Andy Goldrich (Mgr-HR)

Subsidiary (Non-US):

Shanghai Lang Chemical Co.,
Ltd.   (2)
901 room No 970 Dalian Road, Shanghai,
China
Tel.: (86) 2151289991
Web Site: http://www.langyuan.com.cn
Emp.: 20
Pharmaceutical Chemicals Mfr
N.A.I.C.S.: 325998
Charlie Chen (CEO & Mgr)

CDI Shanghai Management Co.,
Ltd.   (1)
Rm W635 Jingjiang Junling Bldg No 59 Ma-
oMing Rd S, Shanghai, 200020,
China   (100%)
Tel.: (86) 2154660915
Web Site:
    http://www.chinadirectinvestments.com
Sales Range: $75-99.9 Million
Management & Financing to Small to Mid-
Sized Chinese Companies
N.A.I.C.S.: 541611
Robert Zhuang (Gen Mgr)
Frank Zhang (Exec VP)

CDII Minerals, Inc.   (1)
431 Fairway Dr Ste 200, Deerfield Beach,
FL 33441
Tel.: (954) 363-7334
Web Site: http://www.cdiitrading.com
Mineral Distr
N.A.I.C.S.: 423520

International Magnesium Group,
Inc.   (1)
431 Fairway Dr Ste 200, Deerfield Beach,
FL 33441-1823
Tel.: (954) 363-7333
Web Site: http://www.magnesiumgroup.com
Emp.: 10
Magnesium Distr
N.A.I.C.S.: 331491
Yuejian James Wang (Chm)
Yuwei Huang (CEO & Vice Chm)

CDTI ADVANCED MATERIALS, INC.
1641 Fiske Pl, Oxnard, CA 93033
Tel.: (805) 486-4649   DE
Web Site: https://www.cdti.com
Year Founded: 1994
CDTI—(NASDAQ)
Sales Range: $25-49.9 Million
Emp.: 97
Harmful Emissions Reduction Tech-
nologies Focusing on Internal Com-
bustion Engines; Fuel Economy &
Engine Power Improvement Tech-
nologies
N.A.I.C.S.: 336310
Peter Chase (COO)
Stephen J. Golden (CTO & VP-Bus
Dev & Strategy)
Kristi Cushing (Mgr-IR)
Kipp Bottorff (VP-Heavy Duty Diesel
Sls-North America)
Lon E. Bell (Chm)
Matthew Beale (Pres & CEO)
Gordon Foster (Dir-Catalyst Sls)
Tracy A. Kern (CFO & Sec)

CDTi Advanced Materials, Inc.—(Continued)

Subsidiaries:

CDTI Sweden AB **(1)**
Olivier Bommenel Baragatan 4, 212 28,
Malmo, Sweden
Tel.: (46) 406701550
Web Site: http://www.cdti.com
Automobile Equipment Mfr
N.A.I.C.S.: 811114
Lena Stenberg (CFO)

CDTi **(1)**
1621 Fiske Pl, Oxnard, CA 93033
Tel.: (805) 486-4649
Web Site: http://www.cdti.com
Sales Range: $25-49.9 Million
Emp.: 100
Emissions Control Systems & Products Mfr
& Distr
N.A.I.C.S.: 336390
Stephen J. Golden (CTO)

Subsidiary (Non-US):

Engine Control Systems Limited **(2)**
83 Commerce Valley Dr E, Thornhill, L3T
7T3, ON, Canada
Tel.: (905) 707-7746
Web Site:
http://www.enginecontrolsystems.com
Sales Range: $25-49.9 Million
Emp.: 100
Industrial & Automotive Emission Control
Systems
N.A.I.C.S.: 334519

Subsidiary (Non-US):

Engine Control Systems Europe
AB **(3)**
Baragatan 4, Box 9015, SE 200 39, Malmo,
Sweden
Tel.: (46) 406701550
Web Site: http://www.ecseurope.se
Sales Range: $1-9.9 Million
Automotive & Industrial Emissions Systems
N.A.I.C.S.: 334519
Lars Hergart (Mng Dir)

Subsidiary (US):

Engine Control Systems Ltd. **(3)**
4910 Longley Ln Ste 103, Reno, NV 89502-
7933
Tel.: (775) 827-3400
Web Site:
http://www.enginecontrolsystems.com
Sales Range: $10-24.9 Million
Emp.: 25
Industrial & Automotive Exhaust Parts
N.A.I.C.S.: 334519
Dennis Davanto (Mgr-Facility)

Clean Diesel Technologies
Limited **(1)**
475 Godstone Road, South Godstone,
CR30BL, Surrey, United Kingdom
Tel.: (44) 1883621048
Web Site: http://www.cdti.com
Sales Range: $10-24.9 Million
Emp.: 1
Vehicle Emissions Control System Mfr
N.A.I.C.S.: 334519

CDW CORPORATION
200 N Milwaukee Ave, Vernon Hills,
IL 60061
Tel.: (847) 465-6000 **IL**
Web Site: https://www.cdw.com
Year Founded: 1904
CDW—(NASDAQ)
Rev.: $23,748,700,000
Assets: $13,131,500,000
Liabilities: $11,528,200,000
Net Worth: $1,603,300,000
Earnings: $1,114,500,000
Emp.: 15,100
Fiscal Year-end: 12/31/22
Software Development Services
N.A.I.C.S.: 449210
Sona Chawla (Chief Growth & Inno-
vation Officer)
Christine A. Leahy (Founder-
Women's Opportunity Network, Chm
& CEO)

Albert J. Miralles (CFO & Sr VP)
Frederick J. Kulevich (Gen Counsel,
Sec & Sr VP)
Sara Granack (VP-Comm)
Elizabeth H. Connelly (Chief HR Offi-
cer, Sr VP-Healthcare & Sr VP-
Coworker Svcs)
Sanjay Sood (CTO & Sr VP)
Steve O'Brien (VP-IR)
Peter R. Locy (Chief Acctg Officer,
VP & Controller)
Michael S. Drory (Sr VP)

Subsidiaries:

CDW Canada, Inc. **(1)**
185 The West Mall Suite 1700, Toronto,
M9C 5L5, ON, Canada
Tel.: (647) 288-5700
Web Site: https://www.cdw.ca
Sales Range: $25-49.9 Million
Retailer of Brandname Technology Services
& Computer Products
N.A.I.C.S.: 423430
Julie Clivio (Mgr-Mktg Comm)
J. D. Hupp (VP & Gen Mgr)
Ginette Adragna (CFO)

CDW Government, Inc. **(1)**
200 N Milwaukee Ave, Vernon Hills, IL
60061
Tel.: (847) 371-6090
Web Site: http://www.cdwg.com
Emp.: 9,000
Computer & Computer Product Whslr
N.A.I.C.S.: 449129

CDW Logistics, Inc. **(1)**
200 N Milwaukee Ave, Vernon Hills, IL
60061
Tel.: (847) 465-6000
Web Site: http://www.cdw.com
Sales Range: $450-499.9 Million
Information Technology Solutions
N.A.I.C.S.: 519290

CDW Technologies, Inc. **(1)**
200 N Milwaukee Ave, Vernon Hills, IL
60061-1577
Tel.: (608) 288-3000
Web Site: http://www.cdw.com
Sales Range: $400-449.9 Million
Computer Integrated Systems Design
N.A.I.C.S.: 541512

Branch (Domestic):

CDW Technologies, Inc. -
Appleton **(2)**
4321 W College Ave Ste 400, Appleton, WI
54914-3968
Tel.: (920) 997-9420
Web Site: http://www.cdw.com
Sales Range: $25-49.9 Million
Emp.: 83
Computer Hardware, Software & Technical
Solution Services
N.A.I.C.S.: 423430

CDW Technologies, Inc. -
Chicago **(2)**
CDW Plz 120 S Riverside, Chicago, IL
60606
Tel.: (847) 465-6000
Web Site: http://www.cdw.com
Sales Range: $25-49.9 Million
Emp.: 87
Computer Hardware Software & Technical
Solution Distr
N.A.I.C.S.: 423430
Steve Winandy (Mgr-Reg)

CDW Technologies, Inc. -
Cincinnati **(2)**
9349 Waterstone Blvd Ste 150, Cincinnati,
OH 45249
Tel.: (513) 677-4100
Web Site: http://www.cdw.com
Sales Range: $25-49.9 Million
Emp.: 34
Computer Hardware Software & Technical
Solution Distr
N.A.I.C.S.: 423430

CDW Technologies, Inc. -
Cleveland **(2)**
6650 W Snowville Rd Unit A, Brecksville,
OH 44141

Tel.: (440) 746-7200
Web Site: http://www.cdw.com
Sales Range: $25-49.9 Million
Emp.: 106
Computer Hardware, Software & Technical
Solution Services
N.A.I.C.S.: 423430

CDW Technologies, Inc. - Detroit **(2)**
1000 Town Ctr Ste 1800, Southfield, MI
48075
Tel.: (248) 223-4500
Web Site: http://www.cdw.com
Sales Range: $25-49.9 Million
Emp.: 46
Computer Hardware, Software & Technical
Solution Services
N.A.I.C.S.: 423430

CDW Technologies, Inc. - Grand
Rapids **(2)**
4690 E Fulton St Ste 203, Ada, MI 49301
Tel.: (616) 464-2700
Web Site: http://www.cdw.com
Sales Range: $25-49.9 Million
Emp.: 58
Computer Hardware, Software & Technical
Solution Services
N.A.I.C.S.: 423430
Brian Donovan (Acct Exec)

CDW Technologies, Inc. -
Indianapolis **(2)**
11711 N Meridian St, Carmel, IN 46032
Tel.: (317) 569-4200
Web Site: http://www.cdw.com
Sales Range: $25-49.9 Million
Emp.: 54
Computer Hardware Software & Technical
Solution Distr
N.A.I.C.S.: 423430

CDW Technologies, Inc. -
Madison **(2)**
5520 Research Park Dr, Fitchburg, WI
53711
Tel.: (608) 288-3000
Web Site: http://www.cdw.com
Sales Range: $75-99.9 Million
Computer Hardware, Software & Technical
Solution Services
N.A.I.C.S.: 423430

CDW Technologies, Inc. -
Milwaukee **(2)**
N19W23993 Ridgeview Pkwy W Ste 120,
Waukesha, WI 53188-1000
Tel.: (262) 521-5600
Web Site: http://www.cdw.com
Computer Hardware Software & Technical
Solution Distr
N.A.I.C.S.: 423430

CDW Technologies, Inc. -
Minneapolis **(2)**
7145 Boone Ave N Ste 140, Brooklyn Park,
MN 55428
Tel.: (763) 592-5800
Web Site: http://www.cdw.com
Sales Range: $25-49.9 Million
Emp.: 112
Computer Hardware, Software & Technical
Solution Services
N.A.I.C.S.: 423430

CDW Technologies, Inc. -
Wausau **(2)**
7402 Stoneridge Dr Ste 1, Weston, WI
54476
Tel.: (715) 359-8100
Web Site: http://www.cdw.com
Sales Range: $25-49.9 Million
Emp.: 42
Computer Hardware, Software & Technical
Solution Services
N.A.I.C.S.: 423430

Enquizit Inc. **(1)**
7927 Jones Branch Dr Ste 400, McLean,
VA 22102
Tel.: (647) 243-3790
Web Site: http://www.enquizit.com
Sales Range: $1-9.9 Million
Information Technology Services
N.A.I.C.S.: 541512
Ravi Sundar (Sr Mgr-Recruiting)

Mission Cloud Services Inc. **(1)**
4470 W Sunset Blvd Ste 107 PMB 94146,
Los Angeles, CA 90027

Web Site: http://www.missioncloud.com
Sales Range: $1-9.9 Million
Emp.: 200
Software Development Services
N.A.I.C.S.: 541511
Simon Anderson (Founder, Chm & CEO)
Stewart Armstrong (CFO)
Jonathan Lacour (CTO)
Ted Stuart (Pres)
Mark Medina (VP-Mktg)

Sirius Computer Solutions, Inc. **(1)**
10100 Reunion Pl Ste 500, San Antonio, TX
78216
Tel.: (800) 460-1237
Web Site: http://www.siriuscom.com
Computer System Design Services
N.A.I.C.S.: 541512
Jim Simpson (Pres-Strategic Initiatives)
Terry Johnson (COO)
Joe Mertens (Pres & CEO)
Muditha Karunatileka (Pres)
Karen Kochheiser (Chief Acctg Officer)
Michael Harwood (Sr VP-Mktg)
Bonnie Cerrito (Sr VP-Contracts & Fin
Svcs)
Chris Mierzwa (Sr VP-Strategic Initiatives)
Rick Bailer (Sr VP-Sls)
Keith Ikels (CIO)
Becky Murphy (Sr VP-Sls-Southwest)
Craig Nelson (Exec VP-Svcs & Networking)
Thomas Neville (Sr VP-Sls-Managed Svcs)
Imran Salim (Sr VP-Sls-West)
Jehad Abdeljawad (VP-Infrastructure Svcs)
Joe Andersen (VP-Tech & Engrg Svcs)
Justin Sobey (Gen Counsel & VP)
Hemant Kapadia (CFO)

Subsidiary (Domestic):

Champion Solutions Group Inc. **(2)**
791 Park of Commerce Blvd Ste 200, Boca
Raton, FL 33487
Tel.: (561) 997-2900
Web Site: http://www.championsg.com
Sales Range: $75-99.9 Million
Emp.: 120
Computer Peripheral Equipment
N.A.I.C.S.: 449210
James Canfield (Dir-Online Svcs)
Lisa Cuthbertson (VP-Svcs Ops)
Chris Pyle (Pres & CEO)
Laura Poblano (CFO)
Michael Lewis Gray (COO)
Mike Piltoff (Sr VP-Strategic Mktg)

Subsidiary (Domestic):

DirecLogix Corp **(3)**
791 Park of Commerce Blvd Ste 200, Boca
Raton, FL 33487
Web Site: http://www.direclogix.com
Sales Range: $1-9.9 Million
Emp.: 15
Full Range IT Professional Consulting Ser-
vices
N.A.I.C.S.: 541690
Aleef Adam (Mng Partner)

Midrange Support & Service, Inc. **(3)**
1122 E Atlantic Ave Ste C, Delray Beach,
FL 33483 **(100%)**
Tel.: (561) 272-5883
Web Site: http://www.midrangesupport.com
Support & Services to the International
Business Machines
N.A.I.C.S.: 423430
Brooke Liccardi (VP-Ops)
Steve Marinak III (Pres)

Subsidiary (Domestic):

Continuum Worldwide
Corporation **(2)**
3333 Farnam St Ste 1, Omaha, NE 68131
Tel.: (402) 916-1800
Information Technology Consulting Services
N.A.I.C.S.: 541512
Christopher Hoke (Mng Dir)
Jeffrey Matza (Pres)

Force 3, Inc. **(2)**
2151 Priest Rdg Dr, Crofton, MD 21114
Tel.: (301) 261-0204
Web Site: https://www.siriusfederal.com
Sales Range: $250-299.9 Million
Emp.: 2,600
Network Security Technology Services
N.A.I.C.S.: 541519

Josh Weiner (*VP-Defense & Intelligence*)
Tammy Little (*Sr Dir-Sls Ops*)
Pat Farr (*VP-Fin*)
Steve Levine (*VP*)
Joe Mertens (*Pres*)
Muditha Karunatileka (*Exec VP*)

Forsythe Technology Inc.   **(2)**
7770 Frontage Rd, Skokie, IL 60077
Tel.: (847) 213-7000
Web Site: http://www.forsythe.com
Sales Range: $400-449.9 Million
Emp.: 1,200
IT Consulting Services
N.A.I.C.S.: 541690
William P. Brennan (*Pres & CEO*)
Albert L. Weiss (*CFO & Exec VP*)
Michelle M. Coffield (*Sr VP-Order Mgmt*)
R. Thomas Hoffman (*Gen Counsel & Sr VP*)
Michael J. Qualley (*Exec VP-Tech Solutions*)
Daniel Rodgers (*VP*)
Gary W. LoMonaco (*Treas & VP*)

Subsidiary (Domestic):

Forsythe McArthur Associates, Inc.   **(3)**
7770 Frontage Rd, Skokie, IL 60077-2634
Tel.: (847) 213-7000
Web Site: http://www.forsythe.com
Sales Range: $25-49.9 Million
Emp.: 500
Technology Infrastructure Services
N.A.I.C.S.: 561499
Albert L. Weiss (*CFO*)

Forsythe Solutions Group, Inc.   **(3)**
11301 Carmel Commons Blvd Ste 211, Charlotte, NC 28226-5305
Tel.: (847) 213-7000
Web Site: http://www.forsythe.com
Sales Range: $25-49.9 Million
Emp.: 23
IT Infrastructure Consulting Services
N.A.I.C.S.: 541512
Michael J. Qualley (*Sr VP-Sys Solutions & Tech Products*)
William P. Brennan (*Pres & CEO*)
John D. Carcone (*Sr VP-Fin Svcs*)
Robert D. Dvorak (*Sr VP & Gen Mgr-Central Area*)

Subsidiary (Non-US):

Forsythe Technology Canada, Inc.   **(3)**
50 Burnhamthorpe Road West, Mississauga, L5B 3C2, ON, Canada
Tel.: (343) 338-3404
Information Technology Consulting Services
N.A.I.C.S.: 541512

Subsidiary (Domestic):

Mentora Group, Inc.   **(3)**
1300 Ridenour Blvd Ste 100, Kennesaw, GA 30152
Tel.: (404) 492-6581
Web Site: http://www.mentora.com
Web Hosting Services
N.A.I.C.S.: 518210
Kathryn Saunders (*Pres & CEO*)
Susan Tutor (*Dir-Hosting Svcs Admin*)
Andrey Dmitriev (*Dir-Hosting Ops*)
Steve Cleary (*Mgr-Bus Dev*)

SOS Security Inc   **(3)**
13333 NW Freeway, Houston, TX 77040
Tel.: (713) 428-4238
Web Site: http://www.securesos.com
Information Technology Consulting Services
N.A.I.C.S.: 541512
Mark Jones (*CEO*)
Kirk Jones (*Pres*)
Leslie Nielsen (*Dir-Enterprise Architecture*)
Deb Weimer (*Reg Mgr-Sls*)
Brett Atwood (*Reg Mgr-Sls*)

Synnefo Technology Solutions, Inc.   **(3)**
1300 E Woodfield Rd Ste 302, Schaumburg, IL 60173
Tel.: (847) 213-7720
Web Site: http://www.synnefo.com
Information Technology Consulting Services
N.A.I.C.S.: 541512
Janell Taraszka (*COO*)
Carmen Santiago-Keenon (*Mgr-Channel*)

CEA INDUSTRIES INC.
385 S Pierce Ave Ste C, Louisville, CO 80027
Tel.: (303) 993-5271
Web Site:
   https://www.ceaindustries.com
Year Founded: 2009
CEAD—(NASDAQ)
Rev.: $6,910,951
Assets: $13,772,083
Liabilities: $1,510,875
Net Worth: $12,261,208
Earnings: ($2,911,551)
Emp.: 10
Fiscal Year-end: 12/31/23
Cultivation Technologies Developer
N.A.I.C.S.: 541713
Stephen B. Keen (*Co-Founder*)
Brandy Marie Keen (*Co-Founder*)
Anthony K. McDonald (*Chm, Pres, CEO & Chief Acctg Officer*)

Subsidiaries:

Hydro Innovations, LLC   **(1)**
1780 55th St Ste A, Boulder, CO 80301
Tel.: (303) 997-6050
Web Site: http://www.hydroinnovations.com
Air Conditioning Equipment Mfr & Distr
N.A.I.C.S.: 333415

CECIL BANCORP, INC.
127 N St, Elkton, MD 21921
Tel.: (410) 398-1650   MD
Web Site: http://www.cecilbank.com
Year Founded: 1994
CECL—(OTCIQ)
Bank Holding Company
N.A.I.C.S.: 551111
Terrie G. Spiro (*Pres & CEO*)
R. Lee Whitehead (*CFO & Exec VP*)
Brian J. Hale (*CIO & Exec VP*)
Robin W. Brueckman (*Sr VP-Bus Dev*)
Thomas L. Hotchkiss (*Exec VP & Chief Credit Officer*)
Thomas J. Ahearn (*Sr VP*)
V. Guy Abell (*Vp & Controller*)
Cheryl A. Artysiewicz (*VP & Officer-Bus Devt*)
Tamara S. Fender (*VP*)
Matthew D. Mryncza (*Asst VP & Credit Analyst*)
William H. Cole IV (*Chm*)
William F. Ariano Jr. (*Vice Chm*)

Subsidiaries:

Cecil Bank   **(1)**
127 N St, Elkton, MD 21921
Tel.: (410) 398-1650
Web Site: http://www.cecilbank.com
Commericial Banking
N.A.I.C.S.: 522110
Terrie G. Spiro (*Pres & CEO*)
R. Lee Whitehead (*CFO & Exec VP*)
Brian J. Hale (*CIO & Exec VP*)
Thomas J. Ahearn (*Chief Credit Officer & Sr VP*)
Robin W. Brueckman (*Sr VP-Bus Dev*)

CECO ENVIRONMENTAL CORP.
14651 Dallas Pkwy Ste 500, Dallas, TX 75254
Tel.: (214) 357-6181   DE
Web Site:
   https://www.cecoenviro.com
Year Founded: 1966
CECO—(NASDAQ)
Rev.: $422,627,000
Assets: $504,721,000
Liabilities: $286,573,000
Net Worth: $218,148,000
Earnings: $17,417,000
Emp.: 1,000
Fiscal Year-end: 12/31/22
Industrial & Commercial Fan & Blower & Air Purification Equipment Manufacturing

N.A.I.C.S.: 333413
Todd R. Gleason (*CEO*)
Peter K. Johansson (*Chief Fin & Strategy Officer & Sr VP*)
Lynn Watkins-Asiyanbi (*Chief Admin & Legal Officer, Gen Counsel & Sec*)
Kiril Kovachev (*Chief Acctg Officer, VP & Controller-Global*)

Subsidiaries:

CECO Environmental Middle East DMCC   **(1)**
AU Gold Tower Floor 28 Office A Cluster I Jumeirah Lake Towers, PO Box 62435, Dubai, United Arab Emirates
Tel.: (971) 44340004
Industrial & Commercial Air Purification Equipment Mfr
N.A.I.C.S.: 333413
Sammy Aquino (*Sr Engr-Process*)

CECO Group Global Holdings LLC   **(1)**
4625 Red Bank Rd Ste 200, Cincinnati, OH 45227
Tel.: (513) 458-2600
Holding Company
N.A.I.C.S.: 551112
Jeff Lang (*CEO*)

Subsidiary (Non-US):

CECO Environmental Netherlands B.V.   **(2)**
Industrieweg 59, PO Box 65, 8070 AB, Nunspeet, Netherlands
Tel.: (31) 341252635
Web Site: http://www.cecoenviro.com
Emp.: 60
Air Filter Mfr
N.A.I.C.S.: 326199

CECO Group, Inc.   **(1)**
4625 Red Bank Rd Ste 200, Cincinnati, OH 45227
Tel.: (513) 458-2600
Web Site: http://www.cecoenviro.com
Air Pollution Control Equipment Mfr
N.A.I.C.S.: 333413

Subsidiary (Domestic):

Adwest Technologies, Inc.   **(2)**
4222 E LA Palma Ave, Anaheim, CA 92807
Tel.: (714) 632-9801
Emp.: 25
Air Filter Mfr
N.A.I.C.S.: 326199
Brian Cannon (*Dir-Sls & Mktg*)
Bruce Plano (*Mgr-Panel Fabrication*)

CECO Filters Inc.   **(2)**
700 Emlen Way, Telford, PA 18969
Tel.: (610) 825-8585
Web Site: https://www.cecoenviro.com
Sales Range: $25-49.9 Million
Emp.: 16
Fiber Bed Filter Elements Mfr
N.A.I.C.S.: 333413

Subsidiary (Domestic):

New Busch Co., Inc.   **(3)**
10431 Perry Hwy Ste 201, Wexford, PA 15090-9200
Tel.: (724) 940-2326
Web Site: http://www.buschintl.com
Emp.: 5
Air Pollution Control Equipment Mfr
N.A.I.C.S.: 333413

Compass Water Solutions, Inc   **(1)**
1732 McGaw Ave, Irvine, CA 92614
Tel.: (949) 222-5777
Web Site: http://www.cworldwater.com
Sales Range: $1-9.9 Million
Emp.: 30
Water & Wastewater Treatment
N.A.I.C.S.: 541380
Dana Trujillo (*Controller*)

Effox, Inc.   **(1)**
9759 Inter Ocean Dr, Cincinnati, OH 45246
Tel.: (513) 874-8915
Web Site: http://www.effox.com
Sales Range: $10-24.9 Million
Emp.: 120

Coal-Fired Electric Plant Dampers & Expansion Joints
N.A.I.C.S.: 332313

Emtrol-Buell Technologies   **(1)**
1440 Veterans Memorial Hwy Ste 100, Islandia, NY 11749
Tel.: (631) 582-9700
Web Site: http://www.emtrolcorp.com
Air Pollution Control Equipment & Supplies
N.A.I.C.S.: 423730

Environmental Integrated Solutions Ltd.   **(1)**
15 The Courtyard Buntsford Drive, Bromsgrove, B60 3DJ, Worcestershire, United Kingdom
Tel.: (44) 1215507079
Web Site: https://www.eisuk.co.uk
Environmental Consultancy Services
N.A.I.C.S.: 541620

Fisher-Klosterman Inc.   **(1)**
10000 Shelbyville Rd Ste 101, Louisville, KY 40223
Tel.: (502) 572-4000
Web Site: https://www.cecoenviro.com
Sales Range: $25-49.9 Million
Emp.: 100
Custom Designed Air Pollution Control & Product Recovery Equipment & Systems
N.A.I.C.S.: 333413

Flextor Inc.   **(1)**
61 chemin du Tremblay, Boucherville, J4B 7L6, QC, Canada
Tel.: (450) 449-9882
Web Site: http://www.essoxflextor.com
Emp.: 1
Air Filter Mfr
N.A.I.C.S.: 326199

HEE Environmental Engineering, LLC   **(1)**
2143 Convention Center Way Ste 180, Ontario, CA 91764
Tel.: (909) 230-6120
Web Site: http://www.hee-llc.com
Sales Range: $10-24.9 Million
Emp.: 35
Air Pollution Control Products Mfr
N.A.I.C.S.: 333413

KBD Technic   **(1)**
11633 Deerfield Rd, Cincinnati, OH 45242
Tel.: (513) 351-6200
Web Site: https://www.kbdtechnic.com
Sales Range: $10-24.9 Million
Emp.: 12
Design, Testing & Analysis of Air Movement Systems
N.A.I.C.S.: 541330

Kemco Systems, Co. LLC   **(1)**
11500 47th St North, Clearwater, FL 33762
Tel.: (727) 573-2323
Web Site: http://www.kemcosystems.com
Industrial Water Reuse, Recycle & Wastewater Treatment Services
N.A.I.C.S.: 333414
Carroll Gorrell (*Pres*)
Rod Kummer (*Mgr-Ops*)
Allen Jennemen (*Exec VP*)
Gerard Van Gils (*VP*)
Brenda Cleary (*Mgr-Acctg*)
Tom Vanden Heuvel (*VP & Gen Mgr*)

Kirk & Blum Manufacturing Company Inc.   **(1)**
6245 Creek Rd, Blue Ash, OH 45242
Tel.: (513) 458-2600
Web Site: http://www.kirkblum.com
Sales Range: $100-124.9 Million
Emp.: 32
Industrial Sheet Metal Contractor; Custom Sheet & Plate Fabricator; Industrial Air System Component Mfr
N.A.I.C.S.: 238390

Division (Domestic):

K&B Duct   **(2)**
8735 W Market St, Greensboro, NC 27409
Tel.: (336) 668-3773
Web Site: http://www.kbduct.com
Sales Range: $25-49.9 Million
Ductwork Systems Design & Mfr
N.A.I.C.S.: 333413

Met-Pro Technologies LLC   **(1)**

CECO Environmental Corp.—(Continued)

160 Cassell Rd PO Box 144, Harleysville, PA 19438
Tel.: (215) 723-6751
Product Recovery & Pollution Control Equipment Mfr & Whlsr
N.A.I.C.S.: 333413

Unit (Domestic):

Burgess-Aarding (2)
50 Cobham Dr, Orchard Park, NY 14127-4121
Tel.: (716) 662-6540
Web Site: https://www.cecoenviro.com
Heat Exchangers, Industrial Silencers & Gas Separators Mfr
N.A.I.C.S.: 335314

Dean Pump (2)
6040 Guion Rd, Indianapolis, IN 46254
Tel.: (317) 293-2930
Web Site: http://www.cecoenviro.com
Sales Range: $25-49.9 Million
Emp.: 32
High Temperature Resistant Pumps Mfr
N.A.I.C.S.: 333914

Flex-Kleen (2)
45 N Brandon Dr, Glendale Heights, IL 60139
Tel.: (630) 775-0707
Web Site: http://www.flex-kleen.com
Sales Range: $25-49.9 Million
Emp.: 15
Fabric Filters Distribution of Dust Collectors
N.A.I.C.S.: 333413

Fybroc (2)
700 Emlen Way, Telford, PA 18969-1773
Tel.: (215) 723-8155
Web Site: https://www.cecoenviro.com
Sales Range: $25-49.9 Million
Emp.: 60
Corrosion Resistant Fiberglass Centrifugal Pumps Mfr
N.A.I.C.S.: 333914

Subsidiary (Domestic):

MPC Inc. (2)
615 N Park St, Madison, WI 54840-7253
Tel.: (262) 275-5791
Air Filter Mfr
N.A.I.C.S.: 326199

Subsidiary (Non-US):

Mefiag B.V. (2)
Magnesiumweg 2, 8445 PJ, Heerenveen, Netherlands (100%)
Tel.: (31) 513630230
Web Site: http://www.mefiag.com
Sales Range: $10-24.9 Million
Emp.: 50
Mfr of Horizontal Disc Filtrations Systems
N.A.I.C.S.: 334419

Unit (Domestic):

Mefiag USA (2)
1550 Industrial Dr, Owosso, MI 48867
Tel.: (989) 725-8184
Web Site: http://www.met-pro.com
Sales Range: $25-49.9 Million
Emp.: 50
Horizontal Disc Filtration Systems Mfr
N.A.I.C.S.: 333914

Pristine Water Solutions Inc. (2)
1570 S Lakeside Dr, Waukegan, IL 60085-8309
Tel.: (847) 689-1100
Web Site:
http://www.pristinewatersolutions.com
Sales Range: $25-49.9 Million
Emp.: 20
Chemicals & Treatment Systems for Corrosion, Iron, Lead, Copper, Manganese & Scale Problems in Municipal Water Systems
N.A.I.C.S.: 325998

PMFG, Inc. (1)
14651 N Dallas Pkwy Ste 500, Dallas, TX 75254
Tel.: (214) 357-6181
Web Site: http://www.cecoenviro.com
Rev.: $158,643,000
Assets: $162,493,000

Liabilities: $74,881,000
Net Worth: $87,612,000
Earnings: ($8,222,000)
Emp.: 500
Fiscal Year-end: 06/27/2015
Moisture Removal Systems, Gas Filtration & Separation Systems & Selective Catalytic Reduction Systems
N.A.I.C.S.: 333248

Subsidiary (Non-US):

Peerless Asia Pacific Pte. Ltd. (2)
No 34 Boon Leat Terrace 04-19, Singapore, 119866, Singapore (100%)
Tel.: (65) 64720020
Web Site: http://www.cecoenviro.com
Filtration & Separation Equipments Mfr & Distr
N.A.I.C.S.: 333248
Yin Hock Lee (Mng Dir)

Peerless China Manufacturing Co. Ltd. (2)
Suite 611 No 1081 Wuzhong Road, Min-hang District, Shanghai, 201103, China (60%)
Tel.: (86) 0511 085308188
Web Site: http://www.cecoenviro.com
Industrial Equipment Whsr
N.A.I.C.S.: 423830

Peerless Europe Ltd. (2)
3rd Floor Endeavour House Coopers End Road, Stansted, CM24 1SJ, Essex, United Kingdom (100%)
Tel.: (44) 1439 330623
Web Site: http://www.cecoenviro.com
Emp.: 1
Separation Filtration Equipment & Environmental Systems Design & Sales
N.A.I.C.S.: 332919

Division (Domestic):

Peerless Manufacturing Co. (2)
2711 Transit Rd Ste 125, Elma, NY 14059 (100%)
Tel.: (716) 662-6540
Web Site: http://www.cecoenviro.com
Heat Exchangers, Industrial Silencers & Gas Separators Mfr
N.A.I.C.S.: 335314

CEL-SCI CORPORATION

8229 Boone Blvd Ste 802, Vienna, VA 22182
Tel.: (703) 506-9460   CO
Web Site: https://www.cel-sci.com
Year Founded: 1983
CVM—(NYSEAMEX)
Assets: $30,528,250
Liabilities: $17,313,360
Net Worth: $13,214,890
Earnings: ($32,194,303)
Emp.: 44
Fiscal Year-end: 09/30/23
Research & Development of Immunotherapy Products in the Treatments of Cancer & Infectious Diseases
N.A.I.C.S.: 325414
Geert R. Kersten (CEO, CFO, Chief Acctg Officer & Treas)
Patricia B. Prichep (Sec & Sr VP-Ops)
Eyal Talor (Chief Scientific Officer)
Daniel H. Zimmerman (Sr VP-Res-Cellular Immunology)
John Cipriano (Sr VP-Regulatory Affairs)
William Brooke Jones (VP-Quality Assurance)
Todd S. Burkhart (VP-Mfg)

CELADON GROUP, INC.

9503 E 33rd St 1 Celadon Dr, Indianapolis, IN 46235
Tel.: (317) 972-7000   DE
Year Founded: 1985
CGIP—(OTCEM)
Sales Range: $1-4.9 Billion
Holding Company; Freight Transportation & Logistics Services

N.A.I.C.S.: 551112
Vincent Donargo (CFO, Chief Acctg Officer & Exec VP)
Michael Gabbei (VP & CIO)
Thomas Stephen Albrecht (Chief Strategy & Comml Officer & Exec VP)
Paul Svindland (CEO)

Subsidiaries:

Celadon E-Commerce, Inc. (1)
9503 E 33rd St, Indianapolis, IN 46235-4207 (100%)
Tel.: (317) 972-7000
Sales Range: $125-149.9 Million
Emp.: 300
Holding Company; Freight Transportation Business-to-Business Electronic Market Operator
N.A.I.C.S.: 551112
Paul A. Will (Pres & CEO)

Affiliate (Domestic):

TruckersB2B, Inc. (2)
9503 E 33rd St, Indianapolis, IN 46235 (35%)
Tel.: (317) 972-7000
Web Site: http://www.truckersb2b.com
Sales Range: $50-74.9 Million
Emp.: 100
Freight Transportation Business-to-Business Electronic Market Operator
N.A.I.C.S.: 425120

Celadon Logistics Services, Inc. (1)
9503 E 33rd St, Indianapolis, IN 46235
Tel.: (317) 972-7000
Web Site: http://www.celadonlogistics.com
Sales Range: $25-49.9 Million
Emp.: 15
Integrated Freight Logistics Services
N.A.I.C.S.: 488510

Celadon Trucking Services, Inc. (1)
9503 E 33rd St, Indianapolis, IN 46235-4207 (100%)
Tel.: (317) 972-7000
Web Site: http://www.celadontrucking.com
Sales Range: $250-299.9 Million
Emp.: 2,500
Freight Trucking Services
N.A.I.C.S.: 484121
Paul A. Will (Vice Chm, Pres & COO)
Richard Stocking (Chief Transformation Officer)

Subsidiary (Non-US):

Celadon Canada Inc. (2)
280 Shoemaker St, Kitchener, N2E 3E1, ON, Canada
Tel.: (519) 748-9773
Web Site: http://www.celadoncanada.com
Sales Range: $25-49.9 Million
Emp.: 550
Provider of Trucking Related Services
N.A.I.C.S.: 484122

Hyndman Transport (1972) Limited (1)
1001 Belmore Line, Wroxeter, Howick, N0G 2X0, ON, Canada
Tel.: (519) 335-3575
Web Site: http://www.hyndman.ca
Emp.: 42
Freight Transportation Services
N.A.I.C.S.: 484121
Mike Campbell (Pres & CEO)
Jeff Sippel (CFO)
John Kellie (Mgr-Safety)
Randy Scott (Mgr-Fleet Maintenance & Livestock)
Steve Thornton (Mgr-Shop)

Stinger Logistics, Inc. (1)
101 Dollar St, Ottoville, OH 45876
Tel.: (419) 453-3774
Emp.: 4
Logistics Consulting Servies
N.A.I.C.S.: 541614
Ron Dixon (Gen Mgr)

CELANESE CORPORATION

222 W Las Colinas Blvd Ste 900N, Irving, TX 75039-5421
Tel.: (972) 443-4000   DE

Web Site: https://www.celanese.com
Year Founded: 2004
CE—(NYSE)
Rev.: $10,940,000,000
Assets: $26,597,000,000
Liabilities: $19,045,000,000
Net Worth: $7,552,000,000
Earnings: $1,960,000,000
Emp.: 12,410
Fiscal Year-end: 12/31/23
Industrial Chemicals Producer
N.A.I.C.S.: 325180
Scott A. Richardson (COO & Exec VP)
Lori J. Ryerkerk (Chm, Pres & CEO)
A. Lynne Puckett (Gen Counsel & Sr VP)
Tom Kelly (Sr VP- Engineered Materials)
Patrick Schumacher (Sr VP-Engineered Materials)
Marcel R. van Amerongen (VP-Cellulose Derivatives)
Mark C. Murray (Sr VP-Acetyls)
Vanessa A. Dupuis (Chief HR Officer & Sr VP)

Subsidiaries:

Celanese (China) Holding Co., Ltd. (1)
4560 Jinke Road, Zhang Jiang Pudong New Area, Shanghai, 201203, China
Tel.: (86) 2138619288
Web Site: http://www.celanese.com.cn
Sales Range: $75-99.9 Million
Chemical Products Mfr
N.A.I.C.S.: 325998

Celanese (Shanghai) Polymers Co., Ltd. (1)
No 275 Huajia Road, Songjiang Industrial Estate, Shanghai, 201600, China
Tel.: (86) 2137746188
Chemical Products Mfr
N.A.I.C.S.: 325998

Celanese (Thailand) Limited (1)
589/123 Bang Na-Trad Road, Bangna, Bangkok, 10260, Thailand
Tel.: (66) 27457342
Chemical Products Mfr
N.A.I.C.S.: 325998

Celanese EVA Performance Polymers Inc. (1)
4405 101 Avenue, Edmonton, T5J 2K1, AB, Canada
Tel.: (780) 468-0800
Emp.: 300
Chemical Products Mfr
N.A.I.C.S.: 325998

Celanese Emulsions B.V. (1)
De Asselen Kuil 20, 6161 RD, Geleen, Netherlands
Tel.: (31) 464389898
Web Site: http://www.celanese.com
Sales Range: $25-49.9 Million
Emp.: 110
Mfr of Specialty Synthetic Polymers
N.A.I.C.S.: 325998

Celanese Emulsions Ltd. (1)
Eastford Rd, Warrington, WA4 6HG, Cheshire, United Kingdom
Tel.: (44) 1925236400
Web Site: http://www.celanese.com
Sales Range: $10-24.9 Million
Emp.: 42
Specialty Synthetic Polymers Mfr
N.A.I.C.S.: 325998

Celanese Emulsions Norden AB (1)
Risebergavagen 12, 284 34, Perstorp, Sweden (100%)
Tel.: (46) 43534060
Web Site: http://www.celanese.com
Sales Range: $25-49.9 Million
Emp.: 100
Mfr of Dyes & Paints
N.A.I.C.S.: 325130
Anita Sindberg (CEO)

Celanese Far East Ltd. (1)
Room F 54 China Oversea Building 139

Hennessy Road, Wanchai, China (Hong Kong)
Tel.: (852) 0025063126
Sales Range: $25-49.9 Million
Emp.: 4
Chemical Products Mfr
N.A.I.C.S.: 325998
Eddie Luen (Gen Mgr)

Celanese GmbH **(1)**
(95%)
Tel.: (49) 69450091777
Web Site: http://www.celanese.com
Sales Range: $1-4.9 Billion
Holding Company: Chemicals, Chemical Intermediates, Acetate Products & Acetyl Products
N.A.I.C.S.: 551112

Subsidiary (Non-US):

Celanese Acetate, LLC **(2)**
Tel.: (972) 443-4000
Web Site: http://www.celaneseacetate.com
Mfr of Cellulose Acetate Filament
N.A.I.C.S.: 313110

Celanese Chemicals, Inc. **(2)**
Tel.: (972) 443-4000
Web Site: http://www.celanese.com
Commodity Chemical Products Mfr
N.A.I.C.S.: 325199

Ticona GmbH **(2)**
Tel.: (49) 6930582490
Web Site: https://ticona.lookchem.com
Sales Range: $1-4.9 Billion
Emp.: 1,800
Provider of Engineering Plastics
N.A.I.C.S.: 326199

Celanese Korea Ltd. **(1)**
4th Fl Songwon Bldg 59-4 Banpo 4-dong, Seocho-gu, Seoul, Korea (South)
Tel.: (82) 234781195
Chemical Products Mfr
N.A.I.C.S.: 325998

Celanese Production Switzerland AG **(1)**
Neumattstrasse 196, 5054, Moosleerau, Switzerland
Tel.: (41) 627388888
Chemical Products Mfr
N.A.I.C.S.: 325998

Celanese Property Germany GmbH & Co. KG **(1)**
Am Unisys-Park 1, Main-Taunus-Kreis, 65843, Sulzbach, Germany
Tel.: (49) 69450090
Chemical Product Mfr & Distr
N.A.I.C.S.: 325199

Celanese Pte. Ltd. **(1)**
Tel.: (65) 65130438
Web Site: https://www.celanese.com
Sales Range: $25-49.9 Million
Emp.: 26
Chemical Products Mfr
N.A.I.C.S.: 325998
Simon Yep (Dir Gen)

Celanese S.A./N.V. **(1)**
Industrieweg 80, 3620, Lanaken, 3620, Belgium
Tel.: (32) 89710111
Chemical Products Mfr
N.A.I.C.S.: 325998

Celanese Services Germany GmbH **(1)**
Am Unisys-Park 1, 65843, Sulzbach, Germany
Tel.: (49) 69450091777
Web Site: https://www.celanese.de
Emp.: 250
Industrial Chemical Mfr & Distr
N.A.I.C.S.: 325199

Celanese Singapore Pte. Ltd. **(1)**
21 Sakra Avenue, Singapore, 627883, Singapore
Tel.: (65) 68676005
Web Site: https://www.celanese.com
Chemical Products Mfr
N.A.I.C.S.: 325998

Celanese Switzerland AG **(1)**
Industriestrasse 17a Station, 6203, Sempach, Switzerland

Tel.: (41) 414696969
Web Site: http://www.elotex.com
Chemical Products Mfr
N.A.I.C.S.: 325998

DuPont Filaments Europe, B.V. **(1)**
Minckelersstraat 8, 6372 PP, Landgraaf, Netherlands
Tel.: (31) 455329105
Web Site: https://dupontfilaments.com
Cosmetic Brush Mfr & Distr
N.A.I.C.S.: 339994

DuPont Performance Solutions (Singapore) Pte. Ltd. **(1)**
10 Marina Boulevard 07-01 Marina Bay Financial Centre Tower 2, Singapore, 018983, Singapore
Tel.: (65) 63225288
Web Site: https://www.dupont.com.sg
Electronic Product Mfr & Distr
N.A.I.C.S.: 334419

DuPont Performans cozumleri Endustriyel urunler Ticaret Limited Sirketi **(1)**
Chemical Products Industry and Trade AS Palladium Tower, Business Center Barbaros Mah Kardelen St No 2 Floor 11 Atasehir, 34746, Istanbul, Turkiye
Tel.: (90) 2166870400
Web Site: https://www.dupont.com.tr
Electronic Product Mfr & Distr
N.A.I.C.S.: 334419

Next Polymers Limited **(1)**
701 C B Square Building Sangam Complex 127 Andheri Kurla Road, Chakala Andheri East, Mumbai, 400 059, India
Tel.: (91) 226 259 6200
Web Site: https://www.nextpolymers.co.in
Synthetic Resin & Plastic Material Mfr
N.A.I.C.S.: 325211
Vedprakash Shukla (CEO)

Polymer Solutions Iberica S.L.U. **(1)**
C/ Burriana 30, 46005, Valencia, Spain
Tel.: (34) 618661127
Web Site: https://polymersolutions.es
Chemical Product Mfr & Distr
N.A.I.C.S.: 325998

PortaGas, Inc. **(1)**
1202 E Sam Houston Pkwy S, Pasadena, TX 77503
Tel.: (713) 928-6477
Web Site: http://www.portagas.com
Medical & Indsutrial Gas Mfr
N.A.I.C.S.: 325120
Joseph Abdoo (VP-Central Reg)
Catie Sheklarevski (Dir-HG Product Mgmt)
Anurag Sharma (Dir-Efficiency & Cost Reduction)

So.F.teR Brasil Compostos Termoplasticos Ltda. **(1)**
Av Edgar Hoffmeister 275, 93700-000, Campo Bom, Brazil
Tel.: (55) 5121232610
Thermo Plastic Mfr & Distr
N.A.I.C.S.: 325211

So.F.teR. S.r.l. **(1)**
Via Mastro Giorgio 1 Zona Industriale Villa Selva, Forli, 47122, Italy
Tel.: (39) 0543790411
Thermo Plastic Distr
N.A.I.C.S.: 423830

So.F.teR. US, Inc. **(1)**
400 Innovative Way, Lebanon, TN 37090
Tel.: (844) 657-6383
Thermo Plastic Distr
N.A.I.C.S.: 423830

Specialty Products Czech Republic s.r.o. **(1)**
Pekarska 14/628, 15500, Prague, Czech Republic
Tel.: (420) 257414211
Industrial Chemical Product Distr
N.A.I.C.S.: 424690

CELCUITY INC.
16305 36th Ave N, Minneapolis, MN 55446
Tel.: (763) 392-0767 DE
Web Site: https://www.celcuity.com
Year Founded: 2012

CELC—(NASDAQ)
Rev.: $7,777,602
Assets: $191,219,398
Liabilities: $51,450,076
Net Worth: $139,769,322
Earnings: ($63,779,116)
Emp.: 55
Fiscal Year-end: 12/31/23
Biotechnology Research & Development Services
N.A.I.C.S.: 541713
Brian F. Sullivan (Co-Founder, Chm & CEO)
Brian F. Sullivan (Co-Founder, Chm & CEO)
Vicky Hahne (CFO)
Lance G. Laing (Co-Founder, Chief Science Officer, Sec & VP)
Igor Gorbatchevsky (Chief Medical Officer)
Nadene Zack (VP)
Bernhard Lampert (VP)
Mark Mannebach (VP)
David Bridge (VP)
Pratima Nayak (VP)
Fred Kerwood (VP)
John R. MacDonald (Sr VP)

CELL MEDX CORP.
123 W Nye Ln Ste 446, Carson City, NV 89706
Tel.: (775) 884-0873 NV
Web Site: https://cellmedx.com
Year Founded: 2010
CMXC—(OTCQB)
Rev.: $6,065
Assets: $41,344
Liabilities: $2,050,375
Net Worth: ($2,009,031)
Earnings: ($697,379)
Fiscal Year-end: 05/31/22
Holding Company; Pharmaceutical Mfr
N.A.I.C.S.: 551112
Frank E. McEnulty (CEO)
Yanika Silina (CFO, Treas & Sec)

CELL SOURCE, INC.
57 W 57th St Ste 400, New York, NY 10019
Tel.: (646) 416-7896 NV
Web Site: http://www.cell-source.com
Year Founded: 2012
CLCS—(OTCQB)
Assets: $409,845
Liabilities: $13,043,740
Net Worth: ($12,633,895)
Earnings: ($5,167,748)
Fiscal Year-end: 12/31/22
Pharmaceuticals Mfr
N.A.I.C.S.: 325413
Itamar Shimrat (Pres, CEO & CFO)

CELL TECH INTERNATIONAL INCORPORATED
565 Century Ct, Klamath Falls, OR 97601
Tel.: (541) 882-5406 DE
EFLI—(OTCIQ)
Nutritional Product Mfr & Distr
N.A.I.C.S.: 325411
Marta A. Kollman (Pres & CEO)

CELLDEX THERAPEUTICS, INC.
53 Frontage Rd Ste 220, Hampton, NJ 08827
Tel.: (908) 454-7120 DE
Web Site: https://www.celldex.com
CLDX—(NASDAQ)
Rev.: $2,357,000
Assets: $352,735,000
Liabilities: $26,531,000
Net Worth: $326,204,000
Earnings: ($112,325,000)
Emp.: 148

Fiscal Year-end: 12/31/22
Medical & Immunotherapeutic Products Mfr
N.A.I.C.S.: 325412
Ronald A. Pepin (Chief Bus Officer & Sr VP)
Richard Wright (Chief Comml Officer & Sr VP)
Margo Heath-Chiozzi (Sr VP-Regulatory Affairs)
Elizabeth Crowley (Chief Product Dev Officer & Sr VP)
Tibor Keler (Co-Founder, Chief Scientific Officer & Exec VP)
Sam Martin (CFO, Treas & Sr VP)
Sarah Cavanaugh (Sr VP-Corp Affairs & Admin)
Diane C. Young (Chief Medical Officer & Sr VP)
Freddy A. Jimenez (Gen Counsel & Sr VP)
Anthony S. Marucci (Founder, Pres & CEO)

Subsidiaries:

CuraGen Corporation **(1)**
119 4th Ave, Needham, MA 02494
Tel.: (781) 433-0771
Web Site: http://www.celldextherapeutics.com
Sales Range: $1-9.9 Million
Emp.: 16
Biotechnology Research
N.A.I.C.S.: 541714
Jonathan M. Rothberg (Founder)

CELLECTAR BIOSCIENCES, INC.
100 Campus Dr Ste 207, Florham Park, NJ 07932
Tel.: (608) 441-8120 DE
Web Site: https://www.cellectar.com
Year Founded: 1996
CLRB—(NASDAQ)
Rev.: $152,519
Assets: $21,589,790
Liabilities: $6,082,271
Net Worth: $15,507,519
Earnings: ($28,601,254)
Emp.: 15
Fiscal Year-end: 12/31/22
Biopharmaceutical Mfr
N.A.I.C.S.: 325412
James V. Caruso (Pres & CEO)
Jarrod Longcor (COO)
Chad Kolean (CFO)
Shane Lea (Chief Comml Officer)
Andrei Shustov (Sr VP)

CELSIUS HOLDINGS, INC.
2424 Federal Hwy Ste 208, Boca Raton, FL 33431
Tel.: (561) 276-2239 NV
Web Site:
https://www.celsiusholdingsinc.com
Year Founded: 2005
CELH—(NASDAQ)
Rev.: $1,318,014,000
Assets: $1,536,396,000
Liabilities: $1,272,356,000
Net Worth: $264,040,000
Earnings: $181,991,000
Emp.: 765
Fiscal Year-end: 12/31/23
Beverages Producer, Marketer & Distr
N.A.I.C.S.: 311411
Ronnie Char (Mng Dir-Asia)
Jarrod Langhans (CFO)
Robin Lybeck (Mng Dir-Europe)
Tony Guilfoyle (Exec VP-Sls-North America)
Matti Takkinen (Dir-Sls-Finland & Baltics)
Marcus Sandifer (Gen Counsel)
Paul Storey (Sr VP)
Brant P. Burchfield (VP)
John Fieldly (Chm, Pres & CEO)

Celsius Holdings, Inc.—(Continued)

Subsidiaries:

Func Food Finland Oy (1)
Mannerheimintie 105, 00280, Helsinki, Finland
Tel.: (358) 201557755
Web Site: https://www.fast.fi
Food Products Mfr
N.A.I.C.S.: 311999
Matti Salo (Brand Mgr-Activation)

Func Food Group Oyj (1)
Mannerheimintie 105, 00280, Helsinki, Finland
Tel.: (358) 20 155 7755
Web Site: http://www.funcfood.com
Food Products Mfr
N.A.I.C.S.: 311999

Peoples Choice AB (1)
Mariehallsvagen 37F, 168 65, Bromma, Sweden
Tel.: (46) 317628380
Food Products Mfr
N.A.I.C.S.: 311999

Suomen Lisaravinne Oy (1)
Mannerheimintie 105, 00280, Helsinki, Finland
Tel.: (358) 503641817
Web Site: http://www.suomenlisaravinne.fi
Food Nutritional Supplement Product Distr
N.A.I.C.S.: 456191

CELULARITY INC.
170 Park Ave, Florham Park, NJ 07039
Tel.: (908) 768-2170 DE
Web Site: https://www.celularity.com
Year Founded: 2016
CELU—(NASDAQ)
Rev.: $22,771,000
Assets: $143,889,000
Liabilities: $102,929,000
Net Worth: $40,960,000
Earnings: ($196,295,000)
Emp.: 120
Fiscal Year-end: 12/31/23
Research & Development in Biotechnology
N.A.I.C.S.: 541714
Robert Joseph Hariri (Founder, Chm & CEO)
David C. Beers (CFO)
Carlos Ramirez (Sr VP-IR)

CEMTREX, INC.
135 Fell Ct, Hauppauge, NY 11788
Tel.: (631) 756-9116 DE
Web Site: https://www.cemtrex.com
Year Founded: 1998
CETX—(NASDAQ)
Rev.: $66,863,884
Assets: $44,115,458
Liabilities: $39,154,616
Net Worth: $4,960,842
Earnings: ($7,678,629)
Emp.: 264
Fiscal Year-end: 09/30/24
Diversified Technology Company;
Electronics & Industrial Air Filtration & Environmental Control Equipment Mfr
N.A.I.C.S.: 333248
Saagar Govil (Chm, Pres, CEO & Sec)

Subsidiaries:

Advanced Industrial Services, Inc. (1)
3250 Susquehanna Trl, York, PA 17406
Tel.: (717) 764-9811
Web Site: https://www.ais-york.com
Sales Range: $10-24.9 Million
Emp.: 120
Industrial Machinery Installation Contractor
N.A.I.C.S.: 238290
Barb Lamer (CFO)
Blythe Pruitt (Dir-HR & Safety)
Stephen Campbell (Dir-Ops)
Jared Haas (Mgr-Bus Dev)
Greg Fasolt (Mgr-Fleet)

Scott Trimmer (Mgr-Safety)
John Fennell (Mgr-Sls & Mktg-Natl)
Mike Jennings (Project Mgr)
Steve Sanders (Project Mgr)
Marty Green (Sr Project Mgr)

Heisey Mechanical, Ltd. (1)
615 Florence St, Columbia, PA 17512
Tel.: (717) 684-4551
Web Site: http://www.heiseymechanical.com
Rev.: $5,000,000
Emp.: 30
Commercial & Institutional Building Construction
N.A.I.C.S.: 236220

Virtual Driver Interactive, Inc. (1)
4505 Golden Foothill Pkwy, El Dorado Hills, CA 95762-9644
Web Site: http://www.driverinteractive.com
Professional Equipment & Supplies Merchant Whslr
N.A.I.C.S.: 423490
Bob Davis (Founder & Gen Mgr)
Andre Luongo (VP-Product Dev)
Van Burns (VP & Gen Mgr)
Pam LeFevre (VP-Mktg)

CENCORA, INC.
1 W 1st Ave, Conshohocken, PA 19428-1800
Tel.: (610) 727-7000 DE
Web Site: https://www.cencora.com
Year Founded: 2001
COR—(NYSE)
Rev.: $293,958,599,000
Assets: $67,101,667,000
Liabilities: $66,314,925,000
Net Worth: $786,742,000
Earnings: $1,519,273,000
Emp.: 42,000
Fiscal Year-end: 09/30/24
Pharmaceuticals & Medical Supplies Distr
N.A.I.C.S.: 424210
Steven H. Collis (Exec Chm)
Robert P. Mauch (Pres & CEO)
Bennett S. Murphy (Sr VP-IR)
Rich Tremonte (Pres-Customer Ops, Animal Health, Community & Specialty Pharmacy)
Silvana Battaglia (Chief HR Officer & Exec VP)
Leslie E. Donato (Chief Strategy Officer & Exec VP)
Kourosh Q. Pirouz (VP, Sec & Assoc Gen Counsel)
Elizabeth S. Campbell (Chief Legal Officer & Exec VP)
Jennifer Dubas (Chief Compliance Officer)
James F. Cleary Jr. (CFO & Exec VP)

Subsidiaries:

APS Enterprises Holding Company, Inc. (1)
309 Henderson Dr, Sharon Hill, PA 19079
Tel.: (610) 727-7000
Holding Company
N.A.I.C.S.: 551112

ASD Specialty Healthcare, Inc. (1)
3101 Gaylord Pkwy, Frisco, TX 75034
Tel.: (972) 490-5551
Web Site: http://www.asdhealthcare.com
Pharmaceutical Drug Distr
N.A.I.C.S.: 424210

American Health Packaging (1)
2550 John Glenn Ave Ste A, Columbus, OH 43217-1188 (100%)
Tel.: (614) 492-8177
Web Site: http://www.healthpack.com
Sales Range: $150-199.9 Million
Emp.: 230
N.A.I.C.S.: 456191

Amerisource Health Services Corporation (1)
2550 John Glenn Ave Ste A, Columbus, OH 43217
Tel.: (614) 492-8177
Web Site:
http://www.americanhealthpackaging.com

Pharmaceutical Drug Mfr
N.A.I.C.S.: 325412

AmerisourceBergen (1)
322 N 3rd St PO Box 330, Paducah, KY 42001-0723 (100%)
Tel.: (270) 575-9245
Sales Range: $125-149.9 Million
Emp.: 200
Wholesale Distribution of Pharmaceutical Products
N.A.I.C.S.: 424210

AmerisourceBergen (1)
6305 Lasalle Dr, Lockbourne, OH 43137 (100%)
Tel.: (614) 409-6000
Sales Range: $125-149.9 Million
Emp.: 250
Wholesale Distribution of Pharmaceutical Products
N.A.I.C.S.: 424210

AmerisourceBergen (1)
2100 Directors Row, Orlando, FL 32809-6234 (100%)
Tel.: (407) 856-6239
Sales Range: $100-124.9 Million
Emp.: 120
Wholesale Distribution of Pharmaceutical Products
N.A.I.C.S.: 424210

AmerisourceBergen (1)
1 W 1st Ave, Conshohocken, PA 19428 (100%)
Tel.: (952) 941-9550
Sales Range: $100-124.9 Million
Emp.: 180
Wholesale Distribution of Pharmaceutical Products
N.A.I.C.S.: 424210

AmerisourceBergen (1)
100 Friars Blvd, Thorofare, NJ 08086-2141 (100%)
Tel.: (856) 848-3400
Sales Range: $125-149.9 Million
Emp.: 250
Wholesale Distribution of Pharmaceutical Products
N.A.I.C.S.: 424210

AmerisourceBergen (1)
172 Cahaba Vly Pkwy, Pelham, AL 35124-1143 (100%)
Tel.: (205) 985-5100
Sales Range: $100-124.9 Million
Emp.: 200
Wholesale Distribution of Pharmaceutical & Health Care Products
N.A.I.C.S.: 424210

AmerisourceBergen (1)
1825 S 43rd Ave, Phoenix, AZ 85009-6051
Tel.: (602) 353-1153
Sales Range: $75-99.9 Million
Emp.: 50
Distribution of Pharmaceutical Products
N.A.I.C.S.: 424210

AmerisourceBergen (1)
1851 California Ave, Corona, CA 92881
Tel.: (951) 371-2000
Sales Range: $75-99.9 Million
Emp.: 90
Distribution of Pharmaceutical Products
N.A.I.C.S.: 424210

AmerisourceBergen (1)
238 Sand Is Access Rd, Honolulu, HI 96819-4913 (100%)
Tel.: (808) 848-6568
Sales Range: $150-199.9 Million
Distribution of Pharmaceutical Products
N.A.I.C.S.: 424210

AmerisourceBergen (1)
PO Box 959, Valley Forge, PA 19482 (100%)
Tel.: (610) 727-7118
Sales Range: $75-99.9 Million
Emp.: 100
Distribution of Pharmaceutical Products
N.A.I.C.S.: 424210

AmerisourceBergen (1)
1765 Fremont Dr, Salt Lake City, UT 84104-4218
Tel.: (801) 972-4131

Sales Range: $50-74.9 Million
Emp.: 50
Distribution of Pharmaceutical Products
N.A.I.C.S.: 424210

AmerisourceBergen (1)
19220 64th Ave S, Kent, WA 98032-1152
Tel.: (206) 575-3343
Sales Range: $350-399.9 Million
Emp.: 100
Distribution of Pharmaceutical Products
N.A.I.C.S.: 424210

AmerisourceBergen (1)
1 Industrial Park Dr, Williamston, MI 48895-1604 (100%)
Tel.: (517) 655-5433
Web Site: http://www.amerisource.com
Sales Range: $75-99.9 Million
Emp.: 100
Distribution of Pharmaceutical Products
N.A.I.C.S.: 424210
Darren Johnston (Pres)

AmerisourceBergen Consulting Services, Inc. (1)
2320 Cascade Point Blvd, Charlotte, NC 28208
Tel.: (704) 357-8869
Web Site: http://www.lashgroup.com
Medical Equipment Distr
N.A.I.C.S.: 541618

AmerisourceBergen Drug Corporation (1)
1300 Morris Dr, Chesterbrook, PA 19087-5594
Tel.: (610) 727-7000
Web Site:
http://www.amerisourcebergen.com
Sales Range: $450-499.9 Million
Emp.: 400
Pharmaceutical Products Distr
N.A.I.C.S.: 424210

AmerisourceBergen Services Corporation (1)
1300 Morris Dr Ste 100, Chesterbrook, PA 19087
Tel.: (610) 727-7000
Sales Range: $400-449.9 Million
Emp.: 800
Healthcare Services
N.A.I.C.S.: 424210

AmerisourceBergen Specialty Group (1)
1300 Morris Dr, Chesterbrook, PA 19087
Tel.: (610) 727-7000
Web Site: http://www.asbg.com
Sales Range: $1-4.9 Billion
Specialty Pharmaceutical Products Distr & Clinical Services
N.A.I.C.S.: 424210

Subsidiary (Domestic):

ASD Healthcare (2)
3101 Gaylord Pkwy 3rd Fl, Frisco, TX 75034
Tel.: (469) 365-8000
Web Site: http://www.asdhealthcare.com
Sales Range: $75-99.9 Million
Emp.: 200
Pharmaceuticals Distr
N.A.I.C.S.: 424210
William Venus (VP & Gen Mgr-Specialty Distr)
Devetta James (Sr VP-Customer Ops)
Michael Gelgor (VP-Ops)
Summer Hichoux (VP-Specialty Sls)

Besse Medical Supply (2)
9075 Ctr Pt Dr Ste 140, West Chester, OH 45069
Tel.: (513) 682-3600
Web Site: http://www.besse.com
Sales Range: $450-499.9 Million
Emp.: 100
Pharmaceutical & Vaccine Distr
N.A.I.C.S.: 424210
Michael E. Besse (Pres)
Michael Besse (Pres)
Jennifer Sherak (Sr VP)
Lisa Harrison (VP)
Eric Besse (VP)
Kevin Long (VP)
Shirley Turner Sapp (VP)

Integrated Commercialization Solutions (2)
3101 Gaylord Pkwy, Frisco, TX 75034
Tel.: (469) 365-7777
Web Site: http://www.icsconnect.com
Sales Range: $10-24.9 Million
Emp.: 250
Specialty Pharmaceutical Outsourcing Logistics & Clinical Services
N.A.I.C.S.: 541614

Integrated Nephrology Network (2)
3101 Gaylord Pkwy 3rd Fl, Frisco, TX 75034
Web Site: http://www.inn-online.com
Sales Range: $150-199.9 Million
Nephrology Physician Services Network
N.A.I.C.S.: 456199

International Oncology Network, LLC (2)
3101 Gaylord Pkwy, Frisco, TX 75034
Tel.: (469) 365-7000
Web Site: http://www.ion.com
Sales Range: $50-74.9 Million
Emp.: 70
Oncology Information & Network Services
N.A.I.C.S.: 541715

Network for Medical Communication & Research, LLC (2)
4114 Woodlands Pkwy Ste 500, Palm Harbor, FL 34685-3450
Tel.: (404) 845-3800
Sales Range: $10-24.9 Million
Emp.: 15
Continuing Medical Education Services
N.A.I.C.S.: 611710

Unit (Domestic):

NMCR Analytics (3)
4114 Woodlands Pkwy Ste 500, Palm Harbor, FL 34685-3450   (100%)
Tel.: (404) 845-3800
Continuing Medical Education Services
N.A.I.C.S.: 611710

Subsidiary (Domestic):

The Lash Group, Inc. (2)
Lake Pointe Corporate Ctr 5 3735 Glen Lake Dr, Charlotte, NC 28208
Tel.: (650) 624-6000
Web Site: http://www.lashgroup.com
Sales Range: $200-249.9 Million
Emp.: 800
Healthcare Reimbursement Consulting & Patient Management Services
N.A.I.C.S.: 541613
Mike Obringer (COO & Sr VP)

US Bioservices Corporation (2)
3200 Internet Blvd, Frisco, TX 75034
Tel.: (214) 572-8300
Web Site: http://www.usbioservices.com
Sales Range: $50-74.9 Million
Emp.: 65
Provider of Pharmaceutical Products
N.A.I.C.S.: 424210

AutoMed Technologies (Canada), Inc. (1)
2015 Fisher Dr, Peterborough, K9J 6X6, ON, Canada
Tel.: (705) 745-6857
Medical Equipment Distr
N.A.I.C.S.: 423450

AutoMed Technologies, Inc. (1)
1400 W Pkwy, Buffalo Grove, IL 60089
Tel.: (847) 808-2600
Web Site: http://www.amerisource.com
Automated Pharmacy Dispensing Services
N.A.I.C.S.: 333248

Bellco Health Corp. (1)
5500 New Horizons Blvd, Amityville, NY 11701-1156
Tel.: (631) 789-6300
Sales Range: $1-4.9 Billion
Emp.: 255
Dialysis Drugs & Other Pharmaceutical Products Mfr & Distr
N.A.I.C.S.: 424210

Subsidiary (Domestic):

Bellco Drug Corp. (2)

5500 New Horizons Blvd, Amityville, NY 11701
Tel.: (631) 789-6900
Web Site: http://www.bellcoonline.com
Sales Range: $450-499.9 Million
Emp.: 150
Pharmeceutical Whlsr
N.A.I.C.S.: 424210

Clinical Outcomes Resource Application Corporation (2)
5500 New Horizon, Amityville, NY 11701
Tel.: (631) 225-8400
Sales Range: $100-124.9 Million
Web-Based Clinical Data Collection & Reporting Services
N.A.I.C.S.: 518210

Good Neighbor Pharmacy (1)
1300 Morris Dr, Chesterbrook, PA 19087
Tel.: (610) 727-7000
Sales Range: $400-449.9 Million
Emp.: 500
Voluntary Organization Providing Member Drugstores With Services Encompassing All Aspects of Their Operations: Advertising, Shipping & Other Services
N.A.I.C.S.: 424210

IHS Acquisition XXX, Inc. (1)
109 Chelsea Pkwy, Boothwyn, PA 19061
Tel.: (610) 586-8514
Women Healthcare Services
N.A.I.C.S.: 621610

Innomar Strategies, Inc. (1)
3470 Superior Court, Oakville, L6L 0C4, ON, Canada
Tel.: (905) 847-4310
Web Site: https://www.innomar-strategies.com
Healtcare Services
N.A.I.C.S.: 621610

International Physicians Network, L.L.C. (1)
11100 Valley Blvd Ste 220, El Monte, CA 91731
Tel.: (818) 659-5082
Web Site: http://www.uscipn.org
Health Care Srvices
N.A.I.C.S.: 621610
Angelia Yang (CEO)

IntrinsiQ, LLC (1)
25 Corporate Dr Ste 300, Burlington, MA 01803-4245
Tel.: (781) 647-1144
Web Site: http://www.intrinsiq.com
Sales Range: $25-49.9 Million
Emp.: 70
Oncology Information & Analysis Services
N.A.I.C.S.: 519290

MWI Veterinary Supply, Co. (1)
3041 W Pasadena Dr, Boise, ID 83705
Tel.: (208) 955-8930
Web Site: http://www.mwiah.com
Sales Range: $1-4.9 Billion
Emp.: 90
Holding Company; Animal Health Products Distr & Services
N.A.I.C.S.: 551112
Paul Mercier (VP-Production Animal Sls)
Stacy Phillips (VP-Mktg)
Kevin Price (VP)
Bridger Tatum (VP)
Steve Shell (Pres)
Julia Loew (Sr VP)

Subsidiary (Non-US):

Centaur Services Ltd. (2)
Centaur House Torbay Road, Castle Cary, BA7 7EU, Somerset, United Kingdom
Tel.: (44) 1963350187
Web Site: http://www.centaurweb.co.uk
Veterinary Medical Equipment & Supplies Whslr
N.A.I.C.S.: 423450
Simon Crawforth (Sr Mgr-North West)
Nick Weaving (Mgr-HR)
Andrew Paull (Dir-Fin)
Paul O'Connor (Head-IT)
Richard Clarkson (Mgr-Wales & West)

Securos Europe GmbH (2)
Take Off Gewerbepark 4, 78579, Neuhausen, Baden-Wurttemberg, Germany
Tel.: (49) 7467947650

Web Site: http://www.securos-europe.eu
Emp.: 5
Veterinary Equipments & Supplies Whslr
N.A.I.C.S.: 423490

PharMEDium Services, LLC (1)
2 Conway Pk 150 N Field Dr Ste 350, Lake Forest, IL 60045-2506
Tel.: (847) 457-2300
Web Site: http://www.pharmedium.com
Pharmaceuticals Mfr
N.A.I.C.S.: 325412
Jeff Nordquist (VP-Mktg, Bus Dev & Customer Svc)

Pharm Plus Acquisition, Inc. (1)
15017-A Califa St, Van Nuys, CA 94111
Tel.: (610) 727-7000
Pharmaceutical Drug Distr
N.A.I.C.S.: 424210

TheraCom LLC (1)
9717 Key West Ave, Rockville, MD 20850
Tel.: (301) 215-7300
Sales Range: $700-749.9 Million
Pharmaceutical Drug Mfr
N.A.I.C.S.: 325412

World Courier Inc. (1)
1313 4th Ave, New Hyde Park, NY 11040
Tel.: (800) 221-6600
Web Site: http://www.worldcourier.com
Air Courier Services
N.A.I.C.S.: 492110
Lief Walling (Reg VP-North America)

Subsidiary (Domestic):

World Courier Management Inc. (2)
1313 4th Ave, New Hyde Park, NY 11040
Tel.: (516) 354-2600
Web Site: http://www.worldcourier.com
Rev.: $17,000,000
Emp.: 1
Air Courier Services
N.A.I.C.S.: 492110

Xcenda, LLC (1)
4114 Woodlands Pkwy Ste 500, Palm Harbor, FL 34685
Tel.: (727) 771-4100
Web Site: http://www.xcenda.com
Emp.: 70
Scientific Marketing & Consulting Services
N.A.I.C.S.: 541613
Robert P. Mauch (Founder)
Matt Sarnes (Sr VP-New Bus Dev & Strategy)
Mike Eaddy (VP-Scientific Consulting)
Luther Hill (VP-Tech & Innovation)
Kristine Flemister (Pres)
Jay Jackson (Sr VP-Consulting Svcs)
Teri Burnell (Sr VP-Field Svcs)
Barb Lennert (Sr VP-Ops)
Trish Monaco (Dir-Mktg)
Ana Stojanovska (VP-Comml Consulting)
Patricia Wolfangel (VP-Customer Engagement)
Jennifer Snow (VP-Reimbursement & Policy Insights)
Amy Duhig (VP-Strategic Market Access & Intelligence)
Evelyn Sarnes (VP-Medical Comm)
Trent McLaughlin (VP-Real-World Evidence)
Kellie Meyer (VP-Health Economics & Outcomes Res-Global)
Bryan Horveath (Sr Dir-Trng & Provider Education)
Warren Dunn (VP-Creative Strategy)
Bryan H. Lawrence (Owner)

CENTAURUS DIAMOND TECHNOLOGIES, INC.
1000 W Bonanza Rd, Las Vegas, NV 89106
Tel.: (702) 382-3385   NV
Web Site:
   http://www.centaurustechnologies inc.com
Year Founded: 2007
CTDT—(OTCIQ)
Assets: $100,425
Liabilities: $560,710
Net Worth: ($460,285)
Earnings: ($341,044)
Fiscal Year-end: 03/31/19

Diamond Exploration Services
N.A.I.C.S.: 212390
Alvin A. Snaper (Founder, Chm, CTO & Chief Science Officer)
Chaslav Radovich (Pres & CEO)
Diran Kludjian (CFO & Treas)
Stephen Saunders (Sec)

CENTENE CORPORATION
7700 Forsyth Blvd, Saint Louis, MO 63105
Tel.: (314) 725-4477   DE
Web Site: https://www.centene.com
Year Founded: 1984
CNC—(NYSE)
Rev.: $153,999,000,000
Assets: $84,641,000,000
Liabilities: $58,704,000,000
Net Worth: $25,937,000,000
Earnings: $2,702,000,000
Emp.: 67,700
Fiscal Year-end: 12/31/23
Health & Medical Insurance Services
N.A.I.C.S.: 524114
Kenneth J. Fasola (Pres)
Sarah M. London (CEO)
Andrew L. Asher (CFO & Exec VP)
Colin Toney (Exec VP-Mergers & Acq)
Gerald J. D. Roberts Jr. (VP-Strategy & Bus Dev)
Alice H. Chen (Chief Health Officer)
Brian LeClaire (CIO)
Tanya McNally (Chief People Officer)
Susan Smith (COO)

Subsidiaries:

AECC Total Vision Health Plan of Texas, Inc. (1)
112 Zebulon Court, Rocky Mount, NC 27804
Tel.: (252) 937-6650
Eye Care Service
N.A.I.C.S.: 456130

AT Medics Holdings LLP (1)
26-28 Streatham Place, London, SW2 4QY, United Kingdom
Tel.: (44) 208 678 5630
Web Site: https://www.atmedics.com
Primary Health Care Services
N.A.I.C.S.: 621610
Liz Perry (CEO)
Omar Din (Mng Dir)
Louise Watson (Chief Integration Officer)
Edward McKenzie-Boyle (CFO)
Elad Duschak (Chief Bus Dev Officer)

AT Medics Ltd. (1)
26-28 Streatham Place, London, SW2 4QY, United Kingdom
Tel.: (44) 2086785624
Web Site: https://www.atmedics.com
Health & Medical Insurance Services
N.A.I.C.S.: 524114

Absolute Total Care, Inc (1)
100 Center Point Cir Ste 100, Columbia, SC 29210
Web Site:
   https://www.absolutetotalcare.com
Medicaid Health Plan Services
N.A.I.C.S.: 923130

AcariaHealth Pharmacy #11, Inc. (1)
1311 W Sam Houston Pkwy N Ste 130, Houston, TX 77043
Tel.: (713) 651-8001
Pharmaceutical Products Distr
N.A.I.C.S.: 424210

AcariaHealth Pharmacy #12, Inc. (1)
5 Skyline Dr Ste 240, Hawthorne, NY 10532
Tel.: (914) 789-5091
Medical Product Distr
N.A.I.C.S.: 423450

AcariaHealth Pharmacy #13, Inc. (1)
3302 Garfield Ave, Commerce, CA 90040-3102
Tel.: (323) 262-9403
Pharmaceutical Products Distr
N.A.I.C.S.: 424210

Centene Corporation—(Continued)

Reina Olsen (Gen Mgr)

AcariaHealth, Inc. (1)
8427 Southpark Cir Ste 400, Orlando, FL 32816
Tel.: (407) 903-1308
Web Site:
https://acariahealth.envolvehealth.com
Pharmaceutical Products Distr
N.A.I.C.S.: 424210
Steve Jensen (Pres)

Agate Resources, Inc. (1)
U O Riverfront Research Park 1800 Millrace Dr, Eugene, OR 97403-1992
Tel.: (541) 762-9088
Life & Health Insurance Services
N.A.I.C.S.: 524114
Rhonda Busek (Sr VP)

Ambetter of Magnolia, Inc. (1)
111 E Capitol St Ste 500, Jackson, MS 39201
Web Site:
http://www.magnoliahealthplan.com
Life & Health Insurance Services
N.A.I.C.S.: 524114

Ambetter of North Carolina, Inc. (1)
13620 FM620 Bldg C Ste 300, Austin, TX 78717
Web Site:
https://www.ambetterofnorthcarolina.com
Health Insurance Marketplace Services
N.A.I.C.S.: 524114

Ambetter of Peach State Inc. (1)
1100 Circle 75 Pkwy Ste 1100, Atlanta, GA 30339
Web Site: https://ambetter.pshpgeorgia.com
Life & Health Insurance Services
N.A.I.C.S.: 524114

Arkansas Health & Wellness Health Plan, Inc. (1)
1 Allied Dr Ste 2520, Little Rock, AR 72202
Web Site: https://www.arhealthwellness.com
Life & Health Insurance Services
N.A.I.C.S.: 524114

Arkansas Total Care, Inc. (1)
PO Box 25010, Little Rock, AR 72221
Tel.: (501) 954-6159
Web Site:
https://www.arkansastotalcare.com
Life & Health Insurance Services
N.A.I.C.S.: 524114

B2B Salud S.L.U. (1)
Avenida Cortes Valencianas 58 Sorolla Center Oficina 0409, 46015, Valencia, Spain
Tel.: (34) 960900500
Web Site: http://www.b2bsalud.com
Management Consulting Services
N.A.I.C.S.: 541611

BMI Southend Private Hospital Ltd. (1)
15-17 Fairfax Drive, Westcliff-On-Sea, SS0 9AG, Essex, United Kingdom
Tel.: (44) 1702662949
Hospital & Health Care Services
N.A.I.C.S.: 622110

BMI Syon Clinic Ltd. (1)
Syon Clinic 941 Great West Road, Brentford, TW8 9DU, Middlesex, United Kingdom
Tel.: (44) 2080032799
Hospital & Health Care Services
N.A.I.C.S.: 622110

Bridgeway Health Solutions of Arizona LLC (1)
1850 W Rio Salado Pkwy Ste 201, Tempe, AZ 85282
Tel.: (480) 567-9000
Health Care Srvices
N.A.I.C.S.: 622110

Buckeye Community Health Plan Inc. (1)
4339 Easton Way Ste 400, Columbus, OH 43219
Web Site:
https://www.buckeyehealthplan.com
Health Care Srvices
N.A.I.C.S.: 621999

CBHSP Arizona, Inc. (1)
875 S Cooper Rd, Gilbert, AZ 85233
Tel.: (480) 456-0942
Web Site: http://www.cenpatico.com
Emp.: 20
Health Care Srvices
N.A.I.C.S.: 622110

CT Presov s.r.o. (1)
CT Department – FNsP Campus Holleho 14, 081 81, Presov, Slovakia
Tel.: (421) 517754146
Web Site: https://www.ctpresov.sk
Diagnostic Imaging Services
N.A.I.C.S.: 621512

California Health & Wellness Plan (1)
1740 Creekside Oaks Dr Ste 200, Sacramento, CA 95833
Tel.: (916) 246-3600
Web Site:
https://www.cahealthwellness.com
Emp.: 200
Health Care Services
N.A.I.C.S.: 622110

Celtic Group, Inc. (1)
Celtic Centre Bldg 3888 S Sherwood Forest Blvd, Baton Rouge, LA 70816
Web Site: https://celticgroup.com
Health & Medical Insurance Services
N.A.I.C.S.: 524114

Celtic Life Insurance Company Inc. (1)
233 E Wacker Dr, Chicago, IL 60601
Tel.: (312) 332-5401
Web Site: http://www.celtic-net.com
Sales Range: $150-199.9 Million
Health & Medical Insurance Services
N.A.I.C.S.: 524114

Cenpatico Behavioral Health LLC (1)
12515-8 Research Blvd Ste 400, Austin, TX 78759
Tel.: (512) 406-7200
Web Site: http://www.cenpatico.com
Emp.: 52
Mental Health & Substance Service
N.A.I.C.S.: 621112

Cenpatico of Arizona Inc. (1)
333 E Wetmore Rd Ste 500, Tucson, AZ 85705
Tel.: (866) 495-6738
Web Site:
http://www.cenpaticointegratedcareaz.com
Life & Health Insurance Services
N.A.I.C.S.: 524114

Centene UK Limited (1)
Rose House Dell Lane Office Village, Little Chalfont, HP6 6FA, Buckinghamshire, United Kingdom
Tel.: (44) 2086785624
Mental Health Care Services
N.A.I.C.S.: 621112

Centro Inmunologcia De La Comunidad Valenciana, S.L. (1)
C/Cristo de la Paz 36-38 Bajos, Sant Joan D'Alacant, 03550, Alicante, Spain
Tel.: (34) 965943133
Web Site: http://www.cialab.com
Diagnostic Clinic Services
N.A.I.C.S.: 621498

Centurion LLC (1)
20569 N Pinehurst St, Rathdrum, ID 83858
Tel.: (208) 687-8880
Health Care Srvices
N.A.I.C.S.: 622110

Centurion of Indiana, LLC (1)
550 N Meridian St 1 Fl, Indianapolis, IN 46204
Tel.: (317) 912-1272
Web Site:
https://www.centurionmanagedcare.com
Emp.: 10,000
Hospital & Health Care Services
N.A.I.C.S.: 622110

Centurion of New Hampshire, LLC (1)
105 Pleasant St Room 301S, Concord, NH 03301
Tel.: (603) 271-7936

Health Care Srvices
N.A.I.C.S.: 621610

Centurion of Pennsylvania, LLC (1)
5115 E Trindle Rd, Mechanicsburg, PA 17050
Tel.: (717) 761-4002
Health Care Srvices
N.A.I.C.S.: 621610

Circle Health 1 Ltd. (1)
Warwick Mill Warwick Mill Business Village Warwick Bridge, Cumbria, Carlisle, CA4 8RR, United Kingdom
Tel.: (44) 1556510576
Web Site: https://circular1.com
Hospital & Health Care Services
N.A.I.C.S.: 622110
Stuart MacLennan (CEO & Chm)
Miranda Kirschel (Dir-Business Development)
Jules Carr (COO)
Rachael Almond (Dir)
Rosie Connolly (Dir)

Circle Health Holdings Limited (1)
32 Welbeck Street, London, W1G 8EU, United Kingdom
Tel.: (44) 2070345250
Web Site: http://www.circlehealth.co.uk
Sales Range: $150-199.9 Million
Holding Company; Healthcare Services
N.A.I.C.S.: 551112
Paolo Pieri (CEO)
Massoud Fouladi (Dir-Medical)
Sarah Marston (Interim CFO)

Subsidiary (Domestic):

BMI Healthcare Limited (2)
1st Floor 30 Cannon Street, London, EC4M 6XH, United Kingdom
Tel.: (44) 20 3283 6771
Web Site: http://www.bmihealthcare.co.uk
Private Hospitals & Healthcare Services
N.A.I.C.S.: 622110
Karen Prins (COO)
Henry Davies (CFO)
Steven Luttrell (Dir-Medical)
David Cooper (Dir-HR)

Subsidiary (Domestic):

BMI The Edgbaston Hospital (3)
22 Somerset Road, Edgbaston, Birmingham, B15 2QQ, United Kingdom
Tel.: (44) 1214562000
Web Site: http://www.bmihealthcare.co.uk
Sales Range: $25-49.9 Million
Emp.: 130
Hospital Services
N.A.I.C.S.: 622110

DMI The Huddersfield Hospital (3)
Birkby Hall Road, Huddersfield, HD2 2BL, United Kingdom
Tel.: (44) 1484533131
Hospital Services
N.A.I.C.S.: 622110

BMI The Lancaster Hospital (3)
Meadowside, Lancaster, LA1 3RH, Lancashire, United Kingdom
Tel.: (44) 0152462345
Web Site: http://www.bmihealthcare.co.uk
Sales Range: $25-49.9 Million
Emp.: 150
Hospital Services
N.A.I.C.S.: 622110

Nuffield Hospital Harrogate (3)
Queens Road, Harrogate, HG2 0HF, North Yorkshire, United Kingdom
Tel.: (44) 1423567136
Web Site: http://www.bmihealthcare.co.uk
Sales Range: $10-24.9 Million
Emp.: 100
Hospital Services
N.A.I.C.S.: 622110

Subsidiary (Domestic):

Circle Health Limited (2)
32 Welbeck Street, London, W1G 8EU, United Kingdom
Tel.: (44) 20 7034 5250
Web Site: http://www.circlehealth.co.uk
Hospital Operator; Rehabilitation & Health Services
N.A.I.C.S.: 622110

Paolo Pieri (CEO)
Sarah Marston (CFO & Head-Fin Ops & Contract Mgmt)
Shane Cobb (Gen Counsel & Sec)
Nick Boyle (Dir-Bus Dev)
Jacqueline Droogan (Dir-Mobilisation)
Massoud Fouladi (Dir-Medical)
Helen Tait (Dir-MSK)

Circle International (1)
Mayfair Point 34 South Molton Street, London, W1K 5RG, United Kingdom
Tel.: (44) 2036330510
Web Site:
https://www.circleinternational.co.uk
Health & Medical Insurance Services
N.A.I.C.S.: 524114

Clinica Santo Domingo De Lugo, S.L. (1)
Plaza Santo Domingo n 24 1 Planta, 27001, Lugo, Spain
Tel.: (34) 982105756
Web Site: http://www.lugoclinica.com
Diagnostic Clinic Services
N.A.I.C.S.: 621498

Coordinated Care Corporation Indiana, Inc., (1)
550 N Meridian St Ste 101, Indianapolis, IN 46204-1041
Web Site: https://www.mhsindiana.com
Managed Health Services
N.A.I.C.S.: 813212

DR Magnet S.R.O. (1)
Centre Kramare ak L Derera Hospital Limbova 5, 833 05, Bratislava, Slovakia
Tel.: (421) 232661251
Web Site:
http://www.magnetickarezonancia.sk
Health Care Srvices
N.A.I.C.S.: 621610

Envolve Dental of Texas, Inc. (1)
2100 S Interstate 35 Ste 202, Austin, TX 78704
Tel.: (844) 431-9565
Life & Health Insurance Services
N.A.I.C.S.: 524114

Envolve Optical, Inc. (1)
1118 Falls Rd, Rocky Mount, NC 27804
Tel.: (252) 544-9296
Web Site: https://www.envolveoptical.com
Eye Care Center & Eyeglass Retailer
N.A.I.C.S.: 456130

Envolve PeopleCare, Inc. (1)
20 Batterson Park Rd, Farmington, CT 06032
Tel.: (800) 293-0056
Web Site:
http://www.envolvepeoplecare.com
Health Care Srvices
N.A.I.C.S.: 621491
Dan Cave (Pres & CEO)

Envolve Pharmacy Solutions, Inc. (1)
8427 S Park Cir Ste 400, Orlando, FL 32819
Web Site:
http://pharmacy.envolvehealth.com
Pharmacy Management & Health Care Services
N.A.I.C.S.: 621399
Drew Asher (CEO)

Envolve Vision Benefits, Inc. (1)
112 Zebulon Ct, Rocky Mount, NC 27804
Tel.: (800) 531-2818
Web Site:
https://visionbenefits.envolvehealth.com
Life & Health Insurance Services
N.A.I.C.S.: 524114

Envolve Vision, Inc. (1)
1151 Falls Rd Ste 2000, Rocky Mount, NC 27804
Tel.: (919) 872-2039
Web Site: https://www.envolvevision.com
Life & Health Insurance Services
N.A.I.C.S.: 524114

Family Nurse Care, LLC (1)
40600 Ann Arbor Rd E Ste 201, Plymouth, MI 48170
Tel.: (810) 732-9307
Health Care Insurance Services

N.A.I.C.S.: 524114

Foundation Care, LLC (1)
4010 Wedgeway Ct, Earth City, MO 63045
Tel.: (314) 291-1122
Web Site: https://www.foundcare.com
Retail Pharmacy Operator
N.A.I.C.S.: 456110

Granite State Health Plan, Inc. (1)
2 Executive Park Dr, Bedford, NH 03110-6915
Tel.: (603) 625-9200
Insurance Management Services
N.A.I.C.S.: 524298

Health Care Enterprises, LLC (1)
5825 Dry Creek Ln NE, Cedar Rapids, IA 52402
Tel.: (319) 368-3619
Web Site: https://www.healthenterprises.org
Health Care Insurance Services
N.A.I.C.S.: 524114
Jeffrey A. Schwaneke (Exec VP)
Sarah M. London (Pres & Exec VP-Advanced Tech)

Health Net Access, Inc. (1)
1850 W Rio Salado Pkwy Ste 211, Tempe, AZ 85281
Web Site:
   https://www.azcompletehealth.com
Health Care Srvices
N.A.I.C.S.: 621491

Health Net, LLC (1)
21650 Burbank Blvd, Woodland Hills, CA 91367
Tel.: (818) 676-6000
Web Site: https://www.healthnet.com
Sales Range: $15-24.9 Billion
Emp.: 2,600
Holding Company; Managed Health Care Services
N.A.I.C.S.: 551112
Brian Ternan (Pres & CEO)
Kerri Balbone (COO)
Alex Y. Chen (Chief Medical Officer)
Christy K. Bosse (VP-Compliance)
Darrel Ng (VP-Comm & Mktg)
David Koenig (VP-Govt Rels, Pub Affairs, and Community Investments)

Subsidiary (Domestic):

Greater Sacramento Surgery Center Limited Partnership (2)
2288 Auburn Blvd Ste 201, Sacramento, CA 95821
Tel.: (916) 929-7229
Web Site:
   https://www.greatersacsurgery.com
Health & Medical Insurance Services
N.A.I.C.S.: 524114

Health Net Federal Services, LLC (2)
2025 Aerojet Rd, Rancho Cordova, CA 95742
Web Site:
   https://www.healthnetfederalservices.com
Health Care Srvices
N.A.I.C.S.: 621491

MHN Services (2)
PO Box 9103, Van Nuys, CA 91409
Web Site: https://www.mhn.com
Health & Medical Insurance Services
N.A.I.C.S.: 524114

HomeScripts.com, LLC (1)
500 Kirts Blvd Ste 300, Troy, MI 48084
Web Site: https://www.homescripts.envolvehealth.com
Health Care Insurance Services
N.A.I.C.S.: 524114

Hospital Polusa, S.A. (1)
Dr Iglesias Otero s/n, 27004, Lugo, Spain
Tel.: (34) 982222854
Web Site: http://www.polusa.es
Women Healthcare Services
N.A.I.C.S.: 621610

Hospital Povisa, S.A. (1)
Calle Salamanca 5, 36211, Vigo, Pontevedra, Spain
Tel.: (34) 98 641 3144
Web Site: http://www.povisa.es
Health Care Srvices
N.A.I.C.S.: 621610

IAH of Florida, LLC (1)
500 Kirts Blvd, Troy, MI 48084
Tel.: (904) 281-1915
Health Care Insurance Services
N.A.I.C.S.: 524114

Interpreta, Inc. (1)
9255 Towne Centre Dr Ste 600, San Diego, CA 92121
Tel.: (858) 795-1900
Web Site: https://www.interpreta.com
Contract Staffing Services
N.A.I.C.S.: 561320
Raghu Sugavanam (Co-Founder & Pres)
Jiong Huang (VP-Quality Mgmt)
Gary Rayner (Co-Founder)
Sachin Patel (CEO)
Haseeb Iqbal (VP-Engrg)

Iowa Total Care, Inc. (1)
1080 Jordan Creek Pkwy Ste 100 S, West Des Moines, IA 50266
Web Site: https://www.iowatotalcare.com
Healthcare & Transportation Services
N.A.I.C.S.: 621999

Kentucky Spirit Health Plan, Inc. (1)
201 E Main St Ste 501, Lexington, KY 40507
Tel.: (859) 226-4700
Web Site:
   http://www.kentuckyspirithealth.com
Insurance Management Services
N.A.I.C.S.: 524298

LifeShare Management Group, LLC (1)
60 Rogers St Ste 2, Manchester, NH 03103
Tel.: (603) 625-8825
Web Site: https://www.lifeshareusa.com
Health Care Srvices
N.A.I.C.S.: 622110
Rachel Boynton (Founder)

Louisiana Health Care Connections, Inc. (1)
8585 Archives Ave Ste 310, Baton Rouge, LA 70809
Tel.: (225) 929-8320
Web Site:
   http://www.louisianahealthconnect.com
Health Care Srvices
N.A.I.C.S.: 622110
James E. Schlottman (CEO & Pres)
Joseph Tidwell (VP)
Michael P. Smith (VP-Product Development)
Joe Sullivan (VP-Operations)
Alesia Wilkins-Braxton (VP-Compliance)
Chris Broussard (VP-Communications)
John Kight (Sr VP)
Jan Rivers (Dir-Human Resources)
Stewart T. Gordon (Chief Medical Officer)
Kia Biller (CFO)

Louisiana Healthcare Connections, Inc. (1)
8585 Archives Ave Ste 310, Baton Rouge, LA 70809
Web Site:
   http://www.louisianahealthconnect.com
Life & Health Insurance Services
N.A.I.C.S.: 524114
Jamie Schlottman (CEO & Pres)
Kendra Case (COO)
Stewart T. Gordon (Chief Medical Officer)
Marcus Wallace (Sr VP-Medical Affairs)
Joseph Tidwell (VP)
Michael P. Smith (VP-Product Development)
Joe Sullivan (VP-Operations)
Alesia Wilkins-Braxton (VP-Compliance)
Chris Broussard (VP-Communications)
John Kight (Sr VP)
Jan Rivers (Dir-Human Resources)
Kia Biller (CFO)

MHM Services, Inc. (1)
1593 Spring Hill Rd Ste 600, Vienna, VA 22182-2231
Tel.: (703) 749-4600
Web Site: https://www.mhm-services.com
Emp.: 10,000
Behavioral Health & Medical Specialty Care Services
N.A.I.C.S.: 813920
Gina Morris (VP-Recruiting)
Melanie de la Rocha (Mgr-Benefits)
Chris McGhee (Mgr-Development)

MR Centrum Melnick, s.r.o. (1)

Prazska 221, 276 01, Melnik, Czech Republic
Tel.: (420) 318690183
Web Site: https://www.mr-melnik.cz
Health & Medical Insurance Services
N.A.I.C.S.: 524114

MR Poprad s.r.o. (1)
Magnetic Resonance Banicka 803/28, Infection Disease Pavilion, 058 01, Poprad, Slovakia
Tel.: (421) 524280060
Web Site: https://magnetickarezonancia.sk
Health Care Srvices
N.A.I.C.S.: 621610

MR Zilina s.r.o. (1)
Vojtecha Spanyola 1739/43, 010 01, Zilina, Slovakia
Tel.: (421) 417002190
Web Site: https://magnetickarezonancia.sk
Health Care Srvices
N.A.I.C.S.: 621610

Magellan Health, Inc. (1)
4801 E Washington St, Phoenix, AZ 85034
Tel.: (602) 572-6050
Web Site: http://www.magellanhealth.com
Rev.: $4,577,531,000
Assets: $3,359,855,000
Liabilities: $1,489,883,000
Net Worth: $1,869,972,000
Earnings: $382,335,000
Emp.: 9,000
Fiscal Year-end: 12/31/2020
Behavioral Health & Employee Assistance Services
N.A.I.C.S.: 621330
Christopher Koster (Sec)
Tom Britt (CIO)
Derrick Duke (CEO)
Anna Sever (Pres-Federal)
Arthur Hennig (Chief Bus Officer & Sr VP)
Sara Pierce (Chief Bus Officer-Employer Market & Sr VP)

Subsidiary (Domestic):

AlphaCare Holdings, Inc. (2)
15 Metrotech Ctr 11th Fl, Brooklyn, NY 11201
Tel.: (212) 466-6000
Holding Company
N.A.I.C.S.: 551112
Joel Landau (Pres)

AlphaCare of New York, Inc. (2)
335 Adams St Ste 2600, Brooklyn, NY 11201
Tel.: (855) 363-6110
Web Site: http://www.alphacare.com
Health Care Srvices
N.A.I.C.S.: 621498

Arizona Biodyne (2)
8825 N 23rd Ave Ste 100, Phoenix, AZ 85021
Tel.: (602) 293-2119
Sales Range: $1-9.9 Million
Emp.: 11
Mental Health Clinic Outpatient
N.A.I.C.S.: 621420
Joyce Kocourek (Dir-Ops & Quality Improvement)

Armed Forces Services Corporation (2)
2800 Shirlington Rd Ste 350, Arlington, VA 22206-3601
Tel.: (703) 379-9311
Web Site: http://www.afsc.com
General Management Consulting Services
N.A.I.C.S.: 541611
Oscar Montes (CEO)
Todd Baker (CFO)
Kate Lyle (VP-HR)
Don Bartholomew (Gen Mgr-HR Solutions)

Cobalt Software, LLC (2)
6650 Park of Commerce Blvd, Boca Raton, FL 33487
Tel.: (561) 453-0200
Web Site:
   https://www.mycobaltsoftware.com
Health & Medical Insurance Services
N.A.I.C.S.: 524114

Employee Assistance Services, Inc. (2)
179 Pierce Ave, Macon, GA 31204-2821

Tel.: (478) 742-1464
Sales Range: $10-24.9 Million
Emp.: 20
Mental Health Counseling Services
N.A.I.C.S.: 621499
Miona Gordon (Pres)

ICORE Healthcare LLC (2)
5850 TG Lee Blvd Ste 510, Orlando, FL 32822
Tel.: (866) 664-2673
Web Site: http://www.icorehealthcare.com
Sales Range: $75-99.9 Million
Emp.: 50
Specialty Pharmacy Management Services
N.A.I.C.S.: 541690

Magellan Behavioral Health of Pennsylvania, Inc. (2)
105 Terry Dr Ste 103, Newtown, PA 18940-0873
Tel.: (215) 504-3930
Web Site: https://www.magellanofpa.com
Sales Range: $25-49.9 Million
Emp.: 100
Psychiatric & Substance Abuse Hospital Services
N.A.I.C.S.: 622210

Magellan Behavioral Health, Inc. (2)
14100 Magellan Plz Ste 400, Maryland Heights, MO 63043-4644
Tel.: (314) 387-4000
Psychiatric & Substance Abuse Hospital Services
N.A.I.C.S.: 622210
Barry Smith (CEO)

Subsidiary (Domestic):

Magellan Behavioral Health of Florida, Inc. (3)
8621 Robert Fulton Dr, Columbia, MD 21046
Web Site: http://www.magellanofflorida.com
Psychiatric & Substance Abuse Hospital Services
N.A.I.C.S.: 622210

Branch (Domestic):

Magellan Health Services (2)
14100 Magellan Plz, Saint Louis, MO 63043
Tel.: (314) 387-4000
Web Site: http://www.magellanprovider.com
Provider of Employee Assistance Programs
N.A.I.C.S.: 624190

Magellan Health Services (2)
199 Pomeroy Rd, Parsippany, NJ 07054
Tel.: (973) 515-5010
Web Site: http://www.magellanassist.com
Sales Range: $50-74.9 Million
Emp.: 235
Mental Health Benefits Manager
N.A.I.C.S.: 621420

Subsidiary (Domestic):

Magellan Healthcare Provider Group, Inc. (2)
6950 Columbia Gateway Dr, Columbia, MD 21046-2706
Tel.: (410) 953-4702
Health Care Srvices
N.A.I.C.S.: 621498
Dave Goldman (Dir-Clinical)

Magellan Healthcare, Inc. (2)
14100 Magellan Plz, Maryland Heights, MO 63043
Tel.: (410) 953-1000
Web Site: https://www.magellanhealth.com
Emp.: 100
Health Care Srvices
N.A.I.C.S.: 621498

Subsidiary (Domestic):

Granite Alliance Insurance Company (3)
2256 S 3600 W Ste A, Salt Lake City, UT 84119
Tel.: (801) 503-3851
Web Site: http://www.mygraniterx.com
Pharmacy Retailer
N.A.I.C.S.: 456110

SWH Holdings, Inc. (3)
58 Charles Str, Cambridge, MA 02141-2128

Centene Corporation—(Continued)

Tel.: (617) 494-5353
Health Assistance Services
N.A.I.C.S.: 621111

Subsidiary (Domestic):

Magellan Life Insurance Company (2)
14100 Magellan Plz, Maryland Heights, MO 63043
Tel.: (314) 387-5602
Property & Casualty Insurance Services
N.A.I.C.S.: 524126

Magellan Method, LLC (2)
130 Bellevue Ave Ste 201, Newport, RI 02840 (100%)
Tel.: (401) 619-5210
Web Site: http://www1.magellanrx.com
Health Care Srvices
N.A.I.C.S.: 621498

Mendota Insurance Company (2)
2805 Dodd Rd Ste 300, Eagan, MN 55121
Tel.: (651) 468-2910
Web Site: http://www.mendota-insurance.com
Property & Casualty Insurance Products & Services
N.A.I.C.S.: 524126

Michael B. Bayless & Associates, LLC (2)
3033 N Central Ave Ste 700, Phoenix, AZ 85012
Tel.: (602) 281-7289
Web Site: http://www.baylesshealthcare.com
Health Care Srvices
N.A.I.C.S.: 621999
Justin M. Bayless (CEO)

National Imaging Associates Inc. (2)
433 Hackensack Ave 6th Fl, Hackensack, NJ 07601
Tel.: (201) 530-3200
Web Site: http://www.radmd.com
Sales Range: $10-24.9 Million
Emp.: 400
Radiology Benefits Management & Solutions
N.A.I.C.S.: 541611

Partners Rx Management, LLC (2)
15950 N 76th Str Ste 200, Scottsdale, AZ 85260
Tel.: (480) 624-9400
Web Site: http://www.partnersrx.com
Sales Range: $200-249.9 Million
Emp.: 50
Health Care Management Services
N.A.I.C.S.: 541618

The Managomont Group LLC (2)
2424 Rimrock Rd Ste 230, Fitchburg, WI 53713 (100%)
Tel.: (608) 255-6441
Web Site: https://www.tmgwisconsin.com
Sales Range: $1-9.9 Million
Emp.: 500
Consumer Directed, Community-Based Long-Term Care Services
N.A.I.C.S.: 621999
Shanna Jensen (Pres)
Maggie McGuire (Sr Dir-Fin)
Gwendolyn Dunkin (Sr Dir-ICA Ops)
Sue Urban (Sr Dir-Clinical Svcs)

VRx, LLC (2)
170 S Main St Ste 900, Salt Lake City, UT 84111
Tel.: (801) 417-9722
Web Site: http://www.myvrx.com
Sales Range: $50-74.9 Million
Emp.: 43
Pharmacy Benefit Management
N.A.I.C.S.: 524298

Subsidiary (Domestic):

VRx Pharmacy, LLC (3)
50 E S Temple Ste 145, Salt Lake City, UT 84111
Tel.: (801) 236-8879
Web Site: https://www.vrxpharmacy.com
Pharmaceutical Products Distr
N.A.I.C.S.: 424210

Subsidiary (Domestic):

Vista Health (2)

4253 N Crossover Rd, Fayetteville, AR 72703-4593 (100%)
Tel.: (479) 521-5731
Web Site: http://www.vistahealthservices.com
Sales Range: $50-74.9 Million
Emp.: 234
General Medical & Surgical Hospitals
N.A.I.C.S.: 622210

Magnolia Health Plan Inc. (1)
1020 Highland Colony Pkwy Ste 502, Ridgeland, MS 39157
Web Site: https://www.magnoliahealthplan.com
Health & Medical Insurance Services
N.A.I.C.S.: 524114

Magnolia Health Plan, Inc. (1)
111 E Capitol St Ste 500, Jackson, MS 39201
Web Site: http://www.magnoliahealthplan.com
Insurance Management Services
N.A.I.C.S.: 524298

Managed Health Network, LLC (1)
2370 Kerner Blvd, San Rafael, CA 94901
Web Site: https://www.mhn.com
Health Utilization Management Services
N.A.I.C.S.: 621999

Subsidiary (Domestic):

Managed Health Network (2)
2370 Kerner Blvd, San Rafael, CA 94901
Web Site: https://www.mhn.com
Commercial Health & Employee Benefits Services Organization
N.A.I.C.S.: 813920

Managed Health Services (1)
1205 S 70th St Ste 500, West Allis, WI 53214-3167
Tel.: (888) 713-6180
Web Site: http://www.managedhealthservices.com
Sales Range: $50-74.9 Million
Emp.: 110
Hospital & Medical Service Plans
N.A.I.C.S.: 524114
Jill Claypool (VP-Network Dev-Contracting)
Bill Wilson (CFO)
Christina Hage (Sr VP)
Geoff Petrie (VP-Compliance)
Patricia Richards (Sr VP)
Kevin O'Toole (Pres & CEO)
Eric A. Yancy (Chief Medical Officer-Medical)
Chirag Patel (VP)
Dana Moell (VP-Operations)
Jill Dusina (VP-Quality)
Shara Wesley (VP)
Chirag Patel (VP)
Dana Moell (VP-Operations)
Jill Dusina (VP-Quality)
Shara Wesley (VP)

Medicina Nove Zamky s.r.o. (1)
Magnetic Resonance Centre Slovenska 11, 940 34, Nove Zamky, Slovakia
Tel.: (421) 356408300
Health Care Srvices
N.A.I.C.S.: 621610

Michigan Complete Health (1)
800 Tower Dr Ste 200, Troy, MI 48098
Web Site: http://mmp.michigancompletehealth.com
Health Care Srvices
N.A.I.C.S.: 621491

Nebraska Total Care, Inc. (1)
2525 N 117th Ave Ste 100, Omaha, NE 68164-9988
Web Site: https://www.nebraskatotalcare.com
Health Care Srvices
N.A.I.C.S.: 621491
Adam Proctor (Pres & CEO)

Novasys Health, Inc. (1)
10801 Executive Center Dr Ste 101, Little Rock, AR 72211
Tel.: (501) 219-4444
Web Site: https://www.novasyshealth.com
Health Care Srvices
N.A.I.C.S.: 622110

Subsidiary (Domestic):

OB Care s.r.o. (1)

Pod Krejcarkem 975/2, 130 00, Prague, 3, Czech Republic
Tel.: (420) 255725121
Health Care Srvices
N.A.I.C.S.: 621610

OB Klinika A.S. (1)
Pod Krejcarkem 975/2, Zizkov, Prague, Czech Republic
Tel.: (420) 25 572 5110
Web Site: https://www.obklinika.cz
Health Care Srvices
N.A.I.C.S.: 621610

Operose Health Ltd. (1)
77 New Cavendish Street, London, W1W 6XB, United Kingdom
Tel.: (44) 2039173496
Web Site: http://www.operosehealth.co.uk
Health Care Srvices
N.A.I.C.S.: 621610

Peach State Health Plan Inc. (1)
1100 Circle 75 Pkwy Ste 1100, Atlanta, GA 30339
Tel.: (678) 556-2300
Web Site: https://www.pshpgeorgia.com
Health Care Srvices
N.A.I.C.S.: 923120

Pennsylvania Health & Wellness, Inc. (1)
300 Corporate Center Dr Ste 600, Camp Hill, PA 17011
Web Site: http://www.pahealthwellness.com
Health Care Srvices
N.A.I.C.S.: 621610

Preamed s.r.o. (1)
Holleho 14, 080 01, Presov, Slovakia
Tel.: (421) 918188804
Web Site: https://www.preamed.sk
Health & Medical Insurance Services
N.A.I.C.S.: 524114

PrimeroSalud, S.L. (1)
Calle Serrano 45 2 2, 28001, Madrid, Spain
Tel.: (34) 913084466
Web Site: https://www.primerosalud.net
Health & Medical Insurance Services
N.A.I.C.S.: 524114

Pro Magnet, s.r.o. (1)
pracovisko magnetickej rezonancie Kosice Rastislavova 43, budova Vychodoslovenskeho Onkologickeho ustavu, 041 91, Kosice, Slovakia
Tel.: (421) 557297101
Web Site: https://magnetickarezonancia.sk
Health & Medical Insurance Services
N.A.I.C.S.: 524114

Pro RTG s.r.o (1)
Poliklinika Mytna 5 - 2 poschodie, 811 07, Bratislava, Slovakia
Tel.: (421) 25 249 9446
Web Site: https://www.prortg.sk
Health Care Srvices
N.A.I.C.S.: 621610

Progress Medical A.S. (1)
Pod Krejcarkem 975/2, Zizkov, 130 00, Prague, Czech Republic
Tel.: (420) 25 572 5100
Web Site: https://www.progressmedical.cz
N.A.I.C.S.: 621610

Qualchoice of Arkansas, Inc. (1)
10825 Financial Centre Pa, Little Rock, AR 72211
Tel.: (501) 228-7111
Web Site: http://www.qualchoice.com
Sales Range: $1-9.9 Million
Emp.: 130
Management Services, Nsk
N.A.I.C.S.: 541611
Mark Johnson (VP-Network Dev)
Barry Fielder (VP-Pharmacy)
Jeff Brinsfield (VP-Info Sys)
Chris O'Dwyer (Dir-Sales)
John Ryan (Pres & CEO)
Chris Perry (CFO)
Melisa Chesney (VP-Ops)
Lubna Maruf (Dir-Medical)
Liz Hubbard (Dir-Compliance)
Billy White (Dir-Dev)

RX Direct, Inc., (1)
5001 Stateline Ave Ste C, Texarkana, TX 75503

Tel.: (903) 735-4011
Web Site: http://www.rxdirect.com
Direct Health Insurance Carrier Services
N.A.I.C.S.: 524114

Ribera Lab, S.L.U. (1)
Nicolas de Bussi Street 18 Torrellano industrial estate, 03203, Elche, Alicante, Spain
Tel.: (34) 965943133
Health & Medical Insurance Services
N.A.I.C.S.: 524114

SilverSummit Healthplan, Inc. (1)
2500 N Buffalo Dr 2nd Fl, Las Vegas, NV 89128
Web Site: https://www.silversummithealthplan.com
Health Care Srvices
N.A.I.C.S.: 621491

Specialty Therapeutic Care Holdings, LLC (1)
601 Lexington Ave 55th Fl, New York, NY 10022
Tel.: (212) 542-1590
Holding Company
N.A.I.C.S.: 551112

Specialty Therapeutic Care, GP, LLC (1)
1311 W Sam Houston Pkwy N Ste 130, Houston, TX 77043
Tel.: (832) 300-1200
Web Site: https://stcare.envolvehealth.com
Emp.: 2,000
Health Care Srvices
N.A.I.C.S.: 622110

Sunshine State Health Plan, Inc. (1)
1301 International Pkwy Ste 400, Sunrise, FL 33323
Web Site: http://www.sunshinehealth.com
Health Care Srvices
N.A.I.C.S.: 524114

Superior HealthPlan Community Solutions, Inc. (1)
5900 E Ben White Blvd, Austin, TX 78741
Web Site: http://www.superiorhealthplan.com
Health Care Srvices
N.A.I.C.S.: 621610
Jeff Dorsey (Sr Mgr-Operations)

Superior HealthPlan Inc. (1)
5900 E Ben White Blvd, Austin, TX 78741
Web Site: https://www.superiorhealthplan.com
Health & Medical Insurance Services
N.A.I.C.S.: 524114

The New York State Catholic Health Plan, Inc. (1)
25-01 Jackson Ave, Long Island City, NY 11101
Tel.: (718) 896-6500
Web Site: https://www.fideliscare.org
Health Insurance Services
N.A.I.C.S.: 524114
Deb Chambers (VP-Quality)

The Pavilion Clinic Ltd. (1)
Stormont Estate Upper Newtownards Road, Belfast, BT4 3TA, United Kingdom
Tel.: (44) 2890767176
Web Site: https://thepavilionclinic.co.uk
Health & Medical Insurance Services
N.A.I.C.S.: 524114

The Practice (Group) Limited (1)
Rose House Bell Lane Office Village Little Chalfont, Little Chalfont, HP6 6FA, Bucks, United Kingdom
Tel.: (44) 2086785624
Health Care Srvices
N.A.I.C.S.: 621491

Three Shires Hospital LP (1)
The Ave Cliftonville, Northampton, NN1 5DR, Northamptonshire, United Kingdom
Tel.: (44) 1604808732
Hospital & Health Care Services
N.A.I.C.S.: 622110

Torrevieja Salud S.L.U. (1)
Ctra Torrevieja San Miguel de Salinas CV-95 Partida La Cenuela, 03186, Torrevieja, Alicante, Spain
Tel.: (34) 965721200
Web Site: http://www.torrevieja-salud.com
Health Care Srvices

N.A.I.C.S.: 621610

Total Carolina Care, Inc. (1)
100 Center Point Cir Ste 100, Columbia, SC 29210
Tel.: (314) 725-4477
Web Site:
https://www.absolutetotalcare.com
Sales Range: $50-74.9 Million
Medicaid Health Plan
N.A.I.C.S.: 621491

Total Vision, Inc. (1)
27271 Las Ramblas Ste 210, Mission Viejo, CA 92691
Tel.: (949) 652-7230
Web Site: https://yourtotalvision.com
Health & Medical Insurance Services
N.A.I.C.S.: 524114

Trillium Community Health Plan, Inc. (1)
555 International Way Bldg B, Springfield, OR 97477
Tel.: (541) 485-2155
Web Site: https://www.trilliumohp.com
Health & Medical Insurance Services
N.A.I.C.S.: 524114

US Medical Management LLC (1)
500 Kirts Blvd Ste 270, Troy, MI 48084-4135
Tel.: (269) 743-4650
Web Site: http://www.usmmllc.com
Emp.: 175
Medical Management Services
N.A.I.C.S.: 541618

US Script, Inc. (1)
8427 Southpark Cir Ste 400, Orlando, FL 32819
Tel.: (559) 244-3700
Web Site: http://www.usscript.com
Sales Range: $25-49.9 Million
Emp.: 100
Pharmacy Services
N.A.I.C.S.: 456110

Vivamed s.r.o. (1)
Holleho 14, 081 81, Presov, Slovakia
Tel.: (421) 517011717
Web Site: https://www.vivamed.sk
Health & Medical Insurance Services
N.A.I.C.S.: 524114

WellCare Health Plans Inc. (1)
8725 Henderson Rd, Tampa, FL 33634
Tel.: (877) 247-6272
Web Site: http://www.wellcare.com
Rev.: $20,414,100,000
Assets: $11,764,700,000
Liabilities: $7,524,700,000
Net Worth: $4,240,300,000
Earnings: $439,800,000
Emp.: 12,000
Fiscal Year-end: 12/31/2018
Hospital & Medical Plan Services
N.A.I.C.S.: 524114
Andrew L. Asher (CFO & Exec VP)
Kelly Munson (Exec VP)
Michael Polen (Exec VP-Operations)
Michael Yount (Chief Compliance Officer & Exec VP)
Michael P. Radu (Exec VP-Business Development)
Darren Ghanayem (CIO & Exec VP)
Timothy Trodden (Chief HR Officer & Exec VP)
Eugenie M. Komives (Chief Medical Officer)
Troy Hildreth (Pres-North Carolina)

Subsidiary (Domestic):

APS Healthcare, Inc. (2)
PO Box 71474, San Juan, PR 00936-8574
Tel.: (787) 641-0773
Web Site: https://apshealth.com
Health & Medical Insurance Services
N.A.I.C.S.: 524114

Accountable Care Coalition of Community Health Centers, LLC (2)
4888 Loop Central Dr Ste 300, Houston, TX 77081
Tel.: (800) 272-5259
Web Site:
http://www.acccommunityhealth.com
Health Care Srvices
N.A.I.C.S.: 621491

Michael Blain (Dir-Medical)
Davin Magno (Officer-Quality Assurance-Improvement)

Accountable Care Coalition of DeKalb, LLC (2)
250 E Ponce De Leon Ave Ste 434, Decatur, GA 30030
Tel.: (855) 243-7301
Web Site: http://www.accdekalb.com
Health Care Srvices
N.A.I.C.S.: 621491
Martha Crenshaw (Dir-Medical & Officer-Quality Assurance & Improvement)

Care 1st Health Plan Arizona, Inc. (2)
1850 W Rio Salado Paky Ste 211, Tempe, AZ 85281
Tel.: (602) 778-1800
Web Site: https://www.care1staz.com
Health Plan Services
N.A.I.C.S.: 524114
Deena Sigel (VP-Finance)
Mike Ferguson (Dir)
Mike Witiuk (Dir-Marketing)
Jessica Sedita-Igneri (VP)
Steffanie Costal (Sr Dir)
Kathy Thurman (Dir)
Angela Balascak (Dir)
Kelly Jordan (Dir-UM)
Maria Cole (Dir)
Mark Shen (Dir-Adult Sys of Care)
Ed Fess (Dir-Medical)
Dee Reny (Dir)
Nicolle Cameron (Partner)
Maria Cole (Dir)
Mark Shen (Dir-Adult Sys of Care)
Ed Fess (Dir-Medical)
Dee Reny (Dir)
Nicolle Cameron (Partner)

Comprehensive Health Management, Inc. (2)
8735 Henderson Rd, Tampa, FL 33634
Tel.: (813) 290-6200
Administrative Services
N.A.I.C.S.: 541611

Exactus Pharmacy Solutions, Inc. (2)
4110 George Rd Ste 100, Tampa, FL 33634
Tel.: (866) 458-9246
Web Site: http://www.exactusrx.com
Health Plan Services
N.A.I.C.S.: 524114

Harmony Health Plan Inc. (2)
200 W Adams St, Chicago, IL 60606 (100%)
Tel.: (312) 516-4985
Sales Range: $50-74.9 Million
Emp.: 125
Healtcare Services
N.A.I.C.S.: 524114

Subsidiary (Domestic):

Harmony Health Plan of Indiana (3)
41 E Washington Ste 310, Indianapolis, IN 46204
Tel.: (317) 423-3036
Sales Range: $10-24.9 Million
Emp.: 25
Health Care Srvices
N.A.I.C.S.: 524114

Subsidiary (Domestic):

Healthease of Florida Inc. (2)
8735 Henderson Rd, Tampa, FL 33634
Tel.: (813) 290-6200
Health Maintenance Organization
N.A.I.C.S.: 524114

Maryland Collaborative Care Transformation Organization, Inc. (2)
4888 Loop Central Dr Ste 300, Houston, TX 77081
Web Site:
https://www.mdcctransformation.com
Medical Care Services
N.A.I.C.S.: 621999

MeridianRx, LLC (2)
1 Campus Martius Ste 750, Detroit, MI 48226
Web Site: https://www.meridianrx.com
Pharmacy & Drug Store Services
N.A.I.C.S.: 456110

Mid-Atlantic Collaborative Care, LLC (2)
4888 Loop Central Dr Ste 300, Houston, TX 77081
Web Site: https://www.midatlanticaco.com
Health Care Srvices
N.A.I.C.S.: 621491
Anuradha Reddy (Officer-Quality Assurance)

Missouri Care, Inc. (2)
2404 Forum Blvd, Columbia, MO 65203
Tel.: (573) 441-2129
Web Site: http://www.missouricare.com
Health Care Srvices
N.A.I.C.S.: 621112

Ohana Health Plan, Inc. (2)
820 Mililani St Ste 200, Honolulu, HI 96813
Tel.: (808) 832-3100
Web Site: https://www.ohanahealthplan.com
Health & Medical Insurance Services
N.A.I.C.S.: 524114

Universal American Corp. (2)
44 S Broadway Ste 1200, White Plains, NY 10601
Tel.: (914) 934-5200
Holding Company; Life & Health Insurance Products & Services
N.A.I.C.S.: 551112
Sarah Bell (VP-Mktg)

Subsidiary (Domestic):

Accountable Care Coalition of Southeast Texas, Inc. (3)
4888 Loop Central Dr Ste 700, Houston, TX 77081
Web Site: https://www.accofsetexas.com
Health & Medical Insurance Services
N.A.I.C.S.: 524114

Golden Triangle Physician Alliance (3)
2300 Hwy 365 Ste 390, Nederland, TX 77627-6282
Tel.: (409) 721-5900
Health Insurance Services
N.A.I.C.S.: 524114

SelectCare of Texas, Inc. (3)
4888 Loop Central Dr Loop Central 1 Ste 300, Houston, TX 77081
Tel.: (713) 843-6720
Health & Life Insurance Services
N.A.I.C.S.: 524114

Worlco Management Services, Inc. (3)
527 Bay Rd, Queensbury, NY 12804
Tel.: (518) 798-0642
Web Site: https://www.worlcoins.com
Insurance Brokerage Services
N.A.I.C.S.: 524210
Jennifer Shaner (Coord-Sls & New Bus)
James Mackenzie (Sr VP-Sls)
Chris Anderson (Dir-Sls & Mktg)

Subsidiary (Domestic):

WellCare Health Plans of Kentucky, Inc. (2)
8725 Henderson Rd, Tampa, FL 33634-1143
Tel.: (813) 206-6251
Emp.: 3,500
Healtcare Services
N.A.I.C.S.: 621491
Kenneth A. Burdick (CEO)

WellCare Specialty Pharmacy, Inc. (2)
8715 Henderson Rd, Tampa, FL 33634
Tel.: (866) 458-9246
Insurance Services
N.A.I.C.S.: 524298

WellCare of Georgia, Inc. (2)
211 Perimeter Ctr Pkwy Ste 800, Atlanta, GA 30346
Tel.: (678) 327-0939
Emp.: 130
Health Insurance Services
N.A.I.C.S.: 524114
Jenifer Allen (Coord-Office)

Windsor Health Group, Inc. (2)
7100 Commerce Way Ste 285, Brentwood, TN 37027

Tel.: (615) 782-7910
Healtcare Services
N.A.I.C.S.: 621491

Wellness By Choice, LLC (1)
201 W Genesee St Ste 231, Fayetteville, NY 13066
Tel.: (315) 432-4689
Web Site: http://www.wellbychoice.com
Wellness & Disease Management Programs
N.A.I.C.S.: 813212

Western Sky Community Care, Inc. (1)
5300 Homestead Rd NE, Albuquerque, NM 87110
Web Site:
https://www.westernskycommunitycare.com
Health & Medical Insurance Services
N.A.I.C.S.: 524114

Winning Security, S.L. (1)
C/San Petersburgo N 19, 10005, Caceres, Spain
Tel.: (34) 628879430
Web Site: https://winningsecurity.es
Health & Medical Insurance Services
N.A.I.C.S.: 524114

nirvanaHealth, LLC (1)
136 Turnpike Rd, Southborough, MA 01772
Tel.: (508) 804-6900
Web Site: https://www.nirvanahealth.com
Health & Medical Insurance Services
N.A.I.C.S.: 524114

CENTERPOINT ENERGY, INC.

1111 Louisiana St, Houston, TX 77002
Tel.: (713) 207-1111
Web Site:
https://www.centerpointenergy.com
Year Founded: 1882
CNP—(NYSE)
Rev.: $8,696,000,000
Assets: $39,715,000,000
Liabilities: $30,048,000,000
Net Worth: $9,667,000,000
Earnings: $867,000,000
Emp.: 8,827
Fiscal Year-end: 12/31/23
Electrical, Power & Gas Services
N.A.I.C.S.: 221122
Kristie L. Colvin (Chief Acctg Officer & Sr VP)
Christopher A. Foster (CFO & Exec VP)
Jason P. Wells (Pres & CEO)
Russell K. Wright (VP-Fin Plng & Analysis)

Subsidiaries:

CenterPoint Energy (1)
470 N Kirkwood Rd, Saint Louis, MO 63122
Tel.: (314) 991-7347
Web Site: http://www.centerpointenergy.com
Sales Range: $10-24.9 Million
Emp.: 11
Finances Purchases By Customers of Gas Burning Equipment
N.A.I.C.S.: 221210

CenterPoint Energy (1)
505 Nicollet Mall, Minneapolis, MN 55459-0038
Tel.: (612) 372-4727
Web Site: http://www.centerpointenergy.com
Sales Range: $1-4.9 Billion
Emp.: 1,400
Natural Gas Distribution & Services; Appliances Sales & Services
N.A.I.C.S.: 221210

CenterPoint Energy Mississippi River Transmission Corporation (1)
1600 S Brentwood, Saint Louis, MO 63144
Tel.: (314) 991-9900
Web Site: http://www.centerpointenergy.com
Rev.: $253,600,000
Emp.: 25
Natural Gas Transmission Services
N.A.I.C.S.: 221210

CenterPoint Energy Services, Inc. (1)
1111 Louisiana St, Houston, TX 77002

CenterPoint Energy, Inc.—(Continued)

Tel.: (713) 207-1111
Web Site: http://www.centerpointenergy.com
Natural Gas Distribution Services
N.A.I.C.S.: 221210

Vectren Corporation (1)
1 Vectren Sq, Evansville, IN 47708
Tel.: (812) 491-4000
Electricity & Natural Gas Distr
N.A.I.C.S.: 551112
Kristie L. Colvin (VP)

Subsidiary (Domestic):

Miller Pipeline, LLC
8850 Crawfordsville Rd, Indianapolis, IN
46234
Tel.: (317) 293-0278
Web Site: http://www.millerpipeline.com
Natural Gas Distr
N.A.I.C.S.: 221210
Dan Short (Sr VP)
Dale Anderson (Pres & COO)
Chris Schuler (VP)
Chad Davis (VP-Construction-South Reg)
Kevin Miller (Pres)
Frank Bracht (VP-Construction-East Coast)
Dave Tucker (VP-Construction-Midwest)
Andy Cleeter (VP-Environmental, Health &
Safety)
Michelle Hall (VP-Claims)
Laura Morrow (VP-Comm)
Justin Sanchez (VP-Fin)
Scott Miller (VP)
Douglas S. Banning Jr. (CEO)

Subsidiary (Domestic):

FH Construction of Marion, LLC (3)
1240 SE 12TH CT, OCALA, FL 34471
Tel.: (352) 236-3355
Oil & Gas Pipeline & Related Structures
Construction
N.A.I.C.S.: 237120
Harvey W. Vandeven (Pres)

Subsidiary (Domestic):

Minnesota Limited, LLC (2)
18640 200th St, Big Lake, MN 55309
Tel.: (763) 262-7000
Web Site: http://www.mnlimited.com
Emp.: 80
Natural Gas Pipeline Construction Services
N.A.I.C.S.: 237120

ProLiance Holdings, LLC (2)
111 Monument Cir Ste 2200, Indianapolis,
IN 46204
Tel.: (317) 231-6800
Web Site: http://www.proliance.com
Investment Management Service
N.A.I.C.S.: 551112

Holding (Domestic):

Vectren Enterprises, Inc. (2)
211 N W Riverside Dr, Evansville, IN
47708 (100%)
Tel.: (812) 491-4000
Natural Gas Distribution
N.A.I.C.S.: 221210
Carl L. Chapman (Pres)

Subsidiary (Domestic):

Energy Realty, Inc. (3)
20 Nw 4th St, Evansville, IN
47708-1724 (100%)
Tel.: (812) 491-4000
Web Site: http://www.vectren.com
Sales Range: $50-74.9 Million
Real Estate Services
N.A.I.C.S.: 531210

Vectren Utility Holdings, Inc. (100%)
1 Vectren Sq, Evansville, IN 47708
Tel.: (812) 491-4000
Web Site: http://www.vectren.com
Rev.: $1,382,600,000
Assets: $5,497,800,000
Liabilities: $3,775,000,000
Net Worth: $1,722,800,000
Earnings: $175,800,000
Emp.: 1,600
Fiscal Year-end: 12/31/2017
Holding Company; Natural Gas & Electric
Generation & Distr
N.A.I.C.S.: 551112

Waskom Gas Processing Co. (1)
155 Private Rd 1133, Waskom, TX
75692 (50%)
Tel.: (903) 687-2513
Sales Range: $25-49.9 Million
Emp.: 40
Industrial Gas Mfr
N.A.I.C.S.: 325120
Jody Castle (Plant Mgr)

CENTERSPACE
3100 10th St SW, Minot, ND 58702-
1988
Tel.: (701) 837-4738 ND
Web Site:
https://centerspacehomes.com
Year Founded: 1970
CSR—(NYSE)
Rev.: $261,309,000
Assets: $1,926,361,000
Liabilities: $995,336,000
Net Worth: $931,025,000
Earnings: $34,897,000
Emp.: 377
Fiscal Year-end: 12/31/23
Real Estate Investment Trust
N.A.I.C.S.: 525990
Anne M. Olson (Pres & CEO)
Susan J. Picotte (Sr VP-Asset Mgmt
& Ops Support)
Grant P. Campbell (Sr VP-
Investments)
Jean Denn (Sr VP-Ops)
Julie Letner (Sr VP-Talent & Culture)
Bhairav Patel (CFO & Exec VP)
Julie Ellis (Chief Acctg Officer & Sr
VP)
Kelly Weber (Sr VP-Strategic Svcs)
Brad Abel (Sr VP-Information Tech-
nology)

Subsidiaries:

CSR - Monticello Crossings, LLC (1)
2205 Meadow Oak Ave, Monticello, MN
55362
Tel.: (651) 372-8454
Web Site:
https://www.monticellocrossings.com
Apartment Rental Services
N.A.I.C.S.: 531110

IRET - Ashland Apartments, LLC (1)
2151 36th Ave S, Grand Forks, ND 58201
Tel.: (701) 203-0268
Web Site: http://www.iret.com
Residential Building Construction Services
N.A.I.C.S.: 236116

IRET - Park Meadows, LLC (1)
408 Park Meadows Dr, Waite Park, MN
56387
Tel.: (320) 253-9638
Residential Building Construction Services
N.A.I.C.S.: 236116

IRET - Valley Park Manor, LLC (1)
3401 28th Ave S, Grand Forks, ND 58201
Tel.: (888) 340-0911
Sales Range: $25-49.9 Million
Emp.: 4
Residential Building Rental & Leasing Ser-
vices
N.A.I.C.S.: 531110

IRET - Whispering Ridge Apartments,
LLC (1)
17551 Pinkney Plz, Omaha, NE 68116
Tel.: (402) 881-8939
Emp.: 10
Residential Building Construction Services
N.A.I.C.S.: 236116
Jennifer Hayes (Mgr)

IRET Properties (1)
1400 31st Ave SW Ste 60, Minot, ND
58702-1988
Tel.: (701) 837-4738
Web Site: http://www.iret.com
Sales Range: $300-349.9 Million
Real Estate Management & Agents
N.A.I.C.S.: 531210

CENTRAL BANCOMPANY, INC.
Tel.: (573) 634-1234 MO

Web Site:
http://www.centralbancompany.com
Year Founded: 1970
CBCYB—(OTCIQ)
Rev.: $538,614,000
Assets: $14,960,940,000
Liabilities: $12,834,877,000
Net Worth: $2,126,063,000
Earnings: $209,643,000
Fiscal Year-end: 12/31/19
Bank Holding Company
N.A.I.C.S.: 551111
Sam Bryan Cook (CEO)
Christine K. Ellinger (Chief HR Officer
& Sr VP)
Daniel H. Westhues (CMQ & Exec
VP-Retail Banking)
Daniel G. Stephen (Chief Risk Offi-
cer, Sr Credit Officer & Exec VP)
John Ross (Pres & COO)
Robert M. Robuck (Bd of Dirs &
Chm)
Piyush Agarwal (CFO)
Russell L. Goldammer (CIO & Exec
VP)
Abby Schafers (Chief HR Officer)
Carey Schoeneberg (Chief Risk Offi-
cer)
Jeremy Colbert (Gen Counsel)

Subsidiaries:

Central Bank of Audrain County (1)
203 E Liberty St, Mexico, MO 65265-2845
Tel.: (573) 581-2381
Web Site: http://www.centralbankac.net
Sales Range: $1-9.9 Million
National Commercial Bank Services
N.A.I.C.S.: 522110
Mike Bunge (Pres)
Rebecca Stansberry (VP)

Central Bank of Lake of the
Ozarks (1)
3848 Hwy 54, Osage Beach, MO
65065-2170 (100%)
Tel.: (573) 348-2761
Web Site: http://www.cbolobank.com
Sales Range: $50-74.9 Million
Emp.: 100
State Commercial Banks
N.A.I.C.S.: 522110
John R. Porth (Sr VP)
Robert C. Frazee (VP)
Mary E. Nelson (Asst VP & Branch Mgr)
Holly J. Woodman (Asst VP & Branch Mgr)
Jill E. Williams (Dir-HR)
Nik D. Perrigo (VP)
Chris McElyea (VP & Branch Mgr)
Chalee B. Crouch (Asst VP)
Tammy J. Darnall (Coord-HR)
Vonda S. Duncan (Supvr-Bookkeeping)
Shanel M. Howard (Asst VP)
Khristina Pahlmann (Branch Mgr)
M. Tracy Peters (Branch Mgr)
Valerie L. Taylor (Branch Mgr)

Central Bank of Oklahoma (1)
8908 S Yale Ave Ste 100, Tulsa, OK 74137
Tel.: (918) 477-7400
Web Site: http://www.centralbank.net
Sales Range: $25-49.9 Million
Commericial Banking
N.A.I.C.S.: 522110
Angie Hobza (Officer-Mortgage Loan)
Aaron Ochoa (Asst VP)

Central Bank of St. Louis (1)
7777 Forsyth Blvd, Clayton, MO 63105-
1809
Tel.: (314) 862-8300
Web Site: http://www.centralbankstl.net
Sales Range: $25-49.9 Million
Emp.: 70
National Commercial Banks
N.A.I.C.S.: 522110
Rick Bagy (Pres)
Rachel Rufkhar (Officer-Mortgage Loan &
Asst VP)
Jean Godi (VP-Mortgage Lending)
Tom Pike (VP-Mortgage Lending)
Alexis I. White (Sr Asst Branch Mgr)
Vickie Agan (Officer-Mortgage Loan)
Lacy Childers (Officer-Mortgage Loan)
Karlyn Brasselmon (Officer-Mortgage Loan)

Glenn Boland (Officer-Mortgage Loan)
Timothy M. Ferrick (Sr VP-Comml Lending)
Michael J. Gardner (Sr VP-Comml Lending)
Daniel G. Kleffner (Exec VP-Comml Lend-
ing)
James W. Kuehn (Exec VP-Comml Lend-
ing)
Jeffrey M. Causey (Sr VP-Comml Lending)
Matthew A. Favazza (Pres-Chesterfield)
James M. Lewis (Exec VP-Comml Lending)
Brian S. Liberman (Sr VP-Comml Lending)
Mark Mesnier (Sr VP-Comml Lending)
Norman F. Mueller (Exec VP)
Kevin R. Olson (Sr VP-Comml Lending)
Nicholas M. Riordan (Sr VP-Comml Loans
& Dental Practice Lending)
Mark E. Sauerwein (Officer-Comml Loan &
Pres-South County)
C. Evan Sowers (Exec VP)
Nancy O'Neal (Chief Compliance Officer &
VP)
Vance Urick (Sr VP & Sr Portfolio Mgr)
Steve Johnson (Sr VP & Sr Portfolio Mgr)
Dawn Federhofer (Sr VP & Mgr-Customer
Rels)
Brian McRae (Officer-Bus Dev Loan & Sr
VP-Residential Lending)
Debbie Wiedner (Sr VP-Residential Lend-
ing)
David Beck (Sr VP-Comml Leasing)
M. Charles Carpenter IV (Sr VP-Comml
Lending)

Central Bank of the Midwest (1)
609 N 291 Hwy, Lees Summit, MO 64086
Tel.: (816) 525-5300
Web Site: http://www.centralbank.net
Federal Savings Bank
N.A.I.C.S.: 522180
Bill Ferguson (Pres & CEO)
Steve Sulzer (CFO)
Tony Yarbrough (Chief Credit Officer)
Kayla Holloway (Dir-HR)
Darren Bell (Dir-Retail)
Chris Tallent (Dir-Bus Solutions)

Central Trust & Investment
Company (1)
7733 Forsyth Blvd, Saint Louis, MO 63105-
1898
Tel.: (314) 725-9055
Web Site: http://www.centrustco.com
Sales Range: $1-4.9 Billion
Emp.: 25
Trust & Investment Asset Management Ser-
vices
N.A.I.C.S.: 523991
Jami Peebles (Exec VP & Reg Mgr-
Southern)
Mary Ellen Muller (VP & Head-Retirement
Svcs)
Nancy O'Neal (Chief Compliance Officer &
VP)
Scott Kellett (Pres & CEO)
Daniel J. Monte (Chief Fiduciary Officer &
Exec VP)
Terry Seboldt (COO & Exec VP)

City Bank & Trust Company of
Moberly (1)
500 W Coates St, Moberly, MO 65270-1504
Tel.: (660) 263-1234
Web Site: http://www.city-bank.com
Rev.: $8,600,000
Emp.: 45
State Commercial Banks
N.A.I.C.S.: 522110
James M. Gardner (Pres & CEO)

First Central Bank (1)
401 N Maguire St, Warrensburg, MO
64093-1815
Tel.: (660) 429-2101
Web Site: http://www.firstcentral.net
Rev.: $2,400,000
Emp.: 15
State Commercial Banks
N.A.I.C.S.: 522110
Kandy Rieachert (Mgr)

Jefferson Bank of Missouri (1)
700 SW Blvd, Jefferson City, MO 65109-
2660
Tel.: (573) 634-0800
Web Site: http://www.jefferson-bank.com
Rev.: $29,854,000
Emp.: 100
State Commercial Banks
N.A.I.C.S.: 522110

Ozark Mountain Bank (1)
PO Box 130, Branson, MO
65615-0130 (100%)
Tel.: (417) 334-4125
Web Site: http://www.ozkmtnbank.com
Rev.: $14,936,000
Emp.: 90
State Commercial Banks
N.A.I.C.S.: 522110
Craig Richards (Pres & CEO)
Steven Bradshaw (VP-Real Estate)

The Boone County National Bank of Columbia (1)
720 E Broadway, Columbia, MO 65201-4444
Tel.: (573) 874-8100
Web Site: http://www.centralbank.net
Rev.: $42,423,000
Emp.: 300
National Commercial Banks
N.A.I.C.S.: 522110
Mary Wilkerson (Mgr-Mktg)
Joseph Henderson (Pres)
Steve Erdel (CEO)
Lorry Myers (Mgr-Centralia)

The Central Trust Bank (1)
238 Madison St, Jefferson City, MO 65101
Tel.: (573) 634-1234
Web Site: http://www.centralbank.net
Sales Range: $100-124.9 Million
Emp.: 345
State Commercial Banks
N.A.I.C.S.: 522110
Sam Bryan Cook (Pres & CEO)
Michael McCoy (VP)
Michael Prenger (Sr VP & Mgr)
Don Perdue (Exec VP)
Amparo Thomas (VP)
Carol R. Scott (COO)

The Third National Bank of Sedalia (1)
301 W Broadway Blvd, Sedalia, MO 65301-5734
Tel.: (660) 827-3333
Web Site: http://www.thirdnationalbank.com
Sales Range: $50-74.9 Million
Emp.: 60
Commercial Banking Services
N.A.I.C.S.: 522110
Larry J. Bahr (Pres)

CENTRAL GARDEN & PET COMPANY
1340 Treat Blvd Ste 600, Walnut
Creek, CA 94597
Tel.: (925) 948-4000   DE
Web Site: https://www.central.com
Year Founded: 1955
CENT—(NASDAQ)
Rev.: $3,200,460,000
Assets: $3,553,439,000
Liabilities: $1,995,894,000
Net Worth: $1,557,545,000
Earnings: $109,313,000
Emp.: 6,100
Fiscal Year-end: 09/28/24
Lawn, Garden & Pet Supply Products
N.A.I.C.S.: 444240
Nicholas Lahanas (CFO & Sr VP)
Ken Elsbury (Sr VP-Central Life Sciences)
Mike McGoohan (Sr VP-Mktg & Strategy)
Dan Pennington (Sr VP-Wild Bird, Chemical, and Fertilizer)
Chris Walter (CIO & Sr VP)
Howard A. Machek (Chief Acctg Officer & Sr VP)
Aron Kolosik (Chief Supply Chain Officer)
John E. Hanson (Pres-Pet Consumer Products)
J. D. Walker (Pres-Garden Consumer Products)
Joyce McCarthy (Gen Counsel & Sec)
Glen Axelrod (Sr VP-Dog & Cat Brands)

Subsidiaries:

B2E Corporation (1)

500 Mamaroneck Ave, Harrison, NY 10528
Tel.: (914) 777-1111
Web Site:
http://www.protectivechemicals.com
Protective Chemicals Mfr
N.A.I.C.S.: 325180
William Mintz (Pres)

Bell Nursery Holdings, LLC (1)
7111 Troy Hill Dr, Elkridge, MD 21075
Tel.: (410) 782-4500
Web Site: http://www.bellnursery.com
Flower, Nursery Stock & Florists' Supplies
Merchant Whslr
N.A.I.C.S.: 424930
Brett Guthrie (COO)

Farnam Companies, Inc. (1)
301 W Osborn Rd, Phoenix, AZ 85013-3921
Tel.: (602) 285-1660
Web Site: http://www.farnam.com
Sales Range: $400-449.9 Million
Emp.: 400
Horse & Livestock Health Care Products
Mfr & Distr
N.A.I.C.S.: 424520

Four Paws Products, Ltd. (1)
1340 Treat Blvd 600, Walnut Creek, CA 94597
Tel.: (925) 948-4000
Web Site: http://www.fourpaws.com
Pet Care Product Mfr
N.A.I.C.S.: 311111

General Pet Supply, Inc. (1)
7711 N 81st St, Milwaukee, WI 53224
Tel.: (414) 365-3400
Web Site: http://www.generalpet.com
Emp.: 200
Provider of Medical & Dental Supplies
N.A.I.C.S.: 424990
Robert Merar (Pres)

Green-It Turf Products Inc. (1)
2389 State Hwy 66, Longmont, CO 80504-9608
Tel.: (303) 678-5060
Sales Range: $50-74.9 Million
Emp.: 10
Fertilizers & Agricultural Chemicals
N.A.I.C.S.: 424910
Duane Phillips (Gen Mgr)

K&H Manufacturing LLC (1)
825 Citadel Dr E Ste 250, Colorado
Springs, CO 80909
Tel.: (719) 591-6950
Web Site: http://www.khmfg.com
Farm Supplies Merchant Whslr
N.A.I.C.S.: 339999
James Koskey (Founder)

Kaytee Products, Inc. (1)
521 Clay St, Chilton, WI 53014-1476
Tel.: (920) 849-2321
Web Site: http://www.kaytee.com
Sales Range: $150-199.9 Million
Emp.: 350
Bird Products & Bird Seed
N.A.I.C.S.: 311119

Matson, LLC (1)
45620 SE N Bend Way, North Bend, WA 98045
Tel.: (425) 888-6212
Agricultural Insecticide Mfr
N.A.I.C.S.: 325320

New England Pottery, LLC (1)
1000 Washington St, Foxboro, MA 02035
Tel.: (508) 543-7700
Gardening Equipment Distr
N.A.I.C.S.: 423820

Pennington Seed Inc. (1)
1280 Atlanta Hwy, Madison, GA 30650-0290
Tel.: (706) 342-1234
Web Site: http://www.pennington.com
Sales Range: $10-24.9 Million
Emp.: 150
Mfr of Consumer Lawn & Garden Products
N.A.I.C.S.: 111422

Sun Pet, Ltd. (1)
3765 Zip Industrial Blvd, Atlanta, GA 30354-2936
Tel.: (404) 476-7260
Web Site: http://www.sunpet.com

Pet & Pet Supplies Whslr
N.A.I.C.S.: 424990

TDBBS LLC. (1)
5701 Eastport Blvd, Richmond, VA 23231
Web Site: http://www.bestbullysticks.com
Sales Range: $10-24.9 Million
Emp.: 36
Dog Treats
N.A.I.C.S.: 311111

TFH Publications, Inc. (1)
PO Box 427, Neptune, NJ 07754
Tel.: (732) 988-5466
Web Site: http://www.tfh.com
Emp.: 200
Infotainment Book Publisher
N.A.I.C.S.: 513130

Wellmark International (1)
1501 E Woodfield Rd Ste 200 W, Schaumburg, IL 60173-5125 (100%)
Tel.: (847) 330-5300
Web Site:
http://www.centrallifesciences.com
Sales Range: $25-49.9 Million
Emp.: 65
Pest Management Products & Services
N.A.I.C.S.: 561710
Kay Schwichtenberg (CEO)

CENTRAL NATURAL RESOURCES, INC.
1044 Main St Ste 502, Kansas City,
MO 64105
Tel.: (816) 842-2430   DE
Web Site:
https://www.centralholdings.com
CTNR—(OTCIQ)
Sales Range: Less than $1 Million
Emp.: 5
Support Activities for Oil & Gas Operations
N.A.I.C.S.: 213112
Phelps C. Wood (Pres & CEO)
Gary J. Pennington (VP & Gen Mgr)
Ray A. Infantino (Treas & Sec)
Vincent L. Gualtier (Asst Sec)

CENTRAL PACIFIC FINANCIAL CORPORATION
220 S King St Ste 2125, Honolulu, HI
96813
Tel.: (808) 544-0500   HI
Web Site: https://www.cpb.bank
Year Founded: 1954
CPF—(NYSE)
Rev.: $282,657,000
Assets: $7,642,796,000
Liabilities: $7,138,981,000
Net Worth: $503,815,000
Earnings: $58,669,000
Emp.: 696
Fiscal Year-end: 12/31/23
Bank Holding Company
N.A.I.C.S.: 551111
Blenn A. Fujimoto (Exec VP)
David S. Morimoto (CFO & Sr Exec VP)
Arnold D. Martines (Pres & CEO)
Ian Tanaka (Sr VP & Mgr-Treasury)
Tim Sakahara (Asst VP & Mgr-Corp Comm)
Kisan Jo (Exec VP)
Diane Murakami (Exec VP)

Subsidiaries:

Central Pacific Bank (1)
220 S King St, Honolulu, HI 96813 (100%)
Tel.: (808) 544-0500
Web Site: http://www.centralpacificbank.com
Sales Range: $125-149.9 Million
Emp.: 850
Commercial Banking Services
N.A.I.C.S.: 522110
Blenn A. Fujimoto (Exec VP-Wealth & Intl Markets)
David S. Morimoto (CFO & Sr Exec VP)
Arnold D. Martines (Pres & CEO)
Ian Tanaka (Sr VP & Mgr-Treasury)
Tim Sakahara (Asst VP & Mgr-Corp Comm)

Rachel I. Cunningham (Officer-Mortgage Loan)
Amery Lam (Officer-Mortgage Loan)
Marife P. Yamamoto (Officer-Mortgage Loan)
Russell J. Rodriguez (Officer-Mortgage Loan)
Rusty Rasmussen (Sr VP & Mgr-Div)
Tracey Lyum (VP)
Gale Lee (Officer-Reverse Mortgage Loan)
Spencer Lee (VP & Mgr-Sls)
Kenneth Leung (VP & Mgr-Sls)
Jennifer Macaraeg (VP)
Matthew Wong (VP)
Duncan Chun (VP)
Desiree Ting (Asst VP)
Donn Y. Hoshide (VP & Mgr-Loan-Mortgage)
Iris Toguchi (VP & Mgr-Loan-Mortgage)
Ian Kemsley (Officer-Mortgage Loan & VP)
Andrew Stuber (Officer-Mortgage Loan & VP)
Juo M. Leung (Officer-Mortgage Loan & VP)
Phuong M. T. Matsuura (Officer-Mortgage Loan & VP)
Linda C. Miyasaki (Officer-Mortgage Loan & Asst VP)
Linda Nakanelua (Officer-Mortgage Loan & Asst VP)
Craig Nakashima (Officer-Mortgage Loan & Asst VP)
Tom Chua (Officer-Loan-Mortgage)
Linda Ribao Fagner (Officer-Loan-Mortgage)
Celia Y. Fujikami (Officer-Loan-Mortgage & Asst VP)
Zachary Gaynor (Officer-Loan-Mortgage)
Mike Lampman (Officer-Loan-Mortgage)
Jon Okabe (Officer-Loan-Mortgage)
Myrna R. Declaro (Officer-Loan-Mortgage)
Keith Y. Amemiya (Exec Dir)

Subsidiary (Domestic):

CPB Properties, Inc. (2)
220 S King St, Honolulu, HI
96813-4526 (100%)
Tel.: (808) 544-0500
Web Site: http://www.centralpacificbank.com
Sales Range: $350-399.9 Million
Emp.: 290
Management of Property
N.A.I.C.S.: 531120

Central Pacific HomeLoans, Inc. (1)
220 S King St, Honolulu, HI 96813
Tel.: (808) 356-4000
Emp.: 96
Real Estate Investment Services
N.A.I.C.S.: 522292

Gentry HomeLoans, LLC (1)
220 S King St, Honolulu, HI 96813
Tel.: (808) 536-8010
Web Site:
https://www.gentryhomeloans.com
Emp.: 4
Real Estate Investment Services
N.A.I.C.S.: 522292
Betty Lewis (VP & Mgr-Mortgage Loan)
Andrew Ramirez (Officer-Mortgage Loan)
Xiaofan Larson (Officer-Mortgage Loan)

Haseko HomeLoans, LLC (1)
91-1001 Kaimalie St Ste 205, Ewa Beach,
HI 96706-6250
Tel.: (808) 544-5480
Web Site:
http://www.hasekohomeloans.com
Real Estate Services
N.A.I.C.S.: 522292

Island Pacific HomeLoans, LLC (1)
Kahala Mall Upper Level 4211 Waialae Ave,
Honolulu, HI 96816
Tel.: (808) 544-5470
Web Site:
https://www.islandpacifichomeloans.com
Real Estate Services
N.A.I.C.S.: 522292

CENTRAL PLAINS BANCSHARES, INC.
221 S Locust St, Grand Island, NE
68801
Tel.: (308) 382-4000   MD
Year Founded: 2023

Central Plains Bancshares, Inc.—(Continued)

CPBI—(NASDAQ)
Emp.: 67
Bank Holding Company
N.A.I.C.S.: 551111

CENTRAL SECURITIES CORPORATION
630 5th Ave, New York, NY 10111
Tel.: (212) 698-2020   DE
Web Site:
  https://www.centralsecurities.com
Year Founded: 1929
CET—(NYSEAMEX)
Rev.: $24,269,191
Assets: $1,037,065,609
Liabilities: $729,115
Net Worth: $1,036,336,494
Earnings: $18,090,322
Fiscal Year-end: 12/31/20
Investment Services
N.A.I.C.S.: 523999
Marlene A. Krumholz *(Sec & VP)*
Lawrence P. Vogel *(Treas & VP)*
Andrew J. O'Neill *(VP)*
John C. Hill *(Pres & CEO)*

CENTRAL SERVICE CORP.
324 W Broadway, Enid, OK 73701
Tel.: (580) 233-3535   DE
Web Site: http://www.cnb-ok.com
CESO—(OTCIQ)
Bank Holding Company
N.A.I.C.S.: 551111
Brud Baker *(CEO)*

CENTRUS ENERGY CORP.
6901 Rockledge Dr Ste 800,
Bethesda, MD 20817
Tel.: (301) 564-3200   DE
Web Site:
  https://www.centrusenergy.com
Year Founded: 1998
LEU—(NYSEAMEX)
Rev.: $320,200,000
Assets: $796,200,000
Liabilities: $763,900,000
Net Worth: $32,300,000
Earnings: $84,400,000
Emp.: 292
Fiscal Year-end: 12/31/23
Holding Company; Uranium Refiner &
Whslr
N.A.I.C.S.: 551112
John M. A. Donelson *(CMO & Sr VP)*
Larry B. Cutlip *(Sr VP-Field Ops)*
Dan Leistikow *(VP-Corp Comm)*
Kevin J. Harrill *(CFO, Treas & Sr VP)*
Shahram Ghasemian *(Chief Compliance Officer, Acting Corp Counsel & Sec)*
Nelson Perez *(VP)*
Amir V. Vexler *(Pres & CEO)*

Subsidiaries:

United States Enrichment
Corporation   (1)
6903 Rockledge Dr 4th Fl, Bethesda, MD
20817
Tel.: (301) 564-3200
Uranium Refiner & Whslr
N.A.I.C.S.: 331410
Robert Van Namen *(COO & Sr VP)*

CENTURY ALUMINUM COMPANY
1 S Wacker Dr Ste 1000, Chicago, IL
60606
Tel.: (312) 696-3101   DE
Web Site:
  https://www.centuryaluminum.com
Year Founded: 1995
CENX—(NASDAQ)
Rev.: $2,777,300,000
Assets: $1,472,000,000
Liabilities: $1,072,700,000

Net Worth: $399,300,000
Earnings: ($14,100,000)
Emp.: 1,956
Fiscal Year-end: 12/31/22
Aluminum Mfr
N.A.I.C.S.: 331313
Jesse E. Gary *(Pres & CEO)*
Gerald C. Bialek *(CFO & Exec VP)*
Peter A. Trpkovski *(Treas & Sr VP-Fin)*
Agust Hafberg *(Chief Comml Officer & Sr VP)*
John DeZee *(Gen Counsel, Sec & Exec VP)*
Kenneth L. Calloway *(Sr VP-Human Resources & VP)*
Matthew F. Aboud *(Sr VP-Strategy & Business Development)*
Robert Hoffman *(Chief Acctg Officer & VP-Information Technology)*
Steinunn Dogg Steinsen *(VP-Sustainability & Mgmt Sys)*
Gauti Hoskuldsson *(VP-Global & Operations)*
Theresa Brainerd *(Corp Controller-Global)*
Gunnar Gudlaugsson *(Exec VP-Global Ops)*

Subsidiaries:

Century Aluminum Sebree, LLC   (1)
9404 State Rte 2096, Robards, KY 42420
Tel.: (270) 521-7811
Emp.: 625
Aluminum Mfr
N.A.I.C.S.: 331313

Century Aluminum of Kentucky   (1)
1627 State Rte 3543, Hawesville, KY 42348
Tel.: (270) 685-2493
Web Site: http://www.centuryca.com
Sales Range: $350-399.9 Million
Emp.: 525
Primary Aluminum Mfr
N.A.I.C.S.: 331313
John Hoerner *(VP)*

Century Aluminum of Kentucky General Partnership   (1)
1627 State Route 3543, Hawesville, KY
42348-6816
Tel.: (270) 685-2493
Sales Range: $125-149.9 Million
Emp.: 700
Aluminum Sheet Mfr
N.A.I.C.S.: 331315

Century Aluminum of South Carolina, Inc.   (1)
508 Meeting St, West Columbia, SC 29169
Tel.: (843) 572-3700
Emp.: 295
Aluminum Mfr
N.A.I.C.S.: 331313

Century Aluminum of West Virginia, Inc.   (1)
PO Box 98, Ravenswood, WV
26164-0098   (100%)
Tel.: (304) 273-7322
Web Site: http://www.centuryaluminum.com
Sales Range: $350-399.9 Million
Emp.: 750
Aluminum Mfr
N.A.I.C.S.: 331313

Century Kentucky, Inc.   (1)
1627 State Rte 3543, Hawesville, KY 42348
Tel.: (270) 685-2493
Emp.: 525
Aluminium Products Mfr
N.A.I.C.S.: 331315

Nordural HF   (1)
Grundartangi, 301, Akranes,
Iceland   (100%)
Tel.: (354) 4301000
Web Site: http://www.nordural.is
Sales Range: $100-124.9 Million
Emp.: 500
Security Brokers & Dealers
N.A.I.C.S.: 523210

Nordural ehf   (1)
Skogarhlio 12, 105, Reykjavik, Iceland

Tel.: (354) 4301000
Web Site: https://www.nordural.is
Emp.: 600
Aluminum Mfr
N.A.I.C.S.: 331313
Gunnar Guolaugsson *(Mng Dir)*
Sigrun Helgadottir *(Mgr-Plant)*
Kristinn Bjarnason *(Mgr-Finance)*
Fjalar Rikharosson *(Mgr-Potroom)*
Birna Bjornsdottir *(Mgr-Rodding Shop)*
Guomundur Oskar Ragnarsson *(Mgr-Casthouse)*
Sigriour Haroardottir *(Mgr-Human Resources)*
Guolaugur Bjarki Luoviksson *(Mgr-Safety, Environment, and Improvements)*
Baldur Bjarnason *(Mgr-Technical Services)*
Solveig Bergmann *(Mgr-Communications & Public Relations)*
Margret Ros *(Project Mgr-Communications & Public Relations)*

CENTURY CASINOS, INC.
455 E Pikes Peak Ave Ste 210, Colorado Springs, CO 80903
Tel.: (719) 527-8300   DE
Web Site: https://www.cnty.com
Year Founded: 1992
CNTY—(NASDAQ)
Rev.: $430,529,000
Assets: $884,967,000
Liabilities: $730,768,000
Net Worth: $154,199,000
Earnings: $7,976,000
Emp.: 2,292
Fiscal Year-end: 12/31/22
Gaming Casinos Management
N.A.I.C.S.: 713210
Andreas Terler *(CIO & Sr VP-Ops-Missouri & West Virginia)*
Nicholas Muscari *(CIO)*
Lyle Randolph *(VP-Operations)*
William Beaumont *(VP-Human Resources)*
Erwin Haitzmann *(Chm & Co-CEO)*
Peter Hoetzinger *(Vice Chm, Pres & Co-CEO)*
Margaret Stapleton *(CFO & Sec)*
Eric Rose *(VP-Ops)*

Subsidiaries:

Century Casino Bath, Ltd.   (1)
Saw Close, Bath, BA1 1EY, United Kingdom
Tel.: (44) 1225308990
Casino Entertainment Services
N.A.I.C.S.: 713210
Philip Keller *(Mgr-Bus Dev)*

Century Casino Calgary Inc.   (1)
1010 42 Ave SE, Calgary, T2G 1Z4, AB,
Canada
Tel.: (403) 287-1183
Web Site: http://www.calgary.cnty.com
Casino Hotel Operator
N.A.I.C.S.: 721120

Century Casino St. Albert, Inc.   (1)
24 Boudreau Road, Saint Albert, T8N 6K3,
AB, Canada
Tel.: (780) 460-8092
Casinos Services
N.A.I.C.S.: 713210

Century Casinos Africa (Pty) Ltd.   (1)
Tel.: (27) 343281777
Sales Range: $1-9.9 Million
Emp.: 100
Hotel & Casino
N.A.I.C.S.: 721120

Subsidiary (Non-US):

Century Casinos Caledon (Pty)
Ltd.   (2)
Tel.: (27) 282145100
Web Site: http://www.cnty.com
Hotel & Casino
N.A.I.C.S.: 721120

Century Casinos Cripple Creek,
Inc.   (1)
200-220 E Bennett Ave, Cripple Creek, CO
80813
Tel.: (719) 689-0333

Web Site: http://www.cnty.com
Sales Range: Less than $1 Million
Emp.: 20
Hotel & Casino
N.A.I.C.S.: 721120

Century Casinos Europe GmbH   (1)
Untere Viaduktgasse 2, Vienna, 1030, Austria
Tel.: (43) 15336333
Web Site: http://www.centurycasinos.com
Sales Range: Less than $1 Million
Emp.: 29
Casino & Hotel Management
N.A.I.C.S.: 721120

Subsidiary (Non-US):

Casinos Poland Ltd.   (2)
Wolnosc 3A, 01-018, Warsaw,
Poland   (66.6%)
Tel.: (48) 22 862 2880
Web Site: https://casinospoland.pl
Emp.: 300
Casino Operator
N.A.I.C.S.: 713210

Century Resorts Alberta, Inc.   (1)
13103 Fort Road, Edmonton, T5A 1C3, AB,
Canada
Tel.: (780) 643-4000
Web Site: http://www.cnty.com
Sales Range: $125-149.9 Million
Hotel & Casino
N.A.I.C.S.: 721120

Century Resorts Management
GmbH   (1)
Untere Viaduktgasse 2, 1030, Vienna, Austria
Tel.: (43) 15336333
Casino Entertainment Services
N.A.I.C.S.: 713210

IOC-Caruthersville, LLC   (1)
777 E 3rd St, Caruthersville, MO 63830
Tel.: (573) 333-6000
Web Site:
  http://www.ladyluckcaruthersville.com
Casino Operator
N.A.I.C.S.: 721120

Mountaineer Park, Inc.   (1)
1420 Mountaineer Cir, New Cumberland,
WV 26047-2651
Tel.: (304) 387-8335
Web Site:
  http://www.moreatmountaineer.com
Casino, Racetrack & Resort Operator
N.A.I.C.S.: 721120

WMCK-Venture Corp.   (1)
200-220 E Bennett Ave, Cripple Creek, CO
80813
Tel.: (719) 689-0333
Casino Hotel Operator
N.A.I.C.S.: 721120

CENTURY COBALT CORP.
10100 Santa Monica Blvd Ste 300,
Los Angeles, CA 90067
Tel.: (310) 772-2209   NV
Web Site:
  http://www.centurycobalt.com
Year Founded: 2008
CCOB—(OTCIQ)
Assets: $159,277
Liabilities: $1,690,104
Net Worth: ($1,530,827)
Earnings: ($912,308)
Emp.: 1
Fiscal Year-end: 11/30/21
Mineral Mining Services
N.A.I.C.S.: 212390

CENTURY COMMUNITIES, INC.
8390 E Crescent Pkwy Ste 650,
Greenwood Village, CO 80111
Tel.: (303) 770-8300   DE
Web Site:
  https://www.centurycommunities.com
Year Founded: 2002

CCS—(NYSE)
Rev.: $3,692,185,000
Assets: $4,139,362,000
Liabilities: $1,752,426,000
Net Worth: $2,386,936,000
Earnings: $259,224,000
Emp.: 1,650
Fiscal Year-end: 12/31/23
Single Family Housing Construction & Development
N.A.I.C.S.: 236115
Dale Francescon (Co-Founder, Chm & Co-CEO)
Robert J. Francescon (Co-Founder, Pres & Co-CEO)
J. Scott Dixon (CFO)
Hunter Wells (VP-Investor Relations)

Subsidiaries:

Augusta Pointe, LLC   (1)
1788 Holmby Ct, Castle Rock, CO 80104
Tel.: (303) 407-5684
Household Product Distr
N.A.I.C.S.: 423220

Avalon at Inverness, LLC   (1)
8390 E Crescent Pkwy Ste 650, Greenwood Village, CO 80111
Tel.: (303) 770-8300
Residential Building Construction Services
N.A.I.C.S.: 236115

BMCH Tennessee, LLC   (1)
2630 Elm Hill Pike Ste 110, Nashville, TN 37214
Tel.: (615) 254-2112
Housing Development Services
N.A.I.C.S.: 236117
Clint Mitchell (VP-Pur)

Centennial Holding Company, LLC   (1)
3348 Peachtree Rd Ne Ste 10, Atlanta, GA 30326
Tel.: (404) 816-8080
Web Site:
   http://www.centennialholdingco.com
Real Estate Services
N.A.I.C.S.: 551112
William P. Payne (Founder & Chm)
Jerry Brewer (CFO)
Shannon Watkins (Sr VP)
C. Read Morton (Exec VP-Bus Dev)
Michelle Wood (Dir-Ops)
Bronson D. Smith (Co-Chief Investment Officer)
Michael Fullmer (Chief Acctg Officer)
Andrew H. Trotter III (Pres & Co-Chief Investment Officer)
W. Porter Payne Jr. (CEO)

Century Group LLC   (1)
1200 17th St Ste 1225, Denver, CO 80202
Tel.: (720) 409-3949
Web Site: http://www.century-group.com
Financial Investment Services
N.A.I.C.S.: 523940
Peter Nelson (Mng Dir-Denver & Colorado)

Century Living, LLC   (1)
4310 Shelbyville Rd, Louisville, KY 40207
Tel.: (502) 253-6922
Web Site: http://www.centuryliving.com
Interior Design Services
N.A.I.C.S.: 541410
John Poynter (Owner)

Cherry Hill Park, LLC   (1)
9800 Cherry Hill Rd, College Park, MD 20740
Tel.: (301) 937-7116
Web Site: http://www.cherryhillpark.com
Emp.: 500
Resort Management Services
N.A.I.C.S.: 721110

Enclave at Pine Grove, LLC   (1)
15905 Filly Ave, Parker, CO 80134
Tel.: (720) 643-1905
Housing Development Services
N.A.I.C.S.: 236117

IHL Home Insurance Agency, LLC   (1)
15801 Brixham Hill Ave Ste 300, Charlotte, NC 28277
Web Site: https://www.ihlinsurance.com

Insurance Agency Services
N.A.I.C.S.: 524210

Inspire Home Loans, Inc.   (1)
4695 MacArthur Ct Ste 350, Newport Beach, CA 92660
Tel.: (949) 420-9889
Emp.: 5
Housing Development Services
N.A.I.C.S.: 236117

Landmark Homes of Tennessee, Inc.   (1)
6064 Central Pike, Mount Juliet, TN 37122
Tel.: (615) 773-0700
Web Site: http://www.yourlandmark.com
Sales Range: $1-9.9 Million
Emp.: 10
Construction Management Services
N.A.I.C.S.: 236115
Gary Wisniewski (Founder, Pres & CEO)
David Huffaker (Mgr-Sls)

Parkway Financial Group, LLC   (1)
Tel.: (850) 696-0133
Web Site:
   https://www.parkwayfinancialgrp.com
Financial Investment Services
N.A.I.C.S.: 523940

Peachtree Communities, LLC   (1)
41 Perimeter Ctr E, Atlanta, GA 30346
Tel.: (678) 533-1160
Web Site:
   http://www.centurycommunities.com
Single-Family Housing
N.A.I.C.S.: 236115

Sundquist Homes LLC   (1)
16108 Ash Way Ste 201, Lynnwood, WA 98087
Tel.: (425) 775-8661
Residential Remodeler
N.A.I.C.S.: 236118

The Retreat at Ridgegate, LLC   (1)
10736 Bluffside Dr, Lone Tree, CO 80124
Tel.: (720) 643-1906
Housing Development Services
N.A.I.C.S.: 236117

CENTURY NEXT FINANCIAL CORPORATION
505 N Vienna St, Ruston, LA 71270
Tel.: (318) 255-3733   LA
Web Site: https://www.cnext.bank
Year Founded: 2010
CTUY—(OTCIQ)
Rev.: $28,604,000
Assets: $515,070,000
Liabilities: $459,550,000
Net Worth: $55,520,000
Earnings: $5,214,000
Emp.: 124
Fiscal Year-end: 12/31/20
Bank Holding Company
N.A.I.C.S.: 551111
William D. Hogan (Pres & CEO)
Mark A. Taylor (CFO & Exec VP)
David Layne Weeks (Chief Credit Officer & Exec VP)
Lorie R. Hamlin (COO & Exec VP)
Scott R. Thompson (Chm)
John Tompkins (VP-Lending & Admin)
Angela Carpenter (Sr VP-Ops & Mktg)
Courtnie Beach (Sr VP-Comml Lending)
Mitsy Huffstetler (Compliance Officer & Sr VP)
Toni Bacon (Sr VP-Comml Lending)
Tammy Walsworth (Sr VP-Loan Admin)
Nicholas Austin (VP-Comml Lending)
Terry Burns (VP-Lending Compliance)
Sheri Burt (VP-Lending)
Christy Bishop (VP-Relationship Banking)
Matt Winkelpleck (VP-Mortgage Lending)
Mallory Taylor (VP-Fin)
Amanda Taunton (VP-IT)

Alan Roberson (VP & Controller)
Carla Raborn (VP-HR)
Denny Lee (VP-Lending)
Johnathan Canley (VP-Lending)
Charles Young (VP-Compliance)
Sarah Cantley (VP-Mortgage)
Christy Martin (VP & Branch Mgr)
Corbitt Holloway (VP-Credit Review)
Angie Johnson (VP)
Connie Kelley (VP-Retail Lending)
Gretchen Tiser (VP-Credit Svcs)
Michael Wilke (VP-Lending & Branch Mgr)

Subsidiaries:

Bank of Ruston   (1)
PO Box 949, Ruston, LA 71273-0949
Tel.: (318) 255-3733
Web Site: http://www.bankruston.com
Sales Range: $25-49.9 Million
Emp.: 40
Banking Services
N.A.I.C.S.: 522110
Mark A. Taylor (CFO)
Chastain Wardlaw (VP-Bus Dev)

CENTURY THERAPEUTICS, INC.
25 N 38th St 11th Fl, Philadelphia, PA 19104
Tel.: (267) 817-5790   DE
Web Site: https://www.centurytx.com
Year Founded: 2018
IPSC—(NASDAQ)
Rev.: $5,199,000
Assets: $486,544,000
Liabilities: $183,806,000
Net Worth: $302,738,000
Earnings: ($130,932,000)
Emp.: 163
Fiscal Year-end: 12/31/22
Research & Development in Biotechnology (except Nanobiotechnology)
N.A.I.C.S.: 541714
Gregory Russotti (Chief Tech & Mfg Officer)
Hy Levitsky (Pres-R&D)
Luis Borges (Chief Scientific Officer)
Adrienne Farid (COO)
Michael Diem (CFO)
Michael Naso (VP-Cell Engrg)
Carl Burke (VP-Dev & Mfg)
Douglas Carr (Interim Principal Fin Officer & Sr VP-Fin & Ops)
Shane Williams (Chief People Officer)
Kenneth J. Dow (VP-Law)
Mark Wallet (VP & Head-Immunology)
Melody L. Eble (VP-Regulatory Affairs)

CEPTON, INC.
399 W Trimble Rd, San Jose, CA 95131
Tel.: (408) 459-7579   DE
Web Site: https://www.cepton.com
Year Founded: 2010
CPTN—(NASDAQ)
Rev.: $7,426,000
Assets: $50,316,000
Liabilities: $48,683,000
Net Worth: $1,633,000
Earnings: $9,380,000
Fiscal Year-end: 12/31/22
Motor Vehicle Parts Mfr
N.A.I.C.S.: 336390
Jun Pei (Chm, Pres & CEO)
Dongyi Liao (CTO)

CERES GLOBAL AG CORP.
701 Xenia Ave S Ste 400, Golden Valley, MN 55416
Tel.: (952) 746-6800   Ca
Web Site:
   https://www.ceresglobalagcorp.com
Year Founded: 2007

CRP—(TSX)
Rev.: $438,396,000
Assets: $212,964,000
Liabilities: $82,200,000
Net Worth: $130,764,000
Earnings: ($16,871,000)
Fiscal Year-end: 06/30/19
Asset Management Services
N.A.I.C.S.: 523940
Carlos Paz (Pres, CEO, VP & Comml Dir)
Blake Amundson (CFO & VP)
Holly Dammer (VP-Human Resources)
Jennifer Henderson (Gen Counsel, Sec & VP)
Paul Backowski (Dir-Commercial)
Dale Heide (Mng Dir)
Jeff Wildeman (Mng Dir)
James T. Vanasek (Chm)

Subsidiaries:

Delmar Commodities Ltd.   (1)
2-915 Navigator Road, PO Box 1055, Winkler, R6W 0L7, MB, Canada
Tel.: (888) 974-7246
Web Site:
   http://www.delmarcommodities.com
Sales Range: $10-24.9 Million
Grain Mfr
N.A.I.C.S.: 493130
Dale Heide (Pres)
Darryl Harder (Office Mgr)
Scott Crick (CFO & Exec VP)

Plant (Domestic):

Delmar Commodities Ltd. - Beausejour Facility   (2)
1094 Selch St, Beausejour, R0E 0C0, MB, Canada
Tel.: (204) 268-9797
Grain Storage Services
N.A.I.C.S.: 493130

Delmar Commodities Ltd. - Gladstone Elevator Facility   (2)
72 Church St, Gladstone, R0J 0T0, MB, Canada
Tel.: (204) 385-2292
Grain Distr
N.A.I.C.S.: 424510
Vaughn Guy (Mgr)

Delmar Commodities Ltd. - Newdale Elevator Facility   (2)
2 Elevator Road, Newdale, R0J 1J0, MB, Canada
Tel.: (204) 849-2228
Oilseed Processing Services
N.A.I.C.S.: 311224
Michael Besser (Mgr)

Delmar Commodities Ltd. - Somerset Elevator Facility   (2)
296 Carlton Avenue, Somerset, R0G 2L0, MB, Canada
Tel.: (204) 744-2126
Oilseed Processing Services
N.A.I.C.S.: 311224
Ken Desrochers (Mgr)

Delmar Commodities Ltd. - Westroc Elevator Facility   (2)
Hwy 50 & Hwy 16 78075, Westbourne, R0H 1P0, MB, Canada
Tel.: (204) 385-2975
Grain Distr
N.A.I.C.S.: 424510
Glenn Bjarnarson (Mgr)

Subsidiary (Domestic):

Jordan Mills Inc   (2)
Hwy 23 & Hwy 3, Roland, R0G 1T0, MB, Canada
Tel.: (204) 343-3456
Grain Storage Services
N.A.I.C.S.: 493130

CERES VENTURES, INC.
430 Pk Ave Ste 702, New York, NY 10022
Tel.: (212) 246-3030
CEVE—(OTCEM)

Ceres Ventures, Inc.—(Continued)

Asset Management Services
N.A.I.C.S.: 523940

CERMETEK MICROELEC-TRONICS, INC.

2211 Fortune Dr Ste B, San Jose, CA
95131
Tel.: (408) 942-2200　　DE
Web Site: https://www.cermetek.com
Year Founded: 1968
CRMK—(OTCIQ)
Electronic Computer Manufacturing
N.A.I.C.S.: 334111
Jim Hansel *(Fin Mgr)*

CERTARA, INC.

100 Overlook Ctr Ste 101, Princeton,
NJ 08540
Tel.: (609) 716-7900
Web Site: https://www.certara.com
CERT—(NASDAQ)
Rev.: $354,337,000
Assets: $1,563,140,000
Liabilities: $516,300,000
Net Worth: $1,046,840,000
Earnings: ($55,357,000)
Emp.: 1,338
Fiscal Year-end: 12/31/23
Drug Development Support Services
N.A.I.C.S.: 541690
William F. Feehery *(CEO)*
John E. Gallagher III *(CFO)*
Amin Rostami *(Chief Scientific Officer)*
Jieun W. Choe *(Chief Strategy & Mktg Officer)*
Jaap Mandema *(Chief Innovation Officer)*
Richard M. Traynor *(Gen Counsel)*
Robert Aspbury *(Pres-Simcyp)*
Leif E. Pedersen *(Pres-Software)*
Ron DiSantis *(Sr VP)*
Nicolette D. Sherman *(Chief HR Officer)*
Patrick F. Smith *(Pres)*
Sheila Rocchio *(CMO)*
James E. Cashman III *(Chm)*

Subsidiaries:

Certara UK Limited　　　　　　(1)
Level 2-Acero 1 Concourse Way, Sheffield,
S1 2BJ, United Kingdom
Tel.: (44) 1144512200
Web Site: http://www.certara.com
Pharmaceutical Development Support Services
N.A.I.C.S.: 541990
Steve Toon *(Pres & Mng Dir)*

Certara USA, Inc. - Saint Louis　(1)
210 N Tucker Blvd Ste 350, Saint Louis,
MO 63101
Tel.: (314) 647-1099
Pharmaceutical Research & Development Services
N.A.I.C.S.: 541715

Pinnacle 21, LLC　　　　　　　(1)
1777 Sentry Pkwy WSte 405, Blue Bell, PA
19422
Web Site: https://www.pinnacle21.com
Computer Related Services
N.A.I.C.S.: 541519
Max Kanevsky *(Founder & CEO)*
Tim Stone *(CTO)*

Synchrogenix Information Strategies
Inc.　　　　　　　　　　　　　(1)
2 Righter Pkwy Ste 205, Wilmington, DE
19803
Tel.: (302) 892-4800
Web Site: http://www.certara.com
Regulatory Writing Services
N.A.I.C.S.: 541690
Kelley Kendle *(Pres-Regulatory Strategy & Head-Writing Div)*
Steven Sibley *(VP-Global Submissions & Submission Leadership)*
Lauren Sobocinski *(Sr Dir-Global Bus Dev)*

CERTIVE SOLUTIONS INC.

8149 N 87th pl, Scottsdale, AZ 85258
Tel.: (480) 922-5327　　　　BC
Web Site: https://certivehealth.com
Year Founded: 2010
CBP—(CNSX)
Rev.: $1,109,687
Assets: $939,374
Liabilities: $7,015,590
Net Worth: ($6,076,216)
Earnings: ($1,065,748)
Fiscal Year-end: 05/31/19
Software Publisher
N.A.I.C.S.: 513210
Van H. Potter *(CMO)*
Michael J. Miller *(Sec)*
Tom Marreel *(CEO)*
Tim Hyland *(CFO & Treas)*
Scott Thomas *(VP-IR)*

Subsidiaries:

Titan Health Management Solutions,
Inc.　　　　　　　　　　　　　(1)
2500 N Pantano Rd Ste 120, Tucson, AZ
85715
Tel.: (520) 258-0560
Web Site: http://www.titan-health.com
Sales Range: $1-9.9 Million
Emp.: 15
Hospital Revenue Cycle Management Services
N.A.I.C.S.: 561499
Thomas J. Hoehner *(CEO)*
Todd E. Hisey *(COO)*
Tom Pepping *(VP-Bus Dev)*

CERUS CORPORATION

1220 Concord Ave, Concord, CA
94520
Tel.: (925) 288-6000　　　　DE
Web Site: https://www.cerus.com
Year Founded: 1970
CERS—(NASDAQ)
Rev.: $162,048,000
Assets: $218,092,000
Liabilities: $149,530,000
Net Worth: $68,562,000
Earnings: ($42,779,000)
Emp.: 362
Fiscal Year-end: 12/31/22
Developer of Blood-Pathogen Inactivation Systems
N.A.I.C.S.: 325412
William M. Greenman *(Pres & CEO)*
Lori L. Roll *(Sec & VP-Admin)*
Kevin D. Green *(CFO & VP-Fin)*
Chrystal Menard *(Chief Legal Officer & Gen Counsel)*
Carol M. Moore *(Sr VP-Regulatory Affairs & Quality)*
Nina Mufti *(VP-Dev)*
Richard J. Benjamin *(Chief Medical Officer)*
Vivek K. Jayaraman *(COO)*
Yasmin Singh *(VP-Dev)*

Subsidiaries:

Cerus Europe B.V.　　　　　　(1)
Stationsstraat 79-D, 3811 MH, Amersfoort,
Netherlands
Tel.: (31) 33 496 0600
Web Site: https://www.cerus.com
Sales Range: $75-00.0 Million
Pharmaceuticals Mfr
N.A.I.C.S.: 325412

CERVOMED INC.

20 Park Plz Ste 424, Boston, MA
02116
Tel.: (617) 744-4400　　　　DE
Web Site: https://www.cervomed.com
CRVO—(NASDAQ)
Rev.: $380,752
Assets: $22,635,052
Liabilities: $2,417,336
Net Worth: $20,217,716
Earnings: ($15,591,428)
Emp.: 7

Fiscal Year-end: 12/31/22
Biopharmaceutical Developer
N.A.I.C.S.: 325412
Robert J. Cobuzzi Jr. *(COO)*
William Elder *(CFO, Principal Acctg Officer, Gen Counsel & Sec)*
Sylvie Gregoire *(Co-Founder & Chm)*
Kelly Blackburn *(Sr VP-Clinical Dev)*
John J. Alam *(Co-Founder & CEO)*

Subsidiaries:

Diffusion Pharmaceuticals LLC　(1)
2020 Avon Ct Ste 4, Charlottesville, VA
22902
Tel.: (434) 220-0718
Web Site: http://www.diffusionpharma.com
Biopharmaceutical Developer
N.A.I.C.S.: 541715

CES SYNERGIES, INC.

Tel.: (813) 783-1688　　　　NV
Web Site: https://www.crossenv.com
Year Founded: 2010
CESX—(OTCEM)
Sales Range: $10-24.9 Million
Emp.: 124
Holding Company; Demolition, Asbestos Removal & Mold Abatement Services
N.A.I.C.S.: 551112
Clyde Alan Biston *(Founder, Pres & CEO)*
James Lee Smith *(VP)*
John Eugene Tostanoski *(CEO)*
Sharon Margaret Rosenbauer *(CFO, Treas & VP)*

Subsidiaries:

Cross Environmental Services,
Inc.　　　　　　　　　　　　　(1)
39646 Fig St, Zephyrhills, FL 33540
Tel.: (813) 783-1688
Web Site: http://www.crossenv.com
Sales Range: $10-24.9 Million
Emp.: 40
Demolition, Asbestos Removal & Mold Abatement Services
N.A.I.C.S.: 562910
Clyde Alan Biston *(Founder & Pres)*
Linda Weyant *(Mgr-Accts Payable)*
Tony Overstreet *(Project Mgr)*

CEVA, INC.

15245 Shady Grove Rd Ste 400,
Rockville, MD 20850
Tel.: (240) 308-8328　　　　DE
Web Site: https://www.ceva-ip.com
Year Founded: 1993
CEVA—(NASDAQ)
Rev.: $134,648,000
Assets: $308,442,000
Liabilities: $49,571,000
Net Worth: $258,871,000
Earnings: ($23,183,000)
Emp.: 485
Fiscal Year-end: 12/31/22
Intellectual Property Solutions for Mobile Internet Devices Designer & Developer
N.A.I.C.S.: 334413
Amir Panush *(CEO)*
Chad Lucien *(VP & Gen Mgr-Sensor Fusion BU)*
Michael Boukaya *(COO)*
Gweltaz Toquet *(Chief Comml Officer)*
Dana Maor-Megiddo *(VP-People)*
Tal Shalev *(VP & Gen Mgr-Wireless IoT BU)*
Guy Keshet *(VP & Gen Mgr-Mobile Broadband BU)*
Iri Trashanski *(Chief Strategy Officer)*
Yaniv Arieli *(CFO & Treas)*

Subsidiaries:

CEVA D.S.P. Limited　　　　　(1)
2 Maskit Street, PO Box 4047, Herzliyya,
4612001, Israel
Tel.: (972) 99613700

Web Site: http://www.ceva-dsp.com
Wireless Application Software Publisher
N.A.I.C.S.: 513210

CEVA France　　　　　　　　　(1)
Les Bureaux Green Side 5 Bat 6 400 avenue Roumanille, Sophia Antipolis, 06410,
Biot, France
Tel.: (33) 483881200
Semiconductor Mfr
N.A.I.C.S.: 334413

CEVA Ireland Limited　　　　　(1)
Unit A2 First Floor Building 6500 Airport
Business Park Kinsale Road, Cork, 2, Ireland
Tel.: (353) 12373900
Electronic Components Mfr
N.A.I.C.S.: 334419

CEVA Limited　　　　　　　　　(1)
Bedeck Building First Floor 463 Lisburn Rd,
Belfast, BT9 7EZ, United Kingdom
Tel.: (44) 2890688800
Logistic Services
N.A.I.C.S.: 541614

Hillcrest Laboratories, Inc.　　(1)
15245 Shady Grove Rd Ste 400, Rockville,
MD 20850
Tel.: (240) 386-0600
Web Site: http://www.hillcrestlabs.com
Electronic Products Mfr
N.A.I.C.S.: 334419
Chad Lucien *(VP & Gen Mgr)*
Steve Scheirey *(Sr Dir-Software)*

Nihon CEVA K.K.　　　　　　　(1)
1-4-24 Taishidou Hagitou Bldg 7F,
Setagaya-ku, Tokyo, 154-0004,
Japan　　　　　　　　　　　(100%)
Tel.: (81) 357799620
Web Site: http://www.ceva-dsp.com
Sales Range: $100-124.9 Million
Emp.: 5
Provider of Telecommunications Equipment
N.A.I.C.S.: 238210

CF BANKSHARES INC.

4960 E Dublin Granville Rd Ste 400,
Columbus, OH 43081
Tel.: (614) 505-5805　　　　DE
Web Site:
　　https://www.cfbankonline.com
Year Founded: 1892
CFBK—(NASDAQ)
Rev.: $70,974,000
Assets: $1,820,174,000
Liabilities: $1,680,926,000
Net Worth: $139,248,000
Earnings: $18,164,000
Emp.: 120
Fiscal Year-end: 12/31/22
Bank Holding Company
N.A.I.C.S.: 551111
Timothy T. O'Dell *(Pres & CEO)*
Kevin J. Beerman *(Officer-Fin & Sr VP)*
Tim Meder *(Sr VP & Sr Mgr-Comml Credit)*

Subsidiaries:

CFBank, National Association　(1)
3009 Smith Rd Ste 100, Fairlawn, OH
44333　　　　　　　　　　　(100%)
Tel.: (330) 666-7979
Web Site: http://www.cfbankonline.com
Sales Range: $10-24.9 Million
Emp.: 50
Federal Savings Bank
N.A.I.C.S.: 522180
Timothy T. O'Dell *(Pres & CEO)*
Robert E. Hoeweler *(Chm)*
Lori Wood *(Officer-Treasury Mgmt & Asst VP)*
Dan Ludwig *(Sr VP-Comml Real Estate)*
Anne Cheh-Falb *(VP & Sr Mgr-Relationship-Cleveland)*
Whitney Lewis *(VP-Treasury Mgmt)*
John J. Catalano *(Pres-Equipment Fin)*
Brad Ringwald *(Chief Comml Banking Officer)*

CF INDUSTRIES HOLDINGS, INC.

2375 Waterview Dr, Northbrook, IL 60062
Tel.: (847) 405-2400   DE
Web Site:
https://www.cfindustries.com
Year Founded: 1946
CF—(NYSE)
Rev.: $6,631,000,000
Assets: $14,376,000,000
Liabilities: $6,003,000,000
Net Worth: $8,373,000,000
Earnings: $1,525,000,000
Emp.: 2,700
Fiscal Year-end: 12/31/23
Chemical Fertilizers Mfr & Whslr
N.A.I.C.S.: 325311
W. Anthony Will (Pres & CEO)
Richard A. Hoker (VP & Controller)
Christopher D. Bohn (CFO, COO & Exec VP)
Eric B. Bergstrom (Dir-Cash Mngmt)
Bert A. Frost (Exec VP-Sls, Market Dev, and Supply Chain)
Ashraf K. Malik (Sr VP-Mfg & Distr)
Chris Close (Dir-Corp Comm)
Susan L. Menzel (Sr VP-HR)
Michael P. McGrane (Gen Counsel, Sec & VP)
Julie Scheck Freigang (CIO & VP)
Linda M. Dempsey (VP-Pub Affairs)
Martin Jarosick (VP-IR)
Mark T. Campbell (VP-Supply Chain)
Jeffrey L. Olin (VP-Tax)
Martin A. Jarosick (VP)

Subsidiaries:

CF Industries Nitrogen, LLC   (1)
4608 Hwy 49 E, Yazoo City, MS 39194
Tel.: (662) 746-4131
Emp.: 275
Nitrogenous Fertilizer Mfr
N.A.I.C.S.: 325311

CF Industries Sales, LLC   (1)
5300 Pine Bend Trail, Rosemount, MN 55068
Tel.: (651) 437-6191
Web Site: https://www.cfindustries.com
Emp.: 50
Fertilizer Distr
N.A.I.C.S.: 424910
Francis G. Meyer (CFO)

CF Industries, Inc.   (1)
4 Pkwy N Ste 400, Deerfield, IL 60015
Tel.: (847) 405-2400
Web Site: https://www.cfindustries.com
Sales Range: $50-74.9 Million
Emp.: 400
Chemical Fertilizers Mfr & Whslr
N.A.I.C.S.: 325311

Plant (Domestic):

CF Industries, Inc. - Donaldsonville Nitrogen Complex   (2)
Hwy 3089, Donaldsonville, LA 70346
Tel.: (225) 473-8291
Web Site: http://www.cfindustries.com
Sales Range: $10-24.9 Million
Emp.: 485
Anhydrous Ammonia & Urea Production Services
N.A.I.C.S.: 325311

CF Industries, Inc. - Woodward Plant   (2)
1000 Terra Dr, Woodward, OK 73801
Tel.: (580) 256-8651
Web Site: http://www.cfindustries.com
Emp.: 160
Ammonia Mfr
N.A.I.C.S.: 325311
David Borzik (Gen Mgr)

CF Industries, Inc. - Yazoo City Plant   (2)
4608 Hwy 49 E, Yazoo City, MS 39194
Tel.: (662) 746-4131
Web Site: http://www.cfindustries.com
Sales Range: $75-99.9 Million
Emp.: 275

Ammonia, Ammonium Nitrate & Other Nitrogen-Based Products Mfr
N.A.I.C.S.: 325311

Point Lisas Nitrogen Limited   (1)
North Caspian Drive, Point Lisas Industrial Estate, Point Lisas, Trinidad & Tobago   (50%)
Tel.: (868) 6363776
Web Site: https://www.plnltt.com
Ammonia Mfr & Distr
N.A.I.C.S.: 325311

Terra Nitrogen Company, L.P.   (1)
4 Pkwy N Ste 400, Deerfield, IL 60015   (75.32%)
Tel.: (847) 405-2400
Rev.: $397,200,000
Assets: $403,900,000
Liabilities: $35,800,000
Net Worth: $368,100,000
Earnings: $153,900,000
Fiscal Year-end: 12/31/2017
Nitrogen Fertilizer Products Mfr
N.A.I.C.S.: 325311
W. Anthony Will (Pres & CEO)

CFN ENTERPRISES INC.

2601 Ocean Park Blvd Ste 310, Santa Monica, CA 90405
Tel.: (949) 548-2253   DE
Web Site:
https://www.cfnenterprisesinc.com
CNFN—(OTCQB)
Rev.: $4,317,490
Assets: $870,551
Liabilities: $10,042,900
Net Worth: ($9,172,349)
Earnings: ($9,922,219)
Emp.: 14
Fiscal Year-end: 12/31/22
Online Marketing Services
N.A.I.C.S.: 541613
Brian Ross (Chm, Pres & CEO)
Allen Park (COO)
Rami Abi (Chief Strategy Officer)
Anness Ziadeh (Chief Sls & Mktg Officer)
Mario Marsillo Jr. (Chief Investment Officer)

CFSB BANCORP, INC.

15 Beach St, Quincy, MA 02170
Tel.: (617) 471-0750   MA
Web Site:
https://www.colonialfed.com
Year Founded: 2022
CFSB—(NASDAQ)
Rev.: $11,342,000
Assets: $349,007,000
Liabilities: $273,118,000
Net Worth: $75,889,000
Earnings: $1,446,000
Emp.: 29
Fiscal Year-end: 06/30/23
Offices of Bank Holding Companies
N.A.I.C.S.: 551111
Michael E. McFarland (Pres & CEO)
Susan Shea (COO & Treas)
James M. O'Leary Jr. (Chm)

CG ONCOLOGY, INC.

400 Spectrum Ctr Dr Ste 2040, Irvine, CA 92618
Tel.: (949) 409-3700   DE
Web Site:
https://www.cgoncology.com
Year Founded: 2010
CGON—(NASDAQ)
Rev.: $204,000
Assets: $199,301,000
Liabilities: $322,401,000
Net Worth: ($123,100,000)
Earnings: ($67,798,000)
Emp.: 61
Fiscal Year-end: 12/31/23
Biotechnology Research & Development Services
N.A.I.C.S.: 541714

CGE ENERGY INC.

7627 Park Pl, Brighton, MI 48116
Tel.: (248) 446-1344   DE
Web Site:
https://www.cgeenergy.com
Year Founded: 1998
CGEI—(OTCIQ)
Offices of Other Holding Companies
N.A.I.C.S.: 551112
Bryan Zaplitny (Pres & CEO)
Kevin B. Cook (Sec)
Mark A. Cecil (Treas)
Paul Schneider (VP-Mktg & Sec)
Derek Spangler (VP-Project Mgmt & Dev)
Gary L. Westerholm (VP-Fin)
Harold Telners (CFO)
Richard Bearup (VP-Lighting Div)
Gary Zaplitny (VP-Field Svcs)

Subsidiaries:

Clean Green Energy, LLC   (1)
7627 Park Pl Ste 401, Brighton, MI 48116
Tel.: (248) 446-1344
Web Site:
http://www.cleangreenenergyllc.com
Alternative Energy Systems Design & Installation Services
N.A.I.C.S.: 238290
Bryan Zaplitny (Pres & CEO)

CGROWTH CAPITAL INC.

4300 Biscayne Blvd Ste 203, Miami, FL 33137
Tel.: (305) 390-1880   DE
Web Site:
https://www.cgrowthcapital.com
Year Founded: 1986
CGRA—(OTCIQ)
Mining-Related Asset Management Services
N.A.I.C.S.: 523999
Nicolas Link (Chm & CEO)

CHAMPION HOMES, INC.

755 W Big Beaver Rd Ste 1000, Troy, MI 48084
Tel.: (248) 614-8211   IN
Web Site:
https://ir.championhomes.com
Year Founded: 1951
SKY—(NYSE)
Rev.: $2,207,229,000
Assets: $1,234,619,000
Liabilities: $409,506,000
Net Worth: $825,113,000
Earnings: $248,044,000
Emp.: 8,400
Fiscal Year-end: 04/02/22
Holding Company; Prefabricated Housing, Mobile Home & Recreational Vehicles Mfr & Distr
N.A.I.C.S.: 551112
Mark J. Yost (Pres & CEO)
Laurel Krueger (Gen Counsel, Sec & Sr VP)
Laurie Hough (CFO, Treas & Exec VP)
Timothy M. Larson (Chief Growth Officer)
Timothy Burkhardt (VP & Controller)
Joseph Kimmell (Exec VP-Operations)
Laurel Krueger (Gen Counsel, Sec & Sr VP)

Subsidiaries:

Champion Enterprises Holdings, LLC   (1)
755 W Big Beaver Rd Ste 1000, Troy, MI 48084
Tel.: (248) 614-8265
Web Site: http://www.championhomes.com
Emp.: 5,200
Holding Company; Real Estate Builders & Brokers
N.A.I.C.S.: 551112
Timothy J. Bernlohr (Chm)

Subsidiary (Domestic):

Champion Home Builders Inc.   (2)
755 W Big Beaver Rd Ste 1000, Troy, MI 48084
Tel.: (248) 614-8200
Web Site: https://www.championhomes.com
Emp.: 8,400
Manufactured House Building Services
N.A.I.C.S.: 321991
Laurel Krueger (Deputy Gen Counsel)

Subsidiary (Domestic):

Athens Park Homes, LLC   (3)
3401 W Corsicana St, Athens, TX 75751
Tel.: (903) 677-0108
Web Site: http://www.athensparkhomes.com
Modular Houses Mfr
N.A.I.C.S.: 321991
Dick Grymonprez (Dir-Park Model Sls)

Scotbilt Homes, Inc.   (3)
2888 Fulford Rd, Waycross, GA 31503
Tel.: (912) 490-7268
Web Site: http://scotbilt.com
Rev.: $7,500,000
Emp.: 43
Residential Remodeler
N.A.I.C.S.: 236118
Shea Jones (VP & Mgr-Sls)
Brandy Tompkins (Coord-Sls)

Subsidiary (Domestic):

Champion Homes of Tennessee   (2)
2073 Evergreen St, Dresden, TN 38225
Tel.: (731) 364-4600
Web Site: http://www.championhomes.com
Mobile Homes Building Services
N.A.I.C.S.: 236115
Mike Barnett (Gen Mgr)

Subsidiary (Non-US):

Moduline Industries (Canada) Ltd.   (2)
1175 Railway St, Penticton, V2A 5X5, BC, Canada
Tel.: (250) 493-0122
Web Site: http://www.moduline.ca
Sales Range: $100-124.9 Million
Emp.: 150
Mobile Home Mfr & Whslr
N.A.I.C.S.: 321991

Subsidiary (Domestic):

Titan Mobile Homes, Inc.   (2)
951 Rte 12 S, Sangerfield, NY 13455
Tel.: (315) 841-4122
Web Site: http://www.titanhomesny.com
Mobile Home Mfr
N.A.I.C.S.: 321991

Homette Corporation   (1)
2520 By-Pass Rd, Elkhart, IN 46515
Tel.: (574) 294-6521
Web Site: http://www.skylinepm.com
Mobile Home Mfr
N.A.I.C.S.: 321991

Skyline Homes, Inc.   (1)
2520 By-Pass Rd, Elkhart, IN 46515
Tel.: (574) 294-6521
Web Site: https://www.skylinehomes.com
Sales Range: $125-149.9 Million
Prefabricated Homes Mfr
N.A.I.C.S.: 321992

CHAMPION INDUSTRIES, INC.

2450-90 1st Ave, Huntington, WV 25705
Tel.: (304) 528-2700   WV
Web Site: https://www.champion-industries.com
Year Founded: 1992
CHMP—(OTCIQ)
Sales Range: $50-74.9 Million
Emp.: 316
Commercial Printer, Business Forms Mfr & Office Products & Office Furniture Supplier
N.A.I.C.S.: 323111
Justin Todd Evans (CFO & Sr VP)
Adam M. Reynolds (Pres & CEO)

Champion Industries, Inc.—(Continued)

Subsidiaries:

Capitol Business Equipment, Inc. (1)
645 S McDonough St, Montgomery, AL
36104
Tel.: (334) 265-8903
Web Site: http://www.cbe-inc.com
Security System Whslr
N.A.I.C.S.: 423610
James Anderson (CFO)

Carolina Cut Sheets, Inc. (1)
2450 1st Ave, Huntington, WV
25703 (100%)
Tel.: (304) 528-2700
Web Site: http://www.champion-
industries.com
Sales Range: $10-24.9 Million
Emp.: 15
Printing Services
N.A.I.C.S.: 323111
Larry Moore (Gen Mgr)

**Champion Graphic
Communications (1)**
10848 Airline Hwy, Baton Rouge, LA 70816
Tel.: (225) 291-9090
Web Site: http://www.champion-
industries.com
Sales Range: $25-49.9 Million
Emp.: 30
Commercial Printing & Wholesale Office
Supplies & Furniture
N.A.I.C.S.: 323111
Marshall T. Reynolds (Chm & CEO)

Champion Industries, Inc. (1)
700 4th St, Clarksburg, WV 26301-4708
Tel.: (304) 623-6688
Web Site: http://www.champion-
industries.com
Sales Range: $50-74.9 Million
Emp.: 7
Commercial Printing & Wholesale Office
Supplies & Furniture
N.A.I.C.S.: 459410

Champion Publishing, Inc. (1)
946 5th Ave, Huntington, WV 25701
Tel.: (304) 526-4000
Newspaper Publishing Services
N.A.I.C.S.: 513110

Donihe Graphics, Inc. (1)
766 Brookside Dr, Kingsport, TN 37660-
6614
Tel.: (423) 246-2800
Sales Range: $10-24.9 Million
Emp.: 53
Commercial Printing, Wholesale Office Sup-
plies & Furniture
N.A.I.C.S.: 323111

Interform Corporation (1)
1901 Mayview Rd, Bridgeville, PA 15017-
1520
Tel.: (412) 221-7321
Web Site: http://www.interformsolutions.com
Manifold Business Forms; Commercial Let-
terpresses & Offset Printing
N.A.I.C.S.: 323111

Division (Domestic):

**Consolidated Graphic
Communications (2)**
1901 Mayview Rd, Bridgeville, PA
15017-1520 (100%)
Tel.: (412) 221-2700
Web Site: http://www.cgc1.com
Sales Range: $10-24.9 Million
Emp.: 30
Distr of Printed Material
N.A.I.C.S.: 323111

River Cities Printing (1)
2450 1st Ave, Huntington, WV 25703
Tel.: (304) 528-5496
Web Site: http://www.rivercitiesprinting.com
Commercial Printing Services
N.A.I.C.S.: 323111
Cindy Crigger (Dir-Mktg & Bus Dev)
Lisa A. Marcum (Sls Mgr-Comml)

Smith & Butterfield Co., Inc. (1)
2800 Lynch Rd, Evansville, IN
47711 (100%)
Tel.: (270) 683-3555

Web Site: http://www.smithbutterfield.com
Sales Range: $25-49.9 Million
Emp.: 15
Retail Store, Office Supplies & Furniture
N.A.I.C.S.: 459410
Marshall T. Reynolds (Chm)
Steve Baren (Pres)

Stationers, Inc. (1)
1945 5th Ave 100 in, Huntington, WV 25702
Tel.: (304) 528-2780
Web Site: http://www.stationers-wv.com
Sales Range: $50-74.9 Million
Emp.: 50
Mfr of Office Products, Furniture & Supplies
N.A.I.C.S.: 459410
Marshall Reynolds (Pres)

Division (Domestic):

Capitol Business Interiors (2)
711 Indiana Ave, Charleston, WV
25302-3311 (100%)
Tel.: (304) 346-3342
Web Site: http://www.cbiwv.com
Sales Range: $25-49.9 Million
Emp.: 15
Office Systems & Design
N.A.I.C.S.: 423210
Janet Clayman (Pres)

Garrison Brewer (2)
405 Ann St, Parkersburg, WV 26101
Tel.: (304) 485-8596
Sales Range: $50-74.9 Million
Emp.: 6
Mfr of Office Supplies, Furniture & Products
N.A.I.C.S.: 459410
Marshall T. Reynolds (Chm)

**The Chapman Printing Company,
Inc. (1)**
2450 1st Ave 90, Huntington, WV 25703-
1218
Tel.: (304) 528-2791
Web Site: http://www.champion-
industries.com
Sales Range: $200-249.9 Million
Emp.: 290
Commercial Printer
N.A.I.C.S.: 323111
Marshall T. Reynolds (Chm & CEO)

Plant (Domestic):

**The Chapman Printing Company, Inc.
- Charleston (2)**
3000 Washington St W, Charleston, WV
25387
Tel.: (304) 341-0676
Web Site: http://www.champion-
industries.com
Sales Range: $25-49.9 Million
Emp.: 30
Commercial Printing & Wholesale Office
Supplies & Furniture
N.A.I.C.S.: 323111

**The Chapman Printing Company, Inc.
- Lexington (2)**
890 Russell Cave Rd, Lexington, KY
40505-3466
Tel.: (859) 252-2661
Web Site:
http://www.championindustries.com
Sales Range: $10-24.9 Million
Emp.: 16
Commercial Printer
N.A.I.C.S.: 323111

**The Chapman Printing Company, Inc.
- Parkersburg (2)**
405 Ann St, Parkersburg, WV 26101-5325
Tel.: (304) 485-8596
Web Site: http://www.champion-
industries.com
Sales Range: $1-9.9 Million
Emp.: 25
Commercial Printing & Wholesale Office
Supplies & Furniture
N.A.I.C.S.: 323111

The Merten Company (1)
1515 Central Pkwy, Cincinnati, OH
45214-2815 (100%)
Tel.: (513) 721-5167
Sales Range: $10-24.9 Million
Emp.: 30
Commercial Printing
N.A.I.C.S.: 323111

US Tag & Ticket (1)
2450-90 1st Ave, Huntington, WV
25703 (100%)
Tel.: (304) 691-5046
Web Site: http://www.champion-
industries.com
Sales Range: $50-74.9 Million
Emp.: 52
Commercial Tags Mfr
N.A.I.C.S.: 323111
Marshall Reynolds (Pres)

CHAMPIONS ONCOLOGY, INC.
1 University Plz Ste 307, Hacken-
sack, NJ 07601
Tel.: (201) 808-8400 DE
Web Site:
https://www.championsoncology.com
CSBR—(NASDAQ)
Rev.: $50,155,000
Assets: $26,132,000
Liabilities: $28,035,000
Net Worth: ($1,903,000)
Earnings: ($7,276,000)
Emp.: 210
Fiscal Year-end: 04/30/24
Pharmaceutical Preparation Mfr
N.A.I.C.S.: 325412
Ronnie Morris (Pres & CEO)
David Miller (CFO)
David DeOrnellis (VP-Laboratory
Ops-Global)
Philip Breitfeld (Chief Strategy & In-
novation Officer)
Michael Ritchie (Chief Comml Officer)
Maria Mancini (VP-Pharmacology)
Karin Abarca Heidemann (VP-
Scientific Ops)
David Sidransky (Chm)
Joel Ackerman (Vice Chm)

CHAMPIONX CORPORATION
2445 Technology Forest Blvd Bldg 4
Ste 1200, The Woodlands, TX 77381
Tel.: (281) 403-5772 DE
Web Site:
https://www.championx.com
Year Founded: 2017
CHX—(NASDAQ)
Rev.: $3,758,285,000
Assets: $3,241,702,000
Liabilities: $1,580,671,000
Net Worth: $1,661,031,000
Earnings: $314,238,000
Emp.: 7,100
Fiscal Year-end: 12/31/23
Pump Mfr & Distr
N.A.I.C.S.: 333996
Kenneth M. Fisher (CFO & Exec VP)
Daniel W. Rabun (Chm)
Sivasankaran Somasundaram (Pres
& CEO)
Paul E. Mahoney (Pres-Production &
Automation Technologies)
Rob K. Galloway (Pres-Drilling Tech-
nologies)
Syed Raza (Chief Digital Officer & Sr
VP)
Julia Wright (Gen Counsel, Sec & Sr
VP)
Jordan Zweig (Chief HR Officer & Sr
VP)
Ross O'Dell (Pres-Oilfield & Specialty
Performance)
Mark Eley (Sr VP-Mktg & Tech,
Chemical Technologies & Corp
Comm)
Kurt Kirchof (Sr VP)
Saurabh Nitin (Sr VP-Strategy & Corp
Dev)
Alina Parast (CIO & Sr VP)
Byron Pope (VP-ESG & IR)
Antoine Marcos (Chief Acctg Officer,
VP & Controller)
Deric Bryant (COO & Pres)
Juan Alvarado (Sr VP-Environment-
Quality)
Marc Kalmes (Sr VP)

Subsidiaries:

**ChampionX Oilfield Solutions Nigeria
Limited (1)**
29 Onitsha Road, Trans Amadi, Port Har-
court, Rivers, Nigeria
Tel.: (234) 8152664336
Pumping Equipment Mfr & Distr
N.A.I.C.S.: 333914

RMSpumptools Limited (1)
North Meadows Oldmeldrum, Aberdeen,
AB51 0GQ, United Kingdom
Tel.: (44) 1651874999
Web Site: https://www.rmspumptools.com
Electrical Pump Mfr
N.A.I.C.S.: 333914

Scientific Aviation, Inc. (1)
335 Airport Rd Ste B, Boulder, CO 80301
Tel.: (720) 408-4001
Web Site: https://www.scientificaviation.com
Research & Development in the Physical,
Engineering & Life Sciences
N.A.I.C.S.: 541715
Stephen A. Conley (Pres)

Windrock, Inc. (1)
1832 Midpark Rd Ste 102, Knoxville, TN
37921
Tel.: (865) 330-1100
Web Site: http://www.windrock.com
Rev.: $8,000,000
Emp.: 32
Electrical Equipment Mfr & Distr
N.A.I.C.S.: 335999

CHARDAN NEXTECH ACQUI-
SITION CORP.
17 State St 21st Fl, New York, NY
10004
Tel.: (646) 465-9000 DE
Year Founded: 2020
CNAQU—(NASDAQ)
Investment Services
N.A.I.C.S.: 523999
Kerry Propper (Co-Founder & Chm)
Jonas Grossman (Co-Founder, Pres,
CEO, Treas & Sec)
Steven Urbach (CFO)
Alex Weil (COO)

CHARGE ENTERPRISES, INC.
125 Park Ave 25th Fl, New York, NY
10017
Tel.: (212) 921-2100
Web Site:
https://www.charge.enterprises
Year Founded: 2003
CRGE—(NASDAQ)
Rev.: $697,833,000
Assets: $168,454,000
Liabilities: $144,204,000
Net Worth: $24,250,000
Earnings: ($30,349,000)
Emp.: 332
Fiscal Year-end: 12/31/22
Web Application Services
N.A.I.C.S.: 541511
James Biehl (Chief Legal Officer,
Chief Compliance Officer & Sec)
Mark LaNeve (Pres)
Leah Schweller (CFO)
Craig Denson (Interim CEO & COO)
James Biehl (Chief Legal Officer)
Marc Rosenwald (Controller)
Jamie Yung (Dir)
Mark Buzzell (VP)
Matt Chee (VP)
Christine Cannella (VP)
Robert Caslin (VP)

Subsidiaries:

BW Electrical Services LLC (1)
239 Homestead Rd Unit 2A, Hillsborough,
NJ 08844
Tel.: (908) 281-0660

Web Site: https://www.bwes.com
Electrical Contractor
N.A.I.C.S.: 238210
Al Gutmore (Dir-Pur)
Charles DePasquale (Sr Project Mgr)
Michael S. Wojtowicz (Mng Partner)

Charge Services, LLC (1)
23 W Industrial Loop, Midland, TX 79701
Tel.: (432) 218-7674
Web Site: https://chargerservices.com
Oil Filed Construction Services
N.A.I.C.S.: 237120
Jake Davis (Co-Founder & Chief Mktg Officer)
Tom Hull (Pres & Co-Founder)
Kyle Davis (CEO & Co-Founder)

NextRidge, Inc. (1)
12 Elmwood Rd, Albany, NY 12204
Tel.: (518) 292-6505
Web Site: http://www.nextridgeinc.com
Sales Range: $10-24.9 Million
Emp.: 62
Telecommunications Equipment Repair &
Consulting Services
N.A.I.C.S.: 238210
Shaun P. Mahoney (Chm, Pres & CEO)
Sarah R. Cozzolino (VP & Controller)
Patrick T. Maney Jr. (Chm)

Subsidiary (Domestic):

**ANS Advanced Network Services,
LLC** (2)
12 Elmwood Rd, Albany, NY 12204
Tel.: (518) 292-6555
Web Site: http://www.anscorporate.com
Sales Range: $1-9.9 Million
Emp.: 69
Electrical Contractor
N.A.I.C.S.: 238210
Erik Reidell (Mgr-Product Line)
Dale Snyder (VP-Ops)
Paul Fettuccia (CEO)
Robert W. Hebert (VP-Admin)
Sue Politi (Controller)

**Greenspeed Energy Solutions,
LLC** (2)
2148 Hills Ave Ste H, Atlanta, GA 30318-
2208
Tel.: (404) 924-7400
Electrical Contractor
N.A.I.C.S.: 238210
Richard L. Dobbs (Dir-Sls & Mktg)

TAG Solutions, LLC (2)
12 Elmwood Rd, Albany, NY
12204-2410 (100%)
Tel.: (518) 254-5173
Web Site: https://tagsolutions.wpengine.com
Information Technology Management Services
N.A.I.C.S.: 541512
Jeff Miller (Mgr-Channel Mktg)

**CHARGEPOINT HOLDINGS,
INC.**
240 E Hacienda Ave, Campbell, CA
95008
Tel.: (408) 841-4500 DE
Web Site:
https://www.chargepoint.com
Year Founded: 2019
CHPT—(NYSE)
Rev.: $506,639,000
Assets: $1,103,363,000
Liabilities: $775,687,000
Net Worth: $327,676,000
Earnings: ($457,609,000)
Emp.: 1,650
Fiscal Year-end: 01/31/24
Investment Services
N.A.I.C.S.: 523999
Lawrence Lee (Sr VP-Ops & Support)
Bill Loewenthal (Sr VP-Product)
Jennifer Bowcock (VP-Comm)
Patrick Hamer (VP-Capital Markets &
IR)
Rick Wilmer (Pres & CEO)
Mansi Khetani (CFO)

Subsidiaries:

ChargePoint Inc. (1)

240 E Hacienda Ave, Campbell, CA 95008
Tel.: (408) 841-4500
Web Site: https://www.chargepoint.com
Electric Vehicle Charging Network Services
N.A.I.C.S.: 441330
Sherice R. Torres (CMO)
Pasquale Romano (CEO)
John Paolo Canton (VP-Comm)
AJ Gosselin (Dir-Corp Comm)
Patrick Hamer (VP-Capital Markets & IR)

CHARLES & COLVARD LTD
170 Southport Dr, Morrisville, NC
27560
Tel.: (919) 468-0399 NC
Web Site:
https://charlesandcolvard.com
Year Founded: 1995
CTHR—(NASDAQ)
Rev.: $29,946,234
Assets: $48,884,088
Liabilities: $9,109,502
Net Worth: $39,774,586
Earnings: ($19,580,794)
Emp.: 48
Fiscal Year-end: 06/30/23
Mfr, Marketer & Distributor of Moissanite Jewels
N.A.I.C.S.: 339910
Neal Ira Goldman (Chm)
Don J. O'Connell (Pres & CEO)

Subsidiaries:

Charles & Colvard Direct, LLC (1)
Tel.: (919) 468-0399
Sales Range: $25-49.9 Million
Emp.: 65
Jewelry Mfr
N.A.I.C.S.: 339910
Michelle M. Jones (Pres)

charlesandcolvard.com, LLC (1)
170 Southport Dr, Morrisville, NC
27560 (100%)
Tel.: (919) 882-5503
Web Site:
http://www.charlesandcolvard.com
Jewelry Mfr & Distr
N.A.I.C.S.: 339910

moissaniteoutlet.com, LLC (1)
11010 Lake Grove Blvd Ste 100-497, Morrisville, NC 27560
Jewelry Retailer
N.A.I.C.S.: 339910

CHARLES RIVER LABORATORIES INTERNATIONAL, INC.
251 Ballardvale St, Wilmington, MA
01887
Tel.: (781) 222-6000 MA
Web Site: https://www.criver.com
Year Founded: 1951
CRL—(NYSE)
Rev.: $4,129,409,000
Assets: $8,195,001,000
Liabilities: $4,592,725,000
Net Worth: $3,602,276,000
Earnings: $474,624,000
Emp.: 20,000
Fiscal Year-end: 12/30/23
Pharmaceutical & Biotechnology Research Services
N.A.I.C.S.: 325414
James C. Foster (Chm, Pres & CEO)
Brian Bathgate (Sr VP-European
Safety Assessment)
John C. Ho (Chief Strategy Officer &
Sr VP-Corp Strategy)
Foster T. Jordan (Sr VP-Microbial Solutions)
William D. Barbo (Exec VP)
Matthew L. Daniel (Chief Compliance
Officer, Gen Counsel, Sec & Sr VP)
Joseph W. LaPlume (Exec VP-Corp
Dev & Strategy)
Birgit Girshick (COO & Exec VP)
Colin Dunn (Sr VP-Global Res Models & Svcs)

Kristen M. Eisenhauer (Chief Comml
Officer & Sr VP)
Michael G. Knell (Chief Acctg Officer
& Sr VP)
Gina Mullane (CMO & Sr VP)
Barbara J. Patterson (Sr VP-
Regulatory Affairs & Compliance)
Toni Ahtoniemi (Assoc Dir-Client
Svcs)
Christopher Dowdy (Portfolio Mgr-
Client & Scientific)
John Dubczak (Exec Dir-Reagent
Dev & Pilot Plant Ops)
Christine Farrance (Dir-R&D)
Ken Henderson (Sr Dir-Laboratory
Scientific Diagnostic Svcs)
Julia Schuler (Dir-Res)
Jill Schultz (Sr Dir-Technical Svcs &
Quality Control)
Clare Lenich (Mgr-Technical Svcs)
Wilbert Frieling (Sr VP-Discovery
Svcs-Global)
Michel Assad (Exec Dir-Orthopedics
& Biomaterials)
Francois Bergeron (Dir-Bus Dev)
Elise M. Lewis (Sr Dir-Toxicology)
Danielle Brown (Dir-Site)
Sandra Love (Dir-Safety Pharmacology)
Miriam A. Rosario (Assoc Dir-
Regulatory Affairs)
Tom Haymaker (Assoc Dir-
Pharmacokinetics)
Alan Hoberman (Exec Dir-Global Developmental & Reproductive)
Tuulia Huhtala (Head-Biomarkers &
Molecular Imaging)
Rhiannon Jenkinson (Dir-Science-
Discovery Svcs)
Edward Marsden (Assoc Dir-
Developmental & Reproductive Toxicology)
Genevieve Normand (Gen Mgr)
Flavia H. Pease (CFO & Exec VP)
Kerstin Dolph (Sr VP)
Mark Mintz (CIO)
Linda Allais (Dir)
Philippe Ancian (Dir)
Elizabeth Anderson (Dir)
Ben Arthur Thompson (Mgr)
Simon Authier (Sr Dir)
Omar Aziz (Dir)
Cristina Ballesteros (Dir)
Duncan Barlow (Mgr)
Amy Bennett (Mgr)
Carline Brands (Dir)
Jean-Philippe Buerckert (Dir)
Sarah Campion (Dir)
Matthieu Carriere (Head)
Mark Chambers (Dir)
Dominic Clarke (Dir)
Pragati S. Coder (Dir)
John Cook (Mgr)
Philip Damiani (Dir)
Kurt Derfler (Exec Dir)
Nancy Doyle (Mgr)
David Eastwood (Mgr)
Will Esmieu (Mgr)

Subsidiaries:

Accugenix, Inc. (1)
614 Interchange Blvd, Newark, DE 19711
Tel.: (302) 292-8888
Web Site: http://www.accugenix.com
Sales Range: $10-24.9 Million
Medical Laboratories
N.A.I.C.S.: 621511

Agilux Laboratories, Inc. (1)
3 Biotech 1 Innovation Dr, Worcester, MA
01605
Tel.: (508) 753-5000
Web Site: http://www.agiluxlabs.com
Biotechnology Research Services
N.A.I.C.S.: 541714

**Beijing Vital River Laboratory Animal
Technology Co. Ltd.** (1)

4F Sangpu Building 10 Dayangfang
Beiyuan Road, Chaoyang District, Beijing,
100012, China
Tel.: (86) 1084744500
Web Site: https://www.vitalriver.com
Biotechnology Research & Development
Services
N.A.I.C.S.: 541714

**CRL Dutch Holding Company
BV** (1)
Darwinweg 24, 2333 CR, Leiden, Netherlands
Tel.: (31) 717020000
Pharmaceutical & Biotechnology Research
Services
N.A.I.C.S.: 541714

Cellero, LLC (1)
672 Suffolk St Ste 300, Lowell, MA 01854
Tel.: (978) 364-0641
Web Site: http://www.cellero.com
Biological Product Mfr & Distr
N.A.I.C.S.: 325414
Edward P. Scott (Co-Founder & Chief Medical Officer)
Anne Lodge (Co-Founder & Chief Science
& Innovation Officer)
Jeffrey D. Allen (Pres & CEO)

Celsis International BV (1)
Europalaan 24, 6199 AB, Maastricht, Netherlands
Tel.: (31) 455696666
Emp.: 3
Pharmaceutical & Biotechnology Research
Services
N.A.I.C.S.: 541714
Yvonne Bos (Mgr)

ChanTest Corporation (1)
14656 Neo Pkwy, Cleveland, OH 44128
Tel.: (216) 332-1665
Testing Laboratory Services
N.A.I.C.S.: 541380

**Charles River Discovery Research
Services Finland** (1)
Microkatu 1, Kuopio, 70210, Pohjois-Savo,
Finland
Tel.: (358) 173680801
Web Site: http://www.criver.com
Biotechnology Research & Development
Services
N.A.I.C.S.: 541714

**Charles River Endotoxin Microbial
Detection Europe SAS** (1)
9 Allee Moulin Berger, 69130, Ecully,
France
Tel.: (33) 437502530
Biotechnology Research & Development
Services
N.A.I.C.S.: 541714

**Charles River Endotoxin and Microbial Detection Singapore Pte.
Ltd.** (1)
33 Ubi Avenue 3 06-17/18 Vertex Tower B,
Singapore, 408868, Singapore
Tel.: (65) 67426007
Web Site: https://criver.com.sg
Emp.: 20
Biological Products Distr
N.A.I.C.S.: 424210

Charles River France S.A. (1)
Domain Des Oncins, 69592, Saint Germain
sur L'Arbresle, Cedex, France (100%)
Tel.: (33) 474016969
Web Site: http://www.crl.com
Sales Range: $150-199.9 Million
Emp.: 200
Microbial QC Products & Testing Solutions
N.A.I.C.S.: 541380

**Charles River Germany GmbH & Co.
KG** (1)
Sandhofer Weg 7, 97633, Sulzfeld, Germany
Tel.: (49) 97614060
Web Site: http://www.criver.de
Sales Range: $25-49.9 Million
Emp.: 120
Biologics Testing Solutions, Avian Vaccine
Services & Microbial Solutions
N.A.I.C.S.: 112910

Subsidiary (Domestic):

Charles River Biopharmaceutical Services GmbH (2)

Charles River Laboratories International, Inc.—(Continued)

Max-Planck-Str 15 A, 40699, Erkrath, Germany
Tel.: (49) 2119255356
Web Site: http://www.criver.com
Sales Range: $25-49.9 Million
Emp.: 10
Drug Development Research Services
N.A.I.C.S.: 541715

Charles River Germany Verwaltungs GmbH (2)
Sandhofer Weg 7, 97633, Sulzfeld, Germany
Tel.: (49) 97614060
Web Site: http://www.criver.com
Emp.: 150
Administrative & Management Consulting Services
N.A.I.C.S.: 541611
Eberhard Rank (CEO)

Charles River Laboratories India Private Limited (1)
No 15 1st Floor Rest House Crescent Road, Bengaluru, 560001, India
Tel.: (91) 8025588175
Web Site: http://www.criver.com
Sales Range: $25-49.9 Million
Drug Development Research Services
N.A.I.C.S.: 541715

Charles River Laboratories Italia Srl (1)
Via Indipendenza 11, I 2050, Calcio, Lecco, Italy
Tel.: (39) 039509915
Web Site: http://www.crl.com
Sales Range: $25-49.9 Million
Biotechnology Research & Development
N.A.I.C.S.: 541714

Charles River Laboratories Japan, Inc. (1)
3-17-6 Shin-Yokohama Innotek Building 11th Floor, Kohoku-ku, Yokohama, 222-0033, Japan
Tel.: (81) 454749340
Web Site: http://www.crj.co.jp
Sales Range: $10-24.9 Million
Biotechnology Research & Development Services
N.A.I.C.S.: 541714

Charles River Laboratories Preclinical Services Ireland Limited (1)
Carrentrelia, Ballina, County Mayo, Ireland
Tel.: (353) 9620800
Drug Development Research Services
N.A.I.C.S.: 541715

Charles River Laboratories Preclinical Services Montreal, ULC (1)
22022 Trans Canadian Hwy, Senneville, H9X 3R3, QC, Canada
Tel.: (514) 630-8200
Web Site: http://www.crl.com
Emp.: 130
Biotechnology Research & Development
N.A.I.C.S.: 541714

Charles River Laboratories SA Netherlands Holdings BV (1)
Hambakenwetering 7, 5231 DD, s-Hertogenbosch, Netherlands
Tel.: (31) 736406700
Pharmaceutical & Biotechnology Research Services
N.A.I.C.S.: 541714

Charles River Laboratories Saint-Constant S.A. (1)
324 Saint Regis N, Saint-Constant, J5A 2E7, QC, Canada
Tel.: (450) 638-1571
Web Site: http://www.criver.com
Sales Range: $25-49.9 Million
Emp.: 100
Biotechnology Research & Development
N.A.I.C.S.: 541714

Charles River Laboratories, Inc. (1)
251 Ballardvale St, Wilmington, MA 01887
Tel.: (978) 658-6000
Web Site: http://www.criver.com
Biological Product Development Laboratories

N.A.I.C.S.: 325414

Branch (Domestic):

Charles River Laboratories (2)
3121 Rte 209, Kingston, NY 12401 **(100%)**
Tel.: (845) 687-7658
Web Site: http://www.crl.com
Sales Range: $25-49.9 Million
Emp.: 160
Animal Research
N.A.I.C.S.: 812910

Charles River Laboratories (2)
401 S New Hope Rd, Raleigh, NC 27610-1400 **(100%)**
Tel.: (919) 231-0511
Sales Range: $50-74.9 Million
Emp.: 180
Animal Research Laboratory
N.A.I.C.S.: 541380
Frank Schmidt (Sr Plant Mgr)

Charles River Laboratories-MI (2)
9801 Shaver Rd Kalamazoo County, Portage, MI 49024 **(100%)**
Tel.: (269) 327-4248
Sales Range: $75-99.9 Million
Animal Research Laboratories
N.A.I.C.S.: 541380

Charles River SPAFAS (1)
106 Rte 32, North Franklin, CT 06254-1811 **(100%)**
Tel.: (860) 889-1389
Web Site: http://www.crl.com
Sales Range: $10-24.9 Million
Emp.: 141
Egg Research
N.A.I.C.S.: 424440

Charles River UK Limited (1)
Manston Road, Margate, CT9 4LT, United Kingdom
Tel.: (44) 1843823388
Sales Range: $25-49.9 Million
Emp.: 100
Biotechnology Research & Development
N.A.I.C.S.: 541714

Subsidiary (Domestic):

BioFocus DPI (Holdings) Limited (2)
Chesterford Park Little Chesterford, Saffron Walden, CB10 1XL, Essex, United Kingdom
Tel.: (44) 1799533500
Sales Range: $25-49.9 Million
Holding Company; Drug Research & Development Services
N.A.I.C.S.: 551112
Angus MacLeod (Dir-Medicinal Chemistry)

Subsidiary (US):

BioFocus DPI (3)
385 Oyster Point Blvd Ste 1, South San Francisco, CA 90480
Tel.: (650) 228-1400
Drug Research & Development Services
N.A.I.C.S.: 541715
Chris Newton (Sr VP)

Subsidiary (Non-US):

BioFocus DPI AG (3)
Gewerbestrasse 16, Allschwil, 4123, Basel, Switzerland
Tel.: (41) 614878585
Pharmaceuticals Product Mfr
N.A.I.C.S.: 325412

Subsidiary (US):

BioFocus, Inc. (3)
3345 Old Salem Rd, Dayton, OH 45415
Tel.: (937) 890-3068
Pharmaceuticals Product Mfr
N.A.I.C.S.: 325412

Subsidiary (Domestic):

Charles River Laboratories (2)
Elpinstone Research Ctr, Tranent, EH33 2NE, East Lothian, United Kingdom
Tel.: (44) 1875614545
Web Site: http://www.inveresk.com
Emp.: 756
Drug Development Services
N.A.I.C.S.: 325412

Charles River Laboratories Preclinical Services Edinburgh Ltd. (2)
Elpinstone Research Centre, Edinburgh, EH33, East Lothian, United Kingdom
Tel.: (44) 1875614545
Web Site: http://www.criver.com
Emp.: 750
Drug Development Research Services
N.A.I.C.S.: 456110
K. V. Suresh (Chm & CEO)

CiToxLAB Group SAS (1)
BP 563, 27005, Evreux, France
Tel.: (33) 232292626
Web Site: http://www.citoxlab.com
Sales Range: $100-124.9 Million
Emp.: 800
Holding Company; Pre-Clinical Research, Biopharmaceutical Development, Non-Clinical Medical & Testing Laboratories
N.A.I.C.S.: 551112
Jean-Francois Le Bigot (Pres & CEO)
Philippe Ancian (Dir)
John Stamatopoulos (Dir)
Robert Tavcar (Sr Dir)
Christian Li (Dir)
Philippe Ancian (Dir)
John Stamatopoulos (Dir)
Robert Tavcar (Sr Dir)
Christian Li (Dir)
Philippe Ancian (Dir)
John Stamatopoulos (Dir)
Robert Tavcar (Sr Dir)
Christian Li (Dir)

Subsidiary (Domestic):

CIT-Citoxlab France SAS (2)
BP 563, Evreux, 27005, France
Tel.: (33) 2 3229 2626
Web Site: http://www.citoxlab.com
Pre-Clinical Research & Biopharmaceutical Development
N.A.I.C.S.: 541715
Olivier Foulon (Dir-Operations-CiToxLAB & Mng Dir)

Subsidiary (Non-US):

CiToxLAB Hungary Ltd. (2)
Szabadsagpuszta, Veszprem, 88200, Hungary
Tel.: (36) 88 545 300
Web Site: http://www.citoxlab.com
Sales Range: $25-49.9 Million
Emp.: 140
Pre-Clinical Research & Biopharmaceutical Development
N.A.I.C.S.: 541715

CiToxLAB North America Inc. (2)
445 Armand Frappier Blvd, Laval, H7V 4B3, QC, Canada
Tel.: (450) 973-2240
Sales Range: $125-149.9 Million
Emp.: 300
Non-Clinical Biological Research & Testing Laboratory
N.A.I.C.S.: 541715
Simon Authier (Dir-Safety Pharmacology & Veterinary Science)
Andrew Graham (VP-Ops)
John Kapeghian (Sr Dir-Toxicology)
Alan Bartlett (Sr Dir-Global Laboratory Ops)

CiToxLAB Scantox A/S (2)
Hestehavevej 36A, Ejby, Lille Skensved, 4623, Denmark
Tel.: (45) 56861500
Web Site: https://scantox.com
Sales Range: $25-49.9 Million
Emp.: 150
Non-Clinical Medical Laboratory
N.A.I.C.S.: 621511
Andrew Makin (Mng Dir)

Cognate BioServices, Inc. (1)
4600 E Shelby Dr Ste 108, Memphis, TN 38118
Tel.: (901) 541-9800
Web Site:
    http://www.cognatebioservices.com
Emp.: 500
Cell-Mediated Gene Development & Mfr
N.A.I.C.S.: 325412
J Kelly Ganjei (CEO & Chm)

Explora Biolabs, Inc. (1)
3030 Bunker Hill St, San Diego, CA 92109
Tel.: (858) 273-6574

Web Site: http://www.explorabiolabs.com
Rev.: $1,800,000
Emp.: 19
Research & Development in Biotechnology
N.A.I.C.S.: 541714

HemaCare Corporation (1)
8500 Balboa Blvd Ste 130, Northridge, CA 91325
Web Site: http://www.hemacare.com
Sales Range: $25-49.9 Million
Blood Products & Services Supplier
N.A.I.C.S.: 621991
Rochelle Martel (CFO)

Subsidiary (Domestic):

Coral Blood Services (2)
15350 Sherman Way Ste 350, Van Nuys, CA 91406
Tel.: (818) 226-1968
Web Site: http://www.hemacare.com
Blood Products & Services Supplier
N.A.I.C.S.: 621991

NAMSCO Inc. (1)
35 Country Ln, Beach Lake, PA 18405
Tel.: (570) 729-7700
Web Site: https://www.namscoinc.com
Industrial Molding Product Whslr
N.A.I.C.S.: 423310

Pathology Associates (1)
15 Wormans Mill Ct Ste I, Frederick, MD 21701 **(100%)**
Tel.: (301) 663-1644
Web Site: http://www.crl.com
Rev.: $33,000,000
Emp.: 80
Biomedical Research & Testing Services & Product Development
N.A.I.C.S.: 541720

Springborn Smithers Labs LLC (1)
790 Main St, Wareham, MA 02571-1037
Tel.: (508) 295-2550
Rev.: $16,295,708
Emp.: 75
Testing Laboratories
N.A.I.C.S.: 541715

Vigene Biosciences, Inc. (1)
5 Research Ct, Rockville, MD 20850
Tel.: (301) 251-6638
Web Site: http://www.vigenebio.com
Biotechnology Research & Development Services
N.A.I.C.S.: 541714
Zairen Sun (CEO)

CHARLIE'S HOLDINGS, INC.
1007 Brioso Dr, Costa Mesa, CA 92627
Tel.: (949) 570-0691   NV
Web Site:
    https://www.charliesholdings.com
Year Founded: 2001
CHUC—(OTCQB)
Rev.: $26,424,000
Assets: $7,061,000
Liabilities: $5,361,000
Net Worth: $1,700,000
Earnings: ($1,592,000)
Emp.: 35
Fiscal Year-end: 12/31/22
Nutritional Supplement Product Developer, Marketer & Distr
N.A.I.C.S.: 325411
Adam Mirkovich (CIO)
Brandon Stump (Co Founder)
Ryan Stump (Co-Founder & COO)
Henry Sicignano III (Pres)
Matthew Montesano (CFO)

Subsidiaries:

Bazi, Inc. (1)
1730 Blake St Ste 305, Denver, CO 80202-1275 **(100%)**
Tel.: (714) 941-2294
Web Site: http://www.drinkbazi.com
Energy Drink Mfr
N.A.I.C.S.: 424210

CHARLOTTE'S WEB HOLDINGS, INC.

700 Tech Ct, Louisville, CO 80027
Tel.: (720) 484-8930
Web Site:
https://www.charlottesweb.com
CWEB—(TSX)
Rev.: $74,139,000
Assets: $187,642,000
Liabilities: $110,137,000
Net Worth: $77,505,000
Earnings: ($59,313,000)
Emp.: 170
Fiscal Year-end: 12/31/22
Pharmaceutical Preparation Manufac-
turing
N.A.I.C.S.: 325412
Joel Stanley *(Co-Founder)*
Jared Stanley *(Co-Founder)*
Cory Pala *(Dir-IR)*
Gregory A. Gould *(CFO, Chief Admin
Officer, Principal Acctg Officer & Exec
VP)*
Andrew Shafer *(CMO)*

CHART INDUSTRIES, INC.

2200 Airport Industrial Dr Ste 100,
Ball Ground, GA 30107
Tel.: (770) 721-8800   DE
Web Site:
https://www.chartindustries.com
Year Founded: 1992
GTLS—(NYSE)
Rev.: $1,612,400,000
Assets: $5,901,900,000
Liabilities: $3,217,600,000
Net Worth: $2,684,300,000
Earnings: $24,000,000
Emp.: 5,178
Fiscal Year-end: 12/31/22
Industrial Process Equipment Mfr
N.A.I.C.S.: 332410
Jillian C. Evanko *(Pres & CEO)*
Gerald F. Vinci *(Chief HR Officer &
VP)*
Joseph Belling *(Chief Comml Officer)*
Brad K. Babineaux *(VP-Ops-North
America)*
Herbert G. Hotchkiss *(Gen Counsel,
Sec & VP)*
Joe Brinkman *(CFO & VP)*
Stephanie Everett *(Chief Acctg Offi-
cer)*
Robin Catalano *(VP-Operational Ex-
cellence)*
Matthew Benkert *(Treas & VP-Fin)*
Jennifer Adams *(Sr VP)*
Massimo Bizzi *(COO)*
Brian Bostrom *(CTO)*
Fred Hearle *(Pres)*
Harry Labbe *(VP)*
Camille Levy *(Pres)*
Sherry Shi *(VP)*
Ali Snyder *(Dir)*
Shane Sumners *(VP)*
Eric Vemer *(Pres)*
John Walsh *(VP)*

Subsidiaries:

BlueInGreen, LLC   **(1)**
700 W Research Ctr Blvd Ste 1207, Fay-
etteville, AR 72701-6948
Tel.: (479) 527-6378
Web Site: http://www.blueingreen.com
Research & Development in the Physical,
Engineering & Life Sciences
N.A.I.C.S.: 541715
Scott Goodson *(CFO)*
Chris Milligan *(Pres & CEO)*
Billy Ammons *(Chief Technical Officer)*
Adrian Beirise *(Engr-Product & Tech Svcs)*
Nick Lombardo *(Production Mgr)*
Theresa Case *(Mgr-Admin & Fin)*
Tyler Elm *(CMO & Chief Bus Sustainability
Officer)*
Cambron Clark *(Mktg Mgr)*
Scott Osborn *(Co-Founder)*
Marty D. Matlock *(Co-Founder)*

Chart Asia, Inc.   **(1)**

1 Infinity Corporate Center Dr Ste 300, Gar-
field Heights, OH 44125
Tel.: (440) 753-1490
Natural & Liquefied Petroleum Gas Distr
N.A.I.C.S.: 221210

Chart Australia Pty Ltd.   **(1)**
Sydney Business and Technology Centre
Unit 44 - 2 Railway Parade, Lidcombe,
2141, NSW, Australia
Tel.: (61) 297494333
Web Site: http://www.chartindustries.com
Emp.: 5
Supplier of Industrial Gas Equipment for
Biomedical Market
N.A.I.C.S.: 423830

Chart Cooler Service Company,
Inc.   **(1)**
3515 Dawson Rd Ste 300, Tulsa, OK 74115
Tel.: (918) 834-0002
Electrical Equipment Distr
N.A.I.C.S.: 423440

Chart Cryogenic Distribution Equip-
ment (Changzhou) Company
Limited   **(1)**
No 12 Fu Kang Road, Changzhou, 213032,
China
Tel.: (86) 51985966190
Electrical Equipment Distr
N.A.I.C.S.: 423440

Chart Distribution & Storage Systems
Inc.   **(1)**
1300 Airport Dr, Ball Ground, GA
30107   **(100%)**
Tel.: (770) 479-6531
Web Site: http://www.chartindustries.com
Mfr of Cryogenic Bulk Storage Systems
N.A.I.C.S.: 333912

Chart Energy & Chemicals Inc.   **(1)**
8665 New Trails Dr, Woodlands, TX 77381
Tel.: (281) 364-8700
Web Site: http://www.chart-ind.com
Sales Range: $25-49.9 Million
Emp.: 100
Mfr of Heat Exchangers, Coldboxes & Liqui-
fied Natural Gas Fuel Systems
N.A.I.C.S.: 332410

Chart Energy and Chemicals Wuxi
Co., Ltd.   **(1)**
No 27 Hongxiang Road, Hudai Town, Wuxi,
China
Tel.: (86) 51068069000
Industrial Machinery Distr
N.A.I.C.S.: 423830
Maximo Ulloa *(Gen Mgr)*

Chart Ferox a.s.   **(1)**
Ustecka 30, 405 30, Decin, Czech Republic
Tel.: (420) 412507111
Web Site: http://www.chart-ferox.cz
Sales Range: $75-99.9 Million
Emp.: 550
Mfr of Industrial Gas Storage Systems
N.A.I.C.S.: 325120

Chart France SAS   **(1)**
3 rue Etienne Collombet, ZAC du Moun-
dron, 31470, Paris, France
Tel.: (33) 561 08 2977
Supplier of Industrial Gas Equipment for
Biomedical Market
N.A.I.C.S.: 423830

Chart Industries Inc.- Distribution &
Storage - Houston   **(1)**
55 Southbelt Industrial Dr, Houston, TX
77047
Tel.: (713) 413-3000
Web Site: http://www.chartindustries.com
Sales Range: $25-49.9 Million
Emp.: 25
Plate Work Mfr
N.A.I.C.S.: 332313
Robert Chen *(Pres-Asia)*

Chart Italy S.r.l.   **(1)**
Via Canada 10, 35127, Padua, Italy
Tel.: (39) 049 644 498
Supplier of Industrial Gas Equipment for
Biomedical Market
N.A.I.C.S.: 423830
Andrea Maggio *(Sls Mgr)*

Chart Japan Co., Ltd.   **(1)**
Aoki Bldg 2F 4-1-10 Toranomon, Minato-ku,

Tokyo, 105 0001, Japan
Tel.: (81) 3 5776 2670
Web Site: http://www.chartjapan.com
Emp.: 2
Import, Sales & Rental of Medical Device &
Cryopreservation Equipment
N.A.I.C.S.: 423830
T. Lalo Hayashi *(Mng Dir)*

Chart Latin America S.A.S.   **(1)**
Edificio Offices 124 Calle 124 No 7-35 Offi-
cina 703, Bogota, Colombia
Tel.: (57) 12142822
Industrial Gas Product Mfr
N.A.I.C.S.: 325120

Chengdu Golden Phoenix Liquid Ni-
trogen Container Company
Limited   **(1)**
No 48 Qingma Road South Area, Chengdu
Modern Industrial Park, Chengdu, 610081,
Sichuan, China
Tel.: (86) 2887805257
Web Site: https://www.mvebio.cn
Emp.: 20
Liquid Nitrogen Containers Mfr
N.A.I.C.S.: 332439

Cofimco Fan (Changshu) Co.,
Ltd.   **(1)**
B2 Jinjang Industrial Park Huangpujiang
Road, Changshu Southeast Economic De-
velopment Zone, Changshu, 215500, Ji-
angsu, China
Tel.: (86) 51252358930
Extruded Aluminum Fan Mfr
N.A.I.C.S.: 333413

Cofimco International (Shanghai)
Trading Co, Inc.   **(1)**
Room 1803 No 3 Building Kai Xuan Hua
Yuan 111 Zhong Cao Road, Shanghai,
200030, China
Tel.: (86) 2164686460
Extruded Aluminum Fan Mfr
N.A.I.C.S.: 333413

Cofimco S.r.l.   **(1)**
via A Gramsci 136, Pombia, 28050, Novara,
NO, Italy
Tel.: (39) 0321968311
Web Site: http://www.cofimco.com
Extruded Aluminum Fan Mfr
N.A.I.C.S.: 333413

Cryo Diffusion S.A.S.   **(1)**
49 rue de Verdun, Lery, 27690, Cote-d'Or,
France
Tel.: (33) 23 259 0368
Web Site: http://www.cryodiffusion.com
Stainless Steel Tank Mfr
N.A.I.C.S.: 332420
Vincent Archeray *(Acct Dir-Mgmt)*

Fema S.r.l.   **(1)**
Via Tibet 5, 21052, Busto Arsizio, Varese,
Italy
Tel.: (39) 03311646099
Web Site: http://www.femasrl.it
Construction Machinery Mfr
N.A.I.C.S.: 333120

Flow Instruments & Engineering
GmbH   **(1)**
Siemensstrasse 19, 40789, Monheim am
Rhein, Germany
Tel.: (49) 2173960590
Web Site: http://www.flow-instruments.de
Emp.: 50
Mfr of Flow Meters for Cryogenics & Other
Liquids
N.A.I.C.S.: 334514

Harsco Industrial Air-X-Changers   **(1)**
5616 S 129th E Ave, Tulsa, OK 74134
Tel.: (918) 619-8000
Web Site: http://www.harscoaxc.com
Sales Range: $125-149.9 Million
Air-Cooled Heat Exchangers & Natural Gas
Processing Equipment Mfr
N.A.I.C.S.: 333415

Howden Group Ltd.   **(1)**
Operations Division Old Govan Road, Ren-
frew, PA4 8XJ, United Kingdom
Tel.: (44) 1418857500
Sales Range: $800-899.9 Million
Emp.: 500
Compressor, Fan & Blower Mfr
N.A.I.C.S.: 333912

Ross B. Shuster *(CEO)*

Subsidiary (Non-US):

Howden Air & Gas India Private
Limited   **(2)**
Tel.: (91) 1244241901
Emp.: 15
Commercial Fan & Blower Mfr
N.A.I.C.S.: 333413

Howden Alphair Ventilating Systems
Inc.   **(2)**
1221 Sherwin Rd, Winnipeg, MB R3H 0V1,
MB, Canada
Tel.: (204) 694-6666
Fan & Compressor Mfr
N.A.I.C.S.: 333413
Mike Brunette *(Gen Mgr-Mining)*

Howden Australia Pty Limited   **(2)**
Suite 6 01 58 Norwest Boulevard,
Baulkham Hills, 2153, NSW, Australia
Tel.: (61) 288449100
Web Site: http://www.howden.com.au
Sales Range: $25-49.9 Million
Emp.: 10
Industrial Machinery Mfr & Whslr
N.A.I.C.S.: 333248

Howden Axial Fans AB   **(2)**
Kvarnvagen 18, 352 41, Vaxjo, Sweden
Tel.: (46) 470594620
Fan & Compressor Mfr
N.A.I.C.S.: 333413
Fredrik Albertson *(CEO)*
Jesper Osterlund *(Dir-Sls-OEM)*
Henrik Gronvold Jensen *(Dir-HAX Aftermar-
ket)*
Henrik Marken *(Gen Mgr-Ops)*

Howden Axial Fans ApS   **(2)**
Industrivej 23, DK-4700, Naestved, Den-
mark
Tel.: (45) 55776262
Fan & Compressor Mfr
N.A.I.C.S.: 333413

Howden BC Compressors   **(2)**
Rue Roland Vachette, PO Box 80001,
60180, Nogent-sur-Oise, France
Tel.: (33) 344744100
Web Site: http://www.howden.com
Emp.: 130
Air & Gas Compressor Mfr & Whslr
N.A.I.C.S.: 333912

Howden CKD Compressors s.r.o   **(2)**
Logistic Park P3 Prague D11 Mstetice
1052, 250 91, Prague, Czech Republic
Tel.: (420) 226543102
Centrifugal & Reciprocating Compressor Mfr
N.A.I.C.S.: 333912

Subsidiary (Domestic):

Howden Compressors Limited   **(2)**
Old Govan Road, Renfrew, PA4 8XJ,
United Kingdom
Tel.: (44) 1418857500
Web Site: http://www.howden.com
Screw Compressor Mfr
N.A.I.C.S.: 333912

Subsidiary (Non-US):

Howden Covent Fans Inc.   **(2)**
Head Office Plant 1381 Hocquart St St
Bruno, Montreal, J3V 6B5, QC, Canada
Tel.: (450) 441-3233
Web Site: http://www.howdenfans.com
Emp.: 60
Fan & Compressor Mfr
N.A.I.C.S.: 333413

Howden Donkin (Proprietary)
Limited   **(2)**
Libertas Street, PO Box 919, Port Elizabeth,
Eastern Cape, South Africa
Tel.: (27) 414091400
Web Site: http://www.donkin.co.za
Sales Range: $25-49.9 Million
Emp.: 100
Commercial Fan & Blower Mfr
N.A.I.C.S.: 333413

Howden FFP (Proprietary)
Limited   **(2)**
1A Booysens Road, Booysens, 2091, Johannesburg, South Africa
Tel.: (27) 112404000

Chart Industries, Inc.—(Continued)

Web Site: http://www.howden.com
Sales Range: $25-49.9 Million
Emp.: 450
Commercial Fan & Blower Mfr
N.A.I.C.S.: 333413
Kavin Johanson *(CFO)*
Mirinella Zigouroux *(CFO)*

Howden France (2)
19 Rue De La Ladrie, BP 90125, Villeneuve
d'Ascq, 59653, France
Tel.: (33) 328 333 230
Web Site: http://www.howden.com
Sales Range: $25-49.9 Million
Emp.: 50
Centrifugal Fan Whslr
N.A.I.C.S.: 423830

Howden Group BV (2)
Lansinkesweg 4, PO Box 975, 7550 AZ,
Hengelo, Netherlands
Tel.: (31) 742556000
Web Site: http://www.howden.com
Emp.: 125
Pump & Pumping Equipment Mfr
N.A.I.C.S.: 333914
Weerden Berg *(Gen Mgr)*

**Howden Group South Africa
Limited** (2)
1A Booysens Road Booysens, 2091, Jo-
hannesburg, South Africa
Tel.: (27) 112404000
Web Site: http://www.howden.com
Holding Company
N.A.I.C.S.: 551112

Holding (Domestic):

Howden Africa Holdings Limited (3)
1A Booysens Road, Booysens, 2091, South
Africa **(55.39%)**
Tel.: (27) 112404000
Web Site: http://www.howden.com
Rev.: $140,760,642
Assets: $172,061,118
Liabilities: $48,243,117
Net Worth: $123,818,002
Earnings: $22,633,475
Emp.: 314
Fiscal Year-end: 12/31/2017
Specialized Fans Mfr
N.A.I.C.S.: 333413

Subsidiary (Non-US):

Howden Japan Limited (2)
3-19-11 Ryogoku, Sumida-ku, Tokyo, 130-
0026, Japan
Tel.: (81) 345400390
Industrial Air Conditioning Equipment Distr
N.A.I.C.S.: 423730

Howden Melbourne Pty Limited (2)
122-124 Freight Drive, Somerton, 3062,
VIC, Australia
Tel.: (61) 399305000
Web Site: http://www.howden.com
Emp.: 60
Blowers & Fan Mfr
N.A.I.C.S.: 333413
Thomas Barwald *(Gen Mgr)*

Howden Middle East FZE (2)
PO Box 262964, Jebel Ali, United Arab
Emirates
Tel.: (971) 48809353
Web Site: http://www.howden.com
Commercial Fan & Blower Mfr
N.A.I.C.S.: 333413

Subsidiary (US):

Howden North America, Inc. (2)
7909 Parklane Rd, Columbia, SC 29223
Tel.: (803) 741-2700
Web Site: http://www.howden.com
Sales Range: $100-124.9 Million
Emp.: 30
Industrial Fan & Blower Mfr
N.A.I.C.S.: 333413

Subsidiary (Domestic):

Howden Compressors Inc (3)
1850 Gravers Rd Ste 200, Plymouth Meeting, PA 19462-2837
Tel.: (610) 313-9800
Web Site: http://www.howden.com

Emp.: 30
Air & Gas Compressor Mfr
N.A.I.C.S.: 333912
Keith Kimmell *(Dir)*

Howden USA Company (3)
2933 Symmes Rd, Fairfield, OH 45014-
2099
Tel.: (513) 874-2400
Web Site: http://www.americanfan.com
Industrial Fans Mfr
N.A.I.C.S.: 333413

Subsidiary (Non-US):

Howden Solyvent (India) Pvt Ltd (2)
147 Poonamallee High Rd Numbal, Ma-
heshtala, Chennai, 600077, West Bengal,
India
Tel.: (91) 4426793500
Web Site: http://www.howden.com
Emp.: 200
Fan & Compressor Mfr
N.A.I.C.S.: 333413
Falguni Datta Roy *(Deputy Gen Mgr-AFM)*
Saurav Ghosh *(Sr Mgr-Mktg & Strategy)*
Soumyajit Chakraborty *(Gen Mgr-Sls-North)*
Mahesh Kinikar *(Asst Gen Mgr-Sls)*
Awadhesh Kumar Singh *(Sr Mgr-Svc)*

**Howden Thomassen
Compressors** (2)
Havalandseweg 8-a, PO Box 99, 6991 AB,
Rheden, Netherlands
Tel.: (31) 264975200
Web Site:
  http://www.howdenthomassencompres
  sors.co.nl
Sales Range: $150-199.9 Million
Emp.: 250
Manufactures, Designs, Installs & Repairs
Compressors & Compression Systems
N.A.I.C.S.: 333912
Henk Hoven *(Mng Dir)*
Hanf Zandergaag *(Mgr-Revamp)*

**Howden Thomassen Compressors
India Private Limited** (2)
Eco Tower Unit 301 Third Floor Behind Sy-
mentic Software Ltd, Baner Pashan Link
Road, Pune, 411 045, Maharashtra, India
Tel.: (91) 2066041001
Air & Gas Compressor Mfr
N.A.I.C.S.: 333912

**Howden Thomassen Far East Pte
Ltd** (2)
Block 219 Henderson Rd 08 04, Singapore,
159556, Singapore
Tel.: (65) 62781712
Fan & Compressor Mfr
N.A.I.C.S.: 333413

**Howden Thomassen Middle East
FZCO** (2)
PO Box 262585, 262585 Block BA, Dubai,
United Arab Emirates
Tel.: (971) 48864393
Web Site: http://www.howden.com
Crude Petroleum & Natural Gas Extraction
Services
N.A.I.C.S.: 211120
Nico Uintébroek *(Gen Mgr)*

Howden Turbo Fans Oy (2)
Karapellontie 12, PO Box 5, 02621, Espoo,
Finland
Tel.: (358) 102874000
Turbo Fan Mfr & Distr
N.A.I.C.S.: 333413

Howden Turbomachinery S.R.L. (2)
Via Nino Bixio 3, 21020, Mornago, Italy
Tel.: (39) 0331903890
Web Site: http://www.howden.com
Emp.: 20
Industrial Air Conditioning Equipment Distr
N.A.I.C.S.: 423730
Massimo De Cicco *(Mng Dir)*

Howden Turbowerke GmbH (2)
Naundorfer Strasse 4, 01640, Coswig, Ger-
many
Tel.: (49) 3523 94 0
Centrifugal & Axial Fan Whslr
N.A.I.C.S.: 423830

Subsidiary (Domestic):

Howden UK Limited (2)

Old Govan Road, Renfrew, PA4 8XJ,
United Kingdom
Tel.: (44) 1418857500
Web Site: http://www.howden.com
Centrifugal Fans Distr
N.A.I.C.S.: 423730

Division (Domestic):

**Howden UK Limited - Carcroft
Division** (3)
Unit 16 17 Adwick Business Park Adwick
Park Court Adwick-Le-Street, Carcroft, Don-
caster, DN6 7HD, United Kingdom
Tel.: (44) 1302 330 263
Web Site: http://www.howden.com
Emp.: 20
Industrial Equipment Repair & Maintenance
Services
N.A.I.C.S.: 811310

**Howden UK Limited - Construction &
Maintenance Division** (3)
Units 6 & 7 Baird House Innovation Centre
Pensnett Estate, Kingswinford, DY6 7FX,
West Midlands, United Kingdom
Tel.: (44) 1384 401 021
Web Site: http://www.howden.com
Industrial Equipment Repair & Maintenance
Services
N.A.I.C.S.: 811310

Subsidiary (Non-US):

Howden Ventilatoren GmbH (2)
Habsburgerstrase7, Aalen, 73432, Germany
Tel.: (49) 7321 3520
Sales Range: $25-49.9 Million
Emp.: 30
Axial Flow Fans Distr
N.A.I.C.S.: 423730
Michael Kleineher *(Mgr-Power Stations
Fans-Ruhrgebial Area)*

Subsidiary (Domestic):

James Howden Group Limited (2)
Old Govan Road, Renfrew, PA4 8XJ,
United Kingdom
Tel.: (44) 1418857500
Web Site: http://www.howden.com
Compressor, Fan & Blower Mfr
N.A.I.C.S.: 333912

Subsidiary (Non-US):

L & T Howden Private Ltd. (2)
Technology Block 2nd Floor Lift Wing, Su-
rat, Gujarat, India
Tel.: (91) 2612805359
Commercial Fan & Blower Mfr
N.A.I.C.S.: 333413

Hudson Products Corporation (1)
9660 Grunwald Rd, Beasley, TX 77417
Tel.: (281) 396-8100
Web Site: http://www.hudsonproducts.com
Axial Flow Fans & Heat Transfer Systems
Mfr
N.A.I.C.S.: 333413

**Industrie Meccaniche di Bagnolo
S.r.l.** (1)
Strada Paullese 2, 26010, Bagnolo Cre-
masco, CE, Italy
Tel.: (39) 0373237611
Web Site: http://www.imbagnolo.com
Air & Gas Compressor Mfr
N.A.I.C.S.: 333912

L.A. Turbine (1)
28557 Industry Dr, Valencia, CA 91355
Tel.: (661) 294-8290
Web Site: http://www.laturbine.com
Oil & Gas Turbine Mfr
N.A.I.C.S.: 333611
Danny Mascari *(Pres)*
Idris Kebir *(Dir-Applications & Project Mgmt)*
Richard Samson *(Product Dir)*
Houman Shokraneh *(Dir-Engrg)*
John Maskaluk *(Founder)*
David Bloss *(Dir-Field Svc)*
Dominique Maskaluk *(CFO)*
Frank Loth *(Mgr-Quality Assurance)*
Julia Budiharso *(Sr Project Mgr)*
Marlene LHeureux *(Mgr-HR)*
Shawne Thiry *(Dir-Mktg)*
Troy O'Steen *(Dir-Sls)*

PT. Thermax (1)

Menara Palma 9 02B and 03 9th Floor Jl H
R Rasuna Said Blok X2 Kav 6, Kuningan,
12950, Jakarta, Indonesia
Tel.: (62) 81110528866
Engineering Consulting Services
N.A.I.C.S.: 541330

Skaff Cryogenics, Inc. (1)
48 Pine Rd, Brentwood, NH 03833
Tel.: (603) 775-0350
Web Site: http://www.skaffcryogenics.com
Commercial & Industrial Machinery &
Equipment (except Automotive & Electronic)
Repair & Maintenance
N.A.I.C.S.: 811310

**Sustainable Energy Solutions,
Inc.** (1)
1489 W 105 N, Orem, UT 84057
Tel.: (801) 528-9509
Web Site: http://www.sesinnovation.com
Engineering Services
N.A.I.C.S.: 541330

VCT Vogel GmbH (1)
Industriestr 6, Gablingen, 86456, Augsburg,
Germany
Tel.: (49) 82308915060
Web Site: http://www.vct-vogel.de
Car Distr
N.A.I.C.S.: 441120

VRV Asia Pacific Private Limited (1)
220 Italia Lane, Sri City, Chittoor, 517 646,
Andhra Pradesh, India
Tel.: (91) 8623304700
Industrial Equipment Distr
N.A.I.C.S.: 423830
G. L. Rangnekar *(Mng Dir)*

VRV S.r.l. (1)
Via Burago 24, 20876, Omago, MB, Italy
Tel.: (39) 03960251
Web Site: http://www.vrv.com
Industrial Equipment Distr
N.A.I.C.S.: 423830

CHARTER COMMUNICATIONS,
INC.
400 Washington Blvd, Stamford, CT
06902
Tel.: (203) 905-7801   DE
Web Site:
  https://corporate.charter.com
Year Founded: 1993
CHTR—(NASDAQ)
Rev.: $54,607,000,000
Assets: $147,193,000,000
Liabilities: $132,475,000,000
Net Worth: $14,718,000,000
Earnings: $4,557,000,000
Emp.: 101,100
Fiscal Year-end: 12/31/23
Cable Television, Internet & Tele-
phone Communications Services
N.A.I.C.S.: 517111
Christopher L. Winfrey *(Pres & CEO)*
Kevin D. Howard *(Chief Acctg Officer,
Exec VP & Controller)*
Catherine C. Bohigian *(Exec VP-Govt
Affairs)*
Paul Marchand *(Chief HR Officer &
Exec VP)*
David L. Kline *(Exec VP)*
Michael Bair *(Exec VP-Spectrum Net-
works)*
Tom Montomagno *(Exec VP
Programming Acquisition)*
Cameron Blanchard *(Sr VP-Comm)*
Bill Archer *(Pres-Spectrum Enterprise
& Exec VP)*
Adam Ray *(Exec VP-Spectrum Com-
munity Solutions)*
Magesh Srinivasan *(Exec VP-
Network Ops)*
Cliff Hagan *(Exec VP-Customer Ops)*
Jake Perlman *(Exec VP-Software
Dev & IT)*
Jessica Fischer *(CFO)*
Richard J. DiGeronimo *(Pres-Product
& Tech)*
Danny L. Bowman *(Exec VP-Product)*

Jamal Haughton *(Gen Counsel, Sec & Exec VP)*
Eric Louis Zinterhofer *(Chm)*

Subsidiaries:

Bay News 9 **(1)**
700 Carillon Pkwy Ste 9, Saint Petersburg, FL 33716
Tel.: (727) 329-2400
Web Site: http://www.baynews9.com
Sales Range: $10-24.9 Million
Emp.: 120
Cable Television News
N.A.I.C.S.: 516210

Bresnan Communications, Inc. **(1)**
1 Manhattanville Rd, Purchase, NY 10577
Tel.: (914) 641-3300
Web Site: http://www.bresnan.com
Phone, Cable & Internet Services
N.A.I.C.S.: 517111

CCO Holdings Capital Corp. **(1)**
400 Atlantic St, Stamford, CT 06901
Tel.: (203) 905-7801
Holding Company
N.A.I.C.S.: 551112
Thomas M. Rutledge *(Chm & CEO)*

CCO Holdings, LLC **(1)**
400 Washington Blvd, Stamford, CT 06902
Tel.: (203) 905-7801
Rev.: $51,674,000,000
Assets: $140,711,000,000
Liabilities: $104,484,000,000
Net Worth: $36,227,000,000
Earnings: $6,311,000,000
Fiscal Year-end: 12/31/2021
Holding Company
N.A.I.C.S.: 551112
Thomas M. Rutledge *(Chm & CEO)*
Kevin D. Howard *(Chief Acctg Officer, Exec VP & Controller)*
Jessica M. Fischer *(CFO)*

Canoe Ventures LLC **(1)**
200 Union Blvd Ste 590, Lakewood, CO 80228
Tel.: (212) 364-3600
Web Site: https://www.canoeventures.com
Television Advertising Services
N.A.I.C.S.: 541890
Tom Huber *(COO)*
Joel Hassell *(CEO)*
Chris Pizzurro *(Sr VP-Sls & Mktg-Global)*
Ed Knudson *(Chief Revenue Officer)*
Sid Gregory *(CTO)*
David Porter *(Sr VP & Gen Mgr-Addressable)*

Charter Cable Partners, L.L.C. **(1)**
12405 Powercourt Dr, Saint Louis, MO 63131-3673
Tel.: (314) 288-3126
Web Site: http://charter.com
Cable Programming Services
N.A.I.C.S.: 516210

Spectrum Management Holding Company, LLC **(1)**
60 Columbus Cir, New York, NY 10023
Tel.: (212) 364-8200
Web Site: http://www.spectrum.com
Holding Company; Cable Television Distribution Services
N.A.I.C.S.: 551112

Joint Venture (Domestic):

Music Choice **(2)**
650 Dresher Rd, Horsham, PA 19044
Tel.: (215) 784-5840
Web Site: http://www.musicchoice.com
Emp.: 60
Music Video Cable Television Programming, Online & Mobile Publishing Services
N.A.I.C.S.: 516210
David Del Beccaro *(Founder, Co-Pres & CEO)*
Christina Tancredi *(Co-Pres & COO)*
Jeremy Rosenberg *(Co-Founder)*

Subsidiary (Domestic):

Oceanic Time Warner Cable LLC **(2)**
PO Box 30050, Honolulu, HI 96820-0050
Tel.: (808) 643-2100
Web Site: http://www.oceanic.com
Cable Television & Internet Services

N.A.I.C.S.: 517111
Gregg Fujimoto *(Pres)*

Unit (Domestic):

Spectrum News NY1 **(2)**
75 9th Ave, New York, NY 10011
Tel.: (212) 379-3311
Web Site: http://www.ny1.com
News Television Broadcasting Network
N.A.I.C.S.: 516120
Melissa Rabinovich *(Asst Dir-News)*

Joint Venture (Domestic):

SportsNet New York, LLC **(2)**
1271 Avenue of the Americas Fl 16, New York, NY 10020 **(26.8%)**
Tel.: (212) 485-4800
Web Site: http://www.sny.tv
Regional Sports Cable Network Operator
N.A.I.C.S.: 516210
Steve Raab *(Pres)*
Gary Morgenstern *(Sr VP-Programming)*
Scott Weinfeld *(CFO & Sr VP-Fin & Admin)*

Subsidiary (Domestic):

Time Warner Cable Enterprises LLC **(2)**
60 Columbus Cir Fl 17, New York, NY 10023
Tel.: (212) 364-8200
Motion Picture & Video Production Services
N.A.I.C.S.: 512110

Spectrum Reach, LLC **(1)**
1633 Broadway Fl 39, New York, NY 10019
Web Site: https://www.spectrumreach.com
Marketing & Advertising Services
N.A.I.C.S.: 541810
Michael Guth *(Sr VP-Mktg)*
David L. Kline *(Pres)*

Tennessee Tractor, LLC - Jackson **(1)**
3621 Hwy 45 N, Jackson, TN 38305-8719
Tel.: (731) 668-8792
Web Site: http://www.tennesseetractor.com
Tractor Distr
N.A.I.C.S.: 423820
Gary Fowler *(Mgr-Parts)*
Josh Gilliam *(Mgr-Svc)*
Randell Mask *(Mgr-Turf Svc)*

CHASE PACKAGING CORPORATION

106 W River Rd, Rumson, NJ 07760
Tel.: (732) 741-1500 **TX**
Web Site:
https://www.chasepackaging
corp.com
Year Founded: 1993
WHLT—(OTCIQ)
Rev.: $14,679
Assets: $388,171
Liabilities: $4,985
Net Worth: $383,186
Earnings: ($403,030)
Fiscal Year-end: 12/31/23
Packaging Products Mfr & Distr
N.A.I.C.S.: 561910
Ann C. W. Green *(CFO, Exec Officer & Asst Sec)*

CHATHAM LODGING TRUST

222 Lakeview Ave Ste 200, West Palm Beach, FL 33401
Tel.: (561) 802-4477 **MD**
Web Site:
https://www.chathamlodging
trust.com
Year Founded: 2009
CLDT—(NYSE)
Rev.: $294,851,000
Assets: $1,343,738,000
Liabilities: $525,741,000
Net Worth: $817,997,000
Earnings: $9,805,000
Emp.: 17
Fiscal Year-end: 12/31/22
Other Financial Vehicles
N.A.I.C.S.: 525990

Jeffrey H. Fisher *(Chm, Pres & CEO)*
Dennis M. Craven *(COO & Exec VP)*
Eric Kentoff *(Gen Counsel, Sec & Sr VP)*
Rick Fenton *(VP-Fin Analysis)*
Jeremy B. Wegner *(CFO & Sr VP)*

CHEESECAKE FACTORY INCORPORATED

26901 Malibu Hills Rd, Calabasas Hills, CA 91301
Tel.: (818) 871-3000 **DE**
Web Site:
https://www.thecheesecakefac
tory.com
Year Founded: 1972
CAKE—(NASDAQ)
Rev.: $3,303,156,000
Assets: $2,775,220,000
Liabilities: $2,483,217,000
Net Worth: $292,003,000
Earnings: $43,123,000
Emp.: 47,500
Fiscal Year-end: 01/03/23
Restaurant Chain & Wholesale Bakery
N.A.I.C.S.: 722511
Scarlett May *(Gen Counsel, Sec & Exec VP)*
David M. Gordon *(Pres)*
David Overton *(Founder, Chm & CEO)*
Cheryl M. Slomann *(Chief Acctg Officer, Sr VP & Controller)*
Matthew E. Clark *(CFO & Exec VP)*

Subsidiaries:

Cheesecake Factory Restaurants of Kansas LLC **(1)**
2900 SW Wanamaker Dr Ste 204, Topeka, KS 66614
Tel.: (913) 451-6272
Restaurant Operating Services
N.A.I.C.S.: 722511

Fox Restaurant Concepts, LLC **(1)**
4455 E Camelback Rd Ste B100, Phoenix, AZ 85018
Tel.: (480) 905-6920
Web Site: https://www.foxrc.com
Full-Service Restaurants
N.A.I.C.S.: 722511
Sam Fox *(Founder & CEO)*
Angela Haning *(VP-HR)*

Grand Lux Cafe LLC **(1)**
3355 Las Vegas Blvd S, Las Vegas, NV 89109
Tel.: (702) 414-3888
Web Site: https://www.grandluxcafe.com
Sales Range: $125-149.9 Million
Emp.: 450
Restaurant
N.A.I.C.S.: 722511

The Cheesecake Factory Bakery Incorporated **(1)**
26901 Malibu Hills Rd, Calabasas, CA 91301
Tel.: (818) 871-3281
Web Site:
https://www.thecheesecakefactoryba
kery.com
Sales Range: $350-399.9 Million
Restaurant Chain Wholesale Bakery
N.A.I.C.S.: 311812
Keith T. Carango *(Pres)*

The Cheesecake Factory Restaurants, Inc. **(1)**
26901 Malibu Hills Rd, Calabasas Hills, CA 91301
Tel.: (818) 871-3000
Sales Range: $150-199.9 Million
Emp.: 350
Restaurant
N.A.I.C.S.: 722511

The Houston Cheesecake Factory Corporation **(1)**
5015 Westheimer Rd, Houston, TX 77056
Tel.: (713) 840-0600
Restaurant Operating Services

N.A.I.C.S.: 722511
David Gorden *(CEO)*

CHEETAH NET SUPPLY CHAIN SERVICE INC,

6201 Fairview Rd Ste 225, Charlotte, NC 28210
Tel.: (704) 826-7280 **NC**
Web Site: https://www.cheetah-net.com
Year Founded: 2016
CTNT—(NASDAQ)
Rev.: $55,153,335
Assets: $14,719,404
Liabilities: $12,874,049
Net Worth: $1,845,355
Earnings: $816,980
Emp.: 20
Fiscal Year-end: 12/31/22
Logistic Services
N.A.I.C.S.: 541614
Walter Folker *(VP-Procurement)*
Huan Liu *(Founder, Chm & CEO)*

CHEGG INC.

3990 Freedom Cir, Santa Clara, CA 95054
Tel.: (408) 855-5700 **DE**
Web Site: https://www.chegg.com
Year Founded: 2005
CHGG—(NYSE)
Rev.: $716,295,000
Assets: $1,727,235,000
Liabilities: $782,617,000
Net Worth: $944,618,000
Earnings: $18,180,000
Emp.: 1,979
Fiscal Year-end: 12/31/23
Online Textbook Rental Services
N.A.I.C.S.: 611710
Nathan Schultz *(Pres & CEO)*
Heather Hatlo Porter *(Cheif Comm Officer)*
Debra Thompson *(Chief People Officer)*
Lauren Glotzer *(Chief Strategy Officer)*
David Longo *(CFO & Treas)*
Colin Coggins *(Sr VP-Chegg Skills)*
Chris Mason *(Sr VP-Bus Ops)*
Daniel L. Rosensweig *(Bd of Dirs, Executives)*

Subsidiaries:

Chegg India Private Limited **(1)**
401 Baani Corporate One, Jasola, New Delhi, 110025, India
Tel.: (91) 1141802240
Web Site: https://www.cheggindia.com
Educational Support Services
N.A.I.C.S.: 611710
Bhanu P. Mishra *(Mng Dir)*

Internships.com, LLC **(1)**
3990 Freedom Cir, Santa Clara, CA 95054
Tel.: (408) 855-5700
Web Site: http://www.internships.com
Software Design Services
N.A.I.C.S.: 513210

The Campus Special, LLC **(1)**
3575 Koger Blvd Ste 150, Duluth, GA 30096
Tel.: (800) 365-8520
Web Site: http://www.campusspecial.com
Sales Range: $10-24.9 Million
Emp.: 30
Print, Mobile & Online Marketing Services for Local Business Recruiting College Students
N.A.I.C.S.: 541613

Thinkful, Inc. **(1)**
31 Penn Plz 12th Fl 132 W 31st St, New York, NY 10001
Tel.: (646) 847-0114
Web Site: https://www.thinkful.com
Emp.: 600
Online Education Provider
N.A.I.C.S.: 611710
Darrell Silver *(CEO & Co-Founder)*
Daniel Friedman *(Co-Pres)*
Benjamin White *(Head)*
Grae Drake *(VP)*

Chegg Inc.—(Continued)

David Eby (COO)
Allison Winston (VP)
Catherine Zuppe (VP-Marketing)
Chris Powers (VP-Engineering)
Darren Laiben (VP)
Erin Rosenblatt (VP)
Joan Meyer (VP)
Jasjit Singh (VP)
Abdul Hanif (Sr Product Mgr)
Adam Levenson (Mgr-Content)
Alethia Halbig (Mgr)
Theresa Freet (Head)
Shannon Gallagher (Mgr)
Stephanie Bermudez (Mgr)
Melissa Bennett (Head)
Noel Duarte (Mgr)
Matt Shull (Product Mgr)
Mayank Mishra (Mgr)
Austen Weinhart (Mgr)
Lauren Jacobson (Mgr)
Kelly Kawa (Mgr)
Josephine Pike (Mgr)
Emma Holland (Mgr)
Emet Ozar (Mgr)
Derrick Foust (Mgr)

CHEMED CORPORATION

Ste 2600 255 E 5th St, Cincinnati,
OH 45202-4726
Tel.: (513) 762-6690   DE
Web Site: https://www.chemed.com
Year Founded: 1935
CHE—(NYSE)
Rev.: $2,264,417,000
Assets: $1,668,095,000
Liabilities: $560,219,000
Net Worth: $1,107,876,000
Earnings: $272,509,000
Emp.: 15,087
Fiscal Year-end: 12/31/23
Plumbing & Drain Cleaning Services
to Residential & Commercial Custom-
ers
N.A.I.C.S.: 238220
Nicholas M. Westfall (Exec VP)
Kevin J. McNamara (Pres & CEO)
Spencer S. Lee (Exec VP)
Thomas C. Hutton (VP)
Joel F. Gemunder (VP & Exec VP)
Michael D. Witzeman (CFO, Principal
Acctg Officer, VP & Controller)
Gregory A. Zarick (VP)
Brian C. Judkins (Chief Legal Officer,
Sec & VP)
Holley R. Schmidt (VP)
Nathan J. McNamara (VP)

Subsidiaries:

Jet Resource, Inc.   (1)
455 Wilmer Ave, Cincinnati, OH 45226-
1833
Tel.: (513) 762-6909
Web Site: http://www.jetresource.com
Sales Range: $10-24.9 Million
Emp.: 6
Aircraft Rental & Mfr.
N.A.I.C.S.: 336411

Roto-Rooter Canada, Ltd.   (1)
817 Allsbrook Rd, Parksville, V9P 2A9, BC,
Canada
Tel.: (250) 248-8743
Plumbing, Heating & Air Conditioning Ser-
vices
N.A.I.C.S.: 238220

Roto-Rooter Group, Inc.   (1)
2500 1st Financial Ctr 255 E 5th St, Cincin-
nati, OH 45202-4726
Tel.: (513) 762-6690
Web Site: https://www.rotorooter.com
Waste Management Services
N.A.I.C.S.: 562998

Subsidiary (Domestic):

Roto-Rooter Services Co   (2)
2500 1st Financial Ctr 255 E 5th St, Cincin-
nati, OH 45202-4726
Tel.: (513) 762-6690
Plumbing Products & Services
N.A.I.C.S.: 238220

Subsidiary (Domestic):

Western Drain Supply, Inc.   (3)
3188 E La Palma Ave, Anaheim, CA 92806-
2802
Web Site:
    http://www.westerndrainsupply.com
Plumbing, Heating & Air-Conditioning Contractors
N.A.I.C.S.: 238220

Roto-Rooter, Corp.   (1)
300 Ashworth Rd, West Des Moines, IA
50265
Tel.: (515) 223-1343
Web Site: http://www.rotorooter.com
Plumbing Contractor
N.A.I.C.S.: 238220

VITAS Hospice Services, LLC   (1)
Tel.: (305) 374-4143
Web Site: https://www.vitas.com
Sales Range: $300-349.9 Million
Emp.: 8,000
Hospice Care Management
N.A.I.C.S.: 622310

Subsidiary (Domestic):

Hospice Care Inc.   (2)
2675 N Mayfair Rd Ste 500, Wauwatosa,
WI 53226
Tel.: (414) 257-2600
Web Site: http://hospice.io
Sales Range: $25-49.9 Million
Emp.: 200
Hospice Care Services
N.A.I.C.S.: 622310

VITAS   (2)
8401 Datapoint Dr Ste 300, San Antonio,
TX 78229
Tel.: (210) 348-4300
Web Site: http://www.vitas.com
Sales Range: $50-74.9 Million
Hospice Care
N.A.I.C.S.: 622310

VITAS   (2)
3055 Kettering Blvd Ste 400, Dayton, OH
45439
Tel.: (937) 299-5379
Web Site: http://www.vitas.com
Sales Range: $50-74.9 Million
Emp.: 200
Hospice Care
N.A.I.C.S.: 622310

VITAS HME Solutions, Inc.   (2)
14651 N Dallas Pkwy Ste 812, Dallas, TX
75254
Tel.: (214) 424-5600
Web Site: http://www.vitas.com
Sales Range: $10-24.9 Million
Emp.: 50
Hospice Care
N.A.I.C.S.: 622310

VITAS Healthcare   (2)
2009 Mackenzie Way ste110, Cranberry, PA
16066
Tel.: (412) 799-2101
Web Site: http://www.vitas.com
Sales Range: $25-49.9 Million
Emp.: 100
Hospice Care
N.A.I.C.S.: 622310
Joel Wherley (COO & Exec VP)
Nicholas M. Westfall (Pres & CEO)
Joseph Shega (Chief Medical Officer & Sr
VP)
Jeffrey M. Kreger (CFO & Exec VP)
Patrick Hale (CIO & Exec VP)
Bob Miller (Chief Compliance Officer &
Exec VP)
Peggy Pettit (Exec VP)
Drew Landmeier (CMO & Sr VP)
Diane Psaras (Chief HR Officer & Exec VP)

VITAS Healthcare Corporation   (2)
201 S Biscayne Blvd Ste 400, Miami, FL
33131
Tel.: (305) 374-4143
Web Site: https://www.vitas.com
Sales Range: $50-74.9 Million
Hospice Care Services
N.A.I.C.S.: 622310
Joel Wherley (Pres, COO & COO)
Patrick Hale (CIO, CIO & Exec VP)
Patty Husted (Exec VP-Ops)

Bob Miller (Chief Compliance Officer, Chief
Compliance Officer & Exec VP)
Joseph Shega (Chief Medical Officer &
Exec VP)
Craig Tidwell (Sr VP-Ops-Midwest)
Nancy Wallent (Sr VP-Ops-Northeast)
Nick Westfall (Chm)
Alexander Fernandez (CFO)
Brian Judkins (Gen Counsel)
Bryan Wysong (Exec VP-Operations)
Jeff Weil (Sr VP-Operations & West)
Jennifer Nygaard (Sr VP-Operations &
Northern Florida)
Mark Hayes (Sr VP-Operations-Southern
Florida, Georgia)

Subsidiary (Domestic):

Hospice of Citrus County, Inc.   (3)
8471 W Periwinkle Ln Ste B, Homosassa
Springs, FL 34446
Tel.: (352) 249-1470
Web Site: http://friendsofcitrus.org
Health Care Srvices
N.A.I.C.S.: 621610

Subsidiary (Domestic):

VITAS Healthcare Corporation of
California   (2)
9655 Granite Ridge Dr Ste 300, San Diego,
CA 92123
Tel.: (858) 499-8901
Web Site: http://www.vitas.com
Women Healthcare Services
N.A.I.C.S.: 621610

VITAS Healthcare Corporation of
Georgia   (2)
2000 Riveredge Pkwy NW Ste GL - 100,
Atlanta, GA 30328
Tel.: (404) 843-6500
Web Site: http://www.vitas.com
Women Healthcare Services
N.A.I.C.S.: 621610

VITAS Healthcare Corporation of
Ohio   (2)
11500 Northlake Dr Ste 400, Cincinnati, OH
45249
Tel.: (513) 742-6310
Emp.: 100
Women Healthcare Services
N.A.I.C.S.: 621610

VITAS Healthcare, Inc.   (2)
521 Fellowship Rd Ste 110, Mount Laurel,
NJ 08054
Tel.: (856) 778-0222
Web Site: http://www.vitas.com
Sales Range: $25-49.9 Million
Hospice Care
N.A.I.C.S.: 622310

VITAS Healthcare, Inc.   (2)
70 S Orange Ave Ste 210, Livingston, NJ
07039
Tel.: (973) 994-4738
Web Site: http://www.vitas.com
Sales Range: $10-24.9 Million
Emp.: 50
Hospice Care
N.A.I.C.S.: 622310

VITAS Hospice Care   (2)
6100 Western Pl Ste 800, Fort Worth, TX
76107
Tel.: (817) 870-7000
Web Site: http://www.vitas.com
Sales Range: $25-49.9 Million
Hospice Care
N.A.I.C.S.: 622310

VITAS Innovative Hospice Care   (2)
11500 Northlake Dr Ste 400, Cincinnati, OH
45249
Tel.: (513) 742-6310
Web Site: http://www.vitas.com
Sales Range: $50-74.9 Million
Emp.: 325
Hospice Care
N.A.I.C.S.: 622310

VITAS Solutions, Inc.   (2)
5430 NW 33rd Ave Ste 106, Fort Lauder-
dale, FL 33309-6349
Tel.: (877) 868-4827
Web Site: http://www.vitos.com
Emp.: 10
Women Healthcare Services

N.A.I.C.S.: 621610

VITAS, Corp.   (2)
1740 Walton Rd Ste 100, Blue Bell, PA
19422
Tel.: (610) 260-6020
Web Site: http://www.viatas.com
Sales Range: $10-24.9 Million
Emp.: 25
Hospice Care
N.A.I.C.S.: 622310

VITAS, Inc.   (2)
17320 Red Oak Dr Ste 102, Houston, TX
77090
Tel.: (281) 895-6351
Web Site: http://www.vitas.com
Sales Range: $50-74.9 Million
Emp.: 40
Hospice Care
N.A.I.C.S.: 622310

VITAS, Inc.   (2)
3131 Eastside Ste 200, Houston, TX 77098
Tel.: (713) 663-4900
Web Site: http://www.vitas.com
Sales Range: $25-49.9 Million
Emp.: 50
Hospice Care Management
N.A.I.C.S.: 622310

CHEMUNG FINANCIAL COR-
PORATION

Tel.: (607) 737-3711   NY
Web Site:
    https://www.chemungcanal.com
Year Founded: 1985
CHMG—(NASDAQ)
Rev.: $102,911,000
Assets: $2,645,553,000
Liabilities: $2,479,165,000
Net Worth: $166,388,000
Earnings: $28,783,000
Emp.: 340
Fiscal Year-end: 12/31/22
State Commercial Banks
N.A.I.C.S.: 522210
Dale M. McKim III (CFO & Treas)
Thomas W. Wirth (Exec VP-Wealth
Mgmt Grp)
Anders M. Tomson (Pres & CEO)
Kimberly A. Hazelton (Exec VP-Retail
Client Div)

Subsidiaries:

CFS Group, Inc.   (1)
1 Chemung Canal Plz, Elmira, NY 14901
Tel.: (607) 737-3967
Web Site: https://cfsgroupny.com
Emp.: 7
Investment Advice
N.A.I.C.S.: 523940
Ronald Bentley (CEO)

Chemung Canal Trust Company   (1)
1 Chemung Canal Plz, Elmira, NY 14901-
3408
Tel.: (607) 737-3711
Web Site: https://www.chemungcanal.com
State Commercial Banks
N.A.I.C.S.: 522110

CHENGHE ACQUISITION I CO.

590 Madison Ave 34th Fl, New York,
NY 10022
Tel.: (212) 547-2600   Ky
Year Founded: 2021
LATG—(NASDAQ)
Rev.: $11,182,832
Assets: $135,786,357
Liabilities: $141,277,734
Net Worth: ($5,491,377)
Earnings: $9,832,611
Emp.: 2
Fiscal Year-end: 12/31/22
Investment Services
N.A.I.C.S.: 523999
Gerard Cremoux (CEO & CFO)
Gerardo Mendoza (Chief Investment
Officer)
Eduardo Cortina (Chm)
Hector Martinez (Mng Dir)
Miguel Olea (Mng Dir)

CHENIERE ENERGY, INC.
845 Texas Ave Ste 1250, Houston, TX 77002
Tel.: (713) 375-5000   DE
Web Site: https://www.cheniere.com
Year Founded: 1996
LNG—(NYSE)
Rev.: $20,394,000,000
Assets: $43,076,000,000
Liabilities: $34,056,000,000
Net Worth: $9,020,000,000
Earnings: $9,881,000,000
Emp.: 1,605
Fiscal Year-end: 12/31/23
Oil Exploration & Production; Liquified Natural Gas Developer
N.A.I.C.S.: 213112
Jack A. Fusco (Pres & CEO)
Charif Souki (Co-Founder)
Anatol Feygin (Chief Comml Officer & Exec VP)
J. Corey Grindal (COO & Exec VP)
Sean N. Markowitz (Chief Legal Officer, Sec & Exec VP)
David Craft (Sr VP-Engrg & Construction)
Michael Dove (Sr VP-Shared Svcs)
David Slack (Chief Acctg Officer & VP)
Julie Nelson (Sr VP)

Subsidiaries:

Cheniere Creole Trail Pipeline, L.P.   (1)
717 Texas Ave ste 3100, Houston, TX 77002
Tel.: (713) 659-1361
Natural Gas Pipeline Distr
N.A.I.C.S.: 486210

Cheniere Energy Partners LP Holdings, LLC   (1)
845 Texas Ave Ste 1250, Houston, TX 77002   (100%)
Tel.: (713) 375-5100
Web Site: https://cqpir.cheniere.com
Sales Range: $100-124.9 Million
Emp.: 1,229
Holding Company; Natural Gas Distr
N.A.I.C.S.: 551112
Michael J. Wortley (CFO & Exec VP)
Leonard E. Travis (Chief Acctg Officer & Sr VP)
Leonard E. Travis (Chief Acctg Officer & Sr VP)

Holding (Domestic):

Cheniere Energy Partners, L.P.   (2)
845 Texas Ave Ste 1250, Houston, TX 77002
Tel.: (713) 375-5100
Web Site: https://www.cheniere.com
Rev.: $9,664,000,000
Assets: $18,102,000,000
Liabilities: $18,886,000,000
Net Worth: ($784,000,000)
Earnings: $4,254,000,000
Emp.: 1,605
Fiscal Year-end: 12/31/2023
LNG Facility Developer, Owner & Operator
N.A.I.C.S.: 213112
Jack A. Fusco (Chm, Pres & CEO)
Vincent Pagano Jr. (Gen Partner)

Cheniere Marketing, Ltd.   (1)
3 rd Floor The Zig Zag Building 70 Victoria Street, London, SW1E 6SQ, United Kingdom
Tel.: (44) 2032142700
Oil & Gas Pipeline Construction Services
N.A.I.C.S.: 237120

Sabine Pass LNG, L.P.   (1)
700 Milam St Ste 1900, Houston, TX 77002-2835
Tel.: (713) 375-5000
Sales Range: $500-549.9 Million
Natural Gas Liquid Extraction Services
N.A.I.C.S.: 211130
Jack A. Fusco (Pres, CEO & Mgr)

CHERRY HILL MORTGAGE INVESTMENT CORPORATION
1451 Rte 34 Ste 303, Farmingdale, NJ 07727   MD
Web Site: https://www.chmireit.com
Year Founded: 2012
CHMI—(NYSE)
Rev.: $49,985,000
Assets: $1,392,992,000
Liabilities: $1,134,617,000
Net Worth: $258,375,000
Earnings: ($35,455,000)
Fiscal Year-end: 12/31/23
Real Estate Investment Trust
N.A.I.C.S.: 525990
Julian Evans (Chief Investment Officer)
Jeffrey B. Lown II (Pres & CEO)

Subsidiaries:

Aurora Financial Group Inc.   (1)
1451 Rte 34 Ste 303, Farmingdale, NJ 07727
Web Site: https://auroralending.com
Loan & Mortgage Services
N.A.I.C.S.: 522310

CHERRY STREET CAPITAL
645 Cherry St SE Ste 200, Grand Rapids, MI 49503
Tel.: (616) 822-0261
Web Site: http://www.cherrystcapital.com
CHSC.P—(TSX)
Financial Investment Services
N.A.I.C.S.: 523999
James Peterson (Owner)

CHERUBIM INTERESTS, INC.
1304 Norwood Dr, Bedford, TX 76022   NV
Web Site: http://www.cherubiminterests.com
Year Founded: 2006
CHIT—(OTCIQ)
Sales Range: Less than $1 Million
Real Estate Development Services
N.A.I.C.S.: 531390
Charles Everett (Chm)
Patrick J. Johnson (Pres & CEO)

Subsidiaries:

Golden Eagle Roofing Company (1)
1308 Teasley Lane Ste 11K, Denton, TX 75048
Tel.: (972) 496-0246
Web Site: http://www.goldeneagleroofing.com
Other Building Finishing Contractors
N.A.I.C.S.: 238390
Chuck Johnson (Owner)

CHESAPEAKE BANCORP
245 High St, Chestertown, MD 21620
Tel.: (410) 778-1600   MD
CPKB—(OTCIQ)
Banking Holding Company
N.A.I.C.S.: 551111
Glenn Wilson (CEO)

CHESAPEAKE FINANCIAL SHARES, INC.
97 N Main St, Kilmarnock, VA 22482
Tel.: (804) 435-4249   VA
Web Site: https://www.chesapeakefinancialshares.com
CPKF—(OTCQX)
Rev.: $58,187,288
Assets: $1,204,733,133
Liabilities: $1,082,066,650
Net Worth: $122,666,483
Earnings: $11,749,391
Emp.: 233
Fiscal Year-end: 12/31/20
Bank Holding Company
N.A.I.C.S.: 551111

Jeffrey M. Szyperski (Chm, Pres & CEO)
Douglas D. Monroe Jr. (Vice Chm)
Rebecca A. Foster (CFO, Sec & Sr VP)

Subsidiaries:

Chesapeake Bank   (1)
97 N Main St, Kilmarnock, VA 22482
Tel.: (804) 435-1181
Web Site: http://www.chesbank.com
Sales Range: $10-24.9 Million
Emp.: 170
State Commercial Banks
N.A.I.C.S.: 522110
Sherry Vanlandingham (Asst Mgr-Info Sys)

Chesapeake Mortgage Company (1)
35 School St, Kilmarnock, VA 22482
Tel.: (804) 435-1181
Web Site: http://www.chesfin.com
Rev.: $3,200,000
Emp.: 40
Mortgage Companies, Urban
N.A.I.C.S.: 522292
Jeffrey M. Szyperski (Pres)

CHESAPEAKE GRANITE WASH TRUST
601 Travis Fl 16, Houston, TX 77002
Tel.: (512) 236-6555   DE
Web Site: https://www.chkgranitewashtrust.com
Year Founded: 2011
CHKR—(OTCIQ)
Rev.: $15,842,000
Assets: $10,822,000
Net Worth: $10,822,000
Earnings: $12,988,000
Fiscal Year-end: 12/31/22
Gas & Oil Investment Services
N.A.I.C.S.: 213112
Sarah Newell (VP)

CHESAPEAKE UTILITIES CORPORATION
500 Energy Ln, Dover, DE 19901
Tel.: (302) 734-6799   DE
Web Site: https://www.chpk.com
Year Founded: 1859
CPK—(NYSE)
Rev.: $680,704,000
Assets: $2,215,037,000
Liabilities: $803,848,000
Net Worth: $1,411,189,000
Earnings: $89,796,000
Emp.: 1,034
Fiscal Year-end: 12/31/22
Propane & Natural Gas Distr
N.A.I.C.S.: 221210
Jeffrey S. Sylvester (COO & Sr VP)
Jeffry M. Householder (Chm, Pres & CEO)
Kevin J. Webber (Chief Dev Officer & Sr VP)
Sydney Hawthorne Davis (Mgr-Digital Comm)
Vikrant A. Gadgil (CIO & VP)
Lindsay Orr (Assoc Gen Counsel & Asst VP)
Brianna Patterson (Mgr-PR & Strategic Comm)
Michael D. Galtman (Chief Acctg Officer & Sr VP)
William Hughston (Chief HR Officer, Sr VP & VP)
James F. Moriarty (Chief Risk Officer, Chief Policy Officer, Gen Counsel, Sec & Exec VP)
Noah Russell (Treas, Asst VP & Asst Treas)
Cheryl M. Martin (Sr VP-Regulatory & External Affairs)
Joseph D. Steinmetz (VP & Controller)
Shane E. Breakie (VP-Sustainability & Organic Growth)

Stacie L. Roberts (VP-Corp Governance)
Michael D. Cassel (VP-Governmental & Regulatory Affairs)
Puru Buddha (VP & Asst VP-Enterprise Applications)
Andrena Burd (VP & Asst VP-Risk Management)
George Navo (VP & Asst VP-Fin Report)
Devon S. Rudloff (Asst VP-HR)
Danielle Mulligan (Asst VP-Strategic Communications & Community Affairs)
Kelley A. Parmer (Asst VP-Customer Care)
Heidi W. Watkins (Mgr-Shareholder Svcs)

Subsidiaries:

Aspire Energy of Ohio, LLC   (1)
300 Tracy Bridge Rd, Orrville, OH 44667
Tel.: (330) 682-7726
Web Site: https://aspireenergyco.com
Natural Gas Distr
N.A.I.C.S.: 221210
Doug Ward (VP)
Craig Provenzano (Mgr-Optimization)

Chesapeake Service Company (1)
909 Silver Lake Blvd, Dover, DE 19904-2409   (100%)
Tel.: (302) 734-6799
Sales Range: $650-699.9 Million
Holding Company
N.A.I.C.S.: 523999

Subsidiary (Domestic):

Chesapeake Investment Company   (2)
Cannon Bldg 909 Silver Lake Blvd Ste 200, Dover, DE 19901
Tel.: (302) 734-6799
Web Site: https://www.chpk.com
Sales Range: $25-49.9 Million
Investment Services
N.A.I.C.S.: 551112
John R. Schimkaitis (Vice Chm & CEO)

Eastern Shore Natural Gas Company   (1)
500 Energy Ln, Dover, DE 19901   (100%)
Tel.: (302) 734-6710
Web Site: https://www.esng.com
Sales Range: $25-49.9 Million
Emp.: 30
Natural Gas Distribution
N.A.I.C.S.: 213111

Elkton Gas Company   (1)
125 E High St, Elkton, MD 21921-5624
Tel.: (315) 437-2881
Web Site: https://www.elktongas.com
Natural Gas Distr
N.A.I.C.S.: 221210
Christie McMullen (Pres)

Florida Public Utilities Company (1)
1641 Worthington Rd, West Palm Beach, FL 33409
Tel.: (561) 832-0872
Web Site: http://www.fpuc.com
Natural & Propane Gas, Electricity & Water Services
N.A.I.C.S.: 221111
Kevin J. Webber (VP)

Grove Energy Inc.   (1)
832 Sarah St, Osceola Mills, PA 16666-9336
Tel.: (814) 339-6380
Web Site: https://www.groveenergyinc.com
Coal Whslr
N.A.I.C.S.: 423520

Marlin Compression, LLC   (1)
15032 Hudson Ave, Spring Hill, FL 34610
Web Site: https://marlincompression.com
Fuel Distr
N.A.I.C.S.: 457210

Marlin Gas Services, LLC   (1)
15032 Hudson Ave, Spring Hill, FL 34610
Tel.: (727) 375-5007
Web Site: https://www.marlingas.com
Natural Gas Pipeline Transportation Services
N.A.I.C.S.: 486210

Chesapeake Utilities Corporation—(Continued)

Kevin McCrackin *(VP & Asst VP-Business Development)*

Peninsula Energy Services Company, Inc. (1)
331 West Central Ave Ste 200, Winter Haven, FL 33880
Tel.: (855) 737-2600
Natural Gas Marketing Business
N.A.I.C.S.: 221210
Bill Hancock *(Asst VP)*

Sharp Energy, Inc. (1)
648 Ocean Hwy, Pocomoke City, MD 21851 **(100%)**
Tel.: (410) 957-1501
Web Site: https://www.sharpenergy.com
Sales Range: $25-49.9 Million
Emp.: 20
Distr of Propane Products
N.A.I.C.S.: 457210

Xeron, Inc. (1)
2500 City W Blvd, Houston, TX 77042
Tel.: (713) 988-0051
Web Site: http://www.chpk.com
Sales Range: $75-99.9 Million
Emp.: 100
Propane Marketing Services
N.A.I.C.S.: 457210

CHESTER BANCORP, INC.
1112 State St, Chester, IL 62233
Tel.: (618) 826-5038   DE
Web Site:
    http://www.chesternationalbank.com
Year Founded: 1996
CNBA—(OTCIQ)
Bank Holding Company
N.A.I.C.S.: 551111
Michael W. Welge *(Pres & CFO)*
Edward K. Collins *(CEO)*

CHESTER MINING CO
905 N Pines Rd Ste A, Spokane Valley, WA 99206
Web Site:
    https://www.chestermining.com
Year Founded: 1900
CHMN—(OTCIQ)
Metal Exploration Services
N.A.I.C.S.: 213114
Travis Campbell *(Pres)*

CHEVRON CORPORATION
5001 Executive Pkwy Ste 200, San Ramon, CA 94583-2324
Tel.: (925) 842-1000   DE
Web Site: https://www.chevron.com
Year Founded: 1879
CVX—(NYSE)
Rev.: $200,949,000,000
Assets: $261,632,000,000
Liabilities: $99,703,000,000
Net Worth: $161,929,000,000
Earnings: $21,369,000,000
Emp.: 45,600
Fiscal Year-end: 12/31/23
Chemical Products Mfr
N.A.I.C.S.: 325998
Eimear P. Bonner *(CFO & VP)*
Mark A. Nelson *(Vice Chm & Exec VP-Oil, Products & Gas)*
Michael K. Wirth *(Chm & CEO)*
Navin K. Mahajan *(Treas & VP)*
Paul Antebi *(Gen Counsel-Tax & VP)*
Alana K. Knowles *(Principal Acctg Officer, VP, VP-Chevron Gas & Midstream & Controller)*
Mary A. Francis *(Chief Governance Officer & Sec)*
R. Hewitt Pate *(Gen Counsel & VP)*
Frank W. Mount *(VP-Corporate Business Development)*
Molly T. Laegeler *(VP-Strategy & Sustainability)*
Jeff B. Gustavson *(VP-Lower Carbon Energies)*
Colin E. Parfitt *(VP-Midstream)*

Subsidiaries:

Advanced Refining Technologies, LLC (1)
7500 Grace Dr, Columbia, MD 21044
Tel.: (410) 531-4000
Web Site:
    https://www.arthydroprocessing.com
Hydroprocessing Catalysts Developer & Mfr; Owned by W. R. Grace & Co. & by Chevron Corporation
N.A.I.C.S.: 325998

Unit (Domestic):

Advanced Refining Technologies, LLC - Catalysts (2)
4099 W 71st St, Chicago, IL 60629
Tel.: (773) 838-3200
Web Site: http://www.artcatalysts.com
Refinery Catalysts Mfr
N.A.I.C.S.: 325998

Chevron (Thailand) Limited (1)
19 Tower 3 SCB Park Plaza Fl 7 Ratchadapisek Road, Chatuchak, Bangkok, 10900, Thailand
Tel.: (66) 20814000
Web Site: http://www.chevron.com
Gasoline, Motor Oils, Greases, Diesel Engine Lubricating Oils & Industrial Lubricants Mfr
N.A.I.C.S.: 324191

Subsidiary (Domestic):

Chevron Thailand Exploration & Production, Ltd. (2)
6th Floor Tower 3 SCB Park Plaza Chatuchak 19 Rachadapisak Road, 19 Ratchadapisek Road, Bangkok, 10900, Thailand
Tel.: (66) 25455555
Web Site: http://www.chevron.com
Crude Petroleum & Natural Gas
N.A.I.C.S.: 211120

Chevron Argentina S.R.L. (1)
Tte Gral Juan Domingo Peron 925 Piso 4 1038, Buenos Aires, Argentina
Tel.: (54) 1143207400
Natural Gas Exploration Service
N.A.I.C.S.: 213112

Chevron Australia Pty Ltd. (1)
QV1 Building 250 St Georges Terrace, Perth, 6000, WA, Australia
Tel.: (61) 89 216 4000
Web Site: https://australia.chevron.com
Emp.: 6,000
Natural Gas Extraction Services
N.A.I.C.S.: 213112

Chevron Belgium NV/SA (1)
Technologiepark Zwijnaarde 2, 9052, Zwijnaarde, Belgium **(100%)**
Tel.: (32) 92937111
Web Site: http://www.texaco.com
Sales Range: $100-124.9 Million
Emp.: 170
Marketing Services in Europe
N.A.I.C.S.: 457210

Chevron Canada Limited (1)
Atlantic Place Suite 700 - 215 Water Street, PO Box 79, Saint John's, A1C 6C9, NL, Canada **(100%)**
Tel.: (709) 757-6100
Web Site: https://www.canada.chevron.com
Exploration Producing Refining & Marketing of Petroleum Products
N.A.I.C.S.: 213111
Frank Cassulo *(Pres)*

Subsidiary (Domestic):

Chevron Canada Finance Ltd. (2)
500 5th Ave SW, Calgary, T2P 0L7, AB, Canada **(100%)**
Tel.: (403) 234-5000
Web Site: http://www.chevron.ca
Financial Services
N.A.I.C.S.: 523940

Chevron Canada Resources (2)
500 - 5th Avenue S W, Calgary, T2P 0L7, AB, Canada **(100%)**
Tel.: (403) 234-5000
Web Site: http://www.chevron.com

Sales Range: $500-549.9 Million
Emp.: 350
Research & Development of Oil
N.A.I.C.S.: 213112

Chevron Exploration & Production Inc. (1)
9525 Camino Media, Bakersfield, CA 93311
Tel.: (925) 842-1000
Sales Range: $300-349.9 Million
Emp.: 300
Petroleum Refining
N.A.I.C.S.: 211120
Jeff Shellebarger *(Pres-North America)*
Stephen W. Green *(Pres-Asia Pacific)*

Chevron France SA (1)
141 rue Michel Carre, 95100, Argenteuil, France **(100%)**
Tel.: (33) 134340355
Web Site: http://www.texaco.com
Sales Range: $25-49.9 Million
Emp.: 15
Petrochemical Marketing & Service
N.A.I.C.S.: 425120

Chevron Funding Corporation (1)
6001 Bollinger Canyon Rd, San Ramon, CA 94583-2324
Tel.: (925) 842-1000
Web Site: http://www.chevron.com
Oil & Gas Extraction Services
N.A.I.C.S.: 213112

Chevron Global Energy Inc. (1)
6001 Bollinger Canyon Rd, San Ramon, CA 94583
Tel.: (925) 842-1000
Oil & Gas Support Services
N.A.I.C.S.: 213112
Guy J. Camarata *(Exec VP)*

Chevron Information Technology Company (1)
6001 Bollinger Cyn Rd, San Ramon, CA 94583-2324 **(100%)**
Tel.: (925) 842-1000
Web Site: http://www.chevron.com
Sales Range: $450-499.9 Million
Emp.: 3,000
Computer Integrated Systems Design Services
N.A.I.C.S.: 541512

Chevron International Pte. Ltd. (1)
30 Raffles Place 21-00 Chevron House, Singapore, 48622, Singapore
Tel.: (65) 63181000
Web Site: http://www.chevron.com
Sales Range: $1-4.9 Billion
Emp.: 700
Petroleum Products Refinery
N.A.I.C.S.: 324110

Joint Venture (Domestic):

Singapore Refining Co. Pte. Ltd. (2)
1 Merlimau Rd, Singapore, 628260, Singapore **(50%)**
Tel.: (65) 63570100
Web Site: https://www.src.com.sg
Petroleum Refiner
N.A.I.C.S.: 324110

Chevron Latin America (1)
Avenida La Estancia Centro Banaven Torre D Piso 7-Chuao, Caracas, Venezuela **(100%)**
Tel.: (58) 2125265400
Web Site: http://www.chevron.com
Sales Range: $75-99.9 Million
Emp.: 150
Mfr of Gasolines, Motor Oils, Greases, Diesel Engine Lubricating Oils & Industrial Lubricants
N.A.I.C.S.: 324191

Chevron Nigeria Limited (1)
2 Chevron Drive Lekki Peninsula Private Mail Bag, 12825, Lagos, Nigeria
Tel.: (234) 412772222
Oil & Gas Support Services
N.A.I.C.S.: 213112
Esimaje Brikins *(Gen Mgr-Policy, Govt & Pub Affairs)*
Edema Collins *(Pres)*
Jeffrey Ewing *(Chm & Mng Dir)*

Chevron Oronite Company LLC (1)
6001 Bollinger Canyon Rd, San Ramon, CA 94583-2324

Tel.: (713) 954-6060
Web Site: https://www.chevron.com
Fuel & Lubricant Additives & Chemicals Mfr
N.A.I.C.S.: 325110
Mitra Kashanchi *(Pres)*
Laura Boudreau *(VP)*
Koon Eng Goh *(VP)*

Chevron Oronite Pte. Ltd. (1)
21 Sakra Road, Singapore, 627890, Singapore
Crude Petroleum & Natural Gas Extraction Services
N.A.I.C.S.: 211120

Chevron Oronite S.A. (1)
1 rue Eugene et Armand Peugeot, CS 10022, 92508, Rueil-Malmaison, Cedex, France **(100%)**
Tel.: (33) 146393600
Web Site: http://www.oronite.com
Sales Range: $50-74.9 Million
Emp.: 100
Lube Oil Additives Mfg
N.A.I.C.S.: 324191
Fourneor Xravur *(Pres)*

Chevron Overseas Petroleum Limited (1)
6001 Bollinger Canyon Rd, San Ramon, CA 94583 **(100%)**
Tel.: (925) 842-1000
Web Site: http://www.chevron.com
Sales Range: $200-249.9 Million
Emp.: 1,500
International Petroleum Exploration & Production
N.A.I.C.S.: 541611

Chevron Philippines Inc. (1)
6/F 6750 Ayala Avenue, Makati, 1226, Philippines
Tel.: (63) 28411000
Crude Petroleum Natural Gas Extraction Services
N.A.I.C.S.: 211120

Chevron Phillips Chemical Company LLC (1)
10001 6 Pines Dr, The Woodlands, TX 77380 **(50%)**
Tel.: (832) 813-4100
Web Site: https://www.cpchem.com
Sales Range: $5-14.9 Billion
Emp.: 4,800
Producer of Olefins & Polyolefins; Supplier of Aromatics, Alpha Olefins, Styrenics & Specialty Chemicals
N.A.I.C.S.: 325110
Tim Hill *(Gen Counsel, Sec & Sr VP-Legal & Pub Affairs)*
Mitch Eichelberger *(Exec VP-Polymers & Specialties)*
Carolyn Burke *(CFO & Exec VP)*
Maricela Caballero *(Sr VP-HR)*
Steve Prusak *(Sr VP-Corp Plng & Tech)*
Bryan Canfield *(Sr VP-Mfg)*
Justine Smith *(Sr VP-Petrochemicals)*
Allison Martinez *(CIO)*

Subsidiary (Non-US):

Chevron Phillips Chemicals International N.V. (2)
Brusselsesteenweg 355 BV, Overijse, 3090, Belgium
Tel.: (32) 26891211
Web Site: http://www.cpch.com
Sales Range: $400-449.9 Million
Emp.: 75
Chemical Products Mfr
N.A.I.C.S.: 325998

Chevron Pipe Line Company (1)
1400 Smith St, Houston, TX 77002 **(100%)**
Tel.: (713) 432-2500
Web Site: http://www.chevron.com
Sales Range: $100-124.9 Million
Emp.: 700
Crude Oil & Petroleum Products Transportation
N.A.I.C.S.: 486110

Chevron Shipping Company LLC (1)
6101 Bollinger Canyon Rd Rm 3432, San Ramon, CA 94583 **(100%)**
Tel.: (925) 842-1000
Web Site: http://www.chevron.com

Sales Range: $100-124.9 Million
Marine Transportation Management
N.A.I.C.S.: 483111

Chevron Trinidad, Inc. (1)
3A Sweet Briar Road, Port of Spain, Trinidad & Tobago (100%)
Tel.: (868) 6226024
Web Site: http://www.chevron.com
Sales Range: $150-199.9 Million
Emp.: 10
Petroleum Distr
N.A.I.C.S.: 213111

Chevron U.S.A. Inc. (1)
6001 Bollinger Canyon Rd, San Ramon, CA 94583
Natural Gas Exploration Service
N.A.I.C.S.: 213112

Chevron United Kingdom Limited (1)
Hill of Rubislaw, Aberdeen, AB15 6XL, United Kingdom (100%)
Tel.: (44) 224334000
Web Site: http://www.chevron.com
Sales Range: $200-249.9 Million
Emp.: 300
Mfr of Gasolines, Motor Oils, Greases, Diesel Engine Lubricating Oils & Industrial Lubricants
N.A.I.C.S.: 324191

Coalinga Cogeneration Company (1)
32812 W Gale Ave, Coalinga, CA 93210
Tel.: (559) 935-8763
Rev.: $20,000,000
Emp.: 8
Electric Power Generation
N.A.I.C.S.: 221118
Kelly Lucas *(Exec Dir)*

Noble Energy, Inc. (1)
1001 Noble Energy Way, Houston, TX 77070
Tel.: (281) 872-3100
Web Site: http://www.nblenergy.com
Sales Range: $1-4.9 Billion
Emp.: 2,282
Exploration, Production & Marketing of Crude Oil & Natural Gas
N.A.I.C.S.: 211120
Kenneth M. Fisher *(CFO & Exec VP)*
David L. Stover *(Executives)*
Dustin A. Hatley *(Chief Acctg Officer, VP & Controller)*
Rachel G. Clingman *(Gen Counsel, Sec & Sr VP)*
Chris Michel *(Sr VP-HR, Admin & Security)*
Jeff B. Gustavson *(Pres)*

Joint Venture (Domestic):

AMPCO Marketing, L.L.C. (2)
16945 Northchase Dr Ste 1950, Houston, TX 77060
Tel.: (281) 872-8324
Web Site: http://www.atlanticmethanol.com
Emp.: 13
Methanol Marketing & Sales
N.A.I.C.S.: 424690

AMPCO Services, LLC (2)
16945 Northchase Dr Ste 1950, Houston, TX 77060
Tel.: (281) 872-8324
Povider of Consulting Services for the Methanol Industry
N.A.I.C.S.: 541618

Subsidiary (Non-US):

EDC Ireland (2)
River House Blackpool Retail Park, Blackpool, Cork, T23 R5TF, Ireland
Tel.: (353) 214280476
Web Site: http://www.edcengineers.com
Sales Range: $25-49.9 Million
Emp.: 22
Engineering Services
N.A.I.C.S.: 541330

Energy Development Corporation (China), Inc. (2)
Suite A 2501 Eagle Run Plaza No 26 Xiaoyun Road, Chaoyang District, Beijing, 100016, China (100%)
Tel.: (86) 1051088210
Sales Range: $10-24.9 Million
Emp.: 10
Producer of Crude Oil & Natural Gas
N.A.I.C.S.: 211120

Subsidiary (Domestic):

HGC, Inc. (2)
8250 Agate Rd, White City, OR 97503
Tel.: (541) 826-3602
Web Site: http://www.hgc-inc.net
Highway & Bridge Construction Services
N.A.I.C.S.: 237990

Subsidiary (Non-US):

NBL International Finance B.V. (2)
Zuid Hollandlaan 7, 2596 AL, Hague, Netherlands
Tel.: (31) 702400800
Financial Services
N.A.I.C.S.: 541611

Subsidiary (Domestic):

NBL Texas, LLC (2)
1001 Noble Energy Way, Houston, TX 77070
Tel.: (281) 872-3100
Oilfield Assets Holding Company
N.A.I.C.S.: 551112
Charles J. Rimer *(Pres)*

Unit (Domestic):

Noble Energy - Ardmore (2)
110 W Broadway St, Ardmore, OK 73401 (100%)
Tel.: (580) 223-4110
Web Site: http://www.nobleenergyinc.com
Sales Range: $100-124.9 Million
Emp.: 125
Engaged in the Exploration, Production & Marketing of Crude Oil & Natural Gas
N.A.I.C.S.: 211120

Noble Energy - Denver (2)
1625 Broadway, Denver, CO 80202 (100%)
Tel.: (303) 228-4321
Web Site: http://www.noble-energy.com
Sales Range: $400-449.9 Million
Emp.: 400
Acquirer, Developer & Producer of Oil & Natural Gas
N.A.I.C.S.: 213112

Subsidiary (Non-US):

Noble Energy Mexico, S. de R.L. de C.V. (2)
Lago Alberto 416 Int A Anahuac Seccion, Miguel Hidalgo, 11320, Mexico, Mexico
Tel.: (52) 5592193076
Web Site: https://nobleenergymexico.com
Natural Gas Distribution Services
N.A.I.C.S.: 221210

Subsidiary (Domestic):

Noble Energy New Ventures, LLC (2)
100 Glenborough Dr Ste 100, Houston, TX 77067-3610
Tel.: (281) 872-3100
Eletric Power Generation Services
N.A.I.C.S.: 221112
David Baumgartner *(Dir-Bus Dev)*
David Stoever *(Dir-Bus Dev)*

Noble Midstream Partners LP (2)
1001 Noble Energy Way, Houston, TX 77070 (100%)
Tel.: (281) 872-3100
Web Site: http://www.nblmidstream.com
Rev.: $764,625,000
Assets: $3,037,196,000
Liabilities: $1,736,845,000
Net Worth: $1,300,351,000
Earnings: $134,031,000
Emp.: 225
Fiscal Year-end: 12/31/2020
Midstream Services
N.A.I.C.S.: 213112

Subsidiary (Non-US):

Oil Insurance Company (2)
3 Bermudiana Road 2nd Floor, Hamilton, HM08, Bermuda
Tel.: (441) 2950905
Web Site: https://www.oil.bm
Insurance Services
N.A.I.C.S.: 524210
Bertil C. Olsson *(Pres & CEO)*
George F. Hutchings *(COO & Sr VP)*

Ricky E. Lines *(CFO & Sr VP)*
Marlene J. Cechini *(VP-Fin & Controller)*
Theresa Dunlop *(VP)*
Matthew Pifer *(Gen Counsel, Sec & Sr VP)*
Fabrizio Mastrantonio *(Deputy Chm)*
Robert Foskey *(Chief Actuary, Chief Data & Analytics Officer & Sr VP)*
Theodore Guidry II *(Chm)*

Subsidiary (Domestic):

Optimized Energy Solutions, LLC (2)
3445 Airway Dr Ste A, Reno, NV 89511
Web Site:
http://www.optimizedenergysolution.com
Information Technology Services
N.A.I.C.S.: 541511

Samedan Methanol (2)
100 Glenborough Ste 100, Houston, TX 77067 (100%)
Tel.: (281) 876-6250
Producer of Crude Oil & Natural Gas
N.A.I.C.S.: 325199

Joint Venture (Domestic):

Atlantic Methanol Associates LLC (3)
16945 Northchase Dr Ste 1950, Houston, TX 77060
Tel.: (281) 872-8324
Web Site: http://www.atlanticmethanol.com
Holding Company; Methanol Mfr
N.A.I.C.S.: 551112

PDC Energy, Inc. (1)
1775 Sherman St Ste 3000, Denver, CO 80203
Tel.: (303) 860-5800
Web Site: https://www.pdce.com
Rev.: $3,845,733,000
Assets: $7,982,765,000
Liabilities: $4,000,020,000
Net Worth: $3,982,745,000
Earnings: $1,778,121,000
Emp.: 616
Fiscal Year-end: 12/31/2022
Natural Gas Developer, Producer & Marketer
N.A.I.C.S.: 213112
David Lillo *(Sr VP-Ops)*
R. Scott Meyers *(CFO & Sr VP)*
Lance A. Lauck *(Exec VP-Corp Dev & Strategy)*
Nathan Anderson *(Sr Dir-Asset)*
Scott Canonico *(VP-Environment, Health & Safety)*
Troy Welling *(Controller)*
Paul Whisenand *(Dir-Land)*
Erik Roach *(Dir-Reservoir Engrg & Tech)*
Rhett Wallace *(Dir-E&P Acctg)*
Julie Blaser *(VP & Asst Gen Counsel)*
Chris Laramie *(Dir-Land Admin)*
Ryan Robison *(Dir-Revenue Acctg)*
Troy M. Welling *(Chief Acctg Officer)*
Jaimie Bell *(Dir)*
Brad BonSalle *(Dir)*
William Crawford *(VP)*
Trish Lovewell-Versaw *(Dir)*
Tricia Neal *(Dir)*
Cristina Sigdestad *(Dir)*
Jason Wojciechowicz *(Dir)*
Kimberly s. McHugh *(Pres)*

Subsidiary (Domestic):

Riley Natural Gas (2)
120 Genesis Blvd, Bridgeport, WV 26330-1706 (100%)
Tel.: (304) 842-8930
Web Site: http://www.rileynaturalgas.com
Sales Range: $50-74.9 Million
Emp.: 5
Natural Gas Marketing
N.A.I.C.S.: 424720
Kathie Bonnell *(Mgr-Pur & Sls)*

Riley Natural Gas Company (2)
120 Genesis Blvd, Bridgeport, WV 26330
Tel.: (304) 842-8930
Web Site: http://www.rileynaturalgas.com
Natural Gas Distr
N.A.I.C.S.: 221210
Kathie Bonnell *(Mgr-Pur & Sls)*

PT Chevron Pacific Indonesia (1)
Sentral Senayan 1 Office Tower Jl Asia Afrika No 8 12th Fl, Jakarta, 10270, Indonesia
Tel.: (62) 2134351230

Sales Range: $750-799.9 Million
Emp.: 500
Oil & Gas
N.A.I.C.S.: 211120

Renewable Energy Group, Inc. (1)
416 S Bell Ave, Ames, IA 50010
Tel.: (515) 239-8000
Web Site: http://www.regi.com
Rev.: $3,244,050,000
Assets: $2,558,944,000
Liabilities: $831,118,000
Net Worth: $1,727,826,000
Earnings: $213,819,000
Emp.: 1,093
Fiscal Year-end: 12/31/2021
Renewable Energy Services
N.A.I.C.S.: 211120
Eric M. Bowen *(Gen Counsel & Sec)*
Natalie Merrill *(Sr VP-Bus Dev)*
Todd Robinson *(Deputy CFO, Treas & VP-IR)*
Doug Lenhart *(VP-Procurement)*
Raymond Richie *(Mng Dir-Intl Bus & VP)*
Trisha Conley *(Sr VP-People Dev)*
Bob Kenyon *(Sr VP-Sls & Mktg)*
Richard Craig Bealmear *(CFO)*
Neville Fernandes *(VP-Corp Affairs & Dev)*
Paul Nees *(VP-Ops)*
Derek Winkel *(VP-Mfg Ops)*

Subsidiary (Domestic):

Mel Dawson Inc. (2)
4325 Pacific St, Rocklin, CA 95677-2104
Tel.: (916) 624-8284
Web Site: http://www.dawsonoil.com
Sales Range: $10-24.9 Million
Emp.: 35
Petroleum Services
N.A.I.C.S.: 424710
Mel C. Dawson *(Pres)*

Subsidiary (Non-US):

Petrotec AG (2)
(87.49%)
Tel.: (49) 2862910019
Web Site: http://www.petrotec.de
Sales Range: $150-199.9 Million
Emp.: 110
Biodiesel Manufacturers
N.A.I.C.S.: 324110

Subsidiary (Non-US):

Petrotec Biodiesel GmbH (3)
Tel.: (49) 2862910019
Web Site: http://www.petrotec.de
Biodiesel Mfr
N.A.I.C.S.: 324199

Subsidiary (Domestic):

REG Albert Lea, LLC (2)
15200 780th Ave, Albert Lea, MN 56007
Tel.: (507) 448-0124
Consumable Fuel Whslr
N.A.I.C.S.: 424720

REG Atlanta, LLC (2)
4334 Tanners Church Rd, Ellenwood, GA 30294
Tel.: (404) 366-8900
Petroleum Product Whslr
N.A.I.C.S.: 424720

REG Danville, LLC (2)
300 N Anderson St, Danville, IL 61832
Tel.: (217) 431-6600
Emp.: 1
Crude Oil Whslr
N.A.I.C.S.: 424720

REG Geismar, LLC (2)
36187 Hwy 30, Geismar, LA 70734
Tel.: (225) 744-1300
Consumable Fuel Whslr
N.A.I.C.S.: 424720

Subsidiary (Non-US):

REG Germany GmbH (2)
Kaiserwerther Str 115, 40880, Ratingen, Germany
Tel.: (49) 2862910083
Web Site: http://www.regi.com
Chemical Products Mfr
N.A.I.C.S.: 325998

Chevron Corporation—(Continued)

Subsidiary (Domestic):

REG Grays Harbor, LLC **(2)**
3122 Port Industrial Rd, Hoquiam, WA
98550
Tel.: (360) 532-3752
Web Site:
http://www.imperiumrenewables.com
Chemical Products Distr
N.A.I.C.S.: 424690

REG Houston, LLC **(2)**
11815 Port Rd, Seabrook, TX 77586
Tel.: (515) 239-8000
Emp.: 7
Crude Oil Whslr
N.A.I.C.S.: 324110

REG Life Sciences, LLC **(2)**
600 Gateway Blvd, South San Francisco,
CA 94080
Tel.: (650) 243-5400
Web Site: http://www.reglifesciences.com
Chemicals Mfr
N.A.I.C.S.: 325998

REG Madison, LLC **(2)**
605 Bassett St, De Forest, WI 53532
Tel.: (608) 842-7112
Web Site: http://www.regfuel.com
Chemical Products Mfr
N.A.I.C.S.: 325998

**REG Marketing & Logistics Group,
LLC** **(2)**
416 S Bell Ave, Ames, IA 50010
Tel.: (515) 239-8000
Web Site: http://www.regi.com
Emp.: 20
Petroleum Product Whslr
N.A.I.C.S.: 424720

REG Mason City, LLC **(2)**
4172 19th St SW, Mason City, IA 50401
Tel.: (641) 421-7590
Emp.: 30
Petroleum Product Whslr
N.A.I.C.S.: 424720

REG New Boston, LLC **(2)**
280 Texas Ave, New Boston, TX 75570
Tel.: (903) 280-7585
Emp.: 9
Petroleum Product Whslr
N.A.I.C.S.: 424720

REG Newton, LLC **(2)**
3426 E 28th St N, Newton, IA 50208
Tel.: (641) 791-1010
Emp.: 21
Petroleum & Petroleum Products Whslr
N.A.I.C.S.: 424720

REG Ralston, LLC **(2)**
33321 215th St, Ralston, IA 51459
Tel.: (712) 667-3232
Web Site: http://www.regi.com
Emp.: 19
Crude Oil Whslr
N.A.I.C.S.: 424720

REG Seneca, LLC **(2)**
614 Shipyard Rd, Seneca, IL 61360-9469
Tel.: (815) 357-6300
Industrial Organic Chemicals Mfr
N.A.I.C.S.: 325199

REG Synthetic Fuels, LLC **(2)**
5416 S Yale Ste 400, Tulsa, OK 74135
Tel.: (918) 592-7900
Sales Range: $1-9.9 Million
Emp.: 15
Synthetic Fuels Mfr
N.A.I.C.S.: 324199
Brad Albin (VP-Mfg)

Sabine Pipe Line LLC **(1)**
4800 Fournace Pl, Bellaire, TX 77401
Tel.: (713) 432-2966
Web Site: http://www.sabinepipeline.com
Sales Range: $10-24.9 Million
Emp.: 5
Natural Gas Pipeline Transportation
N.A.I.C.S.: 486110

Saudi Arabian Chevron Inc. **(1)**
270 Road, PO Box 6, Mina Al Zour, Kuwait,
Kuwait **(100%)**
Tel.: (965) 3950444

Web Site: http://www.chevron.com
Petroleum & Energy Production
N.A.I.C.S.: 324199

**Star Petroleum Refining Public Co.,
Ltd.** **(1)**
No 1 I-3B Road, Map Ta Phut Mueang,
Rayong, 21150, Thailand
Tel.: (66) 38699000
Web Site: https://www.sprc.co.th
Rev.: $6,816,102,610
Assets: $1,904,791,273
Liabilities: $849,084,594
Net Worth: $1,055,706,679
Earnings: ($34,257,632)
Emp.: 553
Fiscal Year-end: 12/31/2023
Crude Oil & Natural Gas Extraction Ser-
vices
N.A.I.C.S.: 211120
Robert Joseph Dobrik (CEO & Dir)

**The Pipelines of Puerto Rico,
Inc.** **(1)**
Carr 28 Zona Portuaria Planta Distribution
Texaco Chevron, Guaynabo, PR
00969 **(40%)**
Tel.: (787) 783-3693
Sales Range: $10-24.9 Million
Emp.: 7
Pipe Line Transportation from Catano to
San Juan International Airport
N.A.I.C.S.: 486910
Robert Rose (Pres)

CHICAGO ATLANTIC REAL
ESTATE FINANCE, INC.
1680 Michigan Ave Ste 700, Miami
Beach, FL 33139
Tel.: (312) 809-7002   **MD**
Web Site: https://www.refi.reit
Year Founded: 2021
REFI—(NASDAQ)
Rev.: $48,857,628
Assets: $343,271,050
Liabilities: $79,238,027
Net Worth: $264,033,023
Earnings: $32,292,477
Fiscal Year-end: 12/31/22
Real Estate Investment Services
N.A.I.C.S.: 531210
John Mazarakis (Co-Founder & Chm)
Anthony Cappell (CEO & Co-
Founder)
Andreas Bodmeier (Co-Pres, Co-
Founder & Chief Investment Officer)
Peter Sack (Co-Pres)
Phillip Silverman (Interim CFO & In-
terim Sec)

CHICAGO RIVET & MACHINE
COMPANY
901 Frontenac Rd, Naperville, IL
60563
Tel.: (630) 357-8500   **IL**
Web Site:
https://www.chicagorivet.com
Year Founded: 1920
CVR—(NYSEAMEX)
Rev.: $33,646,033
Assets: $33,626,127
Liabilities: $2,639,329
Net Worth: $30,986,798
Earnings: $2,867,629
Emp.: 208
Fiscal Year-end: 12/31/22
Bolt, Nut, Screw, Rivet & Washer
Manufacturing
N.A.I.C.S.: 332722
Gregory D. Rizzo (CEO)

Subsidiaries:

Chicago Rivet & Machine Co. **(1)**
901 Frontenac Rd, Naperville, IL
60563 **(100%)**
Tel.: (630) 357-8500
Web Site: https://www.chicagorivet.com
Sales Range: $25-49.9 Million
Emp.: 5
Automated Assembly Systems Design &
Sales Support

N.A.I.C.S.: 541330

**Chicago Rivet & Machine Company-
Albia Division** **(1)**
Hwy 5 N, Albia, IA 52531 **(100%)**
Tel.: (641) 932-7107
Web Site: http://www.chicagorivet.com
Sales Range: $25-49.9 Million
Emp.: 28
Mfr of Cutting Tools
N.A.I.C.S.: 333515

**Chicago Rivet & Machine Company-
Jefferson Division** **(1)**
208 E Central Ave, Jefferson, IA
50129-1304 **(100%)**
Tel.: (515) 386-4114
Sales Range: $25-49.9 Million
Emp.: 30
Mfr of Rivets
N.A.I.C.S.: 332722

**Chicago Rivet & Machine Company-
Tyrone Division** **(1)**
2728 Adams Ave, Tyrone, PA
16686 **(100%)**
Tel.: (814) 684-2430
Web Site: http://www.chicagorivet.com
Sales Range: $50-74.9 Million
Emp.: 100
Tools, Rivets & Rivet Setting Machines Mfr
N.A.I.C.S.: 333517

H&L Tool Company, Inc. **(1)**
32701 Dequindre Rd, Madison Heights, MI
48071 **(100%)**
Tel.: (248) 585-7474
Web Site: https://www.hltool.com
Sales Range: $50-74.9 Million
Emp.: 120
Screw Machine Product Mfr
N.A.I.C.S.: 332722

CHICKEN SOUP FOR THE
SOUL ENTERTAINMENT, INC.
132 E Putnam Ave Fl 2W, Cos Cob,
CT 06807
Tel.: (310) 623-6493   **DE**
Web Site:
https://www.cssentertainment.com
Year Founded: 2017
CSSE—(NASDAQ)
Rev.: $252,810,110
Assets: $883,879,409
Liabilities: $804,131,470
Net Worth: $79,747,939
Earnings: ($101,544,252)
Emp.: 1,329
Fiscal Year-end: 12/31/22
Video Broadcasting Services
N.A.I.C.S.: 516210
Philippe Guelton (Chief Revenue Offi-
cer)
David Fannon (Chief Acquisition Offi-
cer & Chief Distribution Officer)
Jason Meier (CFO & Chief Acctg Offi-
cer)
Elana B. Sofko (Co-Chief Strategy
Officer)
Peter Binazeski (Sr VP-Corporate
Communications)
Zaia Lawandow (Head-Investor Rela-
tions & Dir)
Amy L. Newmark (Publr & Editor-in-
Chief)
William J. Rouhana Jr (Chm & Co-
CEO)

Subsidiaries:

Digital Media Enterprises LLC **(1)**
PO Box 679, Berryville, VA 22611
Web Site:
http://www.digitalmediaenterprises.com
Digital Marketing Services
N.A.I.C.S.: 541613

Pivotshare Inc. **(1)**
120 Newport Ctr Dr, Newport Beach, CA
92660
Tel.: (949) 336-2932
Web Site: http://www.pivotshare.com
Software Publisher
N.A.I.C.S.: 513210

Adam Mosam (Founder)

Recruiter.com Group, Inc. **(1)**
123 Farmington Ave Ste 252, Bristol, CT
06010
Web Site: https://www.recruiter.com
Rev.: $25,372,274
Assets: $14,133,284
Liabilities: $9,054,967
Net Worth: $5,078,317
Earnings: ($18,395,901)
Emp.: 18
Fiscal Year-end: 12/31/2022
Technology Development & Acquisition
N.A.I.C.S.: 551112
Miles Jennings (Founder)
Granger Whitelaw (CEO)

Redbox Entertainment Inc. **(1)**
1 Tower Ln Ste 800, Oakbrook Terrace, IL
60181
Tel.: (866) 733-2693
Web Site: https://www.redbox.com
Rev.: $288,540,000
Assets: $378,032,000
Liabilities: $440,983,000
Net Worth: ($62,951,000)
Earnings: ($140,756,000)
Emp.: 1,408
Fiscal Year-end: 12/31/2021
Investment Services
N.A.I.C.S.: 523999
Galen C. Smith (CEO)

Screen Media Ventures LLC **(1)**
800 3rd Ave 3rd Fl, New York, NY 10017
Tel.: (212) 308-1790
Web Site: http://www.screenmedia.net
Motion Picture Rights Distr
N.A.I.C.S.: 512120
David Fannon (VP-Bus Affairs)
Donna Tracey (Dir-Ops)

Sonar Entertainment, Inc. **(1)**
423 W 55th St 12th Fl, New York, NY
10019
Tel.: (212) 977-9001
Web Site: http://www.sonarent.com
Sales Range: $75-99.9 Million
Emp.: 80
Holding Company; Television Program Pro-
duction & Distribution
N.A.I.C.S.: 551112
Laura Kirrin (VP-HR & Ops)
Jeffrey Smith (Sr VP-Bus & Legal Affairs)
Gabriel de Alba (Chm)
David Ellender (CEO)
Alan Zapakin (Sr VP-Mktg & Publicity)
Andrea Gorfolova (Pres-Family & Factual
Entertainment)
Andres Santos (Sr VP-Intl Distr)
Ashley Rite (VP-Kids & Family)
Carol Eymery (Exec VP-Intl Distr)
Chan Park (Sr VP-Fin)
Cheyanne Dillenberger (VP-Factual Dev)
Jeff Hevert (Sr VP-Factual Dev)
Jenna Santoianni (Exec VP-Television Se-
ries)
Kylie Munnich (Sr VP-Intl Distr)
Marc Kell Whitehead (VP-Factual Produc-
tion)
Roberta Ibba-Hartog (Sr VP-Distr-Intl)
Matt Loze (Exec VP-Dev & Production)

Subsidiary (Domestic):

Sonar Entertainment, LLC **(2)**
423 W 55th St 12th Fl, New York, NY
10019 **(100%)**
Tel.: (212) 977-9001
Web Site: http://www.sonarent.com
Television Programming Production & Distri-
bution Services
N.A.I.C.S.: 512110
Debbie Back (Sr VP-Sls-North America)

Subsidiary (Domestic):

**Sonar Entertainment Distribution,
LLC** **(3)**
423 W 55th St 12th Fl, New York, NY
10019
Tel.: (212) 977-9001
Web Site: http://www.sonarent.com
Television Program Distribution
N.A.I.C.S.: 512120
Paul Jags (Sr VP-Digital & DVD Distr)

CHILEAN COBALT CORP.

1199 Lancaster Ave Ste 107, Berwyn, PA 19312
Tel.: (484) 580-8697   NV
Web Site:
   https://www.chileancobaltcorp.com
Year Founded: 2017
COBA—(OTCQB)
Rev.: $813
Assets: $677,170
Liabilities: $22,896
Net Worth: $654,274
Earnings: ($1,032,295)
Fiscal Year-end: 12/31/22
Copper, Nickel, Lead & Zinc Mining
N.A.I.C.S.: 212230
Duncan T. Blount *(Pres)*
Greg Levinson *(Chm)*

CHILL N OUT CRYOTHERAPY, INC.

1851 San Diego Ave Ste 100A, San Diego, CA 92110
Tel.: (858) 945-2830
Web Site: https://www.chillnout.com
CHNO—(OTCIQ)
Health Care Srvices
N.A.I.C.S.: 621999
Roman Valenzuela *(Mgr-Studio)*

CHIMERA INVESTMENT CORP.

630 5th Ave Ste 2400, New York, NY 10111
Tel.: (212) 626-2300   MD
Web Site:
   https://www.chimerareit.com
Year Founded: 2007
CIM—(NYSE)
Rev.: $773,121,000
Assets: $13,401,991,000
Liabilities: $10,735,188,000
Net Worth: $2,666,803,000
Earnings: ($513,066,000)
Emp.: 39
Fiscal Year-end: 12/31/22
Real Estate Investment Trust
N.A.I.C.S.: 525990
Phillip John Kardis II *(Pres & CEO)*
Subramaniam Viswanathan *(CFO & Principal Acctg Officer)*
Dan Thakkar *(Chief Investment Officer)*

Subsidiaries:

Kah Capital Management, LLC   **(1)**
1750 Tysons Blvd Ste 1500, McLean, VA 22102
Tel.: (703) 677-3424
Web Site: https://www.kahcapital.com
Investment Management Service
N.A.I.C.S.: 523999
Donna Sims Wilson *(COO)*

CHIMERIX, INC.

2505 Meridian Pkwy Ste 100, Durham, NC 27713
Tel.: (919) 806-1074   DE
Web Site: https://www.chimerix.com
Year Founded: 2000
CMRX—(NASDAQ)
Rev.: $33,824,000
Assets: $279,341,000
Liabilities: $22,484,000
Net Worth: $256,857,000
Earnings: $172,167,000
Emp.: 89
Fiscal Year-end: 12/31/22
Pharmaceutical Preparation Manufacturing
N.A.I.C.S.: 325412
Thomas J. Riga *(COO & Chief Comml Officer)*
Odin Naderer *(VP-Clinical Pharmacology & Translational Medicine)*
Michael A. Alrutz *(Gen Counsel & VP)*
David Jakeman *(Principal Acctg Officer & Exec Dir-Fin & Acctg)*

Michelle LaSpaluto *(VP-Strategic Plng & IR)*
Allen Melemed *(Chief Medical Officer)*
Caryn Barnett *(VP-Clinical Ops)*
Christopher L. Jordan *(VP-Regulatory Affairs)*
Joshua E. Allen *(CTO)*
Michael T. Andriole *(Pres & CEO)*

CHINA CARBON GRAPHITE GROUP, INC.

20955 Pathfinder Rd Ste 200, Diamond Bar, CA 91765
Tel.: (909) 843-6518   NV
Web Site:
   https://www.chinacarboninc.com
CHGI—(OTCIQ)
Rev.: $429,335
Assets: $121,642
Liabilities: $2,822,092
Net Worth: ($2,700,450)
Earnings: ($271,401)
Emp.: 9
Fiscal Year-end: 12/31/20
Carbon Graphite Product Mfr
N.A.I.C.S.: 335991
Donghai Yu *(Pres & CEO)*

CHINA HEALTH MANAGEMENT CORP.

3609 Hammerkop Dr N, Las Vegas, NV 89084
Tel.: (415) 841-3570
Web Site:
   https://www.chinahealthcorp.com
Year Founded: 2006
CNHC—(OTCIQ)
Health Care Srvices
N.A.I.C.S.: 621999
Xu Mei *(Pres)*

CHINA INDUSTRIAL STEEL INC.

110 Wall St 11th Fl, New York, NY 10005
Tel.: (646) 328-1502   MD
CDNN—(OTCIQ)
Sales Range: $600-649.9 Million
Emp.: 1,621
Holding Company; Steel Plate, Bar, & Billet Mfr
N.A.I.C.S.: 551112

CHINA LIAONING DINGXU ECOLOGICAL AGRICULTURE DEVELOPMENT, INC.

17800 Castleton St Ste 256, City of Industry, CA 91748
Tel.: (702) 213-8888   NV
Year Founded: 2010
CLAD—(OTCIQ)
Sales Range: Less than $1 Million
Mushrooms & Related Products
N.A.I.C.S.: 111411
Joseph Yentsu Lai *(COO)*
Caren D. Currier *(Fin Mgr)*
Mary Liu *(Office Mgr)*
David He *(Chm, Pres & CEO)*

CHINA MULANS NANO TECHNOLOGY CORP. LTD.

PO Box 110310, Naples, FL 34108-0106
Tel.: (239) 598-2300   NV
CMNT—(OTCIQ)
Software Development Services
N.A.I.C.S.: 541511
Frank Pioppi *(Pres)*
Anna Herbst *(Sec)*

CHINO COMMERCIAL BANCORP

14245 Pipeline Ave, Chino, CA 91710
Tel.: (909) 393-8880   CA

Web Site:
   https://www.chinocommercial
bank.com
CCBC—(OTCIQ)
Rev.: $11,931,476
Assets: $314,839,618
Liabilities: $287,616,437
Net Worth: $27,223,181
Earnings: $2,624,730
Fiscal Year-end: 12/31/20
Offices of Bank Holding Companies
N.A.I.C.S.: 551111
Dann H. Bowman *(Pres & CEO)*

Subsidiaries:

Chino Commercial Bank   **(1)**
14245 Pipeline Ave, Chino, CA 91710
Tel.: (909) 393-8880
Web Site:
   http://www.chinocommercialbank.com
Sales Range: $25-49.9 Million
Emp.: 25
Banking Services
N.A.I.C.S.: 522110
Dan Bowman *(Pres)*

CHIPOTLE MEXICAN GRILL, INC.

610 Newport Ctr Dr, Newport Beach, CA 92660
Tel.: (303) 222-2541   DE
Web Site: https://www.chipotle.com
Year Founded: 1993
CMG—(NYSE)
Rev.: $9,871,649,000
Assets: $8,044,362,000
Liabilities: $4,982,155,000
Net Worth: $3,062,207,000
Earnings: $1,228,737,000
Emp.: 116,068
Fiscal Year-end: 12/31/23
Mexican Restaurant Operator
N.A.I.C.S.: 722511
Christopher Brandt *(CMO)*
Laurie Schalow *(Chief Corp Affairs & Food Safety Officer)*
Marissa Andrada *(Chief Diversity, Inclusion & People Officer)*
Roger Theodoredis *(Chief Legal Officer)*
Curtis Evander Garner III *(CTO)*
Scott Boatwright *(Chm & CEO)*

Subsidiaries:

Chipotle Mexican Grill Canada Corp.   **(1)**
323 Yonge St Unit 114, Toronto, M5B 1R7, ON, Canada
Tel.: (416) 596-8600
Sales Range: $25-49.9 Million
Emp.: 150
Restaurant Operating Services
N.A.I.C.S.: 722511

Chipotle Mexican Grill Germany GMBH   **(1)**
Europ-Allee 6 Shop 00 SH 011, 60327, Frankfurt, Germany
Tel.: (49) 76758116
Web Site: http://www.chipotle.de
Restaurant
N.A.I.C.S.: 722511

Chipotle Mexican Grill Service Co., LLC   **(1)**
1543 Wazee St Ste 200, Denver, CO 80202-1443
Tel.: (303) 595-4000
Web Site: http://www.chipotle.com
Sales Range: $50-74.9 Million
Restaurant Services
N.A.I.C.S.: 722511

Chipotle Mexican Grill U.S. Finance Co., LLC   **(1)**
1401 Wynkoop St Ste 500, Denver, CO 80202
Tel.: (303) 595-4000
Web Site: http://www.chipotle.com
Sales Range: $10-24.9 Million
Emp.: 9
Restaurant Business Support Services

N.A.I.C.S.: 561499
Montgomery F. Moran *(Pres & COO)*

Chipotle Mexican Grill of Berwyn Heights, LLC   **(1)**
5506 Cherrywood Ln Ste G, Greenbelt, MD 20770
Tel.: (301) 982-6722
Restaurant Services
N.A.I.C.S.: 722511

Chipotle Mexican Grill of Colorado, LLC   **(1)**
1401 Wynkoop St Ste 500, Denver, CO 80202
Tel.: (303) 595-4000
Web Site: http://www.chipotle.com
Sales Range: $50-74.9 Million
Restaurant Services
N.A.I.C.S.: 722511

CHOICE HOTELS INTERNATIONAL, INC.

1 Choice Hotels Cir Ste 400, Rockville, MD 20850
Tel.: (301) 592-5000   DE
Web Site:
   https://www.choicehotels.com
Year Founded: 1939
CHH—(NYSE)
Rev.: $1,544,165,000
Assets: $2,394,799,000
Liabilities: $2,359,201,000
Net Worth: $35,598,000
Earnings: $258,507,000
Emp.: 1,836
Fiscal Year-end: 12/31/23
Hotel & Motel Franchising Services
N.A.I.C.S.: 721110
Scott E. Oaksmith *(CFO & Principal Acctg Officer)*
David A. Pepper *(Chief Dev Officer)*
Patrick S. Pacious *(Pres & CEO)*
Patrick J. Cimerola *(Chief HR Officer)*
Robert McDowell *(Chief Comml Officer)*
Janis Cannon *(Sr VP-Upscale Brands)*
Dominic E. Dragisich *(Chief Global Brand Officer & Exec VP-Ops)*
Anna Scozzafava *(Chief Strategy Officer & Sr VP-Tech)*
Megan Brumagim *(VP-Environmental, Social & Governance)*
Noha Abdalla *(CMO)*
Simone Wu *(Gen Counsel, Sec & Sr VP-External Affairs)*

Subsidiaries:

Choice Hotels Asia-Pac Pty. Ltd.   **(1)**
150 Jolimont Road, Melbourne, 3002, VIC, Australia
Tel.: (61) 392432400
Web Site: https://www.choicehotels.com
Hotel Services
N.A.I.C.S.: 561599

Choice Hotels Australasia Pty. Ltd.   **(1)**
150 Jolimont Road, Melbourne, 3002, VIC, Australia
Tel.: (61) 392432400
Web Site: http://www.choicehotels.com.au
Sales Range: $1-9.9 Million
Emp.: 60
Hotels & Motels; Management Consulting Services
N.A.I.C.S.: 721110
Trent Fraser *(CEO)*

Choice Hotels Canada, Inc.   **(1)**
5090 Explorer Drive Suite 500, Mississauga, L4W 4T9, ON, Canada
Tel.: (905) 602-2222
Web Site: https://www.choicehotels.ca
Sales Range: $10-24.9 Million
Emp.: 220
Franchisor of Hotels & Motels
N.A.I.C.S.: 721110

Choice Hotels International, Inc.—(Continued)

Brian Leon *(Mng Dir)*

Choice Hotels France, S.A.S **(1)**
2 rue Christophe Colomb, 91300, Massy,
France
Tel.: (33) 181918100
Home Management Services
N.A.I.C.S.: 721110

Choice Hotels Franchise, GmbH **(1)**
Martin Kollar Str 9, Munchen, 81829, Munich, Germany
Tel.: (49) 894200150
Web Site: https://www.choicehotels.de
Emp.: 16
Home Management Services
N.A.I.C.S.: 721110
Georg Chlegel *(Mng Dir)*

Choice Hotels International Services Corp **(1)**
1 Choice Hotels Cir, Rockville, MD 20850
Tel.: (301) 592-5000
Web Site: https://www.choicehotels.com
Home Management Services
N.A.I.C.S.: 533110

Choice Hotels Limited **(1)**
107 Dickson Road, Blackpool, FY1 2ET,
Lancashire, United Kingdom
Tel.: (44) 8448115570
Web Site: http://www.choicehotels.co.uk
Sales Range: $125-149.9 Million
Emp.: 400
Hotels & Motels
N.A.I.C.S.: 721110

Choice Vacation Rentals LLC **(1)**
4563 Ada Ln, Kissimmee, FL 34746
Hotel Operator
N.A.I.C.S.: 721110

Maxxton B.V. **(1)**
Kousteensedijk 5, 4331 JE, Middelburg,
Netherlands
Tel.: (31) 118671010
Software Development Services
N.A.I.C.S.: 541511
Rob Sonke *(CTO)*
Martijn Houben *(COO)*

Maxxton US Corp. **(1)**
Highland Park Pl 4514 Cole Ave Ste 600,
Dallas, TX 75205
Tel.: (214) 559-7158
Web Site: http://www.maxxton.com
Software Development Services
N.A.I.C.S.: 541511
Chris Connar *(VP-Sls & Mktg)*

**Park Lane Drive Hotel Development,
LLC** **(1)**
1000 Park Ln Dr, Pittsburgh, PA 15275-1107
Tel.: (412) 490-7343
Hotel
N.A.I.C.S.: 721110

Sleep Inn Hotels **(1)**
701 Yorkmont Rd, Charlotte, NC 28217
Tel.: (704) 525-5005
Hotel Operator
N.A.I.C.S.: 721110

CHOICEONE FINANCIAL SERVICES, INC.
Tel.: (616) 887-7366 **MI**
Web Site:
https://www.choiceone.com
COFS—(NASDAQ)
Rev.: $80,132,000
Assets: $2,385,915,000
Liabilities: $2,217,041,000
Net Worth: $168,874,000
Earnings: $23,640,000
Emp.: 332
Fiscal Year-end: 12/31/22
Bank Holding Company
N.A.I.C.S.: 551111
Kelly J. Potes *(CEO)*
Adom J. Greenland *(CFO, Treas &
Sec)*
Michael J. Burke Jr. *(Pres)*

Subsidiaries:

ChoiceOne Bank **(1)**

109 E Division St, Sparta, MI 49345
Tel.: (616) 887-7366
Web Site: http://www.choiceone.com
Sales Range: $25-49.9 Million
Emp.: 165
Commericial Banking
N.A.I.C.S.: 522110
Kelly J. Potes *(CEO)*
Adom J. Greenland *(CFO, Treas & Sec)*
Michael J. Burke Jr. *(Pres)*
Adom J. Greenland *(COO & Sr VP)*
Bradley A. Henion *(Chief Lending Officer &
Sr VP)*
Lee A. Braford *(Chief Credit Officer & Sr
VP)*
Ryan L. Wolthuis *(Sr VP-Grand Rapids
Market)*
Chris Allamon *(VP & Dir-Tech & Innovation)*
Steve Turk *(Asst VP & Project Mgr-IT)*

CHORD ENERGY CORPORATION
1001 Fannin St Ste 1500, Houston,
TX 77002
Tel.: (281) 404-9500 **DE**
Web Site:
https://www.chordenergy.com
Year Founded: 2010
CHRD—(NASDAQ)
Rev.: $3,896,641,000
Assets: $6,926,150,000
Liabilities: $1,849,526,000
Net Worth: $5,076,624,000
Earnings: $1,023,779,000
Emp.: 514
Fiscal Year-end: 12/31/23
Oil & Gas Exploration & Production
Services
N.A.I.C.S.: 211120
Charles J. Rimer *(COO & Exec VP)*
Richard N. Robuck *(CFO & Exec VP)*
Michael H. Lou *(Chief Strategy Officer, Chief Comml Officer & Exec VP)*
Daniel E. Brown *(Pres & CEO)*
Michael H. Lou *(CFO & Exec VP)*
Greg E. Hills *(Sr VP-Mktg & Midstream)*
Richard N. Robuck *(Treas & Sr VP-Fin)*
Robbin Clark *(VP-Permian)*
Jay B. Knaebel *(VP-Reservoir Engrg)*
Lara Kroll *(VP-Acctg & Controller)*
Karla Lundquist *(VP-HR)*
Jason Swaren *(VP-Ops)*
Alex Wall *(VP-Bus Dev)*

Subsidiaries:

Oasis Midstream Partners LP **(1)**
1001 Fannin St Ste 1500, Houston, TX
77002 **(67.5%)**
Tel.: (281) 404-9500
Web Site: http://www.oasismidstream.com
Rev.: $347,859,000
Assets: $1,030,693,000
Liabilities: $507,035,000
Net Worth: $523,658,000
Earnings: $23,075,000
Emp.: 105
Fiscal Year-end: 12/31/2020
Midstream Asset Management Services
N.A.I.C.S.: 213112
Richard N. Robuck *(CFO & Sr VP)*
Danny Brown *(Chm)*

Oasis Midstream Services LLC **(1)**
1001 Fannin St Ste 1500, Houston, TX
77002
Tel.: (281) 404-9500
Petroleum Product Whslr
N.A.I.C.S.: 423520

Oasis Petroleum LLC **(1)**
1001 Fannin St Ste 1500, Houston, TX
77002
Tel.: (281) 404-9500
Sales Range: $100-124.9 Million
Emp.: 174
Crude Petroleum & Natural Gas Extracting
Services
N.A.I.C.S.: 211120

Oasis Petroleum North America
LLC **(1)**

1001 Fannin St Ste 1500, Houston, TX
77002
Tel.: (281) 404-9500
Web Site: http://www.oasispetroleum.com
Crude Petroleum & Natural Gas Extracting
Services
N.A.I.C.S.: 211120

Whiting Holdings LLC **(1)**
1001 Fannin St Ste 1500, Houston, TX
77002
Tel.: (281) 404-9500
Holding Company
N.A.I.C.S.: 551112

Subsidiary (Domestic):

Whiting Petroleum Corporation **(2)**
1700 Broadway Ste 2300, Denver, CO
80290-2300
Tel.: (303) 837-1661
Web Site: http://www.whiting.com
Rev.: $1,533,481,000
Assets: $2,457,931,000
Liabilities: $794,306,000
Net Worth: $1,663,625,000
Earnings: $427,906,000
Emp.: 356
Fiscal Year-end: 12/31/2021
Crude Petroleum & Natural Gas Exploration
& Extraction
N.A.I.C.S.: 551112
Eric K. Hagen *(VP-Corp Affairs)*
Sirikka R. Lohoefener *(VP & Controller)*
Shane A. Fross *(VP-Ops)*
Kevin A. Kelly *(VP-Mktg & Midstream)*
Rick L. Hatcher *(VP-IT)*
John B. Marvin Jr. *(VP-Bus Dev)*

Subsidiary (Domestic):

Whiting Canadian Holding Company
ULC **(3)**
1700 Broadway Ste 2300, Denver, CO
80290-2300
Tel.: (303) 837-1661
Web Site: http://www.whiting.com
Rev.: $904,612,000
Assets: $3,923,770,000
Liabilities: $2,730,698,000
Net Worth: $1,193,072,000
Earnings: $141,416,000
Emp.: 202
Fiscal Year-end: 12/31/2013
Holding Company; Oil & Gas Exploration
Services
N.A.I.C.S.: 551112
James J. Volker *(Chm, Pres & CEO)*

CHP MERGER CORP.
25 Deforest Ave Ste 108, Summit, NJ
07901
Tel.: (212) 508-7090 **DE**
Year Founded: 2019
CHPM—(NASDAQ)
Rev.: $25,824,527
Assets: $188,792,288
Liabilities: $213,051,577
Net Worth: ($24,259,289)
Earnings: $22,219,073
Emp.: 3
Fiscal Year-end: 12/31/21
Investment Services
N.A.I.C.S.: 523999
Joseph R. Swedish *(Chm)*
James T. Olsen *(CEO)*
Benson Jose *(CFO)*

CHRISTOPHER & BANKS CORPORATION
6740 Shady Oak Rd, Eden Prairie,
MN 55344
Tel.: (763) 551-5000 **DE**
Web Site: https://www.christopherand
banks.com
Year Founded: 1956
CBKC—(OTCIQ)
Rev.: $348,850,000
Assets: $189,406,000
Liabilities: $180,298,000
Net Worth: $9,108,000
Earnings: ($16,694,000)
Emp.: 3,800
Fiscal Year-end: 02/01/20

Women's Specialty Apparel Retailer
N.A.I.C.S.: 458110
Donna J. Fauchald *(VP-Real Estate
& Construction)*
Lisa M. Klein *(VP-Plng & Allocation)*
Andrea Kellick *(Chief Mdsg Officer &
Sr VP)*
Carmen L. Wamre *(Chief Stores Officer & Sr VP)*
Richard Heyman *(CIO & Sr VP)*
Rachel Endrizzi *(CMO & Sr VP)*
Maureen A. Reagan *(VP-HR)*
Kara Johnson *(CFO & Sr VP)*

CHROMADEX CORPORATION
10900 Wilshire Blvd Ste 600, Los Angeles, CA 90024
Tel.: (310) 388-6706 **DE**
Web Site:
https://www.chromadex.com
Year Founded: 1999
CDXC—(NASDAQ)
Rev.: $72,050,000
Assets: $54,057,000
Liabilities: $25,385,000
Net Worth: $28,672,000
Earnings: ($16,540,000)
Emp.: 113
Fiscal Year-end: 12/31/22
Holding Company; Medicinal Chemicals & Botanical Products Developer,
Mfr & Whslr
N.A.I.C.S.: 551112
Frank Louis Jaksch Jr. *(Co-Founder)*
Ozan Pamir *(CFO & Principal Acctg
Officer)*
Andrew Shao *(Sr VP-Regulatory-Global & Scientific Affairs)*
Robert N. Fried *(CEO)*
Heather Van Blarcom *(Sec)*

Subsidiaries:

ChromaDex Analytics, Inc. **(1)**
1751 S Fordham St Ste 350, Longmont,
CO 80503
Tel.: (720) 600-0862
Nutraceutical Product Mfr
N.A.I.C.S.: 325411
Amanda Storjohann *(Sr Mgr)*

ChromaDex, Inc. **(1)**
1735 Flight Way Ste 200, Tustin, CA 92782
Tel.: (949) 419-0288
Web Site: http://www.chromadex.com
Medicinal Chemical & Botanical Product
Developer Mfr
N.A.I.C.S.: 325411
Ozan Pamir *(CFO)*

CHROMOCELL THERAPEUTICS CORPORATION
4400 Rte 9 S Ste 1000, Freehold, NJ
07728
Tel.: (732) 514-2636 **DE**
Web Site:
https://www.chromocell.com
Year Founded: 2021
CHRO—(NYSEAMEX)
Assets: $96,391
Liabilities: $6,540,943
Net Worth: ($6,444,552)
Earnings: ($7,380,793)
Emp.: 4
Fiscal Year-end: 12/31/23
Biotechnology Research & Development Services
N.A.I.C.S.: 541714

CHS INC.
5500 Cenex Dr, Inver Grove Heights,
MN 55077
Tel.: (651) 355-6000 **MN**
Web Site: https://www.chsinc.com
Year Founded: 1998
CHSCP—(NASDAQ)
Rev.: $39,261,229,000
Assets: $18,715,075,000

Liabilities: $7,953,151,000
Net Worth: $10,761,924,000
Earnings: $1,102,659,000
Emp.: 10,730
Fiscal Year-end: 08/31/24
Holding Company; Farm Product
Raw Materials, Equipment & Supplies
Whslr
N.A.I.C.S.: 551112
Jay D. Debertin *(Pres & CEO)*
Daniel W. Schurr *(Chm)*
Steve Riegel *(Asst Sec & Asst Treas)*
James S. Loving *(Sr VP-Refining, Pipelines, and Terminals)*
Darin Hunhoff *(Exec VP-Energy)*
Richard A. Dusek *(Exec VP-Country Ops)*
Daniel Lehmann *(Chief Acctg Officer, VP-Fin & Controller)*
Mary Kaul-Hottinger *(Sr VP-HR)*
Russell A. Kehl *(Treas & Sec)*
John Griffith *(Exec VP-Ag Bus)*
Gary Halvorson *(Sr VP-Enterprise Customer Dev)*
Olivia Nelligan *(CFO & Exec VP)*
Brandon Smith *(Gen Counsel & Exec VP)*
Kirstie Foster *(Sr VP-Mktg Comm)*

Subsidiaries:

ADM/CHS, LLC **(1)**
1815 31st Ave NE, Havre, MT 59501
Tel.: (406) 265-2208
Web Site: http://www.admchsllc.com
Emp.: 12
Freight Transportation Services
N.A.I.C.S.: 484230
Chris Herring *(Mgr)*

Ag States Agency, LLC **(1)**
PO Box 64422, Saint Paul, MN
55164 **(100%)**
Tel.: (651) 355-3700
Web Site: http://www.agstatesgroup.com
Sales Range: $1-9.9 Million
Emp.: 40
Commercial Insurance Agency
N.A.I.C.S.: 524210

Agriliance, LLC **(1)**
5500 Cenex Dr, Inver Grove Heights, MN
55077-1733
Tel.: (651) 451-5000
Sales Range: $800-899.9 Million
Emp.: 2,504
Crop Protection Products & Services;
Owned by CHS Inc. & Land O'Lakes, Inc.
N.A.I.C.S.: 423820

Agro Distribution, LLC **(1)**
209 Lovers Ln, Waynesboro, GA 30830
Tel.: (706) 554-9477
Farm Supply Whslr
N.A.I.C.S.: 424910

Allied Agronomy, LLC **(1)**
109 Industrial Park Ste 1, Edgeley, ND
58433-2680
Tel.: (701) 493-2680
Web Site: http://www.alliedag.com
Sales Range: $10-24.9 Million
Emp.: 20
Agricultural Services
N.A.I.C.S.: 325320

Ardent Mills, LLC **(1)**
1875 Lawrence St, Denver, CO
80202 **(12%)**
Tel.: (800) 851-9618
Web Site: http://www.ardentmills.com
Sales Range: $1-4.9 Billion
Flour & Other Grain Mill Products Milling
N.A.I.C.S.: 311211
Dan Dye *(CEO)*

Unit (Domestic):

Ardent Mills **(2)**
905 W Marion St, Lake City, MN 55041-2007
Tel.: (651) 345-3351
Sales Range: $10-24.9 Million
Emp.: 32
Self-Rising Prepared Blended Flour Producer

N.A.I.C.S.: 311211
Deb Roschen *(Mgr-Admin)*

Subsidiary (Domestic):

Hinrichs Trading LLC **(2)**
155 SE Kamiaken St, Pullman, WA 83501
Tel.: (509) 332-8888
Web Site: http://www.hinrichstrading.com
Commodity Contracts Dealing
N.A.I.C.S.: 523160
Phil Hinrichs *(CEO)*

Boort Grain Cooperative Ltd **(1)**
Silo-Woolshed Rd, Boort, 3537, VIC, Australia
Tel.: (61) 354552600
Farm Supply Whslr
N.A.I.C.S.: 424910

Border States Cooperatives **(1)**
PO Box 362, Clinton, MN 56225
Tel.: (320) 325-5466
Web Site: http://www.bscorp.com
Sales Range: $10-24.9 Million
Emp.: 75
Fertilizer & Fertilizer Materials
N.A.I.C.S.: 424910

CHS (Shanghai) Trading Co., LTD **(1)**
Room 3902 Jin Mao Tower No 88 Century
Avenue, Shanghai, 200120, China
Tel.: (86) 2160212511
Agriculture Product Distr
N.A.I.C.S.: 424910

CHS (Taiwan) Commodity Trading Co. Ltd **(1)**
6F No 126 Songjiang Road, Zhongshan
Dist, Taipei, 104, Taiwan
Tel.: (886) 221813588
Farm Supply Whslr
N.A.I.C.S.: 424910

CHS Agritrade Bulgaria Ltd. **(1)**
Str F Joliot Curie nr 16 2nd floor, 1113, Sofia, Bulgaria
Tel.: (359) 28173780
Farm Product Whslr
N.A.I.C.S.: 424910
Adrian Paskalev *(Dir-Fin)*

CHS Agritrade Hungary Ltd. **(1)**
Fenyes Adolf utca 6, 1036, Budapest, Hungary
Tel.: (36) 13457810
Farm Supply Whslr
N.A.I.C.S.: 424910

CHS Agritrade d.o.o **(1)**
Ive Andrica no 4, Brcko, Bosnia & Herzegovina
Tel.: (387) 49232700
Farm Supply Whslr
N.A.I.C.S.: 424910

CHS Agromarket, LLC **(1)**
72 im E Bershanskoy St, 350911, Krasnodar, Russia
Tel.: (7) 8612991300
Web Site: http://www.chsinc.com
Emp.: 6
Agricultural Product Whslr
N.A.I.C.S.: 424910

CHS Broadbent Pty. Ltd. **(1)**
300B Gillies St, Wendouree, 3355, VIC, Australia
Tel.: (61) 343136700
Web Site: http://www.chsbroadbent.com
Global Commodity Marketing Services
N.A.I.C.S.: 926140
Steve Broadbent *(Mng Dir)*
Michael Broadbent *(COO)*
Sam Batters *(Gen Mgr)*
Anthony O'Brien *(CFO)*

CHS Bulgaria Ltd. **(1)**
16 Fr Joliot Curie Str, 1113, Sofia, Bulgaria
Tel.: (359) 28260500
Agriculture Farming Services
N.A.I.C.S.: 115116

CHS Canada LP **(1)**
102-7777 10th Street NE, Calgary, T2E
8X2, AB, Canada
Tel.: (587) 755-2000
Agriculture Product Distr
N.A.I.C.S.: 424910

CHS Capital, LLC **(1)**
5500 Cenex Dr, Inver Grove Heights, MN
55077
Tel.: (651) 355-6000
Web Site: http://www.chsinc.com
Financial Products & Services for Agriculture Industry
N.A.I.C.S.: 522299
Eric Born *(Chief Credit Officer)*

CHS Country Operations Canada, Inc. **(1)**
504 East Road, Standard, T0J 3G0, AB,
Canada
Tel.: (403) 947-3767
Web Site: http://www.chsinc.com
Emp.: 10
Agricultural Product Retailer
N.A.I.C.S.: 444240

CHS Elburn **(1)**
108 N Main St, Sycamore, IL 60178
Tel.: (815) 899-8964
Web Site: http://chselburn.com
Grain Elevators
N.A.I.C.S.: 424510
Phil Farrell *(Gen Mgr)*
Dave Myers *(Mgr-Agronomy Div)*
Chris Gould *(Vice Chm)*
Denise Ramm-Lenz *(Pres)*
Rich Hamilton *(Mgr-Grain Ops)*
Jerry Whalen *(Mgr-Newark Grain Location)*
Ryan Engelbarts *(Mgr-Trucking Logistics)*
Chris Daniels *(Mgr-Darien Location)*

CHS Energy Canada, Inc. **(1)**
2700 350 7th Avenue SW, Calgary, T2P
3N9, AB, Canada
Tel.: (403) 538-3197
Agriculture Product Distr
N.A.I.C.S.: 424910

CHS Hallock, LLC **(1)**
2100 US Hwy 75, Kennedy, MN 56733
Tel.: (218) 843-2531
Farm Supply Whslr
N.A.I.C.S.: 424910
Zack Schaefer *(Mgr-Grain Origination)*

CHS Inc. - Mankato Oilseed Processing Plant **(1)**
2020 S Riverfront Dr, Mankato, MN 56001
Tel.: (507) 625-7911
Sales Range: $100-124.9 Million
Emp.: 200
Soybean Processor
N.A.I.C.S.: 311224
Denny Wendland *(VP-Oilseed Processing)*

CHS Inc.-Faulkton **(1)**
609 9th Ave, Faulkton, SD 57438
Tel.: (605) 598-4532
Web Site: http://www.chsriverplains.com
Soil Preparation Services
N.A.I.C.S.: 115112

CHS Industries Ltd **(1)**
2 Hahadarim St, POB 2230, Ashdod,
77121, Israel
Tel.: (972) 88632111
Farm Supply Whslr
N.A.I.C.S.: 424910

CHS Industries Ltd. **(1)**
2 Hahadarim Street, PO Box 2230, 77121,
Ashdod, Israel
Tel.: (972) 97288632111
Food Products Distr
N.A.I.C.S.: 424490

CHS Italy S.r.l. **(1)**
Galleria Eremitani 4, 35121, Padova, Italy
Tel.: (39) 0492148393
Agriculture Product Distr
N.A.I.C.S.: 424910

CHS Korea, LLC **(1)**
602 Samsung Sim's Bldg 39 Teheran-ro 87
Gil, Gangnam-gi, Seoul, 06166, Korea
(South)
Tel.: (82) 234538379
Emp.: 2
Agricultural Product Whslr
N.A.I.C.S.: 424910

CHS McPherson Refinery Inc. **(1)**
2000 S Main St, McPherson, KS
67460 **(100%)**
Tel.: (620) 241-2340
Web Site: http://www.ncra.coop
Agriculture Product Distr
N.A.I.C.S.: 424910

Emp.: 653
Petroleum Refining & Distribution
N.A.I.C.S.: 324110

Subsidiary (Domestic):

Jayhawk Pipeline, LLC **(2)**
2000 S Main St, McPherson, KS 67460
Tel.: (620) 241-9270
Web Site: http://www.jayhawkpl.com
Sales Range: $25-49.9 Million
Emp.: 12
N.A.I.C.S.: 486910

Kaw Pipe Line Company **(2)**
747 W Witt Ave, Russell, KS 67665
Tel.: (785) 483-2196
Web Site: http://www.jayhawkpl.com
Sales Range: $25-49.9 Million
Emp.: 14
Pipeline Maintenance & Installation Services
N.A.I.C.S.: 486910

CHS Ningbo Protein Foods Ltd. **(1)**
12 Xingye Road Ningbo Free Trade Zone,
Ningbo, 315800, China
Tel.: (86) 57486806680
Soy Protein Distr
N.A.I.C.S.: 424510
Todd Overgard *(Pres)*
Gail McMinn *(Exec VP-Comml Svcs)*
Mary Pinick *(Exec VP-Corp Ops)*
Casey Whelan *(VP-Strategic Initiatives)*

CHS Northwest **(1)**
402 Main St, Lynden, WA 98264
Tel.: (360) 354-2108
Web Site: http://www.chsnw.com
Retail & Convenience Stores, Fuel Stations
& Farm Supplies Whslr
N.A.I.C.S.: 424910
Rod Tjoelker *(Pres)*
Jerry Juergens *(Sec)*
Randy Honcoop *(VP)*

CHS Primeland - Walla Walla **(1)**
928 W Main St, Walla Walla, WA 99362
Tel.: (509) 525-6690
Web Site: http://www.chsprimeland.com
Agriculture Retail & Grain Handling Cooperative
N.A.I.C.S.: 115116

CHS Serbia D.O.O. Novi Sad **(1)**
Hajduk veljkova 11/3 3rd floor, 21000, Novi
Sad, Serbia
Tel.: (381) 212445892
Agricultural Product Whslr
N.A.I.C.S.: 424910

CHS Singapore Trading Company PTE. LTD. **(1)**
1 Finlayson Green 06-01, Singapore,
049246, Singapore
Tel.: (65) 66928100
Commodity Trading Services
N.A.I.C.S.: 523160

Subsidiary (Non-US):

CHS de Paraguay SRL **(2)**
Calle Gabriel Cassacia - Edificio Las Margaritas 3er Piso of 6, Parana Country Club,
Hernandarias, Paraguay
Tel.: (595) 61571101
Soy Protein Distr
N.A.I.C.S.: 424510

CHS South Sioux City, Inc. **(1)**
680 Hale Ave N Ste 110, Saint Paul, MN
55128
Tel.: (651) 493-0250
Soy Protein Distr
N.A.I.C.S.: 424510

CHS Spiritwood Fertilizer LLC **(1)**
5500 Cenex Dr, Inver Grove Heights, MN
55077-1721
Tel.: (651) 355-3710
Chemical Product Mfr & Distr
N.A.I.C.S.: 325998

CHS Tarim ve Gida Sanayii Limited Sirketi **(1)**
Merkez Mahallesi Akar Sokak iTower Residence No 3 Daire13 Bomonti, Istanbul, Turkiye
Tel.: (90) 2128031913
Agriculture Product Distr
N.A.I.C.S.: 424910

CHS INC.—(Continued)

CHS Trading Company Australia Pty. Ltd. (1)
Level 5 9 Castlereagh St, Sydney, 2000, NSW, Australia
Tel.: (61) 282224088
Commodity Trading Services
N.A.I.C.S.: 523160
Melanie Woo (Office Mgr & Mgr-HR)

CHS Ukraine, LLC (1)
33 Petra Sahaidachnoho Street 6th floor, Kiev, Ukraine
Tel.: (380) 443642010
Agriculture Product Distr
N.A.I.C.S.: 424910

CHS Uruguay SRL (1)
Av Italia 7519 esq Barradas Office 407, Montevideo, Uruguay
Tel.: (598) 26008361
Grain Distr
N.A.I.C.S.: 424510

CHS do Brasil Ltda. (1)
Rua Fidencio Ramos 308 - 4 Andar Conjuntos 41 e 43, Vila Olimpia, Sao Paulo, 04551-902, SP, Brazil
Tel.: (55) 1130337700
Web Site: http://www.chsinc.com
Grain & Field Beans
N.A.I.C.S.: 424510

CHS-Corsica (1)
120 E Main St, Corsica, SD 57328
Tel.: (605) 946-6233
Automobile Parts Mfr
N.A.I.C.S.: 336390

CHS-Elkton (1)
109 N Elk ST, Elkton, SD 57026
Tel.: (605) 542-2035
Web Site: http://www.chsmarshall.com
Emp.: 12
Grain & Field Beans Distr
N.A.I.C.S.: 424510
Aaron Coe (Mgr-Location)

CHS-Holdrege, Inc. (1)
310 Logan St, Holdrege, NE 68949-2723
Tel.: (308) 995-8626
Web Site: http://www.chsholdrege.com
Sales Range: $50-74.9 Million
Emp.: 150
Producer of Grain & Field Beans
N.A.I.C.S.: 424510

CHS-LCC Co-op (1)
W5394 Center Valley Rd, Black Creek, WI 54106
Tel.: (920) 734-1409
Grain Storage Service
N.A.I.C.S.: 493110

CHS-M&M, Inc. (1)
101 S Detroit Ave, Yuma, CO 80759
Tel.: (970) 848-5432
Web Site: http://www.chsyuma.com
Sales Range: $150-199.9 Million
Feed, Grain & Farm Supplies Distr
N.A.I.C.S.: 424910

Unit (Domestic):

CHS-M&M, Inc. - Wiggins (2)
114 W Central Ave, Wiggins, CO 80654
Tel.: (970) 483-7328
Web Site: http://www.chsinc.com
Sales Range: $10-24.9 Million
Emp.: 20
Farm Supplies Distr
N.A.I.C.S.: 424910

CHS-Napoleon (1)
407 Independence Dr, Fremont, OH 43545
Tel.: (419) 599-9033
Web Site: http://www.fremontchs.com
Emp.: 4
Health Care Srvices
N.A.I.C.S.: 621610

CHS-Ostrander Farmer Coop Elevator (1)
208 Main St, Ostrander, MN 55961
Tel.: (507) 657-2234
Web Site: http://www.ostranderfarmerscoop.com
Sales Range: $10-24.9 Million
Emp.: 27
Grain Elevators

Lynden Johnson (Exec VP)

CHS-Rochester (1)
1740 3rd Ave SE, Rochester, MI 55904
Tel.: (507) 288-1245
Farm Product Distr
N.A.I.C.S.: 424910

CHS-Shipman, Inc. (1)
3620 Route 16, Shipman, IL 62685
Tel.: (618) 729-9009
Web Site: http://www.chsshipman.com
Agricultural Product Whslr
N.A.I.C.S.: 424910

CHS-Sub Whatcom, Inc (1)
402 Main St, Lynden, WA 98264
Tel.: (360) 354-2108
Farm Product Distr
N.A.I.C.S.: 424910

CHS-Winger (1)
15 S Highland Park Dr, Winger, MN 56592
Tel.: (218) 280-5192
Agricultural Product Whslr
N.A.I.C.S.: 424910

CHSINC Iberica SL (1)
Carrer de la Diputacio 238, 08007, Barcelona, Spain
Tel.: (34) 933249769
Agriculture Product Distr
N.A.I.C.S.: 424910

Carrollton Farmers Elevator Co., Inc. (1)
102 S Main St, Carrollton, IL 62016
Tel.: (217) 942-6922
Web Site: http://www.carrolltonelev.com
Emp.: 10
Other Animal Food Mfr
N.A.I.C.S.: 311119
Chris Howard (Gen Mgr)

Cenex Zip Trip (1)
151 Rosebud Ln, Billings, MT 59101-6503
Tel.: (406) 259-5426
Sales Range: $50-74.9 Million
Emp.: 10
Gasoline Petroleum Dealer
N.A.I.C.S.: 424720
Travis Sears (Mgr-Store)

Central Montana Cooperative (1)
28616 MT-80, Geraldine, MT 59446
Tel.: (406) 737-4480
Web Site: http://www.centralmontanacoop.com
Rev.: $15,492,417
Emp.: 8
Agricultural Cooperative
N.A.I.C.S.: 424510

Central Montana Propane, LLO (1)
Lewistown Mt, Lewistown, MT 59457-0558
Tel.: (406) 538-3953
Heating Oil Dealers
N.A.I.C.S.: 457210

Central Plains Ag Services LLC (1)
10810 7th St SE, Hannaford, ND 58448-0009
Tel.: (701) 769-2665
Web Site: http://www.centralplainsag.net
Emp.: 40
Fright Trucking
N.A.I.C.S.: 484121
Andrew Johnson (Mgr-Sls)
Tim Hornung (Mgr-Ops)
Kelly Hanson (Plant Mgr-Fertilizer)
Welton Cochrane (Controller)

Colorado Retail Ventures Services, LLC (1)
816 Broadway St, Sterling, CO 80751-2829
Tel.: (970) 522-0801
Retail Venture Services
N.A.I.C.S.: 561499

Consumers Supply Distributing, LLC (1)
PO Box 1820, North Sioux City, SD 57049
Tel.: (712) 255-6927
Web Site: http://www.consumers-supply.com
Farm Product Distr
N.A.I.C.S.: 424910

Cooperative Agronomy Services (1)
110 E Aspen Ave, Groton, SD 57445
Tel.: (605) 397-2671

Sales Range: $10-24.9 Million
Emp.: 2
Information Services
N.A.I.C.S.: 519290
Dave Andrefon (Pres)

Cornerstone Ag, LLC (1)
2148 County Rd Q, Colby, KS 67701
Tel.: (785) 462-3354
Web Site: http://www.cornerstone-ag.com
Grain Marketing Services
N.A.I.C.S.: 424510

Country Hedging, Inc. (1)
5500 Cenex Dr Ste 290, Inver Grove Heights, MN 55077-1721
Tel.: (651) 355-6500
Contract Brokers
N.A.I.C.S.: 425120

Creston Bean Processing, L.L.C. (1)
1310 Howard St, Creston, IA 50801-0107
Tel.: (641) 782-2336
Sales Range: $25-49.9 Million
Emp.: 32
Soybean Processing
N.A.I.C.S.: 311224

Dakota Agronomy Partners, LLC (1)
1800 13th St SE, Minot, ND 58701-6061
Tel.: (701) 852-3567
Web Site: http://www.dakotaagronomy.com
Sales Range: $50-74.9 Million
Emp.: 12
Agricultural Services
N.A.I.C.S.: 424910

Farmers Alliance (1)
1320 W Havens St #100, Mitchell, SD 57301-3802
Tel.: (605) 996-9200
Web Site: http://www.farmersalliance.coop
Sales Range: $25-49.9 Million
Emp.: 8
Agricultural Services
N.A.I.C.S.: 111998

Farmers Elevator Co. (1)
Railroad Ave, Circle, MT 59215
Tel.: (406) 485-3313
Web Site: http://www.apps.chsinc.com
Sales Range: $50-74.9 Million
Emp.: 10
Grain Elevators
N.A.I.C.S.: 424510

Fin-Ag Inc. (1)
1211 N Ellis Rd, Sioux Falls, SD 57107-7004
Tel.: (605) 339-1050
Web Site: http://www.chsnutrition.com
Sales Range: $75-99.9 Million
Emp.: 15
Farm Financing Services
N.A.I.C.S.: 523999

Front Range Pipeline, LLC (1)
1 Watson Ln, Great Falls, MT 59404-6116
Tel.: (406) 771-7210
Pipeline Construction Services
N.A.I.C.S.: 237120

Green Bay Terminal Corporation (1)
1031 Hurlbut St, Green Bay, WI 54303-3736
Tel.: (920) 432-7793
Sales Range: $150-199.9 Million
Gas Whslr
N.A.I.C.S.: 424710

Illinois River Energy, LLC (1)
1900 Steward Rd, Rochelle, IL 61068-9508
Tel.: (815) 561-0650
Emp.: 60
Methanol Mfr
N.A.I.C.S.: 325193
Mike Van Houten (Plant Mgr)

Larsen Cooperative Co. (1)
1104 Mulligan Dr, New London, WI 54961
Tel.: (920) 982-1111
Web Site: http://www.chslarsencooperative.com
Sales Range: $25-49.9 Million
Emp.: 80
Distribute Feed, Fertilizer & Grain
N.A.I.C.S.: 424910

Lewis-Clark Terminal, Inc. (1)
1534 3rd Ave N, Lewiston, ID 83501
Tel.: (208) 746-9685

Farm Product Whslr
N.A.I.C.S.: 424910
Scott Zuger (Mgr)

M Tairhaiz Raktairozaisi eis Szolgaltatoi Korlaitolt Felelosseigu Tairsasaig (1)
Szeszfozde u 2, 5900, Oroshaza, Hungary
Tel.: (36) 68412822
Emp.: 25
Agricultural Product Whslr
N.A.I.C.S.: 424910
Anne Szendre (Gen Mgr)

Midwest Ag Supplements, LLC (1)
601 Ontario Rd, Marshall, MN 56258-2727
Tel.: (507) 532-2279
Web Site: https://www.midwestagsupplements.com
Dog & Cat Food Mfr
N.A.I.C.S.: 311111

Mountain Country, LLC (1)
2687 South 2000 W, Rexburg, ID 83440
Tel.: (208) 656-8909
Web Site: http://www.mtncountry.com
Propane Gas Whslr
N.A.I.C.S.: 424720

Northwest Grain (1)
315 N Broadway, Saint Hilaire, MN 56754
Tel.: (218) 964-5252
Web Site: http://www.northwestgrain.com
Emp.: 10
Grain Elevators
N.A.I.C.S.: 424510
Mitch Steven (Gen Mgr)

Subsidiary (Domestic):

CHS-Oklee (2)
806 Elevator Rd, Oklee, MN 56742
Tel.: (218) 796-5125
Web Site: http://www.northwestgrain.com
Sales Range: $10-24.9 Million
Grain Elevators
N.A.I.C.S.: 424510

St. Hilaire Ag Insurance, Inc. (2)
315 Broadway, Saint Hilaire, MN 56754
Tel.: (218) 964-5252
Insurance Services
N.A.I.C.S.: 524128

PGG HSC Feed Company, LLC (1)
1211 N Ellis Rd 201, Sioux Falls, SD 57107
Tel.: (605) 339-1050
Sales Range: $450-499.9 Million
Farm Supply Sales
N.A.I.C.S.: 424910
Kent Hansen (Office Mgr)

Patriot Fuels Biodiesel, LLC (1)
101 Patriot Way, Annawan, IL 61234-9753
Tel.: (309) 935-5700
Emp.: 10
Petroleum Refining Services
N.A.I.C.S.: 324110
Audie Sturtewagen (Mgr-Production)

Patriot Renewable Fuels, LLC (1)
101 Patriot Way, Annawan, IL 61234
Tel.: (309) 935-5700
Scientific & Technical Consulting Services
N.A.I.C.S.: 541690
Jeff Vandevoorde (Co-Founder)

Producer Ag, LLC (1)
307 W Cole St, Moundridge, KS 67107
Tel.: (620) 345-3560
Web Site: https://www.producerag.com
Agriculture Product Distr
N.A.I.C.S.: 424910

S.C. CHS Agritrade Romania SRL (1)
92-96 Izvor Street 8th Floor, 5th District, 050564, Bucharest, Romania
Tel.: (40) 213113863
Web Site: http://www.chsinc.com
Emp.: 60
Commodity Trading Services
N.A.I.C.S.: 523160

S.C. Silotrans S.R.L. (1)
Constanta Port - South Pier 1S Berth 114, Agigea, 907015, Romania
Tel.: (40) 241602291
Emp.: 46
Warehousing & Storage Services
N.A.I.C.S.: 493110

Alexandru Damoc *(Gen Mgr)*

S.C. Transporter S.R.L. (1)
Portului Street no 1 Giurgiu Free Zone,
080013, Giurgiu, Romania
Tel.: (40) 734009804
Trucking Service
N.A.I.C.S.: 484110

Solbar Industries Ltd. (1)
2 Hahadrim Street, Ashdod, 77613, Israel
Tel.: (972) 88632111
Web Site: http://www.solbar.com
Sales Range: $50-74.9 Million
Emp.: 200
Soy Proteins & Soy Isoflavones Mfr
N.A.I.C.S.: 111110

Subsidiary (Non-US):

Solbar Ningbo Food Co., Ltd. (2)
No 12 Xingye Rd, Ningbo Free Trade Zone,
315800, Ningbo, China
Tel.: (86) 57486806652
Web Site: http://solbar.en.ningboexport.com
Soy Proteins & Soy Isoflavones Mfr
N.A.I.C.S.: 311999

Southeast Propane, LLC (1)
101 Dakota St, Colfax, ND 58018-4016
Tel.: (701) 372-3433
Petroleum Refining Services
N.A.I.C.S.: 324110

The Purchasing Group, LLC (1)
4966 El Camino Real Ste 111, Los Altos,
CA 94022-1406
Tel.: (650) 938-3964
Market Consulting Services
N.A.I.C.S.: 541613

United Plains Ag (1)
102 N Front St, Sharon Springs, KS 67758
Tel.: (785) 852-4241
Web Site: http://www.unitedplainsag.com
Sales Range: $25-49.9 Million
Emp.: 32
Producers of Grain & Farm Supplies
N.A.I.C.S.: 424510
Jeff Kahle *(Mng Dir)*

Watertown Crop Nutrients LLC (1)
710 20th Ave SW, Watertown, SD 57201
Tel.: (605) 882-1351
Web Site: http://watertownsd.com
Emp.: 10
Warehousing & Storage Services
N.A.I.C.S.: 493110

West Central Distribution, LLC (1)
2700 Trott Ave SW, Willmar, MN 56201
Tel.: (320) 235-8518
Web Site: http://www.westcentralinc.com
Farm Product Distr
N.A.I.C.S.: 424910
Larry Bruess *(Mgr-Facilities, Fleet & Logistics)*

CHURCH & DWIGHT CO., INC.
Princeton S Corporate Ctr 500
Charles Ewing Blvd, Ewing, NJ
08628
Tel.: (609) 806-1200   NJ
Web Site:
    https://www.churchdwight.com
Year Founded: 1846
CHD—(NYSE)
Rev.: $5,867,900,000
Assets: $8,569,200,000
Liabilities: $4,713,800,000
Net Worth: $3,855,400,000
Earnings: $755,600,000
Emp.: 5,550
Fiscal Year-end: 12/31/23
Household Deodorizing & Cleaning,
Laundry & Personal Care Products &
Specialty Inorganic Chemicals Mfr &
Marketer
N.A.I.C.S.: 325612
Patrick D. de Maynadier *(Gen Counsel, Sec & Exec VP)*
Joseph J. Longo *(VP & Controller)*
Barry A. Bruno *(CMO, Pres-US & Exec VP)*
Brian Buchert *(Exec VP)*
Michael Read *(Exec VP)*

Kevin Gokey *(CIO)*
Carlen Hooker *(Chief Comml Officer)*
Surabhi Pokhriyal *(Chief Digital Growth Officer)*
Matthew Thomas Farrell *(Chm, Pres & CEO)*

Subsidiaries:

Carter Products (N.Z.) Inc. (1)
51 Port View Crescent Moturoa, New Plymouth, 4310, Taranaki, New Zealand
Tel.: (64) 67513879
Soap & Detergent Mfr
N.A.I.C.S.: 325611

Church & Dwight Domestic Consumer Products (1)
469 N Harrison St, Princeton, NJ
08540   **(100%)**
Tel.: (609) 683-5900
Web Site: http://www.churchdwight.com
Household Deodorizing & Cleaning, Laundry & Personal Care Products Mfr
N.A.I.C.S.: 325612

Unit (Domestic):

Arm & Hammer Consumer Products (2)
469 N Harrison St, Princeton, NJ
08543-5297   **(100%)**
Tel.: (609) 683-5900
Web Site: http://www.armhammer.com
Sales Range: $1-4.9 Billion
Household Cleaning & Personal Care Products Mfr & Whslr
N.A.I.C.S.: 325611
Scott Headley *(Dir-Mktg Comm)*

Church & Dwight International Consumer Products (1)
469 N Harrison St, Princeton, NJ
08543-5297   **(100%)**
Tel.: (609) 683-5900
Web Site: http://www.churchdwight.com
Sales Range: $300-349.9 Million
Household Deodorizing & Cleaning, Laundry & Personal Care Products Mfr
N.A.I.C.S.: 325612

Subsidiary (Non-US):

Church & Dwight (Australia) Pty. Ltd. (2)
Level 2 22 Rodborough Road, French's
Forest, 2086, NSW, Australia   **(100%)**
Tel.: (61) 289787878
Web Site: https://www.churchdwight.com.au
Sales Range: $10-24.9 Million
Mfr of Consumer Products
N.A.I.C.S.: 922190

Church & Dwight (UK) Ltd. (2)
Wear Bay Road, Folkestone, CT19 6PG,
Kent, United Kingdom   **(100%)**
Tel.: (44) 8001216080
Web Site: https://www.churchdwight.co.uk
Emp.: 300
Warehousing of Consumer Products
N.A.I.C.S.: 493110

Church & Dwight Canada Corp. (2)
635 Secretariat Court, Mississauga, L5S
0A5, ON, Canada
Tel.: (905) 696-6570
Web Site: http://www.churchdwight.ca
Sales Range: $50-74.9 Million
Emp.: 200
Toiletries & Consumer Products Mfr
N.A.I.C.S.: 325620

Plant (Domestic):

Church & Dwight Canada Corp. (3)
5485 Rue Ferrier, Montreal, H4P 1M6, QC,
Canada   **(100%)**
Tel.: (514) 731-3931
Web Site: http://www.churchdwight.ca
Over-the-Counter Pharmaceutical, Family
Planning & Personal Care Products Mfr &
Distr
N.A.I.C.S.: 325412

Subsidiary (Non-US):

Sofibel S.A.S. (2)
110-114 Rue Victor Hugo, 92686, Levallois-
Perret, Cedex, France
Tel.: (33) 149684100

Web Site: https://sterimar.com
Sales Range: $50-74.9 Million
Emp.: 120
Holding Company
N.A.I.C.S.: 551112

Subsidiary (Domestic):

Fumouze Diagnostics (3)
110-114 rue Victor Hugo Levallois-Perret,
Paris, Cedex, France
Tel.: (33) 149684138
Sales Range: $10-24.9 Million
Emp.: 30
Medical & Pharmaceutical Diagnostic Products Mfr
N.A.I.C.S.: 339112

Church & Dwight Servicios de R.L. de C.V. (1)
Jaime Balmes 8 Piso 6, 11510, Mexico,
Mexico
Tel.: (52) 5555809540
Web Site: http://www.churchdwight.com.mx
Household Products Mfr
N.A.I.C.S.: 325620

Church & Dwight Specialty Products Division (1)
469 N Harrison St, Princeton, NJ 08543
Tel.: (609) 806-1765
Web Site: http://www.ahspecialty.com
Sales Range: $200-249.9 Million
Sodium Bicarbonate, Ammonium Bicarbonate & Potassium Carbonate Products Mfr
N.A.I.C.S.: 325180
Joseph A. Sipia Jr. *(Pres & COO-Specialty Products Div)*

Joint Venture (Domestic):

Armand Products Company (2)
469 N Harrison St, Princeton, NJ 08543-
5297
Tel.: (609) 683-7090
Web Site: https://www.armandproducts.com
Sales Range: $150-199.9 Million
Emp.: 350
Potassium Carbonate & Bicarbonate Products Mfr; Owned by Church & Dwight Co.,
Inc. & Occidental Chemical Corporation
N.A.I.C.S.: 325180

Church & Dwight do Brasil Ltda (1)
Rua Octanol 640, Camacari, 42810-000,
Bahia, Brazil
Tel.: (55) 2125340098
Household Products Mfr
N.A.I.C.S.: 325620

Water Pik, Inc. (1)
1730 E Prospect Rd, Fort Collins, CO
80553-0001   **(100%)**
Tel.: (970) 484-1352
Web Site: https://www.waterpik.com
Dental Care & Pool Products Mfr
N.A.I.C.S.: 339114

CHURCHILL CAPITAL CORP. VII
640 Fifth Ave 12th fl, New York, NY
10019
Tel.: (212) 380-7500
Web Site:
    https://vii.churchillcapitalcorp.com
Year Founded: 2021
CVII—(NYSE)
Miscellaneous Financial Investment
Activities
N.A.I.C.S.: 523999
Michael S. Klein *(Chm & CEO)*

CHURCHILL DOWNS, INC.
600 N Hurstbourne Pkwy Ste 400,
Louisville, KY 40222
Tel.: (502) 636-4400   KY
Web Site:
    https://www.churchilldownsincor
    porated.com
Year Founded: 1875
CHDN—(NASDAQ)
Rev.: $2,461,700,000
Assets: $6,955,500,000
Liabilities: $6,061,900,000
Net Worth: $893,600,000

Earnings: $417,300,000
Emp.: 5,660
Fiscal Year-end: 12/31/23
Horse Racing, Casino & Online Gambling Services
N.A.I.C.S.: 711212
William C. Carstanjen *(CEO)*
William E. Mudd *(COO)*
Benjamin C. Murr *(Pres-TwinSpires & Online Gaming & Sr VP)*
Marcia A. Dall *(CFO & Exec VP)*
Tonya Abeln *(VP-Corp Comm)*
Ryan Jordan *(Sr VP-Real Estate Dev)*
Michael Anderson *(Pres)*
Katherine Armstrong *(Sr VP)*
Jason Sauer *(Sr VP)*
Nate Simon *(CTO)*

Subsidiaries:

Arlington Park (1)
2200 W Euclid Ave, Arlington Heights, IL
60005-1004
Tel.: (847) 385-7500
Web Site: http://www.arlingtonpark.com
Sales Range: $25-49.9 Million
Horse Racetrack
N.A.I.C.S.: 711212

BB Development, LLC (1)
777 Casino Way, Oxford, ME 04270
Tel.: (207) 539-6700
Web Site: https://www.oxfordcasino.com
Hotel & Casino Operator
N.A.I.C.S.: 721120

Bluff Holding Company, LLC (1)
1200 Lake Hearn Dr Ste 450, Atlanta, GA
30319
Tel.: (404) 250-1798
Web Site: http://www.bluff.com
Magazine Publishing Services
N.A.I.C.S.: 459210
Eddy Kleid *(Pres)*

Calder Race Course, Inc. (1)
21001 NW 27th Ave, Miami, FL 33056
Tel.: (305) 625-1311
Web Site: https://www.caldercasino.com
Sales Range: $10-24.9 Million
Emp.: 600
Horse Racetrack
N.A.I.C.S.: 711212
Richard Sukhu *(Pres & Gen Mgr)*

Churchill Downs Management Company, LLC (1)
700 Central Ave, Louisville, KY 40208
Tel.: (502) 636-4400
Operates Thoroughbred Horse Race Track
N.A.I.C.S.: 711212

Churchill Downs Racetrack, LLC (1)
600 N Hurstbourne Pkwy Ste 400, Louisville, KY 40222
Tel.: (502) 394-1000
Professional Scientific & Technical Services
N.A.I.C.S.: 541990
Margaret Robinson *(Mgr-Digital Mktg)*
Randy Prasse *(Sr Dir-Ops)*
William E. Mudd *(Interim Pres)*

Derby City Gaming, LLC (1)
4520 Poplar Level Rd, Louisville, KY 40213
Tel.: (502) 961-7600
Web Site: https://www.derbycitygaming.com
Casino Operator
N.A.I.C.S.: 713210
Michael Wood *(Dir-IT)*

Fair Grounds Corporation (1)
1751 Gentilly Blvd, New Orleans, LA 70119
Tel.: (504) 944-5515
Web Site: http://www.fgno.com
Sales Range: $25-49.9 Million
Emp.: 805
Thoroughbred Horse Racing Tracks Owner & Operator
N.A.I.C.S.: 711212

Miami Valley Gaming & Racing, LLC (1)
6000 SR 63, Lebanon, OH 45036
Tel.: (513) 934-7070
Web Site:
    https://www.miamivalleygaming.com
Hotel & Casino Operator
N.A.I.C.S.: 721120

Churchill Downs, Inc.—(Continued)

Ocean Downs LLC (1)
10218 Racetrack Rd, Berlin, MD 21811
Tel.: (410) 641-0600
Web Site: http://www.oceandowns.com
Racetrack & Casino Operator
N.A.I.C.S.: 711212

Presque Isle Downs, Inc. (1)
8199 Perry Hwy, Erie, PA 16509
Tel.: (814) 860-8999
Web Site:
  https://www.presqueisledowns.com
Casino, Racetrack & Resort Operator
N.A.I.C.S.: 721120

Turfway Park, LLC (1)
7500 Turfway Rd, Florence, KY 41042
Tel.: (859) 371-0200
Web Site: https://www.turfway.com
Racetracks
N.A.I.C.S.: 711212

TwinSpires (1)
801 Corporate Dr 2nd Fl, Lexington, KY 40503
Web Site: https://www.twinspires.com
Advance-Deposit Wagering Service for Churchill Downs
N.A.I.C.S.: 522320

United Tote Canada, Inc. (1)
4837 Albion Rd S, Gloucester, K1X 1A3, ON, Canada
Tel.: (613) 226-3666
Horse Race Betting System Developer
N.A.I.C.S.: 713290

Youbet.com, LLC (1)
5901 De Soto Ave, Woodland Hills, CA 91367
Tel.: (818) 668-2100
Web Site: https://www.youbet.com
Business Support Services
N.A.I.C.S.: 561990

CIB MARINE BANCSHARES, INC.

19601 W Bluemound Rd, Brookfield, WI 53045
Tel.: (262) 695-6010WI
Web Site: https://www.cibmarine.com
Year Founded: 1985
CIBH—(OTCQX)
Rev.: $48,797,000
Assets: $750,982,000
Liabilities: $647,278,000
Net Worth: $103,704,000
Earnings: $8,184,000
Emp.: 179
Fiscal Year-end: 12/31/20
Bank Holding Company
N.A.I.C.S.: 551111
Paul Curtis Melnick (Exec VP & Dir-Special Assets)
J. Brian Chaffin (Pres & CEO)
Patrick J. Straka (CFO & Exec VP)
Daniel J. Rasmussen (Chief Admin Officer, Gen Counsel, Sec & Exec VP)
Mark A. Elste (Chm)
Joanne M. P. Blaesing (Exec VP & Dir-Community Dev)
Michelle M. Bragstad (Chief Compliance Officer & Sr VP)
Scott C. Winkel (Chief Credit Officer, Chief Credit Officer & Exec VP)
Mark V. Wilmington (Exec VP & Dir-Retail Banking)
James P. Mullaney (Exec VP & Dir-Corp Banking)
Gary A. Maughan (Exec VP & Dir-Mortgage Banking)
Dawn M. DeRidder (Exec VP & Dir-Govt Guaranteed Lending)
Lee W. Abner (Sr VP & Dir-Tech Svcs)

Subsidiaries:

CIBM Bank (1)
2913 W Kirby Ave, Champaign, IL 61821-5301 (100%)

Tel.: (217) 355-0900
Web Site: http://www.cibmbank.com
Sales Range: $50-74.9 Million
Emp.: 127
Commericial Banking
N.A.I.C.S.: 522110
Paul Curtis Melnick (Chief Credit Officer & Exec VP)
J. Brian Chaffin (Pres & CEO)
James P. Mullaney (Exec VP/Dir-Corp Banking-Wheaton)
Mark A. Elste (Chm)
Mark Wilmington (Exec VP/Dir-Retail Banking-Peoria)
Gary Maughan (Exec VP/Dir-Mortgage Banking-Naperville)

Subsidiary (Domestic):

Avenue Mortgage Corporation (2)
1700 Park St Ste 106, Naperville, IL 60563
Tel.: (630) 369-7227
Web Site: http://www.avenuemortgage.com
Emp.: 30
Real Estate Credit
N.A.I.C.S.: 522292
David R. Pendley (Pres)
Gary Maughan (Sls Mgr)

CIBL, INC.

165 W Liberty St Ste 220, Reno, NV 89501
Tel.: (775) 329-8555DE
Web Site: https://ciblinc.com
Year Founded: 2007
CIBY—(OTCIQ)
Rev.: $1,909,000
Assets: $25,014,000
Liabilities: $543,000
Net Worth: $24,471,000
Earnings: $287,000
Emp.: 5
Fiscal Year-end: 12/31/23
Telecommunication Servicesb
N.A.I.C.S.: 517810
Kenneth D. Masiello (CFO)
Mario J. Gabelli (Exec Chm)

CIBUS, INC.

6455 Nancy Rdge Dr, San Diego, CA 92121
Tel.: (858) 450-0008DE
Web Site: https://www.cibus.com
Year Founded: 2010
CBUS—(NASDAQ)
Rev.: $157,000
Assets: $22,421,000
Liabilities: $15,188,000
Net Worth: $7,233,000
Earnings: ($16,891,000)
Emp.: 48
Fiscal Year-end: 12/31/22
Food & Agriculture Technology Services
N.A.I.C.S.: 541715
Peter Beetham (Co-Founder, Pres & COO)
Greg Gocal (Co-Founder, Chief Scientific Officer & Exec VP)
Wade King (CFO)
Rory B. Riggs (Co-Founder, Chm & CEO)
Noel Sauer (Sr VP-Res)
Rosa Cheuk Kim (Sr VP-Legal)
Sean O'Connor (Sr VP)
Noel Fong (Dir-Strain Dev)
James Radtke (Sr VP-Product Dev)
Tony Moran (Sr VP-Intl Dev)
Norm Sissons (Sr VP-Seed & Traits)
Dave Voss (VP-Bus Dev)
Andrew Walker (VP-Production)

Subsidiaries:

Cibus Corp. (1)
6455 Nancy Ridge Dr, San Diego, CA 92121
Tel.: (858) 450-0008
Web Site: http://www.cibus.com
Sales Range: $1-9.9 Million
Emp.: 134

Biotechnology Research & Development Services
N.A.I.C.S.: 541714
Tony Moran (VP-Intl Dev)
James Radtke (Sr VP-Product Dev)
Bradley Castanho (Sr VP-Comml & Bus Dev)
Sean O'Connor (Sr VP)
Noel Sauer (VP-Res)
David Sippell (VP)

CIDARA THERAPEUTICS, INC.

6310 Nancy Ridge Dr Ste 101, San Diego, CA 92121
Tel.: (858) 752-6170DE
Web Site: https://www.cidara.com
Year Founded: 2012
CDTX—(NASDAQ)
Rev.: $63,905,000
Assets: $67,030,000
Liabilities: $75,240,000
Net Worth: ($8,210,000)
Earnings: ($22,931,000)
Emp.: 69
Fiscal Year-end: 12/31/23
Pharmaceuticals Mfr
N.A.I.C.S.: 325412
Preetam Shah (CFO, Chief Bus Officer & Principal Acctg Officer)
Daniel D. Burgess (Chm)
Taylor Sandison (Chief Medical Officer)
Laura A. Navalta (Sr VP-Clinical Ops)
Shane M. Ward (COO & Chief Legal Officer)
Allison Lewis (Sr VP)
Carol Waldo (Sr VP)
Nicole Davarpanah (Sr VP-Translational R&D)
Jeffrey L. Stein (Pres & CEO)

CIENA CORPORATION

7035 Ridge Rd, Hanover, MD 21076
Tel.: (410) 694-5700DE
Web Site: https://www.ciena.com
Year Founded: 1992
CIEN—(NYSE)
Rev.: $4,014,955,000
Assets: $5,641,337,000
Liabilities: $2,825,199,000
Net Worth: $2,816,138,000
Earnings: $83,956,000
Emp.: 8,657
Fiscal Year-end: 11/02/24
Network Platforms, Software & Services
N.A.I.C.S.: 541512
Gary B. Smith (Pres & CEO)
Jason M. Phipps (Sr VP-Customer Engagement-Global)
Stephen B. Alexander (CTO & Sr VP)
Andrew C. Petrik (VP & Controller)
Nicole Anderson (Sr Dir-Corp Comm)
David M. Rothenstein (Chief Strategy Officer, Sec & Sr VP)
Jane Hobbs (Chief HR Officer & Sr VP)
Patrick H. Nettles (Founder & Exec Chm)
Rick L. Hamilton (Sr VP-Blue Planet Software)
Joe Cumello (Sr VP-Comm & Mktg-Global)
James E. Moylan Jr. (CFO & Sr VP-Fin)

Subsidiaries:

Blue Planet (1)
1383 N McDowell Blvd Ste 300, Petaluma, CA 94954
Tel.: (707) 735-2300
Software Publisher
N.A.I.C.S.: 513210

CIENA Communications, Inc. (1)
1201 Winterson Rd, Linthicum, MD 21090
Tel.: (410) 694-5700
Web Site: http://www.ciena.com

Sales Range: $100-124.9 Million
Emp.: 755
Developer of Software
N.A.I.C.S.: 334210

CIENA Corporation - Spokane Valley Main Office & Training Center (1)
115 N Sullivan Rd, Spokane Valley, WA 99037
Tel.: (509) 242-9000
Sales Range: $25-49.9 Million
Emp.: 150
Telecommunications Network Platforms
N.A.I.C.S.: 517810

Ciena Canada, Inc. (1)
2351 Alfred-Nobel Boulevard Suite N-300, Saint Laurent, H4S 2A9, QC, Canada
Tel.: (514) 228-2300
Network Engineering Services
N.A.I.C.S.: 541512

Ciena Communications Singapore Pte. Ltd. (1)
12 Marina View Asia Square Tower 2 19-03, Singapore, 018961, Singapore
Tel.: (65) 6 971 6087
Software Development Services
N.A.I.C.S.: 541511

Ciena Limited (1)
43-51 Worship Street, London, EC2A 2DX, United Kingdom
Tel.: (44) 2070125500
Network Engineering Services
N.A.I.C.S.: 541512
Jamie Jefferies (VP & Gen Mgr-Europe, Middle East & Africa)

CIIG MERGER CORP.

40 W 57th St 29th Fl, New York, NY 10019
Tel.: (212) 796-4796DE
Year Founded: 2019
CIICU—(NASDAQ)
Rev.: $1,107,693
Assets: $260,309,654
Liabilities: $255,309,652
Net Worth: $5,000,002
Earnings: ($5,302,800)
Emp.: 3
Fiscal Year-end: 12/31/20
Investment Services
N.A.I.C.S.: 523999
F. Peter Cuneo (Chm & CEO)

CINCINNATI FINANCIAL CORPORATION

6200 S Gilmore Rd, Fairfield, OH 45014-5141
Tel.: (513) 870-2000OH
Web Site: https://www.cinfin.com
Year Founded: 1950
CINF—(NASDAQ)
Rev.: $10,013,000,000
Assets: $32,769,000,000
Liabilities: $20,671,000,000
Net Worth: $12,098,000,000
Earnings: $1,843,000,000
Emp.: 5,426
Fiscal Year-end: 12/31/23
Financial Investment Services
N.A.I.C.S.: 551112
Steven J. Johnston (Chm & CEO)
Stephen M. Spray (Pres)

Subsidiaries:

CFC Investment Company (1)
6200 S Gilmore Rd, Fairfield, OH 45014-5141 (100%)
Tel.: (513) 870-2000
Web Site: http://www.cinfin.com
Rev.: $8,145,570
Emp.: 3,000
Provider of Leasing & Financing Services
N.A.I.C.S.: 532490
Kenneth William Stecher (Chm)

Cincinnati Global Underwriting Limited (1)
1 Minster Court Fenchurch Street, London, EC3R 7AA, United Kingdom
Tel.: (44) 20 7220 8200
Insurance Underwriting Services
N.A.I.C.S.: 524298

Subsidiary (Domestic):

Beaufort Underwriting Agency Limited (2)
3rd Floor One Minster Court Mincing Lane, London, EC3R 7AA, United Kingdom
Tel.: (44) 2072208200
Web Site: https://cinfinglobal.com
Emp.: 60
Property Insurance Underwriting Services
N.A.I.C.S.: 524126
Graham Tuck (Dir-Fin)

The Cincinnati Insurance Company (1)
6200 S Gilmore Rd, Fairfield, OH 45014-5141 (100%)
Tel.: (513) 870-2000
Web Site: http://www.cincinnatifinancial.com
Sales Range: $800-899.9 Million
Emp.: 2,800
Underwriter of Property Casualty Insurance
N.A.I.C.S.: 524126
Steven J. Johnston (Chm & CEO)

Subsidiary (Domestic):

The Cincinnati Casualty Company (2)
6200 S Gilmore Rd, Fairfield, OH 45014-5141 (100%)
Tel.: (513) 870-2000
Web Site: http://www.cinfin.com
Fire & Casualty Insurance
N.A.I.C.S.: 524126

The Cincinnati Indemnity Company (2)
6200 S Gilmore Rd, Fairfield, OH 45014-5141 (100%)
Tel.: (513) 870-2000
Web Site: http://www.cinfin.com
Sales Range: $150-199.9 Million
Emp.: 3,500
Casualty Insurance
N.A.I.C.S.: 524126
Steven J. Johnston (Pres & CEO)

The Cincinnati Life Insurance Company (2)
6200 S Gilmore Rd, Fairfield, OH 45014-5141 (100%)
Tel.: (513) 870-2000
Sales Range: $900-999.9 Million
Life, Accident & Health Insurance
N.A.I.C.S.: 524113
Kenneth William Stecher (Chm)
Roger A. Brown (COO & Sr VP)

CINDERELLA TARGET VALUE ZONES INC.
40 Wall St 28th Fl, New York, NY 10005
Tel.: (212) 660-2285   NV
Year Founded: 1999
CTVZ—(OTCIQ)
Holding Company
N.A.I.C.S.: 551112
Aidan Doyle (CEO)
Katherine L. Menera (VP)

CINEMARK HOLDINGS, INC.
3900 Dallas Pkwy, Plano, TX 75093
Tel.: (972) 665-1000   DE
Web Site: https://ir.cinemark.com
Year Founded: 2006
CNK—(NYSE)
Rev.: $3,066,700,000
Assets: $4,836,800,000
Liabilities: $4,518,000,000
Net Worth: $318,800,000
Earnings: $188,200,000
Emp.: 26,800
Fiscal Year-end: 12/31/23
Holding Company; Motion Picture Theaters Owner

N.A.I.C.S.: 551112
Sean Gamble (Pres, CEO & COO)
Melissa Thomas (CFO & Exec VP)
Michael Cavalier (Gen Counsel, Sec & Exec VP)
Valmir Fernandes (Pres-Intl)
Caren Bedard (Sr VP)

Subsidiaries:

Century Theatres Summit Sierra, L.L.C. (1)
13965 S Virginia St, Reno, NV 89511
Tel.: (775) 851-4347
Emp.: 20
Motion Picture Exhibition Services
N.A.I.C.S.: 512131
Paul Gray (Gen Mgr)

Century Theatres of Canada, ULC (1)
65 Queensway E, Simcoe, N3Y 4M5, ON, Canada
Tel.: (519) 428-2862
Sales Range: $10-24.9 Million
Emp.: 16
Motion Picture Exhibition Services
N.A.I.C.S.: 512131
John Morey (Office Mgr)

Cinemark Argentina, S.R.L. (1)
Antonio Beruti 3399 Piso 5th 1425, Buenos Aires, Argentina
Tel.: (54) 1157771000
Motion Picture Exhibition Services
N.A.I.C.S.: 512131

Cinemark International, LLC (1)
3900 Dallas Pkwy Ste 500, Plano, TX 75093-7865
Tel.: (972) 665-1000
Web Site: http://www.cinemark.com
Owner & Operator of International Motion Picture Theaters
N.A.I.C.S.: 512131

Cinemark Media, Inc. (1)
3900 Dallas Pkwy Ste 500, Plano, TX 75093
Tel.: (972) 665-1000
Web Site: http://www.cinemark.com
Emp.: 300
Motion Picture Exhibition Services
N.A.I.C.S.: 512131
Mark Zoradi (CEO)

Cinemark USA, Inc. (1)
3900 Dallas Pkwy, Plano, TX 75093
Tel.: (972) 665-1000
Web Site: http://www.cinemark.com
Rev.: $3,066,699,999
Assets: $4,655,900,000
Liabilities: $4,055,600,000
Net Worth: $600,300,000
Earnings: $205,300,000
Emp.: 26,799
Fiscal Year-end: 12/31/2023
Motion Picture Exhibition Operator
N.A.I.C.S.: 512110
Michael Cavalier (Gen Counsel, Sec & Exec VP)
Sean Gamble (Pres & COO)
Caren Bedard (Sr VP)
Valmir Fernandes (Pres)

Cinemark, Inc. (1)
3900 Dallas Pkwy, Plano, TX 75093 (100%)
Tel.: (972) 665-1000
Web Site: http://www.cinemark.com
Sales Range: $100-124.9 Million
Emp.: 230
Motion Picture Theaters Owner & Operator
N.A.I.C.S.: 512131
Lee Roy Mitchell (Executives)

CINEVERSE CORP.
224 W 35th St Ste 500 947, New York, NY 10001
Tel.: (212) 206-8600   DE
Web Site: https://www.cineverse.com
Year Founded: 2000
CNVS—(NASDAQ)
Rev.: $49,131,000
Assets: $64,378,000
Liabilities: $32,227,000
Net Worth: $32,151,000

Earnings: ($21,265,000)
Emp.: 176
Fiscal Year-end: 03/31/24
Digital Cinema Software & Content Marketer, Distr & Support Services
N.A.I.C.S.: 512120
Gary S. Loffredo (Pres, COO, Gen Counsel & Sec)
Jill Newhouse Calcaterra (Exec VP-Mktg & Comm)
Christopher J. McGurk (Chm & CEO)
Mark Wayne Lindsey (CFO)
Erick Opeka (Chief Strategy Officer & Pres-Networks)
Yolanda Macias (Chief Content Officer)
Mark Torres (Sr VP-HR & Admin)
Tony Huidor (Chief Tech & Product Officer)
Daniel Coyle (Sr VP-Sls)
Cheryl Odoardi (Sr VP-Fin & Acctg)
Jennifer Soltesz (VP-Bus Dev & Strategy)
Kim Staruk (VP-Mktg)
Russell Schneider (Sr VP-Brand Partnerships)
Erick Opeka (Chief Strategy Officer)
Mark Lindsey (Exec VP-Fin & Acctg)

Subsidiaries:

Cinedigm Entertainment Corp. (1)
45 W 36th St, New York, NY 10018
Tel.: (212) 206-8600
Web Site: http://www.newvideo.com
Movie & Television Program Distr
N.A.I.C.S.: 512120

Cinedigm Entertainment Holdings, LLC (1)
902 Broadway Fl 9, New York, NY 10010
Tel.: (212) 206-8600
Holding Company
N.A.I.C.S.: 551112

FoundationTV, Inc. (1)
1821 S Bascom Ave Ste 137, Campbell, CA 95008
Tel.: (415) 690-8688
Web Site: http://www.thefoundationtv.com
IT Services
N.A.I.C.S.: 541512
Samrat Ganguly (Co-Founder)
Sudipta Ghorui (Co-Founder & VP-Engrg)
Sudeept Bhatnagar (Co-Founder & CTO)
Indranil Mukherjee (Head-Ops)
Sourav Jana (Head-QA)

CINGULATE INC.
1901 W 47th Pl, Kansas City, KS 66205
Tel.: (913) 942-2300   DE
Web Site: https://www.cingulate.com
Year Founded: 2021
CING—(NASDAQ)
Assets: $11,405,057
Liabilities: $7,523,035
Net Worth: $3,882,022
Earnings: ($17,676,232)
Emp.: 15
Fiscal Year-end: 12/31/22
Holding Company
N.A.I.C.S.: 551112
Shane J. Schaffer (Co-Founder, Chm, CEO & Principal Fin Officer)
Laurie A. Myers (COO & Exec VP)
Raul R. Silva (Chief Science Officer & Exec VP)
Matthew Brams (Co-Founder, Chief Medical Officer, Chief Medical Officer & Exec VP)
Jennifer Callahan (CFO)

CINTAS CORPORATION
6800 Cintas Blvd, Cincinnati, OH 45262-5737
Tel.: (513) 459-1200   WA
Web Site: https://www.cintas.com
Year Founded: 1929

CTAS—(NASDAQ)
Rev.: $9,596,615,000
Assets: $9,168,817,000
Liabilities: $4,852,445,000
Net Worth: $4,316,372,000
Earnings: $1,571,592,000
Emp.: 46,500
Fiscal Year-end: 05/31/24
Apparel Product Retailer
N.A.I.C.S.: 315250
Scott D. Farmer (Exec Chm)
Karen L. Carnahan (Executives)
Michael L. Thompson (Chief Admin Officer & Exec VP)
J. Michael Hansen (CFO & Exec VP)
D. Brock Denton (Gen Counsel, Sec & Sr VP)
Christy Nageleisen (Chief Compliance Officer & VP-Environment, Social & Governance)
Michelle Goret (VP-Comml Affairs)
Lizz Summers (Dir-Bus Affairs)
Paul Adler (Treas & VP)
Todd M. Schneider (Pres & CEO)

Subsidiaries:

CC Dutch Property Holding B.V. (1)
Taanderstraat 13, 2222 BG, Katwijk, Netherlands
Tel.: (31) 715215070
Holding Company
N.A.I.C.S.: 551112

Cintas (Guangzhou) Enterprise Services Co., Ltd. (1)
No 4 Third of Jingquan Road, Yonghe District, Guangzhou, 511356, China
Tel.: (86) 2028129988
Business Development Services
N.A.I.C.S.: 541720
Stella Zhang (Supvr-HR & Admin)

Cintas - R.U.S., L.P. (1)
301 Junior Beck Dr, Corpus Christi, TX 78405-4405
Tel.: (361) 289-1781
Industrial Laundry Services
N.A.I.C.S.: 812332
Treveor Fraely (Gen Mgr)

Cintas Canada Limited (1)
3370 Dundas St W, Toronto, M6S 2S2, ON, Canada
Tel.: (416) 763-4400
Industrial Laundry Services
N.A.I.C.S.: 812332

Cintas Corporation No. 3 (1)
1312 Capital Blvd Ste 102, Reno, NV 89502
Tel.: (775) 352-1753
Web Site: https://www.cintas.com
Industrial Laundry Services
N.A.I.C.S.: 812332

Cintas Document Management Inc. (1)
1001 Airbrake Ave, Wilmerding, PA 15148
Tel.: (412) 798-7720
Web Site: http://www.cintas.com
Rev.: $3,100,000
Emp.: 45
Document Management Services
N.A.I.C.S.: 561410
Scott Sarmter (Pres)

Cintas Document Management, LLC (1)
6800 Cintas Blvd, Mason, OH 45040
Tel.: (800) 914-1960
Web Site: http://www.cintas.com
Sales Range: $1-9.9 Million
Emp.: 36
Document Management Services
N.A.I.C.S.: 561410

Cintas Netherlands Holdings B.V. (1)
Koepelweg 3, 2202AJ, Noordwijk, Netherlands
Tel.: (31) 715215070
Industrial Laundry Services
N.A.I.C.S.: 812332

Cintas Corporation—(Continued)

G&K Services, LLC　　　　　　**(1)**
5995 Opus Pkwy Ste 500, Minnetonka, MN
55343
Tel.: (952) 912-5500
Web Site: http://www.gkservices.com
Uniform Supplier & Facilities Services
N.A.I.C.S.: 812331

Subsidiary (Non-US):

G&K Services Canada, Inc.　　　　**(2)**
5935 Airport Road Suite 1105, Mississauga,
L4V 1W5, ON, Canada
Tel.: (905) 677-6161
Web Site: http://www.gkservices.com
Uniform Rental Services
N.A.I.C.S.: 315210

Subsidiary (Domestic):

Les Services G&K　　　　　　　　　**(3)**
8400 19th Avenue, Montreal, H1Z 4J3, QC,
Canada
Tel.: (438) 792-0030
Web Site: http://www.gkservices.com
Uniform Rental Services
N.A.I.C.S.: 812990

Branch (Domestic):

G&K Services, LLC - Laurel　　　　**(2)**
136 Lafayette Ave, Laurel, MD 20707
Tel.: (301) 476-1510
Web Site: http://www.gkservices.com
Industrial Cleaners
N.A.I.C.S.: 812332

JDRJ Inc.
1203 N Barkley Rd, Statesville, NC 28677
Tel.: (704) 394-9289
Web Site: http://www.rentaluniform.com
Rev.: $4,200,000
Emp.: 120
Linen Supply
N.A.I.C.S.: 812331
James Myers *(Mgr-Sls)*

Sally Fourmy & Associates　　　　**(1)**
30 Duncan St 5th Fl, Toronto, M5V 2C3,
ON, Canada　　　　　　　　　　**(100%)**
Tel.: (416) 593-4676
Web Site: http://www.cintas.com
Sales Range: $50-74.9 Million
Emp.: 60
Mfr & Sale of Uniforms
N.A.I.C.S.: 315210
Helen E. Loader *(Pres)*

Sitex Corporation　　　　　　　　**(1)**
1300 Commonwealth Dr, Henderson, KY
42420
Web Site: http://www.sitex-corp.com
Linen Supply
N.A.I.C.S.: 812331
Traci Tyler *(VP-HR)*

**The Millennium Mat Company,
LLC**　　　　　　　　　　　　　　**(1)**
3200 Shawnee Industrial Way, Suwanee,
GA 30024-4623
Tel.: (678) 482-5623
Web Site: https://www.millmats.com
Sales Range: $50-74.9 Million
Emp.: 200
Floor Mats & Carpets Mfr
N.A.I.C.S.: 314110

CION INVESTMENT CORPO-
RATION
100 Park Ave 25th Fl, New York, NY
10017
Tel.: (212) 418-4700　　　　　　**MD**
Web Site: https://www.cionbdc.com
Year Founded: 2011
CION—(NYSE)
Rev.: $194,898,000
Assets: $1,872,411,000
Liabilities: $988,777,000
Net Worth: $883,634,000
Earnings: $88,205,000
Fiscal Year-end: 12/31/22
Financial Investment Management
Services
N.A.I.C.S.: 523940
Gregg A. Bresner *(Pres & Chief In-
vestment Officer)*

Geoff Manna *(Sr Mng Dir)*
Aditi Budhia *(Sr VP)*
Joe Elsabee *(Mng Dir)*
Mark Gatto *(Co-Founder, Co-Pres &
Co-CEO)*
Michael A. Reisner *(Co-Founder, Co-
Pres & Co-CEO)*
Keith S. Franz *(Mng Dir, CFO, CFO-
CION Investment Mgmt & Treas)*
Eric Pinero *(Chief Legal Officer)*
Nicholas Tzoumas *(Dir)*
Charlie Arestia *(Mng Dir & Head-
Investor Relations)*

Subsidiaries:

David's Bridal, LLC　　　　　　**(1)**
1001 Washington St, Conshohocken, PA
19428-2356
Tel.: (610) 943-5000
Web Site: http://www.davidsbridal.com
Sales Range: $650-699.9 Million
Bridal Gowns & Related Apparel & Acces-
sories Sales
N.A.I.C.S.: 458110
Christine Pope *(Chm)*
Bob Walker *(Chief Field Ops & Store Expe-
rience Officer)*
James Marcum *(CEO)*
Kelly Cook *(Chief Mktg & IT Officer)*

CIPHER MINING INC.
1 Vanderbilt Ave Fl 54 Ste C, New
York, NY 10017
Tel.: (332) 262-2300　　　　　　**DE**
Web Site:
　　https://www.ciphermining.com
Year Founded: 2020
CIFR—(NASDAQ)
Rev.: $3,037,000
Assets: $418,463,000
Liabilities: $75,571,000
Net Worth: $342,892,000
Earnings: ($39,053,000)
Emp.: 26
Fiscal Year-end: 12/31/22
Investment Services
N.A.I.C.S.: 523999
Tyler Page *(CEO)*
Cary Grossman *(Founder)*
Patrick Kelly *(Co-Pres & COO)*
William Iwaschuk *(Co-Pres, Chief Le-
gal Officer & Sec)*
Josh Kane *(Head-IR)*
James E. Newsome *(Chm)*
Edward Farrell *(CFO)*

CIRRUS LOGIC, INC.
800 W 6th St, Austin, TX 78701
Tel.: (512) 851-4000　　　　　　**DE**
Web Site: https://www.cirrus.com
Year Founded: 1984
CRUS—(NASDAQ)
Rev.: $1,788,890,000
Assets: $2,231,576,000
Liabilities: $414,562,000
Net Worth: $1,817,014,000
Earnings: $274,572,000
Emp.: 1,625
Fiscal Year-end: 03/30/24
High-Precision Analog & Mixed-Signal
Integrated Circuits Mfr
N.A.I.C.S.: 334413
Carl Alberty *(VP-Mixed-Signal Prod-
ucts)*
Gregory Scott Thomas *(Sec, Sr VP &
Gen Counsel)*
David J. Tupman *(Chm)*
Andy Brannan *(VP-Worldwide Sls)*
Allan Hughes *(VP-Cirrus Logic Inter-
national)*
Jeff Baumgartner *(VP-Research &
Development)*
John M. Forsyth *(Pres & CEO)*
Justin Dougherty *(VP-Engrg Ops)*
Jennifer Krueger *(Dir-Corp Comm)*
Chelsea Heffernan *(VP-IR)*

Subsidiaries:

Acoustic Technologies, Inc.　　　**(1)**
1620 S Stapley Dr Ste 201, Mesa, AZ
85204
Tel.: (480) 507-4300
Web Site: http://www.acoustictech.com
Sales Range: $1-9.9 Million
Emp.: 30
Voice Processing Firmware Technology Mfr
N.A.I.C.S.: 541690

Apex Precision Power　　　　　**(1)**
5980 N Shannon Rd, Tucson, AZ 85741
Tel.: (520) 690-8600
Web Site: https://www.apexanalog.com
Sales Range: $25-49.9 Million
Emp.: 100
Power Amplifiers, Circuits & Motor Control-
lers Mfr
N.A.I.C.S.: 334413

**Cirrus Logic International (UK)
Ltd.**　　　　　　　　　　　　　**(1)**
7B Nightingale Way Quartermile, Edin-
burgh, EH3 9EG, United Kingdom
Tel.: (44) 1312727000
Web Site: https://www.cirrus.com
Emp.: 440
Fabless Semiconductor & Integrated Circuit
Supplier
N.A.I.C.S.: 334413

Cirrus Logic International Ltd.　　**(1)**
Suite 1427 Ocean Centre Harbour City, 5
Canton Road Tsimshatsui, Kowloon, China
(Hong Kong)
Tel.: (852) 2376 0801
Semiconductor Product Mfr
N.A.I.C.S.: 334413

Cirrus Logic K.K.　　　　　　　**(1)**
8f A-Place Shinagawa Higashi 1-7-18 Ko-
nan, Minato-ku, Tokyo, 108-0075,
Japan　　　　　　　　　　　　**(100%)**
Tel.: (81) 357828180
Sales Range: $10-24.9 Million
Emp.: 9
Software Mfr
N.A.I.C.S.: 334413

CIRTRAN CORPORATION
6360 S Pecos Rd Ste 8, Las Vegas,
NV 89120
Tel.: (801) 963-5112　　　　　　**NV**
Web Site: https://www.cirtran.com
CIRX—(OTCIQ)
Rev.: $1,616,148
Assets: $1,848,562
Liabilities: $23,627,247
Net Worth: ($21,778,685)
Earnings: $20,288,360
Emp.: 4
Fiscal Year-end: 12/31/23
Mfr & Distribution Services
N.A.I.C.S.: 339999
Iehab J. Hawatmeh *(Chm, Pres, CEO
& CFO)*
Kathryn Hollinger *(Controller)*

CISCO SYSTEMS, INC.
170 W Tasman Dr, San Jose, CA
95134-1706
Tel.: (408) 526-4000　　　　　　**DE**
Web Site: https://www.cisco.com
Year Founded: 1984
CSCO—(NASDAQ)
Rev.: $50,000,000,000
Assets: $124,413,000,000
Liabilities: $78,956,000,000
Net Worth: $45,457,000,000
Earnings: $10,320,000,000
Emp.: 90,400
Fiscal Year-end: 07/27/24
Telecommunication Servicesb
N.A.I.C.S.: 517112
Charles H. Robbins *(Chm & CEO)*
Sailaja K. Shankar *(Sr VP-Engrg &
Security Bus Grp)*
Francine S. Katsoudas *(Chief People-
,Policy & Purpose Officer & Exec VP)*
Nick Michaelides *(Sr VP-Pub Sector-
U.S)*

Liz Centoni *(Chief Strategy Officer,
Exec VP & Gen Mgr-Applications)*
Eyal Dagan *(Exec VP-Common Hard-
ware Grp)*
Mark Patterson *(Sr VP)*
David Ashley *(Sr VP-Product Ops)*
Andrew Ashton *(Sr VP-Corp Fin)*
Roger Biscay *(Treas, Sr VP & Head-
Global Corp Security)*
Jeff Campbell *(Chief Government
Strategy Officer & Sr VP)*
Derek Idemoto *(Sr VP-Corp Dev &
Investments)*
Rob Johnson *(Sr VP-Taxation-Global)*
Alexandra Lopez *(Chief Procurement
Officer & Sr VP)*
Brian Maddox *(Sr VP-Bus Entity Fin)*
Girish Parekh *(Sr VP-Sls Fin)*
Richard Scott Herren *(CFO & Exec
VP)*
Rodney Clark *(Sr VP-Partnerships &
Small & Medium Bus)*
Maria Poveromo *(Chief Comm Officer
& Sr VP)*
Will Eatherton *(Sr VP-Distributed Sys
Engrg)*
Patrick Morrissey *(Sr VP-Global Spe-
cialists)*
Carrie Palin *(CMO & Sr VP)*
Darren Pleasance *(Sr VP-
Acceleration Center)*
Thimaya Subaiya *(Chief Transforma-
tion Officer)*
John Wunder *(Sr VP-Sls Strategy,
Planning, and Operations)*
Deborah L. Stahlkopf *(Chief Legal
Officer & Exec VP)*
Jeetu Patel *(Exec VP & Gen Mgr-
Security & Collaboration)*
Aruna Ravichandran *(CMO/Chief
Customer Officer-Webex & Sr VP)*
Bill Gartner *(Sr VP/Gen Mgr-Optical
Systems & Optics Group)*
Bret Hull *(Sr VP & Head-Meraki En-
grg)*
Brian Tippens *(Chief Social Impact
Officer & Sr VP)*
Buffy Ransom *(Sr VP-Global CX
Centers)*
Chris Heckscher *(Sr VP-Global Svcs
& Software Sls)*
Christian Bigsby *(Sr VP-Workplace
Resources)*
Dave West *(Pres-Asia Pacific, Japan
& Greater China & Sr VP)*
Ed Paradise *(Sr VP-Security & Trust
Organization)*
Elaine Mason *(Sr VP-Purpose Strat-
egy & Innovation)*
Fletcher Previn *(CIO & Sr VP)*
Greg Dorai *(Sr VP & Gen Mgr-
Networking & Campus Connectivity)*
Guy Diedrich *(Global Innovation
Officer-Country Digital Acceleration &
Cisco Networking Academy & Sr VP)*
Jacqueline Guichelaar *(Sr VP & Gen
Mgr-Customer Experience-Asia Pa-
cific, Japan & Greater China)*
Jeremy Foster *(Sr VP & Gen Mgr-
Cisco Networking　Compute)*
John Dorval *(Sr VP-Svc Provider-
Americas)*
M. Victoria Wong *(Chief Acctg Officer
& Sr VP)*
Oliver Tuszik *(Partner-Sls-Global,
Pres-EMEA, Sr VP & Gen Mgr-
Routes to Market)*
Harry Caldwell *(Sr VP-Americas &
Gen Mgr-Cisco Customer Experience
Americas)*
Gary Steele *(Pres-Go-to,Market)*
Martin Lund *(Exec VP-Common
Hardware Grp)*
Vikas Butaney *(Sr VP & Gen Mgr)*
Vijoy Pandey *(Sr VP)*

Tom Gillis (Sr VP & Gen Mgr)
Tim Coogan (Sr VP-US Comml Sls)
Ted Kezios (Sr VP-People & Communities)
Srini Namineni (Sr VP-Strategic Growth Ops)
Snorre Kjesbu (Sr VP & Gen Mgr)
Ronak Desai (Sr VP & Gen Mgr)
Rebecca Stone (Sr VP-Global Revenue Mktg)
Raj Chopra (Chief Product Officer & Sr VP)
Pastora Valero (Sr VP-Intl Govt Affairs)
Nick Small (Pres-Cisco Capital)
Nathan Jokel (Sr VP-Corporate Strategy & Alliances)
Nancy Scott (Sr VP-Legal & Deputy General Counsel)
Morgan Teachworth (Sr VP-Cisco Wireless & Meraki Hardware)
Masum Mir (Sr VP & Gen Mgr)
Mary de Wysocki (Chief Sustainability Officer & Sr VP)
Marco De Martin (Sr VP-Global Supplier Mgmt)
Lynley Noviello (Sr VP-Global Enterprise Sls)
Leslie McKnew (Sr VP & Deputy Gen Counsel-Regulatory Affairs)
Lawrence Huan (Sr VP & Gen Mgr)
Kristen Nichols (COO & Sr VP)

Subsidiaries:

Acacia Communications, Inc.   (1)
3 Mill and Main Pl Ste 400, Maynard, MA 01754
Tel.: (978) 938-4896
Web Site: http://www.acacia-inc.com
Rev.: $464,663,000
Assets: $721,415,000
Liabilities: $142,992,000
Net Worth: $578,423,000
Earnings: $32,839,000
Emp.: 427
Fiscal Year-end: 12/31/2019
Telecommunication Servicesb
N.A.I.C.S.: 517111
Christian J. Rasmussen (Co-Founder & VP-Digital Signal Processing & Optics)
John F. Gavin (CFO & Treas)
Mehrdad Givehchi (Co-Founder & VP-Hardware & Software)
Bhupendra C. Shah (VP-Engrg)
John J. LoMedico (VP-Corp Dev)
John P. Kavanagh (Sr VP-Ops)
Renee M. Pianka (Chief HR Officer)
Eric L. Fisher (VP-Sls-Global)
Robert C. Bickle (Chief Quality Officer & VP-Quality)

Subsidiary (Non-US):

Acacia Communications (Canada) Limited   (2)
309 Legget Dr, Ottawa, K2K 3A3, ON, Canada
Tel.: (613) 519-4422
Network Service Provider
N.A.I.C.S.: 517810

AppDynamics International Ltd.   (1)
Building 10 9-11 New Square Bedfont Lakes, Feltham, TW14 8HA, United Kingdom
Tel.: (44) 2088240048
Software Development Services
N.A.I.C.S.: 513210

AppDynamics Technologies India Private Limited   (1)
Commerz Building Bagmane Tech Park Krishnappa Garden Rd, C V Raman Nagar, Bengaluru, 560093, Karnataka, India
Tel.: (91) 8046109400
Software Development Services
N.A.I.C.S.: 513210
Venkatesh Ponnuswamy (Mgr-Talent Acquisition)

AppDynamics, LLC   (1)
303 2nd St N Tower 8 Fl, San Francisco, CA 94107
Tel.: (628) 263-8000

Web Site: https://www.appdynamics.com
Sales Range: $150-199.9 Million
Application Software Development Services
N.A.I.C.S.: 541511
Bhaskar Sunkara (Founder)
Danny Winokur (Chief Product Officer)

Armorblox LLC   (1)
100 S Murphy Ave Ste 200, Sunnyvale, CA 94086
Tel.: (650) 260-5352
Web Site: https://www.armorblox.com
Email Security Services
N.A.I.C.S.: 541519

BroadSoft Japan KK   (1)
Koyo Bldg 5f 1-10-17 Hamamatsu-cho, Minato-ku, Tokyo, 105-0013, Japan
Tel.: (81) 345501600
Web Site: http://www.broadsoft.jp
Software Development Services
N.A.I.C.S.: 513210

BroadSoft, Inc.   (1)
9737 Washingtonian Blvd Ste 350, Gaithersburg, MD 20878
Tel.: (301) 977-9440
Web Site: http://www.broadsoft.com
VoIP Application Software Mfr
N.A.I.C.S.: 513210
Mary Ellen Seravalli (Chief Legal Officer)

Subsidiary (Domestic):

BroadSoft Hospitality, Inc.   (2)
800 NW 17th Ave Ste A, Delray Beach, FL 33445-2581
Tel.: (561) 276-7004
Computer Facilities Management Services
N.A.I.C.S.: 541513
Ron Tarro (VP-Hospitality Solutions)

Subsidiary (Non-US):

BroadSoft Technologies Private Limited   (2)
RR Towers II No 94/95 Thiruvika Industrial Estate, Chennai, 600032, Tamil Nadu, India
Tel.: (91) 4445576128
Computer System Design Services
N.A.I.C.S.: 541512
Siva Kumar (Dir)

finocom AG   (2)
Lothringer St 65, 50677, Cologne, Germany
Tel.: (49) 22199998560
Web Site: http://www.finocom.de
Computer Facilities Management Services
N.A.I.C.S.: 541513

Cariden Technolgoies LLC   (1)
840 W California Ave Ste 200, Sunnyvale, CA 94086-4828
Tel.: (650) 564-9200
Software Publishing Services
N.A.I.C.S.: 513210

Castup Israel LLC   (1)
Adgar Tower 11th Floor 35 Efal Street, Kiryat Arye, Petah Tiqwa, 49511, Israel
Tel.: (972) 37917917
Web Site: http://www.castup.net
Video Streaming Services
N.A.I.C.S.: 518210

Cisco (China) Innovation Technology Co., Ltd.   (1)
Unit 04-06 24th Floor Guangzhou Chow Tai, Fook Finance Centre Zhujiang East Road Tianhe District, Guangzhou, 510000, Guangdong, China
Tel.: (86) 41139723033
Computer Equipment & Software Whslr
N.A.I.C.S.: 423430

Cisco (China) Technology Services Co., Ltd.   (1)
Zone 9 Daxin Group Luoqun Section, Chenjiang Village Chenjiang Sub-district Zhongkai Hi-tech District, Huizhou, China
Tel.: (86) 41139723033
Computer Equipment & Software Whslr
N.A.I.C.S.: 423430

Cisco Dutch Holdings B.V.   (1)
Haarlerbergpark Haarlerbergweg 17-19, 1101 CH, Amsterdam, Netherlands
Tel.: (31) 8000200791
Computer Equipment & Software Whslr
N.A.I.C.S.: 423430

Cisco ISH B.V.   (1)
Haarlerbergpark Haarlerbergweg 13 - 19, Petach Tikva, 1101 CH, Amsterdam, Netherlands
Tel.: (31) 203571000
Holding Company
N.A.I.C.S.: 551112

Cisco Norway AS   (1)
Philip Pedersens vei 1, 1366, Lysaker, Norway
Tel.: (47) 207194038
Communication Equipment Mfr
N.A.I.C.S.: 334210

Cisco Norway Holdings AS   (1)
Philip Pedersens vei 1, 1366, Lysaker, Norway
Tel.: (47) 23273600
Holding Company
N.A.I.C.S.: 551112

Cisco Optical GmbH   (1)
Nordostpark 12, 90411, Nuremberg, Germany
Tel.: (49) 91158056200
Information Technology Consulting Services
N.A.I.C.S.: 541618

Cisco Photonics Italy S.R.L.   (1)
Via Philips 12, 20052, Monza, Italy
Tel.: (39) 0396295353
Web Site: http://www.cisco.com
Sales Range: $100-124.9 Million
Networking Hardware, Software & Services
N.A.I.C.S.: 541512

Cisco Systems (Argentina) S.A.   (1)
Ing Enrique Butty 240 Piso 17 Laminar Edificio Laminar, Distrito Federal, Buenos Aires, 1001, Argentina   (100%)
Tel.: (54) 11 4341 0100
Web Site: http://www.cisco.com
Sales Range: $25-49.9 Million
Emp.: 100
Networking Hardware, Software & Services
N.A.I.C.S.: 541512

Cisco Systems (China) Networking Technology Co., Ltd.   (1)
7-12F Building C Yintai Office Tower B No 2 Jianguomenwai Ave, Chaoyang Dist, Beijing, 100022, China
Tel.: (86) 1085155000
Networking Technology Product Mfr & Distr
N.A.I.C.S.: 334210

Cisco Systems (Colombia) Limitada   (1)
Carrera 9 115 - 06 Piso 14 Edificio Tierra Firme, Bogota, Colombia   (100%)
Tel.: (57) 43541555
Web Site: http://www.ciscosystems.com
Sales Range: $25-49.9 Million
Emp.: 100
Provider of Networking Hardware, Software & Services
N.A.I.C.S.: 541512

Cisco Systems (Czech Republic) s.r.o   (1)
Karlovo namesti 2097/10, Nove Mesto, 120 00, Prague, Czech Republic   (100%)
Tel.: (420) 221584800
Web Site: http://www.cisco.com
Sales Range: $10-24.9 Million
Emp.: 80
Provider of Networking Hardware, Software & Services
N.A.I.C.S.: 541512

Cisco Systems (HK), Ltd.   (1)
31/Fl Great Eagle Center 23 Harbour Road, Wanchai, China (Hong Kong)   (100%)
Tel.: (852) 25883100
Sales Range: $25-49.9 Million
Emp.: 100
Provider of Networking Hardware, Software & Services
N.A.I.C.S.: 541512

Cisco Systems (India) Pvt. Ltd.   (1)
25 Barakhamba Road, New Delhi, 110001, India
Tel.: (91) 1142611000
Web Site: http://www.cisco.com
Sales Range: $100-124.9 Million
Provider of Networking Hardware, Software & Services
N.A.I.C.S.: 541512

Vishak Raman (Dir-Security Bus)
Vaibhav Pant (Mgr-Sys Engrg & Collaboration Bus)

Cisco Systems (Italy) S.R.L.   (1)
Palazzo Acero Via Torri Bianche 8, 20871, Vimercate, MB, Italy
Tel.: (39) 0396295353
Web Site: http://www.cisco.com
Networking Hardware, Software & Services Provider
N.A.I.C.S.: 541512

Cisco Systems (Korea) Limited   (1)
Computer Equipment & Software Whslr
N.A.I.C.S.: 423430

Cisco Systems (Scotland) Limited   (1)
Gyleview House 3 Redheughs Rigg Edinburgh West Office Park, South Gyle, Edinburgh, EH12 9DQ, United Kingdom   (100%)
Tel.: (44) 2088242001
Web Site: http://www.cisco.com
Networking Hardware & Software Provider; Computer Consultancy Services
N.A.I.C.S.: 541512

Cisco Systems (Spain) S.L.   (1)
Av de La Vega 15 Edif 3- 4 Arroyo de la Vega, 28109, Alcobendas, Madrid, Spain   (100%)
Tel.: (34) 912012800
Web Site: http://www.cisco.com
Sales Range: $75-99.9 Million
Emp.: 350
Provider of Networking Hardware, Software & Services
N.A.I.C.S.: 541512

Cisco Systems (Sweden) AB   (1)
Arstaangsvagen 21 B, 117 43, Stockholm, Sweden   (100%)
Tel.: (46) 86859000
Web Site: http://www.cisco.com
Sales Range: $25-49.9 Million
Emp.: 125
Provider of Networking Hardware, Software & Services
N.A.I.C.S.: 541512

Cisco Systems (Switzerland) GmbH   (1)
Richtistrasse 7, 8304, Wallisellen, Zurich, Switzerland   (100%)
Tel.: (41) 80 017 9317
Web Site: http://www.cisco.com
Computer Software & Services
N.A.I.C.S.: 541512

Cisco Systems (Thailand) Ltd.   (1)
28 Floor The Offices at Central World Bldg 999/9 Rama I Road, Patumwan, Bangkok, 10330, Thailand   (100%)
Tel.: (66) 2 263 7000
Web Site: https://www.cisco.com
Sales Range: $25-49.9 Million
Emp.: 90
Provider of Networking Hardware, Software & Services
N.A.I.C.S.: 541512

Cisco Systems Australia Pty Limited   (1)
80 Pacific Highway Level 10, North Sydney, 2060, NSW, Australia
Tel.: (61) 284466000
Emp.: 1,139
Electronic Equipment Distr
N.A.I.C.S.: 423690

Cisco Systems Australia Pty., Ltd.   (1)
Level 22-24 177 Pacific Hwy, PO Box 469, North Sydney, 2060, NSW, Australia   (100%)
Tel.: (61) 284466000
Web Site: http://www.cisco.com
Sales Range: $25-49.9 Million
Emp.: 150
Provider of Networking Hardware, Software & Services
N.A.I.C.S.: 541512
Todd Lynton (Mng Dir-Consumer Products-Australia & New Zealand)

Cisco Systems Austria GmbH   (1)
Millennium Tower 30/31st floor Handelskai 94-96, 1200, Vienna, Austria

Cisco Systems, Inc.—(Continued)

Tel.: (43) 1240306000
Communication Equipment Distr
N.A.I.C.S.: 423690

Cisco Systems Belgium S.P.R.L. (1)
Pegasus Park De Kleetlaan 6A, 1831, Di-
egem, Belgium **(100%)**
Tel.: (32) 27042500
Web Site: http://www.cisco.com
Sales Range: $100-124.9 Million
Provider of Networking Hardware, Software
& Services
N.A.I.C.S.: 541512

Cisco Systems Bulgaria EOOD (1)
Tel.: (359) 29375911
Sales Range: $10-24.9 Million
Emp.: 78
Provider of Networking Hardware, Software
& Services
N.A.I.C.S.: 541512

Cisco Systems Canada Co. (1)
88 Queens Quay West Suite 2900, Toronto,
M5J 0B8, ON, Canada **(100%)**
Tel.: (416) 306-7000
Sales Range: $150-199.9 Million
Emp.: 700
Networking Hardware, Software & Services
N.A.I.C.S.: 541512
Bernadette Wightman (Pres)

**Cisco Systems Capital (Australia) Pty.
Ltd.** (1)
Level 10 80 Pacific Hwy, PO Box 469, Syd-
ney, 2060, NSW, Australia **(100%)**
Tel.: (61) 284466000
Web Site: http://www.cisco.com
Sales Range: $25-49.9 Million
Emp.: 100
Provider of Business Capital Services
N.A.I.C.S.: 561499

**Cisco Systems Capital (India) Private
Limited** (1)
2nd Floor Brigade South Parade 10 MG
Road, Bengaluru, 560 001, Karnataka, India
Tel.: (91) 8041593000
Communication & Networking Products Mfr
N.A.I.C.S.: 334290

**Cisco Systems Capital (Korea)
Limited** (1)
5F ASEM Tower World Trade Center 159-1
Samsung-dong, Kangnam-ku, 135-798,
Seoul, Korea (South)
Tel.: (82) 234298000
Web Site: http://www.cisco.com
Sales Range: $150-199.9 Million
Emp.: 300
Provider of Corporate Financial Services
N.A.I.C.S.: 522320

Cisco Systems Capital K.K. (1)
9-7-1 Akasaka Midtown Tower, Minato-ku,
Tokyo, 107-6227, Japan **(100%)**
Tel.: (81) 364346500
Web Site: http://www.cisco.com
Sales Range: $125-149.9 Million
Emp.: 1,300
Corporate Financial Services
N.A.I.C.S.: 522320

Cisco Systems Caribe (1)
235 Federico Costa St Ste 415, Hato Rey,
PR 00918
Tel.: (787) 620-1888
Web Site: http://www.cisco.com
Sales Range: $10-24.9 Million
Emp.: 20
Provider of Networking Hardware, Software
& Services
N.A.I.C.S.: 541512

Cisco Systems Chile S.A. (1)
Edificio El Golf Av Apoquindo 3650 Suites
201 and 301, Santiago, Chile **(100%)**
Tel.: (56) 24314900
Sales Range: $100-124.9 Million
Networking Hardware, Software & Services
N.A.I.C.S.: 541512

Cisco Systems Costa Rica SA (1)
Centro Corporativo Plaza Roble Edificio Los
Balcones A Primer Nivel, Escazu, Costa
Rica **(100%)**
Tel.: (506) 22013600
Web Site: http://www.cisco.com

Sales Range: $10-24.9 Million
Emp.: 60
Provider of Networking Hardware, Software
& Services
N.A.I.C.S.: 541512

Cisco Systems Cyprus Ltd. (1)
81-83 Grivas Digenis Avenue, Nicosia, Cy-
prus
Tel.: (357) 302106381445
Web Site: http://www.cisco.com
Sales Range: $100-124.9 Million
Provider of Networking Hardware, Software
& Services
N.A.I.C.S.: 541512

Cisco Systems Danmark A/S (1)
Lautrupsgade No7, 2100, Copenhagen,
Denmark **(100%)**
Tel.: (45) 39585000
Sales Range: $25-49.9 Million
Emp.: 100
Provider of Networking Hardware, Software
& Services
N.A.I.C.S.: 541512
Niels Munster (Gen Mgr)

Cisco Systems Egypt Ltd. (1)
City Stars Complex Tower 2A Omar Ibn El-
Khattab Street, Heliopolis, Cairo, Egypt
Tel.: (20) 224885300
Web Site: http://www.cisco.com
Provider of Networking Hardware, Software
& Services
N.A.I.C.S.: 541512

Cisco Systems Estonia OU (1)
Viru Valjak 2 III korrus, 10111, Tallinn, Esto-
nia
Tel.: (372) 6675961
Communication Service
N.A.I.C.S.: 517111

**Cisco Systems Finance International
Unlimited Company** (1)
32 Hamelacha St I Z Sapir South, PO Box
8735, Netanya, 42504, Israel
Tel.: (972) 98927197
Computer Equipment & Software Whslr
N.A.I.C.S.: 423430

Cisco Systems Finland Oy (1)
Lars Sonckin Kaari 16, 02600, Espoo,
Finland **(100%)**
Tel.: (358) 2047061
Sales Range: $10-24.9 Million
Emp.: 70
Provider of Networking Hardware, Software
& Services
N.A.I.C.S.: 541512
Esa Korvenmaa (Mgr)

Cisco Systems France SARL (1)
11 rue Camille Desmoulins, 92782, Issy-les-
Moulineaux, Cedex 9, France
Tel.: (33) 158045858
Web Site: http://www.cisco.com
Sales Range: $100-124.9 Million
Provider of Networking Hardware, Software
& Services
N.A.I.C.S.: 541512

Cisco Systems G.K. (1)
Midtown Tower Building 9-7-1 Akasaka,
Minato-Ku, Tokyo, 107-6227, Japan
Tel.: (81) 364346500
Communication Equipment Distr
N.A.I.C.S.: 423690

Cisco Systems G.K. Tokyo (1)
Midtown Tower Building 9-7-1 Akasaka, Mi-
nato ku, Tokyo, 107-6227, Japan
Tel.: (81) 3 6434 6500
Web Site: http://www.cisco.com
Sales Range: $100-124.9 Million
Networking Hardware, Software & Services
N.A.I.C.S.: 541512

Cisco Systems GmbH (1)
12 Etage Kurfurstendamm 22, 10719, Ber-
lin, Germany
Tel.: (49) 3097892700
Web Site: http://www.cisco.com
Sales Range: $100-124.9 Million
Networking Hardware, Software & Services
N.A.I.C.S.: 541512

Cisco Systems Hellas S.A. (1)
Monumental Plaza Bldg C 44 Kifisias Ave,
Maroussi, 15125, Athens, Greece **(100%)**
Tel.: (30) 210 6381300

Web Site: http://www.cisco.gr
Sales Range: $100-124.9 Million
Emp.: 50
Networking Hardware, Software & Services
Solutions
N.A.I.C.S.: 541512

**Cisco Systems Holding GmbH & Co.
KG** (1)
Am Soldnermoos 17, Hallbergmoos, 85399,
Germany
Tel.: (49) 8115543535
Web Site: http://www.cisco.com
Sales Range: $100-124.9 Million
Provider of Networking Hardware, Software
& Services
N.A.I.C.S.: 541512

**Cisco Systems Internetworking (Ire-
land) Limited** (1)
Block P6 East Point Business Park, Dublin,
3, Leinster, Ireland
Tel.: (353) 18192700
Communication Equipment Distr
N.A.I.C.S.: 423690

Cisco Systems Israel Ltd. (1)
32 Hamelacha st I Z Sapir, PO Box 8735,
Netanya, 42504, Israel
Tel.: (972) 98927222
Web Site: http://www.cisco.com
Sales Range: $150-199.9 Million
Emp.: 750
Provider of Networking Hardware, Software
& Services
N.A.I.C.S.: 541512

Cisco Systems LLC (1)
Bait Al Reem Business Centre Office No's
104 105 and 106 Bldg No 81, Block No 234
Plot No 34/19 Al Thaqafa Str Way No 3409
Al Khuwair, Muscat, Oman
Tel.: (968) 24942800
Computer Hardware Mfr
N.A.I.C.S.: 334210

Cisco Systems Limited (1)
9-11 New Square Bedfont Lakes, Feltham,
TW14 8HA, Middlesex, United
Kingdom **(100%)**
Tel.: (44) 2088241000
Sales Range: $100-124.9 Million
Emp.: 3,000
Provider of Networking Hardware, Software
& Services
N.A.I.C.S.: 541512

Cisco Systems Ltd. (1)
Block P6 Eastpoint Business Park, Dublin,
3, Ireland **(100%)**
Tel.: (353) 18192700
Web Site: http://www.cisco.com
Sales Range: $100-124.9 Million
Provider of Networking Hardware, Software
& Services
N.A.I.C.S.: 541512

**Cisco Systems Luxembourg
s.a.r.l.** (1)
Avenue JF Kennedy 46A 4th floor, 1855,
Luxembourg, Luxembourg **(100%)**
Tel.: (352) 26433311
Web Site: http://www.cisco.lu
Sales Range: $1-9.9 Million
Emp.: 10
Provider of Networking Hardware, Software
& Services
N.A.I.C.S.: 541512

**Cisco Systems Macedonia DOOEL
Skopje** (1)
Bul 8-mi Septemvri No 16 Hyperium Busi-
ness Center 2nd floor, 1000, Skopje, North
Macedonia
Tel.: (389) 70383366
Web Site: http://www.cisco.com
Networking Equipment Mfr
N.A.I.C.S.: 334210

Cisco Systems Magyarorszg Kft. (1)
Csorsz Utca 45, Budapest, 1123,
Hungary **(100%)**
Tel.: (36) 1 225 4600
Web Site: http://www.cisco.com
Sales Range: $10-24.9 Million
Emp.: 60
Networking Hardware, Software & Services
N.A.I.C.S.: 541512

**Cisco Systems Malaysia Sdn,
Bhd** (1)

Level 5 One Sentral Jalan Travers Kuala
Lumpur Sentral, 50470, Kuala Lumpur,
Malaysia **(100%)**
Tel.: (60) 3 2081 1800
Web Site: http://www.cisco.com
Sales Range: $10-24.9 Million
Emp.: 50
Networking Hardware, Software & Services
N.A.I.C.S.: 541512
Albert Chai (Mng Dir)

**Cisco Systems Netherlands Holdings
B.V.** (1)
Haarlerbergpark Haarlerbergweg 13 19,
Amsterdam, 1101 CH, Netherlands **(100%)**
Tel.: (31) 203571000
Web Site: http://www.cisco.com
Sales Range: $150-199.9 Million
Emp.: 700
Provider of Networking Hardware, Software
& Services
N.A.I.C.S.: 541512

**Cisco Systems New Zealand
Limited** (1)
Level 3 152 Fanshawe Street, PO Box
6624, Wellesley Street, Auckland, 1010,
New Zealand
Tel.: (64) 93551950
Web Site: http://www.cisco.com
Sales Range: $25-49.9 Million
Emp.: 30
Provider of Networking Hardware, Software
& Services
N.A.I.C.S.: 541512

Cisco Systems Norway AS (1)
Philip Pedersens Vei 1, 1366, Lysaker,
Norway **(100%)**
Tel.: (47) 67125125
Web Site: http://www.cisco.com
Sales Range: $10-24.9 Million
Emp.: 640
Provider of Networking Hardware, Software
& Services
N.A.I.C.S.: 541512

Cisco Systems Peru S.A. (1)
Av Victor Andres Belaunde 147 Via Princi-
pal 123, Edificio Real Uno Piso 13, San
Isidro, LIMA 27, Lima, Peru
Tel.: (51) 12155100
Web Site: http://www.cisco.com
Sales Range: $100-124.9 Million
Provider of Networking Hardware, Software
& Services
N.A.I.C.S.: 541512

Cisco Systems Poland Sp. Z o.o. (1)
Domaniewska 39B, 02-672, Warsaw,
Poland **(100%)**
Tel.: (48) 225722700
Web Site: http://www.cisco.com
Sales Range: $50-74.9 Million
Emp.: 200
Provider of Networking Hardware, Software
& Services
N.A.I.C.S.: 541512

**Cisco Systems Portugal Sistemas
Informaticos Sociedade Unipessoal
Ltda.** (1)
Lagoas Park Edificio 12 3 andar, 2740-269,
Porto Salvo, Portugal **(100%)**
Tel.: (351) 214541000
Web Site: http://www.cisco.com
Sales Range: $10-24.9 Million
Emp.: 65
Provider of Networking Hardware, Software
& Services
N.A.I.C.S.: 541512

Cisco Systems Romania S.R.L. (1)
America House 4-8 Nicolae Titulescu Bd
Sector 1, 011141, Bucharest, Romania
Tel.: (40) 21 302 3550
Web Site: http://www.cisco.com
Sales Range: $100-124.9 Million
Emp.: 70,112
Networking Hardware, Software & Services
N.A.I.C.S.: 541512

**Cisco Systems Slovakia, spol. s
r.o.** (1)
Eurovea Central 3 Pribinova 10, 811 09,
Bratislava, Slovakia **(100%)**
Tel.: (421) 258255500
Web Site: http://www.cisco.com
Sales Range: $10-24.9 Million
Emp.: 35

Provider of Networking Hardware, Software
& Services
N.A.I.C.S.: 541512

Cisco Systems South Korea (1)
5F ASEM Tower, Kangnam-ku, 46164,
Seoul, Korea (South)
Tel.: (82) 234298000
Web Site: http://www.cisco.com
Sales Range: $75-99.9 Million
Emp.: 300
Networking Hardware, Software & Services
N.A.I.C.S.: 541512

Cisco Systems Taiwan Ltd. (1)
Xin Ji Building 12F 460 Xin Yi Road Section
4, Xinyi District, Taipei, 11052,
Taiwan   (100%)
Tel.: (886) 287587100
Web Site: http://www.cisco.com
Sales Range: $100-124.9 Million
Emp.: 100
Networking Hardware, Software & Services
N.A.I.C.S.: 541512

Cisco Systems Venezuela (1)
Avenida La Estancia Centro Banaven Torre
C Piso 7, Chuao, Caracas, 1064,
Venezuela   (100%)
Tel.: (58) 212 902 0221
Web Site: http://www.cisco.com
Networking Hardware, Software & Services
N.A.I.C.S.: 541512

Cisco Systems Vietnam Limited (1)
Phong 2301-2305 tang 23 72 Building
Keangnam Hanoi Landmark Tower, Khu E6
Pham Hung Quan Tu Liem, Hanoi,
Vietnam   (100%)
Tel.: (84) 2439746227
Web Site: http://www.cisco.com
Sales Range: $25-49.9 Million
Emp.: 70
Networking Hardware, Software & Services
N.A.I.C.S.: 541512

**Cisco Systems de Mexico, S.A. de
C.V.** (1)
Paseo de Tamarindos 400A Pisos 14 25 y
30 Torre Arcos, Bosques de las Lomas
Cuajimalpa, 05120, Mexico,
Mexico   (100%)
Tel.: (52) 55 5267 1000
Web Site: http://www.cisco.com
Sales Range: $100-124.9 Million
Networking Hardware, Software Devices &
Services Mfr
N.A.I.C.S.: 541512

Cisco Systems do Brasil Ltda. (1)
United Nations Avenue 12901-United Na-
tions Business Center, West Tower Brooklin
New, Sao Paulo, 04578-910, SP, Brazil
Tel.: (55) 155089999
Web Site: http://www.cisco.com.br
IT; Networking Hardware, Software & Ser-
vices
N.A.I.C.S.: 541512

Cisco THV LLC (1)
2711 Centerville Rd Ste 400, Wilmington,
DE 19808
Tel.: (302) 636-5401
Web Site: http://www.cisco.com
Computer Product Mfr
N.A.I.C.S.: 334118

**Cisco Technologies (Beijing) Co.,
Ltd.** (1)
Floor 7 and 9 Building 3 Yard 2 Jian-
guomenwai Street, Chaoyang District, Bei-
jing, China
Tel.: (86) 41139723033
Computer Equipment & Software Whslr
N.A.I.C.S.: 423430

**Cisco Technologies (Thailand)
Limited** (1)
999/9 Rama I Road, Pathum Wan, Bang-
kok, 10330, Thailand
Tel.: (66) 22637000
Web Site: http://www.cisco.com
Emp.: 100
Communication Equipment Distr
N.A.I.C.S.: 423690

Cisco Technology Belguim BVBA (1)
Cisco Pegasus Park De Kleetlaan 6A,
1831, Diegem, Belgium
Tel.: (32) 80094242

Web Site: http://www.cisco.com
Communication Equipment Distr
N.A.I.C.S.: 423690

Cisco Technology Denmark ApS (1)
Lautrupsgade 7 7th floor, 2100, Copenha-
gen, Denmark
Tel.: (45) 207194037
Communication Equipment Distr
N.A.I.C.S.: 423690

**Cisco Technology Services (Dalian)
Co. Ltd** (1)
Room 302 303 304 & 305 3rd Floor No 5
Software East Rd, Dalian Software Park
Ganjingzi District, Dalian, Liaoning, China
Tel.: (86) 41139723033
Electric Device Mfr
N.A.I.C.S.: 335210

**Cisco Video Technologies India Pri-
vate Limited** (1)
Block 9A & 9B Pritech Park SEZ Sarjapur
Outer Ring Road, Bellandur Village, Benga-
luru, 560 103, India
Tel.: (91) 8030216248
Communication Equipment Mfr
N.A.I.C.S.: 334210

**Cisco Video Technologies Israel
Ltd.** (1)
Shlomo Momo ha-Levi 5 Industrial area Har
Hotzvim 1, Jerusalem, Israel
Tel.: (972) 98927327
Communication Equipment Distr
N.A.I.C.S.: 423690

Cisco WebEx LLC (1)
3979 Freedom Cir, Santa Clara, CA 95054
Tel.: (408) 435-7000
Web Site: http://www.webex.com
Software Publishing Services
N.A.I.C.S.: 513210

Cisco do Brasil Ltda. (1)
Av das Nacoes Unidas 12901 25th Floor,
Brooklin Novo, Sao Paulo, 04578-000, Bra-
zil
Tel.: (55) 1155089999
Web Site: http://www.cisco.com
Communication Equipment Mfr
N.A.I.C.S.: 334290

CloudLock, Inc. (1)
203 Crescent St Ste 105, Waltham, MA
02453
Tel.: (781) 996-4332
Web Site: http://www.cloudlock.com
Software Security Services
N.A.I.C.S.: 541511

Cloudlock, Ltd. (1)
Rothschild Boulevard 3 Psagot Tower, Tel
Aviv, Israel
Tel.: (972) 723369850
Web Site: http://www.cloudlock.com
Computer Equipment & Software Whslr
N.A.I.C.S.: 423430
Ron Zalkind *(Founder & CTO)*

Composite Software, Inc. (1)
2655 Campus Dr Ste 200, San Mateo, CA
94403
Tel.: (650) 227-8200
Web Site: http://www.compositesw.com
Sales Range: $10-24.9 Million
Emp.: 3,570
Low Cost Data Integration Software Mfr
N.A.I.C.S.: 513210

Duo Security LLC (1)
123 N Ashley St Ste 100, Ann Arbor, MI
48104
Internet Security Solutions Developer
N.A.I.C.S.: 513210

Fluidmesh Networks S.r.l. (1)
Via Carlo Farini 5, Milan, Italy
Tel.: (39) 0200616189
Computer Networking Services
N.A.I.C.S.: 541519

**Healthcare Communications UK
Ltd.** (1)
Stewart House Royal Court, Macclesfield,
SK11 7AE, Cheshire, United Kingdom
Tel.: (44) 8459000890
Web Site: https://healthcare-
communications.com
Information Technology Services
N.A.I.C.S.: 541511

Kenny Bloxham *(Mng Dir)*
Sam Sutcliffe *(Acct Mgr)*
Mark Broughton *(Sls Mgr-Commercial)*
Kurt Fitzgerald *(Acct Mgr)*
Ross Hunter *(Mgr-Business Development)*

IMImobile PLC (1)
5 St John's Lane, London, EC1M 4BH,
United Kingdom
Tel.: (44) 1494750500
Web Site: http://www.imimobile.com
Rev.: $224,528,869
Assets: $269,356,734
Liabilities: $166,093,154
Net Worth: $103,263,580
Earnings: $2,659,925
Emp.: 1,114
Fiscal Year-end: 03/31/2020
Holding Company; Mobile Communications
Software Publisher
N.A.I.C.S.: 551112
Jay Patel *(CEO)*
Sudarshan Dharmapuri *(Exec VP-Products)*
Thomas Boesen *(Sr VP-Predicts)*
Chaitanya Devalapally *(Exec VP-APAC)*
Ross Venter *(CEO-South Africa)*
Ashwani Raj Chadha *(Exec VP-MEA)*
Aditya Challa *(Sr VP-AI & Innovation)*

Subsidiary (Domestic):

**IMImobile Intelligent Networks
Limited** (2)
Abbey House 1650 Arlington Business
Park, Farringdon, Theale, RG7 4SA, United
Kingdom
Tel.: (44) 1494 750 500
Web Site: http://imimobile.com
Cloud Communications Software Services
N.A.I.C.S.: 517112

Subsidiary (Non-US):

IMImobile Pvt. Ltd. (2)
Plot No 770 Road No 44, Jubilee Hills,
Hyderabad, 500 033, India
Tel.: (91) 4030858626
Web Site: http://imimobile.com
Sales Range: $150-199.9 Million
Mobile Data & Media Services
N.A.I.C.S.: 518210
Vishwanath Alluri *(Co-Founder)*
Shyam Bhat *(Co-Founder & CTO-Grp)*
Jay Patel *(CEO-Grp)*
Mike Jefferies *(COO-Grp)*

Subsidiary (Non-US):

Skinkers Ltd. (3)
33 Glasshouse Street, London, W1B 5DG,
United Kingdom
Tel.: (44) 20 7036 6580
Web Site: http://www.skinkers.com
Sales Range: $25-49.9 Million
Emp.: 12
Communications Software Developer &
Distr
N.A.I.C.S.: 513210
Tim Heyes *(Head-Tech)*
Matt Bryson *(Head-Dev)*

Subsidiary (Non-US):

Impact Mobile Inc. (2)
460 Richmond Street West Suite 700, To-
ronto, M5V 1Y1, ON, Canada
Tel.: (416) 368-8400
Mobile Marketing Technology & Solutions
N.A.I.C.S.: 513210
Tim Strike *(VP-Ops)*
John Leon *(COO & Gen Mgr)*
Tricia Waters *(VP-Client Svcs)*
Laurie McLean *(VP-Fin & Contract Admin)*

Subsidiary (US):

SUMOTEXT Corp. (2)
201 E Markham Ste 150, Little Rock, AR
72201
Tel.: (501) 372-1347
Web Site: http://www.sumotext.com
Software Publisher
N.A.I.C.S.: 513210
Timothy Miller *(Pres)*
Mason Woods *(CTO)*
Elsbeth Cloninger *(Sr VP-Client Svcs)*

Subsidiary (Domestic):

Txtlocal Ltd. (2)
Pulford House Bell Meadow Bus Park Park

Lane, Pulford, Chester, CH4 9EP, United
Kingdom
Tel.: (44) 1244 752299
Web Site: http://www.textlocal.com
Mobile Application Development & Messag-
ing Services
N.A.I.C.S.: 541511
Alastair Shortland *(Founder)*

Involvio LLC (1)
54 W 40th St, New York, NY 10018
Tel.: (212) 729-6670
Web Site: https://www.involvio.com
Software Development Services
N.A.I.C.S.: 541511

July Systems, LLC (1)
533 Airport Blvd Ste 395, Burlingame, CA
94010
Tel.: (650) 685-2460
Location Analytics Software
N.A.I.C.S.: 513210

Kenna Security, Inc. (1)
3945 Freedom Cir Ste 300, Santa Clara,
CA 95054
Web Site: http://www.kennasecurity.com
Sales Range: $10-24.9 Million
Emp.: 130
Data Protection & Security Services
N.A.I.C.S.: 561621
Ed Bellis *(Co-Founder & CTO)*
Jeff Heuer *(Co-Founder)*
Karim Toubba *(CEO)*
Rick Kramer *(VP-Worldwide Sls)*
Dave Bortz *(VP-Engrg)*

Lancope, LLC (1)
3650 Brookside Pkwy Ste 500, Alpharetta,
GA 30022
Tel.: (770) 225-6500
Web Site: http://www.cisco.com
Software Publisher
N.A.I.C.S.: 513210

Lightwire LLC (1)
1053 E Whitaker Mill Rd Ste 115 Ofc 220,
Raleigh, NC 27604
Tel.: (919) 836-1255
Web Site: https://lightwireinc.com
Computer Hardware Mfr
N.A.I.C.S.: 334210

MaintenanceNet, Inc. (1)
1947 Camino, Carlsbad, CA 92008
Tel.: (760) 496-7564
Web Site: http://www.maintenancenet.com
Sales Range: $1-9.9 Million
Emp.: 25
Software Developer
N.A.I.C.S.: 513210
Scott Herron *(CEO)*
Kelly Crothers *(VP-Mktg)*

Meraki LLC (1)
500 Terry A Francois, San Francisco, CA
94158
Tel.: (415) 937-6671
Web Site: https://meraki.cisco.com
Sales Range: $100-124.9 Million
Emp.: 2,000
Cloud Managed Networking Solutions
N.A.I.C.S.: 513210
Sanjit Biswas *(Co-Founder)*
John Bicket *(Co-Founder)*
Hans Robertson *(Co-Founder)*

**Meraki Networks Australia Pty.
Ltd.** (1)
Level 21 321 Kent St, Sydney, 2000, NSW,
Australia
Tel.: (61) 283979000
Computer Equipment & Software Whslr
N.A.I.C.S.: 423430

NDS Holdings B.V (1)
Nijverheidscentrum 28, Zuidplas, 2761 JP,
Zuid-Holland, Netherlands
Tel.: (31) 180634356
Holding Company
N.A.I.C.S.: 551112

NDS Sweden (1)
Arstaangsvagen 21 B 5tr, 117 43, Stock-
holm, Sweden
Tel.: (46) 40238600
Advertising & Market Research Services
N.A.I.C.S.: 541890

OpenDNS, Inc. (1)
135 Bluxome St, San Francisco, CA 94107

Cisco Systems, Inc.—(Continued)

Tel.: (415) 344-3200
Web Site: https://umbrella.cisco.com
Internet Security Services
N.A.I.C.S.: 518210
David Ulevitch (Founder)

PT Cisco Systems Indonesia (1)
Perkantoran Hijau Arkadia Tower F 5th
Floor JI TB Simatupang Kav 88, Jakarta,
12510, Indonesia (100%)
Tel.: (62) 212 754 7566
Web Site: https://www.cisco.com
Sales Range: $100-124.9 Million
Provider of Networking Hardware, Software
& Services
N.A.I.C.S.: 541512

Pawaa Software Private Limited (1)
No 1133 First Floor Anand Embassy 100 Ft
Road HAL 2nd Stage, Indira Nagar, Benga-
luru, 560038, India
Tel.: (91) 8048669299
Web Site: http://www.securelyshare.com
Emp.: 30
System Integration Design Services
N.A.I.C.S.: 541512

Postpath LLC (1)
1200 Villa St Ste 150, Mountain View, CA
94041-1106
Tel.: (650) 810-8100
Hardware & Server Peripheral Mfr
N.A.I.C.S.: 334112

Rostrvm Solutions Limited (1)
Dukes Court Duke Street, Woking, GU21
5BH, United Kingdom
Tel.: (44) 1494700600
Software Development Services
N.A.I.C.S.: 541511

SA Japan KK (1)
525 Kagiage Shinden, Iwatsuki, Saitama,
339-0025, Japan
Tel.: (81) 645605527
Web Site: https://www.sajapan.net
Computer Hardware Mfr
N.A.I.C.S.: 334210

Scientific-Atlanta, LLC (1)
40 Technology Pkwy S Ste 300, Norcross,
GA 30092-2967
Tel.: (770) 903-5000
Web Site: http://www.scientificatlanta.com
Emp.: 7,652
Communication Equipment Mfr
N.A.I.C.S.: 334210

Subsidiary (Non-US):

Cisco Systems (2)
100 Middlefield Road Unit 1, Scarborough,
M1S 4M6, ON, Canada
Tel.: (416) 299-6888
Web Site: http://www.cisco.com
Sales Range: $125-149.9 Million
Emp.: 140
End-To-End Video Distribution Networks &
Video Systems Integration Services
N.A.I.C.S.: 334310

Socio Labs LLC (1)
115 W Washington St Ste 1190, Indianapo-
lis, IN 46204
Web Site: https://www.socio.events
Event Organizing Services
N.A.I.C.S.: 561920
Kara Gladish (Mgr)
Murat Nalcaci (Dir)

Sourcefire, Inc. (1)
9770 Patuxent Woods Dr, Columbia, MD
21046
Tel.: (410) 290-1616
Web Site: http://www.sourcefire.com
Rev.: $223,090,000
Assets: $364,674,000
Liabilities: $119,548,000
Net Worth: $245,126,000
Earnings: $5,027,000
Emp.: 599
Fiscal Year-end: 12/31/2012
Cybersecurity Software Developer & Ser-
vices
N.A.I.C.S.: 518210

Subsidiary (Non-US):

Godo Kaisha Sourcefire (2)

8F Pacific Century Place Marunouchi 1-11-1
Marunouchi, Chiyoda-ku, Tokyo, 100-6208,
Japan
Tel.: (81) 368608415
Web Site: http://www.sourcefire.com
Sales Range: $25-49.9 Million
Emp.: 100
Cybersecurity Software Whslr & Services
N.A.I.C.S.: 423430

**Sourcefire Brasil Comercio e Segur-
anca de Rede Ltda.** (2)
CN Qd 02 Bloco A Ed Corporate Financial
Center, Salas 502/503/504, Brasilia, 70712-
900, Brazil
Tel.: (55) 6133296014
Web Site: http://www.sourcefire.com
Emp.: 1
Cybersecurity Software Whslr & Services
N.A.I.C.S.: 423430

Sourcefire Canada Ltd. (2)
2424 4th St SW Ste 230, Calgary, T2S 2T4,
AB, Canada
Tel.: (800) 917-4134
Cybersecurity Software Whslr & Services
N.A.I.C.S.: 423430

Sourcefire Limited (2)
One Thames Valley West, Wing Wokingham
Road, Bracknell, RG42 1NG, Berks, United
Kingdom
Tel.: (44) 1189898400
Sales Range: $75-99.9 Million
Emp.: 50
Cybersecurity Software Whslr & Services
N.A.I.C.S.: 423430

Sourcefire Singapore Pte. Ltd. (2)
1 Raffles Pl Ste 29-01 1 Raffles Pl, Singa-
pore, 048616, Singapore
Tel.: (65) 66710455
Cybersecurity Software Whslr & Services
N.A.I.C.S.: 423430

Splunk Inc. (1)
270 Brannan St, San Francisco, CA 94107
Tel.: (415) 848-8400
Web Site: https://www.splunk.com
Rev.: $3,653,708,000
Assets: $6,343,923,000
Liabilities: $6,454,436,000
Net Worth: ($110,513,000)
Earnings: ($277,862,000)
Emp.: 8,000
Fiscal Year-end: 01/31/2023
Software Publisher
N.A.I.C.S.: 513210
Ammar Maraqa (Chief Strategy Officer & Sr
VP)
Brian Kayman (Chief Acctg Officer)
Scott Morgan (Chief Legal Officer-Global
Affairs, Sec & Sr VP)
Christian Smith (Chief Revenue Officer & Sr
VP)
Claire Hockin (CMO & Sr VP)
Simon Davies (Sr VP-Gen Mgr-Asia Pacific)
Gary Steele (Pres & CEO)
Jason Lee (Chief Info Security Officer)
Brian Roberts (CFO & Sr VP)
Brian Roberts (CFO)
Toni Pavlovich (Chief Customer Officer)
Emily Killam (Sr VP)

Subsidiary (Domestic):

Bugsense Inc. (2)
440 N Wolfe Rd, Sunnyvale, CA 94085
Tel.: (801) 357-9388
Emp.: 14
Software Development Services
N.A.I.C.S.: 541511

Caspida, Inc. (2)
2400 Geng Rd Ste 150, Palo Alto, CA
94303
Tel.: (650) 646-9850
Cyber Security Services
N.A.I.C.S.: 541513

Rigor, Inc. (2)
270 Brannan St 1st Fl, San Francisco, CA
94107
Web Site: http://www.rigor.com
Software Development Services
N.A.I.C.S.: 541511

Subsidiary (Non-US):

**Splunk Information Technology
(Shanghai) Co., Ltd.** (2)

Room 901 Tower 11 KIC III No 303 Song
Hu Road, Yangpu District, Shanghai,
200433, China
Tel.: (86) 2180176100
Engineering Research & Development Ser-
vices
N.A.I.C.S.: 541715

Splunk Services FZ-LLC (2)
2507A - 2508A Floor 25 Business Central
Towers, Dubai, United Arab Emirates
Tel.: (971) 42486200
Information Technology Consulting Services
N.A.I.C.S.: 541512

Splunk Services France SAS (2)
3 rue de Stockholm, 75008, Paris, Cedex,
France
Tel.: (33) 148014880
Information Technology Consulting Services
N.A.I.C.S.: 541512

Splunk Services Germany GmbH (2)
Bayerstrasse 85, 80335, Munich, Germany
Tel.: (49) 2032044300
Web Site: http://www.splunk.com
Software Development Services
N.A.I.C.S.: 541511

Splunk Services Hong Kong Ltd. (2)
31/F Tower 5 The Gateway Harbour City,
Tsim Sha Tsui, Kowloon, China (Hong
Kong)
Tel.: (852) 39754000
Information Technology Consulting Services
N.A.I.C.S.: 541512

Splunk Services Japan GK (2)
8F Otemachi Park Building 1-1-1 Otemachi,
Chiyoda-ku, Tokyo, 100-0004, Japan
Tel.: (81) 36 206 3780
Web Site: https://www.splunk.com
Emp.: 45
Information Technology Consulting Services
N.A.I.C.S.: 541512

Splunk Services Korea (2)
27th Fl Trade Tower 511 Young Dong St,
Gangnam-gu, Seoul, 06164, Korea (South)
Tel.: (82) 260222361
Information Technology Consulting Services
N.A.I.C.S.: 541512

Splunk Services Sweden AB (2)
Vasagatan 7, 111 20, Stockholm, Sweden
Tel.: (46) 723886398
Web Site: http://www.splunk.com
Information Technology Consulting Services
N.A.I.C.S.: 541512

Splunk Services UK Limited (2)
Brunel Building 1 2 Canalside Walk, Lon-
don, W2 1DG, United Kingdom
Tel.: (44) 203 204 4300
Web Site: http://www.splunk.com
Information Technology Consulting Services
N.A.I.C.S.: 541512

**Splunk Technology Consulting (Bei-
jing) Co., Ltd.** (2)
Level 9 China Central Place Tower 2 79
Jianguo Road, Chaoyang District, Beijing,
100025, China
Tel.: (86) 106 580 0518
Web Site: http://www.splunk.com
Emp.: 100
Software Development Services
N.A.I.C.S.: 513210

Subsidiary (Domestic):

VictorOps, Inc. (2)
3400 Valmont Rd, Boulder, CO 80301
Scientific & Technical Consulting Services
N.A.I.C.S.: 541690

Springpath LLC (1)
640 W California Ave Ste 110, Sunnyvale,
CA 94086
Tel.: (669) 777-3800
Web Site:
http://www.sandbox.springpathinc.com
Data Storage Services
N.A.I.C.S.: 518210
Mallik Mahalingam (Founder & CTO)
Krishna Yadappanavar (Co-Founder)
Ravi Parthasarathy (VP-Product Mgmt)
Brett Flinchum (VP-Customer Success)
Suresh Ravoor (VP-Engr)

Starent Networks, Corp. (1)

200 Ames Pond Dr Ste 104, Tewksbury, MA
01876-1291 (100%)
Tel.: (978) 851-1100
Sales Range: $250-299.9 Million
Emp.: 774
Wireless Infrastructure Services & Technol-
ogy
N.A.I.C.S.: 334220

Subsidiary (Non-US):

**Starent Networks Beijing Co.,
Ltd.** (2)
Unit 5 Level 3 Tower E1 The Towers Orien-
tal Plaza, No 1 East Chang An Avenue,
Dong Cheng District, Beijing, 100738,
China (100%)
Tel.: (86) 10 851 80050
Wireless Infrastructure Services & Technol-
ogy
N.A.I.C.S.: 334220

TANDBERG ASA (1)
Philip Pedersens vei 20, 1366, Lysaker,
Norway
Tel.: (47) 67125125
Web Site: http://www.tandberg.com
Sales Range: $800-899.9 Million
Emp.: 1,451
Video Conferencing Equipment & Services
N.A.I.C.S.: 334310

Textlocal Ltd. (1)
Pulford House Bell Meadow Bus Park Park
Lane, Pulford, Chester, CH4 9EP, United
Kingdom
Tel.: (44) 1244752299
Web Site: https://www.textlocal.com
Telecommunication Servicesb
N.A.I.C.S.: 334220
Jason Palgrave-Jones (Mng Dir)
Edu Moura (Comml Dir)
Mark Neath (Assoc Dir-Business Develop-
ment)
Dawn Rowley (Sr Mgr)

ThousandEyes Germany GmbH (1)
Park Ring 20, Garching, 85748, Munich,
Germany
Tel.: (49) 8001873652
Web Site: https://www.thousandeyes.com
Telecommunication Servicesb
N.A.I.C.S.: 334220
Mohit Lad (CEO & Co-Founder)
Ricardo Oliveira (Co-Founder & CTO)

ThousandEyes, Inc. (1)
201 Mission St Ste 1700, San Francisco,
CA 94105
Tel.: (650) 331-0091
Web Site: http://www.thousandeyes.com
Software Publisher
N.A.I.C.S.: 513210
Ricardo Oliveira (Co-Founder & CTO)
Mike Staiger (CFO)
Mohit Lad (Co-Founder & CEO)
Jennifer Taylor (VP-People Ops)
Matt Piercy (VP-Sls-Europe, Middle East &
Africa)
Alexander Anoufriev (Chief Info Security
Officer)
Dave Fraleigh (VP-Solutions Architecture)
Joe Vaccaro (VP-Product)
Murtaza Doctor (VP-Engr)
Sanjay Mehta (CMO)
Trevis Schuh (VP-Customer Engrg)

Truviso LLC (1)
1065 E Hillsdale Blvd Ste 215, Foster City,
CA 94404
Tel.: (650) 242-3500
Software Development Services
N.A.I.C.S.: 541511

Valtix LLC (1)
170 E Tasman Dr, San Jose, CA 95134
Tel.: (650) 420-6014
Web Site: https://www.valtix.com
Cloud Network Security Services
N.A.I.C.S.: 518210

**WebEx Communications Japan,
K.K.** (1)
Midtown Tower 9-7-1 Akasaka, Minato-ku,
Tokyo, 107-6227, Japan
Tel.: (81) 364346044
Web Site: http://www.webex.co.jp
Communication Service
N.A.I.C.S.: 517111

WebEx Communications UK, Ltd. **(1)**
20 Garrick Street, London, WC2E 9BT, United Kingdom
Tel.: (44) 1612500706
Web Site: http://www.webex.co.uk
Video Conferencing & Communications Services
N.A.I.C.S.: 517111

WebEx Communications, Inc. **(1)**
3979 Freedom Cir, Santa Clara, CA 95054
Tel.: (408) 435-7000
Web Site: http://www.webex.com
Sales Range: $350-399.9 Million
Emp.: 2,189
Real Time, Interactive Multimedia Communications Services For Websites
N.A.I.C.S.: 513210

Subsidiary (Non-US):

WebEx Communications Deutschland GmbH **(2)**
Hansaallee 249, Dusseldorf, 40549, Germany
Tel.: (49) 211522820
Web Site: http://www.webex.de
Online Collaboration Tools for Small Businesses
N.A.I.C.S.: 541519

WebEx Communications France SARL **(2)**
1 rue de la Haye, Le Dome, 95731, Paris, France
Tel.: (33) 1 70 99 35 10
Web Site: http://www.webex.fr
Online Collaboration Tools for Small Businesses
N.A.I.C.S.: 541519

Subsidiary (Domestic):

WebExOne **(2)**
1 Van de Graaff Dr, Burlington, MA 01803
Tel.: (781) 565-6000
Web Site: http://www.webex.com
Sales Range: $25-49.9 Million
Emp.: 100
Online Collaboration Tools for Small Businesses
N.A.I.C.S.: 541519

sli.do s.r.o. **(1)**
Vajnorska 100/A, 831 04, Bratislava, Slovakia
Tel.: (421) 23 305 7224
Web Site: https://www.sli.do
Emp.: 200
Polling Services
N.A.I.C.S.: 541910

CISO GLOBAL, INC.
6900 E Camelback Rd Ste 900, Scottsdale, AZ 85251
Tel.: (480) 389-3444 **DE**
Web Site: https://www.ciso.inc
Year Founded: 2019
CISO—(NASDAQ)
Rev.: $46,549,617
Assets: $104,496,815
Liabilities: $28,051,724
Net Worth: $76,445,091
Earnings: ($33,775,182)
Emp.: 443
Fiscal Year-end: 12/31/22
Information Technology Management Services
N.A.I.C.S.: 541512
Ashley Devoto (Pres & Chief Info Security Officer)
David Bennett (COO)
Rory V. Sanchez (Pres)
David G. Jemmett (Chm & CEO)
Jim Kleeman (Exec VP-Bus Dev)
Baan Alsinawi (Chief Compliance Officer)
Deb Smith (CFO)
Kyle Young (VP-Ops)
Brian Yelm (Mng Dir & Exec VP-Sls)

Subsidiaries:

Alpine Security, LLC **(1)**

7 Eagle Ctr Ste B-5, O'Fallon, IL 62269
Tel.: (618) 207-4636
Web Site: http://www.alpinesecurity.com
Computer & Network Security Services
N.A.I.C.S.: 541519

CISTERA NETWORKS, INC.
6509 Windcrest Dr Ste 160, Plano, TX 75024
Tel.: (972) 381-4699 **NV**
Web Site: https://www.cistera.com
Year Founded: 2005
CNWT—(OTCIQ)
Communications Solutions
N.A.I.C.S.: 334220
Gregory Thomas Royal (CEO & CTO)
James T. Miller Jr. (Pres)

CITADEL EXPLORATION, INC.
417 31st St Unit A, Newport Beach, CA 92663
Tel.: (949) 612-8040 **NV**
Web Site: http://www.citadelexploration.com
Year Founded: 2009
COIL—(OTCIQ)
Sales Range: $1-9.9 Million
Emp.: 3
Oil & Gas Exploration
N.A.I.C.S.: 211120
James Walesa (Chm)

CITBA FINANCIAL CORP.
33 N Indiana St, Mooresville, IN 46158
Tel.: (317) 831-0110 **DE**
Web Site: https://www.citizens-banking.com
Year Founded: 1931
CBAF—(OTCIQ)
Rev.: $21,495,000
Assets: $588,975,000
Liabilities: $526,326,000
Net Worth: $62,649,000
Earnings: $5,297,000
Emp.: 130
Fiscal Year-end: 12/31/20
Bank Holding Company
N.A.I.C.S.: 551111
Keith A. Lindauer (Pres & CEO)
Larry R. Heydon (Chm)
John Purdie (Chief Credit Officer & Sr VP)
Pennie Stancombe (Chief HR Officer & Sr VP)
Mike Polley (Sr VP-Ops & Facilities)
Cory Palmer (CIO & Sr VP)
Mark Lemieux (Chief Experience Officer & Sr VP)
Beth Pedersen (CFO & Sr VP)

Subsidiaries:

Citizens Bank **(1)**
33 N Indiana St, Mooresville, IN 46158
Tel.: (317) 831-0110
Web Site: http://www.citizens-banking.com
Sales Range: $50-74.9 Million
Emp.: 150
Commercial Banking Services
N.A.I.C.S.: 522110
John Fleener (CFO & VP)
Penny Stancombe (VP-HR)

CITI TRENDS INC.
104 Coleman Blvd, Savannah, GA 31408
Tel.: (912) 236-1561 **DE**
Web Site: https://www.cititrends.com
Year Founded: 1946
CTRN—(NASDAQ)
Rev.: $795,011,000
Assets: $544,258,000
Liabilities: $377,814,000
Net Worth: $166,444,000
Earnings: $58,892,000
Emp.: 2,700
Fiscal Year-end: 01/28/23

Family Apparel & Accessories Retailer
N.A.I.C.S.: 458110
Peter R. Sachse (Chm)
Lisa A. Powell (Chief Mdsg Officer & Exec VP)
Kenneth D. Seipel (Interim CEO)
Charles J. Hynes (Sr VP-Supply Chain)
Heather L. Plutino (CFO, Principal Acctg Officer & Exec VP)

CITIGROUP INC.
388 Greenwich St, New York, NY 10013
Tel.: (212) 559-1000 **DE**
Web Site: https://www.citigroup.com
Year Founded: 1865
C—(NYSE)
Rev.: $133,258,000,000
Assets: $2,411,834,000,000
Liabilities: $2,205,583,000,000
Net Worth: $206,251,000,000
Earnings: $9,228,000,000
Emp.: 239,000
Fiscal Year-end: 12/31/23
Financial Investment Services
N.A.I.C.S.: 551111
Jane Nind Fraser (CEO)
Peter Babej (CEO-Asia Pacific)
Zdenek Turek (Chief Risk Officer)
Mark A. L. Mason (CFO)
Anand Selvakesari (COO)
Sara Wechter (Head-HR)
Ernesto Torres Cantu (CEO-Latin America & Head-International)
Andy Sieg (Head-Wealth)
Tim Ryan (Head-Technology & Bus Enablement)
Vis Raghavan (Vice Chm & Head-Banking)
Andrew Morton (Head-Markets)
Shahmir Khaliq (Head-Svcs)
John C. Dugan (Chm)

Subsidiaries:

Afore Banamex, S.A. de C.V. **(1)**
Av Paseo de la Reforma N 381 Planta Baja, Col Cuauhtemoc Alcaldia Cuauhtemoc, 06500, Mexico, Mexico
Tel.: (52) 5522623673
Web Site: https://www.aforebanamex.com.mx
Financial Services
N.A.I.C.S.: 522320

Banamex USA Bancorp **(1)**
2029 Century Park E 42nd Fl, Los Angeles, CA 90067
Tel.: (310) 203-3400
Banking Services
N.A.I.C.S.: 522110

Banco Citibank S.A. **(1)**
Avenida Paulista 1 111, Sao Paulo, 01311-920, Brazil **(100%)**
Tel.: (55) 1140093000
Web Site: https://corporateportal.brazil.citibank.com
Sales Range: $900-999.9 Million
Emp.: 2,500
Retail & Corporate Banking Services
N.A.I.C.S.: 522110

Subsidiary (Domestic):

Citibank Leasing S.A.-Arrendamento Mercantil **(2)**
Avenue Paulista 1111 12 Andar, Sao Paulo, 01311-920, Brazil
Tel.: (55) 1140093000
Commercial Banking Services
N.A.I.C.S.: 522110

Citibank-Distribuidora de Titulos e Valores Mobiliarios S.A. **(2)**
Avenida Paulista 1111 2Â Andar Parte, Sao Paulo, 01311-920, Brazil
Tel.: (55) 1132327603
Commercial Banking Services
N.A.I.C.S.: 522110

Banco de Honduras S.A. **(1)**

Bulevar Suyapa y Colonia Loma Linda, Tegucigalpa, 3434, Honduras **(97.4%)**
Tel.: (504) 22900100
Web Site: http://www.bancodehonduras.citibank.com
Sales Range: $50-74.9 Million
Emp.: 80
Commercial Bank
N.A.I.C.S.: 522110

Bank Handlowy w Warszawie S.A. **(1)**
Ul Senatorska 16, 00-923, Warsaw, Poland
Tel.: (48) 226577200
Financial Services
N.A.I.C.S.: 522320

CFJ G.K. **(1)**
Shinjuku Eastside Square 6-27-30 Shinjuku, Shinjuku-ku, Tokyo, 160-8812, Japan
Tel.: (81) 367768200
Financial Services
N.A.I.C.S.: 522320

CIGPF LTDA en Liquidacion **(1)**
CA 7 33 42 Piso 7, Bogota, Colombia
Tel.: (57) 17485000
Financial Management Services
N.A.I.C.S.: 541611

Citi Cards Canada Inc. **(1)**
5900 Hurontario Street, Mississauga, L5R 0B8, ON, Canada
Tel.: (905) 285-7309
Credit Card Services
N.A.I.C.S.: 522210

Citi Consumer Banking **(1)**
388 Greenwich St, New York, NY 10013 **(100%)**
Tel.: (212) 559-1000
Sales Range: $15-24.9 Billion
Commercial & Personal Investment Banking & Consumer Lending Services
N.A.I.C.S.: 522110
Manuel Medina-Mora (Global CEO)
Michael Corbat Corbat (CEO)

Subsidiary (Domestic):

CitiFinancial Credit Company **(2)**
6460 Las Colinas Blvd, Irving, TX 75039 **(100%)**
Tel.: (410) 332-3000
Sales Range: $300-349.9 Million
Emp.: 900
Consumer Financial Services
N.A.I.C.S.: 522291

CitiMortgage, Inc. **(2)**
1000 Technology Dr, O'Fallon, MO 63368-2240
Tel.: (800) 283-7918
Web Site: http://www.citimortgage.com
Sales Range: $125-149.9 Million
Residential Mortgage Services
N.A.I.C.S.: 522310
Jane Nind Fraser (Pres)

Division (Domestic):

Citibank, N.A. **(2)**
399 Park Ave, New York, NY 10022 **(100%)**
Tel.: (212) 559-7517
Web Site: http://www.citibank.com
Sales Range: $800-899.9 Million
Savings, Loans, Commercial & Investment Banking Services
N.A.I.C.S.: 522110

Subsidiary (Non-US):

Citibank (China) Co., Ltd. **(3)**
Citi Tower No 33 Hua Yuan Shi Qiao Road, Lu Jia Zui Finance and Trade Zone, Shanghai, 200120, China
Tel.: (86) 212 896 6000
Web Site: https://www.citi.com.cn
Commercial Banking Services
N.A.I.C.S.: 522110

Citibank Maghreb **(3)**
Zenith Millenium Lotissement Attaoufik Immeuble 1, Sidi Maarouf, 20190, Casablanca, Morocco
Tel.: (212) 522489600
Web Site: https://www.citigroup.com
Emp.: 56
Commercial Banking Services
N.A.I.C.S.: 522110

Citigroup Inc.—(Continued)

Hasna Boufkiri *(Officer-Pub Affairs)*

Subsidiary (Domestic):

Citibank Overseas Investment Corporation **(3)**
1 Penns Way Ste 1, New Castle, DE 19720
Tel.: (302) 323-3100
Emp.: 7
Commercial Banking Services
N.A.I.C.S.: 522110

Subsidiary (Non-US):

Bank Handlowy w Warszawie S.A. **(4)**
ul Senatorska 16, 00-923, Warsaw, Poland
Tel.: (48) 22 657 7200
Web Site: https://www.citibank.pl
Commercial Banking Services
N.A.I.C.S.: 522110
Slawomir S. Sikora *(Pres)*
Barbara Sobala *(VP)*
Natalia Bozek *(VP)*
Maciej Kropidlowski *(VP)*
James Foley *(Member-Mgmt Bd)*
Katarzyna Majewska *(Member-Mgmt Bd)*
Dennis Hussey *(VP)*

Subsidiary (Domestic):

CJP Holdings Inc. **(4)**
2083 Hwy 92 S, Fayetteville, GA 30215
Tel.: (404) 247-8524
Emp.: 3
Holding Company
N.A.I.C.S.: 551112

Subsidiary (Non-US):

Canada Square Operations Limited **(4)**
Citigroup Centre 25 Canada Square, London, E14 5LB, United Kingdom
Tel.: (44) 2895954174
Financial Processing & Insurance Services
N.A.I.C.S.: 523160

Citi Overseas Investments Bahamas Inc. **(4)**
110 Thompson Blvd, Nassau, C5, Bahamas
Tel.: (242) 302 8524
Holding Company
N.A.I.C.S.: 551112
Margaret Butler *(Pres)*

Subsidiary (Non-US):

Citigroup Global Markets Finance Corporation & Co. beschrankt haftende KG **(5)**
Reuterweg 16, Frankfurt am Main, Germany
Tel.: (49) 69 1366 1273
Holding Company
N.A.I.C.S.: 551112
Theo Aschenbruecker *(Controller)*

Subsidiary (Domestic):

Citigroup Global Markets Deutschland AG **(6)**
Reuterweg 16, PO Box 11 03 33, 60323, Frankfurt, Germany
Tel.: (49) 6913660
Sales Range: $650-699.9 Million
Financial Services
N.A.I.C.S.: 523150

Subsidiary (Non-US):

Citibank Berhad **(4)**
165 Jalan Ampang, PO Box 11725, 50450, Kuala Lumpur, Malaysia
Tel.: (60) 32 383 0000
Web Site: https://www.citibank.com.my
Commercial Banking Services
N.A.I.C.S.: 522110

Citicorp Finance (India) Limited **(4)**
B7 5th Floor Nirlon Knowledge Park, Goregaon East, Mumbai, 400063, India
Tel.: (91) 2261757241
Web Site: https://www.citicorpfinance.co.in
Commercial Banking Services
N.A.I.C.S.: 522110

Representative Office (Non-US):

Citibank, N.A. **(3)**

Edificio Plaza Panama Calle 50 Piso 11, Panama, 0831 00555, Panama **(100%)**
Tel.: (507) 2105900
Web Site: http://www.latinamerica.citibank.com
Emp.: 255
Full Banking Services
N.A.I.C.S.: 522299

Citibank, N.A. **(3)**
PALIC Building Level 1 Alameda Manuel Enrique Araujo y, Calle Nueva No 1 Col Escalon, San Salvador, El Salvador **(100%)**
Tel.: (503) 22112855
Web Site: https://www.citigroup.com
Sales Range: $25-49.9 Million
Emp.: 100
Commercial Banking Services
N.A.I.C.S.: 522110

Citibank, N.A. **(3)**
3a Avenue 13-78 zone 10 Citi Tower Building Level 1, Nivel 15, 01010, Guatemala, Guatemala **(100%)**
Tel.: (502) 23368001
Web Site: https://www.citigroup.com
Sales Range: $25-49.9 Million
Emp.: 80
Banking, Insurance & Investment Services
N.A.I.C.S.: 522110

Branch (Domestic):

Citibank, N.A. Puerto Rico **(3)**
235 Calle Federico Costa Ste 315, Hato Rey, PR 00918
Tel.: (787) 766-2029
Web Site: http://www.latam.citi.com
Sales Range: $200-249.9 Million
Emp.: 100
Corporate & Investment Banking, Transaction, Finance & Treasury Services
N.A.I.C.S.: 523150
Guillermo Gomez *(Pres)*

Subsidiary (Non-US):

Citicorp International Limited **(3)**
47th-48th Floor Citibank Tower Citibank Plaza 3 Garden Road, Central, China (Hong Kong)
Tel.: (852) 2868 6666
Investment Banking Services
N.A.I.C.S.: 523150
Curt Engler *(Head-Execution Svcs-Asia Pacific)*
Richard Heyes *(Head-Equities-Asia Pacific)*

Diners Club Pty Limited **(3)**
L 10 2 Park St, Sydney, 2000, NSW, Australia
Tel.: (61) 386432210
Web Site: https://www.dinersclub.com.au
Emp.: 4
Consumer Lending Services
N.A.I.C.S.: 522291

Citi Fund Services Ohio, Inc. **(1)**
3435 Stelzer Rd, Columbus, OH 43219
Tel.: (614) 470-8000
Information Technology Consulting Services
N.A.I.C.S.: 541512

Citi Global Cards **(1)**
399 Park Ave, New York, NY 10022 **(100%)**
Tel.: (212) 559-1000
Web Site: http://www.citi.com
Sales Range: $15-24.9 Billion
Emp.: 3,000
Credit Card Issuing & Management Services
N.A.I.C.S.: 522210
Jud Linville *(CEO)*

Subsidiary (Domestic):

Citibank (South Dakota), N.A. **(2)**
701 E 60th St N, Sioux Falls, SD 57117-1251 **(100%)**
Tel.: (605) 331-2626
Web Site: http://www.citicards.com
Sales Range: $400-449.9 Million
Emp.: 1,583
Consumer Credit Card Issuing & Services
N.A.I.C.S.: 522210

Citi Global Wealth Management **(1)**
399 Park Ave, New York, NY 10043 **(100%)**

Tel.: (212) 559-1000
Sales Range: $5-14.9 Billion
Wealth Management Services
N.A.I.C.S.: 523940
John Cardito *(Mgr-Unsecured Program & Head-Credit Process)*

Unit (Domestic):

Citigroup Private Bank **(2)**
153 E 53rd St 16/F Zone 19, New York, NY 10022
Tel.: (212) 559-9124
Web Site: http://www.citigroup.com
Sales Range: $650-699.9 Million
Investment Management Services for Individuals
N.A.I.C.S.: 523999
Ida Liu *(Head)*

Citi Institutional Clients Group **(1)**
399 Park Ave, New York, NY 10043 **(100%)**
Tel.: (212) 559-1000
Web Site: https://icg.citi.com
Emp.: 100
Corporate & Investment Banking, Securities Trading, Transaction & Alternative Investment Services
N.A.I.C.S.: 523150
Francis Genesi *(CFO)*
Stuart Riley *(Head-Ops & Tech)*

Citi International Financial Services, LLC **(1)**
235 Parque Las Americas Federico Costa, San Juan, PR 00918
Tel.: (787) 766-3995
Emp.: 96
Financial & Investment Brokerage Services
N.A.I.C.S.: 524210
Armando Silva *(Pres)*

Citi Islamic Investment Bank EC **(1)**
PO Box 548, Manama, 973, Bahrain **(100%)**
Tel.: (973) 17588330
Web Site: http://www.citiislamic.com
Sales Range: $75-99.9 Million
Emp.: 20
Securities Brokerage, Trade Finance, Fund Management
N.A.I.C.S.: 523150

Citi Ventures, Inc. **(1)**
3101 Park Blvd, Palo Alto, CA 94301
Tel.: (650) 798-8140
Financial Management Services
N.A.I.C.S.: 551112
Deborah C. Hopkins *(Founder, Chm & CEO)*
Deborah C. Hopkins *(Chm)*

CitiFinancial Canada East Corp. **(1)**
75 Elizabeth Dr, PO Box 384, Gander, A1V 1J9, NL, Canada
Tel.: (709) 256-4891
Web Site: http://www.citifinancial.ca
Sales Range: $25-49.9 Million
Emp.: 5
Loan Broker
N.A.I.C.S.: 522310

CitiFinancial Europe plc **(1)**
Citigroup Centre Canada Square Canary Wharf, London, E14 5LB, United Kingdom
Tel.: (44) 2075087706
Financial Consulting Services
N.A.I.C.S.: 523940

Citibanamex Seguros, S.A. de C.V. **(1)**
Av Revolucion 1267 Piso 13, Col Los Alpes Alcaldia Alvaro Obregon, 01010, Mexico, Mexico
Tel.: (52) 5512268100
Web Site: https://www.segurosbanamex.com.mx
Financial Services
N.A.I.C.S.: 522320

Citibank (Costa Rica) S.A. **(1)**
Edificio Citibank Rohrmoser frente a Plaza Mayor, Rhormoser, San Jose, Costa Rica **(100%)**
Tel.: (506) 22010800
Web Site: http://www.bancocmb.fi.cr
Sales Range: $25-49.9 Million
Emp.: 80
Commercial Banking Services

N.A.I.C.S.: 522110

Citibank (Hong Kong) Limited **(1)**
50/F Champion Tower 3 Garden Road, Central, China (Hong Kong) **(100%)**
Tel.: (852) 28688888
Web Site: http://www.citibank.com.hk
Commercial Banking Services
N.A.I.C.S.: 522110
Peter Babej *(CEO-Asia Pacific)*
Peter Babej *(CEO-Asia Pacific)*

Citibank Canada **(1)**
Citigroup Place 123 Front Street W Suite 1900, Toronto, M5J 2M3, ON, Canada
Tel.: (416) 947-5500
Web Site: http://www.citibank.ca
Sales Range: $75-99.9 Million
Emp.: 300
Commercial Banking Services
N.A.I.C.S.: 522110
John Hastings *(CEO)*

Citibank Europe plc **(1)**
1 North Wall Quay, Dublin, Ireland
Tel.: (353) 1 622 2000
Web Site: http://www.citigroup.com
Sales Range: $150-199.9 Million
Emp.: 1,600
Financial Services
N.A.I.C.S.: 522110
Zdenek Turek *(CEO)*

Subsidiary (Non-US):

Citibank (Switzerland) AG **(2)**
Prime Tower Hardstrasse 201, PO Box 8010, 8010, Zurich, Switzerland **(100%)**
Tel.: (41) 587505000
Web Site: https://www.citigroup.com
Corporate & Investment Banking Services
N.A.I.C.S.: 523150
David Livingstone *(CEO-Europe, Middle East, and Africa)*

Representative Office (Non-US):

Citibank Europe plc - Finland Representative Office **(2)**
Aleksanterinkatu 48 A, 00100, Helsinki, Finland
Tel.: (358) 934887101
Web Site: http://www.citigroup.com
Emp.: 30
International Banking
N.A.I.C.S.: 522299

Citibank Europe plc - France Representative Office **(2)**
21-25 rue Balzac, 75406, Paris, Cedex 08, France
Tel.: (33) 170755000
Web Site: https://www.citigroup.com
Sales Range: $76 00.0 Million
Emp.: 200
Banking Services
N.A.I.C.S.: 522299
Cecile Ratcliffe *(Chief Country Officer)*

Citibank Europe plc, organizacni slozka **(2)**
Bucharova 2641/14, 158 02, Prague, Czech Republic
Tel.: (420) 233061111
Web Site: https://www.citigroup.com
Sales Range: $400-449.9 Million
Emp.: 900
Commericial Banking
N.A.I.C.S.: 522110
Philip Wilhelm *(Mng Dir-Fin)*

Subsidiary (Non-US):

Citibank Nigeria Limited **(2)**
Charles S Sankey House 27 Kofo Abayomi Street, Victoria Island, Lagos, Nigeria
Tel.: (234) 12798400
Web Site: https://www.citigroup.com
Emp.: 248
Banking Services
N.A.I.C.S.: 522110
Olayemi Cardoso *(Chm)*
Akinsowon Dawodu *(CEO)*
Funmi Ogunlesi *(Exec Dir)*
Nneka Enwereji *(Head-Global Subsidiaries Grp & Exec Dir)*
Oluwole Awotundun *(Exec Dir & Country Mgr-Risk)*
Bayo Adeyemo *(Treas & Head-Markets)*
Aderonke Adetoro *(Country Mgr-Securities)*

Olusola Fagbure (Sec)
Gboyega Oloyede (Officer-HR)
Sharaf Muhammed (CFO)
Lola Oyeka (Officer-Pub Affairs)

Representative Office (Non-US):

Citibank United Arab Emirates (2)
Dubai International Financial Centre Building 2 Floor 3 & 7, PO Box 506560, Dubai, United Arab Emirates
Tel.: (971) 143114000
Web Site: https://www.citigroup.com
Sales Range: $400-449.9 Million
Emp.: 1,000
Full Banking Services
N.A.I.C.S.: 522110
Shamsa Al-Falasi (CEO)

Citibank Investments Limited (1)
Citigroup Centre Canada Square Canary Wharf, London, E14 5LB, United Kingdom
Tel.: (44) 2079864000
Insurance & Financial Services
N.A.I.C.S.: 524298

Citibank Korea Inc. (1)
50 Saemunan-ro, Jongno-gu, Seoul, 100-180, Korea (South) **(100%)**
Tel.: (82) 234552114
Web Site: http://www.citibank.co.kr
Sales Range: $1-4.9 Billion
Emp.: 3,900
International Banking
N.A.I.C.S.: 522299
Myung-soon Yoo (CEO)
Valentin Valderrabano (Exec VP-Consumer Banking Grp)
Roman Labutin (Exec VP-Fin Div)
Hae Soon Hwang (Compliance Officer)
Hee Sup Park (Chief Information Security Officer & Chief Privacy Officer)
Ji Yong Um (Exec VP-Markets Div)
Kyoung Ho Kim (Exec VP-Corp Banking Grp)

Citibank Singapore Ltd. (1)
Robinson Road, PO Box 356, Singapore, 900706, Singapore **(100%)**
Tel.: (65) 62255225
Web Site: https://www.citibank.com.sg
Sales Range: $1-4.9 Billion
Emp.: 8,000
Commercial Banking Services
N.A.I.C.S.: 522110

Citibank Taiwan Limited (1)
No 8 Siangyang Rd, Jhongjheng District, Taipei, 100, Taiwan
Tel.: (886) 22 371 5181
Web Site: http://www.citibank.com.tw
Sales Range: $250-299.9 Million
Emp.: 5,800
Banking Services
N.A.I.C.S.: 522110

Citibank Tanzania Limited (1)
Citibank House Plot 1962 Toure Drive Oyster Bay, PO Box 71625, Dar es Salaam, Tanzania
Tel.: (255) 222211200
Financial Services
N.A.I.C.S.: 522320

Citibank del Peru S.A. (1)
Avenida Canaval y Moreyra 480 piso 3, San Isidro, Lima, Peru
Tel.: (51) 12152080
Financial Services
N.A.I.C.S.: 522320

Citibank-Colombia S.A. (1)
Carrera 9 A No 99 - 02, Bogota, Colombia **(100%)**
Tel.: (57) 16383838
Web Site: https://www.citigroup.com
Sales Range: $350-399.9 Million
Emp.: 860
Commercial Banking Services
N.A.I.C.S.: 522110

Citicorp Data Systems Incorporated (1)
100 Citibank Dr, San Antonio, TX 78245
Tel.: (210) 677-7443
Commercial Banking Services
N.A.I.C.S.: 522110

Citicorp Insurance Agency Co., Ltd. (1)

13f 16 Nanking E Rd Sec 4, Taipei, 10553, Taipei, Taiwan
Tel.: (886) 225785662
Insurance Related Services
N.A.I.C.S.: 524210

Citicorp Securities International, Inc. (1)
10th Floor Citibank Tower 8741 Paseo De Roxas, Makati, 1227, Philippines
Tel.: (63) 28947823
Web Site: http://www.citibank.com.ph
Sales Range: $400-449.9 Million
Emp.: 1,400
Full Banking Services
N.A.I.C.S.: 522299

Citiflight, Inc. (1)
79 Tower Rd Hngr Ste 2, White Plains, NY 10604
Tel.: (914) 989-2300
Air Freight Transportation Services
N.A.I.C.S.: 481112

Citigroup Acquisition LLC (1)
399 Park Ave, New York, NY 10022
Tel.: (212) 816-0234
Commercial Banking Services
N.A.I.C.S.: 522110

Citigroup Corporate & Investment Banking (1)
388 Greenwich St, New York, NY 10013
Tel.: (212) 816-6000
Web Site: http://www.citigroup.com
Sales Range: $650-699.9 Million
Corporate & Investment Banking Services
N.A.I.C.S.: 523150

Subsidiary (Domestic):

Citigroup Global Markets Holdings, Inc. (2)
388 Greenwich St 38th Fl, New York, NY 10013
Tel.: (212) 816-6000
Sales Range: $1-4.9 Billion
Holding Company
N.A.I.C.S.: 551112

Subsidiary (Non-US):

Citigroup Global Markets (Proprietary) Limited (3)
Citi Plaza 1st Floor 145 West Street, Sandown Sandton, 2196, Johannesburg, South Africa **(100%)**
Tel.: (27) 119441000
Web Site: http://www.citi.com
Sales Range: $150-199.9 Million
Emp.: 300
Full Banking Services
N.A.I.C.S.: 522299
Naveed Riaz (CEO)

Citigroup Global Markets Europe Limited (3)
Citigroup Centre, Canada Square Canary Wharf, London, E14 5LB, United Kingdom
Tel.: (44) 2079864000
Web Site: http://www.citi.com
Sales Range: $1-4.9 Billion
Emp.: 3,620
Investment Banking Services
N.A.I.C.S.: 523150

Subsidiary (Domestic):

Citigroup Global Markets Europe Finance Limited (4)
Citigroup Centre Canada Square, Canary Wharf, London, E14 5LB, United Kingdom
Tel.: (44) 2079864000
Web Site: http://www.citi.com
Sales Range: $250-299.9 Million
Holding Company
N.A.I.C.S.: 551112

Citigroup Global Markets Limited (4)
Citigroup Centre 33 Canada Square, Canary Wharf, London, E14 5LB, United Kingdom
Tel.: (44) 2079864000
Web Site: http://www.citi.com
Sales Range: $650-699.9 Million
Investment Banking Services
N.A.I.C.S.: 523150

Subsidiary (Non-US):

Citigroup Global Markets U.K. Equity Limited (4)

Tel.: (44) 2079864000
Web Site: http://www.citi.com
Sales Range: $800-899.9 Million
Securities Brokerage
N.A.I.C.S.: 523150

Joint Venture (Non-US):

Kelda Group Limited (5)
Tel.: (44) 1274600111
Web Site: https://www.keldagroup.com
Emp.: 3,500
Holding Company; Water, Sewage, Environmental & Land Management Services
N.A.I.C.S.: 551112

Unit (Domestic):

Egg and Citi UK Consumer (4)
1 Waterhouse Sq, London, EC1N 2NA, United Kingdom
Tel.: (44) 75262500
Web Site: http://www.egg.com
Sales Range: $900-999.9 Million
Emp.: 2,300
Online Banking Services
N.A.I.C.S.: 522110

Subsidiary (Domestic):

Citigroup Global Markets Inc. (3)
388 Greenwich St, New York, NY 10013
Tel.: (212) 816-6000
Web Site: http://www.citigroup.com
Sales Range: $1-4.9 Billion
Investment Banking & Asset Management Services
N.A.I.C.S.: 523150

Division (Domestic):

Citigroup Capital Strategies Inc. (4)
24022 Calle De La Plata Ste 100, Laguna Hills, CA 92653
Tel.: (949) 206-5000
Sales Range: $100-124.9 Million
Emp.: 50
Investment Banking Services Specializing in Mergers, Acquisitions & Divestitures
N.A.I.C.S.: 523150

Subsidiary (Non-US):

Citigroup Global Markets Mauritius Private Limited (4)
609 St James Court St Denis Street, Port Louis, 97118, Mauritius
Tel.: (230) 210 1178
Investment Banking Services
N.A.I.C.S.: 523150

Joint Venture (Domestic):

Morgan Stanley Smith Barney LLC (4)
1585 Broadway Ave, New York, NY 10036
Tel.: (212) 761-4000
Web Site: http://www.morganstanleysmithbarney.com
Sales Range: $1-4.9 Billion
Emp.: 12,400
Wealth Management Services; Owned by Morgan Stanley 51% & Citigroup Inc. 49%
N.A.I.C.S.: 523940

Subsidiary (Domestic):

Structured Products Corp. (3)
388 Greenwich St, New York, NY 10013
Tel.: (212) 723-4070
Trust & Fund Management Services
N.A.I.C.S.: 523940
Peter Aherne (Pres)

Citigroup Corporate Aviation (1)
79 Tower Rd, White Plains, NY 10604 **(100%)**
Tel.: (914) 989-2300
Sales Range: $350-399.9 Million
Emp.: 35
Non-Scheduled Passenger Aviation Services
N.A.I.C.S.: 481211
James Moore (Mng Dir)
Alan Goldstein (Treas)

Citigroup Derivatives Markets Inc. (1)
130 Cheshire Ln Ste 102, Minnetonka, MN 55305-1052

Tel.: (952) 475-5500
Emp.: 50
Asset Management Services
N.A.I.C.S.: 531390
Jennifer Anfang (Office Mgr)

Citigroup Energy Inc. (1)
2800 Post Oak Blvd Ste 500, Houston, TX 77056-6156
Tel.: (713) 752-5200
Electric Power Distr
N.A.I.C.S.: 221122

Citigroup First Investment Management Americas LLC (1)
388 Greenwich St, New York, NY 10013
Tel.: (212) 723-4529
Financial Investment Management Services
N.A.I.C.S.: 523940

Citigroup Global Markets Asia Limited (1)
50th Floor Citibank Tower Citibank Plaza 3 Garden Road, Central, China (Hong Kong)
Tel.: (852) 28688888
Financial Management Services
N.A.I.C.S.: 551112

Citigroup Global Markets Australia Pty Limited (1)
Level 26 Citigroup Centre 2 Park St, Sydney, 2000, NSW, Australia
Tel.: (61) 282251000
Banking Services
N.A.I.C.S.: 522110
Ian Campbell (Head-Debt Capital Markets-Australia & New Zealand)

Citigroup Global Markets India Private Limited (1)
1202 12th Floor First International Financial Centre G Block, Bandra Kurla Complex Bandra East, Mumbai, 400 051, India
Tel.: (91) 2261759999
Financial Services
N.A.I.C.S.: 522320

Citigroup Global Markets Korea Securities Limited (1)
17th Floor Citibank Building 39 Da-dong Jung-gu, Seoul, 100180, Korea (South)
Tel.: (82) 237050600
Banking & Investment Services
N.A.I.C.S.: 523150

Citigroup Global Markets Switzerland Holding GmbH (1)
Hofstrasse 1A, 6300, Zug, Switzerland
Tel.: (41) 417291070
Holding Company
N.A.I.C.S.: 551112

Citigroup Investor Services, Inc. (1)
105 Eisenhower Pkwy Ste 2, Roseland, NJ 07068
Tel.: (973) 461-2500
Web Site: http://www.citi.com
Sales Range: $800-899.9 Million
Emp.: 5,000
Fund Management & Alternative Investment Services
N.A.I.C.S.: 525910

Citigroup Japan Holdings Corp. (1)
Otemachi Park Building 1-1-1, Otemachi Chiyoda ku, Tokyo, 100-8132, Japan
Tel.: (81) 367766600
Web Site: http://www.citigroup.jp
Financial Services
N.A.I.C.S.: 523999

Subsidiary (Domestic):

Citibank Japan Ltd. (2)
Otemachi Park Building 1-1-1 Otemachi, Chiyoda-ku, Tokyo, 100-8132, Japan
Tel.: (81) 367765000
Web Site: http://www.citigroup.jp
Sales Range: $300-349.9 Million
Emp.: 1,809
Commericial Banking
N.A.I.C.S.: 522110

Citigroup Capital Partners Japan (2)
Shin-Marunouchi Building 1-5-1 Marunouchi, Chiyoda-ku, Tokyo, 100-6520, Japan **(100%)**
Tel.: (81) 362706970
Web Site: http://www.npi.co.jp
Sales Range: $1-4.9 Billion
Equity Investment & Management Services
N.A.I.C.S.: 523999

Citigroup Inc.—(Continued)

Subsidiary (Non-US):

Citigroup Capital UK Limited (3)
100 Pall Mall, London, SW1Y 5NN, United Kingdom
Tel.: (44) 2077997700
Sales Range: $75-99.9 Million
Emp.: 10
Equity Investment & Management Services
N.A.I.C.S.: 523999

Holding (Domestic):

EMI Group Limited (4)
27 Wrights Lane, London, W8 5SW, United Kingdom
Tel.: (44) 2077957000
Sales Range: $1-4.9 Billion
Holding Company; Music Recording, Publishing & Distr
N.A.I.C.S.: 551112

Subsidiary (Domestic):

Citigroup Global Markets Japan Inc. (2)
Otemachi Park Building 1-1-1 Otemachi, Chiyoda-ku, Tokyo, 100-8132, Japan
Tel.: (81) 36,776 8800
Web Site: https://www.citigroup.jp
Sales Range: $400-449.9 Million
Investment Banking Services
N.A.I.C.S.: 523150
Tatsuo Tanaka (Chm)
Lee Robert Waite (Pres & CEO)
Fumiaki Kurahara (Vice Chm)

Citigroup Overseas Holdings GK (2)
1 5 1 Marunouchi Shimmarunochi Bldg, Chiyoda-Ku, Tokyo, 100-0005, Japan
Tel.: (81) 362706600
Financial Services
N.A.I.C.S.: 522320

Citigroup Management Corp. (1)
701 E 60th St N, Sioux Falls, SD 57104
Tel.: (605) 331-2632
Emp.: 99
Business Management Services
N.A.I.C.S.: 541611
Reinecke Reinecke (Sr VP)

Citigroup Pty Limited (1)
Level 14 2 Park Street, Sydney, 2000, NSW, Australia
Tel.: (61) 28 225 0615
Web Site: https://www1.citibank.com.au
Commercial Banking Services
N.A.I.C.S.: 522110

Citishare Corporation (1)
388 Greenwich St, New York, NY 10005   (100%)
Tel.: (212) 559-9124
Web Site: http://www.citigroup.com
Sales Range: $10-24.9 Million
Emp.: 60
Electronic Funds Transfer Network, Including Switching
N.A.I.C.S.: 522320

GOVCO, LLC (1)
6601 Glengarry Ave NW, Canton, OH 44718
Tel.: (330) 352-6173
Management Consulting Services
N.A.I.C.S.: 541611

JSC Citibank Kazakhstan (1)
Park Palace Building A 2nd Floor 41A Kazibek bi Street, Almaty, 050010, Kazakhstan
Tel.: (7) 7272980400
Sales Range: $50-74.9 Million
Emp.: 10
Banking Services
N.A.I.C.S.: 522110
Asif Zaidi (CEO)

Latin American Investment Bank Bahamas Limited (1)
Oakes Field New Providence, Nassau, Bahamas
Tel.: (242) 3028650
Holding Company
N.A.I.C.S.: 551111

MRC Holdings, Inc. (1)
1666 E Michael Way, Sandy, UT 84093
Tel.: (801) 571-8459

Holding Company
N.A.I.C.S.: 551112

Ret Participacoes S.A. (1)
R Iguatemi 354, 1451010, Sao Paulo, Brazil
Tel.: (55) 21 3231 8200
Investment Management Service
N.A.I.C.S.: 523940
Adriana Maria Mammocci (CFO)

Seguros e Inversiones, S.A. (1)
Edificio Sisa Km 10 1/2 Carretera A, Santa Tecla, La Libertad, El Salvador
Tel.: (503) 22410000
Web Site: https://www.sisa.com.sv
Insurance Services
N.A.I.C.S.: 524210

TRV Holdings LLC (1)
399 Park Ave, New York, NY 10022
Tel.: (347) 648-4734
Holding Company
N.A.I.C.S.: 551111

Subsidiary (Domestic):

TRV Investments LLC (2)
300 N Westwood Ave, Toledo, OH 43607
Tel.: (419) 535-6868
Web Site: http://www.ohiobelting.com
Power Transmission Equipment Whslr
N.A.I.C.S.: 423840

Subsidiary (Non-US):

Grupo Financiero Banamex, S.A. de C.V. (3)
Actuario Roberto Medellin number 800 Torre Norte 2nd floor, Colonia Santa Faith Alvaro Obregon Mayor's Office, 01210, Mexico, DF, Mexico
Tel.: (52) 5512262626
Web Site: http://www.banamex.com
Rev.: $4,622,890,440
Assets: $70,905,649,500
Liabilities: $61,020,811,320
Net Worth: $9,884,838,180
Earnings: $1,002,079,260
Fiscal Year-end: 12/31/2015
Bank Holding Company
N.A.I.C.S.: 551111

Subsidiary (Domestic):

Acciones y Valores Banamex, S.A. de C.V. (4)
Paseo de la Reforma 398, Colonia Juarez, 06600, Mexico, DF, Mexico   (100%)
Tel.: (52) 55 1226 0819
Web Site: http://www.accival.com.mx
Sales Range: $125-149.9 Million
Emp.: 400
Investment Banking & Securities Brokerage
N.A.I.C.S.: 523150

Banco Nacional de Mexico, S.A. (4)
Isabel la Catolica 44 Col Centro Historico CP, Del Cuauhtemoc, 06000, Mexico, Mexico   (100%)
Tel.: (52) 12268867
Web Site: http://www.banamex.com
Banking Services
N.A.I.C.S.: 522110

Seguros Banamex, S.A. de C.V. (4)
Venustiano Carranza no 63, Col Centro C P, 06000, Mexico, 06000, DF, Mexico   (52%)
Tel.: (52) 5512268100
Web Site: http://www.segurosbanamex.com.mx
Sales Range: $75-99.9 Million
Insurance Services
N.A.I.C.S.: 524298

ZAO Citibank (1)
8-10 biuld 1 Gasheka Street, 125047, Moscow, Russia
Tel.: (7) 4956431699
Web Site: http://www.citibank.ru
Commercial Banking Services
N.A.I.C.S.: 522110
Duscai Evelin (CEO)

CITIUS PHARMACEUTICALS, INC.

11 Commerce Dr 1st Fl, Cranford, NJ 07016
Tel.: (908) 967-6677   NV

Web Site: https://www.citiuspharma.com
Year Founded: 2007
CTXR—(NASDAQ)
Assets: $116,651,751
Liabilities: $42,549,921
Net Worth: $74,101,830
Earnings: ($39,425,839)
Emp.: 23
Fiscal Year-end: 09/30/24
Investment Services
N.A.I.C.S.: 523999
Myron S. Czuczman (Chief Medical Officer & Exec VP)
Myron Z. Holubiak (Vice Chm)
Jay Wadekar (Sr VP-Bus Strategy)
Kelly Creighton (Exec VP-Chemistry, Manufacturing, and Controls)
John Westman (VP-Project Mgmt)
Paul Sowyrda (VP-Business Development & Market Intelligence)
Leonard L. Mazur (Co-Founder, Exec Chm, Chm, CEO & Sec)
Gary F. Talarico (Exec VP-Ops)
Ilanit Allen (VP-Corp Comm)
Catherine Kessler (Exec VP-Regulatory Affairs)
Nikolas Burlew (Exec VP-Quality Assurance)

Subsidiaries:

Citius Oncology, Inc. (1)
No 99 Tiangu 7th Road, Yanta District, Xi'an, 71000, Shanxi, China   (92.3%)
Tel.: (86) 3476270058
Web Site: https://www.citiusonc.com
Assets: $84,368,878
Liabilities: $38,228,539
Net Worth: $46,140,339
Earnings: ($21,148,747)
Fiscal Year-end: 09/30/2024
Investment Services
N.A.I.C.S.: 523999
Xiaofeng Yuan (Chm)
Taylor Zhang (CEO & CFO)

CITIZENS & NORTHERN CORPORATION

Tel.: (570) 724-3411   PA
Web Site: https://www.cnbankpa.com
Year Founded: 1987
CZNC—(NASDAQ)
Rev.: $117,079,000
Assets: $2,454,307,000
Liabilities: $2,204,982,000
Net Worth: $249,325,000
Earnings: $26,618,000
Emp.: 336
Fiscal Year-end: 12/31/22
Bank Holding Company
N.A.I.C.S.: 551111
Susan E. Hartley (Atty)

Subsidiaries:

Citizens & Northern Bank (1)
90-92 Main St, Wellsboro, PA 16901-1517   (100%)
Tel.: (570) 724-3411
Web Site: https://www.cnbankpa.com
Sales Range: $75-99.9 Million
Emp.: 346
State Commercial Banks
N.A.I.C.S.: 522110

Subsidiary (Domestic):

C&N Financial Services Corporation (2)
90-92 Main St, Wellsboro, PA 16901
Tel.: (570) 724-3411
General Insurance Services
N.A.I.C.S.: 524113

CITIZENS BANCORP INVESTMENT, INC.

Tel.: (615) 666-2195   TN
Web Site: http://www.citizens-bank.org
Year Founded: 1986

CBTN—(OTCQX)
Sales Range: $50-74.9 Million
Emp.: 283
Bank Holding Company
N.A.I.C.S.: 551111
Joe Carter (Pres)

Subsidiaries:

Citizens Bank of Lafayette (1)
400 Hwy 52 Bypass W, Lafayette, TN 37083
Tel.: (615) 666-2195
Web Site: http://www.citizens-bank.org
Sales Range: $25-49.9 Million
Emp.: 223
Commercial Banking
N.A.I.C.S.: 522110
Joe Carter (Pres)

CITIZENS BANCORP OF VIRGINIA, INC.

126 S Main St, Blackstone, VA 23824
Tel.: (434) 292-8100
CZBT—(OTCIQ)
Emp.: 82
Banking Services
N.A.I.C.S.: 522110
Charles F. Parker Jr. (Chm)

CITIZENS BANCSHARES CORPORATION

230 Peachtree St Ste 2700, Atlanta, GA 30303
Tel.: (678) 406-4000   GA
Web Site: https://www.ctbconnect.com
Year Founded: 1972
CZBS—(OTCIQ)
Bank Holding Company
N.A.I.C.S.: 551111
Cynthia N. Day (Pres & CEO)
Samuel J. Cox (Exec VP & CFO)
Jason A. Eppenger (Pres-Alabama Market)
Iris D. Goodly (Sr VP, Dir-Client Svcs & Ops)
Farrand O. Logan (Sr VP & Mgr-Comml Banking Div)
Wanda F. Nesbit (Sr VP & Dir-HR)
Moira R. Montgomery (VP, Officer-Compliance & Mgr-Special Projects)
Frederick L. Daniels Jr. (Exec VP & Chief Credit Officer)

Subsidiaries:

Citizens Trust Bank (1)
75 Piedmont Ave, Atlanta, GA 30303
Tel.: (404) 575-8400
Web Site: http://www.ctbconnect.com
Commercial Banking
N.A.I.C.S.: 522110
Cynthia N. Day (Pres & CEO)
Samuel J. Cox (CFO)
Eric D. Wilson (Sr Mgr-Comml Relationship)
Jason A. Eppenger (Pres-Alabama)
Tracey A. Boney (Mgr-Client Relationship)
Frederick L. Daniels Jr. (Chief Credit Officer)

CITIZENS BANK

275 SW 3rd St, Corvallis, OR 97339-0030
Tel.: (541) 752-5161   OR
Web Site: https://www.citizensebank.com
Year Founded: 1957
CZBC—(OTCIQ)
Commercial Banking Services
N.A.I.C.S.: 522110
Curtis Davis (VP & Branch Mgr)
Brande Grassel (Asst Branch Mgr)
Darin McLemore (Officer-Comml Loan & VP)
Janice Stehle (Officer-Comml Loan & VP)

CITIZENS COMMUNITY BANCORP, INC.

2174 EastRidge Ctr, Eau Claire, WI
54701
Tel.: (715) 836-9994   MD
Web Site: https://www.ccf.us
Year Founded: 2006
CZWI—(NASDAQ)
Rev.: $79,827,000
Assets: $1,816,386,000
Liabilities: $1,649,298,000
Net Worth: $167,088,000
Earnings: $17,761,000
Emp.: 210
Fiscal Year-end: 12/31/22
Bank Holding Company
N.A.I.C.S.: 551111
Richard W. McHugh *(Chm)*
Stephen M. Bianchi *(Pres & CEO)*
James S. Broucek *(CFO, Treas, Sec
& Exec VP)*

Subsidiaries:

Citizens Community Federal
N.A.   (1)
219 Fairfax St, Altoona, WI 54720
Tel.: (715) 852-2288
Web Site: http://www.ccf.us
Sales Range: $75-99.9 Million
Federal Savings Bank
N.A.I.C.S.: 522180
Stephen M. Bianchi *(Chm, Pres & CEO)*
James S. Broucek *(CFO)*

Subsidiary (Domestic):

Wells Insurance Agency, Inc.   (2)
53 1st St SW, Wells, MN 56097
Tel.: (941) 922-9357
Web Site: https://jwellsinsurance.com
Insurance Agents
N.A.I.C.S.: 524210

CITIZENS FINANCIAL CORP.
211 3rd St, Elkins, WV 26241
Tel.: (304) 636-4095   DE
Web Site: http://www.citizenswv.com
Year Founded: 1986
CIWV—(OTCIQ)
Bank Holding Company
N.A.I.C.S.: 551111
Kathy Leombruno *(Sr VP & COO)*
Franklin Hinzman *(VP & Chief Lend-
ing Officer)*
Deborah Swiger *(VP-HR & Branch
Ops)*

**CITIZENS FINANCIAL CORPO-
RATION**
12910 Shelbyville Rd Ste 300, Louis-
ville, KY 40243
Tel.: (502) 244-2420   KY
Web Site:
   https://www.citizensfinancial
   corp.com
Year Founded: 1990
CIWV—(OTCIQ)
Offices of Other Holding Companies
N.A.I.C.S.: 551112
Randy Ammon *(CFO)*
Karen Eckel *(Vice Pres-Mktg)*
Shawn Lilley *(Chief Bus Dev Officer)*
John D. Cornett *(COO & Exec VP)*

Subsidiaries:

Citizens Security Life Insurance
Company   (1)
The Marketplace Ste 300 12910 Shelbyville
Rd, Louisville, KY 40243
Tel.: (502) 244-2420
Web Site: http://www.citizenssecuritylife.com
Fire Insurance Services
N.A.I.C.S.: 524113

**CITIZENS FINANCIAL GROUP,
INC.**
1 Citizens Plz, Providence, RI 02903
Tel.: (203) 900-6715   DE
Web Site:
   https://www.citizensbank.com
Year Founded: 1984

CFG—(NYSE)
Rev.: $12,187,000,000
Assets: $221,964,000,000
Liabilities: $197,622,000,000
Net Worth: $24,342,000,000
Earnings: $1,491,000,000
Emp.: 17,570
Fiscal Year-end: 12/31/23
Bank Holding Company
N.A.I.C.S.: 551111
Malcolm D. Griggs *(Chief Risk Offi-
cer)*
Bruce W. Van Saun *(Chm & CEO)*
Elizabeth S. Johnson *(Chief Experi-
ence Officer & Head-Environmental,
Social, and Governance)*
Brendan Coughlin *(Head-Consumer
Banking)*
John F. Woods *(Vice Chm CFO &
Interim Chief Acctg Officer)*
Susan LaMonica *(Chief HR Officer)*
Michael Ruttledge *(CIO)*
Ted Swimmer *(Head-Corp Fin &
Capital Markets)*
Eric J. Schuppenhauer *(Head)*
Polly Klane *(Chief Legal Officer)*
Donald H. McCree III *(Head-Comml
Banking)*

Subsidiaries:

CCO Investment Services Corp.   (1)
770 Legacy Pl MLP240, Dedham, MA
02026
Tel.: (617) 994-7544
Investment Management Service
N.A.I.C.S.: 523940
Priscilla Harlan *(VP & Dir-Phone Bank)*

Citizens Bank, N.A.   (1)
1 Citizens Plz, Providence, RI
02903   (100%)
Tel.: (203) 900-6715
Web Site: http://www.citizensbank.com
Banking Services
N.A.I.C.S.: 522220
Eric Schuppenhauer *(Head-Consumer
Lending)*

Subsidiary (Domestic):

Citizens Asset Finance, Inc.   (2)
71 S Wacker Dr 28th Fl, Chicago, IL 60606
Tel.: (312) 777-3500
Web Site: http://www.rbsassetfinance.com
Bank Lending Services
N.A.I.C.S.: 525990

Subsidiary (Domestic):

DH Capital, LLC   (3)
810 Seventh Ave Ste 2005, New York, NY
10019
Tel.: (212) 774-3720
Portfolio Management
N.A.I.C.S.: 523940
Dean Mann *(Mng Dir)*
Peter Hopper *(Founder)*
Paul Vasilopoulos *(Partner)*

Division (Domestic):

Citizens Bank New Hampshire   (2)
875 Elm St, Manchester, NH
03101   (100%)
Tel.: (603) 634-7090
Web Site: http://www.citizensbank.com
Rev.: $11,900,000
Emp.: 54
Investment Advisory Services
N.A.I.C.S.: 523940

Citizens Bank of Massachusetts   (2)
28 State St, Boston, MA 02109   (100%)
Tel.: (617) 725-5900
Web Site: http://www.citizensbank.com
Sales Range: $50-74.9 Million
Emp.: 100
Banking Services
N.A.I.C.S.: 522110

Citizens Bank of Pennsylvania   (2)
130 N 18th St 1 Logan Sq, Philadelphia, PA
19103   (100%)
Tel.: (215) 977-8460
Commericial Banking
N.A.I.C.S.: 522110

Unit (Domestic):

Citizens Business Capital   (2)
53 State St, Boston, MA 02109
Tel.: (617) 725-5830
Web Site: http://citizensbank.com
Asset-Based Lending Services
N.A.I.C.S.: 522251
Christopher Carmosino *(Pres)*

Subsidiary (Domestic):

Citizens Financial Services
Corporation   (2)
1 Citizens Plz, Providence, RI
02903-1344   (100%)
Tel.: (401) 456-7096
Web Site: http://www.citizensbank.com
Personal & Corporate Financial Services
N.A.I.C.S.: 522310
George Graboys *(CEO)*

Citizens Mortgage Corporation   (2)
875 Elm St, Manchester, NH
03101   (100%)
Tel.: (603) 634-7700
Sales Range: $50-74.9 Million
Mortgage Banking Services
N.A.I.C.S.: 522292
Mark Thompson *(CFO)*
Vincent J. Balsamo Jr. *(Sr VP)*

Unit (Domestic):

Citizens One Card Services   (2)
1000 Lafayette Blvd, Bridgeport, CT 06604
Tel.: (203) 551-2573
Credit Card Issuing Services
N.A.I.C.S.: 522210

Subsidiary (Domestic):

Franklin American Mortgage Co.   (2)
6100 Tower Cir Ste 600, Franklin, TN
37067
Tel.: (615) 778-1000
Bond & Mortgage Companies
N.A.I.C.S.: 522292

Citizens JMP Group, LLC   (1)
600 Montgomery St Ste 1100, San Francisco, CA 94111
Real Estate Financial Services
N.A.I.C.S.: 531312

Citizens JMP Securities, LLC   (1)
450 Park Ave 5th Fl, New York, NY 10022
Tel.: (212) 906-3500
Web Site: https://www.jmpsecurities.com
Real Estate Financial Services
N.A.I.C.S.: 531312

Clarfeld Financial Advisors, LLC   (1)
520 White Plains Rd 3rd Fl, Tarrytown, NY
10591
Tel.: (914) 846-0100
Web Site: https://www.clarfeld.com
Sales Range: $1-9.9 Million
Emp.: 46
Financial Planning & Advisory Services
N.A.I.C.S.: 523940
Robert A. Clarfeld *(Founder & Chm)*

Investors Bancorp, Inc.   (1)
101 JFK Pkwy, Short Hills, NJ 07078
Tel.: (973) 924-5100
Web Site: http://www.myinvestorsbank.com
Rev.: $983,101,000
Assets: $27,806,618,000
Liabilities: $24,868,190,000
Net Worth: $2,938,428,000
Earnings: $313,333,000
Emp.: 1,598
Fiscal Year-end: 12/31/2021
Bank Holding Company
N.A.I.C.S.: 551111
Kevin D. Cummings *(Pres & CEO)*

Subsidiary (Domestic):

Investors Bank   (2)
101 JFK Pkwy, Short Hills, NJ 07078
Tel.: (973) 924-5100
Web Site: http://www.myinvestorsbank.com
Sales Range: $250-299.9 Million
Emp.: 160
Retail & Commercial Banking
N.A.I.C.S.: 522180
William E. Brown *(Chief Retail Banking Offi-
cer)*

Richard S. Spengler *(Chief Lending Officer
& Exec VP)*
Paul Kalamaras *(Chief Risk Officer & Exec
VP)*
P. Sean Burke *(CFO & Exec VP)*
Domenick A. Cama *(Pres & COO)*
Kari Pencek *(Mgr-Comm)*
Marianne Wade *(Dir-Fin Reporting)*

Subsidiary (Domestic):

Investors Financial Group, Inc.   (3)
1100 S Clinton Ave Ste C, Dunn, NC 28335
Tel.: (910) 892-7340
Insurance Agency & Brokerage Services
N.A.I.C.S.: 524210
Mike Lee *(Pres)*

Investors Financial Services, Inc.   (3)
10235 W Mlto York Ste 410, Houston, TX
77040
Tel.: (713) 339-3900
Emp.: 4
Account Management Services
N.A.I.C.S.: 541219

JMP Group LLC   (1)
600 Montgomery St Ste 1100, San Fran-
cisco, CA 94111
Tel.: (415) 835-8900
Web Site: http://www.jmpg.com
Rev.: $113,237,000
Assets: $241,331,000
Liabilities: $178,923,000
Net Worth: $62,408,000
Earnings: ($4,697,000)
Emp.: 180
Fiscal Year-end: 12/31/2020
Holding Company; Investment Banking &
Asset Management Services
N.A.I.C.S.: 551112
Raymond S. Jackson *(CFO)*
Thomas R. Wright *(COO-JMP Securities &
Dir-Equities-JMP Securities)*
Gavin Slader *(Co-Head-Investment Banking
Grp & Head-Mergers & Acquisitions)*
Jonathan Dever *(Co-Head-Investment
Banking Grp & Head-Fin Svcs & Real Es-
tate)*

Subsidiary (Domestic):

JMP Group Inc.   (2)
600 Montgomery St Ste 1100, San Fran-
cisco, CA 94111
Tel.: (415) 835-8900
Web Site: http://www.jmpg.com
Sales Range: $150-199.9 Million
Holding Company
N.A.I.C.S.: 551112

Subsidiary (Domestic):

Harvest Capital Strategies LLC   (3)
600 Montgomery St Ste 1100, San Fran-
cisco, CA 94111
Tel.: (415) 835-3900
Web Site: http://www.jmpg.com
Hedge Funds & Asset Management Ser-
vices
N.A.I.C.S.: 523999
Craig Johnson *(Chm)*

JMP Asset Management LLC   (3)
600 Montgomery St Ste 1100, San Fran-
cisco, CA 94111
Tel.: (415) 835-8900
Web Site: https://www.jmpg.com
Investment Management Service
N.A.I.C.S.: 523940
Kent Ledbetter *(Pres)*
Jim Fowler *(Mng Dir)*
James Wilson *(Mng Dir)*

JMP Securities LLC   (3)
600 Montgomery St Ste 1100, San Fran-
cisco, CA 94111
Tel.: (415) 835-8900
Web Site: http://www.jmpsecurities.com
Investment Banking & Securities Brokerage
Services
N.A.I.C.S.: 523150
Maneet S. Saroya *(Executives)*
Mark L. Lehmann *(CEO)*

Citizens Financial Group, Inc.—(Continued)

Branch (Domestic):

JMP Securities LLC - New York   **(4)**
450 Park Ave 5th Fl, New York, NY 10022
Tel.: (212) 906-3500
Web Site: http://www.jmpc.com
Emp.: 40
Investment Banking & Securities Brokerage Services
N.A.I.C.S.: 523150

Subsidiary (Domestic):

JMP Realty Trust Inc.   **(2)**
600 Montgomery St Ste 1100, San Francisco, CA 94111
Tel.: (415) 835-3900
Web Site: https://www.jmpg.com
Real Estate Investment Services
N.A.I.C.S.: 531210

New England Acceptance Corporation   **(1)**
875 Elm St, Manchester, NH 03101
Tel.: (603) 634-7000
Financial Services
N.A.I.C.S.: 541611

RBS Citizens Insurance Agency, Inc.   **(1)**
1215 Superior Ave, Cleveland, OH 44114
Tel.: (216) 566-7049
Insurance Management Services
N.A.I.C.S.: 524298

Trinity Capital, LLC   **(1)**
11755 Wilshire Blvd # 2450, Los Angeles, CA 90025
Tel.: (310) 268-8330
Web Site: http://www.trinitycapitalllc.com
Management Consulting Services
N.A.I.C.S.: 541611
Kevin Burke (Mng Dir)
David Stiles (Mng Dir)
Aaron Edwards (VP)
Kevin Walsh (VP)

Windsor Realty Corp.   **(1)**
9229 Shore Rd Apt 6d, Brooklyn, NY 11209
Tel.: (718) 836-8003
Emp.: 6
Real Estate Development Services
N.A.I.C.S.: 531210

CITIZENS FINANCIAL SERVICES, INC.
15 S Main St, Mansfield, PA 16933
Tel.: (570) 662-2121   **PA**
Web Site:
  https://www.citizensbank.com
Year Founded: 1983
CZFS—(NASDAQ)
Rev.: $93,095,000
Assets: $2,333,393,000
Liabilities: $2,133,246,000
Net Worth: $200,147,000
Earnings: $29,060,000
Emp.: 312
Fiscal Year-end: 12/31/22
Bank Holding Company
N.A.I.C.S.: 551111
Randall E. Black (Vice Chm, Pres & CEO)
Stephen J. Guillaume (CFO & Sr VP)
Jeffrey R. White (COO)

Subsidiaries:

First Citizens Community Bank   **(1)**
15 S Main St, Mansfield, PA 16933
Tel.: (570) 545-6130
Web Site: https://www.firstcitizensbank.com
Sales Range: $25-49.9 Million
Commericial Banking
N.A.I.C.S.: 522110
Randall E. Black (Vice Chm, Pres & CEO)
David Z. Richards Jr. (Sr Exec VP)
Jeffrey R. White (COO)
Jami Tomczuk (Mgr-Cash Mgmt Sls)
Chris Landis (Officer-Lending & Sr VP)
Robert B. Mosso (Sr VP & Mgr-Investments & Trust Svcs)
Florence L. Prough (Officer-Trust & Estate Plng & Asst VP)

Kristen D. D'Angelo (Officer-Investments & Trust & Asst VP)
Sylvia R. Thompson (Asst VP & Mgr-Wealth Mgmt Relationship)

CITIZENS HOLDING COMPANY
521 Main St, Philadelphia, MS 39350
Tel.: (601) 656-4692   **MS**
Web Site:
  https://www.thecitizensbankphila.com
Year Founded: 1982
CIZN—(NASDAQ)
Rev.: $50,586,000
Assets: $1,324,003,000
Liabilities: $1,284,978,000
Net Worth: $39,025,000
Earnings: $9,620,000
Emp.: 271
Fiscal Year-end: 12/31/22
Bank Holding Company
N.A.I.C.S.: 551111
Stacy M. Brantley (Pres & CEO)
Herbert A. King (Co-Chm)
Phillip R. Branch (CFO & Treas)
Mark Taylor (Sec)
David A. King (Co-Chm)

Subsidiaries:

The Citizens Bank of Philadelphia, Mississippi   **(1)**
521 Main St, Philadelphia, MS 39350   **(100%)**
Tel.: (601) 656-4692
Web Site:
  https://www.thecitizensbankphila.com
Sales Range: $125-149.9 Million
Emp.: 250
Commercial Bank
N.A.I.C.S.: 522110
Gregory E. Cronin (Pres-Gulf Coast Area)
Stacy M. Brantley (Pres & CEO)

CITIZENS NATIONAL CORPO-RATION
620 Broadway, Paintsville, KY 41240
Tel.: (606) 789-4001   **KY**
Web Site:
  https://www.wercitizens.bank
Year Founded: 1982
CZNL—(OTCIQ)
Sales Range: $25-49.9 Million
Emp.: 155
Bank Holding Company
N.A.I.C.S.: 551111
V. Burton Bellamy (Pres & CEO)
Darren Gillespie (Sr VP-Bus Banking)
Leisha Maynard (CFO & Sr VP)
Gregory Meade (Chm)

Subsidiaries:

Citizens National Bank of Paintsville   **(1)**
620 Broadway Ave, Paintsville, KY 41240
Tel.: (606) 789-4001
Web Site: http://www.cnbonline.com
Sales Range: $25-49.9 Million
Commericial Banking
N.A.I.C.S.: 522110
V. Burton Bellamy (Pres & CEO)
Leisha Maynard (CFO & Sr VP)
Lee Wilson (Chief Credit Officer & Exec VP)
Ben D. Tackett Jr. (Chief Lending Officer & Exec VP)

CITIZENS, INC.
11815 Alterra Pkwy Ste 1500, Austin, TX 78758
Tel.: (512) 837-7100   **CO**
Web Site:
  https://www.citizensinc.com
Year Founded: 1977
CIA—(NYSE)
Rev.: $232,524,000
Assets: $1,569,970,000
Liabilities: $1,568,927,000
Net Worth: $1,043,000
Earnings: ($6,638,000)
Emp.: 224

Fiscal Year-end: 12/31/22
Holding Company; Insurance Products & Services
N.A.I.C.S.: 551112
Gerald W. Shields (Vice Chm)
Jon Stenberg (CEO)
Harvey J. L. Waite (Chief Actuary-Interim & VP)
Sheryl Kinlaw (Chief Legal Officer, Sec & VP)
Jerry D. Davis Jr. (Chm)
Robert McHardy Mauldin III (CMO & VP)

Subsidiaries:

CICA Life Insurance Company of America   **(1)**
400 E &erson Ln, Austin, TX 78752   **(100%)**
Tel.: (512) 837-7100
Web Site: http://www.cicalife.com
Life Insurance Products & Services
N.A.I.C.S.: 524113

Subsidiary (Domestic):

Citizens National Life Insurance Company   **(2)**
14231 Tandem Blvd, Austin, TX 78728
Tel.: (512) 837-7100
Web Site: http://www.citizensinc.com
Emp.: 200
Life Insurance Products & Services
N.A.I.C.S.: 524113
Kay Elizabeth Osbourn (Pres)

Security Plan Life Insurance Company   **(2)**
201 Railroad Ave, Donaldsonville, LA 70346
Tel.: (225) 473-8654
Web Site: http://www.citizensinc.com
Life, Property & Casualty Insurance Products & Services
N.A.I.C.S.: 524113

Subsidiary (Domestic):

Security Plan Fire Insurance Company   **(3)**
201 Railroad Ave, Donaldsonville, LA 70346
Tel.: (225) 473-8654
Web Site: http://www.citizensinc.com
Property & Casualty Insurace Products & Services
N.A.I.C.S.: 524126

CITY HOLDING COMPANY
25 Gatewater Rd, Charleston, WV 25313
Tel.: (304) 769-1100   **WV**
Web Site: https://www.bankatcity.com
Year Founded: 1983
CHCO—(NASDAQ)
Rev.: $261,765,000
Assets: $5,878,106,000
Liabilities: $5,300,254,000
Net Worth: $577,852,000
Earnings: $102,071,000
Emp.: 909
Fiscal Year-end: 12/31/22
Bank Holding Company
N.A.I.C.S.: 551111
Charles R. Hageboeck (Pres & CEO)
Michael T. Quinlan Jr. (Exec VP-Retail Banking)
David L. Bumgarner (CFO, Chief Acctg Officer & Exec VP)
John A. DeRito (Exec VP-Comml Banking)
Jeffrey Dale Legge (CIO, Chief Admin Officer & Exec VP)
C. Dallas Kayser (Chm)

Subsidiaries:

Citizens Commerce Bancshares, Inc.   **(1)**
PO Box 1028, Versailles, KY 40383
Tel.: (859) 879-9455
Web Site: http://www.citizenscommerce.com
Rev.: $10,623,089
Assets: $264,978,262
Liabilities: $237,913,079

Net Worth: $27,065,183
Earnings: $1,742,379
Fiscal Year-end: 12/31/2019
Bank Holding Company
N.A.I.C.S.: 551111
Frank Stark (Pres)
Michelle Oxley (Treas & Sec)

City National Bank of West Virginia   **(1)**
3601 MacCorkle Ave SE, Charleston, WV 25304   **(100%)**
Tel.: (304) 926-3308
Web Site: http://www.bankatcity.com
Commericial Banking
N.A.I.C.S.: 522110
Charles R. Hageboeck (Pres & CEO)
Craig G. Stilwell (Exec VP-Mktg, HR & Retail Banking)
James A. Bindas (Exec VP-Tech)
John A. DeRito (Exec VP-Comml Banking)
Jeffrey Dale Legge (CIO & Exec VP)
David L. Bumgarner (CFO & Exec VP)

CIVEO CORPORATION
333 Clay St Ste 4980, Houston, TX 77002
Tel.: (713) 510-2400   **DE**
Web Site: https://www.civeo.com
CVEO—(NYSE)
Rev.: $697,052,000
Assets: $566,184,000
Liabilities: $262,483,000
Net Worth: $303,701,000
Earnings: $3,997,000
Emp.: 1,400
Fiscal Year-end: 12/31/22
Facilities Support Services
N.A.I.C.S.: 561210
Peter L. McCann (Sr VP-Australia)
Bradley J. Dodson (Pres & CEO)
Richard A. Navarre (Chm)
Regan Nielsen (Sr Dir-Corp Dev & IR)

Subsidiaries:

Civeo Premium Camp Services Ltd   **(1)**
Stony Plain Rd Nw 17220, Edmonton, T5S 1K6, AB, Canada
Tel.: (780) 733-4900
Prefabricated Wood Building Product Mfr
N.A.I.C.S.: 321992

Civeo Pty Ltd   **(1)**
Level 6 10 Bond Street, Sydney, 2000, NSW, Australia
Tel.: (61) 283469200
Accomodation & Facility Management Services
N.A.I.C.S.: 561210

Civeo Pty Ltd   **(1)**
Level 6 10 Bond Street, Sydney, 2000, NSW, Australia
Tel.: (61) 283469200
Accomodation & Facility Management Services
N.A.I.C.S.: 561210

Civeo Pty Ltd   **(1)**
Level 6 10 Bond Street, Sydney, 2000, NSW, Australia
Tel.: (61) 283469200
Accomodation & Facility Management Services
N.A.I.C.S.: 561210

Civeo Pty Ltd   **(1)**
Level 6 10 Bond Street, Sydney, 2000, NSW, Australia
Tel.: (61) 283469200
Accomodation & Facility Management Services
N.A.I.C.S.: 561210

Civeo USA LLC   **(1)**
390 Mountain View Rd, Berthoud, CO 80513-9149
Tel.: (970) 670-6216
Prefabricated Wood Building Product Mfr
N.A.I.C.S.: 321992
Cindy Lahoda (Mgr-Hospitality Ops)

CIVISTA BANCSHARES, INC.

Tel.: (419) 625-4121   OH
Web Site: https://www.civb.com
Year Founded: 1987
CIVB—(NASDAQ)
Rev.: $150,329,000
Assets: $3,537,830,000
Liabilities: $3,202,995,000
Net Worth: $334,835,000
Earnings: $39,427,000
Emp.: 530
Fiscal Year-end: 12/31/22
Bank Holding Company
N.A.I.C.S.: 551111
Richard J. Dutton (Sr VP)
Michael D. Mulford (Sr VP)
Dennis G. Shaffer (Vice Chm, Pres & CEO)
Charles A. Parcher (Sr VP)
Lance A. Morrison (Gen Counsel, Sec & Sr VP)
John A. Betts (Sr VP)
Donna M. Waltz-Jaskolski (Sr VP)
Robert L. Curry Jr. (Sr VP)
Russell L. Edwards (Sr VP)
Carl A. Kessler III (Sr VP)

Subsidiaries:

Civista Bank   (1)
100 E Water St, Sandusky, OH 44870
Tel.: (419) 625-4121
Web Site: http://www.civista.bank
Sales Range: $50-74.9 Million
Commericial Banking
N.A.I.C.S.: 522110
Dennis E. Murray Jr. (Chm)
Richard J. Dutton (COO & Exec VP)
Paul J. Stark (Chief Credit Officer & Sr VP)
Michael D. Mulford (Chief Credit Officer & Sr VP)
Dennis G. Shaffer (Vice Chm, Pres & CEO)
Charles A. Parcher (Chief Lending Officer & Exec VP)
Lance A. Morrison (Sec)
Todd A. Michel (Sr VP & Controller)
John A. Betts (Sr VP-Risk Mgmt)
Jessica A. Steuk (Sr VP & Mgr-Private Banking)
R. Keith Creech (VP-Port Clinton)
Tim Ott (VP & Mgr-Mortgage)
Paul Koch (Asst VP)
Jason Kuhnle (Sr VP & Dir-Wealth Mgmt)
Tessa Steinemann (Asst VP & Mgr-Customer Rels)
Charlene Bonsignore (VP)
Micha Meyer (VP-Comml Lending)

Subsidiary (Domestic):

First Citizens Capital LLC   (2)
1105 N Market St Ste 1300, Wilmington, DE 19801
Tel.: (302) 656-1240
Commercial Banking Services
N.A.I.C.S.: 522110

First Citizens Investments, Inc.   (2)
1105 N Market St, Wilmington, DE 19801-1216
Tel.: (302) 656-5014
Investment Banking Services
N.A.I.C.S.: 523150

Comunibanc Corp.   (1)
122 E Washington St, Napoleon, OH 43545
Tel.: (419) 599-1065
Bank Holding Company
N.A.I.C.S.: 551111
William L. Wendt (Pres)

Subsidiary (Domestic):

Henry County Bank   (2)
122 East Washington St, Napoleon, OH 43545
Tel.: (419) 599-5170
Web Site:
     http://www.thehenrycountybank.com
Rev.: $10,000,000
Emp.: 35
Commericial Banking
N.A.I.C.S.: 522110
William L. Wendt (Pres)

Vision Financial Group, Inc.   (1)
615 Iron City Dr, Pittsburgh, PA 15205

Tel.: (412) 539-1500
Web Site: http://www.vfgusa.com
Rev.: $6,699,000
Emp.: 16
All Other Nondepository Credit Intermediation
N.A.I.C.S.: 522299
Frederick S. Summers (Founder & Chm)
Louis P. Brill (Sr VP-Ops-Credit)
Conrad J. Eimers (COO)
William P. Gmaz (Chief Risk Officer)
William P. Summers (CEO)

CIVITAS RESOURCES, INC.

555 17th St Ste 3700, Denver, CO 80202
Tel.: (303) 293-9100   DE
Web Site:
     https://www.civitasresources.com
CIVI—(NYSE)
Rev.: $3,479,240,000
Assets: $14,097,319,000
Liabilities: $7,915,998,000
Net Worth: $6,181,321,000
Earnings: $784,288,000
Emp.: 516
Fiscal Year-end: 12/31/23
Oil & Gas Exploration Services
N.A.I.C.S.: 211120
Travis L. Counts (Chief Legal Officer & Sec)
Brian T. Kuck (Sr VP-Corp Plng & Bus Dev)
Kayla D. Baird (Chief Acctg Officer & Sr VP)
Marianella Foschi (CFO)
Brian Cain (Chief Sustainability Officer)
Travis Counts (Chief Legal Officer & Sec)
Hodge Walker (COO)
Brad Johnson (Sr VP)
M. Christopher Doyle (Pres & CEO)

Subsidiaries:

Bonanza Creek Energy Operating Company LLC   (1)
4900 California Ave, Bakersfield, CA 93309
Tel.: (661) 638-2730
Web Site: http://www.bonanzacrk.net
Sales Range: $50-74.9 Million
Emp.: 23
Crude Petroleum & Natural Gas Extraction
N.A.I.C.S.: 211120

Bonanza Creek Energy Resources, LLC   (1)
213 Lafayette 36, Stamps, AR 71860
Tel.: (870) 533-2226
Oil & Natural Gas Exploration Services
N.A.I.C.S.: 211120

Extraction Oil & Gas, Inc.   (1)
370 17th St Ste 5200, Denver, CO 80202
Tel.: (720) 557-8300
Web Site: http://www.extractionog.com
Rev.: $557,904,000
Assets: $2,025,199,000
Liabilities: $3,064,244,000
Net Worth: ($1,039,045,000)
Earnings: ($1,273,694,000)
Emp.: 125
Fiscal Year-end: 12/31/2020
Oil & Gas Extraction Service
N.A.I.C.S.: 211120
Tom L. Brock (Chief Acctg Officer, VP & Controller)
Eric Christ (Gen Counsel, Sec & VP)

Subsidiary (Domestic):

Axis Exploration, LLC   (2)
15 W 6th St Ste 2350, Tulsa, OK 74119
Tel.: (918) 346-6789
Web Site: https://www.axisexploration.com
Oil & Gas Exploration Services
N.A.I.C.S.: 213112
Jack Kueser (VP)
Dave Culbertson (CFO)

HighPoint Resources Corporation   (1)
555 17th St Ste 3700, Denver, CO 80202
Tel.: (303) 293-9100

Web Site: http://www.hpres.com
Oil & Natural Gas Exploration & Development
N.A.I.C.S.: 213111
William M. Crawford (CFO & Principal Acctg Officer)
Kenneth A. Wonstolen (Gen Counsel & Sr VP)
Jerry D. Vigil (VP-IT)
Larry C. Busnardo (VP-IR)
Paul Geiger (COO)

Rocky Mountain Infrastructure, LLC   (1)
410 17th St Ste 1400, Denver, CO 80202
Tel.: (720) 440-6100
Natural Oil & Gas Extraction Services
N.A.I.C.S.: 213112

CKX LANDS, INC.

2417 Shell Beach Dr, Lake Charles, LA 70601
Tel.: (337) 493-2399   LA
Web Site: https://www.ckxlands.com
Year Founded: 1930
CKX—(NYSEAMEX)
Rev.: $1,105,494
Assets: $17,687,590
Liabilities: $267,176
Net Worth: $17,420,414
Earnings: ($1,317,718)
Emp.: 1
Fiscal Year-end: 12/31/22
Land & Mineral Interests Owner
N.A.I.C.S.: 213112
William Gray Stream (Chm, Pres & Treas)
Lee W. Boyer (Sec)
Scott Stepp (CFO)

CLARIM ACQUISITION CORP.

245 5th Ave Ste 1500, New York, NY 10016
Tel.: (917) 636-7925   DE
Year Founded: 2020
CLRMU—(NASDAQ)
Rev.: $4,825,615
Assets: $288,120,604
Liabilities: $308,136,210
Net Worth: ($20,015,606)
Earnings: $2,465,392
Emp.: 4
Fiscal Year-end: 12/31/21
Investment Services
N.A.I.C.S.: 523999
Russell D. Glass (Vice Chm)
James F. McCann (Chm & CEO)
Paul Stamoulis (Exec VP)

CLARION COUNTY COMMUNITY BANK

333 W Main St, Clarion, PA 16214
Tel.: (814) 226-6000
Web Site:
     https://www.clarionbank.com
Year Founded: 2004
CCYY—(OTCIQ)
Rev.: $7,850,444
Assets: $175,386,527
Liabilities: $158,148,671
Net Worth: $17,237,856
Earnings: $819,220
Fiscal Year-end: 12/31/19
Commericial Banking
N.A.I.C.S.: 522110
James L. Kifer (Pres & CEO)

CLARIOS INTERNATIONAL INC.

Florist Tower 5757 N Green Bay Ave, Milwaukee, WI 53201
Tel.: (414) 214-6500   DE
Web Site: http://www.clarios.com
Year Founded: 1885
BTRY—(NYSE)
Emp.: 16,505
Storage Battery Mfr
N.A.I.C.S.: 335910

Mark Wallace (Pres & CEO)
Anthony Moore (VP & Gen Mgr-United States & Canada)
Gerardo Gonzalez-Aleu (VP & Gen Mgr-Latin America)
Jennifer L. Slater (VP & Gen Mgr-Original Equipment & Products)
Leslie Wong (VP & Gen Mgr-China & Asia Pacific)
Werner Benade (VP & Gen Mgr-Europe, Middle East & Africa)
Claudio Morfe (Gen Counsel, Sec & VP)
Wendy Radtke (Chief HR Officer)
Becky Kryger (VP & Controller)
Diarmuid O'Connell (Chm)
Marc Andraca (VP-Strategy & Bus Dev)
Kathryn Campbell (VP-Corp Mktg & IR)
Koben Miceli (VP-Operational Transformation)
Helmut Zodl (CFO)

CLARITAS PHARMACEUTICALS, INC.

4040 Civic Ctr Dr Ste 200, San Rafael, CA 94903
Tel.: (888) 861-2008   BC
Web Site:
     http://www.claritaspharma.com
Year Founded: 2004
CLAS—(TSXV)
Assets: $10,445,000
Liabilities: $8,938,000
Net Worth: $1,507,000
Earnings: $4,210,000
Fiscal Year-end: 12/31/20
Bio Technology Services
N.A.I.C.S.: 541714
Robert Farrell (Pres & CEO)
Nedira Frenkel (Dir-Bus Dev)
Yousif Sahly (Dir-Quality Control)
Gali Guzikevich (Dir-Quality Assurance)
Amos Rosenthal (Head-Chemistry)
Iris Maimon (Dir-Drug Dev)

CLARK COUNTY BANCORPORATION

1400 Washington St Ste 200, Vancouver, WA 98660
Tel.: (360) 993-2265
Year Founded: 1999
CKCB—(OTCIQ)
Commercial Bank Services
N.A.I.C.S.: 522110
Michael A. Worthy (Pres & CEO)

CLAROCITY CORPORATION

2202 N Westshore Blvd Suite 200, Tampa, FL 33607
Tel.: (888) 485-9551   AB
Web Site: https://www.clarocity.com
Year Founded: 2004
CLY—(TSXV)
Sales Range: $10-24.9 Million
Property Photography Services; Appraisal Analysis & Collection Services
N.A.I.C.S.: 541922
Shane Copeland (CEO)
Jim Boyle (Chm)
Dave Guebert (CFO)
Ernie Durbin (Chief Valuation Officer)
Bill Mohler (Chief Product Officer)
Aleksandra James (Pres)

CLARUS CORPORATION

2084 E 3900 S, Salt Lake City, UT 84124
Tel.: (801) 278-5552   DE
Web Site:
     https://www.claruscorp.com

Clarus Corporation—(Continued)

CLAR—(NASDAQ)
Rev.: $448,106,000
Assets: $518,145,000
Liabilities: $226,037,000
Net Worth: $292,108,000
Earnings: ($69,780,000)
Emp.: 900
Fiscal Year-end: 12/31/22
Outdoor Recreation Products Mfr &
Retailer
N.A.I.C.S.: 339920
Michael J. Yates (CFO & Principal
Acctg Officer)
Warren B. Kanders (Chm)
Michael J. Yates (CFO)

Subsidiaries:

Black Diamond Equipment AG   (1)
Hans-Maier-Strasse 9, 6020, Innsbruck,
Austria
Tel.: (43) 125374599333
Web Site:
http://www.blackdiamondequipment.com
Sporting Goods Mfr
N.A.I.C.S.: 339920

Black Diamond Equipment Europe
GmbH   (1)
Hans-Maier-Strasse 9, 6020, Innsbruck,
Austria
Tel.: (43) 12537459333
Web Site:
https://eu.blackdiamondequipment.com
Sporting Goods Retailer Services
N.A.I.C.S.: 459110

Black Diamond Equipment Ltd.   (1)
2084 E 3900 S, Salt Lake City, UT 84124
Tel.: (801) 278-5533
Web Site:
https://www.blackdiamondequipment.com
Sporting & Athletic Equipment Mfr
N.A.I.C.S.: 339920

PIEPS GmbH   (1)
Parkring 4, Lebring, 8403, Leibnitz, Austria
Tel.: (43) 3182525560
Web Site: https://www.pieps.com
Emp.: 5
Avalanche Transceivers Mfr
N.A.I.C.S.: 237990

POC Austria   (1)
Panzerhalle Siezenheimerstrasse 39 D,
5020, Salzburg, Austria
Tel.: (43) 662890090
Outdoor Recreation Services
N.A.I.C.S.: 237990
Hans Schlick (Mng Dir)

POC Sweden AB   (1)
Nackagatan 4, 116 49, Stockholm, Sweden
Tel.: (46) 87174050
Web Site: http://www.pocsports.com
Outdoor Recreation Services
N.A.I.C.S.: 237990
Stefan Ytterborn (CEO)

POC USA LLC   (1)
1755 Prospector Ave Ste 101, Park City,
UT 84060
Tel.: (801) 365-5550
Outdoor Recreation Services
N.A.I.C.S.: 237990

SKINourishment, LLC   (1)
691 La Buena Vista Dr Ste D, Wimberley,
TX 78676
Tel.: (512) 047-2579
Web Site: http://skinourishment.com
Skin Care Products Distr
N.A.I.C.S.: 424210

**CLARUS THERAPEUTICS
HOLDINGS, INC.**
15 E Putnam Ave Ste 363, Green-
wich, CT 06830
Tel.: (646) 303-0737   DE
Year Founded: 2020
CRXT—(NASDAQ)
Rev.: $13,957,000
Assets: $51,708,000
Liabilities: $67,627,000
Net Worth: ($15,919,000)

Earnings: ($40,617,000)
Emp.: 16
Fiscal Year-end: 12/31/21
Investment Services
N.A.I.C.S.: 523999
Kimberly M. Murphy (Chm)
Robert E. Dudley (Pres & CEO)
Zhanna Jumadilova (Chief Clinical
Dev Officer)

Subsidiaries:

Clarus Therapeutics, Inc.   (1)
555 Skokie Blvd Ste 340, Northbrook, IL
60062
Tel.: (847) 562-4300
Web Site:
http://www.clarustherapeutics.com
Pharmaceuticals Mfr
N.A.I.C.S.: 325412
Robert E. Dudley (Pres & CEO)
Steven A. Bourne (CFO, Treas & Sec)

**CLASS ACCELERATION
CORP.**
2925 Woodside Rd, Woodside, CA
94062
Tel.: (650) 235-4777   DE
Year Founded: 2020
CLASU—(NYSE)
Rev.: $5,922,932
Assets: $259,474,235
Liabilities: $278,515,368
Net Worth: ($19,041,133)
Earnings: $4,800,787
Emp.: 3
Fiscal Year-end: 12/31/21
Investment Services
N.A.I.C.S.: 523999
Joseph E. Parsons (Co-Chm &
Treas)
Robert C. Daugherty (Co-Chm &
Sec)
Michael T. Moe (CEO)

**CLAYTON & LAMBERT MANU-
FACTURING CO.**
3813 W Hwy 146, Buckner, KY
40010   DE
Web Site:
http://www.claytonlambert.com
Year Founded: 1888
CLLA—(OTCIQ)
Swimming Pool Construction Ser-
vices
N.A.I.C.S.: 236220
Phillip Lambert (VP)

**CLEAN COAL TECHNOLO-
GIES, INC.**
295 Madison Ave 12th Fl, New York,
NY 10017
Tel.: (646) 710-3549
Web Site:
http://www.cleancoaltechnologies
inc.com
CCTC—(OTCIQ)
Assets: $16,000
Liabilities: $31,482,738
Net Worth: ($31,466,738)
Earnings: ($3,262,353)
Emp.: 2
Fiscal Year-end: 12/31/22
Coal Byproduct Extraction Services
N.A.I.C.S.: 324199
Robin T. Eves (Pres & CEO)
Aiden Neary (CFO & COO)

**CLEAN ENERGY FUELS
CORP.**
4675 MacArthur Ct Ste 800, Newport
Beach, CA 92660
Tel.: (949) 437-1000   DE
Web Site:
https://www.cleanenergyfuels.com
CLNE—(NASDAQ)
Rev.: $420,164,000
Assets: $1,082,357,000

Liabilities: $354,886,000
Net Worth: $727,471,000
Earnings: ($58,733,000)
Emp.: 496
Fiscal Year-end: 12/31/22
Vehicular Natural Gas Supplier
N.A.I.C.S.: 221210
Mitchell W. Pratt (Chief Tech Dev Of-
ficer)
Andrew J. Littlefair (Co-Founder, Pres
& CEO)
Barclay F. Corbus (Sr VP-Strategic
Dev & Co-Head-Renewable Fuels)
J. Nathan Jensen (Chief Legal Offi-
cer, Sr VP & Co-Head-Renewable
Fuels)
Barbara Johnson (VP-Admin)
Robert M. Vreeland (CFO)
Clay Corbus (Sr VP)
Jim Sytsma (Gen Counsel)
Raymond Burke (Sr VP)

Subsidiaries:

Clean Energy-Dallas   (1)
8117 Preston Rd Ste 202, Dallas, TX 75225
Tel.: (214) 572-6580
Web Site: http://www.cleanenergyfuels.com
Sales Range: $10-24.9 Million
Emp.: 140
Vehicular Natural Gas Supplier
N.A.I.C.S.: 221210

Clean Energy-Denver   (1)
4955 Peoria St Unit D, Denver, CO
80239   (100%)
Tel.: (303) 322-4600
Web Site: http://www.cleanenergyfuels.com
Sales Range: $25-49.9 Million
Emp.: 35
Vehicular Natural Gas Supplier
N.A.I.C.S.: 221210

Clean Energy-East Coast   (1)
35 Corporate Dr 4th Fl, Burlington, MA
01803-4223
Tel.: (781) 685-4857
Web Site: http://www.cleanenergyfuels.com
Sales Range: $200-249.9 Million
Vehicular Natural Gas Supplier
N.A.I.C.S.: 221210

I.M.W. CNG Bangladesh Ltd.   (1)
Flat 103-104 hou se 292 Road 3 Mirp, Mo-
hakhali, Dhaka, 1216, Bangladesh
Tel.: (880) 1713062356
Web Site: http://www.cleanenergyfuels.com
Compressed Natural Gas Equipment Prod-
uct Mfr
N.A.I.C.S.: 333912

IMW Colombia Ltd.   (1)
Via 40 NRO 69-58 Parque Comercial E In-
dustrial Via 40, Barranquilla, Colombia
Tel.: (57) 53443171
Sales Range: $25-49.9 Million
Emp.: 90
Compressed Natural Gas Equipment Mfr
N.A.I.C.S.: 237120

NG Advantage LLC   (1)
78 Severance Green Ste 102, Colchester,
VT 05446
Tel.: (802) 760-1167
Web Site: https://www.ngadvantage.com
Oil & Gas Pipeline Construction Services
N.A.I.C.S.: 237120
Tom Evslin (Co-Founder)
Mary Evslin (Co-Founder)
Ben Frost (CTO)
Claudia Ashton (Dir-Mktg)
Enrico Biasetti (CEO)
Kathi Kiernan (Dir-HR)
Kathryn Towle (Dir-Fin & Acctg)

SAFE&CEC S.r.l.   (1)
Via Ferruccio Lamborghini 18, San Gio-
vanni in Persiceto, Bologna, Italy   (49%)
Tel.: (39) 0516878211
Web Site: https://safegas.it
Petroleum & Fuel Industries
N.A.I.C.S.: 324199
Mario Pirraglia (Pres)

Subsidiary (Non-US):

IMW Industries Ltd.   (2)

Unit 610 - 44688 South Sumas Road, Chilli-
wack, V2R 5M3, BC, Canada
Tel.: (604) 795-9491
Web Site: https://imw.ca
Sales Range: $50-74.9 Million
Emp.: 300
Natural Gas Equipment Mfr
N.A.I.C.S.: 333912

**CLEAN ENERGY PATHWAYS,
INC.**
30 MGould St Ste R, Sheridan, WY
82801
Tel.: (929) 459-0949
Web Site:
http://www.cleanenergypathways.com
CPWY—(OTCIQ)
Sales Range: Less than $1 Million
Emp.: 2
Solar Energy Generation Systems
N.A.I.C.S.: 335311

**CLEAN ENERGY SPECIAL
SITUATIONS CORP.**
405 Lexington Ave 11th Fl, New York,
NY 10174
Tel.: (212) 818-8800   DE
Year Founded: 2021
SWSS—(NASDAQ)
Rev.: $2,505,330
Assets: $175,488,391
Liabilities: $175,425,277
Net Worth: $63,114
Earnings: $838,650
Emp.: 3
Fiscal Year-end: 12/31/22
Investment Management Service
N.A.I.C.S.: 523999

**CLEAN ENERGY TECHNOLO-
GIES, INC.**
1340 Reynolds Ave Ste 120, Irvine,
CA 92614
Tel.: (949) 273-4990   NV
Web Site: https://www.cetyinc.com
Year Founded: 1995
CETY—(NASDAQ)
Rev.: $2,663,212
Assets: $8,114,329
Liabilities: $6,236,133
Net Worth: $1,878,196
Earnings: $147,395
Emp.: 27
Fiscal Year-end: 12/31/22
Other Electronic Component Manu
facturing
N.A.I.C.S.: 334419
Jamie Burrows (Dir-Ops)
Calvin Pang (CFO)

Subsidiaries:

Trident Manufacturing, Inc.   (1)
41W275 Railrd St, Pingree Grove, IL
60140-6314
Tel.: (847) 805-3500
Web Site: https://tridentmfg.com
Full Service Assembly & Mfr Services
N.A.I.C.S.: 339999
John Sapiente (CEO)

CLEAN HARBORS, INC.
42 Longwater Dr, Norwell, MA 02061-
9149
Tel.: (781) 792-5000   MA
Web Site:
https://www.cleanharbors.com
Year Founded: 1980
CLH—(NYSE)
Rev.: $5,409,152,000
Assets: $6,382,869,000
Liabilities: $4,135,363,000
Net Worth: $2,247,506,000
Earnings: $377,856,000
Emp.: 21,021
Fiscal Year-end: 12/31/23
Environment & Hazardous Waste
Management Services

N.A.I.C.S.: 541990
Michael L. Battles *(CFO & Exec VP)*
Alan S. McKim *(Founder, Exec Chm & CTO)*
George L. Curtis *(Exec VP-Pricing & Proposals)*
Jim Buckley *(Sr VP-IR)*
Sharon Gabriel *(CIO & Exec VP)*
Melkeya McDuffie *(Chief HR Officer & Exec VP)*
Loan N. Mansy *(Exec VP-Sls & Svc)*

Subsidiaries:

Altair Disposal Services, LLC   (1)
5464 Hwy 71, Altair, TX 77412
Tel.: (979) 234-5749
Sales Range: $25-49.9 Million
Emp.: 5
Hazardous Waste Management Services
N.A.I.C.S.: 562211
Mark Wilson *(Office Mgr)*

Cat Tech Asia Pacific PTE Ltd.   (1)
11 Tuas Avenue 16, Singapore, 638929, Singapore
Tel.: (65) 62646261
Engineering Services
N.A.I.C.S.: 541330

Clean Harbors Arizona, LLC   (1)
1340 W Lincoln St, Phoenix, AZ 85007
Tel.: (602) 462-2300
Web Site: https://www.cleanharbors.com
Emp.: 25
Hazardous Waste Management Services
N.A.I.C.S.: 562211

Clean Harbors BDT, LLC   (1)
13652 County Rd 180, Carthage, MO 64836
Tel.: (716) 759-2868
Web Site: https://www.cleanharbors.com
Sales Range: $10-24.9 Million
Emp.: 2
Handler of Hazardous Waste Collection & Disposal
N.A.I.C.S.: 562211

Clean Harbors Baton Rouge, LLC   (1)
13351 Scenic Hwy, Baton Rouge, LA 70807
Tel.: (225) 778-1234
Sales Range: $25-49.9 Million
Emp.: 45
Handler of Hazardous Waste Collection & Disposal
N.A.I.C.S.: 562219

Clean Harbors Buttonwillow, LLC   (1)
2500 W Lokern Rd, Buttonwillow, CA 93206
Tel.: (661) 762-6200
Web Site: https://www.cleanharbors.com
Sales Range: $25-49.9 Million
Emp.: 30
Hazardous Waste Management Services
N.A.I.C.S.: 562211

Clean Harbors Canada Inc.   (1)
4090 Telfer Road Rural Route 1, Corunna, N0N 1G0, ON, Canada   (100%)
Tel.: (519) 864-1021
Web Site: https://www.cleanharbors.com
Sales Range: $25-49.9 Million
Emp.: 130
Solvent Recycling, Oil Re-Refining & Fuel Blending Services & Transportation
N.A.I.C.S.: 423930

Clean Harbors Caribe, Inc.   (1)
Rd 869 St Ste 2 West Gate Industrial Park Palmas Ward, Catano, PR 00962
Tel.: (787) 641-5393
Hazardous Waste Management Services
N.A.I.C.S.: 562211

Clean Harbors Catalyst Services Trinidad Limited   (1)
403 A Pacific Ave Point Lisas Industrial Estate, Couva, Trinidad & Tobago
Tel.: (868) 8686797369
Hazardous Waste Treatment & Disposal Services
N.A.I.C.S.: 562211

Clean Harbors Catalyst Services, LLC   (1)
18025 S Broadway, Carson, CA 90248
Tel.: (562) 251-0231

Sales Range: $25-49.9 Million
Emp.: 100
Hazardous Waste Management Services
N.A.I.C.S.: 562211
Lani Haley *(Office Mgr)*

Clean Harbors Chattanooga, LLC   (1)
3300 Cummings Rd, Chattanooga, TN 37419
Tel.: (423) 821-6926
Sales Range: $25-49.9 Million
Emp.: 55
Handler of Liquid Waste Collection & Disposal
N.A.I.C.S.: 562920

Clean Harbors Coffeyville, LLC   (1)
2474 Hwy 169 N, Coffeyville, KS 67337
Tel.: (620) 251-6380
Web Site: https://www.cleanharbors.com
Sales Range: $25-49.9 Million
Emp.: 50
Hazardous Waste Management Services
N.A.I.C.S.: 562211

Clean Harbors Colfax, LLC   (1)
3763 Hwy 471, Colfax, LA 71417
Tel.: (318) 627-3443
Web Site: https://www.cleanharbors.com
Emp.: 11
Hazardous Waste Management Services
N.A.I.C.S.: 562211

Clean Harbors Deer Trail, LLC   (1)
108555 E Hwy 36, Deer Trail, CO 80105
Tel.: (970) 386-2293
Sales Range: $1-9.9 Million
Emp.: 12
Handler of Hazardous Waste Collection & Disposal
N.A.I.C.S.: 562211

Clean Harbors El Dorado, LLC   (1)
309 American Cir, El Dorado, AR 71730
Tel.: (870) 863-7173
Sales Range: $350-399.9 Million
Emp.: 320
Environmental & Hazardous Waste Management Services
N.A.I.C.S.: 562211

Clean Harbors Energy & Industrial Services Corp.   (1)
15715 121 A Avenue, Edmonton, T5V 1B1, AB, Canada
Tel.: (780) 451-6969
Web Site: http://www.cleanharbors.com
Oilfield, Environmental & Industrial Services
N.A.I.C.S.: 541360

Clean Harbors Energy and Industrial Services Corp.   (1)
15715-121A Avenue, Edmonton, T5V 1B1, AB, Canada
Tel.: (780) 451-6969
Web Site: https://www.cleanharbors.com
Hazardous Waste Management Services
N.A.I.C.S.: 562112

Clean Harbors Energy and Industrial Services LP   (1)
525 E Dewdney Avenue, Regina, S4N 4E9, SK, Canada
Tel.: (306) 546-3322
Web Site: https://www.cleanharbors.com
Sales Range: $25-49.9 Million
Emp.: 35
Janitorial Services
N.A.I.C.S.: 561720

Clean Harbors Environmental Services, Inc.   (1)
221 Sutton St, North Andover, MA 01845
Tel.: (978) 687-5041
Web Site: http://www.cleanharbors.com
Sales Range: $10-24.9 Million
Emp.: 12
Handler of Liquid Waste Collection & Disposal
N.A.I.C.S.: 562211
Alan S. McKim *(Chm & CEO)*

Clean Harbors Environmental Services, Inc.   (1)
2202 Genoa Red Bluff Rd, Houston, TX 77034
Tel.: (346) 315-8301
Web Site: http://www.cleanharbors.com

Sales Range: $50-74.9 Million
Emp.: 250
Environmental Waste Management Services
N.A.I.C.S.: 562998

Clean Harbors Environmental Services, Inc.   (1)
4101 Industrial Way, Benicia, CA 94510
Tel.: (707) 747-6699
Web Site: http://www.cleanharbors.com
Sales Range: $25-49.9 Million
Emp.: 100
Environment & Hazardous Waste Management Services
N.A.I.C.S.: 562910

Clean Harbors Exploration Services Ltd.   (1)
2700 61 Avenue SE, Calgary, T2C 4V2, AB, Canada   (100%)
Tel.: (403) 984-6254
Web Site: http://www.cleanharbors.com
Emp.: 7,000
Survey & Mapping Operations
N.A.I.C.S.: 541360

Division (Domestic)

Clean Harbors Exploration Services Ltd. - Seismic Services   (2)
33 County Industrial Park, PO Box 49, R R 3 Site 1, Grande Prairie, T8V 5N3, AB, Canada   (100%)
Tel.: (780) 532-0011
Seismic Drilling Operations
N.A.I.C.S.: 213111

Clean Harbors Exploration Services, Inc.   (1)
13116 State Hwy 18, Conneaut Lake, PA 16316
Tel.: (814) 213-0990
Web Site: https://www.cleanharbors.com
Hazardous Waste Management Services
N.A.I.C.S.: 562211

Clean Harbors Florida, LLC   (1)
7001 Kilo Ave, Bartow, FL 33830
Tel.: (863) 533-6111
Web Site: https://www.cleanharbors.com
Sales Range: $25-49.9 Million
Emp.: 75
Hazardous Waste Management Services
N.A.I.C.S.: 562211

Clean Harbors Industrial Services Canada, Inc.   (1)
9808 - 12 Avenue SW, Edmonton, T6X 0J5, AB, Canada
Tel.: (780) 395-5800
Web Site: https://www.cleanharbors.com
Sales Range: $25-49.9 Million
Emp.: 52
Hazardous Waste Management Services
N.A.I.C.S.: 562211
Alan S. McKim *(CEO)*

Clean Harbors Industrial Services, Inc.   (1)
42 Longwater Dr, Norwell, MA 02061-9149
Tel.: (781) 792-5801
Web Site: https://www.cleanharbors.com
Hazardous Waste Management Services
N.A.I.C.S.: 562211

Clean Harbors Kansas, LLC   (1)
2549 N New York St, Wichita, KS 67219
Tel.: (316) 269-7400
Sales Range: $10-24.9 Million
Emp.: 10
Handler of Hazardous Waste Collection & Disposal
N.A.I.C.S.: 811490

Clean Harbors Kimball Realty, LLC   (1)
2247 S Hwy 71, Kimball, NE 69145
Tel.: (308) 235-4012
Waste Management & Recycling Services
N.A.I.C.S.: 562998

Clean Harbors Lodging Services Ltd.   (1)
25963 111 Ave, Acheson, T7X 6C8, AB, Canada
Tel.: (780) 960-1507
Web Site: https://www.cleanharbors.com
Emp.: 40
Hazardous Waste Management Services

N.A.I.C.S.: 562211

Clean Harbors Lone Mountain, LLC   (1)
40355 S County Road 236, Waynoka, OK 73860
Tel.: (580) 697-3500
Web Site: https://www.cleanharbors.com
Sales Range: $25-49.9 Million
Emp.: 50
Hazardous Waste Management Services
N.A.I.C.S.: 562211

Clean Harbors Los Angeles, LLC   (1)
5756 Alba St, Los Angeles, CA 90058
Tel.: (323) 277-2500
Hazardous Waste Management Services
N.A.I.C.S.: 562211
Abby Pourhassanian *(Office Mgr)*

Clean Harbors Mercier, Inc.   (1)
1294 Blvd Sainte-Marguerite, Mercier, J6R 2L1, QC, Canada
Tel.: (450) 691-9610
Web Site: https://www.cleanharbors.com
Hazardous Waste Management Services
N.A.I.C.S.: 562211

Clean Harbors Recycling Services of Chicago, LLC   (1)
1445 W 42nd St, Chicago, IL 60609
Tel.: (773) 247-2828
Hazardous Waste Management Services
N.A.I.C.S.: 562211

Clean Harbors Recycling Services of Ohio LLC   (1)
581 Milliken Dr, Hebron, OH 43025
Tel.: (740) 929-3532
Web Site: https://www.cleanharbors.com
Sales Range: $25-49.9 Million
Emp.: 35
Hazardous Waste Management Services
N.A.I.C.S.: 562211

Clean Harbors Reidsville, LLC   (1)
208 Watlington Industrial Dr, Reidsville, NC 27320
Tel.: (336) 342-6106
Web Site: https://www.cleanharbors.com
Sales Range: $25-49.9 Million
Emp.: 50
Hazardous Waste Management Services
N.A.I.C.S.: 562211

Clean Harbors San Leon, Inc.   (1)
2700 Ave S, San Leon, TX 77539
Tel.: (281) 339-1352
Web Site: https://www.cleanharbors.com
Hazardous Waste Treatment & Disposal Services
N.A.I.C.S.: 562211

Clean Harbors Services, Inc.   (1)
11800 S Stony Is Ave, Chicago, IL 60617
Tel.: (773) 646-0149
Web Site: https://www.cleanharbors.com
Sales Range: $25-49.9 Million
Emp.: 50
Hazardous Waste Management Services
N.A.I.C.S.: 562211
Alan S. McKim *(Chm & CEO)*

Clean Harbors Surface Rentals Ltd.   (1)
Hwy 2 N and Township Road 730, PO Box 3001, Clairmont, T0H 0W0, AB, Canada
Tel.: (780) 567-2992
Web Site: https://www.cleanharbors.com
Hazardous Waste Treatment & Disposal Services
N.A.I.C.S.: 562211

Clean Harbors Surface Rentals Partnership   (1)
530-8th Avenue SW Suite 1800, Calgary, T2P 3S8, AB, Canada
Tel.: (403) 262-4200
Petroleum Equipment Rental Services
N.A.I.C.S.: 423830

Clean Harbors Surface Rentals USA, Inc.   (1)
506 K & P Industrial Dr, Rock Springs, WY 82901
Tel.: (307) 382-4442
Oil & Gas Field Services
N.A.I.C.S.: 213112

Clean Harbors Tennessee, LLC   (1)

Clean Harbors, Inc.—(Continued)

2815 Old Greenbrier Pike, Greenbrier, TN 37073
Tel.: (615) 643-3170
Sales Range: $25-49.9 Million
Emp.: 30
Hazardous Waste Management Services
N.A.I.C.S.: 562211

Clean Harbors Westmorland, LLC (1)
5295 S Garvey Rd, Westmorland, CA 92281
Tel.: (760) 344-9400
Web Site: https://www.cleanharbors.com
Sales Range: $25-49.9 Million
Emp.: 2
Hazardous Waste Management Services
N.A.I.C.S.: 562211

Clean Harbors White Castle, LLC (1)
52735 Clarke Rd, White Castle, LA 70788
Tel.: (225) 545-7800
Web Site: https://www.cleanharbors.com
Sales Range: $25-49.9 Million
Emp.: 18
Hazardous Waste Management Services
N.A.I.C.S.: 562211

Clean Harbors Wichita, LLC (1)
2808 Ohio St, Wichita, KS 67219
Tel.: (316) 226-7480
Industrial Waste Services
N.A.I.C.S.: 562119

Clean Harbors Wilmington, LLC (1)
1737 E Denni St, Wilmington, CA 90744
Tel.: (310) 835-9998
Hazardous Waste Management Services
N.A.I.C.S.: 562211
Mike Gilham *(Gen Mgr)*

Clean Harbors of Baltimore, Inc. (1)
1910 Russell St, Baltimore, MD 21230
Tel.: (410) 244-8200
Web Site: https://www.cleanharbors.com
Hazardous Waste Management Services
N.A.I.C.S.: 562211

Clean Harbors of Braintree, Inc. (1)
1 Hill Ave, Braintree, MA 02184
Tel.: (781) 380-7100
Web Site: https://www.cleanharbors.com
Hazardous Waste Management Services
N.A.I.C.S.: 562211

Clean Harbors of Connecticut, Inc. (1)
51 Broderick Rd, Bristol, CT 06010
Tel.: (860) 583-8917
Hazardous Waste Management Services
N.A.I.C.S.: 562211
Alan S. McKim *(Chm CEO)*
Kristin Mahoney *(Gen Mgr)*

Green View Technologies, Inc. (1)
30 Green View Dr, Rollinsford, NH 03869
Tel.: (603) 742-8700
Web Site: https://www.gvtoil.com
Essential Oil Mfr
N.A.I.C.S.: 325998

Grizzco Camp Services Inc. (1)
4720 Airport Rd, Chetwynd, V0C 1J0, BC, Canada
Tel.: (250) 788-3266
Web Site: http://www.grizzco.com
Hazardous Waste Treatment & Disposal Services
N.A.I.C.S.: 562211

HPC Industrial Services, LLC (1)
900 Georgia Ave, Deer Park, TX 77536
Web Site: https://www.hpc-industrial.com
Industrial Cleaning Services
N.A.I.C.S.: 561740

JL Filtration Inc. (1)
1102 - 6th Street, Nisku, T9E 7N7, AB, Canada
Tel.: (780) 955-8788
Web Site: http://www.jlfiltration.com
Emp.: 25
Filtration Products Mfr
N.A.I.C.S.: 333998
Cory Martin *(Gen Mgr)*

Lonestar Sylvan Inc. (1)
11208 84 AV, Fort Saskatchewan, T8L 3V7,

AB, Canada
Tel.: (780) 370-8685
Industrial Waste Services
N.A.I.C.S.: 562119

Lonestar West Inc. (1)
105 Kuusamo Drive, Red Deer, T4E 2J5, AB, Canada
Tel.: (780) 370-8685
Web Site: http://www.lonestarwest.com
Hydro Vacuum Services
N.A.I.C.S.: 213112

Murphy's Waste Oil Service, Inc. (1)
252 Salem St, Woburn, MA 01801
Tel.: (781) 935-9066
Oil Recycling Services
N.A.I.C.S.: 324110

Peak Energy Services Ltd. (1)
Livingston Place South Tower 740- 222 - 3 Ave SW, Calgary, T2P 0B4, AB, Canada
Tel.: (403) 543-7325
Web Site: http://www.peak-energy.com
Sales Range: $150-199.9 Million
Emp.: 30
Drilling & Production Services
N.A.I.C.S.: 213111

Subsidiary (Domestic):

Anchor King Ltd. (2)
102-116-Clearwill Ave, Red Deer, T4E 0A1, AB, Canada **(100%)**
Tel.: (403) 346-3171
Web Site: http://www.anchorking.ca
Sales Range: $50-74.9 Million
Emp.: 20
Tension Anchoring Services for Service Oil Rigs
N.A.I.C.S.: 213111
Andy Davidson *(Gen Mgr)*
Ron Psikla *(Mgr)*
Ron Psikla *(Mgr)*

Sanitherm Inc. (2)
25963-111 Ave, Acheson, T7X 6C8, AB, Canada
Tel.: (780) 960-2443
Web Site: http://www.sanitherm.com
Sales Range: $25-49.9 Million
Emp.: 30
Water Treatment Equipment Mfr
N.A.I.C.S.: 333310

Plaquemine Remediation Services, LLC (1)
32655 Gracie Ln, Plaquemine, LA 70764-7112
Tel.: (225) 659-2434
Hazardous Waste Management Services
N.A.I.C.S.: 562211

Ricky's Oil & Environmental Services, LLC (1)
PO Box 669295, Miami, FL 33166
Web Site: https://www.synergyrecycling.org
Industrial Cleaning Services
N.A.I.C.S.: 561740

Rosemead Oil Products, Inc. (1)
12912 E Lakeland Rd, Santa Fe Springs, CA 90670-2914
Tel.: (562) 941-3261
Emp.: 15
Industrial Waste Services
N.A.I.C.S.: 562119
Richard Schoensiegel *(Pres)*

SK Holding Company, Inc. (1)
5400 Legacy Dr Cluster Li, Plano, TX 76024
Tel.: (972) 265-2000
Emp.: 4,500
Holding Company
N.A.I.C.S.: 551114

SK Servicios Ambientales Administrativos, S. de R.L. de C.V. (1)
Blvd Manuel Avila Camacho 40, Int 1801 Torre Esmeralda Lomas de Chapultepec, 11000, Mexico, Mexico
Tel.: (52) 5555405558
Hazardous Waste Treatment & Disposal Services
N.A.I.C.S.: 562211

Safety-Kleen de Mexico, S. de R.L. de C.V. (1)

Calle Venados 36, Tlahuac, 13210, Mexico, Mexico
Tel.: (52) 5558506008
Hazardous Waste Treatment & Disposal Services
N.A.I.C.S.: 562211

Safety-Kleen of California, Inc. (1)
4139 N Valentine Ave, Fresno, CA 93722
Tel.: (559) 486-1960
Web Site: https://www.safety-kleen.com
Hazardous Waste Treatment & Disposal Services
N.A.I.C.S.: 562211

Safety-Kleen, Inc. (1)
1651 N Glenville Dr Ste 210, Richardson, TX 75081
Tel.: (972) 265-2000
Web Site: https://www.safety-kleen.com
Sales Range: $1-4.9 Billion
Emp.: 4,200
Holding Company; Industrial & Hazardous Waste Management Services
N.A.I.C.S.: 551112

Subsidiary (Domestic):

Clean Harbors Deer Park, LLC (2)
2027 Independence Pkwy S, La Porte, TX 77571
Tel.: (281) 930-2300
Sales Range: $50-74.9 Million
Emp.: 250
Handles Hazardous Waste Collection & Disposal Services
N.A.I.C.S.: 541618

Clean Harbors Environmental Services, Inc. (2)
1010 Commercial St, San Jose, CA 95112
Tel.: (408) 451-5000
Web Site: http://www.cleanharbors.com
Sales Range: $25-49.9 Million
Emp.: 100
Operates Hazardous Waste Transport Services
N.A.I.C.S.: 562112

Holding (Non-US):

ORM Bergold Chemie GmbH & Co. (2)
Daimlerstrasse 2-4 Gerthe, Bochum, D-44805, Germany **(100%)**
Tel.: (49) 234879080
Web Site: http://www.safetykleen.eu
Solvent Removal & Reclamation
N.A.I.C.S.: 562910
Roland Kowalewski *(Mgr-Key Acct)*

Safety-Kleen Canada, Inc. (2)
300 Woolwich Street South, Breslau, N0B 1M0, ON, Canada
Tel.: (519) 648-2291
Solvent Recycling, Oil Re-Refining & Fuel Blending Services
N.A.I.C.S.: 325998

Division (Domestic):

Safety-Kleen Envirosystems Co. (2)
1500 E Villa St, Elgin, IL 60120-1390 **(100%)**
Tel.: (847) 468-6600
Web Site: http://www.safetykleen.com
Sales Range: $25-49.9 Million
Emp.: 75
Waste Material Recycling Services
N.A.I.C.S.: 562920

Subsidiary (Domestic):

Safety-Kleen Oil Recovery Co. (2)
601 Riley Rd, East Chicago, IN 46312 **(100%)**
Tel.: (219) 397-1131
Web Site: http://www.safety-kleen.com
Sales Range: $25-49.9 Million
Emp.: 80
Operates Oil Recovery & Recycling Facilities
N.A.I.C.S.: 324191

Safety-Kleen Systems, Inc. (2)
6880 Smith Ave, Newark, CA 94560
Tel.: (510) 795-4400
Sales Range: $10-24.9 Million
Waste Oil Refining Services
N.A.I.C.S.: 324110

Sanitherm USA, Inc. (1)
42 Longwater Dr, Norwell, MA 02061
Tel.: (781) 792-5000
Hazardous Waste Management Services
N.A.I.C.S.: 562211

Sawyer Disposal Services, LLC (1)
12400 247th Ave SE, Sawyer, ND 58781
Tel.: (701) 624-5622
Sales Range: Less than $1 Million
Emp.: 19
Handler of Hazardous Waste Collection & Disposal
N.A.I.C.S.: 237210

Service Chemical, LLC (1)
221 Sutton St, North Andover, MA 01845-1639
Tel.: (978) 687-5041
Hazardous Waste Management Services
N.A.I.C.S.: 562211

Spring Grove Resource Recovery, Inc. (1)
4879 Spring Grove Ave, Cincinnati, OH 45232
Tel.: (513) 681-6242
Web Site: https://www.cleanharbors.com
Sales Range: $25-49.9 Million
Emp.: 50
Hazardous Waste Management Services
N.A.I.C.S.: 562211

Synergy Recycling, LLC (1)
PO Box 669295, Miami, FL 33166
Web Site: https://www.synergyrecycling.org
Environmental & Waste Management Services
N.A.I.C.S.: 562998

The Solvents Recovery Service of New Jersey, Inc. (1)
1200 Sylvan St, Linden, NJ 07036
Tel.: (201) 862-2000
Hazardous Waste Treatment & Disposal Services
N.A.I.C.S.: 562211

Tri-vax Enterprises Ltd. (1)
Mod 3 Comp 8 RR1, Fort McMurray, T9H 5B4, AB, Canada
Tel.: (780) 743-1892
Web Site: https://www.cleanharbors.com
Emp.: 70
Hazardous Waste Management Services
N.A.I.C.S.: 562211

CLEAN VISION CORPORATION
123 W NYE Ln Ste 129, Carson City, NV 89706
Tel.: (203) 137-6486
Web Site:
https://www.cleanvisioncorp.com
CLNV—(OTCQB)
Business Services
N.A.I.C.S.: 561499
Chris Percy *(Pres & Chief Comml Officer)*

Subsidiaries:

Fidelity Holding Corp. (1)
Unit 1 14F Bank of East Asia Harbour View Center, Wanchai, 999077, China (Hong Kong)
Tel.: (852) 96916289
Liabilities: $89,000
Net Worth: ($89,000)
Earnings: ($325,000)
Fiscal Year-end: 12/31/2020
Financial Investment Services
N.A.I.C.S.: 523999
Zewu Xuan *(Pres)*
Tze Ling Yeung *(Head-Fin)*

CLEANSPARK, INC.
10624 S Eastern Ave Ste A 638, Henderson, NV 89052
Tel.: (702) 989-7692   NV
Web Site:
https://www.cleanspark.com
Year Founded: 1987
CLSK—(NASDAQ)
Rev.: $378,968,000
Assets: $1,962,662,000

Liabilities: $201,821,000
Net Worth: $1,760,841,000
Earnings: ($145,777,000)
Emp.: 256
Fiscal Year-end: 09/30/24
Investment Services
N.A.I.C.S.: 523999
Zachary K. Bradford (Pres & CEO)
S. Matthew Schultz (Exec Chm)
Gary A. Vecchiarelli (CFO)
Rachel Silverstein (Gen Counsel & VP-Compliance)
Amer Tadayon (Chief Revenue Officer & Pres-Energy Div)
Gary A. Vecchiarelli (CFO)
Bernardo Schucman (Sr VP-Digital Currency Div)
Isaac Holyoak (Chief Comm Officer)
Scott Garrison (COO)
Taylor Monnig (CTO)
Joni McMillan (VP)

Subsidiaries:

CleanSpark, LLC **(1)**
4360 Viewridge Ave Ste C, San Diego, CA 92123
Web Site: http://www.cleanspark.com
Software Development Services
N.A.I.C.S.: 541511

Pioneer Critical Power Inc. **(1)**
9210 Wyoming Ave N Ste 250, Minneapolis, MN 55445
Tel.: (763) 424-6053
Web Site: http://www.pssigear.com
Electric Equipment Mfr.
N.A.I.C.S.: 423610
George Moothedan (Pres)

Solar Watt Solutions Inc. **(1)**
2042 Corte Del Nogal Ste C, Carlsbad, CA 92011
Tel.: (760) 576-5270
Web Site: http://www.solarwattsolutions.com
Plumbing, Heating & Air-Conditioning Contractors
N.A.I.C.S.: 238220
Dave Watt (Mgr)

CLEANTECH ALPHA CORPORATION
1800 NE 135th St, Oklahoma City, OK 73131
Tel.: (770) 886-2734 **DE**
Web Site: https://cleantech-alpha.com
Year Founded: 2003
GERS—(OTCIQ)
Construction Engineering Services
N.A.I.C.S.: 541330

CLEAR CHANNEL OUTDOOR HOLDINGS, INC.
4830 N Loop 1604 W Ste 111, San Antonio, TX 78249
Tel.: (210) 547-8800 **DE**
Web Site: https://www.clearchanneloutdoor.com
Year Founded: 1997
CCO—(NYSE)
Rev.: $2,481,134,000
Assets: $5,086,011,000
Liabilities: $8,348,817,000
Net Worth: ($3,262,806,000)
Earnings: ($96,604,000)
Emp.: 4,700
Fiscal Year-end: 12/31/22
Holding Company; Out-of-Home Display Advertising Products & Services
N.A.I.C.S.: 551112
Scott R. Wells (Pres & CEO)
David Sailer (CFO & Exec VP)
Justin Cochrane (CEO)

Subsidiaries:

Clear Channel (Guangzhou) Ltd. **(1)**
SOHO Office 411 NO 310 Yuangang Road, Tianhe District, Guangzhou, 510650, China
Tel.: (86) 2085279704
Web Site: https://www.clearchannelint.cn
Media Monitoring Services
N.A.I.C.S.: 541840

Clear Channel Nederland BV **(1)**
Mercuriusplein 1, 2132 HA, Hoofddorp, Netherlands
Tel.: (31) 850170070
Web Site: https://www.clearchannel.nl
Marketing & Advertising Services
N.A.I.C.S.: 541810

Clear Channel Outdoor, Inc. **(1)**
2325 E Camelback Rd Ste 400, Phoenix, AZ 85016 **(100%)**
Tel.: (602) 381-5700
Web Site: http://www.clearchanneloutdoor.com
Sales Range: $250-299.9 Million
Out-of-Home Display Advertising Products & Services
N.A.I.C.S.: 541850
Eugene P. Leehan (Exec VP)
Bryan Parker (Exec VP-Real Estate & Pub Affairs)

Subsidiary (Non-US):

Adshel (Brazil) Ltda **(2)**
Rua Funchal 551 9 Andar Cj 91/92, Vila Olimpia, 04551-060, Brazil
Tel.: (55) 1121335800
Web Site: http://www.clearchannel.com.br
Sales Range: $50-74.9 Million
Emp.: 40
Outdoor Advertising Services
N.A.I.C.S.: 541890

Adshel Ireland Limited **(2)**
Beech House Beech Hill Road, Donnybrook, Dublin, Ireland
Tel.: (353) 14784500
Web Site: http://www.clearchannel.ie
Emp.: 22
Advertising Services
N.A.I.C.S.: 541890
Terry Buckley (Mng Dir)
Patrick Wyse (CFO)
Declan O'Carroll (COO)
Padraig Mangan (Dir-IT)
John Quinn (Dir-Dev)
Bairbre Drury Byrne (Sls Dir-Mktg)
Dave Costello (Sls Mgr)
Brian Hughes (Dir-Ops)
Laura Hendrick (Dir-Client Svcs)
Laura Noble (Sr Acct Mgr)

B & P Outdoor BV **(2)**
Geversstraat 30, Oegstgeest, 2342 AA, Netherlands
Tel.: (31) 715157343
Outdoor Advertising Services
N.A.I.C.S.: 541850

Division (Domestic):

Clear Channel Airports **(2)**
205 N Michigan Ave Ste 940, Chicago, IL 60601
Tel.: (312) 647-2938
Web Site: http://www.clearchannelairports.com
Sales Range: $25-49.9 Million
Emp.: 15
Airport Display Advertising Products & Services
N.A.I.C.S.: 541850
Morten Gotterup (Pres)

Subsidiary (Non-US):

Clear Channel Danmark A/S **(2)**
Wildersgade 8 4 sal, 1408, Copenhagen, Denmark
Tel.: (45) 36440244
Web Site: http://www.clearchannel.dk
Emp.: 7
Advertising Services
N.A.I.C.S.: 541810

Clear Channel France SA **(2)**
4 Place Des Ailes, Boulogne-Billancourt, 92641, Boulogne-Billancourt, France
Tel.: (33) 141868686
Web Site: http://www.clearchannel.fr
Outdoor Advertising Services
N.A.I.C.S.: 541890

Clear Channel Holdings Limited **(2)**

33 Golden Square, London, W1F 9JT, United Kingdom **(100%)**
Tel.: (44) 2074782200
Web Site: http://www.clearchannel.co.uk
Sales Range: $250-299.9 Million
Holding Company; Out-of-Home Display Advertising Products & Services
N.A.I.C.S.: 551112

Subsidiary (Domestic):

Clear Channel UK Limited **(3)**
33 Golden Square, London, W1F 9JT, United Kingdom
Tel.: (44) 2074782200
Web Site: https://www.clearchannel.co.uk
Sales Range: $25-49.9 Million
Emp.: 250
Display Advertising Services
N.A.I.C.S.: 541850
Will Ramage (Co-Mng Dir)
Justin Cochrane (CEO)
Richard Bon (Co-Mng Dir)
Martin Corke (CMO)
Louise Stubbings (Dir-Partnership & Creative)
Mark Smith (Sls Dir)
Aimee McKay (Dir-Client Partnership)
David Shepherd (Dir-Trading)
Mead Lee (Dir-Direct Sls)
George Manns (Dir-Portfolio & Strategy)
Salvatore Viola (Dir-Strategy)
Kevin A. Mayer (Executives, Bd of Dirs)

Division (Domestic):

Clear Channel Malls **(2)**
1270 Ave of the Americas, New York, NY 10020-1700
Tel.: (212) 972-0399
Web Site: http://www.clearchannelmalls.com
Sales Range: $100-124.9 Million
Mall Display Advertising Products & Services
N.A.I.C.S.: 541850

Branch (Domestic):

Clear Channel Outdoor - Eastern Regional Office **(2)**
99 Park Ave 2nd Fl, New York, NY 10016
Tel.: (212) 812-0000
Web Site: http://www.clearchanneloutdoor.com
Sales Range: $10-24.9 Million
Emp.: 60
Out-of-Home Display Advertising Products & Services
N.A.I.C.S.: 541850

Branch (Domestic):

Clear Channel Outdoor - Akron/Canton **(3)**
1 Cascade Plz Ste 1400, Akron, OH 44308
Tel.: (330) 762-8848
Web Site: http://www.clearchanneloutdoor.com
Sales Range: $1-9.9 Million
Emp.: 8
Out-of-Home Display Advertising Products & Services
N.A.I.C.S.: 541850

Clear Channel Outdoor - Atlanta **(3)**
1200 Wilson Way Ste C, Smyrna, GA 30082
Tel.: (678) 309-0085
Web Site: http://www.clearchanneloutdoor.com
Sales Range: $10-24.9 Million
Emp.: 48
Out-of-Home Display Advertising Products & Services
N.A.I.C.S.: 541850
Jack Jessen (Reg Pres-North East)

Clear Channel Outdoor - Daytona Beach/Melbourne **(3)**
715 N Dr Ste L, Melbourne, FL 32934
Tel.: (321) 726-6611

Web Site: https://clearchanneloutdoor.com
Sales Range: $10-24.9 Million
Emp.: 15
Out-of-Home Display Advertising Products & Services
N.A.I.C.S.: 541850

Clear Channel Outdoor - Indianapolis **(3)**
511 Madison Ave, Indianapolis, IN 46225-1105
Tel.: (317) 634-1900
Web Site: http://www.clearchanneloutdoor.com
Sales Range: $10-24.9 Million
Emp.: 40
Out-of-Home Display Advertising Products & Services
N.A.I.C.S.: 541850

Clear Channel Outdoor - Jacksonville **(3)**
4601 Touchton Rd Ste 3290, Jacksonville, FL 32246
Tel.: (352) 479-6900
Web Site: https://clearchanneloutdoor.com
Sales Range: $10-24.9 Million
Emp.: 40
Out-of-Home Display Advertising Products & Services
N.A.I.C.S.: 541850

Clear Channel Outdoor - Miami **(3)**
5800 NW 77th Ct, Miami, FL 33166
Tel.: (305) 592-6250
Web Site: http://www.clearchanneloutdoor.com
Out-of-Home Display Advertising Products & Services
N.A.I.C.S.: 541850

Clear Channel Outdoor - Orlando **(3)**
5333 Old Winter Garden Rd, Orlando, FL 32811
Tel.: (407) 298-6410
Web Site: http://www.clearchanneloutdoor.com
Sales Range: $10-24.9 Million
Emp.: 55
Out-of-Home Display Advertising Products & Services
N.A.I.C.S.: 541850

Clear Channel Outdoor - Philadelphia **(3)**
9130 State Rd, Philadelphia, PA 19136
Tel.: (215) 827-1100
Web Site: http://www.clearchannel.com
Out-of-Home Display Advertising Products & Services
N.A.I.C.S.: 541850

Clear Channel Outdoor - Washington, D.C./Baltimore **(3)**
9590 Lynn Buff Ct Ste 5, Laurel, MD 20723
Tel.: (301) 617-2600
Web Site: http://www.clearchanneloutdoor.com
Sales Range: $10-24.9 Million
Emp.: 50
Out-of-Home Display Advertising Products & Services
N.A.I.C.S.: 541850

Clear Channel Outdoor - Wilmington **(3)**
24 Germay Dr, Wilmington, DE 19804
Tel.: (302) 658-5520
Web Site: http://www.clearchanneloutdoor.com
Sales Range: $10-24.9 Million
Emp.: 12
Out-of-Home Display Advertising Products & Services
N.A.I.C.S.: 541850

Branch (Domestic):

Clear Channel Outdoor - Western Regional Office **(2)**
3700 E Randol Mill Rd, Arlington, TX 76011
Tel.: (817) 640-4550
Web Site: http://www.clearchanneloutdoor.com
Sales Range: $25-49.9 Million
Emp.: 105
Out-of-Home Display Advertising Products & Services
N.A.I.C.S.: 541850

Clear Channel Outdoor Holdings, Inc.—(Continued)

Branch (Domestic):

Clear Channel Outdoor - Chicago (3)
4000 S Morgan St, Chicago, IL 60609-2581
Tel.: (773) 843-2000
Web Site:
http://www.clearchanneloutdoor.com
Sales Range: $25-49.9 Million
Emp.: 100
Out-of-Home Display Advertising Products & Services
N.A.I.C.S.: 541850

Clear Channel Outdoor - Houston (3)
12852 Westheimer Rd, Houston, TX 77077
Tel.: (281) 588-4200
Web Site:
http://www.clearchanneloutdoor.com
Sales Range: $10-24.9 Million
Emp.: 75
Out-of-Home Display Advertising Products & Services
N.A.I.C.S.: 541850
Jimmy Hintz (VP)
Nancy Dennis (VP)

Clear Channel Outdoor - Las Vegas (3)
6855 S Cimarron Rd Ste 170, Las Vegas, NV 89113
Tel.: (702) 238-7200
Web Site: https://clearchanneloutdoor.com
Sales Range: $10-24.9 Million
Emp.: 40
Out-of-Home Display Advertising Products & Services
N.A.I.C.S.: 541850
Jerry McElroy (Production Mfg)

Clear Channel Outdoor - Los Angeles (3)
19320 Harborgate Way, Torrance, CA 90501
Tel.: (310) 755-7200
Web Site: https://clearchanneloutdoor.com
Sales Range: $10-24.9 Million
Emp.: 25
Out-of-Home Display Advertising Products & Services
N.A.I.C.S.: 541850
John Moyer (Sr VP)
Tom Britton (VP)
Layne Lawson (VP)
Kyle Huddle (VP)
Jon Sayer (VP)

Clear Channel Outdoor - Milwaukee (3)
908 Silvernail Rd, Pewaukee, WI 53072
Tel.: (262) 506-9000
Web Site: https://clearchanneloutdoor.com
Sales Range: $10-24.9 Million
Emp.: 40
Out-of-Home Display Advertising Products & Services
N.A.I.C.S.: 541850
Diane Veres (Reg Pres)
Eric Hamme (VP)

Clear Channel Outdoor - Sacramento (3)
401 Slobe Ave, Sacramento, CA 95815
Tel.: (916) 492-1303
Web Site: https://clearchanneloutdoor.com
Sales Range: $100-124.9 Million
Out-of-Home Display Advertising Products & Services
N.A.I.C.S.: 541850

Clear Channel Outdoor - San Antonio (3)
3714 N Pan Am Expy, San Antonio, TX 78219
Tel.: (210) 227-3451
Web Site: https://clearchanneloutdoor.com
Sales Range: $10-24.9 Million
Emp.: 36
Out-of-Home Display Advertising Products & Services
N.A.I.C.S.: 541850

Clear Channel Outdoor - San Diego (3)
7257 Ronson Rd Ste E, San Diego, CA 92111

Tel.: (858) 302-5137
Web Site: https://clearchanneloutdoor.com
Sales Range: $1-9.9 Million
Emp.: 7
Out-of-Home Display Advertising Products & Services
N.A.I.C.S.: 541850

Clear Channel Outdoor - San Francisco (3)
555 12th St Ste 950, Oakland, CA 94607
Tel.: (510) 835-5900
Web Site: https://clearchanneloutdoor.com
Sales Range: $10-24.9 Million
Emp.: 50
Out-of-Home Display Advertising Products & Services
N.A.I.C.S.: 541850
Stephanie Saporita (VP)
Erik Neese (VP)
John Moyer (Sr VP)
Jon Sayer (Sr VP)

Clear Channel Outdoor - Wichita (3)
3405 N Hydraulic St, Wichita, KS 67219
Tel.: (316) 838-0871
Web Site:
http://www.clearchanneloutdoor.com
Sales Range: $10-24.9 Million
Emp.: 20
Out-of-Home Display Advertising Products & Services
N.A.I.C.S.: 541850

Lamar Advertising Company - Seattle (3)
3601 Sixth Ave S, Seattle, WA 98134
Tel.: (206) 682-3833
Out-of-Home Display Advertising Products & Services
N.A.I.C.S.: 541850

Subsidiary (Non-US):

Clear Channel Outdoor Company Canada (2)
20 Dundas St W Ste 1001, Toronto, M5G 2C2, ON, Canada
Tel.: (416) 408-0800
Web Site:
http://www.clearchanneloutdoor.ca
Sales Range: $10-24.9 Million
Emp.: 31
Out-of-Home Display Advertising Products & Services
N.A.I.C.S.: 541850

Subsidiary (Domestic):

Clear Channel Spectacolor, LLC (2)
28 Liberty St, New York, NY 10005
Tel.: (212) 221-3100
Web Site: http://www.spectacolor.com
Sales Range: $100-124.9 Million
Emp.: 20
Radio Broadcasting Services
N.A.I.C.S.: 516210

Subsidiary (Non-US):

Paneles Napsa, S.A. (2)
Av Paseo de la Republica 11th floor, Miraflores, 5895, Lima, Peru
Tel.: (51) 980020030
Web Site: https://www.clearchannel.com.pe
Advertising Services
N.A.I.C.S.: 541890

Unit (Domestic):

Quantum Structures & Design (2)
2145 Moen Ave Unit 2, Joliet, IL 60436
Tel.: (815) 744-8663
Sales Range: $1-9.9 Million
Emp.: 7
Billboard Advertising
N.A.I.C.S.: 541850

CLEAR PEAK ENERGY, INC.
3450 N Triumph Blvd Ste 102, Lehi, UT 84043
Tel.: (801) 753-5715   NV
Web Site: https://clpe.com
Year Founded: 1999
CLPE—(OTCIQ)
Renewable Energy Development Services
N.A.I.C.S.: 221111

William Brandon Nash (CEO)
Jeff Jensen (CFO, Treas & Sec)

CLEAR SECURE, INC.
85 10th Ave 9th Fl, New York, NY 10011
Tel.: (646) 723-1404   DE
Web Site: https://www.clearme.com
Year Founded: 2021
YOU—(NYSE)
Rev.: $437,434,000
Assets: $1,037,517,000
Liabilities: $526,596,000
Net Worth: $510,921,000
Earnings: ($65,573,000)
Emp.: 3,056
Fiscal Year-end: 12/31/22
Software Development Services
N.A.I.C.S.: 541511
Chiranjiv S. Jouhal (CTO)
Matthew Levine (Chief Privacy Officer & Gen Counsel)
Maria A. Comella (Head-Pub Affairs)
Dennis Liu (Chief Acctg Officer)
Caryn Seidman-Becker (Chm & CEO)
Kenneth Cornick (Pres & CFO)
Richard N. Patterson Jr. (Chief Info Security Officer)
W. Catesby Perrin III (Exec VP-Growth)

CLEARDAY, INC.
8800 Village Dr, San Antonio, TX 78217
Tel.: (210) 451-0839   DE
Web Site:
https://www.myclearday.com
Year Founded: 1987
CLRD—(OTCQX)
Rev.: $12,881,675
Assets: $46,542,883
Liabilities: $83,335,790
Net Worth: ($36,792,907)
Earnings: ($19,506,675)
Emp.: 225
Fiscal Year-end: 12/31/21
Superconducting Products for Wireless Networks Developer, Mfr & Marketer
N.A.I.C.S.: 334220
Jim Walesa (Chm & CEO)
BJ Parrish (Interim CFO & COO)
Linda L. Carrasco (Pres-Memory Care America LLC)
Richard M. Morris (Exec VP & Gen Counsel)
Gary Sawina (Dir-Real Estate Ops & Exec VP)

Subsidiaries:

Allied Integral United, Inc. (1)
8800 Village Dr Ste 201, San Antonio, TX 78217
Tel.: (210) 451-0839
Web Site: http://www.myclearday.com
Health, Wellness & Fitness Company
N.A.I.C.S.: 456199
Jim Walesa (Pres & CEO)

Subsidiary (Domestic):

Primrose Wellness Group, LLC (2)
6812 Bandera Rd Ste 124, San Antonio, TX 78238-1365
Tel.: (210) 647-8300
Web Site:
http://www.primroselaneadultdaycare.com
Services for the Elderly & Persons with Disabilities
N.A.I.C.S.: 624120
Michelle Garza (Pres)

CLEARFIELD, INC.
7050 Winnetka Ave N Ste 100, Brooklyn Park, MN 55428
Tel.: (763) 476-6866   MN
Web Site:
https://www.seeclearfield.com
Year Founded: 1979

CLFD—(NASDAQ)
Rev.: $166,705,000
Assets: $315,275,000
Liabilities: $39,512,000
Net Worth: $275,763,000
Earnings: ($12,453,000)
Emp.: 400
Fiscal Year-end: 09/30/24
Commercial & Service Industry Machinery Manufacturing
N.A.I.C.S.: 333310
Ronald G. Roth (Chm)
Cheryl Podzimek Beranek (Pres & CEO)
Johnny Hill (COO)
Kevin Morgan (CMO)
Allen Griser (Chief Comml Officer)
Bob Cody (VP)
Skip Hansen (CIO & VP)
Daniel Herzog (CFO, CIO & VP)

Subsidiaries:

Nestor Cables Ltd. (1)
Mittarikuja 5, 90620, Oulu, Finland
Tel.: (358) 207912770
Web Site: https://www.nestorcables.com
Fiber Optic Cable Mfr
N.A.I.C.S.: 335921
Jarmo Rajala (Pres & CEO)

CLEARONE, INC.
5225 Wiley Post Way Ste 500, Salt Lake City, UT 84116
Tel.: (801) 975-7200   UT
Web Site: https://www.clearone.com
CLRO—(NASDAQ)
Rev.: $25,205,000
Assets: $83,750,000
Liabilities: $9,620,000
Net Worth: $74,130,000
Earnings: $20,556,000
Emp.: 82
Fiscal Year-end: 12/31/22
Video Conferencing Products & Services
N.A.I.C.S.: 334210
Eric L. Robinson (Chm)
Simon Brewer (CFO & Principal Acctg Officer)
Derek Graham (Interim CEO & Sr VP-R&D)
David Wang (VP-Sls-Asia Pacific)
Grifiths Zachariah (VP-Sls-Europe, Middle East, India, Africa & Oceania)
Jim Mergens (VP-Sls-Americas)

Subsidiaries:

ClearOne Ltd. (1)
4 Hacharash, Hod Hasharon, 4524075, Israel
Tel.: (972) 97627800
Video & Audio Streaming Services
N.A.I.C.S.: 518210

CLEARPOINT NEURO, INC.
120 S Sierra Ave Ste 100, Solana Beach, CA 92075
Tel.: (949) 900-6833   DE
Web Site:
https://www.clearpointneuro.com
Year Founded: 1998
CLPT—(NASDAQ)
Rev.: $23,955,000
Assets: $42,661,000
Liabilities: $21,488,000
Net Worth: $21,173,000
Earnings: ($22,089,000)
Emp.: 107
Fiscal Year-end: 12/31/23
Medical Device Mfr
N.A.I.C.S.: 339112
Joseph Michael Burnett (Pres & CEO)
Chris Yelley (VP-Ops)
Joseph Michael Burnett (Pres & CEO)
Jacqueline Keller (VP-Mktg)

Danilo D'Alessandro *(CFO)*
Mazin Sabra *(COO)*
Ellisa Cholapranee *(Gen Counsel)*
Jeremy Stigall *(Exec VP)*
Lyubomir Zagorchev *(VP)*
Timothy Orr *(VP)*
Ernesto Salegio *(VP)*
Megan Faulkenberry *(VP)*
Mary McNamara-Cullinane *(VP)*

CLEARSIDE BIOMEDICAL, INC.
900 North Point Pkwy Ste 200, Alpharetta, GA 30005
Tel.: (678) 270-3631   DE
Web Site:
https://www.clearsidebio.com
Year Founded: 2011
CLSD—(NASDAQ)
Rev.: $1,327,000
Assets: $51,303,000
Liabilities: $40,696,000
Net Worth: $10,607,000
Earnings: ($32,947,000)
Emp.: 36
Fiscal Year-end: 12/31/22
Drug Mfr
N.A.I.C.S.: 325412
Charles A. Deignan *(CFO)*
Rick McElheny *(VP-Bus Dev)*
Lester Rodriguez *(VP-Quality)*
Thomas Crawford *(VP-Supply Chain)*
Barbara H. Bauschka *(VP-Regulatory)*
Susan Coultas *(Chief Clinical Officer)*
George M. Lasezkay *(Pres & CEO)*

CLEARSIGN TECHNOLOGIES CORP.
12864 Interurban Ave S, Seattle, WA 98168
Tel.: (918) 236-6461   WA
Web Site: https://www.clearsign.com
Year Founded: 2008
CLIR—(NASDAQ)
Rev.: $2,403,000
Assets: $7,620,000
Liabilities: $2,428,000
Net Worth: $5,192,000
Earnings: ($5,194,000)
Emp.: 15
Fiscal Year-end: 12/31/23
Combustion Systems Mfr
N.A.I.C.S.: 336310
Colin James Deller *(CEO, Interim CFO, Interim Treas & Interim Sec)*
Brent Hinds *(Principal Fin Officer, Principal Acctg Officer, Treas, VP & Controller)*
Robert Thurston Hoffman Sr. *(Chm)*

CLEARTRONIC, INC.
8000 N Federal Hwy, Boca Raton, FL 33487
Tel.: (561) 939-3300   FL
Web Site:
https://www.cleartronic.com
CLRI—(OTCIQ)
Rev.: $2,131,955
Assets: $1,299,802
Liabilities: $1,294,625
Net Worth: $5,177
Earnings: $56,556
Emp.: 2
Fiscal Year-end: 09/30/23
Communication Equipment Mfr
N.A.I.C.S.: 334220
Larry M. Reid *(Founder, Pres, CFO, Chief Acctg Officer & Sec)*
Michael M. Moore *(CEO)*
Richard J. Martin *(Chm)*

Subsidiaries:

ReadyOp Communications, Inc. **(1)**
28050 US Hwy 19 N Ste 310, Clearwater, FL 33761

Tel.: (813) 289-7620
Web Site: https://www.readyop.com
Information Technology Services
N.A.I.C.S.: 541519

CLEARWATER ANALYTICS HOLDINGS, INC.
777 W Main St Ste 900, Boise, ID 83702
Tel.: (208) 433-1200   DE
Web Site:
https://www.clearwateranalytics.com
Year Founded: 2021
CWAN—(NYSE)
Rev.: $303,426,000
Assets: $481,942,000
Liabilities: $143,556,000
Net Worth: $338,386,000
Earnings: ($7,967,000)
Emp.: 1,728
Fiscal Year-end: 12/31/22
Offices of Other Holding Companies
N.A.I.C.S.: 551112
Sandeep Sahai *(CEO)*
Jim Cox *(CFO)*
Scott Erickson *(Chief Revenue Officer)*
Cindy Blendu *(Chief HR & Transformation Officer)*
Souvik Das *(CTO)*
Susan Ganeshan *(CMO)*
Joseph Kochansky *(Pres-Product & Tech)*
James Price *(Chief Quality Officer)*
Subi Sethi *(Chief Client Officer)*
Josh Sullivan *(Chief Strategy Officer)*
Alphonse Valbrune *(Chief Legal Officer)*
Eric Lee *(Chm)*
Scott Erickson *(Chief Revenue Officer)*
Thomas van Cauwelaert *(Reg Mgr-France)*
Sai Perry *(Mgr-Solutions-Europe)*
Sunil Dixit *(Chief Product Officer)*

CLEARWATER PAPER CORPORATION
601 W Riverside Ste 1100, Spokane, WA 99201
Tel.: (509) 344-5900   DE
Web Site:
https://ir.clearwaterpaper.com
CLW—(NYSE)
Rev.: $2,080,100,000
Assets: $1,703,500,000
Liabilities: $1,131,400,000
Net Worth: $572,100,000
Earnings: $46,000,000
Emp.: 3,000
Fiscal Year-end: 12/31/22
Paper & Paper Products Mfr
N.A.I.C.S.: 322299
Michael S. Gadd *(Gen Counsel, Sec & Sr VP)*
Kari G. Moyes *(Sr VP-HR)*
Alexander Toeldte *(Exec Chm)*
Arsen S. Kitch *(Pres & CEO)*
Sherri J. Baker *(CFO & Sr VP)*
Steve M. Bowden *(Sr VP & Gen Mgr-Pulp & Paperboard)*
Rebecca A. Barckley *(Chief Acctg Officer, VP & Controller)*

Subsidiaries:

Clearwater Fiber, LLC **(1)**
601 W Riverside Ste 1100, Spokane, WA 99201
Tel.: (509) 344-5922
Tissue Product Mfr
N.A.I.C.S.: 322291
Jeff Shrewsberry *(Supvr-Log yard)*

Manchester Industries, Inc. of Virginia **(1)**
200 Orleans St, Richmond, VA 23231
Tel.: (804) 226-4250
Web Site: https://www.manind.com

Paperboard Mfr
N.A.I.C.S.: 322130

CLEARWAVE TELECOMMUNICATIONS, INC.
7582 Las Vegas Blvd S, Las Vegas, NV 89123
Tel.: (702) 721-9915
Web Site: http://www.clearwave.com
Year Founded: 1991
CWTC—(OTCIQ)
Corporate Telecommunication Infrastructure Services
N.A.I.C.S.: 517810
Darryl Payne *(CEO)*

CLENE INC.
6550 S Millrock Dr Ste G50, Salt Lake City, UT 84121
Tel.: (801) 676-9695   DE
Web Site: https://www.clene.com
Year Founded: 2012
CLNN—(NASDAQ)
Rev.: $473,000
Assets: $44,493,000
Liabilities: $41,256,000
Net Worth: $3,237,000
Earnings: ($29,918,000)
Emp.: 75
Fiscal Year-end: 12/31/22
Biotechnology Research & Development Services
N.A.I.C.S.: 541714
Morgan R. Brown *(CFO & Principal Acctg Officer)*
Robert Etherington *(Pres & CEO)*

CLEVELAND-CLIFFS, INC.
200 Public Sq Ste 3300, Cleveland, OH 44114-2315
Tel.: (216) 694-5700   OH
Web Site:
https://www.clevelandcliffs.com
Year Founded: 1846
CLF—(NYSE)
Rev.: $21,996,000,000
Assets: $17,537,000,000
Liabilities: $9,415,000,000
Net Worth: $8,122,000,000
Earnings: $399,000,000
Emp.: 28,000
Fiscal Year-end: 12/31/23
Producer & Retailer of Iron Ore Products
N.A.I.C.S.: 212210
Celso L. Goncalves Jr. *(CFO & Exec VP)*
Patricia Persico *(Sr Dir-Corp Comm)*
Clifford T. Smith *(Pres-Steel & Exec VP)*
C. Lourenco Goncalves *(Chm, Pres & CEO)*
Keith A. Koci *(Pres-Svcs & Exec VP)*

Subsidiaries:

AK Steel Holding Corporation **(1)**
9227 Centre Pointe Dr, West Chester, OH 45069
Tel.: (513) 425-5000
Web Site: http://www.aksteel.com
Rev.: $6,359,400,000
Assets: $4,590,600,000
Liabilities: $4,113,300,000
Net Worth: $477,300,000
Earnings: $11,200,000
Emp.: 9,300
Fiscal Year-end: 12/31/2019
Flat-Rolled Carbon, Stainless & Electrical Steel Products & Carbon & Stainless Tubular Steel Products Mfr
N.A.I.C.S.: 331110
Celso L. Goncalves Jr. *(Treas & VP)*
Douglas O. Mitterholzer *(Gen Mgr-IR & Asst Treas)*
Maurice A. Reed *(VP-Strategic Plng & Bus Dev)*
Stephanie S. Bisselberg *(VP-HR)*
Joseph C. Alter *(Gen Counsel, Sec & VP)*

Renee S. Filiatraut *(VP-Litigation, Labor & External Affairs)*
Scott M. Lauschke *(VP-Sls & Customer Svc)*
Brian K. Bishop *(VP-Carbon Steel Ops)*
Michael A. Kercsmar *(VP-Specialty Steel Ops)*
R. Christopher Cebula *(Chief Acctg Officer, Controller & VP)*

Subsidiary (Domestic):

AK Coal Resources, Inc. **(2)**
1134 Stoystown Rd, Friedens, PA 15541-9801
Tel.: (814) 443-2646
Web Site: http://www.aksteel.com
Emp.: 4
Coal Mining Services
N.A.I.C.S.: 212115
Mikel Vaughn *(CFO)*

AK Coatings Inc. **(2)**
9227 Ctr Point Dr, West Chester, OH 45069
Tel.: (513) 425-5000
Web Site: http://www.akcoatings.com
Sales Range: $150-199.9 Million
Emp.: 300
Antimicrobial-Coated Carbon & Stainless Steel Mfr
N.A.I.C.S.: 331221
James L. Wainscott *(Chm, Pres & CEO)*

Subsidiary (Non-US):

AK Steel BV **(2)**
Rat Verleghstraat 2a, 4815 NZ, Breda, Netherlands
Tel.: (31) 765237300
Web Site: https://www.aksteel.nl
Sales Range: $25-49.9 Million
Emp.: 36
Steel Products Mfr
N.A.I.C.S.: 331110
Gerard Baert *(Mng Dir)*

Branch (Domestic):

AK Steel Corp. **(2)**
9227 Ctr Point Dr, West Chester, OH 45069
Tel.: (513) 425-5000
Web Site: http://www.aksteel.com
Sales Range: $25-49.9 Million
Emp.: 300
Steel Mills
N.A.I.C.S.: 331110

Subsidiary (Domestic):

AK Tube LLC **(3)**
30400 E Broadway, Walbridge, OH 43465
Tel.: (419) 661-4150
Web Site: http://www.aktube.com
Sales Range: $50-74.9 Million
Emp.: 300
Welded Tubular Steel Products Mfr
N.A.I.C.S.: 331210
Edward J. Urbaniak *(Pres & CEO)*

Subsidiary (Non-US):

AK Steel GmbH **(2)**
Holzmarkt 1, 50676, Cologne, Germany
Tel.: (49) 221973520
Web Site: http://www.aksteel.de
Sales Range: $10-24.9 Million
Emp.: 14
Steel Products Mfr
N.A.I.C.S.: 331110
Thomas Wolter *(Branch Mgr)*

AK Steel International BV **(2)**
Rat Verleghstraat 2A, 4815 NZ, Breda, Netherlands
Tel.: (31) 765237300
Web Site: http://www.aksteel.eu
Emp.: 40
Carbon & Stainless Steel Product Mfr
N.A.I.C.S.: 331110

AK Steel Limited **(2)**
The Business & Technology Centre Room S04 Bessemer Drive, Stevenage, SG1 2DX, Hertfordshire, United Kingdom
Tel.: (44) 1438842910
Web Site: http://www.aksteel.com
Emp.: 2
Steel Products Mfr
N.A.I.C.S.: 331110

Cleveland-Cliffs, Inc.—(Continued)

Hans Geraeds *(Mng Dir)*

AK Steel Merchandising S.A. **(2)**
Avda Diagonal 640 6th floor, 08017, Barcelona, Spain
Tel.: (34) 932094177
Web Site: http://www.aksteel.eu
Emp.: 6
Steel Products Mfr
N.A.I.C.S.: 331110

AK Steel NV **(2)**
Haven 200 Schouwkensstraat 7, 2030, Antwerp, Belgium
Tel.: (32) 35430640
Web Site: http://www.aksteel.eu
Emp.: 5
Steel Products Mfr
N.A.I.C.S.: 331110

AK Steel S.A.R.L. **(2)**
Immeuble Sezac 1 Rpt Pariwest, 78310, Maurepas, France
Tel.: (33) 130051130
Web Site: http://www.aksteel.fr
Sales Range: $10-24.9 Million
Emp.: 7
Iron & Steel Product Merchant Whslr
N.A.I.C.S.: 423510

AK Steel Srl **(2)**
Piazza della Vittoria 15/31, 16121, Genoa, Italy
Tel.: (39) 010582746
Web Site: http://www.aksteel.eu
Emp.: 12
Steel Products Mfr
N.A.I.C.S.: 331110

Subsidiary (Domestic):

Coal Innovations, LLC **(2)**
329 Yellow Creek Rd, Stoystown, PA 15563
Tel.: (814) 893-5790
Web Site: http://www.coalinnovations.com
Carbon & Stainless Steel Product Mfr
N.A.I.C.S.: 331110

Division (Domestic):

Combined Metals of Chicago LLC **(2)**
2401 W Grant Ave, Bellwood, IL 60104-1660
Tel.: (708) 547-8800
Web Site: http://www.combmet.com
Sales Range: $50-74.9 Million
Emp.: 100
Mfr of Steel
N.A.I.C.S.: 423510

Subsidiary (Domestic):

Mountain State Carbon, LLC **(2)**
1851 Main St, Follansbee, WV 26037
Tel.: (304) 527-5632
Web Site: http://mscarbonllc.com
Emp.: 200
Furnace & Foundry Coke Mfr
N.A.I.C.S.: 324199

Subsidiary (Non-US):

Precision Partners Holding Company **(2)**
1965 Ambassador Dr, Windsor, N9C 3R5, ON, Canada
Tel.: (519) 969-4632
Web Site: http://www.pphc.com
Emp.: 1,000
Holding Company
N.A.I.C.S.: 551112
Desmond Griffiths *(Pres & CEO)*

Subsidiary (Domestic):

Fleetwood Metal Industries, Inc. **(3)**
1885 Blackacre Dr, Windsor, N0R1L0, ON, Canada **(100%)**
Tel.: (519) 737-1919
Web Site: http://www.fleetwoodmetal.com
Sales Range: $25-49.9 Million
Emp.: 40
Metal Stamping & Welding for Automotive Industry
N.A.I.C.S.: 336370
Terry Soanes *(VP-Sls)*
Gary McGuinness *(Mgr-Corp Sls)*

ArcelorMittal Steel USA Inc. **(1)**
1 S Dearborn Ste 1800, Chicago, IL 60603
Tel.: (312) 899-3351
Bar & Flat-Rolled Steel Mfr
N.A.I.C.S.: 331110

Subsidiary (Domestic):

ArcelorMittal Coatesville **(2)**
139 Modena Rd, Coatesville, PA 19320
Tel.: (610) 383-2000
Sales Range: $200-249.9 Million
Emp.: 800
Construction Machinery Mfr
N.A.I.C.S.: 333120

ArcelorMittal East Chicago **(2)**
3001 E Columbus Dr, East Chicago, IN 46312
Tel.: (219) 399-6120
Web Site: http://www.usa.arcelormittal.com
Engineering Research & Development Services
N.A.I.C.S.: 541715

ArcelorMittal LaPlace **(2)**
138 Hwy 3217, La Place, LA 70068
Tel.: (985) 652-4900
Web Site: http://www.bayousteel.com
Sales Range: $250-299.9 Million
Emp.: 524
Light Structural & Merchant Bar Products Mfr
N.A.I.C.S.: 331221

Plant (Domestic):

Bayou Steel Corporation (Tennessee) **(3)**
2404 S Roane St, Harriman, TN 37748
Tel.: (865) 882-5100
Sales Range: $25-49.9 Million
Emp.: 130
Light Structural & Merchant Bar Products Mfr
N.A.I.C.S.: 331221

Subsidiary (Domestic):

ArcelorMittal Steelton LLC **(2)**
215 S Front St, Steelton, PA 17113
Tel.: (717) 986-2000
Sales Range: $150-199.9 Million
Emp.: 700
Railroad Rails Products & Large Expanded Pipe Mfr
N.A.I.C.S.: 813930

ArcelorMittal Tailored Blanks **(2)**
2 Kexon Dr, Pioneer, OH 43554
Tel.: (419) 737-3180
Automotive Welded Blank Mfr
N.A.I.C.S.: 332311

ArcelorMittal Vinton, Inc **(2)**
8001 Border Steel Rd, Canutillo, TX 79835
Tel.: (915) 886-2000
Sales Range: $75-99.9 Million
Emp.: 360
Steel Making Operations
N.A.I.C.S.: 331110
Gerardo Salinas *(Pres)*

Cleveland-Cliffs Burns Harbor LLC **(2)**
250 W US Hwy 12, Burns Harbor, IN 46304
Tel.: (216) 694-5700
Steel Products Mfr
N.A.I.C.S.: 423510

Cleveland-Cliffs Cleveland Works LLC **(2)**
3060 Eggers Ave, Cleveland, OH 44105
Tel.: (216) 429-6000
Rolled Steel Shape Mfr
N.A.I.C.S.: 331221

Cleveland-Cliffs Minorca Mine Inc. **(2)**
5950 Old Hwy 53 N, Virginia, MN 55792
Tel.: (218) 749-5910
Ore Fluxed Pellets Producer
N.A.I.C.S.: 212210

Cleveland-Cliffs Plate LLC **(2)**
139 Modena Rd, Coatesville, PA 19320
Tel.: (610) 383-2000
Carbon Alloy & Clad Plate Steel Mfr
N.A.I.C.S.: 331110

Cleveland-Cliffs Weirton LLC **(2)**

299 Cove Rd, Weirton, WV 26062
Tel.: (304) 797-2000
Flat Rolled Steel Mfr
N.A.I.C.S.: 331110

Joint Venture (Domestic):

Double G Coatings Company, L.P. **(2)**
1096 Mendell Davis Dr, Jackson, MS 39272-9109 **(50%)**
Tel.: (601) 372-4236
Sales Range: $10-24.9 Million
Emp.: 78
Steel Sheeting Mfr
N.A.I.C.S.: 332812

Cliffs Mining Company **(1)**
1100 Superior Ave E Ste 15, Cleveland, OH 44114 **(100%)**
Tel.: (216) 694-5700
Web Site:
http://www.cliffsnaturalresources.com
Sales Range: $125-149.9 Million
Emp.: 125
Metals & Mining Operations
N.A.I.C.S.: 213113

Cliffs Netherlands B.V. **(1)**
De Boelelaan 7, Amsterdam, 1083 HJ, Netherlands
Tel.: (31) 205043800
Emp.: 30
Metal Mining Services
N.A.I.C.S.: 212290

FPT Florida, LLC **(1)**
3700 NW N River Dr, Miami, FL 33142
Tel.: (305) 638-0040
Metal Recycling Services
N.A.I.C.S.: 562920

I/N Kote L.P. **(1)**
30755 Edison Rd, New Carlisle, IN 46552-9728
Tel.: (219) 654-1000
Sales Range: $50-74.9 Million
Emp.: 250
Provider of Hot-Dip & Electrogalvanizing Lines for Flat-Rolled Steel; Joint Venture Between Ispat Inland Inc. & Nippon Steel Corp.
N.A.I.C.S.: 332812

I/N Tek L.P. **(1)**
30755 Edison Rd, New Carlisle, IN 46552-9728
Tel.: (574) 654-1000
Emp.: 516
Continuous Cold Rolling Mill; Joint Venture Between Ispat Inland Inc. & Nippon Steel Corporation
N.A.I.C.S.: 332812

Koil Metals L.L.C. **(1)**
3400 E Lafayette, Detroit, MI 48207
Tel.: (313) 567-4070
Web Site: https://www.koilmetals.com
Rolled Steel Mfr & Distr
N.A.I.C.S.: 331221

Northshore Mining Company **(1)**
10 Outer Dr, Silver Bay, MN 55614
Tel.: (218) 226-4125
Iron Ore Pallets Mfr
N.A.I.C.S.: 331210

Stelco Holdings, Inc. **(1)**
386 Wilcox Street, Hamilton, L8L 8J6, ON, Canada
Tel.: (905) 528-2511
Web Site: https://www.stelco.com
Rev.: $1,186,718,760
Assets: $1,391,676,120
Liabilities: $1,171,855,440
Net Worth: $219,820,680
Earnings: ($124,382,520)
Emp.: 2,200
Fiscal Year-end: 12/31/2020
Holding Company
N.A.I.C.S.: 551112
Paul Scherzer *(CFO)*
Sujit Sanyal *(COO)*

Tilden Mining Company LC **(1)**
PO Box 2000, Ishpeming, MI 49849 **(100%)**
Tel.: (906) 475-3400
Web Site:
http://www.cliffsnaturalresources.com
Rev.: $55,300,000

Emp.: 1,500
Iron Ore Mining
N.A.I.C.S.: 212210

United Taconite, LLC **(1)**
1200 W Hwy 16, Eveleth, MN 55734 **(100%)**
Tel.: (218) 744-7800
Sales Range: $10-24.9 Million
Emp.: 486
Iron Ore Mining & Pelletizing
N.A.I.C.S.: 212210

CLEVER LEAVES HOLDINGS INC.
489 5th Ave 27th Fl, New York, NY 10017
Tel.: (646) 880-4382
Year Founded: 2020
CLVR—(NASDAQ)
Rev.: $17,800,000
Assets: $52,098,000
Liabilities: $11,690,000
Net Worth: $40,408,000
Earnings: ($66,165,000)
Emp.: 400
Fiscal Year-end: 12/31/22
Holding Company
N.A.I.C.S.: 551111
Kyle Detwiler *(CEO)*
Henry R. Hague III *(CFO)*

CLIFTON MINING COMPANY
705 E 50 S, American Fork, UT 84003
Tel.: (801) 756-1414
Web Site:
https://www.cliftonmining.com
Year Founded: 1993
CFTN—(OTCIQ)
Sales Range: Less than $1 Million
Metal Ore Mining Services
N.A.I.C.S.: 212290
Ken Friedman *(Pres)*

CLIKIA CORP.
7117 Florida Blvd Ste 206, Baton Rouge, LA 70806
Tel.: (800) 584-3808
Web Site: http://www.clikia.com
Year Founded: 2002
CLKA—(OTCIQ)
Content Delivery Company; Video Streaming Subscription Service & Original Content Incubator
N.A.I.C.S.: 512199
David Loflin *(Pres)*

CLIMB GLOBAL SOLUTIONS, INC.
32 Wiggins Ave, Bedford, MA 01730
Tel.: (781) 457-9000
Web Site: https://www.anika.com
Year Founded: 1982
CLMB—(NASDAQ)
Rev.: $304,348,000
Assets: $231,856,000
Liabilities: $171,282,000
Net Worth: $60,574,000
Earnings: $12,497,000
Emp.: 284
Fiscal Year-end: 12/31/22
Software Distr & Reseller
N.A.I.C.S.: 423430
Timothy Popovich *(COO & VP)*
Dale Richard Foster *(Pres & CEO)*
Vito Legrottaglie *(CIO & VP)*
Andrew E. Clark *(CFO & VP)*
Charles Bass *(CMO & VP)*
Drew Clark *(CFO)*

Subsidiaries:

Climb Channel Solutions, Inc. **(1)**
4 Industrial Way W 3rd Fl, Eatontown, NJ 07724
Tel.: (732) 389-0037
Web Site: https://www.climbcs.com
Computer Software Services

N.A.I.C.S.: 541511
Timothy Popovich *(Pres & COO)*
Charles Bass *(CMO)*
Tim Popovich *(VP-Sls-US)*

Grey Matter (EMEA) Limited **(1)**
St Gall's House St Gall Gardens South,
Milltown, Dublin, D14 Y882, Ireland
Tel.: (353) 414141001
Computer Software Services
N.A.I.C.S.: 541511

ISP International Software Partners,
Inc. **(1)**
4 Industrial Way W, Eatontown, NJ 07724
Tel.: (732) 389-0932
Web Site: https://www.ispfulfillment.com
Emp.: 3
Software Publishing Services
N.A.I.C.S.: 513210

Lifeboat Distribution, EMEA B.V. **(1)**
Hoogoorddreef 9, 1101 BA, Amsterdam,
Netherlands
Tel.: (31) 202108005
Telemarketing Customer Services
N.A.I.C.S.: 561422
Dale Foster *(Exec VP)*
Vito Legrottaglie *(CIO & VP)*
Michael Vesey *(CFO & VP)*
Kevin Scull *(Chief Acctg Officer & VP)*
Brian Gilbertson *(VP & Gen Mgr)*

Lifeboat Distribution, Inc. **(1)**
4 Industrial Way W 3rd Fl, Eatontown, NJ
07724
Tel.: (800) 847-7078
Web Site: http://www.lifeboatdistribution.com
Sales Range: $50-74.9 Million
Emp.: 100
Customer Support Services
N.A.I.C.S.: 561422
Tim Popovich *(VP-Sls-North America)*
Patrick Castenie *(VP-Mktg)*

Programmer's Paradise, Inc. **(1)**
4 Industrial Way W 3rd floor, Eatontown, NJ
07702-4321
Tel.: (732) 389-8950
Web Site:
    http://www.waysidetechnology.com
Sales Range: $25-49.9 Million
Emp.: 100
Computer Products Distr & Mail-Order
N.A.I.C.S.: 423430

TechXtend, Inc. **(1)**
4 Industrial Way W 3rd Fl, Eatontown, NJ
07724
Tel.: (800) 599-4388
Web Site: https://greymatter.com
Sales Range: $75-99.9 Million
Emp.: 100
Software Development Services
N.A.I.C.S.: 513210
Kevin Askew *(VP & Gen Mgr)*

CLIPPER REALTY INC.
4611 12th Ave Ste 1L, Brooklyn, NY
11219
Tel.: (718) 438-2804   MD
Web Site:
    https://www.clipperrealty.com
Year Founded: 2015
CLPR—(NYSE)
Rev.: $129,746,000
Assets: $1,229,631,000
Liabilities: $1,192,452,000
Net Worth: $37,179,000
Earnings: ($4,764,000)
Emp.: 147
Fiscal Year-end: 12/31/22
Residential & Commercial Property
Development Services
N.A.I.C.S.: 531210
Sam D. Levinson *(Co-Chm)*
David Bistricer *(Co-Chm & CEO)*
Jacob Joseph Bistricer *(COO)*
Jacob Schwimmer *(Chief Property
Mgmt Officer)*

CLOUDFLARE, INC.
101 Townsend St, San Francisco, CA
94107
Tel.: (650) 319-8930   DE

Web Site: https://www.cloudflare.com
Year Founded: 2009
NET—(NYSE)
Rev.: $1,296,745,000
Assets: $2,759,767,000
Liabilities: $1,996,720,000
Net Worth: $763,047,000
Earnings: ($183,949,000)
Emp.: 3,682
Fiscal Year-end: 12/31/23
Online Security Services
N.A.I.C.S.: 541512
Thomas J. Seifert *(CFO)*
Douglas Kramer *(Gen Counsel)*
Janel Riley *(Chief Acctg Officer & VP-
Fin)*
Michelle Zatlyn *(Co-Founder, Pres &
COO)*
Jennifer Taylor *(Chief Product Officer
& Sr VP-Products)*
Matthew Prince *(Co-Founder, Chm &
CEO)*

CLOUDWEB, INC.
800 W El Camino Real Ste 180,
Mountain View, CA 94040
Tel.: (773) 236-8132   FL
Year Founded: 2014
CLOW—(OTCIQ)
Liabilities: $560,442
Net Worth: ($560,442)
Earnings: $102,996)
Emp.: 314
Fiscal Year-end: 12/31/22
Investment Services
N.A.I.C.S.: 523999
Zhi De Liao *(Pres, CEO & CFO)*

**CLOUGH GLOBAL DIVIDEND
& INCOME FUND**
1700 Broadway Ste 1850, Denver,
CO 80290
Tel.: (303) 623-2577   DE
GLV—(NYSEAMEX)
Rev.: $4,408,689
Assets: $176,385,268
Liabilities: $73,714,988
Net Worth: $102,670,280
Earnings: $1,152,057
Fiscal Year-end: 10/31/19
Investment Management Service
N.A.I.C.S.: 525990
Adam D. Crescenzi *(Vice Chm)*
Jeremy May *(Pres)*

**CLOUGH GLOBAL EQUITY
FUND**
1700 Broadway Ste 1850, Denver,
CO 80290   DE
GLQ—(NYSEAMEX)
Rev.: $5,267,961
Assets: $298,479,199
Liabilities: $127,142,209
Net Worth: $171,336,990
Earnings: ($676,852)
Fiscal Year-end: 10/31/19
Investment Management Service
N.A.I.C.S.: 525990
Christopher Moore *(Sec)*
Adam D. Crescenzi *(Vice Chm)*
Robert L. Butler *(Chm)*
Jill Kerschen *(Treas)*
Bradley Swenson *(Chief Compliance
Officer)*

**CLOUGH GLOBAL OPPORTU-
NITIES FUND**
1700 Broadway Ste 1850, Denver,
CO 80290
Tel.: (303) 623-2577   DE
GLO—(NYSEAMEX)
Rev.: $12,662,837
Assets: $609,343,403
Liabilities: $269,065,503
Net Worth: $340,277,900
Earnings: ($1,334,560)

Fiscal Year-end: 10/31/19
Investment Management Service
N.A.I.C.S.: 525990
Christopher Moore *(Sec)*
Adam D. Crescenzi *(Vice Chm)*
Jill Kerschen *(Treas)*
Jeremy May *(Pres)*

**CLOVER HEALTH INVEST-
MENTS, CORP.**
Tel.: (201) 432-2133   DE
Web Site:
    https://www.cloverhealth.com
Year Founded: 2019
CLOV—(NASDAQ)
Rev.: $3,476,687,000
Assets: $808,620,000
Liabilities: $460,882,000
Net Worth: $347,738,000
Earnings: ($338,844,000)
Emp.: 656
Fiscal Year-end: 12/31/22
Cloud-Based Health Care Services
Platform Developer
N.A.I.C.S.: 541511
Peter J. Kuipers *(CFO & Principal
Acctg Officer)*
Andrew Toy *(CEO)*
Rachel Fish *(Chief People Officer)*
Brady Priest *(CEO-Home Care)*
Jamie Reynoso *(CEO-Medicare Ad-
vantage)*
Wendy Richey *(Chief Compliance
Officer)*
Theresa Safe *(Sr VP-Business En-
ablement)*
Karen Soares *(Gen Counsel)*
Aric Sharp *(CEO-Value Based Care)*
Conrad Wai *(CTO)*

**CLOVER LEAF CAPITAL
CORP.**
1450 Brickell Ave Ste 2520, Miami,
FL 33131
Tel.: (305) 577-0031   DE
Web Site: https://cloverlcc.com
Year Founded: 2021
CLOE—(NASDAQ)
Rev.: $1,536,888
Assets: $18,684,974
Liabilities: $26,415,164
Net Worth: ($7,730,190)
Earnings: $60,237
Emp.: 3
Fiscal Year-end: 12/31/22
Investment Services
N.A.I.C.S.: 523999
Felipe MacLean *(Chm, Pres & CEO)*
Luis A. Guerra *(CFO & Treas)*
Markus Puusepp *(COO)*

CLOVIS ONCOLOGY, INC.
5500 Flatiron Pkwy Ste 100, Boulder,
CO 80301
Tel.: (303) 625-5000   DE
Web Site:
    http://www.clovisoncology.com
Year Founded: 2009
CLVS—(NASDAQ)
Rev.: $374,524,000
Assets: $472,833,000
Liabilities: $751,673,000
Net Worth: ($278,840,000)
Earnings: ($264,524,000)
Emp.: 413
Fiscal Year-end: 12/31/21
Biopharmaceutical Researcher, De-
veloper & Mfr
N.A.I.C.S.: 325412
Lindsey Rolfe *(Chief Medical Officer
& Exec VP-Clinical & Preclinical Dev)*
Gillian C. Ivers-Read *(Chief Regula-
tory Officer & Exec VP-Technical
Ops)*
Patrick J. Mahaffy *(Pres & CEO)*
Daniel W. Muehl *(CFO & Exec VP)*

Ann Bozeman *(Exec VP-HR)*
Thomas Fuglsang Harding *(Chief Scientific Officer & Exec VP)*

Subsidiaries:

Clovis Oncology UK Limited **(1)**
Sheraton House Castle Park, Cambridge,
CB3 0AX, United Kingdom
Tel.: (44) 1223370037
Medical Research Services
N.A.I.C.S.: 325412
Alan Newlands *(VP-Regulatory Affairs)*

CLS HOLDINGS USA, INC.
516 S 4th St, Las Vegas, NV 89101   NV
Web Site:
    https://www.clsholdingsinc.com
Year Founded: 2011
CLSH—(OTCQB)
Rev.: $19,961,133
Assets: $7,925,061
Liabilities: $20,833,859
Net Worth: ($12,908,798)
Earnings: ($4,485,236)
Emp.: 79
Fiscal Year-end: 05/31/24
Holding Company; Cannabis Cultiva-
tion & Sales
N.A.I.C.S.: 551112
Andrew J. Glashow *(Chm, Pres &
CEO)*

Subsidiaries:

CLS Labs, Inc. **(1)**
1810 E Sahara Ave Ste 613, Las Vegas,
NV 89104
Cannabis Cultivation & Sales
N.A.I.C.S.: 111419

Serenity Wellness Center, LLC **(1)**
1800 Industrial Rd Ste 180, Las Vegas, NV
89102
Tel.: (702) 420-2405
Web Site: https://www.oasiscannabis.com
Cannabis Dispensary
N.A.I.C.S.: 459999

**CLUBHOUSE MEDIA GROUP,
INC.**
3651 Lindell Rd Ste D517, Las Ve-
gas, NV 89103
Tel.: (702) 479-3016   NV
Web Site:
    https://clubhousemediagroup.com
Year Founded: 2006
CMGR—(OTCIQ)
Rev.: $6,283,691
Assets: $1,243,754
Liabilities: $8,921,990
Net Worth: ($7,678,236)
Earnings: ($7,525,731)
Emp.: 3
Fiscal Year-end: 12/31/22
Hospital Owner & Operator
N.A.I.C.S.: 622110
Simon Yu *(COO)*
Amir Ben-Yohanan *(Chm & CEO)*
Christian J. Young *(Pres & Sec)*

CME GROUP, INC.
20 S Wacker Dr, Chicago, IL 60606
Tel.: (312) 930-1000
Web Site: https://www.cmegroup.com
CME—(NASDAQ)
Rev.: $5,578,900,000
Assets: $129,706,100,000
Liabilities: $102,968,200,000
Net Worth: $26,737,900,000
Earnings: $3,185,600,000
Emp.: 3,565
Fiscal Year-end: 12/31/23
Financial Investment Services
N.A.I.C.S.: 551112
Julie Holzrichter *(Sr Mng Dir & COO)*
Hilda Harris Piell *(Sr Mng Dir & Chief
HR Officer)*
Julie M. Winkler *(Sr Mng Dir & Chief
Comml Officer)*

CME Group, Inc.—(Continued)

Tim McCourt *(Sr Mng Dir & Head-Fin & OTC Products-Global)*
Jack Tobin *(Mng Dir & Chief Acctg Officer)*
Patrick J. Mulchrone *(Vice Chm)*
Julie Holzrichter *(COO)*
Lynne Fitzpatrick *(Sr Mng Dir & CFO)*
Jonathan Marcus *(Sr Mng Dir)*
Suzanne Sprague *(Sr Mng Dir)*
Terrence A. Duffy *(Chm & CEO)*

Subsidiaries:

CME Clearing Europe Limited (1)
Fourth Floor One New Change, London, EC4M 9AF, United Kingdom
Tel.: (44) 2033793100
Web Site:
http://www.cmeclearingeurope.com
Risk Management Solutions
N.A.I.C.S.: 523210

CME Digital Limited (1)
Old Town Close, Beaconsfield, HP9 1LF, Buckinghamshire, United Kingdom
Tel.: (44) 1494680118
Web Site: https://cme.digital
Software Development Services
N.A.I.C.S.: 541511

CME Europe Limited (1)
Fourth Floor 1 New Change, London, EC4M 9AF, United Kingdom
Tel.: (44) 2033793700
Web Site: http://www.cmeeurope.com
Commodity Contract Trading Services
N.A.I.C.S.: 523160

CME Group Asia Holdings Pte. Ltd (1)
10 Marina Boulevard 21-01 Marina Bay Financial Centre Tower 2, Singapore, 018983, Singapore
Tel.: (65) 6 593 5555
Web Site: http://www.cmegroup.com
Financial Risk Management Services
N.A.I.C.S.: 523150

CME Group Australia Pty. Ltd. (1)
Level 36 Gateway Tower 1 Macquarie Place, Sydney, 2000, NSW, Australia
Tel.: (61) 280513210
Financial Investment Services
N.A.I.C.S.: 551112

CME Group Singapore Operations Pte.Ltd. (1)
10 Marina Boulevard 21-01 Marina Bay Financial Centre, Singapore, 018983, Singapore
Tel.: (65) 65935555
Insurance Management Services
N.A.I.C.S.: 524210

Dubai Mercantile Exchange Limited (1)
Bldg 10 4th floor, PO Box 66500, Dubai, United Arab Emirates **(50%)**
Tel.: (971) 43655500
Web Site: http://www.dubaimerc.com
Sales Range: $650-699.9 Million
Emp.: 20
Commodities Exchange; Owned by New York Mercantile Exchange, Inc., by Dubai Holding LLC & by Oman Investment Fund
N.A.I.C.S.: 523210
Shahnaz Qaedi *(Gen Counsel, Sec & Head-Membership)*
Ahmad Sharaf *(Chm)*
Michelle Zhang *(Head-Products & Svcs-Asia)*

GFX Corporation (1)
550 W Washington Blvd Ste Fl 6, Chicago, IL 60661
Tel.: (312) 930-1000
Sales Range: $75-99.9 Million
Emp.: 25
Currency Futures & Electronic Trade Services
N.A.I.C.S.: 523210

NEX Abide Trade Repository AB (1)
Master Samuelsgatan 17, 111 44, Stockholm, Sweden
Tel.: (46) 850541475

Web Site: http://www.natr.abide-financial.com
Trading Exchange Services
N.A.I.C.S.: 561990

NEX Exchange Limited (1)
London Fruit and Wool Exchange 1 Duval Square, London, E1 6PW, United Kingdom
Tel.: (44) 2035976364
Financial Services
N.A.I.C.S.: 523999
Patrick Birley *(CEO)*

NEX Group Limited (1)
2 Broadgate, London, EC2M 7UR, United Kingdom **(100%)**
Tel.: (44) 2078189000
Web Site: http://www.nex.com
Rev.: $797,329,920
Assets: $2,320,486,400
Liabilities: $1,099,532,800
Net Worth: $1,220,953,600
Earnings: $152,450,560
Emp.: 1,934
Fiscal Year-end: 03/31/2018
Securities Brokerage Services
N.A.I.C.S.: 523150

Subsidiary (Domestic):

Aquis Stock Exchange Limited (2)
77 Cornhill, London, EC3V 3QQ, United Kingdom
Tel.: (44) 203 597 6365
Web Site: http://www.aquis.eu
Securities Exchange Operator
N.A.I.C.S.: 523210
Michael Berkeley *(Chm)*

EBS Dealing Resources International Limited (2)
London Fruit And Wool Exchange 1 Duval Square, London, E1 6PW, United Kingdom **(100%)**
Tel.: (44) 2070299000
Sales Range: $400-449.9 Million
Emp.: 1,800
Data Processing Services
N.A.I.C.S.: 518210
Michael Spencer *(CEO)*
Paul Allmark *(Global Head-ECommerce Solutions)*

Subsidiary (US):

EBS Dealing Resources Inc (3)
1 Uppr Pond Rd Bldg F Fl 3, Parsippany, NJ 07054
Tel.: (973) 257-6600
Foreign Exchange Trading Services
N.A.I.C.S.: 522299

Subsidiary (Non-US):

EBS Dealing Resources Japan Limited (3)
Toho Twin Tower Building 3rd Floor, 1-5-2 Yurakucho Chiyoda-ku, 100-0006, Tokyo, Japan **(100%)**
Tel.: (81) 355116696
Web Site: http://www.icap.com
Custom Computer Programming Services
N.A.I.C.S.: 541511

EBS Service Co Limited (3)
Lavaterstrasse 40, 8002, Zurich, 8002, Switzerland
Tel.: (41) 442857585
Electronic Broking Services
N.A.I.C.S.: 425120

Subsidiary (Non-US):

FCD-Harlow Butler Pty Limited (2)
105 Central Street, Houghton, 2041, Johannesburg, South Africa **(55.3%)**
Tel.: (27) 112769000
Sales Range: $50-74.9 Million
Emp.: 40
Investment Advice
N.A.I.C.S.: 523940

ICAP (Hong Kong) Limited (2)
Unit 2902-2909 29th Floor The Center, 99 Queen's Road, Central, China (Hong Kong) **(100%)**
Tel.: (852) 25320888
Sales Range: $100-124.9 Million
Emp.: 120
Securities Brokerage
N.A.I.C.S.: 523150

ICAP AP (Singapore) Pte Limited (2)
50 Raffles Place 41-00, Singapore, 48623, Singapore **(100%)**
Tel.: (65) 68310888
Sales Range: $100-124.9 Million
Emp.: 200
Securities Brokerage
N.A.I.C.S.: 523150

Subsidiary (Domestic):

ICAP America Investments Limited (2)
2 Broadgate, London, EC2M 7UR, United Kingdom
Tel.: (44) 20 7000 5000
Web Site: http://www.icap.com
Emp.: 2,000
Investment Management Service
N.A.I.C.S.: 523999

Subsidiary (Non-US):

ICAP Australia Pty Limited (2)
Level 27 9 Castlereagh Street, Sydney, 2000, NSW, Australia **(100%)**
Tel.: (61) 297770800
Sales Range: $50-74.9 Million
Emp.: 74
Nondepository Credit Intermediation
N.A.I.C.S.: 522299
Brad Howell *(CEO)*

ICAP Brokers Pty Limited (2)
Level 27 9 Castlereagh Street, Sydney, 2000, NSW, Australia **(100%)**
Tel.: (61) 297770800
Web Site: http://www.icap.com
Sales Range: $50-74.9 Million
Emp.: 60
Securities Brokerage
N.A.I.C.S.: 523150
Brad Howell *(CEO)*

ICAP Colombia Investment Corporation (2)
Cra 11 No 93-46 Office 403, Bogota, Colombia **(100%)**
Tel.: (57) 16355489
Investment & Securities Services
N.A.I.C.S.: 523940

ICAP Currency Options Pte Limited (2)
50 Raffles Place 41-00 Singapore Land Tower, Singapore, 048623, Singapore **(100%)**
Tel.: (65) 68316800
Sales Range: $100-124.9 Million
Emp.: 200
Securities Brokerage
N.A.I.C.S.: 523150

ICAP Deutschland GmbH (2)
Stephanstrasse 14 - 16, 60313, Frankfurt, Germany
Tel.: (49) 6913009
Web Site: http://www.icap.com
Securities Brokerage
N.A.I.C.S.: 523150

Subsidiary (Domestic):

ICAP Electronic Broking Limited (2)
2 Broadgate, London, EC2M7UR, United Kingdom **(100%)**
Tel.: (44) 2070005000
Sales Range: $700-749.9 Million
Emp.: 1,800
Securities Brokerage
N.A.I.C.S.: 523150

Subsidiary (Non-US):

ICAP Energy AS (2)
Fantoftvegen 2, 5072, Bergen, Norway **(100%)**
Tel.: (47) 55604400,
Sales Range: $75-99.9 Million
Emp.: 14
Electric Power Distribution
N.A.I.C.S.: 221122
Denise Crum *(Mng Dir)*

Subsidiary (Domestic):

ICAP Energy Limited (2)
2 Broadgate, London, EC2M 7UR, United Kingdom **(100%)**
Tel.: (44) 2070005000

Web Site: http://www.icap.com
Sales Range: $700-749.9 Million
Emp.: 1,200
Securities & Commodity Exchanges
N.A.I.C.S.: 523210

Subsidiary (Non-US):

ICAP Energy Pte Limited (2)
6 Battery Rd No 39-01, 049909, Singapore, Singapore **(100%)**
Tel.: (65) 68203000
Sales Range: $100-124.9 Million
Emp.: 200
Securities Brokerage
N.A.I.C.S.: 523150

ICAP Equities Asia Limited (2)
29/F Center 99 Queen's Road, Central District, Hong Kong, China (Hong Kong)
Tel.: (852) 2532 0856
Investment Advisory Services
N.A.I.C.S.: 523940
Benny Luk *(Gen Mgr)*

Subsidiary (Domestic):

ICAP Europe Limited (2)
2 Broadgate, London, EC2M7UR, United Kingdom **(100%)**
Tel.: (44) 2070005000
Web Site: http://www.icap.com
Sales Range: $700-749.9 Million
Emp.: 1,500
Securities & Commodity Exchanges
N.A.I.C.S.: 523210

Subsidiary (Non-US):

ICAP Foreign Exchange Brokerage Limited (2)
11th Floor Seoul YWCA Building, 1-1 Myeong-dong 1-ga Jung-gu, Seoul, 100-021, Korea (South) **(100%)**
Tel.: (82) 23117604
Web Site: http://www.icap.com
Sales Range: $50-74.9 Million
Emp.: 30
International Trade Financing
N.A.I.C.S.: 522299
Minho Lee *(CEO)*

ICAP Futures (Australia) Pty Ltd (2)
Level 27 9 Castlereagh Street, Sydney, 2000, NSW, Australia
Tel.: (61) 297770800
Securities Brokerage Services
N.A.I.C.S.: 523150

ICAP Holdings (Nederland) B.V. (2)
Kabelweg 37, 1014 BA, Amsterdam, Netherlands **(100%)**
Tel.: (31) 206424747
Real Estate Investment Trust
N.A.I.C.S.: 525990

ICAP India Private Limited (2)
202 Dalamal Towers, Nariman Point, 400021, Mumbai, India **(51%)**
Tel.: (91) 2222855754
Sales Range: $50-74.9 Million
Emp.: 50
Securities Brokerage
N.A.I.C.S.: 523150

Subsidiary (Domestic):

ICAP Management Services Limited (2)
2 Broadgate, London, EC2M7UR, United Kingdom **(100%)**
Tel.: (44) 2070005000
Web Site: http://www.icap.com
Sales Range: $350-399.9 Million
Emp.: 2,000
Activities Related to Credit Intermediation
N.A.I.C.S.: 522390

Subsidiary (Non-US):

ICAP New Zealand Limited (2)
Level 12, Craigs Investment Partners, House 36 Customhouse Quay, Wellington, New Zealand **(80%)**
Tel.: (64) 44990009
Sales Range: $50-74.9 Million
Emp.: 12
Securities Brokerage
N.A.I.C.S.: 523150

Subsidiary (US):

ICAP North America, Inc. (2)
1100 Plz 5, Jersey City, NJ 07311-4996
Tel.: (201) 209-7900
Sales Range: $350-399.9 Million
Emp.: 700
Securities Brokerage & Investment Management Services
N.A.I.C.S.: 523150
Laurent Paulhac *(CEO/Mng Dir-SEF-New York)*
Ivette Colazzo *(Dir-Comm)*
Ted Bragg *(Mng Dir-Fixed Income Product Initiatives-Securities Grp-New York)*

Subsidiary (Domestic):

BrokerTec (3)
Harborside Finl Ctr 1100 Plaza Five 11th Fl, Jersey City, NJ 07311 (100%)
Tel.: (201) 209-7900
Web Site: http://www.icap.com
Sales Range: $300-349.9 Million
Electronic Trading for Fixed Income Markets
N.A.I.C.S.: 523150

First Brokers Securities LLC (3)
Harborside Financial Ctr 1100 Plz 5 12th Fl, Jersey City, NJ 07311-4996 (100%)
Tel.: (212) 341-9900
Web Site: http://www.icap.com
Sales Range: $150-199.9 Million
Emp.: 1,000
Securities Brokerage
N.A.I.C.S.: 523150

Affiliate (Domestic):

Hartfield, Titus & Donnelly LLC (3)
111 Town Sq Pl Ste 1430, Jersey City, NJ 07310 (33%)
Tel.: (201) 217-8045
Web Site: http://www.htdonline.com
Sales Range: $50-74.9 Million
Emp.: 100
Securities Brokerage
N.A.I.C.S.: 523150
Paul Emanuel *(Sr VP & Mgr-Brokering-Natl)*
Ronald Purpora *(Chm)*
Chris Ferreri *(COO)*
Edward J. Smith III *(Chief Compliance Officer, Gen Counsel & Sec)*

Subsidiary (Domestic):

ICAP Capital Markets LLC (3)
Harborside Financial Ctr 1100 Plz 5 12th Fl, Jersey City, NJ 07311-4996 (100%)
Tel.: (212) 341-9900
Web Site: http://www.icap.com
Sales Range: $1-4.9 Billion
Emp.: 900
Securities Brokerage
N.A.I.C.S.: 523150

ICAP Corporates LLC (3)
Harborside Financial Ctr 1100 Plz 5 12th Fl, Jersey City, NJ 07311 (100%)
Tel.: (212) 341-9900
Web Site: http://www.icap.com
Sales Range: $300-349.9 Million
Emp.: 900
Securities Brokerage
N.A.I.C.S.: 523150

Subsidiary (Domestic):

ICAP Futures LLC (4)
75 Montgomery St Ste 601, Jersey City, NJ 07302 (100%)
Tel.: (201) 369-8080
Securities Brokerage
N.A.I.C.S.: 523150

Division (Domestic):

ICAP Energy LLC (5)
9931 Corporate Campus Dr, Louisville, KY 40223 (100%)
Tel.: (502) 327-1400
Web Site: http://www.icapenergy.com
Commodity Contracts Dealing
N.A.I.C.S.: 523160

ICAP United Inc (5)
35 Corporate Dr Ste 150, Burlington, MA 01803 (100%)
Tel.: (781) 272-3000
Web Site: http://www.icap.com

Sales Range: $25-49.9 Million
Emp.: 50
Securities Brokerage
N.A.I.C.S.: 523150

Subsidiary (Domestic):

ICAP Electronic Broking LLC (3)
Harborside Financial Ctr 1100 Plz 5 12th Fl, Jersey City, NJ 07311-4996 (100%)
Tel.: (212) 341-9900
Sales Range: $300-349.9 Million
Securities Brokerage
N.A.I.C.S.: 523150

ICAP Services North America LLC (3)
1100 Plz 5, Jersey City, NJ 07311-4003
Tel.: (212) 732-6900
Web Site: http://www.icap.com
Securities Brokerage Services
N.A.I.C.S.: 523150

ICAP Shipping USA Inc (3)
850 Canal St 3rd Fl, Stamford, CT 06902
Tel.: (203) 487-7000
Web Site: http://www.icapshipping.com
Sales Range: $25-49.9 Million
Emp.: 20
Shipping Brokerage Services
N.A.I.C.S.: 488330

ReMatch Inc (3)
500 5th Ave Ste 830, New York, NY 10110
Tel.: (212) 815-6821
Post Trade Risk Management Services
N.A.I.C.S.: 238990

Traiana, Inc. (3)
4 Times Sq, New York, NY 10036-8002
Tel.: (212) 404-1714
Web Site: http://uat-www.traiana.com
Sales Range: $10-24.9 Million
Emp.: 90
Automated Post-Trade Processing Services
N.A.I.C.S.: 522320

TriOptima North America LLC (3)
4 Times Sq 14th Fl, New York, NY 10036
Tel.: (646) 744-0400
Web Site: http://www.trioptima.com
Post Trade Risk Management Services
N.A.I.C.S.: 238990
Martin Sandstrom *(CTO)*

Wrightson ICAP LLC (3)
Harborside Financial Ctr Plz 5, Jersey City, NJ 07311 (100%)
Tel.: (212) 815-6540
Web Site: http://www.wrightson.com
Sales Range: $300-349.9 Million
Securities Brokerage
N.A.I.C.S.: 523150

Subsidiary (Non-US):

ICAP Philippines Inc (2)
14 Fl RCBC Savings Bank Corporate Centre 26 & 25 street, Taguig, 1634, Philippines
Tel.: (63) 2 888 2333
Sales Range: $50-74.9 Million
Emp.: 50
Foreign Exchange Trading Services
N.A.I.C.S.: 523160

ICAP Scandinavia A/S (2)
Rentemestervej 14, 2400, Copenhagen, Denmark (100%)
Tel.: (45) 77887600
Sales Range: $50-74.9 Million
Emp.: 30
Securities Brokerage
N.A.I.C.S.: 523150
Rene Simonson *(Mng Dir)*

ICAP Scandinavia Fondsmaeglerselskab A/S (2)
Rentemestervej 14, Copenhagen, 2400, Denmark
Tel.: (45) 77887600
Emp.: 30
Investment Management Service
N.A.I.C.S.: 523999
Rene Simonsen *(Gen Mgr)*

Subsidiary (Domestic):

ICAP Securities Limited (2)
2 Broadgate, London, EC2M 7UR, United Kingdom (100%)
Tel.: (44) 2070005000

Sales Range: $700-749.9 Million
Emp.: 1,800
Securities Brokerage
N.A.I.C.S.: 523150

Subsidiary (Non-US):

ICAP Securities Argentina S.A. (3)
Reconquista 365 - 8th Fl, 1003, Buenos Aires, Argentina
Tel.: (54) 1141066900
Securities Brokerage
N.A.I.C.S.: 523150

ICAP Securities Colombia S.A. (3)
Cra 11 No 93 - 46 - 403 Office, Bogota, Colombia (100%)
Tel.: (57) 16355489
Commercial Banking
N.A.I.C.S.: 522110

Subsidiary (Non-US):

ICAP Shipping Limited (2)
Tel.: (44) 20 7459 2229
Ship Broking Services
N.A.I.C.S.: 488390

Subsidiary (Non-US):

ICAP Shipping (Germany) GmbH (3)
Tel.: (49) 4041913330
Emp.: 3
Shipping Brokerage Services
N.A.I.C.S.: 488330

ICAP Shipping (Gibraltar) Limited (3)
Tel.: (350) 200 75480
Emp.: 1
Shipping Brokerage Services
N.A.I.C.S.: 488330

ICAP Shipping (Hong Kong) Limited (3)
Tel.: (86) 2163094580
Shipping Brokerage Services
N.A.I.C.S.: 488330

ICAP Shipping Derivatives Limited (3)
Tel.: (44) 20 7532 4920
Web Site: http://www.icapshipping.com
Freight Derivatives Services
N.A.I.C.S.: 425120

ICAP Shipping International Limited (3)
Tel.: (44) 207 459 2000
Web Site: http://www.icapshipping.com
Sales Range: $50-74.9 Million
Emp.: 150
Ship Broking Services
N.A.I.C.S.: 488330

ICAP Shipping Singapore Pte Limited (3)
Tel.: (65) 6831 0551
Shipping Brokerage Services
N.A.I.C.S.: 488330

Subsidiary (Domestic):

ICAP Shipping Tanker Derivatives Limited (2)
2 Broadgate, London, EC2M 7UR, United Kingdom
Tel.: (44) 2075324920
Web Site: http://www.icapshipping.com
Container Freight Derivative Services
N.A.I.C.S.: 523160

ICAP Wclk Limited (2)
135 Bishopsgate, London, EC2M 3TP, United Kingdom (100%)
Tel.: (44) 2070005000
Sales Range: $700-749.9 Million
Emp.: 1,500
Securities Brokerage
N.A.I.C.S.: 523150
Charles Gregson *(Chm)*
Charles Gregson *(Chm)*

Subsidiary (Non-US):

ICAP del Ecuador S.A. (2)
Eloy Alfaro 2515 Y Catalina Aldaz, Quito, 170201, Ecuador (100%)
Tel.: (593) 23330900
Web Site: http://www.icap.com

Sales Range: $50-74.9 Million
Emp.: 30
Securities Brokerage
N.A.I.C.S.: 523150

ICAP-AP (Thailand) Co. Ltd. (2)
55 Wave Place Building, 13th Floor Wireless Road Lumpi, Bangkok, 10330, Thailand
Tel.: (66) 22560888
Web Site: http://www.icap.com
Sales Range: $50-74.9 Million
Emp.: 30
Commercial Banking
N.A.I.C.S.: 522110
Nichaya Chongvatana *(Sec)*

Link Securities Hong Kong Limited (2)
Suite 2910 29/F The Center 99 Queen's Road, Central District, Hong Kong, China (Hong Kong)
Tel.: (852) 21693363
Web Site: http://www.icap.com
Securities Brokerage Services
N.A.I.C.S.: 523150

Subsidiary (Domestic):

NEX Treasury (2)
1 Duval Square, London, E1 6PW, United Kingdom
Tel.: (44) 20 7000 5163
Web Site: http://www.nex-treasury.com
Electronic Trading Services
N.A.I.C.S.: 561990
Peter McHugh *(CEO)*
Patrik Nagel *(Head-Buy-Side Sls)*
Rhian Ivey *(Head-Relationship Mgmt EMEA)*
Matthew Frankfurt *(Head-Corp FX Sls)*
Toby Michelmore *(Head-Corp FX Sls)*
Joseph Russo *(Global Co-Head-Money Markets)*
Thomas Mykityshyn *(Global Co-Head-Money Markets)*
Joseph Porretta *(Mgr-Corp Fx Sls)*
Sue Hubbard *(Global Head-Client Svcs)*

Subsidiary (Non-US):

PT ICAP Indonesia (2)
Plz 89 3rd Fl, Jl JR Rasuna Said kav X-7/6, 129740, Jakarta, Indonesia (85%)
Tel.: (62) 215220430
Sales Range: $50-74,9 Million
Emp.: 30
Commericial Banking
N.A.I.C.S.: 522110
John Su *(Mng Dir)*

Reset Pte Limited (2)
10 Marina Boulevard 21-01 Marina Bay Financial Centre Tower 2, Singapore, 018983, Singapore
Tel.: (65) 6831 0950
Web Site: http://www.reset.net
Emp.: 56
Matching Engine Mfr
N.A.I.C.S.: 333618
Deron Siddons *(Dir-Sls-Americas)*
Antonio Marques-Casey *(Dir-Sls-Europe)*
Emma Kelly *(Dir-Sls-Europe)*
Charlie Sabel *(Dir-Sls-Europe)*
Stephen MacLennan *(Specialist-Risk)*
Mark Moth Reeves *(Dir-Sls-Asia & Australasia)*
Chris Chumley Swannie *(Dir-Sls-Asia & Australasia)*
Alexandre Dubost *(Dir-Sls-Europe)*
Andrew Livesey *(Dir-Sls-Americas)*
Kate Pacheco *(Dir-Sls)*

Joint Venture (Non-US):

SIF ICAP S.A. de C.V. (2)
Paseo de La Reforma No 255 Piso 7, Col Cuauhtemoc, Cuauhtemoc, 6500, Mexico
Tel.: (52) 55512820
Web Site: http://www.sif.com.mx
Emp.: 35
Securities & Commodity Exchanges
N.A.I.C.S.: 523210
Gabriel Rodriguez *(Gen Mgr)*

Joint Venture (Domestic):

TFS-ICAP Limited (2)
Beaufort House 15 St Botolph Street, London, EC3A 7QX, United Kingdom

CME Group, Inc.—(Continued)

Tel.: (44) 207 422 3500
Web Site: http://www.tradition.com
Sales Range: $350-399.9 Million
Emp.: 700
Securities Brokerage
N.A.I.C.S.: 523150

Subsidiary (US):

TFS-ICAP Holdings LLC (3)
3232 OldSlip 34th Fl, New York, NY 10005-1501
Tel.: (212) 943-6916
Web Site: http://www.tfsbrokerage.com
Sales Range: $50-74.9 Million
Emp.: 15
Holding Company
N.A.I.C.S.: 551112
David Pinchin (Mng Dir)

Subsidiary (Domestic):

TFS-ICAP LLC (4)
32 Oozslip 34th Fl, New York, NY 10005
Tel.: (212) 943-6916
Web Site: http://www.tfsbrokerage.com
Sales Range: $25-49.9 Million
Securities Brokerage
N.A.I.C.S.: 523150
David Pinchin (Mng Dir)

Subsidiary (Domestic):

The Link Asset and Securities Company Limited
135 Bishopsgate, London, EC2M 3TP, United Kingdom
Tel.: (44) 2076634300
Securities Brokerage Services
N.A.I.C.S.: 523150

Subsidiary (Non-US):

Traiana Technologies Limited (2)
132 Menachem Begin Road Azrieli Square Tower Floor 25, Tel Aviv, 63927, Israel
Tel.: (972) 3 610 0300
Emp.: 180
Post Trade Risk Services
N.A.I.C.S.: 238990
Igor Teleshevsky (Gen Mgr)

TriOptima AB (2)
Master Samuelsgatan 17, Stockholm, 11144, Sweden
Tel.: (46) 8 545 25 130
Web Site: http://www.trioptima.com
Emp.: 100
Portfolio Management Services
N.A.I.C.S.: 523940
Raf Pritchard (Head-Triresolve)
Martin Sandstrom (CTO)

TriOptima Asia Pacific Pte Limited (2)
10 Marina Boulevard 21-01 Marina Bay Financial Centre Tower 2, Singapore, 018983, Singapore
Tel.: (65) 63728181
Web Site: http://www.trioptima.com
Post Trade Commodity Brokerage Services
N.A.I.C.S.: 523160

Subsidiary (Domestic):

TriOptima UK Limited (2)
1 Duval Square, London, E1 6PW, United Kingdom
Tel.: (44) 2073822200
Post Trade Risk Management Services
N.A.I.C.S.: 561499

Joint Venture (Non-US):

NEX Services Limited (1)
London Fruit And Wool Exchange 1 Duval Square, London, E1 6PW, United Kingdom
Tel.: (44) 2078189000
Emp.: 1,900
Trading Exchange Services
N.A.I.C.S.: 561990

NEX Services Pte. Ltd. (1)
10 Marina Boulevard 21-01 Marina Bay Financial Tower 2, Singapore, 018983, Singapore
Tel.: (65) 68310997
Commodities Exchange Services
N.A.I.C.S.: 523210

New York Mercantile Exchange, Inc. (1)
300 Vesey Street, New York, NY 10282
Tel.: (212) 299-2000
Web Site: http://www.cmegroup.com
Sales Range: $650-699.9 Million
Emp.: 978
Commodities Exchange
N.A.I.C.S.: 523210

Pivot, Inc. (1)
World Financial Center One North End Avenue 7th floor, New York, NY 10282
Tel.: (212) 299-2701
Software Publishing Services
N.A.I.C.S.: 513210
John H. Eley (CEO)
Bob Barlow (VP-Ops)

The Board of Trade of Kansas City, Missouri, Inc. (1)
4800 Main St Ste 303, Kansas City, MO 64112
Tel.: (816) 753-7500
Web Site: http://www.kcbt.com
Commodities Exchange
N.A.I.C.S.: 523210

TriOptima Japan K.K. (1)
Kasumigaseki Building 3-2-5 Kasumigaseki 6F Room No 622, Chiyoda-ku, Tokyo, Japan
Tel.: (81) 355116688
Security Exchange Services
N.A.I.C.S.: 523210

e-MID SIM S.p.A. (1)
Via Giuseppe Marcora 11, 20121, Milan, Italy
Tel.: (39) 02303451
Trading Exchange Services
N.A.I.C.S.: 561990
Giuseppe Attana (Pres)

CMG HOLDINGS GROUP, INC.

2130 N Lincoln Park W, Chicago, IL 60614
Tel.: (773) 770-3440   NV
Web Site:
https://www.cmgholdingsinc.com
CMGO—(OTCIQ)
Rev.: $2,033,712
Assets: $1,955,403
Liabilities: $1,221,525
Net Worth: $733,878
Earnings: $17,617
Emp.: 3
Fiscal Year-end: 12/31/22
Marketing Consulting Services
N.A.I.C.S.: 541613
Glonn Lakon (Chm, CEO & CFO)

Subsidiaries:

Good Gaming, Inc. (1)
415 McFarlan Rd Ste 108, Kennett Square, PA 19348   (100%)
Web Site: https://www.good-gaming.com
Rev.: $9,609
Assets: $1,055,996
Liabilities: $426,386
Net Worth: $629,610
Earnings: ($2,107,901)
Emp.: 3
Fiscal Year-end: 12/31/2022
Data Hosting Services
N.A.I.C.S.: 518210
David Dorwart (Chm & CEO)
Jordan Majkszak Axt (CMO)

Ship Ahoy LLC (1)
4401 Eastern Ave Bldg 52 Unit 1C, Baltimore, MD 21224
Web Site: https://www.shipsahoyinc.com
Boat Ceramic Coating Services
N.A.I.C.S.: 713930

CMS ENERGY CORPORATION

1 Energy Plz, Jackson, MI 49201
Tel.: (517) 788-0550   MI
Web Site:
https://www.cmsenergy.com
Year Founded: 1886
CMS—(NYSE)
Rev.: $7,462,000,000
Assets: $33,517,000,000

Liabilities: $25,392,000,000
Net Worth: $8,125,000,000
Earnings: $887,000,000
Emp.: 8,356
Fiscal Year-end: 12/31/23
Holding Company; Electric Power Distr
N.A.I.C.S.: 551111
Rejji P. Hayes (CFO & Exec VP)
Glenn P. Barba (Chief Acctg Officer, VP & Controller)
Venkat Dhenuvakonda Rao (Sr VP-Strategy)
Shaun M. Johnson (Gen Counsel & Sr VP)
Catherine A. Hendrian (Sr VP-HR)
Brandon J. Hofmeister (Sr VP-Governmental, Regulatory & Pub Affairs)
Tonya L. Berry (Sr VP-Transformation & Engrg)
Garrick J. Rochow (Pres & CEO)
LeeRoy Wells Jr. (Sr VP-Ops)
Melissa M. Gleespen (Chief Compliance Officer, Sec & VP)
Brian F. Rich (Chief Customer Officer & Sr VP)
Scott McIntosh (Chief Acctg Officer, VP-Tax & Controller)
Tamara Faber-Doty (Chief Digital Officer & Chief Digital Officer-Technology)
Katie Carey (Dir-Media Rels)
Brian Wheeler (Sr Dir-Pub Information)
Kelly M. Hall (VP & Deputy Gen Counsel)
Jeffrey J. Shingler (VP-Consumers Energy)
Angela Thompkins (Chief Diversity Officer & VP)
Amanda M. Wagenschutz (VP-People & Culture Operations)
Tamara J. Faber-Doty (Chief Digital Officer)
Roger A. Curtis (VP)
Norman J. Kapala (VP)
David N. Hicks (VP)
Michael A. Torrey (VP)
Christine M. Wisniewski (VP)

Subsidiaries:

AJD Forest Products Limited Partnership (1)
4440 Four Mile Rd, Grayling, MI 49738
Tel.: (989) 348-5412
Web Site: http://www.ajdforestproducts.com
Sales Range: $25-49.9 Million
Eletric Power Generation Services
N.A.I.C.S.: 221118

CMS Land Company (1)
5544 Charlevoix Rd, Petoskey, MI 49770
Tel.: (231) 753-2333
Emp.: 5
Eletric Power Generation Services
N.A.I.C.S.: 221118

Consumers Energy Company (1)
1 Energy Plz, Jackson, MI 49201   (100%)
Tel.: (517) 788-0550
Web Site:
https://www.consumersenergy.com
Rev.: $7,166,000,000
Assets: $31,852,000,000
Liabilities: $21,052,000,000
Net Worth: $10,800,000,000
Earnings: $865,000,000
Emp.: 8,144
Fiscal Year-end: 12/31/2023
Electric & Natural Gas Distr & Generator
N.A.I.C.S.: 221112
Rejji P. Hayes (CFO & Exec VP)
Glenn P. Barba (Chief Acctg Officer, VP & Controller)
Shaun M. Johnson (Gen Counsel & Sr VP)
Catherine A. Hendrian (Sr VP-HR)
Brandon J. Hofmeister (Sr VP-Governmental, Regulatory & Pub Affairs)
Tonya L. Berry (Sr VP-Transformation & Engrg)

Garrick J. Rochow (Pres & CEO)
LeeRoy Wells Jr. (Sr VP-Ops)
Mary P. Palkovich (VP)
Melissa M. Gleespen (Chief Compliance Officer, Sec & VP)
Brian F. Rich (Chief Customer Officer & Sr VP)
Michael A. Torrey (VP-Rates & Regulation)
David N. Hicks (VP-Renewables Dev & Enterprise Project Mgmt)
Venkat Dhenuvakonda Rao (Sr VP-Strategy)
Tamara J. Faber-Doty (Chief Digital Officer & VP-Tech)
Lauren Youngdahl Snyder (VP-Customer Experience)
John P. Broschak (VP)
Roger A. Curtis (VP-Pub Affairs)
Kelly M. Hall (VP & Deputy Gen Counsel)
Jeffrey J. Shingler (VP-Ops Support)
Amanda M. Wagenschutz (VP-People & Culture Ops)
Christine M. Wisniewski (VP-Ops Performance)
Norman J. Kapala (VP)
Chris Laird (VP-Electric Ops)
David N. Hicks (VP-Renewables Dev & Enterprise Project Mgmt)

Subsidiary (Domestic):

Consumers 2014 Securitization Funding LLC (2)
1 Energy Plz, Jackson, MI 49201
Tel.: (517) 788-1947
Web Site: http://www.consumersenergy.com
Financial Management Services
N.A.I.C.S.: 541611
Rejji P. Hayes (Exec VP & Mgr)
Catherine M. Reynolds (Gen Counsel, Sr VP & Mgr)
Glenn P. Barba (Chief Acctg Officer, Controller & VP)
Melissa M. Gleespen (Sec, VP & Mgr)
Scott B. McIntosh (VP)
Albert J. Fioravanti (Mgr)
Srikanth Maddipati (Pres, CEO, CFO & Treas)
Leonard J. Padula (Mgr)

Exeter Energy Limited Partnership (1)
10 Exeter Dr, Sterling, CT 06377
Tel.: (860) 564-7000
Natural Gas Distr
N.A.I.C.S.: 221210

Grayling Generating Station Limited Partnership (1)
4400 W 4 Mile Rd, Grayling, MI 49738-9779   (50%)
Tel.: (989) 348-4575
Natural Gas Distr
N.A.I.C.S.: 221210

Mid-Michigan Recycling, L.C. (1)
G-5310 N Dort Hwy, Flint, MI 48505-1833
Tel.: (810) 785-4512
Web Site: https://midmichiganrecycling.com
Wood Recycling Services
N.A.I.C.S.: 321999
Scott Morningstar (Owner)

Newport Solar, LLC (1)
300 Old Baptist Rd Ste 2, North Kingstown, RI 02852
Tel.: (401) 352-6155
Web Site: http://www.newportsolarri.com
Solar Power Installation Services
N.A.I.C.S.: 221114
Doug Sabetti (Founder & Owner)
Eric Martin (Sls Mgr-Solar)
Mark Cordeiro (Project Mgr)
Kara Kilmartin (Coord-Client & Program)

NorthStar Clean Energy (1)
1 Energy Plz, Jackson, MI 49201
Tel.: (517) 768-3376
Web Site: https://northstarcleanenergy.com
Sales Range: $1-4.9 Billion
Operator of Independent Power Generating Plants
N.A.I.C.S.: 221122

Subsidiary (Domestic):

Dearborn Industrial Generation, L.L.C. (2)
2400 Miller Rd, Dearborn, MI 48120

Tel.: (313) 336-7189
Sales Range: $25-49.9 Million
Emp.: 36
Electronic Services
N.A.I.C.S.: 221118

Affiliate (Domestic):

Genesee Power Station Limited
Partnership   **(2)**
5315 Energy Dr, Flint, MI 48505
Tel.: (810) 785-4144
Wood Fired Electricity Mfr
N.A.I.C.S.: 221118

T.E.S. Filer City Station Limited
Partnership   **(2)**
700 Mee St, Filer City, MI 49634
Tel.: (231) 723-6573
Natural Gas Extraction Services
N.A.I.C.S.: 213112

CNB BANK SHARES, INC.

450 W Side Sq, Carlinville, IL 62626
Tel.: (217) 854-2674   **IL**
Web Site: https://www.cnbil.com
Year Founded: 2013
CNBN—(OTCQX)
Rev.: $86,184,000
Assets: $1,673,148,000
Liabilities: $1,539,238,000
Net Worth: $133,910,000
Earnings: $15,042,000
Emp.: 254
Fiscal Year-end: 12/31/23
Bank Holding Company
N.A.I.C.S.: 551111
Shawn Davis (Sr VP)
James Ashworth (Pres)
Richard Walden (Chm)
Diana Tone (CFO & VP)
Nancy Ruyle (Sec)
Thomas DeRobertis (VP)
Andrew Tinberg (Exec VP)
James T. Ashworth (Vice Chm, Pres
& Pres-Investor Relations)

Subsidiaries:

CNB Bank & Trust, N.A.   **(1)**
450 W Side Sq, Carlinville, IL 62626
Tel.: (217) 854-2674
Web Site: http://www.cnbil.com
Sales Range: $50-74.9 Million
Federal Savings Bank
N.A.I.C.S.: 522180
Shawn Davis (Pres & CEO)
Larry Franklin (Chief Banking Officer & Sr
Exec VP)
Christopher Williams (Chief Credit Officer &
Sr VP)
Matthew Turley (CIO & VP)
Maureen Oswald (Sr VP & Cashier)
Angel Hopper (VP & Dir-HR)

CNB COMMUNITY BANCORP,
INC.

1 S Howell St, Hillsdale, MI 49242
Tel.: (517) 439-4300
Web Site: https://www.cnbb.bank
Year Founded: 1934
CNBB—(OTCQX)
Rev.: $28,647,000
Assets: $662,067,000
Liabilities: $605,528,000
Net Worth: $56,539,000
Earnings: $8,473,000
Fiscal Year-end: 12/31/18
Bank Holding Company
N.A.I.C.S.: 551111
Stephen J. Maddalena (Gen Mgr)

Subsidiaries:

County National Bank   **(1)**
1 S Howell St, Hillsdale, MI 49242
Tel.: (517) 439-4300
Web Site:
    http://www.countynationalbank.com
Sales Range: $25-49.9 Million
Emp.: 50
Commercial Banking Services
N.A.I.C.S.: 522110

Craig S. Connor (CEO)
Timothy P. Sullivan (Second VP-Trust)
Lois E. Howard (Reg VP-Comml Loans)
John Waldron (Pres)
Ronald J. Haber (VP-Comml Loans)
Sharon L. Burns (Second VP)
Christopher A. Phillips (Officer-Trust & VP)
Brian J. Powers (Asst VP)
Erik Lawson (CFO)

CNB CORPORATION

303 N Main St, Cheboygan, MI
49721
Tel.: (231) 627-7111   **MI**
Web Site:
    https://www.cnbismybank.com
Year Founded: 1985
CNBZ—(OTCIQ)
Rev.: $16,029,000
Assets: $398,878,000
Liabilities: $368,210,000
Net Worth: $30,668,000
Earnings: $2,812,000
Emp.: 74
Fiscal Year-end: 12/31/20
Bank Holding Company
N.A.I.C.S.: 551111
Victoria J. Hand (Sec)
Stephen J. Crusoe (Sr VP-Residential
Banking-Citizens National Bank)
Rebecca L. Tomaski (Asst VP-
Shareholders Rels-Citizens National
Bank)
Nicole M. Drake (Sr VP-Bus Banking-
Citizens National Bank)
Darren M. Selden (VP-Residential
Banking-Citizens National Bank)
Rick A. Tromble (Chm)
Joseph M. Daly (Sr VP-Bus Banking-
Citizens National Bank)
Matthew E. Keene (Pres & CEO)
Michelle M. Miller (Officer-
Residential-Citizens National Bank)
Amy E. Essex (Treas)

Subsidiaries:

Citizens National Bank of
Cheboygan   **(1)**
303 N Main St, Cheboygan, MI
49721   **(100%)**
Tel.: (231) 627-7111
Web Site: http://www.cnbismybank.com
Sales Range: $50-74.9 Million
Emp.: 60
Personal & Commercial Banking & Lending
Services
N.A.I.C.S.: 522110
Victoria J. Hand (Sr VP)
Cyril Drier (Exec VP)
Matthew Keene (Pres & CEO)

CNB CORPORATION

1411 4th Ave, Conway, SC 29526-
0320
Tel.: (843) 248-5721   **SC**
Web Site:
    https://www.conwaynational
    bank.com
Year Founded: 1903
CNBW—(OTCIQ)
Sales Range: Less than $1 Million
Bank Holding Company
N.A.I.C.S.: 551111
Freeman Holmes (Officer-Banking)
Vanessa Bagwell (Head-Teller-
Northside Office)
Stephen Wayne (Auditor-Ops &
Admin-Conway)
Joe Hunter Hyman (Asst VP)
Marsha S. Jordan (Asst VP)
Jackie S. Siratt (Officer-Banking)
Christy H. Broughton (Officer-
Banking)
Angela H. Hearl (Officer-Banking)
P. Alex Clayton Jr. (VP-Ops Mgmt)
James P. Jordan III (VP)

Subsidiaries:

The Conway National Bank Inc.   **(1)**

1400 3rd Ave, Conway, SC 29526
Tel.: (843) 248-5721
Web Site:
    http://www.conwaynationalbank.com
Rev.: $30,040,000
Emp.: 237
National Commercial Banks
N.A.I.C.S.: 522110
Jennings Dunkun (Pres)
Ford Sanders (CFO)

CNB FINANCIAL CORPORA-
TION

1 S 2nd St, Clearfield, PA 16830
Tel.: (814) 765-9621   **PA**
Web Site: https://www.cnbbank.bank
Year Founded: 1983
CCNE—(NASDAQ)
Rev.: $248,504,000
Assets: $5,475,179,000
Liabilities: $4,944,417,000
Net Worth: $530,762,000
Earnings: $63,188,000
Emp.: 722
Fiscal Year-end: 12/31/22
Offices of Bank Holding Companies
N.A.I.C.S.: 551111
Richard L. Greslick Jr. (COO, Sec &
Sr Exec VP)
Michael D. Peduzzi (Pres & CEO)

Subsidiaries:

CNB Bank   **(1)**
1 S 2nd St, Clearfield, PA 16830
Tel.: (814) 765-9621
Sales Range: $25-49.9 Million
Emp.: 500
Banking Services
N.A.I.C.S.: 522110
Richard L. Greslick Jr. (COO & Sr Exec VP)
Michael D. Peduzzi (Pres & CEO)

Division (Domestic):

ERIEBANK, a division of CNB
Bank   **(2)**
7402 Ctr St, Mentor, OH 44060
Tel.: (440) 205-8100
Web Site: https://www.eriebank.bank
Sales Range: $1-9.9 Million
Emp.: 31
Commericial Banking
N.A.I.C.S.: 522110

FCBank, a division of CNB Bank   **(2)**
105 Washington Sq, Bucyrus, OH 44820
Tel.: (419) 562-7040
Web Site: https://www.fcbankohio.com
Emp.: 18
Commericial Banking
N.A.I.C.S.: 522110
Jenny Saunders (Pres)

CNB Securities Corporation   **(1)**
1105 N Market St Ste 1300, Wilmington, DE
19801
Tel.: (302) 427-9149
Holding Company
N.A.I.C.S.: 551112

CNBX PHARMACEUTICALS
INC.

No 3 Bethesda Metro Ctr Ste 700,
Bethesda, MD 20814   **NV**
Web Site: https://cnbxpharma.com
Year Founded: 2004
CNBX—(OTCQB)
Rev.: $130,074
Assets: $31,383
Liabilities: $2,511,363
Net Worth: ($2,479,980)
Earnings: ($695,198)
Emp.: 2
Fiscal Year-end: 08/31/24
Pharmaceuticals Mfr
N.A.I.C.S.: 325412
Uri Ben-Or (CFO & Principal Acctg
Officer)
Lior Eshdat (VP-Intellectual Property)
Ilya Reznik (Head-Neuropsychiatry
Dev)
Gabriel Yariv (Chm)

Eyal Barad (Co-Founder & CEO)
Sanja Goldberg (CTO)
Uri Ben-Or (CFO & Principal Acctg
Officer)

CNO FINANCIAL GROUP, INC.

11299 Illinois St Ste 200, Carmel, IN
46032
Tel.: (317) 817-6100   **DE**
Web Site: https://www.cnoinc.com
Year Founded: 1979
CNO—(NYSE)
Rev.: $4,146,800,000
Assets: $35,102,500,000
Liabilities: $32,886,900,000
Net Worth: $2,215,600,000
Earnings: $276,500,000
Emp.: 3,500
Fiscal Year-end: 12/31/23
Holding Company; Insurance Ser-
vices
N.A.I.C.S.: 551112
Paul H. McDonough (CFO)
Yvonne K. Franzese (Chief HR Offi-
cer)
Eric R. Johnson (Chief Investment
Officer)
Matthew J. Zimpfer (Gen Counsel)
Gary C. Bhojwani (CEO)
Jean Linnenbringer (COO)
Mike Mead (CIO)
Scott L. Goldberg (Pres-Consumer
Div)
Michael B. Byers (Pres-Worksite Div)
Tom Kleyle (Treas & VP-Corp Fin)
Michellen Wildin (Chief Acctg Officer)
Rocco F. Tarasi III (CMO)

Subsidiaries:

40/86 Advisors, Inc.   **(1)**
535 N College Dr, Carmel, IN
46032   **(100%)**
Tel.: (317) 817-2804
Web Site: https://www.4086.com
Sales Range: $125-149.9 Million
Emp.: 90
Investment Consultancy Services
N.A.I.C.S.: 523940
Eric R. Johnson (Pres)
Richard W. Burke (CIO & Sr VP)
Jess E. Horsfall (Sr VP-Portfolio Mgmt)
Eduardo Piedra (VP-Leveraged Loans)
Jerimy Horner (VP-Structured Securities)
Zandra M. de Haai (Sr VP-Fixed Income
Res)

Bankers Life Holding Corp.   **(1)**
600 W Chicago Ave, Chicago, IL
60654-2800   **(100%)**
Tel.: (312) 396-6000
Web Site: http://www.bankers.com
Sales Range: $250-299.9 Million
Holding Company
N.A.I.C.S.: 551112

Subsidiary (Domestic):

Bankers Life & Casualty
Company   **(2)**
303 E Wacker Dr Ste 500, Chicago, IL
60601   **(100%)**
Tel.: (312) 396-6000
Web Site: https://www.bankerslife.com
Sales Range: $1-4.9 Billion
Emp.: 1,200
Life Accident & Health Insurance Services
N.A.I.C.S.: 524114
Scott L. Goldberg (Pres)

Beneficial Standard Life Insurance
Company   **(1)**
11825 N Pennsylvania St, Carmel, IN
46032-4555   **(100%)**
Tel.: (317) 817-6100
Sales Range: $10-24.9 Million
Emp.: 25
Life Insurance
N.A.I.C.S.: 524113

CDOC, Inc.   **(1)**
1201 N Orange St Ste 789, Wilmington, DE
19801-1173
Tel.: (302) 884-6703

CNO Financial Group, Inc.—(Continued)

Insurance Agencies & Brokerage Services
N.A.I.C.S.: 524210

CNO Services, LLC (1)
11825 N Pennsylvania St, Carmel, IN
46032-4555
Tel.: (317) 817-2893
Web Site: https://www.cnoinc.com
Insurance Agencies & Brokerage Services
N.A.I.C.S.: 524210

**Colonial Penn Life Insurance
Company** (1)
399 Market St, Philadelphia, PA
19181 **(100%)**
Tel.: (215) 928-8000
Web Site: https://colonialpenn.com
Sales Range: $300-349.9 Million
Emp.: 500
Insurance Carrier
N.A.I.C.S.: 524114

**Conseco Life Insurance Company of
Texas** (1)
11825 N Pennsylvania St, Carmel, IN
46032-4555 **(100%)**
Tel.: (317) 817-6100
Web Site: https://www.conseco.com
Sales Range: $650-699.9 Million
Emp.: 2,500
Life Insurance
N.A.I.C.S.: 524113

**Conseco Senior Health Insurance
Company** (1)
11815 N Pennsylvania St, Carmel, IN
46032-4555 **(100%)**
Tel.: (317) 817-6100
Sales Range: $150-199.9 Million
Emp.: 300
Life & Health Insurance
N.A.I.C.S.: 524113

Design Benefit Plans, Inc. (1)
4040 Charles St Ste 209, Rockford, IL
61108
Tel.: (815) 399-7007
Insurance Agencies & Brokerage Services
N.A.I.C.S.: 524210

DirectPath, LLC (1)
120 18th St S, Birmingham, AL 35233
Tel.: (205) 397-2800
Web Site: http://www.directpathhealth.com
Insurance Agencies & Brokerages
N.A.I.C.S.: 524210
Marc Salois (Chief Revenue Officer)
Michael Byers (Co-Pres-Worksite Division)

Subsidiary (Domestic):

Flores & Associates, LLC (2)
1218 S Church St, Charlotte, NC 28203
Tel.: (704) 335-8211
Web Site: http://www.flores-associates.com
Human Resource Consulting Services
N.A.I.C.S.: 541612
Kenneth Pekarek (Pres)
Gary J. Trainor (Exec Chm)

**Performance Matters Associates of
Texas, Inc.** (1)
8150 N Central Expy Ste 1300, Dallas, TX
75206-1954
Tel.: (214) 360-1300
Web Site: http://www.pmausa.com
Sales Range: $25-49.9 Million
Emp.: 35
Insurance Agencies & Brokerage Services
N.A.I.C.S.: 524210
Linda Teels (VP)

**Washington National Insurance
Co.** (1)
11825 N Pennsylvania St, Carmel, IN
46032 **(100%)**
Tel.: (317) 817-6100
Web Site:
https://www.washingtonnational.com
Sales Range: $100-124.9 Million
Emp.: 110
Dental & Disability Insurance
N.A.I.C.S.: 524113
Mike Heard (Pres)

**Washington National Insurance
Company** (1)
11299 Illinois St Ste 200, Carmel, IN 46032

Tel.: (312) 396-7467
Web Site:
https://www.washingtonnational.com
Sales Range: $100-124.9 Million
Insurance Services
N.A.I.C.S.: 524210
Mike Heard (Pres)

**Web Benefits Design
Corporation** (1)
4725 W Sand Lake Rd Ste 300, Orlando,
FL 32819
Tel.: (407) 480-5820
Web Site: http://www.wbdcorp.com
Data Outsourcing Services
N.A.I.C.S.: 518210
Bethany Schenk (Co-Founder, Pres & CEO)
Darin Wardwell (Co-Founder & CIO)
Susan Otten (COO)
Steve Herman (Chief Revenue Officer)
Christian Campbell (CTO)

**CNS PHARMACEUTICALS,
INC.**
2100 W Loop S Ste 900, Houston,
TX 77027 　　　　NV
Web Site:
https://www.cnspharma.com
Year Founded: 2017
CNSP—(NASDAQ)
Assets: $13,053,115
Liabilities: $4,920,259
Net Worth: $8,132,856
Earnings: ($15,274,134)
Emp.: 3
Fiscal Year-end: 12/31/22
Biotechnology Research & Development Services
N.A.I.C.S.: 541714
John M. Climaco (CEO)
Sandra L. Silberman (Chief Medical
Officer)
Donald Picker (Chief Science Officer)
Waldemar Priebe (Founder)
Christopher S. Downs (CFO)

CNX RESOURCES CORPORATION
1000 Horizon Vue Dr, Canonsburg,
PA 15317-6506
Tel.: (724) 485-4000 　　　DE
Web Site: https://www.cnx.com
Year Founded: 1860
CNX—(NYSE)
Rev.: $3,434,948,000
Assets: $8,626,657,000
Liabilities: $4,265,640,000
Net Worth: $4,361,017,000
Earnings: $1,720,716,000
Emp.: 470
Fiscal Year-end: 12/31/23
Holding Company; Petroleum & Natural Gas Exploration & Extraction;
Coal Mining
N.A.I.C.S.: 551112
Nicholas J. Deluliis (Pres & CEO)
Jason L. Mumford (VP & Controller)
Audric Dodds (Dir-Community Relations)
Ravi Srivastava (Pres-New Tech)
Hayley F. Scott (Chief Risk Officer)
Brain Aiello (VP-Human Resources)
Navneet Behl (COO)
Timothy S. Bedard (Gen Counsel,
Sec & Exec VP)

Subsidiaries:

CNX Gas Corporation (1)
1000 Consol Energy Dr, Canonsburg, PA
15317-6506 **(81.3%)**
Tel.: (724) 485-4000
Sales Range: $650-699.9 Million
Emp.: 174
Natural Gas Exploration, Development &
Production Services
N.A.I.C.S.: 324199
Nick DeLuliis (Pres & CEO)

CNX Midstream Partners LP (1)

1000 Horizon Vue Dr, Canonsburg, PA
15317-6506 **(100%)**
Tel.: (724) 485-4000
Web Site: http://www.cnxmidstream.com
Sales Range: $300-349.9 Million
Holding Company; Natural Gas Gathering &
Transportation Operations Management
Services
N.A.I.C.S.: 551112
Nicholas J. Deluliis (Chm & CEO)
Chad A. Griffith (Pres & COO)
Donald W. Rush (CFO)

Subsidiary (Domestic):

**CNX Midstream Operating Company
LLC** (2)
1000 Consol Energy Dr, Canonsburg, PA
15317
Tel.: (724) 485-4000
Web Site: http://www.cnxmidstream.com
Natural Gas Gathering & Transportation
Operations Management Services
N.A.I.C.S.: 486210

**Cardinal States Gathering
Company** (1)
Hwy 52 S, Delbarton, WV 25670
Tel.: (304) 426-8870
Web Site: http://www.consolenergy.com
Emp.: 5
Gasoline Services
N.A.I.C.S.: 457120

Coalfield Pipeline Company (1)
105 Mitchell Rd Ste 104, Oak Ridge, TN
37830
Tel.: (865) 481-1902
Web Site: https://www.consolenergy.com
Emp.: 12
Gas Process
N.A.I.C.S.: 325120

CO-DIAGNOSTICS, INC.
2401 S Foothill Dr Ste D, Salt Lake
City, UT 84109
Tel.: (801) 438-1036 　　　NY
Web Site: https://co-dx.com
Year Founded: 2013
CODX—(NASDAQ)
Rev.: $34,218,209
Assets: $123,086,280
Liabilities: $8,566,288
Net Worth: $114,519,992
Earnings: ($14,238,249)
Emp.: 145
Fiscal Year-end: 12/31/22
Medical Diagnostic Equipment Distr
N.A.I.C.S.: 334510
Dwight H. Egan (Chm, Pres & CEO)
Brian L. Brown (CFO & Sec)
Rebecca A. Garcia (VP-Product Dev)
Mark Poritz (Chief Scientific Officer)
Mayuranki Almaula (Sr VP)
Cameron Gundry (Head)
Ivory Chang (Chief Regulatory Affairs
Officer)

**COASTAL CAROLINA
BANCSHARES, INC.**
1012 38th Ave N, Myrtle Beach, SC
29577
Tel.: (843) 839-2265 　　　SC
Web Site: https://www.myccnb.com
Year Founded: 2008
CCNB—(OTCQX)
Sales Range: $1-9.9 Million
Emp.: 38
Bank Holding Company
N.A.I.C.S.: 551111
Henrietta U. Golding (Treas)
Dennis L. Wade (Chm)

Subsidiaries:

Coastal Carolina National Bank (1)
1012 38th Ave N, Myrtle Beach, SC 29577
Tel.: (843) 839-2265
Web Site: http://www.myccnb.com
Commericial Banking
N.A.I.C.S.: 522110

Dawn Kinard (CFO & Exec VP)
Chris Houston (Chief Credit Officer & Sr
VP)
Scott Benninga (Sr VP & Dir-Mortgage
Banking)
Justin Lee (Chief Lending Officer & Sr VP)
Robert Hucks (Sr VP-North Strand Market)
Allison Stout (Sr VP & Controller)
Bobby Sunday (Sr VP & Dir-Retail Ops)
Dave Brunko (Sr VP & Sls Mgr-Mortgage)
Jeremy Baird (Sr VP & Dir-Strategy & Svcs)
Jimmy Kimbell (Sr VP)
Kevin Hagen (Sr VP & Dir-Treasury Svcs)
Steve Hales (Sr VP & Sls Mgr-Mortgage)
W. David Keller (Sr VP)
Laurence S. Bolchoz Jr. (Pres & CEO)

COASTAL FINANCIAL CORPORATION
5415 Evergreen Way, Everett, WA
98203
Tel.: (425) 257-9000 　　　WA
Web Site:
https://www.coastalbank.com
Year Founded: 1997
CCB—(NASDAQ)
Rev.: $316,854,000
Assets: $3,144,467,000
Liabilities: $2,900,973,000
Net Worth: $243,494,000
Earnings: $40,625,000
Emp.: 448
Fiscal Year-end: 12/31/22
Bank Holding Company
N.A.I.C.S.: 551111
Eric M. Sprink (CEO)
Joel G. Edwards (CFO, Sec & Exec
VP)
Thomas D. Lane (Founder)
Andy Stines (Chief Risk Officer)
Jon Sand (Chief Credit Officer)
Curt Queyrouze (Pres)

**COASTAL SOUTH
BANCSHARES, INC.**
5 Bow Cir, Hilton Head Island, SC
29928
Tel.: (843) 341-9900 　　　VA
Year Founded: 2003
COSO—(OTCQX)
Rev.: $115,611,000
Assets: $2,028,599,000
Liabilities: $1,872,556,000
Net Worth: $156,043,000
Earnings: $24,478,000
Fiscal Year-end: 12/31/23
Banking Holding Company
N.A.I.C.S.: 551111
James S. Macleod (Chm)

**COATES INTERNATIONAL,
LTD.**
2100 Hwy 34 & Ridgewood Rd, Wall
Township, NJ 07719
Tel.: (732) 449-7717 　　　DE
Web Site:
http://www.coatesengine.com
Year Founded: 1988
COTE—(OTCIQ)
Sales Range: Less than $1 Million
Emp.: 5
Combustion Engine Mfr
N.A.I.C.S.: 333618
George J. Coates (Chm, Pres &
CEO)
Gregory G. Coates (Pres-Tech &
Sec)
Barry C. Kaye (CFO & Treas)
William Wolf (Gen Counsel)

COBANK, ACB
6340 S Fiddlers Green Cir, Greenwood Village, CO 80111
Tel.: (303) 740-4000
Web Site: http://www.cobank.com
Year Founded: 1916
CKNQP—(OTCIQ)

Sales Range: $1-4.9 Billion
Emp.: 719
Agribusiness & Utilities Lending, Export Financing & Other Financial Services
N.A.I.C.S.: 522299
John Svisco (Chief Bus Svcs Officer)
Robert F. West (Exec VP-Infrastructure Banking)
Todd Wilson (Sr VP-Enterprise Solutions & Svcs)
David P. Burlage (CFO)
James R. Bernsten (Co-CIO & Sr VP)
Antony M. Bahr (Exec VP-Banking Svcs Grp)
Arthur Hodges (Sr VP-Corp Comm)
Daniel T. Kelley (Owner)
Mary E. Fritz (Vice Chm)
Ann Trakimas (COO)
Andrew D. Jacob (Chief Regulatory, Legislative & Compliance Officer)
Mike Hechtner (Reg Pres-Central-Reg Agribusiness Banking Grp)
Mike Vestal (Sr VP & Controller)
Timothy D. Steidle (Treas & Sr VP)
Leili Ghazi (Reg Pres-Western-Reg Agribusiness Banking Grp)
David Sparks (Reg Pres-Eastern-Reg Agribusiness Banking Grp)
Thomas Halverson (Pres & CEO)
Ted R. Koerner (Sr VP-Comm Banking Grp)
Eileen Baines (Co-CIO & Sr VP)
Matthew H. Cammer (Sr VP-Digital Bus Solutions)
Brian Cavey (Sr VP-Govt Affairs)
Katia Hoffer (Sr VP-Enterprise Risk Mgmt)
Horst Kisch (Sr VP-Enterprise Risk Mgmt)
Jo Solonika (VP-Corp Comm)
Eric Itambo (Chief Banking Officer)
Everett M. Dobrinski (Chm)
Thomas Halverson (Pres & CEO)

COCA-COLA CONSOLIDATED, INC.

4100 Coca Cola Plz, Charlotte, NC 28211
Tel.: (980) 392-8298   DE
Web Site:
https://www.cokeconsolidated.com
Year Founded: 1902
COKE—(NASDAQ)
Rev.: $6,200,957,000
Assets: $3,709,545,000
Liabilities: $2,594,157,000
Net Worth: $1,115,388,000
Earnings: $430,158,000
Emp.: 15,000
Fiscal Year-end: 12/31/22
Soft Drink Bottling, Canning & Marketing Services
N.A.I.C.S.: 312111
J. Frank Harrison III (Chm & CEO)
Morgan H. Everett (Vice Chm)
David Michael Katz (Pres & COO)
F. Scott Anthony (CFO & Exec VP)
Matthew J. Blickley (Chief Acctg Officer & Sr VP-Fin Plng)
Jeffrey L. Turney (Sr VP-Strategy & Bus Transformation)
Christine A. Motherwell (Sr VP)
E. Beauregarde Fisher III (Gen Counsel, Sec & Exec VP)

Subsidiaries:

Coca-Cola Bottling Co. Consolidated
- Charleston, WV   (1)
640 Winfield Rd, Saint Albans, WV 25177-1554
Tel.: (304) 759-0300
Web Site: http://www.cokeconsolidated.com
Sales Range: $50-74.9 Million
Emp.: 110
Bottling & Marketing of Soft Drinks
N.A.I.C.S.: 312111

Coca-Cola Bottling Co. Consolidated
- Columbia, TN   (1)
1516 Nashville Hwy, Columbia, TN 38401-2068
Tel.: (931) 388-3455
Web Site: http://www.cokeconsolidated.com
Sales Range: $25-49.9 Million
Emp.: 30
Bottling & Marketing of Soft Drinks
N.A.I.C.S.: 312111

Coca-Cola Bottling Co. Consolidated
- Columbus, GA   (1)
6055 Coca Cola Blvd, Columbus, GA 31909-5532
Tel.: (706) 568-2726
Sales Range: $25-49.9 Million
Emp.: 75
Soft Drink Bottling
N.A.I.C.S.: 312111

Coca-Cola Bottling Co. Consolidated
- Jackson, TN   (1)
2650 N Pkwy E, Jackson, TN 38301
Tel.: (731) 424-2697
Web Site: http://www.cokeconsolidated.com
Sales Range: $75-99.9 Million
Emp.: 100
Bottling & Marketing of Soft Drinks
N.A.I.C.S.: 424490

Coca-Cola Bottling Co. Consolidated
- Mobile, AL   (1)
5300 Coca Cola Rd, Mobile, AL 36619-1922
Tel.: (251) 666-2410
Sales Range: $125-149.9 Million
Emp.: 300
Bottling & Marketing of Soft Drinks
N.A.I.C.S.: 312111
Carlon Lewis (Mgr-Ops)

Coca-Cola Bottling Co. Consolidated
- Panama City, FL   (1)
6130 Bayline Dr, Panama City, FL 32404
Tel.: (850) 781-6171
Sales Range: $25-49.9 Million
Emp.: 50
Distribution of Soft Drinks
N.A.I.C.S.: 312111

Coca-Cola Bottling Co. Consolidated
- Roanoke, VA   (1)
235 Shenandoah Ave NW, Roanoke, VA 24016-2455
Tel.: (540) 343-8041
Sales Range: $150-199.9 Million
Emp.: 400
Bottling & Marketing of Soft Drinks
N.A.I.C.S.: 312111

Consolidated Beverage Co.   (1)
3505 E Virginia Beach Blvd, Norfolk, VA 23502
Tel.: (757) 420-9371
Emp.: 20
Beverage Distr
N.A.I.C.S.: 424490
John Starkes (Gen Mgr)

COCRYSTAL PHARMA, INC.

19805 N Creek Pkwy, Bothell, WA 98011
Tel.: (310) 691-7100   DE
Web Site:
https://www.cocrystalpharma.com
Year Founded: 2006
COCP—(NASDAQ)
Rev.: $575,000
Assets: $31,259,000
Liabilities: $4,875,000
Net Worth: $26,384,000
Earnings: ($17,984,000)
Emp.: 12
Fiscal Year-end: 12/31/23
Holding Company; Pharmaceutical Developer & Mfr
N.A.I.C.S.: 551112
Steven D. Rubin (Vice Chm)
Sam Lee (Pres & Interim Co-CEO)
James J. Martin (Interim Co-CEO & CFO)

Subsidiaries:

Cocrystal Discovery, Inc.   (1)

19805 N Creek Pkwy, Bothell, WA 98011
Tel.: (425) 398-7178
Web Site: http://www.cocrystalpharma.com
Pharmaceutical Developer & Mfr
N.A.I.C.S.: 325412
Sam Lee (Pres)

CODA OCTOPUS GROUP, INC.

3300 S Hiawassee Rd Ste 104-105, Orlando, FL 32835-6350
Tel.: (801) 973-9136   DE
Web Site:
https://www.codaoctopusgroup.com
Year Founded: 1994
CODA—(NASDAQ)
Rev.: $19,352,088
Assets: $51,841,516
Liabilities: $3,412,750
Net Worth: $48,428,766
Earnings: $3,124,149
Emp.: 83
Fiscal Year-end: 10/31/23
Semiconductor & Related Device Manufacturing
N.A.I.C.S.: 334413
Blair Cunningham (Pres-Tech)
Annmarie Gayle (Chm & CEO)
Gayle Jardine (Interim CFO)

Subsidiaries:

Coda Octopus Colmek, Inc.   (1)
6526 S Cottonwood St, Murray, UT 84107
Tel.: (801) 973-9136
Web Site: http://www.colmek.com
Emp.: 20
Electrical, Mechanical & Software Engineering Services
N.A.I.C.S.: 541330
Jason Martin (CTO)
Shelly Reich (Dir-HR & Bus Rels)
Greg Hoepfner (COO)

Coda Octopus Martech Ltd.   (1)
17 Mereside Osprey Quay, Dorset, DT5 1PY, Portland, United Kingdom
Tel.: (44) 1305770440
Web Site: http://www.martechsystems.co.uk
Sales Range: $25-49.9 Million
Emp.: 16
Engineering Services
N.A.I.C.S.: 541330
Paul Baxter (Mng Dir)
Samantha Shuttleworth (Mgr-Ops)
James Wilson (Mgr-Comml)
David Bates (Mgr-Bus Dev)

Coda Octopus Products A/S   (1)
Gammel Strandvej 22C St Tv, DK-2990, Nivaa, Denmark
Tel.: (45) 60571185
Marine Construction Services
N.A.I.C.S.: 237990

Coda Octopus Products Ltd.   (1)
38 S Gyle Crescent South Gyle Business Park, Leith, Edinburgh, EH12 9EB, United Kingdom
Tel.: (44) 1315531380
Web Site: http://www.codaoctopus.com
Sales Range: $25-49.9 Million
Emp.: 25
Navigational Services
N.A.I.C.S.: 334511

Coda Octopus Products, Inc.   (1)
3300 S Hiawassee Rd Ste 104-105, Orlando, FL 32835-6350
Tel.: (407) 735-2400
Marine Construction Services
N.A.I.C.S.: 237990

CODEXIS, INC.

200 Penobscot Dr, Redwood City, CA 94063
Tel.: (650) 421-8100   DE
Web Site: https://www.codexis.com
Year Founded: 2002
CDXS—(NASDAQ)
Rev.: $70,143,000
Assets: $136,561,000
Liabilities: $49,946,000
Net Worth: $86,615,000
Earnings: ($76,240,000)
Emp.: 174

Fiscal Year-end: 12/31/23
Biocatalytic Chemical Processes Developer
N.A.I.C.S.: 325998
Sriram Ryali (CFO & Principal Acctg Officer)
Rob Wilson (Sr VP & Gen Mgr-Performance Enzymes)
Stefan Lutz (Sr VP-Res)
Robert Sato (Sr VP-Pharmaceutical Dev, Quality, and Regulatory)
Kevin Norrett (COO)
Karen Frechou-Armijo (Sr VP)
Alison Moore (Chief Technical Officer)
Stephen G. Dilly (Chm, Pres & CEO)

Subsidiaries:

Codexis Laboratories India Pvt. Ltd.   (1)
G-01 Prestige Loka, 7/1 Brunton Road, Bengaluru, 560 025, Karnataka, India
Tel.: (91) 8066935000
Web Site: http://www.codexis.com
Biotechnology Research & Development Services
N.A.I.C.S.: 541714

CODIAK BIOSCIENCES, INC.

35 Cambridge Park Dr Ste 500, Cambridge, MA 02140
Tel.: (617) 949-4100   DE
Web Site: http://www.codiakbio.com
Year Founded: 2015
CDAK—(NASDAQ)
Rev.: $22,935,000
Assets: $171,670,000
Liabilities: $118,165,000
Net Worth: $53,505,000
Earnings: ($37,157,000)
Emp.: 102
Fiscal Year-end: 12/31/21
Biotechnology Research & Development Services
N.A.I.C.S.: 541714
Linda C. Bain (CFO)
Douglas E. Williams (Pres & CEO)
Nicole Barna (Sr VP-HR)
Richard Brudnick (Chief Bus Officer & Head-Strategy)
Konstantin Konstantinov (CTO)
Sriram Sathyanarayanan (Chief Scientific Officer)
Steven Gillis (Chm)
Jennifer Wheler (Chief Medical Officer)

COEPTIS THERAPEUTICS HOLDINGS, INC.

105 Bradford Rd Ste 420, Wexford, PA 15090
Tel.: (724) 934-6467   DE
Web Site: https://coeptistx.com
Year Founded: 2020
COEP—(NASDAQ)
Rev.: $98,701
Assets: $7,915,689
Liabilities: $3,112,360
Net Worth: $4,803,329
Earnings: ($37,574,217)
Emp.: 4
Fiscal Year-end: 12/31/22
Pharmaceuticals Mfr
N.A.I.C.S.: 325412
Dave Mehalick (Chm, Pres & CEO)
Christine Sheehy (Sec & VP-Compliance)
Dan Yerace (VP & Dir-Ops)
Brian Cogley (CFO)
Colleen Delaney (Chief Scientific Officer & Chief Medical Officer)

COEUR D'ALENE BANCORP, INC.

912 NW Blvd, Coeur D'Alene, ID 83814
Tel.: (208) 665-5999   ID

Coeur D'Alene Bancorp, Inc.—(Continued)

Year Founded: 2008
CDAB—(OTCIQ)
Bank Holding Company
N.A.I.C.S.: 551111
Wes Veach *(Pres & CEO)*
Kimberly L. Nordstrom *(Sr VP)*
William J. Haley *(Chm)*

COEUR MINING, INC.

200 S Wacker Dr Ste 2100, Chicago,
IL 60606
Tel.: (312) 489-5800   DE
Web Site: https://www.coeur.com
Year Founded: 1928
CDE—(NYSE)
Rev.: $785,636,000
Assets: $1,846,143,000
Liabilities: $957,127,000
Net Worth: $889,016,000
Earnings: ($78,107,000)
Emp.: 2,107
Fiscal Year-end: 12/31/22
Precious Metal Ore Exploration &
Mining
N.A.I.C.S.: 212290
Mitchell J. Krebs *(Pres & CEO)*
Casey M. Nault *(Gen Counsel, Sec &
Sr VP)*
Emilie C. Schouten *(Sr VP-HR)*
Kris Venkiteswaran *(VP-Operational
Excellence)*
Thomas S. Whelan *(CFO & Sr VP)*
Michael Routledge *(COO & Sr VP)*
Ken Watkinson *(Chief Acctg Officer)*
Anne Beckelheimer *(Treas & VP-Tax)*
Aoife McGrath *(Sr VP-Exploration)*
Cody Sutherlin *(VP-US Ops)*
Deon de Villiers *(VP-Internal Audit)*
Jeff Wilhoit *(Dir-IR)*
Glen Hogendoorn *(VP-Projects &
Engineering)*

Subsidiaries:

Coeur Capital, Inc.   (1)
104 S Michigan Ave Ste 900, Chicago, IL
60603
Tel.: (312) 489-5800
Silver Mining Services
N.A.I.C.S.: 212220

Coeur Explorations, Inc.   (1)
505 E Frnt Ave, Coeur D'Alene, ID
83814   (100%)
Tel.: (208) 667-3511
Web Site: http://www.coeur.com
Emp.: 30
Precious Metal Exploration Services
N.A.I.C.S.: 213114

Coeur Rochester, Inc.   (1)
PO Box 1057, Lovelock, NV
89419-1057   (100%)
Tel.: (775) 273-7995
Sales Range: $25-49.9 Million
Emp.: 200
Silver & Gold Mine
N.A.I.C.S.: 212220
Greg Robinson *(Asst Gen Mgr)*

Global Royalty Corp.   (1)
1111 W Hastings St Ste 1600, Vancouver,
V6E 2J3, BC, Canada
Tel.: (604) 696-9720
Mineral Mining Services
N.A.I.C.S.: 212323

Wharf Resources (USA) Inc.   (1)
10928 Wharf Rd, Lead, SD 57754   (100%)
Tel.: (605) 584-1441
Web Site: https://www.coeur.com
Emp.: 197
Gold Mining
N.A.I.C.S.: 212220

COFFEE HOLDING COMPANY, INC.

3475 Victory Blvd, Staten Island, NY
10314
Tel.: (718) 832-0800   NV

Web Site:
https://www.coffeeholding.com
Year Founded: 1971
JVA—(NASDAQ)
Rev.: $68,173,404
Assets: $42,191,901
Liabilities: $18,476,810
Net Worth: $23,715,091
Earnings: ($835,576)
Emp.: 96
Fiscal Year-end: 10/31/23
Wholesale Coffee Roaster & Dealer
N.A.I.C.S.: 311920
Andrew Gordon *(Chm, Pres, CEO,
CFO & Treas)*
David Gordon *(COO, Sec & Exec
VP-Ops)*
Sterling Gordon *(Founder)*
Robert Penrose *(COO-Sonofresco)*
Erik Hansen *(Exec VP-Sls)*

Subsidiaries:

Coffee Kinetics, L.L.C.   (1)
1365 Pacific Dr, Burlington, WA
98233   (100%)
Tel.: (360) 757-2800
Web Site: https://www.sonofresco.com
Coffee & Tea Mfr
N.A.I.C.S.: 311920

Comfort Foods, Inc.   (1)
25 Commerce Way, North Andover, MA
01845
Tel.: (978) 557-0009
Web Site:
http://www.harmonybaycoffee.com
Grocery & Related Products Whslr
N.A.I.C.S.: 424490

Organic Products Trading Company,
LLC   (1)
4018 NE 112th Ave Ste D-8, Vancouver,
WA 98682
Tel.: (360) 573-4433
Web Site: https://optco.com
Organic Product Mfr & Distr
N.A.I.C.S.: 325199
Misty Myers *(Mgr-Admin)*
Brian Nicholas *(Mgr-Acct)*
Connie Kolosvary *(Dir-Cafe Femenino Pro-
gram)*
Aron Guterman *(Mgr-Acct)*

Steep & Brew, Inc.   (1)
6656 Odana Rd, Madison, WI 53719
Tel.: (608) 833-6656
Web Site: https://steepnbrewwest.com
Coffee & Tea Mfr
N.A.I.C.S.: 311920
Michael Dineen *(Dir-Territory)*

COFFEE INC.

1901 N Roselle Rd Ste 800 PMB
8080, Schaumburg, IL 60195
Tel.: (630) 250-2708   NV
Web Site:
https://coffeeincorporated.com
Year Founded: 2014
COFE—(OTCIQ)
Sales Range: $10-24.9 Million
Emp.: 409
Coffee Distr
N.A.I.C.S.: 445298
Larry Trachtenberg *(Pres & CEO)*

COGENT BIOSCIENCES, INC.

275 Wyman St 3rd Fl, Waltham, MA
02451
Tel.: (617) 945-5576   DE
Web Site: https://www.cogentbio.com
Year Founded: 2014
COGT—(NASDAQ)
Rev.: $7,598,000
Assets: $300,810,000
Liabilities: $45,075,000
Net Worth: $255,735,000
Earnings: ($140,241,000)
Emp.: 138
Fiscal Year-end: 12/31/22
Immunotherapy Research & Develop-
ment Services

N.A.I.C.S.: 541714
John Green *(CFO)*
Jessica Sachs *(Chief Medical Officer)*
Erin Schellhammer *(Chief People Of-
ficer)*
John Robinson *(Chief Scientific Offi-
cer)*
Brad Barnett *(CTO)*
Brad Fell *(VP)*
Francis Sullivan *(VP)*
Shannon Winski *(VP)*
Evan Kearns *(Chief Legal Officer)*
Dana Martin *(Chief Patient Officer)*
Andrew Robbins *(Pres, CEO & princi-
pal executive officer)*

COGENT COMMUNICATIONS HOLDINGS, INC.

2450 N St NW, Washington, DC
20037
Tel.: (202) 295-4200   DE
Web Site: https://www.cogentco.com
Year Founded: 1999
CCOI—(NASDAQ)
Rev.: $940,922,000
Assets: $3,211,619,000
Liabilities: $2,602,063,000
Net Worth: $609,556,000
Earnings: $1,273,441,000
Emp.: 1,947
Fiscal Year-end: 12/31/23
Holding Company; High-Speed Inter-
net Access & Internet Protocol Com-
munications Services
N.A.I.C.S.: 551112
David Schaeffer *(Founder, Chm, Pres
& CEO)*
Thaddeus Gerard Weed *(CFO, Prin-
cipal Acctg Officer, Treas & VP)*
Deneen Howell *(Bd of Dirs & Atty)*
Jocelyn Johnson *(Sr Mgr-Marketing &
Communications)*

Subsidiaries:

C.C.D. Cogent Communications
Deutschland GmbH   (1)
Atricom Building Lyoner Strasse 15, 60528,
Frankfurt am Main, Germany
Tel.: (49) 692998960
Sales Range: $100-124.9 Million
High-Speed Internet Services
N.A.I.C.S.: 517810

Cogent Canada, Inc.   (1)
220 Yonge Street Suite 211, Toronto, M5B
2I1, ON, Canada
Tel.: (416) 860-8080
Web Site: http://www.cogentco.com
Sales Range: $10-24.9 Million
Emp.: 24
High-Speed Internet Services
N.A.I.C.S.: 517810

Cogent Communications Denmark
ApS   (1)
Holbergsgade 14 2 tv, 1057, Copenhagen,
Denmark
Tel.: (45) 33377979
Internet Service Provider
N.A.I.C.S.: 517111

Cogent Communications Espana
SA   (1)
C/ Jose Bardasano Baos 9 Planta 2a A Edi-
ficio Gorbea III, 28016, Madrid, Spain
Tel.: (34) 911022527
Web Site: http://www.cogentco.com
Sales Range: $100-124.9 Million
Emp.: 30
High-Speed Internet Services
N.A.I.C.S.: 517810

Cogent Communications France
SAS   (1)
77 Boulevard de la Republique, 92257, La
Garenne-Colombes, Cedex, France
Tel.: (33) 14 903 1800
Web Site: http://www.cogentco.com
Sales Range: $25-49.9 Million
Emp.: 25
High-Speed Internet Services
N.A.I.C.S.: 517810

Cogent Communications Netherlands
B.V.   (1)
Haarlemmerstraatweg 135, 1165 MK, Half-
weg, Netherlands
Tel.: (31) 20 462 1440
Web Site: http://www.cogentco.com
Sales Range: $1-9.9 Million
Emp.: 10
High-Speed Internet Services
N.A.I.C.S.: 517810

Cogent Communications Nordics   (1)
Kruislaan 400, 1098 SM, Amsterdam, Neth-
erlands
Tel.: (31) 208884874
Web Site: http://www.cogentco.com
Sales Range: $10-24.9 Million
Emp.: 5
High-Speed Internet Services
N.A.I.C.S.: 517810

Cogent Communications Poland Sp.
z o.o.   (1)
c/o Accace Cybernetyki 10, 02-677, Warsaw, Poland
Tel.: (48) 298149
Internet Services
N.A.I.C.S.: 517111

Cogent Communications Sweden
AB   (1)
Torshamnsgatan 27, 164 40, Kista, Sweden
Tel.: (46) 84441444
Sales Range: $10-24.9 Million
Emp.: 3
Internet Service Provider
N.A.I.C.S.: 517111

Cogent Communications UK Ltd.   (1)
20 Mastmaker Court, London, E14 9UB,
United Kingdom
Tel.: (44) 207 510 9204
Web Site: http://www.cogentco.com
High-Speed Internet Services
N.A.I.C.S.: 517810

Cogent Communications, Inc.   (1)
2450 N St NW, Washington, DC 20037
Tel.: (202) 295-4200
Web Site: https://www.cogentco.com
High-Speed Internet Access & Internet Pro-
tocol Communications Services
N.A.I.C.S.: 517810
Tad Weed *(CFO)*

Cogent Latvia SIA   (1)
Krisjana Valdemara iela 21-11, Riga, 1010,
Latvia
Tel.: (371) 40103312778
Internet Service Provider
N.A.I.C.S.: 517111

COGNEX CORPORATION

1 Vision Dr, Natick, MA 01760-2059
Tel.: (508) 650-3000   MA
Web Site: https://www.cognex.com
Year Founded: 1981
CGNX—(NASDAQ)
Rev.: $837,547,000
Assets: $2,017,812,000
Liabilities: $513,060,000
Net Worth: $1,504,752,000
Earnings: $113,234,000
Emp.: 2,992
Fiscal Year-end: 12/31/23
Machine Vision Systems Used to Re-
place Human Vision in Manufacturing
Processes
N.A.I.C.S.: 334513
Robert J. Willett *(Pres & CEO)*
Marilyn Matz *(Co-Founder)*
Sheila DiPalma *(Exec VP-Corp Em-
ployee Svcs)*
Laura A. MacDonald *(Principal Acctg
Officer & Controller)*
Carl Gerst *(Exec VP-Vision & ID
Products)*
Dennis Fehr *(CFO & Sr VP-Fin)*
Joerg Kuechen *(CTO)*

Subsidiaries:

Chiaro Technologies LLC   (1)
1600 Range St Ste 102, Boulder, CO
80301-2739
Tel.: (303) 554-0557

Web Site: http://www.chiarotech.com
3D Machine Vision Sensors Mfr
N.A.I.C.S.: 334118
Eric Moore (Founder)

Cognex France (1)
Immeuble Le Patio 104 Ave Albert Ter,
92563, Rueil-Malmaison, France
Tel.: (33) 147771550
Web Site: http://www.cognex.fr
Sales Range: $10-24.9 Million
Emp.: 45
Mfr of Machine Vision Sensors & Systems
N.A.I.C.S.: 541512

Cognex Germany, Inc. (1)
Emmy Noether Str 11, 76131, Karlsruhe,
Germany
Tel.: (49) 7219588052
Web Site: https://www.cognex.com
Sales Range: $10-24.9 Million
Emp.: 50
Mfr of Machine Vision Sensors & Systems
N.A.I.C.S.: 541512
Justin Testa (Sr VP-Mktg)
Torsten Zoeller (Mgr-Marketing)

Cognex Hungary Kft. (1)
Tel.: (36) 18088100
Web Site: http://www.cognex.com
Vision Products Mfr
N.A.I.C.S.: 333310

Cognex International, Inc. (1)
1 Vision Dr, Natick, MA 01760-2059
Tel.: (508) 650-3000
Web Site: http://www.cognex.com
Vision Products Mfr
N.A.I.C.S.: 333310

Cognex K.K. (1)
23F Bunkyo Green Court Building 2-28-8,
Honkomagome, Bunkyo-ku, Tokyo, 113-
6591, Japan (100%)
Tel.: (81) 359775400
Sales Range: $25-49.9 Million
Emp.: 100
Mfr of Machine Vision Sensors & Systems
N.A.I.C.S.: 541512

Cognex Malaysia Sdn. Bhd. (1)
73-3-1 iDeal The One Jalan Mahsuri,
11950, Bayan Lepas, 11950, Penang, Malaysia
Tel.: (60) 199165532
Electric Equipment Mfr
N.A.I.C.S.: 335999

Cognex Poland z.o.o (1)
ul Legnicka 48F, 54-202, Wroclaw, Poland
Tel.: (48) 717121086
Industrial Product Distr
N.A.I.C.S.: 423830

**Cognex Singapore Manufacturing
PTE. Ltd.** (1)
238A Thomson Road 13-01/02 Novena
Square Tower A, Singapore, 307684, Singa-
pore
Tel.: (65) 31583322
Machine Part Mfr
N.A.I.C.S.: 333111

Cognex UK Ltd. (1)
Regus Central Boulevard Blythe Valley
Business Park, Silverstone Circuit Silver-
stone, Solihull, B90 8AG, West Midlands,
United Kingdom
Tel.: (44) 121 296 5163
Web Site: https://www.cognex.com
Machine Vision System Mfr
N.A.I.C.S.: 333310

Cognex Vietnam Company Ltd. (1)
7th Floor CEO Building Lot HH2-1 Me Tri
Ha Urban Area Pham Hung Street, Me Tri
Ward Nam Tu Liem District, Hanoi, Vietnam
Tel.: (84) 982405167
Industrial Product Distr
N.A.I.C.S.: 423830

Cognex Vision Thailand Limited (1)
173 Asia Centre Building 27th Floor Wework Office S Sathorn Road, Thung Mahamek Sathorn, Bangkok, Thailand
Tel.: (66) 632309998
Electric Equipment Mfr
N.A.I.C.S.: 335999

MORITEX Corporation (1)

3-13-45 Senzui, Asaka, 351-0024, Saitama,
Japan
Tel.: (81) 482182525
Web Site: http://www.moritex.com
Sales Range: $25-49.9 MIllion
Optical Equipment Mfr & Whslr
N.A.I.C.S.: 333310
Takao Sato (CEO)
Kyoyu Uchida (Operating Officer)
Nobuyuki Kawasaki (Operating Officer)
Hiroshi Misawa (Operating Officer)

Subsidiary (US):

MORITEX North America, Inc. (2)
6862 Santa Teresa Blvd, San Jose, CA
95119
Tel.: (408) 363-2100
Fiber Optic, Machine Vision, Automated Op-
tical Alignment & Automated Bio Equipment
Mfr & Distr
N.A.I.C.S.: 333310

Subsidiary (Non-US):

**MORITEX Technologies (Shenzhen)
Co., Ltd.** (2)
No 20 Gui Yue Road Da Ping Village Guan
Lan, Bao An District, Shenzhen, 518110,
China
Tel.: (86) 755 2798 8282
Glass Products Mfr
N.A.I.C.S.: 327215

Moritex Asia Pacific PTE., Ltd. (1)
60 Paya Lebar Road 06-31, Singapore,
409051, Singapore
Tel.: (65) 68980835
Optical Equipment Mfr & Distr
N.A.I.C.S.: 334610

SuaLab (Suzhou) Co., Ltd. (1)
4-B801 328 Xinghu Street, Creative Indus-
trial Park Suzhou Industrial Park, Suzhou,
China
Tel.: (86) 51262650852
Electric Equipment Mfr
N.A.I.C.S.: 335999

SuaLab Co., Ltd. (1)
6F Majestar Tower2 Seochodaero 38gil 12,
Seocho-gu, Seoul, 06655, Korea (South)
Tel.: (82) 262640366
Web Site: http://www.sualab.com
Electric Equipment Mfr
N.A.I.C.S.: 335999
Eric Eungjin Moon (CEO)
Brandon Lee (Mgr)

Webscan, Inc. (1)
4990 Pearl East Cir Ste 300, Boulder, CO
80301
Tel.: (303) 485-6811
Web Site: https://www.webscaninc.com
Computer Peripheral Equipment Mfr & Mar-
keter
N.A.I.C.S.: 334118

COGNITION THERAPEUTICS, INC.
2500 Wchester Ave, Purchase, NY
10577
Tel.: (412) 481-2210
Web Site: https://www.cogrx.com
CGTX—(NASDAQ)
Rev.: $22,154,000
Assets: $50,425,000
Liabilities: $10,176,000
Net Worth: $40,249,000
Earnings: ($21,397,000)
Emp.: 22
Fiscal Year-end: 12/31/22
Research & Development in Biotech-
nology (except Nanobiotechnology)
N.A.I.C.S.: 541714
John Doyle (CFO & Principal Acctg
Officer)
Jack A. Khattar (Chm)
Lisa Ricciardi (Pres & CEO)
Anthony O. Caggiano (Chief Medical
Officer & Head-R&D)
Mary Hamby (VP-Res)

COGNITIV, INC.

704 N 39th StSte 120, Fort Pierce,
FL 34947
Tel.: (888) 256-3951   FL
Web Site: http://www.4cogv.com
Year Founded: 2001
COGV—(OTCIQ)
Website Development & Internet Mar-
keting
N.A.I.C.S.: 541519
Jeremy Fain (Founder & CEO)
Meredith Tehan (Sr VP-Sls)

COGNIZANT TECHNOLOGY SOLUTIONS CORPORATION
300 Frank W Burr Blvd, Teaneck, NJ
07692
Tel.: (201) 801-0233   DE
Web Site: https://www.cognizant.com
Year Founded: 1994
CTSH—(NASDAQ)
Rev.: $19,353,000,000
Assets: $18,483,000,000
Liabilities: $5,256,000,000
Net Worth: $13,227,000,000
Earnings: $2,126,000,000
Emp.: 347,700
Fiscal Year-end: 12/31/23
Information Technology, Consulting &
Business Outsourcing Services
N.A.I.C.S.: 541513
Robert Telesmanic (Chief Acctg Offi-
cer, Sr VP & Controller)
Gaurav Chand (CMO)
Anil Cheriyan (Exec VP-Strategy &
Tech)
Rob Walker (Pres-Global Growth
Markets)
Ravi Kumar (Executives)
Tyler Scott (VP-IR)
Jeff DeMarrais (VP-Corp Comm)
Ravi Kumar Singisetti (CEO)

Subsidiaries:

AustinCSI, LLC (1)
5340 Legacy Dr Ste 180, Plano, TX 75024
Tel.: (214) 296-0258
Web Site: http://www.austincsi.com
Sales Range: $1-9.9 Million
Emp.: 200
Management Consulting Firm Specializing
in Business Process Optimization, Project &
Portfolio Management & Software Quality
Management Services
N.A.I.C.S.: 541618
Karen Moree (Founder, CEO & Mng Part-
ner)
James Anderson (Head-Strategy &
Project/Portfolio Mgmt)
Rizwan Sheikh (Mng Partner)

Bolder Outreach Solutions, LLC (1)
9200 Shelbyville Rd, Louisville, KY 40222
Tel.: (502) 371-1700
Healthcare Revenue Cycle Management
Services
N.A.I.C.S.: 561499
Michael Shea (CEO)

Subsidiary (Domestic):

Receivables Outsourcing, LLC (2)
1920 Greenspring Dr Ste 200, Timonium,
MD 21093
Tel.: (410) 561-9911
Revenue Cycle Management Services (for
Hospitals)
N.A.I.C.S.: 561440
Christopher G. Wunder (Founder & CEO)

Subsidiary (Domestic):

**Prospective Payment Specialists,
Inc.** (3)
1600 Rosecans Ave Bldg 7 4th Fl, Manhat-
tan Beach, CA 90266
Tel.: (310) 563-1810
Hospital Compliance Consulting Services
N.A.I.C.S.: 561690

Cadient, Inc. (1)
72 E Swedesford Rd, Malvern, PA 19355
Tel.: (484) 351-2800
Web Site: http://www.cadient.com

Digital Marketing Advertising Agency
N.A.I.C.S.: 541810
Charles Walker (COO)
Ben Matus (Exec Dir-Client Services)
Josh Voluck (Client Svcs Dir)
Anja Huebler (Exec Creative Dir)
Tim Nelson (Client Svcs Dir)
Stacy Davis (Dir-Development)
Shweta Neville (Dir-)
Maria Swope (Sr Dir)
Ben Matus (Exec Dir-Client Services)
Josh Voluck (Client Svcs Dir)
Anja Huebler (Exec Creative Dir)
Tim Nelson (Client Svcs Dir)
Stacy Davis (Dir-Development)
Shweta Neville (Dir-)
Maria Swope (Sr Dir)

CogDev Malaysia SDN BHD (1)
Level 30 Menara Shell 211 Jalan Tun Sam-
banthan, Wilayah Persekutuan, 50470,
Kuala Lumpur, Malaysia
Tel.: (60) 327424100
Web Site: https://www.cognizant.com
Information Technology Infrastructure Ser-
vices
N.A.I.C.S.: 541512

**Cognizant Consulting and Services
GmbH** (1)
Europaallee 27-29, Frechen, 50226, Ger-
many
Tel.: (49) 2234933000
Information Technology Consulting Services
N.A.I.C.S.: 541512
Claus P. Dehnbostel (Mgr)

**Cognizant El Salvador, Sociedad
Anonima de Capital Variable** (1)
63 Avenida Sur y Alameda Roosevelt Cen-
tro Financiero Gigante Torre A, Nivel 7, San
Salvador, El Salvador
Tel.: (503) 22029000
Software Development Services
N.A.I.C.S.: 541511

Cognizant Japan KK (1)
PMO Hanzomon 2-1 Kojimachi Level 8,
Chiyoda-ku, Tokyo, 102-0083, Japan
Tel.: (81) 345638300
Computer System Design Services
N.A.I.C.S.: 541512

Cognizant Mobility GmbH (1)
Ingolstadter Str 45, 80807, Munich, Ger-
many
Tel.: (49) 89921614500
Web Site: https://cognizant-mobility.com
Information Technology Infrastructure Ser-
vices
N.A.I.C.S.: 541512

**Cognizant Mortgage Services
Corporation** (1)
5001 Statesman Dr Ofc 107 - Ste 200, Ir-
ving, TX 75063
Tel.: (214) 459-6929
Information Technology Infrastructure Ser-
vices
N.A.I.C.S.: 541512

Cognizant Technology Solutions (1)
Canyon Corporate Plz 2512 W Dunlap Ave
Ste 100 - 600, Phoenix, AZ 85021
Tel.: (480) 366-0400
Web Site: http://www.cognizant.com
Rev.: $1,570,000
Emp.: 10
Custom Computer Programming Services
N.A.I.C.S.: 541511
Tobi M. Edwards Young (Sr VP-Legal,
Regulatory, and Corporate Affairs)

**Cognizant Technology Solutions
(Netherlands) B.V.** (1)
Gustav Mahlerlaan 308 FOZ Building 3rd
Floor, 1082 ME, Amsterdam, Netherlands
Tel.: (31) 205247700
Web Site: http://www.cognizant.com
Software Development Services
N.A.I.C.S.: 513210
Gerard Elkhuizen (Head-Sales-Benelux)
Saket Gulati (Head)
Jitka Beukenkamp (Head)
Wim Van Hennekeler (Head)

**Cognizant Technology Solutions
(Shanghai) Co., Ltd.** (1)
Building 10 No 401 ChuanQiao Road, Pu-
dong New Area, Shanghai, 201206, China

Cognizant Technology Solutions Corporation—(Continued)
Tel.: (86) 2120609555
Web Site: http://www.cognizant.com
Custom Computer Programming Services
N.A.I.C.S.: 541511

Cognizant Technology Solutions A.G. (1)
Prime Tower 18th floor Hardstrasse 201, 8005, Zurich, Switzerland
Tel.: (41) 417246645
Web Site: https://www.cognizant.com
Information Technology Infrastructure Services
N.A.I.C.S.: 541512

Cognizant Technology Solutions Asia Pacific Pte Ltd. (1)
Web Site: https://www.cognizant.com
Computer Programming Services
N.A.I.C.S.: 541511

Cognizant Technology Solutions Australia Pty. Ltd. (1)
Level 37 Tower Two International Towers Sydney 200 Barangaroo Avenue, Barangaroo, Sydney, 2000, NSW, Australia
Tel.: (61) 292233988
Web Site: http://www.cognizant.com
Sales Range: $25-49.9 Million
Emp.: 500
Program Management Consulting Services
N.A.I.C.S.: 541618

Subsidiary (Domestic):

Cognizant Technology Solutions Australia Pty. Ltd. (2)
15 Williams Street Level 6 Suite 2, Melbourne, 3000, VIC, Australia (100%)
Tel.: (61) 39 252 3000
Web Site: https://www.cognizant.com
Sales Range: $10-24.9 Million
Technological Advances in Business
N.A.I.C.S.: 561499

Cognizant Technology Solutions Belgium S.A.
Havenlaan 86C, Box 408, 1000, Brussels, Belgium
Tel.: (32) 27924467
Web Site: http://www.cognizant.com
Custom Computer Programming Services
N.A.I.C.S.: 541511

Cognizant Technology Solutions Benelux B.V. (1)
Cognizant Digital Studio Paul van Vlissingenstraat 10, 1096 BK, Amsterdam, Netherlands
Tel.: (31) 205950550
Web Site: http://www.cognizant.com
Information Technology Infrastructure Services
N.A.I.C.S.: 541512

Cognizant Technology Solutions Denmark ApS (1)
Bredgade 6, 1260, Copenhagen, Denmark
Tel.: (45) 49251234
Web Site: http://www.cognizant.com
Custom Computer Programming Services
N.A.I.C.S.: 541511

Cognizant Technology Solutions France S.A. (1)
50-52 Boulevard Haussmann, 75009, Paris, France
Tel.: (33) 170365657
Web Site: http://www.cognizant.com
Custom Computer Programming Services
N.A.I.C.S.: 541511

Cognizant Technology Solutions GmbH (1)
Torhaus Westhafen Speicherstrasse 57-59, 60327, Frankfurt am Main, Germany
Tel.: (49) 69272269500
Web Site: http://www.cognizant.com
Custom Computer Programming Services
N.A.I.C.S.: 541511

Cognizant Technology Solutions Hungary Kft
Mill Park Office A buliding Soroksari ut 44, 1095, Budapest, Hungary
Tel.: (36) 14567000
Web Site: http://www.cognizant.com

Custom Computer Programming Services
N.A.I.C.S.: 541511

Cognizant Technology Solutions India Pvt. Limited (1)
H-04 Vignesh Hi-tech City-2 Survey No 30 P 35 P & 35 P, Gachibowli Serilingampally Mandal, Hyderabad, 500 019, Telangana, India
Tel.: (91) 18002086999
Information Technology Infrastructure Services
N.A.I.C.S.: 541512

Cognizant Technology Solutions India Pvt. Ltd. (1)
Kensington SEZ A Wing 12th & 13th Floor, Hiranandani Business Park Powai, Mumbai, 400 076, India
Tel.: (91) 2261104312
Web Site: http://www.cognizant.com
Information Technology Consulting Services
N.A.I.C.S.: 541512
Rajesh Nambiar (Chm, Mng Dir & Exec VP)
Lakshmi Narayanan (CEO)

Cognizant Technology Solutions Lithuania, UAB (1)
Savanoriu ave 16, 03159, Vilnius, Lithuania
Tel.: (370) 60454941
Software Development Services
N.A.I.C.S.: 541511

Cognizant Technology Solutions New Zealand Limited (1)
Tel.: (64) 93632871
Web Site: http://www.cognizant.com
Computer System Design Services
N.A.I.C.S.: 541512

Cognizant Technology Solutions Norway A.S. (1)
Snaroyveien 36 Suite Wing 2A, 1364, Oslo, Norway
Tel.: (47) 67826000
Web Site: http://www.cognizant.com
Custom Computer Programming Services
N.A.I.C.S.: 541511

Cognizant Technology Solutions Philippines, Inc. (1)
Science Hub Tower 4 1110 Campus Avenue Mckinley Hill Cyber Park, 1st-4th floor, Taguig, 1634, Philippines
Tel.: (63) 27 976 2270
Web Site: https://www.cognizant.com
Custom Computer Programming Services
N.A.I.C.S.: 541511

Cognizant Technology Solutions Sweden AB (1)
Linnegatan 87D, 115 23, Stockholm, Sweden
Tel.: (46) 850386900
Web Site: https://www.cognizant.com
Sales Range: $25-49.9 Million
Software Publishing Services
N.A.I.C.S.: 513210

Cognizant Technology Solutions U.S. Corporation (1)
211 Quality Cir, College Station, TX 77845
Tel.: (979) 691-7700
Custom Computer Programming Services
N.A.I.C.S.: 541511

Cognizant Technology Solutions UK Limited (1)
280 Bishopsgate, Paddington Central, London, EC2M 4RB, United Kingdom
Tel.: (44) 2072977600
Web Site: http://www.cognizant.com
Custom Computer Programming Services
N.A.I.C.S.: 541511

Cognizant Technology Solutions de Argentina S.R.L. (1)
Moreno 877, C1091AAQ, Buenos Aires, Argentina
Tel.: (54) 1148760900
Software Development Services
N.A.I.C.S.: 541511

Collaborative Solutions Europe Limited (1)
50 St Mary Axe, London, EC3A 8FR, United Kingdom
Tel.: (44) 2038658479
Finance Consulting Services

N.A.I.C.S.: 541611

Devbridge Canada ULC (1)
100 University Avenue Floor 5, Toronto, M5J 1V6, ON, Canada
Tel.: (416) 901-0235
Information Technology Services
N.A.I.C.S.: 541511

Devbridge UK Ltd. (1)
34-57 Liverpool St, London, EC2M 7PP, United Kingdom
Tel.: (44) 2037430717
Information Technology Services
N.A.I.C.S.: 541511

EI-Technologies France SAS (1)
24 rue Jacques Ibert, 92300, Levallois-Perret, France
Tel.: (33) 180038800
Web Site: https://www.ei-technologies.com
Management Consulting Services
N.A.I.C.S.: 541613
Pierre Sarrola (CFO)
Jean De Lasa (Gen Mgr)

Equinox Consulting SAS (1)
63 Boulevard Haussman, Paris, 75008, France
Tel.: (33) 153430643
Web Site: http://www.equinox-cognizant.com
Financial Consulting Services
N.A.I.C.S.: 523940
Antoine Pertriaux (Partner-Capital Markets)

Equinox-Cognizant SARL (1)
N 295 Angle bd Abdelmoumen and street Perseus-3rd floor-C21 Maarif, 20100, Casablanca, Morocco
Tel.: (212) 522863887
Web Site: http://www.equinox-cognizant.com
Financial Services
N.A.I.C.S.: 523991

Hedera Consulting BVBA (1)
Prins Boudewijnlaan 24A, 2550, Kontich, Belgium
Tel.: (32) 821711645
Web Site: http://www.hederaconsulting.com
Consulting & Professional Services
N.A.I.C.S.: 541618

Hunter Technical Resources LLC. (1)
2000 RiverEdge Pkwy Ste 930, Atlanta, GA 30328
Tel.: (404) 459-7373
Web Site: http://www.htrjobs.com
Sales Range: $10-24.9 Million
Emp.: 153
Executive Search Service
N.A.I.C.S.: 501312
Alex Brown (Mng Partner & CFO)
Clint Bailey (Co-Founder, Mng Partner & VP-Sls)
Tracy Bailey (Co-Founder)
Scott Hall (Pres & Mng Partner)
Douglas Kling (Dir)

Idea Couture Latin America, S.A.P.I. de C.V. (1)
Antiguo Camino a la Huasteca No 360 Col Mirador de la Huasteca, 66354, Santa Catarina, NL, Mexico
Tel.: (52) 8182622210
Web Site: https://ideacouturelatinamerica.wordpress.com
Software Development Services
N.A.I.C.S.: 541511

Inawisdom Ltd. (1)
Connexions Building 159 Princes Street, Ipswich, IP1 1QJ, Suffolk, United Kingdom
Tel.: (44) 2081338349
Web Site: https://inawisdom.com
Information Technology Infrastructure Services
N.A.I.C.S.: 541512

Itaas, Inc. (1)
11695 Johns Creek Pkwy Ste 300, Duluth, GA 30097
Tel.: (678) 527-8500
Web Site: http://www.itaas.com
Emp.: 200
Digital Video Solutions & Services
N.A.I.C.S.: 541511

Jaspal Bhasin (COO & Partner)
Vibha Rustagi (Founder, Pres & CEO)
Bob Edwards (VP-Engrg)
Arun Prasad (VP-Ops-Worldwide)
Jim Elayan (VP-Mktg & Bus Dev)
Jatin Desai (CTO & Partner)

Subsidiary (Non-US):

itaas India Private Limited (2)
4th Floor Tower C Logix Techno Park Plot 5 Sector 127, Noida, 201301, UP, India
Tel.: (91) 120 400 1900
Web Site: http://www.itaas.com
Digital Video Solutions & Services
N.A.I.C.S.: 541511

KBACE Technologies, Inc. (1)
6 Trafalgar Sq, Nashua, NH 03063
Tel.: (603) 821-7000
Web Site: http://www.kbace.com
Emp.: 400
Oracle eBusiness Consulting Services
N.A.I.C.S.: 541511
Amit Ajmani (Mng Dir & VP)
Michael Peterson (Pres & COO)
David Sullivan (VP)
Jeff Curtis (Sr VP)

KIS Informatik AG (1)
Vadianstrasse 29, 9000, Saint Gallen, Switzerland
Tel.: (41) 712272992
Web Site: http://www.kis-informatik.ch
Software Development Services
N.A.I.C.S.: 541511

KIS Information Services GmbH (1)
Am Silberpalais 1, Duisburg, 47057, Germany
Tel.: (49) 20379909410
Software Development Services
N.A.I.C.S.: 541511
Joachim Walentowitz (Mng Dir)

Kabushiki Kaisha Brilliant Service (1)
Kita-ku Nishi-tenmu 2 - chome No 6 8 Dojima Building 8 th floor, Osaka, Osaka, Japan
Tel.: (81) 663635735
Software Development Services
N.A.I.C.S.: 541511

LZ Lifescience Limited (1)
A 4 The Courtyard Kilcarbery Business Park Nangor Road, Dublin, Ireland
Tel.: (353) 12910955
Web Site: https://www.lzlifescience.com
Life Science Research & Development Services
N.A.I.C.S.: 541714
Eric Daly (Sys Engr)

LZ Lifescience US Inc. (1)
25 Sentry Pkwy 5 Sentry Park W Bldg Ste 100, Blue Bell, PA 19422
Tel.: (267) 428-2499
Life Science Research & Development Services
N.A.I.C.S.: 541714

Magenic Technologies, Inc. (1)
1600 Utica Ave S Ste 800, Saint Louis Park, MN 55416
Tel.: (763) 398-4800
Web Site: http://www.magenic.com
Software Publisher
N.A.I.C.S.: 513210
Rockford Lhotka (CTO)
Stefanos Daskalakis (Gen Mgr)
Greg Frankenfield (CEO)

Mirabeau B.V. (1)
Groothandelsgebouw Conradstraat 38 - Kamer D8 131, 3013 AP, Rotterdam, Netherlands
Tel.: (31) 205950550
Web Site: http://www.mirabeau.nl
Software Digital Business Services
N.A.I.C.S.: 541511

Mobica Ltd. (1)
Crown House Manchester Road, Wilmslow, SK9 1BH, United Kingdom
Tel.: (44) 1625446140
Web Site: http://www.mobica.com
Sales Range: $10-24.9 Million
Emp.: 400
Software Development & Integration Services
N.A.I.C.S.: 541512

Nick Stammers *(Chm)*
Andy Collis *(CFO)*
Jim Carroll *(CTO)*
Sam Kingston *(CEO)*

Subsidiary (Non-US):

Mobica Limited Sp. z o.o. **(2)**
Oddzial w Warszawie ul Walbrzyska 11,
02-741, Warsaw, Poland
Tel.: (48) 22 852 14 75
Web Site: http://www.mobica.com
Software Development Services
N.A.I.C.S.: 541511

Subsidiary (US):

Mobica US Inc. **(2)**
Silicon Vly Ctr 2570 N 1st St 2nd Flr, San
Jose, CA 95131
Tel.: (408) 273-4557
Web Site: http://www.mobica.com
Emp.: 1,000
Software Development Services
N.A.I.C.S.: 541511
Marcin Kloda *(CEO)*

Netcentric AG **(1)**
Prime Tower Hardstrasse 201, 8005, Zurich,
Switzerland
Tel.: (41) 444447058
Web Site: https://www.netcentric.biz
Software Digital Business Services
N.A.I.C.S.: 541511
Elian Kool *(VP)*

Netcentric Benelux BV **(1)**
Paul van Vlissingenstraat 10C, 1096 BK,
Amsterdam, Netherlands
Tel.: (31) 654362364
Software Digital Business Services
N.A.I.C.S.: 541511
Ronald Baart *(Dir-Bus Dev)*

Netcentric Deutschland GmbH **(1)**
Landsberger Str 110, 80339, Munich, Ger-
many
Tel.: (49) 89121405761
Software Digital Business Services
N.A.I.C.S.: 541511
Gerhard Gerner *(COO)*

**Netcentric Eastern Europe
S.R.L.** **(1)**
165 Splaiul Unirii TN Offices 2 Building, Dis-
trict 3, 030133, Bucharest, Romania
Tel.: (40) 316300869
Software Digital Business Services
N.A.I.C.S.: 541511
Andrei Hobeanu *(Mgr-Svc)*

Netcentric Iberica SLU **(1)**
Cami Antic de Valencia 54 7-9, 08005, Bar-
celona, Spain
Tel.: (34) 932201992
Software Digital Business Services
N.A.I.C.S.: 541511
Vanessa C. Torres Navarro *(Engr-Software)*

New Signature Canada Inc. **(1)**
7th Floor 5140 Yonge Street, Toronto, M2N
7J8, ON, Canada
Tel.: (416) 971-4267
Cloud Services
N.A.I.C.S.: 518210

New Signature UK Limited **(1)**
57 Bermondsey Street Laxmi Building, Lon-
don, SE1 3XJ, United Kingdom
Tel.: (44) 2076453299
Cloud Services
N.A.I.C.S.: 518210

New Signature US, Inc. **(1)**
901 K St NW, Washington, DC 20001
Tel.: (202) 452-5923
Web Site: http://www.newsignature.com
Sales Range: $1-9.9 Million
Emp.: 80
Information Technology Services
N.A.I.C.S.: 541511
Jeffrey Tench *(CEO)*
Pat Paquette *(CFO)*
Jeff Dunmall *(Head)*
Vicki Thomson *(Exec VP-Human Re-
sources)*
Reed Wiedower *(CTO)*
Ed Schwartz *(Head-Operations-North
America)*
Paul Cosgrave *(Chief Strategy Officer)*
Alison Garback *(CMO)*
Dan Scarfe *(Chief Solutions Officer)*

Odecee Pty Limited **(1)**
Level 6 15 William St, Melbourne, 3000,
VIC, Australia
Tel.: (61) 300633233
Web Site: http://www.odecee.com.au
Application Software Development Services
N.A.I.C.S.: 541511
Lynelle Spinks *(Office Mgr)*

Oy Samlink AB **(1)**
Linnoitustie 9, PO Box 130, 02601, Espoo,
Finland
Tel.: (358) 954 8050
Web Site: https://www.samlink.fi
Financial Management Services
N.A.I.C.S.: 541611
Tommi Rilasmaa *(Mgr)*
Simo Heikkinen *(Dir)*
Markku Siikala *(Sls Dir)*
Sami Suuronen *(Dir)*
Matti Sarkkinen *(CFO)*
Paivi Vikstrom *(Dir)*

**SaaSforce Consulting Private
Limited** **(1)**
B-21 Sector-58, Noida, UP, India
Tel.: (91) 1206487856
Web Site: http://www.saasforce.in
Software & Technical Consulting Services
N.A.I.C.S.: 541690
Jaideep Kumar *(CEO)*

**Saband Software Technologies Pri-
vate Limited** **(1)**
127/1b/1 Plot No 1 Gopal House Karve
Road Kothrud, Pune, 411 029, India
Tel.: (91) 2025450495
Web Site: http://www.saband.com
Application Software Development Services
N.A.I.C.S.: 541511
Bryan Hill *(Sr VP-Global Tech)*
Vikram Bapat *(Head-Unit)*

Servian Pty Ltd **(1)**
Level 46 264 George Street, Sydney, 2000,
NSW, Australia
Tel.: (61) 293760700
Web Site: https://www.servian.com
Software Development Services
N.A.I.C.S.: 541511

**ServiceXpert Gesellschaft fur Service
Informationssysteme mbH** **(1)**
Wandsbeker Allee 77, 22041, Hamburg,
Germany
Tel.: (49) 4067 049 0300
Web Site: https://servicexpert.de
Information Technology Services
N.A.I.C.S.: 541511

Solstice SAS **(1)**
73 rue Gabriel Peri, 78114, Magny-les-
Hameaux, France
Tel.: (33) 130528509
Web Site: https://www.solstice-analyse.com
Information Technology Infrastructure Ser-
vices
N.A.I.C.S.: 541512

TMG Health, Inc. **(1)**
100 Four Falls Corporate Ctr Ste 406, Con-
shohocken, PA 19428
Tel.: (610) 878-9111
Web Site: http://www.tmghealth.com
Technology Enabled Business Process Out-
sourcing (BOP) Services for Insurers, Em-
ployers, Health Plans, Medicare, Medicaid
& Group Retiree Health Plans
N.A.I.C.S.: 561499

TQS Integration AG **(1)**
Stucki Park Hochbergerstrasse 70, 4057,
Basel, Switzerland
Tel.: (41) 765474396
Information Technology Services
N.A.I.C.S.: 541511

TriZetto Corporation **(1)**
9655 Maroon Cir, Englewood, CO 80112
Tel.: (303) 495-7000
Web Site: http://www.trizetto.com
Sales Range: $450-499.9 Million
Emp.: 2,000
Healthcare Technology Services
N.A.I.C.S.: 518210

Branch (Domestic):

**TriZetto Corp. - Union Regional
Office** **(2)**

1085 Morris Ave, Union, NJ 07083
Tel.: (908) 351-0700
Web Site: http://www.trizetto.com
Sales Range: $25-49.9 Million
Emp.: 240
Client/Server Software Provider to Health
Care & Managed Care Organizations
N.A.I.C.S.: 812990
Richard Kerian *(Sr VP)*

Subsidiary (Domestic):

TriZetto Provider Solutions, LLC **(2)**
3300 Rider Trail S, Earth City, MO 63045
Tel.: (314) 802-6700
Web Site: https://www.trizettoprovider.com
Medical Industry Electronic Data Inter-
change Services
N.A.I.C.S.: 518210
Eric Schnarr *(Sr IT Project Mgr)*
Michael Emerson *(COO)*
Geoff Felder *(CTO)*

Branch (Domestic):

**TriZetto Provider Solutions, LLC -
NHXS** **(3)**
431 I St Ste 200, Sacramento, CA 95814
Tel.: (916) 231-0670
Emp.: 27
Medical Billing & Revenue Recovery Data
Services
N.A.I.C.S.: 518210
Chris Harber *(Gen Mgr)*

TriZetto India Private Limited **(1)**
Fourth Floor Wing 3 Cluster B EON Free
Zone, MIDC Kharadi Knowledge Park,
Pune, 411 014, India
Tel.: (91) 2046606060
Information Technology Consulting Services
N.A.I.C.S.: 541512

**TriZetto Services India Private
Limited** **(1)**
Office 601 & 602 D Building Weikfield IT-
CITI Info Park Nagar Road, Pune, 411 014,
India
Tel.: (91) 2040104444
Information Technology Consulting Services
N.A.I.C.S.: 541512
Abhijit Nalage *(Engr-Software)*

Utegration, LLC **(1)**
3535 Briarpark Dr #101, Houston, TX
77042
Tel.: (713) 337-3888
Web Site: http://www.utegration.com
Custom Computer Programming Services
N.A.I.C.S.: 541511
Bart Thielbar *(Pres & CEO)*
Henry Bailey *(Chief Strategy Officer & Exec
VP)*
Jerry Cavalieri *(Mng Dir-Regulatory Report-
ing)*

Subsidiary (Domestic):

HPC America LLC **(2)**
111 Deerwood Rd Ste 200, San Ramon, CA
94583
Tel.: (925) 831-4765
Web Site: http://www.hpc-america.com
Rev.: $1,300,000
Emp.: 12
Custom Computer Programming Services
N.A.I.C.S.: 541511
Josef Heck *(Founder)*
Steven Brown *(Dir-Mktg)*

ValueSource NV **(1)**
Havenlaan 2, 1080, Sint-Jans-Molenbeek,
Belgium
Tel.: (32) 15 35 22 51
Emp.: 170
Information Technology Consulting Services
N.A.I.C.S.: 541512

Subsidiary (Non-US):

**ValueSource Technologies Private
Limited** **(2)**
Level 4 IIFL Towers No 143 MGR Road,
Perungudi, Chennai, 600 096, Tamil Nadu,
India
Tel.: (91) 44 24634000
Web Site: http://www.valuesource.in
Sales Range: $25-49.9 Million
Emp.: 15
Financial Software Development Services

N.A.I.C.S.: 541511
Maria de Boeck *(Mng Dir)*

ZT Automation Limited **(1)**
22/F ONE Lujiazui 68 Yin Chen Road Suite
2257, Pudong New Area, Shanghai,
200120, China
Tel.: (86) 2160589232
Life Science Consulting Services
N.A.I.C.S.: 541690

Zenith Technologies BVBA **(1)**
Technology House of the Kempen Cipal-
straat 3, 2440, Geel, 2440, Belgium
Tel.: (32) 16407919
Life Science Consulting Services
N.A.I.C.S.: 541690

Zenith Technologies Limited **(1)**
Unit 4 Portgate Business Park,
Ringaskiddy, Cork, T12 RP29, Ireland
Tel.: (353) 214370200
Life Science Consulting Services
N.A.I.C.S.: 541690

marketRx Inc. **(1)**
1200 US Rte 22 E 3rd Fl, Bridgewater, NJ
08807
Tel.: (908) 541-0045
Sales Range: $10-24.9 Million
Emp.: 430
Analytics, Market Research & Technology to
Global Pharmaceutical & Biotechnology
Companies
N.A.I.C.S.: 561499

Subsidiary (Non-US):

marketRx India Private Limited **(2)**
15th Floor Tower B Signature Towers South
City-i, Gurgaon, 122 001, India
Tel.: (91) 01244160800
Analytics, Market Research & Technology to
Global Pharmaceutical & Biotechnology
Companies
N.A.I.C.S.: 561499

COHBAR, INC.
1455 Adams Dr Ste 1308, Menlo
Park, CA 94025
Tel.: (650) 446-7888   DE
Web Site: https://www.cohbar.com
Year Founded: 2007
CWBR—(NASDAQ)
Assets: $16,365,667
Liabilities: $1,033,638
Net Worth: $15,332,029
Earnings: ($12,175,208)
Emp.: 9
Fiscal Year-end: 12/31/22
Pharmaceuticals Mfr
N.A.I.C.S.: 325412
David A. Sinclair *(Co-Founder)*

COHEN & COMPANY INC.
2929 Arch St Ste 1703, Philadelphia,
PA 19104-2870
Tel.: (215) 701-9555   MD
Web Site:
https://www.cohenandcompany.com
Year Founded: 1999
COHN—(NYSEAMEX)
Rev.: $44,387,000
Assets: $887,055,000
Liabilities: $793,029,000
Net Worth: $94,026,000
Earnings: ($13,389,000)
Emp.: 121
Fiscal Year-end: 12/31/22
Investment Services
N.A.I.C.S.: 523999
Daniel Gideon Cohen *(Chief Invest-
ment Officer & Chm)*
Douglas Listman *(Chief Acctg Officer
& Asst Treas)*
Lester R. Brafman *(CEO)*
John Butler *(Mng Dir & Head-
Insurance Asset Mgmt Platform & ILS
Program-Global)*

Cohen & Company Inc.—(Continued)

Andrew K. Davilman (COO-Asset Mgmt Bus)
Plamen Mitrikov (Mng Dir & Head-Bus Dev & Structured Credit Asset Mgmt)
Dennis J. Crilly (Gen Counsel)
Paul Vernhes (Mng Dir)
Daniel G. Cohen (Exec Chm & Portfolio Mgr)
Joseph W. Pooler Jr. (CFO, Treas & Exec VP)

Subsidiaries:

Cohen & Compagnie, SAS (1)
23 rue de Campo-Formio, 75013, Paris, France
Tel.: (33) 142253504
Web Site: https://cohen-cohen.fr
Investment Management Service
N.A.I.C.S.: 523940
Paul Vernhes (Pres)

JVB Financial Group LLC (1)
1825 NW Corporate Blvd Ste 100, Boca Raton, FL 33431
Tel.: (561) 416-5876
Web Site: https://www.jvbfinancial.com
Sales Range: $25-49.9 Million
Emp.: 20
Investment Advisory Services
N.A.I.C.S.: 523940
Katie Vacca (Chief Compliance Officer)
Stephan Burklin (COO & Exec VP)

COHEN & STEERS CLOSED-END OPP FD, INC.
1166 Ave of the Americas 30th Fl, New York, NY 10036
Tel.: (212) 832-3232   MD
Year Founded: 2006
FOF—(NYSE)
Investment Services
N.A.I.C.S.: 523999

COHEN & STEERS LIMITED DURATION PREFERRED AND INCOME FUND, INC.
1166 Avenue of the Americas 30th Fl, New York, NY 10036
Tel.: (212) 832-3232   MD
Web Site:
http://www.cohenandsteers.com
Year Founded: 2012
LDP—(NYSE)
Sales Range: $50-74.9 Million
Closed-End Fund
N.A.I.C.S.: 525990
Robert Hamilton Steers (Chm)
Robert S. Becker (Sr VP & Portfolio Mgr)
Leonard Geiger (Sr VP & Assoc Portfolio Mgr-United Kingdom)
Elaine Zaharis-Nikas (Sr VP & Portfolio Mgr)
Francis Casimir Poli (Sec)
William F. Scapell (VP)
Adam M. Derechin (Pres & CEO)
Albert Laskaj (CFO & Treas)
Stephen Murphy (Chief Compliance Officer & VP)

COHEN & STEERS MLP INCOME & ENERGY OPP
280 Park Ave 10th Fl, New York, NY 10017
Tel.: (212) 832-3232
Web Site:
http://www.cohenandsteers.com
Year Founded: 1986
MIE—(NYSE)
Real Estate Manangement Services
N.A.I.C.S.: 531390
Martin Cohen (Chm)

COHEN & STEERS REIT &

PREFERRED INCOME FUND, INC.
1166 Ave of the Americas 30th Fl, New York, NY 10036
Tel.: (212) 832-3232   MD
Year Founded: 2003
RNP—(NYSE)
Investment Management Service
N.A.I.C.S.: 525990
Adam M. Derechin (Mgr-Fund)

COHEN & STEERS SELECT PREFERRED & INCOME FUND, INC.
1166 Ave of the Americas 30th Fl, New York, NY 10036
Tel.: (212) 832-3232   MD
Year Founded: 2010
PSF—(NYSE)
Investment Management Service
N.A.I.C.S.: 525990

COHEN & STEERS TOTAL RETURN REALTY FUND, INC.
1166 Ave of the Americas 30th Fl, New York, NY 10036
Tel.: (212) 832-3232   MD
Year Founded: 1992
RFI—(NYSE)
Investment Management Service
N.A.I.C.S.: 525990

COHEN & STEERS, INC.
1166 Avenue of the Americas 30th Fl, New York, NY 10036
Tel.: (212) 832-3232   DE
Web Site:
https://www.cohenandsteers.com
Year Founded: 1986
CNS—(NYSE)
Rev.: $566,906,000
Assets: $673,379,000
Liabilities: $331,771,000
Net Worth: $341,608,000
Earnings: $171,042,000
Emp.: 388
Fiscal Year-end: 12/31/22
Real Estate Investment Trust
N.A.I.C.S.: 523940
Christopher Rhine (Sr VP & Head-Natural Resource Equities & Portfolio Mgr-Strategy)
Martin Cohen (Founder)
Robert Hamilton Steers (Exec Chm)
Benjamin W. Morton (Exec VP, Head-Global Infrastructure & Sr Portfolio Mgr)
Joseph M. Harvey (Pres & CEO)
Adam M. Derechin (COO)
Matthew Scott Stadler (CFO)
Leonard Geiger (Sr VP & Portfolio Mgr-Real Estate-Europe)
Elaine Zaharis-Nikas (Sr VP & Portfolio Mgr-Fixed Income & Preferred Securities)
Francis Casimir Poli (Gen Counsel, Sec & Exec VP)
Jon Y. Cheigh (Chief Investment Officer, Exec VP & Sr Portfolio Mgr)
Vincent L. Childers (Sr VP & Head-Real Assets Multi-Strategy,Portfolio Mgr)
Yigal D. Jhirad (Sr VP & Head-Risk-Quantitative,Derivatives Strategies)
Rogier Quirijns (Sr VP, Head-Real Estate-Europe & Sr Portfolio Mgr)
Jason A. Yablon (Exec VP, Head-Listed Real Estate & Sr Portfolio Mgr-Real Estate Securities)
William Leung (Sr VP & Head-Real Estate-Asia Pacific,Portfolio Mgr ,Global)
Douglas R. Bond (Exec VP & Head-Closed End Funds & Portfolio Mgr)
Anthony Corriggio (Sr VP)

Paul Zettl (CMO & Exec VP-Global Mktg)
James Corl (Exec VP & Head-Private Real Estate)
Jerry Dorost (Sr VP & Portfolio Mgr-Fixed Income & Preferred Securities)
Mathew Kirschner (Sr VP & Portfolio Mgr-U.S Real Estate)
Jeffrey Palma (Sr VP & Head-Multi-Asset Solutions)
Rich Hill (Sr VP & Head-Real Estate Strategy & Research)
Khalid Husain (Sr VP & Head-ESG)
Hamid Tabib (Sr VP & Head-Real Estate Acquisitions-North America)
Ji Zhang (Sr VP & Portfolio Mgr-Global Real Estate)
Robert Kastoff (VP & Portfolio Mgr-Fixed Income & Preferred Securities)
Raquel McLean (VP & Portfolio Mgr-Fixed Income & Preferred Securities)
Arun Sharma (VP & Portfolio Mgr-Thematic Strategies)
Ed Valente (VP & Sls Mgr-Internal)
Brandon Brown (Chief HR Officer)
Daniel Charles (Head-Global Distr)
Raja Dakkuri (CFO)
John Muth (VP)

Subsidiaries:

Cohen & Steers Asia Limited (1)
Suites 1201-02 Champion Tower 3 Garden Road, Central, China (Hong Kong)
Tel.: (852) 36670080
Sales Range: $1-4.9 Billion
Emp.: 10
Investment Management
N.A.I.C.S.: 523150

Cohen & Steers Europe S.A. (1)
Chaussee de la Hulpe 166, Brussels, 1170, Belgium
Tel.: (32) 26790660
Sales Range: $25-49.9 Million
Emp.: 9
Investment Management Service
N.A.I.C.S.: 523940
William Joseph Houlihan (CEO)

Cohen & Steers Japan, LLC (1)
Pacific Century Place 16th Floor 1-11-1 Marunouchi, Chiyoda-Ku, Tokyo, 100-6216, Japan
Tel.: (81) 345304710
Web Site: https://www.cohenandsteers.com
Investment Advice
N.A.I.C.S.: 523940

Cohen & Steers Singapore Private Limited (1)
Marina Bay Financial Centre Tower 1 Suite 11-03 8 Marina Boulevard, Singapore, 018981, Singapore
Tel.: (65) 69648900
Financial Services
N.A.I.C.S.: 523999

Cohen & Steers UK Limited (1)
3 Dering Street 2nd Floor, London, W1S 1AA, United Kingdom
Tel.: (44) 2074606350
Investment Management Service
N.A.I.C.S.: 523940

COHERENT CORP.
375 Saxonburg Blvd, Saxonburg, PA 16066
Tel.: (724) 352-4455   PA
Web Site: https://www.coherent.com
Year Founded: 1971
COHR—(NYSE)
Rev.: $4,707,688,000
Assets: $14,488,634,000
Liabilities: $6,542,355,000
Net Worth: $7,946,279,000
Earnings: ($158,764,000)
Emp.: 26,157
Fiscal Year-end: 06/30/24
Optical Components, Thermo-Electric Systems & Engineered Materials Developer, Mfr & Marketer
N.A.I.C.S.: 333310

Ilaria Mocciaro (Principal Acctg Officer, Sr VP & Controller)
Mark S. Sobey (Pres-Lasers Segment)
Ronald Basso (Sec & Chief Legal & Compliance Officer)
Gary Alan Kapusta (Chief Procurement Officer)
Sunny Sun (Pres-Networking Segment)
Sanjai Parthasarathi (CMO)
Anantha Ganga (CIO)
Shirley Reha (Chief HR Officer)
Chris Theis (Chief Quality Officer)
Sohail Khan (Exec VP-New Ventures-Wide-Bandgap Electronics Technologies)
Paul Silverstein (VP-IR & Corp Comm)
Mark Lourie (VP-Corp Comm)
Young-Kai Chen (Deputy CTO)
James R. Anderson (Pres & CEO)

Subsidiaries:

CoAdna Holdings, Inc. (1)
190 Elgin Avenue, Georgetown, KY1-9005, Grand Cayman, Cayman Islands
Tel.: (345) 2 2656 2356
Web Site: http://www.coadna.com
Rev.: $28,090,280
Assets: $56,864,529
Liabilities: $5,792,545
Net Worth: $51,071,985
Earnings: ($1,658,205)
Emp.: 260
Fiscal Year-end: 12/31/2017
Photonic Solutions
N.A.I.C.S.: 334413

Subsidiary (Non-US):

CoAdna (HK) Limited (2)
Room 1101 11th Floor Easey Commercial Building 253-261 Hennessy Road, Wanchai, China (Hong Kong)
Tel.: (852) 28249890
Fiber Optic Cable Mfr
N.A.I.C.S.: 335921

Subsidiary (US):

CoAdna Photonics, Inc. (2)
375 Saxonburg Blvd, Saxonburg, PA 16056
Tel.: (408) 736-1100
Photonic Component Mfr & Distr
N.A.I.C.S.: 334419

Coherent, Inc. (1)
5100 Patrick Henry Dr, Santa Clara, CA 95054
Tel.: (408) 764-4000
Web Site: http://www.coherent.com
Rev.: $1,487,468,000
Assets: $1,888,930,000
Liabilities: $1,020,745,000
Net Worth: $868,185,000
Earnings: ($106,751,000)
Emp.: 5,085
Fiscal Year-end: 10/02/2021
Photonics Solutions for Commercial & Scientific Research
N.A.I.C.S.: 334516
Garry W. Rogerson (Chm)
Bret M. DiMarco (Chief Legal Officer, Sec & Exec VP)

Subsidiary (Non-US):

Coherent (Beijing) Commercial Company Ltd. (2)
Room 1006-1009 Raycom Info Park Tower B No 2 Kexueyuan South Rd, Haidian District, Beijing, 100190, China
Tel.: (86) 1082153600
Web Site: http://www.coherent.com.cn
Sales Range: $10-24.9 Million
Emp.: 34
Optical & Laser Equipment Sales
N.A.I.C.S.: 423990

Coherent (Deutschland) GmbH (2)
Dieselstrasse 5B, 64807, Dieburg, Germany   (100%)
Tel.: (49) 60719680
Web Site: http://www.coherent.de

Sales Range: $10-24.9 Million
Medical, Industrial & Scientific Lasers Mfr
N.A.I.C.S.: 334517

Coherent (U.K.) Ltd. (2)
Saint Thomas place Cambridgeshire Business Park, Ely, CB7 4EX, United
Kingdom (100%)
Tel.: (44) 1353658833
Web Site: http://www.coherent.com
Sales Range: $10-24.9 Million
Emp.: 12
Medical, Industrial & Scientific Lasers Mfr
N.A.I.C.S.: 334517

Unit (Domestic):

Coherent - Portland (2)
27650 SW 95th Ave, Wilsonville, OR 97070
Tel.: (971) 327-2700
Web Site: http://www.coherent.com
Laser Measurement & Beam Diagnostic
Equipment Mfr & Services
N.A.I.C.S.: 334112

Subsidiary (Non-US):

Coherent BV (2)
Smart Business Park Kanaalweg 18A,
Utrecht, 3526 KL, Netherlands (100%)
Tel.: (31) 302806060
Web Site: http://www.coherent.com
Sales Range: $10-24.9 Million
Emp.: 50
Optical Products
N.A.I.C.S.: 333310
Vander Hoeven (Mng Dir)

Subsidiary (Domestic):

Coherent Crystal Associates (2)
31 Farinella Dr, East Hanover, NJ 07936
Tel.: (973) 240-6851
Web Site: http://www.coherent.com
Sales Range: $10-24.9 Million
Emp.: 85
Irradiation Apparatus Mfr
N.A.I.C.S.: 334517

Coherent DEOS (2)
1280 Blue Hill Ave, Bloomfield, CT 06002
Tel.: (860) 243-9557
Web Site: http://www.coherent.com
Sales Range: $100-124.9 Million
Laser Systems
N.A.I.C.S.: 334510

Subsidiary (Non-US):

Coherent Europe B.V. (2)
Smart Business Park Kanaalweg 18A, 3526
KL, Utrecht, Netherlands
Tel.: (31) 302806060
Web Site: http://www.coherent.nl
Laser Cutting Machinery Mfr & Distr
N.A.I.C.S.: 333517

Coherent France (2)
14-16 Allee du Cantal CE 1831, 91090,
Lisses, Cedex, France
Tel.: (33) 169119400
Web Site: http://www.coherent.fr
Medical, Industrial & Scientific Laser Mfr
N.A.I.C.S.: 334517

Coherent GmbH (2)
Hans-Bockler-Strasse 12, 37079, Gottingen,
Germany
Tel.: (49) 55169380
Professional Equipment Merchant Whslr
N.A.I.C.S.: 423490
Ralph Delmdahl (Product Mgr-Mktg)

Coherent Italia (2)
Viale Lombardia 159, 20900, Monza, Italy
Tel.: (39) 03927291
Web Site: http://www.coherent.it
Sales Range: $1-9.9 Million
Emp.: 4
Diode Laser Mfr
N.A.I.C.S.: 334413

Coherent Japan, Inc. (2)
Shinjuku Maynds Tower 26F 2-1-1 Yoyogi,
Shibuya-ku, Tokyo, 151-0053,
Japan (100%)
Tel.: (81) 353657100
Web Site: http://www.coherent.co.jp
Sales Range: $1-9.9 Million
Emp.: 80
Optical & Laser Product Mfr

N.A.I.C.S.: 333310

Coherent Japan, Inc. (2)
Nissei Shin-Osaka Minamiguchi Bldg 9F
5-14-5 Nishi-Nakajima, Yodogawa-ku,
Osaka, 532-0011, Japan
Tel.: (81) 661017670
Web Site: http://www.coherent.co.jp
Sales Range: $100-124.9 Million
Diode Lasers Mfr
N.A.I.C.S.: 334419

Coherent Kaiserslautern GmbH (2)
Opelstrasse 10, 67661, Kaiserslautern, Germany
Tel.: (49) 630132013180
Electronic Components Mfr
N.A.I.C.S.: 334419
Nina Kirr (Mgr-HR)

Coherent Korea Ltd. (2)
1F 5F 6F Eagle Town 20 Gwangnaru-ro
6-gil, Seongdong-gu, Seoul, 04796, Korea
(South)
Tel.: (82) 24607900
Web Site: https://www.coherent.com
Precision Laser Component Mfr
N.A.I.C.S.: 334510

**Coherent LaserSystems GmbH & Co.
KG** (2)
Bldg 1 Hans Boeckler Strasse 12, 37079,
Gottingen, Germany
Tel.: (49) 55169380
Sales Range: $50-74.9 Million
Emp.: 200
Scientific, Medical & Industrial Lasers Mfr
N.A.I.C.S.: 334517
Martina Schwarze (Asst Gen Mgr)

Subsidiary (Non-US):

Lambda Physik Japan Co., Ltd. (3)
German Industry Ctr 1 18 2 Hakusan, Midori Ku, Yokohama, 226-0006,
Japan (95%)
Tel.: (81) 45 939 7848
Web Site: http://www.lambdaphysik.co.jp
Sales Range: $10-24.9 Million
Emp.: 30
Medical, Industrial & Scientific Lasers Mfr
N.A.I.C.S.: 334517

Subsidiary (Non-US):

Coherent Scotland Ltd. (2)
West of Scotland Science Pk, Todd Campus Maryhill Rd, Glasgow, G20 0XA, United
Kingdom (100%)
Tel.: (44) 01419458150
Sales Range: $10-24.9 Million
Emp.: 130
Laser Mfr
N.A.I.C.S.: 334510

Coherent Singapore PTE Ltd. (2)
1 Kallang Sector 07-01, Singapore, 349276,
Singapore
Tel.: (65) 66717700
Web Site: http://www.coherent.com
Electric Equipment Mfr
N.A.I.C.S.: 335999

Subsidiary (Domestic):

Nuvonyx Incorporated (2)
5100 Patrick Henry Dr, Santa Clara, CA
95054
Tel.: (408) 764-4000
Web Site: http://www.nuvonyx.com
Sales Range: $100-124.9 Million
High-Power Diode Laser Solutions
N.A.I.C.S.: 335999
John R. Ambrossio (Pres & CEO)

Subsidiary (Non-US):

O.R. Lasertechnologie GmbH (2)
Dieselstrasse 5b, 64807, Dieburg, Germany
Tel.: (49) 6071209890
Web Site: http://www.or-laser.com
Laser Material Mfr
N.A.I.C.S.: 333992

Subsidiary (Domestic):

Rofin-Sinar Technologies, Inc. (2)
40984 Concept Dr, Plymouth, MI
48170 (100%)
Tel.: (734) 455-5400
Web Site: http://www.rofin.com

Laser & Laser Systems Mfr
N.A.I.C.S.: 333310
Louis Molnar (COO-North America)
Ingrid Mittelstadt (CFO & Exec VP)
Ulrich Hefter (CTO)
Andreas Ewald (VP-Markets)
Thorsten Frauenpreiss (VP-Macro)
Armin Renneisen (VP-Micro & Marking)

Subsidiary (Non-US):

Coherent Korea Co., Ltd. (3)
Eagle Town 1F 5F 6F Gwangnaru-ro 6gil
20, Seongdong-Gu, Seoul, 04796, Korea
(South)
Tel.: (82) 228371750
Web Site: http://www.rofin.co.kr
Emp.: 20
Laser Equipment Supplier
N.A.I.C.S.: 334413

Coherent Laser India Pvt. Ltd, (3)
1st Floor A-454, TTC Industrial Area Mahape, Navi Mumbai, 400710, India
Tel.: (91) 2241553232
Web Site:
https://www.coherentlaserindia.com
Sales Range: $10-24.9 Million
Emp.: 10
Laser Equipment Supplier
N.A.I.C.S.: 334413
Raj Verma (Gen Mgr)
Manoj Rathod (VP-Sls)

Coherent Singapore Pte., Ltd. (3)
1 Kallang Sector 07-06, Singapore, 349276,
Singapore
Tel.: (65) 66717700
Web Site: http://www.rofin-baasel.com.sg
Emp.: 30
Laser System Mfr
N.A.I.C.S.: 333517
Steaven Wang (Dir-Sls)

Subsidiary (Domestic):

DILAS Diode Laser, Inc. (3)
9070 S Rita Rd Ste 1500, Tucson, AZ
85747
Tel.: (520) 282-6000
Web Site: http://www.dilas.com
Laser Diode Component Mfr
N.A.I.C.S.: 334413

Subsidiary (Non-US):

**Germany Dinas Semiconductor Laser
Co., Ltd.** (3)
Room 102 Building 1 Zhangjiang Guochuang Center No 835,937 Dangui Road, Pudong New Area, Shanghai, 201203, China
Tel.: (86) 2168986200
Web Site: http://www.dilas.com.cn
Laser Product Mfr
N.A.I.C.S.: 333517

Nanjing Eastern Laser Co., Ltd. (3)
Eastern Laser Industry Park No 8-8 Pusi
Road Nanjing New, High Technology Industry Development Zone, Nanjing, 210061,
China
Tel.: (86) 2558840187
Laser Processing System Mfr & Distr
N.A.I.C.S.: 333517

Nanjing Eastern Technologies Company, Ltd. (3)
No 8-8 Pusi Road Pukuo District, Nanjing,
210061, China
Tel.: (86) 2558749160
Laser System Mfr
N.A.I.C.S.: 333517

Subsidiary (Domestic):

Nufern Inc. (3)
7 Airport Park Rd, East Granby, CT 06026
Tel.: (860) 408-5000
Web Site: http://www.nufern.com
Optical Fiber & Laser Developer & Mfr
N.A.I.C.S.: 335921

PRC Laser Corp. (3)
350 N Frontage Rd, Landing, NJ 07850
Tel.: (973) 347-0100
Web Site: http://www.prclaser.com
Industrial Laser Mfr
N.A.I.C.S.: 333517

Subsidiary (Non-US):

ROFIN-BAASEL Canada Ltd. (3)

3600A Laird Rd Unit 15, Mississauga, L5L
6A6, ON, Canada
Tel.: (905) 607-0400
Web Site: http://www.rofin-inc.com
Laser Cutting & Welding Mfr
N.A.I.C.S.: 333517

ROFIN-BAASEL China Co., Ltd. (3)
Room 310 Tower 1 No 1376 Jiang Dong
Road, Pudong New District, Shanghai,
201203, China
Tel.: (86) 2158213715
Laser Equipment Supplier
N.A.I.C.S.: 334413

ROFIN-BAASEL Japan Corp. (3)
1042-4 Toda, Atsugi, 243-0023, Kanagawa,
Japan
Tel.: (81) 462298655
Web Site: http://www.rofin-baasel.co.jp
Laser Equipment Supplier
N.A.I.C.S.: 334413
Nobuyoshi Hirano (Pres)

ROFIN-BAASEL Taiwan Ltd. (3)
4F No 100 Rueiguang Road, Neihu, Taipei,
11491, Taiwan
Tel.: (886) 227901300
Web Site: http://www.rofin.com.tw
Emp.: 20
Laser Equipment Supplier
N.A.I.C.S.: 334413

Subsidiary (Domestic):

ROFIN-BAASEL, Inc. (3)
68 Barnum Rd, Devens, MA 01434-3508
Tel.: (978) 635-9100
Web Site: http://www.rofin-inc.com
Laser Marking System Mfr
N.A.I.C.S.: 333517

ROFIN-SINAR, Inc. (3)
40984 Concept Dr, Plymouth, MI 48170
Tel.: (734) 455-5400
Web Site: http://www.rofin-inc.com
Laser System Mfr
N.A.I.C.S.: 333517

Subsidiary (Non-US):

Rofin-Baasel Korea Co., Ltd. (3)
5F Eagle Town 20 Gwangnaruro 6Gil,
Seongdong-Gu, Seoul, 04796, Korea
(South)
Tel.: (82) 228371750
Web Site: http://www.rofin-baasel.co.kr
Analytical Laboratory Instrument Mfr
N.A.I.C.S.: 334516

Rofin-Sinar Laser GmbH (3)
Berzeliusstrasse 83, 22113, Hamburg,
Germany (100%)
Tel.: (49) 40733630
Web Site: http://www.rofin.de
Industrial Laser Mfr
N.A.I.C.S.: 334513

Subsidiary (Non-US):

Coherent Italia S.r.l. (4)
Viale Lombardia 159, 20900, Monza, MI,
Italy
Tel.: (39) 03927291
Web Site: http://www.rofin.it
Laser Cutting Machinery Mfr
N.A.I.C.S.: 333517

Coherent Switzerland AG (4)
Aemmenmattstrasse 43, 3123, Belp, Switzerland
Tel.: (41) 332274545
Web Site: http://www.rofin-baasel.ch
Electronic Equipment Whslr
N.A.I.C.S.: 423690
Christian Wissing (Mng Dir)

Corelase Oy (4)
Kauhakorvenkatu 52, PO Box 73, 33720,
Tampere, Finland
Tel.: (358) 34476400
Web Site: http://www.coherent.com
Laser Module & Electronic Component Distr
N.A.I.C.S.: 334419

Subsidiary (Domestic):

DILAS Diodenlaser GmbH (4)
Galileo-Galilei-Strasse 10, 55129, Mainz,
Germany
Tel.: (49) 613192260

Coherent Corp.—(Continued)

Web Site: http://www.dilas.com
Laser Diode Component Mfr
N.A.I.C.S.: 334413

Subsidiary (Non-US):

ES Technology Ltd. (4)
Unit 2 Newnham Drive, Daventry, NN11
8YN, Oxfordshire, United Kingdom
Tel.: (44) 1865821818
Sales Range: $10-24.9 Million
Emp.: 20
Industrial Laser Systems Mfr
N.A.I.C.S.: 334413

Optoskand AB (4)
Aminogatan 30, 431 53, Molndal, Sweden
Tel.: (46) 317062750
Web Site: http://www.optoskand.se
Laser Optic & Fiber Mfr
N.A.I.C.S.: 334513

PRC Laser Europe N.V. (4)
Industriepark De Buwaan 89B, 9700, Oud-
enaarde, Belgium
Tel.: (32) 55303196
Web Site: https://prclaser-europe.be
Sales Range: $10-24.9 Million
Emp.: 11
Industrial Laser Mfr
N.A.I.C.S.: 333992

Subsidiary (Domestic):

**RASANT-ALCOTEC Beschichtung-
stechnik GmbH** (4)
Zur Kaule 1, 51491, Overath, Germany
Tel.: (49) 220690250
Web Site: http://www.rasant-alcotec.de
Laser Module & Electronic Component Distr
N.A.I.C.S.: 334419
Bret DiMarco (Member-Mgmt Bd)

Subsidiary (Non-US):

ROFIN-BAASEL UK Ltd. (4)
Unit 2 Newnham Drive, Daventry, NN11
8YN, Northants, United Kingdom
Tel.: (44) 1327701100
Web Site: http://www.rofin.co.uk
Laser Module & Electronic Component Distr
N.A.I.C.S.: 334419

**ROFIN-SINAR Technologies Europe
S.L.** (4)
Poligono Arazuri-Orcoyen Calle C Numero
12, Olza, 31170, Navarra, Barcelona, Spain
Tel.: (34) 934774200
Web Site: http://www.rofin.com
Laser System Mfr
N.A.I.C.S.: 333517

Rofin Baasel Benelux BV (4)
Kanaalweg 18A, 3526 KL, Utrecht,
Netherlands (100%)
Tel.: (31) 302806060
Web Site: http://www.rofin.com
Laser Equipment Services
N.A.I.C.S.: 333992

Rofin-Baasel Espana SL (4)
Poligono Arazuri-Orcoyen Calle C Numero
12, Olza, 31170, Navarra, Arazuri,
Spain (99%)
Tel.: (34) 948324600
Web Site: http://www.rofin.es
Laser Equipment Services
N.A.I.C.S.: 333992

Rofin-Baasel France SA (4)
4 Rue du Cantal, 91090, Lisses,
France (100%)
Tel.: (33) 169119400
Web Site: http://www.rofin.fr
Laser Equipment Supplier
N.A.I.C.S.: 333992

Subsidiary (Domestic):

**Rofin-Baasel Lasertech GmbH & Co.
KG** (4)
Zeppelinstrasse 10, 82205, Gilching, Ger-
many
Tel.: (49) 810539650
Web Site: http://www.rofin.com
Industrial Laser Systems Mfr
N.A.I.C.S.: 334513

WB-PRC Laser Service GmbH (4)

Munchner Str 15b, 85604, Zorneding, Ger-
many
Tel.: (49) 8106306260
Laser Module & Electronic Component Distr
N.A.I.C.S.: 334419

m2k-laser GmbH (4)
Galileo-Galilei-Strasse 10, 55129, Mainz,
Germany
Tel.: (49) 76151587640
Web Site: http://www.m2k-laser.de
Laser Mfr
N.A.I.C.S.: 333992

Epiworks, Inc. (1)
1606 Rion Dr, Champaign, IL 61822
Tel.: (217) 373-1590
Web Site: http://www.epiworks.com
Rev.: $14,000,000
Emp.: 90
Fiscal Year-end: 12/31/2015
Develops & Manufactures Compound Semi-
conductor Epitaxial Wafers
N.A.I.C.S.: 334413
Quesnell Hartmann (CEO)

Finisar Corporation (1)
1389 Moffett Park Dr, Sunnyvale, CA 94089
Tel.: (408) 548-1000
Web Site: http://www.finisar.com
Rev.: $1,280,480,000
Assets: $2,352,167,000
Liabilities: $738,006,000
Net Worth: $1,614,161,000
Earnings: ($53,216,000)
Emp.: 13,000
Fiscal Year-end: 04/28/2019
Telecommunication Optical Subsystems &
Components Designer & Mfr
N.A.I.C.S.: 334290

Unit (Domestic):

Advanced Optical Components (2)
600 Millenium Dr, Allen, TX 75013
Tel.: (214) 509-2700
Web Site: http://www.finisar.com
Sales Range: $75-99.9 Million
Emp.: 175
Semiconductor Wafers Mfr
N.A.I.C.S.: 334413

Subsidiary (Non-US):

Finisar Australia Pty. Ltd. (2)
21 Rosebery Avenue, Rosebery, 2018,
NSW, Australia
Tel.: (61) 295811600
Web Site: http://www.finisar.com
Sales Range: $75-99.9 Million
Emp.: 220
Telecommunication & Cable TV Network
Optical Subsystems Designer & Mfr
N.A.I.C.S.: 334290

Branch (Domestic):

Finisar Corp. - Fremont (2)
41762 Christy St, Fremont, CA 94538
Tel.: (510) 979-3000
Sales Range: $10-24.9 Million
Emp.: 450
Electronic Research
N.A.I.C.S.: 334210

Finisar Corp. - Horsham (2)
200 Precision Rd, Horsham, PA 19044
Tel.: (267) 803-3800
Web Site: http://www.finisar.com
Sales Range: $125-149.9 Million
Emp.: 267
Telecommunication & Cable TV Network
Optical Subsystems Designer & Mfr
N.A.I.C.S.: 334290
Chris Brown (Gen Counsel & VP)

Subsidiary (Non-US):

Finisar Israel Ltd. (2)
3 Golda Meir St Lev Hakongresim Nitzan
Bldg, Nes-Ziona Science Indus Park,
74036, Nes Ziyyona, Israel
Tel.: (972) 89313030
Web Site: http://www.finisar.com
Sales Range: $900-999.9 Million
Emp.: 45
Telecommunication & Cable TV Network
Optical Subsystems Designer & Mfr
N.A.I.C.S.: 334290

Finisar Malaysia Sdn. Bhd. (2)

Plot 1 Kinta Free Industrial Zone Off Jalan
Tunku Abdul Rahman, Chemor, Perak,
31200, Malaysia
Tel.: (60) 52907800
Sales Range: $25-49.9 Million
Emp.: 4,006
Fiber Optic & Communications Equipment
Mfr
N.A.I.C.S.: 334413

Finisar Shanghai Inc. (2)
No 66 Huiqing Rd, East Zhangjiang Hi-Tech
Park, Shanghai, 201201, China
Tel.: (86) 2138559200
Sales Range: $100-124.9 Million
Fiber-Optics Communication Application
Components & Sub-Systems Mfr
N.A.I.C.S.: 334413

Subsidiary (Domestic):

LightSmyth Technologies, Inc. (2)
875 Wilson St Ste C, Eugene, OR 97402
Tel.: (541) 431-0026
Web Site: http://www.lightsmyth.com
Optical Telecommunication Equipment Mfr
N.A.I.C.S.: 334220

Subsidiary (Non-US):

SmartOptics AS (2)
Brynsalleen 2, 0667, Oslo, Norway
Tel.: (47) 21417400
Web Site: https://www.smartoptics.com
Optical Networking Services
N.A.I.C.S.: 541512
Carina Osmund (COO)
Magnus Grenfeldt (CEO)

SmartOptics Holdings AS (2)
Ryensvingen 7, Oslo, 680, Norway
Tel.: (47) 21379180
Web Site: http://www.smartoptics.com
Investment Management Service
N.A.I.C.S.: 551112

First Capital Partners, LLC (1)
1620 Dodge St Ste 800, Omaha, NE 68102
Tel.: (402) 718-8850
Web Site:
 https://www.firstcapitalpartners.com
Emp.: 7
Private Investment Firm
N.A.I.C.S.: 523999
David F. McLeese (Mng Partner)
Young J. Park (Mng Dir)
Andrew B. Kemp (Mng Dir)
David R. Paulmeyer (VP)

Holding (Domestic):

INNOViON Corporation (2)
2121 Zanker Rd, San Jose, CA 95131
Tel.: (408) 501-9100
Web Site: http://www.innovioncorp.com
Microelectronics Manufacturing Support
Services
N.A.I.C.S.: 541330
Gary Holyoak (CEO)

Fuzhou Photop Optics Co., Ltd. (1)
253 Fuxin Road, PO Box 1109, Zhong-
hangji Industrial Area Jin'an District, Fu-
zhou, 350014, Fujian, China
Tel.: (86) 59188052890
Web Site: http://www.photoptech.com
Fiber Optic Product Mfr
N.A.I.C.S.: 335921
John Ling (CEO)

**HIGHYAG Lasertechnologie
GmbH** (1)
Hermann von Helmholtz Ctr 2, 14502,
Kleinmachnow, Germany (74.93%)
Tel.: (49) 332038830
Web Site: http://www.highyag.com
Sales Range: $10-24.9 Million
Emp.: 70
Automated Laser Equipment Designer &
Mfr
N.A.I.C.S.: 333517

**II-VI Advanced Materials Develop-
ment Center** (1)
375 Saxonburg Blvd, Saxonburg, PA 16056
Tel.: (724) 352-5206
Web Site: http://www.iiviamdc.com
Materials Development, Process Develop-
ment & Manufacturing Scale-Up Services
N.A.I.C.S.: 541715

Vincent D. Mattera Jr. (Pres & COO)

II-VI Benelux N.V. (1)
Ottergemsesteenweg Zuid 808 - Bus 300,
9240, Ghent, Belgium (100%)
Tel.: (32) 52458610
Web Site: http://www.ii-vi.be
Sales Range: $10-24.9 Million
Emp.: 5
Optic & Laser Products Distr
N.A.I.C.S.: 423830
Van Goubergen (Mgr)

II-VI Deutschland GmbH (1)
Brunnenweg 19-21, 64331, Weiterstadt,
Germany (100%)
Tel.: (49) 61505439226
Web Site: http://www.ii-vi.com
Sales Range: $10-24.9 Million
Emp.: 6,500
Laser Optical Equipment Mfr & Distr
N.A.I.C.S.: 333310
Martin Benzing (Mng Dir)

II-VI GmbH (1)
Brunnenweg 19-21, 64331, Weiterstadt,
Germany
Tel.: (49) 61505439226
Semiconductor Equipment Mfr & Distr
N.A.I.C.S.: 333242

II-VI Infrared (1)
375 Saxonburg Blvd, Saxonburg, PA 16056
Tel.: (724) 352-1504
Web Site: http://www.iiviinfrared.com
Laser Lenses, Mirrors, Infrared Optical Ma-
terials & Components Designer & Mfr
N.A.I.C.S.: 333310
Gary Alan Kaputsa (VP)

**II-VI Infrared Laser (Suzhou) Co.,
Ltd.** (1)
Block D 01-01/02 No 5 Xing Han Street,
Suzhou Industrial Park, Suzhou, 215101,
China
Tel.: (86) 51267619295
Optical Instrument Mfr
N.A.I.C.S.: 333310

II-VI Italia S.r.l. (1)
Via Andrea Costa 31, 20131, Milan,
Italy (100%)
Tel.: (39) 022828740
Web Site: http://www.ii-vi.it
Sales Range: $25-49.9 Million
Emp.: 5
Laser Optics Distr
N.A.I.C.S.: 423830

II-VI Japan Incorporated (1)
Wbg Marive East 26F Nakase 2-6-1,
Mihama-ku, Chiba, 261-7126,
Japan (100%)
Tel.: (81) 432972693
Web Site: http://www.ii-vi.co.jp
Sales Range: $10-24.9 Million
Emp.: 10
Marketer of Optical & Electro-Optical Com-
ponents, Devices & Materials for Infrared,
Near Infrared, Visible Light & X-Ray Instru-
ments & Applications
N.A.I.C.S.: 423460

II-VI Laser Enterprise GmbH (1)
Binzstrasse 17, 8045, Zurich, Switzerland
Tel.: (41) 444558760
Web Site: http://www.laserenterprise.com
Sales Range: $75-99.9 Million
Emp.: 20
Semiconductor, Laser Diodes & Related
Devices Mfr
N.A.I.C.S.: 334413

II-VI Singapore Pte., Ltd. (1)
Blk 5012 Techplace II 04-07 05-07/12 Ang
Mo Kio Ave 5, Singapore, 569876, Singa-
pore
Tel.: (65) 64818215
Web Site: http://www.iiviinfrared.com
Infrared & Near-Infrared Laser Optical Com-
ponents Mfr & Distr
N.A.I.C.S.: 333310
Ahmad Magad (Mng Dir)

Subsidiary (Non-US):

II-VI Optics (Suzhou) Co., Ltd. (2)
12 Sutong Road, Industrial Zone, Suzhou,
215000, China (100%)
Tel.: (86) 51267619295
Web Site: http://www.ii-vi.com.cn

Sales Range: $50-74.9 Million
Mfr, Designer & Marketer of Optical &
Electro-Optical Components, Devices & Materials for Infrared, Near Infrared, Visible
Light & X-Ray Instruments & Applications
N.A.I.C.S.: 333310

II-VI Technologies (Beijing) Co., (2)
Ltd.
Rm 202 1 Lize 2nd Middle Road, Wangjing,
Beijing, 100102, China   (100%)
Tel.: (86) 1064398226
Web Site: http://www.iivibj.com
Emp.: 10
Radiation Detection & X-ray Imaging Products Research & Development Services
N.A.I.C.S.: 541715
Xiquan Wu (Gen Mgr)

II-VI Suisse S.a.r.l. (1)
Moulin-du-Choc C, Le Mont-sur-Lausanne,
1052, Switzerland   (100%)
Tel.: (41) 218690252
Web Site: http://www.ii-vi.ch
Sales Range: $25-49.9 Million
Emp.: 3
Laser Optics Distr
N.A.I.C.S.: 423830
Andre Galliker (Mng Dir)

II-VI Suwtech, Inc. (1)
2F Building 65 421 Hongcao Road, Shanghai, 200233, China
Tel.: (86) 2164955552
Web Site: http://www.ii-vi-suwtech.com
Electrical Equipment Mfr & Distr
N.A.I.C.S.: 334510

II-VI Taiwan (1)
6F No 288 Ruiguang Rd, Taipei, 114, Taiwan
Tel.: (886) 287512155
Web Site: http://www.ii-vi.com
Opto-Electronic Components Distr
N.A.I.C.S.: 517112

II-VI U.K. Ltd. (1)
Unit 20B Oakham Enterprise Park Ashwell
Road, Oakham, LE15 7TU, Rutland, United
Kingdom   (100%)
Tel.: (44) 1572771778
Web Site: http://www.iivinfrared.com
Sales Range: $10-24.9 Million
Emp.: 7
Marketer of Optical & Electro-Optical Components, Devices & Materials for Infrared,
Near Infrared, Visible Light & X-Ray Instruments & Applications
N.A.I.C.S.: 423460

II-VI Wide Band Gap, Inc. (1)
20 Chapin Rd Ste 1007, Pine Brook, NJ
07058   (100%)
Tel.: (973) 227-1551
Web Site: http://www.iiviwbg.com
Sales Range: $25-49.9 Million
Emp.: 60
Silicon Carbide & Other Bandgap Material
Products Developer, Mfr & Whslr
N.A.I.C.S.: 334419

Integrated Photonics, Inc. (1)
132 Stryker Ln, Hillsborough, NJ 08844
Tel.: (908) 281-8000
Web Site:
http://www.integratedphotonics.com
Sales Range: $1-9.9 Million
Emp.: 75
Photonic Device Mfr
N.A.I.C.S.: 335921

LightWorks Optical Systems, Inc. (1)
36570 Briggs Rd, Murrieta, CA
92563-2347   (100%)
Tel.: (951) 926-2994
Web Site: http://www.exotic-eo.com
Sales Range: $50-74.9 Million
Emp.: 180
Infrared Crystals, Optical Components &
Assemblies Mfr
N.A.I.C.S.: 333310

Branch (Domestic):

LightWorks Optical Systems, Inc. (2)
14192 Chambers Rd, Tustin, CA 92780
Tel.: (714) 247-7100
Web Site: http://www.lightworksoptics.com
Sales Range: $10-24.9 Million
Emp.: 58
Optical Instruments & Lenses

N.A.I.C.S.: 333310

M Cubed Technologies, Inc. (1)
31 Pecks Ln Ste 8, Newtown, CT 06470
Tel.: (203) 452-2333
Web Site: http://www.mmmt.com
Emp.: 130
Ceramic & Metal Composite Materials &
Precision Motion Control Products Mfr
N.A.I.C.S.: 339999

Marlow Industries, Inc. (1)
10451 Vista Park Rd, Dallas, TX 75238-
1645
Tel.: (214) 340-4900
Web Site: http://www.marlow.com
Sales Range: $25-49.9 Million
Emp.: 210
Mfr of Thermoelectric Coolers & Cooling
Systems
N.A.I.C.S.: 334413

Max Levy Autograph, Inc. (1)
2710 Commerce Way, Philadelphia, PA
19154
Tel.: (215) 842-3675
Web Site: http://www.maxlevy.com
Sales Range: $25-49.9 Million
Emp.: 30
Optical Product Mfr
N.A.I.C.S.: 333310
Peter Tran (Engr-Applications)

Pacific Rare Specialty Metals & (1)
Chemicals, Inc.
Cavite Economic Zone Authority, Lot 6 Blk 1
Phase II Rosario, Cavite, 4106, Philippines
Tel.: (63) 27844000
Web Site: http://www.prsmetals.com
Sales Range: $50-74.9 Million
Emp.: 200
Tellurium & Selenium Products Distr
N.A.I.C.S.: 332999

Photop Technologies, Inc. (1)
3640 Westwind Blvd, Santa Rosa, CA
95403
Tel.: (408) 732-1603
Web Site: http://www.ii-vi-photop.com
Fiber Optical Product Distr
N.A.I.C.S.: 423690

Redstone Aerospace Corporation (1)
2410 Trade Ctr Ave, Longmont, CO 80503
Tel.: (720) 372-4150
Web Site:
http://www.redstoneaerospace.com
Radio & Television Broadcasting & Wireless
Communication Equipment Mfr
N.A.I.C.S.: 334220

COHERUS BIOSCIENCES, INC.

333 Twin Dolphin Dr Ste 600, Redwood City, CA 94065
Tel.: (650) 649-3530   DE
Web Site: https://www.coherus.com
Year Founded: 2010
CHRS—(NASDAQ)
Rev.: $211,042,000
Assets: $480,847,000
Liabilities: $618,265,000
Net Worth: ($137,418,000)
Earnings: ($291,754,000)
Emp.: 359
Fiscal Year-end: 12/31/22
Biologics Mfr
N.A.I.C.S.: 325414
Dennis M. Lanfear (Founder, Chm,
Pres & CEO)
Rosh Dias (Chief Medical Officer)
Paul Reider (Chief Comml Officer)
Theresa LaVallee (Chief Dev Officer)
Andy Rittenberg (Gen Counsel &
Exec VP)
Scott Saywell (Exec VP-Corporate
Development)
Bryan McMichael (CFO & Principal
Acctg Officer)

Subsidiaries:

Surface Oncology, Inc. (1)
50 Hampshire St 8th Fl, Cambridge, MA
02139
Tel.: (617) 714-4096

Web Site: https://www.surfaceoncology.com
Rev.: $30,000,000
Assets: $159,910,000
Liabilities: $66,507,000
Net Worth: $93,403,000
Earnings: ($63,586,000)
Emp.: 60
Fiscal Year-end: 12/31/2022
Cancer Therapy Development Services
N.A.I.C.S.: 541714
Shannon Rourke Devens (VP-Clinical Dev
Ops)

COHN ROBBINS HOLDINGS CORP.

1000 NW St Ste 1200, Wilmington,
DE 19801
Tel.: (302) 295-4937   Ky
Web Site:
http://www.cohnrobbins.com
Year Founded: 2020
CRHC—(NYSE)
Rev.: $41,895,681
Assets: $829,046,027
Liabilities: $894,686,593
Net Worth: ($65,640,566)
Earnings: $35,896,310
Fiscal Year-end: 12/31/21
Investment Services
N.A.I.C.S.: 523999
Gary D. Cohn (Co-Founder & Co-
Chm)
Clifton S. Robbins (Co-Founder &
Co-Chm)
Todd R. Marcy (Mng Dir)

COHU, INC.

12367 Crosthwaite Cir, Poway, CA
92064-6817
Tel.: (858) 848-8000   DE
Web Site: https://www.cohu.com
Year Founded: 1957
COHU—(NASDAQ)
Rev.: $887,214,000
Assets: $1,259,044,000
Liabilities: $376,542,000
Net Worth: $882,502,000
Earnings: $167,325,000
Emp.: 3,240
Fiscal Year-end: 12/25/21
Electric Equipment Mfr
N.A.I.C.S.: 334419
Luis A. Muller (Pres & CEO)
Jeffrey D. Jones (CFO & VP-Fin)

Subsidiaries:

Cohu Semiconductor Test GmbH (1)
Geigelsteinstrasse 6, 83059, Kolbermoor,
Germany
Tel.: (49) 80 312 3370
Semiconductor & Related Device Mfr
N.A.I.C.S.: 334413

CohuHD (1)
7330 Trade St, San Diego, CA 92121
Tel.: (858) 391-1800
Web Site: https://costarhd.com
Sales Range: $25-49.9 Million
Emp.: 145
High-Definition Video Surveillance Camera
Systems Mfr
N.A.I.C.S.: 334419

Delta Design, Inc. (1)
12367 Crosthwaite Cir, Poway, CA
92064   (100%)
Tel.: (858) 848-8000
Web Site: http://www.deltad.com
Sales Range: $150-199.9 Million
Emp.: 704
Design & Production of Electro-Mechanical
Test Equipment for Semiconductor Manufacturers & Users
N.A.I.C.S.: 334515

Subsidiary (Non-US):

Delta Design Singapore Pte. Ltd. (2)
Unit 1 -06 Kallang Sec, Singapore, 349278,
Singapore   (100%)
Tel.: (65) 62886949
Web Site: http://www.deltad.com

Sales Range: $10-24.9 Million
Emp.: 40
Sales of Electro-Mechanical Test Equipment
for Semiconductor Manufacturers & Users
N.A.I.C.S.: 334413

Ismeca Semiconductor Holding (2)
SA
283 rue de l'Helvetie, 2301, La Chaux-de-
Fonds, Switzerland
Tel.: (41) 32 925 71 11
Web Site: http://www.ismeca-
semiconductor.com
Sales Range: $75-99.9 Million
Holding Company; Electronic Components
Mfr
N.A.I.C.S.: 551112

Subsidiary (Non-US):

Cohu Malaysia Sdn. Bhd. (3)
No 5203-1 Jalan PAK 2/3 Kawasan Perindustrian Ayer Keroh Fasa 4, 75450, Malacca, Malaysia
Tel.: (60) 62527888
Electric Equipment Mfr
N.A.I.C.S.: 334419

Subsidiary (Domestic):

Ismeca Europe Semiconductor (3)
SA
283 rue de l'Helvetie, 2300, La Chaux-de-
Fonds, Switzerland
Tel.: (41) 32 552 4000
Web Site: http://www.ismeca.com
Electronic Parts & Equipment Whslr
N.A.I.C.S.: 423930

Subsidiary (Non-US):

Ismeca Malaysia Sdn. Bhd. (3)
No 32 Jalan TTC 30, Taman Teknologi
Cheng, 75250, Melaka, Malaysia
Tel.: (60) 6 331 2888
Web Site: http://www.ismeca-
semiconductor.net
Electronic Components Mfr & Distr
N.A.I.C.S.: 334419

Ismeca Semiconductor (Suzhou) Co. (3)
Ltd.
Room 305 3rd Floor Block 5 Xinsu Square
No 5 Xing Han Street, Suzhou, 215021,
China
Tel.: (86) 512 6956 0618
Web Site: http://www.ismeca-
semiconductor.net
Electronic Parts & Equipment Whslr
N.A.I.C.S.: 423930

Subsidiary (US):

Ismeca USA, Inc. (3)
12367 Crosthwaite Cir, Poway, CA 92064-
6817
Tel.: (858) 848-8000
Web Site: http://www.ismeca-
semiconductor.net
Electronic Components Mfr & Distr
N.A.I.C.S.: 334419
Luis A. Muller (Pres-Semiconductor Equipment)

Subsidiary (Non-US):

Rasco GmbH (2)
Geigelsteinstrasse 6, 83059, Kolbermoor,
Germany
Tel.: (49) 803123370
Web Site: http://www.rasco.de
Sales Range: $25-49.9 Million
Emp.: 160
High Speed Integrated Circuit Test Handlers
Developer, Mfr & Distr
N.A.I.C.S.: 333242
Alexander Waldauf (Mng Dir)

Subsidiary (Non-US):

Kita Manufacturing Co., LTD. (3)
4-27 Rinku-Minamihama, Sennan, 590-
0535, Osaka, Japan
Tel.: (81) 72 485 1900
Web Site: https://www.kita-mfg.com
Emp.: 140
Industrial Machinery Mfr
N.A.I.C.S.: 333248

Equiptest Engineering Pte. Ltd. (1)
No 1 Ubi View Focus One 01-08, Singa-

Cohu, Inc.—(Continued)

pore, 408555, Singapore
Tel.: (65) 65789900
Web Site: https://www.equiptest.com.sg
Semiconductor Mfr & Distr
N.A.I.C.S.: 334413

Fisher Research Laboratory, Inc. **(1)**
1120 Alza Dr, El Paso, TX 79907 **(100%)**
Tel.: (915) 225-0333
Web Site: https://www.fisherlab.com
Sales Range: $25-49.9 Million
Emp.: 88
Metal Detector Mfr
N.A.I.C.S.: 334519

Kita USA, Inc. **(1)**
64 Water St, Attleboro, MA 02703
Tel.: (774) 331-2265
Web Site: http://www.kita-usa.net
Spring Product Mfr
N.A.I.C.S.: 332613

MCT Asia (Penang) SDN BHD **(1)**
Plot 82 Lintang Bayan Lepas Phase 4
Bayan Lepas Industrial Park, Bayan Lepas,
11900, Penang, Malaysia
Tel.: (60) 46087099
Semiconductor Mfr & Distr
N.A.I.C.S.: 334413

MCT Worldwide LLC **(1)**
121 S 8th St Ste 960, Minneapolis, MN
55402-2848
Tel.: (612) 436-3240
Web Site: http://www.mctint.com
Sales Range: $10-24.9 Million
Emp.: 50
Integrated Automation Solutions for the
Global Semiconductor Test & Assembly
Industry
N.A.I.C.S.: 334514
John H. Moon *(Pres & CEO)*
Jan Allen Klein *(CFO)*
Douglas K. Park *(COO)*
Kenneth A. Ramsey *(Exec VP-Sls & Bus
Dev)*
Jeffrey S. Morphy *(Sr VP-Engrg & FAE
Ops)*

Plant (Non-US):

**MCT Worldwide LLC - Malaysia
Facility** **(2)**
Plot 82 Lintang Bayan Lepas Phase 4
Bayan Lepas Industrial Zone, Bayan Lepas,
11900, Penang, Malaysia
Tel.: (60) 4 644 4994
Web Site: http://www.mctint.com
Emp.: 60
Strip Test Handler Mfr
N.A.I.C.S.: 334413
Douglas K. Park *(COO)*

Xcerra Corporation **(1)**
825 University Ave, Norwood, MA 02062
Tel.: (781) 461-1000
Web Site: http://www.xcerra.com
Rev.: $390,771,000
Assets: $438,613,000
Liabilities: $124,934,000
Net Worth: $313,679,000
Earnings: $22,555,000
Emp.: 1,640
Fiscal Year-end: 07/31/2017
Semiconductor Testing Equipment Devel-
oper & Mfr
N.A.I.C.S.: 333242

Subsidiary (Non-US):

Credence Systems (M) Sdn Bhd **(2)**
42 1 Perslaran Bayan Indah, Bayan Bay
Sungai Nibong, 11900, Penang, Malaysia
Tel.: (60) 4 642 5485
Sales Range: $10-24.9 Million
Emp.: 8
Semiconductor Testing Equipment Devel-
oper & Mfr
N.A.I.C.S.: 334413

Credence Systems Pte. Ltd. **(2)**
6 Sarangoon N Ave 5 03 05 07, Singapore,
554910, Singapore
Tel.: (65) 64088408
Web Site: http://www.xcerra.com
Sales Range: $100-124.9 Million
Emp.: 100
Semiconductor Products & Devices Mfr &
Distr

N.A.I.C.S.: 334413

Subsidiary (Domestic):

**Everett Charles Technologies
LLC** **(2)**
6 Court Dr, Lincoln, RI 02865 **(100%)**
Tel.: (401) 739-7310
Web Site: https://ect-cpg.com
Sales Range: $25-49.9 Million
Emp.: 100
Production Assemblies & Test Equipment
Mfr
N.A.I.C.S.: 334515

Division (Domestic):

**Everett Charles Test Fixture
Division** **(3)**
487 Jefferson Blvd, Warwick, RI 02886-
1321
Tel.: (401) 739-7320
Web Site: http://www.ectinfo.com
Sales Range: $10-24.9 Million
Emp.: 20
Test Fixtures & Electrical Components Mfr
N.A.I.C.S.: 334515

Subsidiary (Non-US):

**LTX-Credence (Deutschland)
GmbH** **(2)**
Emp.: 20
Electronic Testing Equipment Distr

Subsidiary (Non-US):

Multitest GmbH **(3)**
Tel.: (49) 80314060
Web Site: http://www.multitest.com
Electronic Testing Equipment Mfr
N.A.I.C.S.: 334515

**Multitest elektronische Systeme
GmbH** **(3)**
Tel.: (49) 80314060
Web Site: http://www.multitest.com
Rev.: $106,192,800
Emp.: 350
Semiconductor Technology
N.A.I.C.S.: 334413

atg-Luther & Maelzer Asia Ltd. **(3)**
Tel.: (886) 33138255101
Web Site: https://www.atg-lm.com
Electronic Testing Equipment Distr
N.A.I.C.S.: 423830

Subsidiary (Non-US):

LTX-Credence Armenia L.L.C. **(2)**
48 Mamikoniants Str Building 1, Yerevan,
375051, Armenia
Tel.: (374) 10233122
Semiconductor Testing Equipment Mfr
N.A.I.C.S.: 333242

LTX-Credence Italia S.r.l. **(2)**
via Paracelso 22 Centro Direzionale Col-
leoni, Palazzo Cassiopea Scala 1, 20864,
Agrate Brianza, MB, Italy
Tel.: (39) 0396340501
Web Site: http://www.ltxc.com
Semiconductor Testing Equipment Mfr
N.A.I.C.S.: 334413

**LTX-Credence Singapore Pte
Ltd.** **(2)**
6 Serangoon North Avenue 5 No 03-06,
Singapore, 554910, Singapore
Tel.: (65) 64088408
Sales Range: $25-49.9 Million
Emp.: 70
Semiconductor Testing Equipment Mfr
N.A.I.C.S.: 333242
Pao Gin Yap *(Controller)*

LTX-Credence Systems KK **(2)**
Shin-Mizonokuchi Building 5F 3-5-7 Hisano-
noto, Takatsu-ku, Kawasaki, 213-0011, Ka-
nagawa, Japan **(100%)**
Tel.: (81) 44 812 2761
Web Site: http://www.xcerra.com
Sales Range: $10-24.9 Million
Emp.: 13
Semiconductor Product Mfr
N.A.I.C.S.: 334413

**Multitest Electronic Systems (Pen-
ang) Sdn. Bhd.** **(2)**
Plot 152 Bayan Lepas FTZ Ph 1, Jalan Sul-

tan Azlan Shah, 11900, Penang, Malaysia
Tel.: (60) 46442177
Web Site: http://www.multitest.com
Emp.: 200
Semiconductor Product Mfr
N.A.I.C.S.: 334413

**Multitest Electronic Systems (Philip-
pines) Corporation** **(2)**
Unit 1203-1204 Alabang Business Tower
1216 Acacia Avenue Madrigal, Business
Park Ayala Alabang, Muntinlupa, 1770, Phil-
ippines
Tel.: (63) 28093219
Web Site: http://www.xcerra.com
Emp.: 13
Electronic Testing Equipment Distr
N.A.I.C.S.: 423830

Subsidiary (Domestic):

Multitest Electronic Systems, Inc. **(2)**
3021 Kenneth St, Santa Clara, CA 95054
Tel.: (408) 988-6544
Sales Range: $10-24.9 Million
Emp.: 170
Printed Circuit Boards
N.A.I.C.S.: 334412

Branch (Domestic):

Xcerra Corporation - Milpitas **(2)**
880 N McCarthy Blvd Ste 100, Milpitas, CA
95035
Tel.: (408) 635-4300
Sales Range: $200-249.9 Million
Emp.: 120
Semiconductor Testing Equipment Devel-
oper & Mfr
N.A.I.C.S.: 334413
Pascal Ronde *(VP-Global Field Ops)*

COIN CITADEL INC.
146 Power Dam Way Ste 125, Platts-
burgh, NY 12901
Tel.: (212) 292-7460   NV
Web Site: http://www.coincitadel.net
Year Founded: 1986
CCTL—(OTCIQ)
Online Bitcoin Exchange & Bitcoin
ATM Owner & Operator
N.A.I.C.S.: 522320
Thomas Philsworth *(CEO)*

COINBASE GLOBAL, INC.
1209 Orange St, Wilmington, DE
19801
Tel.: (302) 777-0200
Web Site: https://www.coinbase.com
COIN—(NASDAQ)
Rev.: $3,108,383,000
Assets: $206,982,953,000
Liabilities: $200,701,304,000
Net Worth: $6,281,649,000
Earnings: $94,871,000
Emp.: 3,416
Fiscal Year-end: 12/31/23
Digitial Investment Services
N.A.I.C.S.: 523999
Emilie Choi *(Pres & COO)*
Paul Grewal *(Chief Legal Officer)*
Manish Gupta *(Exec VP-Engrg)*
Alesia J. Haas *(CFO)*
L.J. Brock *(Chief People Officer)*
Jennifer N. Jones *(Chief Acctg Offi-
cer)*
Faryar Shirzad *(Chief Policy Officer)*
Max Branzburg *(VP)*
Will Robinson *(VP)*
Alesia J. Haas *(CFO)*
Brian Armstrong *(Co-Founder &
CEO)*
Frederick Ernest Ehrsam III *(Co-
Founder)*

Subsidiaries:

**Coinbase Asset Management,
LLC** **(1)**
2200 Atlantic St Ste 320, Stamford, CT
06902
Tel.: (203) 489-1450
Web Site: https://www.cbassetmgmt.com

Financial Services
N.A.I.C.S.: 523999

COJAX OIL AND GAS CORPO-
RATION
Wilson Blvd Ste E-605, Arlington, VA
22201
Tel.: (703) 216-8606   VA
Web Site:
   https://www.cojaxoilandgas.com
Year Founded: 2017
CJAX—(OTCIQ)
Rev.: $106,554
Assets: $5,435,257
Liabilities: $2,228,273
Net Worth: $3,206,984
Earnings: ($6,237,615)
Emp.: 2
Fiscal Year-end: 12/31/22
Crude Oil Extraction Services
N.A.I.C.S.: 211120
Jeffrey Joseph Guzy *(Chm, Pres &
CEO)*
Barrett Wellman *(CFO)*

COLGATE-PALMOLIVE COM-
PANY
300 Park Ave, New York, NY 10022
Tel.: (212) 310-2000   DE
Year Founded: 1806
CL—(NYSE)
Rev.: $19,457,000,000
Assets: $16,393,000,000
Liabilities: $15,436,000,000
Net Worth: $957,000,000
Earnings: $2,300,000,000
Emp.: 34,000
Fiscal Year-end: 12/31/23
Household & Personal Care Prod-
ucts, Pet Care Products, Specialty
Hostess & Decorator Accessories Mfr
& Distr
N.A.I.C.S.: 325611
Mukul V. Deoras *(Pres-Asia Pacific)*
Brigitte H. King *(Chief Digital Officer-
Global)*
Kim Faulker *(VP-Latin America)*
Stephan Habif *(CTO)*
Jules Andrew *(Chief Bus Svcs Offi-
cer)*
Alexander Schuchman *(Chief Infor-
mation Security Officer)*
Noel R. Wallace *(Chm, Pres & CEO)*
Cliff Wilkins *(Exec VP, VP-Legal-
Global & Sr Assoc Gen Counsel-
Technology, Reg, and Ext Innov)*
Burc Cankat *(Exec VP & Gen Mgr-
NAMET)*
Betsy Fishbone *(Exec VP & VP-
Legal-Global)*
Ann Tracy *(Chief Sustainability Offi-
cer & Chief Sustainability Officer)*
Brian O. Newman *(Bd of Dirs, CFO &
Exec VP)*
Jennifer M. Daniels *(Chief Legal Offi-
cer & Sec)*
Sally Massey *(Chief HR Officer)*
Derek Gordon *(Chief Diversity , Eq-
uity & Inclusion Officer)*
John Faucher *(Chief IR Officer &
Exec VP-M & A)*
Juan Pablo Zamorano *(Pres-Latin
America)*
Gina Grant *(Treas & Sr VP)*
Nadine Flynn *(Exec VP & VP-Legal-
Global)*
Charalabos Klados *(Gen Counsel-
Asia Pacific, Sr VP & VP-Legal-
Global)*
Gregory Malcolm *(Exec VP, VP &
Controller)*
Ivan Sandoval *(Gen Counsel-Div-
Latin America, Sr VP & VP-Legal-
Global)*
Javier Llinas *(Sr VP-GIT, Infrastruc-
ture, and Operations & VP-IT-Global)*

Warren Pruitt (Sr VP-Global Engrg & VP-Supply Chain-Global)

Julie Dillon (Sr VP-Global Ethics & Compliance, VP & Gen Mgr-Hills Pet Nutrition-Greater Asia,South Pacific)

Eddie Niem (Exec VP, VP & Gen Mgr-Hawley & Hazel)

Pierre Denis (Sr VP-Global Quality & VP-R&D-Global)

Valerie Haliburton (Sr VP-Global Ethics & Compliance & VP-Compliance & Ethics-Global)

Kristi Hutchinson (Exec VP, VP-Legal-Global & Assoc Gen Counsel-Corp & Skin Health)

Iain Kielty (Exec VP-Global Budget & Fin Plng & VP-Fin-Global)

Lia Arvanitidou (Sr VP-Skin Health & VP-R&D-Global)

Jose Borrell (Exec VP-End to End SC Hills & VP-Hills Pet Nutrition)

Yvonne Hsu (Exec VP, VP-Hills Pet Nutrition & Gen Mgr-Hills US)

Cesar Martinez (Exec VP, VP & Gen Mgr-Southern Cone)

Juan Vernaza (Exec VP-Finance-Latin America & VP-North America)

Mauro Watanabe (Exec VP-End to End SC EU & AEA & VP-Europe, Africa, and Eurasia)

Courtney Williams (Gen Counsel-Division-North America, Sr VP & VP-Legal-Global)

Wendy Boise (Sr VP-Global Talent, Learning, and Org Dev & VP-HR-Global)

Gavin du Toit (Exec VP-Mktg Latin America & VP-Latin America)

Sergio Leite (Sr VP-Global Oral Care R&D & VP-R&D-Global)

Daniel Braidatto (Sr VP-Latin America Supply)

Andre Bragantini (Sr VP-Customer Dev Africa & Eurasia)

Carlos Campos (Sr VP-Fin Andina & Gen Mgr-Venezuela)

Gonzalo Canteros Paz (Exec VP-End to End Supply Chain-Latin America)

M. Chandrasekar (Sr VP-Customer Dev-Asia Pacific)

Marty Collins (Exec VP-GI Total Rewards & HR Ops)

Patricia Granda (Sr VP-DEI & Global People Rels)

Mathilde Fleury (Sr VP-Fin North America)

Maria Ryan (Chief Clinical Officer)

Thierry Antona-Traversi (Sr VP, VP & Gen Mgr-Filorga)

Sophie Bailly-Maitre (Sr VP-Mktg Europe & VP)

Claudia Barrera (Sr VP-GIT & Global Applications & VP)

Eutychus Karuru (Sr VP-Audit & VP)

Vance Merolla (Sr VP-Fellow & Global Sustainability & VP)

Catalina Monroy (Sr VP-Global Flavors & Fragrance & VP)

Emma Rolfe (Sr VP-Global Supply, Demand, and eCommerce & VP)

Eoghan Smith (Sr VP-GIT, EU, Africa, and Asia Shared Svcs & VP)

Jenny Zirinsky (Sr VP-Global Market Comm & Media Transformation & VP)

Yun-Po Zhang (Sr VP-Distinguished Fellow & VP)

James Wang (Sr VP-Global Direct Materials & VP)

Ingrid Stewart (Sr VP, VP & Gen Mgr)

Naveen Jayaraman (Sr VP-Global Digital Technologies)

Diana Schildhouse (Chief Analytics Officer & Chief Insights Officer)

Subsidiaries:

CP GABA GmbH   (1)

Beim Strohhause 17, 20097, Hamburg, Germany
Tel.: (49) 407 319 0125
Web Site: https://www.cpgaba-shop.de
Dental Product Distr
N.A.I.C.S.: 423450
Gerald Mastio (Mng Dir)
Anja Kurch (Mng Dir)
Alex Arnstein (Mng Dir)
Ingrid Stewart (Mng Dir)

CPIF Venture, Inc.   (1)
400 SW 8th Ave, Topeka, KS 66603
Tel.: (785) 233-8444
Home Care Products Distr
N.A.I.C.S.: 423990

Colgate Oral Pharmaceutical   (1)
300 Park Ave, New York, NY 10022
Tel.: (212) 310-2000
Web Site: http://www.colgatepalmolive.com
Sales Range: $25-49.9 Million
Emp.: 600
Oral Hygiene Products Mfr & Distr
N.A.I.C.S.: 325412

Colgate Palmolive Argentina S.A. (1)
Av Antartica Argentina 2269 Llavallol, B1836AOI, Buenos Aires, Argentina   (100%)
Tel.: (54) 8104440057
Web Site: http://www.colgatepalmolive.com.ar
Sales Range: $75-99.9 Million
Household Products & Toiletries Mfr
N.A.I.C.S.: 325620

Colgate U.S.A.   (1)
300 Park Ave, New York, NY 10022-7402
Tel.: (212) 310-2000
Web Site: http://www.colgate.co.in
Sales Range: $200-249.9 Million
Mfr of Cosmetics, Perfumes & Toiletries
N.A.I.C.S.: 325611

Colgate-Palmolive (Arkansas)   (1)
5211 Village Pkwy Ste 201, Rogers, AR 72758   (100%)
Tel.: (479) 464-3000
Sales Range: Less than $1 Million
Emp.: 40
Distr of Personal Care & Oral Care Products
N.A.I.C.S.: 325611

Colgate-Palmolive (Central America)   (1)
Av 4 E Chiriqui, PO Box 0819-05220, Panama, 6, Panama   (100%)
Tel.: (507) 77742127
Web Site: http://www.colgate-palmolive.com
Sales Range: $25-49.9 Million
Emp.: 150
Mfr of Soaps & Detergents
N.A.I.C.S.: 325611

Colgate-Palmolive (Central America) S.A.   (1)
Avenida del Ferrocarril 49-65 zone 12, Guatemala, Guatemala   (100%)
Tel.: (502) 8012654283
Web Site: http://www.colgate.com
Sales Range: $450-499.9 Million
Soaps & Detergents Mfr
N.A.I.C.S.: 325620

Colgate-Palmolive (Central America), Inc.   (1)
Km 9 1 2 Blvd Pinza El St 11, Santa Tecla, El Salvador   (100%)
Tel.: (503) 2781213
Web Site: http://www.colgate.com
Sales Range: $25-49.9 Million
Emp.: 50
Mfr of Soaps & Detergents
N.A.I.C.S.: 325611

Colgate-Palmolive (Central America), Inc.   (1)
Edificio Servifiesta Colonia Palmira Segunda calle Casa No 2244, frente a Embajada de Brasil, Tegucigalpa, 3134, Honduras
Tel.: (504) 22903200
Web Site: http://www.colgatepalmolive.com.gt
Mfr Soaps & Detergents
N.A.I.C.S.: 325611

Colgate-Palmolive (Eastern) Pte. Ltd.   (1)

350 Orchard Road 18-08 Shaw House, Singapore, 238868, Singapore   (100%)
Tel.: (65) 8006011251
Web Site: https://www.colgatepalmolive.com.sg
Soaps & Detergents, Personal Care Products Mfr
N.A.I.C.S.: 325611

Colgate-Palmolive (Fiji) Ltd.   (1)
Lot1 Wailekutu Lami, PO Box 1195, Suva, Fiji   (100%)
Tel.: (679) 3369800
Web Site: http://www.colgatepalmolive.com
Soaps & Personal Care Products Mfr
N.A.I.C.S.: 325611
Hiten Lal (Gen Mgr)

Colgate-Palmolive (Guyana) Ltd.   (1)
R 6 Rumiveldt, Georgetown, Guyana   (100%)
Tel.: (592) 2278912
Sales Range: $1-9.9 Million
Emp.: 1
Mfr of Soaps & Detergents
N.A.I.C.S.: 325611

Colgate-Palmolive (Hellas) S.A.I.C.   (1)
Athens 89, 185 41, Piraeus, Greece
Tel.: (30) 8001125100
Web Site: https://www.colgatepalmolive.com.gr
Toilet Preparation & Cosmetic Mfr
N.A.I.C.S.: 325620

Colgate-Palmolive (India) Ltd.   (1)
Hiranandani Gardens Powai, Mumbai, 400 076, India   (100%)
Tel.: (91) 800225599
Web Site: https://www.colgatepalmolive.co.in
Sales Range: $75-99.9 Million
Emp.: 250
Detergents, Personal Care Products Research & Development & Mfr
N.A.I.C.S.: 325611
M. K. Ajay (Exec VP-Human Resources)
V. Ganesh (VP-Customer Service-Logistics)
Ram Raghavan (Mng Dir)
Surender Sharma (VP-)
Arvind Chintamani (VP-Mktg)
K. Randhir Singh (Compliance Officer & Compliance Officer)
Balaji Sreenivasan (Exec VP-HR)
Sarala Menon (Exec VP-Manufacturing)
Ashish Bansal (VP-Customer Service-Logistics)
Ruchir Bhatnagar (VP)
Swati Agarwal (VP)

Colgate-Palmolive (Malaysia) Sdn. Bhd.   (1)
Jalan Semangat / Bersatu Section 13, 46200, Petaling Jaya, Selangor, Malaysia   (100%)
Tel.: (60) 800883918
Web Site: https://www.colgatepalmolive.com.my
Mfr of Toilet Preparations
N.A.I.C.S.: 325620

Colgate-Palmolive (Marketing) Sdn Bhd   (1)
No 2 Jln 13/4 Seksyen 13, 46200, Petaling Jaya, Selangor, Malaysia
Tel.: (60) 379654488
Web Site: http://www.colgatepalmolive.com.my
Personal Care Product Mfr
N.A.I.C.S.: 325612

Colgate-Palmolive (Myanmar) Limited   (1)
Sule Square Office Tower No 221 18th Floor Room 08/09, Sule Pagoda Road Pabedan Township, Yangon, Myanmar
Tel.: (95) 1254186
Toilet Product Mfr
N.A.I.C.S.: 325611
Durgesh Chugh (Gen Mgr)
Han Zaw Lin (Sr Mgr-Customer Dev)

Colgate-Palmolive (Poland) SP. z o.o.   (1)
ul Wybrzeze Gdynskie 6D, 01-531, Warsaw, Poland
Tel.: (48) 80 111 6611
Web Site: https://www.colgatepalmolive.pl

Toilet Preparation & Cosmetic Mfr
N.A.I.C.S.: 325620

Colgate-Palmolive (Romania) SRL   (1)
Str Gara Herastrau nr 4C Green Court Bucharest Cladirea B Etaj 2, Sector 2, Bucharest, Romania
Tel.: (40) 800070027
Bar Soap Mfr
N.A.I.C.S.: 325611

Colgate-Palmolive (Thailand) Limited   (1)
19 Sunthon Kosa Rd Khwaeng Khlong Toei Khet Khlong Toei, Krung Thep Maha Nakhon, Bangkok, 10110, Thailand   (100%)
Tel.: (66) 22298000
Web Site: http://www.colgatepalmolive.co.th
Soaps, Detergents & Personal Care Products Mfr & Dist
N.A.I.C.S.: 325611

Colgate-Palmolive A/S   (1)
Bredevej 2A, 2830, Virum, Denmark   (100%)
Tel.: (45) 80607000
Web Site: http://www.colgatepalmolive.dk
Sales Range: $25-49.9 Million
Household Products & Toiletries Mfr
N.A.I.C.S.: 325620

Colgate-Palmolive AB   (1)
Svardvagen 23, 182 33, Danderyd, Sweden   (100%)
Tel.: (46) 20662200
Web Site: http://www.colgatepalmolive.se
Sales Range: $50-74.9 Million
Emp.: 60
Mfr of Soaps & Detergents
N.A.I.C.S.: 325611

Colgate-Palmolive AG   (1)
Zurcherstrasse 68, 8800, Thalwil, Switzerland   (100%)
Tel.: (41) 447227300
Web Site: http://www.colgate.ch
Sales Range: $25-49.9 Million
Emp.: 26
Mfr of Soaps & Detergents
N.A.I.C.S.: 325611

Colgate-Palmolive Belgium S.A.   (1)
Boulevard du Souverain 165, 1160, Brussels, Belgium   (100%)
Tel.: (32) 80032132132
Web Site: https://www.colgatepalmolive.be
Mfr of Detergents & Personal Care Products
N.A.I.C.S.: 325611

Colgate-Palmolive C.A.   (1)
Av Hans Neumann Corimon Bldg 1st Floor Los Cortijos de Lourdes, 1071, Caracas, Distrito Federal, Venezuela
Tel.: (58) 2126104711
Web Site: https://www.colgatepalmolive.com.ve
Toothpaste & Oral Hygiene Product Mfr
N.A.I.C.S.: 325611

Colgate-Palmolive CIA   (1)
Carrera 1era 40-108, Cali, 750004, Colombia   (100%)
Tel.: (57) 8000520800
Web Site: http://www.colgate.com.co
Soaps & Detergents Mfr
N.A.I.C.S.: 325611

Colgate-Palmolive Canada Inc.   (1)
895 Don Mills Rd, North York, M3C 1W3, ON, Canada   (100%)
Tel.: (416) 421-6000
Household Products & Toiletries Mfr
N.A.I.C.S.: 325620

Colgate-Palmolive Ceska republika, s.r.o.   (1)
Sokolovska 100/94, 180 00, Prague, Czech Republic
Tel.: (420) 257087111
Web Site: http://www.colgate.cz
Toilet Preparation & Cosmetic Mfr
N.A.I.C.S.: 325620

Colgate-Palmolive Chile S.A.   (1)
Av Las Esteras 2800, Quilicura, Santiago, Chile
Tel.: (56) 800200510
Web Site: http://www.colgatepalmolive.cl

Colgate-Palmolive Company—(Continued)

Consumer Products Mfr
N.A.I.C.S.: 325611

Colgate-Palmolive Co., Institutional Products Div. (1)
191 E Hanover Ave, Morristown, NJ 07960-3151
Tel.: (973) 630-1500
Web Site: http://www.colpalcommercial.com
Sales Range: $75-99.9 Million
Emp.: 70
Institutional Products for Housekeeping; Professional Product Sales to Hospitals & Nursing Homes; Bar Soap, Sterno, Degreasers
N.A.I.C.S.: 424690

Colgate-Palmolive Comercial Ltda. (1)
Rua Rio Grande 752, Caixa Postal 1862, Vila Mariana, Sao Paulo, 01059-970, Brazil
Tel.: (55) 800 703 7722
Web Site:
   https://www.colgatepalmolive.com.br
Pharmaceutical Product Merchant Whslr
N.A.I.C.S.: 424210

Colgate-Palmolive Del Ecuador, S.A. (1)
1/2 Via a Daule, Guayaquil, Ecuador
Tel.: (593) 800895020
Web Site:
   http://www.colgatepalmolive.com.ec
Mfr of Soaps & Detergents
N.A.I.C.S.: 325611

Colgate-Palmolive Eeska republika spol. s r.o. (1)
Rohanske nabrezi 678/23 Karlin, 186 00, Prague, Czech Republic
Tel.: (420) 257087111
Web Site: http://www.colgatepalmolive.cz
Brooms Hand & Machine Mfr
N.A.I.C.S.: 339994

Colgate-Palmolive France (1)
9-11 rue du Debarcadere, 92700, Colombes, France (100%)
Tel.: (33) 969320510
Web Site: http://www.colgate.com
Sales Range: $1-4.9 Billion
Emp.: 2,000
Disinfectants & Household Products Mfr
N.A.I.C.S.: 325620

Colgate-Palmolive Ghana Limited (1)
14 Senchi Street LE Pierre Offices Airport Residential, Accra, Ghana
Tel.: (233) 303933500
Toilet Product Mfr
N.A.I.C.S.: 325611

Colgate-Palmolive GmbH (1)
Luebecker Strasse 128, Hamburg, 22087, Germany (100%)
Tel.: (49) 4073191392
Web Site: http://www.colgate.de
Sales Range: $25-49.9 Million
Emp.: 125
Mfr Soaps & Detergents
N.A.I.C.S.: 325611

Colgate-Palmolive GmbH (1)
Leopold Ungar Platz 2 Staircase 4 3 Floor Top 431, 1190, Vienna, Austria
Tel.: (43) 8000123965
Web Site: http://www.colgatepalmolive.at
Mfr of Soaps & Detergents
N.A.I.C.S.: 325611

Colgate-Palmolive Household Products Division (1)
300 Park Ave, New York, NY 10022-7402
Tel.: (212) 310-2000
Web Site: http://www.colgatepalmolive.com
Sales Range: $800-899.9 Million
Emp.: 1,000
Mfr of Household Products; Laundry Detergent & Softeners, Dishwashing Liquids, Bar & Liquid Soaps & Household Cleaners
N.A.I.C.S.: 325611

Colgate-Palmolive Inc. S.A. (1)
Teniente Galeano 3160, Montevideo, Uruguay
Tel.: (598) 4054057
Household & Oral Care Product Mfr

N.A.I.C.S.: 325611

Colgate-Palmolive Ireland (1)
Unit 3054 Lake Drive Citywest Business Campus Naas Road, Dublin, Ireland (100%)
Tel.: (353) 80032132132
Web Site: http://www.colgate-palmolive.com
Sales Range: $25-49.9 Million
Emp.: 120
Consumer & Household Products Mfr
N.A.I.C.S.: 325620

Colgate-Palmolive Italia Srl (1)
Viale Alexandre Gustave Eiffel 15, Rome, 00148, Italy (100%)
Tel.: (39) 0800860047
Mfrs. Soaps & Detergents
N.A.I.C.S.: 325611

Colgate-Palmolive Ltd. (1)
Guildford Business Park Middleton Rd, Guildford, GU2 8JZ, Surrey, United Kingdom (100%)
Tel.: (44) 80032132132
Web Site: http://www.colgate.co.uk
Sales Range: $150-199.9 Million
Emp.: 180
Personal Care & Beauty Products Mfr
N.A.I.C.S.: 325620

Colgate-Palmolive Ltd. (1)
528 Commissioner Street, PO Box 213, Boksburg, 1460, South Africa (100%)
Tel.: (27) 860114146
Web Site: http://www.colgatepalmolive.co.za
Sales Range: $200-249.9 Million
Mfr of Soaps, Detergents & Personal Care Products
N.A.I.C.S.: 325611

Colgate-Palmolive Ltd. (1)
45 Knights Road, PO Box 38077, 5010, Lower Hutt, 5010, Wellington, New Zealand (100%)
Tel.: (64) 800441740
Sales Range: $25-49.9 Million
Emp.: 33
Soaps & Detergents Mfr
N.A.I.C.S.: 325611
John Garside (Gen Mgr)

Colgate-Palmolive Ltda. (1)
Rua Rio Grande 752, Vila Mariana, Sao Paulo, 4366-6600, Brazil (100%)
Tel.: (55) 8007037722
Web Site: http://www.colgate.com.br
Sales Range: $25-49.9 Million
Emp.: 500
Toiletry Manufacturing
N.A.I.C.S.: 325620

Colgate-Palmolive Nederland B.V. (1)
Leeuwenveldseweg 3F, 1382 LV, Weesp, Netherlands
Tel.: (31) 294491949
Web Site: http://www.colgate.nl
Mfr of Soaps & Detergents
N.A.I.C.S.: 325611

Colgate-Palmolive Personal Care Products Division (1)
300 Park Ave, New York, NY 10022-7402
Tel.: (212) 310-2000
Web Site: http://www.colgate.co.in
Sales Range: $1-4.9 Billion
Emp.: 5,000
Mfr of Hair Care Products, Toothpaste & Toothbrushes, Toiletries
N.A.I.C.S.: 325611

Colgate Palmolive Peru A.A. (1)
Grimaldo del solar 346, Miraflores, Lima, Peru
Tel.: (51) 80113636
Web Site:
   http://www.colgatepalmolive.com.pe
Toilet Preparation & Cosmetic Mfr
N.A.I.C.S.: 325620

Colgate-Palmolive Philippines Inc. (1)
11th Floor Three World Square Building No 22, Upper Mckinley Road, Taguig, 1634, Philippines (100%)
Tel.: (63) 88027800
Web Site: http://www.colgatepalmolive.ph
Soaps & Detergents Mfr
N.A.I.C.S.: 325611

Colgate-Palmolive Portuguese Ltda (1)
Lagoas Park Edificio 15-piso, 2740-262, Porto Salvo, Portugal (100%)
Tel.: (351) 80032132132
Web Site: http://www.colgate.pt
Sales Range: $25-49.9 Million
Emp.: 75
Mfr of Personal Care Products & Detergents
N.A.I.C.S.: 325620

Colgate-Palmolive Pty. Ltd. (1)
Level 14 345 George St, Sydney, 2000, NSW, Australia (100%)
Tel.: (61) 292295600
Web Site:
   https://www.colgatepalmolive.com.au
Household & Personal Products Mfr.
N.A.I.C.S.: 325620

Colgate-Palmolive S.p.A. (1)
Viale Alexandre Gustave Eiffel 15, 00148, Rome, Italy
Tel.: (39) 0800860047
Web Site: https://www.colgatepalmolive.it
Toothpaste Soap Toiletries & Cosmetics Mfr
N.A.I.C.S.: 325611

Colgate-Palmolive Services (Belgium) SA/NV (1)
Boulevard du Souverain 165, 1160, Brussels, Belgium
Tel.: (32) 26749211
Web Site: http://www.colgate.be
Sales Range: $25-49.9 Million
Emp.: 40
Cosmetics & Household Products Distr
N.A.I.C.S.: 456120

Colgate-Palmolive Services S.A. (1)
9-11 rue du Debarcadere, 92700, Colombes, France
Tel.: (33) 969320510
Web Site: http://www.colgatepalmolive.fr
Toilet Preparation & Cosmetic Mfr
N.A.I.C.S.: 325620

Colgate-Palmolive Slovensko, s.r.o. (1)
Grosslingova 4, 811 09, Bratislava, Slovakia
Tel.: (421) 257087111
Web Site: http://www.colgateusmev.sk
Toothpaste & Toothbrush Mfr
N.A.I.C.S.: 325620

Colgate-Palmolive Temizlik Urunleri Sanayi ve Ticaret Anonim Sirketi (1)
Centrum Is Merkezi Aydinevler Sanayi Caddesi No 3 Kat 5, Kucukyali-Maltepe, 34854, Istanbul, Turkiye
Tel.: (90) 2165878000
Web Site:
   http://www.colgatepalmolive.com.tr
Toilet Preparation Mfr
N.A.I.C.S.: 325620

Colgate-Palmolive de Puerto Rico, Inc. (1)
300 Park Ave, New York, NY 10022-7402
Tel.: (212) 310-2000
Personal Care Product Mfr
N.A.I.C.S.: 325611

Colgate-Palmolive, (DR), Inc. (1)
C/Rafael Augusto Sanchez 38 Torre Malaga VII Naco, Santo Domingo, Dominican Republic
Tel.: (809) 2001472
Web Site: http://www.colgate.com
Sales Range: $150-199.9 Million
Mfrs. Soaps & Detergents
N.A.I.C.S.: 325611

Colgate-Palmolive, Inc. (1)
Teniente Galeano, 3160, Montevideo, Uruguay
Tel.: (598) 25111100
Web Site:
   https://www.colgatepalmolive.com.uy
Mfr of Soaps & Detergents
N.A.I.C.S.: 325611

Colgate-Palmolive, S.A. De C.V. (1)
Av Mexican National Army 843-B 6th Floor, Col Granada Delegation Miguel Hidalgo, 11520, Mexico, Distrito Federal, Mexico (100%)
Tel.: (52) 91267000

Web Site:
   http://www.colgatepalmolive.com.mx
Soaps & Detergents Mfr
N.A.I.C.S.: 325611

Cotelle S.A. (1)
60 Ave de lEurope, Bois-Colombes, 92270, France
Tel.: (33) 147686000
Web Site: http://www.colgate.com
Emp.: 200
Bleach & Other Detergents Mfr
N.A.I.C.S.: 325130

Elta MD, Inc. (1)
2055 Luna Rd Ste 126, Carrollton, TX 75006
Web Site: https://www.eltamd.com
Broom Machinery Mfr
N.A.I.C.S.: 339994
Jonathan Nugent (Dir-Natl Sls)

Filorga Americas Inc. (1)
429 Lenox Ave, Miami, FL 33139
Tel.: (786) 406-6202
Cosmetic Product Distr
N.A.I.C.S.: 456120
Deborah Feldman Amsellem (Mktg Mgr)

Filorga Portugal, Unipessoal, Lda. (1)
Rua Luz de Almeida n 1D, 1500-473, Lisbon, Portugal
Tel.: (351) 211396310
Cosmetic Product Distr
N.A.I.C.S.: 456120

GABA International AG (1)
Grabetsmattweg, Therwil, 4106, Switzerland
Tel.: (41) 614156060
Web Site: http://www.gaba.com
Sales Range: $50-74.9 Million
Emp.: 300
Oral Care Product Mfr
N.A.I.C.S.: 339114

Subsidiary (Non-US):

GABA B.V. (2)
Leeuwenveldseweg 5n, PO Box 27, 1380 AA, Weesp, Netherlands
Tel.: (31) 80032132132
Web Site: https://www.colgate.nl
Sales Range: $100-124.9 Million
Emp.: 40
Marketing & Sales of Pharmaceutical Products
N.A.I.C.S.: 424210

Hawley & Hazel Chemical Co., (HK) Ltd. (1)
45 Wong Chuk Hang Road, Aberdeen, China (Hong Kong) (50%)
Tel.: (852) 25551338
Web Site: http://www.darlie.com.hk
Sales Range: $25-49.9 Million
Emp.: 110
Toothpaste Product Mfr
N.A.I.C.S.: 325620

Hello Products LLC (1)
363 Bloomfield Ave Ste 2D, Montclair, NJ 07042
Web Site: https://www.hello-products.com
Grocery Product Distr
N.A.I.C.S.: 445110

Hill's Pet Nutrition (NZ) Limited (1)
PO Box 112253, Penrose, Auckland, 1642, New Zealand
Tel.: (64) 800344557
Web Site: https://www.hillspet.co.nz
Pet Food Product Distr
N.A.I.C.S.: 424990

Hill's Pet Nutrition Asia-Pacific, Pte. Ltd. (1)
350 Orchard Road No 18-07 Shaw House, Singapore, 238868, Singapore
Tel.: (65) 67353286
Web Site: http://www.hillspet.com.sg
Pet Food Product Mfr
N.A.I.C.S.: 311111

Hill's Pet Nutrition B.V. (1)
t a v Klantenservice, Postbus 3177, 4800 DD, Breda, Netherlands
Tel.: (31) 8000222466
Web Site: https://www.hillspet.nl
Pet Food Product Distr
N.A.I.C.S.: 424990

Hill's Pet Nutrition Canada Inc. (1)
PO Box 699, Streetsville, L5M 2C2, ON, Canada
Web Site: http://www.hillspet.ca
Pet Accessory Whslr
N.A.I.C.S.: 424990

Hill's Pet Nutrition Denmark ApS (1)
Havretoften 4, 5500, Langeskov, Denmark
Tel.: (45) 72141414
Web Site: http://www.hillspet.dk
Pet Accessory Whslr
N.A.I.C.S.: 424990

Hill's Pet Nutrition Espana, S.L. (1)
Servicio de atencion al cliente c/ Quintana-vides 19 Edif 4 4 planta, 28050, Madrid, Spain
Tel.: (34) 800760179
Web Site: https://www.hillspet.es
Pet Food Product Distr
N.A.I.C.S.: 424990

Hill's Pet Nutrition GmbH (1)
Beim Strohhause 17, 20097, Hamburg, Germany
Tel.: (49) 8004455773
Web Site: https://www.hillspet.de
Pet Food Product Distr
N.A.I.C.S.: 424990

Hill's Pet Nutrition Italia, S.r.l. (1)
Servizio clienti Viale Alexandre Gustave Eiffel 15, 00148, Rome, Italy
Tel.: (39) 0800701702
Web Site: https://www.hillspet.it
Pet Food Product Distr
N.A.I.C.S.: 424990

Hill's Pet Nutrition Korea Ltd. (1)
9th floor National Federation of Businesses 24 Yeoui-daero, Yeongdeungpo-gu, Seoul, 135-880, Korea (South)
Tel.: (82) 1 877 9828
Web Site: https://www.hillspet.co.kr
Pet Food Mfr
N.A.I.C.S.: 311111

Hill's Pet Nutrition Limited (1)
1b Guildford Business Park Midleton Road, Guildford, GU2 8JZ, United Kingdom
Tel.: (44) 0800282438
Pet Food Mfr
N.A.I.C.S.: 311111

Hill's Pet Nutrition Manufacturing, B.V. (1)
Zeedijk 23, PB 522, 4871 NM, Etten-Leur, Netherlands
Tel.: (31) 168375500
Web Site: http://www.hillspet.com
Sales Range: $50-74.9 Million
Emp.: 160
Pet Food Mfr
N.A.I.C.S.: 311111

Hill's Pet Nutrition Norway AS (1)
Kruuse Norge AS, PO Box 150, 1440, Drobak, Norway
Tel.: (47) 64907500
Web Site: http://www.hillspet.no
Pet Food Mfr
N.A.I.C.S.: 311111

Hill's Pet Nutrition Pty. Ltd. (1)
PO Box 3964, Sydney, 2000, NSW, Australia
Tel.: (61) 1800679932
Web Site: https://www.hillspet.com.au
Pet Food Product Distr
N.A.I.C.S.: 424990

Hill's Pet Nutrition S.N.C. (1)
955 route des lucioles, 06904, Sophia-Antipolis, France
Tel.: (33) 80 022 2149
Web Site: http://www.hillspet.fr
Pet Food Product Mfr
N.A.I.C.S.: 311111

Hill's Pet Nutrition South Africa Proprietary Limited (1)
16 Victoria Avenue Hout Bay, Cape Town, South Africa
Tel.: (27) 8600228783
Web Site: https://hillsacademy.co.za
Pet Food Product Distr
N.A.I.C.S.: 424990

Hill's Pet Nutrition Sweden AB (1)
Kruuse Svenska AB Consumer Service Ulls

Vag 30, 756 51, Uppsala, Sweden
Tel.: (46) 4899700
Web Site: http://www.hillspet.se
Pet Food Mfr
N.A.I.C.S.: 311111

Hill's Pet Nutrition Switzerland GmbH (1)
Grabetsmattweg 1, 4106, Therwil, Switzerland
Tel.: (41) 800555456
Web Site: https://www.hillspet.ch
Pet Food Product Distr
N.A.I.C.S.: 424990

Hill's Pet Nutrition de Mexico, S.A. de C.V. (1)
Av Ejercito Nacional Mexicano 843-B Piso 6, Col Granada, 11520, Mexico, Mexico
Tel.: (52) 18000144557
Web Site: https://www.hillsvet.com.mx
Pet Food Product Distr
N.A.I.C.S.: 424990

Hill's Pet Nutrition s.r.o. (1)
Rohanske Nabrezi 678/23, 186 00, Prague, 186 00, Czech Republic
Tel.: (420) 261198500
Web Site: http://www.hillspet.cz
Pet Food Mfr
N.A.I.C.S.: 311111

Hill's Pet Nutrition, Inc. (1)
400 SW 8th St, Topeka, KS 66603
Tel.: (785) 354-8523
Web Site: https://www.hillspet.com
Mfr of Prescription Diet Therapeutic Pet Foods & Science Diet
N.A.I.C.S.: 424990
Noel R. Wallace *(COO)*

Subsidiary (Domestic):

Hill's Pet Nutrition Indiana, Inc. (2)
2325 Union Pike, Richmond, IN 47374
Tel.: (785) 354-8523
Web Site: http://www.hillspet.com
Pet Food Mfr
N.A.I.C.S.: 311111

Hill's Pet Nutrition Sales, Inc. (2)
400 SW 8th Ave Ste 101, Topeka, KS 66603
Tel.: (785) 354-8523
Web Site: http://www.hillspet.com
Grocery Products Mfr
N.A.I.C.S.: 424490

Hill's-Colgate Japan Ltd. (1)
7F Nibancho Center Building 5-25 Nibancho, Chiyoda-Ku, Tokyo, 102-0084, Japan
Tel.: (81) 120211311
Web Site: https://www.hills.co.jp
Emp.: 200
Pet Care Products Mfr
N.A.I.C.S.: 311119

Laboratoires Filorga Cosmetiques Espana S.L.U. (1)
Avenida Diagonal 407 Planta 2 Puerta 2, 08008, Barcelona, Spain
Tel.: (34) 933188072
Cosmetic Product Distr
N.A.I.C.S.: 456120

Laboratoires Filorga Cosmetiques S.A. (1)
2 rue de Lisbonne, 75008, Paris, France
Tel.: (33) 184792929
Web Site: https://fr.filorga.com
Cosmetic Product Distr
N.A.I.C.S.: 456120

Mission Hills, S.A. de C.V. (1)
Carretera Federal No 57 Km 47 Col La Cantera, 37980, San Jose Iturbide, Mexico
Tel.: (52) 4191983600
Toilet Preparation & Cosmetic Mfr
N.A.I.C.S.: 325620

Paramount Research, Inc. (1)
1212 Sadler Dr, North Liberty, IA 52317
Tel.: (319) 338-7210
Web Site:
 https://www.paramountresearch.com
Magazine Publisher
N.A.I.C.S.: 513120

Tom's of Maine, Inc. (1)
302 Lafayette Ctr, Kennebunk, ME 04043 **(84%)**

Tel.: (207) 985-2944
Web Site: https://www.tomsofmaine.com
Sales Range: $25-49.9 Million
Emp.: 175
Natural Toothpaste, Deodorant, Mouthwash, Shaving Cream, Cough & Cold Wellness Products, Glycerin Bars, Liquid Soap & Dental Ribbon Mfr
N.A.I.C.S.: 325611

COLICITY INC.
2300 Carillon Pt, Kirkland, WA 98033
Tel.: (435) 278-7100   DE
Year Founded: 2020
COLI—(NASDAQ)
Rev.: $6,793,419
Assets: $346,043,404
Liabilities: $367,613,736
Net Worth: ($21,570,332)
Earnings: $5,648,973
Emp.: 3
Fiscal Year-end: 12/31/21
Investment Services
N.A.I.C.S.: 523999
Craig McCaw *(Chm & CEO)*
Joseph J. Viraldo *(CFO & Principal Acctg Officer)*

COLISEUM ACQUISITION CORP.
1180 N Town Ctr Dr Ste 100, Las Vegas, NV 89144
Tel.: (702) 781-4313   Ky
Web Site:
 https://www.coliseumacq.com
Year Founded: 2021
MITA—(NASDAQ)
Rev.: $8,847,796
Assets: $152,820,389
Liabilities: $158,498,035
Net Worth: ($5,677,646)
Earnings: $7,596,243
Fiscal Year-end: 12/31/22
Investment Services
N.A.I.C.S.: 523999
Charles E. Wert *(CEO)*
Oanh Do Ngoc Truong *(CFO)*

COLLEGIUM PHARMACEUTICAL, INC.
100 Technology Ctr Dr Ste 300, Stoughton, MA 02072
Tel.: (781) 713-3699   VA
Web Site:
 https://www.collegiumpharma.com
Year Founded: 2002
COLL—(NASDAQ)
Rev.: $566,767,000
Assets: $1,143,308,000
Liabilities: $947,877,000
Net Worth: $195,431,000
Earnings: $48,155,000
Emp.: 197
Fiscal Year-end: 12/31/23
Pharmaceuticals Mfr
N.A.I.C.S.: 325412
Colleen Tupper *(CFO & Exec VP)*
Scott Dreyer *(Chief Comml Officer & Exec VP)*
Bart Dunn *(Exec VP-Strategy & Corp Dev)*
Kelly Clements *(Chief People Officer)*
Thomas B. Smith *(Chief Medical Officer)*
Michael Thomas Heffernan *(Founder, Chm, Interim Pres & Interim CEO)*

Subsidiaries:

BioDelivery Sciences International, Inc. (1)
4131 ParkLake Ave Ste 225, Raleigh, NC 27612
Tel.: (919) 582-9050
Web Site: http://www.bdsi.com
Rev.: $156,471,000
Assets: $239,894,000
Liabilities: $131,660,000
Net Worth: $108,234,000

Earnings: $25,711,000
Emp.: 176
Fiscal Year-end: 12/31/2020
Drug DeliveryTechnologies
N.A.I.C.S.: 325412
Joseph J. Ciaffoni *(Pres & CEO)*
Colleen Tupper *(CFO & Treas)*
Joseph M. Lockhart *(Sr VP-Ops)*
Scott M. Plesha *(Pres & Chief Comml Officer)*
James Vollins *(Chief Compliance Officer, Gen Counsel & Sec)*
Mary Theresa Coelho *(Co-CFO, Treas & Exec VP)*
Thomas B. Smith *(Chief Medical Officer)*
Kevin Ostrander *(Sr VP-Bus Dev)*

COLONY BANKCORP, INC.
115 S Grant St, Fitzgerald, GA 31750
Tel.: (229) 426-6000   GA
Web Site:
 https://www.colonybank.com
CBAN—(NASDAQ)
Rev.: $126,562,000
Assets: $2,936,570,000
Liabilities: $2,706,302,000
Net Worth: $230,268,000
Earnings: $19,542,000
Emp.: 511
Fiscal Year-end: 12/31/22
Bank Holding Company
N.A.I.C.S.: 551111
Derek Shelnutt *(CFO & Exec VP)*
T. Heath Fountain *(CEO)*
Edward G. Canup *(Chief Revenue Officer & Pres-Banking Solutions)*
R. Dallis Copeland Jr. *(Pres)*

Subsidiaries:

Colony Bank (1)
302 S Main St, Fitzgerald, GA
31750 **(100%)**
Tel.: (229) 423-5446
Web Site: http://www.colonybank.com
Banking Services
N.A.I.C.S.: 522110
Brian D. Schmitt *(Exec VP)*
Derek Shelnutt *(CFO & Exec VP)*
Thomas M. Bird *(Mgr-Augusta, Statesboro & Savannah)*

SouthCrest Financial Group, Inc. (1)
1475 Peachtree St NE STE 200, Atlanta, GA 30309
Tel.: (678) 810-1103
Web Site: http://www.southcrestbank.com
Sales Range: $10-24.9 Million
Emp.: 240
Bank Holding Company
N.A.I.C.S.: 551111
Edmond H. Wilson *(Pres-Community Banking Group)*
H. Russell Holland III *(Chief Credit Officer)*
Rebecca Bell *(Chief Risk Officer)*
David Roberts *(Sr VP-HR)*
Shane Mohr *(Sr VP-IT)*
Joseph Rheaves *(Pres-Metro Banking Group)*

Subsidiary (Domestic):

SouthCrest Bank, N.A. (2)
967 N Main St, Cedartown, GA
30125 **(100%)**
Tel.: (770) 748-1750
Web Site: http://www.southcrestbank.com
Sales Range: $25-49.9 Million
Federal Savings Bank
N.A.I.C.S.: 522180
Edmond H. Wilson *(Pres-Community Banking Grp)*
H. Russell Holland III *(Chief Credit Officer)*
Joseph Rheaves *(Pres-Metro Banking Grp)*
Linda Burch *(VP-West)*
Dexter Lummus *(Sr VP-Comml lending)*
Alisha Nasse *(Dir-Private Banking)*
Jane Prescott *(Chief HR Officer & Sr VP)*
Rhonda Grimes *(VP/Mgr-Fayetteville)*
Scott Hudgins *(Sr VP & Mgr-Comml Banking-North Fulton & Forsyth)*
Teresa Baker *(Sr VP & Mgr-Relationship)*

COLOR STAR TECHNOLOGY CO., LTD.

Color Star Technology Co., Ltd.—(Continued)

80 Broad St 5Th Fl, New York, NY
10005
Tel.: (929) 317-2699　　　　NV
Web Site:
　http://www.colorstarinternatio
　nal.com
ADD—(NASDAQ)
Rev.: $6,783,957
Assets: $81,075,167
Liabilities: $4,124,666
Net Worth: $76,950,501
Earnings: ($8,238,513)
Emp.: 55
Fiscal Year-end: 06/30/21
Ready Mix Concrete Materials Mfr
N.A.I.C.S.: 327320
Lili Jiang (CFO)
Biao Lu (Chief Artistic Officer)
Wei Zhang (Chm)
Louis Luo (CEO)

COLUMBIA BANKING SYS-TEM, INC.

1301 A St, Tacoma, WA 98402-2156
Tel.: (253) 305-1900　　　　WA
Web Site:
　https://www.columbiabankingsys
　tem.com
COLB—(NASDAQ)
Rev.: $2,743,254,000
Assets: $52,173,596,000
Liabilities: $47,178,562,000
Net Worth: $4,995,034,000
Earnings: $348,715,000
Emp.: 5,114
Fiscal Year-end: 12/31/23
Bank Holding Company
N.A.I.C.S.: 551111
Cort Lane O'Haver (Exec Chm)
Lisa M. White (Controller)
Clint E. Stein (Pres & CEO)
Kumi Yamamoto Baruffi (Gen Coun-sel, Sec & Exec VP)
David Moore Devine (Chief Mktg & Experience Officer & Exec VP)

Subsidiaries:

Umpqua Bank　　　　　　　(1)
445 SE Main St, Roseburg, OR 97470
Tel.: (541) 440-3961
Web Site: https://www.umpquabank.com
Sales Range: $450-499.9 Million
Emp.: 2,397
State Commercial Bank & Trust Company
N.A.I.C.S.: 522110
Cort Lane O'Haver (CEO)
Anddria Clack-Rogers Varnado (Dir-Publicly-Traded)
Brian J. Read (Exec VP & Head-Retail Banking)
Kevin Skinner (Exec VP & Head-Home Lending)
Rilla S. Delorier (Executives)

Umpqua Bank　　　　　　　(1)
445 SE Main St, Roseburg, OR 97470
Tel.: (541) 440-3961
Web Site: https://www.umpquabank.com
Sales Range: $450-499.9 Million
Emp.: 2,397
State Commercial Bank & Trust Company
N.A.I.C.S.: 522110
Cort Lane O'Haver (CEO)
Anddria Clack-Rogers Varnado (Dir-Publicly-Traded)
Brian J. Read (Exec VP & Head-Retail Banking)
Kevin Skinner (Exec VP & Head-Home Lending)
Rilla S. Delorier (Executives)

Subsidiary (Domestic):

Columbia Trust Company　　(2)
805 SW Broadway Ste 780, Portland, OR
97205
Tel.: (503) 224-2472
Web Site:
　https://www.columbiatrustcompany.com
Trust & Wealth Management Services

N.A.I.C.S.: 523991
Rob Howell (Sr VP & Dir-Investments)
Andrew Hagerty (VP & Portfolio Mgr-Trust)
Gillian Eubanks (VP & Mgr-Trust Relation-ship)
Helen Robinson (VP & Mgr-Trust Relation-ship)
Jessica Bryant (Asst VP & Mgr-Trust Rela-tionship)
Kevin Donovan (Sr VP)
Julio Quinteros (VP)

Financial Pacific Leasing, Inc.　(2)
3455 S 344th Way Ste 300, Federal Way,
WA 98001
Tel.: (253) 568-6000
Web Site: https://www.finpac.com
Sales Range: $25-49.9 Million
Emp.: 150
Equipment Leasing Finance Services
N.A.I.C.S.: 525990
Terey N. Jennings (Pres)
John M. Wright (Sr VP-Portfolio Svcs)
Jodi L. Wilshire (CFO & Exec VP)
Stephen E. Leege (Chief Credit Officer & Sr VP)
Thomas J. McSweeney Jr. (Sr VP-Information Technologies)

Intervest Mortgage Investment
Company　　　　　　　　　(2)
720 4th Ave Ste 120, Kirkland, WA
98033　　　　　　　　　(100%)
Tel.: (425) 828-1404
Web Site: http://www.intervestcref.com
Sales Range: $25-49.9 Million
Emp.: 55
Commercial Real Estate Lending Services
N.A.I.C.S.: 522310

Umpqua Bank　　　　　　　(1)
445 SE Main St, Roseburg, OR 97470
Tel.: (541) 440-3961
Web Site: https://www.umpquabank.com
Sales Range: $450-499.9 Million
Emp.: 2,397
State Commercial Bank & Trust Company
N.A.I.C.S.: 522110
Cort Lane O'Haver (CEO)
Anddria Clack-Rogers Varnado (Dir-Publicly-Traded)
Brian J. Read (Exec VP & Head-Retail Banking)
Kevin Skinner (Exec VP & Head-Home Lending)
Rilla S. Delorier (Executives)

Umpqua Bank　　　　　　　(1)
445 SE Main St, Roseburg, OR 97470
Tel.: (541) 440-3961
Web Site: https://www.umpquabank.com
Sales Range: $450-499.9 Million
Emp.: 2,397
State Commercial Bank & Trust Company
N.A.I.C.S.: 522110
Cort Lane O'Haver (CEO)
Anddria Clack-Rogers Varnado (Dir-Publicly-Traded)
Brian J. Read (Exec VP & Head-Retail Banking)
Kevin Skinner (Exec VP & Head-Home Lending)
Rilla S. Delorier (Executives)

Subsidiary (Domestic):

Columbia Trust Company　　(2)
805 SW Broadway Ste 780, Portland, OR
97205
Tel.: (503) 224-2472
Web Site:
　https://www.columbiatrustcompany.com
Trust & Wealth Management Services
N.A.I.C.S.: 523991
Rob Howell (Sr VP & Dir-Investments)
Andrew Hagerty (VP & Portfolio Mgr-Trust)
Gillian Eubanks (VP & Mgr-Trust Relation-ship)
Helen Robinson (VP & Mgr-Trust Relation-ship)
Jessica Bryant (Asst VP & Mgr-Trust Rela-tionship)
Kevin Donovan (Sr VP)
Julio Quinteros (VP)

Financial Pacific Leasing, Inc.　(2)
3455 S 344th Way Ste 300, Federal Way,
WA 98001
Tel.: (253) 568-6000

Web Site: https://www.finpac.com
Sales Range: $25-49.9 Million
Emp.: 150
Equipment Leasing Finance Services
N.A.I.C.S.: 525990
Terey N. Jennings (Pres)
John M. Wright (Sr VP-Portfolio Svcs)
Jodi L. Wilshire (CFO & Exec VP)
Stephen E. Leege (Chief Credit Officer & Sr VP)
Thomas J. McSweeney Jr. (Sr VP-Information Technologies)

Intervest Mortgage Investment
Company　　　　　　　　　(2)
720 4th Ave Ste 120, Kirkland, WA
98033　　　　　　　　　(100%)
Tel.: (425) 828-1404
Web Site: http://www.intervestcref.com
Sales Range: $25-49.9 Million
Emp.: 55
Commercial Real Estate Lending Services
N.A.I.C.S.: 522310

COLUMBIA FINANCIAL, INC.

19-01 Rte 208 N, Fair Lawn, NJ
07410　　　　　　　　　　DE
Web Site:
　https://www.columbiabankon
　line.com
Year Founded: 1997
CLBK—(NASDAQ)
Rev.: $340,070,000
Assets: $10,408,169,000
Liabilities: $9,354,574,000
Net Worth: $1,053,595,000
Earnings: $86,173,000
Emp.: 748
Fiscal Year-end: 12/31/22
Offices of Bank Holding Companies
N.A.I.C.S.: 551111
Thomas J. Kemly (Pres & CEO)
Noel R. Holland (Chm)
Dennis E. Gibney (CFO & Exec VP)
Damodaram Bashyam (Chief Infor-mation & Digital Officer & Exec VP)
Geri M. Kelly (Officer-HR & Exec VP)
John Klimowich (Chief Risk Officer & Exec VP)
Mark S. Krukar (Chief Credit Officer & Exec VP)
Brian W. Murphy (Officer-Ops & Exec VP-Ops)
Allyson Schlesinger (Exec VP & Head-Consumer Banking)
Tony Rose (Mktg Dir)
Oliver E. Lewis Jr. (Exec VP & Head-Comml Banking)

Subsidiaries:

Columbia Bank　　　　　　(1)
19-01 Rte 208 N, Fair Lawn, NJ 07410
Tel.: (201) 794-5840
Web Site:
　https://www.columbiabankonline.com
Sales Range: $1-4.9 Billion
Emp.: 628
Federal Savings Bank
N.A.I.C.S.: 522180
Thomas J. Kemly (Pres & CEO)

First Jersey Title Services, Inc.　(1)
25-00 Broadway, Fair Lawn, NJ 07410
Tel.: (201) 791-4200
Web Site: https://firstjerseytitle.com
Insurance Services
N.A.I.C.S.: 524210
Douglas Cronk (CEO)

Stewardship Financial
Corporation　　　　　　　(1)
630 Godwin Ave, Midland Park, NJ 07432
Tel.: (201) 444-7100
Web Site: http://www.asbnow.com
Rev.: $39,416,000
Assets: $955,630,000
Liabilities: $875,480,000
Net Worth: $80,150,000
Earnings: $8,030,000
Emp.: 119
Fiscal Year-end: 12/31/2018
Bank Holding Company
N.A.I.C.S.: 551111

Web Site: https://www.finpac.com
Sales Range: $25-49.9 Million
Emp.: 150
Equipment Leasing Finance Services
N.A.I.C.S.: 525990
Terey N. Jennings (Pres)
John M. Wright (Sr VP-Portfolio Svcs)
Jodi L. Wilshire (CFO & Exec VP)
Stephen E. Leege (Chief Credit Officer & Sr VP)
Thomas J. McSweeney Jr. (Sr VP-Information Technologies)

Intervest Mortgage Investment
Company　　　　　　　　　(2)
720 4th Ave Ste 120, Kirkland, WA
98033　　　　　　　　　(100%)
Tel.: (425) 828-1404
Web Site: http://www.intervestcref.com
Sales Range: $25-49.9 Million
Emp.: 55
Commercial Real Estate Lending Services
N.A.I.C.S.: 522310

Subsidiary (Domestic):

Atlantic Stewardship Bank　(2)
630 Godwin Ave, Midland Park, NJ 07432
Tel.: (201) 444-7100
Web Site: http://www.asbnow.com
Sales Range: $25-49.9 Million
Provider of Banking Services
N.A.I.C.S.: 522110
Michael A. Westra (Chm)
William S. Clement (Chief Lending Officer & Sr VP)
Howard R. Yeaton Jr. (Vice Chm)

COLUMBIA SELIGMAN PRE-MIUM TECHNOLOGY GROWTH FUND, INC.

290 Congress St, Boston, MA 02210
Tel.: (612) 671-4321　　　　MD
Year Founded: 2009
STK—(NYSE)
Rev.: $3,493,464
Assets: $373,969,664
Liabilities: $1,906,871
Net Worth: $372,062,793
Earnings: ($258,437)
Fiscal Year-end: 12/31/19
Investment Management Service
N.A.I.C.S.: 525990
Shekhar Pramanick (Mgr-Fund)
Paul Wick (Portfolio Mgr)
Braj Agrawal (Portfolio Mgr)
Jeetil Patel (Portfolio Mgr)
Christopher Boova (Portfolio Mgr)
Vimal Patel (Portfolio Mgr)

COLUMBIA SPORTSWEAR COMPANY

14375 NW Science Park Dr, Port-land, OR 97229
Tel.: (503) 985-4000　　　　OR
Web Site: https://www.columbia.com
Year Founded: 1938
COLM—(NASDAQ)
Rev.: $3,487,203,000
Assets: $2,939,013,000
Liabilities: $1,000,403,000
Net Worth: $1,938,610,000
Earnings: $251,400,000
Emp.: 10,070
Fiscal Year-end: 12/31/23
Active Outdoor Apparel Mfr
N.A.I.C.S.: 424350
Lisa A. Kulok (Chief Supply Chain Officer & Exec VP)
Joseph P. Boyle (Pres-Columbia Brand & Exec VP)
Jim A. Swanson (CFO & Exec VP)
Peter Rauch (Sr VP-Direct-Asia)
Sarah Johnson (Mgr-Raw Materials Planning-Global)
Andrew Burns (VP-IR & Strategic Plng)
Timothy P. Boyle (Chm, Pres & CEO)
Craig Zanon (Sr VP-Emerging Brands)
Skip Potter (Chief Digital Information Officer)
Cory Long (Pres-SOREL Brand)
Richelle T. Luther (Chief HR Officer & Sr VP)

Subsidiaries:

Columbia Brands International
Sarl　　　　　　　　　　　(1)
Geneva Business Center Avenue des
Morgines 12, 1213, Petit-Lancy, Switzerland
Tel.: (41) 228709000
Emp.: 30
Apparel Mfr & Distr
N.A.I.C.S.: 315250

Columbia Brands USA, LLC　(1)
14375 NW Science Pk Dr, Portland, OR
97229
Tel.: (503) 985-4036
Emp.: 14

Apparel Mfr & Distr
N.A.I.C.S.: 315250
Mike Levi *(Dir-Sls-Europe)*

Columbia Sportswear Asia Pacific Sarl   **(1)**
Avenue des Morgines 12, 1213, Lancy, Switzerland
Tel.: (41) 228709000
Sporting Goods Mfr & Distr
N.A.I.C.S.: 339920

Columbia Sportswear Canada LP   **(1)**
1425 Max Brose Drive, London, N6N 0A2, ON, Canada
Tel.: (519) 245-4811
Web Site:
   https://www.columbiasportswear.ca
Active Outdoor Apparel Mfr
N.A.I.C.S.: 424350

Columbia Sportswear Commercial (Shanghai) Co., Ltd.   **(1)**
13/F Xuhuiyuan Building 1089 Zhongshan No 2 Road S, Shanghai, 200030, China   **(100%)**
Tel.: (86) 2161451900
Sporting Goods Distr
N.A.I.C.S.: 423910

Columbia Sportswear Denmark ApS   **(1)**
Holmensvej 5, 3600, Frederikssund, Denmark
Tel.: (45) 47310359
Web Site:
   https://www.columbiasportswear.dk
Active Outdoor Apparel Mfr
N.A.I.C.S.: 424350

Columbia Sportswear Finland OY   **(1)**
Keilaranta 11, 02150, Espoo, Finland
Tel.: (358) 974790265
Web Site: https://www.columbiasportswear.fi
Active Outdoor Apparel Mfr
N.A.I.C.S.: 424350

Columbia Sportswear France S.A.S.   **(1)**
5 Rue De La Haye, Schiltigheim, 67300, France
Tel.: (33) 390220800
Web Site: http://www.columbia.com
Sales Range: $50-74.9 Million
Emp.: 100
Active Outdoor Apparel Mfr
N.A.I.C.S.: 424350

Columbia Sportswear GmbH   **(1)**
Walter-Gropius-Str 23, 80807, Munich, Germany
Tel.: (49) 8924445777
Web Site:
   https://www.columbiasportswear.de
Active Outdoor Apparel Mfr
N.A.I.C.S.: 424350

Columbia Sportswear International Sarl   **(1)**
Avenue des Morgines 12 Geneva Business Center, 1213, Petit-Lancy, Switzerland
Tel.: (41) 22901815
Web Site: http://www.columbiasportswear.be
Sales Range: $25-49.9 Million
Emp.: 75
Active Outdoor Apparel Mfr
N.A.I.C.S.: 424350

Columbia Sportswear Korea   **(1)**
7-10th Floor of Daesung Tower 429 Cheonho-daero, Dongdaemun-gu Jangandong, Seoul, Korea (South)
Tel.: (82) 805400277
Web Site: https://www.columbiakorea.co.kr
Outerwear Product Distr
N.A.I.C.S.: 424350

Columbia Sportswear USA Corporation   **(1)**
3 Monroe Pkwy Ste H, Lake Oswego, OR 97035
Tel.: (503) 636-6593
Web Site: http://www.columbia.com
Active Outdoor Apparel Mfr
N.A.I.C.S.: 424350

Mountain Hardwear, Inc.   **(1)**
1414 Harbour Way S, Richmond, CA 94804

Tel.: (510) 558-3000
Web Site:
   https://www.mountainhardwear.com
Sales Range: $75-99.9 Million
Emp.: 101
Outdoor Gear, Apparel & Accessories Mfr & Distr
N.A.I.C.S.: 423910

OutDry Technologies S.r.l.   **(1)**
Via Del Bosco 41, 21052, Busto Arsizio, Italy
Tel.: (39) 0331677611
Web Site: http://www.outdry.com
Waterproof Clothing Items Mfr
N.A.I.C.S.: 313320
Luca Morlacchi *(CEO & Gen Mgr)*

Pacific Trail Corporation   **(1)**
14375 Nw Science Park Dr, Portland, OR 97229
Tel.: (503) 985-4012
Clothing Store Operator
N.A.I.C.S.: 458110

Pacific Trail Inc.   **(1)**
290 Pine St, Seattle, WA 98101
Tel.: (206) 443-7639
Web Site: http://www.pacifictrail.com
Sales Range: $10-24.9 Million
Emp.: 100
Outerwear Mfr
N.A.I.C.S.: 424350

Piccollo s.r.o.   **(1)**
Revnicka 170/4, Trebonice, 155 21, Prague, Czech Republic   **(100%)**
Tel.: (420) 226254897
Web Site: http://www.columbia.cz
Sales Range: $125-149.9 Million
Emp.: 80
Outdoor Apparel Distr
N.A.I.C.S.: 458110

Sorel Corporation   **(1)**
14375 NW Science Park Dr, Portland, OR 97229-5418
Tel.: (503) 978-2300
Web Site: https://www.sorel.com
Footwear Whslr
N.A.I.C.S.: 424340

prAna Living, LLC   **(1)**
3209 Lionshead Ave, Carlsbad, CA 92010-4710
Tel.: (760) 566-1070
Web Site: https://www.prana.com
Women's & Men's Outdoor Apparel & Accessories Designer, Whslr & Online Retailer
N.A.I.C.S.: 424350
Russ Hopcus *(Pres)*

COLUMBINE VALLEY RESOURCES, INC.
3223 Arapahoe Ave Ste 325, Boulder, CO 80303
Tel.: (303) 956-0226   NV
Web Site: http://www.t-rexoilinc.com
Year Founded: 2004
TRXO—(OTCIQ)
Sales Range: Less than $1 Million
Emp.: 8
Oil & Gas Production Services
N.A.I.C.S.: 211120
Donald L. Walford *(Chm, Pres & CEO)*
Calvin Smiley *(Dir-Business Development)*

COLUMBUS MCKINNON CORPORATION
205 Crosspoint Pkwy, Getzville, NY 14068
Tel.: (716) 689-5400   NY
Web Site: https://www.cmco.com
Year Founded: 1875
CMCO—(NASDAQ)
Rev.: $906,555,000
Assets: $1,685,707,000
Liabilities: $912,904,000
Net Worth: $772,803,000
Earnings: $29,660,000
Emp.: 3,224
Fiscal Year-end: 03/31/22

Construction Machinery Manufacturing
N.A.I.C.S.: 333120
Gerald G. Colella *(Chm)*
Gregory P. Rustowicz *(CFO & Exec VP-Fin)*
Mark Paradowski *(VP-Information Svcs)*
Bert A. Brant *(VP-Mfg Ops-Global)*
Mario Y. Ramos *(VP-Product Dev-Global)*
Appal Chintapalli *(VP-Engineered Products)*
Peter Stipan *(Dir-Automation Div-Global)*
Lynn Bostrom *(Dir-Mktg-Global)*
David J. Wilson *(Pres & CEO)*
Adrienne Williams *(Chief HR Officer & VP)*
Kristine Moser *(Treas & VP-IR)*

Subsidiaries:

CM Chain Division   **(1)**
560 Rush St, Lexington, TN 38351-2231   **(100%)**
Tel.: (731) 968-5271
Web Site: http://www.cmworks.com
Sales Range: $100-124.9 Million
Emp.: 267
Industrial Material Handling Equipment
N.A.I.C.S.: 332111

CM Hoist Division   **(1)**
22364 Jeb Stuart Hwy, Damascus, VA 24236-2504
Tel.: (276) 475-3124
Web Site: http://www.cmworks.com
Sales Range: $75-99.9 Million
Emp.: 200
Hand & Electric Powered Hoists
N.A.I.C.S.: 333923

CM Insurance Company, Inc.   **(1)**
140 John James Audubon Pkwy, Amherst, NY 14228
Tel.: (716) 689-5400
Sales Range: $50-74.9 Million
Emp.: 138
Insurance Brokerage Services
N.A.I.C.S.: 524210
Timothy T. Tevens *(CEO)*

CM Mechanical Handling Systems   **(1)**
140 John James Audubon Pkwy, Amherst, NY 14228-1197   **(100%)**
Tel.: (716) 689-5400
Web Site: http://www.cmworks.com
Sales Range: $50-74.9 Million
Emp.: 100
Industrial Material Handling Equipment
N.A.I.C.S.: 332111

Cady Lifters   **(1)**
140 John James Audubon Pkwy, Amherst, NY 14228
Tel.: (716) 689-5400
Web Site: http://www.cmworks.com
Sales Range: $10-24.9 Million
Emp.: 35
Industrial Material Handling Equipment
N.A.I.C.S.: 811210

Chester Hoist   **(1)**
205 Crosspoint Pkwy, Getzville, NY 14068
Tel.: (716) 424-7248
Web Site: https://www.cmco.com
Emp.: 56
Hoisting Equipment Mfr
N.A.I.C.S.: 333923
Alan Roscoe *(Engr-Application)*
David Rom *(Engr-Application)*
Robert Tracy *(Mgr-Application Engr)*

Columbus McKinnon (Shanghai) International Trading Co. Ltd.   **(1)**
Room 501 Building 6 No 289 Bisheng Road Zhang Jiang Hi-Tech Park, Pudong, Shanghai, 201204, China
Tel.: (86) 2138820620
Industrial Machinery & Equipment Mfr & Distr
N.A.I.C.S.: 333998

Subsidiary (Domestic):

Columbus McKinnon (Hangzhou) Industries Co. Ltd.   **(2)**

No 100 Luofeng Road, Xiaoshan District, Hangzhou, 310053, China
Tel.: (86) 57181025500
Material Handling Product Distr
N.A.I.C.S.: 423830

Columbus McKinnon Asia Pacific Pte. Ltd.   **(1)**
100D Pasir Panjang Road 05-02 Meissa, Singapore, 118520, Singapore
Tel.: (65) 65672166
Material Handling Product Distr
N.A.I.C.S.: 423830

Columbus McKinnon Austria GmbH   **(1)**
Wiener Str 132a, 2511, Pfaffstatten, Austria
Tel.: (43) 2252460660
Web Site: http://www.cmworks.com
Emp.: 40
Material Handling Products Mfr & Distr
N.A.I.C.S.: 423830

Subsidiary (Domestic):

Hebetechnik Gesellschaft GmbH   **(2)**
Wiener Strasse 132A, 2511, Pfaffstatten, Austria
Tel.: (43) 2252221330
Web Site: http://www.hebetechnik.at
Lifting Equipment Mfr
N.A.I.C.S.: 333998

Columbus McKinnon Industrial Products GmbH   **(1)**
Yale-Allee 30, 42329, Wuppertal, Germany
Tel.: (49) 202693590
Web Site: http://www.cmco.eu
Material Handling & Lifting Equipment Mfr & Distr
N.A.I.C.S.: 532490

Subsidiary (Non-US):

CMCO Material Handling (Pty), Ltd.   **(2)**
2 Imola Place, PO Box 15557, Westmead, Pinetown, 3608, Kwazulu-Natal, South Africa
Tel.: (27) 317004388
Web Site: http://www.cmcosa.co.za
Material Handling Equipment Mfr
N.A.I.C.S.: 333998

Columbus McKinnon Asia Pacific Ltd.   **(2)**
Room 501-502 Building 6 289 Bisheng Rd Zhang Jiang Hi-Tech Park, Pudong, Shanghai, 201204, China
Tel.: (86) 2138820620
Web Site: http://www.cmworks.com
Material Handling Equipment Mfr & Distr
N.A.I.C.S.: 423830

Subsidiary (Domestic):

Columbus McKinnon (Hangzhou) Industrial Products Co. Ltd.   **(3)**
No 100 Nuanhuan Road, Xinjiang, 311256, Zhejiang, China
Tel.: (86) 2138820620
Web Site: http://www.cmco-cn.com
Emp.: 200
Material Handling & Lifting Equipment Mfr & Distr
N.A.I.C.S.: 532490

Subsidiary (Non-US):

Columbus McKinnon Singapore Pte. Ltd.   **(3)**
100D Pasir Panjang Road, Singapore, 118520, Singapore
Tel.: (65) 62689228
Construction Machinery Distr
N.A.I.C.S.: 423810

Subsidiary (Non-US):

Columbus McKinnon Corporation Ltd.   **(2)**
Knutsford Way, Sealand Industrial Estate, Chester, CH1 4NZ, Cheshire, United Kingdom
Tel.: (44) 1244375375
Web Site: https://www.cmco.com
Emp.: 50
Material Handling & Lifting Equipment Mfr & Distr
N.A.I.C.S.: 423830

Columbus McKinnon Corporation—(Continued)

Columbus McKinnon Hungary
Kft. (2)
Vasarhelyi Ut 5, 8000, Szekesfehervar,
Hungary
Tel.: (36) 22880540
Web Site: https://www.cmco.hu
Material Handling Products Mfr & Distr
N.A.I.C.S.: 532490

Columbus McKinnon Iberica
S.L.U. (2)
Ctra de la Esclusa 21 Acc A, 41011, Seville,
Spain
Tel.: (34) 954298940
Web Site: https://www.cmiberica.com
Emp.: 100
Material Handling Equipment Mfr & Distr
N.A.I.C.S.: 423830

Columbus McKinnon Industrial Prod-
ucts ME FZE (2)
Warehouse No FZSBD01 Dubai, PO Box
261013, Jebel Ali, United Arab Emirates
Tel.: (971) 48049600
Web Site: http://www.cmco.com
Material Handling & Lifting Equipment Mfr &
Distr
N.A.I.C.S.: 532490

Columbus McKinnon Italia S.r.l. (2)
Via 11 Settembre 26, 20023, Cerro Mag-
giore, MI, Italy
Tel.: (39) 0331576329
Web Site: https://www.cmco-italia.it
Material Handling Equipment Mfr & Distr
N.A.I.C.S.: 423830

Columbus McKinnon Russia LLC (2)
Marshal Govorov st 35 bldg 4 Business
center Propaganda of 413-416, Saint Pe-
tersburg, 198095, Russia
Tel.: (7) 8123226838
Web Site: https://www.cmco.ru
Emp.: 8
Industrial Machinery Mfr & Distr
N.A.I.C.S.: 423830

Yale Industrial Products Asia Co.
Ltd. (2)
54 Bb Building Room 1510 15th Floor
Sukhumvit 21 Asoke Road, Klongtoey Nua
Wattana Wattana, Bangkok, 10110, Thai-
land
Tel.: (66) 26640300
Web Site: http://www.yale-thailand.com
Emp.: 2
Material Handling & Lifting Equipment Mfr &
Distr
N.A.I.C.S.: 423830
Joshua Loh *(Mng Dir)*

Columbus McKinnon Ireland,
Ltd. (1)
Unit 4 South Court Wexford Road Business
Park, Carlow, Ireland
Tel.: (353) 599186605
Web Site: http://www.columbusmckinnon.ie
Material Handling Product Distr
N.A.I.C.S.: 423830

Columbus McKinnon do Brazil
Ltda. (1)
Estrada Da Fazendinha 1 169 Jd, Ana Es-
tela, Carapicuiba, 06351-040, Sao Paulo,
Brazil
Tel.: (55) 1146134900
Web Site: http://www.cmdobrasil.com.br
Sales Range: $50-74.9 Million
Emp.: 30
Material Handling Products Mfr & Distr
N.A.I.C.S.: 532490

Duff-Norton (1)
9415 Pioneer Ave, Charlotte, NC
28273-6318 (100%)
Tel.: (704) 588-4610
Web Site: https://www.cmco.com
Sales Range: $100-124.9 Million
Emp.: 150
Mfr of Lifting Jacks, Mechanical Actuators,
Electromechanical Linear Actuators & Rotat-
ing Joints
N.A.I.C.S.: 333998

Garvey Corporation (1)
208 S Rte 73, Blue Anchor, NJ 08037
Tel.: (609) 561-2450

Web Site: https://www.garvey.com
Rev.: $10,000,000
Emp.: 90
Conveyors & Conveying Equipment Mfr
N.A.I.C.S.: 333922
Jake Garvey *(Sls Dir-OEM)*

Lico Steel, Inc. (1)
9222 E47th St, Kansas City, MO
64133 (100%)
Tel.: (816) 356-8990
Web Site: http://www.licosteel.com
Steel Erection Services
N.A.I.C.S.: 238120

Magnetek Canada ULC (1)
161 Orenda Road Unit 1, Brampton, L6W
1W3, ON, Canada
Tel.: (905) 828-1526
Material Handling Product Distr
N.A.I.C.S.: 423830

Magnetek, Inc. (1)
N49W13650 Campbell Dr, Menomonee
Falls, WI 53051
Tel.: (262) 783-3500
Web Site: https://www.cmco.com
Sales Range: $100-124.9 Million
Emp.: 350
Digital Electronic Power & Motion Control
Products Mfr
N.A.I.C.S.: 334519

Division (Non-US):

Magnetek (UK) Ltd. (2)
Unit 3 Bedford Business Centre Mile Road,
Bedford, MK42 9TW, United Kingdom
Tel.: (44) 1234349191
Web Site: http://www.elevatordrives.com
Sales Range: $100-124.9 Million
DC Elevator Drive Mfr
N.A.I.C.S.: 335312

Division (Domestic):

Magnetek Elevators (2)
N50 W13775 Overview Dr, Menomonee
Falls, WI 53051
Tel.: (262) 252-6999
Web Site: http://www.magnetekmh.com
Emp.: 350
DC Elevator Drive Mfr
N.A.I.C.S.: 335312

Magnetek Material Handling (2)
N49 W13650 Campbell Dr, Menomonee
Falls, WI 53051
Tel.: (262) 783-3500
Web Site: http://www.magnetekmh.com
Emp.: 350
Power Control, Delivery Systems & Solu-
tions Services
N.A.I.C.S.: 221118

Magnetek Mining (2)
N50 W13775 Overview Dr, Menomonee
Falls, WI 53051
Tel.: (262) 783-3500
Web Site: http://www.magnetekmining.com
Industrial Power Controller Designer & Mfr
N.A.I.C.S.: 334519

Pfaff Beteiligungs GmbH (1)
Am Silberpark 2-8, Friedberg, 86438, Ger-
many
Tel.: (49) 82178010
Web Site: http://www.pfaff-silberblau.com
Emp.: 180
Material Handling Products Mfr & Distr
N.A.I.C.S.: 532490

Subsidiary (Domestic):

Columbus McKinnon Engineered
Products GmbH (2)
Am Silberpark 2-8, 86438, Kissing, Ger-
many
Tel.: (49) 823321210
Web Site: http://www.pfaff-silberblau.com
Emp.: 200
Material Handling & Lifting Equipment Mfr
N.A.I.C.S.: 333998
Ulrich Hintermeier *(Mng Dir)*
Alan Scott Korman *(Mng Dir)*

Subsidiary (Non-US):

Columbus McKinnon Switzerland
AG (3)
Dallikerstrasse 25, PO Box 29, 8107, Bu-

chs, Switzerland
Tel.: (41) 448515577
Web Site: http://www.cmco.ch
Sales Range: $25-49.9 Million
Emp.: 6
Material Handling Equipment Distr
N.A.I.C.S.: 423830

Pfaff-silberblau Hebezeugfabrik
GmbH (1)
Am Silberpark 2 8, 86438, Kissing, Ger-
many
Tel.: (49) 823321210
Web Site: http://www.pfaff-silberblau.com
Sales Range: $25-49.9 Million
Emp.: 200
Industrial Component Mfr
N.A.I.C.S.: 333248

STAHL CraneSystems GmbH (1)
Daimlerstr 6, 74653, Kunzelsau, Germany
Tel.: (49) 79401280
Web Site: http://www.stahlcranes.com
Crane Hoisting Technologies & Systems
Designer & Mfr
N.A.I.C.S.: 333923
Werner Wagner *(Mng Dir)*
Natalie Muller *(Mgr-Personnel)*

Subsidiary (Non-US):

STAHL CraneSystems (India) Pvt.
Ltd. (2)
No 8 50th Street 7th Avenue, Chennai, 600
083, Tamil Nadu, India
Tel.: (91) 4443523955
Web Site: http://www.stahlcranes.com
Industrial Crane Component Mfr
N.A.I.C.S.: 333923

Subsidiary (US):

STAHL CraneSystems Inc. (2)
2284 Clements Ferry Rd Ste E, Charleston,
SC 29492-7729
Tel.: (843) 767-1951
Web Site: http://www.stahlcranes.com
Crane Component Distr
N.A.I.C.S.: 423830

Subsidiary (Non-US):

STAHL Cranesystems Shanghai Co.
Ltd. (2)
Room 901 No 399, Putuo District, Shang-
hai, 200333, China
Tel.: (86) 2166083737
Crane Component Distr
N.A.I.C.S.: 423810

Stahl CraneSystems FZE (2)
Warehouse No RA08 / SC08 Jebel Ali Free
Zone, PO Box 261271, Dubai, United Arab
Emirates
Tel.: (971) 48053700
Web Site: http://www.stahlcranes.com
Sales Range: $25-49.9 Million
Emp.: 23
Crane Component Distr
N.A.I.C.S.: 423830

Stahl CraneSystems Ltd. (2)
Unit 2 Forge Mills Park, Coleshill, B46 1JH,
Warwickshire, United Kingdom
Tel.: (44) 1675437280
Web Site: http://www.stahlcranes.com
Emp.: 700
Crane Component Distr
N.A.I.C.S.: 423830

Stahl CraneSystems S.A.S. (2)
5 rue Jean-Pierre Timbaud, PO Box 50236,
95106, Argenteuil, France
Tel.: (33) 1 3998 5060
Web Site: http://www.stahlcranes.com
Material Handling Component Distr
N.A.I.C.S.: 423830
Thomas Bouvet *(Gen Dir)*

Stahl CraneSystems S.L. (2)
Avda de la Industria 53 Nave 11, 28108,
Alcobendas, Spain
Tel.: (34) 91 484 08 65
Web Site: http://www.stahlcranes.com
Crane Component Distr
N.A.I.C.S.: 423830

Stahl CraneSystems Trading (Shang-
hai) Co. Ltd. (2)
Room 901 No 399 North Nu Jiang Road,

Putuo District, Shanghai, 200331, China
Tel.: (86) 21 66083737
Web Site: http://www.stahlcranes.com.cn
Overhead Crane Mfr
N.A.I.C.S.: 333923

Stahlhammer Bommern GmbH (1)
Carl-Zeiss-Str 7, 59077, Hamm, Germany
Tel.: (49) 2381914980
Web Site: https://www.stahlhammer.de
Steel Forging Mfr
N.A.I.C.S.: 331110

Unified Industries, Inc. (1)
740 Advance St, Brighton, MI 48116
Tel.: (517) 546-3220
Web Site: https://www.cmco.com
Sales Range: $10-24.9 Million
Emp.: 36
Crane & Lifting System Mfr
N.A.I.C.S.: 333923

Yale Engineering Products (Pty.)
Ltd. (1)
12 Laser Park Square 34 Zeiss Road Rand-
burg, Honeydew, 2170, South Africa
Tel.: (27) 117942910
Web Site: http://www.yalejhb.co.za
Sales Range: $25-49.9 Million
Emp.: 20
Railway Equipment Mfr & Dist
N.A.I.C.S.: 423830
Kevin Hoy *(Mng Dir)*

Yale Lifting & Mining Products (Pty.)
Ltd. (1)
No 7 Rustenburg Road, PO Box 592, 1791,
Magaliesburg, Gauteng, South Africa
Tel.: (27) 145772607
Web Site: http://www.yale.co.za
Sales Range: $50-74.9 Million
Emp.: 42
Material Handling & Lifting Equipment Mfr &
Distr
N.A.I.C.S.: 532490

Yale Lifting Solutions (Pty.) Ltd. (1)
PO Box 592, Magaliesburg, 1791, Gauteng,
South Africa
Tel.: (27) 145772607
Web Site: https://www.yale.co.za
Emp.: 70
Material Handling Machinery Mfr & Distr
N.A.I.C.S.: 423830

COM-GUARD.COM, INC.
1106 2nd St Ste 201, Encinitas, CA
92024
Tel.: (858) 381-7800　　　　　NV
Web Site: https://www.com-
guard.com
Year Founded: 1008
CGUD—(OTCIQ)
Software Development Services
N.A.I.C.S.: 541511

COMCAST CORPORATION
1701 JFK Blvd, Philadelphia, PA
19103
Tel.: (215) 286-1700　　　　　PA
Web Site:
https://corporate.comcast.com
Year Founded: 1963
CMCSA—(NASDAQ)
Rev.: $121,572,000,000
Assets: $264,811,000,000
Liabilities: $181,585,000,000
Net Worth: $83,226,000,000
Earnings: $15,388,000,000
Emp.: 186,000
Fiscal Year-end: 12/31/23
Cable Television, Internet & Digital
Phone Services
N.A.I.C.S.: 516210
Sean Gamble *(Executives)*
Michael J. Cavanagh *(Pres)*
Brian L. Roberts *(Chm & CEO)*
Greg R. Butz *(Pres-Connectivity Svcs
& Consumer Experience-Comcast
Cable)*
Kristine Dankenbrink *(Exec VP-Tax)*
Lynn R. Charytan *(Exec VP)*
Anand Kini *(Exec VP-Corp Strategy)*

Daniel C. Murdock (Chief Acctg Officer, Exec VP & Controller)
Dalila Wilson-Scott (Chief Diversity Officer & Exec VP)
Lisa Bonnell (Exec VP-Audit-Global)
Robert L. Eatroff (Exec VP-Strategy & Global Corp Dev)
Jennifer Khoury Newcomb (Chief Comm Officer & Exec VP)
David A. Scott (Chm/CEO-Comcast Spectator)
Rocky Gupta (Treas & Exec VP)
Thomas J. Reid (Chief Legal Officer & Sec)
Kristen Gohr (Exec Dir-Corp Comm-Experience, Multicultural & Privacy-Xfinity)
Karen Dougherty Buchholz (Exec VP-Admin)
Kimberley D. Harris (Exec VP)
Carolyne Hannan (Sr VP-New England West)
Christine Whitaker (Pres-Central Div)
Marci Ryvicker (Exec VP-IR)
Sophia Marshall (Sr VP-Comm-Central Div)
Quiana Pinckney (VP-Employee Comm-Central Div)
Jason S. Armstrong (CFO)
Mitch Rose (Exec VP-Federal Govt Affairs)
Mark Woodbury (Chm & CEO)
Daniel J. Hilferty (Chm & CEO-Comcast Spectacor)
Dana Strong (Grp CEO-Sky)
JD Buckley (CEO-Ireland)
Cecile Frot-Coutaz (CEO-Sky Studios & Officer)
Barny Mills (CEO-Sky-Deutschland)
Sena Fitzmaurice (Sr VP-Corp Comm)
Sena Fitzmaurice (Sr VP-Corp Comm)

Subsidiaries:

Active Voices Limited (1)
Peter House Oxford St, Manchester, M1 5AN, United Kingdom
Tel.: (44) 3336667366
Web Site: https://activevoice.uk
Software Development Services
N.A.I.C.S.: 541511

Albatros Datenservice GmbH (1)
Werftstrasse 12/Hafenkontor, 76189, Karlsruhe, Germany
Tel.: (49) 7211834944
Web Site: https://www.albatros.net
Software Development Services
N.A.I.C.S.: 541511

Blast ! Films Limited (1)
Unit 100 Highgate Studios 53-79 Highgate Road, London, NW5 1TL, United Kingdom
Tel.: (44) 2038416000
Web Site: https://www.blastfilms.co.uk
Film Production Services
N.A.I.C.S.: 512110

Blueface Italia S.r.l. (1)
Via Marsala n 29 H/I, 00815, Rome, Italy
Tel.: (39) 0662277630
Software Development Services
N.A.I.C.S.: 541511

Blueface Ltd. (1)
10/11 Exchange Place IFSC, Dublin, Ireland
Tel.: (353) 1 524 2000
Web Site: http://www.blueface.com
Web-Based Telecommunication Services
N.A.I.C.S.: 517810
Feargal Brady (Co-Founder)
Alan Foy (CEO)
Nameer Kazzaz (CTO)
Brian Martin (Sr VP)
Amy Coghlan (VP)
Colleen Gallagher (Head-Project Mgmt)
Luca Caralvi (Dir-Wholesale)

Subsidiary (US):

Star2Star Communications, LLC (2)

301 N Cattlemen Rd Ste 300, Sarasota, FL 34232
Tel.: (256) 428-6000
Web Site: https://www.sangoma.com
Telephone System & Integrated Communications Products Mfr
N.A.I.C.S.: 334210
Norman Worthington (Founder, Chm & CEO)
Graham D. Potter (Chief Knowledge Officer)
Bruce Illes (Chief Legal Officer)
William M. Rogers (Officer-Govt Contract)
Sergey Galchenko (CTO)
Bobby Mohanty (Chief Product Officer)
David Portnowitz (CMO)

Canoe Ventures LLC (1)
200 Union Blvd Ste 590, Lakewood, CO 80228
Tel.: (212) 364-3600
Web Site: https://www.canoeventures.com
Television Advertising Services
N.A.I.C.S.: 541890
Tom Huber (COO)
Joel Hassell (CEO)
Chris Pizzurro (Sr VP-Sls & Mktg-Global)
Ed Knudson (Chief Revenue Officer)
Sid Gregory (CTO)
David Porter (Sr VP & Gen Mgr-Addressable)

Carnival Film & Television Limited (1)
6 Agar Street, London, WC2N 4HN, United Kingdom
Tel.: (44) 2036186600
Web Site: https://www.carnivalfilms.co.uk
Television Program & Film Production Services
N.A.I.C.S.: 512110

Comcast Cable Communications, LLC (1)
1500 Market St, Philadelphia, PA 19102-2100 (100%)
Tel.: (856) 638-4000
Web Site: http://www.comcast.com
Sales Range: $15-24.9 Billion
Emp.: 59,000
Developer, Manager & Operator of Broadband Communications Networks
N.A.I.C.S.: 516210
Steven Andrew White (Pres)
David N. Watson (CEO)
Marcien Jenckes (Mng Dir-Comcast Adv)
William J. T. Strahan (Exec VP-HR)
Noopur Davis (Chief Product & Information Security Officer & Exec VP)
Kathy Kelly-Brown (Sr VP-Strategic Initiatives)
Dana Strong (Pres-Consumer Svcs)
James Rooke (Pres-Comcast Adv)

Division (Domestic):

Comcast Spotlight (2)
5 Times Sq 9th Fl, New York, NY 10036
Tel.: (917) 934-1936
Web Site: http://www.comcastspotlight.com
Sales Range: $10-24.9 Million
Emp.: 70
Advertising Sales
N.A.I.C.S.: 541890
Chris Ellis (Sr Dir-Comm)
Michael Ruggiere (Dir-Sls-Indiana)
Marina McQueary (Dir-Res & Promos)
Jeanine Socha (Dir-Res)
Kevin Patrick Smith (VP-Adv Sls Dev)
Steve Feingold (Sr VP-Ops & Strategic Plng)
Mark Altschuler (VP-Natl Adv Sls)
Bill Haase (VP-Fin & Admin)
Lucette Mercer (Sr Dir-Res & Mktg-West Div)
Adam LaRose (VP-Tech & Ops)
Mark Ebetino (VP-Ops SE Div)
Tom Straszewski (VP-Interactive Sls)
Kellie Grutko (VP-Mktg)
Sherry Avara (Mgr-Local Sls-Fort Wayne)
Dana Runnells (Sr Dir-Comm)
Charlie Thurston (Pres)
Hank Oster (Sr VP & Gen Mgr)
John Tierney (VP-Reg-Natl Sls)
Dan Sinagoga (VP-Political Adv Sls)
Teresa Lucido (Sr VP-Sls Excellence)
Justin Evans (VP-Data Strategy)
Maria Weaver (Sr VP-Mktg)
Hank Oster (COO & Sr VP)
Brendan Condon (Chief Revenue Officer)

Megan Latham (VP-Customer Experience)
Dawn Lee Williamson (VP-Southeast)
Kathy DeAmicis (CFO & VP-Fin)
Travis Parrill (Sr VP-Tech & Ops)
Rick Stanley (Sr VP-Sls Strategy)
John Tierney (Sr VP-Sls-Natl)
Michael Miller (VP-Video Strategy)
Melanie Hamilton (VP-Natl Sls)
Kelly Perone (VP-Product Strategy)
Andrea Zapata (VP-Data Innovation & Insights)

Joint Venture (Domestic):

Music Choice (2)
650 Dresher Rd, Horsham, PA 19044
Tel.: (215) 784-5840
Web Site: http://www.musicchoice.com
Emp.: 60
Music Video Cable Television Programming, Online & Mobile Publishing Services
N.A.I.C.S.: 516210
David Del Beccaro (Co-Founder,Co-Pres & CEO)
Christina Tancredi (Co-Pres & COO)
Jeremy Rosenberg (Co-Founder)

Comcast Cablevision Investment Corporation (1)
1701 JFK Blvd, Philadelphia, PA 19103
Tel.: (215) 665-1700
Sales Range: $700-749.9 Million
Emp.: 4,000
Investment Company
N.A.I.C.S.: 516210

Comcast Corp. (1)
6850 S Tucson Way, Englewood, CO 80112
Tel.: (303) 930-2000
Sales Range: $125-149.9 Million
Emp.: 500
Cable TV Systems
N.A.I.C.S.: 516210
Steve Lang (Sr VP-Commun)
William Schineder (CEO)
Lynn Folkersen (Dir-Enterprise Sls)
Jennifer Price (Dir-Govt Affiars-West)

Comcast Corp. (1)
1255 W N Ave, Chicago, IL 60622
Tel.: (847) 585-6595
Sales Range: $75-99.9 Million
Emp.: 250
Broadband Services
N.A.I.C.S.: 517121
Reji Tharakan (VP-Engrg-Greater Chicago)
Julie Maleski (VP-HR)

Comcast Corp. (1)
650 Centerton Rd, Moorestown, NJ 08057
Tel.: (856) 638-4000
Web Site: http://www.comcast.com
Sales Range: $125-149.9 Million
Emp.: 500
Telephone Communication, Except Radio
N.A.I.C.S.: 516210

Division (Domestic):

CN8, The Comcast Network (2)
650 Centerton Rd, Moorestown, NJ 08057
Tel.: (856) 206-0651
Web Site: http://www.cn8.tv
Cable Networks
N.A.I.C.S.: 516210

Comcast Corp. (1)
3500 Patterson Ave Southeast, Grand Rapids, MI 49512-5699
Tel.: (616) 977-7200
Web Site: http://www.comcast.com
Sales Range: $50-74.9 Million
Emp.: 180
Provider of Cable Television Services
N.A.I.C.S.: 516210
Rick Collman (Opers Mgr)

Comcast Corp. (1)
1111 Andersen Dr, San Rafael, CA 94901-5336
Tel.: (415) 459-5333
Web Site: http://www.comcast.com
Sales Range: $25-49.9 Million
Emp.: 150
Cable Television Services
N.A.I.C.S.: 516210

Comcast Corp. (1)
900 132nd St SW, Everett, WA 98204 (100%)

Tel.: (334) 585-9643
Sales Range: $125-149.9 Million
Emp.: 500
Cable Television Services
N.A.I.C.S.: 516210
John Diretrich (Gen Mgr)
Leonard Rozak (Sr VP)
Matthew Fassnacht (VP-Bus)
Rick Comeau (Asst Gen Mgr & Dir-Ops-Comcast Arena)

Comcast Enterprise Services, LLC (1)
4400 Port Union Rd, West Chester, OH 45011
Tel.: (513) 860-2573
Web Site: http://www.contingent.com
Information Techonolgy Services
N.A.I.C.S.: 541513
Glenn Katz (VP & Gen Mgr)

Comcast Interactive Capital, L.P. (1)
1701 JFK Blvd, Philadelphia, PA 19103-2196
Tel.: (215) 981-8450
Web Site: http://www.civentures.com
Sales Range: $1-9.9 Million
Emp.: 5,000
Venture Capital Fund; Internet & Other Interactive Technology Companies Investor
N.A.I.C.S.: 516210

Comcast MO of Delaware, LLC (1)
1500 Market St, Philadelphia, PA 19103-2148
Tel.: (215) 665-1700
Cable & Progeramming Services
N.A.I.C.S.: 516210

Comcast Phone of Colorado, LLC (1)
183 Inverness Dr W, Englewood, CO 80112
Tel.: (720) 267-4406
Telecommunication Servicesb
N.A.I.C.S.: 517810

Comcast Phone of D.C., LLC (1)
335 Raleigh St SE, Washington, DC 20032
Tel.: (202) 621-9972
Wireless Telecommunication Services
N.A.I.C.S.: 517111

Comcast Spectacor, L.P. (1)
3601 S Broad St, Philadelphia, PA 19148
Tel.: (215) 336-3600
Web Site: http://www.comcastspectacor.com
Sales Range: $1-4.9 Billion
Sports & Entertainment Holding Company
N.A.I.C.S.: 551112
David A. Scott (Chm & CEO)
Phil Weinberg (Gen Counsel & Exec VP-Admin)
Peter Ranere (Mgr-Corp Comm)
Betsy McGill (Sr VP & Deputy Gen Counsel)
Laurie Kleinman (VP-Risk Mgmt)

Subsidiary (Domestic):

Comcast-Spectacor Foundation (2)
Wells Fargo Ctr 3601 S Broad St, Philadelphia, PA 19148
Tel.: (215) 389-9426
Web Site: http://www.comcastspectacorfoundation.org
Emp.: 4
Charitable Foundation
N.A.I.C.S.: 813219
Mary Ann Saleski (Sr VP)
Russ Chandler (CFO & Exec VP-Fin)
Fred Shabel (Vice Chm)
Shawn Tilger (Sr VP-Philadelphia Flyers)
Phil Weinberg (Exec VP)
Lisa Cataldo (Mgr-Fin)

Paciolan, Inc. (2)
5291 California Ave Ste 100, Irvine, CA 92617
Web Site: http://www.paciolan.com
Collegiate Athletic Ticketing, Marketing & Fundraising Solutions
N.A.I.C.S.: 513210
Craig Ricks (CMO)
Jane Kleinberger (Founder)
Kim Damron (Pres & CEO)
Christian Lewis (Sr VP-Bus Dev)
Kim Boren (CFO)
Keith White (Chief Product & Tech Officer)
Deana Barnes (Sr VP-Client Engagement)

Comcast Corporation—(Continued)

Philadelphia Flyers, LLC (2)
3601 S Broad St, Philadelphia, PA 19148
Tel.: (215) 952-5763
Web Site: http://flyers.nhl.com
Holding Company; Professional Hockey
Teams Operator
N.A.I.C.S.: 551112

Subsidiary (Domestic):

Philadelphia Flyers, L.P. (3)
3601 S Broad St, Philadelphia, PA 19148
Tel.: (215) 465-4500
Web Site: http://flyers.nhl.com
Sales Range: $10-24.9 Million
Emp.: 500
Professional Hockey Team
N.A.I.C.S.: 711211
Cindy Stutman (Sr VP-Bus Ops)
Rob Baer (Mgr-Youth & Amateur Hockey)
Dave Brown (Head-Pro Scout)
Bryan Hardenbergh (Sr Dir-Team Svcs)
Zack Hill (Sr Dir-Comm)
Anthony Gioia (Sr Dir-Game Presentation)
Angelo Cardone (Sr VP-Fin Plng & Strategy)
Chuck Fletcher (Pres-Hockey Ops & Gen Mgr)
Valerie Camillo (Pres-Bus Ops)
Brent Flahr (VP & Asst Gen Mgr)
Ian Anderson (Dir-Hockey Analytics)
Jim McCrossin (Dir-Medical Svcs)
Harry Bricker (Mgr-Equipment)
Anthony Oratorio (Asst Mgr-Equipment)
Mike Craytor (Asst Mgr-Equipment)
Joe Siville (Dir-Player Rels)
Brian Smith (Mgr-Brdcst & Media)
Jason Tempesta (Dir-Community Rels)
Christopher DelleMonache (Coord-Creative Content)
Courtney Fedena (Dir-Fan Experience)
Sarah Bosnjak (Dir-Special Events)
Julian Franklin (Acct Mgr-Memberships)
Ryan Gillies (Dir-FP&A)
Maxwell Farrara (Mgr-Video Production)
Brad Marsh (Dir-Community Dev)
Sarah Schwab (Sr Dir-Comm)
Lauren McNally (VP-HR)
Cynthia Punsalan (VP-Bus Admin)
Mike Schwartz (Sr VP-Corp Partnerships)
Mike Shane (Chief Bus Officer)
Blair Listino (CFO)
Phil Weinberg (Gen Counsel & Exec VP-Admin)
Phil Laws (Sr VP & Gen Mgr-Wells Fargo Center)
Sean Coit (VP-Comm)
Sam Ebb (VP-Bus Strategy & Analytics)
James Darlington (Dir-Ticket Market Strategy)
Joanna Levy (Dir-Strategy & Analytics)
Brendan Stone (Mgr-Bus Strategy & Analytics)
Patrick Dornan (Mgr-Data Engrg)
Dakota Marshall (Coord-CRM)
Meghan Flanagan (Dir-Comm)
Lauren Capone (Comm Mgr)
Shannon Rostick (Comm Mgr)
Steve Coskey (Dir-Partnership Activation)
Davey Chadwick (Dir-Partnership Analytics & Strategy)
Stephanie Jacobson (Dir-Partnership Sls)
Taylor Kennedy (Mgr-Partnership Activation)
Yvonne Stephenson (Dir-Partnership Activation)
Juliana Carfagno (Mgr-Partnership Activation)
Jason Williams (Coord-Fan Experience)
Susan Calabrese (Sr Mgr-Acctg)
Mike Plunkett (Mgr-Acctg)
Megan Gallagher (Accountant-Staff)
Candy McKnight (Accountant-Staff)
Jessica Vagnoni (Accountant-Sys)
Jamie Rossi (Coord-Acctg)

Subsidiary (Domestic):

Flyers Skate Zone, L.P. (4)
3601 S Broad St, Philadelphia, PA 19148
Tel.: (215) 952-5217
Web Site:
https://www.flyerstrainingcenter.com
Emp.: 40
Fitness & Recreational Sports Centers
N.A.I.C.S.: 713940
Nancy LaBarre (Office Mgr-Atlantic City)
Brian Lusardi (Mgr-Voorhees Store)

Jamie Oswald (Gen Mgr-Pennsauken)
Pat Mudge (Dir-Figure Skating-Pennsauken)
Jay Freeman (Gen Mgr-Voorhees)
Jeremy Hall (Dir-Hockey Dev)
Bob Sweet (Sr Mgr-Ops)
Tom Evans (Mgr-Gear Zone-Voorhees)
Pam Dreyer (Dir-Learn To Skate-Voorhees)
Scott Martinez (Dir-Gear Zone Retail)
Mary Kate Snyder (Coord-Sls)

Phantoms Hockey, LLC (4)
701 Hamilton St, Allentown, PA 18101
Tel.: (610) 224-4625
Web Site: http://www.phantomshockey.com
Professional Hockey Team
N.A.I.C.S.: 711211
Jim Brooks (Co-Owner & Governor)
Rob Brooks (Co-Owner & Governor)
Chris Porreca (Exec VP)
Richard Lintker (VP-Ticket Sls)
Dennis Begley (VP-Partnerships & Premium Seating)
Mike Musialowski (Mgr-Retention)
Tommy DeCore (Mgr-Premium Seating)
Bev Saunders (Mgr-Mdse)
Bill Downey (Mgr-Hockey Ops)
Michael Ianniello (Mgr-Community Engagement & PR)
Nicolet Danese (Mgr-Client Svcs)
Jennifer Keeble (Exec Dir-Phantoms Charities)
George Kerth (Editor-Video)
Alex Schempp (Editor)
Patrick Keppel (Editor)
Trevor Herrick (Dir-Ticket Sls)
Nicole Repetto (Dir-Premium Seating)
Kevin Heilman (Dir-Partnerships)
Shawn Hackman (Dir-Partnerships)
Katie Nork (Dir-Mktg)
Eric Fuzer (Dir-Fun)
Russ Hryvnak (Dir-Digital & Social Media)
Amy Keller (Dir-Creative)
Heather Holston (Coord-Ticket)
Michelle DeLong (Coord-Creative)
Tyler Deane (Controller)
Nolan Bowker (Asst Mgr-Equipment)
Philip Saveri (Accountant-Staff)

Joint Venture (Domestic):

Spectra Venue Management (2)
3601 S Broad St, Philadelphia, PA 19148
Tel.: (215) 389-9477
Web Site:
http://www.spectraexperiences.com
Commercial Facilities Maintenance Services
N.A.I.C.S.: 561210

Comcast Venture LLC (1)
1 Comcast Ctr 55F 1701 John F Kennedy
Blvd, Philadelphia, PA 19103
Tel.: (215) 286-8450
Web Site: http://www.comcastventures.com
Advertising Services Provider
N.A.I.C.S.: 541810
Kim Armor (Mng Dir & CFO)
Chandler Cribe (Accountant)
Chris King (Deputy Gen Counsel)
Kyle Peters (Dir-Fin)
Derek Squire (Gen Counsel)
Madura Wijewardena (Head-Bus Dev)

Comcast of Arizona, Inc. (1)
8251 N Cortaro Rd, Tucson, AZ 85743
Tel.: (520) 744-5474
Cable Television & Internet Services
N.A.I.C.S.: 516210
Allen Price (Gen Mgr)

Comcast of Colorado/Pennsylvania/West Virginia, LLC (1)
221 W Philadelphia St, York, PA 17401
Tel.: (215) 286-3345
Emp.: 99
Cable & Programming Services
N.A.I.C.S.: 516210

Comcast of Delmarva, Inc. (1)
5729 W Dennys Rd, Dover, DE 19904
Tel.: (301) 531-9383
Web Site: http://www.comcast.com
Sales Range: $25-49.9 Million
Emp.: 100
Cable Television & Internet Services
N.A.I.C.S.: 516210

Comcast of Garden State, L.P. (1)
1250 Berlin Rd, Cherry Hill, NJ 08034

Tel.: (856) 821-6100
Emp.: 30
Cable & Programming Services
N.A.I.C.S.: 516210

Comcast of Harford County, LLC (1)
30 N Parke St, Aberdeen, MD 21001
Tel.: (215) 286-3345
Emp.: 300
Cable & Programming Services
N.A.I.C.S.: 516210

Comcast of Illinois/Indiana/Ohio, LLC (1)
8101 183rd St, Tinley Park, IL 60487-6295
Tel.: (708) 444-8661
Sales Range: $1-4.9 Billion
Emp.: 7,000
Cable Television & Internet Services
N.A.I.C.S.: 516210

Comcast of Maine/New Hampshire, Inc. (1)
676 Island Pond Rd, Manchester, NH 03109
Tel.: (215) 851-3345
Cable & Programming Services
N.A.I.C.S.: 516210

Comcast of Potomac, LLC (1)
11800 Tech Rd 200, Silver Spring, MD 20904
Tel.: (301) 273-3418
Emp.: 99
Cable & Programming Services
N.A.I.C.S.: 516210

Comcast of Southern New England, Inc. (1)
440 Myles Standish Blvd, Taunton, MA 02780
Tel.: (603) 628-2572
Trucking Service
N.A.I.C.S.: 484110

Deep Blue Communications, LLC (1)
433 River St Ste 4002, 12180, Troy, NY 02122
Tel.: (518) 434-4300
Web Site:
http://www.deepbluecommunications.com
Wireless Network Installation Services
N.A.I.C.S.: 238210

Digital Golf Solutions SAS (1)
8 rue Hans List, 78290, Croissy-sur-Seine, France
Tel.: (33) 185761220
Web Site: https://www.dgsgolf.com
Software Development Services
N.A.I.C.S.: 541511

E Holdings, LLC (1)
1801 Ctr Ave Ste 313, Pittsburgh, PA 15219
Tel.: (412) 434-6571
Web Site: https://eholdingsinc.com
Real Estate & Construction Services
N.A.I.C.S.: 236220

E! Distribution, L.L.C. (1)
2805 Market St Ste 187, Garland, TX 75041
Web Site: https://www.e-dist.com
Warehouse Services
N.A.I.C.S.: 236220

Entertainment for All, LLC (1)
1755 N 13th St, Philadelphia, PA 19122
Tel.: (267) 225-9057
Web Site:
https://www.allentertainmentllc.com
Music Entertainment Services
N.A.I.C.S.: 711130

FM Production Services LLC (1)
900 Mix Ave Ste 19, Hamden, CT 06514
Tel.: (860) 944-4662
Web Site: https://fm-productions-llc.ueniweb.com
Entertainment Services
N.A.I.C.S.: 711190

FreeWheel Media Inc. (1)
231 Second Ave, San Mateo, CA 94401
Tel.: (415) 295-4550
Web Site: http://www.freewheel.tv
Emp.: 90
Online Video Advertising Solutions
N.A.I.C.S.: 513210
Diane Yu (Co-Founder)
Jonathan Heller (Co-Founder)

James Rothwell (VP-Agency, Brand & Industry Rels-Global)
Soo Jin Oh (Chief Strategy Officer)
Sarah Foss (Sr VP-Strategic Initiatives)
Hong Cai (VP-Engrg & Gen Mgr-Beijing)
Yuling Ma (CTO)
Mark McKee (Gen Mgr)
Katy Loria (Chief Revenue Officer-US)
Michael Lawlor (Chief Ops & Svc Officer)
Chris Rouser (Head-HR)
Douglas S. Knopper (Co-Founder)

GuideWorks, LLC (1)
150 N Radnor Chester Rd Ste C300, Radnor, PA 19087
Tel.: (610) 535-4400
Cable Television Services
N.A.I.C.S.: 516210
John Baxter (Engr-Software Quality)

Hilltop Services LLC (1)
122 Mann Rd, Yorktown, TX 78164
Tel.: (361) 564-9511
Web Site: https://hilltopservicesllc.com
Structural Metal Product Mfr
N.A.I.C.S.: 332311

In Demand L.L.C. (1)
345 Hudson St 17th Fl, New York, NY 10014
Tel.: (646) 638-8200
Web Site: http://www.indemand.com
Emp.: 150
Cable Television Services
N.A.I.C.S.: 516210
Stacie Gray (Chief Creative Officer & Exec VP)
John Vartanian (CTO & Sr VP)
Bill Wolstromer (VP & Controller)
Craig Helmstetter (VP-Fin)
Sean Murray (VP-Audit)
Michael Diana (VP-Affiliate Mktg)
Dale Hopkins (Pres & CEO)

International Media Distribution, LLC (1)
4100 E Dry Creek Rd, Centennial, CO 80122
Tel.: (303) 712-5400
Web Site: http://www.imediadistribution.com
Cable Television Services
N.A.I.C.S.: 516210
Mike Scott (VP-Affiliate Sls & Mktg)
Katie Daniels (VP-Programming Dev)
Patrick Dodge (VP-Acctg & Fin)
Colleen Hunt (Sr Mgr-Accounts Receivable)
Alexa DeGennaro (Project Mgr-Mktg)
Alison Clausen (Mgr-Content Ops)
Erin O'Brien (Exec Dir-Legal & Bus Affairs)
Nicole Wang (Dir-Sls & Mktg)
Adrienne Alwag (Dir-Affiliate Mktg)
Doug Bourdon (Assoc Dir-Plng & Analysis)

International Networks, LLC (1)
4100 E Dry Creek Rd, Centennial, CO 80122 (100%)
Tel.: (303) 712-5400
Web Site:
https://www.imediadistribution.com
Sales Range: $200-249.9 Million
Cable Networks
N.A.I.C.S.: 516210

Jones Communications, Inc. (1)
312 W 1st St Ste 503, Sanford, FL 32771-7805
Tel.: (407) 448-6615
Construction Machinery Mfr
N.A.I.C.S.: 333120

Love Productions USA, Inc. (1)
3415 S Sepulveda Blvd Ste 1200, Los Angeles, CA 90034
Tel.: (310) 294-9491
Television Program Production Services
N.A.I.C.S.: 512110

Matchbox Pictures Pty Ltd. (1)
92 High Street, Windsor, 3181, VIC, Australia
Tel.: (61) 395198201
Web Site:
https://www.matchboxpictures.com
Television Program & Film Production Services
N.A.I.C.S.: 512110

Midcontinent Communications (1)
3901 N Louise Ave, Sioux Falls, SD 57107 (50%)

Web Site: http://www.midco.com
Cable Television, Telephone, High-speed
Internet Access, Cable Advertising & Data
Network Services
N.A.I.C.S.: 517121

Monkey Kingdom Limited (1)
Tea Building Unit 5 01 / 56 Shoreditch High
Street, London, E1 6JJ, United Kingdom
Tel.: (44) 2036188400
Web Site: https://www.monkeykingdom.com
Television Program Production Services
N.A.I.C.S.: 512110

**NBCUniversal Entertainment Japan
LLC** (1)
8F Atago Green Hills Mori Tower, 2-5-1
Atago, Tokyo, 105-6208, Japan
Tel.: (81) 5036126030
Web Site: https://nbcuni.co.jp
Entertainment Services
N.A.I.C.S.: 711190

NBCUniversal Media, LLC (1)
30 Rockefeller Plz, New York, NY
10112 (100%)
Tel.: (212) 664-4444
Web Site: http://www.nbcuniversal.com
Rev.: $34,021,000,000
Assets: $83,048,000,000
Liabilities: $32,662,000,000
Net Worth: $50,386,000,000
Earnings: $5,784,000,000
Emp.: 66,000
Fiscal Year-end: 12/31/2019
Digital Marketing Services
N.A.I.C.S.: 551112
Anand Kini *(CFO)*
Kimberley D. Harris *(Gen Counsel & Exec
VP)*
Mark H. Lazarus *(Chm)*
Mark Hoffman *(Chm-CNBC)*
Matt Bond *(Chm-Content Distr)*
Adam Miller *(Exec VP)*
Craig Robinson *(Chief Diversity Officer &
Exec VP)*
Kathy Kelly-Brown *(Sr VP-Strategic Initia-
tives)*
Maggie McLean Suniewick *(Pres-
NBCUniversal Digital Enterprises)*
Thomas L. Williams *(Chm/CEO-Universal
Parks & Resorts)*
Donna Langley *(Chm-Universal Filmed En-
tertainment Grp)*
Paul Telegdy *(Chm-NBC Entertainment)*
Matt Strauss *(Chm-Peacock & NBCUniver-
sal Digital Enterprises)*
Pete Bevacqua *(Pres-NBC Sports Grp)*
Pearlena Igbokwe *(Chm-Universal Studio
Grp)*
Susan Rovner *(Chm-Entertainment
Content-Television & Streaming)*
Jimmy Horowitz *(Vice Chm-Bus Affairs &
Ops)*
Valari Dobson Staab *(Pres-Owned Televi-
sion Stations)*
Vicki Williams *(Chief HR Officer)*
Kelly Campbell *(Pres-Peacock)*
Jordan Moblo *(Exec VP-Creative Acq & IP
Mgmt-Universal Studio Grp)*
Erin Underhill *(Pres-UTV)*
Beatrice Springborn *(Pres-UCP & UIS)*
Toby Gorman *(Pres-UTAS)*
Corie Henson *(Exec VP-Entertainment Un-
scripted Content-Television & Streaming
Grp)*
Matt Schnaars *(Pres-Content Distr)*
Cesar Conde *(Chm-NBCUniversal News
Grp)*

Subsidiary (Domestic):

Bravo Media LLC (2)
145 W 28th St 2nd Fl, New York, NY 10001
Tel.: (212) 563-0054
Web Site: http://www.bravomedia.com
Food, Fashion, Beauty, Design & Pop Cul-
ture Cable Programming Network
N.A.I.C.S.: 516210
Rachel Smith *(Sr VP-Dev)*

DreamWorks Animation, LLC (2)
1000 Flower St, Glendale, CA 91201
Tel.: (818) 695-5000
Web Site: https://www.dreamworks.com
Computer-Generated Animated Feature
Films Producer & Developer
N.A.I.C.S.: 512110

E! Entertainment Television, LLC (2)

5750 Wilshire Blvd Ste 560, Los Angeles,
CA 90036
Tel.: (213) 954-2400
Web Site: http://www.eonline.com
Cable Television Network & Online Enter-
tainment News Publisher
N.A.I.C.S.: 516210
Winsome Walker *(Assoc Editor)*

G4 Media, LLC (2)
5750 Wilshire Blvd 4th Fl, Los Angeles, CA
90036-7201
Tel.: (310) 979-5000
Cable Network Operator & Internet Publisher
N.A.I.C.S.: 516210

Group (Domestic):

NBC News Worldwide LLC (2)
30 Rockefeller Plz, New York, NY 10112
Tel.: (207) 843-8700
Web Site: http://www.nbcumv.com
Holding Company; News Syndicate & Inter-
net Publisher
N.A.I.C.S.: 551112
Ali Zelenko *(Sr VP-Comm)*
Rebecca Blumenstein *(Pres-Editorial)*
Libby Leist *(Exec VP-Today & Lifestyle)*
Janelle Rodriguez *(Exec VP-NBC News
Now)*

Subsidiary (Domestic):

CNBC LLC (3)
900 Sylvan Ave, Englewood Cliffs, NJ
07632
Tel.: (201) 735-2622
Web Site: http://www.cnbc.com
Sales Range: $100-124.9 Million
Business News & Personal Finance Cable
Programming & Internat Publisher
N.A.I.C.S.: 516210
Mark Hoffman *(Chm)*
Satpal Brainch *(Pres-Bus News Worldwide)*
Spencer Kimball *(Dir-Polling)*
Jay Yarow *(Sr VP & Exec Editor-Digital)*
Dan Colarusso *(Sr VP-Bus News)*
John Casey *(Pres/Mng Dir-Intl)*
Deirdre Bianchi *(Sr VP-Program Strategy &
Acquisitions)*
Patricia Pomeroy *(CFO)*
Angi Seitzer *(Sr VP-HR)*
Kevin Wright *(Sr VP-Res)*
Brian W. Steel *(Exec VP-PR)*

MSNBC Cable LLC (3)
30 Rockefeller Plz, New York, NY 10112
Tel.: (212) 664-6605
Web Site: http://www.msnbc.com
News & Information Cable Network
N.A.I.C.S.: 516210
Phil Griffin *(Pres)*
Jeff Kepnes *(Mng Editor)*

NBC News Bureaus LLC (3)
30 Rockefeller Plz, New York, NY 10112
Tel.: (212) 956-2395
Web Site: http://www.nbcnews.com
News Syndicates
N.A.I.C.S.: 516210

NBC News Digital LLC (3)
30 Rockefeller Plz, New York, NY 10112
Tel.: (212) 413-6142
Web Site: http://www.nbcnews.com
News Internet Publisher
N.A.I.C.S.: 516210
Jason Abbruzzese *(Sr Editor-Tech)*
Meredith Bennett-Smith *(Sr Editor-THINK)*
Joy Wang *(Sr Editor-Plng)*
Anna Brand *(Sr Editor-News Projects)*
Matthew Grimson *(Sr Editor-Homepage)*
Julie Shapiro *(Sr Editor-Enterprise)*
Megan Carpentier *(Editor-THINK)*
Hilary Krieger *(Editor-THINK)*
Zach Haberman *(Editor-Politics)*
Matthew Korade *(Editor-Politics)*
Alana Satlin *(Editor-Politics)*
Jessica Simeone *(Editor-News)*
Joe Murphy *(Editor-Data)*
Dipti Coorg *(Editor-Copy)*
Alex Johnson *(Editor-Copy)*
Maia Davis *(Editor-Breaking News)*
Gavon Laessig *(Editor-Breaking News)*
Margaret O'Malley *(Editor-BETTER)*
Kara Haupt *(Dir-Art)*

Group (Domestic):

NBC Sports Ventures LLC (2)

30 Rockefeller Plz, New York, NY 10112-
0015
Tel.: (212) 664-4444
Web Site: http://www.mbcuni.com
Holding Company; Sports Cable Broadcast-
ing Networks Operator & Internet Publisher
N.A.I.C.S.: 551112
Mark H. Lazarus *(Chm & Pres)*

Subsidiary (Domestic):

**Comcast Sports Management Ser-
vices, LLC** (3)
3601 S Broad St, Philadelphia, PA 19148
Tel.: (215) 336-3500
Web Site: http://www.csnphilly.com
Regional Sports Cable Programming Net-
works Operator
N.A.I.C.S.: 516210

Subsidiary (Domestic):

**Comcast SportsNet Mid-Atlantic,
L.P.** (4)
7700 Wisconsin Ave Ste 200, Bethesda,
MD 20814
Tel.: (301) 718-3200
Web Site: http://www.csnwashington.com
Sales Range: $25-49.9 Million
Emp.: 50
Regional Sports Cable Network Operator
N.A.I.C.S.: 516210

**Comcast SportsNet New England,
LLC** (4)
42 3rd Ave, Burlington, MA 01803
Tel.: (781) 270-7200
Web Site: http://www.csnne.com
Emp.: 130
Regional Sports Cable Network Operator
N.A.I.C.S.: 516210

**Comcast SportsNet Philadelphia,
L.P.** (4)
3601 S Broad St, Philadelphia, PA 19148
Tel.: (215) 952-2200
Web Site: http://www.csnphilly.com
Emp.: 15
Regional Sports Cable Network Operator
N.A.I.C.S.: 516210

NBC Sports Bay Area (4)
360 3rd St 2nd Fl, San Francisco, CA
94107
Tel.: (415) 296-8900
Web Site: http://www.nbcsports.com
Regional Sports Cable Network Operator
N.A.I.C.S.: 516210
Jason Liu *(Mgr-Local Sls)*
Hilary Allan *(Mgr-Digital Sls)*

Joint Venture (Domestic):

SportsNet New York, LLC (4)
1271 Avenue of the Americas Fl 16, New
York, NY 10020
Tel.: (212) 485-4800
Web Site: http://www.sny.tv
Regional Sports Cable Network Operator
N.A.I.C.S.: 516210
Steve Raab *(Pres)*
Gary Morgenstern *(Sr VP-Programming)*
Scott Weinfeld *(CFO & Sr VP-Fin & Admin)*

Subsidiary (Domestic):

NBC Olympics LLC (3)
30 Rockefeller Plz Fl 52, New York, NY
10112-0002
Tel.: (212) 664-4444
Television Broadcasting Services
N.A.I.C.S.: 516120
Phil Parrish *(Sr Editor)*
Molly Solomon *(Pres)*

NBC Sports Network, L.P. (3)
30 Rockefeller Plz, New York, NY 10112
Tel.: (212) 664-4444
Web Site: http://www.nbcsports.com
Cable Sports & Entertainment Network
N.A.I.C.S.: 516210

The Golf Channel, LLC (3)
7580 Golf Channel Dr, Orlando, FL 32819
Tel.: (407) 355-4653
Web Site: http://www.golfchannel.com
Golf Cable Programming Network
N.A.I.C.S.: 516210
Mike McCarley *(Pres)*
Jay Madara *(CFO)*

Jeff Foster *(Sr VP-New Media)*
Tom Knapp *(Exec VP-Partnerships & Pro-
gramming)*
Will McIntosh *(Exec VP-Digital)*
Christopher Murvin *(Gen Counsel & Sr VP-
Bus Affairs)*
Molly Solomon *(Exec VP-Content)*
David Schaefer *(VP-Comm)*
Julie Lusk *(VP-HR)*
Geoff Russell *(Sr VP & Exec Editor)*
Pepper White *(Sr VP-Mktg)*
Nick Menta *(Editor-Contributing)*
Jay Coffin *(Dir-Editorial)*
Brandon Tucker *(Mng Editor-Travel)*
Mercer Baggs *(Mng Editor)*
Amanda Norvell *(VP-Direct to Consumer
Products & Svcs)*
Will Gray *(Assoc Editor-Community & Con-
tent)*
Jason Crook *(Assoc Editor)*
Brentley Romine *(Assoc Editor)*
Samantha Marks *(Assoc Editor)*
Carson Williams *(Assoc Editor)*

Subsidiary (Domestic):

EZLinks Golf LLC (4)
401 S La Salle St Ste 302, Chicago, IL
60605
Tel.: (888) 885-4657
Web Site: http://www.ezlinksgolf.com
Software & IT Services for Golf Industry
N.A.I.C.S.: 513210

Subsidiary (Domestic):

**Integrated Business Systems
Inc.** (5)
12201 Gayton Rd Ste 100, Richmond, VA
23238
Tel.: (804) 754-3200
Web Site: http://www.goibs.com
Sales Range: $10-24.9 Million
Emp.: 75
Business Support Software & Services
N.A.I.C.S.: 513210
Kevin Pillsbury *(Controller)*
Hillary Campbell *(Coord-Events & Travel)*
Anthony Strange *(Founder & Pres)*

Joint Venture (Domestic):

**World Championship Sports Network,
Inc.** (3)
12100 Wilshire Blvd, Los Angeles, CA
90025
Tel.: (310) 921-7001
Sports Cable Network
N.A.I.C.S.: 516210

Subsidiary (Domestic):

**NBC Stations Management II
LLC** (2)
30 Rockefeller Plz, New York, NY 10112-
0015
Tel.: (212) 664-4444
Web Site: http://www.nbcstations.com
Television Broadcasting Stations Operator
N.A.I.C.S.: 516120
Valari Dobson Staab *(Pres)*

Unit (Domestic):

KNBC-TV (3)
100 Universal City Plz, Universal City, CA
91608
Tel.: (818) 684-4321
Web Site: http://www.nbclosangeles.com
Television Broadcasting Station
N.A.I.C.S.: 516120

KNSD-TV (3)
9680 Granite Ridge Dr, San Diego, CA
92123
Tel.: (619) 578-0201
Web Site: http://www.nbcsandiego.com
Television Broadcasting Station
N.A.I.C.S.: 516120
Richard Kelley *(Pres & Gen Mgr)*

KNTV-TV (3)
360 3rd St Ste 103, San Francisco, CA
94107
Tel.: (408) 432-6221
Web Site: http://www.nbcbayarea.com
Television Broadcasting Station
N.A.I.C.S.: 516120

KXAS-TV (3)

Comcast Corporation—(Continued)

3900 Barnett St, Fort Worth, TX 76103
Tel.: (817) 654-6300
Web Site: http://www.nbcdfw.com
Television Broadcasting Station
N.A.I.C.S.: 516120
Thomas Ehlmann (Pres & Gen Mgr)
John Stone (VP-News)

WCAU-TV (3)
1800 Arch St, Philadelphia, PA 19103
Tel.: (610) 668-5510
Web Site: http://www.nbcphiladelphia.com
Emp.: 300
Television Broadcasting Station
N.A.I.C.S.: 516120

WMAQ-TV (3)
454 N Columbus Dr, Chicago, IL 60611
Tel.: (312) 836-5555
Web Site: http://www.nbcchicago.com
Television Broadcasting Station
N.A.I.C.S.: 516120

WNBC-TV (3)
30 Rockefeller Plz, New York, NY 10112
Tel.: (212) 664-4444
Web Site: http://www.nbcnewyork.com
Television Broadcasting Station
N.A.I.C.S.: 516120

WRC-TV (3)
4001 Nebraska Ave NW, Washington, DC
20016
Tel.: (202) 885-4000
Web Site: http://www.nbcwashington.com
Emp.: 200
Television Broadcasting Station
N.A.I.C.S.: 516120

WTVJ-TV (3)
15000 SW 27th St, Miramar, FL 33027
Tel.: (954) 622-6000
Web Site: http://www.nbcmiami.com
Emp.: 350
Television Broadcasting Station
N.A.I.C.S.: 516120

WVIT-TV (3)
1422 New Britain Ave, West Hartford, CT
06110-1632
Tel.: (860) 521-3030
Web Site: http://www.nbcconneticut.com
Television Broadcasting Station
N.A.I.C.S.: 516120

Group (Domestic):

**NBC Universal Digital Solutions
LLC** (2)
30 Rockefeller Plz, New York, NY 10112
Tel.: (212) 664-4444
Web Site: http://www.nbcuni.com
Holding Company; Digital Media & Market
Development Services
N.A.I.C.S.: 551112
Lauren Zalaznick (Chm)

Subsidiary (Domestic):

DailyCandy, LLC (3)
584 Broadway Ste 201, New York, NY
10012
Tel.: (646) 435-9199
Web Site: http://www.dailycandy.com
Emp.: 244
Fashion, Gadgets & Shopping Guides Email
Newsletter & Internet Publishing Services
N.A.I.C.S.: 513199

Fandango, LLC (3)
407 N Maple Dr Ste 300, Beverly Hills, CA
90210
Tel.: (310) 954-0278
Web Site: http://www.fandango.com
Online, Mobile & Telephone Entertainment
Information & Ticketing Services
N.A.I.C.S.: 519290
Sandro Corsaro (Chief Creative Officer & Sr
VP)
Jason Davis (Sr VP & Gen Mgr-Rewards
Programs)
Kerry Samovar (Sr VP & Head-Bus & Legal
Affairs)
Mark Young (Sr VP-Strategy & Bus Dev)
Lori Pantel (CMO)
Lisa Holleran (Sr VP-PMO)
Dee Patel (CFO)
Dana Benson (Sr VP-Comm)
Katie Ibay (Head-HR)
Paul Yanover (Pres)

Subsidiary (Domestic):

MovieTickets.Com, LLC (4)
2255 Glades Rd Ste 100 E, Boca Raton,
FL 33431
Tel.: (561) 322-3200
Web Site: http://www.movietickets.com
Online Movie Ticket Retailer
N.A.I.C.S.: 459999
Shari E. Redstone (Co-Chm)

Subsidiary (Non-US):

MovieTickets.co.UK, Ltd. (5)
1 Central St Giles St Giles High Street,
London, WC2H 8NU, United Kingdom
Tel.: (44) 2035149556
Online Movie Ticket Retailer
N.A.I.C.S.: 561599

Subsidiary (Domestic):

VUDU Inc. (4)
2980 Bowers Ave, Santa Clara, CA 95051-
0919
Tel.: (408) 492-1010
Web Site: http://www.vudu.com
Sales Range: $50-74.9 Million
Emp.: 100
Internet-Based Movie Rental & Download
Services
N.A.I.C.S.: 532282

Subsidiary (Domestic):

iVillage LLC (3)
30 Rockseller Pl, New York, NY 10112-4502
Tel.: (212) 664-4444
Web Site: http://www.ivillage.com
Sales Range: $75-99.9 Million
Emp.: 300
Online Content Platform Publisher for
Women
N.A.I.C.S.: 518210
David Sailer (CFO & VP)

Subsidiary (Non-US):

**NBCUniversal International
Limited** (2)
1 Central St Giles St Giles High Street,
London, WC2H 8NU, United Kingdom
Tel.: (44) 2073076600
Web Site: http://nbcuintl.com
Holding Company; Television Programming,
Broadcasting & Syndication
N.A.I.C.S.: 551112
Jeff Wachtel (Pres-Studios-Los Angeles)

Subsidiary (Domestic):

NBCUniversal, LLC (2)
30 Rockefeller Plz, New York, NY 10112
Tel.: (212) 664-4444
Emp.: 3,000
Radio Station Operator
N.A.I.C.S.: 516110
Mark H. Lazarus (Chm)
Dina Juliano (Sr VP-Consumer Product
Strategy)
Gregory M. Resh (Sr VP-Fin-Hispanic En-
terprises & Content)
Denise Colella (Sr VP-Advanced Adv Prod-
ucts & Strategy-Adv Sls)
Chika Chukudebelu (VP-Programming &
Diversity-NBCUniversal Cable Entertain-
ment)
Ed Kozek (Sr VP-Ad Tech)
Pankaj Kumar (Sr VP-Measurement & Inno-
vation)
Ryan McConville (Exec VP-Ad Platforms &
Ops)
Krishan Bhatia (Exec VP-Bus Ops & Strat-
egy)
Ronald Day (Pres-Entertainment & Content
Strategy-Telemundo Enterprises)
Sandra Smester (Exec VP-Programming &
Content Dev-Telemundo Enterprises)

New England Cable News (2)
189 B St, Needham, MA 02494
Tel.: (617) 630-5000
Web Site: http://www.necn.com
Sales Range: $200-249.9 Million
Emp.: 180
Cable Television News Network
N.A.I.C.S.: 516210
Michael St. Peter (Sr VP & Gen Mgr)

Oxygen Media LLC (2)

30 Rockefeller Plz, New York, NY, 10112
Tel.: (212) 651-2000
Web Site: http://www.oxygen.com
Sales Range: $350-399.9 Million
Emp.: 400
Cable Television Network & Website Pub-
lisher
N.A.I.C.S.: 516210
Lisa Gersh (Co-Founder)
Rod Aissa (Exec VP-Original Programming)

SportsEngine, Inc. (2)
2808 Hennepin Ave S, Minneapolis, MN
55408
Tel.: (612) 379-1030
Web Site: http://www.sportsengine.com
Sports Management Software Solutions
N.A.I.C.S.: 513210
Justin Kaufenberg (Co-Founder)
Carson Kipfer (Co-Founder)
Greg Blasko (Co-Founder)
Brett MacKinnon (Sr VP & Gen Mgr)
Jody Vogelaar (Chief Customer Officer)
Jason Cuthbertson (CFO)
Sarah Barber (VP-Fin)
Valerie Just (VP-HR)
Ken McGinley (VP-Customer Success)

Subsidiary (Domestic):

TeamUnify, LLC (3)
PO Box 7136, Bend, OR 97708
Tel.: (541) 317-8462
Web Site: http://www.teamunify.com
Emp.: 60
Software to Help Swim Teams Manage
Business Operations
N.A.I.C.S.: 513210
Tom Fristoe (Founder & CEO)

Subsidiary (Domestic):

Syfy LLC (2)
30 Rockefeller Plz 21st FL, New York, NY
10112
Tel.: (212) 413-5000
Web Site: http://www.syfy.com
Sales Range: $75-99.9 Million
Emp.: 300
Cable Television Network Operator
N.A.I.C.S.: 516210
Mark Miller (Sr VP-Cable Entertainment Sls)

Telemundo Network LLC (2)
2290 W 8th Ave, Hialeah, FL 33010-2017
Tel.: (305) 884-8200
Web Site:
  http://www.msnlatino.telemundo.com
Sales Range: $550-599.9 Million
Emp.: 1,700
Spanish-Language Television Broadcasting
Network & Marketing Services
N.A.I.C.S.: 516120
Millie Carrasquillo (Sr VP-Res)
Alfredo Richard (Sr VP-Corp Comm)
Johanna Guerra (Sr VP-News)
Peter Blacker (Exec VP-Digital Media &
Emerging Bus)
Susan Solano Vila (Exec VP-Mktg)
Ken Wilkey (Sr VP-Brdcst Network Ops &
TV Stations Tech)
Jorge Hidalgo (Sr Exec VP-Sports)
Borja Perez (VP-Integrated Solutions &
Digital Media)
Mike Rodriguez (Sr VP-Sls)
Jacqueline Hernandez (COO)
Lee Flaster (Sr VP-Plng & Bus Ops-
Telemundo Ad Sls)
Anjelica Cohn (Sr VP-Bus Affairs)
Alina Falcon (Exec VP-News & Alternative
Programming)
Mike Chico (Sr VP-Sls-Station Grp)
Allan Infeld (VP Client Dev Media)
Eli Velazquez (Sr VP-Sports-Media,Miami)
Michael Guariglia (VP-Sls)
Javier I. Ortiz (VP-HR-Station Grp)
Danny Martinez (Editor-Assignment-KVDA
60)
Mirta Ojito (Dir-New Standards)
Luis Silberwasser (Pres)
Maria Isabel Figueroa (VP-Mktg)
Humberto Duran (VP-News Ops & Produc-
tion Mgmt)
Mauricio Piccone (Sr VP-Reality Program-
ming)
Jacinto Vargas (Dir-Bus Dev & Special
Events-Washington)
Luis Fernandez (Exec VP-Network News)
Lia Silkworth (Sr VP-Insights & Consumer
Dev)

Richard Borjas (VP-Production)
Jesus Torres Viera (Exec VP-Entertainment)
Vanessa Pombo (VP-Production Mgmt &
Business News)
Claudia Foghini (Exec VP-Talent & Produc-
tion Mgmt Svcs)
Mara Arakelian (Sr VP-Casting & Talent
Mgmt)
Francisco Ponce (VP-On-Air Talent Mgmt)
Claudia Franklin (VP-Entertainment Public-
ity)

Subsidiary (Non-US):

USJ LLC (2)
2-1-33 Sakurajima, Konohana-ku, Osaka,
554-0031, Japan
Tel.: (81) 664654005
Web Site: http://www.usj.co.jp
Theme Park Operator
N.A.I.C.S.: 713110
J. L. Bonnier (Pres & CEO)

Subsidiary (Domestic):

Universal Studios LLC (2)
110 Universal City Plz 2160 Ste 7C, Univer-
sal City, CA 91608-1002
Tel.: (818) 777-1000
Web Site:
  http://www.universalstudioshollywood.com
Holding Company; Motion Picture, Home
Video & Music Production, Distribution &
Licensing Services; Entertainment Theme
Parks Operator
N.A.I.C.S.: 551112
Donna Langley (Chm-Universal Pictures)

Subsidiary (Domestic):

Focus Features LLC (3)
110 Universal City Plz 2160 Ste 7C, Los
Angeles, CA 90401
Tel.: (818) 777-1000
Web Site: http://www.focusfeatures.com
Sales Range: $150-199.9 Million
Emp.: 100
Motion Picture Production & Distribution
Services
N.A.I.C.S.: 512110
Peter Kujawski (Chm)
Kiska Higgs (Pres-Production & Acq)

Unit (Domestic):

Focus Features LLC - New York (4)
5 Times Sq 11th Fl, New York, NY 10112
Tel.: (212) 664-4444
Web Site: http://www.focusfeatures.com
Motion Picture Production & Distribution
Services
N.A.I.C.S.: 512110

Subsidiary (Domestic):

Universal City Studios LLC (3)
100 Universal City Plz Bldg 2160 8H, Uni-
versal City, CA 91608
Tel.: (818) 777-1000
Web Site: http://www.nbcuniversal.com
Television Broadcasting Services
N.A.I.C.S.: 516120

Universal City Travel Partners (3)
100 Universal City Plz Bldg 2160 8H, Uni-
versal City, CA 91608-1002
Tel.: (407) 363-8220
Motion Picture & Video Production Services
N.A.I.C.S.: 512110

**Universal Network Television
LLC** (3)
30 Rockefeller Plz, New York, NY 10112
Tel.: (212) 664-4444
Web Site: http://www.nbcuniversal.com
Wireless Telecommunication Services
N.A.I.C.S.: 517111

**Universal Parks & Resorts Manage-
ment Services LLC** (3)
10 Universal City Plz, Universal City, CA
91608-1002
Tel.: (818) 777-1000
Web Site: http://www.nbcuni.com
Amusement Theme Park Operator
N.A.I.C.S.: 713110
Mark Woodbury (Chm & CEO)

Subsidiary (Domestic):

**Universal City Development Partners,
Ltd.** (4)

1000 Universal Studios Plz, Orlando, FL
32819-7610
Tel.: (407) 224-4233
Web Site: http://www.universalorlando.com
Amusement Theme Park Operator
N.A.I.C.S.: 713110
Jim Timon (Sr VP-Entertainment)

Subsidiary (Domestic):

UCDP Finance, Inc.   (5)
1000 Universal Studios Plz, Orlando, FL
32819
Tel.: (407) 363-8000
Web Site: http://www.universalorlando.com
Business Support Services
N.A.I.C.S.: 561499

Subsidiary (Domestic):

Universal Studios Hollywood   (4)
100 Universal City Plz, Universal City, CA
91608
Tel.: (818) 622-1548
Web Site:
    http://www.universalstudioshollywood.com
Amusement Theme Park Operator
N.A.I.C.S.: 713110

Wet 'n Wild Orlando   (4)
6200 International Dr, Orlando, FL 32819
Tel.: (407) 351-1800
Web Site: http://www.wetnwildorlando.com
Sales Range: $50-74.9 Million
Emp.: 400
Water Slide Amusement Park Operator
N.A.I.C.S.: 713110

Subsidiary (Non-US):

Universal Pictures International Enter-
tainment Limited   (3)
1 Central Saint Giles Saint Giles High
Street, London, WC2H 8NU, United King-
dom
Tel.: (44) 2036188000
Web Site:
    http://www.universalpicturesinterna
tional.com
Holding Company; Motion Picture & Video
Production & Distribution Services
N.A.I.C.S.: 551112

Joint Venture (Domestic):

United International Pictures   (4)
Bldg 5 Chiswick Park 566 Chiswick High
Road, London, W4 5YF, United
Kingdom   (67%)
Tel.: (44) 20 3184 2500
Web Site: http://www.uip.com
International Movie & Video Distr & Mar-
keter
N.A.I.C.S.: 512120
Kristy Grant-Hart (Chief Compliance Officer)

Subsidiary (Non-US):

Universal Studios International
B.V.   (4)
Moermanskkade 421, 1013 BC, Amster-
dam, Netherlands
Tel.: (31) 206177575
Web Site: https://www.universalpictures.nl
Motion Picture Production & Distribution
Services
N.A.I.C.S.: 512120
Jo Yan (Mng Dir & Exec VP-China)

Subsidiary (Domestic):

Universal Studios Home Entertain-
ment LLC   (3)
100 Universal City Plz, Universal City, CA
91608
Tel.: (818) 777-5159
Web Site: https://www.uphe.com
Home Video Production & Distribution Ser-
vices
N.A.I.C.S.: 512120
Eddie Cunningham (Pres-Worldwide Home
Entertainment)

National Center for Safety Initiatives,
LLC   (1)
PO Box 39008, Cleveland, OH 44139
Web Site: https://solutions.ncsisafe.com
Software Development Services
N.A.I.C.S.: 541511

Northern Entertainment Productions
LLC   (1)
PO Box 1354, Ceiba, PR 00735
Tel.: (646) 349-3125
Web Site: http://www.crossbonespr.com
Motion Picture & Video Production Services
N.A.I.C.S.: 512110

Open 4 Business Productions
LLC   (1)
2621 W 15th Pl, Chicago, IL 60608
Tel.: (773) 521-9196
Emp.: 6
Motion Picture & Tape Distr
N.A.I.C.S.: 512120
Carlo Corwin (Principal)

Patron Solutions, L.P.   (1)
930 E Lincoln Hwy, Exton, PA 19341
Tel.: (484) 875-7300
Web Site: http://www.neweratickets.com
Emp.: 30
Online Ticketing Services
N.A.I.C.S.: 513199
Steve Geib (VP-Professional Svcs)
Kim Damron (Pres & CEO)
Steve Demots (Chief Revenue Officer)
Keith White (CTO)
Kim Boren (CFO)
Craig Ricks (Sr VP-Mktg)
Christian Lewis (VP-Bus Dev)
Erik Janis (VP-Tech Svcs)
Chad Phillips (VP-Customer Svc)
Jane Kleinberger (Founder)

Pennebaker LLC   (1)
504 W 9th St, Houston, TX 77007
Tel.: (713) 963-8607
Web Site: https://pennebaker.com
Marketing Communication Services
N.A.I.C.S.: 541613

Plaxo, Inc.   (1)
203 Ravendale Dr, Mountain View, CA
94043
Tel.: (650) 254-5400
Web Site: http://www.plaxo.com
Sales Range: $100-124.9 Million
Social Networking Products & Services
N.A.I.C.S.: 334610

Rider Productions LLC   (1)
260 Mountain Rd, North Granby, CT 06060
Tel.: (860) 413-9067
Web Site: https://www.riderevents.com
Event Management Services
N.A.I.C.S.: 561920

Sky Limited   (1)
Grant Way, Isleworth, TW7 5QD, Mddx,
United Kingdom
Tel.: (44) 3331000333
Web Site: http://www.skygroup.sky
Sales Range: $15-24.9 Billion
Holding Company; Television Broadcasting,
Multimedia Entertainment Publishing & Tele-
communications Services
N.A.I.C.S.: 551112
Chris Stylianou (COO-Ireland)
Stephen van Rooyen (CEO & Exec VP)
Gary Davey (CEO-Studios)
Luke Bradley-Jones (CMO-UK)
Karl Holmes (COO)
Lyssa McGowan (Chief Consumer Officer)
Debbie Klein (CMO & Chief Corp Affairs
Officer)
Simon Robson (CFO)
Mohamed Hammady (CTO)
Colin Smith (Co-CFO)
Brendan Lynch (Co-CTO)
Patrick Behar (Chief Bus Officer)
Lucy Thomas (Chief Data Officer)
Natalie Peters (Mng Dir-Customer Svc Grp)
Claire Canning (Gen Counsel)
Joanna Manning-Cooper (Grp Dir-Corp Af-
fairs)
Claudia Osei-Nsafoah (Dir-People)
Zai Bennett (Mng Dir-Content)
Mai Fyfield (Chief Comml Officer)

Joint Venture (Domestic):

DTV Services Limited   (2)
Broadcast Centre BC3 D5, 201 Wood Lane,
London, W12 7TP, United Kingdom
Tel.: (44) 8708809980
Web Site: http://www.freeview.co.uk
Holding Company; Digital Television Ser-
vices

N.A.I.C.S.: 551112

Subsidiary (Non-US):

Sky Deutschland Gmbh   (2)
Medienallee 26, 85774, Unterfohring,
Germany   (100%)
Tel.: (49) 89995802
Web Site: https://www.skygroup.sky
Sales Range: $1-4.9 Billion
Television Station Operator
N.A.I.C.S.: 516120
Julia Buchmaier (Dir-Corp Comm)
Holger Ensslin (Mng Dir, Chief Legal
Officer-Regulatory & Distr & Member-Mgmt
Bd)
Thomas Kuhnert (Sr Mgr-Sports Comm)
Moritz Wetter (VP-Product & Content
Comm)
Birgit Ehmann (Sr Mgr-Fiction & Entertain-
ment Comm)
Judith Mayr (Head-Comm-Sky Osterreich)
Matthew McDonald (CTO)
Elke Walthelm (Exec VP-Content)
Jens Bohl (Sr Mgr-Sports Comm)
Shoshannah Peter (Sr Mgr-Consumer
Comm-Sky Film & Series Channel)
Dirk Bohm (Dir-Sports Comm)
Siegfried Schneider (Pres)
Barbara Haase (CMO)
Devesh Raj (CEO & Member-Mgmt Bd)
Toni Huemer (Sr Mgr-Sports Comm)
Thomas Schoffner (Sr Mgr-Fiction & Enter-
tainment Comm)
Stephanie Teicher (Sr Mgr-Fiction & Enter-
tainment Comm)
Dominik Lehner (Sr Mgr-Event & Program
Comm)
Alexandra Fexer (Sr Mgr-Corp Comm)
Andreas Stumptner (Head-Product Comm)
Thomas Henkel (Exec VP-Strategy)
Jacques Raynaud (Exec VP-Sports & Adv)
Danja Frech (Exec VP-People & Organisa-
tion)
Christian Hindennach (Chief Comml Officer)
Colin Jones (CFO, COO & Member-Mgmt
Bd)
Barny Mills (Co-CFO)
Charly Classen (Exec VP-Sports)

Subsidiary (Domestic):

Sky Deutschland Service Center
GmbH   (3)
Eckdrift 109, 19061, Schwerin,
Germany   (100%)
Tel.: (49) 385 64105 0
Web Site: http://www.servicecenter.sky.de
Emp.: 650
Call Center Operator
N.A.I.C.S.: 561421
Daniela See (Mng Dir)

Sky Media GmbH   (3)
Medienallee 26, 85774, Unterfohring,
Germany   (100%)
Tel.: (49) 8999727900
Web Site: https://www.skymedia.de
Television & Other Media Advertising Ser-
vices
N.A.I.C.S.: 541890
Martin Michel (Mng Dir)

Subsidiary (Non-US):

Sky Osterreich GmbH   (3)
Rivergate Handelskai 92 Gate 1, 1200, Vi-
enna, Austria   (100%)
Tel.: (43) 1 880210
Television Broadcasting Services
N.A.I.C.S.: 516120
Holger Ensslin (Gen Mgr)

Subsidiary (Domestic):

Sky Osterreich Fernsehen
GmbH   (4)
Rivergate Handelskai 92 Gate 1, 1200, Vi-
enna, Austria
Web Site: http://www.sky.at
Television Broadcasting Services
N.A.I.C.S.: 516120

Sky Osterreich Verwaltung
GmbH   (4)
Schonbrunner Strasse 297/2, 1120, Vienna,
Austria
Tel.: (43) 149166200
Television Broadcasting Services
N.A.I.C.S.: 516120

Werner Liska (Mgr-Strategy & Ops)

Subsidiary (Domestic):

Sky Home Communications
Limited   (2)
260 Bath Road, Slough, SL1 4DX, United
Kingdom
Tel.: (44) 2074795000
Web Site: http://www.bethere.co.uk
Internet Service Provider
N.A.I.C.S.: 517810
Chris Stening (Mng Dir)

Subsidiary (Non-US):

Sky Italia S.r.l.   (2)
Via Monte Penice 7, 20138, Milan, Italy
Tel.: (39) 02 30801
Web Site: http://www.sky.it
Television Broadcasting & Media Services
N.A.I.C.S.: 516120
Maximo Ibarra (CEO)
Gabriella Vacca (CTO)

Subsidiary (Domestic):

Sky Publications Limited   (2)
Grant Way, Isleworth, TW7 5QD, Mddx,
United Kingdom
Tel.: (44) 2077053000
Multimedia Publishing Services
N.A.I.C.S.: 513199

Subsidiary (Domestic):

Challenge TV   (3)
1 Braham Street, London, E1 8EP, United
Kingdom   (100%)
Tel.: (44) 20 7032 8000
Web Site: http://www.challenge.co.uk
Digital Television Broadcasting
N.A.I.C.S.: 516120

Sky Living   (3)
123 Buckingham Palace Road 2nd Floor,
London, SW1W 9SL, United Kingdom
Tel.: (44) 20 7032 2000
Web Site: http://www.sky.com
Sales Range: $25-49.9 Million
Emp.: 50
Television Broadcasting
N.A.I.C.S.: 516120

Subsidiary (Domestic):

Sky UK Limited   (2)
Grant Way, Isleworth, TW7 5QD, United
Kingdom
Tel.: (44) 3331000333
Web Site: http://www.sky.com
Television Broadcasting
N.A.I.C.S.: 516120

The Cloud Networks Limited   (2)
Third Floor 4 Victoria Square, Saint Albans,
AL1 3TF, United Kingdom
Tel.: (44) 333 202 0931
Web Site: http://www.thecloud.net
Sales Range: $10-24.9 Million
Emp.: 70
Wireless Broadband Services
N.A.I.C.S.: 517810

TVWorks, LLC   (1)
2 Belvedere Pl Ste 200, Mill Valley, CA
94941
Tel.: (415) 380-6200
Web Site: http://www.tvworks.com
Cable Television & Internet Services
N.A.I.C.S.: 516210

Telemundo 314 Redwood LLC   (1)
314 S Redwood Rd, Salt Lake City, UT
84104
Tel.: (801) 956-2020
Web Site: https://www.telemundoutah.com
Online Television Broadcasting Services
N.A.I.C.S.: 334220

Telemundo Las Vegas LLC   (1)
6380 Polaris Ave, Las Vegas, NV 89118
Tel.: (702) 258-0039
Web Site:
    https://www.telemundolasvegas.com
Online Television Broadcasting Services
N.A.I.C.S.: 334220

Telemundo Rio Grande Valley,
LLC   (1)
200 S 10th St 2nd Fl, McAllen, TX 78501

Comcast Corporation—(Continued)

Tel.: (956) 686-0040
Web Site: https://www.telemundo40.com
Online Television Broadcasting Services
N.A.I.C.S.: 334220

Telemundo of Arizona LLC (1)
4625 S 33rd Pl, Phoenix, AZ 85040
Tel.: (602) 648-3900
Web Site:
https://www.telemundoarizona.com
Online Television Broadcasting Services
N.A.I.C.S.: 334220

Telemundo of Chicago LLC (1)
454 N Columbus Dr, Chicago, IL 60611
Tel.: (312) 836-1444
Web Site:
https://www.telemundochicago.com
Online Television Broadcasting Services
N.A.I.C.S.: 334220

Telemundo of Denver LLC (1)
4100 E Dry Creek Rd, Centennial, CO
80122
Tel.: (720) 897-9025
Web Site:
https://www.telemundodenver.com
Online Television Broadcasting Services
N.A.I.C.S.: 334220

Telemundo of Fresno LLC (1)
2441 N Grove Industrial Dr, Fresno, CA
93727
Tel.: (559) 252-5101
Web Site: https://www.telemundofresno.com
Online Television Broadcasting Services
N.A.I.C.S.: 334220

Telemundo of New England LLC (1)
189 B St, Needham, MA 02494
Tel.: (617) 630-3300
Web Site:
https://www.telemundonuevainglaterra.com
Online Television Broadcasting Services
N.A.I.C.S.: 334220

Telemundo of New Mexico LLC (1)
2400 Monroe St NE, Albuquerque, NM
87110
Tel.: (505) 884-5353
Web Site:
https://www.telemundonuevomexico.com
Online Television Broadcasting Services
N.A.I.C.S.: 334220

**Telemundo of Northern California
LLC** (1)
500 Middle Pl, Sacramento, CA 95815
Tel.: (916) 567-3300
Web Site: https://www.telemundo33.com
Online Television Broadcasting Services
N.A.I.C.S.: 334220

Telemundo of Puerto Rico LLC (1)
383 Roosevelt Ave, Hato Rey, PR 00918
Tel.: (787) 641-2222
Web Site: https://www.telemundopr.com
Online Television Broadcasting Services
N.A.I.C.S.: 334220

Telemundo of San Diego LLC (1)
9680 Granite Ridge Dr, San Diego, CA
92123
Tel.: (619) 578-0200
Web Site: https://www.telemundo20.com
Online Television Broadcasting Services
N.A.I.C.S.: 334220

True North Productions Limited (1)
Marshalls Mill Marshall Street, Leeds, LS11
0YJ, United Kingdom
Tel.: (44) 1133945494
Web Site: https://www.truenorth.tv
Television Program Production Services
N.A.I.C.S.: 512110

**United International Pictures of
Panama, Inc.** (1)
Edificio Aventura Quinto Piso Local No 501,
Avenida Ricardo J Alfaro, Panama, Panama
Tel.: 507 790324
Film Production Entertainment Services
N.A.I.C.S.: 512120

Universal Pictures Home Entertainment LLC (1)
400 R St Ste 1080, Sacramento, CA 95814
Tel.: (916) 445-1254

Web Site: https://www.uphe.com
Film Production Entertainment Services
N.A.I.C.S.: 512120

Vehix, Inc. (1)
19 E 200 S 10th Fl Ter, Salt Lake City, UT
84111
Tel.: (801) 401-6060
Used Automobile Dealer
N.A.I.C.S.: 441120

Working Title Films Limited (1)
26 Aybrook Street, London, W1U 4AN,
United Kingdom
Tel.: (44) 2073073000
Web Site: https://www.workingtitlefilms.com
Television Program & Film Production Services
N.A.I.C.S.: 512110

COMERA LIFE SCIENCES HOLDINGS, INC.
12 Gill St 4650, Woburn, MA 01801
Tel.: (617) 871-2101 DE
Web Site:
https://ir.comeralifesciences.com
Year Founded: 2014
CMRA—(NASDAQ)
Rev.: $633,102
Assets: $3,727,113
Liabilities: $9,974,201
Net Worth: ($6,247,088)
Earnings: ($18,377,954)
Emp.: 12
Fiscal Year-end: 12/31/22
Holding Company
N.A.I.C.S.: 551112
Jeffrey S. Hackman *(Chm, Pres & CEO)*
Michael G. Campbell *(CFO & Exec VP)*
Janice McCourt *(Chief Bus Officer)*
Neal Muni *(COO & Exec VP)*

COMERICA INCORPORATED
1717 Main St MC 6404, Dallas, TX
75201 DE
Web Site: https://www.comerica.com
Year Founded: 1849
CMA—(NYSE)
Rev.: $5,253,000,000
Assets: $85,834,000,000
Liabilities: $79,428,000,000
Net Worth: $6,406,000,000
Earnings: $854,000,000
Emp.: 7,496
Fiscal Year-end: 12/31/23
Financial Investment Services
N.A.I.C.S.: 551111
Christine M. Moore *(Exec VP)*
Curtis Chatman Farmer *(Pres & CEO)*
Megan D. Burkhart *(Chief Admin Officer & Sr Exec VP)*
James H. Weber *(Chief Experience Officer & Exec VP)*
Megan D. Crespi *(COO & Sr Exec VP)*
J. McGregor Carr *(Exec VP & Exec Dir-Wealth Mgmt)*
Allysun Fleming *(Exec VP-Payments)*
Corey R. Bailey *(Exec VP & Exec Dir-Middle Market & Bus Banking)*
Michael I. Ritchie *(Exec VP & Exec Dir-Natl & Specialty Banking)*
Bruce Mitchell *(CIO & Exec VP)*
Brian S. Goldman *(Chief Risk Officer & Sr Exec VP)*
Larry Franco *(Exec VP & Natl Dir-Retail & Small Bus Banking)*

Subsidiaries:

Comerica Bank (1)
1717 Main St, Dallas, TX 75201 **(100%)**
Tel.: (214) 462-6723
Web Site: https://www.comerica.com
Sales Range: $400-449.9 Million
Banking Services
N.A.I.C.S.: 522110

Christine M. Moore *(Exec VP & Gen Auditor)*
Curtis Chatman Farmer *(Pres & CEO)*
Cassandra M. McKinney *(Exec VP)*
Paul R. Obermeyer *(Exec VP-Operations)*
Steve Richins *(Pres-Arizona Market)*
Wendy Bridges *(Exec VP & Exec Dir-Corp Responsibility)*
Beatrice Kelly *(Dir & Sr VP)*
Kevin Watkins *(VP & Mgr-External Affairs-Southeast Michigan)*
Sandra Felegy *(Sr VP & Dir-Small Bus Banking-California)*
Brent Harraman *(Sr VP & Dir-Small Bus Banking-Texas)*
Meghan Storey *(Sr VP & Dir-Small Bus Banking-Michigan)*
Omar Salah *(Exec VP & Dir-Small Bus Banking)*
Von E. Hays *(Chief Legal Officer)*
J. McGregor Carr *(Exec VP)*
Melinda A. Chausse *(Chief Credit Officer)*
Megan D. Crespi *(COO)*
James J. Herzog *(CFO)*
Cassandra M. McKinney *(Exec VP)*
Morgan Rector *(Pres)*
Steve Davis *(Pres)*
Brian P. Foley *(Pres)*
Dave Galbreath *(Pres)*
Cassandra M. McKinney *(Exec VP-Retail)*
Irvin Ashford Jr. *(Chief Community Officer)*

Subsidiary (Domestic):

**Comerica Bank & Trust, National
Association** (2)
101 N Main St, Ann Arbor, MI 48104-1475
Tel.: (734) 930-2421
Web Site: http://www.comerica.com
Sales Range: $10-24.9 Million
Emp.: 28
Bank & Trust
N.A.I.C.S.: 522110

Division (Domestic):

**Comerica Bank - Michigan
Market** (2)
411 W Lafayette MC 3262, Detroit, MI
48226-3416
Tel.: (313) 222-4000
Web Site: http://www.comerica.com
Regional Managing Office; Retail, Commercial & Investment Banking
N.A.I.C.S.: 551114
Christine M. Moore *(Exec VP)*
Steve Davis *(Pres)*

**Comerica Bank - Western
Market** (2)
333 W Santa Clara St Fl 1, San Jose, CA
95113
Tel.: (400) 550-5300
Web Site: http://www.comerica.com
Rev.: $106,000,000
Emp.: 2,000
Regional Managing Office; Retail, Commercial & Investment Banking
N.A.I.C.S.: 551114

Subsidiary (Non-US):

Comerica Bank Mexico, S.A. (2)
Edificio Torre Comercial America Batallon
de San Patricio 111 Piso 17, Colonia Valle
Oriente Garza Garcia, 66269, Nuevo Leon,
66269, CP, Mexico
Tel.: (52) 8183680316
Web Site: http://www.comerica.com
Banking Services
N.A.I.C.S.: 522110
Dalia Apodaca *(Sr VP)*

Comerica Holdings Incorporated (1)
500 Woodward Ave, Detroit, MI 48226
Tel.: (313) 222-4000
Commercial Banking Services
N.A.I.C.S.: 522110
Ralph W. Babb Jr. *(Chm, Pres & CEO)*

Comerica Insurance Group, Inc. (1)
Comerica Tower at Detroit Ctr, Detroit, MI
48226
Tel.: (248) 371-5000
Insurance Services
N.A.I.C.S.: 524298

**Comerica Insurance Services,
Inc.** (1)

35405 Grand River, Farmington, MI
48335 **(100%)**
Tel.: (248) 603-3600
Web Site:
https://comerica.insuranceaisle.com
Sales Range: Less than $1 Million
Insurance Services
N.A.I.C.S.: 524210

Comerica Leasing Corporation (1)
411 W Lafayette Blvd Lower Lvl 1, Detroit,
MI 48226-3120
Tel.: (313) 222-1212
Web Site: http://www.comerica.com
Equipment Leasing & Financing Services to
Businesses
N.A.I.C.S.: 551111

Comerica Securities, Inc. (1)
201 W Fort St, Detroit, MI 48226-3137
Tel.: (313) 222-5580
Web Site: http://www.comerica.com
Sales Range: $650-699.9 Million
Securities Brokerage
N.A.I.C.S.: 523150
Michael W. Malone *(Pres & CEO)*

Comerica Wire Transfer (1)
500 Woodward Ave, Detroit, MI 48226
Tel.: (313) 222-4000
Sales Range: $1-4.9 Billion
Wire Transfer Company
N.A.I.C.S.: 525990

**Professional Life Interlink
Securities** (1)
2155 Butterfield Dr, Troy, MI
48084 **(100%)**
Tel.: (248) 356-7587
Web Site:
http://www.plusfinancialnetwork.com
Sales Range: $1-9.9 Million
Emp.: 16
Life Insurance, Annuities & Disability Insurance
N.A.I.C.S.: 524210

W.Y. Campbell & Company (1)
1 Woodward Ave Fl 26, Detroit, MI
48226 **(100%)**
Tel.: (313) 496-9000
Web Site: http://www.wycampbell.com
Sales Range: $75-99.9 Million
Emp.: 20
Investment Banking Services
N.A.I.C.S.: 523160

Wilson, Kemp & Associates, Inc. (1)
255 E Brown St Ste 200, Birmingham, MI
48009-6208 **(100%)**
Tel.: (313) 259-6210
Sales Range: $50-74.9 Million
Emp.: 10
Investment Services
N.A.I.C.S.: 523940
John Capuano *(VP & Sr Portfolio Mgr)*

COMERTON CORP.
17888-67th Ct N, Loxahatchee, FL
33470
Tel.: (727) 877-6747 FL
Web Site:
http://www.comertoncorp.com
Year Founded: 2004
COCM—(OTCIQ)
Wind Power Services
N.A.I.C.S.: 221115

COMF5 INTERNATIONAL, INC.
7477 W Lake Mead Blvd Ste 260,
Las Vegas, NV 89128
Tel.: (702) 938-9300 FL
CMFV—(OTCIQ)
Information Technology Services
N.A.I.C.S.: 541512
Tracy Sperry *(CFO)*

COMFORT SYSTEMS USA, INC.
675 Bering Dr Ste 400, Houston, TX
77057
Tel.: (713) 830-9600 DE
Web Site:
https://www.comfortsystemsusa.com
Year Founded: 1997

FIX—(NYSE)
Rev.: $4,140,364,000
Assets: $2,597,478,000
Liabilities: $1,597,555,000
Net Worth: $999,923,000
Earnings: $245,947,000
Emp.: 14,100
Fiscal Year-end: 12/31/22
Commercial HVAC Sales & Services
N.A.I.C.S.: 238220
William George (CFO & Exec VP)
Brian E. Lane (Pres & CEO)
Julie S. Shaeff (Chief Acctg Officer & Sr VP)
Terrance Reed (Sr VP)

Subsidiaries:

ACI Mechanical, Inc. (1)
2182 231st Ln, Ames, IA 50014-6343
Tel.: (515) 232-1236
Web Site: https://www.acimechinc.com
Sales Range: $25-49.9 Million
Emp.: 80
Mechanical Contracting Service
N.A.I.C.S.: 238990
Michael G. McCoy (Pres)

Acorn Industrial, Inc. (1)
7311 ACC Blvd, Raleigh, NC 27617
Tel.: (919) 256-6505
Mechanical & Plumbing Services
N.A.I.C.S.: 238220

Advance Technology, Inc. (1)
4 Washington Ave, Scarborough, ME 04070-6834
Tel.: (207) 883-6364
Web Site:
    http://www.advancetechnology.com
Computer System Design Services
N.A.I.C.S.: 541512

Air Systems Engineering, Inc. (1)
3602 S Pine St, Tacoma, WA 98409
Tel.: (253) 572-9484
Web Site: https://www.asei.ws
Sales Range: $25-49.9 Million
Emp.: 105
Heating, Ventilation & Air Conditioning Services
N.A.I.C.S.: 238220

AirTemp, Inc. (1)
20 Thomas Dr, Westbrook, ME 04092
Tel.: (207) 774-2300
Web Site: https://airtempmaine.com
Automotive Environmental Comfort Services
N.A.I.C.S.: 238220

Amteck, LLC (1)
1387 E New Cir Rd Ste 120, Lexington, KY 40509
Tel.: (859) 255-9546
Web Site: http://www.amteck.com
Holding Company; Electrical Contractor
N.A.I.C.S.: 551112
Daren L. Turner (CEO)
Pete Bierden (COO)
Jeri Tackett (VP-HR)
Roger Hamilton (VP-Technology)
Wayne Boyd (VP-Engrg)
Corey Bard (Pres)
Jennifer Green (CFO)
Dean Delano (Exec VP)
Rodney Sallee (VP)
Pam Thompson (VP)
Ed Erny (Pres)

Subsidiary (Domestic):

Amteck of Kentucky, LLC (2)
1387 E New Cir Rd Ste 130, Lexington, KY 40505
Tel.: (859) 255-9546
Web Site: https://www.amteck.com
Electrical Contractor
N.A.I.C.S.: 238210
Corey Bard (CFO)
David Wagner (Pres)
Jon Dougherty (Mgr)
Pamela Thompson (VP)
Wayne Boyd (Mgr-Engineering-Construction)
Greg Carr (Mgr)
Dean Delano (COO)
Kent Gibson (Mgr)
Mike Gorlow (Mgr)

Corey Jones (Mgr-Marketing)
Rodney Sallee (Mgr)
Kurtis Strauel (Dir-Human Resources)
Daniel Swintosky (Gen Mgr)
Daren L. Turner (CEO)

Southeastern Automatic Sprinkler Co., Inc. (2)
124 Enterprise Dr, Madison, MS 39110-8701
Tel.: (601) 898-9385
Web Site:
    https://www.southeasternautomaticsprinkler.com
Sprinkler Systems Contractor
N.A.I.C.S.: 238220
Harlon Sistrunk (Owner)

Wallace Engineering, Inc. (2)
PO Box 1021, Dothan, AL 36302
Tel.: (334) 793-4974
Web Site:
    http://www.wallaceengineeringinc.com
Sales Range: $1-9.9 Million
Emp.: 15
Electrical Contractor
N.A.I.C.S.: 238210
Terry L. Wallace (Founder)

Atlantic Electric, LLC (1)
7320 Cross County Rd, North Charleston, SC 29418
Tel.: (843) 460-1202
Web Site: http://www.atlanticelectric.com
Sales Range: $1-9.9 Million
Emp.: 75
Electrical Contractor
N.A.I.C.S.: 238210
Michael Richardson (VP)

Atlas Comfort Systems USA, Inc. (1)
1225 E Crosby Rd Ste B14, Carrollton, TX 75006
Tel.: (972) 466-4161
Heating & Air Conditioning Contracting Services
N.A.I.C.S.: 238220

BCH Mechanical LLC (1)
6350/6354 118th Ave, Largo, FL 33773
Tel.: (727) 546-3561
Web Site: http://www.bchmechanical.com
Plumbing, Heating & Air Conditioning Services
N.A.I.C.S.: 238220
Dan Allen (VP-Ops)
John Fields (Pres)
Carmandy Garber (CFO)

BCM Controls Corporation (1)
30 Commerce Way, Woburn, MA 01801
Tel.: (781) 933-8878
Web Site: https://www.bcmcontrols.com
Emp.: 30
Automotive Environmental Comfort Services
N.A.I.C.S.: 238220

Blue C, LLC (1)
PO Box 77, Heron, MT 59844-9545
Web Site: http://www.hvacredu.net
Education Services
N.A.I.C.S.: 611710
Chris Compton (Founder, CEO & Dir)

Building Temperature Solutions, LLC (1)
9326 Yeager Dr, Fort Wayne, IN 46809
Tel.: (260) 449-9201
Web Site:
    http://www.buildingtemperaturesolutions.com
Building Construction Services
N.A.I.C.S.: 236210

Century Mechanical Solutions, Inc. (1)
419 Elliott Ave, Cincinnati, OH 45215
Tel.: (513) 681-5700
Web Site:
    http://www.comfortsystemsusaohio.com
Mechanical Engineering Services
N.A.I.C.S.: 541330

ColonialWebb Contractors Company (1)
2820 Ackley Ave, Richmond, VA 23228
Tel.: (804) 916-1400
Web Site: https://colonialwebb.com
Automotive Environmental Comfort Services
N.A.I.C.S.: 238220

Mitch Haddon (CEO)
Joe Piacentino (CFO)
Brett Mutnick (VP-)
John Zilla (Reg VP-)
Ray Battani (Reg VP-)
Nathan Wethington (VP-)
Tyler Sinsabaugh (VP-)

Comfort Systems USA (Arkansas), Inc. (1)
116 Commercial Dr, Lowell, AR 72745
Tel.: (479) 770-8992
Web Site: https://www.comfortar.com
Emp.: 45
Automotive Environmental Comfort Services
N.A.I.C.S.: 238220
Tad Hankins (VP & Project Mgr)
Daniel Pierce (Project Mgr)
Jerry Floyd (Project Mgr)
Gary Love (Project Mgr)
Dawn McElyea (Controller)
Sean Cross (Project Mgr)
Joe Loomis (Project Mgr)
Jon Davis (Project Mgr)
Cris Thompson (Superintendent-Field)
Keith Daniels (Dir-Safety)
Barbara Eggleston (VP-Svc Dept)
Josh Zuber (Project Mgr)

Comfort Systems USA (Bristol), Inc. (1)
294 Blevins Blvd, Bristol, VA 24202
Tel.: (276) 669-3138
Automotive Environmental Comfort Services
N.A.I.C.S.: 238220
Will Nulton (VP-Svc)

Comfort Systems USA (Carolinas), LLC (1)
1600 Crossbeam Dr, Charlotte, NC 28217
Tel.: (704) 426-1069
Web Site:
    http://www.comfortsystemsusa.com
Sales Range: $25-49.9 Million
Emp.: 7
Automotive Environmental Comfort Services
N.A.I.C.S.: 238220

Comfort Systems USA (Intermountain), Inc. (1)
2035 S Milestone Dr, Salt Lake City, UT 84104
Tel.: (801) 907-6700
Web Site: https://comfortsystemutah.com
Emp.: 100
Automotive Environmental Comfort Services
N.A.I.C.S.: 238220

Comfort Systems USA (Kentucky), Inc. (1)
5051 Commerce Crossings Dr Ste 1, Louisville, KY 40229
Tel.: (502) 363-2654
Web Site:
    https://comfortsystemsusakentucky.com
Sales Range: $25-49.9 Million
Emp.: 47
Automotive Environmental Comfort Services
N.A.I.C.S.: 238220
Dan Lemons (Pres)

Comfort Systems USA (MidAtlantic), LLC (1)
1057 Bill Tuck Hwy, South Boston, VA 24592
Tel.: (434) 572-6986
Web Site: https://csusamidatlantic.com
Automotive Environmental Comfort Services
N.A.I.C.S.: 238220
Mark R. Glasscock (Exec VP)
Mark A. Gosney (Mgr-Piping Div)
Robert M. Marks Jr. (CFO)
David N. Allen (VP-Operations)
Stephen W. Kent Jr. (VP)

Comfort Systems USA (Northwest), Inc. (1)
18702 N Creek Pkwy Ste 110, Bothell, WA 98011
Tel.: (425) 883-9224
Web Site:
    http://www.comfortsystemsusanorthwest.com
Emp.: 160
Mechanical Contractor Services
N.A.I.C.S.: 238220

Comfort Systems USA (Ohio), Inc. (1)

7401 First Pl, Oakwood Village, OH 44146
Tel.: (440) 703-1600
Web Site:
    https://comfortsystemsusaohio.com
Sales Range: $25-49.9 Million
Emp.: 75
Automotive Environmental Comfort Services
N.A.I.C.S.: 238220

Comfort Systems USA (South Central), Inc. (1)
9745 Bent Oak Dr, Houston, TX 77040
Tel.: (832) 590-5700
Web Site: https://www.csusasc.com
Sales Range: $50-74.9 Million
Emp.: 200
Automotive Environmental Comfort Services
N.A.I.C.S.: 238220
Travis Welch (Pres)
Doug Robicheaux (Controller)
Ted Bashinski (Dir-Safety-Risk Management)
Monisha Haskell (Partner)
Ken Villarrubia (Pres)
Jerri Anh Wright (VP)

Comfort Systems USA (Southeast), Inc. (1)
8633 Elm Fair Blvd, Tampa, FL 33610
Tel.: (813) 272-2809
Web Site: http://www.comfortsystems.com
Sales Range: $25-49.9 Million
Emp.: 40
Automotive Environmental Comfort Services
N.A.I.C.S.: 238220
Kimberlee Anderson (Pres)
Duane Haley (Sr VP)

Comfort Systems USA (Southwest), Inc. (1)
6875 W Galveston St, Chandler, AZ 85226
Tel.: (480) 940-8400
Web Site: https://csusasw.com
Emp.: 300
Automotive Environmental Comfort Services
N.A.I.C.S.: 238220
Joe Nichter (Pres)
Nate Nelson (Pres)
Scott Sawyer (CFO)
Tim Plaster (Exec VP)
Todd Stanfield (VP)
Mike Smith (VP)

Comfort Systems USA (Syracuse), Inc. (1)
6500 New Venture Gear Dr, East Syracuse, NY 13057
Tel.: (315) 425-7100
Web Site: https://www.csusasyr.com
Emp.: 200
Automotive Environmental Comfort Services
N.A.I.C.S.: 238220
Thomas J. Billone (Pres & CEO)

Comfort Systems USA Energy Services, Inc. (1)
7 Waterside Crossing, Windsor, CT 06095
Tel.: (877) 898-2086
Automotive Environmental Comfort Services
N.A.I.C.S.: 238220

Control Concepts, LLC (1)
119 N Post Oak Rd, Sulphur, LA 70663
Tel.: (337) 626-0130
Web Site:
    https://www.controlconceptsllc.com
Plumbing Heating & Air-Conditioning Related Services
N.A.I.C.S.: 238220

Decco Inc. (1)
PO Box 330282, Tulsa, OK 74133-0282
Tel.: (918) 481-8722
Industrial Machinery & Equipment Merchant Whslr
N.A.I.C.S.: 423830
Bob Stewart (Mgr-Estimating)

Design Mechanical Incorporated (1)
312 CTC Blvd, Louisville, CO 80027
Tel.: (303) 449-2092
Web Site: https://designmech.com
Emp.: 250
Automotive Environmental Comfort Services
N.A.I.C.S.: 238220

Dilling Group, Inc. (1)
111 E Mildred St, Logansport, IN 46947-0047
Tel.: (574) 753-3182

Comfort Systems USA, Inc.—(Continued)

Web Site: https://www.dillinggroup.com
Engineering Construction Services
N.A.I.C.S.: 541330
Eric Ott *(CEO)*
Mark Parmeter *(Pres)*
Frank Freeman *(Sr VP-Engineering)*
Mike Thrush *(VP-)*
Jerry Hamilton *(VP-)*
Billy Smith *(VP- &)*
Jeff Secrist *(Pres)*

Dyna Ten Corporation (1)
4375 Diplomacy Rd, Fort Worth, TX 76155
Tel.: (817) 616-2200
Web Site: https://dynaten.com
Sales Range: $50-74.9 Million
Emp.: 100
Engineering & Mechanical Contracting Services
N.A.I.C.S.: 541330
Dewayne White *(Controller)*
Matt Morrow *(VP)*
Kyle Hogue *(Pres)*
Michael Jolly *(VP-)*
Larry Elledge *(VP-)*
James Belota *(VP-)*
Barry Koontz *(Mgr)*
Steve Jones *(Dir-Safety)*
Mark Faulkenberry *(Superintendent)*
Wesley Baker *(Exec VP-)*
Grant Grubb *(VP-)*

Dyna Ten Maintenance Services, LLC (1)
4375 Diplomacy Rd, Fort Worth, TX 76155
Tel.: (817) 595-1391
Web Site: http://www.dynaten.com
Electrical Contracting Services
N.A.I.C.S.: 238210

Eastern Heating & Cooling, Inc. (1)
880 Broadway, Albany, NY 12207-1316
Tel.: (518) 465-8878
Web Site: https://easternheatingcooling.com
Sales Range: $25-49.9 Million
Emp.: 90
Automotive Environmental Comfort Services
N.A.I.C.S.: 238220
Richard Kraus *(Mgr-Controls)*
Buddy Tricarick *(Pres)*

Edwards Electrical & Mechanical, Inc. (1)
2350 N Shadeland Ave, Indianapolis, IN 46219
Tel.: (317) 543-3460
Web Site: https://www.edwards-elec.com
Electronic Services
N.A.I.C.S.: 238210
Dale Caldwell *(VP-Charlotte)*
Mike Chapman *(VP-Greenville)*
Allen McKinney *(Pres & CEO)*
Stephen Reynolds *(CFO)*
Corey Arledge *(Exec Dir-Safety)*
Joel Langhals *(VP-Charleston)*
Leland Busby *(VP-Birmingham)*
Michelle Reed *(Mgr-HR)*

Environmental Air Systems, LLC (1)
250 Swathmore Ave, High Point, NC 27263
Tel.: (336) 273-1975
Web Site: https://con.easinc.net
Mechanical Contractor
N.A.I.C.S.: 238220

Envirotrol, LLC (1)
250 Swathmore Ave, High Point, NC 27263
Tel.: (336) 273-9587
Web Site: https://www.envirotrol.net
Emp.: 75
Automotive Environmental Comfort Services
N.A.I.C.S.: 238220

EnvirotrolSC, LLC (1)
7148 Cross County Rd, North Charleston, SC 29418
Tel.: (843) 277-0375
Web Site: http://www.etrol.net
Automation Control System Distr
N.A.I.C.S.: 423610

Granite State Plumbing & Heating, LLC (1)
17 Oil Mill Rd, Weare, NH 03281
Tel.: (603) 529-3322
Web Site: http://www.gsphinc.com
Emp.: 56
Automotive Environmental Comfort Services
N.A.I.C.S.: 238220
Ken Duchesne *(Pres & CEO)*

H & M Mechanical, Inc. (1)
3100 Richard Arrington Jr Blvd N, Birmingham, AL 35203-1313
Tel.: (205) 664-0620
Emp.: 250
Automotive Environmental Comfort Services
N.A.I.C.S.: 238220
Tim Head *(Pres)*

Hayes & Lunsford Electric, LLC (1)
2048 Gibbs Shoals Rd, Greer, SC 29650
Tel.: (864) 297-3198
Web Site: https://hayesandlunsford.com
Electrical Contracting Services
N.A.I.C.S.: 238210

MJ Mechanical Services, Inc. (1)
95 Pirson Pkwy, Tonawanda, NY 14150
Tel.: (716) 874-9200
Web Site: https://www.mjmechanical.com
Automotive Environmental Comfort Services
N.A.I.C.S.: 238220
Dan Fetes *(Pres)*
Nancy Pohlman *(VP)*
Paul Kwiatkowski *(Mgr-HR)*
Sharon Boyer *(Dir-Safety)*
Tom Bauer *(Engr-Project Design)*
Mike Clancy *(Engr-Project Design)*
Terry Clancy *(Engr-Project Design)*
Mark Poole *(Engr-Project Design)*
Roger Hoffman *(Engr-Project Design)*
Dick Lynch *(Engr-Project Design)*
Tom Dempsey *(Gen Mgr-Svc)*
Mike Kriegbaum *(Mgr-Acct)*
Rick Krakomberger *(Engr-Controls)*
Tim McKillen *(Gen Mgr-Controls)*
Scott Bochocki *(Gen Mgr-Ops)*
Dave Schasel *(Mgr-Project)*
Steve Neureuther *(Mgr-Warehouse)*
Scott Kazmierczak *(Superintendent-Piping)*
Bob Flegal *(Project Mgr)*
Pete Haen *(Mgr-Shop)*

Mechanical Technical Services, Inc. (1)
1720 Royston Ln, Round Rock, TX 78664
Tel.: (512) 929-7090
Web Site: https://mtechtexas.com
Emp.: 150
Automotive Environmental Comfort Services
N.A.I.C.S.: 238220

Quality Air Heating and Cooling, Inc. (1)
3395 Kraft Ave SE, Grand Rapids, MI 49512
Tel.: (616) 956-0200
Automotive Environmental Comfort Services
N.A.I.C.S.: 238220
Tim Albers *(Pres)*

Riddleberger Brothers, Inc. (1)
6127 S Valley Pike, Mount Crawford, VA 22841
Tel.: (540) 434-1731
Web Site: https://www.rbiva.com
Construction Engineering Services
N.A.I.C.S.: 541330
Daniel Blosser *(Pres)*
Wayne Gibson *(VP-)*
Kirk Adams *(VP- & Business Development)*
Connie Newman *(CFO)*
Matt Landes *(VP-)*

Royalaire Mechanical Services, LLC (1)
101 Dunbar Ave Ste D, Oldsmar, FL 34677
Tel.: (813) 749-2370
Web Site: https://www.royalaire.com
Mechanical Contractor Services
N.A.I.C.S.: 238220

S.I. Goldman Co., Inc. (1)
799 Bennett Dr, Longwood, FL 32750-7591
Tel.: (407) 830-5000
Web Site: https://www.sigoldmanco.com
Sales Range: $10-24.9 Million
Emp.: 160
Mechanical Contractor Plumbing, Heating & Air Conditioning

N.A.I.C.S.: 238220
Roy L. Burkett *(Pres)*
Sandro Cornelio *(VP-Business Development)*
Mark Woehrle *(Dir-Operations)*
Dustin Prill *(VP-Operations)*
Jacquie Brooks *(Dir-Human Resources)*

S.M. Lawrence Company, Inc. (1)
245 Preston St, Jackson, TN 38301-4966
Tel.: (731) 423-0112
Web Site: https://smlawrence.com
Sales Range: $75-99.9 Million
Emp.: 300
Automotive Environmental Comfort Services
N.A.I.C.S.: 238220

Seasonair, Inc. (1)
16001 Industrial Dr Ste A, Gaithersburg, MD 20877-1448
Tel.: (301) 670-4750
Web Site: https://seasonairinc.com
Automotive Environmental Comfort Services
N.A.I.C.S.: 238220

Shoffnerkalthoff Mechanical Electrical Service, LLC (1)
3600 Papermill Dr, Knoxville, TN 37909
Tel.: (865) 523-1129
Web Site: http://www.skmes.com
Emp.: 500
Plumbing, Heating & Air-Conditioning Services
N.A.I.C.S.: 238220

Starr Electric Co. Inc. (1)
6 Battleground Ct, Greensboro, NC 27408-8007
Tel.: (336) 275-0241
Web Site: https://www.starrelectric.net
Sales Range: $100-124.9 Million
Emp.: 1,000
Electrical Contracting Services
N.A.I.C.S.: 238210
Philip A. Campolo *(CFO)*
Harley Garrison *(CEO)*
Dan Thomas *(Sr VP-Operations)*
Allen Holloman *(VP)*
Leon Smith *(VP)*
Mark Mercer *(VP)*
Dan Thomas *(Sr VP-Operations)*
Allen Holloman *(VP)*
Leon Smith *(VP)*
Mark Mercer *(VP)*

Subsidiary (Domestic):

Starr Electric Company (2)
1808 Norland Rd, Charlotte, NC 28205-5708 (100%)
Tel.: (704) 568-6600
Web Site: https://www.starrelectric.net
Sales Range: $10-24.9 Million
Emp.: 40
Providers of Electrical Services
N.A.I.C.S.: 238210
Dan Thomas *(Sr VP-Ops)*
Mark Mercer *(VP-Preconstruction)*
Kevin Berkebile *(VP)*

TAS Energy, Inc. (1)
6110 Cullen Blvd, Houston, TX 77021
Tel.: (713) 877-8700
Web Site: https://www.tas.com
Sales Range: $10-24.9 Million
Emp.: 100
Turbine Mfr
N.A.I.C.S.: 333611
J.T. Grumski *(Pres & CEO)*

The Capital Refrigeration Company (1)
619 E Jefferson St, Montgomery, AL 36104
Tel.: (334) 263-0201
Emp.: 50
Automotive Environmental Comfort Services
N.A.I.C.S.: 238220
Jeffrey Lambert *(VP)*

Thermal Equipment Service, Inc. (1)
680 Bizzell Dr, Lexington, KY 40510
Tel.: (859) 255-9665
Web Site: https://www.thermaleq.com
Industrial Equipment Distr
N.A.I.C.S.: 423730
Chris Taylor *(CEO)*
Tom Erpenbeck *(Sys Engr)*
Jodie Beadles *(Sys Engr)*
John Puryear *(VP)*
Paul Mattingly III *(Sys Engr)*

Trumbo Electric, Incorporated (1)
258 N Timber Way, Broadway, VA 22815-3636
Tel.: (540) 896-7095
Web Site: https://trumboelectric.com
Electrical Contractor Services
N.A.I.C.S.: 238210
Shanna Billhimer *(Pres)*
Jeremy Sonifrank *(VP-Bus Dev)*
Tim Kimberlain *(VP-Ops)*

COMMERCE BANCSHARES, INC.
1000 Walnut, Kansas City, MO 64106
Tel.: (816) 234-2000   MO
Web Site:
  https://www.commercebank.com
Year Founded: 1966
CBSH—(NASDAQ)
Rev.: $1,954,336,000
Assets: $31,701,061,000
Liabilities: $28,736,831,000
Net Worth: $2,964,230,000
Earnings: $477,060,000
Emp.: 4,592
Fiscal Year-end: 12/31/23
Bank Holding Company
N.A.I.C.S.: 551111
David W. Kemper *(Exec Chm)*
Charles G. Kim *(CFO & Exec VP)*
Patricia R. Kellerhals *(Sr VP)*
John W. Kemper *(Pres & CEO)*
Robert S. Holmes *(Exec VP)*
David L. Roller *(CIO & Sr VP)*
Paul A. Steiner *(Chief Acctg Officer & Controller)*
David L. Orf *(Chief Credit Officer & Exec VP)*
Derrick R. Brooks *(Sr VP)*
Kim L. Jakovich *(Sr VP)*

Subsidiaries:

Capital for Business, Inc. (1)
11 S Meramec Ste 1330, Saint Louis, MO 63105 (99%)
Tel.: (314) 746-7427
Web Site: https://www.cfb.com
Sales Range: $50-74.9 Million
Emp.: 3,400
Private Investment Firm
N.A.I.C.S.: 523999
Stephen P. Broun *(Mng Partner)*
William S. Witzofsky *(Sr VP)*
Chris Redmond *(Sr VP)*
Tim Buening *(VP)*
Matt Leinauer *(VP)*
Eddie Trigo *(VP)*
Jim Frazer *(Operating Partner)*
Don Hickerson *(Operating Partner)*

Holding (Domestic):

DIT-MCO International (2)
5612 Brighton Ter, Kansas City, MO 64130
Tel.: (816) 444-9700
Web Site: https://www.ditmco.com
Electronic Test Equipment Mfr
N.A.I.C.S.: 334515
Karl Sweers *(Sls Mgr-Intl)*
Brent Stringham *(Dir-Sls, Mktg & Customer Svc)*

Perennial Energy, LLC (2)
1375 County Rd 8690, West Plains, MO 65775
Tel.: (417) 256-2002
Web Site: https://perennialenergy.com
Sales Range: $1-9.9 Million
Waste Gas Processing Systems & Equipment Designer, Mfr & Distr
N.A.I.C.S.: 333998

Commerce Bank, N.A. (1)
922 Walnut st, Kansas City, MO 64106-2123 (100%)
Tel.: (816) 234-2000
Web Site: https://www.commercebank.com
Sales Range: $500-549.9 Million
Emp.: 4,000
National Bank
N.A.I.C.S.: 522110
A. Bayard Clark *(CFO)*

Subsidiary (Domestic):

Commerce Brokerage Services, Inc. (2)

1000 Walnut Ste 201, Kansas City, MO
64106
Tel.: (816) 234-2416
Web Site: https://www.commerce-
brokerage.com
Sales Range: $1-9.9 Million
Emp.: 4
Discount Brokerage Service, Trading
Stocks, Options, Mutual Funds, Bonds
N.A.I.C.S.: 522110

Commerce Insurance Services, **(2)**
Inc.
8000 Forsyth Blvd, Saint Louis, MO
63105 **(100%)**
Tel.: (314) 726-2255
Web Site:
https://www.commerceinsurance.com
Sales Range: $75-99.9 Million
Emp.: 4
Credit Life Reinsurance
N.A.I.C.S.: 524298

Commerce Mortgage Corp. **(2)**
922 Walnut St Ste 1100, Kansas City, MO
64106-2166 **(100%)**
Tel.: (816) 234-2990
Web Site: http://www.commercialbank.com
Sales Range: $50-74.9 Million
Emp.: 125
Mortgage Bankers & Loan Correspondents
N.A.I.C.S.: 522310
Jeff Gerner *(VP)*
Mark Heider *(VP)*

COMMERCE GROUP CORP.
N8 W22577 Johnson Dr, Waukesha,
WI 53186
Tel.: (262) 522-8139   WI
Web Site:
http://www.commercegroup
corp.com
Year Founded: 1962
CGCO—(OTCEM)
Emp.: 20
Gold Mining Services
N.A.I.C.S.: 551112
Sidney Sodos *(Treas & VP)*
Christine M. Wolski *(Sec)*
John H. Curry *(Exec VP)*

Subsidiaries:

Commerce/Sanseb Joint Venture **(1)**
6001 N 91st St N 8 W 22577 Johnson Dr,
Waukesha, WI 53186-1721 **(90%)**
Tel.: (414) 462-5310
Web Site:
http://www.commercegroupcorp.com
Sales Range: Less than $1 Million
Emp.: 2
Gold Ore Mining
N.A.I.C.S.: 212220

Ecomm Group, Inc. **(1)**
6001 N 91st St, Milwaukee, WI
53225-1721 **(100%)**
Tel.: (414) 462-5310
Web Site:
http://www.commercegroupcorp.com
Sales Range: Less than $1 Million
Emp.: 3
Organizer of Mergers & Acquisitions in the
Internet Portal Industry
N.A.I.C.S.: 531210

Homespan Realty Co., Inc. **(1)**
6001 N 91st St, Milwaukee, WI
53225-1721 **(100%)**
Tel.: (414) 462-5310
Sales Range: $25-49.9 Million
Emp.: 3
Real Estate Sales: Inactive
N.A.I.C.S.: 459120

Mineral San Sebastian, S.A. de
C.V.
Apdo Postal 01-166, Av Antiguo Cuscatlan
13, Colonia La Sultano, San Salvador, El
Salvador
Tel.: (503) 26693646
Emp.: 10
Gold Mining
N.A.I.C.S.: 212220

San Sebastian Gold Mines, Inc. **(1)**

N 8 W 22577 Johnson Dr, Waukesha, WI
53186 **(82.5%)**
Tel.: (414) 462-5310
Sales Range: $1-9.9 Million
Emp.: 4
Gold Mining-Gold Ore Reserves
N.A.I.C.S.: 212220

COMMERCEWEST BANK
2445 McCabe Way Ste 300, Irvine,
CA 92614
Tel.: (949) 251-6959   CA
Web Site: https://www.cwbk.com
Year Founded: 2001
CWBK—(OTCIQ)
Commercial Banking Services
N.A.I.C.S.: 522110
Ivo Tjan *(Chm & CEO)*
Leeann Cochran *(CFO)*

COMMERCIAL METALS COM-
PANY
6565 N MacArthur Blvd Ste 800, Ir-
ving, TX 75039
Tel.: (214) 689-4300   DE
Web Site: https://www.cmc.com
Year Founded: 1915
CMC—(NYSE)
Rev.: $7,925,972,000
Assets: $6,817,839,000
Liabilities: $2,517,815,000
Net Worth: $4,300,024,000
Earnings: $485,491,000
Emp.: 13,178
Fiscal Year-end: 08/31/24
Low-Cost Metals Recycling, Manufac-
turing, Fabricating & Trading Services
N.A.I.C.S.: 423510
Ty Garrison *(Sr VP-Operational &
Comml Excellence)*
Tim Bourcier *(VP-Central Reg)*
Brad Cottrell *(Chief Supply Chain Of-
ficer & VP)*
Ty Garrison *(Sr VP-Ops & VP-Ops &
Strategy)*
Steve Henderson *(VP-West Reg)*
Kolin Keller *(VP-Ops Support)*
Paul J. Lawrence *(CFO & VP)*
Jerzy Kozicz *(Mng Dir-Poland)*
Billy Milligan *(VP-Mktg & Enterprise
Support)*
Jody K. Absher *(Chief Legal Officer,
Sec & Sr VP)*
Jennifer J. Durbin *(Chief Comm Offi-
cer, Chief HR Officer & Sr VP)*
Lindsay L. Sloan *(Chief Acctg Officer
& VP)*
Peter R. Matt *(Pres & CEO)*

Subsidiaries:

Advanced Steel Recovery LLC **(1)**
14451 Whittram Ave, Fontana, CA 92335
Tel.: (909) 355-2372
Web Site: http://www.advancedsteel.com
Hazardous Waste Treatment & Disposal
N.A.I.C.S.: 562111

CMC (Australia) Pty Limited **(1)**
Tel.: (61) 295856222
Web Site: http://www.cmcaustralia.com.au
Sales Range: $25-49.9 Million
Emp.: 60
Mfr of Steel Products
N.A.I.C.S.: 331110

Branch (Non-US):

CMC (Australia) Pty Limited **(2)**
(100%)
Tel.: (61) 398050400
Web Site: http://www.cmcaustralia.com.au
Sales Range: $10-24.9 Million
Emp.: 20
Mfr of Steel Products
N.A.I.C.S.: 331110

CMC (Beijing) International Trade
Company Ltd. **(1)**
Suite 2208 22nd Floor One Indigo 20 Jiuxianqiao Road, Chaoyang District, Beijing,
100016, China

Tel.: (86) 1059540000
Web Site: http://www.cmc.com
Sales Range: $25-49.9 Million
Emp.: 42
Steel Products Mfr
N.A.I.C.S.: 331110
Weston Liu *(Pres)*

CMC Centrozlom Sp. z o.o. **(1)**
ul Surowcowa 30, Katowice, 40-431, Poland
Tel.: (48) 322557321
Web Site: http://www.cmc.com
Scrap Processing & Recycling Services
N.A.I.C.S.: 331492

CMC Construction Services **(1)**
8901 E Almeda Rd, Houston, TX 77054
Tel.: (713) 794-9802
Web Site:
http://www.cmcconstructionservices.com
Sales Range: $200-249.9 Million
Emp.: 500
Concrete Accessories Forming & Shoring
N.A.I.C.S.: 423510

CMC Construction Services Inc **(1)**
2300 1st St NW, Albuquerque, NM 87102-
1083
Tel.: (505) 247-4344
Sales Range: $25-49.9 Million
Emp.: 26
Rebar Fabricating Shop
N.A.I.C.S.: 423510

CMC Europe AG **(1)**
Lindenstrasse 14, CH-6340, Baar,
Switzerland **(100%)**
Tel.: (41) 417669666
Web Site: http://www.cmc.com
Sales Range: $25-49.9 Million
Emp.: 40
Metals Service Centers & Offices
N.A.I.C.S.: 423510

Subsidiary (Non-US):

CMC Poland Sp. z o.o. **(2)**
ul Pilsudskiego 82, 42-400, Zawiercie, Po-
land
Tel.: (48) 326721621
Web Site: http://www.cmcpoland.com
Seal Products Distr
N.A.I.C.S.: 423510
Dorota Apostel-Krzyzaniak *(Member-Mgmt
Bd)*
Jerzy Kozicz *(Chm-Mgmt Bd & Mng Dir)*
Adam Guzy *(Member-Mgmt Bd)*
Wojciech Wieclawik *(Vice Chm-Mgmt Bd)*
Tomasz Flak *(Member-Mgmt Bd)*
Marcin Kulesza *(Member-Mgmt Bd)*
Jolanta Czeczko *(Member-Mgmt Bd)*
Monika Bien-Tomaszewska *(Member-Mgmt
Bd)*
Barbara Kaleta *(Member-Mgmt Bd)*
Tracy Porter *(Chm-Supervisory Bd)*

Subsidiary (Domestic):

Scrapena S.A. **(3)**
ul Lubliniecka 41, Herby, 42-284, Poland
Tel.: (48) 343574242
Scrap Metal Services
N.A.I.C.S.: 423510

Subsidiary (Non-US):

CMC UK Ltd. **(2)**
Building 1 Trident Park Glass Ave Ocean
Way, Cardiff, CF24 5EN, United Kingdom
Tel.: (44) 2920 895260
Web Site: http://www.cmc.com
Sales Range: $1-9.9 Million
Emp.: 5
Steel Distr & Processor
N.A.I.C.S.: 238120
John Elmore *(Pres-CMC Intl Div & Sr VP)*

Commercial Metals Deutschland
GmbH **(2)**
Web Site: http://www.cmc.com
Mfr of Steel Products
N.A.I.C.S.: 331221

CMC Europe GmbH **(1)**
Lindenstrasse 14, 6340, Baar, Switzerland
Tel.: (41) 417669666
Metal Mining Services
N.A.I.C.S.: 212290

CMC Fareast Limited **(1)**
Unit C 12th Fl Neich Tower, 128 Gloucester

Rd, Wanchai, China (Hong Kong) **(100%)**
Tel.: (852) 25110218
Web Site: http://www.cmc.com
Sales Range: $150-199.9 Million
Metals Service Centers & Offices
N.A.I.C.S.: 423510

CMC GH Sisak d.o.o. **(1)**
Ulica Grada Vukovara 269S, Zagreb,
10000, Croatia
Tel.: (385) 16199930
Metal Mining Services
N.A.I.C.S.: 212290

CMC Putex Sp.z o.o. **(1)**
ul Paderewskiego 61, 42-400, Zawiercie,
Poland
Tel.: (48) 326725227
Web Site: https://www.putex.pl
Tourism & Catering Services
N.A.I.C.S.: 561591

CMC Rebar **(1)**
4846 Singleton Blvd, Dallas, TX 75212
Tel.: (214) 631-5250
Sales Range: $50-74.9 Million
Emp.: 100
Metals Service Centers & Offices
N.A.I.C.S.: 423510

Subsidiary (Domestic):

CMC Rebar **(2)**
18 Lavelle Ladner Rd, Lumberton, MS
39455
Tel.: (601) 796-5474
Rev.: $5,000,000
Emp.: 11
Rebar Fabrication
N.A.I.C.S.: 332322

CMC Receivables, Inc. **(1)**
6565 N MacArthur Blvd Ste 800, Irving, TX
75039
Tel.: (214) 689-4300
Metal Products Services
N.A.I.C.S.: 423510

CMC Recycling **(1)**
6565 N MacArthur Blvd Ste 800, Irving, TX
75039 **(100%)**
Tel.: (214) 689-4300
Web Site: http://www.cmc.com
Sales Range: $1-4.9 Billion
Emp.: 1,377
Ferrous & Non-Ferrous Metal Recycling
N.A.I.C.S.: 562920

Subsidiary (Domestic):

CMC Recycling **(2)**
7100 Broadway St, Galveston, TX
77554 **(100%)**
Tel.: (409) 744-3695
Sales Range: $25-49.9 Million
Emp.: 35
Scrap Ferrous & Non-Ferrous Metals Recy-
cler & Merchant
N.A.I.C.S.: 423930

CMC Recycling **(2)**
2308 2 Notch Rd, Lexington, SC 29072-
8996
Tel.: (803) 359-6137
Web Site: http://www.cmcrecycling.com
Sales Range: $25-49.9 Million
Emp.: 100
Metal Scrap & Metal Products Distr
N.A.I.C.S.: 333998

CMC Steel Distribution Pty Ltd **(1)**
73-90 Lenore Ln, Erskine Park, 2761, NSW,
Australia
Tel.: (61) 296708400
Steel Product Distr
N.A.I.C.S.: 423510
Neil Lobb *(Gen Mgr-Sheet & Coil & Pro-
cessing)*

CMC Steel Fabricators, Inc. **(1)**
1 Steel Mill Dr, Seguin, TX 78155 **(100%)**
Tel.: (830) 372-8200
Steel Products Fabrication Services
N.A.I.C.S.: 331222

Subsidiary (Domestic):

MMFX Technologies Corp. **(2)**
11444 E Germann Rd, Mesa, AZ 85212
Tel.: (866) 466-7878
Steel Mfrs

Commercial Metals Company—(Continued)
N.A.I.C.S.: 331513
Thomas Russo (Gen Mgr)

CMC Steel Group (1)
6565 N MacArthur Blvd Ste 800, Irving, TX
75039
Tel.: (830) 372-8214
Web Site: http://www.cmcsg.com
Sales Range: $150-199.9 Million
Holding Company
N.A.I.C.S.: 331221

Unit (Domestic):

CMC Alamo Steel (2)
2784 Old Dallas Rd, Waco, TX
76705-4849 (100%)
Tel.: (254) 799-2471
Web Site: http://www.cmc.com
Sales Range: $75-99.9 Million
Emp.: 120
Steel Fabrication
N.A.I.C.S.: 332312

CMC Alamo Victoria (2)
255 Skytop Rd, Victoria, TX 77905
Tel.: (361) 575-4561
Web Site: http://www.cmc.com
Sales Range: $50-74.9 Million
Emp.: 100
Steel Fabrication
N.A.I.C.S.: 336510

CMC Metal Recycling (Augusta) (2)
1890 Old Savannah Rd, Augusta, GA
30901-3730 (100%)
Tel.: (706) 434-2450
Sales Range: $50-74.9 Million
Emp.: 28
Scrap Ferrous & Non-Ferrous Metals Recycler & Merchant
N.A.I.C.S.: 441330

CMC Metal Recycling (Cayce) (2)
603 Godley St, Cayce, SC
29033-3708 (100%)
Tel.: (803) 926-0060
Web Site:
http://www.cmcmetalrecycling.com
Sales Range: $50-74.9 Million
Emp.: 10
Scrap Ferrous & Non-Ferrous Metal Recycler & Merchant
N.A.I.C.S.: 562920

CMC Metal Recycling (Lexington) (2)
2308 2 Notch Rd, Lexington, SC
29072 (100%)
Tel.: (803) 359-6137
Sales Range: $50-74.9 Million
Emp.: 80
Scrap Ferrous & Non-Ferrous Metal Recycler & Merchants
N.A.I.C.S.: 562920

CMC Metal Recycling (Seguin) (2)
1558 N Austin St, Seguin, TX
78155-2646 (100%)
Tel.: (830) 372-8550
Sales Range: $25-49.9 Million
Emp.: 15
Scrap Ferrous & Non-Ferrous Metals Recycler & Merchant
N.A.I.C.S.: 562920

CMC Rebar (2)
12451 Arrow Route, Etiwanda, CA
91739 (100%)
Tel.: (909) 899-9993
Web Site: http://www.cmc.com
Sales Range: $100-124.9 Million
Emp.: 300
Reinforced Steel Engineering, Fabricating & Placing
N.A.I.C.S.: 238190

CMC Rebar (2)
6802 Safety Steel Dr, Corpus Christi, TX
78414-5755
Tel.: (361) 991-2510
Web Site: http://www.cmcsg.com
Sales Range: $25-49.9 Million
Emp.: 20
Reinforcing Steel Fabricator
N.A.I.C.S.: 238220

CMC Rebar Carolinas (2)
2105 S Beltline Blvd, Columbia, SC 29201

Tel.: (803) 254-4660
Web Site: http://www.cmc.com
Sales Range: $25-49.9 Million
Emp.: 45
Rebar Fabrication
N.A.I.C.S.: 332312

CMC Rebar Florida (2)
9625 Florida Mining Blvd, Jacksonville, FL
32257 (100%)
Tel.: (904) 262-9770
Sales Range: $25-49.9 Million
Emp.: 13
Providers of Steel Fabrication Services
N.A.I.C.S.: 332312

CMC Rebar Georgia (2)
251 Hosea Rd, Lawrenceville, GA 30046
Tel.: (770) 963-6251
Sales Range: $50-74.9 Million
Emp.: 100
Steel Products Mfr
N.A.I.C.S.: 332312

CMC Rebar North Carolina (2)
2528 N Chester St, Gastonia, NC
28052-1808 (100%)
Tel.: (704) 865-8571
Web Site: http://www.cmc.com
Sales Range: $50-74.9 Million
Emp.: 50
Mfr of Steel Products
N.A.I.C.S.: 332312

CMC Rebar Virginia (2)
9434 Crossroads Pkwy, Fredericksburg, VA
22408-1734 (100%)
Tel.: (540) 898-1111
Web Site: http://www.cmc.com
Sales Range: $50-74.9 Million
Emp.: 45
Mfr of Steel Products
N.A.I.C.S.: 332312

CMC Steel Alabama (2)
101 S 50th St, Birmingham, AL
35212-3525 (100%)
Tel.: (205) 592-8981
Sales Range: $200-249.9 Million
Emp.: 420
Steel Products Mfr
N.A.I.C.S.: 331110

CMC Steel Arkansas (2)
100 Columbia 7-B, Magnolia, AR
71753 (100%)
Tel.: (870) 234-8703
Web Site: http://www.cmcsteelar.com
Sales Range: $125-149.9 Million
Emp.: 287
Steel Products Mfr
N.A.I.C.S.: 332312

CMC Steel South Carolina (2)
310 New State Rd, Cayce, SC
29033-3704 (100%)
Tel.: (803) 936-3700
Sales Range: $75-99.9 Million
Emp.: 290
Steel Products Mfr
N.A.I.C.S.: 331110

CMC Steel Texas (2)
1 Steel Mill Dr, Seguin, TX 78155 (100%)
Web Site: http://www.cmcsteeltexas.com
Sales Range: $400-449.9 Million
Emp.: 856
Steel Products Mfr
N.A.I.C.S.: 331110
Phil Seidenberger (Exec VP & Gen Mgr)

CMC Sterling Steel (2)
2001 Brittmoore Rd, Houston, TX 77043-
2208
Tel.: (713) 225-4446
Web Site: http://www.cmcststl.com
Sales Range: $50-74.9 Million
Emp.: 85
Steel Bar Fabrication
N.A.I.C.S.: 332312

CMC Texas Cold Finished Steel, Inc. (2)
235 Port Wall St, Houston, TX 77029-1208
Tel.: (713) 225-4446
Web Site: http://www.cmcsg.com
Sales Range: $50-74.9 Million
Emp.: 60
Steel Fabrication
N.A.I.C.S.: 332312

Unit (Non-US):

South Carolina Steel (2)
(100%)
Tel.: (864) 244-2860
Sales Range: $75-99.9 Million
Emp.: 165
Steel Fabrication
N.A.I.C.S.: 332312

Unit (Domestic):

Southern Post Company (2)
100 Columbia 7B, Magnolia, AR 71753
Tel.: (870) 234-8703
Sales Range: $300-349.9 Million
Emp.: 280
Mfr of Steel Products
N.A.I.C.S.: 324199
Pete Dichak (VP-Sls)
Jimmy Glass (Mgr-Mill)

Subsidiary (Domestic):

Southern Post Company-Texas (3)
440 Wonder World Dr, San Marcos, TX
78666-5941
Tel.: (512) 396-0300
Sales Range: $25-49.9 Million
Emp.: 25
Mfrof Steel Products
N.A.I.C.S.: 331110

Southern Post Company-Utah (3)
920 W 600 N, Brigham City, UT
84302-1771 (100%)
Tel.: (435) 734-2785
Sales Range: $25-49.9 Million
Emp.: 25
Mfr of Steel Products
N.A.I.C.S.: 331110
Jason Jimson (Plant Mgr)

Southern Post South Carolina (3)
850 Taylor St, Cayce, SC 29033
Tel.: (803) 926-7100
Sales Range: $25-49.9 Million
Emp.: 22
Mfr of Steel Products
N.A.I.C.S.: 332312

CMC Steel Oklahoma, LLC (1)
584 Old Hwy 70, Durant, OK 74701
Tel.: (580) 634-5200
Metal Merchant Whslr
N.A.I.C.S.: 423510

Coil Steels Group Pty Limited (1)
Tel.: (61) 296821266
Sales Range: $250-299.9 Million
Holding Company
N.A.I.C.S.: 551112

Subsidiary (Non-US):

Coil Steels (Aust) Pty Limited (2)
Tel.: (61) 296821266
Sales Range: $100-124.9 Million
Steel Processing
N.A.I.C.S.: 332111

Coil Steels Long Products (2)
Tel.: (61) 894532033
Web Site: http://www.coilsteels.com
Sales Range: $50-74.9 Million
Emp.: 100
Steel Producer
N.A.I.C.S.: 332111

Coil Steels Processing (2)
Tel.: (61) 732774523
Web Site: http://www.coilsteels.com
Sales Range: $75-99.9 Million
Emp.: 150
Steel Processing
N.A.I.C.S.: 332111

Coil Steels Trading Pty Ltd (2)
Tel.: (61) 0296708400
Web Site: http://www.coilsteels.com.au
Coated & Uncoated Sheet & Coil Steels
Processor & Distr
N.A.I.C.S.: 332111

Cometals Far East, Inc. (2)
6565 N MacArthur Blvd Ste 800, Irving, TX
75039
Tel.: (214) 689-4300
Web Site: http://www.cmc.com
Sales Range: $100-124.9 Million
Emp.: 4,500
Steel Processing

N.A.I.C.S.: 332111

Commercial Metals (International) AG (1)
Lindenstrasse 14, Baar, 6340, ZG, Switzerland
Tel.: (41) 417669666
Web Site: http://www.cmceu.com
Sales Range: $25-49.9 Million
Emp.: 57
Metals Processing
N.A.I.C.S.: 423510

Commercial Metals SF/JV Company (1)
6565 N Macarthur Blvd, Irving, TX 75039-
2490
Tel.: (214) 689-4300
Sales Range: $150-199.9 Million
Emp.: 500
Metal Products Services
N.A.I.C.S.: 423510

Edsco Fasteners, LLC (1)
2200 Worthington Dr, Denton, TX 76207
Tel.: (866) 443-3726
Web Site: http://www.edsco.com
Quality Anchor Bolts Mfr
N.A.I.C.S.: 332722
Jim Cox (Dir-Quality & Safety)
Cullen Johnson (Dir-Ops & Continuous Improvement)
Miley Akers (Dir-Sls & New Bus Dev)
Darron Chrane (Dir-Supply Chain)
Susan Heckendorn (Mgr-Acctg)

Europickling NV (1)
Durmakker 31, 9940, Evergem, Belgium
Tel.: (32) 92570630
Web Site: https://www.europickling.com
Sales Range: $25-49.9 Million
Emp.: 45
Toll Processing & Coil Pickling
N.A.I.C.S.: 332312

G.A.M. Steel Pty. Ltd. (1)
557 Mount Derrimut Road, Derrimut, 3030,
VIC, Australia
Tel.: (61) 383681555
Web Site: http://www.gamsteel.com.au
Steel Product Distr
N.A.I.C.S.: 423510
Andrew Dickson (Gen Mgr)
Loucas Ananidis (Mgr-Pur)
Greg Brennan (Ops Mgr)
Mark Samson (Mgr-Customer Svc)

Gerdau Knoxville Steel Mill (1)
1919 Tennessee Ave NW, Knoxville, TN
37921-2696
Tel.: (865) 546-5472
Web Site: http://www.gerdau.com
Sales Range: $25-40.0 Million
Emp.: 100
Steel Mills
N.A.I.C.S.: 331110

Gerdau Rancho Cucamonga Steel Mill (1)
PO Box 325, Rancho Cucamonga, CA
91739-0325
Tel.: (909) 899-0660
Sales Range: $75-99.9 Million
Emp.: 300
Mfr of Steel Reinforcing Bar, Rod
N.A.I.C.S.: 331110
Carl Krepper (VP-Sls)
Luis Del Rosario (Mgr-Quality Control)
Dennis Fachler (VP-Pur)
Charlie Perry (VP-HR)

Gerdau Sayreville Steel Mill (1)
1 Crossman Rd, Sayreville, NJ 08872
Tel.: (732) 721-6600
Web Site: http://www.gerdau.com
Sales Range: $125-149.9 Million
Emp.: 300
Rolled Steel & Rebar Mfr
N.A.I.C.S.: 331110

Howell Metal Company (1)
574 New Market Depot Rd, New Market,
VA 22844
Tel.: (540) 740-4700
Web Site: http://www.howellmetal.com
Sales Range: $50-74.9 Million
Emp.: 160
Metals Mfr
N.A.I.C.S.: 332117

MC Impacts Metals   (1)
PO Box U, Chicora, PA
16025-0491   (100%)
Tel.: (724) 445-2155
Web Site: http://www.cmc.com
Sales Range: $25-49.9 Million
Emp.: 68
Heat Treatment of Steel
N.A.I.C.S.: 332811

**Owen Electric Steel Company of
South Carolina**   (1)
310 New State Rd, Cayce, SC 29033
Tel.: (803) 936-3700
Web Site: http://www.cmc.com
Emp.: 100
Steel Mills
N.A.I.C.S.: 331110

SMI Steel Inc.   (1)
101 S 50th St, Birmingham, AL 35212
Tel.: (205) 592-8981
Web Site: http://www.cmc.com
Steel Mfr & Distr
N.A.I.C.S.: 331110

Safety Railway Service   (1)
Warehouse Rd, Victoria, TX 77905-1819
Tel.: (361) 576-2141
Sales Range: $50-74.9 Million
Emp.: 130
Producer of Fabricated Structural Metal
N.A.I.C.S.: 336510
Dennis McReynolds *(Gen Mgr)*
Tommy Loest *(Mgr-Pur)*

Tendon Systems, LLC   (1)
7340 McGinnis Ferry Rd Ste 100, Suwanee, GA 30024
Tel.: (678) 835-1100
Web Site: http://www.tendonllc.com
Single-Family Housing
N.A.I.C.S.: 236115
Bradford J. Raffensperger *(CEO)*

Tensar Corporation, LLC   (1)
2500 Northwinds Pkwy Ste 500, Alpharetta, GA 30009-2247
Tel.: (770) 344-2090
Sales Range: $150-199.9 Million
Specialty Products & Engineering Services for the Mining, Erosion Prevention & Solid Waste Industries
N.A.I.C.S.: 541330
Robert F. Briggs *(Gen Counsel, Sec & VP-Admin)*
Bryan Gee *(Dir-Education & Training)*
Mark Koepsel *(Exec VP-Ops)*
Joe Cavanaugh *(Exec VP-Tech & Product Mktg)*
Tim Oliver *(VP-Global Product Mgmt & Tech)*

Subsidiary (Domestic):

Geopier Foundation Company   (2)
130 Harbour Place Dr Ste 280, Davidson, NC 28036
Tel.: (704) 439-1790
Web Site: https://www.geopier.com
Sales Range: $1-9.9 Million
Emp.: 10
Engineering Services
N.A.I.C.S.: 541330
Kord Wissmann *(Pres)*

North American Green Inc.   (2)
5401 St Wendel-Cynthiana Rd, Poseyville, IN 47633
Tel.: (812) 867-6632
Web Site: http://www.tensarnagreen.com
Emp.: 100
Erosion & Sediment Control Products & Systems Mfr & Distr
N.A.I.C.S.: 325320
I. Tim Lancaster *(Mgr-Sls-ND,SD,NE,KS,MO,IL,IA,MN,WI)*

**Tensar Geosynthetics (China)
Limited**   (1)
6 Checheng Avenue, Wuhan Economic and Technical Development Zone HanYang District, Wuhan, 430056, China
Tel.: (86) 2784236383
Civil Engineering Services
N.A.I.C.S.: 541330

Tensar International B.V.   (1)
Helftheuvelweg 11, 5222 AV, 's-Hertogenbosch, Netherlands

Tel.: (31) 736241916
Web Site: https://www.tensar.nl
Polymer Grid Product Mfr & Distr
N.A.I.C.S.: 325211

Tensar International Gmbh   (1)
Lengsdorfer Hauprstr 75, 53127, Bonn, Germany
Tel.: (49) 228913920
Web Site: https://www.tensar.de
Civil Engineering Services
N.A.I.C.S.: 541330

Tensar International Limited   (1)
Units 2-4 Cunningham Court Shadsworth Business Park, Blackburn, BB1 2QX, United Kingdom
Tel.: (44) 1254262431
Web Site: https://www.tensar.co.uk
Civil Engineering Services
N.A.I.C.S.: 541330

Tensar International SARL   (1)
46 Rue Victor Hugo, 69200, Venissieux, France
Tel.: (33) 669632020
Web Site: https://www.tensar.fr
Polymer Grid Product Mfr & Distr
N.A.I.C.S.: 325211

COMMERCIAL NATIONAL FINANCIAL CORPORATION
900 Ligonier St, Latrobe, PA 15650-1834
Tel.: (724) 539-3501   PA
Web Site:
    https://www.cnbthebankonline.com
Year Founded: 1986
CNAF—(OTCIQ)
Rev.: $16,048,000
Assets: $425,431,000
Liabilities: $356,004,000
Net Worth: $69,427,000
Earnings: $5,713,000
Emp.: 80
Fiscal Year-end: 12/31/20
Bank Holding Company
N.A.I.C.S.: 551111
Gregg E. Hunter *(Vice Chm, Pres & CEO)*
George V. Welty *(Chm)*

Subsidiaries:

**Commercial Bank & Trust of
Pennsylvania**   (1)
900 Ligonier St, Latrobe, PA 15650
Tel.: (724) 539-3501
Web Site: http://www.cbthebank.com
Sales Range: $50-74.9 Million
Emp.: 120
State Commercial Banks
N.A.I.C.S.: 522110
Gregg E. Hunter *(Vice Chm, Pres & CEO)*
Wendy S. Schmucker *(Sec & Sr VP)*
Susan R. Skoloda *(VP, Asst Sec & Asst Treas)*

COMMERCIAL VEHICLE GROUP, INC.
7800 Walton Pkwy, New Albany, OH 43054
Tel.: (614) 289-5360   DE
Web Site: https://www.cvgrp.com
Year Founded: 2002
CVGI—(NASDAQ)
Rev.: $981,553,000
Assets: $470,268,000
Liabilities: $350,228,000
Net Worth: $120,040,000
Earnings: ($21,971,000)
Emp.: 7,600
Fiscal Year-end: 12/31/22
Motor Vehicle Seating & Interior Trim Manufacturing
N.A.I.C.S.: 336360
Kristin Mathers *(Chief HR Officer)*
Minja Zahirovic *(Pres-Warehouse Automation)*
Chung Kin Cheung *(CFO & Exec VP)*
Jeff Tritapoe *(COO)*
James R. Ray Jr. *(Pres & CEO)*

Subsidiaries:

CVG - Alabama   (1)
50 Nances Creek Ind Blvd, Piedmont, AL 36272
Tel.: (256) 447-9051
Web Site: http://www.bostromseating.com
Sales Range: $25-49.9 Million
Emp.: 135
Truck & Off-Highway Vehicle Suspension Seats
N.A.I.C.S.: 336360

CVG - Vonore   (1)
200 National Dr, Vonore, TN 37885-2124
Tel.: (423) 884-6651
Web Site: http://www.cvgrp.com
Sales Range: $200-249.9 Million
Emp.: 500
Mfr of Bus & Truck Seating
N.A.I.C.S.: 336390

**CVG Electrical Systems -
Monona**   (1)
301 W Spruce St, Monona, IA 52159-8035
Tel.: (563) 539-2011
Web Site: http://www.cvg.com
Sales Range: $150-199.9 Million
Emp.: 300
Electrical & Electronic Wire Harness & Related Assemblies Mfr
N.A.I.C.S.: 332618

CVG Sprague Devices, LLC   (1)
527 W Us Hwy 20, Michigan City, IN 46360
Tel.: (800) 245-7691
Commercial Vehicle Parts Mfr
N.A.I.C.S.: 336390

CVS Holdings, Inc.   (1)
310 S Saint Marys St Ste 1515, San Antonio, TX 78205
Tel.: (210) 226-1188
Commercial Vehicle Interior Systems Supplier
N.A.I.C.S.: 336360

KAB Seating AB   (1)
Fagelviksvagen 9 6trp, Stockholm, Sweden
Tel.: (46) 855442700
Seat Designer & Mfr
N.A.I.C.S.: 336360

KAB Seating Limited   (1)
Round Spinney, Northampton, NN3 8RS, United Kingdom
Tel.: (44) 160 479 0500
Web Site: https://www.kabseating.com
Emp.: 250
Seat Designer & Mfr
N.A.I.C.S.: 336360

KAB Seating PTY. LTD.   (1)
Unit 1-3 Building 4 29-41 Lysaght Street, Acacia Ridge, 4110, QLD, Australia
Tel.: (61) 73 344 0500
Web Site: https://www.kabseating.com.au
Seat Designer & Mfr
N.A.I.C.S.: 336360

KAB Seating SA   (1)
Avenue Ernest Solvay 90, 1480, Saintes, Belgium
Tel.: (32) 2 367 1310
Web Site: http://www.kabseating.com
Seat Designer & Mfr
N.A.I.C.S.: 336360

PEKM Kabeltechnik s.r.o.   (1)
Svarovska 698, Straz nad Nisou, 463 03, Liberec, Czech Republic
Tel.: (420) 48 524 8111
Web Site: https://www.pekm.eu
Sales Range: $50-74.9 Million
Emp.: 300
Wire Harness Products Mfr
N.A.I.C.S.: 336320
Milan Hejral *(Mng Dir)*

Sprague Devices, Inc.   (1)
527 W US 20, Michigan City, IN 46360
Tel.: (219) 872-7295
Web Site: https://sprague-devices.com
Emp.: 150
Commercial Vehicle Interior Systems Supplier
N.A.I.C.S.: 336360

Trim Systems Operating Corp.   (1)
7800 Walton Pkwy, New Albany, OH 43054
Tel.: (614) 880-2100

Web Site: http://www.cvgrp.com
Sales Range: $350-399.9 Million
Emp.: 1,000
Mfr & Designer of Truck Interiors & Exterior Trims
N.A.I.C.S.: 336390

Subsidiary (Domestic):

CVG Sprague Division   (2)
527 W US Hwy 20, Michigan City, IN 46360
Tel.: (219) 872-7295
Web Site: http://www.cvgrp.com
Sales Range: $300-349.9 Million
Emp.: 100
Mfr of Windshield Wiper Systems for the Heavy-Duty Truck Market
N.A.I.C.S.: 336390

COMMSCOPE HOLDING COMPANY, INC.
3642 E US Hwy 70, Claremont, NC 28610
Tel.: (828) 459-5000   DE
Web Site:
    https://www.commscope.com
Year Founded: 2010
COMM—(NASDAQ)
Rev.: $5,789,200,000
Assets: $9,371,900,000
Liabilities: $12,340,700,000
Net Worth: ($2,968,800,000)
Earnings: ($1,512,700,000)
Emp.: 20,000
Fiscal Year-end: 12/31/23
Holding Company; Wireless Communications
N.A.I.C.S.: 551112
Charles L. Treadway *(Pres & CEO)*
Kyle Lorentzen *(Chief Transformation Officer & Sr VP)*
Kyle D. Lorentzen *(CFO & Exec VP)*
Claudius E. Watts IV *(Chm)*

Subsidiaries:

ARRIS International plc   (1)
3871 Lakefield Dr Ste 300, Suwanee, GA 30024
Tel.: (678) 473-2000
Web Site: http://www.arris.com
Sales Range: $5-14.9 Billion
Holding Company; Communications Technology & Broadband Network Products Designer, Mfr & Distr
N.A.I.C.S.: 551112

Subsidiary (Domestic):

ARRIS Enterprises LLC   (2)
3871 Lakefield Dr, Suwanee, GA 30024
Tel.: (678) 473-2000
Holding Company; Communications Technology & Broadband Network Products Designer, Mfr & Distr
N.A.I.C.S.: 551112

Subsidiary (Non-US):

ARRIS Belgium BVBA   (3)
Diegem Industrie Excelsiorlaan 89 Pac 813, Zaventem, 1930, Belgium
Tel.: (32) 27216742
Telecommunication Equipment Distr
N.A.I.C.S.: 423690

Division (Domestic):

**ARRIS Group, Inc. - Global
Strategies**   (3)
1825 NW 167th Pl, Beaverton, OR 97006
Tel.: (503) 495-9240
Web Site: http://www.arrisi.com
Sales Range: $25-49.9 Million
Emp.: 30
Broadband Management Services
N.A.I.C.S.: 541512

ARRIS Group, Inc. - Operations   (3)
15 Sterling Dr, Wallingford, CT 06492
Tel.: (203) 303-6400
Web Site: http://www.arrisi.com
Sales Range: $75-99.9 Million
Emp.: 200
Global Supplier of Network Equipment
N.A.I.C.S.: 423610

CommScope Holding Company, Inc.—(Continued)

Subsidiary (Non-US):

ARRIS Solutions U.K., Ltd. (3)
710 Wharfedale Road, Wokingham, RG41
5TP, Berkshire, United Kingdom
Tel.: (44) 1189215500
Communication Equipment Mfr
N.A.I.C.S.: 335929

Subsidiary (Non-US):

ARRIS Sweden A.B. (4)
Teknikringen 2, 583 30, Linkoping, Sweden
Tel.: (46) 13367600
Communication Equipment Mfr
N.A.I.C.S.: 335929

ARRIS Taiwan, Ltd. (4)
1 Lane 232 Baoqiao Rd, Xindian, New Tai-
pei City, 23145, Taiwan
Tel.: (886) 229189145
Communication Equipment Mfr
N.A.I.C.S.: 335929
Bryan Lai (Sr Mgr)

Subsidiary (Domestic):

ARRIS Solutions, Inc. (3)
3871 Lakefield Dr Ste 300, Suwanee, GA
30024
Tel.: (678) 473-2000
Web Site: http://www.arrisi.com
Communications Technology & Broadband
Network Products Designer, Mfr & Distr
N.A.I.C.S.: 334220

Subsidiary (Non-US):

ARRIS Broadband Solutions,
Ltd. (4)
28 Ha Barzel Street, Tel Aviv, 69710, Israel
Tel.: (972) 36071111
Communication Equipment Mfr
N.A.I.C.S.: 335929

ARRIS Group B.V. (4)
Atlas Arena Building Azie Hoogoorddreef 5,
1101 BA, Amsterdam, 1101 BA, Nether-
lands
Tel.: (31) 203112500
Web Site: http://www.arris.com
Electronic Parts & Equipment Distr
N.A.I.C.S.: 449210

ARRIS Group Europe Holding
B.V. (4)
Hoogoorddreef 5, Amsterdam Zuidoost,
1101 BA, Amsterdam, Netherlands
Tel.: (31) 203112500
Holding Company
N.A.I.C.S.: 551112

Subsidiary (Non-US):

ARRIS International Iberia S.L. (5)
Calle Ochandiano 8 - Piso 1 Dr B, Madrid,
28023, Spain
Tel.: (34) 914233855
Web Site: http://www.arris.com
Telecommunication Equipment Distr
N.A.I.C.S.: 423690

Subsidiary (Non-US):

ARRIS Group de Mexico S.A. de
C.V. (4)
Av La Paz 11721 Parque Industrial Pacifico,
22643, Tijuana, 22643, BC, Mexico
Tel.: (52) 6641047200
Web Site: http://www.arris.com
Sales Range: $150-199.9 Million
Emp.: 500
RF Equipment Mfr
N.A.I.C.S.: 423690

Branch (Domestic):

ARRIS Solutions, Inc. - Chicago (4)
2400 Ogden Ave Ste 180, Lisle, IL 60532
Tel.: (630) 281-3000
Web Site: http://www.arrisi.com
Sales Range: $25-49.9 Million
Emp.: 100
Telecommunications Department
N.A.I.C.S.: 334220

ARRIS Solutions, Inc. - Horsham (4)
101 Tournament Dr, Horsham, PA 19044
Tel.: (215) 323-1000

Web Site: http://www.arris.com
Sales Range: $250-299.9 Million
Emp.: 850
Wireless Communications Equipment De-
veloper, Mfr & Distr
N.A.I.C.S.: 334220

Subsidiary (Non-US):

C-COR Argentina S.R.L. (4)
Calle Ortiz 1974 B1852OJB Almirante
Brown - Burzaco 1852, Buenos Aires, Ar-
gentina
Tel.: (54) 1142399000
Communication Equipment Distr
N.A.I.C.S.: 423690

Subsidiary (Domestic):

C-COR Incorporated (4)
60 Decibel Rd, State College, PA 16801
Tel.: (814) 238-2461
Web Site: http://www.arris.com
Sales Range: $450-499.9 Million
Emp.: 1,260
Integrated Network Solutions
N.A.I.C.S.: 334210

Subsidiary (Domestic):

ARRIS Technology, Inc. (3)
101 Tournament Dr, Horsham, PA 19044
Tel.: (215) 323-1000
Communication Equipment Distr
N.A.I.C.S.: 423690

Subsidiary (Domestic):

ARRIS Enterprises, Inc. (4)
3871 Lakefield Dr, Suwanee, GA 30024
Tel.: (678) 473-2000
Communication Equipment Mfr
N.A.I.C.S.: 335929

Subsidiary (Non-US):

ARRIS Communications Ireland
Limited (5)
4300 Cork Airport Business Park Kinsale
Road, Cork, Ireland
Tel.: (353) 217305800
Communication Equipment Mfr
N.A.I.C.S.: 335929

ARRIS Group Japan K.K. (5)
Shinagawa East One Tower 21F 2-16-1 Ko-
nan, Minato-ku, Tokyo, 108-0075, Japan
Tel.: (81) 354617300
Web Site: http://www.arris.com
Emp.: 40
Communication Equipment Distr
N.A.I.C.S.: 423690

ARRIS Technology (Shenzhen) Co.,
Ltd. (5)
South & East Wing 4/F Block 2 Vision
Shenzhen Business Park, Shenzhen, China
Tel.: (86) 75526716300
Communication Equipment Mfr
N.A.I.C.S.: 335929

ARRIS Telecomunicacoes do Brasil
Ltda (5)
Cond Edificio Dumez Av Alfredo Egidio de
Souza Aranha 75, 4 andar conjunto 42,
04726-170, Sao Paulo, Brazil
Tel.: (55) 1127376206
Emp.: 25
Telecommunication Equipment Distr
N.A.I.C.S.: 423690

Subsidiary (Non-US):

ARRIS France S.A.S. (4)
381 Avenue du General de Gaulle, Clamart,
92140, Paris, France
Tel.: (33) 145373661
Communication Equipment Mfr
N.A.I.C.S.: 335929

ARRIS Group Korea, Inc. (4)
1507 Parkview Office Tower Jeongja-dong,
Bundang-gu, Seongnam, Gyeonggi-Do, Ko-
rea (South)
Tel.: (82) 317404217
Communication Equipment Distr
N.A.I.C.S.: 423690

ARRIS Singapore Pte. Ltd. (4)
28 Yan Kit Rd, Singapore, 088271, Singapore

Tel.: (65) 90074274
Building Rental Services
N.A.I.C.S.: 531110

ARRIS Solutions Spain S.L. (4)
Calle Garrotxa Num 10-12 Floor 1 Mod 4B
Oceano 1, Barcelona, Spain
Tel.: (34) 933789140
Telecommunication Equipment Distr
N.A.I.C.S.: 423690
Pablo Guaglianone (Acct VP & Mng Dir)

ARRIS Telecomunicaciones Chile
Ltda. (4)
Avda Cerro el Plomo 5680 Torre 6 oficina
1901, Las Condes, Chile
Tel.: (56) 26784500
Telecommunication Equipment Distr
N.A.I.C.S.: 423690

ARRIS de Mexico S.A. de C.V. (4)
Via de la Innovacion 402 Parque de Investi-
gacion e Innovacion Tecnolog, 66628, Apo-
daca, Nuevo Leon, Mexico
Tel.: (52) 8128818500
Communication Equipment Distr
N.A.I.C.S.: 423690
Jorge Ibarra (Supvr-Production Control)

General Instrument Corporation India
Private Limited (4)
Level 7 8 Lake View Building Blocka No 66
1 Bagmane Tech Parkc, V Raman Nagar
656 KN KR Puram whitefield, Bengaluru,
Karnataka, India
Tel.: (91) 7503991677
Communication Equipment Mfr
N.A.I.C.S.: 335929

Affiliate (Domestic):

ActiveVideo Networks, Inc. (3)
333 W San Carlos St Ste 900, San Jose,
CA 95110 (65%)
Tel.: (408) 931-9200
Web Site: https://www.activevideo.com
Software Publisher
N.A.I.C.S.: 513210
Jeff Miller (Pres & CEO)
Ronald Brockmann (CTO)
Chris Linden (COO)
Matt Andrade (CFO)
Tyler Bell (VP)
Ed Lee (Sr VP-Global)
Martin Gibson (VP)
Amy Ross (VP)
Martin Gibson (VP)
Amy Ross (VP)
Anton Stokes (VP)

Subsidiary (Non-US):

Arris Global Ltd. (3)
Viotoria Road, Saltaire, Chipley, BD10 0LT,
West Yorkshire, United Kingdom
Tel.: (44) 1274532000
Web Site: http://www.arris.com
Digital Television Products & Technology
Designer & Mfr
N.A.I.C.S.: 334310

Subsidiary (US):

ARRIS - Boca Raton (4)
3701 FAU Blvd Ste 200, Boca Raton, FL
33431
Tel.: (561) 995-6000
Web Site: http://www.arris.com
Holding Company; Regional Managing Of-
fice
N.A.I.C.S.: 551112

Subsidiary (Non-US):

ARRIS - Hong Kong (4)
Unit 1011-1013 Tower 1 Grand Central
Plaza, 138 Shatin Rural Committee Road,
Sha Tin, NT, China (Hong Kong)
Tel.: (852) 26900723
Electrical Apparatus, Equipment Wiring
Supplies & Construction Material Whslr
N.A.I.C.S.: 423610

ARRIS Group India Private
Limited (4)
The Senate 3rd Floor 33/1 Ulsoor Road,
Bengaluru, 560042, Karnataka, India
Tel.: (91) 8067737908
Telecommunication Product Distr
N.A.I.C.S.: 423690

Subsidiary (Non-US):

General Instrument LLC (3)
Testovskaya 10 13th Floor, 123317, Mos-
cow, Russia
Tel.: (7) 4959884764
Telecommunication Equipment Distr
N.A.I.C.S.: 423690

Subsidiary (Domestic):

Ruckus Wireless, Inc. (3)
350 W Java Dr, Sunnyvale, CA 94089
Tel.: (650) 265-4200
Smart Wi-Fi Products & LAN Systems De-
signer, Mfr & Marketer
N.A.I.C.S.: 334220

Subsidiary (Non-US):

ARRIS Group Russia LLC (2)
Registered Smolenskiy square 3 Floor 7
Premises 1 Office 63, Moscow, 121099,
Russia
Tel.: (7) 4999813499
Telecommunication Product Distr
N.A.I.C.S.: 423690

Ruckus Wireless Private Ltd. (2)
B2 2nd Floor Diamond District Building Old
Airport Road, Bengaluru, 560 008, India
Tel.: (91) 8049134104
Web Site: http://www.ruckuswireless.com
Software Development Services
N.A.I.C.S.: 541511

CommScope Technologies LLC (1)
19700 Janelia Farm Blvd, Ashburn, VA
20147
Tel.: (703) 726-5500
Web Site: http://www.comsearch.com
Wireless Communication Equipment Mfr
N.A.I.C.S.: 334220

CommScope, Inc. (1)
1100 CommScope Pl SE, Hickory, NC
28602
Tel.: (828) 324-2200
Web Site: https://www.commscope.com
Sales Range: $1-4.9 Billion
Emp.: 12,500
High Speed, High Bandwidth Cables &
Other Telecommunications Applications Mfr
N.A.I.C.S.: 334220
Frank M. Drendel (Chm)

Subsidiary (Non-US):

Andrew Satcom Aftica (Pty.) Ltd. (2)
Woodland Office Park Building 11 Entrance
A, PO Box 786117, Sandton, 2146, South
Africa
Tel.: (27) 117196000
Web Site: http://www.commscope.com
Sales Range: $10-24.9 Million
Emp.: 28
Telecommunications Equipment
N.A.I.C.S.: 334290

Andrew Telecommunications India
Pvt. Ltd. (ATGV) (2)
Plot No N-2 Phase IV Verna Industrial Es-
tate Verna Salcette, Goa, 403722, India
Tel.: (91) 8326685200
Web Site: http://www.commscope.com
Sales Range: $400-449.9 Million
Emp.: 1,000
Antenna & Cable Equipment Mfr
N.A.I.C.S.: 334290

Andrew Telecommunications de Rey-
nosa S de RL de CV (2)
Av Industrial Reynosa Lte 2 al 5 Parque
Industrial Center, Industrial Center CP.
88780, 88780, Tamaulipas, 88780, Mexico
Tel.: (52) 8999211700
Web Site: http://www.commscope.com
Sales Range: $1-9.9 Million
Emp.: 80
Antenna Mfr
N.A.I.C.S.: 334220

Subsidiary (Domestic):

Cable Devices Incorporated (2)
3008 S Crody Way, Santa Ana, CA 92704
Tel.: (714) 554-4370
Web Site: http://www.4cablex.com
Emp.: 200
Fiber Optic & Copper Assemblies Mfr &
Distr

N.A.I.C.S.: 335921

Subsidiary (Non-US):

CommScope Asia (Suzhou) Technologies Co., Ltd. **(2)**
68 Su Hong Xi Lu, Suzhou, 215021, Jiangsu, China
Tel.: (86) 51267610069
Web Site: http://www.andrew.com
Sales Range: $750-799.9 Million
Emp.: 2,700
Broadband Cable Mfr
N.A.I.C.S.: 335921

Subsidiary (Domestic):

CommScope International Holdings, LLC **(2)**
1100 CommScope Pl SE, Hickory, NC 28602
Tel.: (828) 324-2200
Sales Range: $50-74.9 Million
Emp.: 200
High Speed, High Bandwidth Cables for Video & Other Telecommunications Applications Mfr
N.A.I.C.S.: 335929

CommScope Nevada, LLC **(2)**
1285 Southern Way, Sparks, NV 89431
Tel.: (775) 351-1717
Sales Range: $150-199.9 Million
Mfr of High Speed, High Bandwidth Cables for Video & Other Telecommunications Applications
N.A.I.C.S.: 335921

CommScope Optical Technologies, Inc. **(2)**
1100 CommScope Pl SE, Hickory, NC 28602
Tel.: (828) 324-2200
Web Site: http://www.commscope.com
Sales Range: $50-74.9 Million
Emp.: 225
Mfr of High Speed, High Bandwidth Cables for Video & Other Telecommunications Applications
N.A.I.C.S.: 335929

Subsidiary (Non-US):

CommScope Solutions Germany GmbH **(2)**
Industriering 10, 86675, Buchdorf, Germany
Tel.: (49) 909969346
Sales Range: $75-99.9 Million
Emp.: 270
Antenna System Mfr
N.A.I.C.S.: 334220

CommScope Solutions International, Inc. - Bachenbulach **(2)**
Baechliwis 2B, 8184, Bachenbulach, Switzerland
Tel.: (41) 448637373
Web Site: http://www.andrew.com
Sales Range: $10-24.9 Million
Emp.: 15
Telecommunications Equipment
N.A.I.C.S.: 334290

CommScope Solutions Ireland Ltd. **(2)**
Corke Abbey Ave, Bray, A98FY03, Co Dublin, Ireland
Tel.: (353) 12042000
Sales Range: $25-49.9 Million
Emp.: 150
Communication Equipment Mfr
N.A.I.C.S.: 334290
William O'Connell *(Dir-Technical-Enterprise Solutions-EMEA)*

Unit (Domestic):

CommScope, Inc. - Westchester **(2)**
3 Westbrook Corporate Ctr Ste 900, Westchester, IL 60154
Tel.: (708) 236-6616
Web Site: http://www.commscope.com
Emp.: 50
Communications Equipment Systems Mfr
N.A.I.C.S.: 334290

Subsidiary (Domestic):

CommScope, Inc. of North Carolina **(2)**

3642 E US Hwy 70, Claremont, NC 28610
Tel.: (828) 324-2200
Sales Range: $700-749.9 Million
Emp.: 4,500
Mfr of High Speed, High Bandwidth Cables for Video & Other Telecommunications Applications
N.A.I.C.S.: 335929

Subsidiary (Non-US):

Commscope Cabos do Brasil Ltda **(2)**
Av Com Camilo Julio 1256 Jardim Ibiti do Paco, Sorocaba, 18086-000, SP, Brazil
Tel.: (55) 1521024000
Web Site: http://www.commscope.com
Sales Range: $100-124.9 Million
Emp.: 70
Telecommunications Equipment Mfr
N.A.I.C.S.: 334290

Subsidiary (Domestic):

Itracs Corp. **(2)**
1501 W Fountainhead Pkwy Ste 190, Tempe, AZ 85282
Tel.: (480) 557-8000
Web Site: http://www.itracs.com
Sales Range: $10-24.9 Million
Emp.: 30
Custom Computer Programing
N.A.I.C.S.: 541511

COMMUNITIES FIRST FINANCIAL CORPORATION

7690 N Palm Ave, Fresno, CA 93711
Tel.: (559) 439-0200
Web Site:
http://www.fresnofirstbank.com
CFST—(OTCIQ)
Rev.: $35,807,349
Assets: $871,895,232
Liabilities: $803,347,991
Net Worth: $68,547,241
Earnings: $11,512,250
Emp.: 49
Fiscal Year-end: 12/31/20
Bank Holding Company
N.A.I.C.S.: 551111
Steven R. Canfield *(CFO & Exec VP)*
Robert Lee Reed *(Chief Credit Officer & Exec VP)*
Mark D. Saleh *(Chm)*
Jared Martin *(Vice Chm)*
Steven Kenneth Miller *(Pres & CEO)*

Subsidiaries:

Fresno First Bank **(1)**
7690 N Palm Ave Ste 101, Fresno, CA 93711
Tel.: (559) 439-0200
Web Site: http://www.fresnofirstbank.com
Emp.: 40
Commercial Banking Services
N.A.I.C.S.: 522110
Evangelina Gonzalez *(Sr VP)*
Robert Lee Reed *(Sr VP)*
Steve Canfield *(CFO)*
David Price *(Chm)*
Dave Kraechan *(Sr VP-Comml Lending)*
Steve Miller *(Pres & CEO)*

COMMUNITY BANCORP, INC.

4811 US Rte 5, Newport, VT 05855
Tel.: (802) 334-7915   VT
Web Site:
https://www.communitybancorp vt.com
Year Founded: 1982
CMTV—(OTCQX)
Rev.: $43,757,704
Assets: $1,056,032,147
Liabilities: $980,855,784
Net Worth: $75,176,363
Earnings: $13,739,940
Emp.: 122
Fiscal Year-end: 12/31/22
Bank Holding Company
N.A.I.C.S.: 551111

Kathryn M. Austin *(Pres & CEO)*
Christopher L. Caldwell *(VP)*
Louise M. Bonvechio *(Treas & Sec)*

Subsidiaries:

Community National Bank **(1)**
4811 US Route 5, Derby, VT 05829   **(100%)**
Tel.: (802) 334-7915
Web Site:
    https://www.communitynationalbank.com
Sales Range: $50-74.9 Million
Emp.: 140
Commercial Bank
N.A.I.C.S.: 522110
Kathryn M. Austin *(CEO)*
Christopher L. Caldwell *(Pres)*
Louise M. Bonvechio *(CFO, Sec & Exec VP)*

COMMUNITY BANCSHARES, INC.

112 W Main St, McArthur, OH 45651
Tel.: (740) 596-2525   OH
Web Site:
    https://www.vcnbfamily.bank
Year Founded: 1981
CNUN—(OTCIQ)
Offices of Bank Holding Companies
N.A.I.C.S.: 551111
Thomas D. Will *(Chm, Pres & CEO)*
Ronald B. Collins *(Pres/CEO-Bank)*
J. Benjamin Crow *(Treas & Sec)*

Subsidiaries:

The Vinton County National Bank **(1)**
112 W Main St, Mc Arthur, OH 45651
Tel.: (740) 596-2525
Web Site: http://www.vintoncountybank.com
Commericial Banking
N.A.I.C.S.: 522110
Thomas D. Will *(Chm)*
Ronald B. Collins *(Pres & CEO)*
Kim Ward *(CFO)*
Annamarie Qualls *(Exec VP-HR)*
Mark Erslan *(Exec VP-Lending)*
Emily Oyer *(Exec VP-Retail Banking)*
Jane Nickels *(Sr VP)*
Audra Johnson *(Dir-Mktg)*

COMMUNITY BANK OF SANTA MARIA

2739 Santa Maria Way, Santa Maria, CA 93455
Tel.: (805) 922-2900   CA
Web Site: https://www.yourcbsm.com
Year Founded: 2000
CYSM—(OTCIQ)
Rev.: $13,055,000
Assets: $338,796,000
Liabilities: $310,689,000
Net Worth: $28,107,000
Earnings: $2,209,000
Emp.: 59
Fiscal Year-end: 12/31/20
Commericial Banking
N.A.I.C.S.: 522110
James D. Glines *(Co-Founder & Chm)*
Janet Silveria *(Pres & CEO)*
Lisa R. Ramser *(CFO & Exec VP)*
Leah West *(Officer-Comml Loan & VP)*
Lisa R. Canale *(Chief Credit Officer & Exec VP)*
Mark Adam *(Co-Founder)*
Fran Aughtman *(Co-Founder)*
Dan Blough *(Co-Founder)*
Peggy Blough *(Co-Founder)*
Bill Bogue *(Co-Founder)*
John Branquinho *(Co-Founder)*
Brandy Branquinho *(Co-Founder)*
Tony Cossa *(Co-Founder)*
Ron Edwards *(Co-Founder)*
Marcia Edwards *(Co-Founder)*
John Eggert *(Co-Founder)*
Barbara Eggert *(Co-Founder)*
Phil F. Fee *(Co-Founder)*

A. Milo Ferini *(Co-Founder)*
Georganne Ferini *(Co-Founder)*
Ruth L. Fletcher *(Co-Founder)*
Angela Freitas *(Co-Founder)*
Parnell Fuhrer *(Co-Founder)*
Sandra Fuhrer *(Co-Founder)*
Joe Gallas *(Co-Founder)*
Chris Gallas *(Co-Founder)*
George Wittenburg *(Co-Founder)*
Kathryn A. Glines *(Co-Founder)*
Milt Guggia *(Co-Founder)*
Angela Guggia *(Co-Founder)*

COMMUNITY BANK SYSTEM, INC.

5790 Widewaters Pkwy, De Witt, NY 13214
Tel.: (315) 445-2282   DE
Web Site: https://www.cbna.com
Year Founded: 1983
CBU—(NYSE)
Rev.: $702,454,000
Assets: $15,835,651,000
Liabilities: $14,283,946,000
Net Worth: $1,551,705,000
Earnings: $188,081,000
Emp.: 2,839
Fiscal Year-end: 12/31/22
Bank Holding Company
N.A.I.C.S.: 551111
Dimitar A. Karaivanov *(Pres & CEO)*
Michael N. Abdo *(Gen Counsel & Exec VP)*
Daniel L. Bailey *(Chief Risk Officer)*
Maureen Gillan-Myer *(Chief HR Officer)*
Jeffrey M. Levy *(Pres)*

Subsidiaries:

Benefit Plans Administrative Services, Inc. **(1)**
6 Rhoads Dr Ste 7, Utica, NY 13502-5104
Tel.: (315) 735-8322
Web Site: https://www.bpas.com
Sales Range: $25-49.9 Million
Emp.: 240
Pension Administration & Consulting Firm Servicing Sponsors of Defined Benefit & Defined Contribution Plans
N.A.I.C.S.: 541611

Subsidiary (Domestic):

Harbridge Consulting Group, LLC **(2)**
1 Lincoln Ctr Fl 12, Syracuse, NY 13202
Tel.: (315) 703-8900
Sales Range: $10-24.9 Million
Emp.: 30
Employee Benefit Consulting Services
N.A.I.C.S.: 541612
Steve Chase *(VP-Health Care Consulting)*
Sarah E. Dam *(Chief Actuary & VP)*
Kenneth M. Prell *(VP)*
Sheila L. Yoensky *(VP)*
Kevin J. Wade *(VP-Client Svc)*

Community Bank, N.A. **(1)**
5790 Widewaters Pkwy, De Witt, NY 13214
Tel.: (315) 445-2282
Web Site: https://www.cbna.com
Sales Range: $400-449.9 Million
Emp.: 3,000
Savings Bank
N.A.I.C.S.: 522180
Sally A. Steele *(Chm)*
Bernadette R. Barber *(Chief HR Officer & Sr VP)*
Harold M. Wentworth *(Sr VP-Retail Banking, Sls, and Mktg)*
Paul J. Ward *(Chief Risk Officer & Sr VP)*
Scott J. Boser *(Sr VP-Consumer Lending)*
Susan S. Fox *(CIO & Sr VP)*
Dimitar A. Karaivanov *(Pres & CEO)*
Michael N. Abdo *(Gen Counsel & Exec VP)*
Paul A. Restante *(CEO)*
Theresa Kalil-Lennon *(Sr VP)*

Subsidiary (Domestic):

Community Investment Services, Inc. **(2)**

Community Bank System, Inc.—(Continued)

5790 Widewaters Pkwy Ste 170, Syracuse, NY 13214-1883
Tel.: (315) 445-2282
Web Site:
　https://www.communityinvestmentser
　vices.com
Sales Range: $50-74.9 Million
Emp.: 4
Investment Services
N.A.I.C.S.: 523940

Elmira Savings Bank　　　　　　　(2)
333 E Water St, Elmira, NY 14901
Tel.: (607) 734-3374
Web Site:
　http://www.elmirasavingsbank.com
Rev.: $28,034,000
Assets: $606,829,000
Liabilities: $548,218,000
Net Worth: $58,611,000
Earnings: $3,486,000
Emp.: 124
Fiscal Year-end: 12/31/2019
Commercial Banking Services
N.A.I.C.S.: 522110
Bradley V. Serva (Sr VP-HR)
Gary O. Short (Sr VP-Lending)
Susan M. Cook (Asst VP-Credit)
Joseph L. Walker (VP-Mgmt Info Sys)
Phillip J. Collins (Asst VP-Mgmt Information Sys)
Donna J. Tangorre (Sr VP-Retail Svcs)
Margaret A. Phillips (VP-Ops)
Kevin J. Berkley (Officer-Loan & Exec VP-Lending)
Jason T. Sanford (CFO & Sr VP-Fin)
John J. Stempin (VP-Fin & Controller)
Carrie L. Spencer (Sr VP-Credit)
Judy A. Woodruff (Asst VP-Fin)
Stacy Ward (Asst Sec-HR)
John Strong (Asst VP-Retail Svcs)
Renee A. Wheeler (VP-Retail Svcs)
Anne M. Lavancher (Asst Sec)
Michele Corby (Asst VP-Audit & Control)
Meredith Tigue (VP-Compliance & BSA)
Eric Dejesus (Asst VP-Collections)
Dawn V. Siglin (VP-Credit)
Kathleen Bange (Asst Sec-Credit)
Erin Thomas-Allen (Asst Sec-Credit)
Taryn Schwartz (Asst Sec-Credit)
Christopher J. Giammichele (Sr VP-Lending)
Ellaminda Leader (Asst Sec-Retail Svcs)
Lindsay McCutcheon (Asst Treas-Retail Svcs)
Valerie Friedrich (Asst Treas-Retail Svcs)
Chrissie Allen (Asst Treas-Retail Svcs)
Deborah French (Asst VP-Retail Svcs)
Cory Eddy (Asst VP-Retail Svcs)
Linda S. Confer (Asst VP-Retail Svcs)
Frank P. Spena Jr. (Asst VP-Credit)
Robert W. Hazelton III (Sr VP-Lending)

OneGroup NY, Inc.　　　　　　　(2)
182 Main St, Oneida, NY 13421
Tel.: (315) 457-1830
Web Site: http://www.onegroup.com
Emp.: 90
Insurance & Financial Services
N.A.I.C.S.: 524298
Pierre J. Morrisseau (CEO)
Ron Heath (CMO & Chief Sls Officer)
Chris Mason (Pres)

Oneida Wealth Management, Inc.　　　　　　　　　　　　(2)
706 N Clinton St, Syracuse, NY 13204
Tel.: (315) 474-1707
Web Site: http://www.bcgcny.com
Emp.: 20
Employee Benefits Consulting & Retirement Planning Services
N.A.I.C.S.: 541612

Workplace Health Solutions Inc.　(2)
706 N Clinton St, Syracuse, NY 13204
Tel.: (315) 413-4409
Web Site: http://www.whsny.com
Emp.: 3
Risk Managemeng Srvices
N.A.I.C.S.: 524298

Global Trust Company, Inc.　　　(1)
12 Gill St Ste 2600, Woburn, MA 01801
Tel.: (781) 938-9595
Web Site: https://www.globaltrustco
　com
Investment Trust Services
N.A.I.C.S.: 523991

Chris Hulse (COO & Exec VP)
Diane Murphy (Chief Compliance Officer & VP)
Peter Lyons (VP & Gen Counsel)
Don Doherty (VP & Dir-Bus Dev)
Chris Ellis (CFO & VP)
Vincent Manning (Sr VP-Corporate Dev)
Tim Smith (Sr VP)
Scott Graham (Sr VP)
Freddie Jacobs Jr. (Officer-Risk & VP)

Gordon B. Roberts Agency, LLC　(1)
22-26 Watkins Ave, Oneonta, NY 13820
Tel.: (607) 432-2022
Web Site: http://gbrobertsagency.com
Sales Range: $1-9.9 Million
Emp.: 16
Insurance Management Services
N.A.I.C.S.: 524210
Vince Foti (Acct Exec-Insurance)

Northeast Retirement Services, LLC　　　　　　　　　　　(1)
12 Gill St Ste 2600, Woburn, MA 01801
Tel.: (781) 938-9595
Web Site: https://www.nrstpa.com
Financial Investment Services
N.A.I.C.S.: 523991
Chris Hulse (COO & Exec VP)
Peter Lyons (VP & Gen Counsel)
Don Doherty (VP & Dir-Bus Dev)
Diane Murphy (VP-Ops)
Chris Ellis (CFO & VP)
Vincent Manning (Sr VP-Corporate Dev)
Tom Lombardo (Sr VP-Donor Acctg Svcs)
Freddie Jacobs Jr. (COO, Officer-Risk, Exec VP & VP)

Nottingham Advisors, Inc.　　　(1)
100 Corporate Pkwy Ste 338, Amherst, NY 14226
Tel.: (716) 633-3800
Web Site:
　https://www.nottinghamadvisors.com
Sales Range: $50-74.9 Million
Emp.: 11
Investment Advisory Services
N.A.I.C.S.: 523940
Lawrence V. Whistler (Pres & Chief Investment Officer)
Timothy D. Calkins (Dir-Fixed Income & Sr Portfolio Mgr)
Matthew J. Krajna (Dir-Equity Res & Sr Portfolio Mgr)
Nicholas Dirienzo (Dir-Ops)
Meagan M. Reimann (Mktg Mgr)
Thomas Quealy Jr. (CEO)
Nicole Hendrix (Dir-Institutional & Advisor Solutions)
Michael Skrzypczyk (Sr Portfolio Mgr)
Peter Kazmierczak (Sr Portfolio Mgr)
Cara Bland (Client Svcs Mgr)
Meagan Reimann (Coord-Wealth Mgmt Content)
Conner Gyllenhammer (Assoc Portfolio Mgr)

OneGroup Wealth Partners, Inc.　(1)
5790 Widewaters Pkwy, Syracuse, NY 13214
Tel.: (561) 472-2312
Web Site:
　https://www.onegroupwealthpartners.com
Advisory Services
N.A.I.C.S.: 541618
Paul A. Restante (Pres)
Chasity Jaynes (COO)
Tony Van Ore (Chief Compliance Officer)

The Carta Group, Inc.　　　　　(1)
5790 Widewaters Pkwy Ste 100B, Syracuse, NY 13214
Tel.: (315) 445-7384
Web Site: https://www.cartagroup.com
Financial Services
N.A.I.C.S.: 523940
Garry R. M. Payne (Founder & Mng Partner)
Jeremy T. Caza (Partner)
Mary Ellen Sharpe (Dir-Administration)
Gary Casab (Partner)

Town & Country Agency LLC　　(1)
2590 Hamilton Mill Rd Ste 101, Buford, GA 30519
Tel.: (678) 889-2150
Web Site:
　https://www.townandcountryagency.com
Emp.: 1

Insurance Services
N.A.I.C.S.: 524210
Deborah Lee (VP)

COMMUNITY BANKERS

Tel.: (724) 464-2265　　　　　　PA
Year Founded: 1905
CTYP—(OTCIQ)
Bank Holding Company
N.A.I.C.S.: 551111
Trisha Brewer (CFO)
George Karlheim (Pres)
Anna M. Mano (Sec)
Michelle L. Peterson (Asst Sec)
Katie Rescenete (Officer-Marketing)
John D. Gandolfi (Chm)
Robert R. Packer (Vice Chm)

COMMUNITY CAPITAL BANCSHARES, INC.

2815 Meredyth Dr, Albany, GA 31707
Tel.: (229) 446-2265　　　　　　GA
Web Site: http://www.abtgold.com
Year Founded: 1998
ALBY—(OTCQX)
Rev.: $9,929,596
Assets: $281,840,540
Liabilities: $263,843,913
Net Worth: $17,996,627
Earnings: $1,772,900
Emp.: 32
Fiscal Year-end: 12/31/20
Bank Holding Company
N.A.I.C.S.: 551111

Subsidiaries:

AB&T National Bank　　　　　　(1)
2815 Meredyth Dr, Albany, GA 31707
Tel.: (229) 446-2265
Web Site: http://www.abtgold.com
Sales Range: $1-9.9 Million
Emp.: 25
Retail & Commercial Banking Services
N.A.I.C.S.: 522180
T. Wayne Whitfield (Sr VP & Dir-Mortgage Banking)
Nita Gaines (Asst Admin-Pres)
James Luke Flatt (Pres & CEO)
Dana White (Sr VP-Ops, Risk Mgmt, Compliance, and IT)
Stan W. Edmonds (VP & Mgr-Fin)
Gayle B. Woolard (VP-Comml & Private Banking)
Perry Revell (VP-Comml Banking)
Matt Rushton (VP-Comml Banking)
Joseph Pierce (VP & Credit Officer)
Johnnie Benton (Officer-Banking & Customer Svc)
John P. Ventulett Jr. (Vice Chm)

COMMUNITY FIRST BANCORPORATION

449 Hwy 123 Bypass, Seneca, SC 29678
Tel.: (864) 886-0206　　　　　　SC
Web Site: http://www.c1stbank.com
Year Founded: 1997
CFOK—(OTCIQ)
Rev.: $26,004,000
Assets: $543,988,000
Liabilities: $493,200,000
Net Worth: $50,788,000
Earnings: $1,801,000
Emp.: 93
Fiscal Year-end: 12/31/20
Bank Holding Company
N.A.I.C.S.: 551111
William M. Brown (Sec)
Jennifer M. Champagne (CFO & Exec VP-Community First Bank)
Richard D. Burleson Jr. (Pres & CEO-Community First Bank)

COMMUNITY HEALTH SYSTEMS, INC.

4000 Meridian Blvd, Franklin, TN 37067
Tel.: (615) 465-7000　　　　　　DE

Web Site: https://www.chs.net
Year Founded: 1985
CYH—(NYSE)
Rev.: $12,490,000,000
Assets: $14,455,000,000
Liabilities: $15,602,000,000
Net Worth: ($1,147,000,000)
Earnings: ($133,000,000)
Emp.: 48,000
Fiscal Year-end: 12/31/23
Holding Company; Hospital & Ambulatory Surgery Center Operator
N.A.I.C.S.: 551112
Brad Cash (Sr VP-Financial Ops)
Kevin J. Hammons (Pres & CFO)
Michael M. Lynd (Sr VP-Fin Svcs)
Tim L. Hingtgen (CEO)
Tomi Galin (Exec VP-Corp Comm, Mktg, and Pub Affairs)
Pamela T. Rudisill (Chief Nursing Officer & Sr VP)
Jason K. Johnson (Chief Acctg Officer & Sr VP)
Susan Schrupp (Chief Pur Officer & Sr VP)
Beth Witte (Officer-Corp Compliance & Privacy & Sr VP)
J. Anton Hie (VP-IR)
Drew Mason (Pres)
Kevin Stockton (Pres)
Mark Medley (Pres)
Chad Campbell (Pres)
Miguel S. Benet (Sr VP)
Chris Cobb (Sec)
Craig Conti (VP)
Jim Horrar (Sr VP)
Gabe Ottinger (Treas)
Craig Pickard (VP)
Nathaniel Summar (VP)
Miguel S. Benet (Chief Medical Officer & Pres/Exec VP-Clinical Ops)

Subsidiaries:

A Woman's Place, LLC　　　　　(1)
215 S Power Rd St 218 S, Mesa, AZ 85206-5235
Tel.: (480) 325-5885
Web Site: http://www.awpgynmesa.com
Health Care Srvices
N.A.I.C.S.: 622110

ARMC, L.P.　　　　　　　　　　(1)
6250 US-83, Abilene, TX 79606
Tel.: (325) 428-1000
Web Site: http://www.abileneregional.com
Emp.: 800
Women Healthcare Services
N.A.I.C.S.: 621610
Michale Murphy (CEO)

AdventHealth Ocala　　　　　　(1)
1500 SW 1st Ave, Ocala, FL 34471
Tel.: (352) 351-7200
Web Site: https://www.adventhealth.
　com
Health Care Srvices
N.A.I.C.S.: 622110
Terry D. Shaw (Co-Pres & Co-CEO)
David Banks (Chief Strategy & Organizational Transformation Officer)
Joe Johnson (Co-Pres & Co-CEO)
Michael Torres (Chief Medical Officer)
Fran Crunk (Co-CFO)
Patricia Price (Chief Nursing Officer)
Jim Burkhart (COO)
Ron Smith (Chm)
Olesea Azevedo (Chief HR Officer & Sr VP)
Ken Bacon (Pres-State Div,CEO-,Multi,State Div & Sr Exec VP)
Trish Celano (Sr VP)
Bryan Stiltz (Exec VP)
Vickie White (Chief Brand & Consumer Officer & Sr VP)
Ron Smith (Chm)
Olesea Azevedo (Chief HR Officer & Sr VP)
Ken Bacon (Pres-State Div,CEO-,Multi,State Div & Sr Exec VP)
Trish Celano (Sr VP)
Bryan Stiltz (Exec VP)
Vickie White (Chief Brand & Consumer Officer & Sr VP)

Advocate Sherman Hospital, L.P.　(1)
1425 N Randall Rd, Elgin, IL 60123

Tel.: (847) 742-9800
General Medical & Surgical Hospitals
N.A.I.C.S.: 622110

Affinity Cardio-Thoracic Specialists, LLC (1)
2871 Acton Rd Ste 100, Vestavia Hills, AL 35243-2559
Tel.: (205) 716-6900
Hospital Healthcare Services
N.A.I.C.S.: 621491

Affinity Cardiovascular Specialists, LLC (1)
3680 Grandview Pkwy Ste 200, Birmingham, AL 35243
Tel.: (205) 971-7500
Web Site: https://www.alcardio.com
Hospital Healthcare Services
N.A.I.C.S.: 621491

Affinity Health Systems, LLC (1)
1506 S Oneida St, Appleton, WI 54915
Tel.: (920) 738-2000
Web Site: https://www.affinityhealth.org
Health Care Srvices
N.A.I.C.S.: 622110

Affinity Hospital, LLC (1)
3690 Grandview Pkwy, Birmingham, AL 35243
Tel.: (205) 971-1000
Web Site: https://www.grandviewhealth.com
Health Care Srvices
N.A.I.C.S.: 622110

Affinity Orthopedic Services, LLC (1)
720 Montclair Rd, Birmingham, AL 35213-1964
Tel.: (205) 397-5200
Health Care Services
N.A.I.C.S.: 622110
Katie Reaves *(Office Mgr)*

Affinity Physician Services, LLC (1)
840 Montclair Rd Ste 500, Birmingham, AL 35213
Tel.: (205) 599-3477
Health & Allied Services
N.A.I.C.S.: 812199

Ambulance Services of Dyersburg, Inc. (1)
400 E Tickle St, Dyersburg, TN 38024-3120
Tel.: (731) 285-2237
Emp.: 40
Ambulance Service
N.A.I.C.S.: 621910
Chuck Latimer *(Reg Dir)*

Ambulance Services of McNairy, Inc. (1)
705 E Poplar Ave, Selmer, TN 38375
Tel.: (731) 646-0239
Sales Range: $10-24.9 Million
Emp.: 25
Ambulance Service
N.A.I.C.S.: 621910
Chuck Latimer *(Dir-Reg)*

BH Trans Company, LLC (1)
199 Reecevile Rd, Coatesville, PA 19320
Tel.: (717) 464-0724
Ambulance Service
N.A.I.C.S.: 621910

Barberton Health System, LLC (1)
PO Box 714139, Columbus, OH 43271
Tel.: (330) 745-1611
Health Care Srvices
N.A.I.C.S.: 622110

Bartow HMA Physician Management, LLC (1)
4000 Meridian Blvd, Franklin, TN 37067
Tel.: (615) 465-7000
Medical Group Practice
N.A.I.C.S.: 621111

Bayfront Health System, Inc. (1)
2333 34th St S, Saint Petersburg, FL 33711
Tel.: (727) 865-4650
Web Site: https://healthystpete.foundation
Sales Range: $75-99.9 Million
Emp.: 1,900
Hospitals & Medical Centers
N.A.I.C.S.: 622110

Subsidiary (Domestic):

Bayfront Ambulatory Surgical Center, LLC (2)

701 6th St S, Saint Petersburg, FL 33701
Tel.: (727) 823-1234
Web Site: https://www.bayfrontstpete.com
Health Care Srvices
N.A.I.C.S.: 622110

Bayfront HMA Convenient Care, LLC (2)
7601 Seminole Blvd, Seminole, FL 33772
Tel.: (727) 394-8442
Web Site: https://www.bayfrontclinics.com
Emp.: 6
Health Care Srvices
N.A.I.C.S.: 622110

Bayfront HMA Medical Center, LLC (2)
701 6th St S, Saint Petersburg, FL 33701
Tel.: (727) 823-1234
Health Care Srvices
N.A.I.C.S.: 622110

Bayfront HMA Physician Management, LLC (2)
603 7th St S Ste 101, Saint Petersburg, FL 33701-4719
Tel.: (727) 553-7450
Health Care Srvices
N.A.I.C.S.: 622110

Bayfront Health Brooksville (2)
17240 Cortez Blvd, Brooksville, FL 34601
Tel.: (352) 796-5111
Web Site:
 http://www.bayfrontbrooksville.com
Hospitals & Medical Care Services
N.A.I.C.S.: 622110
Karen Nicolai *(Vice Chm)*
Sharon D. Hayes *(Chm & CEO)*
C. J. Hamilton *(COO)*
Amber Lipe *(CFO)*

Bayfront Health Imaging Center, LLC (2)
2201 Central Ave, Saint Petersburg, FL 33713-8844
Tel.: (727) 893-6050
Hospital Healthcare Services
N.A.I.C.S.: 621491

Bayfront Health Port Charlotte (2)
2500 Harbor Blvd, Port Charlotte, FL 33952
Tel.: (941) 766-4122
Web Site: http://www.bayfrontcharlotte.com
Hospitals & Medical Centers Operator
N.A.I.C.S.: 622110
Terry Shambles *(CFO)*
Eric Kaplan *(COO)*
Tara McCoy *(CEO)*
Michael Poli *(Chief Admin Officer)*
Russ Schroeder *(Chief Nursing Officer)*

Bayfront Health Spring Hill (2)
10461 Quality Rd, Spring Hill, FL 34609
Tel.: (352) 688-8200
Web Site: https://www.braverahealth.com
Hospitals & Medical Centers Operator
N.A.I.C.S.: 622110
Karen Nicolai *(Vice Chm)*
Amber Lipe *(CFO)*
C. J. Hamilton *(COO)*
Sharon D. Hayes *(Chm & CEO)*

Berwick Hospital Company, LLC (1)
701 E 16th St, Berwick, PA 18603
Tel.: (570) 759-5000
Web Site: https://berwickhospitalcenter.com
Health Care Srvices
N.A.I.C.S.: 622110

Big Bend Home Care Services, LLC (1)
2707 W Hwy 90, Alpine, TX 79830-2002
Tel.: (432) 837-3467
Web Site: http://www.bigbendhomecare.com
Emp.: 11
Women Healthcare Services
N.A.I.C.S.: 621610

Biloxi HMA, Inc. (1)
150 Reynoir St, Biloxi, MS 39530
Tel.: (228) 432-1571
Web Site: https://www.merithealthbiloxi.com
Sales Range: $50-74.9 Million
Hospital Services
N.A.I.C.S.: 622110

Birmingham Holdings, LLC (1)
5800 Tennyson Pkwy, Plano, TX 75024
Tel.: (214) 473-7000

Holding Company
N.A.I.C.S.: 551112

Birmingham Home Care Services, LLC (1)
345 Walker Chapel Plz, Fultondale, AL 35068
Tel.: (205) 783-7900
Health Care Srvices
N.A.I.C.S.: 622110

Birmingham Orthopedics & Sports Specialists, LLC (1)
4600 Hwy 280 Ste 210, Birmingham, AL 35242
Tel.: (205) 971-8000
Web Site: https://bossorthopedics.com
Hospital Healthcare Services
N.A.I.C.S.: 621491

Black Creek Medical Consultants LLC (1)
149 E Carolina Ave, Hartsville, SC 29550
Tel.: (843) 383-5312
Web Site:
 https://www.blackcreekaesthetics.com
Health Care Srvices
N.A.I.C.S.: 622110

Blackwell HMA, LLC (1)
710 S 13th St, Blackwell, OK 74631
Tel.: (580) 363-2311
Health Care Srvices
N.A.I.C.S.: 622110

Blue Island Home Care Services, LLC (1)
11600 S Kedzie Ave, Merrionette Park, IL 60803-6307
Tel.: (708) 371-7777
Emp.: 15
Health Care Srvices
N.A.I.C.S.: 622110
Lida Hanewrch *(Gen Mgr)*

Bluefield Clinic Company, LLC (1)
2111 College Ave, Bluefield, VA 24605
Tel.: (276) 322-4661
Health Care Srvices
N.A.I.C.S.: 622110

Bluefield HBP Medical Group, LLC (1)
500 Cherry St, Bluefield, WV 24701-3306
Tel.: (304) 327-1100
Health Care Srvices
N.A.I.C.S.: 622110

Bluffton Health System, LLC (1)
303 S Main St, Bluffton, IN 46714
Tel.: (260) 824-3210
Web Site: https://www.blufftonregional.com
Health Care Srvices
N.A.I.C.S.: 622110

Brandon HMA, LLC (1)
350 Crossgates Blvd, Brandon, MS 39042
Tel.: (601) 825-2811
Web Site:
 https://www.merithealthrankin.com
Hospital Services
N.A.I.C.S.: 622110
Cynthia Ellis *(Chief Nursing Officer)*
Justin Stroud *(CFO)*

Brandon Physician Management, LLC (1)
187 Doctors Dr, Pearl, MS 39208
Tel.: (601) 932-8722
Hospital Healthcare Services
N.A.I.C.S.: 621491

Brevard HMA Home Health, LLC (1)
8060 Spyglass Hill Rd Viera, Melbourne, FL 32940-7983
Tel.: (321) 253-2200
Women Healthcare Services
N.A.I.C.S.: 621610
Raelene Pratte *(Bus Mgr)*

Brevard HMA Hospice, LLC (1)
8060 Spyglass Hill Rd Viera, Melbourne, FL 32940-7983
Tel.: (321) 253-2200
Women Healthcare Services
N.A.I.C.S.: 621610

Brevard HMA Nursing Home, LLC (1)

8050 Spyglass Hill Rd, Melbourne, FL 32940-7983
Tel.: (321) 752-1000
Web Site: http://www.greystonehealth.com
Women Healthcare Services
N.A.I.C.S.: 621610

Brooksville HMA Physician Management, LLC (1)
8425 Northcliffe Blvd Ste 101, Spring Hill, FL 34606-1107
Tel.: (352) 796-5111
Women Healthcare Services
N.A.I.C.S.: 621610

Brownsville Hospital Corporation (1)
4000 Meridian Blvd, Franklin, TN 37067
Tel.: (615) 465-7000
General Medical & Surgical Hospitals
N.A.I.C.S.: 622110

Bullhead City Clinic Corp. (1)
1225 Hancock Rd Ste 204, Bullhead City, AZ 86442-5948
Tel.: (928) 704-3712
Health Care Srvices
N.A.I.C.S.: 622110

Bullhead City Hospital Corporation (1)
2735 Silver Creek Rd, Bullhead City, AZ 86442
Tel.: (928) 763-2273
Web Site: http://www.warmc.com
Emp.: 110
Health Care Srvices
N.A.I.C.S.: 622110

CHS/Community Health Systems, Inc. (1)
22675 Alessandro Blvd, Moreno Valley, CA 92553
Tel.: (951) 571-2350
Web Site: https://www.chsica.org
Health Care Srvices
N.A.I.C.S.: 622110

CHSPSC, LLC (1)
4000 Meridian Blvd, Franklin, TN 37067 **(100%)**
Tel.: (615) 465-7000
Web Site: https://www.chs.net
Hospital Management & Healthcare Services
N.A.I.C.S.: 622110
Wayne T. Smith *(Chm & CEO)*
Miguel S. Benet *(Sr VP)*
Kevin Hammons *(Pres)*
Lynn T. Simon *(Pres)*
Brad Cash *(Exec VP)*
Tomi Galin *(Exec VP)*
James M. Hayes *(Chief HR Officer)*
Justin Pitt *(Exec VP)*
Drew Mason *(Pres)*
Kevin Stockton *(Pres)*
Mark Medley *(Pres)*
Chad Campbell *(Pres)*
Chris Cobb *(Sec)*
Craig Conti *(VP)*
Jason K. Johnson *(Chief Acctg Officer)*
Edward W. Lomicka *(VP-Strategic Analytics)*
Gabe Ottinger *(Treas)*
Pam Rudisill *(Sr VP)*
Susan Schrupp *(Sr VP)*
Nathan Summar *(VP)*
Richard T. Willis *(VP)*
Beth Witte *(Sr VP)*

Subsidiary (Domestic):

Brownwood Hospital, L.P. (2)
1501 Burnett Rd, Brownwood, TX 76801
Tel.: (325) 646-8541
Web Site: http://www.brmc-cares.com
Hospital & Health Care Services
N.A.I.C.S.: 622110
Jay Smith *(Dir)*

Subsidiary (Domestic):

Brownwood Medical Center, LLC (3)
1501 Burnet Rd, Brownwood, TX 76801-8520
Tel.: (325) 897-4263
Web Site: https://www.brmc-cares.com
General Medical And Surgical Hospitals
N.A.I.C.S.: 459420

Unit (Domestic):

Walker Cancer Center (4)

Community Health Systems, Inc.—(Continued)

1501 Burnet Dr, Brownwood, TX 76801
Tel.: (325) 649-5000
Sales Range: $1-9.9 Million
Emp.: 15
Oncology Services
N.A.I.C.S.: 621111

Subsidiary (Domestic):

Detar Hospital, LLC　　(2)
506 E San Antonio St, Victoria, TX 77901
Tel.: (361) 575-7441
Web Site: https://www.detar.com
Medical & Surgical Hospital
N.A.I.C.S.: 622110

Gateway Health System　　(2)
651 Dunlop Ln, Clarksville, TN
37040　　(80%)
Tel.: (931) 502-1000
Web Site: http://www.todaysgateway.com
Surgical Hospital
N.A.I.C.S.: 622110

Unit (Domestic):

Clarksville Medical Center, G.P.　(3)
651 Dunlop Ln, Clarksville, TN
37040　　(100%)
Tel.: (931) 502-1000
Web Site: http://www.todaysgateway.com
Sales Range: $50-74.9 Million
Surgical Hospital
N.A.I.C.S.: 622110

Subsidiary (Domestic):

Kay County Oklahoma Hospital Company, LLC　(2)
1900 N 14th St, Ponca City, OK 74601
Tel.: (580) 765-3321
Web Site:
　https://www.alliancehealthponcacity.com
Sales Range: $25-49.9 Million
Hospital
N.A.I.C.S.: 622110
Andy Wachtel (CEO)

Medical Center Enterprise
400 N Edwards St, Enterprise, AL 36330
Tel.: (334) 347-0584
Web Site: https://www.mcehospital.com
Sales Range: $50-74.9 Million
Medical Hospital
N.A.I.C.S.: 622110

Navarro Regional, LLC　　(2)
3201 W Hwy 22, Corsicana, TX 75110-2450
Tel.: (903) 654-6800
Web Site: https://www.navarrohospital.com
Hospital Operations
N.A.I.C.S.: 622110

Subsidiary (Domestic):

Navarro Hospital, L.P.　　(3)
3201 W Hwy 22, Corsicana, TX 75110-2450
Tel.: (903) 654-6800
Web Site: https://www.navarrohospital.com
Women Healthcare Services
N.A.I.C.S.: 621610

Subsidiary (Domestic):

Northwest Hospital, LLC　　(2)
6200 N LaCholla Blvd, Tucson, AZ 85741
Tel.: (520) 742-9000
Web Site: https://www.healthiertucson.com
Sales Range: $75-99.9 Million
Hospital
N.A.I.C.S.: 622110

Affiliate (Domestic):

San Angelo Hospital, L.P.　　(2)
3501 Knickerbocker Rd, San Angelo, TX
76904
Tel.: (325) 949-9511
Web Site: https://www.sacmc.com
Hospital Operator
N.A.I.C.S.: 622110
T. Richey Oliver (Chm)
David Lupton (Vice Chm)
Rodney Schumacher (CEO & Sec)

Subsidiary (Domestic):

Woodland Heights Medical Center,
LLC　　(2)
505 S John Redditt Dr, Lufkin, TX 75904

Tel.: (936) 634-8311
Web Site: https://www.woodlandheights.net
Sales Range: $75-99.9 Million
General Medical & Surgical Hospitals
N.A.I.C.S.: 622110

Cahaba Orthopedics, LLC　　(1)
720 Montclair Rd Ste 200, Birmingham, AL
35213
Tel.: (205) 592-5000
Health Care Srvices
N.A.I.C.S.: 622110

Campbell County HMA, LLC　　(1)
923 E Central Ave, La Follette, TN 37766
Tel.: (423) 907-1200
Web Site: https://www.tennova.com
Health Care Srvices
N.A.I.C.S.: 622110

Carlsbad Medical Center, LLC　　(1)
2430 W Pierce St, Carlsbad, NM 88220
Tel.: (575) 887-4100
Web Site:
　https://www.carlsbadmedicalcenter.com
Health Care Srvices
N.A.I.C.S.: 622110

Cedar Park Health System, L.P.　(1)
1401 Medical Pkwy, Cedar Park, TX 78613
Tel.: (512) 528-7000
Web Site:
　https://www.cedarparkregional.com
Sales Range: $25-49.9 Million
Emp.: 600
General Medical & Surgical Hospitals
N.A.I.C.S.: 622110

Cedar Park Surgery Center, LLC　(1)
351 Cypress Creek Rd Ste 102, Cedar
Park, TX 78613
Tel.: (512) 498-9006
Web Site:
　https://cedarparksurgerycenter.com
Physician Health Care Services
N.A.I.C.S.: 621111

Center for Adult Healthcare, LLC　(1)
1629 Woodlawn Ave, Dyersburg, TN 38024
Tel.: (731) 288-7250
Web Site: http://www.adult-healthcare.com
Emp.: 3
Health Care Srvices
N.A.I.C.S.: 622110

Center for Medical Interoperability,
Inc.　　(1)
8 City Blvd Ste 203, Nashville, TN 37209
Tel.: (615) 257-6400
Web Site:
　http://www.medicalinteroperability.org
Health Care Srvices
N.A.I.C.S.: 622110
Ed Cantwell (Pres & CEO)
Ed Miller (CTO)
Aaron Goldmuntz (COO)
Kelly Aldrich (Chief Clinical Digital Officer)
Meredith Karney (VP)

Champion Sports Medicine Birmingham, LLC　(1)
200 Montgomery Hwy Ste 150, Birmingham, AL 35216
Tel.: (205) 822-0067
Web Site:
　https://www.csmsportsmedicine.com
Hospital & Health Care Services
N.A.I.C.S.: 622110

Chesterton Surgery Center, LLC　(1)
3111 Village Pt, Chesterton, IN 46304-9689
Tel.: (219) 983-1401
Health Care Srvices
N.A.I.C.S.: 622110

Claremore Anesthesia, LLC　　(1)
1202 N Muskogee Plz, Claremore, OK
74017-3058
Tel.: (918) 392-4456
Health Care Srvices
N.A.I.C.S.: 622110

Claremore Internal Medicine,
LLC　　(1)
1501 N Florence Ave Ste 201, Claremore,
OK 74017
Tel.: (918) 341-1886
General Medical & Surgical Hospitals
N.A.I.C.S.: 622110

Clarksville Home Care Services,
LLC　　(1)

647 Dunlop Ln Ste 305, Clarksville, TN
37040
Tel.: (931) 647-3553
Women Healthcare Services
N.A.I.C.S.: 621610

Cleveland Home Care Services,
LLC　　(1)
2440 Oakland Dr NW, Cleveland, TN
37311-3826
Tel.: (423) 559-6092
Home Health Services
N.A.I.C.S.: 621610

Cleveland Hospital Corporation　(1)
2800 Westside Dr NW, Cleveland, TN
37312-3501
Tel.: (423) 339-4100
Emp.: 190
Health Care Srvices
N.A.I.C.S.: 622110
Coleman Foss (CEO)

Cleveland Medical Clinic, Inc.　(1)
2305 Chambliss Ave, Cleveland, TN 37320
Tel.: (423) 559-6000
Health Care Srvices
N.A.I.C.S.: 622110

Clinton HMA, LLC　　(1)
100 N 30th St, Clinton, OK 73601
Tel.: (580) 323-2363
Web Site:
　https://www.alliancehealthclinton.com
Emp.: 175
General Hospital Operator
N.A.I.C.S.: 622110
Jay Johnson (CFO)
Kimberly Todd (Chief Nursing Officer)
Landon E. Hise (CEO)
Kim Hunter (Mgr)
Jill Atchley (Dir-Quality)
Julie Graumann (Dir-Human Resources)
Lori Messenger (Dir-Marketing)
Tracy P. Byers (CEO)
Gwendolyn Fuchs (Chief Nursing Officer)
Melinda Brock (Dir-Human Resources)
Doug Ross (Mktg Dir)
Tracy P. Byers (CEO)
Gwendolyn Fuchs (Chief Nursing Officer)
Melinda Brock (Dir-Human Resources)
Doug Ross (Mktg Dir)
Tracy P. Byers (CEO)
Gwendolyn Fuchs (Chief Nursing Officer)
Melinda Brock (Dir-Human Resources)
Doug Ross (Mktg Dir)

Cocke County HMA, LLC　　(1)
435 2nd St, Newport, TN 37821
Tel.: (423) 625-2200
Web Site: https://www.tennovanewport.com
Health Care Srvices
N.A.I.C.S.: 622110

College Station Hospital, L.P.　(1)
1604 Rock Prairie, College Station, TX
77845
Tel.: (979) 764-5100
Web Site: https://stjoseph.stlukeshealth.org
Health Care Srvices
N.A.I.C.S.: 622110

College Station RHC Company,
LLC　　(1)
600 N Park St, Brenham, TX 77833
Tel.: (979) 337-5800
Web Site: http://www.brenhamclinic.com
General Medical & Surgical Hospitals
N.A.I.C.S.: 622110

Collier HMA Neurological Vascular
Medical Group, LLC　　(1)
5811 Pelican Bay Blvd Ste 500, Naples, FL
34108-2733
Tel.: (239) 598-3131
Health Care Srvices
N.A.I.C.S.: 622110

Commonwealth Health Cancer Network, LLC　(1)
Saint Joseph Cancer Ctr 1708 Forest Dr
Ste 101, Corbin, KY 40701
Tel.: (606) 528-5000
Web Site:
　https://www.commonwealthcancercen
　ter.com
Health Care Srvices
N.A.I.C.S.: 622110

Commonwealth Physician Network,
LLC　　(1)

4 E Main St, Nanticoke, PA 18634
Tel.: (570) 735-7474
Web Site:
　https://www.commonwealthhealth.net
Health Care Srvices
N.A.I.C.S.: 622110

Compass Imaging, LLC　　(1)
14245 Dedeaux Rd, Gulfport, MS 39503
Tel.: (228) 314-7226
Hospital Healthcare Services
N.A.I.C.S.: 621491

Cottage Home Options, L.L.C.　(1)
184 S River Ave Ste 204, Holland, MI
49423
Tel.: (616) 393-9460
Web Site: https://cottagehome.com
Women Healthcare Services
N.A.I.C.S.: 621610

Crane Creek Surgical Partners,
LLC　　(1)
2222 S Harbor City Blvd Ste 540, Melbourne, FL 32901
Tel.: (321) 541-1776
Web Site:
　http://www.cranecreeksurgerycenter.com
Sales Range: $1-9.9 Million
Emp.: 19
Health Care Srvices
N.A.I.C.S.: 622110

Crestwood Hospital, LLC　　(1)
1 Hospital Dr, Huntsville, AL 35801
Tel.: (256) 429-4000
Web Site:
　https://www.crestwoodmedcenter.com
Emp.: 1,000
General Medical & Surgical Hospitals
N.A.I.C.S.: 622110

Crestwood Physician Services,
LLC　　(1)
4810 Whitesport Cir SW Ste 200, Huntsville, AL 35801-7419
Tel.: (256) 429-5248
Health Care Srvices
N.A.I.C.S.: 622110

Crossroads Home Care Services,
LLC　　(1)
1109 Vicente St Ste 101, San Francisco,
CA 94116
Tel.: (415) 682-2111
Web Site: http://www.crossroadshh.com
General Medical & Surgical Hospitals
N.A.I.C.S.: 622110

Deaconess Holdings, LLC　　(1)
Switch 5501 Northportlind, Oklahoma City,
OK 73112
Tel.: (405) 604-6000
Holding Company
N.A.I.C.S.: 551112

Deaconess Physician Services,
LLC　　(1)
5701 N Portland Ave Ste 126, Oklahoma
City, OK 73112
Tel.: (405) 713-7422
Web Site:
　https://www.deaconessphysicians.com
Health Care Srvices
N.A.I.C.S.: 622110

Diagnostic Clinic of Longview　(1)
707 Hollybrook Dr Ste 500, Longview, TX
75605
Tel.: (903) 232-8276
Web Site: https://www.dcol.net
Health Care Srvices
N.A.I.C.S.: 622110

Diagnostic Imaging of Brandywine
Valley, LP　(1)
1244 Cornerstone Blvd, Downingtown, PA
19335
Tel.: (610) 518-3428
Health Care Srvices
N.A.I.C.S.: 622110

Dukes Physician Services, LLC　(1)
1000 N Broadway, Peru, IN 46970-1070
Tel.: (765) 472-5335
Health Care Srvices
N.A.I.C.S.: 622110

Durant H.M.A., LLC　　(1)
1800 University Blvd, Durant, OK 74701-
3006

Tel.: (580) 924-3080
Web Site: http://www.myalliancehealth.com
Hospital Services
N.A.I.C.S.: 622110
Rick Wigington (Chm)
Joe Barrett (Vice Chm)
Kevin Samrow (CEO)
Gary Bull (CFO)

Dyersburg Hospital Corporation   (1)
400 E Tickle St, Dyersburg, TN 38024
Tel.: (731) 285-2410
General Medical & Surgical Hospitals
N.A.I.C.S.: 622110

East Georgia Regional Medical Center, LLC   (1)
1499 Fair Rd, Statesboro, GA 30458
Tel.: (912) 486-1000
Web Site:
   https://www.eastgeorgiaregional.com
Health Care Srvices
N.A.I.C.S.: 622110
Marie Burdett (Chief Nursing Officer)
Stephen Pennington (CEO)
Beth Simmons (Chief Quality Officer)
John White (CFO)
David Schott (COO)

East Tennessee Clinic Corp.   (1)
502 W 7th N St, Morristown, TN 37814
Tel.: (423) 586-1818
Web Site:
   https://www.easttennesseehealthcen
   ter.com
General Medical & Surgical Hospitals
N.A.I.C.S.: 622110

Emporia Home Care Services, LLC   (1)
201 Hicksford Ave, Emporia, VA 23847-2126
Tel.: (434) 348-3459
Health Care Srvices
N.A.I.C.S.: 622110

FMG PrimeCare, LLC   (1)
4126 W Main St, Dothan, AL 36305-9310
Tel.: (334) 793-2120
Hospital Healthcare Services
N.A.I.C.S.: 621491

Fallbrook Hospital Corporation   (1)
624 E Elder St, Fallbrook, CA 92028-3004
Tel.: (760) 728-1191
Web Site: https://www.fallbrookhospital.com
Sales Range: $25-49.9 Million
Emp.: 434
Medical & Surgical Hospitals
N.A.I.C.S.: 622110

Fayetteville Arkansas Hospital Company, LLC   (1)
3873 N Parkview Dr, Fayetteville, AR 72703
Tel.: (479) 571-7070
Hospital Healthcare Services
N.A.I.C.S.: 621491

First Choice Health Plan of Mississippi, LLC   (1)
309 Newpointe Dr Ste A, Ridgeland, MS 39157
Tel.: (601) 856-0997
Web Site: http://www.firstchoicems.com
Health Care Srvices
N.A.I.C.S.: 622110

Florida Endoscopy and Surgery Center, LLC   (1)
12900 Cortez Blvd Ste 103, Brooksville, FL 34613
Tel.: (352) 596-1145
Web Site: https://www.myfesc.com
Health Care Srvices
N.A.I.C.S.: 622110

Foley Hospital Corporation   (1)
1613 N McKenzie St, Foley, AL 36535
Tel.: (251) 949-3400
Web Site: https://www.southbaldwinrmc.com
Emp.: 800
Health Care Srvices
N.A.I.C.S.: 622110

Fort Payne Home Care Corporation   (1)
1706 Glenn Blvd SW Ste 3, Fort Payne, AL 35968
Tel.: (256) 844-2882
Emp.: 10

Women Healthcare Services
N.A.I.C.S.: 621610
June Brown (Mgr-Admin)

Fort Smith HMA, LLC   (1)
1001 Towson Ave, Fort Smith, AR 72901-4921
Tel.: (479) 441-4000
Web Site: https://www.sparkshealth.com
Health Care Srvices
N.A.I.C.S.: 621610

Franklin Clinic Corp.   (1)
2000 Meade Pkwy, Suffolk, VA 23434
Tel.: (757) 562-7301
Emp.: 8
Health Care Srvices
N.A.I.C.S.: 622110

Franklin Home Care Services, LLC   (1)
100 Fairview Dr, Franklin, VA 23851-1238
Tel.: (757) 569-6360
Emp.: 15
Women Healthcare Services
N.A.I.C.S.: 621610
Sandy Edwards (Gen Mgr)

Gadsden Home Care Services, LLC   (1)
300 Medical Center Dr Ste 403, Gadsden, AL 35903
Tel.: (256) 538-2273
Emp.: 15
Health Care Srvices
N.A.I.C.S.: 621610

Gadsden Regional Medical Center, LLC   (1)
1007 Goodyear Ave, Gadsden, AL 35903
Tel.: (256) 494-4000
Web Site: https://www.gadsdenregional.com
Sales Range: $50-74.9 Million
Emp.: 2,000
Health & Medical Services
N.A.I.C.S.: 622110

Gadsden Regional Primary Care, LLC   (1)
1026 Goodyear Ave Ste 100, Gadsden, AL 35903
Tel.: (256) 492-8250
Health Care Srvices
N.A.I.C.S.: 622110

Galesburg Home Care Corporation   (1)
799 N Henderson St, Galesburg, IL 61401-2515
Tel.: (309) 343-9031
Web Site: http://www.chs.net
Emp.: 20
Health Care Srvices
N.A.I.C.S.: 621610

Granbury Hospital Corporation   (1)
1310 Paluxy Rd, Granbury, TX 76048
Tel.: (817) 573-2273
Web Site:
   https://www.lakegranburymedicalcen
   ter.com
Health Care Srvices
N.A.I.C.S.: 622110
Jerry Petterson (VP)

Granite City Home Care Services, LLC   (1)
2100 Madison Ave, Granite City, IL 62040-4701
Tel.: (618) 798-3200
Web Site: http://www.chs.net
Emp.: 25
Health Care Srvices
N.A.I.C.S.: 621610

Green Clinic, LLC   (1)
1200 S Farmerville St, Ruston, LA 71270
Tel.: (318) 255-3690
Web Site: https://www.green-clinic.com
Emp.: 400
Medical Devices
N.A.I.C.S.: 622110
Gary E. Luffey (Partner)

Gulf Coast HMA Physician Management, LLC   (1)
540 The Rialto, Venice, FL 34285
Web Site:
   https://www.gulfcoastmedicalgroup.com

Sales Range: $10-24.9 Million
Healthcare & Medical Services
N.A.I.C.S.: 621111

Gulf Coast Medical Center, LLC   (1)
10141 US 59 Rd, Wharton, TX 77488
Tel.: (979) 532-2500
Web Site: http://www.gcmc-pc.com
Health Care Srvices
N.A.I.C.S.: 622110

Gulf Oaks Therapeutic Day School, LLC   (1)
180c Debuys Rd, Biloxi, MS 39531
Tel.: (228) 388-0679
Education Services
N.A.I.C.S.: 611110

Gulf South Surgery Center, LLC   (1)
1206 31st Ave, Gulfport, MS 39501
Tel.: (228) 864-0008
Web Site: http://www.gsscllc.com
Health Care Srvices
N.A.I.C.S.: 622110

HMA Bayflite Services, LLC   (1)
701 6th St S, Saint Petersburg, FL 33701
Tel.: (727) 893-6803
Web Site: https://www.bayflite.com
Aviation Services
N.A.I.C.S.: 488119

HMA Santa Rosa Medical Center, Inc.   (1)
6002 Berryhill Rd, Milton, FL 32570
Tel.: (850) 626-7762
Web Site: https://www.srmcfl.com
Sales Range: $50-74.9 Million
Emp.: 300
Hospital Services
N.A.I.C.S.: 622110

Haines City HMA Urgent Care, LLC   (1)
7375 Cypress Gardens Blvd, Winter Haven, FL 33884
Tel.: (863) 325-8185
Web Site:
   https://centracare.adventhealth.com
Medical Devices
N.A.I.C.S.: 622110

Harris Medical Clinics, Inc.   (1)
1200 Mclain St, Newport, AR 72112-3534
Tel.: (870) 523-2320
Health Care Srvices
N.A.I.C.S.: 622110

Harrison HMA, Inc.   (1)
180 DeBuys Rd, Biloxi, MS 39531
Tel.: (228) 388-6711
Hospital Services
N.A.I.C.S.: 622110

Health Education Services, LLC   (1)
1000 Varian St Ste A, San Carlos, CA 94070
Sales Range: $1-9.9 Million
Emp.: 22
First Aid Training Services
N.A.I.C.S.: 611699

Health Management Associates of West Virginia, Inc.   (1)
859 Alderson St, Williamson, WV 25661
Tel.: (304) 235-2500
Web Site:
   http://www.williamsonmemorial.net
Hospital Services
N.A.I.C.S.: 622110

Health Management Associates, LLC   (1)
230 Lexington Green Cir Ste 605, Lexington, KY 40503-3326
Tel.: (859) 219-3939
Web Site: https://www.hmacorp.com
Sales Range: $50-74.9 Million
Hospital Management Services
N.A.I.C.S.: 921120

Heritage Healthcare Innovation Fund II, LP   (1)
20 Burton Hills Blvd, Nashville, TN 37215-6197
Tel.: (615) 665-8220
Hospital Healthcare Services
N.A.I.C.S.: 621491

Hernando HMA, Inc.   (1)
17240 Cortez Blvd, Brooksville, FL 34601

Tel.: (352) 544-6129
Web Site:
   https://www.brooksvilleregionalhospital.org
Sales Range: $50-74.9 Million
Hospital Services
N.A.I.C.S.: 622110

Subsidiary (Domestic):

Citrus HMA, Inc.   (2)
6201 N Suncoast Blvd, Crystal River, FL 34428-6712
Tel.: (352) 795-5560
Web Site:
   https://www.bayfrontsevenrivers.com
Hospital Services
N.A.I.C.S.: 622110
Linda Stockton (CEO)
Martha Smith (Chief Nursing Officer)
Chris Benson (CFO)

Branch (Domestic):

Hernando HMA, Inc.   (2)
10461 Quality Dr, Spring Hill, FL 34609
Tel.: (352) 688-8200
Sales Range: $50-74.9 Million
Emp.: 400
Hospital Services
N.A.I.C.S.: 622110
Patrick Maloney (CEO)

Hill Regional Clinic Corp.   (1)
117 Jane Ln, Hillsboro, TX 76645-2673
Tel.: (254) 582-8006
Health Care Srvices
N.A.I.C.S.: 622110

Hood Medical Group   (1)
1308 Paluxy Rd, Granbury, TX 76049
Tel.: (817) 578-8906
Web Site:
   https://www.lakesidephysicians.com
Women Healthcare Services
N.A.I.C.S.: 621610
Linda Childress (Gen Mgr)

Hospital Laundry Services, Inc.   (1)
3322 Cavalier Dr, Fort Wayne, IN 46808
Tel.: (260) 482-3540
Web Site: https://www.hls-fw.com
Laundry Services
N.A.I.C.S.: 812331
Bill Jones (Gen Mgr)
Troy Snyder (Plant Mgr)
Andrew Hamilton (Dir-Linen Distr)
Tina Stabler (Controller)
Scott Steen (Mgr-Facilities & Safety)
Huberto Vasquez (Mgr-Parkview Linen Distr)
Jay Cruz (Mgr-Methodist Linen Distr)
Monica Wilson (Supvr-Production)

Hospital of Fulton, Inc.   (1)
2000 Holiday Ln, Fulton, KY 42041
Tel.: (270) 472-2522
Web Site:
   https://www.parkwayregionalhospital.com
Health Care Srvices
N.A.I.C.S.: 622110

Hospital of Morristown, Inc.   (1)
726 McFarland St, Morristown, TN 37814-3989
Tel.: (423) 522-6000
Web Site:
   https://www.lakewayregionalhospital.com
Sales Range: $25-49.9 Million
Emp.: 390
General Medical & Surgical Hospitals
N.A.I.C.S.: 622110

Innovations Surgery Center, LLC   (1)
3206 Tower Oaks Blvd, Rockville, MD 20852
Tel.: (240) 669-3134
Web Site: https://www.innovationsasc.com
Health Care Srvices
N.A.I.C.S.: 622110

Intermountain Medical Group, Inc.   (1)
610 Wyoming Ave, Kingston, PA 18704
Tel.: (570) 288-5441
Web Site:
   http://www.intermountainhealthcare.org
Emp.: 5,000
Health Care Srvices
N.A.I.C.S.: 622110
F. Ann Millner (Vice Chm)
Kevan Mabbutt (Chief Consumer Officer & Sr VP)

Community Health Systems, Inc.—(Continued)

Jackson HB Medical Services, LLC (1)
1850 Chadwick Dr, Jackson, MS 39204
Tel.: (601) 376-1000
Web Site:
https://www.merithealthcentral.com
Hospital Operator
N.A.I.C.S.: 622110

Jackson HMA, LLC (1)
1850 Chadwick Dr, Jackson, MS 39204
Tel.: (601) 376-1000
Web Site:
https://www.merithealthcentral.com
Hospital Services
N.A.I.C.S.: 622110
Justin Stroud (CFO)
David C. Henry (Interim CEO)
Dana Clark (Chief Nursing Officer)

Jackson, Tennessee Hospital Company, LLC (1)
367 Hospital Blvd, Jackson, TN 38305
Tel.: (731) 661-2000
General Medical & Surgical Hospitals
N.A.I.C.S.: 622110

Jefferson County HMA, LLC (1)
110 Hospital Dr, Jefferson City, TN 37760
Tel.: (865) 471-2718
Health Care Srvices
N.A.I.C.S.: 622110
Gina Leath (Chief Nursing Officer)

Jourdanton Home Care Services, LLC (1)
1907 E Hwy 97 Ste 230, Jourdanton, TX 78064
Tel.: (830) 281-8136
Health Care Srvices
N.A.I.C.S.: 621610

Kay County Clinic Company, LLC (1)
Doctors Park 415 Fairview Ste 201, Ponca City, OK 74601-2035
Tel.: (580) 762-0202
Web Site: https://www.poncamedcenter.com
Sales Range: $25-49.9 Million
Emp.: 410
Health Care Srvices
N.A.I.C.S.: 621610

Kennett HMA, Inc. (1)
1301 1st St, Kennett, MO 63857
Tel.: (573) 888-4522
Web Site: http://www.twinriversregional.com
Sales Range: $50-74.9 Million
Emp.: 400
Hospital Services
N.A.I.C.S.: 622110

Key West I IMA, Inc. (1)
5900 College Rd, Key West, FL 33040-4023
Tel.: (305) 294-5531
Web Site: https://www.lkmc.com
Sales Range: $50-74.9 Million
Hospital Services
N.A.I.C.S.: 622110

Kirksville Academic Medicine, LLC (1)
800 W Jefferson St, Kirksville, MO 63501-1443
Tel.: (660) 626-2235
Health Care Srvices
N.A.I.C.S.: 622110

Kirksville Clinic Corp. (1)
1607 S Baltimore St, Kirksville, MO 63501-4506
Tel.: (660) 627-3363
Health Care Srvices
N.A.I.C.S.: 622110

Kirksville Missouri Hospital Company, LLC (1)
315 S Osteopathy, Kirksville, MO 63501-6401
Tel.: (660) 785-1000
Web Site: https://www.nermc.com
Emp.: 500
Health Care Srvices
N.A.I.C.S.: 621399
Patrick Avila (CEO)
Jete Edmisson (Interim CFO)
Elizabeth Guffey (Chief Nursing Officer)
Tami Western (Chief Quality Officer)

Kirksville Physical Therapy Services, LLC (1)
2814 S Baltimore St, Kirksville, MO 63501-4640
Tel.: (660) 785-1834
Sales Range: $10-24.9 Million
Emp.: 30
General Medical & Surgical Hospitals
N.A.I.C.S.: 622110
Nancy Averil (Gen Mgr)

Knoxville HB Medical Services, LLC (1)
7565 Dannaher Dr, Powell, TN 37849
Tel.: (865) 859-8000
Web Site:
https://www.tennovanorthknoxville.com
Hospital Operator
N.A.I.C.S.: 622110

Knoxville HMA Cardiology PPM, LLC (1)
1225 E Weisgarber Rd Ste 190, Knoxville, TN 37909-2604
Tel.: (865) 602-6700
Emp.: 3
Health Care Srvices
N.A.I.C.S.: 622110

Knoxville HMA Physician Management, LLC (1)
900 E Oak Hill Ave, Knoxville, TN 37917-4505
Tel.: (865) 545-8000
Health Care Srvices
N.A.I.C.S.: 622110

Knoxville Home Care Services, LLC (1)
7447 &ersonville Pike, Knoxville, TN 37938-4238
Tel.: (865) 925-5500
Web Site: https://www.tennovahospice.com
Emp.: 30
Health Care Srvices
N.A.I.C.S.: 622110

LaPorte Medical Group Surgical Center, LLC (1)
900 I St Ste 1, La Porte, IN 46350
Tel.: (219) 324-1670
Web Site: https://www.laportesurgery.com
Health Care Srvices
N.A.I.C.S.: 622110

Lake Area Physician Services, LLC (1)
4150 Nelson Rd Bldg G, Lake Charles, LA 70605
Tel.: (337) 562-3732
Web Site:
http://www.lakeareaphysicians.com
Health Care Srvices
N.A.I.C.S.: 622110

Lake Granbury Hospital-Based Professional Services (1)
1310 Paluxy Rd, Granbury, TX 76048
Tel.: (817) 573-2273
Web Site:
https://www.lakegranburymedicalcenter.com
Hospital Operator
N.A.I.C.S.: 622110

Lake Wales Clinic Corp. (1)
340 W Central Ave, Lake Wales, FL 33853-4203
Tel.: (863) 676-3445
Web Site:
https://business.lakewaleschamber.com
Health Care Srvices
N.A.I.C.S.: 622110
Skip Alford (CEO)
Allison Snyder (CFO)

Lakeland Home Care Services, LLC (1)
1120 Carlton Ave Ste 2300, Lake Wales, FL 33853
Tel.: (863) 603-9777
Health Care Srvices
N.A.I.C.S.: 622110
Marie Abbatoy (Supvr-Clinic)

Lakeway Regional Hospital (1)
726 McFarland St, Morristown, TN 37814
Tel.: (423) 522-6000
Web Site: http://www.tennovaeast.com

Healthcare & Medical Services
N.A.I.C.S.: 622110

Lancaster Clinic Corp. (1)
838 W Meeting St Ste A, Lancaster, SC 29720-6233
Tel.: (803) 285-2700
Web Site: https://www.lancasterclinics.com
Health Care Srvices
N.A.I.C.S.: 622110

Lancaster Emergency Medical Services Association (1)
1829 Lincoln Hwy E, Lancaster, PA 17602
Tel.: (717) 481-4841
Web Site: https://www.lemsa.com
Emergency Medical Services
N.A.I.C.S.: 621493
C. Robert May (Exec Dir)
Teresa M. Mullhausen (Coord-Benefits)
Tina M. D'Imperio (Coord-Scheduling & Special Events)
Edward M. Crawford (Coord)
Richard M. Pearson (Dir-Education)
Andrew Gilger (Officer-Performance Improvement)
Andrew G. Weitzel (Supvr-IT)
Michael Johnson (Treas)
Dick Moriarty (Sec)
Joanne Weidman (CFO)
Jerry Schramm (Dir-Ops)
Carli Moua (Dir)
Gladdie McMurtrie (Chm)
Robert G. Burrs Jr. (Officer-Logistics)

Lancaster Home Care Services, LLC (1)
901 Meeting St Ste 201, Lancaster, SC 29720-6209
Tel.: (803) 286-1472
Emp.: 50
Health Care Srvices
N.A.I.C.S.: 622110
Raymond Helms (Dir-Admin)

Lancaster Imaging Center, LLC (1)
1037 W Meeting St, Lancaster, SC 29720
Tel.: (803) 313-3170
Emp.: 8
Health Care Srvices
N.A.I.C.S.: 622110

Lancaster Medical Group, LLC (1)
1600 Cloister Dr, Lancaster, PA 17601-2390
Tel.: (888) 579-3499
Emp.: 100
Medical Related Services
N.A.I.C.S.: 622110
Lee Meyers (CEO)

Lancaster Outpatient Imaging, LLC (1)
2170 Noll Dr Ste 200, Lancaster, PA 17603
Tel.: (717) 230-3700
Medical Devices
N.A.I.C.S.: 622110
Karen Branner (Mgr)

Las Cruces Medical Center, LLC (1)
4311 E Lohman Ave, Las Cruces, NM 88011
Tel.: (575) 556-7600
Web Site:
http://www.mountainviewregional.com
Emp.: 1,200
Health Care Srvices
N.A.I.C.S.: 622110

Las Cruces Physician Services, LLC (1)
2301 Saturn Cir, Las Cruces, NM 88012
Tel.: (575) 521-4006
Emp.: 99
Health Care Srvices
N.A.I.C.S.: 622110

Las Cruces Surgery Center - Telshor, LLC (1)
1205 S Telshor Blvd, Las Cruces, NM 88011
Tel.: (575) 522-6144
Web Site:
https://www.lascrucessurgerycenter.com
Health Care Srvices
N.A.I.C.S.: 622110
Trina Mosley (Dir-Surgical Svcs)
Eve Tonkin (Mgr-Bus Office)
Nicole McCalop (Mgr-Nurse)

Lebanon HMA Surgery Center, LLC (1)

1414 W Baddour Pkwy, Lebanon, TN 37087-2514
Tel.: (615) 444-8262
Web Site: https://www.chs.net
Medical Devices
N.A.I.C.S.: 622110

Lebanon HMA, Inc. (1)
1411 W Baddour Pkwy, Lebanon, TN 37087-2513
Tel.: (615) 444-8262
Web Site:
https://www.universitymedicalcenter.com
Sales Range: $150-199.9 Million
Emp.: 900
Hospital Services
N.A.I.C.S.: 622110

Lebanon Surgery Center, LLC (1)
1840 Quentin Rd, Lebanon, PA 17042
Tel.: (717) 272-0007
Web Site:
http://www.physicianssurgicalcenteroflebanon.com
Health Care Srvices
N.A.I.C.S.: 622110

Little Rock HMA, Inc. (1)
11401 I 30, Little Rock, AR 72209
Tel.: (501) 455-7100
Web Site:
https://www.southwestregional.com
Holding Company; Hospital Operator
N.A.I.C.S.: 551112

Live Oak HMA, LLC (1)
1100 SW 11th St, Live Oak, FL 32064
Tel.: (386) 362-0800
Web Site: https://www.shandsliveoak.com
Emp.: 170
Medical Devices
N.A.I.C.S.: 622110
Donna Ragan (Chief Nursing Officer)
Jennifer Grafton (CFO)

Lock Haven Home Care Services, LLC (1)
208 E Church St Ste 200, Lock Haven, PA 17745-2025
Tel.: (615) 465-7488
Health Care Srvices
N.A.I.C.S.: 622110

Longview Regional Medical Center (1)
2901 N 4th St, Longview, TX 75605
Tel.: (903) 758-1818
Web Site: https://www.longviewregional.com
Emp.: 180
General Medical & Surgical Hospitals
N.A.I.C.S.: 622110

Louisa Home Care Services, LLC (1)
306 Commerce Dr Ste 400, Louisa, KY 41230-1409
Tel.: (606) 638-0521
Web Site: http://www.louisahomecare.com
Health Care Srvices
N.A.I.C.S.: 622110

Louisburg HMA, Inc. (1)
100 Hospital Dr, Louisburg, NC 27549-2256
Tel.: (919) 496-5131
Web Site: http://www.franklinregional.org
Sales Range: $50-74.9 Million
Emp.: 400
Hospital Services
N.A.I.C.S.: 622110

Lutheran Medical Group, LLC (1)
7910 W Jefferson Blvd Ste 120, Fort Wayne, IN 46804
Tel.: (260) 458-3500
Web Site:
http://www.lutheranhealthphysicians.com
Health Care Srvices
N.A.I.C.S.: 622110

MCSA, L.L.C. (1)
700 W Grove St, El Dorado, AR 71730
Tel.: (870) 863-2000
Web Site: https://www.themedcenter.net
Emp.: 700
General Medical & Surgical Hospitals
N.A.I.C.S.: 622110

MEDSTAT, LLC (1)
1500 Provident Dr Ste A, Warsaw, IN 46580

Tel.: (574) 372-7637
Emp.: 20
Health Care Srvices
N.A.I.C.S.: 622110
Megan Martin (Gen Mgr)

Madison HMA, LLC (1)
161 River Oaks Dr, Canton, MS 39046
Tel.: (601) 855-4000
Health Care Srvices
N.A.I.C.S.: 622110
Brith Thelps (Exec Dir)

Marion Physician Services, LLC (1)
1080A E Main St, Latta, SC 29565-1617
Tel.: (843) 752-1234
Health Care Srvices
N.A.I.C.S.: 622110

Marshall County HMA, LLC (1)
901 S 5th Ave, Madill, OK 73446
Tel.: (580) 795-3384
Web Site:
https://www.alliancehealthdurant.com
Health Care & Medical Services
N.A.I.C.S.: 622110
Scott Landgraf (Chm)
Keith Long (Vice Chm)
Walter Bruce Bigger (Executives)
Sharon Roberts (Chief Nursing Officer)
Jeff Tarrant (CEO)
David Rogers (COO)
Marc Nakagawa (CFO)
Keaton Francis (Interim Chief Admin Officer)
Keaton Francis (Interim Chief Admin Officer)

Marshall County HMPN, LLC (1)
2 Hospital Dr, Madill, OK 73446
Tel.: (580) 795-0191
Health Care Srvices
N.A.I.C.S.: 622110

Martin Clinic Corp. (1)
143 Kennedy Dr Ste A, Martin, TN 38237-3309
Tel.: (731) 587-5321
Emp.: 20
Health Care Srvices
N.A.I.C.S.: 622110
Sandy Brundage (Gen Mgr)

Martin Hospital Company, LLC (1)
161 Mount Pelia Rd, Martin, TN 38237
Tel.: (731) 588-3204
Web Site: https://www.tennova.com
Health Care Srvices
N.A.I.C.S.: 622110

Mayes County HMA, LLC (1)
111 N Bailey St, Pryor, OK 74361
Tel.: (918) 825-1600
Health Care Srvices
N.A.I.C.S.: 622110

Mayes County HMPN, LLC (1)
1301 NE 1st St, Pryor, OK 74361
Tel.: (918) 824-7714
Health Care Srvices
N.A.I.C.S.: 622110

McNairy Hospital Corporation (1)
705 Poplar Ave, Selmer, TN 38375
Tel.: (731) 645-3221
Web Site:
https://www.mcnairyregionalhospital.com
Emp.: 37
Health Care Srvices
N.A.I.C.S.: 622110

Medical Imaging Center of Ocala, LLP (1)
1490 SE Magnolia Ave Ext, Ocala, FL 34471
Tel.: (352) 671-4300
Web Site: http://www.raocala.com
Health Care Srvices
N.A.I.C.S.: 622110

Merritt Island ASC, LLC (1)
220 N Sykes Creek Pkwy Ste 101, Merritt Island, FL 32953
Tel.: (321) 459-0015
Web Site:
https://www.merrittislandsurgerycenter.com
Health Care Srvices
N.A.I.C.S.: 622110

Metro Knoxville HMA, LLC (1)

900 E Oak Hill Ave, Knoxville, TN 37917
Tel.: (865) 545-8000
Health Care Srvices
N.A.I.C.S.: 622110

Midwest Regional Medical Center, LLC (1)
2825 Parklawn Dr, Midwest City, OK 73110
Tel.: (405) 610-4411
Web Site: https://www.myalliancehealth.com
Emp.: 300
Medical Devices
N.A.I.C.S.: 622110
Clay Franklin (CEO)
Darrell Hardy (CFO)
Patrick Dunn (Chief Nursing Officer)

Mississippi HMA DME, LLC (1)
4290 Lakeland Dr Ste B, Flowood, MS 39232
Tel.: (601) 932-8880
Health Care Srvices
N.A.I.C.S.: 622110

Mississippi HMA Hospitalists, LLC (1)
161 River Oaks Dr, Canton, MS 39046-5375
Tel.: (601) 855-4001
Health Care Srvices
N.A.I.C.S.: 622110

Moberly HBP Medical Group, LLC (1)
1515 Union Ave, Moberly, MO 65270-9407
Tel.: (660) 263-8400
Emp.: 150
Health Care Srvices
N.A.I.C.S.: 622110
Ranee Brayton (Gen Mgr)

Moberly Medical Clinics, Inc. (1)
300 N Morley St, Moberly, MO 65270
Tel.: (660) 263-1513
Health Care Srvices
N.A.I.C.S.: 622110

Mooresville Hospital Management Associates, Inc. (1)
171 Fairview Rd, Mooresville, NC 28117
Tel.: (704) 660-4000
Web Site: http://www.lnrmc.com
Sales Range: $150-199.9 Million
Emp.: 900
Hospital Services
N.A.I.C.S.: 622110

MountainView Regional Home Health (1)
3948 E Lohman Ave Ste3, Las Cruces, NM 88011
Tel.: (575) 652-3867
Web Site:
http://www.mountainviewregionalhh.com
Women Healthcare Services
N.A.I.C.S.: 621610

Muir/Diablo Occupational Medicine (1)
2231 Galaxy Ct, Concord, CA 94520
Tel.: (925) 685-7744
Web Site: http://www.ushealthworks.com
Occupational Health Services
N.A.I.C.S.: 621340

NHCI of Hillsboro, Inc. (1)
101 Cir Dr, Hillsboro, TX 76645
Tel.: (254) 580-8500
Web Site:
https://www.hillregionalhospital.com
General Medical & Surgical Hospitals
N.A.I.C.S.: 622110

Naples HMA, Inc. (1)
8300 Collier Blvd, Naples, FL 34114-3549
Tel.: (239) 354-6000
Web Site:
http://www.physiciansregionalcollier.com
Sales Range: $50-74.9 Million
Hospital Services
N.A.I.C.S.: 622110
Gary Newsome (CEO)

Natchez Hospital Company, LLC (1)
54 Sergeant Prentiss Dr, Natchez, MS 39120-4726
Tel.: (601) 443-2100
Web Site:
https://www.merithealthnatchez.com
Health Care Srvices

N.A.I.C.S.: 622110
Lee Hinson (Chief Nursing Officer)
Amy Campbell (Officer-Facility Compliance)
Garett May (CEO)
Deena Keasler (CFO)

National Healthcare of Leesville, Inc. (1)
1020 Fertitta Blvd, Leesville, LA 71446
Tel.: (337) 239-9041
Web Site: https://www.byrdregional.com
Emp.: 35
Health Care Srvices
N.A.I.C.S.: 622110

Neuroskeletal Imaging, LLC (1)
1315 S Orange Ave Ste 1B, Orlando, FL 32806
Tel.: (407) 999-9977
Web Site: http://www.nsimri.com
Diagnostic Imaging Services
N.A.I.C.S.: 621512
Lou Ann Meli (Office Mgr)
Lisa Faucett (Office Mgr)
Matt Start (COO)
Mark Rouleau (CTO)

New Gulf Coast Surgery Center, LLC (1)
3882 Bienville Blvd, Ocean Springs, MS 39564
Tel.: (228) 872-6290
Web Site: http://www.gulfcoastsc.com
Medical & Surgery Services
N.A.I.C.S.: 622110

North Carolina HMA Regional Service Center, LLC (1)
170 Medical Park Rd Ste 300, Mooresville, NC 28117-8540
Tel.: (704) 660-4482
Health Care Srvices
N.A.I.C.S.: 622110

North Okaloosa Clinic Corp. (1)
550 Redstone Ave Ste 370, Crestview, FL 32536-6428
Tel.: (850) 306-2710
Emp.: 4
Health Care Srvices
N.A.I.C.S.: 622110

Northampton Clinic Company, LLC (1)
7100 Commerce Way Ste 180, Brentwood, TN 37027
Tel.: (615) 465-7626
Health Care Srvices
N.A.I.C.S.: 622110

Northampton Home Care, LLC (1)
3001 Emrick Blvd Ste 303, Bethlehem, PA 18020-8041
Tel.: (610) 866-2882
Women Healthcare Services
N.A.I.C.S.: 621610

Northwest Allied Physicians, LLC (1)
3630 W Tangerine Rd Ste 100, Marana, AZ 85658
Tel.: (520) 744-3206
Web Site:
https://www.nwalliedphysicians.com
Health Care Srvices
N.A.I.C.S.: 622110

Northwest Arkansas Hospitals, LLC (1)
3000 Medical Center Pkwy, Bentonville, AR 72712
Tel.: (479) 553-1000
Web Site: http://www.northwesthealth.com
Health Care Srvices
N.A.I.C.S.: 622110

Northwest Benton County Physician Services, LLC (1)
803 Quandt Ave, Springdale, AR 72764
Tel.: (479) 756-9199
Health Care Srvices
N.A.I.C.S.: 622110

Northwest Physicians, LLC (1)
601 W Maple Ave Ste 703, Springdale, AR 72764
Tel.: (479) 750-2203
Web Site: https://www.nw-physicians.com
Women Healthcare Services
N.A.I.C.S.: 621610

Norton HMA, Inc. (1)
4311 E Lohman Ave, Las Cruces, NM 88011
Tel.: (575) 556-7600
Web Site:
https://www.mountainviewregional.com
Sales Range: $25-49.9 Million
Emp.: 200
Hospital Services
N.A.I.C.S.: 622110
David Brash (CEO)

Oak Hill Clinic Corp. (1)
320 Jones Ave, Oak Hill, WV 25901-2909
Tel.: (304) 469-2500
Health Care Srvices
N.A.I.C.S.: 622110
Patricia Davis (Gen Mgr)

Oak Hill Hospital Corporation (1)
430 Main St, Oak Hill, WV 25901
Tel.: (304) 469-8600
Web Site: http://www.plateauhealth.com
Health Care Srvices
N.A.I.C.S.: 622110

Oklahoma City Home Care Services, LLC (1)
5300 N Grand Ste 100, Oklahoma City, OK 73112-5517
Tel.: (405) 778-6900
Web Site: http://www.chs.net
Emp.: 30
Home Care Services
N.A.I.C.S.: 621999

Osler HMA Medical Group, LLC (1)
2222 S Harbor City Blvd Ste 420, Melbourne, FL 32901-5594
Tel.: (321) 725-5050
Health Care Srvices
N.A.I.C.S.: 622110

Palmetto Tri-County Medical Specialists, LLC (1)
201 W Meeting St Ste A, Lancaster, SC 29720-2379
Tel.: (803) 286-4666
Health Care Srvices
N.A.I.C.S.: 622110

Parkway Regional Medical Clinic, Inc. (1)
2006 Holiday Ln Ste 100, Fulton, KY 42041-8468
Tel.: (270) 472-8399
Health Care Srvices
N.A.I.C.S.: 622110

Peckville Hospital Company, LLC (1)
810 Jasmine St, Omak, WA 98841
Tel.: (509) 826-1760
Web Site: https://www.mvhealth.org
Health Care Srvices
N.A.I.C.S.: 622110
Randy Coffell (Dir-Human Resources)
Holly Stanley (CFO)
Jennifer Thill (Chief Medical Officer)
Richard Johnson (Chm)
John White (CEO)
Carol Neely (Chief Nursing Officer)
Christina Wagar (COO)

Pecos Valley of New Mexico, LLC (1)
2420 W Pierce Ste 104, Carlsbad, NM 88220
Tel.: (575) 628-5051
Web Site: https://www.pecosvalleydocs.com
Health Care Srvices
N.A.I.C.S.: 622110

Pennington Gap HMA, Inc. (1)
W Morgan Ave, Pennington Gap, VA 24277
Tel.: (276) 546-1440
Sales Range: $50-74.9 Million
Hospital Services
N.A.I.C.S.: 622110

Petersburg Clinic Company, LLC (1)
436 Claremont Ct Ste 100, Colonial Heights, VA 23834-1765
Tel.: (804) 526-2121
Health Care Srvices
N.A.I.C.S.: 622110

Physician Practice Support, Inc. (1)
500 Wilson Pike Cir Ste 360, Brentwood, TN 37027
Tel.: (615) 465-7000
Emp.: 98

Community Health Systems, Inc.—(Continued)

Health Care Srvices
N.A.I.C.S.: 622110

Physicians Regional Marco Island, LLC (1)
1839 San Marco Rd, Marco Island, FL 34145
Tel.: (239) 354-6501
Web Site:
https://www.physiciansregional.com
Health Care Srvices
N.A.I.C.S.: 622110

Physicians Specialty Hospital, LLC (1)
3873 N Parkview Dr Ste 1, Fayetteville, AR 72703
Tel.: (479) 571-7010
Healthcare, Surgical & Diagnostic Imaging Services
N.A.I.C.S.: 621512

Piedmont Surgical Center of Excellence, LLC (1)
5 Memorial Medical Ct, Greenville, SC 29605
Tel.: (864) 272-3409
Web Site:
https://www.piedmontsurgerycenter.com
Surgical Hospital Services
N.A.I.C.S.: 622110

Ponca City Home Care Services, Inc. (1)
1900 N 14th St, Ponca City, OK 74601-2035
Tel.: (580) 765-8155
Health Care Srvices
N.A.I.C.S.: 622110

Poplar Bluff Regional Medical Center, Inc. (1)
2620 N Westwood Blvd, Poplar Bluff, MO 63901
Tel.: (573) 776-2000
Sales Range: $50-74.9 Million
Hospital Services
N.A.I.C.S.: 622110

Precision Surgery Center, LLC (1)
1857 N Webb Rd, Wichita, KS 67206
Tel.: (316) 866-2540
Hospital Healthcare Services
N.A.I.C.S.: 621491
Mary Ann Talman (Mgr-Clinical)

PremierCare of Northwest Arkansas, LLC (1)
417 W Maple Ave, Springdale, AR 72764
Tel.: (479) 750-6579
Web Site: https://pcnwa.net
General Medical & Surgical Hospitals
N.A.I.C.S.: 622110
Jesse Mangham (Dir-Ops & Contracting)

Punta Gorda HMA, Inc. (1)
809 E Marion Ave, Punta Gorda, FL 33950
Tel.: (941) 639-3131
Web Site:
https://www.shorepointhealthcharlotte.com
Sales Range: $150-199.9 Million
Hospital Services
N.A.I.C.S.: 622110

Subsidiary (Domestic):

Punta Gorda HMA Physician Management, LLC (2)
1951b Tamiami Trl, Port Charlotte, FL 33948-2112
Tel.: (041) 010 0000
Emp.: 5
Medical Devices
N.A.I.C.S.: 622110

QHG of Enterprise, Inc. (1)
400 N Edwards St, Enterprise, AL 36330
Tel.: (334) 347-0584
Web Site: http://www.mcehospital.com
General Medical & Surgical Hospitals
N.A.I.C.S.: 622110

QHG of Fort Wayne Company, LLC (1)
7333 W Jefferson Blvd, Fort Wayne, IN 46804
Tel.: (260) 458-3830
Web Site: https://www.redimedclinics.com

Health Care Srvices
N.A.I.C.S.: 622110

QHG of Hattiesburg, Inc. (1)
5001 Hardy St, Hattiesburg, MS 39402-1308
Tel.: (601) 268-8000
Health Care Srvices
N.A.I.C.S.: 622110

QHG of South Carolina, Inc. (1)
805 Pamplico Hwy, Florence, SC 29505
Tel.: (843) 674-5000
Web Site: https://www.carolinashospital.com
Health Care Srvices
N.A.I.C.S.: 622110

QHG of Springdale, Inc. (1)
609 W Maple Ave, Springdale, AR 72764
Tel.: (479) 751-5711
Health Care Srvices
N.A.I.C.S.: 622110

Red Bud Home Care Services, LLC (1)
325 Spring St, Red Bud, IL 62278
Tel.: (618) 282-3338
Emp.: 15
Women Healthcare Services
N.A.I.C.S.: 621610
Angella Randla (Gen Mgr)

Regional Cancer Treatment Center, Ltd. (1)
102 N Magdalen Ste 120, San Angelo, TX 76903
Tel.: (325) 653-2010
Web Site: https://www.shannonhealth.com
Health Care Srvices
N.A.I.C.S.: 622110

Regional Employee Assistance Program (1)
5730 Sherwood Way, San Angelo, TX 76901-5642
Tel.: (325) 944-3851
Web Site: https://www.regionalhealth.com
General Medical & Surgical Hospitals
N.A.I.C.S.: 622110

River Oaks Hospital, Inc. (1)
1030 River Oaks Dr, Flowood, MS 39232-9729
Tel.: (601) 932-1030
Web Site:
https://www.merithealthriveroaks.com
Hospital Services
N.A.I.C.S.: 622110

Subsidiary (Domestic):

Madison River Oaks Medical Center (2)
161 River Oaks Dr, Canton, MS 39046
Tel.: (601) 855-4000
Web Site: http://www.madisonriveroaks.com
Sales Range: $10-24.9 Million
Emp.: 55
Hospital Services
N.A.I.C.S.: 622110
Randall Strong (Chm)
Brit Phelps (CEO, Treas & Sec)
Ashley Hindman (CFO)
Tim Lolley (Chief Nursing Officer)
Sabrina Bryant (Dir-HR)
Athena Chapin (Dir-Quality & Risk)

ROH, LLC (2)
1026 N Flowood Dr, Jackson, MS 39232-9532
Tel.: (601) 933-6401
Web Site: http://www.roh-inc.com
Sales Range: $50-74.9 Million
Hospital Services
N.A.I.C.S.: 622110

Riverpark ASC, LLC (1)
107 Front St, Vidalia, LA 71373
Tel.: (318) 336-2218
Web Site: https://www.riverparkmedical.com
General Medical & Surgery Services
N.A.I.C.S.: 622110

Riverpark Community Cath Lab, LLC (1)
107 Frnt St, Vidalia, LA 71373-2836
Tel.: (601) 445-1703
Health Care Srvices
N.A.I.C.S.: 622110

Roswell Hospital Corporation (1)

405 W Country Club Rd, Roswell, NM 88201-5209
Tel.: (575) 622-8170
Web Site: http://www.enmmc.com
Emp.: 150
Health Care Srvices
N.A.I.C.S.: 622110

Ruston Clinic Company, LLC (1)
1401 Ezelle St, Ruston, LA 71270
Tel.: (318) 251-8316
Sales Range: $50-74.9 Million
Emp.: 550
General Medical & Surgical Hospitals
N.A.I.C.S.: 622110

Ruston Louisiana Hospital Company, LLC (1)
401 E Vaughn Ave, Ruston, LA 71270
Tel.: (318) 254-2100
Web Site:
https://www.northernlouisianamedical
center.com
Sales Range: $50-74.9 Million
General Medical & Surgical Hospitals
N.A.I.C.S.: 622110

Salem Home Care Services, LLC (1)
390 N BroadwayÂ Ste 900, Pennsville, NJ 08070
Tel.: (856) 678-8500
Web Site:
http://www.memorialhomecarenj.com
Emp.: 45
Women Healthcare Services
N.A.I.C.S.: 621610

Salem Hospital Corporation (1)
310 Woodstown Rd, Salem, NJ 08079
Tel.: (856) 935-1000
Web Site: https://www.smc.health
Health Care Srvices
N.A.I.C.S.: 622110
Steven Rosefsky (VP)
Manuel Guantez (Sec)
William J. Colgan (Chm)
Wamiq S. Sultan (Chief Medical Officer)
Tammy Torres (CEO)
Vincent Riccitelli (CFO)
Justine Murphy (Interim Chief Nursing Officer)
George J. Gennaoui (Dir-Marketing-Public Relations)
Patricia Palmieri (Assoc VP-Operations)
Michele Pawlowski (Dir)
James Piper (Assoc VP)
Lynn Righter-Shookla (Assoc VP)

San Angelo Community Medical Center, LLC (1)
3501 Knickerbocker Rd, San Angelo, TX 76904
Tel.: (325) 949-9511
Web Site: http://www.sacmc.org
Emp.: 170
Health Care Srvices
N.A.I.C.S.: 622110
Rod Schumacher (CEO)

Scott County HMA, LLC (1)
201 Albert Ave, Scott City, KS 67871
Tel.: (620) 872-5811
Web Site: https://www.scotthospital.net
Health Care Srvices
N.A.I.C.S.: 622110
D. Mark Burnett (Pres & CEO)
Suzanne Beaver (Chm)

Scranton Clinic Company, LLC (1)
157 Scranton Carbondale Hwy, Eynon, PA 18403-1027
Tel.: (570) 230-0038
Health Care Srvices
N.A.I.C.S.: 622110

Scranton Emergency Physician Services, LLC (1)
746 Jefferson Ave, Scranton, PA 18510-1624
Tel.: (570) 348-7957
Health Care Srvices
N.A.I.C.S.: 622110

Scranton Hospitalist Physician Services, LLC (1)
746 Jefferson Ave 4th Fl, Scranton, PA 18510-1624
Tel.: (570) 340-5079
Health Care Srvices

N.A.I.C.S.: 622110

Scranton Quincy Ambulance, LLC (1)
1000 Remington Ave, Scranton, PA 18505
Tel.: (570) 558-4911
Health Care Srvices
N.A.I.C.S.: 622110

Scranton Quincy Clinic Company, LLC (1)
748 Quincy Ave Ste 1a, Scranton, PA 18510
Tel.: (570) 347-9600
Web Site: https://www.chs.net
Emp.: 3
Health Care Srvices
N.A.I.C.S.: 622110

Scranton Quincy Hospital Company, LLC (1)
700 Quincy Ave, Scranton, PA 18510
Tel.: (570) 770-5000
Web Site:
http://www.commonwealthhealth.net
Emp.: 400
Health Care Srvices
N.A.I.C.S.: 622110

Select Specialty Hospital - Tucson, LLC (1)
2025 W Orange Grove Rd 2nd Fl, Tucson, AZ 85704
Tel.: (520) 584-4500
Hospital & Health Care Services
N.A.I.C.S.: 622110

Seminole HMA, LLC (1)
2401 Wrangler Blvd, Seminole, OK 74868
Tel.: (405) 303-4000
Web Site:
https://www.alliancehealthseminole.com
Health Care Srvices
N.A.I.C.S.: 622110
Steve Saxon (Mgr-City)
Damon Brown (CEO)
Christy Gehr (CFO)
Sharon Carr (Chief Nursing Interim Officer)
Breane Griffith (Chief Nursing Officer)

Sharon Clinic Company, LLC (1)
740 E State St, Sharon, PA 16146-3328
Tel.: (724) 983-1980
Health Care Srvices
N.A.I.C.S.: 622110

Sharon Home Care Services, LLC (1)
850 S Hermitage Rd Ste C, Hermitage, PA 16148-3679
Tel.: (724) 983-2350
Emp.: 50
Health Care Srvices
N.A.I.C.S.: 622110
Andi Bosshart (Gen Mgr)

Sharon Regional Health System, Inc. (1)
740 E State St, Sharon, PA 16146
Tel.: (724) 983-3911
Web Site: https://www.sharonregional.com
Emp.: 1,750
Health Care Srvices
N.A.I.C.S.: 622110

Shelbyville Clinic Corp. (1)
120 Frank Martin Rd Ste 103, Shelbyville, TN 37160
Tel.: (931) 684-4074
Web Site:
https://www.tennovamedicalgroup.com
General Medical & Surgical Hospitals
N.A.I.C.S.: 622110

Shelbyville Home Care Services, LLC (1)
635 N Main St Ste D, Shelbyville, TN 37160-3257
Tel.: (931) 684-2118
Emp.: 15
Health Care Srvices
N.A.I.C.S.: 622110
Channa Johnson (Gen Mgr)

Shelbyville Hospital Corporation (1)
2835 US-231, Shelbyville, TN 37160
Tel.: (931) 685-5433
Web Site:
http://www.heritagemedicalcenter.com

Sales Range: $25-49.9 Million
Emp.: 326
General Medical & Surgical Hospitals
N.A.I.C.S.: 622110

Silver Creek MRI, LLC (1)
2735 Silver Creek Rd, Bullhead City, AZ
86442-7924
Tel.: (928) 704-8973
Health Care Srvices
N.A.I.C.S.: 622110

**SkyRidge Clinical Associates,
LLC** (1)
1060 Peerless Crossing Ste 200, Cleveland, TN 37312-3861
Tel.: (423) 479-4165
Emp.: 75
Health Care Srvices
N.A.I.C.S.: 622110

**South Arkansas Physician Services,
LLC** (1)
460 W Oak St Ste 402, El Dorado, AR
71730-4567
Tel.: (870) 863-2515
Health Care Srvices
N.A.I.C.S.: 622110

Sparks PremierCare, L.L.C. (1)
810 Lexington Ave, Fort Smith, AR 72901
Tel.: (479) 441-5870
Health Care Srvices
N.A.I.C.S.: 622110
Tracy Hester (Gen Mgr)

**Spokane Valley Washington Hospital
Company, LLC** (1)
12606 E Mission Ave, Spokane Valley, WA
99216
Tel.: (509) 924-6650
Web Site: https://www.multicare.org
Sales Range: $50-74.9 Million
Emp.: 600
General Medical & Surgical Hospitals
N.A.I.C.S.: 622110

**St. Cloud Physician Management,
LLC** (1)
1600 Budinger Ave Ste D, Saint Cloud, FL
34769-6008
Tel.: (407) 891-2946
Web Site: http://www.stcloudphysicians.com
Health Care Srvices
N.A.I.C.S.: 621610

Statesboro HMA, Inc. (1)
1499 Fair Rd, Statesboro, GA 30458-1683
Tel.: (912) 486-1000
Web Site:
http://www.eastgeorgiaregional.net
Sales Range: $125-149.9 Million
Emp.: 725
Hospital Services
N.A.I.C.S.: 622110

Subsidiary (Domestic):

Statesville HMA, Inc. (2)
218 Old Mocksville Rd, Statesville, NC
28625
Tel.: (704) 873-0281
Web Site: https://www.davisregional.com
Emp.: 350
Hospital Services
N.A.I.C.S.: 622110

**Surgery Center of Key West,
LLC** (1)
931 Toppino Dr, Key West, FL 33040
Tel.: (305) 293-1801
Web Site:
https://surgerycenterofkeywest.com
General Medical & Surgery Services
N.A.I.C.S.: 622110

**Surgery Center of Midwest City,
LLC** (1)
8121 National Ave Ste 108, Midwest City,
OK 75228
Tel.: (405) 732-7905
Web Site: http://www.scmwc.com
Health Care Srvices
N.A.I.C.S.: 622110

**Surgicare Outpatient Center of Lake
Charles, Inc.** (1)
2100 Lk St, Lake Charles, LA 70601
Tel.: (337) 436-6941
Web Site: https://surgicarelc.com

Emp.: 32
Health Care Srvices
N.A.I.C.S.: 622110

Symbol Health Solutions, LLC. (1)
3765-A Government Blvd, Mobile, AL 36693
Tel.: (251) 338-2942
Web Site: https://www.symbolhealth.com
Women Healthcare Services
N.A.I.C.S.: 621610
Michael G. Molyneux (Founder, Pres &
CEO)
Richard M. Mazey (Chief Medical Officer)

**Tomball Texas Home Care Services,
LLC** (1)
13530 Michel Rd, Tomball, TX 77375-3305
Tel.: (281) 401-7680
Web Site: http://www.tomballhomecare.com
Women Healthcare Services
N.A.I.C.S.: 621610

Triad of Alabama, LLC (1)
4370 W Main St, Dothan, AL 36305
Tel.: (334) 793-5000
Web Site: https://www.flowershospital.com
Emp.: 1,400
Health Care Srvices
N.A.I.C.S.: 622110

Tullahoma HMA, Inc. (1)
1801 N Jackson St, Tullahoma, TN 37388
Tel.: (931) 393-3000
Web Site:
http://www.hartonmedicalcenter.com
Sales Range: $50-74.9 Million
Emp.: 300
Hospital Services
N.A.I.C.S.: 622110

**Tunkhannock Clinic Company,
LLC** (1)
5950 SR 6, Tunkhannock, PA 18657-7905
Tel.: (570) 996-1134
Emp.: 3
Health Care Srvices
N.A.I.C.S.: 622110

**United Vascular of Huntsville,
LLC** (1)
4700 Whitesburg Dr Ste 300, Huntsville, AL
35802
Tel.: (256) 692-5100
Web Site:
https://www.unitedvascularhuntsville.com
Dialysis Healthcare Services
N.A.I.C.S.: 621492

**Vanderbilt-Ingram Cancer Center at
Tennova Healthcare-Clarksville** (1)
375 Alfred Thun Rd, Clarksville, TN 37040
Tel.: (931) 221-0479
General Medical & Surgery Services
N.A.I.C.S.: 622110

Venice HMA, Inc. (1)
540 The Rialto, Venice, FL 34285
Tel.: (941) 485-7711
Web Site:
https://www.shorepointhealthvenice.com
Sales Range: $50-74.9 Million
Hospital Services
N.A.I.C.S.: 622110
Karen Fordham (CEO)

Vicksburg Healthcare, LLC (1)
2100 US-61, Vicksburg, MS 39183
Tel.: (601) 883-5000
Web Site:
https://www.merithealthriverregion.com
General Medical & Surgical Hospitals
N.A.I.C.S.: 622110

**Victoria Texas Home Care Services,
LLC** (1)
101 W Goodwin Ave Ste 850, Victoria, TX
77901
Tel.: (361) 578-2436
Hospital Healthcare Services
N.A.I.C.S.: 621491

Victoria of Texas, L.P. (1)
506 E San Antonio St, Victoria, TX 77901
Tel.: (361) 575-7441
Web Site: http://www.detar.com
Health Care Srvices
N.A.I.C.S.: 622110

WA-SPOK DH CRNA, LLC (1)
800 W 5th Ave, Spokane, WA 99204-2803

Tel.: (509) 479-7286
Health Care Srvices
N.A.I.C.S.: 622110

WA-SPOK Medical Care, LLC (1)
801 W 5th Ave Ste 422, Spokane, WA
99204-2841
Tel.: (509) 473-7250
Health Care Srvices
N.A.I.C.S.: 622110

WA-SPOK Primary Care, LLC (1)
1603 N Belt, Spokane, WA 99205-4038
Tel.: (509) 473-7060
Health Care Srvices
N.A.I.C.S.: 622110

**WA-SPOK Pulmonary & Critical Care,
LLC** (1)
910 W 5th Ave Ste 500, Spokane, WA
99204-2967
Tel.: (509) 625-1915
General Medical & Surgical Hospitals
N.A.I.C.S.: 622110

WA-SPOK VH CRNA, LLC (1)
12606 E Mission Ave, Spokane Valley, WA
99216-3421
Tel.: (509) 473-5405
Health Care Srvices
N.A.I.C.S.: 622110
Greg Repetti (CEO)

Waukegan Hospice, LLC (1)
36100 Brooksdie Dr, Gurnee, IL 60031
Tel.: (847) 672-9225
Web Site:
http://www.vistahomehealthandhospice.com
Community Home Healthcare Provider
N.A.I.C.S.: 621610

**Weatherford Home Care Services,
LLC** (1)
208 N Main St Ste 200, Weatherford, TX
76086-6422
Tel.: (817) 341-4663
Web Site:
http://www.brazosriverhomehealth.com
Home Health Care & Rehabilitation Services
N.A.I.C.S.: 623110

Wesley Health System, LLC (1)
5001 Hardy St, Hattiesburg, MS 39402
Tel.: (601) 268-8000
Web Site:
https://www.merithealthwesley.com
Emp.: 200
General Medical & Surgical Hospitals
N.A.I.C.S.: 622110
Phebe McKay (Chief Nursing Officer)
Ron Cain (VP-Physician Svcs)
Debbie Johnson (Officer-Patient Safety &
VP-Quality & Clinical Transformation)
Traci Rouse (VP-Mktg)
Jesse Folds (Dir & Officer)
David Muns (COO)
Tammy Schramm (CFO)
Steve Branton (Dir & Officer)
Rodney Gresham (Officer-Facility Safety &
Dir-Plant Ops)
Curtis Herrin (CFO)
Rick Kolaczek (COO)
Angela Parker (Officer-)
Todd Blanchard (CEO)

**Western Reserve Health Education,
Inc.** (1)
1350 E Market St, Warren, OH 44483
Tel.: (330) 884-3983
Web Site: https://www.wrhe-edu.org
Emp.: 80
Health Care Srvices
N.A.I.C.S.: 622110

**Wilkes-Barre Academic Medicine,
LLC** (1)
2 Sharpe St, Kingston, PA 18704-3715
Tel.: (570) 552-8900
Emp.: 50
Health Care Srvices
N.A.I.C.S.: 622110
Annette Craig (Gen Mgr)

**Wilkes-Barre Home Care Services,
LLC** (1)
900 Rutter Ave Ste 8, Forty Fort, PA 18704-
4962
Tel.: (570) 718-4400
Health Care Srvices

N.A.I.C.S.: 622110

**Wilkes-Barre Hospital Company,
LLC** (1)
575 N River St, Wilkes Barre, PA 18764
Tel.: (570) 829-8111
Web Site: http://www.wilkesbarregeneral.net
Emp.: 400
Health Care Srvices
N.A.I.C.S.: 622110

Wilkes-Barre Skilled Nursing Services, LLC (1)
80 E Northampton St, Wilkes Barre, PA
18701-3035
Tel.: (570) 826-1031
Health Care Srvices
N.A.I.C.S.: 622110

Women's Health Partners, LLC (1)
6859 SW 18th St Ste 200, Boca Raton, FL
33433
Tel.: (561) 368-3775
Web Site: http://www.myobgynoffice.com
Health Care Srvices
N.A.I.C.S.: 622110

Womens Health Partners, LLC (1)
6859 SW 18th St Ste 200 300, Boca Raton,
FL 33433
Tel.: (561) 368-3775
Web Site: https://www.toplinemd.com
Health Care Srvices
N.A.I.C.S.: 622110

Womens Health Specialists of Birmingham, Inc. (1)
3686 Grandview Pkwy Ste 300, Birmingham, AL 35243
Tel.: (205) 536-7676
Web Site: https://whsbham.com
Health Care Srvices
N.A.I.C.S.: 622110

Womens Health Specialists of Carlisle, LLC (1)
19 Sprint Dr Ste 2, Carlisle, PA 17015
Tel.: (717) 218-8888
Web Site: http://www.whscarlisle.com
Health Care Srvices
N.A.I.C.S.: 622110

Woodward Health System, LLC (1)
900 17th St, Woodward, OK 73801
Tel.: (580) 256-5511
Web Site:
https://www.alliancehealthwoodward.com
Emp.: 124
Health Care Srvices
N.A.I.C.S.: 622110
Landon E. Hise (CEO)
Melinda Brock (Dir-Human Resources)
Kim Nickelson (Dir)
Shonda Logan (Chief Nursing Officer)
Holly Holland (Dir)

**Woodward Home Care Services,
LLC** (1)
1611 Main St Ste 103, Woodward, OK
73801-3021
Tel.: (580) 254-9275
Emp.: 10
General Medical & Surgical Hospitals
N.A.I.C.S.: 622110
Shelly Spray (Office Mgr)

York Anesthesiology Physician Services, LLC (1)
325 S Belmont St, York, PA 17403-2608
Tel.: (717) 843-8623
Health Care Srvices
N.A.I.C.S.: 622110

York Clinic Company, LLC (1)
1232 GreenSprings Dr, York, PA 17402-
8825
Tel.: (717) 755-6166
Web Site: https://www.mhyork.com
Health Care Srvices
N.A.I.C.S.: 622110

York Home Care Services, LLC (1)
1412 6th Ave, York, PA 17403-2648
Tel.: (717) 843-5091
Emp.: 20
Health Care Srvices
N.A.I.C.S.: 622110
Beth Markowitz (Office Mgr)

COMMUNITY HEALTHCARE

COMMUNITY HEALTHCARE —(CONTINUED)

TRUST INCORPORATED
3326 Aspen Grove Dr Ste 150,
Franklin, TN 37067
Tel.: (615) 771-3052　　　　　　MD
Web Site: https://www.chct.reit
Year Founded: 2014
CHCT—(NYSE)
Rev.: $112,845,000
Assets: $945,412,000
Liabilities: $432,156,000
Net Worth: $513,256,000
Earnings: $7,714,000
Emp.: 37
Fiscal Year-end: 12/31/23
Real Estate Investment Trust
N.A.I.C.S.: 525990
David H. Dupuy *(Pres & CEO)*
Timothy L. Meyer *(Exec VP-Asset Mgmt)*
William G. Monroe IV *(CFO)*
Bill Davis *(Founder)*
Leigh Ann Stach *(Chief Acctg Officer & Exec VP)*

COMMUNITY HERITAGE FINANCIAL, INC.
24 W Main St, Middletown, MD
21769
Tel.: (301) 371-6700　　　　　　MD
Web Site:
　https://www.communityheritage
　inc.com
Year Founded: 1907
CMHF—(OTCIQ)
Sales Range: $10-24.9 Million
Bank Holding Company
N.A.I.C.S.: 551111
John A. Scaldara Jr. *(CFO & Exec VP)*
James G. Pierne *(Chm)*
Brenda McComas *(COO & Exec VP)*
Dawn Lowe *(Chief Talent Officer & Chief Culture Officer & Exec VP)*
Ryan Lampton *(Reg Pres & Exec VP)*
Jerry Merrick *(Pres & Exec VP)*
Michelle Lease *(Asst Sec-Corp)*
Todd M. Snook *(Vice Chm)*
Dustin Watson *(Chief Credit Officer & Exec VP)*
Robert E. Goetz Jr. *(Pres & CEO)*

Subsidiaries:

Middletown Valley Bank　　　　　(1)
24 W Main St, Middletown, MD 21769
Tel.: (301) 371-6700
Web Site: http://www.mvbbank.com
Sales Range: $1-9.9 Million
Commercial Banking
N.A.I.C.S.: 522110
John A. Scaldara Jr. *(Exec VP-Fin)*
Chad Tasker *(VP-IT & Bank Support Svcs)*
Robert J. Goetz *(Pres & CEO)*
Micheal Line *(VP & Mgr-Comml Relationship)*
Dawn Woods *(Sec)*
Emily Radaker *(VP & Controller)*
Linda Kinslow *(VP & Ops Mgr)*
J. Michael Hill *(Chief Risk Officer & Exec VP)*
Angela Shubert *(COO & Sr VP)*
Whitney Dangerfield *(VP-HR & Branch Admin)*
George Chaney *(VP & Mgr-Comml Relationship)*
Dustin Watson *(VP-Credit & Loan Admin)*

COMMUNITY INVESTORS BANCORP, INC.
119 S Sandusky Ave, Bucyrus, OH
44820
Tel.: (419) 562-7066　　　　　　OH
Web Site: https://www.ffcb.com
Year Founded: 1995
CIBN—(OTCIQ)
Rev.: $13,808,000
Assets: $271,874,000
Liabilities: $255,054,000

Net Worth: $16,820,000
Earnings: $716,000
Emp.: 81
Fiscal Year-end: 06/30/23
Bank Holding Company
N.A.I.C.S.: 551111
Phillip W. Gerber *(Vice Chm)*
Dawn S. Ratliff *(Chm)*
Brandy L. Hoepf *(Chief Lending Officer-Portfolio & VP)*
Eric J. Savidge *(Chief Lending Officer-Secondary Market & VP)*
Sonya Coffman *(Asst VP-Lending)*
Steven R. Crall *(CFO)*

Subsidiaries:

First Federal Community Bank of
Bucyrus　　　　　　　　　　　　　(1)
119 S Sandusky Ave, Bucyrus, OH 44820
Tel.: (419) 562-7055
Web Site: http://www.ffcb.com
Rev.: $6,745,000
Assets: $125,273,000
Liabilities: $114,751,000
Net Worth: $10,522,000
Earnings: $172,000
Fiscal Year-end: 12/31/2013
Federal Savings Institutions
N.A.I.C.S.: 522180

COMMUNITY REDEVELOPMENT INC.
14673 Midway Rd Ste 220, Addison,
TX 75001
Web Site: https://www.comredev.com
CRDV—(OTCIQ)
Rev.: $93,750
Assets: $7,584,318
Liabilities: $7,950,450
Net Worth: ($366,132)
Earnings: ($10,821,237)
Fiscal Year-end: 12/31/22
Renewable Energy Consulting Services
N.A.I.C.S.: 541690
Myron Jones *(Head-Dev)*
Richard Balles *(Pres)*

COMMUNITY SAVINGS BANCORP, INC.
425 Main St, Caldwell, OH 43724
Tel.: (740) 732-5678　　　　　　MD
Year Founded: 2016
CCSB—(OTCIQ)
Rev.: $2,384,000
Assets: $52,222,000
Liabilities: $44,533,000
Net Worth: $7,689,000
Earnings: ($159,000)
Emp.: 16
Fiscal Year-end: 06/30/19
Bank Holding Company
N.A.I.C.S.: 551111
Alvin Barry Parmiter *(Pres & CEO)*
Sherman Crum *(Controller)*
Michael Schott *(Chm)*
Ladawn Spring *(Compliance Officer)*
Amanda Jones *(Officer-Collection)*

COMMUNITY TRUST BANCORP INC
2501 Ring Rd, Elizabethtown, KY
42701
Tel.: (606) 432-1414　　　　　　KY
Web Site: https://www.ctbi.com
Year Founded: 1980
CTBI—(NASDAQ)
Rev.: $255,658,000
Assets: $5,380,316,000
Liabilities: $4,752,269,000
Net Worth: $628,047,000
Earnings: $81,814,000
Emp.: 985
Fiscal Year-end: 12/31/22
Bank Holding Company
N.A.I.C.S.: 551111

James J. Gartner *(Exec VP)*
Mark A. Gooch *(Chm, Pres & CEO)*
Richard W. Newsom *(Exec VP)*
Kevin J. Stumbo *(CFO, Treas & Exec VP)*
Ricky D. Sparkman *(Exec VP)*
Eugenia Crittenden Luallen *(Vice Chm)*
David Andrew Jones *(Exec VP)*
David I. Tackett *(Exec VP)*
Charles Wayne Hancock II *(Sec)*
Billie J. Dollins *(Exec VP)*

Subsidiaries:

Community Trust Bank, Inc.　　　(1)
346 N Mayo Trl, Pikeville, KY
41501　　　　　　　　　　　　　(100%)
Tel.: (606) 432-1414
Web Site: https://www.ctbi.com
Sales Range: $50-74.9 Million
Emp.: 120
Commercial Bank
N.A.I.C.S.: 522110
Mark A. Gooch *(Chm & CEO)*
Richard W. Newsom *(Pres)*
David I. Tackett *(Pres-Eastern Region)*
Kevin J. Stumbo *(CFO & Exec VP)*
David Andrew Jones *(Pres-Northeastern Reg)*
John Caldwell *(Pres-Market-Floyd, Johnson & Knott Counties)*

Community Trust and Investment
Company　　　　　　　　　　　　(1)
100 E Vine St Ste 501, Lexington, KY
40507　　　　　　　　　　　　　(100%)
Tel.: (859) 389-5300
Web Site: https://www.ctbi.com
Investment Management Services, Estate
Planning, Trust & Administrative Services
N.A.I.C.S.: 523940
Andy D. Waters *(Pres & CEO)*
H. Trigg Mitchell *(VP-Wealth & Trust Mgmt)*
Jason L. Lee *(Sr VP & Mgr-Private Wealth Svcs)*
Jeffrey S. Thomison *(VP & Sr Mgr-Equity)*
E. Barrett Coleman *(VP & Portfolio Mgr)*
Tammy R. Provost *(VP & Portfolio Mgr)*
Andrew Windsor *(VP & Portfolio Mgr)*
Sumer Miller *(Asst VP & Portfolio Mgr)*
Brenda H. Brammer *(Sr VP)*
Sandy Combs *(Sr VP)*
R. Christopher Meng *(Sr VP-Investment Mgmt Group)*
Derek Stivers *(Portfolio Mgr)*
Cade King *(Portfolio Mgr)*
David Sever *(Sr VP-Community Trust Financial Svcs)*
Susan Langlois *(Sr VP-Community Trust Financial Svcs)*
Robert B. Stadelman *(Sr VP)*
Gerrie Clark *(VP)*
Taylor Curtis *(VP)*
Chad Maynard *(Asst VP)*
Nicole Record *(Asst VP-Wealth Advisor)*
Sabrina Lequire *(Asst VP-Wealth Advisor)*
Tim Little *(Asst VP-Wealth Advisor)*

COMMUNITY WEST BANCSHARES
7100 N Financial Dr Ste 101, Fresno,
CA 93720
Tel.: (559) 298-1775　　　　　　CA
Web Site: https://www.cvcb.com
Year Founded: 2000
CWBC—(NASDAQ)
Rev.: $88,012,000
Assets: $2,422,519,000
Liabilities: $2,247,859,000
Net Worth: $174,660,000
Earnings: $26,645,000
Emp.: 253
Fiscal Year-end: 12/31/22
Bank Holding Company
N.A.I.C.S.: 551111
Robert H. Bartlein *(Vice Chm)*
James J. Kim *(CEO)*
Martin E. Plourd *(Pres)*
Shannon R. Avrett *(CFO & Exec VP)*
Patrick A. Luis *(Chief Credit Officer & Exec VP)*
Dawn P. Crusinberry *(Exec VP)*

Steven D. McDonald *(Sec)*
Dawn Cagle *(Chief HR Officer & Exec VP)*

Subsidiaries:

COMMUNITY WEST
BANCSHARES　　　　　　　　　(1)
445 Pine Ave, Goleta, CA 93117
Tel.: (805) 692-5821
Web Site: http://www.communitywest.com
Rev.: $49,138,000
Assets: $1,091,502,000
Liabilities: $978,852,000
Net Worth: $112,650,000
Earnings: $13,449,000
Emp.: 134
Fiscal Year-end: 12/31/2022
Financial Services Holding Company
N.A.I.C.S.: 551111
Richard Pimentel *(CFO & Exec VP)*

Subsidiary (Domestic):

Community West Bank　　　　　　(2)
5827 Hollister Ave, Goleta, CA 93117
Tel.: (805) 683-4944
Web Site:
　https://www.communitywestbank.com
Sales Range: $50-74.9 Million
Full Service Community Bank
N.A.I.C.S.: 522310
Robert H. Bartlein *(Founder & Vice Chm)*
William R. Peeples *(Chm)*
Susan C. Thompson *(Sr VP & Interim Mgr-SEC Reporting)*
Richard Pimentel *(CFO & Exec VP)*
Martin E. Plourd *(CEO)*
William F. Filippin *(Pres & Chief Credit Officer)*
T. Joseph Stronks *(COO & Exec VP)*
Richard Pimentel *(CFO & Exec VP)*

Central Valley Community Bank　(1)
7100 N Financial Dr Ste 101, Fresno, CA
93720
Tel.: (559) 298-1775
Web Site: https://www.cvcb.com
Sales Range: $50-74.9 Million
Commercial Bank
N.A.I.C.S.: 522110
Robert H. Bartlein *(Vice Chm)*
Daniel J. Doyle *(Chm)*
James J. Kim *(Pres & CEO)*
Shannon R. Avrett *(CFO & Exec VP)*
Dawn P. Crusinberry *(Exec VP)*
James J. Kim *(Pres & CEO)*
Blaine Lauhon *(Chief Banking Officer & Exec VP)*
Dawn Cagle *(Sr VP-HR)*
Robert H. Bartlein *(Vice Chm)*
Shannon R. Livingston *(CFO)*
William F. Filippin *(Exec VP)*
Jeff Martin *(Chief Banking Officer)*
T. Joseph Stronks *(Chief Risk Officer)*

COMMVAULT SYSTEMS, INC.
1 Commvault Way, Tinton Falls, NJ
07724
Tel.: (732) 728-5310　　　　　　DE
Web Site:
　https://www.commvault.com
Year Founded: 1988
CVLT—(NASDAQ)
Rev.: $839,247,000
Assets: $943,913,000
Liabilities: $665,828,000
Net Worth: $278,085,000
Earnings: $168,906,000
Emp.: 2,882
Fiscal Year-end: 03/31/24
Data Management Software Applications & Related Services
N.A.I.C.S.: 513210
Sanjay Mirchandani *(Pres & CEO)*
Nicholas A. Adamo *(Chm)*
Michael J. Melnyk *(Dir-IR)*
Alan Atkinson *(Chief Partner Officer)*
Anthony Anzevino *(Sr VP-Americas Field Organization)*
Jennifer DiRico *(CFO)*
Gary Merrill *(Chief Comml Officer)*

Subsidiaries:

CV Simpana Software (Proprietary)
Limited　　　　　　　　　　　　　(1)

Palazzo Towers West Montecasino, William Nicol Drive Fourways, Johannesburg, 2005, South Africa
Tel.: (27) 115100040
Sales Range: $10-24.9 Million
Emp.: 8
Data Management Software
N.A.I.C.S.: 513210

Comm Vault Systems International B.V.   (1)
Europalaan 516, Utrecht, 3526 KS, Netherlands
Tel.: (31) 307117200
Web Site: http://www.commvault.com
Data & Information Management Software Publisher
N.A.I.C.S.: 513210

CommVault Systems (Australia) Pty. Ltd.   (1)
Suite 24 01 Level 24 207 Kent Street, Sydney, 2000, NSW, Australia
Tel.: (61) 281977700
Software Application Development Services
N.A.I.C.S.: 513210

CommVault Systems (Canada) Inc.   (1)
Tel.: (732) 728-5310
Sales Range: $100-124.9 Million
Emp.: 1
Data Management Software Mfr
N.A.I.C.S.: 513210

CommVault Systems (India) Private Limited   (1)
Block-A 7th Floor Quay Building Bagmane Tech Park C V Raman Nagar, Bengaluru, 560093, Karnataka, India
Tel.: (91) 8067879900
Web Site: http://www.commvault.com
Sales Range: $100-124.9 Million
Data Management Software
N.A.I.C.S.: 513210

CommVault Systems (New Zealand) Limited   (1)
Level 15 Pwc Tower 15 Customs Street West, Auckland, 1010, New Zealand
Tel.: (64) 93575059
Data & Information Management Software Publisher
N.A.I.C.S.: 513210

CommVault Systems (Singapore) Private Limited   (1)
Tel.: (65) 68179590
Web Site: https://www.commvault.com
Sales Range: $100-124.9 Million
Data Management Software Mfr
N.A.I.C.S.: 513210

CommVault Systems AB   (1)
Frosundaviks alle 1, 169 70, Solna, Sweden
Tel.: (46) 841064990
Web Site: http://www.largestcompanies.com
Sales Range: $10-24.9 Million
Emp.: 19
Data Management Software
N.A.I.C.S.: 513210

CommVault Systems Belgium BVBA   (1)
Philipssite 5 / bus 1, 3000, Leuven, Belgium
Tel.: (32) 27882570
Software, Prerecorded Compact Disc & Tape Record Reproducing Services
N.A.I.C.S.: 334610

CommVault Systems Gmbh   (1)
Tel.: (49) 6950607691
Web Site: http://www.commvault.de
Sales Range: $25-49.9 Million
Emp.: 120
Data Management Software Mfr
N.A.I.C.S.: 513210

CommVault Systems Iberia Srl   (1)
C/ Copenhague 6 Edificio Al-Andalus Poligono Europolis Las Rozas, Madrid, 28230, Spain
Tel.: (34) 916266042
Sales Range: $1-9.9 Million
Emp.: 10
Data Management Software Mfr
N.A.I.C.S.: 334610
Richard Gerard (Mng Dir)

CommVault Systems Italia S.r.l.   (1)

Tel.: (39) 03386315232
Computer Software Services
N.A.I.C.S.: 513210

CommVault Systems Limited   (1)
Apex Plaza Forbury Road, Reading, RG1 1AX, United Kingdom
Tel.: (44) 1189516500
Web Site: http://www.commvault.co.uk
Sales Range: $10-24.9 Million
Emp.: 250
Data Management Software Mfr
N.A.I.C.S.: 513210

CommVault Systems Mexico S. de R.L. de C.V.   (1)
Patriotismo No 229 Piso 8, Col San Pedro de los Pinos, 3800, Mexico, Mexico
Tel.: (52) 55528810240
Data Management Software
N.A.I.C.S.: 513210

CommVault Systems Netherlands B.V.   (1)
Papendorpseweg 99, 3528 BJ, Utrecht, Netherlands
Tel.: (31) 307117200
Web Site: http://www.commvault.com
Sales Range: $10-24.9 Million
Emp.: 25
Data Management Software Mfr
N.A.I.C.S.: 513210

CommVault Systems Sarl   (1)
13 Rue Madeleine Michelis, 92200, Neuilly-sur-Seine, France
Tel.: (33) 173130012
Data & Information Management Software Publisher
N.A.I.C.S.: 513210

Commvault Systems (South Africa) (Pty) Ltd.   (1)
Regus Bryanston The Campus Cnr Main and Sloane Street The Campus, Twickenham Building, Johannesburg, 2021, South Africa
Tel.: (27) 861114625
Software Development Services
N.A.I.C.S.: 541511

COMPASS DIGITAL ACQUISITION CORP.
195 US Hwy 50 Ste 208, Zephyr Cove, NV 89448
Tel.: (214) 306-4001   Ky
Web Site:
    https://www.compassdigitalspac.com
Year Founded: 2021
CDAQ—(NASDAQ)
Rev.: $10,499,202
Assets: $216,798,844
Liabilities: $225,154,427
Net Worth: ($8,355,583)
Earnings: $9,295,239
Emp.: 2
Fiscal Year-end: 12/31/22
Investment Services
N.A.I.C.S.: 523999
Thomas D. Hennessy (CEO)
Nick Geeza (CFO)
Daniel J. Hennessy (Chm)

COMPASS DIVERSIFIED HOLDINGS
301 Riverside Ave 2nd Fl, Westport, CT 06880
Tel.: (203) 221-1703   DE
Web Site:
    https://compassdiversified.com
Year Founded: 2005
CODI—(NYSE)
Rev.: $2,264,044,000
Assets: $3,849,631,000
Liabilities: $2,487,669,000
Net Worth: $1,361,962,000
Earnings: $36,387,000
Emp.: 1,022
Fiscal Year-end: 12/31/22
Offices of Other Holding Companies
N.A.I.C.S.: 551112

Larry L. Enterline (Chm)
Ryan J. Faulkingham (CFO & Exec VP)
Elias Joseph Sabo (CEO & Partner)
Patrick A. Maciariello (Partner & COO)
Katie Melzer (Mng Dir & Head-Bus Dev)
David Abate (Treas)
Kaajal Ali (Dir)
Barbara Anderson (Mgr)
Jennifer Cerminaro (VP)
Morgan Christiansen (Controller)
Bridgette Clark-Johnson (Mgr)
Raj Dalal (Principal)
Ke Ding (Dir)
Sarah Henry (Sr Dir)
Rachel Koh (VP)
Zoe Koskinas (VP)
Gabe LePera (Sr VP)
Phelan McCormack (VP)
Macartan McElroy (Mgr)
Joseph Milana (Chief Admin Officer)
Nicolette Nguyen (Mgr)
Cara Ramm (Dir)
Jill Ritchie (Chief Compliance Officer)
Kurt Roth (Partner)
Carrie Ryan (Chief Compliance Officer)
Nadia Sahin (Sr Dir)
Lucas Scholhamer (VP)
David Swanson (Partner)
Kerri Tiernan (Sr VP)
Ami Vearrier (Sr Dir)
Ryan Thorp (Principal)

Subsidiaries:

5.11 Acquisition Corp.   (1)
4300 Spyres Way, Modesto, CA 95356
Tel.: (209) 527-4511
Financial Investment Services
N.A.I.C.S.: 523940

5.11 International A.B.   (1)
Geijersgatan 2B, 216 18, Limhamn, Sweden
Tel.: (46) 40467388
Clothing Material Distr
N.A.I.C.S.: 458110

5.11 Sourcing, Limited   (1)
53 Granville Road, Tsim Tsa Tsui, China (Hong Kong)
Tel.: (852) 23461158
Web Site: http://www.511tactical.com
Apparel Product Distr
N.A.I.C.S.: 458110

9G Products, Inc.   (1)
6878 Martindale Rd, Shawnee, KS 66218
Tel.: (913) 422-7400
Administrative Management & General Management Consulting Services
N.A.I.C.S.: 541611

AERC Acquisition Corporation   (1)
2591 Mitchell Ave, Allentown, PA 18103
Tel.: (610) 797-7608
Web Site: https://www.cleanearthinc.com
Recycling Services
N.A.I.C.S.: 562920

AES Asset Acquisition Corporation   (1)
310 7 Fields Blvd Ste 210, Seven Fields, PA 16046
Tel.: (724) 933-4100
Waste Treatment & Disposal Services
N.A.I.C.S.: 562219

AFM Holding Corporation   (1)
320 W 45th St, New York, NY 10036
Tel.: (212) 582-4001
Holding Company
N.A.I.C.S.: 551112

Advanced Circuits, Inc.   (1)
229 S Clark Dr, Tempe, AZ 85281
Waste Collection Services
N.A.I.C.S.: 562119

Altor Solutions Inc.   (1)
8722 E San Alberto Dr Ste 200, Scottsdale, AZ 85258-4353

Tel.: (480) 607-7330
Mfr & Distributor of Plastics Foam Products
N.A.I.C.S.: 326150
Michael Hays (VP)
Terry Moody (CEO)
Zach Sawtelle (Chm)

Subsidiary (Domestic):

Foam Concepts Inc.   (2)
44 Rivulet St, Uxbridge, MA 01569
Tel.: (508) 278-7255
Web Site: http://www.foamconcepts.com
Sales Range: $1-9.9 Million
Emp.: 28
Protective Packaging Products Mfr
N.A.I.C.S.: 326150
Mark Villamaino (Pres)

Plant (Domestic):

Foam Fabricators Inc. - Molding Plant   (2)
900 E Keller Pkwy, Keller, TX 76248
Tel.: (817) 379-6520
Web Site:
    http://www.foamfabricatorsinc.com
Plastic Foam Product Mfr
N.A.I.C.S.: 326199

Arnold Magnetic Technologies AG   (1)
Hubelacherstrasse 15, 5242, Lupfig, Switzerland
Tel.: (41) 564642100
Web Site: http://www.arnoldmagnetics.com
Electrical Equipment Mfr & Distr
N.A.I.C.S.: 334515

BOA Technology (Shenzen) Ltd.   (1)
2/F Building A 139 Da Bao Road, District 33M Bao An, Shenzhen, 518133, China
Tel.: (86) 75527856299
Sporting Goods Mfr
N.A.I.C.S.: 339920

BOA Technology Japan Inc.   (1)
Tokiwa Bld 8F 1-14-11, Fujimi Chuo-Ku, Chiba, 260-0015, Japan
Tel.: (81) 433046526
Sporting Goods Mfr
N.A.I.C.S.: 339920

BOA Technology Korea Inc.   (1)
5F Dorim Bldg 40 Dosin-Ro 15-gil, Yeongdeungpo-gu, Seoul, 07374, Korea (South)
Tel.: (82) 24645008
Sporting Goods Mfr
N.A.I.C.S.: 339920

Baby Tula Poland   (1)
Komunalna 5, 15-197, Bialystok, Poland
Tel.: (48) 798527943
Web Site: https://www.babytula.pl
Baby Carrier Bag Mfr
N.A.I.C.S.: 339930

Beyond Clothing, LLC   (1)
6363 6th Ave S, Seattle, WA 98108-3437
Tel.: (206) 767-0307
Web Site: https://www.beyondclothing.com
Clothing Mfr & Distr
N.A.I.C.S.: 315250

Boatechnology GmbH   (1)
Prielhofstrasse 10, A-5310, Mondsee, Austria
Tel.: (43) 623293080
Sporting Goods Mfr
N.A.I.C.S.: 339920

CEHI Acquisition Corporation   (1)
61 Wilton Rd 2nd Fl, Westport, CT 06880
Tel.: (203) 221-1703
Environmental Consulting Services
N.A.I.C.S.: 541620

Candle Lamp Company, LLC   (1)
2483 Harbor Ave, Memphis, TN 38106
Tel.: (901) 942-8870
Candle Distr
N.A.I.C.S.: 424990

Clean Earth Holdings, Inc.   (1)
334 S Warminster Rd, Hatboro, PA 19040
Tel.: (215) 734-1400
Holding Company
N.A.I.C.S.: 551112

Clean Earth of Cateret, LLC   (1)

Compass Diversified Holdings—(Continued)

24 Middlesex Ave, Carteret, NJ 07008
Tel.: (732) 541-8909
Waste Treatment & Disposal Services
N.A.I.C.S.: 562219

Clean Earth of Michigan, LLC **(1)**
550 Lycaste St, Detroit, MI 48214
Tel.: (313) 824-5840
Waste Collection Services
N.A.I.C.S.: 562119

Clean Earth of West Virginia, Inc. **(1)**
85 Olin St, Morgantown, WV 26501
Tel.: (724) 933-4100
Web Site: http://www.cleanearthinc.com
Waste & Recycling Services
N.A.I.C.S.: 562111

Compass Group Diversified Holdings LLC **(1)**
301 Riverside Ave 2nd FL, Westport, CT 06880
Tel.: (203) 221-1703
Web Site: http://www.compassequity.com
Emp.: 640
Fiscal Year-end: 12/31/2018
Investment Holding Company
N.A.I.C.S.: 551112
Elias Joseph Sabo (CEO & Partner)
Stephen Keller (CFO & Exec VP)

Holding (Domestic):

5.11, Inc. **(2)**
4300 Spyres Way, Modesto, CA 95356
Tel.: (209) 527-4511
Web Site: http://www.511tactical.com
Law Enforcement, Military & Firefighter
Clothing & Safety Equipment Mfr & Distr
N.A.I.C.S.: 458110
Francisco Morales (Founder)
Troy R. Brown (CEO)

Arnold Magnetic Technologies Corporation **(2)**
770 Linden Ave, Rochester, NY 14625-2716
Tel.: (585) 385-9010
Web Site: https://www.arnoldmagnetics.com
Sales Range: $25-49.9 Million
Emp.: 100
Precision Magnetic, Electronic & Mechanical Devices Mfr
N.A.I.C.S.: 334416

Subsidiary (Non-US):

Arnold Magnetic Technologies Ltd. **(3)**
Vector 31 Waleswood Way, Wales Bar, Sheffield, S26 5NU, United Kingdom
Tel.: (44) 1909772021
Emp.: 6
Mfr of Magnetic Assemblies
N.A.I.C.S.: 332999

Subsidiary (Domestic):

Flexmag Industries Inc. **(3)**
107 Industry Rd, Marietta, OH 45750-9355
Tel.: (740) 374-8024
Sales Range: $25-49.9 Million
Emp.: 100
Flexible Magnetic Sheets & Strips Mfr
N.A.I.C.S.: 332999

Division (Domestic):

Ogallala Electronics **(3)**
601 W 1st, Ogallala, NE 69153
Tel.: (308) 284-4093
Web Site: http://www.arnoldmagnetics.com
Sales Range: $25-49.9 Million
Emp.: 25
Electromagnets & Magnetic Assemblies Mfr
N.A.I.C.S.: 332999

Holding (Domestic):

BOA Holdings Inc. **(2)**
2010 Main St Ste 1220, Irvine, CA 92614
Tel.: (949) 333-5033
Holding Company
N.A.I.C.S.: 551112

Subsidiary (Domestic):

BOA Technology Inc. **(3)**

3575 Ringsby Ct Ste 200, Denver, CO 80216
Tel.: (303) 455-5126
Web Site: https://www.boafit.com
Emp.: 230
Sporting & Athletic Goods Mfr
N.A.I.C.S.: 339920
Shawn Neville (CEO)

Holding (Domestic):

Liberty Safe & Security Products, Inc. **(2)**
1199 W Utah Ave, Payson, UT 84651
Tel.: (801) 925-1000
Web Site: https://www.libertysafe.com
Sales Range: $75-99.9 Million
Emp.: 400
Residential Security Product Mfr
N.A.I.C.S.: 332999
Alan B. Offenberg (Chm)

The ERGO Baby Carrier, Inc. **(2)**
617 W 7th St Ste 1000, Los Angeles, CA 90017
Tel.: (213) 283-2090
Web Site: https://www.ergobaby.com
Baby Carrier & Backpack Mfr
N.A.I.C.S.: 314910
William B. Chiasson (Exec Chm)

Subsidiary (Domestic):

Orbit Baby, Inc. **(3)**
8445 Central Ave, Newark, CA 94560
Tel.: (510) 793-5007
Web Site: https://orbitbabyusa.com
Sales Range: $1-9.9 Million
Women's, Children's & Infants' Clothing & Accessories Merchant Whslr
N.A.I.C.S.: 424350

Ergobaby Europe GmBH **(1)**
Gaussstrasse 120, 22765, Hamburg, Germany
Tel.: (49) 404210650
Web Site: https://ergobaby.de
Baby Carrier Bag Mfr
N.A.I.C.S.: 339930
Gunnar Dahl (Mng Dir)

Foam Fabricators Queretaro, S. de R.L. de C.V. **(1)**
Parque Industrial Queretaro Ave, La Montana No 112 Edeficio 3 Modulos 4-6 St Rosa Jaurequi, Queretaro, Mexico
Tel.: (52) 115242420200
Foam Products Mfr
N.A.I.C.S.: 326140

LBM S.R.L. **(1)**
Via A Volta 238, Sustinente, 46030, Mantua, Italy
Tel.: (39) 0386437212
Web Site: https://www.lbmfiltri.it
Hydraulic Accessory Mfr & Distr
N.A.I.C.S.: 333996

Lugano Diamonds & Jewelry, Inc. **(1)**
620 Newport Ctr Dr Ste 100, Newport Beach, CA 92660-8044
Tel.: (949) 720-1258
Web Site: http://www.luganodiamonds.com
Precious Stone & Precious Metal Merchant Whslr
N.A.I.C.S.: 423940
Idit Ferder (VP)
Stuart Winston (CMO & Exec Dir-Retail)
Moti Ferder (Co-Founder & CEO)

Marucci Clubhouse, LLC **(1)**
158 Caprice Ct, Castle Rock, CO 80109
Tel.: (303) 955-5838
Web Site:
  https://www.marucciclubhouse.com
Metal Product Distr
N.A.I.C.S.: 423510

Marucci Elite Training L.L.C. **(1)**
9222 Burbank Dr, Baton Rouge, LA 70820
Tel.: (225) 761-4321
Web Site: http://www.maruccielite.com
Indoor & Outdoor Sport Training Services
N.A.I.C.S.: 611620

Marucci Hitters House, LLC **(1)**
2141 Rosecrans Ave Ste 5100, El Segundo, CA 90245
Tel.: (310) 408-2562

Web Site: http://www.hittershouse.com
Metal Product Distr
N.A.I.C.S.: 423510

Rimports, LLC **(1)**
201 E Bay Blvd, Provo, UT 84606
Tel.: (801) 437-4300
Web Site: https://www.rimports.com
Holding Company Services
N.A.I.C.S.: 551114

Sterno Products, LLC **(1)**
6900 N Dallas PKWY Ste 870, Plano, TX 75024
Tel.: (951) 682-9600
Web Site: https://www.sterno.com
Food Warming Equipment Mfr
N.A.I.C.S.: 333310
Donna Moad (CEO)

Swift Levic Magnets
Arnold Building High Hazels Road, Barlborough Links, Barlborough, S43 4UZ, Derbyshire, United Kingdom
Tel.: (44) 1246570500
Electronic Coil, Transformer & Other Inductor Mfr
N.A.I.C.S.: 334416

The Arnold Engineering Co. **(1)**
300 Northwest St, Marengo, IL 60152
Tel.: (815) 568-2000
Emp.: 168
Electronic Coil, Transformer & Other Inductor Mfr
N.A.I.C.S.: 334416

Velocity Outdoor Inc. **(1)**
7629 State 5 and 20, Bloomfield, NY 14469
Tel.: (585) 657-6161
Web Site: https://www.velocity-outdoor.com
Emp.: 300
Holding Company Services
N.A.I.C.S.: 551114

COMPASS MINERALS INTERNATIONAL, INC.
9900 W 109th St Ste 100, Overland Park, KS 66210
Tel.: (913) 344-9200   DE
Web Site:
  https://www.compassminerals.com
CMP—(NYSE)
Rev.: $1,117,400,000
Assets: $1,640,100,000
Liabilities: $1,323,500,000
Net Worth: $316,600,000
Earnings: ($206,100,000)
Emp.: 1,894
Fiscal Year-end: 09/30/24
Producer of Rock Salt, General Trade Salt & Sulfate of Potash
N.A.I.C.S.: 212390
Edward C. Dowling Jr. (Pres & CEO)
Rick Axthelm (Chief Pub Affairs & Sustainability Officer)
Mary L. Frontczak (Chief Admin Officer, Chief Legal Officer & Sec)
Rob Fisher (CIO & Sr VP)
Douglas Kris (Sr Dir-IR)
Teresa D. Cook (Interim VP-Fin & Acctg)
Brent Collins (VP-IR)
Lorin Crenshaw (CFO)
Chris Yandell (Head)
Jeffrey C. Cathey (CFO & Chief Accty Officer)

Subsidiaries:

Big Quill Resources Inc. **(1)**
2 Big Quill Rd, PO Box 1059, Wynyard, S0A 4T0, SK, Canada
Tel.: (306) 554-3322
Web Site: http://www.bigquill.com
Sales Range: $25-49.9 Million
Emp.: 3
Packaged Frozen Food Whslr
N.A.I.C.S.: 424420

Compass Minerals (UK) Limited **(1)**
Astbury House Bradford Road, Winsford, CW7 2PA, Cheshire, United Kingdom
Tel.: (44) 370 532 9723

Web Site:
  http://www.compassmineralsuk.com
Rock Salt Mining & Distribution Services
N.A.I.C.S.: 212390

Compass Minerals America Inc. **(1)**
9900 W 109th St Ste 100, Overland Park, KS 66210
Tel.: (913) 344-9200
Web Site:
  https://www.compassminerals.com
Sales Range: $125-149.9 Million
Emp.: 200
Salt Mfr
N.A.I.C.S.: 212390

Compass Minerals Louisiana Inc. **(1)**
1382 Cote Blanche Is, Franklin, LA 70538
Tel.: (337) 923-7514
Chemical & Fertilizer Mineral Mining Services
N.A.I.C.S.: 212390

Compass Minerals Manitoba Inc. **(1)**
800 One Research Road, Winnipeg, R3T 6E3, MB, Canada
Tel.: (204) 237-9653
Crop Farming Services
N.A.I.C.S.: 111998

Compass Minerals Odgen Inc. **(1)**
765 N 10500 W, Ogden, UT 84404
Tel.: (801) 731-3100
Web Site: http://www.compassminerals.com
Chemical & Fertilizer Mineral Mining Services
N.A.I.C.S.: 212390

Compass Minerals Storage & Archives Limited **(1)**
Salt Union, Winsford, CW7 2PA, Cheshire, United Kingdom
Tel.: (44) 8450565759
Chemical & Fertilizer Mineral Mining Services
N.A.I.C.S.: 212390

Compass Minerals UK Holdings Limited **(1)**
Astbury House Bradford Road, Bradford Road, Winsford, CW7 2PA, Cheshire, United Kingdom
Tel.: (44) 1606861850
Holding Company
N.A.I.C.S.: 551112
Mike Stacey (Mgr-Pur)

Compass Minerals USA Inc. **(1)**
9900 W 109th St Ste 100, Overland Park, KS 66210
Tel.: (913) 344-9200
Web Site: http://www.compassminerals.com
Chemical & Fertilizer Mineral Mining Services
N.A.I.C.S.: 212390

Compass Minerals Winnipeg Unlimited Liability Company **(1)**
327 Smith Road, Nappan, Amherst, B4H 3Y4, Canada
Tel.: (902) 667-3388
Table Salt Mfr & Distr
N.A.I.C.S.: 311942

Compass Minerals Wynyard Inc. **(1)**
2 Big Quill Road, Wynyard, S0A 4T0, SK, Canada
Tel.: (306) 554-3322
Crop Farming Services
N.A.I.C.S.: 111998

Curlew Valley Farms, LLC **(1)**
185 S State St, Salt Lake City, UT 84111
Tel.: (913) 940-3491
Web Site: http://www.agrilicious.org
Crop Farming Services
N.A.I.C.S.: 111998

GSL Corporation **(1)**
701 Utica Ave, Brooklyn, NY 11203
Tel.: (718) 778-0023
Emp.: 7
Chemical Mineral Mining Mfr
N.A.I.C.S.: 325180

Salt Union Limited **(1)**
Astbury House Bradford Road, Winsford, CW7 2PA, Cheshire, United Kingdom
Tel.: (44) 1606596530
Web Site:
  http://www.compassminerals.co.uk

Chemical Mineral Mining Distr
N.A.I.C.S.: 212390

Sifto Canada, Inc. (1)
6700 Century Ave Ste 202, Mississauga,
L5N 6A4, ON, Canada
Tel.: (905) 567-0231
Web Site: http://www.siftocanada.com
Sales Range: $200-249.9 Million
Emp.: 500
Salt Mfr
N.A.I.C.S.: 212390

COMPASS THERAPEUTICS INC.
80 Guest St Ste 601, Boston, MA
02135
Tel.: (617) 500-8099   DE
Web Site:
   https://www.compasstherapeu
   tics.com
Year Founded: 2018
CMPX—(NASDAQ)
Rev.: $2,430,000
Assets: $199,645,000
Liabilities: $18,007,000
Net Worth: $181,638,000
Earnings: ($39,225,000)
Emp.: 26
Fiscal Year-end: 12/31/22
Oncology-focused Biopharmaceutical
Company
N.A.I.C.S.: 541714
Thomas J. Schuetz (Co-Founder &
CEO)
Vered Bisker-Leib (Pres & COO)
Jonathan Anderman Jonathan Ander-
man (VP, Sec & Head-Legal)
Thomas J. Schuetz (Co-Founder,
Vice Chm, Co-CEO, Principal Acctg
Officer & Pres-R&D)
Minori Rosales (Sr VP & Head-
Clinical Dev)
Ian Chia (VP-Business Development
& Strategy)
Karin Herrera (VP & Head-Clinical
Ops)
James Kranz (VP & Head-Chemistry
Mfg & Controls)
Neil Lerner (VP-Finance)
Kris Sachsenmeier (VP-Translational
Sciences)
Bing Gong (Sr VP-Discovery Res &
VP-Protein Sciences & Protein Ana-
lytics)

COMPASS, INC.
110 5th Ave 3rd Fl, New York, NY
10011
Tel.: (646) 982-0353
Web Site: https://www.compass.com
Year Founded: 2012
COMP—(NYSE)
Rev.: $4,885,000,000
Assets: $1,160,300,000
Liabilities: $728,300,000
Net Worth: $432,000,000
Earnings: ($321,300,000)
Emp.: 2,549
Fiscal Year-end: 12/31/23
Online Home Searching Services
N.A.I.C.S.: 519290
Scott Wahlers (Chief Acctg Officer)
Robert Reffkin (Co-Founder, Chm &
CEO)
Ori Allon (Co-Founder & Chief Strat-
egy Officer)
Neda Nevab (Pres)
Kalani Reelitz (CFO)

Subsidiaries:

Alain Pinel Realtors, Inc. (1)
12772 Sunnyvale-Saratoga Rd Ste 1000,
Saratoga, CA 95070
Tel.: (408) 741-1111
Sales Range: $1-9.9 Million
Emp.: 152
Offices of Real Estate Agents & Brokers

N.A.I.C.S.: 531210
Carol Burnett (VP)
Greg Terry (Mgr-Sls)
Joe Cutrufelli (VP)
Lisa Crosby-Torres (Mgr-Danville)
Phil Weingrow (Mgr-Real Estate)
Ron Gable (VP & Mgr)
Steve Dickason (Mgr-Marin & Novato)
Barry L. Baltor (VP & Mgr-Bus Ops)
Bill Lewis (Mgr-Los Altos)
Bob Gerlach (Mgr-Palo Alto)
Bob Profeta (Mgr-Morgan Hill & Carmel)
David Bellamy (CFO & Chief Admin Officer)
David Walsh (Mgr-Almaden)
Don Faught (Mgr-Pleasanton & Livermore)
Jan Jaramillo (Dir-Career Dev-Peninsula)
Jeff Barnett (Mgr-Los Gatos)
Jim Pojda (Dir-Career Dev-South Bay)
Joanne Wondolowski (Mgr-Burlingame)
Judith Profeta (Mgr-Carmel)
Linda Granger (Mgr-Lake Tahoe)
Lori Legler (Mgr-Orinda)
Mark Bonn (Mgr-APR Investment Grp)
Mary Gebhardt (Mgr-Menlo Park & Wood-
side)
Michi Olson (VP-Relocation & Bus Dev)
Mike Hulme (Pres)
Rainy Hake (COO & Exec VP)
Ron Kurkendall (Mgr-Carmel)
Tom Flanagan (VP-IT)
Will Klopp (Mgr-Morgan Hill)
Heidi Dittloff (VP-Mktg)

Latter & Blum, Inc. (1)
430 Notre Dame St, New Orleans, LA
70130-3610
Tel.: (504) 525-1311
Web Site: http://www.latterblum.com
Sales Range: $1-4.9 Billion
Real Estate Brokerage Services
N.A.I.C.S.: 531210
Robert W. Merrick (Chm)
Joseph S. Pappalardo (Pres-Latter & Blum
Property Management Inc)
Patrick J. Egan (Exec VP)
Richard P. Stone (Exec VP)
Robert C. Penick (Vice Chm)
Lacey Merrick Conway (CEO)

Subsidiary (Domestic):

Latter & Blum of Texas, LLC (2)
1223 Antoine Dr, Houston, TX 77055
Tel.: (713) 464-5656
Web Site:
   http://www.realtyassociatestex.com
Emp.: 1,700
Real Estate Brokerage Services
N.A.I.C.S.: 531210
Peter Merritt (Pres)

Realty Austin, LLC (1)
1209 W 5th St Ste 300, Austin, TX 78703
Tel.: (512) 241-1300
Web Site: http://www.realtyaustin.com
Residential Property Managers
N.A.I.C.S.: 531311
Gabe Richter (CEO)

COMPLETE FINANCIAL SOLU-TIONS, INC.
7629 Purfoy Rd Ste 105, Fuquay Va-
rina, NC 27526
Tel.: (919) 552-4286   NV
Web Site:
   https://completefinancialsolu
   tions.org
Year Founded: 2006
CFSU—(OTCIQ)
Sales Range: $10-24.9 Million
Financial Services Investment Hold-
ing Company
N.A.I.C.S.: 551112
Allen Ringer (Founder, Chm & CEO)
Kenneth Stephenson (Pres)
Sandy Stephenson (Dir-Finance &
Office Mgr)
Krystle Stalnecker (Dir-Bus Ops)
Susan Denise (Specialist-Client Ser-
vices)

Subsidiaries:

**Acceptance Capital Mortgage
Corporation** (1)

113 E Magnesium Rd Unit D, Spokane, WA
99208
Tel.: (714) 595-3661
Web Site: http://www.acceptancecapital.com
Mortgage Banker
N.A.I.C.S.: 522310
Frank Taylor (Pres)

COMPLETE SOLARIA, INC.
45700 Northport Loop E, Fremont,
CA 94538
Tel.: (510) 270-2507   Ky
Web Site:
   https://www.completesolaria.com
CSLR—(NASDAQ)
Rev.: $10,389,398
Assets: $350,120,913
Liabilities: $361,611,211
Net Worth: ($11,490,298)
Earnings: $5,982,340
Emp.: 1
Fiscal Year-end: 12/31/22
Solar Electric Power Generation
N.A.I.C.S.: 221114
Thurman John Rodgers (CEO)
William J. Anderson (Founder)

COMPOSECURE, INC.
309 Pierce St, Somerset, NJ 08873
Tel.: (908) 518-0500   DE
Web Site:
   https://www.composecure.com
Year Founded: 2020
CMPO—(NASDAQ)
Rev.: $378,476,000
Assets: $162,943,000
Liabilities: $1,055,175,000
Net Worth: ($892,232,000)
Earnings: $18,657,000
Emp.: 850
Fiscal Year-end: 12/31/22
Miscellaneous Financial Investment
Activities
N.A.I.C.S.: 523999
Dixon Doll Jr. (CEO)
David M. Cote (Exec Chm)

Subsidiaries:

Arculus Holdings, L.L.C. (1)
309 Pierce St, Somerset, NJ 08873
Tel.: (202) 807-1406
Web Site: https://www.getarculus.com
Wallet Mfr & Distr
N.A.I.C.S.: 339910

COMPUMED, INC.
5777 W Century Blvd, Los Angeles,
CA 90045
Tel.: (310) 258-5000   DE
Web Site: https://compumedinc.com
Year Founded: 1973
CMPD—(OTCIQ)
Rev.: $5,048,000
Assets: $2,908,000
Liabilities: $1,057,000
Net Worth: $1,851,000
Earnings: $973,000
Emp.: 8
Fiscal Year-end: 09/30/19
Computer Aided Diagnostic Systems
N.A.I.C.S.: 325413
David W. Pointer (Chm)
Laura Carroll (CFO & Sec)
Lee D. Keddie (Pres & CEO)

COMPUTER SERVICES, INC.
3901 Technology Dr, Paducah, KY
42001-5201
Tel.: (270) 442-7361   KY
Web Site: http://www.csiweb.com
Year Founded: 1965
CSVI—(OTCIQ)
Rev.: $291,337,000
Assets: $384,349,000
Liabilities: $139,658,000
Net Worth: $244,691,000
Earnings: $55,404,000
Emp.: 1,268

Fiscal Year-end: 02/28/21
Financial Technology Solutions
N.A.I.C.S.: 518210
Steven A. Powless (Chm)
David Culbertson (Pres & CEO)
Paul Koziarz (Chief Dev Officer)
Keith Monson (Chief Risk Officer)
Brian K. Brown (CFO)
Giovanni Mastronardi (Pres-
Enterprise Banking-Grp)
Kurt Guenther (Pres-Bus Solutions)
Charmaine Smith (Chief People Offi-
cer)
Vijayaraghava Reddy (CTO)
Jennifer Werner (CMO)
Patrick MacCartney (Chief Data Offi-
cer)
Steve Sanders (Chief Information Se-
curity Officer)
Tammy Souder (Chief Admin Officer
& Sec)

Subsidiaries:

Computer Services, Inc (1)
1248 O St 5th Fl, Lincoln, NE 68508
Tel.: (270) 442-7361
Sales Range: $10-24.9 Million
Emp.: 35
Core Processing, Managed Services, Mo-
bile & Internet Solutions
N.A.I.C.S.: 541511

COMSCORE, INC.
11950 Democracy Dr, Reston, VA
20190
Tel.: (703) 438-2000   DE
Web Site: https://www.comscore.com
Year Founded: 1997
SCOR—(NASDAQ)
Rev.: $376,423,000
Assets: $580,586,000
Liabilities: $436,424,000
Net Worth: $144,162,000
Earnings: ($66,561,000)
Emp.: 1,382
Fiscal Year-end: 12/31/22
Digital Marketing Intelligence Ser-
vices
N.A.I.C.S.: 541613
Jonathan Carpenter (CEO)
Gregory T. Dale (CQO)
Linda Boland Abraham (Co-Founder)
Sara Dunn (Chief People Officer)
David Algranati (Chief Innovation Offi-
cer)
Carol Hinnant (Chief Revenue Offi-
cer)
Mary Margaret Curry (CFO, Chief
Acctg Officer & Treas)
Tania Yuki (CMO & Exec VP-Digital)
Joris Goossens (Sr VP-Comml-
Europe & APAC)
Brian Pugh (CIO)
William P. Livek (Vice Chm)

Subsidiaries:

Proximic, Inc. (1)
4400 Bohannon Dr Ste 150, Menlo Park,
CA 94025
Tel.: (650) 549-7800
Web Site: http://www.proximic.com
Advertising Software Developer
N.A.I.C.S.: 513210

TMRG, Inc. (1)
11950 Democracy Dr Ste 600, Reston, VA
20190
Tel.: (703) 438-2000
Web Site: https://www.tmrginc.com
Digital Marketing Intelligence Services
N.A.I.C.S.: 541810

comScore Canada, Inc. (1)
1 University Avenue 3rd floor, Toronto, M5J
2P1, ON, Canada
Tel.: (416) 985-5237
Web Site: https://www.comscore.com
Sales Range: $100-124.9 Million
Digital Marketing Intelligence Services
N.A.I.C.S.: 541810

comScore, Inc.—(Continued)

comScore Europe, Inc. (1)
6-7 Saint Cross Street 3rd Floor, London,
EC1N 8UA, United Kingdom
Tel.: (44) 2070991760
Web Site: http://www.comscore.com
Sales Range: $100-124.9 Million
Digital Marketing Intelligence Services
N.A.I.C.S.: 541810

comScore Media Metrix, Inc. (1)
11950 Demorcy Dr Ste 600, Reston, VA
20190
Tel.: (703) 438-2000
Web Site: https://www.comscore.com
Sales Range: $75-99.9 Million
Emp.: 550
Marketing & Research Services
N.A.I.C.S.: 541910

COMSOVEREIGN HOLDING CORP.
6890 E Sunrise Dr Ste 120-506, Tucson, AZ 85750
Tel.: (206) 796-0173   NV
Web Site:
https://www.comsovereign.com
Year Founded: 1997
COMS—(NASDAQ)
Rev.: $9,878,000
Assets: $24,918,000
Liabilities: $39,919,000
Net Worth: ($15,001,000)
Earnings: ($80,391,000)
Emp.: 25
Fiscal Year-end: 12/31/22
Aircraft Manufacturing
N.A.I.C.S.: 336411
David Knight (Pres & CEO)
Kevin M. Sherlock (Gen Counsel & Sec)
Daniel L. Hodges (Co-Founder)
Brian M. Kelly (Exec VP-Bus Dev)
Dustin H. McIntire (CTO)
Bud Patterson (COO)
John E. Howell (Co-Founder)
Jeffrey L. Landers (Chief Creative Officer & VP-Mktg)
Scott Velazquez (Chief Res Officer)
Keith Kaczmarek (Chief Revenue Officer)
Steve Gersten (Dir-IR)

Subsidiaries:

Dragonwave-X Canada, Inc. (1)
362 Terry Fox Drive Suite 100, Ottawa, K2K 2P5, ON, Canada
Tel.: (613) 295-1879
Packet Microwave Equipment Mfr
N.A.I.C.S.: 335999

Elitise LLC (1)
1668 S Research Loop Ste 332, Tucson, AZ 85710
Tel.: (520) 499-3799
Web Site: http://www.elitise.com
Research & Development Services
N.A.I.C.S.: 541715
Sergei Begliarov (Co-Founder, Pres & CEO)
Kagum Zakharyan (Co-Founder & VP)

Fast Plastic Parts LLC (1)
880A Elkton Dr, Colorado Springs, CO 80907
Tel.: (719) 418-5100
Web Site: http://www.fastplasticparts.com
Plastic Parts Mfr
N.A.I.C.S.: 326199

Innovation Digital, LLC (1)
15373 Innovation Dr 180, San Diego, CA 92128
Tel.: (858) 240-2500
Web Site: https://www.innovationdigital.com
Digital Signal Design & Consulting Services
N.A.I.C.S.: 541810

RVision Inc. (1)
3033 5th Ave Ste 400, San Diego, CA 95131
Tel.: (619) 233-1403
Web Site: http://www.rvisionusa.com
Photographic Equipment Mfr

N.A.I.C.S.: 333310
Brian Kelly (CEO)

SAGUNA Networks Ltd. (1)
3 Hakidma St, Yokneam, 206673, Israel
Tel.: (972) 545787144
Web Site: https://www.saguna.net
Mobile Edge Computing Services
N.A.I.C.S.: 531190

Silver Bullet Technology, Inc. (1)
240 E Intendencia St, Pensacola, FL 32502
Tel.: (850) 437-5880
Web Site: http://www.sbullet.com
Software Services
N.A.I.C.S.: 541511
Bryan Clark (Founder & CEO)

Sky Sapience Ltd. (1)
Tavor Building Yokneam Hi-Tech Park, PO Box 170, Yokneam, 20692, Israel
Tel.: (972) 49591777
Web Site: https://www.skysapience.com
Emp.: 45
Aircraft Mfr
N.A.I.C.S.: 336411
Limor Barak-Tanchuma (VP-Mktg & HR)
Meir Vazana (VP-Sls)

Skyline Partners Technology, LLC (1)
2595 Canyon Blvd Ste 420, Boulder, CO 80302
Tel.: (408) 998-1444
Web Site: http://www.fastbacknetworks.com
Communication Equipment Mfr
N.A.I.C.S.: 334290

COMSTOCK HOLDING COMPANIES, INC.
1900 Reston Metro Plz 10th Fl, Reston, VA 20190
Tel.: (703) 230-1985   DE
Web Site: https://www.comstock.com
Year Founded: 1985
CHCI—(NASDAQ)
Rev.: $39,313,000
Assets: $42,473,000
Liabilities: $13,619,000
Net Worth: $28,854,000
Earnings: $9,393,000
Emp.: 152
Fiscal Year-end: 12/31/22
Residential Real Estate Developer
N.A.I.C.S.: 531390
Joseph M. Squeri (Exec VP-Corp Dev & Strategy)
Christopher Clemente (Chm & CEO)
Jubal R. Thompson (Gen Counsel & Exec VP)
Timothy J. Steffan (Exec VP-Asset Mgmt, Leasing & Dev)
Michael Gualtieri (Sr VP-Fin & Controller)
Tracy Schar (Sr VP-Mktg & Brand Mgmt)
John Harrison (Sr VP-Dev)
Christopher Guthrie (CFO & Exec VP)
Mike Daugard (Sr VP-Acquisition)
Kristoffer Green (VP-Residential Property Mgmt)
Dylan Clemente (VP-Parking Mgmt)
James Mandich (VP & Controller)
Chris Facas (Sr VP-Human Resources-Comml Real Estate Svcs)

Subsidiaries:

Comstock Maxwell Square, L.C. (1)
1886 Metro Center Dr, Reston, VA 20190
Tel.: (703) 883-1700
Real Estate Asset Management Services
N.A.I.C.S.: 531390

COMSTOCK INC.
117 American Flat Rd, Virginia City, NV 89440
Tel.: (775) 847-5272   NV
Web Site: https://comstock.inc
Year Founded: 1999

LODE—(NYSEAMEX)
Rev.: $178,150
Assets: $100,053,759
Liabilities: $43,690,300
Net Worth: $56,363,459
Earnings: ($45,948,744)
Emp.: 33
Fiscal Year-end: 12/31/22
Precious Metal Mining Services
N.A.I.C.S.: 212220
Corrado F. De Gasperis (Exec Chm & CEO)
Laurence G. Martin (Dir-Exploration & Mineral Dev)
Kevin E. Kreisler (Pres & CFO)
Zach M. Spencer (Treas, Sec & Dir-External Rels)
Chris Peterson (Dir-Health, Safety & Environmental Protection & Gen Mgr-Site)
William J. McCarthy (COO)

Subsidiaries:

Gold Hill Hotel, Inc. (1)
1540 Main St, Virginia City, NV 89440
Tel.: (775) 847-0111
Web Site: https://goldhillhotel.net
Sales Range: $10-24.9 Million
Emp.: 15
Home Management Services
N.A.I.C.S.: 721110

COMSTOCK RESOURCES, INC.
5300 Town and Country Blvd Ste 500, Frisco, TX 75034
Tel.: (972) 668-8800   NV
Web Site:
https://www.comstockresources.com
Year Founded: 1983
CRK—(NYSE)
Rev.: $1,565,109,000
Assets: $6,253,623,000
Liabilities: $3,870,432,000
Net Worth: $2,383,191,000
Earnings: $211,894,000
Emp.: 251
Fiscal Year-end: 12/31/23
Oil & Gas Producer
N.A.I.C.S.: 211120
Roland O. Burns (Pres, CFO & Sec)
Daniel K. Presley (Treas, VP-Acctg & Controller)
LaRae L. Sanders (VP-Land)
Daniel S. Harrison (COO)
Patrick H. McGough (VP-Ops)
Ronald E. Mills (VP-Fin & IR)
Brian C. Claunch (VP)
Clifford D. Newell (VP)
Miles Jay Allison (Chm & CEO)

Subsidiaries:

Comstock Oil and Gas (1)
5300 Town & Country Blvd Ste 500, Frisco, TX 75034
Tel.: (972) 668-8800
Sales Range: $50-74.9 Million
Emp.: 90
Independent Energy Company
N.A.I.C.S.: 221122
Jay Allison (Pres)

COMTECH TELECOMMUNICATIONS CORP.
68 S Service Rd Ste 230, Melville, NY 11747
Tel.: (480) 333-2200   DE
Web Site: https://www.comtech.com
Year Founded: 1967
CMTL—(NASDAQ)
Rev.: $540,403,000
Assets: $912,434,000
Liabilities: $606,181,000
Net Worth: $306,253,000
Earnings: ($99,985,000)
Emp.: 1,718
Fiscal Year-end: 07/31/24

Communications Products, Systems & Services
N.A.I.C.S.: 334220
Michael A. Bondi (CFO)
John Ratigan (Interim CEO & Chief Corp Dev Officer)
Kent Hellebust (Pres-Safety & Security Technologies)
Jay F. Whitehurst (Pres-Location Technologies)
Michael Plourde (VP-Programs & Engrg-Global)
Nancy M. Stallone (Treas)
Roger Seaton (Pres-Comtech Systems Inc)
Michael Hrybenko (Pres-PST Corp)
Marcus Alston (Chief Trade Compliance Officer)
Jennie Reilly (VP-HR)
Donald Walther (Chief Legal Officer)
Ken Peterman (Chm, Pres & CEO)
Maria Hedden (COO)
Nicole Robinson (Chief Strategy Officer)

Subsidiaries:

CGC Technology Limited (1)
1 Beechwood Chineham Business Park
Lime Tree Avenue, Chineham, Basingstoke, RG24 8WA, Hampshire, United Kingdom
Tel.: (44) 1252724274
Web Site: http://www.cgctech.com
Software Development Services
N.A.I.C.S.: 541511

Comtech EF Data Corp. (1)
2114 W 7th St, Tempe, AZ 85281-7227   (100%)
Tel.: (480) 333-2200
Web Site: https://www.comtechefdata.com
Sales Range: $250-299.9 Million
Emp.: 800
Satellite Communications Products & Systems Mfr
N.A.I.C.S.: 517410
Mark Toppenberg (Co-Pres-Tempe)
Jeffrey Harig (Co-Pres-Tempe)
Marcos Jannuzzi (VP-Sls-Latin America)
Magid Bengatta (Dir-Sls-France-North Africa)
Daniel Gizinski (Pres-Govt Grp)

Subsidiary (Non-US):

Beijing Comtech EF Data Equipment Repair Services, Co., Ltd. (2)
RM 807 Canway Bldg No 66 Nanlish Road, Xicheng District, Beijing, 100045, China
Tel.: (86) 1068080081
Web Site: http://www.comtechefdata.com
Sales Range: $10-24.9 Million
Emp.: 10
Telecommunication Equipment Repair & Maintenance Services
N.A.I.C.S.: 811210

Group (Domestic):

Comtech EF Data Corp. - Vipersat Networks Group (2)
3215 Skyway Ct, Fremont, CA 94539-5951
Tel.: (510) 252-1462
Satellite Capacity Management Solutions
N.A.I.C.S.: 517410

Subsidiary (Non-US):

Comtech EF Data Pte. Ltd. (2)
Web Site: http://www.comtechefdata.com
Emp.: 10
Satellite Modem & Communication Equipment Mfr
N.A.I.C.S.: 335999
Patrick Wong (Mng Dir-Asia-Pacific)

Memotec Inc. (2)
7755 Henri Bourassa Blvd West, Saint Laurent, H4S 1P7, QC, Canada
Tel.: (514) 738-4781
Web Site: http://www.memotec.com
Emp.: 21
Telecommunication Services
N.A.I.C.S.: 517810
Michael Wrobel (Dir-Customer Svcs)

Comtech Mobile Datacom Corp. (1)

20430 Century Blvd, Germantown, MD
20874-1202   **(100%)**
Tel.: (240) 686-3300
Web Site: http://www.comtechmobile.com
Sales Range: $25-49.9 Million
Emp.: 100
Mobile Satellite-Based Data Communications Services
N.A.I.C.S.: 517111
Greg Handermann (CTO & Sr VP-Ops)

Branch (Domestic):

Comtech Mobile Datacom Corp.   **(2)**
7606 N Union Blvd Ste D, Colorado
Springs, CO 80920
Tel.: (240) 686-3300
Web Site: http://www.comtechmobile.com
Sales Range: $1-9.9 Million
Advanced Geospatial Systems
N.A.I.C.S.: 541360

Comtech PST Corp.   **(1)**
105 Baylis Rd, Melville, NY
11747-3833   **(100%)**
Tel.: (631) 777-8900
Web Site: https://www.comtechpst.com
Sales Range: $50-74.9 Million
Emp.: 180
Mfr of Solid State High Power Amplifiers for
Communications, Instrumentation & Government Defense Applications
N.A.I.C.S.: 334220
Michael Hrybenko (Pres)

Comtech Satellite Network Technologies, Inc.   **(1)**
305 N 54th St, Chandler, AZ 85226
Tel.: (480) 333-2200
Web Site: https://www.comtechefdata.com
Satellite Infrastructure Equipment Mfr
N.A.I.C.S.: 334220

Comtech Systems, Inc.   **(1)**
212 Out Pt Dr 100 St, Orlando, FL
32809   **(100%)**
Tel.: (407) 854-1950
Web Site: http://www.comtechsystems.com
Sales Range: $10-24.9 Million
Emp.: 100
Mfr of Troposcatter & Satellite Communication Systems & Equipment
N.A.I.C.S.: 334220
Alan Swan (CFO-Div & VP-Fin)
Dan Ammar (VP-Engrg)
Aaron Ross (VP-Program Mgmt)
John Boelke (VP-Contracts)
Doug Houston (Sr VP-Programs & Ops)
Paul Scardino (Sr VP-Govt Sls)
Tim Giroux (VP-Contracts & Trade Compliance)
Donja Long (VP-HR)
Mike Smith (Dir-IT Svcs)

Comtech Xicom Technology, Inc. **(1)**
3550 Bassett St, Santa Clara, CA 95054-2704
Tel.: (408) 213-3000
Web Site: http://www.xicomtech.com
Sales Range: $50-74.9 Million
Emp.: 150
High Power Amplifier Supplier
N.A.I.C.S.: 334220
Kevin Kirkpatrick (VP-Mktg & Sls)
Eric Schmidt (VP-Sls)
Jason Launius (Sls Dir-Western US &
Canada)
Jon Davis (Sls Dir-Western US & Canada)
Mark Littlejohn (VP-Sls & Govt
Programs-US & Canada)
Tony Jones (Sls Dir-Eastern US & Canada)
Mark Schmeichel (Pres)
Sanjay Nagpal (VP-Bus Dev)
Gerry Pieters (Engr-Sls Application)
Rollin Hughes (Dir-Govt Channel Sls)
Mike Lange (Sls Dir-Southern US)
Steve Segura (Mgr-Network Solutions Sls)

Subsidiary (Non-US):

Xicom Technology Europe, Ltd.   **(2)**
4 Portland Business Center Manor House
Lane, Datchet, SL3 9EG, Berkshire, United
Kingdom
Tel.: (44) 1753549999
Emp.: 4
Electrical Equipment & Component Mfr
N.A.I.C.S.: 335999
Ann Mullan (Reg Sls Mgr-Europe & Turkey)

Sheet Metal Precision Limited   **(1)**
Unit 7b Woolmer Way, Bordon, GU35 9QE,
Hants, United Kingdom
Tel.: (44) 1420488488
Web Site:
   http://www.sheetmetalprecision.ltd.uk
Sheet Metal Mfr
N.A.I.C.S.: 332322
David Lewis (Engr-Sls)
Jim Livermore (Gen Mgr)

Solacom Technologies (US), Inc. **(1)**
3020 Woodcreek Dr Ste A, Downers Grove,
IL 60515
Tel.: (819) 205-8100
Web Site: https://www.solacom.com
Personal Sound Amplification Product Mfr
N.A.I.C.S.: 334290
Pierre Plangger (Pres)

COMTEX NEWS NETWORK, INC.

625 N Washington St Ste 301, Alexandria, VA 22314
Tel.: (703) 820-2000   DE
Web Site: https://www.comtex.com
Year Founded: 1980
CMTX—(OTCIQ)
Sales Range: $1-9.9 Million
Emp.: 26
Online News Distribution Services
N.A.I.C.S.: 516210
Chip Brian (Pres & CEO)
Kan Devnani (CTO & VP)

CONAGRA BRANDS, INC.

222 W Merchandise Mart Plz Ste
1300, Chicago, IL 60654
Tel.: (312) 549-5000   DE
Web Site:
   https://www.conagrabrands.com
Year Founded: 1919
CAG—(NYSE)
Rev.: $12,050,900,000
Assets: $20,862,300,000
Liabilities: $12,351,000,000
Net Worth: $8,511,300,000
Earnings: $347,700,000
Emp.: 18,500
Fiscal Year-end: 05/26/24
Flour Milling Product Mfr
N.A.I.C.S.: 311211
Sean M. Connolly (Pres & CEO)
David S. Marberger (CFO & Exec
VP)
Thomas M. McGough (Co-COO &
Exec VP)
Derek De La Mater (Chief Customer
Officer & Exec VP)
Jonathan J. Harris (Chief Comm Officer & Sr VP)
Charisse Brock (Chief HR Officer &
Exec VP)
Carey Bartell (Gen Counsel, Sec &
Exec VP)
William E. Johnson (Principal Acctg
Officer, Sr VP & Controller)
Alexandre Eboli (Chief Supply Chain
Officer & Exec VP)
Noelle O'Mara (Pres-New Platforms
& Acquisitions & Exec VP)
Tracy Schaefer (CIO & Sr VP)

Subsidiaries:

Agro Tech Foods Ltd.   **(1)**
Tower C 15th Floor Building No 10 DLF
Phase - II DLF Cyber City, Gurgaon,
122002, India
Tel.: (91) 1244593700
Web Site: https://www.atfoods.com
Rev.: $125,442,272
Assets: $84,448,865
Liabilities: $21,370,577
Net Worth: $63,078,288
Earnings: $3,528,116
Emp.: 548
Fiscal Year-end: 03/31/2022
Food Products Mfr & Distr
N.A.I.C.S.: 311999

Sachin Gopal (Mng Dir)
N. Narasimha Rao (Sr VP-HR & Corp
Comm)
Asheesh Kumar Sharma (VP-Mktg)
Gulshan Gandhi (Head-Res, Quality & Innovation)
Lalit Vij (Head-Procurement Oils, Pkg Materials & Bus Dev Crystal)
Rikesh Ramesh Kotwal (Head-Sls)
Jyoti Chawla (Compliance Officer & Sec)
K. P. N. Srinivas (CFO)
Dharmesh Kumar Srivastava (VP-Supply
Chain)
Sanjay Srivastava (Head-Mfg)

American Italian Pasta Company **(1)**
1251 NW Briarcliff Pkwy Ste 500, Kansas
City, MO 64116
Tel.: (816) 584-5000
Web Site: http://www.aipc.com
Sales Range: $600-649.9 Million
Emp.: 750
Pasta Mfr & Marketer
N.A.I.C.S.: 311824
Kevin A. Hall (VP-Continuous Improvement)

Subsidiary (Non-US):

Pasta Lensi, S.r.l.   **(2)**
Via Don L Sturzo 21-23, Verolanuova BS,
25028, Brescia, Italy
Tel.: (39) 030936441
Web Site: https://www.pastalensi.it
Pasta Based Products Canning Services
N.A.I.C.S.: 311422

Ardent Mills, LLC   **(1)**
1875 Lawrence St, Denver, CO
80202   **(44%)**
Tel.: (800) 851-9618
Web Site: http://www.ardentmills.com
Sales Range: $1-4.9 Billion
Flour & Other Grain Mill Products Milling
N.A.I.C.S.: 311211
Dan Dye (CEO)

Unit (Domestic):

Ardent Mills   **(2)**
905 W Marion St, Lake City, MN 55041-
2007
Tel.: (651) 345-3351
Sales Range: $10-24.9 Million
Emp.: 32
Self-Rising Prepared Blended Flour Producer
N.A.I.C.S.: 311211
Deb Roschen (Mgr-Admin)

Subsidiary (Domestic):

Hinrichs Trading LLC   **(2)**
155 SE Kamiaken St, Pullman, WA 83501
Tel.: (509) 332-8888
Web Site: http://www.hinrichstrading.com
Commodity Contracts Dealing
N.A.I.C.S.: 523160
Phil Hinrichs (CEO)

Bremner Food Group, Inc.   **(1)**
1475 US Hwy 62 W, Princeton, KY 42445
Tel.: (270) 365-5505
Cookie & Cracker Mfr
N.A.I.C.S.: 311821

ConAgra Foods - Compton   **(1)**
PO Box 4188, Compton, CA 90221
Tel.: (310) 223-1499
Web Site: http://www.conagrafoods.com
Sales Range: $10-24.9 Million
Emp.: 20
Ethnic & Frozen Foods
N.A.I.C.S.: 311412

ConAgra Foods - Council Bluffs **(1)**
1023 S 4th Ave, Council Bluffs, IA 51501-
4030
Tel.: (712) 322-0203
Web Site: http://www.conagrafoods.com
Sales Range: $400-449.9 Million
Emp.: 800
Marketer of Frozen Items
N.A.I.C.S.: 311412

ConAgra Foods - Gilroy   **(1)**
1350 Pacheco Pass Hwy, Gilroy, CA 95020
Tel.: (408) 846-3200
Sales Range: $250-299.9 Million
Emp.: 675
Dehydration of Onion, Garlic & Capsicum
Products

N.A.I.C.S.: 311423

ConAgra Foods - Hamburg   **(1)**
2301 Washington St, Hamburg, IA
51640   **(100%)**
Tel.: (712) 382-2634
Web Site: http://www.vogelpopcorn.com
Sales Range: $25-49.9 Million
Emp.: 24
Popcorn Production
N.A.I.C.S.: 311999

ConAgra Foods - Hebrew National
Kosher Foods   **(1)**
4551 Squires Rd, Quincy, MI
49082   **(100%)**
Tel.: (517) 689-2221
Web Site: http://www.conagrafoods.com
Sales Range: $150-199.9 Million
Emp.: 300
Meat Producer
N.A.I.C.S.: 311612

ConAgra Foods - Indianapolis   **(1)**
4300 W 62nd St, Indianapolis, IN 46268-
2520
Tel.: (317) 329-3700
Web Site: http://www.conagrafoods.com
Sales Range: $75-99.9 Million
Emp.: 280
Mfr & Production of Dairy & Cheese Products
N.A.I.C.S.: 541715

ConAgra Foods - Modesto   **(1)**
705 E Whitmore Ave, Modesto, CA 95358-
9408
Tel.: (209) 538-1071
Web Site: http://www.conagrafoods.com
Sales Range: $150-199.9 Million
Emp.: 350
Dehydration of Vegetables
N.A.I.C.S.: 311423

ConAgra Foods - Rossville   **(1)**
1 Creative Way, Rossville, IL
60963   **(100%)**
Tel.: (217) 748-6784
Web Site: http://www.conagrafoods.com
Sales Range: $50-74.9 Million
Emp.: 140
Edible Fats & Oils
N.A.I.C.S.: 311611

ConAgra Foods Food Ingredients
Company, Inc.   **(1)**
1 Conagra Dr, Omaha, NE 68102
Tel.: (402) 595-4000
Web Site: http://www.conagrafoods.com
Other Miscellaneos Food Mfr
N.A.I.C.S.: 311999

Plant (Domestic):

ConAgra Food Ingredients Co.   **(2)**
110 South Nebraska Ave, Tampa, FL 33602
Tel.: (813) 223-4741
Web Site: http://www.conagrafoods.com
Flour Milling
N.A.I.C.S.: 311211

ConAgra Foods Ltd.   **(1)**
570 Cure Boivin, Boisbriand, J7G 2A7, QC,
Canada
Tel.: (450) 433-1322
Web Site: http://www.conagrafoods.com
Sales Range: $100-124.9 Million
Emp.: 250
Frozen Snacks & Prepared Foods
N.A.I.C.S.: 311919

Subsidiary (Domestic):

ConAgra Foods Canada, Inc.   **(2)**
5055 Satellite Drive, Mississauga, L4W
5K7, ON, Canada   **(100%)**
Tel.: (416) 679-4200
Web Site: http://www.conagrafoods.ca
Sales Range: $50-74.9 Million
Emp.: 100
Canned Foods, Snack Foods & Frozen
Foods Mfr & Distr
N.A.I.C.S.: 311422

ConAgra Foods Packaged Foods,
LLC   **(1)**
1 Conagra Dr, Omaha, NE 68102
Tel.: (402) 240-4000
Food Preparations Mfr
N.A.I.C.S.: 311999

Conagra Brands, Inc.—(Continued)

ConAgra Grocery Products Company, LLC (1)
215 W Diehl Rd, Naperville, IL 60563
Tel.: (630) 857-1000
Web Site: http://www.conagrafoods.com
Sales Range: $300-349.9 Million
Emp.: 650
Grocery Products Mfr & Marketing
N.A.I.C.S.: 311421

ConAgra Store Brands (1)
21340 Hayes Ave, Lakeville, MN 55044-6802
Tel.: (952) 469-4981
Web Site: http://www.conagrafoods.com
Sales Range: $150-199.9 Million
Emp.: 725
Mfr of Granola Cereals & Bars, Fruit Snacks, Graham Cracker Pie Crusts, Candy Bars & RTE Cereals
N.A.I.C.S.: 311423

Conagra Brands Canada Inc. (1)
5055 Satellite Drive, Mississauga, L4W 5K7, ON, Canada
Tel.: (416) 679-4200
Web Site: https://www.conagrabrands.ca
Food & Beverage Mfr
N.A.I.C.S.: 333241

Harvest Manor Farms LLC (1)
Tel.: (319) 841-4170
Sales Range: $150-199.9 Million
Emp.: 300
Holding Company; Nut Producer
N.A.I.C.S.: 311911

Division (Non-US):

Jimbo's Jumbos (2)
Tel.: (252) 482-2193
Web Site: http://www.jimbosjumbos.com
Sales Range: $50-74.9 Million
Emp.: 127
Peanut Processor
N.A.I.C.S.: 311911

Original Nut House (2)
Tel.: (319) 841-4170
Web Site: http://www.originalnuthouse.com
Sales Range: $75-99.9 Million
Emp.: 250
Peanut Processing
N.A.I.C.S.: 311911

Linette Quality Chocolates, Inc. (1)
336 Hill Rd, Womelsdorf, PA 19567
Tel.: (610) 589-4526
Candy & Other Confectionary Products
N.A.I.C.S.: 311351

Medallion Foods, Inc. (1)
3636 Medallion Pl, Newport, AR 72112
Tel.: (870) 523-3500
Snack Product Mfr
N.A.I.C.S.: 311919

National Pretzel Company (1)
2060 Old Philadelphia Pike, Lancaster, PA 17602-3413
Tel.: (717) 299-2321
Web Site: http://www.nationalpretzel.com
Sales Range: $25-49.9 Million
Emp.: 200
Pretzels Mfr
N.A.I.C.S.: 311919

Subsidiary (Domestic):

California Pretzel Company (2)
7607 Goshen Ave, Visalia, CA 93278
Tel.: (559) 651-0600
Sales Range: $25-49.9 Million
Emp.: 200
Mfr of Pretzels
N.A.I.C.S.: 311919

Petri Baking Products, Inc. (1)
18 Main St, Silver Creek, NY 14136
Tel.: (716) 934-2661
Web Site: http://www.petribaking.com
Cookie Mfr
N.A.I.C.S.: 311821

Pinnacle Foods Inc. (1)
399 Jefferson Rd, Parsippany, NJ 07054
Tel.: (973) 541-6620
Web Site: http://www.pinnaclefoods.com
Rev.: $3,144,002,000

Assets: $6,578,264,000
Liabilities: $4,198,026,000
Net Worth: $2,380,238,000
Earnings: $532,049,000
Emp.: 4,900
Fiscal Year-end: 12/31/2017
Holding Company; Branded Food Products Mfr & Whslr
N.A.I.C.S.: 551112

Subsidiary (Domestic):

Pinnacle Foods Finance LLC (2)
399 Jefferson Rd, Parsippany, NJ 07054
Tel.: (973) 541-6620
Web Site: http://www.pinnaclefoods.com
Sales Range: $1-4.9 Billion
Emp.: 3,700
Holding Company; Food Mfr, Distr & Marketer
N.A.I.C.S.: 551112

Subsidiary (Domestic):

Pinnacle Foods Group LLC (3)
399 Jefferson Rd, Parsippany, NJ 07054
Tel.: (973) 541-6620
Web Site: http://www.pinnaclefoods.com
Sales Range: $800-899.9 Million
Emp.: 3,100
Holding Company for Dry/Frozen Food Brands
N.A.I.C.S.: 551112

Subsidiary (Domestic):

Birds Eye Foods LLC (4)
399 Jefferson Rd, Parsippany, NJ 07054
Tel.: (973) 541-6620
Web Site: http://www.birdseye.com
Rev.: $935,644,000
Assets: $673,597,000
Liabilities: $917,402,000
Net Worth: ($243,805,000)
Earnings: $53,645,000
Emp.: 1,700
Fiscal Year-end: 06/27/2009
Frozen & Canned Vegetables Mfr & Marketer
N.A.I.C.S.: 311421

Pinnacle Foods Fort Madison LLC (4)
2467 Henry Ladyn Dr, Fort Madison, IA 52627
Tel.: (319) 463-7111
Food Products Mfr
N.A.I.C.S.: 311999
Paul Lovell (Mgr-Ops)

Pinnacle Foods International Corp. (4)
1 Old Bloomfield Ave, Mountain Lakes, NJ 07046
Tel.: (973) 541-6620
Food Products Mfr
N.A.I.C.S.: 311999

Subsidiary (Non-US):

Pinnacle Foods Canada Corporation (5)
6555 Mississauga Rd, Mississauga, L5N 1A6, ON, Canada
Tel.: (905) 821-8500
Emp.: 5
Specialty Foods Mfr
N.A.I.C.S.: 311412
David Johnston (VP & Gen Mgr)

Subsidiary (Domestic):

Garden Protein International Inc. (6)
200-12751 Vulcan Way, Richmond, V6V 3C8, BC, Canada
Tel.: (604) 278-7300
Web Site: http://www.gardein.com
Specialty Foods Mfr
N.A.I.C.S.: 311412

Ralcorp Receivables, LLC (1)
1055 E Greg St, Sparks, NV 89431
Tel.: (775) 355-8115
Investment Management Service
N.A.I.C.S.: 523940

Ralston Foods (1)
800 Market St Ste 2900, Saint Louis, MO 63101 (100%)
Tel.: (314) 877-7000
Web Site: http://www.ralstonfoods.com

Sales Range: $75-99.9 Million
Emp.: 300
Private Label & Store Brand Breakfast Cereals Mfr
N.A.I.C.S.: 311230

Plant (Domestic):

Ralston Foods, Inc. (2)
150 McCamly St S, Battle Creek, MI 49017-3522 (100%)
Tel.: (269) 968-6181
Sales Range: $100-124.9 Million
Emp.: 180
Cereal Breakfast Foods
N.A.I.C.S.: 311230

Ralston Foods, Inc. (2)
276 Bremen Rd, Lancaster, OH 43130-7873
Tel.: (740) 654-8880
Breakfast Cereal Mfr
N.A.I.C.S.: 311230
Petsy Monday (Gen Mgr)

Ralston Foods, Inc. (2)
800 Market St, Saint Louis, MO 63101
Tel.: (314) 877-7000
Web Site: http://www.ralcorp.com
Breakfast Cereal Mfr
N.A.I.C.S.: 311230

Ralston Foods, Inc. (2)
1055 E Greg St, Sparks, NV 89431-6535
Tel.: (775) 359-4000
Web Site: http://www.ralcorp.com
Sales Range: $75-99.9 Million
Emp.: 170
Breakfast Cereal Mfr
N.A.I.C.S.: 311230

Sepp's Gourmet Foods Ltd. (1)
529 Annance Ct, Delta, V3M 6Y7, BC, Canada
Tel.: (604) 524-2540
Web Site: http://www.seppsfoods.com
Sales Range: $25-49.9 Million
Emp.: 150
Frozen Food Mfr
N.A.I.C.S.: 311999
Alan V. Maddox (Pres)
James D. Pratt (CEO)
Debbie Cullum (Comm Mgr)

Western Waffles Corp. (1)
175 Savannah Oaks Drive, Rural Route No 6, Brantford, N3V 1E8, ON, Canada
Tel.: (519) 759-2025
Frozen Waffles Mfr
N.A.I.C.S.: 311412

CONAIR CORPORATION
246 Broadway, Garden City Park, NY 11040 NY
Web Site: https://www.conairhvacfranchise.com
Year Founded: 1963
CNGA—(OTCIQ)
All Other Health & Personal Care Retailers
N.A.I.C.S.: 456199
Mary J. George (Owner)
Barry Stransky (Pres & CEO-Bus Dev)

CONCENTRIX CORPORATION
44111 Nobel Dr, Fremont, CA 94538
Tel.: (800) 747-0583 DE
Web Site: http://www.concentrix.com
Year Founded: 1983
CNXC—(NASDAQ)
Rev.: $7,114,706,000
Assets: $12,491,827,000
Liabilities: $8,348,533,000
Net Worth: $4,143,294,000
Earnings: $313,842,000
Emp.: 440,000
Fiscal Year-end: 11/30/23
Information Technology Services
N.A.I.C.S.: 519290
Christopher L. Caldwell (Pres & CEO)
Andre Valentine (CFO)
Rick Rosso (Exec VP-Sls & Acct Mgmt)

Monica Egger (Sr VP-Fin Plng & Analysis)
Jane C. Fogarty (Sec & Exec VP-Legal)
Diane Hanson (VP)
Kathryn V. Marinello (Chm)

Subsidiaries:

Concentrix Insurance Administration Solutions Corporation (1)
2000 Wade Hampton Blvd, Greenville, SC 29615
Tel.: (864) 248-9202
Insurance Related Services
N.A.I.C.S.: 524298
Kathryn Shepherd (Project Mgr)

Concentrix SREV, Inc. (1)
707 17th St 25th Fl, Denver, CO 80202
Tel.: (720) 889-8500
Web Site: http://www.servicesource.com
Rev.: $195,704,000
Assets: $132,448,000
Liabilities: $65,414,000
Net Worth: $67,034,000
Earnings: ($14,721,000)
Emp.: 2,900
Fiscal Year-end: 12/31/2021
Service Revenue Management Solutions
N.A.I.C.S.: 541512
Gary B. Moore (Chm & CEO)

Subsidiary (Non-US):

ServiceSource International Bulgaria EOOD (2)
Capital Fort Building Tsarigradsko Shausse 90, Sofia, 1784, Bulgaria
Tel.: (359) 24471199
Business Management Consulting Services
N.A.I.C.S.: 541611

ServiceSource International Japan G.K. (2)
11 F MM Park Building, 3-6-3 Minatomirai Nishi-ku, Yokohama, 220-0012, Japan
Tel.: (81) 456700400
Web Site: http://www.servicesource.com
Information Technology Services
N.A.I.C.S.: 519290

ServiceSource International Singapore Pte. Ltd. (2)
80 Pasir Panjang Road 15-83 to 84 Mapletree Business City, Singapore, 117372, Singapore
Tel.: (65) 6 594 3900
Web Site: https://www.servicesource.com
Sales Range: $75-99.9 Million
Emp.: 180
Computer System Design Services
N.A.I.C.S.: 541512
Gwen Wight (Dir Gen)

Convergys Corporation (1)
201 E 4th St, Cincinnati, OH 45202
Tel.: (513) 723-7000
Web Site: http://www.convergys.com
Rev.: $2,792,100,000
Assets: $2,414,700,000
Liabilities: $1,037,000,000
Net Worth: $1,377,700,000
Earnings: $121,400,000
Emp.: 115,000
Fiscal Year-end: 12/31/2017
Holding Company; Business & Operational Support Systems, Automated & Agent Assisted Customer Service Support & Human Resource Outsourcing Services
N.A.I.C.S.: 561110

Subsidiary (Domestic):

Ceon Corporation (2)
1600 Seaport Blvd Ste 160, Redwood City, CA 94063 (100%)
Tel.: (650) 817-6300
Web Site: http://www.ceon.com
Sales Range: $10-24.9 Million
Product Lifecycle Management Software Publisher
N.A.I.C.S.: 513210

Subsidiary (Non-US):

Concentrix International Services Europe B.V. (2)

Kabelweg 43, 1014 BA, Amsterdam, Netherlands
Tel.: (31) 205864700
Customer Management Services
N.A.I.C.S.: 541613

Subsidiary (Domestic):

Convergys Customer Management Group Inc. (2)
201 E 4th St, Cincinnati, OH
45202   (100%)
Tel.: (513) 723-7000
Web Site: http://www.convergys.com
Sales Range: $75-99.9 Million
Automated & Agent-Assisted Customer Service Support
N.A.I.C.S.: 561499
Marife B. Zamora *(Mng Dir-Asia Pacific & EMEA)*

Subsidiary (Non-US):

Convergys France SAS (2)
32 avenue Charles de Gaulle, 92200,
Neuilly-sur-Seine, France
Tel.: (33) 155244300
Data Processing Services
N.A.I.C.S.: 518210

Convergys Global Services GmbH (2)
Komturstrasse 18, Berlin, 12099, Germany
Tel.: (49) 3075763000
Customer Relationship Management Services
N.A.I.C.S.: 561422
Anette Gelbe *(Mgr-Ops)*

Convergys Group Servicios de Apoyo Informatico, S.L. (2)
Calle Newton 7 A Coruna, 15008, La Coruna, Spain
Tel.: (34) 902501331
Customer Relationship Management Services
N.A.I.C.S.: 561422

Convergys Holdings (UK) Ltd. (2)
70 Atlantic Street, Altrincham, WA14 5FY,
Cheshire, United Kingdom
Tel.: (44) 1616160537
Holding Company
N.A.I.C.S.: 551112

Convergys International Bulgaria EOOD (2)
Business Park, Sofia-grad - Yugozapaden,
1766, Sofia, Bulgaria
Tel.: (359) 24003499
Customer Relationship Management Services
N.A.I.C.S.: 561422
Emil Gueorguiev *(Sr Mgr-Team)*

Convergys International Nordic AB (2)
Ronnowsgatan 8, Helsingborg, 252 25,
Sweden
Tel.: (46) 424957700
Emp.: 200
Customer Relationship Management Services
N.A.I.C.S.: 561422

Convergys Ireland Limited (2)
Woodford Business Park Turnepin Lane
Santry, Dublin, Ireland
Tel.: (353) 18440000
Customer Relationship Management Services
N.A.I.C.S.: 561422

Convergys Malaysia Sdn Bhd (2)
Level 3 1 Tech Park Tanjung Bandar
Utama, Petaling Jaya, 47800, Malaysia
Tel.: (60) 376821000
Customer Relationship Management Services
N.A.I.C.S.: 561422

Convergys Netherlands LLC (2)
Kabelweg 43, 1014 BA, Amsterdam, Netherlands
Tel.: (31) 205864700
Web Site: http://www.convergys.com
Emp.: 550
Information Technology Services
N.A.I.C.S.: 541512

Convergys Philippines Inc. (2)
8F to 12F Vector One Building Northgate
Cyberzone Filinvest Corporate, City Alabang, Muntinlupa, 1770, Philippines
Tel.: (63) 27581588
Web Site: http://www.convergys.com
Customer Relationship Management Services
N.A.I.C.S.: 561422

Subsidiary (Domestic):

Convergys Services Philippines, Inc. (3)
UP-AyalaLand TechnoHub UP Diliman
Commonwealth Avenue, UP North Science
& Technology, Quezon City, 1121, Philippines
Tel.: (63) 29816478
Customer Relationship Management Services
N.A.I.C.S.: 561422

eTelecare Philippines, Inc. (3)
22nd Floor CyberOne Building Eastwood
City Cyberpark, Bagumbayan, Quezon City,
1110, Metro Manila, Philippines
Tel.: (63) 29165670
Customer Relationship Management Services
N.A.I.C.S.: 561422

Subsidiary (Non-US):

Convergys Philippines Services Corporation (2)
Convergys 1 Building 6796 Ayala Avenue,
Corner Salcedo Street Legaspi Village,
Makati, 1200, Philippines
Tel.: (63) 27923031
Web Site: http://www.convergys.com
Data Processing Services
N.A.I.C.S.: 518210

Convergys Services Singapore Pte. Ltd. (2)
180 Clemenceau Avenue 05-03 Hawpar
Centre, Singapore, 239922, Singapore
Tel.: (65) 65572277
Customer Relationship Management Services
N.A.I.C.S.: 561422

Convergys Stream Pvt. Ltd. (2)
14th Floor G Corp Gb Road Kasarvadavali,
Near Kasarvadavali Next to Big Mall,
Thane, 400 615, India
Tel.: (91) 2239311600
Customer Relationship Management Services
N.A.I.C.S.: 561422
Rajvin Tarwale *(Engr-HP)*

Subsidiary (Domestic):

Encore Receivable Management, Inc. (2)
400 N Rogers Rd, Olathe, KS 66062
Tel.: (913) 782-3333
Web Site: http://www.convergys.com
Data Processing Services
N.A.I.C.S.: 518210

Finali Corporation (2)
10225 Westmoor Dr Ste 100, Westminster,
CO 80021-2703
Tel.: (720) 887-7800
Sales Range: $10-24.9 Million
Emp.: 30
Data Processing Services
N.A.I.C.S.: 518210

Subsidiary (Non-US):

SGS Tunisie S.A.R.L. (2)
Rue 8612 Impasse no 5 La Charguia, 2035,
Tunis, Tunisia
Tel.: (216) 71205100
Web Site: http://www.sgs.tn
Inspection & Testing Services
N.A.I.C.S.: 541990

Subsidiary (Domestic):

Stream Global Services - AZ, Inc. (2)
1801 E Camelback Rd Ste 300, Phoenix,
AZ 85016
Tel.: (509) 826-0300

Customer Relationship Management Services
N.A.I.C.S.: 561422

Subsidiary (Non-US):

Stream Global Services El Salvador, S.A. de C.V. (2)
65 Ave Sur y Alameda Roosevelt, Colonia
Escalon, San Salvador, El Salvador
Tel.: (503) 25003701
Customer Relationship Management Services
N.A.I.C.S.: 561422

Stream Global Services Honduras, S.A. (2)
Tower 2 Km 2 NO Boulevard Armenta, Altia
Business Park, San Pedro Sula, Honduras
Tel.: (504) 25802550
Customer Relationship Management Services
N.A.I.C.S.: 561422
Jose Eduardo Medina *(Mgr-Ops)*

Stream Global Services Nicaragua, S.A. (2)
Rotonda El Periodista 150 mts al sur Ofiplaza El Retiro Edificio 3 Rot, Managua,
Nicaragua
Tel.: (505) 22809620
Customer Relationship Management Services
N.A.I.C.S.: 561422

Stream International Canada ULC (2)
540 Dundas St W, Belleville, K8P 1B8, ON,
Canada
Tel.: (613) 961-5400
Customer Relationship Management Services
N.A.I.C.S.: 561422

Stream International Costa Rica S.A. (2)
26g 600 Mts Norte Del Mall Real Cariari,
Zona Franca America Edificio, Heredia,
Costa Rica
Tel.: (506) 83491954
Customer Relationship Management Services
N.A.I.C.S.: 561422

Stream International Sp. z.o.o. (2)
Al Wojska Polskiego 62, 70-470, Szczecin,
West Pomeranian, Poland
Tel.: (48) 914881323
Web Site: http://www.convergys.pl
Customer Relationship Management Services
N.A.I.C.S.: 561422

Subsidiary (Domestic):

Stream New York Inc. (2)
146 Arsenal St, Watertown, NY 13601
Tel.: (315) 785-9200
Office Administrative Services
N.A.I.C.S.: 561110

Subsidiary (Non-US):

Stream Tunisie, S.A.R.L. (2)
16 Rue Des Metiers Zi Charguia Ii, 2035,
Tunis, Tunisia
Tel.: (216) 70839700
Customer Relationship Management Services
N.A.I.C.S.: 561422

Patientys SAS (1)
32 Avenue Pierre Grenier, 92100,
Boulogne-Billancourt, France
Tel.: (33) 177702500
Web Site: https://www.patientys.com
Health Care Management Services
N.A.I.C.S.: 621610

ProKarma Inc. (1)
8705 SW Nimbus Ave Ste 118, Beaverton,
OR 97008
Tel.: (971) 317-0700
Web Site: https://catalyst.concentrix.com
Business Support & IT Services
N.A.I.C.S.: 561499
Thomas L. Monahan III *(Chm)*
Vivek Kumar *(Co-Founder & Co-Pres)*
Jeff Miller *(Co-Founder)*
Vijay Ijju *(Co-Founder & Co-Pres)*

Manish Mehta *(Co-Founder & Vice Chm)*
Nancy Peterson *(Exec VP-Global Resource)*
Bonnie Page *(Chief Legal Officer)*
Kris Klein *(CMO)*
Courtney Klein *(Head-M&A & Integration)*
Kelly Heather *(VP-HR)*
Cam Dyer *(Mng Dir)*
Dinesh Venugopal *(CEO)*
Anjan Sur *(CFO)*

Subsidiary (Domestic):

Lenati LLC (2)
1905 Queen Anne Ave N Ste 300, Seattle,
WA 98109
Web Site: http://www.pkglobal.com
Business Support & IT Services
N.A.I.C.S.: 561990

ProKarma Inc. - Washington (2)
13555 SE 36th St Ste 200, Bellevue, WA
98006
Tel.: (425) 250-0400
Web Site: http://www.prokarma.com
Business Support & IT Services
N.A.I.C.S.: 561499
Bonnie Page *(Chief Legal Officer)*
Steve Simion *(CMO & Chief Sls Officer)*

Telecats B.V. (1)
Colosseum 42, 7521 PT, Enschede, Netherlands
Tel.: (31) 534889900
Web Site: https://www.telecats.com
Telecommunication Servicesb
N.A.I.C.S.: 517111

Tetel SA de CV (1)
Avenida Albert Einstein y Bulevar, San Salvador, El Salvador
Tel.: (503) 5011806141011
Software Development Services
N.A.I.C.S.: 541511

Wge SAS (1)
4 Rue De La Chair, 95300, Livilliers, France
Tel.: (33) 680630049
Web Site: https://wgefrance.fr
Shaping Equipment Maintenance Services
N.A.I.C.S.: 811310

CONCORD ACQUISITION CORP.
477 Madison Ave, New York, NY
10022
Tel.: (212) 883-4330   DE
Year Founded: 2020
CND—(NYSE)
Rev.: $1,233,168
Assets: $276,458,650
Liabilities: $314,529,084
Net Worth: ($38,070,434)
Earnings: ($27,611,291)
Fiscal Year-end: 12/31/21
Investment Services
N.A.I.C.S.: 523999
Bob Diamond *(Chm)*
Jeff Tuder *(CEO)*
Michele Cito *(CFO)*
Jeffrey M. Tuder *(Executives)*

CONCORDIS GROUP, INC.
211 Regency Dr, Wylie, TX 75098
Tel.: (214) 810-3419   MD
Web Site: https://concordisgrp.com
Year Founded: 2009
CNGI—(OTCIQ)
Financial Investment Services
N.A.I.C.S.: 523999
Atif Rafique *(Pres, CEO & Dir-Operations)*
Joseph Donahue *(Chm & Dir)*

CONCRETE LEVELING SYSTEMS, INC.
5046 E Blvd NW, Canton, OH 44718
Tel.: (330) 966-8120   NV
Web Site:
https://www.clsfabricating.com
Year Founded: 2007
CLEV—(OTCIQ)
Rev.: $778

Concrete Leveling Systems, Inc.—(Continued)

Assets: $18,666
Liabilities: $578,925
Net Worth: ($560,259)
Earnings: ($65,985)
Fiscal Year-end: 07/31/24
Concrete Leveling Device Mfr
N.A.I.C.S.: 333120
Edward A. Barth *(Pres)*
Suzanne I. Barth *(Founder, CEO, CFO & Principal Acctg Officer)*
Eugene H. Swearengin *(Sec)*

CONCRETE PUMPING HOLDINGS, INC.

500 E 84th Ave Ste A-5, Thornton, CO 80229
Tel.: (303) 289-7497   DE
Web Site:
   https://www.concretepumpingholdings.com
Year Founded: 1983
BBCP—(NASDAQ)
Rev.: $442,241,000
Assets: $904,525,000
Liabilities: $596,285,000
Net Worth: $308,240,000
Earnings: $31,790,000
Emp.: 1,720
Fiscal Year-end: 10/31/23
Investment Services
N.A.I.C.S.: 523999
Howard D. Morgan *(Chm)*
Brian Hodges *(Vice Chm)*
Bruce F. Young *(Pres & CEO)*
Mark Young *(Pres)*
David Anthony Faud *(Mng Dir)*
Tom O'Malley *(Sr VP-Sales & Marketing)*
Iain Humphries *(CFO & Sec)*
Casey Mendenhall *(Pres-ECo-Pan)*

Subsidiaries:

Camfaud Concrete Pumps
Limited   **(1)**
High Road, Thornwood Common, Epping, CM16 6LU, United Kingdom
Tel.: (44) 1992560898
Web Site: http://www.camfaud.co.uk
Construction Services
N.A.I.C.S.: 236220

Capital Pumping, LP   **(1)**
8217 Shoal Creek Blvd Ste 201, Austin, TX 78757
Tel.: (512) 276 0116
Web Site: https://www.capitalpumping.com
Construction Services
N.A.I.C.S.: 236220

Coastal Carolina Pumping, Inc.   **(1)**
1326 N Teachey Rd, Wallace, NC 28466
Tel.: (704) 552-6000
Web Site: http://www.ccpumping.com
Rev.: $8,900,000
Emp.: 100
Poured Concrete Foundation & Structure Contractors
N.A.I.C.S.: 238110
Chris Boergert *(CFO)*

Eco-Pan Limited   **(1)**
High Road Thornwood Common, Epping, CM16 6LU, United Kingdom
Tel.: (44) 1608610740
Web Site: https://www.eco-pan.co.uk
Concrete Waste Containment & Recycling Services
N.A.I.C.S.: 562119

Eco-Pan, Inc.   **(1)**
500 E 84th Ave Ste A-5, Thornton, CO 80229-5300
Tel.: (303) 853-4995
Web Site: http://www.eco-pan.com
Environmental Services
N.A.I.C.S.: 541620
Casey Mendenhall *(Gen Mgr)*
Paul Sulman *(Dir-Natl Sls & Bus Dev)*
Lloyd Lyver *(Reg Dir & Mgr-Field Ops)*
Tim Walker *(Reg Dir & Branch Mgr)*
Cody Howlett *(Reg Dir)*

Premier Concrete Pumping
Limited   **(1)**
Greenfield Farm Howe Lane, White Waltham, Maidenhead, SL6 3JP, Berkshire, United Kingdom
Tel.: (44) 1189343772
Web Site:
   http://www.premierconcretepumping.co.uk
Construction Services
N.A.I.C.S.: 236220
Mark Henshaw *(Natl Sls Mgr)*

CONDOR HOSPITALITY TRUST, INC.

1800 W Pasewalk Ave Ste 120, Norfolk, NE 68701
Tel.: (301) 861-3305   MD
Web Site:
   http://www.condorhospitality.com
Year Founded: 1994
CDOR—(NYSEAMEX)
Rev.: $35,188,000
Assets: $275,193,000
Liabilities: $198,912,000
Net Worth: $76,281,000
Earnings: ($19,681,000)
Emp.: 6
Fiscal Year-end: 12/31/20
Hospitality Real Estate Investment Trust
N.A.I.C.S.: 525990
Daphne J. Dufresne *(Chm)*
Jill Burger *(Pres, CEO, CFO & Chief Acctg Officer)*

CONDUENT INCORPORATED

100 Campus Dr Ste 200, Florham Park, NJ 07932
Tel.: (203) 849-2339   NY
Web Site: https://www.conduent.com
Year Founded: 2016
CNDT—(NASDAQ)
Rev.: $3,722,000,000
Assets: $3,162,000,000
Liabilities: $2,529,000,000
Net Worth: $633,000,000
Earnings: ($296,000,000)
Emp.: 59,000
Fiscal Year-end: 12/31/23
Holding Company; Business Process Services
N.A.I.C.S.: 551112
Scott Letier *(Chm)*
Burhan Jaffer *(Head-Strategy & Corp Dev-Global)*
Clifford A. Skelton *(Pres & CEO)*
Mark Brewer *(Pres-Transportation Solutions, Exec VP & Head-Enterprise Accounts)*
Louis Keyes *(Chief Revenue Officer & Exec VP)*
Chris Kujawa *(Chief HR Officer)*
Mark Prout *(CIO)*
Dharma Rajagopalan *(Grp Pres-Comml Solutions)*
Tracy Yelencsics *(CMO)*
Randal King *(Grp Pres-Customer Experience Mgmt)*
Michael Krawitz *(Gen Counsel, Sec & Exec VP)*
Adam Appleby *(Head-Ops-Global)*
Jeff Browning *(Chief Risk Officer)*
Pat Costa *(Grp Pres-Healthcare Solutions)*
Walter Frye *(Head-Diversity & Inclusion-Global)*
Stephen Wood *(CFO & Exec VP)*

Subsidiaries:

ACS Solutions Poland Sp. z.o.o. **(1)**
ul Gdanska 47 49, 91-001, Lodz, Poland
Tel.: (48) 422917000
Management Services
N.A.I.C.S.: 541611

Affiliated Computer Services
GmbH   **(1)**

Freiburgstrasse 251, 3018, Bern, Switzerland
Tel.: (41) 448100353
Business Process Outsourcing & Information Technology Services
N.A.I.C.S.: 518210

Conduent Credit Balance Solutions,
LLC   **(1)**
100 Campus Dr Ste 200, Florham Park, NJ 07932
Tel.: (410) 560-6700
Management Consulting Services
N.A.I.C.S.: 541618

Conduent Education Services,
LLC   **(1)**
100 Campus Dr Ste 200, Florham Park, NJ 07932
Web Site:
   https://www.conduenteducation.com
Education Services
N.A.I.C.S.: 611710

Conduent Federal Solutions,
LLC   **(1)**
100 Campus Dr Ste 200, Florham Park, NJ 07932
Tel.: (844) 663-2638
All Other Business Support Services
N.A.I.C.S.: 561499

Conduent Germany Holding
GmbH   **(1)**
Deichstrabe 1, 20459, Hamburg, Germany
Tel.: (49) 43153039090
Fire Insurance Services
N.A.I.C.S.: 611710

Conduent Healthcare Information
Services, Inc.   **(1)**
100 Campus Dr Ste 200, Florham Park, NJ 07932
Tel.: (844) 663-2638
Health Care Information Services
N.A.I.C.S.: 519290

Conduent Healthcare Knowledge Solutions, LLC   **(1)**
2457 Care Dr, Tallahassee, FL 32308
Tel.: (850) 385-7915
Custom eLearning Solutions
N.A.I.C.S.: 541511

Conduent Mortgage Services,
Inc.   **(1)**
100 Campus Dr Ste 200, Florham Park, NJ 07932
Tel.: (844) 663-2638
Business Support Services
N.A.I.C.S.: 561499

Conduent Parking Enforcement Solutions Limited   **(1)**
Asghar House Hayward Business Centre New Lane, Havant, PO9 2NL, United Kingdom
Tel.: (44) 2392455564
Software Services
N.A.I.C.S.: 513210

Conduent Payment Integrity Solutions, Inc.   **(1)**
1301 Basswood Rd, Schaumburg, IL 60173
Tel.: (847) 839-7700
Collection Agency
N.A.I.C.S.: 561440

Conduent Payment Integrity Solutions, Inc.   **(1)**
PO Box 30114, Salt Lake City, UT 84130-0114
Software Development Services
N.A.I.C.S.: 513210

Conduent Securities Services,
Inc.   **(1)**
100 Campus Dr Ste 200, Florham Park, NJ 07932
Software Development Services
N.A.I.C.S.: 541511

Conduent State & Local Solutions,
Inc.   **(1)**
100 Campus Dr Ste 200, Florham Park, NJ 07932
Tel.: (844) 663-2638
Custom Computer Programming Services
N.A.I.C.S.: 541511

Subsidiary (Domestic):

Consilience Software, Inc.   **(2)**
11305 4 Points Dr Ste 150, Austin, TX 78726
Tel.: (512) 795-1300
Case Management Software Publisher
N.A.I.C.S.: 513210

Conduent State Healthcare, LLC **(1)**
9040 Roswell Rd, Atlanta, GA 30350
Tel.: (770) 594-7799
Health Care Srvices
N.A.I.C.S.: 621491

Conduent Transport Solutions,
Inc.   **(1)**
3100 Medlock Bridge Rd, Norcross, GA 30071
Tel.: (770) 368-2003
Software Services
N.A.I.C.S.: 513210

Invoco Communication Center
GmbH   **(1)**
Lubsche Str 95, 23966, Wismar, Germany
Tel.: (49) 8000000725
Telecommunication Servicesb
N.A.I.C.S.: 517810

Invoco Customer Service GmbH **(1)**
Lubsche Str 95, 23966, Wismar, Germany
Tel.: (49) 800 0000725
Telecommunication Servicesb
N.A.I.C.S.: 517810

Invoco Holding GmbH   **(1)**
Friedrich-Ebert-Damm 111, 22047, Hamburg, Germany
Tel.: (49) 43153039090
Web Site: http://conduentdeutschland.de
Holding Company
N.A.I.C.S.: 551112
Michael Krawitz *(Mng Dir)*

Sia Rigas Karte   **(1)**
Cesu str 31/ 3 entrance 8 3 floor, Riga, 1012, Latvia   **(49%)**
Tel.: (371) 67326300
Web Site: https://rigaskarte.lv
Smart Payment Services
N.A.I.C.S.: 522320
Pavels Tulovskis *(Dir-Technical)*
Katherine Gauran *(Chm)*

Unamic/HCN B.V.   **(1)**
PJ Oudweg 7, 1314CH, Almere, Netherlands
Tel.: (31) 365459000
Financial & Transaction Management Services
N.A.I.C.S.: 541611

CONDUIT PHARMACEUTICALS INC.

4995 Murphy Canyon Rd Ste 300, San Diego, CA 92123
Tel.: (760) 471-8536   DE
Web Site:
   https://www.conduitpharma.com
Year Founded: 2021
CDT—(NASDAQ)
Rev.: $1,976,183
Assets: $137,517,822
Liabilities: $141,817,908
Net Worth: ($4,300,086)
Earnings: $398,639
Emp.: 3
Fiscal Year-end: 12/31/22
Investment Services
N.A.I.C.S.: 523999
Freda Lewis-Hall *(Chm)*
David Tapolczay *(CEO)*
Joanne Holland *(Chief Scientific Officer)*
Bill Begien *(VP-Investor Relations)*
Adam Sragovicz *(CFO & Treas)*

CONECTISYS CORP.

14308 S Goss Rd, Cheney, WA 99004
Tel.: (949) 929-5455   CO
Year Founded: 1986
CONC—(OTCIQ)

Application Software Development Services
N.A.I.C.S.: 541511
Robert A. Spigno *(Chm, CEO & CFO)*
Patricia A. Spigno *(CTO & Sec)*

CONFLUENT, INC.
899 W Evelyn Ave, Mountain View, CA 94041 **DE**
Web Site: https://www.confluent.io
Year Founded: 2014
CFLT—(NASDAQ)
Rev.: $776,952,000
Assets: $2,460,809,000
Liabilities: $1,650,394,000
Net Worth: $810,415,000
Earnings: ($442,746,000)
Emp.: 2,744
Fiscal Year-end: 12/31/23
Software Development Services
N.A.I.C.S.: 541511
Jun Rao *(Co-Founder)*
Erica Ruliffson Schultz *(Pres-Field Ops)*
Stephanie Buscemi *(CMO)*
Cheryl Dalrymple *(Chief People Officer & Head-Corp Dev)*
Roger Scott *(Chief Customer Officer)*
Ganesh Srinivasan *(Chief Product & Engrg Officer)*
Rohan Sivaram *(CFO)*
Neha Narkhede *(Co-Founder)*
Jay Kreps *(Co-Founder, Chm & CEO)*

CONIFER HOLDINGS, INC.
3001 W Big Beaver Rd Ste 200, Troy, MI 48084
Tel.: (248) 559-0840 **MI**
Web Site: https://www.cnfrh.com
Year Founded: 2009
CNFR—(NASDAQ)
Rev.: $104,889,000
Assets: $312,350,000
Liabilities: $293,400,000
Net Worth: $18,950,000
Earnings: ($10,681,000)
Emp.: 109
Fiscal Year-end: 12/31/22
Holding Company; Insurance Services
N.A.I.C.S.: 551112
James G. Petcoff *(Co-Founder)*
Andrew D. Petcoff *(Sr VP-Personal Lines)*
Nicholas J. Petcoff *(Co-Founder, CEO & Exec VP)*
Brian J. Roney *(Pres)*
Harold J. Meloche *(CFO & Treas)*

Subsidiaries:

American Colonial Insurance Company **(1)**
260 Wekiva Springs Rd Ste 2060, Longwood, FL 32779
Tel.: (877) 214-3970
Web Site: http://www.american-colonial.com
Homeowners & Auto Insurance
N.A.I.C.S.: 524126

Red Cedar Insurance Company **(1)**
855 Jefferson Ave Ste 2669, Redwood City, CA 94063
Tel.: (650) 596-5900
Web Site: https://www.redcedaragency.com
Insurance Services
N.A.I.C.S.: 524210

White Pine Insurance Company **(1)**
209 Georgian Pl, Somerset, PA 15501
Tel.: (814) 445-8905
Web Site: http://www.whitepineins.com
Insurance Services
N.A.I.C.S.: 524210
James G. Petcoff *(Chm)*
Andrew D. Petcoff *(Sr VP-Personal Lines)*
Nicholas J. Petcoff *(Pres)*

CONIHASSET CAPTIAL PARTNERS, INC.

2 International Pl 16th Fl, Boston, MA 02110
Tel.: (617) 235-7215
CNHA—(OTCIQ)
Investment Management Service
N.A.I.C.S.: 525990
Edward M. Mulherin *(CFO)*

CONMED CORPORATION
11311 Concept Blvd, Largo, FL 33773
Tel.: (727) 392-6464 **NY**
Web Site: https://www.conmed.com
Year Founded: 1970
CNMD—(NYSE)
Rev.: $1,045,472,000
Assets: $2,297,592,000
Liabilities: $1,552,047,000
Net Worth: $745,545,000
Earnings: ($80,582,000)
Emp.: 4,100
Fiscal Year-end: 12/31/22
Electrosurgery & Other Medical Products Mfr
N.A.I.C.S.: 334511
Curt R. Hartman *(Chm, Pres & CEO)*
Todd W. Garner *(CFO & Exec VP)*
Johonna Pelletier *(Treas & VP-Tax)*
Sarah M. Oliker *(Asst Sec & Asst Gen Counsel)*
Shanna Cotti-Osmanski *(CIO & Exec VP-IT)*
Patrick J. Beyer *(COO)*

Subsidiaries:

Aspen Laboratories, Inc. **(1)**
7211 S Eagle St, Englewood, CO 80112-4203 **(100%)**
Tel.: (303) 699-7600
Web Site: http://www.conmed.com
Sales Range: $50-74.9 Million
Emp.: 140
Mfr of Medical Supplies
N.A.I.C.S.: 334510

Buffalo Filter LLC **(1)**
5900 Genesee St, Lancaster, NY 14086
Tel.: (716) 835-7000
Web Site: http://www.buffalofilter.com
Sales Range: $10-24.9 Million
Emp.: 70
Medical Device Mfr & Supplier of Surgical Smoke Evacuation Equipment
N.A.I.C.S.: 333413

CONMED Corporation - Denmark **(1)**
Naverland 2 - 1 sal, 2600, Glostrup, Denmark **(100%)**
Tel.: (45) 43636460
Web Site: http://www.conmed.com
Medical Supplies Whslr
N.A.I.C.S.: 423450

Subsidiary (Non-US):

Linvatec Sweden AB **(2)**
Datavagen 10D, Askim, 436 32, Gothenburg, Sweden
Tel.: (46) 313379030
Web Site: http://www.conmed.com
Emp.: 20
N.A.I.C.S.: 456199
Patrick Erricson *(Mng Dir)*

CONMED Denmark ApS **(1)**
Naverland 2 - 1 sal, DK-2600, Glostrup, Denmark
Tel.: (45) 43636460
Pharmaceutical Products Distr
N.A.I.C.S.: 424210

CONMED Deutschland GmbH **(1)**
Frankfurter Strasse 74, 64521, Gross-Gerau, Germany
Tel.: (49) 61529370
Web Site: https://www.conmed.com
Medical Device Mfr
N.A.I.C.S.: 334510

CONMED Europe BV **(1)**
WA Mozartlaan, B-1620, Drogenbos, Belgium
Tel.: (32) 5260560
Surgical & Patient Care Product Mfr
N.A.I.C.S.: 339112

CONMED France SAS **(1)**
575 655 Allee des Parcs Batiment D, 69800, Saint-Priest-en-Jarez, France
Tel.: (33) 472474030
Medical Device Mfr
N.A.I.C.S.: 334510

CONMED Iberia SL **(1)**
Gran Via Carles III 124 3, 08034, Barcelona, Spain
Tel.: (34) 932064070
Medical Equipment Whslr
N.A.I.C.S.: 423450

CONMED Linvatec Australia Pty. Ltd **(1)**
Unit 4 10 Rodborough Road, French's Forest, 2086, NSW, Australia
Tel.: (61) 2 972 4000
Web Site: https://www.conmed.com
Sales Range: $25-49.9 Million
Emp.: 4
Medical Equipment & Supplies Mfr
N.A.I.C.S.: 334510
Ralph Jennings *(Mng Dir)*

CONMED Linvatec Biomaterials Oy **(1)**
Hermiankatu 6-8 L, 33720, Tampere, Finland
Tel.: (358) 207871333
Web Site: https://www.conmed.com
Medical Device Mfr
N.A.I.C.S.: 334510

CONMED U.K. Ltd. **(1)**
73/74 Shrivenham Hundred Business Park, Swindon, SN6 8TY, Wiltshire, United Kingdom
Tel.: (44) 1793787910
Web Site: https://www.conmed.com
Emp.: 30
Medical Device Mfr
N.A.I.C.S.: 334510

Linvatec Biomaterials, Ltd. **(1)**
Hermiankatu 6-8 L, 33721, Tampere, Finland
Tel.: (358) 207871333
Web Site: http://www.conmed.com
Sales Range: $25-49.9 Million
Emp.: 3
Pharmaceutical Preparation Mfr
N.A.I.C.S.: 325412

Linvatec Corporation **(1)**
11311 Concept Blvd, Largo, FL 33773 **(100%)**
Tel.: (727) 392-6464
Web Site: http://www.linvatec.com
Sales Range: $450-499.9 Million
Emp.: 1,200
Mfr of Surgical Devices
N.A.I.C.S.: 339112

Linvatec Europe SPRL **(1)**
W A Mozartlaan 3, 1620, Drogenbos, Belgium
Tel.: (32) 25268480
Web Site: http://www.conmed.com
Sales Range: $25-49.9 Million
Emp.: 30
Pharmaceutical Preparation Mfr
N.A.I.C.S.: 325412

Linvatec Korea Ltd. **(1)**
16F Kumha Bldg 41-2 Cheongdam-dong, Gangnam-gu, Seoul, 135-766, Korea (South)
Tel.: (82) 2 3483 2600
Web Site: http://www.conmed.com
Surgical Appliance & Supplies Mfr
N.A.I.C.S.: 339113

Linvatec U.K. Ltd. **(1)**
73/74 Shrivenham Hundred Business Park, Watchfield, Swindon, SN6 8TY, Wiltshire, United Kingdom
Tel.: (44) 1793787910
Web Site: http://www.conmed.com
Emp.: 35
Medical Equipment Mfr
N.A.I.C.S.: 339112

SurgiQuest, Inc. **(1)**
488 Wheelers Farms Rd, Milford, CT 06461
Tel.: (203) 799-2400
Web Site: http://www.surgiquest.com
Emp.: 124
Developer, Marketer & Mfr Of The AirSeal System for use in Minimally Invasive Surgeries
N.A.I.C.S.: 339112

N.A.I.C.S.: 339112

CONN'S, INC.
2445 Technology Forest Blvd Ste 800, The Woodlands, TX 77381
Tel.: (936) 230-5899 **DE**
Web Site: https://www.conns.com
Year Founded: 1890
CONN—(NASDAQ)
Rev.: $1,342,527,000
Assets: $1,716,215,000
Liabilities: $1,213,805,000
Net Worth: $502,410,000
Earnings: ($59,292,000)
Emp.: 3,800
Fiscal Year-end: 01/31/23
Home Appliances, Consumer Electronics, Home Computers, Computer Peripherals & Accessories, Lawn & Garden Products & Mattresses Retailer
N.A.I.C.S.: 441330
Timothy Santo *(CFO, Chief Acctg Officer & VP)*
Norman L. Miller *(Pres & CEO)*

Subsidiaries:

W.S. Badcock LLC **(1)**
200 NW Phosphate Blvd, Mulberry, FL 33860-2328
Tel.: (863) 425-4921
Web Site: https://www.badcock.com
Sales Range: $450-499.9 Million
Emp.: 1,200
Retailer of Home Furnishings, Appliances, Electronics & Floor Coverings
N.A.I.C.S.: 449110

CONNECTM TECHNOLOGY SOLUTIONS, INC.
419 Webster St, Monterey, CA 93940
Tel.: (831) 649-7388 **DE**
Web Site:
https://www.montereycap.com
Year Founded: 2021
MCAC—(NASDAQ)
Rev.: $1,289,804
Assets: $94,222,525
Liabilities: $102,277,085
Net Worth: ($8,054,560)
Earnings: ($3,763,638)
Emp.: 3
Fiscal Year-end: 12/31/22
Investment Services
N.A.I.C.S.: 523999
Vivek Soni *(Exec VP)*
Daniel Davis *(CFO)*
Bala Padmakumar *(Chm & CEO)*

CONNECTONE BANCORP, INC.
301 Sylvan Ave, Englewood Cliffs, NJ 07632
Tel.: (201) 816-8900 **NJ**
Web Site:
https://www.connectonebank.com
Year Founded: 1982
CNOB—(NASDAQ)
Rev.: $386,989,000
Assets: $9,644,948,000
Liabilities: $8,466,197,000
Net Worth: $1,178,751,000
Earnings: $125,211,000
Emp.: 507
Fiscal Year-end: 12/31/22
Bank Holding Company
N.A.I.C.S.: 551111
Frank S. Sorrentino III *(Chm & CEO)*
William S. Burns *(CFO & Exec VP)*
Laura Criscione *(Sec & Exec VP)*

Subsidiaries:

BoeFly, Inc. **(1)**
50 W 72nd St C4, New York, NY 10023
Web Site: https://www.boefly.com
Business Loan Brokerage Services
N.A.I.C.S.: 522310

ConnectOne Bancorp, Inc.—(Continued)

Brian O'Boyle *(Founder & CTO)*
Nancy Broudo *(Sr VP)*
Greg Clower *(Sr VP)*
Doug Cullinan *(Sr VP)*

ConnectOne Bank   **(1)**
301 Sylvan Ave, Englewood Cliffs, NJ
07632
Tel.: (201) 816-8900
Web Site: http://www.connectonebank.com
Emp.: 15
Commericial Banking
N.A.I.C.S.: 522110
Frank S. Sorrentino III *(Chm & CEO)*
Elizabeth Magennis *(Pres)*

**ConnectOne Preferred Funding
Corp.**   **(1)**
301 Sylvan Ave, Englewood Cliffs, NJ
07632
Tel.: (201) 816-4460
Web Site: http://www.connectonebank.com
Real Estate Investment Services
N.A.I.C.S.: 531390

Twin Bridge Capital Corporation   **(1)**
2455 Morris Ave Ste 100, Union, NJ 07083
Tel.: (908) 688-9500
Commercial Banking Services
N.A.I.C.S.: 522110

CONNECTYX TECHNOLOGIES HOLDINGS GROUP, INC.

1825 NW Corporate Blvd Ste 110,
Boca Raton, FL 33431
Tel.: (561) 418-7725   **FL**
CTYX—(OTCIQ)
Pharmaceutical & Medical Device Mfr
N.A.I.C.S.: 339112
Paul M. Michaels *(CEO)*

CONNEXA SPORTS TECHNOLOGIES INC.

2709 N Rolling Rd Unit 138, Windsor
Mill, MD 21244
Tel.: (443) 407-7564   **MD**
Web Site:
https://www.connexasports.com
Year Founded: 2016
YYAI—(NASDAQ)
Rev.: $8,398,049
Assets: $21,622,624
Liabilities: $12,022,810
Net Worth: $9,599,814
Earnings: ($15,636,418)
Emp.: 8
Fiscal Year-end: 04/30/24
Sports Brand
N.A.I.C.S.: 459110
Paul McKeown *(Chief Bus Integration
Officer)*

Subsidiaries:

Slinger Bag Americas, Inc.   **(1)**
2709 N Rolling Rd Ste 138, Windsor Mill,
MD 21244
Web Site: https://slingerbag.com
Slinger Bag Mfr & Distr
N.A.I.C.S.: 339920

CONNEXIONONE CORP.

39899 Balentine Dr Ste 200, Newark,
CA 94560
Tel.: (408) 533-8155   **NC**
AFTC—(OTCIQ)
Assets: $385,032
Liabilities: $1,744,957
Net Worth: ($1,359,925)
Earnings: ($92,490)
Fiscal Year-end: 12/31/22
Fuel Injection Equipment Mfr
N.A.I.C.S.: 336310

CONOCOPHILLIPS

925 N Eldridge Pkwy, Houston, TX
77079-2703
Tel.: (281) 293-1000   **DE**
Web Site:
https://www.conocophillips.com

Year Founded: 1917
COP—(NYSE)
Rev.: $58,574,000,000
Assets: $95,924,000,000
Liabilities: $46,645,000,000
Net Worth: $49,279,000,000
Earnings: $10,957,000,000
Emp.: 9,900
Fiscal Year-end: 12/31/23
Petroleum Products, Natural Gas &
Chemicals Explorer, Refiner & Marketer
N.A.I.C.S.: 324110
Andrew D. Lundquist *(Sr VP-Govt
Affairs)*
Ryan M. Lance *(Chm & CEO)*
Kelly B. Rose *(Gen Counsel & Sr VP-
Legal)*
Heather Sirdashney *(VP-HR, Real
Estate & Facilities Svcs)*
Christopher P. Delk *(VP, Controller &
Counsel-Gen Tax)*
Heather G. Sirdashney *(Sr VP)*
Andy O'Brien *(Sr VP)*
William L. Bullock Jr. *(CFO & Exec
VP)*

Subsidiaries:

Concho Resources, Inc.   **(1)**
1 Concho Ctr 600 W Illinois Ave, Midland,
TX 79701
Tel.: (432) 683-7443
Web Site: http://www.conchoresources.com
Oil & Natural Gas Exploration Services
N.A.I.C.S.: 211120
Chris Spies *(VP-Geoscience & Tech)*
Jack F. Harper *(Pres)*
Erick W. Nelson *(Sr VP-Ops & Production)*
M. Ray Peterson *(VP-Drilling)*
Clay Bateman *(Sr VP-Assets)*
Megan P. Hays *(VP-IR & Pub Affairs)*
Mary T. Starnes *(Mgr-IR)*
Mary Ann Berry *(VP & Asst Sec)*
James Caputo *(VP-Bus Dev)*
Kang Chen *(CIO & VP)*
Keith Corbett *(Sr VP-Corp Engrg & Plng)*
Scott Kidwell *(Sr VP-Admin)*
Jacob P. Gobar *(Chief Acctg Officer & VP)*
Jeff Gasch *(VP-Delaware Basin)*
Chris Gatjanis *(VP-Horizontal Completions)*
Aaron Hunter *(VP-Midland Basin)*
Jere Thompson *(VP-Plng)*
C. William Giraud IV *(COO & Exec VP)*

Subsidiary (Domestic):

Marbob Energy Corp.   **(2)**
2208 W Main St, Artesia, NM 88210
Tel.: (505) 748-3303
Crude Petroleum & Natural Gas Exploration
Services
N.A.I.C.S.: 211120

**Three Rivers Operating Company
LLC**   **(2)**
5301 SW Pkwy Ste 400, Austin, TX 78735
Tel.: (512) 600-3190
Web Site: https://3roc.com
Sales Range: $100-124.9 Million
Emp.: 91
Oil & Natural Gas Exploration, Development
& Extraction
N.A.I.C.S.: 213112
Michael A. Wichterich *(Pres & CEO)*
David Goodman *(VP-Land)*
Drew Pinzur *(CFO)*
Leanne Churchward *(VP-Bus Dev)*

**ConocoPhillips (Browse Basin) Pty
Ltd**   **(1)**
53 Ord st Level 3, West Perth, 6005, WA,
Australia
Tel.: (61) 894236666
Emp.: 300
Natural Gas Extraction Services
N.A.I.C.S.: 211130

**ConocoPhillips (U.K.) Marketing &
Trading Limited**   **(1)**
20th Floor 1 Angel Court Throgmorton St,
London, EC2 7HJ, United Kingdom
Tel.: (44) 2074086000
Emp.: 40
Oil & Natural Gas Distr
N.A.I.C.S.: 424710

ConocoPhillips Alaska, Inc.   **(1)**
700 G St, Anchorage, AK
99501-3439   **(100%)**
Tel.: (907) 276-1215
Web Site:
   http://www.conocophillipsalaska.com
Sales Range: $75-99.9 Million
Emp.: 1,200
Exploration & Production of Crude Oil,
Natural Gas Liquids & Natural Gas in
Alaska
N.A.I.C.S.: 486110

**ConocoPhillips Asia Ventures Pte.
Ltd.**   **(1)**
1 Temasek Avenue 40-01 Millenia Tower,
Singapore, 39192, Singapore
Tel.: (65) 65360010
Business Consulting Services
N.A.I.C.S.: 541611

ConocoPhillips Australia Gas Holdings Pty Ltd   **(1)**
53 Ord st, West Perth, 6005, WA, Australia
Tel.: (61) 862187100
Emp.: 300
Natural Gas Extraction Services
N.A.I.C.S.: 211130

ConocoPhillips Australia Pty Ltd   **(1)**
37 Woods st, PO Box 2266, Darwin, 800,
NT, Australia
Web Site: http://www.conocophillips.com.au
Petroleum & Natural Gas Mfr
N.A.I.C.S.: 211120

**ConocoPhillips Austria Ges,
m.b.H.**   **(1)**
Samergasse 27, 5020, Salzburg,
Austria   **(100%)**
Tel.: (43) 6628778800
Web Site: http://www.getthntstellen.at
Sales Range: $10-24.9 Million
Emp.: 30
N.A.I.C.S.: 324110

ConocoPhillips Canada   **(1)**
401 9th Ave SW, PO Box 130, Calgary,
T2P 2H7, AB, Canada   **(100%)**
Tel.: (403) 233-4000
Web Site: http://www.conocophillips.ca
Sales Range: $1-4.9 Billion
Emp.: 2,000
Exploration of Crude Oil & Natural Gas
N.A.I.C.S.: 211120

Subsidiary (Domestic):

ConocoPhillips Canada   **(2)**
2100 250 Sixth Avenue Southwest, Calgary,
T2P 3H7, AB, Canada
Tel.: (403) 260-8000
Web Site: http://www.conocophillips.ca
Sales Range: $1-4.9 Billion
Emp.: 2,000
Exploration, Development & Production of
Oil & Gas
N.A.I.C.S.: 211120
Stephen Bradley *(VP-Operations)*
Khoa Dao *(VP-Development)*
Stephen Lee *(Gen Counsel & Gen Counsel)*
Sandra Stillwell *(VP)*
James Makowecki *(VP-Health, Safety, Environment & Sustainable Dev)*
Ross Stalker *(VP-Finance)*
Kirk Johnson *(Pres)*
Bijan Agarwal *(VP)*
David Boyle *(VP-Operations)*
Christopher Malkin *(VP-Commercial)*
Billie Korsunskiy *(VP)*
Kenny Brunette *(VP-Finance)*

ConocoPhillips China Inc   **(1)**
Room 1201 Hyundai Motor Tower No 38
Xiaoyun Road, Chaoyang District, Beijing,
100027, China
Tel.: (86) 1059184600
Web Site: http://www.conocophillips.com.cn
Oil & Gas Exploration Services
N.A.I.C.S.: 211120

ConocoPhillips Co.   **(1)**
925 N Eldridge Pkwy, Houston, TX
77079-2703   **(100%)**
Tel.: (281) 293-1000
Web Site: https://www.conocophillips.com
Rev.: $58,574,000,000
Assets: $95,924,000,000
Liabilities: $46,645,000,000

Net Worth: $49,279,000,000
Earnings: $10,957,000,000
Emp.: 9,900
Fiscal Year-end: 12/31/2023
Filling Stations Operations
N.A.I.C.S.: 457120

ConocoPhillips Norge   **(1)**
Ekofiskvegen 35, 4056, Tananger, Norway
Tel.: (47) 52020000
Web Site: https://www.conocophillips.no
Emp.: 1,800
Holding Company; Oil & Gas Exploration
Services
N.A.I.C.S.: 551112

Subsidiary (Domestic):

ConocoPhillips Skandinavia AS   **(2)**
Ekofiskvegen 35, 4056, Tananger,
Norway   **(100%)**
Tel.: (47) 52020000
Web Site: https://www.conocophillips.no
Emp.: 1,800
Exploration & Production of Petroleum; Development of Mineral Lands
N.A.I.C.S.: 211120

ConocoPhillips Russia Inc.   **(1)**
Lesnaya 5 B, Moscow, 125047, Russia
Tel.: (7) 4957852800
Web Site: http://www.conocophillips.ru
Oil & Gas Exploration Services
N.A.I.C.S.: 424710

ConocoPhillips Russia, Inc.   **(1)**
Gasheka Str 6 1300 Ducat Pl 3 Office 300,
Moscow, 125047, Russia   **(100%)**
Tel.: (7) 4957852800
Web Site: http://www.conocophillips.com
Sales Range: $25-49.9 Million
Emp.: 40
Development of Mineral Lands
N.A.I.C.S.: 211120
Don Wallette *(CFO & Exec VP-Finance-
Commercial)*

Dubai Petroleum Company   **(1)**
Al Safa Street, Dubai, United Arab
Emirates   **(100%)**
Tel.: (971) 43012579
Web Site: http://www.dubhaipetroleum.ae
Sales Range: $900-999.9 Million
Emp.: 600
Exploration & Production of Petroleum
N.A.I.C.S.: 211120

Marathon Oil Corporation   **(1)**
990 Town and Country Blvd, Houston, TX
77024-2217
Tel.: (713) 629-6600
Web Site: https://www.marathonoil.com
Rev.: $6,407,000,000
Assets: $19,575,000,000
Liabilities: $8,370,000,000
Net Worth: $11,205,000,000
Earnings: $1,554,000,000
Emp.: 1,681
Fiscal Year-end: 12/31/2023
Holding Company; Petroleum & Natural
Gas Exploration, Development & Extraction
N.A.I.C.S.: 551112
Ryan M. Lance *(Chm & CEO)*
Bruce A. McCullough *(CIO & Sr VP-Tech &
Innovation)*
Patrick J. Wagner *(Exec VP-Corp Dev &
Strategy)*
Zach Dailey *(Chief Acctg Officer, VP & Controller)*
Reginald D. Hedgebeth *(Chief Admin Officer & Exec VP)*
Mike Henderson *(Exec VP-Ops)*
Martin Stuart *(VP-Ops)*
Rob L. White *(CFO & Exec VP)*
Tom Hellman *(VP)*
Dale Kokoski *(VP)*
Kimberly O. Warnica *(Gen Counsel, Sec &
Exec VP)*

Joint Venture (Domestic):

AMPCO Marketing, L.L.C.   **(2)**
16945 Northchase Dr Ste 1950, Houston,
TX 77060
Tel.: (281) 872-8324
Web Site: http://www.atlanticmethanol.com
Emp.: 13
Methanol Marketing & Sales
N.A.I.C.S.: 424690

AMPCO Services, LLC (2)
16945 Northchase Dr Ste 1950, Houston, TX 77060
Tel.: (281) 872-8324
Povider of Consulting Services for the Methanol Industry
N.A.I.C.S.: 541618

Atlantic Methanol Associates LLC (2)
16945 Northchase Dr Ste 1950, Houston, TX 77060
Tel.: (281) 872-8324
Web Site: http://www.atlanticmethanol.com
Holding Company; Methanol Mfr
N.A.I.C.S.: 551112

Subsidiary (Domestic):

FWA Equipment & Mud Company, Inc. (2)
5555 San Felipe St, Houston, TX 77056
Tel.: (713) 296-2805
Emp.: 4
Holding Company
N.A.I.C.S.: 551112

GRT, Inc. (2)
861 Ward Dr, Santa Barbara, CA 93111
Tel.: (772) 538-3971
Chemical Engineering Services
N.A.I.C.S.: 541330

Glacier Drilling Company (2)
75 Commerce Cir, Durham, CT 06422-1002
Tel.: (860) 349-0397
Web Site: https://www.glacierdrilling.com
Natural Gas Extraction Services
N.A.I.C.S.: 211130

MOC Portfolio Delaware, Inc. (2)
990 Town Country Blvd, Houston, TX 77024-2217
Tel.: (713) 629-6600
Sales Range: $500-549.9 Million
Producer of Crude Oil: Petroleum Production
N.A.I.C.S.: 561499

Subsidiary (Non-US):

Marathon International Oil Company (2)
Tel.: (713) 629-6600
Sales Range: $1-4.9 Billion
Crude Petroleum Production
N.A.I.C.S.: 211120

Marathon International Petroleum Indonesia Limited (2)
Beltway Office Park Building A 4th Floor Jalan T B Simatupang No 41, Jakarta, 12550, Indonesia
Tel.: (62) 217891622
Sales Range: $150-199.9 Million
Emp.: 50
Petroleum Exploration & Production
N.A.I.C.S.: 211120

Marathon Oil Exploration (U.K.) Limited (2)
Capital House 25 Chapel St, London, NW1 5DQ, United Kingdom
Tel.: (44) 2072982500
Web Site: http://www.marathonoil.com
Emp.: 20
Oil & Gas Exploration Services
N.A.I.C.S.: 213112
Carri Lockhart *(Mng Dir)*

Marathon Oil Holdings U.K. Limited (2)
Capital House 25 Chapel Street, London, NW1 5DQ, United Kingdom
Tel.: (44) 2072982500
Holding Company
N.A.I.C.S.: 551112

Marathon Oil Supply Company (U.S.) Limited (2)
Capital House, London, NW1 5DQ, United Kingdom
Tel.: (44) 2072982500
Crude Petroleum Natural Gas Extraction
N.A.I.C.S.: 211120

Subsidiary (Domestic):

Marathon Petroleum Investment, Ltd. (2)

539 S Main St, Findlay, OH 45840-3295
Tel.: (419) 422-2121
Web Site: http://www.marathonoil.com
Producer of Crude Oil: Petroleum Production
N.A.I.C.S.: 211120

Subsidiary (Non-US):

Marathon Service (G.B.) Limited (2)
Capital House 25 Chapel St, London, 5DQNW1, United Kingdom
Tel.: (44) 2072982500
Oil & Gas Extraction Services
N.A.I.C.S.: 211120

Subsidiary (Domestic):

Pennaco Energy, Inc. (2)
1050 17th St Ste 700, Denver, CO 80265
Tel.: (303) 629-6700
Emp.: 30
Fossil Fuel Extraction Services
N.A.I.C.S.: 211120

Polar Tankers, Inc. (2)
925 N Eldridge Pkwy, Houston, TX 77079
Tel.: (281) 293-1000
Web Site: https://polartankers.conocophillips.com
Emp.: 272
Freight Transportation & Logistics Services
N.A.I.C.S.: 483113

SWEPI LP (1)
PO Box 576, Houston, TX 77001-0576
Tel.: (281) 544-2121
Holding Company
N.A.I.C.S.: 551112

Subsidiary (Domestic):

Shell Robert Training & Conference Center (2)
23260 Shell Ln, Robert, LA 70455
Tel.: (985) 543-1200
Web Site: https://www.shell.us
Sales Range: $25-49.9 Million
Emp.: 15
Skills Training, Skills Development & Technical Consulting Services
N.A.I.C.S.: 611430

Shell Technology Ventures, Inc. (2)
PO Box 2463, Houston, TX 77002
Tel.: (713) 241-6161
Web Site: http://www.shelltechnologyventures.com
Sales Range: $200-249.9 Million
Emp.: 150
Environment, Exploration & Production Technology Services
N.A.I.C.S.: 213112

CONRAD INDUSTRIES, INC.
1100 Brashear Ave Ste 200, Morgan City, LA 70380
Tel.: (985) 702-0195   DE
Web Site:
   https://www.conradindustries.com
Year Founded: 1948
CNRD—(OTCIQ)
Rev.: $158,661,000
Assets: $155,864,000
Liabilities: $47,688,000
Net Worth: $108,176,000
Earnings: ($4,036,000)
Emp.: 432
Fiscal Year-end: 12/31/20
Shipbuilding & Repairing
N.A.I.C.S.: 336611
Gary Lipely *(Dir-Sls & Mktg)*
Daniel T. Conrad *(Sr VP)*
Brett Wolbrink *(COO, Exec VP & VP-LNG)*
Carl Hebert *(CFO & VP)*
Eric Bland *(Dir-LNG Ops)*
Lynn Falgout *(Gen Mgr-Deepwater South)*
Pete Orlando *(Gen Mgr-Deepwater Repair)*
Rene Leonard *(VP-Engrg & Product Dev)*
Robert Sampey *(VP-Bus Dev)*
Robert Socha *(VP-Sls & Mktg)*

Robert Scully *(Gen Mgr)*
Cecil A. Hernandez Jr. *(Pres)*
Johnny P. Conrad Jr. *(Chm & CEO)*

Subsidiaries:

Conrad Aluminum, L.L.C. (1)
9752 Hwy 182 E, Morgan City, LA 70380
Tel.: (985) 631-2395
Web Site: http://www.conradindustries.com
Sales Range: $300-349.9 Million
Aluminum Vessel Fabrication & Repair Services
N.A.I.C.S.: 336611

Conrad Shipyard, L.L.C. (1)
1501 Front St, Morgan City, LA 70380
Tel.: (985) 384-3060
Web Site: http://www.conradindustries.com
Sales Range: $25-49.9 Million
Emp.: 100
Ship Repair & Construction Services
N.A.I.C.S.: 336611
Gary Lipely *(Dir-Mktg & Sls)*

Orange Shipbuilding Company, Inc. (1)
710 Market St, Orange, TX 77630
Tel.: (409) 883-6666
Web Site: http://www.conradindustries.com
Sales Range: $50-74.9 Million
Emp.: 150
Shipbuilding & Repair Services
N.A.I.C.S.: 336611
Wolcrink Brett *(Gen Mgr)*

CONSENSUS CLOUD SOLUTIONS, INC.
700 S Flower St Ste 1500, Los Angeles, CA 90017
Tel.: (323) 860-9200   DE
Web Site:
   https://www.consensus.com
Year Founded: 2021
CCSI—(NASDAQ)
Rev.: $362,422,000
Assets: $633,899,000
Liabilities: $889,160,000
Net Worth: ($255,261,000)
Earnings: $72,714,000
Emp.: 581
Fiscal Year-end: 12/31/22
Custom Computer Programming Services
N.A.I.C.S.: 541511
James C. Malone *(CFO)*
Jeffrey Sullivan *(CTO)*
John Nebergall *(COO)*
Johnny Hecker *(Exec VP)*
Scott R. Turicchi *(CEO)*

CONSERVATIVE BROADCAST MEDIA & JOURNALISM INC.NV
Web Site: http://www.cbmjince.com
Year Founded: 2014
CBMJ—(OTCIQ)
Investment Services
N.A.I.C.S.: 523999
Mark Schaftlein *(CEO)*
Tracey Clarksons *(Sec)*

CONSOL ENERGY INC.
275 Technology Dr Ste 101, Canonsburg, PA 15317-9565
Tel.: (724) 416-8300   DE
Web Site:
   https://www.consolenergy.com
Year Founded: 2017
CEIX—(NYSE)
Rev.: $2,101,937,000
Assets: $2,704,377,000
Liabilities: $1,538,551,000
Net Worth: $1,165,826,000
Earnings: $466,979,000
Emp.: 1,860
Fiscal Year-end: 12/31/22
Offices of Other Holding Companies
N.A.I.C.S.: 551112
Kurt R. Salvatori *(Chief Admin Officer)*
James A. Brock *(CEO)*

William P. Powell *(Chm)*
Mitesh B. Thakkar *(Pres & CFO)*
Martha A. Wiegand *(Gen Counsel & Sec)*
James J. McCaffrey *(Sr VP)*
John M. Rothka *(Chief Acctg Officer)*
Eric V. Schubel *(Sr VP-Operations)*
Zach Smith *(Mgr)*
Nathan Tucker *(Dir-Finance-Investor Relations)*
Daniel Connell *(Sr VP-Strategy)*
Mitesh Thakkar *(Pres)*

Subsidiaries:

CONSOL Coal Resources LP (1)
1000 CONSOL Energy Dr Ste 100, Canonsburg, PA 15317-6506   **(100%)**
Tel.: (724) 416-8300
Web Site: http://www.ccrlp.com
Rev.: $332,928,000
Assets: $496,094,000
Liabilities: $284,233,000
Net Worth: $211,861,000
Earnings: $45,551,000
Fiscal Year-end: 12/31/2019
Coal Operations
N.A.I.C.S.: 213113
James A. Brock *(Chm & CEO)*

CONSOL Financial Inc. (1)
2751 Centerville Rd, Wilmington, DE 19808
Tel.: (302) 225-5068
Financial Services
N.A.I.C.S.: 523999

CONSOL Marine Terminals LLC (1)
3800 Newgate Ave, Baltimore, MD 21224
Tel.: (410) 631-6400
Transport Services
N.A.I.C.S.: 336999

Little Eagle Coal Company, LLC (1)
1000 Consol Energy Dr Ste 100, Canonsburg, PA 15317
Tel.: (724) 416-8300
Bituminous Coal Mining Services
N.A.I.C.S.: 212115

CONSOLIDATED COMMUNICATIONS HOLDINGS, INC.
2116 S 17th St, Mattoon, IL 61938-5973
Tel.: (217) 235-3311   DE
Web Site:
   https://www.consolidated.com
Year Founded: 1894
CNSL—(NASDAQ)
Rev.: $1,191,263,000
Assets: $3,887,094,000
Liabilities: $3,170,325,000
Net Worth: $716,769,000
Earnings: $99,981,000
Emp.: 3,200
Fiscal Year-end: 12/31/22
Holding Company; Voice & Data Telecommunications & Directory Services
N.A.I.C.S.: 551112
Fred Albert Graffam III *(CFO & Exec VP)*
C. Robert Udell Jr. *(Pres & CEO)*
Dan Stoll *(Pres & Pres-Commercial & Carrier)*
Garrett Van Osdell *(Chief Legal Officer & Sec)*
Gabe Waggoner *(Chief Network Officer & Exec VP-Ops)*
Jennifer Spaude *(Sr VP-Corp Comm)*

Subsidiaries:

Communication Technologies, Inc. (1)
11710 Plz America Dr Ste 2000, Reston, VA 20190   **(100%)**
Tel.: (207) 797-9123
Web Site: https://www.comtechnologies.com
IT Services & Customer Support
N.A.I.C.S.: 519290
Sandi Pasalic *(Pres)*

Consolidated Communications Holdings, Inc.—(Continued)

Consolidated Communications of Pennsylvania, LLC (1)
4008 Gibsonia Rd, Gibsonia, PA 15044-9311
Tel.: (724) 443-9600
Web Site: http://www.consolidated.com
Sales Range: $25-49.9 Million
Emp.: 140
Telephone Communication, Except Radio
N.A.I.C.S.: 517121

Consolidated Communications of Texas Company (1)
350 S Loop 336 W, Conroe, TX 77304
Tel.: (936) 756-0611
Web Site: http://www.consolidated.com
Sales Range: $200-249.9 Million
Telecommunication Servicesb
N.A.I.C.S.: 517111

Consolidated Communications, Inc. (1)
Tel.: (217) 235-3311
Web Site: http://www.consolidated.com
Voice & Data Telecommunications & Directory Services
N.A.I.C.S.: 517111
C. Robert Udell Jr. (Pres & CEO)

East Texas Fiber Line, Inc. (1)
102 W Frank Ave, Lufkin, TX 75904
Tel.: (936) 634-1011
Emp.: 4
Telecommunication Servicesb
N.A.I.C.S.: 517810

Ellensburg Telephone Company (1)
305 N Ruby St, Ellensburg, WA 98926
Tel.: (509) 925-1425
Web Site: http://www.consolidated.com
Local Telephone Communications
N.A.I.C.S.: 517121

FairPoint Carrier Services, Inc. (1)
521 E Morehead St Ste 250, Charlotte, NC 28202
Tel.: (800) 298-3100
Telecommunication Servicesb
N.A.I.C.S.: 517810

Illinois Consolidated Telephone Company (1)
121 S 17th St, Mattoon, IL 61938-3987
Tel.: (217) 235-3311
Web Site: http://www.consolidated.com
Telecommunication Servicesb
N.A.I.C.S.: 517111

Sunflower Telephone Co. (1)
908 W Frontview St, Dodge City, KS 67801
Tel.: (620) 227-4400
Web Site: http://www.consolidated.com
Telecommunication Servicesb
N.A.I.C.S.: 517111
Patrick L. Morse (Sr VP-Govt Affairs)

SureWest Communications (1)
8150 Industrial Ave Bldg A, Roseville, CA 95678
Tel.: (916) 786-6141
Web Site: http://www.surewest.com
Emp.: 812
Telecommunications, Digital Video, Internet & Other Related Services
N.A.I.C.S.: 551112

Subsidiary (Domestic):

SureWest Kansas, Inc. (2)
14859 W 95th St, Lenexa, KS 66215
Tel.: (913) 825-3000
Cable & Other Subscription Programming Services
N.A.I.C.S.: 516210

SureWest Long Distance Company (2)
8150 Industrial Ave, Roseville, CA 95678-5903
Tel.: (916) 772-7000
Wired Telecommunication Services
N.A.I.C.S.: 517111

SureWest Telephone (2)
211 Lincoln St, Roseville, CA 95678
Tel.: (916) 786-6141
Emp.: 78
Local Exchange Telephone Services

N.A.I.C.S.: 517111

CONSOLIDATED EDISON, INC.
4 Irving Pl Rm 700, New York, NY 10003
Tel.: (212) 460-4600   **NY**
Web Site:
    https://www.conedison.com
Year Founded: 1998
ED—(NYSE)
Rev.: $14,663,000,000
Assets: $66,331,000,000
Liabilities: $45,173,000,000
Net Worth: $21,158,000,000
Earnings: $2,516,000,000
Emp.: 14,592
Fiscal Year-end: 12/31/23
Energy Holding Company
N.A.I.C.S.: 551112
Robert N. Hoglund (CFO & Sr VP)
Timothy P. Cawley (Chm, Pres & CEO)
Yukari Saegusa (Treas & VP)
Joseph Miller (Chief Acctg Officer, VP & Controller)
Jan C. Childress (Dir-IR)
Sylvia V. Dooley (Sec & VP)
Deneen L. Donnley (Gen Counsel & Sr VP)

Subsidiaries:

Consolidated Edison Company of New York, Inc. (1)
4 Irving Pl RM 1875, New York, NY 10003 **(100%)**
Tel.: (212) 460-4600
Web Site: https://www.coned.com
Rev.: $13,268,000,000
Assets: $57,445,000,000
Liabilities: $40,567,000,000
Net Worth: $16,878,000,000
Earnings: $1,390,000,000
Emp.: 14,318
Fiscal Year-end: 12/31/2022
Electric & Gas Utility
N.A.I.C.S.: 221118
Robert N. Hoglund (CFO & Sr VP)
Timothy P. Cawley (Chm & CEO)
Yukari Saegusa (Treas & VP)
Joseph Miller (Principal Acctg Officer, VP & Controller)
Mat Ketschke (Pres)

Orange & Rockland Utilities, Inc. (1)
1 Blue Hill Plz, Pearl River, NY 10965
Tel.: (845) 577-3661
Web Site: http://www.oru.com
Sales Range: $700-749.9 Million
Emp.: 1,200
Electric & Gas Utility Services
N.A.I.C.S.: 221122

Subsidiary (Domestic):

Rockland Electric Company (2)
1 Blue Hill Plz, Pearl River, NY 10965 **(100%)**
Web Site: http://www.oru.com
Sales Range: $350-399.9 Million
Electric Utility
N.A.I.C.S.: 221122

CONSTELLATION BRANDS, INC.
207 High Point Dr Bldg 100, Victor, NY 14564
Tel.: (585) 678-7100   **DE**
Web Site: https://www.cbrands.com
Year Founded: 1945
STZ—(NYSE)
Rev.: $9,961,800,000
Assets: $25,691,700,000
Liabilities: $15,627,100,000
Net Worth: $10,064,600,000
Earnings: $1,727,400,000
Emp.: 10,600
Fiscal Year-end: 02/29/24
Wine, Spirits & Imported Beer Marketer & Distr
N.A.I.C.S.: 312130

Richard Sands (Vice Chm)
F. Paul Hetterich (Chm-Beer Div & Exec VP)
James O. Bourdeau (Chief Legal Officer, Sec & Exec VP)
Bill Renspie (Chief Customer Officer-Beer Div)
Jeff LaBarge (Gen Counsel & Sr VP-Beer Div)
Tiffanie De Liberty (Chief Compliance Officer, Gen Counsel & Sr VP-Wine & Spirits Div)
Ann Legan (VP-Brand Mktg-Beer Div)
Mallika Monteiro (Chief Growth, Strategy & Digital Officer & Exec VP)
Brian Berlin (VP-Data Solutions)
Karena Breslin (Sr VP-Digital & Media)
Matt Stanton (Sr VP-Pub Affairs)
Michael McGrew (Chief Comm, CSR & Diversity Officer & Exec VP)
John Kester (Sr VP-Ops Svcs-Beer Div)
Amy Martin (VP-Corp Reputation & CSR)
Alex Wagner (VP-Comm-Wine & Spirits Div)
Michelle Christensen (VP-Analytics & Comml Insights)
Heide Tierney (Sr VP-Bus Intelligence)
Andrew Zrike (VP-Mktg)
Meghan Erickson (Dir-Mktg Enablement-Wine & Spirits Div)
Greg Gallagher (VP-Brand Mktg-Beer Div)
Kevin Kramnic (VP-Trade Mktg)
Rene Ramos (VP-Events, Sponsorships & Field Mktg)
Julie Rossman (VP-Brand Mktg-Wine & Spirits Div)
Wayne Duan (VP-E-Commerce)
Mark Buri (VP & Deputy Gen Counsel)
Abdon Hernandez (VP & Deputy Gen Counsel)
Tracey Quick Smith (VP & Deputy Gen Counsel)
Dan Towner (Sr VP-HR Ops-Global)
Jeff Viviano (Sr VP-Global Total Rewards)
Sam Glaetzer (Sr VP-Global Ops & Intl Sls-Wine & Spirits Div)
Tom McCorry (Sr VP-Wine & Spirits Div)
Melina Param (Sr VP-HR-Wine & Spirits Div)
Darrell Hearne (VP-Internal Audit & Advisory Svcs)
Steve King (VP-Corp Dev)
Bukky Ekundayo (Dir-Wine & Spirits Innovation)
Jennifer Evans (VP-Ventures)
Paula Fitzgerald (VP-Business Transformation)
John Seethoff (VP-Mktg Innovation-Wine & Spirits Div)
James A. Sabia Jr. (Pres-Beer Div & Exec VP)
Patty Yahn-Urlaub (Sr VP-IR)

Subsidiaries:

24 Ligne LLC (1)
1344 University Ave Ste 7000, Rochester, NY 14607
Tel.: (585) 730-4512
Web Site:
    https://www.blackbuttondistilling.com
Soft Drinks Mfr
N.A.I.C.S.: 312111

CB Spirits Canada, Inc. (1)
Suite 8-C 219 Dufferin Street, Toronto, M6K 1Y9, ON, Canada
Tel.: (416) 626-0100
Web Site: http://www.spiritscanada.ca
Food & Beverage Mfr
N.A.I.C.S.: 312140

Catoctin Creek Distilling Company LLC (1)
120 W Main St, Purcellville, VA 20132
Tel.: (540) 751-8404
Web Site: https://catoctincreekdistilling.com
Alcoholic Beverages Mfr
N.A.I.C.S.: 312130
Scott Harris (Co-Founder & Gen Mgr)
Becky Harris (Co-Founder)

Constellation Beers Ltd. (1)
1 South Dearborn St Ste 1700, Chicago, IL 60603
Tel.: (312) 346-9200
Web Site: http://www.constellation.com
Emp.: 350
Alcoholic Beverages Mfr312130
N.A.I.C.S.: 312130
William A. Newlands (CEO)

Constellation Brands Beach Holdings, Inc. (1)
207 High Point Dr Bldg 100, Victor, NY 14564
Tel.: (585) 678-7100
Holding Company
N.A.I.C.S.: 551112

Constellation Brands Europe Trading S.a r.l. (1)
73-75 Parc d Activites, 8308, Capellen, Luxembourg
Tel.: (352) 26102829
Alcoholic Beverage Distr
N.A.I.C.S.: 424810

Constellation Brands New Zealand Limited (1)
45 Station Road, PO Box 471, Kumeu Huapai, Auckland, 0841, New Zealand
Tel.: (64) 94126666
Web Site: http://www.constellationnz.com
Emp.: 132
Alcoholic Beverage Mfr & Distr
N.A.I.C.S.: 312120
Shane Whiting (VP-Fin)
Simon Towns (Pres & Mng Dir)
Stephen Cheadle (VP-Ops)
Jacqui Cormack (Dir-Legal)

Constellation Brands Schenley, Inc. (1)
One Salaberry Rd, Salaberry-de-Valleyfield, J6T 2G9, QC, Canada **(100%)**
Tel.: (450) 373-3230
Sales Range: $75-99.9 Million
Emp.: 200
Distilled & Blended Liquors
N.A.I.C.S.: 312140
Jenis Labelle (Pres)
Lori Williams-Freeman (Coord-Production)

Constellation Wines U.S. (1)
235 N Bloomfield Rd, Canandaigua, NY 14424-1059
Tel.: (585) 396-7600
Web Site: http://www.franciscan.com
Wine Mfr
N.A.I.C.S.: 312130
Joel Peterson (Sr VP)

Division (Domestic):

Franciscan Estate Winery (2)
1178 Galleron Rd Hwy 29, Saint Helena, CA 94574
Tel.: (707) 967-3830
Web Site: http://www.franciscan.com
Wine Mfr
N.A.I.C.S.: 312130

Ravenswood Winery, Inc. (2)
18701 Gehricke Rd, Sonoma, CA 95476
Tel.: (707) 933-2332
Web Site:
    http://www.ravenswoodwinery.com
Wineries
N.A.I.C.S.: 312130
Joel E. Peterson (Founder)

Robert Mondavi Winery (2)
7801 Saint Helena Hwy, Oakville, CA 94562
Tel.: (707) 226-1395
Web Site:
    http://www.robertmondaviwinery.com
Premium Table Wine Producer
N.A.I.C.S.: 312130

Simi Winery (2)
16275 Healdsburg Ave, Healdsburg, CA
95448-9075
Tel.: (707) 473-3232
Web Site: https://www.simiwinery.com
Sales Range: $50-74.9 Million
Emp.: 75
Producers of Wines
N.A.I.C.S.: 312130

Copper & Kings American Brandy Company (1)
1121 E Washington St, Louisville, KY 40206
Tel.: (502) 561-0267
Web Site: http://www.copperandkings.com
Alcoholic Beverages Mfr
N.A.I.C.S.: 312130

Crew Wine Company LLC (1)
12300 County Rd 92b, Zamora, CA 95698
Tel.: (530) 662-1032
Emp.: 10
Wine & Alcoholic Beverage Mfr
N.A.I.C.S.: 312130
Steve Crosta (Gen Mgr-Sls)

Crown Imports LLC (1)
1 S Dearborn St Ste 1700, Chicago, IL
60603   (100%)
Tel.: (312) 873-9600
Web Site: http://www.cbrands.com
Sales Range: $350-399.9 Million
Emp.: 300
Beer Distr
N.A.I.C.S.: 424810

Declan Distillers, LLC (1)
300 W 6th St Ste 1540, Austin, TX 78701
Tel.: (512) 364-1636
Web Site: http://www.austincocktails.com
Cocktail Distr
N.A.I.C.S.: 424820
Jill Burns (Co-Founder)
Kelly Gasink (Co-Founder)
Amanda Valdez (Sr Mgr-Sls & Mktg)
Kate Canty (Mgr-Mktg)
John Callihan (VP-Sls)

Durham Distillery LLC (1)
711 Washington St, Durham, NC 27701
Tel.: (919) 937-2121
Web Site: https://www.durhamdistillery.com
Food & Beverage Mfr
N.A.I.C.S.: 312140

El Silencio Holdings, Inc. (1)
1625 17th St Ste 5, Santa Monica, CA
90404
Tel.: (310) 396-9004
Web Site: https://www.silencio.com
Food & Beverage Mfr
N.A.I.C.S.: 312140

Four Corners Brewing Co. (1)
1311 S St, Dallas, TX 75215
Tel.: (214) 748-2739
Web Site: https://www.fcbrewing.com
Craft Brewery
N.A.I.C.S.: 722410

Franciscan Vineyards, Inc. (1)
18701 Gehricke Rd, Sonoma, CA 95476-4710
Tel.: (707) 938-1960
Alcoholic Beverages Mfr
N.A.I.C.S.: 312130

Funky Buddha Brewery LLC (1)
1201 NE 38th St, Oakland Park, FL 33334-4504
Tel.: (954) 440-0046
Web Site: https://funkybuddha.com
Wine & Distilled Spirit Distr
N.A.I.C.S.: 424820
Kristopher C. Sentz (Co-Owner)
Ryan Sentz (Co-Owner)

High West Distillery, LLC (1)
27649 Old Lincoln Hwy Wanship, Park City,
UT 84017
Tel.: (435) 649-8300
Web Site: https://www.highwest.com
Alcoholic Beverages Mfr
N.A.I.C.S.: 312130

Industria Vidriera de Coahuila, S. de R.L. de C.V. (1)
Via Jose Lopez Portillo No 7, Tultitlan,
54940, Hidalgo, Mexico
Tel.: (52) 5553715700

Glass Container Mfr
N.A.I.C.S.: 327213

L.O. Smith AB (1)
Fabriksgatan 5, Gotene, 533 33, Sweden
Tel.: (46) 511773200
Web Site: http://www.losmith.se
Wine & Alcoholic Beverage Mfr & Whslr
N.A.I.C.S.: 312130
Henrik Sundewall (CEO)

Montanya Distillers, LLC (1)
204 Elk Ave, Crested Butte, CO 81224
Tel.: (970) 799-3206
Web Site: https://www.montanyarum.com
Food & Beverage Mfr
N.A.I.C.S.: 312140
Karen Hoskin (Founder & Owner)
Jenny Foust (Mgr-PR)
Alissa Jhonson (VP-Corp Comm)
Rob Richardson (Sls Dir)

My Favorite Neighbor, LLC (1)
2644 Anderson Rd, Paso Robles, CA 93446
Tel.: (805) 237-7367
Web Site:
https://www.myfavoriteneighbor.com
Wine Distr
N.A.I.C.S.: 445320

Nelson's Green Brier Distillery, LLC (1)
1414 Clinton St, Nashville, TN 37203
Tel.: (615) 913-8800
Web Site:
https://www.greenbrierdistillery.com
Alcoholic Beverage Merchant Whslr
N.A.I.C.S.: 424820

Old Line Spirits, LLC (1)
200 S Janney St, Baltimore, MD 21224
Tel.: (443) 218-9984
Web Site: https://www.oldlinespirits.com
Soft Drinks Mfr
N.A.I.C.S.: 312111

Polyphenolics LLC (1)
5631 E Olive Ave, Fresno, CA 93727
Tel.: (559) 243-6078
Web Site: https://www.polyphenolics.com
Sales Range: $10-24.9 Million
Emp.: 50
Grape & Grape Products Mfr & Distr
N.A.I.C.S.: 541910
Steve Kupina (Dir-Quality & Tech)

Ruffino S.r.l. (1)
Ple Ruffino I, 50065, Pontassieve, FI, Italy
Tel.: (39) 05583605
Web Site: https://www.ruffino.it
Sales Range: $25-49.9 Million
Emp.: 300
Alcoholic Beverages Mfr
N.A.I.C.S.: 312130

Schrader Cellars, LLC (1)
PO Box 1004, Calistoga, CA 94515
Tel.: (707) 942-1540
Web Site: https://www.schradercellars.com
Alcoholic Beverages Mfr
N.A.I.C.S.: 312130
Fred Schrader (Founder)

Stanton South LLC (1)
140 S Dearborn St, Chicago, IL 60603-5225
Tel.: (847) 491-9800
Web Site:
http://www.crafthousecocktails.com
Alcoholic Beverage Merchant Whslr
N.A.I.C.S.: 424820
William Skelly (Sr Mng Dir)

Tenute Ruffino S.r.l. (1)
Via Poggio Al Mandorlo 1, Bagno a Ripoli,
50012, Firenze, Italy
Tel.: (39) 03029721
Web Site: http://www.rufino.it
Alcoholic Beverage Distr
N.A.I.C.S.: 424810

CONSTELLATION ENERGY CORPORATION
1310 Point St, Baltimore, MD 21231-3380
Tel.: (610) 765-5959   **PA**
Web Site:
https://www.constellationenergy.com
Year Founded: 2021

CEG—(NASDAQ)
Rev.: $24,918,000,000
Assets: $50,758,000,000
Liabilities: $39,472,000,000
Net Worth: $11,286,000,000
Earnings: $1,623,000,000
Emp.: 13,813
Fiscal Year-end: 12/31/23
Clean Energy & Carbon-Free Electricity, Generation & Distribution Services
N.A.I.C.S.: 221122
Joseph Dominguez (Pres & CEO)
Bryan C. Hanson (Chief Generation
Officer & Exec VP)
Daniel L. Eggers (CFO & Exec VP)
James McHugh (Chief Comml Officer
& Sr VP)
Matthew N. Bauer (Sr VP & Controller)
Robert J. Lawless (Chm)

Subsidiaries:

Constellation Energy Generation, LLC (1)
200 Exelon Way, Kennett Square, PA
19348-2473
Tel.: (610) 765-5959
Web Site: http://www.exeloncorp.com
Rev.: $24,439,999,999
Assets: $46,908,999,999
Liabilities: $35,536,999,999
Net Worth: $11,371,999,999
Earnings: ($167,000,000)
Emp.: 13,369
Fiscal Year-end: 12/31/2022
Electricity & Natural Gas Services
N.A.I.C.S.: 221122
Joseph Dominguez (CEO)
Bryan C. Hanson (Chief Generation Officer
& Exec VP)
Daniel L. Eggers (CFO & Exec VP)
Christopher M. Crane (Principal Executive
Officer)
Kathleen L. Barron (Chief Strategy Officer)
David O. Dardis (Gen Counsel)
Mike Koehler (Chief Admin Officer)
James McHugh (Chief Comml Officer)
Susie Kutansky (Chief HR Officer)

Subsidiary (Domestic):

AV Solar Ranch 1, LLC (2)
10 S Dearborn St Ste 49, Chicago, IL
60603
Tel.: (610) 765-5619
Air Conditioning Equipment Installation Services
N.A.I.C.S.: 238220

Annova LNG, LLC (2)
1221 Lamar St Ste 750, Houston, TX 77010
Tel.: (713) 201-1700
Natural Gas Exploration Service
N.A.I.C.S.: 211130

Big Top, LLC (2)
77226 Mader Rust Ln, Hermiston, OR
97826
Tel.: (541) 376-8246
Eletric Power Generation Services
N.A.I.C.S.: 221118

C3, LLC (2)
1400 Seaport Blvd, Redwood City, CA
94063
Tel.: (650) 503-2200
Web Site: https://www.c3.ai
Emp.: 125
Software Development Services
N.A.I.C.S.: 541511
Stephen Maurice Ward Jr. (Founder)
Thomas M. Siebel (Chm & CEO)
Tod Weber (Sr VP/Gen Mgr-Federal Sys
Grp)

CECG International Holdings, Inc. (2)
100 Constellation Way 700 C, Baltimore,
MD 21202
Tel.: (410) 470-2800
Holding Company
N.A.I.C.S.: 551112

CER-Colorado Bend Energy Partners LP (2)

3863 S State Hwy 60, Wharton, TX 77488
Tel.: (979) 531-8017
Electric Power Generation ServicesElectric
Power Generation Services
N.A.I.C.S.: 221118

CER-Quail Run Energy Partners LP (2)
2950 E Interstate 20, Odessa, TX 79766
Tel.: (432) 332-3197
Eletric Power Generation Services
N.A.I.C.S.: 221118

CEU Paradigm, LLC (2)
100 Constellation Way Ste 500C, Baltimore,
MD 21202
Tel.: (410) 470-2555
Eletric Power Generation Services
N.A.I.C.S.: 221118

CLT Energy Services Group, L.L.C. (2)
2090 Greentree Rd, Pittsburgh, PA 15220
Tel.: (412) 489-9447
Electric Power Distribution Services
N.A.I.C.S.: 221122

CNE Gas Holdings, LLC (2)
9960 Corporate Campus Dr Ste 2000, Louisville, KY 40223
Tel.: (502) 426-4500
Emp.: 100
Holding Company
N.A.I.C.S.: 551112
Tim Lynch (Gen Mgr)

California PV Energy, LLC (2)
100 Constellation Way, Baltimore, MD
21202
Tel.: (410) 783-2800
Emp.: 2,012
Eletric Power Generation Services
N.A.I.C.S.: 221118

Canton Crossing District Energy LLC (2)
1520 S Clinton St, Baltimore, MD 21224
Tel.: (410) 563-0690
Eletric Power Generation Services
N.A.I.C.S.: 221118

CoLa Resources LLC (2)
416 Travis St 700, Shreveport, LA 71101
Tel.: (318) 227-9299
Emp.: 4
Electric Power Distribution Services
N.A.I.C.S.: 221122

Cogenex Corporation (2)
1 Vision Dr, Natick, MA 01760-2059
Tel.: (508) 650-4100
Web Site: https://www.cognex.com
Eletric Power Generation Services
N.A.I.C.S.: 221118

Affiliate (Domestic):

Constellation Energy Nuclear Group, LLC (2)
100 Constellation Way, Baltimore, MD
21202   (100%)
Tel.: (410) 470-2800
Web Site: http://www.cengllc.com
Holding Company; Nuclear Power Plants
Operator
N.A.I.C.S.: 551112

Subsidiary (Domestic):

R.E. Ginna Nuclear Power Plant, LLC (3)
1503 Lake Rd, Ontario, NY 14519
Tel.: (585) 771-5402
Web Site: http://www.cengllc.com
Nuclear Power Plant Operator
N.A.I.C.S.: 221113

Subsidiary (Domestic):

Constellation Energy Resources, LLC (2)
111 Market Pl Ste 500, Baltimore, MD
21202-3142
Tel.: (866) 237-7693
Web Site: http://www.constellation.com
Electricity & Natural Gas Services
N.A.I.C.S.: 221122
Joseph Nigro (CEO)

Subsidiary (Domestic):

BGE Home Products & Services, LLC (3)

Constellation Energy Corporation—(Continued)

1409 A Tangier Dr, Baltimore, MD 21220
Tel.: (410) 918-5600
Web Site:
　https://www.constellationhome.com
Electric & Natural Gas Distr
N.A.I.C.S.: 221122

Constellation Energy Control and Dis-
patch, LLC　　　　　　　　　(3)
1331 Lamar St 4 Houston Ctr Ste 560,
Houston, TX 77010
Tel.: (713) 332-2901
Eletric Power Generation Services
N.A.I.C.S.: 221118

Constellation Energy Partners Hold-
ings, LLC　　　　　　　　　(3)
111 Market Pl, Baltimore, MD 21202
Tel.: (410) 470-3500
Holding Company
N.A.I.C.S.: 551112

Constellation Energy Projects & Services Group Advisors, LLC　　(3)
100 Constellation Way Ste 1200C, Baltimore, MD 21202
Tel.: (410) 470-2504
Eletric Power Generation Services
N.A.I.C.S.: 221118

Constellation Mystic Power, LLC　(3)
100 Constellation Way, Baltimore, MD
21202
Tel.: (410) 783-2800
Eletric Power Generation Services
N.A.I.C.S.: 221118

Constellation NewEnergy-Gas Divi-
sion, LLC　　　　　　　　　(3)
9960 Corporate Campus Dr Ste 2000, Lou-
isville, KY 40223　　　　　(100%)
Tel.: (502) 426-4500
Natural Gas Distr
N.A.I.C.S.: 221210
J. Kevin Watson (VP & Gen Mgr)
Mark P. Huston (Pres)
David Ellsworth (COO)

Constellation Operating Services　(3)
11258 California 65, McFarland, CA 93250
Tel.: (661) 792-3048
Eletric Power Generation Services
N.A.I.C.S.: 221118

Joint Venture (Domestic):

Safe Harbor Water Power
Corporation　　　　　　　　(3)
1 Powerhouse Rd, Conestoga, PA 17516
Tel.: (717) 872-5441
Web Site: http://www.shwpc.com
Hydroelectric Power Plant
N.A.I.C.S.: 221111
Wyatt F. Morrison (Treas & Sec)

Subsidiary (Domestic):

Star Electricity, Inc.　　　　　(3)
3200 SW Frwy, Houston, TX 77027
Tel.: (713) 357-2800
Web Site: http://www.startexpower.com
Energy Supplier
N.A.I.C.S.: 221122

Subsidiary (Domestic):

Constellation Energy Services,
Inc.　　　　　　　　　　　(2)
1716 Lawrence Dr, De Pere, WI 54115
Tel.: (920) 617-6100
Web Site: http://www.constellation.com
Energy Management & Related Products
Services
N.A.I.C.S.: 221122

DL Windy Acres, LLC　　　　(2)
78597 370th Ave, Okabena, MN 56161
Tel.: (507) 853-4496
Motor & Generator Mfr
N.A.I.C.S.: 335312

Exelon Nuclear Partners, LLC　(2)
200 Exelon Way, Kennett Square, PA
19348
Tel.: (610) 765-5100
Web Site:
　http://www.exelonnuclearpartners.com
Electric Power Distribution Services
N.A.I.C.S.: 221122

Bryan Hanson (Pres & Chief Nuclear Officer)

Exelon PowerLabs, LLC　　　(2)
175 N Caln Rd, Coatesville, PA 19320
Tel.: (610) 380-2478
Web Site: http://www.exelonpowerlabs.com
Emp.: 54
Electric Power Distribution Services
N.A.I.C.S.: 221122
Janice Yakonick (Supvr-Customer Care)
Jeff Hilker (Mgr-Mid-Atlantic)
Jessica Harper (Sr Mgr-Sls)
Cory Peters (Project Mgr-Strategic)

Fourmile Wind Energy, LLC　　(2)
191 Main St, Annapolis, MD 21401
Tel.: (410) 267-9200
Electric Power Distribution Services
N.A.I.C.S.: 221122

Greensburg Wind Farm, LLC　　(2)
6400 NW 86th St, Johnston, IA 50131
Tel.: (515) 267-3871
Electric Power Distribution Services
N.A.I.C.S.: 221122

Outback Solar, LLC　　　　　(2)
TI 2000 Christmas Vly H, Silver Lake, OR
97638
Tel.: (503) 245-8800
Emp.: 5
Electric Power Distribution Services
N.A.I.C.S.: 221122

Shooting Star Wind Project, LLC　(2)
10 S Dearborn St, Chicago, IL 60603
Tel.: (312) 394-3625
Eletric Power Generation Services
N.A.I.C.S.: 221118

Wolf Hollow I, LP　　　　　　(2)
9201 Wolf Hollow Ct, Granbury, TX 76048
Tel.: (817) 579-8201
Sales Range: $1-9.9 Million
Emp.: 30
Eletric Power Generation Services
N.A.I.C.S.: 221118

Constellation PowerLabs, LLC　(1)
175 N Caln Rd, Coatesville, PA 19320
Web Site:
　https://constellationpowerlabs.com
Calibration & Testing Services
N.A.I.C.S.: 541380

Constellation Solar Maryland MC,
LLC　　　　　　　　　　　(1)
10 S Dearborn St Fl 49, Chicago, IL 60603
Tel.: (630) 821-5335
Eletric Power Generation Services
N.A.I.C.S.: 221114
Andrew Berdy (VP-Comml Ops)
Rodger Krakau (VP-Customer Care Ops)
David Leone (VP)

CONSTRUCTION PARTNERS, INC.
290 HealthW Dr Ste 2, Dothan, AL
36303
Tel.: (334) 673-9763　　　　DE
Web Site:
　https://www.constructionpartners.net
Year Founded: 2007
ROAD—(NASDAQ)
Rev.: $1,823,889,000
Assets: $1,542,135,000
Liabilities: $968,395,000
Net Worth: $573,740,000
Earnings: $68,935,000
Emp.: 1,484
Fiscal Year-end: 09/30/24
Civil Engineering Services
N.A.I.C.S.: 541330
Fred Julius Smith III (Pres & CEO)
Charles E. Owens (Co-Founder &
Vice-Chm)
R. Alan Palmer (Co-Founder)
Brett Armstrong (Sr VP)
Bob Flowers (Sr VP)
John Harper (Sr VP)
John Walker (Sr VP)
Todd K. Andrews (Chief Acctg Officer)

Ryan Brooks (Sr VP-Legal)
Gregory A. Hoffman (CFO)
Ned N. Fleming III (Founder & Exec
Chm)

Subsidiaries:

C.W. Roberts Contracting, Inc.　(1)
3660 Hartsfield Rd, Tallahassee, FL 32303
Tel.: (850) 385-5060
Web Site: http://www.cwrcontracting.com
Highway & Road Construction Services
N.A.I.C.S.: 237310
Robert Flowers (Pres)
Robert Delisle (CFO & Sec)
Jimmy Strain (Area Mgr-Tallahassee & Hos-
ford Div)
Chris Riley (VP)

Subsidiary (Domestic):

Mancil's Tractor Service, Inc.　(2)
8530 SW Jayme Way, Palm City, FL 34990
Tel.: (772) 288-0951
Asphalt Paving & Maintenance Services
N.A.I.C.S.: 324121

Ferebee Asphalt Corporation　　(1)
10045 Metromont Industrial Blvd, Charlotte,
NC 28269
Tel.: (704) 509-2586
Web Site: https://www.ferebee.com
Asphalt Mfr & Distr
N.A.I.C.S.: 327999

Ferebee Corporation　　　　　(1)
10045 Metromont Industrial Blvd, Charlotte,
NC 28269
Tel.: (704) 509-2586
Sales Range: $10-24.9 Million
Emp.: 100
Contractor of Highway & Street Construc-
tion
N.A.I.C.S.: 237310
Joseph B. Ferebee (Chm)
Chris Ferebee (Pres)
Erin Puls (Asst Controller)

Fred Smith Construction, Inc.　(1)
6105 Chapel Hill Rd, Raleigh, NC 27607
Tel.: (919) 783-5700
Web Site: http://www.fredsmithcompany.net
Commercial Construction Services
N.A.I.C.S.: 237310

Gelder & Associates, Inc.　　　(1)
3901 Gelder Dr, Raleigh, NC 27603
Tel.: (919) 772-6895
Web Site:
　http://www.gelderandassociates.com
Highway, Street & Bridge Construction
N.A.I.C.S.: 237310

Hubbard Paving & Grading, Inc.　(1)
698 Rock Crusher Rd, Walhalla, SC 29691
Tel.: (864) 647-6410
Sales Range: $1-9.9 Million
Emp.: 13
Highway, Street & Bridge Construction
N.A.I.C.S.: 237310
David Hubbard (Pres)

King Asphalt, Inc.　　　　　　(1)
2127 Greenville Hwy, Liberty, SC 29657
Tel.: (864) 855-0338
Web Site: http://www.kingasphaltinc.com
Sales Range: $1-9.9 Million
Emp.: 80
Asphalt Mfr & Paving Maintenance Services
N.A.I.C.S.: 324121
Douglas Limbaugh (Mgr-Milling Ops Proj-
ect)
Michael Crenshaw (Pres)

PLT Construction Co., Inc.　　(1)
1282 New Bethel Rd, Garner, NC 27529
Tel.: (919) 359-9971
Rev.: $1,100,000
Emp.: 20
Engineering Services
N.A.I.C.S.: 541330
Mark Proctor (Pres)

Riley Paving, Inc.　　　　　　(1)
6644 Glendon Carthage Rd, Carthage, NC
28327
Tel.: (910) 947-5376
Rev.: $6,700,000
Emp.: 60
Highway, Street & Bridge Construction
N.A.I.C.S.: 237310

James Riley (VP)
Rhonda Good (Controller)

Robinson Paving Company　　　(1)
5425 Schatulga Rd, Columbus, GA 31917
Tel.: (706) 563-7959
Web Site: http://www.robinsonpavingco.com
Sales Range: $25-49.9 Million
Emp.: 200
Highway & Street Paving Contractor
N.A.I.C.S.: 237310
Darrell Robinson (VP)
Jeff D. Robinson (VP)
Patrick L. Pugh (VP)

Sunbelt Asphalt Surfaces, Inc　(1)
1383 Duncan Ln, Auburn, GA 30011
Tel.: (770) 867-5312
Web Site: http://www.sunbeltasphalt.com
Rev.: $3,800,000
Emp.: 31
Gasket, Packing & Sealing Device Mfr
N.A.I.C.S.: 339991

CONSUMER AUTOMOTIVE FI-
NANCE, INC.
751NDrSte11, Melbourne, FL 32934
Tel.: (702) 576-9864　　　　NV
Web Site: http://www.cafius.com
CAFI—(OTCIQ)
Rev.: $33,817
Assets: $110,056
Liabilities: $109,909
Net Worth: $147
Earnings: ($34,840)
Fiscal Year-end: 06/30/20
Automobile Financing Services
N.A.I.C.S.: 522220
Nicholas Konopka (Pres & CEO)
Robert Clark (CEO)
Brandon Spikes (Pres & Sec)

CONSUMER PORTFOLIO SER-
VICES, INC.
3800 Howard Hughes Pkwy, Las Ve-
gas, NV 89169
Tel.: (949) 753-6800　　　　CA
Web Site:
　https://www.consumerportfolio.com
Year Founded: 1991
CPSS—(NASDAQ)
Rev.: $329,709,000
Assets: $2,752,768,000
Liabilities: $2,524,379,000
Net Worth: $228,389,000
Earnings: $85,983,000
Emp.: 792
Fiscal Year-end: 12/31/22
Automotive Financial Services Com-
pany
N.A.I.C.S.: 522291
John P. Harton (Sr VP-Program Dev)
Steve Schween (Sr VP-Sys)
Catrina Ralston (Sr VP-Human Re-
sources)
Michael T. Lavin (Pres, COO & Chief
Legal Officer)
Denesh Bharwani (CFO, Exec VP-
Finance & Sr VP-Fin)
Lisette Reynoso (Gen Counsel & Sr
VP)
Susan Ryan (Sr VP-Servicing)
Charles E. Bradley Jr. (Chm & CEO)

Subsidiaries:

Consumer Portfolio Services　　(1)
700 Independence Pky Ste 400, Chesa-
peake, VA 23320
Tel.: (757) 962-1426
Web Site:
　http://www.consumerportfolioservices.com
Sales Range: $75-99.9 Million
Emp.: 150
Purchaser & Servicer of Installment Loans
for Automobiles & Motorcycles
N.A.I.C.S.: 562111

Consumer Portfolio Services,
Inc.　　　　　　　　　　　(1)
860 Greenbriar Cir Tower One Ste 600,
Norfolk, VA 23320-2640

Tel.: (757) 523-3909
Web Site:
   https://www.consumerportfolio.com
Sales Range: $75-99.9 Million
Emp.: 276
Automotive Financial Services Company
N.A.I.C.S.: 522291

CONSUMERS BANCORP, INC.
614 E Lincoln Way, Minerva, OH 44657
Tel.: (330) 868-7701   OH
Web Site:
   https://www.consumers.bank
Year Founded: 1994
CBKM—(OTCQX)
Rev.: $49,218,000
Assets: $1,097,089,000
Liabilities: $1,033,404,000
Net Worth: $63,685,000
Earnings: $8,580,000
Emp.: 169
Fiscal Year-end: 06/30/24
Offices of Bank Holding Companies
N.A.I.C.S.: 551111
Frank L. Paden *(Chm)*
Richard T. Kiko Jr. *(Vice Chm)*
Ralph J. Lober II *(Pres & CEO)*

Subsidiaries:

Consumers National Bank   (1)
614 E Lincoln Way, Minerva, OH 44657   (100%)
Tel.: (330) 868-7701
Web Site: https://www.consumersbank.com
Sales Range: $75-99.9 Million
Emp.: 52
Savings, Loans, Investment & Commercial Banking Services
N.A.I.C.S.: 522180
Frank L. Paden *(Chm)*
Richard T. Kiko Jr. *(Vice Chm)*
Ralph J. Lober II *(Pres & CEO)*
Vicki Hall *(Officer-Bus Banking-Columbiana County & VP)*
Suzanne Mikes *(Chief Credit Officer & Sr VP)*
Derek Williams *(Sr VP-Retail Banking & Ops)*
Anthony Mattioli *(Officer-Bus Banking-Fairlawn Office)*
Debbie Miller *(Specialist-Comml Deposit)*
Joe Shemasek *(VP-Bus Banking-Lisbon Office-Columbiana)*
Kim Chuckalovchak *(CIO & Sr VP)*
Mike Benson *(Officer-Bus Banking, VP & Mgr-Akron Metro)*
Sarah Grubbs *(Officer-Agricultural Lending & VP)*
Scott E. Dodds *(Officer-Loan & Exec VP)*
Beth McBride *(Asst VP)*
Joshua Ondo *(Asst VP & Mgr-Electronic Mktg)*
Matt Hogue *(Asst VP & Mgr-Network)*
Christina Kugler *(Asst VP & Asst Controller)*
Denise Molinari *(Asst VP & Mgr-Credit Dept)*
Scott Lawrence *(Officer-Bus Dev & Asst VP)*
James Wigington *(Asst VP)*
John Holland III *(Officer-Bus Banking & VP-Wooster Office-Wayne County)*

Subsidiary (Domestic):

Community Title Agency, Inc.   (2)
1115 Canton Rd NW Ste A1, Carrollton, OH 44615-9498
Tel.: (330) 627-2293
Web Site: http://www.community-title.net
Sales Range: $1-9.9 Million
Emp.: 2
Provides Title Insurance for Mortgage Loan & Real Estate Purchase Customers
N.A.I.C.S.: 522110

Peoples Bancorp of Mt. Pleasant, Inc.   (1)
298 Union St, Columbus, OH 43939
Tel.: (740) 769-2377
Web Site: http://www.peoplesnbmp.com
Bank Holding Company
N.A.I.C.S.: 551111
Robert C. Hargrave *(Chm & CEO)*
Gail E. Fisher *(Pres)*

Subsidiary (Domestic):

The Peoples National Bank of Mount Pleasant   (2)
298 Union St, Mount Pleasant, OH 43939
Tel.: (740) 769-2377
Web Site:
   http://www.peoplesnationalbankon line.com
Sales Range: $1-9.9 Million
Emp.: 21
Commericial Banking
N.A.I.C.S.: 522110
Robert C. Hargrave *(Chm & CEO)*

CONTANGO ORE, INC.
3700 Buffalo Speedway Ste 925, Houston, TX 77098
Tel.: (713) 877-1311   DE
Web Site:
   https://www.contangoore.com
CTGO—(NYSEAMEX)
Rev.: $29,651
Assets: $25,662,739
Liabilities: $30,436,177
Net Worth: ($4,773,438)
Earnings: ($39,741,300)
Emp.: 11
Fiscal Year-end: 06/30/23
Gold, Associated Mineral & Rare Earth Element Exploration & Mining Services
N.A.I.C.S.: 212220
Michael Clark *(CFO & Sec)*
John Juneau *(Chm)*
Rick Van Nieuwenhuyse *(Pres & CEO)*
Chris Kennedy *(Gen Mgr-Lucky Shot Mine)*

CONTEXT THERAPEUTICS INC.
2001 Market St Ste 3915 Unit 15, Philadelphia, PA 19103
Tel.: (267) 225-7416   DE
Web Site:
   https://www.contexttherapeutics.com
Year Founded: 2015
CNTX—(NASDAQ)
Rev.: $547,268
Assets: $37,965,943
Liabilities: $3,207,577
Net Worth: $34,758,366
Earnings: ($14,835,939)
Emp.: 9
Fiscal Year-end: 12/31/22
Research & Development in Biotechnology (except Nanobiotechnology)
N.A.I.C.S.: 541714
Richard Berman *(Chm)*
Jennifer Minai-Azary *(CFO)*
Martin Lehr *(Pres & CEO)*
Tarek Sahmoud *(Chief Medical Officer)*
Evan G. Dick *(Sr VP-R&D)*
Eileen Kittrick *(Controller)*
Alex Levit *(Chief Legal Officer)*
Jennifer Minai-Azary *(CFO)*
Christopher Beck *(Sr VP-Ops)*
Mark Fletcher *(VP-R&D)*

CONTINENTAL RESOURCES, INC.
175 Middlesex Tpke Ste 1, Bedford, MA 01730-9137
Tel.: (781) 275-0850   MA
Web Site: http://www.conres.com
Year Founded: 1962
CLR—(NYSE)
Rev.: $5,719,318,000
Assets: $18,591,111,000
Liabilities: $10,734,786,000
Net Worth: $7,856,325,000
Earnings: $1,660,968,000
Emp.: 1,254
Fiscal Year-end: 12/31/21
Computer Related Services

N.A.I.C.S.: 541519
James M. Bunt *(CFO)*
Mary Nardella *(CEO)*
Kevin E. McCann *(COO)*
Richard Wright *(Controller)*
James D. Keady *(VP-Test Equipment Div)*
James F. McCann Jr. *(Pres)*

Subsidiaries:

Continental Leasing Company, Inc.   (1)
175 Middlesex Tpke Ste 1, Bedford, MA 01730-9137
Tel.: (781) 275-0850
Computer Rental & Leasing Services
N.A.I.C.S.: 532420
James M. Bunt *(CFO)*

CONTRAFECT CORPORATION
28 Wells Ave 3rd Fl, Yonkers, NY 10701
(914) 207-2300   DE
Web Site: http://www.contrafect.com
Year Founded: 2008
CFRX—(NASDAQ)
Rev.: $81,000
Assets: $20,679,000
Liabilities: $32,531,000
Net Worth: ($11,852,000)
Earnings: ($65,153,000)
Emp.: 23
Fiscal Year-end: 12/31/22
Pharmaceuticals Mfr
N.A.I.C.S.: 325412
Roger J. Pomerantz *(Chm, Pres & CEO)*

CONVERSIONPOINT HOLDINGS, INC.
840 Newport Center Dr Ste 450, Newport Beach, CA 92660   DE
Year Founded: 2018
CPTI—(NASDAQ)
Emp.: 85
Holding Company
N.A.I.C.S.: 551112
Robert Tallack *(Pres & CEO)*

CONX CORP.
5701 S Santa Fe Dr, Littleton, CO 80120
Tel.: (303) 472-1542   NV
Year Founded: 2020
CONX—(NASDAQ)
Rev.: $26,296,717
Assets: $85,663,787
Liabilities: $117,417,750
Net Worth: ($31,753,963)
Earnings: $24,194,750
Emp.: 1
Fiscal Year-end: 12/31/22
Investment Services
N.A.I.C.S.: 523999
Charles W. Ergen *(Founder & Chm)*
Jason Kiser *(CEO)*

COOL TECHNOLOGIES, INC.
8875 Hidden River Pkwy Ste 300, Tampa, FL 33637
Tel.: (813) 975-7467   NV
Web Site:
   https://www.cooltechnologiesinc.com
Year Founded: 2002
WARM—(OTCQB)
Assets: $1,043,122
Liabilities: $8,531,451
Net Worth: ($7,488,329)
Earnings: ($1,843,623)
Emp.: 2
Fiscal Year-end: 12/31/22
Automobile Parts Mfr
N.A.I.C.S.: 336390
Judson William Bibb *(Interim CFO, Treas, Sec & VP)*

Timothy Hassett *(Co-Founder, Chm & CEO)*
Mark Michael Hodowanec *(Co-Founder)*
Judson Bibb *(Interim CFO, Treas, Sec & VP)*

Subsidiaries:

Ultimate Power Truck, LLC   (1)
13800 US Hwy 19 N, Clearwater, FL 33764
Tel.: (727) 303-3884
Web Site: https://a34568.cmorecars.com
Truck Rental Services
N.A.I.C.S.: 532120

COOPER-STANDARD HOLDINGS INC.
40300 Traditions Dr, Northville, MI 48168
Tel.: (248) 596-5900   DE
Web Site:
   https://www.cooperstandard.com
Year Founded: 2004
CPS—(NYSE)
Rev.: $2,525,391,000
Assets: $1,963,529,000
Liabilities: $1,862,337,000
Net Worth: $101,192,000
Earnings: ($215,384,000)
Emp.: 23,000
Fiscal Year-end: 12/31/22
Holding Company; Automotive Fluid Handling, Body Sealing & Anti-Vibration Systems & Components Mfr & Distr
N.A.I.C.S.: 551112
Jeffrey S. Edwards *(Chm & CEO)*
Larry E. Ott *(Chief HR Officer & Sr VP)*
Jonathan P. Banas *(CFO & Exec VP)*
Christopher E. Couch *(CTO & Sr VP)*
Alison Nudd *(Chief Acctg Officer & VP)*
Ramsey Changoo *(Mng Dir)*
Shannon B. Quinn *(Chief Comml Officer)*
Soma Venkat *(Chief IT Officer)*

Subsidiaries:

CSF Poland Sp. z o.o.   (1)
Ul Legionow 244, Czestochowa, 42-202, Silesia, Poland
Tel.: (48) 343907700
Motor Vehicle Parts Distr
N.A.I.C.S.: 423120

Cooper Standard Europe GmbH   (1)
Fred-Joachim-Schoeps-Str 55, Baden-Wurttemberg, 68535, Edingen-Neckarhausen, 68535, Germany
Tel.: (49) 6214702514
Automobile Parts Distr
N.A.I.C.S.: 423140
Gerd Fleissig *(Sr Mgr-Energy & Facility Mgmt)*

Cooper Standard France SAS
194 Route de Lorient, PO Box 74321, Brittany, Rennes, 35043, France   (51%)
Tel.: (33) 223465656
Automobile Parts Mfr
N.A.I.C.S.: 336390

Subsidiary (Non-US):

CSF Poland z o.o.   (2)
Legion 244, Czestochowa, Poland (100%)
Tel.: (48) 343604700
Automobile Parts Mfr
N.A.I.C.S.: 336390

Cooper Standard Sealing (Guangzou) Co. Ltd.   (1)
Room 1 Longxiu Road Hualong Town Panyu, Guangzhou, Guangdong, China
Tel.: (86) 2039118080
Motor Vehicle Parts Distr
N.A.I.C.S.: 423120

Cooper Standard Srbija DOO Sremska Mitrovica   (1)
Dimitrija Davidovica 1, Srem, Sremska Mitrovica, 22000, Serbia
Tel.: (381) 22638334
Motor Vehicle Parts Distr

Cooper-Standard Holdings Inc.—(Continued)

N.A.I.C.S.: 423120
Danijela Timotic *(Accountant)*

Cooper-Standard Automotive (Changchun) Co., Ltd. (1)
Industrial Building 2-2 1977 Guanggudajie Chaoyang, Changchun, 130012, China
Tel.: (86) 4317039099
Motor Vehicle Parts Distr
N.A.I.C.S.: 423120

Cooper-Standard Automotive France S.A.S. (1)
2 Rue Saint Omer, 57150, Creutzwald, 57150, France
Tel.: (33) 387298912
Motor Vehicle Parts Distr
N.A.I.C.S.: 423120

Cooper-Standard Automotive Inc. (1)
39555 Orchard Hill Pl Ste 320 3rd Fl, Novi, MI 48375
Tel.: (248) 596-5900
Web Site: http://www.cooperstandard.com
Sales Range: $1-4.9 Billion
Emp.: 16,266
Rubber & Plastic Automotive Parts
N.A.I.C.S.: 336390

Subsidiary (Non-US):

Cooper Standard Automotive France S.A.S. (2)
2 Rue Saint Omer Creutzwald, Lorraine, F-57150, Metz, France
Tel.: (33) 0387298912
Web Site: http://www.cooperstandard.com
Automotive Components Mfr
N.A.I.C.S.: 423120

Cooper Standard Automotive Japan K.K. (2)
Yokohama Mitsui Building 2403 1-1-2 Takashima, Nishi-ku, Yokohama, 220-0011, Kanagawa, Japan
Tel.: (81) 452275700
Emp.: 6
Motor Vehicle Parts & Accessory Mfr
N.A.I.C.S.: 336390
Mike Masuko *(Pres)*

Cooper Standard Automotive Polska Sp. z.o.o. (2)
Piekarska 77, Bielsko-Biala, 43-300, Silesia, Poland
Tel.: (48) 338289101
Web Site: http://www.cooperstandard.com
Sales Range: $125-149.9 Million
Emp.: 700
Automotive & Industrial Parts Mfr
N.A.I.C.S.: 332999

Cooper-Standard Automotive (Deutschland) GmbH (2)
Ehinger Strasse 28, 89601, Schelklingen, Germany
Tel.: (49) 73942420
Web Site: http://cooperstandard.com
Emp.: 250
Motor Vehicle Parts Whslr
N.A.I.C.S.: 423120

Cooper-Standard Automotive Brasil Sealing Ltda. (2)
Av Manoel Vida 1000, Distr Industrial Miguel de Lucca, Varginha, 37070-015, Minas Gerais, Brazil
Tel.: (55) 353 219 4000
Web Site: http://www.cooperstandard.com
Sales Range: $10-24.9 Million
Emp.: 700
Rubber Automotive Products & Plastic Seals & Trim Mfr
N.A.I.C.S.: 326291

Plant (Domestic):

Cooper-Standard Automotive Brasil Sealing Ltda. - Camacari Plant (3)
Av Henry Ford 2000 Parte 1 Polo Petroquimico, Camacari, 42810-970, Bahia, Brazil
Tel.: (55) 3521054037
Rubber Automotive Products
N.A.I.C.S.: 326291

Subsidiary (Non-US):

Cooper-Standard Automotive Canada Limited (2)
703 Douro Street, Stratford, N5A 3T1, ON, Canada
Tel.: (519) 271-3360
Automobile Parts Mfr
N.A.I.C.S.: 336390

Cooper-Standard Automotive Ceska Republika s.r.o. (2)
Prumyslova 1419, Bystrice, 591 01, Czech Republic
Tel.: (420) 567122118
Automobile Parts Mfr
N.A.I.C.S.: 336390

Plant (Domestic):

Cooper-Standard Automotive Inc. - Bowling Green Plant (2)
400 Van Camp Rd, Bowling Green, OH 43402
Tel.: (419) 353-2500
Web Site: http://www.cooperstandard.com
Sales Range: $100-124.9 Million
Emp.: 500
Mfr of Hoses
N.A.I.C.S.: 326220

Subsidiary (Non-US):

Cooper-Standard Automotive International Holdings B.V. (2)
Stroombaan 10 3rd Floor, 1181 VX, Amstelveen, 1181 VX, Netherlands
Tel.: (31) 205453322
Automobile Parts Mfr
N.A.I.C.S.: 336390

Cooper-Standard Automotive Italy SpA (2)
Via Torino 140, Piedmont, Cirie, 10073, Turin, Italy
Tel.: (39) 0119216111
Web Site: http://cooperstandard.com
Automobile Parts Mfr
N.A.I.C.S.: 336390

Cooper-Standard Automotive Korea Inc. (2)
#303 C Dong Pangyo Inno Valley 621 Sampyeong, Bundang-gu, Seongnam, 463-400, Korea (South)
Tel.: (82) 3180180701
Web Site: http://www.cooperstandard.com
Rubber Automotive Products
N.A.I.C.S.: 326291

Cooper-Standard Automotive Piotrkow sp zoo (2)
Ul Dmowskiego 30/e, Lodz, 97-300, Piotrkow Trybunalski, Wojewodztwo lodzkie, Poland
Tel.: (48) 446493823
Automobile Parts Mfr
N.A.I.C.S.: 336390

Cooper-Standard Automotive Services, S.A. de C.V. (2)
Ave Mexico 101 Parque Industrial San Francisco, San Francisco De Los Romo, Aguascalientes, 20300, Mexico
Tel.: (52) 4499222000
Automobile Parts Mfr
N.A.I.C.S.: 336390

Cooper-Standard Automotive UK Limited (2)
Cooper Standard Orchard Court 8, Binley Business Park, Coventry, CV3 2TQ, United Kingdom
Tel.: (44) 2476 437 820
Web Site: http://www.cooperstandard.com
Rubber Automotive Produto
N.A.I.C.S.: 326291

Cooper-Standard Automotive de Mexico S.A. de C.V. (2)
Poniente 150 No 956, Mexico, 20300, Mexico
Tel.: (52) 5557298834
Automobile Parts Mfr
N.A.I.C.S.: 336390

Subsidiary (Domestic):

Cooper-Standard Automotive Fluid Systems de Mexico, S. de R.L. de C.V. (3)
Calle Num 17, Sin Numero Zona Industrial, Atlacomulco, 50450, Mexico, Mexico

Tel.: (52) 7121229400
Automobile Parts Mfr
N.A.I.C.S.: 336390

Subsidiary (Non-US):

Cooper-Standard Chongqing Automotive Co., Ltd. (2)
2nd Floor G Building Industrial Park of Automotive Components for Ford, 2 Changfu Road Chongqing Economic & Technological Development Zone, Chongqing, 401122, China
Tel.: (86) 2386000600
Automobile Parts Distr
N.A.I.C.S.: 423120

Subsidiary (Domestic):

Cooper-Standard Rockford Inc. (2)
2460 Stock Creek Blvd, Rockford, TN 37853
Tel.: (865) 573-0122
Automobile Parts Mfr
N.A.I.C.S.: 336390

Subsidiary (Non-US):

Metzeler Automotive Profile Systems GmbH (2)
Bregenzer Strasse 133, 88131, Lindau, Germany
Tel.: (49) 83827070
Web Site: http://www.cooperstandard.com
Emp.: 950
Automobile Parts Mfr
N.A.I.C.S.: 336390

Joint Venture (Domestic):

Nishikawa Cooper LLC (2)
324 Morrow St, Topeka, IN
46571-9076 (40%)
Tel.: (260) 593-2156
Web Site: https://niscoseals.com
Sales Range: $125-149.9 Million
Emp.: 500
Fabricated Rubber Products
N.A.I.C.S.: 326299
Naoki Masukuni *(Pres)*
Scott Keys *(VP)*
Masahiro Okamine *(VP)*
Glenn Seiji Iwahara *(VP)*
Yoshio Fujimura *(VP)*
Ed Carpenter *(VP)*

Subsidiary (Domestic):

Westborn Service Center, Inc. (2)
39550 Orchard Hill Pl, Novi, MI 48375
Tel.: (248) 735-0049
Automobile Parts Mfr
N.A.I.C.S.: 336390

Cooper-Standard Sealing (Shenyang) Co. Ltd. (1)
No12 Dongyue Street Dadong, Shenyang, Liaoning, China
Tel.: (86) 2431951080
Motor Vehicle Parts Distr
N.A.I.C.S.: 423120

Huayu-Cooper Standard Sealing Systems Co., Ltd. (1)
No 4600 Qingsong Road, Qingpu District, Shanghai, 201712, China
Tel.: (86) 2159221580
Web Site: http://www.huayu-auto.com
Emp.: 710
Passenger Vehicles Mfr & Distr
N.A.I.C.S.: 336999

Lauren Plastics LLC (1)
17155 Van Wagoner Rd, Spring Lake, MI 49456
Tel.: (616) 844-2888
Plastic Component Mfr
N.A.I.C.S.: 326199

Liveline Technologies Inc. (1)
11820 Globe St, Livonia, MI 48105
Tel.: (734) 542-6341
Web Site: https://www.liveline.tech
Industrial Automation Services
N.A.I.C.S.: 541330

Sujan Barre Thomas AVS Private Limited (1)
Building No 1 Plot No 1 & 2 Behind Blue Chip Industrial Estate, Village Waliv Sativali

Udyog Nagar Vasai Dist, Thane, 401208, India
Tel.: (91) 2502456743
Web Site: http://www.sujanbarrethomas.com
Motor Vehicle Body Mfr
N.A.I.C.S.: 336390

COPART, INC.
14185 Dallas Pkwy Ste 400, Dallas, TX 75254
Tel.: (972) 391-5000 **CA**
Web Site: https://www.copart.com
Year Founded: 1982
CPRT—(NASDAQ)
Rev.: $4,236,823,000
Assets: $8,427,764,000
Liabilities: $879,209,000
Net Worth: $7,548,555,000
Earnings: $1,362,347,000
Emp.: 11,700
Fiscal Year-end: 07/31/24
Used & Salvage Vehicle Sales & Remarketing Services
N.A.I.C.S.: 441120
Leah C. Stearns *(CFO & Sr VP)*
Willis J. Johnson *(Founder)*
A. Jayson Adair *(Exec Chm)*
Robert H. Vannuccini *(Chief Sls Officer)*
Gregory R. DePasquale *(Gen Counsel & Sec)*
Scott Booker *(CMO & Chief Product Officer)*
Steve Powers *(COO)*
Rama Prasad *(CTO)*
Paul Kirkpatrick *(Chief Legal Officer)*
Gavin Renfrew *(Interim Principal Acctg Officer & VP-Global Acctg)*
Adiel Avelar *(Pres, Pres, Mng Dir, Chief Medical Officer, Exec VP, Exec VP & Exec VP)*
Colin Cordery *(Pres, Pres, Mng Dir, Mng Dir, Chief Medical Officer, Exec VP, Exec VP & Exec VP)*
Jan Johansson *(Mng Dir)*
Steve MacAluso *(Mng Dir)*
Jane Pocock *(Mng Dir)*
Kai Siersleben *(Mng Dir)*
Santiago Zamit *(Mng Dir)*
Jeffrey Liaw *(CEO)*

Subsidiaries:

Autoresiduos S.L.U. (1)
Calle Malaga 4 Planta 5a, 14003, Cordoba, Spain
Tel.: (34) 957958063
Web Site: https://www.autoresiduos.com
Automobile Parts Distr
N.A.I.C.S.: 423110

COPART OF ARIZONA, INC. (1)
615 So 51st Ave, Phoenix, AZ 85043-4706
Tel.: (602) 484-7075
Emp.: 30
Salvage Auctions & Online Auctions Services
N.A.I.C.S.: 425120

COPART OF ARKANSAS, INC. (1)
703 Main St, Conway, AR 72032-9428
Tel.: (501) 796-2812
Automobile Auctions & Whslr
N.A.I.C.S.: 423110

COPART OF HOUSTON, INC. (1)
1655 Rankin Rd, Houston, TX 77073-4903
Tel.: (281) 214-7800
Automobile Auction Retailer
N.A.I.C.S.: 441330

COPART OF TENNESSEE, INC. (1)
865 Stumpy Ln, Lebanon, TN 37090
Tel.: (615) 449-6195
Automobile Auctions & Whslr
N.A.I.C.S.: 425120

COPART OF WASHINGTON, INC. (1)
3333 N Railroad Ave, Pasco, WA 99301-9394
Tel.: (509) 547-1701
Automobile Auction Operator & Whslr

N.A.I.C.S.: 423110

Copart Canada, Inc. (1)
175 Osborne Rd, Courtice, L1E 2R3, ON, Canada
Tel.: (905) 436-2045
Web Site: http://www.copart.ca
Sales Range: $25-49.9 Million
Emp.: 15
Administrator of Salvage Automobile Auctions
N.A.I.C.S.: 441120

Copart Deutschland GmbH (1)
Zulpicher Str 150, 52349, Duren, Germany
Tel.: (49) 2421480920
Online Auction Services
N.A.I.C.S.: 423120

Copart Excavation, Inc. (1)
501 E US Hwy 80, Forney, TX 75126
Tel.: (972) 564-5525
Web Site: http://www.brightexcavation.com
Excavation Contractor Services
N.A.I.C.S.: 238910
Dwaine Bright (Pres)
Brian Carpenter (COO)
Tom Ishmael (VP)

Copart Salvage Auto Auctions, Inc. (1)
8100 McCoy Rd, Orlando, FL 32822-5503
Tel.: (407) 888-2424
Web Site: http://www.copart.com
Sales Range: $150-199.9 Million
Emp.: 40
Administrator of Salvage Automobile Auctions
N.A.I.C.S.: 423110

Copart UAE Auctions LLC (1)
Dic plot 500-663 Seih Shuaib 3, PO Box 334292, Sheikh Mohammad Bin Zayed Road 311, Dubai, United Arab Emirates
Tel.: (971) 44592700
Web Site: http://www.copartmea.com
Online Auction Services
N.A.I.C.S.: 423120

Copart UK Limited (1)
Acrey Fields Woburn Road, Wootton, MK43 9EJ, Bedfordshire, United Kingdom
Tel.: (44) 1234766500
Web Site: https://www.copart.co.uk
Emp.: 200
Automobiles & Automotive Parts Sales
N.A.I.C.S.: 423110

Copart of Connecticut, Inc. (1)
138 Christian Ln, New Britain, CT 06051-4123
Tel.: (860) 666-1183
Sales Range: $25-49.9 Million
Emp.: 38
Administrator of Salvage Automobile Auctions
N.A.I.C.S.: 423110
James Costello (Gen Mgr)
Lisa Doherty (Reg Mgr)

Copart of Kansas, Inc. (1)
8440 Gibbs Rd, Kansas City, KS 66111-2124
Tel.: (913) 548-0818
Sales Range: $10-24.9 Million
Emp.: 20
Administrator of Salvage Automobile Auctions
N.A.I.C.S.: 561499

Copart of Louisiana, Inc. (1)
14600 Old Gentilly Rd, New Orleans, LA 70129-2348
Tel.: (504) 254-3944
Sales Range: $150-199.9 Million
Emp.: 79
Administrator of Salvage Automobile Auctions
N.A.I.C.S.: 423110

Copart of Oklahoma, Inc, (1)
2408 W 21st St, Tulsa, OK 74107-3402
Tel.: (918) 582-3828
Sales Range: $150-199.9 Million
Administrator of Salvage Automobile Auctions
N.A.I.C.S.: 423110
Rachel Fashing (Gen Mgr)
Peter Greenwood (Reg Mgr)

Copart of Texas, Inc. (1)

505 Idlewild Rd, Grand Prairie, TX 75051-2410
Tel.: (972) 263-2711
Sales Range: $50-74.9 Million
Emp.: 40
Administrator of Salvage Automobile Auctions
N.A.I.C.S.: 532120

Crashed Toys LLC (1)
7777 John W Carpenter Fwy, Dallas, TX 75247-4828
Tel.: (214) 920-9664
Web Site: https://www.crashedtoys.com
Online Auction Services
N.A.I.C.S.: 423120

Cycle Express, LLC (1)
12400 Stowe Dr, Poway, CA 92064
Web Site: http://www.npauctions.com
Powersport Auction Services
N.A.I.C.S.: 423120
Brandon McDonald (Gen Mgr-Ops)
Trevor Nicely (Reg Mgr-Sls)
Dominick Catalfamo (Reg Mgr-Sls)
Michael McDonald (Mgr-Online Auctions)
Cliff Clifford (Chm)
Jim Woodruff (CEO)
Devin Deforest (CFO)
Michael Harlan (CTO)
Jeff Kinney (VP-Ops)
Mike Murray (VP-Sls)
Tony Altieri (VP-Bus Dev)
Ryan Keefe (VP-Mktg)
Al Sands (Dir-Customer Care)
Mark Clifford (Ops Mgr-East)
Jeff Stalder (Ops Mgr-West)
Buffy Huffman (Gen Mgr-Ops)
Colleen Baldwin (Mgr-Bus Dev)
Damon Puckett (Mgr-Bus Dev)
Gerry Houseman (Mgr-Transportation)

Dallas Copart Salvage Auto Auctions LP (1)
505 Idlewild Rd, Grand Prairie, TX 75051
Tel.: (972) 263-2711
Sales Range: $25-49.9 Million
Emp.: 50
Administrator of Salvage Automobile Auctions
N.A.I.C.S.: 423110

Houston Copart Salvage Auto Auctions LP (1)
3046 Hwy 322 S, Longview, TX 75603-7006
Tel.: (903) 643-9705
Web Site: http://www.copart.com
Sales Range: $100-124.9 Million
Emp.: 10
Administrator of Salvage Automobile Auctions
N.A.I.C.S.: 561499
Jeff King (Gen Mgr)
Timothy Smith (Reg Mgr)

Motors Auction Group, Inc. (1)
2323 N Dupont Hwy, New Castle, DE 19720
Tel.: (877) 605-9105
Web Site: http://www.dpaa2.com
Car Auction Services
N.A.I.C.S.: 423110
John Budzyn (Mgr-Shop)
Brandon Price (Gen Mgr)
Megan Dixon (Controller)
Jackie Dmytrus (Mgr-Fin)
Zuly Cortes (Office Mgr)

VB2, INC. (1)
9895 Double R Blvd, Reno, NV 89521
Tel.: (775) 770-1700
Automotive Part Whslr
N.A.I.C.S.: 423110

WOM WreckOnlineMarket GmbH (1)
Im Stockmadle 13, 76307, Karlsbad, Germany
Tel.: (49) 7248931310
Web Site:
  http://www.wreckonlinemarket.com
Emp.: 65
Online Auction Services
N.A.I.C.S.: 423120

COPPER PROPERTY CTL PASS THROUGH TRUST
6501 LEGACY DRIVE, PLANO, TX 75024

Tel.: (972) 243-1100   NY
CPPTL—(OTC)
N.A.I.C.S.:

COPT DEFENSE PROPERTIES
6711 Columbia Gateway Dr Ste 300, Columbia, MD 21046
Tel.: (443) 285-5400   MD
Web Site: https://www.copt.com
Year Founded: 1999
OFC—(NYSE)
Rev.: $739,030,000
Assets: $4,257,275,000
Liabilities: $2,535,820,000
Net Worth: $1,721,455,000
Earnings: $173,029,000
Emp.: 395
Fiscal Year-end: 12/31/22
Fully-Integrated & Self-Managed Real Estate Investment Trust
N.A.I.C.S.: 525990
Robert L. Denton Sr. (Co-Founder)
Stephen E. Budorick (Pres & CEO)
Anthony Mifsud (CFO & Exec VP)
Michelle Layne (Mgr-IR)
Matthew T. Myers (Chief Acctg Officer, Sr VP & Controller)
Venkat Kommineni (VP)

Subsidiaries:

COPT DC-6, LLC (1)
6711 Columbia Gateway Dr, Columbia, MD 21046
Tel.: (443) 285-5400
Professional, Scientific & Technical Services
N.A.I.C.S.: 541990

COPT Northcreek, LLC (1)
5755 Mark Dabling Blvd, Colorado Springs, CO 80919-2228
Tel.: (443) 285-5400
Real Estate Investment Services
N.A.I.C.S.: 531110

COPT Property Management Services, LLC (1)
6711 Columbia Ste 300, Columbia, MD 21046
Tel.: (410) 931-6922
Real Estate Investment Services
N.A.I.C.S.: 531110

Corporate Development Services, LLC (1)
6711 Columbus Gate Way Dr Ste 300, Columbia, MD 21046   (100%)
Tel.: (443) 285-5400
Web Site: http://www.copt.com
Sales Range: Less than $1 Million
Emp.: 10
Provider of Comprehensive Development & Construction Services with a Specialization in Suburban Office Buildings
N.A.I.C.S.: 237210
Mary Ellen Fowler (Treas & Sr VP)

Corporate Office Properties, L.P. (1)
6711 Columbia Gtwy Dr Ste 300, Columbia, MD 21046
Tel.: (443) 285-5400
Rev.: $609,364,999
Assets: $4,073,996,000
Liabilities: $2,380,284,000
Net Worth: $1,693,712,000
Earnings: $98,854,000
Fiscal Year-end: 12/31/2020
Real Estate Investment Services
N.A.I.C.S.: 531210
Stephen E. Budorick (Pres & CEO)

TRC Pinnacle Towers, L.L.C. (1)
6711 Columbia Gateway Dr 3rd Fl, Columbia, MD 21046
Tel.: (703) 790-5114
Real Estate Investment Services
N.A.I.C.S.: 531110

Towerview, LLC (1)
500 Pk Ave, New York, NY 10022
Tel.: (212) 935-7640
Real Estate Investment Services
N.A.I.C.S.: 531110
Daniel Richard Tisch (CFO)

CORBUS PHARMACEUTICALS

HOLDINGS, INC.
500 River Ridge Dr, Norwood, MA 02062
Tel.: (617) 963-0100   DE
Web Site:
  https://www.corbuspharma.com
Year Founded: 2013
CRBP—(NASDAQ)
Rev.: $3,389,440
Assets: $28,272,393
Liabilities: $35,177,115
Net Worth: ($6,904,722)
Earnings: ($44,603,316)
Emp.: 19
Fiscal Year-end: 12/31/23
Holding Company; Pharmaceutical Mfr & Whslr
N.A.I.C.S.: 551112
Yuval Cohen (Co-Founder & CEO)
Sean F. Moran (CFO)
Bruce Mackle (Mng Dir)
Christina Bertsch (Head)

Subsidiaries:

Corbus Pharmaceuticals, Inc. (1)
500 River Rdg Dr, Norwood, MA 02062
Tel.: (617) 963-0100
Web Site: https://www.corbuspharma.co
Pharmaceuticals Product Mfr
N.A.I.C.S.: 325412
Yuval Cohen (CEO & Dir)
Sean Moran (CFO)
Rachael Brake (Chief Scientific Officer)

CORCEPT THERAPEUTICS INCORPORATED
101 Redwood Shores Pkwy, Redwood City, CA 94065
Tel.: (650) 327-3270   DE
Web Site: https://www.corcept.com
Year Founded: 1998
CORT—(NASDAQ)
Rev.: $401,858,000
Assets: $583,430,000
Liabilities: $81,588,000
Net Worth: $501,842,000
Earnings: $101,288,000
Emp.: 299
Fiscal Year-end: 12/31/22
Pharmaceutical Preparation Manufacturing
N.A.I.C.S.: 325412
Joseph K. Belanoff (Co-Founder, Pres & CEO)
Gary Charles Robb (Chief Bus Officer)
Joseph Douglas Lyon (Chief Acctg Officer)
Atabak Mokari (CFO)
William Guyer (Chief Dev Officer)
Amy Flood (Chief HR Officer)

CORDIA CORP.
401 Ryland St, Reno, NV 89502
Tel.: (213) 915-6673   NV
Year Founded: 1998
CORG—(OTCIQ)
Restaurant Operators
N.A.I.C.S.: 722511
Peter Klamka (Pres & CEO)
Smit Shah (CEO)

CORE & MAIN, INC.
1830 Craig Park Ct, Saint Louis, MO 63146
Tel.: (314) 432-4700   DE
Web Site:
  https://www.coreandmain.com
Year Founded: 2021
CNM—(NYSE)
Rev.: $6,702,000,000
Assets: $5,069,000,000
Liabilities: $3,545,000,000
Net Worth: $1,524,000,000
Earnings: $371,000,000
Emp.: 5,000
Fiscal Year-end: 01/24/24

Core & Main, Inc.—(Continued)

Wastewater Related Product Distr
N.A.I.C.S.: 423390
Stephen O. LeClair *(Chm & CEO)*
Jack Schaller *(Pres)*
Bradford A. Cowles *(Pres-Fire Protection)*
Mark R. Witkowski *(CFO)*
Laura K. Schneider *(Chief HR Officer)*
Mark G. Whittenburg *(Gen Counsel & Sec)*
Yvonne Bland *(VP-Sls & Bus Dev)*
Bill Driskill *(VP-Vendor Rels, Sourcing & Ops)*
Jeffrey D. Giles *(VP-Corp Dev)*
John R. Schaller *(Pres-Waterworks)*
John Stephens *(VP & Controller)*
Robyn Bradbury *(VP-Fin Plng, Analysis & IR)*
Carrie Busbee *(CIO)*

Subsidiaries:

Catalone Pipe & Supply Co. (1)
10752 Bennetts Vly Hwy, Penfield, PA 15849
Tel.: (814) 637-5851
Web Site: http://www.catalonepipe.com
Metal Service Centers & Other Metal Merchant Whslr
N.A.I.C.S.: 423510
Craig Catalone *(Owner)*

Dana Kepner Company, LLC (1)
700 Alcott St, Denver, CO 80204
Tel.: (303) 623-6161
Web Site: https://www.danakepner.com
Sales Range: $10-24.9 Million
Emp.: 300
Waterworks Supplies
N.A.I.C.S.: 423510
Dave Wickett *(CEO)*
Deron Johnson *(Pres)*

Dodson Engineered Products, Inc. (1)
33 Marand Rd, Glenwood Springs, CO 81602-9327
Tel.: (970) 945-2233
Web Site: http://www.dodsonpipe.com
Water Supply & Irrigation Systems
N.A.I.C.S.: 221310
David Dodson *(Pres)*

Foster Supply Inc. (1)
9374 Teays Valley Rd, Scott Depot, WV 25560
Tel.: (304) 755-8241
Web Site: https://www.fostersupply.com
Lumber, Plywood & Millwork
N.A.I.C.S.: 423310
Ronald P. Foster *(CEO)*
Sarah Foster *(CFO)*
Geoff Foster *(Ops Mgr)*
Opie Taylor *(Asst Ops Mgr)*
Jesse Hodge *(Supvr-Yard)*
Kerry Cole *(Mgr-Special Projects & Estimating)*
Matt Gibson *(Pres-ECI)*

Granite Water Works, Inc. (1)
635 28th Ave S, Waite Park, MN 56387
Tel.: (320) 253-8587
Web Site:
http://www.granitewaterworks.com
Commercial & Service Industry Machinery Mfr
N.A.I.C.S.: 333310
Ed Molitor *(Pres)*

Green Equipment Company (1)
2563 Gravel Dr, Fort Worth, TX 76118
Tel.: (817) 589-2704
Web Site: http://www.greenequipco.com
Rev.: $1,200,000
Emp.: 10
Oil & Gas Field Machinery & Equipment Mfr
N.A.I.C.S.: 333132
Ed Green *(Owner & Pres)*
Zane Smith *(VP)*

Heidler Holdings, Inc. (1)
106 Cherry St, Horse Cave, KY 42749
Tel.: (270) 786-3010
Web Site: http://www.geothermalsupply.com

Sales Range: $1-9.9 Million
Emp.: 32
Warm Air Heating & Air Conditioning Equipment & Supplies Whslr
N.A.I.C.S.: 423730
David McCool *(Mgr-Sls)*
Matt Lile *(Mgr-Ops)*
Todd Highbaugh *(Mgr-Supply Chain)*
Michael Doyle *(Mgr-Production)*

Inland Water Works Supply Co. (1)
2468 N Miramonte Dr, San Bernardino, CA 92405
Tel.: (909) 883-8941
Web Site: http://www.inlandwaterworks.com
Durable Goods Merchant Whslr
N.A.I.C.S.: 423990

J & J Municipal Supply, Inc. (1)
900 N Baker Rd, Boonville, IN 47601-9509
Tel.: (812) 897-8888
Web Site: http://www.jjsupply1.com
House Service Supply
N.A.I.C.S.: 423620
John Fleener *(Pres)*

J.W. D'Angelo Co., Inc. (1)
601 S Harbor Blvd, La Habra, CA 90631-6187
Tel.: (562) 690-1000
Web Site: http://www.dangelo.net
Waterworks & Fire Protection Products Distr
N.A.I.C.S.: 922160

Lee Supply Company Inc. (1)
305 1st St, Charleroi, PA 15022-1427
Tel.: (724) 483-3543
Web Site: http://www.leesupply.com
Sales Range: $10-24.9 Million
Emp.: 102
Provider of Industrial Supply Services
N.A.I.C.S.: 423840
Joe Santangelo *(Mgr-Environmental Sls)*

Long Island Pipe Supply, Inc. (1)
586 Commercial Ave, Garden City, NY 11530
Tel.: (516) 222-8008
Web Site: http://www.lipipe.com
Sales Range: $10-24.9 Million
Emp.: 50
Fabricated Pipe & Fitting Mfr
N.A.I.C.S.: 332996
Robert Moss *(Pres)*
Larry Greenberg *(Gen Mgr)*
Ryan Eckert *(Reg Mgr-Wholesale)*

Subsidiary (Domestic):

Neill Supply Co., Inc (2)
700 Schuyler Ave, Lyndhurst, NJ 07071
Tel.: (201) 939-1100
Web Site: http://www.neillsupply.com
Sales Range: $10-24.9 Million
Emp.: 32
Industrial Supplies Merchant Whslr
N.A.I.C.S.: 423840

Maskell Pipe & Supply, Inc. (1)
560 N Rincon St, Corona, CA 92880
Tel.: (909) 574-8662
Web Site: http://www.mr-inc.com
Rev.: $8,000,000
Emp.: 14
Fiscal Year-end: 12/31/2015
Distr & Fittings Fabricator of Polyethylene Pipe
N.A.I.C.S.: 332996
Salma Bushala *(Pres)*
Mel Reeves *(Mgr-Ops)*

R&B Company (1)
605 Commercial, San Jose, CA 95112
Tel.: (408) 436-1699
Web Site: http://www.rbcompany.com
Pipe, Valve & Fitting Whslr
N.A.I.C.S.: 423840
Reed Mack *(Pres)*
Tom Gribbin *(VP)*
Peggy Stockwell *(CFO)*
Raul Soria *(Mgr-Applications Dev)*
Kurt Vincelette *(COO)*
Chris Jacobsen *(VP-Sls)*
Ryan Evans *(Mgr-Chico)*
Roger Hamilton *(Mgr-Manteca)*
Richie Aliotti *(Mgr-Oakley)*
Obie Gomez *(Mgr-Redwood City)*
Bob Barstad *(Mgr-Sacramento)*
Max Yates *(Mgr-Salinas)*
Paul Harrington *(Mgr-San Jose Fusion)*

Ramiro Cardenas *(Mgr-Warehouse)*
Oscar Hernandez *(Mgr-Warehouse)*
Fernando Valdez *(Mgr-Warehouse)*
Mo Yusuff *(Mgr-Warehouse)*
Vanessa Diricco *(Office Mgr)*
Tiffany Mayhue *(Office Mgr)*
Kevin Chambers Jr. *(Mgr-Bakersfield)*

Water Works Supply Company (1)
660 State Rt 23, Pompton Plains, NJ 07444
Tel.: (973) 835-2153
Metal Service Centers & Other Metal Merchant Whslr
N.A.I.C.S.: 423510
Jim C. Schmutz *(Owner & Pres)*
Walter Siubis *(Mgr-Ops)*

CORE MOLDING TECHNOLOGIES, INC.
800 Manor Park Dr, Columbus, OH 43228
Tel.: (614) 870-5000   DE
Web Site: https://www.coremt.com
Year Founded: 1996
CMT—(NYSEAMEX)
Rev.: $377,376,000
Assets: $198,615,000
Liabilities: $82,490,000
Net Worth: $116,125,000
Earnings: $12,203,000
Emp.: 1,986
Fiscal Year-end: 12/31/22
Mfr of Plastic & Fiberglass Molded Products
N.A.I.C.S.: 339113
John P. Zimmer *(CFO & Exec VP)*
Eric L. Palomaki *(Exec VP-Ops & R&D)*
David L. Duvall *(Pres & CEO)*
J. Christopher Highfield *(Exec VP-Sls & Mktg)*
Renee R. Anderson *(Exec VP-HR)*

Subsidiaries:

Core Molding Technologies Inc (1)
24 Commerce Dr Meadow Creek Industrial Pk, Gaffney, SC 29340
Tel.: (864) 488-4620
Web Site: http://www.coremt.com
Sales Range: $10-24.9 Million
Emp.: 75
Mfr of Molded Plastic Products
N.A.I.C.S.: 326199

Horizon Plastics International Inc. (1)
Building 3 Northam Industrial Park, PO Box 474, Cobourg, K9A 4L1, ON, Canada
Tel.: (905) 372-2291
Web Site: http://www.horizonplastics.ca
Foam Plastic Products Mfr
N.A.I.C.S.: 326150

CORE RESOURCE MANAGEMENT, INC.
34522 N Scottsdale Rd Ste 120-409, Scottsdale, AZ 85266
Tel.: (602) 314-3230   NV
Web Site:
http://www.coreresource.net
Year Founded: 1999
CRMIQ—(OTCIQ)
Sales Range: Less than $1 Million
Emp.: 8
Investment Management Service
N.A.I.C.S.: 523999
James D. Clark *(Pres & Interim CEO)*
Alexander B. Campbell *(Interim Chm)*
Neal Duncan *(CFO)*

CORE-MARK HOLDING CO. INC.
1500 Solana Blvd Ste 3400, Westlake, TX 76262
Tel.: (940) 293-8600   DE
Web Site: http://www.core-mark.com
Year Founded: 1888
CORE—(NASDAQ)
Rev.: $16,957,900,000
Assets: $1,954,700,000

Liabilities: $1,322,800,000
Net Worth: $631,900,000
Earnings: $63,200,000
Emp.: 7,534
Fiscal Year-end: 12/31/20
Packaged Consumables Mfr
N.A.I.C.S.: 424410
Eric J. Rolheiser *(Pres-Canada & Sr VP-Northern Div)*
William G. Stein *(Sr VP-Enterprise Growth)*
Christopher M. Miller *(CFO, Exec VP & Sr VP)*
Alan T. Thomas *(Sr VP-Western Div)*
Jennifer Hulett *(Chief HR Officer & Sr VP)*
Andy Newkirk *(Sr VP-Ops)*
Christopher K. Hobson *(Pres & CEO)*

Subsidiaries:

Core-Mark (1)
7800 Riverfront Gate, Burnaby, V5J 5L3, BC, Canada   (100%)
Tel.: (604) 430-2181
Web Site: http://www.core-mark.com
Sales Range: $75-99.9 Million
Emp.: 30
Packaged Consumer Products Distr
N.A.I.C.S.: 541614
Eric J. Rolheiser *(Pres)*

Core-Mark Distributors, Inc. (1)
4820 N Church Ln SE, Atlanta, GA 30339
Tel.: (404) 792-2000
Food & Staples Retail Services
N.A.I.C.S.: 445110

Core-Mark International (1)
355 Main St, Whitinsville, MA 01588
Tel.: (508) 791-9000
Web Site: http://www.core-mark.com
Sales Range: $250-299.9 Million
Emp.: 175
Merchandise Distr
N.A.I.C.S.: 424940

Subsidiary (Domestic):

Core-Mark Distributors, Inc. (2)
4820 N Church Ln SE, Atlanta, GA 30339
Tel.: (404) 792-2000
Web Site: http://www.core-mark.com
Grocery Retailer
N.A.I.C.S.: 424490
Randy Hall *(Mgr-Pur)*

Core-Mark Interrelated Companies, Inc. (2)
353 Meyer Cir, Corona, CA 92879-1349
Tel.: (951) 736-1591
Web Site: http://www.coremark.com
Consumer Products Distr & Logistics Services
N.A.I.C.S.: 541614

Core-Mark Midcontinent, Inc. (2)
395 Oyster Point Blvd Ste 415, South San Francisco, CA 94080-1928
Tel.: (650) 589-9445
Consumer Products Distr & Logistics Services
N.A.I.C.S.: 541614
Tom Purken *(CEO)*

Farner-Bocken Co. (1)
1751 Hwy 30 E, Carroll, IA 51401
Tel.: (712) 792-3503
Web Site: http://www.farner-bocken.com
Convenience & Food Service Products Distr
N.A.I.C.S.: 424490

CORECARD CORPORATION
1 Meca Way, Norcross, GA 30093
Tel.: (770) 381-2900   GA
Web Site: https://www.corecard.com
Year Founded: 1973
CCRD—(NYSE)
Rev.: $69,765,000
Assets: $63,232,000
Liabilities: $10,469,000
Net Worth: $52,763,000
Earnings: $13,881,000
Emp.: 1,200
Fiscal Year-end: 12/31/22

Investor & Operator: Business Knowledge, Financial Capital & Incubator Programs
N.A.I.C.S.: 551112
James Leland Strange *(Chm, Pres & CEO)*
Matthew A. White *(CFO & Sec)*
Mark Raleigh *(COO)*
Eswaraprasad Dontu *(CTO)*
Dan Stavros *(Exec VP)*
Prakash Kadiyala *(Exec VP-Processing)*
Anupam Pathak *(Sr VP-India Ops)*
Brian Beuning *(Sr VP-Platform & Architecture)*
John Chandy *(VP-Innovation)*

Subsidiaries:

CoreCard Software, Inc.   **(1)**
1 Meca Way, Norcross, GA 30093   **(85%)**
Tel.: (770) 564-8000
Web Site: https://www.corecard.com
Sales Range: $100-124.9 Million
Developer of Financial Software Products
N.A.I.C.S.: 541511
Leland Strange *(Pres & CEO)*
Dan Stavros *(Exec VP)*
Eswaraprasad Dontu *(VP)*
Brian Beuning *(VP-Platform & Architecture)*
Mark Raleigh *(VP)*
Prakash Kadiyala *(VP)*

ISC Software Pvt. Ltd.   **(1)**
7th Floor V Time Square CBD Belapur, Shahpura, Navi Mumbai, 400 614, Maharashtra, India
Tel.: (91) 7553292414
Web Site: https://isc-software-pvt-ltd.business.site
Emp.: 20
Software Development Services
N.A.I.C.S.: 513210
Anupam Pathak *(Mng Dir)*

CORECIVIC, INC.
5501 Virginia Way Ste 110, Brentwood, TN 37027
Tel.: (615) 263-3000   MD
Web Site: https://www.corecivic.com
Year Founded: 1983
CXW—(NYSE)
Rev.: $1,845,329,000
Assets: $3,244,769,000
Liabilities: $1,812,361,000
Net Worth: $1,432,408,000
Earnings: $122,320,000
Emp.: 10,653
Fiscal Year-end: 12/31/22
Prisons, Correctional & Detention Facilities Manager
N.A.I.C.S.: 922140
Damon T. Hininger *(Pres & CEO)*
David M. Garfinkle *(CFO & Exec VP)*
Steve Owen *(VP-Comm)*
Brad Regensis *(VP-Partnership Rels)*
David Churchill *(Chief HR Officer & Exec VP)*
Brian Hammonds *(VP-Fin & Controller)*
Patrick Swindle *(COO & Exec VP)*
William Dalius *(VP-Facility Ops-Bus Unit 1)*
Brian K. Ferrell *(VP-Proposal Dev)*
Daren Swenson *(VP-Reentry Partnerships & Innovation)*
John Paul Wooden *(VP-Treasury & Tax)*
Cole Carter *(Gen Counsel & Exec VP)*
Scott Craddock *(Chief Ethics & Compliance Officer & VP)*
Jason Medlin *(VP-Facility Ops-Bus Unit 2)*
Ron Charpentier *(VP-Health Svcs)*
Don Murray *(VP-Quality Assurance)*
Erik Rasmussen *(VP-Strategic Dev)*
Shannon Carst *(VP-Community Corrections)*
Tony Grande *(Chief Dev Officer)*

Libby Craver *(VP)*
Harold Shannon *(CIO)*
Brigham Sloan *(VP)*

Subsidiaries:

Avalon Corpus Christi Transitional Center, LLC   **(1)**
1515 N Tancahua St, Corpus Christi, TX 78401
Tel.: (361) 883-1004
Civic & Social Organization Services
N.A.I.C.S.: 813410

Avalon Correctional Services, Inc.   **(1)**
1017 N Bryant Ave, Edmond, OK 73034   **(100%)**
Tel.: (405) 330-6800
Web Site: http://www.avaloncorrections.com
Private Community Correctional Facilities Owner & Operator
N.A.I.C.S.: 922140
Brian T. Costello *(Pres & COO)*

Avalon Staffing, LLC   **(1)**
3390 Auto Mall Dr, Westlake Village, CA 91362
Tel.: (805) 367-3260
Web Site: http://www.avalonstaffing.com
Human Resource Consulting Services
N.A.I.C.S.: 541612

Avalon Transitional Center Dallas, LLC   **(1)**
1554 E Langdon Rd, Dallas, TX 75141
Tel.: (214) 742-1971
Civic & Social Organization Services
N.A.I.C.S.: 813410

Avalon Tulsa, LLC   **(1)**
302 W Archer St, Tulsa, OK 74103
Tel.: (918) 583-9445
Civic & Social Organization Services
N.A.I.C.S.: 813410

CCA Inc   **(1)**
10 Burtonhills Blvd, Nashville, TN 37215   **(100%)**
Tel.: (615) 263-3000
Web Site: http://www.cca.com
Sales Range: $75-99.9 Million
Emp.: 300
Consulting & Management Services
N.A.I.C.S.: 541618
Damon T. Hininger *(Pres & CEO)*

CCA TRS, LLC   **(1)**
10 Burton Hills Blvd, Nashville, TN 37215
Tel.: (615) 263-3000
Facility Management & Support Services
N.A.I.C.S.: 561210

Carver Transitional Center, LLC   **(1)**
400 S May Ave, Oklahoma City, OK 73108
Tel.: (405) 232-8233
Civic & Social Organization Services
N.A.I.C.S.: 813410

Corecivic, Inc. - Fox Facility   **(1)**
570 W 44th Ave, Denver, CO 80216
Tel.: (303) 477-5190
Web Site: http://www.corecivic.com
Residential Care Facilities
N.A.I.C.S.: 623990
Terence Matthews *(Dir-Facility & Mgr-Compliance)*

Correctional Alternatives, LLC   **(1)**
551 S 35th St, San Diego, CA 92113
Tel.: (619) 232-8600
Facility Management & Support Services
N.A.I.C.S.: 561210
Bessy Glaske *(Pres & COO)*

Fort Worth Transitional Center, LLC   **(1)**
600 N Henderson St, Fort Worth, TX 76107
Tel.: (817) 335-6053
Civic & Social Organization Services
N.A.I.C.S.: 813410

New Beginnings Treatment Center Inc.   **(1)**
2445 N Oracle Rd, Tucson, AZ 85705
Tel.: (520) 624-0075
Community Corrections Services
N.A.I.C.S.: 623990

Southern Corrections System of Wyoming, LLC   **(1)**

5501 Virginia Way Ste 110, Brentwood, TN 37027
Tel.: (307) 632-9096
Management Consulting Services
N.A.I.C.S.: 541618

Thrivur Health, LLC   **(1)**
730 W Hampden Ave Ste 205, Englewood, CO 80110
Tel.: (720) 716-5256
Web Site: https://thrivurhealth.com
Healthcare & Education Services
N.A.I.C.S.: 524128

TransCor America, LLC   **(1)**
646 Melrose Ave, Nashville, TN 37211
Tel.: (615) 251-7008
Web Site: https://www.transcor.com
Sales Range: $10-24.9 Million
Emp.: 50
Prisoner & Detainee Transportation Services
N.A.I.C.S.: 485999
Curtiss Sullivan *(Pres & Gen Mgr)*
David Spence *(Mng Dir-DOT Compliance & Fleet Mgmt)*
Michael Swinton *(COO & VP)*
James Crouch *(Mng Dir-Strategic Planning)*
Amy Cutshaw *(Controller)*
Jody Campbell *(Dir-Fleet Mgmt)*
Vivian Marsh *(Dir-Transportation Clinical Svcs)*
Randall Milks *(Dir-Operational Compliance & Quality Assurance)*
Stephanie Takishita *(Dir-Ops)*
Charles Westbrook Sr. *(Dir-Operations)*

Turley Residential Center, LLC   **(1)**
6101 N Martin Luther King Jr Blvd, Tulsa, OK 74126
Tel.: (539) 424-5361
Management Consulting Services
N.A.I.C.S.: 541618

CORENERGY INFRASTRUCTURE TRUST, INC.
1100 Walnut Ste 3350, Kansas City, MO 64106
Tel.: (816) 875-3705   MD
Web Site: https://corenergy.reit
Year Founded: 2005
CORRQ—(OTCIQ)
Rev.: $131,567,907
Assets: $229,103,232
Liabilities: $262,048,271
Net Worth: ($32,945,039)
Earnings: ($272,830,090)
Emp.: 151
Fiscal Year-end: 12/31/23
Oil & Gas Investment Services
N.A.I.C.S.: 523999
David John Schulte *(Chm & CEO)*
Robert L. Waldron *(Pres, CEO & CFO)*
John D. Grier *(COO)*
Chris Huffman *(Chief Acctg Officer)*

CORMEDIX INC.
300 Connell Dr 4th Fl Ste 4200, Berkeley Heights, NJ 07922
Tel.: (908) 517-9500   DE
Web Site: https://www.cormedix.com
Year Founded: 2006
CRMD—(NASDAQ)
Rev.: $65,408
Assets: $62,038,259
Liabilities: $6,978,523
Net Worth: $55,059,736
Earnings: ($29,701,705)
Emp.: 40
Fiscal Year-end: 12/31/22
Cardiac & Renal Dysfunction Pharmaceutical Researcher, Developer & Mfr
N.A.I.C.S.: 325412
Joseph Todisco *(CEO)*
Myron M. Kaplan *(Chm)*
Liz Masson-Hurlburt *(Exec VP & Head-Clinical Ops)*
Matthew David *(CFO & Exec VP)*
Beth Zelnick Kaufman *(Chief Legal Officer, Sec & Exec VP)*

CORNER GROWTH ACQUISITION CORP.
251 Lytton Ave Ste 200, Palo Alto, CA 94301
Tel.: (650) 543-8180   Ky
Web Site:
https://www.cornergrowth.com
Year Founded: 2020
COOL—(NASDAQ)
Assets: $15,789,790
Liabilities: $21,572,562
Net Worth: ($5,782,772)
Earnings: $17,687,623
Emp.: 6
Fiscal Year-end: 12/31/22
Investment Services
N.A.I.C.S.: 523999
John Cadeddu *(Co-Chm)*
Marvin Tien *(Co-Chm, CEO & Acting CFO)*
Jane Batzofin *(Pres)*
David Kutcher *(Chief Investment Officer)*
Kevin Tanaka *(Dir-Corp Dev)*

Subsidiaries:

Walsin Liwha Corp.   **(1)**
25F No 1 Songzhi Rd, Taipei, 11047, Taiwan
Tel.: (886) 287262211
Web Site: https://www.walsin.com
Electric Wire & Cable Mf
N.A.I.C.S.: 335929

CORNERSTONE COMMUNITY BANCORP
192 Hartnell Ave, Redding, CA 96002
Tel.: (530) 222-1460   CA
Year Founded: 2014
CRSB—(OTCIQ)
Banking Holding Company
N.A.I.C.S.: 551111
Jeffrey P. Finck *(Chm)*
Matthew B. Moseley *(Pres & CEO)*
Les Melburg *(Vice Chm)*

CORNERSTONE STRATEGIC VALUE FUND, INC.
225 Pictoria Dr Ste 450, Cincinnati, OH 45246
Tel.: (513) 587-3400
Web Site:
https://www.cornerstonestrategic
valuefund.com
CLM—(NYSEAMEX)
Rev.: $16,682,970
Assets: $815,703,476
Liabilities: $5,105,273
Net Worth: $810,598,203
Earnings: $7,612,871
Fiscal Year-end: 12/31/19
Closed-End Investment Fund
N.A.I.C.S.: 525990
Ralph W. Bradshaw *(Pres)*
Joshua G. Bradshaw *(Co-Portfolio Mgr & Asst Sec)*
Daniel W. Bradshaw *(Asst Sec)*
Rachel L. McNabb *(Chief Compliance Officer)*
Hoyt M. Peters *(Sec & Asst Treas)*
Theresa M. Bridge *(Treas)*

CORNERSTONE TOTAL RETURN FUND, INC.
225 Pictoria Dr Ste 450, Cincinnati, OH 45246   NY
Web Site:
https://www.cornerstonetotalreturn
fund.com
Year Founded: 1973
CRF—(NYSEAMEX)
Rev.: $8,783,760
Assets: $417,310,256
Liabilities: $1,750,637
Net Worth: $415,559,619
Earnings: $3,964,660
Fiscal Year-end: 12/31/19
Investment Management Service

Cornerstone Total Return Fund, Inc.—(Continued)

N.A.I.C.S.: 525990
Ralph W. Bradshaw *(Chm & Pres)*
Joshua G. Bradshaw *(Co-Portfolio Mgr & Asst Sec)*
Daniel W. Bradshaw *(Co-Portfolio Mgr & Asst Sec)*
Rachel L. McNabb *(Chief Compliance Officer)*
Brian J. Lutes *(Treas)*
Hoyt M. Peters *(Sec & Asst Treas)*

CORNING INCORPORATED

1 Riverfront Plz, Corning, NY 14831
Tel.: (607) 974-9000   **NY**
Web Site: https://www.corning.com
Year Founded: 1851
GLW—(NYSE)
Rev.: $12,588,000,000
Assets: $28,500,000,000
Liabilities: $16,632,000,000
Net Worth: $11,868,000,000
Earnings: $581,000,000
Emp.: 49,800
Fiscal Year-end: 12/31/23
Specialty Glass & Ceramic Products Mfr
N.A.I.C.S.: 327212
Lewis A. Steverson *(Chief Legal & Admin Officer & Exec VP)*
Wendell P. Weeks *(Chm & CEO)*
Stefan Becker *(Principal Acctg Officer, Sr VP-Fin & Controller)*
Michael A. Bell *(Sr VP & Gen Mgr-Optical Comm)*
Li Fang *(Co-Pres & Sr VP-Corning Intl & New Bus Dev-Solar)*
Edward A. Schlesinger *(CFO & Exec VP)*
Jordana Kammerud *(Chief HR Officer & Sr VP)*
Michael P. O'Day *(Sr VP & Gen Mgr-Optical Comm)*
Michaune D. Tillman *(Gen Counsel & Sr VP)*
Avery Nelson III *(Sr VP & Gen Mgr-Automotive)*

Subsidiaries:

Axygen, Inc.   (1)
33210 Central Ave, Union City, CA 94587
Tel.: (510) 494-8900
Web Site: http://www.axygen.com
Sales Range: $75-99.9 Million
Plastic Laboratory Equipment Mfr
N.A.I.C.S.: 339113
Hemant Gupta *(Pres & CEO)*

Subsidiary (Domestic):

Axygen BioScience, Inc.   (2)
33210 Central Ave, Union City, CA 94587
Tel.: (510) 494-8900
Pharmaceutical & Biotechnology Products Mfr
N.A.I.C.S.: 325411

Subsidiary (Non-US):

Corning Life Sciences B.V.   (2)
Fojostraat 12, 1060 LJ, Amsterdam, Netherlands   (100%)
Tel.: (31) 206596051
Web Site: http://www.corning.com
Sales Range: $25-49.9 Million
Emp.: 80
Laboratory & Filtration Products & Disposable Labware Distr
N.A.I.C.S.: 423490
Nils Kan *(Mng Dir)*

Subsidiary (Domestic):

Mediatech, Inc.   (2)
9345 Discovery Blvd, Manassas, VA 20109
Tel.: (703) 471-5955
Web Site: http://www.cellgro.com
Biological Pharma Products Developer, Mfr & Whslr
N.A.I.C.S.: 325414

Corning (Hainan) Optical Communications Co., Ltd.   (1)
C02-C06 HaiKou Free Trade Zone Nanhai Avenue 168, Haikou, 570216, Hainan, China
Tel.: (86) 89866832031
Glass Product Distr
N.A.I.C.S.: 423460

Corning (Shanghai) Co., Ltd.   (1)
358 Lu Qiao Road Jinqiao Export Processing Zone, Pudong, Shanghai, 201206, China
Tel.: (86) 2150554888
Web Site: http://www.corning.com
Automobile Parts Mfr
N.A.I.C.S.: 336390

Corning B.V.   (1)
Fogostraat 12, 1060 LJ, Amsterdam, Netherlands
Tel.: (31) 206596051
Web Site: https://www.corning.com
Scientific Laboratory Products Mfr
N.A.I.C.S.: 327910

Corning Cable Systems Pty. Ltd.   (1)
211 Wellington Road Building C Level 2, Mulgrave, 3170, VIC, Australia
Tel.: (61) 395382300
Emp.: 60
Flat Glass Mfr
N.A.I.C.S.: 327211
Noel Davidson *(Mgr-Logistics)*

Corning China (Shanghai) Regional Headquarter   (1)
358 Lu Qiao Road Jinqiao Export Processing Zone, Pudong, Shanghai, 201206, China
Tel.: (86) 2122152888
Glass Product Mfr & Distr
N.A.I.C.S.: 327215

Corning Display Technologies (China) Co., Ltd.   (1)
No 26 Kechuang 10th Street, Beijing Economic & Technological Development Area, Beijing, 100176, China
Tel.: (86) 1067873838
Web Site: http://www.corning.com
Glass Substrate Mfr
N.A.I.C.S.: 327215

Corning Display Technologies (Chongqing) Co., Ltd.   (1)
No 8 Yunhan Avenue Shuitu High-Tech Industry Park, Beibei District, Chongqing, 400714, China
Tel.: (86) 2388939888
Glass Product Distr
N.A.I.C.S.: 423460

Corning Display Technologies (Hefei) Co., Ltd.   (1)
No 3399 Wolong Road, Xinzhan District, Hefei, 230012, China
Tel.: (86) 55169111703
Glass Product Distr
N.A.I.C.S.: 423460

Corning Gilbert Inc.   (1)
5310 W Camelback Rd, Glendale, AZ 85301
Tel.: (623) 845-5613
Web Site: http://www.corning.com
Sales Range: $10-24.9 Million
Emp.: 71
Electric Cord Connectors Mfr
N.A.I.C.S.: 335931

Corning Holding GmbH   (1)
Wiesbaden, 65189, Wiesbaden, Germany
Tel.: (49) 61173660
Web Site: http://www.corning.com
Holding Company
N.A.I.C.S.: 551112
Klaus Wellstein *(Mng Dir)*

Subsidiary (Domestic):

Corning GmbH   (2)
Carl-Billand-Strasse 1, 67661, Kaiserslautern, Germany
Tel.: (49) 63135250
Sales Range: $250-299.9 Million
Emp.: 1,200
Optical Component Mfr
N.A.I.C.S.: 327212
Klaus Wellstein *(Mng Dir)*

Corning Optical Communications Germany   (2)
Leipziger Str 121, 10117, Berlin, Germany
Tel.: (49) 3053032100
Communication Equipment Mfr
N.A.I.C.S.: 335929

Corning Holding Japan GK   (1)
Akasaka Intercity 1-11-44 Akasaka, Minato-Ku, Tokyo, 107-0052, Japan
Tel.: (81) 355622605
Web Site: http://www.corning.co.jp
Holding Company
N.A.I.C.S.: 551112

Subsidiary (Domestic):

Corning Japan K.K.   (2)
Akasaka Intercity 1-11-44 Akasaka, Minato-ku, Tokyo, 107-0052, Japan   (100%)
Tel.: (81) 355622260
Web Site: http://www.corning.com
Sales Range: $200-249.9 Million
Homefurnishings
N.A.I.C.S.: 449129
Akihisa Mitsuhashi *(Pres)*

Corning Inc. - Harrodsburg Plant   (1)
680 E Office St, Harrodsburg, KY 40330
Tel.: (859) 734-3341
Web Site: http://www.corning.com
Sales Range: $100-124.9 Million
LCD Glass Mfr
N.A.I.C.S.: 334419

Corning India   (1)
2nd Floor Pioneer Square Sector 62 CPRF Road, Near Golf Course Extension Road, Gurgaon, 122005, Haryana, India   (50%)
Tel.: (91) 1244604000
Web Site: http://www.corning.com
Sales Range: $50-74.9 Million
Emp.: 100
Glass for TV & Display Tubes Mfr
N.A.I.C.S.: 327212
Sudhir Pillai *(Mng Dir)*

Corning International Corporation   (1)
1 Riverfront Plz, Corning, NY 14831-0001   (100%)
Tel.: (607) 974-9000
Web Site: http://www.corning.com
Sales Range: $600-649.9 Million
Holding Company
N.A.I.C.S.: 551112
Wendell P. Weeks *(Chm, Pres & CEO)*

Corning Life Sciences (Wujiang) Co., Ltd.   (1)
T03/17 No 1801 Pang Jin Road Wujiang Economic Development Zone, Wujiang, 215200, Jiang Su, China
Tel.: (86) 51263196555
Lab Instrument Mfr
N.A.I.C.S.: 334516

Corning NetOptix, Inc.   (1)
69 Island St, Keene, NH 03431
Tel.: (603) 357-7662
Optomedical Components Mfr
N.A.I.C.S.: 333310

Corning Optical Communications - UK   (1)
Elwy House Lakeside Business Village, Saint David's Park, Ewloe, CH5 3XD, Flintshire, United Kingdom
Tel.: (44) 1244525325
Emp.: 20
Fiber Optic Cable Whslr
N.A.I.C.S.: 423690

Corning Optical Communications LLC   (1)
1164 23rd St SE, Hickory, NC 28602   (100%)
Tel.: (828) 901-5000
Web Site: http://www.corning.com
Supplier of Fiber Optic Cables, Connectors, Splices, Hardware, Test Equipment & Network Interfaces
N.A.I.C.S.: 335921

Subsidiary (Non-US):

Corning MobileAccess, Inc.   (2)
8391 Old Courthouse Rd, 22182, Vienna, Austria
Tel.: (43) 7038480200
Web Site: http://www.mobileaccess.com

Sales Range: $50-74.9 Million
Emp.: 150
Wireless Network Equipment & Solutions
N.A.I.C.S.: 334220

Corning Optical Communications LLC   (1)
800 17th St NW, Hickory, NC 28601
Tel.: (828) 901-5000
Fiber Optic Cable Mfr
N.A.I.C.S.: 335921

Corning Optical Communications Polska Sp. z o.o.   (1)
Tulipan Park ul Smolice 1e, 95-010, Strykow, Poland
Tel.: (48) 422301100
Fiber Optic Cable Mfr
N.A.I.C.S.: 335921
Piotr Templin *(Mgr-Strategic Sourcing)*

Corning Optical Communications Pty. Ltd.   (1)
211 Wellington Road Building C Level 2, Mulgrave, 3170, VIC, Australia
Tel.: (61) 395382300
Fiber Optic Cable & Display Glass Mfr
N.A.I.C.S.: 335921
Greg Whiffin *(Dir-Comml Ops & Enterprise Networks)*

Corning Optical Communications S. de R.L. de C.V.   (1)
Ant Carr A Roma Km 3 6, San Nicolas de los Garza, 66480, Monterrey, Mexico
Tel.: (52) 8181588400
Glass Products Mfr
N.A.I.C.S.: 327215

Corning Optical Fiber Cable (Chengdu) Co., Ltd.   (1)
1 Siemens Rd High-tech Development Zone, Chengdu, 610042, Sichuan, China
Tel.: (86) 2885182968
Fiber Optic Cable & Display Glass Mfr
N.A.I.C.S.: 335921

Corning Pharmaceutical Glass S.p.A.   (1)
Via Montelungo 4, 56122, Pisa, Italy
Tel.: (39) 050566611
Pharmaceutical Glass Mfr
N.A.I.C.S.: 327212

Corning Pharmaceutical Glass, LLC   (1)
563 Crystal Ave, Vineland, NJ 08360
Tel.: (856) 794-7100
Glass Products Mfr
N.A.I.C.S.: 327215
Matthew Simon *(Mgr-Logistics)*

Corning Precision Materials Company Ltd.   (1)
Asan Plant Manjeondang-Gil 30, Asan, 31452, Tangjeong-Myeon, Korea (South)   (100%)
Tel.: (82) 415201114
Web Site: http://www.scp.samsung.com
Electronics Glass Substrates Mfr
N.A.I.C.S.: 327212

Corning S.A.   (1)
7 bis avenue de Valvins, CS70156, Samois-sur-Seine, 77215, Avon, Cedex, France   (100%)
Tel.: (33) 164697111
Web Site: http://www.corning.com
Sales Range: $25-49.9 Million
Emp.: 100
Ophthalmic Optics Mfr
N.A.I.C.S.: 339113

Corning Specialty Materials, Inc.   (1)
1 Riverfront Plz, Corning, NY 14831
Tel.: (607) 974-9000
Fiber Optic Cable Mfr
N.A.I.C.S.: 335921

Corning Technologies India Private Limited   (1)
D-237 MIDC Phase 2, Chakan Varale, Pune, 410 501, Maharashtra, India
Tel.: (91) 2135667201
Glass Product Distr
N.A.I.C.S.: 423460

Corning Tropel Corp.   (1)
60 O'Connor Rd, Fairport, NY 14450
Tel.: (585) 388-3500

Web Site: http://www.tropel.com
Rev.: $17,300,000
Emp.: 180
Optical Subsystems & Metrology Instrument Mfr
N.A.I.C.S.: 333310

Eurokera (Thailand) Limited (1)
Hemaraj Eastern Seaboard No 500/61 Moo3, Tambol Tasit Amphur P Luakdaeng, Rayong, 21140, Thailand
Tel.: (66) 38950138
Web Site: http://www.eurokera.com
Glass Product Distr
N.A.I.C.S.: 423460

Eurokera Guangzhou Co., Ltd. (1)
Number 11 Building American Industrial Park 48 Hongmian Road, Xinhua Town, Guangzhou, China
Tel.: (86) 2036872266
Flat Glass Mfr
N.A.I.C.S.: 327211

Eurokera North America, Inc. (1)
140 Chase Blvd, Fountain Inn, SC 29644-8082
Tel.: (864) 963-8082
Web Site: http://pyro.eurokera.com
Sales Range: $25-49.9 Million
Emp.: 50
Flat Glass Mfr
N.A.I.C.S.: 327211

Eurokera S.N.C. (1)
1 Avenue du General de Gaulle, Chierry, 02400, Essomes-sur-Marne, France
Tel.: (33) 323848500
Web Site: http://eurokera.com
Glass Product Mfr & Distr
N.A.I.C.S.: 327215

Hemlock Semiconductor, LLC (1)
1805 Salzburg St, Midland, MI 48640
Tel.: (989) 301-5000
Web Site: https://www.hscpoly.com
Polysilicon Material Mfr & Distr
N.A.I.C.S.: 325199
Mark R. Bassett (Chm & CEO)
Philip D. Dembowski (Chief Comml Officer & Sr VP)
Steven M. Sklenar (CFO)
Greggory M. Lubben (Sr Exec VP)
George M. Mesrey (Gen Counsel & Sec)
Mark J. Loboda (Sr VP-Science & Tech)

Subsidiary (Domestic):

Hemlock Semiconductor Operations LLC (2)
12334 Geddes Rd, Hemlock, MI 48626-9409
Tel.: (989) 301-5000
Web Site: https://www.hscpoly.com
Polysilicon Materials Mfr & Whslr
N.A.I.C.S.: 325180
Mark R. Bassett (Chm & CEO)

Innovative Technical Solutions, Inc. (1)
3049 Ualena St Ste 504, Honolulu, HI 96819
Tel.: (808) 839-0646
Web Site: http://www.nova-sol.com
Sales Range: $1-9.9 Million
Emp.: 65
Optical Systems Research & Engineering Services
N.A.I.C.S.: 541990

Keraglass SNC (1)
Rue du Saint Laurent, 77167, Bagneaux-sur-Loing, France
Tel.: (33) 164784700
Web Site: http://www.eurokera.com
Sales Range: $50-74.9 Million
Emp.: 200
Flat Glass Mfr
N.A.I.C.S.: 327211
Gilles Grandpierre (Gen Mgr)

Nine Point Medical (1)
12 Oak Park Dr, Bedford, MA 01730
Tel.: (617) 250-7190
Web Site: http://www.ninepointmedical.com
Surgical & Medical Instrument Mfr
N.A.I.C.S.: 339112
Tom Miller (Chm)
Judith Huber (CFO)
Eman Namati (Pres & CEO)

STRAN Technologies Inc. (1)
39 Great Hill Rd, Naugatuck, CT 06770
Tel.: (203) 720-6500
Web Site: https://www.strantech.com
Electrical Equipment & Component Mfr
N.A.I.C.S.: 335999

Subsidiary (Domestic):

Shane Industries, Inc. (2)
39 Great Hill Rd, Naugatuck, CT 06770
Tel.: (203) 720-6500
Web Site: https://www.shaneindustries.com
Sales Range: $1-9.9 Million
Emp.: 110
Cable Reel Mfr
N.A.I.C.S.: 335999

Shanghai Corning Engineering Corporation (1)
Flat B 6th Floor San Wei Building, No 1266 Nan Jing Road West, Shanghai, 200040, China (50%)
Tel.: (86) 2132224666
Sales Range: $150-199.9 Million
Mfr of Glassware
N.A.I.C.S.: 327212
Eric S. Musser (CEO)

Sorenson Bioscience, Inc. (1)
6507 S 400 W, Salt Lake City, UT 84107
Tel.: (801) 266-9334
Web Site: https://www.sorbio.com
Plastic Liquid Handling Product Mfr
N.A.I.C.S.: 326199

SpiderCloud Wireless, Inc. (1)
475 Sycamore Dr, Milpitas, CA 95035
Tel.: (408) 235-2900
Web Site: http://www.spidercloud.com
Wireless Telecommunication Services
N.A.I.C.S.: 517112

TR Manufacturing, LLC (1)
33210 Central Ave, Union City, CA 94587
Tel.: (510) 494-8900
Web Site: http://www.trmfginc.com
Electronic Connector Mfr
N.A.I.C.S.: 334417

iBwave Solutions Inc. (1)
400 avenue Sainte-Croix Suite 2100, Saint Laurent, H4N 3L4, QC, Canada
Tel.: (514) 397-0606
Web Site: http://www.ibwave.com
Wireless Telecommunication Services
N.A.I.C.S.: 517112

CORNWALL RESOURCES, INC.
301 Carlson Pkwy Ste 301, Minnetonka, MN 55305
Tel.: (952) 258-5500
CORC—(OTCIQ)
Oil & Gas Distr
N.A.I.C.S.: 424720
Robert C. Rhodes (Chm)

CORO GLOBAL INC.
78 SW 7th St Ste 500, Miami, FL 33130 NV
Web Site: http://coro.global
Year Founded: 2005
CGLO—(OTCIQ)
Rev.: $694
Assets: $987,764
Liabilities: $685,751
Net Worth: $302,013
Earnings: ($5,518,401)
Emp.: 2
Fiscal Year-end: 12/31/20
Technology Development Company; Blockchain & Directed Acyclic Graph Mfr
N.A.I.C.S.: 334118
Brian Dorr (COO)

CORPAY, INC.
3280 Peachtree Rd Ste 2400, Atlanta, GA 30305
Tel.: (770) 449-0479 DE
Web Site: https://www.corpay.com
Year Founded: 2000

CPAY—(NYSE)
Rev.: $3,757,719,000
Assets: $15,476,252,000
Liabilities: $12,193,893,000
Net Worth: $3,282,359,000
Earnings: $981,890,000
Emp.: 10,500
Fiscal Year-end: 12/31/23
Financial Investment Services
N.A.I.C.S.: 522320
Ronald F. Clarke (Chm, Pres & CEO)
Armando L. Netto (Pres-Brazil-Grp)
Alan King (Pres-Fuel-Europe,Australia,New Zealand)
Thomas E. Panther (CFO)
Alissa B. Vickery (Chief Acctg Officer)
Dan Csont (CMO)
Mark Schatz (Pres-Prepaid-Grp)

Subsidiaries:

ALE Solutions, Inc. (1)
1 W Illinois St Ste 300, Saint Charles, IL 60174
Tel.: (630) 513-6434
Web Site: http://www.alesolutions.com
Home Insurance Services
N.A.I.C.S.: 524298
Christa Landgraf (VP)
Darlene Adams (Mgr-Client Svcs)
Robert Zimmers (CEO)
Rowena Zimmers (Founder & Pres)
Jessica Knox (Dir-Housing Solutions)
Rene Lindorff (VP-Acctg & Fin)
Matt Nelson (CIO)
Shari Nelson (Dir-HR)

Buyatab Online Inc. (1)
B1 - 788 Beatty Street, Vancouver, V6B 2M1, BC, Canada
Web Site: https://www.web.buyatab.com
Electronic Gift Card Whslr
N.A.I.C.S.: 424990
Moneca Lo (VP-Fin)
Jarnail Dadial (VP-Software Engrg)

CCS Ceska spolecnost pro platebni karty sro (1)
Voctarova 2500/20a, 180 00, Prague, 8, Czech Republic
Tel.: (420) 26 610 8108
Web Site: https://www.ccs.cz
Bank Credit Card Service
N.A.I.C.S.: 522210

CGMP Centro de Gestao de Meios de Pagamentos Ltda. (1)
Minas Bogasian Street 253-Centro, Osasco, Brazil
Tel.: (55) 40021552
Web Site: http://www.semparar.com.br
Commercial Management Services
N.A.I.C.S.: 541618

CH Jones Limited (1)
Unit 3 St James Business Park Grimball Crag Court, Knaresborough, HG5 8QB, North Yorkshire, United Kingdom
Tel.: (44) 1922704455
Web Site: http://www.keyfuels.co.uk
Emp.: 40
Fuel Cards & Fuel Management Solutions
N.A.I.C.S.: 561499

CLC Group, Inc. (1)
8111 E 32nd St N Ste 300, Wichita, KS 67226-2614
Tel.: (316) 636-5055
Web Site: http://www.clclodging.com
Emp.: 220
Lodging Management Services
N.A.I.C.S.: 561599

Cambridge Mercantile (Australia) Pty. Ltd. (1)
35 Clarence Street Level 13 Suite 13 02, Sydney, 2000, NSW, Australia
Tel.: (61) 280766500
Cross-Border Payment Services
N.A.I.C.S.: 522320

Cambridge Mercantile Corp. (1)
212 King Street West Suite 400, Toronto, M5H 1K5, ON, Canada
Tel.: (416) 646-6401
Web Site: http://www.cambridgefx.com
Business-to-Business Payment Services

N.A.I.C.S.: 522320

Subsidiary (US):

Cambridge Mercantile Corp. (U.S.A.) (2)
1350 Broadway Ste 810, New York, NY 10018
Tel.: (212) 594-2200
Web Site: https://www.corpay.com
Business-to-Business Payment Services
N.A.I.C.S.: 522320

Cambridge Mercantile Corp. (U.K.) Ltd. (1)
8-10 Moorgate 4th Floor, London, EC2R 6DA, United Kingdom
Tel.: (44) 2073985700
Cross-Border Payment Services
N.A.I.C.S.: 522320

Cardlink Systems Limited (1)
Private Bag 99918, Newmarket, Auckland, 1149, New Zealand
Tel.: (64) 80 072 7863
Web Site: https://www.cardlink.co.nz
Business Management Services
N.A.I.C.S.: 561110

Comdata Corporation (1)
5301 Maryland Way, Brentwood, TN 37027-5055
Tel.: (615) 370-7000
Web Site: https://www.comdata.com
Sales Range: $250-299.9 Million
Payment Processing Services
N.A.I.C.S.: 522320

Consel Consorzio Elis (1)
Via Sandro Sandri 81, 00159, Rome, Italy
Tel.: (39) 0645924447
Web Site: https://www.elis.org
Educational Institution & Management Training Services
N.A.I.C.S.: 611430

Creative Lodging Solutions, LLC (1)
8111 E 32nd St N Ste 300, Wichita, KS 67226-2614
Tel.: (316) 636-5055
Web Site: https://www.yourcls.com
Corporate Travel & Lodging Solutions
N.A.I.C.S.: 561599
Carolyn Hundley (Chief Culture & Dev Officer)

Crew Transportation Specialists, Inc. (1)
3280 Peachtree Rd Ste 2400, Atlanta, GA 30305
Tel.: (316) 219-4292
Transportation Services
N.A.I.C.S.: 488999

Epyx France SAS (1)
Zone Paris Nord 2 Le Cezanne 35 allee des Impressionnistes CDG, PO Box 58233, 95956, Roissy-en-France, Cedex, France
Tel.: (33) 149900100
Web Site: http://www.epyx.fr
Business Management Services
N.A.I.C.S.: 561110

Epyx Limited (1)
Heath Farm Hampton Lane, Meriden, CV7 7LL, United Kingdom
Tel.: (44) 167 659 1020
Web Site: https://www.epyx.co.uk
Emp.: 95
Business Management Services
N.A.I.C.S.: 561110

FleetCor Czech Republic sro (1)
Voctarova 2500/20a, Liben, 180 00, Prague, Czech Republic
Tel.: (420) 296181204
Web Site: https://fleetcor.cz
Fuel Card & Shell Card Whslr
N.A.I.C.S.: 424720

FleetCor Deutschland GmbH (1)
Frankenstrasse 150c, 90461, Nuremberg, Germany
Tel.: (49) 9111 495 5287
Web Site: https://www.fleetcor.de
Business Management Services
N.A.I.C.S.: 561110
Andrew Blazye (Mng Dir)

FleetCor Europe Limited (1)

Corpay, Inc.—(Continued)

64-65 Vincent Square, London, SW1P 2NU,
United Kingdom
Tel.: (44) 2079329312
Web Site: http://www.FleetCor.com
Sales Range: $25-49.9 Million
Emp.: 20
Financial Transaction Processing Services
N.A.I.C.S.: 522320

FleetCor Fuel Cards (Europe)
Limited   (1)
Richmond House, Sproughton Road, Ips-
wich, IP1 5AN, Suffolk, United Kingdom
Tel.: (44) 1473466666
Web Site:
http://www.thefuelcardcompany.co.uk
Sales Range: $50-74.9 Million
Emp.: 86
Fuel Card Services
N.A.I.C.S.: 424720

FleetCor Slovakia s.r.o.   (1)
Galvaniho 15/C, Ruzinov, 821 04, Brati-
slava, Slovakia
Tel.: (421) 233527874
Web Site: https://fleetcor.sk
Fuel Card & Shell Card Whslr
N.A.I.C.S.: 424720

Fleetcor Poland Spoeka Z Ografni-
zona Odpowiedzialnoscia   (1)
Generation Park Z ul, 00-839, Warsaw,
Poland
Tel.: (48) 222441256
Fuel Card & Shell Card Whslr
N.A.I.C.S.: 424720

Global Processing Companies Rus,
Limited Liability Company   (1)
Dolomanovsky lane 70d, 344011, Rostov-
na-Donu, Russia
Tel.: (7) 8632689315
Web Site: http://www.gpc-rus.ru
Fuel Card & Shell Card Whslr
N.A.I.C.S.: 424720

LJK Companies Inc.   (1)
3600 American Blvd W Ste 300, Blooming-
ton, MN 55431
Tel.: (952) 944-5462
Web Site: http://travellianceinc.com
Comprehensive Lodging Administrative Ser-
vices
N.A.I.C.S.: 721310
Ted Scislowski (CEO)

Subsidiary (Domestic):

Intermotel Leasing, Inc.   (2)
10225 Yellow Cir Dr, Minnetonka, MN
55343
Tel.: (952) 944-2963
Web Site: http://www.travellianceinc.com
Lodging House
N.A.I.C.S.: 721310
Lisa Wing (CEO)

Mannatec, Inc.   (1)
5445 Triangle Pkwy Ste 400, Norcross, GA
30092
Web Site: https://www.mannatec.com
Emp.: 12
Fleet Card Programs for Petroleum Market-
ers
N.A.I.C.S.: 522210

Masternaut B.V.   (1)
Ceresstraat 1, 4811 CA, Breda, Netherlands
Tel.: (31) 852732100
Vehicle Tracking Services
N.A.I.C.S.: 488410

Masternaut Iberica SL   (1)
Calle Lopez de Hoyos 42, 28006, Madrid,
Spain
Tel.: (34) 916509930
Vehicle Tracking Services
N.A.I.C.S.: 488410

Nvoicepay, Inc.   (1)
8905 SW Nimbus Ave Ste 240, Beaverton,
OR 97008
Web Site: http://www.nvoicepay.com
Electronic Payment Services
N.A.I.C.S.: 522320
Karla Friede (Co-Founder & CEO)
John Ewert (CFO & COO)
Shaun McAravey (Co-Founder & CTO)
Tana Law (Co-Founder & Sr VP)
Derek Halpern (Sr VP-Sls)

P97 Networks Inc.   (1)
2050 W Sam Houston Pkwy S Ste 900,
Houston, TX 77042
Web Site: https://www.p97.com
Mobile Commerce & Digital Marketing Ser-
vices
N.A.I.C.S.: 541613
Donald Frieden (Chm, Pres & CEO)
Bryan Olivier (COO)
Sharon Brown (Sec & VP-Fin)
Steve Moses (VP-Compliance)
Dae Kim (Chief Strategy Officer)
Paul Cwalina (Sr VP-Sls)
David Nichamoff (VP-Innovation)
Saurabh Choudhary (VP-Engrg)
Kevin Halloran (Gen Counsel)

Plugsurfing GmbH   (1)
Weserstrasse 175, 12045, Berlin, Germany
Tel.: (49) 30959981410
Web Site: http://www.plugsurfing.com
Electric Vehicle Charging Services
N.A.I.C.S.: 457120

R2C Online Limited   (1)
2 Vantage Drive, Sheffield, S9 1RG, South
Yorkshire, United Kingdom
Tel.: (44) 114 399 2430
Web Site: https://www.r2conline.com
Information Technology Services
N.A.I.C.S.: 541519
Nick Walls (Mng Dir)
Laurence Vaughan (Chm)
Paul Waterhaouse (Fin Dir)
Tim Griffiths (Dir-Ops)
Jason Fitzgerald (Sls Dir)

Stored Value Solutions International
B.V.   (1)
Hoogoorddreef 15, 1101 BA, Amsterdam,
Netherlands
Tel.: (31) 205222555
Business Management Services
N.A.I.C.S.: 561110

The Fuelcard Company UK Ltd.   (1)
St James Business Park Grimbald Crag
Court, Knaresborough, HG5 8QB, Suffolk,
United Kingdom
Tel.: (44) 845 456 1400
Web Site: https://www.fuelcards.co.uk
Sales Range: $50-74.9 Million
Emp.: 10
Petroleum Product Whslr
N.A.I.C.S.: 424720

TravelCard, B.V.   (1)
P J Oudweg 4, PO Box 1314, 1300 BH,
Almere, Netherlands
Tel.: (31) 881105000
Web Site: https://www.travelcard.nl
Traveling Card Services
N.A.I.C.S.: 522210

VB SERVICIOS, COMERCIO E AD-
MINISTRACAO LTDA   (1)
Rua Vitoria 211 Sala 01, Sao Paulo, 06529-
200, Brazil
Tel.: (55) 1133512020
Business Management Services
N.A.I.C.S.: 561110

Venturo Technologies S.a.r.l.   (1)
46A Avenue JF Kennedy, 1855, Luxem-
bourg, Luxembourg
Tel.: (352) 28261456
Commercial Payment Services
N.A.I.C.S.: 541214

CORPORATE RESTAURANT CONCEPTS, INC.

6721 W 121st St Ste 200, Overland
Park, KS 66209
Tel.: (913) 808-3673   DE
Year Founded: 2008
CRSQ—(OTCIQ)
Restaurant Operators
N.A.I.C.S.: 722511
Mary L. Bell (Pres)
Shelly Williams (Asst Sec)

CORPORATE UNIVERSE, INC.

1 World Trade Ctr 85th Fl, New York,
NY 10007
Tel.: (302) 273-1150   DE
Year Founded: 1986

COUV—(OTCEM)

Assets: $2,419,502
Liabilities: $3,861,034
Net Worth: ($1,441,532)
Earnings: ($2,155,240)
Emp.: 8
Fiscal Year-end: 12/31/22
Finance Investment Services
N.A.I.C.S.: 523999
Jack Brooks (Pres)

CORRELATE ENERGY CORP.

176 S Capitol Blvd 2nd Fl, Boise, ID
83702
Tel.: (318) 425-5000   NV
Web Site:
https://www.correlate.energy
CIPI—(OTCQB)
Rev.: $3,403,648
Assets: $2,256,955
Liabilities: $5,062,629
Net Worth: ($2,805,674)
Earnings: ($7,162,908)
Emp.: 9
Fiscal Year-end: 12/31/22
Bioceutical Research & Development
N.A.I.C.S.: 325412
Matthew C. Flemming (Pres)
Channing F. Chen (CFO)
Todd Michaels (CEO)
Dave Bailey (Chief Revenue Officer)
Jed Freedlander (Chief Dev Officer)
Roger Baum (Exec VP-Operations)
Jason Loyet (Dir-Solar Energy &
Storage)
Tom Kunhardt (Dir-Customer Suc-
cess)

CORSAIR GAMING, INC.

115 N McCarthy Blvd, Milpitas, CA
95035
Tel.: (510) 657-8747   DE
Web Site: https://www.corsair.com
Year Founded: 2017
CRSR—(NASDAQ)
Rev.: $1,375,098,000
Assets: $1,297,245,000
Liabilities: $641,811,000
Net Worth: $655,434,000
Earnings: ($54,388,000)
Emp.: 2,480
Fiscal Year-end: 12/31/22
Hardware Component Distr
N.A.I.C.S.: 423430
Michael G. Potter (CFO)
Carina Tan (Gen Counsel & VP)
Pete Hilliard (Chief HR Officer)
Andrew J. Paul (Founder & CEO)
Thi L. La (Pres & COO)

CORSAIR PARTNERING COR-PORATION

717 5th Ave 24th Fl, New York, NY
10022
Tel.: (212) 224-9400   Ky
Web Site: https://www.corsair-
capital.com
Year Founded: 2020
CORS—(NYSE)
Rev.: $4,275,995
Assets: $285,735,367
Liabilities: $300,381,450
Net Worth: ($14,646,083)
Earnings: $13,194,575
Emp.: 2
Fiscal Year-end: 12/31/22
Investment Services
N.A.I.C.S.: 523999
Jeremy S. Schein (Pres & CFO)
D.T. Ignacio Jayanti (CEO)

CORTEVA, INC.

9330 Zionsville Rd, Indianapolis, IN
46268   DE
Web Site: https://www.corteva.com
Year Founded: 2018

CTVA—(NYSE)

Rev.: $17,226,000,000
Assets: $42,996,000,000
Liabilities: $17,717,000,000
Net Worth: $25,279,000,000
Earnings: $735,000,000
Emp.: 22,500
Fiscal Year-end: 12/31/23
Holding Company; Agricultural Solu-
tions Services
N.A.I.C.S.: 551112
Rajan Gajaria (Exec VP)
Timothy P. Glenn (Chief Comml Offi-
cer & Exec VP)
Meghan Cassidy (Chief HR & Diver-
sity Officer, Chief Diversity Officer &
Chief HR & Diversity Officer)
Sam Eathington (CTO & Sr VP)
Cornel B. Fuerer (Gen Counsel & Sr
VP)
Debra King (CIO & Sr VP)
Charles Victor Magro (CEO)
Brian Titus (Principal Acctg Officer,
VP & Controller)
Robert King (Exec VP)
Brook Cunningham (Chief Strategy
Officer)
Audrey Grimm (Sr VP)
David P. Johnson (CFO & Exec VP)

Subsidiaries:

AG (Shanghai) Agriculture Technol-
ogy Co., Ltd.   (1)
Room 806 No 488 Yaohua Road Pudong
NewArea, Shanghai, 200126, China
Tel.: (86) 2168869130
Web Site: http://www.agsh.com.cn
Biopharmaceutical Product Research & De-
velopment Services
N.A.I.C.S.: 541714

Agrigenetics, Inc.   (1)
9330 Zionsville Rd, Indianapolis, IN
46268   (88.11%)
Web Site: http://www.mycogen.com
Agronomic Crop Research Services
N.A.I.C.S.: 541715

Subsidiary (Domestic):

Corteva Agriscience LLC   (2)
9330 Zionsville Rd, Indianapolis, IN
46268-1053   (51%)
Tel.: (317) 337-3000
Web Site: http://engage.corteva.com
Rev.: $3,400,000,000
Emp.: 5,500
Agricultural Chemical Mfr
N.A.I.C.S.: 325320

Subsidiary (Domestic):

Alforex Seeds LLC   (3)
18369 County Rd 96, Woodland, CA 95695
Tel.: (530) 666-3331
Web Site: https://www.alforexseeds.com
Seed Producer
N.A.I.C.S.: 311224

Division (Domestic):

Alforex Seeds LLC   (4)
N4505 County Rd M, West Salem, WI
54669
Tel.: (608) 786-1554
Web Site: http://www.alforexseeds.com
Seed Distr
N.A.I.C.S.: 424450

Subsidiary (Non-US):

Nantong DAS Chemical Co., Ltd.   (3)
No 60 Yongxing Road Gangzha Econo, De-
velopment Zone, Nantong, 226003, China
Tel.: (86) 51385305353
Agricultural Chemical Mfr
N.A.I.C.S.: 325320

Caszyme, UAB   (1)
Sauletekio av 7C, 10257, Vilnius, Lithuania
Tel.: (370) 69400210
Web Site: https://caszyme.com
Software Development Services
N.A.I.C.S.: 541511

Centen AG LLC (1)
974 Ctr Rd, Wilmington, DE 19805
Tel.: (302) 485-3000
Holding Company
N.A.I.C.S.: 551112

Corteva Agriscience (Cambodia) Co., Ltd. (1)
Regency Square C Ground Floor Unit 30C/168 Mao Tse Tong Blvd 245, Phum 3 Tumnob Tuek Khan Chamkamon, Phnom Penh, 120108, Cambodia
Tel.: (855) 92777527
Web Site: https://www.kh.corteva.com
Agricultural Services
N.A.I.C.S.: 926140

Corteva Agriscience (Singapore) Pte. Ltd. (1)
21 Biopolis Road Nucleos South Tower 07-21, Singapore, 138567, Singapore
Tel.: (65) 64611000
Agrochemical Product Mfr & Distr
N.A.I.C.S.: 325320

Corteva Agriscience (Thailand) Co., Ltd. (1)
6 Floor M Thai Tower All Season Place 87 Wireless Rd, Lumpini Plathumwan, Bangkok, 10300, Thailand
Tel.: (66) 27922913
Web Site: https://www.th.corteva.com
Farming Services
N.A.I.C.S.: 115116

Corteva Agriscience Australia PTY Ltd. (1)
Locked Bag 2002, Chatswood, 2057, NSW, Australia
Tel.: (61) 1800700096
Web Site: https://www.corteva.com.au
Farming Services
N.A.I.C.S.: 115116

Corteva Agriscience Bulgaria EOOD (1)
Mladost IV Business Park Sofia Building No 1A 1st Floor, 1766, Sofia, Bulgaria
Tel.: (359) 24899160
Web Site: http://www.corteva.bg
Farm Management Services
N.A.I.C.S.: 115116

Corteva Agriscience Canada Company (1)
Suite 2450 215-2nd Street SW, Calgary, T2P 1M4, AB, Canada
Web Site: https://www.corteva.ca
Agricultural Services
N.A.I.C.S.: 926140

Corteva Agriscience Croatia LLC (1)
Florijana Andraseca 18 A, 10000, Zagreb, Croatia
Tel.: (385) 12958000
Web Site: https://www.corteva.hr
Agricultural Services
N.A.I.C.S.: 926140

Corteva Agriscience Czech s.r.o. (1)
Pekarska 14/628, Jinonice, 155 00, Prague, 5, Czech Republic
Tel.: (420) 602129528
Web Site: http://www.corteva.cz
Farm Management Services
N.A.I.C.S.: 115116

Corteva Agriscience Egypt LLC (1)
Fourth Floor Fifth Settlement 67 El Tessein Street, New Cairo, Egypt
Tel.: (20) 226131885
Web Site: http://www.eg.corteva.com
Farm Management Services
N.A.I.C.S.: 115116

Corteva Agriscience Germany GmbH (1)
Riedenburger Str 7, 81677, Munich, Germany
Tel.: (49) 89455330
Web Site: https://www.corteva.de
Agricultural Services
N.A.I.C.S.: 926140

Corteva Agriscience Hellas S.A. (1)
2 Hydras and 280 Kifissias Ave, Chalandri, 15232, Athens, Greece
Tel.: (30) 2106889717
Web Site: http://www.corteva.gr
Farm Management Services

N.A.I.C.S.: 115116

Corteva Agriscience Kenya Limited (1)
Keystone Park Wing B 3rd Floor Riverside Drive, PO Box 53384, Nairobi, Kenya
Tel.: (254) 709142000
Web Site: https://www.corteva.co.ke
Farming Services
N.A.I.C.S.: 115116

Corteva Agriscience Korea Ltd. (1)
HSBC Building 15F 37 Chilpae-ro, Jung-gu, Seoul, Korea (South)
Tel.: (82) 222238900
Web Site: http://www.corteva.co.kr
Farm Management Services
N.A.I.C.S.: 115116

Corteva Agriscience Lithuania UAB (1)
Spaces verslo centras Gedimino pr 44A, Vilnius, 01110, Lithuania
Tel.: (370) 52100260
Web Site: http://www.corteva.lt
Farm Management Services
N.A.I.C.S.: 115116

Corteva Agriscience Maroc SARL (1)
Oasis Square Building 6 2nd floor - No 217 Oasis, 20410, Casablanca, Morocco
Tel.: (212) 529055192
Web Site: https://www.corteva.ma
Agricultural Services
N.A.I.C.S.: 926140

Corteva Agriscience Netherlands B.V. (1)
Zuid-Oostsingel 24 D, 4611 BB, Bergen-op-Zoom, Netherlands
Tel.: (31) 164444000
Web Site: https://www.corteva.nl
Farming Services
N.A.I.C.S.: 115116

Corteva Agriscience New Zealand Ltd. (1)
Private Bag 2017, New Plymouth, 4342, New Zealand
Tel.: (64) 67577812
Web Site: https://www.corteva.co.nz
Farming Services
N.A.I.C.S.: 115116

Corteva Agriscience Pakistan Limited (1)
26-FCC 2nd Floor Syed Maratab Ali Road Gulberg IV, Lahore, Pakistan
Tel.: (92) 42357113039
Web Site: http://www.corteva.pk
Farm Management Services
N.A.I.C.S.: 115116

Corteva Agriscience Philippines, Inc. (1)
8th Floor ISquare Building 15 Meralco Avenue, Pasig, 1605, Metro Manila, Philippines
Tel.: (63) 28189911
Web Site: https://www.corteva.ph
Farming Services
N.A.I.C.S.: 115116

Corteva Agriscience Poland Sp. z o.o. (1)
Jozefa Piusa Dziekonskiego 1, 00-728, Warsaw, Poland
Tel.: (48) 225487300
Web Site: https://www.corteva.pl
Farming Services
N.A.I.C.S.: 115116

Corteva Agriscience Romania S.R.L. (1)
Soseaua Bucuresti-Ploiesti nr 42 -44, Baneasa Business Technology Park cladirea B etaj 2 Sector 1, Bucharest, Romania
Tel.: (40) 316204100
Web Site: https://www.corteva.ro
Agricultural Services
N.A.I.C.S.: 926140

Corteva Agriscience SRB d.o.o. (1)
Kis Ernea 4, 21000, Novi Sad, Serbia
Tel.: (381) 216742240
Web Site: https://www.corteva.rs
Agricultural Services
N.A.I.C.S.: 926140

Corteva Agriscience Uruguay S.A. (1)
Eduardo Carbajal 2972, 11800, Montevideo, Uruguay
Tel.: (598) 22005899
Web Site: https://www.corteva.uy
Farming Services
N.A.I.C.S.: 115116

Corteva Agriscience Vietnam Co., Ltd. (1)
Tang 12 toa nha Central Plaza 17 Le Duan, Phuong Ben Nghe Quan 1, Ho Chi Minh City, Vietnam
Tel.: (84) 2838288921
Web Site: https://www.corteva.vn
Agricultural Services
N.A.I.C.S.: 926140

Corteva Agriscience Zambia Limited (1)
Plot No 35283 Mwembeshi Road, PO Box 33282, Heavy Industrial Area, Lusaka, Zambia
Tel.: (260) 211846299
Web Site: https://www.zm.corteva.com
Farming Services
N.A.I.C.S.: 115116

Corteva Crop Solutions HUN Kft. (1)
Boldizsar U 4, 1112, Budapest, Hungary
Tel.: (36) 12727888
Web Site: https://www.corteva.hu
Farming Services
N.A.I.C.S.: 115116

DASER AGRO S.A. (1)
Ruta 26 km 42 5, 3153, Victoria, Entre Rios, Argentina (50%)
Tel.: (54) 3436424800
Web Site: https://daseragro.com.ar
Farm Supplies Whslr
N.A.I.C.S.: 424910
Omar Perea (Mgr-JV)

Dow AgroSciences B.V (1)
Herbert H Dowweg 5, PO Box 522, 4530 AM, Terneuzen, Netherlands (100%)
Tel.: (31) 115674320
Sales Range: >$250-299.9 Million
Emp.: 1,000
Agricultural Chemical Mfr
N.A.I.C.S.: 325320
Arnd Thomas (Mng Dir-Ops)

Subsidiary (Non-US):

Ambito DAS S.A. (2)
Dr Carlos Sodini 423, Alejandro Roca, 2686, Argentina
Tel.: (54) 3584980253
Chemical Products Distr
N.A.I.C.S.: 424690

ChacoDAS S.A. (2)
San Martin 926 1st Floor, Reconquista, Santa Fe, Argentina
Tel.: (54) 3482420768
Web Site: http://www.chacodas.com
Chemical Products Distr
N.A.I.C.S.: 424690

Corteva Agriscience Argentina S.R.L. (2)
Avenida Libertador 101 Piso 1, Vicente Lopez, 1638, Buenos Aires, Argentina
Tel.: (54) 1141100202
Web Site: https://www.corteva.com.ar
Agricultural Chemical Mfr
N.A.I.C.S.: 325320

Corteva Agriscience Bolivia S.A. (2)
Av San Martin 1800 Edificio Tacuaral 2o Piso Of 205, Santa Cruz, 95060, Bolivia
Tel.: (591) 33416464
Web Site: https://www.corteva.bo
Chemical Products Mfr
N.A.I.C.S.: 325199

Corteva Agriscience Czech s.r.o. (2)
Pekarska 14/628, Jinonice, 155 00, Prague, 5, Czech Republic
Tel.: (420) 602129528
Web Site: https://www.corteva.cz
Chemical Products Mfr
N.A.I.C.S.: 325199

Corteva Agriscience Denmark A/S (2)

Langebrogade 3H, 1411, Copenhagen, Denmark (100%)
Tel.: (45) 280800
Web Site: https://www.corteva.dk
Agricultural Chemicals Sales
N.A.I.C.S.: 325998

Corteva Agriscience France SAS (2)
1 bis avene du 8 mai 1945 Immeuble Equinoxe II, PO Box 1220, Sophia Antipolis, 7280, Guyancourt, France (100%)
Tel.: (33) 800470810
Web Site: https://www.corteva.fr
Agro Products & Services
N.A.I.C.S.: 325998

Corteva Agriscience Germany GmbH (2)
Riedenburger Str 7, 81677, Munich, Germany (100%)
Tel.: (49) 89455330
Web Site: https://www.corteva.de
Agricultural Chemical Mfr
N.A.I.C.S.: 325320

Corteva Agriscience UK Limited (2)
CPC2 Capital Park Fulbourn, Cambridge, CB21 5XE, Cambridgeshire, United Kingdom
Tel.: (44) 1462457272
Web Site: https://www.corteva.co.uk
Agricultural Chemical Mfr
N.A.I.C.S.: 325320

Corteva Agriscience de Colombia S.A.S. (2)
Teleport Calle 113 7-21 oficina 1401, Bogota, Colombia
Tel.: (57) 6012595900
Web Site: https://www.corteva.co
Crop Protection Services
N.A.I.C.S.: 115112

Desab S.A. (2)
1846 Av San Martin, Buenos Aires, Argentina
Tel.: (54) 3382438300
Web Site: http://www.desab.com.ar
Agricultural Develpment Services
N.A.I.C.S.: 926140
Raul Zaratiegui (Branch Mgr-Marcos Juarez)

Dintec Agroquimica Produtos Quimicos, Lda. (2)
Avenida Arriaga 77 Sala 504, Ilha Da Madeira, Funchal, 9000-060, Portugal
Tel.: (351) 291223254
Emp.: 2
Chemical Products Mfr
N.A.I.C.S.: 325199

Dow AgroSciences (Malaysia) Sdn Bhd (2)
Level 6 CP Tower Jalan 16/11 Pusat Dagang Section 16, 46350, Petaling Jaya, Selangor Darul Ehsan, Malaysia (100%)
Tel.: (60) 379655300
Animal Feeds, Fertilizers, Agricultural Chemicals & Other Farm Supplies Distr
N.A.I.C.S.: 325320

Dow AgroSciences (NZ) Limited (2)
Private Bag 2017, New Plymouth, 4342, New Zealand (100%)
Tel.: (64) 67577812
Web Site: https://www.corteva.co.nz
Agricultural Chemicals Sales & Distr
N.A.I.C.S.: 325320

Dow AgroSciences Australia Limited (2)
Locked Bag 2002, Chatswood, 2057, NSW, Australia (100%)
Tel.: (61) 80 070 0096
Web Site: https://www.corteva.com.au
Crop Protection Services
N.A.I.C.S.: 115112

Subsidiary (Domestic):

Advantage Wheats Pty Ltd (3)
56 Araba Street, Aranda, Canberra, 2614, ACT, Australia
Tel.: (61) 415931464
Web Site: http://www.hrzwheats.com.au
Wheat Farming Services
N.A.I.C.S.: 111140
Paul Kelly (Sec)
Neil Comben (Gen Mgr)

Corteva, Inc.—(Continued)

Subsidiary (Non-US):

Dow AgroSciences B.V.-Philippines (2)
8th Floor Isquare Building 15 Meralco Avenue, Pasig, 1605, Metro Manila, Philippines
Tel.: (63) 28189911
Web Site: https://www.corteva.ph
Organic & Inorganic Chemicals Mfr
N.A.I.C.S.: 325998

Dow AgroSciences Canada Inc. (2)
Suite 2400 215-2nd Street SW, Calgary, T2P 1M4, AB, Canada (100%)
Tel.: (708) 998-4833
Web Site: http://www.corteva.ca
Agricultural Chemicals & Biological Products Developer, Mfr & Distr
N.A.I.C.S.: 325320
Bryce Eger (Pres)

Unit (Domestic):

Dow AgroSciences Canada Inc. - Saskatoon (3)
101 421 Downey Rd, Saskatoon, S7N 4L8, SK, Canada (100%)
Tel.: (306) 657-3351
Web Site: http://www.dowagro.ca
Sales Range: $10-24.9 Million
Emp.: 40
Agricultural Chemical Mfr
N.A.I.C.S.: 325320

Subsidiary (Non-US):

Dow AgroSciences Chile S.A. (2)
Gran Avenida 1621, Metropolitan Region, Santiago, Paine, Chile (100%)
Tel.: (56) 22 836 7000
Web Site: https://www.corteva.cl
Agricultural Chemical Distr
N.A.I.C.S.: 325320

Dow AgroSciences Costa Rica S.A. (2)
Edificio Torre Mercedes 6th Floor, Paseo Colon, San Jose, Costa Rica (100%)
Tel.: (506) 22587110
Web Site: http://www.corteva.cr
Agricultural Chemicals Sales & Distr
N.A.I.C.S.: 325320

Dow AgroSciences Iberica S.A. (2)
Ribera Del Loira N 4-6 Edificio Iris - 4 Planta, 28042, Madrid, Spain (100%)
Tel.: (34) 977 54 36 20
Web Site: http://www.corteva.es
Agricultural Chemical Mfr
N.A.I.C.S.: 325320
Anton Valero (Mng Dir)

Dow AgroSciences Industrial Ltda. (2)
Alameda Itapecuru 506 Alphaville Industrial, Barueri, Sao Paulo, 06454-080, Brazil
Tel.: (55) 800 772 2492
Web Site: https://www.corteva.com.br
Crop Protection Services
N.A.I.C.S.: 115112

Dow AgroSciences Pacific Limited (2)
47/F Sun Hung Kai Ctr 30 Harbour Rd, Wanchai, China (Hong Kong)
Tel.: (852) 28797333
Crop Protection Services
N.A.I.C.S.: 115112

Dow AgroSciences Paraguay S.A. (2)
Lopez Moreira Casi Aviadores Del Chaco Edificio Royal Tower Piso 4, Asuncion, 1766, Paraguay
Tel.: (595) 21613412
Web Site: http://www.corteva.com.py
Chemical Products Mfr
N.A.I.C.S.: 325199

Dow AgroSciences Polska Sp z.o.o. (2)
Jozefa Piusa Dziekonskiego 1, 00-728, Warsaw, Poland (100%)
Tel.: (48) 225487300
Web Site: https://www.corteva.pl
Agricultural Chemicals Sales
N.A.I.C.S.: 325320

Paluch Andrzej (Pres)

Dow AgroSciences Switzerland S.A. (2)
Bachtobelstrasse 4, Horgen, 8810, Switzerland (100%)
Tel.: (41) 447282111
Web Site: http://www.ch.dow.com
Crop Protection Services
N.A.I.C.S.: 115112
Heinz Haller (Pres-EMEA & Exec VP)

Dow AgroSciences Taiwan Ltd. (2)
14 F 167 DunHwa N Rd, 105, Taipei, Taiwan
Tel.: (886) 87711101
Organic & Inorganic Chemicals Mfr
N.A.I.C.S.: 325998

Dow AgroSciences Technology GmbH (2)
Bachtobelstrasse 4, 8810, Horgen, Switzerland
Tel.: (41) 447282111
Chemical Products Mfr
N.A.I.C.S.: 325199

Dow AgroSciences de Mexico S.A. de C.V. (2)
Carretera Guadalajara-Morelia Km21 No 8601-B C P, Tlajomulco de Zuniga, 45645, Guadalajara, Morelia, Mexico (100%)
Tel.: (52) 36797979
Web Site: https://www.corteva.mx
Crop Protection Services
N.A.I.C.S.: 115112

Dow Agrosciences (Thailand) Ltd. (2)
6 Floor M Thai Tower All Season Place 87 Wireless Rd, Lumpini Plathumwan, Bangkok, 10300, Thailand
Tel.: (66) 27922913
Polystyrene Resins & Polyurethanes Mfr
N.A.I.C.S.: 325211

Dow Venezuela, C.A. (2)
Ave Principal La Castellana Edif Banco Lara Piso 7 Of A1 y A2, La Castellana, Caracas, Venezuela
Tel.: (58) 22653371
Web Site: http://www.corteva.com.ve
Chemical Mfr & Distr
N.A.I.C.S.: 424690

Fedea S.A. (2)
Av San Martin 1151 Norte, 6360, General Pico, La Pampa, Argentina
Tel.: (54) 2302438200
Web Site: https://www.fedea.com.ar
Pesticide Mfr
N.A.I.C.S.: 325320

Forratec Argentina S.A. (2)
Monsenor Magliano 3061, San Isidro, B1642GLA, Buenos Aires, Argentina
Tel.: (54) 11 5230 2800
Web Site: http://www.forratec.com.ar
Agricultural Farming Services
N.A.I.C.S.: 111199

Rindes y Cultivos DAS S.A. (2)
Tel.: (54) 2494446850
Web Site: http://www.rycdas.com.ar
Agricultural Farming Services
N.A.I.C.S.: 111199

Ubajay DAS S.A. (2)
Ruta 18 Km 150 5, CP 3240, Villaguay, Entre Rios, Argentina
Tel.: (54) 345515456104
Web Site: https://www.ubajaydas.com.ar
Chemical Products Distr
N.A.I.C.S.: 424690

Dow AgroSciences India Pvt. Ltd. (1)
1st floor Block B Gate 02 Godrej IT Park, Godrej Business District Pirojshanagar L B S Marg Vikhroli West, Mumbai, 400079, India (100%)
Tel.: (91) 9833496732
Web Site: https://www.corteva.in
Agricultural Chemicals Mfr & Whslr
N.A.I.C.S.: 325320

Dow AgroSciences Southern Africa (Proprietary) Limited (1)
272 West Avenuew Lakefield Office Park

Building A 2nd Floor, Centurion, 157, South Africa (100%)
Tel.: (27) 126835700
Web Site: https://www.corteva.co.za
Crop Protection Whslr
N.A.I.C.S.: 424910

DuPont Hellas S.A. (1)
Halandri Ydras 2 and Kifisias Avenue 280r, 15232, Athens, Greece
Tel.: (30) 2106889700
Chemicals Mfr
N.A.I.C.S.: 325998

DuPont Magyarorszag Kft (1)
Neumann Janos u 1, 2040, Budaors, Hungary
Tel.: (36) 23447400
Web Site: http://www.corteva.hu
Farm Management Services
N.A.I.C.S.: 115116

DuPont Poland Sp z o.o. (1)
Ul Postepu 17B, 02-676, Warsaw, Poland
Tel.: (48) 223200900
Web Site: http://www.dupont.pl
Chemicals Mfr
N.A.I.C.S.: 325998

DuPont Romania S.R.L. (1)
Bucharest-Ploiesti road no 42-44, Baneasa Business & Technology Park building B 2nd floor Sector 1, 013685, Bucharest, Romania
Tel.: (40) 316204100
Web Site: https://www.corteva.ro
Electronic Products Mfr
N.A.I.C.S.: 334419

DuPont Turkey Endustri Urunleri Limited Sirketi (1)
Barbaros Mah Kardelen Sok Palladium Tower Is Merkezi No 2 K 12, Atasehir, 34746, Istanbul, Turkiye
Tel.: (90) 216 687-0400
Web Site: https://www.dupont.com.tr
Organic Chemical Mfr
N.A.I.C.S.: 325199

EIDP, Inc. (1)
9330 Zionsville Rd, Indianapolis, IN 46268
Web Site: https://www.corteva.com
Rev.: $17,225,999,999
Assets: $43,373,000,000
Liabilities: $17,713,000,000
Net Worth: $25,660,000,000
Earnings: $730,000,000
Emp.: 22,499
Fiscal Year-end: 12/31/2023
Miscellaneous Chemical Products & Preparation Mfr
N.A.I.C.S.: 325211
Brian Titus (VP & Controller)

Subsidiary (Non-US):

Du Pont Far East, Inc. (2)
8th Floor iSquare Building 15 Meralco Avenue, Pasig, 1605, Metro Manila, Philippines
Tel.: (63) 28189911
Web Site: http://www.dupont.ph
Industrial Chemical Whslr
N.A.I.C.S.: 424690

DuPont (Australia) Ltd. (2)
Level 3 7 Eden Park Drive, Macquarie Park, 2113, NSW, Australia (100%)
Tel.: (61) 299236111
Web Site: http://www.dupont.com.au
Textile Fibers, Pigments & Agricultural Chemicals Mfr
N.A.I.C.S.: 314999
James C. Collins Jr. (Exec VP & Sr VP)
David Fawcett (Mgr-MCC)

DuPont (Thailand) Limited (2)
6-7th Floor M Thai Tower All Seasons Place 87 Wireless Road, Lumpini Phatumwan, Bangkok, 10330, Thailand
Tel.: (66) 26594000
Web Site: http://www.dupont.co.th
Industrial Solution Provider
N.A.I.C.S.: 541611

DuPont (U.K.) Ltd. (2)
4th Floor Kings Court London Road, Stevenage, SG1 2NG, Hertfordshire, United Kingdom (100%)
Tel.: (44) 1438734000
Chemicals Mfr
N.A.I.C.S.: 325998

Division (Domestic):

DuPont Agriculture & Nutrition (2)
974 Ctr Rd, Wilmington, DE 19805
Tel.: (302) 485-3000
Insecticides, Fungicides, Herbicides & Animal Feed Supplements Mfr
N.A.I.C.S.: 325320

Subsidiary (Domestic):

Dupont Agricultural Products (3)
2830 US Hwy 24 E, El Paso, IL 61738
Tel.: (309) 527-5115
Agriculture Product Distr
N.A.I.C.S.: 424910

Pioneer Hi-Bred International, Inc. (3)
7300 NW 62nd Ave, Johnston, IA 50131 (100%)
Tel.: (515) 535-3200
Web Site: http://www.pioneer.com
Hybrid Seed Corn, Wheat, Alfalfa, Sunflower, Sorghum, Soybean, Microbial Genetic Inoculants, Hay & Livestock Mfr
N.A.I.C.S.: 424910
Bethany Drendel (Mgr-Territory)
Jeffrey W. Crom (Mgr-Acct)
Garrett Carver (Mgr-Territory)
Luke Stamp (Mgr-Acct)
Chad Arp (Mgr-Territory)
Brian Renze (Mgr-Acct)

Subsidiary (Non-US):

MISR Pioneer Seeds Company S.A.E. (4)
67 El Tessein Street Fifth Settlement, New Cairo, Helwan, Egypt
Tel.: (20) 1 2744 2933
Corn, Wheat & Other Hybrid Agricultural Seeds & Related Products Distr
N.A.I.C.S.: 424910

PHI Seeds Private Limited (4)
3rd Floor Babukhans Millenium Centre H No 6-3-1099/1100, Raj Bhavan Road Somajiguda, Hyderabad, 500 082, India
Tel.: (91) 4030434400
Corn, Wheat & Other Hybrid Agricultural Seeds & Related Products Distr
N.A.I.C.S.: 424910

Pioneer Argentina, S.R.L. (4)
Ing Butty 240 piso 11, Buenos Aires, Argentina
Tel.: (54) 11 4717 9100
Corn, Soybeans, Sunflowers, Sorghum & Other Agricultural Products Distr
N.A.I.C.S.: 424910

Pioneer Hi-Bred (Thailand) Co. Limited (4)
6-7th Floor M Thai Tower All Seasons Place 87 Wireless Road Lumpini, Phatumwan, Bangkok, 10300, Thailand
Tel.: (66) 27922900
Corn & Other Hybrid Agricultural Seeds & Related Products Distr
N.A.I.C.S.: 424910

Pioneer Hi-Bred Australia, Pty Ltd. (4)
204 Toowoomba Karara Rd, Toowoomba, 4350, QLD, Australia
Tel.: (61) 746372966
Web Site: https://www.pioneerseeds.com.au
Corn, Wheat & Other Hybrid Agricultural Seeds & Related Products Distr
N.A.I.C.S.: 424910

Pioneer Hi-Bred Canada Company (4)
7398 Queen's Line, Chatham, N7M 5L1, ON, Canada
Tel.: (519) 352-6350
Web Site: https://www.pioneer.com
Corn, Wheat & Other Hybrid Agricultural Seeds & Related Products Distr
N.A.I.C.S.: 424910

Plant (Domestic):

Pioneer Hi-Bred Ltd. (5)
Site 600 RR#6, PO Box 12, Saskatoon, S7K 3J9, SK, Canada
Tel.: (306) 668-9992

Agricultural Research Services
N.A.I.C.S.: 541715

Subsidiary (Domestic):

Pioneer Hi-Bred Production Company (5)
7398 Queens Line, Chatham, N7M 5L1, ON, Canada
Tel.: (519) 352-6350
Hybrid Seeds Mfr
N.A.I.C.S.: 424910

Branch (Domestic):

Pioneer Hi-Bred International (4)
1000 Jefferson St, Tipton, IN 46072
Tel.: (765) 675-2101
Agricultural Product Whslr
N.A.I.C.S.: 424590
Pete Letsinger (Acct Mgr)
Frederick Kramer (Acct Mgr)

Pioneer Hi-Bred International (4)
3258 Hwy 52, Rushville, IN 46173
Tel.: (765) 932-3911
Agricultural Product Whslr
N.A.I.C.S.: 424590
Nathan Osting (Mgr-Territory)

Pioneer Hi-Bred International (4)
3239 Hwy 8, Dysart, IA 52224
Tel.: (319) 476-2390
Agricultural Services
N.A.I.C.S.: 444240
Rob Roose (Mgr-Territory)
Joseph Pickard (Acct Mgr)
Matthew Wilson (Acct Mgr)

Pioneer Hi-Bred International (4)
2112 County Rd 1600 N, Saint Joseph, IL 61873
Tel.: (217) 469-7000
Agricultural Product Whslr
N.A.I.C.S.: 424510
Greg Jarling (Mgr-Territory)
Drew Wright (Mgr-Territory)
Mark Griffin (Mgr-Territory)

Pioneer Hi-Bred International (4)
R617 County Rd 13A, Napoleon, OH 43545
Tel.: (419) 599-5316
Agricultural Research Services
N.A.I.C.S.: 541715
Chasitie Euler (Acct Mgr)

Pioneer Hi-Bred International (4)
3445 Progressive Rd, Seward, NE 68434
Tel.: (402) 643-2012
Agricultural Product Whslr
N.A.I.C.S.: 424910

Pioneer Hi-Bred International (4)
12937 US Hwy 281, Doniphan, NE 68832
Tel.: (402) 744-3271
Agricultural Product Whslr
N.A.I.C.S.: 111998

Pioneer Hi-Bred International (4)
1365 S Washington St, Constantine, MI 49042
Tel.: (269) 435-2855
Agricultural Product Whslr
N.A.I.C.S.: 424910
Kevin Hoffman (Acct Mgr)

Pioneer Hi-Bred International (4)
15180 Henry Wood County Rd, Grand Rapids, OH 43522
Tel.: (419) 748-8051
Agricultural Product Whslr
N.A.I.C.S.: 424910

Pioneer Hi-Bred International (4)
121 3rd St NE, New Richland, MN 56072
Tel.: (507) 465-3320
Agricultural Product Whslr
N.A.I.C.S.: 424910
Joel Dorn (Acct Mgr)

Pioneer Hi-Bred International (4)
11329 US-70, Proctor, AR 72376
Tel.: (870) 702-7180
Crop Farming Services
N.A.I.C.S.: 444240
Chad Kirkley (Mgr-Territory)
Jeff Lambert (Mgr-Territory)

Pioneer Hi-Bred International (4)
317 Industrial Pkwy, Ithaca, MI 48847
Tel.: (989) 875-2220
Agricultural Research Services

N.A.I.C.S.: 541715
Kevin Thiel (Acct Mgr)

Pioneer Hi-Bred International (4)
10150 Hwy 149, Fremont, IA 52561
Tel.: (641) 933-4281
Miscellaneous Crop Farming Services
N.A.I.C.S.: 111998
Garrett Carver (Mgr-Territory)

Pioneer Hi-Bred International (4)
182 Industrial Park, Jackson, MN 56143
Tel.: (507) 847-5522
Agricultural Product Whslr
N.A.I.C.S.: 424590
Chad Anderson (Mgr-Territory)
Brad Weber (Mgr-Territory)

Pioneer Hi-Bred International (4)
1740 45th St SE, Willmar, MN 56201
Tel.: (320) 235-2422
Agricultural Product Whslr
N.A.I.C.S.: 424910
Steve Sieg (Acct Mgr)

Pioneer Hi-Bred International (4)
1901 Hwy 169 N, Algona, IA 50511
Tel.: (515) 295-9411
Miscellaneous Crop Farming Services
N.A.I.C.S.: 111998
Katie Ricklefs (Acct Mgr)
Ben Hinners (Mgr-Territory)
Kevin Lauver (Mgr-Territory)

Pioneer Hi-Bred International (4)
1920 E McGregor Rd, Algona, IA 50511
Tel.: (515) 295-7283
Crop Farming Services
N.A.I.C.S.: 111998

Pioneer Hi-Bred International (4)
3261 N Alburnett Rd, Marion, IA 52302
Tel.: (319) 377-2870
Agricultural Services
N.A.I.C.S.: 444240
Matthew Wilson (Acct Mgr)

Pioneer Hi-Bred International (4)
110 Hwy 175, Reinbeck, IA 50669
Tel.: (319) 788-6411
Agricultural Services
N.A.I.C.S.: 444240
Colby Entriken (Mgr-Production Location)

Pioneer Hi-Bred International (4)
2240 County Rd 60, Plainview, TX 79072
Tel.: (806) 293-5231
Hybrid Seeds Mfr
N.A.I.C.S.: 424910
Kevin Kerr (Mgr-Territory)

Pioneer Hi-Bred International (4)
9940 US 50, Garden City, KS 67846
Tel.: (620) 271-0662
Agricultural Product Whslr
N.A.I.C.S.: 424910

Pioneer Hi-Bred International (4)
982 N New Holland Rd, New Holland, PA 17557
Tel.: (717) 354-6044
Crop Farming Services
N.A.I.C.S.: 424910

Pioneer Hi-Bred International (4)
115 Meyer St, Taft, TX 78390
Tel.: (361) 528-3575
Hybrid Seeds Mfr
N.A.I.C.S.: 424910

Pioneer Hi-Bred International (4)
17835 Hwy 13, Wahpeton, ND 58075
Tel.: (701) 642-5300
Agricultural Product Whslr
N.A.I.C.S.: 424910

Pioneer Hi-Bred International (4)
1410 Hwy 34, York, NE 68467
Tel.: (402) 362-3349
Agricultural Product Whslr
N.A.I.C.S.: 111998
Chris Woerner (Acct Mgr)

Pioneer Hi-Bred International (4)
18285 County Rd 96, Woodland, CA 95695
Tel.: (530) 666-1182
Miscellaneous Crop Farming Services
N.A.I.C.S.: 111998
Jason Root (Mgr-Territory)

Pioneer Hi-Bred International (4)
68 Industrial Rd, Elizabethtown, PA 17022

Tel.: (717) 367-9055
Hybrid Seeds Mfr
N.A.I.C.S.: 424910

Pioneer Hi-Bred International (4)
300 SW 5th St, Woodhull, IL 61490
Tel.: (309) 334-2835
Farm Product Raw Material Whslr
N.A.I.C.S.: 424590
Ryan Ricketts (Mgr-Territory)
Ryan Hartstirn (Mgr-Territory)

Pioneer Hi-Bred International (4)
S 5380 Cemetary Rd, Eau Claire, WI 54701
Tel.: (715) 834-0061
Hybrid Seeds Whslr
N.A.I.C.S.: 424910

Pioneer Hi-Bred International (4)
1039 Milton Shopiere Rd, Janesville, WI 53546
Tel.: (608) 756-4030
Hybrid Seeds Whslr
N.A.I.C.S.: 424910

Pioneer Hi-Bred International (4)
2300 Pioneer Dr, Plymouth, IN 46563
Tel.: (574) 936-3243
Agricultural Product Whslr
N.A.I.C.S.: 424590
Paul Georgen (Acct Mgr)

Pioneer Hi-Bred International (4)
18259 W Frontage Rd, Litchfield, IL 62056
Tel.: (217) 324-6507
Agricultural Product Whslr
N.A.I.C.S.: 424510
Mark Winkler (Acct Mgr)

Pioneer Hi-Bred International (4)
390 Union Blvd Ste 500A, Lakewood, CO 80228
Tel.: (303) 716-3960
Miscellaneous Crop Farming Services
N.A.I.C.S.: 111998

Pioneer Hi-Bred International (4)
14150 Carole Dr, Bloomington, IL 61705
Tel.: (309) 663-4086
Farm Product Raw Material Whslr
N.A.I.C.S.: 424590

Pioneer Hi-Bred International (4)
21781 Skwy Church Rd, Maxton, NC 28364
Tel.: (910) 844-3648
Agricultural Product Whslr
N.A.I.C.S.: 424590
Randy Graves (Mgr-Plant)

Pioneer Hi-Bred International (4)
2208 Yankee Ave, Durant, IA 52747
Tel.: (563) 785-4446
Agricultural Product Whslr
N.A.I.C.S.: 444240
Michael Tierney (Mgr-Territory)

Pioneer Hi-Bred International (4)
21888 N 950th Rd, Adair, IL 61411
Tel.: (309) 653-2401
Agricultural Research Services
N.A.I.C.S.: 541690
Ryan Gentle (Sls Mgr-Territory)

Subsidiary (Non-US):

Pioneer Hi-Bred Italia Srl (4)
Via Pari Opportunita 2, Gadesco Pieve Delmona, 26030, Parma, CR, Italy
Tel.: (39) 0372841611
Corn, Wheat & Other Hybrid Agricultural Seeds & Related Products Distr
N.A.I.C.S.: 424910

Branch (Domestic):

Pioneer Hi-Bred Puerto Rico (4)
3 Cll Puerto Rico, Salinas, PR 00751
Tel.: (787) 824-4440
Crop Farming Services
N.A.I.C.S.: 111998

Pioneer Hi-Bred Research Center (4)
4200 W Service Rd Unit 4, Evans, CO 80620
Tel.: (970) 506-9219
Agricultural Research Services
N.A.I.C.S.: 541715

Subsidiary (Non-US):

Pioneer Hi-Bred Services GmbH (4)

Pioneerstrasse Industriegelande, 7111, Parndorf, Austria
Tel.: (43) 216625250
Corn, Wheat & Other Hybrid Agricultural Seeds & Related Products Distr
N.A.I.C.S.: 424910

Subsidiary (Domestic):

Pioneer Seeds Inc. (4)
404 S County Rd, Toledo, IA 52342
Tel.: (641) 484-2141
Miscellaneous Crop Farming Services
N.A.I.C.S.: 444240

Subsidiary (Non-US):

Pioneer Semences S.A.S (4)
1131 Chemin de l'Enseigure, 31840, Aussonne, France
Tel.: (33) 561062000
Web Site: http://www.france.pioneer.com
Corn, Wheat & Other Hybrid Agricultural Seeds & Related Products Distr
N.A.I.C.S.: 424910

Pioneer Tohumculuk A.S. (4)
Kiza Is Merkezi Onur Mahallesi Turhan Cemal Beriker Bulvari, No 437 A5 Blok Kat 6 Seyhan, Adana, Turkiye
Tel.: (90) 3223556800
Web Site: http://www.pioneer.com
Corn & Other Hybrid Agricultural Seeds & Related Products Distr
N.A.I.C.S.: 424910
Kubilay Guzeler (Reg Mgr-Tarsus)

Subsidiary (Domestic):

Terral Seed, Inc. (4)
117 Ellington Dr, Rayville, LA 71269
Tel.: (318) 559-2840
Web Site: http://www.terralseed.com
Seeds, Soybeans, Rice, Wheat, Oats & Corn Distr
N.A.I.C.S.: 424910
Suzanne Sitton (Office Mgr)
Chad Ervin (Dir-Sls)
Austin Jackson (Mgr-Ops)
Mike Martien (Gen Mgr)
Bert Mann (District Sls Mgr)
Blake Strnadel (District Sls Mgr)
Clint Williams (District Sls Mgr)
Jeremy Hawkins (District Sls Mgr)
John Burt Strider (District Sls Mgr)
Steve Woodham (District Sls Mgr)
Warren Cobb (District Sls Mgr)
William Schultz (District Sls Mgr)
Willie Remore (District Sls Mgr)
Phil Michener (Dir-Agronomic Svcs)
Charles Johnston (Coord-Supply Chain & Logistics)

Subsidiary (Non-US):

DuPont Asturias, S.L. (2)
Valle de Tamon-Nubledo, Carreno, 33469, Asturias, Spain
Tel.: (34) 985124000
Web Site: https://www.dupont.es
Electroplating Chemical Whslr
N.A.I.C.S.: 424690
Antonia Regales (Head-HR)

Subsidiary (Domestic):

DuPont Capital Management Corporation (2)
Delaware Corporate Ctr 1 Righter Pkwy Ste 3200, Wilmington, DE 19803
Tel.: (302) 477-6000
Web Site: http://www.dupontcapital.com
Investment Management Service
N.A.I.C.S.: 523999
Valerie J. Sill (Pres & CEO)
Krzysztof A. Kowal (Mng Dir-Fixed Income Investments)
Robin P. Sachs (COO)
Paul Leahy (Head-Relationship Mgmt)
Brendan P. Naughton (Principal-Bus Dev)
Lode J. Devlaminck (Mng Dir-Equities)
Westin T. Dinsel (Head-Portfolio Risk & Analytics & Portfolio Mgr)
Jeffrey M. Fasino (Dir-Bus Dev)
Kimberly A. Fetterman (Mgr-Client Svcs)
Ted Hu (Portfolio Mgr)
Antonis Mistras (Mng Dir-Alternative Investments)
William J. Perrone (Dir-Bus Dev)

Corteva, Inc.—(Continued)

Ming Shao *(Dir-Fixed Income Investments)*
William Flores *(Chief Compliance Officer)*
William W. Smith Jr. *(Mng Dir-Bus Dev & Rels Mgmt)*

Subsidiary (Non-US):

DuPont Iberica, S.L. **(2)**
Barcelona Avda Diagonal 571 Edificio L illa Diagonal, 08029, Barcelona, Spain
Tel.: (34) 932276000
Industrial Chemicals Mfr
N.A.I.C.S.: 541611

DuPont Singapore Pte. Ltd. **(2)**
10 Marina Boulevard 07-01 Marina Bay Financial Centre Tower 2, Singapore, 018983, Singapore
Tel.: (65) 65863688
Web Site: http://www.sg.dupont.com
Textiles & Textile Chemicals & Engineering Plastics Mfr
N.A.I.C.S.: 313310

DuPont Ukraine LLC **(2)**
St Petra Sagaidachnoho 1, Kiev, 04070, Ukraine
Tel.: (380) 44 498 9000
Web Site: https://www.corteva.com.ua
Pesticide & Agricultural Chemical Mfr
N.A.I.C.S.: 325320

Subsidiary (Domestic):

DuPont Washington Works **(2)**
8480 Dupont Rd, Washington, WV 26181
Tel.: (304) 863-2000
Plastics Processing Services
N.A.I.C.S.: 326199

Subsidiary (Non-US):

DuPont de Nemours (France) S.A.S, Cernay Plant **(2)**
82 rue de Wittelsheim, 68701, Cernay, France **(100%)**
Tel.: (33) 389383838
Agricultural Product Mfr
N.A.I.C.S.: 325320

DuPont de Nemours South Africa (Pty) Ltd. **(2)**
1st Level Block B 34 Whiteley Road Melrose Arch, Atholl, Johannesburg, 2196, South Africa
Tel.: (27) 11 218 8600
Web Site: https://www.dupont.co.za
Pesticide & Agricultural Chemical Mfr
N.A.I.C.S.: 325320

DuPont do Brasil S.A. **(2)**
Al Itapecuru 506 Alphaville, Barueri, 06454-080, San Paulo, Brazil
Tel.: (55) 1141668000
Web Site: http://www.dupont.com.br
Chemicals Mfr
N.A.I.C.S.: 325998

E.I. DuPont Canada Company **(2)**
1919 Minnesota Court, Mississauga, L5N 0C9, ON, Canada
Tel.: (905) 816-3300
Web Site: http://www.dupont.ca
Chemicals Mfr
N.A.I.C.S.: 325998

Subsidiary (Domestic):

Kingston Distribution Center **(3)**
505 Front Road, Kingston, K7L 5A1, ON, Canada **(100%)**
Tel.: (613) 548-5500
Noncellulosic Organic Fibers Warehouse
N.A.I.C.S.: 325220

Subsidiary (Non-US):

E.I. DuPont India Private Limited **(2)**
7th Floor Tower C DLF Cyber Greens Sector-25A, DLF City Phase III, Gurgaon, 122002, Haryana, India
Tel.: (91) 124 4091818
Web Site: http://www.dupont.co.in
Chemical Products Mfr
N.A.I.C.S.: 325998

Plant (Domestic):

E.I. DuPont de Nemours & Co. **(2)**
3115 River Rd, Buffalo, NY 14207 **(100%)**

Tel.: (716) 876-4420
Solid Surface Company
N.A.I.C.S.: 325220

E.I. DuPont de Nemours & Co. **(2)**
801 35th St, Fort Madison, IA 52627-2011 **(100%)**
Tel.: (319) 372-1430
Ink Mfr
N.A.I.C.S.: 325910

E.I. DuPont de Nemours & Co. **(2)**
800 Dupont Rd, Circleville, OH 43113 **(100%)**
Tel.: (740) 474-0111
Web Site: https://www.dupont.com
Seed Mfr
N.A.I.C.S.: 325211

Subsidiary (Domestic):

NuTech Seed LLC **(2)**
201 Knollwood Dr Ste A, Champaign, IL 61820
Web Site: https://nutechseed.com
Corn & Soybeans Mfr & Dist
N.A.I.C.S.: 111110
Brad Johnson *(Head-Sls Agronomy)*

Subsidiary (Domestic):

Pfister Seeds LLC **(3)**
201 Knollwood Dr Ste A, Champaign, IL 61820
Tel.: (888) 647-3478
Web Site: http://www.pfisterseeds.com
Grain Crops Whslr
N.A.I.C.S.: 111150

Grainit S.R.L. **(1)**
Viale dell'Industria 23, 35129, Padova, PD, Italy
Tel.: (39) 03388836195
Web Site: http://www.grainit.it
Electronic Products Mfr
N.A.I.C.S.: 334419

Hoegemeyer Hybrids, Inc. **(1)**
2905 E Morningside Rd, Fremont, NE 68025
Web Site: https://www.therightseed.com
Agricultural Services
N.A.I.C.S.: 926140

Lavie Bio Ltd. **(1)**
PO Box 4173, 7638517, Ness Ziona, Israel
Tel.: (972) 89311900
Web Site: https://lavie-bio.com
Biotechnology Research Services
N.A.I.C.S.: 541714

Pioneer Hi-Bred Magyarorszag Kft **(1)**
Boldizsar u 4, 1112, Budapest, Hungary
Tel.: (36) 12707000
Agricultural Services
N.A.I.C.S.: 926140

Pioneer Hi-Bred Northern Europe Service Division GmbH **(1)**
Riedenburger Str 7, 81677, Munich, Germany
Tel.: (49) 89455330
Agricultural Services
N.A.I.C.S.: 926140

Pioneer Hi-Bred Poland Sp z o.o. **(1)**
Jozefa Piusa Dziekonskiego 1, 00-728, Warsaw, Poland
Tel.: (48) 225487300
Web Site: https://www.pioneer.com
Agricultural Services
N.A.I.C.S.: 926140

Pioneer Hi-Bred R.S.A. (Pty) Ltd. **(1)**
272 West Avenue Lakefield Office Park Block A 2nd Floor, Centurion, Gauteng, South Africa
Tel.: (27) 126835700
Web Site: http://www.pioneer.com
Farm Management Services
N.A.I.C.S.: 115116
Jaco Snyman *(Sls Mgr)*
Emile Van Den Berg *(Mgr-Agronomy)*

Pioneer Hi-Bred Romania S.R.L. **(1)**
D N 2 Km 19 O P Afumati, Ilfov, 077010, Bucharest, Romania
Tel.: (40) 213035300
Agricultural Services

N.A.I.C.S.: 926140

Seed Consultants Inc. **(1)**
648 Miami Trace Rd SW, Washington Court House, OH 43160
Web Site: http://www.seedconsultants.com
Tutoring Services
N.A.I.C.S.: 611699
Chris Jeffries *(Owner)*
Bill McDonald *(Dir-Agronomic Svcs)*
Daniel Call *(Gen Mgr)*
Stuart Yensel *(Dir-Sls & Mktg)*
Alissa Armstrong *(Mgr-Mktg Comm)*

Stoller Colombia S.A. **(1)**
Kilometro 2 via de Briceno - Zipaquira Parque Industrial Tibitoc, Bodega 22B, Tocancipa, Colombia
Tel.: (57) 18697739
Web Site: https://www.stollercolombia.com
Agricultural Product Mfr & Distr
N.A.I.C.S.: 325311

Stoller Enterprises, Inc. **(1)**
9090 Katy Fwy Ste 400, Houston, TX 77024
Tel.: (713) 461-1493
Web Site: https://www.stolleragro.com
Agricultural Product Cultivation Services
N.A.I.C.S.: 541690

Stoller Europe, S.L.U. **(1)**
Elche Parque Empresarial C/ Max Planck 1, 03203, Elche, Alicante, Spain
Tel.: (34) 965110522
Web Site: https://stollereurope.com
Agricultural Product Mfr & Distr
N.A.I.C.S.: 325311

Stoller Group, Inc. **(1)**
9090 Katy Fwy Ste 400, Houston, TX 77024-1696
Tel.: (713) 461-1493
Web Site: http://www.stollerusa.com
Rev.: $50,000,000
Emp.: 250
Agricultural Chemical Mfr
N.A.I.C.S.: 325320
Jerry Stoller *(Pres)*

Subsidiary (Non-US):

DBJ Enterprises de Colombia S.A. **(2)**
Carrera 14 No 7611 Oficiania 401, Bogota, 37927, Colombia
Tel.: (57) 1 218 2442
Web Site: http://www.stollerme.com
Mfr of Agricultural Chemicals
N.A.I.C.S.: 325320

NAP-Stoller Thailand **(2)**
293-293/1-2 Surawongse Rd, Bangkok, 10500, Thailand
Tel.: (66) 22376540
Web Site: http://www.napnoutiscience.com
Sales Range: $10-24.9 Million
Emp.: 25
Mfr of Agricultural Chemicals
N.A.I.C.S.: 325320

Quimicas Stoller de Centroamerica, S.A. **(2)**
Avenida Petapa 52-50 zona 12, Oficina 102, Guatemala, Guatemala
Tel.: (502) 22041100
Web Site: https://www.stoller.com.gt
Mfr of Agricultural Chemicals
N.A.I.C.S.: 325320

Stoller - Peru S.A. **(2)**
Sales Range: $10-24.9 Million
Emp.: 30
Mfr of Agricultural Chemicals
N.A.I.C.S.: 325320

Stoller Argentina **(2)**
Calle Publica 7156 Aeropuerto, B Ferreyra X, 5019, Cordoba, Argentina
Tel.: (54) 3514977797
Web Site: https://www.stoller.com.ar
Sales Range: $10-24.9 Million
Emp.: 26
Agricultural Chemical Mfr
N.A.I.C.S.: 325320

Stoller Australia Pty. Ltd. **(2)**
6 Todd St, PO Box 420, 5015, Port Adelaide, SA, Australia
Tel.: (61) 884402420
Web Site: http://www.stoller.com.au

Mfr of Agricultural Chemicals
N.A.I.C.S.: 325320

Stoller Chemical Company of Canada Ltd. **(2)**
940 Sheldon Court, Burlington, L7L 5K6, ON, Canada
Tel.: (905) 632-8503
Web Site: http://stollercanada.ca
Sales Range: $10-24.9 Million
Emp.: 4
Agricultural Chemical Mfr
N.A.I.C.S.: 325320
Wayne Izumi *(Owner & Mgr)*

Stoller Do Brasil, Ltda. **(2)**
Torre II-Av Carlos Grimaldi 1701-3 Andar-Jardim Conceicao, PO Box 55, Campinas, Sao Paulo, 13091-908, Brazil
Tel.: (55) 1937071200
Web Site: https://www.stoller.com.br
Sales Range: $10-24.9 Million
Emp.: 100
Mfr of Agricultural Chemicals
N.A.I.C.S.: 325320
Rodrigo Ferraire *(Pres)*

Stoller Enterprises de Mexico, SA DE CV **(2)**
Escultura No 108 Fracc Industrial La Capilla, 37927, Leon, Guanajuato, Mexico **(100%)**
Tel.: (52) 4777808347
Web Site: http://www.stollermexico.com
Sales Range: $10-24.9 Million
Emp.: 7
Mfr of Agricultural Chemicals
N.A.I.C.S.: 325320

Stoller Enterprises, Ltd. **(2)**
284 Industrial Drive, Regina, S4R 8R6, SK, Canada
Tel.: (305) 545-4414
Web Site: https://stollerenterprises.ca
Mfr & Distr of Agricultural Chemicals
N.A.I.C.S.: 325320

Stoller Iberica, S.L. **(2)**
Apartado De Correo N 5 424, 03080, Alicante, Spain
Tel.: (34) 965110522
Web Site: http://www.stollerspain.com
Sales Range: $10-24.9 Million
Emp.: 5
Mfr of Agricultural Chemicals
N.A.I.C.S.: 325320

Stoller Phillipinnes, Inc. **(2)**
Unit 801 8 Fl Manila Luxury Pearl Dr, Corner Goldloop St, Pasig, 1600, Philippines
Tel.: (63) 26342121
Web Site: http://www.stoller.com.ph
Sales Range: $10-24.9 Million
Emp.: 23
Mfr of Agricultural Chemicals
N.A.I.C.S.: 325320
Jerry Stoller *(Pres & CEO)*

Stoller de Chile, S.A. **(2)**
El Juncal 500, Loteo Buenaventura, Quilicura, Santiago, Chile **(100%)**
Tel.: (56) 27335411
Web Site: http://www.stoller.cl
Sales Range: Less than $1 Million
Emp.: 11
Agricultural Chemical Mfr
N.A.I.C.S.: 325320

Stoller Mexico S.A. de C.V **(1)**
Av Autotransportistas No 203 Col El Palote, 37208, Leon, Guanajuato, Mexico
Tel.: (52) 8008215444
Web Site: https://stollermexico.com
Crop Farming Services
N.A.I.C.S.: 111998

Stoller South Africa (Pty) Ltd. **(1)**
Die Gewels Murray and Van Der Merwe Street, Nelspruit, 1200, South Africa
Tel.: (27) 130071678
Web Site: https://stollersouthafrica.co.za
Agricultural Research Services
N.A.I.C.S.: 541713

Stoller Turkey Organik Tarim Sanayi Ticaret A.S. **(1)**
Mustafa Kemal Ataturk Mah 35/1 Sokak No 13/1, Kemalpasa, 35735, Izmir, Turkiye
Tel.: (90) 2328734445
Web Site: https://stoller.com.tr

Agriculture Product Distr
N.A.I.C.S.: 424590

Stoller USA, Inc. (1)
9090 Katy Fwy Ste 400, Houston, TX
77024
Web Site: https://stollerusa.com
Agricultural Product Cultivation Services
N.A.I.C.S.: 541690

**Symborg (Shanghai) Trading Co.,
Ltd.** (1)
1999 Jinxiu East Road Maiteng Wisdom
World Room 326, Pudong New District,
Shanghai, 201206, China
Tel.: (86) 2161096082
Agricultural Biotechnology Research & De-
velopment Services
N.A.I.C.S.: 541714

Symborg Chile, SPA (1)
El Bosque Norte 107 OF 81, Las Condes,
Santiago, Chile
Tel.: (56) 225822356
Agricultural Biotechnology Research & De-
velopment Services
N.A.I.C.S.: 541714

Symborg Participacoes Ltda. (1)
Av Marcos Penteado de Ulhoa Rodrigues
939 8 andar Torre Jacaranda, Sala 898,
Barueri, 06460-040, Sao Paulo, Brazil
Tel.: (55) 1128442536
Agricultural Biotechnology Research & De-
velopment Services
N.A.I.C.S.: 541714

Symborg Peru S.A.C. (1)
Av Circunvalacion del Club Golf Los Inkas
No 208 Torre III, Interior 705B Santiago de
Surco, Lima, Peru
Tel.: (51) 225822356
Agricultural Biotechnology Research & De-
velopment Services
N.A.I.C.S.: 541714

Symborg Turkey Tarim A.S. (1)
Etiler Mah 839 Sok Platin Is Merkezi No
17/401, Muratpasa, Antalya, Turkiye
Tel.: (90) 2422447700
Agricultural Biotechnology Research & De-
velopment Services
N.A.I.C.S.: 541714

Symborg, Inc. (1)
300 E Esplanade Dr 9th Fl, Oxnard, CA
93036
Tel.: (805) 765-4801
Agricultural Biotechnology Research & Development Services
N.A.I.C.S.: 541714

Symborg, S.L.U. (1)
Cabezo Cortado Avenida Jesus Martinez
Cortado 51, Espinardo, 30100, Murcia,
Spain
Tel.: (34) 968899250
Web Site: https://symborg.com
Agricultural Biotechnology Research & De-
velopment Services
N.A.I.C.S.: 541714

CORVEL CORPORATION

5128 Apache Plume Rd Ste 400, Fort
Worth, TX 76109
Tel.: (817) 390-1416   DE
Web Site: https://www.corvel.com
Year Founded: 1988
CRVL—(NASDAQ)
Rev.: $646,230,000
Assets: $415,246,000
Liabilities: $202,851,000
Net Worth: $212,395,000
Earnings: $66,410,000
Emp.: 4,233
Fiscal Year-end: 03/31/22
Managed Health Care Services
N.A.I.C.S.: 524114
Victor Gordon Clemons Sr. *(Chm)*
Sharon O'Connor *(VP-Legal-Human)*
Michael G. Combs *(Pres & CEO)*
Maxim Shishin *(CIO)*
Brandon T. O'Brien *(CFO)*
Jennifer L. Yoss *(Chief Acctg Officer
& VP-Accounting)*
Jeff Gurtcheff *(Chief Claims Officer)*

Subsidiaries:

CorVel Healthcare Corporation (1)
601 SW Second Ave Ste 1400, Portland,
OR 97204
Tel.: (503) 222-3144
Web Site: http://www.corvel.com
Sales Range: $1-9.9 Million
Emp.: 350
Healthcare Managed Services
N.A.I.C.S.: 524298
Victor Gordon Clemons Sr. *(CEO & Chm)*

Eagle Claims Services, Inc. (1)
251 Salina Meadows Pkwy Ste 150, North
Syracuse, NY 13212
Tel.: (315) 457-6212
Workers Compensation Administrative Ser-
vices
N.A.I.C.S.: 923130
Nancy Cardella *(Gen Mgr)*

Symbeo, Inc. (1)
1800 SW 1st Ave Ste 600, Portland, OR
97201
Tel.: (503) 242-4210
Web Site: https://www.symbeo.com
Software Development Services
N.A.I.C.S.: 541511

CORVUS PHARMACEUTI-
CALS, INC.

863 Mitten Rd Ste 102, Burlingame,
CA 94010
Tel.: (650) 900-4520
Web Site:
https://www.corvuspharma.com
Year Founded: 2014
CRVS—(NASDAQ)
Rev.: $587,000
Assets: $68,240,000
Liabilities: $12,125,000
Net Worth: $56,115,000
Earnings: ($41,307,000)
Emp.: 29
Fiscal Year-end: 12/31/22
Clinical-Stage Biopharmaceutical
Development
N.A.I.C.S.: 325412
Peter A. Thompson *(Co-Founder)*
Richard A. Miller *(Co-Founder, Chm,
Pres & CEO)*
Long Kwei *(Sr VP-Biometrics)*
Mehrdad Mobasher *(Chief Medical
Officer & Sr VP)*
James W. Janc *(VP-Pharmacology)*
Debra Horen *(VP-HR)*
Leiv Lea *(CFO)*
William Ben Jones *(Sr VP-
Pharmaceutical Dev)*

COSCIENS BIOPHARMA INC.

315 Sigma Dr, Summerville, SC
29486
Tel.: (843) 900-3223   Ca
Web Site:
https://www.cosciensbio.com
Year Founded: 1990
CSCI—(NASDAQ)
Rev.: $5,640,000
Assets: $56,026,000
Liabilities: $20,250,000
Net Worth: $35,776,000
Earnings: ($22,727,000)
Emp.: 21
Fiscal Year-end: 12/31/22
Pharmaceutical Product Developer
N.A.I.C.S.: 325412
Gilles Gagnon *(Pres & CEO)*
Eckhard G. Guenther *(Mng Dir & Sr
VP-Bus Dev-Aeterna Zentaris GmbH)*
Michael Teifel *(Chief Scientific Officer
& Sr VP-Non-Clinical Dev)*
Giuliano La Fratta *(CFO & Sr VP)*

Subsidiaries:

AEterna Zentaris GmbH (1)
Weismullerstrasse 50, 60314, Frankfurt,
Germany (100%)
Tel.: (49) 69426023228

Web Site: https://www.zentaris.com
Sales Range: $25-49.9 Million
Pharmaceutical Product Developer
N.A.I.C.S.: 325412

Ceapro Inc. (1)
7824-51 Avenue NW, Edmonton, T6E 6W2,
AB, Canada
Tel.: (780) 421-4555
Web Site: https://www.cosciensbio.com
Rev.: $11,829,076
Assets: $22,861,140
Liabilities: $3,843,939
Net Worth: $19,017,201
Earnings: $1,451,990
Emp.: 17
Fiscal Year-end: 12/31/2020
Biotechnology & Pharmaceutical Products
Mfr
N.A.I.C.S.: 325412
Gilles R. Gagnon *(Pres & CEO)*
Glenn R. Rourke *(Chm)*
Stacy Prefontaine *(CFO)*
Leoni DeJoya *(VP-Bioprocessing Bus Unit)*
Paul Moquin *(Dir-Scientific Affairs & Bus
Dev)*
Bernhard Seifried *(Dir-Engrg Res & Tech-
nologies)*
Sigrun Watson *(Chief Revenue Officer)*
Michel Regnier *(Sr VP)*

Subsidiary (Domestic):

JuventeDC Inc. (2)
175 Avenue des Ateliers, Montmagny, G5V
0G8, QC, Canada
Tel.: (418) 241-2235
Web Site: https://www.juventedc.com
Pharmaceuticals Product Mfr
N.A.I.C.S.: 325412
Jean-Guy Boulet *(Gen Mgr)*

Zentaris IVF GmbH (1)
Weismullerstrasse 50, 60314, Frankfurt,
Germany
Tel.: (49) 69426023228
Pharmaceutical Research & Development
Services
N.A.I.C.S.: 541714

COSMOS HEALTH INC.

141 W Jackson Blvd Ste 4236, Chi-
cago, IL 60604
Tel.: (312) 536-3102   NV
Web Site:
https://www.cosmoshealthinc.com
Year Founded: 2009
COSM—(NASDAQ)
Rev.: $50,347,652
Assets: $68,038,621
Liabilities: $28,754,326
Net Worth: $39,284,295
Earnings: ($63,945,285)
Emp.: 102
Fiscal Year-end: 12/31/22
Commercial & Residential Real Es-
tate & Real Estate Related Assets
Acquirer & Operator
N.A.I.C.S.: 531390
Grigorios Siokas *(Chm)*
Demetrios G. Demetriades *(Sec)*
Georgios Terzis *(CFO)*

Subsidiaries:

Cosmofarm Ltd. (1)
Gonata Stilianou 15, Peristeri Attiki, 12133,
Athens, Greece
Tel.: (30) 2112112270
Web Site: https://www.cosmofarm.gr
Pharmaceutical Products Distr
N.A.I.C.S.: 424210

Decahedron Ltd. (1)
Unit 11 Spire Green Centre, Harlow, CM19
5TR, Essex, United Kingdom
Tel.: (44) 1279435591
Web Site: https://www.dhnltd.com
Pharmaceutical Products Distr
N.A.I.C.S.: 424210

SkyPharm, S.A. (1)
St Georgiou 5, Pylaia, 57001, Thessaloniki,
Greece
Tel.: (30) 2313080710
Web Site: https://www.skypremiumlife.com
Pharmaceutical Products Distr

N.A.I.C.S.: 424210
Grigorios Siokas *(CEO & Ops Mgr)*

COSTAR GROUP, INC.

1331 L St NW, Washington, DC
20005
Tel.: (202) 346-6500   DE
Web Site:
https://www.costargroup.com
Year Founded: 1987
CSGP—(NASDAQ)
Rev.: $2,455,000,000
Assets: $8,919,700,000
Liabilities: $1,581,100,000
Net Worth: $7,338,600,000
Earnings: $374,700,000
Emp.: 6,152
Fiscal Year-end: 12/31/23
Information Services to the Commer-
cial Real Estate Industry
N.A.I.C.S.: 561499
Frank A. Simuro *(CTO)*
Fred G. Saint *(Pres-Marketplaces)*
Andrew Thomas *(Pres & Mgr-CoStar
Real Estate)*
Michael Desmarais *(Chief HR Officer)*
Jason Butler *(CIO)*
Gene Boxer *(Gen Counsel)*
Christian M. Lown *(CFO & Principal
Acctg Officer)*
Andrew C. Florance *(Founder &
CEO)*

Subsidiaries:

Apartments, LLC (1)
175 W Jackson Blvd Ste 800, Chicago, IL
60604
Tel.: (312) 601-5000
Web Site: http://www.apartments.com
Sales Range: $750-799.9 Million
Emp.: 200
Online Apartment Advertising Services
N.A.I.C.S.: 531390

Business Immo S.A.S. (1)
81 Rue Taitbout, 75009, Paris, France
Tel.: (33) 144838383
Web Site: https://www.businessimmo.com
Real Estate Information & Database Ser-
vices
N.A.I.C.S.: 531390

CoStar Espana, S.L. (1)
Velazquez number 157, Madrid, 28002,
Spain
Tel.: (34) 912793322
Web Site: https://www.belbex.com
Software Development Services
N.A.I.C.S.: 541511

CoStar Limited (1)
1 Chapel Place, London, W1G 0BG, United
Kingdom
Tel.: (44) 20 7009 2900
Web Site: http://www.costar.co.uk
Sales Range: $25-49.9 Million
Emp.: 80
Holding Company
N.A.I.C.S.: 551111

Subsidiary (Domestic):

CoStar UK Limited (2)
26th Floor The Shard 32 London Bridge
Street, London, SE1 9SG, United Kingdom
Tel.: (44) 2032054600
Web Site: http://www.costar.co.uk
Sales Range: $50-74.9 Million
Emp.: 100
Commercial Real Estate Information Ser-
vices
N.A.I.C.S.: 531390

Branch (Domestic):

CoStar UK Limited (3)
1st Floor 131 West Nile Street, Glasgow,
G1 2RX, Scotland, United Kingdom
Tel.: (44) 1413540600
Web Site: http://www.costar.co.uk
Commercial & Industrial Real Estate Infor-
mation Services
N.A.I.C.S.: 531390

CoStar Portfolio Strategy, LLC (1)

CoStar Group, Inc.—(Continued)

1331 L St NW, Washington, DC 20005
Tel.: (617) 443-3100
Web Site:
    http://www.costarportfoliostrategy.com
Real Estate Manangement Services
N.A.I.C.S.: 531390

CoStar Realty Information, Inc. (1)
1331 L St NW, Washington, DC 20005
Tel.: (202) 346-6500
Web Site: http://www.costar.com
Commercial Real Estate Information
N.A.I.C.S.: 531390
Andrew C. Florance (Pres & CEO)

ForRent, LLC (1)
3438 Peachtree Rd NE Ste 1500, Atlanta,
GA 30326
Web Site: http://www.forrent.com
Real Estate Rental Services
N.A.I.C.S.: 531110

Grecam S.A.S. (1)
81 rue Taitbout, 75009, Paris, France
Tel.: (33) 147559900
Web Site: https://www.grecam.com
Sales Range: $25-49.9 Million
Emp.: 10
Commercial Real Estate Information Ser-
vices
N.A.I.C.S.: 531390
Hugues Kirichian (Co-Founder)
Claude Ogier (Co-Founder)

LoopNet, Inc. (1)
101 California St, San Francisco, CA 94111
Tel.: (415) 243-4200
Web Site: http://www.loopnet.com
Emp.: 354
Commercial Real Estate Online Information
Services
N.A.I.C.S.: 531390

Division (Domestic):

BizBuySell.com (2)
101 California St 43rd Fl, San Francisco,
CA 94111
Tel.: (888) 777-9892
Web Site: http://www.bizbuysell.com
Online Business Directory
N.A.I.C.S.: 425120
Bob House (Pres)

Subsidiary (Domestic):

Cityfeet.com (2)
101 California St Fl 43, San Francisco, CA
94111-5899
Tel.: (212) 447-4313
Web Site: https://www.cityfeet.com
Sales Range: $1-9.9 Million
Emp.: 16
Online Real Estate Listing Network
N.A.I.C.S.: 531390

Off Campus Partners (1)
PO Box 5664, Charlottesville, VA 22905-
5664
Tel.: (434) 817-0721
Web Site:
    https://www.offcampuspartners.com
Marketing & Advertising Services
N.A.I.C.S.: 541810
James W. Jones (Pres)
Trina Jones Rogers (Sr VP)
Brittaney Deighan (Dir)
Chris Stafford (Mgr)
Tom Tran (Mgr)
Kenneth Jones (Mgr)
Tiffany Crosby (Mgr)
Olivia Berry (Coord)
Cassandra Barnett (Coord)
Kerry Brown (Mktg Dir)
Brittaney Deighan (Dir)
Chris Stafford (Mgr)
Tom Tran (Mgr)
Kenneth Jones (Mgr)
Tiffany Crosby (Mgr)
Olivia Berry (Coord)
Cassandra Barnett (Coord)
Kerry Brown (Mktg Dir)

OnTheMarket Plc (1)
155-157 High Street, PO Box 450, Alder-
shot, GU11 9FZ, United Kingdom
Web Site: https://www.plc.onthemarket.com
Rev.: $43,197,255
Assets: $34,601,515

Liabilities: $10,046,162
Net Worth: $24,555,353
Earnings: ($207,381)
Emp.: 171
Fiscal Year-end: 01/31/2023
Asset Management Services
N.A.I.C.S.: 523999

STR Columbia SAS (1)
Centro Empresarial Calle 98 21-50 office
201, Bogota, Colombia
Tel.: (57) 3166200795
Real Estate Services
N.A.I.C.S.: 531210

STR, Inc. (1)
735 E Main St, Hendersonville, TN 37075
Tel.: (615) 824-8664
Web Site: http://www.str.com
Sales Range: $10-24.9 Million
Emp.: 103
Hotel Industry Marketing Analysis Services
N.A.I.C.S.: 541910
Randy Smith (Founder)
Amanda W. Hite (Pres)
Brad Garner (Sr VP-Client Services)
Bobby Bowers (Sr VP-Operations)
Jan D. Freitag (Natl Dir-CoStar Grp)
Debbie Gryszko (CFO)
Steve Hood (Dir & Sr VP)
Vail R. Brown (Sr VP-Marketing)
Jonathan Bell (VP)
Chris Crenshaw (VP)
Duane Vinson (VP)
Chad Church (VP-Client Svcs)
Kay Caudle (Gen Counsel)
Veronica Andrews (Dir)
Jon Timmons (COO)
Felicity Collins (Dir-Operations)
Thomas Emanuel (Dir)
Elizabeth Randall Winkle (Chief Strategy
Officer)
Robin Rossmann (Mng Dir)
Scott Hendryx (CIO)
Isaac Collazo (VP-Analytics)
Alison Hoyt (Sr Dir)
Carter Wilson (Sr VP)

Ten-X, LLC (1)
17600 Laguna Canyon Rd, Irvine, CA
92618
Web Site: https://www.ten-x.com
Real Estate Brokerage Services
N.A.I.C.S.: 531210
Monte J. M. Koch (Co-Founder)
Steven Jacobs (Pres)
Brandon Lewe (VP-Sls)
Victor Gutierrez (VP-Platform Ops)
David Nance (VP-IT)
Joseph Cuomo (Sr Mng Dir)

The Screening Pros, LLC (1)
PO Box 3338, Chatsworth, CA 91313
Web Site:
    https://www.thescreeningpros.com
Software Development Services
N.A.I.C.S.: 541511

Thomas Daily GmbH (1)
Ingeborg-Krummer-Schroth-Str 30, 79106,
Freiburg, Germany
Tel.: (49) 761385590
Web Site: https://www.thomas-daily.de
Emp.: 1,800
Online Information Services
N.A.I.C.S.: 531390
Matthew Green (Mng Dir)

VirtualPremise, Inc. (1)
3438 Peachtree Rd NE Ste 1500, Atlanta,
GA 30326 (100%)
Tel.: (404) 267-1781
Web Site: https://costarmanager.com
Sales Range: $25-49.9 Million
Emp.: 35
Real Estate Information Management Tech-
nology Solutions
N.A.I.C.S.: 513210
Andy Thomas (Pres)
Andrew Hamilton (Sr VP)
Robbin Wemyss (VP)
Mark McDonald (VP)
David Gibson (VP)
Justin Rubner (VP)

Visual Lease, LLC (1)
100 Woodbridge Ctr Dr Ste 200, Wood-
bridge, NJ 07095
Web Site: http://www.visuallease.com
Sales Range: $1-9.9 Million
Emp.: 200
Payroll & Accounting Services

N.A.I.C.S.: 541214
Marc E. Betesh (Founder & CEO)
Clark Convery (COO)
Erinn Tarpey (CMO)
Joe Fitzgerald (Sr VP-Lease Market Strat-
egy)
Alexandra Betesh (VP-Client Svcs)
Guy Zerega (Sr VP-Sls)

Westside Rentals, LLC (1)
1020 Wilshire Blvd, Santa Monica, CA
90401
Web Site: http://www.westsiderentals.com
Real Estate Rental Services
N.A.I.C.S.: 531110

COSTAS, INC.
1008 N Pine Hills Rd, Orlando, FL
32808
Tel.: (321) 465-9899   NV
Web Site: http://www.costasinc.com
Year Founded: 1998
CSSI—(OTCIQ)
Sales Range: Less than $1 Million
Emp.: 1
Digital Currency Services
N.A.I.C.S.: 522320
Fredrick Paul Waid (Pres)
James Donald Brooks (CEO)
Jeffrey Don Turner (Gen Counsel)

COSTCO WHOLESALE COR-
PORATION
999 Lake Dr, Issaquah, WA 98027
Tel.: (425) 313-8100   WA
Web Site: https://www.costco.com
Year Founded: 1976
COST—(NASDAQ)
Rev.: $242,290,000,000
Assets: $68,994,000,000
Liabilities: $43,936,000,000
Net Worth: $25,058,000,000
Earnings: $6,292,000,000
Emp.: 316,000
Fiscal Year-end: 09/03/23
Consumer Goods Sales
N.A.I.C.S.: 455211
Richard A. Galanti (Exec VP)
James P. Murphy (COO-Intl Div &
Exec VP)
Timothy L. Rose (Exec VP-Ancillary
Businesses, Mfg & Bus Centers)
Ali Moayeri (Sr VP-Construction &
Pur)
Russell D. Miller (Sr Exec VP-Ops-
U.S.)
Patrick J. Callans (Exec VP-Admin)
Jeffrey Abadir (Sr VP & Gen Mgr-Bay
Area)
Richard Chang (Sr VP & Gen Mgr-
Asia)
Daniel M. Hines (Sr VP & Controller)
James C. Klauer (COO-Northern Div
& Exec VP)
Mario Omoss (Sr VP & Gen Mgr-
Northwest Reg)
John Sullivan (Gen Counsel, Sec &
Sr VP)
Richard Wilcox (Sr VP & Gen Mgr-
San Diego)
Claudine Adamo (Sr VP-Mdsg-Non-
Foods & Ecommerce)
David Skinner (Sr VP & Gen Mgr-
Western Canada)
Darby Greek (Sr VP & Gen Mgr-
Texas)
Gary Millerchip (CFO & Exec VP)
Gino Dorico (Sr VP & Gen Mgr-
Eastern Canada)
Nancy Griese (Sr VP-Mdsg-Foods &
Sundries)
Dave Messner (Sr VP-Real Estate
Dev)
Mike Parrott (Sr VP-Ecommerce)
Azmina Virani (Sr VP-Non-Foods,
E-commerce, Membership & Mktg-
Canada)

Josh Dahmen (Dir-Financial Plng &
IR)
Yoon Kim (Sr VP-Mdsg-Non-Foods &
Ecommerce)
Adam Self (Sr VP & Gen Mgr-
Northeast Reg)
Sarah Wehling (Sr VP-Mdsg-Fresh
Foods)
Terry Williams (Sr VP-Information
Sys)
Yoram Rubananko (Exec VP-
Northeast & Southeast)
Jim Sinegal (Founder)
Jon Raper (Chief Info Security Offi-
cer)
Marc-Andre Bally (COO, Exec VP &
Sr VP)
Greg Carter II (CFO, Exec VP, Sr VP
& Gen Mgr)
Jeff Cole (Sr VP)
Sarah George (Sr VP)
William Koza (Sr VP)
Pietro Nenci (Sr VP)
Robert Parker (Sr VP)
Walt Shafer (Sr VP)
Geoff Shavey (Sr VP)
Louie Silveira (Sr VP)
Richard Stephens (Sr VP)
Sandy Torrey (Sr VP)
Brenda Weber (Sr VP)
Ron M. Vachris (Pres & CEO)

Subsidiaries:

Costco Canada Holdings Inc. (1)
415 W Hunt Club Rd, Ottawa, K2E 1C5,
ON, Canada
Tel.: (613) 221-2000
Web Site: http://www.costco.ca
Sales Range: $150-199.9 Million
Emp.: 600
Home Appliance Whslr
N.A.I.C.S.: 449129

Costco Insurance Agency, Inc. (1)
999 Lake Dr, Issaquah, WA 98027
Tel.: (425) 313-8100
Insurance Agency & Brokerage Services
N.A.I.C.S.: 524210

Costco Wholesale Canada Ltd. (1)
415 West Hunt Club, Ottawa, K2E 1C5,
ON, Canada   (100%)
Tel.: (613) 221-2000
Web Site: http://www.costco.ca
Sales Range: $1-4.9 Billion
Emp.: 600
Consumer Goods Whslr
N.A.I.C.S.: 455211
Richard A. Galanti (CFO & Exec VP)

**Costco Wholesale Employee
Club** (1)
999 Lake Dr, Issaquah, WA 98027
Tel.: (425) 313-6461
Sales Range: $1-9.9 Million
Employee Discount Shopping Club
N.A.I.C.S.: 813990
Richard A. Galanti (Pres)
Monica Smith (Sec & VP)

Costco Wholesale Japan, Inc. (1)
3-1-4 Ikegami-Shincho Kawasaki Ku, Kawa-
saki, 210-0832, Kanagawa, Japan
Tel.: (81) 442701140
Web Site: http://www.costco.co.jp
Warehouse Club & Services
N.A.I.C.S.: 455211
Ken Monasterio (Pres)

Costco Wholesale Korea, Ltd. (1)
40 Iljik-ro, Gwangmyeong, 14347, Gyeo-
nggi, Korea (South)
Tel.: (82) 18999900
Web Site: https://www.costco.co.kr
Warehouse Club & Services
N.A.I.C.S.: 455211

**Costco Wholesale Membership,
Inc.** (1)
6750 Stanford Ranch Rd, Roseville, CA
95678-1907
Tel.: (916) 789-1616
Web Site: http://www.costco.com

Sales Range: $75-99.9 Million
Emp.: 300
Provider of Membership Services
N.A.I.C.S.: 813410

Costco Wholesale UK Limited (1)
Hartspring Lane, Watford, WD25 8JS, Hertfordshire, United Kingdom
Web Site: http://www.costco.co.uk
Sales Range: $1-4.9 Billion
Emp.: 3,539
Consumer Goods Whslr
N.A.I.C.S.: 455211
Steve Pippils (Mng Dir)

Costco de Mexico, S.A. de C.V. (1)
Av Magnocentro No 4 San Fernando la Herradura, 52760, Huixquilucan, Mexico
Tel.: (52) 5552008214
Web Site: https://www.costco.com.mx
Consumer Goods Distr
N.A.I.C.S.: 424990

Price Costco Canada Holdings Inc. (1)
415 W Hunt Club Rd, Ottawa, K2E 1C5, ON, Canada (100%)
Tel.: (613) 221-2000
Sales Range: $250-299.9 Million
Emp.: 500
Wholesale Services
N.A.I.C.S.: 459110
Joseph P. Portera (CEO)

COTERRA ENERGY INC.
3 Memorial City Plz 840 Gessner Rd Ste 1400, Houston, TX 77024
Tel.: (281) 589-4600   DE
Web Site: https://www.coterra.com
Year Founded: 1989
CTRA—(NYSE)
Rev.: $5,914,000,000
Assets: $20,415,000,000
Liabilities: $7,376,000,000
Net Worth: $13,039,000,000
Earnings: $1,625,000,000
Emp.: 894
Fiscal Year-end: 12/31/23
Natural Gas Explorer & Producer
N.A.I.C.S.: 211130
Todd M. Roemer (Chief Acctg Officer & VP)
Shannon E. Young III (CFO & Exec VP)
Michael D. Deshazer (VP-Bus Units)
Kevin W. Smith (CTO & VP)
Andrea M. Alexander (Chief HR Officer & Sr VP)
Stephen P. Bell (Exec VP)
Gary J. Hlavinka (VP)
Adam Vela (Gen Counsel)
Thomas E. Jorden (Chm, Pres & CEO)
Blake A. Sirgo (Sr VP-Ops)
Stephen P. Bell (Exec VP)

Subsidiaries:

Cabot Petroleum North Sea Limited (1)
1200 Enclave Pkwy, Houston, TX 77077-1764 (100%)
Tel.: (281) 589-4600
Web Site: http://www.cabotog.com
Sales Range: $200-249.9 Million
Petroleum Exploration
N.A.I.C.S.: 221210

Cimarex Energy Co. (1)
1700 Lincoln St Ste 3700, Denver, CO 80203
Tel.: (303) 295-3995
Web Site: http://www.cimarex.com
Oil & Natural Gas Production
N.A.I.C.S.: 213112
Francis B. Barron (Gen Counsel & Sr VP)
Gary R. Abbott (VP-Corp Engrg)
Joe Albei (CEO)
Mark G. Burford (CFO & Sr VP)
John A. Lambuth (Exec VP-Exploration)
Timothy A. Ficker (Chief Acctg Officer, VP, Controller & Asst Sec)
Thomas F. McCoy (Sr VP-Production)

Subsidiary (Domestic):

Cimarex Energy Co. of Colorado (2)

1700 Lincoln St Ste 1800, Denver, CO 80203
Tel.: (303) 295-3995
Natural Gas Extraction Services
N.A.I.C.S.: 211130

Cimarex Energy, Inc. (2)
15 E 5th St Ste 1000, Tulsa, OK 74103
Tel.: (918) 585-1100
Sales Range: $25-49.9 Million
Emp.: 30
Oil & Gas Drilling; Exploration & Production
N.A.I.C.S.: 211120

Cimarex Resolute LLC (2)
1700 Lincoln St Ste 2800, Denver, CO 80203
Tel.: (303) 534-4600
Web Site: http://www.resoluteenergy.com
Rev.: $303,478,000
Assets: $641,922,000
Liabilities: $716,331,000
Net Worth: ($74,409,000)
Earnings: ($1,233,000)
Emp.: 128
Fiscal Year-end: 12/31/2017
Gas & Oil Exploitation & Development Services
N.A.I.C.S.: 211120

Subsidiary (Domestic):

Resolute Natural Resources Company, LLC (3)
1700 Lincoln St Ste 2800, Denver, CO 80202
Tel.: (303) 534-4600
Web Site: http://www.resoluteenergy.com
Oil & Natural Gas Exploration Services
N.A.I.C.S.: 211130

Subsidiary (Domestic):

Key Production Company, Inc. (2)
1700 Lincoln St Ste 3700, Denver, CO 80203-4537
Tel.: (303) 295-3995
Web Site: http://www.cimarex.com
Emp.: 100
Crude Petroleum & Natural Gas Extraction Services
N.A.I.C.S.: 211120

Cranberry Pipeline Corporation (1)
840 Gessner Rd Ste 1400, Houston, TX 77024-4152 (100%)
Tel.: (281) 589-4600
Web Site: http://www.cabotog.com
Sales Range: $350-399.9 Million
Emp.: 110
Petroleum & Natural Gas Extraction
N.A.I.C.S.: 211120

GasSearch Drilling Services Corporation (1)
8283 State Route 29, Montrose, PA 18801
Tel.: (570) 278-7118
Web Site: https://www.gassearchdrilling.com
Sales Range: $75-99.9 Million
Emp.: 100
Oil & Gas Drilling Services
N.A.I.C.S.: 213111

COUCHBASE, INC.
3250 Olcott St, Santa Clara, CA 95054
Tel.: (650) 417-7500   DE
Web Site:
   https://www.couchbase.com
Year Founded: 2008
BASE—(NASDAQ)
Emp.: 51
Database Management Software Developer
N.A.I.C.S.: 513210
Greg Henry (CFO & Sr VP)
Matt Cain (Chm, Pres & CEO)
Scott Anderson (Sr VP-Cloud, Growth, and Bus Ops)
Fidelma Butler (Chief People Officer & Sr VP)
Margaret Chow (Chief Legal Officer & Sr VP)
Gopi Duddi (Sr VP-Engineering)
Julie Irish (CIO & Sr VP)
Josh Harbert (CMO & Sr VP)
Bill Carey (Chief Acctg Officer & VP)

COUNTER PRESS ACQUISITION CORPORATION
1981 Marcus Ave Ste 227, Lake Success, NY 11042
Tel.: (718) 775-3013   Ky
Year Founded: 2021
CPAQU—(NASDAQ)
Emp.: 2
Investment Services
N.A.I.C.S.: 523999
Paul Conway (CEO)
Michael Kalt (CFO)
Randy Frankel (Chm)

COURSERA, INC.
381 E Evelyn Ave, Mountain View, CA 94041
Tel.: (650) 963-9884   DE
Web Site: https://www.coursera.org
Year Founded: 2011
COUR—(NYSE)
Rev.: $635,764,000
Assets: $920,533,000
Liabilities: $304,339,000
Net Worth: $616,194,000
Earnings: ($116,554,000)
Emp.: 1,295
Fiscal Year-end: 12/31/23
Education Services
N.A.I.C.S.: 611710
Jeffrey Nacey Maggioncalda (Pres & CEO)
Andrew Y. Ng (Co-Founder & Chm)
Kenneth R. Hahn (CFO, Treas & Sr VP)
Marni Baker Stein (Chief Content Officer)
Tim Hannan (CMO)
Daphne Koller (Co-Founder)
Marcelo Modica (Chief People Officer)
Karine Allouche (Gen Mgr-Enterprise)
Michele M. Meyers (Chief Acctg Officer & VP-Acctg)
Alan Cardenas (Gen Counsel & Sec)
Mustafa Furniturewala (CTO & Head)

COUSINS PROPERTIES INCORPORATED
3344 Peachtree Rd NE Ste 1800, Atlanta, GA 30326-4802
Tel.: (404) 407-1000   GA
Web Site: https://www.cousins.com
Year Founded: 1958
CUZ—(NYSE)
Rev.: $802,874,000
Assets: $7,634,474,000
Liabilities: $3,086,161,000
Net Worth: $4,548,313,000
Earnings: $82,963,000
Emp.: 305
Fiscal Year-end: 12/31/23
Real Estate Development & Investment Services
N.A.I.C.S.: 525990
John S. McColl (Exec VP-Dev)
Tim Hendricks (Sr VP & Mng Dir)
Pamela F. Roper (Gen Counsel, Sec & Exec VP)
Gregg D. Adzema (CFO & Exec VP)
Michael Colin Connolly (Pres & CEO)
Matthew S. Mooney (Mng Dir & Sr VP)
Kyle Burd (Sr VP & Mng Dir)
J. Kennedy Hicks (Chief Investment Officer, Exec VP-Investments & Mng Dir-Investments)
Jeffrey D. Symes (Chief Acctg Officer & Sr VP)
Steve Hallmark (VP)
Jarett Brock (VP)
Yesenia Felix (VP)
Patrick Gehm (VP)
Heather Haney (VP)
Richard G. Hickson IV (Exec VP-Ops)

Subsidiaries:

Cousins - San Jacinto Center LLC (1)
98 San Jacinto Blvd, Austin, TX 78701
Tel.: (512) 279-2170
Web Site: http://www.sanjacintocenter.com
Real Estate Investment Services
N.A.I.C.S.: 525990
Tim Hendricks (Mng Dir & Sr VP)
Samantha Ingram (Asst Mgr-Property)
Dan Jones (Sr Mgr-Property)
Anyssa Hoyle (Mgr-Admin)

Cousins Properties LP (1)
3344 Peachtree Rd NE Ste 1800, Atlanta, GA 30326
Tel.: (404) 407-1000
Real Estate Investment Services
N.A.I.C.S.: 531120

Cousins Properties Palisades LLC (1)
6300 Bee Cave Rd, Austin, TX 78746
Tel.: (512) 477-3434
Real Estate Management Services
N.A.I.C.S.: 531190

Cousins Properties Services LLC (1)
6565 N Macarthur Blvd, Irving, TX 75039
Tel.: (972) 401-3550
Real Estate Management Services
N.A.I.C.S.: 531190
John Wehmeyer (Sr Mgr-Property)

Cousins Realty Services, LLC (1)
2202 N Westshore Blvd, Tampa, FL 33607
Tel.: (813) 421-8702
Web Site: http://cousinsproperties.com
Property Management Services; Full-Service Leasing, Management, Construction, Acquisition, Disposition & Tenant Representation Services
N.A.I.C.S.: 531312

Cousins Terminus LLC (1)
3280 Peachtree Rd NE, Atlanta, GA 30305
Tel.: (404) 407-2000
Web Site: http://www.terminusatlanta.com
Real Estate Development & Investment Services
N.A.I.C.S.: 531390

TIER REIT, Inc. (1)
5950 Sherry Ln, Dallas, TX 75225
Tel.: (972) 483-2400
Web Site: http://www.cousins.com
Sales Range: $200-249.9 Million
Real Estate Investment Trust
N.A.I.C.S.: 525990

COVENANT LOGISTICS GROUP, INC.
400 Birmingham Hwy, Chattanooga, TN 37419
Tel.: (423) 821-1212   NV
Web Site:
   https://www.covenantlogistics.com
Year Founded: 1985
CVLG—(NASDAQ)
Rev.: $1,216,858,000
Assets: $796,645,000
Liabilities: $419,517,000
Net Worth: $377,128,000
Earnings: $108,682,000
Emp.: 4,607
Fiscal Year-end: 12/31/22
Truckload Carrier Services
N.A.I.C.S.: 484121
David R. Parker (Chm & CEO)
Dustin Koehl (COO)
James S. Grant III (CFO & Exec VP)
M. Paul Bunn (Pres)
Joey Ballard (Exec VP-People & Safety)
Sam Hough (Exec VP-Expedited Ops)
Lynn Doster (Exec VP-Dedicated & Warehouse Ops)
Eric Whitton (Sr VP-Technology)
Brande Tweed (Sr VP-Fin Improvement)
Dan Porterfield (Sr VP-Maintenance & Equipment Control)

Covenant Logistics Group, Inc.—(Continued)

Jim Massengill (Sr VP-Warehouse Ops)
Lyndal Harper (Sr VP-Managed Freight Ops)
Billy Cartright (Sr VP-Dedicated Ops)
George Yates (Sr VP-Brokerage)
Matisse Long (Chief Acctg Officer)
Troy Robertson (Gen Counsel & Sr VP)
E. J. Johnson (Sr VP-Dedicated Ops)
Rob Coffman (Sr VP-Expedited Ops)

Subsidiaries:

AAT Carriers, Inc.   (1)
1110 Market St Warehouse Row Ste 316b, Chattanooga, TN 37402
Web Site: http://www.aatcarriers.com
General Freight Trucking
N.A.I.C.S.: 484121
Nina Wilson (VP-Sls)

Covenant Properties, LLC   (1)
22107 Whitestone Ct, Smithsburg, MD 21783
Tel.: (301) 371-8780
Emp.: 3
Nonresidential Building Operators
N.A.I.C.S.: 531312

Covenant Transport, Inc.   (1)
400 Birmingham Hwy, Chattanooga, TN 37419   (100%)
Tel.: (423) 821-1212
Web Site: http://www.covenanttransport.com
Sales Range: $150-199.9 Million
Truckload Carrier Services
N.A.I.C.S.: 484121

Heritage Insurance Inc   (1)
24401 104th Ave SE Ste 102, Kent, WA 98030
Tel.: (253) 638-8142
Web Site: https://www.heritageadvises.com
Insurance Services
N.A.I.C.S.: 522220

IQS Insurance Retention Group, Inc.   (1)
76 Saint Paul St Ste 500, Burlington, VT 05401
Tel.: (802) 862-4400
Insurance Agents
N.A.I.C.S.: 524210

Southern Refrigerated Transport   (1)
8055 Hwy 67 N, Texarkana, AR 71854
Tel.: (870) 772-4581
Web Site: http://www.covenanttransport.com
Refrigerated Truck Service
N.A.I.C.S.: 484230

Star Transportation, LLC   (1)
1234 Bridgestone Pkwy, La Vergne, TN 37086-3509
Tel.: (615) 256-4336
Web Site: http://www.covenanttransport.com
Irregular Route Truck Load Carrier
N.A.I.C.S.: 484121

Transport Enterprise Leasing, LLC   (1)
400 Birmingham Hwy, Chattanooga, TN 37419
Tel.: (423) 214-3910
Web Site: https://tel360.com
Truck & Trailer Equipment Management Services
N.A.I.C.S.: 532490
Doug Carmichael (OCO)
Jud Alexander (Pres)
Sheri Aaberg (COO)
Jeff Berger (CIO)
Aaron Thompson (VP-Maintenance)
Brandon Lairsen (VP-Trailer Leasing)
Jacob Brazier (VP-Fleet Leasing)
David Gernhard (VP-Credit & Collections)
Ashley Smith (VP-Finance & Accounting)

COYA THERAPEUTICS, INC.

5850 San Felipe St Ste 500, Houston, TX 77057   DE
Web Site:
  https://coyatherapeutics.com
Year Founded: 2020

COYA—(NASDAQ)
Rev.: $63,673
Assets: $8,395,566
Liabilities: $16,789,111
Net Worth: ($8,393,545)
Earnings: ($12,244,776)
Emp.: 6
Fiscal Year-end: 12/31/22
Biotechnology Research & Development Services
N.A.I.C.S.: 541714
Arun Swaminathan (CEO & Chief Bus Officer)
Fred Grossman (Pres & Chief Medical Officer)
David Snyder (CFO & COO)
Michelle Frazier (Sr VP-Regulatory)
Daniel Barvin (VP-Operations & Patient Advocacy)
Howard Berman (Co-Founder & Exec Chm)

COYNI, INC.

3131Camino DelRio N Ste 1400, San Diego, CA 92108
Tel.: (609) 514-5136   NV
Web Site: https://www.coyni.com
Year Founded: 2001
LOGQ—(OTCIQ)
Assets: $511
Liabilities: $28,962
Net Worth: ($28,451)
Earnings: ($227,096)
Fiscal Year-end: 12/31/22
IT Outsourcing Services
N.A.I.C.S.: 541519
Yew Siong Cheng (CFO & Principal Acctg Officer)

CPI AEROSTRUCTURES, INC.

91 Heartland Blvd, Edgewood, NY 11717
Tel.: (631) 586-5200   NY
Web Site: https://www.cpiaero.com
Year Founded: 1980
CVU—(NYSEAMEX)
Rev.: $83,335,764
Assets: $59,447,080
Liabilities: $55,250,050
Net Worth: $4,197,030
Earnings: $9,176,225
Emp.: 208
Fiscal Year-end: 12/31/22
Other Aircraft Parts & Auxiliary Equipment Manufacturing
N.A.I.C.S.: 336413
Dorith Hakim (Pres & CEO)
Andrew L. Davis (CFO, Principal Acctg Officer & Sec)
Carey E. Bond (Vice Chm)
Clint Allnach (Dir-Engineering-Technology)
Nazzareno Palmerini (VP-Programs)
James Mulhall (VP-Business Development)

Subsidiaries:

Welding Metallurgy, Inc.   (1)
110 Plant Ave, Hauppauge, NY 11788
Tel.: (631) 253-0500
Web Site: http://www.weldingmet.com
Sales Range: $1-9.9 Million
Emp.: 30
Aerospace Industry Sheet Metal Mfr
N.A.I.C.S.: 332322
Dorith Hakim (Pres & CEO)

Subsidiary (Domestic):

Compac Development Corporation   (2)
110 Plant Ave, Hauppauge, NY 11788
Tel.: (631) 881-4906
Metal Enclosure Mfr
N.A.I.C.S.: 332119
Dorith Hakim (Pres & CEO)

CPS TECHNOLOGIES CORPORATION

111 S Worcester St, Norton, MA 02766
Tel.: (508) 222-0614   DE
Web Site:
  https://www.cpstechnologysolutions.com
Year Founded: 1984
CPSH—(NASDAQ)
Rev.: $22,449,065
Assets: $18,800,719
Liabilities: $5,634,408
Net Worth: $13,166,311
Earnings: $3,215,877
Emp.: 90
Fiscal Year-end: 12/25/21
Advanced Materials Mfr
N.A.I.C.S.: 325998
Brian Mackey (Pres & CEO)
Charles K. Griffith Jr. (CFO)
Gregg Weatherman (Mgr-Sls-Natl)
Anthony Koski (Officer)

CRA INTERNATIONAL, INC.

200 Clarendon St, Boston, MA 02116-5092
Tel.: (617) 425-3000   MA
Web Site: https://www.crai.com
Year Founded: 1965
CRAI—(NASDAQ)
Rev.: $565,933,000
Assets: $555,360,000
Liabilities: $349,526,000
Net Worth: $205,834,000
Earnings: $41,679,000
Fiscal Year-end: 01/01/22
Business Consulting Services
N.A.I.C.S.: 541611
Daniel K. Mahoney (CFO, Chief Acctg Officer, Treas & Exec VP)
Robert Broadnax (VP-London)
Michael Hunter (VP)
Jonathan D. Yellin (Gen Counsel & Exec VP)
David P. Lamoreaux (VP-Tallahassee)
James J. Donohue (VP-New York)
Craig T. Elson (VP-Chicago)
Joanna Tsai (VP-Washington)
Walter Colasante (VP-Life Sciences Practice-Cambridge)
Richard V. L. Cooper (VP-Chicago)
Hitesh Chawda (CIO)
Stephanie M. Andrews (Principal)
Ana L. Balcarcel (Principal)
Ken Beers (VP)
Tiago Duarte Silva (VP-London)
Lev Gerlovin (VP-Boston)
Kira Gordon (Principal)
John J. Griffin (VP)
Adam J. Hart (Principal)
Miguel Herce (Principal)
Rhett Johnson (VP-Boston)
Brian Langan (VP-Boston)
Robert J. Lee (VP-Boston)
Matthew P. List (VP-Boston)
Sam Lynch (VP-Boston)
Sean May (VP-Boston)
Jim McMahon (VP-Boston)
Monica Noether (VP)
Chad M. Holmes (Chief Corp Dev Officer & Exec VP)
Raquel Tamez (Chief Inclusion & Engagement Officer)
Margaret F. Sanderson (VP-Antitrust & Competition Economics Practice)
Gregory D. Adams (VP-Salt Lake City)
Renee McMahon (VP-Chicago)
Jeffrey Prisbrey (VP-Washington DC)
David Skanderson (VP-Washington)
Yianis Sarafidis (VP-Washington)
Aaron Dolgoff (VP)
Kristofer Swanson (VP-Chicago)
Bill Hardin (VP-Chicago)
G. Scott Solomon (VP-Chicago)
Cuyler Robinson (VP-Chicago)
Gopal Das Varma (VP-Washington)
Seabron Adamson (VP)
Mukarram Attari (VP-Oakland)
Arthur P. Baines (VP-Washington)
Peter Boberg (VP)
Christopher J. Bokhart (VP-Chicago)
Simon Chisholm (VP-London)
Joanne Clark (VP-Cambridge-Cambridge)
Andrew R. Dick (VP-Washington-Washington)
Marsha J. Courchane (VP-Washington)
Sandra Chan (Principal)
Brian M. Daniel (VP-Chicago)
Raphael De Coninck (VP-Brussels)
Dan Donath (VP-London)
Sean Durkin (VP-Chicago)
Simon Ede (VP-London-London)
Laurent Flochel (VP-Paris)
Fei Deng (VP-Oakland)
Gregory K. Leonard (VP-Oakland)
Mario A. Lopez (VP-Oakland)
Stephen P. Rusek (VP-Oakland)
Noah Schwartz (VP-Oakland)
Sandy David (Chief Acctg Officer, VP & Controller)
Nicholas Davies (VP-Life Sciences Practice)
Becky Davis (Principal)
Eyal Dvir (Principal)
Dimitri Kordonis (Principal)
Zawadi Lemayian (Principal)
Josh Lustig (Principal)
Maria Tripolski-Kimel (Principal)
Griff Vinton (VP)
Allison Wiese (Principal)
Mary Beth Savio (VP)
Erin McDermott (Principal)
Matthew M. Bennett (VP-London)
Paul A. Maleh (Chm, Pres & CEO)

Subsidiaries:

CRA International (Netherlands) BV   (1)
Koninginneweg 11, 1217 KP, Hilversum, Netherlands
Tel.: (31) 208081320
Emp.: 1
Financial & Business Consulting Services
N.A.I.C.S.: 541611

CRA International Ltd.   (1)
401 Bay Street Suite 900, PO Box 46, Toronto, M5H 2Y4, ON, Canada   (100%)
Tel.: (416) 413-4070
Sales Range: $1-9.9 Million
Emp.: 12
Provider of Business Consulting Services
N.A.I.C.S.: 541611

CRA International UK Ltd.   (1)
8 Finsbury Circus, London, EC2M 7EA, United Kingdom   (100%)
Tel.: (44) 207 664 3700
Web Site: http://www.crai.co.uk
Sales Range: $25-49.9 Million
Emp.: 125
Provider of Business Consulting Services
N.A.I.C.S.: 541611

Marakon Associates, Inc.   (1)
1411 Broadway 35th Fl, New York, NY 10018
Tel.: (212) 520-7120
Web Site: https://www.marakon.com
Sales Range: $50-74.0 Million
Emp.: 300
Management Consulting Services
N.A.I.C.S.: 541611
Happy Liu (Principal)

Welch Consulting   (1)
1716 Briarcrest Dr, Bryan, TX 77802
Tel.: (979) 268-3143
Web Site: http://www.welchcon.com
Sales Range: $1-9.9 Million
Emp.: 48
Business Consulting, Nec, Nsk
N.A.I.C.S.: 541618
Finis Welch (Founder)

bioStrategies Group, Inc.   (1)
20 S Clark St, Chicago, IL 60603
Tel.: (312) 482-8292

Web Site: http://www.biostrategies.com
Rev.: $4,250,000
Emp.: 25
Administrative & General Management Consulting Services
N.A.I.C.S.: 541611
Phillip Benson (Partner)
Lisa Kaestle (Principal)
Julie VanEenenaam (Mgr-Recruiting & Res)

CRACKER BARREL OLD COUNTRY STORE, INC.
305 Hartmann Dr, Lebanon, TN 37087-4779
Tel.: (615) 444-5533   **TN**
Web Site:
  https://www.crackerbarrel.com
Year Founded: 1998
CBRL—(NASDAQ)
Rev.: $3,470,762,000
Assets: $2,161,494,000
Liabilities: $1,721,345,000
Net Worth: $440,149,000
Earnings: $40,930,000
Emp.: 77,600
Fiscal Year-end: 08/02/24
Restaurant Holding Company
N.A.I.C.S.: 722511
Sandra Brophy Cochran (Pres & CEO)
Laura A. Daily (Sr VP-Retail)
Richard M. Wolfson (Gen Counsel, Sec & Sr VP)
Donna L. Roberts (Chief HR Officer & VP)
Bruce A. Hoffmeister (CIO & Sr VP)
Craig Pommells (CFO, Interim Principal Acctg Officer & Sr VP)
Mark Spurgin (Sr VP-Officer)
Chris Edwards (Chief Strategy Officer & Sr VP)
Sarah Moore (CMO & Sr VP)
Julie Felss Masino (Pres & CEO)

Subsidiaries:

CBOCS Distribution, Inc.   (1)
305 Hartmann Dr, Lebanon, TN 37087
Tel.: (615) 444-5533
Transportation Support Services
N.A.I.C.S.: 488999

CBOCS Texas, LLC   (1)
307 Hartman Dr, Lebanon, TN 37087-2519
Tel.: (615) 235-4096
Web Site: http://www.crackerbarrel.com
Sales Range: $50-74.9 Million
Emp.: 500
Restaurant Operating Services
N.A.I.C.S.: 722511

CBOCS West, Inc.   (1)
3993 Howard Hughes Pkwy Ste 250, Las Vegas, NV 89169-6754
Tel.: (702) 866-2252
Investment Management Service
N.A.I.C.S.: 551112

CBOCS, Inc.   (1)
305 Hartmann Dr, Lebanon, TN 37087   (100%)
Tel.: (615) 444-5533
Restaurant & Gift Shop Operator
N.A.I.C.S.: 722511
Michael A. Woodhouse (Chm & CEO)

CRANE COMPANY
100 1st Stamford Pl, Stamford, CT 06902
Tel.: (203) 363-7300   **DE**
Web Site: https://www.craneco.com
Year Founded: 1855
CR—(NYSE)
Rev.: $2,086,400,000
Assets: $2,333,600,000
Liabilities: $973,300,000
Net Worth: $1,360,300,000
Earnings: $255,900,000
Emp.: 7,300
Fiscal Year-end: 12/31/23
Engineering Services
N.A.I.C.S.: 541330

Max H. Mitchell (Chm, Pres & CEO)
Ann Vinci (CIO)
Richard A. Maue (CFO)
Tami Polmanteer (Chief HR Officer)

Subsidiaries:

Technifab Products, Inc.   (1)
10339 N Industrial Pk Dr, Brazil, IN 47834-7322
Tel.: (812) 442-0520
Web Site: http://www.technifab.com
Rev.: $5,800,000
Emp.: 68
Industrial Machinery Mfr
N.A.I.C.S.: 333248
Phil Redenbarger (VP)

Vian Enterprises, Inc.   (1)
1501 Industrial Dr, Auburn, CA 95603
Tel.: (530) 885-1997
Sales Range: $1-9.9 Million
Emp.: 50
Business Services, Nec, Nsk
N.A.I.C.S.: 711410

CRANE NXT, CO.
100 1st Stamford Pl, Stamford, CT 06902
Tel.: (203) 363-7300   **DE**
Web Site: https://www.cranenxt.com
Year Founded: 1855
CXT—(NYSE)
Rev.: $1,391,300,000
Assets: $2,129,400,000
Liabilities: $1,165,400,000
Net Worth: $964,000,000
Earnings: $188,300,000
Emp.: 4,000
Fiscal Year-end: 12/31/23
Security, Micro-optics Technology Solution Services
N.A.I.C.S.: 334513
Max H. Mitchell (Pres & CEO)
Richard A. Maue (CFO & Sr VP)
Paul G. Igoe (Gen Counsel-Crane NXT, Sec-Crane NXT & Sr VP-Crane NXT)
Alex Alcala (Pres-ChemPharma & Energy)
Hari Jinaga (Pres-Crane India)
John O'Sullivan (Pres-Crane Composites)
Brian P. Sweeney (Pres-Crane Pumps & Systems)
Richard C. Tuck (Pres-BS&U)
Michelle Yan (Pres-Crane China)
Mark Youssef (Pres-Crane Middle East & Africa)
Kumar C. Mathuria (VP-Financial Plng & Analysis)
Jason D. Feldman (VP-IR)
Christina Cristiano (Principal Acctg Officer, VP & Controller)
Chris Mitchell (Pres-Valve Svcs)
Aaron W. Saak (Pres-Crane NXT & CEO-Crane NXT)
David Jones (VP-Bus System)
Alejandro Alcala (Exec VP)
Gustavo Cruz (Pres)
John J. Higgs (Pres)
Subramanya Prasad (Pres)
Tamara S. Polmanteer (Chief HR Officer)
Diane Byron (VP)
Scott A. Grisham (Sr VP)
Sina Passarelli (VP)
Ann Vinci (CIO)
Tricia Wise (VP)

Subsidiaries:

Crane Aerospace & Electronics   (1)
16700 13th Ave W, Lynnwood, WA 98037-8503
Tel.: (425) 743-1313
Web Site: http://www.craneae.com
Holding Company; Aerospace & Electronics Products Mfr
N.A.I.C.S.: 551112

Subsidiary (Domestic):

Crane Aerospace, Inc.   (2)
16700 13th Ave W, Lynnwood, WA 98037-8503
Tel.: (425) 743-1313
Web Site: http://www.craneae.com
Aerospace Products Mfr
N.A.I.C.S.: 334419

Unit (Domestic):

Crane Aerospace & Electronics, Keltec Operation   (3)
84 Hill Ave NW, Fort Walton Beach, FL 32548   (100%)
Tel.: (850) 244-0043
Web Site: http://www.crane.com
Sales Range: $75-99.9 Million
Emp.: 250
Power Supply, Amplifier & Transmitter Designer & Mfr
N.A.I.C.S.: 334419

Crane Aerospace STC Microwave System Olektron   (3)
28 Tozer Rd, Beverly, MA 01915   (100%)
Tel.: (978) 524-7200
Web Site: http://www.craneae.com
Sales Range: $25-49.9 Million
Emp.: 100
Space Electronic Components Designer & Mfr
N.A.I.C.S.: 334220

Subsidiary (Domestic):

Crane Lear Romec Corp.   (3)
241 S Abbe Rd, Elyria, OH 44035
Tel.: (440) 323-3211
Web Site: http://www.learromec.com
Emp.: 250
Aircraft Pumps, Parts & Auxiliary Equipment Mfr
N.A.I.C.S.: 336413

ELDEC Corporation   (3)
16700 13th Ave W, Lynnwood, WA 98037-8503   (100%)
Tel.: (425) 743-1313
Web Site: http://www.craneae.com
Aerospace Component Mfr
N.A.I.C.S.: 334511

Subsidiary (Non-US):

ELDEC France S.A.R.L.   (4)
18 rue du 35 Regiment d'Aviation, 69500, Bron, France   (100%)
Tel.: (33) 478261010
Web Site: http://www.craneae.com
Sales Range: $1-9.9 Million
Emp.: 50
Electronic Products Designer & Mfr
N.A.I.C.S.: 334513

Subsidiary (Domestic):

Hydro-Aire Inc.   (3)
3000 Winona Ave, Burbank, CA 91504-2540   (100%)
Tel.: (818) 526-2600
Web Site: http://www.craneae.com
Fuel & Hydraulic Systems for Aircraft & Missile Industry Mfr
N.A.I.C.S.: 336413

P.L. Porter Controls, Inc.   (3)
3000 Winona Ave, Burbank, CA 91504
Tel.: (818) 526-2500
Web Site: http://www.craneae.com
Sales Range: $25-49.9 Million
Emp.: 300
Position Control Mechanisms Mfr
N.A.I.C.S.: 336413

Subsidiary (Domestic):

Crane Electronics, Inc.   (2)
10301 Willows Rd PO Box 97005, Redmond, WA 98073-9705
Tel.: (425) 882-3100
Web Site: http://www.craneae.com
Electronic Products Mfr
N.A.I.C.S.: 334419

Subsidiary (Non-US):

Crane Electronics Corporation   (3)
No 198 Xin-Sheng Rd, Qianzhen District, Kaohsiung, 80672, Taiwan   (100%)

Tel.: (886) 7 811 2131
Web Site: http://www.craneae.com
Sales Range: $50-74.9 Million
Emp.: 200
Microcircuit Products Mfr
N.A.I.C.S.: 334413

Subsidiary (Domestic):

Crane Nuclear, Inc.   (3)
2825 Cobb International Blvd, Kennesaw, GA 30152   (100%)
Tel.: (770) 424-6343
Web Site: http://www.cranenuclear.com
Sales Range: $25-49.9 Million
Emp.: 60
Industrial Machinery & Equipment Distr
N.A.I.C.S.: 423830

Subsidiary (Non-US):

Interpoint U.K. Ltd.   (3)
8 Reading Road, Yateley, GU46 7RX, Hampshire, United Kingdom   (100%)
Tel.: (44) 1252872266
Web Site: http://www.interpoint.com
Sales Range: $1-9.9 Million
Emp.: 3
Microcircuit Products Mfr
N.A.I.C.S.: 334413

Crane Controls, Inc.   (1)
100 First Stamford Pl, Stamford, CT 06902
Tel.: (203) 363-7300
Industrial Control Mfr
N.A.I.C.S.: 334513

Subsidiary (Domestic):

Azonix Corporation   (2)
900 Middlesex Tpke Bldg 6, Billerica, MA 01821   (100%)
Tel.: (978) 670-6300
Web Site: http://www.azonix.com
Sales Range: $10-24.9 Million
Emp.: 47
Control & Measurement Devices Mfr
N.A.I.C.S.: 334513

Barksdale, Inc.   (2)
3211 Fruitland Ave, Los Angeles, CA 90058-1234   (100%)
Tel.: (323) 589-6181
Web Site: https://www.barksdale.com
Sales Range: $50-74.9 Million
Emp.: 150
Valves, Transducers, Temperature & Pressure Switches & Electronics Mfr
N.A.I.C.S.: 334519

Subsidiary (Non-US):

Barksdale GmbH   (3)
Dorn-Assenheimer Str 27, 61203, Reichelsheim, Germany   (100%)
Tel.: (49) 6 035 9490
Web Site: https://www.barksdale.de
Sales Range: $10-24.9 Million
Emp.: 65
Level, Temperature & Pressure Switches, Valves & Transducers Mfr
N.A.I.C.S.: 335931
Michael Weileder (Mng Dir)

Subsidiary (Domestic):

Dynalco Controls Corporation   (2)
3690 NW 53rd St, Fort Lauderdale, FL 33309   (100%)
Tel.: (954) 739-4300
Web Site: http://www.dynalco.com
Sales Range: $25-49.9 Million
Emp.: 80
Electronic Flow Controls
N.A.I.C.S.: 334519

Westlock Controls Holdings, Inc.   (2)
280 N Midland Ave Ste 258, Saddle Brook, NJ 07663
Tel.: (201) 794-7650
Web Site: http://www.westlockcontrols.com
Investment Management Service
N.A.I.C.S.: 523999

Subsidiary (Non-US):

Westlock Controls Limited   (3)
1st Floor Chapman House Chapman Way, Tunbridge Wells, TN2 3EF, Kent, United Kingdom
Tel.: (44) 1892516277

Crane NXT, Co.—(Continued)

Web Site: https://www.westlockcontrols.com
Valve Position Monitor Mfr
N.A.I.C.S.: 334519

Crane Engineered Materials (1)
100 First Stamford Pl, Stamford, CT 06902
Tel.: (203) 263-7300
Web Site: http://www.craneco.com
Sales Range: $125-149.9 Million
Building Composites Mfr
N.A.I.C.S.: 444180

Subsidiary (Domestic):

Crane Composites Inc. (2)
23525 W Eames St, Channahon, IL
60410 **(100%)**
Tel.: (815) 467-8600
Web Site: http://www.cranecomposites.com
Sales Range: $75-99.9 Million
Emp.: 500
Fiberglass Reinforced Plastic Panel Mfr
N.A.I.C.S.: 326199
Mike Cheney (VP-Recreational Vehicles)
Matt Shields (VP-Building Products)
Drew Franzen (VP-Transportation)
John O'Sullivan (Pres)
Matt Mackin (VP)
Michael Richardson (VP)
Michael Ridge (VP)
Omar Haddadin (VP)

Subsidiary (Domestic):

Crane Composites, Inc. (3)
2424 E Kercher Rd, Goshen, IN 46526
Tel.: (574) 534-0010
Web Site: http://www.cranecomposites.com
Sales Range: $25-49.9 Million
Emp.: 157
Mfr of Composite Siding & Exterior Panels
for Recreational Vehicles
N.A.I.C.S.: 332322

Lasco Composites, LP (3)
8015 Dixon Dr, Florence, KY 41042
Tel.: (859) 371-7720
Sales Range: $50-74.9 Million
Emp.: 145
Reinforced Plastic Panel Mfr & Retailer
N.A.I.C.S.: 326191

Subsidiary (Domestic):

Polyflon Company (2)
1 Willard Rd, Norwalk, CT 06851
Tel.: (203) 840-7555
Web Site: http://www.polyflon.com
Sales Range: $25-49.9 Million
Emp.: 20
Electroplates & Teflon Mfr
N.A.I.C.S.: 332912

Crane Fluid Handling (1)
100 First Stamford Pl, Stamford, CT 06902
Tel.: (203) 363-7300
Web Site: http://www.craneco.com
Sales Range: $125-149.9 Million
Emp.: 75
Pumps & Pumping Equipment
N.A.I.C.S.: 333914

Subsidiary (Domestic):

**Crane ChemPharma Flow
Solutions** (2)
4444 Cooper Rd, Cincinnati, OH
45242 **(100%)**
Tel.: (513) 745-6000
Web Site:
   http://www.cranechempharma.com
Sales Range: $75-99.9 Million
Industrial Valves & Actuators Mfr
N.A.I.C.S.: 332911

Subsidiary (Non-US):

Xomox Canada Ltd. (3)
9429 41 Ave, Edmonton, T6E 5X7, AB,
Canada **(100%)**
Tel.: (780) 462-3100
Web Site:
   http://www.craneflowsolutions.com
Sales Range: $25-49.9 Million
Emp.: 12
Industrial Valves & Pipe Fittings Mfr
N.A.I.C.S.: 332911

Xomox Corporation (3)
39213 Hwy 74 Ste B, Gonzales, LA 70737-
6406
Tel.: (225) 644-2300
Web Site: http://www.xomox.com
Sales Range: $25-49.9 Million
Emp.: 6
Industrial Valve Distr
N.A.I.C.S.: 332911

Subsidiary (Non-US):

Xomox France S.A. (3)
8 Rue De L III, PO Box 29, Brunstatt, Mul-
house, 68350, France **(100%)**
Tel.: (33) 389611361
Web Site: http://www.xomox.de
Sales Range: $25-49.9 Million
Emp.: 26
Valves, Actuators & Flow Control Products
Mfr
N.A.I.C.S.: 332911
Christian Beyer (Mng Dir)

Xomox Hungary Kft. (3)
Czech u 1, PL 354, 8000, Szekesfehervar,
Hungary **(100%)**
Tel.: (36) 622513100
Mfr of Industrial Valves, Actuators & Flow
Control Products
N.A.I.C.S.: 332911

**Xomox International GmbH &
Co.** (3)
Von-Behring-Str 15, Bodensee, 88131, Lin-
dau, Germany **(100%)**
Tel.: (49) 83827020
Web Site:
   http://www.cranechempharma.com
Sales Range: $75-99.9 Million
Emp.: 200
Industrial Valves, Actuators & Flow Control
Products Mfr
N.A.I.C.S.: 332911

Xomox Japan Ltd. (3)
691-2 Nippa-Cho, Kouhoku-ku, Yokohama,
223-0057, Kanagawa, Japan
Tel.: (81) 45 534 1450
Web Site: http://www.japan.xomox.com
Emp.: 21
Industrial Valves & Pipe Fittings Mfr
N.A.I.C.S.: 332911

Xomox Korea Ltd. (3)
2nd Fl 583-4 Hwajeon-Dong, Gangseo-Gu,
Busan, 618-280, Korea (South) **(100%)**
Tel.: (82) 518316930
Web Site: http://www.xomox.com
Sales Range: $25-49.9 Million
Emp.: 4
Mfr of Industrial Valves, Actuators & Flow
Control Products
N.A.I.C.S.: 332911

Joint Venture (Non-US):

Xomox Sanmar Ltd. (3)
9 Cathedral Road, Chennai, 600 086, India
Tel.: (91) 4428128400
Web Site: http://www.sunmargroup.com
Emp.: 240
Industrial Valve Mfr; Owned by Sanmar
Holdings Ltd. & Xomox Corporation
N.A.I.C.S.: 332911
M. N. Radhakrishnan (Mng Dir)

Subsidiary (Non-US):

Crane Ningjin Valve Co (2)
No 496 Jing Long Street, Ningjin, 055550,
Hebei, China **(90%)**
Tel.: (86) 319 580 8686
Web Site: https://www.craneco.com.cn
Sales Range: $100-124.9 Million
Mfr of Industrial Valves
N.A.I.C.S.: 332911

Subsidiary (Domestic):

Crane Pumps & Systems Inc. (2)
420 3rd St, Piqua, OH 45356-3918 **(100%)**
Tel.: (937) 773-2442
Web Site: http://www.cranepumps.com
Sales Range: $100-124.9 Million
Pumps & Cleaning Systems Mfr
N.A.I.C.S.: 333914

Subsidiary (Non-US):

**Crane Pumps and Systems Canada,
Inc.** (3)
83 West Dr, Bramalea, L6T 2J6, ON,
Canada **(100%)**
Tel.: (905) 457-6223
Web Site: http://www.cranepumps.com
Sales Range: $125-149.9 Million
Emp.: 40
Pumps Mfr
N.A.I.C.S.: 333914

Subsidiary (Domestic):

Crane Resistoflex/Industrial (2)
1 Quality Way, Marion, NC 28752 **(100%)**
Tel.: (828) 724-4000
Web Site: http://www.resistoflex.com
Sales Range: $50-74.9 Million
Plastic-Lined Pipes & Fittings Mfr
N.A.I.C.S.: 326122

Unit (Domestic):

Parker Hannifin (3)
2575 W 5th St, Jacksonville, FL 32254-
2066
Tel.: (904) 389-3400
Sales Range: $50-74.9 Million
Emp.: 76
Separable Lip Seal Fittings & Teflon-Lined
Braided Hose Mfr for the Aerospace Indus-
try
N.A.I.C.S.: 332912

Subsidiary (Domestic):

Crane Valve Services (2)
2825 Cobb International Blvd, Kennesaw,
GA 30152-4352
Tel.: (770) 424-6343
Web Site: http://www.craneco.com
Sales Range: $50-74.9 Million
Emp.: 40
ValveWatch Condition Monitoring Systems
for Oil & Gas, Petrochemical, Chemical &
Pipeline Applications
N.A.I.C.S.: 332912

Subsidiary (Domestic):

Pacific Valves (3)
3201 Walnut Ave, Signal Hill, CA 90755
Tel.: (562) 426-2531
Web Site: http://www.craneenergy.com
Sales Range: $25-49.9 Million
Valve Mfr
N.A.I.C.S.: 332919

Subsidiary (Domestic):

Stockham Valves & Fittings, Inc. (2)
2129 3rd Ave SE, Cullman, AL
35055-5477 **(100%)**
Tel.: (256) 775-3800
Web Site: http://www.crane.com
Sales Range: $50-74.9 Million
Emp.: 50
Flow Control Devices & Valves Mfr
N.A.I.C.S.: 332919

**Crane International Holdings,
Inc.** (1)
100 1st Stamford Pl, Stamford, CT
06902 **(100%)**
Tel.: (203) 363-7300
Web Site: http://www.craneco.com
Sales Range: $50-74.9 Million
Emp.: 70
Holding Company
N.A.I.C.S.: 551112
Max H. Mitchell (Pres & CEO)

Subsidiary (Non-US):

Crane (Asia Pacific) Pte. Ltd. (2)
16 Gul Link, Singapore, 629386, Singapore
Tel.: (65) 68631559
Industrial Machinery Whslr
N.A.I.C.S.: 423830

Crane Australia Pty. Ltd. (2)
146-154 Dunheved Circuit, Saint Marys,
2760, NSW, Australia
Tel.: (61) 288890100
Emp.: 109
Industrial Machinery Whslr
N.A.I.C.S.: 423830

Crane Currency Malta Ltd. (2)

HHF 402 Hal Far Industrial Estate, Birzeb-
buga, BBG 3000, Malta
Tel.: (356) 27782300
Web Site: https://www.cranecurrency.com
Commercial Printing Services
N.A.I.C.S.: 323111
Sam Keayes (Sr VP)
Jon Ngin (VP-Ops)
Mike Fitzgerald (CFO & VP-Fin)
Mike Prout (VP-Global Security)
Wael Mrad (VP-Sls)

Crane Global Holdings S.L. (2)
Calle Via Augusta 158 2, Barcelona, 08918,
Spain
Tel.: (34) 933004163
Industrial Products Mfr
N.A.I.C.S.: 332911
Sergio Rueda (Gen Mgr)

**Crane Holdings (Germany)
GmbH** (2)
Heerdter Lohweg 63-71, 40549, Dusseldorf,
Germany **(100%)**
Tel.: (49) 21159560
Industrial Machinery Distr
N.A.I.C.S.: 423830

Subsidiary (Domestic):

**Crane Process Flow Technologies
GmbH** (3)
Heerdter Lohweg 63 71, 40512, Dusseldorf,
Germany **(100%)**
Tel.: (49) 21159560
Web Site: http://www.craneflow.de
Emp.: 80
Industrial Valve Mfr
N.A.I.C.S.: 332911
Hans Ptak (Gen Mgr)

Subsidiary (Non-US):

**Crane Process Flow Technologies
S.P.R.L.** (3)
Avenue Leonard de Vinci 11, 1300, Wavre,
Belgium
Tel.: (32) 10818440
Industrial Machinery Whslr
N.A.I.C.S.: 423830
Patrick Germentier (Mng Dir)

Subsidiary (Non-US):

Crane Limited (2)
Crane House Epsilon Terrace West Road,
Ipswich, IP3 9FJ, Suffolk, United Kingdom
Tel.: (44) 1473277300
Web Site: http://www.cranefs.com
Valves & Flow Control Products Mfr
N.A.I.C.S.: 332911

Division (Domestic):

**Crane Building Services &
Utilities** (3)
Crane House at Epsilon Terrace W Rd, Ips-
wich, IP3 9FJ, Suffolk, United Kingdom
Tel.: (44) 1473277300
Web Site: http://www.cranebsu.com
Emp.: 100
Fluid Valves, Fittings & Engineered Prod-
ucts Mfr
N.A.I.C.S.: 332913

Subsidiary (Domestic):

**Crane Merchandising Systems
Ltd.** (3)
Pipsmore Park, Bumpers Farm Industrial
Estate, Chippenham, SN14 6NQ, Wiltshire,
United Kingdom
Tel.: (44) 1249444807
Web Site: https://www.cranems.co.uk
Vending Machine Mfr
N.A.I.C.S.: 333310

**Crane Process Flow Technologies
Ltd.** (3)
Grange Road, Cwmbran, NP44 3XX,
Gwent, United Kingdom
Tel.: (44) 1633486666
Web Site: http://www.cranecpe.com
Valves & Fittings Designer & Mfr
N.A.I.C.S.: 332912

Crane Stockham Valve Ltd. (3)
6 Alexander Road, Belfast, BT6 9HJ, United
Kingdom
Tel.: (44) 2890704222

Mfr of Valves
N.A.I.C.S.: 332911

ELDEC Electronics Ltd. (3)
Whittle Close, Daventry, NN11 8YE,
Northants, United Kingdom
Tel.: (44) 327307200
Web Site: http://www.grenson.com
Sales Range: $10-24.9 Million
Emp.: 30
Power Supplies Mfr
N.A.I.C.S.: 335999

Subsidiary (Non-US):

Crane National Vendors Co., Ltd. (2)
51 B Caldari Road Unit 6, Concord, L4K
4G3, ON, Canada (100%)
Tel.: (416) 291-7600
Web Site: http://www.cranems.com
Sales Range: $10-24.9 Million
Emp.: 6
Welding Machine Distr
N.A.I.C.S.: 423440

**Crane Process Flow Technologies
S.r.l.** (2)
Via Pusiano 2, 20900, Monza, 20052, Italy
Tel.: (39) 0392704314
Industrial Machinery Whslr
N.A.I.C.S.: 423830

Crane Resistoflex GmbH (2)
Industriestrasse 96, 75181, Pforzheim,
75181, Germany
Tel.: (49) 72317850
Industrial Machinery Whslr
N.A.I.C.S.: 423830

Hattersly Newman Hender Ltd. (2)
Epsilon Terrace West Road, Ipswich, IP3
9FJ, Suffolk, United Kingdom
Tel.: (44) 1473277410
Web Site: https://www.hattersley.com
Pipe Fitting & Hose Mfr
N.A.I.C.S.: 326122

Mondais Holdings B.V. (2)
Naritaweg 165, 1043 BW, Amsterdam,
Netherlands
Tel.: (31) 205722300
Holding Company
N.A.I.C.S.: 551112

P.T. Crane Indonesia (2)
Delta Silicon 1 Industrial Park Jalan Akasia
2 Block AE 49, AE 49 Lippo Cikarang,
Bekasi, 17550, Indonesia
Tel.: (62) 2189907980
Web Site: http://www.cranecpe.com
Sales Range: $50-74.9 Million
Emp.: 30
Fluid & Pollution Controls Mfr
N.A.I.C.S.: 332912

Viking Johnson Ltd. (2)
46-48 Wilbury Way, Hitchin, SG4 0UD,
Hertfordshire, United Kingdom
Tel.: (44) 1462443322
Web Site: https://www.vikingjohnson.com
Pipe Fitting & Hose Mfr
N.A.I.C.S.: 326122

Wade Couplings Ltd. (2)
Crane House Epsilon Terrace West Road,
Ipswich, IP3 9FJ, Suffolkshire, United King-
dom
Tel.: (44) 1473277460
Web Site: http://www.wadefittings.com
Industrial Fitting & Valve Mfr
N.A.I.C.S.: 333996

Wask Ltd. (2)
46-48 Wilbury Way, Hitchin, SG4 0UD,
Hertfordshire, United Kingdom
Tel.: (44) 1462443225
Web Site: https://www.wask-uk.com
Pipe Fitting & Hose Mfr
N.A.I.C.S.: 326122

Xomox Chihuahua S.A. de C.V. (2)
Juan Ruiz de Alarcon 313 Complejo Indus-
trial Chihuahua, 31136, Chihuahua, Mexico
Tel.: (52) 6144429860
Industrial Machinery Whslr
N.A.I.C.S.: 423830

Xomox France S.A.S. (2)
8 Rue de I ill Brunstatt, PO Box 29, 68350,
Mulhouse, 68350, France
Tel.: (33) 389611361

Industrial Machinery Whslr
N.A.I.C.S.: 423830

Crane Merger Co. LLC (1)
100 First Stamford Pl, Stamford, CT 06902-
6740
Tel.: (203) 363-7300
Hydraulic Fittings & Valve Mfr
N.A.I.C.S.: 333996

Crane NXT Private Limited (1)
8th Floor M Agile S No 33/1 Samarth
Colony, Baner, Pune, 411045, India
Tel.: (91) 2069127120
Financial & Payment Technology Services
N.A.I.C.S.: 522320

Crane Overseas LLC (1)
100 1st Stamford Pl, Stamford, CT 06902
Tel.: (203) 363-7300
Industrial Products Mfr
N.A.I.C.S.: 332911
Max Mitchell (CEO)

**Crane Payment & Merchandising
Technologies** (1)
3222 Phoenixville Pike Ste 200, Malvern,
PA 19355
Tel.: (610) 430-2700
Web Site: http://www.craneco.com
Commercial & Service Industry Machinery
Mfr
N.A.I.C.S.: 333310

Subsidiary (Domestic):

**Crane Merchandising Systems,
Inc.** (2)
3330 Crane Way, Williston, SC
29853 (100%)
Tel.: (314) 298-3500
Web Site: http://www.cranems.com
Vending Machine Mfr
N.A.I.C.S.: 339999

Subsidiary (Domestic):

**Automatic Products International
Ltd.** (3)
165 Bridgepoint Dr, South Saint Paul, MN
55075
Tel.: (651) 288-2975
Web Site:
http://www.automaticproducts.com
Sales Range: $200-249.9 Million
Emp.: 525
Automatic Vending Machines
N.A.I.C.S.: 423850

Subsidiary (Non-US):

Automatic Products (UK) Ltd. (4)
International Office Stirling House Church
Road, Wombourne, WV5 9DJ, West Mid-
lands, United Kingdom
Tel.: (44) 1902324400
Web Site:
https://www.automaticproducts.com
Vending Machine Mfr
N.A.I.C.S.: 333310

Subsidiary (Domestic):

Streamware Corporation (3)
55 Providence Hwy Ste 1, Norwood, MA
02062 (100%)
Tel.: (781) 551-0010
Web Site: http://www.streamware.com
Sales Range: $10-24.9 Million
Emp.: 19
Vending & Delivery Software Publisher
N.A.I.C.S.: 513210

Subsidiary (Domestic):

Crane Payment Innovations, Inc. (2)
3222 Phoenixville Pike Ste 200, Malvern,
PA 19355
Tel.: (610) 430-2700
Fluid Power Valve & Hose Fitting Mfr
N.A.I.C.S.: 332912

Subsidiary (Non-US):

**Crane Payment Innovations
GmbH** (3)
Harburger Strasse 47-51, D-21614, Buxte-
hude, Germany (100%)
Tel.: (49) 41617290

Sales Range: $75-99.9 Million
Emp.: 150
Mfr of Fluid & Pollution Controls
N.A.I.C.S.: 332912

Crane Payment Innovations Srl (3)
Via Torquato Tasso 50, 24121, Bergamo,
Italy
Tel.: (39) 03316503302
Web Site: https://www.cranepi.com
Welding Machine Distr
N.A.I.C.S.: 423440

Plant (Domestic):

**Crane Payments Innovations,
Inc.** (3)
3222 Phoenixville Pike Ste 200, Malvern,
PA 19355
Tel.: (610) 430-2700
Web Site: https://www.cranepi.com
Payment Technologies Products Mfr
N.A.I.C.S.: 333310

Subsidiary (Domestic):

Cummins-Allison Corporation (3)
851 N Addison Ave, Elmhurst, IL 60126
Tel.: (630) 833-2285
Web Site: http://www.cumminsallison.com
Sales Range: $75-99.9 Million
Emp.: 750
Holding Company Services
N.A.I.C.S.: 551112
Kevin Frampton (Acct Mgr-Natl)
Linda Lortz (Dir-Credit & Customer Svcs)
Sharon Burr (Dir-Tax)
Glenn Gordon (Engr-Mechanical Design)
Will Hsiung (Engr-Software)
Sergio Solomon (Engr-Software)
Frank Janezic (Exec VP)
Donald Bodziak (Exec VP-Mfg)
Bill Klotz (Mgr-Eastern)
Riana Jimenez (Mgr-Intl Reg Channel Sls)
Henry Pielach (Mgr-Pur)
Mike Stodola (Mgr-Warehouse)
Marty Barrett (Sr Dir-Mfg)
Patrick Guardyak (Sr Dir-Software Architec-
ture & Design)
Jim Carson (Supvr-Facilities Maintenance)
Rico Parro (Supvr-Quality)
Marianne Krbec (VP-Coin Product & Engr-
Mechanical)
Darcy Devore (Reg Mgr)
Bob Jordan (CFO & Exec VP)
Soumyabrata Bhattacharya (Engr-Software
Design)
Pam Moellenkamp (Supvr-PMIA)
Doris Hiller (Acct Mgr-Natl)
Jeffrey Weickart (Engr-Software)
Doug Mennie (Pres)

Subsidiary (Non-US):

Cummins Allison Pty Ltd (4)
PO Box 7051, Silverwater, 2128, NSW,
Australia
Tel.: (61) 296486661
Web Site: http://www.cumminsallison.com
Emp.: 5
Electronic Equipment Distr
N.A.I.C.S.: 423690
Peter Gardner (Gen Mgr)

Cummins Allison SAS (4)
Parc Des Nations-Paris Nord 2 385 Rue de
la Belle Etoile, 95974, Roissy-en-France,
France
Tel.: (33) 148196160
Web Site: https://www.cumminsallison.fr
Emp.: 10
Electronic Equipment Mfr & Distr
N.A.I.C.S.: 333310
Phillippe Rabier (Gen Mgr)

Cummins-Allison GmbH (4)
Arnold Sommerfeld Ring 2, Baesweiler,
52499, Germany (100%)
Tel.: (49) 2401805252
Web Site: https://www.cumminsallison.de
Sales Range: Less than $1 Million
Emp.: 10
Mfr of Small Business Machines, Coin
Counters & Wrappers; Coupon Books
N.A.I.C.S.: 333310

Cummins-Allison Inc. (4)
6725 Millcreek Drive - Unit 2, Mississauga,
L5N 5V3, ON, Canada (100%)
Web Site: http://www.cumminsallison.ca

Mfr of Small Business Machines, Coin
Counters & Wrappers; Coupon Books
N.A.I.C.S.: 333310

Cummins-Allison Ltd. (4)
William H Klotz House Colonnade Point,
Central Boulevard Prologis Park, Coventry,
CV46 BU, United Kingdom (100%)
Tel.: (44) 2476 339810
Web Site: http://www.cumminsallison.co.uk
Sales Range: $10-24.9 Million
Emp.: 25
Mfr of Small Business Machines, Coin
Counters & Wrappers; Coupon Books
N.A.I.C.S.: 333310
Andy Crowson (Gen Mgr)

Cummins-Allison ULC (4)
3350 Ridgeway Drive, Mississauga, L5L
5Z9, ON, Canada
Tel.: (905) 814-6184
Money Processing Services
N.A.I.C.S.: 522320
Harry Patrinos (Mng Dir)

Subsidiary (Domestic):

Glenview State Bank (4)
800 Waukegan Rd, Glenview, IL
60025-4381 (95%)
Tel.: (847) 729-1900
Web Site: http://www.gsb.com
Sales Range: $75-99.9 Million
Emp.: 225
State Bank
N.A.I.C.S.: 522110
Paul A. Jones (Pres & CEO)
Joan Cantrell (Sr VP & Dir-HR)
David Kreimann (Exec VP & Dir-Mktg)
Susan Schroll (Sr VP-Electronic Banking)
Marimel Lim (Sr VP & Mgr-Retail Banking)
William Campbell (Sr VP-Retail Banking)
Scott Limper (Sr VP-Trust & Investment
Dept)
Michael Bartochowski (Sr VP-Trust & In-
vestment Dept)
Bethany R. Prociuk (Officer-Trust Admin)

Subsidiary (Non-US):

**MEI Auto Payment System (Shang-
hai) Ltd.** (4)
Room 603 Zhuoyue Building Fu Hua One
Road No 98, Futian District, Shenzhen,
518048, China
Tel.: (86) 75582028032
Web Site: http://www.cranepi.com
Payment Technologies Products Mfr
N.A.I.C.S.: 333310

MEI Queretaro S. de R.L. de CV (3)
MEI Av Santa Rosa de Viterbo 10 Parque
Industrial Finsa, Bernardo Quintana, 76246,
El Marques, 76246, Queretaro, Mexico
Tel.: (52) 4422382000
Durable Goods Whslr
N.A.I.C.S.: 423990

MEI Sarl (3)
41 Rue Ampere ZI, 16440, Nersac, France
Tel.: (33) 682127028
Web Site: https://www.sarl-mei.fr
Industrial Machinery Mfr
N.A.I.C.S.: 332911

Nippon Conlux Co. Ltd. (3)
5-3-8 Chiyoda, Sakado, 350-0214, Saitama,
Japan
Tel.: (81) 492831185
Web Site: https://www.conlux.co.jp
Emp.: 188
Vending Machinery Mfr & Distr
N.A.I.C.S.: 333310
Yuichi Koike (CEO)

Crane Payment Innovations AG (1)
Chemin Du Pont-Du-Centenaire 109 Plan-
les-Ouates 2, PO Box 2650, 1211, Geneva,
Switzerland
Tel.: (41) 228840505
Financial & Payment Technology Services
N.A.I.C.S.: 522320

Merrimac Industries Inc. (1)
41 Fairfield Pl, West Caldwell, NJ 07006
Tel.: (973) 575-1300
Web Site: http://www.merrimacind.com
Sales Range: $25-49.9 Million
Emp.: 207

Crane NXT, Co.—(Continued)

Microwave & Radio Frequency Components & Subsystems Mfr
N.A.I.C.S.: 334419

OpSec Security Group Ltd (1)
40 Phoenix Road, Washington, NE38 0AD, Tyne & Wear, United Kingdom
Tel.: (44) 1914175434
Web Site: http://www.opsecsecurity.com
Sales Range: $75-99.9 Million
Security Systems
N.A.I.C.S.: 238210
Mike W. Angus (Sec & Dir-Fin)
David Bowden (Dir-Ops-EMEA)
Christine Holmes (Dir-Ops-USA)
Bill Patterson (Dir-Mktg)
Riya Sood (Chief HR Officer)
Lisa Arrowsmith (Chief Product Officer)
Selva Selvaratnam (CEO)

Subsidiary (US):

Global Trim Sales Inc. (2)
22835 Savi Ranch Pkwy, Yorba Linda, CA 92887
Tel.: (714) 998-4400
Web Site: http://www.globaltrim.com
Rev.: $1,430,000
Emp.: 10
Commercial Flexographic Printing Services
N.A.I.C.S.: 323111
Hersh Cherson (CEO)
David Cherson (VP-Sls)
Lori Griffin (VP-Ops)

Subsidiary (Domestic):

OpSec Security Limited (2)
40 Phoenix Rd, Washington, NE38 0AD, Tyne & Wear, United Kingdom
Tel.: (44) 1914175434
Web Site: http://www.opsecsecurity.com
Hologram Mfr
N.A.I.C.S.: 323111
Michael Currie (Dir-Fin)

Terminal Manufacturing Co. (1)
707 Gilman St, Berkeley, CA 94710
Tel.: (510) 526-3071
Web Site:
   https://www.terminalmanufacturing.com
Industrial Machinery Mfr
N.A.I.C.S.: 332911

Westlock Controls Corporation (1)
280 N Midland Ave Ste 258, Saddle Brook, NJ 07663
Tel.: (201) 794-7650
Web Site: https://www.westlockcontrols.com
Industrial Equipment Mfr
N.A.I.C.S.: 332912

CRAWFORD & COMPANY

5335 Triangle Pkwy, Peachtree Corners, GA 30302
Tel.: (404) 300-1000   **GA**
Web Site: https://www.crawco.com
Year Founded: 1941
CRD.B—(NYSE)
Rev.: $1,231,226,000
Assets: $791,507,000
Liabilities: $668,129,000
Net Worth: $123,378,000
Earnings: ($18,305,000)
Emp.: 10,400
Fiscal Year-end: 12/31/22
Claims Management Solutions
N.A.I.C.S.: 524298
Rohit Verma (Pres & CEO)
Larry C. Thomas (Pres-Platform Solutions-Global)
Tim Jarman (Pres-Australia)
Lisa Bartlett (Pres-UK & Ireland)
Ken Tolson (Pres-Network Solutions-Global)
Mike Hoberman (Pres-TPA, Broadspire-North America)
Pat Van Bakel (Pres-Loss Adjusting-North America)
Benedict Burke (Chief Client Officer-Global Client Dev)
Michelle Montgomery (CMO)

Nidhi Verma (Chief People ESG Officer)
Daniel Volk (CIO)
Meredith Brogan (Pres)
Erica Fichter (COO)
Larry Milburn (CTO)
Greg Youngblood (Sr VP)
W. Bruce Swain Jr. (CFO & Exec VP)

Subsidiaries:

Broadspire Services, Inc. (1)
1391 NW 136th Ave, Sunrise, FL 33323-2800
Tel.: (954) 452-4000
Web Site:
   https://www.choosebroadspire.com
Sales Range: $125-149.9 Million
Emp.: 616
Medical Management Company
N.A.I.C.S.: 541611

Crawford & Company (Bermuda) Limited (1)
1001 Summit Blvd, Atlanta, GA 30319-1334
Tel.: (404) 256-0830
Web Site:
   http://www.crawfordandcompany.com
Rev.: $210,000
Emp.: 4,000
Insurance Agents, Brokers & Services
N.A.I.C.S.: 524298

Crawford & Company (Canada) Inc. (1)
539 Riverbend Drive, Kitchener, N2K 3S3, ON, Canada   (100%)
Tel.: (519) 578-5540
Web Site:
   http://ca.crawfordandcompany.com
Sales Range: $10-24.9 Million
Emp.: 80
Insurance Adjusters Services
N.A.I.C.S.: 524298
Greg Smith (COO)
Pat Van Bakel (Pres)
Jim Eso (Sr VP-Crawford Claims Solutions)
Paul Hancock (VP-Technical Svcs-Global)
Heather Matthews (Chief Client Officer)
Cortney Young (VP-Broadspire Svcs)
Jeff Setterington (VP-Sls)
Kelly Stevens (VP-Acct Mgmt)
Andrea Aitken (VP-TPA)

Crawford & Company (Canada), Inc. (1)
880 North Service Road East Building 100 Unit 103, Windsor, N8X 3J5, ON, Canada
Tel.: (519) 974-5911
Insurance Agencies & Brokerage Services
N.A.I.C.S.: 524210
Steve DelGreco (Dir-Toronto GTS & Loss Adjusting)
Greg Smith (Pres)
Andrea Aitken (VP)
Kelly Stevens (Sr VP-Loss Adjusting)
Cortney Young (VP-Platform Solutions & Contractor Connection)
Jeff Setterington (VP-Sales)
Walter Waugh (VP-Loss Adjusting & GTS)

Crawford & Company Adjusters Limited (1)
106 Fenchurch Street The Hallmark Building, London, EC3M 5JE, United Kingdom
Tel.: (44) 2072654000
Web Site: https://www.crawco.co.uk
Claims Management Services
N.A.I.C.S.: 524291
Rohit Verma (CEO)
Joooph Blanco (Pres)
Benedict Burke (Chief Client Officer)
Michelle Montgomery (CMO)
Tami Stevenson (Gen Counsel)
W. Bruce Swain Jr. (CFO)
Nidhi Verma (Chief People ESG Officer)
Daniel Volk (CIO)

Crawford & Company International Pte Ltd (1)
6 Shenton Way OUE Downtown 2 19-10, Singapore, 068809, Singapore   (100%)
Tel.: (65) 62254211
Web Site: https://www.crawco.com
Sales Range: $25-49.9 Million
Emp.: 50
Loss Adjustors & Appraisers
N.A.I.C.S.: 488390

Richard Desker (Mng Dir)

Crawford & Company UK (1)
106 Fenchurch Street The Hallmark Building, London, EC3M 5JE, United Kingdom   (100%)
Tel.: (44) 2072654000
Web Site: http://www.crawford.com
Sales Range: $10-24.9 Million
Emp.: 120
Provider of Insurance Brokerage Services
N.A.I.C.S.: 524298
Lee Sadowski (Mng Dir-Contractor Connection)
Joseph Blanco (Pres)
Andrew Bart (CEO)
Michelle Montgomery (CMO)
W. Bruce Swain Jr. (CFO)
Daniel Volk (CIO)

Praxis Consulting Inc. (1)
333 E Main St, Muncie, IN 47305
Web Site: http://www.praxisconsulting.com
Insurance Agencies & Brokerages
N.A.I.C.S.: 524210
Robert Ford (Founder)

Risk Sciences Group, Inc. (1)
1900 E Golf Rd Ste 700, Schaumburg, IL 60173-5032
Tel.: (847) 619-7475
Web Site: http://www.risksciencesgroup.com
Sales Range: $50-74.9 Million
Emp.: 100
Computer Software Applications; Builder & Maintenance Solutions for Large Corporate Database Operations Primarily in the Insured & Self-Insured Industries
N.A.I.C.S.: 541513

WeGoLook, LLC (1)
100 NE 5th St, Oklahoma City, OK 73104
Tel.: (405) 795-5665
Web Site: http://www.wegolook.com
Emp.: 130
Application Software Development Services
N.A.I.C.S.: 541511
Kenneth Knoll (COO)
Brian Clubb (Dir-Engrg)
Christopher Harrell (Dir-Bus Dev)
Robin Smith (Co-Founder & CEO)
Robin Roberson (Co-Founder)

CRAWFORD UNITED CORPORATION

10514 Dupont Ave, Cleveland, OH 44108
Tel.: (216) 243-2614   **OH**
Web Site:
   https://www.crawfordunited.com
Year Founded: 1915
CRAWA—(OTCIQ)
Rev.: $143,885,934
Assets: $93,639,598
Liabilities: $35,914,251
Net Worth: $57,725,347
Earnings: $13,294,793
Emp.: 405
Fiscal Year-end: 12/31/23
Precision Indicating Instruments & Automotive Diagnostic Test Equipment Mfr, Developer & Marketer
N.A.I.C.S.: 334513
Brian E. Powers (Pres & CEO)
Jeffrey J. Salay (CFO & VP)

Subsidiaries:

Advanced Industrial Coatings, Inc. (1)
950 Industrial Dr, Stockton, CA 95206
Tel.: (209) 234-2700
Web Site: http://www.aic-coatings.com
Sales Range: $1-9.9 Million
Emp.: 53
Metal Coating, Engraving (except Jewelry & Silverware) & Allied Services to Mfr
N.A.I.C.S.: 332812
David Arney (Founder, COO & VP)
Steve Hockett (VP-Production)

CAD Enterprises, Inc. (1)
302 N 52nd Ave, Phoenix, AZ 85043
Tel.: (602) 278-4407
Web Site: https://www.cadenterprises.com
Engineering Services

N.A.I.C.S.: 541330

Data Genomix LLC (1)
10514 Dupont Ave, Cleveland, OH 44108
Tel.: (216) 710-4901
Web Site: https://www.datagenomix.com
Advertising & Marketing Services
N.A.I.C.S.: 541810
G. Jeremiah (Sr Dir-Ops & Bus Dev)

Global-Tek-Manufacturing LLC (1)
315 Avenida Lauro Pinero, Ceiba, PR 00735
Tel.: (787) 468-0682
Web Site: https://www.globaltekllc.com
Precision Machinery Parts Mfr
N.A.I.C.S.: 332721

Heany Industries, Inc. (1)
249 Briarwood Ln, Scottsville, NY 14546
Tel.: (585) 889-2700
Web Site: http://www.heany.com
Sales Range: $10-24.9 Million
Emp.: 35
Miscellaneous Nonmetallic Mineral Product Mfr
N.A.I.C.S.: 327999
Charles Aldridge (Exec VP)

Hickok AE LLC (1)
735 Glaser Pkwy, Akron, OH 44306
Tel.: (330) 794-9770
Web Site: https://www.airenterprises.com
Air Handling Product Mfr
N.A.I.C.S.: 333413

KT Acquisition LLC (1)
40 Rockdale St, Worcester, MA 01606-1908
Tel.: (508) 853-4500
Web Site: http://www.komtek.com
Sales Range: $50-74.9 Million
Emp.: 70
Die Forging & Investment Casting Services
N.A.I.C.S.: 332111

Kent Island Mechanical, LLC (1)
13340 Mid Atlantic Blvd, Laurel, MD 20708-1432
Tel.: (301) 776-3035
Web Site:
   http://www.kentislandmechanical.com
Plumbing, Heating & Air-Conditioning Contractors
N.A.I.C.S.: 238220
Mark E. Bowen (Pres)

Marine Products International LLC (1)
34929 Curtis Blvd, Eastlake, OH 44095
Web Site: https://www.marinehose.com
Marine Hose Mfr & Distr
N.A.I.C.S.: 326220

Reverso Pumps, Inc. (1)
4001 SW 47th Ave Ste 201, Davie, FL 33314
Tel.: (954) 522-0882
Web Site: http://reversopumps.com
Sales Range: $1-9.9 Million
Emp.: 14
Diesel Filtration, Transfer Pumps & Oil Change Systems Distr
N.A.I.C.S.: 333914

Waekon Corp. (1)
10514 Dupont Ave, Cleveland, OH 44108   (100%)
Tel.: (216) 541-8060
Web Site: https://www.waekon.com
Sales Range: $25-49.9 Million
Mfr of Test Equipment Used by Automotive Technicians
N.A.I.C.S.: 334515

CRAZY WOMAN CREEK BANCORP, INC.

106 Fort St, Buffalo, WY 82834
Tel.: (307) 684-5591   **WY**
Web Site:
   https://www.buffalofed.bank
Year Founded: 1995
CRZY—(OTCIQ)
Rev.: $6,994,000
Assets: $142,244,000
Liabilities: $128,754,000
Net Worth: $13,490,000
Earnings: $920,000
Emp.: 50

Fiscal Year-end: 09/30/20
Bank Holding Company
N.A.I.C.S.: 551111
Paul M. Brunkhorst (Pres & CEO)
Greg L. Goddard (Sec)
Sandra K. Todd (Treas)
Carolyn S. Kaiser (CFO & Sr VP)
Richard B. Griffith (Officer-Loan & Sr VP)

Subsidiaries:

Buffalo Federal Savings Bank   (1)
106 Fort St, Buffalo, WY 82834
Tel.: (307) 684-5591
Web Site: http://www.buffalofed.com
Sales Range: $10-24.9 Million
Emp.: 37
Commercial Banking
N.A.I.C.S.: 522110
Wes Haskins (Pres-Branch)

CREATD, INC.
419 Lafayette St 6th Fl, New York, NY 10003
Tel.: (201) 258-3770   NV
Web Site: https://www.creatd.com
Year Founded: 1999
VOCL—(OTCQB)
Rev.: $4,796,474
Assets: $4,819,749
Liabilities: $17,322,948
Net Worth: ($12,503,199)
Earnings: ($32,293,271)
Emp.: 14
Fiscal Year-end: 12/31/22
Commercial Real Estate Investment
N.A.I.C.S.: 531390
Robert Tal (CIO)
Jeremy Frommer (Co-Founder, Chm, CEO & CFO)
Justin Maury (Co-Founder, Pres & COO)
Erica Wagner (Head-Literary & IP Dev-Creatd Studios)

Subsidiaries:

Seller's Choice, LLC   (1)
2050 Center Ave 640, Fort Lee, NJ 07024
Tel.: (203) 903-9949
Web Site: https://www.sellerschoiceusa.com
Digital Marketing Services
N.A.I.C.S.: 541613
Dana Dench (Sr Acct Mgr)
Sophia Spiridakis (Mgr-Design)
Jay Goldberg (Founder)

CREATIVE EDGE NUTRITION, INC.
313 S Central Ave, Scarsdale, NY 10583
Tel.: (914) 419-5586   NV
Web Site:
http://www.cenergynutrition.com
Year Founded: 2002
FITX—(OTCIQ)
Holding Company; Health & Fitness Nutritional Supplements Developer & Marketer
N.A.I.C.S.: 551112
James L. Robinson (Pres)

CREATIVE MEDIA & COMMUNITY TRUST CORPORATION
4700 Wilshire Blvd, Los Angeles, CA 90010
Tel.: (972) 349-3200   TX
Web Site:
https://www.cimcommercial.com
Year Founded: 1979
CMCT—(NASDAQ)
Rev.: $101,906,000
Assets: $690,248,000
Liabilities: $328,215,000
Net Worth: $362,033,000
Earnings: $5,918,000
Emp.: 5
Fiscal Year-end: 12/31/22

Commercial Real Estate Investment Services
N.A.I.C.S.: 531390
Barry N. Berlin (CFO, CFO-Lending Div, Sec & Sec-Lending Div)
David A. Thompson (CEO)
Shaul Kuba (Chief Investment Officer)

Subsidiaries:

Western Financial Capital Corporation   (1)
17950 Preston Rd Ste 600, Dallas, TX 75252-5656
Tel.: (972) 349-3200
Web Site: https://pmcsba.com
Emp.: 30
Construction Lending Services
N.A.I.C.S.: 522292

CREATIVE MEDICAL TECHNOLOGY HOLDINGS, INC.
211 E Osborn Rd, Phoenix, AZ 85012
Tel.: (480) 399-2822   NV
Web Site:
https://www.creativemedicaltechnology.com
Year Founded: 1998
CELZ—(NASDAQ)
Rev.: $88,600
Assets: $19,186,326
Liabilities: $3,321,652
Net Worth: $15,864,674
Earnings: ($10,144,044)
Emp.: 4
Fiscal Year-end: 12/31/22
Holding Company; Medical Products Developer
N.A.I.C.S.: 551112
Timothy Warbington (Founder, Chm, Pres & CEO)
Donald Dickerson (CFO)

Subsidiaries:

Creative Medical Technologies, Inc.   (1)
211 E Osborn Rd, Phoenix, AZ 85012
Tel.: (480) 399-2822
Medical Technologies Developer
N.A.I.C.S.: 325414
Timothy Warbington (Chm, Pres & CEO)

CREATIVE REALITIES, INC.
13100 Magisterial Dr Ste 100, Louisville, KY 40223
Tel.: (502) 791-8800   MN
Web Site: https://www.cri.com
Year Founded: 2000
CREX—(NASDAQ)
Rev.: $43,350,000
Assets: $66,015,000
Liabilities: $40,436,000
Net Worth: $25,579,000
Earnings: $1,876,000
Emp.: 120
Fiscal Year-end: 12/31/22
Wireless Communications Development
N.A.I.C.S.: 541512
Dennis A. McGill (Chm)
Richard C. Mills (CEO)
Beth Warren (Sr VP-Mktg & Retail Practice)
Will Logan (CFO)
Mike McKim (VP-Ops)
Rodrick Glass (Exec VP-Bus & Dev)
Dave Petricig (Dir-Channel Sls)

Subsidiaries:

Allure Global Solutions, Inc.   (1)
400 Embassy Row Ste 580, Atlanta, GA 30328
Tel.: (770) 951-0000
Web Site: http://www.allureglobal.com
Software Publisher
N.A.I.C.S.: 513210

Conexus World Global LLC   (1)

1240 E Campbell Rd Ste 200, Richardson, TX 75081
Tel.: (972) 372-0304
Web Site: http://www.conexusworld.com
Wireless Network Installation Services
N.A.I.C.S.: 517112

Reflect Systems, Inc.   (1)
2934 Taylor St, Dallas, TX 75226
Tel.: (214) 413-3200
Web Site: http://www.reflectsystems.com
Sales Range: $1-9.9 Million
Emp.: 34
Software Publisher
N.A.I.C.S.: 513210

Wireless Ronin Technologies (Canada), Inc.   (1)
4510 Rhodes Dr Unit 800, Windsor, N8W 5C2, ON, Canada
Tel.: (519) 974-2363
Sales & Development of Interactive Software for E-Learning & Digital Signage Applications
N.A.I.C.S.: 513210

CREDIT ACCEPTANCE CORPORATION
25505 W 12 Mile Rd, Southfield, MI 48034-8339
Tel.: (248) 353-2700   MI
Web Site:
https://www.creditacceptance.com
Year Founded: 1972
CACC—(NASDAQ)
Rev.: $1,901,900,000
Assets: $7,610,200,000
Liabilities: $5,856,500,000
Net Worth: $1,753,700,000
Earnings: $286,100,000
Emp.: 2,232
Fiscal Year-end: 12/31/23
Financial Services
N.A.I.C.S.: 522210
Daniel A. Ulatowski (Chief Sls Officer)
Arthur L. Smith (Chief Analytics Officer)
Jay D. Martin (CFO & Principal Acctg Officer)
Ravi Mohan (CTO)
Douglas W. Busk (Chief Treasury Officer)
Jonathan L. Lum (COO)
Erin J. Kerber (Chief Legal Officer)
Kenneth S. Booth (Pres & CEO)

Subsidiaries:

Arlington Investment Company   (1)
1815 4th St Ste D, Berkeley, CA 94710-1943
Tel.: (510) 652-1252
Investment Management Service
N.A.I.C.S.: 523940

Buyers Vehicle Protection Plan, Inc.   (1)
25505 W 12 Mile Rd Ste 3000, Southfield, MI 48034   (100%)
Tel.: (248) 353-2700
Web Site: http://www.creditacceptance.com
Sales Range: $75-99.9 Million
Automotive Insurance Protection Plans
N.A.I.C.S.: 524298
Brett A. Roberts (CEO)

CREDITRISKMONITOR.COM, INC.
704 Executive Blvd Ste A, Valley Cottage, NY 10989
Tel.: (845) 230-3000   NV
Web Site:
https://www.creditriskmonitor.com
CRMZ—(OTCQX)
Rev.: $17,979,317
Assets: $22,468,070
Liabilities: $14,898,335
Net Worth: $7,569,735
Earnings: $1,360,238
Emp.: 90
Fiscal Year-end: 12/31/22
Online Financial Information Services

N.A.I.C.S.: 519290
Jerome S. Flum (Chm)
Peter Roma (Sr VP-Sls & Svc)
Michael I. Flum (Pres & CEO)
Michael Broos (CTO & Sr VP)
Kirk Ellis (Sr VP-Quality Assurance)
Michael Clark (Sr VP-IT)
Chris Chach (VP-Client Svcs)
Brain Beckley (VP-Sls)
Jennifer Gerold (CFO)
David Reiner (Chief Acctg Officer)
Marcos Bentolila (VP-Software Dev)
Jean Coichy (VP-Quality Assurance)
Eddy Huerta (VP-FRISK Analytics)
Charles Wang (VP-Offshore Rels-Global Svcs)
Julio Clerveaux (VP-Private Company Data)
Brian Sanders (Asst VP-Technical Solutions)

CREDO TECHNOLOGY GROUP HOLDING LTD.
1600 Technology Dr, San Jose, CA 95110
Tel.: (408) 664-9329   Ky
Year Founded: 2014
CRDO—(NASDAQ)
Rev.: $184,194,000
Assets: $397,289,000
Liabilities: $49,654,000
Net Worth: $347,635,000
Earnings: ($16,547,000)
Emp.: 438
Fiscal Year-end: 04/29/23
Holding Company
N.A.I.C.S.: 551112
Katherine E. Schuelke (Chief Legal Officer & Sec)
William Brennan (Pres & CEO)
Daniel Fleming (CFO)
Chi Fung Cheng (CTO)
Yat Tung Lam (COO)
Adam Thorngate-Gottlund (Sec & Gen Counsel)

CRESCENT CAPITAL BDC, INC.
11100 Santa Monica Blvd Ste 2000, Los Angeles, CA 90025
Tel.: (310) 235-5900   DE
Web Site:
https://www.crescentbdc.com
Year Founded: 2015
CCAP—(NASDAQ)
Rev.: $184,134,000
Assets: $1,627,379,000
Liabilities: $884,785,000
Net Worth: $742,594,000
Earnings: $82,541,000
Emp.: 200
Fiscal Year-end: 12/31/23
Investment Services
N.A.I.C.S.: 523999
Erik Barrios (Chief Compliance Officer & Sr VP)
Jason A. Breaux (Pres & CEO)
Raymond F. Barrios (Mng Dir)
Henry Chung (Chm)
Gerhard Lombard (CFO)

Subsidiaries:

Alcentra Capital Corporation   (1)
200 Park Ave 7th Fl, New York, NY 10166
Tel.: (212) 922-8240
Web Site: http://www.alcentra.com
Debt & Equity Financing Solutions; Investment Services
N.A.I.C.S.: 525990
Brandon Chao (Mng Dir)
Jonathan DeSimone (CEO)

First Eagle Alternative Capital BDC, Inc.   (1)
500 Boylston St Ste 1200, Boston, MA 02116
Tel.: (800) 450-4424

Crescent Capital BDC, Inc.—(Continued)

Web Site: http://www.feacbdc.com
Rev.: $31,404,000
Assets: $417,761,000
Liabilities: $227,055,000
Net Worth: $190,706,000
Earnings: $11,996,000
Fiscal Year-end: 12/31/2021
Investment Services
N.A.I.C.S.: 523999

CRESCO LABS, INC.

600 W Fulton Ste 800, Chicago, IL 60661
Tel.: (312) 929-0993
Web Site:
https://www.crescolabs.com
Year Founded: 1990
CRLBF—(OTCQX)
Rev.: $842,681,000
Assets: $1,583,692,000
Liabilities: $996,009,000
Net Worth: $587,683,000
Earnings: ($212,047,000)
Emp.: 3,200
Fiscal Year-end: 12/31/22
Gold Ore & Silver Ore Mining
N.A.I.C.S.: 212220
Charles Bachtell (Founder & CEO)
Tom Manning (Chm)
Jason Erkes (Chief Comm Officer)
Megan Kulick (Sr VP-IR)
Dennis Olis (CFO)
Angie Demchenko (Chief People Officer)
Greg Brings (Chief Transformation Officer)
Zach Marburger (CIO)
John Schetz (Gen Counsel)

CRESTWOOD EQUITY PARTNERS LP

811 Main St Ste 3400, Houston, TX 77002
Tel.: (832) 519-2200   DE
Web Site:
https://www.crestwoodlp.com
Year Founded: 1996
CEQP—(NYSE)
Rev.: $6,000,700,000
Assets: $6,567,000,000
Liabilities: $4,659,800,000
Net Worth: $1,907,200,000
Earnings: $31,300,000
Emp.: 753
Fiscal Year-end: 12/31/22
Holding Company; Midstream Energy Assets Owner & Operator
N.A.I.C.S.: 551112
Joel Christian Lambert (Chief Legal, Safety & Compliance Officer & Exec VP)
Will Moore (Exec VP-Corp Strategy)
John J. Sherman (Executives, Bd of Dirs)
Diaco Aviki (COO & Exec VP)
John Black (CFO & Exec VP)
Rob de Cardenas (Sr VP-Crude & Gas Mktg)
Ben Hansen (Sr VP-Ops)
Curt Van Hoorn (Sr VP-Bakken Ops)
Deana Werkowitch (Sr VP-Audit, Tech & Implementation Svcs)
Joanne Howard (Sr VP-Sustainability & Corp Comm)
Donna Schmidt (VP-Tax)
Casey Rosengarten (VP-Risk Mgmt)
Andrew Thorington (VP-Fin & IR)
Robert Hallett (Sr VP)
Robert Thornbury Halpin III (Pres)
Robert G. Phillips (Founder, Chm & CEO)

Subsidiaries:

Arrow Midstream Holdings, LLC   (1)
801 Cherry St Unit 20 Ste 3800, Fort Worth, TX 76102

Tel.: (817) 339-5400
Holding Company
N.A.I.C.S.: 551112

Central New York Oil & Gas Company, LLC   (1)
800 Robinson Rd, Owego, NY 13827   (100%)
Tel.: (607) 689-0993
Web Site:
http://www.stagecoachstorage.com
Sales Range: $125-149.9 Million
Emp.: 70
Natural Gas Storage Facility Operator & Pipeline Distr
N.A.I.C.S.: 424710

Crestwood Appalachia Pipeline LLC   (1)
700 Louisiana St Ste 2060, Houston, TX 77002
Tel.: (832) 519-2200
Web Site: http://www.crestwoodlp.com
Emp.: 70
Natural Gas Transmission Services
N.A.I.C.S.: 486210

Crestwood Arkansas Pipeline LLC   (1)
124 W Capitol Ave Ste 1900, Little Rock, AR 72201
Tel.: (501) 556-3091
Emp.: 9
Natural Gas Pipeline Transmission Services
N.A.I.C.S.: 486210

Crestwood Crude Services LLC   (1)
700 Louisiana St Ste 2550, Houston, TX 77002
Tel.: (832) 519-2200
Web Site: http://www.crestwoodlp.com
Crude Oil & Natural Gas Distr
N.A.I.C.S.: 424720

Crestwood Crude Transportation LLC   (1)
12590 23rd St NW, Watford City, ND 58854
Tel.: (701) 842-4771
Natural Gas Transportation Services
N.A.I.C.S.: 486210

Crestwood Dakota Pipelines LLC   (1)
2 Brush Creek Blvd, Kansas City, MO 64112
Tel.: (816) 842-8181
Natural Gas Transportation Services
N.A.I.C.S.: 486210

Crestwood Gas Services Operating LLC   (1)
700 Louisiana St Ste 2550, Houston, TX 77002
Tel.: (832) 519-2200
Web Site: http://www.crestwoodlp.com
Emp.: 80
Natural Gas Pipeline Transmission Services
N.A.I.C.S.: 486210

Crestwood Panhandle Pipeline LLC   (1)
1200 Summit Ave Ste 320, Fort Worth, TX 76102
Tel.: (817) 339-5470
Web Site: http://www.crestwoodlp.com
Emp.: 50
Natural Gas Pipeline Transmission Services
N.A.I.C.S.: 486210

Crestwood Partners LLC   (1)
8626 NE 24th St, Clyde Hill, WA 98004
Tel.: (206) 232-4111
Emp.: 4
Investment Management Service
N.A.I.C.S.: 523940

Inergy Gas Marketing, LLC   (1)
Two Brush Creek Blvd Ste 200, Kansas City, MO 64112   (100%)
Tel.: (816) 842-8181
Web Site: http://www.crestwoodlp.com
Sales Range: $50-74.9 Million
Emp.: 140
Propane Marketing & Wholesale Services
N.A.I.C.S.: 424720

L&L Transportation, LLC   (1)
3825 US Hwy 6, Waterloo, IN 46793
Tel.: (260) 837-7826
Sales Range: $150-199.9 Million
Emp.: 30
Propane & Natural Gas Trucking Services

N.A.I.C.S.: 484230
Joe H. Donnell (Pres)

Steuben Gas Storage Company   (1)
4979 Downes Rd, Canisteo, NY 14823
Tel.: (607) 695-2618
Web Site:
http://www.steubengasstorage.com
Natural Gas Bulk Storage Facility Operator
N.A.I.C.S.: 424710

US Salt, LLC   (1)
3580 Salt Point Rd, Watkins Glen, NY 14891
Tel.: (607) 535-2067
Web Site: https://www.ussaltllc.com
Sales Range: $150-199.9 Million
Salt Mining, Processing & Distr
N.A.I.C.S.: 311942

CREXENDO, INC.

1615 S 52nd St, Tempe, AZ 85281
Tel.: (602) 714-8500   DE
Web Site: https://www.crexendo.com
Year Founded: 1995
CXDO—(NASDAQ)
Rev.: $37,554,000
Assets: $55,634,000
Liabilities: $14,175,000
Net Worth: $41,459,000
Earnings: ($35,413,000)
Emp.: 176
Fiscal Year-end: 12/31/22
Web-Based Technology Solutions
N.A.I.C.S.: 513210
Doug Gaylor (Pres & COO)
Ronald Vincent (CFO)
Nishith Chudasama (VP-Engrg)
Brian Spitler (VP-Ops)
David Wang (CTO)
Jim Murphy (Sr VP)
Bryan J. Dancer (Exec VP)
Jeffrey G. Korn (Exec Chm, Chm & CEO)
Jon D. Brinton (Chief Revenue Officer)
Chris Aaker (Sr VP-Engineering)
Jason Byrne (Sr VP-Marketing)
Michael Czernaeda (Sls Dir)
Tim Wilbourn (Sr VP-Support & Customer Success)
Anand Buch (Chief Strategy Officer & Gen Mgr-Software Div)

Subsidiaries:

Allegiant Networks, LLC   (1)
14643 W 95th St, Shawnee Mission, KS 66215-5216
Tel.: (913) 599-6900
Web Site: http://www.allegiantusa.com
Data Processing, Hosting & Related Services
N.A.I.C.S.: 518210
Mark Spence (Mgr-Svc)

CRIMSON WINE GROUP, LTD.

5901 Silverado Trl, Napa, CA 94558
Tel.: (707) 257-4721   DE
Web Site:
https://www.crimsonwinegroup.com
CWGL—(OTCQB)
Rev.: $74,244,000
Assets: $218,760,000
Liabilities: $31,760,000
Net Worth: $187,000,000
Earnings: $1,077,000
Emp.: 164
Fiscal Year-end: 12/31/22
Holding Company; Wineries & Vineyards Operator
N.A.I.C.S.: 551112
John D. Cumming (Chm)
Nicolas Michel Eric Quille (Chief Winemaking & Ops Officer)
Jennifer L. Locke (CEO)
Alexis Walsh (Sr VP-Brand Mktg & Sls-Global)
Alexa Fox (VP-Direct to Consumer & Revenue Mktg)

Subsidiaries:

Pine Ridge Winery, LLC   (1)
5901 Silverado Trl, Napa, CA 94558-9417   (100%)
Tel.: (707) 253-7500
Web Site: http://www.pineridgewinery.com
Sales Range: $750-799.9 Million
Emp.: 50
Winery
N.A.I.C.S.: 312130

CRINETICS PHARMACEUTICALS, INC.

6055 Lusk Blvd, San Diego, CA 92121
Tel.: (858) 450-6464   DE
Web Site: https://www.crinetics.com
Year Founded: 2008
CRNX—(NASDAQ)
Rev.: $4,737,000
Assets: $352,176,000
Liabilities: $35,848,000
Net Worth: $316,328,000
Earnings: ($163,918,000)
Emp.: 210
Fiscal Year-end: 12/31/22
Pharmaceutical Preparation Mfr & Distr
N.A.I.C.S.: 325412
Wendell D. Wierenga (Chm)
Alan S. Krasner (Chief Medical Officer)
Dana Pizzuti (Chief Dev Officer)
Jeff E. Knight (COO)
Garlan Adams (Gen Counsel)
Naomi Yamamoto (Fin Mgr)
Hypatia Tong (Mgr)
Kika Teudt (Sr Dir)
Cindy Silva (Assoc Dir)
Greg Solis (Mgr)
Eric Spoor (Sr Dir)
Brian Schultz (Dir)
Brian Russell (Sr Dir)
Natalie Rossingnol (VP)
Donna Rainwater (Dir)
Matthew Dansey (Dir)
Chris Robillard (Chief Bus Officer)
Deepak Dalvie (VP)
Beth Fleck (Assoc Dir)
Sun Hee Kim (Assoc Dir)
Jim Leonard (VP)
Stacy Markison (VP)
Joseph Pontillo (Dir)
Collin Regan (Assoc Dir)
Emmanuel Sturchler (Assoc Dir)
Jian Zhao (Sr Dir)
Heather Budetti (Assoc Dir)
Anna Covington (Assoc Dir)
Shirley Cruz (Dir)
Scott Henley (VP)
R. Scott Struthers (Co-Founder, Pres & CEO)

CROCS, INC.

13601 Via Varra, Broomfield, CO 80020
Tel.: (303) 848-7000   DE
Web Site: http://www.crocs.com
CROX—(NASDAQ)
Rev.: $3,962,347,000
Assets: $1,613,834,000
Liabilities: $3,189,911,000
Net Worth: $1,453,923,000
Earnings: $792,566,000
Emp.: 7,030
Fiscal Year-end: 12/31/23
Footwear Designer, Mfr & Marketer
N.A.I.C.S.: 316210
Terence Reilly (Pres-HEYDUDE Brand & Exec VP)
Susan L. Healy (CFO & Exec VP)
Anne Mehlman (Pres-Brand & Exec VP)
Anne Mehlman (CFO & Exec VP)
Adam Michaels (Chief Digital officer & Sr VP)

Shannon Sisler (*Chief People Officer*)
Cori Lin (*VP-Corp Fin*)
Lori Foglia (*Chief Product & Mdsg Officer & Sr VP*)
Erinn Murphy (*Sr VP-IR & Corp Strategy*)
Andrew Rees (*Interim CEO*)

Subsidiaries:

Crocs Asia Pte. Ltd.   (1)
150 Cecil Street 03-00, Singapore, 069543, Singapore
Tel.: (65) 64117641
Web Site: http://www.crocs.com.sg
Footwear Designer & Marketer
N.A.I.C.S.: 316210

Crocs Australia Pty. Ltd   (1)
Level 3 47 Wellington St St Kilda, Melbourne, 3182, VIC, Australia
Tel.: (61) 80 046 9382
Web Site: https://www.crocsaustralia.com.au
Footwear Designer & Marketer
N.A.I.C.S.: 316210

Crocs Australia Pty. Ltd.   (1)
7477EDry Creek Pkwy, Longmont, CO 80503-7167
Tel.: (303) 848-7000
Web Site: http://www.crocs.com
Sales Range: $125-149.9 Million
Emp.: 200
Footwear Mfr
N.A.I.C.S.: 316210

Crocs Canada, Inc.   (1)
1455 16th Avenue Unit 7, Richmond Hill, L4B 4W5, ON, Canada
Tel.: (905) 747-3366
Web Site: https://www.crocs.ca
Footwear Designer & Marketer
N.A.I.C.S.: 316210

Crocs Hong Kong Ltd.   (1)
No 21 G/F Excelsior Plaza Chee On Building No 24 East Point Road, Causeway Bay, China (Hong Kong)
Tel.: (852) 21740122
Web Site: http://www.crocs.hk
Footwear Designer & Marketer
N.A.I.C.S.: 316210

Crocs India Private Limited   (1)
The Peach Tree 101/102 2nd Floor Block-C, Sushant Lok-1, Gurgaon, 122002, India
Tel.: (91) 1244384290
Web Site: http://www.shopcrocs.in
Footwear Designer & Marketer
N.A.I.C.S.: 316210

Crocs NZ Limited   (1)
142A Broadway Newmarket, Auckland, 1023, New Zealand
Tel.: (64) 99120888
Web Site: http://www.crocs.co.nz
Casual Footwear Mfr & Distr
N.A.I.C.S.: 316210

Crocs Nordic Oy   (1)
Hatanpaan Valtatie 18, 33100, Tampere, Finland
Tel.: (358) 33 454 3400
Web Site: https://www.crocs.fi
Emp.: 100
Footwear Mfr
N.A.I.C.S.: 316210

Crocs Online, Inc.   (1)
6328 Monarch Park Pl, Longmont, CO 80503-7167
Tel.: (303) 648-4260
Web Site: http://www.crocs.com
Sales Range: $150-199.9 Million
Online Footwear Retailer
N.A.I.C.S.: 424340

Crocs Puerto Rico, Inc.   (1)
2050 Ponce Bypass Space 169, Ponce, PR 00717
Tel.: (787) 259-1815
Footwear Designer & Marketer
N.A.I.C.S.: 316210

Crocs Retail, Inc.   (1)
6328 Monarch Park Pl, Longmont, CO 80503-7167
Tel.: (303) 648-4260
Web Site: http://www.crocs.com

Sales Range: $150-199.9 Million
Footwear Retailer
N.A.I.C.S.: 424340

Crocs Singapore Pte. Ltd.   (1)
11 North Buona Vista 04-07, Singapore, 138589, Singapore
Tel.: (65) 3 163 9943
Web Site: https://www.crocs.com.sg
Footwear Designer & Marketer
N.A.I.C.S.: 316210

Crocs South Africa   (1)
22 Mansfield Cres, Gordon's Bay, 7150, Western Cape, South Africa
Tel.: (27) 218568460
Web Site: https://www.crocssa.co.za
Sales Range: $25-49.9 Million
Emp.: 35
Footwear Designer & Marketer
N.A.I.C.S.: 316210

Crocs Stores Ireland   (1)
32 Liffey Street Upper, Dublin, Ireland
Tel.: (353) 218818436
Men & Women Clothing Store Operator
N.A.I.C.S.: 458110
Evelyn Gaynor (*Mgr*)

Exo Italia, S.r.l.   (1)
Via Villa Albarella 8, 35020, Masera di Padova, Italy
Tel.: (39) 0498862882
Web Site: http://www.exoitalia.it
Sales Range: $25-49.9 Million
Emp.: 100
Footwear Designer & Marketer
N.A.I.C.S.: 316210
Marco Ferniani (*Mng Dir*)

Ocean Minded, Inc.   (1)
3005 S El Camino Real, San Clemente, CA 92672
Tel.: (949) 369-5057
Web Site: http://www.oceanminded.com
Footwear Designer & Mfr
N.A.I.C.S.: 316210

CROGHAN BANCSHARES, INC.
323 Croghan St, Fremont, OH 43420
Tel.: (419) 332-7301   **OH**
Web Site: https://www.croghan.com
Year Founded: 1984
CHBH—(OTCIQ)
Rev.: $46,873,000
Assets: $1,028,452,000
Liabilities: $892,603,000
Net Worth: $135,849,000
Earnings: $13,719,000
Emp.: 199
Fiscal Year-end: 12/31/20
Banking Services
N.A.I.C.S.: 522210
Kendall W. Rieman (*Pres & CEO*)
Jodi A. Albright (*VP & Reg Mgr-Retail, Fremont*)
Stacy A. Cox (*COO & Sr VP*)
Daniel N. Schloemer (*Sec*)
Melissa A. Walker (*VP & Mgr-Retail Ops*)
Laura M. Whipple (*VP & Mgr-HR*)
Brad Elfring (*Treas*)
Amy LeJeune (*Asst Sec*)

Subsidiaries:

The Croghan Colonial Bank   (1)
323 Croghan St, Fremont, OH 43420
Tel.: (419) 332-7301
Web Site:
  http://www.croghanbancshares.com
Sales Range: $25-49.9 Million
Emp.: 150
Provider of Banking Services
N.A.I.C.S.: 522110
Rick M. Robertson (*Pres & CEO*)

CROSS COUNTRY HEALTHCARE, INC.
6551 Park of Commerce Blvd, Boca Raton, FL 33487
Tel.: (561) 998-2232   **DE**

Web Site:
  https://www.crosscountry.com
Year Founded: 1986
CCRN—(NASDAQ)
Rev.: $2,806,609,000
Assets: $947,839,000
Liabilities: $490,620,000
Net Worth: $457,219,000
Earnings: $188,461,000
Emp.: 12,980
Fiscal Year-end: 12/31/22
Healthcare Staffing Services
N.A.I.C.S.: 561320
William J. Burns (*CFO & Exec VP*)
Phillip Noe (*CIO*)
Kevin C. Clark (*Founder*)
Karen Mote (*Pres-Cross Country Locums*)
Colin McDonald (*Chief HR Officer*)
Henry Drummond (*Chief Clinical Officer & Sr VP*)
Marc Krug (*Grp Pres-Delivery*)
John A. Martins (*Pres & CEO*)
Gerald Purgay (*CMO*)
Liz Cantwell (*Chief Nursing Officer & Sr VP-Workforce Solutions*)
James V. Redd III (*Chief Acctg Officer & Sr VP*)
Cynthia Grieco (*Treas*)
Michael Skovira (*Chief Medical Officer*)

Subsidiaries:

Advantage On Call, LLC   (1)
17592 17th St Ste 110, Tustin, CA 92780
Tel.: (888) 748-3711
Employment Agency Services
N.A.I.C.S.: 561311

Advantage RN, LLC   (1)
9021 Meridian Way, West Chester, OH 45069
Tel.: (513) 603-3822
Web Site: http://www.advantagern.com
Healthcare Professional Staffing Services
N.A.I.C.S.: 561311
Marianne Heatherly (*VP-Recruitment*)
Nikki Tudor (*Sr Dir-Acct Mgmt*)

Allied Health Group, LLC   (1)
145 Technology Pkwy NW, Norcross, GA 30092
Tel.: (770) 734-2488
Web Site: http://www.alliedhealth.com
Medical Staffing Services
N.A.I.C.S.: 561320

Assent Consulting   (1)
10054 Pasadena Ave, Cupertino, CA 95014
Tel.: (408) 366-8820
Web Site: http://www.assentconsulting.com
Medical Staffing Services
N.A.I.C.S.: 561320

Assignment America, LLC   (1)
6551 Park of Commerce Blvd, Boca Raton, FL 33487-8247
Tel.: (561) 998-8533
Medical Staffing Services
N.A.I.C.S.: 561320

CC Staffing, Inc.   (1)
6551 Park of Cmmrce Blvd Nw, Boca Raton, FL 33487
Tel.: (561) 998-2232
Web Site: http://www.ccstaffing.com
Emp.: 25
Medical Staffing Services
N.A.I.C.S.: 561320

Cejka Search, Inc.   (1)
4 Cityplace Dr Ste 300, Saint Louis, MO 63141
Web Site: https://www.cejkasearch.com
Emp.: 85
Employment Placement Agencies
N.A.I.C.S.: 561311
Paul Esselman (*Pres & Mng Dir*)
Rebecca Kapphahn (*VP*)
Joyce E. Tucker (*Mng Principal & Exec VP*)
Alan D. Johns (*Mng Principal & Exec VP*)
Mark Madden (*Mng Principal & Exec VP*)
Martha Regan (*VP*)
Todd Wozniak (*VP*)
John Elffer (*VP-Exec Search Svcs*)

Cross Country Infotech, Pvt. Ltd.   (1)
4th Floor 401 402 NextGen Avenue Sr No 103 Bahiratwadi Near ICC Tower, S B Road, Pune, 411016, Maharashtra, India
Tel.: (91) 7276610002
Web Site: https://www.crosscountry.in
Software Development Services
N.A.I.C.S.: 541511

Cross Country Staffing, Inc.   (1)
6551 Park of Commerce Blvd, Boca Raton, FL 33487
Tel.: (877) 818-8401
Web Site:
  https://www.crosscountrystaffing.com
Employment Placement Services
N.A.I.C.S.: 561311

Cross Country TravCorps, Inc.   (1)
6551 Park of Commerce Blvd, Boca Raton, FL 33487-8247
Tel.: (561) 998-2232
Web Site: https://www.crosscountry.com
Medical Staffing Services
N.A.I.C.S.: 561320

Intellify Talent Solutions, LLC   (1)
6551 Park of Commerce Blvd, Boca Raton, FL 33487-8247
Web Site: https://www.intellify.com
Information Technology & Management Services
N.A.I.C.S.: 541519

MRA Search, Inc.   (1)
40 Eastern Ave, Malden, MA 02148
Web Site: http://www.mrasearch.com
Medical Staffing Services
N.A.I.C.S.: 561320

Med-Staff, Inc.   (1)
3805 W Chester Pike Ste 200, Newtown Square, PA 19073
Medical Staffing Services
N.A.I.C.S.: 561320

Mediscan Diagnostic Services, LLC   (1)
21050 Califa St Ste 100, Woodland Hills, CA 91367
Tel.: (818) 758-4224
Web Site:
  https://www.crosscountryeducation.com
Diagnostic Services
N.A.I.C.S.: 621999

Mint Medical Physician Staffing, LP   (1)
1077 Westheimer, Houston, TX 77042
Tel.: (713) 541-1177
Web Site: http://www.mintphysicians.com
Temporary Help Service
N.A.I.C.S.: 561320
Stuart McKelvey (*Pres*)

NovaPro   (1)
1408 N Westshore Blvd Ste 300, Tampa, FL 33607   **(100%)**
Tel.: (813) 636-5050
Web Site: http://www.novaprostaffing.com
Sales Range: $10-24.9 Million
Emp.: 28
Temporary Staffing to Healthcare Industry
N.A.I.C.S.: 561311

Workforce Solutions Group, Incorporated   (1)
26090 Towne Ctr Dr, Foothill Ranch, CA 92610
Tel.: (949) 709-1883
Web Site:
  http://www.workforcesolutionsgroup.com
Human Resources & Executive Search Consulting Services
N.A.I.C.S.: 541612
Colleen Jones (*Exec VP*)
Karen Tarca-Cowan (*Sr VP-Bus Dev*)
Irene Simpson (*VP-HR*)
Pamela K. Jung (*Founder & CEO*)
Stacy Burt (*Sr VP-Ops*)

CROSS TIMBERS ROYALTY TRUST
3838 Oak Lawn Ave Ste 1720, Dallas, TX 75219   **TX**
Web Site: https://crt-crosstimbers.com
Year Founded: 1991

Cross Timbers Royalty Trust—(Continued)

CRT—(NYSE)
Rev.: $12,509,191
Assets: $4,863,965
Liabilities: $1,902,010
Net Worth: $2,961,955
Earnings: $11,743,236
Fiscal Year-end: 12/31/22
Venture Capital Services
N.A.I.C.S.: 523910
Nancy Willis *(VP)*

CROSSAMERICA PARTNERS LP

645 Hamilton St Ste 400, Allentown, PA 18101
Tel.: (610) 625-8000   DE
Web Site:
  https://www.crossamericapart
  ners.com
CAPL—(NYSE)
Rev.: $4,386,263,000
Assets: $1,181,682,000
Liabilities: $1,178,675,000
Net Worth: $3,007,000
Earnings: $42,592,000
Emp.: 244
Fiscal Year-end: 12/31/23
Petroleum Distr
N.A.I.C.S.: 424720
Bob Brecker *(Exec VP-Operations)*
Glenn C. Faust *(VP-Wholesale Ops)*
Jacques Mitchell *(VP)*
Tracy Derstine *(Exec VP-Human Resources)*
Joseph V. Topper Jr. *(Chm)*
John B. Reilly III *(Vice Chm)*
Charles M. Nifong Jr. *(Pres & CEO)*

Subsidiaries:

LGP Operations LLC   (1)
702 W Hamilton St Ste 203, Allentown, PA 18101
Tel.: (610) 625-8000
Natural Gas Distr
N.A.I.C.S.: 221210

Petroleum Marketers, Inc.   (1)
3000 Ogden Rd, Roanoke, VA 24014-2418
Tel.: (540) 772-4900
Petroleum & Petroleum Products Retailer; Convenience Store Owner & Operator
N.A.I.C.S.: 457210
Tammy Shifflett *(Mgr)*

Subsidiary (Domestic):

PM Foods Inc.   (2)
3000 Ogden Rd, Roanoke, VA 24018   (100%)
Tel.: (540) 772-3000
Emp.: 100
Fuel Station Food Markets
N.A.I.C.S.: 457210
Ron Hare *(CEO)*

PM Properties Inc.   (2)
3000 Ogden Rd, Roanoke, VA 24018   (100%)
Tel.: (540) 772-4900
Sales Range: $25-49.9 Million
Emp.: 77
Retail & Wholesale Petroleum Products
N.A.I.C.S.: 531120

PM Terminals, Inc.   (2)
3000 Ogden Rd, Roanoke, VA 23234   (100%)
Tel.: (540) 772-4900
Sales Range: $10-24.9 Million
Emp.: 4
Petroleum Products Terminalling
N.A.I.C.S.: 457210

Stop In Food Stores, Inc.   (2)
3000 Ogden Rd, Roanoke, VA 24018   (100%)
Tel.: (540) 772-4700
Sales Range: $10-24.9 Million
Emp.: 45
Retail Gasoline & Convenience Stores
N.A.I.C.S.: 445131
Ronald R Hare *(Pres)*

CROSSFIRST BANKSHARES, INC.

11440 Tomahawk Crk Pkwy, Leawood, KS 66211
Tel.: (913) 312-6800   KS
Web Site:
  https://investors.crossfirstbank
  shares.com
Year Founded: 2017
CFB—(NASDAQ)
Rev.: $265,794,000
Assets: $6,601,086,000
Liabilities: $5,992,487,000
Net Worth: $608,599,000
Earnings: $61,599,000
Emp.: 465
Fiscal Year-end: 12/31/22
Bank Holding Company
N.A.I.C.S.: 551111
Michael J. Maddox *(Pres & CEO)*
Benjamin R. Clouse *(CFO)*
W. Randy Rapp *(Pres-CrossFirst Bank)*

CROSSROADS SYSTEMS, INC.

2247 Central Dr, Bedford, TX 76021
Tel.: (415) 404-2539   DE
Web Site: https://crossroads.com
Year Founded: 1994
CRSS—(OTCIQ)
Rev.: $37,704,000
Assets: $179,503,000
Liabilities: $128,458,000
Net Worth: $51,045,000
Earnings: $2,370,000
Emp.: 5
Fiscal Year-end: 10/31/19
Computer Terminal & Other Computer Peripheral Equipment Manufacturing
N.A.I.C.S.: 334118
Eric Donnelly *(CEO)*
Farzana Giga *(CFO)*

Subsidiaries:

Crossroads Systems (Texas), Inc.   (1)
11000 N MoPac Bld 6 Ste 100, Austin, TX 78759
Tel.: (512) 349-0300
Web Site: http://www.crossroads.com
Sales Range: $50-74.9 Million
Provider of Computer Peripheral Equipment
N.A.I.C.S.: 334118
Don Pearce *(Chm)*

CROWDSTRIKE HOLDINGS, INC.

206 E 9th St Ste 1400, Austin, TX 78701
Tel.: (888) 512-8906   DE
Web Site:
  https://www.crowdstrike.com
Year Founded: 2011
CRWD—(NASDAQ)
Rev.: $3,055,555,000
Assets: $6,646,520,000
Liabilities: $4,309,431,000
Net Worth: $2,337,089,000
Earnings: $89,327,000
Emp.: 7,925
Fiscal Year-end: 01/31/24
Holding Company
N.A.I.C.S.: 551112
Gerhard Watzinger *(Chm)*
George R. Kurtz *(Pres & CEO)*
Colin Black *(COO)*
Burt W. Podbere *(CFO)*
Michael Carpenter *(Pres-Global Sls & Field Ops)*
Amol Kulkarni *(Chief Product & Engrg Officer)*
Michael Sentonas *(CTO)*
Adam Meyers *(Sr VP-Intelligence)*
Jerry Dixon *(Chief Information Security Officer)*

Cathleen Anderson *(Gen Counsel)*
J. C. Herrera *(Chief HR Officer)*
Marianne Budnik *(CMO)*
Gerhard Watzinger *(Chm)*
Johanna Flower *(CMO)*
Geoff Swaine *(VP-Asia Pacific & Japan)*

Subsidiaries:

Hybrid Analysis GmbH   (1)
Mainzer Landstrasse 41, 60329, Frankfurt am Main, Germany
Tel.: (49) 24193688811
Web Site: https://www.hybrid-analysis.com
Computer Software Services
N.A.I.C.S.: 541511
Burt Podbere *(Mng Dir)*
Michael Forman *(Mng Dir)*

CROWN CASTLE INC.

8020 Katy Fwy, Houston, TX 77024-1908
Tel.: (713) 570-3000   DE
Web Site:
  https://www.crowncastle.com
CCI—(NYSE)
Rev.: $6,981,000,000
Assets: $38,527,000,000
Liabilities: $32,146,000,000
Net Worth: $6,381,000,000
Earnings: $1,502,000,000
Emp.: 4,700
Fiscal Year-end: 12/31/23
Owner, Operator & Leaser of Wireless Communication Towers & Broadcast Transmission Networks
N.A.I.C.S.: 517112
Catherine Piche *(COO-Towers & Exec VP)*
P. Robert Bartolo *(Chm)*
Philip M. Kelley *(Exec VP-Corp Dev & Strategy)*
Laura Nichol *(Exec VP-Bus Support)*
Ben Lowe *(VP-Corp Fin)*
Kenneth J. Simon *(Gen Counsel & Exec VP)*
Christopher D. Levendos *(COO-Towers & Fiber & Exec VP)*
Robert S. Collins *(VP & Controller)*
Chris Levendos *(COO-Towers & Fiber & Exec VP)*
Dan Schlanger *(CFO)*
Kris Hinson *(Treas & VP)*
Steven J. Moskowitz *(Pres & CEO)*

Subsidiaries:

CCATT LLC   (1)
550 Sunol St, San Jose, CA 95126
Tel.: (724) 416-2000
Wireless Telecommunication Services
N.A.I.C.S.: 517112

Crown Castle Operating Company   (1)
510 Bering Dr St 600, Houston, TX 77057
Tel.: (713) 570-3000
Web Site: https://www.crowncastle.com
Site Leasing, Tower & Rooftop Development
N.A.I.C.S.: 236210

Crown Castle USA Inc.   (1)
2000 Corporate Dr, Canonsburg, PA 15317-8538
Tel.: (724) 416-2000
Web Site: https://www.crowncastle.com
Radiotelephone Communication
N.A.I.C.S.: 237130

Subsidiary (Domestic):

Crown Castle NG West LLC   (2)
890 Tasman Dr, Milpitas, CA 95035
Tel.: (408) 468-5521
Wireless Telecommunication Services
N.A.I.C.S.: 517112

Towers Development Corporation   (1)
4378 Auburn Blvd Ste 300, Sacramento, CA 95841
Tel.: (916) 978-0800

Wireless Telecommunication Services
N.A.I.C.S.: 517112

CROWN CRAFTS, INC.

916 S Burnside Ave, Gonzales, LA 70737
Tel.: (225) 647-9100   DE
Web Site:
  https://www.crowncrafts.com
Year Founded: 1957
CRWS—(NASDAQ)
Rev.: $87,632,000
Assets: $82,706,000
Liabilities: $31,105,000
Net Worth: $51,601,000
Earnings: $4,894,000
Emp.: 162
Fiscal Year-end: 03/31/24
Juvenile & Infant Textile Products Mfr
N.A.I.C.S.: 313210
Zenon S. Nie *(Chm)*
Olivia W. Elliott *(Pres & CEO)*
Craig J. Demarest *(CFO, Principal Acctg Officer & VP)*

Subsidiaries:

Carousel Designs LLC   (1)
4519 Bankhead Hwy, Douglasville, GA 30134
Tel.: (770) 949-2187
Web Site: http://www.babybedding.com
Baby Furniture Mfr
N.A.I.C.S.: 337122

Crown Crafts Infant Products, Inc.   (1)
916 Burnside Ave, Gonzales, LA 70707   (100%)
Tel.: (225) 647-9100
Web Site: http://www.crowncrafts.com
Infant Bedding & Accessories Mfr
N.A.I.C.S.: 313210

Hamco, Inc.   (1)
916 Burnside Ave, Gonzales, LA 70737   (100%)
Tel.: (225) 647-9100
Web Site: http://www.hamcobaby.com
Sales Range: $50-74.9 Million
Emp.: 25
Mfr of Infant Bedding
N.A.I.C.S.: 424350
E. Randall Chestnut *(Pres & CEO)*
Janet Talbot *(VP-Sls)*

Manhattan Group LLC   (1)
300 1st Ave N Ste 200, Minneapolis, MN 55401-1744
Tel.: (012) 007-9000
Web Site: http://www.manhattantoy.com
Provider of Toys & Hobby Supplies
N.A.I.C.S.: 423920

Manhattan Toy Europe Limited   (1)
Suite 3 5 Robin Hood Lane, Sutton, SM1 2SW, Surrey, United Kingdom
Tel.: (44) 2089443160
Web Site: https://www.manhattantoy.com
Toy Mfr & Distr
N.A.I.C.S.: 335311

CROWN ELECTROKINETICS CORP.

1110 NE Cir Blvd, Corvallis, OR 97330
Tel.: (213) 600-4250   DE
Web Site: http://www.crownek.com
CRKN—(NASDAQ)
Rev.: $793,000
Assets: $6,590,000
Liabilities: $6,060,000
Net Worth: $530,000
Earnings: ($14,370,000)
Emp.: 6
Fiscal Year-end: 12/31/22
Automotive Glass Mfr
N.A.I.C.S.: 327215
Timothy Koch *(Founder & CTO)*
Douglas Croxall *(Chm & CEO)*
Joel Krutz *(CFO & COO)*
Kai Sato *(CMO)*

CROWN EQUITY HOLDINGS INC.

11226 Pentland Downs St, Las Vegas, NV 89141
Tel.: (702) 683-8946
Web Site:
https://www.crownequityhold
ings.com
Year Founded: 1995
CRWE—(OTCIQ)
Rev.: $1,916
Assets: $2,448
Liabilities: $227,767
Net Worth: ($225,319)
Earnings: ($383,111)
Fiscal Year-end: 12/31/15
Online Advertising & Marketing Services
N.A.I.C.S.: 541890
Kenneth Bosket (Vice Chm, Vice Chm, CFO & Head/Head-Ops)

CROWN EQUITY HOLDINGS INC.

11226 Pentland Downs St, Las Vegas, NV 89141
Tel.: (702) 683-8946   NV
Web Site:
https://crownequityholdings.com
Year Founded: 1995
CRWE—(OTCIQ)
Rev.: $2,935
Assets: $5,437
Liabilities: $1,385,768
Net Worth: ($1,380,331)
Earnings: ($739,975)
Fiscal Year-end: 12/31/22
Holding Company; Investment Services
N.A.I.C.S.: 551112
Montse Zaman (COO & Sec)
Mike Zaman (Chm, Pres & CEO)
Kenneth Bosket (CFO)
Shahram Khial (VP-Mktg)
Mohammad Sadrolashrafi (VP-Ops)
Malcolm Ziman (VP-Fin)

CROWN HOLDINGS, INC.

14025 Riveredge Dr Ste 300, Tampa, FL 33637-2015
Tel.: (215) 698-5100   PA
Web Site:
https://www.crowncork.com
Year Founded: 1892
CCK—(NYSE)
Rev.: $12,010,000,000
Assets: $15,034,000,000
Liabilities: $12,170,000,000
Net Worth: $2,864,000,000
Earnings: $450,000,000
Emp.: 25,000
Fiscal Year-end: 12/31/23
Holding Company; Consumer Packaging Products Mfr
N.A.I.C.S.: 551112
Torsten J. Kreider (VP-Plng & Dev)
Rosemary M. Haselroth (Asst Sec)
Michael J. Rowley (Asst Sec & Asst Gen Counsel)
Kevin Charles Clothier (CFO & Sr VP)
Gerard H. Gifford (COO & Exec VP)
Adam J. Dickstein (Gen Counsel, Sec & Sr VP)
Christopher A. Blaine (VP-Corp Risk Mgmt)
Thomas T. Fischer (VP-IR & Corp Affairs)
Joseph C. Pearce (VP-Corp Tax)
David A. Beaver (Treas & VP)
Christy L. Kalaus (VP & Controller)
John Rost (VP-Global Sustainability & Regulatory Affairs)
Sidonie Lecluse (Sr VP-Diversity & Inclusion)

Claudine Schelp (Sr VP-Global Procurement)
Anthony Vitello (Chief Information Security Officer)
Timothy J. Donahue (Chm, Pres & CEO)
Deborah L. Jaskel (Controller & Asst Controller-Corp)

Subsidiaries:

Crown Cork & Seal Co., Inc.   (1)
1 Crown Way, Philadelphia, PA
19154-4599   (100%)
Tel.: (215) 698-5100
Web Site: http://www.crowncork.com
Sales Range: $1-4.9 Billion
Emp.: 300
Mfr of Packaging Products for Consumer Goods
N.A.I.C.S.: 332431

Subsidiary (Non-US):

Adularia Inversiones 2010 S.L.   (2)
Poligono Industrial Pinos, Las Torres de Cotillas, 30565, Spain
Tel.: (34) 968364400
Financial Investment Services
N.A.I.C.S.: 523999

Butimove   (2)
67 Rue Arago, 93400, Saint-Ouen, France
Tel.: (33) 149184000
Metal Tank Mfr
N.A.I.C.S.: 332431

CROWN Aerosols Nederland BV (2)
Veenweg 161, Mijdrecht, 3641, Netherlands
Tel.: (31) 297273275
Web Site: http://www.crowncork.com
Sales Range: $25-49.9 Million
Emp.: 30
Metal Can Mfr & Whslr
N.A.I.C.S.: 332431

CROWN Aerosols UK Limited   (2)
Oddicroft Lane, Sutton in Ashfield, NG17 5FS, Notts, United Kingdom
Tel.: (44) 1623528427
Web Site: http://www.crowncork.com
Metal Tank Mfr
N.A.I.C.S.: 332431

Subsidiary (Domestic):

CROWN Americas LLC   (2)
1 Crown Way, Philadelphia, PA 19154-4501
Tel.: (215) 698-5100
Web Site: http://www.crowncork.com
Holding Company; Regional Managing Office
N.A.I.C.S.: 551112

Subsidiary (Domestic):

CROWN Cork & Seal USA, Inc. (3)
770 Township Line Rd, Yardley, PA 19067
Tel.: (215) 698-5100
Web Site: http://www.crowncork.com
Packaging Products Mfr & Distr
N.A.I.C.S.: 322220

Plant (Domestic):

Crown Cork & Seal Avery Technical Center   (4)
5555 W 15th St, Alsip, IL 60803
Tel.: (708) 239-5555
Web Site: http://www.crowncork.com
Mfr of Packaging Products for Consumer Goods
N.A.I.C.S.: 332119

Crown Cork & Seal USA, Inc. - Massillon   (4)
700 16th St SE, Massillon, OH 44646
Tel.: (330) 833-1011
Web Site: http://www.crowncork.com
Mfr of Packaging Products for Consumer Goods
N.A.I.C.S.: 332431

Unit (Domestic):

Crown Cork & Seal Co Inc. -Sugar Land   (3)
12910 Jess Pirtle Blvd, Sugar Land, TX
77478   (100%)
Tel.: (281) 240-4838

Web Site: http://www.crowncork.com
Mfr of Packaging Products for Consumer Goods
N.A.I.C.S.: 332431

Subsidiary (Domestic):

Crown Specialty Packaging USA, Inc.   (3)
4606 Richlyn Dr, Belcamp, MD 21017
Tel.: (410) 273-1880
Metal Tank Mfr
N.A.I.C.S.: 332431

Subsidiary (Non-US):

CROWN Bevcan Espana S.L.   (2)
Avenida Ebro Parc 34 35 A, Agoncillo, 26160, Spain
Tel.: (34) 941431026
Metal Can Mfr & Supplies
N.A.I.C.S.: 332431

CROWN Bevcan France SAS   (2)
203 Boulevard De Finlandec, PO Box 18, Parc Eiffel Energie BP 18, Custines, 54670, France
Tel.: (33) 383494000
Emp.: 550
Metal Tank Mfr
N.A.I.C.S.: 332431

CROWN Bevcan Turkiye Ambalaj Sanayi Ve Ticaret   (2)
Suadiye Belediyesi 332 Cepni Caddesi, Kocaeli, 41170, Turkiye
Tel.: (90) 2623522660
Web Site: http://www.crowncork.com
Emp.: 120
Metal Tank Mfr
N.A.I.C.S.: 332431

CROWN Beverage Cans (Cambodia) Limited   (2)
Chom Chao St 217 in Front of Honda Factory, Chom Chao Village, 12405, Phnom Penh, Cambodia
Tel.: (855) 23995977
Emp.: 260
Metal Tank Mfr
N.A.I.C.S.: 332431

CROWN Beverage Cans Beijing Limited   (2)
No 1 Anxiang Road B Area Tianzhu Konggang Industrial Zone, Beijing, 100101, China
Tel.: (86) 1080497999
Metal Tank Mfr
N.A.I.C.S.: 332431

CROWN Beverage Cans Malaysia Sdn Bhd   (2)
No 2a Jalan P/1a, 43650, Bandar Baru Bangi, 43650, Selangor Darul Ehsan, Malaysia
Tel.: (60) 389258921
Sales Range: $25-49.9 Million
Emp.: 150
Metal Tank Mfr
N.A.I.C.S.: 332431
Simon Tan (Gen Mgr)

CROWN Beverage Cans Sihanoukville Limited   (2)
National Road No 4 Village 1 Sangkat 1, Sihanoukville, 955, Preah Sihanouk, Cambodia
Tel.: (855) 34900119
Web Site: http://www.crowncork.com
Emp.: 140
Metal Container Mfr
N.A.I.C.S.: 332439

CROWN Beverage Cans Singapore Pte. Ltd.   (2)
455 Jln Ahmad Ibrahim, Singapore, 639936, Singapore
Tel.: (65) 6863 2555
Web Site: http://www.crowncork.com
Emp.: 115
Metal Tank Mfr
N.A.I.C.S.: 332431

CROWN Commercial France SAS   (2)
67 Rue Arago, 93400, Saint-Ouen, France
Tel.: (33) 899868208
Non-Durable Goods Whslr
N.A.I.C.S.: 424310

CROWN Commercial Germany GmbH & Co. KG   (2)
Fritz Zuchner Str 8, Lower Saxony, 38723, Seesen, Germany
Tel.: (49) 53817810
Packaging & Labeling Services
N.A.I.C.S.: 561910
Sebastien Duriez (Mgr-Customer Svc)

CROWN Commercial Netherlands B.V.   (2)
Anodeweg 3, 1627 LJ, Hoorn, Netherlands
Tel.: (31) 229280300
Metal Product Merchant Whslr
N.A.I.C.S.: 423510

Joint Venture (Non-US):

CROWN Embalagens Metalicas da Amazonia S.A.   (2)
Rua Jutai 405, Distrito Industrial, Manaus, 69075-130, Amazonas, Brazil
Tel.: (55) 1145291000
Web Site:
http://www.crownembalagens.com.br
Emp.: 15
Metal Tank Mfr
N.A.I.C.S.: 332431
Johan Van Rompaey (Office Mgr)

Subsidiary (Non-US):

CROWN Emballage France SAS (2)
67 Rue Arago - Le Colisee 1, 93400, Saint-Ouen, France
Tel.: (33) 149 184 000
Metal Tank Mfr
N.A.I.C.S.: 332431

CROWN Emirates Company Limited   (2)
Round About 11 Jebel Ali Free Zone, Jebel Ali, 17030, United Arab Emirates
Tel.: (971) 4 8835452
Metal Tank Mfr
N.A.I.C.S.: 332431
Ashwini Kotwal (Gen Mgr)

CROWN Foodcan Germany GmbH   (2)
Fritz Zuchner Str 8 Harz, Seesen, Germany
Tel.: (49) 53817810
Web Site: http://www.crowncork.com
Holding Company
N.A.I.C.S.: 551112

CROWN Hellas Can Packaging SA   (2)
Ethnikis Antistaseos 57, 152-31, Chalandri, Greece
Tel.: (30) 2106799100
Web Site: http://www.crownhellascan.gr
Metal Tank Mfr
N.A.I.C.S.: 332431

CROWN Hellas Packaging Can SA   (2)
National Resistance 57A, Chalandri, Athens, 15231, Greece
Tel.: (30) 2106799100
Web Site: http://www.crownhellascan.gr
Metal Container Mfr
N.A.I.C.S.: 332439
Angeliki A. Nikaki (Fin Dir & VP)

CROWN Middle East Can Co. Ltd.   (2)
Amman Industrial City Sahab Str No 17, PO Box 260, Amman, 11512, Jordan
Tel.: (962) 6 4023986
Web Site: http://www.mecanjo.com
Metal Tank Mfr
N.A.I.C.S.: 332431

CROWN Packaging Polska Sp.z.o.o.   (2)
Maszewska 20, 71-100, Goleniow, Poland
Tel.: (48) 914697801
Web Site: https://crown-packaging-opakowania.business.site
Metal Packaging Materials Mfr
N.A.I.C.S.: 339999
Wieslaw Baczek (Plant Mgr)

CROWN SIEM   (2)
Boulevard Giscard d Zone 3 Valery Estaing, BP 1242, Abidjan, Cote d'Ivoire
Tel.: (225) 21 750900
Metal Tank Mfr

Crown Holdings, Inc.—(Continued)

N.A.I.C.S.: 332431
Michel Moreau (Dir Gen)

CROWN Senegal **(2)**
PO Box 3850, Dakar, Senegal
Tel.: (221) 33 849 32 32
Web Site: http://www.crowncork.com
Metal Tank Mfr
N.A.I.C.S.: 332431

CROWN Vogel AG **(2)**
Industriestrasse 37, 4147, Aesch, Switzerland
Tel.: (41) 617561313
Emp.: 90
Metal Can Mfr & Whslr
N.A.I.C.S.: 332431
Johannes Rehm (Mng Dir)

CarnaudMetalbox Engineering Ltd **(2)**
Dockfield Road, Shipley, BD17 7AY, West Yorkshire, United Kingdom
Tel.: (44) 127 484 6200
Web Site:
   https://www.carnaudmetalboxengineer
   ing.co.uk
Emp.: 200
Metal Tank Mfr
N.A.I.C.S.: 332431

CarnaudMetalbox Finance SA **(2)**
67 Rue Arago, 93400, Saint-Ouen, France
Tel.: (33) 1 49 18 40 00
Web Site: http://www.crowncork.com
Emp.: 80
Metal Tank Mfr
N.A.I.C.S.: 332431

CarnaudMetalbox Food South Africa (Pty) Limited **(2)**
Sacks Circle, Bellville, 7530, Western Cape, South Africa
Tel.: (27) 219511186
Web Site: http://www.crowncork.com
Emp.: 25
Metal Tank Mfr
N.A.I.C.S.: 332431

Crown Asia Pacific Holdings, Ltd. **(2)**
1 HarbourFront Place 03-01 HarbourFront Tower One, Singapore, 098633, Singapore **(100%)**
Tel.: (65) 6 423 9798
Web Site: http://www.crowncork.com
Sales Range: $10-24.9 Million
Emp.: 30
Consumer Goods Mfr
N.A.I.C.S.: 326199

Crown Beverage Cans HK Ltd. **(2)**
Ste 1315 Tower 1 Grand Central Plz, Sha Tin, China (Hong Kong) **(51%)**
Tel.: (852) 26656312
Sales Range: $10-24.9 Million
Emp.: 10
Metal Tank Mfr
N.A.I.C.S.: 332431

Subsidiary (Non-US):

Foshan Continental Can Co. Limited **(3)**
20 Qinggong San Rd, Foshan, 528000, China **(51%)**
Tel.: (86) 75783376948
Sales Range: $50-74.9 Million
Emp.: 190
Can Mfr
N.A.I.C.S.: 332431

Subsidiary (Non-US):

Crown Canadian Holdings ULC **(2)**
10000 Rue Meilleur, Montreal, H3L 3J7, QC, Canada
Tel.: (514) 389-5961
Holding Company
N.A.I.C.S.: 551112

Crown Closures Spain, S.L. **(2)**
Calle turdetanos pol ind la isla 1, 41703, Dos Hermanas, Spain
Tel.: (34) 954979500
Web Site: http://www.crowncork.com
Emp.: 100
Metal Container Mfr
N.A.I.C.S.: 332439

Crown Colombiana, S.A. **(2)**
Carrera 64 C No 96 26, Medellin, Antioquia, Colombia **(100%)**
Tel.: (57) 42670031
Web Site:
   http://www.drodembasdscrown.com
Sales Range: $125-149.9 Million
Emp.: 200
Mfr of Packaging Products for Consumer Goods
N.A.I.C.S.: 332431

Crown Comercial de Envases, S.L. **(2)**
Avenida Ebro Pol Industrial Par 9, Agoncillo, 26160, Spain
Tel.: (34) 941486550
Metal Tank Mfr
N.A.I.C.S.: 332431

Crown Commercial Polska Sp. z.o.o. **(2)**
Ul Maszewska 20 Wojewodztwo Zachodniopomorskie, 72-100, Goleniow, Poland
Tel.: (48) 914697801
Emp.: 5
Non-Durable Goods Whslr
N.A.I.C.S.: 424310

Crown Cork & Seal Deutschland Holdings GmbH **(2)**
Fritz-Zuchner-Str 8, Seesen, 38723, Germany
Tel.: (49) 5381 7810
Web Site: http://www.crowncork.com
Metal Tank Mfr
N.A.I.C.S.: 332431
Rolf Willke (Mng Dir)

Crown Cork & Seal de Portugal Embalagens S.A. **(2)**
Estrada Nacional - Monte Das Cardeeiras, 2890-152, Alcochete, Portugal **(100%)**
Tel.: (351) 212348230
Sales Range: $100-124.9 Million
Emp.: 250
Mfr of Packaging Products for Consumer Goods
N.A.I.C.S.: 332431

Crown Envases Mexico, S.A. de C.V. **(2)**
2239 Alfonso Reyes Avenue, 07850, Monterrey, DF, Mexico **(100%)**
Tel.: (52) 5557474100
Emp.: 650
Packaging Products Mfr
N.A.I.C.S.: 332431

Crown European Holdings SA **(2)**
67 RUE ARAGO, Cedex 17, 75830, Paris, France
Tel.: (33) 149184000
Metal Tank Mfr
N.A.I.C.S.: 332431

Crown Holdings Italia Srl **(2)**
Strada Ugozzolo 100/A, 43122, Parma, Italy
Tel.: (39) 0521909335
Sales Range: $10-24.9 Million
Emp.: 24
Metal Tank Mfr
N.A.I.C.S.: 332431

Subsidiary (Domestic):

Crown Imgallaggi Italia Srl **(3)**
Strada Ugozzolo 100/A, 43122, Parma, Italy
Tel.: (39) 0521909311
Web Site: http://www.crownimballaggi.it
Sales Range: $150-199.9 Million
Metal Tank Mfr
N.A.I.C.S.: 332431
Guglielmo Prati (VP-Food)

Subsidiary (Non-US):

Crown Metal Packaging Canada Ltee. **(2)**
7900 Keele St, Concord, L4K 2A3, ON, Canada **(100%)**
Tel.: (905) 669-1401
Web Site: http://www.crowncork.com
Sales Range: $25-49.9 Million
Emp.: 100
Mfr of Packaging Products for Consumer Goods
N.A.I.C.S.: 332431

Crown Obrist AG **(2)**

Romerstrasse 83, 4153, Reinach, Switzerland
Tel.: (41) 0617152424
Web Site: http://www.hyfoma.com
Mfr of Plastic Bottle Caps
N.A.I.C.S.: 326199

Crown Packaging Europe GmbH **(2)**
Baarermatte, CH-6340, Baar, Switzerland
Tel.: (41) 41 759 10 00
Metal Tank Mfr
N.A.I.C.S.: 332431

Crown Packaging Ireland Ltd. **(2)**
Woodstock Industrial Estate, Athy, Co Kildare, Ireland **(100%)**
Tel.: (353) 59830210
Sales Range: $100-124.9 Million
Packaging Products for Consumer Goods Mfr
N.A.I.C.S.: 332431

Crown Packaging Lux I S.a.r.l. **(2)**
Cote dEich 73, 1450, Luxembourg, Luxembourg
Tel.: (352) 27848431
Packaging Machinery Mfr
N.A.I.C.S.: 333993

Crown Packaging Maroc **(2)**
Route Secondaire No 110 Km 10 Chefchaouni, Casablanca, 20250, Morocco
Tel.: (212) 522667530
Metal Tank Mfr
N.A.I.C.S.: 332431

Crown UK Holdings Ltd **(2)**
Downsview Rd, Wantage, OX12 9BP, Oxon, United Kingdom
Tel.: (44) 1235772929
Sales Range: $250-299.9 Million
Beverage Packaging Mfr & Distr
N.A.I.C.S.: 327213
Alan Walter Rutherford (Mng Dir)

Subsidiary (Domestic):

Crown Packaging UK plc **(3)**
Downsview Road, Wantage, OX12 9BP, Oxfordshire, United Kingdom **(100%)**
Tel.: (44) 1235772929
Web Site: http://www.crowncork.com
Sales Range: $200-249.9 Million
Emp.: 500
Holding Company; Mfr of Packaging Products for Consumer Goods
N.A.I.C.S.: 551112

Crown Speciality Packaging UK Plc **(3)**
Crown Farm Way Forest down, Mansfield, NG 19 0FT, Notts, United Kingdom
Tel.: (44) 1623622651
Web Site: http://www.crowngroup.com
Sales Range: $50-74.9 Million
Emp.: 130
Metal Tank Mfr
N.A.I.C.S.: 332431

Subsidiary (Non-US):

Crown Verpakking Belgie NV **(2)**
Krugerstraat 232, 2660, Antwerp, Belgium
Tel.: (32) 33604811
Web Site: http://www.crowncork.com
Sales Range: $50-74.9 Million
Emp.: 400
Management Consulting Services
N.A.I.C.S.: 541611

Subsidiary (Domestic):

Crown Speciality Packaging Belgie NV **(3)**
Krugerstraat 232, Antwerp, 2660, Belgium
Tel.: (32) 382001911
Sales Range: $75-99.9 Million
Emp.: 135
Metal Tank Mfr
N.A.I.C.S.: 332431

Subsidiary (Non-US):

Crown Verpakking Nederland N.V. **(2)**
Anodeweg 3, 1627 LJ, Hoorn, Netherlands
Tel.: (31) 229280320
Management Consulting Services
N.A.I.C.S.: 541611

Subsidiary (Domestic):

Crown Speciality Packaging B.V. **(3)**
Anodeweg 3, PO Box 485, 1627 LJ, Hoorn, Netherlands
Tel.: (31) 229280300
Sales Range: $100-124.9 Million
Metal Products Mfr
N.A.I.C.S.: 332431

Joint Venture (Non-US):

Crown Vinalimex Packaging Ltd. **(2)**
Km 24 Highway 1, Quat Dong, Houng Tin Hatay, Hanoi, Vietnam
Tel.: (84) 34852003
Sales Range: $25-49.9 Million
Emp.: 88
Packaging Products for Consumer Goods;
Joint Venture of Crown Cork & Seal Co., Inc. & Swire Pacific Limited Mfr
N.A.I.C.S.: 326199

Subsidiary (Non-US):

Fabricas Monterrey, S.A. de C.V. **(2)**
Carretera Mexico Toluca Km 60, 50000, Toluca, Mexico
Tel.: (52) 17222755800
Sheet Metal Mfr
N.A.I.C.S.: 332322

Foshan Crown Easy-Opening End Co. Limited **(2)**
Ron 711 4th Avenue, Foshan, 528000, China **(51%)**
Tel.: (86) 75782219400
Resealable Plastic Bag & Other Packaging Products Mfr
N.A.I.C.S.: 326111

Glass & Silice, S.A. DE C.V. **(2)**
Avenida Alfonso Reyes 2239, 64220, Monterrey, Mexico
Tel.: (52) 8183286600
Building Materials Mfr
N.A.I.C.S.: 327120

Joint Venture (Non-US):

Jeddah Beverage Can Making Co. Ltd. **(2)**
Industrial city phase 3 Rd 153 Street 31, PO Box 16626, Jeddah, B21474, Saudi Arabia
Tel.: (966) 26361750
Web Site: http://www.jbcmc.com
Sales Range: $75-99.9 Million
Emp.: 256
Mfr of Packaging Products for Consumer Goods; Joint Venture of Crown Cork & Seal Co., Inc. & A.H. Algosaibi & Bros.
N.A.I.C.S.: 326199

Subsidiary (Non-US):

Mivisa Envases S.A.U. **(2)**
Poligono Industrial Los Pinos, Carretera de Mula s/n, 30565, Las Torres de Cotillas, Murcia, Spain
Tel.: (34) 968 364 400
Web Site: http://www.mivisa.com
Sales Range: $750-799.9 Million
Metal Tank Mfr
N.A.I.C.S.: 332431

Subsidiary (Non-US):

Mivisa Hungary Kft. **(3)**
Uveggyar Utca 0318/15 hrsz, Tatabanya - Kornye Ipari Park, 2851, Kornye, Hungary
Tel.: (36) 34 57 3320
Web Site: http://www.mivisa.com
Metal Tank Mfr
N.A.I.C.S.: 332431

Mivisa Maroc, S.A. **(3)**
Lot no B 646 Zone Industriele Ait Melloul, Agadir, Morocco
Tel.: (212) 5 28 24 8100
Web Site: http://www.mivisa.com
Metal Tank Mfr
N.A.I.C.S.: 332431

Subsidiary (Non-US):

Prolatamex, S.A. DE C.V. **(2)**
Av Alfonso Reyes Norte 2239, 64450, San Nicolas, Mexico
Tel.: (52) 8183286697
Emp.: 50

Industrial Machinery & Equipment Whslr
N.A.I.C.S.: 423830

Silice Del Istmo, S.A. DE C.V. (2)
Km 10 de la Carretera Sayula-San Juan
Evangelista, Acayucan, Veracruz, Mexico
Tel.: (52) 9242457420
Industrial Machinery & Equipment Whslr
N.A.I.C.S.: 423830

**Superior Investment Holdings Pte.
Ltd.** (2)
7 Benoi Sector, Singapore, 629842, Singa-
pore
Tel.: (65) 62683933
Web Site: http://www.smpl.com.sg
Holding Company
N.A.I.C.S.: 551112

Superior Multi-Packaging Limited (2)
7 Benoi Sector, Singapore, 629842, Singa-
pore
Tel.: (65) 6 268 3933
Web Site: https://www.smpl.com.sg
Sales Range: $125-149.9 Million
Emp.: 190
Metal Containers & Flexible Packaging Ma-
terials Mfr
N.A.I.C.S.: 332431

Subsidiary (Non-US):

**Kunshan Huade Metal Packaging
Container Co., Ltd.** (3)
No 55 Zhong Huan Road Civil Hi-tech In-
dustrial Park, Kunshan, 215316, China
Tel.: (86) 512 57780584
Web Site: http://www.smpl.com.sg
Metal Container Mfr
N.A.I.C.S.: 332431

**Langfang Huade Metal Packaging
Container Co., Ltd.** (3)
No 30 Quan Xing Road Langfang Economic
Tech Dev Zone, Langfang, 065001,
China   (100%)
Tel.: (86) 3166070233
Web Site: http://www.smpl.com.sg
Customized Metal Printing
N.A.I.C.S.: 332999

**Neo Tech Packaging (Shanghai) Co.,
Ltd** (3)
No 429 Li Hang Road Pudong Wang Qiao
Industrial Park New Area, Shanghai,
201201, China
Tel.: (86) 2158385823
Web Site: http://www.neo-tech.cn
Laminated Metal Plates Mfr
N.A.I.C.S.: 332999

**Superior (Chengdu) Multi-Packaging
Co., Ltd.** (3)
Blk A Longteng Industry Estate Row 7,
Chengdu Economic & Technological Devel-
opment Zone, Chengdu, 610100, China
Tel.: (86) 2884848201
Flexible Packaging Mfr
N.A.I.C.S.: 326112

**Superior (LangFang) Multi-Packaging
Co., Ltd.** (3)
No 30 Quan Xing Road Langfang Economic
Tech Dev Zone, Langfang, 065001, Hebei
Province, China
Tel.: (86) 3166070234
Flexible Packaging Mfr
N.A.I.C.S.: 326112

**Superior (Tianjin) Multi-Packaging
Co., Ltd.** (3)
Wuqing District Tianjin Jinbin Industrial Park
10 Tai Yuan Road, Tianjin, 301712, China
Tel.: (86) 2222198321
Flexible Packaging Mfr
N.A.I.C.S.: 326112

**Superior Cans & Pails Containers
(Pune) Private Limited** (3)
Plot D-246 & D-247 Ranjangaon MIDC Vil-
lage Karegaon, Tal-Shirur Maharashtra,
Pune, 412220, India
Tel.: (91) 2138 610001
Web Site: http://www.smpindia.co.in
Metal Pails Mfr
N.A.I.C.S.: 332999

Subsidiary (Domestic):

**Superior Investments Holdings Pte
Ltd** (3)

7 Benoi Sector, Singapore, 629842,
Singapore   (100%)
Tel.: (65) 6 268 3933
Web Site: http://www.smpl.com.sg
Investment Management Service
N.A.I.C.S.: 523999

Subsidiary (Non-US):

**Superior Metal Printing (Huiyang)
Co., Ltd.** (3)
Dong Jiang Industrial Zone, Shui Kou Zhen,
Huiyang, 516255, China   (100%)
Tel.: (86) 752 2311613
Web Site: http://www.smpl.com.sg
Sales Range: $25-49.9 Million
Emp.: 70
Metal Pails & Cans Mfr
N.A.I.C.S.: 332431

**Superior Multi-Packaging (Vietnam)
Co., Ltd** (3)
Tan Hiep Tan Binh Commune, Di An, Binh
Duong, Vietnam   (100%)
Tel.: (84) 6503782268
Metal Pails & Cans & Plastic Pails Mfr
N.A.I.C.S.: 332431

**Zhejiang Gaote Metal Decorating Co.,
Ltd.** (3)
No 309 Tongyu Road Tudian Light Textile
Industrial Park, Tongxiang, 314503, Zheji-
ang, China
Tel.: (86) 57388865856
Flexible Packaging Mfr
N.A.I.C.S.: 326112

Crown Food Espana, S.A.U. (1)
Poligono Industrial Silvota S/n 33420,
33420, Asturias, Spain
Tel.: (34) 985732030
Packaging Can Distr
N.A.I.C.S.: 424490

**Crown Packaging European Division
GmbH** (1)
Baarermatte, 6340, Baar, Switzerland
Tel.: (41) 417591000
Packaging Can Distr
N.A.I.C.S.: 424490

Litec France S.A.S. (1)
ZI des Joncs, BP 24, 71700, Tournus,
France
Tel.: (33) 385322380
Aluminium Cans Mfr
N.A.I.C.S.: 332431

**SMB Schwede Maschinenbau
GmbH** (1)
Markgrafenstrasse 2, 95497, Goldkronach,
Germany
Tel.: (49) 92739820
Web Site: https://www.smb.biz
Industrial Machinery Mfr
N.A.I.C.S.: 333248
Ellen Fleischmann *(Mng Dir)*
Markus Petersam *(Sr Mgr-Sls)*

**SMP Schwede Maschinenbau Weis-
chlitz GmbH** (1)
Bodenfeldstrasse 4, Weischlitz, 08538,
Leipzig, Germany
Tel.: (49) 37 436 9110
Web Site: https://www.smp-
    maschinenbau.de
Industrial Machinery Mfr
N.A.I.C.S.: 333248

Shippers Europe Srl (1)
66 Rue Louis de Brouckere, 7100, La Lou-
viere, Belgium
Tel.: (32) 64430511
Web Site: http://www.shipperseurope.com
Dunnage Bag Mfr & Retailer
N.A.I.C.S.: 322220

Signode Brasileira Ltda. (1)
Rodovia Dom Gabriel P B Couto Km 78,
Bairro Cabreuva, Jacarei, 13318-000, Sao
Paulo, Brazil
Tel.: (55) 1145298400
Web Site: https://www.signode.com.br
Packaging & Container Services
N.A.I.C.S.: 561910
Marcio Cardoso *(Plant Mgr)*

Signode Denmark ApS (1)
Literbuen 9, 2740, Skovlunde, Denmark
Tel.: (45) 44850600

Web Site: http://www.signode.dk
Wrapping Machine Mfr
N.A.I.C.S.: 333993
Heinrich Hansen *(Sls Mgr)*
Jan Vernersen *(Sls Mgr-Area)*
Arne Thomsen *(Sls Mgr-Area)*
Steffen Koch *(Mgr-Svc)*
Torsten Thomsen *(Controller)*

Signode Finland Oy (1)
Ayritie 12 A, 01510, Vantaa, Finland
Tel.: (358) 24376111
Web Site: http://www.signode.fi
Emp.: 180
Wrapping Machine Mfr
N.A.I.C.S.: 333993
Matti Hamalainen *(Country Mgr-Sls)*

Signode Industrial Group AB (1)
Hantverkarvagen 6, 187 66, Taby, Sweden
Tel.: (46) 86309960
Web Site: http://www.signode.se
Packaging & Container Services
N.A.I.C.S.: 561910

Signode Industrial Group GmbH (1)
Silbernstrasse 14, 8953, Dietikon, Switzer-
land
Tel.: (41) 447455050
Packaging & Container Services
N.A.I.C.S.: 561910

Signode Industrial Group LLC (1)
3650 W Lake Ave, Glenview, IL 60026-1215
Tel.: (847) 724-6100
Web Site: http://www.signodegroup.com
Holding Company; Industrial Packaging
Consumables, Tools & Equipment & Global
Bulk Goods Transportation
N.A.I.C.S.: 551112
Robert H. Bourque Jr. *(Pres)*

Unit (Domestic):

Fleetwood-Signode (2)
3624 W Lake Ave, Glenview, IL 60026
Tel.: (847) 657-5111
Web Site: https://www.signode.com
Sales Range: $125-149.9 Million
Emp.: 50
Mfr & Distr of Protective Packaging Sys-
tems that Apply Plastic & Steel Strapping,
Stretch Film & Pressure Sensitive Tape
N.A.I.C.S.: 333993

Subsidiary (Non-US):

**ITW Packaging (Shanghai) Co.,
Ltd.** (2)
Room 907 Jindu Building 277 Wu Xin
Road, Xuhui District, Shanghai, 200030,
China
Tel.: (86) 2164739322
Web Site: http://www.signode.com
Packaging Material Distr
N.A.I.C.S.: 423840

SPG Packaging Systems GmbH (2)
Westring 13, 40721, Hilden, Germany
Tel.: (49) 2103960670
Web Site: http://www.sigpse.com
Emp.: 100
Packaging Machinery Mfr & Distr
N.A.I.C.S.: 333993

Subsidiary (Domestic):

Signode Acme Inc. (2)
3624 W Lake St, Glenview, IL 60026
Tel.: (630) 589-5100
Web Site: http://www.signodeacme.com
Sales Range: $100-124.9 Million
Emp.: 50
Steel & Plastic Strapping, Strapping Seals,
Strapping Tools & Other Packaging Sup-
plies Sales & Distr
N.A.I.C.S.: 423840

Unit (Domestic):

**Signode Industrial Group -
Angleboard** (2)
595 Telser Rd Ste 100, Lake Zurich, IL
60047-6720   (100%)
Tel.: (847) 719-9200
Web Site: http://www.signodegroup.com
Sales Range: $300-349.9 Million
Emp.: 1,000
Protective Packaging & Transportation Sys-
tems Mfr
N.A.I.C.S.: 322220

Subsidiary (Non-US):

**Signode Packaging Group (Malaysia)
Sdn Bhd** (2)
No 10 Jalan Tiara 1, Taman Perindustrian
Sime UEP, 47620, Subang Jaya, Selangor,
Malaysia
Tel.: (60) 380259363
Web Site: http://www.signode.com
Packaging Machinery Mfr
N.A.I.C.S.: 333993

Unit (Domestic):

Signode Packaging Systems (2)
3650 W Lake Ave, Glenview, IL 60026
Tel.: (847) 724-7500
Web Site: http://www.signode.com
Sales Range: $150-199.9 Million
Emp.: 450
Steel & Plastic Strapping, Stretch Film &
Application Equipment & Accessories Mfr &
Whslr
N.A.I.C.S.: 333993

Subsidiary (Non-US):

Signode (Espana) S.A. (3)
Ctra Del Mig 83-87, Cornella del Llobregat,
8940, Barcelona, Spain   (100%)
Tel.: (34) 934800720
Web Site: http://www.signode-europe.com
Sales Range: $10-24.9 Million
Emp.: 90
Machines & Hand Tools Parts & Services
N.A.I.C.S.: 333517
Rosa Maria Perez *(Mng Dir)*

Signode BVBA (3)
Ikaros park Ikaroslaan 33, B-1930,
Zaventem, Belgium   (100%)
Tel.: (32) 27163620
Web Site: http://www.signode-europe.com
Sales Range: $1-9.9 Million
Emp.: 20
Steel & Plastic Strapping, Stretch Film,
Pressure Sensitive Carton Sealing Tape
Equipment & Accessories
N.A.I.C.S.: 326199

Signode Canada (3)
241 Gough Road, Markham, L3R 5B3, ON,
Canada   (100%)
Tel.: (905) 479-9754
Web Site: https://www.signode.ca
Sales Range: $25-49.9 Million
Emp.: 40
Steel & Plastic Strapping, Stretch Film,
Pressure Sensitive Carton Sealing Tape
Equipment & Accessories Mfr
N.A.I.C.S.: 333993

Signode France S.A.S. (3)
4 Allee des Erables, 94 042, Creteil, Cedex,
France
Tel.: (33) 820208208
Web Site: http://www.signodeeurope.com
Sales Range: $150-199.9 Million
Packaging Machinery & Equipment Distr
N.A.I.C.S.: 423830

Signode Hong Kong Limited (3)
Unit 2A 2F Block 4 Tai Ping Industrial Cen-
tre, 51A Ting Kok Rd, Tai Po, NT, China
(Hong Kong)   (100%)
Tel.: (852) 27852328
Web Site: http://www.signode.com.hk
Sales Range: $50-74.9 Million
Emp.: 5
Steel & Plastic Strapping, Stretch Film,
Pressure Sensitive Carton Sealing Tape
Equipment & Accessories
N.A.I.C.S.: 333993

Signode India Limited (3)
3rd Floor Jyothi Majestic 8-2-120/84 Road
No 2 Banjara Hills, Hyderabad, 500034,
Telangana, India   (100%)
Tel.: (91) 4067468900
Web Site: http://www.signodeindia.com
Emp.: 200
Steel & Plastic Strapping, Stretch Film &
Packaging Systems Mfr
N.A.I.C.S.: 326112
Rohit Gupta *(CFO)*

Signode Kabushiki Kaisha (3)
1-2-4 Minatojima Nakamachi, Chuo-ku,
Kobe, 650-0046, Japan   (100%)
Tel.: (81) 783065501

Crown Holdings, Inc.—(Continued)

Web Site: http://www.signode.co.jp
Sales Range: $25-49.9 Million
Emp.: 52
Steel & Plastic Strapping, Stretch Film
Packaging Systems & Automatic Binding
Machine & Various Devices
N.A.I.C.S.: 333993
Eiji Tsukamoto *(Pres)*
Rama Krishna *(Dir-RVS)*

Signode Limited (3)
Florestfach Queensway, Swansea, SA5
4ED, United Kingdom
Tel.: (44) 7192563229
Web Site: http://www.signode.com
Steel & Plastic Strapping, Stretch Film,
Pressure Sensitive Carton Sealing Tape
Equipment & Accessories
N.A.I.C.S.: 325520

Signode Singapore Pte. Ltd. (3)
10 Tampines North Drive 4 07-12 JTC
Space Tampines North, Singapore, 528553,
Singapore (100%)
Tel.: (65) 68617677
Web Site: http://www.signode.com
Sales Range: $50-74.9 Million
Emp.: 5
Packaging Evaluation & Testing
N.A.I.C.S.: 541380

Signode System GmbH (3)
Magnusstrasse 18, 46524, Dinslaken,
Germany (100%)
Tel.: (49) 206469408
Packaging Systems After Sales Services
N.A.I.C.S.: 333993
Reinhard Bittner *(Mgr-HR & Grp Controller)*
Rainer Kammer *(Mng Dir & Grp VP-Metals-Europe)*

Unit (Non-US):

**Signode Packaging Systems Europe
- UK & Ireland** (2)
Unit 51 Empire Industrial Park Brickyard
Road, Aldridge, WS9 8UQ, United
Kingdom (100%)
Tel.: (44) 1922742500
Web Site: http://www.sigpse.com
Strapping & Packaging Machinery Mfr
N.A.I.C.S.: 333993

Subsidiary (Non-US):

Strapex Holding GmbH (2)
Silbernstrasse 14, Postfach 595, 8953, Di-
etikon, Switzerland
Tel.: (41) 447455080
Web Site: http://www.strapex.ch
Stretch Wrapping Machines & Strapping
Tools Mfr & Distr
N.A.I.C.S.: 423830

**Signode Industrial Group Mexico,
R.L. de C.V.** (1)
Carretera Monterrey-Laredo km 22 7, Cien-
ega de Flores, 65550, Nuevo Leon, Mexico
Tel.: (52) 8183298400
Web Site: http://www.signodemexico.com
Packaging Machinery Mfr
N.A.I.C.S.: 333993

Signode Industrial Group US Inc. (1)
3650 W Lake Ave, Glenview, IL 60026
Web Site: http://www.signode.com
Packaging Machinery Mfr
N.A.I.C.S.: 333993
Michael Watts *(VP-Dev & Head-Mktg-Global)*

Signode Norway AS (1)
Ryghgata 4B, 3051, Mjondalen, Norway
Tel.: (47) 32231880
Web Site: http://www.signode.no
Wrapping Machine Mfr
N.A.I.C.S.: 333993
Odd Einar Mortensen *(Sls Mgr)*
Stig Arve Bjorkas *(Sls Mgr)*
Terje Bruserud *(Sls Mgr)*
Arne Koldingsnes *(Sls Mgr)*
Per-Terje Fredriksen *(Coord-Svc)*

Signode Polska Sp. z o.o. (1)
ul Gen L Okulickiego 7/9, 05-500,
Piasecino, Poland
Tel.: (48) 222331041
Web Site: http://signode.pl
Packaging Machinery Mfr

N.A.I.C.S.: 333993

Signode UK Ltd. (1)
Unit 51 Brickyard Road, Empire Industrial
Park Aldridge, Walsall, WS9 8UQ, United
Kingdom
Tel.: (44) 1922742500
Web Site: http://www.signodegroup.co.uk
Wrapping Machine Mfr
N.A.I.C.S.: 333993

CROWN PROPTECH ACQUISI-TIONS
Tel.: (212) 563-6400 Ky
Web Site:
https://www.crownproptech.com
Year Founded: 2020
CPTK—(NYSE)
Rev.: $19,039,525
Assets: $280,118,377
Liabilities: $281,631,032
Net Worth: ($1,512,655)
Earnings: $14,797,454
Emp.: 2
Fiscal Year-end: 12/31/22
Miscellaneous Financial Investment
Activities
N.A.I.C.S.: 523999
Michael Minnick *(CEO, Principal
Acctg Officer & Principal Fin Officer)*

CRUCIBLE ACQUISITION CORPORATION
1050 Walnut St Ste 210, Boulder, CO
80302
Tel.: (401) 216-7635 DE
Web Site:
http://www.crucibleacquisition.com
Year Founded: 2020
CRUU—(NYSE)
Investment Services
N.A.I.C.S.: 523999
James M. Lejeal *(CEO)*
Brad Feld *(Chm)*
Jason M. Lynch *(Chief Admin Officer)*

CRYO-CELL INTERNATIONAL, INC.
700 Brooker Creek Blvd Ste 1800,
Oldsmar, FL 34677
Tel.: (813) 749-2100 DE
Web Site: https://www.cryo-cell.com
Year Founded: 1992
CCEL—(NYSE)
Rev.: $28,884,902
Assets: $60,662,076
Liabilities: $56,477,762
Net Worth: $4,184,314
Earnings: $2,083,521
Emp.: 83
Fiscal Year-end: 11/30/21
Medical Technologies Developer
N.A.I.C.S.: 541690
David I. Portnoy *(Chm & Co-CEO)*
Mark L. Portnoy *(Co-CEO)*
Joanne Kurtzberg *(Dir-Medical)*
Todd Schuesler *(Dir-Laboratory Ops)*
Andrea Darrow *(Sr Mgr-Quality As-
surance & Regulatory)*
Thomas Moss *(Dir-Infusion Svcs)*
Jill Taymans *(CFO)*

Subsidiaries:

CU Blood, Inc. (1)
555 Winderley Pl Ste 300, Maitland, FL
32751
Tel.: (407) 667-3000
Blood & Organ Banks
N.A.I.C.S.: 621991
Hal Broxmeyer *(Founder)*

**Saneron CCEL Therapeutics,
Inc.** (1)
16704 Tobacco Rd, Lutz, FL 33558
Tel.: (813) 977-7664
Web Site: https://www.saneron-ccel.com
Cell Therapy Researcher & Developer
N.A.I.C.S.: 541715

Paul R. Sanberg *(Co-Founder)*
Don F. Cameron *(Co-Founder)*
Bernard R. Skerkowski *(Treas)*

CRYOMASS TECHNOLOGIES INC.
1001 Bannock St Ste 612, Denver,
CO 80204
Tel.: (303) 222-8092 NV
Web Site: https://www.cryomass.com
Year Founded: 2011
CRYM—(OTCQB)
Rev.: $13,552
Assets: $972,506
Liabilities: $6,821,748
Net Worth: ($5,849,242)
Earnings: ($12,955,728)
Fiscal Year-end: 12/31/23
Other Activities Related to Real Es-
tate
N.A.I.C.S.: 531390
Philip Blair Mullin *(CFO)*
Delon Human *(Chm)*
Patricia I. Kovacevic *(Gen Counsel,
Sec & Head-External Affairs)*
Christian Noel *(CEO)*

Subsidiaries:

Good Meds, Inc. (1)
8420 W Colfax Ave, Lakewood, CO 80215
Tel.: (303) 238-1253
Web Site: http://www.goodmeds.com
Cannabis Distr
N.A.I.C.S.: 459991

CRYOPORT, INC.
112 Westwood Pl Ste 350, Brent-
wood, TN 37027
Tel.: (949) 470-2300 NV
Web Site: https://www.cryoport.com
CYRX—(NASDAQ)
Rev.: $237,277,000
Assets: $1,038,746,000
Liabilities: $482,908,000
Net Worth: $555,838,000
Earnings: ($45,333,000)
Emp.: 960
Fiscal Year-end: 12/31/22
Cryogenic Shipping Services
N.A.I.C.S.: 493120
Edward J. Zecchini *(CTO, Chief Digi-
tal Officer & Sr VP)*
Bret Bollinger *(CTO-Cryoport Sys)*
Robert S. Stefanovich *(CFO, Treas &
Sec)*
Jerrell W. Shelton *(Chm, Pres &
CEO)*
Mark W. Sawicki *(Chief Scientific Offi-
cer)*
Thomas J. Heinzen *(VP-Corp Dev)*
Phil Wilson *(COO-Cryoport Sys)*
Rob Jones *(VP-Bioservices-Global-
Cryoport Sys)*

Subsidiaries:

Cryo Express GmbH (1)
Schonauerstrasse 111, 04207, Leipzig, Ger-
many
Tel.: (49) 3414278461
Logistic Services
N.A.I.C.S.: 488510

Cryo Express Sp. z o.o. (1)
Al Krakowska 4/6, 02-284, Warsaw, Poland
Tel.: (48) 228680933
Logistic Services
N.A.I.C.S.: 488510

CryoPort Systems, Inc. (1)
225 Broadway, San Diego, CA 92101
Tel.: (619) 481-6800
Web Site: http://cryoport.com
Emp.: 9
Cold Storage Locker Services
N.A.I.C.S.: 493120

Subsidiary (Domestic):

Bluebird Express, LLC (2)
145 Hook Creek Blvd, Valley Stream, NY
11581

Tel.: (516) 255-0800
Sales Range: $1-9.9 Million
Emp.: 18
Expedited Courier Service
N.A.I.C.S.: 488510
Heather Holstein *(Office Mgr)*

I.C.S. Dry-Ice Express B.V. (1)
Verzetstraat 10, 5171 PT, Kaatsheuvel,
Netherlands
Tel.: (31) 416283331
Web Site: https://www.icsdryice.com
Dry Ice Mfr & Distr
N.A.I.C.S.: 325120

**MVE Biological Solutions US,
LLC** (1)
112 Westwood Pl Ste 350, Brentwood, TN
37027
Web Site: https://www.mvebio.com
Cryogenic Freezer Distr
N.A.I.C.S.: 423740

CRYSTAL VALLEY FINANCIAL CORP.
111 S Main St, Middlebury, IN 46540
Tel.: (574) 825-2166 IN
Year Founded: 1910
CYVF—(OTCIQ)
Financial Investment Services
N.A.I.C.S.: 523999
D. Joe Caffee *(Pres & CEO)*
Sam Hoover Jr. *(COO)*
Jared Sponseller *(CFO)*
Erik Romzek *(Sr VP)*
Lance Weirich *(Chief Legal Officer)*
Joe Smucker *(Chm)*

CS DISCO, INC.
111 Congress Ave Ste 900, Austin,
TX 78701 DE
Web Site: https://www.csdisco.com
Year Founded: 2013
LAW—(NYSE)
Rev.: $138,090,000
Assets: $231,547,000
Liabilities: $31,212,000
Net Worth: $200,335,000
Earnings: ($42,150,000)
Emp.: 543
Fiscal Year-end: 12/31/23
Custom Computer Programming Ser-
vices
N.A.I.C.S.: 541511
Kiwi Camara *(Co-Founder)*
Kent Radford *(Co-Founder & Chief
Ethics & Compliance Officer)*
Michael Lafair *(CFO)*
Melanie Antoon *(Sr VP-Professional
Svcs)*
Melissa Fruge *(Gen Counsel & Sr
VP)*
Krishna Srinivasan *(Chm)*
Jignasha Amin Grooms *(Chief HR
Officer & Exec VP)*

Subsidiaries:

CS Disco India Private Ltd. (1)
DLF Forum DLF Cybercity Phase III, Gur-
gaon, 122002, Haryana, India
Tel.: (91) 8336534726
Professional & Management Services
N.A.I.C.S.: 611430

CSB BANCORP, INC.
91 N Clay St, Millersburg, OH 44654
Tel.: (330) 674-9015
Web Site: https://www.csb1.com
CSBB—(OTCIQ)
Rev.: $41,530,000
Assets: $1,159,108,000
Liabilities: $1,063,188,000
Net Worth: $95,920,000
Earnings: $13,313,000
Emp.: 154
Fiscal Year-end: 12/31/22
Bank Holding Company
N.A.I.C.S.: 551111

Paula J. Meiler *(CFO & Sr VP)*
Eddie L. Steiner *(Pres & CEO)*
Brett A. Gallion *(COO, CIO & Exec VP)*
Pamela S. Basinger *(Chief Acctg Officer & VP)*
Andrea R. Miley *(Chief Risk Officer)*
Harland Bud Stebbins *(Sr VP)*

Subsidiaries:

CSB Investment Services, LLC **(1)**
409 Tenney, Kewanee, IL 61434
Tel.: (309) 853-3696
Web Site: http://www.csbinvestments.com
Emp.: 4,168
Financial Investment Services
N.A.I.C.S.: 523940

The Commercial and Savings Bank of Millersburg, Ohio **(1)**
91 N Clay St, Millersburg, OH 44654
Tel.: (330) 674-9015
Web Site: https://www.csb1.com
Banking Services
N.A.I.C.S.: 522110
Eddie L. Steiner *(Chm & CEO)*
Brett A. Gallion *(Pres, COO & CIO)*

CSG SYSTEMS INTERNATIONAL, INC.

169 Inverness Dr W Ste 300, Englewood, CO 80112
Tel.: (303) 200-2000   DE
Web Site: https://www.csgi.com
Year Founded: 1994
CSGS—(NASDAQ)
Rev.: $1,169,258,000
Assets: $1,443,046,000
Liabilities: $1,169,720,000
Net Worth: $273,326,000
Earnings: $66,246,000
Emp.: 6,000
Fiscal Year-end: 12/31/23
Holding Company
N.A.I.C.S.: 551112
Brian A. Shepherd *(Pres & CEO)*
Hai V. Tran *(CFO & Exec VP)*
Chad Dunavant *(Chief Strategy & Product Officer)*
Rasmani Bhattacharya *(Chief Legal Officer)*
Lori J. Szwanek *(Chief Acctg Officer)*

Subsidiaries:

Ascade Middle East FZ-LLC **(1)**
Dubai Internet City Building 11 Office G-11 12 and 13, PO Box 500 463, Dubai, United Arab Emirates
Tel.: (971) 43754704
Computer Programming Services
N.A.I.C.S.: 513210

CSG Interactive Messaging, Inc. **(1)**
2525 N 117th Ave, Omaha, NE 68164
Tel.: (402) 398-4100
Sales Range: $200-249.9 Million
Interactive Messaging Services
N.A.I.C.S.: 517810

CSG International Colombia SAS **(1)**
Calle 82 10 50 Piso 5, Bogota, 805, Colombia
Tel.: (57) 16341500
Computer Programming Services
N.A.I.C.S.: 513210

CSG International DP, Inc. **(1)**
1000 Town Center Dr Ste 300, Oxnard, CA 93036
Tel.: (805) 278-7430
Computer Programming Services
N.A.I.C.S.: 513210

CSG International Pty Limited **(1)**
Ground Floor 545 Queen Street, Brisbane, 4000, QLD, Australia
Tel.: (61) 732188888
Data Processing Services
N.A.I.C.S.: 541511

CSG Systems **(1)**
1455 Broad St Ste 110, Bloomfield, NJ 07003-3039
Tel.: (973) 396-4500

Sales Range: $25-49.9 Million
Emp.: 109
Print & Electronic Customer Communications Support Services
N.A.I.C.S.: 541511

CSG Systems, Inc. **(1)**
1000 Town Center Dr Ste 300, Oxnard, CA 93036
Tel.: (888) 214-6680
Web Site: http://www.csgi.com
Rev.: $10,323,505
Emp.: 65
Direct Mail & Billing Statement Services
N.A.I.C.S.: 541860

Division (Domestic):

CSG Systems **(2)**
1000 Town Center Dr Ste 300, Oxnard, CA 93036
Tel.: (888) 214-6680
Web Site: http://www.csgi.com
Sales Range: $10-24.9 Million
Emp.: 4
Business Support Services to Generate Revenues, Maximizing Customer Values & Managing Business Efficiencies
N.A.I.C.S.: 561499

DGIT Systems Pty. Ltd. **(1)**
313 La Trobe Street, Melbourne, 3000, VIC, Australia
Tel.: (61) 38 820 5200
Web Site: https://www.dgitsystems.com
Software Services
N.A.I.C.S.: 541511
Michael Lawrey *(Chm)*
Greg Tilton *(CEO)*
Doug Nixon *(COO)*

Designgen, Comunicacao Visual, Unipessoal Lda. **(1)**
Edificio Liberdade Street Fashion Av da Liberdade 615 3 Salas 10-12, 4710-251, Braga, Portugal
Tel.: (351) 253217900
Software Development Services
N.A.I.C.S.: 541511

Forte Payment Systems, Inc. **(1)**
2121 Providence Dr Ste 151, Fort Worth, TX 76106
Tel.: (469) 675-9920
Web Site: https://www.forte.net
Payment Processing & Check Verification Requests for Banks & Financial Institutions
N.A.I.C.S.: 522210
Jeff Thorness *(CEO)*

Intec Telecom Systems Limited **(1)**
Spaces Unit 6 Albion House High Street, Albert Drive, Woking, GU21 6BG, Surrey, United Kingdom
Tel.: (44) 148 374 5800
Web Site: https://www.csgi.com
Operational Support Systems for Telecommunications Companies
N.A.I.C.S.: 561499
Fred Brott *(Pres)*

Subsidiary (Non-US):

Intec Billing Ireland **(2)**
Martin House IDA Business Park, Dangan, H91 A06C, Galway, Ireland
Tel.: (353) 91526611
Web Site: http://www.csgi.com
Sales Range: $25-49.9 Million
Emp.: 100
Operational Support Systems for Telecommunications Companies
N.A.I.C.S.: 561499

PT DGIT Indonesia **(1)**
Jl Pura Mertasari No 7 Sunset Road Abian Base, Kuta Badung, 80361, Bali, Indonesia
Tel.: (62) 361 475 2333
Computer System Design Services
N.A.I.C.S.: 541512

Tango Telecom Limited **(1)**
Walton House Lonsdale Road National Technology Park, Limerick, Ireland
Tel.: (353) 61 501900
Web Site: http://www.tangotelecom.com
Telecommunication Servicesb
N.A.I.C.S.: 517112
Jim Mountjoy *(Chm)*
Colm Ward *(CEO)*

Kieran Kelly *(CTO)*
Kay Mulqueen *(Dir-Engineering)*
Robi Axiata Ltd *(CTO)*

CSLM ACQUISITION CORP.

2400 E Commercial Blvd Ste 900, Fort Lauderdale, FL 33308
Tel.: (954) 315-9380   Ky
Web Site: https://www.cimspac.com
Year Founded: 2021
CSLM—(NASDAQ)
Rev.: $6,275,220
Assets: $52,162,898
Liabilities: $60,480,635
Net Worth: ($8,317,737)
Earnings: $4,626,782
Fiscal Year-end: 12/31/23
Investment Management Service
N.A.I.C.S.: 523999

CSP INC.

175 Cabot St Ste 210, Lowell, MA 01854
Tel.: (978) 954-5038   MA
Web Site: https://www.cspi.com
Year Founded: 1968
CSPI—(NASDAQ)
Rev.: $55,219,000
Assets: $69,436,000
Liabilities: $22,166,000
Net Worth: $47,270,000
Earnings: ($326,000)
Emp.: 111
Fiscal Year-end: 09/30/24
Peripheral Computer Equipment Designer & Mfr
N.A.I.C.S.: 541512
C. Shelton James *(Chm)*
Gary Southwell *(Gen Mgr-Cybersecurity Div)*
Michael Newbanks *(Chief Acctg Officer & VP-Fin)*
Gary W. Levine *(CFO)*

Subsidiaries:

CSP Inc. Securities Corp. **(1)**
43 Manning Rd, Billerica, MA 01821
Tel.: (978) 663-7598
Software Development Services
N.A.I.C.S.: 541511

Modcomp, Inc. **(1)**
1182 E Newport Center Dr, Deerfield Beach, FL 33442-8185
Tel.: (954) 571-4600
Web Site: http://www.cspitechsolutions.com
Process Control, Data Acquisition & System Integration Services
N.A.I.C.S.: 541512

Subsidiary (Non-US):

Modcomp, Ltd. **(2)**
12A Oaklands Business Center, Oaklands Pk, Wokingham, RG41 2FD, Berks, United Kingdom   **(100%)**
Tel.: (44) 1189893843
Web Site: http://www.modcomp.co.uk
Sales Range: $10-24.9 Million
Emp.: 15
International Computer Sales & Services
N.A.I.C.S.: 541512
Kevin Magee *(Gen Mgr)*

Myricom, Inc. **(1)**
3871 E Colorado Blvd Ste 101, Pasadena, CA 91107
Tel.: (626) 821-5555
Web Site: http://ww.myricom.com
Sales Range: $25-49.9 Million
Emp.: 50
Computer Processors Mfr
N.A.I.C.S.: 334118
Michele Merrell *(VP-Global Mktg & Comm)*
Dennis Chan *(Dir-Production)*

CSW INDUSTRIALS, INC.

5420 Lyndon B Johnson Fwy Ste 500, Dallas, TX 75240
Tel.: (214) 884-3777   DE
Web Site:
https://www.cswindustrials.com

Year Founded: 2014
CSWI—(NASDAQ)
Rev.: $792,840,000
Assets: $1,043,326,000
Liabilities: $427,603,000
Net Worth: $615,723,000
Earnings: $102,539,000
Emp.: 2,600
Fiscal Year-end: 03/31/24
Holding Company
N.A.I.C.S.: 551112
Joseph Brooks Armes *(Chm, Pres & CEO)*
Luke E. Alverson *(Sec, Sr VP & Gen Counsel)*
Don J. Sullivan *(Exec VP & Gen Mgr-Industrial Products)*
Adrianne D. Griffin *(Treas & VP-IR)*
James E. Perry *(CFO & Exec VP)*
Danielle R. Garde *(Chief People Officer & Sr VP)*

Subsidiaries:

Balco, Inc. **(1)**
410 E 37th St N Ste A, Wichita, KS 67219
Tel.: (316) 945-9328
Web Site: https://www.balcousa.com
Injection Mold Product Mfr
N.A.I.C.S.: 333248
Ronnie Leonard *(Pres & CEO)*
John Harder *(VP-Ops)*
Steve Cooper *(VP)*

Greco Aluminum Railings (U.S.A.) Inc. **(1)**
9410 Eden Ave, Hudson, FL 34667
Tel.: (727) 372-1100
Web Site: https://www.grecorailings.com
Architectural Railing & Metal Product Mfr
N.A.I.C.S.: 332323
Tyler Kelshaw *(Sls Mgr)*

Greco Aluminum Railings, Ltd. **(1)**
3255 Wyandotte St East, Windsor, N8Y 1E9, ON, Canada
Tel.: (519) 966-4210
Architectural Railing & Metal Product Mfr
N.A.I.C.S.: 332323

Jet-Lube of Canada Ltd. **(1)**
Units 8 9 1260-34 Avenue, Nisku, T9E 1K7, AB, Canada
Tel.: (780) 463-7441
Drilling Compound Mfr
N.A.I.C.S.: 325998

RectorSeal Australia Proprietary Limited **(1)**
Tel.: (61) 1300772878
Web Site: https://www.rectorseal.com.au
Heating & Air Conditioning Equipment Maintenance & Repair Services
N.A.I.C.S.: 238220
Craig Bicket *(Gen Mgr)*

RectorSeal LLC **(1)**
2601 Spenwick Dr, Houston, TX 77055
Tel.: (713) 263-8001
Web Site: https://rectorseal.com
Sales Range: $50-74.9 Million
Sealant Whslr
N.A.I.C.S.: 424690
Angela Kohl *(VP)*
Dallas Mabry *(Sr VP)*
Dave Blood *(Sr VP)*
Jeff Underwood *(Sr VP)*
Marshall Blackham *(VP)*
Tom Fluker *(VP)*
Travis Weirich *(VP)*

Subsidiary (Domestic):

Dust Free, LP **(2)**
1112 Industrial Dr, Royse City, TX 75189
Tel.: (972) 635-9564
Web Site: http://www.dustfree.com
Sales Range: $1-9.9 Million
Emp.: 45
Mfg Blowers/Fans
N.A.I.C.S.: 333413

Sure-Seal LLC **(2)**
1628 S Mildred St Ste 205, Tacoma, WA 98465-1629

CSW Industrials, Inc.—(Continued)

Tel.: (253) 564-0624
Web Site: http://www.thesureseal.com
Waterless Floor Drain Trap Seals Mfr &
Distr
N.A.I.C.S.: 339991

TA Industries Inc. (2)
11130 Bloomfield Ave, Santa Fe Springs,
CA 90670
Tel.: (562) 466-1000
Web Site: http://www.truaire.com
Miscellaneous General Purpose Machinery
Mfr
N.A.I.C.S.: 333998
Ken Grubbs *(VP-Sls)*

Shoemaker Manufacturing, Co. (1)
618 E 1st St, Cle Elum, WA 98922
Tel.: (509) 674-4414
Web Site: https://www.shoemakermfg.com
Ornamental & Architectural Metal Work Mfr
N.A.I.C.S.: 332323
Jerry Hein *(Pres)*
Claire Nicholls *(VP)*

Smoke Guard, Inc. (1)
287 N Maple Grove Rd, Boise, ID 83704
Tel.: (208) 850-1618
Web Site: https://www.smokeguard.com
Fire Protection Product Mfr
N.A.I.C.S.: 334290

**The Whitmore Manufacturing
Company** (1)
930 Whitmore Dr, Rockwall, TX 75087
Tel.: (972) 771-1000
Web Site: https://www.whitmores.com
Lubricants, Coatings & Sealants Mfr
N.A.I.C.S.: 325510

Subsidiary (Domestic):

Strathmore Products Inc. (2)
1970 W Fayette St, Syracuse, NY 13204
Tel.: (315) 488-5401
Web Site:
   http://www.strathmoreproducts.com
Paints & Paint Additives
N.A.I.C.S.: 325510

Whitmore Europe Limited (1)
Unit 9 Foster Avenue, Woodside Park In-
dustrial Estate, Dunstable, LU5 5TA, Bed-
fordshire, United Kingdom
Tel.: (44) 1707379870
Automotive Lubricant Product Mfr
N.A.I.C.S.: 324191
Sean Harsent *(Dir-Ops)*

CSX CORPORATION

500 Water St 15th Fl, Jacksonville,
FL 32202
Tel.: (904) 359-3200   **VA**
Web Site: https://www.csx.com
Year Founded: 1980
CSX—(NASDAQ)
Rev.: $14,657,000,000
Assets: $42,408,000,000
Liabilities: $30,275,000,000
Net Worth: $12,133,000,000
Earnings: $3,715,000,000
Emp.: 23,000
Fiscal Year-end: 12/31/23
Holding Company; Line-Haul Railroad
& Intermodal Freight Transportation
Operations
N.A.I.C.S.: 551112
Joseph R. Hinrichs *(Pres & CEO)*
Michael A. Cory *(COO & Exec VP)*
Nathan D. Goldman *(Chief Legal Offi-
cer, Sec & Exec VP)*
Diana B. Sorfleet *(Chief Admin Offi-
cer & Exec VP)*
Paul C. Hilal *(Vice Chm)*
Angela C. Williams *(Chief Acctg Offi-
cer & VP)*
Kevin S. Boone *(Chief Comml Officer
& Exec VP)*
Sean R. Pelkey *(CFO & Exec VP)*
Casey Albright *(Sr VP-Network Ops &
Svc Design)*
Ricky Johnson *(Sr VP-Ops)*

Joseph R. Hinrichs *(Pres & CEO)*
Stephen Fortune *(CTO, Chief Digital
Officer & Exec VP)*

Subsidiaries:

CSX Intermodal, Inc. (1)
500 Water St, Jacksonville, FL
32202   **(100%)**
Tel.: (904) 633-1000
Web Site: http://www.csxi.com
Sales Range: $100-124.9 Million
Emp.: 200
Transcontinental Intermodal Transportation
N.A.I.C.S.: 484230

CSX Real Property Inc. (1)
301 W Bay St Ste 800, Jacksonville, FL
32202
Tel.: (904) 633-4500
Web Site: http://www.csx.com
Sales Range: $400-449.9 Million
Emp.: 61
Real Estate Services
N.A.I.C.S.: 482111

CSX Transportation, Inc. (1)
500 Water St, Jacksonville, FL
32202-4423   **(100%)**
Tel.: (904) 359-3100
Web Site: http://www.csx.com
Sales Range: $5-14.9 Billion
Freight Transportation Services
N.A.I.C.S.: 488510

Subsidiary (Domestic):

**Allegheny & Western Railway
Co.** (2)
500 Water St, Jacksonville, FL 32202-4420
Tel.: (904) 359-3100
Railroad Freight Shipment Services
N.A.I.C.S.: 488210
Jerry A. Davis *(Pres)*
Patricia Aftoora *(Sec)*

Dayton & Michigan Railroad Co. (2)
500 Water St, Jacksonville, FL 32202
Tel.: (904) 359-3100
Freight Transportation Services
N.A.I.C.S.: 488510
Michael A. Ward *(Chm, Pres & CEO)*
Oscar Munoz *(Exec VP)*

Conrail Inc. (1)
1717 Arch St 13th Fl, Philadelphia, PA
19103   **(50%)**
Tel.: (215) 209-2000
Web Site: http://www.conrail.com
Sales Range: $1-4.9 Billion
Emp.: 22,000
Holding Company; Line Haul Railroad Op-
erator
N.A.I.C.S.: 551112
Joseph D. Soto *(Gen Mgr-Field Ops)*
Rodney Gordon *(Gen Mgr-Svc Delivery)*
Anthony D. Carlini *(Treas & VP-Fin & IT)*
Jocelyn Gabrynowicz Hill *(Gen Counsel &
Sec)*
Eric B. Levin *(VP-Engrg, Mechanical & Real
Estate)*
Brian Gorton *(Pres & COO)*

Affiliate (Domestic):

Albany Port Railroad Co. (2)
101 Raft St, Albany, NY 12202   **(50%)**
Tel.: (518) 463-8679
Rev.: $1,029,000
Emp.: 11
Railroad; Switching & Terminal Company
N.A.I.C.S.: 488210

Subsidiary (Domestic):

CRC Properties Inc. (2)
1717 Arch St 13th Fl, Philadelphia, PA
19103
Tel.: (215) 209-2000
Web Site: http://www.conrail.com
Rev.: $6,049,000
Own & Lease Real Estate
N.A.I.C.S.: 482111

CRR Industries, Inc. (2)
2001 Market St 16th Fl, Philadelphia, PA
19103
Tel.: (215) 209-5000
Sales Range: $75-99.9 Million
Investment Holding Company
N.A.I.C.S.: 488510

CRR Investments, Inc. (2)
1000 Howard Blvd 4th Fl, Mount Laurel, NJ
08054   **(100%)**
Tel.: (856) 231-7224
Web Site: http://www.conrail.com
Rev.: $65,019,000
Cash Management Company
N.A.I.C.S.: 238220

Consolidated Rail Corporation (2)
330 Fellowship Rd Ste 300, Mount Laurel,
NJ 08054   **(100%)**
Tel.: (856) 231-6401
Web Site: http://www.conrail.com
Sales Range: $100-124.9 Million
Line Haul Railroad Operator
N.A.I.C.S.: 482111

Indiana Harbor Belt Railroad Co. (2)
2721 161st St, Hammond, IN 46323
Tel.: (219) 989-4703
Web Site: http://www.ihbrr.com
Rev.: $72,417,000
Emp.: 728
Railroads; Switching & Terminal Company
N.A.I.C.S.: 488210
Steve Denby *(Mgr-Accounting & Treas)*
Leo Pauwels *(Dir-Sls & Industrial Dev)*
Paula Wratten *(Mgr)*
James Gidney *(Superintendent)*
Michael Kapitan *(Mgr-Risk Management)*
Patrick McShane *(Asst Dir-Business Devel-
opment)*
Michael Schroeter *(Mgr-Customer Service)*
Dawn Geeve *(Mgr-Car Mgmt-Demurrage)*
John Wright *(Gen Mgr)*
Darrell Snyder *(Gen Dir-Mechanical & En-
grg)*
Joel Cornfeld *(Gen Counsel)*
Donald Bolster *(Dir-Safety)*
Dan Kelley *(Dir-Human Resources)*
Nicole Moore Parchem *(Dir-HR & Labor
Rels)*
Tammy Winterfeldt *(Dir-Customer Service)*
Jim Wilson *(Comptroller)*
Tony Kazakevicius *(Asst Dir-Business De-
velopment)*
Richard Katterman *(Asst Mgr)*
Matthew Peagler *(Dir-Customer Service)*
Michael Pavlopoulos *(Mgr-Customer Ser-
vice)*
Eric Ritter *(Dir-Safety)*
Cindy Morley *(Mgr-Accounting & Treas)*
Joshua Sanchez *(Dir-Risk Management)*
James Pecyna *(Sr Mgr-Labor Relations)*

**Penn Central Communications
Corp.** (2)
2001 Market St, Philadelphia, PA
19103-7044   **(100%)**
Tel.: (215) 209-5000
Sales Range: $400-449.9 Million
Repository for Radio & Communication Li-
censing
N.A.I.C.S.: 482111

Affiliate (Domestic):

**Peoria & Pekin Union Railway
Co.** (2)
301 Wesley Rd, Creve Coeur, IL 61610
Tel.: (802) 527-3499
Rev.: $13,030,000
Emp.: 99
Railroad; Switching & Terminal Company
N.A.I.C.S.: 488210

Pan Am Railways, Inc. (1)
1700 Iron Horse Park, North Billerica, MA
01862
Tel.: (978) 663-1065
Web Site: http://www.panamrailways.com
Freight Services
N.A.I.C.S.: 482111
Eric Lawler *(CFO & Sr VP)*
Michael Bostwick *(Chief Commercial Officer
& Exec VP)*
Jeff Turner *(Dir-Sls & Intermodal)*
Michael Clements *(VP-Mktg & Strategic
Planning)*
Ted Krug *(Chief Engr-Design & Construc-
tion)*
Peter Cooper *(CEO)*
Nicholas Brickley *(Dir-Manpower)*
Tim Doherty *(Sr Dir-Industrial Dev)*

**Total Distribution Services, Inc.
(TDSI)** (1)
500 Water St J980, Jacksonville, FL 32202

Tel.: (904) 783-4481
Web Site: http://www.csx.com
Vehicle Logistics & Customer Service
N.A.I.C.S.: 493190
Greg Stephens *(Dir)*

Transflo Corporation (1)
3796 Warrington St, Jacksonville, FL 32254
Tel.: (904) 332-3745
Web Site: https://www.transflo.net
Sales Range: $75-99.9 Million
Emp.: 32
Multi-modal Transloading, Materials Man-
agement & Logistics
N.A.I.C.S.: 484121

CTO REALTY GROWTH, INC.

369 N New York Ave Ste 201, Winter
Park, FL 32789
Tel.: (386) 274-2202   **FL**
Web Site: https://www.ctoreit.com
Year Founded: 1902
CTO—(NYSE)
Rev.: $109,119,000
Assets: $989,668,000
Liabilities: $532,142,000
Net Worth: $457,526,000
Earnings: $758,000
Emp.: 33
Fiscal Year-end: 12/31/23
Real Estate, Income Properties &
Golf Operations
N.A.I.C.S.: 531390
Philip R. Mays *(CFO, Treas & Sr VP)*
George R. Brokaw *(Vice Chm)*
Laura M. Franklin *(Chm)*
Lisa M. Vorakoun *(Chief Acctg Officer
& Sr VP)*
John P. Albright *(Pres & CEO)*

Subsidiaries:

Indigo Development Inc. (1)
1530 Cornerstone Blvd Ste 100, Daytona
Beach, FL 32117   **(100%)**
Tel.: (386) 274-2202
Web Site: https://www.indigodev.com
Sales Range: $1-9.9 Million
Sale & Development of Land
N.A.I.C.S.: 237210

Indigo Group Inc. (1)
1530 Cornerstone Blvd Ste 100, Daytona
Beach, FL 32117   **(100%)**
Tel.: (386) 274-2202
Web Site: https://www.ctlc.com
Sales Range: $1-9.9 Million
Development & Sale of Commercial Real
Estate
N.A.I.C.S.: 237210

Indigo International Inc. (1)
1000 Champions Dr, Daytona Beach, FL
32124   **(100%)**
Tel.: (386) 523-2040
Web Site:
   http://www.consolidatedtomoka.com
Sales Range: $1-9.9 Million
Golf Operations
N.A.I.C.S.: 713910
Gary Moothart *(Controller)*

CTR INVESTMENTS & CON-
SULTING, INC.

1003 10 Mile Rd NW, Sparta, MI
49345
Tel.: (843) 424-8146   **NV**
Year Founded: 1999
CIVX—(OTCIQ)
Information Technology Services
N.A.I.C.S.: 541990
Cavan Christian Carlson *(Pres)*

CTS CORPORATION

4925 Indiana Ave, Lisle, IL 60532
Tel.: (630) 577-8800   **IN**
Web Site: https://www.ctscorp.com
Year Founded: 1896
CTS—(NYSE)
Rev.: $586,869,000

Assets: $748,487,000
Liabilities: $242,263,000
Net Worth: $506,224,000
Earnings: $59,575,000
Emp.: 4,209
Fiscal Year-end: 12/31/22
Electronic Components Designer, Mfr & Distr
N.A.I.C.S.: 334419
Kieran M. O'Sullivan *(Chm, Pres & CEO)*
Thomas M. White *(Principal Acctg Officer)*
Martin Baumeister *(Sr VP)*
Doug Ford *(VP-Corporate Development & Marketing)*
Ashish Agrawal *(CFO, Principal Acctg Officer & VP)*

Subsidiaries:

CTS (Tianjin) Electronics Company Ltd.   (1)
No 1 Muning Road Teda, Tianjin, 300457, China
Tel.: (86) 2265201810
Web Site: http://www.ctscorp.com
Electronic Components Distr
N.A.I.C.S.: 423610

CTS Automotive   (1)
Business Unit 1100 Roosevelt St, Brownsville, TX 78521   **(100%)**
Tel.: (956) 542-6897
Web Site: http://www.ctscorp.com
Sales Range: $10-24.9 Million
Emp.: 8
Mfr of Electronic Components
N.A.I.C.S.: 334416

CTS Automotive, L.L.C.   (1)
1142 West Beardsley Ave, Elkhart, IL 46514
Tel.: (574) 295-3575
Emp.: 150
Electronic Components Mfr
N.A.I.C.S.: 334419

CTS Corporation - Automotive Products   (1)
1142 W Beardsley Ave, Elkhart, IN 46514-2224   **(100%)**
Tel.: (574) 295-3575
Web Site: http://www.ctscorp.com
Sales Range: $150-199.9 Million
Emp.: 387
Motor Vehicle Electronic Components Mfr
N.A.I.C.S.: 336320

CTS Corporation U.K. Ltd.   (1)
13 Queens Road, Aberdeen, AB15 4YL, United Kingdom
Tel.: (44) 1698505050
Web Site: http://www.ctscorp.com
Electronic Components Distr
N.A.I.C.S.: 423610

CTS Electronic Components   (1)
2375 Cabot Dr, Lisle, IL 60532-3631   **(100%)**
Tel.: (630) 577-8865
Web Site: http://www.ctscorp.com
Sales Range: $10-24.9 Million
Emp.: 53
Quartz Crystals & Crystal Oscillators Clocks Mfr
N.A.I.C.S.: 517112

CTS Electronic Components, Inc.   (1)
2375 Cabot Dr, Lisle, IL 60532   **(100%)**
Tel.: (630) 577-8800
Web Site: http://www.ctscorp.com
Sales Range: $25-49.9 Million
Emp.: 50
Mfr of Wireless Electronic Components & Assemblies
N.A.I.C.S.: 334310

CTS Electronic Components, Inc.   (1)
4800 Alameda Blvd NE, Albuquerque, NM 87113   **(100%)**
Tel.: (505) 346-3329
Web Site: http://www.ctscorp.com
Wireless Electronic Components Mfr
N.A.I.C.S.: 334310
William Cahill *(VP)*

CTS India Private Limited   (1)
Plot No 70 Sector 3 IMT Manesar, Gurgaon, 122050, Haryana, India
Tel.: (91) 8813876933
Web Site: http://www.ctscorp.com
Electric Component Whslr
N.A.I.C.S.: 423610

CTS Japan, Inc.   (1)
TVP Building 2 Floor 3-9-13 Moriya-Cho, Kanagawa-ku, Yokohama, 221-0022, Kanagawa, Japan
Tel.: (81) 454502363
Web Site: http://www.ctscrop.com
Electronic Components Distr
N.A.I.C.S.: 423610
Ichiio Osawa *(Dir Gen)*

CTS Singapore Pte., Ltd.   (1)
6 Serangoon North Ave 5 Ste 04-09, Singapore, 554910, Singapore
Tel.: (65) 65517551
Electronic Components Distr
N.A.I.C.S.: 423610

CTS Valpey Corporation   (1)
75 S St, Hopkinton, MA 01748-2204
Tel.: (508) 435-6831
Web Site: http://www.ctscorp.com
Electronic Components Mfr
N.A.I.C.S.: 334419

CTS of Canada Co.   (1)
80 Thomas St, Mississauga, L5M 1Y9, ON, Canada
Tel.: (905) 826-1141
Electric Component Whslr
N.A.I.C.S.: 423610

CTS of Canada, Ltd.   (1)
80 Thomas St, Streetsville, L5M 1Y9, ON, Canada   **(100%)**
Tel.: (905) 826-1141
Web Site: http://www.ctscorp.com
Sales Range: $100-124.9 Million
Emp.: 250
Mfr of Automotive Sensors & Actuators
N.A.I.C.S.: 333995

Filter Sensing Technologies, Inc.   (1)
7 Bow St, Malden, MA 02148
Tel.: (617) 379-7330
Web Site: http://www.fstcorporation.com
Electric Component Whslr
N.A.I.C.S.: 423610

International Electronic Research Corp.   (1)
413 N Moss St, Burbank, CA 91502   **(100%)**
Tel.: (818) 842-7277
Web Site: http://www.anemostat.com
Sales Range: $10-24.9 Million
Emp.: 28
Electronic Components Mfr
N.A.I.C.S.: 334419

Noliac AS   (1)
Hejreskovvej 18B, 3490, Kvistgaard, Denmark
Tel.: (45) 49125030
Web Site: http://www.noliac.com
Emp.: 100
Piezoelectric Product Mfr
N.A.I.C.S.: 334419

Quality Thermistor, Inc.   (1)
2108 Century Way, Boise, ID 83709
Tel.: (208) 377-3373
Web Site: https://www.qtisensing.com
Instruments & Related Products Manufacturing for Measuring, Displaying & Controlling Industrial Process Variables
N.A.I.C.S.: 334513

Sensor Scientific, Inc.   (1)
6 Kingsbridge Rd, Fairfield, NJ 07004
Tel.: (973) 227-7790
Web Site: https://www.sensorsci.com
Measuring and Controlling Devices, Nec, N
N.A.I.C.S.: 334513
Bob Brinley *(Pres)*

SyQwest, LLC   (1)
30 Kenney Dr, Cranston, RI 02920
Tel.: (401) 921-5170
Web Site: http://www.syqwestinc.com
Rev.: $1,000,000
Emp.: 9
Hazardous Waste Collection
N.A.I.C.S.: 562112

Robert Tarini *(CEO)*
Michael Curran *(Pres)*

Technologia Mexicana S.A. de C.V.   (1)
Ave Instituto Tecnologico Suite 298, 84065, Nogales, Sonora, Mexico
Tel.: (52) 3132614
Electric Component Whslr
N.A.I.C.S.: 423610

Tusonix Inc.   (1)
7741 N Business Park Dr, Tucson, AZ 85743
Tel.: (520) 744-0400
Web Site: http://www.tusonix.com
Sales Range: $25-49.9 Million
Emp.: 120
Electronic Component Designer Mfr
N.A.I.C.S.: 334419

iFire Group Ltd.   (1)
1400 Cornwall Road Unit 5, Oakville, M9W 5A5, ON, Canada   **(97.5%)**
Tel.: (905) 491-6855
Web Site: http://www.ifire.com
Sales Range: $50-74.9 Million
Emp.: 160
Electronics Mfr
N.A.I.C.S.: 423620

CTT PHARMACEUTICAL HOLDINGS INC.
3853 Northdale Blvd Ste 268, Tampa, FL 33624
Tel.: (604) 312-6874   DE
Web Site:
   http://www.cttpharmaceuticals.com
Year Founded: 1996
CTTH—(OTCIQ)
Liabilities: $19,000
Net Worth: ($19,000)
Earnings: ($35,000)
Emp.: 2
Fiscal Year-end: 12/31/23
Investment Services
N.A.I.C.S.: 523999
Pankaj Modi *(CEO & Chief Science Officer)*

CTX VIRTUAL TECHNOLOGIES, INC.
2385 NW Executive Centre Dr Ste 100, Boca Raton, FL 33431
Tel.: (702) 851-5808   DE
Web Site:
   https://www.ctxtechnologies.com
Year Founded: 2004
CTXV—(OTCIQ)
Sales Range: $100-124.9 Million
Mobile Telecommunication Equipment Mfr
N.A.I.C.S.: 334220
Saad Medleg *(Chm)*
Stephen Lee *(VP & Gen Mgr-Mfg)*
David Lithwick *(CTO)*
D. S. Moon *(Dir-Fin)*
Jason Yu *(VP)*

CUBA BEVERAGE COMPANY
PO Box 121089, San Diego, CA 92112
Tel.: (866) 431-2822
Web Site: http://www.cubabev.com
CUBV—(OTCIQ)
Sales Range: Less than $1 Million
Herbal Energy Juice Mfr
N.A.I.C.S.: 311999
Alex C. Procopio *(Pres & Sec)*

CUBESMART
5 Old Lancaster Rd, Malvern, PA 19355
Tel.: (610) 535-5000   MD
Web Site:
   https://www.cubesmart.com
Year Founded: 2004
CUBE—(NYSE)
Rev.: $1,050,334,000
Assets: $6,225,020,000

Liabilities: $3,404,488,000
Net Worth: $2,820,532,000
Earnings: $410,757,000
Emp.: 3,040
Fiscal Year-end: 12/31/23
Self-Storage Facilities; Real Estate Investment Trust
N.A.I.C.S.: 525990
Christopher P. Marr *(Pres & CEO)*
Timothy M. Martin *(CFO)*
Joel D. Keaton *(COO)*
Matthew DeNarie *(Chief Acctg Officer & Sr VP)*
Jennifer Schulte *(Chief HR Officer)*

Subsidiaries:

12902 South 301 Highway, LLC   (1)
5 Old Lancaster Rd, Malvern, PA 19355
Tel.: (813) 556-6900
Self Storage Facility Services
N.A.I.C.S.: 531130

2701 S. Congress Avenue, LLC   (1)
2701 S Congress Ave, Austin, TX 78704
Tel.: (512) 410-2703
Self Storage Facility Services
N.A.I.C.S.: 531130

4211 Bellaire Blvd., LLC   (1)
4211 Bellaire Blvd, Houston, TX 77025
Tel.: (832) 356-3633
Self Storage Facility Services
N.A.I.C.S.: 531130

4370 Fountain Hills Drive NE, LLC   (1)
4370 Fountain Hills Dr NE, Prior Lake, MN 55372
Tel.: (612) 439-0010
Self Storage Facility Services
N.A.I.C.S.: 531130

500 Mildred Avenue Primos, LLC   (1)
500 Mildred Ave, Clifton Heights, PA 19018
Tel.: (610) 713-5380
Self Storage Facility Services
N.A.I.C.S.: 531130

5700 Washington Avenue, LLC   (1)
5700 Washington Ave, Houston, TX 77007
Tel.: (713) 861-6004
Self Storage Facility Services
N.A.I.C.S.: 531130

5715 Burnet Road, LLC   (1)
5715 Burnet Rd, Austin, TX 78756
Tel.: (512) 206-3139
Self Storage Facility Services
N.A.I.C.S.: 531130

610 Sawdust Road, LLC   (1)
610 Sawdust Rd, Spring, TX 77380
Tel.: (281) 882-3848
Self Storage Facility Services
N.A.I.C.S.: 531130

CubeSmart Alexandria, LLC   (1)
4650 Eisenhower Ave, Alexandria, VA 22304
Tel.: (703) 751-8100
Real Estate Asset Management Services
N.A.I.C.S.: 531390

CubeSmart Wilton, LLC   (1)
111 Danbury Rd, Wilton, CT 06897
Tel.: (203) 834-5033
Web Site: http://www.cubesmart.com
Emp.: 3
Real Estate Investment Services
N.A.I.C.S.: 525990

CubeSmart, L.P.   (1)
5 Old Lancaster Rd, Malvern, PA 19355
Tel.: (610) 535-5000
Web Site: https://www.cubesmart.com
Rev.: $1,009,623,999
Assets: $6,325,829,999
Liabilities: $3,485,448,999
Net Worth: $2,840,380,999
Earnings: $293,194,000
Emp.: 2,803
Fiscal Year-end: 12/31/2022
Real Estate Manangement Services
N.A.I.C.S.: 531210

Fontana Self Storage TRS, LLC   (1)
10533 Beech Ave, Fontana, CA 92337
Tel.: (909) 350-3500

CubeSmart—(Continued)

Web Site:
https://www.fontanaselfstorage.com
Convenient Storage Facility Services
N.A.I.C.S.: 531130

LAACO, Ltd. (1)
431 W 7th St, Los Angeles, CA 90014-1601
Tel.: (213) 622-1254
Membership Sports & Recreation Clubs
N.A.I.C.S.: 713940
Karen Hathaway (Pres & Mng Partner)
Bill Odell (Controller)
Bryan Cusworth (CFO)
Charles Michaels (Gen Counsel)
Carla Grose (VP-Storage Admin)
Don McLaurin (Mgr-Payroll)
Fred Zepeda (VP)
Joan Valencia (Coord-Membership)
Robert School (Mgr-Computer & Network)

U-Store-It Mini Warehouse Co. (1)
6801 Engle Rd, Middleburg, OH 44130-7993
Tel.: (440) 325-4384
Sales Range: $150-199.9 Million
General Warehousing & Self-Storage Services
N.A.I.C.S.: 493110
Christopher P. Marr (Pres, COO & Chief Investment Officer)

CUE BIOPHARMA, INC.
40 Guest St, Boston, MA 02135
Tel.: (617) 949-2680   DE
Web Site:
https://www.cuebiopharma.com
Year Founded: 2014
CUE—(NASDAQ)
Rev.: $1,245,227
Assets: $91,283,452
Liabilities: $25,600,877
Net Worth: $65,682,575
Earnings: ($53,010,382)
Emp.: 51
Fiscal Year-end: 12/31/22
Research & Development in Biotechnology (except Nanobiotechnology)
N.A.I.C.S.: 541714
Kenneth Pienta (Chief Medical Officer-Acting)
Rodolfo J. Chaparro (Co-Founder)
Colin Sandercock (Gen Counsel & Sr VP)
Kerri-Ann Millar (CFO)
Anish Suri (Pres & Chief Scientific Officer)
Steven Almo (Co-Founder)
Marie Campinel (Sr Dir-Corp Comm)
Ronald D. Seidel III (Co-Founder)
Patricia Nasshorn (Chief Bus Officer)
Daniel R. Passeri (CEO)

CUE HEALTH INC.
4980 Carroll Canyon Rd Ste 100, San Diego, CA 92121
Tel.: (858) 412-8151   DE
Web Site: https://www.cuehealth.com
Year Founded: 2010
HLTH—(NASDAQ)
Rev.: $483,476,000
Assets: $694,580,000
Liabilities: $118,086,000
Net Worth: $576,494,000
Earnings: ($194,056,000)
Emp.: 1,515
Fiscal Year-end: 12/31/22
Medical Diagnostic Product Mfr
N.A.I.C.S.: 334510
Randall E. Pollard (Chief Acctg Officer, Interim Principal Fin Officer & Controller)
Ayub Khattak (Co-Founder)
Clint Sever (Co-Founder & CEO)
David Arida (COO)
Andy Hudak (VP-Program Mgmt)
Erica Palsis (Gen Counsel & Sec)
Elizabeth Swanson (VP-People & Culture)

Glenn Wada (Chief Comml Officer)
David Tsay (Chief Medical Officer)
Chris Achar (Chief Bus Officer)

CUENTAS INC.
19 W. Flagler St Ste 902, Miami, FL 33130   FL
Web Site: http://www.cuentas.com
Year Founded: 2005
CUEN—(NASDAQ)
Rev.: $2,994,000
Assets: $1,499,000
Liabilities: $2,223,000
Net Worth: ($724,000)
Earnings: ($14,531,000)
Emp.: 3
Fiscal Year-end: 12/31/22
Digital Banking Services
N.A.I.C.S.: 523150
Shlomo Zakai (CFO)
Arik Maimon (Co-Founder & Chm)
Adiv Baruch (Chief Strategy Officer)
Michael A. De Prado (Co-Founder, Vice Chm & Pres)

Subsidiaries:

Accent Intermedia, LLC (1)
300 Missouri Ave, Jeffersonville, IN 47130
Tel.: (812) 206-2475
Web Site: http://www.accentintermedia.com
Commercial Flexographic Printing
N.A.I.C.S.: 323111

CUISINE SOLUTIONS, INC.
4106 Wheeler Ave, Alexandria, VA 22304
Tel.: (703) 270-2900   DE
Web Site:
https://www.cuisinesolutions.com
Year Founded: 1972
CUSI—(OTCIQ)
Sales Range: $75-99.9 Million
Emp.: 347
Frozen Specialty Food Manufacturing
N.A.I.C.S.: 311412
Thomas Donohoe (CMO)

Subsidiaries:

Cuisine Solutions France (1)
Ecopard Dheudebouville 1 Allee Des Tilleuls, 27400, Louviers, France   (100%)
Tel.: (33) 232250606
Web Site: http://www.cusinesolutions.com.fr
Sales Range: $50-74.9 Million
Emp.: 50
Mfr of Prepared Foods
N.A.I.C.S.: 311991
Plat Christian (Mng Dir)

CULLEN/FROST BANKERS, INC.
Tel.: (210) 220-4011   TX
Web Site: https://www.frostbank.com
Year Founded: 1977
CFR—(NYSE)
Rev.: $2,646,258,000
Assets: $50,845,038,000
Liabilities: $47,128,591,000
Net Worth: $3,716,447,000
Earnings: $591,298,000
Emp.: 5,495
Fiscal Year-end: 12/31/23
Bank Holding Company
N.A.I.C.S.: 551111
Phillip D. Green (Chm & CEO)
Paul H. Bracher (Pres)
Robert A. Berman (Exec VP-Res & Strategy-Frost Bank)
Kenneth L. Wilson (Chief Wealth Officer & Exec VP)
A. B. Mendez (Dir-Investor Relations)
Coolidge E. Rhodes Jr. (Sec, Exec VP & Gen Counsel)

Subsidiaries:

Frost Bank (1)
111 W Houston St Ste 100, San Antonio, TX 78205   (100%)

Tel.: (210) 220-4011
Web Site: http://www.frostbank.com
Sales Range: $900-999.9 Million
Commercial Banking
N.A.I.C.S.: 522110
Phillip D. Green (Chm & CEO)
Paul H. Bracher (Chief Banking Officer)
Robert A. Berman (Exec VP-Res & Strategy-Grp)
William L. Perotti (Exec VP-Grp)
Annette Alonzo (Chief HR Officer & Exec VP)
Carol Severyn (Chief Risk Officer & Exec VP)
Jimmy Stead (Chief Consumer Banking Officer & Exec VP)
Candace Wolfshohl (Exec VP-Culture & People Dev)

Subsidiary (Domestic):

Frost Brokerage Services, Inc. (2)
100 W Houston St Ste 100, San Antonio, TX 78205-1400
Tel.: (210) 220-5000
Web Site: http://www.frostbank.com
Sales Range: $50-74.9 Million
Emp.: 100
Securities Brokerage Services
N.A.I.C.S.: 523150
Karen Banks (Pres)

Unit (Domestic):

Frost HR Consulting (2)
5555 San Felipe St Ste 850, Houston, TX 77056
Tel.: (713) 622-3330
Web Site: http://www.frostbank.com
Sales Range: $1-9.9 Million
Emp.: 20
Human Resources Consulting & Outsourcing Services
N.A.I.C.S.: 541612

Subsidiary (Domestic):

Tri-Frost Corporation (2)
100 W Houston St, San Antonio, TX 78205
Tel.: (210) 220-4841
Web Site: http://www.frostbank.com
Sales Range: $600-649.9 Million
Emp.: 2,000
Financial Management Services
N.A.I.C.S.: 523999

Frost Securities, Inc. (1)
2950 N Harwood St Ste 1000, Dallas, TX 78201
Tel.: (214) 515-4435
Investment Banking & Securities Dealing
N.A.I.C.S.: 523150
C. Brian Coad (Co-Founder)

CULLINAN THERAPEUTICS
1 Main St Ste 1350, Cambridge, MA 02142
Tel.: (617) 410-4650   DE
Web Site:
https://cullinantherapeutics.com
Year Founded: 2016
CGEM—(NASDAQ)
Rev.: $6,611,000
Assets: $561,117,000
Liabilities: $26,088,000
Net Worth: $535,029,000
Earnings: $111,214,000
Emp.: 62
Fiscal Year-end: 12/31/22
Oncology Therapeutics
N.A.I.C.S.: 541714
Jeffrey Jones (Chief Medical Officer)
Owen Patrick Hughes Jr. (Co-Founder)
Mary Kay Fenton (CFO & Principal Acctg Officer)
Ansbert K. Gadicke (Chm)
Patrick A. Baeuerle (Co-Founder)
Jennifer Michaelson (Chief Dev Officer-Biologics)
Corinne Savill (Chief Bus Officer-Interim)
Leigh Zawel (Chief Scientific Officer-Small Molecules)
Jacquelyn Sumer (Chief Legal Officer)

CULLMAN BANCORP, INC.
316 2nd Ave SW, Cullman, AL 35055
Tel.: (256) 734-1740
Web Site:
https://www.cullmansavings bank.com
CULL—(NASDAQ)
Rev.: $18,215,000
Assets: $423,229,000
Liabilities: $323,047,000
Net Worth: $100,182,000
Earnings: $4,183,000
Emp.: 59
Fiscal Year-end: 12/31/22
Bank Holding Company
N.A.I.C.S.: 551111
Robin Parson (COO & Exec VP)
Katrina Stephens (CFO & Sr VP)
John A. Riley III (Chm, Pres & CEO)

Subsidiaries:

Cullman Savings Bank (1)
316 2nd Ave SW, Cullman, AL 35055
Tel.: (256) 734-1740
Web Site:
https://www.cullmansavingsbank.com
Sales Range: $100-124.9 Million
Banking Services
N.A.I.C.S.: 522110
John A. Riley III (Pres & CEO)

CULP, INC.
1823 Echester Dr, High Point, NC 27265
Tel.: (336) 889-5161   NC
Web Site: https://www.culp.com
Year Founded: 1972
CULP—(NYSE)
Rev.: $225,333,000
Assets: $132,054,000
Liabilities: $55,925,000
Net Worth: $76,129,000
Earnings: ($13,819,000)
Emp.: 1,000
Fiscal Year-end: 04/28/24
Upholstery Fabrics & Mattress Ticking Mfr & Sales
N.A.I.C.S.: 313210
Franklin N. Saxon (Chm)
Kenneth R. Bowling (CFO, Treas & Sr VP)
Ashley C. Durbin (Sec, VP & Gen Counsel)
Robert G. Culp IV (Pres & CEO)

Subsidiaries:

Culp Europe (1)
UL Chabrowa 23, 64-610, Rogozno, Poland
Tel.: (48) 603076765
Commercial & Institutional Building Construction Services
N.A.I.C.S.: 236220

Culp Fabrics (Shanghai) Co., Ltd. (1)
Building A-25 Waiqingsong Road 5399, Qingpu, Shanghai, 201707, China
Tel.: (86) 2169210358
Web Site: https://www.culp.com
Mattress Mfr
N.A.I.C.S.: 337910
Boyd Chumbley (Exec VP-Upholstery Fabrics)

Rayonese Textiles, Inc. (1)
500 MGR Dubois, Saint-Jerome, J7Y 3L8, QC, Canada
Tel.: (450) 476-1991
Web Site: http://www.culp.com
Sales Range: $10-24.9 Million
Emp.: 200
Fabric Mill
N.A.I.C.S.: 313210

Read Window Products, LLC (1)
5900 Weisbrook Ln, Knoxville, TN 37909
Tel.: (865) 675-4086

Web Site: https://www.readwindow.com
Furniture Installation Services
N.A.I.C.S.: 238350
Dale Read *(CEO)*

eLuxury, LLC (1)
2625 Kotter Ave, Evansville, IN 47715
Web Site: http://www.eluxury.com
Bedding Online Retailer; Mattress Pad Mfr
N.A.I.C.S.: 313210
Paul Saunders *(Founder & CEO)*

CUMBERLAND PHARMACEU-TICALS, INC.
1600 W End Ave Ste 1300, Nashville,
TN 37203
Tel.: (615) 255-0068 **TN**
Web Site:
https://www.cumberlandpharma.com
Year Founded: 1999
CPIX—(NASDAQ)
Rev.: $42,010,949
Assets: $92,925,158
Liabilities: $56,951,152
Net Worth: $35,974,006
Earnings: ($5,570,241)
Emp.: 85
Fiscal Year-end: 12/31/22
Pharmaceuticals Mfr
N.A.I.C.S.: 325412
Martin S. Brown Jr. *(Executives, Bd of Dirs)*
A. J. Kazimi *(Founder, Chm & CEO)*
Tan Cheow Choon *(Sr Dir-Intl Bus Dev)*
Adam S. Mostafa *(Mng Dir-Consulting)*
John H. Hammergren *(CFO, Principal Acctg Officer & Sr Dir-Fin & Acctg)*

CUMMINS INC.
500 Jackson St, Columbus, IN
47202-3005
Tel.: (812) 377-5000 **IN**
Web Site: https://www.cummins.com
Year Founded: 1919
CMI—(NYSE)
Rev.: $34,065,000,000
Assets: $32,005,000,000
Liabilities: $22,101,000,000
Net Worth: $9,904,000,000
Earnings: $735,000,000
Emp.: 75,500
Fiscal Year-end: 12/31/23
Diesel & Natural Gas Engine Designer, Mfr & Distributor
N.A.I.C.S.: 333618
Sharon R. Barner *(Chief Admin Officer & Interim Chief HR Officer)*
Mark A. Smith *(CFO & VP)*
Srikanth Padmanabhan *(Pres-Operations & VP)*
Jeff Wiltrout *(Sr VP & VP-Corporate Strategy)*
Nicole Y. Lamb-Hale *(Chief Legal Officer, Gen Counsel, Sec & VP)*
Brett Merritt *(Pres-Engine Bus)*
Jonathan Wood *(CTO)*
Marvin Boakye *(Chief HR Officer)*
Jennifer W. Rumsey *(Chm, Pres & CEO)*

Subsidiaries:

Centro de Fomento para Inclusion, S. de R.L. de C.V. (1)
Federal Electricity Commission 230, Industrial Zone, 78395, San Luis Potosi, Mexico
Tel.: (52) 4441325689
Web Site: https://www.cefi.com.mx
Freight Transportation Services
N.A.I.C.S.: 484110

Consolidated Diesel, Inc. (1)
9377 N US Hwy 301, Whitakers, NC 27891-8621
Tel.: (252) 437-6611
Diesel Engine Whlsr
N.A.I.C.S.: 423830

Cummins Africa Middle East (Pty.) Ltd. (1)
23 Magwa Cr West Allandale Waterfall City, 2090, Johannesburg, South Africa
Tel.: (27) 115898400
Web Site: http://www.africa.cummins.com
Motor Vehicle Gasoline Engine & Engine Part Mfr
N.A.I.C.S.: 336310

Cummins Americas, inc. (1)
3350 Sw 148th Ave Ste 205, Miramar, FL 33027-3239
Tel.: (954) 431-5511
Diesel Engine Whlsr
N.A.I.C.S.: 423830

Cummins Argentina-Servicios Mineros S.A. (1)
Ruta Panamericana Km 32 5 Colect Este El Talar, C1618DDR, Buenos Aires, Argentina
Tel.: (54) 1147366400
Web Site: http://www.cummins.com.ar
Emp.: 120
Automobile Parts Distr
N.A.I.C.S.: 423120

Cummins Atlantic LLC (1)
11101 Nations Ford Rd, Charlotte, NC 28273
Tel.: (704) 588-1240
Web Site:
http://www.salesandservice.cummins.com
Industrial Machinery & Equipment Distr
N.A.I.C.S.: 423830

Cummins Austria GmbH (1)
Bahnstrasse 57, Theresienfeld, 2604, Wiener Neustadt, Austria
Tel.: (43) 2622774180
Web Site: https://www.cummins.at
Diesel Engine Mfr
N.A.I.C.S.: 336310
Christian Kogler *(Mng Dir)*

Cummins BLR LLC (1)
Minsk Region Papernyanskii S/S 50/1-7 Dubovlyany, 223043, Minsk, Belarus
Tel.: (375) 172181068
Motor & Generator Mfr
N.A.I.C.S.: 335312

Cummins Belgium N.V. (1)
Catenbergstraat 1, 2840, Rumst, Belgium
Tel.: (32) 15479100
Web Site: http://www.cummins.com
Sales Range: $25-49.9 Million
Deisel Engines Distr & Mfr
N.A.I.C.S.: 333618

Cummins Brasil Ltda. (1)
Rua Jati 310 Jardim Cubica, Guarulhos, 07180-140, SP, Brazil (100%)
Tel.: (55) 11218649
Web Site: http://www.cummins.com.br
Natural Gas Engine Mfr
N.A.I.C.S.: 333618

Cummins Bridgeway LLC (1)
722 N Outer Dr, Saginaw, MI 48601
Tel.: (989) 752-5200
Sales Range: $50-74.9 Million
Emp.: 243
Repair Facility
N.A.I.C.S.: 811114

Subsidiary (Domestic):

Cummins Bridgeway Columbus, LLC (2)
4000 Lyman Dr, Hilliard, OH 43026
Tel.: (614) 771-1000
Power Generation Equipment Distr
N.A.I.C.S.: 423830
Dean Headley *(Mgr-Ops)*

Cummins Bridgeway Grove City, LLC (2)
2297 SW Blvd Ste K, Grove City, OH 43123-1822
Tel.: (614) 604-6000
Power Generation Equipment Distr
N.A.I.C.S.: 423830

Cummins Bridgeway Toledo, LLC (2)
801 Illinois Ave, Maumee, OH 43537
Tel.: (419) 893-8711

Web Site:
http://www.cummindbridgeway.com
Emp.: 26
Power Generation Equipment Distr
N.A.I.C.S.: 423830
Urban Jared *(Gen Mgr)*

Plant (Domestic):

Cummins Bridgeway, LLC - Hilliard (2)
4000 Lyman Dr, Hilliard, OH 43026-1212
Tel.: (614) 771-1000
Web Site:
http://www.cumminsbridgeway.com
Sales Range: $50-74.9 Million
Emp.: 60
Diesel Engines & Parts Distr & Repair
N.A.I.C.S.: 423120

Cummins Canada Limited (1)
7175 Pacific Circle, Mississauga, L5T 2A5, ON, Canada
Tel.: (905) 795-0050
Web Site: http://www.cummins.com
Diesel & Gas Engine Whlsr
N.A.I.C.S.: 423830

Cummins Central Power (1)
10088 S 136th St, Omaha, NE 68138-3902
Tel.: (402) 551-7678
Web Site: http://www.cummins.com
Sales Range: $75-99.9 Million
Emp.: 140
Industrial Machinery & Equipment
N.A.I.C.S.: 423830

Cummins Child Development Center, Inc. (1)
650 Pleasant Grv, Columbus, IN 47201
Tel.: (812) 378-5833
Web Site: https://cumminscdc.com
Child Day Care Services
N.A.I.C.S.: 624410
Cindy Reed *(Dir-Center)*
Jennifer Milan *(Office Mgr)*
Becky Smith *(Coord-Developmental)*
Jackie Dixon *(Coord-Educational)*
Taylor Baker *(Asst Dir-Center)*

Cummins Corporation (1)
Tower A 28 Fl Gateway Pz No18 N Rd E 3rd Ring Rd, Beijing, 100027, China (100%)
Tel.: (86) 1065051658
Web Site: http://www.cummins.com
Sales Range: $25-49.9 Million
Emp.: 400
Truck, Industrial & Marine Engines
N.A.I.C.S.: 333618
Earl Newsome Jr. *(CIO)*

Cummins Crosspoint (1)
2301 Nelson Miller Pkwy, Louisville, KY 40223-2191
Tel.: (317) 484-2168
Sales Range: $25-49.9 Million
Emp.: 25
Diesel Engines & Industrial Equipment
N.A.I.C.S.: 423830
Donald Beal *(Mgr-Parts)*

Cummins Czech Republic s.r.o. (1)
Obchodni 110, 251 70, Cestlice, Czech Republic
Tel.: (420) 272680110
Web Site: https://www.cummins.cz
Motor Vehicle Parts Mfr
N.A.I.C.S.: 336390

Cummins Deutschland GmbH (1)
Peter-Traiser-Strasse 1, PO Box 1134, 64521, Gross-Gerau, Germany
Tel.: (49) 61521740
Web Site: http://www.cumminseurope.com
Diesel Engine Mfr
N.A.I.C.S.: 333618

Cummins Diesel Sales Corporation (1)
1000 5th St, Columbus, IN 47201-6319
Tel.: (812) 377-5401
Engine Parts Whslr
N.A.I.C.S.: 423830

Cummins Distribution Holdco Inc. (1)
500 Jackson St, Columbus, IN 47201
Tel.: (812) 377-5000
Emp.: 15

Sporting Goods Mfr
N.A.I.C.S.: 339920

Cummins Eastern Canada LP (1)
7200 Trans-Canada Highway, Pointe-Claire, H9R 1C2, QC, Canada
Tel.: (514) 695-8410
Web Site:
http://www.estducanada.cummins.com
Automobile Parts Distr
N.A.I.C.S.: 423120

Cummins Eastern Marine, Inc. (1)
50 Simmonds Dr, Dartmouth, B3B 1R3, NS, Canada
Tel.: (902) 468-7938
Automobile Parts Distr
N.A.I.C.S.: 423110

Cummins Emission Solutions Inc. (1)
525 Jackson St, Columbus, IN 47203
Tel.: (800) 343-7357
Engine & Generator Distr
N.A.I.C.S.: 423120
Amy M. Adams *(VP & Gen Mgr)*
Mahesh Narang *(VP)*

Cummins Energy Solutions Business Iberia (1)
Calle de Josefa Valcarcel 8, 28027, Madrid, Spain
Tel.: (34) 913200771
Engine & Generator Distr
N.A.I.C.S.: 423120

Cummins Engine Company Pty Limited (1)
2 Caribbean Drive, Scoresby, 3179, VIC, Australia (100%)
Tel.: (61) 397653222
Web Site: http://www.cummins.com
Sales Range: $100-124.9 Million
Emp.: 1,600
Remanufactured Engines & Components
N.A.I.C.S.: 333618
Peter Jensen-Muir *(CEO)*

Division (Non-US):

Diesel ReCon UK (2)
2-10 Napier Pl Wardpark N, Cumbernauld, G68 0BP, Glascow, United Kingdom (100%)
Tel.: (44) 1236725981
Web Site: http://www.cummings.com
Sales Range: $25-49.9 Million
Emp.: 75
Remanufactured Engines & Components
N.A.I.C.S.: 333618

Cummins Filtration International Corp. (1)
Cummins Filtration Waterfall Commercial Park, Pretoria Main Road and Beatty Street Woodmead, Johannesburg, 2191, Gauteng, South Africa
Tel.: (27) 102850200
Motor & Generator Mfr
N.A.I.C.S.: 335312

Cummins Filtration, Inc. (1)
26 Century Blvd, Nashville, TN 37214 (100%)
Tel.: (615) 367-0040
Web Site: http://www.cumminsfiltration.com
Sales Range: $150-199.9 Million
Natural Gas Engine Designer Mfr
N.A.I.C.S.: 333618

Subsidiary (Non-US):

Cummins Distributor Belgium SA (2)
Egide Walschaertsstraat 2 Industriepark Zuid, 2800, Mechelen, 2800, Belgium
Tel.: (32) 15479100
Web Site: http://www.cummins.com
Sales Range: $125-149.9 Million
Emp.: 50
Engine & Hydraulic Filtration
N.A.I.C.S.: 333618

Subsidiary (Non-US):

Cummins Filtration Co. Ltd. (3)
409-6 Yookil-Ri Songsan-Myeon, Hwaseong, 445-873, Gyeonggi-Do, Korea (South)
Tel.: (82) 313695900

Cummins Inc.—(Continued)
Web Site: http://www.fleetguard.co.kr
Sales Range: $125-149.9 Million
Emp.: 16
Engine & Hydraulic Filtration Systems
N.A.I.C.S.: 333618

Cummins Filtration SARL (3)
Z I du Grand Guelen, 29556, Quimper, Cedex, France (100%)
Tel.: (33) 298764949
Web Site: http://www.cumminsfiltration.com
Sales Range: $125-149.9 Million
Natural Gas Engine Designer Mfr
N.A.I.C.S.: 333618

Cummins Sales & Service Singapore Pte Ltd (3)
85 Tuas South Avenue 1, Singapore, 609019, Singapore (100%)
Tel.: (65) 62613555
Web Site: http://www.cumminsfiltration.com
Air, Fuel, Hydraulic & Lube Filtration Designer & Mfr
N.A.I.C.S.: 333618

Fleetguard Filters Pvt. Ltd. (3)
136 Park Marina Road Baner, Pune, 411 045, Maharashtra, India
Tel.: (91) 2067179111
Web Site: https://www.fleetguard-filtrum.com
Sales Range: $100-124.9 Million
Emp.: 150
Engine & Hydraulic Filtration Systems Mfr
N.A.I.C.S.: 333618

Shanghai Fleetguard Filter Co., Ltd. (3)
3595 North Yang Gao Road Pudong, Shanghai, 201208, China
Tel.: (86) 2158657950
Web Site:
http://www.shanghaifleetguard.com
Sales Range: $100-124.9 Million
Industrial Machinery Mfr
N.A.I.C.S.: 333248

Plant (Domestic):

Cummins Filtration (2)
1200 Fleetguard Rd, Cookeville, TN 38506-6258
Tel.: (931) 526-9551
Web Site: http://www.cumminsfiltration.com
Sales Range: $50-74.9 Million
Emp.: 100
Engine & Hydraulic Filtration Systems
N.A.I.C.S.: 336390

Cummins Filtration (2)
26 Century Blvd, Nashville, TN 37214
Tel.: (615) 367-0040
Web Site: https://www.cumminsfiltration.com
Sales Range: $200-249.9 Million
Emp.: 500
Engine & Hydraulic Filters
N.A.I.C.S.: 336340

Subsidiary (Non-US):

Cummins Filtration GmbH (2)
Im Neugrund 13, Gross-Gerau, 64521, Germany
Tel.: (49) 61521740
Web Site: http://www.cumminsfiltration.com
Emp.: 9
Industrial Machinery & Equipment Whslr
N.A.I.C.S.: 423830

Cummins Fuel Systems (Wuhan) Co. Ltd. (1)
No 1 East Kejiyuan Rd Zhuankou, Wuhan, 430056, Hubei, China
Tel.: (86) 2768847188
Power Generator Distr
N.A.I.C.S.: 423120

Cummins Generator Technologies (1)
Fountain Court Lynch Wood, PO Box 17, Peterborough, PE2 6FZ, Lincolnshire, United Kingdom
Tel.: (44) 1733395300
Web Site:
http://www.cumminsgeneratortechnologies.com
Sales Range: $250-299.9 Million
Emp.: 500
Diesel & Natural Gas Engine Designer Mfr

Cummins Generator Technologies Co., Ltd. (1)
No 11 Xiang Jiang Road High-Tech Ind Dev Zone, Wuxi, 214028, Jiangsu, China
Tel.: (86) 51081103088
Web Site:
http://www.cumminsgeneratortechnologies.com.cn
Generator Manufacturing
N.A.I.C.S.: 335312
Jason Wang (Gen Mgr)

Cummins Generator Technologies GmbH (1)
Bunsenstrasse 17, D-85053, Ingolstadt, Germany
Tel.: (49) 8417920
Sales Range: $50-74.9 Million
Emp.: 280
Electrical Power Generation System Mfr
N.A.I.C.S.: 335312

Cummins Generator Technologies Italy SRL (1)
Via Carducci 125 Sesto San Giovanni, Milan, 20099, MI, Italy
Tel.: (39) 0238000714
Power Generator Whslr
N.A.I.C.S.: 423120

Cummins Generator Technologies Mexico S de R.L. de C.V. (1)
Av Circuito Mexico No 185 Parque Industrial 3 Naciones, San Luis Potosi, 78395, Mexico
Tel.: (52) 4448704400
Web Site: http://www.cummins.com
Emp.: 30
Power Generator Mfr
N.A.I.C.S.: 335312

Cummins Generator Technologies Norway (1)
Osloveien 20, As, 1431, Akershus, Norway
Tel.: (47) 64974540
Alternate Current Generator Mfr
N.A.I.C.S.: 335312

Cummins Generator Technologies Romania S.A. (1)
B-dul Decebal Nr 116A, Dolj, 200746, Craiova, Dolj, Romania
Tel.: (40) 351443444
Web Site: http://www.stamford-avk.com
Alternate Current Generator Mfr
N.A.I.C.S.: 335312

Cummins Generator Technologies Singapore Pte Ltd. (1)
10 Toh Guan Rd Suite 05-04 Tt International Tradepark, PO Box 10 02, Singapore, 608838, Singapore
Tel.: (65) 63053150
Web Site: http://www.stamford-avk.com
Generator Distr
N.A.I.C.S.: 423120

Cummins Generator Technologies Spain S.A. (1)
Av del Sistema Solar 27 Naves-1-2, San Fernando de Henares, 28830, Madrid, Spain
Tel.: (34) 916787600
Alternate Current Generator Mfr
N.A.I.C.S.: 335312

Cummins Ghana Limited (1)
Odorkor-Sakaman Off Kaneshie-Mallam Road, Accra, 233, Ghana
Tel.: (233) 302301451
Industrial Machinery Distr
N.A.I.C.S.: 423830

Cummins Holland B.V. (1)
Olivijn 800, 3316 KH, Dordrecht, Netherlands
Tel.: (31) 786181200
Web Site: http://cumminseurope.com
Diesel Engine Mfr
N.A.I.C.S.: 333618

Cummins Hong Kong Ltd. (1)
4 Lok Tung Street On Lok Tsuen, 11 Wo Shing Street Fo Tan, Kowloon, China (Hong Kong)
Tel.: (852) 26065678
Web Site: http://www.cummins.com.cn

Sales Range: $25-49.9 Million
Emp.: 50
Diesel & Natural Gas Engine Designer Mfr
N.A.I.C.S.: 333618

Cummins Inc. (1)
(100%)
Tel.: (716) 456-2111
Web Site: https://www.cummins.com
Sales Range: $400-449.9 Million
Emp.: 75,500
Truck & Bus Engines
N.A.I.C.S.: 333611

Cummins India Limited (1)
Cummins India Office Campus Tower A & B Survey No 21 Balewadi, Pune, 411 045, Maharashtra, India
Tel.: (91) 2067067000
Web Site: http://www.cummins.com
Sales Range: $1-4.9 Billion
Diesel Engines
N.A.I.C.S.: 336310
Ashwath Ram (Mng Dir)
Aditi Sharma (VP-ABO Quality, Mfg & HSE)
Binu John (Head-Interim-IT)
Anupama Kaul (Head-HR)
Steven Chapman (Chm)

Cummins Italia S.P.A. (1)
Via Liguria 3/2, Peschiera Borromeo, 20068, Milan, MI, Italy
Tel.: (39) 025165581
Web Site: http://www.cumminseurope.com
Power Generation Equipment & Engine Mfr
N.A.I.C.S.: 333618

Cummins Japan Ltd. (1)
15F New Pier Takeshiba South Tower 1-16-1, Kaigan Minato-ku, Tokyo, 105-0022, Japan
Tel.: (81) 366316400
Web Site: http://www.cummins.jp
Industrial Machinery Mfr
N.A.I.C.S.: 336350

Cummins Juarez, S.A. de C.V. (1)
Blvd Juan Pablo Ii No 1951, Ciudad Juarez, 32550, Mexico
Tel.: (52) 6561463200
Diesel Engine Mfr
N.A.I.C.S.: 333618

Cummins Komatsu Engine Company (1)
800 E 3rd St, Seymour, IN 47274-3906
Tel.: (812) 524-6693
Web Site: http://www.komatsu.com
Sales Range: $25-49.9 Million
Emp.: 52
Mfr of Large Sized Diesel Engines
N.A.I.C.S.: 333611

Cummins Korea Ltd. (1)
25th Fl Trade Center ASEM Tower 517 Yeongdong-daero, Gangnam-gu, Seoul, 06164, Korea (South) (100%)
Tel.: (82) 234524313
Web Site: http://www.cummins.co.kr
Sales Range: $25-49.9 Million
Generator Set & Marine Engine Mfr
N.A.I.C.S.: 332322

Cummins Makina Sanayi ve Ticaret Limited Sirketi (1)
Deri Osb Vakum cad Optik Sok No 6, Istanbul, 34957, Turkiye
Tel.: (90) 2165817300
Power Generation Equipment & Engines Mfr
N.A.I.C.S.: 333618

Cummins Mercruiser Diesel Marine LLC (1)
4500 Leeds Ave Ste 301, North Charleston, SC 29405
Tel.: (843) 745-2700
Sales Range: $300-349.9 Million
Marine Diesel Engines Mfr
N.A.I.C.S.: 336310

Cummins Middle East FZE (1)
South Zone 2 Jebel Ali Free Zone, PO Box 17636, Dubai, United Arab Emirates
Tel.: (971) 48809911
Web Site:
http://www.middleeast.cummins.com
Diesel Engine Mfr
N.A.I.C.S.: 333618
Rachib Ouenniche (Mng Dir)

Cummins N.V. (1)
Catenbergstraat 1 Industriezone 2, Rumst, 2840, Belgium (100%)
Tel.: (32) 34563000
Emp.: 500
Natural Gas Engine Designer Mfr
N.A.I.C.S.: 333618

Cummins Natural Gas Engines, Inc. (1)
8713 Airport Freeway Ste 316, Fort Worth, TX 76180
Tel.: (817) 581-7575
Web Site: http://www.cummins.com
Sales Range: $50-74.9 Million
Emp.: 47
Diesel & Natural Gas Engine Designer Mfr
N.A.I.C.S.: 333618

Cummins Nigeria Ltd. (1)
Plot Y Mobolaji Johnson Avenue, Alausa Ikeja, Lagos, Nigeria
Tel.: (234) 2866467
Web Site: http://www.cumminsnigeria.com
Power Generator Machinery Distr
N.A.I.C.S.: 423120

Cummins Northeast Inc. (1)
100 Allied Dr, Dedham, MA 02026
Tel.: (781) 329-1750
Web Site:
http://www.cumminsnortheast.com
Sales Range: $50-74.9 Million
Emp.: 100
Natural Gas Engine Designer Mfr
N.A.I.C.S.: 333618
David Letts (Owner & Pres)

Cummins Norway AS (1)
Osloveien 20, PO Box 97, 1430, Oslo, Norway
Tel.: (47) 64974500
Web Site: http://www.cummins.no
Automotive & Industrial Products Sls & Mfr
N.A.I.C.S.: 423830

Cummins Npower LLC (1)
1600 Buerkle Rd, White Bear Lake, MN 55110
Tel.: (651) 636-1000
Web Site: http://www.cumminsnpower.com
Sales Range: $25-49.9 Million
Emp.: 65
Industrial Equipment Whsr
N.A.I.C.S.: 423830

Cummins Power Generation (1)
1400 73rd Ave NE, Minneapolis, MN 55432 (100%)
Tel.: (763) 574-5000
Web Site: http://power.cummins.com
Sales Range: $125-149.9 Million
Emp.: 1,800
Portable & Stand-By Electric Generators & Gasoline Engines Mfr
N.A.I.C.S.: 335312
Antonio Leitao (VP-Bus Organization-Europe)

Cummins Power Generation (S) Pte. Ltd. (1)
44 Pioneer Sector 2, Singapore, 628395, Singapore
Tel.: (65) 68615715
Diesel Engine Whslr
N.A.I.C.S.: 423830

Cummins Power Generation (U.K.) Limited (1)
Unit 44 Gwash Way Industrial Estate Ryhall Road, Stamford, PE9 1XP, United Kingdom
Tel.: (44) 1780481666
Power Generator Whslr
N.A.I.C.S.: 423120

Cummins Power Systems (1)
890 Zerega Ave, Bronx, NY 10473
Tel.: (718) 892-2400
Web Site:
http://www.powersystems.cummins.com
Rev.: $75,000,000
Emp.: 30
Electrical Apparatus & Equipment & Diesel Engines
N.A.I.C.S.: 423610

Cummins Power Systems Inc. (1)
2727 Ford Rd, Bristol, PA 19007-6805
Tel.: (215) 785-6005
Web Site:
http://www.powersystems.cummins.com
Rev.: $78,000,000

Emp.: 600
Industrial Machinery & Equipment
N.A.I.C.S.: 425120

Cummins Rocky Mountain LLC (1)
8211 E 96th Ave, Henderson, CO 80640
Tel.: (303) 287-0201
Web Site:
    http://www.cumminsrockymountain.com
Sales Range: $75-99.9 Million
Emp.: 200
Industrial Machinery & Equipment Services
N.A.I.C.S.: 423830

Branch (Domestic):

Cummins Rocky Mountain (2)
2167 S 5370 W, Salt Lake City, UT 84120
Tel.: (801) 355-6500
Sales Range: $50-74.9 Million
Emp.: 100
Mfr & Distributor of Diesel Engines & Parts;
Refrigeration Units; Motor Vehicles
N.A.I.C.S.: 459999

Cummins Romania Srl (1)
No 27 Turistilor Str, Ilfov, 077040, Chiajna,
Romania
Tel.: (40) 733559042
Web Site: http://www.cummins.com
Diesel Engine Mfr
N.A.I.C.S.: 333618

Cummins Sales and Service (1)
8201 NE Parvin Rd, Kansas City, MO
64161-9553
Tel.: (816) 414-8200
Web Site: http://www.cummins.com
Diesel Engine Repair Services
N.A.I.C.S.: 333618

Cummins Sales and Service (Singapore) Pte. Ltd. (1)
85 Tuas South Avenue 1, Singapore,
637419, Singapore
Tel.: (65) 62613555
Web Site: http://www.cummins.com.sg.com
Electrical Components Whslr
N.A.I.C.S.: 423610

Cummins Sales and Service Philippines Inc. (1)
Lots 1 2 Block 15 LIIP Avenue Laguna International Industrial Park, Mamplasan, Binan, 4024, Laguna, Philippines
Tel.: (63) 26676500
Industrial Machinery & Equipment Whslr
N.A.I.C.S.: 423830

Cummins Sales and Service Private Limited (1)
B-69 Sector 63 Near Fortis Hospital, Noida,
201 301, Uttar Pradesh, India
Tel.: (91) 1204792444
Web Site: https://www.csspl.org
Motor Vehicle Parts Mfr
N.A.I.C.S.: 336390

Cummins Scott & English Malaysia Sdn. Bhd. (1)
No 53 Jalan IM 14/7 Kawasan Industri
Ringan Sektor 3, Bandar Indera Mahkota,
Kuantan, Malaysia
Tel.: (60) 95701185
Web Site: http://www.cummins.com
Industrial Machinery Mfr
N.A.I.C.S.: 333998

Cummins South Africa (Pty.) Ltd. (1)
Harrowdene Office Park Block 8 First Floor
Western Service Road, Woodmead, 2196,
South Africa
Tel.: (27) 115898517
Web Site: http://www.cummins.com
Alternate Current Generator Mfr
N.A.I.C.S.: 335312
Gino Puttera (CEO)

Cummins South Inc. (1)
5125 Hwy 85, Atlanta, GA 30349
Tel.: (404) 763-0151
Web Site:
    http://www.cumminspowersouth.com
Sales Range: $50-74.9 Million
Emp.: 80
Engines & Parts, Diesel
N.A.I.C.S.: 423830

Cummins South Pacific Pty. Limited (1)

2 Caribbean Drive, Scoresby, 3179, VIC,
Australia
Tel.: (61) 397653222
Web Site: http://www.cummins.com.au
Emp.: 1,600
Power Generator Whslr
N.A.I.C.S.: 423120
Stephanie Disher (Mng Dir)

Cummins Southeastern Power, Inc. (1)
5421 N 59th St, Tampa, FL 33610
Tel.: (813) 621-7202
Web Site: http://www.cspi.cummins.com
Sales Range: $900-999.9 Million
Emp.: 300
Diesel Engines & Parts
N.A.I.C.S.: 423830

Cummins Southern Plains, LLC (1)
600 N Watson Rd, Arlington, TX 76011
Tel.: (817) 640-6801
Web Site: http://www.cummins-sp.com
Sales Range: $50-74.9 Million
Natural Gas Engine Designer Mfr
N.A.I.C.S.: 333618

Cummins Spain, S.L. (1)
C/Vidrieros 9, San Fernando de Henares,
28830, Madrid, Spain
Tel.: (34) 916787600
Web Site: http://www.cumminsspain.com
Generator Whslr
N.A.I.C.S.: 423120

Cummins Sweden AB (1)
Ostra Bangatan 18, 195 60, Arlandastad,
Sweden
Tel.: (46) 859513390
Power Generator Machinery Distr
N.A.I.C.S.: 423120

Cummins Technologies India Limited (1)
Campus Tower A and B Survey No 21,
Balewadi, Pune, 411 045, Maharashtra,
India
Tel.: (91) 2067067000
Web Site: http://www.cumminsindia.com
Industrial Machinery Mfr & Distr
N.A.I.C.S.: 335312

Cummins Turbo Technologies Ltd. (1)
Saint Andrews Road, Huddersfield, HD1
6RA, W Yorkshire, United
Kingdom (100%)
Tel.: (44) 1484422244
Web Site: http://www.holset.co.uk
Sales Range: $100-124.9 Million
Emp.: 900
Diesel & Natural Gas Engine Designer Mfr
N.A.I.C.S.: 333618

Subsidiary (Non-US):

Cummins Turbo Technologies (2)
Rua Jati 310, Guarulhos, 07180-900, SP,
Brazil
Tel.: (55) 8002866467
Web Site: http://www.holset.co.uk
Sales Range: $75-99.9 Million
Turbocharger Engineering
N.A.I.C.S.: 541330

Unit (US):

Cummins Turbo Technologies (2)
500 Central Ave, Columbus, IN 47201
Tel.: (812) 377-9221
Sales Range: $75-99.9 Million
Emp.: 160
Engineering Services
N.A.I.C.S.: 541330
Thomas Innis (Engr-Svcs)

Subsidiary (Non-US):

Wuxi Cummins Turbo Technologies Co., Ltd. (2)
28 Xinxi Rd, Wuxi New District, Wuxi,
214028, Jiangsu, China (55%)
Tel.: (86) 51085200800
Web Site: http://www.cummins.com.cn
Sales Range: $75-99.9 Million
Diesel & Natural Gas Engine Designer Mfr
N.A.I.C.S.: 333618

Cummins U.K. Pension Plan Trustee Ltd. (1)

Yarm Road, Darlington, DL1 4PW, United
Kingdom
Tel.: (44) 1325556000
Web Site:
    http://www.mycummins.cummins.com
Emp.: 1,500
Diesel Engine Whlsr
N.A.I.C.S.: 423830
Chris Willoughby (Plant Mgr)

Cummins West Africa Limited (1)
8 Ijora Cause Way, Ijora, Lagos, Nigeria
Tel.: (234) 15878820
Web Site: http://africa.cummins.com
Power Generation Equipment Distr
N.A.I.C.S.: 423830
Tosin Tomori (Mng Dir)

Cummins Western Canada Limited Partnership (1)
18452 96 Ave, Surrey, V4N 3P8, BC,
Canada
Tel.: (604) 882-5000
Web Site:
    http://www.westerncanada.cummins.com
Emp.: 530
Natural Gas Engine Designer Mfr
N.A.I.C.S.: 333618
Charles Masters (Pres)

Cummins Westport Inc. (1)
1750 West 75th Ave Suite 101, Vancouver,
V6P 6G2, BC, Canada (50%)
Tel.: (604) 718-8100
Web Site: http://www.cumminswestport.com
Sales Range: $25-49.9 Million
Emp.: 60
Alternative Fuel Engines Mfr
N.A.I.C.S.: 336310
Roe C. East (Gen Mgr-On-Highway Natural
Gas Bus)

Cummins Zambia Ltd. (1)
Plot 3763 Chibuluma Rd Industrial Area,
Kitwe, 10101, Copperbelt, Zambia
Tel.: (260) 212310050
Web Site: http://www.cummins.com
Sales Range: $25-49.9 Million
Generator Whlsr
N.A.I.C.S.: 423120
Jacques Sourie (CEO)

Cummins Zimbabwe Pvt. Ltd. (1)
No 2 Edison Crescent Kelvin Rd South, PO
Box ST 363, Graniteside, Harare, Zimbabwe
Tel.: (263) 4777802
Web Site: http://www.zimapantrucks.com
Generator Distr
N.A.I.C.S.: 423120

Cummins, Ltd. (1)
Royal Oak Way S, Daventry, N11 8NU,
Northhampshire, United Kingdom (100%)
Tel.: (44) 1327886000
Sales Range: $300-349.9 Million
Emp.: 1,100
Diesel Engine Mfr
N.A.I.C.S.: 333618
Peter Glover (Plant Mgr)

Diesel ReCon Company (1)
2680 Pershing Ave, Memphis, TN 38112
Tel.: (901) 320-3396
Web Site: http://www.cnge.com
Sales Range: $75-99.9 Million
Emp.: 14
Remanufactured Engines & Components
N.A.I.C.S.: 488510

Distribuidora Cummins Centroamerica Costa Rica, S.de R.L. (1)
Avenida 59 Calle 54 a Lo Que es Igual a
100 Metros, Norte De La Agencia KIA Contiguo a Disitali, San Jose, Costa Rica
Tel.: (506) 41031600
Motor Vehicle Parts Whslr
N.A.I.C.S.: 423120

Distribuidora Cummins Centroamerica El Salvador, S.de R.L. (1)
Carretera Puerto de La Libertad Km 11 1/2
A un Costado de C Imberton, Frente a la
Gasolinera Uno Antiguo Cuscatlan, San
Salvador, El Salvador
Tel.: (503) 25554000
Motor Vehicle Parts Whslr
N.A.I.C.S.: 423120

Distribuidora Cummins Centroamerica Guatemala, Ltda. (1)
Calzada Atanasio Tzul 22-00 Zona 12 Empresarial Cortijo Ii No 500, Guatemala, Guatemala
Tel.: (502) 46727454
Automotive & Construction Services
N.A.I.C.S.: 811310

Distribuidora Cummins Centroamerica Honduras, S.de R.L. (1)
Desvio Colonia la Pradera Contiguo a
Gasolinera UNO, Comayaguela MDC, Tegucigalpa, Honduras
Tel.: (504) 22025600
Motor Vehicle Parts Whslr
N.A.I.C.S.: 423120

Distribuidora Cummins S.A. Sucursal Bolivia (1)
Av Cristo Redentor Km 6 5 de la Sierra,
Santa Cruz, Bolivia
Tel.: (591) 33120279
Diesel Engine Distr
N.A.I.C.S.: 423830

Distribuidora Cummins de Panama, S. de R.L. (1)
Panama Pacifico PanAmerica Corporate
Center Edificio 9130, Local 1 Arraijan,
Panama, Panama
Tel.: (507) 3779000
Motor Vehicle Parts Whslr
N.A.I.C.S.: 423120

Dongfeng Cummins Engine Co., Ltd. (1)
Automobile Industry Development Zone,
Xiangcheng, 441004, China
Tel.: (86) 7103320888
Web Site: http://www.dfac.com
Sales Range: $500-549.9 Million
Emp.: 2,400
Engine Mfr
N.A.I.C.S.: 333618

Efficient Drivetrains Inc. (1)
1181 Cadillac Ct, Milpitas, CA 95035
Tel.: (408) 624-1231
Web Site: http://www.efficientdrivetrains.com
General Automotive Repair
N.A.I.C.S.: 811111
Andrew Frank (CTO)
Joerg Ferchau (CEO)

Hydrogenics Corporation (1)
220 Admiral Boulevard, Mississauga, L5T
2N6, ON, Canada (100%)
Tel.: (905) 361-3660
Web Site: http://www.hydrogenics.com
Rev.: $33,896,000
Assets: $49,924,000
Liabilities: $38,963,000
Net Worth: $10,961,000
Earnings: ($13,339,000)
Emp.: 187
Fiscal Year-end: 12/31/2018
Fuel Cell & Hydrogen Generation Products
Mfr
N.A.I.C.S.: 335999
Daryl C. F. Wilson (CEO)

Division (Domestic):

Hydrogenics Test Systems (2)
Unit C 4242 Phillips Avenue, Burnaby, V5A
2X2, BC, Canada (100%)
Tel.: (604) 676-4000
Sales Range: $25-49.9 Million
Emp.: 35
Testing & Diagnostic Equipment for the Fuel
Cell Industry
N.A.I.C.S.: 334515

Hydrogenics Europe N.V. (1)
Nijverheidsstraat 48c, 2260, Oevel, Belgium
Tel.: (32) 14462110
Industrial Gas Mfr
N.A.I.C.S.: 325120

Hydrogenics USA, Inc. (1)
2870 Whiptail Loop Ste 106, Carlsbad, CA
92010
Tel.: (858) 386-8930
Industrial Gas Mfr
N.A.I.C.S.: 325120

Industrial Power Alliance, Ltd. (1)
400 Yokokura Shinden, Oyama, 323-8558,
Tochigi, Japan

Cummins Inc.—(Continued)

Tel.: (81) 28 528 8210
Web Site: https://www.ipalliance.co.jp
Emp.: 340
Engine Equipment Mfr
N.A.I.C.S.: 333618
Yasuyuki Onodera *(Pres)*

Jacobs Vehicle Systems, Inc.   **(1)**
22 E Dudley Town Rd, Bloomfield, CT
06002
Tel.: (860) 243-1441
Web Site: http://www.jakebrake.com
Engine Retarder Mfr
N.A.I.C.S.: 333618

Subsidiary (Non-US):

Jacobs (Suzhou) Vehicle Systems
Co., Ltd   **(2)**
19 building 99 Gangtian Road, Suzhou In-
dustrial Park, Suzhou, 215024, China
Tel.: (86) 51262993200
Web Site:
  http://www.jacobsvehiclesystems.com
Automotive Parts Mfr & Distr
N.A.I.C.S.: 336390
Harbort Wu *(Dir-Bus Dev & Engrg-Asia)*

Komatsu Cummins Chile Ltda. **(1)**
Americo Vespucio Avenue 0631 3rd Floor,
Quilicura, Santiago, Chile
Tel.: (56) 226557777
Web Site:
  http://www.komatsulatinoamerica.com
Sales Range: $150-199.9 Million
Emp.: 350
Holding Company; Joint Venture of
Komatsu Ltd. & Cummins Engine Company,
Inc.
N.A.I.C.S.: 551112

Komatsu Cummins Engine Co.,
Ltd.   **(1)**
400 Yokokurashinden, Oyama, 323-8558,
Tochigi, Japan   **(50%)**
Tel.: (81) 285288380
Web Site: http://www.komatsu.com
Sales Range: $25-49.9 Million
Emp.: 100
Diesel Engine Mfr
N.A.I.C.S.: 333618

Meritor, Inc.   **(1)**
2135 W Maple Rd, Troy, MI 48084-7186
Tel.: (248) 435-1000
Web Site: http://www.meritor.com
Rev.: $3,833,000,000
Assets: $2,938,000,000
Liabilities: $2,323,000,000
Net Worth: $615,000,000
Earnings: $199,000,000
Emp.: 9,600
Fiscal Year-end: 10/03/2021
Integrated Systems, Modules & Compo-
nents Supplier to the Motor Vehicle Industry
N.A.I.C.S.: 336390
Timothy Earl Joseph Bowes *(Pres-*
Electrification & Industrial-North America &
Sr VP)
William R. Newlin *(Chm)*
John Nelligan *(Pres-Truck-Americas & Sr*
VP)
Krista L. Sohm *(Chief Mktg & Comm Officer*
& VP)
Paul D. Bialy *(Chief Acctg Officer & VP)*
Scott M. Confer *(Interim Chief Legal Officer*
& Sec)
Ken Hogan *(Pres-Truck-Europe & Asia Pa-*
cific & Sr VP)
Darrell Whitney *(Chief HR Officer & VP)*

Division (Domestic):

AVM, Inc.   **(2)**
3108 Hwy 76 E, Marion, SC
29571   **(100%)**
Tel.: (843) 464-7823
Web Site: https://www.avmind.com
Sales Range: $150-199.9 Million
Emp.: 400
Actuators & Gas Spring Lift Supports Mfr
N.A.I.C.S.: 336390

Subsidiary (Non-US):

Arvin European Holdings (UK)
Limited   **(2)**

Grange Road Cwmbran, Gwent, NP44 3XU,
United Kingdom
Tel.: (44) 1633834040
Web Site: http://www.meritor.com
Emp.: 450
Automobile Brakes Installation Services
N.A.I.C.S.: 336390

Arvin International Holland B.V. **(2)**
Keulsebaan 507, Roermond, 6045 GG,
Netherlands
Tel.: (31) 475884242
Emp.: 450
Investment Services
N.A.I.C.S.: 523150
Dirk Stoll *(Gen Mgr)*

Arvin Motion Control Limited   **(2)**
Grange Road, Cwmbran, NP44 3XU, South
Wales, United Kingdom   **(100%)**
Tel.: (44) 162743600
Gas springs, Struts Dampers & End Fittings
N.A.I.C.S.: 334519

ArvinMeritor B.V.   **(2)**
Antareslaan 47, 2132 JE, Hoofddorp,
Netherlands   **(100%)**
Tel.: (31) 235690300
Web Site: http://www.arvinmerito.com
Sales Range: $25-49.9 Million
Emp.: 80
Braking & Suspension Systems
N.A.I.C.S.: 336340

ArvinMeritor CV Aftermarket
GmbH   **(2)**
Hagenauerstr 59, 65203, Wiesbaden, Hes-
sen, Germany
Tel.: (49) 61156507821
Vehicle Parts Mfr
N.A.I.C.S.: 336390

ArvinMeritor CVS (Shanghai) Co.,
Ltd.   **(2)**
B Part No 48 Taigu Road Gaoqiao Bonded
Ar, Shanghai, 200131, China
Tel.: (86) 2158685095
Vehicle Parts Mfr
N.A.I.C.S.: 336390

ArvinMeritor Heavy Vehicle Systems
Espania S.A.   **(2)**
Carretera De Granollers A Sabadell Km 15
3, 08401, Barcelona, Spain   **(100%)**
Tel.: (34) 938439568
Sales Range: $10-24.9 Million
Emp.: 4
Braking & Suspension Systems Sales
N.A.I.C.S.: 336340

Division (Domestic):

ArvinMeritor Light Vehicle Aftermarket
Group   **(2)**
2135 W Maple Rd, Troy, MI 48084
Tel.: (248) 435-1000
Web Site: http://www.meritor.com
Sales Range: $10-24.9 Million
Emp.: 25
Mfr of Aftermarket Automotive Shock Ab-
sorbers, Exhaust Systems & Filters
N.A.I.C.S.: 336390

Subsidiary (Non-US):

ArvinMeritor Light Vehicle
Systems-France   **(3)**
18 Rue De Gauriers, 45600, Sully-sur-Loire,
France   **(100%)**
Tel.: (33) 238298800
Web Site: http://www.arvinmeritor.com
Emp.: 500
Motor Vehicle Parts Mfr
N.A.I.C.S.: 336390
Stephan Land *(Chm)*

Meritor LVS Zhenjiang Co. Ltd. **(3)**
2 Jingwu Road Dingmao Development
Zone, Jingkou District, Zhenjiang, 212009,
China   **(100%)**
Tel.: (86) 51188885999
Braking & Suspension Systems
N.A.I.C.S.: 336340

Subsidiary (Domestic):

Meritor Light Vehicle Technology,
LLC   **(3)**
2135 W Maple Rd, Troy, MI 48084-7121
Tel.: (248) 273-4698

Web Site: http://www.arvinmeritor.com
Vehicle Mfr
N.A.I.C.S.: 336340

Subsidiary (Non-US):

Arvinmeritor Sweden AB   **(2)**
Ishockeygatan 3, 711 34, Lindesberg, 711
34, Sweden
Tel.: (46) 58184000
Web Site: http://www.meritor.com
Emp.: 800
Vehicle Parts Mfr
N.A.I.C.S.: 336390
Laila Osterholm *(Pres)*

Joint Venture (Non-US):

Automotive Axles Limited   **(2)**
Hootagalli Industrial Area Off Hunsur Road,
Mysore, 570 018, Karnataka, India
Tel.: (91) 8217197500
Web Site: http://www.autoaxle.com
Rev.: $279,194,293
Assets: $138,669,145
Liabilities: $47,628,679
Net Worth: $91,040,465
Earnings: $19,426,773
Emp.: 988
Fiscal Year-end: 03/31/2023
Motor Vehicle Rear Drive Axle Assemblies
Mfr; Owned by Kalyani Group & by Arvin-
Meritor, Inc.
N.A.I.C.S.: 336390
Chrishan Villavarayan *(Bd of Dirs, Execu-*
tives)
Babasaheb Neelkanth Kalyani *(Chm)*
R. Shivakumar *(Member-Mgmt Bd, VP-Ops*
& Mgr-Factory)
Ranganathan S. *(CFO & Member-Mgmt Bd)*
Debadas Panda *(Compliance Officer & Sec)*
K. S. Satish *(Member-Mgmt Bd, Head-*
Quality & Svc & Gen Mgr)
Srinivasan Kumaradevan *(Member-Mgmt*
Bd & Sr VP)

Subsidiary (Domestic):

AxleTech International Holdings,
Inc.   **(2)**
1400 Rochester Rd, Troy, MI 48083
Tel.: (248) 658-7200
Web Site: http://www.axletech.com
Sales Range: $250-299.9 Million
Holding Company; Off-Highway & Specialty
Vehicle Drivetrain Systems & Components
Mfr & Whslr
N.A.I.C.S.: 551112
Tom Buley *(VP-Pur & Program Mgmt)*

Subsidiary (Non-US):

AxleTech International SAS   **(3)**
4 Rue Jean Servanton, PO Box 656,
42042, Saint Etienne, France
Tel.: (33) 477928800
Web Site: http://www.axletech.com
Off-Highway & Specialty Vehicle Drivetrain
Systems & Components Mfr & Whslr
N.A.I.C.S.: 336350
Mathieu Fidel *(Pres & VP-Ops-Intl)*

Subsidiary (Domestic):

AxleTech International, LLC   **(3)**
1400 Rochester Rd, Troy, MI 48083
Tel.: (248) 658-7200
Web Site: http://www.axletech.com
Off-Highway & Specialty Vehicle Drivetrain
Systems & Components Mfr & Whslr
N.A.I.C.S.: 336350
Joseph L. Mejaly *(CEO)*

Subsidiary (Non-US):

AxleTech do Brasil Sistemas Automo-
tivos Ltda.   **(3)**
Rua Marechal Rondon 840, Sao Paulo,
Osasco, 06093-010, SP, Brazil
Tel.: (55) 11 3653 1420
Web Site: http://www.axletech.com
Emp.: 36
Off-Highway & Specialty Vehicle Drivetrain
Systems & Components Whslr
N.A.I.C.S.: 423120

Subsidiary (Non-US):

Gabriel Europe   **(2)**
Le Clos aux Moines, BP 63, 28800, Bon-
neval, France

Tel.: (33) 237444800
Web Site: http://www.gabrieleurope.com
Sales Range: $25-49.9 Million
Emp.: 160
Gas & Hydraulic Shock Absorbers Mfr
N.A.I.C.S.: 336390

Meritor Aftermarket Spain, S.A. **(2)**
Medes 4 Bjo, Barcelona, 08023, Spain
Tel.: (34) 935519736
Web Site: http://www.meritor.com
Emp.: 4
Automobile Parts Mfr
N.A.I.C.S.: 423120

Meritor Aftermarket Switzerland
AG   **(2)**
Neugutstrasse 89, Dubendorf, 8600, Swit-
zerland
Tel.: (41) 41448248200
Vehicle Parts & Equipment Mfr
N.A.I.C.S.: 336390

Meritor Automotive B.V.   **(2)**
Antareslaan 47, 2132 JE, Hoofddorp,
Netherlands   **(100%)**
Tel.: (31) 235690300
Web Site: http://www.meritor.com
Sales Range: $25-49.9 Million
Emp.: 80
N.A.I.C.S.: 336340

Subsidiary (Domestic):

Meritor Brake Holdings, Inc.   **(2)**
2135 W Maple Rd, Troy, MI 48084-7121
Tel.: (248) 435-1000
Web Site: http://www.meritor.com
Sales Range: $75-99.9 Million
Emp.: 200
Braking & Suspension Systems
N.A.I.C.S.: 336340

Subsidiary (Non-US):

Meritor HVS   **(2)**
Emmeuble Vinci 13 Rue Henni Becquerel,
77290, Mitry-Mory, France   **(100%)**
Tel.: (33) 164274461
Sales Range: $10-24.9 Million
Emp.: 3
Axles & Mechanical & Air Suspensions
N.A.I.C.S.: 336350

Meritor HVS AB   **(2)**
Ishockeygatan 3, 711 34, Lindesberg,
Sweden   **(100%)**
Tel.: (46) 58184000
Web Site: http://www.meritor.com
Sales Range: $150-199.9 Million
Emp.: 900
Mfr of Truck & Trailer Products
N.A.I.C.S.: 333924

Meritor HVS India Ltd.   **(2)**
Plot No 36 Off Hunsur Road, Hootagalli In-
dustrial area, Mysore, 570 018, Karnataka,
India   **(51%)**
Tel.: (91) 8217197800
Web Site: https://www.mhvsil.com
Sales Range: $250-299.9 Million
Emp.: 90
Design, Research & Development, Sales &
Marketing & Export of Automotive Compo-
nents, Including Drive Axles, Brakes & Ag-
gregates
N.A.I.C.S.: 336340
Raghunathan Sundararajan *(Sr VP)*

Meritor Heavy Vehicle Systems Cam-
eri SpA   **(2)**
Strada Provinciale Cameri Bellinzago, Km
5, 28062, Novara, 28062, Italy   **(100%)**
Tel.: (39) 03214231
Web Site: http://www.meritor.com
Sales Range: $300-349.9 Million
Emp.: 600
Mfr of Commercial Vehicle Aftermarket
Products; Bus & Coach Products; Air Cam,
Wedge & Disc Brakes & Axles for Trucks
N.A.I.C.S.: 336340

Subsidiary (Domestic):

Meritor Heavy Vehicle Systems,
LLC   **(2)**
7975 Dixie Hwy, Florence, KY 41042-2793
Tel.: (859) 525-3500
Web Site: http://www.meritor.com
Emp.: 300

Motor Vehicle Parts & Accessories Mfr
N.A.I.C.S.: 336390

Subsidiary (Non-US):

Meritor Holdings Netherlands B.V. (2)
Antareslaan 47, Hoofddorp, Netherlands
Tel.: (31) 235690300
Vehicle Parts Mfr
N.A.I.C.S.: 336390

Meritor Huayang Vehicle Braking Company, Ltd. (2)
No 32-1 Che Cheng South Road, Shiyan, 442000, Hu Bei, China
Tel.: (86) 7198876100
Vehicle Parts & Equipment Mfr
N.A.I.C.S.: 423120

Meritor Japan K.K. (2)
MetLife Bldg 6F 25-15 Yamashita-cho, Naka-ku, Yokohama, 231-0023, Japan
Tel.: (81) 456405820
Automotive Repair & Services
N.A.I.C.S.: 336390
Michihiro Emuematsu (Gen Mgr)

Subsidiary (Domestic):

Meritor Management Corp. (2)
2135 W Maple Rd, Troy, MI 48084
Tel.: (248) 435-4709
Motor Vehicle Parts Mfr
N.A.I.C.S.: 336390

Subsidiary (Non-US):

Meritor Mexicana, S.A. de C.V. (2)
Ave Del Tepeyac 110 Col Parque Industrial El Tepeyac El Marquez, Queretaro, 76020, Mexico
Tel.: (52) 4422781200
Automobile Mfr
N.A.I.C.S.: 336390

Joint Venture (Domestic):

Meritor Suspension Systems Company (2)
6401 W Fort St, Detroit, MI 48209
Tel.: (313) 551-2735
Web Site: http://www.mitsubishisteel.co.jp
Sales Range: $10-24.9 Million
Emp.: 6
Automotive Coil Springs, Torsion Bars, Stabilizer Bars & Automobile Assemblies
N.A.I.C.S.: 336340

Subsidiary (Non-US):

Meritor, Inc. (2)
Km 9 5 Carretera Queretaro, CP 76100, San Luis Potosi, QRO, Mexico (100%)
Tel.: (52) 8181507580
Web Site: http://www.meritor.com
Sales Range: $150-199.9 Million
Emp.: 400
Motor Vehicle Parts & Accessories Mfr
N.A.I.C.S.: 336340

Subsidiary (Domestic):

Transportation Power, Inc. (2)
2145 Auto Pkwy, Escondido, CA 92029
Tel.: (858) 248-4255
Web Site: http://www.transpowerusa.com
Motor Vehicle Transmission & Power Train Parts Manufacturing
N.A.I.C.S.: 336350
Michael Simon (Pres & CEO)

Subsidiary (Non-US):

Wilmot-Breeden Holdings Limited (2)
Unit 21 Sutton Park Ave, Suttons Business Park, Reading, RG6 1LA, Berks, United Kingdom (100%)
Tel.: (44) 1189359074
Sales Range: $50-74.9 Million
Emp.: 100
Holding Company
N.A.I.C.S.: 551112

OOO Cummins (1)
1G Klyazma Khimki, Moscow, 141402, Russia
Tel.: (7) 4959268624
Web Site: http://www.cummins.ru
Industrial Machinery Distr

N.A.I.C.S.: 423830

Pacific World Trade Inc. (1)
8604 Allisonville Rd Ste 160, Indianapolis, IN 46250
Tel.: (317) 570-8846
Web Site: http://www.pacificworldtrade.com
Sales Range: $75-99.9 Million
Emp.: 3
Automotive Parts Importer & Exporter
N.A.I.C.S.: 425120
Dennis B. Kelley (Pres)

SYTECH (1)
500 Central Ave, Columbus, IN 47201 (100%)
Tel.: (812) 377-8105
Sales Range: $10-24.9 Million
Emp.: 20
Engine Components
N.A.I.C.S.: 333248
Jason Irwin (Gen Mgr)

Shanghai Cummins Trading Co., Ltd. (1)
Room 2308 Metro Mansion No 30 Ti, Shanghai, 200030, China
Tel.: (86) 2160852600
Emp.: 50
Power Generator Whslr
N.A.I.C.S.: 423120

Taiwan Cummins Sales & Services Co. Ltd. (1)
49 Ting Hu Road, Kuei Shan Dist, Taoyuan, 33327, Taiwan
Tel.: (886) 33188999
Motor Vehicle Electrical & Electronic Equipment Mfr
N.A.I.C.S.: 336320

Turbo Drive Ltd. (1)
4 Lok Tung Street On Lok Tsuen, Fanling, New Territories, China (Hong Kong)
Tel.: (852) 26065678
Industrial Machinery Distr
N.A.I.C.S.: 423830

WABCO Compressor Manufacturing Co. (1)
8225 Lincoln Patriot Blvd, North Charleston, SC 29418
Tel.: (843) 745-1158
Web Site: http://www.wabco-auto.com
Sales Range: $125-149.9 Million
Air Compressors
N.A.I.C.S.: 333912

CUMULUS MEDIA INC.

780 Johnson Ferry Rd NE Ste 500, Atlanta, GA 30342
Tel.: (404) 949-0700   DE
Web Site:
    https://www.cumulusmedia.com
Year Founded: 1997
CMLS—(NASDAQ)
Rev.: $953,506,000
Assets: $1,609,031,000
Liabilities: $1,200,626,000
Net Worth: $408,405,000
Earnings: $16,235,000
Emp.: 2,455
Fiscal Year-end: 12/31/22
Holding Company; Radio Broadcasting Stations & Radio Network Owner & Operator
N.A.I.C.S.: 551112
Suzanne M. Grimes (Exec VP-Corp Mktg)
Richard S. Denning (Gen Counsel, Sec & Exec VP)
Mary G. Berner (Pres & CEO)
David H. Milner (Pres-Ops)
Francisco J. Lopez-Balboa (CFO & Exec VP)
Bob Walker (Exec VP-Ops)

Subsidiaries:

Cumulus Media Holdings, Inc. (1)
3280 Peachtree Rd NW Ste 2300, Atlanta, GA 30305
Tel.: (404) 949-0700
Web Site: http://www.cumulus.com
Holding Company
N.A.I.C.S.: 551112

Subsidiary (Domestic):

Broadcast Software International Inc. (2)
909 International Way, Springfield, OR 97477 (100%)
Tel.: (541) 338-8588
Web Site: https://bsiusa.com
Radio Automation & Broadcasting Software Publisher
N.A.I.C.S.: 513210

Cumulus Broadcasting LLC (2)
3280 Peachtree Rd NW Ste 2300, Atlanta, GA 30305 (100%)
Tel.: (404) 949-0700
Web Site: http://www.cumulus.com
Radio Broadcasting Stations Operator
N.A.I.C.S.: 516110
Lewis W. Dickey Jr. (Chm, Pres & CEO)

Subsidiary (Domestic):

Atlanta Radio, LLC (3)
780 Johnson Ferry Rd NE 5th Fl, Atlanta, GA 30342
Tel.: (404) 497-4700
Web Site: http://atlanta.cumulusradio.com
Sales Range: $25-49.9 Million
Radio Broadcasting Stations
N.A.I.C.S.: 516110

Chicago Radio, LLC (3)
455 N Cityfront Plz Dr Ste 1700, Chicago, IL 60611
Tel.: (312) 984-0890
Web Site: http://chicago.cumulusradio.com
Sales Range: $25-49.9 Million
Emp.: 100
Radio Broadcasting Stations
N.A.I.C.S.: 516110

Unit (Domestic):

Cumulus Broadcasting Inc. - Indianapolis, IN (3)
6810 N Shadeland Ave, Indianapolis, IN 46220
Tel.: (317) 842-9550
Web Site: http://www.cumulusmedia.com
Radio Broadcasting Stations
N.A.I.C.S.: 516110

Cumulus Broadcasting LLC - Abilene, TX (3)
2525 S Danville Dr, Abilene, TX 79605
Tel.: (325) 793-9700
Sales Range: $10-24.9 Million
Emp.: 30
Radio Broadcasting Stations
N.A.I.C.S.: 516110
Lori Morris (Bus Mgr)
Chris Andrews (Engr)

Cumulus Broadcasting LLC - Allentown, PA (3)
2158 Ave C Ste 100, Bethlehem, PA 18017
Tel.: (610) 266-7600
Web Site: http://allentown.cumulusradio.com
Sales Range: $1-9.9 Million
Emp.: 35
Radio Broadcasting Stations
N.A.I.C.S.: 516110

Cumulus Broadcasting LLC - Ann Arbor, MI (3)
1100 Victors Way Ste 100, Ann Arbor, MI 48108
Tel.: (734) 302-8100
Web Site: http://www.cumulusradio.com
Sales Range: $10-24.9 Million
Emp.: 25
Radio Broadcasting Stations
N.A.I.C.S.: 516110

Cumulus Broadcasting LLC - Baton Rouge, LA (3)
631 Main St, Baton Rouge, LA 70806
Tel.: (225) 926-1106
Web Site: http://www.cumulus.com
Radio Broadcasting Stations
N.A.I.C.S.: 516110

Cumulus Broadcasting LLC - Buffalo, NY (3)
50 James E Casey Dr, Buffalo, NY 14206
Tel.: (716) 881-4555
Web Site: http://buffalo.cumulusradio.com
Emp.: 70
Radio Broadcasting Stations

N.A.I.C.S.: 516110

Cumulus Broadcasting LLC - Cincinnati, OH (3)
4805 Montgomery Rd, Cincinnati, OH 45212
Tel.: (513) 241-9898
Web Site: http://cincinnati.cumulusradio.com
Sales Range: $25-49.9 Million
Emp.: 65
Radio Broadcasting Stations
N.A.I.C.S.: 516110

Cumulus Broadcasting LLC - Colorado Springs, CO (3)
6805 Corporate Dr Ste 130, Colorado Springs, CO 80919
Tel.: (719) 593-2700
Web Site: http://www.cumulusmedia.com
Radio Broadcasting Stations
N.A.I.C.S.: 516110
Scott Jones (Gen Mgr)

Cumulus Broadcasting LLC - Columbia, MO (3)
503 Old Hwy 63 N, Columbia, MO 65201
Tel.: (573) 449-4141
Web Site: http://columbia.cumulusradio.com
Sales Range: $25-49.9 Million
Emp.: 75
Radio Broadcasting Stations
N.A.I.C.S.: 516110

Unit (Domestic):

Cumulus Broadcasting LLC - Jefferson City, MO (4)
1002 Diamond Rdg Ste 400, Jefferson City, MO 65109
Tel.: (573) 893-5100
Web Site: http://www.cumulus.com
Emp.: 20
Radio Broadcasting Stations
N.A.I.C.S.: 516110

Unit (Domestic):

Cumulus Broadcasting LLC - Columbia, SC (3)
1301 Gervais St Ste 700, Columbia, SC 29201
Tel.: (803) 796-7600
Web Site: http://www.cumulus.com
Sales Range: $25-49.9 Million
Emp.: 50
Radio Broadcasting Stations
N.A.I.C.S.: 516110

Cumulus Broadcasting LLC - Dallas, TX (3)
3090 Nowitzki Way W Victory Plz Ste 400, Dallas, TX 75219
Tel.: (214) 526-2400
Web Site: http://www.cumulusmedia.com
Radio Broadcasting Stations
N.A.I.C.S.: 516110
Dan Bennett (Reg VP)
Tom Dailey (Bus Mgr)
Austin Maddox (Dir-Digital Ops)
Janet DuPree (Sls Mgr-Digital)
Dawn Girocco (VP-Sls)
Rebecca Silvers (Dir-Mktg & Promos)

Cumulus Broadcasting LLC - Dubuque, IA (3)
5490 Saratoga Rd, Dubuque, IA 52002-2593
Tel.: (563) 557-1040
Web Site: http://dubuque.cumulusradio.com
Sales Range: $25-49.9 Million
Emp.: 15
Radio Broadcasting Stations
N.A.I.C.S.: 516110
Daniel Sullivan (Pres & Gen Mgr)

Cumulus Broadcasting LLC - Fayetteville, NC (3)
1009 Drayton Rd, Fayetteville, NC 28303
Tel.: (910) 864-5222
Web Site:
    http://www.fayettevillenc.cumulusradio.com
Sales Range: $25-49.9 Million
Emp.: 30
Radio Broadcasting Stations

Cumulus Media Inc.—(Continued)

N.A.I.C.S.: 516110
Linda Schulte *(Mgr-Promotion)*
Eric McCart *(VP & Gen Mgr)*

Cumulus Broadcasting LLC - Harrisburg, PA (3)
2300 Vartan Way, Harrisburg, PA 17110
Tel.: (717) 238-1041
Web Site:
    http://www.harrisburg.cumulusradio.com
Emp.: 50
Radio Broadcasting Stations
N.A.I.C.S.: 516110
John O'Dea *(Ops Mgr-Harrisburg Stations)*
Janelle Kachtik *(Dir-Promos-Harrisburg Stations)*

Unit (Domestic):

Cumulus Broadcasting LLC - York, PA (4)
5989 Susquehanna Plz Dr, York, PA 17406
Tel.: (717) 764-1155
Web Site: http://newstalkwsba.com
Radio Broadcasting Stations
N.A.I.C.S.: 516110

Unit (Domestic):

Cumulus Broadcasting LLC - Houston, TX (3)
9801 Westheimer Rd Ste 700, Houston, TX 77042-3950
Tel.: (713) 266-1000
Web Site: https://www.krbe.com
Radio Broadcasting Stations
N.A.I.C.S.: 516110
Leslie Whittle *(Program Dir)*

Cumulus Broadcasting LLC - Kansas City, KS (3)
8900 Indian Creek Pkwy 3rd Fl, Overland Park, KS 66210
Tel.: (913) 514-3000
Web Site: http://www.cumulusmedia.com
Radio Broadcasting Stations
N.A.I.C.S.: 516110
Jon Taylor *(Dir-Broadcast Production-KCFX-FM)*
Donna Baker *(Reg VP-Midwest)*
Bill Ryan *(Sls Mgr-KCFX-FM, KCMO-FM)*
Jared Robb *(Sls Mgr-KCMO-HD2)*
Ashley Coppock *(Dir-Mktg & Promos)*
Ryan Britland *(Sls Mgr-KCJK-FM)*

Cumulus Broadcasting LLC - Kokomo, IN (3)
519 N Main St, Kokomo, IN 46901
Tel.: (765) 459-4191
Web Site: https://www.wwki.com
Sales Range: $1-9.9 Million
Emp.: 25
Radio Broadcasting Stations
N.A.I.C.S.: 516110
John Spilman *(Mgr-Market)*

Cumulus Broadcasting LLC - Lafayette, LA (3)
202 Galbert Rd, Lafayette, LA 70506
Tel.: (337) 232-1311
Web Site: http://www.cumulus.com
Sales Range: $25-49.9 Million
Emp.: 50
Radio Broadcasting Stations
N.A.I.C.S.: 516110

Cumulus Broadcasting LLC - Little Rock, AR (3)
124 W Capitol Ave Ste 1900, Little Rock, AR 72201
Tel.: (501) 401-0200
Web Site: http://www.power923.com
Radio Broadcasting Stations
N.A.I.C.S.: 516110

Cumulus Broadcasting LLC - Modesto/Stockton, CA (3)
3127 Transworld, Stockton, CA 95206
Tel.: (209) 766-5000
Web Site: http://modesto.cumulusradio.com
Sales Range: $25-49.9 Million
Emp.: 85
Radio Broadcasting Stations
N.A.I.C.S.: 516110

Cumulus Broadcasting LLC - Muncie, IN (3)
1134 W State Rd 38, New Castle, IN 47362

Tel.: (765) 529-2600
Web Site:
    http://www.muncie.cumulusradio.com
Sales Range: $10-24.9 Million
Emp.: 25
Radio Broadcasting Stations
N.A.I.C.S.: 516110
Chris Carter *(Dir-Program)*

Cumulus Broadcasting LLC - New Orleans, LA (3)
201 Saint Charles Ave Ste 201, New Orleans, LA 70170
Tel.: (504) 581-7002
Web Site: http://www.cumulusradio.com
Radio Broadcasting Stations
N.A.I.C.S.: 516110

Cumulus Broadcasting LLC - Oklahoma City, OK (3)
4045 NW 64th St Ste 600, Oklahoma City, OK 73116
Tel.: (405) 848-0100
Web Site:
    http://www.oklahomacity.cumulusradio.com
Emp.: 100
Radio Broadcasting Stations
N.A.I.C.S.: 516110
Jake Daniels *(Dir-Program & Mgr-Ops)*
Jay Davis *(Mgr-Sls Local)*

Cumulus Broadcasting LLC - Saginaw, MI (3)
1740 Champagne Dr N, Saginaw, MI 48604
Tel.: (989) 776-2100
Web Site: http://www.cumulus.com
Emp.: 40
Radio Broadcasting Stations
N.A.I.C.S.: 516110

Cumulus Broadcasting LLC - Salt Lake City, UT (3)
434 Bearcat Dr, Salt Lake City, UT 84115
Tel.: (801) 485-6700
Web Site: http://www.cumulus.com
Sales Range: $25-49.9 Million
Emp.: 120
Radio Broadcasting Stations
N.A.I.C.S.: 516110

Cumulus Broadcasting LLC - Syracuse, NY (3)
1064 James St, Syracuse, NY 13203
Tel.: (315) 472-0200
Sales Range: $25-49.9 Million
Emp.: 60
Radio Broadcasting Stations
N.A.I.C.S.: 516110

Cumulus Broadcasting LLC - Wichita Falls, TX (3)
4302 Call Field Rd, Wichita Falls, TX 76308
Tel.: (940) 691-2311
Web Site: http://www.cumulus.com
Sales Range: $25-49.9 Million
Emp.: 17
Radio Broadcasting Stations
N.A.I.C.S.: 516110

Cumulus Broadcasting LLC - Worcester, MA (3)
250 Commercial St, Worcester, MA 01608
Tel.: (508) 752-1045
Web Site:
    http://worcester.cumulusradio.com
Sales Range: $1-9.9 Million
Emp.: 40
Radio Broadcasting Stations
N.A.I.C.S.: 516110

Subsidiary (Domestic):

DC Radio Assets, LLC (3)
4400 Jenifer St NW, Washington, DC 20015-2113
Tel.: (202) 895-2327
Holding Company; Radio Broadcasting Stations
N.A.I.C.S.: 551112

Detroit Radio, LLC (3)
3011 W Grand Blvd Fisher Bldg Ste 800, Detroit, MI 48202
Tel.: (313) 871-3030
Web Site:
    http://www.detroitcumulusradio.com
Sales Range: $25-49.9 Million
Emp.: 95
Radio Broadcasting Stations

N.A.I.C.S.: 516110
LA Radio, LLC (3)
3321 La Cienaga Blvd, Los Angeles, CA 90016-3114
Tel.: (310) 840-4900
Web Site:
    http://losangeles.cumulusradio.com
Radio Broadcasting Stations
N.A.I.C.S.: 516110

Subsidiary (Domestic):

Radio Networks, LLC (2)
261 Madison Ave, New York, NY 10016
Tel.: (212) 735-1700
Web Site:
    http://www.cumulusmedianetworks.com
Sales Range: $150-199.9 Million
Radio Networks Operator
N.A.I.C.S.: 516210

Branch (Domestic):

Radio Networks, LLC - Dallas Office (3)
13725 Montfort Dr, Dallas, TX 75240
Tel.: (972) 991-9200
Web Site:
    http://affiliates.citadelmedianetworks.com
Radio Networks Operations
N.A.I.C.S.: 516210

Subsidiary (Domestic):

Westwood One, Inc. (2)
300 Vesey St 11th Fl, New York, NY 10282
Tel.: (212) 967-2888
Web Site: http://www.westwoodone.com
Rev.: $239,019,000
Assets: $340,612,000
Liabilities: $401,781,000
Net Worth: ($61,169,000)
Earnings: ($146,692,000)
Emp.: 425
Fiscal Year-end: 12/31/2012
Radio Network & Advertising Services
N.A.I.C.S.: 516210

Dial Commuications Global Media, LLC (1)
Candle Tower 220 W 42nd St, New York, NY 10036
Tel.: (212) 967-2888
Commercial Radio Broadcasting Services
N.A.I.C.S.: 516210

POP Radio, LP (1)
100 Federal St 30th Fl, Boston, MA 02110
Tel.: (617) 576-9700
Web Site: http://www.popradio.com
Radio Station Operator
N.A.I.C.S.: 516110
Jeff Shapiro *(Chm)*
Gary Seem *(Pres)*

CURALEAF HOLDINGS, INC.
290 Harbor Dr, Stamford, CT 06902
Tel.: (781) 451-0150 BC
Web Site: http://www.curaleaf.com
Year Founded: 2014
CURA—(TSX)
Rev.: $1,346,632,000
Assets: $3,096,576,000
Liabilities: $1,925,284,000
Net Worth: $1,171,292,000
Earnings: $281,197,000
Emp.: 5,650
Fiscal Year-end: 12/31/23
Cannabis Pharmacist Product Distr
N.A.I.C.S.: 456110
Joseph Lusardi *(Founder & Vice Chm)*
Matt Darin *(CEO)*
Ed Kremer *(CFO)*
Peter Clateman *(Chief Legal Officer)*

CURATIVE BIOSCIENCES, INC.
2 S Biscayne Blvd Ste 3760, Miami, FL 33131
Tel.: (949) 287-3164 NV
Web Site: http://www.curativebio.com
Year Founded: 1996
CBDX—(OTCIQ)
Beverage Mfr & Sales
N.A.I.C.S.: 312111

CURIOSITYSTREAM INC.
8484 Georgia Ave Ste 700, Silver Spring, MD 20910
Tel.: (310) 755-2050 DE
Web Site: https://curiositystream.com
Year Founded: 2019
CURI—(NASDAQ)
Rev.: $78,043,000
Assets: $154,113,000
Liabilities: $36,487,000
Net Worth: $117,626,000
Earnings: ($50,917,000)
Emp.: 78
Fiscal Year-end: 12/31/22
Media & Entertainment Company
N.A.I.C.S.: 512110
Tia Cudahy *(COO & Gen Counsel)*
Andre Silva *(CTO)*
P. Brady Hayden *(CFO)*
Ludo Dufour *(VP-Licensing)*
John Hendricks *(Founder & Chm)*
Clint Stinchcomb *(Pres & CEO)*

CURIS, INC.
128 Spring St Bldg C- Ste 500, Lexington, MA 02421
Tel.: (617) 503-6500 DE
Web Site: https://www.curis.com
Year Founded: 2000
CRIS—(NASDAQ)
Rev.: $10,023,000
Assets: $77,282,000
Liabilities: $57,612,000
Net Worth: $19,670,000
Earnings: ($47,413,000)
Emp.: 48
Fiscal Year-end: 12/31/23
Therapeutic Drug Developer
N.A.I.C.S.: 325414
Robert E. Martell *(Head-R&D)*
Rachel Blasbalg *(Sr Dir-HR)*
Reinhard von Roemeling *(Sr VP-Clinical Dev)*
Dora Ferrari *(VP-Clinical Ops)*
Mark Noel *(VP)*
Jonathan Zung *(Chief Dev Officer)*
James E. Dentzer *(Pres & CEO)*

Subsidiaries:

Curis Securities Corporation (1)
4 Maguire Rd, Lexington, MA 02421-3112
Tel.: (701) 001-0007
Sales Range: $25-49.9 Million
Biotechnology Research & Development Laboratories Services
N.A.I.C.S.: 541714

CURO GROUP HOLDINGS CORP.
200 W Hubbard St 8th Fl, Chicago, IL 60654
Tel.: (312) 470-2741 DE
Web Site: https://www.curo.com
Year Founded: 1997
CURO—(NYSE)
Rev.: $1,025,918,000
Assets: $2,789,193,000
Liabilities: $2,040,327,000
Net Worth: ($54,134,000)
Earnings: ($185,484,000)
Emp.: 4,000
Fiscal Year-end: 12/31/22
Financial Management Services
N.A.I.C.S.: 551112
Tamara Schulz *(Chief Acctg Officer)*
Ismail Dawood *(CFO)*
Chad Faulkner *(Founder & Chm)*
Gary Fulk *(COO)*
Peter Kalen *(CEO)*
Jennifer Mathissen *(CMO)*
Rebecca Fox *(Chief Legal Officer)*
Phil Gitler *(Chief Strategy Officer)*
Shu Chen *(Chief Credit Risk Officer)*

Kerry Palombo *(Chief Compliance Officer)*

Subsidiaries:

Ad Astra Recovery Services Inc.   **(1)**
3527 N Ridge Rd, Wichita, KS 67205-9370
Web Site:
   http://www.adastrarecoveryservicesinc.com
Emp.: 80
Collection Agencies
N.A.I.C.S.: 561440

Attain Finance Canada, Inc.   **(1)**
400 Carlingview Drive, Toronto; M9W 5X9,
ON, Canada
Financial Management Services
N.A.I.C.S.: 551112

Avio Credit, Inc.   **(1)**
3615 N Ridge Rd, Wichita, KS 67205
Web Site: http://www.aviocredit.com
Consumer Lending & Loan Services
N.A.I.C.S.: 522291

Cash Colorado, LLC   **(1)**
3615 N Ridge Rd, Wichita, KS 67205
Tel.: (316) 425-1175
Web Site: http://www.speedycash.com
Payday & Installment Loan Services
N.A.I.C.S.: 522310

Cash Money Cheque Cashing,
Inc.   **(1)**
4-2880 Queen Street East Suite 316,
Brampton, L6S 6E8, ON, Canada
Web Site: https://www.cashmoney.ca
Payday Lender & Cheque Cashing Services
N.A.I.C.S.: 522390
Dave Hews *(Owner)*

Ennoble Finance, LLC   **(1)**
PO Box 319, Maize, KS 67101
Web Site: https://www.revolvefinance.com
Finance Banking Services
N.A.I.C.S.: 522220

First Heritage Credit LLC   **(1)**
605 Crescent Blvd Ste 101, Ridgeland, MS
39157-8659
Tel.: (601) 898-8611
Web Site: http://www.1stheritagecredit.com
Credit Union
N.A.I.C.S.: 522130

Heights Finance Corporation   **(1)**
101 N Main Street Ste 600, Greenville, SC
29601   **(100%)**
Web Site: https://www.heightsfinance.com
Sales Range: $75-99.9 Million
Emp.: 35
Consumer Lending & Sales Financing Ser-
vices
N.A.I.C.S.: 522291
Wendy L. Kisler *(Sec)*
Timothy L. Stanley *(CEO)*

LendDirect Corp.   **(1)**
4-2880 Queen Street East Suite 316,
Brampton, L6S 6E8, ON, Canada
Web Site: https://www.lenddirect.ca
Personal & Investment Loan Services
N.A.I.C.S.: 522291

CURRENC GROUP INC.

32 Broadway Ste 401, New York, NY
10004
Tel.: (212) 287-5010   Ky
Web Site: https://www.infintspac.com
Year Founded: 2021
CURR—(NASDAQ)
Rev.: $2,932,192
Assets: $209,298,900
Liabilities: $217,787,204
Net Worth: ($8,488,304)
Earnings: ($1,111,964)
Emp.: 2
Fiscal Year-end: 12/31/22
Investment Services
N.A.I.C.S.: 523999
Sheldon Brickman *(CFO)*

Subsidiaries:

Seamless Group Inc.   **(1)**
9F Olympia Plaza 255 Kings Road, North
Point, Hong Kong, China (Hong Kong)
Tel.: (852) 39516288

Web Site: http://www.tngfintech.com
Investment Services
N.A.I.C.S.: 523999
Haggai Ravid *(CFO)*
Alex Kong *(Co-Founder)*
Takis Wong *(Co-Founder & COO)*
Ronnie Hui *(CEO)*

Subsidiary (Non-US):

Tranglo Sdn. Bhd.   **(2)**
Unit 10-1 Tower 9 Avenue 5 Bangsar South
8 Jln Kerinchi, 59200, Kuala Lumpur,
Malaysia   **(60%)**
Tel.: (60) 322414188
Web Site: http://www.tranglo.com
Mobile Financial Transaction Processing
Platform Developer & Operator
N.A.I.C.S.: 518210
Hui Yong Sia *(CEO)*

CURRENCY EXCHANGE IN-TERNATIONAL, CORP.

6649 Westwood Blvd Ste 250, Or-
lando, FL 32821
Tel.: (407) 240-0224
Web Site: https://www.ceifx.com
Year Founded: 1998
CXI—(TSX)
Rev.: $41,784,043
Assets: $82,729,716
Liabilities: $16,400,679
Net Worth: $66,329,037
Earnings: $2,924,720
Emp.: 350
Fiscal Year-end: 10/31/19
Currency Exchange, Travelers'
Checks, Foreign Check Clearing &
International Wire Payments
N.A.I.C.S.: 522320
Randolph W. Pinna *(Pres & CEO)*
Matthew A. Schillo *(COO)*
Wade A. Bracy *(VP-Process Improve-
ment)*
Khatuna Bezhitashvili *(VP-HR)*
Irene Vomvolakis *(VP-Ops)*
Paul Ohm *(VP-IT)*
Stephen Fitzpatrick *(CFO)*
Katelyn Brown *(Fin Dir)*
Chirag Bhavsar *(Chm)*
Dennis Winkel *(Chief Risk Officer)*

Subsidiaries:

eZforex.com, Inc.   **(1)**
213 N Fredonia St Ste 240, Longview, TX
75601
Tel.: (903) 663-3056
Web Site: http://www.ezforex.com
Foreign Exchange Service Provider
N.A.I.C.S.: 523160

CURTISS MOTORCYCLE COMPANY, INC.

8114 Pkwy Dr, Leeds, AL 35094-2225
Tel.: (205) 460-5855   DE
Web Site:
   https://www.curtissmotorcycles.com
Year Founded: 1991
CMOT—(OTCIQ)
Rev.: $99
Assets: $600,998
Liabilities: $1,675,573
Net Worth: ($1,074,575)
Earnings: ($1,253,725)
Fiscal Year-end: 03/31/23
Motorcyle Designer & Mfr
N.A.I.C.S.: 336991
H. Matthew Chambers *(Chm& CEO)*

CURTISS-WRIGHT CORPORATION

130 Harbour Pl Dr Ste 300, David-
son, NC 28036
Tel.: (704) 869-4600   DE
Web Site:
   https://www.curtisswright.com
Year Founded: 1929
CW—(NYSE)
Rev.: $2,845,373,000

Assets: $4,620,969,000
Liabilities: $2,292,556,000
Net Worth: $2,328,413,000
Earnings: $354,509,000
Emp.: 8,600
Fiscal Year-end: 12/31/23
Motion & Flow Control Components
Mfr
N.A.I.C.S.: 333310
K. Christopher Farkas *(CFO)*
Lynn M. Bamford *(Chm & CEO)*
Gary A. Ogilby *(VP & Controller)*
Robert F. Freda *(Treas & VP)*
John C. Watts *(VP)*

Subsidiaries:

901D, LLC   **(1)**
360 Rt 59, Airmont, NY 10952
Tel.: (845) 369-1111
Web Site: http://www.901d.com
Mfg Racks
N.A.I.C.S.: 337126

Curtiss-Wright Controls, Inc.   **(1)**
15800 John J Delaney Dr Ste 200, Char-
lotte, NC 28277
Tel.: (704) 869-4600
Web Site: http://www.cwcontrols.com
Sales Range: $10-24.9 Million
Emp.: 32
Control Products, Embedded Computers &
Subsystems Mfr
N.A.I.C.S.: 334519

Subsidiary (Domestic):

Autronics Corporation   **(2)**
665 N Baldwin Park Blvd, City of Industry,
CA 91746-6807   **(100%)**
Tel.: (626) 851-3100
Web Site: http://www.autronics.com
Mfr of Electronic Controls & Power Supplies
N.A.I.C.S.: 334511

Subsidiary (Non-US):

Curtiss-Wright Antriebstechnik
GmbH   **(2)**
Badstrasse 5, 8212, Neuhausen, Switzer-
land
Tel.: (41) 526746522
Industrial Supplies Whslr
N.A.I.C.S.: 423840

Curtiss-Wright Controls Defense So-
lutions - Ottawa   **(2)**
333 Palladium Drive, Kanata, K2V 1A6, ON,
Canada   **(100%)**
Tel.: (613) 599-9199
Web Site: http://www.curtisswright.com
Aerospace, Ground & Naval Defense Sys-
tems & Support
N.A.I.C.S.: 541512

Curtiss-Wright Controls Embedded
Computing-High Wycombe   **(2)**
Manor Courtyard, Hughenden Avenue, High
Wycombe, HP13 5RE, United
Kingdom   **(100%)**
Tel.: (44) 1494476000
Web Site: http://www.curtisswright.com
Computer Systems Products & Services
N.A.I.C.S.: 541519

Subsidiary (Domestic):

Curtiss-Wright Controls Integrated
Sensing   **(2)**
5875 Obispo Ave, Long Beach, CA 90805
Tel.: (562) 531-6500
Web Site: http://www.curtisswright.com
Mfr of Linear Motion Transducers
N.A.I.C.S.: 334416

Curtiss-Wright Flight Systems,
Inc.   **(2)**
201 Old Boling Spring World, Shelby, NC
28152   **(100%)**
Tel.: (704) 481-1150
Web Site: http://www.curtisswright.com
Emp.: 400
Motion Control Integrated Systems & Com-
ponents Designer & Mfr for the Aerospace,
Defense & Industrial Markets
N.A.I.C.S.: 336412

Subsidiary (Non-US):

Curtiss-Wright Valve
Group-Farris   **(2)**

15 Shaver Street, Brantford, N3T 5T3, ON,
Canada
Tel.: (519) 756-4800
Web Site: http://www.cw-valvegroup.com
Metal Valve & Pipe Fitting Mfr
N.A.I.C.S.: 332919

Subsidiary (Domestic):

IMC Magnetics Corp.   **(2)**
1900 E 5th St, Tempe, AZ 85281
Tel.: (480) 968-4441
Web Site: http://www.curtisswright.com
Valve, Fuel Atomizer, Pressure Switch, Ac-
tuator, Precision Solenoid Mfr
N.A.I.C.S.: 335314

Subsidiary (Non-US):

Indal Technologies Inc.   **(2)**
3570 Hawkestone Rd, Mississauga, L5C
2V8, ON, Canada   **(100%)**
Tel.: (905) 275-5300
Web Site: http://www.indaltech.com
Shipboard Helicopter Handling Systems Mfr
for Naval Applications
N.A.I.C.S.: 336611

Novatronics, Inc.   **(2)**
677 Erie St, Stratford, N4Z1A1, ON,
Canada
Tel.: (519) 271-3880
Engineeering Services
N.A.I.C.S.: 541330

Subsidiary (Domestic):

Parvus Corp.   **(2)**
3222 S Washington St, Salt Lake City, UT
84115
Tel.: (801) 483-1533
Web Site: http://www.parvus.com
Sales Range: $10-24.9 Million
Computers & Communication Subsystems
Mfr
N.A.I.C.S.: 334118

Subsidiary (Non-US):

Penny & Giles Controls Ltd.   **(2)**
15 Enterprise Way Aviation Park West
Bournemouth International Airport,
Christchurch, BH23 6HH, Dorset, United
Kingdom   **(100%)**
Tel.: (44) 1202409409
Web Site: http://www.pennyandgiles.com
Mfr of Position Sensors
N.A.I.C.S.: 334513

Subsidiary (Domestic):

Penny & Giles Aerospace Ltd.   **(3)**
15 Enterprise Way Aviation Park West
Bournemouth International Airport,
Christchurch, BH23 6HH, United
Kingdom   **(100%)**
Tel.: (44) 1202481771
Web Site: http://www.pennyandgiles.com
Sales Range: $50-74.9 Million
Emp.: 400
Mfr of Aircraft Flight Recorders
N.A.I.C.S.: 334511

Subsidiary (US):

Penny & Giles Controls Inc.   **(3)**
665 N Baldwin Park Blvd, City of Industry,
CA 91746-1502   **(100%)**
Tel.: (562) 531-6500
Web Site: http://www.pennyandgiles.com
Sales Range: $10-24.9 Million
Emp.: 5
Marketing & Sales of Position Sensors
N.A.I.C.S.: 334513

Subsidiary (Domestic):

Penny & Giles Controls Ltd.   **(3)**
15 Airfield Road, Bournemouth Airport,
Christchurch, BH23 3TG, United Kingdom
Tel.: (44) 1202409499
Web Site: http://www.cw-
industrialgroup.com
Mfr of Position Sensors & Industrial Joystick
Controllers
N.A.I.C.S.: 334513

Curtiss-Wright Corporation—(Continued)

Subsidiary (Non-US):

Penny & Giles GmbH (3)
Schleissheimer Strasse 91a, 85748, Garching, Germany (100%)
Tel.: (49) 8418855670
Web Site: http://www.penny-giles.de
Sales Range: $1-9.9 Million
Emp.: 15
Distr of Measuring & Control Products
N.A.I.C.S.: 334513

**Curtiss-Wright Flow Control
Corporation** (1)
2941 Fairview Park Dr Ste 850, Falls
Church, VA 22042 (100%)
Tel.: (703) 286-2000
Web Site: https://www.cwfc.com
Rev.: $548,121,024
Emp.: 200
Nuclear Valve, Pump, Motor, Generator &
Electronics Designer & Mfr
N.A.I.C.S.: 332911

Subsidiary (Domestic):

A.P. Services, LLC (2)
203 Armstrong Dr, Freeport, PA 16229
Tel.: (724) 295-6200
Web Site: http://www.apservicesinc.com
Sales Range: $10-24.9 Million
Emp.: 84
Mechanical Valve, Pump, Gasket & Fluid
Sealing Products Mfr & Distr
N.A.I.C.S.: 332919

EST Group, Inc. (2)
2701 Township Line Rd, Hatfield, PA 19440-
1770
Tel.: (215) 721-1100
Web Site: http://www.estgroup.cwsc.com
Sales Range: $25-49.9 Million
Emp.: 100
Mfr of Specialty Maintenance Tools, Caps,
Heat Exchanger & Pipe Plugs, Pressure
Pumps, Tube Testing & Plugging Equipment
N.A.I.C.S.: 334519

**Curtiss-Wright Flow Control Service,
LLC** (1)
2550 Market Str, Aston, PA 19014-3426
Tel.: (610) 494-8000
Electronic Product Mfr & Distr
N.A.I.C.S.: 334111

Dy4 Systems, Inc. (1)
333 Palladium Dr M/S 252, Kanata, K2V
1A6, ON, Canada
Tel.: (613) 599-9199
Emp.: 350
Aerospace Embedded System Mfr
N.A.I.C.S.: 334511
Cathy Pomery (VP)

**Engineered Arresting Systems
Corporation** (1)
2550 Market St, Aston, PA 19014-3426
Tel.: (610) 494-8000
Military Aircraft Arresting Gear & Commerical Aviation Runway Safety Systems
N.A.I.C.S.: 336413

Exlar Corp. (1)
18400 W 77th St, Chanhassen, MN 55317
Tel.: (952) 500-6200
Web Site: http://www.exlar.com
Sales Range: $50-74.9 Million
Emp.: 150
Roller Screw Linear Actuators, Rotary Servo
Motors & Electronic Products Mfr
N.A.I.C.S.: 332721

IMR Test Labs Inc. (1)
131 Woodsedge Dr, Lansing, NY 14882
Tel.: (607) 533-7000
Web Site: https://www.imrtest.com
Sales Range: $10-24.9 Million
Emp.: 115
Testing Laboratories
N.A.I.C.S.: 541380
Alexis Puerta (Mgr-Quality)

**Metal Improvement Company,
LLC** (1)
80 Rte 4 E Ste 310, Paramus, NJ
07652 (100%)
Tel.: (201) 843-7800
Web Site: https://www.cwst.com

Sales Range: $700-749.9 Million
Emp.: 1,000
Industrial Shot Peening , Laser Peening,
Specialty Coatings & Heat Treatment
N.A.I.C.S.: 332811
Dave Adams (Pres)

PG Drives Technology Ltd. (1)
10 Airspeed Road, Christchurch, BH23
4HD, Dorset, United Kingdom (100%)
Tel.: (44) 1425271444
Web Site: http://www.pgdt.com
Sales Range: $50-74.9 Million
Emp.: 186
Controllers for Medical & Industrial Mobility
Mfr
N.A.I.C.S.: 335314

Subsidiary (US):

PG Drives Technology Inc. (2)
2532 E Cerritos Ave, Anaheim, CA 92806-
5627
Tel.: (714) 712-7911
Web Site: http://www.pgdt.com
Motor Speed Controllers Mfr & Distr
N.A.I.C.S.: 334514

Peerless Instrument Co., Inc. (1)
2030 Coolidge St, Hollywood, FL 33020
Tel.: (954) 921-6006
Web Site:
https://www.peerlessinstrument.com
Sales Range: $25-49.9 Million
Emp.: 100
Electronic Components Mfr
N.A.I.C.S.: 334419

**Tactical Communications Group,
LLC** (1)
2 Highwood Dr, Tewksbury, MA 01876-1157
Tel.: (978) 654-4800
Software Publisher
N.A.I.C.S.: 513210

Tapco International Inc. (1)
16315 Market St, Channelview, TX 77530
Tel.: (281) 247-8100
Industrial Valve Mfr
N.A.I.C.S.: 332911

Teletronics Technology Corp. (1)
15 Terry Dr, Newtown, PA 18940
Tel.: (267) 352-2020
Web Site: http://www.ttcdas.com
Emp.: 200
Computer Software & Hardware for Aerospace & Defense Applications
N.A.I.C.S.: 541519

Williams Controls, Inc. (1)
14100 SW 72nd Ave, Portland, OR 97224
Tel.: (503) 684-8600
Web Site: http://www.curtisswright.com
Rev.: $64,372,000
Assets: $36,418,000
Liabilities: $19,747,000
Net Worth: $16,671,000
Earnings: $3,364,000
Emp.: 284
Fiscal Year-end: 09/30/2012
Electronic Throttle Controls for Commercial
Vehicles
N.A.I.C.S.: 336211

Subsidiary (Non-US):

Williams Controls Europe GmbH (2)
Schleissheimer Strasse 91a, 85748, Garching, Germany
Tel.: (49) 8104628780
Web Site: http://www.wmco.eu
Sales Range: $10-24.9 Million
Emp.: 5
Automotive Electronic Component Mfr
N.A.I.C.S.: 336320

**Williams Controls India Private
Limited** (2)
J-1 S Block Midc Bhosari, Pune, 411 026,
India
Tel.: (91) 2067319100
Web Site: http://www.cw-industrial.com
Sales Range: $25-49.9 Million
Emp.: 50
Automotive Electronic Component Mfr
N.A.I.C.S.: 336320

Subsidiary (Domestic):

Williams Controls Industries, Inc. (2)

14100 SW 72nd Ave, Portland, OR 97224-
8009
Tel.: (503) 684-8600
Web Site: http://www.wimco.com
Sales Range: $50-74.9 Million
Emp.: 200
Electronic Throttle Controls, Pneumatic &
Hydraulic Controls Mfr
N.A.I.C.S.: 336390

**CUSTOM DESIGNED COM-
PRESSOR SYSTEMS, INC.**
PO Box 37, Bloomfield, NM
87413 DE
Year Founded: 2004
CPYJ—(OTCIQ)
Natural Gas Compressor Mfr
N.A.I.C.S.: 333912
Shelby E. Ball (Chm & CEO)
Craig H. Williams (Pres)
Paulette Ball (CFO & Treas)

**CUSTOM TRUCK ONE
SOURCE, INC.**
7701 Independence Ave Building H,
Kansas City, MO 64125
Tel.: (816) 241-4888 DE
Web Site:
https://www.customtruck.com
Year Founded: 2017
CTOS—(NYSE)
Rev.: $1,573,086,000
Assets: $2,938,212,000
Liabilities: $2,049,769,000
Net Worth: $888,443,000
Earnings: $38,905,000
Emp.: 2,270
Fiscal Year-end: 12/31/22
Holding Company; Equipment Rental
& Leasing Services
N.A.I.C.S.: 551112
Christopher J. Eperjesy (CFO)
Fred Ross (Founder)
R. Todd Barrett (Chief Acctg Officer)
Marshall A. Heinberg (Chm)
Ryan McMonagle (Pres, CEO &
COO)

Subsidiaries:

1104816 Ontario Limited (1)
29 Perini Road, Elliot Lake, P5A 2T1, ON,
Canada
Tel.: (705) 848-0170
Web Site: https://www.hirailleasing.com
Railroad Leasing Services
N.A.I.C.S.: 532411

**A&D Maintenance Leasing & Repairs,
Inc.** (1)
118 Wyandanch Ave, Wyandanch, NY
11798
Tel.: (631) 491-6906
Rev.: $1,200,000
Emp.: 17
Fiscal Year-end: 12/31/2006
Truck Repair
N.A.I.C.S.: 811111

Custom Truck & Equipment, LLC (1)
7701 E 24 Hwy, Kansas City, MO 64125
Tel.: (816) 241-4888
Web Site: http://www.customtruck.com
Utility & Energy Truck & Equipment Whslr
N.A.I.C.S.: 333924
Fred Ross (Founder)
Chris Ross (COO & VP-Ops)
Fred Ross (Pres)
Steve Creal (Mgr-Facilities)
Joe Ross (VP-Sls)
Jim Ross (CFO)

NESCO LLC (1)
6714 Pointe Inverness Way Ste 220, Fort
Wayne, IN 46804
Tel.: (260) 824-6340
Web Site: http://www.nescosales.com
Equipment Rental & Leasing Services
N.A.I.C.S.: 532412
Jacobson Lee (CEO)
Bruce Heinemann (CFO)

Truck Utilities, Inc. (1)
2370 English St, Saint Paul, MN 55109

Tel.: (651) 484-3305
Web Site: http://www.truckutilities.com
Truck Bodies Provider
N.A.I.C.S.: 336211
Craig Capeder (Pres)
Jay Langer (VP)

CUSTOMERS BANCORP, INC.
701 Reading Ave, Reading, PA 19611
Tel.: (610) 933-2000 PA
Web Site:
http://www.customersbank.com
CUBI—(NYSE)
Rev.: $1,437,925,000
Assets: $21,316,265,000
Liabilities: $19,677,871,000
Net Worth: $1,638,394,000
Earnings: $250,143,000
Emp.: 711
Fiscal Year-end: 12/31/23
Bank Holding Company
N.A.I.C.S.: 551111
Jay S. Sidhu (Chm & CEO)
Mary Lou Scalese (Exec VP &
Auditor-Customers Bank)
Timothy D. Romig (Pres/Mng Dir-
Market-Pennsylvania & Exec VP-
Customers Bank)
Lyle P. Cunningham (Chief Lending
Officer & Exec VP-Customers Bank)
William J. Pizzichil (Chief Compliance
Officer & Exec VP-Customers Bank)
Tammy Sibalic (Sr VP & Dir-Corp
Plng-Customers Bank)
Jessie John Velasquez (Chief Acctg
Officer & Sr VP-Customers Bank)
Andrew B. Sachs (Gen Counsel, Sec
& Exec VP)
Karen Kirchner (Sr VP & Dir-Svcs-
Customers Bank)
David Patti (Dir-Comm)
Joan Cheney (Chief Risk Officer &
Exec VP)
Thomas Kasulka (Chief Credit Officer
& Exec VP)
Phil Watkins (CFO & Exec VP)
Nicholas Harris (CIO & Exec VP)
Glenn Hedde (Exec VP-Banking-
Mortgage Companies)
Jesse Honigberg (Exec VP-Products
& Platforms)
Samuel H. Smith III (Pres)
Lisa Walsh (Chief People Officer &
Exec VP)

Subsidiaries:

Customers Bank (1)
1015 Penn Ave, Wyomissing, PA 19610
Tel.: (610) 933-2000
Web Site: http://www.customersbank.com
Retail & Commercial Banking
N.A.I.C.S.: 522110
Samvir S. Sidhu (Pres & CEO)
Endre Walls (Chief Ops and Tech Officer)
Phil Watkins (Exec VP)

CUTERA, INC.
3240 Bayshore Blvd, Brisbane, CA
94005
Tel.: (415) 657-5500 DE
Web Site: https://www.cutera.com
Year Founded: 1998
CUTR—(NASDAQ)
Rev.: $252,399,000
Assets: $520,988,000
Liabilities: $536,169,000
Net Worth: ($15,181,000)
Earnings: ($82,340,000)
Emp.: 540
Fiscal Year-end: 12/31/22
Laser & Other Light Based Product
Mfr
N.A.I.C.S.: 334510
Jeffrey S. Jones (COO)
Stephana Patton (Chief Legal Officer)
Greg Barker (VP-Corp FP, A, and Investor Relations)

Kevin Cameron *(Chm)*
Michael Karavitis *(CTO & Exec VP)*
Taylor C. Harris *(Pres & CEO)*

Subsidiaries:

Cutera Australia Pty Ltd **(1)**
24/1 O'Connell St, Sydney, 2000, NSW,
Australia
Tel.: (61) 1800288372
Web Site: https://cuteraanz.com
Light Based Product Mfr
N.A.I.C.S.: 334510

Cutera France SARL **(1)**
1 rue Georges Charpak Bat C, 77127, Lieu-
saint, France
Tel.: (33) 160622440
Web Site: https://cutera.fr
Medical Equipment Whslr
N.A.I.C.S.: 423450

Cutera Japan KK **(1)**
12-10 Sakuragaoka-cho Shibuya Info Annex
3F, Shibuya-ku, Tokyo, 150-0031, Japan
Tel.: (81) 354566325
Web Site: https://cutera.jp
Medical Equipment Whslr
N.A.I.C.S.: 423450

Cutera Spain SL **(1)**
Cmo Viejo de Cobena 14, Paracuellos de
Jarama, 28860, Madrid, Spain
Tel.: (34) 650533808
Web Site: https://cutera.es
Medical Equipment Whslr
N.A.I.C.S.: 423450

Cutera Switzerland GmbH **(1)**
Zollikerstrasse 27, 8032, Zurich, Switzer-
land
Tel.: (41) 41789635800
Medical Equipment Whslr
N.A.I.C.S.: 423450

CV SCIENCES, INC.

9530 Padgett St Ste 107, San Diego,
CA 92126   TX
Web Site:
    https://www.cvsciences.com
Year Founded: 2010
CVSI—(OTCQB)
Rev.: $16,205,000
Assets: $12,736,000
Liabilities: $13,513,000
Net Worth: ($777,000)
Earnings: ($9,134,000)
Emp.: 42
Fiscal Year-end: 12/31/22
Drug Development, Mfr & Sales
N.A.I.C.S.: 325412
Joseph D. Dowling *(CEO & Sec)*
Joerg Grasser *(CFO)*
Jesse Karagianes *(Sr VP-Revenue
Growth)*
Michael J. Mona III *(Founder)*

CVB FINANCIAL CORP.

701 N Haven Ave, Ontario, CA 91764
Tel.: (909) 980-4030   CA
Web Site: https://www.cbbank.com
Year Founded: 1981
CVBF—(NASDAQ)
Rev.: $665,660,000
Assets: $16,020,993,000
Liabilities: $13,943,021,000
Net Worth: $2,077,972,000
Earnings: $221,435,000
Emp.: 1,107
Fiscal Year-end: 12/31/23
Bank Holding Company
N.A.I.C.S.: 551111
Elsa I. Zavala *(Chief Info Security
Officer & Exec VP-Bank)*
George A. Borba Jr. *(Vice Chm)*
David C. Harvey *(COO & Exec VP)*
David A. Brager *(Pres & CEO)*
David F. Farnsworth *(Chief Credit Of-
ficer & Exec VP-Citizens Business
Bank)*
Richard H. Wohl *(Gen Counsel &
Exec VP)*

Francene LaPoint *(Chief Acctg Officer
& Sr VP)*
Susan M. Mlot *(Exec VP)*
Timothy B. Noone *(Exec VP)*
Jeffrey S. Boyer *(Sr VP)*
Michael K. Currie *(CIO)*
Gilbert W. Estrada *(Sr VP)*
Donald E. Evenson *(Chief Investment
Officer)*
Richard M. Favor *(Sr VP)*
Deborah G. Gallagher *(Sr VP)*
Derrick I. Hong *(Sr VP)*
Joyce Y. Kwon *(Sr VP)*
Daniel Limon *(Sr VP)*
Rudy I. Ramirez *(Chief Information
Security Officer)*
Mark C. Richardson *(Sr VP)*
LaVon Short *(Sr VP)*
Michael D. Stain *(Sr VP)*
David S. Stong *(Sr VP)*
Robert E. Zeltner *(Sr VP)*

Subsidiaries:

Citizens Business Bank **(1)**
701 N Haven Ave, Ontario, CA 91764
Tel.: (909) 980-4030
Web Site: https://www.cbbank.com
Commericial Banking
N.A.I.C.S.: 522110
George A. Borba Jr. *(Vice Chm)*
Hal W. Oswalt *(Chm)*
David C. Harvey *(COO & Exec VP)*
David A. Brager *(Pres & CEO)*
David F. Farnsworth *(Chief Credit Officer &
Exec VP)*
Yamynn De Angelis *(Chief Risk Officer &
Exec VP)*
Timothy B. Noone *(Exec VP & Mgr-
Specialty Banking Grp)*
Michael D. Stain *(Sr VP & Reg Mgr-Central
Valley)*
Ted J. Dondanville *(Exec VP)*
Hector G. Gutierrez *(Exec VP)*
Mark C. Richardson *(Sr VP-Real Estate
Banking Grp)*
Michael B. Mulcahy *(Sr VP & Reg Mgr-Los
Angeles-Metro)*
Robert E. Zeltner *(Sr VP & Mgr-Orange
County)*
E. Allen Nicholson *(CFO & Exec VP)*
Gilbert W. Estrada *(Sr VP-Inland Empire)*
Richard M. Favor *(Sr VP-Central Coast)*
Joyce Y. Kwon *(Sr VP & Dir-HR)*
Daniel Limon *(Sr VP & Gen Mgr-Specialty
Lending-Grp)*
Lavon Short *(Sr VP & Mgr-Sls Support-Grp)*
David S. Stong *(Sr VP-San Diego)*
Jeffrey S. Boyer *(Sr VP-Los Angeles-North)*
Donald E. Evenson *(Sr VP)*
Deborah G. Gallagher *(Sr VP & Mgr-SBA
Grp)*
Susan M. Mlot *(Sr VP & Head-Ops)*
Richard H. Wohl *(Gen Counsel)*
R. Daniel Banis *(Exec VP)*
Walter J. Smiechewicz *(Sr VP)*
Rudy I. Ramirez *(Chief Information Security
Officer)*
Mike K. Currie *(CIO)*

Unit (Domestic):

Citizens Business Bank - BankCard
Services **(2)**
701 N Haven Ave, Ontario, CA 91764
Tel.: (909) 980-4030
Web Site: http://www.cbbank.com
Emp.: 50
Bank & Credit Card Services
N.A.I.C.S.: 522390

Group (Domestic):

Citizens Business Bank - Dairy &
Livestock Industries Group **(2)**
12808 Central Ave, Chino, CA 91710
Tel.: (909) 627-7316
Web Site: http://www.cbbank.com
Sales Range: $25-49.9 Million
Emp.: 10
Dairy & Livestock Farm Lending Services
N.A.I.C.S.: 522299
Mike Maciel *(VP & Mgr-Relationship-Visalia)*
Wanda Jones *(Sr VP & Mgr-Center)*
Sandra Mendes *(VP & Mgr-Svc)*
Rick Rehm *(Officer-Portfolio & VP)*
Roger Brossman *(VP & Mgr-Svc)*

Citizens Business Bank - Wealth
Management Group **(2)**
1010 Colorado Blvd 2nd Fl, Pasadena, CA
91106
Tel.: (626) 405-4915
Web Site: http://www.cbbank.com
Financial Assets Management Services
N.A.I.C.S.: 523940

CVD EQUIPMENT CORPORA-TION

355 S Technology Dr, Central Islip,
NY 17722
Tel.: (631) 981-7081   NY
Web Site:
    https://www.cvdequipment.com
Year Founded: 1982
CVV—(NASDAQ)
Rev.: $25,813,000
Assets: $37,912,000
Liabilities: $8,513,000
Net Worth: $29,399,000
Earnings: ($224,000)
Emp.: 136
Fiscal Year-end: 12/31/22
Customized Equipment & Solutions in
Solar, Nano & Advanced Electronic
Components
N.A.I.C.S.: 334417
Lawrence J. Waldman *(Chm)*
Karlheinz Strobl *(VP-Bus Dev)*
Kevin R. Collins *(VP & Gen Mgr-SDC
Div)*
William S. Linss *(VP-Ops-CVD Equip-
ment & Firstnano)*
Emmanuel Lakios *(Pres & CEO)*
Maxim Shatalov *(VP-Engrg & Tech)*
Jeff Brogan *(VP-Sls & Mktg)*
Richard Catalano *(CFO, Treas, Sec &
VP)*

Subsidiaries:

Conceptronic **(1)**
355 S Technology Dr, Central Islip, NY
11722
Tel.: (631) 981-7081
Mfr of Solder Reflow Ovens, Forced Con-
vection Rework Stations & Customized
Thermal Processing Equipment for Customers in the Electronics Manufacturing Industry
N.A.I.C.S.: 333242

Stainless Design Concepts **(1)**
1117 Kings Hwy, Saugerties, NY 12477
Tel.: (845) 246-3631
Web Site: https://www.stainlessdesign.com
Sales Range: $25-49.9 Million
Emp.: 30
Provider & Installer of Gas & Chemical
Management Equipment
N.A.I.C.S.: 333248

CVRX, INC.

9201 W Broadway Ave Ste 650, Min-
neapolis, MN 55445
Tel.: (763) 416-2840
Web Site: https://www.cvrx.com
Year Founded: 2000
CVRX—(NASDAQ)
Rev.: $39,295,000
Assets: $115,229,000
Liabilities: $39,282,000
Net Worth: $75,947,000
Earnings: ($41,199,000)
Emp.: 200
Fiscal Year-end: 12/31/23
Medical Device Mfr
N.A.I.C.S.: 339112
Kevin Hykes *(Pres & CEO)*
John Brintnall *(CFO)*
Dean Bruhn-Ding *(VP-Regulatory Af-
fairs)*
Philippe Wanstok *(Chief Comml Offi-
cer)*
Joseph DuPay *(VP-R&D Ops)*
Paul Verrastro *(CMO)*
Thomas Hengsteler *(VP-Sls & Mktg-
Europe)*
Robert Kieval *(CTO & Exec VP)*

CVS HEALTH CORPORATION

1 CVS Dr, Woonsocket, RI 02895
Tel.: (401) 765-1500   DE
Web Site: https://www.cvshealth.com
Year Founded: 1963
CVS—(NYSE)
Rev.: $357,776,000,000
Assets: $249,728,000,000
Liabilities: $173,092,000,000
Net Worth: $76,636,000,000
Earnings: $8,344,000,000
Emp.: 300,000
Fiscal Year-end: 12/31/23
Holding Company; Pharmacy Opera-
tion & Franchising, Benefit Manage-
ment, Drug Distribution & Specialty
Care Services
N.A.I.C.S.: 551112
Michelle A. Peluso *(Chief Customer
Officer & Co-Pres-Pharmacy & Con-
sumer Wellness)*
Thomas F. Cowhey *(CFO & Exec VP)*
Laurie P. Havanec *(Chief People Offi-
cer & Exec VP)*
Anita M. Allemand *(Executives)*
James D. Clark *(Chief Acctg Officer,
Sr VP & Controller)*
Valerie C. Haertel *(Sr VP-Investor
Relations)*
Kimberly White *(Chief Comm Officer
& Sr VP)*
Michael Pykosz *(Pres-Health Care
Delivery & Exec VP)*
Dan Finke *(Exec VP)*
Tilak Mandadi *(Chief Data, Digital &
Tech Officer & Exec VP)*
Mario Rivera *(Sr VP-Supply Chain)*
Sree Chaguturu *(Chief Medical Offi-
cer & Exec VP)*
David A. Falkowski *(Chief Compli-
ance Officer & Exec VP)*
John P. Kennedy *(Chief Tax Officer &
Sr VP)*
Prem Shah *(Chief Pharmacy Officer
& Exec VP)*
Thomas S. Moffatt *(Asst Sec & VP)*
Sam Khichi *(Chief Policy Officer, Gen
Counsel & Exec VP)*
Larry McGrath *(Sr VP)*
Neela Montgomery *(Exec VP)*
J. David Joyner *(Pres & CEO)*

Subsidiaries:

Accordant Health Services, Inc. **(1)**
4900 Koger Blvd Ste 100, Greensboro, NC
27407-2710
Tel.: (336) 855-5870
Web Site: http://www.accordant.net
Sales Range: $25-49.9 Million
Emp.: 200
Disease Management Services
N.A.I.C.S.: 621999
Mark A. Duke *(VP-Sls)*

Advanced Care Scripts, Inc. **(1)**
6251 Chancellor Dr Ste 101, Orlando, FL
32809
Web Site: https://www.acs-rx.com
Health Care Srvices
N.A.I.C.S.: 621610

Aetna Better Health Premier Plan
MMAI Inc. **(1)**
3200 Highland Ave MC F661, Downers
Grove, IL 60515
Web Site:
    https://www.aetnabetterhealth.com
Health & Wellness Services
N.A.I.C.S.: 525120

Aetna Better Health of Florida
Inc. **(1)**
8200 NW 41st St Ste 125, Doral, FL 33166
Web Site:
    https://www.aetnabetterhealth.com
Health Care Srvices
N.A.I.C.S.: 621999

Aetna Global Benefits (Middle East)
LLC **(1)**
Office 503 Level 5 Standard Chartered
Tower Opp Emaar Square, PO Box 6380,

CVS Health Corporation—(Continued)

Dubai Downtown, Dubai, United Arab Emirates
Tel.: (971) 44387500
Health Care Srvices
N.A.I.C.S.: 621610

Aetna Inc. **(1)**
151 Farmington Ave, Hartford, CT 06156
Tel.: (860) 273-0123
Web Site: http://www.aetna.com
Sales Range: $50-74.9 Billion
Emp.: 47,950
Health Maintenance & Insurance Services
N.A.I.C.S.: 524114
Alec Cunningham (COO)
Kyu Rhee (Chief Medical Officer & Sr VP)

Subsidiary (Domestic):

Active Health Management, Inc. **(2)**
233 Spring St, New York, NY 10013
Tel.: (212) 651-8200
Web Site: https://www.activehealth.com
Health Care Srvices
N.A.I.C.S.: 621610

Active Health Management, Inc. **(2)**
233 Spring St, New York, NY 10013
Tel.: (212) 651-8200
Web Site: http://www.activehealth.com
Health Management & Data Analytics Products & Services
N.A.I.C.S.: 518210
Carol B. Ingher (Chief Customer Solutions Officer, Chief Sls Officer & Exec VP)
Larry Siegel (Exec VP-Reporting & Informatics)
Mohamed Diab (Pres & CEO)
Miriam Ferreira (COO)
Jonathan S. Rubens (Chief Medical Officer)
Matt Asmus (CFO)
Beth Austin (Dir-Clinical Svcs)
Wadida J. Murib-Holmes (Sr VP-Acct Mgmt)
Matt Hoffman (CMO)

Subsidiary (Domestic):

Health Data & Management Solutions, Inc. **(3)**
10 S Riverside Plz Ste 1540, Chicago, IL 60606
Tel.: (312) 701-1320
Web Site: http://www1.hdms.com
Software Development Services
N.A.I.C.S.: 541511
Mark Magnuson (CTO & VP)
Keith A. Wilton (VP-Product Mgmt)
Robert Corrigan (Sr Dir-Advisory Svcs)
Matt Asmus (CFO)
Mohamed Diab (CEO)

Subsidiary (Non-US):

Futrix Limited **(4)**
Level 2 330 Lambton Quay, Wellington, 6011, New Zealand
Tel.: (64) 44991327
Web Site: http://www.futrix.com
Data Analysis Solution Services
N.A.I.C.S.: 518210

Subsidiary (Non-US):

Aetna (Shanghai) Enterprise Services Co. Ltd. **(2)**
Suite 702 757 Meng Zi Road, Gopher Center Huang Pu District, Shanghai, China
Tel.: (86) 4008811269
Health Care Srvices
N.A.I.C.S.: 621610

Aetna (Shanghai) Enterprise Services Co. Ltd. **(2)**
Suite 702 757 Meng Zi Road Gopher Center, Huang Pu District, Shanghai, 200001, China
Tel.: (86) 4008811269
Employee Benefit Insurance Services
N.A.I.C.S.: 525120

Subsidiary (Domestic):

Aetna Better Health of Michigan Inc. **(2)**
28588 Northwestern Hwy Ste 380B, Southfield, MI 48034
Health Care Srvices
N.A.I.C.S.: 621610

Aetna Capital Management, LLC **(2)**
29 S Main St Ste 304, West Hartford, CT 06107
Tel.: (860) 380-1230
Web Site:
    http://www.aetnacapitalmanagement.com
Health & Welfare Fund Services
N.A.I.C.S.: 525120
Mark Garber (Pres & CIO)

Subsidiary (Non-US):

Aetna Global Benefits (Asia Pacific) Limited **(2)**
Suite 11021 11/F Tower 535 535 Jaffe Road, Causeway Bay, China (Hong Kong)
Tel.: (852) 28608021
Web Site: http://www.aetnainternational.com
Medical Insurance Services
N.A.I.C.S.: 524114

Aetna Global Benefits (Europe) Limited **(2)**
169 Park Lane 1st Floor, Croydon, CR9 1BG, United Kingdom
Tel.: (44) 8704424386
Medical Insurance Services
N.A.I.C.S.: 524114

Aetna Global Benefits (UK) Limited **(2)**
25 Templer Avenue, Farnborough, GU14 6FE, United Kingdom
Tel.: (44) 2037883288
Health Care Srvices
N.A.I.C.S.: 621610

Aetna Global Benefits Limited **(2)**
28th Floor Media One Tower Building, PO Box 6380, Dubai Media City, 6380, United Arab Emirates
Tel.: (971) 44387500
Employee Benefit Insurance Services
N.A.I.C.S.: 525120

Subsidiary (Domestic):

Aetna Health Holdings, LLC **(2)**
151 Farmington Ave, Hartford, CT 06156-0001
Tel.: (860) 273-0123
Holding Company
N.A.I.C.S.: 551112

Subsidiary (Domestic):

Aetna Better Health Inc. **(3)**
151 Farmington Ave, Hartford, CT 06156
Tel.: (860) 273-0123
Web Site: http://www.aetna.com
Insurance Services
N.A.I.C.S.: 524113
Keith Wisdom (CEO-Kansas)

Aetna Better Health of California Inc. **(3)**
10260 Meanley Dr, San Diego, CA 92131
Web Site:
    https://www.aetnabetterhealth.com
Health Care Management Services
N.A.I.C.S.: 621999
Chet Uma (CEO)

Aetna Better Health of Florida Inc. **(3)**
8200 NW 41st St Ste 125, Doral, FL 33166
Direct Health & Medical Insurance Carriers Services
N.A.I.C.S.: 524114

Aetna Better Health of Kansas Inc. **(3)**
9401 Indian Creek Pkwy Ste 1300, Overland Park, KS 66210
Web Site:
    https://www.aetnabetterhealth.com
Health Care Management Services
N.A.I.C.S.: 621999
Kimberly Glenn (COO)

Aetna Better Health of Kentucky Insurance Company **(3)**
9900 Corporate Campus Dr Ste 1000, Louisville, KY 40223
Web Site:
    https://www.aetnabetterhealth.com
Health Care Management Services
N.A.I.C.S.: 621999
Jonathan Copley (CEO)

Aetna Better Health of Michigan Inc. **(3)**
28588 Northwestern Hwy Ste 380B, Southfield, MI 48034
Web Site:
    https://www.aetnabetterhealth.com
Sales Range: $150-199.9 Million
Emp.: 250
Health Maintenance Organization
N.A.I.C.S.: 524114

Aetna Better Health, Inc. **(3)**
2400 Veterans Memorial Blvd Ste 200, Kenner, LA 70062
Health Care Management Services
N.A.I.C.S.: 621999

Aetna Health Inc. **(3)**
3838 N Causeway Blvd Ste 3350, Metairie, LA 70002
Tel.: (504) 834-0840
Sales Range: $25-49.9 Million
Emp.: 60
HMO
N.A.I.C.S.: 524114

Aetna Health Inc. **(3)**
333 Earle Ovington Blvd Ste 104, Uniondale, NY 11553
Tel.: (516) 229-2500
Health & Medical Insurance Carriers
N.A.I.C.S.: 524114

Aetna Health Inc. (Connecticut) **(3)**
151 Farmington Ave, Hartford, CT 06156
Tel.: (860) 273-0123
Web Site: http://www.aetna.com
Health Care Srvices
N.A.I.C.S.: 524113

Subsidiary (Domestic):

Aetna Better Health Inc. **(4)**
3 Independence Way Ste 400, Princeton, NJ 08540-6626
Health Care Management Services
N.A.I.C.S.: 621999
Glenn MacFarlane (CEO)

Aetna Better Health Inc. **(4)**
7400 W Campus Rd, New Albany, OH 43054
Health Care Management Services
N.A.I.C.S.: 621999

Aetna Better Health Inc. **(4)**
333 W Wacker Dr Ste 2100, Chicago, IL 60606
Health Care Management Services
N.A.I.C.S.: 621999
Robert Kritzler (Chief Medical Officer)

Aetna Better Health Inc. **(4)**
2000 Market St Ste 050, Philadelphia, PA 19103
Health Care Management Services
N.A.I.C.S.: 621999
Jason Rottman (CEO)

Aetna Better Health Inc. **(4)**
55 W 125th St Ste 1300, New York, NY 10027
Health Care Management Services
N.A.I.C.S.: 621999

Subsidiary (Domestic):

Aetna Health Inc. (New York) **(3)**
100 Park Ave, New York, NY 10017-1601 **(100%)**
Tel.: (212) 457-0700
Web Site: http://www.aetna.com
Sales Range: $75-99.9 Million
Emp.: 150
Group Health Insurance
N.A.I.C.S.: 524114

Aetna Health Inc. (Pennsylvania) **(3)**
980 Jolly Rd, Blue Bell, PA 19422
Tel.: (212) 286-0670
Healthcare & Medical Services
N.A.I.C.S.: 524114

Aetna Health of California Inc. **(3)**
2625 Shadelands Dr, Walnut Creek, CA 94598
Tel.: (800) 756-7039
Web Site: http://www.aetna.com
Health Maintenance Organization
N.A.I.C.S.: 524114

Aetna Health of Iowa Inc. **(3)**
4320 114th St, Urbandale, IA 50322-5408
Tel.: (515) 225-1234
Web Site:
    http://www.coventryhealthcare.com
Health Care Management Services
N.A.I.C.S.: 621999
Janet Clausen (Mgr-Health services)

Aetna Health of Utah Inc. **(3)**
10150 S Centennial Pkwy, Sandy, UT 84070-4166
Tel.: (801) 933-3500
Healthcare & Medical Services
N.A.I.C.S.: 524114

Aetna Medicaid Administrators LLC **(3)**
4500 E Cotton Center Blvd, Phoenix, AZ 85040
Tel.: (602) 659-1100
Web Site: http://www.aetnabetterhealth.com
Administrative Management Consulting Services
N.A.I.C.S.: 541611

Aetna Specialty Pharmacy, LLC **(3)**
503 Sunport Ln, Orlando, FL 32809-7874
Tel.: (407) 513-6400
Web Site: http://www.aetna.com
Insurance Services
N.A.I.C.S.: 524113

Aetna Student Health Agency Inc. **(3)**
151 Farmington Ave, Hartford, CT 06156
Tel.: (617) 218-8400
Web Site:
    http://www.aetnastudenthealth.com
Direct Life Insurance Services
N.A.I.C.S.: 524113
Peter Diniaco (Exec Dir-Natl)

Carefree Insurance Services, Inc. **(3)**
261 N University Dr Ste 100, Plantation, FL 33324
Tel.: (772) 220-7525
Web Site: https://carefreeagency.com
Direct Health & Medical Insurance Carriers Services
N.A.I.C.S.: 524114
Tim Ipema (VP-Sls)
Mike Penney (Pres)
Anthony Del Oso (Dir-Sls)
Trina Burnette (Dir-Natl Sls)

Cofinity, Inc. **(3)**
28588 Northwestern Hwy, Southfield, MI 48034
Tel.: (248) 357-7766
Web Site: http://www.cofinity.net
Healthcare Technology Services
N.A.I.C.S.: 541512

Coventry Financial Management Services, Inc. **(3)**
300 Delaware Ave, Wilmington, DE 19801
Tel.: (302) 576-2882
Business Support Services
N.A.I.C.S.: 561499

Coventry Health Care of Delaware, Inc. **(3)**
750 Prides Crossing Ste 200, Newark, DE 19713 **(100%)**
Tel.: (302) 995-6100
Web Site: http://www.chcde.com
Sales Range: $50-74.9 Million
Emp.: 100
Health Care Srvices
N.A.I.C.S.: 524114

Coventry Health Care of Georgia, Inc. **(3)**
1100 Cir 75 Pkwy SE Ste 1400, Atlanta, GA 30339-3067 **(100%)**
Tel.: (678) 202-2100
Web Site: http://www.cvty.com
Sales Range: $50-74.9 Million
Emp.: 130
Health Care Srvices
N.A.I.C.S.: 524114
Frank Ulibarri (Gen Mgr)

Coventry Health Care of Illinois, Inc. **(3)**
2110 Fox Dr Ste A, Champaign, IL 61820
Tel.: (217) 366-5551

Web Site: http://coventry-
medicare.coventryhealthcare.com
Employee Benefit Insurance Services
N.A.I.C.S.: 525120

**Coventry Health Care of Iowa,
Inc.** (3)
4320 114 St, Urbandale, IA 50322 (100%)
Tel.: (515) 225-1234
Web Site: http://www.cvty.com
Sales Range: $25-49.9 Million
Emp.: 75
HMO
N.A.I.C.S.: 524114

**Coventry Health Care of Kansas,
Inc.** (3)
6720-B Rockledge Dr Ste 800, Bethesda,
MD 20817 (100%)
Tel.: (301) 581-0600
Web Site:
http://www.coventryhealthcare.com
Healtcare Services
N.A.I.C.S.: 621610

**Coventry Health Care of Missouri,
Inc.** (3)
1285 Fern Ridge Pkwy Ste 200, Saint
Louis, MO 63141 (100%)
Tel.: (314) 506-1700
Web Site:
http://chcmissouri.coventryhealthcare.com
Sales Range: $200-249.9 Million
Emp.: 500
Health Maintenance Organization
N.A.I.C.S.: 524114
John Otten (VP-Sls & Mktg)

**Coventry Health Care of Nebraska,
Inc.** (3)
15950 W Dodge Rd Ste 400, Omaha, NE
68118-4030 (100%)
Tel.: (402) 498-9090
Sales Range: $25-49.9 Million
Emp.: 52
Insurance Company
N.A.I.C.S.: 524114

**Coventry Health Care of Texas,
Inc.** (3)
3900 Rogers Rd, San Antonio, TX 78251
Tel.: (210) 525-3400
Web Site:
http://www.chctexas.coventryhealth
care.com
Ambulatory Health Care Services
N.A.I.C.S.: 621999

**Coventry Health Care of Virginia,
Inc.** (3)
9881 Mayland Dr, Richmond, VA
23233 (100%)
Tel.: (804) 747-3700
Web Site:
http://coventrycaresoh.coventryhealth
care.com
Sales Range: $100-124.9 Million
Health Maintenance Organization
N.A.I.C.S.: 524114

**Coventry Health Care of West Vir-
ginia, Inc.** (3)
500 Virginia St E Ste 400, Charleston, WV
25301
Tel.: (304) 348-2900
Web Site:
http://coventrycaresoh.coventryhealth
care.com
Medical Insurance Services
N.A.I.C.S.: 524114

**Coventry Health Care of the Caroli-
nas, Inc.** (3)
2801 Slater Rd Ste 200, Morrisville, NC
27560 (100%)
Tel.: (800) 935-7284
Web Site: http://chccarolinas.coventryhealth
care.com
Sales Range: $10-24.9 Million
Emp.: 63
HMO
N.A.I.C.S.: 621491

**Coventry Health Plan of Florida,
Inc.** (3)
1340 Concord Terrace, Sunrise, FL 33323
Tel.: (954) 858-3000
Direct Health & Medical Insurance Carriers
Services

N.A.I.C.S.: 524114

**Coventry Prescription Management
Services, Inc.** (3)
2215 Renaissance Dr, Las Vegas, NV
89119-6163
Tel.: (702) 932-4908
Direct Health & Medical Insurance Carriers
Services
N.A.I.C.S.: 524114

First Health Group Corp. (3)
3200 Highland Ave, Downers Grove, IL
60515-1223
Tel.: (630) 737-7900
Web Site:
https://providerlocator.firsthealth.com
Sales Range: $800-899.9 Million
Emp.: 6,000
Group Health, Workers' Compensation &
Government Medical Services
N.A.I.C.S.: 524114
Paul Lavin (Exec Dir)
Kara Dornig (VP-Bus Dev)

HealthAmerica Health Insurance (3)
11 Stanwix St Ste 2300, Pittsburgh, PA
15222 (100%)
Tel.: (412) 553-7300
Web Site:
http://www.healthamerica.cvty.com
Sales Range: $25-49.9 Million
Emp.: 200
Health Maintenance Organization
N.A.I.C.S.: 621111

Division (Domestic):

**HealthAmerica Pennsylvania,
Inc.** (4)
3721 Techport Dr, Harrisburg, PA 17106-
9373
Tel.: (717) 540-4260
Web Site:
http://www.healthamerica.cvty.com
Health Maintenance Organization
N.A.I.C.S.: 524114

Subsidiary (Domestic):

**HealthCare USA of Missouri,
LLC** (3)
10 S Broadway Ste 1200, Saint Louis, MO
63102-1825 (100%)
Tel.: (314) 241-5300
Sales Range: $25-49.9 Million
Emp.: 125
Health Maintenance Organization
N.A.I.C.S.: 813920
Brian Bovinns (CEO)

MetraComp, Inc. (3)
3721 TecPort Dr, Harrisburg, PA 17106
Web Site: http://www.metracomp.com
Direct Health & Medical Insurance Carriers
Services
N.A.I.C.S.: 524114

Prodigy Health Group, Inc. (3)
1 Penn Plz Ste 1510, New York, NY 10119
Tel.: (212) 698-2220
Web Site:
http://www.prodigyhealthgroup.com
Health Services Holding Company
N.A.I.C.S.: 551112

Holding (Domestic):

American Health Holding Inc. (4)
7400 W Campus Rd Ste 300, New Albany,
OH 43054-8768
Tel.: (614) 818-3222
Web Site:
https://www.americanhealthholding.com
Sales Range: $50-74.9 Million
Medical Management Services
N.A.I.C.S.: 541611
Paul Lavin (Pres & CEO)
Ivan S. Gilbert (Co-Founder)
Michael J. Reidelbach (Co-Founder)
Roland Griggs (Dir-Medical)
Richard Hodsdon (VP-Sls)
Stephanie Mills (VP)
Dennis Bryant (VP-Bus Support)
Ron Gibb (COO & Exec VP)
Lynda Davis (VP)
Anne Klie (Dir-Bus Dev)
Suzanne Wade (Dir-Svc Ops)
Kari Ruthig (Dir-Disease Mgmt & Wellness)

Liz Rorapaugh (Mgr-Svc Ops-AHH Call
Center)
Carrie Raethke (VP-Sls)
Deanna Duvall (Mgr-Program, Strategy &
Mktg)
Adam Anticola (Dir-Strategy & Mktg)
Suzanne Allford Wade (Dir-Svc Ops)
Rob Dubois (Sr Dir-Client Svcs)

Meritain Health, Inc. (4)
300 Corporate Pkwy, Amherst, NY 14226
Tel.: (716) 446-5500
Web Site: http://www.meritain.com
Sales Range: $500-549.9 Million
Emp.: 1,350
Self-Funded Healthcare Plans Administra-
tive, Medical, Disease, Network & Cost
Management Services
N.A.I.C.S.: 524292

Subsidiary (Domestic):

U.S Healthcare Holdings, LLC (5)
9769 Silverleaf Dr, North Royalton, OH
44133
Tel.: (440) 230-1232
Holding Company
N.A.I.C.S.: 551112

Holding (Domestic):

Scrip World, Inc. (4)
10150 S Centennial Pkwy Ste 450, Sandy,
UT 84070
Tel.: (801) 359-5326
Sales Range: $25-49.9 Million
Emp.: 13
Prescription Plan Management
N.A.I.C.S.: 524114

Subsidiary (Domestic):

Strategic Resource Company (3)
PO Box 14079, Lexington, KY 40512-4079
Tel.: (803) 865-4700
Web Site: http://www.aetna.com
Insurance Agency Services
N.A.I.C.S.: 524210

Subsidiary (Non-US):

**Aetna Health Insurance (Thailand)
Public Company Limited** (3)
98 Sathorn Square Office Tower 14th-15th
Floor North Sathorn Road, Silom Bangrak,
Bangkok, 10500, Thailand
Tel.: (66) 26770000
Web Site: http://www.aetna.co.th
Health & Travel Insurance Products & Ser-
vices
N.A.I.C.S.: 524114

**Aetna Health Services (UK)
Limited** (2)
8 Eastcheap, London, EC3M 1AE, United
Kingdom
Tel.: (44) 2076186060
Insurance Services
N.A.I.C.S.: 524113

**Aetna Insurance (Singapore) Pte.
Ltd.** (2)
80 Robinson Road 23-02/03, Singapore,
068898, Singapore
Tel.: (65) 67016912
Medical Insurance Services
N.A.I.C.S.: 524114

**Aetna Insurance Company
Limited** (2)
50 Cannon Street, London, EC4N 6JJ,
United Kingdom
Tel.: (44) 1252745910
Health Care Insurance Provider
N.A.I.C.S.: 524114

Subsidiary (Domestic):

Aetna Intelihealth Inc. (2)
151 Farmington Ave, Hartford, CT 06156
Tel.: (860) 273-0123
Direct Health & Medical Insurance Carriers
N.A.I.C.S.: 524114

Aetna Multi-Strategy 1099 Fund (2)
29 S Main St Ste 304, West Hartford, CT
06107-2449
Tel.: (860) 380-1230
Capital Market Investment Services
N.A.I.C.S.: 523940

Aetna Service Center (2)
980 Jolly Rd Aetna Bldg 1, Blue Bell, PA
19422-0770 (100%)
Tel.: (215) 775-4800
Web Site: http://www.aetna.com
Sales Range: $900-999.9 Million
Emp.: 3,000
Healthcare Support Center
N.A.I.C.S.: 561990
Mark T. Bertolini (Chm & CEO)

**Continental Life Insurance Company
of Brentwood, Tennessee** (2)
800 Crescent Centre Dr Ste 200, Franklin,
TN 37067-7285 (100%)
Tel.: (800) 264-4000
Fire Insurance Services
N.A.I.C.S.: 524113
Ty Woolridge (Gen Mgr)

Subsidiary (Domestic):

**American Continental Insurance
Company** (3)
800 Crescent Centre Dr Ste 200, Franklin,
TN 37067-7285
Tel.: (800) 264-4000
Supplement Insurance Services
N.A.I.C.S.: 524113

Subsidiary (Domestic):

**Health Data & Management Solu-
tions, Inc.** (2)
233 Spring St, New York, NY 10013
Tel.: (312) 701-1320
Web Site: https://www.hdms.com
Health Care Srvices
N.A.I.C.S.: 621610

Horizon Behavioral Services, Inc. (2)
1965 S Lake Pointe Dr Ste 100, Lewisville,
TX 75057
Tel.: (972) 420-8200
Sales Range: $25-49.9 Million
Emp.: 133
Employee Assistance Programs & Psychiat-
ric Managed Care
N.A.I.C.S.: 622210
Jack Devaney (Pres)

CVS Pharmacy, Inc. (1)
1 CVS Dr, Woonsocket, RI 02895
Tel.: (888) 607-4287
Web Site: http://www.cvshealth.com
Pharmaceutical Product Merchant Whslr
N.A.I.C.S.: 424210

Subsidiary (Domestic):

CVS Transportation, LLC (2)
21455 Melrose Ave Ste 20, Southfield, MI
48075
Tel.: (248) 352-8380
Web Site: http://cvstransportation.com
Medical Transportation Services
N.A.I.C.S.: 621910

Red Oak Sourcing, LLC (2)
2 Hampshire St Ste 200, Foxborough, MA
02035
Tel.: (508) 216-1000
Web Site: http://redoaksourcing.com
Business Development Services
N.A.I.C.S.: 541720
Punit Patel (Pres)
Daniel Rocha (VP-Fin)
Mike Shea (VP-Strategic Pharmaceutical
Sourcing)
Charles Rubin (VP-Strategy & Analytics)

Caremark Rx, LLC (1)
1 CVS Dr, Woonsocket, RI 02895
Tel.: (401) 765-1500
Web Site: http://www.caremark.com
Prescription Benefits Management Services
N.A.I.C.S.: 424210
Larry Merlot (Pres)

Subsidiary (Domestic):

Caremark, LLC (2)
1 CVS Dr, Woonsocket, RI 02895
Tel.: (480) 314-8319
Web Site: http://www.caremark.com
Pharmaceutical Services
N.A.I.C.S.: 524114

CaremarkPCS Health LLC (1)
PO Box 6590, Lees Summit, MO 64064-
6590

CVS Health Corporation—(Continued)

Tel.: (401) 652-0893
Web Site: http://www.caremark.com
Pharmaceutical Products Distr
N.A.I.C.S.: 456110
Alan Lotvin (Pres)

Garfield Beach CVS, L.L.C. (1)
1835 Newport Blvd Ste C137, Costa Mesa, CA 92627
Tel.: (949) 722-1750
Restaurant Services
N.A.I.C.S.: 722511

Geneva Woods Pharmacy, LLC (1)
501 W International Airport Rd Ste 6, Anchorage, AK 99518
Tel.: (907) 565-6100
Web Site: https://www.genevawoods.com
Fiscal Year-end: 12/31/2006
Health Care Srvices
N.A.I.C.S.: 621610
Justin Soltani (CTO & VP)

Holiday CVS, L.L.C. (1)
2400 Enterprise Rd, Orange City, FL 32763-7902
Tel.: (386) 774-5547
Health Care Srvices
N.A.I.C.S.: 524114

Subsidiary (Domestic):

Home Care Pharmacy, LLC (1)
6 Florida Park Dr N Ste A, Palm Coast, FL 32137
Tel.: (386) 445-1212
Web Site: https://www.home-care-pharmacy.com
Health Care Srvices
N.A.I.C.S.: 621610

Martin Health Services, LLC (1)
700 S State St, Denver, IA 50622
Tel.: (319) 984-5680
Web Site: http://www.martinhealthservices.com
Residential Care Facility Services
N.A.I.C.S.: 621610

MemberHealth LLC (1)
29100 Aurora Rd Ste 301, Solon, OH 44139
Tel.: (440) 248-8448
Sales Range: $200-249.9 Million
Emp.: 400
Prescription Benefit Management Services
N.A.I.C.S.: 456110

Navarro Discount Pharmacies, LLC (1)
9400 NW 104th St, Miami, FL 33178-1333
Tel.: (786) 245-8524
Web Site: http://www.navarro.com
Pharmacies Operator & Drug Distr
N.A.I.C.S.: 456110

Oak Street Health, Inc. (1)
30 W Monroe St Ste 1200, Chicago, IL 60603
Tel.: (312) 733-9730
Web Site: https://www.oakstreethealth.com
Rev.: $2,160,900,000
Assets: $2,054,700,000
Liabilities: $2,322,000,000
Net Worth: ($267,300,000)
Earnings: ($509,200,000)
Emp.: 6,000
Fiscal Year-end: 12/31/2022
Health Care Srvices
N.A.I.C.S.: 621610
Michael Pykosz (Co-Founder & Chm)
Geoffrey Price (Chief Innovation Officer)
Griffin Myoro (Executive, Bd of Dirs)
Drew Crenshaw (Chief Population Health Officer)
Tamara Jurgenson (Chief Growth Officer)
Cynthia Hiskes (Chief HR Officer)
Jason Van den Eeden (CTO)
James Chow (Pres-Managed Care Ops)
David Buchanan (Chief Clinical Officer)
Brian Clem (COO)
Caroline Sommers (Sr VP-Clinical Quality)
Grace Chen (Sr VP-Care Svcs)
Deb Edberg (Chief Wellness Officer)
Julie Silverstein (Chief Medical Officer-Care Delivery)
Erica Frank (VP-PR)
Sarah Cluck (Head-IR)

Omnicare, Inc. (1)

900 Omnicare Ctr 201 E 4th St, Cincinnati, OH 45202 **(100%)**
Tel.: (513) 719-2600
Web Site: http://www.omnicare.com
Pharmaceutical Services
N.A.I.C.S.: 456110

Subsidiary (Domestic):

Advanced Care Scrips, Inc. (2)
6251 Chancellor Dr Ste 101, Orlando, FL 32809
Web Site: http://www.acs-rx.com
Pharmacy Services
N.A.I.C.S.: 456110

Badger Acquisition of Orlando LLC (2)
6 Florida Park Dr N Ste A, Palm Coast, FL 32137
Tel.: (386) 445-1212
Web Site: https://www.home-care-pharmacy.com
Health Care Srvices
N.A.I.C.S.: 621610

CIC Services LLC (2)
9721 Cogdill Rd Ste 202, Knoxville, TN 37932
Tel.: (865) 248-3044
Web Site: https://www.captivatingthinking.com
Health Care Srvices
N.A.I.C.S.: 621610

CSR, Inc. (2)
901 N Stuart St Ste 904A, Arlington, VA 22203-1674
Tel.: (703) 312-5220
Web Site: http://www.csrincorporated.com
Consulting Services
N.A.I.C.S.: 541611

Compscript, LLC (2)
100 Business Park Dr, Ridgeland, MS 39157
Tel.: (601) 956-6228
Pharmaceutical Services
N.A.I.C.S.: 456110

Heartland Pharmacy of Illinois LLC (2)
940 S Frontage Rd, Woodridge, IL 60517
Tel.: (630) 427-1534
Pharmacy Services
N.A.I.C.S.: 456110

LifeMed Alaska, LLC (2)
3838 W 50th Ave, Anchorage, AK 99502
Tel.: (907) 563-6633
Web Site: http://www.lifemedalaska.com
Pharmacy Services
N.A.I.C.S.: 456110
Marie Bingham (CFO)
Russ Edwards (CEO)
Steve Heyano (COO)
Erik Lewis (Dir-Clinical Svcs)
Bill Chaplin (Dir-Safety & Quality)
Will Halleran (Mgr-Ground Ops)
Ed Saclayan (Mgr-Ops Support)
Andrew Pratt (Mgr-Fleet & Facilities)
Kimberley Johnson (Coord-Trng Center)
Seth Ransom (Mgr-Bus Dev)

Management & Network Services LLC (2)
6500 Emerald Pkwy Ste 310, Dublin, OH 43016
Tel.: (614) 789-2000
Web Site: http://www.mnsnetwork.com
Pharmacy Services
N.A.I.C.S.: 325412
Jonathan Hoffman (COO)
Heather Tausel (Chief Dev Officer)
Melissa Shandor (Dir-Bus Dev)
Brian Deeley (Pres & CEO)
Voni Hope (Dir-Care Coordination)
Joyce Wehner (Dir-Managed Care Contracting & Compliance)
Jennifer Lee (Dir-Fin Plng & Analysis)

NCS Healthcare of Montana, Inc. (2)
2747 Enterprise Ave Ste 1, Billings, MT 59102-7412
Tel.: (406) 896-3399
Pharmaceutical Services
N.A.I.C.S.: 456110

NeighborCare of Indiana, LLC (2)

3402 Congressional Pkwy, Fort Wayne, IN 46808
Tel.: (260) 484-7366
Pharmaceutical Services
N.A.I.C.S.: 456110

Subsidiary (Domestic):

Grandview Pharmacy, LLC (3)
474 Southpoint Cir, Brownsburg, IN 46112
Web Site: http://grandrx.com
Health Care Srvices
N.A.I.C.S.: 621610
Mark Prifogle (CEO)
Glenn Eldridge (Dir-Clinical Svcs)
John Jones (Dir-Quality Assurance)
Brooke Bradley (Dir-Pharmacy)
Christian Marr (Mgr-Billing & Accounts Receivable)

Subsidiary (Domestic):

NeighborCare of Virginia, LLC (2)
8575 Magellan Pkwy Ste 100, Richmond, VA 23227
Tel.: (757) 399-2046
Nursing Care Facilities
N.A.I.C.S.: 623110

Omnicare Pharmacies of Pennsylvania West, LLC (2)
1152 Gardeb St, Greensburg, PA 15601
Tel.: (724) 832-1233
Pharmaceutical Products Distr
N.A.I.C.S.: 424210

Omnicare Pharmacy of Pueblo, LLC (2)
4602 N Elizabeth St Ste 190, Pueblo, CO 81008
Tel.: (719) 544-2146
Pharmaceutical Services
N.A.I.C.S.: 456110

Shore Pharmaceutical Providers, Inc. (2)
55 W Ames Ct Ste 200, Plainview, NY 11803
Tel.: (516) 938-8080
Pharmaceutical Services
N.A.I.C.S.: 456110

Sterling Healthcare Services, Inc. (2)
19925 Stevens Creek Blvd Ste 100, Cupertino, CA 95014
Tel.: (502) 601-0081
Web Site: https://www.sterlinghcs.com
Health Care Srvices
N.A.I.C.S.: 621610

Superior Care Pharmacy, Inc. (2)
161 E Main St, El Cajon, CA 92020
Web Site: https://www.superiorcarerx.com
Health Care Facility Services
N.A.I.C.S.: 622310

Value Health Care Services, LLC (2)
3545 Cruse Rd Ste 103, Lawrenceville, GA 30044
Tel.: (404) 975-4135
Web Site: https://valuehealthcareservices.com
Health Care Srvices
N.A.I.C.S.: 621610

Pennsylvania CVS Pharmacy, L.L.C. (1)
1535 W 26th St, Erie, PA 16508
Tel.: (814) 461-1215
Emp.: 4
Pharmacy & Drug Store Operator
N.A.I.C.S.: 456110

Pt. Aetna Global Benefits Indonesia (1)
Sentral Senayan 2 Building 16th Floor Suite West 16 Jl Asia Afrika, No 8 Gelora Bung Karno, Jakarta Pusat, 10270, Indonesia
Tel.: (62) 85230715022
Health Care Srvices
N.A.I.C.S.: 621610

RxAmerica LLC (1)
221 N Charles Lindbergh Dr, Salt Lake City, UT 84116
Tel.: (801) 961-6000
Web Site: http://www.rxamerica.com
Sales Range: $250-299.9 Million
Emp.: 400

Pharmacy Benefits Management; Mail Order Prescription Drugs
N.A.I.C.S.: 456110

Signify Health, Inc. (1)
4055 Valley View Ln Ste 700, Dallas, TX 75244
Tel.: (203) 541-4600
Web Site: https://www.signifyhealth.com
Rev.: $805,500,000
Assets: $1,744,100,000
Liabilities: $923,500,000
Net Worth: $820,600,000
Earnings: ($576,800,000)
Emp.: 2,100
Fiscal Year-end: 12/31/2022
Holding Company
N.A.I.C.S.: 551112
Bradford Kyle Armbrester (CEO)
Steven Senneff (Pres)
Adam McAnaney (Corp Counsel)
Susan Yun (Chief HR Officer)
Josh Builder (CTO)
David Pierre (COO)
Marc Rothman (Chief Medical Officer)
Laurel Douty (Exec VP)

SilverScript Insurance Company (1)
445 Great Circle Rd, Nashville, TN 37228
Tel.: (615) 743-6600
Web Site: http://www.silverscript.com
Pharmacy & Drug Store Services
N.A.I.C.S.: 456110

bswift Resources LLC (1)
10 S Riverside Plz Ste 1100, Chicago, IL 60606
Web Site: https://www.bswift.com
Information Technology Services
N.A.I.C.S.: 541511

CW PETROLEUM CORP.
2717 Commercial Ctr Blvd Ste E200 PMB 264, Katy, TX 77494
Tel.: (281) 817-8099 TX
Web Site: https://www.cwpetroleumcorp.com
Year Founded: 2011
CWPE—(OTCQB)
Rev.: $9,313,358
Assets: $1,032,394
Liabilities: $894,176
Net Worth: $138,218
Earnings: $449,293
Emp.: 4
Fiscal Year-end: 12/31/23
Fuel Distr
N.A.I.C.S.: 457210
Christopher Williams (Pres & CEO)
Graham Williams (CFO)

CXAPP INC.
4 Palo Alto Sq 3000 El Camino Real, Palo Alto, CA 94306
Tel.: (650) 575-4456 DE
Web Site: https://www.cxapp.com
CXAI—(NASDAQ)
Assets: $4,151,829
Liabilities: $3,952,948
Net Worth: $198,881
Earnings: $17,634,910
Fiscal Year-end: 12/31/22
Software Development Services
N.A.I.C.S.: 518210
Naresh H. Soni (CTO)
Leon Papkoff (Co-Founder)
Khurram Parviz Sheikh (Co-Founder, Chm & CEO)

CYANOTECH CORPORATION
73-4460 Queen Kaahumanu Hwy Ste 102, Kailua Kona, HI 96740
Tel.: (808) 326-1353 NV
Web Site: https://www.cyanotech.com
Year Founded: 1983
CYAN—(NASDAQ)
Rev.: $23,071,000
Assets: $25,112,000
Liabilities: $13,298,000
Net Worth: $11,814,000

Earnings: ($5,267,000)
Emp.: 77
Fiscal Year-end: 03/31/24
Microalgae Products Researcher, Developer & Mfr
N.A.I.C.S.: 325411
Gerald R. Cysewski *(Co-Founder & Chief Scientific Officer)*
Glenn D. Jensen *(VP-Operations)*
Michael A. Davis *(Chm)*
Jen Johansen *(VP-Quality-Regulatory-Govt Affairs)*
Matthew K. Custer *(Pres & CEO)*
Amy Nordin *(Sec & VP-Human Resources)*

Subsidiaries:

Nutrex, Inc.   **(1)**
73 4460 Queen Kaahamanu Hwy Ste 102, Kailua Kona, HI 96740   **(100%)**
Tel.: (808) 326-1353
Web Site: http://www.nutrex-hawaii.com
Sales Range: $75-99.9 Million
Emp.: 70
Sales & Marketing of Nutritional Consumer Products
N.A.I.C.S.: 424490
Gerald R. Cysewski *(Chief Scientific Officer & Exec VP)*

CYBER ENVIRO-TECH, INC.
6991 E Camelback Rd Ste D 300, Scottsdale, AZ 85251
Tel.: (307) 200-2803   WY
Web Site:
https://www.cyberenviro.tech
Year Founded: 1992
CETI—(OTCIQ)
Rev.: $85,356
Assets: $2,871,855
Liabilities: $958,496
Net Worth: $1,913,359
Earnings: $1,479,362
Fiscal Year-end: 12/31/22
Custom Computer Programming Services
N.A.I.C.S.: 541511
Dan Leboffe *(Principal Acctg Officer)*
Kim D. Southworth *(CEO)*
T. J. Agardy *(Pres)*

CYBERFORT SOFTWARE, INC.
388 Market St Ste 1300, San Francisco, CA 94111
Tel.: (415) 295-4507   NV
Web Site:
http://www.cyberfortsoftware.com
Year Founded: 2010
CYBF—(OTCIQ)
Liabilities: $710,650
Net Worth: ($710,650)
Earnings: ($656,677)
Emp.: 1
Fiscal Year-end: 03/31/19
Software Security Services
N.A.I.C.S.: 513210

CYBERLOQ TECHNOLOGIES, INC.
4837 Swift Rd Ste 210-1, Sarasota, FL 34231
Tel.: (612) 961-4536   NV
Web Site: https://www.cyberloq.com
Year Founded: 2008
CLOQ—(OTCQB)
Rev.: $2,671
Assets: $341,118
Liabilities: $324,132
Net Worth: $16,986
Earnings: ($979,048)
Emp.: 2
Fiscal Year-end: 12/31/22
Technology-Based Credit Management Processing Services
N.A.I.C.S.: 513210
Christopher Jackson *(Co-Founder, Pres, Treas & Sec)*
Enrico Giordano *(Co-Founder & VP)*

CYBERLUX CORPORATION
800 Park Offices Dr Ste 3209, Research Triangle Park, NC 27709
Tel.: (984) 363-6894   NV
Web Site: https://www.cyberlux.com
Year Founded: 2000
CYBL—(OTCIQ)
Sales Range: $1-9.9 Million
Emp.: 13
Lighting Systems Mfr
N.A.I.C.S.: 335139
Mark D. Schmidt *(Pres & CEO)*
David D. Downing *(CFO & Treas)*
John W. Ringo *(Chm, Chm, Gen Counsel, Gen Counsel & Sec)*

Subsidiaries:

Datron World Communications, Inc.   **(1)**
3055 Enterprise Ct, Vista, CA 92081
Tel.: (760) 597-1500
Web Site: http://www.dtwc.com
Sales Range: $25-49.9 Million
Emp.: 170
Radio Communication Equipment Mfr
N.A.I.C.S.: 334220
John Biljan *(Dir-Land Mobile Radio)*
Arthur Barter *(Pres & CEO)*

CYBRA CORPORATION
1 Executive Blvd, Yonkers, NY 10701
Tel.: (914) 963-6600   NY
Web Site: http://www.cybra.com
Year Founded: 1985
CYRP—(OTCIQ)
Sales Range: $1-9.9 Million
Emp.: 12
Software Development Services
N.A.I.C.S.: 541511
Harold L. Brand *(Founder, Chm, Pres, CEO & CFO)*
Robert J. Roskow *(Exec VP)*
Paul Holm *(CTO)*
Michael J. Shabet *(VP-Sls & Mktg)*
Charles M. Roskow *(VP-Ops)*

CYCLACEL PHARMACEUTI-CALS, INC.
200 Connell Dr Ste 1500, Berkeley Heights, NJ 07922
Tel.: (908) 517-7330   DE
Web Site: https://www.cyclacel.com
Year Founded: 1996
CYCC—(NASDAQ)
Rev.: $1,741,000
Assets: $27,501,000
Liabilities: $11,992,000
Net Worth: $15,509,000
Earnings: ($21,198,000)
Fiscal Year-end: 12/31/22
Immune System Therapies Developer
N.A.I.C.S.: 325412
Spiro Rombotis *(Pres & CEO)*
Robert J. Spiegel *(Vice Chm)*
Christopher S. Henney *(Chm)*
Paul McBarron *(CFO, COO, Sec & Exec VP-Fin)*
Brian M. Schwartz *(Interim Chief Medical Officer)*

Subsidiaries:

ALIGN Pharmaceuticals, LLC   **(1)**
200 Connell Dr Ste 1500, Berkeley Heights, NJ 07922
Tel.: (908) 834-0960
Web Site: http://www.alignpharma.com
Pharmaceutical Preparation Mfr
N.A.I.C.S.: 325412

Cyclacel Limited   **(1)**
1 James Lindsay Place, Dundee, DD1 5JJ, United Kingdom
Tel.: (44) 1382206062
Web Site: http://www.cyclacel.com
Sales Range: $1-9.9 Million
Biopharmaceutical Products Mfr for Cancer & Other Diseases Involving Abnormal Cell Proliferation
N.A.I.C.S.: 325412

Spiro Rombotis *(Pres & CEO)*

CYCLERION THERAPEUTICS, INC.
245 1st St Riverview II 18th Fl, Cambridge, MA 02142
Tel.: (857) 327-8778   MA
Web Site: https://www.cyclerion.com
Year Founded: 2018
CYCN—(NASDAQ)
Rev.: $1,625,000
Assets: $18,079,000
Liabilities: $7,627,000
Net Worth: $10,452,000
Earnings: ($44,078,000)
Emp.: 16
Fiscal Year-end: 12/31/22
Research & Development in Biotechnology (except Nanobiotechnology)
N.A.I.C.S.: 541714
Peter M. Hecht *(CEO)*
Cheryl Gault *(COO)*
Todd Milne *(VP-Corp Dev)*

CYCLO THERAPEUTICS, INC.
6714 NW 16th St Ste B, Gainesville, FL 32653
Tel.: (386) 418-8060   FL
Web Site:
https://www.cyclotherapeutics.com
Year Founded: 1990
CYTH—(NASDAQ)
Rev.: $1,375,760
Assets: $4,215,213
Liabilities: $3,480,669
Net Worth: $734,544
Earnings: ($15,450,888)
Emp.: 9
Fiscal Year-end: 12/31/22
Holding Company; Chemical Products Mfr & Distr
N.A.I.C.S.: 551112
C. E. Strattan *(Founder)*
Jeffrey L. Tate *(COO & Chief Quality Officer)*
Francis Patrick Ostronic *(Vice Chm)*
Markus W. Sieger *(Chm)*
Joshua M. Fine *(CFO)*
Michael Lisjak *(Chief Regulatory Officer & Sr VP-Bus Dev)*
Russ Belden *(Chief Comml Officer-Acting)*
Lori McKenna Gorski *(Head-Patient Advocacy-Global)*
Karen Mullen *(Interim Chief Medical Officer)*
N. Scott Fine *(CEO)*

Subsidiaries:

Applied Molecular Transport Inc.   **(1)**
450 E Jamie Ct, South San Francisco, CA 94080
Tel.: (650) 392-0420
Web Site: https://www.appliedmt.com
Rev.: $898,000
Assets: $107,446,000
Liabilities: $46,608,000
Net Worth: $60,838,000
Earnings: ($126,325,000)
Emp.: 79
Fiscal Year-end: 12/31/2022
Biotechnology Research & Development Services
N.A.I.C.S.: 541714
Shawn Cross *(Chm & CEO)*
Tahir Mahmood *(Co-Founder)*
Randall Mrsny *(Co-Founder)*
Elizabeth Bhatt *(Chief Bus & Strategy Officer)*
Brandon Hants *(CFO & Principal Acctg Officer)*
Derek Maclean *(Sr VP-Pharmaceutical Sciences)*
Chuck Olson *(Sr VP-Ops)*
Andy Whitney *(VP-Preclinical Dev & Translational Science)*
Douglas Rich *(Chief Technical Officer)*
Andrew Chang *(Head-IR & Corp Comm)*

CYCLONE POWER TECH-NOLOGIES, INC.
601 NE 26th Ct, Pompano Beach, FL 33064
Tel.: (954) 943-8721   FL
Web Site:
http://www.cyclonepower.com
Year Founded: 2004
CYPW—(OTCIQ)
Sales Range: Less than $1 Million
Emp.: 6
Engineering Research & Development Services
N.A.I.C.S.: 541715
Frankie Fruge *(Pres)*
Bruce Schames *(CFO)*

CYGNUS OIL & GAS CORPO-RATION
520 Post Oak Blvd Ste 320, Houston, TX 77027
Tel.: (713) 784-1113
CYNS—(OTCEM)
Oil & Gas Exploration Services
N.A.I.C.S.: 213112
H. Malcolm Lovett *(Pres & Chief Restaurant Officer)*

CYIOS CORPORATION
258 S Military Trl, Deerfield Beach, FL 33442
Tel.: (617) 504-3635   NV
Web Site: https://www.cyios.com
CYIO—(OTCIQ)
Sales Range: Less than $1 Million
Emp.: 15
Knowledge Management Solutions
N.A.I.C.S.: 541512
Timothy W. Carnahan *(Founder, Pres & CEO)*
Scott DiStefano *(Program Mgr)*
Traci Anderson *(CFO)*

CYNGN INC.
1015 O'Brien Dr, Menlo Park, CA 94025
Tel.: (650) 924-5905   DE
Web Site: https://www.cyngn.com
Year Founded: 2013
CYN—(NASDAQ)
Rev.: $262,000
Assets: $25,505,012
Liabilities: $1,387,485
Net Worth: $24,117,527
Earnings: ($19,236,509)
Emp.: 66
Fiscal Year-end: 12/31/22
Custom Computer Programming Services
N.A.I.C.S.: 541511
Sean Stetson *(VP-Engrg)*
Lior Tal *(Chm & CEO)*
Donald Alvarez *(CFO)*
Ben Landen *(VP-Engrg)*
Biao Ma *(VP-Bus Dev)*
Marc Brown *(VP-HR)*
Chris Wright *(Head-Sls)*
Felix Singh *(VP-Engrg Svcs)*

CYPRESS ENVIRONMENTAL PARTNERS, L.P.
5727 S Lewis Ave Ste 300, Tulsa, OK 74105
Tel.: (918) 748-3900   DE
Web Site:
http://www.cypressenvironmental.biz
Year Founded: 2013
CELP—(NYSE)
Rev.: $117,317,000
Assets: $96,978,000
Liabilities: $62,418,000
Net Worth: $34,560,000
Earnings: ($14,732,000)
Emp.: 472
Fiscal Year-end: 12/31/21
Oil & Gas Industry Services

Cypress Environmental Partners, L.P.—(Continued)

N.A.I.C.S.: 213112
Peter C. Boylan III *(Founder, Chm, Pres & CEO)*

Subsidiaries:

Brown Integrity, LLC (1)
1743 Hwy 77 S, Giddings, TX 78942
Tel.: (979) 542-3813
Web Site: http://www.brownintegrity.com
Hydro Testing Services
N.A.I.C.S.: 541380

Cypress Energy Partners, LLC (1)
5727 S Lewis Ave Ste 300, Tulsa, OK 74105
Tel.: (918) 748-3900
Energy Consulting Services
N.A.I.C.S.: 541690

Tulsa Inspection Resources, LLC (1)
5727 S Lewis Ave Ste 300, Tulsa, OK 74105
Tel.: (918) 274-1100
Web Site: http://www.tulsainspection.com
Sales Range: $1-9.9 Million
Emp.: 200
Pipeline Inspection Services
N.A.I.C.S.: 213112
Randall Lorett *(Pres & CEO)*
Richard Grogan *(Sr VP-Integrity)*
Chris Hartnell *(VP-Integrity Svcs)*
Rodney Einer *(COO & Exec VP)*
James Allen III *(Dir-Acct Mgmt)*

Subsidiary (Non-US):

Foley Inspection Services, ULC (2)
5920 Macleod Trail SW Suite 501, Calgary, T2H 0K2, AB, Canada
Tel.: (403) 258-2999
Web Site: http://www.foleyinspection.com
Emp.: 5
Pipeline Inspection Services
N.A.I.C.S.: 213112

Tulsa Inspection Resources - Canada, ULC (2)
501-5920 Macleod Trl SW, Calgary, T2H 0K2, AB, Canada
Tel.: (403) 258-2999
Web Site: http://www.tircanada.com
Hydro Testing Services
N.A.I.C.S.: 541380

CYTEIR THERAPEUTICS, INC.
128 Spring St Bldg A Ste 510, Lexington, MA 02421
Tel.: (857) 285-4140 DE
Web Site: http://www.cyteir.com
Year Founded: 2012
CYT—(NASDAQ)
Rev.: $2,109,000
Assets: $153,232,000
Liabilities: $6,946,000
Net Worth: $146,286,000
Earnings: ($46,061,000)
Emp.: 46
Fiscal Year-end: 12/31/22
Biotechnology Research & Development Services
N.A.I.C.S.: 541714
Markus Renschler *(Pres & CEO)*
Tom OShea *(Sr VP-Clinical Pharmacology & Preclinical Dev)*
Judson Englert *(Sr VP-Clinical Research & Dev)*
Barbara Wan *(VP-Research & Dev Project Leadership)*
Jean-Marc Lapierre *(VP-Chemistry)*
Susan Doleman *(VP-Clinical Ops)*
David Gaiero *(CFO)*
Lisa Hayes *(VP-IR & Comm)*
Gale Cohen *(VP-HR)*
David Gaiero *(CFO)*

CYTEK BIOSCIENCES, INC.
47215 Lakeview Blvd, Fremont, CA 94538-6407 DE
Web Site: https://www.cytekbio.com
Year Founded: 2014

CTKB—(NASDAQ)
Rev.: $164,036,000
Assets: $519,476,000
Liabilities: $93,930,000
Net Worth: $425,546,000
Earnings: $2,484,000
Emp.: 583
Fiscal Year-end: 12/31/22
Research & Development in Biotechnology (except Nanobiotechnology)
N.A.I.C.S.: 541714
William McCombe *(CFO)*
Patrik Jeanmonod *(Head-Corp Dev Analytics)*
Valerie Barnett *(Gen Counsel & Sec)*
Ken RileyRiley *(Gen Mgr)*
Melik Ulusu *(VP-Ops & Integrated Supply Chain)*
Raymond A. Lannigan *(VP-Sls & Svc)*
Maria Jaimes *(VP-Applications)*
Allen Poirson *(Sr VP-Mktg & Corp Dev)*
Mark Edinger *(VP-Scientific Affairs)*
Chris Williams *(COO)*
Philippe Busque *(Sr VP-Global Sls & Svcs)*
Paul Goodson *(Head-IR)*
Wenbin Jiang *(Co-Founder, Chm & CEO)*
Ming Yan *(Co-Founder & CTO)*

CYTODYN INC.
1111 Main St Ste 660, Vancouver, WA 98660
Tel.: (360) 980-8524 CO
Web Site: https://www.cytodyn.com
Year Founded: 2002
CYDY—(OTCQB)
Assets: $11,136,000
Liabilities: $127,894,000
Net Worth: ($116,758,000)
Earnings: ($49,841,000)
Emp.: 9
Fiscal Year-end: 05/31/24
Biopharmaceutical Mfr
N.A.I.C.S.: 325412
Tanya Durkee Urbach *(Chm)*
Mahboob U. Rahman *(Chief Scientific Officer)*
Christopher P. Recknor *(Sr Exec VP-Clinical Ops)*
Antonio Migliarese *(CFO, Principal Acctg Officer, Treas & Sec)*
Seenu Srinivasan *(Exec Dir-CMC Regulatory Affairs)*
Cyrus Arman *(Sr VP-Bus Ops)*
Jacob P. Lalezari *(CEO)*

CYTOKINETICS, INC.
350 Oyster Point Blvd, South San Francisco, CA 94080
Tel.: (650) 624-3000 DE
Web Site:
https://www.cytokinetics.com
Year Founded: 1997
CYTK—(NASDAQ)
Rev.: $94,588,000
Assets: $1,014,775,000
Liabilities: $1,122,675,000
Net Worth: ($107,900,000)
Earnings: ($388,955,000)
Emp.: 409
Fiscal Year-end: 12/31/22
Research & Development in the Social Sciences & Humanities
N.A.I.C.S.: 541720
James H. Sabry *(Co-Founder)*
Robert I. Blum *(Pres & CEO)*
James A. Spudich *(Co-Founder)*
David W. Cragg *(Chief Admin & HR Officer)*
Elisabeth A. Schnieders *(Sr VP-Bus Dev)*
Bradley Paul Morgan *(Sr VP-Res & Non-Clinical Dev)*

Bonnie A. Charpentier *(Sr VP-Regulatory Affairs & Compliance)*
Diane Weiser *(Sr VP-Corp Comm & IR)*
Daniel R. Casper *(VP-IT)*
Lawrence Goldstein *(Co-Founder)*
Ronald D. Vale *(Co-Founder)*
Eric Terhaerdt *(VP-Dev Ops)*
Robert C. Wong *(Chief Acctg Officer & VP)*
Sung H. Lee *(CFO & Exec VP)*
Erin Donnelly *(VP-Portfolio & Project Mgmt)*
Daniel E. Kates *(VP-Medical Affairs)*
Stuart Kupfer *(Chief Medical Officer & Sr VP)*
Anne N. Murphy *(VP-Biology)*
Andrew Callos *(Chief Comml Officer)*
Steven M. Cook *(Sr VP)*
YulyMae DiNapoli *(VP)*
Genie Dubuk *(VP)*
John Faurescu *(Sec)*
Stephen B. Heitner *(VP)*
John Jacoppi *(VP)*
Kari K. Loeser *(Chief Compliance Officer)*
Jeff Lotz *(VP)*
Fady I. Malik *(Exec VP)*
Lisa Meng *(VP)*
Diann Potestio *(VP)*
Stacy A. Rudnicki *(VP)*
Norma Tom *(VP)*
Brett A. Pletcher *(Chief Legal Officer & Exec VP)*
Andrew A. Wolff *(Sr VP)*

CYTOMX THERAPEUTICS, INC.
151 Oyster Point Blvd Ste 400, South San Francisco, CA 94080
Tel.: (650) 515-3185 DE
Web Site: https://www.cytomx.com
Year Founded: 2008
CTMX—(NASDAQ)
Rev.: $53,163,000
Assets: $260,891,000
Liabilities: $346,642,000
Net Worth: ($85,751,000)
Earnings: ($99,317,000)
Emp.: 116
Fiscal Year-end: 12/31/22
Pharmaceuticals Mfr
N.A.I.C.S.: 325412
Sean A. McCarthy *(Chm & CEO)*
Sridhar Viswanathan *(Sr VP-Process Sciences & Mfg Ops)*
Danielle Olander *(Sr VP-Talent & Sys Dev)*
Frederick W. Gluck *(Co-Founder)*
Alison Joly *(Sr VP-Program & Alliance Mgmt)*
Patrick Daugherty *(Co-Founder)*
Marcia P. Belvin *(Sr VP & Head-Res)*
Lloyd A. Rowland Jr. *(Chief Compliance Officer, Gen Counsel, Sec & Sr VP)*

CYTOSORBENTS CORPORATION
305 College Rd E, Princeton, NJ 08540
Tel.: (732) 329-8885 NV
Web Site:
https://www.cytosorbents.com
Year Founded: 2002
CTSO—(NASDAQ)
Rev.: $34,688,809
Assets: $63,231,530
Liabilities: $27,856,557
Net Worth: $35,374,973
Earnings: ($32,812,583)
Emp.: 198
Fiscal Year-end: 12/31/22
Medical Device Mfr
N.A.I.C.S.: 339112

Peter J. Mariani *(CFO)*
Vincent J. Capponi *(Pres & COO)*
Christopher Cramer *(VP-Bus Dev)*
Kathleen P. Bloch *(CFO)*
Efthymios N. Deliargyris *(Chief Medical Officer)*
Phillip P. Chan *(CEO)*

Subsidiaries:

CytoSorbents Europe GmbH (1)
Muggelseedamm 131, 12587, Berlin, Germany
Tel.: (49) 3065499145
Web Site: https://cytosorb-therapy.com
Medical & Hospital Equipment Whslr
N.A.I.C.S.: 423450
Christian Steiner *(Mng Dir & VP-Sls & Mktg)*
Phillip P. Chan *(CEO)*
Vincent Capponi *(Pres)*
Christopher Cramer *(VP-Business Development)*
Kathleen Bloch *(CFO)*
Efthymios N. Deliargyris *(Chief Medical Officer)*

CYTTA CORP.
5450 W Sahara Ave Ste 300A, Las Vegas, NV 89146
Tel.: (702) 900-7022 NV
Year Founded: 2006
CYCA—(OTCQB)
Rev.: $30,059
Assets: $2,301,134
Liabilities: $2,561,493
Net Worth: ($260,359)
Earnings: ($4,728,473)
Fiscal Year-end: 09/30/23
Electronic Components Mfr
N.A.I.C.S.: 334419
Gary M. Campbell *(Founder, CEO, CFO, Principal-Finance, Sec & Exec Dir)*
Erik Stephansen *(Pres & Dir)*
Michael Collins *(CTO & Chief Visionary Officer)*
Gary R. Brown *(Sr VP-Product & Technology)*

CYXTERA TECHNOLOGIES, INC.
2333 Ponce De Leon Blvd Ste 900, Coral Gables, FL 33134
Tel.: (305) 537-9500 DE
Web Site: https://www.cyxtera.com
Year Founded: 2019
CYXT—(NASDAQ)
Rev.: $746,000,000
Assets: $3,063,300,000
Liabilities: $2,679,000,000
Net Worth: $384,300,000
Earnings: ($355,100,000)
Emp.: 752
Fiscal Year-end: 12/31/22
Investment Services
N.A.I.C.S.: 523999
Kenneth R. Marlin *(CFO)*
Victor Semah *(Chief Legal Officer)*
Nelson Fonseca *(CEO)*
Manuel D. Medina *(Chm)*

Subsidiaries:

Cyxtera Technologies, Inc. (1)
2333 Ponce De Leon Blvd Ste 900, Coral Gables, FL 33134
Tel.: (305) 537-9500
Web Site: http://www.cyxtera.com
Security & Data Analytics Technology Solutions
N.A.I.C.S.: 518210
Manuel D. Medina *(Founder & Chm)*
Nelson Fonseca *(CEO)*
Barry Field *(Chief Revenue Officer)*
Rene A. Rodriguez *(CFO)*
Randy Rowland *(COO)*
Victor Semah *(Chief Legal Officer)*
Frank Barnett *(Chief HR Officer)*
Leo Casusol *(CIO)*

Gregory J. Touhill *(Pres-Cyxtera Federal Grp)*
Leo Taddeo *(Chief Information Security Officer)*
David Keasey *(Exec VP-Data Center Sls)*
Thomas Cannady *(VP-Network Svcs)*
Ben Stewart *(VP-Engrg & Innovation)*
Jason Lochhead *(CTO-Infrastructure)*
Carlos Sagasta *(CFO)*

Subsidiary (Domestic):

Immunity, Inc. (2)
2 Alhambra Plz Ste PH-1-B, Coral Gables, FL 33134
Tel.: (786) 220-0600
Web Site: https://www.immunityinc.com
Internet Security Services
N.A.I.C.S.: 541519

D & Z MEDIA ACQUISITION CORP.
2870 Peachtree Rd NW Ste 509, Atlanta, GA 30305
Tel.: (404) 585-8233   DE
Year Founded: 2020
DNZ'U—(NYSE)
Investment Services
N.A.I.C.S.: 523999
Betty Liu *(Chm, Pres, CEO & CFO)*

D.R. HORTON, INC.
1341 Horton Cir, Arlington, TX 76011
Tel.: (817) 390-8200   TX
Web Site: https://www.drhorton.com
Year Founded: 1978
DHI—(NYSE)
Rev.: $36,801,400,000
Assets: $36,104,300,000
Liabilities: $10,279,900,000
Net Worth: $25,824,400,000
Earnings: $4,806,000,000
Emp.: 14,766
Fiscal Year-end: 09/30/24
Residential Home Builder
N.A.I.C.S.: 236117
Paul J. Romanowski *(Co-COO & Exec VP)*
Paul J. Romanowski *(Pres & CEO)*
Donald R. Horton *(Founder & Chm)*
Bill W. Wheat *(CFO & Exec VP)*
David V. Auld *(Vice Chm)*
Michael J. Murray *(Co-COO & Exec VP)*
Bethany Carle *(Mgr-IR)*
Aron M. Odom *(VP & Controller)*
Jessica Hansen *(VP-IR)*

Subsidiaries:

Austin Data, Inc. (1)
505 E Huntland Dr Ste 470, Austin, TX 78752
Tel.: (512) 454-5141
Web Site: http://www.austindata.com
Building & Construction Services
N.A.I.C.S.: 561790

Braselton Homes, Inc. (1)
5337 Yorktown Blvd, Corpus Christi, TX 78413
Tel.: (361) 991-4710
Web Site: http://www.braseltonhomes.com
Sales Range: $10-24.9 Million
Emp.: 45
Developer & Home Builder
N.A.I.C.S.: 236115
Fred Braselton *(Pres)*

Cane Island, LLC (1)
5251 Cane Is Loop, Kissimmee, FL 34746
Tel.: (407) 397-0128
Web Site: http://www.caneislandliving.com
Sales Range: $10-24.9 Million
Emp.: 3
Vacation Home Services
N.A.I.C.S.: 531110

Classic Builders, Inc. (1)
1910 SW Plz Shops Ln, Ankeny, IA 50023
Tel.: (515) 965-7876
Web Site:
http://www.classicbuildersiowa.com
Home Design & Construction Services

N.A.I.C.S.: 236115
Josh Moulton *(Pres)*

Crown Communities, Inc. (1)
1371 Dogwood Dr SW, Conyers, GA 30012
Tel.: (678) 509-0555
Web Site: http://www.crownus.com
Sales Range: $250-299.9 Million
Emp.: 133
Residential Home Construction Services
N.A.I.C.S.: 236117

D.R. Horton (1)
20410 N 19th Ave Ste 100, Phoenix, AZ 85027   **(100%)**
Tel.: (480) 483-0006
Web Site: http://www.drhorton.com
Sales Range: $50-74.9 Million
Emp.: 100
Constructs, Sells & Finances Single-Family Homes
N.A.I.C.S.: 236115

Subsidiary (Domestic):

Continental Homes of Austin, L.P. (2)
10700 Pecan Park Blvd Ste 400, Austin, TX 78750   **(100%)**
Tel.: (512) 345-4663
Web Site: http://www.drhorton.com
Sales Range: $50-74.9 Million
Emp.: 100
Builder of Single Family Homes
N.A.I.C.S.: 236115
Mark Ferguson *(Pres)*

Subsidiary (Domestic):

DHI Title (3)
10700 Pecan Park Blvd Ste 210, Austin, TX 78750   **(100%)**
Tel.: (512) 345-5535
Web Site: http://www.dhititle.com
Sales Range: $25-49.9 Million
Emp.: 20
Real Estate Closings; Issues Titles
N.A.I.C.S.: 522310
Kim Minks *(Reg Mgr)*

Subsidiary (Domestic):

D.R. Horton Homes (2)
1245 S Military Trl Ste 100, Deerfield Beach, FL 33442   **(100%)**
Tel.: (954) 428-4854
Web Site: http://www.drhorton.com
Sales Range: $100-124.9 Million
Emp.: 50
Residential Construction
N.A.I.C.S.: 236220

D.R. Horton, Inc (2)
2280 Wardlow Cir Ste 100, Corona, CA 92880   **(100%)**
Tel.: (951) 272-9000
Web Site: http://www.drhorton.com
Sales Range: $50-74.9 Million
Emp.: 80
Custom Home Building
N.A.I.C.S.: 236117
Steve Sitzpatrick *(Pres)*

D.R. Horton/Continental Series (2)
7600 E Orchard Rd Ste 350F, Greenwood Village, CO 80111-2556   **(100%)**
Tel.: (303) 488-0061
Web Site: http://www.drhorton.com
Sales Range: $10-24.9 Million
Emp.: 50
Mortgage Services
N.A.I.C.S.: 541611

D.R. Horton - Colorado, LLC (1)
9555 S Kingston Ct Ste 200, Englewood, CO 80112
Tel.: (303) 488-0061
Web Site: http://www.drhorton.com
Residential Building Construction Services
N.A.I.C.S.: 531110

D.R. Horton - Crown, LLC (1)
301 Commerce St, Fort Worth, TX 76102
Tel.: (817) 390-8200
Real Estate Related Services
N.A.I.C.S.: 531390

D.R. Horton - Georgia, LLC (1)
1371 Dogwood Dr SW, Conyers, GA 30012
Tel.: (678) 509-0555
Residential Building Construction Services

N.A.I.C.S.: 531110

D.R. Horton - Indiana, LLC (1)
9210 N Meridian St, Indianapolis, IN 46260
Tel.: (317) 844-0433
Residential Building Construction Services
N.A.I.C.S.: 531110

D.R. Horton - Iowa, LLC (1)
1910 SW Plaza Shops Ln, Ankeny, IA 50023
Tel.: (515) 620-4240
Home Construction Services
N.A.I.C.S.: 236117

D.R. Horton Insurance Agency, Inc. (1)
1341 Horton Cir, Arlington, TX 76011
Web Site: http://www.drhortoninsurance.com
Insurance Services
N.A.I.C.S.: 524128

D.R. Horton Realty, LLC (1)
9555 S Kingston Ct, Englewood, CO 80218
Tel.: (720) 326-3774
Real Estate Related Services
N.A.I.C.S.: 531390

D.R. Horton, Inc. - Conroe Office (1)
400 Carriage Hills Blvd, Conroe, TX 77384
Tel.: (281) 465-7000
Web Site: http://www.drhorton.com
Sales Range: $50-74.9 Million
Emp.: 150
Single-Family Housing Construction
N.A.I.C.S.: 236115

D.R. Horton, Inc. - DFW East Division Office (1)
4306 Miller Rd, Rowlett, TX 75088
Tel.: (214) 607-4244
Web Site: http://www.drhorton.com
Sales Range: $50-74.9 Million
Emp.: 40
Residential Construction
N.A.I.C.S.: 236115
Derek Ammerman *(Pres)*

D.R. Horton, Inc. - Fresno (1)
5050 Hopyard Rd Ste 180, Pleasanton, CA 94588
Tel.: (925) 225-7400
Residential Building Construction Services
N.A.I.C.S.: 236116

D.R. Horton, Inc. - Huntsville (1)
415-H Church St NW Ste 202, Huntsville, AL 35801-5573
Tel.: (256) 513-8600
Real Estate Related Services
N.A.I.C.S.: 531390
Jason Paul *(Pres)*

D.R. Horton, Inc. - Minnesota (1)
20860 Kenbridge Ct Ste 100, Lakeville, MN 55044
Tel.: (952) 985-7272
Real Estate Related Services
N.A.I.C.S.: 531390
Jim Slaikeu *(Pres)*

D.R. Horton, Inc. - San Antonio Office (1)
211 N Loop 1604 E Ste 130, San Antonio, TX 78232-1242
Tel.: (210) 496-2668
Web Site: http://www.continentalhomes.com
Sales Range: $75-99.9 Million
Emp.: 160
Residential Construction
N.A.I.C.S.: 236115
James Kyle *(Pres)*

D.R. Horton, Inc. -Chicago (1)
750 E Bunker Ct, Vernon Hills, IL 60061
Tel.: (847) 362-9100
Real Estate Related Services
N.A.I.C.S.: 531390

D.R. Horton, inc. - Seattle Office (1)
12931 NE 126th Pl, Kirkland, WA 98034
Tel.: (425) 821-3400
Web Site: http://www.drhorton.com
Speculative Builder, Single-Family Houses
N.A.I.C.S.: 236115
Jan Lungren *(VP)*

DHI Communities, Inc. (1)
1341 Horton Cir, Arlington, TX 76011
Tel.: (817) 390-8200
Web Site: https://www.dhicommunities.com

Home Construction Services
N.A.I.C.S.: 236117

DHI Mortgage Company GP, Inc. (1)
10700 Pecan Park Blvd Ste 450, Austin, TX 78750
Tel.: (512) 502-0545
Credit Intermediation Services
N.A.I.C.S.: 522390

DHI Mortgage Company Ltd. (1)
10700 Pecan Park Blvd Ste 450, Austin, TX 78750
Tel.: (512) 502-0545
Web Site: http://www.dhimortgage.com
Sales Range: $25-49.9 Million
Emp.: 50
Mortgage Services
N.A.I.C.S.: 522310

DHI Title of Alabama, Inc. (1)
25355 Profit Dr, Daphne, AL 36526
Tel.: (251) 621-9621
Real Estate Related Services
N.A.I.C.S.: 531390

DHI Title of Arizona, Inc. (1)
7025 W Bell Rd Ste 2, Glendale, AZ 85308
Tel.: (623) 878-8600
Emp.: 6
Title Insurance Services
N.A.I.C.S.: 524127
Angela Hukill *(Branch Mgr)*

DHI Title of Minnesota, Inc. (1)
20860 Kenbridge Ct Ste 110, Lakeville, MN 55044
Tel.: (952) 985-7875
Web Site: http://www.dhititle.com
Sales Range: $25-49.9 Million
Emp.: 2
Title Insurance Services
N.A.I.C.S.: 524127
Carla Jensen *(Branch Mgr)*

DHI Title of Nevada, Inc. (1)
1081 Whitney Ranch Dr Ste 121, Henderson, NV 89014
Tel.: (702) 260-6505
Home Construction Services
N.A.I.C.S.: 236117

DHI Title of Ohio, LLC (1)
10700 Pecan Park Blvd Ste 130, Austin, TX 78750
Tel.: (512) 345-5535
Home Construction Services
N.A.I.C.S.: 236117

DHI Title of Washington, Inc. (1)
11241 Slater Ave Ste 200, Kirkland, WA 98033
Tel.: (425) 947-4420
Family House Construction Services
N.A.I.C.S.: 236115
Sharonda Harris *(Branch Mgr-Ops)*

DHIC - Pioneer Hill, LLC (1)
10014 Baden Ln, Austin, TX 78754
Tel.: (512) 605-0406
Home Construction Services
N.A.I.C.S.: 236115

DHIC - Ridgewood, LLC (1)
11645 Saw Palmetto Ln, Riverview, FL 33569
Home Construction Services
N.A.I.C.S.: 236115

DHIR - Amber Creek, LLC (1)
13438 Oneida Ln, Thornton, CO 80229
Tel.: (720) 357-7731
Residential Building Construction Services
N.A.I.C.S.: 236115

DHIR - Arabella, LLC (1)
4927 E Village Dr, Scottsdale, AZ 85254
Tel.: (480) 922-2178
Residential Building Construction Services
N.A.I.C.S.: 236115

DHIR - Bridge Harbor, LLC (1)
107 Bridge Harbor Dr, Callaway, FL 32404
Tel.: (850) 215-2694
Home Construction Services
N.A.I.C.S.: 236115

DHIR - Brookside at Pleasant Valley, LLC (1)
3747 SW Snowberry Ave, Gresham, OR 97080
Tel.: (971) 279-9276
Residential Building Construction Services
N.A.I.C.S.: 236115

D.R. Horton, Inc.—(Continued)

DHIR - Cedar Station, LLC (1)
300 Carr Ln, Lebanon, TN 37087
Tel.: (615) 283-6013
Residential Building Construction Services
N.A.I.C.S.: 236115

DHIR - Cypress Bay, LLC (1)
2203 Capital Dr SE, Palm Bay, FL 32909
Tel.: (321) 482-3228
Residential Building Construction Services
N.A.I.C.S.: 236115

DHIR - Fountain Park, LLC (1)
167 Monroe Creek Blvd, Asheville, NC 28806
Residential Building Construction Services
N.A.I.C.S.: 236115

DHIR - Lakeshore Villages, LLC (1)
3604 Spruce Key Ln, Slidell, LA 70461
Tel.: (985) 231-0493
Residential Building Construction Services
N.A.I.C.S.: 236115

DHIR - Millbrook Park, LLC (1)
208 Fairfax Ave, San Marcos, TX 78666
Tel.: (512) 605-0406
Residential Building Construction Services
N.A.I.C.S.: 236115

DHIR - Riverstone at Westpointe, LLC (1)
14302 Flint Path, San Antonio, TX 78253
Tel.: (210) 645-5522
Residential Building Construction Services
N.A.I.C.S.: 236115

DRH Cambridge Homes, Inc. (1)
800 S Milwaukee Ave Ste 250, Libertyville, IL 60048
Tel.: (847) 362-9100
Web Site: http://www.drhorton.com
Rev.: $14,800,000
Emp.: 50
New Home Construction
N.A.I.C.S.: 236115

DRH Construction, Inc. (1)
2401A Waterman Blvd Ste 4, Fairfield, CA 94534
Tel.: (707) 372-6864
Web Site: https://drhconstructioninc.com
Emp.: 12
Home Construction Services
N.A.I.C.S.: 236117

DRH Southwest Construction, Inc. (1)
4400 Alameda Blvd NE Ste B, Albuquerque, NM 87113-1520
Tel.: (505) 797-4245
Building Construction Services
N.A.I.C.S.: 238390

DRH Tucson Construction, Inc. (1)
3580 W Ina Rd Ste 100, Tucson, AZ 85741-7407
Tel.: (520) 790-6005
Residential Construction
N.A.I.C.S.: 236115

Emerald Realty of Northwest Florida, LLC (1)
2450 Highway 29 S, Cantonment, FL 32533
Tel.: (850) 937-0445
Real Estate Related Services
N.A.I.C.S.: 531390

Founders Oil & Gas, LLC (1)
1341 Horton Cir, Arlington, TX 76011
Tel.: (817) 390-1800
Web Site: http://www.foundersoil.com
Oil & Gas Operation Services
N.A.I.C.S.: 213112
Paten Morrow (Pres)
Mark Wright (VP-Ops)
Jonathan Holmes (VP-Land)
Mike Williams (VP-Reservoir Engrg)
Jeff Turner (VP-Fin & Acctg)

Iao Partners (1)
3613 Perkins Rd Ste E, Baton Rouge, LA 70808
Tel.: (225) 771-8265
Web Site: http://www.iaopartners.com
Facilities Maintenance Supplier
N.A.I.C.S.: 423990
Brandon Dufrene (CEO & Mng Dir)

Metro Title, LLC (1)
6402 Railroad Ave, Crestwood, KY 40014
Tel.: (502) 243-8132
Emp.: 15
Real Estate Services
N.A.I.C.S.: 531390

SRHI LLC (1)
232 Madison Ave Rm 608, New York, NY 10016-2901
Tel.: (646) 366-0500
Apartment Building Rental Services
N.A.I.C.S.: 531110

Terramor Homes, Inc. (1)
7208 Falls of Neuse Rd 201, Raleigh, NC 27615
Tel.: (919) 728-9742
Single-Family Housing
N.A.I.C.S.: 236115

The Club at Hidden River, LLC (1)
13564 Cypress Glen Ln Ste 101, Tampa, FL 33637
Tel.: (813) 437-9322
Web Site:
http://www.hiddenriveraptstampa.com
Real Estate Related Services
N.A.I.C.S.: 531390

The Club at Pradera, Inc. (1)
5225 Raintree Dr, Parker, CO 80134
Tel.: (303) 607-5672
Web Site: http://www.theclubatpradera.com
Golf Club Services
N.A.I.C.S.: 713910

Truland Homes, LLC (1)
29891 Woodrow Ln Ste 100, Spanish Fort, AL 36527
Tel.: (251) 621-0850
Web Site: http://www.trulandhomes.com
Sales Range: $75-99.9 Million
Emp.: 56
Real Estate Services
N.A.I.C.S.: 531390
Nathan Cox (Founder)
Charles Schetter (Pres)
Wesley Rider (Dir-Ops)
Debra Townson (Dir-Acctg)
Erica Pounder (Mgr-Mktg & Adv)

Vidler Water Resources, Inc. (1)
3480 GS Richards Blvd Ste 101, Carson City, NV 89703
Tel.: (775) 885-5000
Web Site: http://www.vidlerwater.com
Rev.: $29,398,000
Assets: $181,089,000
Liabilities: $2,834,000
Net Worth: $178,255,000
Earnings: $11,526,000
Emp.: 14
Fiscal Year-end: 12/31/2019
Holding Company
N.A.I.C.S.: 551112

Westport Homes, Inc. (1)
9210 N Meridian St, Indianapolis, IN 46260
Tel.: (317) 844-0433
New Multifamily Housing Construction, except Operative Builders
N.A.I.C.S.: 236116

D7 ENTERPRISES, INC.
7685 S Fairplay Ct, Aurora, CO 80003
Tel.: (303) 681-1994 DE
Web Site:
http://www.d7enterprises.com
DGIF—(OTCIQ)
Assets: $1,368,818
Liabilities: $257,746
Net Worth: $1,111,072
Earnings: ($93,534)
Information Technology Services
N.A.I.C.S.: 541519
Anthony J. Panasuk (CEO & CFO)
David Lynn Williams (VP)
Matthew Mackintosh (Sec & VP)

DA32 LIFE SCIENCE TECH ACQUISITION CORP.
345 Park Ave S 12th Fl, New York, NY 10010
Tel.: (212) 551-1600 DE

Year Founded: 2021
DALS—(NASDAQ)
Rev.: $2,902,010
Assets: $203,855,661
Liabilities: $208,591,496
Net Worth: ($4,735,835)
Earnings: $599,215
Emp.: 2
Fiscal Year-end: 12/31/22
Investment Services
N.A.I.C.S.: 523999
Steve Kafka (CEO)
Christopher Wolfe (CFO & Sec)

DAC TECHNOLOGIES GROUP INTERNATIONAL, INC.
100 Gamble Rd Ste 1, Little Rock, AR 72211
Tel.: (501) 661-9100 FL
Web Site: https://www.dactec.com
Year Founded: 1990
DAAT—(OTCIQ)
Power-Driven Handtool Manufacturing
N.A.I.C.S.: 333991
Kim Woodruff (Mgr)

DACOTAH BANKS, INC.
Tel.: (605) 225-5611 SD
Web Site:
https://www.dacotahbank.com
Year Founded: 1955
DBIN—(OTCQX)
Rev.: $141,593,000
Assets: $4,164,125,000
Liabilities: $3,776,609,000
Net Worth: $387,516,000
Earnings: $26,167,000
Emp.: 630
Fiscal Year-end: 12/31/23
Bank Holding Company
N.A.I.C.S.: 551111
Chad D. Bergan (CFO & Sr VP)
Paige Bjronson (Pres-North Reg)
Richard L. Westra (Vice Chm)
Joseph A. Senger (Pres & CEO)
Robert J. Fouberg (Chm)
Diana Pfister (Gen Counsel & Sr VP)
Kristen N. Fauth (COO & Exec VP)

Subsidiaries:

Dacotah Bank (1)
308 S Main St, Aberdeen, SD 57401
Tel.: (605) 225-5611
Web Site: http://www.dacotahbank.com
Commercial Banking
N.A.I.C.S.: 522110
Richard L. Westra (Chm)

DAILY JOURNAL CORPORATION
915 E 1st St, Los Angeles, CA 90012
Tel.: (213) 229-5300 SC
Web Site:
https://www.dailyjournal.com
Year Founded: 1986
DJCO—(NASDAQ)
Rev.: $69,931,000
Assets: $403,763,000
Liabilities: $124,979,000
Net Worth: $278,784,000
Earnings: $78,113,000
Emp.: 400
Fiscal Year-end: 09/30/24
Legal Newspaper Publisher
N.A.I.C.S.: 513110
Laurinda Keys (Assoc Editor)
Melanie Brisbon (Editor-Special Reports)
Ilan Isaacs (Assoc Editor-Legal)
Silva Demirjian (Editor-Rulings)
Nicole Tyau (Editor-Digital)
Steven Myhill-Jones (Chm & CEO)
Tu To (CFO)
Matthew Sasaki (Editor)
Diana Bosetti (Editor)
Jessica Murray (Assoc Editor)

Arin Mikailian (Editor)
Lisa Churchill (Editor)
Marites Santiago (Coord)

Subsidiaries:

Journal Technologies, Inc. (1)
843 S 100 W, Logan, UT 84321
Tel.: (435) 713-2100
Web Site: https://www.journaltech.com
Sales Range: $1-9.9 Million
Emp.: 150
Case Management Solutions
N.A.I.C.S.: 513210
Maryjoe Rodriguez (COO & VP)
Jarl Salzman (Pres)

New Dawn Technologies, Inc. (1)
843 South 100 W, Logan, UT 84321
Tel.: (435) 713-2100
Web Site: http://www.newdawn.com
Computer System Design Services
N.A.I.C.S.: 541512

Sustain Technologies, Inc. (1)
949 E 2nd St, Los Angeles, CA 90012 (100%)
Tel.: (213) 229-5400
Web Site: http://www.sustain.net
Sales Range: $100-124.9 Million
Legal Information Services
N.A.I.C.S.: 541199

DAKOTA GOLD CORP.
106 Glendale Dr Ste A, Lead, SD 57754
Tel.: (605) 717-2540 NV
Web Site: https://dakotagoldcorp.com
Year Founded: 2017
DC—(NYSEAMEX)
Rev.: $414,168
Assets: $108,202,540
Liabilities: $4,666,089
Net Worth: $103,536,451
Earnings: ($36,449,199)
Emp.: 41
Fiscal Year-end: 12/31/23
Gold Exploration Services
N.A.I.C.S.: 212220
Robert A. Quartermain (Chm)
Jonathan T. Awde (Pres & CEO)
Gerald Michael Aberle (COO)

DAKTRONICS, INC.
Tel.: (605) 692-0200 SD
Web Site:
https://www.daktronics.com
Year Founded: 1968
DAKT—(NASDAQ)
Rev.: $818,083,000
Assets: $527,884,000
Liabilities: $289,092,000
Net Worth: $238,792,000
Earnings: $34,621,000
Emp.: 2,520
Fiscal Year-end: 04/27/24
Electronic Display Systems Designer & Mfr
N.A.I.C.S.: 339950
Duane E. Sander (Founder)
Reece A. Kurtenbach (Chm, Pres & CEO)
Sheila M. Anderson (CFO & Treas)

Subsidiaries:

ADFLOW Networks, Inc. (1)
3425 Harvester Road Suite 105, Burlington, L7N 3N1, ON, Canada
Tel.: (905) 333-0200
Web Site: http://www.adflownetworks.com
Information Technology Support Services
N.A.I.C.S.: 541512

Daktronics Australia Pty Ltd. (1)
Tel.: (61) 294534600
Web Site: https://www.daktronics.com
Electronic Scoreboards Mfr
N.A.I.C.S.: 339950

Daktronics FZE (1)
Dubai Investment Park European Business

Center, PO Box 437505, Dubai, United Arab Emirates
Tel.: (971) 48135250
Sales Range: $10-24.9 Million
Emp.: 8
Electronic Scoreboards Mfr
N.A.I.C.S.: 334419
Ahmad Dahmash (Gen Mgr)

Daktronics France SARL (1)
52 Rue d'Emerainville Lot 219 Building D, Parc de l Esplanade, 77183, Croissy-Beaubourg, France
Tel.: (33) 160314678
Web Site: http://www.daktronics.com
Electronic Scoreboards Mfr
N.A.I.C.S.: 334419

Daktronics Ireland Co. Ltd. (1)
Deerpark Industrial Estate, County Clare, Ennistymon, V95 X6WV, Co. Clare, Ireland
Tel.: (353) 65 707 2600
Web Site: https://www.daktronics.com
Emp.: 140
LCD Display Mfr
N.A.I.C.S.: 334419

Daktronics Japan, Inc. (1)
6F Sumitomo Kanda Iwamotocho Building 3-1-5 Iwamotocho, Chiyoda-ku, Tokyo, 101-0032, Japan
Tel.: (81) 358353177
Web Site: https://www.daktronics.com
Emp.: 3
Electronic Scoreboards Mfr
N.A.I.C.S.: 334419

Daktronics Shanghai Ltd. (1)
No 99 Lane 2891 South Qi Lian Shan Road, Putuo District, Shanghai, 200331, China
Tel.: (86) 2166619600
Web Site: http://www.daktronics.com
Emp.: 100
Electronic Scoreboards Mfr
N.A.I.C.S.: 334419

Daktronics UK, Ltd. (1)
Kestrel Court Waterwells Drive, Quedgeley, Gloucester, GL2 2AT, United Kingdom
Tel.: (44) 1454413606
Web Site: https://www.daktronics.com
Sales Range: $10-24.9 Million
Emp.: 15
Electronic Scoreboards Mfr
N.A.I.C.S.: 334419

Daktronics, GmbH (1)
Klingholzstrasse 7, 65189, Wiesbaden, Germany
Tel.: (49) 61171186100
Web Site: https://www.daktronics.com
Sales Range: $10-24.9 Million
Emp.: 15
Electronic Scoreboards Mfr
N.A.I.C.S.: 334419

DALLASNEWS CORPORATION
1954 Commerce St, Dallas, TX 75201
Tel.: (214) 977-8222　　　　DE
Web Site:
　　https://www.dallasnewscorporation.com
Year Founded: 2007
DALN—(NASDAQ)
Rev.: $150,651,000
Assets: $72,265,000
Liabilities: $59,902,000
Net Worth: $12,363,000
Earnings: ($9,786,000)
Emp.: 663
Fiscal Year-end: 12/31/22
Holding Company; Newspaper Publisher
N.A.I.C.S.: 551112
Grant S. Moise (CEO)
Kathryn Mary Murray (Pres, CFO & Treas)
John Kiker (Pres-Medium Giant)
Chris Patheiger (Chief Product & Innovation Officer)

Subsidiaries:

AHC California Dispositions, Inc. (1)

1825 Chicago Ave Ste 100, Riverside, CA 92507
Tel.: (909) 684-1200
Web Site: http://www.pe.com
Newspaper Publishing Services
N.A.I.C.S.: 513110

Belo Enterprises, Inc. (1)
3906 Hwy 7, Iron, MN 55751-7100
Tel.: (218) 744-3748
Newspaper Publishing Services
N.A.I.C.S.: 513110

Belo Interactive, Inc. (1)
900 Jackson St Ste 400, Dallas, TX 75202
Tel.: (214) 977-4000
Web Site: http://www.belointeractive.com
Sales Range: $25-49.9 Million
Emp.: 100
Online News & Information Services
N.A.I.C.S.: 513199

Distribion, Inc. (1)
8350 N Central Expy Ste 1600, Dallas, TX 75206
Tel.: (214) 826-6290
Web Site: http://m.distribion.com
Marketing Software
N.A.I.C.S.: 513210

The Dallas Morning News, Inc. (1)
1954 Commerce St, Dallas, TX 75201
Tel.: (214) 745-8383
Web Site: https://dallasnews.zendesk.com
Newspaper Publishers
N.A.I.C.S.: 513110
Grant S. Moise (Pres)
Leezel Tanglao (Sr Dir-Digital)

Subsidiary (Domestic):

Al Dia, Inc. (2)
508 Young St, Dallas, TX 75202
Tel.: (469) 977-3600
Web Site: http://www.aldiatx.com
Sales Range: $10-24.9 Million
Emp.: 50
Newspapers
N.A.I.C.S.: 513110

DFW Printing Company, Inc. (2)
3900 W Plano Pkwy, Plano, TX 75075-7807
Tel.: (214) 977-7458
Web Site:
　　https://www.dfwprintingcompany.com
Emp.: 300
Commercial Printing Services
N.A.I.C.S.: 513110

True North Real Estate LLC (1)
30 Weeping Willow Ln, Milford, CT 06461-2239
Tel.: (203) 314-6487
Web Site:
　　http://www.truenorthrealestate.com
Newspaper Publishing Services
N.A.I.C.S.: 513110

Your Speakeasy LLC (1)
800 Jackson St Ste B-100, Dallas, TX 75202　　　　　　　　　　　　**(100%)**
Tel.: (214) 628-9700
Marketing & Advertising Services
N.A.I.C.S.: 541613

DALRADA FINANCIAL CORPORATION
600 La Terraza Blvd, Escondido, CA 92025
Tel.: (858) 283-1253　　　　DE
Web Site: https://www.dalrada.com
Year Founded: 1982
DFCO—(OTCQB)
Rev.: $29,738,969
Assets: $25,169,115
Liabilities: $20,916,279
Net Worth: $4,252,836
Earnings: ($20,627,721)
Emp.: 75
Fiscal Year-end: 06/30/23
Holding Company; Human Resources & Other Administrative & Business Support Services
N.A.I.C.S.: 561110
Brian Bonar (Founder & CEO)
Kyle McCollum (CFO)

Brian C. McGoff (Pres & COO)
Jose Arrieta (Chief Strategy Officer & Pres-Technologies)

Subsidiaries:

Genefic (1)
600 Laterraza Blvd, Escondido, CA 92505
Tel.: (858) 283-1135
Web Site: https://genefic.com
Research & Development in the Physical, Engineering & Life Sciences
N.A.I.C.S.: 541715
Harvey Hershkowitz (Chm, Pres & CEO)

Subsidiary (Domestic):

International Health Group Inc. (2)
8787 Complex Dr Ste 130, San Diego, CA 92123-1451
Tel.: (858) 278-9818
Web Site:
　　http://www.internationalhealthgroup.net
Offices of All Other Miscellaneous Health Practitioners
N.A.I.C.S.: 621399

Quik Pix, Inc. (1)
7050 Village Dr Ste F, Buena Park, CA 90621　　　　　　　　　　　**(85%)**
Tel.: (714) 522-8255
Web Site: http://www.colorvisuals.com
Mfr of Photofinishing Technologies
N.A.I.C.S.: 812921

DANA INCORPORATED
3939 Technology Dr, Maumee, OH 43537
Tel.: (419) 887-3000　　　　DE
Web Site: https://www.dana.com
Year Founded: 1904
DAN—(NYSE)
Rev.: $10,156,000,000
Assets: $7,449,000,000
Liabilities: $5,846,000,000
Net Worth: $1,603,000,000
Earnings: $242,000,000
Emp.: 41,800
Fiscal Year-end: 12/31/22
Holding Company; Motor Vehicle Parts Designer, Mfr & Whslr
N.A.I.C.S.: 551112
Byron S. Foster (Pres-Light Vehicle Drive Sys)
Christophe Dominiak (CTO & Sr VP)
James Kevin Kamsickas (Chm, Pres & CEO)
Douglas H. Liedberg (Chief Compliance Sustainability Officer, Gen Counsel, Sec & Sr VP)
James D. Kellett (Chief Acctg Officer & VP)
Chris Clark (Sr VP-Ops-Global)
Timothy R. Kraus (CFO & Sr VP)
Maureen Pittenger (Chief HR Officer)
Andrea Siudara (CIO)
Brian Pour (Pres-Motion Sys & Comml Vehicle Drive & Sr VP)
Craig Price (Pres-Off-Highway Drive & Motion Sys & Sr VP)
Jeroen Decleer (Pres-Off-Highway Drive & Motion Sys & Sr VP)

Subsidiaries:

Allied Transmissions (S.E.A.) PTE LTD (1)
01-36 2-8 Penjuru Tech Hub Penjuru Place, Singapore, 608780, Singapore
Tel.: (65) 63568922
Web Site: http://www.allied-transmissions.com
Industrial Coupling Mfr & Distr
N.A.I.C.S.: 333613

BPE SRL (1)
Viale Dell Olma 22, Reggio nell'Emilia, 42012, Italy
Tel.: (39) 0522662357
Web Site: http://www.bpe.it
Industrial Electronic Mfr & Distr
N.A.I.C.S.: 334419

Brevini Australia Pty Ltd (1)

147-149 Gilba Road, Girraween, 2145, NSW, Australia
Tel.: (61) 288484000
Web Site: http://www.brevini.com.au
Industrial Gear Box Drive Mfr & Distr
N.A.I.C.S.: 333612

Brevini Canada Limited (1)
236 Galaxy Boulevard, Toronto, M9W 5R8, ON, Canada
Tel.: (416) 674-2591
Web Site: http://www.brevini.ca
Industrial Gear Box Drive Mfr & Distr
N.A.I.C.S.: 333612

Brevini Espana S.A. (1)
Pol Industrial Los Huertecillos C Abedul S n Ciempozuelos, 28350, Madrid, Spain
Tel.: (34) 918015165
Web Site: http://www.breviniespana.com
Industrial Gear Box Drive Mfr & Distr
N.A.I.C.S.: 333612

Brevini Finland Oy (1)
Koskelonkuja 1, 2920, Espoo, Finland
Tel.: (358) 207431828
Industrial Gear Box & Drive Distr
N.A.I.C.S.: 423840

Brevini Fluid Power Beijing Co. Ltd. (1)
140 Lilianghe Village Temple Town, Huairou District, Beijing, 101401, China
Tel.: (86) 1061605089
Hydraulic Electronic Component Distr
N.A.I.C.S.: 423830

Brevini Fluid Power Distribution S.r.l. (1)
Via Roma 103, 20873, Cavenago di Brianza, Italy
Tel.: (39) 02052297
Hydraulic Electronic Component Distr
N.A.I.C.S.: 423830

Brevini Fluid Power France SAS (1)
7 Rue Des Entrepreneurs - Parc De La Vertonne, BP 2217, 44120, Vertou, France
Tel.: (33) 240332348
Web Site: https://www.brevinifluidpower.fr
Hydraulic Electronic Component Mfr & Distr
N.A.I.C.S.: 333996

Brevini Fluid Power GmbH (1)
Benzstrasse 7, 82291, Mammendorf, Germany
Tel.: (49) 814592830
Web Site: http://www.brevinifluidpower.de
Hydraulic Electronic Component Mfr & Distr
N.A.I.C.S.: 333996

Brevini Fluid Power UK Limited (1)
Kestrel Court Centre Park Warrington, Cheshire, WA1 1QX, United Kingdom
Tel.: (44) 1925624800
Fluid Power Valve Distr
N.A.I.C.S.: 423120

Brevini Fluid Power Veneto S.r.l. (1)
Via della tecnica 25-27, 35035, Mestrino, PD, Italy
Tel.: (39) 0498987277
Hydraulic Electronic Component Distr
N.A.I.C.S.: 423830

Brevini India Ltd (1)
101 Faizan Apartments Above Syndicate Bank 134 S V Road Jogeshwari, Mumbai, 400 102, Maharashtra, India
Tel.: (91) 2226794262
Fluid Power Valve Distr
N.A.I.C.S.: 423120

Brevini Ireland Limited (1)
Allenwood Enterprise Park Allenwood Kildare, Naas, Ireland
Tel.: (353) 45890100
Web Site: http://www.brevinifluidpower.ie
Hydraulic Electronic Component Mfr & Distr
N.A.I.C.S.: 333996

Brevini Japan Ltd (1)
KIBC Bldg 5F 5-5-2 Minatojima Minami-machi, Chuo-ku, Kobe, 650-0047, Japan
Tel.: (81) 783045377
Web Site: http://www.brevini.jp
Industrial Gear Box Drive Mfr & Distr
N.A.I.C.S.: 333612

Brevini Korea Co., Ltd. (1)
Shintri Technotown Room 305 1254 Shin

Dana Incorporated—(Continued)

Jung3-Dong Yang Chon-Ku, Seoul, Korea (South)
Tel.: (82) 220659563
Web Site: http://www.brevini.kr
Industrial Gear Box Drive Mfr & Distr
N.A.I.C.S.: 333612

Brevini Latino-Americana Ind. & Co. Ltd. (1)
Via Pref Jurandyr Paixao 1900-Jd Campo
Belo Limeira, 13481-149, Sao Paulo, Brazil
Tel.: (55) 1934468600
Web Site: http://brevini.com.br
Industrial Gear Box Drive Mfr & Distr
N.A.I.C.S.: 333612

Brevini New Zealand Limited (1)
9 Bishop Croke Place East Tamaki Botany
Manukau, PO Box 58-148, 2163, Auckland, New Zealand
Tel.: (64) 92500050
Web Site: http://www.brevini.co.nz
Hydraulic Electronic Component Mfr & Distr
N.A.I.C.S.: 333996

Brevini Norge AS (1)
Elveveien 38, 3262, Larvik, Norway
Tel.: (47) 33117100
Web Site: http://www.brevini.no
Industrial Gear Box Drive Mfr & Distr
N.A.I.C.S.: 333612

Brevini Power Transmission France (1)
198 Avenue Franklin Roosevelt, 69516, Vaulx-en-Velin, France
Tel.: (33) 472812555
Web Site: http://www.brevini.fr
Industrial Gear Box Drive Mfr & Distr
N.A.I.C.S.: 333612

Brevini Power Transmission Reduktor Sanayi ve Ticared Limited Sirteki (1)
Kubilay Caddesi No 94 Kartal, Topselvi Ma-hallesi, 34873, Istanbul, Turkiye
Tel.: (90) 2165405909
Web Site: http://www.brevini.com.tr
Electronic Components Mfr
N.A.I.C.S.: 336350

Brevini Svenska AB (1)
Zinkgatan 2, 602 23, Norrkoping, Sweden
Tel.: (46) 114009000
Hydraulic Electronic Component Mfr & Distr
N.A.I.C.S.: 333996

Brevini Thailand Co. Ltd. (1)
88 17 Kallaprapruk Road Khwaeng Bang-kae Khet Bangkae Metropolis, Bangkok, 10160, Thailand
Tel.: (66) 21108060
Web Site: http://www.brevini.co.th
Industrial Gear Box Drive Mfr & Distr
N.A.I.C.S.: 333612

Brevini USA Inc. (1)
14141 W Brevini Dr, Yorktown, IN 47396
Tel.: (765) 759-2300
Web Site: http://www.brevini.us
Industrial Gear Box Drive Mfr & Distr
N.A.I.C.S.: 333612

Brevini Yancheng Planetary Drives Co. Ltd. (1)
15 South Hope Ave Yancheng Economic Development Zone, Jiangsu, 224007, China
Tel.: (86) 51588289326
Industrial Gear Box Drive Mfr & Distr
N.A.I.C.S.: 333612

Dana (Deutschland) Grundstuckver-waltungo GmbH (1)
Plant 2 Schnieringstrasse 49, 45329, Es-sen, Germany
Tel.: (49) 2 018 1240
Web Site: http://www.gwbdriveshaft.com
Emp.: 2
Industrial Product Distr
N.A.I.C.S.: 423830

Dana Australia (Holdings) Pty. Ltd. (1)
39 45 Wedgewood Road, Hallam, 3803, VIC, Australia
Tel.: (61) 392135555
Web Site: https://www.dana.com.au
Sales Range: $75-99.9 Million
Emp.: 160
Holding Company

N.A.I.C.S.: 551112
Peter Langworthy *(Mng Dir)*

Dana Australia Pty. Ltd. (1)
8 Hudson Court, Keysborough, 3173, VIC, Australia
Tel.: (61) 1300003262
Web Site: https://www.dana.com.au
Sales Range: $125-149.9 Million
Vehicle Parts Services
N.A.I.C.S.: 336390

Dana Austria GmbH (1)
Max-Planck-Strasse 1, 9100, Volkermarkt, Austria
Tel.: (43) 423251480
Web Site: http://www.dana.com
Sales Range: $25-49.9 Million
Emp.: 70
Vehicle Parts Mfr
N.A.I.C.S.: 336390

Dana Automocion, S.A. (1)
P Indal Landaben Calle E, 31012, Pam-plona, Navarre, Spain
Tel.: (34) 94 828 9100
Web Site: http://www.danaautomocion.sa
Motor Vehicle Parts Mfr
N.A.I.C.S.: 336390

Dana Automotive Aftermarket, Inc. (1)
3939 Technology Dr, Maumee, OH 43537
Tel.: (419) 887-3550
Web Site: http://www.dana.com
Motor Vehicle Parts Mfr
N.A.I.C.S.: 336390

Dana Belgium BVBA (1)
Ten Briele 3, 8200, Brugge, West-Vlaanderen, Belgium
Tel.: (32) 50402211
Web Site: https://www.dana.com
Sales Range: $125-149.9 Million
Emp.: 450
Motor Vehicle Parts Mfr
N.A.I.C.S.: 336390

Dana Belgium NV (1)
Ten Briele 3, 8200, Brugge, B 8200, Bel-gium
Tel.: (32) 50402211
Web Site: http://www.dana.be
Automotive Industrial Parts Mfr& Distr
N.A.I.C.S.: 336390

Dana Brevini Power - Transmission S.p.A. (1)
Via Luciano Brevini 1 / A, 42124, Reggio Emilia, Italy
Tel.: (39) 05229281
Web Site: http://www.brevinipowertransmission.com
Industrial Gear Box Drive Mfr & Distr
N.A.I.C.S.: 333612

Dana Canada Corporation (1)
PO Box 3029, Saint Catharines, L2R 7k9, ON, Canada **(100%)**
Tel.: (905) 635-2210
Web Site: https://www.danacanada.com
Sales Range: $25-49.9 Million
Emp.: 50
Automotive & Heavy Truck Parts Mfr
N.A.I.C.S.: 336390

Division (Domestic):

Dana Canada Corporation (2)
656 Kerr St, Oakville, L6K 3E4, ON, Canada **(100%)**
Tel.: (905) 849-1200
Web Site: http://www.dana.com
Sales Range: $75-99.9 Million
Heat Exchanger Mfr
N.A.I.C.S.: 333310

Dana Corporation Automotive Sys-tems Group (1)
3939 Technology Dr, Maumee, OH 43537
Tel.: (419) 535-4500
Automotive Products Mfr
N.A.I.C.S.: 441330
Roger J. Wood *(Pres & CEO)*

Subsidiary (Domestic):

Coupled Products, Inc. (2)
2709 Bond St, Rochester Hills, MI 48309-3513 **(100%)**
Tel.: (248) 293-7300

Web Site: http://www.dana.com
Sales Range: $350-399.9 Million
Emp.: 1,015
Plastic Lines, Metal Tubing, Rubber Hose & Fuel Rails Mfr
N.A.I.C.S.: 336390

Dana Fluid Power Distribution S.r.l. (1)
Via Roma 103, 20873, Cavenago di Bri-anza, MB, Italy
Tel.: (39) 02052297
Motor Vehicle Parts Distr
N.A.I.C.S.: 423140

Dana Heavy Vehicle Technologies & Systems (1)
6201 Trust Dr, Holland, OH 43538-8427 **(100%)**
Tel.: (419) 866-3900
Web Site: http://www.dana.com
Sales Range: $50-74.9 Million
Emp.: 150
Front-Steer & Rear-Drive Trailer & Auxiliary Axles, Driveshafts, Steering Shafts, Brakes, Suspensions & Related Systems, Modules & Services Designer, Marketer & Mfr
N.A.I.C.S.: 336390

Dana Holding GmbH (1)
Reinzstr 3-7, 89233, Neu-Ulm, Germany
Tel.: (49) 73170460
Web Site: https://www.reinz.com
Sales Range: $200-249.9 Million
Emp.: 1,100
Motor Vehicle Parts Mfr & Whslr
N.A.I.C.S.: 336390

Dana Inc. - Paris Plant (1)
100 Plumley Dr, Paris, TN 38242-8022
Tel.: (731) 642-5582
Web Site: http://www.dana.mediaroom.com
Emp.: 300
Rubber Hoses & Sealing Devices Mfr
N.A.I.C.S.: 339991

Dana India Technical Centre Pvt. Ltd. (1)
Pride Silicon Plaza 5th Floor Office No 503 Senapati Bapat Road, Near Chturshrungi Temple Pune University, Pune, 411007, MH, India **(100%)**
Tel.: (91) 2030211700
Web Site: https://www.dana.com
Motor Vehicle Parts Whslr
N.A.I.C.S.: 423120

Dana Italia, SpA (1)
Via Torino 10, 13044, Crescentino, Italy
Tel.: (39) 046 183 3311
Web Site: https://www.dana.com
Industrial Transmission Supplies Distr
N.A.I.C.S.: 423840

Dana Motion Systems Italia S.r.l. (1)
Via Luciano Brevini 1/A, 42124, Reggio Emilia, Italy
Tel.: (39) 0522928100
Web Site: http://www.brevini.com
Electronic Components Mfr
N.A.I.C.S.: 336350

Dana Off-Highway Products (1)
123 Phoenix Pl, Fredericktown, OH 43019 **(100%)**
Tel.: (740) 694-2055
Web Site: http://www.dana.com
Sales Range: $50-74.9 Million
Emp.: 120
Transaxles & Brake Mfr
N.A.I.C.S.: 336390

Plant (Domestic):

Dana Off-Highway Products (2)
139 E Broad St, Statesville, NC 28877 **(100%)**
Tel.: (704) 873-2811
Web Site: http://www.dana.com
Sales Range: $25-49.9 Million
Emp.: 35
Axles, Transaxles, Driveshafts & End-Fittings, Transmissions, Torque Converters, Electronic Controls, Brakes & Replacement Parts Designer, Marketer & Mfr
N.A.I.C.S.: 336350

Dana Power Transmission France (1)
1 Esplanade Myriam Makeba Cs 40297

69100, Villeurbanne, Cedex, France
Tel.: (33) 472812555
Web Site: http://www.brevini.fr
Electronic Components Mfr
N.A.I.C.S.: 336350

Dana SAC Australia Pty. Ltd. (1)
147 -149 Gilba Road, Girraween, 2145, NSW, Australia
Tel.: (61) 288484000
Web Site: http://www.brevini.com.au
Electronic Components Mfr
N.A.I.C.S.: 336350

Dana SAC Benelux B.V. (1)
Rontgenweg 24, 2408 AB, Alphen aan den Rijn, Netherlands
Tel.: (31) 172428080
Web Site: https://www.dana-sac-benelux.com
Motor Vehicle Parts Mfr
N.A.I.C.S.: 336390

Dana SAC Canada Limited (1)
860 Denison Street, Markham, L3R 4H1, ON, Canada
Tel.: (905) 474-3262
Industrial Equipment Distr
N.A.I.C.S.: 423830
Allen Murphy *(Gen Mgr)*

Dana SAC Germany GmbH (1)
Benzstrasse 7, 82291, Mammendorf, Ger-many
Tel.: (49) 814592830
Industrial Equipment Distr
N.A.I.C.S.: 423830
Claudio Schultze *(Gen Mgr)*

Dana SAC Korea Co., Ltd. (1)
13-38 Sinheung-ro 511beon-gil, Bucheon, Gyeonggi-do, Korea (South)
Tel.: (82) 326729563
Web Site: https://www.dana.com
Industrial Equipment Distr
N.A.I.C.S.: 423830

Dana SAC Mexico, S.A. de C.V. (1)
Acceso III 7-C Parque Industrial Benito Juarez, Santiago de Queretaro, Mexico
Tel.: (52) 4424834727
Web Site: http://www.brevinidemexico.com
Motor Vehicle Parts Mfr
N.A.I.C.S.: 336390

Dana SAC New Zealand Limited (1)
9 Bishop Croke Place East, Tamaki, Auck-land, 2013, New Zealand
Tel.: (64) 92500050
Industrial Equipment Distr
N.A.I.C.S.: 423830

Dana SAC Norway AS (1)
Elvovoion 38, 3262, Larvik, Norway
Tel.: (47) 33117100
Web Site: http://www.brevini.no
Electronic Components Mfr
N.A.I.C.S.: 336350

Dana SAC S.E. Asia Pte. Ltd. (1)
8B Buroh Street, Singapore, Singapore
Tel.: (65) 63568922
Industrial Equipment Distr
N.A.I.C.S.: 423830
K. Khaing *(Reg Sls Mgr)*

Dana SAC South Africa (Pty) Ltd. (1)
38A Apex Road 1540 Benoni, Johannes-burg, South Africa
Tel.: (27) 114219949
Web Site: http://www.brevini.co.za
Electronic Components Mfr
N.A.I.C.S.: 336350

Dana SAC Turkey Reduktor Sanayi Ve Ticaret Limited Sirketi (1)
Topselvi Mahallesi Kubilay Caddesi No 94, Kartal, Istanbul, Turkiye
Tel.: (90) 2165405909
Industrial Equipment Distr
N.A.I.C.S.: 423830

Dana SAC UK Limited (1)
Kestrel Court Centre Park, Warrington, WA1 1QX, Cheshire, United Kingdom
Tel.: (44) 1925636682
Web Site: https://dana-sac.co.uk
Electronic Components Mfr
N.A.I.C.S.: 336350

Dana San Luis S.A. (1)
Avenida J Vives Catasus Sin N Naschel
D5759, San Luis, Argentina
Tel.: (54) 2656491095
Motor Vehicle Parts Mfr
N.A.I.C.S.: 336390

Dana Sealing Products (1)
1945 Ohio St, Lisle, IL 60532
Tel.: (630) 960-4200
Web Site: http://www.victorreinz.com
Sales Range: $25-49.9 Million
Emp.: 100
Sealing Solution Mfr
N.A.I.C.S.: 339991

Dana Spicer Axle South Africa (Pty) Ltd. (1)
Bricksfield Road, Uitenhage, 6229, South
Africa
Tel.: (27) 419947200
Motor Vehicle Parts Mfr
N.A.I.C.S.: 326220
Paul Myburgh (Mng Dir)

Dana Structural Products, LLC (1)
3939 Technology Dr, Maumee, OH 43537-
9194
Tel.: (419) 887-3000
Power Transmission Equipment Distr
N.A.I.C.S.: 423830

Dana TM4 Inc. (1)
135 J A Bombardier Suite 25, Boucherville,
J4B 8P1, QC, Canada
Tel.: (450) 645-1444
Web Site: http://www.danatm4.com
Automobile Parts Mfr
N.A.I.C.S.: 336390

Dana TM4 Italia S.r.l. (1)
Via della Tecnica Z I 40, 36071, Arzignano,
VI, Italy
Tel.: (39) 0444470511
Automobile Parts Mfr
N.A.I.C.S.: 336390

Dana TM4 UK (1)
Bridgeway House Bridgeway, Upon Avon,
Stratford, CV37 6YX, United Kingdom
Tel.: (44) 1392340184
Automobile Parts Mfr
N.A.I.C.S.: 336390

Dana Torque Technology (1)
2100 W State St, Fort Wayne, IN
46808 (100%)
Tel.: (260) 483-7174
Sales Range: $300-349.9 Million
Emp.: 800
Axles, Limited-Slip Differentials & Lock-Out
Hubs Mfr
N.A.I.C.S.: 336390
Mark Howard (Gen Mgr)

Dana de Mexico Corporacion, S. de R.L. de C.V. (1)
Accesso 3 No 7 Parque Ind'l Benito Juarez,
76120, Queretaro, 76120, Mexico
Tel.: (52) 4422117100
Motor Vehicle Parts Mfr
N.A.I.C.S.: 336390

Fujian Spicer Drivetrain System Co., Ltd. (1)
Qing Kou Industrial Zone, Minhou, Fuzhou,
350119, Fujian, China
Tel.: (86) 59187013399
Web Site: https://www.roc-spicer.com.tw
Sales Range: $50-74.9 Million
Emp.: 260
Gear Set Mfr
N.A.I.C.S.: 333612

GK Drive Systems (Suzhou) Co., Ltd. (1)
No 118 Dongshenxu Road, Suzhou Indus-
trial Park, Suzhou, 215027, Jiangsu, China
Tel.: (86) 51262892377
Web Site: https://www.gkdrive.com
Industrial Equipment Mfr
N.A.I.C.S.: 333415
Wen Zhang (CEO)

Graziano Transmissioni UK Ltd. (1)
9 Harley Ind Park Paxton Hill, Saint Neots,
PE19 6TA, United Kingdom
Tel.: (44) 1480403453
Web Site: http://www.grazianouk.co.uk
Industrial Equipment Distr

N.A.I.C.S.: 423830
Ross Brown (Mng Dir)

H.B. S.R.L. (1)
Via Vespucci 7 Vicenza, 36071, Arzignano,
Italy
Tel.: (39) 0444451744
Web Site: https://www.hbchemicals.com
Chemical Mfr & Distr
N.A.I.C.S.: 325199

Industria de Ejes y Transmissiones S.A. (1)
Zona Ind L De Giron Km 7 Calle 32 No 15-
23, Giron, Colombia
Tel.: (57) 76468288
Web Site: https://www.transejes.com
Emp.: 9
Motor Vehicle Parts Mfr
N.A.I.C.S.: 336390

O.T. Oil Technology S.r.l. (1)
Strada Romitaggio 23, Bianconese di Fon-
tevivo, 43010, Parma, PR, Italy
Tel.: (39) 0521628761
Web Site: https://www.ot-oiltechnology.com
Motor & Pump Mfr & Distr
N.A.I.C.S.: 333996

PIV Drives GmbH (1)
Werner-Reimers-Strasse 6, 61352, Bad
Homburg, Germany
Tel.: (49) 61721020
Fluid Power Valve Distr
N.A.I.C.S.: 423120

Pi Innovo LLC (1)
47023 W 5 Mile Rd, Plymouth, MI 48170-
3765
Tel.: (734) 656-0140
Web Site: http://www.pi-innovo.com
Electronic Components Mfr
N.A.I.C.S.: 334419
Walter Lucking (CEO)
Ken Olson (VP-Engineering)
Dwight Hansell (VP-Business Development)
Jonathan Hurden (Dir)
Cheryl Samarco (CFO)

ROC Spicer, Ltd. (1)
No 822 Guangfu Road, Bade District,
Taoyuan, 334, Taiwan
Tel.: (886) 33616184
Web Site: https://www.roc-spicer.com.tw
Sales Range: $50-74.9 Million
Emp.: 304
Automobiles Products Mfr
N.A.I.C.S.: 333612

Rational Motion GmbH (1)
Horbeller Strasse 19, 50858, Cologne, Ger-
many
Tel.: (49) 22349791200
Web Site: http://www.rationalmotion.de
Electrical Products Distr
N.A.I.C.S.: 423610
Benoit Vareille (Mng Dir)

Reinz-Dichtungs-GmbH & Co KG (1)
Reinzstrasse 3-7, 89233, Neu-Ulm,
Germany (100%)
Tel.: (49) 7 317 0460
Web Site: https://www.reinz.com
Sales Range: $200-249.9 Million
Flat Gaskets & Gasket Materials, Metallic &
Metalloplastic Gaskets, Gasket Sets for En-
gine Overhaul, Protective Shields & Univer-
sal Sealing Compounds Mfr
N.A.I.C.S.: 339991
Olivier Lassurguere (Gen Mgr)

SME Deutschland GmbH (1)
Sauerwiesen 6, 67661, Kaiserslautern, Ger-
many
Tel.: (49) 630171230
Web Site: http://www.schwarzmueller-
inverter.com
Industrial Equipment Mfr
N.A.I.C.S.: 333415
Johnnie Rask Jensen (Mng Dir)

SME Shanghai Co., Ltd. (1)
No 2 Bldg 8 1st Floor 388 Xujing Shuan-
glian Road, Qingpu District, Shanghai,
201702, China
Tel.: (86) 2160253818
Industrial Equipment Mfr
N.A.I.C.S.: 333415

Shenyang Spicer Driveshaft Co. Ltd. (1)

iG 5-19 Yulin Street Dong-Ling District,
Shenyang, 110045, Liaoning, China
Tel.: (86) 2488201801
Web Site: https://www.roc-spicer.com.tw
Motor Vehicle Parts Mfr
N.A.I.C.S.: 326220

Spicer Off-Highway Belgium N.V. (1)
Ten Briele 3, 8200, Brugge, Belgium
Tel.: (32) 50402211
Web Site: http://www.dana.com
Emp.: 450
Motor Vehicle Parts Mfr
N.A.I.C.S.: 336110

Taiway Industry Co., Ltd. (1)
No 14 Kwang Fu Rd, Hukou, 303, Hsian-
chu, Taiwan
Tel.: (886) 35983601
Web Site: http://www.roc-spicer.com.tw
Automotive Front-wheel Drive Shaft, Hub
Bearings & Other Precision Mechanical
Parts & Components Mfr
N.A.I.C.S.: 336390

Talesol S.A. (1)
Juan Quevedo 5640, Montevideo, 12200,
Ituzaingo, Uruguay
Tel.: (598) 25143901
Motor Vehicle Parts Mfr
N.A.I.C.S.: 336390

Transejes Transmissiones Homoci-neticas de Columbia S.A. (1)
Calle 32 15 23, Giron, Colombia
Tel.: (57) 31647158
Web Site: http://www.transejes.com
Automotive Components Mfr
N.A.I.C.S.: 336390

DANAHER CORPORATION
2200 Pennsylvania Ave NW Ste
800W, Washington, DC 20037-1701
Tel.: (202) 828-0850. DE
Web Site: https://www.danaher.com
Year Founded: 1979
DHR—(NYSE)
Rev.: $23,890,000,000
Assets: $84,488,000,000
Liabilities: $30,998,000,000
Net Worth: $53,490,000,000
Earnings: $4,743,000,000
Emp.: 61,000
Fiscal Year-end: 12/31/23
Biotechnological, Life Science & Di-
agnostic Products Developer & Mfr
N.A.I.C.S.: 334513
John Marotta (Executives)
Daniel A. Raskas (Sr VP-Corp Dev)
Rainer M. Blair (Pres & CEO)
Steven M. Rales (Co-Founder)
Robert S. Lutz (Sr VP-Fin)
Mitchell P. Rales (Co-Founder)
Matthew R. McGrew (CFO & Exec
VP)
Brian W. Ellis (Gen Counsel & Sr VP)
Georgeann F. Couchara (Sr VP-HR)
Julie Sawyer Montgomery (Exec VP-
Danaher Diagnostics Platform)
Chris Riley (Exec VP-BioTech Grp)
William H. King IV (Sr VP-Strategic
Dev)

Subsidiaries:

AB Sciex LLC (1)
500 Old Connecticut Path, Framingham,
MA 01701
Tel.: (508) 383-7700
Web Site: https://sciex.com
Sales Range: $75-99.9 Million
Emp.: 63
Biomedical Research Services
N.A.I.C.S.: 541714
Gordon Logan (Sr VP-Research & Develop-
ment)
Andrew Clark (CFO & VP-Information
Technology-Operations-Global)
Joe Fox (Pres)
Fraser McLeod (VP & Gen Mgr-Software)
Mike Cowhig (Gen Counsel & VP)
Mani Krishnan (VP & Gen Mgr-CE-
BioPharma)
Chris Lock (VP-LCMS-Research & Develop-
ment)

Nichole Riek (VP-Quality-Regulatory Affairs)
Chris Apicerno (CFO & VP-Finance-
Information Technology-Global)
Brenda Newton (VP)
Carli Stoller (VP)
Kerry Larkin (VP)
Mark Cafazzo (VP)
Micael Morvik (VP)
Usman Habib (VP)
Kevin Roberts (VP)

Subsidiary (Non-US):

AB Sciex Germany GmbH (2)
Landwehrstrasse 54, 64293, Darmstadt,
Germany
Tel.: (49) 6151352005815
Web Site: http://www.sciex.com
Emp.: 150
Medical Equipment Distr
N.A.I.C.S.: 325412

AB Sciex KK (2)
4-7-35 Kitashinagawa, Shinagawa-ku, To-
kyo, 140-0001, Japan
Tel.: (81) 120318551
Web Site: https://sciex.jp
Emp.: 134
Drug Discovery & Development Services
N.A.I.C.S.: 325412

AB Sciex LP (2)
71 Four Valley Dr, Concord, L4K 4V8, ON,
Canada
Tel.: (905) 660-9006
Web Site: http://www.sciex.com
Medical Analytical Instrument Designer &
Mfr
N.A.I.C.S.: 334516

AB Sciex Netherlands B.V. (2)
Eerste Tochtweg 11 3rd Floor, PO Box 330,
2910 AH, Nieuwerkerk, Netherlands
Tel.: (31) 25033802
Web Site: https://www.sciex.com
Sales Range: $25-49.9 Million
Emp.: 50
Laboratory Services
N.A.I.C.S.: 541380

API Delevan, Inc. (1)
270 Quaker Rd, East Aurora, NY 14052
Tel.: (716) 652-3600
Web Site: https://www.delevan.com
Sales Range: $25-49.9 Million
Emp.: 100
Mfr of Electronic & Inductive Components &
Electronic Coils
N.A.I.C.S.: 334220

Abcam Limited (1)
Discovery Drive Cambridge Biomedical
Campus, Cambridge, CB2 0AX, United
Kingdom
Tel.: (44) 1223696000
Web Site: https://corporate.abcam.com
Rev.: $491,087,324
Assets: $1,434,566,952
Liabilities: $447,640,284
Net Worth: $986,926,668
Earnings: ($11,540,620)
Emp.: 1,760
Fiscal Year-end: 12/31/2022
Medical, Dental & Hospital Equipment &
Supplies Merchant Wholesalers
N.A.I.C.S.: 423450
Michael S. Baldock (CFO)
Emma Sceats (Sr VP)
Juan Carlos Sacristan (Sr VP)
Subham Basu (Dir)
Rich Lane (Dir)
John Baker (Sr VP)
Brent Thomson (Mgr)
Jac Price (Sr VP)
Nick Skinner (Sr VP)
Yi Sun (Mgr)
Alejandra Solache (Sr VP)

Subsidiary (Non-US):

Abcam (Hong Kong) Limited (2)
Unit 3328 33/F China Merchants Tower 168
Connaught Road Central, Hong Kong,
China (Hong Kong)
Tel.: (852) 37933454
Antibody Tool Mfr & Distr
N.A.I.C.S.: 339112

Abcam Australia Pty. Limited (2)
Level 16 414 La Trobe Street, Melbourne,

Danaher Corporation—(Continued)

3000, VIC, Australia
Tel.: (61) 390704707
Biotechnology Research Services
N.A.I.C.S.: 541714

Abcam KK (2)
2F Sumitomo Fudosan Ningyocho Building
2-2-1 Horidomecho, Nihonbashi Chuo-ku,
Tokyo, 103-0012, Japan
Tel.: (81) 362310940
Web Site: https://www.abcam.co.jp
Antibodies Mfr & Distr
N.A.I.C.S.: 325412

Abcam Singapore Pte. Limited (2)
11 North Buona Vista Drive 16-08 The Metropolis Tower Two, Singapore, 138589,
Singapore
Tel.: (65) 67349252
Antibody Tool Mfr & Distr
N.A.I.C.S.: 339112

Subsidiary (US):

BioVision, Inc.
155 S Milpitas Blvd, Milpitas, CA 95035
Tel.: (408) 493-1800
Web Site: http://www.biovision.com
Life Science Company; Assay Kits, Antibodies, Recombinant Proteins & Enzymes &
other Innovative Research Tools Mfr
N.A.I.C.S.: 541714

Epitomics Holdings, Inc. (2)
152 Grove St, Waltham, MA 02453
Biotechnology Research Services
N.A.I.C.S.: 541714

Marker Gene Technologies, Inc. (2)
1850 Millrace Dr, Eugene, OR 97403
Tel.: (541) 342-3760
Web Site: http://www.markergene.com
Pharmaceutical Preparation Mfr
N.A.I.C.S.: 325412
Alisa A. Naleway (COO)
John J. Naleway (Pres & CEO)

MitoSciences Inc. (2)
1850 Millrace Dr, Eugene, OR 97403
Web Site: https://www.mitosciences.com
Monoclonal Antibodies Mfr & Distr
N.A.I.C.S.: 325414

Accu-Sort Systems, Inc. (1)
511 School House Rd, Telford, PA 18969-1148
Tel.: (215) 723-0981
Mfr of Optical Scanners & Computer Systems for Scanners
N.A.I.C.S.: 334118

Advanced Vision Technology Ltd. (1)
6 Hanagar St, Hod Hasharon, 4527703,
Israel
Tel.: (972) 9 7614444
Web Site: http://www.avt-inc.com
Rev.: $57,274,000
Assets: $51,326,000
Liabilities: $21,131,000
Net Worth: $30,195,000
Earnings: $4,135,000
Emp.: 244
Fiscal Year-end: 12/31/2016
Commercial Printing Services
N.A.I.C.S.: 323111
Barry Ben-Ezra (CTO)
Alan Then (Gen Mgr-Dallas)
Merav Yanai (VP-Ops & HR)
Amir Sheinman (VP-Mktg)
Yair Shaharabany (COO)
Roy Porat (Pres)
Michael Almagor (VP-Digital Print Solutions
& OEM)
Hadar Ben-Moshe (CFO)
Lior Haviv (VP-R&D)
Uri Kapuler (VP-Global Customer Svcs)

Aguasin SpA (1)
Panamericana 18 900, Lampa, Santiago,
Chile
Tel.: (56) 222709500
Web Site: https://www.aguasin.com
Waste Treatment Services
N.A.I.C.S.: 221310

Aldevron, LLC (1)
4055 41st Ave S, Fargo, ND 58104
Tel.: (701) 297-9256

Web Site: http://www.aldevron.com
Rev.: $3,333,333
Emp.: 20
Biological Product, except Diagnostic, Mfr
N.A.I.C.S.: 325414
Kevin J. Ballinger (CEO)
Cindy Biffert (VP)
John Ballantyne (Cp-Founder & Chief Scientific Officer)
Jenny Stafford (VP & Gen Mgr)
Fritz Grunert (Chief Scientific Officer)
Ally Hauser (Mgr)
Stefan Lang (Dir-Business Development)
Henry Hebel (COO)
Diane Rogers (Sr VP)
Vijay Surapaneni (VP)
Ellen Shafer (Sr Dir-Marketing-Communications)
James Brown (Pres)
Michael Chambers (Co-Founder & Chm)

Alltec Angewandte Laserlicht Technologie GmbH (1)
An der Trave 27-31, 23923, Selmsdorf,
Germany
Tel.: (49) 38823550
Laser Marking Equipment Mfr
N.A.I.C.S.: 334510

Alpha Biotec Ltd. (2)
Kiryat Aryeh St swing 4, PO Box 3936, Jerusalem, 49510, Israel
Tel.: (972) 39291000
Web Site: http://www.alpha-bio.net
Emp.: 200
Surgical Equipment Mfr & Distr
N.A.I.C.S.: 339113
Ethan Nash (CFO)
Ofer Zigman (VP-Research & Development)
Avi Lev (VP-Sales-Local)
Ronit Steiner (Sr Mgr)

**Applied Imaging International
Ltd.** (1)
Bioscience Centre Times Square Scotswood Road, Newcastle upon Tyne, NE1
4EP, Tyne & Wear, United Kingdom
Tel.: (44) 191 202 3100
Sales Range: $25-49.9 Million
Emp.: 20
Automated Imaging System Mfr
N.A.I.C.S.: 334516

Aquafine Corporation (1)
29010 Ave Paine, Valencia, CA 91355-4198
Tel.: (661) 257-4770
Web Site: http://www.aquafineuv.com
Water Treatment Equipment Mfr
N.A.I.C.S.: 333310

Aquafine GmbH (1)
Ramskamp 77-85, 25337, Elmshorn, Germany
Tel.: (49) 41215780613
Web Site: http://www.aquafineuv.com
Ultraviolet Equipment Mfr
N.A.I.C.S.: 334516

Arbor Networks UK Ltd (1)
Western Peninsula Western Road, Bracknell, RG12 1RF, Berkshire, United Kingdom
Tel.: (44) 2071278147
Network Engineering Services
N.A.I.C.S.: 541512
Colin Gray (VP-EMEA Sls)

Beckman Australia ApS (1)
Akandevej 21, Bronshoj, 2700, Copenhagen, Hovedstaden, Denmark
Tel.: (45) 87434431
Electronic Equipment Whslr
N.A.I.C.S.: 423620

**Beckman Coulter Saudi Arabia
Co.Ltd.** (1)
King Abdallah Road Exit 10 Al Mugharazat
Area, Riyadh, Saudi Arabia
Tel.: (966) 114519100
Health Care Srvices
N.A.I.C.S.: 621610

Beckman Coulter, Inc. (1)
250 S Kraemer Blvd, Brea, CA 92821-6232
Tel.: (714) 993-5321
Web Site: http://www.beckmancoulter.com
Sales Range: $1-4.9 Billion
Emp.: 11,900
Biomedical Testing Equipment Designer, Mfr
& Marketer
N.A.I.C.S.: 334516

Subsidiary (Non-US):

Beckman Coulter AB (2)
Ekbacksvagen 28, 168 69, Bromma, Sweden
Tel.: (46) 856485900
Drug Discovery & Development Services
N.A.I.C.S.: 325412

**Beckman Coulter Australia Pty.
Ltd.** (2)
23-27 Chaplin Drive, Lane Cove, 2066,
NSW, Australia
Tel.: (61) 80 006 0880
Web Site: http://www.beckman.com
Biomedical Testing Equipment Retailer &
Marketer
N.A.I.C.S.: 423450

**Beckman Coulter Biomedical
GmbH** (2)
Sauerbruchstr 50, 81377, Munich, Germany
Tel.: (49) 895795890
Web Site: http://www.beckmancoulter.com
Emp.: 120
Drug Discovery & Development Services
N.A.I.C.S.: 325412

**Beckman Coulter Biyomedikal Urunler Sanayi ve Ticaret Limited
Sirketi** (2)
Askent Sokak No 3A Kosifler Is Merkezi A
Blok Kat 8, Icerenkoy Atasehir, 34752, Istanbul, Turkiye
Tel.: (90) 2165701717
Web Site: http://www.beckmancoulter.com.tr
Infrared Optical Lens Mfr
N.A.I.C.S.: 334516

Beckman Coulter Canada, Inc. (2)
7075 Financial Drive, PO Box 1059, Mississauga, L5N 6V8, ON, Canada
Tel.: (905) 819-1234
Sales Range: $75-99.9 Million
Emp.: 180
Biomedical Testing Equipment Distr
N.A.I.C.S.: 423450

**Beckman Coulter Ceska republika
s.r.o.** (2)
Radiova 1, 10 - Hostivar, 102 27, Prague,
Czech Republic
Tel.: (420) 272017999
Web Site: http://www.beckman.cz
Emp.: 80
Pharmaceuticals Product Mfr
N.A.I.C.S.: 325412

Beckman Coulter Commercial Enterprise (China) Co., Ltd. (2)
4/F Building 2 518 North Fuquan Road IBP,
Changning District, Shanghai, 200335,
China
Tel.: (86) 400 821 8899
Web Site: http://beckman.cnpowder.com.cn
Pharmaceuticals Product Mfr
N.A.I.C.S.: 325412

Beckman Coulter Espana, S.A. (2)
Torre Realia 4 Planta Plaza de Europa 41-
43, L'Hospitalet de Llobregat, 08908, Barcelona, Spain
Tel.: (34) 900802008
Web Site: https://www.beckman.com
Biomedical Testing Equipment Mfr
N.A.I.C.S.: 334516

**Beckman Coulter Eurocenter
S.A.** (2)
22 Rue Juste-olivier, PO Box 0301, 1260,
Nyon, 1260, Switzerland
Tel.: (41) 223653808
Medical Instrument Distr
N.A.I.C.S.: 423450

Beckman Coulter France S.A. (2)
Paris-Nord 2 22 Av Des Nations, BP 54359,
Roissy CDG, 95942, Villepinte, Cedex,
France
Tel.: (33) 149909000
Sales Range: $25-49.9 Million
Emp.: 50
Retailer & Servicer of Biomedical Testing
Equipment
N.A.I.C.S.: 423450

Beckman Coulter GmbH (2)
Europark Fichtenhain B 13, 47807, Krefeld,
Germany (100%)
Tel.: (49) 21513335

Sales Range: $150-199.9 Million
Emp.: 200
Retailer & Servicer of Biomedical Testing
Equipment
N.A.I.C.S.: 423450

**Beckman Coulter Hong Kong
Ltd.** (2)
22/F AXA Tower Landmark East 100 How
Ming Street, Kwun Tong, Kowloon, China
(Hong Kong) (100%)
Tel.: (852) 2 814 7431
Web Site: https://www.beckmancoulter.com
Sales Range: $50-74.9 Million
Emp.: 60
Medical Equipment Mfr
N.A.I.C.S.: 334510

**Beckman Coulter India Private
Limited** (2)
Unit No 3rd floor B wing Art Guild House
Phoenix Market City LBS Marg, Kurla West,
Mumbai, 400070, India
Tel.: (91) 2268385130
Emp.: 56
Pharmaceuticals Product Mfr
N.A.I.C.S.: 325412
Chandrashekar Payannavar (Gen Mgr)

**Beckman Coulter International
S.A.** (2)
22 rue Juste-Olivier, Case postal 1059,
1260, Nyon, Switzerland
Tel.: (41) 800850810
Sales Range: $150-199.9 Million
Emp.: 330
Retailer & Servicer of Biomedical Testing
Equipment
N.A.I.C.S.: 423450

Beckman Coulter Ireland Inc. (2)
Maryfort O'callaghans Mills Co Clare, Ennis,
Ireland
Tel.: (353) 14073081
Pharmaceuticals Product Mfr
N.A.I.C.S.: 325412

Beckman Coulter K. K. (2)
TOC Ariake West Tower 3-5-7 Ariake, Koto-
Ku, Tokyo, 135-0063, Japan
Tel.: (81) 36 745 4704
Web Site: http://www.beckmancoulter.co.jp
Biomedical Testing Equipment Mfr & Distr
N.A.I.C.S.: 423450

Beckman Coulter Korea Ltd. (2)
3rd Fl Suseo Bldg 281 Gwangpyeong-ro,
Gangnam-gu, Seoul, 135-884, Korea
(South)
Tel.: (82) 264203142
Pharmaceuticals Product Mfr
N.A.I.C.S.: 325412

**Beckman Coulter Laboratory Systems
(Suzhou) Co. Ltd.** (2)
No 181 West Suhong Road china-sing, Suzhou, 215021, China
Tel.: (86) 51267425505
Infrared Optical Lens Mfr
N.A.I.C.S.: 334516

Subsidiary (Domestic):

Beckman Coulter Life Sciences (2)
5350 Lakeview Pkwy S Dr, Indianapolis, IN
46268
Tel.: (800) 742-2345
Web Site: http://www.beckman.com
Diagnostics & Life Sciences
N.A.I.C.S.: 541715
Richard Ellson (CTO)
Casey Garamoni (VP-HR)
Adam Mandelbaum (Gen Counsel & VP)
Nicolas Cindric (VP-Global Svc)
Deborah Gonyea (CFO & VP-Fin)
Giles Snare (VP-Sls)
Mike Musgnug (VP & Gen Mgr-Biotechnology Bus Unit)
Tim Kerr (VP-Res & Dev)
Jason Lanie (VP-Global Mktg)
Mario Koksch (VP & Gen Mgr-Flow Cytometry Bus Unit)
Sidharth Kapileshwar (VP-Strategy & Innovation)

Subsidiary (Domestic):

Labcyte, Inc. (3)
170 Rose Orchard Wy, San Jose, CA
95134

Tel.: (408) 747-2000
Laboratory Instrument Mfr
N.A.I.C.S.: 334516

Subsidiary (Non-US):

Beckman Coulter Limited Liability Company (2)
Tel.: (7) 4952286700
Web Site: https://www.beckmancoulter.ru
Medical Equipment Distr
N.A.I.C.S.: 423450

Beckman Coulter Magyarorszag Kft (2)
Papirgyr str 58-59, 1038, Budapest, Hungary
Tel.: (36) 12509300
Biomedical Testing Equipment Mfr
N.A.I.C.S.: 334516

Beckman Coulter Mishima K.K. (2)
454-32 Higashino Nagaizumi-cho, Suntogun, Nagaizumi, 411-0931, Shizuoka, Japan
Tel.: (81) 367454704
Medical Equipment Mfr
N.A.I.C.S.: 334516

Beckman Coulter Nederland B.V. (2)
Pelmolenlaan 15, 3447 GW, Woerden, Netherlands
Tel.: (31) 348462462
Pharmaceuticals Product Mfr
N.A.I.C.S.: 325412
Ruud Huisman *(Mgr-Distributors)*

Beckman Coulter Polska sp. z.o.o. (2)
Aleje Jerozolimskie 181A, 02-222, Warsaw, Poland
Tel.: (48) 223551500
Web Site: http://www.beckmancoulter.com
Pharmaceuticals Product Mfr
N.A.I.C.S.: 325412

Subsidiary (Domestic):

Beckman Coulter Puerto Rico Inc. (2)
Carr Ste 1 Int 175 - Lot 33 Rio Canas Industrial Park, Caguas, PR 00725
Tel.: (787) 653-5426
Web Site: https://www.mybeckman.in
Emp.: 35
Analytical Instrument Mfr
N.A.I.C.S.: 334516

Subsidiary (Non-US):

Beckman Coulter S.p.A. (2)
Via Roma 108 Palazzo F1 Centro Cassina Plaza, Cassina De' Pecchi, Milan, 20060, Italy
Tel.: (39) 02953921
Web Site: http://www.beckman.com
Sales Range: $50-74.9 Million
Emp.: 150
Biomedical Testing Equipment Retailer & Marketer
N.A.I.C.S.: 423450

Beckman Coulter Singapore Pte. Ltd. (2)
Unit No 07-01 Hyflux Innovation Centre 80 Bendemeer Road, Singapore, 339949, Singapore
Tel.: (65) 63407100
Medical Equipment Mfr
N.A.I.C.S.: 334516

Beckman Coulter Slovenska republika s.r.o. (2)
Digital Park II Einsteinova 23, 851 01, Bratislava, Slovakia
Tel.: (421) 220903911
Web Site: http://www.beckman.cz
Pharmaceuticals Product Mfr
N.A.I.C.S.: 325412

Beckman Coulter South Africa (Proprietary) Limited (2)
Stand 1A Growthpoint Business Park Tonnetti Street Halfway House, Midrand, 1685, KwaZulu-Natal, South Africa
Tel.: (27) 115643000
Web Site: https://www.beckman.com
Medical Equipment Mfr
N.A.I.C.S.: 334516
Lorinda Palmer *(Sec)*

Beckman Coulter Srl (2)
Via Roma 108 - Palazzo F1/F2 Centro Cassina Plaza, Cassina De' Pecchi, 20051, Milan, Italy
Tel.: (39) 02953921
Medical Equipment Mfr
N.A.I.C.S.: 334516

Beckman Coulter Taiwan Inc. (2)
No 216 Sec 2 8th Floor Dunhua S Road, Da-an District, Taipei, 106, Taiwan
Tel.: (886) 227302599
Web Site: http://www.beckmancoulter.com
Emp.: 80
Medical Equipment Mfr
N.A.I.C.S.: 334516

Beckman Coulter United Kingdom Ltd. (2)
Oakley Court Kingsmead Business Park London Road, High Wycombe, HP11 1JU, Buckinghamshire, United Kingdom
Tel.: (44) 1494441181
Sales Range: $50-74.9 Million
Emp.: 150
Retailer & Servicer of Biomedical Testing Equipment
N.A.I.C.S.: 423450

Beckman Coulter d.o.o. (2)
Avenija Veceslava Holjevca 40, 10020, Zagreb, Croatia
Tel.: (385) 15501220
Pharmaceuticals Product Mfr
N.A.I.C.S.: 325412

Beckman Coulter de Mexico, S.A. de C.V. (2)
Av Popocatepetl no 396 Col Graal Pedro Ma Anaya, 03340, Mexico, 03340, Mexico
Tel.: (52) 5591832800
Medical Instrument Distr
N.A.I.C.S.: 423450

Beckman Coulter do Brasil Comercio e Importacao de Produtos de Laboratorio Ltda. (2)
Edificio West Towers - 15 andar- Torre B, Alameda Rio Negro 500- Alphaville, Barueri, Brazil
Tel.: (55) 1141542207
Web Site: http://www.beckmancoulter.com
Pharmaceuticals Product Mfr
N.A.I.C.S.: 325412

Subsidiary (Domestic):

IRIS International, Inc. (2)
250 S Kraemer Blvd, Brea, CA 92821-6232
Tel.: (714) 993-5321
Web Site: https://www.beckmancoulter.com
Imaging Automation Designer & Vitro Diagnostic Equipment Mfr
N.A.I.C.S.: 334516

Subsidiary (Domestic):

Arista Molecular, Inc. (3)
10455 Pacific Ctr Ct, San Diego, CA 92121-4339
Tel.: (877) 554-5004
Pharmaceuticals Product Mfr
N.A.I.C.S.: 325412

Subsidiary (Non-US):

Iris Diagnostics (UK) Ltd. (3)
St Johns Innovation Centre St Johns Innovation Park Cowley Road, Cambridge, CB4 0WS, United Kingdom
Tel.: (44) 1223421590
Diagnostic Equipment Mfr
N.A.I.C.S.: 334516
Alain Richard *(Gen Mgr)*

Iris Diagnostics France S.A. (3)
Micropark D Paris Nord II, 33 rue Chardonnerets, 95933, Roissy-en-France, France
Tel.: (33) 1 82 71 30 10
Web Site: http://www.irisdiagnostics.com
Diagnostic Equipment Mfr
N.A.I.C.S.: 334516

Subsidiary (Domestic):

StatSpin, Inc. (3)
60 Glacier DrSte 2000, Westwood, MA 02090 **(100%)**
Tel.: (781) 251-0421
Web Site: http://www.statspin.com

Sales Range: $25-49.9 Million
Emp.: 40
Developer, Mfr & Marketer of Sample Preparation Devices & Instrumentation for Laboratories
N.A.I.C.S.: 334516
Robert A. Mello *(Pres)*

Subsidiary (Domestic):

Lumigen, Inc (2)
22900 W 8 Mile Rd, Southfield, MI 48033
Tel.: (248) 351-5600
Web Site: https://www.lumigen.com
Rev.: $33,000,000
Emp.: 45
Clinical Diagnostics & Life Science
N.A.I.C.S.: 325180

BioTector Analytical Systems Ltd (1)
Raffeen House, Ringaskiddy, County Cork, Ireland
Tel.: (353) 214374237
Web Site: http://www.biotector.com
Emp.: 40
Electronic Testing Equipment Mfr
N.A.I.C.S.: 334515

Blue Software LLC (1)
8430 W Bryn Mawr Ave Ste 1100, Chicago, IL 60631
Tel.: (773) 957-1600
Web Site: https://www.bluesoftware.com
Software Development Services
N.A.I.C.S.: 541511

BrightTech Inc. (1)
1529 S Robertson Blvd, Los Angeles, CA 90035
Tel.: (310) 927-8026
Electric Lamp Bulb & Part Mfr
N.A.I.C.S.: 335139

Cepheid (1)
904 Caribbean Dr, Sunnyvale, CA 94089
Tel.: (408) 541-4191
Microfluidic Systems to Analyze Biological Samples
N.A.I.C.S.: 334516

Subsidiary (Non-US):

Cepheid AB (2)
Rontgenvagen 5, 171 54, Solna, Sweden
Tel.: (46) 10 555 9060
Web Site: http://www.cepheid.com
Clinical Molecular Diagnostic Assays Distr Services
N.A.I.C.S.: 541380

Cepheid Europe SAS (2)
Vira Solelh, 81470, Maurens-Scopont, France
Tel.: (33) 563825319
Biotechnology Research & Development
N.A.I.C.S.: 541714

Subsidiary (Non-US):

Cepheid Benelux (3)
Kleinhoefstraat 5 bus 26, 2440, Geel, Belgium
Tel.: (32) 14713913
Web Site: http://www.cepheid.com
Biotechnological Research Services
N.A.I.C.S.: 541714

Cepheid UK (3)
Oakley Court, Kingsmead Business Park Frederick Place, High Wycombe, HP11 1JU, United Kingdom
Tel.: (44) 330 333 2533
Web Site: http://www.cepheid.com
Medical Laboratories
N.A.I.C.S.: 621511

Subsidiary (Non-US):

Cepheid GK (2)
Burex Toranomon 703 2-7-5 Toranomon, Minato-ku, Tokyo, 105-0001, Japan
Tel.: (81) 8888383222
Web Site: http://www.cepheid.com
Biotechnology Research & Development
N.A.I.C.S.: 541714

Cepheid GmbH (2)
Europark Fichtenhain A 4, 47807, Krefeld, Germany
Tel.: (49) 2151 328 0100
Web Site: http://www.cepheid.com

Biotechnology Research & Development Services
N.A.I.C.S.: 541714

Cepheid South Africa (2)
Famous Grouse House Kildrummy Office Park, Cnr Witkoppen Rd & Uhmlanga Ave Paulshof, Johannesburg, 2191, South Africa
Tel.: (27) 112349636
Web Site: http://www.cepheid.com
Biotechnology Research & Development
N.A.I.C.S.: 541714

Cepheid Italy Srl (1)
Via Figino 20 22 Pero, Milan, 20016, Italy
Tel.: (39) 0287223850
Web Site: http://www.cepheid.com
Surgical Instrument Mfr
N.A.I.C.S.: 334513

Cepheid Proprietary Limited (1)
Building 3 Culross on Main Corner Main Road and Culross Road, Johannesburg, 2191, Bryanston, South Africa
Tel.: (27) 870061550
Surgical Instrument Mfr
N.A.I.C.S.: 334513

ChemTreat International, Inc. (1)
4701 Cox Rd Ste 301, Glen Allen, VA 23060
Tel.: (804) 965-0784
Pharmaceuticals Product Mfr
N.A.I.C.S.: 325412

ChemTreat, Inc. (1)
5640 Cox Rd, Glen Allen, VA 23060
Tel.: (804) 935-2000
Web Site: https://www.chemtreat.com
Sales Range: $200-249.9 Million
Emp.: 500
Water Treatment Products & Services
N.A.I.C.S.: 325998

Citicon (Hong Kong) Limited (1)
Room 1202 12/f Olympia Plaza 255 Kings Road, North Point, China (Hong Kong)
Tel.: (852) 21274693
Web Site: http://www.citicon.com.hk
Dental Equipment Distr
N.A.I.C.S.: 423450

DANRAD Holding ApS (1)
Akandevej 21, Bronshoj, 2700, Denmark
Tel.: (45) 38273827
Web Site: http://www.radiometer.com
Holding Company
N.A.I.C.S.: 551112

DH Denmark Holding ApS (1)
Akandevej 21, 2700, Bronshoj, Denmark
Tel.: (45) 8273827
Bank Holding Company
N.A.I.C.S.: 551111

DH Europe Finance SA (1)
1b Heienehaff, Senningerberg, 1736, Luxembourg
Tel.: (352) 27848058
Industrial Measuring Instrument Mfr
N.A.I.C.S.: 334513

DH Holdings Corp. (1)
1250 24th St NW, Washington, DC 20037
Tel.: (202) 828-0850
Holding Company
N.A.I.C.S.: 551112
Daniel A. Raskas *(Sr VP-Corp Dev)*
Steven M. Rales *(Chm)*
James H. Ditkoff *(Sr VP-Fin & Tax)*

DHR Finland Oy (1)
Nuutisarankatu 4, Tampere, 33900, Finland
Tel.: (358) 32311200
Sales Range: $25-49.9 Million
Emp.: 7
Automation Products Retailer
N.A.I.C.S.: 811191

DHR Holding India Pvt. Ltd. (1)
77 North Avenue 3 7th Floor Maker Maxity Bandra Kurla Complex Bandra E, Mumbai, 400 051, India
Tel.: (91) 2261382000
Medical Appliance Distr
N.A.I.C.S.: 423450

Danaher Controls (1)
1675 N Delany Rd, Gurnee, IL 60031-1237 **(100%)**
Tel.: (847) 662-2666

Danaher Corporation—(Continued)

Web Site: http://www.dancon.com
Sales Range: $25-49.9 Million
Emp.: 105
Mfr of Digital & Microprocessor-Based Controls for the Speed, Motion & Position of Industrial Machinery
N.A.I.C.S.: 334514

Danaher Controls Corp. (1)
2100 W Broad St, Elizabethtown, NC 28337
Tel.: (910) 862-2511
Web Site:
http://www.specialtyproducttechnologies.com
Industrial Instruments for Measurement
N.A.I.C.S.: 522130

Danaher Holding B.V. (1)
Science Park 5110 Son En Breugel, Eindhoven, 5692 EC, Netherlands
Tel.: (31) 402675100
Holding Company
N.A.I.C.S.: 551112

Danaher Industrial Controls (1)
1675 N Delany Rd, Gurnee, IL 60031-1237   (100%)
Tel.: (847) 662-2666
Web Site: http://www.dynapar.com
Sales Range: $25-49.9 Million
Emp.: 110
Factory Automatic & Process Controls Mfr
N.A.I.C.S.: 334514

Danaher Motion Company (1)
201A W Rock Rd, Radford, VA 24141   (100%)
Tel.: (540) 633-3545
Web Site: http://www.danahermotion.com
Sales Range: $200-249.9 Million
Emp.: 2,025
Mfr of Specialty Motion Control Systems & Components
N.A.I.C.S.: 335312

Division (Domestic):

America Precision Industry - Surface Mount Division (2)
95 North St, Arcade, NY 14009-9196
Tel.: (585) 496-6052
Sales Range: $25-49.9 Million
Emp.: 90
Mfr of Surface Mounted Inductive Components
N.A.I.C.S.: 334416

Unit (Domestic):

Danaher Motion (2)
628 N Hamilton St, Saginaw, MI 48602-4301
Tel.: (989) 776-5111
Sales Range: $125-149.9 Million
Electromagnetic, Mechanical & Control Technologies
N.A.I.C.S.: 332991

Danaher Motion (2)
110 Westtown Rd, West Chester, PA 19382-4978   (100%)
Tel.: (610) 692-2700
Web Site: http://www.portescap.com
Rev.: $16,000,000
Emp.: 100
Mechanical & Electronic Motors & Components Mfr
N.A.I.C.S.: 423830

Danaher Motion (2)
50 Alexander Ct, Ronkonkoma, NY 11770   (100%)
Tel.: (631) 467-8000
Web Site: http://www.danahermotion.com
Sales Range: $25-49.9 Million
Emp.: 105
Aircraft Parts & Equipment
N.A.I.C.S.: 335312

Subsidiary (Non-US):

Danaher Motion China (2)
Rm 2205 Scitech Tower 22 Jianguomen Wai Street, 22 Jianguomen Wai Street, Beijing, 100004, China
Tel.: (86) 10 65150260
Sales Range: $125-149.9 Million
Mfr of Brushless DC Motor Systems
N.A.I.C.S.: 333996

Danaher Motion Saro AB (2)
Saro, Kungsbacka, 429 80, Sweden
Tel.: (46) 31938000
Navigation Systems Mfr
N.A.I.C.S.: 334111

Subsidiary (Domestic):

Dover (2)
159 Swanson Rd, Boxborough, MA 01719-1040   (100%)
Tel.: (508) 475-3400
Web Site: http://www.dovermotion.com
Sales Range: $50-74.9 Million
Emp.: 160
Mfr of Special Dies, Tools, Jigs & Fixtures
N.A.I.C.S.: 333514

Subsidiary (Non-US):

Hach Lange GmbH (2)
Willstatterstrasse 11, 40549, Dusseldorf, Germany   (100%)
Tel.: (49) 21152880
Web Site: http://www.de.hach.com
Sales Range: $25-49.9 Million
Emp.: 280
Industrial Machinery Whslr
N.A.I.C.S.: 423830
Gert Schaumburg (Mng Dir)

Subsidiary (Domestic):

Portescap (2)
110 Westtown Rd, West Chester, PA 19382   (100%)
Tel.: (610) 235-5499
Web Site: https://www.portescap.com
Sales Range: $125-149.9 Million
Emp.: 100
Mfr & Designer of Brushless DC Miniature Motors
N.A.I.C.S.: 333996

Subsidiary (Non-US):

Portescap (2)
Rue Jardiniere 157, 2301, La Chaux-de-Fonds, Switzerland   (100%)
Tel.: (41) 329256111
Web Site: http://www.portescap.com
Sales Range: $10-24.9 Million
Emp.: 30
Mfr & Designer of Brushless DC Miniature Motors
N.A.I.C.S.: 333996

Portescap (2)
Unit No 2 SDF-1 SEEPZ-SEZ, Andheri East, Mumbai, 400 096, India   (100%)
Tel.: (91) 2242004165
Web Site: http://www.portescap.com
Sales Range: $125-149.9 Million
Emp.: 125
Mfr of Brushless DC Miniature Motors
N.A.I.C.S.: 333996

Portescap India Private Limited (2)
Unit 2 S D F-1 Seepz-sez, Andheri East, Mumbai, 400 096, Maharashtra, India
Tel.: (91) 2242004165
Web Site: http://www.portescap.com
Sales Range: $150-199.9 Million
Motor & Other Equipment Mfr
N.A.I.C.S.: 335312

Portescap SA (2)
Rue Jardiniere 157, 2300, La Chaux-de-Fonds, 2301, Switzerland
Tel.: (41) 329256240
Web Site: http://www.portescap.com
Emp.: 20
Motor Product Mfr
N.A.I.C.S.: 335312

Portescap Singapore Pte. Ltd. (2)
30 Cecil Street 19-08 Prudential Tower, Singapore, 049712, Singapore   (100%)
Tel.: (65) 67474888
Sales Range: $125-149.9 Million
Mfr of Brushless DC Miniature Motors
N.A.I.C.S.: 333996

Precision Technologies Pte Ltd (2)
211 Henderson Road 13 - 02 Henderson Industrial Park, Singapore, 159552, Singapore   (100%)
Tel.: (65) 62734573
Web Site: https://www.pretech.com.sg
Sales Range: $10-24.9 Million
Emp.: 2

Designs, Manufactures & Markets Industrial Process & Environmental Controls & Tools & Components
N.A.I.C.S.: 334513

Sika Interplant Systems Ltd. (2)
3 Gangadharchetty Rd, Bengaluru, 560 042, India   (100%)
Tel.: (91) 8049299144
Web Site: https://www.sikaglobal.com
Sales Range: $1-9.9 Million
Emp.: 100
Motion Control Products Mfr
N.A.I.C.S.: 335312

Dental Complex (1)
Apothecary Lane 6, Saint Petersburg, 191186, Russia
Tel.: (7) 8123247414
Web Site: http://dentalcomplex.com
Dental Equipment Distr
N.A.I.C.S.: 423450

Dental Equipment, LLC (1)
11727 Fruehauf Dr, Charlotte, NC 28273
Tel.: (704) 588-2126
Web Site: http://www.marus.com
Dental Equipment Mfr
N.A.I.C.S.: 339114

Dental Imaging Technologies Corporation (1)
1910 N Penn Rd, Hatfield, PA 19440
Tel.: (215) 997-5661
Dental Equipment Mfr
N.A.I.C.S.: 339114

Devicor Medical Europe GmbH (1)
Sudportal 5, 22848, Norderstedt, Germany
Tel.: (49) 4059355910
Surgical Instrument Mfr
N.A.I.C.S.: 334513

Devicore Medical Products Inc. (1)
300 E Business Way 5th Fl, Cincinnati, OH 45241
Tel.: (513) 864-9000
Web Site: https://www.mammotome.com
Pharmaceuticals Product Mfr.
N.A.I.C.S.: 325412

Dolan-Jenner Industries Inc. (1)
159M Swanson Rd, Boxboro, MA 01719   (100%)
Tel.: (978) 263-1400
Web Site: https://www.dolan-jenner.com
Process Control Instruments Mfr
N.A.I.C.S.: 334513
Charles G. Clarkson (Pres)

Dr. Lange Nederland B.V. (1)
Laan van Westroijen 2a, 4003 AZ, Tiel, 4003 AZ, Netherlands
Tel.: (31) 344631130
Web Site: http://www.nl.nach.com
Emp.: 40
Water Analysis Equipment Distr
N.A.I.C.S.: 423830

ELE International (1)
Chartmore Rd Chartwell Business Pk, Leighton Buzzard, LU7 4WG, Bedfordshire, United Kingdom   (100%)
Tel.: (44) 1525249200
Web Site: http://www.ele.com
Sales Range: $10-24.9 Million
Emp.: 50
Provider of Environmental Measuring Instrumentation
N.A.I.C.S.: 334516
Tony Tower (Mng Dir)

Subsidiary (US):

ELE International, Inc (2)
PO Box 389, Loveland, CO 80539
Tel.: (970) 663-3780
Web Site: http://www.ele.com
Mfr Engineering Test Equipment for Construction Materials, Including Soils, Rock, Concrete & Asphalt
N.A.I.C.S.: 334516

Esko BVBA (1)
Kortrijksesteenweg 1095, BE-9051, Gent, Belgium
Tel.: (32) 92169211
Web Site: http://www.esko.com
Sales Range: $200-249.9 Million
Commercial Printing & Professional Publishing Services

N.A.I.C.S.: 323111
Mattias Bystrom (Pres)
Charles Ravetto (VP & Gen Mgr-Supplier Solutions)
Andy Warnement (VP & Gen Mgr-Brand Solutions)
Joel Depernet (CTO)
Felix Hornicek (CFO)
Jan Bouwen (VP-HR)
Steve Toseland (VP-DBS)

Subsidiary (Domestic):

Enfocus NV (2)
The Loop - Building Networks Raymonde de Larochelaan 13, 9051, Gent, Belgium
Tel.: (32) 92169801
Web Site: https://www.enfocus.com
Sales Range: $25-49.9 Million
Emp.: 37
Printing Solutions
N.A.I.C.S.: 323111

Subsidiary (Non-US):

Esko Brno S.r.o (2)
Videnska 101 119, 619 00, Brno, Czech Republic
Tel.: (420) 545422031
Metalworking Machines Mfr
N.A.I.C.S.: 333519
Karel Novacek (Plant Mgr)

Esko Graphics Imaging GmbH (2)
Heerskamp 6, 25524, Itzehoe, 25524, Germany
Tel.: (49) 482177010
Web Site: http://www.eskographics.com
Sales Range: $25-49.9 Million
Packaging, Commercial Printing & Professional Publishing Services
N.A.I.C.S.: 323111

Esko Graphics Kongsberg AS (2)
Kirkegardsveien 45, PO Box 1016, 3616, Kongsberg, Norway
Tel.: (47) 32289900
Packaging, Commercial Printing & Professional Publishing Services
N.A.I.C.S.: 323111

Subsidiary (Domestic):

Esko-Graphics BVBA (2)
Kortrijksesteenweg 1095, 9051, Gent, Belgium
Tel.: (32) 92169211
Web Site: http://www.esko.com
Emp.: 380
Software Publishing Services
N.A.I.C.S.: 513210
Bernard Zwaenepoel (CIO & CTO-Software)
Mattias Bystrom (Pres)
Andy Warnement (VP & Gen Mgr-Brand Solutions)
Charles Ravetto (VP & Gen Mgr-Supplier Solutions)
Joel Depernet (CTO)
Felix Hornicek (CFO)
Steve Toseland (VP-DBS)
Jan Bouwen (VP-HR)

Subsidiary (Non-US):

Esko-Graphics GmbH (2)
Zusestrasse 4a, 25524, Itzehoe, Germany
Tel.: (49) 482177010
Web Site: http://www.esko.com
Computer Peripheral Equipment & Software Merchant Whslr
N.A.I.C.S.: 423430

Esko-Graphics Pte Ltd. (2)
1 Kaki Bukit View 04-15/17 Techview, Singapore, 415941, Singapore
Tel.: (65) 64200399
Web Site: http://www.esko.com
Emp.: 25
Software Publishing Services
N.A.I.C.S.: 513210

Esko-Graphics Inc. (1)
8535 Gander Creek Dr, Miamisburg, OH 45342
Tel.: (937) 454-1721
Web Site: https://www.esko.com
Emp.: 100
Software Development Services
N.A.I.C.S.: 541511

Filtronic AB (1)

Hissgatan 2, Box 2284, SE-531 02, Lidkoping, Sweden
Tel.: (46) 510 208 10
Web Site: http://www.filtronic.se
Electronic Products Mfr
N.A.I.C.S.: 334419

Fluke Operations B.V. (1)
1st Road 11, Nieuwerkerk ad Ijssel, 2913 LN, Son en Breugel, Netherlands
Tel.: (31) 402675200
Electronic Components Mfr
N.A.I.C.S.: 334419

G. Lufft Mess- und Regeltechnik GmbH (1)
Gutenbergstr 20, 70736, Fellbach, Germany
Tel.: (49) 711518220
Web Site: https://www.lufft.com
Electronic Components Mfr
N.A.I.C.S.: 334419
Tobias Weil (Mktg Dir)
Thomas Bolling (Mng Dir)
Patrick Gierman (Mng Dir)
Nina von Sivers (Mng Dir)

Gasboy International, Inc. (1)
7300 W Friendly Ave, Greensboro, NC 27410 (100%)
Tel.: (336) 547-5000
Web Site: http://www.gildarco.com
Sales Range: $300-349.9 Million
Emp.: 1,000
Mfr of Fuel Dispensing Equipment
N.A.I.C.S.: 333914

Gendex Dental Systems (1)
901 W Oakton St, Des Plaines, IL 60018-1843
Tel.: (847) 364-2420
Web Site: http://www.gendexxray.com
Sales Range: $75-99.9 Million
Emp.: 300
Mfr, Designer, Developer & Marketer of X-Ray Systems & Various Support Equipment for the Dental Market
N.A.I.C.S.: 334517

Genedata AG (1)
Margarethenstrasse 38, Basel, Switzerland
Tel.: (41) 615118400
Web Site: https://www.genedata.com
Biopharmaceutical Services
N.A.I.C.S.: 541713

Genetix Corp. (1)
120 Baytech Dr, San Jose, CA 95134-2302
Tel.: (408) 719-6400
Sales Range: $10-24.9 Million
Emp.: 65
Automated Chromosomal Image Analysis Systems to Clinical & Research Laboratories
N.A.I.C.S.: 334516

Genetix GmbH (1)
12 Humboldtstr, Dornach bei, 85609, Munich, Germany
Tel.: (49) 8994490275
Sales Range: $25-49.9 Million
Emp.: 2
Genetic Research Equipment & Supplies Mfr; Research Services for Life Sciences & Pharmaceutical Development
N.A.I.C.S.: 541715

Glabarco Leader Group Inc. (1)
4262 Kellway Cir, Addison, TX 75001-4232
Tel.: (972) 732-6965
Sales Range: $25-49.9 Million
Emp.: 3
Gasoline Pumps Measuring Or Dispensing
N.A.I.C.S.: 424720

Global Life Sciences Solutions Singapore Pte Ltd (1)
1 Maritime Square 11-01 HarbourFront Center, Singapore, 099253, Singapore
Tel.: (65) 67737303
Research & Development Services
N.A.I.C.S.: 541714

Global Life Sciences Solutions USA LLC (1)
100 Results Way, Marlborough, MA 01752
Web Site:
   https://www.cytivalifesciences.com
Research & Development Services
N.A.I.C.S.: 541714

Global Life Sciences Technologies Japan KK (1)

Sanken Bldg 3-25-1 Hyakunincho, Shinjuku-ku, Tokyo, 169-0073, Japan
Tel.: (81) 353319336
Research & Development Services
N.A.I.C.S.: 541714

Hach Company (1)
5600 Lindbergh Dr, Loveland, CO 80538-8842
Tel.: (970) 669-3050
Web Site: https://www.hach.com
Sales Range: $75-99.9 Million
Emp.: 1,000
Chemical & Laboratory Testing Equipment, Process Analyzers & Water Test Kits Mfr
N.A.I.C.S.: 334516

Subsidiary (Domestic):

Hach International Foreign Sales Co., Inc. (2)
5600 Lindbergh Dr, Loveland, CO 80538-8842 (100%)
Tel.: (970) 669-3050
Web Site: http://www.hach.com
Sales Range: $200-249.9 Million
Emp.: 900
Sales of Chemical & Laboratory Testing Equipment, Process Analyzers & Water Test Kits
N.A.I.C.S.: 334516

Subsidiary (Non-US):

Hach Lange ApS (2)
Akandevej 21 Bronshoj, 2700, Copenhagen, Denmark
Tel.: (45) 36772911
Web Site: http://www.dk.hach.com
Sales Range: $25-49.9 Million
Emp.: 20
Water Aanalysis Services
N.A.I.C.S.: 221310

Hach Lange France S.A.S. (2)
8 mail Barthelemy Thimonnier - Lognes, 77437, Marne-la-Vallee, France
Tel.: (33) 169673496
Web Site: http://www.fr.hach.com
Electric Equipment Mfr
N.A.I.C.S.: 335999

Hach Lange S.L. (2)
Edif Arteaga Centrum Antiguo Seminario Derio C Larrauri 1C- 2a Pl, Derio, 48160, Spain
Tel.: (34) 946573388
Web Site: http://www.hach.com
Emp.: 15
Water Analysis Services
N.A.I.C.S.: 327910

Hach Lange S.r.l. (2)
Via Rossini 1/A, 20020, Lainate, MI, Italy
Tel.: (39) 0293575400
Web Site: https://www.it.hach.com
Electric Equipment Mfr
N.A.I.C.S.: 335999

Hach Lange Spain S.L. (2)
Edificio Seminario C/Larrauri 1C-2 Pl, 48160, Derio, Bizkaia, Spain
Tel.: (34) 946573388
Web Site: http://www.hach-lange.es
Electric Equipment Mfr
N.A.I.C.S.: 335999

Hach Sales & Service Canada Ltd. (2)
400 Britannia Road East Unit 1, Mississauga, L4Z 1X9, ON, Canada (100%)
Tel.: (204) 632-5598
Web Site: http://www.hach.com
Sales Range: Less than $1 Million
Emp.: 10
Designs, Manufactures & Markets Industrial Process & Environmental Controls & Tools & Components
N.A.I.C.S.: 334512

Hach Ultra Japan KK (2)
5F TD Building 1-29-9 Takadanobaba, Shinjuku-ku, Tokyo, 169-0075, Japan
Tel.: (81) 362055510
Web Site: https://jp.hach.com
Electronic Equipment Distr
N.A.I.C.S.: 423690

Subsidiary (Domestic):

Sutron Corporation (2)

22400 Davis Dr, Sterling, VA 20164
Tel.: (703) 406-2800
Web Site: http://www.sutron.com
Emp.: 80
Remote Site Systems, Sensors, Data Acquisition Units, Telemetry & Software for Data Collection & Control Projects
N.A.I.C.S.: 334519

Subsidiary (Domestic):

IPS MeteoStar, Inc. (3)
99 Inverness Dr E Ste 130, Englewood, CO 80112
Tel.: (303) 242-5002
Web Site: http://www.meteostar.com
Environmental Analysis, Display & Integration Systems Designer & Mfr
N.A.I.C.S.: 334519

Hach Lange Finance GmbH (1)
Konigsweg 10, 14163, Berlin, Germany
Tel.: (49) 30809860
Industrial Measuring Instrument Mfr
N.A.I.C.S.: 334513

Hexis Cientifica S.A. (1)
Av Antonieta Piva Barranqueiros 385, PO Box 2130, Distrito Industrial Sao Paulo, Jundiai, 13213-009, SP, Brazil
Tel.: (55) 1145892600
Web Site: https://www.hexis.com.br
Emp.: 250
Medical Equipment Distr
N.A.I.C.S.: 423450

Imaging Sciences International LLC (1)
1910 N Penn Rd, Hatfield, PA 19440
Tel.: (215) 997-5666
Dental Radiography Products Mfr
N.A.I.C.S.: 339114
Dana Lawfer (Mgr-Acctg)

Immunotech SAS (1)
130 Avenue de Lattre de Tassigny, PO Box 177, 13276, Marseille, 13276, France
Tel.: (33) 491172700
Biomedical Testing Equipment Mfr
N.A.I.C.S.: 334516

Immunotech Sro (1)
Radiova 1122/1, Hostivar, 102 00, Prague, Czech Republic
Tel.: (420) 27 201 7200
Web Site: https://www.immunotech.cz
Pharmaceuticals Product Mfr
N.A.I.C.S.: 325412

Implant Direct Sybron International LLC (1)
3050 E Hillcrest Dr, Thousand Oaks, CA 91362
Tel.: (818) 444-3333
Web Site: http://www.implantdirect.com
Dental Equipment Mfr
N.A.I.C.S.: 339114

Subsidiary (Domestic):

Implant Direct Sybron Manufactuing LLC (2)
27030 Malibu Hills Rd, Calabasas Hills, CA 91301
Tel.: (818) 444-3300
Web Site: http://www.implantdirect.com
Medicinal Product Mfr
N.A.I.C.S.: 339112

Joslyn Clark Controls, Inc. (2)
2100 West Broad St, Elizabethtown, NC 28337 (100%)
Tel.: (800) 390-6405
Sales Range: $50-74.9 Million
Emp.: 600
Mfr of Industrial Controls & Systems
N.A.I.C.S.: 335314

Integrated DNA Technologies BVBA (1)
Interleuvenlaan 12A, 3001, Leuven, Belgium
Tel.: (32) 16282260
Pharmaceuticals Product Mfr
N.A.I.C.S.: 325412
Anna Tanda (CEO & Mng Dir)

Integrated DNA Technologies, Inc. (1)
1710 Commercial Park, Coralville, IA 52241

Tel.: (319) 626-8400
Web Site: http://www.idtdna.com
Provider of Chemical Laboratory Services
N.A.I.C.S.: 325414
Demaris Mills (Pres)
Linda De Jesus (VP)
Hanna Dust (VP)
Norm Fuller (VP)
Steven Henck (VP)
Sandy Ottensmann (VP)
Nichole Riek (VP)
Jamey Robbins (VP)
Erik Swenson (CFO)
Steve Wowk (VP)

Subsidiary (Non-US):

Integrated DNA Technologies Pte. Ltd. (2)
41 Science Park Road 01-28 The Gemini, Singapore Science Park II, Singapore, 117610, Singapore
Tel.: (65) 67759187
Web Site: http://sg.idtdna.com
Organic Chemical Mfr
N.A.I.C.S.: 325199

Subsidiary (Domestic):

Swift Biosciences, Inc. (2)
58 Parkland Plz Ste 100, Ann Arbor, MI 48103
Tel.: (734) 330-2568
Web Site: http://www.swiftbiosci.com
Biotechnology Health Care Services
N.A.I.C.S.: 541714
Steve Spotts (Chief Comml Officer)
Vladimir Makarov (Chief Scientific Officer)
Eric Halverson (VP-Finance)
Timothy Harkins (Pres & CEO)
Candia Brown (VP)
Dan Kidle (Chm)

JS Technology Inc. (1)
3000 W Kingsley Rd, Garland, TX 75041-2313
Tel.: (770) 475-8011
Web Site: http://www.danaher.com
Rev: $7,800,000
Emp.: 80
Mfr of Hand & Edge Tools
N.A.I.C.S.: 332216

KAVO Dental GmbH (1)
Bismarckring 39, 88400, Biberach, Germany
Tel.: (49) 7351560
Web Site: https://www.kavo.com
Emp.: 580
Dental Equipment Mfr
N.A.I.C.S.: 339114

KAVO Dental Ltd. (1)
St Mary's Court The Broadway, Amersham, HP7 0UT, Bucks, United Kingdom
Tel.: (44) 1494733000
Web Site: http://www.kavo.com
Emp.: 10
Dental Equipment Mfr
N.A.I.C.S.: 339114
Don Gilchrist (Mgr-Midlands & East-England)
Julie Cullen (Mgr-)

KaVo do Brasil Industria e Comercio Ltda. (1)
Rua Chapeco 86 Saguacu, 89221-040, Joinville, Santa Catarina, Brazil
Tel.: (55) 4734510100
Web Site: http://www.kavo.com.br
Dental Equipment Mfr
N.A.I.C.S.: 339114

Kaltenbach & Voigt GmbH (1)
Bismarckring 39, Biberach, 88400, Germany
Tel.: (49) 7351560
Web Site: http://www.kavo.com
Emp.: 100
Medicinal Product Mfr
N.A.I.C.S.: 339112

Kavo Dental Technologies, LLC (1)
11727 Fruehauf Dr, Charlotte, NC 28273
Web Site: https://www.kavo.com

Danaher Corporation—(Continued)

Dental Equipment Mfr
N.A.I.C.S.: 339114

Subsidiary (Domestic):

Aribex, Inc. (2)
11727 Fruehauf Dr, Charlotte, NC 28273
Tel.: (801) 226-5522
Web Site: http://www.aribex.com
Sales Range: $1-9.9 Million
Emp.: 33
Dental Equipment & Supplies Mfr
N.A.I.C.S.: 339114

Kerr Corporation (1)
200 S Kraemer Blvd Bldg E2, Brea, CA 92821
Web Site: https://www.kerrdental.com
Emp.: 250
Dental Equipment Mfr
N.A.I.C.S.: 339114

Kerr GmbH (1)
Konrad-Zuse-Strasse 6, 52134, Herzogen-rath, Germany
Tel.: (49) 80030323032
Web Site: http://www.kerrdental.de
Dental Equipment Mfr & Distr
N.A.I.C.S.: 339114

Kerr Italia S.r.l. (1)
Via Passanti 332, 84018, Scafati, Italy
Tel.: (39) 0818508327
Web Site: https://www.kerrdental.com
Dental Equipment Mfr
N.A.I.C.S.: 339114

Kreatech Biotechnology BV (1)
Vlierweg 20, 1032 LG, Amsterdam, 1032 LG, Netherlands
Tel.: (31) 206919181
Surgical Instrument Mfr
N.A.I.C.S.: 334513
Marjolijn van Aalderen (Office Mgr)

Lachat Instruments (1)
6645 W Mill Rd, Milwaukee, WI 53218
Tel.: (414) 358-4200
Web Site: http://www.lachatinstruments.com
Sales Range: $50-74.9 Million
Emp.: 226
Mfr of Toxic & Flammable Gas & Fire De-tection Systems
N.A.I.C.S.: 334516

Leica Biosystems Imaging Inc. (1)
1700 Leider Ln, Buffalo Grove, IL 60089
Tel.: (844) 534-2262
Web Site: http://www.leicabiosystems.com
Surgical Instrument Mfr
N.A.I.C.S.: 334513

Leica Microsystems Cambridge Limited (1)
19 Jessops Riverside 800 Brightside Lane, Sheffield, S9 2RX, United Kingdom
Tel.: (44) 1223411411
Microscope Mfr & Repair Services
N.A.I.C.S.: 334516

Leica Microsystems Canada (1)
71 Four Valley Drive, Concord, L4K 4V8, ON, Canada
Medical Appliance Distr
N.A.I.C.S.: 423450

Leica Microsystems GmbH (1)
Ernst-Leitz-Strasse 17-37, 35578, Wetzlar, Germany
Tel.: (49) 6441290
Web Site: https://www.leica-microsystems.com
Sales Range: $650-699.9 Million
Emp.: 3,050
Microscopes & Laboratory Equipment Mfr
N.A.I.C.S.: 334516
Maxim Mamin (VP)
Christine Munz (VP)
Mark Wetzel (VP-Global)
Dominikus Hamann (Gen Counsel)

Subsidiary (Domestic):

Leica Biosystems Nussloch GmbH (1)
Heidelberger Strasse 17-19, 69226, Nus-sloch, Germany
Tel.: (49) 6 224 1430
Web Site: https://www.leicabiosystems.com

Medicinal Product Mfr
N.A.I.C.S.: 339112

Subsidiary (US):

Aperio Technologies, Inc. (3)
1360 Park Ctr Dr Ste 106, Vista, CA 92081
Tel.: (760) 539-1100
Web Site: http://www.aperio.com
Sales Range: $10-24.9 Million
Emp.: 85
Surgical & Medical Instrument Mfr
N.A.I.C.S.: 339112

Devicor Medical Products, Inc. (3)
300 E Business Way 5th Fl, Cincinnati, OH 45241
Tel.: (513) 864-9000
Web Site: https://www.mammotome.com
Surgical & Medical Instrument Mfr
N.A.I.C.S.: 339112

Subsidiary (Non-US):

Leica Biosystems Newcastle Limited (3)
Balliol Business Park West Benton Lane, Newcastle upon Tyne, NE12 8EW, United Kingdom
Tel.: (44) 1912150567
Sales Range: $25-49.9 Million
Emp.: 10
Medicinal Product Mfr
N.A.I.C.S.: 339112

Subsidiary (US):

Leica Biosystems Richmond, Inc. (3)
5205 Rte 12, Richmond, IL 60071
Tel.: (815) 678-2000
Sales Range: $25-49.9 Million
Emp.: 185
Surgical Appliances & Supplies
N.A.I.C.S.: 339113

Subsidiary (Domestic):

Bioptigen, Inc. (4)
633 Davis Dr Ste 480, Morrisville, NC 27560
Tel.: (919) 314-5500
Web Site: http://www.bioptigen.com
Optical Coherence Tomography Technolo-gies Developer & Mfr
N.A.I.C.S.: 339115

Subsidiary (Non-US):

Leica Microsystems (SEA) Pte Ltd (2)
12 Teban Gardens Crescent, Singapore, 608924, Singapore
Tel.: (65) 65505999
Analytical Instrument Mfr
N.A.I.C.S.: 334516

Leica Microsystems B.V. (2)
Vlierweg 20, 1032 LG, Amsterdam, 1032 LG, Netherlands
Tel.: (31) 704132100
Analytical Instrument Mfr
N.A.I.C.S.: 334516

Subsidiary (Domestic):

Leica Microsystems IR GmbH (2)
Ernst-Leitz-Str 17-37, 35578, Wetzlar, 35578, Germany
Tel.: (49) 6441294000
Medicinal Product Mfr
N.A.I.C.S.: 339112

Subsidiary (Non-US):

Leica Microsystems KK (2)
1-29-9 Takadanobaba, Shinjuku-ku, Tokyo, 169-0075, Japan
Tel.: (81) 367585656
Web Site: http://www.leica-microsystems.co.jp
Medical Equipment Mfr
N.A.I.C.S.: 339112

Leica Microsystems Limited (2)
Office Building 858 Beijing New Century Nikko Hotel, No 6 South Capital Gymna-sium Road, Beijing, 100044, China
Tel.: (86) 4006506632
Web Site: http://www.leicamicrosystems.com
Emp.: 74

Medicinal Product Mfr
N.A.I.C.S.: 339112

Subsidiary (US):

Leica Microsystems, Inc. (2)
10 Pkwy N, Deerfield, IL 60015-1515
Tel.: (847) 405-0123
Web Site: https://www.leica-microsystems.com
Microscopes & Scientific Instruments Mfr
N.A.I.C.S.: 334516

Subsidiary (Domestic):

Leica Mikrosysteme Vertrieb GmbH (2)
Ernst-Leitz-Strasse 17-37, 35578, Wetzlar, Germany
Tel.: (49) 644 129 4099
Web Site: http://www.leica-microsystems.com
Medicinal Product Mfr
N.A.I.C.S.: 339112

Leica Microsystems Trading (Shang-hai) Ltd. (1)
5th Floor Building 2 No 518 Fuquan North Road, Changning District, Shanghai, 200335, China
Tel.: (86) 4006506632
Web Site: http://www.leica-microsystems.com
Microscope Instrument Mfr
N.A.I.C.S.: 334513

Leica Mikrosysteme (Austria) GmbH (1)
Hernalser Hauptstrasse 219, 1170, Vienna, Austria
Tel.: (43) 148680500
Web Site: http://www.leica-microsystems.com
Infrared Optical Lens Mfr
N.A.I.C.S.: 334516
Christian Hofmann (Mgr-Sales)

Life Sciences Holdings France SAS (1)
Silic 703 16 Avenue Du Quebec, 91961, Courtaboeuf, Cedex, France
Tel.: (33) 160198600
Holding Company
N.A.I.C.S.: 551112

Linx Printing Technologies Limited (1)
Linx House 8 Stocks Bridge Way, Compass Point Business Park, Saint Ives, PE27 5JL, Cambridgeshire, United Kingdom
Tel.: (44) 148 030 2100
Web Site: https://www.linxglobal.com
Emp.: 220
Printing Products Mfr
N.A.I.C.S.: 333248

Lipesa Colombia SA (1)
Carretera Central Bogota Tunja km 21 Cun-dinamarca, Tocancipa, Colombia
Tel.: (57) 6018786600
Web Site: http://www.lipesa.com
Chemical Preparations Mfr
N.A.I.C.S.: 325199

McCrometer Inc. (1)
3255 W Stetson Ave, Hemet, CA 92545 (100%)
Tel.: (951) 652-6811
Web Site: https://www.mccrometer.com
Sales Range: $25-49.9 Million
Emp.: 110
Mfr of Flow Meters for Agricultural, Indus-trial & Municipal Applications with Electronic Batching & Remote Recording Systems
N.A.I.C.S.: 334514
David Splatt (Sls Dir-)

Metrex Research, LLC (1)
1717 W Collins Ave, Orange, CA 92867
Tel.: (714) 516-7788
Web Site: https://www.metrex.com
Pharmaceuticals Product Mfr
N.A.I.C.S.: 325412

Molecular Devices LLC (1)
1311 Orleans Dr, Sunnyvale, CA 94089
Tel.: (408) 747-1700
Web Site: http://www.moleculardevices.com
Sales Range: $150-199.9 Million
Emp.: 300

Drug Measurement Systems Developer & Mfr
N.A.I.C.S.: 334516

Branch (Domestic):

Molecular Devices Corporation - Downingtown (2)
402 Boot Rd, Downingtown, PA 19335
Tel.: (408) 747-1700
Web Site: https://www.moleculardevices.com
Sales Range: $25-49.9 Million
Emp.: 38
Laboratory Instrument Mfr
N.A.I.C.S.: 334516

Subsidiary (Non-US):

Molecular Devices GmbH (2)
Sauerbruchstr 50, 81377, Munich, Germany
Tel.: (49) 1189448000
Sales Range: $50-74.9 Million
Emp.: 250
Laboratory Instruments
N.A.I.C.S.: 334516

Molecular Devices Ltd. (2)
660-665 Eskdale Road Winnersh Triangle, Wokingham, RG41 5TS, Berkshire, United Kingdom
Tel.: (44) 1189448000
Web Site: http://www.moleculardevices.com
Sales Range: $25-49.9 Million
Emp.: 40
Laboratory Instruments
N.A.I.C.S.: 334516

Namco Controls Corporation (1)
6095 Parkland Blvd Ste 310 2100 W Broad St, Elizabethtown, NC 28337 (100%)
Tel.: (440) 460-1360
Web Site: http://www.namcocontrols.com
Sales Range: $75-99.9 Million
Emp.: 300
Limit Switches; Proximity Switches; Sole-noids; Coils; Logic Drivers, Electrical & Electronic Controls; Fiber Optic Switches & Photoelectric Switches; Lasernet Sensors
N.A.I.C.S.: 334419

Negele Messtechnik GmbH (1)
Raiffeisenweg 7, 87743, Egg an der Gunz, Germany
Tel.: (49) 833392040
Web Site: https://www.anderson-negele.com
Electric Equipment Mfr
N.A.I.C.S.: 335999

Nihon Pall Manufacturing Limited (1)
46 Kasumi-no-sato Ami-Cho, Inashiki-gun, Ibaraki, 300-0315, Japan
Tel.: (81) 298890001
Emp.: 280
Semiconductor Mfr
N.A.I.C.S.: 333242

Nobel Biocare Holding AG (1)
Tel.: (41) 432114200
Sales Range: $650-699.9 Million
Emp.: 2,552
Aesthetic Dental Products Mfr
N.A.I.C.S.: 339114

Subsidiary (Non-US):

Alpha-Bio Tec Ltd. (2)
Tel.: (972) 39291000
Web Site: https://alpha-bio.net
Emp.: 200
Dental & Surgical Equipment Mfr
N.A.I.C.S.: 339112

Medicim NV (2)
Tel.: (32) 15443200
Web Site: https://www2.medicim.com
Sales Range: $25-49.9 Million
Emp.: 100
Medical Image Computing Services
N.A.I.C.S.: 541990

Nobel Biocare AB (2)
Tel.: (46) 31818800
Web Site: http://www.nobelbiocare.com
Sales Range: $50-74.9 Million
Emp.: 150
Dental Implants & Prosthetics
N.A.I.C.S.: 339114

Nobel Biocare Asia-Africa Holding AG (2)

Tel.: (41) 432114200
Holding Company & Investment Management Services
N.A.I.C.S.: 551112

Nobel Biocare Commercial (Shanghai) Co. Ltd. (2)
Tel.: (86) 4000817707
Emp.: 80
Medical & Surgical Equipment Mfr
N.A.I.C.S.: 339112

Nobel Biocare Danmark A/S (2)
Tel.: (45) 39404846
Emp.: 3
Dental Implants & Prosthetics
N.A.I.C.S.: 423450

Nobel Biocare Distribution Center BV (2)
Tel.: (31) 774757420
Emp.: 150
Medical & Surgical Equipment Distr
N.A.I.C.S.: 423450

Nobel Biocare Holding USA Inc. (2)
Tel.: (714) 282-4800
Sales Range: $200-249.9 Million
Emp.: 300
Investment Management Service
N.A.I.C.S.: 523999

Nobel Biocare India Pvt. Ltd. (2)
Tel.: (91) 2267519964
Web Site: http://myimplant.in
Sales Range: $25-49.9 Million
Emp.: 35
Medical & Surgical Equipment Mfr & Distr
N.A.I.C.S.: 339112

Nobel Biocare Magyarorszag Kft. (2)
Tel.: (36) 17010409
Emp.: 7
Dental Implants & Prosthetics Distr
N.A.I.C.S.: 423450

Nobel Biocare Management AG (2)
Tel.: (41) 43 211 42 00
Management & Administrative Services
N.A.I.C.S.: 561499

Nobel Biocare Mexico S.A. de C.V. (2)
Tel.: (52) 5552497460
Web Site: http://www.nobelbiocare.com
Emp.: 18
Dental Implants & Prosthetics
N.A.I.C.S.: 423450

Nobel Biocare Nederland BV (2)
Tel.: (31) 306354949
Medical & Surgical Equipment Mfr
N.A.I.C.S.: 339112

Nobel Biocare Norway AS (2)
Tel.: (47) 64 95 75 55
Emp.: 6
Dental Implants & Prosthetics Distr
N.A.I.C.S.: 423450

Nobel Biocare Portugal S.A. (2)
Tel.: (351) 223747350
Emp.: 18
Dental Implants & Prosthetics Sales
N.A.I.C.S.: 423450

Nobel Biocare Procera K.K. (2)
Tel.: (81) 474550171
Sales Range: $25-49.9 Million
Emp.: 5
Developer, Mfr & Marketer of Dental Equipment for Restorative & Aesthetic Dentistry
N.A.I.C.S.: 339114

Nobel Biocare Procera Services Inc. (2)
Tel.: (418) 683-8435
Health Care Srvices
N.A.I.C.S.: 621999

Nobel Biocare Russia LLC (2)
Tel.: (7) 4959747755
Emp.: 5
Dental Implants & Prosthetics Distr
N.A.I.C.S.: 423450

Nobel Biocare Services AG (2)
Tel.: (41) 432114200
Sales Range: $25-49.9 Million
Emp.: 200

Medical & Dental Products Packaging, Labeling, Logistics & Distr
N.A.I.C.S.: 423450

Nobel Biocare Singapore Pte Ltd. (2)
Tel.: (65) 64083904
Sales Range: $50-74.9 Million
Emp.: 5
Dental & Medical Equipment Distr
N.A.I.C.S.: 423450

Nobel Biocare South Africa (2)
Tel.: (27) 510111520
Web Site: http://www.nobelbiocare.com
Surgical Equipment Distr
N.A.I.C.S.: 423450

Nobel Biocare South Africa (Pty) Ltd (2)
Tel.: (27) 11 802 0112
Emp.: 16
Medical & Surgical Equipment Mfr
N.A.I.C.S.: 339112

Nobel Biocare Suomi Oy (2)
Tel.: (358) 207406100
Dental & Medical Equipment Distr
N.A.I.C.S.: 423450

Nobel Biocare UAB (2)
Tel.: (370) 52683448
Web Site: http://www.nobelbiocare.com
Emp.: 6
Medical & Surgical Equipment Distr
N.A.I.C.S.: 423450

Normond info SAS (1)
7 Rue Frederic Degeorge Bat B - 2eme etage, CS 10451, 62028, Arras, Cedex, France
Tel.: (33) 149908600
Web Site: http://www.normand-info.fr
Healthcare Software Development Services
N.A.I.C.S.: 541511

OTT Hydromet Corp. (1)
22400 Davis Dr, Sterling, VA 20164
Tel.: (703) 406-2800
Health Care Srvices
N.A.I.C.S.: 621610

OTT Hydromet GmbH (1)
Ludwigstrasse 16, 87437, Kempten, Germany
Tel.: (49) 83156170
Web Site: https://www.ott.com
Electric Equipment Mfr
N.A.I.C.S.: 335999

Ormco BV (1)
Basicweg 20, Amersfoort, 3821 BR, Netherlands
Tel.: (31) 334536161
Medicinal Product Mfr
N.A.I.C.S.: 339112

Ormco Europe BV (1)
Basicweg 20, 3821 BR, Amersfoort, Netherlands
Tel.: (31) 80030323032
Health Care Srvices
N.A.I.C.S.: 621610

Ormco LLC (1)
Maloohtinskij Pr 64 Lit V, 195112, Saint Petersburg, Russia
Tel.: (7) 8123247414
Web Site: http://www.ormco.ru
Orthodontic Product Mfr
N.A.I.C.S.: 334513

PLS Pacific Laser Systems LLC (1)
2550 Kerner Blvd, San Rafael, CA 94901
Tel.: (415) 453-5780
Web Site: http://www.plslaser.com
Laser Tool Mfr
N.A.I.C.S.: 333517

Pall Corporation (1)
25 Harbor Park Dr, Port Washington, NY 11050 **(100%)**
Tel.: (516) 703-1819
Web Site: http://www.pall.com
Filtration, Separation & Purification Products Mfr & Marketer
N.A.I.C.S.: 334514
Naresh Narasimhan *(Pres)*
Rajan Beera *(CTO)*
Aaron Rivers *(VP)*
Joseph Siniscalchi *(CFO)*

Shangaza Dasent *(VP)*
Dan Huntsberger *(VP)*
Greg Sears *(VP)*
David Stein *(VP)*

Subsidiary (Non-US):

Nihon Pall Ltd. (2)
6-5-1 Nishishinjuku, Shinjuku-ku, Tokyo, 163-1325, Japan
Tel.: (81) 36 901 5860
Web Site: http://www.pall.com
Filtration, Separation & Purification Products Mfr & Sales
N.A.I.C.S.: 333310

PT Pall Filtration Indonesia (2)
Perkantoran Hijau Arkadia Tower F 2nd Floor, JI Let Jend TB Simatupang Kav 88, Jakarta, 12520, Indonesia
Tel.: (62) 2178830088
Web Site: http://www.pall.com
Filtration, Separation & Aerospace Purification Products Development, Mfr & Sales
N.A.I.C.S.: 333310

Pall (Canada) Limited (2)
3450 Ridgeway Drive Unit 6, Mississauga, L5L 0A2, ON, Canada
Tel.: (905) 542-0330
Web Site: http://www.pall.com
Filtration Equipment Mfr
N.A.I.C.S.: 333998

Pall (Schweiz) AG (2)
Schaeferweg 16, 4057, Basel, Switzerland
Tel.: (41) 61 638 3900
Web Site: http://www.pall.com
Filtration, Separation & Purification Products Mfr & Sales
N.A.I.C.S.: 333413

Subsidiary (Domestic):

Pall Aeropower Corporation (2)
10540 Ridge Rd, New Port Richey, FL 34654
Tel.: (727) 849-9999
Web Site: https://www.pall.com
Separation & Purification Product Mfr
N.A.I.C.S.: 333998

Subsidiary (Non-US):

Pall Asia International Ltd. (2)
Room 2003-4 Tower 1 33 Canton Road, Tsim Tsa Tsui, Kowloon, China (Hong Kong)
Tel.: (852) 25839610
Web Site: https://www.pall.com
Filtration, Separation & Purification Products Mfr & Distr
N.A.I.C.S.: 333310

Pall Australia Pty Ltd (2)
1-2 Wandarri Court, Cheltenham, Melbourne, 3192, VIC, Australia
Tel.: (61) 80 063 5082
Web Site: http://www.pall.com
Filtration, Separation & Purification Products Development, Mfr & Sales
N.A.I.C.S.: 333413

Pall Austria Filter GmbH (2)
Handelskai 94-96 Top 422, 1200, Vienna, Austria
Tel.: (43) 149 1920
Web Site: http://www.pall.com
Filtration Solutions; Separation & Purification Products Development, Mfr & Distr
N.A.I.C.S.: 333413

Subsidiary (Domestic):

Pall Biomedical, Inc. (2)
25 Harbor Park Dr, Port Washington, NY 11050
Tel.: (516) 484-3600
Web Site: http://www.pall.com
Surgical & Medical Instrument Mfr
N.A.I.C.S.: 339112

Subsidiary (Non-US):

Pall Corporation Filtration & Separations Ltd. (2)
Unit 2501 Rasa Tower 25th Floor 555 Phaholyothin Road, Kwang/Khet Chatuchak, Bangkok, 10900, Thailand
Tel.: (66) 29371055
Web Site: http://www.pall.com

Filtration, Separation & Purification Products Development, Mfr & Sales
N.A.I.C.S.: 333310

Subsidiary (Domestic):

Pall Cortland (2)
3643 State Route 281, Cortland, NY 13045
Tel.: (607) 753-6041
Web Site: http://www.pall.com
Filtration, Separation & Purification Products Mfr & Distr
N.A.I.C.S.: 333310

Subsidiary (Non-US):

Pall Espana S.A.U. (2)
Valgrande 8 Floor 1 Thanworth Building, 28108, Alcobendas, Madrid, Spain
Tel.: (34) 916579815
Web Site: http://www.pall.com
Filtration, Separation & Purification Products Development, Mfr & Sales
N.A.I.C.S.: 333413
Juan Martinez de Lara *(Fin Dir)*

Pall Europe Ltd. (2)
5 Harbourgate Business Park Southampton Road, Portsmouth, PO6 4BQ, Hampshire, United Kingdom
Tel.: (44) 239 233 8000
Web Site: http://www.pall.com
Filtration, Separation & Purification Products Development, Mfr & Sales
N.A.I.C.S.: 333310

Pall Filter (Beijing) Co., Ltd. (2)
No 12 Hongda South Rd, Daxing District, Beijing, 100176, China
Tel.: (86) 1087225588
Web Site: http://www.pall.com
Filtration, Separation & Purification Products Mfr & Distr
N.A.I.C.S.: 333413

Pall Filtersystems GmbH (2)
Werk Schumacher Crailsheim Zur Fluegelau 70, 74564, Crailsheim, Germany
Tel.: (49) 79519664610
Web Site: https://www.pall.com
Industrial Machinery Equipment Mfr
N.A.I.C.S.: 333248
Arndt Nottrott *(Dir-Ops & Engrg-Europe)*

Pall Filtration Pte Ltd. (2)
1 Science Park Road 05-09/15 East Wing The Capricorn, Singapore Science Park II, Singapore, Singapore
Tel.: (65) 6 388 8688
Web Site: http://www.pall.com
Filtration Solutions; Separation & Purification Products Mfr & Distr
N.A.I.C.S.: 333413

Subsidiary (Domestic):

Pall Filtration and Separations Group (2)
2118 Greenspring Dr, Lutherville Timonium, MD 21093-3112
Tel.: (410) 252-0800
Filtration Products Mfr
N.A.I.C.S.: 333998

Subsidiary (Non-US):

Pall France (2)
3 Rue des Gaudines, PO Box 5253, 78102, Saint Germain-en-Laye, Cedex, France
Tel.: (33) 13 061 3800
Web Site: http://www.pall.com
Industrial Filtration Equipment Distr
N.A.I.C.S.: 333310

Pall GmbH (2)
Philipp-Reis-Strasse 6, 63303, Dreieich, Germany
Tel.: (49) 6 103 3070
Web Site: http://www.pall.de
Fluid Process, Fluid Power & Aerospace Products Mfr & Sales
N.A.I.C.S.: 334511

Pall India Pvt. Ltd. (2)
Survey No 237 IT Park Phase 1 Hinjwadi, Pune, 411057, Maharashtra, India
Tel.: (91) 2066751300
Web Site: http://www.pall.com
Industrial Machinery Mfr
N.A.I.C.S.: 333310

Danaher Corporation—(Continued)

Pall International Sarl (2)
Avenue de Tivoli 3, 1700, Fribourg, Switzerland
Tel.: (41) 80022557255
Web Site: https://www.oil-gas.pall.com
Commercial & Industrial Machinery Mfr
N.A.I.C.S.: 333415

Pall Italia S.R.L. (2)
Via Emilia 26, Buccinasco, 20090, Milan, Italy
Tel.: (39) 020 070 7400
Web Site: http://www.pall.com
Biomedical & Fluid Process; Aerospace Filter & Fluid Clarification Products Mfr & Distr
N.A.I.C.S.: 333310

Pall Korea Limited (2)
4th Fl Ildong Bldg 968-5 Daechi 2-Dong, Kangnam-Gu, Seoul, Korea (South)
Tel.: (82) 2 560 8756
Web Site: http://www.pall.com
Filtration, Separation & Purification Products Development, Mfr & Sales
N.A.I.C.S.: 333998

Pall Life Sciences Belgium BVBA (2)
Reugelstraat 2, 3320, Hoegaarden, Belgium
Tel.: (32) 16768070
Plastics Product Mfr
N.A.I.C.S.: 326199
Ingrid Leroy (VP-Bioprocess Dev)

Subsidiary (Domestic):

Pall Life Sciences Puerto Rico, LLC
Ochoa Bldg 500 Calle de la Tanca Ste 514, San Juan, PR 00901
Tel.: (787) 863-1124
Filtration, Separation & Purification Products Mfr & Distr
N.A.I.C.S.: 333998

Subsidiary (Non-US):

Pall Manufacturing UK Limited (2)
5 Harbourgate Business Park Southampton Road, Portsmouth, PO6 4BQ, Hampshire, United Kingdom
Tel.: (44) 2392338000
Filtration, Separation & Purification Product Mfr
N.A.I.C.S.: 333998

Pall Medistad BV (2)
Nijverheidsweg 1, 1671 GC, Medemblik, 1671, Netherlands
Tel.: (31) 227546600
Emp.: 22
Industrial Machinery Equipment Mfr
N.A.I.C.S.: 333248
Timo Kreike (Project Mgr-Sls-Inside)

Pall New Zealand Ltd. (2)
Warehouse - Unit 3/33 Spartan Rd, PO Box 10 492, Auckland, 2105, Takanini, New Zealand
Tel.: (64) 79593200
Web Site: http://www.medical.pall.com
Filtration, Separation & Purification Products Development, Mfr & Sales
N.A.I.C.S.: 333310

Pall Norden AB (2)
Aldermansgatan 10, Lund, Sweden
Tel.: (46) 46198400
Web Site: http://www.medical.pall.com
Industrial & Commercial Fan Mfr
N.A.I.C.S.: 333413

Pall Norge A/S (2)
Hvervenmovelen 45, 3511, Honefoss, Norway
Tel.: (47) 32181470
Web Site: http://www.pall.com
Filtration, Separation & Purification Products Development, Mfr & Sales
N.A.I.C.S.: 333310

Pall Poland Ltd. (2)
st Wenecka 12, 03-244, Warsaw, Poland
Tel.: (48) 225102100
Web Site: http://www.pall.com
Filtration, Separation & Purification Products Mfr, Development & Sales
N.A.I.C.S.: 333413

Pall Singapore Taiwan Branch Holding Company Pte Ltd. (2)
14F-5 No 207 Tun Hwa North Road, Taipei, 105, Taiwan
Tel.: (886) 225455991
Web Site: http://www.pall.com
Filtration, Separation & Purification Products Mfr & Sales
N.A.I.C.S.: 333310

Pall South Africa (Pty) Limited (2)
Birchwood Court 43 Montrose Road, Vorna Valley, Midrand, South Africa
Tel.: (27) 112662300
Web Site: http://www.pall.com
Aerospace Filtration, Separation & Purification Products Development & Mfr
N.A.I.C.S.: 333310

Pall Technologies SA (2)
Riobamba 1236 Piso 8 of C, Buenos Aires, Argentina
Tel.: (54) 1141295300
Web Site: http://www.pall.com
Filtration, Separation & Purification Products Development, Mfr & Sales
N.A.I.C.S.: 333310

Pall do Brasil Ltda. (2)
Av Luigi Papaiz 239 - 1 andar, Diadema, Sao Paulo, 09931-610, Brazil
Tel.: (55) 1140996100
Web Site: https://www.pall.com
Fluid Separation & Purification Product Mfr
N.A.I.C.S.: 334514

Pall SAS (1)
26-28 avenue de Winchester, 78100, Saint Germain-en-Laye, France
Tel.: (33) 130613900
Oil Extraction Services
N.A.I.C.S.: 213112

Pall Technology UK Limited (1)
Unit 5 Harbour Gate Business Park Southampton Road, Portsmouth, PO6 4BQ, United Kingdom
Tel.: (44) 2392338000
Radiometer Instrument Mfr
N.A.I.C.S.: 334513

PaloDEx Group Oy (1)
Nahkelantie 160, PO Box 54, 04300, Tuusula, 4300, Finland
Tel.: (358) 102702000
Web Site: http://www.palodexgroup.com
Sales Range: $100-124.9 Million
Emp.: 380
Dental Equipment & Supplie Mfr
N.A.I.C.S.: 339114

Subsidiary (US):

Instrumentarium Dental Inc. (2)
1245 W Canal St, Milwaukee, WI 53233
Tel.: (414) 747-1030
Web Site:
http://www.instrumentariumdental.com
Sales Range: $25-49.9 Million
Emp.: 75
Dental X-Ray Equipment Whslr
N.A.I.C.S.: 423450

Subsidiary (Non-US):

Instrumentarium Dental S.A.R.L. (2)
PA des Petits Carreaux 12 Avenue de Coquelicots, Bonneuil-sur-Marne, 94380, France
Tel.: (33) 141941610
Web Site: http://www.palodex.fi
Retailer of Dental Imaging Technology
N.A.I.C.S.: 551114

PaloDEx Holding OY (1)
Nahkelantie 160, 04301, Tuusula, Finland
Tel.: (358) 102702000
Web Site: http://www.palodex.com
Sales Range: $75-99.9 Million
Emp.: 350
Medicinal Product Mfr
N.A.I.C.S.: 339112

Phenomenex, Inc. (2)
411 Madrid Ave, Torrance, CA 90501-1430
Tel.: (310) 212-0555
Web Site: https://www.phenomenex.com
Industrial Measuring Instrument Mfr
N.A.I.C.S.: 334513

Precision Nanosystems ULC (1)

50 655 W Kent Ave N, Vancouver, V6P 6T7, BC, Canada
Web Site:
https://www.precisionnanosystems.com
Biotechnology Research Services
N.A.I.C.S.: 541714
James Taylor (Founder & Gen Mgr)

Prest, LLC (1)
11727 Fruehauf Dr, Charlotte, NC 28273
Tel.: (704) 588-2126
Web Site: http://www.marus.com
Emp.: 300
Dental Equipment Mfr
N.A.I.C.S.: 339114

Prozess und Maschinen Automation GmbH (1)
Miramstrasse 87, 34123, Kassel, Germany
Tel.: (49) 5615051307
Web Site: http://www.west-cs.de
Measuring Instruments Mfr
N.A.I.C.S.: 334515

Radiometer A/S (1)
Akandevej 21, 2700, Bronshoj, Denmark (100%)
Tel.: (45) 38273827
Web Site: http://www.radiometer.com
Sales Range: $550-599.9 Million
Emp.: 2,400
Blood Gas Analyzer Mfr
N.A.I.C.S.: 334516

Subsidiary (Non-US):

HemoCue AB (2)
Kuvettgatan 1, 262 71, Angelholm, Sweden
Tel.: (46) 77 570 0210
Web Site: https://www.hemocue.se
Sales Range: $75-99.9 Million
Emp.: 300
Point-Of-Care Blood Chemistry Test Systems Mfr
N.A.I.C.S.: 334510

Subsidiary (Non-US):

HemoCue Australia Pty. Ltd. (3)
35 Longview Close, Wamberal, 2260, NSW, Australia
Tel.: (61) 243846855
Web Site: https://www.cossetgroup.com
Sales Range: $10-24.9 Million
Emp.: 15
Medical Test Kit Mfr
N.A.I.C.S.: 334515
Steven Hensley (Mng Dir)

HemoCue GmbH (3)
Babenhauser Strasse 39A, Grossostheim, 63762, Germany
Tel.: (49) 602699890
Web Site: http://www.hemocue.com
Sales Range: $100-124.9 Million
Medical Test Kit Mfr
N.A.I.C.S.: 334515

HemoCue Oy (3)
Kivenlahdenkatu 1B, 02320, Espoo, Finland
Tel.: (358) 98190070
Web Site: http://www.hemocue.com
Sales Range: $10-24.9 Million
Emp.: 5
Medical Test Kit Mfr
N.A.I.C.S.: 334515

Subsidiary (US):

HemoCue, Inc. (3)
11331 Valley View St, Cypress, CA 90630-5366
Tel.: (949) 859-2630
Web Site: http://www.hemocue.com
Sales Range: $25-49.9 Million
Emp.: 50
Medical Test Kit Mfr
N.A.I.C.S.: 334515

Subsidiary (Non-US):

Radiometer (UK) Ltd. (2)
Manor Court Manor Royal, Crawley, RH10 9FY, West Sussex, United Kingdom (100%)
Tel.: (44) 1293517599
Web Site: https://www.radiometer.co.uk
Sales Range: $25-49.9 Million
Emp.: 40
Holding Company
N.A.I.C.S.: 551112

Subsidiary (US):

Radiometer America Inc. (2)
250 S Kraemer Blvd, Brea, CA 92821
Web Site:
https://www.radiometeramerica.com
Sales Range: $75-99.9 Million
Emp.: 200
Blood Gas Analyzer Mfr
N.A.I.C.S.: 334516

Subsidiary (Non-US):

Radiometer Basel AG (2)
Austrasse 25, 4051, Basel, 4051, Switzerland (100%)
Tel.: (41) 612788111
Web Site: http://www.radiometer.ch
Sales Range: $25-49.9 Million
Emp.: 34
Industrial Gas Mfr
N.A.I.C.S.: 325120

Subsidiary (Domestic):

Radiometer Danmark A/S (2)
Akandevej 21, Bronshoj, 2700, Denmark (100%)
Tel.: (45) 38273827
Web Site: https://www.radiometer.dk
Sales Range: $200-249.9 Million
Emp.: 2,000
Mfr of Surgical & Medical Instruments & Apparatus
N.A.I.C.S.: 339112

Subsidiary (Non-US):

Radiometer GmbH (2)
Europark Fichtenhain A 4, 47807, Krefeld, Germany (100%)
Tel.: (49) 21518933100
Web Site: http://www.radiometer.de
Sales Range: $25-49.9 Million
Emp.: 50
Provider of Holding Company Services
N.A.I.C.S.: 551112

Radiometer Iberica S.L. (2)
Avda de Valgrande 8 - Planta 2a, 28108, Madrid, Alcobendas, Spain
Tel.: (34) 916559950
Web Site: https://www.radiometer.es
Surgical & Medical Equipment Retailer
N.A.I.C.S.: 423450

Radiometer K.K. (2)
Gotenyama Trust Tower 15F 4-7-35 Kita-shinagawa, Shinagawa-ku, Tokyo, 140-0001, Japan
Tel.: (81) 343313500
Web Site: https://www.radiometer.co.jp
Medical Equipment Distr
N.A.I.C.S.: 423450

Radiometer Limited (2)
Manor Court Manor Royal, Crawley, RH10 9FY, West Sussex, United Kingdom
Tel.: (44) 1293517599
Web Site: http://www.radiometer.co.uk
Emp.: 40
Testing Equipment Mfr
N.A.I.C.S.: 334516
Anders Wallseth (Mng Dir)

Subsidiary (Domestic):

Radiometer Medical A/S (2)
Akandevej 21, PO Box 2700, 2700, Bronshoj, Denmark (100%)
Tel.: (45) 38273827
Web Site: https://www.radiometer.com
Sales Range: $400-449.9 Million
Emp.: 3,400
Provider of Research, Development, Production & Export of Medical Instruments & Accessories
N.A.I.C.S.: 339112
Henrik Schimmell (Pres)
Rikke Tengberg (VP-Human Resources-Communications)
Lena Munk Sorensen (VP-Regulatory Affairs & Quality Assurance)
Henrik Brandborg (VP-Sales)
Rikke Birkelund Christiansen (VP-Marketing-Global)
Marianne Helstrup (Gen Counsel & VP)
Sannna Wallenborg (VP & Gen Mgr)
Jesper Kjae Hansen (CIO & VP)
Michael Reinholt Andersen (VP-)
Jose Antunes (VP)
Gitte Hesselholt (VP)

Subsidiary (Non-US):

Radiometer Medical Equipment (Shanghai) Co. Ltd. (2)
3rd Floor Building 1 No 518 Fuquan North Road, Changning District, Shanghai, 200335, China
Tel.: (86) 2160158498
Web Site: https://www.radiometer.cn
Emp.: 40
Medical Equipment Distr
N.A.I.C.S.: 423450

Radiometer Nederland B.V. (2)
Chroomstraat 8, PO Box 233, 2718 RR, Zoetermeer, Netherlands
Tel.: (31) 793614593
Web Site: https://www.radiometer.nl
Sales Range: $25-49.9 Million
Emp.: 22
Sales of Laboratory & Medical Analysis Equipment
N.A.I.C.S.: 456199

Radiometer Pacific Ltd. (2)
Unit 2 1 Site 3 30 Saint Benedicts Street Eden Terrace, PO Box 331211, Auckland, 2110, New Zealand
Tel.: (64) 800723722
Web Site: https://www.radiometer.co.nz
Sales Range: $50-74.9 Million
Emp.: 30
Sales of Laboratory & Medical Analytical Equipment
N.A.I.C.S.: 456199
Rose-Marie Daniel (Mng Dir)

Radiometer Pacific Pty. Ltd. (2)
1st Floor 96 Ricketts Road, PO Box 5134, Mount Waverley, 3149, VIC, Australia (100%)
Tel.: (61) 392117333
Web Site: https://www.radiometer.com.au
Sales Range: $10-24.9 Million
Emp.: 55
Surgical & Medical Equipment
N.A.I.C.S.: 339112
Simon Eldred (Product Mgr)

Radiometer RSCH GmbH (2)
Zurcherstrasse 66, PO Box 124, 8800, Thalwil, Switzerland (100%)
Tel.: (41) 447231160
Web Site: https://www.radiometer.ch
Sales Range: $10-24.9 Million
Emp.: 10
Sales of Medical Equipment
N.A.I.C.S.: 423450

Radiometer S.A. (2)
8 rue Edmond Michelet, 93360, Neuilly-Plaisance, France (100%)
Tel.: (33) 149443550
Web Site: https://www.radiometer.fr
Sales Range: $50-74.9 Million
Emp.: 35
Sales of Scientific & Electromedical Analysis Equipment
N.A.I.C.S.: 456199

Radiometer South Africa (2)
19 Lanner Falcon Road, PO Box 4019, Samrand, Centurion, 0157, Gauteng, South Africa (100%)
Tel.: (27) 760920994
Web Site: https://www.radiometer.co.za
Sales Range: $10-24.9 Million
Emp.: 12
Surgical & Medical Equipment
N.A.I.C.S.: 339112

Subsidiary (US):

SenDx Medical, Inc. (2)
1945 Palomar Oaks Way, Carlsbad, CA 92009-1307
Tel.: (760) 930-6300
Web Site: http://www.radiometer.com
Sales Range: $25-49.9 Million
Emp.: 100
Provider of Research, Development, Production & Export of Medical Instruments & Accessories
N.A.I.C.S.: 334516

Radiometer K.K. (1)
Gotenyama Trust Tower 15F 4-7-35 Kitashinagawa, Shinagawa-ku, Tokyo, 140-0001, Japan
Tel.: (81) 343313500

Health Care Srvices
N.A.I.C.S.: 621610

Radiometer Medical ApS (1)
Akandevej 21, 2700, Bronshoj, Denmark
Tel.: (45) 38273827
Web Site: https://www.radiometer.com
Emp.: 3,200
Radiometer Instrument Mfr
N.A.I.C.S.: 334513
Henrik Schimmell (Pres)
Anders Myhre (VP-Marketing)
Claus Lonborg (VP-Finance-Information Technology)
Henrik Brandborg (VP-Sales)
Rikke Tengberg (VP-Human Resources-Communications)
Niels Fogelstrom (VP-Global)
Lena Munk Sorensen (VP-RA-QA)
Rikke Birkelund Christiansen (VP-Marketing-Global)
Kasper Oktavio Schweitz (VP-Global & Gen Mgr-Global)
Marianne Helstrup (VP & Gen Counsel)
Sanna Wallenberg (VP)
Rikke Bergstedt (VP-Human Resources-Communications)
Soumitra Dev Burman (VP-Sales)
Jesper Kjaer Hansen (CIO & VP)
Michael Reinholt Andersen (VP)
Rikke Bergstedt (VP-Human Resources-Communications)
Soumitra Dev Burman (VP-Sales)
Jesper Kjaer Hansen (CIO & VP)
Michael Reinholt Andersen (VP)

Radiometer Turku Oy (1)
Biolinja 12, 20750, Turku, Finland
Tel.: (358) 22784000
Radiometer Instrument Mfr
N.A.I.C.S.: 334513

Sedaru, Inc. (1)
168 E Arrow Hwy 101, San Dimas, CA 91773
Web Site: https://sedaru.com
Software Development Services
N.A.I.C.S.: 541511
Sree Sreedhar (CTO)
Kevin Koshko (Chief Product Officer)
Paul Hauffen (Pres & CEO)
Jennifer Wood (Dir)
Dave Harrington (Dir)

Shanghai Shilu Instrument Co. Ltd. (1)
139 Lane 2638 Hongmei South Rd Minhang District, Shanghai, 200241, China
Tel.: (86) 2154401908
Electric Equipment Mfr
N.A.I.C.S.: 335999

Skyland Analytics Inc. (1)
7916 Niwot Rd Ste 200, Niwot, CO 80503
Tel.: (720) 773-8800
Web Site: https://skylandanalytics.net
Software Development Services
N.A.I.C.S.: 541511
Dave Withers (CEO & Co-Founder)
Dan Mitchell (Mng Dir)
Robert Di Scipio (CEO)

Sonix, Inc. (1)
8700 Morrissette Dr, Springfield, VA 22152
Tel.: (703) 440-0222
Web Site: https://www.sonix.com
Electric Equipment Mfr
N.A.I.C.S.: 335999

Spline Gauges Ltd. (1)
Spline Gauges Piccadilly, Tamworth, B78 2ER, Staffordshire, United Kingdom (100%)
Tel.: (44) 1827872771
Web Site: https://splinegauges.com
Sales Range: $50-74.9 Million
Emp.: 70
Gauges & Gear Machines
N.A.I.C.S.: 332216
Ian Garrett (Mng Dir)
Jeremy Green (Mgr-Design)
Joanne Johnson (Mgr-Fin)
Darren Massey (Mgr-Sls Admin)
Gareth Jones (Mgr-Inspection)
Steve Dick (Sr Mgr-Comml)
Dean Grice (Production Mgr)

SpofaDental a.s. (1)
Markova 238, 506 46, Jicin, 506 46, Hradec Kralove, Czech Republic

Tel.: (420) 493583251
Dental Equipment Mfr
N.A.I.C.S.: 339114

Sybron Canada LP (1)
55 Laurier Dr, Morrisburg, K0C 1X0, ON, Canada
Tel.: (613) 543-3791
Dental Equipment Mfr
N.A.I.C.S.: 339114

Sybron Dental Specialties, Inc. (1)
1717 W Collims Ave, Orange, CA 92687 (94%)
Tel.: (714) 516-7400
Web Site: http://www.sybrondental.com
Sales Range: $600-649.9 Million
Emp.: 4,117
Orthodontic Supply & Dental Product Mfr
N.A.I.C.S.: 339114

Subsidiary (Domestic):

Ormco Corporation (2)
200 S Kraemer Blvd, Brea, CA 92821
Tel.: (714) 516-7400
Web Site: https://ormco.com
Sales Range: $10-24.9 Million
Emp.: 50
Orthodontic Products
N.A.I.C.S.: 339114

TGA Industries Limited (1)
The Hyde Business Park, Brighton, BN2 4JU, E Sussex, United Kingdom
Tel.: (44) 1273606271
Web Site: https://www.west-cs.com
Specialized Temperature Control Equipment Mfr
N.A.I.C.S.: 334512

Trojan Technologies Group ULC (1)
3020 Gore Road, London, N5V 4T7, ON, Canada
Tel.: (519) 457-3400
Web Site: http://www.trojantechnologies.com
Waste Treatment Services
N.A.I.C.S.: 221320
Stephen Bell (Pres)
Christian Williamson (VP-Marketing)
Kathy Davis (VP)
Daniel Benitez (Gen Mgr-Pall Water)
Wesley D. From (VP-Research & Development)
Dan Rinehart (VP-Marketing-Global)
Kevin Spehr (VP)
Jo Anne Van Hooydonk (Interim Pres, Interim CFO & Interim VP-Finance-Information Technology)
Natalia Yurkevich (VP-Human Resources)

Trojan Technologies, Inc. (1)
3020 Gore Rd, London, N5V 4T7, ON, Canada
Tel.: (519) 457-3400
Web Site: http://www.trojanuv.com
Sales Range: $75-99.9 Million
Emp.: 300
Ultraviolet Disinfection Systems Mfr
N.A.I.C.S.: 335139
Kathy Davis (VP)
Wesley D. From (VP-R&D)
Daniel Benitez (Gen Mgr-Pall Water)
Natalia Yurkevich (VP-HR)
Sikander Gill (VP)
Tom Siller (Pres)

Subsidiary (Non-US):

Salsnes Filter AS (2)
Havnegata 12, 7800, Namsos, Norway
Tel.: (47) 74274860
Web Site: https://www.salsnes-filter.no
Filtration System Mfr
N.A.I.C.S.: 237110
Tor Olav Lyng (Dir-)
Hans Jorgen Sandnes (Gen Mgr)
Stefano Salvatore (Dir-Business Development-Sales-Global)

TrojanUV Technolgies Limited (2)
Unit 5 De Salis Court Hampton Lovett, Droitwich, WR9 0QE, United Kingdom (100%)
Tel.: (44) 01905771117
Web Site: http://www.trojanuv.com
Sales Range: $1-9.9 Million
Emp.: 6
Provider of Lighting Equipment

N.A.I.C.S.: 335139

U.S. Peroxide, LLC (1)
1375 Peachtree St NE Ste 300 N, Atlanta, GA 30309
Tel.: (404) 352-6070
Web Site: http://www.h2o2.com
Waste Water Treatment Services
N.A.I.C.S.: 562211

Universal Technic SAS (1)
1 Rue Robert Et Sonia Delaunay, 75011, Paris, France
Tel.: (33) 143700800
Electronic Components Mfr
N.A.I.C.S.: 334413

VSS Monitoring, Inc. (1)
1850 Gateway Dr Ste 500, San Mateo, CA 94404
Tel.: (650) 697-8770
Web Site: https://www.vssmonitoring.com
Software Development Services
N.A.I.C.S.: 541511

Vanrx Pharmasystems Inc. (1)
200 - 3811 North Fraser Way, Burnaby, V5J 5J2, BC, Canada
Tel.: (604) 453-8660
Web Site: https://www.vanrx.com
Pharmaceuticals Mfr
N.A.I.C.S.: 325412
Ross Gold (Dir & Gen Dir)
Steve Pratt (Head-Engineering)
John Harmer (Head-Sales-Marketing)
Myles Degenstein (Head-Finance)
Neil Fulgueras (Head-Operations)

Veeder-Root Finance Company (1)
19 Jessops Riverside 800 Brightside Lane, Sheffield, S9 2RX, South Yorkshire, United Kingdom
Tel.: (44) 12715651062
Financial Investment Services
N.A.I.C.S.: 523999

Videojet Argentina S.R.L. (1)
Calle 122 Villa Ballester, 4785, Buenos Aires, 4785, Argentina
Tel.: (54) 1147686638
Emp.: 47
Commercial & Industrial Machinery Mfr
N.A.I.C.S.: 333415

Videojet Technologies (I) Pvt. Ltd (1)
101/102 Rupa Solitaire Sector 1, Millennium Business Park Mahape, Navi Mumbai, 400710, Maharashtra, India
Tel.: (91) 7506345599
Web Site: https://www.videojet.in
Bar Code Printing Services
N.A.I.C.S.: 561499

Videojet Technologies (S) Pte. Ltd. (1)
1 Kaki Bukit View 04-15/17 Techview, Singapore, 415941, Singapore
Tel.: (65) 31382040
Web Site: https://www.videojet.sg
Emp.: 3,000
Health Care Srvices
N.A.I.C.S.: 621610

Videojet Technologies Inc. (1)
1500 N Mittel Blvd, Wood Dale, IL 60191-1073
Tel.: (630) 860-7300
Web Site: http://www.videojet.com
Sales Range: $400-449.9 Million
Emp.: 4,000
Commercial & Service Industry Machinery Mfr
N.A.I.C.S.: 333310

Subsidiary (Non-US):

Videojet Chile Codificadora Limited (2)
Exequiel Fernandez 2831, Macul, Chile
Tel.: (56) 224762890
Web Site: http://www.videojet.com
Emp.: 35
Printing Equipment Mfr
N.A.I.C.S.: 333248

Videojet Italia Srl (2)
Via XXV Aprile 66/C, 20068, Peschiera Borromeo, Italy
Tel.: (39) 0255376811
Web Site: https://www.videojet.it
Emp.: 3,000

Danaher Corporation—(Continued)

Health Care Services
N.A.I.C.S.: 621610

**Videojet Technologies (Shanghai)
Co., Ltd.** (2)
6F Building 2 518 North Fuquan Road,
Changning District, Shanghai, 200335,
China
Tel.: (86) 2164959222
Health Care Srvices
N.A.I.C.S.: 621610

Videojet Technologies B.V. (2)
Gildenstraat 33, 4143 HS, Leerdam, Neth-
erlands
Tel.: (31) 345636500
Web Site: https://www.videojet.nl
Emp.: 40
Laser Marking Equipment Mfr
N.A.I.C.S.: 334510

**Videojet Technologies Canada
L.P.** (2)
7075 Financial Dr, Toronto, L5N 6V8, ON,
Canada
Tel.: (905) 673-1212
Laser Marking Equipment Mfr
N.A.I.C.S.: 334510

**Videojet Technologies Europe
B.V.** (2)
Strijkviertel 39, 3454 PJ, De Meern, Nether-
lands
Tel.: (31) 306693000
Web Site: http://www.videojet.com
Laser Marking Equipment Mfr
N.A.I.C.S.: 334510

**Videojet Technologies Europe
B.V.** (2)
EMEA Strijkviertel 39, 3454 PJ, De Meern,
Netherlands
Tel.: (31) 306693000
Health Care Srvices
N.A.I.C.S.: 621610

Videojet Technologies GmbH (2)
An Der Meil 2, 65555, Limburg, Germany
Tel.: (49) 6 431 9940
Web Site: https://www.videojet.de
Sales Range: $50-74.9 Million
Emp.: 150
Medicinal Product Mfr
N.A.I.C.S.: 311999

Subsidiary (Domestic):

ALLTEC GmbH (3)
An der Trave 27-31, 23923, Selmsdorf,
Germany
Tel.: (49) 38823550
Web Site: http://www.alltec-laser.com
Sales Range: $25-49.9 Million
Emp.: 160
Laser Marking Systems Mfr
N.A.I.C.S.: 339940
Stefan Heczko (Pres)
Sebastian Bloesch (CEO)
Peter Fuchs (CFO)

Subsidiary (Non-US):

Videojet Technologies Inc. (2)
4&5 Ermine Centre Lancaster Way,
Huntington, PE29 6XX, Cambridgeshire,
United Kingdom **(100%)**
Tel.: (44) 3301235007
Web Site: http://www.videojet.in
Sales Range: $10-24.9 Million
Emp.: 3,000
Ink Jet Printing & Coding; Industrial &
Graphics Design Printing Machines
N.A.I.C.S.: 323111

Videojet Technologies JSC (2)
BC Rumyantcevo CLD 4 block E EN22
FL7, Rumyantcevo, Moscow, 142784, Rus-
sia
Tel.: (7) 4952317090
Web Site: http://www.videojet.ru
Laser Marking Equipment Mfr
N.A.I.C.S.: 334510

Videojet Technologies LTD (2)
4&5 Ermine Centre Lancaster Way,
Huntington, PE29 6XX, Cambridgeshire,
United Kingdom
Tel.: (44) 3301235007
Web Site: http://www.videojet.com

Emp.: 100
Electronic Products Mfr
N.A.I.C.S.: 334417

**Videojet Technologies Mexico S. de
R.L. de C.V.** (2)
Av Revolucion 1267 Los Alpes 18th floor,
01040, Mexico, Mexico
Tel.: (52) 53517450
Laser Marking Equipment Mfr
N.A.I.C.S.: 334510

Videojet Technologies S.A.S. (2)
Silic 703-16 avenue du Quebec ZA Courta-
boeuf Bat Lys 1 2, 91140, Villebon-sur-
Yvette, France
Tel.: (33) 169197000
Web Site: https://www.videojet.fr
Medical Instrument Mfr
N.A.I.C.S.: 339112

Videojet X-Rite K.K. (2)
Telecom Center Building West Wing 6F
2-5-10 Aomi, Koto-ku, Tokyo, 135-0064,
Japan
Tel.: (81) 120487036
Web Site: https://www.videojet.co.jp
Laser Marking Equipment Mfr
N.A.I.C.S.: 334510

Viqua (1)
425 Clair Rd W, Guelph, N1L 1R1, ON,
Canada
Tel.: (519) 763-1032
Web Site: http://www.viqua.com
Sales Range: $25-49.9 Million
Emp.: 105
Waste Treatment Services
N.A.I.C.S.: 221310

Water Quality GmbH (1)
Konigsweg 10, Zehlendorf, 14163, Berlin,
Germany
Tel.: (49) 74241400
Analytical Instrument Mfr & Distr
N.A.I.C.S.: 334516

Wolke Inks & Printers GmbH (1)
Ostbahnstrasse 116, Hersbruck, 91217,
Germany
Tel.: (49) 915181610
Web Site: http://www.wolke.com
Sales Range: $25-49.9 Million
Emp.: 40
Inks & Printers Mfr
N.A.I.C.S.: 325910

X-Ray Optical Systems, Inc. (1)
15 Tech Valley Dr, East Greenbush, NY
12061
Tel.: (518) 880-1500
Web Site: https://www.xos.com
Medical Equipment Distr
N.A.I.C.S.: 423450

X-Rite Europe GmbH (1)
Althardstrasse 70, 8105, Regensdorf, Swit-
zerland
Tel.: (41) 8007 003 0001
Web Site: https://www.xrite.com
Paint Product Mfr
N.A.I.C.S.: 325510

X-Rite, Incorporated (1)
4300 44th St SE, Grand Rapids, MI 49512
Tel.: (616) 803-2100
Web Site: http://www.xrite.com
Sales Range: $150-199.9 Million
Emp.: 747
Quality Control Instruments & Software De-
signer, Mfr & Marketer for Companies in the
Paint, Plastic, Textile, Photographic,
Graphic Arts & Medical Industries
N.A.I.C.S.: 333310
Ondrej Kruk (Pres)
Dustin Bowersox (Mgr-Bus Dev-Textile &
Apparel)
Mike Soriano (Dir-Consumer Products &
Matls Bus)

Subsidiary (Domestic):

Pantone, Inc. (2)
590 Commerce Blvd, Carlstadt, NJ 07072-
3098
Tel.: (201) 935-5500
Web Site: https://www.pantone.com
Sales Range: $25-49.9 Million
Emp.: 140
Color Products, Services & Technology
N.A.I.C.S.: 541490

Subsidiary (Non-US):

X-Rite Asia Pacific Limited (2)
Suite 2801 28th Floor AXA Tower Landmark
East 100 How Ming Street, Kwun Tong,
Kowloon, China (Hong Kong)
Tel.: (852) 25686283
Health Care Srvices
N.A.I.C.S.: 621610

X-Rite Europe AG (2)
Althardstrasse 70, 8105, Regensdorf, Swit-
zerland
Tel.: (41) 80070030001
Web Site: http://www.xrite.com
Sales Range: $25-49.9 Million
Emp.: 150
Color Systems & Software Developer
N.A.I.C.S.: 334610

Subsidiary (Non-US):

X-Rite GmbH (3)
Siemensstrasse 12 B, 63263, Neu-
Isenburg, Germany
Tel.: (49) 6102795710
Web Site: http://www.xrite.com
Sales Range: $10-24.9 Million
Emp.: 15
Color Technology Products Mfr
N.A.I.C.S.: 334610

Subsidiary (Non-US):

X-Rite Limited (2)
Suite 14F MiOC Styal Road, Poynton, Man-
chester, M22 5WB, Cheshire, United King-
dom
Tel.: (44) 1625871100
Web Site: http://www.xrite.com
Emp.: 16
Photometer Equipment Mfr
N.A.I.C.S.: 423490

**Young's L&S Dental Supplies
Ltd.** (1)
Rm 1010 10/f Hung Hom Coml Ctr Twr A,
39 Ma Tau Wai Rd, Hung Hom, China
(Hong Kong)
Tel.: (852) 27661332
Dental Equipment Mfr
N.A.I.C.S.: 339114

**Zhuhai S.E.Z. Videojet Electronics
Ltd.** (1)
8 Xinghan Road Sanzao Science and Tech-
nology Park, Zhuhai, 519040, Guangdong,
China
Tel.: (86) 7567512800
Medical Instrument Mfr
N.A.I.C.S.: 339112

DANIELS CORPORATE ADVI-
SORY COMPANY, INC.
Parker Towers 104-60, Forest Hills,
NY 11375
Tel.: (347) 242-3148   NV
Web Site:
http://www.danielscorporateadvi
soryco.com
Year Founded: 2002
DCAC—(OTCIQ)
Rev.: $4,384,842
Assets: $1,250,363
Liabilities: $4,473,803
Net Worth: ($3,223,440)
Earnings: ($250,007)
Fiscal Year-end: 11/30/21
Corporate Advisory Services
N.A.I.C.S.: 561400
Arthur D. Viola (Chm, Pres & Co-
CEO)
Nicholas D. Viola (Co-CEO)
Keith L. Voigts (CFO)

DANIMER SCIENTIFIC, INC.
140 Industrial Blvd, Bainbridge, GA
39817
Tel.: (229) 243-7075   DE
Web Site:
https://www.danimerscientific.com
Year Founded: 2019
DNMR—(NYSE)
Rev.: $53,218,000
Assets: $712,270,000

Liabilities: $334,658,000
Net Worth: $377,612,000
Earnings: ($179,758,000)
Emp.: 271
Fiscal Year-end: 12/31/22
Investment Services
N.A.I.C.S.: 523999
Michael A. Hajost (CFO)
Richard J. Hendrix (Interim Exec
Chm)
Stephen E. Croskrey (CEO)
Michael Smith (COO)
Phillip Van Trump (Chief Science &
Tech Officer)
Scott C. Tuten (Chief Mktg & Sustain-
ability Officer)
John Moore (Sr VP-Bus Dev)
Jeff Uhrig (Pres-Scientific Catalytic
Process & Gen Mgr)
John A. Dowdy III (Sr VP-Fin Plng &
Analysis)
Richard J. Hendrix (Interim Exec
Chm)

Subsidiaries:

Meredian Holdings Group Inc. (1)
140 Industrial Blvd, Bainbridge, GA 39817
Tel.: (229) 243-7075
Web Site: http://www.danimerscientific.com
Synthetic Rubber Mfr
N.A.I.C.S.: 325212
Stephen E. Croskrey (CEO)

Novomer, Inc. (1)
Reservoir Pl 1601 Trapelo Rd Ste 152,
Waltham, MA 02451
Tel.: (781) 672-2525
Web Site: http://www.novomer.com
Chemicals Mfr
N.A.I.C.S.: 325998

DARDEN RESTAURANTS, INC.
1000 Darden Center Dr, Orlando, FL
32837
Tel.: (407) 245-4000   FL
Web Site: https://www.darden.com
Year Founded: 1968
DRI—(NYSE)
Rev.: $11,390,000,000
Assets: $11,323,000,000
Liabilities: $9,080,500,000
Net Worth: $2,242,500,000
Earnings: $1,027,600,000
Emp.: 191,105
Fiscal Year-end: 05/26/24
Restaurant Owner & Operator
N.A.I.C.S.: 722511
Matthew R. Broad (Chief Legal Offi-
cer, Chief Compliance Officer, Sec &
Gen Counsel)
Todd A. Burrowes (Pres-Bus Dev)
John W. Madonna (Sr VP & Control-
ler)
Chris Chang (CIO & Sr VP)
Susan M. Connelly (Chief Comm &
Pub Affairs Officer & Sr VP)
Sarah H. King (Chief People & Diver-
sity Officer & Sr VP)
Douglas J. Milanes (Chief Supply
Chain Officer & Sr VP)
Richard L. Renninger (Chief Dev Offi-
cer & Sr VP)
Ricardo Cardenas (Pres & CEO)
Daniel J. Kiernan (Pres-Olive Gar-
den)
Ali Charri (Sr VP-Strategy & Insights)
Rajesh Vennam (CFO & Sr VP)
John Martin (Pres-Specialty Restau-
rant Grp)
Lindsay L. Koren (Gen Counsel-Div &
Sr VP)

Subsidiaries:

Bahama Breeze (1)
1000 Darden Ctr Dr, Orlando, FL
32837   **(100%)**
Tel.: (407) 245-4000

Web Site: https://www.bahamabreeze.com
Sales Range: $50-74.9 Million
Restaurant Operators
N.A.I.C.S.: 722511
Eugene I. Lee Jr. *(Executives)*
Gene Lee *(CEO)*

Cheddar's Scratch Kitchen **(1)**
1000 Darden Ctr Dr, Orlando, FL 32837
Tel.: (407) 245-4000
Web Site: https://www.cheddars.com
Restaurant Owner, Operator & Franchiser
N.A.I.C.S.: 722511
Eugene I. Lee Jr. *(Executives)*

Chuy's Holdings, Inc. **(1)**
1623 Toomey Rd, Austin, TX 78704
Tel.: (512) 473-2783
Web Site: https://www.chuys.com
Rev.: $461,310,000
Assets: $476,634,000
Liabilities: $226,787,000
Net Worth: $249,847,000
Earnings: $31,510,000
Emp.: 7,400
Fiscal Year-end: 12/31/2023
Holding Company; Mexican & Tex-Mex Restaurants
N.A.I.C.S.: 551112
Jon W. Howie *(CFO & VP)*
Steven J. Hislop *(Chm, Pres & CEO)*
John Mountford *(COO)*

Olive Garden Italian Restaurant **(1)**
1000 Darden Ctr Dr, Orlando, FL 32837   **(100%)**
Tel.: (407) 245-4000
Web Site: https://www.olivegarden.com
Sales Range: $50-74.9 Million
Italian Food Restaurants Operator
N.A.I.C.S.: 722511
David George *(Pres)*

Ruth's Hospitality Group, Inc. **(1)**
1030 W Canton Ave Ste 100, Winter Park, FL 32789
Tel.: (407) 333-7440
Web Site: http://www.rhgi.com
Rev.: $505,858,000
Assets: $521,806,000
Liabilities: $389,475,000
Net Worth: $132,331,000
Earnings: $38,621,000
Emp.: 430
Fiscal Year-end: 12/25/2022
Holding Company; Full-Service Restaurants Owner, Operator & Franchisor
N.A.I.C.S.: 551112
Marcy Norwood Lynch *(Gen Counsel)*
David Hyatt *(Chief People Officer)*

Division (Domestic):

RCSH Operations, LLC **(2)**
1030 W Canton Ave Ste 100, Winter Park, FL 32789
Tel.: (407) 333-7440
Web Site: http://www.ruthschris.com
Sales Range: $50-74.9 Million
Emp.: 12
Steak House Restaurant Operator
N.A.I.C.S.: 722511
Michael P. O'Donnell *(Chm & CEO)*

Subsidiary (Domestic):

Ruth's Chris Steak House Franchise, LLC **(3)**
1030 W Canton Ave Ste 100, Winter Park, FL 32789
Tel.: (407) 333-7440
Web Site: http://www.ruthschris.com
Restaurant Franchise
N.A.I.C.S.: 533110

Yard House USA, Inc. **(1)**
620 Spectrum Ctr Dr, Irvine, CA 92618   **(70%)**
Tel.: (949) 753-9373
Web Site: http://www.yardhouse.com
Sales Range: $150-199.9 Million
Holding Company; Branded Restaurants Owner & Operator
N.A.I.C.S.: 551112

Subsidiary (Domestic):

Yard House Restaurants, LLC **(2)**
620 Spectrum Ctr Dr, Irvine, CA 92618
Tel.: (949) 753-9373
Web Site: http://www.yardhouse.com

Restaurants Operator & Administrative Support Services
N.A.I.C.S.: 561110

Subsidiary (Domestic):

The Yard House, L.P. **(3)**
401 Shoreline Vlg Dr, Long Beach, CA 90802
Tel.: (562) 628-0455
Web Site: http://www.yardhouse.com
Sales Range: $1-9.9 Million
Full-Service Restaurant & Bar
N.A.I.C.S.: 722511
Steele Platt *(Founder & Chm)*

Yard House Irvine Spectrum, LLC **(3)**
620 Spectrum Ctr Dr, Irvine, CA 92618
Tel.: (949) 753-9373
Web Site: http://www.yardhouse.com
Sales Range: $1-9.9 Million
Full-Service Restaurant & Bar
N.A.I.C.S.: 722511

Yard House Rancho Mirage, LLC **(3)**
71800 Hwy 111 Spc B-101, Rancho Mirage, CA 92270
Tel.: (760) 779-1415
Sales Range: $1-9.9 Million
Full-Service Restaurant & Bar
N.A.I.C.S.: 722511

Yard House San Diego, LLC **(3)**
1023 4th Ave, San Diego, CA 92101
Tel.: (619) 233-9273
Web Site: http://www.yardhouse.com
Sales Range: $1-9.9 Million
Full-Service Restaurant & Bar
N.A.I.C.S.: 722511

Yard House Triangle Square, LLC **(3)**
1875 Newport Blvd Ste A219, Costa Mesa, CA 92627
Tel.: (949) 642-0090
Web Site: https://www.yardhouse.com
Sales Range: $1-9.9 Million
Full-Service Restaurant & Bar
N.A.I.C.S.: 722511

DARE BIOSCIENCE, INC.
3655 Nobel Dr Ste 260, San Diego, CA 92122
Tel.: (858) 926-7655   DE
Web Site:
    https://www.darebioscience.com
Year Founded: 2005
DARE—(NASDAQ)
Rev.: $10,000,000
Assets: $43,826,383
Liabilities: $32,714,273
Net Worth: $11,112,110
Earnings: ($30,947,738)
Emp.: 25
Fiscal Year-end: 12/31/22
Pharmaceuticals Mfr
N.A.I.C.S.: 325412
Sabrina Martucci Johnson *(Co-Founder, Pres, CEO & Principal Fin Officer)*
Sabrina Martucci Johnson *(Co-Founder, Pres, CEO & Co-Sec)*
David Friend *(Chief Scientific Officer)*
Mark Walters *(Co-Founder & VP-Ops)*
MarDee Haring-Layton *(Chief Acctg Officer)*
Lisa Walters-Hoffert *(Co-Founder)*
Christine Mauck *(Dir-Medical)*
Nadene Zack *(VP-Clinical Ops)*

DARIEN ROWAYTON BANK
1001 Post Rd, Darien, CT 06820 CT
Web Site: http://www.drbank.com
Year Founded: 2006
DRWB—(OTCIQ)
Commercial Banking Services
N.A.I.C.S.: 522110
Robert Kettenmann *(Pres)*
Syd Ally *(COO)*
Robert Herrmann *(Chief Credit Officer & Exec VP)*

John Barbalaco *(Chief Banking Officer & Exec VP)*
Lindsey Kopp *(CFO)*

DARIOHEALTH CORP.
322 W 57th St Ste 33B, New York, NY 10019
Tel.: (646) 665-4667   DE
Web Site: https://www.mydario.com
Year Founded: 2011
DRIO—(NASDAQ)
Rev.: $20,352,000
Assets: $96,389,000
Liabilities: $38,245,000
Net Worth: $58,144,000
Earnings: ($59,427,000)
Emp.: 276
Fiscal Year-end: 12/31/23
Medical Device Mfr
N.A.I.C.S.: 339112
Erez Raphael *(CEO)*
Yoav Shaked *(Chm)*
Omar Manejwala *(Chief Medical Officer)*
Josh Fischer *(Sr VP-Ops & Compliance)*
Limor Drezner *(VP-HR)*
Eitan Shay *(Chief Product Officer)*
Matt Alberico *(Sr VP)*
Galya Gorodinksy *(Sr VP)*
Brian Harrigan *(Sr VP)*
Michal Hershkovitz *(VP)*
Dave Auslander *(VP)*
Ariel Rubashkin *(VP)*
Katy Guilfoile *(VP)*
Mary Mooney *(VP)*
Steven Nelson *(Chief Comml Officer)*
Zvi Ben David *(CFO, Treas & Sec)*

Subsidiaries:

Labstyle Innovation Ltd. **(1)**
Rehov Menachem Begin 7, 52681, Ramat Gan, Israel
Tel.: (972) 36222929
Software Development Services
N.A.I.C.S.: 541511
Erez Raphael *(CEO)*

DARKPULSE, INC.
815 Walker St Ste 1155, Houston, TX 77002   DE
Web Site: https://www.darkpulse.com
Year Founded: 1989
DPLS—(OTCIQ)
Rev.: $2,020,971
Assets: $4,112,352
Liabilities: $20,787,671
Net Worth: ($16,675,319)
Earnings: ($21,723,043)
Emp.: 3
Fiscal Year-end: 12/31/23
Digital Media Products Developer
N.A.I.C.S.: 513210
Dennis M. O'Leary *(Founder, Chm, Pres, CEO, CFO, Chief Acctg Officer, Treas & Sec)*
Anthony Brown *(Chief Science Officer)*
Joseph Catalino *(Chief Strategy Officer-Govt Rels Liaison)*
Kenneth B. Davidson *(COO & Dir-Ops-Oil & Gas-Renewable Energies-US)*
Rick Gibson *(Dir-Strategic Initiatives)*

Subsidiaries:

TJM Electronics West, Inc. **(1)**
2640 W Medtronic Way, Tempe, AZ 85281-5136
Tel.: (480) 446-3150
Web Site: https://www.tjmwest.com
Sales Range: $1-9.9 Million
Emp.: 35
Ret Radio/Tv/Electronics
N.A.I.C.S.: 449210
Adán Ortiz *(Mgr)*

DARLING INGREDIENTS INC.
5601 N MacArthur Blvd, Irving, TX 75038
Tel.: (972) 717-0300   DE
Web Site: https://www.darlingii.com
Year Founded: 1882
DAR—(NYSE)
Rev.: $6,788,080,000
Assets: $11,061,084,000
Liabilities: $6,367,393,000
Net Worth: $4,693,691,000
Earnings: $647,726,000
Emp.: 15,800
Fiscal Year-end: 12/30/23
Animal By-Products & Used Cooking Oil Processor
N.A.I.C.S.: 311225
Randall C. Stuewe *(Chm & CEO)*
Brad Phillips *(CFO & Exec VP)*
John F. Sterling *(Gen Counsel, Sec & Exec VP)*
Matt Jansen *(COO-North America)*
Jan van der Velden *(Exec VP-Rendering & Specialties-Intl)*
Sandra Dudley *(Exec VP-Renewable Energy & Specialty Ops)*
Jeroen Colpaert *(Exec VP)*
Suann Guthrie *(Sr VP)*
Patrick McNutt *(Chief Admin Officer)*
Joseph Manzi *(Chief Acctg Officer)*

Subsidiaries:

B.V. CTH Groep **(1)**
Bolderweg 38, 1332 AW, Almere, Netherlands
Tel.: (31) 36 532 2552
Web Site: https://www.cth.biz
Investment Management Service
N.A.I.C.S.: 523940

BestHides GmbH **(1)**
Wasserbruck 3, 84174, Eching, Germany
Tel.: (49) 8709928116
Web Site: https://www.besthides.com
Organic Food Whslr
N.A.I.C.S.: 424990

CTH GmbH **(1)**
Fallenriede 4, Holdorf, 49451, Vechta, Germany
Tel.: (49) 5494980200
Web Site: http://www.cth-web.de
Nondurable Goods Merchant Whslr
N.A.I.C.S.: 424990

CTH Porto - Industria Alimentar Unipessoal Lda **(1)**
Rua Dr Antonio Francisco Oliveira 155, 4485-846, Vilar do Pinheiro, Portugal
Tel.: (351) 229272844
Web Site: http://www.cth.biz
Nondurable Goods Merchant Whslr
N.A.I.C.S.: 424990

CTH US Inc. **(1)**
406 E Butler Ave, Clinton, NC 28328
Tel.: (910) 299-0940
Emp.: 4
Food Mfr
N.A.I.C.S.: 311999

Custom Blenders, Inc. **(1)**
9766 S Carlisle St, Terre Haute, IN 47802
Tel.: (812) 299-0233
Web Site: http://www.customblenders.net
Emp.: 5
All Other Miscellaneous Chemical Product & Preparation Mfr
N.A.I.C.S.: 325998
Barry Cowan *(Owner & CEO)*
Jeffrey Lammey *(Pres)*

DarPro Storage Solutions LLC **(1)**
5601 N MacArthur Blvd, Irving, TX 75038
Tel.: (972) 717-0300
Web Site: http://www.darpro-solutions.com
Used Cooking Oil Collection & Recycling Services
N.A.I.C.S.: 562920

Darling AWS LLC **(1)**
251 O Connor Ridge Blvd Ste 300, Irving, TX 75038
Tel.: (972) 717-0300
Organic Food Whslr

Darling Ingredients Inc.—(Continued)
N.A.I.C.S.: 424990

Darling Ingredients International Holding B.V. (1)
Kanaaldijk Noord 20, 5691 NM, Son, Netherlands
Tel.: (31) 499364800
Web Site: http://www.darlingii.com
Sales Range: $1-4.9 Billion
Emp.: 5,700
Animal By-Products Processor
N.A.I.C.S.: 311613
Dirk Kloosterboer (Vice Chm-Exec Bd, VION Ingredients & COO)

Subsidiary (Domestic):

Rendac B.V. (2)
Kanaaldijk Noord 20, 5691 NM, Son, Netherlands
Tel.: (31) 49 936 4500
Web Site: https://www.rendac.nl
Sales Range: $25-49.9 Million
Emp.: 220
Meat Meal & Animal Fat Processor
N.A.I.C.S.: 311613
Dirk Kloosterboer (CEO)

Sonac B.V. (2)
Kanaaldijk Noord 20, 5691 NM, Son, Netherlands
Tel.: (31) 499364820
Web Site: http://www.sonac.biz
Sales Range: $25-49.9 Million
Emp.: 60
Protein Products Derived from Hemoglobin & Plasma Mfr
N.A.I.C.S.: 311613

Plant (US):

Sonac USA (3)
1299 E Maple St, Maquoketa, IA 52060 (100%)
Tel.: (563) 652-4951
Sales Range: $10-24.9 Million
Emp.: 26
Food Mfr
N.A.I.C.S.: 311999
Kent Fuglsang (Plant Mgr)

Darling Ingredients International Rendering and Specialties B.V.
Kanaaldijk Noord 20, 5691 NM, Son en Breugel, Netherlands
Tel.: (31) 499364500
Animal Feed Product Distr
N.A.I.C.S.: 424490

Darling International Netherlands B.V.
N C B Weg 10, 5681 RH, Best, Netherlands
Tel.: (31) 499364555
Nondurable Goods Merchant Whslr
N.A.I.C.S.: 424990
Gert Mulderij (Dir-Mktg & Sls)

EV Acquisition Inc. (1)
201 S Denver Ave, Russellville, AR 72801
Tel.: (479) 498-0500
Food Mfr
N.A.I.C.S.: 311999

Ecoson B.V. (1)
Kanaaldijk Noord 20, 5691 NM, Son, Netherlands
Tel.: (31) 499364800
Web Site: https://www.ecoson.biz
Organic Food Whslr
N.A.I.C.S.: 424990

EnviroFlight, LLC (1)
118 Progress Way, Maysville, KY 41056
Tel.: (606) 956-0269
Web Site: http://www.enviroflight.net
Animal Feed Mfr
N.A.I.C.S.: 311119
Liz Koutsos (Pres & CEO)
Carrie Kuball (VP-Sls & Mktg)
Alejandra McComb (Dir-R&D & Regulatory Affairs)
Donna Hicks (CFO)

Global Ceramic Materials Ltd (1)
Milton Works Diamond Crescent, Milton, Stoke-on-Trent, ST2 7PX, United Kingdom
Tel.: (44) 178 253 7297
Web Site: https://www.globalcm.co.uk
Organic Food Whslr

N.A.I.C.S.: 424990

Griffin Industries LLC (1)
4221 Alexandria Pike, Cold Spring, KY 41076
Tel.: (859) 781-2010
Web Site: http://www.griffinind.com
Organic Food Whslr
N.A.I.C.S.: 424990

Griffin Industries, Inc. (1)
4221 Alexandria Pike, Cold Spring, KY 41076-1821
Tel.: (859) 781-2010
Web Site: http://www.griffinind.com
Sales Range: $250-299.9 Million
Emp.: 1,122
Animal By-Products & Bakery By-Products Recycling; Inedible Grease & Tallow Rendering
N.A.I.C.S.: 311613
Randall C. Stuewe (Pres)

HR-Service Nederland B.V. (1)
Kanaaldijk Noord 20-21, 5691 NM, Son, Netherlands
Tel.: (31) 499364500
Nondurable Goods Merchant Whslr
N.A.I.C.S.: 424990

Hepac B.V. (1)
Kieveen 18, 7371 GD, Loenen, Netherlands
Tel.: (31) 55 505 8641
Web Site: https://www.hepac.biz
Nondurable Goods Merchant Whslr
N.A.I.C.S.: 424990

Kanzler GmbH (1)
Rochusstrasse 47, Pempelfort, 40479, Dusseldorf, Germany
Tel.: (49) 211164510
Web Site: http://www.kklaw.de
Nondurable Goods Merchant Whslr
N.A.I.C.S.: 424990

LARU GmbH (1)
Weusterstr 25, 46240, Bottrop, Germany
Tel.: (49) 20 417 4730
Web Site: https://www.laru-food.com
Food Product Mfr & Distr
N.A.I.C.S.: 311412

Przedsiebiorstwo Produkcyjno Handlowe Conto Sp. z o.o. (1)
Ul Grodziska 39, 60 363, Poznan, Poland
Tel.: (48) 618679598
Web Site: http://www.conto.com.pl
Animal Origin Product Mfr
N.A.I.C.S.: 311613

Rendac BVBA (1)
Fabriekstraat 2, 9470, Denderleeuw, Belgium
Tel.: (32) 5 364 0211
Web Site: http://www.rendac.be
Organic Food Whslr
N.A.I.C.S.: 424990

Rendac Icker GmbH & Co. KG (1)
Engterstrasse 101, Belm-Icker, 49191, Osnabruck, Germany
Tel.: (49) 546893970
Web Site: http://www.rendac.de
Nondurable Goods Merchant Whslr
N.A.I.C.S.: 424990

Rousselot (Da'an) Gelatin Co. Ltd (1)
No 5 Anbei Street, Daan City, Jilin, 131300, China
Tel.: (86) 4365291002
Organic Food Whslr
N.A.I.C.S.: 424990

Rousselot (Guangdong) Gelatin Co. Ltd (1)
No 68 Xingchong Road Sanbu, Kaiping, China
Tel.: (86) 7502212323
Organic Food Whslr
N.A.I.C.S.: 424990

Rousselot (M) SDN.BHD (1)
Block P3-21 Plaza Damas Jalan Sri Hartamas 1, 50480, Kuala Lumpur, Malaysia
Tel.: (60) 362018282
Organic Food Whslr
N.A.I.C.S.: 424990

Rousselot (Whenzou) Gelatin Co, Ltd (1)

No 1 Meipu Road Qiancang office, Aojiang Town Pingyang, Wenzhou, 325411, Zhejiang, China
Tel.: (86) 57763688888
Organic Food Whslr
N.A.I.C.S.: 424990
Jiuliang Yang (Gen Mgr)

Rousselot (Zhejiang) Gelatin Co. Ltd (1)
No 188 Jiangkou Aojiang Pingyang, Wenzhou, 325401, Zhejiang, China
Tel.: (86) 57763668288
Organic Food Whslr
N.A.I.C.S.: 424990

Rousselot Angouleme SAS (1)
Rue de Saint Michel a Angouleme, 16000, Angouleme, France
Tel.: (33) 545642222
Organic Food Whslr
N.A.I.C.S.: 424990

Rousselot Argentina SA (1)
Avenida Gobernador Vergara 2532 1688 Villa Tesei, Hurlingham, Buenos Aires, Argentina
Tel.: (54) 1144898100
Organic Food Whslr
N.A.I.C.S.: 424990
Fernando Bluguermann (Dir-Technical)

Rousselot BVBA (1)
Meulestedekaai 81, 9000, Gent, Belgium
Tel.: (32) 92551818
Organic Food Whslr
N.A.I.C.S.: 424990

Rousselot Gelatin SL (1)
Paratge Pont de Torrent S/N, Cervia de Ter, 17464, Girona, Spain
Tel.: (34) 972496700
Organic Food Whslr
N.A.I.C.S.: 424990
Javier Canete Egea (Mgr-Fin)

Rousselot Isle sur La Sorgue SAS (1)
Chemin Moulin Premier, 84800, L'Isle-sur-la-Sorgue, France
Tel.: (33) 490213141
Organic Food Whslr
N.A.I.C.S.: 424990

Rousselot Japan KK (1)
Ishikin-nihonbashi Bldg 6F 4-14-7 Nihonbashihoncho, Chuo-ku, Tokyo, 103-0023, Japan
Tel.: (81) 356437701
Organic Food Whslr
N.A.I.C.S.: 424990

Sonac Almere BV (1)
Bolderweg 40, 1332 AW, Almere, Netherlands
Tel.: (31) 365322424
Animal Feed Product Distr
N.A.I.C.S.: 424490

Sonac Australia PTY, Ltd (1)
281 Maryborough Dunolly Road, Maryborough, 3465, VIC, Australia
Tel.: (61) 354604855
Animal Feed Product Distr
N.A.I.C.S.: 424490

Sonac Burgum B.V. (1)
Kanaaldijk Noord 20, 5691 NM, Son, Netherlands
Tel.: (31) 49 936 4820
Web Site: https://www.sonac.biz
Meat Product Processing Services
N.A.I.C.S.: 311613

Sonac Eindhoven B.V. (1)
Meerenakkerweg 7, 5652 AR, Eindhoven, Netherlands
Tel.: (31) 402380240
Nondurable Goods Merchant Whslr
N.A.I.C.S.: 424990

Sonac Gent BVBA (1)
Braamtweg 2, 9042, Gent, East Flanders, Belgium
Tel.: (32) 93377009
Nondurable Goods Merchant Whslr
N.A.I.C.S.: 424990

Sonac Harlingen B.V. (1)
Damsingel 27-30, Sumar, 9262 NB, Netherlands

Tel.: (31) 571272631
Nondurable Goods Merchant Whslr
N.A.I.C.S.: 424990

Sonac Kiel GmbH (1)
Ottostrasse 8, Kiel, 24145, Germany
Tel.: (49) 431717560
Nondurable Goods Merchant Whslr
N.A.I.C.S.: 424990

Sonac Lubien Kujawski spolka z ograniczona odpowiedzialnoscia (1)
Kaliska 146, Lubien Kujawski, 87-840, Bydgoszcz, Poland
Tel.: (48) 544413001
Web Site: https://sonac.pl
Pet Food Product Mfr
N.A.I.C.S.: 311119

Sonac Osetnica Sp.z o.o. (1)
Osetnica 1C, 59-225, Chojnow, Poland
Tel.: (48) 76 818 8643
Web Site: http://www.sonac.pl
Frozen Meat Product Mfr
N.A.I.C.S.: 311612

Sonac Usnice Sp.z o.o. (1)
Usnice 27, 82-400, Sztum, Poland
Tel.: (48) 55 277 1179
Web Site: https://www.sonac.pl
Animal Food Product Mfr
N.A.I.C.S.: 311119

T&K Spolka z.o.o. (1)
Ul Budowlanych 50, 45-124, Opole, Poland
Tel.: (48) 774531470
Web Site: http://www.t-k.com.pl
Frozen Meat Product Distr
N.A.I.C.S.: 424470

Triple-T Foods Inc. (1)
209 W McKay St, Frontenac, KS 66763
Tel.: (620) 231-8460
Web Site: http://www.tripletfoods.com
Dog & Cat Food Mfr
N.A.I.C.S.: 311111
Joe Claffey (Mgr-Warehouse)

Vada BVBA (1)
Smalle Weg 6, 2940, Stabroek, Belgium
Tel.: (32) 36646431
Web Site: http://www.vada-vetten.com
Nondurable Goods Merchant Whslr
N.A.I.C.S.: 424990

Valley Proteins, Inc. (1)
151 Valpro Dr, Winchester, VA 22603-3607
Tel.: (540) 877-2590
Web Site: http://www.valleyproteins.com
Sales Range: $150-199.9 Million
Emp.: 1,400
Mfr of Poultry & Animal Feeds
N.A.I.C.S.: 311119
Gerald F. Smith Jr. (Chm, Pres & CEO)

Division (Domestic):

Valley Proteins, Inc. (2)
2410 Randolph Ave, Greensboro, NC 27406-2910
Tel.: (336) 333-3030
Emp.: 52
Holding Company; Manufacturer of Chemicals, Animal Feed Supplements, Animal Fats & Proteins
N.A.I.C.S.: 311613

Valley Proteins, Inc. (2)
5533 York Hwy, Gastonia, NC 28052-8729
Tel.: (704) 864-9941
Sales Range: $25-49.9 Million
Emp.: 100
Mfr of Chemicals & Animal Feed Supplements
N.A.I.C.S.: 311613

Valley Proteins, Inc. (2)
1309 Industrial Dr, Fayetteville, NC 28301-1659
Tel.: (910) 483-0473
Sales Range: $50-74.9 Million
Emp.: 180
Mfr Chemicals & Animal Feed Supplements
N.A.I.C.S.: 311119
Wayne Johnson (Engr-Maintenance)
Rodney Cheatham (Mgr-Fleet)

Valley Proteins, Inc. (2)
9300 Johnson Rd, Strawberry Plains, TN 37871-1111
Tel.: (865) 933-3481

Sales Range: $25-49.9 Million
Emp.: 55
N.A.I.C.S.: 311611

DATA CALL TECHNOLOGIES, INC.
700 S Friendswood Dr Ste E, Friendswood, TX 77546
Tel.: (832) 230-2376   NV
Web Site:
    https://www.datacalltech.com
Year Founded: 2002
DCLT—(OTCIQ)
Rev.: $553,846
Assets: $92,120
Liabilities: $18,845
Net Worth: $73,275
Earnings: $4,782
Emp.: 2
Fiscal Year-end: 12/31/22
Digital Information Services
N.A.I.C.S.: 519290
Timothy E. Vance (Chm, CEO & COO)
Gary D. Woerz (CFO)

DATA I/O CORPORATION
6645 185th Ave NE Ste 100, Redmond, WA 98052
Tel.: (425) 881-6444   WA
Web Site: https://www.dataio.com
Year Founded: 1972
DAIO—(NASDAQ)
Rev.: $24,217,000
Assets: $27,165,000
Liabilities: $8,056,000
Net Worth: $19,109,000
Earnings: ($1,120,000)
Emp.: 85
Fiscal Year-end: 12/31/22
Designs, Manufactures & Sells Programming Systems for Electronic Device Manufacturers
N.A.I.C.S.: 339999
Rajeev Gulati (CTO & VP-Engrg)
Michael Tidwell (VP-Mktg & Bus Dev)
Gerald Ng (CFO, Treas, Sec & VP)
Jennifer Higgins (Mgr-Mktg & Comm)
William Wentworth (Pres & CEO)

Subsidiaries:

Data I/O Canada Corporation   (1)
6725 Airport Road Suite 102, Mississauga, L4V 1V2, ON, Canada
Tel.: (905) 678-0761
Semiconductor Devices Mfr
N.A.I.C.S.: 334413

Data I/O China, Ltd.   (1)
Unit 2401A 24/F Park-in Commercial Centre, 56 Dundas Street Mongkok, Kowloon, China (Hong Kong)   (100%)
Tel.: (852) 3519 0116
Web Site: http://www.dataio.com
Designs, Manufactures & Sells Programming Systems for Electronic Device Manufacturers
N.A.I.C.S.: 339999

Data I/O Electronics (Shanghai) Co., Ltd.   (1)
6th Floor Building 3 No 188 Pingfu Road, Xuhui District, Shanghai, 200231, China   (100%)
Tel.: (86) 2158827686
Web Site: https://www.dataio.cn
Designs, Manufactures & Sells Programming Systems for Electronic Device Manufacturers
N.A.I.C.S.: 339999

Data I/O GmbH   (1)
Am Haag 10, 82166, Grafelfing, Germany   (100%)
Tel.: (49) 89858580
Web Site: https://www.dataio.de
Sales Range: $10-24.9 Million
Emp.: 20
Mfr of Customized Software
N.A.I.C.S.: 334610

Data I/O International, Inc.   (1)

6645 185th Ave NE Ste 100, Redmond, WA 98052
Tel.: (425) 881-6444
Web Site: http://www.dataio.com
Semiconductor Devices Mfr
N.A.I.C.S.: 334413

DATA STORAGE CORPORATION
225 Broadhollow Rd Ste 307, Melville, NY 11747
Tel.: (631) 608-1200   NV
Web Site: https://www.cloudfirst.host
Year Founded: 2001
DTST—(NASDAQ)
Rev.: $23,870,837
Assets: $24,086,235
Liabilities: $5,139,040
Net Worth: $18,947,195
Earnings: ($4,356,802)
Emp.: 45
Fiscal Year-end: 12/31/22
Computer Storage Devices
N.A.I.C.S.: 334112
Charles M. Piluso (Chm, CEO, Co-CFO & Treas)
Harold J. Schwartz (Pres)
Thomas C. Kempster (Exec VP)
Chuck Paolillo (CTO)
Wendy Schmittzeh (Mgr-Admin)
Chris Panagiotakos (Co-CFO)
Lawrence A. Maglione Jr. (Co-Founder)

DATA443 RISK MITIGATION, INC.
4000 Sancar Dr Ste 400, Research Triangle Park, NC 27709
Tel.: (919) 858-6542   NV
Web Site: https://www.data443.com
Year Founded: 1998
ATDS—(OTCIQ)
Rev.: $2,627,123
Assets: $4,183,265
Liabilities: $12,950,118
Net Worth: ($8,766,853)
Earnings: ($9,818,098)
Emp.: 22
Fiscal Year-end: 12/31/22
Real Estate Asset Management Services
N.A.I.C.S.: 531390
Jason Remillard (Founder, Chm, Pres & CEO)
Gregory McCraw (CFO)
Dieter Orlowski (Chief Revenue Officer)

Subsidiaries:

DMBGroup, LLC   (1)
1401 Shoal Creek Ste 250, Highland Village, TX 75077
Tel.: (972) 899-3460
Custom Computer Programming Services
N.A.I.C.S.: 541511

Wala, Inc.   (1)
1324 N Hearne Ave Ste 150, Shreveport, LA 71107
Tel.: (318) 841-1151
Web Site: http://www.arcmail.com
Email Data Archiving Appliances & Software Developer & Whslr
N.A.I.C.S.: 334112
Rory T. Welch (Pres & CEO)

DATADOG, INC.
620 8th Ave 45th Fl, New York, NY 10018
Tel.: (866) 329-4466   DE
Web Site: https://www.datadog.com
Year Founded: 2010
DDOG—(NASDAQ)
Rev.: $2,128,359,000
Assets: $3,936,072,000
Liabilities: $1,910,718,000
Net Worth: $2,025,354,000
Earnings: $48,568,000
Emp.: 5,200

Fiscal Year-end: 12/31/23
Software Development Services
N.A.I.C.S.: 541511
David Obstler (CFO)
Michelle Goldstein (VP-Customer Success)
Adam Blitzer (COO)
Emilio Escobar (Chief Information Security Officer)
Sean Walters (Chief Revenue Officer)
Kerry Acocella (Gen Counsel)
Alexis Le-Quoc (Co-Founder & CTO)
Olivier Pomel (Co-Founder & CEO)

DATATRAK INTERNATIONAL, INC.
5900 Landerbrook Dr, Mayfield Heights, OH 44124
Tel.: (440) 443-0082   OH
Web Site: http://www.datatrak.net
Year Founded: 1995
DTRK—(OTCIQ)
Rev.: $7,742,000
Assets: $8,373,000
Liabilities: $7,227,000
Net Worth: $1,146,000
Earnings: $386,000
Emp.: 51
Fiscal Year-end: 12/31/19
Software Devolopment
N.A.I.C.S.: 334610
Jim Bob Ward (Pres & CEO)
Julia Henderson (CFO)
Alex Tabatabai (Chm)
Scott DeMell (VP-Sls)
Tim Lyons (VP-Product Dev & Ops)
Niki Kutac (VP-Mktg & Product Mgmt)

Subsidiaries:

DATATRAK Deutschland, GmbH   (1)
Bolsgasse 34, Swisttal, 53913, Bonn, Germany
Tel.: (49) 2226169540
Web Site: http://www.datatrak.net
Electronic Data Storage
N.A.I.C.S.: 518210

DATCHAT, INC.
65 Church St, New Brunswick, NJ 08901
Tel.: (732) 374-3529   NV
Web Site: https://www.datchat.com
Year Founded: 2014
DATS—(NASDAQ)
Rev.: $46,214
Assets: $13,113,690
Liabilities: $557,114
Net Worth: $12,556,576
Earnings: ($12,138,572)
Emp.: 15
Fiscal Year-end: 12/31/22
Digital Marketing Services
N.A.I.C.S.: 541810
Darin M. Myman (Pres, CEO, Co-Founder & Chm)
Peter Shelus (Co-Founder & CTO)
Brett Blumberg (CFO)

DAVE INC.
1265 S Cochran Ave, Los Angeles, CA 90019   DE
Web Site: https://www.dave.com
Year Founded: 2016
DAVE—(NASDAQ)
Rev.: $204,838,000
Assets: $321,492,000
Liabilities: $214,932,000
Net Worth: $106,560,000
Earnings: ($128,906,000)
Emp.: 320
Fiscal Year-end: 12/31/22
Financial Services
N.A.I.C.S.: 522320
Kyle Beilman (CFO)
Shannon Sullivan (Chief People Officer)
Gopi Kuchimanchi (VP-Technology)

Grahame Fraser (Head-Product Mgmt)
Joan Aristei (Chief Legal Officer)
Jason Wilk (Founder, Chm, Pres & CEO)

DAVI LUXURY BRAND GROUP, INC.
9426 Dayton Way, Beverly Hills, CA 90210
Tel.: (310) 288-8393   NV
Web Site: https://www.daviskin.com
Year Founded: 2007
MDAV—(OTCIQ)
Investment Services; Skin Care Products Developer
N.A.I.C.S.: 523999
Parrish Medley (CEO & Sec)

DAVITA INC.
2000 16th St, Denver, CO 80202
Tel.: (720) 631-2100   DE
Web Site: https://www.davita.com
Year Founded: 1995
DVA—(NYSE)
Rev.: $12,140,147,000
Assets: $16,893,578,000
Liabilities: $15,649,516,000
Net Worth: $1,244,062,000
Earnings: $691,535,000
Emp.: 70,000
Fiscal Year-end: 12/31/23
Dialysis Related Services
N.A.I.C.S.: 621492
Joel Ackerman (CFO & Treas)
Javier J. Rodriguez (CEO)
Christopher M. Berry (Chief Acctg Officer & Grp VP-Acctg)
Robert Lang (Pres/CEO-Intl)
Kathleen A. Waters (Chief Legal Officer)
James O. Hearty (Chief Compliance Officer)
Kenny Gardner (Chief People Officer)
Bruce Ware (VP, VP & Grp Head/Grp Head-Joint Venture Capital Raising)
Bruce Ware (VP & Grp Head-Joint Venture Capital Raising)
Jeffrey A. Giullian (Chief Medical Officer)
Pamela M. Arway (Chm)

Subsidiaries:

ABQ Health Partners Endoscopy Center, LLC   (1)
PO Box 25207, Albuquerque, NM 87125-0207
Tel.: (505) 262-7600
Web Site:
Emp.:
Health Care Srvices
N.A.I.C.S.: 621493

Aberdeen Dialysis, LLC   (1)
780 W Bel Air Ave, Aberdeen, MD 21001-2236
Tel.: (410) 273-9333
Web Site: https://www.davita.com
Medical Care Services
N.A.I.C.S.: 621492

Afton Dialysis, LLC   (1)
2000 Boca Chica Blvd, Brownsville, TX 78521-2226
Tel.: (956) 544-1158
Web Site: https://www.davita.com
Kidney Dialysis Center Operator
N.A.I.C.S.: 621492

Ahern Dialysis, LLC   (1)
1360 Blair Dr Ste L And M, Odenton, MD 21113-1343
Tel.: (410) 674-3918
Web Site: https://www.davita.com
Kidney Dialysis Center Operator
N.A.I.C.S.: 621492

Alamosa Dialysis, LLC   (1)
612 Del Sol Dr, Alamosa, CO 81101-8548
Tel.: (303) 405-2400
Web Site: https://www.davita.com

DaVita Inc.—(Continued)

Dialysis Treatment Services
N.A.I.C.S.: 621492

American Fork Dialysis, LLC (1)
1175 E 50 S Ste 111, American Fork, UT
84003-2846
Tel.: (801) 763-1304
Web Site: https://www.davita.com
Emp.: 12
Kidney Dialysis Services
N.A.I.C.S.: 621492
Darren Shultz *(Gen Mgr)*

Andrews Dialysis, LLC (1)
1110 SW B Ave, Lawton, OK 73501-4229
Tel.: (580) 595-4987
Web Site: https://www.davita.com
Emp.: 21
Kidney Dialysis Center Operator
N.A.I.C.S.: 621492

Animas Dialysis, LLC (1)
950 S Eastern Ave, Los Angeles, CA
90022-4801
Tel.: (310) 536-2400
Web Site: https://www.davita.com
Kidney Dialysis Services
N.A.I.C.S.: 621492

Argyle Dialysis, LLC (1)
51 Palomba Dr, Enfield, CT 06082-3801
Tel.: (860) 749-0476
Web Site: https://www.davita.com
Kidney Dialysis Center Operator
N.A.I.C.S.: 621492

Artesia Dialysis, LLC (1)
1903 W Main St, Artesia, NM 88210-3718
Kidney Dialysis Services
N.A.I.C.S.: 621492

Athio Dialysis, LLC (1)
6101 Windhaven Pkwy Ste 165, Plano, TX
75093-8197
Tel.: (615) 341-6472
Web Site: https://www.davita.com
Kidney Dialysis Center Operator
N.A.I.C.S.: 621492

Atlantic Dialysis, LLC (1)
1802 Commerce Dr, North Mankato, MN
56003-1800
Tel.: (303) 876-6622
Web Site: https://www.davita.com
Kidney Dialysis Services
N.A.I.C.S.: 621492

Babler Dialysis, LLC (1)
2660 S Broadway Ste A, Rochester, MN
55904-6264
Tel.: (507) 288-1617
Web Site: https://www.davita.com
Kidney Dialysis Center Operator
N.A.I.C.S.: 621492

Baker Dialysis, LLC (1)
2107 Fort Worth Hwy, Weatherford, TX
76086-4808
Tel.: (817) 599-6954
Web Site: https://www.davita.com
Emp.: 17
Kidney Dialysis Center Operator
N.A.I.C.S.: 621492

Bannon Dialysis, LLC (1)
5329 W University Dr, McKinney, TX
75071-8186
Tel.: (615) 341-6472
Web Site: https://www.davita.com
Medical Care Services
N.A.I.C.S.: 621492

Basin Dialysis, LLC (1)
3050 S Dixie Dr, Kettering, OH 45409-1516
Tel.: (937) 643-2337
Web Site: https://www.davita.com
Emp.: 41
Kidney Dialysis Services
N.A.I.C.S.: 621492

Bear Creek Dialysis, L.P. (1)
4978 Hwy 6 N Ste I, Houston, TX 77084
Tel.: (281) 859-5020
Sales Range: $50-74.9 Million
Emp.: 20
Medical Care Services
N.A.I.C.S.: 621492
Maritza Troche *(Gen Mgr)*

Bedell Dialysis, LLC (1)

2000 16th St, Denver, CO 80202
Tel.: (301) 890-8976
Kidney Dialysis Center Operator
N.A.I.C.S.: 621492

Belfair Dialysis, LLC (1)
1629 Treasure Hills Blvd, Harlingen, TX
78550-8907
Tel.: (956) 364-2120
Emp.: 10
Kidney Dialysis Center Operator
N.A.I.C.S.: 621492

Beverly Hills Dialysis Partnership (1)
50 N La Cienega Blvd 3Rd Fl Ste 300, Bev-
erly Hills, CA 90211-2284
Tel.: (310) 289-1612
Sales Range: $10-24.9 Million
Emp.: 50
Kidney Dialysis Center Services
N.A.I.C.S.: 621492

Bidwell Dialysis, LLC (1)
201 S Jupiter Rd, Allen, TX 75002
Tel.: (469) 342-6709
Kidney Dialysis Services
N.A.I.C.S.: 621492

Birch Dialysis, LLC (1)
9050 N Church Dr, Parma Heights, OH
44130-4701
Tel.: (253) 382-1186
Web Site: http://www.davita.com
Sales Range: $10-24.9 Million
Medical Care Services
N.A.I.C.S.: 621492

Bliss Dialysis, LLC (1)
4800 W San Antonio St Ste 201, Broken
Arrow, OK 74012
Tel.: (918) 249-9716
Web Site: https://www.davita.com
Kidney Dialysis Services
N.A.I.C.S.: 621492

Bogachiel Dialysis, LLC (1)
5201 San Mateo Blvd NE, Albuquerque, NM
87109-2414
Tel.: (505) 884-4820
Kidney Dialysis Center Operator
N.A.I.C.S.: 621492

Bollinger Dialysis, LLC (1)
220 Cottonwood Dr, Hempstead, TX 77445
Tel.: (979) 826-0477
Kidney Dialysis Center Operator
N.A.I.C.S.: 621492

Brache Dialysis, LLC (1)
2000 16th St, Denver, CO 80202
Tel.: (253) 382-1493
Kidney Dialysis Center Operator
N.A.I.C.S.: 621492

Brook Dialysis, LLC (1)
2711 Centerville Rd Ste 400, Wilmington,
DE 19808
Tel.: (301) 932-9874
Web Site: http://www.davita.com
Kidney Dialysis Services
N.A.I.C.S.: 621492

Brownsville Kidney Center, Ltd (1)
2945 Central Blvd, Brownsville, TX 78520-
8958
Tel.: (956) 542-8094
Web Site: http://www.davita.com
Kidney Dialysis Services
N.A.I.C.S.: 621492

Buford Dialysis, LLC (1)
1550 Buford Hwy Ste 1E, Buford, GA
30518-3666
Tel.: (770) 831-2379
Web Site: https://www.davita.com
Kidney Dialysis Centers
N.A.I.C.S.: 621492

Burney Dialysis, LLC (1)
401 Northside Dr Ste A, Valdosta, GA
31602-1871
Tel.: (229) 247-9286
Web Site: http://www.davitadialysis.com
Sales Range: $10-24.9 Million
Emp.: 2
Health Care Srvices
N.A.I.C.S.: 622110

Butano Dialysis, LLC (1)
440 N 11th Ave, Hanford, CA 93230-4404
Tel.: (559) 587-0105

Kidney Dialysis Services
N.A.I.C.S.: 621492

Cagles Dialysis, LLC (1)
10511 S Harlem Ave, Chicago Ridge, IL
60415-1291
Tel.: (615) 341-6657
Kidney Dialysis Center Operator
N.A.I.C.S.: 621492

Canyon Springs Dialysis, LLC (1)
22555 Alessandro Blvd Bldg 5, Moreno Val-
ley, CA 92553
Tel.: (951) 653-6400
Web Site: https://www.davita.com
Emp.: 20
Medical Care Services
N.A.I.C.S.: 621492

Capital Dialysis Partnership (1)
9267 Greenback Ln Ste A2, Orangevale,
CA 95662-4864
Tel.: (916) 988-5666
Web Site: https://www.davita.com
Kidney Dialysis Services
N.A.I.C.S.: 621492

Carlsbad Dialysis, LLC (1)
1275 Cleveland Ave Fl 1, East Point, GA
30344
Tel.: (404) 305-9080
Web Site: https://www.davita.com
Kidney Dialysis Services
N.A.I.C.S.: 621492

**Carroll County Dialysis Facility Lim-
ited Partnership** (1)
193 Stoner Ave Ste 120, Westminster, MD
21157
Tel.: (410) 871-1762
Web Site: https://www.davita.com
Emp.: 20
Medical Care Services
N.A.I.C.S.: 621492

Caswell Dialysis, LLC (1)
2812 W 10th St, Greeley, CO 80634-5425
Tel.: (970) 352-9072
Kidney Dialysis Center Operator
N.A.I.C.S.: 621492

Centennial LV, LLC (1)
8775 W Deer Springs Way, Las Vegas, NV
89149-0416
Tel.: (615) 320-4435
Kidney Dialysis Services
N.A.I.C.S.: 621492

**Central Carolina Dialysis Centers,
LLC** (1)
1607 N Main St, Kannapolis, NC 28081
Tel.: (704) 933-0809
Web Site: https://www.davita.com
Kidney Dialysis Services
N.A.I.C.S.: 621492

**Central Kentucky Dialysis Centers,
LLC** (1)
180 E Lincoln Trail Blvd, Radcliff, KY
40160-1254
Tel.: (270) 352-2252
Kidney Dialysis Services
N.A.I.C.S.: 621492

Centrum Dializa II Sp. z o.o. (1)
Jabloniowa 27, 41-214, Sosnowiec, Poland
Tel.: (48) 322901060
Web Site: http://www.centrumdializa.pl
Kidney Dialysis Services
N.A.I.C.S.: 621492

Cerito Dialysis Partners, LLC (1)
2000 16th St, Denver, CO 80202-5117
Tel.: (901) 751-3120
Web Site: http://www.davita.com
Kidney Dialysis Centers
N.A.I.C.S.: 621492

Chadron Dialysis, LLC (1)
14512 Lee Rd, Humble, TX 77396
Tel.: (281) 441-5016
Kidney Dialysis Services
N.A.I.C.S.: 621492

Champions Dialysis, LLC (1)
2220 Commerce Rd Ste 1, Forest Hill, MD
21050-2560
Tel.: (410) 638-6020
Dialysis Treatment Services
N.A.I.C.S.: 621492

Cheraw Dialysis, LLC (1)
3380 San Pablo Dam Rd Ste C-D, San
Pablo, CA 94803-7218
Tel.: (510) 262-9230
Kidney Dialysis Center Operator
N.A.I.C.S.: 621492

Chicago Heights Dialysis, LLC (1)
177 W Joe Orr Rd Ste B, Chicago Heights,
IL 60411-1733
Tel.: (708) 755-9000
Web Site: https://www.davita.com
Dialysis Treatment Services
N.A.I.C.S.: 621492

Chipeta Dialysis, LLC (1)
4141 Katella Ave, Los Alamitos, CA 90720
Tel.: (714) 952-0175
Web Site: https://www.davita.com
Emp.: 20
Kidney Dialysis Services
N.A.I.C.S.: 621492

Churchill Dialysis, LLC (1)
894 FM 3168, Raymondville, TX 78580-
4519
Tel.: (956) 389-9084
Sales Range: $10-24.9 Million
Emp.: 8
Kidney Dialysis Services
N.A.I.C.S.: 621492
Laura Yates *(Gen Mgr)*

Cimarron Dialysis, LLC (1)
7335 Yankee Rd, Liberty Township, OH
45044-0006
Tel.: (513) 755-2524
Kidney Dialysis Services
N.A.I.C.S.: 621492

Cleburne Dialysis, LLC (1)
4797 Marlboro Pike, Capitol Heights, MD
20743
Tel.: (615) 320-4230
Web Site: https://www.davita.com
Kidney Dialysis Services
N.A.I.C.S.: 621492

Clifton Dialysis, LLC (1)
16750 Hwy 3, Webster, TX 77598
Tel.: (281) 332-4719
Emp.: 21
Kidney Dialysis Services
N.A.I.C.S.: 621492

Clinica Central do Bonfim S.A (1)
Praca D Joao I n 25 2, 4000-295, Porto,
Portugal
Tel.: (351) 220044500
Web Site: https://drpintoleite.pt
Health Care Srvices
N.A.I.C.S.: 621493

**Clinica Medica DaVita Londrina Sor-
vicos de Nefrologia Ltda.** (1)
Av Duque De Caxias 1371, Londrina,
86015-000, Jd Petropolis, Brazil
Tel.: (55) 4333732700
Kidney Dialysis Services
N.A.I.C.S.: 621492

Clinton Township Dialysis, LLC (1)
15918 19 Mile Rd Ste 110, Clinton Town-
ship, MI 48038-1101
Tel.: (586) 412-9195
Web Site: https://www.davita.com
Sales Range: $10-24.9 Million
Dialysis Treatment Services
N.A.I.C.S.: 621492

Clough Dialysis, LLC (1)
6116 Sports Village Rd, Frisco, TX 75035
Tel.: (972) 624-7302
Kidney Dialysis Center Operator
N.A.I.C.S.: 621492

Clover Dialysis, LLC (1)
275 Di Salvo Ave, San Jose, CA 95128
Tel.: (408) 297-0103
Kidney Dialysis Services
N.A.I.C.S.: 621492
Justin Mason *(Mgr-Clinic)*

**Colorado Innovative Physician Solu-
tions, Inc.** (1)
5575 Tech Crt Dr Ste 106, Colorado
Springs, CO 80919
Tel.: (719) 388-7678
Physician Health Care Services
N.A.I.C.S.: 621111

Colorado Springs Health Partners, LLC (1)
2 S Cascade Ave Ste 140, Colorado Springs, CO 80903
Tel.: (719) 538-2900
Web Site: https://www.cshp.net
Health Care Srvices
N.A.I.C.S.: 621491

Columbus-RNA-DaVita, LLC (1)
415 E Mound St, Columbus, OH 43215-5532
Tel.: (614) 228-1773
Medical Care Services
N.A.I.C.S.: 621492
Kelly Grines *(CEO)*

Commerce Township Dialysis Center, LLC (1)
120 W Commerce Rd, Commerce Township, MI 48382-3915
Tel.: (248) 363-4862
Web Site: https://www.davita.com
Dialysis Treatment Services
N.A.I.C.S.: 621492

Continental Dialysis Center of Springfield-Fairfax, Inc. (1)
100 Shockoe Slip Fl 2, Richmond, VA 23219-4100
Tel.: (703) 644-7500
Health Care Srvices
N.A.I.C.S.: 621492

Coral Dialysis, LLC (1)
1810 S Fresno Ave, Stockton, CA 95206-1861
Tel.: (209) 946-0738
Kidney Dialysis Center Operator
N.A.I.C.S.: 621492

Cowell Dialysis, LLC (1)
3934 W 24th St, Chicago, IL 60623-3371
Tel.: (773) 306-9069
Kidney Dialysis Services
N.A.I.C.S.: 621492

Croft Dialysis, LLC (1)
1245 W Pacheco Blvd, Los Banos, CA 93635-8619
Tel.: (209) 827-3934
Web Site: https://www.davita.com
Kidney Dialysis Center Operator
N.A.I.C.S.: 621492

Curecanti Dialysis, LLC (1)
1763 E Main St, Dothan, AL 36301
Tel.: (334) 673-0246
Emp.: 4
Kidney Dialysis Services
N.A.I.C.S.: 621492
Kim Hall *(Gen Mgr)*

DNH Medical Management, Inc. (1)
100 N Sepulveda Blvd Ste 600, El Segundo, CA 90245
Tel.: (310) 320-3990
Investment Banking Services
N.A.I.C.S.: 523150
Laura Jacobs *(Pres)*

DV Care Netherlands B.V. (1)
Herengracht 160 II, 1016 BN, Amsterdam, Netherlands
Tel.: (31) 611439707
Emp.: 15
Kidney Dialysis Services
N.A.I.C.S.: 621492

DVA Healthcare Renal Care, Inc. (1)
1185 Monroe St, Dearborn, MI 48124-2814
Tel.: (253) 382-1493
Emp.: 20
Medical Care Services
N.A.I.C.S.: 621492

DVA Healthcare of Massachusetts, Inc. (1)
660 Harrison Ave, Boston, MA 02118-2304
Tel.: (617) 859-7000
Web Site: http://www.davita.com
Kidney Dialysis Services
N.A.I.C.S.: 621492

DVA Healthcare of New London, LLC (1)
5 Shaws Cove Ste 100, New London, CT 06320-4974
Web Site: http://www.davita.com
Medical Care Services

DVA Healthcare of Norwich, LLC (1)
113 Salem Tpke, Norwich, CT 06360-6484
Tel.: (860) 887-1632
Emp.: 21
Kidney Dialysis Services
N.A.I.C.S.: 621492

DVA Healthcare of Pennsylvania, Inc. (1)
3823 Market St, Philadelphia, PA 19104-3145
Medical Care Services
N.A.I.C.S.: 621492

DVA Healthcare of Tuscaloosa, LLC (1)
220 15th St, Tuscaloosa, AL 35401-3523
Tel.: (205) 345-6004
Kidney Dialysis Services
N.A.I.C.S.: 621492

DVA Laboratory Services, Inc. (1)
3000 Davita Way, Deland, FL 32724
Tel.: (954) 585-1100
Laboratory Services
N.A.I.C.S.: 541380

DVA Renal Healthcare, Inc. (1)
601 Hawaii St, El Segundo, CA 90245-4814
Tel.: (310) 297-2699
Kidney Dialysis Services
N.A.I.C.S.: 621492

DVA/Washington University Healthcare of Greater St. Louis, LLC (1)
400 N Lindbergh Blvd, Saint Louis, MO 63141-7814
Tel.: (314) 989-0886
Web Site: http://www.davita.com
Kidney Dialysis Centers
N.A.I.C.S.: 621492

DaVita APAC Holding B.V. (1)
Claude Debussylaan 11, 1082 MC, Amsterdam, Netherlands
Tel.: (31) 202402790
Kidney Dialysis Services
N.A.I.C.S.: 621492

DaVita Aguas Claras Servicos de Nefrologia Ltda. (1)
Av Sibipiruna lote 14 loja 1 Aguas Claras, Brasilia, 71928-720, Distrito Federal, Brazil
Tel.: (55) 6135783379
Clinical Services
N.A.I.C.S.: 621999

DaVita Amery Dialysis, LLC (1)
970 Elden Ave, Amery, WI 54001-1448
Web Site: https://www.davita.com
Kidney Dialysis Centers
N.A.I.C.S.: 621492

DaVita Amherst Dialysis Center (1)
3200 Cooper Foster Park Rd W, Lorain, OH 44053-3654
Tel.: (440) 989-1410
Kidney Dialysis Services
N.A.I.C.S.: 621492

DaVita Bauru Servicos de Nefrologia Ltda. (1)
Rua Baptista Antonio de Angelis 1-49 Vila Regina, Bauru, 17012-641, Sao Paulo, Brazil
Tel.: (55) 1430129600
Clinical Services
N.A.I.C.S.: 621999

DaVita Beverly Dialysis (1)
8109 S Western Ave, Chicago, IL 60620
Tel.: (610) 722-6019
Web Site: https://www.davita.com
Kidney Dialysis Services
N.A.I.C.S.: 621492

DaVita Care (India) Private Limited (1)
1/1 First Floor Berlie Street Langford Town, Shanthi Nagar, Bengaluru, 560025, India
Tel.: (91) 9740426060
Web Site: http://www.davita.in
Emp.: 50
Kidney Dialysis Center Operator
N.A.I.C.S.: 621492
Shriram Vijayakumar *(Mng Dir)*

DaVita Ceilandia Servicos de Nefrologia Ltda. (1)

CNM 1 bloco i lote 3 loja 1 Ceilandia, Brasilia, 72215-509, Distrito Federal, Brazil
Tel.: (55) 6137971340
Clinical Services
N.A.I.C.S.: 621999

DaVita Clinical Research (1)
825 S 8th St Ste 300, Minneapolis, MN 55404
Tel.: (612) 347-6367
Web Site: https://www.davitaclinicalresearch.com
Sales Range: $10-24.9 Million
Emp.: 25
Provider of Clinical Research Services
N.A.I.C.S.: 541720
Amy Young *(VP & Gen Mgr)*
Steven Brunelli *(VP & Dir-Medical-Health Economics & Outcomes Res)*
Tara Kelley *(VP)*
Francesca Tentori *(VP)*

DaVita Dakota Dialysis Center, LLC (1)
4474 23rd Ave S Ste M, Fargo, ND 58104-8795
Tel.: (701) 281-3900
Emp.: 20
Kidney Dialysis Services
N.A.I.C.S.: 621492
Kris Vorwerk *(Gen Mgr)*

DaVita Desert Springs Dialysis (1)
2110 E Flamingo Rd Ste 108, Las Vegas, NV 89119-5191
Tel.: (702) 696-9768
Web Site: http://www.davita.com
Kidney Dialysis Centers
N.A.I.C.S.: 621492

DaVita Deutschland GmbH (1)
Mittelweg 110 B, 20149, Hamburg, Germany
Tel.: (49) 4041462950
Web Site: https://www.davita.de
Kidney Dialysis Center Operator
N.A.I.C.S.: 621492

DaVita Dialysis, LLC (1)
1619 W McClain Ave, Scottsburg, IN 47170-1161
Tel.: (812) 752-5249
Web Site: http://www.davita.com
Sales Range: $10-24.9 Million
Emp.: 4
Kidney Dialysis Centers
N.A.I.C.S.: 621492

DaVita El Paso East, L.P. (1)
11989 Pellicano Dr, El Paso, TX 79936-6287
Tel.: (915) 856-6363
Sales Range: $10-24.9 Million
Emp.: 30
Kidney Dialysis Centers
N.A.I.C.S.: 621492

DaVita HealthCare Partners Plan, Inc. (1)
2000 16th St, Denver, CO 80202
Tel.: (310) 536-2400
Health Care Srvices
N.A.I.C.S.: 621493

DaVita Highland Ranch Dialysis Center (1)
7223 Church St Ste A14, Highland, CA 92346-6837
Tel.: (909) 862-9670
Web Site: http://www.davita.com
Health Care Srvices
N.A.I.C.S.: 622110

DaVita Key West Dialysis (1)
1122 Key Plz, Key West, FL 33040-4076
Tel.: (305) 294-8453
Web Site: http://www.davita.com
Sales Range: $10-24.9 Million
Emp.: 10
Health Care Srvices
N.A.I.C.S.: 621492

DaVita Kidney Care (1)
2000 16th St, Denver, CO 80202
Tel.: (303) 405-2100
Kidney Care & Dialysis Services
N.A.I.C.S.: 621492
Kenny Gardner *(Chief People Officer)*
Mandy Hale *(Chief Nursing Officer)*

DaVita Medical ACO California, LLC (1)

2175 Park Pl, El Segundo, CA 90245
Tel.: (310) 354-4200
Web Site: http://www.healthcarepartners.com
Healtcare Services
N.A.I.C.S.: 621491
Amar A. Desai *(Pres & CEO)*
Craig Dyer *(CFO)*
Derek H. Chao *(Chief Medical Officer)*
Leigh Hutchins *(COO)*

DaVita Medical Center (1)
5610 Almeda Rd, Houston, TX 77004-7515
Tel.: (713) 520-6878
Web Site: http://www.davita.com
Sales Range: $25-49.9 Million
Emp.: 120
Provider of Dialysis Services
N.A.I.C.S.: 621492

DaVita Nephrolife (India) Private Limited (1)
Suite 2 Setlur Street Shantinagar, Bengaluru, 560027, Karnataka, India
Tel.: (91) 9686670420
Web Site: http://www.davita.in
Emp.: 75
Health Care Srvices
N.A.I.C.S.: 621493

DaVita Northwest Dialysis Center (1)
2245 Rolling Run Dr Ste 1, Windsor Mill, MD 21244-1858
Tel.: (410) 265-0158
Web Site: http://www.davita.com
Kidney Dialysis Services
N.A.I.C.S.: 621492

DaVita PDI Johnstown (1)
344 Budfield St, Johnstown, PA 15904-3214
Tel.: (814) 266-4949
Web Site: http://www.davita.com
Sales Range: $10-24.9 Million
Emp.: 30
Dialysis Services
N.A.I.C.S.: 621492

DaVita Pasadena Foothills Dialysis (1)
3722 E Colorado Blvd, Pasadena, CA 91107-3872
Tel.: (626) 432-4331
Web Site: http://www.davita.com
Sales Range: $10-24.9 Million
Emp.: 30
Dialysis Treatment Services
N.A.I.C.S.: 621492

DaVita Pryor Dialysis (1)
309 E Graham Ave, Pryor, OK 74361-2434
Tel.: (918) 825-3100
Web Site: http://www.davita.com
Sales Range: $10-24.9 Million
Emp.: 12
Dialysis Treatment Services
N.A.I.C.S.: 621492

DaVita Riddle Dialysis Center (1)
100 Granite Dr Ste 106, Media, PA 19063-5134
Tel.: (610) 892-2769
Web Site: http://www.davita.com
Kidney Dialysis Centers
N.A.I.C.S.: 621492

DaVita S.A.S. (1)
Av Carrera 45 No 108-27 22nd Floor Tower 3, Bogota, 822, Colombia
Tel.: (57) 8000417222
Web Site: https://www.davita.com.co
Kidney Dialysis Services
N.A.I.C.S.: 621492

DaVita Servicos de Nefrologia Boa Vista Ltda. (1)
Rua Padre Ingles 288, Boa Vista, Recife, 50050-230, Pernambuco, Brazil
Tel.: (55) 8132041900
Clinical Services
N.A.I.C.S.: 621999

DaVita Servicos de Nefrologia Botafogo Ltda. (1)
Rua Dona Mariana 166, 22280-020, Rio de Janeiro, Brazil
Tel.: (55) 2125391881
Kidney Dialysis Services
N.A.I.C.S.: 621492

DaVita Inc.—(Continued)

DaVita Servicos de Nefrologia Campo Grande Ltda. (1)
Rua Treze de Maio 4361 San Francisco, Campo Grande, 79002-353, Mato Grosso do Sul, Brazil
Tel.: (55) 6730449100
Clinical Services
N.A.I.C.S.: 621999

DaVita Servicos de Nefrologia Cuiaba Ltda. (1)
Av Senador Filinto Muller n 2001, Quilombo, Cuiaba, 78043-500, Mato Grosso, Brazil
Tel.: (55) 6536222122
Clinical Services
N.A.I.C.S.: 621999

DaVita Servicos de Nefrologia Jardim das Imbuias Ltda. (1)
R Prof Eneas De Siqueira Neto 549, Sao Paulo, 04829-300, Brazil
Tel.: (55) 1159714545
Kidney Dialysis Services
N.A.I.C.S.: 621492

DaVita Servicos de Nefrologia Joao Dias Ltda. (1)
Rua Braganca Paulista 718 Vila Cruzeiro, Sao Paulo, 04727-001, Brazil
Tel.: (55) 2121271613
Kidney Dialysis Services
N.A.I.C.S.: 621492

DaVita Servicos de Nefrologia Pacini Ltda. (1)
SPES EQ 715/915 set A Block E 1st Floor Rooms 101 to 110 2nd Floor, Rooms 201 to 210 Pacini Building Asa Sul, Brasilia, 70390-911, Distrito Federal, Brazil
Tel.: (55) 6132027010
Clinical Services
N.A.I.C.S.: 621999

DaVita Servicos de Nefrologia Penha Ltda. (1)
R Major Angelo Zanchi 725 Penha De Franca, Sao Paulo, 03633-000, Brazil
Tel.: (55) 1122932350
Kidney Dialysis Services
N.A.I.C.S.: 621492

DaVita Servicos de Nefrologia Recife Ltda. (1)
Av Cruz Cabuga 1563, Recife, 50040-000, Santo Amaro, Brazil
Tel.: (55) 8134214906
Kidney Dialysis Services
N.A.I.C.S.: 621492

DaVita Servicos de Nefrologia Santos Dumont Ltda. (1)
Rua Antonio Saes 77 - Centro, Sao Jose dos Campos, 12210-040, Sao Paulo, Brazil
Tel.: (55) 1239434292
Clinical Services
N.A.I.C.S.: 621999

DaVita Servicos de Nefrologia Santos Ltda. (1)
Rua Monsenhor De Paula Rodrigues 200, Santos, 11075-350, Vila Belmiro, Brazil
Tel.: (55) 1332241256
Kidney Dialysis Services
N.A.I.C.S.: 621492

DaVita Servicos de Nefrologia Sumare Ltda. (1)
Av Da Amizade n 2 953 Parque Virgilio Viel, Cumare, 10177 C0C, Cao Paulo, Brazil
Tel.: (55) 1938039100
Clinical Services
N.A.I.C.S.: 621999

DaVita Servicos de Nefrologia de Araraquara Ltda. (1)
Avenida Papa Bento XV 30, Sao Paulo, 14807-240, Jardim Higienopolis, Brazil
Tel.: (55) 1633016071
Kidney Dialysis Services
N.A.I.C.S.: 621492

DaVita Tidewater-Virginia Beach, LLC (1)
1800 Camelot Dr Ste 100, Virginia Beach, VA 23454-2440
Tel.: (757) 481-6879

Web Site: http://www.davita.com
Dialysis Treatment Services
N.A.I.C.S.: 621492

DaVita Town & County West At Home (1)
12855 N 40 Dr Ste 340, Saint Louis, MO 63141-8665
Tel.: (610) 722-6019
Web Site: http://www.davita.com
Home Hemodialysis Services
N.A.I.C.S.: 621492

DaVita VillageHealth of Ohio, Inc. (1)
10600 Mckinley Rd, Blue Ash, OH 45242
Tel.: (513) 733-8215
Emp.: 20
Kidney Dialysis Services
N.A.I.C.S.: 621492

DaVita-Riverside II, LLC (1)
11161 Magnolia Ave, Riverside, CA 92505-3605
Tel.: (909) 682-2700
Medical Care Services
N.A.I.C.S.: 621492

Damon Dialysis, LLC (1)
9210 Rockville Rd Ste D, Indianapolis, IN 46234-2670
Tel.: (317) 209-2544
Web Site: http://www.davita.com
Medical Care Services
N.A.I.C.S.: 621492

Daroga Dialysis, LLC (1)
2592 E Aurora Rd Ste 200, Twinsburg, OH 44087-0000
Tel.: (615) 341-6311
Health Care Srvices
N.A.I.C.S.: 621493

Davis Dialysis, LLC (1)
5865 Sunnybrook Dr, Sioux City, IA 51106-4203
Tel.: (712) 274-8068
Emp.: 4
Kidney Dialysis Services
N.A.I.C.S.: 621492
Dianna North (Gen Mgr)

Dawson Dialysis, LLC (1)
587 N Mountain Ave, Upland, CA 91786-5016
Tel.: (909) 931-4515
Kidney Dialysis Center Operator
N.A.I.C.S.: 621492

Desoto Dialysis, LLC (1)
2702 Navarre Ave Ste 203, Oregon, OH 43616-3224
Tel.: (419) 691-1514
Web Site: http://www.davita.com
Kidney Dialysis Services
N.A.I.C.S.: 621492
Ken Phiru (Pres)

Diablo Dialysis, LLC (1)
1923 Marsha Sharp Fwy Ste 102, Lubbock, TX 79415-4036
Tel.: (806) 744-2790
Kidney Dialysis Services
N.A.I.C.S.: 621492

Dialyse-Zentrum Hamburg-Ost GmbH (1)
Mittelweg 110 B, Rotherbaum, 20149, Hamburg, Germany
Tel.: (49) 4073924060
Kidney Dialysis Services
N.A.I.C.S.: 621492

Dialysis Specialists of Dallas, Inc. (1)
8101 Brookriver Dr, Dallas, TX 75247-4003
Tel.: (214) 951-7789
Emp.: 20
Kidney Dialysis Center Operator
N.A.I.C.S.: 621492

Dialysis of Des Moines, LLC (1)
501 SW 7th St Ste B, Des Moines, IA 50309-4538
Tel.: (515) 283-1300
Emp.: 20
Kidney Dialysis Services
N.A.I.C.S.: 621492

Dome Dialysis, LLC (1)

241 W Schrock Rd, Westerville, OH 43081-2874
Tel.: (614) 882-1734
Sales Range: $10-24.9 Million
Emp.: 10
Kidney Dialysis Services
N.A.I.C.S.: 621492
Stephanie Sayers (Office Mgr)

Downriver Centers, Inc. (1)
5600 Allen Rd, Allen Park, MI 48101-2604
Kidney Dialysis Services
N.A.I.C.S.: 621492

Downtown Houston Dialysis Center, L.P. (1)
2207 Crawford St, Houston, TX 77002-8915
Tel.: (713) 655-0900
Emp.: 20
Kidney Dialysis Services
N.A.I.C.S.: 621492
Elizabeth Looney (Gen Mgr)

Dresher Dialysis, LLC (1)
3424 Donnell Dr, Forestville, MD 20747-3209
Tel.: (301) 568-0381
Kidney Dialysis Center Operator
N.A.I.C.S.: 621492

Durango Dialysis Center, LLC (1)
72 Suttle St Ste D, Durango, CO 81303-6829
Tel.: (970) 385-8608
Sales Range: $10-24.9 Million
Emp.: 12
Kidney Dialysis Centers
N.A.I.C.S.: 621492

Dworsher Dialysis, LLC (1)
1426 Kingwood Dr, Kingwood, TX 77339
Tel.: (281) 312-1301
Kidney Dialysis Center Operator
N.A.I.C.S.: 621492

East End Dialysis Center, Inc. (1)
2000 16th St, Denver, CO 80202-5117
Tel.: (804) 643-3050
Web Site: http://www.davita.com
Kidney Dialysis Services
N.A.I.C.S.: 621492

East Ft. Lauderdale, LLC (1)
1301 S Andrews Ave Ste 101, Fort Lauderdale, FL 33316-1823
Tel.: (954) 761-1273
Web Site: http://www.davita.com
Kidney Dialysis Services
N.A.I.C.S.: 621492

Edisto Dialysis, LLC (1)
13054 N Harbor Blvd, Garden Grove, CA 92843-1744
Tel.: (714) 539-3395
Kidney Dialysis Center Operator
N.A.I.C.S.: 621492

Elberton Dialysis Facility, Inc. (1)
894 Elbert St, Elberton, GA 30635-2628
Tel.: (706) 283-9833
Web Site: http://www.davita.com
Emp.: 20
Kidney Dialysis Services
N.A.I.C.S.: 621492

Eldrist Dialysis, LLC (1)
721 W Huntington Dr, Arcadia, CA 91007-6734
Tel.: (626) 294-9682
Kidney Dialysis Center Operator
N.A.I.C.S.: 621492

Elk Grove Dialysis Center, LLC (1)
9281 Office Park Cir Ste 105, Elk Grove, CA 95758-8069
Web Site: http://www.davita.com
Kidney Dialysis Services
N.A.I.C.S.: 621492

Especialistas en Salud-Esensa S.A.S. (1)
CA 7 Bis 124 29, Bogota, Colombia
Tel.: (57) 16028311
Renal Dialysis Services
N.A.I.C.S.: 621492

Etowah Dialysis, LLC (1)
1021 Park Ave, Quakertown, PA 18951-1573
Tel.: (215) 538-4665
Medical Care Services

N.A.I.C.S.: 621492

Eufaula Dialysis, LLC (1)
953 Belmont Ave, North Haledon, NJ 07508-2548
Tel.: (973) 427-4675
Kidney Dialysis Services
N.A.I.C.S.: 621492

Eurodial-Centro de Nefrologia e Dialise de Leiria, S.A. (1)
Rua Da Carrasqueira 19 Parceiros, 2400-441, Leiria, Portugal
Tel.: (351) 244819030
Web Site: http://www.davita.pt
Health Care Services
N.A.I.C.S.: 621493

Everett MSO, Inc. (1)
3901 Hoyt Ave, Everett, WA 98201
Tel.: (425) 304-8400
Web Site: http://www.everettclinic.com
Kidney Dialysis Services
N.A.I.C.S.: 621492
Aric Coffman (CEO)
Michael L. Rohrenbach (Assoc Dir-Medical-Medical Subspecialty & Family Medicine)

Everglades Dialysis, LLC (1)
125 E Michigan Ave, Grayling, MI 49738-1740
Tel.: (303) 876-6622
Kidney Dialysis Services
N.A.I.C.S.: 621492

Extracorp Aktiengesellschaft (1)
Mittelweg 110 B, 20149, Hamburg, Germany
Tel.: (49) 4041462950
Web Site: https://www.davita.de
Emp.: 8
Health Care Srvices
N.A.I.C.S.: 621493

Fairfield Dialysis, LLC (1)
4660 Central Way, Fairfield, CA 94534
Tel.: (707) 863-7369
Sales Range: $10-24.9 Million
Emp.: 40
Health Care Srvices
N.A.I.C.S.: 622110

Farragut Dialysis, LLC (1)
2958 Dorchester Dr, Montgomery, AL 36116-3193
Tel.: (334) 280-4980
Web Site: http://www.davita.com
Emp.: 12
Medical Care Services
N.A.I.C.S.: 621492

Five Star Dialysis, LLC (1)
2400 Tech Ctr Ct, Las Vegas, NV 89128-0004
Tel.: (702) 869-3771
Web Site: http://www.davita.com
Sales Range: $10-24.9 Million
Medical Care Services
N.A.I.C.S.: 621492

Fjords Dialysis, LLC (1)
9310 Spring Rd, Ocala, FL 34472-2913
Tel.: (352) 687-0403
Kidney Dialysis Services
N.A.I.C.S.: 621492

Flagler Dialysis, LLC (1)
22620 Goldencrest Dr Ste 101, Moreno Valley, CA 92553-9032
Tel.: (951) 656-3804
Web Site: http://www.davita.com
Kidney Dialysis Services
N.A.I.C.S.: 621492

Flamingo Park Kidney Center, Inc. (1)
901 E 10th Ave Bay 17, Hialeah, FL 33010-3762
Tel.: (305) 884-5677
Web Site: http://www.davita.com
Sales Range: $10-24.9 Million
Kidney Dialysis Services
N.A.I.C.S.: 621492

Flandrau Dialysis, LLC (1)
1301 Custer Rd Ste 524, Plano, TX 75075-9400
Tel.: (972) 578-7047
Kidney Dialysis Center Operator
N.A.I.C.S.: 621492

Foss Dialysis, LLC (1)
2550 S Telshor Blvd, Las Cruces, NM
88011
Tel.: (575) 532-9437
Kidney Dialysis Services
N.A.I.C.S.: 621492

Frontenac Dialysis, LLC (1)
260 Scranton Carbondale Hwy, Eynon, PA
18403-1029
Tel.: (570) 876-1874
Kidney Dialysis Center Operator
N.A.I.C.S.: 621492

Frontier Dialysis, LLC (1)
7316 W Cheyenne Ave, Las Vegas, NV
89129-6201
Tel.: (702) 395-0227
Kidney Dialysis Center Operator
N.A.I.C.S.: 621492

Fullerton Dialysis Center, LLC (1)
3214 Yorba Linda Blvd, Fullerton, CA
92831-1707
Tel.: (714) 577-6940
Web Site: http://www.davitainc.com
Kidney Dialysis Services
N.A.I.C.S.: 621492

Gertrude Dialysis, LLC (1)
402 N Carrier Pkwy Ste 102, Grand Prairie,
TX 75050-5426
Tel.: (972) 237-6724
Kidney Dialysis Center Operator
N.A.I.C.S.: 621492

Geyser Dialysis, LLC (1)
2625 N Ankeny Blvd, Ankeny, IA 50023-
4704
Tel.: (515) 963-3174
Emp.: 8
Kidney Dialysis Services
N.A.I.C.S.: 621492
Lori Weeks (Gen Mgr)

Givhan Dialysis, LLC (1)
526 Broad St, Sumter, SC 29150-3306
Tel.: (803) 773-5891
Web Site: http://www.davita.com
Emp.: 18
Kidney Dialysis Services
N.A.I.C.S.: 621492

Glassland Dialysis, LLC (1)
3901 S Western Ave, Los Angeles, CA
90062
Tel.: (323) 294-0670
Emp.: 20
Kidney Dialysis Services
N.A.I.C.S.: 621492

Golden Sun Bear, LLC (1)
2000 16th St, Denver, CO 80202
Tel.: (813) 971-3064
Health Care Srvices
N.A.I.C.S.: 622110
Nicole Gravely (Mgr)

Goldendale Dialysis, LLC (1)
1200 Brookstone Ctr Pkwy, Columbus, GA
31904
Tel.: (706) 322-2935
Emp.: 5
Kidney Dialysis Services
N.A.I.C.S.: 621492
James K. Hilger (Chief Acctg Officer)

Goliad Dialysis, LLC (1)
251 Lathrop Way Ste A, Sacramento, CA
95815-4223
Tel.: (916) 922-4721
Web Site: http://www.davita.com
Medical Care Services
N.A.I.C.S.: 621492

**Gonzales Dialysis Centers - South-
east, LP** (1)
1406 E Sarah Dewitt Dr, Gonzales, TX
78629
Tel.: (830) 672-4377
Web Site: http://www.davita.com
Sales Range: $1-9.9 Million
Emp.: 10
Provider of Dialysis Services
N.A.I.C.S.: 621492

Goodale Dialysis, LLC (1)
2302 Chester Blvd, Richmond, IN 47374-
1221
Tel.: (765) 935-5128
Kidney Dialysis Center Operator

N.A.I.C.S.: 621492

Grand Home Dialysis, LLC (1)
14671 W Mountain View Blvd Ste 106, Sur-
prise, AZ 85374-4840
Tel.: (623) 546-6120
Sales Range: $10-24.9 Million
Emp.: 5
Kidney Dialysis Services
N.A.I.C.S.: 621492

Greater Las Vegas Dialysis, LLC (1)
653 N Town Ctr Dr Bldg 2 Ste 70, Las Ve-
gas, NV 89144-5140
Tel.: (702) 360-6908
Kidney Dialysis Services
N.A.I.C.S.: 621492
Neville Pokroy (Dir-Medical)

**Greater Los Angeles Dialysis Cen-
ters, LLC** (1)
3986 S Figueroa St, Los Angeles, CA
90037
Tel.: (213) 749-8297
Emp.: 23
Kidney Dialysis Services
N.A.I.C.S.: 621492

Greenleaf Dialysis, LLC (1)
2000 16th St, Denver, CO 80202
Tel.: (352) 378-4960
Web Site: http://www.davita.com
Emp.: 10
Kidney Dialysis Services
N.A.I.C.S.: 621492

Greenwood Dialysis, LLC (1)
1345 N Lansing Ave, Tulsa, OK 74106-5911
Tel.: (918) 585-8811
Web Site: https://www.davita.com
Emp.: 20
Kidney Dialysis Services
N.A.I.C.S.: 621492

Griffin Dialysis, LLC (1)
8243 E Stockton Blvd Ste 100, Sacra-
mento, CA 95828-8204
Tel.: (916) 682-6655
Web Site: http://www.davita.com
Kidney Dialysis Services
N.A.I.C.S.: 621492

Griffs Dialysis, LLC (1)
5660 Nimtz Pkwy, South Bend, IN 46628-
6205
Tel.: (574) 234-8870
Web Site: https://www.davita.com
Kidney Dialysis Services
N.A.I.C.S.: 621492
James K. Hilger (Chief Admin Officer)

Guntersville Dialysis, LLC (1)
2711 Centerville Rd Ste 400, Wilmington,
DE 19808
Tel.: (706) 429-4731
Kidney Dialysis Services
N.A.I.C.S.: 621492

Hanford Dialysis, LLC (1)
402 W 8th St, Hanford, CA 93230-4536
Tel.: (559) 582-5464
Web Site: https://www.davita.com
Kidney Dialysis Services
N.A.I.C.S.: 621492

Harmony Dialysis, LLC (1)
1800 N Texas St, Fairfield, CA 94533-3874
Tel.: (707) 399-9984
Web Site: https://www.davita.com
Emp.: 25
Kidney Dialysis Services
N.A.I.C.S.: 621492
Shenay Bennett (Gen Mgr)

Harris Dialysis, LLC (1)
16236 Lucas Ferry Rd, Athens, AL 35611-
3931
Tel.: (256) 233-3965
Emp.: 5
Kidney Dialysis Services
N.A.I.C.S.: 621492
Kent Thiry (Pres)

Hawaiian Gardens Dialysis, LLC (1)
12191 226th St, Hawaiian Gardens, CA
90716
Tel.: (562) 421-4016
Emp.: 21
Kidney Dialysis Services
N.A.I.C.S.: 621492
Robert Maylad (Gen Mgr)

Hazelton Dialysis, LLC (1)
1950 Sunnycrest Dr Ste 1300, Fullerton, CA
92835
Tel.: (714) 578-0015
Kidney Dialysis Services
N.A.I.C.S.: 621492

Headlands Dialysis, LLC (1)
5832 S Hulen St, Fort Worth, TX 76132-
2684
Tel.: (817) 370-7642
Web Site: https://www.davita.com
Emp.: 9
Kidney Dialysis Center Operator
N.A.I.C.S.: 621492

**HealthCare Partners ASC-LB,
LLC** (1)
2600 Redondo Ave, Long Beach, CA
90806-2325
Tel.: (562) 988-7147
Health Care Srvices
N.A.I.C.S.: 621999

**HealthCare Partners Colorado,
LLC** (1)
717 17th St 26th Fl, Denver, CO 80202
Tel.: (719) 633-2762
Health Care Srvices
N.A.I.C.S.: 621610
Dennis Schneider (Chief Medical Officer)

**HealthCare Partners Holdings
LLC** (1)
19191 S Vermont Ave Ste 200, Torrance,
CA 90502
Tel.: (310) 536-2400
Web Site:
  http://www.healthcarepartners.com
Sales Range: $1-4.9 Billion
Emp.: 3,450
Medical Facility Operator
N.A.I.C.S.: 622110
Derek H. Chao (Chief Medical Officer)
Craig Dyer (CFO)

**HealthCare Partners South Florida,
LLC** (1)
11000 Optum Cir, Eden Prairie, MN 55344
Tel.: (954) 755-5504
Emp.: 10
Health Care Srvices
N.A.I.C.S.: 621999

HealthCare Partners, LLC (1)
19191 S Vermont Ave Ste 200, Torrance,
CA 90502
Tel.: (310) 354-4200
Web Site:
  http://www.healthcarepartners.com
Health Care Srvices
N.A.I.C.S.: 621999

Heavener Dialysis, LLC (1)
2401 Shelby St, Columbus, GA 31903
Tel.: (706) 682-5327
Kidney Dialysis Services
N.A.I.C.S.: 621492
Sarah Shreder (Reg Dir-Ops)

Heideck Dialysis, LLC (1)
3410 Belle Chase Way Ste 600, Lansing,
MI 48911
Tel.: (989) 275-0362
Kidney Dialysis Center Operator
N.A.I.C.S.: 621492

Helmer Dialysis, LLC (1)
1140 S Ben Maddox Way, Visalia, CA
93292
Tel.: (559) 635-1938
Kidney Dialysis Center Operator
N.A.I.C.S.: 621492

Heyburn Dialysis, LLC (1)
2447 Hilliard Rome Rd, Hilliard, OH 43026-
8194
Tel.: (615) 341-6311
Web Site: https://www.davita.com
Kidney Dialysis Services
N.A.I.C.S.: 621492

Hochatown Dialysis, LLC (1)
1216 E 8th St, Odessa, TX 79761-4638
Tel.: (615) 341-5895
Web Site: https://www.davita.com
Kidney Dialysis Services
N.A.I.C.S.: 621492

Holiday Dialysis, LLC (1)

2410 Alft Ln Ste 101, Elgin, IL 60124-8090
Tel.: (847) 289-5628
Emp.: 5
Kidney Dialysis Services
N.A.I.C.S.: 621492
Marie Rose (Gen Mgr)

Holten Dialysis, LLC (1)
1800 Medical Ctr Dr Ste 150, San Ber-
nardino, CA 92411-1218
Tel.: (909) 887-6869
Web Site: https://www.davita.com
Kidney Dialysis Center Operator
N.A.I.C.S.: 621492

**Houston Kidney Center/Total Renal
Care Integrated Service Network Lim-
ited Partnership** (1)
221 Fm 1960 Rd W Ste H, Houston, TX
77090
Tel.: (281) 880-8821
Dialysis Treatment Services
N.A.I.C.S.: 621492

Humboldt Dialysis, LLC (1)
2214 Osborne St, Humboldt, TN 38343-
3044
Tel.: (610) 722-6019
Web Site: https://www.davita.com
Kidney Dialysis Services
N.A.I.C.S.: 621492

Hummer Dialysis, LLC (1)
713 E Lk Mead Blvd, North Las Vegas, NV
89030-6751
Tel.: (702) 642-0216
Web Site: https://www.davita.com
Kidney Dialysis Center Operator
N.A.I.C.S.: 621492

**Huntington Artificial Kidney Center,
Ltd.** (1)
2000 16TH St, Denver, CO 80202
Tel.: (516) 379-5000
Web Site: http://www.davita.com
Medical Care Services
N.A.I.C.S.: 621492

Huntington Park Dialysis, LLC (1)
5942 Rugby Ave, Huntington Park, CA
90255-2803
Tel.: (323) 585-7605
Web Site: https://www.davita.com
Emp.: 20
Dialysis Treatment Services
N.A.I.C.S.: 621492

Hyde Dialysis, LLC (1)
8231 E Stockton Blvd Ste A, Sacramento,
CA 95828-8202
Web Site: https://www.davita.com
Medical Care Services
N.A.I.C.S.: 621492

ISD Canton, LLC (1)
260 Hospital Rd, Canton, GA 30114-2409
Tel.: (678) 880-3939
Web Site: https://www.davita.com
Health Care Srvices
N.A.I.C.S.: 622110
Jenifer Gabrielili (Mgr-HR)

ISD Kansas City, LLC (1)
3947 Broadway St, Kansas City, MO 64111-
2516
Tel.: (816) 531-1181
Health Care Srvices
N.A.I.C.S.: 622110

ISD Kendallville, LLC (1)
602 N Sawyer Rd, Kendallville, IN 46755-
2566
Tel.: (260) 599-0423
Web Site: https://www.davita.com
Emp.: 10
Health Care Srvices
N.A.I.C.S.: 622110
Hillary Hathway (Gen Mgr)

Indian River Dialysis Center, LLC (1)
2150 45th St Unit 102, Vero Beach, FL
32967-6281
Web Site: https://www.davita.com
Emp.: 20
Dialysis Treatment Services
N.A.I.C.S.: 621492

Ionia Dialysis, LLC (1)
2622 Heartland Blvd, Ionia, MI 48846-8757
Tel.: (616) 522-0265
Web Site: https://www.davita.com

DaVita Inc.—(Continued)

Kidney Dialysis Services
N.A.I.C.S.: 621492
Cecily Sherlock (Gen Mgr)

Iroquois Dialysis, LLC (1)
5200 Virginia Way, Riverside, CA 37027-7569
Tel.: (615) 341-5895
Kidney Dialysis Center Services
N.A.I.C.S.: 621492

JSA Healthcare Nevada, LLC. (1)
1776 E Warm Springs Rd Ste 302, Las Vegas, NV 89119
Tel.: (702) 932-8500
Emp.: 5
Holding Company
N.A.I.C.S.: 551112

JSA P5 Nevada, LLC. (1)
700 E Warm Springs Rd Ste 110, Las Vegas, NV 89119
Tel.: (702) 932-8561
Health Care Srvices
N.A.I.C.S.: 621999

Jedburg Dialysis, LLC (1)
2897 W 5th N St, Summerville, SC 29483-9674
Tel.: (843) 873-1638
Web Site: https://www.davita.com
Dialysis Treatment Services
N.A.I.C.S.: 621492

Joshua Dialysis, LLC (1)
626 S Andover Rd ste 900, Andover, KS 67002-8910
Tel.: (316) 733-2984
Web Site: https://www.davita.com
Kidney Dialysis Services
N.A.I.C.S.: 621492

Kamakee Dialysis, LLC (1)
635 Bay Ave Ste 215, Toms River, NJ 08753-3349
Tel.: (732) 341-2730
Web Site: https://www.davita.com
Kidney Dialysis Center Operator
N.A.I.C.S.: 621492

Kamiah Dialysis, LLC (1)
2703 S Towne Ave, Pomona, CA 91766
Tel.: (909) 590-4930
Kidney Dialysis Center Operator
N.A.I.C.S.: 621492

Kavett Dialysis, LLC (1)
7150 W 20th Ave Ste 109, Hialeah, FL 33016-5509
Tel.: (305) 827-8399
Web Site: https://www.davita.com
Kidney Dialysis Services
N.A.I.C.S.: 621492

Kearn Dialysis, LLC (1)
201 Fm 971, Georgetown, TX 78626-4631
Tel.: (512) 819-9636
Health Care Srvices
N.A.I.C.S.: 622110

Kerricher Dialysis, LLC (1)
2400 Lands End Blvd Ste 131, Fort Worth, TX 76116
Tel.: (817) 570-0916
Emp.: 29
Kidney Dialysis Center Operator
N.A.I.C.S.: 621492

Kidney Centers of Michigan, LLC (1)
3410 Belle Chase Way Ste 600, Lansing, MI 48911
Tel.: (248) 356-8079
Web Site: http://www.davita.com
Kidney Dialysis Services
N.A.I.C.S.: 621492

Kidney Home Center, LLC (1)
2711 Centerville Rd Ste 400, Wilmington, DE 19808
Tel.: (410) 265-6515
Web Site: http://www.davita.com
Kidney Dialysis Services
N.A.I.C.S.: 621492

Knickerbocker Dialysis, Inc. (1)
80 State St, Albany, NY 12207
Medical Care Services
N.A.I.C.S.: 621492

Kobuk Dialysis, LLC (1)

1005 Pennsylvania Ave Ste 101, Ottumwa, IA 52501-4130
Tel.: (641) 682-1531
Kidney Dialysis Services
N.A.I.C.S.: 621492
Shari Baustiemir (Gen Mgr)

Lapham Dialysis, LLC (1)
449 Industrial Blvd, Ellijay, GA 30540
Tel.: (706) 276-6040
Kidney Dialysis Services
N.A.I.C.S.: 621492

Las Olas De Sequoia, LLC (1)
3 W Hawthorn Pkwy Ste 410, Vernon Hills, IL 60061-1446
Tel.: (847) 388-2001
Kidney Dialysis Services
N.A.I.C.S.: 621492

Las Vegas Pediatric Dialysis, LLC (1)
7271 W Sahara Ave Ste 120, Las Vegas, NV 89117
Tel.: (702) 227-3049
Emp.: 5
Kidney Dialysis Services
N.A.I.C.S.: 621492
Ryan Welter (Office Mgr)

Las Vegas Solari Hospice Care, LLC (1)
5550 S Jones Blvd, Las Vegas, NV 89118
Tel.: (702) 870-0000
Health Care Srvices
N.A.I.C.S.: 621610

Lassen Dialysis, LLC (1)
3410 Belle Chase Way Sre 600, Lansing, MI 48911
Tel.: (734) 283-4513
Kidney Dialysis Services
N.A.I.C.S.: 621492

Lathrop Dialysis, LLC (1)
3812 E Belknap St, Fort Worth, TX 76111
Tel.: (615) 320-4550
Kidney Dialysis Services
N.A.I.C.S.: 621492
Kent Thiry (Pres)

Latrobe Dialysis, LLC (1)
2000 16th St, Denver, CO 80202-5117
Tel.: (615) 341-5819
Medical Care Services
N.A.I.C.S.: 621492

Lawrenceburg Dialysis, LLC (1)
721 Rudolph Way, Lawrenceburg, IN 47025
Tel.: (812) 537-4240
Dialysis Treatment Services
N.A.I.C.S.: 621492

Lees Dialysis, LLC (1)
2000 16th St, Denver, CO 80202
Tel.: (703) 339-6050
Kidney Dialysis Center Services
N.A.I.C.S.: 621492

Liberty RC, Inc. (1)
80 State St, Albany, NY 12207
Tel.: (800) 424-6589
Health Care Srvices
N.A.I.C.S.: 621999

Lifeline Pensacola, LLC (1)
1 Pkwy N Ste 200S, Deerfield, IL 60015
Tel.: (847) 388-2001
Medical Care Services
N.A.I.C.S.: 621492

Lifeline Vascular Center - Orlando, LLC (1)
1511 Sligh Blvd, Orlando, FL 32806
Tel.: (407) 835-0196
Medical Care Services
N.A.I.C.S.: 621492

Lifeline Vascular Center of South Orlando, LLC (1)
1511 Sligh Blvd Ste A, Orlando, FL 32806
Tel.: (847) 949-3845
Kidney Dialysis Services
N.A.I.C.S.: 621492

Lifeline Vascular Center- Albany, LLC (1)
2300 Dawson Rd Ste, Albany, GA 31707-2803
Tel.: (847) 388-2001
Kidney Dialysis Center Services

N.A.I.C.S.: 621492

Lincoln Park Dialysis Services, Inc. (1)
2484 N Elston Ave, Chicago, IL 60647-2002
Sales Range: $1-9.9 Million
Provider of Dialysis Services
N.A.I.C.S.: 621492

Lincolnton Dialysis, LLC (1)
10994 Baltimore St NE, Blaine, MN 55449
Tel.: (763) 786-5026
Kidney Dialysis Services
N.A.I.C.S.: 621492

Little Rock Dialysis Centers, LLC (1)
300 Spring Bvld Sit 900 30 S Spring St, Little Rock, AR 72201
Tel.: (501) 945-2323
Emp.: 15
Kidney Dialysis Services
N.A.I.C.S.: 621492

Llano Dialysis, LLC (1)
5200 Virginia Way L & C Dept, Brentwood, TN 37027-7569
Tel.: (615) 341-5895
Kidney Dialysis Services
N.A.I.C.S.: 621492

Lockhart Dialysis, LLC (1)
330 S Lola Ln Ste 100, Pahrump, NV 89048-0879
Tel.: (775) 751-4300
Web Site: http://www.davita.com
Kidney Dialysis Services
N.A.I.C.S.: 621492

Long Beach Dialysis Center, LLC (1)
3744 Long Beach Blvd, Long Beach, CA 90807-3310
Tel.: (562) 435-3637
Medical Care Services
N.A.I.C.S.: 621492

Longworth Dialysis, LLC (1)
508 Meeting St, West Columbia, SC 29169
Tel.: (864) 877-9157
Kidney Dialysis Services
N.A.I.C.S.: 621492

Lord Baltimore Dialysis, LLC (1)
2711 Centerville Rd Ste 400, Wilmington, DE 19808
Tel.: (303) 876-6622
Dialysis Related Services
N.A.I.C.S.: 621492
James Hall (Mgr-Facility)

Loup Dialysis, LLC (1)
1011 Bowles Ave Ste 210, Fenton, MO 63026
Tel.: (636) 326-7130
Emp.: 15
Kidney Dialysis Services
N.A.I.C.S.: 621492

Lourdes Dialysis, LLC (1)
2000 16th St, Denver, CO 80202
Tel.: (407) 833-8667
Kidney Dialysis Services
N.A.I.C.S.: 621492
James K. Hilger (Chief Acctg Officer)

MVZ DaVita Alzey GmbH (1)
Am Damm 17, 55232, Alzey, Germany
Tel.: (49) 6731547440
Kidney Dialysis Center Operator
N.A.I.C.S.: 621492
Birgit Gaubatz (Head-Admin)

MVZ DaVita Ambulantes Kardiologisches Zentrum Peine GmbH (1)
Duttenstedter Street 11, 31224, Peine, Germany
Tel.: (49) 517176730
Web Site: http://www.kardiologie-peine.de
Cardiology Medicine Services
N.A.I.C.S.: 621111

MVZ DaVita Bad Aibling GmbH (1)
Fruhlingstrasse 2, 83043, Bad Aibling, Germany
Tel.: (49) 806130072
Cardiology Medicine Services
N.A.I.C.S.: 621111

MVZ DaVita Cardio Centrum Dusseldorf GmbH (1)
Konigsallee 61, 40215, Dusseldorf, Germany

Tel.: (49) 2119152990
Web Site: http://www.cardio-centrum.com
Cardiology Clinical Services
N.A.I.C.S.: 621111

MVZ DaVita Dillenburg GmbH (1)
Von Arnoldi Strasse 1, 35683, Dillenburg, Germany
Tel.: (49) 277187060
Web Site: https://www.davita.de
Cardiology Medicine Services
N.A.I.C.S.: 621111

MVZ DaVita Dinkelsbuhl GmbH (1)
Luitpoldstrasse 16, 91550, Dinkelsbuhl, Germany
Tel.: (49) 4041462950
Web Site: http://www.davita.de
Diagnosis & Kidney Disease Services
N.A.I.C.S.: 621492

MVZ DaVita Emden GmbH (1)
Bolardusstrasse 20, 26721, Emden, Germany
Tel.: (49) 2194400
Web Site: http://www.dialyse-emden.de
Kidney Dialysis Center Operator
N.A.I.C.S.: 621492

MVZ DaVita Geilenkirchen GmbH (1)
Herzog-Wilhelm-Strasse 105, 52511, Geilenkirchen, Germany
Tel.: (49) 245 190 3210
Web Site: https://www.davita.de
Cardiology & Nephrology Clinical Services
N.A.I.C.S.: 621111

MVZ DaVita Gera GmbH (1)
Strasse des Friedens 122, 07548, Gera, Germany
Tel.: (49) 36552780270
Web Site: https://www.davita.de
Kidney Dialysis Center Operator
N.A.I.C.S.: 621492

MVZ DaVita Neuss GmbH (1)
Am Hasenberg 44, 41462, Neuss, Germany
Tel.: (49) 213166591100
Web Site: http://www.dialyse-neuss.de
Kidney Dialysis Center Operator
N.A.I.C.S.: 621492

MVZ DaVita Nierenzentrum Berlin-Britz GmbH (1)
Britzer Damm 185, 12347, Berlin, Germany
Tel.: (49) 307 010 0910
Web Site: https://www.davita.de
Kidney Dialysis Services
N.A.I.C.S.: 621492

MVZ DaVita Rhein Ruhr GmbH (1)
Am Lichtbogen 43, 45141, Essen, Germany
Tel.: (49) 201863230
Web Site: http://www.ruhr-dialyse-essen.de
Kidney Dialysis Center Operator
N.A.I.C.S.: 621492

MVZ DaVita Rhein-Ahr GmbH (1)
Walporzheimer Str 30, 53474, Bad Neuenahr-Ahrweiler, Germany
Tel.: (49) 2641202640
Web Site: http://www.dialyse-rhein-ahr.de
Kidney Dialysis Services
N.A.I.C.S.: 621492

MVZ DaVita Salzgitter-Seesen GmbH (1)
Hinter dem Salze 33, 38259, Salzgitter, Germany
Tel.: (49) 53413013012
Kidney Dialysis Center Operator
N.A.I.C.S.: 621492

MVZ DaVita Viersen GmbH (1)
Ransberg 25, 41751, Viersen, Germany
Tel.: (49) 2162938900
Web Site: http://www.dialyse-viersen.de
Kidney Dialysis Services
N.A.I.C.S.: 621492

MVZ Dresden Betriebs GmbH (1)
Caspar-David-Friedrich-Str 10a, 01217, Dresden, Germany
Tel.: (49) 351876980
Web Site: http://www.mdb-dresden.de
Health Care Srvices
N.A.I.C.S.: 621999

Madigan Dialysis, LLC (1)
2000 16th St, Denver, CO 80202

Tel.: (813) 948-8157
Kidney Dialysis Center Operator
N.A.I.C.S.: 621492

Magnolia Dialysis, LLC   (1)
2000 16th St, Denver, CO 80202
Tel.: (941) 362-2864
Kidney Dialysis Center Operator
N.A.I.C.S.: 621492
Heather Fitzgerald (Mng Dir)

Magoffin Dialysis, LLC   (1)
107 Trenton Rd, Browns Mills, NJ 08015-
7050
Tel.: (615) 320-4414
Kidney Dialysis Center Operator
N.A.I.C.S.: 621492

Mahoney Dialysis, LLC   (1)
491 Colemans Xing Coleman s Crossing
Ctr, Marysville, OH 43040
Tel.: (937) 642-0676
Kidney Dialysis Services
N.A.I.C.S.: 621492

Mammoth Dialysis, LLC   (1)
2000 16th St, Denver, CO 80202
Tel.: (813) 960-3751
Web Site: http://www.davita.com
Kidney Dialysis Services
N.A.I.C.S.: 621492

Manchester Dialysis, LLC   (1)
3845 E Loop 820 S, Fort Worth, TX 76119
Tel.: (817) 496-9035
Kidney Dialysis Center Operator
N.A.I.C.S.: 621492

Manito Dialysis, LLC   (1)
750 W Route 66 Ste Q, Glendora, CA
91740-4164
Tel.: (626) 335-2063
Web Site: https://www.davita.com
Kidney Dialysis Center Operator
N.A.I.C.S.: 621492

Manzano Dialysis, LLC   (1)
1266 N Broad St, Fairborn, OH 45324-5549
Tel.: (937) 879-0433
Web Site: https://www.davita.com
Emp.: 36
Kidney Dialysis Services
N.A.I.C.S.: 621492

Maples Dialysis, LLC   (1)
300 Spring Bvld Sit 900 30 S Spring St,
Little Rock, AR 72201
Tel.: (870) 563-4901
Web Site: http://www.davita.com
Emp.: 10
Dialysis Treatment Services
N.A.I.C.S.: 621492

Marlton Dialysis Center, LLC   (1)
769 Route 70 E Ste C100, Marlton, NJ
08053-2361
Tel.: (856) 797-7044
Web Site: https://www.davita.com
Medical Care Services
N.A.I.C.S.: 621492

Marysville Dialysis Center, LLC   (1)
1015 8th St, Marysville, CA 95901-5271
Tel.: (530) 741-9801
Emp.: 15
Dialysis Treatment Services
N.A.I.C.S.: 621492

Mazonia Dialysis, LLC   (1)
2977 Redondo Ave, Long Beach, CA
90806-2445
Tel.: (562) 988-3418
Web Site: https://www.davita.com
Kidney Dialysis Center Operator
N.A.I.C.S.: 621492

Meadows Dialysis, LLC   (1)
1566 Sierra Vista Plz, Saint Louis, MO
63138-2040
Tel.: (314) 438-0864
Kidney Dialysis Center Operator
N.A.I.C.S.: 621492

Meesa Dialysis, LLC   (1)
245 Isle St W, Isle, MN 56342
Tel.: (320) 676-3593
Emp.: 16
Kidney Dialysis Center Operator
N.A.I.C.S.: 621492

Memorial Dialysis Center, L.P.   (1)
11621 Katy Fwy, Houston, TX 77079-1801

Tel.: (281) 558-5702
Web Site: https://www.davita.com
Medical Care Services
N.A.I.C.S.: 621492

Mena Dialysis Center, LLC   (1)
1200 Crestwood Cir, Mena, AR 71953-5516
Tel.: (479) 394-8085
Web Site: https://www.davita.com
Emp.: 8
Dialysis Treatment Services
N.A.I.C.S.: 621492

Mendocino Dialysis, LLC   (1)
3211 Interstate 45 N Ste 500, Conroe, TX
77304-2187
Tel.: (303) 876-6622
Web Site: https://www.davita.com
Kidney Dialysis Services
N.A.I.C.S.: 621492

Mesilla Dialysis, LLC   (1)
1430 E US Hwy 36, Urbana, OH 43078-
9112
Tel.: (937) 484-4600
Medical Care Services
N.A.I.C.S.: 621492

Minam Dialysis, LLC   (1)
8604 S Coulter St, Amarillo, TX 79119-7379
Tel.: (806) 358-0051
Web Site: https://www.davita.com
Kidney Dialysis Services
N.A.I.C.S.: 621492

Mission Dialysis Services, LLC   (1)
5200 Virginia Way, Brentwood, TN 37027-
7569
Tel.: (615) 341-6472
Kidney Dialysis Services
N.A.I.C.S.: 621492

Mocca Dialysis, LLC   (1)
1601 Spring St, Jeffersonville, IN 47130-
2903
Tel.: (812) 284-2098
Web Site: https://www.davita.com
Kidney Dialysis Center Operator
N.A.I.C.S.: 621492

**Moncrief Dialysis Center/Total Renal
Care Limited Partnership**   (1)
800 W 34th St Ste 101, Austin, TX 78705-
1143
Tel.: (512) 485-7872
Web Site: http://www.davita.com
Emp.: 20
Dialysis Treatment Services
N.A.I.C.S.: 621492

Montauk Dialysis, LLC   (1)
719 Bunny Trl, Sun Prairie, WI 53590-8507
Tel.: (608) 825-6556
Web Site: https://www.davita.com
Kidney Dialysis Center Operator
N.A.I.C.S.: 621492

Moraine Dialysis, LLC   (1)
2000 16th St, Denver, CO 80202
Tel.: (951) 808-9068
Kidney Dialysis Center Operator
N.A.I.C.S.: 621492

Morro Dialysis, LLC   (1)
290 Alexandersville Rd, Miamisburg, OH
45342-3611
Tel.: (937) 393-3852
Web Site: http://www.davita.com
Sales Range: $10-24.9 Million
Health Care Srvices
N.A.I.C.S.: 622110

Mountain View Medical Group   (1)
2 S Cascade Ave, Colorado Springs, CO
80903
Tel.: (719) 590-1177
Web Site: https://www.mvmg.com
Offices of Physicians (except Mental Health
Specialists)
N.A.I.C.S.: 621111

Mulgee Dialysis, LLC   (1)
14204 Prairie Ave, Hawthorne, CA 90250
Tel.: (310) 349-1174
Emp.: 18
Kidney Dialysis Services
N.A.I.C.S.: 621492
Frenaida Lina (Gen Mgr)

Muskogee Dialysis, LLC   (1)

2316 W Shawnee St, Muskogee, OK
74401-2228
Tel.: (918) 687-0016
Web Site: http://www.davita.com
Sales Range: $10-24.9 Million
Emp.: 10
Dialysis Treatment Services
N.A.I.C.S.: 621492

Myrtle Dialysis, LLC   (1)
2000 16th St, Denver, CO 80202
Tel.: (612) 852-7130
Kidney Dialysis Center Operator
N.A.I.C.S.: 621492

National Trail Dialysis, LLC   (1)
171 S Tuttle Rd, Springfield, OH 45505-
1560
Tel.: (615) 320-4458
Web Site: http://www.davita.com
Emp.: 10
Health Care Srvices
N.A.I.C.S.: 622110

Natomas Dialysis, LLC   (1)
30 Golden Land Ct Bldg G, Sacramento,
CA 95834-2423
Tel.: (916) 285-6452
Web Site: http://www.davita.com
Medical Care Services
N.A.I.C.S.: 621492

Navarro Dialysis, LLC   (1)
764 Hwy 34 Ste A, Matawan, NJ 07747-
6614
Tel.: (732) 583-1085
Kidney Dialysis Center Operator
N.A.I.C.S.: 621492

Naville Dialysis, LLC   (1)
1424 E Whitmore Ave, Ceres, CA 95307-
9215
Tel.: (209) 541-0112
Kidney Dialysis Center Operator
N.A.I.C.S.: 621492

Neff Dialysis, LLC   (1)
1710 Ctr Ave W, Dilworth, MN 56529
Tel.: (218) 233-3354
Kidney Dialysis Services
N.A.I.C.S.: 621492

**Nephrology Medical Associates of
Georgia, LLC**   (1)
334 Smith Ave, Thomasville, GA 31792
Tel.: (229) 227-1595
Web Site: https://gakidney.com
Sales Range: $1-9.9 Million
Emp.: 40
Kidney Dialysis Center Services
N.A.I.C.S.: 621492

New Bay Dialysis, LLC   (1)
720 W Broadway, Louisville, KY 40202-
2240
Tel.: (502) 584-2059
Web Site: http://www.davita.com
Kidney Dialysis Services
N.A.I.C.S.: 621492

Nolia Dialysis, LLC   (1)
900 N Blue Mound Rd Ste 192, Saginaw,
TX 76131-4810
Tel.: (817) 232-1502
Kidney Dialysis Center Operator
N.A.I.C.S.: 621492

Norte Dialysis, LLC   (1)
7650 River Rd Ste 150, North Bergen, NJ
07047
Tel.: (201) 861-1031
Kidney Dialysis Center Operator
N.A.I.C.S.: 621492

**North Colorado Springs Dialysis,
LLC**   (1)
6011 E Woodmen Rd Ste 120, Colorado
Springs, CO 80923
Tel.: (719) 571-8600
Web Site: http://www.davita.com
Dialysis Treatment Services
N.A.I.C.S.: 621492

Northwest Tucson Dialysis, LLC   (1)
8825 N 23rd Ave Ste 100, Phoenix, AZ
85021
Tel.: (520) 797-0049
Web Site: http://www.davita.com
Sales Range: $10-24.9 Million
Emp.: 15
Health Care Srvices

N.A.I.C.S.: 622110

Noster Dialysis, LLC   (1)
8080 Limonite Ave, Jurupa Valley, CA
92509-6107
Tel.: (951) 361-9405
Kidney Dialysis Center Operator
N.A.I.C.S.: 621492

Oasis Dialysis, LLC   (1)
1213 Hermann Dr Ste 180, Houston, TX
77004-7018
Tel.: (713) 529-5155
Kidney Dialysis Training Services
N.A.I.C.S.: 621492

Okanogan Dialysis, LLC   (1)
5200 Virginia Way L & C Dept, Brentwood,
TN 37027-7569
Tel.: (615) 341-6406
Medical Care Services
N.A.I.C.S.: 621492

Olive Dialysis, LLC   (1)
105 Michael Martin Rd, Mount Olive, NC
28365-1112
Tel.: (610) 722-6019
Kidney Dialysis Services
N.A.I.C.S.: 621492

Orange Dialysis, LLC   (1)
10055 Whittwood Dr, Whittier, CA 90603-
2313
Tel.: (562) 947-1808
Kidney Dialysis Services
N.A.I.C.S.: 621492

Osage Dialysis, LLC   (1)
6225 Atlanta Hwy Ste 117, Alpharetta, GA
30004
Tel.: (770) 569-1275
Emp.: 8
Kidney Dialysis Services
N.A.I.C.S.: 621492

Owasso Dialysis, LLC   (1)
9521 N Owasso Expy, Owasso, OK 74055-
5414
Tel.: (918) 376-9479
Web Site: http://www.davita.com
Emp.: 5
Health Care Srvices
N.A.I.C.S.: 622110

Owyhee Dialysis, LLC   (1)
601 Hawaii, El Segundo, CA 90245
Tel.: (316) 773-1400
Kidney Dialysis Services
N.A.I.C.S.: 621492

Pacheco Dialysis, LLC   (1)
1007 E Kearney St, Springfield, MO 65803-
3433
Tel.: (417) 873-9926
Web Site: http://www.davita.com
Kidney Dialysis Services
N.A.I.C.S.: 621492

Palmetto Dialysis, LLC   (1)
5200 Virginia Way, Brentwood, TN 37027-
7569
Tel.: (615) 341-5893
Kidney Dialysis Services
N.A.I.C.S.: 621492

Palomar Dialysis, LLC   (1)
3201 Doolan Rd Ste 175, Livermore, CA
94551-9610
Tel.: (303) 876-6622
Kidney Dialysis Services
N.A.I.C.S.: 621492

Parker Dialysis, LLC   (1)
225 Plaza Dr, Monroe, GA 30655-3184
Tel.: (770) 207-0850
Web Site: http://www.davita.com
Kidney Dialysis Services
N.A.I.C.S.: 621492

Parkside Dialysis, LLC   (1)
2711 Centerville Rd Ste 400, Wilmington,
DE 19808
Tel.: (410) 358-1745
Kidney Dialysis Center Operator
N.A.I.C.S.: 621492

Patient Pathways, LLC   (1)
1551 Wewatta St, Denver, CO 80202-6173
Tel.: (310) 536-2506
Kidney Dialysis Services
N.A.I.C.S.: 621492

DaVita Inc.—(Continued)

Patoka Dialysis, LLC (1)
2000 16th St, Denver, CO 80202
Tel.: (954) 426-3350
Kidney Dialysis Services
N.A.I.C.S.: 621492

Pearl Dialysis, LLC (1)
14050 Pilot Knob Rd Ste 100, Apple Valley,
MN 55124-6470
Tel.: (952) 423-4062
Medical Care Services
N.A.I.C.S.: 621492

Pedernales Dialysis, LLC (1)
213 Delores St, Colquitt, GA 39837
Tel.: (229) 758-1985
Kidney Dialysis Center Operator
N.A.I.C.S.: 621492

Pekin Dialysis, LLC (1)
1021 Court St Ste A, Pekin, IL 61554-4817
Tel.: (309) 346-0159
Emp.: 10
Kidney Dialysis Services
N.A.I.C.S.: 621492
Rana Ritchie (Gen Mgr)

Pendster Dialysis, LLC (1)
7769 Old Country Ct, Huber Heights, OH
45424-0970
Tel.: (937) 237-0769
Kidney Dialysis Center Operator
N.A.I.C.S.: 621492

Percha Dialysis, LLC (1)
74 Camaritas Ave S, San Francisco, CA
94080-3133
Tel.: (650) 589-8562
Kidney Dialysis Services
N.A.I.C.S.: 621492

**Philadelphia-Camden Integrated Kid-
ney Care, LLC.** (1)
2000 16th St, Denver, CO 80202
Web Site:
http://www.philadelphiacamdenesco.com
Kidney Dialysis Services
N.A.I.C.S.: 621492

Physicians Choice Dialysis, LLC (1)
211 Commerce Ct Ste 104, Pottstown, PA
19464
Tel.: (610) 495-8900
Web Site: https://phychoice.com
Kidney Dialysis Services
N.A.I.C.S.: 621492
Thomas J. Karl (Chm, Pres & CEO)
Cindy Locklear (Chief Clinical Officer)
Kelly Smith (Dir-Contracts & HR)
Kimbery Pfeffer (Mgr-Reimbursement)
Stephanie Domurat (Supvr-Collection)

**Physicians Dialysis of Lancaster,
LLC** (1)
1412 E King St, Lancaster, PA 17602-3240
Tel.: (717) 392-1552
Web Site: http://www.davita.com
Kidney Dialysis Services
N.A.I.C.S.: 621492

Pible Dialysis, LLC (1)
5200 Virginia Way, Brentwood, TN 80011
Tel.: (615) 341-6765
Kidney Dialysis Services
N.A.I.C.S.: 621492

Pittsburg Dialysis Partners, LLC (1)
5200 Virginia Way L & C Dept, Brentwood,
TN 37027-7569
Tel.: (615) 320-4414
Kidney Dialysis Services
N.A.I.C.S.: 621492

Plaine Dialysis, LLC (1)
1525 Plumas Ct Ste A, Yuba City, CA
95991-2971
Tel.: (530) 671-3652
Sales Range: $10-24.9 Million
Emp.: 32
Kidney Dialysis Services
N.A.I.C.S.: 621492

Platte Dialysis, LLC (1)
305 S J T Stites St, Sallisaw, OK 74955-
9302
Tel.: (918) 235-0290
Web Site: http://www.davita -
Kidney Dialysis Services
N.A.I.C.S.: 621492

Pluribus Dialise - Benfica, S.A. (1)
Rua dos Arneiros 64, 1500-060, Lisbon,
Portugal
Tel.: (351) 211166030
Web Site: https://www.davita.pt
Kidney Dialysis Services
N.A.I.C.S.: 621492

Pluribus Dialise - Cascais, S.A. (1)
Rua Fernao Lopes 60 Cobre, 2750-663,
Cascais, Portugal
Tel.: (351) 211166000
Web Site: https://www.davita.pt
Kidney Dialysis Services
N.A.I.C.S.: 621492

Pluribus Dialise - Sacavem, S.A. (1)
Rua Cooperativa a Sacavenense 21, 2685-
005, Sacavem, Portugal
Tel.: (351) 211166020
Clinical Services
N.A.I.C.S.: 621999

Pobello Dialysis, LLC (1)
21026 W Bellfort St, Richmond, TX 77406
Tel.: (832) 595-0187
Health Care Srvices
N.A.I.C.S.: 621999

Pointe Dialysis, LLC (1)
508 Meeting St, West Columbia, SC 29169
Tel.: (843) 852-3537
Web Site: http://www.davita.com
Emp.: 15
Health Care Srvices
N.A.I.C.S.: 622110

Pokagon Dialysis, LLC (1)
100 W Washington Blvd, Montebello, CA
90640
Tel.: (323) 728-2984
Kidney Dialysis Center Services
N.A.I.C.S.: 621492

Ponca Dialysis, LLC (1)
1290 Tully Rd Ste 60, San Jose, CA 95122-
3069
Tel.: (408) 275-0105
Kidney Dialysis Services
N.A.I.C.S.: 621492

Portola Dialysis, LLC (1)
323 N Michigan Ave, Saginaw, MI 48602-
4240
Tel.: (989) 791-3624
Web Site: http://www.davita.com
Sales Range: $10-24.9 Million
Kidney Dialysis Services
N.A.I.C.S.: 621492

Powerton Dialysis, LLC (1)
5200 Virginia Way L & C Dept, Brentwood,
TN 37027-7569
Tel.: (615) 341-6311
Kidney Dialysis Services
N.A.I.C.S.: 621492

Prairie Dialysis, LLC (1)
721 W 1st St, Tustin, CA 92780-9030
Tel.: (714) 544-0079
Kidney Dialysis Center Operator
N.A.I.C.S.: 621492

Priday Dialysis, LLC (1)
725 Ridder Park Dr Ste 50, San Jose, CA
95131-2431
Tel.: (303) 876-6622
Kidney Dialysis Services
N.A.I.C.S.: 621492

Quality Dialysis Care Sdn. Bhd. (1)
No 63 Jalan Wangsa Delima 5 Seksyen 5
Wangsa Maju Wilayah Persekutuan, 53300,
Kuala Lumpur, Malaysia
Tel.: (60) 162267972
Emp.: 4
Kidney Dialysis Services
N.A.I.C.S.: 621492

RMS Lifeline, Inc. (1)
1 Pkwy N Ste 200S, Deerfield, IL 60015
Tel.: (847) 388-2019
Web Site: https://lifelinevascular.com
Health Care Srvices
N.A.I.C.S.: 621999
Jeff Peo (Mng Partner)
Jason Lohmeyer (CFO)

RNA-DaVita Dialysis, LLC (1)
601 Hawaii St, El Segundo, CA 90245
Tel.: (310) 536-2400

Emp.: 20
Kidney Dialysis Services
N.A.I.C.S.: 621492

Rancho Dialysis, LLC (1)
899 E Iron Ave, Dover, OH 44622
Tel.: (253) 382-1493
Web Site: http://www.davita.com
Emp.: 15
Dialysis Treatment Services
N.A.I.C.S.: 621492
David Smith (Chief Admin Officer)

Red Willow Dialysis, LLC (1)
7198 Castor Ave, Philadelphia, PA 19149-
1105
Tel.: (215) 745-4060
Kidney Dialysis Services
N.A.I.C.S.: 621492

Redcliff Dialysis, LLC (1)
5200 Virginia Way, Brentwood, TN 37027
Tel.: (615) 320-4414
Medical Care Services
N.A.I.C.S.: 621492

Reef Dialysis, LLC (1)
2000 16th St, Denver, CO 80202
Tel.: (850) 969-9082
Kidney Dialysis Services
N.A.I.C.S.: 621492
Ryan Smith (Gen Mgr)

**Renal Center of Flower Mound,
LLC** (1)
4941 Long Prairie Rd, Flower Mound, TX
75028-2782
Kidney Care & Hemodialysis Services
N.A.I.C.S.: 621492

Renal Center of Frisco, LLC (1)
10850 Frisco St Ste 300, Frisco, TX 75033-
3586
Web Site: https://www.davita.com
Kidney Care & Hemodialysis Services
N.A.I.C.S.: 621492

Renal Center of Lewisville, LLC (1)
1600 Waters Rdg Dr B, Lewisville, TX
75057
Tel.: (972) 436-7211
Web Site: https://www.davita.com
Emp.: 30
Kidney Dialysis Services
N.A.I.C.S.: 621492

Renal Center of Nederland, LLC (1)
8797 9th Ave, Port Arthur, TX 77642-8011
Kidney Dialysis Services
N.A.I.C.S.: 621492

**Renal Center of North Denton,
L.L.L.P.** (1)
4309 Mesa Dr, Denton, TX 76207
Tel.: (940) 566-2701
Web Site: https://www.davita.com
Emp.: 25
Kidney Dialysis Services
N.A.I.C.S.: 621492
Tracy Weed (Dir-Nursing)

Renal Center of Port Arthur, LLC (1)
3730 Dryden Rd, Port Arthur, TX 77642
Tel.: (409) 983-4110
Web Site: https://www.davita.com
Kidney Dialysis Services
N.A.I.C.S.: 621492

**Renal Center of Storm Lake,
LLC** (1)
1426 Lake Ave, Storm Lake, IA 50588-1910
Kidney Dialysis Services
N.A.I.C.S.: 021492

Renal Life Link, Inc. (1)
2000 16th St, Denver, CO 80202
Kidney Dialysis Services
N.A.I.C.S.: 621492

**Renal Treatment Centers - Hawaii,
Inc.** (1)
1003 Bishop St Ste 1600 Pauahi Tower,
Honolulu, HI 96813
Tel.: (808) 521-8061
Sales Range: $50-74.9 Million
Provider of Dialysis Services
N.A.I.C.S.: 621492

**Renal Treatment Centers-California,
Inc.** (1)

40945 County Center Dr Ste G, Temecula,
CA 92591-6006
Dialysis Treatment Services
N.A.I.C.S.: 621492

**Renal Treatment Centers-Illinois,
Inc.** (1)
3410 Belle Chase Way Ste 600, Lansing,
MI 48911
Tel.: (810) 733-5004
Kidney Dialysis Services
N.A.I.C.S.: 621492

**Renal Treatment Centers-Mid-
Atlantic, Inc.** (1)
4861 Tesla Dr Ste G H J, Bowie, MD 20715
Tel.: (301) 809-5342
Web Site: http://www.davita.com
Medical Care Services
N.A.I.C.S.: 621492

**Renal Treatment Centers-West,
Inc.** (1)
1315 E 4th Ave, Winfield, KS 67156-2457
Tel.: (620) 221-4100
Web Site: https://www.davita.com
Sales Range: $10-24.9 Million
Emp.: 10
Medical Care Services
N.A.I.C.S.: 621492

Rio Dialysis, LLC (1)
3461 W Broadway Ave, Robbinsdale, MN
55422-2955
Tel.: (763) 521-4865
Web Site: http://www.davita.com
Kidney Dialysis Services
N.A.I.C.S.: 621492

Ripley Dialysis, LLC (1)
854 Hwy 51 S, Ripley, TN 38063
Tel.: (731) 221-1883
Emp.: 25
Kidney Dialysis Centers
N.A.I.C.S.: 621492

Rita Ranch Dialysis, LLC (1)
7355 S Houghton Rd No 101, Tucson, AZ
85747-9379
Tel.: (520) 663-4035
Kidney Dialysis Services
N.A.I.C.S.: 621492
Julie Rex (Mgr)

River Valley Dialysis, LLC (1)
3121 W 2nd Ct, Russellville, AR 72801-
4504
Tel.: (859) 371-1263
Web Site: http://www.davita.com
Sales Range: $10-24.9 Million
Kidney Dialysis Services
N.A.I.C.S.: 621492

Robinson Dialysis, LLC (1)
1215 N Allen St Ste B, Robinson, IL 62454-
1100
Tel.: (618) 544-7092
Web Site: http://www.davita.com
Emp.: 8
Kidney Dialysis Centers
N.A.I.C.S.: 621492

Roushe Dialysis, LLC (1)
1420 Trinity Pl, Mishawaka, IN 46545-5005
Tel.: (253) 382-1869
Kidney Dialysis Services
N.A.I.C.S.: 621492

Russell Dialysis, LLC (1)
941 S Westgate Way, Wylie, TX 75098-
4947
Tel.: (972) 429-4315
Web Site: http://www.davita.com
Kidney Dialysis Services
N.A.I.C.S.: 621492

Rye Dialysis, LLC (1)
377 Boxwood Ln, Pearisburg, VA 24134-
1660
Tel.: (540) 921-1384
Kidney Dialysis Services
N.A.I.C.S.: 621492

Saddleback Dialysis, LLC (1)
2377 Hwy 196 W, Hinesville, GA 31313-
8036
Tel.: (912) 368-2710
Web Site: http://www.davita.com
Kidney Dialysis Centers
N.A.I.C.S.: 621492

San Marcos Dialysis, LLC (1)
2135 Montiel Rd Bldg B, San Marcos, CA 92069
Tel.: (610) 722-6019
Emp.: 20
Kidney Dialysis Services
N.A.I.C.S.: 621492

Sandusky Dialysis, LLC (1)
211 Lakeside Park, Sandusky, OH 44870-8639
Tel.: (419) 609-1847
Web Site: http://www.davita.com
Kidney Dialysis Services
N.A.I.C.S.: 621492

Santa Fe Springs Dialysis, LLC (1)
11147 Washington Blvd, Whittier, CA 90606
Tel.: (562) 695-0827
Emp.: 20
Dialysis Treatment Services
N.A.I.C.S.: 621492
Carlos Benologa (Gen Mgr)

Santiam Dialysis, LLC (1)
5923 Westheimer Rd, Houston, TX 77057-6030
Tel.: (281) 358-3071
Kidney Dialysis Services
N.A.I.C.S.: 621492

Seasons Dialysis, LLC (1)
720 Cog Cir, Crystal Lake, IL 60014-7301
Tel.: (815) 459-4945
Kidney Dialysis Services
N.A.I.C.S.: 621492

Seminole Dialysis, LLC (1)
76 Highland Pavilion Ct Ste 129, Hiram, GA 30141-3170
Tel.: (678) 384-1180
Web Site: http://www.davita.com
Kidney Dialysis Services
N.A.I.C.S.: 621492

Seneca Dialysis, LLC (1)
10 St Lawrence Dr, Tiffin, OH 44883
Tel.: (419) 443-1051
Kidney Dialysis Services
N.A.I.C.S.: 621492

Shadow Dialysis, LLC (1)
6406 Tupelo Dr Ste A, Citrus Heights, CA 95621-1780
Tel.: (253) 382-1869
Emp.: 20
Kidney Dialysis Services
N.A.I.C.S.: 621492

Shawano Dialysis, LLC (1)
W 7305 Elm Ave, Shawano, WI 54166
Kidney Dialysis Services
N.A.I.C.S.: 621492

Shayano Dialysis, LLC (1)
15555 E 14th St Ste 520, San Leandro, CA 94578-1949
Tel.: (510) 317-6510
Web Site: http://www.davita.com
Sales Range: $10-24.9 Million
Dialysis Treatment Services
N.A.I.C.S.: 621492

Shelby Dialysis, LLC (1)
13525 E Fwy Ste A, Houston, TX 77015-5902
Tel.: (615) 341-6472
Kidney Dialysis Center Services
N.A.I.C.S.: 621492

Shelling Dialysis, LLC (1)
1197 S Redondo Ctr Dr, Yuma, AZ 85365
Tel.: (928) 329-4340
Kidney Dialysis Center Operator
N.A.I.C.S.: 621492

Shining Star Dialysis, Inc. (1)
525 Jack Martin Blvd Ste 200, Brick, NJ 08724-7737
Tel.: (732) 836-9669
Web Site: http://www.davita.com
Medical Care Services
N.A.I.C.S.: 621492

Shoals Dialysis, LLC (1)
101 Okatie Ctr Blvd S, Bluffton, SC 29909
Tel.: (843) 706-9900
Emp.: 26
Kidney Dialysis Services
N.A.I.C.S.: 621492

Shone Dialysis, LLC (1)

10132 Carlin Ave, Covington, GA 30014
Tel.: (770) 385-8008
Kidney Dialysis Center Operator
N.A.I.C.S.: 621492

Shoshone Dialysis, LLC (1)
46360 Gratiot Ave, Chesterfield, MI 48051
Tel.: (586) 949-5417
Kidney Dialysis Center Operator
N.A.I.C.S.: 621492

Siena Dialysis Center, LLC (1)
2865 Siena Hts Dr Ste 141, Henderson, NV 89052-4168
Tel.: (702) 260-0348
Web Site: http://www.davita.com
Medical Care Services
N.A.I.C.S.: 621492

Silverwood Dialysis, LLC (1)
1208 N Arlington Ave, Indianapolis, IN 46219-3203
Tel.: (317) 353-6315
Kidney Dialysis Services
N.A.I.C.S.: 621492

Smithgall Dialysis, LLC (1)
425 M-b Ln, Chilton, WI 53014-1604
Tel.: (920) 849-3441
Kidney Dialysis Center Operator
N.A.I.C.S.: 621492

Soledad Dialysis Center, LLC (1)
901 Los Coches Dr, Soledad, CA 93960-2995
Tel.: (831) 678-4310
Emp.: 15
Dialysis Treatment Services
N.A.I.C.S.: 621492

Somerville Dialysis Center, LLC (1)
2000 16th St, Denver, CO 80202-5117
Tel.: (610) 722-6019
Kidney Dialysis Services
N.A.I.C.S.: 621492

South Central Florida Dialysis Partners, LLC (1)
2000 16th St, Denver, CO 80202
Tel.: (407) 532-3109
Medical Care Services
N.A.I.C.S.: 621492

South Florida Integrated Kidney Care, LLC (1)
2000 16th St, Denver, CO 80202
Web Site: http://www.southfloridaesco.com
Kidney Dialysis Services
N.A.I.C.S.: 621492

South Shore Dialysis Center. L.P. (1)
212 Gulf Fwy S Ste G3, League City, TX 77573-3956
Tel.: (281) 554-6050
Dialysis Treatment Services
N.A.I.C.S.: 621492

Southcrest Dialysis, LLC (1)
10921 E 81st St, Tulsa, OK 74133-4227
Tel.: (918) 249-8402
Emp.: 20
Medical Care Services
N.A.I.C.S.: 621492

Southern Hills Dialysis Center, LLC (1)
9280 W Sunset Rd Ste 110, Las Vegas, NV 89148-4861
Tel.: (610) 722-6019
Kidney Dialysis Services
N.A.I.C.S.: 621492

Southwest Atlanta Dialysis Centers, LLC (1)
3620 Martin Luther King Dr SW, Atlanta, GA 30331-3711
Kidney Care & Hemodialysis Services
N.A.I.C.S.: 621492
Cynthia Marsh (Gen Mgr)

Southwest Indiana Dialysis, LLC (1)
1136 N Baldwin Ave, Marion, IN 46952
Tel.: (765) 662-1245
Kidney Dialysis Services
N.A.I.C.S.: 621492

Star Dialysis, LLC (1)
201 Sw L St, Grants Pass, OR 97526
Tel.: (541) 474-0776
Kidney Dialysis Services

N.A.I.C.S.: 621492
Kandall Springer (Mgr)

Starks Dialysis, LLC (1)
2301 Martin Luther King Jr Blvd, Tampa, FL 33606
Tel.: (615) 320-4214
Kidney Dialysis Center Operator
N.A.I.C.S.: 621492

Stearns Dialysis, LLC (1)
1601 Prospect Pkwy Unit J, Fort Collins, CO 80525-9992
Tel.: (202) 256-1324
Kidney Dialysis Center Operator
N.A.I.C.S.: 621492

Stewart Dialysis, LLC (1)
4200 Macdonald Ave, Richmond, CA 94805-2315
Tel.: (510) 236-8861
Kidney Dialysis Services
N.A.I.C.S.: 621492

Stines Dialysis, LLC (1)
2000 16th St, Denver, CO 80202-0000
Tel.: (757) 518-9439
Kidney Dialysis Services
N.A.I.C.S.: 621492
Cynthia Whiting (Gen Mgr)

Stockton Dialysis, LLC (1)
620 S Santa Fe Ave Ste C, Moore, OK 73160
Tel.: (405) 799-2439
Kidney Dialysis Center Operator
N.A.I.C.S.: 621492

Storrie Dialysis, LLC (1)
2200 N Limestone St Ste 104, Springfield, OH 45503-2692
Tel.: (937) 390-3125
Web Site: http://www.davita.com
Medical Care Services
N.A.I.C.S.: 621492

Strongsville Dialysis, LLC (1)
17792 Pearl Rd, Strongsville, OH 44136
Tel.: (440) 238-9270
Dialysis Treatment Services
N.A.I.C.S.: 621492

Sugarite Dialysis, LLC (1)
4600 Shelbyville Rd, Louisville, KY 40207-3326
Tel.: (502) 893-4791
Web Site: http://www.davita.com
Sales Range: $10-24.9 Million
Emp.: 4
Health Care Srvices
N.A.I.C.S.: 622110

Sugarloaf Dialysis, LLC (1)
1705 Belle Meade Ct Ste 110, Lawrenceville, GA 30043-5895
Tel.: (770) 513-2833
Web Site: https://www.davita.com
Medical Care Services
N.A.I.C.S.: 621492

Summit Dialysis Center, L.P. (1)
1139 Spruce Dr, Mountainside, NJ 07092-2221
Tel.: (610) 722-6019
Web Site: https://www.davita.com
Kidney Dialysis Centers
N.A.I.C.S.: 621492

Sun City Dialysis Center, LLC (1)
14664 N Del Webb Blvd, Sun City, AZ 85351-2137
Tel.: (623) 583-6550
Emp.: 20
Dialysis Treatment Services
N.A.I.C.S.: 621492

Sun City West Dialysis Center LLC (1)
13907 W Camino Del Sol Ste 103, Sun City, AZ 85375-4405
Tel.: (623) 214-7088
Web Site: http://www.davita.com
Dialysis Treatment Services
N.A.I.C.S.: 621492

Sun Desert Dialysis, LLC (1)
2711 Centerville Rd Ste 400, Wilmington, DE 19808
Tel.: (610) 722-6019
Kidney Dialysis Services
N.A.I.C.S.: 621492

Sunset Dialysis, LLC (1)
3071 Gold Canal Dr, Rancho Cordova, CA 95670-6129
Tel.: (916) 638-8429
Web Site: https://www.davita.com
Dialysis Treatment Services
N.A.I.C.S.: 621492

TRC - Indiana, LLC (1)
222 Douglas St, Hammond, IN 46320-1960
Tel.: (219) 932-1199
Dialysis Treatment Services
N.A.I.C.S.: 621492

TRC West, Inc. (1)
21250 Hawthrone Blvd Ste 800, Torrance, CA 90503-5517
Tel.: (310) 792-2600
Sales Range: $10-24.9 Million
Emp.: 70
Kidney Dialysis Center Services
N.A.I.C.S.: 621492

TRC of New York, Inc. (1)
2000 16th St, Denver, CO 80202
Tel.: (914) 949-5371
Kidney Dialysis Services
N.A.I.C.S.: 621492

TRC-Four Corners Dialysis Clinics, LLC (1)
610 E Main St Ste C, Cortez, CO 81321-3308
Tel.: (970) 565-4302
Kidney Dialysis Centers
N.A.I.C.S.: 621492

TRC-Petersburg, LLC (1)
5200 Virginia Way L & C Dept, Brentwood, TN 37027-7569
Tel.: (615) 341-5875
Health Care Srvices
N.A.I.C.S.: 621999

Taylor Dialysis, LLC (1)
3100 W 2nd St, Taylor, TX 76574-4647
Tel.: (512) 352-2549
Web Site: https://www.davita.com
Emp.: 12
Dialysis Treatment Services
N.A.I.C.S.: 621492
Brenda Cox (Gen Mgr)

Tennessee Valley Dialysis Center, LLC (1)
107 Woodlawn Dr Ste 2, Johnson City, TN 37604-6287
Tel.: (423) 926-2976
Web Site: https://www.davita.com
Dialysis Treatment Services
N.A.I.C.S.: 621492

Tonka Bay Dialysis, LLC (1)
1221 Delaware Ave, Marion, OH 43302-4190
Tel.: (740) 375-0849
Kidney Dialysis Center Operator
N.A.I.C.S.: 621492

Tortugas Dialysis, LLC (1)
2000 16th St, Denver, CO 80202-5117
Tel.: (901) 348-1931
Medical Care Services
N.A.I.C.S.: 621492

Total Renal Care North Carolina, LLC (1)
3147 S 17th St, Wilmington, NC 28412
Tel.: (910) 395-4856
Kidney Dialysis Services
N.A.I.C.S.: 621492

Total Renal Care Texas Limited Partnership (1)
9110 Jones Rd Ste 110, Houston, TX 77065
Tel.: (281) 517-0527
Health Care Srvices
N.A.I.C.S.: 621999

Total Renal Care/Crystal River Dialysis, L.C. (1)
2000 16th St, Denver, CO 80202
Tel.: (352) 564-8400
Web Site: http://www.davita.com
Emp.: 20
Health Care Srvices
N.A.I.C.S.: 622110

Total Renal Care/Eaton Canyon Dialysis Center Partnership (1)

DaVita Inc.—(Continued)

2551 E Washington Blvd, Pasadena, CA
91107-1446
Tel.: (626) 798-8896
Emp.: 50
Kidney Dialysis Services
N.A.I.C.S.: 621492

Total Renal Laboratories, Inc. (1)
3000 DaVita Way, Deland, FL 32724
Tel.: (386) 738-1809
Web Site: https://davitalabs.com
Sales Range: $75-99.9 Million
Emp.: 300
Provider of Medical Research Services
N.A.I.C.S.: 621511
Mike Hahn (Gen Mgr)

Townsend Dialysis, LLC (1)
2000 16th St, Denver, CO 80202
Tel.: (954) 473-9138
Emp.: 4
Kidney Dialysis Services
N.A.I.C.S.: 621492
Rosalyn Tanudtanud (Gen Mgr)

Trailstone Dialysis, LLC (1)
2403 S Vineyard Ave Ste D, Ontario, CA
91761-6471
Tel.: (615) 341-5895
Kidney Dialysis Center Operator
N.A.I.C.S.: 621492

Transmountain Dialysis, L.P. (1)
5800 Woodrow Bean, El Paso, TX 79924-
5060
Tel.: (915) 751-5400
Web Site: https://www.davita.com
Emp.: 20
Medical Care Services
N.A.I.C.S.: 621492
Dina Martinez (Office Mgr)

Tree City Dialysis, LLC (1)
3410 Belle Chase Way Ste 600, Lansing,
MI 48911
Tel.: (248) 352-3137
Kidney Dialysis Services
N.A.I.C.S.: 621492

Tross Dialysis, LLC (1)
2000 16th St, Denver, CO 80202
Tel.: (253) 382-1493
Kidney Dialysis Center Operator
N.A.I.C.S.: 621492

Tulsa Dialysis, LLC (1)
5636 E Skelly Dr, Tulsa, OK 74135-6473
Tel.: (253) 382-1186
Web Site: https://www.davita.com
Dialysis Treatment Services
N.A.I.C.S.: 621492
Kristen Monroe (Office Mgr)

Tunnel Dialysis, LLC (1)
319 Lake Ave, Metuchen, NJ 08840
Tel.: (732) 906-5714
Kidney Dialysis Center Operator
N.A.I.C.S.: 621492

Turlock Dialysis Center, LLC (1)
50 W Syracuse Ave, Turlock, CA 95380-
3143
Tel.: (610) 722-6019
Web Site: https://www.davita.com
Dialysis Treatment Services
N.A.I.C.S.: 621492

Tustin Dialysis Center, LLC (1)
2090 N Tustin Ave Ste 100, Santa Ana, CA
92705-7869
Tel.: (714) 835-2450
Web Site: https://www.davita.com
Kidney Dialysis Centers
N.A.I.C.S.: 621492

Tyler Dialysis, LLC (1)
5200 Virginia Way L & C Dept, Brentwood,
TN 37027-7569
Tel.: (615) 341-6410
Kidney Dialysis Services
N.A.I.C.S.: 621492

**USC-DaVita Dialysis Center,
LLC** (1)
2310 Alcazar St, Los Angeles, CA 90033-
5327
Tel.: (323) 441-9966
Web Site: https://www.davita.com
Dialysis Treatment Services

N.A.I.C.S.: 621492

**UT Southwestern DVA Healthcare,
LLP** (1)
3402 N Buckner Blvd Ste 308, Dallas, TX
75228-5656
Tel.: (214) 941-7807
Dialysis Treatment Services
N.A.I.C.S.: 621492
Jeff Daniels (CEO)

Ukiah Dialysis, LLC (1)
17191 St Lukes Way Ste 100, The Wood-
lands, TX 77384-0420
Tel.: (614) 341-6472
Kidney Dialysis Services
N.A.I.C.S.: 621492

Unicoi Dialysis, LLC (1)
629 Cranbury Rd Ste 101, East Brunswick,
NJ 08816-4096
Tel.: (615) 320-4414
Web Site: http://www.davita.com
Kidney Dialysis Services
N.A.I.C.S.: 621492

University Dialysis Center, LLC (1)
333 University Ave Ste 100, Sacramento,
CA 95825
Tel.: (916) 920-0877
Health Care Srvices
N.A.I.C.S.: 621492

Upper Valley Dialysis, L.P (1)
7933 N Mesa St Ste H, El Paso, TX 79932-
1699
Web Site: https://www.davita.com
Kidney Dialysis Services
N.A.I.C.S.: 621492

Valley Springs Dialysis, LLC (1)
3855 S Jones Blvd Ste 101, Las Vegas, NV
89103-2296
Web Site: https://www.davita.com
Kidney Dialysis Services
N.A.I.C.S.: 621492

Victory Dialysis, LLC (1)
2401 Shelby St, Columbus, GA 31903-3360
Tel.: (410) 553-6951
Web Site: https://www.davita.com
Sales Range: $10-24.9 Million
Emp.: 20
Kidney Dialysis Services
N.A.I.C.S.: 621492

VillageHealth DM, LLC (1)
Three Hawthorn Pkwy Ste 410, Vernon
Hills, IL 60061
Tel.: (847) 388-2001
Web Site: http://www.villagehealth.com
Health Care Srvices
N.A.I.C.S.: 621999
Bryan Becker (Chief Medical Officer)
Martha Wofford (VP-Grp)
Briah Carey (VP)
David Roer (VP-Medical Affairs)
Elise Lyons-Prasad (Sr Dir-Clinical Ops)
Rebecca Olsen (Sr Dir-Ops)

Volo Dialysis, LLC (1)
400 W Black Horse Pike Ste 3, Pleasant-
ville, NJ 08232
Tel.: (609) 646-7202
Kidney Dialysis Center Operator
N.A.I.C.S.: 621492

Wakoni Dialysis, LLC (1)
4700 Springboro Pike A, Moraine, OH
45439
Tel.: (937) 294-7188
Emp.: 21
Kidney Dialysis Services
N.A.I.C.S.: 621492

Walcott Dialysis, LLC (1)
4300 Von Karman Ave, Newport Beach, CA
92660-2004
Tel.: (949) 863-1382
Kidney Dialysis Center Operator
N.A.I.C.S.: 621492

Walton Dialysis, LLC (1)
13250 Service Rd, Walton, KY 41094-9565
Tel.: (770) 207-0850
Web Site: https://www.davita.com
Kidney Dialysis Center Operator
N.A.I.C.S.: 621492

Wauseon Dialysis, LLC (1)

721 S Shoop Ave, Wauseon, OH 43567-
1729
Tel.: (610) 722-6019
Kidney Dialysis Services
N.A.I.C.S.: 621492

Weldon Dialysis, LLC (1)
1836 Sierra Gardens Dr Ste 150, Roseville,
CA 95661-2943
Tel.: (916) 772-0306
Kidney Dialysis Center Operator
N.A.I.C.S.: 621492

Wesley Chapel Dialysis, LLC (1)
2255 Green Hedges Way, Wesley Chapel,
FL 33544-8183
Tel.: (610) 722-6019
Web Site: https://www.davita.com
Kidney Dialysis Services
N.A.I.C.S.: 621492

West Bloomfield Dialysis, LLC (1)
6010 W Maple Rd Ste 215, West Bloom-
field, MI 48322-4406
Tel.: (248) 539-1025
Web Site: https://www.davita.com
Emp.: 18
Kidney Dialysis Services
N.A.I.C.S.: 621492

West Elk Grove Dialysis, LLC (1)
2208 Kausen Dr Ste 100, Elk Grove, CA
95758-7174
Tel.: (916) 683-5992
Medical Care Services
N.A.I.C.S.: 621492

West Sacramento Dialysis, LLC (1)
3450 Industrial Blvd Ste 100, West Sacra-
mento, CA 95691-5053
Tel.: (916) 371-4947
Web Site: http://www.davita.com
Kidney Dialysis Centers
N.A.I.C.S.: 621492

Weston Dialysis Center, LLC (1)
2685 Executive Park Dr Ste 1, Weston, FL
33331-3651
Tel.: (954) 389-1290
Emp.: 6
Kidney Dialysis Centers
N.A.I.C.S.: 621492

Willowbrook Dialysis Center, L.P. (1)
12120 Jones Rd Ste G, Houston, TX
77070-5280
Web Site: http://www.davitadialysis.com
Kidney Dialysis Services
N.A.I.C.S.: 621492

Winds Dialysis, LLC (1)
5036 Tennyson Pkwy, Plano, TX 75024-
3002
Tel.: (310) 536-2575
Web Site: http://www.davita.com
Sales Range: $10-24.9 Million
Kidney Dialysis Services
N.A.I.C.S.: 621492

Wood Dialysis, LLC (1)
19265 Vernier Rd, Harper Woods, MI
48225-1010
Tel.: (610) 722-6019
Kidney Dialysis Services
N.A.I.C.S.: 621492

Wyandotte Central Dialysis, LLC (1)
3737 State Ave, Kansas City, KS 66102-
3830
Tel.: (913) 233-0536
Web Site: http://www.davita.com
Kidney Dialysis Centers
N.A.I.C.S.: 621492

Yargol Dialysis, LLC (1)
5200 Virginia Way, Brentwood, TN 37027
Tel.: (615) 341-6475
Kidney Dialysis Services
N.A.I.C.S.: 621492

Ybor City Dialysis, LLC (1)
2000 16th St, Denver, CO 80202
Tel.: (813) 872-8216
Emp.: 10
Medical Care Services
N.A.I.C.S.: 621492
Teresa McElhattan (Office Mgr)

Yucaipa Dialysis, LLC (1)

33487 Yucaipa Blvd, Yucaipa, CA 92399-
2064
Tel.: (610) 722-6019
Kidney Dialysis Services
N.A.I.C.S.: 621492

Zephyrhills Dialysis Center, LLC (1)
36819 Eiland Blvd Unit 2, Zephyrhills, FL
33542-0600
Tel.: (303) 876-6622
Kidney Dialysis Services
N.A.I.C.S.: 621492

DAXOR CORPORATION
350 5th Ave Ste 4740, New York, NY
10118-7120
Tel.: (212) 330-8500 NY
Web Site: http://www.daxor.com
Year Founded: 1971
DXR—(NYSEAMEX)
Medical Instrumentation & Biotechnol-
ogy Investment Services
N.A.I.C.S.: 523999
Diane M. Meegan (Sec)
Gary Fischman (VP-R&D)
Donald Margouleff (Dir-Nuclear Medi-
cine)
Michael R. Feldschuh (Chm, Pres &
CEO)
Lisa Quartley (Sr VP-Mktg & Comml
Dev)
Jonathan Feldschuh (Chief Scientific
Officer)
Kathryn A. Kornafel (VP-Mktg &
Comml Dev)
Robert J. Michel (CFO)

Subsidiaries:

Idant Laboratory (1)
350 5th Ave Ste 4740, New York, NY 10118
Tel.: (212) 244-0555
Web Site: http://www.idant.com
Emp.: 6
Sperm Bank
N.A.I.C.S.: 621111
Diane M. Meegan (Sec)

Scientific Medical Systems Corp. (1)
350 5th Ave Ste 7120, New York, NY 10118
Tel.: (212) 244-0555
Surgical & Medical Instrument Mfr
N.A.I.C.S.: 339112

DAY ONE BIOPHARMACEUTI-
CALS, INC.
2000 Sierra Pt Pkwy Ste 501, Bris-
bane, CA 94005
Tel.: (650) 484-0899 DE
Web Site:
https://www.dayonebio.com
Year Founded: 2018
DAWN—(NASDAQ)
Rev.: $4,746,000
Assets: $349,062,000
Liabilities: $17,023,000
Net Worth: $332,039,000
Earnings: ($142,181,000)
Emp.: 121
Fiscal Year-end: 12/31/22
Research & Development in Biotech-
nology (except Nanobiotechnology)
N.A.I.C.S.: 541714
Samuel Blackman (Co-Founder &
Head-R&D)
Jeremy Bender (Pres & CEO)
Mike Preigh (Chief Technical Officer)
Lisa Bowers (Chief Comml Officer)
Davy Chiodin (Chief Dev Officer)
Julie Grant (Co-Founder)
Charles N. York II (COO & CFO)

DAYBREAK OIL AND GAS,
INC.
1414 S Friendswood Dr Ste 212,
Friendswood, TX 77546
Tel.: (281) 996-4176 WA
Web Site:
https://www.daybreakoilandgas.com

Year Founded: 1955
DBRM—(OTCIQ)
Rev.: $680,107
Assets: $975,704
Liabilities: $4,322,908
Net Worth: ($3,347,204)
Earnings: ($398,450)
Emp.: 4
Fiscal Year-end: 02/28/22
Oil & Gas Exploration Services
N.A.I.C.S.: 213112
James F. Westmoreland *(Chm, Pres, CEO & Interim Chief Fin & Acctg Officer)*
Bennett W. Anderson *(COO)*

DAYFORCE, INC.
3311 E Old Shakopee Rd, Minneapolis, MN 55425
Tel.: (952) 853-8100   DE
Web Site: https://www.dayforce.com
Year Founded: 2013
DAY—(NYSE)
Rev.: $1,513,700,000
Assets: $9,010,900,000
Liabilities: $6,612,700,000
Net Worth: $2,398,200,000
Earnings: $54,800,000
Emp.: 9,084
Fiscal Year-end: 12/31/23
Software Publishing Services
N.A.I.C.S.: 513210
David D. Ossip *(Chm & CEO)*
Joe Korngiebel *(Chief Product & Tech Officer & Exec VP)*
Sam Alkharrat *(Chief Revenue Officer)*
Donnebra McClendon *(Head)*
Bill McDonald *(Gen Counsel)*
Stephen Moore *(Mng Dir)*
Wendy Muirhead *(Mng Dir)*
Carrie Rasmussen *(CIO)*
Stephen H. Holdridge *(Pres & COO)*
Christopher R. Armstrong *(Chief Customer Officer & Exec VP)*

Subsidiaries:

Ceridian (Mauritius) Ltd.   (1)
Level 9 Cyber Tower 1 Cyber City, Ebene, Mauritius
Tel.: (230) 4544036
Capital Management Services
N.A.I.C.S.: 523940
Yogesh Jankee *(Head-Implementation)*

Ceridian Cares U.S.   (1)
3311 E Old Shakopee Rd, Bloomington, MN 55425-1640
Healtcare Services
N.A.I.C.S.: 621610

Ceridian Dayforce Germany GmbH   (1)
Kaiserswerther Strasse 135, 40474, Dusseldorf, Germany
Tel.: (49) 21186943051
Web Site: http://www.ceridian.com
Software Development Services
N.A.I.C.S.: 541511

Ceridian Europe Limited   (1)
Suite 3A 3rd Floor Skypark 5 45 Finnieston Street, Glasgow, G3 8JU, United Kingdom
Tel.: (44) 1415847100
Capital Management Services
N.A.I.C.S.: 523940

Excelity Australia Pty Ltd   (1)
Level 12 90 Arthur Street, North Sydney, 2060, NSW, Australia
Tel.: (61) 280051191
Software Development Services
N.A.I.C.S.: 541511

Excelity HCM Solutions Sdn. Bhd.   (1)
Suite 3B-08-06 and 7 Level 8 Block 3B Plaza Sentral 2A, Jalan Stesen Sentral 5 KL Sentral, 50470, Kuala Lumpur, Malaysia
Tel.: (60) 327307400
Software Development Services
N.A.I.C.S.: 541511

Excelity Philippines, Inc.   (1)
12F Unit B Menarco Tower 32nd St, Bonifacio Global City, Taguig, 1634, Philippines
Tel.: (63) 285807700
Software Development Services
N.A.I.C.S.: 541511

Pinfeng (Shanghai) Information Technology Co., Ltd.   (1)
Unit 03-06 17 F Centro Building 568 Heng Feng Road, Shanghai, 200070, China
Tel.: (86) 2123248188
Software Development Services
N.A.I.C.S.: 541511

DEBT RESOLVE, INC.
1133 Westchester Ave Ste S-223, White Plains, NY 10604
Tel.: (914) 949-5500   DE
Web Site:
    http://www.debtresolve.com
Year Founded: 1997
DRSV—(OTCIQ)
Sales Range: $1-9.9 Million
Emp.: 2
Web-Based Debt Management Solutions for Creditors & Debtors
N.A.I.C.S.: 513210
William M. Mooney Jr. *(Chm)*
Rene A. Samson *(VP-Tech)*

DECENTRAL LIFE, INC.
6400 S Fiddlers Green Cir Ste 1180, Greenwood Village, CO 80111   NV
Web Site: http://www.social-life-network.com
Year Founded: 1985
WDLF—(OTCIQ)
Rev.: $944,413
Assets: $845,666
Liabilities: $252,093
Net Worth: $593,573
Earnings: $727,386
Emp.: 7
Fiscal Year-end: 12/31/22
Information Technology Consulting Services
N.A.I.C.S.: 541512
Kenneth Shawn Tapp *(Chm, CEO & CTO)*

DECKER MANUFACTURING CORP.
703 N Clark St, Albion, MI 49224
Tel.: (517) 629-3955
Web Site: https://www.deckernut.com
Year Founded: 1927
DMFG—(OTCIQ)
Sales Range: $10-24.9 Million
Emp.: 120
Bolts, Nuts, Rivets & Washers Mfr
N.A.I.C.S.: 332722
Steven Konkle *(Pres)*

DECKERS OUTDOOR CORPORATION
250 Coromar Dr, Goleta, CA 93117
Tel.: (805) 967-7611   DE
Web Site: https://www.deckers.com
Year Founded: 1972
DECK—(NYSE)
Rev.: $4,287,763,000
Assets: $3,135,579,000
Liabilities: $1,028,111,000
Net Worth: $2,107,468,001
Earnings: $759,563,000
Emp.: 4,800
Fiscal Year-end: 03/31/24
Footwear Designer, Marketer & Distr
N.A.I.C.S.: 316210
Steven J. Fasching *(CFO)*
Michael F. Devine III *(Chm)*
Brad Willis *(CTO & Sr VP)*
Stefano Caroti *(Pres-Omni-Channel)*
Thomas Garcia *(Chief Admin Officer-ESG & Gen Counsel)*
Erinn Kohler *(VP-Investor Relations-Corporate Planning)*

Andy Poljak *(Mgr-IR & Corp Plng)*
Pascale Meyran *(Chief HR Officer)*
Anne Spangenberg *(Pres-Fashion Lifestyle)*
Angela Ogbechie *(Chief Supply Chain Officer)*
Stefano Caroti *(Pres & CEO)*

Subsidiaries:

Deckers Asia Pacific Limited   (1)
Units 2604-06 26/F One Harbourfront 18 Tak Fung Street, Hunghom, Kowloon, China (Hong Kong)
Tel.: (852) 29562929
Web Site: http://www.deckers.com
Fashion Apparels Retailer
N.A.I.C.S.: 315990

Deckers Asia Pacific Retail Limited   (1)
Unit 2604-06 One Harbourfront 18 Tak Fung Street Whampoa, Kowloon, Hong Kong, China (Hong Kong)
Tel.: (852) 29562929
Footwear Mfr
N.A.I.C.S.: 316210

Deckers Benelux BV   (1)
Danzigerkade 211 Unit 2B, 1013 AP, Amsterdam, Netherlands
Tel.: (31) 103401200
General & Sports Shoes Mfr
N.A.I.C.S.: 316210

Deckers Consumer Direct Corporation   (1)
123 N Leroux St, Flagstaff, AZ 86001
Tel.: (928) 779-5938
Web Site: http://www.deckers.com
Footwear Mfr
N.A.I.C.S.: 316210

Deckers Europe Ltd.   (1)
130 Shaftesbury Avenue, London, W1D 5EU, Surrey, United Kingdom - England
Tel.: (44) 2070162200
Web Site: http://www.deckers.com
Sales Range: $25-49.9 Million
Emp.: 4
Footwear Mfr
N.A.I.C.S.: 424340

Deckers Footwear (Shanghai) Co., Ltd.   (1)
21/F No 757 Mengzi Road, Huangpu, Shanghai, 200003, China
Tel.: (86) 2180130200
Footwear Mfr & Distr
N.A.I.C.S.: 316210

Deckers France 2 SAS   (1)
26 Rue Vieille du Temple/9 Rue du Tresor, 75004, Paris, France
Tel.: (33) 142711502
Footwear Mfr
N.A.I.C.S.: 316210

Deckers France SAS   (1)
14-18 Rue Volney, 75002, Paris, France
Tel.: (33) 144500900
Footwear Mfr
N.A.I.C.S.: 316210

Deckers Japan GK   (1)
Yebisu Garden Place Tower 15th Floor Ebisu 4-20-3, Shibuya-ku, Tokyo, 150-6015, Japan
Tel.: (81) 345775000
Web Site: http://www.deckers.com
Fashion Apparels Retailer
N.A.I.C.S.: 315990

Deckers Outdoor International Limited   (1)
Units 2604-06 26/F One Harbourfront 18 Tak Fung Street, Hunghom, Kowloon, China (Hong Kong)
Tel.: (852) 29562929
Footwear Distr
N.A.I.C.S.: 424340

Deckers Retail, LLC   (1)
250 Coromar Dr, Goleta, CA 93117
Tel.: (212) 207-8006
Footwear Whslr
N.A.I.C.S.: 424340

Deckers UK, LTD   (1)
130 Shaftesbury Avenue, London, W1D

5EU, United Kingdom
Tel.: (44) 2070162200
Emp.: 200
Footwear Mfr
N.A.I.C.S.: 316210

Holbrook Ltd.   (1)
35/F Tower Two Times Square Causeway Bay, Central, China (Hong Kong)
Tel.: (852) 35898899
Sales Range: $75-99.9 Million
Footwear
N.A.I.C.S.: 316210
Ziv Zohar *(CEO)*

DEEP BLUE MARINE, INC.
696 W 1St St, Midvale, UT 84047
Tel.: (801) 568-1873   NV
DPBE—(OTCIQ)
Marine Engineering Services
N.A.I.C.S.: 541330
Randy Champion *(Pres)*

DEEP GREEN WASTE & RECYCLING, INC.
3524 Central Pike Ste 310, Hermitage, TN 37076
Web Site:
    https://www.deepgreenwaste.com
Year Founded: 2011
DGWR—(OTCQB)
Rev.: $2,682,762
Assets: $2,121,542
Liabilities: $5,421,592
Net Worth: ($3,300,050)
Earnings: ($690,140)
Emp.: 2
Fiscal Year-end: 12/31/23
Waste & Recycling Services; Waste Handling Equipment Sales & Service
N.A.I.C.S.: 562998
Lloyd T. Spencer *(Pres & Sec)*
Bill Edmonds *(Founder, Chm, CEO & Interim CFO)*
David Bradford *(COO)*

Subsidiaries:

Compaction & Recycling Equipment, Inc.   (1)
12250 SE Capps Rd, Clackamas, OR 97015-8961
Tel.: (503) 594-6900
Web Site: https://www.waste-equipment.com
Waste Handling Equipment Mfr
N.A.I.C.S.: 333310

DEEP LAKE CAPITAL ACQUISITION CORP.
930 Tahoe Blvd Ste 802 PMB 381, Incline Village, NV 89451
Tel.: (415) 307-2340   Ky
Year Founded: 2020
DLCAU—(NASDAQ)
Investment Services
N.A.I.C.S.: 523999
Mark Lavelle *(Co-Founder, Chm & CEO)*
Gary Marino *(Co-Founder & Pres)*
Michael Cyrus *(Co-Founder & CFO)*

DEEP MEDICINE ACQUISITION CORP.
595 Madison Ave 12th Fl, New York, NY 10017
Tel.: (917) 289-2776   DE
Year Founded: 2020
DMAQ—(NASDAQ)
Assets: $128,953,272
Liabilities: $132,729,212
Net Worth: ($3,775,940)
Earnings: ($414,045)
Emp.: 2
Fiscal Year-end: 03/31/22
Investment Services
N.A.I.C.S.: 523999

Deep Medicine Acquisition Corp.—(Continued)

Humphrey P. Polanen (Chm & CEO)
Weixuan Luo (CFO)

DEERE & COMPANY
1 John Deere Pl, Moline, IL 61265
Tel.: (309) 765-8000   DE
Web Site: https://www.deere.com
Year Founded: 1837
DE—(NYSE)
Rev.: $61,251,000,000
Assets: $104,087,000,000
Liabilities: $82,298,000,000
Net Worth: $21,789,000,000
Earnings: $10,166,000,000
Emp.: 83,000
Fiscal Year-end: 10/29/23
Commercial & Farm Tractor, Mower,
Truck & Utility Vehicle Developer &
Mfr; Financial Services
N.A.I.C.S.: 423820
Rajesh Kalathur (CIO & Pres-John
Deere Fin)
Mary K. W. Jones (Gen Counsel & Sr
VP)
John C. May (Chm, Pres & CEO)
Markwart von Pentz (Pres-Agriculture
& Turf Div-Europe, CIS, Asia & Af-
rica)
Ryan D. Campbell (Pres-Worldwide
Construction & Forestry & Power
Sys)
Joshua A. Jepsen (CFO & Sr VP)
Jahmy J. Hindman (CTO)
Justin R. Rose (Pres)

Subsidiaries:

Arrendadora John Deere S.A. de
C.V.   (1)
Boulevard Diaz Ordaz No 500 interior A,
Colonia La Leona San Pedro, Garza Gar-
cia, 66210, Nuevo Leon, Mexico
Tel.: (52) 8180407272
Web Site: http://www.deere.com
Provider of Financial Services
N.A.I.C.S.: 522320

Banco John Deere S.A.   (1)
Rod Engenheiro Ermenio Oliveira Penteado
S/N-Km 57 Bldg 1 1St Floor, Bairro Helvetia
Cep, Indaiatuba, 13337-300, Sao Paulo,
Brazil
Tel.: (55) 1038259300
Web Site: http://www.deere.com.br
Sales Range: $100-124.9 Million
Farm Machinery & Equipment Mfr & Com-
mercial & Credit Financing Services
N.A.I.C.S.: 333111
Jorge David Sivina (Pres)

Blue River Technology, Inc.   (1)
550 E Weddell Dr Ste 10, Sunnyvale, CA
94089
Tel.: (408) 745-7550
Web Site: http://www.bluerivert.com
Emp.: 60
General Purpose Machinery Mfr
N.A.I.C.S.: 333998
Lee Redden (Co-Founder & CTO)
Jorge Heraud (Co-Founder & CEO)
Jim Ostrowski (VP-Engrg)
Ben Chostner (Gen Mgr-See & Spray)
Mac Keely (VP-Market Dev)
Scott Kimmel (VP-Fin & Admin)

Chamberlain Holdings Limited   (1)
166-170 Magnesium Dr, Crestmead, 4132,
OLD, Australia
Tel.: (61) 738023222
Web Site: http://www.deere.com.au
Emp.: 190
Farm & Garden Machinery Distr
N.A.I.C.S.: 423820

Hagie Manufacturing Company   (1)
721 Central Ave W, Clarion, IA 50525-1335
Tel.: (515) 532-2861
Web Site: http://www.hagie.com
Sales Range: $75-99.9 Million
Emp.: 300
Agricultural Sprayers & High Clearance Ag-
ricultural Equipment Mfr
N.A.I.C.S.: 333111

Kent Klemme (Pres)

Industrias John Deere S.A. de
C.V.   (1)
Blvd Diaz Ordaz 500, Garza Garcia, 66210,
NL, Mexico
Tel.: (52) 8182881212
Web Site: http://www.johndeere.com.mx
Agricultural, Garden & Lawn Equipment
N.A.I.C.S.: 444230

JDAMC   (1)
10789 S Ridgeview Rd, Olathe, KS
66062   (100%)
Tel.: (913) 310-8100
Web Site: http://www.johndeere.com
Sales Range: $125-149.9 Million
Emp.: 300
Retail Farm Equipment
N.A.I.C.S.: 423820

John Deere (Pty.) Ltd.   (1)
38 Oscar Street Extension 37, Hughes,
Boksburg, 1459, Gauteng, South
Africa   (100%)
Tel.: (27) 114372600
Web Site: http://www.johndeere.co.za
Sales Range: $1-9.9 Million
Emp.: 110
Tillage Equipment Distr
N.A.I.C.S.: 423820
Jason Brantley (Dir-A&T Sls & Mktg-Africa
Middle East)
Jaco Beyers (Mng Dir-Mktg & Sls-Africa
Middle East)

John Deere Bank S.A.   (1)
43 avenue, PO Box 1685, 1016, Luxem-
bourg, Luxembourg
Tel.: (352) 262 9901
Web Site: https://www.deere.eu
Emp.: 75
Farm Machinery & Equipment Mfr
N.A.I.C.S.: 333111

John Deere Brasil Ltda.   (1)
Rodovia Ermenio de Oliveira Penteado 57 5
km Predio 1, Indaiatuba, 13337-300, Sao
Paulo, Brazil
Tel.: (55) 1933188100
Web Site: http://www.deere.com.br
Emp.: 600
Agricultural Machinery Mfr
N.A.I.C.S.: 333111
Paulo Herrmann (Pres)

John Deere Canada ULC   (1)
295 Hunter Road, PO Box 1000, Grimsby,
L3M 4H5, ON, Canada
Tel.: (905) 945-7425
Agricultural Machinery Distr
N.A.I.C.S.: 423820
Michael Blonski (Pres & Mgr-Global Seg-
mentation Dev & Integration)

John Deere Capital Corporation   (1)
PO Box 5328, Madison, WI
53705-0328   (100%)
Tel.: (775) 786-5527
Rev.: $4,940,000,000
Assets: $62,514,600,000
Liabilities: $56,287,400,000
Net Worth: $6,227,200,000
Earnings: $581,300,000
Emp.: 1,338
Fiscal Year-end: 10/27/2024
Licensed Small Loan Lenders
N.A.I.C.S.: 522210
Rajesh Kalathur (Pres)
John C. May (Chm & CEO)
Ryan D. Campbell (Sr VP)

John Deere Coffeyville Works
Inc   (1)
Hwy 169 N Industrial Park, Coffeyville, KS
67337
Tel.: (620) 251-3400
Web Site: http://www.deere.com
Sales Range: $150-199.9 Million
Emp.: 400
Specialty Hydraulic & Mechanical Power
Transmissions Pump Drives
N.A.I.C.S.: 336350

John Deere Commercial Worksite
Products, Inc.   (1)
1 John Deere Pl, Moline, IL 61265
Tel.: (309) 765-8000
Web Site: http://www.johndeere.com
Sales Range: $15-24.9 Billion
Emp.: 45,000
Provider of Commercial Machinery

N.A.I.C.S.: 333111

John Deere Consumer & Commercial
Equipment, Inc.   (1)
2000 John Deere Run, Cary, NC
27513   (100%)
Tel.: (919) 804-2000
Web Site: http://www.johndeere.com
Sales Range: $100-124.9 Million
Emp.: 350
Sales, Customer Service & Marketing For
John Deere Products
N.A.I.C.S.: 333112

John Deere Credit Company   (1)
6400 NW 86th St, Johnston, IA 50131-6600
Tel.: (515) 267-3000
Web Site: http://www.deere.com
Loan Brokers-Agricultural Construction &
Consumer Equipment
N.A.I.C.S.: 522299

John Deere Credit OY   (1)
Lokomonkatu 21, Tampere, 33900, Finland
Tel.: (358) 20584162
Web Site: http://www.johndeere.com
Investment Advisory Services
N.A.I.C.S.: 523940

John Deere Credit Services, Inc.   (1)
8402 Excelsior Dr, Madison, WI 53717-
1923
Tel.: (608) 821-2000
Web Site:
http://www.johndeerefinancial.com
Sales Range: $200-249.9 Million
Emp.: 250
N.A.I.C.S.: 333112

John Deere Engine Works   (1)
3801 Richway Ave, Waterloo, IA 50704
Tel.: (319) 292-4311
Web Site: http://www.deere.com
Sales Range: $125-149.9 Million
Farm & Garden Machinery & Equipment
N.A.I.C.S.: 333111

John Deere Financial Inc.   (1)
3430 Superior Ct, Oakville, L6L 0C4, ON,
Canada
Tel.: (905) 319-9100
Financial Management Services
N.A.I.C.S.: 541611

John Deere Financial Limited   (1)
166-170 Magnesium Drive, Crestmead,
4132, QLD, Australia   (100%)
Tel.: (61) 738023100
Web Site: http://www.johndeere.com.au
Sales Range: $10-24.9 Million
Emp.: 50
Financial Services
N.A.I.C.S.: 522320
Thil Stainley (Mng Dir)

John Deere Financial Mexico, S.A. de
C.V. Sofom, E.N.R.   (1)
Blvd Diaz Ordaz No 500 Interior A Colonia
La Leona, San Pedro Garza Garcia, 66210,
Nuevo Leon, Mexico
Tel.: (52) 8182887272
Web Site: https://www.deere.com.mx
Financial Services
N.A.I.C.S.: 522320

John Deere Financial, f.s.b.   (1)
8402 Excelsior Dr, Madison, WI
53717-1909   (100%)
Tel.: (608) 821-2000
Web Site: http://www.deere.com
Sales Range: $25-49.9 Million
Emp.: 95
Acquires, Finances & Services Merchant
Receivables in the Agricultural Retail Indus-
try
N.A.I.C.S.: 522220

John Deere Foreign Sales Corpora-
tion Limited   (1)
1 John Deere Pl, Moline, IL 61265-8010
Tel.: (309) 765-8000
Web Site: http://www.johndeere.com
Sales Range: $150-199.9 Million
Emp.: 1,800
Provider of Business Services
N.A.I.C.S.: 423830

John Deere GmbH & Co. KG   (1)
John-Deere-Str 8, 76646, Bruchsal, Germany

Tel.: (49) 72519240
Web Site: http://www.deere.de
Agricultural Machinery Distr
N.A.I.C.S.: 423820

John Deere GmbH & Co. KG   (1)
John-Deere-Str 8, 76646, Bruchsal,
Germany   (100%)
Tel.: (49) 72519240
Web Site: http://www.deere.de
Sales Range: $50-74.9 Million
Emp.: 120
Holding Company: Farm & Lawn Machinery
N.A.I.C.S.: 551112

John Deere Horicon Works   (1)
300 N 9th St, Horicon, WI 53032-1062
Tel.: (920) 485-4411
Web Site: http://www.johndeere.com
Sales Range: $300-349.9 Million
Emp.: 850
Farm & Garden Machinery & Equipment
N.A.I.C.S.: 333112

John Deere Iberica S.A.   (1)
Centro Integral de Formacion y Marketing
Bulevar John Deere 2, Parla, 28984, Ma-
drid, Spain   (100%)
Tel.: (34) 914958200
Web Site: http://www.deere.es
Mfr & Distributor of Farm Equipment
N.A.I.C.S.: 333111

John Deere India Private Limited   (1)
Tower 14 Cybercity Magarpatta City,
Hadapsar, Pune, 411013, India
Tel.: (91) 2066425000
Web Site: https://www.deere.co.in
Agricultural Equipment Distr
N.A.I.C.S.: 423820

John Deere Intercontinental
GmbH   (1)
John Deere Strasse 70, 68163, Mannheim,
Germany   (100%)
Tel.: (49) 62182901
Web Site: http://www.johndeere.com
Sales Range: $75-99.9 Million
Emp.: 200
Provider of Agricultural, Gardening & Lawn
Equipment
N.A.I.C.S.: 444230

John Deere International GmbH   (1)
Rheinweg 11, 8200, Schaffhausen,
Switzerland   (100%)
Tel.: (41) 526329600
Web Site: http://www.jdonline.deere.com
Sales Range: $25-49.9 Million
Emp.: 60
Provider of Agricultural, Gardening & Lawn
Equipment
N.A.I.C.S.: 444230

John Deere Lawn and Grounds Care
Holdings, Inc.   (1)
1 John Deere Pl, Moline, IL 61265-8010
Tel.: (309) 765-8000
Web Site: http://www.johndeere.com
Sales Range: $150-199.9 Million
Holding Company
N.A.I.C.S.: 423830

John Deere Limited Australia   (1)
166-170 Magnesium Drive, Crestmead,
4132, QLD, Australia   (100%)
Tel.: (61) 738023222
Web Site: http://www.deere.com.au
Sales Range: $50-74.9 Million
Provider of Agricultural, Gardening & Lawn
Equipment
N.A.I.C.S.: 444230
Mike Park (Mng Dir)

John Deere Ltd.   (1)
Harby Road Langar, Nottingham, NG13
9HT, United Kingdom   (100%)
Tel.: (44) 1949860491
Web Site: http://www.deere.co.uk
Sales Range: $50-74.9 Million
Emp.: 100
Provider of Agricultural, Gardening & Lawn
Equipment
N.A.I.C.S.: 444230
Jonathan Henry (Mng Dir)

John Deere Ltd.   (1)
295 Hunter Road, PO Box 1000, Grimsby,
L3M 4H5, ON, Canada   (100%)
Tel.: (905) 945-9281

Web Site: http://www.johndeere.com
Sales Range: $1-4.9 Billion
Emp.: 300
Mfr & Distr of Industrial & Farm Equipment
N.A.I.C.S.: 333111

John Deere Mexico S.A. de C.V. **(1)**
Boulevard Diaz Ordaz 500, Garza Garcia,
66210, NL, Mexico **(100%)**
Tel.: (52) 8182881212
Web Site: http://www.deere.com
Sales Range: $150-199.9 Million
Provider of Agricultural, Lawn & Garden
Equipment
N.A.I.C.S.: 444230

John Deere Polska Sp. Zo.o **(1)**
ul Poznanska 1B, 62 080, Tarnowo
Podgorne, Poland
Tel.: (48) 618115196
Web Site: https://www.deere.pl
Agricultural Equipment Distr
N.A.I.C.S.: 423820

John Deere Polska Sp. z o.o. **(1)**
ul Poznanska 1b, 62-080, Tarnowo
Podgorne, Poland
Tel.: (48) 61 811 5196
Web Site: https://www.deere.pl
Agricultural Machinery Distr
N.A.I.C.S.: 423820

John Deere Power Products, Inc. **(1)**
1630 Howell Henard Rd, Greeneville, TN
37743
Tel.: (423) 636-1500
Web Site: http://www.johndeere.com
Sales Range: $150-199.9 Million
Emp.: 600
Lawn & Garden Tractors & Home Lawn &
Garden Equipment
N.A.I.C.S.: 333111

John Deere Receivables, Inc. **(1)**
1 E 1st St Ste 600, Reno, NV 89501-1610
Tel.: (775) 786-5527
Sales Range: $750-799.9 Million
N.A.I.C.S.: 531390
James A. Israel *(Pres)*

John Deere S.A. de C.V. **(1)**
Blvd Diaz Ordaz 500 Col Laleona, San Pe-
dro, 66210, Nuevo Leon, Mexico **(49%)**
Tel.: (52) 8182881212
Web Site: http://www.johndeere.com
Sales Range: $75-99.9 Million
Emp.: 200
Mfr & Distributor of Farm Equipment
N.A.I.C.S.: 333111

John Deere S.A.S. **(1)**
23 Rue du Paradis Ormes, PO Box 219,
Cedex, Saint Jean-de-la-Ruelle,
France **(100%)**
Tel.: (33) 238723000
Web Site: http://www.johndeere.com
Sales Range: $75-99.9 Million
Emp.: 60
Provider of Agricultural, Gardening & Lawn
Equipment
N.A.I.C.S.: 444230

John Deere Technologies Center **(1)**
1 John Deere Pl, Moline, IL 61265 **(100%)**
Tel.: (309) 765-3700
Web Site: http://www.johndeere.com
Sales Range: $25-49.9 Million
Emp.: 80
Engineering Services
N.A.I.C.S.: 541611

John Deere Walldorf GmbH & Co.
KG **(1)**
John Deere Street 1, 69190, Walldorf, Ger-
many
Tel.: (49) 62277873600
Web Site: https://www.deere.de
Agricultural Services
N.A.I.C.S.: 423820
Richard Johnson *(Mng Dir)*
Csaba Lejko *(Mng Dir)*
Dirk Stratmann *(Mng Dir)*

John Deere Worldwide Agricultural
Equipment **(1)**
1 John Deere Pl, Moline, IL 61265-8098
Tel.: (309) 765-8000
Web Site: http://www.johndeere.com
Sales Range: $125-149.9 Million
Farm Machinery & Equipment Manufactur-
ing

N.A.I.C.S.: 333111

Subsidiary (Non-US):

Industrias John Deere Argentina
S.A. **(2)**
Juan Orsetti 481, Granadero Baigorria,
Santa Fe, Argentina **(100%)**
Tel.: (54) 3414101800
Web Site: http://www.deere.com
Agricultural, Gardening & Lawn Equipment
N.A.I.C.S.: 444230

Subsidiary (Domestic):

John Deere Agricultural Holdings,
Inc. **(2)**
1 John Deere Pl, Moline, IL 61265-8010
Tel.: (309) 765-8000
Holding Company
N.A.I.C.S.: 423830

John Deere Electronic Solutions,
Inc. **(2)**
1441 44th St N, Fargo, ND 58102
Tel.: (701) 277-6100
Web Site: http://www.deere.com
Engine Controls, Transmission Controls,
GPS receivers, Telematics & Gauge &
Switch Panels
N.A.I.C.S.: 334519

Plant (Domestic):

John Deere Harvester Works **(2)**
1100 13th Ave, East Moline, IL 61244-1455
Tel.: (309) 765-8000
Web Site: http://www.deere.com
Farm & Garden Machinery & Equipment
N.A.I.C.S.: 333111

John Deere Ottumwa Works **(2)**
928 E Vine St, Ottumwa, IA 52501
Tel.: (641) 684-4641
Web Site: http://www.deere.com
Emp.: 50
Farm & Garden Machinery & Equipment
N.A.I.C.S.: 333111

Subsidiary (Domestic):

John Deere Thibodaux, Inc. **(2)**
244 Hwy 3266, Thibodaux, LA 70301-1602
Tel.: (985) 447-7285
Web Site: http://www.johndeereonline.com
Sales Range: $125-149.9 Million
Emp.: 500
Mfr of Sugarcane Harvesters, Scrapers &
Landscape Loaders Machinery
N.A.I.C.S.: 333111

Plant (Domestic):

John Deere Waterloo Works **(2)**
300 W Comm, Waterloo, IA 50701-5343
Tel.: (319) 292-4634
Web Site: http://www.deere.com
Farm & Garden Machinery & Equipment
N.A.I.C.S.: 333111

Subsidiary (Domestic):

Monosem, Inc. **(2)**
1001 Blake St, Edwardsville, KS 66111
Tel.: (913) 438-1700
Web Site: http://www.monosem-inc.com
Agricultural Planting Equipment Mfr
N.A.I.C.S.: 333111
Don Niehs *(Gen Sls Mgr)*
Ben Ross *(Mgr-Sls-Western)*
Chad Compton *(Mgr-Sls-Territory)*

NavCom Technology Inc **(2)**
20780 Madrona Ave, Torrance, CA 90503
Tel.: (310) 381-2000
Web Site: http://www.navcomtech.com
Sales Range: $25-49.9 Million
Emp.: 100
Communications Consultant
N.A.I.C.S.: 541618

Subsidiary (Non-US):

The Vapormatic Co., Ltd. **(2)**
Kestrel Way Sowton Industrial Est, Exeter,
EX27NB, Devon, United Kingdom
Tel.: (44) 392435461
Web Site: http://www.vapormatic.com

Sales Range: $50-74.9 Million
Emp.: 75
Tractor Parts & Equipment Distr
N.A.I.C.S.: 423830

John Deere Worldwide Construction
& Forestry **(1)**
1 John Deere Pl, Moline, IL 61265
Tel.: (309) 765-8000
Web Site: http://www.deere.com
Sales Range: $900-999.9 Million
Construction & Forestry Equipment Manu-
facturing & Marketing
N.A.I.C.S.: 333120

Joint Venture (Domestic):

Deere-Hitachi Construction Machinery
Corporation **(1)**
1000 Deere Hitachi Rd, Kernersville, NC
27284
Tel.: (336) 996-8100
Web Site: http://www.deerehitachi.com
Sales Range: $125-149.9 Million
Emp.: 315
Mfr of Hydraulic Excavators & Track Log
Loaders; Owned 50% by Hitachi Construc-
tion Machinery Co., Ltd. & 50% by Deere &
Company
N.A.I.C.S.: 333120

Subsidiary (Domestic):

John Deere Construction & Forestry
Company **(2)**
1 John Deere Pl, Moline, IL 61265-8010
Tel.: (309) 765-8000
Web Site: http://www.johndeere.com
Sales Range: $100-124.9 Million
Mfr of Construction Equipment
N.A.I.C.S.: 333111

Plant (Domestic):

John Deere Davenport Works **(2)**
1175 E 90th St, Davenport, IA 52808
Tel.: (563) 388-4200
Web Site: http://www.deere.com
Sales Range: $350-399.9 Million
Emp.: 1,100
Mfr of Construction Machinery & Equipment
N.A.I.C.S.: 333120

John Deere Dubuque Works **(2)**
18600 S John Deere Rd, Dubuque, IA
52001
Tel.: (563) 589-5151
Web Site: http://www.johndeere.com
Sales Range: $550-599.9 Million
Emp.: 2,000
Mfr of Farm & Garden Machinery & Equip-
ment
N.A.I.C.S.: 333111

Subsidiary (Domestic):

John Deere Forestry Group LLC **(2)**
1 John Deere Pl, Moline, IL 61265
Tel.: (309) 765-8000
Web Site: http://www.johndeere.com
Construction Machinery Mfr & Distr
N.A.I.C.S.: 333120

John Deere-Lanz
Verwaltungs-Aktiengesellschaft **(1)**
Steubenstrasse 36-42, Mannheim, 68163,
Germany
Tel.: (49) 62182901
Real Estate Management Services
N.A.I.C.S.: 531210

Motores John Deere S.A. de
C.V. **(1)**
Carretera Amieleras Km 6 5 SN, Torreon,
27400, Mexico **(100%)**
Tel.: (52) 8717055000
Web Site: http://www.deere.com
Sales Range: $200-249.9 Million
Emp.: 500
Diesel Engine Mfr
N.A.I.C.S.: 336310

Sunbelt Outdoor Products Inc. **(1)**
5100 H W W T Harris Blvd, Charlotte, NC
28269
Tel.: (888) 432-3373
Sales Range: $25-49.9 Million
Emp.: 30
Mfr of Material Handling Products
N.A.I.C.S.: 423820

Valuepart Inc. **(1)**
100 Lakeview Pkwy, Vernon Hills, IL 60061-
1547
Tel.: (847) 918-6090
Web Site: http://www.valuepart.com
Sales Range: $1-9.9 Million
Emp.: 10
Parts & Accessories for Internal Combustion
Engines
N.A.I.C.S.: 333618

Waratah Forestry Equipment Canada
Limited **(1)**
930 Laval Cres, Kamloops, V2C 5P5, BC,
Canada
Tel.: (250) 377-4333
Web Site: https://www.waratah.com
Emp.: 16
Farm Machinery & Equipment Mfr
N.A.I.C.S.: 333111

Western Sales (1986) Ltd. **(1)**
405 Highway 7 West, PO Box 968, Rose-
town, S0L 2V0, SK, Canada
Tel.: (306) 882-4291
Web Site: http://www.westernsales.ca
Farm Equipment & Technology
N.A.I.C.S.: 333111

Wirtgen Group Holding GmbH **(1)**
Reinhard-Wirtgen-Strasse 2, 53578, Wind-
hagen, Germany
Tel.: (49) 26451310
Web Site: http://www.wirtgen-group.com
Sales Range: $1-4.9 Billion
Emp.: 8,000
Holding Company; Road Construction Ma-
chinery Mfr & Whslr
N.A.I.C.S.: 551112
Jurgen Wirtgen *(Mng Partner)*
Stefan Wirtgen *(Mng Partner)*

Subsidiary (Domestic):

Hamm AG **(2)**
Hammstrasse 1, 95643, Tirschenreuth, Ger-
many
Tel.: (49) 9631800
Web Site: http://www.hamm.eu
Emp.: 900
Road Construction Roller & Compactor Mfr
& Whslr
N.A.I.C.S.: 333120
Reinhold Baisch *(Member-Mgmt Bd)*
Stefan Klumpp *(Member-Mgmt Bd)*

Joseph Vogele AG **(2)**
Joseph-Vogele-Strasse 1, 67075, Lud-
wigshafen, Germany
Tel.: (49) 62181050
Web Site: http://www.voegele.info
Road Paving Machinery Mfr & Whslr
N.A.I.C.S.: 333120

Kleemann GmbH **(2)**
Manfred-Worner-Strasse 160, 73037, Gop-
pingen, Germany
Tel.: (49) 71612060
Web Site: http://www.kleemann.info
Stone Crushing Machinery Mfr & Whslr
N.A.I.C.S.: 333120

Wirtgen GmbH **(2)**
Reinhard-Wirtgen Strasse 2, 53578, Wind-
hagen, Germany
Tel.: (49) 026451310
Web Site: https://www.wirtgen-group.com
Road Construction Machinery Mfr & Whslr
N.A.I.C.S.: 333120
Frank G. Betzelt *(Member-Mgmt Bd)*

Subsidiary (Non-US):

PIK Wirtgen Ukraine **(3)**
Pyrogivskyy shlyakh Str. 28, 03083, Kiev,
Ukraine
Tel.: (380) 445030191
Web Site: http://www.wirtgen.ua
Construction Machinery Distr
N.A.I.C.S.: 423810

Wirtgen (China) Machinery Co.,
Ltd. **(3)**
No 395 Chuang Ye Road Langfang Eco &
Tech Dev Zone, 65001, Langfang, Hebei,
China
Tel.: (86) 3162250100
Web Site: http://www.wirtgen-china.com.cn
Construction Machinery Distr
N.A.I.C.S.: 423810

Deere & Company—(Continued)

Ulrich Reichert (CEO)
Tim Xie (Gen Mgr-Mktg)
Betsy Wang Bojin (Mgr-HR)
Liu Jianjun (Mgr-Pur)
Shirly Zhu Yongmei (Dir-PR & Exec Affairs)
Gary Qi Sheng (Sls Mgr-Used Machine)

Wirtgen (Thailand) Co. Ltd. (3)
99/9 Moo 6, Bangna-Trad Km. 24 Rd.,
T.Bang Sao Thong, A. Bang Sao Thong,
Bangplee, 10540, Samut Prakan, Thailand
Tel.: (66) 27502908
Web Site: http://www.wirtgen.co.th
Construction Machinery Distr
N.A.I.C.S.: 423810
Sarun Veangsong (Member-Mgmt Bd)
Tatiya Singhasut (Sec)
Chalit Padoongcheep (Mng Dir)
Phichet Sukkanha (Sls Mgr-Quarry & Mining)
Virote Juhong (Sls Mgr-Road Tech)
Somsak Klangarun (Engr-Sls)
Nirun Lohitsiri (Engr-Sls)
Kuson Thaorat (Engr-Sls)
Salinla Sirikulpotitong (Mgr-Fin & Acct)
Patcharee Sasakul (Asst Mgr-Fin)
Chalaoluck Sagawee (Coord-Customer)
Theeraphong Chaikham (Mgr-Jobsite & Svc Dept)
Patsarun Pongsathabordee (Supvr-Svc Admin)
Piya Prommachan (Supvr-Workshop Admin)
Chaloempon Kam-In (Engr-Technical)
Chayanit Renumarn (Engr-Technical)

Subsidiary (US):

Wirtgen America Inc. (3)
6030 Dana Way, Antioch, TN 37013
Tel.: (615) 501-0600
Web Site: http://www.wirtgenamerica.com
Construction Machinery Distr
N.A.I.C.S.: 423810
Tim Kowalski (Mgr-Applications Support-HAMM)
Jim McEvoy (Pres & CEO)
Brad McKinney (CFO)
Matthew Graves (Mktg Dir-Comm)
Austin Evans (Coord-Mktg Comm)
Janie Gallagher (Coord-Mktg)
Allen Parton (Dir-HR)
Ed Asbury (Mgr-IT)
Steve Howard (Mgr-Safety & Facilities)

Subsidiary (Non-US):

Wirtgen Ankara Makina Sanayi ve Ticaret Ltd, Sti. (3)
Ankara Cad No 223 Bahcelievler
MahallesiKonya-Ankara Yolu 3 km, Golbasi,
6830, Ankara, Turkiye
Tel.: (90) 3124853939
Web Site: https://www.wirtgen-group.com
Construction Machinery Distr
N.A.I.C.S.: 423810

Wirtgen Australia Pty Ltd (3)
Lot 2 Great Eastern Highway, Guildford,
6055, WA, Australia
Tel.: (61) 862792200
Web Site: http://www.wirtgen-aust.com.au
Construction Machinery Distr
N.A.I.C.S.: 423810

Wirtgen Belgium B.V.B.A. (3)
Schoonmansveld 19A, 2870, Puurs, Belgium
Tel.: (32) 38609535
Web Site: http://www.wirtgen.be
Construction Machinery Distr
N.A.I.C.S.: 423810

Wirtgen Eesti OU (3)
Saha-Loo tee 14 Iru kula, Joelahtme vald,
74206, Harjumaa, Estonia
Tel.: (372) 6066188
Web Site: http://www.wirtgen.ee
Construction Machinery Distr
N.A.I.C.S.: 423810

Wirtgen France SAS (3)
7 rue Marc Seguin, BP 31633, 95696,
Goussainville, France
Tel.: (33) 130189595
Web Site: http://www.wirtgen.fr
Construction Machinery Distr
N.A.I.C.S.: 423810

Wirtgen India Pvt. Ltd. (3)
Gat No 301 & 302 Bhandgaon Khor Road,
Village Bhandgaon Taluka Daund, Pune,
412214, Maharashtra, India
Tel.: (91) 2117302600
Web Site: http://www.wirtgenindia.co
Construction Machinery Distr
N.A.I.C.S.: 423810
Ramesh Palagiri (CEO & Mng Dir)
Anshum Jain (COO)
Nilesh Jajodia (CFO)
Krishna Prasad Shetty (VP & Head-Sls & Customer Support)
Sanjay Bajaj (VP-Bus Dev & Road Technologies)
Ashok Nambiar (Head-HR & Admin)

Wirtgen Macchine Srl. (3)
Via delle Industrie 7, Noviglio, 20082, Milan,
Italy
Tel.: (39) 029057941
Web Site: http://www.wirtgen.it
Construction Machinery Distr
N.A.I.C.S.: 423810

Wirtgen Norway AS (3)
Gallebergveien 28, 3070, Sande, Vestfold,
Norway
Tel.: (47) 33786600
Web Site: http://www.wirtgen.no
Construction Machinery Distr
N.A.I.C.S.: 423810

Wirtgen Osterreich GmbH (3)
Dr Linsinger Str 5, 4662, Steyrermuhl, Austria
Tel.: (43) 76132480
Web Site: http://www.wirtgen.at
Construction Machinery Distr
N.A.I.C.S.: 423810

Wirtgen Singapore Pte. Ltd. (3)
11 Tuas View Cresent, Multico Building,
Singapore, 637643, Singapore
Tel.: (65) 68632863
Web Site: http://www.wirtgen.com.sg
Construction Machinery Distr
N.A.I.C.S.: 423810

Wirtgen South Africa (Pty) Ltd. (3)
52 Maple Street, Pomona, Kempton Park,
1619, South Africa
Tel.: (27) 114521838
Web Site: http://www.wirtgen.co.za
Construction Machinery Distr
N.A.I.C.S.: 423810
Heinrich Schulenburg (Mng Dir)
Waylon Kukard (Mgr-Sls)
Paul van Wyk (Mgr-Technical Svc)
Johan Pretorius (Mgr-Parts)
Claire Poole (Mgr-Fin)
Anwar Hoosen (Reg Mgr-Kwazulu Natal)

Subsidiary (Domestic):

Wirtgen Zwickau Vertriebs- und Service GmbH (3)
Moseler Weg 2, 08393, Meerane, Germany
Tel.: (49) 376440170
Web Site: http://www.wirtgen-zwickau.de
Construction Machinery Distr
N.A.I.C.S.: 423810

Subsidiary (Non-US):

Wirtgen-Srbija d.o.o. (3)
Batajnicki drum 4 deo 14, Beograd-Zemun,
11080, Serbia
Tel.: (381) 112280368
Web Site: http://www.wirtgen.rs
Construction Machinery Distr
N.A.I.C.S.: 423810

DEFENSE TECHNOLOGIES INTERNATIONAL CORP.
2683 Via De La Valle Ste G418, Del
Mar, CA 92014   NV
Web Site:
  https://www.defensetechnologies
  intl.com
Year Founded: 1998
DTII—(OTCIQ)
Rev.: $49,012
Assets: $7,770
Liabilities: $2,370,132
Net Worth: ($2,362,362)
Earnings: ($575,766)

Emp.: 5
Fiscal Year-end: 04/30/24
Security & Defense Products Mfr
N.A.I.C.S.: 561621
Merrill W. Moses (Pres, CEO, Interim CFO & Sec)

DEFENTECT GROUP, INC.
364 Rowayton Ave, Norwalk, CT
06853
Tel.: (203) 803-1736   DE
Web Site: https://defentect.com
Year Founded: 2006
DFTC—(OTCIQ)
Telecommunication Servicesb
N.A.I.C.S.: 517111
Edmund L. Resor (VP)

DEFINITIVE HEALTHCARE CORP.
492 Old Connecticut Path Ste 401,
Framingham, MA 01701
Tel.: (508) 720-4224   DE
Web Site:
  https://www.definitivehc.com
Year Founded: 2021
DH—(NASDAQ)
Rev.: $222,653,000
Assets: $2,120,993,000
Liabilities: $633,772,000
Net Worth: $1,487,221,000
Earnings: ($6,037,000)
Emp.: 946
Fiscal Year-end: 12/31/22
Offices of Other Holding Companies
N.A.I.C.S.: 551112
Richard D. Booth (CFO)
Jason Krantz (Founder & Chm)
Kevin Coop (CEO)
Jonathan Maack (Pres)
Carrie Lazorchak (Chief Revenue Officer)
Richard Booth (CFO)
David Samuels (Chief Legal Officer)
Kate Shamsuddin (Chief Product Officer)
Jon Maack (Pres)

Subsidiaries:

Definitive Healthcare LLC (1)
492 Old Connecticut Path Ste 401,
Framingham, MA 01701
Web Site: https://www.definitivehc.com
Sales Range: $25-49.9 Million
Emp.: 133
Healthcare Software Development Services
N.A.I.C.S.: 541511
Robert W. Musslewhite (CEO)
Jon Maack (Pres)
Rick Booth (CFO)
Joe Mirisola (Chief Revenue Officer)
Matt Ruderman (Chief Legal Officer)
Kate Shamsuddin Jensen (Chief Product Officer)
Justin Steinman (CMO)
Tom Penque (Chief Talent Officer)
Scott Oberlink (CTO)
Ram Sharma (Exec VP)

Subsidiary (Domestic):

Analytical Wizards, Inc. (2)
100 S Wood Ave Ste 208, Iselin, NJ 08830
Tel.: (732) 902-2032
Web Site: http://www.analyticalwizards.com
Sales Range: $1-9.9 Million
Emp.: 100
Management Consulting Services
N.A.I.C.S.: 541611
Ram Sharma (Chm & CEO)
Ashish Jha (Mng Principal)
Sanjeev Bhalla (CTO)
Jimmy Cerveaux (CFO)
Jaya Subramaniam (Chief Strategy Officer)

DELAWARE ENHANCED GLOBAL DIVIDEND & INCOME FUND
2005 Market St 6th Fl, Philadelphia,
PA 19103-7094

DEX—(NYSE)
Rev.: $9,511,573
Assets: $197,872,683
Liabilities: $65,419,263
Net Worth: $132,453,420
Earnings: $4,764,056
Fiscal Year-end: 11/30/19
Investment Management Service
N.A.I.C.S.: 525990
Roger A. Early (Mgr-Fund)

DELAWARE INVESTMENTS COLORADO INSURED MUNICIPAL INCOME FUND
2005 Market St, Philadelphia, PA
19103-7057
Tel.: (215) 255-1200
VCF—(NYSEAMEX)
Investment Management Service
N.A.I.C.S.: 525990
Denise A. Franchetti (Mgr-Fund)

DELAWARE INVESTMENTS DIV & INCOME FUND
2005 Market St, Philadelphia, PA
19103
Tel.: (215) 255-1333
DDF—(NYSE)
Rev.: $5,031,513
Assets: $123,485,022
Liabilities: $39,003,686
Net Worth: $84,481,336
Earnings: $2,405,403
Fiscal Year-end: 11/30/19
Investment Management Service
N.A.I.C.S.: 525990
Robert A. Vogel Jr. (Mgr-Fund)

DELAWARE INVESTMENTS MINNESOTA MUNICIPAL INCOME FUND II, INC.
2005 Market St, Philadelphia, PA
19103-7057
Tel.: (215) 255-1200
VMM—(NYSEAMEX)
Fund Management Services
N.A.I.C.S.: 523940
Denise A. Franchetti (Mgr-Fund)

DELCATH SYSTEMS, INC.
566 Queensbury Ave, Queensbury,
NY 12804
Tel.: (212) 409-2100   DE
Web Site: https://www.delcath.com
Year Founded: 1988
DCTH—(NASDAQ)
Rev.: $2,719,000
Assets: $17,862,000
Liabilities: $23,721,000
Net Worth: ($5,859,000)
Earnings: ($36,508,000)
Emp.: 52
Fiscal Year-end: 12/31/22
Medical Device & Pharmaceuticals
Developer & Mfr
N.A.I.C.S.: 339112
Gerard J. Michel (CEO)
Anthony C. Dias (VP-Fin)
Martha S. Rook (COO)
David Hoffman (Chief Compliance Officer, Gen Counsel & Sec)
Sandra Pennell (Principal Fin Officer, Principal Acctg Officer & Sr VP-Fin)
Johnny John (Sr VP-Clinical Ops & Medical Affairs)
Vojislav Vukovic (Chief Medical Officer)

DELHI BANK CORP.
124 Main St, Delhi, NY 13753
Web Site: https://www.dnbd.bank
Year Founded: 1994
DWNX—(OTCIQ)
Commericial Banking

N.A.I.C.S.: 522110
Timothy C. Townsend *(Chm)*

DELL TECHNOLOGIES INC.
1 Dell Way, Round Rock, TX 78682
Tel.: (800) 289-3355   DE
Web Site:
   https://www.delltechnologies.com
Year Founded: 1984
DELL—(NYSE)
Rev.: $88,425,000,000
Assets: $82,089,000,000
Liabilities: $84,398,000,000
Net Worth: ($2,309,000,000)
Earnings: $3,211,000,000
Emp.: 120,000
Fiscal Year-end: 02/02/24
Software Development Services
N.A.I.C.S.: 551112
Brunilda Rios *(Chief Acctg Officer)*
Michael S. Dell *(Founder, Chm & CEO)*
Julie Sanders *(Sr VP)*
Richard J. Rothberg *(Gen Counsel)*
Vivek Mohindra *(Executives)*
Allison Dew *(CMO)*
William F. Scannell *(Pres-Sls-Global,Customer Ops)*
Yvonne McGill *(CFO)*
Jim Kelly *(Sr VP-Federal Sls-North America)*
John Byrne *(Pres-Sls-North America)*
Jennifer Saavedra *(Chief HR Officer)*
Edward D. Ward *(Pres-Client Product Grp)*
William Francis Scannell *(Pres-Global Sls & Customer Ops)*
Jeffrey W. Clarke *(Vice Chm & COO)*

Subsidiaries:

AirWatch LLC   **(1)**
8114 Storrow Dr, Westerville, OH 43081
Tel.: (614) 259-7554
Information Technology Equipment Services
N.A.I.C.S.: 541511

Avi Networks B.V.   **(1)**
Diana Vesta Amsterdam Zuidoost ArenA Herikerbergweg 292, 1101 CT, Amsterdam, Netherlands
Tel.: (31) 202251283
Software Development Services
N.A.I.C.S.: 541511

Avi Networks Germany GmbH   **(1)**
Franz-Mayer-Strasse 1, 93053, Regensburg, Germany
Tel.: (49) 94146297551
Software Development Services
N.A.I.C.S.: 541511

Avi Networks India Private Limited   **(1)**
4th floor B wing Salarpuria Softzone Green Glen Layout, Bellandur, Bengaluru, 560103, Karnataka, India
Tel.: (91) 8067537500
Software Development Services
N.A.I.C.S.: 541511

CloudHealth Technologies Australia Pty. Ltd.   **(1)**
WeWork Building at 5 Martin Place, Sydney, 2000, NSW, Australia
Tel.: (61) 79863900
Software Development Services
N.A.I.C.S.: 541511

DFS B.V.   **(1)**
Rudonk 7, 4824 AJ, Breda, Netherlands
Tel.: (31) 854861000
Computer Hardware Mfr
N.A.I.C.S.: 334118

Dell (China) Company Limited   **(1)**
Unit 507 5/F Tower A Full Link Plaza, No 18 Chaoyangmenwai Avenue, Beijing, China
Tel.: (86) 1058261389
Web Site: http://www.dell.com
Computer Mfr
N.A.I.C.S.: 334118
Zeena Fruitwala *(VP)*

Dell GmbH   **(1)**

Main Airport Center Unterschweinstiege 10, 60549, Frankfurt am Main, Germany
Tel.: (49) 6997927350
Computer Hardware Mfr
N.A.I.C.S.: 334118

Dell Inc.   **(1)**
1 Dell Way, Round Rock, TX 78682   **(71%)**
Tel.: (512) 728-7800
Web Site: http://www.dell.com
Sales Range: $50-74.9 Billion
Computer Products Developer, Mfr & Sales
N.A.I.C.S.: 334111

Subsidiary (Non-US):

ACS (India) Limited   **(2)**
House of Industrial Automation ACS Plot No 144 A Sector 7 PCNDTA, MIDC Bhosari, Pune, 411 026, India
Tel.: (91) 7588228065
Web Site: https://www.acs-india.com
Computer Hardware Mfr
N.A.I.C.S.: 334118

Alienware Limited   **(2)**
Unit 1 Blyry Court Blyry Industrial Estate, Athlone, Ireland
Tel.: (353) 12044359
Computer Peripherals Mfr
N.A.I.C.S.: 334118

Subsidiary (Domestic):

Boomi, Inc.   **(2)**
1400 Liberty Ridge Dr, Chesterbrook, PA 19087
Tel.: (610) 854-0700
Web Site: https://www.boomi.com
Sales Range: $10-24.9 Million
Emp.: 35
Cloud Integration Software Developer
N.A.I.C.S.: 513210
Arlen R. Shenkman *(Pres & CFO)*
Steve Lucas *(CEO)*
Sean Wechter *(CIO)*
Matt Heinz *(Chief Revenue Officer)*
Alison Vigan *(CMO)*
Adrian Trickett *(VP-Sls-Europe, Middle East & Africa & Gen Mgr-Europe, Middle East & Africa)*
Jim Fisher *(VP-Channels & Partners-Asia Pacific & Japan)*
Thomas Lai *(VP-Asia Pacific & Japan & Gen Mgr-Asia Pacific & Japan)*
Dan McAllister *(Sr VP-Global Alliances & Channels)*
Jasmine Ee *(Head-Media & Analyst Rels-Asia Pacific & Japan)*
Josh Rutberg *(Chief Customer Officer)*
Greg Wolfe *(Chief Comml Officer)*
Troy Anderson *(VP-Global Comml Markets)*
Rahim Bhatia *(Chief Strategy Officer)*
Jessica Soisson *(Chief Acctg Officer)*

Clerity Solutions, Inc.   **(2)**
1 Lincoln Centre 18 W 140 Butterfield Rd 15th Fl, Oakbrook Terrace, IL 60181
Tel.: (630) 981-6100
Sales Range: $1-9.9 Million
Emp.: 20
Computer System Design Services
N.A.I.C.S.: 541512

Subsidiary (Non-US):

DELL Computer spol. s r.o.   **(2)**
V Parku 16, 148 00, Prague, Czech Republic
Tel.: (420) 22 577 2711
Web Site: https://www.dell.cz
Computer Products Sales & Services
N.A.I.C.S.: 423430

Dell (China) Company Limted   **(2)**
No 2388 Jinshang Road, Xiamen, 361011, China
Tel.: (86) 8008582999
Web Site: http://www.dell.com
Sales Range: $1-4.9 Billion
Emp.: 4,000
Computer Products Sales & Services
N.A.I.C.S.: 423430

Dell A.S.   **(2)**
Lysaker Torg 8, PO Box 176, 1366, Lysaker, Norway   **(100%)**
Tel.: (47) 67106448
Web Site: http://www.dell.no

Computer & Laptop Distr
N.A.I.C.S.: 423430

Dell A/S   **(2)**
Arne Jacobsons Alle 15-17, 2300, Copenhagen, Denmark   **(100%)**
Tel.: (45) 32871200
Web Site: http://www.dell.dk
Computer Products Sales & Services
N.A.I.C.S.: 423430

Dell AB   **(2)**
Frosundaleden 2B, 169 70, Solna, Sweden   **(100%)**
Tel.: (46) 859005100
Web Site: http://www.dell.se
Sales Range: $75-99.9 Million
Emp.: 200
Computer Component Distr
N.A.I.C.S.: 423430

Dell Asia Pacific Sdn.   **(2)**
Plot P27 Bayan Lepas Industrial Zone, Bayan Lepas, Bayan Lepas, 11900, Malaysia   **(100%)**
Tel.: (60) 46334888
Web Site: http://www.dell.com.my
Sales Range: $900-999.9 Million
Emp.: 2,000
Computer Component Distr
N.A.I.C.S.: 423430

Dell Australia Pty. Limited   **(2)**
Building 3 14 Aquatic Drive, French's Forest, 2086, NSW, Australia   **(100%)**
Tel.: (61) 299303355
Web Site: http://www.dell.com.au
Sales Range: $200-249.9 Million
Emp.: 867
Computer Component Distr
N.A.I.C.S.: 423430

Dell B.V.   **(2)**
Transformatorweg 38-72, Amsterdam, 1014, Netherlands   **(100%)**
Tel.: (31) 206745500
Web Site: http://www.dell.nl
Sales Range: $250-299.9 Million
Emp.: 600
Computer Component Distr
N.A.I.C.S.: 423430

Dell Canada Inc.   **(2)**
155 Gordon Baker Rd Suite 501, North York, M2H 3N5, ON, Canada   **(100%)**
Tel.: (416) 773-5055
Web Site: http://www.dell.ca
Sales Range: $200-249.9 Million
Emp.: 400
Computer Component Distr
N.A.I.C.S.: 423430

Dell Computadores do Brasil Ltda.   **(2)**
Av Industrial Belgraf 400-a/c Paulo Gome, Eldorado do Sul, Porto Alegre, 92990 000, Brazil
Tel.: (55) 5134998821
Web Site: http://www.dell.com.br
Computer Component Distr
N.A.I.C.S.: 423430

Dell Computer (Proprietary) S.A.   **(2)**
Sloane St 57 The Campus Wembley Bldg 2nd Fl, Bryanston, 2021, Johannesburg, South Africa   **(100%)**
Tel.: (27) 117097700
Web Site: http://www.dell.co.za
Sales Range: $75-99.9 Million
Emp.: 150
Computer Products Sales & Services
N.A.I.C.S.: 423430

Dell Computer India Private Limited   **(2)**
Divyashree Greens Ground Floor SNo 12/1 12/2A 13/1A, Koramangala Inner Ring Road, Bengaluru, 560068, India   **(100%)**
Tel.: (91) 8025357311
Web Site: http://www.dell.co.in
Sales Range: $1-4.9 Billion
Emp.: 23,000
Computer Products Sales & Services
N.A.I.C.S.: 423430

Dell Computer S.A.   **(2)**
Basauri 17 Bloque B 1 Plant Urbanizacion La Florida, Madrid, 28023, Spain   **(100%)**
Tel.: (34) 902 100 130
Web Site: http://www.dell.es

Sales Range: $75-99.9 Million
Emp.: 250
Computer Component Distr
N.A.I.C.S.: 423430

Dell Computer de Chile Ltda   **(2)**
Av Ricardo Lyon 222 11th Floor, Providencia, Santiago, Chile
Tel.: (56) 2 2685 6800
Web Site: http://www.dell.com
Computer Products Mfr & Sales
N.A.I.C.S.: 423430

Dell Corporation (Thailand) Co., Ltd.   **(2)**
No 1 Empire Tower 22nd Floor South Sathorn Road, Yannawa Sathorn, Bangkok, 10120, Thailand
Tel.: (66) 26707250
Web Site: http://www.dell.co.th
Sales Range: $75-99.9 Million
Emp.: 150
Computer Component Distr
N.A.I.C.S.: 423430

Dell Corporation Limited   **(2)**
Dell House The Boulevard Cain Road, Bracknell, RG12 1LF, Berks, United Kingdom   **(100%)**
Tel.: (44) 1344860456
Web Site: http://www.dell.co.uk
Computer Component Distr
N.A.I.C.S.: 423430

Subsidiary (Domestic):

Dell Funding L.L.C.   **(2)**
4050 Pacific Harbors Dr, Las Vegas, NV 89169
Tel.: (702) 369-1094
Financial Services
N.A.I.C.S.: 522291

Subsidiary (Non-US):

Dell Gesm.b.H.   **(2)**
Wienerbergstrasse 41 43 Euro Plaza 4 Stock, 1120, Vienna, Austria
Tel.: (43) 12058113
Computer Hardware Mfr
N.A.I.C.S.: 334118

Dell GmbH   **(2)**
Main Airport Center Unterschweinstiege 10, 60549, Frankfurt am Main, Germany   **(100%)**
Tel.: (49) 699 7920
Web Site: https://www.dell.com
Computer Component Distr
N.A.I.C.S.: 423430

Dell Halle GmbH   **(2)**
Raffineriestrasse 28, 06112, Halle, Germany
Tel.: (49) 34578220
Computer Component Distr
N.A.I.C.S.: 423430

Branch (Domestic):

Dell Inc. - Fremont   **(2)**
6591 Dumbarton Cir, Fremont, CA 94555
Tel.: (510) 818-5500
IT Desktop Management Services
N.A.I.C.S.: 541512

Dell Inc. - Nashua   **(2)**
300 Innovative Way Ste 301, Nashua, NH 03062
Tel.: (603) 579-9762
Web Site: http://www.dell.com
Sales Range: $50-74.9 Million
Emp.: 1,000
Internet Protocol-Based Data Storage Systems Developer
N.A.I.C.S.: 541513

Dell Inc. - Nashville   **(2)**
1 Dell Pkwy, Nashville, TN 37217
Tel.: (615) 361-4214
Web Site: http://www.dell.com
Personal Computer Mfr
N.A.I.C.S.: 334111

Subsidiary (Non-US):

Dell India Private Ltd.   **(2)**
Divyashree Greens S No 12/1 12/2A 13/1A Ground Floor Varthur-Hobli, Bengaluru, 560071, India

Dell Technologies Inc.—(Continued)

Tel.: (91) 1600338044
Web Site: http://www.dell.com
Computer Related Equipment & Software Mfr
N.A.I.C.S.: 334118

Dell International Services India Private Limited (2)
Divyashree Greens Ground Floor Sys Nos 12/1 12/2A and 13/1A, Challaghatta Village Varthur Hobli, Bengaluru, 560 071, Karnataka, India
Tel,: (91) 18004254026
Computer Component Distr
N.A.I.C.S.: 423430

Dell International Services Philippines Inc. (2)
CyberPark E Rodriguez, Rodriguez Jr Avenue Bagumbayan, 1110, Quezon City, Metro Manila, Philippines
Tel.: (63) 27283355
Web Site: http://www.dellinternational.com
Computer Component Distr
N.A.I.C.S.: 423430

Dell Japan Inc. (2)
Solid Square Bldg Higashi-kan 20F 580 Horikawacho, Saiwai-Ku, Kawasaki, 212-0013, Kanagawa, Japan
Tel.: (81) 445564300
Web Site: http://www.dell.com
Computer Component Distr
N.A.I.C.S.: 423430

Unit (Domestic):

Dell MessageOne (2)
11044 Research Blvd Bldg C Fl 5, Austin, TX 78759
Tel.: (512) 652-4500
Web Site: http://www.messageone.com
Sales Range: $25-49.9 Million
Emp.: 100
E-Mail Management, Archiving & Business Continuity Services
N.A.I.C.S.: 513210

Subsidiary (Non-US):

Dell N.V. (2)
Koningin Astridlaan 164, 1780, Wemmel, Belgium (100%)
Tel.: (32) 24819100
Web Site: http://www.dell.be
Sales Range: $50-74.9 Million
Emp.: 130
Computer Component Distr
N.A.I.C.S.: 423430

Dell New Zealand Limited (2)
Unit 1A Pacific Office Park 4 Pacific Rise Mount Wellington, Auckland, New Zealand (100%)
Tel.: (64) 800289335
Web Site: http://www.dell.com
Computer Component Distr
N.A.I.C.S.: 423430

Dell S.A. (2)
7 R Eugene Et Armand Peugeot, 92500, Rueil-Malmaison, Cedex, France (100%)
Tel.: (33) 155947100
Web Site: http://www.dell.com
Computer Component Distr
N.A.I.C.S.: 423430

Dell S.A. (2)
Route De L Aeroport 29, PO Box 216, Geneva, Switzerland (100%)
Tel.: (41) 227990101
Web Site: http://www.dell.ch
Sales Range: $125-149.9 Million
Emp.: 300
Computer Component Distr
N.A.I.C.S.: 423430

Dell SA (2)
West Side Village 89D rue Pafebruch, 8308, Capellen, Luxembourg
Tel.: (352) 26 304 766
Web Site: http://www1.euro.dell.com
Sales Range: $50-74.9 Million
Emp.: 15
Computer Peripheral Mfr & Whslr
N.A.I.C.S.: 423430

Dell Singapore Pte. Ltd. (2)
180 Clemenceau Avenue Suite 06-01 Haw

Par Centre, Singapore, 239922, Singapore
Tel.: (65) 63353388
Computer Component Distr
N.A.I.C.S.: 423430

Dell Sp.z.o.o (2)
Inflancka 4A, 00-189, Warsaw, Poland
Tel.: (48) 22 579 59 99
Web Site: http://www.dell.com.pl
Computer Component Distr
N.A.I.C.S.: 423430

Dell s.r.o. (2)
Fazuiova 7, 811 07, Bratisiava, Slovakia
Tel.: (421) 257502014
Web Site: https://www.dell.sk
Emp.: 1,800
Computer Component Distr
N.A.I.C.S.: 423430

Subsidiary (Domestic):

Gale Technologies, Inc. (2)
2350 Mission College Blvd Ste 825, Santa Clara, CA 95054
Tel.: (408) 213-4900
Web Site: http://www.galetechnologies.com
Sales Range: $25-49.9 Million
Emp.: 50
Laboratory Automation & Test Lifecycle Management Software Developer & Publisher
N.A.I.C.S.: 513210

InSite One, Inc. (2)
135 N Plains Industrial Rd, Wallingford, CT 06492-2332
Tel.: (203) 265-6111
Web Site: https://insiteone.com
Computer Data Archiving Storage & Recovery Services
N.A.I.C.S.: 541519

License Technologies Group, Inc. (2)
840 Asbury Dr, Buffalo Grove, IL 60089
Tel.: (800) 883-8573
Software Licensing Services
N.A.I.C.S.: 611420

Subsidiary (Non-US):

Oy Dell A.B. (2)
Linnoitustie 2 A, Espoo, 2600, Finland (100%)
Tel.: (358) 207533538
Web Site: http://www.dell.fi
Sales Range: $50-74.9 Million
Emp.: 100
Computer Component Distr
N.A.I.C.S.: 423430

Subsidiary (Domestic):

SecuroWorks Corp. (2)
1 Concourse Pkwy NE Ste 500, Atlanta, GA 30328
Tel.: (404) 327-6339
Web Site: https://www.secureworks.com
Rev.: $463,475,000
Assets: $840,870,000
Liabilities: $282,909,000
Net Worth: $557,961,000
Earnings: ($114,499,000)
Emp.: 2,149
Fiscal Year-end: 02/03/2023
Computer Systems Security
N.A.I.C.S.: 541513
Alpana Wegner (CFO)
Michael S. Dell (Chm)
Mike Aiello (CTO)
Allan Peters (Chief Revenue Officer)
George Hanna (Chief Legal Officer & Chief Admin Officer)
Steve Fulton (Pres & Pres-Customer Success)
Chris Bell (Chief Strategy Officer)
Nash Borges (VP-Global Engrg)
Stacy Leidwinger (VP-Marketing)
Wendy K. Thomas (CEO)

Subsidiary (Non-US):

SonicWALL B.V. (2)
Business Park E 19, Battelsesteenweg 455 A2, 2800, Mechelen, Belgium
Tel.: (32) 15280985
Web Site: http://www.sonicwall.com
Sales Range: $150-199.9 Million
Integrated Network Security, Identity, Mobility & Productivity Solutions

N.A.I.C.S.: 423430
Will Benton (Dir-Northern Europe)
Tristan Bateup (Mgr-Ireland)
Terry Greer-King (VP-Sls-Europe, the Middle East & Africa)
Osca St Marthe (VP-Pre-Sls & Sls Engrg-Europe, the Middle East & Africa)
Bob VanKirk (Pres & CEO)
Christine Bartlett (CMO & Sr VP)

Subsidiary (Domestic):

StatSoft, Inc. (2)
2300 E 14th St, Tulsa, OK 74104
Tel.: (918) 749-1119
Web Site: http://www.statsoft.com
Sales Range: $10-24.9 Million
Analytic Software Publisher
N.A.I.C.S.: 513210

Subsidiary (Non-US):

Wyse Technology Inc. (2)
Tel.: (408) 473-1200
Web Site: http://www.wyse.com
Sales Range: $150-199.9 Million
Emp.: 500
Cloud Software Services
N.A.I.C.S.: 541511

Subsidiary (Non-US):

Wyse Technology (UK) Limited (3)
Tel.: (44) 1189342200
Web Site: http://www.wyse.com
Sales Range: $25-49.9 Million
Emp.: 30
Computers, Monitors, Software & Terminals Mfr
N.A.I.C.S.: 334111

Wyse Technology Australia Pty Limited (3)
Tel.: (61) 1300889973
Web Site: http://www.wyse.com.au
Computers, Monitors, Software & Terminals Mfr
N.A.I.C.S.: 334111

EMC Corporation (1)
176 South St, Hopkinton, MA 01748
Tel.: (508) 435-1000
Web Site: http://www.dellemc.com
Holding Company; Information Technology Storage Systems & Software Mfr; Data Management Services
N.A.I.C.S.: 551112

Subsidiary (Non-US):

EMC Australia Pty Limited (2)
Level 14 333 Collins Street, Melbourne, 3000, VIC, Australia
Tel.: (61) 390287444
Web Site: https://www.emcaustralia.com.au
Mfr of Computers; Field Engineering; Product Repair Center; Logistics & Continuing Products
N.A.I.C.S.: 334111

Division (Non-US):

EMC New Zealand Corporation Limited (3)
5-7 Willeston Street Level 8 EMC House, PO Box 9735, Wellington, 6011, New Zealand
Tel.: (64) 44733914
Web Site: http://www.dellemc.com
Sales Range: $10-24.9 Million
Emp.: 8
Data Processing Services
N.A.I.C.S.: 518210

Subsidiary (Non-US):

EMC Brasil Servicos De Ti LTDA (2)
Rua Verbo Divino St 1488 4 Fl, Sao Paulo, 04719902, Brazil (100%)
Tel.: (55) 1151895000
Web Site: http://www.dellemc.com
Computer Product Sales
N.A.I.C.S.: 449210

EMC Chile S.A. (2)
Avenida Ricardo Lyon 222 11th Floor, Santiago, CP7510125, Chile (100%)
Tel.: (56) 23733100
Web Site: http://www.dellemc.com
Sales of Computer Systems
N.A.I.C.S.: 449210

EMC Computer Systems (Benelux) B.V. (2)
Edisonbaan 14 B Gebouw 8, Nieuwegein, 3639MN, Netherlands (100%)
Web Site: http://www.dellemc.com
Computer Equipment Sls
N.A.I.C.S.: 449210

EMC Computer Systems (FE) Limited (2)
18/F Oxford House taikoo Place 979 Kings Road, Island East, Hong Kong, China (Hong Kong) (100%)
Tel.: (852) 28399600
Web Site: http://www.dellemc.com
Computer Component Distr
N.A.I.C.S.: 423430

EMC Computer Systems (South Asia) PTE Ltd (2)
1 Changi Business Park Central 1 08-101 ONE, Changi, Singapore, 486036, Singapore (100%)
Tel.: (65) 68232106
Web Site: http://www.dellemc.com
Computer Component Distr
N.A.I.C.S.: 423430
Ron Goh (Pres-South Asia)

EMC Computer Systems A/S (2)
Linde Alle 9A & 9B, 2850, Naerum, Denmark (100%)
Tel.: (45) 70106878
Web Site: http://www.emc.com
Sales Range: $25-49.9 Million
Emp.: 70
Computer Mfr, Software Publisher & Cloud Infrastructure
N.A.I.C.S.: 334118

EMC Computer Systems AS, Norway (2)
Lilleakerveien 2b, Oslo, 0283, Norway (100%)
Tel.: (47) 23207700
Web Site: http://www.dellemc.com
Mfr of Computers
N.A.I.C.S.: 334111

EMC Computer Systems Austria GmbH (2)
At Euro place 1/4, Vienna, 1120, Austria
Tel.: (43) 159952500
Web Site: http://www.dellemc.com
Computer Component Distr
N.A.I.C.S.: 423430

EMC Computer Systems Danmark A/S (2)
Linde Alle 9A and 9B Ground and 1st Floor Naerum, Copenhagen, 2850, Denmark
Tel.: (45) 70106878
Web Site: http://www.dellemc.com
Computer Device Distr
N.A.I.C.S.: 423430

EMC Computer Systems France (2)
River Ouest 80 Quai Voltaire CS 21002, 95870, Bezons, Cedex, France
Tel.: (33) 805113759
Web Site: http://france.emc.com
Computer Component Distr
N.A.I.C.S.: 423430

EMC Computer Systems Italia S.p.A (2)
Via Spadolini 5, Milan, 20141, Italy (100%)
Tel.: (39) 02409081
Web Site: http://www.dellemc.com
Computer Services
N.A.I.C.S.: 541512

EMC Computer Systems Poland Sp. z.o.o. (2)
ul Inflancka 4A, Warsaw, Poland
Tel.: (48) 224178761
Web Site: http://www.dellemc.com
Information Technology Services
N.A.I.C.S.: 541511

EMC Computer Systems Spain, S.A.U. (2)
Calle Ribera del Loira 8 Olivar de la Hinojosa, Madrid, 28042, Spain (100%)
Tel.: (34) 914103800
Web Site: http://www.dellemc.com
Computer Component Distr
N.A.I.C.S.: 423430
Jose L. Solla (Mng Dir)

EMC Computer Systems Venezuela, S.A. (2)
Francisco de Miranda Avenue Multicentro Empresarial del Este Building, Miranda Tower Core A Floor 6 Office A-64, Caracas, 1060, Venezuela **(100%)**
Tel.: (58) 2122066911
Web Site: http://www.emc.com
Computer Assembly, Peripheral Assembly & Testing
N.A.I.C.S.: 334111

EMC Computer-Systems OY (2)
Keilaranta 13 A, 2150, Espoo, Finland
Tel.: (358) 201202200
Web Site: https://www.dell.com
Computer Device Distr
N.A.I.C.S.: 423430

Branch (Domestic):

EMC Corporation - Santa Clara (2)
2831 Mission College Blvd, Santa Clara, CA 95054
Tel.: (408) 566-2000
Web Site: http://www.dellemc.com
Computer & Computer Peripheral Equipment & Software Merchant Whslr
N.A.I.C.S.: 423430

EMC Corporation - Southborough (2)
32 Coslin Dr Bldg 5, Southborough, MA 01772
Tel.: (508) 898-4296
Web Site: http://www.emc.com
Field Engineering, Technical Support Functions, Custom Software, Educational Services
N.A.I.C.S.: 334112

Subsidiary (Non-US):

EMC Corporation of Canada (2)
2680 Skymark Avenue 10th Floor Suite 1000, Mississauga, L4W 5L6, ON, Canada
Tel.: (416) 628-5973
Web Site: http://www.dellemc.com
Computer Device Distr
N.A.I.C.S.: 423430

EMC Corporation of Canada (2)
120 Adelaide Street West Suite 1400, Toronto, M5H 1T1, ON, Canada **(100%)**
Tel.: (416) 628-5973
Web Site: http://www.dellemc.com
Sales; Field Engineering Product Repair & Logistics Center
N.A.I.C.S.: 449210

EMC Czech Republic s.r.o. (2)
V Parku 2335/20 1st Floor Chodov, Prague, 14800, Czech Republic
Tel.: (420) 272089410
Web Site: http://www.dellemc.com
Computer Device Distr
N.A.I.C.S.: 423430

EMC Deutschland GmbH (2)
Am Kronberger Hang 2a, Schwalbach am Taunus, 65824, Germany **(100%)**
Tel.: (49) 8001016944
Web Site: http://www.dellemc.com
Computer Component Distr
N.A.I.C.S.: 423430

EMC Information Systems (Thailand) Limited (2)
57 Wireless Road Lumpini Level 10 Park Ventures Ecoplex Pathumwan, Bangkok, 10330, Thailand
Tel.: (66) 23423600
Web Site: http://www.dellemc.com
Computer Device Distr
N.A.I.C.S.: 423430

EMC Information Systems Colombia Ltda. (2)
Oficina Central Calle 116 7-15 Interioir 2 Oficina 402 & 405, Bogota, Colombia
Tel.: (57) 16580900
Web Site: http://www.dellemc.com
Computer Device Distr
N.A.I.C.S.: 423430

EMC Information Systems N.V. (2)
Imperiastraat 18, Zaventem, 1930, Belgium
Tel.: (32) 27006032
Web Site: http://www.dellemc.com
Computer Device Distr

N.A.I.C.S.: 423430

EMC Information Systems Pakistan (Private) Limited (2)
Suite No 403 4th Floor Green Trust Tower Jinnah Avenue Sector F6, Blue Area, Islamabad, 44000, Pakistan
Tel.: (92) 518744155
Computer Device Distr
N.A.I.C.S.: 423430

EMC Information Systems Sweden AB (2)
Telegrafgatan 4, Solna, 16972, Sweden **(100%)**
Tel.: (46) 855512000
Web Site: http://www.dellemc.com
Computer Component Distr
N.A.I.C.S.: 423430

Division (Domestic):

EMC Sales & Marketing (2)
176 S St, Hopkinton, MA 01748
Tel.: (508) 435-1000
Web Site: http://www.emc.com
Sales & Marketing of Data General Computers, Software & Peripherals
N.A.I.C.S.: 541519
Joseph M. Tucci (Chm, Pres & CEO)

Subsidiary (Non-US):

EMC del Peru S.A. (2)
Av Republica De Panama No 3531 Fl 8, Lima, 27, Peru **(100%)**
Tel.: (51) 14210670
Web Site: http://www.dellemc.com
Data Processing Services Mfr & Supplier
N.A.I.C.S.: 518210

Subsidiary (Domestic):

Isilon Systems, LLC (2)
505 1st Ave S, Seattle, WA 98104
Tel.: (206) 315-7500
Web Site: http://www.dellemc.com
Computer Storage
N.A.I.C.S.: 334112

Lastline G.K. (1)
Level 20 Marunouchi Trust Tower Main 1-8-3 Marunouchi, Chiyoda-ku, Tokyo, 100-0005, Japan
Tel.: (81) 352885386
Software Development Services
N.A.I.C.S.: 541511

More I.T. Resources Ltd. (1)
1 Ben Gurion BSR 2, Bnei Brak, 51201, Israel
Tel.: (972) 36142199
Information Technology Equipment Services
N.A.I.C.S.: 541511

SecureWorks Europe S.R.L. (1)
4A Timisoara Blvd AFI PARK 4&5 5th floor, 6th District, 061328, Bucharest, Romania
Tel.: (40) 312291014
Computer Hardware Mfr
N.A.I.C.S.: 334118

SecureWorks, Inc. (1)
1 Concourse Pkwy NE 500, Atlanta, GA 30328
Web Site: https://www.secureworks.com
Software Development Services
N.A.I.C.S.: 513210

VMware Argentina S.R.L. (1)
Alicia Moreau de Justo 140 piso 2, Puerto Madero, Buenos Aires, Argentina
Tel.: (54) 1152350928
Software Development Services
N.A.I.C.S.: 541511

VMware Global, Inc. (1)
Willy-Brandt-Platz 2, 81829, Munich, Germany
Tel.: (49) 89370617000
Software Development Services
N.A.I.C.S.: 513210

VMware International Spain, S.L. (1)
Calle Rafael Boti 26 2nd Floor, 28023, Madrid, Spain
Tel.: (34) 914125000
Software Development Services
N.A.I.C.S.: 541511

VMware Malaysia SDN. BHD. (1)
Lot 7 02B Level 7 Menara BRDB 285 Jalan

Maarof, Bukit Bandaraya, 59000, Kuala Lumpur, Malaysia
Tel.: (60) 322964301
Computer Hardware Mfr
N.A.I.C.S.: 334118

VMware Poland Sp. z o.o. (1)
4 Inflancka str Gdanski Business Center Building B 1st floor, 00-189, Warsaw, Poland
Tel.: (48) 223225300
Computer Hardware Mfr
N.A.I.C.S.: 334118

VMware Rus LLC (1)
30 Floor Nordstar Tower Business Centre 3/1 Begovaya St, Moscow, 125284, Russia
Tel.: (7) 4952122900
Software Development Services
N.A.I.C.S.: 513210

VMware South Africa (Pty.) Ltd. (1)
3021 William Nicol Dr Block A 1st Floor, Bryanston, Johannesburg, 2021, South Africa
Tel.: (27) 115134800
Computer Hardware Mfr
N.A.I.C.S.: 334118

Vmware Mexico S. de R.L. de C.V. (1)
Paseo de la Reforma 250 Capital Reforma Torre A Piso 9, Col Juarez CDMX, 06600, Mexico, Mexico
Tel.: (52) 5536007200
Computer Hardware Mfr
N.A.I.C.S.: 334118

DELPHAX TECHNOLOGIES INC.
5000 W 36th St Ste 130, Minneapolis, MN 55416
Tel.: (952) 939-9000   MN
Web Site: https://www.delphax.com
Year Founded: 1981
DLPX—(OTCIQ)
Sales Range: $25-49.9 Million
Emp.: 280
Digital Document Printing Equipment Mfr
N.A.I.C.S.: 333248
Gregory S. Furness (CFO)
Steve Hubbard (VP-Sls)

Subsidiaries:

Delphax Technologies Ltd. (1)
Unit 1 Vector Point Newton Road, West Suxxex, Crawley, RH10 9AU, West Sussex, United Kingdom **(100%)**
Tel.: (44) 1293551051
Web Site: http://www.delphax.com
Sales Range: $10-24.9 Million
Emp.: 210
Mfr of Computerized Financial Document Production Systems
N.A.I.C.S.: 333248

DELTA AIR LINES, INC.
PO Box 20706, Atlanta, GA 30320-6001
Tel.: (404) 715-2600   DE
Web Site: https://www.delta.com
Year Founded: 1924
DAL—(NYSE)
Rev.: $58,048,000,000
Assets: $73,644,000,000
Liabilities: $62,539,000,000
Net Worth: $11,105,000,000
Earnings: $4,609,000,000
Emp.: 103,000
Fiscal Year-end: 12/31/23
Air Transportation & Air Cargo Services
N.A.I.C.S.: 481111
Alicia L. Tillman (CMO-Global)
Glen W. Hauenstein (Pres)
Joanne D. Smith (Chief People Officer & Exec VP)
Tim Mapes (Chief Mktg & Comm Officer & Sr VP)
William P. Lentsch (Chief Customer Experience Officer)

Ranjan Goswami (VP)
Peter W. Carter (Exec VP-External Affairs)
Rahul Samant (CIO & Exec VP)
Joe Esposito (Sr VP)
Perry Cantarutti (Sr VP-International)
Brandi Thomas (VP)
Prashant Sharma (VP)
William Charles Carroll (Sr VP-Finance & Controller)
Richard Cox Jr. (Sr VP-Reser Sales & Customer Care)
Henry Ting (Chief Health Officer)
Dwight James (CEO-Delta Vacations & Sr VP)
Alex Antilla (VP-Latin America)
Pamela Fletcher (Chief Sustainability Officer-Corp Innovation & Sr VP)
Daniel C. Janki (CFO & Exec VP)
Alain M. Bellemare (Pres-Intl)

Subsidiaries:

DAL Global Services (1)
980 Virginia Ave 4th Fl Department 937, Atlanta, GA 30354
Tel.: (404) 715-4300
Web Site: http://www.deltaglobalstaffing.com
Sales Range: $25-49.9 Million
Emp.: 1,500
Employment Placement Agency Services
N.A.I.C.S.: 561311

Delta Air Lines France (1)
2 Rue Robert Esnault Pelterie, 75007, Paris, France **(100%)**
Tel.: (33) 811640005
Web Site: http://www.delta.com
Sales Range: $600-649.9 Million
Emp.: 240
Cargo & Passenger Ticketing Services
N.A.I.C.S.: 481111

Delta Air Lines Frankfurt (1)
Frankfurt Airport, Cargo City South Bldg 556B, 60549, Frankfurt, Germany **(100%)**
Tel.: (49) 6969028604
Web Site: http://www.deltacargo.com
Sales Range: $350-399.9 Million
Emp.: 25
Cargo & Passenger Transportation
N.A.I.C.S.: 481112

Delta Air Lines UK (1)
24 Buckinghamgate, SW1E6LB, London, United Kingdom **(100%)**
Tel.: (44) 2079328300
Sales Range: $350-399.9 Million
Emp.: 30
Cargo & Passenger Transportation
N.A.I.C.S.: 481111

Delta Material Services, LLC (1)
1775 M H Jackson Service Rd, Atlanta, GA 30354
Tel.: (404) 714-2376
Web Site: http://www.dms.aero
Aviation Equipment Mfr
N.A.I.C.S.: 336413
Jeff Keisling (Chief Comml Officer & Exec VP)
Mark Benson (VP-Technical Ops)
Bill Thompson (Sr VP-Comml)
Mohan Perumal (Sr VP-Operational Excellence & IT)
V. R. Sridhar (VP-Programs & Plng)
Bob Bietz (VP-Ops)
Doug Nowinski (VP-Supplier Procurement)
Josh Abelson (Pres)

Delta Technology Inc. (1)
1020 Delta Blvd Dept 810, Atlanta, GA 30354-1989 **(100%)**
Tel.: (404) 714-1500
Rev.: $214,300,000
Emp.: 1,200
Travel Technology Solutions for Air Travel Industry
N.A.I.C.S.: 541512

Endeavor Air, Inc. (1)
7500 Airline Dr, Minneapolis, MN 55450-1101
Tel.: (612) 266-1470
Web Site: https://www.endeavorair.com
Emp.: 4,400
Oil Transportation Services

Delta Air Lines, Inc.—(Continued)
N.A.I.C.S.: 481111
Joe Miller (COO)
Russ Elander (VP-Ops)
Bill Donohue (VP-Tech Ops)
Jodie Douglas (VP-HR)
Jay Furnish (VP-Network & Crew Resources)
Patty Allen (VP-Inflight Svcs)
Brian Darsow (VP-Fin & Supply Chain)
David Garrison (CEO)

Endeavour Air, Inc.   (1)
7500 Airline Dr, Minneapolis, MN 55450-1101
Tel.: (612) 266-1470
Web Site: https://www.endeavorair.com
Emp.: 7,797
Airline Holding Company
N.A.I.C.S.: 551112
Edward M. Christie III (Executives)
Jodie A. Douglas (VP-HR)
Jay Furnish (VP-Network & Crew Resources)
Patty Allen (VP-Inflight Svcs)
Jim Graham (CEO)
Phillip Underwood (COO)
Cara Marx (Mng Dir)
Todd Tilbury (Mng Dir)

Epsilon Trading, Inc.   (1)
1030 Delta Blvd, Atlanta, GA 30354-1989
Tel.: (404) 715-2600
Sales Range: $150-199.9 Million
Aircraft Refueling Services
N.A.I.C.S.: 457210
Richard Anderson (Pres)

MIPC, LLC   (1)
920 Cherry Tree Rd, Aston, PA 19014
Tel.: (610) 485-3709
Web Site: https://www.monroepipeline.com
Pipeline Transportation Services
N.A.I.C.S.: 486990

MLT Vacations, Inc.   (1)
700 S Central Ave, Atlanta, GA 30354
Tel.: (404) 559-2270
Web Site: http://www.mltvacations.com
Sales Range: $50-74.9 Million
Emp.: 500
Vacation Travel Packages Whslr
N.A.I.C.S.: 561510

Monroe Energy, LLC   (1)
4101 Post Rd, Trainer, PA 19061
Tel.: (610) 364-8000
Web Site: https://www.monroe-energy.com
Petroleum Product Distr
N.A.I.C.S.: 324110
Brian Carlson (VP-Reliability & Optimization)
Mark Schuck (VP-Refinery Ops)
Christine Shorokey (VP & Gen Mgr-MIPC)
Jeff Warmann (Pres & CEO)
Christopher Ruggiero (Gen Counsel, Sec & VP)
Bill McEnroe (Dir-HSS)
Matthew O'Mahoney (CFO)
Regan Howell (COO)
Sharon Watkins (VP)

Montana Enterprises, Inc.   (1)
1509 Rio Vista Ave, Los Angeles, CA 90023
Tel.: (213) 749-2600
Web Site: http://www.1826jeann.com
Sales Range: $25-49.9 Million
Emp.: 5
Oil Transportation Services
N.A.I.C.S.: 481111
Tony Javidzad (Pres)

Northwest Training Center   (1)
2600 Lone Oak Point, Eagan, MN 55121
Tel.: (612) 726-6100
Emp.: 50,000
Flight Training Unit
N.A.I.C.S.: 611512

Tomisato Shoji Kabushiki Kaisha (1)
650-35 Nanae, Tomisato, Chiba, 286-0221, Japan
Tel.: (81) 476931234
Oil Transportation Services
N.A.I.C.S.: 481111

DELTA APPAREL, INC.
2750 Premiere Pkwy Ste 100, Duluth, GA 30097

Tel.: (864) 232-5200   GA
Web Site:
   https://www.deltaapparelinc.com
Year Founded: 1999
DLA—(NYSEAMEX)
Rev.: $415,351,000
Assets: $455,238,000
Liabilities: $305,043,000
Net Worth: $150,195,000
Earnings: ($33,213,000)
Emp.: 6,811
Fiscal Year-end: 09/30/23
Knit Apparel Designer, Mfr & Marketer
N.A.I.C.S.: 424310
Nancy P. Bubanich (Chief Acctg Officer, Principal Fin Officer, VP, Asst Treas & Asst Sec)
Jeffery N. Stillwell (Pres-Salt Life Group)
S. Lauren Satterfield (Sec & Deputy Gen Counsel)
Carlos E. Encalada Arjona (VP-Mfg)
Patrick Bowman (Sr Dir-DTG2Go)
Jason Bates (VP-Fin-Delta Grp)

Subsidiaries:

DTG2Go, LLC   (1)
3631 131st Ave N, Clearwater, FL 33762
Tel.: (727) 800-9767
Web Site: http://www.dtg2go.com
Printing
N.A.I.C.S.: 323113

Subsidiary (Domestic):

Silk Screen Ink LTD.   (2)
512 Geneseo St, Storm Lake, IA 50588
Tel.: (712) 732-9457
Web Site: http://www.ssidps.com
Textile Product Mill Services
N.A.I.C.S.: 314999

FunTees   (1)
245 Manor Ave SW, Concord, NC 28025-5711
Tel.: (704) 788-3003
Web Site: http://www.funtees.com
Sales Range: $125-149.9 Million
Emp.: 65
Private-Label Knit Goods
N.A.I.C.S.: 315250
Lewis Reid (Pres)

Junkfood Clothing Company   (1)
5770 W Jefferson Blvd, Los Angeles, CA 90016
Tel.: (310) 445-7776
Web Site: http://www.junkfoodclothing.com
Sales Range: $150-199.9 Million
Emp.: 65
Licensed & Branded Apparel Sales
N.A.I.C.S.: 315990

M. J. Soffe, LLC   (1)
1 Soffe Dr, Fayetteville, NC 28312 (100%)
Tel.: (910) 483-2500
Web Site: http://www.soffe.com
Sales Range: $600-649.9 Million
Emp.: 2,000
Casual & Active Apparel Designer, Mfr & Marketer
N.A.I.C.S.: 315250

TCX, LLC   (1)
115 E 3rd St, Wendell, NC 27591-9791
Tel.: (919) 365-5900
Sales Range: $50-74.9 Million
Emp.: 160
Fashion Apparel Mfr & Distr
N.A.I.C.S.: 424350

To The Game, LLC   (1)
1147 6th Ave, Columbus, GA 31901
Web Site: https://www.saltlife.com
Emp.: 75
Fashion Apparel Mfr & Distr
N.A.I.C.S.: 424350

DELTAGEN, INC.
1900 S Norfolk St Ste 105, San Mateo, CA 94403
Tel.: (650) 345-7601   DE
Web Site: http://www.deltagen.com
DGEN—(OTCIQ)

Sales Range: $10-24.9 Million
Genetic Technology Developer
N.A.I.C.S.: 541715
Robert J. Driscoll (Pres & CEO)

DELUXE CORPORATION
801 S Marquette Ave, Minneapolis, MN 55402-2807
Tel.: (651) 483-7111   MN
Web Site: https://www.deluxe.com
Year Founded: 1915
DLX—(NYSE)
Rev.: $2,238,010,000
Assets: $3,076,520,000
Liabilities: $2,472,296,000
Net Worth: $604,224,000
Earnings: $65,395,000
Emp.: 5,863
Fiscal Year-end: 12/31/22
Fraud Prevention, Customer Loyalty & Brand Building Products & Services
N.A.I.C.S.: 561499
Tracey G. Engelhardt (Pres-Checks & Sr VP)
Chip Zint (CFO & Sr VP)
Jean Herrick (Chief HR Officer & Sr VP)
Barry C. McCarthy (Pres & CEO)
Jeffrey L. Cotter (Chief Admin Officer, Gen Counsel, Sec & Sr VP)
Yogaraj Jayaprakasam (CTO, Chief Digital Officer & Sr VP)
Cheryl E. Mayberry McKissack (Chm)
Debra A. Bradford (Pres-Merchant Svcs & Sr VP)
Kristopher D. Lazzaretti (Pres-Data & Sr VP)
Garry L. Capers (Pres-Cloud Solutions & Sr VP)

Subsidiaries:

Anchor Systems Pty Ltd   (1)
Level 11 201 Elizabeth St, Sydney, 2000, NSW, Australia
Tel.: (61) 282965111
Web Site: https://www.anchor.com.au
Web Hosting Services
N.A.I.C.S.: 518210

Bnbs, Inc.   (1)
11600 Otter Creek Rd S, Mabelvale, AR 72103   (100%)
Tel.: (501) 224-1992
Web Site: http://www.bnbsolutionsinc.com
Sales Range: $25-49.9 Million
Emp.: 100
Printing & Promotional Business Services
N.A.I.C.S.: 323111

Company 3 LA   (1)
1661 Lincoln Blvd Ste 400, Santa Monica, CA 90404
Tel.: (310) 255-6600
Web Site: http://www.company3.com
Sales Range: $100-124.9 Million
Emp.: 75
Motion Picture Sound Effects & Music Production Services
N.A.I.C.S.: 512191

Crucial Paradigm Pty Ltd   (1)
Suite 2 Level 3 104-106 Commonwealth Street, Surry Hills, 2010, NSW, Australia
Tel.: (61) 1300884839
Web Site: http://www.crucial.com.au
Web Hosting Services
N.A.I.C.S.: 518210

Datamyx LLC   (1)
2300 Glades Rd Ste 400E, Boca Raton, FL 33432
Tel.: (800) 488-9113
Web Site: https://www.datamyx.com
Emp.: 35
Marketing Consulting Services
N.A.I.C.S.: 541613

Deluxe Small Business Sales, Inc. (1)
3680 Victoria St N, Shoreview, MN 55126
Tel.: (651) 483-7111
Web Site: https://www.deluxe.com
Commercial Printing Services

N.A.I.C.S.: 323111

Deluxe Small Business Services   (1)
500 Main St, Groton, MA 01471   (100%)
Tel.: (978) 448-6111
Web Site: http://www.deluxe.com
Sales Range: $550-599.9 Million
Emp.: 600
Check, Envelope, Label, Greeting Card, Sign, Stationery & Related Printing Services
N.A.I.C.S.: 424120

Subsidiary (Non-US):

NEBS Business Products Limited   (2)
330 Cranston Crescent, Midland, L4R 4V9, ON, Canada
Web Site: https://www.deluxe.ca
Personalized Business Products Mfr & Distr; Cheques, Forms & Web Services
N.A.I.C.S.: 459410

NEBS Payroll Service Limited   (2)
102-420 Sheldon Dr, Cambridge, N1T 2H9, ON, Canada   (100%)
Tel.: (519) 621-3570
Web Site: http://www.payweb.ca
Sales Range: $10-24.9 Million
Emp.: 30
Payroll Services
N.A.I.C.S.: 561499

Subsidiary (Domestic):

Rapidforms, Inc.   (2)
PO Box 64235, Saint Paul, MN 55164-0235
Tel.: (651) 483-7111
Web Site: http://www.rapidforms.com
Sales Range: $350-399.9 Million
Emp.: 382
Office Management & Promotional Product Retailer
N.A.I.C.S.: 424120

Subsidiary (Non-US):

Safeguard Business Systems Limited (2)
330 Cranston Crescent, Midland, L4R 4V9, ON, Canada
Tel.: (705) 526-4233
Web Site: https://www.gosafeguard.ca
Sales Range: $50-74.9 Million
Emp.: 20
Stationery & Office Supplies Whslr
N.A.I.C.S.: 424120

Subsidiary (Domestic):

Safeguard Business Systems, Inc.   (2)
8585 Stemmons Fwy Ste 600N, Dallas, TX 75247
Tel.: (214) 905-3935
Web Site: http://www.gosafeguard.com
Sales Range: $150-199.9 Million
Check, Check-Writing System & Business Form Mfr & Marketer
N.A.I.C.S.: 323111

Subsidiary (Domestic):

Brand Advantage Group   (3)
5097 Nathan Ln N, Minneapolis, MN 55442
Tel.: (763) 559-4330
Web Site:
   http://www.brandadvantagegroup.com
Office Equipment Supplies Distr
N.A.I.C.S.: 424120
Tom Lyngdal (CFO)
Brian Selvig (Dir-IT)
David Daoust (CEO)
Darryl Breckheimer (Mgr-Customer Svc)

Fontis Solutions, Inc.   (3)
60 Bunsen, Irvine, CA 92618
Tel.: (949) 754-9000
Web Site: http://www.fontissolutions.com
Marketing Communication Services
N.A.I.C.S.: 541613
Chris Paul (CFO)
Jim Spellman (VP-Sls)
Tammi McCullough (Dir-Ops)

Deluxe Strategic Sourcing, Inc.   (1)
1406 Dunn Dr, Carrollton, TX 75006
Tel.: (800) 869-0992
Web Site:
   http://www.accusourcesolutions.net

Office Equipment & Stationery Supplies Whslr
N.A.I.C.S.: 424120
Mark Wood *(Pres & CEO)*

Digital Pacific Pty Ltd (1)
Level 11 201 Elizabeth Street, Sydney, 2000, NSW, Australia
Tel.: (61) 288231020
Web Site: https://www.digitalpacific.com.au
Web Hosting Services
N.A.I.C.S.: 518210

Direct Checks Unlimited Sales, Inc (1)
PO Box 19000, Colorado Springs, CO 80935-9000
Tel.: (719) 531-3900
Web Site: http://www.checksunlimited.com
Sales Range: $75-99.9 Million
Office Supply Mfr
N.A.I.C.S.: 459410

Encore Hollywood (1)
6344 Fountain Ave, Hollywood, CA 90028
Tel.: (323) 466-7663
Web Site: http://www.encorehollywood.com
Sales Range: $100-124.9 Million
Editing, Visual Effects, Coloring & Digital Intermediate Services
N.A.I.C.S.: 512191

First American Payment Systems, L.P. (1)
100 Throckmorton St Ste 1800, Fort Worth, TX 76102-2802
Tel.: (817) 317-9100
Web Site: https://www.first-american.net
Sales Range: $250-299.9 Million
Credit Card Authorization & Payment Systems to Retail Merchants
N.A.I.C.S.: 522390
Neil L. Randel *(Chm & CEO)*
Debra A. Bradford *(Pres & CFO)*
Michael Lawrence *(CIO & Exec VP)*
Rick Rizenbergs *(Exec VP-Sls & Mktg)*
Brian Dorchester *(Exec VP-Ops)*
Latiffa Sharpe *(VP-Merchant Svcs)*
Kathy Dorchester *(VP-Compliance & Merchant Settlement)*
Bill Lodes *(Exec VP-Bus Dev & Strategy)*
Alan R. Struble *(Gen Counsel & Exec VP)*
Sarah Adams *(VP-Global Product)*
Angela Carranza *(Mgr-Strategic Partnerships)*
Dana Odom *(VP-Integrated Software Vendors)*
Mike LoMurro *(Pres-Certified Payments)*
Matthew Landers *(VP-Sls-Certified Payments)*
Chuck Springer *(VP-Info Security & Compliance)*
Ashley Rangel *(VP-Bus Ops Support)*
Michael Bradford *(VP-Ops)*
Chris Yurko *(VP-Integrated Payments)*

First Manhattan Consulting Group, LLC (1)
90 Park Ave, New York, NY 10016
Tel.: (212) 557-0500
Web Site: https://www.fmcgdirect.com
Consulting Services for Financial Services Industry
N.A.I.C.S.: 541611
Tad C. LeBlond *(Exec VP)*
Derek S. Elmerick *(VP)*
Kristopher D. Lazzaretti *(Exec VP)*
Stephen Ryan *(VP)*
John Tracy *(VP)*
Elissa Rodd *(VP)*
Alexandra Moss *(VP)*
Amy Herguth *(COO)*
Maureen Cawley *(Head-Talent & Culture)*
David Brauntuch *(VP)*

Form Systems, Inc. (1)
15575 SW Sequoia Pkwy, Portland, OR 97224
Tel.: (503) 624-5879
Commercial Printing Services
N.A.I.C.S.: 323111

Hostopia.com Inc. (1)
110 E Broward Blvd Ste 1650, Fort Lauderdale, FL 33301
Tel.: (954) 463-3080
Web Site: http://www.hostopia.com
Sales Range: $10-24.9 Million
Emp.: 300
Web Hosting Services

N.A.I.C.S.: 518210

InkHead Promotional Products (1)
138 Park Ave Ste 300, Winder, GA 30680
Tel.: (678) 905-5629
Web Site: http://www.inkhead.com
Online Merchandise Distr
N.A.I.C.S.: 541890

Innovative Print & Media Group, Inc. (1)
500 Schell Ln, Phoenixville, PA 19460
Tel.: (610) 489-4800
Web Site: https://safeguardbyinnovative.com
Emp.: 50
Commercial Printing Services
N.A.I.C.S.: 323111
Betsy McBride *(Mgr-HR)*

Level Three Post (1)
2901 W Alameda Ave, Burbank, CA 91505
Tel.: (818) 840-7200
Web Site: http://www.level3post.com
Sales Range: $100-124.9 Million
Editing, Visual Effects, Coloring & Digital Intermediate Services
N.A.I.C.S.: 512191

NetClime-Bulgaria EOOD (1)
bul Tsarigradsko Shose 127B fl 5 and fl 6, 1784, Sofia, Bulgaria
Tel.: (359) 24922963
Software Development Services
N.A.I.C.S.: 541511

Orangesoda, Inc. (1)
732 E Utah Valley Dr, American Fork, UT 84003
Tel.: (801) 610-2500
Web Site: http://www.orangesoda.com
Sales Range: $10-24.9 Million
Emp.: 182
Online Marketing Services
N.A.I.C.S.: 541613

Payce, Inc. (1)
1220-B E Joppa Rd Ste 324, Towson, MD 21286
Tel.: (443) 279-9000
Web Hosting Services
N.A.I.C.S.: 518210
Josh Lindenmuth *(CIO)*

RDM Corporation (1)
619A Kumpf Drive, Waterloo, N2V 1K8, ON, Canada
Tel.: (519) 746-8483
Web Site: http://www.rdmcorp.com
Electronic Check & Bill Payment Solutions Services
N.A.I.C.S.: 522320

Subsidiary (Domestic):

Research, Development & Manufacturing Corporation (2)
619A Kumpf Drive, Waterloo, N2V 1K8, ON, Canada
Tel.: (800) 567-6227
Web Site: http://www.rdmcorp.com
Computer Programming Developers
N.A.I.C.S.: 541511

Rushes Postproduction Ltd (1)
66 Old Compton Street, London, W1D 4UH, United Kingdom
Tel.: (44) 2074378676
Web Site: http://www.rushes.co.uk
Sales Range: $100-124.9 Million
Emp.: 50
Motion Picture Sound Effects & Music Production Services
N.A.I.C.S.: 512191
Joce Capper *(Mng Dir)*

Safeguard Franchise Sales, Inc. (1)
8585 N Stemmons Freeway Ste 600N, Dallas, TX 75247
Tel.: (214) 905-3935
Commercial Printing Services
N.A.I.C.S.: 323111

The Johnson Group (1)
2801 E Rock Dr, Rockford, IL 61109
Tel.: (815) 397-0800
Web Site: http://www.johngroup.com
Sales Range: $10-24.9 Million
Emp.: 130
Commercial Printing Services
N.A.I.C.S.: 323111

Subsidiary (Domestic):

Cardinal Printing Co., Inc. (2)
341 Vincennes St, New Albany, IN 47150
Tel.: (812) 945-6611
Web Site: http://www.cardinalprint.com
Commercial Printing Services
N.A.I.C.S.: 323111
Kelly Horrell *(Mgr-Production)*

DEMAND BRANDS, INC.
160 Spear St Ste 415, San Francisco, CA 94105
Tel.: (415) 685-0317   WA
Year Founded: 2005
DMAN—(OTCIQ)
Oil & Gas Operation Services
N.A.I.C.S.: 213112
Dawn R. Loos *(COO & Sec-Corp)*
Ankit Jain *(Chief Acctg Officer)*
Kevin Sparks *(Pres & CEO)*

DEMOCRASOFT HOLDINGS, INC.
50 Old Courthouse Sq Ste 407, Santa Rosa, CA 95404
Web Site:
https://www.democrasoft.com
DEMO—(OTCIQ)
Information Technology Services
N.A.I.C.S.: 541511
Richard Lang *(Founder, Chm & CEO)*

DENALI BANCORP INC.
119 N Cushman St, Fairbanks, AK 99701
Tel.: (907) 456-1400
Web Site:
https://www.denalistatebank.com
DENI—(OTCIQ)
Bank Holding Company
N.A.I.C.S.: 551111
Steven Lundgren *(Pres & CEO)*
Aaron Hines *(Sr VP & Mgr-Comml Loan)*
Andra Lozano *(Sr VP & COO)*
Aaron Pletnikoff *(Chief Lending Officer & Exec VP)*
Randy Weaver *(CFO & Exec VP)*

Subsidiaries:

Denali State Bank (1)
119 N Cushman St, Fairbanks, AK 99701
Tel.: (907) 456-1400
Web Site: http://www.denalistatebank.com
Rev.: $12,856,000
Assets: $260,845,000
Liabilities: $236,087,000
Net Worth: $24,758,000
Earnings: $1,804,000
Emp.: 60
Fiscal Year-end: 12/31/2013
Banking Services
N.A.I.C.S.: 522110
Steven Lundgren *(Pres & CEO)*

DENALI CAPITAL ACQUISITION CORP.
437 Madison Ave 27th Fl, New York, NY 10022
Tel.: (646) 978-5180   Ky
Year Founded: 2022
DECAU—(NASDAQ)
Investment Services
N.A.I.C.S.: 523150
Lei Huang *(CEO)*
You Sun *(CFO)*

DENALI THERAPEUTICS INC.
161 Oyster Pt Blvd, South San Francisco, CA 94080
Tel.: (650) 866-8548   DE
Web Site:
https://www.denalitherapeutics.com
Year Founded: 2013
DNLI—(NASDAQ)
Rev.: $108,463,000
Assets: $1,460,242,000

Liabilities: $417,812,000
Net Worth: $1,042,430,000
Earnings: ($325,991,000)
Emp.: 427
Fiscal Year-end: 12/31/22
Biotechnology Research & Development Services
N.A.I.C.S.: 541714
Marc Tessier-Lavigne *(Co-Founder)*
Ryan J. Watts *(Co-Founder, Pres & CEO)*
Alexander O. Schuth *(Co-Founder, Chief Operating & Fin Officer & Sec)*
Cindy Dunkle *(Chief People Officer)*
Joe Lewcock *(Chief Scientific Officer)*
Dana Andersen *(Chief Tech & Mfg Officer)*
Kimberly Scearce-Levie *(VP-Translational Sciences)*
Laura Hansen *(VP-IR)*
Michelle Polowski *(Sr VP)*
Anthony Delucchi *(VP)*
Wei Dong *(VP)*
Leah Frautschy *(VP)*
Kirk Henne *(VP)*
Mark Kafka *(VP)*
Fabian Model *(VP)*
Michael Ostland *(VP)*
Mark Rowen *(VP)*
Carole Ho *(Chief Medical Officer & Head-Dev)*
Katie Peng *(Chief Comml Officer)*

DENHAM SUSTAINABLE PERFORMANCE ACQUISITION CORP.
185 Dartmouth St 7th Fl, Boston, MA 02116
Tel.: (617) 531-7200   Ky
Year Founded: 2021
DSPQ—(NYSE)
Investment Services
N.A.I.C.S.: 523999
Jordan Marye *(CEO)*
James Obulaney *(CFO)*
Stuart Porter *(Founder & Chm)*
Saurabh Anand *(Exec VP)*

DENNY'S CORPORATION
203 E Main St, Spartanburg, SC 29319
Tel.: (864) 597-8000   DE
Web Site: https://www.dennys.com
Year Founded: 1989
DENN—(NASDAQ)
Rev.: $398,174,000
Assets: $435,527,000
Liabilities: $500,792,000
Net Worth: ($65,265,000)
Earnings: $78,073,000
Emp.: 3,300
Fiscal Year-end: 12/29/21
Food Service & Restaurant Franchise Owner & Operator
N.A.I.C.S.: 722511
J. Scott Melton *(Asst Sec & Asst Gen Counsel)*
Ross B. Nell *(Treas & VP-Tax)*
Kelli F. Valade *(Pres & CEO)*
Stephen C. Dunn *(Chief Global Dev Officer & Sr VP)*
Thomas M. Starnes *(Chief Food Safety Officer & VP-Brand Protection & Quality)*
Jay C. Gilmore *(Chief Acctg Officer, Sr VP & Controller)*
R. Gregory Linford *(VP-Pur)*
Robert P. Verostek *(CFO & Exec VP)*
David W. Coltrin *(VP-Guest Experience & Mktg Tech)*
Laurie R. Curtis *(VP-Mktg & Menu Innovation)*
Erik P. Jensen *(VP-Brand Engagement)*
Fasika Melaku-Peterson *(Chief Learning & Dev Officer & VP)*

Denny's Corporation—(Continued)

Mark S. Burgess *(VP-Real Estate & Bus Dev)*
Ethan R. Gallagher *(VP-Field Fin & Growth Strategies)*
Pankaj Patra *(Chief Digital & Tech Officer)*
Gail Sharps Myers *(Chief Legal Officer, Chief People Officer & Exec VP)*
Kelli Valade *(CEO)*
Stephanie Davidson *(Chief People Officer)*
Curtis L. Nichols Jr. *(VP-IR, Fin Plng & Analysis)*
Ramon Torres *(VP-Ops Svcs)*

Subsidiaries:

DFO, LLC   **(1)**
203 E Main St, Spartanburg, SC 29319-0001
Tel.: (864) 597-8000
Web Site: http://www.dennysfranchising.com
Food Processing & Export Services
N.A.I.C.S.: 722310

Denny's, Inc.   **(1)**
203 E Main St, Spartanburg, SC 29319   **(100%)**
Tel.: (864) 597-8000
Web Site: http://www.dennys.com
Sales Range: $900-999.9 Million
Emp.: 300
Operator of Family Style Restaurants
N.A.I.C.S.: 722511

Keke's Breakfast Cafe Inc.   **(1)**
1032 Montgomery Rd, Altamonte Springs, FL 32714-7420
Tel.: (407) 951-7770
Web Site:
   http://www.kekesbreakfastcafe.com
Limited-Service Restaurants
N.A.I.C.S.: 722513
Sebastien DeFabrique *(Owner & Mgr)*
David Schmidt *(Pres)*

DENTAL PATIENT CARE AMERICA, INC.
41 N Rio Grande St Ste 100, Salt Lake City, UT 84101
Tel.: (801) 456-0444   UT
Web Site:
   https://www.dentalcoop.com
Year Founded: 1998
DPAT—(OTCIQ)
Dental Care Services
N.A.I.C.S.: 621210
Michael Silva *(Chm & CEO)*
Brandon Berrett *(Dir-Financing & Patient Programs)*
Nicole Green *(Dir-HR Benefits)*
Camille Mauerhan *(Dir-Merchant Svcs)*
Erica Gordon *(Dir-Insurance Fee Maximization)*
Drew McIlveen *(Dir-Vendor Partnerships)*
Jeff Harmon *(Dir-Transitions & Financing)*
Marlon Berrett *(Pres)*
Andrew Eberhardt *(COO)*
Jared Hansen *(VP)*
Teresa Jardine *(Dir-Idaho Area)*
Ray Landry III *(Dir-Northern Utah & Nevada Area)*
Mark Damron *(Dir-Central & Southern Utah Area)*
Rio Padilla *(Dir-Pennsylvania Area)*

DENTSPLY SIRONA INC.
13320 Ballantyne Corporate Pl, Charlotte, NC 28277-3607
Tel.: (717) 845-7511   DE
Web Site:
   https://www.dentsplysirona.com
Year Founded: 1899
XRAY—(NASDAQ)
Rev.: $3,965,000,000
Assets: $7,370,000,000

Liabilities: $4,076,000,000
Net Worth: $3,294,000,000
Earnings: ($132,000,000)
Emp.: 15,000
Fiscal Year-end: 12/31/23
Holding Company; Dental Equipment & Supplies Mfr & Whslr
N.A.I.C.S.: 551112
Lisa Yankie *(Chief HR Officer & Sr VP)*
Chidam Chidambaram *(Chief Digital Officer & Sr VP)*
Matthew Coggin *(Chief Strategy & Bus Dev Officer & Exec VP)*
Simon D. Campion *(Pres & CEO)*
Andrea Daley *(VP-IR)*
Tony Johnson *(Sr VP)*
Andrew Robinson *(Sr VP)*
Rich Rosenzweig *(Gen Counsel)*
Glenn G. Coleman *(CFO & Exec VP)*
Erania S. Brackett *(Sr VP-Customer Experience & Orthodontic Aligner Solu & Head-Environment & Social Governance)*

Subsidiaries:

CCRI, Inc.   **(1)**
2903 15th St S, Moorhead, MN 56560
Tel.: (218) 236-6730
Web Site: http://www.ccrimoorhead.org
Emp.: 500
Health Care Srvices
N.A.I.C.S.: 621330
Shannon Bock *(Exec Dir)*
Mark McGuigan *(Mgr-Bus)*
Jody Hudson *(Dir-Dev)*
Eric Hilber *(Dir-SLS)*
Melanie Eidsmoe *(Asst Dir-SLS)*
Kent Schultz *(Dir-IT)*
Lynette Weber *(Dir-Ops)*
Dave Pompe *(Asst Dir-Ops)*
Bethany Berkeley *(Pres)*
Heather Rye *(VP)*
Marit Haman *(Treas)*

DENTSPLY SIRONA Inc. - Preventive Division   **(1)**
1301 Smile Way, York, PA 17404
Tel.: (717) 767-8500
Mfr of Dental Equipment
N.A.I.C.S.: 339114

DENTSPLY SIRONA Inc. - Restorative   **(1)**
38 W Clarke Ave, Milford, DE 19963-1805
Tel.: (302) 422-4511
Web Site: http://www.dentsply.com
Mfr & Wholesale Distributor of Dental Supplies
N.A.I.C.S.: 339114

DENTSPLY Sirona K.K.   **(1)**
4F 1-8-10 Azabudai, Minato-ku, Tokyo, 106-0041, Japan
Tel.: (81) 120789123
Web Site: http://www.dentsplysirona.com
Dental Equipment Provider
N.A.I.C.S.: 339114
Yuko Kitamoto *(Pres & CEO)*

Dental Implant Training Center Corp.   **(1)**
18-00 Fair Lawn Ave, Fair Lawn, NJ 07410
Tel.: (201) 797-9144
Web Site: http://www.ditcusa.com
Dental Training Services
N.A.I.C.S.: 611310

Dentaply Prosthetics Austria GmbH   **(1)**
Wahringerstrasse 11/Turm A/27, 1100, Vienna, Austria
Tel.: (43) 16004930304
Medical Equipment Mfr
N.A.I.C.S.: 339112

Dentsply (Singapore) Pte. Ltd.   **(1)**
80 Bendemeer Rd 07-05/06, Singapore, 339949, Singapore
Tel.: (65) 68869555
Web Site: http://www.dentsplymaillefer.com
Dental Equipment Distr
N.A.I.C.S.: 339114

Dentsply (Thailand) Ltd.   **(1)**

23/F Panjathani Tower 127/28 Ratchadapisek Road Chongnonsee, Yannawa, Bangkok, 10120, Thailand   **(100%)**
Tel.: (66) 22953744
Web Site: http://www.dentsplymaillefer.com
Dental Equipment Distr
N.A.I.C.S.: 327910

Dentsply Argentina   **(1)**
661 Gral Enrique Martinez, C1426BBI, Buenos Aires, Argentina
Tel.: (54) 1145550808
Dental Equipment Distr
N.A.I.C.S.: 339114
Raul Ripoll *(Country Mgr)*

Dentsply DeTrey GmbH   **(1)**
De-Trey-Str 1, 78467, Konstanz, Germany
Tel.: (49) 75315830
Web Site: http://www.dentsplysirona.com
Distr of Dental Supplies & Equipment
N.A.I.C.S.: 423450

Dentsply GAC Europe SAS   **(1)**
1 Rue des Messagers, 37210, Rochecorbon, France
Tel.: (33) 247402330
Dental Equipment Distr
N.A.I.C.S.: 423450
Patricia Dorriere *(Controller-Fin-European)*

Dentsply Germany Investments GmbH   **(1)**
Steinzeugstrasse 50, Mannheim, 68229, Germany
Tel.: (49) 6214302000
Dental Equipment Distr
N.A.I.C.S.: 339114

Subsidiary (Non-US):

Zhermack S.p.A.   **(2)**
Bovazecchino street 100, 45021, Badia Polesine, RO, Italy
Tel.: (39) 042 559 7611
Web Site: https://www.zhermack.com
Dental Equipment & Supplies Mfr
N.A.I.C.S.: 339114

Dentsply IH A/S   **(1)**
Hummeltoftevej 49, 2830, Virum, Denmark
Tel.: (45) 43624332
Web Site: http://www.wellspect.dk
Medical Equipment Distr
N.A.I.C.S.: 423450

Dentsply IH AB   **(1)**
Aminogatan 1, 431 53, Molndal, Sweden
Tel.: (46) 313764000
Web Site: https://www.wellspect.com
Dental Equipment Distr
N.A.I.C.S.: 339114

Dentsply IH AB   **(1)**
Aminogatan 1, 431 53, Molndal, Sweden
Tel.: (46) 313764000
Web Site: https://www.wellspect.com
Dental Equipment Distr
N.A.I.C.S.: 339114

Dentsply IH AB   **(1)**
Aminogatan 1, 431 53, Molndal, Sweden
Tel.: (46) 313764000
Web Site: https://www.wellspect.com
Dental Equipment Distr
N.A.I.C.S.: 339114

Dentsply IH AB   **(1)**
Aminogatan 1, 431 53, Molndal, Sweden
Tel.: (46) 313764000
Web Site: https://www.wellspect.com
Dental Equipment Distr
N.A.I.C.S.: 339114

Dentsply IH GmbH   **(1)**
Wienerbergstrabe 11/Turm A/27, 1100, Austria
Tel.: (43) 1 6004930 301
Web Site: http://www.dentsplyimplants.at
Dental Equipment Distr
N.A.I.C.S.: 339114

Dentsply IH GmbH   **(1)**
Fabrikstrasse 31, 64625, Bensheim, Germany
Tel.: (49) 643198690
Web Site: https://www.dentsplysirona.com
Medical Equipment Distr
N.A.I.C.S.: 423450

Dentsply IH Inc   **(1)**

590 Lincoln St, Waltham, MA 02451
Tel.: (781) 890-6800
Dental Equipment Distr
N.A.I.C.S.: 339114

Dentsply IH Ltd   **(1)**
Building 3 The Heights Brooklands, Weybridge, KT13 0NY, Gloucestershire, United Kingdom
Tel.: (44) 1453791763
Medical Equipment Distr
N.A.I.C.S.: 423450

Dentsply IH Oy   **(1)**
Piispansilta 9B, 02230, Espoo, Finland
Tel.: (358) 986761626
Web Site: http://implants.dentsplysirona.com
Medical Equipment Distr
N.A.I.C.S.: 423450

Dentsply Implants Manufacturing GmbH   **(1)**
Steinzeugstrasse 50, 68229, Mannheim, Germany
Tel.: (49) 6214302006
Dental Equipment Distr
N.A.I.C.S.: 339114
Norbert Rabenstein *(Head-Implant Production)*

Dentsply Implants Taiwan Co, Ltd.   **(1)**
12Floor No 216 Sec 1 Sanmin Rd, Banciao District, New Taipei City, 22069, Taiwan
Tel.: (886) 229613655
Dental Equipment Distr
N.A.I.C.S.: 339114

Dentsply Implants Turkey A.S.   **(1)**
Nisbetiye Caddesi Levent is Merkezi No 6 Kat 2 1 Levent, PK 34340, Istanbul, Turkiye
Tel.: (90) 2122198400
Web Site: http://implants.dentsplysirona.com
Medical Equipment Mfr
N.A.I.C.S.: 339112

Dentsply India Pvt. Ltd.   **(1)**   **(100%)**
Tel.: (91) 2262510000
Web Site: http://dentsply.co.in
Dental Supplies & Equipment Mfr & Distr
N.A.I.C.S.: 339114

Dentsply Italia S.r.L.   **(1)**
Piazza dell Indipendenza 11B, 00185, Rome, Italy   **(100%)**
Tel.: (39) 0067264031
Web Site: http://www.dentsplysirona.com
Dental Equipment & Supplies Sales
N.A.I.C.S.: 456199

Dentsply Limited   **(1)**
Building 3 The Heights Brooklands, Weybridge, KT13 0NY, Surrey, United Kingdom
Tel.: (44) 1932838343
Web Site: https://www.dentsply.co.uk
Mfr & Marketer of Dental Supplies & Equipment
N.A.I.C.S.: 339114

Dentsply Mexico, S.A. de C.V.   **(1)**   **(100%)**
Tel.: (52) 55876488
Web Site: http://www.dentsply.com.mx
Dental Supplies & Equipment Mfr
N.A.I.C.S.: 339114

Dentsply Sirona (Phils.), Inc.   **(1)**
Offices 16/F Tower 6789 Ayala Ave Brgy Bel-Air, Legazpi Village, Makati, 1209, Metro Manila, Philippines   **(100%)**
Tel.: (63) 288636833
Dental Supplies & Equipment Distr
N.A.I.C.S.: 423450
Victor Malillin *(Country Mgr)*

Dentsply Sirona - Norway   **(1)**
Karihaugveien 89, 1086, Oslo, Norway
Tel.: (47) 67839610
Web Site: http://www.dentsply-gac.no
Medical Equipment Mfr
N.A.I.C.S.: 339112

Dentsply Sirona Benelux B.V.   **(1)**
Signal red 55, 2718 SG, Zoetermeer, Netherlands
Tel.: (31) 880245200
Medical Equipment Mfr & Distr
N.A.I.C.S.: 339112
Heidi Kok-Benoist *(Sr Mgr-HR)*

Dentsply Sirona Canada **(1)**
161 Vinyl Ct, Woodbridge, L4L 4A3, ON,
Canada **(100%)**
Web Site: http://www.dentsplysirona.com
Wholesale Distributor of Dental Supplies &
Equipment
N.A.I.C.S.: 423450

Dentsply Sirona Endodontics **(1)**
5100 E Skelly Dr #300, Tulsa, OK 74135
Tel.: (800) 662-1202
Dental Equipment Distr
N.A.I.C.S.: 339114

Dentsply Sirona Europe GmbH **(1)**
Sirona Strasse 1 Himmelreich, 5071,
Salzburg, Austria
Tel.: (43) 66224500
Dental Equipment Distr
N.A.I.C.S.: 423450

Dentsply Sirona France S.A.S. **(1)**
Tel.: (33) 130976500
Emp.: 600
Dental Supplies & Equipment Distr
N.A.I.C.S.: 423450

**Dentsply Sirona Implants
Norway** **(1)**
Karihaugveien 89, 1086, Oslo, Norway
Tel.: (47) 81559119
Web Site: http://implants.dentsplysirona.com
Medical Equipment Mfr
N.A.I.C.S.: 339112

Dentsply Sirona Korea **(1)**
7F Daemyung Tower 135 Beobwon-ro,
Songpa-Gu, Seoul, 005-836, Korea (South)
Tel.: (82) 220087600
Web Site: http://www.dentsplysirona.com
Provider of Pharmaceutical Products
N.A.I.C.S.: 325412

Dentsply Sirona Pty. Ltd. **(1)**
30 Friar John Way West, Pinjarra, 6208,
WA, Australia **(100%)**
Tel.: (61) 89418274230
Web Site: http://www.dentsply.com.au
Distr of Dental Supplies & Equipment
N.A.I.C.S.: 423450

Dentsply Sirona Pty. Ltd. **(1)**
Unit 19 39 Herbert St, Saint Leonards,
2065, NSW, Australia
Tel.: (61) 294965100
Web Site: http://www.dentsplysirona.com
Dental Equipment Distr
N.A.I.C.S.: 423450

Dentsply Sirona Switzerland Sarl **(1)**
Chemin Du Verger 3, 1338, Ballaigues,
Switzerland
Tel.: (41) 218439292
Dental Equipment Distr
N.A.I.C.S.: 423450

GAC Deutschland GmbH **(1)**
Am Kirchenholzl 15, 82166, Grafelfing, Ger-
many
Tel.: (49) 895402690
Web Site: https://www.dentsplysirona.com
Dental Equipment Distr
N.A.I.C.S.: 339114

LLC Dentsply IH **(1)**
2 Maly Mogiltsevky Lane, 119002, Moscow,
Russia
Tel.: (7) 4959882808
Web Site:
    http://www.dentsplyimplants.com.ru
Medical Equipment Distr
N.A.I.C.S.: 423450

LLC Dentsply Russia **(1)**
6 Mira Ave, 129090, Moscow, Russia
Tel.: (7) 4959882808
Web Site:
    http://www.dentsplyimplants.com.ru
Dental Equipment & Supplies Mfr
N.A.I.C.S.: 339114

**Medical 3 Importacion Service Iberica
S.L.** **(1)**
Sigfrido 1 2nd Floor Office 3, 29006,
Malaga, Spain
Tel.: (34) 935122457
Web Site: http://www.misiberica.es
Medical Equipment Mfr
N.A.I.C.S.: 339114

**New Britain Medical Supplies,
Inc.** **(1)**

Tel.: (860) 224-9017
Web Site: https://www.newbritainmedicalsup
plies.com
Medical Equipment Distr
N.A.I.C.S.: 456199
Joseph Paladino *(Founder)*

OraMetrix, Inc. **(1)**
2350 Campbell Creek Blvd Ste 400, Rich-
ardson, TX 75082
Tel.: (972) 728-5900
Web Site: http://www.suresmile.com
Orthodontic Treatment Services
N.A.I.C.S.: 339114
Jay Widdig *(CFO)*

Orthodental International, Inc. **(1)**
1000 Porton Dr, Calexico, CA 92231
Tel.: (760) 357-8070
Dental Equipment Distr
N.A.I.C.S.: 339114
Justin H. McCarthy II *(Sec)*

Sirona Dental Systems, Inc. **(1)**
30-30 47th Ave Ste 500, Long Island City,
NY 11101
Tel.: (718) 937-5765
Web Site: http://www.sirona.com
Sales Range: $1-4.9 Billion
Dental Equipment Distr
N.A.I.C.S.: 339114
Lynn Blankenship *(VP-HR & Svcs-USA)*

Subsidiary (Non-US):

FONA Dental s.r.o. **(2)**
Sevcenkova 34, 85101, Bratislava, Slovakia
Tel.: (421) 2 322 32 455
Web Site: http://www.fonadental.com
Dental Equipment & Supplies Mfr
N.A.I.C.S.: 339114

FONA s.r.l. **(2)**
Via Galileo Galilei 11, 20057, Assago, MI,
Italy
Tel.: (39) 0245712171
Web Site: https://www.fonadental.com
Dental Equipment Distr
N.A.I.C.S.: 339114

MHT Optic Research AG **(2)**
Mandachstrasse 50, 8155, Niederhasli,
Switzerland
Tel.: (41) 448529000
Web Site: http://www.mht.ch
Medical Equipment Mfr
N.A.I.C.S.: 339112
Markus Berner *(Co-Founder & Pres)*
Carlo Gobbetti *(Co-Founder)*

MHT S.r.l. **(2)**
Via Enrico Fermi 22, 37135, Verona, Italy
Tel.: (39) 0456020842
Web Site: http://www.mht.it
Medical Equipment Mfr
N.A.I.C.S.: 339112

SICAT GmbH & Co. KG **(2)**
Schwertberger Str 14-16, 53177, Bonn,
Germany
Tel.: (49) 22885469712
Web Site: http://www.sicat.com
Development of Three-Dimensional Imaging
Software, Products & Solutions for Dental
Implantology & Oral-Maxillofacial Surgery
N.A.I.C.S.: 622110
Jochen Kusch *(Co-Founder, Mng Dir & Gen
Mgr)*
Joachim Hey *(Co-Founder, Mng Dir & Gen
Mgr)*
Felix Uckert *(Specialist-3D Application)*
Stephanie Myers *(Dir-Mktg)*

SiCAT Verwaltungs GmbH **(2)**
Schwertberger Str 14-16, 53177, Bonn,
Germany
Tel.: (49) 2888546971
Web Site: http://www.sicat.com
Surgical Equipment Mfr
N.A.I.C.S.: 339112

Sirona Dental A/S **(2)**
Rho 10, 8382, Hinnerup, Denmark
Tel.: (45) 87439060
Web Site: http://www.sirona.com
Medical Equipment Mfr
N.A.I.C.S.: 339112

Sirona Dental GmbH **(2)**
Sirona Strasse 1, 5071, Wals-Siezenheim,
Salzburg, Austria

Tel.: (43) 66224500
Web Site: http://www.sirona-connect.com
Emp.: 130
Surgical Equipment Distr
N.A.I.C.S.: 423450

Sirona Dental Limited Sirketi **(2)**
Tel.: (90) 2166883672
Web Site: http://www.sirona.com.tr
Dental Equipment & Supplies Mfr
N.A.I.C.S.: 339114

**Sirona Dental Mexico S. de R.L. de
C.V.** **(2)**
German Centre 2 2 10-14 Av Santa Fe, No
170 Colonia Lomas de Santa Fe Del Alvaro
Obregon, 01219, Mexico, Mexico
Tel.: (52) 5552929856
Web Site: http://www.sirona.com.tr
Surgical Equipment Distr
N.A.I.C.S.: 423450

Sirona Dental Systems GmbH **(2)**
Fabrikstrasse 31, D-64625, Bensheim, Ger-
many
Tel.: (49) 6251161690
Dental Equipment Distr
N.A.I.C.S.: 339114

Sirona Dental Systems K.K. **(2)**
5F Sumitomo Fudosan Shiodome
Hamarikyu Bldg 8-21-1 Ginza, Chuo-ku,
Tokyo, 104-0016, Japan
Tel.: (81) 351487895
Web Site: http://www.sirona.co.jp
Dental Equipment Distr
N.A.I.C.S.: 423450

**Sirona Dental Systems Korea,
Ltd.** **(2)**
140-884 1F Hannam Plaza Hannam-dong
85 Dokseodang-ro, Yongsan-gu, Seoul, Ko-
rea (South)
Tel.: (82) 7040355467
Web Site: http://www.sirona.co.kr
Surgical Equipment Distr
N.A.I.C.S.: 423450

Sirona Dental Systems Ltd. **(2)**
Lakeside House 1 Furzeground Way Stock-
ley Park, Stockley Park, Heathrow, UB11
1BD, United Kingdom
Tel.: (44) 8450715040
Web Site: http://www.sirona.com.tr
Dental Equipment Distr
N.A.I.C.S.: 339114

Sirona Dental Systems O.O.O. **(2)**
German Centre for Industry and Trade Of-
fice 10-04, Prospekt Andropova 18 b 6,
115432, Moscow, Russia
Tel.: (7) 4957251087
Web Site: http://www.sirona.ru
Dental Equipment & Supplies Mfr
N.A.I.C.S.: 339114

**Sirona Dental Systems Private
Ltd.** **(2)**
GA 10 11 Phoenix Market City Lal Bahadur
Shastra Marg Kurla West, Art Guild House,
Mumbai, 400070, Maharashtra, India
Tel.: (91) 2262510000
Web Site: http://www.sirona.com
Surgical Equipment Distr
N.A.I.C.S.: 423450

Sirona Dental Systems Pte. Ltd **(2)**
6 Battery Road #15-06, Singapore,
'049909, Singapore
Tel.: (65) 31575160
Web Site: http://www.sirona.com.tr
Surgical Equipment Distr
N.A.I.C.S.: 423450

Sirona Dental Systems SAS **(2)**
7 Ter Rue de la Porte de Buc, 78000, Ver-
sailles, France
Tel.: (33) 130976500
Surgical Equipment Marketing Services
N.A.I.C.S.: 423450

**Sirona Dental Systems South Africa
(Pty) Ltd.** **(2)**
Building 11A Lower Ground Floor The
Woodlands Woodlands Drive, Woodmead,
Sandton, 2080, Johannesburg, South Africa
Tel.: (27) 100012827
Web Site: http://www.sirona.com.tr
Surgical Equipment Distr
N.A.I.C.S.: 423450

**Sirona Dental Systems Trading
(Shanghai) Co. Ltd** **(2)**
283 West Jianguo Road Shangjie Loft
Building 1, 6th Floor Unit 1618, Shanghai,
200031, China
Tel.: (86) 2161352788
Web Site: http://www.sirona.com.tr
Dental Equipment & Supplies Mfr
N.A.I.C.S.: 339114

Sirona Dental Systems s.r.l. **(2)**
Via Enrico Fermi 22, Verona, 37136, Italy
Tel.: (39) 0458281811
Web Site: http://www.sirona.it
Dental Equipment Distr
N.A.I.C.S.: 339114

Subsidiary (Domestic):

Sirona Dental, Inc. **(2)**
13320 B Ballantyne Corporate Pl, Charlotte,
NC 28277
Tel.: (704) 587-0453
Dental Equipment Mfr
N.A.I.C.S.: 339114

Subsidiary (Non-US):

**Sirona Technologie GmbH & Co.
KG** **(2)**
Fabrikstrasse 31, 64625, Bensheim, Ger-
many
Tel.: (49) 6251161610
Dental Equipment & Supply Mfr
N.A.I.C.S.: 339114

Sirona Verwaltungs GmbH **(2)**
Fabrikstr 31, 64625, Bensheim, Germany
Tel.: (49) 6251160
Surgical Equipment Distr
N.A.I.C.S.: 423450

infiniDent Services GmbH **(2)**
Berliner Allee 58, Darmstadt, 64295, Ger-
many
Tel.: (49) 61513961818
Web Site: http://www.infinidentservices.com
Dental Equipment Distr
N.A.I.C.S.: 339114

Tuzodent S.A. de C.V. **(1)**
Mega Comercial Mexicana Local 16, Blvd
Luis Donaldo Colosio No 2003 Col Exhaci-
enda de Coscotitlan, 42083, Pachuca, Hi-
dalgo, Mexico
Tel.: (52) 17717196510
Web Site: http://www.tuzodent.com.mx
Dental Care Services
N.A.I.C.S.: 621210

**VIPI Industria, Comercio, Exportacao
e Importacao de Produtos Odonto-
logicos Ltda.** **(1)**
Carlos St Tassoni 4521, PO Box 48, Indus-
trial District, Pirassununga, 13633-418, Bra-
zil
Tel.: (55) 8007712226
Web Site: http://www.vipi.com.br
Dental Product Mfr
N.A.I.C.S.: 339114

Wellspect B.V. **(1)**
Signal red 55, 2718 SG, Zoetermeer, Neth-
erlands
Tel.: (31) 79 363 7010
Web Site: https://www.wellspect.nl
Medical Equipment Mfr
N.A.I.C.S.: 339112
Toine Vermeer *(Area Mgr)*

Wellspect Healthcare AB **(1)**
Aminogatan 1, PO Box 14, SE 431 21,
Molndal, Sweden
Tel.: (46) 313764000
Web Site: http://www.wellspect.com
Emp.: 1,100
Medical Equipment & Supplies Mfr & Distr
N.A.I.C.S.: 339114

Subsidiary (Non-US):

Dentsply IH S.A. **(2)**
Rue Galilee 6 CEI3 Y-Parc, 1400, Yverdon-
les-Bains, Switzerland
Tel.: (41) 800845844
Dental Equipment Distr
N.A.I.C.S.: 339114

Subsidiary (US):

**Wellspect HealthCare - Urology
Division** **(2)**

DENTSPLY SIRONA Inc.—(Continued)

590 Lincoln St, Waltham, MA 02451
Tel.: (877) 445-6374
Web Site: http://www.wellspect.us
Medical Equipment & Supplies Mfr & Distr
N.A.I.C.S.: 423450

Wellspect HealthCare - Urology
Division　　　　　　　　　　　　　(2)
21535 Hawthorne Blvd Ste 525, Torrance,
CA 90503
Tel.: (310) 316-2626
Web Site: http://www.wellspect.us
Medical Equipment Mfr
N.A.I.C.S.: 423450

Subsidiary (Non-US):

Wellspect HealthCare GmbH　　　(2)
Wienerbergstrasse 11 Turm A/21, A-1100,
Vienna, Austria
Tel.: (43) 121461500
Web Site: https://www.wellspect.at
Medical Equipment & Supplies Mfr & Distr
N.A.I.C.S.: 339114

Wellspect Healthcare Norway　　(2)
Karihaugveien 89, NO 1086, Oslo, Norway
Tel.: (47) 67920550
Web Site: http://www.wellspect.no
Medical Equipment & Supplies Mfr & Distr
N.A.I.C.S.: 339112

Wellspect Ltd.　　　　　　　　　(1)
Stroudwater Business Park, Stonehouse,
GL10 3GB, United Kingdom
Tel.: (44) 1453791763
Web Site: http://www.wellspect.co.uk
Medical Equipment Mfr
N.A.I.C.S.: 339112
Steve Harwood (Mng Dir)

Zhermack GmbH　　　　　　　　(1)
Ohlmuhle 10, 49448, Marl, Germany
Tel.: (49) 544320330
Web Site: http://www.zhermack.de
Dental Equipment & Supplies Mfr
N.A.I.C.S.: 339114

Zhermapol SP Zoo　　　　　　　(1)
Augustowka 14, 02-981, Warsaw, Poland
Tel.: (48) 228588272
Web Site: http://www.zhermapol.pl
Dental Equipment & Supplies Mfr
N.A.I.C.S.: 339114

DENVER BANKSHARES, INC.
1534 California St, Denver, CO
80202
Tel.: (303) 572-3600
DNVB—(OTCIQ)
Bank Holding Company
N.A.I.C.S.: 551111
Linda M. Rock-Kreutz (COO)

Subsidiaries:

The Bank of Denver　　　　　　(1)
810 E 17th Ave, Denver, CO 80218
Tel.: (303) 572-3600
Web Site: http://www.thebankofdenver.com
Commericial Banking
N.A.I.C.S.: 522110
Linda M. Rock-Kreutz (Chm, COO & Exec
VP)
Lori Radcliffe (Pres & CEO)
Edith E. Shell (Sec & Sr VP-Comml & Real
Estate Loans)
Loretta A. Smith (VP-Security & Personnel)
Donna Gutierrez (VP-Acctg & Controller)
Lisa S. Page (Sr VP-Mktg)

DERMATA THERAPEUTICS,
INC.
3525 Del Mar Hts Rd Ste 322, San
Diego, CA 92130
Tel.: (858) 800-2543　　　　　DE
Web Site: https://www.dermatarx.com
Year Founded: 2014
DRMA—(NASDAQ)
Assets: $6,944,488
Liabilities: $922,634
Net Worth: $6,021,854
Earnings: ($9,610,913)
Emp.: 8
Fiscal Year-end: 12/31/22

Research & Development in Biotech-
nology (except Nanobiotechnology)
N.A.I.C.S.: 541714
Gerald T. Proehl (Chm, Pres & CEO)
Maria Bedoya Toro Munera (Sr VP-
Regulatory Affairs & Quality Assur-
ance)
Christopher J. Nardo (Chief Dev Offi-
cer & Sr VP)
Kyri K. Van Hoose (CFO & Sr VP)

DERMISONICS, INC.
4 Tower Bridge 200 Bar Harbor Dr,
West Conshohocken, PA 19428
Tel.: (610) 941-2780
DMSI—(OTCIQ)
Biotechnology Research & Develop-
ment Services
N.A.I.C.S.: 541714
Bruce K. Redding (VP-Licensing &
Corp Strategy)

DESIGN THERAPEUTICS, INC.
6005 Hidden Valley Rd Ste 110,
Carlsbad, CA 92011
Tel.: (858) 293-4900　　　　　DE
Web Site: https://www.designtx.com
Year Founded: 2017
DSGN—(NASDAQ)
Rev.: $4,285,000
Assets: $341,137,000
Liabilities: $13,827,000
Net Worth: $327,310,000
Earnings: ($63,308,000)
Emp.: 132
Fiscal Year-end: 12/31/22
Biotechnology Research & Develop-
ment Services
N.A.I.C.S.: 541714
Julie D. Burgess (Chief Acctg Officer)
Pratik Shah (Founder & Chm)
Joao Siffert (Pres & CEO)
Sean Jeffries (COO)
Jae Kim (Chief Medical Officer)
Dawn Giangiulio (Controller)

DESKTOP METAL, INC.
63 3rd Ave, Burlington, MA 01803
Tel.: (978) 224-1244　　　　　DE
Web Site:
　https://www.desktopmetal.com
Year Founded: 2018
DM—(NYSE)
Rev.: $209,023,000
Assets: $754,347,000
Liabilities: $226,845,000
Net Worth: $527,502,000
Earnings: ($740,343,000)
Emp.: 1,200
Fiscal Year-end: 12/31/22
Miscellaneous Financial Investment
Activities
N.A.I.C.S.: 523999
Ric Fulop (Founder, Chm & CEO)
Steve Billow (Pres)
Arjun Aggarwal (Chief Product Offi-
cer)
Meg Broderick (Sec & Gen Counsel)
Jonah Myerberg (CTO)
Jason Cole (CFO & Treas)
Thomas Nogueira (COO)

Subsidiaries:

The ExOne Company　　　　　　(1)
127 Industry Blvd, North Huntingdon, PA
15642
Tel.: (724) 863-9663
Web Site: http://www.exone.com
Rev.: $59,253,000
Assets: $107,289,000
Liabilities: $30,986,000
Net Worth: $76,303,000
Earnings: ($14,924,000)
Emp.: 263
Fiscal Year-end: 12/31/2020
3D Printing Machines & Printing Products
Mfr & Supplier
N.A.I.C.S.: 333248

Rick Lucas (CTO & VP-New Markets)
Jared Helfrich (VP-Bus Dev)
Douglas D. Zemba (CFO & Treas)
Loretta L. Benec (Gen Counsel, Sec & VP)
Sarah A. Webster (CMO)
Andreas Nagy (VP-Printing Sys)

Subsidiary (Domestic):

ExOne Americas LLC　　　　　　(2)
2341 Alger Dr, Troy, MI 48083
Tel.: (248) 740-1580
Web Site: http://www.exone.com
3D Printing Machines & Printing Products
Mfr & Supplier
N.A.I.C.S.: 333248

Subsidiary (Non-US):

ExOne GmbH　　　　　　　　　(2)
Daimlerstrasse 22, 86368, Gersthofen, Ger-
many
Tel.: (49) 821650630
Web Site: https://www.exone.com
3D Printing Machines & Printing Products
Mfr & Supplier
N.A.I.C.S.: 333248
Eric Bader (Mng Dir)

Subsidiary (Non-US):

ExOne Sweden AB　　　　　　　(3)
Banarpsgatan 43 B, Jonkoping, 55333,
Sweden
Tel.: (46) 700628916
Printing Machinery & Equipment Mfr
N.A.I.C.S.: 333248

Subsidiary (Non-US):

ExOne Italy S.r.l　　　　　　　　(2)
Via Galileo Galilei 68 Localita La Pigna,
25015, Desenzano del Garda, Italy
Tel.: (39) 0309119415
Web Site: http://www.exone.com
Emp.: 4
Printing Machinery Mfr
N.A.I.C.S.: 333248

ExOne KK　　　　　　　　　　(2)
161-5 Haneo, Odawara, 256-0804, Kana-
gawa, Japan
Tel.: (81) 465441303
Emp.: 29
3D Printing Machines & Printing Products
Mfr & Supplier
N.A.I.C.S.: 333248

ExOne Property GmbH　　　　　(2)
Daimlerstrasse 22 Gersthofen, 86368,
Munich, Germany
Tel.: (49) 82174760
Web Site: http://www.oxono.com
Printing Machinery Mfr
N.A.I.C.S.: 333248

Subsidiary (Domestic):

Rocktech Systems, LLC　　　　(2)
56568 N Bay Dr, Chesterfield, MI 48051
Tel.: (586) 646-5955
Web Site: https://www.rocktech.com
Specialty Machine Shop
N.A.I.C.S.: 332710
Ricardo Arredondo (Mgr-Engrg)

DESTINATION MATERNITY
CORPORATION
232 Strawbridge Dr, Moorestown, NJ
08057
Tel.: (856) 291-9700　　　　　DE
Web Site:
　http://www.destinationmaternity
　corp.com
Year Founded: 1982
DEST—(NASDAQ)
Rev.: $383,750,000
Assets: $146,174,000
Liabilities: $119,023,000
Net Worth: $27,151,000
Earnings: ($14,327,000)
Emp.: 1,100
Fiscal Year-end: 02/02/19
Maternity Apparel Designer & Retailer
N.A.I.C.S.: 315210

Eugene Irwin Davis (Chm)
Rodney Schriver (Chief Acctg Officer
& Sr VP)
Marla A. Ryan (Pres-Product Design,
Sourcing & Mdsg)
David J. Helkey (CFO & COO)
Douglas Goeke (Chief Transformation
Officer)

Subsidiaries:

Cave Springs, Inc.　　　　　　(1)
2751 Centerville Rd, Wilmington, DE 19808
Tel.: (302) 225-5091
Maternity Apparel Distr
N.A.I.C.S.: 458110

Mothers Work Canada, Inc.　　(1)
232 Strawbridge Dr, Moorestown, NJ 08057
Tel.: (215) 873-2200
Maternity Apparel Distr
N.A.I.C.S.: 458110

DESTINATION XL GROUP, INC.
555 Turnpike St, Canton, MA 02021
Tel.: (781) 828-9300　　　　　DE
Web Site: https://www.dxl.com
Year Founded: 1976
DXLG—(NASDAQ)
Rev.: $545,838,000
Assets: $350,598,000
Liabilities: $213,370,000
Net Worth: $137,228,000
Earnings: $89,123,000
Emp.: 1,480
Fiscal Year-end: 01/28/23
Men's Clothing Retailer
N.A.I.C.S.: 458110
James Reath (CMO)
Anthony J. Gaeta (Chief Stores &
Real Estate Officer)
Lionel Findlay Conacher (Chm)
Harvey S. Kanter (Pres & CEO)
Stacey Jones (Chief HR Officer)
Rob Bogan (CTO)
Peter H. Stratton Jr. (CFO, Treas &
Exec VP)

Subsidiaries:

CMRG Apparel, LLC　　　　　　(1)
555 Turnpike St, Canton, MA
02021　　　　　　　　　　　(100%)
Tel.: (781) 828-9300
Web Site: http://www.desyinationxl.com
Sales Range: $100-124.9 Million
Emp.: 500
Men's Clothing Sales
N.A.I.C.S.: 458110

Casual Male Direct, LLC　　　　(1)
555 Turnpike St, Canton, MA
02021　　　　　　　　　　　(100%)
Tel.: (781) 828-9300
Web Site: http://www.destinationxl.com
Sales Range: $75-99.9 Million
Emp.: 500
Men's Clothing Sales
N.A.I.C.S.: 458110

Casual Male RBT, LLC　　　　　(1)
555 Turnpike St, Canton, MA
02021　　　　　　　　　　　(100%)
Tel.: (781) 828-9300
Web Site: http://www.destinationxl.com
Sales Range: $100-124.9 Million
Men's Clothing Retailer
N.A.I.C.S.: 458110

Casual Male Retail Store, LLC　(1)
555 Turnpike St, Canton, MA
02021　　　　　　　　　　　(100%)
Tel.: (781) 828-9300
Web Site: http://www.casualmalexl.com
Sales Range: $100-124.9 Million
Emp.: 500
Men's Clothing Sales
N.A.I.C.S.: 458110

Casual Male Store, LLC　　　　(1)
962 S Randall Rd Ste D, Saint Charles, IL
60174

Tel.: (630) 584-4575
Web Site: http://www.destinationxl.com
Emp.: 45
Men Apparel Retailer
N.A.I.C.S.: 458110

DETROIT LEGAL NEWS COMPANY

2001 W Lafayette Blvd, Detroit, MI 48216
Tel.: (313) 961-3949
Web Site: https://dlnco.com
Year Founded: 1895
DTRL—(OTCIQ)
Newspaper Publishers
N.A.I.C.S.: 513110
Bradley L. Thompson (Chm, Pres & CEO)
Gary J. Greenfelder (CFO)

Subsidiaries:

Detroit Legal News Publishing LLC   (1)
1409 Allen Rd Ste B, Troy, MI 48083
Tel.: (248) 577-6100
Web Site: http://www.legalnews.com
Emp.: 200
Commercial Printing & Newspaper Publisher
N.A.I.C.S.: 513110
Bradley L. Thompson (Pres)
Suzanne Favale (Publr)
Tom Kirvan (Editor-in-Chief)
Brian Cox (Editor)

Subsidiary (Domestic):

Macomb County Legal News   (2)
148 S Main St Ste 100, Mount Clemens, MI 48043
Tel.: (586) 463-4300
Web Site: http://www.legalnews.com
Emp.: 50
Weekly Local Newspaper Publisher
N.A.I.C.S.: 513110
Melanie Deeds (Editor)
Brad Thompson (Pres)
Suzanne Favale (Publr)
Tom Kirvan (Editor-in-Chief)

Graphics East, Inc.   (1)
25430 Terra Industrial Dr, Chesterfield, MI 48051
Tel.: (586) 598-1500
Web Site: http://www.graphicseast.com
Sales Range: $1-9.9 Million
Emp.: 25
Books Printing
N.A.I.C.S.: 323117
John Griffin (CFO)

DETWILER FENTON GROUP, INC.

225 Franklin St Ste 2300, Boston, MA 02110
Web Site:
   http://www.detwilerfenton.com
Year Founded: 1962
DMCD—(OTCIQ)
Financial Support Services
N.A.I.C.S.: 541611
Peter Fenton (Chm & CEO)
Alex Arnold (Pres)
Stephen Martino (CFO & COO)

DEVON ENERGY CORPORATION

333 W Sheridan Ave, Oklahoma City, OK 73102-5015
Tel.: (405) 235-3611   DE
Web Site:
   https://www.devonenergy.com
Year Founded: 1971
DVN—(NYSE)
Rev.: $15,258,000,000
Assets: $24,490,000,000
Liabilities: $12,273,000,000
Net Worth: $12,217,000,000
Earnings: $3,747,000,000
Emp.: 1,900
Fiscal Year-end: 12/31/23

Petroleum & Natural Gas Explorer, Extractor & Distr
N.A.I.C.S.: 211120
Richard E. Muncrief (Pres & CEO)
Jeffrey L. Ritenour (CFO & Exec VP)
Tana K. Cashion (Exec VP-HR & Admin)
Scott Coody (VP-IR)
Alana Tetrick (Treas & VP-Corp Fin)
Chris Kirt (Sec, VP-Corp Governance & Assoc Gen Counsel)
Jeremy Colby (VP-Total Rewards & Employee Svcs)
Garrett Jackson (VP-ESG & EHS)
Glen Maynard (VP-Corp Svcs & Assoc Gen Counsel)
Jeremy Webb (VP & Assoc Gen Counsel)
Clay Gaspar (COO & Exec VP)
Dennis Cameron (Gen Counsel & Exec VP)
William Westler (VP-Rockies Bus Unit)

Subsidiaries:

Devon Energy Production Company, L.P.   (1)
333 W Sheridan Ave, Oklahoma City, OK 73102
Tel.: (405) 235-3611
Web Site: http://www.devonenergy.com
Sales Range: $1-4.9 Billion
Energy Services
N.A.I.C.S.: 211120

Devon Midstream Partners, L.P.   (1)
333 W Sheridan Ave, Oklahoma City, OK 73102
Tel.: (405) 231-3611
Oil & Gas Operations
N.A.I.C.S.: 213112
Darryl G. Smette (COO)
David A. Hager (Pres & CEO)

Devon OEI Operating, Inc   (1)
1001 Fannin St Ste 1600, Houston, TX 77002-6714
Tel.: (713) 951-4700
Web Site: http://www.devonenergy.com
Sales Range: $25-49.9 Million
Emp.: 100
Natural Gas Distribution Services
N.A.I.C.S.: 221210

LPC Crude Oil Marketing LLC   (1)
408 W Wall, Midland, TX 79701
Tel.: (432) 789-1188
Web Site: https://lpccrudeoil.com
Crude Oil Transportation Services
N.A.I.C.S.: 486110
Steven Goudeau (Principal)
Derek Shive (Co-Founder)

WPX Energy, Inc.   (1)
3500 One Williams Ctr, Tulsa, OK 74172-0172
Tel.: (918) 573-2000
Web Site: http://www.wpxenergy.com
Rev.: $2,292,000,000
Assets: $8,413,000,000
Liabilities: $3,898,000,000
Net Worth: $4,515,000,000
Earnings: $256,000,000
Emp.: 590
Fiscal Year-end: 12/31/2019
Natural Gas & Oil Exploration Services
N.A.I.C.S.: 211120
J. Kevin Vann (Exec VP)
Bryan K. Guderian (Exec VP-Business Development)
Dennis C. Cameron (Exec VP & Gen Counsel)

Subsidiary (Domestic):

WPX Energy Appalachia, LLC   (2)
6000 Town Ctr Blvd Ste 210, Canonsburg, PA 15317-5841
Tel.: (724) 873-3400
Web Site: http://www.wpxenergy.com
Oil & Gas Production & Exploration Services
N.A.I.C.S.: 211120

WPX Energy Williston, LLC   (2)

1801 Burdick Expy W, Minot, ND 58701-5667
Tel.: (701) 837-2900
Oil & Gas Production & Exploration Services
N.A.I.C.S.: 211120

DEVVSTREAM CORP.

1345 Avenue of the Americas 33rd Fl, New York, NY 10105
Tel.: (647) 689-6041   AB
Year Founded: 2021
DEVS—(NASDAQ)
Rev.: $14,110,388
Assets: $238,831,185
Liabilities: $248,786,395
Net Worth: ($9,955,210)
Earnings: $11,530,114
Emp.: 2
Fiscal Year-end: 12/31/22
Investment Services
N.A.I.C.S.: 523999
Westley Moore (Chm)
Carl Stanton (CEO)
Ernest Lyles (CFO)
Wray Thorn (Chief Investment Officer)

Subsidiaries:

DevvStream Holdings Inc.   (1)
2133-1177 W Hastings Street, Vancouver, V6E 2K3, BC, Canada
Tel.: (818) 683-2765
Web Site: https://devvstream.com
Holding Company
N.A.I.C.S.: 551112

DEXCOM INC

6340 Sequence Dr, San Diego, CA 92121
Tel.: (858) 200-0200   DE
Web Site: https://www.dexcom.com
Year Founded: 1999
DXCM—(NASDAQ)
Rev.: $3,622,300,000
Assets: $6,264,500,000
Liabilities: $4,195,900,000
Net Worth: $2,068,600,000
Earnings: $541,500,000
Emp.: 9,500
Fiscal Year-end: 12/31/23
Glucose Monitoring System Designer & Developer
N.A.I.C.S.: 339112
Donald M. Abbey (Exec VP-Quality and Information Technology)
Jacob S. Leach (COO & Exec VP)
Jereme M. Sylvain (CFO & Exec VP)
Sadie Stern (Chief HR Officer & Exec VP)
Kevin Ronald Sayer (Chm, Pres, Pres & CEO)

Subsidiaries:

DXCM Sweden AB   (1)
Scheelevagen 17, Beta 6, 223 70, Lund, Sweden
Tel.: (46) 2865950
Medical Equipment & Supplies Mfr
N.A.I.C.S.: 456199

DexCom (UK) Limited   (1)
Suite 1 5 Building 3Watchmoor Park Riverside Way, Camberley, GU15 3YL, United Kingdom
Tel.: (44) 8000315761
Web Site: http://www.dexcom.com
User Friendly Glucose Monitor Whslr
N.A.I.C.S.: 423450
Caroline Knott Chivers (Head-Mktg)

DexCom Deutschland GmbH   (1)
Haifa-Allee 2, 55128, Mainz, Germany
Tel.: (49) 800 724 6447
Web Site: https://www.dexcom.com
User Friendly Glucose Monitor Whslr
N.A.I.C.S.: 423450
Lars Kalfhaus (Mng Dir)

DexCom International Ltd.   (1)
Suite 2 12 Building 3 Watchmoor Park,

Camberley, GU15 3YL, United Kingdom
Tel.: (44) 2071391980
Hospital Equipment Distr
N.A.I.C.S.: 423450

DexCom Suisse GmbH   (1)
Allmendstr 18, Horw, 6048, Lucerne, Switzerland
Tel.: (41) 800002810
Web Site: https://www.dexcom.com
User Friendly Glucose Monitor Whslr
N.A.I.C.S.: 423450

Nintamed Handels GmbH   (1)
Leopold-Gattringer-Strasse 25, 2345, Brunn am Gebirge, Austria
Tel.: (43) 22367106710
User Friendly Glucose Monitor Whslr
N.A.I.C.S.: 423450

DH ENCHANTMENT, INC.

6228 Dartle St, Las Vegas, NV 89130
Tel.: (210) 547-0736   NV
Year Founded: 2004
ENMI—(OTCIQ)
Rev.: $15,098
Assets: $15,220
Liabilities: $837,080
Net Worth: ($821,860)
Earnings: ($385,877)
Emp.: 3
Fiscal Year-end: 03/31/23
Crude Petroleum Extraction Services
N.A.I.C.S.: 211120

DHB CAPITAL CORP.

5 Brewster St Ste 2105, Glen Cove, NY 11542
Tel.: (646) 450-5664   DE
Web Site: http://www.dhbcap.com
Year Founded: 2020
DHBCU—(NASDAQ)
Rev.: $2,657,449
Assets: $288,237,797
Liabilities: $308,635,412
Net Worth: ($20,397,615)
Earnings: $335,708
Emp.: 3
Fiscal Year-end: 12/31/21
Investment Services
N.A.I.C.S.: 523999
Richard M. DeMartini (Co-Chm)
Robert J. Hurst (Co-Chm)
Alex Binderow (Pres & CEO)

DHI GROUP, INC.

6465 S Greenwood Plz Ste 400, Centennial, CO 80111
Tel.: (212) 448-6605   DE
Web Site:
   https://www.dhigroupinc.com
Year Founded: 2005
DHX—(NYSE)
Rev.: $151,878,000
Assets: $225,202,000
Liabilities: $117,660,000
Net Worth: $107,542,000
Earnings: $3,491,000
Emp.: 460
Fiscal Year-end: 12/31/23
Holding Company; Online Recruiting Sites Operator & Services
N.A.I.C.S.: 551112
Pam Bilash (Chief HR Officer)
Raime Leeby Muhle (CFO)
Art Zeile (Pres & CEO)
Paul Farnsworth (CTO)
Arie Kanofsky (Chief Revenue Officer)
Evan Lesser (Pres-ClearanceJobs)
Rachel Ceccarelli (VP-Engagement)

Subsidiaries:

Dice Careers GmbH   (1)
Friedensstrasse 2, 60311, Frankfurt am Main, Germany
Tel.: (49) 6966774600
Web Site: https://www.efinancialcareers.de
Online Recruitment Services
N.A.I.C.S.: 561311

DHI Group, Inc.—(Continued)

Bianca Knittel *(Mgr-Sls)*

Dice Careers Limited (1)
2nd Floor 41-44 Great Windmill Street, London, W1D 7NB, United Kingdom
Tel.: (44) 2072923899
Online Recruitment Services
N.A.I.C.S.: 561311

Dice Inc. (1)
225 W Santa Clara St Ste 1150, San Jose, CA 95113
Tel.: (212) 725-6550
Web Site: http://www.dice.com
Information Technology Talent & Job Search Engine Operator
N.A.I.C.S.: 518210
Bob Melk *(Pres)*

Subsidiary (Domestic):

Dice Career Solutions, Inc. (2)
12150 Meredith Dr, Urbandale, IA 50323
Tel.: (515) 280-1144
Web Site: http://www.dice.com
Sales Range: $25-49.9 Million
Emp.: 90
Online Staffing & Recruitment Services for Computer Professionals
N.A.I.C.S.: 561311
Bob Melk *(Pres)*

Targeted Job Fairs, Inc. (1)
4441 Glenway Ave, Cincinnati, OH 45205
Tel.: (800) 695-1939
Web Site: http://www.targetedjobfairs.com
Sales Range: $25-49.9 Million
Emp.: 6
Employment Placement Agencies
N.A.I.C.S.: 561311

eFinancialCareers GmbH (1)
Friedensstrasse 2, 60311, Frankfurt am Main, Germany
Tel.: (49) 696677460012
Web Site: https://www.efinancialcareers.de
Staffing & Recruiting Services
N.A.I.C.S.: 561311

DIAMEDICA THERAPEUTICS INC.
301 Carlson Pkwy Ste 210, Minneapolis, MN 55305
Tel.: (763) 496-5454
Web Site:
https://www.diamedica.com
DMAC—(NASDAQ)
Rev.: $353,000
Assets: $34,395,000
Liabilities: $2,568,000
Net Worth: $31,827,000
Earnings: ($13,676,000)
Emp.: 16
Fiscal Year-end: 12/31/22
Pharmaceutical Preparation Mfr
N.A.I.C.S.: 325412
Rick Pauls *(Pres & CEO)*
Richard Pilnik *(Chm)*
Scott Kellen *(CFO & Sec)*
Edward G. Calamai *(Head-Mfg Consulting)*
David Wambeke *(Chief Bus Officer)*

DIAMOND DISCOVERIES INTERNATIONAL CORP.
45 Rockefeller Plz Ste 2000, New York, NY 10111
Tel.: (212) 332-8016 DE
Year Founded: 2000
DMDD—(OTCIQ)
Mineral Mining Services
N.A.I.C.S.: 213115
Antonio Sciacca *(Co-CEO)*
Edward A. Williams *(CFO)*
John Michael Kowalchuk *(Pres & Co-CEO)*

DIAMOND HILL INVESTMENT GROUP, INC.
325 John H McConnell Blvd Ste 200, Columbus, OH 43215

Tel.: (614) 255-3333 OH
Web Site: https://www.diamond-hill.com
Year Founded: 1990
DHIL—(NASDAQ)
Rev.: $154,496,019
Assets: $249,821,410
Liabilities: $86,149,165
Net Worth: $163,672,245
Earnings: $40,434,107
Emp.: 129
Fiscal Year-end: 12/31/22
Investment Advisory & Portfolio Management Services
N.A.I.C.S.: 523940
Thomas E. Line *(CFO & Treas)*
Heather E. Brilliant *(Pres & CEO)*
Jo Ann Quinif *(Chief Client Officer)*

Subsidiaries:

Diamond Hill Capital Management, Inc. (1)
325 John H McConnell Blvd Ste 200, Columbus, OH 43215 **(100%)**
Tel.: (614) 255-3333
Web Site: https://www.diamond-hill.com
Sales Range: $75-99.9 Million
Emp.: 110
Investment Advisory Services
N.A.I.C.S.: 523940
Thomas E. Line *(CFO)*
Henry Song *(Portfolio Mgr)*
Mark Jackson *(Portfolio Mgr)*
Chris Bingaman *(Portfolio Mgr)*
Bill Zox *(Portfolio Mgr)*
Jo Ann Quinif *(Pres & Chief Client Officer)*
Chuck Bath *(Mng Dir-Investments & Portfolio Mgr)*
Grady Burkett *(Portfolio Mgr)*
Austin Hawley *(Portfolio Mgr)*
John McClain *(Portfolio Mgr)*
Krishna Mohanraj *(Portfolio Mgr)*
Aaron Monroe *(Portfolio Mgr)*
Rick Snowdon *(Portfolio Mgr)*
Chris Welch *(Mng Dir & Portfolio Mgr)*
Anna Corona *(Chief People Officer)*
Nate Palmer *(Dir-Trading)*
Matt Swager *(Dir-Trading)*
James Bishop *(Natl Dir-Accounts)*
Mike Bowser *(Assoc Dir-Bus Dev)*
Christopher Brunner *(Assoc Dir-Mktg)*
Kristen Christman *(Assoc Dir-Institutional Relationships)*
Padraig Connolly *(Dir-Institutional Relationships)*
Alex Gardner *(Mng Dir-Product & Strategy)*
Lynette Hart *(Mktg Dir)*
Lara Hoffmans *(Mng Dir-Mktg)*
Matthew Lehner *(Dir-Bus Dev)*
Maggie McGinnis *(Assoc Dir-Mktg)*
Brad Milavsky *(Dir-Bus Dev)*
Joe Penner *(Dir-Bus Dev)*
Kelsey Powell *(Assoc Dir-Relationship Mgmt)*
Colin Prescott *(Dir-Bus Dev)*
Eric Reinhardt *(Dir-Bus Dev)*
Amanda Robinette *(Dir-Distr Admin)*
Trey Rouse *(Dir-Institutional Relationships)*
Sarah Saxton *(Assoc Dir-Accounts-Natl)*
Scott Stapleton *(Dir-Consultant Comm)*
Faith Stevenson *(Dir-Institutional Relationship)*
Carlotta King *(Gen Counsel & Sec)*
Matthew Stadelman *(Chief Investment Officer)*
Micah Martin *(Dir-Res)*
Derek Colston *(Assoc Dir-Relationship Mgmt)*
Nate Hall *(Reg Dir-Bus Dev)*
Max Pauly *(Dir-Bus Dev)*
James Smith *(Mng Dir-Institutional Relationship)*
Craig Tann *(Dir-Natl Accounts)*
Ed Vukmirovich *(Dir-Relationship Mgmt)*
Ron Walker *(Dir-Distr Enablement)*
Kristen White *(Assoc Dir-Institutional Relationships)*
Emily Wlos *(Dir-Natl Accounts)*
Julie Deisler *(Dir-Compliance)*
Erin Dillon *(Dir-Compliance & Admin)*
Andy DiLuciano *(Dir-Fin & Acctg)*
Mike Evans *(Assoc Dir-Mutual Fund Admin)*
John Kroeger *(Mng Dir-IT)*
Kelsey Newman *(Assoc Dir-IT)*
Brian Risinger *(Dir-Compliance)*

Julie Roach *(Treas-Diamond Hill Funds)*
Michelle Tucker *(Office Mgr)*
Jill Williams *(Dir-HR)*
Gary Young *(Chief Compliance & Risk Officer)*

DIAMOND LAKE MINERALS, INC.
8 E Broadway Ste 609, Salt Lake City, UT 84111 UT
Web Site:
https://diamondlakeminerals.com
Year Founded: 1954
DLMI—(OTCIQ)
Construction Services
N.A.I.C.S.: 237990
Brian J. Esposito *(CEO)*
Douglas Borthwick *(Chief Token Strategist Officer)*
Michael Reynolds *(Pres & Dir)*

DIAMOND OFFSHORE DRILLING, INC.
777 N Eldridge Pkwy Ste 1100, Houston, TX 77079-4500
Tel.: (281) 492-5300 DE
Web Site:
https://www.diamondoffshore.com
DO—(NYSE)
Rev.: $841,278,000
Assets: $1,527,956,000
Liabilities: $848,286,000
Net Worth: $679,670,000
Earnings: ($103,211,000)
Emp.: 2,100
Fiscal Year-end: 12/31/22
Oil Tankers; Offshore Drilling Contractors
N.A.I.C.S.: 213111
Jon L. Richards *(COO & Sr VP)*
David L. Roland *(Gen Counsel, Sec & Sr VP)*
Dominic A. Savarino *(Chief Acctg & Tax Officer & VP)*
Bernie G. Wolford Jr. *(Pres & CEO)*
Neal P. Goldman *(Chm)*

DIAMONDBACK ENERGY, INC.
500 W Texas Ste 100, Midland, TX 79701
Tel.: (432) 221-7400 DE
Web Site:
https://www.diamondbackenergy.com
Year Founded: 2007
FANG—(NASDAQ)
Rev.: $8,412,000,000
Assets: $29,001,000,000
Liabilities: $11,571,000,000
Net Worth: $17,430,000,000
Earnings: $3,143,000,000
Emp.: 1,023
Fiscal Year-end: 12/31/23
Oil & Gas Exploration
N.A.I.C.S.: 211120
Travis D. Stice *(Chm & CEO)*
Teresa L. Dick *(Chief Acctg Officer & Asst Sec)*
Joe Niederhofer *(Sr VP-Midstream Ops)*
Al Barkmann *(Sr VP-Reservoir Engrg)*
Adam T. Lawlis *(VP-IR)*
Kara B. Blubaugh-Few *(Sr VP-Acctg)*
David L. Cannon *(Sr VP-Tech & Geoscience)*
Yong Cho *(Sr VP-Drilling)*
W. Marc Dingler IV *(Sr VP)*
Bill B. Caraway *(Sr VP)*
Jere W. Thompson III *(Sr VP)*
Chris R. Curry *(VP)*
Greg Dolezal *(VP)*
Johnny D. Dossey *(VP)*
Hunter F. Landers *(VP)*
Nathan D. Luoma *(VP)*
Ben Ragsdale *(VP)*

Subsidiaries:

CRAFT Co., Ltd. (1)
1-1-2 Hirokawa-cho, Nakagawa-ku, Nagoya, 454-0027, Aichi, Japan
Tel.: (81) 52 352 9111
Web Site: https://www.craft-web.co.jp
Automobile Parts Distr
N.A.I.C.S.: 423120
Tadashi Seko *(Pres)*

Diamondback E&P LLC (1)
500 W Texas Ave Ste 1200, Midland, TX 79701-4205
Tel.: (432) 221-7400
Web Site:
http://www.diamondbackenergy.com
Sales Range: $25-49.9 Million
Oil & Natural Gas Exploration Services
N.A.I.C.S.: 211120

Energen Corporation (1)
605 Richard Arrington Jr Blvd N, Birmingham, AL 35203-2707
Tel.: (205) 326-2700
Rev.: $961,045,000
Assets: $5,033,895,000
Liabilities: $1,595,438,000
Net Worth: $3,438,457,000
Earnings: $306,828,000
Emp.: 390
Fiscal Year-end: 12/31/2017
Natural Gas & Oil Exploration
N.A.I.C.S.: 221210
John S. Richardson *(Pres & COO)*
Charles W. Porter *(CFO, Treas & VP)*
David A. Godsey *(Sr VP-Exploration & Geology)*
Joe Niederhofer *(VP-Permian Basin Ops)*
Julie S. Ryland *(VP-IR)*
Davis E. Richards *(VP-Ops)*
David Bolton *(VP-Land)*
Edwin Lovelady *(VP-IT)*
John K. Molen *(VP, Asst Sec & Assoc Gen Counsel)*
Mike Allison *(VP-Reservoir Engrg)*
Cynthia T. Dillard *(VP-Admin)*
Russell E. Lynch Jr. *(VP & Controller)*

Subsidiary (Domestic):

Energen Resources Corporation (2)
605 Richard Arrington Jr Blvd N, Birmingham, AL 35203-2707 **(100%)**
Tel.: (205) 326-2710
Sales Range: $150-199.9 Million
Emp.: 200
Oil & Gas Exploration & Production
N.A.I.C.S.: 211120
Joe E. Cook *(VP-Legal & Land)*
D. Paul Sparks *(Sr VP-Resource Dev & Tech)*
Charles W. Porter *(CFO, Treas & VP-Fin)*
James T. McManus II *(Chm & CEO)*
David A. Godsey *(Sr VP-Exploration & Geology)*
J. David Woodruff Jr. *(Gen Counsel, Sec & VP-Dev)*
Edwin Lovelady *(VP-IT)*
David Bolton *(VP-Land-Oil, Gas Exploration & Production)*

QEP Resources, Inc. (1)
1050 17th St Ste 800, Denver, CO 80265
Tel.: (303) 672-6900
Web Site: http://www.qepres.com
Rev.: $724,400,000
Assets: $5,114,200,000
Liabilities: $2,444,000,000
Net Worth: $2,670,200,000
Earnings: $3,200,000
Emp.: 257
Fiscal Year-end: 12/31/2020
Oil & Gas Exploration
N.A.I.C.S.: 211120
Christopher K. Woosley *(Gen Counsel, Sec & Exec VP)*
Alice B. Ley *(Chief Acctg Officer, VP & Controller)*
William J. Buese *(CFO, Treas & VP)*
Joseph T. Redman *(VP-Energy)*
William I. Kent *(Dir-IR)*
Lauren K. Baer *(VP-HR & Community Investments)*

Rattler Midstream LP (1)
500 W Texas Ste 1200, Midland, TX 79701 **(100%)**
Tel.: (432) 221-7400

Web Site: http://www.rattlermidstream.com
Rev.: $396,341,000
Assets: $1,921,135,000
Liabilities: $753,816,000
Net Worth: $1,167,319,000
Earnings: $36,780,000
Fiscal Year-end: 12/31/2021
Gas & Oil Generation Services
N.A.I.C.S.: 211130
Travis D. Stice (CEO)

Viper Energy, Inc. (1)
500 W Texas Ste 1200, Midland, TX 79701
Tel.: (432) 221-7400
Web Site: https://www.viperenergy.com
Rev.: $827,697,000
Assets: $3,974,093,000
Liabilities: $1,116,539,000
Net Worth: $2,857,554,000
Earnings: $200,088,000
Fiscal Year-end: 12/31/2023
Oil & Natural Gas Exploration
N.A.I.C.S.: 211120
Travis D. Stice (CEO)
Matt Zmigrosky (Gen Counsel)
Adam Lawlis (VP)

DIAMONDHEAD CASINO COR-PORATION
1013 Princess St, Alexandria, VA 22314
Tel.: (703) 683-6800   DE
Year Founded: 1988
DHCC—(OTCIQ)
Rev.: $855,019
Assets: $5,532,062
Liabilities: $17,526,938
Net Worth: ($11,994,876)
Earnings: ($1,855,705)
Emp.: 1
Fiscal Year-end: 12/31/22
Casino Operator
N.A.I.C.S.: 721120
Deborah A. Vitale (Pres, CEO, CFO, Treas & Sec)
Gregory A. Harrison (Chm & VP)
Benjamin J. Harrell (VP)

DIAMONDROCK HOSPITALITY COMPANY
2 Bethesda Metro Ctr Ste 1400, Bethesda, MD 20814
Tel.: (240) 744-1150   MD
Web Site: https://www.drhc.com
Year Founded: 2010
DRH—(NYSE)
Rev.: $1,001,503,000
Assets: $3,207,540,000
Liabilities: $1,611,362,000
Net Worth: $1,596,178,000
Earnings: $109,328,000
Emp.: 30
Fiscal Year-end: 12/31/22
Home Management Services
N.A.I.C.S.: 531390
Briony R. Quinn (CFO, Treas & Exec VP)
Jeffrey J. Donnelly (CEO)
Justin L. Leonard (Pres & COO)
Troy G. Furbay (Chief Investment Officer)
William W. McCarten (Co-Founder)
Mark W. Brugger (Co-Founder)
Anika C. Fischer (Gen Counsel, Sec & Sr VP)

Subsidiaries:

Chico Hot Springs Resort, Inc. (1)
Old Chico Rd, Pray, MT 59065
Tel.: (406) 333-4933
Web Site: http://www.chicohotsprings.com
Sales Range: $1-9.9 Million
Emp.: 130
Hotel/Motel Operation Drinking Place
N.A.I.C.S.: 721110
Michael Art (Pres)

Conrad Chicago Hotel (1)
101 E Erie St, Chicago, IL 60611
Tel.: (312) 667-6700

Web Site: https://www.chicago-hotels-now.com
Sales Range: $1-9.9 Million
Luxury Hotel
N.A.I.C.S.: 721110

DiamondRock DC M Street Tenant, LLC (1)
1400 M St NW, Washington, DC 20005-2704
Tel.: (202) 429-1700
Emp.: 7
Hotel Services
N.A.I.C.S.: 721110

DiamondRock San Diego Tenant, LLC (1)
400 W Broadway, San Diego, CA 92101
Tel.: (619) 239-4500
Web Site: http://www.westinsandiego.com
Hotel Services
N.A.I.C.S.: 721110

DIANTHUS THERAPEUTICS, INC.
203 Crescent St Building 17 Ste 102B, Waltham, MA 02453
Tel.: (857) 242-0170   DE
Web Site: https://dianthustx.com
Year Founded: 2015
DNTH—(NASDAQ)
Rev.: $4,440,000
Assets: $146,645,000
Liabilities: $40,687,000
Net Worth: $105,958,000
Earnings: ($76,462,000)
Emp.: 67
Fiscal Year-end: 12/31/22
Biotechnology Research & Development Services
N.A.I.C.S.: 541714
Marino Garcia (Pres & CEO)
John DiPersio (Co-Founder)
Luigi Naldini (Co-Founder)
Robert Negrin (Co-Founder)
Alan Tyndall (Co-Founder)
Thomas Beetham (Chief Legal Officer)
Jeffrey Stavenhagen (Chief Scientific Officer)
Jennifer Davis Ruff (VP & Head-IR & Corp Affairs)
David T. Scadden (Co-Founder)

DICERNA PHARMACEUTI-CALS, INC.
75 Hayden Ave, Lexington, MA 02421
Tel.: (617) 621-8097   DE
Web Site: http://www.dicerna.com
Year Founded: 2006
DRNA—(NASDAQ)
Rev.: $164,307,000
Assets: $707,846,000
Liabilities: $570,092,000
Net Worth: $137,754,000
Earnings: ($112,747,000)
Emp.: 302
Fiscal Year-end: 12/31/20
Pharmaceuticals Mfr
N.A.I.C.S.: 325412
Bob D. Brown (Chief Scientific Officer & Exec VP-R&D)
James B. Weissman (COO & Exec VP)
Jennifer Lockridge (Sr VP-Program Dev)
Regina DeTore Paglia (Chief HR Officer)
Rob Ciappenelli (Chief Comml Officer)
Douglas W. Pagan (CFO)
Ling Zeng (Chief Legal Officer & Sec)
Shreeram Aradhye (Chief Medical Officer & Exec VP)
James Powell (Sr VP-Technical Ops)
Douglas M. Fambrough III (Pres & CEO)

DICK'S SPORTING GOODS, INC.

345 Court St, Coraopolis, PA 15108
Tel.: (724) 273-3400   DE
Web Site: https://www.dickssporting goods.com
Year Founded: 1948
DKS—(NYSE)
Rev.: $12,984,399,000
Assets: $9,311,752,000
Liabilities: $6,694,471,000
Net Worth: $2,617,281,000
Earnings: $1,046,519,000
Emp.: 18,900
Fiscal Year-end: 02/03/24
Sports Related Product Distr
N.A.I.C.S.: 459110
Edward W. Stack (Chm)
William J. Colombo (Vice Chm)
Will Swisher (Sr VP-Plng, Allocation, Replenishment & Mdsg Hardlines)
Stephen P. Miller (Sr VP-Strategy, eCommerce & Analytics)
Joe Pietropola (Sr VP-eCommerce)
Toni Roeller (Sr VP-In-Store Environment, Visual Mdsg & House-Sport)
Ray Sliva (Exec VP-Stores)
Vladimir Rak (CTO & Exec VP)
Peter Land (Chief Comm & Sustainability Officer & Sr VP)
Chad Kessler (Exec VP)
Vincent Corno (Sr VP)
Denise Karkos (Chief eCommerce Officer)
Emily Silver (CMO)
Sean Whitehouse (Sr VP)
Navdeep Gupta (CFO & Exec VP)
Lauren R. Hobart (Pres & CEO)
John Edward Hayes III (Gen Counsel, Sec & Sr VP)

Subsidiaries:

Chick's Sporting Goods Inc. (1)
979 Village Oaks Dr, Covina, CA 91724
Tel.: (626) 915-1685
Web Site: http://www.chickssportinggoods.com
Sales Range: $100-124.9 Million
Emp.: 1,400
Sports Goods Distr
N.A.I.C.S.: 458110

Golf Galaxy GolfWorks, Inc. (1)
4820 Jacksontown Rd, Newark, OH 43056-3008
Tel.: (740) 328-4193
Web Site: http://www.golfworks.com
Golf Components Mfr
N.A.I.C.S.: 339920

Golf Galaxy, Inc. (1)
345 Court St, Coraopolis, PA 15108   (100%)
Tel.: (724) 273-3400
Web Site: http://www.golfgalaxy.com
Golf Equipment, Apparel & Accessories Retailer
N.A.I.C.S.: 459110

DIEBOLD NIXDORF, INC.
350 Orchard Ave NE, North Canton, OH 44720
Tel.: (330) 490-4000   DE
Web Site: https://www.dieboldnixdorf.com
Year Founded: 1859
DBD—(NYSE)
Rev.: $2,131,900,000
Assets: $4,162,000,000
Liabilities: $3,082,800,000
Net Worth: $1,079,200,000
Earnings: $17,800,000
Emp.: 21,000
Fiscal Year-end: 12/31/23
Holding Company; ATM & Security Products & Services
N.A.I.C.S.: 551112
Olaf Heyden (COO & Sr VP)
James A. Barna (Exec VP-Transformation)
Thomas S. Timko (CFO, Principal Acctg Officer & Exec VP)

Joe Myers (Exec VP-Global Banking)
James A. Barna (Exec VP-Transformation)
Octavio Marquez (Pres & CEO)
James Barna (CFO)
Ilhami Cantadurucu (Exec VP)
Elizabeth Radigan (Exec VP)
Susan Malcolm (VP)
Teresa Ostapower (CIO)

Subsidiaries:

Aevi International GmbH (1)
Ahornallee 9, 33106, Paderborn, Germany
Tel.: (49) 52516941554
Web Site: https://www.aevi.com
Information Technology Services
N.A.I.C.S.: 541511

Subsidiary (Non-US):

Aevi CZ s.r.o (2)
Laurinova 2800/4 Stodulky, 155 00, Prague, Czech Republic
Tel.: (420) 273131900
Information Technology Services
N.A.I.C.S.: 541511
Martin Havel (Project Mgr)

Aevi UK Limited (1)
The Bloomsbury Building 10 Bloomsbury Way, London, WC1A 2SL, United Kingdom
Tel.: (44) 7553818806
Information Technology Services
N.A.I.C.S.: 541511

Altus Bilisim Hizmetleri Anonim Sirketi (1)
Asagi Ovecler Mh 8 Cad 1332 Sok No 8, Cankaya, 06460, Ankara, Turkiye
Tel.: (90) 3123871169
Web Site: http://www.altusbilisim.com.tr
Emp.: 130
Software Development Services
N.A.I.C.S.: 541511

Cable Print B.V.B.A. (1)
J Cardijnstraat 14/16, 9420, Erpe-Mere, Belgium
Tel.: (32) 53720100
Information Technology Services
N.A.I.C.S.: 541511

Cryptera A/S (1)
Fabriksparken 20, 2600, Glostrup, Denmark
Tel.: (45) 43434395
Web Site: https://www.cryptera.com
Emp.: 90
Automatic Teller Machine Mfr
N.A.I.C.S.: 334118

Diebold (Thailand) Co., Ltd. (1)
No 1 Q House Lumpini Building Floor 1101, South Sathorn Rd Thungmahamek, Bangkok, 10120, Thailand   (100%)
Tel.: (66) 26101010
Web Site: http://www.diebold.com
Sales Range: $25-49.9 Million
Emp.: 500
ATM & Self-service Computer Terminal Mfr
N.A.I.C.S.: 334118

Diebold ATM Cihazlari Sanayi Ve Ti-caret A.S. (1)
Serifali Mahallesi Kiz Kalesi Sokak No 20, Umraniye, 34775, Istanbul, Turkiye
Tel.: (90) 2166000773
Automatic Teller Machine Mfr
N.A.I.C.S.: 334118

Diebold Australia Pty. Ltd. (1)
Cumberland Green Estate Unit 7 2 8 South Street, Rydalmere, 2116, NSW, Australia   (100%)
Tel.: (61) 2 9684 3500
Web Site: http://www.dieboldaustralia.com.au
Sales Range: $100-124.9 Million
ATM & Self-Service Computer Terminal Mfr
N.A.I.C.S.: 334118

Diebold Global Finance Corp (1)
5995 Mayfair Rd, North Canton, OH 44720   (100%)
Tel.: (330) 490-4000
Web Site: http://www.diebold.com

Diebold Nixdorf, Inc.—(Continued)

Consumer Lending Services
N.A.I.C.S.: 522291

Diebold Information and Security Systems, LLC (1)
2302 S Presidents Dr Ste B, West Valley City, UT 84120
Tel.: (801) 956-1200
Sales Range: $25-49.9 Million
Emp.: 50
Computer & Data Processing Equipment Repair
N.A.I.C.S.: 811210

Diebold International Limited (1)
St Pauls House Park Square South, Leeds, LS1 2ND, West Yorkshire, United Kingdom (100%)
Tel.: (44) 1133888700
Web Site: http://www.diebold.com
Sales Range: $25-49.9 Million
Emp.: 30
Holding Company; Regional Managing Office
N.A.I.C.S.: 551112

Subsidiary (Non-US):

Diebold Belgium (2)
Brusselsesteenweg 494 Chaussee De Bruxelles, 1731, Zellik, Belgium (100%)
Tel.: (32) 24643111
Web Site: http://www.diebold.com
Sales Range: $50-74.9 Million
Emp.: 120
ATM & Self-service Computer Terminal Mfr
N.A.I.C.S.: 334118

Branch (Non-US):

Diebold Luxembourg (3)
Z A Op Zaemer 43-45, 4959, Bascharage, Luxembourg (100%)
Tel.: (352) 4535111
Web Site: http://www.diebold.com
Sales Range: $25-49.9 Million
Emp.: 13
ATM & Self-service Computer Terminal Mfr
N.A.I.C.S.: 334118

Subsidiary (Non-US):

Diebold France (2)
Immeuble Le Crystal 6 Rue Helene Boucher, 6 Rue Helene Boucher, Guyancourt, 78280, France
Tel.: (33) 161084500
Web Site: http://www.diebold.com
Sales Range: $50-74.9 Million
ATM & Self-Service Computer Terminal Mfr
N.A.I.C.S.: 334118

Diebold Hungary Ltd. (2)
Budaorsi Ut 146, Budapest, H1112, Hungary (100%)
Tel.: (36) 013095540
Web Site: http://www.diebold.com
Sales Range: $25-49.9 Million
Emp.: 30
ATM & Self-service Computer Terminal Mfr
N.A.I.C.S.: 334118

Diebold Latin America Holding Company, LLC (1)
5995 Mayfair Rd, Canton, OH 44720 (100%)
Tel.: (330) 489-4000
Sales Range: $1-4.9 Billion
Emp.: 14,000
Holding Company
N.A.I.C.S.: 551112

Unit (Domestic):

Diebold Latin America Operational Headquarters (2)
8010 Woodland Ctr Blvd Ste 1800, Tampa, FL 33614-2405
Tel.: (813) 888-1100
Web Site: http://www.diebold.com
Sales Range: $25-49.9 Million
Emp.: 20
ATM & Self-Service Computer Terminal Mfr.
N.A.I.C.S.: 334118

Subsidiary (Non-US):

Diebold Bolivia S.R. L. (3)
Av 6 de Agosto Numero 2577 Edificio Las

Dos Torres, Mezanine Oficina 3, La Paz, Bolivia
Tel.: (591) 22971409
Web Site: http://www.diebold.com
Software Development Services
N.A.I.C.S.: 513210

Diebold Brasil LTDA (3)
Avenida Francisco Matarazzo1350 Agua Branca, Sao Paulo, 05001-100, SP, Brazil
Tel.: (55) 1136433000
Software Development Services
N.A.I.C.S.: 513210
Elias R. Da Silva *(VP)*

Subsidiary (Domestic):

Diebold Mexico Holding Company, Inc. (3)
5995 Mayfair Rd, North Canton, OH 44720 (100%)
Tel.: (330) 489-4000
Web Site: http://www.diebold.com
Holding Company
N.A.I.C.S.: 551112

Subsidiary (Non-US):

Diebold Mexico, S.A. de C.V. (4)
Paseo de la Reforma no 505 Piso 16, Col Cuauhtemoc, Mexico, 6500, Mexico (100%)
Tel.: (52) 5533007000
Sales Range: $25-49.9 Million
Emp.: 70
Software Development Services
N.A.I.C.S.: 513210

Subsidiary (Non-US):

Diebold OLTP (3)
Av La Estancia Centro Banaven Piso 1D-11, Chuao, Caracas, 1060, Venezuela (100%)
Tel.: (58) 2129595012
Web Site: http://www.diebold-oltp.com.ve
Sales Range: $25-49.9 Million
ATM & Self-Service Computer Terminal Mfr
N.A.I.C.S.: 334118

Diebold Paraguay (3)
Cruz del Chaco 1245 c/ de las Palmeras, Villa Morra, Asuncion, Paraguay
Tel.: (595) 21606200
ATM & Self-Service Computer Terminal Mfr
N.A.I.C.S.: 334118

Procomp Industria Eletronica LTDA (3)
Avenue Kenkiti Simomoto 767 Neighborhood Jaguare, Sao Paulo, 05347-901, Brazil
Tel.: (55) 1137672400
Web Site: http://www.dieboldnixdorf.com
Software Development Services
N.A.I.C.S.: 513210

Diebold Nixdorf (Thailand) Company Limited (1)
No1 Q House Lumpini Building Floor 1101 South Sathorn Road, Thungmahamek Sathorn, Bangkok, 10120, Thailand
Tel.: (66) 28384600
Information Technology Services
N.A.I.C.S.: 541511
Jiraporn Vivian *(Pres-Sls)*

Diebold Nixdorf AG (1)
Heinz-Nixdorf-Ring 1, 33106, Paderborn, Germany (100%)
Tel.: (49) 525169330
Web Site: http://www.dieboldnixdorfag.com
Fiscal Year-end: 12/31/2019
Cash Handling & Supply Chain Management Solutions & Consulting for the Retail & Banking Industries
N.A.I.C.S.: 334118

Subsidiary (Non-US):

Diebold Nixdorf AB (2)
Vretenvagen 10, 171 54, Solna, Sweden
Tel.: (46) 84700900
Web Site: http://www.wincor-nixdorf.com
Software Development Services
N.A.I.C.S.: 513210

Diebold Nixdorf AG (2)
Stationsstrasse 5, 8306, Bruttisellen, Switzerland
Tel.: (41) 448353400

Web Site: http://www.wincor-nixdorf.com
Cash Handling & Supply Chain Management Solutions & Consulting for the Retail & Banking Industries
N.A.I.C.S.: 334118

Diebold Nixdorf B.V. (2)
Papendorpseweg 100, 3528 BJ, Utrecht, Netherlands
Tel.: (31) 881028988
Web Site: http://www.wincor-nixdorf.com
Provider of Cash Handling & Supply Chain Management Solutions & Consulting for the Retail & Banking Industries
N.A.I.C.S.: 334118

Subsidiary (Domestic):

SecurCash Nederland B.V. (3)
Postbus 244, Houten, 3990, Netherlands
Tel.: (31) 306395959
Financial Transaction Services
N.A.I.C.S.: 522320

Subsidiary (Non-US):

Diebold Nixdorf GmbH (2)
Modecenterstrasse 17-19, 1110, Vienna, Austria
Tel.: (43) 174330300
Web Site: http://www.wincor-nixdorf.com
Provider of Cash Handling & Supply Chain Management Solutions & Consulting for the Retail & Banking Industries
N.A.I.C.S.: 449210

Diebold Nixdorf S.r.l. (2)
Via Ludovico il Moro 6/B Palazzo Torricelli, Basiglio, 20080, Milan, Italy
Tel.: (39) 02528631
Web Site: http://www.dieboldnixdorfag.com
Cash Handling & Supply Chain Management Solutions & Consulting for the Retail & Banking Industries
N.A.I.C.S.: 334118

Diebold Nixdorf SAS (2)
6 avenue Morane Saulnier, 78140, Velizy, Villacoublay, France
Tel.: (33) 130670707
Web Site: http://www.dieboldnixdorf.com
Software Development Services
N.A.I.C.S.: 513210

Diebold Nixdorf SL (2)
Avenida de Manoteras 6 Building Cetil II, 28050, Madrid, Spain
Tel.: (34) 914843800
Web Site: http://www.wincor-nixdorf.com
Provider of Cash Handling & Supply Chain Management Solutions & Consulting for the Retail & Banking Industries
N.A.I.C.S.: 334118

Subsidiary (Domestic):

Dynasty Technology Group S.A. (3)
C/maria Pedraza 30 Planta 3, Madrid, 28039, Spain
Tel.: (34) 913846480
Financial Transaction Services
N.A.I.C.S.: 522320

Subsidiary (Non-US):

Wincor Nixdorf Ltd. (2)
One The Boulevard Cain Road, Bracknell, RG12 1WP, Berkshire, United Kingdom
Tel.: (44) 1344384800
Web Site: http://www.wincor-nixdorf.com
IT Services, Solutions & Consulting for the Retail & Banking Industries
N.A.I.C.S.: 519290

Wincor Nixdorf N.V. (2)
Ikaros Business Park Ikaroslaan 45, 1930, Zaventem, Belgium
Tel.: (32) 27129460
Web Site: http://www.wincor-nixdorf.com
Provider of Cash Handling & Supply Chain Management Solutions & Consulting for the Retail & Banking Industries
N.A.I.C.S.: 334118

Diebold Nixdorf Australia Pty. Ltd. (1)
Ground Floor Building C 1 Homebush Bay Drive, Rhodes, 2138, NSW, Australia
Tel.: (61) 297673500
Information Technology Services
N.A.I.C.S.: 541511

Diebold Nixdorf B.V.B.A (1)
Brusselsesteenweg 494, 1731, Zellik, Belgium
Tel.: (32) 24643111
Information Technology Services
N.A.I.C.S.: 541511
Michel Nyssen *(Gen Mgr-Retail Benelux)*

Diebold Nixdorf Global Solutions B.V. (1)
Papendorpseweg 100, 3528 BJ, Utrecht, Netherlands
Tel.: (31) 881028988
Web Site: http://www.wincor-nixdorf.com
Information Technology Services
N.A.I.C.S.: 541511

Diebold Nixdorf India Private Limited (1)
5th Floor Rolta Tower 1 Plot No 39 MIDC Marol Andheri East, Mumbai, 400 093, India
Tel.: (91) 2266774900
Information Technology Services
N.A.I.C.S.: 541511

Diebold Nixdorf Myanmar Limited (1)
Unit F MIMOSA Building Ground Floor 196A, West Shwe Gone Dine 5th Street Bahan Township, Yangon, Myanmar
Tel.: (95) 9772404084
Information Technology Services
N.A.I.C.S.: 541511

Diebold Nixdorf Portugal Unipessoal, Lda. (1)
Rua Nossa Senhora da Conceicao 5, 2794-086, Carnaxide, Portugal
Tel.: (351) 214201800
Information Technology Development Services
N.A.I.C.S.: 541511

Diebold Nixdorf Retail Solutions s.r.o. (1)
Sedmdesata 7055 House 64, 760 01, Zlin, Czech Republic
Tel.: (420) 577050111
Web Site: http://www.tpomm.cz
Emp.: 800
Information Technology Services
N.A.I.C.S.: 541511

Diebold Nixdorf South Africa (Pty) Ltd. (1)
Meadowbrook Business Estate, 972 Jacaranda Avenue, Olivedale Extension 18, Randburg, South Africa
Tel.: (27) 113482900
Information Technology Services
N.A.I.C.S.: 541511
Max Stone *(Sls Mgr)*

Diebold Nixdorf Srl (1)
17 Ceasornicului Street district 1, Bucharest, 014111, Romania
Tel.: (40) 737970788
Computer Peripheral Equipment Mfr
N.A.I.C.S.: 334118

Diebold Nixdorf Technologies LLC (1)
Building N16 Floor 1, Dubai, United Arab Emirates
Tel.: (971) 44582320
Banking Services
N.A.I.C.S.: 522110

Diebold Nixdorf Vietnam Company Limited (1)
Room No 6 21st Floor Charmvit Tower 117 Tran Duy Hung Street, 10000, Hanoi, Vietnam
Tel.: (84) 2439364361
Information Technology Services
N.A.I.C.S.: 541511

Diebold Pacific, Limited (1)
Unit 2506 25 Floor AIA Tower 183 Electric Road, Kowloon, North Point, China (Hong Kong) (100%)
Tel.: (852) 29709888
Web Site: http://www.dieboldnixdorf.com
Software Development Services
N.A.I.C.S.: 513210

Diebold Self-Service Solutions Industrial and Servicing Rom Srl. (1)
Calea Floreasca 169A, Bucharest, Romania
Tel.: (40) 213177919

Software Development Services
N.A.I.C.S.: 513210

Diebold Software Solutions, Inc. **(1)**
8024 Glenwood Ave Ste 305, Raleigh, NC
27612
Tel.: (919) 788-8665
Web Site: http://www.dieboldnixdorf.com
Software Reproducing
N.A.I.C.S.: 334610
Susan Babash (Controller)

Diebold Uruguay S.A. **(1)**
Br Artigas 561, 11300, Montevideo,
Uruguay **(100%)**
Tel.: (598) 27125430
Web Site: http://www.diebold.com
Sales Range: $900-999.9 Million
Emp.: 13
Software Development Services
N.A.I.C.S.: 513210

**Diebold Vietnam Company
Limited** **(1)**
117 Tran Duy Hung Street Room No 6 21st
Floor, Charmvit Tower, Hanoi, 10000, Viet-
nam
Tel.: (84) 439364361
Automatic Teller Machine Mfr
N.A.I.C.S.: 334118
Thang Dinh Quyet (Country Mgr)

Diebold of Nevada, Inc. **(1)**
55 Glen Carran Cir, Sparks, NV 89431
Tel.: (775) 355-1007
Sales Range: $50-74.9 Million
Emp.: 11
ATM & Self-service Computer Terminal Mfr
N.A.I.C.S.: 334118

Diebold-Corp Systems Sdn Bhd **(1)**
A - 33-2 Menara UOA Bangsar No 5, Jalan
Bangsar Utama 1, 59000, Kuala Lumpur,
Malaysia
Tel.: (60) 322895888
Web Site: http://www.diebold.com
Sales Range: $150-199.9 Million
Emp.: 50
Computer Terminal Mfr & Retailer
N.A.I.C.S.: 423430

**Inspur Financial Information System
Co., Ltd.** **(1)**
10F Huasting Building No 88 Lane 777
West Guangzhong Road, Shanghai,
200072, China
Tel.: (86) 4006701188
Banking Services
N.A.I.C.S.: 522110

LLC Wincor Nixdorf **(1)**
RF Krasnoproletarskaya Str 16 Bld 2 En-
trance 5, 127473, Moscow, Russia
Tel.: (7) 4957392300
Information Technology Services
N.A.I.C.S.: 541511
Vladimir Ivanov (Mgr-Key Acct)

Moxx B.V. **(1)**
Industrielaan 18, 6951 KG, Dieren, Nether-
lands
Tel.: (31) 852100230
Web Site: http://www.moxx-mobility.com
Mobile Communications Services
N.A.I.C.S.: 517810

Phoenix Interactive Design Inc. **(1)**
300 Wellington Street 3rd Floor, London,
N6B 2L5, ON, Canada
Tel.: (519) 679-2913
Software Development Services
N.A.I.C.S.: 513210

**The Diebold Company of Canada
Limited** **(1)**
6630 Campobello Rd, Mississauga, L5N
2L8, ON, Canada **(100%)**
Tel.: (905) 817-7600
Web Site: http://www6.diebold.com
Sales Range: $10-24.9 Million
Emp.: 60
Diebold Computer Products Retailer
N.A.I.C.S.: 449210

**WINCOR NIXDORF International
GmbH** **(1)**
Heinz Nixdorf Ring 1, 33106, Paderborn,
Germany
Tel.: (49) 525169330
Information Technology Services

N.A.I.C.S.: 541511
Jess Ralston (CIO & Comml Dir)

Subsidiary (Domestic):

**Bankberatung Organisationsu IT-
Beratungfur Banken AG** **(2)**
Karl-Wiechert-Allee 1, 30625, Hannover,
Germany
Tel.: (49) 5118986680
Web Site: https://www.bankberatung.com
Banking Consulting Services
N.A.I.C.S.: 541611
Thorsten M. Adam (Chm)

Subsidiary (Non-US):

**Diebold Nixdorf (Hong Kong)
Ltd.** **(2)**
Units 2506-10 25 / F Tower 2 Ever Gain
Plaza, 88 Container Port Road New Territo-
ries, Kwai Chung, China (Hong Kong)
Tel.: (852) 28041089
Information Technology Services
N.A.I.C.S.: 541511
Fiona Fu (Mng Dir)

Diebold Nixdorf (UK) Limited **(2)**
One The Boulevard Cain Road, Bracknell,
RG12 1WP, Berkshire, United Kingdom
Tel.: (44) 1344384800
Information Technology Services
N.A.I.C.S.: 541511
Lucy Jenkins (Mktg Mgr)

Subsidiary (Domestic):

**Diebold Nixdorf Business Administra-
tion Center GmbH** **(2)**
Gaertnerstr 12, 04425, Taucha, Germany
Tel.: (49) 342982990
Information Technology Services
N.A.I.C.S.: 541511

Subsidiary (Non-US):

Diebold Nixdorf EURL **(2)**
Panorama Business Center, 33 Rue de
Pins 2eme Etage Hydra, Algiers, 16035,
Algeria
Tel.: (213) 21600474
Information Technology Services
N.A.I.C.S.: 541511
Djamel Babay (Mgr-Import)

**Diebold Nixdorf Information Systems
(Shanghai) Co. Ltd.** **(2)**
10F Huasting Building No 88 Lane 777,
West Guangzhong Road, Shanghai,
200072, China
Tel.: (86) 8008191188
Information Technology Services
N.A.I.C.S.: 541511
Luke Chen (Head-Retail)

Diebold Nixdorf Kft. **(2)**
Nepfurdo Str 22nd B Tower 11th Floor,
1138, Budapest, Hungary
Tel.: (36) 14302550
Information Technology Services
N.A.I.C.S.: 541511

**Diebold Nixdorf Middle East
FZ-LLC** **(2)**
Building N16 Floor 1 Premises 129 Dubai
Internet City, Dubai, United Arab Emirates
Tel.: (971) 44582320
Information Technology Development Ser-
vices
N.A.I.C.S.: 541511
Aftab A. Khan (Mgr-Sls Ops-Middle Est)

Diebold Nixdorf Oy **(2)**
Building 10 Karakaari 5 E, 02610, Espoo,
Finland
Tel.: (358) 207520520
Financial Transaction Services
N.A.I.C.S.: 522320

Diebold Nixdorf S.A. **(2)**
226 Boulevard Zerktouni, 20000, Casa-
blanca, Morocco
Tel.: (212) 522490909
Information Technology Services
N.A.I.C.S.: 541511
Khalid Cherradi (Acct Mgr)

**Diebold Nixdorf Singapore Pte.
Ltd.** **(2)**
30A Kallang Place 04-01, Singapore,
339213, Singapore

Tel.: (65) 67402599
Business Management Consulting Services
N.A.I.C.S.: 541611

Diebold Nixdorf Sp. z.o.o. **(2)**
Al Jerozolimskie 142B, 02-305, Warsaw,
Poland
Tel.: (48) 225724200
Information Technology Services
N.A.I.C.S.: 541511
Grzegorz Slominski (Dir-Cashless Payment
Solutions)

Diebold Nixdorf Taiwan Ltd. **(2)**
6F No 12 WenHu St Neihu District, Taipei,
114, Taiwan
Tel.: (886) 277203780
Information Technology Services
N.A.I.C.S.: 541511
Victor Wu (Head-Retail)

Subsidiary (Domestic):

**Diebold Nixdorf Technology
GmbH** **(2)**
Joliot Curie Str 4 d, 98693, Ilmenau, Ger-
many
Tel.: (49) 36778620
Information Technology Services
N.A.I.C.S.: 541511

Subsidiary (Non-US):

Diebold Nixdorf Teknoloji A.S. **(2)**
Kosuyolu Mahallesi Cenap Sahabettin Sok
No 43, Kadikoy, 34718, Istanbul, Turkiye
Tel.: (90) 2165441000
Information Technology Services
N.A.I.C.S.: 541511
Hakan Soylu (Gen Mgr-Retail)

Diebold Nixdorf s.r.o. **(2)**
Siemensova 2, Stodulky, 155 00, Prague,
13, Czech Republic
Tel.: (420) 233037474
Software Security Services
N.A.I.C.S.: 541511

**Diebold Nixdorf s.r.o. (Czech
Republic)** **(2)**
Luzna 591, 160 00, Prague, Czech Repub-
lic
Tel.: (420) 233037474
Information Technology Services
N.A.I.C.S.: 541511
Irena Bilavcikova (Dir-HR)

Diebold Nixdorf s.r.o. (Slovakia) **(2)**
Mokran zahon 4, 821 04, Bratislava, Slova-
kia
Tel.: (421) 249258111
Information Technology Services
N.A.I.C.S.: 541511
Peter Uhrin (Mgr-Customer Svc)

Subsidiary (Domestic):

Prosystems IT GmbH **(2)**
Rabinstrasse 4, 53111, Bonn, Germany
Tel.: (49) 22833660
Web Site: https://www.prosystemsit.de
Information Technology Services
N.A.I.C.S.: 541511
Jurgen Wunram (Mng Dir)

Subsidiary (Non-US):

Pt. Diebold Nixdorf Indonesia **(2)**
Plaza 89 Building Ground Floor Suite 101
Jalan HR Rasuna Said, Kav X-7 No 6, Ja-
karta, 12940, Indonesia
Tel.: (62) 2125527900
Information Technology Development Ser-
vices
N.A.I.C.S.: 541511

**DIEGO PELLICER WORLD-
WIDE, INC.**
6160 Plumas St, Reno, NV 89519
Tel.: (516) 900-3799 **DE**
Web Site: http://www.diego-
pellicer.com
Year Founded: 2012
DPWW—(OTCIQ)
Rev.: $1,652,419
Assets: $3,046,111
Liabilities: $13,552,551
Net Worth: ($10,506,440)
Earnings: ($3,000,427)

Emp.: 4
Fiscal Year-end: 12/31/20
Investment Services
N.A.I.C.S.: 523999
Christopher Strachan (CFO)
Joseph J. Tomasek (Gen Counsel)
Nello Gonfiantini III (CEO & COO)

**DIGERATI TECHNOLOGIES,
INC.**
8023 Vantage Dr Ste 660, San Anto-
nio, TX 78230
Tel.: (210) 614-7240 **NV**
Web Site: https://www.digerati-
inc.com
Year Founded: 1994
DTGI—(OTCQB)
Rev.: $31,623,000
Assets: $38,372,000
Liabilities: $69,276,000
Net Worth: ($30,904,000)
Earnings: ($8,299,000)
Emp.: 78
Fiscal Year-end: 07/31/23
Holding Company; VoIP & Other
Cloud Communications Services
N.A.I.C.S.: 551112
Arthur L. Smith (Founder, Pres &
CEO)
Craig K. Clement (Chm)
Kenneth E. Ryon (Chief Technical
Officer)
Felipe Lahrssen (Exec VP-Sls & Ops)
Antonio Estrada Jr. (CFO)
Patti Cuthill (VP)
George Robyn (VP)

Subsidiaries:

Nextlevel Internet, Inc. **(1)**
3914 Murphy Canyon Rd, San Diego, CA
92123
Tel.: (858) 836-0703
Web Site: http://www.nextlevelinternet.com
Sales Range: $1-9.9 Million
Emp.: 10
Internet Service Provider
N.A.I.C.S.: 517810

Synergy Telecom, Inc. **(1)**
1600 NE Loop 410 Ste 126, San Antonio,
TX 78216
Tel.: (210) 438-8647
Web Site: http://www.synergytele.com
VoIP Telecommunications Services
N.A.I.C.S.: 517810

T3 Communications, Inc. **(1)**
2401 1st St Ste 300, Fort Myers, FL 33901
Tel.: (239) 333-0000
Web Site: http://www.t3com.com
Wired Telecommunications Carriers
N.A.I.C.S.: 517111

Subsidiary (Domestic):

ITVantage, Inc. **(2)**
5288 Summerlin Commons Way Ste 901-
902, Fort Myers, FL 33907
Tel.: (239) 694-8324
Web Site: http://www.itvantage.com
IT Services
N.A.I.C.S.: 541519
Jeremy Stakely (Pres & CEO)
Josh Stevens (COO)
Wendi Fowler (Dir-Mktg & Comm)
Josh Katine (Mgr-Svc)
Justin Taylor (Sr Engr-Solutions)
Jim McDonald (Sr Engr-Solutions)
Matt Rhodes (Engr-Solutions)
Charisse Nabors (Coord-Client Experience)
Joe Morris (CTO)

Verve Cloud, Inc. **(1)**
8023 Vantage Dr Ste 660, San Antonio, TX
78230
Web Site: https://vervecloud.com
International Telecommunication Services
N.A.I.C.S.: 541618

DIGI INTERNATIONAL INC.
9350 Excelsior Blvd Ste 700, Hopkins, MN 55343
Tel.: (952) 912-3444 **DE**

Digi International Inc.—(Continued)

Web Site: https://www.digi.com
Year Founded: 1985
DGII—(NASDAQ)
Rev.: $424,046,000
Assets: $815,075,000
Liabilities: $234,040,000
Net Worth: $581,035,000
Earnings: $22,505,000
Emp.: 805
Fiscal Year-end: 09/30/24
Data Communications, Computer
Hardware & Software Mfr & Distr
N.A.I.C.S.: 334111
Ronald E. Konezny *(Pres & CEO)*
James J. Loch *(CFO, Treas & Sr VP)*
Terrence G. Schneider *(VP-Supply Chain Mgmt)*
Brian Kirkendall *(Gen Mgr-Infrastructure Mgmt)*
Justin Schmid *(Gen Mgr-Cellular Routers)*
Mandi Karasek *(VP-HR)*
Guy Yehiav *(Sr VP)*

Subsidiaries:

Accelerated Concepts Pty. Ltd. **(1)**
Level 3 8 Gardner Close, Milton, 4064,
QLD, Australia
Tel.: (61) 738711800
Hardware Designer & Mfr
N.A.I.C.S.: 332510

Accelerated Concepts, Inc. **(1)**
1120 E Kennedy Blvd Ste 227, Tampa, FL
33602
Tel.: (813) 699-3110
Hardware Designer & Mfr
N.A.I.C.S.: 332510

Bluenica Corporation **(1)**
St Paul St 1, Saint Catharines, L2R 3M3,
ON, Canada
Tel.: (289) 273-2090
Computer & Software Retailer
N.A.I.C.S.: 541511
Jim Showalter *(Mng Partner)*

Ctek, Inc. **(1)**
1891 N Gaffey St Ste E, San Pedro, CA
90731
Tel.: (310) 241-2973
Web Site: http://www.ctekproducts.com
Sales Range: $1-9.9 Million
Emp.: 15
Telecommunications Resellers
N.A.I.C.S.: 517121
William Buchan *(Pres)*

Digi International **(1)**
411 Waverley Oaks Rd Ste 304, Waltham,
MA 02452
Tel.: (781) 647-1234
Web Site: http://www.digi.com
Sales Range: $25-49.9 Million
Emp.: 20
Develops & Markets Semiconductor De-
vices & Software Solutions
N.A.I.C.S.: 334413

Digi International (HK) Ltd. **(1)**
Unit 21B Lee and Man Commercial Center
169 Electric Road North Point, Hong Kong,
China (Hong Kong)
Tel.: (852) 228331008
Web Site: http://www.digi.com
Sales Range: $25-49.9 Million
Emp.: 8
Networking Component Mfr
N.A.I.C.S.: 541512

Digi International GmbH **(1)**
Lise-Meitner-Strasse 9, 85737, Ismaning,
Germany
Tel.: (49) 895404280
Sales Range: $25-49.9 Million
Emp.: 26
Networking Component Mfr
N.A.I.C.S.: 541512

Digi International
Kabushikikaisha **(1)**
NES Building South 8F 22-14 Sakuragaoka-
cho, Shibuya-ku, Tokyo, 150-0031, Japan
Tel.: (81) 354280261

Networking Component Mfr
N.A.I.C.S.: 541512

Digi International Limited **(1)**
21 Serangoon North Avenue 5 Ban Teck
Han Building 05-02, Singapore, 554864,
Singapore
Tel.: (65) 66039898
Web Site: http://www.digiland.com.sg
Electronic Product Distr
N.A.I.C.S.: 423690

Digi International SARL **(1)**
31 rue des Poissonniers, 92200, Neuilly-
sur-Seine, France
Tel.: (33) 155619898
Web Site: http://www.digi.com
Sales Range: $25-49.9 Million
Emp.: 9
Networking Component Mfr
N.A.I.C.S.: 541512

Digi International Spain S.A. **(1)**
Milicias 13-Bajo, 26003, Logrono, La Rioja,
Spain
Tel.: (34) 941270060
Web Site: http://www.digi.com
Emp.: 18
Electronic Product Distr
N.A.I.C.S.: 423690

Digi m2m Solutions India Pvt.
Ltd. **(1)**
Leela Landmark 7 1st Cross 3rd Main Ash-
wini Layout, Ejipura, Bengaluru, 560 047,
India
Tel.: (91) 8042879887
Web Site: http://company.monsterindia.com
Networking Component Mfr
N.A.I.C.S.: 541512

Etherios Design Services Inc. **(1)**
110 N 5th St Ste 400, Minneapolis, MN
55403
Tel.: (612) 435-0789
Engineering Services
N.A.I.C.S.: 541330

Opengear Limited **(1)**
3rd Floor Chancery House St Nicholas
Way, Sutton, SM1 1JB, Surrey, United
Kingdom
Tel.: (44) 2081334255
Software Services
N.A.I.C.S.: 541511
Alan Stewart-Brown *(VP-Sls)*

Opengear Pty. Ltd. **(1)**
Level 3 8 Gardner Close, Milton, 4064,
QLD, Australia
Tel.: (61) 738711800
Software Services
N.A.I.C.S.: 541511
Gary Marks *(Pres)*
Bill Levering *(VP)*
Douglas Wadkins *(VP)*
Tracy Collins *(VP)*
Alan Stewart-Brown *(VP)*
Analisa Dominic *(VP)*
Simon Pincus *(VP)*
Charlie Knudsen *(VP)*

Opengear, Inc. **(1)**
110 Fieldcrest Ave 2nd Fl, Edison, NJ
08837
Tel.: (801) 282-1387
Web Site: http://www.opengear.com
Sales Range: $25-49.9 Million
Emp.: 136
Computer & Computer Peripheral Equip-
ment & Software Merchant Whslr
N.A.I.C.S.: 423430
Gary Marks *(Pres)*
William Levering *(CFO)*
Charlie Knudsen *(VP-Ops)*
Simon Pincus *(VP-Engrg)*
Steve Cummins *(VP-Mktg)*
Todd Rychecky *(VP-Sls)*

SmartSense **(1)**
4101 Edison Lakes Pkwy, Mishawaka, IN
46545
Web Site: https://www.smartsense.co
Instruments & Related Products Mfr
N.A.I.C.S.: 334513

DIGIMARC CORPORATION
8500 SW Creekside Pl, Beaverton,
OR 97008

Tel.: (503) 469-4800
Web Site: https://www.digimarc.com
DMRC—(NASDAQ)
Rev.: $30,197,000
Assets: $113,777,000
Liabilities: $16,187,000
Net Worth: $97,590,000
Earnings: ($59,798,000)
Emp.: 277
Fiscal Year-end: 12/31/22
Commercial Printing (except Screen
& Books)
N.A.I.C.S.: 323111
Charles Beck *(CFO, Treas & Exec VP)*
Tom Benton *(Chief Revenue Officer)*
Joel Meyer *(VP-Intellectual Property & Innovation Strategy)*
Tony Rodriguez *(CTO & Exec VP)*
George Rieck *(VP-Govt Programs)*
George Karamanos *(Chief Legal Offi-
cer, Sec & Exec VP)*
Jill Elliott *(Chief People Officer)*
Jennah Jevning *(VP)*
Judy Moon *(VP)*
Lucy Oulton *(VP)*
Ken Sickles *(Chief Product Officer)*
Riley McCormack *(Pres & CEO)*

Subsidiaries:

Digimarc GmbH **(1)**
Im Mediapark 8, 50670, Cologne, Germany
Tel.: (49) 22155405110
Software Development Services
N.A.I.C.S.: 541511

DIGITAL ALLY, INC.
14001 Marshall Dr, Lenexa, KS
66215
Tel.: (913) 814-7774   NV
Web Site:
  https://www.digitalallyinc.com
Year Founded: 2000
DGLY—(NASDAQ)
Rev.: $37,009,895
Assets: $56,668,062
Liabilities: $20,327,539
Net Worth: $36,340,523
Earnings: ($21,666,691)
Emp.: 201
Fiscal Year-end: 12/31/22
Audio & Video Equipment Manufac-
turing
N.A.I.C.S.: 334310
Stanton E. Ross *(Chm & CEO)*
Thomas J. Heckman *(CFO, Chief
Acctg Officer, Treas & Sec)*
Charles A. Ross Jr. *(Founder)*
Christa Johnson *(VP-Ops)*
Peng Han *(COO)*
Brody Green *(Pres)*
Erik Dahl *(CTO)*

**DIGITAL ASSET MONETARY
NETWORK, INC.**
3265 Johnson Ave Ste 301, River-
dale, NY 10463
Tel.: (929) 526-3459
Web Site:
  https://www.digitalamn.com
DATI—(OTCIQ)
Venture Capital Funding Services
N.A.I.C.S.: 523910
Ajene Watson *(Chm, Pres & CEO)*

**DIGITAL BRAND MEDIA &
MARKETING GROUP, INC.**
845 3rd Ave 6th Fl, New York, NY
10022
Tel.: (646) 722-2706   FL
Web Site:
  https://www.dbmmgroup.com
Year Founded: 1998
DBMM—(OTCIQ)
Rev.: $237,868
Assets: $61,417

Liabilities: $7,642,588
Net Worth: ($7,581,171)
Earnings: ($1,045,142)
Emp.: 7
Fiscal Year-end: 08/31/24
Investment Services
N.A.I.C.S.: 523999
Linda Perry *(CEO & CFO)*
Reggie James *(COO & Sr VP-Mktg & Comm)*

**DIGITAL BRANDS GROUP,
INC.**
1400 Lavaca St, Austin, TX 78701
Tel.: (209) 651-0172   DE
Web Site:
  https://www.digitalbrandsgroup.co
Year Founded: 2013
DBGI—(NASDAQ)
Rev.: $13,971,178
Assets: $33,738,056
Liabilities: $41,191,230
Net Worth: ($7,453,174)
Earnings: ($38,043,362)
Emp.: 58
Fiscal Year-end: 12/31/22
Apparel Retailer
N.A.I.C.S.: 458110
John Hilburn Davis IV *(Chm, Pres & CEO)*
Reid Yeoman *(CFO)*
Laura Dowling *(CMO)*

DIGITAL LOCATIONS, INC.
1117 State St, Santa Barbara, CA
93101
Tel.: (805) 456-7000   NV
Web Site:
  https://www.digitallocations.com
Year Founded: 2006
DLOC—(OTCIQ)
Rev.: $23,068
Assets: $37,613
Liabilities: $1,917,056
Net Worth: ($1,879,443)
Earnings: $969,014
Emp.: 2
Fiscal Year-end: 12/31/22
Non-Harmful Greenhouse Gas, Car-
bon Dioxide (CO_2) Conversion Tech-
nology
N.A.I.C.S.: 213112
Byron H. Elton *(Chm)*
William Edward Beifuss Jr. *(Pres,
CEO, CFO-Acting & Sec)*

**DIGITAL MEDIA SOLUTIONS,
INC.**
4800 140th Ave N Ste 101, Clearwa-
ter, FL 33762
Tel.: (727) 287-0426   Ky
Web Site:
  https://digitalmediasolutions.com
Year Founded: 2017
DMS—(NYSE)
Rev.: $391,148,000
Assets: $227,201,000
Liabilities: $311,228,000
Net Worth: ($83,947,000)
Earnings: ($31,952,000)
Emp.: 454
Fiscal Year-end: 12/31/22
Investment Services
N.A.I.C.S.: 523999
Joseph Marinucci *(Co-Founder & CEO)*
Fernando Borghese *(Co-Founder,
Pres & COO)*
Mary Ellen Minnick *(Chm)*
Vanessa Guzman-Clark *(CFO)*
Tony Saldana *(Sec, Exec VP-
Compliance & Gen Counsel)*

Amber Paul *(Sr VP-Distr)*
Chris Pink *(Sr VP-Sls)*
Matthew Goodman *(CIO)*
Jason Rudolph *(Chief Product Officer)*
Billy Hubbard *(Sr VP-Strategic Accts)*
Taryn Lomas *(Exec VP-Insurance)*

Subsidiaries:

Car Loan Pal Holdings LLC   (1)
5850 Coral Ridge Dr Ste 105, Coral
Springs, FL 33076
Web Site: http://www.carloanpal.com
Financial Services
N.A.I.C.S.: 523999

Digital Media Solutions, LLC   (1)
4800 140th Ave N Ste 101, Clearwater, FL
33762
Tel.: (727) 287-0426
Advertising Media Services
N.A.I.C.S.: 541840
Joseph Marinucci *(Co-Founder)*
Fernando Borghese *(Co-Founder)*

Subsidiary (Domestic):

Best Rate Referrals   (2)
4800 140th Ave N Ste 101, Clearwater, FL
33761
Tel.: (702) 262-1690
Web Site: https://www.mortgageadvisor.com
Direct Marketing Consulting Services
N.A.I.C.S.: 541613
Raymond Bartreau *(Founder)*

Fosina Marketing Group   (2)
51-53 Kenosia Ave, Danbury, CT 06810-
2304
Tel.: (203) 790-0030
Marketing Consulting Services
N.A.I.C.S.: 541613

DIGITAL REALTY TRUST, INC.
5707 SW Pkwy Bldg 1 Ste 275, Austin, TX 78735
Tel.: (737) 281-0101   MD
Web Site:
    https://www.digitalrealty.com
DLR—(NYSE)
Rev.: $5,477,061,000
Assets: $44,113,258,000
Liabilities: $24,511,751,000
Net Worth: $19,601,507,000
Earnings: $948,838,000
Emp.: 3,664
Fiscal Year-end: 12/31/23
Real Estate Investment Trust
N.A.I.C.S.: 525990
Laurence A. Chapman *(Chm)*
Andrew P. Power *(Pres, CEO & CFO)*
Chris Sharp *(CTO)*
Cindy Fiedelman *(Chief HR Officer)*
Matthew Mercier *(CFO)*
Greg Wright *(Chief Investment Officer)*
Peter Olson *(Interim Chief Acctg Officer)*
Jeannie Lee *(Gen Counsel)*
Serene Nah *(Mng Dir)*
Jeff Tapley *(Co-Mng Dir)*
Jan-Pieter Anten *(Co-Mng Dir)*
Camilla A. Harris *(Chief Acctg Officer)*

Subsidiaries:

Ascenty Data Centers e Telecomunicoes S.A   (1)
Av Joao Batista Nunes 50, Distrito Industrial
Benedito Storani, Vinhedo, 13288-162, SP,
Brazil
Tel.: (55) 1935177600
Web Site: https://www.ascenty.com
Data Processing Services
N.A.I.C.S.: 518210
Chris Torto *(CEO)*
Gilson Granzier *(VP-Admin)*
Pablo Campagnac *(VP-Bus Dev)*
Marcos Siqueira *(VP-Ops)*
Felipe Caballero *(VP-DC Design, Engrg, and Construction)*
Alexandre Demarchi *(Dir-Engrg & Construction)*

Fabio Matos *(Exec Mgr-Data Center Ops)*
Eduardo A. Pereira *(Exec Mgr-Engrg)*
Vincus Minetto *(Sls Dir)*
Rodrigo Radaieski *(Dir-Svcs)*
Jose Carlos M. Queiroz *(Dir-Occupational Health & Safety)*
Sergio Abela *(Dir-Data Center Ops)*
Roberto Rio Branco *(VP-Mktg & Institutional Rels)*

Digital Core REIT Ltd.   (1)
10 Collyer Quay 42-06 Ocean Financial
Centre, Singapore, 049315, Singapore
Tel.: (65) 62309682
Web Site: https://www.digitalcorereit.com
Real Estate Investment Services
N.A.I.C.S.: 531210

Digital Realty Austria GmbH   (1)
Louis-Hafliger-Gasse 10, 1210, Vienna,
Austria
Tel.: (43) 129036360
Web Site: https://www.digitalrealty.at
Data Processing & Consulting Services
N.A.I.C.S.: 541513

Digital Realty Switzerland GmbH   (1)
Baulerwisenstrasse 6, 8152, Glattbrugg,
Switzerland
Tel.: (41) 445623000
Web Site: https://ch.digitalrealty.com
Data Processing & Consulting Services
N.A.I.C.S.: 541513

Digital Realty Trust, L.P.   (1)
5707 Southwest Pkwy Bldg 1 Ste 275, Austin, TX 78735 .   (97.8%)
Tel.: (737) 281-0101
Web Site: https://www.digitalrealty.com
Rev.: $5,477,060,999
Assets: $44,113,257,999
Liabilities: $24,511,750,999
Net Worth: $19,601,506,999
Earnings: $969,548,000
Emp.: 3,663
Fiscal Year-end: 12/31/2023
Real Estate Investment Services
N.A.I.C.S.: 525990
Arthur William Stein *(CEO)*
Andrew P. Power *(Pres & CFO)*

Subsidiary (Domestic):

2001 Sixth LLC   (2)
2001 6th Ave, Seattle, WA 98121
Tel.: (206) 443-1800
Web Site: http://www.westinbldg.com
Sales Range: $25-49.9 Million
Emp.: 24
Real Estate Services
N.A.I.C.S.: 531390
Kyle Peters *(Gen Mgr)*
Lance Forgey *(Dir-Ops)*
Jason Roseen *(Mgr-Ops)*
Dean Collins *(Dir-Projects)*
Steve Kanuch *(Mgr-Construction)*
Mike Rushing *(Mgr-Bus Dev)*

Collins Technology Park Partners,
LLC   (2)
2323 Bryan St Ste 2300, Dallas, TX 75201-
2605
Tel.: (214) 878-4787
Real Estate Services
N.A.I.C.S.: 531390

Digital East Cornell, LLC   (2)
4 Embarcadero Ctr Ste 3200, San Francisco, CA 94111-4106
Tel.: (415) 738-6500
Real Estate Related Services
N.A.I.C.S.: 531390

Digital Winter, LLC   (2)
200 S 6th St Ste 1140, Minneapolis, MN
55402
Tel.: (612) 371-9474
Web Site: https://www.digitalwinter.com
Real Estate Agencies & Brokerage Services
N.A.I.C.S.: 531390

Global Miami Acquisition Company,
LLC   (2)
150 California St 4th Fl Ste 400, San Francisco, CA 94111
Tel.: (305) 372-3648
Emp.: 4
Real Estate Services
N.A.I.C.S.: 531390

Icolo Limited   (1)

LRC Road off Langata South Road, PO
Box 1649, Karen, 00502, Nairobi, Kenya
Tel.: (254) 709182000
Web Site: https://www.icolo.io
Data Processing Services
N.A.I.C.S.: 518210

Icolo Mozambique, Limitada   (1)
COOP AV Vladimir Lenine Lote 140 AD,
Maputo, Mozambique
Tel.: (258) 848587256
Data Processing Services
N.A.I.C.S.: 518210

InterXion Holding N.V.   (1)
Pudongweg 37, 1437 EM, Rozenburg,
Netherlands
Tel.: (31) 20 8807700
Web Site: http://www.interxion.com
Sales Range: $600-649.9 Million
Holding Company; Data Center, Co-Location & Managed Services
N.A.I.C.S.: 551112
David C. Ruberg *(Vice Chm, Pres & CEO)*
Jan-pieter Anten *(Mng Dir-Grp)*
Adriaan Oosthoek *(Sr VP-Ops)*

Subsidiary (Domestic):

Interxion N.V.   (2)
Scorpius 30, 2132 LR, Hoofddorp, Netherlands
Tel.: (31) 80000999222
Web Site: http://www.interxion.com
Sales Range: $200-249.9 Million
Emp.: 50
Data Center, Co-Location & Managed Services
N.A.I.C.S.: 518210
Michael van den Assem *(Mng Dir)*

Subsidiary (Non-US):

Interxion (Schweiz) AG   (3)
Esbogatan 11, PO Box 56, 164 94, Stockholm, 16474, Sweden
Tel.: (46) 850102700
Web Site: http://www.interxion.ch
Data Center, Co-Location & Managed Services
N.A.I.C.S.: 518210

Interxion Belgium N.V.   (3)
Wezembeekstraat 2 Bus 1, 1930,
Zaventem, Belgium
Tel.: (32) 27090360
Data Center, Co-Location & Managed Services
N.A.I.C.S.: 518210

Interxion Danmark ApS   (3)
Industriparken 20A, 2750, Ballerup, Denmark
Tel.: (45) 44822300
Web Site: http://www.interxion.dk
Emp.: 25
Data Center, Co-Location & Managed Services
N.A.I.C.S.: 518210

Interxion Deutschland GmbH   (3)
Hanauer Landstrasse 298, 60314, Frankfurt, Germany
Tel.: (49) 69401470
Web Site: http://www.interxion.de
Data Center, Co-Location & Managed Services
N.A.I.C.S.: 518210

Interxion Espana SA   (3)
Calle Albasanz 71, 28037, Madrid, Spain
Tel.: (34) 917894850
Web Site: http://www.interxion.com
Sales Range: $25-49.9 Million
Emp.: 23
Data Center, Co-Location & Managed Services
N.A.I.C.S.: 518210

Interxion Europe Ltd.   (3)
5th Floor 60 London Wall, London, EC2M
5TQ, United Kingdom
Tel.: (44) 2073757000
Data Center, Co-Location & Managed Services
N.A.I.C.S.: 518210
Giuliano Di Vitantonio *(Chief Mktg & Strategy Officer)*

Interxion France SAS   (3)

129 boulevard Malesherbes, 75017, Paris,
France
Tel.: (33) 153563610
Data Center, Co-Location & Managed Services
N.A.I.C.S.: 518210

Interxion Ireland Ltd.   (3)
Grange Castle Business Park Nangor
Road, Dublin, 22, Ireland
Tel.: (353) 14344900
Web Site: http://www.interxion.com
Emp.: 20
Data Center, Co-Location & Managed Services
N.A.I.C.S.: 518210

Interxion Osterreich GmbH   (3)
Louis Hafliger Gasse 10, 1210, Vienna,
Austria
Tel.: (43) 129036360
Web Site: https://www.interxion.com
Sales Range: $25-49.9 Million
Emp.: 18
Data Center, Co-Location & Managed Services
N.A.I.C.S.: 518210

Interxion Sverige AB   (3)
Esbogatan 11, PO Box 56, 164 94, Kista,
Sweden
Tel.: (46) 850102700
Web Site: http://www.interxion.com
Data Center, Co-Location & Managed Services
N.A.I.C.S.: 518210

Subsidiary (Non-US):

Lamda Hellix S.A   (2)
37 A Kifissias Ave, Maroussi, 151 23, Athens, Greece   (80%)
Tel.: (30) 2107450600
Web Site: http://www.lamdahellix.com
Sales Range: $25-49.9 Million
Emp.: 20
Other Communications Equipment Mfr
N.A.I.C.S.: 334290
Alexandros Bechrakis *(Chief Comml & Tech Officer)*
Apostolos Kakkos *(Co-Founder, Chm & CEO)*
Ioanna-Elena Markou *(Co-Founder & Vice Chm)*
Dimitris Kantaros *(VP-Data Center Ops)*
Giannis Noulis *(Dir-Integration & Consulting Svcs)*
Spyros Fenerlis *(Dir-Fin & Admin)*
Giannis Koukis *(Sr Mgr-Fin & Admin)*

Telx - Dallas, LLC   (1)
2323 Bryan St 2424, Dallas, TX 75201
Tel.: (214) 871-9191
Real Estate Investment Services
N.A.I.C.S.: 531120

Teraco Data Environments Proprietary Limited   (1)
5 Brewery Street, Isando, Johannesburg,
1600, South Africa
Tel.: (27) 115732800
Web Site: https://www.teraco.co.za
Data Protection & Security Services
N.A.I.C.S.: 561621

DIGITAL TURBINE, INC.
110 San Antonio St Ste 160, Austin,
TX 78701
Tel.: (512) 387-7717   DE
Web Site:
    https://www.digitalturbine.com
Year Founded: 1998
APPS—(NASDAQ)
Rev.: $747,596,000
Assets: $1,458,509,000
Liabilities: $942,294,000
Net Worth: $516,215,000
Earnings: $35,546,000
Emp.: 844
Fiscal Year-end: 03/31/22
Entertainment Content Including Images, Video, TV Programming &
Games Publisher & Distr
N.A.I.C.S.: 713990
Robert M. Deutschman *(Chm)*
James Barrett Garrison *(CFO & Exec VP)*

Digital Turbine, Inc.—(Continued)

Barrett Garrison (CFO & Exec VP)
Matt Tubergen (Exec VP-Corp Dev & Strategy)
Sylvia Krzmarzick (Chief People Officer)
Matthew Gillis (Pres)
William Gordon Stone III (CEO)

Subsidiaries:

AdColony, Inc. (1)
11400 W Olympic Blvd Ste 1200, Los Angeles, CA 90064
Tel.: (310) 775-8085
Web Site: http://www.adcolony.com
Sales Range: $10-24.9 Million
Emp.: 70
Mobile Video Advertising Development Services
N.A.I.C.S.: 541890
Lars Boilesen (CEO)
Camila Franklin (COO)
Tabitha Britt (Chief HR Officer)
Jude O'Connor (Chief Revenue Officer)
Tom Simpson (Sr VP-Asia-Pacific)
Adrian Watkins (Dir-Mktg & Growth-Asia-Pacific)
Thomas Bullen (CFO)
Andrzej Dzius (CTO)

Digital Turbine (EMEA) Ltd. (1)
3 Hasadnaot St, Herzliya Pituach, 46140, Israel
Tel.: (972) 732525252
Software Development Services
N.A.I.C.S.: 541511

Fyber N.V. (1)
Wallstrasse 9-13, 10179, Berlin, Germany (95%)
Tel.: (49) 306098555
Web Site: http://www.fyber.com
Rev.: $257,650,361
Assets: $299,647,572
Liabilities: $281,393,469
Net Worth: $18,254,103
Earnings: ($19,037,720)
Emp.: 220
Fiscal Year-end: 12/31/2020
Software Publisher
N.A.I.C.S.: 513210
Ziv Elul (CEO & Member-Mgmt Bd)
Dani Sztern (Deputy CEO, COO & Member-Mgmt Bd)
Yaron Zaltsman (CFO & Member-Mgmt Bd)
Offer Yehudai (Pres)
Yoni Argaman (Sr VP-Mktg & Corp Strategy)
David Simon (Chief Revenue Officer)
Gal Aviv (CTO & Sr VP-Tech)
Tzurit Golan (Sr VP-HR)
Alon Golan (VP-Product Mgmt)
Itai Cohen (VP-Mktg & Corp Strategy)

Subsidiary (Domestic):

Fyber GmbH (2)
Wallstrasse 9-13, 10179, Berlin, Germany
Tel.: (49) 3060985550
Web Site: http://advertilemobile.com
Mobile Advertising Services
N.A.I.C.S.: 541890

Mobile Posse, Inc. (1)
1010 N Glebe Rd Ste 800, Arlington, VA 22201
Tel.: (703) 348-4084
Web Site: http://www.mobileposse.com
Sales Range: $10-24.9 Million
Emp.: 20
Advertising Services
N.A.I.C.S.: 541810
Jon Jackson (Founder & CEO)

Twistbox Entertainment, Inc. (1)
14242 Ventura Blvd 3rd Fl, Sherman Oaks, CA 91423
Tel.: (818) 301-6200
Web Site: http://www.twistbox.com
Sales Range: $25-49.9 Million
Emp.: 120
Mobile Content Production & Publishing
N.A.I.C.S.: 513210

Twistbox Games Ltd. & Co KG (1)
Lohbachstr 12, 58239, Schwerte, Germany
Tel.: (49) 2304200121

Telecommunication Services Provider
N.A.I.C.S.: 517810

WAAT Media Corp. (1)
14242 Ventura Blvd 3rd Fl, Sherman Oaks, CA 91423
Tel.: (818) 301-6200
Web Site: http://www.waatmedia.com
Telecommunication Services Provider
N.A.I.C.S.: 517810

DIGITAL UTILITIES VENTURES, INC.

40 Good Counsel Dr Ste 200, Mankato, MN 56001
Tel.: (952) 400-6045
Web Site:
https://www.duventures.com
Year Founded: 1991
DUTV—(NASDAQ)
Emp.: 2
Investment Management Service
N.A.I.C.S.: 525910
Mark Knute Gaalswyk (CEO)

DIGITALBRIDGE GROUP, INC.

750 Park of Commerce Dr Ste 210, Boca Raton, FL 33487
Tel.: (561) 570-4644   MD
Web Site:
https://www.digitalbridge.com
DBRG—(NYSE)
Rev.: $1,144,572,000
Assets: $11,028,503,000
Liabilities: $6,559,014,000
Net Worth: $4,469,489,000
Earnings: ($321,797,000)
Emp.: 300
Fiscal Year-end: 12/31/21
Real Estate Investment Trust
N.A.I.C.S.: 525990
Marc C. Ganzi (Pres & CEO)
Neale W. Redington (Mng Dir & CFO-Non-Digital Bus)
Jonathan H. Grunzweig (Chief Investment Officer-Non-Digital)
Thomas B. Mayrhofer (CFO & Treas)
Ronald M. Sanders (Exec VP)
Richard S. Welch (Mng Dir & Head-Healthcare)
Kevin Smithen (Chief Comml & Strategy Officer)
Ann B. Harrington (Mng Dir & Deputy Gen Counsel)
Severin White (Mng Dir & Head-Pub IR)
Jacky Wu (CFO & Exec VP)
Kay Papantoniou (Mng Dir & Head-HR-Global)
Tae E. Ahn (Mng Dir-Investment Mgmt & Head-Asia Capital Formation-Investment Mgmt)
T. Criares (Mng Dir)
Matt Evans (Mng Dir)
Jeff Ginsberg (Chief Admin Officer)
Leslie Wolff Golden (Mng Dir)
Geoffrey Goldschein (Chief Legal Officer)
Jon Mauck (Sr Mng Dir)
Francisco Sorrentino (Chief People Officer)
Steven Sonnenstein (Sr Mng Dir)
Stephen Stryker (Mng Dir)
Bernardo Vargas Gibsone (Mng Dir)
Kristen Whealon (Mng Dir)
Jonathan S. Adelstein (Mng Dir)
Parker Anderson (Mng Dir)
Gerhard Ang (Mng Dir)
Haig Bezian (Mng Dir)
Alan Bezoza (Mng Dir)
Hayden Boucher (Principal)
James Burke (Mng Dir)
Wilson Chung (Mng Dir)

Subsidiaries:

Colony Global Acquisition Corp. (1)

515 S Flower St Fl 44, Los Angeles, CA 90071
Tel.: (310) 282-8820
Emp.: 5
Investment Holding Company
N.A.I.C.S.: 551112
Neale W. Redington (CFO)
Jonathan H. Grunzweig (Chief Investment Officer & Sec)
Philippe M. Costeletos (CFO)
Thomas Joseph Barrack Jr. (Chm)

Colony Realty Partners, LLC (1)
2 International Pl Ste 2500, Boston, MA 02110
Tel.: (617) 235-6300
Web Site:
http://www.colonyrealtypartners.com
Emp.: 40
Commercial Real Estate Consulting Services
N.A.I.C.S.: 531210
Scott D. Freeman (Co-Founder & Principal)

Digital Colony Management, LLC (1)
750 Park of Commerce Dr Ste 210, Boca Raton, FL 33487
Tel.: (561) 544-7475
Web Site: http://digitalcolony.com
Investment Firm; Mobile & Internet Infrastructure
N.A.I.C.S.: 551112
Marc C. Ganzi (CEO)
Steven Sonnenstein (Mng Dir)
Sadiq Malik (Principal)
Ben Jenkins (Mng Partner)
Tom Yanagi (Mng Dir)
Hayden Boucher (VP)
Scott McBride (VP)
Leslie Wolff Golden (Mng Dir)
Liam Stewart (COO & Mng Dir)
Jeff Ginsberg (Chief Admin Officer)

Subsidiary (Non-US):

Beanfield Technologies, Inc. (2)
418-67 Mowat Ave, Toronto, M6K 3E3, ON, Canada
Tel.: (416) 532-1555
Web Site: https://www.beanfield.com
Telecommunication Network
N.A.I.C.S.: 517810

Subsidiary (Domestic):

Urban Communications Inc. (3)
4647 Hastings Street, Burnaby, V5C 2K6, BC, Canada
Tel.: (604) 439-8530
Web Site: http://urbanfibre.ca
Telecommunication Network Services
N.A.I.C.S.: 517810

Subsidiary (Domestic):

Boingo Wireless, Inc. (2)
10960 Wilshire Blvd 23rd Fl, Los Angeles, CA 90024
Tel.: (310) 586-5180
Web Site: http://www.boingo.com
Rev.: $237,416,000
Assets: $576,479,000
Liabilities: $494,558,000
Net Worth: $81,921,000
Earnings: ($17,093,000)
Emp.: 390
Fiscal Year-end: 12/31/2020
WiFi Software & Services
N.A.I.C.S.: 517112
Peter Hovenier (CFO)
Michael J. Finley (CEO)
Dawn Callahan (CMO)
Derek Peterson (CTO)
Bruce Crair (Sr VP & Gen Mgr-Military Bus Unit)
Melody Walker (Sr Dir-Mktg Comm)
Tanya Lynch (VP-HR)
Michael J. Zeto III (Chief Comml Officer)

Subsidiary (Non-US):

Boingo Limited (3)
Regus Building 3 Chiswick Park 566 Chiswick High Road, London, W4 5YA, United Kingdom
Tel.: (44) 2034506554
Wireless Telecommunication Services
N.A.I.C.S.: 517112

Subsidiary (Domestic):

Electronic Media Systems, Inc. (3)

10460 NW 46th St, Miami, FL 33178
Tel.: (305) 876-0843
Web Site:
http://www.electronicmediasystems.com
Wireless Telecommunication Services
N.A.I.C.S.: 517121

Endeka Group, Inc. (3)
12526 High Bluff Dr Ste 300, San Diego, CA 92130
Tel.: (858) 227-9434
Wireless Telecommunication Services
N.A.I.C.S.: 517121

New York Telecom Partners, LLC (3)
3000 Marcus Ave Ste 2e6, Lake Success, NY 11042
Tel.: (516) 328-3790
Emp.: 5
Wireless Telecommunication Services
N.A.I.C.S.: 517121

Subsidiary (Non-US):

Cogeco Peer 1 (2)
191 The West Mall, Etobicoke, Toronto, M9C 5K8, ON, Canada
Tel.: (416) 361-5700
Web Site: http://www.cogecopeer1.com
Managed Hosting, Cloud Services & IT Managed Services
N.A.I.C.S.: 518210
Susan Bowen (Pres)
Ted Smith (VP-Engrg & Ops)
Bertrand Labelle (VP-Mktg)
Scott Davis (VP-Customer Experience)
Paul Dyck (VP-HR)

Subsidiary (Domestic):

Peer 1 Network Enterprises, Inc. (3)
Suite 1000 555 W Hastings Street, Vancouver, V6B 4N5, BC, Canada
Tel.: (604) 683-7747
Web Site: http://www.peer1.com
Sales Range: $125-149.9 Million
Emp.: 540
Internet Infrastructure Solutions
N.A.I.C.S.: 517810
Scott Davis (VP-Customer Experience)
Ted Smith Jr. (Sr VP-Engrg & Ops)

Subsidiary (Domestic):

Peer 1 Network (Toronto) Inc. (4)
1 Yonge St, Toronto, M5E 1E5, ON, Canada
Tel.: (416) 815-7027
Sales Range: $25-49.9 Million
Emp.: 5
Web Hosting Services
N.A.I.C.S.: 518210

Subsidiary (US):

Peer 1 Network (USA), Inc. (4)
75 Broad St Rm 280, New York, NY 10004
Tel.: (866) 579-9690
Web Site: http://www.peer1.com
Telecommunication Servicesb
N.A.I.C.S.: 517810

Division (Domestic):

ServerBeach (5)
8500 Vicar Ste 500, San Antonio, TX 78218-1532
Tel.: (210) 798-4400
Web Site: http://www.serverbeach.com
Sales Range: $10-24.9 Million
Emp.: 50
Web Hosting Services
N.A.I.C.S.: 518210

Subsidiary (Domestic):

Landmark Dividend LLC (2)
400 Continental Blvd Ste 500, El Segundo, CA 90245
Tel.: (310) 294-8160
Web Site: http://www.landmarkdividend.com
Lessors of Other Real Estate Property
N.A.I.C.S.: 531190
Kristan Orr (Office Mgr)
John Wing (Sr VP-Sls-West)
Matthew Scott (VP-Acq-San Diego)
Sean Burke (VP-Acq-San Francisco)
Rob Phillips (VP-Acq-San Diego)

Don Reitz (VP-Acq-San Diego)
Veronica Gathagan (Coord-Sls-San Diego)
Jacob Alves (Mgr-Mktg)

Subsidiary (Domestic):

**Landmark Infrastructure Partners
LP** (3)
400 Continental Blvd Ste 500, El Segundo,
CA 90245 (100%)
Tel.: (310) 598-3173
Web Site: http://www.landmarkmlp.com
Rev.: $58,839,000
Assets: $894,778,000
Liabilities: $523,389,000
Net Worth: $371,389,000
Earnings: $29,086,000
Emp.: 182
Fiscal Year-end: 12/31/2020
Real Estate Investment Trust
N.A.I.C.S.: 525990
Steven Sonnenstein (Chm)

Subsidiary (Domestic):

LD Acquisition Company 8 LLC (4)
2141 Rosecrans Ave Ste 2100, El Segundo,
CA 90245
Tel.: (310) 598-3173
Real Estate Related Services
N.A.I.C.S.: 531190

Subsidiary (Non-US):

Poster Property Limited (4)
22 Berghem Mews Blythe Road, London,
W14 0HN, United Kingdom
Tel.: (44) 2038762380
Web Site: http://www.posterproperty.com
Property Management Services
N.A.I.C.S.: 531311

Subsidiary (Domestic):

Vertical Bridge, LLC (2)
750 Park of Commerce Dr, Boca Raton, FL
33487
Tel.: (561) 948-6367
Web Site: http://www.verticalbridge.com
Wireless Telecommunications Infrastructure
Development & Management Services
N.A.I.C.S.: 517810
Alex Gellman (Co-Founder & CEO)
Bernard Borghei (Co-Founder & Sr VP-Ops)
Michael Belski (Co-Founder & Sr VP-
Leasing & Dev)
Robert Paige (Sr VP-Mergers & Acquisi-
tions)
Daniel Marinberg (Gen Counsel & Sr VP)
Johnny Crawford (VP-Dev)
Jim McCulloch (Sr VP-Real Estate)
Buddy Norman (VP-Real Estate Dev)
Daniela Giannoccoli (Dir-Fin Plng & Analy-
sis)
Michael Romaniw (CFO)
Allan Tantillo (VP-Technologies)

Joint Venture (Domestic):

Zayo Group Holdings, Inc. (2)
1821 30th Unit A, Boulder, CO 80301
Tel.: (303) 381-4683
Web Site: http://www.zayo.com
Rev.: $2,578,000,000
Assets: $9,334,600,000
Liabilities: $7,993,100,000
Net Worth: $1,341,500,000
Earnings: $150,000,000
Emp.: 3,781
Fiscal Year-end: 06/30/2019
Holding Company; Bandwidth Infrastructure
N.A.I.C.S.: 551112
Michael Strople (Pres-Allstream-Zayo Group
LLC)
Jack F. Waters (COO & Pres-Networks)
Julie Tschida Brown (Chief People & Cul-
ture Officer)
Steve Smith (CEO)
Ginna Raahauge (CIO)
Frank Cittadino (Sr VP-Edge Services)
Jeffrey Noto (CFO)

Subsidiary (Domestic):

Indiana Fiber Network, LLC (3)
722 North High School Rd, Indianapolis, IN
46214-2076
Tel.: (317) 280-4636
Web Site: http://www.indianafiber.net
Rev.: $7,700,000
Emp.: 8

Electrical Contractor
N.A.I.C.S.: 238210
Kelly Dyer (Pres & CEO)
Ralph Cunha (CFO)
Keith Jones (Mgr-Svc Transition)
Tom Bechtel (VP-Network Plng)
August Zehner (VP-Sls & Mktg)
Darryl Smith (VP-Network Ops)

Latisys-Ashburn, LLC (3)
21635 Red Rum Dr Ste 100, Ashburn, VA
20147-7504
Tel.: (703) 574-7223
Emp.: 20
Data Management Services
N.A.I.C.S.: 518210

Latisys-Chicago, LLC (3)
1808 Swift Dr Unit C, Oak Brook, IL 60523
Tel.: (630) 242-3500
Data Management Services
N.A.I.C.S.: 518210

QOS Networks LLC (3)
5 Park Plz Ste 350, Irvine, CA 92614
Tel.: (310) 436-6970
Web Site: http://www.qosnet.com
Information Technology Consulting Services
N.A.I.C.S.: 541512
Frank Cittadino (CEO)
Tyler Nau (COO)
Chris Nein (Chief Revenue Officer)
Michael Brennan (VP-Strategic & Enterprise
Sls)
Chris Weston (VP-Fin)

Subsidiary (Non-US):

Serenisys SARL (3)
19 - 21 Rue Poissonniere, 75002, Paris,
France
Tel.: (33) 176772740
Web Site: https://www.serenisys.com
Management Consulting Services
N.A.I.C.S.: 541611
Jean-Claude Janvier (CEO)

Zayo France SAS (3)
19/21 Rue Poissonniere, 75002, Paris,
France
Tel.: (33) 179979646
Web Site: http://www.zayo.com
Software Development Services
N.A.I.C.S.: 541511

Subsidiary (Domestic):

Zayo Group, LLC (3)
1821 30th St Ste A, Boulder, CO 80301
Tel.: (303) 381-4683
Web Site: https://www.zayo.com
Emp.: 3,000
Wired & Wireless Telecommunications Infra-
structure Developer & Operator
N.A.I.C.S.: 517121
Daniel P. Caruso (Co-Founder, Chm &
CEO)
Sandi Mays (Co-Founder & Chief Customer
Experience & Information Officer)
Steve Smith (CEO)
Andres Irlando (Pres)
Bill Long (Chief Product Officer)
Brian Daniels (Chief Sls Officer)
Bryan Fleming (Sr VP)
Ginna Raahauge (CIO)
Jeff Noto (CFO)
Julie Tschida Brown (Chief People Officer)
Troy Lupe (Chief Network Officer)
Kimberly Storin (CMO)
Mike Nold (Exec VP)

Subsidiary (Non-US):

Allstream Inc. (4)
5160 Orbitor Drive, Mississauga, L4W 5H2,
ON, Canada
Web Site: http://www.allstream.com
Telecommunication Servicesb
N.A.I.C.S.: 517111

Subsidiary (Domestic):

IdeaTek Systems, Inc. (4)
111 Old Mill St, Buhler, KS 67522-0258
Web Site: https://www.ideatek.com
Holding Company; Fiber-Based Telecommu-
nications Services
N.A.I.C.S.: 551112
Jerrod Reimer (Pres & CEO)
Daniel P. Friesen (Founder & Chief Innova-
tion Officer)

Kent Hoskinson (Partner)
Nathan Oswald (Sls Dir)
Daniel Solomon (CFO)
Megan Shearer (VP)

Subsidiary (Domestic):

IdeaTek Telecom, LLC (5)
111 Old Mill Ln, Buhler, KS 67522
Web Site: https://www.ideatek.com
Fiber-Based Telecommunications Services
N.A.I.C.S.: 517121

Subsidiary (Non-US):

Zayo Group UK Limited (4)
100 New Bridge Street, London, EC4V 6JA,
United Kingdom
Tel.: (44) 2072203822
Web Site: http://www.zayo.com
High Bandwidth Connectivity Solutions
N.A.I.C.S.: 517810

Subsidiary (Domestic):

Zayo Group, LLC-Louiseville (4)
400 Centennial Pkwy Ste 200, Louisville,
CO 80027
Tel.: (303) 381-4683
Web Site: http://www.zayo.com
Bandwidth & Telecom Services
N.A.I.C.S.: 517112

Subsidiary (Non-US):

**upstreamNet Communications
GmbH** (3)
Ruckergasse 30 - 32, 1120, Vienna, Austria
Tel.: (43) 50182180
Web Site: https://www.upstreamnet.at
Electronic Components Mfr
N.A.I.C.S.: 334419

JTOWER, Inc. (1)
Hulic Aoyama Gaien Higashi-dori Bldg 3F
2-2-3 Minamiaoyama, Minato-Ku, Tokyo,
107-0062, Japan (75.62%)
Tel.: (81) 364472614
Web Site: https://www.jtower.co.jp
Rev.: $40,811,238
Assets: $242,048,613
Liabilities: $94,719,090
Net Worth: $147,329,523
Earnings: $6,237,656
Fiscal Year-end: 03/31/2022
Telecommunication Servicesb
N.A.I.C.S.: 517810
Yusuke Kiriya (Sr Mng Dir & VP)
Ryosuke Nakamura (Mng Dir, CFO & VP)

NSAM US LLC (1)
399 Park Ave 18th Fl, New York, NY 10022
Tel.: (212) 547-2600
Real Estate Investment & Portfolio Manage-
ment Services
N.A.I.C.S.: 531390
David T. Hamamoto II (Chm)
Debra A. Hess (CFO)
Albert Tylis (Pres)
Daniel R. Gilbert (COO & Chief Investment
Officer)

**NorthStar Healthcare Income,
Inc.** (1)
16 E 34th St 18th Fl, New York, NY 10016
Tel.: (929) 777-3125
Web Site:
https://www.northstarhealthcarereit.com
Rev.: $185,136,000
Assets: $1,237,835,000
Liabilities: $936,763,000
Net Worth: $301,072,000
Earnings: ($54,100,000)
Fiscal Year-end: 12/31/2022
Healthcare Real Estate Investment Trust
N.A.I.C.S.: 525990
Ann B. Harrington (Gen Counsel & Sec)
Nicholas R. Balzo (CFO & Treas)
Kendall K. Young (Pres & CEO)

Joint Venture (Domestic):

Trilogy Health Services LLC (2)
303 N Hurstbourne Pkwy Ste 200, Louis-
ville, KY 40222 (30%)
Tel.: (502) 412-5847
Web Site: https://www.trilogyhs.com
Women Healthcare Services
N.A.I.C.S.: 532283
Randall J. Bufford (Pres & CEO)

Switch, Inc. (1)
7135 S Decatur Blvd, Las Vegas, NV 89118
Tel.: (702) 444-4111
Web Site: http://www.switch.com
Rev.: $592,045,000
Assets: $2,918,618,000
Liabilities: $2,299,977,000
Net Worth: $618,641,000
Earnings: $5,412,000
Emp.: 829
Fiscal Year-end: 12/31/2021
Internet Service Provider
N.A.I.C.S.: 517121
Rob Roy (Founder, Chm & CEO)
Gabe Nacht (CFO)
Missy Young (CIO)
Lesley McVay (COO)
Kristi Overgaard (Chief Awesomeness Offi-
cer)
Chris Donnelly (Chief Connectivity Officer)
Cindy Zimpfer (Sr VP-Colocation Sls)
Lisa Hurless (Sr VP-Brand)
Brian Boles (Exec VP-Network Ops)
Sam Castor (Exec VP-Policy & Deputy Gen
Counsel)
Jessica Battaglia (VP-HR)
Shanna Williams (Sr VP-Procurement)
Jay Liebe (Exec VP-Dev)
Scott Gutierrez (Sr VP-Connectivity Sls)
Jeff Oberschelp (Head-Client Architecture)
Terri Cooper (Sr VP-Bus Dev)
Jennifer Arias (VP-Acctg & Controller)
Thomas Van Kempen (VP-Sls Engrg)
Michael Wiley (Exec VP-Security)
Brian Huff (Exec VP-Prime Campus Eco-
system Oversight)
Heather Ellerbe (VP-Mktg)
Betsy Fretwell (Sr VP-Switch Cities)
Chris Osiecki (Sr VP-Construction)
Shannon Bischel (Sr Mgr-Acct)
Dave Glover (Gen Mgr-Ops-Las Vegas-
East)
Chelsea Phillips (VP-Engagement)
Rob Elliott (Sr VP-Govt & Pub Affairs)
Natalie Stewart (VP-Govt & Pub Affairs)
Alise Porto (Dir-Strategy Projects)
Eddie Schutter (CTO)
Thomas Morton (Pres & Chief Legal Officer)
Laura Mach (Controller-Tour Traffic & EA)
Hugo Andraus (Sr VP-Network Ops)
Heather Kinder (VP-Connectivity)
Bill Kleyman (Exec VP-Digital Solutions)
Jeffery Bryce (Sr VP-Solutions Architecture)
Karlee Richardson (Engr-Sls)
Wendy Pope (Sr Mgr-Channel Ops)
Raleigh Midura (Sr VP-Client Experience &
Svcs)

Subsidiary (Domestic):

Data Foundry, Inc. (2)
2700 Via Fortuna Ste 500, Austin, TX
78746
Tel.: (512) 684-9000
Web Site: http://www.datafoundry.com
Sales Range: $1-9.9 Million
Emp.: 105
Internet Service Provider
N.A.I.C.S.: 517810
Edward Henigin (CTO)
Nick Parker (VP-Engrg)
Shane Menking (Pres & CFO)
William Mccormick (Mgr-Network)

InNEVation, LLC (2)
6795 S Edmond St 3rd Fl, Las Vegas, NV
89118
Tel.: (702) 444-1111
Web Site: http://www.innevation.com
Internet Publishing & Broadcasting Services
N.A.I.C.S.: 516210

DIGITALOCEAN HOLDINGS,
INC.
101 6th Ave, New York, NY 10013
Tel.: (646) 827-4366   DE
Web Site:
https://www.digitalocean.com
Year Founded: 2012
DOCN—(NYSE)
Rev.: $692,884,000
Assets: $1,460,967,000
Liabilities: $1,774,665,000
Net Worth: ($313,698,000)
Earnings: $19,409,000
Emp.: 1,156

DigitalOcean Holdings, Inc.—(Continued)

Fiscal Year-end: 12/31/23
Holding Company
N.A.I.C.S.: 551112
W. Matthew Steinfort (CFO & Interim Chief Acctg Officer)
Warren Adelman (Exec Chm)
Padmanabhan Srinivasan (CEO)
Bratin Saha (CTO & Chief Product Officer)
Cynthia Carpenter (Sr VP-People)
Larry D'Angelo (Chief Revenue Officer)
Wade Wegner (Chief Ecosystem Officer & Chief Growth Officer)

DIGITALTOWN, INC.
2155 112th Ave NE, Bellevue, WA 98004
Tel.: (425) 577-7766 MN
Web Site: http://www.digitaltown.com
DGTW—(OTCIQ)
Rev.: $34,473
Assets: $59,822
Liabilities: $2,991,936
Net Worth: ($2,932,114)
Earnings: ($7,403,426)
Fiscal Year-end: 02/28/19
School & Community Online Network
N.A.I.C.S.: 516210
Kevin Wilson (CFO, Treas & Sec)
Sam Ciacco (Chm & CEO)

DIH HOLDING US, INC.
77 Accord Park Drive; Ste D-1, Norwell, MA 02061
Tel.: (617) 871-2101 DE
Web Site: https://www.dih.com
Year Founded: 2021
DHAI—(NASDAQ)
Rev.: $8,309,470
Assets: $207,355,603
Liabilities: $214,976,481
Net Worth: ($7,620,878)
Earnings: $6,604,155
Emp.: 3
Fiscal Year-end: 12/31/22
Software Publisher
N.A.I.C.S.: 513210
Jason Chen (Pres & CEO)

DILA CAPITAL ACQUISITION CORP.
1395 Brickell Ave Ste 950, Miami, FL 33131
Tel.: (786) 785-1715 DE
Year Founded: 2020
DILAU—(NASDAQ)
Rev.: $15,319
Assets: $59,034,725
Liabilities: $58,600,678
Net Worth: $434,047
Earnings: ($579,194)
Emp.: 3
Fiscal Year-end: 12/31/21
N.A.I.C.S.:
Eduardo Clave (Chm & CEO)
Alejandro Diez Barroso (COO)
Jorge Velez (CFO)

DILLARD'S INC.
1600 Cantrell Rd, Little Rock, AR 72201
Tel.: (817) 831-5482 DE
Web Site: https://www.dillards.com
Year Founded: 1938
DDS—(NYSE)
Rev.: $6,874,420,000
Assets: $3,448,906,000
Liabilities: $1,751,838,000
Net Worth: $1,697,068,000
Earnings: $738,847,000
Emp.: 20,200
Fiscal Year-end: 03/02/24
Departmental Store Operator
N.A.I.C.S.: 455110

Alex Dillard (Pres)
Mike Dillard (Exec VP)
Drue Matheny (Exec VP)
Chris B. Johnson (Co-CFO & Sr VP)
Denise Mahaffy (Sr VP)
James D. Stockman (VP-Ladies Apparel)
Tom Bolin (VP-Stores)
Mike Litchford (VP-Stores)
Phillip R. Watts (Co-CFO, Chief Acctg Officer & Sr VP)
William T. Dillard III (Sr VP)
Dean L. Worley (Gen Counsel & VP)
Annemarie Jazic (VP-Online Experience)
Alexandra Lucie (VP-Ladies, Juniors & Children's Exclusive Brands)

Subsidiaries:

CDI Contractors, LLC (1)
3000 Cantrell Rd, Little Rock, AR 72202-2010
Tel.: (501) 666-4300
Web Site: https://www.cdicon.com
Sales Range: $300-349.9 Million
Emp.: 500
Commercial Construction Services
N.A.I.C.S.: 236220
Lloyd Garrison (Pres & CEO)
Andy Blush (VP & Dir-Construction)
Chris Johnson (CFO, Treas & Sec)
Jonathan Semans (Dir-Central Arkansas)
Mark Beach (COO & VP)
Matt Bodishbaugh (VP & Dir-Ops-Northwest Arkansas)
Kelly Freeman (Dir-Industry & Infrastructure Solutions)
Jill Floyd (Dir-Community & Client Engagement)
Andre King (Mgr-BIM & VDC)
Daniel Bowen (Dir-Preconstruction)
Kory Fortune (Dir-Safety)
Blake Helm (Sr Project Mgr)
John Deramus (Sr Project Mgr)
Matt Orender (Sr Project Mgr)
Justin Brodnax (Sr Project Mgr)
Daniel Hunt (Sr Project Mgr)
David Cooan (Sr Project Mgr)
Dlorah deVore (Mktg Mgr)
Jeff Sharp (Coord-Mktg)
James Gardner (Project Mgr)
John Schnebelen (Coord-Field Safety)
Kelli Morse (Project Mgr)
Laura McKinney (Controller)
Kylie Canarina (Project Mgr)
Mark Etherington (Mgr-Warranty)
Michael Troeger (Project Mgr)
Mike Trulove (Sr Project Mgr)
Rocky King (Dir-Ops-Natl Div)
Phillip Goodhart (Project Mgr)
Morgan Ussery (Project Mgr-Industrial)
Ryan Heiges (Project Mgr)
Sara Hedge (Coord-BIM & VDC)
Shawn Rosbrough (Mgr-Natl Div)
Ted Garrison (Project Mgr)

Dillard Investment Co., Inc. (1)
1600 Cantrell Rd, Little Rock, AR 72201-1110 (100%)
Tel.: (817) 831-5482
Web Site: http://www.dillards.com
Sales Range: $125-149.9 Million
Investment Services
N.A.I.C.S.: 522299
Alex Dillard (Pres)

Dillard's Fort Worth Division (1)
4501 N Beach St, Fort Worth, TX 76137-3218 (100%)
Tel.: (817) 831-5111
Web Site: http://www.dillards.com
Sales Range: $400-449.9 Million
Emp.: 1,000
Divisional Executive Office; Warehouse Facilities
N.A.I.C.S.: 921110

Dillard's Saint Louis Division (1)
145 Crestwood Plz, Saint Louis, MO 63126 (100%)
Tel.: (314) 301-6890
Web Site: http://www.dillards.com
Sales Range: $50-74.9 Million
Emp.: 200
Executive Office & Buying Office
N.A.I.C.S.: 921110

Dillard's Southeast Division (1)
6990 Tyrone Sq, Saint Petersburg, FL 33710 (100%)
Tel.: (727) 344-4611
Web Site: http://www.dillards.com
Sales Range: $50-74.9 Million
Emp.: 150
Division Executive Office for Department Stores & Buying Office
N.A.I.C.S.: 921110

DIME COMMUNITY BANCSHARES, INC.
898 Veterans Memorial Hwy, Hauppauge, NY 11788
Tel.: (631) 537-1000 NY
Web Site: https://www.dime.com
Year Founded: 1988
DCOM—(NASDAQ)
Rev.: $439,225,000
Assets: $13,189,921,000
Liabilities: $12,020,338,000
Net Worth: $1,169,583,000
Earnings: $152,556,000
Emp.: 823
Fiscal Year-end: 12/31/22
Offices of Bank Holding Companies
N.A.I.C.S.: 551111
James J. Manseau (Chief Banking Officer & Exec VP)
Kenneth J. Mahon (Exec Chm)
Avinash Reddy (CFO & Sr Exec VP)
Conrad J. Gunther Jr. (Chief Lending Officer & Sr Exec VP)
Stuart H. Lubow (Pres & CEO)
Christopher Porzelt (Chief Risk Officer & Exec VP)
Michael J. Fegan (Chief Tech & Ops Officer & Sr Exec VP)
Austin Stonitsch (Chief HR Officer & Exec VP)
Tamara Gavrielof (Sr VP)
Steven Miley (CMO & Exec VP)

Subsidiaries:

Dime Abstract LLC (1)
2200 Montauk Hwy, Bridgehampton, NY 11932
Tel.: (631) 537-5750
Commercial Banking & Financial Services
N.A.I.C.S.: 522110

Dime Community Bank (1)
2200 Montauk Hwy, Bridgehampton, NY 11932
Tel.: (631) 537-8834
Web Site: https://www.bridgenb.com
Sales Range: $75-99.9 Million
Commericial Banking
N.A.I.C.S.: 522110
Kevin M. O'Connor (Pres & CEO)
Kenneth J. Mahon (Chm)
Avinash Reddy (CFO & Sr Exec VP)
Christopher Porzelt (Chief Risk Officer & Exec VP)

Subsidiary (Domestic):

Bridge Abstract LLC (2)
2200 Montauk Hwy, Bridgehampton, NY 11932
Tel.: (631) 537-5750
Web Site: https://www.bridgetitle.com
Sales Range: $75-99.9 Million
Emp.: 6
Title Insurance Services
N.A.I.C.S.: 524298

DIMECO INC.
820 Church St, Honesdale, PA 18431
Tel.: (570) 253-1970 PA
Web Site:
http://www.thedimebank.com
Year Founded: 1905
DIMC—(OTCQX)
Rev.: $39,727,000
Assets: $882,804,000
Liabilities: $787,189,000
Net Worth: $95,615,000
Earnings: $8,856,000
Emp.: 142

Fiscal Year-end: 12/31/20
Bank Holding Company
N.A.I.C.S.: 551111
James M. Gardas (Sr VP)
Sonale Edelmann (Sr VP)
Jeremy J. Patten (Asst VP)
Peter Bochnovich (Pres & CEO)

Subsidiaries:

The Dime Bank (1)
820 Church St, Honesdale, PA 18431 (100%)
Tel.: (570) 253-1970
Web Site: http://www.thedimebank.com
Sales Range: $10-24.9 Million
Emp.: 50
Banking Services
N.A.I.C.S.: 522110
Maureen H. Beilman (CFO)
Peter Bochnovich (Sr VP & Asst Sec)
L. Jill George (VP)
Thomas M. Didato (VP)
Cheryl A. Smith (VP)
Deborah L. Unflat (VP)
Rory McGhie (Mgr-Carbondale)
Rebecca Fama (Asst Mgr-Carbondale)
Pamela Kerber Gehman (Asst VP)
Effie Slattery (Sec)

DINE BRANDS GLOBAL, INC.
10 W Walnut St 4th Fl, Pasadena, CA 91103
Tel.: (818) 240-6055 DE
Web Site:
https://www.dinebrands.com
Year Founded: 1958
DIN—(NYSE)
Rev.: $909,402,000
Assets: $1,881,491,000
Liabilities: $2,182,575,000
Net Worth: ($301,084,000)
Earnings: $81,111,000
Emp.: 637
Fiscal Year-end: 12/31/22
Holding Company; Restaurant Owner & Franchisor
N.A.I.C.S.: 551112
Gregory R. Bever (Sr VP)
John W. Peyton (CEO)
Susan Nelson (Sr VP-Global Comm)
Christine K. Son (Gen Counsel, Sec & Sr VP-Legal)
Justin Skelton (CIO)
Vance Y. Chang (CFO)
Brett Levy (VP-IR)
Scott Gladstone (Pres-Intl & Corp Dev)
Sarah Cannon-Foster (Chief People Officer)
Gary DuBois (VP)
Paul Damico (Pres)

Subsidiaries:

Applebee's Franchisor LLC (1)
450 N Brand Blvd FL 7, Glendale, CA 91203
Tel.: (913) 890-0100
Restaurant Operators
N.A.I.C.S.: 722511

Applebee's International, Inc. (1)
600-A N Wellwood Ave, Lindenhurst, NY 11757-2001
Tel.: (631) 226-2200
Web Site: http://www.applebees.com
Restaurant Operating Services
N.A.I.C.S.: 722511

Applebee's Restaurants North, LLC (1)
15015 Cimarron Ave, Rosemount, MN 55068
Tel.: (651) 423-0544
Restaurant Operating Services
N.A.I.C.S.: 722511

Applebee's Restaurants Texas, LLC (1)
341 Tanger Dr, Terrell, TX 75160
Tel.: (972) 551-1400
Web Site: http://www.applebees.com

Emp.: 40
Restaurant Operating Services
N.A.I.C.S.: 722511

Applebee's Restaurants Vermont, Inc. (1)
155 Dorset St University Mall, Burlington, VT 05403
Tel.: (802) 862-2818
Web Site: http://restaurants.applebees.com
Restaurant Operating Services
N.A.I.C.S.: 722511

Applebee's Services, Inc. (1)
10 W Walnut St, Pasadena, CA 91103
Tel.: (913) 890-0100
Web Site: http://www.applebees.com
Sales Range: $1-4.9 Billion
Franchise Restaurant Management Services
N.A.I.C.S.: 541611

IHOP Franchisor, LLC (1)
450 N Brand Blvd, Glendale, CA 91203
Tel.: (818) 240-6055
Restaurant Operators
N.A.I.C.S.: 722511

IHOP Property Leasing, LLC (1)
450 N Brand Blvd, Glendale, CA 91203
Tel.: (818) 240-6055
Property Rental & Leasing Services
N.A.I.C.S.: 533110

IHOP Restaurants, LLC (1)
3760 N Halsted St, Chicago, IL 60613-3907
Tel.: (773) 296-0048
Web Site: https://www.ihop.com
Restaurant Operators
N.A.I.C.S.: 722511
Brad Haley (CMO)
Jay Johns (Pres)

International House of Pancakes, Inc. (1)
605 N Glendale Ave, Glendale, CA 91206 (100%)
Tel.: (818) 242-0922
Web Site: https://restaurants.ihop.com
Sales Range: $50-74.9 Million
Emp.: 160
Restaurants Owners & Lessors
N.A.I.C.S.: 722511
Jay Johns (Pres)
Michael Kaufman (VP-Strategy & Bus Analytics)

DINEWISE, INC.
730 Peachtree St NE Ste 570, Atlanta, GA 30308
Tel.: (650) 228-0680   NV
Year Founded: 1959
DWIS—(OTCIQ)
Sales Range: $10-24.9 Million
Emp.: 16
Prepared Meal Producer & Distr
N.A.I.C.S.: 311991
Paul A. Roman (Chm & CEO)
Christina Arlene Moore (Pres, Treas & Sec)

DIODES INCORPORATED
4949 Hedgcoxe Rd Ste 200, Plano, TX 75024
Tel.: (972) 987-3900   DE
Web Site: https://www.diodes.com
Year Founded: 1959
DIOD—(NASDAQ)
Rev.: $2,000,580,000
Assets: $2,288,312,000
Liabilities: $705,393,000
Net Worth: $1,582,919,000
Earnings: $331,283,000
Emp.: 8,257
Fiscal Year-end: 12/31/22
Discrete Semiconductors Mfr, Whslr & Distr
N.A.I.C.S.: 334413
Francis Tang (Sr VP-Worldwide Discrete Products)
Emily Yang (Sr VP-Worldwide Sls & Mktg)
Gary Yu (Pres)

Brett R. Whitmire (CFO & Principal Acctg Officer)
Tim Monaghan (Pres-Europe)
Keh-Shew Lu (Chm & CEO)

Subsidiaries:

BCD (Shanghai) Micro-Electronics Limited (1)
No 1600 Zi Rd Shanghai ZiZhu Science based Industrial Park, Minhang, Shanghai, 200241, China
Tel.: (86) 2124162266
Semiconductor & Related Device Mfr
N.A.I.C.S.: 334413

BCD Semiconductor Manufacturing Limited (1)
No 1600 Zi Xing Road Shanghai Zizhu Science-Based Industrial Park, Shanghai, 200241, China
Tel.: (86) 2124162266
Web Site: http://www.bcdsemi.com
Sales Range: $250-299.9 Million
Emp.: 1,300
Semiconductor Device Whslr
N.A.I.C.S.: 423690
Jean-Claude Zhang (CFO)
Zhongyuan Jin (VP-Procurement, Foundry Svcs & Other Products)
Chong Ren (VP-Ops)
Simon Szeto (CTO)
Ernest Lin (Sr VP-Sls)

Subsidiary (Non-US):

BCD Semiconductor (Taiwan) Company Limited (2)
4F 298-1 Rui Guang Road, Nei-Hu District, Taipei, Taiwan
Tel.: (886) 226562808
Semiconductor Devices Mfr
N.A.I.C.S.: 334413

BCD Semiconductor Limited (2)
Room 101-1112 Digital-Empire II 486 Sindong, Yeongtong-Gu, Suwon, 443-734, Gyeonggi-do, Korea (South)
Tel.: (82) 31 695 8430
Sales Range: $10-24.9 Million
Emp.: 4
Semiconductor Devices Mfr
N.A.I.C.S.: 334413

Subsidiary (US):

BCD Semiconductor Corp (3)
48460 Kato Rd, Fremont, CA 94538
Tel.: (510) 668-1950
Semiconductor Devices Mfr
N.A.I.C.S.: 334413

Subsidiary (Domestic):

Shanghai SIM-BCD Semiconductor Manufacturing Co., Ltd. (2)
800 Yishan Road, Shanghai, 200233, China
Tel.: (86) 21 6485 1491
Semiconductor Device Whslr
N.A.I.C.S.: 423690

Canyon Semiconductor Inc. (1)
5th Floor No 24-2 Industrial East Fourth Road, Hsinchu Science Industrial Park, Hsinchu, Taiwan
Tel.: (886) 35797868
Semiconductor Devices Mfr
N.A.I.C.S.: 334413

Diodes Co. Ltd. (1)
7Fl No 50 Minchuan Road, Hsin Tien District, Taipei, 23141, ROC, Taiwan (100%)
Tel.: (886) 289146000
Sales Range: $10-24.9 Million
Emp.: 50
Mfr, Seller & Distributor of Discrete Semiconductors; Provider of Customer Support to the Automotive, Electronics, Computing & Telecommunications Industries.
N.A.I.C.S.: 334413

Diodes FabTech Inc. (1)
777 NW Blue Pkwy Ste 350, Lees Summit, MO 64086
Tel.: (816) 446-4800
Web Site: http://www.diodes.com
Semiconductor Device Whslr
N.A.I.C.S.: 423690

Diodes Japan K.K. (1)

8F Humax Ebisu Bldg 1-1-1 Ebisu-Minami, Shibuya-ku, Tokyo, 150-0022, Japan
Tel.: (81) 368719388
Electronic Parts & Equipment Distr
N.A.I.C.S.: 423690

Diodes Taiwan S.a.r.l (1)
7Fl No 50 Minchuan Road, New Taipei City, 23141, ROC, Taiwan
Tel.: (886) 289146000
Semiconductor & Electronic Component Distr
N.A.I.C.S.: 423690

Diodes Zetex Semiconductors Ltd (1)
Zetex Technology Pk Chadderton, Oldham, OL9 9LL, United Kingdom
Tel.: (44) 1616224444
Web Site: http://www.diodes.com
Sales Range: $100-124.9 Million
Emp.: 350
Semiconductor & Related Device Mfr
N.A.I.C.S.: 334413

Subsidiary (Non-US):

Diodes Zetex GmbH (2)
Kustermann-Park Balanstrasse 59 8th Floor, 81541, Munich, Germany
Tel.: (49) 894549490
Web Site: http://www.diodes.com
Sales Range: $100-124.9 Million
Emp.: 7
Semiconductor & Related Device Mfr
N.A.I.C.S.: 334413

Subsidiary (Domestic):

Diodes Zetex Neuhaus GmbH (3)
Waldweg 7, 98724, Neuhaus am Rennweg, Germany
Tel.: (49) 36797720
Web Site: http://www.diodes.com
Sales Range: $25-49.9 Million
Emp.: 115
Semiconductor Mfr & Whslr
N.A.I.C.S.: 334413
Rutiter Tabst (Mng Dir)

Subsidiary (US):

Zetex Inc. (2)
3500 Sunrise Hwy Bldg 200 Ste 111B, Great River, NY 11739
Tel.: (631) 360-2222
Web Site: http://www.diodes.com
Sales Range: $100-124.9 Million
Semiconductor Mfr & Whslr
N.A.I.C.S.: 334413

Dyna Image Corporation (1)
10F No 205 Sec 3 Beixin Rd, Xindian Dist, New Taipei City, 231, Taiwan
Tel.: (886) 289131128
Web Site: https://www.dyna-image.com
Optical Sensor Mfr
N.A.I.C.S.: 334513
Tommy Chien (CEO)

Eris Technology Co (1)
222 6F No 17 Lane 155 Sec 3 Beishen Rd, Shenkeng Dist, New Taipei City, 22203, Taiwan
Tel.: (886) 226620011
Web Site: https://www.eris.com.tw
Semiconductor & Electronic Component Mfr & Distr
N.A.I.C.S.: 334413
Jonathan Chang (Chm)

FabTech Inc. (1)
777 NW Blue Pkwy Ste 350, Lees Summit, MO 64086 (100%)
Tel.: (816) 525-2550
Web Site: http://www.diodes.com
Sales Range: $25-49.9 Million
Emp.: 200
N.A.I.C.S.: 334413

Savitech Corp. (1)
5F-1 No 100 Minquan Rd, Xindian Dist, New Taipei City, 231, Taiwan
Tel.: (886) 277283580
Web Site: https://www.savitech.co
Audio Equipment Distr
N.A.I.C.S.: 423620

Shanghai Kaihong Electronic Co., Ltd. (1)

No 999 Chenchun Road Xinqiao Town Songjiang, Songjiang County Xingqiao Town, 20161-1612, Shanghai, China (95%)
Tel.: (86) 2157647888
Sales Range: $200-249.9 Million
Emp.: 700
Semiconductor & Related Device Mfr
N.A.I.C.S.: 334413

Texas Instruments (UK) Limited (1)
Larkfield Ind Est, Greenock, PA16 0EQ, Renfrewshire, United Kingdom
Tel.: (44) 1475633733
Web Site: http://www.texasinstruments.com
Sales Range: $100-124.9 Million
Emp.: 450
Integrated Circuits & Microprocessors Mfr
N.A.I.C.S.: 334413

Yea Shin Technology Co., Ltd. (1)
No 51 Neixi Rd, Luzhu Township, Taoyuan, 338, Taiwan
Tel.: (886) 33245885
Web Site: http://www.yeashin.com
Emp.: 100
Semiconductor Assembly Product Mfr
N.A.I.C.S.: 334413

DIRECT COMMUNICATION SOLUTIONS, INC.
11021 Via Frontera Ste C, San Diego, CA 92127
Tel.: (858) 798-7100   FL
Web Site:
https://www.dcsbusiness.com
Year Founded: 2006
DCSI—(CNSX)
Rev.: $13,027,675
Assets: $3,059,005
Liabilities: $10,666,567
Net Worth: ($7,607,562)
Earnings: ($5,088,024)
Emp.: 27
Fiscal Year-end: 12/31/23
Information Technology Services
N.A.I.C.S.: 541512
Mike Lawless (VP-Sls)
Chris Bursey (Founder & CEO)
Dave Scowby (COO)
Rich Gomberg (CFO)
Eric Placzek (CTO)

DIRECT DIGITAL HOLDINGS, INC.
1177 W Loop S Ste 1310, Houston, TX 77027
Tel.: (832) 402-1051   DE
Web Site:
https://directdigitalholdings.com
Year Founded: 2018
DRCT—(NASDAQ)
Rev.: $157,110,000
Assets: $70,672,000
Liabilities: $74,354,000
Net Worth: ($3,682,000)
Earnings: ($6,844,000)
Emp.: 90
Fiscal Year-end: 12/31/23
Holding Company
N.A.I.C.S.: 551112
Diana P. Diaz (CFO)
Mark D. Walker (Co-Founder, Chm & CEO)
Keith W. Smith (Co-Founder & Pres)
Anu Pillai (CTO)
Calvin Scharffs (VP-Mktg)
Maria Vilchez Lowrey (Chief Growth Officer)
Duyen Le (VP-People & Culture)

DIRECT SELLING ACQUISITION CORP.
5800 Democracy Dr, Plano, TX 75024
Tel.: (214) 380-6020   DE
Web Site:
http://www.dsacquisition.com
Year Founded: 2021

Direct Selling Acquisition Corp.—(Continued)

DSAQ—(NYSE)
Rev.: $14,056,260
Assets: $240,632,028
Liabilities: $251,712,748
Net Worth: ($11,080,720)
Earnings: $11,578,910
Emp.: 3
Fiscal Year-end: 12/31/22
Investment Services
N.A.I.C.S.: 523999
Dave Wentz *(Chm & CEO)*
Mike Lohner *(Pres & CFO)*
Wayne Moorehead *(Chief Strategy Officer)*

DISC MEDICINE, INC.
321 Arsenal St Ste 101, Watertown, MA 02472
Tel.: (617) 674-9274   DE
Web Site:
  https://www.discmedicine.com
Year Founded: 2017
IRON—(NASDAQ)
Rev.: $14,795,000
Assets: $367,996,000
Liabilities: $22,875,000
Net Worth: $345,121,000
Earnings: ($76,330,000)
Fiscal Year-end: 12/31/23
Precision Medicine Company
N.A.I.C.S.: 325411
Donald W. Nicholson *(Exec Chm)*
John D. Quisel *(Pres & CEO)*
Jean M. Franchi *(CFO, Principal Acctg Officer & Treas)*

DISCOVER FINANCIAL SERVICES
2500 Lake Cook Rd, Riverwoods, IL 60015
Tel.: (224) 405-0900   DE
Web Site: https://www.discover.com
Year Founded: 1986
DFS—(NYSE)
Rev.: $17,845,000,000
Assets: $151,522,000,000
Liabilities: $136,694,000,000
Net Worth: $14,828,000,000
Earnings: $2,940,000,000
Emp.: 21,100
Fiscal Year-end: 12/31/23
Financial Investment Services
N.A.I.C.S.: 522210
John B. Owen *(Interim Pres & Interim CEO)*
J. Michael Shepherd *(Interim Pres & Interim CEO)*
Carlos M. Minetti *(Pres-Consumer Banking & Exec VP)*
Daniel Peter Capozzi *(Pres-Cards & Exec VP)*
R. Andrew Eichfeld *(Chief HR & Admin Officer & Exec VP)*
John Thomas Greene *(CFO & Exec VP)*
Keith E. Toney *(Chief Data & Analytics Officer & Exec VP)*
Shifra C. Kolsky *(Chief Acctg Officer, Sr VP & Controller)*
Amir S. Arooni *(CIO & Exec VP)*
Jason Hanson *(Pres-Payment Svcs & Exec VP)*

Subsidiaries:

DFS Services LLC   **(1)**
2500 Lake Cook Rd, Riverwoods, IL 60015
Tel.: (224) 405-0900
Web Site:
  http://www.discoverglobalnetwork.com
Sales Range: $750-799.9 Million
Prepaid Payment Services
N.A.I.C.S.: 522390

DINIT d.o.o.   **(1)**
Industrijska cesta 23, 6310, Izola, Slovenia
Tel.: (386) 56600700

Web Site: http://www.dinitcs.com
Financial Services
N.A.I.C.S.: 523940
Primoz Patru *(Mng Dir)*
Davide Rigamonti *(Chm-Supervisory Bd)*
Simone Tettamanti *(Vice Chm-Supervisory Bd)*
Miha Svetek *(Dir-Fin & Acctg)*
Tomaz Lesnik *(Dir-Bus Dev & Sls)*
Darko Zajdela *(Dir-Application Dev & IT Ops)*
Jani Gorup *(Mng Dir)*

Diners Club Italia S.r.l.   **(1)**
Piazza Santa Maria delle Grazie 1, Postale 10077, Casella, 20123, Milan, Italy
Tel.: (39) 063575333
Web Site: https://www.dinersclub.it
Financial Services
N.A.I.C.S.: 523940

Discover Bank   **(1)**
12 Reads Way, New Castle, DE 19720-1649
Web Site: https://www.discover.com
Sales Range: $125-149.9 Million
Emp.: 1,000
Banking Services
N.A.I.C.S.: 522110
John B. Owen *(Pres)*
J. Michael Shepherd *(Interim Pres)*

Subsidiary (Domestic):

Discover Student Loans   **(2)**
750 Washington Blvd, Stamford, CT 06901   **(80%)**
Tel.: (203) 975-6320
Web Site:
  http://www.discoverstudentloans.com
Sales Range: $900-999.9 Million
Emp.: 248
Educational Credit Services
N.A.I.C.S.: 522291

Discover Card   **(1)**
2500 Lake Park Blvd, Salt Lake City, UT 84120-8219
Tel.: (801) 902-4500
Web Site: http://www.discover.com
Sales Range: $400-449.9 Million
Emp.: 1,000
Credit Card Financial Services
N.A.I.C.S.: 522210

Discover Home Loans, Inc.   **(1)**
173 Technology Dr, Irvine, CA 92618
Tel.: (800) 756-0789
Web Site: http://www.discover.com
Sales Range: $150-199.9 Million
Emp.: 600
Residential Mortgage Loan Origination Services
N.A.I.C.S.: 522310

PULSE EFT Association   **(1)**
1301 McKinney Ste 2500, Houston, TX 77010
Tel.: (832) 214-0100
Sales Range: $25-49.9 Million
Emp.: 90
ATM Network Services
N.A.I.C.S.: 522320

PULSE Network LLC   **(1)**
1301 McKinney Ste 600, Houston, TX 77010
Tel.: (713) 223-1400
Web Site: https://www.pulsenetwork.com
Credit Card Services
N.A.I.C.S.: 522210
Diane E. Offereins *(CEO & Exec VP-Payment Svcs Discover Fin Svcs)*
David Schneider *(Pres)*
Jennifer Schroeder *(Exec VP-Product Mgmt)*
Steve Sievert *(Exec VP-Marketing-Brand Management)*
Mike Urquizu *(Exec VP-Sales-Account Management)*
Jim Lerdal *(Exec VP-Operations)*

DISCOVERY ENERGY CORP.
1 Riverway Dr Ste 1700, Houston, TX 77056
Tel.: (713) 840-6495   NV
Web Site: http://discoveryenergy.com
Year Founded: 2006
DENR—(OTCEM)

Assets: $2,942,940
Liabilities: $12,428,945
Net Worth: ($9,486,005)
Earnings: ($2,335,117)
Emp.: 3
Fiscal Year-end: 02/28/22
Petroleum Exploration Services
N.A.I.C.S.: 211120
Keith D. Spickelmier *(Chm)*
William E. Begley *(Pres, CFO & COO)*
Keith J. McKenzie *(CEO)*
Sean Austin *(Treas & Sec)*
Woody Leel *(Mgr-Exploration)*

Subsidiaries:

Discovery Energy SA Pty Ltd   **(1)**
350 Collins Street Level 8, Melbourne, 3000, VIC, Australia
Tel.: (61) 386011131
Web Site: https://discoveryenergy.com
Oil & Gas Exploration Services
N.A.I.C.S.: 213112
Andrew Adams *(Mng Dir)*
Melanie Leydin *(Sec)*
Keith McKenzie *(CEO)*

DISCOVERY MINERALS LTD.
429 W Plumb Ln, Reno, NV 89509
Tel.: (310) 607-8252   NV
Web Site:
  http://www.discoveryminerals.com
Year Founded: 2005
DSCR—(OTCIQ)
Assets: $83,000
Liabilities: $1,531,000
Net Worth: ($1,448,000)
Earnings: ($793,000)
Fiscal Year-end: 09/30/19
Mineral Exploration Services
N.A.I.C.S.: 213114

DISTRIBUTION SOLUTIONS GROUP, INC.
301 Commerce St Ste 1700, Fort Worth, TX 76102
Tel.: (773) 304-5050   DE
Web Site:
  https://www.distributionsolutions group.com
Year Founded: 1952
DSGR—(NASDAQ)
Rev.: $1,151,422,000
Assets: $1,215,610,000
Liabilities: $652,615,000
Net Worth: $562,995,000
Earnings: $7,406,000
Emp.: 3,133
Fiscal Year-end: 12/31/22
Screws, Rivets & Related Fastener Distr
N.A.I.C.S.: 423840
Ronald J. Knutson *(CFO, Treas, Exec VP & Controller)*
John Bryan King *(Chm, Pres & CEO)*
David S. Lambert *(Chief Acctg Officer, VP & Controller)*
Matt Boyce *(Sr VP)*

Subsidiaries:

C.B. Lynn Company   **(1)**
1666 E Touhy Ave, Des Plaines, IL 60018-3607   **(100%)**
Tel.: (847) 827-9666
Sales Range: $200-249.9 Million
Emp.: 500
Speciality Products Distr
N.A.I.C.S.: 423840

His Company, Inc.   **(1)**
6650 Concord Park Dr, Houston, TX 77040-4098
Tel.: (713) 934-1700
Web Site: https://www.hisco.com
Sales Range: $25-49.9 Million
Emp.: 248
Electronic Parts & Equipment
N.A.I.C.S.: 423690

Subsidiary (Domestic):

Adhesive Materials Group   **(2)**
9327 Hwy 6 N Ste 150, Houston, TX 77095
Tel.: (281) 885-3828
Web Site: https://www.hisco.com
Emp.: 25
Packaging Services
N.A.I.C.S.: 561910
Gary Baird *(Gen Mgr)*

Division (Non-US):

His Company, Inc. - HiscoMex Division   **(2)**
Calle 7 Sur Ste 9057-2 Cuidad Industrial Otay, 22444, Tijuana, Mexico
Tel.: (52) 6646236893
Emp.: 36
Industrial Supplies Distr
N.A.I.C.S.: 423840
Richard French *(Branch Mgr)*

Subsidiary (Domestic):

Hisco, Inc.   **(2)**
6650 Concord Park Dr, Houston, TX 77040-4098
Tel.: (713) 934-1700
Web Site: https://www.hisco.com
Sales Range: $250-299.9 Million
Emp.: 385
Industrial Supply Distr
N.A.I.C.S.: 423840
Michael Marks *(Chm)*
William Bland *(VP-Sls-North America)*
Tommy O'Connor *(VP & Mgr-Zone)*
Nelson Picard *(VP-Ops)*
Ellis E. Moseley *(CFO & Sr VP)*
Gary Niemand *(Sr VP-IT)*
Jeff Plath *(Sr VP-Ops, Supply Chain & Quality)*
Greg Smith *(VP-Natl Accts)*

Subsidiary (Domestic):

All-Spec Industries, Inc.   **(3)**
5228 US Hwy 421 N, Wilmington, NC 28401
Tel.: (910) 763-8111
Web Site: http://www.all-spec.com
Sales Range: $1-9.9 Million
Emp.: 40
Distr of Products for Electronic Service, Repair & Testing
N.A.I.C.S.: 423610
Michael Lafleur *(Mgr-Warehouse)*
Todd Hoyle-Harris *(Ops Mgr)*
David Weitner *(VP-Mktg)*
Julianne Kurpiewski Stewart *(Mgr-eCommerce)*

Lawson Products Inc. (Ontario)   **(1)**
7315 Rapistan Court, Mississauga, L5N 5Z4, ON, Canada   **(100%)**
Tel.: (905) 567-1717
Sales Range: $25-49.9 Million
Emp.: 38
Automotive & Industrial Products Distr
N.A.I.C.S.: 423830

Lawson Products, Inc.   **(1)**
1381 Capital Blvd, Reno, NV 89502   **(100%)**
Tel.: (775) 856-1381
Web Site: http://www.lawson.com
Sales Range: $50-74.9 Million
Emp.: 100
Automotive & Electrical Equipment & Supplies Distr
N.A.I.C.S.: 423710

Lawson Products, Inc.   **(1)**
1197 Satellite Blvd NW, Suwanee, GA 30024   **(100%)**
Tel.: (770) 814-7786
Web Site: http://www.lawsonproducts.com
Sales Range: $25-49.9 Million
Emp.: 55
Automotive & Electrical Equipment & Supplies Distr
N.A.I.C.S.: 423710

Lawson Products, Inc.   **(1)**
28 Industrial Rd, Fairfield, NJ 07004   **(100%)**
Tel.: (973) 227-2720
Web Site: http://www.lawsonprod.com
Sales Range: $250-299.9 Million
Emp.: 600

Automotive & Electrical Equipment & Supplies Distr
N.A.I.C.S.: 423830

Lawson Products, Inc. (1)
8770 W Bryn Mawr Ste 900, Chicago, IL 60631 (100%)
Tel.: (847) 827-9666
Web Site: https://www.lawsonproducts.com
Sales Range: $25-49.9 Million
Emp.: 65
Automotive & Industrial Equipment & Supplies Distr
N.A.I.C.S.: 423830

Lawson Products, Inc. (1)
8770 W Bryn Mawr Ave Ste 900, Chicago, IL 60631 (100%)
Tel.: (216) 642-5973
Web Site: http://www.lawsonproducts.com
Sales Range: $50-74.9 Million
Emp.: 75
Hardware, Industrial Supplies
N.A.I.C.S.: 332722

Partsmaster, Inc. (1)
2727 Chemsearch Blvd, Dallas, TX 75265
Tel.: (972) 438-0523
Web Site: http://www.partsmaster.com
Tools & Tool Parts Mfr & Distr
N.A.I.C.S.: 333515
Kenny Smoak (Sr VP)

TestEquity LLC (1)
6100 Condor Dr, Moorpark, CA 93021
Tel.: (805) 498-9933
Web Site: https://www.testequity.com
Electronic Test Equipment Mfr & Distr
N.A.I.C.S.: 334515

Subsidiary (Domestic):

InterWorld Highway, LLC (2)
205 Westwood Ave, Long Branch, NJ 07740
Tel.: (732) 222-7077
Web Site: https://www.tequipment.net
Sales Range: $25-49.9 Million
Emp.: 40
Miscellaneous Retail Stores
N.A.I.C.S.: 459999

Techni-Tool Inc. (2)
1547 N Trooper Rd, Worcester, PA 19490-1117
Tel.: (610) 828-5623
Web Site: https://www.techni-tool.com
Electric Tools Whlsr
N.A.I.C.S.: 423840
Mike Hade (Pres)

DIVERSICARE HEALTHCARE SERVICES, INC.
1621 Galleria Blvd, Brentwood, TN 37027
Tel.: (615) 771-7575   DE
Web Site: http://www.dvcr.com
Year Founded: 1994
DVCR—(OTCIQ)
Rev.: $475,718,000
Assets: $439,852,000
Liabilities: $471,157,000
Net Worth: ($31,305,000)
Earnings: $5,159,000
Emp.: 2,700
Fiscal Year-end: 12/31/20
Long-Term Care Services for the Elderly
N.A.I.C.S.: 623110
Chad A. McCurdy (Chm)
Kerry D. Massey (CFO & Exec VP)
Rebecca B. Bodie (COO & Exec VP)
James R. McKnight Jr. (Pres & CEO)

Subsidiaries:

Diversicare Afton Oaks, LLC (1)
7514 Kingsley, Houston, TX 77087-4412
Tel.: (713) 644-8393
Web Site: http://www.aftonoaks.com
Sales Range: $25-49.9 Million
Emp.: 150
Health Care Srvices
N.A.I.C.S.: 622110

Diversicare Briarcliff, LLC (1)

100 Elmhurst Dr, Oak Ridge, TN 37830-7621
Tel.: (865) 481-3367
Web Site: http://www.dvcr.com
Health Care Srvices
N.A.I.C.S.: 622110

Diversicare Clinton, LLC (1)
106 Padgett Dr, Clinton, KY 42031-1313
Tel.: (270) 653-5558
Web Site: http://www.dvcr.com
Emp.: 76
Health Care Srvices
N.A.I.C.S.: 622110

Diversicare Estates, LLC (1)
201 Sycamore School Rd, Fort Worth, TX 76134-5009
Tel.: (817) 293-7610
Emp.: 40
Health Care Srvices
N.A.I.C.S.: 622110
Tammy Brown (Mgr-HR)

Diversicare Hartford, LLC (1)
217 Toro Rd, Hartford, AL 36344-1459
Tel.: (334) 588-3842
Web Site: http://www.dvcr.com
Health Care Srvices
N.A.I.C.S.: 622110

Diversicare Hillcrest, LLC (1)
208 Maple St, Luling, TX 78648
Tel.: (830) 875-5219
Web Site: http://www.dvcr.com
Emp.: 40
Health Care Srvices
N.A.I.C.S.: 622110

Diversicare Humble, LLC (1)
8450 Will Clayton Pkwy, Humble, TX 77338
Tel.: (281) 446-8484
Web Site: http://www.dvcr.com
Sales Range: $25-49.9 Million
Emp.: 130
Health Care Srvices
N.A.I.C.S.: 622110

Diversicare Katy, LLC (1)
1525 Tull Dr, Katy, TX 77449-5099
Tel.: (281) 578-1600
Web Site: http://www.dvcr.com
Sales Range: $25-49.9 Million
Emp.: 100
Health Care Srvices
N.A.I.C.S.: 622110
Sarah Eivling (Mng Dir)

Diversicare Management Services Co. (1)
1006 Flagpole Ct, Brentwood, TN 37027
Tel.: (615) 221-9090
Web Site:
http://www.diversicaremanagement.com
Sales Range: $25-49.9 Million
Emp.: 100
Health Care Srvices
N.A.I.C.S.: 622110

Subsidiary (Domestic):

Advocat Finance, Inc. (2)
1621 Galleria Blvd, Brentwood, TN 37027
Tel.: (615) 771-7575
Web Site:
http://www.diversicaremanagement.com
Sales Range: $10-24.9 Million
Emp.: 60
Management Services
N.A.I.C.S.: 541611

Subsidiary (Domestic):

Diversicare Leasing Corp. (3)
1621 Galleria Blvd, Brentwood, TN 37027
Tel.: (615) 771-7575
Web Site: http://www.advocat.com
Nursing Home Management Services
N.A.I.C.S.: 541611
Kelly Gale (CEO)

Diversicare Normandy Terrace, LLC (1)
841 Rice Rd, San Antonio, TX 78220-3513
Tel.: (210) 648-0101
Health Care Srvices
N.A.I.C.S.: 622110

Diversicare Therapy Services, LLC (1)
1621 Galleria Blvd, Brentwood, TN 37027

Tel.: (615) 771-7575
Web Site:
http://www.diversicaretherapy.com
Health Care Srvices
N.A.I.C.S.: 621610

Diversicare Treemont, LLC (1)
5550 Harvest Hill Rd Ste 500, Dallas, TX 75230-1684
Tel.: (972) 661-1862
Web Site: http://www.dvcr.com
Sales Range: $25-49.9 Million
Emp.: 100
Health Care Srvices
N.A.I.C.S.: 622110

Diversicare Windsor House, LLC (1)
4411 McAllister Dr, Huntsville, AL 35805-3205
Tel.: (256) 837-8585
Health Care Srvices
N.A.I.C.S.: 622110

Diversicare Yorktown, LLC (1)
670 W 4th St, Yorktown, TX 78164-5092
Tel.: (361) 564-2275
Web Site: http://www.yorktownnursing.com
Emp.: 60
Health Care Srvices
N.A.I.C.S.: 622110

Diversicare of Arab, LLC (1)
235 3rd St SE, Arab, AL 35016
Tel.: (256) 586-3111
Long-term Care Services
N.A.I.C.S.: 623110

Diversicare of Batesville, LLC (1)
154 Woodland Rd, Batesville, MS 38606
Tel.: (662) 563-5636
Long-term Care Services
N.A.I.C.S.: 623110

Diversicare of Bessemer, LLC (1)
820 Golf Course Rd, Bessemer, AL 35023
Tel.: (205) 425-5241
Long-term Care Services
N.A.I.C.S.: 623110

Diversicare of Big Springs, LLC (1)
500 Saint Clair Ave SW, Huntsville, AL 35801-5021
Tel.: (256) 539-5111
Nursing Care Services
N.A.I.C.S.: 623110

Diversicare of Boaz, LLC (1)
600 Corley Ave, Boaz, AL 35957
Tel.: (256) 593-8380
Long-term Care Services
N.A.I.C.S.: 623110

Diversicare of Bradford Place, LLC (1)
1302 Millville Ave, Hamilton, OH 45013-3961
Tel.: (513) 867-4100
Nursing Care Services
N.A.I.C.S.: 623110
Linsy Speed (Gen Mgr)

Diversicare of Brookhaven, LLC (1)
519 Brookman Dr, Brookhaven, MS 39601
Tel.: (601) 833-2881
Long-term Care Services
N.A.I.C.S.: 623110

Diversicare of Chanute, LLC (1)
530 W 14th St, Chanute, KS 66720
Tel.: (620) 431-4940
Web Site:
http://www.diversicareofchanute.com
Sales Range: $25-49.9 Million
Emp.: 95
Healthcare & Rehabilitation Facility & Services
N.A.I.C.S.: 623110

Diversicare of Chateau, LLC (1)
811 N 9th St, Saint Joseph, MO 64501
Tel.: (816) 233-5164
Health Care Srvices
N.A.I.C.S.: 622110

Diversicare of Council Grove, LLC (1)
400 Sunset Dr, Council Grove, KS 66846
Tel.: (620) 767-5172
Web Site:
http://www.diversicareofcouncilgrove.com
Emp.: 65

Healthcare & Rehabilitation Facility & Services
N.A.I.C.S.: 623110

Diversicare of Eupora, LLC (1)
156 E Walnut Ave, Eupora, MS 39744
Tel.: (662) 258-8293
Long-term Care Services
N.A.I.C.S.: 623110

Diversicare of Foley, LLC (1)
1701 N Alston St, Foley, AL 36535
Tel.: (251) 943-2781
Long-term Care Services
N.A.I.C.S.: 623110

Diversicare of Haysville, LLC (1)
215 N Lamar Ave, Haysville, KS 67060
Tel.: (316) 524-3211
Web Site:
http://www.diversicareofhaysville.com
Healthcare & Rehabilitation Facility & Services
N.A.I.C.S.: 623110

Diversicare of Hueytown, LLC (1)
190 Brooklane Dr, Hueytown, AL 35023
Tel.: (205) 491-2905
Long-term Care Services
N.A.I.C.S.: 623110

Diversicare of Hutchinson, LLC (1)
1202 E 23rd Ave, Hutchinson, KS 67502-5656
Tel.: (620) 669-9393
Nursing Care Services
N.A.I.C.S.: 623110

Diversicare of Lanett, LLC (1)
702 S 13th St, Lanett, AL 36863
Tel.: (334) 644-1111
Long-term Care Services
N.A.I.C.S.: 623110

Diversicare of Larned, LLC (1)
1114 W 11th St, Larned, KS 67550
Tel.: (620) 285-6914
Web Site:
http://www.diversicareoflarned.com
Healthcare & Rehabilitation Facility & Services
N.A.I.C.S.: 623110

Diversicare of Mansfield, LLC (1)
2124 Park Ave W, Ontario, OH 44906-3807
Tel.: (419) 529-6447
Web Site: http://www.diversicare.com
Health Care Srvices
N.A.I.C.S.: 622110

Diversicare of Meridian, LLC (1)
4728 Hwy 39 N, Meridian, MS 39301
Tel.: (601) 482-8151
Long-term Care Services
N.A.I.C.S.: 623110

Diversicare of Montgomery, LLC (1)
2020 N Country Club Dr, Montgomery, AL 36106
Tel.: (334) 263-1643
Long-term Care Services
N.A.I.C.S.: 623110

Diversicare of Nicholasville, LLC (1)
100 Sparks Ave, Nicholasville, KY 40356-1004
Tel.: (859) 885-4171
Nursing Care Services
N.A.I.C.S.: 623110

Diversicare of Oneonta, LLC (1)
215 Valley Rd, Oneonta, AL 35121
Tel.: (205) 274-2365
Long-term Care Services
N.A.I.C.S.: 623110

Diversicare of Oxford, LLC (1)
1130 S Hale St, Oxford, AL 36203
Tel.: (256) 831-0481
Long-term Care Services
N.A.I.C.S.: 623110

Diversicare of Pell City, LLC (1)
510 Wolf Creek Rd N, Pell City, AL 35125
Tel.: (205) 338-3329
Long-term Care Services
N.A.I.C.S.: 623110

Diversicare of Providence, LLC (1)
4915 Charlestown Rd, New Albany, IN 47150
Tel.: (812) 945-5221

Diversicare Healthcare Services, Inc.—(Continued)

Nursing Care Services
N.A.I.C.S.: 623110

Diversicare of Ripley, LLC (1)
101 Cunningham Dr, Ripley, MS 38663
Tel.: (662) 837-3011
Long-term Care Services
N.A.I.C.S.: 623110

Diversicare of Riverchase, LLC (1)
2500 Riverhaven Dr, Birmingham, AL 35244
Tel.: (205) 987-0901
Long-term Care Services
N.A.I.C.S.: 623110

Diversicare of Riverside, LLC (1)
1616 Weisenborn Rd, Saint Joseph, MO 64507-2527
Tel.: (816) 232-9874
Health Care Srvices
N.A.I.C.S.: 622110

Diversicare of Sedgwick, LLC (1)
712 N Monroe Ave, Sedgwick, KS 67135
Tel.: (316) 772-5185
Web Site:
   http://www.diversicareofsedgwick.com
Healthcare & Rehabilitation Facility & Services
N.A.I.C.S.: 623110

Diversicare of Selma, LLC (1)
100 Park Pl, Selma, AL 36701
Tel.: (334) 872-3471
Long-term Care Services
N.A.I.C.S.: 623110

Diversicare of Seneca Place, LLC (1)
3526 Dutchmans Ln, Louisville, KY 40205
Tel.: (502) 452-6331
Health Care Srvices
N.A.I.C.S.: 622110

Diversicare of Siena Woods, LLC (1)
6125 N Main St, Dayton, OH 45415
Tel.: (937) 278-8211
Nursing Care Services
N.A.I.C.S.: 623110

Diversicare of St. Joseph, LLC (1)
3002 N 18th St, Saint Joseph, MO 64505
Tel.: (816) 364-4200
Nursing Care Services
N.A.I.C.S.: 623110

Diversicare of St. Theresa, LLC (1)
7010 Rowan Hill Dr, Cincinnati, OH 45227
Tel.: (513) 271-7010
Emp.: 99
Nursing Care Services
N.A.I.C.S.: 623110

Diversicare of Tupelo, LLC (1)
2273 S Eason Blvd, Tupelo, MS 38804
Tel.: (662) 842-2461
Long-term Care Services
N.A.I.C.S.: 623110

Diversicare of Tylertown, LLC (1)
200 Medical Cir, Tylertown, MS 39667
Tel.: (601) 876-2107
Long-term Care Services
N.A.I.C.S.: 623110

Diversicare of Winfield, LLC (1)
144 County Hwy 14, Winfield, AL 35594
Tel.: (205) 487-4211
Long-term Care Services
N.A.I.C.S.: 623110

Senior Care Cedar Hills, LLC (1)
602 E Belt Line Rd, Cedar Hill, TX 75104
Tel.: (972) 291-5000
Web Site: http://cedarhillsliving.net
Health Care Srvices
N.A.I.C.S.: 622110

DIVERSIFIED ENERGY COMPANY PLC

1600 Corporate Dr, Birmingham, AL 35242
Tel.: (205) 408-0909   UK
Web Site: https://www.div.energy
Year Founded: 2001

DEC—(LSE)
Rev.: $868,263,000
Assets: $3,474,022,000
Liabilities: $2,875,612,000
Net Worth: $598,410,000
Earnings: $759,701,000
Emp.: 1,603
Fiscal Year-end: 12/31/23
Holding Company; Oil & Gas Properties Development & Production Services
N.A.I.C.S.: 551112
Bradley G. Gray (COO & Exec VP)
Eric M. Williams (CFO & Exec VP)
David Myers (CIO)
Ben Sullivan (Gen Counsel, Sec & Exec VP)
James P. Rode (Chief Comml Officer & Exec VP)
Maverick Bentley (Sr VP-Southern Ops)
Bob Cayton (Sr VP-Northern Ops)
Paul Espenan (VP-Environmental, Helath & Safety)
Bill Kurtz (Sr VP- Land, Engrg & Measurement)
Randall Barron (Sr VP-Strategy & Fin)
Michael Garrett (Sr VP-Acctg & Controller)
Mark S. Kirkendall (Sr VP-HR)
John Crain (VP-Treasury)
Teresa Odom (VP-IR)
Rusty R. Hutson Jr. (Co-Founder & CEO)

Subsidiaries:

Diversified Gas & Oil
Corporation (1)
1100 Corporate Dr, Birmingham, AL 35242
Tel.: (205) 408-0909
Web Site: https://www.dgoc.com
Oil & Gas Development & Production
N.A.I.C.S.: 213112
Bradley G. Gray (COO)
Bobby J. Cayton (Sr VP- Northern Ops)
Rusty Houston (Pres)

DIVERSIFIED ENERGY HOLDINGS, INC.

3445 Lawrence Ave, Oceanside, NY 11572
Tel.: (646) 768-8417   NV
DIEN—(OTCIQ)
Drilling Oil & Gas Well Exploration Services
N.A.I.C.S.: 213111
David Lazar (CEO)

DIVERSIFIED HEALTHCARE TRUST

2 Newton Pl 225 Washington St Ste 300, Newton, MA 02458-1634
Tel.: (617) 796-8350   MD
Web Site: https://www.dhcreit.com
DHC—(NASDAQ)
Rev.: $1,283,566,000
Assets: $6,002,093,000
Liabilities: $3,363,482,000
Net Worth: $2,638,611,000
Earnings: ($15,774,000)
Fiscal Year-end: 12/31/22
Real Estate Investment Trust
N.A.I.C.S.: 525990
Jennifer B. Clark (Sec)
Christopher J. Bilotto (Pres & CEO)
Matthew C. Brown (CFO & Treas)

DIVERSIFIED OIL & GAS HOLDINGS, LTD.

1520 Rice Rd Ste 200, Tyler, TX 75703
Tel.: (903) 581-4053   NV
Year Founded: 2001
DVFI—(OTCIQ)
Oil & Gas Exploration Services

N.A.I.C.S.: 213112
James Lancaster (CEO)

DIVIDE DRIVES, INC.

1416 Perrys Hollow Dr, Salt Lake City, UT 84103
Tel.: (801) 595-0998   NV
Year Founded: 1988
DVDR—(OTCIQ)
Financial Management Services
N.A.I.C.S.: 523999
Andrew Bebbington (CFO)

DIVIDEND & INCOME FUND

11 Hanover Sq 12th Fl, New York, NY 10005
Tel.: (212) 785-0900
Web Site:
   http://www.dividendandincome fund.com
DNI—(NYSE)
Rev.: $5,554,855
Assets: $239,508,345
Liabilities: $37,161,136
Net Worth: $202,347,209
Earnings: $1,998,234
Fiscal Year-end: 12/31/19
Investment Management Service
N.A.I.C.S.: 525990
Thomas Bassett Winmill (Chm, Pres, CEO & Chief Legal Officer)

DLH HOLDINGS CORP.

3565 Piedmont Rd NE Bldg 3 Ste 700, Atlanta, GA 30305
Tel.: (770) 554-3545   NJ
Web Site: https://www.dlhcorp.com
Year Founded: 1969
DLHC—(NASDAQ)
Rev.: $395,937,000
Assets: $314,381,000
Liabilities: $204,249,000
Net Worth: $110,132,000
Earnings: $7,397,000
Emp.: 2,800
Fiscal Year-end: 09/30/24
Payroll Services, Contract Employment, Employee Leasing & Temporary Medical Staffing
N.A.I.C.S.: 561311
Frederick Gerald Wasserman (Chm)
Zachary C. Parker (Pres & CEO)
Kathryn M. JohnBull (CFO & Principal Acctg Officer)
Donioo Ciotti (Sr VP)
Jeanine Christian (Pres-Pub Health & Scientific Res)
Sandra Halverson (VP)

Subsidiaries:

BrightLane.com, Inc. (1)
925B Peachtree St NE Ste 191, Alpharetta, GA 30309
Tel.: (770) 653-5136
Web Site: http://www.brightlane.com
Financial, Management & Administrative Services for Businesses Online
N.A.I.C.S.: 541990
Chris Johnson (Owner & Mng Dir)
Nancy LaFoy (Mng Dir)

DLH Solutions, Inc. (1)
3525 Hwy 81 S Ste 101, Loganville, GA 30052
Tel.: (770) 554-3545
Web Site: http://www.dlhcorp.com
Sales Range: $10-24.9 Million
Emp.: 20
Contract Staffing Services to Federal Government
N.A.I.C.S.: 561320

Danya International, LLC (1)
Two Piedmont Ctr 3565 Piedmont Rd Bldg 3 Ste 700, Atlanta, GA 30305 (100%)
Tel.: (404) 679-7900
Web Site: http://www.danya.com
Emp.: 209
Administrative Management & General Management Consulting Services

N.A.I.C.S.: 541611
Rosemarie C. Franchi (VP-Monitoring & Compliance)
Gil Tadmor (CTO)
Helene Fisher (Pres)
Kimberly Brock (Dir-Health Mktg & Comm-Atlanta)
Leslie Graves (Sr Dir-HR)
Laurie Mankin (Sr Dir-Monitoring & Compliance)
Ashkwin K. Manne (Dir-IT Solutions & Architecture)
Cynthia Northington (Sr Dir-Ops & Head Start Monitoring)
Sharon R. Novey (Sr Dir-High Impact Prevention)
Joy Vithespongse Trejo (Sr Dir-Bus Dev)

Grove Resource Solutions
Incorporated (1)
6720B Rockledge Dr, Ste 777, Bethesda, MD 20817
Tel.: (240) 236-0800
Web Site: https://www.dlhcorp.com
Sales Range: $10-24.9 Million
Emp.: 300
Business Consulting Services
N.A.I.C.S.: 541618
Deborah Grove (Partner)
Kelly Baldwin (Sr VP-Defense Programs & Gen Mgr-Charleston)

Irving Burton Associates, LLC (1)
3130 Fairview Park Dr Ste 250, Falls Church, VA 22042
Tel.: (703) 575-8359
Web Site: http://www.ibacorp.us
Technical Consulting Services
N.A.I.C.S.: 541690
Mary Dowdall (Pres)
Eric Peterson (VP-Federal IT Svcs)
Linh Ly (CFO)
Cleveland Cooke (VP-Tech)
Quinn Smith (Dir-Ops)

Social & Scientific Systems, Inc. (1)
8757 Georgia Ave 12th Fl, Silver Spring, MD 20910
Tel.: (301) 628-3000
Web Site: http://www.s-3.com
Sales Range: $50-74.9 Million
Emp.: 400
Custom Computer Programming Services
N.A.I.C.S.: 541511
Bruce Beddow (Co-CFO)
Howard Ruddell (Co-CFO)
Jeanine M. Christian (Pres-Operating Unit)

Division (Domestic):

SSS Biomedical Research Support
Division (2)
8757 Georgia Ave 12th Fl, Silver Spring, MD 20910
Tel.: (301) 628-3000
Web Site: http://www.s-3.com
Sales Range: $50-74.9 Million
Custom Computer Programming Services
N.A.I.C.S.: 541511

SSS Computer Systems and Data
Analysis Division (2)
8757 Georgia Ave 12th Fl, Silver Spring, MD 20910
Tel.: (301) 628-3000
Web Site: http://www.s-3.com
Sales Range: $25-49.9 Million
Emp.: 275
Custom Computer Programming Services
N.A.I.C.S.: 541511
Kevin Beverly (Pres)

DLT RESOLUTION INC.

5940 S Rainbow Blvd Ste 400-32132, Las Vegas, NV 89118
Tel.: (702) 796-6363
Web Site:
   https://www.dltresolution.com
Year Founded: 2007
DLTI—(OTCEM)
Rev.: $218,707
Assets: $325,716
Liabilities: $1,202,670
Net Worth: ($876,954)
Earnings: ($1,153,244)
Emp.: 1
Fiscal Year-end: 12/31/22

Hemorrhoid Treatment Services
N.A.I.C.S.: 622110
Drew A. Reid (Chm, Pres, CEO, CFO, Treas & Sec)
Charles Brofman (Gen Counsel & Dir)
Lino Fera (Dir)
Chen Xi Liao (Dir)

DMC GLOBAL INC.
11800 Ridge Pkwy Ste 300, Broomfield, CO 80021
Tel.: (303) 665-5700   DE
Web Site:
    https://www.dmcglobal.com
Year Founded: 1966
BOOM—(NASDAQ)
Rev.: $719,188,000
Assets: $884,495,000
Liabilities: $474,200,000
Net Worth: $410,295,000
Earnings: $26,259,000
Emp.: 1,800
Fiscal Year-end: 12/31/23
Clad Metal Plates Mfr for Heavy-Duty Industrial Uses
N.A.I.C.S.: 331110
Michael L. Kuta (Pres & CEO)
Michelle H. Shepston (Chief Legal Officer & Exec VP)
Eric Walter (CFO)
Brett Seger (Chief Acctg Officer)
Jeff Fithian (CIO)

Subsidiaries:
Arcadia Inc.   (1)
2301 East Vernon Ave, Vernon, CA 90058   (60%)
Tel.: (323) 771-9819
Web Site: http://www.arcadiainc.com
Aluminium Products Mfr
N.A.I.C.S.: 331318
Khan Chow (CFO)
Dan Spielberger (Gen Mgr)
Pat Homkaew (Mgr-Corp Credit)
Michael Teek (Mgr-Engrg)

DYNAenergetics GmbH & Co. KG   (1)
Kaiserstrasse 3, 53840, Troisdorf, Germany
Tel.: (49) 22411236700
Web Site: https://www.dynaenergetics.com
Sales Range: $50-74.9 Million
Emp.: 6
Explosives Mfr
N.A.I.C.S.: 325920

Nobelclad Europe GmbH & Co., KG   (1)
Graf-Zeppelin-Strasse 11, Liebenscheid, 56479, Rennerod, Germany
Tel.: (49) 2736509780
Web Site: http://www.nobelclad.com
Iron & Ferroalloy Whslr
N.A.I.C.S.: 423510

Perfoline   (1)
105 Yamskaya St, Tyumen, 625017, Russia
Tel.: (7) 3452434058
Web Site: http://www.dynaenergetics.com
Sales Range: $25-49.9 Million
Emp.: 22
Industrial Explosives Mfr
N.A.I.C.S.: 325920

DMK PHARMACEUTICALS CORPORATION
11682 El Camino Real Ste 300, San Diego, CA 92130
Tel.: (858) 997-2400   DE
Web Site:
    https://www.adamispharmaceuticals.com
Year Founded: 1989
DMK—(NASDAQ)
Rev.: $4,756,078
Assets: $10,930,840
Liabilities: $11,738,908
Net Worth: ($808,068)
Earnings: ($26,478,273)
Emp.: 11

Fiscal Year-end: 12/31/22
Biopharmaceutical Product Mfr
N.A.I.C.S.: 325412
David J. Marguglio (Pres & CEO)
Richard C. Williams (Chm)
David C. Benedicto (CFO)

Subsidiaries:
Adamis Corporation   (1)
11455 El Camino Real Ste 310, San Diego, CA 92130
Tel.: (858) 722-4242
Sales Range: $150-199.9 Million
Biopharmaceutical Developer
N.A.I.C.S.: 325412

U.S. Compounding, Inc.   (1)
1270 Don s Ln, Conway, AR 72032   (100%)
Tel.: (501) 327-1222
Web Site: http://www.uscompounding.com
Pharmaceutical Preparation Mfr
N.A.I.C.S.: 325412
Kristen Riddle (Pres & Dir-Clinical Svcs)

DMY SQUARED TECHNOLOGY GROUP, INC.
80 N Town Center Dr Ste 100, Las Vegas, NV 89144
Tel.: (702) 781-4313   MA
Web Site:
    https://www.dmysquared.com
Year Founded: 2022
DMYY—(NYSEAMEX)
Rev.: $4,716,849
Assets: $67,700,900
Liabilities: $72,779,918
Net Worth: ($5,079,018)
Earnings: $2,296,931
Fiscal Year-end: 12/31/23
Investment Management Service
N.A.I.C.S.: 523999

DNA BRANDS, INC.
3577 Powerline Rd, Oakland Park, FL 33309
Tel.: (561) 654-5722   CO
Web Site:
    https://www.dnabrandsinc.com
Year Founded: 2007
DNAX—(OTCIQ)
Rev.: $18,000
Assets: $49,000
Liabilities: $2,600,000
Net Worth: ($2,551,000)
Earnings: ($180,000)
Fiscal Year-end: 12/31/19
All Other Miscellaneous Food Manufacturing
N.A.I.C.S.: 311999

DNOW INC.
7402 N Eldridge Pkwy, Houston, TX 77041
Tel.: (281) 823-4700   DE
Web Site: https://www.dnow.com
Year Founded: 2013
DNOW—(NYSE)
Rev.: $2,136,000,000
Assets: $1,320,000,000
Liabilities: $476,000,000
Net Worth: $844,000,000
Earnings: $128,000,000
Emp.: 2,325
Fiscal Year-end: 12/31/22
Holding Company; Industrial Supplies Distr
N.A.I.C.S.: 551112
Toby Eoff (Pres-Process Solutions)
David A. Cherechinsky (Pres & CEO)
Mark B. Johnson (CFO & Sr VP)
Brad Wise (VP-Digital Strategy & IR)
Kelly Munson (Chief Admin & Information Officer)
Dan Pratt (Sr VP-Energy Centers)
Timm Bohnert (VP-Supply Chain)
Raymond Chang (Gen Counsel)
Clent Rawlinson (Sr VP)

Subsidiaries:
DNOW Australia Pty. Ltd.   (1)
49 Campbell Ave, Wacol, Brisbane, 4076, QLD, Australia
Tel.: (61) 737188500
Web Site: http://www.distributionnow.com
Industrial Supplies Distr
N.A.I.C.S.: 423840

DNOW Canada ULC   (1)
696 Cree Dr, Kamloops, V2H 1G7, BC, Canada
Tel.: (250) 372-5650
Web Site: https://www.dnow.com
Emp.: 100
Industrial Supplies Distr
N.A.I.C.S.: 423830

DNOW L.P.   (1)
7402 N Eldridge Pkwy, Houston, TX 77041
Tel.: (281) 823-4700
Web Site: https://www.dnow.com
Industrial Supplies Distr
N.A.I.C.S.: 423840
Merrill A. Miller Jr. (Chm)

DNOW de Mexico S de RL de CV   (1)
Edzna No 65, 24150, Ciudad del Carmen, Campeche, Mexico
Tel.: (52) 9383820851
Industrial Machinery & Equipment Whslr
N.A.I.C.S.: 423830
Pedro Lopez (Engr-Sls-Multiplex)

Distribution NOW FZE   (1)
S1700 Free Trading St Plot S61202 JAFZA South 6, PO Box 263176, Jebel Ali, Dubai, United Arab Emirates
Tel.: (971) 4 889 1200
Web Site: http://www.distributionnow.com
Industrial Valve Manufacturing
N.A.I.C.S.: 332911

Group KZ LLP   (1)
Govorov Street 50 Industrial Zone, 060005, Atyrau, Kazakhstan
Tel.: (7) 7122457055
Web Site: http://www.groupkz.com
Sales Range: $50-74.9 Million
Emp.: 56
Industrial Supplies Distr
N.A.I.C.S.: 423840

MacLean Electrical (Australia) Pty Ltd.   (1)
93 Inspiration Drive, PO Box 1032, Wangara, 6065, WA, Australia
Tel.: (61) 893032248
Web Site: https://www.maclean-electrical.com.au
Electrical & Electronic Appliance Whslr
N.A.I.C.S.: 423620
Joshua Fox (Project Mgr)
Shawn Taylor (Mgr-Sls-Natl)
Shijo Samuel (Mgr-Bus Dev)
Roy van Straaten (Mgr-Bus Dev)

MacLean Electrical Inc.   (1)
7402 N Eldridge Pkwy, Houston, TX 77041
Tel.: (281) 796-3711
Web Site: http://www.maclean-electrical.com
Electrical Contractor Services
N.A.I.C.S.: 238210

MacLean International Group Limited   (1)
Peterseat Park Peterseat Dr, Altens, Aberdeen, AB12 3HT, United Kingdom
Tel.: (44) 122 489 4212
Web Site: https://www.dnow.com
Electrical Equipment Distr
N.A.I.C.S.: 423610

NOW Distribution India Private Limited   (1)
Office No 509 Rupa Solitaire Bldg A1, Millennium Business Park Thane Belapur Highway Mahape, Navi Mumbai, 400710, Maharashtra, India
Tel.: (91) 2239243000
Web Site: http://www.indiamart.com
Emp.: 10
Surgical Appliance & Supplies Manufacturing
N.A.I.C.S.: 339113

NOW Netherlands B.V.   (1)

Gooiland 12, 1948 RC, Beverwijk, Netherlands
Tel.: (31) 251240504
Web Site: http://www.nnow.nl
Electronic Equipment Whslr
N.A.I.C.S.: 423620

NOW Norway AS   (1)
Dvergsnes Bakken 25, 4639, Kristiansand, Norway
Tel.: (47) 48298411
Emp.: 14
Construction Machinery & Equipment Mfr
N.A.I.C.S.: 333120

North Sea Cables Norge AS   (1)
Moseidveien 9, 4033, Stavanger, Norway
Tel.: (47) 51961660
Web Site: http://www.cables.no
Industrial Cable Distr
N.A.I.C.S.: 423510

Oaasis Group Limited   (1)
Merchants House Gapton Hall Road, Great Yarmouth, NR31 0NL, Norfolk, United Kingdom
Tel.: (44) 1493660690
Web Site: http://www.oaasisgroup.com
Safety Equipment Distr
N.A.I.C.S.: 423450

Odessa Pumps and Equipment Inc.   (1)
3209 N County Rd West, Odessa, TX 79764
Tel.: (432) 333-2817
Web Site: http://www.odessapumps.com
Industrial Machinery & Equipment Maintenance Services
N.A.I.C.S.: 811310

Power Service, Inc.   (1)
5625 Chapman Pl, Casper, WY 82604
Web Site: https://www.dnow.com
Industrial Machinery & Equipment Merchant Whslr
N.A.I.C.S.: 423830
Tony Cercy (Owner)
Jake Hagar (VP)

Power Transportation, LLC   (1)
4410 Wolf Creek Rd, Casper, WY 82604
Tel.: (307) 472-7782
General Trucking Services
N.A.I.C.S.: 484110
Nick Shaughnessy (Pres)

Whitco Supply, LLC   (1)
200 N Morgan Ave, Broussard, LA 70518
Tel.: (337) 837-2440
Web Site: http://www.whitcosupply.com
Rev.: $7,500,000
Emp.: 31
Valves, Pipes, Gaskets & Fittings Distr
N.A.I.C.S.: 332919
Tommy Kyle (Mgr)
Jeff White (Mgr)
Brent Berard (CFO)
Mark Navarre (Mgr)
Timmy Boudreaux (Mgr)

DNP SELECT INCOME FUND INC.
PO Box 32760, Louisville, KY 40232
Tel.: (312) 368-5510   MD
Web Site: http://www.dpimc.com
Year Founded: 1986
DNP—(NYSE)
Rev.: $126,924,178
Assets: $4,181,651,960
Liabilities: $1,022,717,848
Net Worth: $3,158,934,112
Earnings: $59,726,720
Emp.: 12
Fiscal Year-end: 10/31/19
Closed-End Investment Services
N.A.I.C.S.: 523999
David J. Vitale (Chm)
Connie M. Luecke (Chief Investment Officer, VP & Sr Portfolio Mgr)
Daniel J. Petrisko (Sr VP & Asst Sec)
Alan M. Meder (Treas & Asst Sec)
Dianna P. Wengler (VP & Asst Sec)
Kathleen L. Hegyi (Chief Compliance Officer)
Jennifer S. Fromm (Sec & VP)
Eileen A. Moran (Vice Chm)

Do It Again Corp.—(Continued)

DO IT AGAIN CORP.
1144 S Lewis Ave, Tulsa, OK 74104
Tel.: (918) 583-2955 — DE
Year Founded: 2021
DOITU—(NASDAQ)
Investment Services
N.A.I.C.S.: 523999
Clifford Hudson (Chm & CEO)
Kathy Taylor (Pres & Sec)
Scott McKinney (CFO & Treas)

DOCGO INC.
35 W 35th St, New York, NY 10001
Tel.: (212) 818-8800 — DE
Web Site: https://www.docgo.com
Year Founded: 2020
DCGO—(NASDAQ)
Rev.: $440,515,746
Assets: $393,277,628
Liabilities: $114,350,237
Net Worth: $278,927,391
Earnings: $34,584,498
Emp.: 2,064
Fiscal Year-end: 12/31/22
Investment Services
N.A.I.C.S.: 523999
James M. Travers (Chm)
Michael Burdiek (CEO)
Lee Bienstock (CEO)
Ely D. Tendler (Gen Counsel & Sec)

DOCUSIGN, INC.
221 Main St Ste 1550, San Francisco, CA 94105
Tel.: (415) 489-4940 — WA
Web Site: https://www.docusign.com
Year Founded: 2003
DOCU—(NASDAQ)
Rev.: $2,761,882,000
Assets: $2,971,290,000
Liabilities: $1,841,551,000
Net Worth: $1,129,739,000
Earnings: $73,980,000
Emp.: 6,840
Fiscal Year-end: 01/31/24
Software Development Services
N.A.I.C.S.: 541511
James P. Shaughnessy (Chief Legal Officer)
Lambert Walsh (Sr VP-Customer Success)
Joan Burke (Chief People Officer)
Steve Krause (Sr VP-Strategy & Product Mktg)
Blake J. Grayson (CFO)
Vivian Chow (Sr VP-Strategic Ops & Execution)
Emily Heath (Chief Trust & Security Officer)
Shanthi Iyer (CIO)
Annie Leschin (VP-IR)
Robert Chatwani (Co-Pres & Gen Mgr-Growth)
Paula Hansen (Co-Pres & Chief Revenue Officer)
Sagnik Nandy (CTO & Exec VP-Engrg)
Allan C. Thygesen (CEO)

Subsidiaries:

ARX Inc. (1)
855 Folsom St Ste 939, San Francisco, CA 94107
Tel.: (415) 839-8161
Web Site: http://www.arx.com
Digital Signature Solutions
N.A.I.C.S.: 513210

DocuSign Brasil Solucoes Em Tecnologia Ltda. (1)
Tower Bridge Corporate Avenida Jornalista Roberto Marinho 85 2 andar, Cj 21 Cidade Moncoes, Sao Paulo, 04576-010, Brazil
Tel.: (55) 1133301000
Web Site: https://www.docusign.com
Software Publishing Services

N.A.I.C.S.: 513210

DocuSign France SAS (1)
Immeuble Central Park 9-15 rue Maurice Mallet, 92130, Issy-les-Moulineaux, France
Tel.: (33) 173052950
Software Development Services
N.A.I.C.S.: 541511

DocuSign International (Asia-Pacific) Private Limited (1)
71 Robinson Road, Singapore, 068895, Singapore
Tel.: (65) 64071102
Software Development Services
N.A.I.C.S.: 541511

DocuSign UK Limited (1)
100 Liverpool St, London, EC2M 2RH, United Kingdom
Tel.: (44) 2037144800
Web Site: https://www.docusign.co.uk
Software Development Services
N.A.I.C.S.: 541511

Docusign Brasil Participacoes Ltda. (1)
Rua Gomes de Carvalho 1306 6 andar Cj, 61 Vila Olimpia, Sao Paulo, 04547-005, Brazil
Tel.: (55) 1133301000
Software Development Services
N.A.I.C.S.: 541511

Seal Software Inc. (1)
1990 N California Blvd Ste 500, Walnut Creek, CA 94596
Tel.: (650) 938-7325
Web Site: http://www.seal-software.com
Computer Software Services
N.A.I.C.S.: 541511

SpringCM Inc. (1)
180 N LaSalle St Fl 12, Chicago, IL 60601
Web Site: https://www.springcm.com
Software Development Services
N.A.I.C.S.: 541511

DOGWOOD STATE BANK
5401 Six Forks Rd Ste 100, Raleigh, NC 27609
Tel.: (919) 863-2293
Web Site:
https://www.dogwoodstatebank.com
Year Founded: 2017
DSBX—(OTCQX)
Emp.: 154
Banking Services
N.A.I.C.S.: 522110

DOLBY LABORATORIES, INC.
1275 Market St, San Francisco, CA 94103-1410
Tel.: (415) 558-0200 — DE
Web Site: https://www.dolby.com
Year Founded: 1965
DLB—(NYSE)
Rev.: $1,299,744,000
Assets: $2,979,766,000
Liabilities: $607,582,000
Net Worth: $2,372,184,000
Earnings: $200,656,000
Emp.: 2,246
Fiscal Year-end: 09/29/23
Sound Processing & Noise Reduction Technology Developer
N.A.I.C.S.: 326199
Kevin J. Yeaman (Pres & CEO)
Andy Sherman (Gen Counsel, Sec & Exec VP)
Doug Darrow (Sr VP-Cinema Bus Grp)
Linda Rogers (Chief People Officer & Sr VP)
Giles Baker (Sr VP-Consumer Entertainment)
Todd Pendleton (CMO & Sr VP)
Ryan Nicholson (Chief Acctg Officer, VP & Controller)
John Couling (Sr VP-Comml Partnerships)
Robert Park (CFO & Sr VP)
Ashley Schwenoha (Sr Mgr-IR)

Marie Huwe (Sr VP-Dolby.io)
Shriram Revankar (Sr VP)
Peter C. Gotcher (Chm)

Subsidiaries:

Dolby Australia Pty. Ltd. (1)
Level 3 35 Mitchell Street, McMahons Point, 2060, NSW, Australia
Tel.: (61) 291017900
Web Site: http://www.dolby.com
Audio Technology Services
N.A.I.C.S.: 334310

Dolby International AB (1)
Gavlegatan 12a, 113 30, Stockholm, Sweden
Tel.: (46) 84429160
Web Site: http://www.dolby.com
Audio & Video Equipment Mfr
N.A.I.C.S.: 334310

Dolby Laboratories Licensing Corporation (1)
Tel.: (415) 558-0200
Web Site: http://www.dolby.com
Property Rental & Leasing Services
N.A.I.C.S.: 533110

Doremi Labs, Inc. (1)
1020 Chestnut St, Burbank, CA 91506
Tel.: (818) 562-1101
Web Site: http://www.doremilabs.com
Sales Range: $10-24.9 Million
Emp.: 45
Digital Cinema Server Designer & Mfr
N.A.I.C.S.: 334310
Camille Rizko (Founder, Pres & CEO)
Brent Jones (CFO)
Safar Ghazal (Exec VP-Quality Assurance)
Adrian Arriaga (Supvr-Production-IMB)

DOLLAR GENERAL CORPORATION
100 Mission Rdg, Goodlettsville, TN 37072
Tel.: (615) 855-4000 — TN
Web Site:
https://www.dollargeneral.com
Year Founded: 1955
DG—(NYSE)
Rev.: $38,691,609,000
Assets: $30,795,591,000
Liabilities: $24,046,472,000
Net Worth: $6,749,119,000
Earnings: $1,661,274,000
Emp.: 185,800
Fiscal Year-end: 02/02/24
Department Store Retailer
N.A.I.C.S.: 455110
Kelly M. Dilts (CFO & Exec VP)
Anita C. Elliott (Chief Acctg Officer & Sr VP)
Todd J. Vasos (CEO)
Rhonda M. Taylor (Gen Counsel & Exec VP)
Carman R. Wenkoff (CIO & Exec VP)
Kathy Reardon (Chief People Officer & Exec VP)
Emily Taylor (Chief Mdsg Officer & Exec VP)
Sanja Krajnovic (Sr VP-Store Ops)
Tim Jagneaux (VP-Construction)
Rod West (Exec VP-Global Supply Chain)

Subsidiaries:

DC Financial, LLC (1)
100 Mission Rdg, Goodlettsville, TN 37072-2171
Tel.: (615) 855-4000
Financial Services
N.A.I.C.S.: 541611

DOLLAR TREE, INC.
500 Volvo Pkwy, Chesapeake, VA 23320
Tel.: (757) 321-5000 — VA
Web Site: https://www.dollartree.com
Year Founded: 1986
DLTR—(NASDAQ)
Rev.: $30,603,800,000

Assets: $22,023,500,000
Liabilities: $14,710,400,000
Net Worth: $7,313,100,000
Earnings: ($998,400,000)
Emp.: 211,826
Fiscal Year-end: 02/03/24
Department Store Retailer
N.A.I.C.S.: 551112
Jonathan B. Leiken (Chief Legal Officer, Sec & Exec VP)
Richard L. McNeely (Chief Mdsg Officer)
Aditya Maheshwari (Chief Acctg Officer & Sr VP)
Jeffrey A. Davis (CFO)
Rick Dreiling (Chm)
Randy Guiler (VP-IR)
Pedro Voyer (Chief Dev Officer)
Mike Kindy (Chief Supply Chain Officer)
Jennifer Silberman (Chief Sustainability Officer)
Emily Turner (CMO)
Robert A. LaFleur (Sr VP-IR)
Michael C. Creedon Jr. (Interim CEO)

Subsidiaries:

Dollar Tree Distribution, Inc. (1)
500 Volvo Pkwy, Chesapeake, VA 23320-1604
Tel.: (757) 321-5000
Web Site: http://www.dollartreeinfo.com
Sales Range: $150-199.9 Million
Emp.: 900
Distribution & Warehousing Services
N.A.I.C.S.: 493110
Bob Sasser (CEO)

Dollar Tree Management, Inc. (1)
500 Volvo Pkwy, Chesapeake, VA 23320
Tel.: (757) 321-5000
Web Site: http://www.dollartree.com
Sales Range: $75-99.9 Million
Emp.: 15
Management Services
N.A.I.C.S.: 541611
Bob Sasser (CEO)

Dollar Tree Stores, Inc. (1)
500 Volvo Pkwy, Chesapeake, VA 23320
Tel.: (757) 321-5000
Web Site: http://www.dollartree.com
Discount Variety Stores Services
N.A.I.C.S.: 455110
Bob Sasser (CEO)

Family Dollar Stores, Inc. (1)
10401 Monroe Rd, Matthews, NC 28105
Tel.: (704) 847-6961
Web Site: http://www.familydollar.com
Sales Range: $5-14.9 Billion
Holding Company; Discount Retail Stores Operator & Franchisor
N.A.I.C.S.: 551112
John Flanigan (Chief Supply Chain Officer)
Larry Gatta (Chief Mdsg Officer)

Subsidiary (Domestic):

Family Dollar, Inc. (2)
10401 Monroe Rd, Matthews, NC 28105
Tel.: (704) 814-5276
Web Site: https://www.familydollar.com
General Merchandise Store Operator
N.A.I.C.S.: 455219

Greenbrier International, Inc. (1)
500 Volvo Pkwy, Chesapeake, VA 23320-1604
Tel.: (757) 321-5000
Web Site: http://www.dollartree.com
Sales Range: $100-124.9 Million
Sourcing Services
N.A.I.C.S.: 561499

DOLPHIN ENTERTAINMENT, INC.
150 Alhambra Cir Ste 1200, Miami, FL 33134
Tel.: (305) 774-0407

Web Site:
https://dolphinentertainment.com
Year Founded: 1995
DLPN—(NASDAQ)
Rev.: $40,505,558
Assets: $75,376,832
Liabilities: $41,285,740
Net Worth: $34,091,092
Earnings: ($4,780,135)
Emp.: 244
Fiscal Year-end: 12/31/22
Other Services Related to Advertising
N.A.I.C.S.: 541890
William O'Dowd IV (Chm, Pres & CEO)
Nelson E. Famadas (Executives)
Mirta A. Negrini (CFO & COO)

Subsidiaries:

42West LLC   (1)
600 3rd Ave 23rd Fl, New York, NY 10016
Tel.: (212) 277-7555
Web Site: https://www.42west.net
Advertising, Entertainment, Public Relations, Strategic Planning/Research
N.A.I.C.S.: 541820
Allan Mayer (Co-CEO)
Leslee Dart (Co-CEO)

Division (Domestic):

B/HI Communications, Inc.   (2)
11500 W Olympic Blvd Ste 655, Los Angeles, CA 90064-1530
Tel.: (310) 473-4147
Web Site: http://www.bhimpact.com
Public Relations Agency
N.A.I.C.S.: 541820
Shawna Lynch (Co-Pres)
Dean Bender (Co-Pres)

Branch (Domestic):

Bender/Helper Impact, Inc.   (3)
150 W 30th St Ste 1201, New York, NY 10001
Tel.: (212) 689-6360
Web Site: http://www.bhimpact.com
Public Relations Agency
N.A.I.C.S.: 541820
Steve Solomon (Acct Supvr)

CLUB CONNECT LLC   (1)
2151 LeJeune Rd Ste 150, Coral Gables, FL 33134
Tel.: (903) 340-6071
Web Site: http://www.clubconnectkids.org
Educational Support Services
N.A.I.C.S.: 611710

HANK PRODUCTIONS LLC   (1)
3090 Penny Ln, Johns Island, SC 29455-8760
Tel.: (843) 442-4265
Motion Picture Production Services
N.A.I.C.S.: 512110

Viewpoint Computer Animation, Incorporated   (1)
55 Chapel St, Newton, MA 02458
Tel.: (617) 597-6667
Web Site:
https://www.viewpointcreative.com
Emp.: 28
Brands & Creative Solutions
N.A.I.C.S.: 541840

DOMA HOLDINGS, INC.
760 NW 107th Ave Ste 401, Miami, FL 33172
Tel.: (650) 419-3827   DE
Web Site: https://www.doma.com
DOMA—(NYSE)
Rev.: $440,181,000
Assets: $378,508,000
Liabilities: $296,716,000
Net Worth: $81,792,000
Earnings: ($302,209,000)
Emp.: 1,062
Fiscal Year-end: 12/31/22
Financial Investment Services
N.A.I.C.S.: 523999
Mike Smith (CFO)
Christopher Morrison (Chief Bus Officer)
Max Simkoff (Founder & CEO)

Subsidiaries:

States Title Holding, Inc.   (1)
101 Mission St Ste 740, San Francisco, CA 94105
Tel.: (650) 419-3827
Web Site: http://www.statestitle.com
Real Estate Solutions & Services
N.A.I.C.S.: 531390
Max Simkoff (CEO)
Noamad Ahmad (CFO)
Christopher Morrison (COO)
Mini Peiris (CMO)

Subsidiary (Domestic):

States Title, Inc.   (2)
1151 Mission St, San Francisco, CA 94103
Tel.: (650) 419-3827
Web Site: http://statestitle.com
Software Publisher; Activities Related to Mortgage Insurance & Lending
N.A.I.C.S.: 518210
Max Simkoff (Co-Founder & CEO)
Adrienne Harris (Gen Counsel & Chief Bus Dev Officer)
Christopher Morrison (COO)
Andy Mahdavi (Chief Data Science Officer)
Daniel Demetri (Co-Founder & Chief Product Officer)
Noaman Ahmad (CFO)
Kirk J. Wells (Gen Mgr-States Title Central)
Doug Aunkst (VP-Natl Operational Svcs-North American Title Co. Div)

Subsidiary (Domestic):

North American Title Group, LLC   (3)
760 Northwest 107th Ave Ste 401, Miami, FL 33172
Tel.: (305) 229-6500
Web Site: http://www.nat.com
Real Estate Transaction Services
N.A.I.C.S.: 531390

Subsidiary (Domestic):

North American Advantage Insurance Services, LLC   (4)
1707 Marketplace Blvd Ste 100, Irving, TX 75063
Tel.: (972) 759-1187
Web Site: http://www.naadvantage.com
Insurance Brokerage Services
N.A.I.C.S.: 524210
Emilio Fernandez (Founder & Pres)
J. Marie Drake (Mgr-Retention)
Brian Duke (Dir-Comml Lines)
Alyssa Thomas (Mgr-Natl Mktg)
Jorge Pacheco (Asst VP)
Josie Garcia Saenz (Mgr-Svc)
Ondrea Connolly (Mgr-Retail Ops)

North American Title Company   (4)
760 NW 107th Ave Ste 401, Miami, FL 33172
Tel.: (305) 485-2551
Web Site: https://www.doma.com
Sales Range: $200-249.9 Million
Emp.: 1,200
Title Insurance Services
N.A.I.C.S.: 524127
Mark J. Loterstein (Corp Counsel & VP)
Claudio D'Ugard (Dir-Tech)

Branch (Domestic):

North American Title Company (AZ)   (5)
3200 E Camelback Rd Ste 200, Phoenix, AZ 85018
Tel.: (602) 280-7500
Web Site: http://www.nat.com
Insurance Brokerage Services
N.A.I.C.S.: 524210

North American Title Company (MD)   (5)
1393 Progress Way Ste 911, Eldersburg, MD 21784
Tel.: (410) 760-9600
Web Site: http://www.nat.com
Insurance Brokerage Services
N.A.I.C.S.: 524127

North American Title Company (MN)   (5)
1720 Adams St Ste 300, Mankato, MN 56001
Tel.: (507) 385-0227

Web Site: http://www.nat.com
Emp.: 3
Real Estate & Title Insurance Services
N.A.I.C.S.: 531210
Douglas J. Christian (Chief Title Officer)
Alex A. Grundhoffer (Mng Dir)
Janean M. Winter (Branch Mgr)
Jenny Koenig (Officer-Escrow)
Thomas D. Christensen (VP)
Robyn Wacholz (Branch Mgr)
Connie Y. Hines (Branch Mgr)
Shane Ruths (Branch Mgr)
Timothy J. Lloyd (Branch Mgr)
Todd M. Anderson (VP)

North American Title Company (NV)   (5)
8485 W Sunset Ste 111, Las Vegas, NV 89113
Tel.: (702) 726-8000
Web Site: http://www.nat.com
Emp.: 18
Insurance Brokerage Services
N.A.I.C.S.: 531210
Jason McDonald (Sr VP & Mgr-San Francisco & San Mateo)

North American Title Company (TX)   (5)
8070 Park Ln Ste 200, Dallas, TX 75231
Tel.: (214) 720-1020
Web Site: http://www.nat.com
Real Estate & Title Insurance Services
N.A.I.C.S.: 531210
Pam Butler (VP & Mgr-Application Support Team)
Christopher Baca (Gen Counsel & Sr VP)
Blake Utley (CFO & Sr VP)

Subsidiary (Domestic):

North American Title Company of Colorado   (4)
12000 N Pecos St Ste 300, Westminster, CO 80234
Tel.: (303) 920-3677
Web Site: http://www.nat.com
Insurance Brokerage Services
N.A.I.C.S.: 524127
Duane Martin (VP & Mgr-Title Ops)
Natalie Koonce (Pres-Div)
Mickey Sanders (VP & Reg Dir-Education)
Felecia Burke (VP-Sls-Northern Colorado)
Neal Paul (VP-Comml, Builder & Transit Grp)
Michael A. Chagnon (VP & Mgr-Bus Dev)
Stevie Schaefer-Hill (Mgr-Bus Dev)
Joann Sandoval (Mgr-Bus Dev)

North American Title Company, Inc.   (4)
520 S El Camino Real Ste 150, San Mateo, CA 94402
Tel.: (650) 343-6282
Web Site: http://www.nat.com
Real Estate Title & Escrow Services
N.A.I.C.S.: 541191
Lisa Fitzpatrick (Officer-Escrow & Asst Branch Mgr)
Mona Bajalia (Officer-Escrow)
Donna Andersen (Officer-Escrow)
Katie Berggren (Officer-Escrow & Sr Mgr-Residential & Comml)
Jason McDonald (Sr VP & Mgr-San Francisco & San Mateo)

North American Title Insurance Company   (4)
1855 Gateway Blvd Ste 600, Concord, CA 94520
Tel.: (925) 935-5599
Web Site: http://www.natic.com
Real Estate Title Insurance Underwriting Services
N.A.I.C.S.: 524127
Emilio Fernandez (Pres)
Margery Q. Lee (Exec VP & Mgr-Claims & Litigation-Natl)
Michael Holden (VP & Mgr-Strategic Agency)
Sara DePhillips (VP & Dir-Ops)
Kelly McCarel (VP-Education & Content)
Rich Griffin (Sr VP-Agency)
Valerie Jahn-Grandin (Exec VP)
Shawn Neely (Mgr-Illinois State Agency)
Kathy Hulbert (Mgr-Agency-Indiana)
Claudio D'Ugard (VP & Dir-IT)
Adam Cotler (VP & Dir-Audit & Compliance Svcs)

Donna Anderson (Asst VP & Mgr-Agency Dev)
Tara Begg (Mgr-Agency-Ohio & Northeast Kentucky)
Veronica Brizuela (VP & Dir-Financial Reporting)
Pamalla Lanaux (Mgr-Agency Relationship)

DOMINION ENERGY, INC.
120 Tredegar St, Richmond, VA 23219
Tel.: (804) 771-3623   VA
Web Site:
https://www.dominionenergy.com
Year Founded: 1983
D—(NYSE)
Rev.: $14,393,000,000
Assets: $109,032,000,000
Liabilities: $81,503,000,000
Net Worth: $27,529,000,000
Earnings: $1,994,000,000
Emp.: 17,700
Fiscal Year-end: 12/31/23
Holding Company; Electric Power Generation, Distribution & Natural Gas Transmission Services
N.A.I.C.S.: 551112
Mark O. Webb (Chief Innovation Officer & Sr VP)
Diane Leopold (COO & Exec VP)
Carter M. Reid (Pres-Svcs, Sec & Exec VP)
Michele L. Cardiff (Chief Acctg Officer, Sr VP & Controller)
Robert M. Blue (Chm, Pres & CEO)
P. Rodney Blevins (Pres-South Carolina)
Mark D. Mitchell (Sr VP-Project Construction)
Carlos M. Brown (Chief Legal Officer, Sec & Exec VP)
William L. Murray (Sr VP-Corp Affairs & Comm)
Edward H. Baine (Pres-Virginia)
Corynne S. Arnett (Sr VP-Regulatory Affairs & Customer Experience)
Charlene J. Whitfield (Sr VP-Power Delivery-Virginia)
Steven D. Ridge (CFO & Exec VP)
Regina Elbert (Sr VP)
Cedric F. Green (Sr VP)
Keith Windle (Sr VP)

Subsidiaries:

Dominion Capital, Inc.   (1)
120 Tredegar St, Richmond, VA 23219
Tel.: (804) 819-2000
Financial Services
N.A.I.C.S.: 541611

Dominion Cove Point LNG LP   (1)
2100 Cove Point Rd, Lusby, MD 20657
Tel.: (410) 286-5100
Web Site: http://www.dom.com
Sales Range: $25-49.9 Million
Emp.: 120
Natural Gas Transmission
N.A.I.C.S.: 486210

Dominion East Ohio Energy   (1)
120 Tredegar St, Richmond, VA 23219
Tel.: (800) 362-7557
Web Site: http://www.dom.com
Sales Range: $1-4.9 Billion
Emp.: 1,700
Gas Utility
N.A.I.C.S.: 221210

Dominion Energy Brayton Point, LLC   (1)
1 Brayton Point Rd, Somerset, MA 02725
Tel.: (804) 787-5600
Web Site: http://www.dom.com
Emp.: 7,000
Management Consulting Services
N.A.I.C.S.: 541618

Dominion Energy Holdings, Inc.   (1)
120 Tredegar St, Richmond, VA 23219-4306
Tel.: (804) 819-2000
Web Site: http://www.dom.com

Dominion Energy, Inc.—(Continued)

Custom Printed Business Services
N.A.I.C.S.: 541890

**Dominion Energy Kewaunee,
Inc.** (1)
N490 Hwy 42, Kewaunee, WI 54216
Tel.: (920) 388-2560
Emp.: 24
Electric Power Distribution Services
N.A.I.C.S.: 221122

**Dominion Energy Midstream Part-
ners, LP** (1)
120 Tredegar St, Richmond, VA
23219 (100%)
Tel.: (804) 819-2000
Sales Range: $450-499.9 Million
Natural Gas
N.A.I.C.S.: 211130
Diane Leopold (Pres/CEO-Gas Infrastruc-
ture Grp & Exec VP)

Joint Venture (Domestic):

**Iroquois Gas Transmission System,
LP** (2)
1 Corporate Dr Ste 600, Shelton, CT
06484-6209
Tel.: (203) 925-7200
Web Site: http://www.iroquois.com
Sales Range: $25-49.9 Million
Emp.: 109
Natural Gas Pipelines
N.A.I.C.S.: 486210
Jeffrey A. Bruner (Pres)
Paul R. Amato (VP-Engrg, Ops & EH&S)
Scott E. Rupff (VP-Mktg, Dev & Comml
Ops)
Michelle Wieler (CFO & Sr Dir-Fin Svcs)

**Dominion Energy Questar
Corporation** (1)
333 S State St, Salt Lake City, UT 84145-
0433
Tel.: (801) 324-5900
Web Site: http://www.questar.com
Rev.: $1,134,900,000
Assets: $4,377,800,000
Liabilities: $3,062,700,000
Net Worth: $1,315,100,000
Earnings: $208,700,000
Emp.: 1,759
Fiscal Year-end: 12/31/2015
Holding Company
N.A.I.C.S.: 551112

Dominion Energy Solutions, Inc. (1)
PO Box 6090, Glen Allen, VA 23058-6090
Tel.: (888) 216-3718
Web Site:
http://www.dominionenergysolutions.com
Holding Company Services
N.A.I.C.S.: 551112

Dominion Energy, Inc. (1)
120 Tredegar St, Richmond, VA 23219-
4306
Tel.: (804) 819-2000
Web Site: http://www.dom.com
Sales Range: $5-14.9 Billion
Utility & Mechant Power Generation
N.A.I.C.S.: 221122

Subsidiary (Domestic):

**Dominion Generation
Corporation** (2)
PO Box 26532, Richmond, VA 23261-6532
Tel.: (804) 819-2205
Web Site: http://www.dominionenergy.com
Sales Range: $200-249.9 Million
Electric Power Distribution Services
N.A.I.C.S.: 221122

Dominion Transmission, Inc. (2)
445 W Main St, Clarksburg, WV
26301 (100%)
Tel.: (304) 627-3000
Web Site: http://www.dom.com
Sales Range: $250-299.9 Million
Emp.: 600
Natural Gas Storage Facilities & Related
Services, Involved in the Administration of
Appalachian Supply Contracts
N.A.I.C.S.: 221210

**Dominion Home Protection Services,
Inc.** (1)

120 Tredegar St, Richmond, VA 23219
Tel.: (866) 803-0132
Home Protection Services
N.A.I.C.S.: 561790

Dominion Hope Gas (1)
347 W Main St, Clarksburg, WV
26301-2947 (100%)
Tel.: (304) 623-8600
Sales Range: $400-449.9 Million
Emp.: 353
Gas Utility
N.A.I.C.S.: 221210

Dominion Investments, Inc. (1)
120 Tredegar St, Richmond, VA 23219-
4306
Tel.: (757) 321-7537
Electric Power Distribution Services
N.A.I.C.S.: 221122

**Dominion Kincaid Generation
L.L.C.** (1)
4 Mi W Kincaid Rte 104, Kincaid, IL
62540 (100%)
Tel.: (217) 237-4311
Web Site: http://www.dom.com
Sales Range: $100-124.9 Million
Emp.: 140
Power Generation
N.A.I.C.S.: 423610

**Dominion Nuclear Connecticut,
Inc.** (1)
Rope Ferry Rd Rr 156, Waterford, CT
06385
Tel.: (860) 447-1791
Electrical Installation Services
N.A.I.C.S.: 238210

**Dominion Privatization Florida,
LLC** (1)
120 Tredegar St, Richmond, VA 23219
Tel.: (757) 857-2851
Water & Sewer Line Construction Services
N.A.I.C.S.: 237110

**Dominion Privatization Texas,
LLC** (1)
120 Tredegar St, Richmond, VA 23219
Tel.: (757) 812-0935
Emp.: 99
Water & Sewer Line Construction Services
N.A.I.C.S.: 237110

**Dominion Technical Solutions,
Inc.** (1)
1 James River Plz 701 E Cary St, Rich-
mond, VA 23219
Tel.: (804) 771-4795
Web Site: http://www.dominion.com
Engineering, Procurement & Construction
Services
N.A.I.C.S.: 541330
Thomas F. Farrell II (Chm, Pres & CEO)

**Eastern Energy Gas Holdings,
LLC** (1)
6603 W Broad St, Richmond, VA 23230
Tel.: (804) 613-5100
Rev.: $2,059,000,000
Assets: $12,700,000,000
Liabilities: $5,172,000,000
Net Worth: $7,528,000,000
Earnings: $474,000,000
Emp.: 1,500
Fiscal Year-end: 12/31/2023
Holding Company
N.A.I.C.S.: 551112

Kincaid Generation, L.L.C. (1)
4 Miles W Kincaid Rte 104, Kincaid, IL
62540
Tel.: (217) 237-4311
Web Site: http://www.dom.com
Sales Range: $50-74.9 Million
Emp.: 142
Electric Power Distr
N.A.I.C.S.: 221122

Mulberry Farm, LLC (1)
50101 Governors Dr Ste 280, Chapel Hill,
NC 27517
Tel.: (919) 960-6015
Web Site: http://www.mulberryfarms.com
Electric Power Distribution Services
N.A.I.C.S.: 221122

Questar Energy Services, Inc. (1)
1210 D St, Rock Springs, WY 82902

Web Site: http://www.questarenergy.com
Energy Research & Development Services
N.A.I.C.S.: 926110

SCANA Corporation (1)
100 SCANA Pkwy, Cayce, SC 29033
Tel.: (803) 217-9000
Web Site: http://www.scana.com
Rev.: $4,052,000,000
Assets: $17,654,000,000
Liabilities: $6,357,000,000
Net Worth: $11,297,000,000
Earnings: ($528,000,000)
Emp.: 5,200
Fiscal Year-end: 12/31/2018
Electric, Natural Gas & Public Transporta-
tion Services
N.A.I.C.S.: 221111
Thomas F. Farrell II (Chm)
P. Rodney Blevins (Pres & CEO)
Michele L. Cardiff (Chief Acctg Officer, VP &
Controller)

Subsidiary (Domestic):

**Dominion Energy South Carolina,
Inc.** (2)
400 Otarre Pkwy, Cayce, SC
29033 (100%)
Tel.: (804) 819-2284
Web Site: https://www.dominionenergy.com
Rev.: $3,783,000,000
Assets: $15,749,000,000
Liabilities: $11,083,000,000
Net Worth: $4,666,000,000
Earnings: $503,000,000
Emp.: 2,300
Fiscal Year-end: 12/31/2022
Electric & Gas Generation, Transmission &
Distribution Services
N.A.I.C.S.: 221122
James R. Chapman (Treas & Exec VP)
Michele L. Cardiff (Chief Acctg Officer, Sr
VP & Controller)
Carter M. Reid (Pres)
Corynne S. Arnett (Sr VP)
Carlos M. Brown (Chief Legal Officer)
William L. Murray (Sr VP)
Steven D. Ridge (CFO)

**Public Service Company of North
Carolina, Incorporated** (2)
800 Gaston Rd, Gastonia, NC 28056-9486
Tel.: (704) 864-6731
Web Site: http://www.psncenergy.com
Natural Gas Extraction Services
N.A.I.C.S.: 211130

SCANA Energy (2)
3344 Peach Tree Rd Ste 2150, Atlanta, GA
30326 (100%)
Tel.: (803) 217-9000
Web Site: http://www.scanaenergy.com
Sales Range: $200-249.9 Million
Natural Gas Marketer
N.A.I.C.S.: 221210

**SCANA Energy Marketing Inc.
(SEMI)** (2)
2 Office Pk Ct Ste 103, Columbia, SC
29223 (100%)
Tel.: (803) 217-9000
Web Site:
http://www.scanaenergymarketing.com
Sales Range: $200-249.9 Million
Natural Gas Marketer & Distr
N.A.I.C.S.: 221210

ServiceCare, Inc. (2)
PO Box 7815, Columbia, SC 29202-7815
Tel.: (803) 217-4654
Web Site: http://www.servicecare.com
Sales Range: $1-9.9 Million
Emp.: 25
Heating & Air Conditioning Service Con-
tracts
N.A.I.C.S.: 811412

Sedona Corp. (1)
1003 W 9th Ave Second Fl, King of Prussia,
PA 19406
Tel.: (610) 337-8400
Web Site: http://www.sedonacorp.com
Financial Holding Company Services
N.A.I.C.S.: 551112
David R. Vey (Chm & CEO)
Timothy A. Rimlinger (Pres & CTO)
Kimberly M. Thomas (Exec VP & Dir-
Product Strategy)

Summit Farms Solar, LLC (1)
192 Raceway Dr, Mooresville, NC 28117
Tel.: (704) 662-0375
Other Electric Power Generation Services
N.A.I.C.S.: 221118

**Virginia Electric and Power
Company** (1)
120 Tredegar St, Richmond, VA
23219 (100%)
Tel.: (804) 819-2284
Web Site: https://www.dominionenergy.com
Rev.: $9,654,000,000
Assets: $53,194,000,000
Liabilities: $35,949,000,000
Net Worth: $17,245,000,000
Earnings: $1,215,000,000
Emp.: 8,600
Fiscal Year-end: 12/31/2022
Electric Power Distribution Services
N.A.I.C.S.: 221122
Michele L. Cardiff (Chief Acctg Officer, Sr
VP & Controller)

Subsidiary (Domestic):

Dominion Clearinghouse (2)
120 Tredegar St, Richmond, VA 23219
Tel.: (804) 819-2000
Sales Range: $200-249.9 Million
Emp.: 150
Electric Power & Natural Gas Production
N.A.I.C.S.: 221122

**Virginia Power Energy Marketing,
Inc.** (1)
120 Tredegar St, Richmond, VA 23219-
4306
Tel.: (804) 787-5600
Web Site: http://www.dom.com
Natural Gas Distribution Services
N.A.I.C.S.: 221210

DOMINION RESOURCES BLACK WARRIOR TRUST

2911 Turtle Creek Blvd, Dallas, TX
75219
Web Site: http://www.dom-
dominion.com
Year Founded: 1994
DOMR—(OTCIQ)
Investment Trust Management Ser-
vices
N.A.I.C.S.: 523940
Ron E. Hooper (Sr VP)

DOMINO'S PIZZA, INC.

30 Frank Lloyd Wright Dr, Ann Arbor,
MI 48105
Tel.: (734) 930-3030 MI
Web Site: https://ir.dominos.com
Year Founded: 1960
DPZ—(NYSE)
Rev.: $4,479,358,000
Assets: $1,674,899,000
Liabilities: $5,745,266,000
Net Worth: ($4,070,367,000)
Earnings: $519,118,000
Emp.: 6,500
Fiscal Year-end: 12/31/23
Food Products Distr
N.A.I.C.S.: 424420
David Allen Brandon (Chm)
Kevin S. Morris (Gen Counsel, Sec &
Exec VP)
Russell J. Weiner (CEO)
Lisa V. Price (Chief HR Officer &
Exec VP)
Sandeep Reddy (CFO & Exec VP)
Cynthia A. Headen (Exec VP-Supply
Chain Svcs)
Jessica L. Parrish (Chief Acctg Offi-
cer, Treas & VP)
Frank R. Garrido (Exec VP)
Kelly E. Garcia (CTO & Exec VP)
Joseph H. Jordan (Pres-U.S. &
Global Svcs)

Subsidiaries:

Domino's IP Holder LLC (1)
30 Frank Lloyd Wright Dr, Ann Arbor, MI
48106

Tel.: (734) 930-3030
Web Site: http://www.dominos.com
Sales Range: $10-24.9 Million
Emp.: 400
Business Services
N.A.I.C.S.: 561499

Domino's Pizza Distribution LLC **(1)**
40600 Ann Arbor Rd E Ste 201, Plymouth, MI 48170
Tel.: (866) 282-3872
Pizza Delivery Services
N.A.I.C.S.: 722513

Domino's Pizza International LLC **(1)**
716 Packard St, Ann Arbor, MI 48104
Tel.: (734) 769-4444
Web Site: http://www.dominos.com
Sales Range: $50-74.9 Million
Emp.: 450
Pizza Restaurant Operating & Franchising Services
N.A.I.C.S.: 722513

Domino's Pizza LLC **(1)**
30 Frank Lloyd Wright Dr, Ann Arbor, MI 48106
Tel.: (734) 930-3030
Web Site: http://www.dominos.com
Sales Range: $10-24.9 Million
Emp.: 50
Pizza Restaurant Operating & Franchising Services
N.A.I.C.S.: 722513

DOMINOVAS ENERGY CORPORATION
1170 Peachtree St 12th Fl, Atlanta, GA 30309
Tel.: (800) 679-1249   NV
Web Site:
      http://www.dominovasenergy.com
Year Founded: 2005
DNRG—(OTCIQ)
Emp.: 10
Fuel Cell Systems
N.A.I.C.S.: 335311
Neal Allen *(Chm, Pres & CEO)*
Michael Robinson Watkins *(COO)*
Emilio De Jesus *(Pres-Africa Div)*
Alejandro Contreras *(Mgr-Fin)*
Shamiul Islam *(Exec VP-Fuel Cell Ops)*

DOMO, INC.
802 E 1050 S, American Fork, UT 84003
Tel.: (801) 899-1000   DE
Web Site: https://www.domo.com
Year Founded: 2010
DOMO—(NASDAQ)
Rev.: $308,645,000
Assets: $242,116,000
Liabilities: $388,516,000
Net Worth: ($146,400,000)
Earnings: ($105,551,000)
Emp.: 967
Fiscal Year-end: 01/31/23
Business Intelligence & Software Development Services
N.A.I.C.S.: 513210
Joshua G. James *(Founder)*
Daren Thayne *(CTO & Exec VP-Engrg & Product)*
Chris Willis *(Chief Design Officer)*
John Mellor *(CEO)*
Mohammed Aaser *(Chief Data Officer)*
Carine S. Clark *(Chm)*
Jeff Skousen *(Pres & Chief Revenue Officer)*
Adam Landefeld *(Sr VP-Product)*
Gina Ventimiglia *(VP-Procurement)*
Alexis Coll *(Chief Legal Officer)*
Madison McCord *(VP-Human Resources)*
Ben Schein *(Sr VP-Product)*
Jim Kowalski *(Gen Mgr-Enterprise-North America)*

DONALDSON COMPANY, INC.
1400 W 94th St, Minneapolis, MN 55431
Tel.: (952) 887-3131   DE
Web Site: https://ir.donaldson.com
Year Founded: 1915
DCI—(NYSE)
Rev.: $3,586,300,000
Assets: $2,914,300,000
Liabilities: $1,425,200,000
Net Worth: $1,489,100,000
Earnings: $414,000,000
Emp.: 14,000
Fiscal Year-end: 07/31/24
Filtration Systems & Replacement Parts Mfr
N.A.I.C.S.: 333413
Tod E. Carpenter *(Chm & CEO)*
Wim J. V. Vermeersch *(VP-Europe, Middle East & Africa)*
Amy C. Becker *(Chief Legal Officer & Sec)*
Scott J. Robinson *(CFO & Sr VP)*
Todd Smith *(VP-Global IAF)*
Michael Wynblatt *(CTO & VP)*
David E. Wood *(VP-Life Sciences Bus Dev)*
Sheila G. Kramer *(Chief HR Officer & VP)*
Bart Driesen *(Pres)*
Tammylynne Jonas *(CIO)*
Angela Zurick *(VP)*
Andrew C. Dahlgren *(Pres-Mobile Solutions)*
Richard B. Lewis *(Pres-Life Sciences)*

Subsidiaries:

Advanced Filtration Systems, Inc. **(1)**
3206 Farber Dr, Champaign, IL 61822
Tel.: (217) 351-3073
Web Site: https://www.afsifilters.com
Sales Range: $75-99.9 Million
Emp.: 180
Manufactures & Markets Diesel Engine Filters; Joint Venture of Caterpillar, Inc. (50%) & Donaldson Company, Inc. (50%)
N.A.I.C.S.: 336390

Subsidiary (Non-US):

AFSI Europe s.r.o. **(2)**
Industrial zone Joseph 139, Havran, 434 01, Most, 1, Czech Republic
Tel.: (420) 476456411
Web Site: https://www.afsifilters.cz
Sales Range: $25-49.9 Million
Emp.: 150
Filters
N.A.I.C.S.: 333618
Michael Svitak *(Mng Dir)*

BOFA Americas Inc. **(1)**
303 S Madison St, Staunton, IL 62088
Tel.: (618) 205-5007
Filtration System & Replacement Parts Mfr
N.A.I.C.S.: 333413

BOFA International Ltd. **(1)**
19-20 Balena Close Creekmoor Industrial Estate, Poole, BH17 7DU, Dorset, United Kingdom
Tel.: (44) 1202699444
Filtration System & Replacement Parts Mfr
N.A.I.C.S.: 333413
Douglas Gray *(Sls Mgr-Intl)*

Donaldson (China) Trading Co., Ltd **(1)**
15/Floor Tower 1 New Richport Centre No 763 Mengzi Road, Shanghai, 200-023, China
Tel.: (86) 2123137000
Emp.: 100
Industrial Machinery Distr
N.A.I.C.S.: 423830
Rebecca Yang *(Mgr-Sls)*

Donaldson (Wuxi) Filters Co., Ltd. **(1)**
16 Xindu Road, Wuxi New District, Wuxi, 214028, Jiangsu, China
Tel.: (86) 51085282010
Web Site: https://www.donaldson.cn

Air Purification Products Mfr
N.A.I.C.S.: 333413

Donaldson Australasia Pty. Ltd. **(1)**
1 Lucca Road, PO Box 153, Wyong, 2259, NSW, Australia
Tel.: (61) 243502000
Web Site:
      http://www.donaldsonfilters.com.au
Air Filtration Units Mfr
N.A.I.C.S.: 333310

Donaldson Co., Inc. **(1)**
5200 Coye Dr, Stevens Point, WI 54481   **(100%)**
Tel.: (715) 341-5311
Web Site: http://www.donaldson.com
Sales Range: $150-199.9 Million
Emp.: 400
Air Cleaning Systems, Liquid Filters & Exhaust Products Mfr
N.A.I.C.S.: 336390

Donaldson Colombia S.A.S. **(1)**
Edificio Argos Torre 3 Oficina 204, Bogota, Colombia
Tel.: (57) 3108506380
Web Site:
      http://www.donaldsoncolombia.com.co
Factory Equipment Mfr
N.A.I.C.S.: 333248

Donaldson Europe, b.v.b.a. **(1)**
Research Park No 1303 Interleuvenlaan 1, 3001, Leuven, Belgium
Tel.: (32) 16383811
Sales Range: $50-74.9 Million
Emp.: 300
Holding Company; Regional Managing Office
N.A.I.C.S.: 551112

Subsidiary (Non-US):

Donaldson Filter Components Ltd. **(2)**
1 Oslo Rd, Hull, HU7 0YN, United Kingdom   **(100%)**
Tel.: (44) 482835213
Air Purification Products Mfr
N.A.I.C.S.: 333413

Donaldson Filtration (GB) Ltd. **(2)**
Humberstone Ln, Thurmaston, Leicester, LE4 8HP, United Kingdom
Tel.: (44) 162696161
Web Site: http://www.ultrafilter.com
Filter Mfr
N.A.I.C.S.: 333413

Donaldson Filtration Magyarorszag Kft. **(2)**
Zahony u 7, H-1031, Budapest, Hungary
Tel.: (36) 14532865
Emp.: 3
Air Purification Equipment Mfr
N.A.I.C.S.: 333413

Donaldson Filtration Norway a.s. **(2)**
Postbus 196, N-1501, Moss, Norway
Tel.: (47) 69215300
Filtration Systems & Replacement Parts Distr
N.A.I.C.S.: 333413

Donaldson Filtration Osterreich, GmbH **(2)**
Gutheil-Schoder-G 8-12, Vienna, 1100, Austria
Tel.: (43) 16165291
Emp.: 5
Industrial Supplies Whslr
N.A.I.C.S.: 423840

Donaldson Filtration Systems (Pty.) Ltd. **(2)**
4 Lake Road Longmeadow Business Estate EXT8, PO Box 149, Modderfontein, 1609, Gauteng, South Africa   **(100%)**
Tel.: (27) 119976000
Web Site: http://www.donaldson.co.za
Sales Range: $100-124.9 Million
Emp.: 250
Air Filtration Units Mfr
N.A.I.C.S.: 333310

Donaldson Filtros Iberica S.L. **(2)**
Avenida de Castilla 2 Edificio Dublin, Madrid, 28830, Spain
Tel.: (34) 916768668

Web Site: http://www.donaldson.com
Sales Range: $10-24.9 Million
Emp.: 5
Air Purification Products Mfr
N.A.I.C.S.: 333413

Subsidiary (Domestic):

Donaldson Iberica Soluciones en Filtracion, S.L. **(3)**
Colom 391 - 3A, Terassa, 08223, Barcelona, Spain
Tel.: (34) 937843834
Sales Range: $10-24.9 Million
Emp.: 35
Air Purification Products Mfr
N.A.I.C.S.: 333413

Subsidiary (Non-US):

Donaldson France, s.a.s. **(2)**
33 rue des Nations Roissy CDG, Ilot E Batiment C, 95958, Charles de Gaulle, Cedex, France
Tel.: (33) 149389930
Emp.: 20
Air Purification Equipment Mfr
N.A.I.C.S.: 333413

Subsidiary (Domestic):

Ultrafilter s.a.s. **(3)**
6 rue de la Croix Jacquebot, BP 80012, 95450, Vigny, France
Tel.: (33) 134486080
Web Site: http://www.donaldson.com
Sales Range: $25-49.9 Million
Emp.: 60
Air Purification Products Mfr
N.A.I.C.S.: 333413

Subsidiary (Non-US):

Donaldson GmbH **(2)**
Industriestrasse 11, 48249, Dulmen, Germany   **(100%)**
Tel.: (49) 25947810
Web Site: http://www.donaldson.com
Sales Range: $75-99.9 Million
Emp.: 190
Air Purification Products Mfr
N.A.I.C.S.: 333413

Subsidiary (Domestic):

Donaldson Filtration Deutschland GmbH **(3)**
Bussingstrasse 1, 42781, Haan, Germany
Tel.: (49) 21295690
Web Site: http://www.donaldson.com
Sales Range: $250-299.9 Million
Emp.: 250
Holding Company; Designer & Manufacturer of Components, Replacement Parts & Complete Systems for the Compressed Air Purification Industry
N.A.I.C.S.: 551112

Torit DCE GmbH **(3)**
Industriestrasse 11, D-48249, Dulmen, Germany   **(100%)**
Tel.: (49) 25947810
Web Site: http://www.donaldson.com
Sales Range: $25-49.9 Million
Emp.: 30
Air Purification Products Mfr
N.A.I.C.S.: 333413
Henk Houf *(Mng Dir)*

Subsidiary (Non-US):

Donaldson Nederland B.V. **(2)**
Transistorstraat 44 III, Postbus 212, 1322 CG, Almere, Netherlands
Tel.: (31) 365480840
Sales Range: $10-24.9 Million
Emp.: 10
Heater & Air Conditioner Whslr
N.A.I.C.S.: 423730

Donaldson Scandinavia a.p.s. **(2)**
Lyngso Alle 3A, DK - 2970, Horsholm, Denmark
Tel.: (45) 45570077
Web Site: https://www.emea.donaldson.com
Sales Range: $10-24.9 Million
Emp.: 8
Filtration Systems & Replacement Parts Mfr
N.A.I.C.S.: 333413

Donaldson Schweiz GmbH **(2)**

Donaldson Company, Inc.—(Continued)

Muhlebachstrasse 2, CH - 8008, Zurich, Switzerland
Tel.: (41) 443020715
Air Purification Equipment Mfr
N.A.I.C.S.: 333413

Subsidiary (Domestic):

Ultrafilter AG (3)
Leutschenbachstrasse 45, CH-8050, Zurich, Switzerland (100%)
Tel.: (41) 442246060
Web Site: http://www.ultrafilter.ch
Sterile, Stem & Ventilation Filter Mfr
N.A.I.C.S.: 333413

Subsidiary (Non-US):

Le Bozec Filtration et Systemes, s.a.s. (2)
2 Rue de la Pature, Carrieres Sur Seine Ile-de-France, 78420, Paris, France
Tel.: (33) 130866666
Air Purification Equipment Mfr
N.A.I.C.S.: 333413

Donaldson Far East Ltd. (1)
Suites 05-06 124 tower 6 Tsim Sha Tsui, 338 Castle Peak Road, Hong Kong, China (Hong Kong)
Tel.: (852) 24022830
Air Purification Equipment Mfr
N.A.I.C.S.: 333413

Donaldson Filtration (Asia Pacific) Pte. Ltd. (1)
3 Temasek Avenue 18-00 Centennial Tower, Districentre, Singapore, 039190, Singapore (100%)
Tel.: (65) 63117373
Sales Range: $125-149.9 Million
Air Purification Products Mfr
N.A.I.C.S.: 333413

Subsidiary (Non-US):

Donaldson Filtration Malaysia Sdn Bhd (2)
Unit 11-01 Level 11 Tower 2B UOA Business Park No 1, Jalan Pengaturcara U1/51A Section U1, 40150, Shah Alam, Selangor Darul Ehsan, Malaysia
Tel.: (60) 355681110
Web Site: https://www.donaldson.com.my
Sales Range: $25-49.9 Million
Emp.: 28
Industrial Supplies Mfr
N.A.I.C.S.: 333413

PT. Donaldson Filtration Indonesia (2)
South Quarter Tower B 16/F Unit E JI RA Kartini Kav 8, Cilandak Barat, Jakarta, 12430, Indonesia
Tel.: (62) 2122702462
Web Site: https://www.donaldson.com
Sales Range: $125-149.9 Million
Emp.: 25
Air Purification Products Mfr
N.A.I.C.S.: 333413

Donaldson Korea Co., Ltd. (1)
11th floor Office Building Hyundai Department Store Pangyo Branch 20, Pangyo Station-ro 146beongil Bundang-gu, Seongnam, 13529, Gyeonggi-do, Korea (South)
Tel.: (82) 8225197552
Web Site: https://www.donaldson.co.kr
Sales Range: $10-24.9 Million
Emp.: 50
Air Purification Products Mfr
N.A.I.C.S.: 333413

Donaldson S.A. de C.V. (1)
Av Japan 303 Industrial Park, Saint Francis of the Romo, 20300, Aguascalientes, Mexico (100%)
Tel.: (52) 4499106150
Filtration Systems & Replacement Parts Mfr
N.A.I.C.S.: 333310

ENV Services, Inc. (1)
2880 Bergey Rd, Hatfield, PA 19440 (100%)
Tel.: (215) 997-5080
Web Site: http://www.envservices.com
Sales Range: $900-999.9 Million
Calibration, Validation, HPV Decontamination of Clean Air Equipment

---

N.A.I.C.S.: 333310

Filtros Partmo S.A.S. (1)
Calle 1 No 3-15 Km 7 Via Palenque - Cafe Madrid Parque Industrial 2, 680011, Bucaramanga, Colombia
Tel.: (57) 6076443775
Web Site: https://partmo.com
Filter Mfr & Distr
N.A.I.C.S.: 336390

Hy-Pro Corporation (1)
6810 Layton Rd, Anderson, IN 46011
Tel.: (317) 849-3535
Web Site: http://www.hyprofiltration.com
Sales Range: $1-9.9 Million
All Other Miscellaneous General Purpose Machinery Mfr
N.A.I.C.S.: 333998

Nippon Donaldson Ltd. (1)
Tachikawa Nishikicho Bldg 3F 1-8-7 Nishikicho Tachikawa, Tokyo, 190-0022, Japan (100%)
Tel.: (81) 425404111
Web Site: http://www.donaldson.co.jp
Sales Range: $75-99.9 Million
Emp.: 330
Air Cleaning Equipment Mfr
N.A.I.C.S.: 333310

Northern Technical, L.L.C. (1)
107B8 Industrial City of Abu Dhabi, PO Box 46958, Abu Dhabi, United Arab Emirates
Tel.: (971) 25501200
Web Site: http://www.northern.ae
Air Filter Mfr & Distr
N.A.I.C.S.: 336390

P.T. Panata Jaya Mandiri (1)
Jl Raya Curug No 88 Desa Kadujaya, Bitung, Tangerang, 14440, Banten, Indonesia
Tel.: (62) 215980155
Web Site: http://www.asia.donaldson.com
Sales Range: $125-149.9 Million
Air Purification Products Mfr
N.A.I.C.S.: 333413

Rashed Al-Rashed & Sons-Donaldson Company Ltd. (1)
PO Box 550, Riyadh, 11421, Saudi Arabia
Tel.: (966) 012767676
Web Site: http://www.alrashed.com
Sales Range: $125-149.9 Million
Air Purification Products Mfr
N.A.I.C.S.: 333413

Western Filter Corporation (1)
26235 Technology Dr, Valencia, CA 91355
Tel.: (661) 295-0800
Web Site: http://www.westernfilter.com
Sales Range: $25-49.9 Million
Emp.: 140
Design, Manufacturer & Sale of Precision Fluid Control Components; Fluid & Airbag Filters; Valves & Control Component Systems; Ultraviolet Water & Air Purification Systems
N.A.I.C.S.: 333413

DONEGAL GROUP INC.

1195 River Rd, Marietta, PA 17547-0302 DE
Web Site:
https://www.donegalgroup.com
Year Founded: 1986
DGICA—(NASDAQ)
Rev.: $848,220,546
Assets: $2,243,349,335
Liabilities: $1,759,756,323
Net Worth: $483,593,012
Earnings: ($1,959,405)
Emp.: 876
Fiscal Year-end: 12/31/22
Other Insurance Funds
N.A.I.C.S.: 525190
Kevin Gerard Burke *(Chm, Pres & CEO)*
Noland R. Deas Jr. *(Sr VP)*
W. Daniel DeLamater *(COO & Exec VP)*
Kristi S. Altshuler *(Sr VP)*
Jeffery T. Hay *(Sr VP)*
Matthew T. Hudnall *(Sr VP)*
Robert R. Long Jr. *(Gen Counsel)*

David B. Bawel *(VP)*
Jason M. Crumbling *(VP)*
Karen L. Groff *(VP)*

Subsidiaries:

Donegal Insurance Group (1)
200 W Main St, Greenville, OH 45331-1483
Tel.: (937) 548-5111
Web Site: http://www.donegalgroup.com
Sales Range: Less than $1 Million
Emp.: 13
Property & Casualty Insurance Carrier
N.A.I.C.S.: 524210
Vince Black *(VP-Southeast Reg)*
William M. Anderson *(VP-Marietta Mktg Reg)*
Matthew Hudnall *(Sr VP-Comml Lines)*

Donegal Insurance Group (1)
360 Alps Rd, Athens, GA 30604 (100%)
Tel.: (770) 291-4580
Web Site: http://www.donegalgroup.com
Sales Range: $10-24.9 Million
Emp.: 20
Property & Casualty Insurance Carrier
N.A.I.C.S.: 524126

Donegal Mutual Insurance Company (1)
1195 River Rd, Marietta, PA 17547
Tel.: (717) 426-1931
Web Site: http://www.donegalgroup.com
Sales Range: $200-249.9 Million
Emp.: 400
Mutual Property & Casualty Insurance Carrier Providing Lines of Personal, Farm & Commercial Products
N.A.I.C.S.: 524126
Kevin Gerard Burke *(Pres & CEO)*
Noland R. Deas Jr. *(Sr VP-Field Ops & Natl Accts)*
Jay S. Martin *(VP-Information Security Officer)*

Subsidiary (Domestic):

Atlantic States Insurance Company (2)
1195 River Rd, Marietta, PA 17547-0302 (100%)
Tel.: (937) 548-5111
Web Site: http://www.donegal.com
Sales Range: $10-24.9 Million
Emp.: 20
Property & Casualty Insurance Services
N.A.I.C.S.: 524126

Atlantic States Insurance Company (2)
1195 River Rd, Marietta, PA 17547-0302 (100%)
Tel.: (937) 548-5111
Web Site: http://www.donegal.com
Sales Range: $10-24.9 Million
Emp.: 20
Property & Casualty Insurance Services
N.A.I.C.S.: 524126

Atlantic States Insurance Company (2)
1195 River Rd, Marietta, PA 17547-0302 (100%)
Tel.: (937) 548-5111
Web Site: http://www.donegal.com
Sales Range: $10-24.9 Million
Emp.: 20
Property & Casualty Insurance Services
N.A.I.C.S.: 524126

Atlantic States Insurance Company (2)
1195 River Rd, Marietta, PA 17547-0302 (100%)
Tel.: (937) 548-5111
Web Site: http://www.donegal.com
Sales Range: $10-24.9 Million
Emp.: 20
Property & Casualty Insurance Services
N.A.I.C.S.: 524126

Mountain States Insurance Company (2)
5051 Journal Ctr Blvd NE, Albuquerque, NM 87109
Tel.: (505) 764-1400
Web Site: https://www.donegalgroup.com
Casualty Insurance Carrier
N.A.I.C.S.: 524126

Stacey Scherer *(Gen Counsel)*

Le Mars Insurance Company (1)
1 Park Ln, Le Mars, IA 51031-1608
Tel.: (712) 546-7847
Web Site: http://www.lemm.com
Sales Range: $1-9.9 Million
Emp.: 55
Insurance Services
N.A.I.C.S.: 524210

Michigan Insurance Company (1)
1700 E Beltline NE Ste 100, Grand Rapids, MI 49525 (100%)
Web Site:
https://www.michiganinsurance.com
Personal & Commercial Insurance
N.A.I.C.S.: 524210

Peninsula Insurance Company (1)
112 E Market St, Salisbury, MD 21803
Tel.: (800) 492-1205
Web Site: http://www.donegalgroup.com
Sales Range: $25-49.9 Million
Emp.: 50
Insurance Services
N.A.I.C.S.: 524210

Subsidiary (Domestic):

Peninsula Indemnity Company (2)
112 E Market St, Salisbury, MD 21803-0108
Tel.: (410) 742-5132
Web Site:
http://www.peninsulainsurance.com
Emp.: 50
Personal & Commercial Insurance Products
N.A.I.C.S.: 524126

Sheboygan Falls Insurance Company (1)
511 Water St, Sheboygan Falls, WI 53085-0159 (100%)
Tel.: (920) 467-4613
Web Site: http://www.donegalgroup.com
Emp.: 25
Personal & Commercial Insurance
N.A.I.C.S.: 524210

Southern Insurance Company of Virginia (1)
801 Virginia Village Dr, Glen Allen, VA 23060-1279
Tel.: (804) 266-7012
Web Site: http://www.donegalgroup.com
Sales Range: $10-24.9 Million
Emp.: 25
Property & Casualty Insurance Carrier
N.A.I.C.S.: 524126

DONNELLEY FINANCIAL SOLUTIONS, INC.

35 W Wacker Dr, Chicago, IL 60601
Tel.: (203) 047-6100 DE
Web Site:
https://www.dfinsolutions.com
Year Founded: 1983
DFIN—(NYSE)
Rev.: $833,600,000
Assets: $828,300,000
Liabilities: $498,800,000
Net Worth: $329,500,000
Earnings: $102,500,000
Emp.: 2,150
Fiscal Year-end: 12/31/22
Holding Company; Financial Communications, Data & Analytics Software & Services
N.A.I.C.S.: 551112
Daniel N. Leib *(Pres & CEO)*
David A. Gardella *(CFO)*
Kami S. Turner *(Chief Acctg Officer, Sr VP & Controller)*
Craig Clay *(Pres-Capital Markets-Global)*
Eric Johnson *(Pres-Investment Companies-Global)*
Floyd Strimling *(Chief Product Officer)*
Kirk Williams *(Chief HR Officer)*
Eric Foster *(CIO)*
Leah Trzcinski *(Chief Legal & Compliance Officer & Sec)*
Andrea Aktan *(VP)*

Marcel Defreitas *(Sr VP)*
Bryan Garabo *(Sr VP)*
Jolecia Marigny *(VP)*
Kathleen Shelton *(Sr VP)*
Dennis Siglin *(VP)*
Euphemia Arbizzani *(Sr VP)*
Dawnet Beverley *(Exec VP)*
David Birch *(VP)*
Jeffrey Catt *(Sr VP)*
Ned Gannon *(Sr VP)*
Bridget Hughes *(VP)*
Mahesh Bommireddy *(Dir)*
Dannie Combs *(Chief Information Security Officer)*
Aravinda Kilaru *(VP)*
Chad Kohl *(VP)*
Katherine Rice *(VP)*
Desi Sendaydiego *(VP)*
LaTonya Caldwell *(Dir)*
Michael King *(Sr VP)*
Stephen Schnaufer *(VP)*
Timothy Hargesheimer *(VP)*
Ted Hershey *(Sr VP)*
Noah Rogers *(Sr VP)*
Robert Wilson *(Sr VP)*
Amy Braun *(VP)*

Subsidiaries:

Donnelley Financial Solutions
Canada Corporation   (1)
220 Bay St Ste 200, Toronto, M5J 2W4,
ON, Canada
Tel.: (416) 383-4545
Financial Management Services
N.A.I.C.S.: 551112

Donnelley Financial Solutions UK
Limited   (1)
55 Ludgate Hill, London, EC4M 7JW,
United Kingdom
Tel.: (44) 2030476100
Financial Management Services
N.A.I.C.S.: 551112

Donnelley Financial, LLC   (1)
35 W Wacker Dr, Chicago, IL 60601
Tel.: (312) 326-8000
Web Site: http://www.dfinsolutions.com
Financial Communications, Data & Analytics
Software & Services
N.A.I.C.S.: 561499

Subsidiary (Domestic):

EDGAR Online   (2)
300 Vesey St, New York, NY 10282
Tel.: (212) 896-4428
Web Site: https://www.edgar-online.com
Online Financial & Business Information
Services
N.A.I.C.S.: 518210

Donnelley Translation Services
(Shanghai) Co., Ltd.   (1)
Unit 2356 Level 23 China World Tower B 1
Jianguomenwai Ave, Chaoyang District,
Beijing, 100004, China
Tel.: (86) 1085098532
Financial Services
N.A.I.C.S.: 541611

eBrevia, Inc.   (1)
55 Water St 11th Fl, New York, NY 10041
Tel.: (203) 870-3000
Web Site: http://www.ebrevia.com
Computer Software Development Services
N.A.I.C.S.: 541511
Ned Gannon *(Co-Founder & Pres)*
Adam Nguyen *(Co-Founder & Sr VP)*
Jacob Mundt *(CTO)*

DOORDASH, INC.

303 2nd St S Tower 8th Fl, San Francisco, CA 94107
Tel.: (650) 487-3970   DE
Web Site: https://www.doordash.com
Year Founded: 2013
DASH—(NASDAQ)
Rev.: $8,635,000,000
Assets: $10,839,000,000
Liabilities: $4,033,000,000
Net Worth: $6,806,000,000
Earnings: ($558,000,000)

Emp.: 19,300
Fiscal Year-end: 12/31/23
Online Food Delivery Services
N.A.I.C.S.: 492210
Prabir Adarkar *(Pres & COO)*
Keith Yandell *(Chief Bus Officer)*
Kofi Amoo-Gottfried *(CMO)*
Tia Sherringham *(Gen Counsel, Sec, VP & Head-Legal)*
Ravi Inukonda *(CFO)*
Tom Pickett *(Chief Revenue Officer)*
Tony Xu *(Co-Founder, Chm & CEO)*
Stanley Tang *(Co-Founder & Head-Labs)*
Andy Fang *(Co-Founder)*

DORCHESTER MINERALS, L.P.

3838 Oak Lawn Ave Ste 300, Dallas,
TX 75219-4541
Tel.: (214) 559-0300   DE
Web Site: https://www.dmlp.net
Year Founded: 1982
DMLP—(NASDAQ)
Rev.: $163,799,000
Assets: $191,065,000
Liabilities: $5,508,000
Net Worth: $185,557,000
Earnings: $114,117,000
Emp.: 27
Fiscal Year-end: 12/31/23
Oil & Gas Exploration Services
N.A.I.C.S.: 211120
James E. Raley *(Vice Chm)*
Robert C. Vaughn *(Founder)*
Bradley J. Ehrman *(CEO)*
Leslie A. Moriyama *(CFO)*

Subsidiaries:

Maecenas Minerals LLP   (1)
3838 Oak Lawn Ave ste300, Dallas, TX
75219
Tel.: (214) 559-0300
Sales Range: $50-74.9 Million
Crude Petroleum & Natural Gas Extraction
Services
N.A.I.C.S.: 211120

DORIAN LPG LTD.

27 Signal Rd, Stamford, CT 06902
Tel.: (203) 674-9900   MH
Web Site: https://www.dorianlpg.com
LPG—(NYSE)
Rev.: $274,221,448
Assets: $1,607,362,093
Liabilities: $687,210,678
Net Worth: $920,151,415
Earnings: $71,935,018
Emp.: 541
Fiscal Year-end: 03/31/22
Deep Sea Freight Transportation
N.A.I.C.S.: 483111
John C. Hadjipateras *(Chm, Pres & CEO)*
John C. Lycouris *(Head-Energy Transition)*
Theodore B. Young *(CFO, Principal Acctg Officer & Treas)*
Tim T. Hansen *(Chief Comml Officer)*
Alexander C. Hadjipateras *(COO & Exec VP-Bus Dev)*

Subsidiaries:

Dorian LPG (DK) ApS   (1)
Overgaden Oven Vandet 62A 3rd Floor,
1415, Copenhagen, Denmark
Tel.: (45) 69159012
Web Site: https://www.dorianlpg.com
Deep Sea Freight Transportation Services
N.A.I.C.S.: 483111

DORMAN PRODUCTS, INC.

3400 E Walnut St, Colmar, PA 18915
Tel.: (215) 997-1800   PA
Web Site:
   https://www.dormanproducts.com
Year Founded: 1978

DORM—(NASDAQ)
Rev.: $1,345,249,000
Assets: $1,673,119,000
Liabilities: $740,383,000
Net Worth: $932,736,000
Earnings: $131,532,000
Emp.: 3,360
Fiscal Year-end: 12/25/21
Aftermarket Auto Parts Distr
N.A.I.C.S.: 336390
Kevin M. Olsen *(Pres & CEO)*
Joseph P. Braun *(Gen Counsel, Sec & Sr VP)*
Michael P. Dickerson *(VP)*
Eric B. Luftig *(Sr VP-Product)*
Brian Borradaile *(Sr VP)*
Paul E. Anderson *(Co-Pres)*
David M. Hession *(CFO, Principal Acctg Officer, Treas & Sr VP)*
Donna M. Long *(CIO & Sr VP)*
Jeffrey L. Darby *(Sr VP-Sls & Mktg)*
Scott D. Leff *(Chief HR Officer & Sr VP)*

Subsidiaries:

Dayton Parts, LLC   (1)
1300 Cameron St, Harrisburg, PA 17103
Tel.: (717) 255-8518
Web Site: https://www.daytonparts.com
Steel & Wire Spring Mfr
N.A.I.C.S.: 332613
Pamela Kreamer *(Mgr-Purchasing)*
Paul Anderson *(Pres & CEO)*

DOUBLEVERIFY HOLDINGS, INC.

462 Broadway, New York, NY 10013
Tel.: (212) 631-2111   DE
Web Site: https://ir.doubleverify.com
Year Founded: 2017
DV—(NYSE)
Rev.: $572,543,000
Assets: $1,243,031,000
Liabilities: $169,092,000
Net Worth: $1,073,939,000
Earnings: $71,466,000
Emp.: 1,101
Fiscal Year-end: 12/31/23
Holding Company
N.A.I.C.S.: 551112
Mark S. Zagorski *(CEO)*
Nicola Allais *(CFO)*
Andy Grimmig *(Chief Legal Officer)*
Julie Eddleman *(Chief Comml Officer)*
R. Davis Noell *(Chm)*
Rose Velez-Smith *(Chief HR Officer & Exec VP)*
Steven Woolway *(Exec VP-Bus Dev)*
Mimi Wotring *(Sr VP-Publr Sls & Client Svcs)*

DOUGLAS DYNAMICS, INC.

11270 W Park Pl Ste 300, Milwaukee, WI 53224
Tel.: (414) 354-2310   DE
Web Site:
   https://www.douglasdynamics.com
PLOW—(NYSE)
Rev.: $616,068,000
Assets: $596,891,000
Liabilities: $359,789,000
Net Worth: $237,102,000
Earnings: $38,609,000
Emp.: 1,813
Fiscal Year-end: 12/31/22
Snow & Ice Control Equipment Mfr & Sales
N.A.I.C.S.: 336390
James L. Janik *(Interim Pres & Interim CEO)*
Sarah C. Lauber *(CFO, Sec-Milwaukee & Exec VP)*
Mark Van Genderen *(COO & Pres-Work Truck Attachments)*

Subsidiaries:

Dejana Truck & Utility Equipment Co.,
Inc.   (1)

490 Pulaski Rd, Kings Park, NY
11754   **(100%)**
Tel.: (631) 967-5399
Web Site: https://www.dejana.com
Sales Range: $1-9.9 Million
Emp.: 45
Light Truck & Utility Vehicle Mfr
N.A.I.C.S.: 336110
Rich Idtensohn *(Dir-Marketing)*
Greg Markert *(Mgr-Business Development-Utility Equipment)*

Douglas Dynamics Finance
Company   (1)
7777 N 73rd St, Milwaukee, WI 53233
Tel.: (414) 354-2310
Web Site: http://www.douglasdynamics.com
Construction Machinery Mfr
N.A.I.C.S.: 333120

Fisher, LLC   (1)
50 Gordon Dr, Rockland, ME 04841-2139
Tel.: (207) 701-4200
Web Site: http://www.fisherplows.com
Sales Range: $50-74.9 Million
Emp.: 250
Construction Machinery Mfr & Distr
N.A.I.C.S.: 333120

Henderson Products, Inc.   (1)
1085 S 3rd St, Manchester, IA 52057
Tel.: (563) 927-2828
Web Site:
   http://www.hendersonproducts.com
Emp.: 250
Holding Company; Heavy-Duty Truck Snow
Removal & Ice Control Equipment Mfr
N.A.I.C.S.: 551112

Trynex, Inc.   (1)
531 Ajax Dr, Madison Heights, MI 48071
Tel.: (248) 414-2026
Sales Range: $1-9.9 Million
Emp.: 15
Snow Removal, Turf Maintenance &
Sweeping Solutions
N.A.I.C.S.: 541990

DOUGLAS ELLIMAN INC.

575 Madison Ave, New York, NY
10022
Tel.: (305) 579-8000   DE
Web Site: https://www.elliman.com
Year Founded: 2021
DOUG—(NYSE)
Rev.: $1,153,177,000
Assets: $550,402,000
Liabilities: $279,945,000
Net Worth: $270,457,000
Earnings: ($6,399,000)
Emp.: 957
Fiscal Year-end: 12/31/22
Real Estate Investment Services
N.A.I.C.S.: 531190
Howard M. Lorber *(Chm, Pres & CEO)*
J. Bryant Kirkland III *(CFO & Sr VP)*
J. David Ballard *(CTO, Gen Counsel, Sec & Sr VP)*
Richard J. Lampen *(COO & Exec VP)*
Susan de France *(CEO-DE Dev Mktg)*
Stephen T. Larkin *(Chief Comm Officer & Exec VP-Communications)*
Connie Mui-Reilly *(CIO & Exec VP)*
Stephanie Garbarini *(CMO & Exec VP)*
Lisa Seligman *(Sr VP-Human Resources)*
Jeffrey Scott Stanton *(Sr VP-Learning & Development)*
Christine Haney *(Sr VP-Global Relocation & Referral Svcs)*
Daniel A. Sachar *(VP-Innovation)*
Israel Abitbol *(Treas, VP & Dir-Finance)*
Deborah A. Fasanelli *(VP-Finance)*
Fredrick W. Schmid III *(VP & Controller)*

DOUGLAS EMMETT, INC.

Douglas Emmett, Inc.—(Continued)

1299 Ocean Ave Ste 1000, Santa
Monica, CA 90401
Tel.: (310) 255-7700   **MD**
Web Site:
   https://www.douglasemmett.com
Year Founded: 1971
DEI—(NYSE)
Rev.: $829,945,000
Assets: $9,644,218,000
Liabilities: $5,798,821,000
Net Worth: $3,845,397,000
Earnings: ($42,706,000)
Emp.: 750
Fiscal Year-end: 12/31/23
Self-Administered & Self-Managed
Real Estate Investment Trust
N.A.I.C.S.: 525990
Jordan L. Kaplan *(Pres & CEO)*
Kenneth M. Panzer *(COO)*
Kevin Andrew Crummy *(Chief Invest-ment Officer)*
Stuart McElhinney *(VP-IR)*
Daniel A. Emmett *(Founder & Chm)*
Peter D. Seymour *(CFO)*

Subsidiaries:

DE 100 Wilshire, LLC
100 Wilshire Blvd, Santa Monica, CA 90401
Tel.: (310) 255-7777
Real Estate Investment Trust Services
N.A.I.C.S.: 525990

DE 8484 Wilshire, LLC   **(1)**
8484 Wilshire Blvd, Beverly Hills, CA 90211
Tel.: (310) 255-7777
Real Estate Investment Trust Services
N.A.I.C.S.: 525990

DE Park Avenue 10880, LLC   **(1)**
10880 Wilshire Blvd Ste 1, Los Angeles, CA 90024
Tel.: (310) 441-1763
Real Estate Property Management Services
N.A.I.C.S.: 531120

DE Park Avenue 10960, LLC   **(1)**
10960 Wilshire Blvd, Los Angeles, CA 90024
Tel.: (818) 321-6546
Real Estate Property Management Services
N.A.I.C.S.: 531120

DEG, LLC   **(1)**
1132 Bishop St Ste 1404, Honolulu, HI 96813
Tel.: (808) 599-5009
Emp.: 3
Real Estate Investment Services
N.A.I.C.S.: 531390

Douglas Emmett 1998, LLC   **(1)**
1299 Ocean Ave, Santa Monica, CA 90401
Tel.: (310) 255-7777
Web Site: http://www.douglasemmett.com
Sales Range: $25-49.9 Million
Emp.: 20
Property Development & Management Services
N.A.I.C.S.: 531110

Douglas Emmett Builders   **(1)**
808 Wilshire Blvd 1st Fl, Santa Monica, CA 90401
Tel.: (310) 255-7800
Web Site: http://www.douglasemmett.com
Sales Range: $150-199.9 Million
Building Construction Services
N.A.I.C.S.: 236220
Jordan L. Kaplan *(Pres & CEO)*

Douglas Emmett Management Hawaii, LLC   **(1)**
55 Merchant St C100, Honolulu, HI 96819
Tel.: (808) 541-4380
Property Development & Management Services
N.A.I.C.S.: 531110

Douglas Emmett Management, Inc.   **(1)**
808 Wilshire Blvd 2nd Fl, Santa Monica, CA 90401
Tel.: (310) 255-7700
Web Site: http://www.douglasemmett.com

Sales Range: $25-49.9 Million
Emp.: 100
Management Services
N.A.I.C.S.: 541611
Jordan L. Kaplan *(Pres & CEO)*

Douglas Emmett Management, LLC   **(1)**
9601 Wilshire Blvd, Beverly Hills, CA 90201
Tel.: (310) 255-7777
Web Site: http://www.douglasemmett.com
Sales Range: $25-49.9 Million
Emp.: 12
Property Development & Management Services
N.A.I.C.S.: 531110

Douglas Emmett Realty Fund, LLC   **(1)**
15821 Ventura Blvd, Encino, CA 91436
Tel.: (818) 990-8410
Real Estate Management Services
N.A.I.C.S.: 531390

HNLC, Inc.   **(1)**
932 Ward Ave 7th Fl, Honolulu, HI 96814
Tel.: (808) 585-9626
Web Site: http://www.HoClub.com
Sales Range: $650-699.9 Million
Real Estate Investment Services
N.A.I.C.S.: 531390

DOVER CORPORATION
3005 Highland Pkwy, Downers
Grove, IL 60515
Tel.: (630) 541-1540   **DE**
Web Site:
   https://www.dovercorporation.com
Year Founded: 1941
DOV—(NYSE)
Rev.: $8,438,134,000
Assets: $11,348,513,000
Liabilities: $6,241,908,000
Net Worth: $5,106,605,000
Earnings: $1,056,828,000
Emp.: 25,000
Fiscal Year-end: 12/31/23
Holding Company; Diversified Industrial, Production & Servicing Equipment Mfr
N.A.I.C.S.: 551112
Brad M. Cerepak *(CFO & Sr VP)*
Ivonne M. Cabrera *(Gen Counsel, Sec & Sr VP)*
James M. Moran *(Treas & VP)*
Richard Joseph Tobin *(Chm, Pres & CEO)*
Girish Juneja *(Chief Digital Officer & Sr VP)*
Anthony K. Kosinski *(VP-Tax)*
Andrey Galiuk *(VP-Corp Dev & IR)*
Jack Dickens *(Sr Dir-IR)*
Adrian Sakowicz *(VP-Comm)*

Subsidiaries:

Accelerated Artificial Lift Systems, LLC   **(1)**
4441 E 146th St N, Skiatook, OK 74070
Tel.: (855) 396-2356
Web Site: http://www.dynafloals.com
Electrical Submersible Pumping System Mfr
N.A.I.C.S.: 238220
Matt Gipson *(Pres)*

Accelerated Companies, LLC   **(1)**
2002 Timberloch Pl Ste 500, The Woodlands, TX 77380-1350
Tel.: (918) 396-0558
Emp.: 4
Electrical Submersible Pumping System Mfr
N.A.I.C.S.: 238220

Accelerated Production Systems Limited   **(1)**
Unit 9C Webb Ellis Business Park, Rugby, CV21 2NP, Warwickshire, United Kingdom
Tel.: (44) 1788568086
Web Site: http://www.aplsystems.com
Emp.: 12
Lift Equipemt Mfr
N.A.I.C.S.: 333998

Accelerated Production Systems, Inc.   **(1)**

2445 Technology Forest Blvd Bldg 4 12th
Fl, The Woodlands, TX 77381
Tel.: (281) 403-5772
Web Site: http://www.accelerateddps.com
Emp.: 500
Oil & Gas Field Services
N.A.I.C.S.: 213112

Acme Cryogenics Inc.   **(1)**
2801 Mitchell Ave, Allentown, PA 18103-7111
Tel.: (610) 791-7909
Web Site: https://www.acmecryo.com
Gas & Liquid Handling Equipment Mfr
N.A.I.C.S.: 333248
David Fritz *(Pres & CEO)*

Advansor A/S   **(1)**
Rosbjergvej 7A, 8220, Brabrand, Denmark
Tel.: (45) 70250030
Emp.: 220
Thermal System Mfr
N.A.I.C.S.: 334513

Alfred Fueling Systems Inc.   **(1)**
3814 Jarrett Way, Austin, TX 78728
Tel.: (512) 388-8311
Pipe Testing & Oil Field Services
N.A.I.C.S.: 213112

Anthony Equity Holdings, Inc.   **(1)**
65 E 55th St 18th Fl, New York, NY 10022
Tel.: (212) 593-6958
Holding Company Operator
N.A.I.C.S.: 551114

Anthony Mexico Holdings S. DE R.L.
DE C.V.   **(1)**
Forest Of Plums No 180 Int-101, Federal
District, Mexico, 11700, Mexico
Tel.: (52) 5522821000
Holding Company
N.A.I.C.S.: 551114

Anthony Refresh Group, LLC   **(1)**
812 Athens Rd, Crawford, GA 30630
Tel.: (706) 743-3352
Glass Products Mfr
N.A.I.C.S.: 327215

Anthony Specialty Glass LLC   **(1)**
1101 Sovis Rd, Madison, GA 30650
Tel.: (706) 342-9300
Emp.: 4
Building Materials Whslr
N.A.I.C.S.: 444180
David Burbach *(Gen Mgr)*

Anthony Technical Glass (Shanghai)
Co. Ltd   **(1)**
No 28 Lane 928 Zhennan Rd, Shanghai, 200331, China
Tel.: (86) 2162848855
Glass Products Mfr
N.A.I.C.S.: 327215

AvaLAN Wireless Systems, Inc.   **(1)**
125A Castle Dr, Madison, AL 35758
Tel.: (650) 384-0000
Web Site: http://www.avalanwireless.com
Electrical Equipment & Component Mfr
N.A.I.C.S.: 335999
Mike Derby *(Founder & CTO)*

BELVAC CR, spol s.r.o.   **(1)**
Tylova 1/57 Hall 2 3 1 Sector II, 301 00, Plzen, Czech Republic
Tel.: (420) 378011322
Web Site: https://www.belvac.com
Packaging Machinery Mfr
N.A.I.C.S.: 333993
Marc Monteil *(Dir)*
Pavel Hlavka *(Mgr)*

BSC Filters   **(1)**
Dover House Units 10-11 Stirling Park Bleriot Way, Clifton Moor, York, YO30 4WU, United Kingdom
Tel.: (44) 1904694250
Web Site: https://www.mpgdover.com
Sales Range: $25-49.9 Million
Emp.: 64
Microwave Filters Mfr
N.A.I.C.S.: 339999
Martyn Lee *(Mng Dir)*

Background2 Limited   **(1)**
Crown House Hammersmith Road, London,
W14 8TH, United Kingdom
Tel.: (44) 2075336520

Web Site:
   http://www.flow.background2.co.uk
Heating Oil & Liquefied Petroleum Whslr
N.A.I.C.S.: 457210

Belanger, Inc.   **(1)**
1001 Doheny Ct, Northville, MI 48167-1957
Tel.: (248) 349-7010
Web Site: http://www.belangerinc.com
Sales Range: $10-24.9 Million
Emp.: 212
Car Wash Equipment Mfr
N.A.I.C.S.: 333310

Belvac Middle East FZE   **(1)**
Jafza show room south Business Centre
building FC04, PO Box 18334, JAFZA South,
Dubai, United Arab Emirates
Tel.: (971) 48808337
Motion Rotary Machinery Mfr
N.A.I.C.S.: 333993
Ahmed Nabil *(Regional Mgr-Ops)*

Butler Engineering & Marketing
S.P.A.   **(1)**
Via DellEcologia 6, Rolo, 42047, Reggio
Emilia, 42047, Italy
Tel.: (39) 0522647911
Web Site: https://www.butler.it
Tyre & Vehicle Mfr
N.A.I.C.S.: 326211

CDS Visual, Inc.   **(1)**
65 Grove St Ste 202, Watertown, MA 02472
Tel.: (408) 550-8820
Web Site: https://cdsvisual.com
Software Development Services
N.A.I.C.S.: 541511

Caldera, Inc.   **(1)**
1850 E 121st St Ste 108, Burnsville, MN 55337
Tel.: (612) 216-5212
Emp.: 8
Fiscal Year-end: 06/30/2014
Industrial Equipment Distr
N.A.I.C.S.: 423830
Tricia Snell *(Exec Dir)*
Turiya Autry *(Dir-Education)*
Michelle Meyer *(Dir-Dev)*
David Nolfi *(Dir-Fin)*
Alisha Miller *(Mgr-Education Ops)*
Cristy Lanfri *(Co-Chm)*
Dan Wieden *(Co-Chm)*

Cook Compression Limited   **(1)**
1-3 Helix Business Park New Bridge Road,
Cheshire, Ellesmere Port, CH65 4LR,
United Kingdom
Tel.: (44) 1513555937
Web Site: http://www.cookcompression.com
Packing Cases & Rod Ring Compressor Mfr
N.A.I.C.S.: 333912

Cook Compression, LLC   **(1)**
11951 N Spectrum Blvd, Houston, TX 77047
Tel.: (713) 433-2002
Web Site: http://www.cookcompression.com
Compressor Component Mfr
N.A.I.C.S.: 333912

Criteria Labs, Inc.   **(1)**
706 Brentwood St, Austin, TX 78752
Tel.: (512) 637-4500
Web Site: http://www.criterialabs.com
Semiconductor Machinery Mfr
N.A.I.C.S.: 333242
Doug Myron *(Pres & CEO)*
Tracy Fuller *(CFO)*
Kathleen Whitcher *(VP-Sls)*
Lori Simpson *(Gen Mgr-Tape & Reel Plant)*
Yolanda Guillory *(Mgr-Ops)*
Nate Woodard *(Dir-Sls)*

DESTACO UK Limited   **(1)**
Unit 7 Laches Close Four Ashes, Calibre
Industrial Park, Wolverhampton, WV10
7DZ, United Kingdom
Tel.: (44) 1902797980
Industrial Product Distr
N.A.I.C.S.: 423840

Dositec Sistemas SL   **(1)**
P I La Fabrica C/ Timo 29, Folguueroles,
08519, Barcelona, Spain
Tel.: (34) 93 812 0028
Web Site: https://dositecsistemas.com
Emp.: 18

Chemical Products Mfr
N.A.I.C.S.: 325199
Toni Torres *(CEO)*
Manel Sanchez *(COO)*

Dosmatic U.S.A., Inc. **(1)**
1230 Crowley Cir, Carrollton, TX 75006
Tel.: (972) 245-9765
Web Site: http://www.dosmatic.com
Sales Range: $1-9.9 Million
Emp.: 30
General Industrial Machinery, Nec, Nsk
N.A.I.C.S.: 333998

**Dover (Shanghai) Trading
Company** **(1)**
No 1528 Century Ave, Shanghai, 200131,
China
Tel.: (86) 2160812822
Business Support Services
N.A.I.C.S.: 561110

**Dover (Suzhou) Industrial Equipment
Manufacturing Co., Ltd.** **(1)**
No 11 Wei Wen Road Suzhou Industrial
Park, Suzhou, 215122, Jiangsu, China
Tel.: (86) 51269368587
Web Site: http://www.dovercorp.com
Emp.: 300
Vehicle Parts & Accessory Mfr
N.A.I.C.S.: 332510

**Dover Artificial Lift International,
LLC** **(1)**
1585 Sawdust Rd Ste 210, The Woodlands,
TX 77380
Tel.: (281) 403-5763
Emp.: 4
Oil & Gas Field Machinery Mfr
N.A.I.C.S.: 333132

Dover Artificial Lift Pty Ltd **(1)**
44 Bernoulli St, Darra, 4076, QLD, Australia
Tel.: (61) 737274000
Mining Machinery Mfr
N.A.I.C.S.: 333131

Dover Artificial Lift, LLC **(1)**
1585 Sawdust Rd Ste 210, The Woodlands,
TX 77380
Tel.: (281) 403-5742
Web Site: http://www.doverals.com
Artificial Lift Equipment Mfr
N.A.I.C.S.: 333998

Dover Asia Trading Private Ltd. **(1)**
8 Marina Boulevard Suite 05-02, Singapore,
018981, Singapore
Tel.: (65) 96792686
Emp.: 100
Printing Equipment Mfr
N.A.I.C.S.: 333248
Doris Ng *(Gen Mgr)*

Dover BMCS Acquisition Corp. **(1)**
1320 S 1600 W, Orem, UT 84058
Tel.: (801) 437-9310
Construction Machinery & Equipment Whslr
N.A.I.C.S.: 423810

**Dover Communication Technologies,
Inc.** **(1)**
17542 E 17th St Ste 470, Tustin, CA 92780
Tel.: (714) 415-4110
Sales Range: $1-4.9 Billion
Emp.: 3
Holding Company; Electronic Technologies
Mfr
N.A.I.C.S.: 551112

Subsidiary (Domestic):

Ceramic & Microwave Products **(2)**
4822 McGrath St, Ventura, CA 93003
Tel.: (714) 415-4110
Sales Range: $100-124.9 Million
Microwave Products Mfr
N.A.I.C.S.: 334419

Subsidiary (Domestic):

K&L Microwave, Inc. **(3)**
2250 Northwood Dr, Salisbury, MD
21801 **(100%)**
Tel.: (410) 749-2424
Web Site: http://www.klmicrowave.com
Sales Range: $100-124.9 Million
Emp.: 300
Microwave Filters Mfr
N.A.I.C.S.: 334419
Jeff Burkett *(Dir-Sls & Mktg)*

Subsidiary (Domestic):

Colder Products Company **(2)**
2820 Cleveland Ave N, Roseville, MN
55113
Tel.: (651) 645-0091
Web Site: https://www.cpcworldwide.com
Sales Range: $50-74.9 Million
Emp.: 300
Couplings & Connectors Mfr
N.A.I.C.S.: 332912

Subsidiary (Non-US):

Colder Products Company LTD **(3)**
Level 19 Two International Finance Centre
8 Finance Street, Cheung Sha Wan, Cen-
tral, China (Hong Kong)
Tel.: (852) 29875272
Web Site: http://www.cpcworldwide.com
Couplings & Fittings Mfr
N.A.I.C.S.: 332912

**Dover Corporation (Canada)
Limited** **(1)**
Brookfield Place TD Canada Trust Tower
161 Bay St 27th Flr, PO Box 508, Toronto,
M5J 2S1, ON, Canada
Tel.: (416) 572-2011
Printing Equipment Mfr
N.A.I.C.S.: 333248

**Dover Corporation Regional
Headquarters** **(1)**
Unit 1-11 19th Floor Chamtime Intl Financial
Center, 1589 Century Avenue, Shanghai,
200122, China
Tel.: (86) 2160812888
Diversified Industrial Product Mfr
N.A.I.C.S.: 333131

Dover Energy Automation, LLC **(1)**
11122 W Little York Rd, Houston, TX 77041
Tel.: (409) 842-0300
Web Site: http://www.tlinemfg.com
Chemical Metering Pump Mfr
N.A.I.C.S.: 333914

Dover Energy, Inc. **(1)**
1100 31st St Ste 520, Oak Brook, IL 60515-
5509
Tel.: (630) 725-9347
Sales Range: $700-749.9 Million
Emp.: 6
Bearing Mfr
N.A.I.C.S.: 333613

Subsidiary (Domestic):

Blackmer Pump **(2)**
1809 Century Ave SW, Grand Rapids, MI
49503
Tel.: (616) 241-1611
Web Site: https://www.blackmer.com
Sales Range: $150-199.9 Million
Rotary Pumps Mfr
N.A.I.C.S.: 213112

Cook-MFS, Inc. **(2)**
2540 Centennial Blvd, Jeffersonville, IN
47130
Tel.: (502) 515-6900
Web Site: http://www.cookcompression.com
Sales Range: $50-74.9 Million
Piston Rings, Packings & Valves for Natural
Gas Compressors Mfr
N.A.I.C.S.: 332919

OPW Fueling Components **(2)**
9393 Princeton-Glendale Rd, Hamilton, OH
45011
Tel.: (513) 870-3315
Web Site: http://www.opwglobal.com
Sales Range: $50-74.9 Million
Gasoline Nozzles, Valves & Fittings Mfr
N.A.I.C.S.: 332919
Kevin Long *(Pres)*

Subsidiary (Domestic):

Marshall Excelsior Company **(3)**
1506 George Brown Dr, Marshall, MI 49068
Tel.: (297) 896-6700
Web Site: http://www.marshallexcelsior.com
Heating Equipment Mfr
N.A.I.C.S.: 333414
Mike Domingo *(Mgr-Pur)*

Subsidiary (Domestic):

Koch & Associates Inc. **(4)**

3230 Darby Com, Fremont, CA 94539-3225
Tel.: (510) 490-0487
Web Site: http://www.kochassoc.com
Landscaping Services
N.A.I.C.S.: 561730
Douglas Koch *(Founder & Pres)*

Subsidiary (Domestic):

OPW Engineered Systems, Inc. **(3)**
9393 Princeton-Glendale Rd, Hamilton, OH
45011
Tel.: (513) 461-0113
Web Site: https://www.opwglobal.com
Hazardous Products Handling Services
N.A.I.C.S.: 488999
Dave Morrow *(Dir-Sls & Mktg)*

Subsidiary (Non-US):

**OPW Fluid Transfer Group Europe
B.V.** **(3)**
Roggestraat 38, 2153 GC, Nieuw-Vennep,
Netherlands
Tel.: (31) 252660300
Web Site: https://www.opwglobal.com
Industrial Equipment Merchant Whslr
N.A.I.C.S.: 423830

Subsidiary (Domestic):

**OPW Fuel Management Systems,
Inc.** **(3)**
6900 Santa Fe Dr, Hodgkins, IL 60525
Tel.: (708) 485-4200
Tank Gauges Mfr
N.A.I.C.S.: 332420

Subsidiary (Non-US):

**OPW Fueling Components (SuZhou)
Co., Ltd.** **(3)**
No 11 Weiwen Road, Suzhou Industrial
Park, Suzhou, 215122, China
Tel.: (86) 51262745328
Web Site: http://www.opwglobal.com
Fluid Components Mfr
N.A.I.C.S.: 332311

Subsidiary (Domestic):

Quartzdyne Inc. **(2)**
4334 W Links Dr, Salt Lake City, UT 84120
Tel.: (801) 839-1000
Web Site: http://www.quartzdyne.com
Sales Range: $25-49.9 Million
Quartz Pressure Transducer Designer & Mfr
N.A.I.C.S.: 333132

Tulsa Winch, Inc. **(2)**
11135 S James Ave, Jenks, OK 74037-1130
Tel.: (918) 298-8300
Web Site: https://www.dovertwg.com
Sales Range: $25-49.9 Million
Winch Mfr
N.A.I.C.S.: 333923

Subsidiary (Domestic):

DP Winch **(3)**
11135 S James Ave, Jenks, OK 74037
Tel.: (918) 298-8300
Web Site: http://www.team-twg.com
Sales Range: $50-74.9 Million
Winch Mfr
N.A.I.C.S.: 333923

Gear Products Inc. **(3)**
1111 N 161st E Ave, Tulsa, OK 74116-4035
Tel.: (918) 234-3044
Sales Range: $50-74.9 Million
Rotation Bearings & Mechanical Power
Transmission Components for Off-Road Ve-
hicles Mfr
N.A.I.C.S.: 332111

Subsidiary (Domestic):

US Synthetic Corporation **(2)**
1260 S 1600 W, Orem, UT 84058
Tel.: (801) 235-9001
Web Site: http://www.ussynthetic.com
Sales Range: $100-124.9 Million
Oil & Gas Field Machinery Manufacturing
N.A.I.C.S.: 333132

Waukesha Bearings Corp. **(2)**
N17 W24222 Riverwood Dr Ste 140,
Waukesha, WI 53188 **(100%)**
Tel.: (262) 506-3000
Web Site: https://www.waukbearing.com

Sales Range: $25-49.9 Million
Bearings for Marine & Industrial Purposes
Mfr
N.A.I.C.S.: 333613

Subsidiary (Domestic):

**FW Murphy Production Controls
LLC** **(3)**
5757 Farinon Dr, San Antonio, TX 78249
Tel.: (918) 317-4100
Web Site: http://www.fwmurphy.com
Sales Range: $25-49.9 Million
Emp.: 200
Quality Controls & Instrumentation Systems
Services
N.A.I.C.S.: 333912
Frank W. Murphy Jr. *(Chm)*
Frank W. Murphy III *(Pres)*

**Dover Engineered Systems UK
Ltd** **(1)**
Unit 7 Laches Close Four Ashes Dorset,
Bournemouth, BH2 5QY, United Kingdom
Tel.: (44) 1902797980
General Purpose Machinery Mfr
N.A.I.C.S.: 333998

Dover Engineered Systems, Inc. **(1)**
3005 Highland Pkwy, Downers Grove, IL
60515 **(100%)**
Tel.: (630) 541-1540
Web Site: http://www.dovercorporation.com
Sales Range: $600-649.9 Million
Emp.: 67
Refrigeration & Industrial System Mfr
N.A.I.C.S.: 333415

Subsidiary (Domestic):

**Belvac Production Machinery,
Inc.** **(2)**
237 Graves Mill Rd, Lynchburg, VA 24502-
4203
Tel.: (434) 239-0358
Web Site: https://www.belvac.com
Motion Rotary Machinery Mfr
N.A.I.C.S.: 333248

Hill Phoenix Inc. **(2)**
2016 Gees Mill Rd, Conyers, GA 30013
Tel.: (770) 285-3264
Web Site: https://www.hillphoenix.com
Sales Range: $450-499.9 Million
Refrigeration Condensing Systems Mfr
N.A.I.C.S.: 333415
Brad Roche *(VP-Mktg Comm)*
Kim Camp *(Mgr-Mktg Comm & Learning
Center Programs)*

Hydro Systems Company **(2)**
3798 Round Bottom Rd, Cincinnati, OH
45244
Tel.: (513) 271-8800
Web Site: https://www.hydrosystemsco.com
Industrial Supplies Distr
N.A.I.C.S.: 423840
Serge Joris *(Pres & CEO)*

PDQ Manufacturing, Inc. **(2)**
1698 Scheuring Rd, De Pere, WI 54115
Tel.: (920) 983-8333
Web Site: http://www.pdqinc.com
Vehicle Washing Systems & Equipment Mfr
& Whslr
N.A.I.C.S.: 333310

Subsidiary (Non-US):

SWEP International AB **(2)**
Hjalmar Brantings vag 5, PO Box 105, 261
22, Landskrona, Sweden **(100%)**
Tel.: (46) 41 840 0400
Web Site: https://www.swep.net
Sales Range: $100-124.9 Million
Emp.: 1,000
Heat Exchanger Mfr
N.A.I.C.S.: 332410

Subsidiary (Domestic):

Vehicle Service Group, LLC **(2)**
2700 Lanier Dr, Madison, IN 47250-0560
Tel.: (812) 265-9423
Web Site: https://www.vsgdover.com
Vehicle Lift Systems Mfr
N.A.I.C.S.: 333310
Niclas Ytterdahl *(Pres)*

Unit (Domestic):

Rotary Lift **(3)**

Dover Corporation—(Continued)

2700 Lanier Dr, Madison, IN 47250
Tel.: (812) 273-1622
Web Site: https://www.rotarylift.com
Sales Range: $100-124.9 Million
Mfr of Automatic Hydraulic Lifts
N.A.I.C.S.: 333310

Subsidiary (Domestic):

Warn Industries, Inc.   **(2)**
12900 SE Capps Rd, Clackamas, OR
97015-8903
Tel.: (503) 722-1200
Web Site: https://www.warn.com
Automotive & Industrial Winches & Hoists
Designer, Mfr & Distr
N.A.I.C.S.: 336390

Dover Fluids UK Ltd   **(1)**
11 Albany Rd, Granby Industrial Estate,
Weymouth, DT4 9TH, Dorset, United King-
dom
Tel.: (44) 1305208327
General Purpose Machinery Mfr
N.A.I.C.S.: 333998
Jillian C. Evanko (CFO & VP)
David Crouse (Co-Pres)
Bill Spurgeon (Co-Pres & CEO)

Dover France Holdings, S.A.S.   **(1)**
40 Avenue Hoche, 75008, Paris, France
Tel.: (33) 149971761
Web Site: http://www.dovercorporation.com
Industrial Components & Products Mfr
N.A.I.C.S.: 333924

**Dover Fueling Solutions UK
Limited**   **(1)**
Unit 3 Baker Road West Pitkerro Industrial
Estate, Dundee, DD5 3RT, United Kingdom
Tel.: (44) 1382598000
Fuel Dispenser Equipment Mfr
N.A.I.C.S.: 333914

**Dover Luxembourg Finance
S.a.r.l.**   **(1)**
7 Avenue Gaston Diderich, 1420, Luxem-
bourg, Luxembourg
Tel.: (352) 26262561
General Purpose Machinery Mfr
N.A.I.C.S.: 333998

Dover PCS Holding LLC   **(1)**
1585 Sawdust Rd Ste 210, Spring, TX
77380
Tel.: (281) 403-5742
Emp.: 2
Holding Services
N.A.I.C.S.: 551112

Dover Pump Solutions Group   **(1)**
1815 S Meyers Rd, Oakbrook Terrace, IL
00101
Tel.: (630) 487-2240
Web Site: http://www.psgdover.com
Pumps, Systems & Related Flow-Control
Technology Mfr
N.A.I.C.S.: 333996

Subsidiary (Domestic):

All-Flo Pump Company, Limited   **(2)**
22069 Van Buren St, 92313, Grand Terrace,
CA
Tel.: (440) 354-1700
Web Site: https://www.psgdover.com
Fluid Power Pumps Mfr
N.A.I.C.S.: 333996

**Dover Pump Solutions Group (Eu-
rope) GmbH**   **(1)**
Aspstrasse 12, 8154, Oberglatt, 7H, Switz-
zerland
Tel.: (41) 442788400
General Purpose Machinery Mfr
N.A.I.C.S.: 333998

**Dover Refrigeration & Food Equip-
ment, Inc.**   **(1)**
3005 Highland Pkwy Ste 200, Downers
Grove, IL 60515-5682   **(100%)**
Tel.: (513) 878-4400
Sales Range: $50-74.9 Million
Emp.: 190
Food Equipment Mfr
N.A.I.C.S.: 333241

Subsidiary (Non-US):

DEK Printing Machines Limited   **(2)**

11 Albany Road Granby Industrial Estate,
Weymouth, DT4 9TH, United Kingdom
Tel.: (44) 1305760760
Emp.: 300
Screen Printing Equipment Mfr
N.A.I.C.S.: 333248
Michael Brianda (Pres)

Subsidiary (Non-US):

DEK Asia Pacific Private Limited   **(3)**
115a Commonwealth Drive 04-01 Tanglin
Halt Industrial Estate, Singapore, 149596,
Singapore
Tel.: (65) 64847010
Web Site: http://www.dek.com
Printed Circuit Board Mfr
N.A.I.C.S.: 334412

DEK Printing Machines GmbH   **(3)**
Theodor-Heuss-Str 57, 61118, Bad Vilbel,
Germany
Tel.: (49) 610152270
Screen Printing Machines Mfr
N.A.I.C.S.: 333248
Milomir Djokic (Mgr-Global Svc)
Dietmar Hillebrand (Mgr-Sls-Southern Ger-
many)

Subsidiary (Non-US):

Markem-Imaje SAS   **(2)**
16 rue Brillat Savarin, PO Box 110, Cha-
teauneuf Sur Isere, 26300, Bourg-les-
Valence, France
Tel.: (33) 825803904
Web Site: https://www.markem-imaje.com
Coding & Marking Equipment Mfr & Distr
N.A.I.C.S.: 339940
Vincent Vanderpoel (Pres & CEO)

Subsidiary (Non-US):

Imaje Nordic AB   **(3)**
Manskarsuagen 9, 141 75, Kungens Kurva,
Sweden
Tel.: (46) 853470780
Web Site: http://www.markem-imaje.se
Sales Range: $25-49.9 Million
Emp.: 30
Coding & Marking Equipment Mfr & Distr
N.A.I.C.S.: 339940

**Markem-Imaje (Hong Kong)
Limited**   **(3)**
Workshop 11-12 10/F Block B New Trade
Plaza 6 On Ping Street, Sha Tin, China
(Hong Kong)
Tel.: (852) 25667202
Web Site: http://hk.markem-imaje.com
Sales Range: $10-24.9 Million
Emp.: 3,000
Coding & Marking Equipment Mfr & Distr
N.A.I.C.S.: 339940

Markem-Imaje (Taiwan) Ltd.   **(3)**
6 F 50 Jing-an Road Chung Ho City,
23575, Taipei, China
Tel.: (886) 222461199
Web Site: http://www.markem-imaje.com
Sales Range: $10-24.9 Million
Emp.: 18
Coding & Marking Equipment Mfr & Distr
N.A.I.C.S.: 339940

Markem-Imaje A/S   **(3)**
Herstedostervej 27-29, 2620, Albertslund,
Denmark
Tel.: (45) 44942100
Web Site: http://www.markem-imaje.dk
Sales Range: $10-24.9 Million
Coding & Marking Equipment Mfr & Distr
N.A.I.C.S.: 339940

Markem-Imaje AG   **(3)**
Aspstrasse 12, 8154, Oberglatt, Switzerland
Tel.: (41) 449566600
Sales Range: $75-99.9 Million
Coding & Marking Equipment Mfr & Distr
N.A.I.C.S.: 339940

Markem-Imaje AS   **(3)**
Karihaugveien 89, 1086, Oslo, Norway
Tel.: (47) 67912600
Web Site: http://www.markem-imaje.no
Sales Range: $50-74.9 Million
Coding & Marking Equipment Mfr & Distr
N.A.I.C.S.: 339940

Markem-Imaje BV   **(3)**

Hullenbergweg 278, 1101 BV, Amsterdam,
Netherlands
Tel.: (31) 29 446 0420
Web Site: https://www.markem-imaje.com
Sales Range: $10-24.9 Million
Coding & Marking Equipment Mfr & Distr
N.A.I.C.S.: 339940

Markem-Imaje Co., Ltd.   **(3)**
Web Site: http://www.kr.markem-imaje.com
Sales Range: $10-24.9 Million
Coding & Marking Equipment Mfr & Distr
N.A.I.C.S.: 339940
Gu Yeol Jeong (Pres)

Subsidiary (US):

Markem-Imaje Corporation   **(3)**
100 Chastain Ctr Blvd Ste 165, Kennesaw,
GA 30144
Tel.: (770) 421-7700
Web Site: https://www.markem-imaje.com
Sales Range: $200-249.9 Million
Product Marking, Coding & Tracking Sys-
tems Equipment & Software Mfr
N.A.I.C.S.: 333248

Unit (Domestic):

Markem-Imaje USA   **(4)**
1650 Airport Rd Ste 101, Kennesaw, GA
30144
Tel.: (770) 421-7700
Web Site: http://www.markem-imaje.us
Sales Range: $25-49.9 Million
Emp.: 150
Coding & Marking Equipment Mfr & Distr
N.A.I.C.S.: 339940

Subsidiary (Non-US):

Markem-Imaje GmbH   **(3)**
Schockenriedstr 8 C, 70565, Stuttgart, Ger-
many
Tel.: (49) 71 178 4030
Web Site: https://www.markem-imaje.com
Sales Range: $25-49.9 Million
Coding & Marking Equipment Mfr & Distr
N.A.I.C.S.: 339940

Branch (Non-US):

Markem-Imaje GmbH - Austria   **(4)**
Europaplatz 2 1 2, 1150, Vienna, Austria
Tel.: (43) 18655130
Web Site: http://www.markem-imaje.com
Sales Range: $50-74.9 Million
Emp.: 5
Coding & Marking Equipment Mfr & Distr
N.A.I.C.S.: 339940

Subsidiary (Non-US):

Markem-Imaje Inc.   **(3)**
2233 Argentia Road East Tower-Suite 302,
Mississauga, L5N 2X7, ON, Canada
Tel.: (514) 633-8848
Web Site: https://www.markem-imaje.ca
Sales Range: $10-24.9 Million
Coding & Marking Equipment Mfr & Distr
N.A.I.C.S.: 339940

**Markem-Imaje India Private
Limited**   **(3)**
H-23 Sector-63, Gautam Budh Nagar,
Noida, 201 301, Uttar pradesh, India
Tel.: (91) 1204099500
Web Site: http://www.in.markem-imaje.com
Sales Range: $50-74.9 Million
Coding & Marking Equipment Mfr & Distr
N.A.I.C.S.: 339940

Markem-Imaje K.K.   **(3)**
Time 24 Building 10F 2-4-32 Aomi, Koto-ku,
Tokyo, 135-0064, Japan   **(100%)**
Tel.: (81) 359621936
Web Site: http://jp.markem-imaje.com
Coding & Marking Equipment Mfr & Distr
N.A.I.C.S.: 339940 (339940)

Markem-Imaje LLC   **(3)**
Semenovskaya Square - 7,building 15,
105318, Moscow, Russia
Tel.: (7) 4952258140
Sales Range: $10-24.9 Million
Emp.: 25
Coding & Marking Equipment Mfr & Distr
N.A.I.C.S.: 339940

Markem-Imaje Ltd.   **(3)**
4th Floor Centenary House 1 Centenary

Way, Manchester, M50 1RF, United King-
dom
Tel.: (44) 1618648100
Web Site: http://www.markem-imaje.co.uk
Engineering Component Mfr
N.A.I.C.S.: 335999

Markem-Imaje N.V.   **(3)**
Jagersdreef 1 F, 2900, Schoten, Belgium
Tel.: (32) 36339999
Web Site: http://www.markem-imaje.be
Sales Range: $25-49.9 Million
Printing Equipment Mfr
N.A.I.C.S.: 333248

Markem-Imaje Oy   **(3)**
Ayritie 12 c, 01510, Vantaa, Finland
Tel.: (358) 98387780
Web Site: http://www.markem-imaje.fi
Sales Range: $10-24.9 Million
Emp.: 9
Coding & Marking Equipment Mfr & Distr
N.A.I.C.S.: 339940

Markem-Imaje Pte. Ltd.   **(3)**
9 Toh Guan Road East, 04-01 Alliance
Building, Singapore, 608604, Singapore
Tel.: (65) 67605388
Web Site: http://www.markem-imaje.com
Sales Range: $10-24.9 Million
Emp.: 55
Coding & Marking Equipment Mfr & Distr
N.A.I.C.S.: 339940

Markem-Imaje Pty Ltd.   **(3)**
Suite 201 - T1 Building 14-16 Lexington
Drive, Bella Vista, 2153, NSW, Australia
Tel.: (61) 30 073 0428
Web Site: http://www.au.markem-imaje.com
Sales Range: $25-49.9 Million
Coding & Marking Equipment Mfr & Distr
N.A.I.C.S.: 339940

Markem-Imaje S.A. de C.V.   **(3)**
Av Gustavo Baz No 309 - Edificio B2 - Piso
1 101, Colonia La Loma, 54060, Tlal-
nepantla, Estado de Mexico, Mexico
Tel.: (52) 551 086 9840
Web Site: http://www.mx.markem-imaje.com
Sales Range: $10-24.9 Million
Coding & Marking Equipment Mfr & Distr
N.A.I.C.S.: 339940

Markem-Imaje S.r.l a socio unico   **(3)**
Via Marconi 2, 20090, Assago, MI, Italy
Tel.: (39) 024407121
Web Site: http://www.markem-imaje.it
Coding & Marking Equipment Mfr & Distr
N.A.I.C.S.: 339940

Markem-Imaje Sdn Bhd   **(3)**
NO 1 - Jalan PJU 3/48 - Sunway, Daman-
sara, 47810, Petaling Jaya, Selangor, Ma-
layoia
Tel.: (60) 378025000
Web Site: http://my.markem-imaje.com
Coding & Marking Equipment Mfr & Distr
N.A.I.C.S.: 541511

Markem-Imaje Spain S.A.   **(3)**
Avda Can Fatjo dels Aurons 9 - 2 Planta,
Sant Cugat del Valles, 08174, Barcelona,
Spain
Tel.: (34) 93 712 3990
Web Site: http://www.markem-imaje.com
Sales Range: $10-24.9 Million
Emp.: 80
Coding & Marking Equipment Mfr & Distr
N.A.I.C.S.: 339940
Jordi Bernabeu (Mng Dir)

Markem-Imaje Unipessoal, Lda   **(3)**
Rua Armando Cortez 7C, 2770-233, Paco
d'Arcos, Portugal
Tel.: (351) 219 25 2700
Sales Range: $25-49.9 Million
Emp.: 50
Coding & Marking Equipment Mfr & Distr
N.A.I.C.S.: 339940

Subsidiary (Domestic):

OK International, Inc.   **(2)**
10800 Valley View St, Cypress, CA
90630   **(100%)**
Tel.: (714) 799-9910
Web Site: https://www.okinternational.com
Sales Range: $125-149.9 Million
Precision Electrical Systems
N.A.I.C.S.: 444180

Subsidiary (Non-US):

OK International (UK) Ltd. **(3)**
Eagle Close Chandlers Ford, Eastleigh,
SO53 4NF, Hampshire, United Kingdom
Tel.: (44) 2380489100
Web Site: http://www.okinternational.com
Emp.: 25
Soldering Tools & Equipment Mfr
N.A.I.C.S.: 333992

**Dover Southeast Asia (Thailand)
Ltd.** **(1)**
Bangkok Square Building A Room No A 540
No 762/2 Rama 3 Road, Bang Phong
Phang Subdistrict Yannawa District, Bang-
kok, 10120, Thailand
Tel.: (66) 22952788
Web Site: https://www.doversea.co.th
Air Control Valve Mfr
N.A.I.C.S.: 332912

Dover Spain Holdings, S.L. **(1)**
Calle Espronceda 53-57, 08005, Barcelona,
Spain
Tel.: (34) 937098041
Holding Company
N.A.I.C.S.: 551114

Ebs-Ray Pumps Pty. Ltd. **(1)**
156 South Creek Road, Cromer, 2099,
NSW, Australia
Tel.: (61) 29 905 0234
Web Site: https://www.psgdover.com
Pump & Pumping Equipment Mfr
N.A.I.C.S.: 333914

**Ettlinger Kunststoffmaschinen
GmbH** **(1)**
Messerschmittring 49, 86343, Konigsbrunn,
Germany
Tel.: (49) 82313490800
Filtration System & Injection Molding Ma-
chine Mfr
N.A.I.C.S.: 333248

Ettlinger North America LP **(1)**
1555 Senoia Rd, Tyrone, GA 30290
Tel.: (770) 703-8541
Filtration System & Injection Molding Ma-
chine Mfr
N.A.I.C.S.: 333248

Fairbanks Environmental Limited **(1)**
The Technology Management Centre Moss
Lane View, Lancashire, Skelmersdale, WN8
9TN, United Kingdom
Tel.: (44) 169551775
Web Site: http://www.fairbanks.co.uk
Fuel Management & Fueling Retailer
N.A.I.C.S.: 457210

FindeR Pompes **(1)**
4 Rue Fernand Pelloutier BP 583, 69200,
Venissieux, France
Tel.: (33) 472212400
Web Site: http://www.finderpompes.fr
Pump & Pumping Equipment Mfr
N.A.I.C.S.: 333914

Finder Pompe S.P.A. **(1)**
Via Bergamo 65, 23807, Merate, Italy
Tel.: (39) 03999821
Pump & Pumping Equipment Mfr
N.A.I.C.S.: 333914
Alex Lampo *(Mgr-Logistics & EHS)*

Gala Industries Asia Limited **(1)**
Pinthong Industrial Estate 789/156 Moo 1,
Si Racha, 20230, Chonburi, Thailand
Tel.: (66) 38190840
Industrial Machinery & Equipment Mfr
N.A.I.C.S.: 332999
Samanyar Tongnat *(Mgr-Mktg)*

**Gala Kunststoff- Und Kautschuk-
maschinen GmbH** **(1)**
Bruchweg 28-30, 46509, Xanten, Germany
Tel.: (49) 28019800
Web Site: https://www.kunststoffweb.de
Industrial Machinery & Equipment Mfr
N.A.I.C.S.: 332999
Berthold Druschel *(Sr Engr-Tech)*

Griswold Acquisition Company **(1)**
22069 Van Buren St, Grand Terrace, CA
92313-5607
Tel.: (909) 512-1275
Electrical Submersible Pumping System Mfr
N.A.I.C.S.: 238220

Hard Parts Direct B.V. **(1)**
Pesetaweg 32, 2153 PJ, Nieuw-Vennep,
Netherlands
Tel.: (31) 853001600
Web Site: http://www.hardpartsdirect.com
Vehicle Parts & Accessory Supply Services
N.A.I.C.S.: 423710

**Hill Phoenix Costa Rica, Sociedad De
Responsabilidad Limitada** **(1)**
No 13 Calle Potrerillos San Rafael de, Ala-
juela, Costa Rica
Tel.: (506) 22820900
Display Case & Specialty Product Mfr
N.A.I.C.S.: 333415

Hiltap Fittings Ltd. **(1)**
1-3140 14th Avenue NE, Calgary, T2A 6J4,
AB, Canada
Tel.: (403) 250-2986
Web Site: http://www.hiltap.com
Industrial Supply Merchant Whslr
N.A.I.C.S.: 423840
Myles Herda *(Engr-Mechanical)*
Carlos Cosse *(Mgr-Quality)*
Colin Bielesch *(Plant Mgr)*

Hydro Nova Europe, Ltd. **(1)**
Unit 3 The Sterling Centre Eastern Road,
Bracknell, RG12 2PW, United Kingdom
Tel.: (44) 1344488880
Detecting System Mfr
N.A.I.C.S.: 333914
Johan Shelton *(Gen Mgr)*

Hydro Systems Europe, Ltd. **(1)**
Unit 3 The Sterling Centre Eastern Road,
Bracknell, RG12 2PW, Berkshire, United
Kingdom
Tel.: (44) 1344488880
Web Site:
    http://www.hydrosystemseurope.com
Proportioning & Dispensing System Mfr
N.A.I.C.S.: 333914

Hydromotion, Inc. **(1)**
85 E Bridge St, Spring City, PA 19475
Tel.: (610) 948-4150
Web Site: https://www.hydromotion.com
Electrical Engineering Services
N.A.I.C.S.: 541330

Hydronova Australia-NZ Pty Ltd **(1)**
Unit A 1 Kellham Place, Glendenning, 2761,
NSW, Australia
Tel.: (61) 296258122
Dispensing Systems Mfr
N.A.I.C.S.: 333914

Innovative Control Systems, Inc. **(1)**
81 Highland Ave Ste 300, Bethlehem, PA
18017
Tel.: (610) 881-8000
Web Site:
    https://www.icscarwashsystems.com
Electronic Car Wash Control System Distr
N.A.I.C.S.: 423690
Rob Wingard *(Reg Mgr-Sls)*
Kevin Detrick *(Founder & Pres)*
Rob Deal *(VP-Corp & Intl Sls)*
Jeff Wizer *(Reg Mgr-Sls)*
Brian Bath *(VP-Sls)*
Bill Myers *(Dir-Support & Car Wash Ops)*
Jason Sears *(Dir-Bus Dev)*
Sham Devarunda *(Dir-Sys Engrg)*
Kolinn Kramer *(Supvr-Production)*
Cindy Penchishen *(Controller)*
Tom Bagnara *(Dir-Sls-Petroleum-North
America)*
Kristy Smith *(Sls Mgr-Retail Petroleum-Natl)*

Inpro/Seal LLC **(1)**
4221 81st Ave W, Rock Island, IL 61201
Tel.: (309) 787-4971
Web Site: https://www.inpro-seal.com
Bearing Mfr
N.A.I.C.S.: 333613

JK Group SPA **(1)**
SP32 Novedratese 33, 22060, Novedrate,
CO, Italy
Tel.: (39) 031 207 4400
Web Site: https://www.kiiandigital.com
Printing Ink Mfr
N.A.I.C.S.: 325910
Alberto De Matthaeis *(CEO)*

JK Group USA, Inc. **(1)**
106 Industrial Park Dr, Soddy Daisy, TN
37379

Tel.: (423) 486-9376
Printing Ink Mfr
N.A.I.C.S.: 325910
Ken Chase *(Mgr-Logistics)*

**KPS (Beijing) Petroleum Equipment
Trading Co, Ltd.** **(1)**
Room 205 G Floor 2 23 Dongzhimenwai St
Chaoyang District, Beijing, 100600, China
Tel.: (86) 1065326342
Storage Equipment Mfr
N.A.I.C.S.: 334112

KPS CEE s.r.o. **(1)**
Nadrazna 1387/65, 92041, Leopoldov, Slo-
vakia
Tel.: (421) 1337341410
Liquid Handling & Storage Equipment Mfr
N.A.I.C.S.: 484220

KPS France SARL **(1)**
73 Avenue Carnot, 94230, Cachan, France
Tel.: (33) 146630400
Liquid Handling & Storage Equipment Mfr
N.A.I.C.S.: 484220

KPS Fueling Solutions Sdn. Bhd. **(1)**
L-07-01 Solaris Mont Kiara, No. 2 Jalan So-
laris Mont Kiara, 50480, Kuala Lumpur,
Wilayah Persekutuan, Malaysia
Tel.: (60) 3 6200 0630
Liquid Handling & Storage Equipment Mfr
N.A.I.C.S.: 321992

KPS UK Limited **(1)**
Unit 2 Mid Suffolk Business Park Progress
Way, Eye, IP23 7HU, Suffolk, United King-
dom
Tel.: (44) 1379870725
Web Site: http://kpspiping.com
Liquid Handling & Storage Equipment Mfr
N.A.I.C.S.: 484220

Kiian Digital (Shanghai) Co., Ltd. **(1)**
6 Fl Bldg D Suite 603 New Bund World
Trade Center N 6 lane 227, Dongyu Road,
Shanghai, China
Tel.: (86) 2160812890
Web Site: https://www.kiiandigital.com
Printing Ink Mfr
N.A.I.C.S.: 325910

Knappco Corporation **(1)**
4304 Mattox Rd, Kansas City, MO 64150
Tel.: (816) 741-6600
Web Site: http://www.knappco.com
Industrial Equipment Merchant Whslr
N.A.I.C.S.: 423830

LIQAL, B.V. **(1)**
Rudonk 7, 4824 AJ, Breda, Netherlands
Tel.: (31) 85 486 1000
Web Site: https://www.liqal.com
Fuel Distr
N.A.I.C.S.: 457210

**Lianyang Jump Petroleum and
Chemical Machinery Co., Ltd.** **(1)**
The pearl river road no 2 sinpo develop-
ment zone, Lianyungang, 222000, Jiangsu,
China
Tel.: (86) 13805122552
Web Site:
    http://www.jumpjs.gmc.globalmarket.com
General Purpose Machinery Mfr
N.A.I.C.S.: 333998

Liquip International Pty Limited **(1)**
148 Newton Road, Wetherill Park, Sydney,
2164, NSW, Australia
Tel.: (61) 297259000
Web Site: https://www.liquip.com
Liquid Handling & Storage Equipment Distr
N.A.I.C.S.: 423830

MARKEM Pte. Ltd. **(1)**
9 Toh Guan Road East 04-01 Alliance
Building, Singapore, 608604, Singapore
Tel.: (65) 67605388
Web Site: http://sg.markem-imaje.com
General Purpose Machinery Mfr
N.A.I.C.S.: 333998

MS Printing Solutions S.R.L. **(1)**
Via Bergamo 1910, 21042, Caronno Pertu-
sella, VA, Italy
Tel.: (39) 02 965 0169
Web Site: https://www.msitaly.com
Printing System Mfr
N.A.I.C.S.: 333248

Maag Automatik GmbH **(1)**
Ostring 19, 63762, Grossostheim, Germany
Tel.: (49) 60265030
Gear Pump & Filtration System Mfr
N.A.I.C.S.: 333914

Maag Pump Systems AG **(1)**
Aspstrasse 12, 8154, Oberglatt, Switzerland
Tel.: (41) 442788200
Web Site: https://www.maag.com
Sales Range: $125-149.9 Million
Gear Pumps & Systems Developer, Mfr &
Whslr
N.A.I.C.S.: 333914

Subsidiary (Non-US):

**Automatik Plastics Machinery (Tai-
wan) Ltd.** **(2)**
Room 619 6F No 6 Hsinyi Rd Sec 4, Da-an
District, New Taipei City, 106, Taiwan
Tel.: (886) 227036336
Web Site: http://www.psgdover.com
Pumps & Pumping Equipment Sales, Pur-
chasing & Servicing
N.A.I.C.S.: 423830

**Automatik Plastics Machinery
GmbH** **(2)**
Ostring 19, Grossostheim, 63762, Germany
Tel.: (49) 60265030
Sales Range: $50-74.9 Million
Emp.: 230
Pelletizing System Mfr
N.A.I.C.S.: 333248
Harald Zang *(Mng Dir)*
Frank Sittinger *(Head-Supply Chain)*

**Automatik Plastics Machinery Sdn.
Bhd.** **(2)**
37 PJU Street 1A 14 Taman Perindustrian
Jaya Ara Damansara, 47301, Petaling Jaya,
Selangor Darul Ehsan, Malaysia
Tel.: (60) 378422116
Web Site: http://www.maag.com
Emp.: 4
Pumps & Pumping Equipment Sales & Ser-
vicing
N.A.I.C.S.: 423830

**Automatik do Brazil Maquinas Para
Industria do Plastico Ltda.** **(2)**
Alameda Rio Preto 165 Sala 3, Centro Em-
presarial Tambore, Barueri, 06460-050, SP,
Brazil
Tel.: (55) 11 4166 4975
Web Site: http://www.psgdover.com
Pumps & Pumping Equipment Sales & Ser-
vicing
N.A.I.C.S.: 423830

Subsidiary (US):

Gala Industries, Inc. **(2)**
181 Pauley St, Eagle Rock, VA 24085
Tel.: (540) 884-2589
Web Site: http://www.gala-industries.com
Emp.: 170
Centrifugal Dryers & Pelletizing Systems
Mfr
N.A.I.C.S.: 333248
Martin Baumann *(VP)*

Subsidiary (Non-US):

**Maag Automatik Plastics Machinery
(Shanghai) Co., Ltd.** **(2)**
No 88 Chenxiang Road, Nanxiang Town
Jiading District, Shanghai, 201802, China
Tel.: (86) 2180333200
Web Site: http://www.psgdover.com
Emp.: 70
Sales & Service for Pump Equipment
N.A.I.C.S.: 423830

Maag Automatik Srl **(2)**
Viale Romagna 7, 20089, Rozzano, MI,
Italy
Tel.: (39) 025759321
Sales, Purchasing & Service of Pelletizing
Systems & Gear Pumps
N.A.I.C.S.: 423830

Subsidiary (US):

Maag Automatik, Inc. **(2)**
3700 Arco Corporate Dr Ste 490, Charlotte,
NC 28273
Tel.: (704) 716-9000

Dover Corporation—(Continued)

Sales Range: $25-49.9 Million
Emp.: 50
Hydraulic & Pneumatic Fluid Power Control
Valves & Pumps Sales & Servicing
N.A.I.C.S.: 423830

Subsidiary (Domestic):

Maag Pump Systems (Switzerland)
AG (2)
Aspstrasse 12, 8154, Oberglatt, Switzerland
Tel.: (41) 442788200
Web Site: http://www.maag.com
Emp.: 160
Advisory, Financing, Management & Planning Services
N.A.I.C.S.: 561499
Ulrich Thuerit (CEO)

Subsidiary (Non-US):

Maag Pump Systems GmbH (2)
Ostring 19, 63762, Grossostheim, Germany
Tel.: (49) 60265030
Web Site: http://www.maag.com
Sales Range: $10-24.9 Million
Emp.: 22
Develops, Manufactures & Supplies Gear
Pumps & Systems
N.A.I.C.S.: 333914

Maag Pump Systems Pte. Ltd. (2)
25 International Business Park No 04-73
German Center, Singapore, 609916, Singapore
Tel.: (65) 65628720
Sales Range: $25-49.9 Million
Emp.: 4
Pumps & Pumping Equipment Sales & Servicing
N.A.I.C.S.: 423830
Ueli Thurig (CEO)

Maag Pump Systems SAS (2)
111 Rue Du 1er Mars 1943, 69100, Villeurbanne, France
Tel.: (33) 472686730
Web Site: https://maag.com
Emp.: 4
Pumps & Pumping Equipment Sales & Servicing
N.A.I.C.S.: 423830

Malema Engineering Corp. (1)
1060 S Rogers Cir, Boca Raton, FL 33487
Tel.: (561) 995-0595
Web Site: http://www.malema.com
Sales Range: $1-9.9 Million
Emp.: 35
Instruments & Related Products Mfr for
Measuring, Displaying & Controlling Industrial Process Variables
N.A.I.C.S.: 334513
Deepak Malani (CEO)
Alvin Chua (Mgr-Bus Dev)

Markem-Imaje CSAT GmbH (1)
Daimlerstrasse 32, Eggenstein-Leopoldshafen, 76344, Eggenstein, Germany
Tel.: (49) 721973150
Web Site: https://csat.markem-imaje.com
General Purpose Machinery Mfr
N.A.I.C.S.: 333998

Markem-Imaje Holding (1)
9 Rue Gaspard Monge Markem Imaje,
26500, Bourg-les-Valence, France
Tel.: (33) 475755500
Web Site: http://www.markem-imaje.com
Emp.: 700
Holding Company
N.A.I.C.S.: 551112
Lambert Oliver (Mng Dir)

Markem-Imaje Industries (1)
9 Rue Gaspard Monge, 26500, Bourg-les-Valence, France
Tel.: (33) 475755500
General Purpose Machinery Mfr
N.A.I.C.S.: 333998

Markem-Imaje Industries Limited (1)
Alexander Fleming Building Nottingham Science Park, Nottingham, NG7 2QN, Nottinghamshire, United Kingdom
Tel.: (44) 1159430055
Web Site: http://www.markem-imaje.com
Emp.: 55

Bar Code Printing Services
N.A.I.C.S.: 561499

Markem-Imaje Limited (1)
Workshop 11-12 10/F Block B New Trade
Plaza 6 On Ping Street, Sha Tin, China
(Hong Kong)
Tel.: (852) 25667202
Web Site: http://hk.markem-imaje.com
General Purpose Machinery Mfr
N.A.I.C.S.: 333998

Markem-Imaje Ltd. (1)
6F No 50 Jing An Road, Chung Ho District,
23575, New Taipei City, Taiwan
Tel.: (886) 222461199
Web Site: http://www.markem-imaje.com
Printing Machinery & Equipment Mfr
N.A.I.C.S.: 333248

Markem-Imaje Ltd. (1)
2nd Floor RN Building 961 Rama 3 Rd,
Bangpongpang Yannawa, Bangkok, 10120,
Thailand
Tel.: (66) 26897333
Thermal Printing Equipment Mfr
N.A.I.C.S.: 333248

Markem-Imaje S.A. (1)
Av De Los Constituyentes 2240, General
Pacheco, B1617ABW, Buenos Aires, Argentina
Tel.: (54) 1152803600
Web Site: http://www.markem-imaje.com.ar
General Purpose Machinery Mfr
N.A.I.C.S.: 333998

Markem-Imaje Spain S.A.U (1)
Avda Can Fatjo dels Aurons 9 2 Planta,
Sant Cugat del Valles, 08174, Barcelona,
Spain
Tel.: (34) 937123990
Thermal Printing Equipment Mfr
N.A.I.C.S.: 333248

Mouvex SASU (1)
ZI La Plaine Des Isles 2 Rue Des Caillottes,
89000, Auxerre, France
Tel.: (33) 386498630
Web Site: https://www.psgdover.com
Sales Range: $25-49.9 Million
Pumps & Compressor Mfr
N.A.I.C.S.: 333914

Norris Production Solutions Colombia
SAS (1)
CI 82, Bogota, 1050, Colombia
Tel.: (57) 16341500
Oil & Gas Exploration Services
N.A.I.C.S.: 211120

Norris Production Solutions Middle
East LLC (1)
Alghubra bank of Beirut, PO Box 1204,
Muscat, 131, Oman
Tel.: (968) 24496903
Web Site: http://www.nps.com
Emp.: 200
Oil & Gas Service Provider
N.A.I.C.S.: 213112
Aaron Grimley (Gen Mgr)

Norris Rods, Inc. (1)
3745 Triway Ln, Wooster, OH 44691
Tel.: (330) 202-7637
Electrical Submersible Pumping System
Services
N.A.I.C.S.: 238220
Jason Spenser (Mgr-Gulf Coast Area)

Novacap LLC (1)
25111 Anza Dr, Valencia, CA 91355
Tel.: (661) 295-5920
Web Site: http://www.novacap.com
Capacitor Mfr
N.A.I.C.S.: 334416
Mark Skoog (Pres)

OPW Fluid Transfer Solutions (Jiang
Su) Co., Ltd. (1)
Lianyungang JUMP Petroleum No 2 Zhujiang Middle Road, XinPu Development
Zone, Lianyungang, 222346, Jiangsu,
China
Tel.: (86) 13805122552
Oil & Energy Related Equipment Mfr
N.A.I.C.S.: 333132

OPW France (1)
73 avenue Carnot, 94230, Cachan, France
Tel.: (33) 146630400

Fuel Management & Fueling Retailer
N.A.I.C.S.: 457210

OPW Malaysia Sdn. Bhd. (1)
Lot P T 27259 Jalan Sigma U6/14 Bukit
Cerakah Seksyen U6, 40150, Shah Alam,
Selangor Darul Ehsan, Malaysia
Tel.: (60) 377701000
Liquid Handling & Storage Equipment Mfr
N.A.I.C.S.: 326111

OPW Slovakia s.r.o. (1)
Antolska 4, 85107, Bratislava, Slovakia
Tel.: (421) 1911886613
Plumbing & Heating Valve Whslr
N.A.I.C.S.: 423720
Ronald Pinka (Dir-Tech Support)

OPW Sweden AB (1)
Box 70, 736 22, Kungsor, Sweden
Tel.: (46) 22742200
Web Site: http://www.opwsweden.com
Liquid Handling & Storage Equipment Mfr
N.A.I.C.S.: 484220
Christian Niejahr (Mgr-Quality)

Officine Meccaniche Sirio S.R.L. (1)
Via Brunelleschi 9, 44020, Ostellato, San
Giovanni, Italy
Tel.: (39) 0516781511
Web Site: http://www.sirioequipment.com
Synthetic Rubber & Tire Mfr
N.A.I.C.S.: 326211

Oil Lift Technology Pty Ltd (1)
Tenancy 3 Building 1 261-269 Gooderham
Road, Willawong, Brisbane, 4110, QLD,
Australia
Tel.: (61) 737274000
Web Site: https://www.championx.com
Emp.: 67
Mining Machinery & Equipment Mfr
N.A.I.C.S.: 333131

PCS Ferguson Canada Inc. (1)
950 64 Ave NE, Calgary, T2E 8S8, AB,
Canada
Tel.: (403) 266-6139
Emp.: 3
Industrial Machinery & Equipment Whslr
N.A.I.C.S.: 423830
Mike Atencio (Controller)

PSD Codax Limited (1)
Axis 8 Hawkfield Business Park Hawkfield
Way, Whitchurch, Bristol, BS14 0BY, United
Kingdom
Tel.: (44) 1275866910
Web Site: http://www.psdcodax.com
Software Development Services
N.A.I.C.S.: 541511

PSG California LLC (1)
22009 Van Duren St, Grand Terrace, CA
92313-5607
Tel.: (909) 422-1700
Fluid Pump Mfr
N.A.I.C.S.: 333996

PSG Germany GmbH (1)
Hochstrasse 150-152, 47228, Duisburg,
Germany
Tel.: (49) 2065892050
Web Site: https://www.psgdover.com
Pumps Mfr
N.A.I.C.S.: 333914

Petro Vend Sp. z o.o. (1)
Ul Gen B Zielinskiego 22, Wegrzce, 30-320,
Krakow, Poland
Tel.: (48) 124106610
Oil & Energy Related Equipment Mfr
N.A.I.C.S.: 333132

Pro-Rod Inc. (1)
Suite 400 600 6th Ave SW, Calgary, T2P
0T8, AB, Canada
Tel.: (403) 269-5116
Web Site: http://www.prorod.com
Industrial Machinery & Equipment Whslr
N.A.I.C.S.: 423830

RAV Equipos Espana, S.L. (1)
Avenida Europa 17 Parcela 1 Nave 1 Poligono Industrial de Costanti, Tarragona,
Spain
Tel.: (34) 977524525
Car & Commercial Vehicle Repair Equipment Mfr
N.A.I.C.S.: 336390

RAV France (1)
4 rue de Longue Raie Zac de la Tremblaie,
91220, Le Plessis-Pate, France
Tel.: (33) 160868815
Car & Commercial Vehicle Repair Equipment Mfr
N.A.I.C.S.: 336390

Ravaglioli Deutschland GmbH (1)
Kirchenpoint 22, 85354, Freising, Germany
Tel.: (49) 8165646956
Car & Commercial Vehicle Repair Equipment Mfr
N.A.I.C.S.: 336390

Ravaglioli S.P.A. (1)
via I Maggio n 3 Frazione di Pontecchio
Marconi, 40037, Sasso Marconi, Italy
Tel.: (39) 0516781511
Web Site: https://ravaglioli.com
Car & Commercial Vehicle Repair Equipment Mfr
N.A.I.C.S.: 336390

SWEP Germany GmbH (1)
Gropiusstr 3, 31137, Hildesheim, Germany
Tel.: (49) 5121998670
Customer Service Management Consulting
Services
N.A.I.C.S.: 541613

Simmons Sirvey Corporation (1)
106 E Main St, Richardson, TX 75081-3327
Tel.: (972) 497-9002
Emp.: 30
Fuel Dispensing Systems Mfr
N.A.I.C.S.: 333914
Myra Canterbury (Pres)
Kevin H. Dockery (VP-Sls)
Robert Dentremont (Engr-Electrical)

So Cal Soft-Pak, Inc. (1)
8525 Gibbs Dr 300, San Diego, CA 92123
Tel.: (619) 283-2330
Web Site: http://www.soft-pak.com
Sales Range: $1-9.9 Million
Software Publisher
N.A.I.C.S.: 513210
Brian Porter (Pres)
Steve Belt (Acct Mgr-Western US &
Canada Reg)
Eddie Garratt (VP-Dev)
Dawn Wittig (VP-Ops)
Chester Howe (VP-IT)
Sandy Geerdes (VP-Support Svcs)
Chris Anselmo (Acct Mgr-Eastern US)

Solaris Laser S.A. (1)
Farbiarska 39, 02-862, Warsaw, Poland
Tel.: (48) 228568970
Web Site: https://www.solarislaser.com.pl
Electrical & Electronic Product Mfr
N.A.I.C.S.: 335999
Lech Boruc (Pres)

Space S.R.L. (1)
Via Sangano 48, Trana, 10090, Turin, Italy
Tel.: (39) 01193440300
Web Site: https://www.spacetest.com
Wheel Balancers & Electronic Product Mfr
N.A.I.C.S.: 336320

Spirit Global Energy Solutions
Canada Ltd. (1)
Bay 3 1206-10 st, Nisku, T9E 8K2, AB,
Canada
Tel.: (780) 979-9934
Artificial Lift Equipment Mfr
N.A.I.C.S.: 333998

Spirit Global Energy Solutions,
Inc. (1)
3406 S State Hwy 349, Midland, TX 79706
Tel.: (432) 522-2288
Web Site:
http://www.spiritenergysolutions.com
Industrial Equipment Merchant Whslr
N.A.I.C.S.: 423830

Systech Solutions, Inc. (1)
214 Carnegie Ctr Ste 101, Princeton, NJ
08540
Tel.: (609) 395-8400
Web Site: https://www.systechone.com
Computer Peripheral Equipment Mfr
N.A.I.C.S.: 334118
Joe Belenardo (Sr VP-Global Sls)

TQC Quantium Quality, S.A. de
C.V. (1)

Carretera federal Mexico Puebla km 100
bodega 3 San Juan Tlautla, San Pedro
Cholula, Puebla, Mexico
Tel.: (52) 2222216429
Web Site:
    https://www.quantiumquality.com.mx
Equipment Repair & Maintenance Services
N.A.I.C.S.: 811310

Tartan Textile Services, Inc.   (1)
333 N Sam Houston Pkwy E Ste 200,
Houston, TX 77060-2414
Tel.: (281) 716-2000
Linen Distr
N.A.I.C.S.: 812331

The Curotto-Can, LLC   (1)
201 W Main St Ste 300, Chattanooga, TN
37408
Tel.: (707) 939-2802
Web Site: https://www.thecurottocan.com
Waste Hauler Mfr
N.A.I.C.S.: 562211

The Espy Corp.   (1)
3698 Rr 620 S Ste 110-111, Austin, TX
78738-1568
Tel.: (512) 443-4847
Web Site: http://www.espy.com
Sales Range: $1-9.9 Million
Emp.: 12
Custom Computer Programming Services
N.A.I.C.S.: 541511
Mark Smith (Pres)

Tokheim Belgium   (1)
Everdongenlaan 31, 2300, Turnhout, Bel-
gium
Tel.: (32) 14448500
Fuel Dispensing Equipment Mfr
N.A.I.C.S.: 333996

Tokheim Guardian Venture Sdn.
Bhd   (1)
No 21 21-1 Jalan Neutron U16 Q Seksyen
U16, Denai Alam, 40160, Shah Alam, Se-
langor, Malaysia
Tel.: (60) 6378597080
Web Site: https://namtech.com.my
Fuel Dispenser Mfr
N.A.I.C.S.: 333914

Tokheim Hengshan Technologies
(Guangzhou) Co. Ltd.   (1)
No 66 Nanxiang 1st Road Science City,
Huangpu District, Guangzhou, Guangdong,
China
Tel.: (86) 4007001128
Web Site: http://www.tokheim.com.cn
Car Washing Machinery & Commercial
Equipment Mfr
N.A.I.C.S.: 333310
Jianming Chen (VP)

Tokheim India Private Limited   (1)
A174 TTC Industrial area MIDC, Village
Khairane, Navi Mumbai, 400709, India
Tel.: (91) 2267614100
Fuel Dispenser Mfr
N.A.I.C.S.: 333914

Tokheim Netherlands B.V.   (1)
Industrieweg 5, 5531 AD, Bladel, Nether-
lands
Tel.: (31) 497389500
Fuel Dispenser Mfr
N.A.I.C.S.: 333914

Tokheim Sofitam Applications   (1)
Route de Soliers, Grentheville, 14540,
Villepinte, France
Tel.: (33) 231151515
Fuel Dispenser Mfr
N.A.I.C.S.: 333914

Val Glass US LLC   (1)
12391 Montero Ave, Sylmar, CA 91342
Tel.: (818) 365-9451
Flat Glass Mfr
N.A.I.C.S.: 327211

WSCR Corp.   (1)
1325 S Colorado Blvd Bldg B Ste 400, Den-
ver, CO 80222
Tel.: (303) 777-2663
Web Site:
    http://www.westernstatesncorp.org
Cancer Research Development Services
N.A.I.C.S.: 813212
Lisa Switzer (CEO & Exec Dir)
Kris Castagnaro (COO)
Trish Gleason (CFO)
David Sevick (Dir-Dev & Comm)

Warn Automotive, LLC   (1)
13270 SE Pheasant Ct, Milwaukie, OR
97222
Tel.: (503) 659-8750
Web Site: https://www.warnauto.com
Car Parts & Accessory Mfr
N.A.I.C.S.: 336390

Wayne Fueling Systems LLC   (1)
3814 Jarrett Way, Austin, TX 78728
Tel.: (512) 388-8311
Web Site: http://www.wayne.com
Fuel Dispensing Systems Mfr
N.A.I.C.S.: 333914

Wayne Fueling Systems Sweden
AB   (1)
Hanogatan 10, 211 24, Malmo, Sweden
Tel.: (46) 40360500
Fuel Dispenser Mfr
N.A.I.C.S.: 333914

em-tec GmbH   (1)
Lerchenberg 20, Finning, 86923, Lands-
berg, Germany
Tel.: (49) 880692360
Web Site: http://www.em-tec.de
Electronics Mfr
N.A.I.C.S.: 334111

uniclip Verpackungstechnik
GmbH   (1)
Wilhelm-bergner-str 9a, Glinde, Germany
Tel.: (49) 407277040
General Purpose Machinery Mfr
N.A.I.C.S.: 333998

DOW INC.
2211 H H Dow Way, Midland, MI
48674
Tel.: (989) 636-1000   DE
Web Site: https://www.dow.com
Year Founded: 2018
DOW—(NYSE)
Rev.: $44,622,000,000
Assets: $57,967,000,000
Liabilities: $38,859,000,000
Net Worth: $19,108,000,000
Earnings: $660,000,000
Emp.: 35,900
Fiscal Year-end: 12/31/23
Holding Company
N.A.I.C.S.: 551112
Jeffrey L. Tate (CFO)
James R. Fitterling (Chm & CEO)
Ronald C. Edmonds (VP-Controllers
& Tax & Controller)
John M. Sampson (Sr VP-Ops, Mfg,
and Engrg)
Jack Broodo (Pres-Feedstocks & En-
ergy)
Neil Carr (Pres-Europe, Middle East,
Africa & India)
Karen S. Carter (Chief HR Officer &
Chief Inclusion Officer)
Diego Donoso (Pres-Pkg & Specialty
Plastics)
Mauro Gregorio (Pres-Performance
Materials & Coatings)
Melanie Kalmar (CIO, Chief Digital
Officer & VP)
Torsten Kraef (Sr VP-Corp Dev)
Jane M. Palmieri (Pres-Industrial In-
termediates & Infrastructure-Asia Pa-
cific oversight)
A. N. Sreeram (CTO & Sr VP-R&D)
Amy E. Wilson (Gen Counsel & Sec)

Subsidiaries:

Dow (Shanghai) Holding Co.,
Ltd.   (1)
Suite 2804 Building C Tiley Central Plaza
Hai De San Street, Shenzhen, 518054,
China
Tel.: (86) 75582816800
Chemical Product Mfr & Distr
N.A.I.C.S.: 325998

Dow Material Sciences Ltd.   (1)
Atrium Building 18th floor 2 Jabotinsky Rd,
Ramat Gan, Israel
Tel.: (972) 733903726

Chemical Product Mfr & Distr
N.A.I.C.S.: 325998

Dow Toray Co., Ltd.   (1)
Tennoz Central Tower 10F 2-24 Higashi
Shinagawa 2-chome, Shinagawa-ku, Tokyo,
140-8617, Japan
Tel.: (81) 354604380
Chemical Product Mfr & Distr
N.A.I.C.S.: 325998

Industrienetzgesellschaft Schkopau
mbH   (1)
Strasse B 13, 06258, Schkopau, Germany
Tel.: (49) 3461490
Petrochemical Mfr
N.A.I.C.S.: 325110

The Dow Chemical Company   (1)
1790 Bldg, Midland, MI 48667
Tel.: (989) 636-1000
Rev.: $44,621,999,999
Assets: $58,015,000,000
Liabilities: $38,609,000,000
Net Worth: $19,406,000,000
Earnings: $556,000,000
Emp.: 35,899
Fiscal Year-end: 12/31/2023
Holding Company; Chemicals, Petrochemi-
cals, Agricultural Chemicals, Plastics, Spe-
cialty Coatings & Products Mfr & Whslr
N.A.I.C.S.: 551112
James R. Fitterling (Chm & CEO)

Joint Venture (Non-US):

Arabian Chemical Company (Latex)
Ltd.   (2)
Juffali Head Office Building 4th Floor Madi-
nah Rd, PO Box 5728, Jeddah, 21432,
Saudi Arabia
Tel.: (966) 26633516
Web Site: http://www.juffali.com
Styrene/Butadiene Latex (for the carpet,
paper & construction sectors) Mfr
N.A.I.C.S.: 424690

Arabian Chemical Company (Polysty-
rene) Limited   (2)
Madinah Road, PO Box 5728, Jeddah,
21432, Saudi Arabia
Tel.: (966) 26633516
Web Site: http://www.eajb.com.sa
Chemical Distr
N.A.I.C.S.: 424690

Subsidiary (Domestic):

DC Alabama, Inc.   (2)
1940 Ohio Ferro Rd, Mount Meigs, AL
36057
Tel.: (334) 215-7560
Petrochemical Mfr
N.A.I.C.S.: 325110

Dorinco Reinsurance Company   (2)
2211 H H Dow Way, Midland, MI 48674
Tel.: (989) 636-0047
Web Site: http://www.dorinco.com
Reinsurance Services
N.A.I.C.S.: 524126
D. E. Chamberlain (Exec VP)
Julie M. Premo (VP & Controller)
G. J. McGuire (Pres & CEO)
E. C. Nicholas (Asst Sec)
Veronica Dejeu (VP-Ops)
J. Blaha (Treas)

Subsidiary (Non-US):

Dow Austria Gesellschaft m.b.H   (2)
Donau-City-Strasse 7/OG 40, 1220, Vienna,
Austria
Tel.: (43) 15121694
Petrochemical Mfr
N.A.I.C.S.: 325110

Dow Brasil Industria e Comercio de
Produtos Quimicos Ltda.   (2)
Av das Nacoes Unidas 14171 Diamond
Tower, Sao Paulo, 04795-000, SP, Brazil
Tel.: (55) 1151889000
Web Site: https://br.dow.com
Chemical Products Distr
N.A.I.C.S.: 424690

Dow Brasil Sudeste Industrial
Ltda.   (2)
Av das Nacoes Unidas 14171 4 Floor Part
Diamond Tower, Santo Amaro, Sao Paulo,

04794-000, Brazil
Tel.: (55) 1135634300
Petrochemical Mfr
N.A.I.C.S.: 325110

Dow Chemical (Australia) Pty
Ltd.   (2)
541-583 Kororoit Creek Road, Altona, 3018,
VIC, Australia
Tel.: (61) 392263500
Web Site: http://www.dow.com
Basic Chemicals Mfr
N.A.I.C.S.: 325998

Dow Chemical (China) Investment
Company Limited   (2)
Room 1101 Oriental Plaza 1 East Changan
Avenue, Dongcheng District, Beijing,
100738, China
Tel.: (86) 1085279199
Web Site: https://cn.dow.com
Holding Company
N.A.I.C.S.: 551112

Subsidiary (Domestic):

Dow Chemical (Sichuan) Co.,
Ltd.   (3)
Chengmei Petrochemical Industrial Park,
Xiejia Town Pengshan, Meishan, 620860,
Sichuan, China
Tel.: (86) 2837720417
Petrochemical Mfr
N.A.I.C.S.: 325110

Subsidiary (Non-US):

Dow Chemical (NZ) Limited   (2)
Level 13 7 City Road, Grafton, Auckland,
1010, New Zealand
Tel.: (64) 93799664
Web Site: http://www.dow.com
Basic Chemicals Sales
N.A.I.C.S.: 325998

Dow Chemical (Zhangjiagang) Co.,
Ltd.   (2)
No 3 Nanjing Road, Yangtze River Interna-
tional, Yangtze River International Chemical
Industrial Park, Zhangjiagang, 215633,
China
Tel.: (86) 51258321122
Web Site: http://www.dow.com
Organic Chemical Product Whslr
N.A.I.C.S.: 424690

Dow Chemical Bangladesh Private
Limited   (2)
Office No 316 Regus Bangladesh SE D 22
Level 3 Road 140, Gulshan South Avenue
Gulshan 1, Dhaka, 1212, Bangladesh
Tel.: (880) 9611888605
Petrochemical Mfr
N.A.I.C.S.: 325110

Dow Chemical Canada ULC   (2)
Suite 2400 215-2nd Street SW, Calgary,
T2P 1M4, AB, Canada
Tel.: (403) 267-3500
Web Site: http://www.dow.com
Chemical Products Mfr
N.A.I.C.S.: 325199

Dow Chemical Canada ULC   (2)
Suite 2400 215 -2nd Street S W, Calgary,
T2P 1M4, AB, Canada
Tel.: (403) 267-3500
Web Site: https://ca.dow.com
Industrial Chemicals & Plastics Mfr & Sales
N.A.I.C.S.: 424690

Branch (Domestic):

Dow Chemical Canada ULC   (3)
Prentiss Site, PO Box 5501, Red Deer, T4N
6N1, AB, Canada
Tel.: (403) 885-7000
Web Site: http://www.dow.com
Industrial Organic Chemicals Mfr
N.A.I.C.S.: 325199

Joint Venture (Domestic):

MEGlobal Canada Inc.   (3)
Hwy 597 & Prentiss Road, Red Deer, T4N
6N1, AB, Canada   (50%)
Tel.: (403) 885-8536
Web Site: https://www.meglobal.biz
Chemicals Mfr

Dow Inc.—(Continued)
N.A.I.C.S.: 325998

Subsidiary (Domestic):

Dow Chemical Inter-American Limited (2)
638 Aldebaran BDE Building Ste HQ06, San Juan, PR 00920
Tel.: (787) 781-1122
Web Site: http://www.dow.com
Plastics Materials & Resins Mfr
N.A.I.C.S.: 424690

Subsidiary (Non-US):

Dow Chemical International Pvt. Ltd. (2)
Unit No 801 8th Floor Building No 9 Gigaplex, TTC Industrial Area MIDC Airoli, Mumbai, 400 708, Maharashtra, India
Tel.: (91) 2266741500
Web Site: http://www.dow.com
Chemical Products Mfr
N.A.I.C.S.: 325199

Dow Chemical Japan Limited (2)
Tennoz Central Tower 10F 2-24 Higashi Shinagawa 2-chome, Shinagawa-ku, Tokyo, 140-8617, Japan
Tel.: (81) 120103742
Web Site: https://jp.dow.com
Emp.: 150
Chemicals Distr & Sales
N.A.I.C.S.: 424690

Dow Chemical Korea Limited (2)
4-5F I-Park Tower 520, Yeongdong-daero Gangnam-gu, Seoul, Korea (South)
Tel.: (82) 23 490 0700
Web Site: http://www.dow.com
Chemicals Mfr
N.A.I.C.S.: 325998

Dow Chemical Pacific (Singapore) Pte Ltd. (2)
260 Orchard Rd 18-01 The Heeren, Singapore, 238855, Singapore
Tel.: (65) 68353773
Web Site: http://www.dow.com
Chemicals & Plastics Sales & Services
N.A.I.C.S.: 325998

Subsidiary (Non-US):

Dow Chemical (Guangzhou) Company Limited (3)
No 2 Jinhua Er St Jinxiu Road GETDD, Guangzhou, 510730, Guangdong, China
Tel.: (86) 2082 220 3223
Web Site: http://www.dow.com
Chemicals Mfr
N.A.I.C.S.: 325998

Dow Chemical (Malaysia) Sdn. Bhd. (3)
Level 6 C P Tower Jalan 16/11 Pusat Dagang Section 16, 46350, Petaling Jaya, Selangor, Malaysia
Tel.: (60) 37 965 5200
Web Site: http://www.dow.com
Chemicals Mfr
N.A.I.C.S.: 325998

PT Dow Indonesia (3)
World Trade Center 3 32nd Floor Jl Jend Sudirman Kav 29, Jakarta, 12920, Indonesia
Tel.: (62) 2129956200
Web Site: http://www.dow.com
Chemical Sales
N.A.I.C.S.: 325998

Subsidiary (Non-US):

Dow Chemical Pacific Limited (2)
47th Floor Sun Hung Kai Centre 30 Harbour Road, PO Box 711, Wanchai, China (Hong Kong)
Tel.: (852) 28797333
Web Site: http://www.dow.com
Chemicals & Allied Products Mfr & Sales
N.A.I.C.S.: 424690

Dow Chemical Philippines, Inc. (2)
23rd Floor 6750 Ayala Avenue, Makati, 1226, Philippines
Tel.: (63) 28191986
Web Site: http://www.dow.com
Chemicals & Plastics Sales

N.A.I.C.S.: 325998

Dow Chemical Romania S.R.L. (2)
6-8 Corneliu Coposu Boulevard Unirii View Building 2nd Floor, Rooms 202 203 204 Sector 3, 030167, Bucharest, Romania
Tel.: (40) 318609118
Petrochemical Mfr
N.A.I.C.S.: 325110

Dow Chemical Silicones Korea, Ltd. (2)
5F I-Park Tower520, Yeongdong-daero Gangnam-gu, Seoul, Korea (South)
Tel.: (82) 234898700
Petrochemical Mfr
N.A.I.C.S.: 325110

Dow Chemical Taiwan Limited (2)
No 9 Kung Yeah Nan 1st Road Nankang Industrial Park, Nantou, 54066, Taiwan
Tel.: (886) 49 225 5535
Web Site: http://www.dow.com
Chemicals Mfr
N.A.I.C.S.: 325998

Dow Chemical Thailand Ltd. (2)
10 Moo 2 Asia Industrial Estate, PO Box 71, Banchang Sub-District Banchang District, Rayong, 21130, Thailand
Tel.: (66) 38925500
Petrochemical Mfr
N.A.I.C.S.: 325110

Dow Chemical Vietnam LLC (2)
Unit 503 5th Floor CentrePoint Building, 106 Nguyen Van Troi Street Ward 8 Phu Nhuan District, Ho Chi Minh City, Vietnam
Tel.: (84) 2862845588
Petrochemical Mfr
N.A.I.C.S.: 325110

Dow Corning Singapore Pte. Ltd. (2)
1 Fusionopolis Walk Suite 07-11 Solaris North Tower, Singapore, 138628, Singapore
Tel.: (65) 63593356
Organic Chemical Mfr
N.A.I.C.S.: 325199

Dow Egypt Services Limited (2)
Katameya Heights Business Center - Office G01 Fifth Settlement, New Cairo, Egypt
Tel.: (20) 220200683
Petrochemical Mfr
N.A.I.C.S.: 325110

Subsidiary (Domestic):

Dow Financial Holdings Inc. (2)
2030 Dow Ctr, Midland, MI 48674
Tel.: (989) 636-1000
Web Site: http://www.dow.com
Holding Company
N.A.I.C.S.: 551112

Subsidiary (Domestic):

Dow Holdings LLC (3)
2030 Dow Ctr, Midland, MI 48674 **(100%)**
Tel.: (989) 636-1000
Web Site: http://www.dow.com
Sales Range: $50-74.9 Million
Emp.: 120
Holding Company
N.A.I.C.S.: 551112

Subsidiary (Domestic):

Dow Pipe Line Company (4)
1000 County Rd 340, Angleton, TX 77515-9597
Tel.: (979) 849-5101
Gasoline Pipelines
N.A.I.C.S.: 486910

Unit (Domestic):

Dow Pipe Line Company (5)
986 County Rd 340 Brazoria, Angleton, TX 77515
Tel.: (979) 849-5101
Gasoline Pipelines
N.A.I.C.S.: 213112

Dow Pipe Line Company (5)
727 Old Underwood Rd, La Porte, TX 77571
Tel.: (281) 471-9440
Web Site: http://www.dow.com
Gasoline Pipelines Operator
N.A.I.C.S.: 486910

Dow Pipe Line Company (5)
2009 Crescent Heights St, Freeport, TX 77541
Tel.: (979) 238-2011
Web Site: http://www.dow.com
Refined Petroleum Pipelines Operations
N.A.I.C.S.: 486910

Subsidiary (Domestic):

Dow Silicones Corporation (4)
5300 11 Mile Rd, Auburn, MI 48611
Tel.: (989) 496-4400
Web Site: http://www.dow.com
Silicone-Based Products, Adhesives, Lubricants & Insulating Materials Mfr
N.A.I.C.S.: 325180

Subsidiary (Domestic):

DC Alabama, Inc. (5)
1940 Ohio Ferro Rd, Mount Meigs, AL 36057
Tel.: (334) 215-7560
Web Site: http://corporate.dow.com
Rubber Products Mfr
N.A.I.C.S.: 325199

Subsidiary (Non-US):

Dow Corning Australia Pty Ltd (5)
F17 Melbourne Commercial Centre 8 Exhibition St, Melbourne, 3000, VIC, Australia
Tel.: (61) 399567500
Glassware Mfr
N.A.I.C.S.: 327212

Joint Venture (Non-US):

Dow Corning Toray Silicon Co., Ltd. (5)
AIG Bldg 1 1 3 4th Fl Dow Corning Toray Marunouchi Chiyoda Ku, Tokyo, 1000005, Japan **(50%)**
Tel.: (81) 332871011
Web Site: http://www.dowcorning.co.jp
Silicon & Organosilicon Polymer Products & Compounds Mfr & Whslr
N.A.I.C.S.: 325211

Division (Domestic):

Dow Silicones Corporation - Kendallville Site (5)
111 S Progress Dr E, Kendallville, IN 46755-3268
Tel.: (260) 347-5813
Web Site: http://www.dow.com
Rubber Products Mfr
N.A.I.C.S.: 325199

Subsidiary (Non-US):

Multibase India Limited (5)
74 / 5&6 Daman Industrial Estate, Kadaiya, Mumbai, 400051, India
Tel.: (91) 2602220627
Web Site: https://www.multibaseindia.com
Rev.: $7,855,234
Assets: $17,170,349
Liabilities: $1,658,530
Net Worth: $15,511,819
Earnings: $916,748
Emp.: 23
Fiscal Year-end: 03/31/2021
Thermoplastic Compound Mfr
N.A.I.C.S.: 325211
Deepak Arun Dhanak *(Mng Dir)*
Sunaina Goraksh *(Compliance Officer & Sec)*
Pankaj Holani *(CFO)*

Joint Venture (Domestic):

Hemlock Semiconductor, LLC (4)
1805 Salzburg St, Midland, MI 48640
Tel.: (989) 301-5000
Web Site: https://www.hscpoly.com
Polysilicon Material Mfr & Distr
N.A.I.C.S.: 325199
Mark R. Bassett *(Chm & CEO)*
Philip D. Dembowski *(Chief Comml Officer & Sr VP)*
Steven M. Sklenar *(CFO)*
Greggory M. Lubben *(Sr Exec VP)*
George M. Mesrey *(Gen Counsel & Sec)*
Mark J. Loboda *(Sr VP-Science & Tech)*

Subsidiary (Domestic):

Hemlock Semiconductor Operations LLC (5)

12334 Geddes Rd, Hemlock, MI 48626-9409
Tel.: (989) 301-5000
Web Site: https://www.hscpoly.com
Polysilicon Materials Mfr & Whslr
N.A.I.C.S.: 325180
Mark R. Bassett *(Chm & CEO)*

Subsidiary (Domestic):

Dow International Holdings Company (2)
2030 Dow Ctr, Midland, MI 48674
Tel.: (989) 636-1000
Web Site: http://www.dow.com
Holding Company
N.A.I.C.S.: 551112

Subsidiary (Non-US):

Dow International Holdings S.A. (3)
Bachtobelstrasse 3, 8810, Horgen, Switzerland **(100%)**
Tel.: (41) 17282111
Web Site: http://ch.dow.com
Holding Company
N.A.I.C.S.: 551112

Subsidiary (Domestic):

Dow Europe GmbH (4)
Bachtobelstrasse 3, 8810, Horgen, Switzerland **(100%)**
Tel.: (41) 447282111
Web Site: https://ch.dow.com
Chemicals Mfr & Sales
N.A.I.C.S.: 325180
Heinz Haller *(Pres-EMEA & Exec VP)*

Subsidiary (Non-US):

Dow Belgium B.V.B.A (5)
Grote Steenweg 214, 2600, Antwerp, Belgium **(100%)**
Tel.: (32) 34502011
Chemicals Mfr
N.A.I.C.S.: 325998

Dow Chemical Company Limited (5)
5 Oakwater Avenue Cheadle Royal Business Park, Cheadle, SK8 3SR, United Kingdom **(100%)**
Tel.: (44) 1615138400
Web Site: https://gb.dow.com
Basic Chemicals Mfr
N.A.I.C.S.: 325998

Dow Chemical Iberica S.A. (5)
Calle Jose Abascal 56 5 planta; 28042, Madrid, Spain **(100%)**
Tel.: (34) 917407800
Web Site: http://es.dow.com
Chemicals Mfr
N.A.I.C.S.: 325998

Dow Deutschland Anlagengesellschaft mbH (5)
Rheingaustr 34, 65201, Wiesbaden, Germany **(100%)**
Tel.: (49) 611237007
Web Site: https://de.dow.com
Emp.: 3,600
Chemical Products Mfr
N.A.I.C.S.: 325320
Ralf Brinkman *(Chm)*
Claudio Ciuchini *(Mng Dir)*
Neides Hovestad *(Mng Dir)*
Jana Kramer *(Mng Dir)*
Klaus Rudert *(Mng Dir)*
Jorg Schmitz *(Mng Dir)*
Dieter Schnepel *(Mng Dir)*
Marc van den Biggelaar *(Mng Dir)*

Subsidiary (Domestic):

Dow Deutschland Beteiligungsgesellschaft mbH (6)
Werk Stade Buetzflether Sand 9, 21683, Stade, Germany
Tel.: (49) 4146910
Web Site: http://de.dow.com
Chemicals Mfr
N.A.I.C.S.: 325998
Dieter Schnepes *(Mng Dir & Dir-Global Bus Mfg)*

Dow Olefinverbund GmbH (6)
Strasse B 13, 06258, Schkopau, Germany **(100%)**
Tel.: (49) 3461490
Web Site: https://de.dow.com

Plastics Product Mfr
N.A.I.C.S.: 326199

Subsidiary (Non-US):

Dow Europe Holdings B.V. (5)
Herbert H Dowweg 5, Postbus 48, 4542
NM, Terneuzen, Netherlands
Tel.: (31) 115671234
Web Site: http://corporate.dow.com
Holding Company
N.A.I.C.S.: 551112
Peter Holicki (Sr VP-Ops, Mfg & Engrg)

Subsidiary (Domestic):

Dow Benelux B.V. (6)
Heemskesweg 45-47, 9936 HE, Delfzijl,
Netherlands (100%)
Tel.: (31) 596675000
Web Site: https://nl.dow.com
Chemicals Mfr
N.A.I.C.S.: 325998
Neldes Hovestad (VP-Ops)

Subsidiary (Domestic):

**Valuepark Terneuzen Beheer
B.V.** (7)
Schelpenpad 2, 4531 PD, Terneuzen, Neth-
erlands
Tel.: (31) 115647400
Web Site: http://www.vpterneuzen.com
Chemical Products Mfr
N.A.I.C.S.: 325199

Subsidiary (Non-US):

Dow Chemical Romania S.R.L. (6)
6-8 Corneliu Coposu Boulevard 030167
Uniril View Building 2nd Floor, Rooms 202
203 204 Sector 3, Bucharest, Romania
Tel.: (40) 318609118
Chemical Products Distr
N.A.I.C.S.: 423830

Subsidiary (Domestic):

Dow Interbranch B.V. (6)
Herbert H Dowweg 5, 4542 NM, Hoek,
Netherlands
Tel.: (31) 115671234
Holding Company
N.A.I.C.S.: 551112

Subsidiary (Non-US):

Dow France S.A.S. (5)
23 Avenue Jules Rimet, 93200, Saint Denis,
France (100%)
Tel.: (33) 149217878
Web Site: https://fr.dow.com
Chemicals & Plastics Mfr & Sales
N.A.I.C.S.: 325998
Helena Guerreiro (Dir-HR)

Dow Hellas SA (5)
Atrina Center 32 Kifisias Avenue, 15125,
Maroussi, Greece (100%)
Tel.: (30) 2144449910
Web Site: http://corporate.dow.com
Plastics & Resins Mfr & Sales
N.A.I.C.S.: 325211

Dow Hungary Ltd. (5)
WestEnd Centre Regus Vaci ut 22 24 7th
Floor, 1132, Budapest, Hungary
Tel.: (36) 18089437
Web Site: http://hu.dow.com
Chemicals Sales & Distr
N.A.I.C.S.: 325998

Dow Italia s.r.l. (5)
Via Carpi 29, 42015, Correggio, RE, Italy
Tel.: (39) 05226451
Web Site: http://it.dow.com
Chemical, Polyurethane & Fabricated Prod-
ucts Mfr
N.A.I.C.S.: 326150

Unit (Domestic):

Dow Italia S.r.l. (6)
Via Francesco Albani 65, 20148, Milan, Italy
Tel.: (39) 0248221
Web Site: https://it.dow.com
Chemicals Mfr
N.A.I.C.S.: 325998

Subsidiary (Non-US):

Dow Polska Sp.z.o.o. (5)

Ul Woloska 22 / 22a, 02-675, Warsaw,
Poland (100%)
Tel.: (48) 225431800
Chemical Sales & Distr
N.A.I.C.S.: 325998

**Dow Portugal - Produtos Quimicos
Unipessoal, Lda.** (5)
Rua Do Rio Antua 1, Estarreja, 3850-529,
Portugal (100%)
Tel.: (351) 234811000
Chemicals Mfr
N.A.I.C.S.: 325998

Dow Southern Africa (Pty) Ltd. (5)
8 Schafer Rd, New Germany KwaZulu-
Nata, Durban, 3610, South Africa (100%)
Tel.: (27) 317165900
Chemicals & Plastics Mfr & Sales
N.A.I.C.S.: 325998

Dow Sverige AB (5)
Ringvagen 163, 261 52, Landskrona,
Sweden (100%)
Tel.: (46) 418450400
Latex, Specialty Chemicals & Resins Sales
N.A.I.C.S.: 325998

**Dow Turkiye Kimya Sanayi ve Ticaret
Ltd Sti** (5)
Dilovasi Organize Sanayi Bolgesi 2 Kisim
D-2001, Sok No 1 Dilovasi, Kocaeli, 41455,
Kisim, Turkiye
Tel.: (90) 2626489600
Web Site: http://www.dow.com
Chemicals Sales & Distr
N.A.I.C.S.: 325998

Subsidiary (Non-US):

Dow Investment Argentina S.R.L. (6)
Boulevard Cecilia Grierson 355 Dique IV,
Piso 25 Puerto Madero, C1107CPG, Bue-
nos Aires, Argentina
Tel.: (54) 1143190100
Web Site: https://ar.dow.com
Chemicals Mfr
N.A.I.C.S.: 325998

Subsidiary (Domestic):

PBBPolisur S.R.L. (3)
Boulevard Cecilia Grierson 355 Dique IV
Piso 25, Puerto Madero, C1107CPG, Bue-
nos Aires, Argentina
Tel.: (54) 1143190100
Web Site: http://www.ar.dow.com
Chemicals Mfr
N.A.I.C.S.: 325998

Subsidiary (Non-US):

**Dow Italia Divisione Commerciale
s.r.l** (2)
Via Francesco Albani 65, 20148, Milan, Italy
Tel.: (39) 0248221
Petrochemical Mfr
N.A.I.C.S.: 325110

**Dow Materials Science Saudi Arabia
Limited** (2)
Adeer Tower - 12th Floor Prince Turkey
Street, PO Box 2171, Al Yarmouk Corniche,
Al Khobar, 34413, Saudi Arabia
Tel.: (966) 138068757
Petrochemical Mfr
N.A.I.C.S.: 325110

**Dow Performance Materials (Austra-
lia) Pty. Ltd.** (2)
Hays Road Point Henry, Geelong, 3221,
VIC, Australia
Tel.: (61) 35 227 6300
Web Site: http://www.dow.com
Organic Chemical Mfr
N.A.I.C.S.: 325199

Dow Peru S.A. (2)
Calle Esquilache 371 Piso 13 Oficina 1302,
San Isidro, 27, Lima, Peru
Tel.: (51) 12084700
Petrochemical Mfr
N.A.I.C.S.: 325110

Dow Quimica Chilena S.A. (2)
Americo Vespucio Sur 100 - Piso 6, Las
Condes, Santiago, 7580154, Chile
Tel.: (56) 24404800
Web Site: http://www.dow.com
Chemicals, Plastics & Raw Materials Sales
N.A.I.C.S.: 424690

**Dow Quimica Mexicana S.A. de
C.V.** (2)
Blvd Emilio Sanchez Piedras No 302 Cd
Industrial Xicohtencatl, Tetla, 90434, Tlax-
cala, Mexico
Tel.: (52) 2414189300
Petrochemical Mfr
N.A.I.C.S.: 325110

Dow Quimica de Colombia S.A. (2)
Calle 127 A 53 A 45 Tower 3 - Floor 7 Cen-
tro Empresarial Colpatria, Bogota, 75240
75241, Colombia
Tel.: (57) 1 219 6000
Web Site: http://www.dow.com
Sales & Administration
N.A.I.C.S.: 424690

**Dow Silicones (Shanghai) Co.,
Ltd.** (2)
448 Eastern Avenue, Songjiang Industrial
Zone, Shanghai, 201613, China
Tel.: (86) 2137741116
Petrochemical Mfr
N.A.I.C.S.: 325110

**Dow Silicones (Zhangjiagang) Co.,
Ltd.** (2)
No 18 Beihai Road, Yangtze River Interna-
tional Chemical Industrial Park, Zhangjia-
gang, 215633, Jiangsu, China
Tel.: (86) 51258101111
Petrochemical Mfr
N.A.I.C.S.: 325110

Dow Silicones Belgium SPRL (2)
Rue Jules Bordet, 7180, Seneffe, Belgium
Tel.: (32) 64888000
Web Site: http://www.dow.com
Organic Chemical Mfr
N.A.I.C.S.: 325199

**Dow Silicones Deutschland
GmbH** (2)
Rheingaustr 34, 65201, Wiesbaden, Ger-
many
Tel.: (49) 6112371
Petrochemical Mfr
N.A.I.C.S.: 325110

Dow Silicones UK Limited (2)
Cardiff Road, Barry, CF63 2YL, Vale of
Glamorgan, United Kingdom
Tel.: (44) 144 673 2350
Web Site: http://www.dow.com
Organic Chemical Mfr
N.A.I.C.S.: 325199

**Dow Siloxanes (Zhangjiagang) Co.,
Ltd.** (2)
No 2 Nanjing Road, Yangtze River Interna-
tional Chemical Industrial Park, Zhangjia-
gang, 215633, Jiangsu, China
Tel.: (86) 51258101888
Petrochemical Mfr
N.A.I.C.S.: 325110

**Dow Verwaltungsgesellschaft
mbH** (2)
Berthastr 13, Schkopau, Germany
Tel.: (49) 3461490
Web Site: http://www.dow.com
Chemical Products Mfr
N.A.I.C.S.: 325199

DuPont Asia Pacific Limited (2)
26f Tower 6 the Gateway 9 Canton Road,
Tsim Sha Tsui, Kowloon, China (Hong
Kong)
Tel.: (852) 27345345
Web Site: http://www.dupoint.com
Explosives, Finishes, Photo Products, Tex-
tile Fibers, Agrichemicals, Pharmaceuticals,
Polymer Products, Electronic Material &
Other Lines of Chemicals Distr
N.A.I.C.S.: 314999

Joint Venture (Non-US):

**EQUATE Petrochemical Company
K.S.C.C.** (2)
PO Box 4733, Safat, 13048, Kuwait
Tel.: (965) 1898888
Web Site: http://www.equate.com
Petrochemical Products Mfr
N.A.I.C.S.: 325998
Ramesh Ramachandran (Pres & CEO)
Dawood Al-Abduljalil (CFO)
Sulaiman Al-Marzouqi (Chm)
Raja Zeidan (Vice Chm)

Subsidiary (Domestic):

Global Industrial Corporation (2)
11 Harbor Park Dr, Port Washington, NY
11050
Web Site: https://www.globalindustrial.com
Petrochemical Mfr
N.A.I.C.S.: 325110

Subsidiary (Non-US):

Japan Acrylic Chemical Co., Ltd. (2)
1-64 Funami-cho, Minato-ku, Nagoya, 455-
0027, Aichi, Japan
Tel.: (81) 526110127
Web Site: http://www.dow.com
Chemicals Mfr
N.A.I.C.S.: 325998

Subsidiary (Domestic):

NuvoSun, Inc. (2)
1565 Barber Ln, Milpitas, CA 95035-7409
Tel.: (408) 514-6200
Web Site: http://www.nuvosun.com
Chemical Products Mfr
N.A.I.C.S.: 325199

POLY-CARB, Inc. (2)
8440 Tower Dr, Twinsburg, OH 44087
Tel.: (440) 248-1223
Web Site: http://www.olinpolycarb.com
Sealer, Coating & Adhesive Mfr
N.A.I.C.S.: 325211

Subsidiary (Non-US):

**Palmyra do Brasil Industria e Comer-
cio de Silicio Metalico e Recursos
Naturais Ltda.** (2)
Rua Carlo Pareto 73, Santos Dumont,
36240-000, Minas Gerais, Brazil
Tel.: (55) 3232519100
Silicon Metal Mfr
N.A.I.C.S.: 331110

Subsidiary (Domestic):

Photon Systems, Inc. (2)
1512 Industrial Park St, Covina, CA 91722-
3417
Tel.: (626) 967-6431
Web Site: http://www.photonsystems.com
Professional Equipment Merchant Whslr
N.A.I.C.S.: 423490
Ray D Reid (VP-Ops)
William F. Hug (Pres)

Rofan Services LLC (2)
2030 Dow Ctr, Midland, MI 48674-0001
Tel.: (989) 636-1000
Holding Company
N.A.I.C.S.: 551112

Rohm & Haas Company (2)
100 Independence Mall W, Philadelphia, PA
19106
Tel.: (215) 592-3000
Web Site: http://www.rohmhaas.com
Chemicals Mfr
N.A.I.C.S.: 325998

Subsidiary (Non-US):

PT Rohm and Haas Indonesia (3)
Jl Eropa III Kav M2 Krakatau Industrial Es-
tate, Cilegon, 42443, Jawa Barat, Indonesia
Tel.: (62) 254380631
Organic & Inorganic Chemicals Mfr
N.A.I.C.S.: 325998

Subsidiary (Domestic):

Rohm and Haas Chemicals LLC (3)
Hayward Plant 25500 Whitesell St, Hay-
ward, CA 94545
Tel.: (510) 786-0100
Organic & Inorganic Chemicals Mfr
N.A.I.C.S.: 325180

Subsidiary (Non-US):

Dow France S.A.S. (4)
23 Avenue Jules Rimet, 93200, Saint Denis,
France
Tel.: (33) 149217878
Web Site: http://www.dow.com
Emp.: 400
Specialty Chemicals Mfr
N.A.I.C.S.: 325998

Rohm and Haas Canada LP (4)

Dow Inc.—(Continued)

2 Manse Rd, Scarborough, Toronto, M1E
3T9, ON, Canada
Tel.: (416) 284-4711
Web Site: http://www.dow.com
Chemicals Mfr
N.A.I.C.S.: 325998

Plant (Domestic):

**Rohm and Haas Chemicals LLC -
Bristol Plant** (4)
Bristol Complex 200 Rte 413, Bristol, PA
19007
Tel.: (215) 785-8000
Paints & Coatings Ingredients Mfr
N.A.I.C.S.: 325180

Subsidiary (Non-US):

**Rohm and Haas Chemicals Singa-
pore Pte Ltd.** (4)
250 Ayer Merbau Road, Singapore, 628281,
Jurong Island, Singapore
Tel.: (65) 68675467
Web Site: http://www.dow.com
Organic & Inorganic Chemicals Mfr
N.A.I.C.S.: 325998

Rohm and Haas Finland Oy (4)
Forcitintie 37, Hanko, 10960, Finland
Tel.: (358) 0207578600
Chemical Products Distr
N.A.I.C.S.: 424690

Rohm and Haas Italia Srl (4)
Via Trieste 25, 22076, Como, Mozzate, Italy
Tel.: (39) 0331839111
Web Site: http://www.dow.com
Agricultural Chemical Mfr
N.A.I.C.S.: 325320

Subsidiary (Domestic):

**Rohm and Haas Texas
Incorporated** (4)
1900 Tidal Rd, Deer Park, TX 77536
Tel.: (281) 228-8100
Web Site: http://www.dow.com
Organic & Inorganic Chemicals Mfr
N.A.I.C.S.: 325998

Subsidiary (Non-US):

**Rohm and Haas Espana Production
Holding, S.L.** (3)
Calle Jose Abascal 56 5 planta, Madrid,
28042, Spain
Tel.: (34) 917407800
Chemical Products Mfr
N.A.I.C.S.: 325199

**Rohm and Haas International Trading
(Shanghai) Co., Ltd.** (3)
Room 2401-03 Guangzhou International
Finance Center No 5 West, Zhujiang Road
Zhujiang New Town, Guangzhou, 510623,
China
Tel.: (86) 20 3813 0600
Organic Chemical Product Whslr
N.A.I.C.S.: 424690

**Rohm and Haas Malaysia Sdn.
Bhd.** (3)
Unit 39-6 The Boulevard Mid Valley City,
Lingkaran Syed Putra, 59200, Kuala Lum-
pur, Malaysia
Tel.: (60) 329383866
Web Site: http://www.dow.com
Organic & Inorganic Chemicals Mfr
N.A.I.C.S.: 325998

**Rohm and Haas Singapore (Pte.)
Ltd.** (3)
260 Orchard Road 18-01 The Heeren, Sin-
gapore, 238855, Singapore
Tel.: (65) 68353773
Chemcials Mfr
N.A.I.C.S.: 325998

Subsidiary (Non-US):

**Rohm and Haas (Foshan) Specialty
Materials Co., Ltd.** (2)
Sanshui Central S T Industrial Park No 12
Xile Avenue, Sanshui, Foshan, 528137,
Guangdong, China
Tel.: (86) 75787381822
Chemicals Mfr

N.A.I.C.S.: 325998

**Rohm and Haas Chemical (Thailand)
Limited** (2)
No 17 Soi G-14 Prakornsongkrohrarj Road,
Map Ta Phut Muang, Rayong, 21150, Thai-
land
Tel.: (66) 33012800
Chemicals Mfr
N.A.I.C.S.: 325998

Rohm and Haas Chile Limitada. (2)
Americo Vespucio Sur 100 - Piso 6, San-
tiago, Chile
Tel.: (56) 24404800
Chemicals Mfr
N.A.I.C.S.: 325998

**Rohm and Haas Kimya Sanayi Lim-
ited Sirketi** (2)
DOSB 1 Kisim Liman Cad No 7, Mevkii
Gebze, 41455, Dilovasi, Kocaeli, Türkiye
Tel.: (90) 2626784600
Petrochemical Mfr
N.A.I.C.S.: 325110

**Rohm and Haas Mexico, S. de R.L.
de C.V.** (2)
Av La Noria Prolongacion 122 Parque In-
dustrial Queretaro, KM 28 5 Carretera
QRO-S L P Santa Rosa Jauregui, 76220,
Queretaro, Mexico
Tel.: (52) 4422964917
Web Site: http://www.dow.com
Agricultural Chemical Product Distr
N.A.I.C.S.: 424910

SD Group Service Company Ltd. (2)
8th 14-16th Floor The White Group Building
2, 75 Soi Rubia Sukhumvit 42 Road Prakanong Klongtoey, Bangkok, 10110, Thailand
Tel.: (66) 2 365 7000
Holding Company
N.A.I.C.S.: 551112

SKC Haas Polska Sp.z o. o. (2)
Strefowa 16, Dzierzoniow, 58-200, Poland
Tel.: (48) 74 646 2603
Chemical Products Mfr
N.A.I.C.S.: 325199
Ki young Do (Mgr-Sls)

Siam Polystyrene Co., Ltd. (2)
75 White Group Building 11 14-15th Floor
Soi Rubia, Sukhumvit 42 Rd Khlong Toei,
10110, Bangkok, Thailand
Tel.: (66) 38683215
Organic & Inorganic Chemicals Mfr
N.A.I.C.S.: 325998

Plant (Domestic):

**The Dow Chemical Co. - Bayport
Plant** (2)
13300 Bay Area Blvd, La Porte, TX 77571
Tel.: (281) 474-4495
Web Site: http://www.dow.com
Chemicals Mfr
N.A.I.C.S.: 325320

**The Dow Chemical Co. - Hayward
Plant** (2)
25500 Whitesell St, Hayward, CA 94545
Tel.: (510) 786-0100
Chemical Plant
N.A.I.C.S.: 325998

**The Dow Chemical Company - Knox-
ville Plant** (2)
730 Dale Ave, Knoxville, TN 37921
Tel.: (865) 521-8200
Web Site: http://www.dow.com
Chemicals Mfr
N.A.I.C.S.: 325998

Unit (Domestic):

**The Dow Chemical Company - Loui-
siana Operations** (2)
21255 Louisiana Hwy 1, Plaquemine, LA
70764
Tel.: (225) 353-8000
Web Site: http://www.dow.com
Plastics & Resins Mfr
N.A.I.C.S.: 325199

**The Dow Chemical Company -
Marietta** (2)
1881 W Oak Pkwy, Marietta, GA 30062

Tel.: (770) 428-2684
Web Site: http://www.dow.com
Industrial Inorganic Chemical Mfr
N.A.I.C.S.: 456110

**The Dow Chemical Company -
Norwich** (2)
1761 Rte 12, Gales Ferry, CT 06335
Tel.: (860) 464-7211
Chemicals & Allied Products Mfr
N.A.I.C.S.: 424690

**The Dow Chemical Company -
Russellville** (2)
3230 Dow Rd, Russellville, AR 72802
Tel.: (479) 968-3404
Chlor-Alkali Cell Components Mfr
N.A.I.C.S.: 334516

**The Dow Chemical Company - Texas
Operations** (2)
2301 Brazosport Blvd APB Bldg, Freeport,
TX 77541
Tel.: (979) 238-2011
Chemicals Mfr
N.A.I.C.S.: 325180

**The Dow Chemical Company -
Washington, DC** (2)
19th St NW, Washington, DC 20006
Tel.: (202) 429-3400
Chemical Products Mfr
N.A.I.C.S.: 325320

**The Dow Chemical
Company-Midland** (2)
1790 Bldg, Midland, MI 48667
Tel.: (989) 636-1000
Polyurethane Products Mfr
N.A.I.C.S.: 326150

Subsidiary (Non-US):

Hyperlast Limited (3)
Station Rd High Peak, SK22 1BR, Birch
Vale, Derbs, United Kingdom - England
Tel.: (44) 1663746518
Polyurethane Elastomers, Coatings & Lubri-
cants Mfr
N.A.I.C.S.: 326150

Subsidiary (Domestic):

Union Carbide Corporation (2)
7501 State Hwy 185 N, Seadrift, TX 77983
Tel.: (361) 553-2997
Web Site: http://www.unioncarbide.com
Rev.: $4,296,000,000
Assets: $5,272,000,000
Liabilities: $3,107,000,000
Net Worth: $2,165,000,000
Earnings: $381,000,000
Emp.: 349
Fiscal Year-end: 12/31/2023
Chemicals & Plastics Mfr
N.A.I.C.S.: 325199
Richard A. Wells (Pres & CEO)
Ignacio Molina (CFO, Treas & VP)
Ronald C. Edmonds (VP-Controllers-Tax &
Controller)

Subsidiary (Domestic):

Amerchol Corporation (3)
136 Talmadge Rd, Edison, NJ 08817
Tel.: (732) 248-6000
Chemical Allied Product Merchant Whslr
N.A.I.C.S.: 424690

Subsidiary (Non-US):

**Carbide Chemical (Thailand)
Limited** (3)
99/1 BJC 2 Building Soi Saengchan-Rubia
Sukhumvit 42 Road, Prakanong Klongtoey,
Bangkok, 10110, Thailand
Tel.: (66) 2 365 7000
Web Site: http://th.dow.com
Chemical Products Mfr
N.A.I.C.S.: 325199

Subsidiary (Domestic):

**UCAR Emulsion Systems Interna-
tional, Inc.** (3)
19206 Hawthorne Blvd, Torrance, CA 90503
Tel.: (310) 214-5300
Paint & Allied Product Mfr
N.A.I.C.S.: 325510

**UNISON Transformer Services,
Inc.** (3)
3126 Brinkerhoff Rd, Kansas City, KS
66115
Tel.: (913) 321-3155
Chemical Products Mfr
N.A.I.C.S.: 325199

Umetco Minerals Corporation (3)
2764 Compass Dr 114, Grand Junction, CO
81506 (100%)
Tel.: (970) 245-3700
Environmental Services
N.A.I.C.S.: 541620

Unit (Domestic):

Union Carbide Corporation (3)
171 River Rd, Piscataway, NJ 08854
Tel.: (732) 563-5000
Web Site: http://www.dow.com
Industrial Chemicals Mfr
N.A.I.C.S.: 325211

Union Carbide Corporation (3)
437 MacCorkle Ave SW, South Charleston,
WV 25303-2544
Tel.: (304) 747-7000
Sales Range: $1-4.9 Billion
Industrial Organic Chemicals Mfr
N.A.I.C.S.: 325199

Subsidiary (Domestic):

Univation Technologies, LLC (3)
5555 San Felipe Ste #1950, Houston, TX
77056 (100%)
Tel.: (281) 966-2500
Web Site: http://www.univation.com
Polyethylene Chemicals Mfr & Whslr
N.A.I.C.S.: 325998

Joint Venture (Domestic):

Viance, LLC (2)
8001 IBM Dr Bldg 403, Charlotte, NC
28262
Tel.: (704) 522-0825
Web Site: http://www.treatwood.com
Timber Treatment Products Mfr
N.A.I.C.S.: 325180
Steve Furr (Dir-Engrg & Tech Svcs)
John Hussa (Pres)
Edie Kello (Dir-Mktg)
Jonathan Moyes (CFO)
Kevin Archer (Dir-R&D)

DOXIMITY, INC.
500 3rd St Ste 510, San Francisco,
CA 94107
Tel.: (650) 549-4330 DE
Web Site: https://www.doximity.com
Year Founded: 2010
DOCS—(NYSE)
Rev.: $475,422,000
Assets: $1,079,374,000
Liabilities: $177,977,000
Net Worth: $901,397,000
Earnings: $147,582,000
Emp.: 827
Fiscal Year-end: 03/31/24
Health Care Srvices
N.A.I.C.S.: 621610
Jeffrey Tangney (Co-Founder & CEO)
Shari Buck (Co-Founder & Sr VP-
People & Ops)
Nate Gross (Co-Founder & Chief
Strategy Officer)
Anna Bryson (CFO)
Jey Balachandran (CTO)
Paul Jorgensen (Sr VP & Gen Mgr-
Hospital Solutions)
Jennifer Chaloemtiarana (Gen Coun-
sel)
Joel Davis (Sr VP-Product)
Bruno Miranda (Sr VP-Engrg)
JR Ordonez (VP-Design)
Ben Greenberg (Sr VP-Comml Prod-
ucts & Gen Mgr)

Subsidiaries:

Amion, LLC (1)
248 Park St, Newton, MA 02458
Tel.: (617) 575-2733
Web Site: https://amion.doximity.com

Software Publishing Services
N.A.I.C.S.: 423430

DRAFTKINGS INC.
222 Berkeley St 5th Fl, Boston, MA
02116
Tel.: (617) 986-6744　　　　　　NV
Web Site: https://www.draftkings.com
Year Founded: 2021
DKNG—(NASDAQ)
Rev.: $3,665,393,000
Assets: $3,944,866,000
Liabilities: $3,104,560,000
Net Worth: $840,306,000
Earnings: ($802,142,000)
Emp.: 4,400
Fiscal Year-end: 12/31/23
Holding Company; Digital Sports Entertainment & Gaming Services
N.A.I.C.S.: 551112
Jason D. Robins *(Chm & CEO)*
Matthew P. Kalish *(Pres-North America)*
Paul Liberman *(Pres-Tech & Product-Global)*
Jason K. Park *(Chief Transformation Officer)*
Harry Evans Sloan *(Vice Chm)*
Alan Ellingson *(CFO)*
Erik Bradbury *(Chief Acctg Officer)*

Subsidiaries:

DraftKings Holdings Inc.　　　　(1)
222 Berkeley St 5th Fl, Boston, MA 02116
Tel.: (617) 986-6744
Rev.: $1,296,025,000
Assets: $4,069,054,000
Liabilities: $2,390,526,000
Net Worth: $1,678,528,000
Earnings: ($1,523,195,000)
Emp.: 3,400
Fiscal Year-end: 12/31/2021
Holding Company
N.A.I.C.S.: 551112
Jason D. Robins *(Chm & CEO)*
David Lebow *(Head-Staff)*
Brian Angiolet *(Chief Media Officer)*
Jennifer Aguiar *(Chief Compliance Officer)*
Travis Dunn *(CTO)*
Graham Walters *(Chief People Officer)*
Ezra Kucharz *(Chief Bus Officer)*
Shay Berka *(Chief Intl Officer)*

Subsidiary (Non-US):

Blue Ribbon Software Malta
Limited　　　　　　　　　　　　(2)
Level G Office 1/3866 Quantum House 75
Abate Rigord St, Ta' Xbiex, 1120, Malta
Tel.: (356) 54 610 0010
Web Site: https://www.bluerbn.com
Gaming Software Development Services
N.A.I.C.S.: 513210
Amir Askarov *(CEO & Co-Founder)*
Dan Fischer *(Co-Founder & CMO)*
Idan Fridman *(CTO)*

Subsidiary (Domestic):

DK Crown Holdings Inc.　　　　(2)
125 Summer St Fl 5, Boston, MA 02110
Tel.: (508) 690-0014
Holding Company; Online Fantasy Sports & Gambling Services
N.A.I.C.S.: 551112
R. Stanton Dodge *(Chief Legal Officer & Sec)*
Ezra Kucharz *(Chief Bus Officer)*
Stephanie Sherman *(CMO)*

DK-FH Inc.　　　　　　　　　　(2)
408 S Main St, Lennox, SD 57039
Tel.: (605) 647-5163
Web Site: https://www.dkfuneralhome.com
Funeral Services
N.A.I.C.S.: 812210
Jay Klusmann *(Co-Owner & Co-Dir-Funeral)*
Joel Klusmann *(Co-Owner & Co-Dir-Funeral)*

Golden Nugget Online Gaming,
Inc.　　　　　　　　　　　　　(2)
222 Berkeley St, Boston, MA 02116
Web Site:
　https://www.goldennuggetcasino.com

Online Gambling Services
N.A.I.C.S.: 713990

Subsidiary (Domestic):

Golden Nugget Online Gaming,
LLC　　　　　　　　　　　　　(3)
222 Berkeley St, Boston, MA 02116
Web Site:
　https://www.goldennuggetcasino.com
Online Gambling Services
N.A.I.C.S.: 713990

Subsidiary (Non-US):

Software Co-Work LLC　　　　(2)
BC Astarta Block A Yaroslavska Street 58,
04071, Kiev, Ukraine
Tel.: (380) 930902569
Web Site: https://softwarecowork.com
Software Development Services
N.A.I.C.S.: 541511

DRAGONFLY ENERGY HOLD-INGS CORP.
1190 Trademark Dr Ste 108, Reno,
NV 89521
Tel.: (775) 622-3448　　　　　NV
Web Site:
　https://dragonflyenergy.com
DFLI—(NASDAQ)
Rev.: $86,251,000
Assets: $88,762,000
Liabilities: $77,430,000
Net Worth: $11,332,000
Earnings: ($39,571,000)
Emp.: 177
Fiscal Year-end: 12/31/22
Battery Manufacturing
N.A.I.C.S.: 335910
Denis Phares *(Chm, Pres & CEO)*
Wade Seaburg *(Chief Revenue Officer)*
Tyler Bourns *(CMO)*

DREAM FINDERS HOMES, INC.
14701 Philips Hwy Ste 300, Jacksonville, FL 32256
Tel.: (904) 644-7670　　　　　DE
Web Site: https://www.dreamfinders
homes.com
Year Founded: 2020
DFH—(NYSE)
Rev.: $3,342,335,000
Assets: $2,371,137,000
Liabilities: $1,570,444,000
Net Worth: $800,693,000
Earnings: $262,313,000
Emp.: 1,170
Fiscal Year-end: 12/31/22
Holding Company
N.A.I.C.S.: 551112
Lorena Anabel Fernandez *(CFO)*
L. Anabel Fernandez *(CFO & Principal Acctg Officer)*
Robert Riva *(Gen Counsel)*
Patrick O. Zalupski *(Chm, Pres & CEO)*

Subsidiaries:

DF Title, LLC　　　　　　　　(1)
14701 Philips Hwy Ste 101, Jacksonville,
FL 32256
Tel.: (904) 503-5170
Web Site: https://www.dreamfinderstitle.com
Financial Services
N.A.I.C.S.: 523999

H&H Constructors of Fayetteville,
LLC　　　　　　　　　　　　　(1)
2919 Breezewood Ave Ste 400, Fayetteville, NC 28303
Tel.: (910) 486-4864
Web Site: http://www.hhhomes.com
Real Estate Services
N.A.I.C.S.: 531390

Village Park Homes, LLC　　　(1)
4454 Bluffton Park Crescent, Bluffton, SC
29910
Tel.: (843) 836-9700

Web Site:
　https://www.villageparkhomes.com
Real Estate Services
N.A.I.C.S.: 531390

DREAM HOMES & DEVELOP-MENT CORP.
314 S Main St, Forked River, NJ
08731
Tel.: (609) 693-8881　　　　　NV
Web Site:
　https://www.dreamhomesltd.com
Year Founded: 2009
DREM—(OTCIQ)
Rev.: $5,656,452
Assets: $10,108,509
Liabilities: $9,475,244
Net Worth: $633,265
Earnings: ($97,379)
Emp.: 8
Fiscal Year-end: 12/31/23
Construction Services
N.A.I.C.S.: 236115
Vincent C. Simonelli *(Chm, Pres, CEO, CFO & Chief Acctg Officer)*
Dave Shaheen *(Gen Counsel-Real Estate)*
Mark Sampson *(Supvr-Reg Construction)*

DRIL-QUIP, INC.
2050 W Sam Houston Pkwy S Ste
1100, Houston, TX 77042
Tel.: (713) 939-7711　　　　　DE
Web Site: https://www.dril-quip.com
Year Founded: 1981
DRQ—(NYSE)
Rev.: $362,070,000
Assets: $972,515,000
Liabilities: $97,599,000
Net Worth: $874,916,000
Earnings: $443,000
Emp.: 1,356
Fiscal Year-end: 12/31/22
Offshore Drilling & Production Equipment Mfr
N.A.I.C.S.: 333132
James C. Webster *(Gen Counsel, Sec & VP)*
Jeffrey J. Bird *(Pres & CEO)*
Kyle F. McClure *(CFO & VP)*
Donald Underwood *(VP-Subsea Products)*
Steve Chauffe *(VP-Downhole Tools)*
Bruce Witwer *(VP-Subsea Services)*
John Mossop *(VP-Technology & Energy Transition)*
Mahesh Puducheri *(Chief HR Officer & VP)*
Halden Zimmermann *(VP-Bus Sys)*

Subsidiaries:

DQ Holdings (Australia) PTY Ltd　(1)
The Forrest Center Level 17 221 St
Georges TCE, Perth, 6000, WA, Australia
Tel.: (61) 893228600
Web Site: https://www.drill-quip.com
Sales Range: $10-24.9 Million
Emp.: 20
Offshore Drilling & Production Equipment Mfr
N.A.I.C.S.: 333132

Dril-Quip (Europe) Limited　　(1)
Stoneywood Park, Dyce, Aberdeen, AB21
7DZ, United Kingdom
Tel.: (44) 1224727000
Web Site: https://www.dril-quip.com
Sales Range: $50-74.9 Million
Emp.: 200
Offshore Drilling & Production Equipment Mfr
N.A.I.C.S.: 333132

Dril-Quip (Europe) Limited　　(1)
Park street 83, 2514 JG, Hague, Netherlands
Tel.: (31) 251229250
Web Site: http://www.drilquip.com

Sales Range: $25-49.9 Million
Emp.: 3
Offshore Drilling & Production Equipment
Mfr
N.A.I.C.S.: 333132

Dril-Quip (Europe) Limited　　(1)
Limfjordsvej 8, 6715, Esbjerg, Denmark
Tel.: (45) 75180944
Sales Range: $10-24.9 Million
Emp.: 20
Offshore Drilling & Production Equipment
Mfr
N.A.I.C.S.: 333132
Peter Nelson *(Gen Mgr)*

Dril-Quip (Europe) Limited　　(1)
Lagerveien 31, 4033, Stavanger, Norway
Tel.: (47) 51443700
Web Site: http://www.drilquip.com
Sales Range: $10-24.9 Million
Emp.: 37
Offshore Drilling & Production Equipment
Mfr
N.A.I.C.S.: 333132

Dril-Quip (Nigeria) Ltd　　　　(1)
Plot 232 Iyowuna Drive Off Peter Odili
Road, Trans Amadi Industrial Layout, Port
Harcourt, Nigeria
Tel.: (234) 8037418228
Sales Range: $125-149.9 Million
Industrial Machinery & Equipment Whslr
N.A.I.C.S.: 423830

Dril-Quip Asia Pacific PTE Ltd　(1)
80 Tuas West Drive, Singapore, 638417,
Singapore
Tel.: (65) 68610600
Web Site: https://www.dril-quip.com
Sales Range: $125-149.9 Million
Offshore Drilling & Production Equipment
Mfr
N.A.I.C.S.: 333132

Dril-Quip DO Brasil LTDA　　(1)
Estrada Melquiades Ribeiro de Almeida
853-Imboassica, 27925-530, Macae, Rio de
Janeiro, Brazil
Tel.: (55) 222 791 8950
Web Site: http://www.drilquip.com
Sales Range: $25-49.9 Million
Emp.: 100
Offshore Drilling & Production Equipment
Mfr
N.A.I.C.S.: 333132

Dril-Quip London　　　　　　(1)
Victoria House Desborough St, High Wycombe, HP11 2NF, Bucks, United Kingdom
Tel.: (44) 1494601086
Web Site: http://www.dril-quip.com
Sales Range: $25-49.9 Million
Emp.: 80
Offshore Drilling & Production Equipment
Mfr
N.A.I.C.S.: 333132

Dril-Quip New Orleans　　　　(1)
701 Poydras St, New Orleans, LA 70139
Tel.: (504) 522-5566
Web Site: http://www.dril-quip.com
Sales Range: $125-149.9 Million
Offshore Drilling & Production Equipment
Mfr
N.A.I.C.S.: 333132

Dril-Quip TIW Mexico S.A. de
C.V.　　　　　　　　　　　　(1)
Km 6 Carretera Villahermosa Cardenas,
86280, Villahermosa, Tabasco, Mexico
Tel.: (52) 9933379625
Drilling Bits Mfr
N.A.I.C.S.: 333131

Honing Inc.　　　　　　　　　(1)
12226 Taylor Rd, Houston, TX 77041
Tel.: (713) 466-0205
Oil & Gas Field Machinery & Equipment Mfr
N.A.I.C.S.: 333132

TIW Corporation　　　　　　　(1)
6401 N Eldridge Pkwy, Houston, TX 77041
Tel.: (713) 939-7711
Web Site: https://www.tiwoiltools.com
Sales Range: $1-9.9 Million
Emp.: 130
Oil & Gas Field Machinery & Equipment Mfr
N.A.I.C.S.: 333132

TIW Hungary LLC　　　　　　(1)

Dril-Quip, Inc.—(Continued)

Mester 35, 5000, Szolnok, Hungary
Tel.: (36) 309355719
Oil & Gas Field Machinery & Equipment Mfr.
N.A.I.C.S.: 333132

TIW International, LLC (1)
12300 Main St, Houston, TX 77035
Tel.: (713) 729-2110
Oil & Gas Field Machinery & Equipment Mfr.
N.A.I.C.S.: 333132

Texas Iron Works Inc. (1)
PO Box 35729, Houston, TX 77235-5729
Tel.: (713) 729-2110
Web Site: http://www.tiwoiltools.com
Industrial Machinery Whslr
N.A.I.C.S.: 423830

The Technologies Alliance, Inc. (1)
1424 N Sam Houston Pkwy E Ste 100,
Houston, TX 77032-2941
Tel.: (713) 939-7711
Web Site: https://oilpatchtech.com
Sales Range: $10-24.9 Million
Emp.: 20
Fiscal Year-end: 12/31/2011
Oil Field Services
N.A.I.C.S.: 541330
Kevin Gendron (Co-Founder)
Paul Berner Jr. (Co-Founder)

DRILLING TOOLS INTERNATIONAL CORP.

3701 Briarpark Dr Ste 150, Houston,
TX 77042
Tel.: (832) 742-8500   DE
Web Site:
    https://www.drillingtools.com
Year Founded: 2021
DTI—(NASDAQ)
Assets: $213,858,117
Liabilities: $215,827,952
Net Worth: ($1,969,835)
Earnings: $1,015,702
Emp.: 2
Fiscal Year-end: 12/31/22
Investment Services
N.A.I.C.S.: 523999
R. Wayne Prejean (Pres & CEO)
David Johnson (CFO)
Mike Domino (Pres-Directional Tool
Rentals Division)
Aldo Rodriguez (VP-Sales)
Trent Pope (VP-Wellbore Optimization)
Jim Rowell (VP-Premium Tools)
Ashley Lane (VP-Intl Bus Dev)
David Stephenson (VP-DTI)
David Cotton (VP-Technical Services
& QHSE)
Veda Ragsdill (VP-Human Resources)
Christian Middleton (VP-Finance)
Jameson Parker (VP-Corporate Development)

Subsidiaries:

Drilling Tools International, Inc. (1)
3701 Briarpark Dr Ste 150, Houston, TX
77042
Tel.: (832) 742-8500
Web Site: http://www.drillingtools.com
Emp.: 16
Mfr & Distr of Drilling Tools for Oil & Gas
Operations
N.A.I.C.S.: 213112
R. Wayne Prejean (Pres & CEO)
Mike Domino (VP-Bus Dev)
David Johnson (CFO)
Aldo Rodriguez (VP-Sls)
Geoff Bartley (District Mgr-Ops)
Tim Eldredge (District Mgr-Ops)
Cory Grover (District Mgr)
Chris Higdon (Mgr-Ops & Sls-Western
Canada)
Jeff Middleton (District Mgr-Ops)
Barry Romero (Plant Mgr)
Steve Stimpson (Mgr-Ops-Northeast)
Rick Young (Mgr-Gulf Coast East Reg)
Ashley Lane (VP-Bus Unit-Eastern)

Buck Smith (District Mgr-Ops)
Thomas Hicks (Chm)
Ron Richardson Sr. (VP-Ops)

Subsidiary (Domestic):

Reamco, Inc. (2)
1149 Smede Hwy, Broussard, LA 70518
Tel.: (337) 364-9244
Web Site: https://www.reamcoinc.com
Sales Range: $10-24.9 Million
Drilling Equipment Mfr
N.A.I.C.S.: 333132
Brent Milam (Pres)

Superior Drilling Products, Inc. (1)
1583 S 1700 E, Vernal, UT 84078
Tel.: (435) 789-0594
Web Site: https://www.sdpi.com
Rev.: $20,973,551
Assets: $27,036,618
Liabilities: $10,381,810
Net Worth: $16,654,808
Earnings: $7,436,045
Emp.: 75
Fiscal Year-end: 12/31/2023
Polycrystalline Diamond Compact Drill Bits
& Horizontal Drill String Enhancement Tools
Mfr For the Oil, Natural Gas & Mining Services Industry
N.A.I.C.S.: 333132

Subsidiary (Domestic):

Extreme Technologies, LLC (2)
809 N 10th St, Millville, NJ 08332
Tel.: (856) 506-8768
Web Site:
    https://www.extremetechnologiesllc.com
Oil Well Machinery Mfr
N.A.I.C.S.: 333132

Superior Drilling Solutions, LLC (2)
1583 S 1700 E, Vernal, UT 84078
Tel.: (435) 781-4881
Emp.: 50
Machine Tools Mfr
N.A.I.C.S.: 333517

DRIVE SHACK INC.

10670 N Central Expy Ste 700, Dallas, TX 75231
Tel.: (469) 862-0139   MD
Web Site: https://ir.driveshack.com
Year Founded: 2002
DS—(NYSE)
Rev.: $281,864,000
Assets: $482,790,000
Liabilities: $452,935,000
Net Worth: $29,855,000
Earnings: ($31,369,000)
Emp.: 3,370
Fiscal Year-end: 12/31/21
Leisure & Entertainment Business
Owner & Operator
N.A.I.C.S.: 713940
Mike Compton (Interim CEO)
Wesley Robert Edens (Chm)

Subsidiaries:

American Golf of Atlanta (1)
4001 Powers Ferry Rd NW, Atlanta, GA
30342
Tel.: (404) 239-9429
Golf Component Distr
N.A.I.C.S.: 339920

Drive Shack Orlando LLC (1)
7285 Corner Dr, Orlando, FL 32827-7144
Tel.: (407) 553-8820
Golf & Country Club Services
N.A.I.C.S.: 713910

**IMPAC Commercial Assets
Corporation** (1)
1401 Dove St, Newport Beach, CA 92660
Tel.: (714) 556-0122
Real Estate Investment Services
N.A.I.C.S.: 525990

NGP Realty Sub GP, LLC (1)
21055 Westheimer Pkwy, Katy, TX 77450
Tel.: (281) 579-6262
Real Estate Investment Services
N.A.I.C.S.: 525990

NGP Realty Sub, L.P. (1)

2951 28th St Ste 3000, Santa Monica, CA
90405
Tel.: (310) 664-4292
Emp.: 5
Real Estate Services
N.A.I.C.S.: 531320

New AGC LLC (1)
601 Baronne St Ste C-1, New Orleans, LA
70113-1066
Tel.: (504) 524-8689
Real Estate Investment Services
N.A.I.C.S.: 525990

Persimmon Golf Club LLC (1)
500 SE Butler Rd, Gresham, OR 97080
Tel.: (503) 667-7500
Golf Courses & Country Club Services
N.A.I.C.S.: 713910

DRIVEITAWAY HOLDINGS, INC.

3201 Market St Ste 200/201, Philadelphia, PA 10104
Tel.: (203) 491-4283   DE
Web Site:
    https://www.driveitaway.com
DWAY—(OTCIQ)
Rev.: $307,284
Assets: $230,790
Liabilities: $2,185,149
Net Worth: ($1,954,359)
Earnings: ($930,137)
Fiscal Year-end: 09/30/23
Children's Learning Centers Franchiser & Operator
N.A.I.C.S.: 611710
John Possumato (CEO)
Adam Potash (COO)

Subsidiaries:

BFK Franchise Company, LLC (1)
5995 W State Ste B, Garden City, ID 73703
Tel.: (904) 824-3133
Web Site: http://www.bricks4kidz.com
Preschool Recreational & Vacation Camp
Center Operator
N.A.I.C.S.: 624410

DRIVEN BRANDS HOLDINGS INC.

440 S Church St Ste 700, Charlotte,
NC 28202
Tel.: (704) 377-8855   DE
Web Site:
    https://www.drivenbrands.com
Year Founded: 2015
DRVN—(NASDAQ)
Rev.: $2,304,029,000
Assets: $5,910,804,000
Liabilities: $5,004,081,000
Net Worth: $906,723,000
Earnings: ($744,962,000)
Emp.: 10,600
Fiscal Year-end: 12/30/23
Holding Company
N.A.I.C.S.: 551112
Jonathan Fitzpatrick (Pres & CEO)
Neal K. Aronson (Chm)
Scott O'Melia (Gen Counsel & Exec
VP)
Shawn Heitz (Chief Comml Officer &
Sr VP)
Dennis Elliott (Sr VP-Dev & M&A)
Suzanne Smith (Sr VP-Driven Insights)
Danny Rivera (Pres-Maintenance-Grp
& Exec VP)
Gabe Mendoza (Exec VP)
Michael Macaluso (Exec VP & Grp
Pres-Paint, Collisio & Glass)
Kyle Marshall (Pres-Platform Svcs)
Michael Beland (Chief Acctg Officer &
Sr VP)
Michael F. Diamond (CFO & Exec
VP)

Subsidiaries:

Auto Glass Now LLC (1)

1258 W Grand Ave, Oakland, CA 94607
Tel.: (510) 451-4111
Web Site: http://www.autoglassnow.com
Other Building Material Dealers
N.A.I.C.S.: 444180

**Automotive Training Institute,
LLC** (1)
705 Digital Dr Ste V, Linthicum, MD 21090
Tel.: (410) 834-0929
Web Site: https://www.autotraining.net
Rev.: $5,100,000
Emp.: 60
General Automotive Repair Services
N.A.I.C.S.: 541611
Chris Fredrick (CEO)
Bryan Stasch (VP-Product & Content Dev)
Karen Dee (VP-Programs-Natl)
Craig Montgomery (Pres)
Ron Greenman (COO)
Chris Frederick Jr. (Sr VP)
Keith Manich (VP-Collision Svcs)
Erin Adero (Dir-Marketing & Virtual Sls)

K & K Glass, Inc. (1)
5938 7th St, Zephyrhills, FL 33542
Tel.: (813) 783-1169
Web Site: http://www.kkglass.com
Sales Range: $1-9.9 Million
Emp.: 15
Automotive Glass Replacement Shops
N.A.I.C.S.: 811122
Daniel Knowlton (Owner)
Brian Higgins (VP)

DROPBOX, INC.

1800 Owens St, San Francisco, CA
94158
Tel.: (415) 857-6800   DE
Web Site: https://www.dropbox.com
Year Founded: 2007
DBX—(NASDAQ)
Rev.: $2,501,600,000
Assets: $2,983,500,000
Liabilities: $3,149,300,000
Net Worth: ($165,800,000)
Earnings: $453,600,000
Emp.: 2,693
Fiscal Year-end: 12/31/23
File Sharing & Synchronization Services
N.A.I.C.S.: 513210
Bart Volkmer (Chief Legal Officer)
Timothy J. Regan (CFO & Chief
Acctg Officer)
Andrew W. Houston (Founder, Chm &
CEO)
Saman Asheer (Chief Comm Officer)
Amber L. Cottle (VP-Global Public
Policy, Govt Affairs, and Social Impact)
Melanie Rosenwasser (Chief People
Officer)

DROR ORTHO-DESIGN, INC.

100 Merrick Rd Ste 400W, Rockville
Centre, NY 11570   DE
Web Site: http://www.novint.com
DROR—(OTCIQ)
Assets: $60,429
Liabilities: $784,285
Net Worth: ($723,856)
Earnings: ($178,750)
Emp.: 609
Fiscal Year-end: 12/31/22
Computer Peripheral Equipment Distr
N.A.I.C.S.: 423430
Orin Hirschman (Pres)

DSA FINANCIAL CORP.

595 W Eads Pkwy, Lawrenceburg, IN
47025
Tel.: (812) 537-0940
Web Site:
    http://www.dearbornsavings.com
DSFN—(OTCIQ)
Bank Holding Company
N.A.I.C.S.: 551111
John P. Young (Pres & CEO)
Joe Ventre (VP & Chief Lending Officer)

Derrick Taylor *(VP & CFO)*
Ray Gruner *(VP-Compliance)*
Janet Faller *(VP-Ops-Dearborn Savings Bank)*

Subsidiaries:

Dearborn Savings Bank   (1)
595 W Eads Pkwy, Lawrenceburg, IN 47025
Tel.: (812) 537-0940
Web Site: http://www.dearbornsavings.com
Rev.: $4,851,000
Assets: $117,180,000
Liabilities: $100,801,000
Net Worth: $16,379,000
Earnings: $960,000
Emp.: 25
Fiscal Year-end: 12/31/2013
Savings Institutions
N.A.I.C.S.: 522180

DSS, INC.
275 Wiregrass Pkwy, West Henrietta, NY 14586
Tel.: (585) 325-3610   **NY**
Web Site: https://www.dssworld.com
Year Founded: 1984
DSS—(NYSEAMEX)
Rev.: $30,258,000
Assets: $153,192,000
Liabilities: $69,979,000
Net Worth: $83,213,000
Earnings: ($97,503,000)
Emp.: 95
Fiscal Year-end: 12/31/23
Computer System Design Services
N.A.I.C.S.: 541512
Jason T. Grady *(Interim CEO & COO)*
Michael S. Caton *(CTO-R&D & Emerging Technologies)*
Todd D. Macko *(Interim CFO & VP-Fin)*
Heng Fai Chan *(Chm)*

Subsidiaries:

DSS Administrative Group, Inc.   (1)
1560 Emerson St, Rochester, NY 14606
Tel.: (585) 341-3100
Emp.: 14
Software Development Services
N.A.I.C.S.: 513210

DSS International Inc.   (1)
Ste 560 Peoples Plz 203, Newark, DE 19702
Tel.: (302) 836-0270
Web Site:
   http://www.dssassociatesbear.com
Financial Investment Services
N.A.I.C.S.: 523940

ExtraDev, Inc.   (1)
3445 Winton Pl Ste 219, Rochester, NY 14623
Tel.: (585) 241-3000
Sales Range: $25-49.9 Million
Emp.: 20
Computer System Design Services
N.A.I.C.S.: 541512

Premier Packaging Corporation   (1)
6 Framark Dr, Victor, NY 14564
Tel.: (585) 924-8460
Web Site:
   http://www.premiercustompkg.com
Sales Range: $25-49.9 Million
Emp.: 30
Packaging & Labeling Services
N.A.I.C.S.: 561910

Securprint Inc.   (1)
1560 Emerson St, Rochester, NY 14606-3118
Tel.: (585) 341-3100
Sales Range: $25-49.9 Million
Emp.: 20
Commercial Lithographic Printing Services
N.A.I.C.S.: 323111

DT MIDSTREAM, INC.
500 Woodward Ave Ste 2900, Detroit, MI 48226-1279
Tel.: (313) 402-8532   **DE**

Web Site:
   https://www.dtmidstream.com
DTM—(NYSE)
Rev.: $922,000,000
Assets: $8,982,000,000
Liabilities: $4,702,000,000
Net Worth: $4,280,000,000
Earnings: $384,000,000
Emp.: 402
Fiscal Year-end: 12/31/23
Natural Gas Midstream Owner & Operator
N.A.I.C.S.: 213112
David Slater *(Pres & CEO)*
Jeffrey A. Jewell *(CFO & Exec VP)*
Dwayne A. Wilson *(Owner)*

Subsidiaries:

Millennium Pipeline Company, LLC   (1)
1 Blue Hill Plz Ste 7, Pearl River, NY 10965-3104   **(52.5%)**
Tel.: (845) 620-1300
Web Site:
   http://www.millenniumpipeline.com
Natural Gas Infrastructure Services
N.A.I.C.S.: 486210
Mark Bering *(Pres)*

DTE ENERGY COMPANY
1 Energy Plz, Detroit, MI 48226-1279
Tel.: (313) 235-4000   **MI**
Web Site: https://www.dteenergy.com
Year Founded: 1996
DTE—(NYSE)
Rev.: $12,745,000,000
Assets: $44,755,000,000
Liabilities: $33,700,000,000
Net Worth: $11,055,000,000
Earnings: $1,397,000,000
Emp.: 9,950
Fiscal Year-end: 12/31/23
Holding Company; Electric & Gas Utilities Owner
N.A.I.C.S.: 551112
David Slater *(Pres, COO, Exec VP & Sr VP-Gas Storage & Pipelines Div)*
Mark C. Rolling *(VP-Finance & Controller)*
Gerardo Norcia *(Chm & CEO)*
Joi M. Harris *(Pres & COO)*
Lisa A. Muschong *(Sec & VP)*
JoAnn Chavez *(Chief Legal Officer & Sr VP)*
David S. Ruud *(CFO & Sr VP)*
Lynette Dowler *(VP-Pub Affairs)*
Diane M. Antishin *(Chief Diversity & Inclusion Officer & VP-HR)*
Shawn P. Patterson *(VP-Environmental Mgmt & Safety)*
Heather D. Rivard *(Sr VP)*
Camilo Serna *(VP-Regulatory Affairs)*
Don M. Stanczak *(VP-Development)*
Tony Tomczak *(VP-Electric Sls & Mktg)*
Steven B. Ambrose *(CIO & VP)*
Peter Dietrich *(Chief Nuclear Officer & Sr VP)*
John Dermody *(Mgr-IR)*
Mark Stiers *(Pres)*
Chuck Conlen *(VP-Renewable Energy)*
Sharon Pfeuffer *(VP-Distr Engrg & Construction)*
Angie Pizzuti *(Chief Customer Officer-Customer Svc Ops & VP)*
Ryan Stowe *(VP-Distr Ops)*
Monique Wells *(Dir-Diversity)*
Rodney Cole *(Dir-Pub Affairs)*
Tracy J. Myrick *(Chief Acctg Officer)*
Christopher J. Allen *(Treas & VP)*
Robert Feldmann *(VP-Gas)*
Cedric Flowers *(VP-Operations-Gas)*
Jodi L. Frisicaro *(VP)*
Patrick Lee *(Chief Tax Officer & VP)*
Joseph Musallam *(VP)*
Michael Seischab *(Sr VP-Corporate Strategy)*

Jaspreet Singh *(VP)*
Angela Wojtowicz *(VP-Development)*
Khalil Rahal *(Dir-Economic Dev)*
Benjamin F. Felton *(Sr VP-Energy Supply)*
Richard L. Redmond Jr. *(Pres)*

Subsidiaries:

Citizens Gas Fuel Company   (1)
127 N Main St, Adrian, MI 49221-2711   **(100%)**
Tel.: (517) 265-2144
Web Site: http://www.citizensgasfuel.com
Rev.: $17,469,000
Emp.: 30
Transmission, Distribution & Storage of Natural Gas
N.A.I.C.S.: 211120

DTE Electric Company   (1)
1 Energy Plz, Detroit, MI 48226-1279
Tel.: (313) 235-4000
Web Site: https://www.dteenergy.com
Rev.: $5,804,000,000
Assets: $32,185,000,000
Liabilities: $21,961,000,000
Net Worth: $10,224,000,000
Earnings: $772,000,000
Emp.: 4,450
Fiscal Year-end: 12/31/2023
Electricity Generation & Distr
N.A.I.C.S.: 221122
Mark C. Rolling *(VP & Controller)*
Gerardo Norcia *(CEO)*
David Ruud *(CFO)*
Tracy Myrick *(Chief Acctg Officer)*

DTE Energy Trading, Inc.   (1)
3410 Belle Chase Way Ste 600, Lansing, MI 48911
Tel.: (734) 887-2000
Emp.: 250
Electric Power Distr
N.A.I.C.S.: 221122
Steven Mabry *(Pres)*

DTE Gas Company   (1)
1 Energy Plz 570 SB, Detroit, MI 48226
Tel.: (313) 235-4000
Natural Gas Distr
N.A.I.C.S.: 221210

MichCon Pipeline Company   (1)
One Energy Plz Rm 2084 WCB, Detroit, MI 48226   **(100%)**
Tel.: (313) 235-1108
Web Site: http://www.mgat.dteenergy.com
Sales Range: $1-4.9 Billion
Emp.: 2,093
Interstate Pipeline, Storage & Gas Distribution
N.A.I.C.S.: 221210
Peter B. Oleksiak *(Chief Acctg Officer & Controller)*
Anthony F. Earley Jr. *(Chm)*

Midwest Energy Resources Company   (1)
2400 W Winter St, Superior, WI 54880   **(100%)**
Tel.: (715) 392-9807
Web Site: https://www.dteenergy.com
Sales Range: $10-24.9 Million.
Emp.: 3
Owns & Operates Coal Dock in Superior, WI
N.A.I.C.S.: 221210
Marshall A. Elder *(Dir-Terminal Ops)*
Jeff D. Papineau *(Pres)*

Vector Pipeline, L.P.   (1)
38705 7th Mile Rd Ste 490, Livonia, MI 48152
Tel.: (734) 462-0230
Web Site: https://www.vector-pipeline.com
Sales Range: $25-49.9 Million
Emp.: 10
Gas Pipeline; Owned 50% by DTE Energy Company & 50% by Enbridge, Inc.
N.A.I.C.S.: 486210
Peter Cianci *(Pres)*
Belinda Friis *(Chief Compliance Officer)*
Amy Back *(Chief Compliance Officer)*

DTF TAX-FREE INCOME 2028 TERM FUND INC.

10 S Wacker Dr Ste 1900, Chicago, IL 60606   **MD**
Year Founded: 1991
DTF—(NYSE)
Investment Management Service
N.A.I.C.S.: 525990

DTHERA SCIENCES
7310 Miramar Rd Ste 350, San Diego, CA 92126
Tel.: (858) 215-6360   **NV**
Web Site: http://www.dthera.com
Year Founded: 2012
DTHR—(OTCIQ)
Emp.: 1
Medical Research & Development Services
N.A.I.C.S.: 541715
Edward M. Cox *(Chm, Pres, CEO & CFO)*
David Keene *(CTO)*
Jonathan Feldschuh *(Chief Scientific Officer)*

DTRT HEALTH ACQUISITION CORP.
1415 W 22nd St Tower Fl, Oak Brook, IL 60523
Tel.: (312) 316-5473   **DE**
Web Site: http://www.dtrthealth.com
Year Founded: 2021
DTRT—(NASDAQ)
Investment Services
N.A.I.C.S.: 523999
Donald Klink *(CFO)*
Mark Heaney *(CEO)*
Arion Robbins *(COO)*

DU-ART FILM LABS, INC.
245 W 55th St, New York, NY 10019
Tel.: (212) 757-4580
Web Site: http://www.duart.com
Year Founded: 1922
DAFL—(OTCIQ)
Digital Media Marketing Services
N.A.I.C.S.: 541613
Linda Young *(Pres & CEO)*

DUCOMMUN INCORPORATED
600 Anton Blvd Ste 1100, Costa Mesa, CA 92626-7100
Tel.: (657) 335-3665   **DE**
Web Site:
   https://www.ducommun.com
Year Founded: 1849
DCO—(NYSE)
Rev.: $712,537,000
Assets: $1,021,506,000
Liabilities: $495,546,000
Net Worth: $525,960,000
Earnings: $28,789,000
Emp.: 2,465
Fiscal Year-end: 12/31/22
Other Aircraft Parts & Auxiliary Equipment Manufacturing
N.A.I.C.S.: 336413
Stephen G. Oswald *(Chm, Pres & CEO)*
Jerry L. Redondo *(Sr VP-Ops)*
Rajiv A. Tata *(Gen counsel, Sec & VP)*
Laureen S. Gonzalez *(Chief HR Officer)*

Subsidiaries:

American Electronics, Inc.   (1)
44423 Airport Rd Ste 102, California, MD 20619
Tel.: (301) 862-5500
Web Site: https://www.amelexinc.com
Engineeering Services
N.A.I.C.S.: 541330

BLR Aerospace, LLC   (1)
11002 29th Ave W Bldg C-19, Everett, WA 98204-1314
Tel.: (425) 353-6591
Web Site: https://www.blraerospace.com

Ducommun Incorporated—(Continued)

Aerospace Equipment Mfr
N.A.I.C.S.: 336413

Ducommun (1)
1885 N Batavia St, Orange, CA
92865-4105 **(100%)**
Tel.: (714) 637-4401
Web Site: http://www.aerochem.com
Sales Range: $75-99.9 Million
Emp.: 150
Close Tolerance Chemical Milling Service to
the Aircraft & Aerospace Industries
N.A.I.C.S.: 333998

Ducommun Aerostructures Inc. (1)
200 Sandpointe Ave Ste 700, Santa Ana,
CA 92707-5759 **(100%)**
Tel.: (310) 380-5390
Web Site: http://www.ducommun.com
Stretch Forming, Thermal Forming & Computer Numerically Controlled Machining &
Assembly for the Aerospace Industry
N.A.I.C.S.: 336413

Plant (Domestic):

Ducommun AeroStructures (2)
4001 El Mirage Rd, Adelanto, CA
92301-9489 **(100%)**
Tel.: (760) 246-4191
Web Site: http://www.ducommun.com
Chemical Milling
N.A.I.C.S.: 333414

Subsidiary (Domestic):

**Ducommun AeroStructures New York,
Inc.** (2)
171 Stacey Rd, Coxsackie, NY 12051-2801
Tel.: (518) 731-2791
Web Site: https://www.ducommun.com
Aircraft Sheet Metal Component Mfr
N.A.I.C.S.: 332322

Ducommun AeroStructures, LLC (2)
23301 Wilmington Ave, Carson, CA 90745
Tel.: (310) 513-7200
Web Site: https://www.ducommun.com
Aircraft Parts & Equipment Mfr
N.A.I.C.S.: 336413

Plant (Domestic):

Ducommun Aerostructures (2)
3333 Main St, Parsons, KS 67357
Tel.: (620) 421-8400
Web Site: http://www.ducommun.com
Rotating Electrical Power Equipment Mfr
N.A.I.C.S.: 336413

**Lightning Diversion Systems,
Inc.** (1)
16572 Burke Ln, Huntington Beach, CA
92647-4538
Tel.: (714) 841-1080
Web Site:
https://www.lightningdiversion.com
Aircraft Part & Auxiliary Equipment Mfr
N.A.I.C.S.: 336413

Nobles Worldwide, Inc. (1)
1105 E Pine St, Saint Croix Falls, WI 54024
Tel.: (715) 483-3079
Web Site: https://www.noblesworldwide.com
Ammunition Chutes & Weapon Systems Mfr
N.A.I.C.S.: 332993

DUFF & PHELPS UTILITY AND
INFRASTRUCTURE FUND INC.

200 S Wacker Dr Ste 500, Chicago,
IL 00000
Tel.: (312) 263-2610 MD
Web Site: http://www.dpimc.com
DPG—(NYSE)
Rev.: $24,433,597
Assets: $883,488,458
Liabilities: $261,526,840
Net Worth: $621,961,618
Earnings: $4,480,935
Fiscal Year-end: 10/31/19
Investment Services
N.A.I.C.S.: 523999
David J. Vitale *(Chm)*
Alan Michael Meder *(Sr Mng Dir,
Chief Risk Officer, Treas & Asst Sec)*
Eileen A. Moran *(Vice Chm)*

Eric Elvekrog *(Sr Portfolio Mgr)*
Daniel J. Petrisko *(Exec Mng Dir,
Exec VP, Head-Portfolio Solutions, Sr
Portfolio Mgr & Asst Sec)*
Kathleen L. Hegyi *(Chief Compliance
Officer)*
Jennifer S. Fromm *(Sec & VP)*
Nikita K. Thaker *(VP & Asst Treas)*
William Patrick Bradley III *(VP & Asst
Treas)*
David Grumhaus Jr. *(Chief Investment Officer)*

DUKE ENERGY CORPORATION

525 S Tryon St, Charlotte, NC 28202-
1803
Tel.: (407) 629-1010 NC
Web Site: https://www.duke-
energy.com
Year Founded: 1904
DUK—(NYSE)
Rev.: $29,060,000,000
Assets: $176,893,000,000
Liabilities: $126,706,000,000
Net Worth: $50,187,000,000
Earnings: $2,735,000,000
Emp.: 27,037
Fiscal Year-end: 12/31/23
Power Plants & Natural Gas Pipelines Operator & Electricity & Natural
Gas Distr
N.A.I.C.S.: 221122
Lynn J. Good *(Chm & CEO)*
Brian D. Savoy *(CFO & Exec VP)*
Melody Birmingham-Byrd *(Chief Admin Officer & Sr VP)*
Regis Repko *(Chief Fossil & Hydro
Officer & Sr VP)*
Kodwo Ghartey-Tagoe *(Chief Legal
Officer, Sec & Exec VP)*
T. Preston Gillespie *(Chief Generation
Officer & Exec VP-Enterprise Operational Excellence)*
Stan Pinegar *(Pres-Indiana)*
Harry K. Sideris *(Pres)*
Amy B. Spiller *(Pres-Ohio & Kentucky)*
Michael Callahan *(Pres-South Carolina)*
Kelley Karn *(VP-Regulatory Affairs &
Policy-Indiana)*
George Hamrick *(Chief Transmission
Officer & Sr VP)*
Kelvin Henderson *(Chief Nuclear Officer & Sr VP)*
Cynthia S. Lee *(Chief Acctg Officer,
VP & Controller)*
Cameron McDonald *(Chief Diversity
& Inclusion Officer & VP-Talent Agility
Acq)*
Paul Draovitch *(Sr VP)*
Melissa M. Feldmeier *(VP)*
Sharene Pierce *(VP)*
Bonnie Titone *(CIO)*

Subsidiaries:

Baker House Apartments LLC (1)
207 E 14th St 100, Lumberton, NC 28358
Tel.: (910) 272-8565
Apartment Building Operating Services
N.A.I.C.S.: 531110

Berkley East Solar, LLC (1)
1716 Lawrence Dr, De Pere, WI 54115
Tel.: (484) 654-1877
Solar Heating Contractor Services
N.A.I.C.S.: 238220

Bison Insurance Agency (1)
3725 Walden Ave, Lancaster, NY 14086
Tel.: (716) 681-2845
Web Site: http://www.bisoninsurance.com
Insurance Services
N.A.I.C.S.: 524210

CST Limited, LLC (1)
302 Washington St Ste 202E, Moorestown,
NJ 08057

Web Site: https://www.cstllc.com
Electric Power Distribution Services
N.A.I.C.S.: 221122

Capitan Corporation (1)
4405 SCR 1270, Midland, TX 79706
Tel.: (432) 561-9356
Web Site: http://www.capitancorp.com
Perforating & Mechanical Services
N.A.I.C.S.: 213112

CaroHome, LLC (1)
526 S Church St, Charlotte, NC 28202-
4200
Tel.: (850) 688-9724
Web Site: https://www.carohome.com
Electric Power Distribution Services
N.A.I.C.S.: 221122

Cinergy Technology, Inc. (1)
100 Plainfield Ave Ste 7, Edison, NJ 08817
Web Site: http://www.cinergytech.com
Software Development & Technical Services
N.A.I.C.S.: 541511

Dogwood Solar, LLC (1)
1501 Creekwood Pkwy Ste 110, Columbia,
MO 65202
Tel.: (573) 447-6527
Web Site: https://www.dogwoodsolar.com
Solar Heating Contractor Services
N.A.I.C.S.: 238160

Duke Capital Corporation (1)
526 S Church St, Charlotte, NC 28202-
1904
Tel.: (704) 382-8000
Web Site: http://www.duke-energy.com
Sales Range: $350-399.9 Million
Emp.: 600
Financial Services
N.A.I.C.S.: 525990

Duke Energy Americas, LLC (1)
5400 Westheimer Ct, Houston, TX 77056
Tel.: (713) 627-5307
Electricity & Natural Gas Generation Services
N.A.I.C.S.: 221113

**Duke Energy Business Services
LLC** (1)
526 S Church St, Charlotte, NC 28202
Tel.: (704) 594-6200
Eletric Power Generation Services
N.A.I.C.S.: 221118

Duke Energy Carolinas, LLC (1)
526 S Church St, Charlotte, NC 28202-
1803
Tel.: (704) 382-3853
Electric Power Distribution Services
N.A.I.C.S.: 221122

Duke Energy Carolinas, LLC (1)
526 S Church St, Charlotte, NC 28202-
1803
Tel.: (704) 382-3853
Rev.: $7,857,000,000
Assets: $50,346,000,000
Liabilities: $34,904,000,000
Net Worth: $15,442,000,000
Earnings: $1,600,000,000
Emp.: 27,858
Fiscal Year-end: 12/31/2022
Electricity Generator & Transmission Services
N.A.I.C.S.: 221113
Lynn J. Good *(CEO)*
Julie S. Janson *(Pres)*
Brian D. Savoy *(CFO)*
Cynthia S. Lee *(Chief Acctg Officer)*

Duke Energy Corp. - Seneca (1)
7812 Rochester Hwy, Seneca, SC 29672-
0752
Tel.: (864) 885-3000
Web Site: http://www.dukepower.com
Sales Range: $1-4.9 Billion
Emp.: 1,300
Nuclear Power Facility
N.A.I.C.S.: 221118

Duke Energy Florida, LLC (1)
299 1st Ave N, Saint Petersburg, FL
33701 **(100%)**
Tel.: (704) 382-3853
Web Site: http://www.duke-energy.com
Rev.: $6,353,000,000
Assets: $25,554,000,000
Liabilities: $16,531,000,000

Net Worth: $9,023,000,000
Earnings: $909,000,000
Emp.: 27,858
Fiscal Year-end: 12/31/2022
Electric Power Generation & Distribution
N.A.I.C.S.: 221118
Lynn J. Good *(CEO)*

**Duke Energy Generation
Services** (1)
139 E 4th St, Cincinnati, OH 45202
Tel.: (513) 419-6982
Web Site: http://www.dukeenergy.com
Sales Range: $200-249.9 Million
Alternative Source Energy Production
N.A.I.C.S.: 221118

Duke Energy Indiana, LLC (1)
1000 E Main St, Plainfield, IN 46168
Tel.: (704) 382-3853
Rev.: $3,922,000,000
Assets: $14,654,000,000
Liabilities: $9,951,000,000
Net Worth: $4,703,000,000
Earnings: $137,000,000
Emp.: 27,858
Fiscal Year-end: 12/31/2022
Electric Utility Services
N.A.I.C.S.: 221122
Lynn J. Good *(CEO)*
Steven K. Young *(CFO & Exec VP)*
Kodwo Ghartey-Tagoe *(Chief Legal Officer)*
T. Preston Gillespie *(Chief Generation Officer)*
Dhiaa M. Jamil *(COO)*
Ronald R. Reising *(Chief HR Officer)*
Louis Renjel *(Exec VP)*
Harry K. Sideris *(Exec VP)*
Paul Draovitch *(Sr VP)*
Melissa M. Feldmeier *(VP)*
George Hamrick *(Chief Transmission Officer)*
Kelvin Henderson *(Sr VP)*
Cynthia S. Lee *(Chief Acctg Officer)*
Sharene Pierce *(VP)*
Bonnie Titone *(CIO)*

Duke Energy International, LLC (1)
5400 Westheimer Ct, Houston, TX 77056-
5310
Tel.: (713) 627-5600
Electricity & Natural Gas Generation Services
N.A.I.C.S.: 221113

Duke Energy Kentucky, Inc. (1)
139 E 4th St, Cincinnati, OH 45202
Tel.: (704) 382-3853
Web Site: http://www.duke-energy.com
Eletric Power Generation Services
N.A.I.C.S.: 221118
Amy Spiller *(Pres-Ohio & Kentucky)*

Duke Energy NGL Services LP (1)
85 Mechanic Ste, Lebanon, NH 03766
Tel.: (603) 448-2825
Sales Range: $50-74.9 Million
Emp.: 41
Petroleum Bulk Services
N.A.I.C.S.: 457210

**Duke Energy North America,
LLC** (1)
5400 Westheimer Ct, Houston, TX 77056-
5310
Tel.: (713) 627-5400
Electricity Generator & Transmission Services
N.A.I.C.S.: 221113

Duke Energy Ohio, Inc (1)
139 E 4th St, Cincinnati, OH 45202
Tel.: (704) 382-3853
Rev.: $2,514,000,000
Assets: $11,506,000,000
Liabilities: $6,740,000,000
Net Worth: $4,766,000,000
Earnings: $302,000,000
Emp.: 27,858
Fiscal Year-end: 12/31/2022
Electric Power & Natural Gas Distr
N.A.I.C.S.: 221122
Lynn J. Good *(CEO)*
Steven K. Young *(Exec VP)*
Brian D. Savoy *(CFO)*
Cynthia S. Lee *(Chief Acctg Officer)*

Duke Energy Ohio, Inc. (1)
139 E 4th St, Cincinnati, OH 45202
Tel.: (704) 382-3853

Electric Power Distribution Services
N.A.I.C.S.: 221122

Duke Energy Renewable Services, LLC (1)
302 1st St E, Canby, MN 56220
Tel.: (507) 223-5000
Wind & Solar Power Electricity Generating Services
N.A.I.C.S.: 221114

Duke Energy Royal, LLC (1)
2503 White St, Greensboro, NC 27405
Tel.: (336) 375-5178
Natural Gas Distr
N.A.I.C.S.: 486210

Fresh Air Energy X, LLC (1)
101 2nd St, San Francisco, CA 94103-6245
Tel.: (415) 626-1802
Emp.: 50
Solar Electric Power Generation Services
N.A.I.C.S.: 221114
Nathan Rogers (Project Mgr-Dev)

Grove Arcade Restoration LLC (1)
1 Page Ave, Asheville, NC 28801
Tel.: (828) 252-7799
Web Site: https://www.grovearcade.com
Building Rental & Leasing Services
N.A.I.C.S.: 531120

High Noon Solar, LLC (1)
569 S Westgate Dr Ste 2, Grand Junction, CO 81505
Tel.: (970) 241-0209
Web Site: https://highnoonsolar.com
Solar Panel Installation & Maintenance Services
N.A.I.C.S.: 238210

Highlander Solar 1, LLC (1)
550 S Tryon St Dec 45, Charlotte, NC 28202
Tel.: (704) 382-8251
Electricity Generation Services
N.A.I.C.S.: 221113

Historic Property Management LLC (1)
1 Page Ave Ste 222, Asheville, NC 28801
Tel.: (828) 225-5100
Real Estate Agency Services
N.A.I.C.S.: 531210

Martins Creek Solar NC, LLC (1)
327 Hillsborough St, Raleigh, NC 27603
Tel.: (904) 251-4910
Solar Heating Contractor Services
N.A.I.C.S.: 238220

North Carolina Renewable Properties, LLC (1)
176 Mine Lake Ct 100, Raleigh, NC 27615
Tel.: (407) 536-5346
Semiconductor Devices Mfr
N.A.I.C.S.: 334413

Ocotillo Windpower, LP (1)
700 N Mopac Ste 475, Austin, TX 78731
Tel.: (512) 241-0495
Electricity Generation Services
N.A.I.C.S.: 221113

PT Attachment Solutions, LLC (1)
526 S Church St, Charlotte, NC 28202
Tel.: (727) 471-5680
Web Site: http://www.ptaccess.net
Emp.: 10
Financial Investment Services
N.A.I.C.S.: 523150

PT Holding Company, LLC (1)
526 S Church St, Charlotte, NC 28202
Tel.: (727) 441-5023
Holding Company
N.A.I.C.S.: 551112

PeakNet, LLC (1)
9887 4th St N Ste 100, Saint Petersburg, FL 33702-2445
Tel.: (727) 547-3655
Web Site: https://www.peaknet.com
Wireless Collocation Services
N.A.I.C.S.: 517112
Allan Bakalar (VP & Gen Mgr)
Tonya R. Swindell (VP-Fin)
Michael Whitley (VP-Bus Dev)

Piedmont Natural Gas Company, Inc. (1)

4720 Piedmont Row Dr, Charlotte, NC 28210
Tel.: (704) 364-3120
Web Site: http://www.piedmontng.com
Rev.: $2,124,000,000
Assets: $10,335,000,000
Liabilities: $6,662,000,000
Net Worth: $3,673,000,000
Earnings: $323,000,000
Emp.: 27,858
Fiscal Year-end: 12/31/2022
Natural Gas Distr
N.A.I.C.S.: 221210
Lynn J. Good (CEO)
Ronald J. Turner (Asst Treas)
Headen B. Thomas (Investor Rels Dir)
Brian D. Savoy (CFO)
Cynthia S. Lee (Chief Acctg Officer)

Subsidiary (Domestic):

Piedmont Energy Partners, Inc. (2)
4720 Piedmont Row Dr, Charlotte, NC 28210 (100%)
Tel.: (704) 364-3120
Web Site: http://www.piedmontng.com
Holding Company
N.A.I.C.S.: 551112

Subsidiary (Domestic):

Piedmont Interstate Pipeline Company (3)
4720 Piedmont Row Dr, Charlotte, NC 28210
Tel.: (704) 364-3120
Web Site: http://www.piedmontng.com
Liquified Natural Gas Peak Demand Facility
N.A.I.C.S.: 211130

Progress Energy, Inc. (1)
410 S Wilmington St, Raleigh, NC 27601-1748
Tel.: (704) 382-3853
Web Site: http://www.progress-energy.com
Rev.: $13,125,000,000
Assets: $66,079,000,000
Liabilities: $44,673,000,000
Net Worth: $21,406,000,000
Earnings: $1,828,000,000
Emp.: 27,858
Fiscal Year-end: 12/31/2022
Public Utility Holding Company; Electric Energy Generation & Distr
N.A.I.C.S.: 221111
Lynn J. Good (CEO)
Brian D. Savoy (CFO)
Cynthia S. Lee (Chief Acctg Officer)

Subsidiary (Domestic):

Duke Energy Progress, LLC (2)
410 S Wilmington St, Raleigh, NC 27601-1748 (100%)
Tel.: (704) 382-3853
Web Site: https://www.progress-energy.com
Rev.: $6,753,000,000
Assets: $36,752,000,000
Liabilities: $26,443,000,000
Net Worth: $10,309,000,000
Earnings: $1,008,000,000
Emp.: 27,859
Fiscal Year-end: 12/31/2022
Energy Services
N.A.I.C.S.: 221118
Lynn J. Good (CEO)
Steven K. Young (CFO & Exec VP)
Cynthia S. Lee (Chief Acctg Officer)
T. Preston Gillespie (Chief Generation Officer)
Ronald R. Reising (Chief HR Officer)
Louis Renjel (Exec VP)
Harry K. Sideris (Exec VP)
Kendal C. Bowman (Pres)
Paul Draovitch (Sr VP)
Melissa M. Feldmeier (VP)
George Hamrick (Chief Transmission Officer)
Kelvin Henderson (Chief Nuclear Officer)
Sharene Pierce (VP)
Bonnie Titone (CIO)

Florida Progress Corporation (2)
410 S Wilmington St, Raleigh, NC 27601
Tel.: (919) 546-6000
Web Site: http://www.progressenergy.com
Electric Power Generation & Distribution Services
N.A.I.C.S.: 221118

Pumpjack Solar I, LLC (1)
550 S Tryon St, Charlotte, NC 28202
Tel.: (704) 382-9151
Plumbing & Heating Equipment Contract Services
N.A.I.C.S.: 238220

REC Solar Commercial Corporation (1)
Topa Financial Ctr 745 Fort St Tower Ste 1950, Honolulu, HI 96813
Tel.: (808) 756-4824
Web Site: http://www.recsolar.com
Solar Electric Power Generation Services
N.A.I.C.S.: 221114

REC Solar, Inc. (1)
3450 Broad St Ste 105, San Luis Obispo, CA 93401
Web Site: http://www.recsolar.com
Commercial Solar Power Equipment Design, Mfr & Installation Services
N.A.I.C.S.: 334413
Matthew Walz (Pres & CEO)
Chris Fallon (VP-Duke Energy Renewables)
Chris Licciardi (Sr Dir-Project Mgmt)
Jesse Elliott (Sr Dir-Safety Constructions & Ops)
Brian Meichtry (Dir-Engrg)
Ann Kroll (Dir-Mktg & Demand Generation)
Art Villa (CIO)
Matt Thomas (Fin Dir)
David O'Grady (Sr Dir-HR)
Craig Noxon (Dir-Enterprise Sls)
Jared Friedman (Dir-Comml & Industrial Sls)
Joslyn Broome (Dir-Operational Excellence & Procurement)
Jama Bond (Dir-Inside Sls)
Billy Heidt (Dir-Ops & Maintenance)

Seaboard Solar LLC (1)
550 S Tryon St, Charlotte, NC 28202
Tel.: (704) 382-9151
Solar Power Generation Services
N.A.I.C.S.: 221114

Shirley Wind, LLC (1)
526 S Church St, Charlotte, NC 28202-1802
Tel.: (920) 864-2522
Electricity Generation Services
N.A.I.C.S.: 221113

South Construction Company, Inc. (1)
279 Firetower Rd, Dublin, GA 31021-2614
Tel.: (478) 272-8351
Web Site: http://www.lentileconstruction.com
Emp.: 15
Industrial Building Construction Services
N.A.I.C.S.: 236210

Sweetwater Development LLC (1)
PO Box 335, Lakewood, WI 54138
Tel.: (920) 621-1557
Web Site:
http://www.sweetwaterrealestatellc.com
Real Estate Services
N.A.I.C.S.: 531210

TX Solar I LLC (1)
1805 29th St Unit 2054, Boulder, CO 80301-1068
Tel.: (720) 838-2289
Heating & Air-Conditioning Contract Services
N.A.I.C.S.: 238220

DULUTH HOLDINGS INC.
100 W Main St, Mount Horeb, WI 53572
Tel.: (608) 437-8655
Web Site:
https://www.duluthtrading.com
Year Founded: 1989
DLTH—(NASDAQ)
Rev.: $653,307,000
Assets: $527,454,000
Liabilities: $300,257,000
Net Worth: $227,197,000
Earnings: $2,246,000
Emp.: 964
Fiscal Year-end: 01/29/23
Apparel Distr
N.A.I.C.S.: 458110

Stephen L. Schlecht (Founder)
Samuel M. Sato (Pres & CEO)
Neala Shepherd (Sr VP)
A. J. Sutera (CTO & Sr VP)

DUN & BRADSTREET HOLDINGS, INC.
5335 Gate Pkwy, Jacksonville, FL 32256
Tel.: (904) 648-6350   DE
Web Site: https://www.dnb.com
Year Founded: 1841
DNB—(NYSE)
Rev.: $2,314,000,000
Assets: $9,135,900,000
Liabilities: $5,704,300,000
Net Worth: $3,431,600,000
Earnings: ($47,000,000)
Emp.: 6,414
Fiscal Year-end: 12/31/23
Holding Company
N.A.I.C.S.: 551112
Virginia Green Gomez (Pres-North America)
Anthony M. Jabbour (CEO)
Bryan T. Hipsher (CFO)
Anthony Pietrontone (Chief Acctg Officer)
Joe A. Reinhardt III (Chief Legal Officer)
William P. Foley II (Exec Chm)

Subsidiaries:

Dun & Bradstreet Estonia AS (1)
Liivalaia 45, 10145, Tallinn, Estonia
Tel.: (372) 6414910
Commercial Data & Analytic Services
N.A.I.C.S.: 518210

Dun & Bradstreet Slovakia, s.r.o. (1)
Ruzinovska 3, Ruzinov District, 821 02, Bratislava, Slovakia
Tel.: (421) 327462640
Commercial Data & Analytic Services
N.A.I.C.S.: 518210

DUO WORLD, INC.
170 S Green Valley Pkwy Ste 300, Henderson, NV 89012
Tel.: (870) 505-6540   NV
Web Site: https://www.duoworld.com
Year Founded: 2014
DUUO—(OTCIQ)
Rev.: $50,564
Assets: $466,859
Liabilities: $2,289,522
Net Worth: ($1,822,663)
Earnings: $667,005
Emp.: 20
Fiscal Year-end: 03/31/23
Software Development Services
N.A.I.C.S.: 541511
Muhunthan Canagasooryam (Founder, Pres, CEO & Chief Architect)
Suzannah Jennifer Samuel Perera (CFO)
Ajeewan Arumugam (Head-Product-Market Dev)
Sudarshini Rajaratnam (Head-HR Dev)
Nilakshini Goonawardena (Officer-Legal)

Subsidiaries:

Duo Software (Pvt.) Limited (1)
No 403 Galle Road, Colombo, Sri Lanka
Tel.: (94) 112375000
Business Management Services
N.A.I.C.S.: 561110
Muhunthan Canagey (CEO)

DUOLINGO, INC.

Duolingo, Inc.—(Continued)

5900 Penn Ave, Pittsburgh, PA 15206
Tel.: (412) 567-6602   DE
Web Site: https://www.duolingo.com
Year Founded: 2011
DUOL—(NASDAQ)
Rev.: $369,495,000
Assets: $747,347,000
Liabilities: $205,269,000
Net Worth: $542,078,000
Earnings: $59,574,000
Emp.: 600
Fiscal Year-end: 12/31/22
Software Development Services
N.A.I.C.S.: 541511
Matthew Skaruppa (CFO)
Robert Meese (Chief Bus Officer)
Stephen Chen (Gen Counsel)
Molly Lindsay (Chief People Officer)
Manu Orssaud (CMO)
Luis Von Ahn (Co-Founder, Chm, Pres & CEO)
Severin Hacker (Co-Founder & CTO)

DUOS TECHNOLOGIES GROUP, INC.

7660 Centurion Pkwy Ste 100, Jacksonville, FL 32256
Tel.: (904) 296-2807   FL
Web Site: https://www.duostech.com
Year Founded: 1994
DUOT—(NASDAQ)
Rev.: $15,012,366
Assets: $13,089,119
Liabilities: $9,038,648
Net Worth: $4,050,471
Earnings: ($6,864,783)
Emp.: 67
Fiscal Year-end: 12/31/22
Mobile Data Center Management Services
N.A.I.C.S.: 518210
Adrian Graham Goldfarb (Pres & CFO)
Kenneth S. Ehrman (Chm)
Charles P. Ferry (CEO)

DUPONT DE NEMOURS, INC.

974 Centre Rd, Wilmington, DE 19805
Tel.: (302) 295-5783   DE
Web Site:
    https://www.investors.dupont.com
Year Founded: 2015
DD—(NYSE)
Rev.: $12,068,000,000
Assets: $38,552,000,000
Liabilities: $13,827,000,000
Net Worth: $24,725,000,000
Earnings: $423,000,000
Emp.: 24,000
Fiscal Year-end: 12/31/23
Holding Company; Chemicals, Resins, Coatings & Other Related Products Developer, Mfr & Whslr
N.A.I.C.S.: 551112
Lori D. Koch (CEO)
Edward D. Breen (Exec Chm & Chm)
Leland Weaver (Pres & Pres-Water & Protection)
Antonella Franzen (CFO & Sr VP)
Steven Larrabee (CIO & Sr VP)
Christopher Raia (Chief HR Officer & Sr VP)
Alexa Dembek (Chief Sustainability Officer, Chief Tech Officer & Sr VP)
Jon Kemp (Pres-Electronics & Industrial)
Erik Hoover (Gen Counsel & Sr VP)
Daryl Roberts (COO, Chief Engrg Officer, Chief Operations Officer & Sr VP)

Subsidiaries:

Belco Technologies Corporation   (1)
9 Entin Rd 1, Parsippany, NJ 07054

Tel.: (973) 884-4700
Chemical Product Whslr
N.A.I.C.S.: 424690
Joseph Stehn (CFO & Sr VP)
Richard A. Jackson (Chief Engr-Structural)
Scott Eagleson (Mgr-Global Dev)

Coastal Training Technologies Corp.   (1)
4023 Kennett Pike Ste 282, Wilmington, DE 19807-2018
Tel.: (757) 498-9014
Web Site: http://www.training.dupont.com
Safety Training & Consulting Services
N.A.I.C.S.: 541618

DPNL BV   (1)
Baanhoekweg 22, 3313 LA, Dordrecht, Netherlands
Tel.: (31) 786219400
Paint & Wallpaper Whslr
N.A.I.C.S.: 444120

DSP Singapore Holdings Pte. Ltd.   (1)
260 Orchard Road 18-01 The Heeren, Singapore, 238855, Singapore
Tel.: (65) 65863688
Construction Material Mfr & Distr
N.A.I.C.S.: 326299

Danisco Brasil Ltda.   (1)
506 Alphaville, Barueri, 06454-080, Brazil
Tel.: (55) 1141668000
Personal Protective Equipment Whslr
N.A.I.C.S.: 423450

Danisco Deutschland GmbH   (1)
Busch-Johannsen-Str 1, 25899, Niebull, Germany
Tel.: (49) 46619570000
Web Site: https://www.du-fuer-danisco.de
Food Chemical Product Mfr
N.A.I.C.S.: 325199

Donatelle Plastics, Inc.   (1)
501 County Rd E2 Ext, Saint Paul, MN 55112
Tel.: (651) 633-4200
Web Site: http://www.donatellemedical.com
Sales Range: $1-9.9 Million
Emp.: 130
Medical Device Mfr
N.A.I.C.S.: 339112
Charles S. Donatelle (Pres)

Du Pont (Australia) PTY LTD.   (1)
Level 3 7 Eden Park Drive, Macquarie Park, 2113, NSW, Australia
Tel.: (61) 299236111
Web Site: https://www.dupont.com.au
Inorganic Chemical Mfr
N.A.I.C.S.: 325180

Du Pont Apollo (Shenzhen) Limited   (1)
DuPont Apollo Hi-Tech Industrial Park East Guangming, Hi-Tech Zone Guangming New District, Shenzhen, 518107, Guangdong, China
Tel.: (86) 755 89 49 5388
Solar Electric System Services
N.A.I.C.S.: 221118

Du Pont China Holding Company Ltd.   (1)
18/F Tower A Gemdale Plaza No 91 Jianguo Road, Chaoyang District, Beijing, 100022, China
Tel.: (86) 108 557 1000
Web Site: http://www.dupont.com.cn
Synthetic Fiber, Agriculture, Chemical & Electronic Products Mfr
N.A.I.C.S.: 325998

Du Pont de Nemours (Belgium) BVBA   (1)
Antoon Spinoystraat 6, 2800, Mechelen, Belgium
Tel.: (32) 15441011
Web Site: https://www.dupontdenemours.be
Production of Synthetic Resins, Refrigerants & Fluoroproducts
N.A.I.C.S.: 325211

DuPont (Korea) Inc.   (1)
Asia Tower 4-5th floor 430 Nonhyeon-ro, Gangnam-gu, Seoul, 06223, Korea (South)
Tel.: (82) 222225200
Web Site: https://www.dupont.co.kr

Chemicals Mfr
N.A.I.C.S.: 325998

DuPont (U.K.) Industrial Limited   (1)
Maydown Works 60 Clooney Road, PO Box 15, Londonderry, BT47 6TH, United Kingdom
Tel.: (44) 28 71 864400
Crop Protection Product Mfr
N.A.I.C.S.: 325320

DuPont Deutschland Holding GmbH & Co. KG   (1)
Friedrichstrasse 154, 10117, Berlin, Germany
Tel.: (49) 30225050160
Personal Protective Equipment Whslr
N.A.I.C.S.: 423450

DuPont Kabushiki Kaisha   (1)
Sanno Park Tower 1-16-1 Nagata-cho, Chiyoda-ku, Tokyo, 100-6111, Japan
Tel.: (81) 355218500
Web Site: http://www.dupont.co.jp
Chemicals Mfr
N.A.I.C.S.: 325998

Joint Venture (Domestic):

Du Pont-Toray Co., Ltd.   (2)
1-1-1 Nihonbashi Honcho METLIFE Nihonbashi Honcho Building, Chuo-ku, Tokyo, 103-0023, Japan   (50%)
Tel.: (81) 332455081
Web Site: https://www.td-net.co.jp
Producer of Synthetic Fiber & Film
N.A.I.C.S.: 325220
Shinichiro Hata (Pres & CEO)

DuPont Mitsui Fluorochemicals Co., Ltd.   (2)
1-5-18 Sarugaku-cho Chiyoda-ku, Tokyo, 101-0064, Japan   (50%)
Tel.: (81) 352815800
Web Site: http://www.md-fluoro.co.jp
Sales Range: $150-199.9 Million
Fluorocarbon Compounds & Resins Mfr
N.A.I.C.S.: 325211

DuPont Mitsui Polychemicals Co., Ltd.   (2)
1-5-2 Siodome City Center Higashi-Shimbashi, Minato-ku, Tokyo, 105-7117, Japan   (50%)
Tel.: (81) 362534000
Web Site: http://www.mdp.jp
Polyolefin Resins, Coating Resins & Foam Sheeting Mfr
N.A.I.C.S.: 325211

Teijin DuPont Films Japan Limited   (2)
Kasumigaseki Common Gate West Tower 3-2-1 Kasumigaseki, Chiyoda-ku, Tokyo, 100-8585, Japan   (40%)
Tel.: (81) 3 3506 4243
Polyester Film Mfr & Whslr
N.A.I.C.S.: 326113

DuPont Nutrition & Biosciences Iberica S.L.U.   (1)
Avenida de Espioca 22, 46460, Valencia, Spain
Tel.: (34) 961212111
Personal Protective Equipment Whslr
N.A.I.C.S.: 423450

DuPont Nutrition Biosciences ApS   (1)
Langebrogade 1, 1411, Copenhagen, Denmark
Tel.: (45) 32662000
Web Site:
    http://www.dupontnutritionandbiosciences.com
Food Ingredients, Sugar & Sweetening Products Mfr
N.A.I.C.S.: 311313

Subsidiary (Non-US):

Danisco (UK) Ltd.   (2)
Wiltshire Market House Ailesbury Court, PO Box 777, High Street, Marlborough, SN8 1AA, Wilts, United Kingdom
Tel.: (44) 1672517777
Food Enzyme Mfr
N.A.I.C.S.: 325199

Plant (Domestic):

Danisco (UK) Ltd. - Beaminster   (3)

6 North Street, Beaminster, DT8 3DZ, Dorset, United Kingdom
Tel.: (44) 1308862216
Food Culture & Enzyme Mfr
N.A.I.C.S.: 325199

Danisco (UK) Ltd. - Reigate   (3)
Reigate Place 43 London Road, Maydown, Reigate, RH2 9PW, Surrey, United Kingdom
Tel.: (44) 1737227720
Special Sweeteners Mfr
N.A.I.C.S.: 325199

Subsidiary (Non-US):

Danisco Australia Pty. Ltd.   (2)
GF 97 Waterloo Rd, Macquarie Park, 2113, NSW, Australia
Tel.: (61) 293845000
Food Stabilizers & Emulsifiers, Spray Dried Ingredients & Food Enzymes Mfr
N.A.I.C.S.: 311423

Danisco Japan Ltd.   (2)
Sanno Park Tower 11 1 Nagata-cho 2 chome, Chiyoda-ku, Tokyo, 100-6111, Japan
Tel.: (81) 355212302
Enzyme, Sweeteners & Food Culture Mfr
N.A.I.C.S.: 325199

Subsidiary (US):

Danisco USA, Inc.   (2)
925 Page Mill Rd, Palo Alto, CA 94304
Tel.: (650) 846-7500
Food Ingredients Production Services
N.A.I.C.S.: 311423

Branch (Domestic):

Danisco USA, Inc. - New Century   (3)
4 New Century Pkwy, New Century, KS 66031
Tel.: (913) 764-8100
Functional Food Ingredients Mfr & Retailer
N.A.I.C.S.: 325199

Subsidiary (Domestic):

Solae LLC   (3)
4300 Duncan Ave, Saint Louis, MO 63110
Tel.: (314) 659-3385
Web Site: http://www.tasteofsolae.com
Isolated Soy Protein Mfr
N.A.I.C.S.: 325199

Plant (Domestic):

Solae LLC - Pryor Office   (4)
5532 Hunt St, Pryor, OK 74361
Tel.: (918) 476-5825
Uncompounded Natural Vitamins Mfr
N.A.I.C.S.: 325111

Division (Domestic):

DuPont Nutrition Biosciences - Brabrand   (2)
Edwin Rahrs Vej 38, 8220, Brabrand, Denmark
Tel.: (45) 89435000
Food Cultures Mfr
N.A.I.C.S.: 311423

Division (US):

Genencor International, Inc.   (2)
925 Page Mill Rd, Palo Alto, CA 94304
Tel.: (650) 846-7500
Genetically-Based Biotechnology Products Mfr
N.A.I.C.S.: 325412

Branch (Domestic):

Genencor International Inc. - Rochester   (3)
1700 Lexington Ave, Rochester, NY 14606
Tel.: (585) 277-4300
Genetically-Based Biotechnology Products Mfr
N.A.I.C.S.: 325412

Subsidiary (Non-US):

Genencor International Oy   (3)
Tiilikantie 15, PO Box 13, 42300, Jamsankoski, Finland
Tel.: (358) 14749411
Food Enzyme Mfr

N.A.I.C.S.: 325199

Branch (Domestic):

Genencor International Oy - Hanko (4)
Orioninkatu 5, PO Box 34, 10900, Hanko, Finland
Tel.: (358) 104317600
Food Enzyme Mfr
N.A.I.C.S.: 325199

DuPont Pakistan Operations (Pvt.) Limited (1)
5th Floor Citi Towers Block-6 Main Shara-e-Faisal, PECHS, Karachi, 75350, Pakistan
Tel.: (92) 2135209428
Chemical Products Mfr
N.A.I.C.S.: 325998
G. Hassan (Mgr-Mktg Comm)

DuPont Specialty Products GmbH & Co. KG (1)
Street B13, 06258, Schkopau, Germany
Tel.: (49) 34612446
Communication Equipment Technology Services
N.A.I.C.S.: 541990

DuPont Specialty Products India Private Limited (1)
82 83 8th Floor 2 North Avenue Maker Maxity Bandra Kurla Complex, Bandra East, Mumbai, 400051, Maharashtra, India
Tel.: (91) 2240716000
Plastic Materials Mfr
N.A.I.C.S.: 325211

DuPont Stylo Corporation (1)
Sanno Park Tower 2-11-1 Nagatcho, Chiyoda-ku, Tokyo, 100-6111, Japan (65%)
Tel.: (81) 3 5521 0111
Web Site: http://www.dupontstyro.co.jp
Plastics Product Mfr
N.A.I.C.S.: 326199
Hideki Yano (Pres)

DuPont Styro Corporation (1)
Sanno Park Tower 2-11-1 Nagatcho, Chiyoda-ku, Tokyo, 100-6111, Japan
Tel.: (81) 355210111
Web Site: https://www.dupontstyro.co.jp
Plastic Materials Mfr
N.A.I.C.S.: 325211

DuPont Taiwan Ltd. (1)
13F No 167 Tun Hwa North Rd, Taipei, 10549, Taiwan
Tel.: (886) 227191999
Web Site: https://www.dupont.com.tw
Chemical Products Mfr
N.A.I.C.S.: 325998

DuPont Uentrop GmbH (1)
Frielinghauser Strasse 5 Uentrop, 59071, Hamm, Germany
Tel.: (49) 2388920
Personal Protective Equipment Whslr
N.A.I.C.S.: 423450

DuPont de Nemours (Deutschland) GmbH (1)
Hugenottenallee 175, 63263, Neu-Isenburg, Germany
Tel.: (49) 6102180
Web Site: https://www.dupont.de
Formulates Conductive Compositions; Fiber, Photographic Products, Nylon Resins, Instrument Products Mfr
N.A.I.C.S.: 325211
Marion Weigand (Chm & Mng Dir)
Bernhard Daiber (Mng Dir)
Jan-Peter Scharfenberg (Mng Dir)
Patrick S. Schriber (Chm-Supvr Bd)

DuPont de Nemours (Luxembourg) SARL (1)
Rue General Patton, 5326, Contern, Luxembourg
Tel.: (352) 36661000
Polyester Film Mfr
N.A.I.C.S.: 326113

DuPont de Nemours (Nederland) B.V. (1)
Baanhoekweg 22, 3313 LA, Dordrecht, Netherlands
Tel.: (31) 786219400
Web Site: https://www.dupontnederland.nl

Production of Synthetic Resins, Refrigerants & Fluoroproducts
N.A.I.C.S.: 325211

DuPont, S.A. de C.V. (1)
Homero 206 Polanco V Seccion, 11570, Mexico, Mexico
Tel.: (52) 5557221000
Web Site: http://www.dupont.mx
Produces Finishes & Agricultural Chemicals & Distributes DuPont Products
N.A.I.C.S.: 325320

Subsidiary (Domestic):

DuPont Mexico, S.A. de C.V. (2)
Homero 206 Polanco V Seccion, 11570, Mexico, Mexico
Tel.: (52) 5557221000
Web Site: https://www.dupont.mx
Chemical Products Mfr
N.A.I.C.S.: 325998

Dupont (China) Research & Development and Management Co., Ltd. (1)
No 600 Cailun Road Zhangjiang High-Tech Park, Shanghai, 201203, China
Tel.: (86) 21 28921002
Business Support Services
N.A.I.C.S.: 561499

Dupont Teijin Films China Ltd. (1)
Units 1B-3A 37/F 148 Electric Road, North Point, China (Hong Kong)
Tel.: (852) 27345345
Web Site: http://www.dupontteijinfilms.com
Polyester Film Mfr & Distr
N.A.I.C.S.: 326113
Tim Leung (Pres)

E.I. DuPont Canada - Thetford Inc. (1)
1045 Monfette Est, Thetford Mines, G6G 5T1, QC, Canada
Tel.: (418) 334-1450
Chemical Product Whslr
N.A.I.C.S.: 424690

EKC Technology, Inc. (1)
2520 Barrington Ct, Hayward, CA 94545
Tel.: (510) 784-9105
Specialty Chemical Product Services
N.A.I.C.S.: 325998

FMC Corp. - Health & Nutrition (1)
2929 Walnut St, Philadelphia, PA 19104
Tel.: (215) 299-6000
Web Site: http://www.fmcbiopolymer.com
Sales Range: $700-749.9 Million
Health & Nutrition Chemicals & Products Mfr & Sales
N.A.I.C.S.: 325998
Eric Norris (Pres)

Subsidiary (Non-US):

Dupont Nutrition Manufacturing UK Limited (2)
Ladyburn Works, Girvan, KA26 9JN, United Kingdom
Tel.: (44) 1655333000
Chemical & Pharmaceutical Product Mfr
N.A.I.C.S.: 325412

FMC BioPolymer AS (2)
Industriveien 33, Sandvika, 1337, Norway
Tel.: (47) 67815500
Chemical Product Whslr
N.A.I.C.S.: 424690

FilmTec Corporation (1)
5400 Dewey Hill Rd, Edina, MN 55439
Tel.: (952) 897-4200
Water Filtration Systems Mfr
N.A.I.C.S.: 325211

Finnfeeds Oy (1)
Myllykatu 20, PO Box 461, 65100, Vaasa, Finland
Tel.: (358) 10431020
Organic Basic Chemicals Mfr
N.A.I.C.S.: 325199

Subsidiary (Domestic):

Finnfeeds Finland Oy (2)
Sokeritehtaantie 20, 02460, Kantvik, Finland
Tel.: (358) 10431020
Chemical Products Mfr
N.A.I.C.S.: 325199

Division (Domestic):

Finnfeeds Finland Oy-Naantali (3)
Satamatie 2, 21100, Naantali, Finland
Tel.: (358) 10431020
Enzyme Mfr
N.A.I.C.S.: 325199

Laird Limited (1)
100 Pall Mall, London, SW1Y 5NQ, United Kingdom
Tel.: (44) 2074684040
Web Site: http://lairdtech.com
Rev.: $1,263,585,792
Assets: $1,510,339,840
Liabilities: $729,873,920
Net Worth: $780,465,920
Earnings: $96,866,816
Emp.: 10,132
Fiscal Year-end: 12/31/2017
Holding Company; Electronic Devices Mfr
N.A.I.C.S.: 551112
Gerhard du Plessis (Gen Counsel & Sec)
Tony Quinlan (CEO)
Kevin Dangerfield (CFO)
Steve Brown (Pres-Connected Vehicle Solutions)
Carmen Chua (Pres-Performance Materials)
Kevin White (Sr VP-Wireless & Thermal Sys)
Melanie Curtis (Interim Chief HR Officer)
Christine Mcgourty (Chief Corp Affairs Officer)
Graeme Watt (Chief Risk Officer & Chief Governance Officer)
Mike Bell (CTO)

Subsidiary (US):

Antenex, Inc (2)
205 Bloomingdale Rd Ste 2000, Glendale Heights, IL 60139
Tel.: (630) 351-9007
Telecommunications Equipment Mfr
N.A.I.C.S.: 334220

Subsidiary (Non-US):

Centurion Electronics (Shanghai) Limited (2)
No 150 Cailun Road Zhangjiang Industrial Park Pudong New Area, Shanghai, 201203, China
Tel.: (86) 2158550827
Telecommunications Equipment Mfr
N.A.I.C.S.: 334220

Subsidiary (US):

LS Research, LLC (2)
W66 N220 Commerce Ct, Cedarburg, WI 53012
Tel.: (262) 375-4400
Web Site: http://www.lsr.com
Wireless Product Development, Certification & Mfr
N.A.I.C.S.: 334220
Jen Sarto (VP-Sls)
David Lockhood (CEO)
Daniel Plach (VP-Ops)

Subsidiary (Domestic):

Laird Controls UK Limited (2)
Ground Floot Lock House 58 Hamm Moor Lane, Weybridge, KT15 2SF, Surrey, United Kingdom
Tel.: (44) 1932247511
Web Site: http://www.lairdtech.com
Portable Remote Control Systems Mfr
N.A.I.C.S.: 335314

Subsidiary (Non-US):

Laird Technologies (M) SDN BHD (2)
Plot No 522 Lorong Perusahaan Baru 3, Perai Industrial Estate, 13600, Perai, Penang, Malaysia
Tel.: (60) 43989298
Telecommunications Equipment Mfr
N.A.I.C.S.: 334220
Lim Kim Chai (Gen Mgr)

Laird Technologies (SEA) PTE Limited (2)
750E Chai Chee Rd 03-07/08 Technopark Chai Chee, Singapore, 469005, Singapore
Tel.: (65) 62438022
Web Site: http://www.lairdtech.com

Sales Range: $25-49.9 Million
Emp.: 30
Telecommunications Equipment Mfr
N.A.I.C.S.: 334220

Laird Technologies (Shanghai) Limited (2)
No 398 Yuan Dian Road Xin Zhuang Industrial Zone, Shanghai, China
Tel.: (86) 2164428018
Web Site: https://www.dupont.com
Radio Antenna Mfr
N.A.I.C.S.: 334419

Laird Technologies (Shenzhen) Limited (2)
Building 1 Dejin Industrial Park Fuyuanyi Road Zhancheng Community Fuhai Street, Fuyong Town Bao An District, Shenzhen, 518103, Guangdong, China
Tel.: (86) 75527141166
Web Site: https://www.dupont.com
Electronic Components Mfr
N.A.I.C.S.: 334419

Laird Technologies Japan, Inc. (2)
Shin Yokohama Business Ctr Bldg 7F 2-6 Shin Yokohama 3-chome, Kohoku-ku, Yokohama, 222-0033, Kanagawa, Japan
Tel.: (81) 454736808
Web Site: http://www.lairdtech.com
Sales Range: $25-49.9 Million
Emp.: 6
Telecommunications Equipment Mfr
N.A.I.C.S.: 334220

Laird Technologies Korea Y.H (2)
160-1 4F Dodang-dong, Wonmi-gu, Bucheon, 420-805, Gyeonggi, Korea (South)
Tel.: (82) 327207900
Web Site: www.lairdtech.com
Sales Range: $25-49.9 Million
Emp.: 24
Electric Equipment Mfr
N.A.I.C.S.: 334419

Laird Technologies S. de R. L. de C. V. (2)
Avenida Industrial Drive Sin Numero Edificio 10 Prologis Park, Reynosa, 88780, Tamaulipas, Mexico
Tel.: (52) 899 921 9000
Electronic Parts & Equipment Mfr
N.A.I.C.S.: 334419

Laird Technologies S.R.O. (2)
Prumyslova 497, 462 11, Liberec, Czech Republic
Tel.: (420) 488575111
Emp.: 100
Telecommunications Equipment Mfr
N.A.I.C.S.: 334290
Leon Bertjens (Gen Mgr)
Peter Stros (Gen Mgr)

Laird Technologies Taiwan, Inc. (2)
No 22 Wucyuan 6th Road, Wugu District, Taipei, 24889, Taiwan
Tel.: (886) 2 2290 1234
Communication Equipment Mfr
N.A.I.C.S.: 334220

Subsidiary (US):

Laird Technologies, Inc. (2)
16401 Swingley Rdg Rd Ste 700, Chesterfield, MO 63017
Tel.: (636) 898-6000
Web Site: https://www.laird.com
Electromagnetic Interference Shielding Materials, Thermal Interface Products & Wireless Antennas Mfr
N.A.I.C.S.: 334419

Subsidiary (Non-US):

Laird Technologies Ltd (3)
Birches Industrial Est, East Grinstead, RH19 1XH, West Sussex, United Kingdom (100%)
Tel.: (44) 1342314044
Web Site: http://www.lairdtech.com
Sales Range: $25-49.9 Million
Emp.: 42
Stamping Metal, Compliance & Evaluation
N.A.I.C.S.: 332119

Laird Techonolgies (SEA) Pte., Ltd. (3)
750 E Chai Chee Rd, Chai Chee Industrial

DuPont de Nemours, Inc.—(Continued)

Park, Singapore, 469005,
Singapore   **(100%)**
Tel.: (65) 62438022
Web Site: http://www.lairdtech.com
Sales Range: $25-49.9 Million
Emp.: 12
Stamping Metal, Compliance & Evaluation
N.A.I.C.S.: 332119
Seika Gunji (Gen Mgr)

Subsidiary (Non-US):

**Tianjin Laird Technologies
Limited** **(2)**
Building C3 / C4 Hongtai Industrial Park No
87 Taifeng Road, Teda, 300457, China
Tel.: (86) 2266298160
Web Site: https://www.dupont.com
Electronic Components Mfr
N.A.I.C.S.: 334419

MECS, Inc. **(1)**
14522 S Outer Forty Rd Ste 100, Chester-
field, MO 63017
Tel.: (314) 275-5700
Sulfuric Acid & Environmental Technology
Products & Serivces
N.A.I.C.S.: 325180

Subsidiary (Non-US):

MECS Europe/Africa BVBA **(2)**
Hoeilaart Office Park Building B I Van-
dammestraat 7, 1560, Hoeilaart, Belgium
Tel.: (32) 26582620
Design & Construction of Sulfuric Acid
Plants; Sulfuric Acid Process Technologies
& Related Products Mfr
N.A.I.C.S.: 333248

Multibase S.A. **(1)**
ZI Chartreuse Guiers, 38380, Saint-Laurent-
du-Pont, France
Tel.: (33) 476671212
Communication Equipment Technology Ser-
vices
N.A.I.C.S.: 541990

NITTA DuPont Incorporated **(1)**
4-4-26 Sakuragawa, Naniwa-ku, Osaka,
556-0022, Japan   **(50%)**
Tel.: (81) 665631291
Web Site: https://www.nittadupont.co.jp
Emp.: 300
Organic Chemical Product Whslr
N.A.I.C.S.: 424690
Mitsutaka Chiba (Pres & CEO)
Rainer Irle (CFO)
Martin Schoder (Sr VP)
Christoph von Plotho (Pres)

**Performance Specialty Products (In-
dia) Private Limited** **(1)**
3rd Floor Tower A DLF Building No 8 DLF
Cyber City DLF Phase II, Gurgaon, 122
002, Haryana, India
Tel.: (91) 1244091818
Communication Equipment Technology Services
N.A.I.C.S.: 541990

**Performance Specialty Products (Sin-
gapore) Pte. Ltd.** **(1)**
10 Marina Boulevard 07-01 Marina Bay Financial Centre Tower 2, Singapore, 018983,
Singapore
Tel.: (65) 63225288
Communication Equipment Technology Services
N.A.I.C.S.: 541990

**Productos Especializados De Mexico
S. De R.L. De C.V** **(1)**
Lago Alberto 319-PH2 Colonia Granada,
11520, Mexico, Mexico
Tel.: (52) 5557221000
Semiconductor Machinery Mfr
N.A.I.C.S.: 333242

**Rohm & Haas Electronic Materials
CMP Korea Ltd.** **(1)**
3-5th Asia Tower 430 Nonhyeon-ro,
Gangnam-gu, Seoul, 06223, Korea (South)
Tel.: (82) 2 2222 5200
Electronic Components Mfr
N.A.I.C.S.: 334419

**Rohm & Haas Electronic Nemerials
K.K.** **(1)**

300 Onnado, Agano, 959-1914, Niigata,
Japan
Tel.: (81) 250621295
Communication Equipment Technology Ser-
vices
N.A.I.C.S.: 541990

**Rohm & Haas Electronic Materials
Singapore Pte. Ltd.** **(1)**
260 Orchard Road Suite18-01 Heeren, Sin-
gapore, 238855, Singapore
Tel.: (65) 68353773
Chemical Product Whslr
N.A.I.C.S.: 424690

**Rohm and Haas Electronic Materials
Asia Pacific Co., Ltd.** **(1)**
No 6 Kesi 2nd Road Jhunan Miaoli Jhunan
Site, Hsinchu Science-Based Industrial
Park, Miao-li, 35053, Taiwan
Tel.: (886) 37539100
Organic Chemical Product Whslr
N.A.I.C.S.: 424690

**Rohm and Haas Electronic Materials
CMP Inc,** **(1)**
451 Bellevue Rd, Newark, DE 19713
Tel.: (302) 366-0500
Chemical Product Whslr
N.A.I.C.S.: 424690

**Rohm and Haas Electronic Materials
Korea, Ltd.** **(1)**
56 1-ro 3 Gongdan, Seobuk-gu, Cheonan,
31093, Chungnam-do, Korea (South)
Tel.: (82) 416219321
Organic Chemical Product Whslr
N.A.I.C.S.: 424690

**Rohm and Haas Electronic Materials
LLC** **(1)**
455 Forest St, Marlborough, MA 01752
Tel.: (508) 481-7950
Chemicals Mfr
N.A.I.C.S.: 325998

**Rohm and Haas Electronic Materials
Taiwan Ltd.** **(1)**
No 6 Lane 280 Zhongshan North Road
Dayuan Industrial Zone, Taoyuan, 33759,
Dayuan, Taiwan
Tel.: (886) 33858000
Organic Chemical Mfr
N.A.I.C.S.: 325199

**Rohm and Haas Shanghai Chemical
Industry Co., Ltd.** **(1)**
8605 Songze Avenue Qingpu Industrial
Park, Shanghai, 201707, China
Tel.: (86) 2169211018
Agricultural Chemical Product Distr
N.A.I.C.S.: 424910

**Specialty Products Turkey Endustri
Urunleri Limited Sirketi** **(1)**
Barbaros Mah Kardelen Sok Palladium
Tower is Merkezi No 2 K 12, Atasehir,
34746, Istanbul, Turkiye
Tel.: (90) 2166870400
Communication Equipment Technology Ser-
vices
N.A.I.C.S.: 541990

Spectrum Plastics Group, Inc. **(1)**
2500 Northwinds Pkwy Ste 472, Alpharetta,
GA 30009
Tel.: (404) 564-8560
Web Site:
    http://www.spectrumplasticsgroup.com
Injection Molding Of Plastics
N.A.I.C.S.: 326199
Rahul Goyal (Chm)

Subsidiary (Domestic):

**Apex Resource Technologies,
Inc.** **(2)**
17 Downing Industrial Pkwy Ste 1, Pittsfield,
MA 01201-3872
Tel.: (413) 442-1414
Custom Injection Plastic Molding Products
Design Engineering & Mfr
N.A.I.C.S.: 326199

Laser Light Technologies, LLC **(2)**
5 Danuser Dr, Hermann, MO 65041
Tel.: (573) 486-5500
Web Site: http://www.laserusa.com
Sales Range: $1-9.9 Million
Emp.: 17
Commercial Printing

N.A.I.C.S.: 323111
Frank Hannan (CEO)

**Zhejiang OMEX Environmental Engi-
neering Co., Ltd.** **(1)**
688 Chuangye Ave Economic Technology
Dvpt Zone, Huzhou, 313000, China
Tel.: (86) 13819232702
Chemical Products Mfr
N.A.I.C.S.: 424690

inge GmbH **(1)**
Flurstrasse 27, 86926, Greifenberg, Ger-
many
Tel.: (49) 8192 997 700
Water Purification Membrane Mfr
N.A.I.C.S.: 339999

DURECT CORPORATION
10240 Bubb Rd, Cupertino, CA
95014-4166
Tel.: (408) 777-1417   DE
Web Site: https://www.durect.com
Year Founded: 1998
DRRX—(NASDAQ)
Rev.: $19,283,000
Assets: $60,100,000
Liabilities: $35,115,000
Net Worth: $24,985,000
Earnings: ($35,333,000)
Emp.: 79
Fiscal Year-end: 12/31/22
Pharmaceutical Preparations Devel-
oper
N.A.I.C.S.: 325412
James E. Brown (Pres & CEO)
David R. Hoffmann (Chm)
Andrew R. Miksztal (VP-
Pharmaceutical & R&D)
David J. Ellis (VP-Clinical Dev)
Judy R. Joice (Sr VP-Ops & Corp
Quality Assurance)
Steve Helmer (VP)
WeiQi Lin (Exec VP-R&D)
Norman L. Sussman (Chief Medical
Officer)
Timothy M. Papp (CFO)
Dorothy Engelking (VP)

DUTCH BROS INC.
110 SW 4th St, Grants Pass, OR
97526
Tel.: (541) 955-4700   DE
Web Site: https://www.dutchbros.com
Year Founded: 2021
BROS—(NYSE)
Rev.: $739,012,000
Assets: $1,186,360,000
Liabilities: $934,384,000
Net Worth: $251,976,000
Earnings: ($4,753,000)
Emp.: 22,000
Fiscal Year-end: 12/31/22
Holding Company
N.A.I.C.S.: 551112
Victoria Tullett (Chief Legal Officer)
Jess Elmquist (Chief People Officer)
Sumitro Ghosh (Pres-Ops)
Joshua Guenser (CFO)
Christine Barone (Pres & CEO)
Travis Boersma (Founder & Chm)
Brian Maxwell (Vice Chm)
Andrew Conway (Sr VP-Ops Systems
& Standard)
Christine Schmidt (Chief Admin Offi-
cer)
Keith Thomajan (Chief Social Impact
Officer)

DWS MUNICIPAL INCOME
TRUST
875 3rd Ave, New York, NY 10022-
6225
Tel.: (212) 454-4500   MA
KTF—(NYSE)
Rev.: $30,445,891
Assets: $756,747,407
Liabilities: $259,748,420

Net Worth: $496,998,987
Earnings: $19,675,570
Fiscal Year-end: 11/30/19
Investment Management Service
N.A.I.C.S.: 525990

DWS STRATEGIC MUNICIPAL
INCOME TRUST
875 3rd Ave, New York, NY 10022-
6225
Tel.: (212) 454-4500
KSM—(NYSE)
Rev.: $9,903,894
Assets: $239,077,527
Liabilities: $96,872,937
Net Worth: $142,204,590
Earnings: $5,904,212
Fiscal Year-end: 11/30/19
Investment Management Service
N.A.I.C.S.: 525990

DXC TECHNOLOGY COMPANY
20408 Bashan Dr Ste 231, Ashburn,
VA 20147
Tel.: (703) 245-9700   NV
Web Site: https://dxc.com
Year Founded: 2017
DXC—(NYSE)
Rev.: $13,667,000,000
Assets: $13,871,000,000
Liabilities: $10,805,000,000
Net Worth: $3,066,000,000
Earnings: $91,000,000
Emp.: 130,000
Fiscal Year-end: 03/31/24
Software Development Services
N.A.I.C.S.: 551112
Raul J. Fernandez (Pres & CEO)
Matthew K. Fawcett (Gen Counsel &
Exec VP)
Robert F. Del Bene (CFO & Exec VP)
Seelan Nayagam (VP & Gen Mgr-
Asia Pacific)
Mark Hughes (Sr VP-Offerings &
Strategic Partners)
Mary E. Finch (Chief HR Officer &
Exec VP)
Vinod Bagal (Exec VP-Transformation
& Delivery-Global)
Chris Drumgoole (COO & Exec VP)
Dmitry Loschinin (Exec VP)
Tim Weir (VP-Asset Protection-
Global)
Jim Brady (COO & Exec VP)
Michael Corcoran (Chief Strategy Of-
ficer & Exec VP)
Zafar Hasan (Sec, VP & Head-Corp
Legal)
Michael McDaniel (VP & Gen Mgr-
Modern Workplace)
Tom Pettit (VP & Gen Mgr-Europe,
Middle East & Africa)
Christopher A. Voci (Principal Acctg
Officer, Sr VP & Controller)
Kristie Grinnell (CIO & Sr VP)

Subsidiaries:

BusinessNow Copenhagen ApS **(1)**
Vandtårnsvej 62A 3 sal, 2860, Søborg, Den-
mark
Tel.: (45) 70230231
Web Site: http://www.businessnow.dk
Information Technology Support Services
N.A.I.C.S.: 541512
Bo Wilchen-Pedersen (CEO & Partner)
Lasse Wilen Kristensen (Partner)
Peter Ravnholt (Partner)
Mette Abildgaard (Mgr-Office)
Christoffer Kock Petersen (Controller-Fin)
Allan Kent Jorgensen (Chief Comml Officer)
Michelle Lindahl Staffensen (Mktg Mgr)

CMORE Automotive GmbH **(1)**
Kemptener Strasse 99 Bodensee, 88131,
Lindau, Germany
Tel.: (49) 8382304930

Web Site: http://www.cmore-automotive.com
Emp.: 250
Software Services
N.A.I.C.S.: 541511
Richard Woller *(Co-Founder, Co-CEO & Mng Dir)*
Gregor Matenaer *(Co-Founder, Co-CEO & Mng Dir)*

Cleartech Brasil Ltda (1)
Al Rio Rio 585 Padauiri Building Alphaville, Barueri, Sao Paulo, Brazil
Tel.: (55) 1135764500
Web Site: http://www.cleartech.com.br
Information Technology Management Services
N.A.I.C.S.: 541512

Computer Sciences Corporation (1)
1775 Tysons Blvd, Tysons, VA 22102
Tel.: (703) 245-9700
Computer Products & Services
N.A.I.C.S.: 541512
Ruth Ann Burger *(Dir-Pension Admin)*
Alexandrina McAfee *(Dir-Compensation & Benefits)*
Sandra McKean *(Dir-Corp Risk Mngmt)*
Thomas Newman *(Dir-Admin Svcs)*
Mike Estrin *(Mgr-Corp Real Estate & Construction)*

Subsidiary (Non-US):

Bad Homburger Inkasso GmbH (2)
Konrad-Adenauer-Allee 1-11, 61118, Bad Vilbel, Germany
Tel.: (49) 6101989110
Web Site: https://www.bad-homburger-inkasso.com
Finance Services
N.A.I.C.S.: 522291
Karsten Schneider *(Mng Dir)*
Sonja Kardorf *(Chm-Supervisory Bd)*
Thomas Schneider *(Mng Dir)*

Subsidiary (Domestic):

CSC Agility Platform, Inc. (2)
233 Wilshire Blvd Ste 990, Santa Monica, CA 90401
Tel.: (310) 729-1864
Software Publisher Services
N.A.I.C.S.: 513210

Subsidiary (Non-US):

CSC Computer Sciences (South Africa) (Pty) Limited (2)
Canal Walk 6th Floor West Tower Century City, Cape Town, 7441, South Africa
Tel.: (27) 215296500
Computer Related Services
N.A.I.C.S.: 541519

CSC Computer Sciences Brasil S/A (2)
Domo Corporate Rua Jose Versolato 20th Floor - Torre A, Sao Bernardo do Campo, 09750-730, SP, Brazil
Tel.: (55) 1125029657
System Integration & Consulting Services
N.A.I.C.S.: 541512

CSC Computer Sciences Consulting Austria GmbH (2)
Donaufelder Str 73-79, 1210, Vienna, Austria
Tel.: (43) 12592908
Computer Consulting Services
N.A.I.C.S.: 541611

CSC Computer Sciences Limited (2)
Royal Pavilion Wellesley Road, Aldershot, GU11 1PZ, Hants, United Kingdom
Tel.: (44) 330575100
Computer Related Services
N.A.I.C.S.: 541512
Steve Turpie *(Sr VP & Reg Mgr)*
Adrienne Doyle *(VP-Developed Markets)*
Sukhbinder Gill *(CTO)*
Tina Gough *(VP-Advanced Markets)*
Purusharth Tripathi *(VP-Reg Acct)*

Subsidiary (Domestic):

Xchanging Limited (3)
30th Floor The Gherkin 30 St Mary Axe, London, EC3A 8EP, United Kingdom
Tel.: (44) 113680837
Business Process Outsourcing Services

N.A.I.C.S.: 561499
Tony Walker *(Head-Technical-Marine)*

Subsidiary (Non-US):

Xchanging Solutions Limited (4)
Kalyani Tech Park Survey No 1 6 24, Kundanhalli Village K R Puram, Bengaluru, 560 066, Karnataka, India **(75%)**
Tel.: (91) 8033870001
Web Site: http://www.xchanging.com
Rev.: $27,291,600
Assets: $80,210,200
Liabilities: $10,756,200
Net Worth: $69,454,000
Earnings: $7,658,000
Emp.: 164
Fiscal Year-end: 03/31/2020
Information Technology & Business Process Outsourcing Services
N.A.I.C.S.: 541511

Subsidiary (Non-US):

CSC Computer Sciences S.A. (2)
12D Impasse Drosbach, L-1653, Luxembourg, Luxembourg
Tel.: (352) 24 83 41
System Integration & Consulting Services
N.A.I.C.S.: 541512

Subsidiary (Domestic):

CSC Enterprises L.P. (2)
8404 W Center Rd, Omaha, NE 68124
Tel.: (402) 391-3223
Transportation Services
N.A.I.C.S.: 541614

Subsidiary (Non-US):

CSC Japan, Ltd. (2)
Kyobashi Edogran 17th Floor 2-2-1 Kyobashi, Chuo-ku, Tokyo, 104-0031, Japan
Tel.: (81) 3 6665 0222
Computer System Design Services
N.A.I.C.S.: 541512

Branch (Domestic):

Computer Sciences Corporation (2)
1550 Crystal Dr Ste 1300, Arlington, VA 22202
Tel.: (703) 413-9200
Web Site: http://www.dxc.technology
Computer Related Services
N.A.I.C.S.: 541519

Computer Sciences Corporation (2)
10301 Wilson Blvd, Blythewood, SC 29016
Tel.: (803) 333-4000
Computer Related Services
N.A.I.C.S.: 541512

Subsidiary (Non-US):

Computer Sciences Corporation India Private Limited (2)
Galaxy Business Park Noida Towers A 44/45 Sector 62, Noida, 201301, India
Tel.: (91) 1206700002
Computer Related Services
N.A.I.C.S.: 541519
Shashi Shekhar *(Mgr-Ops)*

Computer Sciences Corporation Services (Pty) Limited (2)
Canal Walk 6th Floor West Tower Century City, Cape Town, 7441, South Africa
Tel.: (27) 215296500
Computer System Design Services
N.A.I.C.S.: 541512

Continuum SOCS S.A.S. (2)
Tour Carpe Diem 31 Place Des Corolles CS 40075, 92098, Paris, Cedex, France
Tel.: (33) 157980011
Financial Services
N.A.I.C.S.: 523999

Covansys S.L. (2)
Las Rozas C/ Jose Echegaray 8, Las Rozas, Madrid, 28232, Spain
Tel.: (34) 912157362
Computer System Integration & Designing Services
N.A.I.C.S.: 541512

DXC Technology Australia Holdings Pty Limited (2)
26 Talavera Road, Macquarie Park, 2113,

NSW, Australia
Tel.: (61) 290343000
Computer System Design Services
N.A.I.C.S.: 541519

DXC Technology Australia Pty. Limited (2)
26 Talavera Road, Macquarie Park, 2113, NSW, Australia
Tel.: (61) 300765144
Web Site: https://dxc.com
Computer Related Services
N.A.I.C.S.: 541519
Seelan Nayagam *(Mng Dir)*
Daniel Biondi *(CTO)*
Russell Hatton *(VP-Reg Sls)*
Paul Tasker *(Dir-Reg Delivery)*
Nick Mescher *(Sr Partner-Digital Transformation)*
Alex Ratkovsky *(Dir & Gen Mgr-Banking & Capital Market)*
Kevin Jury *(Sr Mng Partner)*
Mary Siourounis *(Dir-Bus Tech)*
Ralph Pickering *(Dir-Merger & Acq)*
Clodagh Farrell *(CFO)*
Natasha Copley *(Dir-HR)*
Bernice Muncaster *(Dir-Mktg & Comm)*

Subsidiary (Domestic):

DXC United Pty. Limited (3)
L15 17-19 360 Collins Street, Melbourne, 3000, VIC, Australia
Tel.: (61) 392245777
Information Technology, Facilities Management & Intellectual Property Services
N.A.I.C.S.: 541519

Subsidiary (Domestic):

DXC Eclipse Pty Ltd (4)
26 Talavera Road, Macquarie Park, Sydney, 2113, NSW, Australia
Tel.: (61) 290343000
Business Software Development Services
N.A.I.C.S.: 541511
Martin Wildsmith *(Dir-DXC Eclipse Microsoft Practice)*

Subsidiary (US):

UXC Eclipse (USA) Inc. (5)
1775 Tysons Blvd, Tysons, VA 22102
Tel.: (703) 289-3400
Computer System Design Services
N.A.I.C.S.: 541512
Ivan Cole *(CTO)*

Subsidiary (Domestic):

Oxygen Business Solutions Pty. Ltd (4)
Level 19 360 Collins Street, Melbourne, 3000, VIC, Australia
Tel.: (61) 361216931
Software Consulting Services
N.A.I.C.S.: 541511
Stuart Dickinson *(Mgr)*

Red Rock Consulting Pty Ltd (4)
L19-21 135 King Street, Sydney, 2000, NSW, Australia
Tel.: (61) 292355600
Business Management Consulting Services
N.A.I.C.S.: 541611
Richard James *(Dir-Oracle Practice)*

Group (Domestic):

UXC BSG Holdings Pty. Ltd. (4)
L15 17-19 360 Collins Street, Melbourne, 3000, VIC, Australia
Tel.: (61) 392245777
Information Technology Infrastructure Services
N.A.I.C.S.: 541519

Subsidiary (Domestic):

UXC Professional Solutions Holdings Pty Ltd (4)
L15 17-19 360 Collins Street, Melbourne, 3000, VIC, Australia
Tel.: (61) 392245777
Information Technology Consulting Services
N.A.I.C.S.: 541512

Subsidiary (Non-US):

DXC Technology Bulgaria E.O.O.D. (2)

8 General Yordan Venedikov St, Sofia, 1784, Bulgaria
Tel.: (359) 29 74 33 16
System Integration & Consulting Services
N.A.I.C.S.: 541512

DXC Technology Danmark A/S (2)
Retortvej 8, 2500, Valby, Denmark
Tel.: (45) 36144000
Computers & Information Technology Services
N.A.I.C.S.: 541513

DXC Technology Deutschland GmbH (2)
Alfred-Herrhausen-Allee 3-5, 65760, Eschborn, Germany
Tel.: (49) 61722687674
System Integration & Consulting Services
N.A.I.C.S.: 541512

DXC Technology Hong Kong Limited (2)
Room 1905-13 19th Floor Cityplaza One 1111 Kings Road, Taikoo Shing, Hong Kong, China (Hong Kong)
Tel.: (852) 29188888
Computer Facilities Management Services
N.A.I.C.S.: 541513

DXC Technology Scandihealth A/S (2)
Retortvej 8, Valby, 2500, Copenhagen, Denmark
Tel.: (45) 36144000
Computer System Design Services
N.A.I.C.S.: 541513

DXC Technology Slovakia s.r.o (2)
Galvaniho 5890/7, 821 04, Bratislava, Slovakia
Tel.: (421) 257525555
Computer Related Services
N.A.I.C.S.: 541519

DXC Technology Switzerland GmbH (2)
Neue Winterthurerstrasse 99, Wallisellen, 8304, Zurich, Switzerland
Tel.: (41) 435471900
Computer Related Services
N.A.I.C.S.: 541519

DXC Techonology Norge AS (2)
Folke Bernadottesvei 38, Fyllingsdalen, 5147, Bergen, Norway
Tel.: (47) 21634000
Computer Facilities Management Services
N.A.I.C.S.: 541513

Experteam S.A./N.V. (2)
Place Marcel Broodthaers, 1060, Brussels, Belgium
Tel.: (32) 2 648 45 10
Information Technology Consulting Services
N.A.I.C.S.: 519290

Fixnetix Ltd. (2)
31st Floor The Gherkin 30 St Mary Axe, London, EC3A 8EP, United Kingdom
Tel.: (44) 2030088999
Web Site: http://www.fixnetix.com
Financial & Investment Software Developer
N.A.I.C.S.: 513210
Shaun Jackson *(Chief Comml Officer)*
Steve Hewson *(Head-Product & Platform)*
Jacob Beeman *(Gen Mgr)*
Matt Cartwright *(Sr Mgr-Contracts)*
Marlena Efstratopoulou *(Chief Info & Security Officer)*
Aidan Houlihan *(Global Head-Bus Dev)*

ISI (China) Co., Ltd. (2)
3/F Technology Building 3 Crown Square, Tianbao Industrial Area Airport Industrial Park, Tianjin, 300308, China
Tel.: (86) 2258218228
Information Service Management Provider
N.A.I.C.S.: 519290

Innovative Banking Solutions AG (2)
Bahnhofstrasse 27-33, 65185, Wiesbaden, Germany
Tel.: (49) 6113410100
Web Site: https://www.ibs-banking.com
Business Process Outsourcing Services
N.A.I.C.S.: 561440

Innovative Banking Solutions AG (2)
Bahnhofstr 27-33, 65185, Wiesbaden, Germany

DXC Technology Company—(Continued)

Tel.: (49) 6113410100
Web Site: https://www.ibs-banking.com
Software Publishing Services
N.A.I.C.S.: 513210
Markus Rhein *(Chm-Exec Bd & CEO)*
Claus Schunemann *(Chm-Supervisory Bd)*
Dietmar Dhar Roy *(Head-Product & Solution Mgmt)*
Yves Zorb *(CFO & Head-Fin)*

Subsidiary (Domestic):

Technology Service Partners, Inc. (2)
4651 Salisbury Rd Ste 155, Jacksonville, FL 32256
Tel.: (904) 296-2312
Staffing & Recruiting Services
N.A.I.C.S.: 561311

Subsidiary (Non-US):

UltraGenda N.V (2)
Blarenberglaan 2, 2800, Mechelen, Belgium
Tel.: (32) 93263030
Web Site: http://www.ultragenda.com
Information Technology Support Services
N.A.I.C.S.: 541512

Subsidiary (Domestic):

iSOFT Inc. (2)
213 W 35th St Ste 908, New York, NY 10001
Tel.: (212) 760-5800
Web Site: https://isoftinc.net
Business Process Outsourcing Services
N.A.I.C.S.: 561440

Subsidiary (Non-US):

iSOFT Solutions (International) Pty Ltd. (2)
26 Talavera Road Macquarie Park, Sydney, 2113, NSW, Australia
Tel.: (61) 290343000
Computer System Design Services
N.A.I.C.S.: 541512

iSOFT eHealth Pty Ltd (2)
26 Talavera Road, Macquarie Park, Sydney, 2113, NSW, Australia
Tel.: (61) 290343000
Information Technology Services for Healthcare Industry
N.A.I.C.S.: 541511

Concerto Cloud Services, LLC (1)
4830 W Kennedy Blvd Ste 350, Tampa, FL 33609
Tel.: (844) 760-1842
Cloud Data Management Services
N.A.I.C.S.: 518210

DXC Connect Pty Ltd (1)
26 Talavera Road, Macquarie Park, 2113, NSW, Australia
Tel.: (61) 1300765144
Integrated Computer Systems Design
N.A.I.C.S.: 541512

Subsidiary (Domestic):

Integ Group Pty. Ltd. (2)
L15 17-19 360 Collins Street, Melbourne, 3000, VIC, Australia
Tel.: (61) 0392245777
Data Networking & Communication Services
N.A.I.C.S.: 517810

Integ Queensland Pty Ltd (2)
L1 East Tower Cathedral Square 410 Ann Street, Brisbane, 4000, QLD, Australia
Tel.: (61) 739098400
Information Technology Consulting Services
N.A.I.C.S.: 541512

DXC Insurance Solutions Australia Pty Ltd (1)
26 Talavera Road, Macquarie Park, 2113, NSW, Australia
Tel.: (61) 290343000
Business Process Outsourcing Services
N.A.I.C.S.: 561440

DXC Technology Australia Pty. Limited (1)
26 Talavera Road, Macquarie Park, 2113,

NSW, Australia
Tel.: (61) 1300765144
Web Site: https://dxc.com
Business Process Outsourcing Services
N.A.I.C.S.: 561440

DXC Technology Baltic UAB (1)
V Gerulaicio Str 1 ALFA Building 4th and 3rd Floors, Vilnius, Lithuania
Tel.: (370) 852522101
Data Processing Services
N.A.I.C.S.: 518210

DXC Technology SARL (1)
Building B9 Sala Al Jadida, Technopolis, 11 100, Rabat, Morocco
Tel.: (212) 530576400
Web Site: https://www.dxc-maroc.com
Information Technology Services
N.A.I.C.S.: 541511

DXC Technology Services Vietnam Company Limited (1)
3Etown 5 Building 364 Cong Hoa Street Ward 13 Tan Binh District, Ho Chi Minh City, Vietnam
Tel.: (84) 2839238520
Computer System Design Services
N.A.I.C.S.: 541512

DXC Techonology Information Services Slovakia s.r.o. (1)
Galvaniho 7 Ruzinov, 820 02, Bratislava, Slovakia
Tel.: (421) 257525555
Information Technology Services
N.A.I.C.S.: 541512

ES Field Delivery France SAS (1)
Niveau RDC Aile C 4 avenue Pablo Picasso, 92000, Nanterre, France
Tel.: (33) 634210781
Business Process Outsourcing Services
N.A.I.C.S.: 561440

ES Field Delivery Nederland B.V. (1)
Laan van Zuid Hoorn 70, 2289 DE, Rijswijk, Netherlands
Tel.: (31) 884474574
Business Process Outsourcing Services
N.A.I.C.S.: 561440

ES Field Delivery Spain, S.L.U. (1)
Calle Jose Echegaray 8, Las Rozas, 28232, Madrid, Spain
Tel.: (34) 916311684
Business Process Outsourcing Services
N.A.I.C.S.: 561440

ES Immobilien GmbH (1)
Bismarckstrasse 13, 74613, Ohringen, Germany
Tel.: (49) 79419631831
Web Site: https://www.es-immobilien24.de
Business Process Outsourcing Services
N.A.I.C.S.: 561440

ESIT Advanced Solutions Inc. (1)
1101-4464 Markham St, Victoria, V8Z 7X8, BC, Canada
Tel.: (250) 405-4500
Web Site: https://dxcas.com
Emp.: 250
Information Technology Services
N.A.I.C.S.: 541512
Ashley Namur *(Exec Dir-HR)*
Serge Bourdage *(Acct Gen Mgr)*
Keith McKinnon *(VP)*
Elaine Bell *(CFO)*

EdgeIQ, Inc. (1)
200 Berkeley St 19th Fl, Boston, MA 02116
Tel.: (857) 999-3343
Web Site: https://www.edgeiq.ai
Business Process Outsourcing Services
N.A.I.C.S.: 561440

EntServ Schweiz GmbH (1)
Neue Winterthurerstrasse 99, Wallisellen, 8304, Zurich, Switzerland
Tel.: (41) 435471900
Information Technology Services
N.A.I.C.S.: 541512

Enterprise Services Nederland B.V. (1)
Laan van Zuid Hoorn 70, 2289 DE, Rijswijk, Netherlands
Tel.: (31) 884474574
Information Technology Services
N.A.I.C.S.: 541512

Excelian Luxoft Financial Services (Switzerland) AG (1)
Gubelstrasse 24 Park Tower, 6300, Zug, Switzerland
Tel.: (41) 415470110
Information Technology Services
N.A.I.C.S.: 541511

Fruition Partners B.V. (1)
Laan van Zuid Hoorn 70, 2289 DE, Rijswijk, Netherlands
Tel.: (31) 707990030
Web Site: http://www.fruitionpartners.nl
Information Technology Support Services
N.A.I.C.S.: 541512

Fruition Partners Canada Ltd. (1)
1300-350 Bay St, Toronto, M5H 2S6, ON, Canada
Tel.: (416) 483-5166
Business Management Services
N.A.I.C.S.: 561110

JAPAN SYSTEMS CO., LTD. (1)
Yoyogi 1-chome Bldg 1-22-1 Yoyogi, Shibuya-Ku, Tokyo, 151-8404, Japan **(53.67%)**
Tel.: (81) 353090300
Web Site: http://www.japan-systems.co.jp
Rev.: $92,502,080
Assets: $67,895,520
Liabilities: $12,971,200
Net Worth: $54,924,320
Earnings: $3,949,440
Fiscal Year-end: 12/31/2020
Software Application Development Services
N.A.I.C.S.: 541512
Tomohiro Kawada *(COO)*

Luxoft Bulgaria E.O.O.D. (1)
Floor 6 Building 8A Business Park, 1766, Sofia, Bulgaria
Tel.: (359) 29043900
Business Process Outsourcing Services
N.A.I.C.S.: 561440

Luxoft Holding, Inc. (1)
Gubelstrasse 24, 6300, Zug, Switzerland
Tel.: (41) 417262060
Web Site: https://www.luxoft.com
Emp.: 210
Software Development, Support, Product Engineering, Testing & Technology Consulting
N.A.I.C.S.: 513210
Dmitry Loschinin *(Pres & CEO)*
Michael Friedland *(COO)*
Samuel Mantle *(Sr VP-Digital Engrg)*
Elena Goryunova *(Sr VP-Talent Acq & Mgmt)*
Vasiliy Suvorov *(VP-Tech Strategy)*
Natasha Ziabkina *(Gen Counsel & VP)*
Ilya Gruzdev *(CFO)*
Luz G. Mauch *(Exec VP-Automotive)*
Nigel Cairns *(Head-Banking & Capital Market)*
Yuri Mazitov *(CIO)*

Subsidiary (Non-US):

Excelian Limited (2)
One Aldermanbury Square, London, EC2V 7HY, United Kingdom
Tel.: (44) 2079930737
Web Site: http://www.luxoft.com
IT Consulting Services
N.A.I.C.S.: 541690
Nick Thomas *(Head-Vendor Solutions-Global)*
Pierre Castagne *(Head-Sls Vendor Solutions)*
Nic Arnold *(Head-Tech Svcs & Solutions-Global)*
David Coe *(Mng Dir-Fin Svcs Market Utilities)*
Robert Easter *(Mng Dir & Head-Engrg Svcs Sls)*

Subsidiary (US):

INSYS Group, Inc. (2)
395 W Passaic St Ste 400, Rochelle Park, NJ 07662 **(100%)**
Tel.: (201) 621-4797
Web Site: http://www.luxoft.com
Marketing Consulting Services
N.A.I.C.S.: 541613

Subsidiary (Non-US):

Luxoft GmbH (2)

Stadionstrasse 66, 70771, Leinfelden-Echterdingen, Germany
Tel.: (49) 71149049200
Web Site: https://www.luxoft.com
Information Technology Services
N.A.I.C.S.: 541511

Luxoft India LLP (2)
Outer Ring Road Gardenia 2D Building, Embassy Tech Village, Bengaluru, 560 103, India
Tel.: (91) 8069349600
Information Technology Services
N.A.I.C.S.: 541511
Ramya Bharadwaj *(Dir-HR)*

Luxoft Korea LLC (2)
Level 22 10 Gukjegeumyung-ro, Yeongdeungpo-gu, Seoul, 7326, Korea (South)
Tel.: (82) 260013316
Information Technology Services
N.A.I.C.S.: 541511
James Yi *(Head-Sls & Bus Dev-Korea)*

Luxoft Malaysia Sdn. Bhd. (2)
Jalan Sultan Ahmad Shah 5, George Town, 10050, Pulau Penang, Malaysia
Tel.: (60) 6042879900
Information Technology Services
N.A.I.C.S.: 541511
Ewan Manamohan *(Mng Dir)*

Luxoft Mexico S.A. de C.V. (2)
La Perla 1 2 Amado Nervo 2200 Edificio Bio I P 1, Zapopan, 45050, Guadalajara, Mexico
Tel.: (52) 3330019510
Information Technology Services
N.A.I.C.S.: 541511

Luxoft Sweden AB (2)
Lilla Bommen 6 floor 7, 411 04, Gothenburg, Sweden
Tel.: (46) 317605801
Information Technology Services
N.A.I.C.S.: 541511

Luxoft Vietnam Company Limited (2)
eTown Room 3 Mezzanine Floor Business Center e town Building, 364 Cong Hoa Street Ward 13 Tan Binh District, Ho Chi Minh City, Vietnam
Tel.: (84) 2839651789
Information Technology Services
N.A.I.C.S.: 541511
An Nguyen *(Mng Dir)*

Luxoft Italy S.r.l. (1)
Via Nizza 262/56, 10126, Turin, Italy
Tel.: (39) 01119872448
Software Services
N.A.I.C.S.: 541511

Luxoft UK Limited (1)
51 Eastcheap, London, EC3M 1DT, United Kingdom
Tel.: (44) 2079930737
Business Process Outsourcing Services
N.A.I.C.S.: 561440

Luxoft Ukraine LLC (1)
10/14 Radishcheva Str, Business Center IRVA B, 03680, Kiev, Ukraine
Tel.: (380) 444810060
Business Process Outsourcing Services
N.A.I.C.S.: 561440

M-Power Solutions Pty Ltd (1)
1139 Hay Street, West Perth, 6005, WA, Australia
Tel.: (61) 1300113013
Business Consulting Services
N.A.I.C.S.: 541611
Sue Bush *(Mgr-Support)*
Ahmed Hafez *(Dir-Solutions)*
Sylvain Guillaume *(Mgr-Practice)*

SME - Science Management & Engineering AG (1)
Parking Ring 17, 85748, Garching, Germany
Tel.: (49) 893267400
Web Site: http://www.sme.de
Management Consulting Services
N.A.I.C.S.: 541618

Sable37 DMCC (1)
905 X3 Tower Cluster X, PO Box 410563, Jumeriah Lake Towers, Dubai, United Arab Emirates

Tel.: (971) 45546231
Web Site: http://www.sable37.com
Data Processing Services
N.A.I.C.S.: 518210

Saltbush Consulting Pty Ltd (1)
Innovation House Tenancy 4 50 Mawson
Lakes Boulevard, Mawson Lakes, 5095,
SA, Australia
Tel.: (61) 410021979
Web Site: http://saltbushconsulting.com.au
Business Process Outsourcing Services
N.A.I.C.S.: 561440

Spikes Cavell Analytic Inc. (1)
1775 Tysons Blvd Ste 900, Tysons, VA
22102-4285
Tel.: (800) 990-0228
Information Technology Services
N.A.I.C.S.: 541512

Syscom AS (1)
Sorkedalsveien 6, PO Box 35, Majorstuen,
0330, Oslo, Norway
Tel.: (47) 23205100
Web Site: http://www.syscomworld.com
IT Management Services
N.A.I.C.S.: 541611
Ola Bryhn *(Founder & Chm)*

TESM Limited (1)
Chancery House 53-64 Chancery Lane,
London, WC2A 1QS, United Kingdom
Tel.: (44) 2038746760
Web Site: http://www.tesm.com
Information Technology Support Services
N.A.I.C.S.: 541512

TESM/NL B.V. (1)
Honderdland 220, 2676 LV, Maasdijk, Neth-
erlands
Tel.: (31) 174525176
Web Site: https://www.tesm.nl
Information Technology Support Services
N.A.I.C.S.: 541512

UXC Consulting Pte Ltd (1)
33 Ubi Ave 3 08-08B, Vertex, Singapore,
408868, Singapore
Tel.: (65) 68153113
Web Site: https://www.uxconsulting.com.sg
Information Technology Consulting Services
N.A.I.C.S.: 541512
Raven Chai *(Founder)*

**UXC Eclipse Solutions (Canada)
Ltd** (1)
355 Burrard Street Suite 250, Vancouver,
V6C 2G8, BC, Canada
Tel.: (604) 899-6092
Information Technology Consulting Services
N.A.I.C.S.: 541512

Virtual Clarity Limited (1)
2-7 Clerkenwell Green, London, EC1R 0DE,
United Kingdom
Tel.: (44) 2031313152
Web Site: http://www.virtualclarity.com
Business Consulting Services
N.A.I.C.S.: 541611
Rens Troost *(CTO)*
Steve Peskin *(Mng Dir)*
Ryan Schoenfeld *(Chief Revenue Officer-
Americas)*
Wendy Woodford *(Mgr-People)*
Brian Glasser *(CEO-US)*
Ashley Cvrkel *(Sr Mgr-Strategic Acct-North
America)*

Wrap Media, LLC (1)
550 15th St Ste 27-28, San Francisco, CA
94103
Tel.: (415) 302-6400
Web Site: https://www.wrap.co
Information Technology Support Services
N.A.I.C.S.: 541512

**Xchanging Global Insurance Solu-
tions Limited** (1)
Endeavor Drive, Basildon, SS14 3WF, Es-
sex, United Kingdom
Tel.: (44) 2036043700
Information Technology Management Ser-
vices
N.A.I.C.S.: 541512

Xchanging Italy S.p.A. (1)
Via A Grandi 4, Cernusco sul Naviglio,
20063, Milan, Italy
Tel.: (39) 0287315908
Business Process Outsourcing Services

N.A.I.C.S.: 561110
Fabia Patellani *(Gen Mgr)*

Xchanging, Inc. (1)
55 W Monroe Ste 200, Chicago, IL 60603
Tel.: (312) 662-1859
Web Site: http://www.xchanging.com
Business Process Outsourcing Services
N.A.I.C.S.: 561110

**eBECS Business Solutions (Ireland)
Limited** (1)
Liffey Technology Park, Kildare, Leixlip,
Ireland
Tel.: (353) 15314450
Web Site: http://www.ebecs.com
Data Processing Services
N.A.I.C.S.: 518210

eBECS Company Limited (1)
Building 3269 Office no 1221 El Amir Mam-
dooh Bin Abdulaziz, PO Box 58524, Al Su-
laimaniah, 12241, Riyadh, Saudi Arabia
Tel.: (966) 11920007299
Web Site: http://www.ebecs.com
Data Processing Services
N.A.I.C.S.: 518210

DXP ENTERPRISES, INC.

5301 Hollister St, Houston, TX 77040
Tel.: (713) 996-4700   **TX**
Web Site: https://www.dxpe.com
DXPE—(NASDAQ)
Rev.: $1,480,832,000
Assets: $1,037,280,000
Liabilities: $671,888,000
Net Worth: $365,392,000
Earnings: $48,155,000
Emp.: 2,675
Fiscal Year-end: 12/31/22
Industrial Supply Distribution Man-
agement Services
N.A.I.C.S.: 423830
David R. Little *(Chm, Pres & CEO)*
John J. Jeffery *(Sr VP-Supply Chain
Svcs, Mktg & IT)*
Todd Hamlin *(Sr VP-Sls, Svc Centers
& Innovation Pumping Solutions)*
Kent Yee *(CFO & Sr VP)*
Chris Gregory *(CIO & Sr VP-IT)*
Nick Little *(COO & Sr VP)*
Paz Maestas *(CMO & CTO)*
David Molero *(Chief Acctg Officer)*

Subsidiaries:

ALEDco, Inc. (1)
1810 E Race St, Allentown, PA 18109
Tel.: (610) 266-2555
Web Site: https://www.aledco.com
Industrial, Sanitary & Oilfield Pumps Distr
N.A.I.C.S.: 333914

**APO Pumps & Compressors,
LLC** (1)
6607 Chittenden Rd, Hudson, OH 44236
Tel.: (330) 366-1326
Web Site: https://www.apopc.com
Fiscal Year-end: 06/30/2006
Pump & Compressor Equipment Mfr
N.A.I.C.S.: 333912
Ted Mailey *(VP)*

Alaska Pump & Supply, Inc. (1)
8400 Sandlewood Plc, Anchorage, AK
99507
Tel.: (907) 563-3424
Web Site: https://www.alaskapump.com
Sales Range: $1-9.9 Million
Emp.: 21
Industrial Machinery & Equipment Merchant
Whslr
N.A.I.C.S.: 423830
Jerry Pilgrim *(Gen Mgr & Mgr-Alaska)*
Gerad Walker *(Coord-Rental)*

Application Specialties, Inc. (1)
3941 B St NW, Auburn, WA 98001
Tel.: (253) 872-0305
Web Site: https://www.1asi.com
Metal Cutting Tool Mfr & Distr
N.A.I.C.S.: 333517

B27, LLC (1)
1417 Gables Ct Ste 201, Plano, TX 75075
Tel.: (214) 473-8580

Sales Range: $25-49.9 Million
Emp.: 150
Flow Control Equipment Distr
N.A.I.C.S.: 333914
Michael Madison *(CFO)*

Subsidiary (Domestic):

**Best Equipment Service & Sales
Company, LLC** (2)
8885 Monroe Rd, Houston, TX 77061
Tel.: (713) 956-2002
Web Site: https://www.pumpworks.com
Sales Range: $10-24.9 Million
Emp.: 50
Pump & Pumping Equipment Mfr
N.A.I.C.S.: 333914

C.W. Rod Tool Co., Inc. (1)
15050 Northgreen Dr, Houston, TX 77032
Tel.: (281) 449-0881
Web Site: http://www.cwrodtool.com
Sales Range: $50-74.9 Million
Emp.: 115
Industrial Machinery & Equipment
N.A.I.C.S.: 423830

Cisco Air Systems, Inc. (1)
214 27th St, Sacramento, CA 95816
Tel.: (916) 444-2525
Web Site: http://www.ciscoair.com
Sales Range: $1-9.9 Million
Emp.: 35
Whol Industrial Equipment Repair Services
N.A.I.C.S.: 423830
William Frkovich *(CEO)*

**Corporate Equipment Company,
LLC** (1)
607 Redna Ter Ste 100, Cincinnati, OH
45215
Tel.: (513) 771-6696
Web Site: https://www.corpequip.com
Pump Distr
N.A.I.C.S.: 423840
Jeff Sackett *(Pres)*
Jim Altonen *(Gen Sls Mgr-Industrial)*

Cortech Engineering, Inc. (1)
1241 N Lakeview Ave Ste T, Anaheim, CA
92807
Tel.: (714) 779-0911
Sales Range: $25-49.9 Million
Emp.: 55
Industrial Machinery & Equipment Merchant
Whslr
N.A.I.C.S.: 423830

D&F Distributors Inc. (1)
800 Canal St, Evansville, IN 47713
Tel.: (812) 867-2441
Web Site: https://www.dfdistrib.com
Pumps & Pumping Equipment Whslr & Distr
N.A.I.C.S.: 423830

Delta Process Equipment Inc. (1)
8275 Florida Blvd, Denham Springs, LA
70726
Tel.: (225) 665-1666
Web Site: https://www.deltaprocess.com
Sales Range: $25-49.9 Million
Emp.: 44
Pump, Compressor, Turbine & Filter Distr
N.A.I.C.S.: 423830

Drydon Equipment, Inc. (1)
2445 Westfield Dr Ste 100, Elgin, IL 60124-
7840
Tel.: (224) 629-4060
Web Site: http://www.drydon.com
Sewage Treatment Facilities
N.A.I.C.S.: 221320
Harold G. Wolff *(Pres)*

HSE Integrated Ltd. (1)
Suite 2200 645 7th Ave SW, Calgary, T2P
4G8, AB, Canada
Tel.: (403) 266-1833
Web Site: https://www.hseintegrated.com
Sales Range: $350-399.9 Million
Emp.: 700
Health, Safety & Environmental Services for
Oil & Gas Industry
N.A.I.C.S.: 213112

Hartwell Environmental Corp. (1)
22115 Hufsmith Kohrville Rd, Tomball, TX
77375
Tel.: (281) 351-8501
Web Site: http://www.hartwellenv.com

Industrial Machinery & Equipment Merchant
Whslr
N.A.I.C.S.: 423830
Bob Russell *(Partner)*

Hennesy Mechanical Sales, LLC (1)
201 S 26th St, Phoenix, AZ 85034-2608
Tel.: (602) 996-3444
Web Site: http://hennesymech.com
Sales Range: $10-24.9 Million
Plumbing & Heating Equipment & Supplies
(Hydronics) Merchant Whslr
N.A.I.C.S.: 423720

**Industrial Paramedic Services,
Ltd.** (1)
Suite 2200 645 7th Ave SW, Calgary, T2P
4G8, AB, Canada
Tel.: (403) 264-6435
Web Site: https://www.ipsems.com
Emp.: 500
Paramedical Services
N.A.I.C.S.: 621399
Brett Herniuk *(Pres)*

Integrated Flow Solutions, LLC (1)
6461 Reynolds Rd, Tyler, TX 75708
Tel.: (903) 595-6511
Web Site: https://www.ifsolutions.com
Emp.: 100
Liquid & Gas Process System Mfr
N.A.I.C.S.: 334513

Kappe Associates, Inc. (1)
100 Wormans Mill Ct, Frederick, MD 21701
Tel.: (301) 846-0200
Web Site: http://www.kappe-inc.com
Plumbing, Heating & Air-Conditioning Con-
tractors
N.A.I.C.S.: 238220
George L. Long *(VP)*

Kenneth Crosby, LLC (1)
1001 Lexington Ave, Rochester, NY 14606
Tel.: (585) 719-9720
Web Site: https://www.kennethcrosby.com
Sales Range: $25-49.9 Million
Emp.: 56
Tools, Abrasives, Fasteners & Gauges Distr
N.A.I.C.S.: 423710

M.W. Smith Equipment, Inc. (1)
4419 W Loop 281, Longview, TX 75604
Tel.: (903) 757-0533
Web Site: https://www.smithequip.com
Sales Range: $100-124.9 Million
Emp.: 20
Pump Equipment Mfr, Sales & Repair
N.A.I.C.S.: 333914
Mark W. Smith *(Reg VP)*
Tim Turner *(Mgr-Customer Svc)*
Steve Allen *(Mgr-Svc)*

Mid-Continent SAFETY LLC (1)
8225 E 36th St N, Wichita, KS 67278
Tel.: (316) 522-0900
Web Site: http://www.midsafe.com
Sales Range: $1-9.9 Million
Emp.: 12
Construction & Mining, except Oil Well, Ma-
chinery & Equipment Merchant Whslr
N.A.I.C.S.: 423810

**National Process Equipment,
Inc.** (1)
128 9 Burbidge Street, Coquitlam, V3K
7B2, BC, Canada
Tel.: (604) 472-3300
Web Site: http://www.natpro.com
Emp.: 50
Pump & Compressor Mfr
N.A.I.C.S.: 333914
Carrie Canty *(CEO)*

PMI Operating Company, Ltd. (1)
13424 Hempstead Hwy, Houston, TX 77040
Tel.: (713) 462-3176
Web Site: https://www.pmi-pump.com
Sales Range: $25-49.9 Million
Emp.: 30
Pumping Equipment Mfr
N.A.I.C.S.: 333914

Production Pump Systems, Inc. (1)
2710 25th St, Snyder, TX 79550-0160
Tel.: (325) 573-1741
Web Site: https://www.productionpump.com
Sales Range: $100-124.9 Million
Gear & Pump Mfr & Distr
N.A.I.C.S.: 333914

DXP Enterprises, Inc.—(Continued)

Mike Goebel *(VP)*

Pump & Power Equipment, LLC **(1)**
5285 Schurmier Rd, Houston, TX 77048
Tel.: (713) 783-8530
Web Site: http://www.pumppower.com
Pump Mfr & Distr
N.A.I.C.S.: 333914

Pumping Solutions, Inc. **(1)**
1906 S Quaker Ridge Pl, Ontario, CA 91761
Tel.: (909) 930-6600
Web Site: https://www.apumpstore.com
Sales Range: $1-9.9 Million
Emp.: 15
Pump Distr
N.A.I.C.S.: 423830

Quadna Inc. **(1)**
2803 E Chambers St, Phoenix, AZ 85040
Tel.: (602) 323-2370
Web Site: https://www.quadna.com
Sales Range: $10-24.9 Million
Emp.: 25
Pumps & Pumping Equipment Mfr
N.A.I.C.S.: 333914

R.A. Mueller, Inc. **(1)**
11270 Cornell Park Dr, Cincinnati, OH 45242
Tel.: (513) 489-5200
Web Site: https://www.ramueller.com
Sales Range: $25-49.9 Million
Emp.: 40
Fluid Processing Equipment
N.A.I.C.S.: 423830

Riordan Materials Corporation **(1)**
6198 Butler Pike Ste 150, Blue Bell, PA 19422-2600
Tel.: (215) 628-9936
Web Site: http://www.riordanmat.com
Transportation Equipment & Supplies Merchant Whslr
N.A.I.C.S.: 423860
Carl E. Janson *(Pres)*

Rocky Mountain Supply Inc. **(1)**
2021 1st Ave, Greeley, CO 80631
Tel.: (970) 351-8220
Web Site: https://www.rockymtnsupply.com
Sales Range: $10-24.9 Million
Emp.: 16
Industrial Supplies Whslr
N.A.I.C.S.: 423840

Tool Supply, Inc. **(1)**
20150 SW Avery Ct, Tualatin, OR 97062
Tel.: (503) 691-1900
Web Site: https://www.toolsupply.com
Sales Range: $1-9.9 Million
Emp.: 10
Industrial Tool & Supplies Distr
N.A.I.C.S.: 423840
Patrick Davis *(Pres)*

Turbo Machinery Repair, Inc. **(1)**
1130 Potrero Ave, Richmond, CA 94804
Tel.: (510) 236-5481
Web Site: http://turboindustrial.net
Electronic & Precision Equipment Repair & Maintenance
N.A.I.C.S.: 811210

DYADIC INTERNATIONAL, INC.
1044 N Hwy 1 Ste 201, Jupiter, FL 33477-5094
Tel.: (561) 743-8333　　　　　　　**DE**
Web Site: https://www.dyadic.com
Year Founded: 1979
DYAI—(NASDAQ)
Rev.: $2,930,303
Assets: $13,712,818
Liabilities: $2,625,079
Net Worth: $11,087,739
Earnings: ($9,735,258)
Emp.: 7
Fiscal Year-end: 12/31/22
Biological Product Mfr
N.A.I.C.S.: 325414
Ping Wang Rawson *(CFO)*
Joseph Hazelton *(Chief Bus Officer)*
Doug Pace *(Exec VP-Bus Dev)*
Mark A. Emalfarb *(Founder, Pres & CEO)*

Subsidiaries:

Dyadic Nederland B.V. **(1)**
Utrechtseweg 48, 3704 HE, Zeist, Netherlands　　　　　　　　　　**(100%)**
Tel.: (31) 306944454
Web Site: http://www.dyadic.com
Sales Range: $75-99.9 Million
Biotechnological Research
N.A.I.C.S.: 541714

DYCOM INDUSTRIES, INC.
11780 US Hwy 1 Ste 600, Palm Beach Gardens, FL 33408
Tel.: (561) 627-7171　　　　　　　**FL**
Web Site: https://www.dycomind.com
Year Founded: 1969
DY—(NYSE)
Rev.: $4,175,574,000
Assets: $2,516,885,000
Liabilities: $1,462,229,000
Net Worth: $1,054,656,000
Earnings: $218,923,000
Emp.: 15,611
Fiscal Year-end: 01/27/24
Holding Company; Telecommunications & Electrical Engineering Services
N.A.I.C.S.: 551112
H. Andrew DeFerrari *(CFO, Principal Acctg Officer & Sr VP)*
Heather M. Floyd *(Chief Acctg Officer & VP)*
Ryan F. Urness *(Gen Counsel, Sec & VP)*
Jason T. Lawson *(Chief HR Officer & VP)*
Daniel S. Peyovich *(Pres & CEO)*

Subsidiaries:

Ansco & Associates, LLC **(1)**
1220 Old Alpharetta Rd Ste 380, Alpharetta, GA 30005
Tel.: (404) 508-5700
Web Site: https://www.anscollc.com
Sales Range: $1-9.9 Million
Emp.: 20
Telecommunications, Power & Cable Contractor
N.A.I.C.S.: 237130

Bigham Cable Construction, Inc. **(1)**
1023 Woodlore Cir, Gulf Breeze, FL 32563
Tel.: (850) 932-8098
Web Site: http://www.bighamcable.com
Sales Range: $1-9.9 Million
Emp.: 75
Power & Communication Line & Related Structures Construction
N.A.I.C.S.: 237130
Margaret Bigham *(Pres)*

Blair Park Services, LLC **(1)**
405 Caredean Dr Ste G & H, Horsham, PA 19044
Tel.: (267) 388-2612
Web Site: https://blairpark.com
Emp.: 45
Telecommunications Infrastructure Maintenance, Repair & Engineering Services
N.A.I.C.S.: 811310

C-2 Utility Contractors, LLC **(1)**
33005 Roberts Ct, Coburg, OR 97408
Tel.: (541) 741-2211
Web Site: https://www.c-2utility.com
Sales Range: $25-49.9 Million
Emp.: 98
Underground Cable Installation
N.A.I.C.S.: 237130

CAN-AM Communications, Inc. **(1)**
208 Leisure St, Yorkville, IL 60560
Tel.: (630) 553-1228
Web Site: http://www.canamcomm.com
Sales Range: $150-199.9 Million
Providers of Electrical Services
N.A.I.C.S.: 238210

Cable Connectors, LLC **(1)**
111 Connector Way, Greenwood, SC 29649
Tel.: (864) 227-0055
Web Site: http://www.cableconnectors.net
Electrical Contractor
N.A.I.C.S.: 238210

CableCom, LLC **(1)**
19910 N Creek Pkwy Ste 100, Bothell, WA 98011
Tel.: (360) 668-1300
Web Site: https://www.cablecomllc.us
Sales Range: $1-9.9 Million
Emp.: 2
Communication Line Engineering, Construction & Testing Services
N.A.I.C.S.: 811310

Subsidiary (Domestic):

CableCom of California, Inc. **(2)**
2110-C Smith Flat Rd, Placerville, CA 95667
Tel.: (530) 622-7762
Web Site: http://www.cablecomllc.us
Communication Line Engineering, Construction & Testing Services
N.A.I.C.S.: 811310

Cavo Broadband Communications, LLC **(1)**
12191 S Rhea Dr, Plainfield, IL 60585-9734
Tel.: (815) 439-8289
Web Site: https://cavocommunications.com
Emp.: 1,500
Cable Laying Construction Services
N.A.I.C.S.: 237130

CertusView Technologies, LLC **(1)**
3960 RCA Blvd Ste 8000, Palm Beach Gardens, FL 33410-4289
Web Site: http://www.certusview.com
Sales Range: $25-49.9 Million
Emp.: 125
Damage Prevention Software Development Services
N.A.I.C.S.: 541511

Communications Construction Group, LLC **(1)**
111 Greenmont Rd, Rising Sun, MD 21911
Tel.: (610) 696-1800
Web Site: https://www.ccgcatv.com
Sales Range: $25-49.9 Million
Emp.: 400
Communications Contractor
N.A.I.C.S.: 237130

Engineering Associates, Inc. **(1)**
1220 Old Alpharetta Rd Ste 318, Alpharetta, GA 30005-3990
Tel.: (678) 455-7266
Web Site: http://www.engineeringassociates.com
Emp.: 50
Telecommunications Engineering Design & Support Services Contractor
N.A.I.C.S.: 238210
Mike Martin *(VP)*
Anthony Pugh *(Pres)*
Nicholas Burkhart *(VP)*
Chris Shaddock *(VP)*

Subsidiary (Domestic):

E A Technical Services, Inc. **(2)**
1220 Old Alpharetta Rd Ste 390, Alpharetta, GA 30005
Tel.: (678) 455-7116
Web Site: https://www.eatechnical.com
Electrical & Telecommunications Infrastructure Contracting Services
N.A.I.C.S.: 238210

Ervin Cable Construction, LLC **(1)**
450 Pryor Blvd, Sturgis, KY 42459
Tel.: (270) 333-3366
Web Site: https://www.ervincable.com
Sales Range: $75-99.9 Million
Emp.: 200
Cable TV Design & Engineering Construction Contractor
N.A.I.C.S.: 238210
Gary Ervin *(Founder & Chm)*
Brad Ervin *(Pres)*
Tim Ervin *(VP)*
Robert Ervin *(Dir-Ops)*
Lyle Pinkston *(VP)*
Bo Gresham *(VP)*

Fiber Technologies Solutions, LLC **(1)**
2675 Mall of Georgia Blvd Ste 301, Buford, GA 42459
Tel.: (770) 554-2220
Power, Communication Line & Related Structure Construction Services

N.A.I.C.S.: 237130

Globe Communications, LLC **(1)**
950 48th Ave N Ste 100, Myrtle Beach, SC 29577
Tel.: (843) 839-5544
Web Site: https://www.globeinc.us
Sales Range: $250-299.9 Million
Emp.: 185
Provider of Communication Services
N.A.I.C.S.: 237130

Ivy H. Smith Company, LLC **(1)**
1220 Old Alpharetta Rd Ste 380, Alpharetta, GA 30005
Tel.: (404) 508-5703
Web Site: https://www.ivysmith.com
Sales Range: $1-9.9 Million
Emp.: 264
Specialized Construction Services
N.A.I.C.S.: 237120

Kanaan Communications, LLC **(1)**
40665 Koppernick Rd, Canton, MI 48187
Tel.: (734) 606-4111
Web Site: https://www.kanaancomm.com
Electrical & Communication Services
N.A.I.C.S.: 238210
Daniel P. Kanaan *(Pres)*

Kohler Construction Company Inc. **(1)**
6425 53rd St, Pinellas Park, FL 33781-5629　　　　　　　　　　**(100%)**
Tel.: (727) 527-2077
Web Site: http://www.kohlerconstruction.us
Sales Range: $10-24.9 Million
Emp.: 10
Above-Ground Fiber Optic Installation Services
N.A.I.C.S.: 237130

Lambert's Cable Splicing Company, LLC **(1)**
2521 S Wesleyan Blvd, Rocky Mount, NC 27803-8847
Tel.: (252) 442-9777
Web Site: https://www.lambertcable.com
Sales Range: $1-9.9 Million
Emp.: 30
Long Distance Telecommunication Lines Utility Contractor
N.A.I.C.S.: 237130
Thomas W. Lambert *(Pres)*

Subsidiary (Domestic):

K.H. Smith Communications, Inc. **(2)**
1651 S Wesleyan Blvd, Rocky Mount, NC 27803
Tel.: (252) 442-1331
Web Site: https://khsmith.com
Cable Splicing
N.A.I.C.S.: 238990
Kenneth H. Smith *(Pres)*

Locating, Inc. **(1)**
2575 Westside Pkwy Ste 100, Alpharetta, GA 30004
Tel.: (678) 461-3900
Web Site: https://locatinginc.com
Sales Range: $75-99.9 Million
Provider of Water & Sewer Services
N.A.I.C.S.: 541330

Midtown Express, LLC **(1)**
55-60 58th St, Maspeth, NY 11378
Tel.: (718) 628-3420
Web Site: http://www.midtownexpress.com
Electrical Contractor
N.A.I.C.S.: 238210

NeoCom Solutions, Inc. **(1)**
10064 Main St, Woodstock, GA 30188
Tel.: (678) 238-1818
Web Site: http://www.neocom.biz
Sales Range: $10-24.9 Million
Emp.: 70
Scientific & Technical Consulting Services
N.A.I.C.S.: 541690

Nichols Construction, LLC **(1)**
1098 Clear Creek Rd, Vansant, VA 24656
Tel.: (276) 597-7441
Web Site: http://www.nicholsconllc.com
Sales Range: $10-24.9 Million
Emp.: 120
Plant Utility Contractor
N.A.I.C.S.: 237130

Niels Fugal Sons Company, LLC **(1)**

1005 S Main St, Pleasant Grove, UT 84062
Tel.: (801) 785-3152
Web Site: https://www.fugal.com
Sales Range: $10-24.9 Million
Emp.: 465
Telecommunications & Natural Gas Construction Contractor
N.A.I.C.S.: 237110

North Sky Communications, Inc. (1)
16701 SE McGillivray Blvd Ste 200, Vancouver, WA 98683
Tel.: (360) 254-6920
Web Site: https://www.northskycomm.com
Telecommunications Contractor
N.A.I.C.S.: 238210

Parkside Utility Construction,
LLC (1)
219 Ruth Rd, Harleysville, PA 19438
Tel.: (215) 513-9500
Web Site: https://www.parksideutil.com
Emp.: 350
Electric, Telecommunications & Water Infrastructure Construction Services
N.A.I.C.S.: 237990

Subsidiary (Domestic):

Parkside Utility Construction
Corp. (2)
2229 Plainfield Pike, Johnston, RI 02919-5600
Tel.: (401) 944-1919
Electrical & Telecommunications Infrastructure Contracting Services
N.A.I.C.S.: 238210

Pauley Construction Inc. (1)
22023 N 20th Ave Ste B, Phoenix, AZ 85027
Tel.: (623) 581-1200
Web Site: http://www.pauleyc.com
Sales Range: $25-49.9 Million
Emp.: 200
Electrical & Communication Line Construction & Maintenance Services
N.A.I.C.S.: 237130

Point to Point Communications,
Inc. (1)
Ste 450 2151 Northwest Pkwy SE, Marietta, GA 30067-8790
Tel.: (337) 837-0090
Web Site: http://www.ppcila.com
Sales Range: $10-24.9 Million
Emp.: 10
Provider of Data Communication Services
N.A.I.C.S.: 517810

Precision Valley Communications of
Vermont, LLC (1)
36 Precision Dr Ste 200, North Springfield, VT 05150
Tel.: (802) 885-9317
Web Site: https://www.pvc2.com
Sales Range: $1-9.9 Million
Emp.: 60
Telecommunications & Utilities Map, Engineer & Design Construction
N.A.I.C.S.: 516120
J. Roger Cawvey (Project Coord)

Prince Telecom LLC (1)
551 A Mews Dr, New Castle, DE 19720-2798
Tel.: (302) 324-1800
Web Site: https://www.princetelecom.com
Sales Range: $450-499.9 Million
Emp.: 1,500
Cable Television Installation
N.A.I.C.S.: 517810

Professional Teleconcepts, Inc. (1)
5132 State Hwy 12, Norwich, NY 13815
Tel.: (607) 336-1689
Web Site: http://www.pro-tel.com
Emp.: 50
Telecommunications Infrastructure Engineering & Construction Services
N.A.I.C.S.: 811310

RJE Telecom, LLC (1)
5905 Breckenridge Pkwy Ste F, Tampa, FL 33610
Tel.: (239) 454-1944
Web Site: https://www.rjetelecom.com
Emp.: 20
Telecommunication Servicesb
N.A.I.C.S.: 517810

S.T.S., LLC (1)
2575 Westside Pkwy Ste 100, Alpharetta, GA 30004 (100%)
Tel.: (678) 461-3900
Web Site: http://www.stsus.net
Sales Range: $1-9.9 Million
Emp.: 50
Engineering, Installation & Utility Locating Services for Telephone Companies & Utilities
N.A.I.C.S.: 237130
Dennis Tarosky (Pres)

Sage Telecommunications Corp. of
Colorado, LLC (1)
6700 Race St, Denver, CO 80229
Tel.: (303) 227-0986
Web Site: https://www.sagecom.net
Power, Communication Line & Related Structure Construction Services
N.A.I.C.S.: 237130
Robert Gudka (Pres)

Spectrum Wireless Solutions,
Inc. (1)
7399 S Tucson Way Ste C-5, Centennial, CO 80112
Tel.: (303) 799-4994
Web Site: https://www.spectrumwi.com
Telecommunications Structure & Equipment Engineering & Installation Services
N.A.I.C.S.: 237130

Division (Domestic):

Spectrum Wireless Solutions, Inc. -
EF&I Division (2)
1406 N McDonald St Ste E, McKinney, TX 75071
Tel.: (469) 385-3900
Web Site: http://spectrumwi.com
Emp.: 75
Wireless Telecommunications Structure Engineering & Installation Services
N.A.I.C.S.: 237130

Star Construction, LLC (1)
6621 Asheville Hwy, Knoxville, TN 37924
Tel.: (865) 521-6795
Web Site: https://www.star-llc.net
Sales Range: $25-49.9 Million
Emp.: 910
Telecommunications, Power & Cable TV Contractor
N.A.I.C.S.: 237130
Bill Heisler (VP)

Stevens Communications, LLC (1)
995 Cripple Creek Dr, Lawrenceville, GA 30043
Tel.: (770) 339-8066
Web Site: http://www.dycom.com
Sales Range: $1-9.9 Million
Emp.: 35
Cable TV & Telecommunications Construction Contractor
N.A.I.C.S.: 237130

TCS Communications, LLC (1)
2045 W Union Ave Ste E, Englewood, CO 80110
Tel.: (303) 377-3800
Web Site: https://www.tcscomm.com
Sales Range: $10-24.9 Million
Emp.: 165
CATV Construction Contractor
N.A.I.C.S.: 516210
Bob Hargrove (Dir-Sls & Bus Dev)
Michael Escollies (Mgr-Ops-IN, TX & KY)

Telcom Construction, Inc. (1)
2218 200th St E, Clearwater, MN 55320
Tel.: (320) 547-1099
Web Site:
https://www.telcomconstruction.com
Emp.: 1,100
Tele Construction Services
N.A.I.C.S.: 237130
Mark Muller (Pres)
David Rantasha (Sr VP)
Steve Brings (VP)

Tesinc LLC (1)
5905 Breckenridge Pkwy Ste F, Tampa, FL 33610
Tel.: (813) 623-1233
Web Site: https://www.tesinc-llc.com
Sales Range: $1-9.9 Million
Emp.: 200
Telecommunication Servicesb

N.A.I.C.S.: 541330
Anita Ptak (Mgr-Office)

Texstar Enterprises, Inc. (1)
17090 Jordan Rd, Selma, TX 78154
Tel.: (210) 656-8775
Web Site: http://www.texstarenterprises.com
Tele Construction Services
N.A.I.C.S.: 237130

Tjader & Highstrom Utility Services,
LLC (1)
541 Industrial Blvd, New Richmond, WI 54017
Tel.: (715) 246-3440
Web Site:
http://www.tjaderandhighstrom.com
Site Preparation Contracting Services
N.A.I.C.S.: 238910
Ancel Highstrom (Co-Founder)

Subsidiary (Domestic):

Fiber Technologies, Inc. (2)
3190 Hwy 78, Loganville, GA 30052
Tel.: (770) 554-2220
Emp.: 25
Fiber Optic Telecommunications Services
N.A.I.C.S.: 517810
Doug Myers (VP)

Tjader & Highstrom Utility Services,
LLC (1)
541 Industrial Blvd, New Richmond, WI 54017
Tel.: (715) 246-3440
Web Site:
http://www.tjaderandhighstrom.com
Emp.: 185
Power, Communication Line & Related Structure Construction Services
N.A.I.C.S.: 237130

Trawick Construction Company,
LLC (1)
1555 S Blvd, Chipley, FL 32428
Tel.: (850) 638-0429
Web Site:
https://www.trawickconstruction.com
Telecommunication Construction Services
N.A.I.C.S.: 237130
Douglas Trawick (Pres)

Triple-D Communications, LLC (1)
3006 Park Central Ave, Nicholasville, KY 40356-9102
Tel.: (859) 887-4683
Web Site: https://www.tdllc.com
Telecommunications & Electrical Contractor
N.A.I.C.S.: 238210

Underground Specialties, LLC (1)
33005 Roberts Ct, Coburg, OR 97408
Tel.: (541) 741-2211
Web Site: http://www.usiwa.com
Sales Range: $150-199.9 Million
Emp.: 40
Utility Contractor
N.A.I.C.S.: 238210

UtiliQuest, LLC (1)
2575 Westside Pkwy Ste 100, Alpharetta, GA 30004
Tel.: (678) 461-3900
Web Site: http://www.utiliquest.com
Emp.: 75
Water/Sewer/Utility Construction
N.A.I.C.S.: 237110
Terry L. Fordham (Pres)

VCI Construction, Inc. (1)
1921 W 11th St, Upland, CA 91786
Tel.: (909) 949-1350
Web Site: http://www.vcicom.com
Emp.: 400
Electrical & Telecommunications Infrastructure Engineering & Construction Services
N.A.I.C.S.: 811310
John Xanthos (Pres)
James Staab (VP-Ops)
Edgar Escobar (Principal Acctg Officer & VP)
Robert Espinosa (Dir-Ops)
Carlos Bugarin (Dir-Safety)
Keith Manning (Dir-HR)
Rene Madrid (Mgr-Fleet & Equipment)

White Mountain Cable Construction,
LLC (1)
2113 Dover Rd, Epsom, NH 03234 (100%)

Tel.: (603) 736-4766
Web Site: https://www.wmc1.com
Sales Range: $1-9.9 Million
Emp.: 90
Telecommunications Construction
N.A.I.C.S.: 237130

DYNA GROUP INTERNATIONAL INC.
1661 S Seguin Ave, New Braunfels, TX 78130
Tel.: (830) 620-4400   NV
Web Site: https://www.gap1.com
DGIX—(OTCIQ)
Holding Company; Novelties, Souvenirs & Gifts Mfr & Distr
N.A.I.C.S.: 551112
Jeffrey L. Smith (VP & Gen Mgr)
Ralph Gabriel (Dir-Mdsg)
Marisa Pacheco (Coord-Drop Ship)

Subsidiaries:

Great American Products Inc. (1)
1661 S Seguin Ave, New Braunfels, TX 78130
Tel.: (830) 620-4400
Web Site: http://www.gap1.com
Novelties & Specialties, Metal
N.A.I.C.S.: 332999
Bryan Oyler (Dir-E-Commerce-Internet Sls)
Ralph Gabriel (Dir-Mdsg)

DYNARESOURCE, INC.
222 W Las Colinas Blvd Ste 1910 N Tower, Irving, TX 75039
Tel.: (972) 868-9066   DE
Web Site:
https://www.dynaresource.com
Year Founded: 1937
DYNR—(OTCQB)
Rev.: $39,767,460
Assets: $40,942,912
Liabilities: $27,750,771
Net Worth: $13,192,141
Earnings: $6,451,503
Emp.: 205
Fiscal Year-end: 12/31/22
Precious Metals
N.A.I.C.S.: 212290
Koy Wilber Diepholz (Chm, Pres, CEO, CFO-Acting & Treas)
Bradford J. Saulter (VP-IR)
Jose Vargas Lugo (Dir-Ops-Mexico)
Pedro Ignacio Teran Cruz (Exec VP & Dir-Exploration & Resource Dev)
Rene L. F. Mladosich (Exec VP & Dir-Exploration & Resource Dev)

DYNASTAR HOLDINGS, INC.
2544 Route 534, Albrightsville, PA 18210
Tel.: (646) 383-0883   NV
Year Founded: 2005
DYNA—(OTCIQ)
Natural Gas Distribution Services
N.A.I.C.S.: 221210

DYNATRACE, INC.
1601 Trapelo Rd Ste 116, Waltham, MA 02451
Tel.: (781) 530-1000   DE
Web Site: https://ir.dynatrace.com
Year Founded: 2014
DT—(NYSE)
Rev.: $1,430,530,000
Assets: $3,409,779,000
Liabilities: $1,394,289,000
Net Worth: $2,015,490,000
Earnings: $154,632,000
Emp.: 4,700
Fiscal Year-end: 03/31/24
Software Development Services
N.A.I.C.S.: 541511
Rick McConnell (CEO)
Jim Benson (CFO)
Matthias Dollentz-Scharer (Chief Customer Officer)

Dynatrace, Inc.—(Continued)

Nicole Fitzpatrick *(Chief Legal Officer & Sec)*
Bernd Greifeneder *(Founder & CTO)*

Subsidiaries:

Dynatrace LLC **(1)**
1601 Trapelo Rd Ste 116, Waltham, MA 02451
Tel.: (781) 530-1000
Web Site: https://www.dynatrace.com
Information Technology Monitoring Application Software Developer & Publisher
N.A.I.C.S.: 513210
Rick M. McConnell *(CEO)*
Bernd Greifeneder *(CTO & Sr VP)*
Rick McConnell *(CEO)*
Jim Benson *(CFO)*
Laura Heisman *(CMO)*
Colleen Kozak *(Chief Transformation Officer)*
Sue Quackenbush *(Chief People Officer)*
Daniel Yates *(Chief Acctg Officer, Sr VP & Controller)*
Nicole Fitzpatrick *(Chief Legal Officer, Gen Counsel & Sec)*
Steve Tack *(Chief Product Officer & Sr VP-Product Mgmt)*
Dan Zugelder *(Chief Revenue Officer)*

Subsidiary (Non-US):

Dynatrace Asia Pacific Limited **(2)**
51/F Hopewell Centre 183 Queens Road East, Wanchai, China (Hong Kong)
Tel.: (852) 91978690
Web Site: http://www.dynatrace.com
Applications Software Programming Services
N.A.I.C.S.: 541511

Dynatrace Asia-Pacific Pty. Ltd **(2)**
Level 16 Lumley House 309 Kent Street, Sydney, 2000, NSW, Australia
Tel.: (61) 2 8875 5000
Web Site: http://www.dynatrace.com
Sales Range: $25-49.9 Million
Emp.: 50
Applications Software Programming Services
N.A.I.C.S.: 541511
Erwan Paccard *(Dir-Omnichannel Strategy)*

Dynatrace Austria GmbH **(2)**
Freistadter Str 313/2, 4040, Linz, Austria
Tel.: (43) 732 908208
Web Site: http://www.dynatrace.com
Emp.: 12
Information Technology Monitoring Application Software Developer & Publisher
N.A.I.C.S.: 513210
Florian Ortner *(Chief Product Officer)*

Dynatrace BV **(2)**
Graadt van Roggenweg 328, 3531 AH, Utrecht, Netherlands **(100%)**
Tel.: (31) 203118800
Web Site: http://www.dynatrace.com
Software Applications Mfr
N.A.I.C.S.: 513210

Dynatrace India Software Operations Pvt. Ltd. **(2)**
Regus Business Center 22 Fl World Trade Center Brigate Gateway, Malleshwaram, Bengaluru, 560055, Karnataka, India
Tel.: (91) 8041481900
Web Site: http://www.dynatrace.com
Emp.: 20
Applications Software Programming Services
N.A.I.C.S.: 541511
Neeraj Dotel *(Mng Dir)*
Rajasrikiran Nibhanapuri *(Mgr-Inside Sls)*
Ashok Swaminathan *(Head-Presales)*
Ram Varadarajan *(Gen Mgr)*

Dynatrace Ireland Limited **(2)**
Alexander House The Sweepstakes, Ballsbridge, Dublin, 4, Ireland
Tel.: (353) 16319335
Web Site: http://www.dynatrace.com
Applications Software Programming Services
N.A.I.C.S.: 541511

Dynatrace Sp. Z.o.o **(2)**

Al Grunwaldzka 411, 80-309, Gdansk, Poland
Tel.: (48) 585247800
Web Site: http://www.dynatrace.com
Applications Software Programming Services
N.A.I.C.S.: 541511

Dynatrace de Mexico **(2)**
Av Insurgentes Sur 863 piso 7 Col Napoles, 03810, Mexico, Mexico
Tel.: (52) 55 5005 6887
Web Site: http://www.dynatrace.com
Applications Software Programming Services
N.A.I.C.S.: 541511

Dynaware Asia Pacific Pte. Ltd. **(2)**
250 North Bridge Road #14-01 Raffles City Tower, Singapore, 179101, Singapore
Tel.: (65) 6653 1919
Web Site: http://www.dynatrace.com
Emp.: 25
Applications Software Programming Services
N.A.I.C.S.: 541511

Subsidiary (Domestic):

Keynote LLC **(2)**
777 Mariners Island Blvd, San Mateo, CA 94404
Tel.: (650) 403-2400
Web Site: http://www.keynote.com
Sales Range: $100-124.9 Million
Emp.: 495
Internet Performance Management Services & Cloud-Based Solutions for Mobile Applications
N.A.I.C.S.: 541519
Shawn White *(VP-Digital Experience & Cloud Ops)*
Howard Wilson *(Gen Mgr)*
Laura Malinasky *(Gen Counsel & Exec VP)*

DYNATRONICS CORPORATION

1200 Trapp Rd, Eagan, MN 55121
Tel.: (801) 568-7000 UT
Web Site:
https://www.dynatronics.com
Year Founded: 1983
DYNT—(OTCQB)
Rev.: $32,533,965
Assets: $25,940,559
Liabilities: $11,780,115
Net Worth: $14,160,444
Earnings: ($2,697,719)
Emp.: 111
Fiscal Year-end: 06/30/24
Rehab Technology & Equipment Mfr-;Physical Therapy
N.A.I.C.S.: 622310
Brian D. Baker *(Pres & CEO)*
Sarah Mealman *(VP-Marketing)*
Michael Withers *(CIO)*
Erin S. Enright *(Chm)*

Subsidiaries:

Bird & Cronin, LLC **(1)**
1200 Trapp Rd, Eagan, MN 55121
Tel.: (651) 683-1111
Web Site: http://www.birdcronin.com
Orthopedic Soft Goods, Sports Medicine Related Items Mfr & Distr
N.A.I.C.S.: 339113
Jason Anderson *(Pres)*

Hausmann Industries, Inc. **(1)**
130 Union St, Northvale, NJ 07647
Tel.: (201) 767-0255
Web Site: http://www.hausmann.com
Laminate Medical, Therapeutic & Athletic Furniture & Equipment Mfr
N.A.I.C.S.: 337127
David H. Hausmann *(CEO)*

DYNAVAX TECHNOLOGIES CORPORATION

2100 Powell St Ste 720, Emeryville, CA 94608
Tel.: (510) 848-5100 DE
Web Site: https://www.dynavax.com

DVAX—(NASDAQ)
Rev.: $722,683,000
Assets: $985,850,000
Liabilities: $404,837,000
Net Worth: $581,013,000
Earnings: $293,156,000
Emp.: 351
Fiscal Year-end: 12/31/22
Developers of Products for the Treatment of Allergies
N.A.I.C.S.: 325412
David F. Novack *(Pres & COO)*
Robert Janssen *(Chief Medical Officer & Sr VP-Clinical Dev)*
Steven N. Gersten *(Chief Ethics & Compliance Officer, Gen Counsel, Sec & Sr VP)*
Ryan Spencer *(Co-Pres, CEO & Interim CFO)*
Justin Burgess *(Principal Acctg Officer & Controller)*
Dong Yu *(Sr VP-Vaccine Res)*
Eric Frings *(Mng Dir, VP & Head-Site)*
Meg Smith *(VP-Sls & Ops)*
John L. Slebir *(Sr VP)*
Paul Cox *(VP)*
Friedhelm Helling *(VP)*
Ouzama Henry *(VP)*
Eleni Constantinidis Kornblatt *(VP)*
Patricia Novy *(VP)*
Alex Oh *(Assoc Gen Counsel)*

Subsidiaries:

Dynavax Europe GmbH **(1)**
Eichsfelderstrasse 11, 40595, Dusseldorf, Germany
Tel.: (49) 211758450
Web Site: https://www.dynavax.com
Pharmaceuticals Mfr
N.A.I.C.S.: 325412

Dynax GmbH **(1)**
Eichsfelderstrasse 11, 40595, Dusseldorf, D-40595, Germany
Tel.: (49) 211758450
Biopharmaceutical Drug Mfr
N.A.I.C.S.: 325412
David F. Novack *(Sr VP-Ops & Quality)*
Robert Janssen *(Chief Medical Officer & Sr VP)*

DYNE THERAPEUTICS, INC.

1560 Trapelo Rd, Waltham, MA 02451
Tel.: (781) 786-8230 DE
Web Site: https://www.dyne-tx.com
Year Founded: 2017
DYN—(NASDAQ)
Rev.: $2,917,000
Assets: $306,325,000
Liabilities: $53,961,000
Net Worth: $252,364,000
Earnings: ($168,099,000)
Emp.: 123
Fiscal Year-end: 12/31/22
Biotechnology Research & Development Services
N.A.I.C.S.: 541714
Jason P. Rhodes *(Co-Founder & Chm)*
John G. Cox *(Pres & CEO)*
Romesh Subramanian *(Co-Founder)*
Chris Mix *(Sr VP-Clinical Dev)*
John Davis *(VP & Head-Preclinical Dev)*
Debra Feldman *(VP & Head-Regulatory)*
Rick Scalzo *(VP-Acctg & Admin)*
Gene Kim *(VP-Fin)*
Amy Reilly *(VP-Corp Comm & IR)*
John Najim *(VP-Chemistry, Mfg & Controls)*
Molly White *(VP-Medical Comm & Advocacy)*
Daniel Wilson *(VP & Head-Intellectual Property)*
Wildon Farwell *(Chief Medical Officer)*

Ashish Dugar *(Sr VP & Head-Medical Affairs-Global)*
Phillip Samayoa *(Co-Founder)*
Francesco Bibbiani *(Sr VP & Head-Dev)*
Oxana Beskrovnaya *(Chief Scientific Officer)*

DYNEX CAPITAL, INC.

4991 Lake Brook Dr Ste 100, Glen Allen, VA 23060-9245
Tel.: (804) 217-5800 VA
Web Site:
https://www.dynexcapital.com
Year Founded: 1987
DX—(NYSE)
Rev.: $86,695,000
Assets: $3,605,234,000
Liabilities: $2,703,906,000
Net Worth: $901,328,000
Earnings: $135,467,000
Emp.: 19
Fiscal Year-end: 12/31/22
Mortgage & Consumer Finance Services
N.A.I.C.S.: 525990
Byron L. Boston *(Chm & CEO)*
Robert S. Colligan *(CFO, Sec & Exec VP)*
Smriti Laxman Popenoe *(Pres, Co-CEO & Chief Investment Officer)*
Alisson Griffin *(VP-IR)*
Jeffrey L. Childress *(VP & Controller)*

DYNTEK, INC.

5241 California Ave Ste 150, Irvine, CA 92617
Tel.: (949) 271-6700 DE
Web Site: http://www.dyntek.com
Year Founded: 1989
DYNE—(OTCIQ)
Sales Range: $150-199.9 Million
Emp.: 188
Information Technology Solutions & Business Process Outsource Services
N.A.I.C.S.: 541511
Joe Rubino *(Sr VP)*
Dan Minella *(VP-Sls-West)*
Timothy Montgomery *(CEO)*
Adam LaChant *(VP-Sls-East)*
Wes Brown *(VP-Architecture)*
Peter Walsh *(VP-Fin)*
Donico Leonard *(VP Sls & Ops)*

Subsidiaries:

DynTek Inc. **(1)**
1250 Broadway Ste 3801, New York, NY 10001
Tel.: (518) 207-3400
Web Site: http://www.dyntek.com
Rev.: $3,000,000
Emp.: 75
Computer Software Development
N.A.I.C.S.: 541511
Ron Ben-Yishay *(CEO)*

DZS INC.

5700 Tennyson Pkwy Ste 400, Plano, TX 75024
Tel.: (510) 777-7000 DE
Web Site: https://dzsi.com
Year Founded: 1999
DZSI—(OTCEM)
Rev.: $244,541,000
Assets: $249,381,000
Liabilities: $226,822,000
Net Worth: $22,559,000
Earnings: ($135,218,000)
Emp.: 660
Fiscal Year-end: 12/31/23
Communications Network Equipment Mfr
N.A.I.C.S.: 334220
Laura Larsen-Misunas *(Chief People Officer)*

Charles Daniel Vogt (Pres & CEO)
Jay Hilbert (Exec VP-Sls-Americas,
Europe, Middle East & Africa)
Andrew Bender (CTO)
Justin Ferguson (Chief Legal Officer
& Sec)
Tom Carter (Chief Customer Officer)
Tuncay Cil (Chief Strategy Officer)
Gunter Reiss (CMO)
Norm Foust (Sr VP)
Raghu Marthi (COO)

Subsidiaries:

DASAN India Private Limited   (1)
D No 40-1-140/3 4th Floor Sri Pothuri Tow-
ers MG Road, Vijayawada, 522010, Andra
Pradesh, India
Tel.: (91) 9866536768
Web Site: https://dasans.com
Research & Development Services
N.A.I.C.S.: 541715

DASAN Network Solutions, Inc.   (1)
5000 Research Ct Ste 700, Suwanee, GA
30024
Tel.: (770) 674-0302
Web Site: http://www.dasannetworks.com

DASAN Vietnam Company
Limited   (1)
Richy Tower - No 35 Mac Thai To Street,
Yen Hoa Ward Cau Giay District, Hanoi,
Vietnam
Tel.: (84) 2437689330
Research & Development Services
N.A.I.C.S.: 541715

DASAN Zhone Solutions, Inc. -
Middle East, Africa & Pakistan   (1)
Business Central Towers Tower B - Office
2701, PO Box 9456, Dubai, United Arab
Emirates
Tel.: (971) 44494017
Web Site: http://www.dasanzhone.com
Provider of Telecommunications Infrastruc-
ture Products for Local Access Networks
N.A.I.C.S.: 517111

DZS Japan Inc.   (1)
13F Parkwest 6-12-1Nishi, Shinjuku, Tokyo,
160-0023, Japan
Tel.: (81) 362581565
Research & Development Services
N.A.I.C.S.: 541715

KEYMILE GmbH   (1)
Wohlenbergstr 3, 30179, Hannover, Ger-
many
Tel.: (49) 511 67 47 0
Web Site: http://www.keymile.com
Data Transmission System Mfr
N.A.I.C.S.: 334220
Wolfgang Spahn (CTO)

Subsidiary (Domestic):

HYTEC Geratebau GmbH   (2)
Power Grids, PO Box 10 03 51, 68128,
Mannheim, Germany
Tel.: (49) 6213813000
Web Site: http://www.hytec.de
Data Transmission System Mfr
N.A.I.C.S.: 334220

Subsidiary (Non-US):

KEYMILE AG   (2)
Schwarzenburgstrasse 73, 3097, Bern,
Switzerland
Tel.: (41) 31 377 1111
Web Site: http://www.keymile.com
Emp.: 120
Data Transmission System Distr
N.A.I.C.S.: 423690

KEYMILE Kft.   (2)
Beg utca 3-5, 1022, Budapest, Hungary
Tel.: (36) 1 457 0105
Data Transmission System Distr
N.A.I.C.S.: 423690

KEYMILE LLC   (2)
4-th Dobryninsky Per Bld 8 BC Dobrynya
Office 200, 119049, Moscow, Russia
Tel.: (7) 495 725 2630
Web Site: http://www.keymile.com
Data Transmission System Distr
N.A.I.C.S.: 423690

KEYMILE Ltd.   (2)
Tate House Watermark Way Foxholes Busi-
ness Park, Hertford, SG13 7TZ, United
Kingdom
Tel.: (44) 1992507000
Web Site: https://dzsi.com
Data Transmission System Distr
N.A.I.C.S.: 423690

KEYMILE Ltda.   (2)
Rua Victor Civita 66 Bl 05 Salas 605/608,
22775-044, Rio de Janeiro, Brazil
Tel.: (55) 2135359320
Web Site: http://www.keymile.com
Emp.: 15
Data Transmission System Distr
N.A.I.C.S.: 423690

Subsidiary (Domestic):

KEYMILE Networks GmbH   (2)
Blumenstrasse 24, 71522, Backnang, Ger-
many
Tel.: (49) 7191344072620
Data Transmission System Mfr
N.A.I.C.S.: 334220

Subsidiary (Non-US):

KEYMILE Sp. z o.o.   (2)
Poloneza 89b, 02-826, Warsaw, Poland
Tel.: (48) 226371640
Data Transmission System Distr
N.A.I.C.S.: 423690
Jaroslaw Starega (Project Mgr)

KEYMILE Systems JLT   (2)
Jumeirah Lake Towers Building JBC-5 Of-
fice 608, PO Box 18355, Dubai, 18355,
United Arab Emirates
Tel.: (971) 4 360 5947
Web Site: http://www.keymile.com
Emp.: 12
Data Transmission System Distr
N.A.I.C.S.: 423690

KEYMILE Systems Pty. Ltd   (2)
Level 5 150 Albert Road, Melbourne, 3205,
VIC, Australia
Tel.: (61) 1 800 080 476
Web Site: http://www.keymile.com
Data Transmission System Distr
N.A.I.C.S.: 423690

KEYMILE Teknoloji Sistemleri Ltd.
Sti.   (2)
Istiklal mah Adalar sok 21/7, 26010, Eskise-
hir, Turkiye
Tel.: (90) 222 220 45 65
Data Transmission System Distr
N.A.I.C.S.: 423690

Optelian Access Networks, Inc.   (1)
1 Brewer Hunt Way, Ottawa, K2K 2B5, ON,
Canada
Tel.: (770) 690-9575
Web Site: http://www.optelian.com
Optical Networking Solution Provider
N.A.I.C.S.: 517810
David Weymouth (CEO)

Zhone Technologies S. de R.L. de
C.V.   (1)
Reforma 350 Piso 11, Col Juarez, Mexico,
6600, Mexico   (100%)
Tel.: (52) 5591711480
Web Site: http://dasanzhone.com
Communication Equipment Mfr
N.A.I.C.S.: 334290

E MED FUTURE, INC.

4054 Sawyer Rd, Sarasota, FL 34233
Tel.: (813) 785-8687   NV
Year Founded: 1990
EMDF—(OTCIQ)
Medical Safety Product Mfr
N.A.I.C.S.: 339112
Gary Kompothecras (CEO)
Michael W. Nole (Pres)

E.L.F. BEAUTY, INC.

570 10th St, Oakland, CA 94607
Tel.: (510) 778-7787   DE
Web Site: https://www.elfbeauty.com
Year Founded: 2013
ELF—(NYSE)
Rev.: $392,155,000

Assets: $494,632,000
Liabilities: $182,203,000
Net Worth: $312,429,000
Earnings: $21,770,000
Emp.: 303
Fiscal Year-end: 03/31/22
Cosmetics, Beauty Supplies & Per-
fume Retailers
N.A.I.C.S.: 456120
Tarang P. Amin (Chm, Pres & CEO)
Jennie Laar (Chief Comml Officer &
Sr VP)
Mandy Fields (CFO, Principal Acctg
Officer & Sr VP)

Subsidiaries:

W3ll People LLC   (1)
215 S Lamar Blvd, Austin, TX 78704-1038
Tel.: (512) 366-7963
Web Site: http://www.w3llpeople.com
Cosmetics, Beauty Supplies & Perfume
Stores
N.A.I.C.S.: 456120

E.MERGE TECHNOLOGY AC-
QUISITION CORP.

533 Airport Blvd Ste 400, Burlingame,
CA 94010
Tel.: (619) 736-6855   DE
Year Founded: 2020
ETAC—(NASDAQ)
Rev.: $19,529,944
Assets: $600,447,360
Liabilities: $634,640,021
Net Worth: ($34,192,661)
Earnings: $18,117,666
Emp.: 2
Fiscal Year-end: 12/31/21
Investment Services
N.A.I.C.S.: 523999
S. Steven Singh (Chm)
Jeff Clarke (Co-CEO & CFO)
Guy Gecht (Co-CEO)

EACO CORPORATION

5065 E Hunter Ave, Anaheim, CA
92807
Tel.: (714) 876-2490   FL
Web Site: https://www.eacocorp.com
Year Founded: 1982
EACO—(OTCIQ)
Rev.: $356,231,000
Assets: $188,538,000
Liabilities: $64,907,000
Net Worth: $123,631,000
Earnings: $14,951,000
Emp.: 604
Fiscal Year-end: 08/31/24
Holding Company; Electronic Compo-
nents, Fasteners & Electromechanical
Hardware Distr
N.A.I.C.S.: 551112
Glen F. Ceiley (Chm & CEO)
Michael Narikawa (CFO, Chief Acctg
Officer & Controller)

Subsidiaries:

Bisco Industries, Inc.   (1)
1500 N Lakeview Ave, Anaheim, CA
92807-1819   (100%)
Tel.: (714) 693-2901
Web Site: http://www.biscoind.com
Sales Range: $1-9.9 Million
Emp.: 265
Electronic Components, Fasteners & Elec-
tromechanical Hardware Distr
N.A.I.C.S.: 423690
Don Wagner (COO & Exec VP)

Division (Domestic):

National Precision   (2)
1500 N Lakeview Ave, Anaheim, CA 92807-
1819
Tel.: (714) 867-2440
Fastener & Electromechanical Hardware
Distr
N.A.I.C.S.: 423710

EAGLE BANCORP MONTANA,
INC.

1400 Prospect Ave, Helena, MT
59604
Tel.: (406) 442-3080   DE
Web Site:
   https://www.opportunitybank.com
Year Founded: 2009
EBMT—(NASDAQ)
Rev.: $95,682,000
Assets: $1,948,384,000
Liabilities: $1,789,968,000
Net Worth: $158,416,000
Earnings: $10,701,000
Emp.: 399
Fiscal Year-end: 12/31/22
Bank Holding Company
N.A.I.C.S.: 551111
Laura F. Clark (Pres & CEO)
Thomas J. McCarvel (Vice Chm)
Shavon R. Cape (Founder)
Mark A. O'Neill (Chief Lending Officer
& Sr VP)
Miranda J. Spaulding (CFO & Sr VP)
Rachel R. Amdahl (COO & Sr VP)
Alana Binde (Chief HR Officer & Sr
VP)
Linda M. Chilton (Chief Retail Officer
& Sr VP)
Rick F. Hays (Chm)

Subsidiaries:

First Community Bancorp, Inc.   (1)
540 2nd Ave S, Glasgow, MT 59230
Tel.: (406) 228-8231
Web Site: http://www.fcbank.net
Sales Range: $1-9.9 Million
Emp.: 60
Commericial Banking
N.A.I.C.S.: 522110
Jean Dreikosen (Mgr)

Opportunity Bank of Montana   (1)
1400 Prospect Ave, Helena, MT 59601
Tel.: (406) 442-3080
Web Site: https://www.opportunitybank.com
Commericial Banking
N.A.I.C.S.: 522110
Laura F. Clark (Pres & CEO)
Jenica Held (Mgr-Retail-Butte)

EAGLE BANCORP, INC.

7830 Old Georgetown Rd, Bethesda,
MD 20814
Tel.: (301) 986-1800   MD
Web Site:
   https://www.eaglebankcorp.com
Year Founded: 1997
EGBN—(NASDAQ)
Rev.: $448,267,000
Assets: $11,150,854,000
Liabilities: $9,922,533,000
Net Worth: $1,228,321,000
Earnings: $140,930,000
Emp.: 496
Fiscal Year-end: 12/31/22
Bank Holding Company
N.A.I.C.S.: 551111
Susan G. Riel (Pres & CEO)
Charles D. Levingston (CFO & Exec
VP)
Lindsey S. Rheaume (Exec VP)
Paul Saltzman (Chief Legal Officer &
Exec VP)

Subsidiaries:

EagleBank   (1)
7735 Old Georgetown Rd Ste 100,
Bethesda, MD 20814
Tel.: (240) 497-2044
Web Site: https://www.eaglebankcorp.com
Sales Range: $150-199.9 Million
Commericial Banking
N.A.I.C.S.: 522110

Eagle Bancorp, Inc.—(Continued)

Susan G. Riel (Pres & CEO)
Norman Robert Pozez (Chm)
Janice L. Williams (Chief Credit Officer & Sr Exec VP)

EAGLE EXPLORATION CO.
93 Spyglass Dr, Littleton, CO 80123
Tel.: (303) 797-6816   CO
EGXP—(OTCIQ)
Natural Gas Exploration Service
N.A.I.C.S.: 213112
Raymond A. Joeckel (Pres & CEO)

EAGLE FINANCIAL SERVICES, INC.
2 E Main St, Berryville, VA 22611
Tel.: (540) 955-2510   VA
Web Site:
   https://www.bankofclarke.bank
Year Founded: 1991
EFSI—(OTCQX)
Rev.: $68,031,000
Assets: $1,616,717,000
Liabilities: $1,514,988,000
Net Worth: $101,729,000
Earnings: $14,521,000
Emp.: 237
Fiscal Year-end: 12/31/22
Bank Holding Company
N.A.I.C.S.: 551111
Joseph T. Zmitrovich (Chief Banking Officer & Exec VP)
Brandon Craig Lorey (Pres & CEO)
Kaley P. Crosen (Sec & Exec VP)
Robert W. Smalley Jr. (Vice Chm)
Kathleen J. Chappell (CFO & Exec VP)

Subsidiaries:

Bank of Clarke County   (1)
2 E Main St, Berryville, VA 22611 (100%)
Tel.: (540) 955-2510
Web Site: https://www.bankofclarke.bank
Sales Range: $75-99.9 Million
Emp.: 125
Savings, Loans & Commercial Banking Services
N.A.I.C.S.: 522180
Joseph T. Zmitrovich (Chief Banking Officer)
Brandon Craig Lorey (Pres & CEO)
Kaley P. Crosen (Chief HR Officer & Exec VP)
James S. George II (Chief Credit Officer)
Debra L. Purrington (Exec VP)
Kathleen J. Chappell (CFO)
Kathleen Croson (Exec VP)
Marianne Schmidt (Chief Mktg Officer)
Mary Liz McCauley (VP)
James S. George II (Chief Credit Officer & Sr VP)

Eagle Investment Services Inc.   (1)
124 N 1st Ave, Iowa City, IA 52245
Tel.: (319) 358-2142
Web Site:
   https://www.eagleinvestmentservices.com
Rev.: $150,000
Emp.: 10
Security Brokers & Dealers
N.A.I.C.S.: 523150

EAGLE FORD OIL AND GAS CORP
1110 Nasa Pkwy Ste 311, Houston, TX 77058
Tel.: (281) 383-9648   NV
ECCE—(OTCIQ)
Oil & Natural Gas Services
N.A.I.C.S.: 213112

EAGLE MATERIALS INC.
5960 Berkshire Ln Ste 900, Dallas, TX 75225
Tel.: (214) 432-2000   DE
Web Site:
   https://www.eaglematerials.com
Year Founded: 1963

EXP—(NYSE)
Rev.: $2,259,297,000
Assets: $2,947,019,000
Liabilities: $1,638,484,000
Net Worth: $1,308,535,000
Earnings: $477,639,000
Emp.: 2,500
Fiscal Year-end: 03/31/24
Holding Company; Cement, Gypsum & Other Construction Products Mfr
N.A.I.C.S.: 551112
Eric M. Cribbs (Exec VP-Concrete & Aggregates, Advanced Cementitious Materials, Logistics & Procurement & Materials)
Michael R. Nicolais (Chm)
D. Craig Kesler (CFO & Exec VP-Finance-Administration)
William R. Devlin (Chief Acctg Officer, Sr VP & Controller)
Richard R. Stewart (Vice Chm)
Michael R. Haack (Pres & CEO)
Matt Newby (Gen Counsel, Sec & Exec VP)

Subsidiaries:

AUDUBON MATERIALS LLC   (1)
2200 Courtney Rd, Sugar Creek, MO 64050
Tel.: (816) 257-3683
Web Site:
   https://www.centralplainscement.com
Cement Plant Construction Services
N.A.I.C.S.: 236210
Kameron Williams (VP-Sales & Marketing)
Reid Skinner (Reg Sls Mgr)
Megan Dangel (Engr-Technical Services)
Aaron Meyer (Mgr-Logistics)
Ann Lehane (Coord-Logistics)
Kelly Lemons (Coord-Operations)
Zac Brummal (Mgr-Oklahoma Territory, Oilwell & Contract Sls)
Jim Wiley (Mgr-Arkansas Territory)
Jeremy Larsen (Mgr-Iowa-Missouri Territory)
Joel Sedlacek (Mgr-Nebraska-Iowa Territory)
Scott Navarro (Mgr-Kansas-Missouri Territory)
Peter Jabbour (Mgr-Kansas-Missouri Territory)
Chris Miller (VP-Operations-Sugar Creek)
Chris Thrower (VP-Operations-Tulsa)
Adam Doppenberg (Plant Mgr-Tulsa Cement Plant)
Jennifer Smith (Mgr-Environmental)

AUDUBON READYMIX LLC   (1)
15100 E Courtney Atherton Rd, Sugar Creek, MO 64058
Tel.: (816) 257-4000
Web Site: https://quicksilverrmx.com
Cement Plant Construction Services
N.A.I.C.S.: 236210

American Gypsum Company LLC   (1)
5960 Berkshire Ln Ste 800, Dallas, TX 75225 (100%)
Tel.: (214) 530-5500
Web Site:
   https://www.americangypsum.com
Rev.: $45,000,000
Emp.: 250
Mfr & Distributor of Gypsum Wallboard Products
N.A.I.C.S.: 327420
Eric M. Cribbs (Pres)

Subsidiary (Domestic):

AG South Carolina LLC   (2)
2007 Pennyroyal Rd, Georgetown, SC 29440 (100%)
Tel.: (843) 520-7727
Sales Range: $25-49.9 Million
Emp.: 80
Synthetic Gypsum Products Mfr
N.A.I.C.S.: 327420

Plant (Domestic):

American Gypsum Co. LLC - Duke Plant   (2)
18972 US Hwy 62, Duke, OK 73532
Tel.: (580) 679-3391
Sales Range: $25-49.9 Million
Emp.: 225
Gypsum Board Mfr

N.A.I.C.S.: 327420

CRS Proppants LLC   (1)
777 Post Oak Blvd Ste 250, Houston, TX 77056
Tel.: (832) 203-8322
Emp.: 50
Raw & Partially Pre-Cured Resin Coated Sand to Oilfield, Exploration & Production Companies
N.A.I.C.S.: 212322
Steven Cobb (Chm & Pres)
Brian Myer (Controller)

Centex Materials LLC   (1)
3019 Alvin Devane Blvd Bldg 1 Ste 100, Austin, TX 78741
Tel.: (512) 460-3003
Web Site: https://www.centexmaterials.com
Emp.: 20
Concrete Building Products Whslr
N.A.I.C.S.: 423320

Fairborn Cement Company LLC   (1)
3250 Linebaugh Rd, Xenia, OH 45385
Tel.: (937) 878-8651
Web Site: https://www.fairborncement.com
Building Materials Distr
N.A.I.C.S.: 423830
Jeff Thomas (Mgr-Packaged Products)
Blase Mahon (Mgr-Northwest-Southwest Ohio)
Tim Kaiser (Mgr-Technical Svcs)
Steve Chaney (Mgr-Quarry)
Rusty Strader (Mgr-Quality Control)
Thomas Byrne (Mgr-Environmental)
Misty Cooper (Mgr-Procurement)
John Miller (VP-Ops)
Ray Meier (VP-Fin)
Michael Snoddy (Mgr-Logistics)
Mike Benroth (Mgr-Contract Sls & Eastern Ohio)
Morgan Hughes (Mgr-Safety)
Spencer Rohr (Mgr-Maintenance)
Armando Leyva (Production Mgr)
Tyler Southworth (Territory Mgr-SW Ohio)

Illinois Cement Company LLC   (1)
1601 Rockwell Rd, La Salle, IL 61301 (100%)
Tel.: (815) 224-2112
Web Site: https://www.illinoiscement.com
Sales Range: $50-74.9 Million
Emp.: 183
Masonry Cement Mfr
N.A.I.C.S.: 327310
Todd Surrarrer (VP-Sales & Marketing)
Jim Gallagher (Sls Mgr)
Ben Bufmack (VP-Operations)
Shawn Mages (Plant Mgr)
Brad Fischer (Production Mgr)
Nick Varani (Mgr-Terminal)
Dan Miller (Mgr-Terminal)
Josh Farr (Plant Mgr)
Robert Carrillo (Mgr-Q/C & Logistics)

KANSAS CITY AGGREGATE LLC   (1)
16400 E Kentucky Rd, Independence, MO 64058
Tel.: (816) 796-9488
Brick, Stone & Related Construction Material Merchant Whslr
N.A.I.C.S.: 423320

KANSAS CITY FLY ASH LLC   (1)
15100 E Courtney-Atherton Rd, Sugar Creek, MO 64058
Tel.: (816) 257-4084
Web Site: https://www.kcflyash.com
Brick, Stone & Related Construction Material Merchant Whslr
N.A.I.C.S.: 423320

Mountain Cement Company   (1)
5 Sand Creek Rd, Laramie, WY 82070 (100%)
Tel.: (307) 745-4879
Web Site: https://www.mountaincement.com
Sales Range: $50-74.9 Million
Emp.: 100
Cement Mfr, Stone Quarrying & Kiln Services
N.A.I.C.S.: 327310
Bob McCollum (Mgr-Production)
Mark Andrews (Mgr-Environmental)
Mike Seaton (Mgr-Pur)
Russell Dickson (Mgr-Safety)
Cesar Millan (VP)
Dan Peda (VP)

NORTHERN WHITE SAND LLC   (1)
2504 Joe Fulton International Trade Corridor, Corpus Christi, TX 78402
Tel.: (361) 687-2112
Brick, Stone & Related Construction Material Merchant Whslr
N.A.I.C.S.: 423320
Michael Crnkovich (VP-Sls & Mktg)

Nevada Cement Company   (1)
1290 W Main St, Fernley, NV 89408 (100%)
Tel.: (775) 575-2281
Web Site: https://www.nevadacement.com
Sales Range: $50-74.9 Million
Emp.: 100
Cement Mfr & Limestone Quarrying
N.A.I.C.S.: 327310

RIO GRANDE DRYWALL SUPPLY CO LLC   (1)
7705 Tiburon St NE, Albuquerque, NM 87109
Tel.: (505) 821-0201
Web Site: http://www.drywallriogrande.com
Building Materials Distr
N.A.I.C.S.: 423830

Raptor Materials LLC   (1)
8120 Gage St, Frederick, CO 80516
Tel.: (303) 666-6657
Web Site: https://www.varracompanies.com
Gravel & Ready Mix Concrete Mfr
N.A.I.C.S.: 327320

Republic Paperboard Company LLC   (1)
8801 SW Lee Blvd, Lawton, OK 73505 (100%)
Tel.: (580) 510-2200
Web Site:
   https://www.republicpaperboard.com
Sales Range: $50-74.9 Million
Emp.: 130
Producer of 100% Recycled Paperboard
N.A.I.C.S.: 322130

Skyway Cement Company LLC   (1)
5960 Berkshire Ln Ste 900, Dallas, TX 75225-6068
Tel.: (214) 432-2105
Web Site: https://www.skywaycement.com
Cement Mfr & Distr
N.A.I.C.S.: 327310
Jan Prusinski (VP-Mktg)
Josh Farr (Plant Mgr)
Robert Carrillo (Mgr-Q/C & Logistics)
Andrew Schuler (Mgr-Logistics Distr)

TULSA CEMEMT LLC   (1)
2609 N 145th E Ave, Tulsa, OK 74116
Tel.: (405) 388-1471
Web Site:
   https://www.centralplainscement.com
Cement Plant Construction Services
N.A.I.C.S.: 236210

Texas Lehigh Cement Company LP   (1)
701 Cement Plant Rd, Buda, TX 78610-0610
Tel.: (512) 295-6111
Web Site: https://www.texaslehigh.com
Construction & Well Cements Mfr; Owned 50% by Eagle Materials Inc. & 50% by Lehigh Cement Company
N.A.I.C.S.: 327310

Wildcat Minerals LLC   (1)
1746 Cole Blvd Bldg 21 Ste 265, Lakewood, CO 80401
Tel.: (303) 747-6200
Web Site: https://www.wildcatminerals.com
Transloading, Distribution & Logistics Services
N.A.I.C.S.: 541614

EAGLE PHARMACEUTICALS, INC.
50 Tice Blvd Ste 315, Woodcliff Lake, NJ 07677
Tel.: (201) 326-5300   DE
Web Site: https://www.eagleus.com
Year Founded: 2007
EGRX—(NASDAQ)
Rev.: $316,610,000
Assets: $406,160,000
Liabilities: $172,600,000

Net Worth: $233,560,000
Earnings: $35,642,000
Emp.: 135
Fiscal Year-end: 12/31/22
Pharmaceuticals Mfr
N.A.I.C.S.: 325412
Michael Graves *(Interim Exec Chm & Principal Exec Officer)*
Scott L. Tarriff *(Founder)*
Daniel J. O'Connor *(Chief Strategy Officer & Head-Corp Dev)*
Steven B. Ratoff *(Interim CFO & Principal Acctg Officer)*
Michael Graves *(Chm)*
Ryan Debski *(Chief Compliance Officer)*
Reed McClung *(Exec VP)*

Subsidiaries:

Acacia Pharma Group PLC   **(1)**
The Officers Mess Royston Road, Duxford, Cambridge, CB22 4QH, United Kingdom
Tel.: (44) 1223919760
Web Site: http://www.acaciapharma.com
Rev.: $211,000
Assets: $102,835,000
Liabilities: $42,350,000
Net Worth: $60,485,000
Earnings: ($33,478,000)
Emp.: 47
Fiscal Year-end: 12/31/2020
Pharmaceuticals Product Mfr
N.A.I.C.S.: 325412
Patrick V. J. J. Vink *(Chm)*
Mike Bolinder *(CEO)*

Subsidiary (US):

Acacia Pharma Inc.   **(2)**
8440 Allison Pointe Blvd Ste 100, Indianapolis, IN 46250
Tel.: (201) 326-5300
Pharmaceuticals Product Mfr
N.A.I.C.S.: 325412

EAGLE POINT CREDIT COMPANY INC.
600 Steamboat Rd Ste 202, Greenwich, CT 06830
Tel.: (203) 340-8510   DE
Web Site:
  https://eaglepointcreditcompany.com
Year Founded: 2014
ECC—(NYSE)
Rev.: $63,546,242
Assets: $512,589,535
Liabilities: $150,928,847
Net Worth: $361,660,688
Earnings: $60,886,226
Fiscal Year-end: 12/31/20
Investment Services
N.A.I.C.S.: 523999
Thomas P. Majewski *(Founder, CEO & Mng Partner)*
James R. Matthews *(Chm)*
Kenneth P. Onorio *(CFO & COO)*
Nauman S. Malik *(Chief Compliance Officer)*
Courtney B. Fandrick *(Sec)*
Karan Chabba *(Head-ABS, MBS, SRT & Specialty Fin)*

EAGLE POINT INCOME COMPANY INC.
600 Steamboat Rd Ste 202, Greenwich, CT 06830
Tel.: (203) 340-8510   DE
Web Site:
  https://www.eaglepointincome.com
Year Founded: 2018
EIC—(NYSE)
Investment Holding Company
N.A.I.C.S.: 551112
Thomas P. Majewski *(Chm & CEO)*
Kenneth P. Onorio *(CFO & COO)*
Nauman S. Malik *(Chief Compliance Officer)*
Courtney B. Fandrick *(Sec)*

EALIXIR, INC.
40 SW 13th St Ph 1, Miami, FL 33130
Tel.: (303) 768-9221   NV
Web Site: https://www.ealixir.com
Year Founded: 1996
EAXR—(OTC)
Information Technology Services
N.A.I.C.S.: 541512
Mark Corrao *(CFO)*
Enea Angelo Trevisan *(Founder & CEO)*
Venkatesh Patrachari *(Pres & CEO)*
Eleonora Ramondetti *(Chm & Sec)*

EARTH GEN-BIOFUEL INC.
1375 Front St NE, Salem, OR 97301
Tel.: (626) 964-8808   NV
Web Site: https://earthgenbiofuel.com
Year Founded: 2012
EGBB—(OTCIQ)
Castor Bean Oil Mfr
N.A.I.C.S.: 311224
Sean Bryant *(CFO)*
Scott Robert DeBo *(Pres & Sec)*

EARTH LIFE SCIENCES, INC.
Ste 880 50 W Liberty St, Reno, NV 89501
Tel.: (514) 500-4111   NV
Web Site:
  https://www.earthlifesciences.net
Year Founded: 2001
CLTS—(OTCIQ)
Software Services
N.A.I.C.S.: 541511
Angelo Marino *(Pres & VP)*

EARTH SCIENCE TECH, INC.
8950 SW 74 CT Ste 101, Miami, FL 33156
Tel.: (305) 724-5684   FL
Web Site:
  https://www.earthsciencetech.com
Year Founded: 2010
ETST—(OTCIQ)
Rev.: $11,953,635
Assets: $3,881,336
Liabilities: $1,632,031
Net Worth: $2,249,305
Earnings: $812,139
Emp.: 32
Fiscal Year-end: 03/31/24
Pharmaceuticals Mfr
N.A.I.C.S.: 325412
Giorgio R. Saumat *(CEO & Chm)*

EAST KANSAS AGRI ENERGY LLC
1304 S Main St, Garnett, KS 66032
Tel.: (785) 448-2888
Web Site: https://www.ekaellc.com
Year Founded: 2001
ETKNU—(OTCIQ)
Fuel Oil Distr
N.A.I.C.S.: 457210
Scott Burkdoll *(Chm)*

EAST MORGAN HOLDINGS, INC.
3100 NE 48 St Ste 917, Fort Lauderdale, FL 33308
Tel.: (954) 380-4600   DE
Web Site:
  http://www.eastmorgan.com
Year Founded: 2001
EMHI—(OTCIQ)
Environmental Remediation Technologies Including Coal Burning Power Plants & Solar Technology
N.A.I.C.S.: 213113
Richard A. Runco *(Pres)*

EAST SIDE FINANCIAL, INC.
9399 W Commercial Blvd, Tamarac, FL 33351

Tel.: (954) 721-3400   DE
ESDF—(OTCIQ)
Banking Services
N.A.I.C.S.: 522110
Diane Raddatz *(Pres & CEO)*

EAST STONE ACQUISITION CORPORATION
25 Mall Rd Ste 330, Burlington, MA 01803
Tel.: (781) 202-9128   VG
Year Founded: 2018
ESSCU—(NASDAQ)
Rev.: $13,076
Assets: $33,569,160
Liabilities: $43,797,168
Net Worth: ($10,228,008)
Earnings: ($4,891,067)
Emp.: 2
Fiscal Year-end: 12/31/21
Investment Services
N.A.I.C.S.: 523999
Xiaoma Lu *(CEO)*
Chunyi Hao *(Chm & CFO)*

EAST WEST BANCORP, INC.
135 N Los Robles Ave 7th Floor, Pasadena, CA 91101
Tel.: (626) 768-6000   DE
Web Site:
  https://www.eastwestbank.com
Year Founded: 1973
EWBC—(NASDAQ)
Rev.: $3,693,805,000
Assets: $69,612,884,000
Liabilities: $62,662,050,000
Net Worth: $6,950,834,000
Earnings: $1,161,161,000
Emp.: 3,206
Fiscal Year-end: 12/31/23
Commercial Banking Services
N.A.I.C.S.: 551111
Douglas P. Krause *(Vice Chm & Chief Corp Officer)*
Christopher J. Del Moral-Niles *(CFO & Exec VP)*
Irene H. Oh *(Chief Risk Officer & Exec VP)*
Dominic Ng *(Chm & CEO)*
Lisa L. Kim *(Gen Counsel, Sec & Exec VP)*

Subsidiaries:

East West Bank   **(1)**
135 N Los Robles Ave 7th Fl, Pasadena, CA 91101   **(100%)**
Tel.: (626) 768-6000
Web Site: http://www.eastwestbank.com
Sales Range: $75-99.9 Million
Emp.: 200
Federal Savings & Loan
N.A.I.C.S.: 522110
Christopher J. Del Moral-Niles *(CFO & Exec VP)*
Irene H. Oh *(Chief Risk Officer & Exec VP)*
Dominic Ng *(Chm & CEO)*

East West Bank (China) Limited   **(1)**
33/F Jin Mao Tower 88 Century Boulevard, Shanghai, 200121, China
Tel.: (86) 2150499999
Web Site: http://www.eastwestbank.com
Commercial Banking Services
N.A.I.C.S.: 522110

EASTERLY GOVERNMENT PROPERTIES, INC.
2001 K St NW Ste 775 N, Washington, DC 20006
Tel.: (202) 595-9500   MD
Web Site:
  https://www.easterlyreit.com
DEA—(NYSE)
Rev.: $293,606,000
Assets: $2,829,385,000
Liabilities: $1,418,403,000
Net Worth: $1,410,982,000
Earnings: $35,562,000

Emp.: 54
Fiscal Year-end: 12/31/22
Real Estate Investment Services
N.A.I.C.S.: 525990
Darrell W. Crate *(Founder & CEO)*
Darrell W. Crate *(CEO)*
Michael P. Ibe *(Vice Chm & Exec VP-Dev & Acquisition)*
Andrew G. Pulliam *(Exec VP-Portfolio Mgmt & Acquisitions)*
Russell A. Dalin *(Sr VP-Asset Mgmt)*
Nick A. Nimerala *(Sr VP & Head-Asset Mgmt)*
Arthur Robertson *(VP-Dev)*
Allison E. Marino *(CFO, Chief Acctg Officer & Exec VP)*
Daniel Morris *(VP-Internal Audit)*
Allison E. Marino *(Chief Acctg Officer & Sr VP)*
Stuart Burns *(Exec VP)*
Daniel Powers *(VP)*
Stephanie Smarr *(VP)*
Ray Blake *(Dir)*
Carthon Davis *(Dir)*
James F. Dunn *(Dir)*
Chevalle Hardison *(Dir)*
Danielle O'Brien *(Dir-Accounting)*
Colin Oppenheimer *(Dir)*
Michael Tonelli *(Dir)*

Subsidiaries:

EGP 2297 Otay LLC   **(1)**
2001 K St NW Ste 775 N, Washington, DC 20006
Tel.: (202) 595-9500
Real Estate Prorperty Leasing Services
N.A.I.C.S.: 531190

USGP Albany DEA, LLC   **(1)**
2001 K St NW Ste 775 N, Washington, DC 20006
Tel.: (202) 741-8400
Emp.: 8
Real Estate Services
N.A.I.C.S.: 531390

USGP Dallas DEA LP   **(1)**
2001 K St NW Ste 775 N, Washington, DC 20006
Tel.: (202) 596-3920
Nonresidential Property Managing Services
N.A.I.C.S.: 531312

EASTERN BANKSHARES, INC.
265 Franklin St, Boston, MA 02110
Tel.: (781) 598-7920   MA
Web Site:
  https://www.easternbank.com
EBC—(NASDAQ)
Rev.: $781,342,000
Assets: $22,646,858,000
Liabilities: $20,175,068,000
Net Worth: $2,471,790,000
Earnings: $199,759,000
Emp.: 2,146
Fiscal Year-end: 12/31/22
Bank Holding Company
N.A.I.C.S.: 551111
Robert F. Rivers *(Chm & CEO)*
Quincy L. Miller *(Pres)*
David Rosato *(CFO & Treas)*
Donald M. Westermann *(CIO & Exec VP)*
Sujata Yadav *(CMO, Chief Product Officer & Exec VP)*
Geogery R. Buscone *(Chief Comml Banking Officer & Exec VP)*
Martha A. Dean *(Exec VP & Sr Dir-Operations)*

Subsidiaries:

Century Bancorp, Inc.   **(1)**
400 Mystic Ave, Medford, MA 02155
Tel.: (781) 391-4000
Web Site: http://www.centurybank.com
Rev.: $149,036,000
Assets: $6,358,834,000
Liabilities: $5,988,425,000
Net Worth: $370,409,000

Eastern Bankshares, Inc.—(Continued)

Earnings: $42,209,000
Emp.: 418
Fiscal Year-end: 12/31/2020
Bank Holding Company
N.A.I.C.S.: 551111
David B. Woonton (Exec VP-Century Bank & Trust Company)
Richard L. Billig (Exec VP)
Jason J. Melius (Exec VP)
James M. Flynn Jr. (Exec VP)

Eastern Bank   (1)
265 Franklin St, Boston, MA 02110
Tel.: (617) 897-1101
Commericial Banking
N.A.I.C.S.: 522110
Robert F. Rivers (Chm, Pres, CEO, COO & Chief Banking Officer)
Quincy L. Miller (Vice Chm)
Sujata Yadav (CMO & Exec VP)
Kathleen C. Henry (Chief HR Officer)
Matthew A. Osborne (Exec VP)
Donald M. Westermann (Exec VP)

EASTERN GOLDFIELDS, INC.
303 Robeson St, Fall River, MA 02720
Tel.: (512) 850-9131   NV
Year Founded: 2005
EGDD—(OTCIQ)
Gold Mining Services
N.A.I.C.S.: 212220
John Michael Johnson (Pres, CEO, CFO & Sec)

EASTERN MICHIGAN FINANCIAL CORP
37 N Howard Ave, Croswell, MI 48422
Tel.: (810) 679-3620
Web Site: https://www.emb.bank
Year Founded: 1984
EFIN—(OTCIQ)
Sales Range: $10-24.9 Million
Emp.: 87
State Commercial Banks
N.A.I.C.S.: 522110

Subsidiaries:

Eastern Michigan Bank   (1)
65 N Howard Ave, Croswell, MI 48422
Tel.: (810) 679-2500
Web Site:
  http://www.easternmichiganbank.com
Rev.: $3,222,112
Emp.: 150
State Trust Companies Accepting Deposits, Commercial
N.A.I.C.S.: 522110
Timothy M. Ward (Vice Chm & CEO)
Earl E. DesJardins (Chm)
Errin M. McMillan (CFO & VP)
Julie A. Chapdelaine (Officer-Bank Secrecy Act)
Rachel L. Galbraith (Officer-Comml Loan)
Alexander J. Messing (Officer-Comml Loan)
William G. Oldford Jr. (Pres)

EASTGROUP PROPERTIES, INC.
400 W Pkwy Pl Ste 100, Ridgeland, MS 39157
Tel.: (601) 354-3555   MD
Web Site: https://www.eastgroup.net
Year Founded: 1969
EGP—(NYSE)
Rev.: $570,591,000
Assets: $4,519,213,000
Liabilities: $1,910,579,000
Net Worth: $2,608,634,000
Earnings: $200,491,000
Emp.: 96
Fiscal Year-end: 12/31/23
Real Estate Investment Trust
N.A.I.C.S.: 525990
Brent W. Wood (CFO, Treas & Exec VP)
John F. Coleman (Exec VP & Head-Eastern Reg)

William D. Gray (VP-Property Mgmt)
Brian Laird (CIO)
Michael P. Sacco (VP-Ops Phoenix, Tucson & Las Vegas markets)
Staci H. Tyler (Chief Acctg Officer, Sec & Sr VP)
David Y. Hicks (VP-Ops-Austin, Dallas & San Antonio Markets)
Farrah Kennedy (VP & Dir-Internal Audit)
Kevin M. Sager (VP-Ops-Houston, El Paso & New Orleans Markets)
Marshall A. Loeb (Pres & CEO)
Ryan M. Collins (Sr VP & Head-Western Reg)
R. Reid Dunbar (Sr VP & Head-Texas)
Michelle Rayner (VP & Controller)
Barry T. Anderson (VP-Property Acctg)
Stephanie Shaw (VP-Dev Acctg)
John I. Ratliff (VP-Ops-Atlanta, Greenville & Charlotte markets)

EASTMAN CHEMICAL COMPANY
200 S Wilcox Dr, Kingsport, TN 37660
Tel.: (423) 229-2000   DE
Web Site: https://www.eastman.com
Year Founded: 1920
EMN—(NYSE)
Rev.: $9,210,000,000
Assets: $14,633,000,000
Liabilities: $9,103,000,000
Net Worth: $5,530,000,000
Earnings: $894,000,000
Emp.: 14,000
Fiscal Year-end: 12/31/23
Fine Chemicals Mfr
N.A.I.C.S.: 325998
Brad A. Lich (Chief Comml Officer)
Mark J. Costa (Chm, Pres & CEO)
Mark K. Cox (Chief Mfg & Engrg Officer & Sr VP)
Kellye L. Walker (Chief Legal Officer & Exec VP)
Michelle R. Stewart (Chief Acctg Officer, VP & Controller)
Travis Smith (Sr VP-Additives & Functional Products)
William T. McLain Jr. (CFO & Sr VP)

Subsidiaries:

CP Films Vertriebs GmbH   (1)
Katzbergstrasse 1a, 40764, Langenfeld, Germany
Tel.: (49) 21739935000
Chemical & Allied Product Whslr
N.A.I.C.S.: 424690

Commonwealth Laminating & Coating (Hong Kong) Limited   (1)
Sun Hing Flat 5 LG8Tsing Yeung Circuit, Tak Lee Industrial Center, Tuen Mun, China (Hong Kong)
Tel.: (852) 24689702
Plastic Material & Resin Mfr
N.A.I.C.S.: 325211

Commonwealth Laminating & Coating (Shanghai) Co., Ltd.   (1)
No 391 Wen'er Road, Hangzhou, China
Tel.: (86) 57188306601
Plastic Material & Resin Mfr
N.A.I.C.S.: 325211
Jacob Johnsen (Acct Mgr)

Commonwealth Laminating & Coating, Inc.   (1)
345 Beaver Creek Dr, Martinsville, VA 24112
Tel.: (276) 632-4991
Web Site:
  http://www.commonwealthlaminating.com
Solar Control Window Film Mfr
N.A.I.C.S.: 334413

Eastman (Shanghai) Chemical Commercial Co., Ltd.   (1)

No 7 Lane 887 Zuchongzhi Road Zhangjiang High-Tech Park, Shanghai, 201203, China
Tel.: (86) 2138764555
Other Chemical Allied Products Merchant Whslr
N.A.I.C.S.: 424690

Eastman Chemical (China) Co., Ltd.   (1)
Building 3 Yaxin Science & Technology Park Lane 399 Shengxia Road, Pudong New Area, Shanghai, 201210, China
Tel.: (86) 2161208700
Plastic Material & Resin Mfr
N.A.I.C.S.: 325211

Eastman Chemical (China) Co., Ltd.   (1)
Room 703 Taikoo Hui Tower 1 385 Tianhe Road, Tianhe District, Guangzhou, 510620, China
Tel.: (86) 2038682188
Chemical Products Distr
N.A.I.C.S.: 424690
Polly Ma (Sr Mgr-Sls Dev)

Eastman Chemical (Malaysia) Sdn. Bhd.   (1)
Tel.: (60) 95856100
Web Site: http://www.eastman.com
Sales Range: $25-49.9 Million
Emp.: 100
Chemicals Mfr
N.A.I.C.S.: 325998

Eastman Chemical (Nanjing) Co., Ltd.   (1)
No 168 Fenghua Road Nanjing Chemical Industry Park, Luhe District, Nanjing, 210047, Jiangsu, China
Tel.: (86) 2558657783
Chemical Products Distr
N.A.I.C.S.: 424690

Eastman Chemical Advanced Materials B.V.   (1)
Fascinatio Boulevard 602-614, 2909 VA, Capelle aan den IJssel, Netherlands
Tel.: (31) 102402111
Emp.: 130
Chemical & Allied Product Whslr
N.A.I.C.S.: 424690

Eastman Chemical Asia Pacific Pte. Ltd.   (1)
9 North Buona Vista Drive 05-04/05/06 The Metropolis Tower 1, Singapore, 138558, Singapore   (100%)
Tel.: (65) 68313100
Sales Range: $25-49.9 Million
Emp.: 70
Chemical & Allied Products Whslr
N.A.I.C.S.: 424690

Eastman Chemical B.V.   (1)
Watermanweg 70, 3067 GG, Rotterdam, Netherlands
Tel.: (31) 10 240 2111
Web Site: http://www.eastman.com
Sales Range: $150-199.9 Million
Emp.: 150
Chemicals Mfr
N.A.I.C.S.: 325998

Subsidiary (Non-US):

Eastman Chemical Italia S.r.l.   (2)
Via Ippolito Rosellini 12, Milan, 20124, Italy
Tel.: (39) 02 6991 151
Web Site: http://www.eastman.com
Sales Range: $150-199.9 Million
Emp.: 8
Chemical Products Sales
N.A.I.C.S.: 424690
Roberto Aroldi (Mng Dir)

Eastman Chemical B.V., The Hague, Zug Branch   (1)
Hertizentrum 6, 6300, Zug, Switzerland
Tel.: (41) 417266100
Chemical Products Mfr
N.A.I.C.S.: 325998

Eastman Chemical Barcelona, S.L.   (1)
Ctra C-35 Km 61, La Batlloria Sant Celoni, 08476, Barcelona, Spain
Tel.: (34) 938470011
Chemical Products Mfr

N.A.I.C.S.: 325998
Joan Llorenc Iglesias Campeny (Area Mgr)

Eastman Chemical Canada, Inc.   (1)
5915 Airport Rd Suite 602, Mississauga, L4V 1T1, ON, Canada
Tel.: (905) 405-0908
Sales Range: $10-24.9 Million
Emp.: 2
Chemical & Allied Products Whslr
N.A.I.C.S.: 424690

Eastman Chemical Company   (1)
300 Kodak Blvd, Longview, TX 75602   (100%)
Tel.: (903) 237-5000
Web Site: http://www.eastman.com
Sales Range: $900-999.9 Million
Emp.: 1,500
Texanol Ester Alcohol & Other Related Chemicals Mfr
N.A.I.C.S.: 325998

Eastman Chemical Company Foundation, Inc.   (1)
100 Eastman Rd, Kingsport, TN 37660
Tel.: (423) 229-2000
Web Site: http://www.eastman.com
Sales Range: $100-124.9 Million
Emp.: 3,700
Charitable Giving Services
N.A.I.C.S.: 561499

Eastman Chemical Company Investments, Inc.   (1)
103 Foulk Rd, Wilmington, DE 19803
Tel.: (302) 622-9876
Plastic Material & Resin Mfr
N.A.I.C.S.: 325211

Eastman Chemical Company South Carolina Operations   (1)
500 K Ave, Gaston, SC 29053   (100%)
Tel.: (803) 794-9200
Sales Range: $400-449.9 Million
Emp.: 800
Chemical & Man-Made Fiber Mfr
N.A.I.C.S.: 325211

Eastman Chemical Germany GmbH   (1)
Charlottenstrasse 61, Cologne, 51149, Germany
Tel.: (49) 220317050
Plastic Material & Resin Mfr
N.A.I.C.S.: 325211
Michaela Knoop (Mng Dir)

Eastman Chemical GmbH   (1)
Katzbergstrasse 1a, 40764, Langenfeld, Germany
Tel.: (49) 21739935000
Web Site: https://www.eastman.com
Sales Range: $150-199.9 Million
Emp.: 35
Chemical Products
N.A.I.C.S.: 325998

Eastman Chemical HTF GmbH   (1)
Paul-Baumann-Strasse 1, 45772, Marl, Germany
Tel.: (49) 23654986233
Plastic Packing Goods Mfr
N.A.I.C.S.: 326112

Eastman Chemical Iberica, S.L.   (1)
Calle Pinar 5, 28006, Madrid, Spain
Tel.: (34) 917456803
Chemical Products Mfr
N.A.I.C.S.: 325000

Eastman Chemical India Private Limited   (1)
801-804 Powai Plaza, Central Avenue Hiranandani Business Park Powai, Mumbai, 400 076, India
Tel.: (91) 2267519000
Plastic Material & Resin Mfr
N.A.I.C.S.: 325211
Vishal Kolhe (Bus Mgr)

Eastman Chemical International AG   (1)
Hertizentrum 6, PO Box 3263, 6303, Zug, Switzerland
Tel.: (41) 7275800
Web Site: http://www.eastman.com

Sales Range: $10-24.9 Million
Emp.: 20
Chemical Products Mfr
N.A.I.C.S.: 325998

Eastman Chemical International GmbH (1)
Hertizentrum 6, 6303, Zug, Switzerland
Tel.: (41) 417275800
Plastic Material & Resin Mfr
N.A.I.C.S.: 325211

Eastman Chemical Japan Limited (1)
BIZCORE Shibuya 3F 1-3-15 Shibuya, Shibuya-ku, Tokyo, 150-0002, Japan
Tel.: (81) 354697600
Sales Range: $150-199.9 Million
Chemical Products
N.A.I.C.S.: 424690

Eastman Chemical Korea Ltd. (1)
6th Floor S-Tower 82 Saemoonan-Ro, Jongno-Gu, Seoul, 110-700, Korea (South)
Tel.: (82) 2 720 1103
Web Site: http://www.eastman.com
Sales Range: $50-74.9 Million
Emp.: 17
Chemical Products
N.A.I.C.S.: 424690

Eastman Chemical Middelburg, B.V. (1)
Herculesweg 35, 4338 PL, Middelburg, Netherlands
Tel.: (31) 118678000
Web Site: http://www.eastman.com
Sales Range: $150-199.9 Million
Emp.: 240
Chemical Products Mfr
N.A.I.C.S.: 325998

Eastman Chemical Products Singapore Pte. Ltd. (1)
9 North Buona Vista Drive 13 Queenstown, Singapore, Singapore
Tel.: (65) 68313100
Chemical Products Mfr
N.A.I.C.S.: 325998

Eastman Chemical Resins, Inc. (1)
2200 State Rt 837, Jefferson Hills, PA 15025
Tel.: (412) 384-2520
Web Site: http://www.eastman.com
Plastics Material & Resin Mfr
N.A.I.C.S.: 325211

Eastman Chemical Singapore Pte. Ltd. (1)
50 Sakra Avenue, Singapore, 627891, Singapore
Tel.: (65) 62636800
Web Site: http://www.eastman.com
Sales Range: $25-49.9 Million
Emp.: 100
Chemical Products Mfr
N.A.I.C.S.: 325998

Eastman Chemical Texas City, Inc. (1)
201 Bay St S, Texas City, TX 77590
Tel.: (409) 945-4431
Plastic Material & Resin Mfr
N.A.I.C.S.: 325211
Debra Pease (Mgr-HSE)

Eastman Chemical Uruapan, S.A. de C.V. (1)
Paseo General Lazaro Cardenas No 844, Col La Magdalena, 60080, Uruapan, Michoacan, Mexico
Tel.: (52) 4525244420
Web Site: http://www.eastman.com
Emp.: 50
Chemical Products Mfr
N.A.I.C.S.: 325180

Eastman Chemical Workington Limited (1)
Siddick, Workington, CA14 1LG, Cumbria, United Kingdom
Tel.: (44) 1900609236
Web Site: http://www.eastman.com
Sales Range: $150-199.9 Million
Emp.: 170
Chemical & Allied Product Whslr
N.A.I.C.S.: 424690

Eastman Chemical do Brasil Ltda. (1)

Rua Alexandre Dumas 1711 Cj 701, Chacara Santo Antonio, Sao Paulo, 04717-004, SP, Brazil
Tel.: (55) 1135791800
Chemical Products Sales
N.A.I.C.S.: 424690

Eastman Cogeneration L.P. (1)
Hwy 149 Kodak Blvd, Longview, TX 75602 **(100%)**
Tel.: (903) 237-5333
Web Site: http://www.eastman.com
Plastic Material & Resin Mfr
N.A.I.C.S.: 325211

Eastman Company UK Limited (1)
Corporation Road, Newport, NP19 4XF, United Kingdom
Tel.: (44) 1633754200
Sales Range: $10-24.9 Million
Emp.: 29
Chemical & Allied Product Whslr
N.A.I.C.S.: 424690

Eastman Espana S.L. (1)
Edificio Kodak Ctra Nal 6 Km 23, Las Rozas, 28230, Madrid, Spain **(100%)**
Tel.: (34) 900973121
Web Site: http://www.eastman.com
Sales Range: $100-124.9 Million
Printing Ink Mfr
N.A.I.C.S.: 325998

Eastman Fibers Korea, Ltd. (1)
234 Yongyeon-ro, Nam-Gu, Ulsan, 44784, Korea (South)
Tel.: (82) 52 701 1600
Web Site: http://www.eastman.com
Emp.: 100
Tobacco Product Mfr
N.A.I.C.S.: 312230

Eastman France S.a.r.l. (1)
Tour Pacific 11-13 Cours Valmy, Paris La Defense, 92977, Paris, Cedex, France
Tel.: (33) 149682000
Chemical Products Distr
N.A.I.C.S.: 424690

Eastman MFG Japan Ltd. (1)
1 Sunayama, Kamisu, 314-0255, Ibaraki, Japan
Tel.: (81) 479463521
Rubber Tire Chemical Product Mfr
N.A.I.C.S.: 325998

Eastman Mazzucchelli Plastics (Shenzhen) Company Limited (1)
No 3 Building Longquan Science & Technology Park Huarong Rd Dalang St, Longhua New District, Shenzhen, China
Tel.: (86) 75561132791
Cellulose Acetate Pellet Mfr
N.A.I.C.S.: 325211
Chun Mei Peng (Gen Mgr)

Eastman Servicios Corporativos, S.A. de C.V. (1)
Av Insurgentes Sur 1605 Piso 23 Damas Y Mercaderes, San Jose Insurgentes, 03900, Mexico, Mexico
Tel.: (52) 5556629962
Web Site: http://www.mx.eastman.com
Sales Range: $50-74.9 Million
Emp.: 200
Chemical & Allied Product Whslr
N.A.I.C.S.: 424690

Eastman Shuangwei Fibers Company Limited (1)
No 3988 Lianhua Road, Economic and Technological Development Zone, Hefei, Anhui, China
Acetate Tow Mfr
N.A.I.C.S.: 325220

Eastman Specialties AS (1)
Uus-Tehase 8, 30328, Kohtla-Jarve, Estonia
Tel.: (372) 3325900
Web Site: http://www.eastman.com
Sales Range: $50-74.9 Million
Emp.: 14
Chemical Product Whslr
N.A.I.C.S.: 424690

Eastman Specialties Corporation (1)
10380 Worton Rd, Chestertown, MD 21620
Tel.: (410) 778-1991
Other Chemical Allied Products Merchant Whslr

N.A.I.C.S.: 424490

Eastman Specialties OU (1)
Uus Tehase 8, 30328, Kohtla-Jarve, Estonia
Tel.: (372) 3325900
Plastic Material & Resin Mfr
N.A.I.C.S.: 325211
Hannes Reinula (Mgr-Site)

Flexsys America Co. (1)
575 Maryville Centre Dr, Saint Louis, MO 63141
Tel.: (314) 674-1000
Plastic Material & Resin Mfr
N.A.I.C.S.: 325211

Genovique Specialties Wuhan Youji Chemical Co., Ltd. (1)
10 Gongnong Road, Qiaokou District, Wuhan, 430035, Hubei, China
Tel.: (86) 27 8341 2932
Chemical & Allied Products Whslr
N.A.I.C.S.: 424690

Huper Optik International Pte. Ltd. (1)
05-01 The Metropolis Tower 1, 9 North Buona Vista Drive, Singapore, 138588, Singapore
Tel.: (65) 68313064
Automotive Repair & Maintenance Services
N.A.I.C.S.: 811198

Huper Optik U.S.A., L.P. (1)
13011 Misty Willow Dr, Houston, TX 77070
Tel.: (832) 467-1170
Web Site: https://www.huperoptikusa.com
Automotive Repair & Maintenance Services
N.A.I.C.S.: 811198
Faisal Nazir (CEO)

Industriepark Nienburg GmbH (1)
Grosse Drakenburger Str 93-97, 31582, Nienburg, Germany
Tel.: (49) 50219880
Web Site: http://www.industriepark-nienburg.de
Automotive Repair & Maintenance Services
N.A.I.C.S.: 811198

Knowlton Technologies LLC (1)
213 Factory St, Watertown, NY 13601
Tel.: (315) 782-0600
Web Site: https://www.knowlton-co.com
Sales Range: $1-9.9 Million
Emp.: 130
Wet-Laid Nonwovens Designer & Mfr
N.A.I.C.S.: 322120
Jamie Lee (VP-New Bus & Tech)
Kirk Denny (Mgr-Friction-Sls)
A. J. Garza (Mgr-Sls & Mktg)

Nanjing Yangzi Eastman Chemical Ltd. (1)
5th Floor B/Research Development BLD 2 Lijing Road, New High Tech Development Zone, Nanjing, 210061, China
Tel.: (86) 256 660 9268
Web Site: https://www.njyec.com.cn
Emp.: 87
Chemical Products Mfr
N.A.I.C.S.: 325998

Novomatrix International Trading (Shanghai) Co. Ltd. (1)
Room 1602 Xu Hui Jing Dian Tower, No 2281 Zhong Shan Xi Road, Shanghai, 200235, China
Tel.: (86) 2151105595
Web Site: http://www.nanolux.com
International Trade Financing Services
N.A.I.C.S.: 522299

Qilu Eastman Specialty Chemicals Ltd. (1)
6-1 Xinhua Road Linzi, Zibo, 255400, Shandong, China
Tel.: (86) 533 7512705
Web Site: http://www.eastmanchemical.com
Sales Range: $25-49.9 Million
Emp.: 70
Chemical Products Mfr
N.A.I.C.S.: 325998

Scandiflex do Brasil Ltda. (1)
Avenida Papa Joao XXIII 4502 Sertaozinho, Maua, 09370-904, Sao Paulo, Brazil
Tel.: (55) 1145129710
Chemical Products Mfr
N.A.I.C.S.: 325998

Shanghai Eastman Consulting Company Ltd. (1)
Building 3 Lane 399 Shengxia Road, Shanghai, 201210, Pudong, China
Tel.: (86) 2161208700
Web Site: http://www.eastman.com
Sales Range: $10-24.9 Million
Emp.: 50
Consulting Services
N.A.I.C.S.: 541690

Solutia (Thailand) Ltd. (1)
33/4 The 9th Tower Grand Rama 9 Tower A 24th Fl TNA 05, Rama 9 Rd Huaykwang, Bangkok, 10310, Thailand
Tel.: (66) 21189700
Chemical Products Mfr
N.A.I.C.S.: 325998

Solutia Argentina S.R.L. (1)
Alicia Moreau de Justo 1960 Oficina 203, Buenos Aires, C1107AFN, Argentina
Tel.: (54) 1153536613
Chemical Products Mfr
N.A.I.C.S.: 325998

Solutia Australia Pty. Ltd. (1)
101 Thomson Road, 19-01/02 United Square, Singapore, 307591, Singapore
Tel.: (65) 63576213
Chemical Products Mfr
N.A.I.C.S.: 325998
Geoff Rankin (Mgr-Comml)

Solutia Europe BVBA/SPRL (1)
Ottergemsesteenweg Zuid 707, 9000, Gent, Belgium
Tel.: (32) 92436211
Laminated Glass Product Mfr
N.A.I.C.S.: 327215

Solutia Hong Kong Limited (1)
101 Thomson Road, 19-01/02 United Square, Singapore, 307591, Singapore
Tel.: (65) 63576155
Chemical Products Mfr
N.A.I.C.S.: 325998

Solutia Hong Kong Limited (1)
Unit 1001 10/F Mira Place Tower A 132 Nathan Road, Tsimshatsui, Kowloon, China (Hong Kong)
Tel.: (852) 25656373
Chemical Products Distr
N.A.I.C.S.: 424690

Solutia Inc. (1)
575 Maryville Centre Dr, Saint Louis, MO 63141
Tel.: (314) 674-1000
Web Site: http://www.solutia.com
Sales Range: $1-4.9 Billion
Emp.: 3,400
Detergent, Rubber, Specialty Chemicals, Man-Made Fibers, Plastics, Resins, Elastomers, Pharmaceuticals & Fabricated Products
N.A.I.C.S.: 325211

Subsidiary (Domestic):

CPFilms Inc. (2)
4210 The Great Rd, Fieldale, VA 24089 **(100%)**
Tel.: (276) 627-3000
Web Site: http://www.cpfilms.com
Sales Range: $125-149.9 Million
Emp.: 600
Window Films
N.A.I.C.S.: 326113

Subsidiary (Non-US):

Flexsys SA/NV (2)
Woluwedal 24, Leonardo Da Vinci Lane 1, 1932, Zaventem, Belgium **(100%)**
Tel.: (32) 27143257
Web Site: http://www.solutia.com
Sales Range: $700-749.9 Million
Emp.: 100
Supplier of Chemicals for the Rubber Industrial
N.A.I.C.S.: 325998

Subsidiary (Non-US):

Flexsys (3)
Zona Industriale A SNC, 86039, Termoli, CB, Italy
Tel.: (39) 0875751714

Eastman Chemical Company—(Continued)

Sales Range: $150-199.9 Million
Rubber Chemicals
N.A.I.C.S.: 325998

Subsidiary (US):

Flexsys America L.P. **(3)**
500 Monsanto Ave, Sauget, IL
62206-1198 **(100%)**
Tel.: (618) 271-5835
Web Site: http://www.eastman.com
Sales Range: $25-49.9 Million
Emp.: 40
Reclaimed Rubber & Specialty Rubber
Compounds
N.A.I.C.S.: 326299

Subsidiary (Non-US):

Flexsys Chemicals (M) Sdn Bhd **(3)**
Lot 118 119 Jalan Gebeng 2/4, Gebeng In-
dustrial Estate, Kuantan, 26080, Pahang
Darul, Malaysia
Tel.: (60) 95856100
Mfr of Chemicals for Rubber Industry
N.A.I.C.S.: 325998

Flexsys Verkauf GmbH **(3)**
Grosse Drakenburgerstrasse 93-97, PO
Box 1440, 31582, Nienburg, Germany
Tel.: (49) 5021988334
Distr of Chemicals Used for Rubber Manu-
facturing & Rubber Articles
N.A.I.C.S.: 424690

Subsidiary (Non-US):

Solutia Brasil Ltda. **(2)**
Rua Alexandre Dumas 1711 Cj 701, 04717-
004, Sao Paulo, 04717-004, SP, Brazil
Tel.: (55) 1135791800
Chemical & Allied Product Whslr
N.A.I.C.S.: 424690

Solutia Europe SPRL/BVBA **(2)**
Scheldelaan 460, 2040, Antwerp,
Belgium **(100%)**
Tel.: (32) 35685111
Sales Range: $25-49.9 Million
Emp.: 70
Specialty Chemical Products
N.A.I.C.S.: 325998

Solutia Performance Products (Su-
zhou) Co., Ltd. **(2)**
No 129 Wang Jiang Road, Weiting Town
SIP, Suzhou, 215121, China
Tel.: (86) 51266968302
Chemicals Mfr
N.A.I.C.S.: 325998

Solutia Solar GmbH **(2)**
Industriestrasse 3, 89165, Dietenheim, Ger-
many
Tel.: (49) 734792230
Chemical & Allied Product Whslr
N.A.I.C.S.: 424690

Solutia Therminol Co., Ltd. **(2)**
No 825 Zhujiang Road, Suzhou New Dis-
trict, Suzhou, 215011, Jiangsu,
China **(60%)**
Tel.: (86) 51266628764
Emp.: 50
Fluid Power Transmission Equipment Mfr
N.A.I.C.S.: 423830

Solutia Tlaxcala S.A. de C.V. **(2)**
Km 32 5 Carretera Tlaxcala-Puebla Santo
Toribio, Xicohtzinco, 90780, Tlaxcala,
Mexico **(100%)**
Tel.: (52) 2222237100
Sales Range: $150-199.9 Million
Chemical & Allied Product Whslr
N.A.I.C.S.: 424690

Solutia U.K. Limited **(2)**
Corporation Road, South Wales, Newport,
NP19 4XF, Gwent, United Kingdom
Tel.: (44) 1633754200
Chemical Products Mfr
N.A.I.C.S.: 325998
Steve Hampson *(Mgr)*

Subsidiary (Domestic):

Southwall Technologies Inc. **(2)**
3788 Fabian Way, Palo Alto, CA 94303
Tel.: (650) 798-1200
Web Site: http://www.eastman.com

Sales Range: $25-49.9 Million
Emp.: 145
Thin-Film Coatings Mfr on Flexible Sub-
strates, Designer, Developer & Marketer
N.A.I.C.S.: 326113

Subsidiary (Domestic):

Crown Operations International,
Ltd. **(3)**
347 Business Park Dr, Sun Prairie, WI
53590
Tel.: (608) 837-7771
Web Site: http://www.eastman.com
Sales Range: $25-49.9 Million
Emp.: 15
Laminated Plastics Plate & Sheet Mfr
N.A.I.C.S.: 326130

Solutia Italia S.r.l. **(1)**
Via Agnello 8, Milan, 20121, Italy
Tel.: (39) 0248024841
Web Site: http://www.solutiapack.com
Chemical & Allied Product Whslr
N.A.I.C.S.: 424690
Eraldo Della Santa *(CEO)*
Silvia Spadotto *(Mgr-Sls)*

Solutia Japan Limited **(1)**
Sowa Bldg 7F 2-3-6 Nihonbashi, Kayaba-
cho Chuo-ku, Tokyo, 103-0025, Japan
Tel.: (81) 3 5847 7180
Chemical & Allied Product Whslr
N.A.I.C.S.: 424690
Daisuke Koyama *(Mgr-Comml)*

Solutia Singapore Pte. Ltd. **(1)**
101 Thomson Road, 19-04/05 United
Square, Singapore, 307591, Singapore
Tel.: (65) 63576100
Chemical & Allied Product Whslr
N.A.I.C.S.: 424690

Solutia UK Investments Ltd. **(1)**
Corporation Road, Newport, NP19 4XF,
Gwent, United Kingdom
Tel.: (44) 1633278221
Chemical & Allied Products Whslr
N.A.I.C.S.: 424690

Solutia Venezuela, S.R.L. **(1)**
Rua Gomes de Carvalho, 1306 - 6 Andar,
04547-005, Sao Paulo, Brazil
Tel.: (55) 4123403675
Chemical Products Mfr
N.A.I.C.S.: 325998

Southwall Europe GmbH **(1)**
Southwallstrasse 1, 01900, Grossrohrsdorf,
Germany
Tel.: (49) 35952440
Chemical Products Mfr
N.A.I.C.S.: 325998
Joris Paul Kuijpers *(Mng Dir)*

St. Gabriel CC Company, LLC **(1)**
3830 Hwy 30, Saint Gabriel, LA 70776
Tel.: (626) 287-9671
Chemical Products Mfr
N.A.I.C.S.: 325998

SunTek Australia Pty. Ltd. **(1)**
Unit 4/40 Carrington Road, Castle Hill,
2154, NSW, Australia
Tel.: (61) 296346377
Web Site: https://www.suntekfilms.com
Chemical & Allied Product Whslr
N.A.I.C.S.: 424690

SunTek Europe GmbH **(1)**
Wahlerstrasse 18, 40472, Dusseldorf, Ger-
many
Tel.: (49) 2114155450
Chemical Products Mfr
N.A.I.C.S.: 325998
Owen Lloyd *(Mgr-Comml)*

SunTek Films Canada, Inc. **(1)**
3620 B Laird Rd Ste 9, Mississauga, L5L
6A9, ON, Canada
Tel.: (855) 569-2221
Web Site: http://www.suntekfilms.com
Chemical Products Mfr
N.A.I.C.S.: 325998

SunTek UK Limited **(1)**
Tel.: (44) 1279419191
Web Site: https://www.suntekfilms.com
Chemical Product & Preparation Mfr
N.A.I.C.S.: 325998

Taminco Argentina SA **(1)**
Av Libertador 2442, Piso 4 Olivos,
B1636DSR, Buenos Aires, Argentina
Tel.: (54) 1147118717
Chemical Products Mfr
N.A.I.C.S.: 325998

Taminco BVBA **(1)**
Pantserschipstraat 207, 9000, Gent, Bel-
gium
Tel.: (32) 92541411
Chemical Products Mfr
N.A.I.C.S.: 325998
Chee Yong Liew *(Bus Mgr)*

Taminco Choline Chloride (Shanghai)
Co., Ltd. **(1)**
Zhuang Hang W Fengxian, Shanghai,
201415, China
Tel.: (86) 2157466585
Chemical Products Mfr
N.A.I.C.S.: 325998

Taminco Finland Oy **(1)**
Typpitie 1, 90620, Oulu, Finland
Tel.: (358) 207108300
Chemical & Allied Product Whslr
N.A.I.C.S.: 424690

Taminco Germany GmbH **(1)**
Am Haupttor Bau 8314, 06237, Leuna, Ger-
many
Tel.: (49) 3461434502
Chemical Products Mfr
N.A.I.C.S.: 325998
Joris Paul Kuijpers *(Mng Dir)*

Taminco Global Chemical
Corporation **(1)**
7540 Windsor Dr Ste 411, Allentown, PA
18195
Tel.: (610) 366-6730
Chemical Products Mfr
N.A.I.C.S.: 325998

Taminco UK Limited **(1)**
36 Leigh Road, Eastleigh, SO50 9DT,
United Kingdom
Tel.: (44) 2380641826
Chemical Products Mfr
N.A.I.C.S.: 325998

Taminco do Brasil Comercio e Indus-
tria de Aminas Ltda. **(1)**
Rua Nafta 717 Polo Petroquimico, Cama-
cari, 42810-210, Bahia, Brazil
Tel.: (55) 71 3642 8059
Chemical & Allied Product Whslr
N.A.I.C.S.: 424690

Taminco do Brazil Produtos Quimicos
Ltda. **(1)**
Alameda Santos 211 - 1905 Cerqueira Ce-
sar, 01419-000, Sao Paulo, Brazil
Tel.: (55) 1135091700
Chemical Products Mfr
N.A.I.C.S.: 325998

Tennessee Eastman Division **(1)**
200 S Wilcox Dr, Kingsport, TN
37660 **(100%)**
Tel.: (423) 229-2000
Web Site: http://www.eastman.com
Sales Range: $1-4.9 Billion
Chemicals, Fibers & Plastics Mfr
N.A.I.C.S.: 325211

V-Kool International Pte. Ltd. **(1)**
9 North Buona Vista Drive The Metropolis
Tower 1 5-01, Singapore, 138588, Singa-
pore
Tel.: (65) 62760555
Web Site: http://www.v-kool.com.sg
Chemical Product & Preparation Mfr
N.A.I.C.S.: 325998

aminco Choline Chloride (Shanghai)
Co., Ltd. **(1)**
Zhuang Hang W, Shanghai, 201415, China
Tel.: (86) 2157466585
Chemical Products Mfr
N.A.I.C.S.: 325998

EASTMAN KODAK COMPANY
343 State St, Rochester, NY 14650
Tel.: (585) 724-4000 NJ
Web Site: https://www.kodak.com
Year Founded: 1880

KODK—(NYSE)
Rev.: $1,205,000,000
Assets: $2,285,000,000
Liabilities: $1,244,000,000
Net Worth: $1,041,000,000
Earnings: $26,000,000
Emp.: 4,200
Fiscal Year-end: 12/31/22
B2B Commercial Imaging, Packaging
& Functional Printing Solutions Devel-
oper, Marketer & Mfr
N.A.I.C.S.: 333310
Terry R. Taber *(CTO, Sr VP-*
Advanced Materials & Chemicals &
VP)
James V. Continenza *(Exec Chm &*
CEO)
Kim E. VanGelder *(CIO)*
David E. Bullwinkle *(CFO, Pres-*
Eastman Bus Park & Sr VP)
Randy D. Vandagriff *(Sr VP-Digital*
Print & VP)
Roger W. Byrd *(Gen Counsel, Sec &*
Sr VP)
Todd Bigger *(VP-Print)*
Steven Bellamy *(Pres-Motion Picture*
& Entertainment)
Cumar Sreekumar *(VP-Advanced*
Materials & Chemicals & Dir-
Advanced Technologies)
Jeff Zellmer *(VP-Sls & Strategy-*
Global)
Matthew C. Ebersold *(Treas)*
Richard Michaels *(Chief Acctg Officer*
& Controller)
Laura Cole *(VP)*
Jim Barnes *(Chief IT Implementation*
Officer)
Denisse Goldbarg *(CMO)*
Jeanne Hilley *(VP)*
Jenine Rose-Johnson *(VP)*
Paul Dils *(VP)*

Subsidiaries:

BASO Precision Optics Ltd. **(1)**
14 Chien-Kuo Road Taichung Export Pro-
cessing Zone Tantzu, Tantzu Hsiang, Taic-
hung, Taiwan
Tel.: (886) 425320168
Web Site: http://www.baso.com.tw
Sales Range: $100-124.9 Million
Emp.: 300
Camera Lenses Mfr
N.A.I.C.S.: 333310

ESL Federal Credit Union **(1)**
225 Chestnut St, Rochester, NY 14604
Tel.: (585) 336-1000
Web Site: https://www.esl.org
Sales Range: $800-899.9 Million
Credit Union
N.A.I.C.S.: 522130
Casey Saucke *(Sr Mgr-Comml Real Estate*
Rels)
Francene Alexander *(Mgr-Cobblestone)*
Faheem A. Masood *(Pres & CEO)*
Joseph S. Buscaglia *(CIO, Sr VP & Dir-Sys*
& Tech)
Keith E. Cleary *(Sr VP & Dir-Bus Banking)*
Marcelina Nobrega Courtney *(Sr VP & Dir-*
Retail Banking)
Theodore T. Heinrich *(VP & Dir-Audit)*
Leo Iacobelli *(Sr VP & Dir-Wealth Mgmt)*
Celeste A. Kier *(Sr VP & Dir-Mktg & Cus-*
tomer Experience)
Steven G. Schmidt *(VP & Dir-Credit Mgmt &*
Admin)
Maureen R. Wolfe *(Sr VP & Dir-HR & Com-*
munity Impact)
Caytie Bowser *(VP & Dir-Product Dev &*
Mgmt)
Ajamu Kitwana *(VP & Dir-Community Im-*
pact)
Tina M. Knapp *(VP & Dir-Payments & Svc*
Support)
Jeremy Newman *(VP & Deputy Gen Coun-*
sel)
Tony Holmes *(VP/Dir-Mortgage Lending)*
Edward French *(VP)*
James Miller *(VP)*

Eastman Kodak Holdings B.V. **(1)**

De Kronkels 16 A Spakenburg, Postbus 56, 3752 LM, Bunschoten, Netherlands **(100%)**
Tel.: (31) 206545257
Web Site: http://www.kodak.nl
Sales Range: $1-9.9 Million
Emp.: 2
Photographic Equipment & Services
N.A.I.C.S.: 512110

Subsidiary (Non-US):

Kodak IL Ltd **(2)**
Hatnufa 7, 49002, Petach Tikva, Israel
Tel.: (972) 3 916 7222
Web Site: http://www.kodak.com
Printing Equipment Mfr
N.A.I.C.S.: 333248

Eastman Kodak International Capital Company, Inc. **(1)**
343 State St, Rochester, NY 14650-0001
Tel.: (800) 698-3324
Web Site: http://www.kodak.com
Sales Range: $50-74.9 Million
Emp.: 1
Financial Services
N.A.I.C.S.: 523999

Eastman Kodak Printing **(1)**
3000 Research Blvd, Dayton, OH 45420
Tel.: (937) 259-3256
Web Site: http://www.kodak.com
Sales Range: $200-249.9 Million
Emp.: 620
Digital Printer Mfr
N.A.I.C.S.: 323111

Graphic Systems Services, Inc. **(1)**
400 S Pioneer Blvd, Springboro, OH 45066
Tel.: (937) 746-0708
Web Site: https://www.gsspress.com
Printing Trades Machinery
N.A.I.C.S.: 333248
Daniel L. Green *(Pres & CEO)*
John Sillies *(Exec VP)*

KODAK Alaris Germany GmbH **(1)**
Hedelfinger Strasse 60, 70327, Stuttgart, Germany **(100%)**
Tel.: (49) 71125281941
Web Site: http://www.kodak.com
Photographic Equipment & Supplies Mfr
N.A.I.C.S.: 333310

Kodak (Australasia) Pty. Ltd. **(1)**
181 Victoria Parade, Collingwood, 3066, VIC, Australia **(100%)**
Tel.: (61) 131514
Web Site: http://www.kodak.com.au
Photographic Equipment Distr
N.A.I.C.S.: 423410

Kodak (China) Ltd. **(1)**
A05 4F Building D CATIC Plaza 15 South Ronghua Rd, Chaoyang District, Beijing, 100022, China
Tel.: (86) 1065616561
Sales Range: $900-999.9 Million
Emp.: 5,000
Photographic Equipment Distr
N.A.I.C.S.: 423410
Ying Yeh *(Chm)*
Ying Yeh *(Chm)*

Kodak (Hong Kong) Limited **(1)**
19th 633 Kings Rd, North Point, China (Hong Kong) **(100%)**
Tel.: (852) 25649333
Web Site: http://www.kodak.com.hk
Sales Range: $50-74.9 Million
Emp.: 200
Photographic Equipment & Supplies
N.A.I.C.S.: 325992

Kodak (Japan) Ltd. **(1)**
KDX Higashi-Shinagawa Bldg 4-10-13 Higashi-Shinagawa, Shinagawa-ku, Tokyo, 140-0002, Japan
Tel.: (81) 5038191470
Web Site: https://www.kodak.com
Photographic Equipment Distr
N.A.I.C.S.: 423410

Subsidiary (Domestic):

K.K. Kodak Information Systems **(2)**
Gotenayama Mori Bldg. 4-7-35 Kita-Shinagawa, Shinagawa-ku, Tokyo, 140, Japan
Tel.: (81) 355402202

Photographic Equipment & Supplies
N.A.I.C.S.: 325998

Kodak Japan Industries Ltd. **(2)**
2-27-1 Shinkawa Chuo-ku Sumitomo Twin Building East, Tokyo, 104-0033, Japan **(100%)**
Tel.: (81) 355402761
Web Site: http://www.kodak.com
Photographic Equipment & Supplies
N.A.I.C.S.: 333310
Hiroshi Fujiwara *(Pres)*

Yamanashi RPB Supply Co. **(2)**
2-9 Kandasurugadai, Chiyoda-ku, Tokyo, 101-0062, Japan
Tel.: (81) 3 5282 1621
Photographic Equipment Distr
N.A.I.C.S.: 423410

Kodak (Kenya) Limited **(1)**
Funzi Rd, PO Box 18210, Nairobi, Kenya **(100%)**
Tel.: (254) 2530164
Sales Range: $10-24.9 Million
Emp.: 40
Photographic Equipment & Supplies
N.A.I.C.S.: 333310

Kodak (Singapore) Pte. Limited **(1)**
151 Lorong Chuan 05-01 New Tech Park, Singapore, 556741, Singapore **(100%)**
Tel.: (65) 63713388
Web Site: http://graphics.kodak.com
Sales Range: $50-74.9 Million
Emp.: 100
Photographic Equipment & Supplies
N.A.I.C.S.: 425120

Kodak (Taiwan) Limited **(1)**
Shin Kong Life Neihu Technology Building 3F 1 No 301 Sector 2, Tiding Boulevard, Taipei, 11493, Taiwan **(100%)**
Tel.: (886) 287518282
Web Site: http://www.kodak.com.tw
Photographic Equipment & Supplies
N.A.I.C.S.: 425120

Kodak (Thailand) Limited **(1)**
41/33 Moo 6, Bang Chalong Subdistrict, Bang Phli, Samut Prakan, Thailand
Tel.: (66) 655193405
Web Site: http://www.kodakthailand.com
Photographic Equipment & Supplies Mfr
N.A.I.C.S.: 425120

Kodak A/S **(1)**
Ny Banegardsgade 55 3 Sal, 8000, Aarhus, Denmark
Tel.: (45) 70260606
Web Site: http://www.kodak.dk
Sales Range: $50-74.9 Million
Emp.: 15
Photographic Equipment & Supplies
N.A.I.C.S.: 423410

Kodak Americas Ltda. **(1)**
Calle 12-C No 76-49 Entrada 2, Parque Industrial VIII Alzacia, Bogota, Colombia
Tel.: (57) 14125550
Web Site: http://www.kodakexpress.co.za
Photographic Equipment & Supplies
N.A.I.C.S.: 333310

Kodak Argentina S.A.I.C. **(1)**
Bonpland 1930, Buenos Aires, C1414CMZ, Argentina
Tel.: (54) 111559894605
Web Site: http://www.kodak.com.ar
Sales Range: $10-24.9 Million
Emp.: 70
Photographic Equipment
N.A.I.C.S.: 333310

Kodak Canada Inc. **(1)**
6 Monogram Pl Ste 200, Toronto, M9R 0A1, ON, Canada **(100%)**
Tel.: (416) 766-8233
Web Site: http://www.kodak.ca
Sales Range: $450-499.9 Million
Emp.: 1,400
Photographic Equipment & Supplies
N.A.I.C.S.: 333310

Kodak Digital Products Center **(1)**
23-11 Naka Oshio, Chino, 391 0293, Nagano, Japan **(59.02%)**
Tel.: (81) 266822000
Sales Range: $100-124.9 Million
Camera Mfr
N.A.I.C.S.: 333310

Kodak Electronic Products (Shanghai) Company Limited **(1)**
Building 8 Jinqiao Office Park 27 Xinjinqiao Road, Pudong, Shanghai, 201206, China
Tel.: (86) 2158841818
Photographic & Photocopying Equipment Mfr
N.A.I.C.S.: 333310

Kodak Gesellschaft m.b.H. **(1)**
Albert Schweitzer Gasse 5, 1140, Vienna, Austria
Tel.: (43) 01970010
Web Site: http://www.kodak.co.at
Sales Range: $25-49.9 Million
Emp.: 300
Photographic Equipment & Supplies
N.A.I.C.S.: 423410

Kodak GmbH **(1)**
Hedelfinger Str 54-60, 70327, Stuttgart, Germany
Tel.: (49) 7114065430
Web Site: http://www.kodak.com
Wide-Format Printer Mfr
N.A.I.C.S.: 323111

Kodak Graphic Communications Canada Company **(1)**
4255 Kincaid St, Burnaby, V5G 4P5, BC, Canada
Tel.: (604) 451-2700
Web Site: http://www.kodak.com
Sales Range: $25-49.9 Million
Emp.: 450
Photographic & Photocopying Equipment Mfr
N.A.I.C.S.: 333310

Kodak Graphic Communications GmbH **(1)**
An der Bahn 80, 37520, Osterode am Hartz, Germany
Tel.: (49) 55229970
Photographic Equipment Distr
N.A.I.C.S.: 423410
Stefan Kull *(Dir-R&D)*

Kodak Graphic Communications Group **(1)**
343 State St, Rochester, NY 14650
Tel.: (585) 724-4000
Web Site: http://www.kodak.com
Printing Software & Supplies
N.A.I.C.S.: 333248

Subsidiary (Non-US):

Kodak Graphic Communications **(2)**
4225 Kincaid Street, Burnaby, V5G 4P5, BC, Canada
Tel.: (604) 451-2700
Web Site: http://www.graphics.kodak.com
Sales Range: $650-699.9 Million
Emp.: 500
Prepress Systems & Digital Solutions Developer & Mfr
N.A.I.C.S.: 333248

Subsidiary (Non-US):

Creo II Ltd. **(3)**
3 Hamada Street, 46103, Herzliyya, Israel
Tel.: (972) 99597222
Web Site: http://graphics.kodak.com
Sales Range: $350-399.9 Million
Prepress Systems & Digital Solutions Developer & Mfr
N.A.I.C.S.: 333248

Subsidiary (US):

Eastman Kodak Company, Small Sales and Cust Serv Office **(3)**
3 Federal St, Billerica, MA 01821-3568
Tel.: (978) 439-7000
Web Site: http://www.graphics.kodak.com
Sales Range: $200-249.9 Million
Prepress Systems & Digital Solutions Developer & Mfr
N.A.I.C.S.: 333248

Subsidiary (Non-US):

Kodak Graphic Communications **(3)**
4-10-13 Higashishinagawa, Shinagawa-ku, Tokyo, 140-0002, Japan
Tel.: (81) 3 6837 7275
Web Site: http://www.kodak.com

Prepress Systems & Digital Solutions Developer & Mfr
N.A.I.C.S.: 333248

Kodak Holding GmbH **(1)**
Hedelfinger Str 54-60, 70327, Stuttgart, Germany
Tel.: (49) 7114065430
Web Site: http://www.kodak.com
Holding Company
N.A.I.C.S.: 551112

Kodak Imaging Network, Inc. **(1)**
1480 64th St Ste 300, Emeryville, CA 94608
Tel.: (510) 229-1200
Web Site: http://www.kodakgallery.com
Sales Range: $75-99.9 Million
Emp.: 300
Online Photography Merchandise & Services
N.A.I.C.S.: 333310

Kodak India Limited **(1)**
Ground Floor Dani Corporate Park 158 Dani Compound, Vidyanagari Marg Kalina Santacruz East, Mumbai, 400 098, Maharashtra, India **(100%)**
Tel.: (91) 2249720222
Web Site: http://www.kodak.com
Sales Range: $25-49.9 Million
Emp.: 100
Photographic Equipment & Supplies
N.A.I.C.S.: 333310

Kodak Korea Ltd. **(1)**
5th Floor DMC Iaan Sangam 2 Danii 1653 Sangam-dong, Mapo-Gu, Seoul, 121-270, Korea (South)
Tel.: (82) 234382625
Web Site: https://www.kodak.co.kr
Photographic Equipment & Supplies
N.A.I.C.S.: 423410

Kodak Limited **(1)**
Building 8 Croxley Green Business Park Hatters Lane, Watford, WD18 8PX, Herts, United Kingdom
Tel.: (44) 8456025991
Web Site: http://www.kodak.co.uk
Sales Range: $100-124.9 Million
Photographic Equipment & Supplies
N.A.I.C.S.: 333310

Kodak Mexicana, S.A. de C.V. **(1)**
Amado Nervo 2200 Torre BIO 301, Ciudad del Sol Distrito La Perla Zapopan, 45050, Mexico, Jalisco, Mexico
Tel.: (52) 333 678 6200
Web Site: http://www.kodak.com
Photographic Equipment Mfr & Distr
N.A.I.C.S.: 334419

Subsidiary (Non-US):

Kodak de Colombia, SAS **(2)**
Carrera 33 25D-20 Oficina 3, Bogota, Colombia
Tel.: (57) 3206788281
Camera Lenses Mfr
N.A.I.C.S.: 333310

Kodak Nederland BV **(1)**
De Maanlander 14-5D, 3824 MP, Amersfoort, Netherlands
Tel.: (31) 20 654 5414
Web Site: http://www.motion.kodak.com
Photographic & Digital Imaging Products Mfr
N.A.I.C.S.: 333310

Kodak New Zealand Limited **(1)**
Auckland 1140, Auckland, New Zealand
Tel.: (64) 800456325
Web Site: http://www.kodak.com
Photographic Equipment & Supplies
N.A.I.C.S.: 423410

Kodak Nordic AB **(1)**
Vallgatan 9, 170 67, Solna, Sweden
Tel.: (46) 855563500
Web Site: http://www.se.kodak.com
Sales Range: $150-199.9 Million
Emp.: 50
Photographic Equipment Distr
N.A.I.C.S.: 423410

Kodak Norge A/S **(1)**
PO Box 507, N-1411, Kolbotn, Norway **(100%)**
Tel.: (47) 66816000

Eastman Kodak Company—(Continued)

Web Site: http://www.kodak.no
Sales Range: $50-74.9 Million
Emp.: 130
Photographic Equipment & Supplies

Kodak OOO (1)
Smolensky Passage Smolenskaya Sq 3
office 9004, 115114, Moscow, Russia
Tel.: (7) 4959378328
Web Site: http://www.kodak.ru
Sales Range: $25-49.9 Million
Emp.: 20
Electric Equipment Mfr
N.A.I.C.S.: 334419

Kodak Oy (1)
Teknobulevardi 3-5, 01530, Vantaa, Finland
Tel.: (358) 46 712 2280
Web Site: http://www.kodak.fi
Sales Range: $125-149.9 Million
Photographic & Digital Imaging Products
Developer, Marketer & Mfr
N.A.I.C.S.: 334118

Kodak Philippines, Ltd. (1)
2901 88 Corporate Center, Makati, 1227,
Metro Manila, Philippines (100%)
Tel.: (63) 28100331
Web Site: http://www.kodak.com.ph
Sales Range: $50-74.9 Million
Emp.: 12
Photographic Equipment Distr
N.A.I.C.S.: 423410

Kodak Rahola, Inc. (1)
208 Ave Ponce De Leon Ste 15, San Juan,
PR 00918-1012
Tel.: (787) 722-0165
Print & Enterprise Inkjet Systems, Micro 3D
Printing & Packaging & Software & Technology Solutions
N.A.I.C.S.: 513210

Kodak S.p.A (1)
Viale Matteotti 62, 20092, Cinisello Balsamo, MI, Italy
Tel.: (39) 0266028304
Web Site: http://www.kodak.com
Sales Range: $150-199.9 Million
Photo Equipment & Supplies Sales
N.A.I.C.S.: 423410

Kodak SA/NV (1)
Excelsiorlaan 87, 1930, Zaventem, Belgium
Tel.: (32) 2 352 2511
Web Site: http://www.kodak.com
Photographic & Digital Imaging Products
Developer, Marketer & Mfr
N.A.I.C.S.: 334118

Kodak Societe Anonyme (1)
Route de Denges 40, 1027, Lonay, Switzerland
Tel.: (41) 223541400
Web Site: http://www.kodak.ch
Sales Range: $150-199.9 Million
Photographic Equipment Distr
N.A.I.C.S.: 423410

Kodak da Amazonia Industria e Comercio Ltda. (1)
Av Dos Oitis 760, Manaus, 69075, Amazonas, Brazil
Tel.: (55) 9236175000
Emp.: 49
Photographic Film Mfr
N.A.I.C.S.: 325992

Kodak de Mexico S.A. de C.V. (1)
Prol Mariano Otero 408 interior 2 Col Ciudad del Sol, CP 45050, Zapopan, Mexico
Tel.: (52) 5553517383
Web Site: http://www.alarisworld.com
Photographic Equipment & Supplies
N.A.I.C.S.: 333310

Kodak, S.A. (1)
Paseo de la Castellana 216 planta 8,
28046, Madrid, Spain
Tel.: (34) 916267100
Web Site: http://www.kodak.com
Photographic Equipment & Supplies
N.A.I.C.S.: 333310

Kodak-Pathe SAS (1)
26 rue Villiot, 75012, Paris, Cedex,
France (100%)
Tel.: (33) 140013000

Web Site: http://www.kodak.fr
Sales Range: $450-499.9 Million
Emp.: 1,239
Photographic Equipment & Supplies
N.A.I.C.S.: 333310

Laser-Pacific Media Corporation (1)
809 N Cahuenga Blvd, Los Angeles, CA 90038
Tel.: (323) 462-6266
Web Site: http://www.laserpacific.com
Emp.: 226
Motion Picture Production Services
N.A.I.C.S.: 512191

EASTSIDE DISTILLING, INC.
2321 NE Argyle Dr Unit D, Portland,
OR 97211
Tel.: (971) 888-4264   NV
Web Site:
https://www.eastsidedistilling.com
Year Founded: 2004
EAST—(NASDAQ)
Rev.: $14,327,000
Assets: $21,476,000
Liabilities: $22,992,000
Net Worth: ($1,516,000)
Earnings: ($16,416,000)
Emp.: 50
Fiscal Year-end: 12/31/22
Bourbon, Whiskey, Rum & Vodka
Distiller
N.A.I.C.S.: 312140
Geoffrey C. Gwin (CEO & CFO)

EATON VANCE CALIFORNIA MUNICIPAL INCOME TRUST
2 International Pl, Boston, MA 02110
Tel.: (617) 482-8260   MA
CEV—(NYSEAMEX)
Rev.: $5,989,437
Assets: $161,991,999
Liabilities: $59,806,015
Net Worth: $102,185,984
Earnings: $3,688,578
Fiscal Year-end: 11/30/19
Investment Management Service
N.A.I.C.S.: 525990

EATON VANCE ENHANCED EQUITY INCOME FUND
2 International Pl, Boston, MA 02110
Tel.: (617) 482-8260   MA
EOI—(NYSE)
Rev.: $10,440,963
Assets: $601,669,849
Liabilities: $10,657,000
Net Worth: $591,012,840
Earnings: $3,990,933
Fiscal Year-end: 09/30/19
Investment Management Service
N.A.I.C.S.: 525990

EATON VANCE ENHANCED EQUITY INCOME II
Two International Pl, Boston, MA 02110
EOS—(NYSE)
Rev.: $7,480,604
Assets: $871,337,970
Liabilities: $12,022,969
Net Worth: $859,315,001
Earnings: ($1,264,080)
Fiscal Year-end: 12/31/19
Investment Management Service
N.A.I.C.S.: 525990
Michael A. Allison (Mgr-Fund)

EATON VANCE FLOATING-RATE 2022 TARGET TERM TRUST
2 International Pl, Boston, MA 02110
EFL—(NYSE)
Rev.: $19,467,626
Assets: $354,856,759
Liabilities: $130,698,605
Net Worth: $224,158,154
Earnings: $11,864,847

Fiscal Year-end: 06/30/19
Investment Management Service
N.A.I.C.S.: 525990
George J. Gorman (Chm)
Paul M. O'neil (Mgr-Fund)

EATON VANCE FLOATING-RATE INCOME PLUS FUND
Two International Pl, Boston, MA 02110
EFF—(NYSE)
Investment Management Service
N.A.I.C.S.: 525990
William H. Park (Chm)
Scott H. Page (Mgr-Fund)

EATON VANCE FLOATING-RATE INCOME TRUST
2 International Pl, Boston, MA 02110
Tel.: (617) 482-8260   MA
EFT—(NYSE)
Rev.: $53,955,357
Assets: $945,715,559
Liabilities: $339,308,038
Net Worth: $606,407,521
Earnings: $33,780,998
Fiscal Year-end: 05/31/19
Investment Management Service
N.A.I.C.S.: 525990
George J. Gorman (Chm)

EATON VANCE LIMITED DU-RATION INCOME FUND
2 International Pl, Boston, MA 02110
Tel.: (617) 482-8260   MA
EVV—(NYSEAMEX)
Rev.: $131,947,232
Assets: $2,210,369,445
Liabilities: $629,100,604
Net Worth: $1,581,268,841
Earnings: $88,499,011
Fiscal Year-end: 03/31/19
Investment Management Service
N.A.I.C.S.: 525990
William H. Park (Chm)

EATON VANCE MUNICIPAL BOND FUND
2 International Pl, Boston, MA 02110
Tel.: (617) 482-8260   MA
EIM—(NYSEAMEX)
Rev.: $68,257,531
Assets: $1,940,301,586
Liabilities: $826,065,853
Net Worth: $1,114,235,733
Earnings: $40,765,020
Fiscal Year-end: 09/30/19
Investment Management Service
N.A.I.C.S.: 525990

EATON VANCE MUNICIPAL INCOME TRUST
2 International Pl, Boston, MA 02110
Tel.: (617) 482-8260   MA
EVY—(NYSEAMEX)
Rev.: $32,461,015
Assets: $867,495,780
Liabilities: $320,511,437
Net Worth: $546,984,343
Earnings: $20,134,524
Fiscal Year-end: 11/30/19
Investment Management Service
N.A.I.C.S.: 525990
George J. Gorman (Chm)

EATON VANCE NATIONAL MU-NICIPAL OPPORTUNITIES TRUST
2 International Pl, Boston, MA 02110
Tel.: (617) 482-8260   MA
EOT—(NYSE)
Rev.: $15,748,896
Assets: $342,659,504
Liabilities: $28,338,534
Net Worth: $314,320,970

Earnings: $12,732,212
Fiscal Year-end: 03/31/20
Investment Management Service
N.A.I.C.S.: 525990
William H. Park (Chm)

EATON VANCE RISK-MANAGED DIVERSIFIED EQ-UITY INCOME FUND
2 International Pl, Boston, MA 02110
Tel.: (617) 482-8260   MA
ETJ—(NYSE)
Rev.: $10,778,180
Assets: $602,211,214
Liabilities: $6,740,688
Net Worth: $595,470,526
Earnings: $4,207,192
Fiscal Year-end: 12/31/19
Investment Management Service
N.A.I.C.S.: 525990

EATON VANCE SENIOR FLOATING-RATE TRUST
2 International Pl, Boston, MA 02110
Tel.: (617) 482-8260   MA
EFR—(NYSE)
Rev.: $51,048,149
Assets: $856,941,645
Liabilities: $246,410,258
Net Worth: $610,531,387
Earnings: $36,357,861
Fiscal Year-end: 10/31/19
Investment Management Service
N.A.I.C.S.: 525990

EATON VANCE SENIOR IN-COME TRUST
2 International Pl, Boston, MA 02110
Tel.: (617) 482-8260   MA
EVF—(NYSE)
Rev.: $23,988,265
Assets: $424,862,523
Liabilities: $120,327,485
Net Worth: $304,535,038
Earnings: $15,520,463
Fiscal Year-end: 06/30/19
Investment Management Service
N.A.I.C.S.: 525990

EATON VANCE SHORT DURA-TION DIVERSIFIED INCOME FUND
2 International Pl, Boston, MA 02110
Tel.: (617) 482-8260   MA
EVG—(NYSE)
Investment Management Service
N.A.I.C.S.: 525990

EATON VANCE TAX MAN-AGED GLOBAL BUY WRITE OPPORTUNITIES FUND
2 International Pl, Boston, MA 02110
Tel.: (617) 482-8260   MA
ETW—(NYSE)
Rev.: $25,887,621
Assets: $1,145,980,768
Liabilities: $20,477,534
Net Worth: $1,125,503,234
Earnings: $13,839,784
Fiscal Year-end: 12/31/19
Investment Management Service
N.A.I.C.S.: 525990

EATON VANCE TAX-ADVANTAGED DIVIDEND IN-COME FUND
2 International Pl, Boston, MA 02110
Tel.: (617) 482-8260   MA
EVT—(NYSE)
Rev.: $74,927,611
Assets: $2,238,753,144
Liabilities: $454,376,743
Net Worth: $1,784,376,401
Earnings: $42,105,593
Fiscal Year-end: 10/31/19

Investment Management Service
N.A.I.C.S.: 525990
William H. Park *(Chm)*

**EATON VANCE TAX-
ADVANTAGED GLOBAL DIVI-
DEND INCOME FUND**
2 International Pl, Boston, MA 02110
Tel.: (617) 482-8260   MA
ETG—(NYSE)
Investment Management Service
N.A.I.C.S.: 525990

**EATON VANCE TAX-
ADVANTAGED GLOBAL DIVI-
DEND OPPORTUNITIES FUND**
2 International Pl, Boston, MA 02110
Tel.: (617) 482-8260   MA
ETO—(NYSE)
Rev.: $14,588,966
Assets: $481,287,142
Liabilities: $121,490,899
Net Worth: $359,796,243
Earnings: $6,646,692
Fiscal Year-end: 10/31/19
Investment Management Service
N.A.I.C.S.: 525990
William H. Park *(Chm)*

**EATON VANCE TAX-
MANAGED BUY-WRITE IN-
COME FUND**
2 International Pl, Boston, MA 02110
Tel.: (617) 482-8260   MA
ETB—(NYSE)
Investment Management Service
N.A.I.C.S.: 525990

**EATON VANCE TAX-
MANAGED BUY-WRITE OP-
PORTUNITIES FUND**
1 Post Office Sq, Boston, MA 02110
Tel.: (617) 482-8260
Web Site:
    https://www.eatonvance.com
ETV—(NYSE)
Rev.: $19,374,683
Assets: $1,297,788,049
Liabilities: $29,642,092
Net Worth: $1,268,145,957
Earnings: $6,814,106
Fiscal Year-end: 12/31/19
Investment Management Service
N.A.I.C.S.: 525990
Thomas C. Seto *(Mgr-Fund)*

**EATON VANCE TAX-
MANAGED DIVERSIFIED EQ-
UITY INCOME FUND**
2 International Pl, Boston, MA 02110
Tel.: (617) 482-8260   MA
ETY—(NYSE)
Rev.: $33,869,702
Assets: $1,810,462,531
Liabilities: $28,098,784
Net Worth: $1,782,363,747
Earnings: $15,065,428
Fiscal Year-end: 10/31/19
Investment Management Service
N.A.I.C.S.: 525990

**EATON VANCE TAX-
MANAGED GLOBAL DIVERSI-
FIED EQUITY INCOME FUND**
2 International Pl, Boston, MA 02110
Tel.: (617) 482-8260   MA
EXG—(NYSE)
Rev.: $57,562,715
Assets: $2,662,075,436
Liabilities: $28,135,961
Net Worth: $2,633,939,475
Earnings: $30,091,672
Fiscal Year-end: 10/31/19
Asset Management Services
N.A.I.C.S.: 523940

EAU TECHNOLOGIES, INC.
1890 Cobb International Blvd, Kenne-
saw, GA 30152
Tel.: (678) 384-3715   DE
Web Site:
    https://www.eautechnologies.com
Year Founded: 1998
EAUI—(OTCEM)
Sales Range: Less than $1 Million
Emp.: 5
Life Sciences Innovation Technology
N.A.I.C.S.: 541715
Paul R. Johnson *(Pres & CEO)*
Earl Boyce *(VP-R&D & R&D)*
Huy Huynh *(VP-Technology)*
David Holmes *(VP-Operations)*

EBAY INC.
2025 Hamilton Ave, San Jose, CA
95125
Tel.: (408) 376-7108   DE
Web Site: https://www.ebay.com
Year Founded: 1995
EBAY—(NASDAQ)
Rev.: $10,112,000,000
Assets: $21,620,000,000
Liabilities: $15,224,000,000
Net Worth: $6,396,000,000
Earnings: $2,767,000,000
Emp.: 12,300
Fiscal Year-end: 12/31/23
Online Shopping Services
N.A.I.C.S.: 455219
Pierre M. Omidyar *(Founder)*
Marie Oh Huber *(Chief Legal Officer,
Gen Counsel, Sec & Sr VP)*
Mazen Rawashdeh *(CTO & Sr VP)*
Julie A. Loeger *(Chief Growth Officer
& Sr VP)*
Cornelius Boone *(Chief People Offi-
cer & Sr VP)*
Stefanie Jay *(Chief Bus & Strategy
Officer)*
Steve Priest *(CFO & Sr VP)*
Jamie Iannone *(Pres & CEO)*

Subsidiaries:

ASFD, Inc.   (1)
20 Penrose St, Reno, NV 89503-2432
Tel.: (775) 747-4542
Data Processing Services
N.A.I.C.S.: 518210

Affiliate Traction   (1)
2125 Delaware Ave Ste E, Santa Cruz, CA
95060-5752
Tel.: (831) 464-1441
Web Site: http://www.affiliatetraction.com
Sales Range: $1-9.9 Million
Emp.: 20
Full-Service Marketing Agency
N.A.I.C.S.: 541613

Bil Markedet ApS   (1)
Axel Kiers Vej 11, 8270, Hojbjerg, Denmark
Tel.: (45) 70220077
Web Site: http://www.bilbasen.dk
New & Used Car Auction Services
N.A.I.C.S.: 541810
Jan Lang *(Officer-PR)*

Den Bla Avis A/S   (1)
Falkoner Alle 1-3 Copenhagen, Frederiks-
berg, 2000, Denmark
Tel.: (45) 44854444
Online Shopping Services
N.A.I.C.S.: 513110

Marktplaats B.V.   (1)
Wibautstraat 224, 1097 DN, Amsterdam,
Netherlands
Tel.: (31) 204622500
Web Site: https://www.marktplaats.nl
Advertising Agency Services
N.A.I.C.S.: 541810

MicroPlace Inc.   (1)
1071 Davis Rd, Elgin, IL 60123
Tel.: (847) 608-6678
Web Site: https://www.microplace.net
Electronic Products Mfr
N.A.I.C.S.: 334419

Promotions Distributor Service
Corporation   (1)
PO Box 310, San Fernando, CA 91341
Tel.: (818) 834-8800
Merchandise & Retail Services
N.A.I.C.S.: 459999

Shopping.com Inc.   (1)
8000 Marina Blvd 5th Fl, Brisbane, CA
94005
Tel.: (650) 616-6500
Web Site: http://www.shopping.com
Online Shopping Services
N.A.I.C.S.: 425120

StackMob, LLC   (1)
541 8th St, San Francisco, CA 94103
Tel.: (415) 547-0093
Data Processing Services
N.A.I.C.S.: 518210

VendorNet, Inc.   (1)
1903 S Congress Ave Ste 460, Boynton
Beach, FL 33426
Tel.: (561) 737-5151
Web Site: http://www.vendornet.com
Emp.: 16
Order Processing Services
N.A.I.C.S.: 561422

Venmo Inc.   (1)
2038 Locust St, Philadelphia, PA 19103
Tel.: (215) 908-8942
Payroll Management Services
N.A.I.C.S.: 541214

WHI Solutions, Inc.   (1)
5 International Dr Ste 210, Rye Brook, NY
10573-7016
Tel.: (914) 697-9301
Web Site: https://www.whisolutions.com
Sales Range: $10-24.9 Million
Business Management Software
N.A.I.C.S.: 513210

Zvents, Inc.   (1)
1875 S Grant St Ste 800, San Mateo, CA
94402
Tel.: (650) 288-0900
Software Publishing Services
N.A.I.C.S.: 513210

eBay Canada Limited   (1)
500 King Street West Suite 200, Toronto,
M5V 1L9, ON, Canada
Tel.: (866) 278-1053
Web Site: http://www.ebay.ca
Online Auction Services
N.A.I.C.S.: 425120

eBay Gmarket Co., Ltd.   (1)
LIG Tower 8th Floor 649-11 Yeoksam-Dong,
Gangnam-Gu, Seoul, 135-912, Korea
(South)
Tel.: (82) 215665701
Web Site: http://www.gmarket.co.kr
Sales Range: $150-199.9 Million
Emp.: 624
Online Retailer
N.A.I.C.S.: 518210

eBay GmbH   (1)
Albert-Einstein-Ring 2-6, 14532, Kleinmach-
now, Germany
Tel.: (49) 3320 385 1021
Web Site: http://www.ebay.de
Custom Computer Programming Services
N.A.I.C.S.: 541511

Subsidiary (Domestic):

eBay Corporate Services GmbH   (2)
J9 Albert - Einstein - Ring 26, 14532, Klein-
machnow, Germany
Tel.: (49) 3320325788
Data Processing Services
N.A.I.C.S.: 518210

mobile.de GmbH   (2)
Marktplatz 1, Dreilinden, 14532, Kleinmach-
now, Germany
Tel.: (49) 3081097601
Web Site: http://www.mobile.de
Online Marketing Services
N.A.I.C.S.: 541613
Malte Kruger *(Mng Dir)*

mobile.international GmbH   (2)
Marktplatz 1, Dreilinden, 14532, Kleinmach-
now, Germany
Tel.: (49) 3081097601

Web Site: http://www.mobile.de
Trading Support Services
N.A.I.C.S.: 561990
Malte Kruger *(Mng Dir)*

eBay Insurance Services, Inc.   (1)
2145 Hamilton Ave, San Jose, CA 95125
Tel.: (408) 376-7400
Emp.: 5
Insurance Agency & Brokerage Services
N.A.I.C.S.: 524210

eBay Marketing (Thailand) Company
Limited   (1)
399 Interchange 21 Buiding Level 32
Sukhumvit Rd, Watthana, Bangkok, 10110,
Thailand
Tel.: (66) 26603682
Electronic Shopping Services
N.A.I.C.S.: 459999

eBay Motors India Private
Limited   (1)
14th Floor North Block R-TECH Park West-
ern, Mumbai, 400063, Maharashtra, India
Tel.: (91) 2266690000
Web Site: http://www.ebay.in
Sales Range: $25-49.9 Million
Emp.: 140
Automotive Services
N.A.I.C.S.: 811198

eBay Singapore Services Private
Limited   (1)
1 Raffles Quay 18-00, Singapore, 048583,
Singapore
Tel.: (65) 65104500
Web Site: http://www.ebay.com.sg
Apparel Accessory Services
N.A.I.C.S.: 458110

eBay Spain International, S.L.   (1)
C/ Don Ramon De La Cruz 84, 28006, Ma-
drid, Spain
Tel.: (34) 915021091
Advertising Agency Services
N.A.I.C.S.: 541810

eBay Taiwan Company Ltd.   (1)
21f 460 Hsin Yi Rd Sec 4, Taipei, 11052,
TAP, Taiwan
Tel.: (886) 287296686
Electronic Shopping Services
N.A.I.C.S.: 459999

EBET, INC.
197 California Ave Ste 302, Las Ve-
gas, NV 89104
Tel.: (702) 481-1779   NV
Web Site:
    http://www.esportstechnologies.com
Year Founded: 2020
EBET—(OTCQB)
Rev.: $39,177,504
Assets: $15,104,638
Liabilities: $63,524,706
Net Worth: ($48,420,068)
Earnings: ($88,330,696)
Emp.: 28
Fiscal Year-end: 09/30/23
Game Development Services
N.A.I.C.S.: 541511
Aaron Speach *(Chm, Pres & CEO)*
Matthew Lourie *(Interim CFO)*

EBIX INC.
1 Ebix Way, Johns Creek, GA 30097
Tel.: (678) 281-2020   DE
Web Site: https://www.ebix.com
Year Founded: 1976
EBIX—(NASDAQ)
Rev.: $1,050,146,000
Assets: $1,537,555,000
Liabilities: $878,115,000
Net Worth: $659,440,000
Earnings: $64,645,000
Emp.: 10,521
Fiscal Year-end: 12/31/22
Insurance & Financial Software Prod-
ucts & Services
N.A.I.C.S.: 541512
Robin Raina *(Chm, Pres & CEO)*
Leon d'Apice *(Mng Dir-Ebix Australia
Grp & Exec VP)*

Ebix Inc.—(Continued)

Tony Wisniewski *(Mng Dir-Ebix New Zealand)*
Amit Kumar Garg *(CFO)*
Ash Sawhney *(Pres-Insurance Solutions-North America)*
James Senge Sr. *(Sr VP-EbixHealth)*

Subsidiaries:

A.D.A.M., INC.   (1)
10 10th St NE Ste 500, Atlanta, GA 30309
Tel.: (404) 604-2757
Web Site: http://www.adam.com
Sales Range: $25-49.9 Million
Emp.: 197
Software Services
N.A.I.C.S.: 513210

Doctors Exchange, Inc.   (1)
19399 Helenburg Rd Ste 1, Covington, LA 70433
Tel.: (985) 220-1212
Web Site: https://www.doctors-exchange.com
Healthcare Support Services
N.A.I.C.S.: 621491

Ebix Australia (VIC) Pty. Ltd.   (1)
Suite 7 670 Canterbury Road, PO Box 203, Surrey Hills, Melbourne, 3127, VIC, Australia
Tel.: (61) 39 899 3388
Web Site: http://www.ebix.com.au
Emp.: 15
Software Development Services
N.A.I.C.S.: 513210

Ebix Australia Pty,. Ltd.   (1)
Ground Floor 754 Pacific Hwy, Chatswood, 2067, NSW, Australia
Tel.: (61) 28 467 3000
Web Site: https://www.ebix.com.au
Emp.: 60
Software Development Services
N.A.I.C.S.: 513210

Ebix BPO Division   (1)
151 N Lyon Ave, Hemet, CA 92543
Tel.: (619) 308-8600
Web Site: http://www.confirmnet.com
Sales Range: $10-24.9 Million
Emp.: 16
Software & E Commerce Development Services
N.A.I.C.S.: 513210

Ebix Consulting   (1)
One Liberty Sq 3rd Fl, New Britain, CT 06051
Tel.: (860) 827-9090
Web Site: http://www.ebix.com
Emp.: 125
Computer System Design Services
N.A.I.C.S.: 541512

Ebix Europe Limited   (1)
4th Floor Dashwood House 69 Old Broad St, London, EC2M 1QS, United Kingdom
Tel.: (44) 2072640440
Web Site: http://www.ebixeurope.co.uk
Emp.: 60
Software Development Services
N.A.I.C.S.: 541511
Mark Griffith *(Dir-Programme)*

Ebix Latin America Technologia e Consultoria LTDA   (1)
Av Eng Luiz Carlos Berrini 1700 - 8 Floor Brooklin, Sao Paulo, Brazil
Tel.: (55) 1155611044
Web Site: https://www.ebixlatinamerica.com.br
Software Development Services
N.A.I.C.S.: 513210

Ebix New Zealand   (1)
Level 2 Imperial Buildings 44-56 Queen Street, Auckland, New Zealand
Tel.: (64) 9 915 0060
Web Site: http://www.ebix.co.nz
Sales Range: $25-49.9 Million
Emp.: 12
Developer of Insurance Software
N.A.I.C.S.: 513210

Ebix Singapore Pte Ltd   (1)
143 Cecil Street 22-01 GB Building, Singapore, 069542, Singapore

Tel.: (65) 63915988
Web Site: http://www.ebix.com
Sales Range: $10-24.9 Million
Emp.: 10
Developer of Insurance Software
N.A.I.C.S.: 513210

EbixCash World Money Ltd.   (1)
EBIX House Manek Plaza Kalina CST Road, Kolivery Village Marg Santacruz East, Mumbai, 400 098, Maharashtra, India
Tel.: (91) 892 948 5250
Web Site: https://www.buyforex.com
Insurance & Financial Software Products & Services
N.A.I.C.S.: 541512
T. C. Guruprasad *(Mng Dir)*

Subsidiary (Domestic):

Essel Finance VKC Forex Limited   (2)
Jeyam Kondar Apartments Unit 2A Second Floor No 40/12, Murrays Gate Road Alwarpet, Chennai, 600 018, India
Tel.: (91) 44 43144106
Web Site: http://www.esselforex.com
Emp.: 400
Financial Management Services
N.A.I.C.S.: 523999
N. Nageswaran *(Mng Dir)*
R. Venkatasubramanian *(Exec Dir)*
Viral Berawala *(Chief Investment Officer-Essel Mutual Fund)*
Amitabh Chaturvedi *(Mng Dir)*
Salil Datar *(CEO)*

Weizmann Forex Limited   (2)
192 2nd floor Kitab Mahal Dr D N Road Fort, Mumbai, 400001, Maharashtra, India   **(89.94%)**
Tel.: (91) 9769926450
Web Site: http://www.weizmannforex.com
Rev.: $1,317,760,978
Assets: $42,036,204
Liabilities: $27,023,486
Net Worth: $15,012,718
Earnings: ($1,955,288)
Emp.: 2,200
Fiscal Year-end: 03/31/2019
Foreign Exchange Services
N.A.I.C.S.: 522320
Sadashiv Shetty *(Head-Treasury)*
Anant Yadav *(CFO)*
Sankalp Waingankar *(CTO)*
Rakesh J. M. *(Asst VP-IT)*
Shantharam Shetty *(Exec Dir)*
K. Mohan Bhaktha *(Exec Dir)*
Vispi Patel *(Exec VP & Head-Bus-Forex)*

EbixExchange   (1)
607 Herndon Pkwy Ste 300, Herndon, VA 20170
Tel.: (703) 234-0150
Web Site: http://www.ebix.com
Sales Range: $10-24.9 Million
Software Products, Tools & Solutions for Insurance Industry
N.A.I.C.S.: 541511

Subsidiary (Domestic):

Connective Technologies, Inc.   (2)
7676 Hillmont St Ste 120, Houston, TX 77040-6468
Tel.: (713) 690-6789
Web Site: http://www.connectivetech.com
Computer Integrated Systems Design
N.A.I.C.S.: 541512

EbixLife Inc.   (1)
2121 S McClelland St Ste 301, Salt Lake City, UT 84106
Tel.: (385) 215-2740
Web Site: http://www.ebix.com
Sales Range: $10-24.9 Million
Emp.: 30
Insurance Sales Software Application Provider
N.A.I.C.S.: 513210
Robin Raina *(Pres & CEO)*

Flight Raja MiddleEast FZ LLC   (1)
DICBuilding 16, PO Box 85284, Dubai, United Arab Emirates
Tel.: (971) 44427917
Oil Transportation Services
N.A.I.C.S.: 481111

Flight Raja Travels Philippines   (1)

Unit 405-407 4F Five E-com Center Building Blk 18 Pacific Drive, Mall of Asia Complex, 1300, Pasay, Manila, Philippines
Tel.: (63) 29900999
Oil Transportation Services
N.A.I.C.S.: 481111
Sheryl Ph *(Mgr-Team)*

Itz Cash Card Limited   (1)
Top 14th Fl Times Tower Kamala City Senapati Bapat Marg Lowr Parel, Mumbai, 400013, India
Tel.: (91) 61125700
Web Site: http://itzcash.com
Other Computer Related Services
N.A.I.C.S.: 541519

Lawson Travels & Tours (India) Private Limited   (1)
201 Elite Square 274 Perin Nariman Street, Fort, Mumbai, 400 001, India
Tel.: (91) 2249193333
Web Site: http://www.lawsononline.com
Software Development Services
N.A.I.C.S.: 513210

Leisure Corp Private Limited   (1)
B-59A Sector - 60, Noida, 201307, Uttar Pradesh, India
Tel.: (91) 1242385260
Web Site: https://www.leisurecorp.in
Travel Agency Services
N.A.I.C.S.: 561510
Naveen Kundu *(Founder & Mng Dir)*
Naresh Gupta *(Dir-Mice & Luxury)*
Arun Gupta *(VP-Fin & Corp Affairs)*
Girish Iti *(Assoc VP)*
Saloney Sabherwal *(VP-Sls-Mumbai)*
Nupur Chauhan *(Assoc VP-Events)*
Rajesh Vasant Navalkar *(Assoc VP-Key Accounts)*

Mercury Himalayan Explorations Ltd.   (1)
Jeevan Tara Building Parliament Street, New Delhi, 101001, India
Tel.: (91) 1143565425
Web Site: http://www.mheadventures.com
Adventure Travel Services
N.A.I.C.S.: 561510
Narinder Kumar *(Founder)*
Akshay Kumar *(CEO)*
Dilshad Master *(Head-Bus Dev & Mktg)*
Anug Sharma *(Sr Mgr-Ops)*

Miles Software Solutions FZ - LLC   (1)
Office 123 Building No 2 Dubai Internet City, PO Box 502662, Dubai, United Arab Emirates
Tel.: (971) 44225817
Software Development Services
N.A.I.C.S.: 541511

Miles Software Solutions Inc.   (1)
5/F Phinma Plaza 39 Plaza Drive Rockwell Center Brgy Poblacion, Makati, Philippines
Tel.: (63) 22244393
Software Development Services
N.A.I.C.S.: 541511

Miles Software Solutions Pvt. Ltd.   (1)
Suraksha Ace 34/3 Andheri Kurla Road Chakala JB Nagar, Andheri East, Mumbai, 400059, India
Tel.: (91) 2268331464
Web Site: https://www.milessoft.com
Software Development Services
N.A.I.C.S.: 513210
Rakesh Sakaria *(CFO)*

Miles Software Solutions UK Limited   (1)
24 Holborn Viaduct, London, EC1A 2BN, United Kingdom
Tel.: (44) 7502515657
Software Development Services
N.A.I.C.S.: 541511

Oakstone Publishing, LLC   (1)
1 Ebix Way, Johns Creek, GA 30097
Web Site: https://www.oakstone.com
Professional Reference & Educational Book Publisher
N.A.I.C.S.: 513130
Sandy Mardant *(Mgr-Continuing Education)*
Rich Frankel *(VP-Program Dev)*

PT. Adya Tours - Indonesia   (1)

Jl Tanah Abang III No 23-25-27 Pakarti Centre Lt 6, Jakarta Pusat Daerah Khusus Ibukota, Jakarta, 10160, Indonesia
Tel.: (62) 212 980 0800
Web Site: https://viacom-indonesia.business.site
Travel Agency Services
N.A.I.C.S.: 561510

WAAH Taxis Private Limited   (1)
B - 59A Sector - 60 Noida Gautam Buddha Nagar, Noida, 201307, Uttar Pradesh, India
Tel.: (91) 8010021822
Web Site: https://www.ahataxis.com
Transportation Services
N.A.I.C.S.: 485310
Amit Grover *(Co-Founder)*
Shivam Mishra *(Co-Founder)*
Kunal Krishna *(Co-Founder)*

WDEV Solucoes em Tecnologia S.A.   (1)
Rua Visconde de Inhauma 37 6 andar Centro, Rio de Janeiro, 20091-007, Brazil
Tel.: (55) 2135539338
Web Site: http://www.wdev.com.br
Emp.: 250
Software Development Services
N.A.I.C.S.: 541511
Carlos Eduardo Rosas *(Dir-Ops)*
Gullermo Reid *(Pres)*
Leonardo Borges *(Dir-New Bus)*

Zillious Solutions Private Limited   (1)
122 123 NSEZ Phase II, National Capital Region, Noida, 201305, India
Tel.: (91) 965 005 3297
Web Site: https://www.zillious.com
Information Technology Services
N.A.I.C.S.: 541511
Shantu Chatterjee *(Head-Support & Implementation)*
Vishesh Kumar *(Head-Infrastructure)*
Sakshi Chaturvedi *(Engr-Quality Accurance)*

via Philippines Travel Corporation   (1)
Level 4 Block B Magnolia Manyata Embassy Business Park, Outer Ring Road Nagawara, Bengaluru, 560045, India
Tel.: (91) 8040433000
Web Site: http://ph.via.com
Travel Agency Services
N.A.I.C.S.: 561510

ECB BANCORP, INC.
419 Broadway, Everett, MA 02149
Tel.: (617) 387-1110   **MD**
Web Site:
https://www.everettbank.com
Year Founded: 2022
ECBK (NASDAQ)
Rev.: $30,550,000
Assets: $1,064,462,000
Liabilities: $901,732,000
Net Worth: $162,730,000
Earnings: $2,720,000
Emp.: 66
Fiscal Year-end: 12/31/22
Offices of Bank Holding Companies
N.A.I.C.S.: 551111
Richard J. O'Neil *(Pres & CEO)*

ECC CAPITAL CORPORATION
2600 E Coast Hwy Ste 250, Corona Del Mar, CA 92625
Tel.: (949) 954-7052   **MD**
Web Site: https://www.ecccapital.com
Year Founded: 2004
ECRO—(OTCIQ)
Other Financial Vehicles
N.A.I.C.S.: 525990
Steven G. Holder *(Chm & CEO)*
Larry E. Moretti *(Chief Admin Officer & Exec VP)*

ECHO THERAPEUTICS, INC.
99 Wood Ave S Ste 302, Iselin, NJ 08830
Tel.: (732) 201-4189   **MN**
Web Site: http://www.echotx.com
Year Founded: 2002
ECTE—(OTCIQ)

Emp.: 17
Medical Device & Pharmaceutical Developer & Mfr
N.A.I.C.S.: 339112
Daniel Sunday (VP-Mfg & Supply Chain-Global)
Thomas H. Bishop (VP-Ops & Product Dev)
Alan W. Schoenbart (CFO & Sec)
Christine H. Olimpio (Dir-IR & Corp Comm)

ECHOSTAR CORPORATION

100 Inverness Ter E, Englewood, CO 80112-5308
Tel.: (303) 706-4000   NV
Web Site: https://www.echostar.com
Year Founded: 2008
SATS—(NASDAQ)
Rev.: $17,015,598,000
Assets: $57,108,894,000
Liabilities: $37,158,984,000
Net Worth: $19,949,910,000
Earnings: ($1,702,057,000)
Emp.: 15,300
Fiscal Year-end: 12/31/23
Satellite Broadcaster & Digital Receiver Mfr
N.A.I.C.S.: 334220
James DeFranco (Exec VP)
Charles W. Ergen (Exec Chm)
Dean A. Manson (Gen Counsel, Sec & Exec VP)
Jeffrey S. Boggs (Principal Acctg Officer)
Hamid Akhavan-Malayer (Pres & CEO)
Veronika Takacs (Controller)
Paul Gaske (COO)
Adrian Morris (CTO)
Ramesh Ramaswamy (Exec VP)

Subsidiaries:

DISH Network Corporation   (1)
9601 S Meridian Blvd, Englewood, CO 80112
Tel.: (303) 723-1000
Web Site: https://www.dish.com
Rev.: $16,679,407,000
Assets: $52,606,562,000
Liabilities: $34,197,922,000
Net Worth: $18,408,640,000
Earnings: $2,303,233,000
Emp.: 14,200
Fiscal Year-end: 12/31/2022
Holding Company; Satellite Television Broadcasting
N.A.I.C.S.: 551112
James DeFranco (Co-Founder)
Charles W. Ergen (Co-Founder)
T. Paul Gaske (COO)
Cantey M. Ergen (Co-Founder)
Paul W. Orban (CFO & Exec VP)
W. Erik Carlson (Pres & CEO)
John W. Swieringa (COO, Pres-Tech & Pres-DISH Wireless)
James S. Allen (Chief Acctg Officer & Sr VP)
Gary Schanman (Grp Pres-Video Svcs & Exec VP)

Subsidiary (Domestic):

Boost Mobile, LLC   (2)
8845 Irvine Center Dr Ste 200, Irvine, CA 92618
Tel.: (949) 748-3200
Web Site: http://www.boostmobile.com
Communication Products & Services
N.A.I.C.S.: 517112

DBSD North America, Inc.   (2)
9601 S Meridian Blvd, Englewood, CO 80112   (100%)
Tel.: (303) 723-1000
Sales Range: $10-24.9 Million
Emp.: 40
Integrated Satellite & Terrestrial Mobile Services
N.A.I.C.S.: 517410

DISH Network L.L.C.   (2)

9601 S Meridian Blvd, Englewood, CO 80112
Web Site: https://www.dish.com
Satellite Telecommunication Services
N.A.I.C.S.: 517410

Dish Network Service, L.L.C.   (2)
9601 S Meridian Blvd, Englewood, CO 80112-5905   (100%)
Tel.: (303) 723-1000
Web Site: http://www.dishnetwork.com
Sales Range: $1-4.9 Billion
Emp.: 1,800
Pay TV services
N.A.I.C.S.: 517111
Charles W. Ergen (Chm)

EchoStar Satellite Services LLC   (2)
90 Inverness Cir E, Englewood, CO 80112
Tel.: (303) 706-4000
Web Site: http://www.echostarsatelliteservices.com
Sales Range: $800-899.9 Million
Satellite Broadcasting Services
N.A.I.C.S.: 516210
Anders N. Johnson (Pres)
Derek de Bastos (CTO)
Richard Mortellaro (Sr VP-Satellite Svcs)
Jaime Londono (VP-Advanced Programs & Spectrum Mgmt)

Echosphere L.L.C.   (2)
9601 S Meridian Blvd, Englewood, CO 80112   (100%)
Tel.: (303) 723-1000
Pay TV services
N.A.I.C.S.: 517111

Ting Inc.   (2)
421 Dr Martin Luther King Jr Dr E 2, Starkville, MS 39759
Tel.: (855) 846-4389
Web Site: http://www.ting.com
Mobile Phone & Wireless Network Services
N.A.I.C.S.: 517112
Elliot Noss (CEO)
Jess Johannson (VP-People)
Michael Goldstein (VP-Sls & Mktg)

Subsidiary (Domestic):

Ting Virginia, LLC   (3)
321 E Main St Ste 200, Charlottesville, VA 22902
Tel.: (434) 817-0707
Internet & Telecommunication Service Provider
N.A.I.C.S.: 517112

Subsidiary (Domestic):

Fiber Roads, LLC   (4)
321 E Main St Ste 200, Charlottesville, VA 22902
Tel.: (434) 531-4141
Web Site: http://www.fiberroads.com
Internet & Telecommunication Service Provider
N.A.I.C.S.: 517112

Subsidiary (Domestic):

Virgin Mobile USA, Inc.   (2)
10 Independence Blvd, Warren, NJ 07059
Tel.: (908) 607-4000
Web Site: http://www.virginmobileusa.com
Sales Range: $1-4.9 Billion
Emp.: 420
Mobile Telecommunications Services
N.A.I.C.S.: 517112

Subsidiary (Domestic):

Helio LLC   (3)
10960 Wilshire Blvd Ste 700, Los Angeles, CA 90024
Tel.: (310) 445-7000
Sales Range: $200-249.9 Million
Wireless Telecom Service
N.A.I.C.S.: 517112

Subsidiary (Domestic):

Wright Travel Corporation   (2)
9601 S Meridian Blvd, Englewood, CO 80112   (100%)
Tel.: (303) 723-4000
Web Site: http://www.wrighttravel.net
Sales Range: $100-124.9 Million
Provider of Travel Services
N.A.I.C.S.: 561510

EchoStar Broadcasting Corporation   (1)
100 Inverness Ter E, Englewood, CO 80112
Tel.: (301) 428-5893
Satellite Communication Services
N.A.I.C.S.: 517410

EchoStar Data Networks Corporation   (1)
211 Perimeter Ctr Pkwy, Atlanta, GA 30346
Tel.: (404) 978-8000
Web Site: http://www.echostar.com
Sales Range: $50-74.9 Million
Emp.: 300
Broadband Satellite Technologies Design & Development Services
N.A.I.C.S.: 334220

EchoStar International Corporation   (1)
90 Inverness Cir E, Englewood, CO 80112
Tel.: (303) 706-4000
Web Site: http://www.echostar.com
Sales Range: $450-499.9 Million
Emp.: 1,000
Provider of Satellite Broadcasting Services
N.A.I.C.S.: 516210

EchoStar Mobile Limited   (1)
25/28 North Wall Quay, Dublin, Ireland
Tel.: (353) 16401859
Web Site: http://echostarmobile.com
Satellite Telecommunication Services
N.A.I.C.S.: 517410

EchoStar Satellite Operating Corporation   (1)
100 Inverness Ter E, Englewood, CO 80112
Tel.: (303) 723-1000
Satellite Communication Services
N.A.I.C.S.: 517410

EchoStar Technologies LLC   (1)
100 Inverness Terr E, Englewood, CO 80112
Tel.: (303) 706-4000
Web Site: https://www.echostar.com
Sales Range: $1-4.9 Billion
Satellite Receiving
N.A.I.C.S.: 516210
Michael T. Dugan (VP-Engrg)

EchoStar Ukraine, LLC   (1)
Kolomenska 63, Kharkiv, 61166, Ukraine
Tel.: (380) 577280281
Web Site: http://www.echostar.com
Engineering Services
N.A.I.C.S.: 541330

HNS Americas Communicacoes, Ltda.   (1)
Av Brigadeiro Faria Lima 201 - 7 andar Pinheiros, ES 05426 100, Sao Paulo, Brazil
Tel.: (55) 1138187500
Satellite Communication Services
N.A.I.C.S.: 517410

HNS de Mexico S.A. de C.V.   (1)
Blvd Manuel Avila Camacho 36 Piso 10 Torre Esmeralda 2, Col Lomas de Chapultepec D F, 11000, Mexico, Mexico
Tel.: (52) 5591711691
Satellite Communication Services
N.A.I.C.S.: 517410

Hughes Communications India Private Ltd.   (1)
Plot No 1 Sector 18 Electronic City, Gurgaon, 122 015, Haryana, India
Tel.: (91) 1247132500
Web Site: https://www.hughes.in
Telecommunication Servicesb
N.A.I.C.S.: 517810
Partho Banerjee (Pres & Mng Dir)
Alok Goyal (CFO)
Shivaji Chatterjee (Sr VP)
Pranav Roach (Gen Counsel)

Hughes Communications, Inc.   (1)
11717 Exploration Ln, Germantown, MD 20876
Tel.: (301) 428-5500
Emp.: 2,254
Satellite Communication Services
N.A.I.C.S.: 517410
Pradman P. Kaul (Pres & CEO)
Grant A. Barber (CFO & Exec VP)
Bahram Pourmand (Exec VP)
Adrian Morris (VP-Engrg)
T. Paul Gaske (Exec VP & Gen Mgr-North America Div)

Hughes Network Systems Europe, Ltd.   (1)
Hughes House Rockingham Drive Linford Wood, Milton Keynes, MK14 6PD, Buckinghamshire, United Kingdom
Tel.: (44) 1908425300
Web Site: https://europe.hughes.com
Emp.: 50
Satellite Communication Services
N.A.I.C.S.: 517410

Hughes Network Systems India, Ltd.   (1)
1 Shivji Marg Westend Greens NH - 8, New Delhi, 110 037, India
Tel.: (91) 9953329507
Web Site: http://www.hughes.com
Emp.: 3
Satellite Communication Equipment Services
N.A.I.C.S.: 517410

Hughes Network Systems, LLC   (1)
11717 Exploration Ln, Germantown, MD 20876
Tel.: (301) 428-5500
Web Site: https://www.hughes.com
Sales Range: $1-4.9 Billion
Emp.: 2,254
Satellite Communication Services
N.A.I.C.S.: 517410
Jeffrey S. Boggs (Sr VP-Global Fin)
T. Paul Gaske (Exec VP & Gen Mgr-North America)
Adrian Morris (Exec VP-Engrg)
Pradman Kaul (Pres)

Hughes Satellite Systems Corporation   (1)
100 Inverness Ter E, Englewood, CO 80112-5308
Tel.: (303) 706-4000
Rev.: $2,003,343,000
Assets: $4,817,283,000
Liabilities: $2,669,420,000
Net Worth: $2,147,863,000
Earnings: $149,413,000
Fiscal Year-end: 12/31/2022
Satellite Communication Services
N.A.I.C.S.: 517410
Hamid Akhavan-Malayer (Pres)
Michael T. Dugan (CEO)
Charles W. Ergen (Chm)
Dean A. Manson (Gen Counsel, Sec & Exec VP)
Jeffrey S. Boggs (Interim Principal Acctg Officer)

NagraStar, LLC   (1)
90 Inverness Cir E, Englewood, CO 80112   (50%)
Tel.: (303) 706-5700
Web Site: https://www.nagrastar.com
Sales Range: $25-49.9 Million
Emp.: 90
Satellite Television Conditional Access & Smart Card Products Mfr & Whslr
N.A.I.C.S.: 334610
Pascal Lenoir (CEO)

Sling Media, Inc.   (1)
1051 E Hillsdale Blvd Ste 500, Foster City, CA 94404
Tel.: (650) 293-8000
Web Site: http://www.slingbox.com
Electronic Products Mfr
N.A.I.C.S.: 334419
Paddy Rao (Sr VP-Product & Engrg)

Solaris Mobile Ltd.   (1)
3 Dublin Landings North Wall Quay, Dublin, DO1C4E0, Ireland
Tel.: (353) 1908422900
Web Site: https://www.echostarmobile.com
Mobile Satellite Operating Services
N.A.I.C.S.: 517410
Telemaco Melia (VP)

ECO DEPOT, INC.

800 2300 W Sahara Ave, Las Vegas, NV 89102
Tel.: (226) 757-1085   NV
Web Site:
http://www.solarenergyspokane.com
ECDP—(OTCIQ)
Eletric Power Generation Services
N.A.I.C.S.: 221114

Eco Depot, Inc.—(Continued)

Hadelin Carlos Diericx Trouyet *(Pres)*
Alexander Muntean *(Officer & VP)*
Pablo Oyanguren *(CFO)*
Kristina Chams *(Chief Admin Officer & Sec)*
Bill Shafley *(Dir-Development)*

ECO INNOVATION GROUP, INC.

18414 Eddy Street, Northridge, CA 91325
Tel.: (833) 464-3334
Web Site: http://www.digitunder.com
ECOX—(OTCIQ)
Rev.: $95,880
Assets: $373,074
Liabilities: $4,653,703
Net Worth: ($4,280,629)
Earnings: ($6,635,436)
Fiscal Year-end: 12/31/21
Holding Company; Consumer Services
N.A.I.C.S.: 551112
Julia Otey-Raudes *(Pres, CEO, CFO, Chm, Treas & Sec)*

Subsidiaries:

Expressions Chiropractic & Rehab, P.A. **(1)**
510 W FM 1382, Cedar Hill, TX 75104-5322 **(100%)**
Tel.: (972) 291-4455
Web Site:
http://www.expressionschiropractic.com
Emp.: 50
Sports Medicine, Rehabilitation, Family Chiropractic Care & Preventative Wellness
N.A.I.C.S.: 621310
Kirtland Speaks *(Owner & Pres)*

ECO SAFE SYSTEMS USA, INC.

19528 Ventura Blvd Ste 159, Tarzana, CA 91356
Tel.: (661) 755-3865 **DE**
Web Site:
https://ecosafesystemsusa.com
ESFS—(OTCIQ)
Water Supply & Irrigation Systems
N.A.I.C.S.: 221310
Michael Elliot *(CEO)*

ECO-STIM ENERGY SOLUTIONS, INC.

1773 Westborough Dr, Katy, TX 77449
Tel.: (281) 531-7200 **NV**
Web Site: http://www.ecostim-es.com
Year Founded: 2003
ESES—(OTCIQ)
Rev.: $40,709,621
Assets: $31,155,144
Liabilities: $34,561,236
Net Worth: ($3,406,092)
Earnings: ($87,867,070)
Emp.: 5
Fiscal Year-end: 12/31/18
Oil & Gas Field Services
N.A.I.C.S.: 213112
Brian R. Stewart *(Chm)*
Carlos A. Fernandez *(Exec VP-Corp Bus Dev & Gen Mgr-Latin America)*
Alexander Nickolatos *(Interim CEO & Interim CFO)*
John Hageman *(Chief Legal Officer & Sec)*

ECOLAB INC.

1 Ecolab Pl, Saint Paul, MN 55102**DE**
Web Site: https://www.ecolab.com
Year Founded: 1923
ECL—(NYSE)
Rev.: $15,320,200,000
Assets: $21,846,600,000
Liabilities: $13,774,400,000

Net Worth: $8,072,200,000
Earnings: $1,372,300,000
Emp.: 48,000
Fiscal Year-end: 12/31/23
Food Service Related Equipment Distr
N.A.I.C.S.: 423440
Larry L. Berger *(Chief Technical Officer & Exec VP)*
Christophe Beck *(Chm & CEO)*
Darrell R. Brown *(Pres & COO)*
Laurie M. Marsh *(Exec VP-HR)*
Nicholas Alfano *(Pres-Global Industrial Grp & Exec VP)*
Scott D. Kirkland *(CFO)*
Jeff Bulischeck *(Exec VP)*
Sam De Boo *(Pres-Global Markets & Exec VP)*
Machiel Duijser *(Chief Supply Chain Officer & Exec VP)*
Jennifer Bradway *(Principal Acctg Officer, Sr VP, Controller & Controller-North America)*
Tiffany Atwell *(Exec VP-Government Relations)*
Missy Blais *(VP-Global Tax)*
Hayley Crowe *(Exec VP & Gen Mgr-Global Life Sciences)*
Soraya Hlila *(Exec VP & Gen Mgr-Global Pest Elimination)*
Joshua Magnuson *(Exec VP & Gen Mgr-Global Light Water Sector)*
Marcello Napol *(Sr VP & Gen Mgr-Global Healthcare)*
Harpreet Saluja *(Exec VP-Corporate Strategy & Business Development)*

Subsidiaries:

AK Kraus und Hiller Schadlingsbekampfung GmbH **(1)**
Munchener Strasse 23, Allershausen, Allershausen, 85391, Germany
Tel.: (49) 8166996500
Web Site: http://www.ak-gmbh.de
Emp.: 37
Pest Control Services
N.A.I.C.S.: 561710
Dirk-Peter Maurer *(Mng Dir)*

Adecom Quimica LTDA **(1)**
Rua Joaquim Suma 110 Parque Corrientes, 28053-400, Campos dos Goytacazes, Rio de Janeiro, Brazil
Tel.: (55) 2227325077
Water Treatment & Distribution Services
N.A.I.C.S.: 221310

Amboile Services SAS **(1)**
35 rue Camille Desmoulins, 92130, Issy-les-Moulineaux, France
Tel.: (33) 800310410
Web Site: http://www.amboileservices.fr
Emp.: 40
Killing Insects & Rats
N.A.I.C.S.: 561990

Aquasign **(1)**
4 Points Commercial Centre Craigshaw Road Tullos, Aberdeen, AB12 3AP, United Kingdom
Tel.: (44) 1224897060
Web Site: http://www.aquasign.com
Subsea Marker Mfr
N.A.I.C.S.: 339950

BIOQUELL Plc **(1)**
52 Royce Close West Portway, Andover, SP10 3TS, Hampshire, United Kingdom
Tel.: (44) 1264 835 900
Web Site: http://www.bioquellplc.com
Bio-Decontamination & Containment Equipment, Related Products & Services
N.A.I.C.S.: 325414
Georgina Pope *(Sec)*

Subsidiary (US):

BIOQUELL Inc. **(2)**
702 Electronic Dr Ste 200, Horsham, PA 19044
Tel.: (215) 682-0225
Web Site: http://www.bioquell.com
Sales Range: $25-49.9 Million
Emp.: 20

Design, Manufacture & Supply of Bio-Decontamination & Containment Equipment, Related Products & Services
N.A.I.C.S.: 541714

Subsidiary (Domestic):

BIOQUELL UK Limited **(2)**
52 Royce Cl, Andover, SP10 3TS, United Kingdom
Tel.: (44) 126 483 5835
Web Site: http://www.bioquell.com
Sales Range: $75-99.9 Million
Emp.: 120
Design, Manufacture & Supply of Bio-Decontamination & Containment Equipment, Related Products & Services
N.A.I.C.S.: 325414

Subsidiary (Non-US):

Bioquell Asia Pacific Pte Ltd **(2)**
21 Gul Lane, Singapore, 629416, Singapore
Tel.: (65) 6 505 6758
Web Site: http://www.bioquell.net
Laboratory Equipments & Supplies Distr
N.A.I.C.S.: 423450

Bioquell Global Logistics (Ireland) Ltd. **(2)**
Unit E4 Eastway Business Park Ballysimon Road, Limerick, V94 XF1H, Munster, Ireland
Tel.: (353) 61 603622
Web Site: http://www.bioquell.ie
Sales Range: $50-74.9 Million
Emp.: 5
Laboratory Equipments & Supplies Distr
N.A.I.C.S.: 423450

Subsidiary (Domestic):

TRaC EMC & Safety Ltd **(2)**
100 Frobisher Business Park, Leigh Sinton Road, Malvern, WR14 1BX, Worcestershire, United Kingdom
Tel.: (44) 1684571700
Sales Range: $25-49.9 Million
Emp.: 15
Electromagnetic Compatibility Testing Services
N.A.I.C.S.: 541380

TRaC Environmental & Analysis Ltd. **(2)**
Rothwell Road, Warwick, CV34 5JX, United Kingdom
Tel.: (44) 1926478478
Web Site: http://www.tracglobal.com
Sales Range: $25-49.9 Million
Emp.: 68
Environmental Testing & Analysis Laboratories
N.A.I.C.S.: 541380

Subsidiary (Domestic):

TRL Compliance Services Limited **(3)**
Long Green, Forthampton, GL19 4QH, Gloucester, United Kingdom
Tel.: (44) 1684835818
Web Site: http://www.trlcompliance.com
EMC, Radio, Safety & Calibration Testing Services
N.A.I.C.S.: 541380

Subsidiary (Domestic):

TRaC Telecoms & Radio Ltd **(2)**
Unit E Hull N Humbers Hull, Kingston upon Hull, HU9 1NJ, Yorkshire, United Kingdom
Tel.: (44) 1482801801
Sales Range: $25-49.9 Million
Emp.: 30
Medical Diagnostic Equipment Mfr
N.A.I.C.S.: 334510

Barclay Water Management, Inc. **(1)**
55 Chapel St, Newton, MA 02458
Tel.: (617) 926-3400
Web Site: http://www.barclaywater.com
Emp.: 82
Water Treatment Equipment Mfr
N.A.I.C.S.: 333310
Joseph J. Berns *(VP-Fin)*
Michael F. Davidson *(VP-Ops)*
Donald W. Carney Jr. *(Pres & CEO)*

Bioquell GmbH **(1)**

Nattermannallee 1, 50829, Cologne, Germany
Tel.: (49) 4539296333
Hydrogen Peroxide Vapor Mfr & Whslr
N.A.I.C.S.: 325180

Bioquell SAS **(1)**
153 quai du Rancy, 94380, Bonneuil-sur-Marne, France
Tel.: (33) 143781594
Hydrogen Peroxide Vapor Mfr & Whslr
N.A.I.C.S.: 325180

Bioquell Technology (Shenzhen) Ltd. **(1)**
Room 416 Kingson Building No 1 Chuangsheng Road, Xili Nanshan District, Shenzhen, 518055, China
Tel.: (86) 75586352622
Hydrogen Peroxide Vapor Mfr & Whslr
N.A.I.C.S.: 325180

CID LINES NV **(1)**
Waterpoortstraat 2, 8900, Ieper, Belgium
Tel.: (32) 57217877
Web Site: http://www.cidlines.com
Animal Health Products Mfr
N.A.I.C.S.: 311119

CID Lines Iberica SL **(1)**
Felipe Prieto 1 F, 34001, Palencia, Spain
Tel.: (34) 24354637
Animal Health Products Mfr
N.A.I.C.S.: 311119

CID Lines Sp. z o. o. **(1)**
Ul Swierkowa 20, Niepruszew, 64-320, Buk, Poland
Tel.: (48) 618968190
Animal Health Products Mfr
N.A.I.C.S.: 311119

Chemstaff, Inc. **(1)**
3180 Theodore St Ste 205, Joliet, IL 60435
Web Site: http://www.chemstaff.biz
Ecological Restoration Consulting Services
N.A.I.C.S.: 541620
Joe Bates *(Pres)*

Chemstar Corp. **(1)**
120 Interstate W Pkwy, Lithia Springs, GA 30122
Tel.: (770) 732-0700
Web Site: http://www.chemstarcorp.com
Polish & Sanitation Good Mfr
N.A.I.C.S.: 325612
Tom Daniel *(Grp VP)*
Tom Happ *(Reg VP)*
Tom Oldham *(Reg VP)*
Jill Hollingsworth *(VP-Food Safety)*
Steve Wood *(Reg VP)*
Ashley Blottenberger *(Reg VP)*
Jim Schurman *(Founder)*

Deren Ilac Sanayl ve Dis Ticaret Anonim Sirketi **(1)**
Melek Aras Bulvari Aromatik Cd No 59 Aydinli-Kosb Tuzla, 34956, Istanbul, Turkiye
Tel.: (90) 2166804444
Web Site: http://www.derenilac.com
Pharmaceutical Product Mfr & Distr
N.A.I.C.S.: 325412

Derypol SA **(1)**
Plato n 6 Entlo 5, 08021, Barcelona, Spain
Tel.: (34) 93 238 9090
Web Site: https://www.derypol.com
Emp.: 60
Chemical Product & Preparation Mfr
N.A.I.C.S.: 325998
Guillem Sole Ristol *(Mng Dir)*

Ecolab (China) Investment Co., Ltd. **(1)**
1208 Tower B City Centre of Shanghai 100 Zunyi Road, Shanghai, 200051, China
Tel.: (86) 2162371000
Food Service Equipment Whslr
N.A.I.C.S.: 423440

Ecolab (Guam) LLC **(1)**
193 Rojas St Harmon Industrial Park, Tamuning, GU 96931
Tel.: (671) 648-5221
Web Site: http://www.ecolab.com
Sales Range: $25-49.9 Million
Emp.: 7
Food Product Machinery Mfr & Consulting
N.A.I.C.S.: 311423

Ecolab (Pty) Ltd. **(1)**

1 Ampere Street, Chloorkop, Edenglen, 1613, South Africa
Tel.: (27) 11 578 5000
Web Site: http://www.ecolab.com
Sales Range: $25-49.9 Million
Emp.: 60
Commercial Cleaning & Sanitizing Products
N.A.I.C.S.: 325611

Ecolab (Schweiz) GmbH (1)
Kagenstrasse 10, 4153, Reinach, Basel-Landschaft, Switzerland
Tel.: (41) 61 466 9466
Web Site: https://www.ecolabhealthcare.ch
Food Product Machinery Mfr
N.A.I.C.S.: 333241
Roland Schmitt (Mng Dir)

Ecolab (Trinidad & Tobago)Unlimited (1)
LP 7 Guayamare Link Road, Warner Village, Trincity, Trinidad & Tobago
Tel.: (868) 2254116
Chemical Product Whslr
N.A.I.C.S.: 424690

Ecolab A/S (1)
Innspurten 9, PO Box 6440, Etterstad, 0605, Oslo, Norway
Tel.: (47) 22681800
Web Site: http://no-no.ecolab.com
Food Product Machinery Mfr
N.A.I.C.S.: 333241

Ecolab AB (1)
Gotalandsvagen 230 Hus 23, 125 24, Alvsjo, Sweden
Tel.: (46) 86032200
Web Site: http://www.ecolab.com
Sales Range: $25-49.9 Million
Emp.: 100
Commercial Cleaning & Sanitizing Products
N.A.I.C.S.: 325611

Ecolab AS (1)
Hoffdingsvej 36, 2500, Valby, Denmark
Tel.: (45) 36158585
Web Site: http://www.da-dk.ecolab.com
Sales Range: $50-74.9 Million
Emp.: 150
Commercial Cleaning & Sanitizing Products
N.A.I.C.S.: 325611

Ecolab ApS (1)
Hoffdingsvej 36, 2500, Valby, Denmark
Tel.: (45) 3 615 8585
Web Site: http://www.ecolab.com
Emp.: 75
Chemical Product & Preparation Mfr
N.A.I.C.S.: 325998

Ecolab Argentina S.R.L. (1)
Victoria Ocampo 360 - Piso 3, 1107, Buenos Aires, Argentina
Tel.: (54) 8009998313
Water, Hygiene & Energy Technology Service Provider
N.A.I.C.S.: 541715

Ecolab Asia Pacific Pte. Ltd. (1)
21 Gul Lane, Singapore, 629416, Singapore
Tel.: (65) 65004900
Water, Hygiene & Energy Technology Service Provider
N.A.I.C.S.: 541715
Serene Chiong (Mgr-Procurement)

Ecolab B.V. (1)
Oude Rhijnhofweg 17, 2342 BB, Oegstgeest, Netherlands
Tel.: (31) 71 524 1100
Web Site: https://nl-nl.ecolab.com
Sales Range: $25-49.9 Million
Emp.: 200
Cleaning & Sanitizing Products Mfr
N.A.I.C.S.: 333241

Ecolab B.V.B.A./S.P.R.L. (1)
Noordkustlaan 16C, 1702, Groot-Bijgaarden, Belgium
Tel.: (32) 2 467 5111
Web Site: http://www.ecolab.com
Emp.: 180
Food Product Machinery Mfr & Consulting
N.A.I.C.S.: 311999

Ecolab Canada (1)
5105 Tomken Rd, Mississauga, L4W 2X5, ON, Canada   (100%)
Tel.: (905) 238-0171

Web Site: http://www.ecolab.com
Sales Range: $250-299.9 Million
Emp.: 550
Mfr of Detergents & Other Cleaning Agents
N.A.I.C.S.: 325611

Ecolab Co. (1)
5105 Tomken Road, Mississauga, L4W 2X5, ON, Canada
Tel.: (905) 238-0171
Web Site: http://en-ca.ecolab.com
Emp.: 200
Food Product Machinery Mfr & Consulting
N.A.I.C.S.: 311999
Christophe Beck (CEO)
Darrell Brown (Pres)
Jennifer Bradway (Sr VP)

Ecolab Colombia S.A. (1)
Avenida Carrera 62 22-75 Interior 7 Santafe de, Bogota, Colombia
Tel.: (57) 14142394
Food Product Machinery Mfr & Consulting
N.A.I.C.S.: 333241

Ecolab Credit Union (1)
370 Wabasha St N Ste 100, Saint Paul, MN 55102
Tel.: (651) 293-2441
Rev.: $210,000
Emp.: 3
Federal & Federally Sponsored Credit Agencies
N.A.I.C.S.: 522130
Samuel Wiederholt (Pres)

Ecolab Deutschland GmbH (1)
Ecolab-Allee 1, 40789, Monheim am Rhein, Germany
Tel.: (49) 2173 599 1900
Web Site: https://en-de.ecolab.com
Water Treatment Equipment Mfr
N.A.I.C.S.: 333310

Ecolab EOOD (1)
Tsarigradsko chaussee Blv 115A, 1784, Sofia, Bulgaria
Tel.: (359) 2 976 8030
Web Site: http://www.ecolab.com
Emp.: 25
Food Product Machinery Mfr
N.A.I.C.S.: 333241

Ecolab East Africa (Kenya) Limited (1)
Tulip House Mombasa Road, PO Box 63497, Next to Sameer Business Park, 00619, Nairobi, Kenya
Tel.: (254) 20 354 0625
Web Site: http://www.ecolab.com
Water, Hygiene & Energy Technologies & Services
N.A.I.C.S.: 221310

Ecolab Ecuador CIA. LTDA. (1)
Sebastian Moreno OE1-195 Y Francisco Garcia, Panamericana Norte Km 6 1/2, Quito, Ecuador
Tel.: (593) 993857931
Food Product Machinery Mfr & Consulting
N.A.I.C.S.: 333241

Ecolab Engineering GmbH (1)
Raiffeisenstrasse 7, 83313, Siegsdorf, Germany   (100%)
Tel.: (49) 866 2610
Web Site: https://www.ecolab-engineering.de
Sales Range: $50-74.9 Million
Emp.: 200
Development, Production & Sales of Measuring, Metering & Application Systems
N.A.I.C.S.: 334519
Markus Niederbichler (Dir)

Ecolab Europe GmbH (1)
Richtistrasse 7, 8304, Wallisellen, Switzerland
Tel.: (41) 44 877 2000
Web Site: https://de-ch.ecolab.com
Food Product Machinery Mfr
N.A.I.C.S.: 333241

Ecolab Export GmbH (1)
Ecolab-Allee 1, 40789, Monheim am Rhein, Germany
Tel.: (49) 2173 599 1900
Web Site: http://www.export.ecolab.com
Water Treatment Equipment Mfr
N.A.I.C.S.: 333310
Stavros Kollias (Mng Dir)

Ecolab G.K. (1)
Harumi Triton Square Tower Y 1-8-11 Harumi, Chuo-ku, Tokyo, 104-6137, Japan
Tel.: (81) 34 236 6700
Web Site: http://www.ecolab.com
Sales Range: $10-24.9 Million
Emp.: 500
Commercial Cleaning & Sanitizing Products
N.A.I.C.S.: 325611
Kenentaro Aatanabe (CEO)

Ecolab Global Institutional Group (1)
1 Ecolab Pl, Saint Paul, MN 55102-1307
Tel.: (651) 293-2233
Web Site: http://www.ecolab.com
Specialized Cleansers & Sanitizers Mfr
N.A.I.C.S.: 325611

Ecolab GmbH (1)
Rivergate D1/4O G Handelskai 92, 1200, Vienna, Austria
Tel.: (43) 1 715 2550
Web Site: https://de-at.ecolab.com
Emp.: 200
Food Product Machinery Mfr & Consulting
N.A.I.C.S.: 333241

Ecolab Hispano-Portuguesa S.L. (1)
Avenida Del Baix Llobregat 3-5, 08970, Sant Joan Despi, Barcelona, Spain
Tel.: (34) 93 475 8900
Web Site: http://www.es.ecolab.eu
Waste Treatment Services
N.A.I.C.S.: 221310

Ecolab Holding Italy Srl (1)
Administrative Centre Colleoni Via Paracelsus 6, CP 3789, 20865, Agrate Brianza, MB, Italy
Tel.: (39) 03960501
Web Site: http://www.it.ecolab.eu
Cooking Equipment Whslr
N.A.I.C.S.: 423440

Ecolab Hygiene Kft. (1)
Vaci ut 81-83 Point II, 1139, Budapest, Hungary
Tel.: (36) 1 550 5290
Web Site: https://hu-hu.ecolab.com
Chemical Products Distr
N.A.I.C.S.: 424690

Ecolab Hygiene Systems GmbH (1)
Auf dem Tigge 60c, Beckum, 59269, Germany
Tel.: (49) 252193640
Food Product Machinery Mfr
N.A.I.C.S.: 333241

Ecolab Hygiene d.o.o. (1)
Tosin Bunar 270 / V Floor, Novi Beograd, 11070, Belgrade, Serbia
Tel.: (381) 11 207 6800
Web Site: http://www.rs-rs.ecolab.com
Emp.: 25
Food Product Machinery Mfr
N.A.I.C.S.: 333241

Ecolab Hygiene s.r.o. (1)
Voctarova 2449/5, 180 00, Prague, 8, Czech Republic
Tel.: (420) 296114040
Web Site: http://www.ecolab.com
Food Product Machinery Mfr & Consulting
N.A.I.C.S.: 311999

Ecolab Korea Ltd. (1)
8F Daemyung Tower Beobwon-Ro, Songpa-gu, Seoul, 05836, Korea (South)
Tel.: (82) 15887595
Chemical Products Distr
N.A.I.C.S.: 424690

Ecolab LLC (1)
4 Heroiv Kosmosu street Office 805, 03148, Kiev, Ukraine
Tel.: (380) 44 494 3120
Web Site: https://ua-ua.ecolab.com
Sales Range: $25-49.9 Million
Emp.: 40
Soaps & Other Detergents Except Specialty Cleaning Service
N.A.I.C.S.: 325611

Ecolab Limited (1)
Winnington Avenue, Northwich, CW8 4DX, Cheshire, United Kingdom   (100%)
Tel.: (44) 160674488
Web Site: https://www.ecolab.com
Sales Range: $25-49.9 Million
Emp.: 600
Supplier to the Cleaning Industry

N.A.I.C.S.: 333310
Christophe Beck (Chm & CEO)
Darrell Brown (Pres & COO)
Scott Kirkland (CFO)
Adrian Studer (Exec VP-Marketing)

Ecolab Limited (1)
15/F Lu Plaza 2 Wing Yip Street, Kwun Tong, Kowloon, China (Hong Kong)
Tel.: (852) 2 341 4202
Web Site: http://www.ecolab.com
Sales Range: $150-199.9 Million
Emp.: 200
Commercial Cleaning & Sanitizing Products
N.A.I.C.S.: 325611

Ecolab Limited (1)
6 Elgin Road, Kingston, Jamaica
Tel.: (876) 8769260750
Food Equipment Distr
N.A.I.C.S.: 423440

Ecolab Limited (1)
15th Floor President Tower 971 973 Ploenchit Road Lumpini, Pathumwan, Bangkok, Thailand
Tel.: (66) 21269499
Food Equipment Distr
N.A.I.C.S.: 423440
Somnit Padungek (Mgr-Field Sls)

Ecolab Limited (1)
Forest Park Mullingar Industrial Estate Mullingar Co, Westmeath, Mullingar, Ireland
Tel.: (353) 12763500
Food Equipment Distr
N.A.I.C.S.: 423440
Ruaidhri O. Broin (Mgr-Acct)

Ecolab Limited (1)
Airport Industrial Park, Nassau, Bahamas
Tel.: (242) 3775121
Food Equipment Distr
N.A.I.C.S.: 423440

Ecolab Ltd. (1)
10 F No 172 Sec 4 Cheng De Rd, Shih Lin Dist, Taipei, Taiwan
Tel.: (886) 289781234
Waste Treatment Services
N.A.I.C.S.: 221310

Ecolab Manufacturing Inc. (1)
Rd 28 Luchetti Indus Pa, Bayamon, PR 00960
Tel.: (787) 796-1290
Web Site: http://www.ecolab.com
Sales Range: $25-49.9 Million
Emp.: 100
Cleaning Service
N.A.I.C.S.: 561720

Ecolab Maroc S.A. (1)
Lot Mounir 1 Parc Industriel Attawfik Route 1029 Sidi Maarouf, Casablanca, Morocco
Tel.: (212) 2258253035
Waste Treatment Services
N.A.I.C.S.: 221310

Ecolab Maroc Societe A Responsabilite Limitee D'associe Unique (1)
Lot Mounir 1 Parc Industriel Attawfik Route 1029, Sidi Maarouf, Casablanca, Morocco
Tel.: (212) 22582530
Web Site: http://en-in.ecolab.com
Water, Hygiene & Energy Technology Service Provider
N.A.I.C.S.: 541715

Ecolab NL 10 B.V. (1)
Iepenhoeve 7, 3438 MR, Nieuwegein, Netherlands
Tel.: (31) 306082222
Web Site: http://www.ecolab.com
Emp.: 250
Waste Treatment Services
N.A.I.C.S.: 221310

Ecolab New Zealand Ltd. (1)
2 Daniel Place, PO Box 10061, Te Rapa, Hamilton, 3241, New Zealand   (100%)
Tel.: (64) 7 958 2333
Web Site: https://en-nz.ecolab.com
Sales Range: $75-99.9 Million
Emp.: 280
Cleaning & Sanitizing Products Developer & Distr
N.A.I.C.S.: 325611

Ecolab Pest Elimination (1)

Ecolab Inc.—(Continued)

3535 South 31st St PO Box 6007, Grand Forks, ND 58201 **(100%)**
Tel.: (701) 775-6283
Web Site: http://www.ecolab.com
Rev.: $1,371,800,000
Emp.: 180
Pest Elimination Service
N.A.I.C.S.: 561710

Ecolab Pest France SAS **(1)**
25 Avenue Aristide Briand, CS 70106, 94112, Arcueil, Cedex, France
Tel.: (33) 80 031 0410
Web Site: http://www.ecolab.com
Pest Control Services
N.A.I.C.S.: 561710

Ecolab Production Belgium BVBA
Havenlaan 4, 3980, Tessenderlo, Belgium
Tel.: (32) 13670511
Chemical Product Whslr
N.A.I.C.S.: 424690

Ecolab Pte. Ltd. **(1)**
21 Gul Lane, Singapore, 629416, Singapore **(100%)**
Tel.: (65) 6 500 4900
Web Site: https://en-sg.ecolab.com
Sales Range: $1-9.9 Million
Emp.: 100
Mfr Detergents for Commercial & Industrial Uses
N.A.I.C.S.: 325611

Ecolab Pty. Ltd. **(1)**
2 Drake Avenue, Macquarie Park, 2113, NSW, Australia **(100%)**
Tel.: (61) 28 870 8100
Web Site: https://www.ecolab.com
Sales Range: $25-49.9 Million
Emp.: 500
Detergents Mfr
N.A.I.C.S.: 325611

Ecolab Quimica Ltda. **(1)**
Av Gupe 10 933 Jardim Belval, Barueri, 06422-120, Sao Paulo, Brazil
Tel.: (55) 1121348457
Food Service Equipment Whslr
N.A.I.C.S.: 423440

Ecolab S. A. **(1)**
Constituyente 1467 Apto 1407 Torre El Gaucho, Montevideo, 11200, Uruguay
Tel.: (598) 2 403 2300
Web Site: http://www.ecolab.com
Sales Range: $10-24.9 Million
Emp.: 5
Food Product Machinery Mfr & Consulting
N.A.I.C.S.: 333241
Roberto Arias *(CEO)*

Ecolab S.A. **(1)**
Av Francisco de Miranda cruce con Av El Parque Urb Campo Alegre, Torre Edicampo Piso 1 of 11 Chacao, Caracas, 1060, Venezuela
Tel.: (58) 2122637878
Sales Range: $25-49.9 Million
Emp.: 7
Food Product Machinery Mfr & Consulting
N.A.I.C.S.: 333241
Luis Muro *(CEO)*

Ecolab S.R.L. **(1)**
Via Trento 26, 20871, Vimercate, MB, Italy
Tel.: (39) 03960501
Web Site: http://www.it.ecolab.com
Chemical Product & Preparation Mfr
N.A.I.C.S.: 325998

Ecolab SAS **(1)**
10 Avenue Aristide Briand, 92220, Bagneux, France
Tel.: (33) 149696500
Chemical Product Whslr
N.A.I.C.S.: 424690

Ecolab SNC **(1)**
23 Avenue Aristide Briand, CS 70107, 94112, Arcueil, Cedex, France
Tel.: (33) 149696500
Web Site: http://en-fr.ecolab.com
Chemical Products Distr
N.A.I.C.S.: 424690

Ecolab Sdn Bhd **(1)**

Suite 12-01 12-02 & 12-03A Level 12 The Pinnacle Persiaran Lagoon, Bandar Sunway, 46150, Petaling Jaya, Selangor, Malaysia
Tel.: (60) 376285200
Web Site: http://www.ecolab.com
Water, Hygiene & Energy Technologies
N.A.I.C.S.: 221310

Ecolab Services Argentina S.R.L. **(1)**
Victoria Ocampo 360 - Piso 3 CABA, 1107, Buenos Aires, Argentina
Tel.: (54) 1155522566
Hygiene Water & Energy Technology Services
N.A.I.C.S.: 926130

Ecolab Services Poland Sp. z o o **(1)**
ul Opolska 114, 31-323, Krakow, Poland
Tel.: (48) 122616100
Web Site: http://en-pl.ecolab.com
Waste Treatment Services
N.A.I.C.S.: 221310

Ecolab Sp. z o.o. **(1)**
Ul Opolska 114, 31-323, Krakow, Poland
Tel.: (48) 122616100
Web Site: http://pl-pl.ecolab.com
Food Product Machinery Mfr
N.A.I.C.S.: 333241
Agnieszka Malinowska *(Pres)*

Ecolab Srl **(1)**
Via Trento 26, 20871, Vimercate, Monza and Brianza, Italy
Tel.: (39) 03960501
Food Product Machinery Mfr & Consulting Services
N.A.I.C.S.: 333241

Ecolab Srl **(1)**
Parque Industrial BES Planta No 60 Del Aeropuerto Juan Santamaria, Alajuela, Costa Rica
Tel.: (506) 24363900
Food Equipment Distr
N.A.I.C.S.: 423440

Ecolab USA Inc. **(1)**
1 Ecolab Pl, Saint Paul, MN 55102-2233
Tel.: (651) 293-2233
Web Site: http://www.ecolab.com
Sales Range: $300-349.9 Million
Emp.: 2,000
Food Product Machinery Mfr & Consulting
N.A.I.C.S.: 333241
Douglas M. Baker Jr. *(Chm)*

Unit (Domestic):

Ecolab USA Inc. - Food & Beverage Processing **(2)**
1 Ecolab Pl, Saint Paul, MN 55102
Tel.: (651) 293-2233
Web Site: http://www.ecolab.com
Sales Range: $1-4.9 Billion
Environment Sanitation Products & Services
N.A.I.C.S.: 325611

Subsidiary (Domestic):

Ecovation, Inc. **(3)**
Eastgate Sq Ste 200 50 Square Dr, Victor, NY 14564
Tel.: (585) 421-3500
Sales Range: $50-74.9 Million
Emp.: 70
Renewable Energy Solutions & Effluent Management Systems for Food & Beverage Industries
N.A.I.C.S.: 562998

Branch (Domestic):

Ecolab USA Inc. - Tucson **(2)**
4775 S Butterfield Dr, Tucson, AZ 85714-3449
Tel.: (520) 571-0909
Sales Range: $10-24.9 Million
Emp.: 42
Polish Mfr
N.A.I.C.S.: 325612

Ecolab Vietnam Company Limited **(1)**
Unit 8 2 E-Town 2 Building 364 Cong Hoa Street, Tan Binh District, Ho Chi Minh City, Vietnam
Tel.: (84) 35285100
Sanitation Goods Mfr

N.A.I.C.S.: 325612
Hoai Nguyen *(Mgr-Field Sls)*

Ecolab d.o.o. **(1)**
Vajngerlova 4, PO Box 190, 2001, Maribor, Slovenia
Tel.: (386) 2 429 3100
Web Site: http://www.ecolab.com
Hospital Hygiene, Textile Care, Commercial Cleaning & Sanitizing Products
N.A.I.C.S.: 325611

Ecolab s.r.o. **(1)**
Cajkova 18, 811 05, Bratislava, Slovakia
Tel.: (421) 25 720 4915
Web Site: https://sk-sk.ecolab.com
Emp.: 34
Waste Treatment Services
N.A.I.C.S.: 221310

Ecolab y Compania Colectiva de Responsabilidad Limitada **(1)**
Km 16 7 Carretera a Ticuantepe 200 mts Camino a la Comunida San Pedro, Ticuantepe, Managua, Nicaragua
Tel.: (505) 22796431
Waste Treatment Services
N.A.I.C.S.: 221310

Ecolab, S. de R.L. de C.V. **(1)**
Corporativo Century Plaza Av Santa Fe No 440 Piso 6, Col Santa Fe Del Cuajimalpa, CP 05348, Mexico, Mexico
Tel.: (52) 8003262000
Web Site: http://www.es-es.ecolab.com
Waste Treatment Services
N.A.I.C.S.: 221310

Ecolab, S.A. de C.V. **(1)**
12 Calle Poniente 23 Avenida Sur N 700, San Salvador, El Salvador
Tel.: (503) 24363930
Cooking Equipment Whslr
N.A.I.C.S.: 423440
Marlene Guerrerro *(Office Mgr)*

Ecolabone B.V. **(1)**
Iepenhoeve 7A, 3438, Nieuwegein, Netherlands
Tel.: (31) 306082222
Web Site: http://www.ecolab.com
Emp.: 60
Investment Management Service
N.A.I.C.S.: 523999

Enviroflo Engineering Limited **(1)**
Winnington Avenue, PO Box 11, Northwich, CW8 4DX, Cheshire, United Kingdom
Tel.: (44) 16 067 4488
Web Site: https://www.envirofloeng.com
Waste Treatment Services
N.A.I.C.S.: 221310

Food Protection Services, L.L.C. **(1)**
510 Fox Ln, Carmel, IN 46032
Tel.: (855) 377-3444
Web Site:
http://www.foodprotectionservices.net
Pest Control Services
N.A.I.C.S.: 115112

Four-State Hygiene, Inc. **(1)**
9155 Marshall Rd ste 1, Cranberry Township, PA 16066
Tel.: (724) 453-1220
Housekeeping Services
N.A.I.C.S.: 561720

GCS Service, Inc. **(1)**
8356 Sterling St, Irving, TX 75063 **(100%)**
Tel.: (972) 906-0307
Web Site: http://www.gcsparts.com
Retail Restaurant Equipment Repair
N.A.I.C.S.: 423440

Branch (Domestic):

GCS Service, Inc. **(2)**
696 Larch Ave, Elmhurst, IL 60126
Tel.: (630) 941-7800
Web Site: http://www.gcsparts.com
Food Service Equipment Distr
N.A.I.C.S.: 423440

Gallay Medical & Scientific NZ Pty Ltd **(1)**
7A Pacific Rise Mt Wellington, Auckland, 1060, New Zealand
Tel.: (64) 92824266
Web Site: http://www.gallay.co.nz
Medical Equipment Distr

N.A.I.C.S.: 423450
Dustin Habeck *(Mgr-New Zealand)*

Gallay Medical & Scientific Pty Ltd **(1)**
13-19 Dunlop Road, Mulgrave, 3170, VIC, Australia
Tel.: (61) 130 042 5529
Web Site: http://www.gallay.com.au
Emp.: 100
Medical Equipment Distr
N.A.I.C.S.: 423450
Geraldine Bell *(Mgr-Mktg Comm)*

Guangzhou Green Harbour Environmental Operation Ltd. **(1)**
Room 201-209 No 6 Huajing Road, Tian He District, Guangzhou, 510630, China
Tel.: (86) 2085560954
Web Site: http://www.ghgroup.com.hk
Pest Control Services
N.A.I.C.S.: 561710

Holchem Laboratories Limited **(1)**
Gateway House Pilsworth Road, Bury, BL9 8RD, Lancashire, United Kingdom
Tel.: (44) 1706222288
Web Site: https://www.holchem.co.uk
Cleaning Product Whslr
N.A.I.C.S.: 423850
John Holah *(Dir-Technical)*
Nick Edwards *(Dir-Sls)*
Stuart Middleton *(Mng Dir)*
Steve Bagshaw *(Mktg Dir)*
Iain Robertson *(Dir-Ops)*

Kay BVBA **(1)**
Havenlaan 4, Tessenderlo, 3980, Limburg, Belgium
Tel.: (32) 13670690
Web Site: http://www.ecolab.com
Emp.: 3
Home Furnishing Material Whslr
N.A.I.C.S.: 423220

Kay Chemical Company **(1)**
8300 Capital Dr, Greensboro, NC 27409
Tel.: (336) 931-2000
Web Site: http://www.ecolab.com
Sales Range: $150-199.9 Million
Emp.: 320
Specialty Cleaning
N.A.I.C.S.: 325612

Krofta Technologies, LLC **(1)**
401 S St, Dalton, MA 01226-1758
Tel.: (413) 236-5634
Web Site: https://www.krofta.com
Waste Treatment Services
N.A.I.C.S.: 221310

LHS (UK) Limited **(1)**
Duke Ave, Cheadle, SK8 6RB, United Kingdom
Tel.: (44) 1614856166
Chemical Product Whslr
N.A.I.C.S.: 424690

Laboratoires Anios S.A. **(1)**
1 rue de l'Espoir, 59260, Lezennes, France
Tel.: (33) 32 067 6767
Web Site: https://www.anios.com
Emp.: 600
Hygiene & Disinfectant Products Mfr
N.A.I.C.S.: 325612

Les Produits Chimiques ERPAC Inc. **(1)**
2099 Boul Fernand-Lafontaine, Longueuil, J4G 2J4, QC, Canada
Tel.: (450) 218-7753
Web Site: https://www.erpac.ca
Chemical Products Distr
N.A.I.C.S.: 424690

Master Chemicals OOO **(1)**
St Zinina 8, Tatarstan, 420097, Kazan, Russia
Tel.: (7) 8432228600
Web Site: http://www.m-chem.ru
Chemical Product & Preparation Mfr
N.A.I.C.S.: 325998

Meratech Rus Group LLC **(1)**
25 Kazanskoe Ave Building 2, 603087, Nizhniy Novgorod, Russia
Tel.: (7) 88003335888
Web Site: http://www.meratech.ru
Food Industry Machinery & Equipment Mfr
N.A.I.C.S.: 333310

Microtek Medical BV (1)
Hekkehorst 24, PO Box 234, 7207 BN, Zutphen, Netherlands
Tel.: (31) 575599200
Web Site: http://www.microtekmed.com
Surgical Products & Equipment Mfr
N.A.I.C.S.: 339113

Microtek Medical Malta Limited (1)
Sorbonne Centre F20, Mosta, MST 3000, Malta
Tel.: (356) 22584800
Surgical Appliance Whslr
N.A.I.C.S.: 423450

Microtek Medical, Inc. (1)
512 Lehmberg Rd, Columbus, MS 39702
Tel.: (662) 327-1863
Web Site: http://www.microtekmed.com
Sales Range: $75-99.9 Million
Emp.: 300
Surgical Appliance Whslr
N.A.I.C.S.: 423450
Jerry S. Wilson (CFO)

Mobotec Europe AB (1)
Armborstv 1, 125 44, Alvsjo, Sweden
Tel.: (46) 31218834
Waste Treatment Services
N.A.I.C.S.: 221310

NDC LLC (1)
6312 S 27th St Ste 202, Oak Creek, WI 53154
Tel.: (414) 761-2040
Web Site: https://www.ndcllc.com
Real Estate Manangement Services
N.A.I.C.S.: 531390
Brian McGarry (Pres)
Mark Lampe (VP & Mgr)

NLC Process & Water Services SARL (1)
N 1 Cooperative Rahma Dely Brahim, 16302, Algiers, Algeria
Tel.: (213) 21335056
Waste Treatment Services
N.A.I.C.S.: 221310

Nalco Holding Company (1)
1601 W Diehl Rd, Naperville, IL 60563-1198
Tel.: (630) 305-1000
Web Site: http://www.nalco.com
Holding Company; Integrated Water Treatment & Process Improvement Services
N.A.I.C.S.: 551112
Stephen N. Landsman (Gen Counsel, Sec & VP)

Subsidiary (Domestic):

Nalco Company LLC (2)
1601 W Diehl Rd, Naperville, IL 60563-1198
Cleaning Service
N.A.I.C.S.: 561720

Subsidiary (Domestic):

Abednego Environmental Services, LLC (3)
27175 Haggerty Rd Ste 125, Novi, MI 48377
Tel.: (248) 567-7700
Web Site: http://www.ecolab.com
Environmental Consulting Services·
N.A.I.C.S.: 541620

Subsidiary (Non-US):

Nalco (China) Environmental Solution Co. Ltd. (3)
18 Waterfront Place 168 Daduhe Rd, Shanghai, 200062, China
Tel.: (86) 2161832500
Waste Treatment Services
N.A.I.C.S.: 221310

Nalco AB (3)
Glasfibergatan 10, 125 24, Alvsjo, Sweden
Tel.: (46) 86032200
Web Site: https://www.ecolab.com
Waste Treatment Services
N.A.I.C.S.: 221310

Nalco Africa (PTY.) LTD. (3)
1 Ampere Street, Chloorkop Eden Glen, Johannesburg, 1613, Gauteng, South Africa
Tel.: (27) 11 578 5000
Web Site: http://www.ecolab.com
Waste Treatment Services
N.A.I.C.S.: 221310

Nalco Anadolu Kimya Sanayi ve Ticaret Limited Sirketi (3)
Esentepe Mahallesi E5 Yanyol Caddesi Vizyon No 13/65 Kat 1 TR, Bulvar No 13 Kat 1 No 65 Kartal, 34870, Istanbul, Kartal, Turkiye
Tel.: (90) 216 458 6900
Web Site: http://www.nowco.com
Emp.: 100
Waste Treatment Services
N.A.I.C.S.: 221310

Nalco Argentina S.R.L. (3)
Victoria Ocampo 360 3er Piso Edificios Colonos Plaza, Torre Sur, C1107BGA, Buenos Aires, Puerto Madero, Argentina
Tel.: (54) 11 5552 2566
Web Site: http://www.nalco.com
Sales Range: $50-74.9 Million
Emp.: 200
Chemicals & Services for Water Treatment, Pollution Control, Papermaking, Energy Conservation, Oil Production & Refining, Steelmaking, Metalworking & Other Industrial Processes
N.A.I.C.S.: 325998

Nalco Australia Pty. Ltd. (3)
2 Drake Avenue, Macquarie Park, 2113, NSW, Australia
Tel.: (61) 288708100
Web Site: http://www.nalco.com
Sales Range: $75-99.9 Million
Emp.: 300
Chemicals Mfr
N.A.I.C.S.: 325998

Nalco Azerbaijan LLC (3)
31 Matbuat Avenue, Baku, Azerbaijan
Tel.: (994) 124976106
Chemical Product & Preparation Mfr
N.A.I.C.S.: 325998

Nalco Belgium BVBA (3)
Noordkustlaan 16 C, 1702, Groot-Bijgaarden, Belgium
Tel.: (32) 24675111
Waste Treatment Services
N.A.I.C.S.: 221310

Subsidiary (Domestic):

Nalco Cal Water, LLC (3)
704 S Richfield Ave, Placentia, CA 92870
Tel.: (714) 792-0708
Web Site: http://www.cal-water.com
Emp.: 23
Water Purification Equipment Whslr
N.A.I.C.S.: 423440

Subsidiary (Non-US):

Nalco Canada Company (3)
1055 Truman Street, Burlington, L7R 3V7, ON, Canada
Tel.: (905) 333-6191
Web Site: http://www.nalco.com
Sales Range: $25-49.9 Million
Emp.: 80
Water Treatment & Process Improvement
N.A.I.C.S.: 325998

Nalco Chemicals India Limited (3)
20 A Pk St, Kolkata, 700 016, West Bengal, India
Tel.: (91) 3322172494
Web Site: http://www.nalco.com
Sales Range: $50-74.9 Million
Emp.: 200
Water, Hygiene & Energy Technologies & Services
N.A.I.C.S.: 237110

Branch (Domestic):

Nalco Company - Sugar Land (3)
11177 S Stadium Dr, Sugar Land, TX 77478
Tel.: (281) 263-7391
Web Site: http://www.nalco.com
Emp.: 100
Chemicals Mfr
N.A.I.C.S.: 424690

Subsidiary (Non-US):

Nalco Company OOO (3)
Letnikovskaya Str 10 Bld 4 6th Floor, 115114, Moscow, Russia
Tel.: (7) 4959807280
Waste Treatment Services

N.A.I.C.S.: 221310

Subsidiary (Domestic):

Nalco Crossbow Water LLC (3)
320 W 194th St, Glenwood, IL 60425
Tel.: (708) 754-2550
Web Site: http://www.nalco.ecolab.com
Emp.: 40
Water Purification Equipment Whslr
N.A.I.C.S.: 423440

Subsidiary (Non-US):

Nalco Czechia s.r.o. (3)
Voctarova 2449/5, Praha 8, 180 00, Prague, Czech Republic
Tel.: (420) 296114003
Web Site: http://www.nalco.com
Emp.: 10
Waste Treatment Services
N.A.I.C.S.: 221310

Nalco Danmark APS (3)
Hoffdingsvej 36 3rd, 2500, Valby, Denmark
Tel.: (45) 36158585
Web Site: http://www.nalco.com
Emp.: 6
Water Treatment Equipment Mfr
N.A.I.C.S.: 333310

Nalco De Colombia LTDA (3)
Av Calle 100 No 19-54 Piso 4, Bogota, Colombia
Tel.: (57) 16186000
Web Site: http://www.nalco.com
Chemical Product & Preparation Mfr
N.A.I.C.S.: 325998

Nalco De Mexico, S. de R. L. de C.V. (3)
Ave Santa Fe 505-4th Fl Santa Fe Col Cruz Manca Cuajimalpa, Col Cruz Manca Santa Fe, Mexico, Cuajimalpa, Mexico
Tel.: (52) 5550816170
Waste Treatment Services
N.A.I.C.S.: 221310

Subsidiary (Domestic):

Nalco Delaware Company (3)
1105 N Market St, Wilmington, DE 19801
Tel.: (302) 427-2681
Emp.: 4
Waste Treatment Services
N.A.I.C.S.: 221310

Subsidiary (Non-US):

Nalco Deutschland GMBH (3)
Ecolab-Allee 1, 40789, Monheim am Rhein, Germany
Tel.: (49) 69153253340
Waste Treatment Services
N.A.I.C.S.: 221310

Subsidiary (Domestic):

Nalco Deutschland Manufacturing GMBH UND CO. KG (4)
Justus-Von-Liebig-Strasse 11, 64584, Biebesheim am Rhein, Germany
Tel.: (49) 62588050
Chemical Product & Preparation Mfr
N.A.I.C.S.: 325998

Subsidiary (Non-US):

Nalco Dutch Holdings B.V. (3)
Rhijnhofweg 17, 2342 BB, Oegstgeest, Netherlands
Tel.: (31) 715235851
Holding Company
N.A.I.C.S.: 551112

Nalco Egypt, LTD. (3)
Building No 67 90th st Southern 5th Settlement-First Sector, Cairo, Egypt
Tel.: (20) 226131755
Waste Treatment Services
N.A.I.C.S.: 221310

Nalco Energy Services Limited (3)
Tern Place Denmore Road Bridge of Don, Aberdeen, AB23 8JX, United Kingdom
Tel.: (44) 1224617000
Waste Treatment Services
N.A.I.C.S.: 221310

Subsidiary (Domestic):

Nalco Energy Services Middle East Holdings, Inc. (3)

7701 Hwy 90-A, Sugar Land, TX 77478
Tel.: (281) 263-7000
Waste Treatment Services
N.A.I.C.S.: 424690

Nalco Energy Services, L.P. (3)
7705 Hwy 90 A, Sugar Land, TX 77478
Tel.: (281) 263-7000
Web Site: http://www.nalco.com
Sales Range: $200-249.9 Million
Specialty Chemicals & Programs for the Oilfield, Refining & Chemical Process Industries & Additives for Gasoline & Diesel Fuel
N.A.I.C.S.: 325998

Nalco Environmental Solutions LLC (3)
7705 Highway 90-A, Sugar Land, TX 77478
Tel.: (281) 263-7709
Web Site: http://www.nalcoesllc.com
Waste Treatment Services
N.A.I.C.S.: 221310

Subsidiary (Non-US):

Nalco Espanola, S.L. (3)
Avda Baix Llobregat 3 Planta 1A, Sant Joan Despi, 08970, Barcelona, Spain
Tel.: (34) 934758900
Waste Treatment Services
N.A.I.C.S.: 221310

Subsidiary (Domestic):

Nalco Espanola Manufacturing, S.L.U. (4)
Pol Industrial S/N, 17460, Celra, Girona, Spain
Tel.: (34) 972497400
Emp.: 50
Waste Treatment Services
N.A.I.C.S.: 221310
Rei Abreu (Gen Mgr)

Subsidiary (Non-US):

Nalco Europe BV (3)
Ir Tjalmaweg 1, PO Box 627, Oegstgeest, 2342 BV, Netherlands
Tel.: (31) 715241100
Web Site: http://www.nalco.com
Sales Range: $25-49.9 Million
Emp.: 110
Provider of Chemicals & Services for Water Treatment, Pollution Control, Papermaking, Energy Conservation, Oil Production & Refining, Steelmaking, Metalworking & Other Industrial Processes
N.A.I.C.S.: 325998

Nalco Finland OY (3)
Palkkatilanportti 1, PO Box 123, 00241, Helsinki, Finland
Tel.: (358) 925195600
Chemical Product & Preparation Mfr
N.A.I.C.S.: 325998

Nalco France (3)
23 avenue Aristide Briand, 94112, Arcueil, Cedex, France
Tel.: (33) 14 969 6500
Web Site: https://fr-fr.ecolab.com
Waste Treatment Services
N.A.I.C.S.: 221310

Nalco Hellas S.A. (3)
280 Kifisias Av & 2 Idras str, Chalandri, Athens, 15232, Greece
Tel.: (30) 2106873700
Web Site: http://www.gr-gr.ecolab.com
Waste Treatment Services
N.A.I.C.S.: 221310

Nalco Holdings G.m.b.H. (3)
Rivergate D1/4OG Handelskai 92, 1200, Vienna, Austria
Tel.: (43) 17152550
Web Site: http://www.nalco.com
Emp.: 25
Holding Company
N.A.I.C.S.: 551112

Nalco Industrial Services (Nanjing) Co., Ltd. (3)
No 19 Hanfu Rd Jiangjun Ave 7th Bldg Room 901 Jiangning, Nanjing, 210004, China
Tel.: (86) 15312064139
Water Treatment Chemicals Whslr
N.A.I.C.S.: 424690

Ecolab Inc.—(Continued)

Nalco Industrial Services (Suzhou) Co., Ltd. (3)
88 Ta Yuan Road, Suzhou New Development Zone, Suzhou, 215009, Jiangsu, China
Tel.: (86) 51281873000
Waste Treatment Services
N.A.I.C.S.: 221310

Nalco Industrial Services (Thailand) Co., Ltd. (3)
14/9 Rayong Highway 3191, Mabtaphut, Rayong, 21150, Thailand
Tel.: (66) 3 864 3400
Web Site: http://www.nalco.com
Sales Range: $10-24.9 Million
Emp.: 50
Chemicals
N.A.I.C.S.: 237110

Nalco Industrial Services Chile Limitada (3)
Av Las Esteras Norte 2341, Quilicura, Santiago, Chile
Tel.: (56) 2 640 2000
Web Site: http://www.nalco.com
Emp.: 120
Waste Treatment Services
N.A.I.C.S.: 221310

Nalco Industrial Services Malaysia SDN. BHD (3)
79 Sibiyu-Jaya Mile 6 Jalan Bintulu-Sibu, 97000, Bintulu, Sarawak, Malaysia
Tel.: (60) 86314976
Web Site: http://www.nalco.com
Waste Treatment Services
N.A.I.C.S.: 221310

Nalco International Holdings B.V. (3)
Ir G Tjalmaweg 1, Oegstgeest, 2342 BV, Netherlands
Tel.: (31) 651181447
Holding Company
N.A.I.C.S.: 551112

Nalco Israel Industrial Services Ltd. (3)
4 Hama'ayan Sreet, Modi'in-Maccabim-Re'ut, 71700, Israel
Tel.: (972) 8 970 5202
Web Site: http://www.nalco.com
Waste Treatment Services
N.A.I.C.S.: 221310

Nalco Korea Limited (3)
2F Jung-hun Bldg 516 Teheran-ro, Gangnam-gu, Seoul, 006-180, Korea (South)
Tel.: (82) 2 559 3676
Web Site: http://www.ecolab.com
Water Treatment & Process Improvements & Energy & Technology Services
N.A.I.C.S.: 221310

Nalco Latin American Operations (3)
Av Das Nacoes Unidas 17 891 6th Floor, Santo Amaro, Sao Paulo, 04795 100, SP, Brazil
Tel.: (55) 1156446500
Web Site: http://www.nalco.com
Sales Range: $25-49.9 Million
Emp.: 100
Provider of Chemicals & Services for Water Treatment, Pollution Control, Papermaking, Energy Conservation, Oil Production & Refining, Steelmaking, Metalworking & Other Industrial Processes
N.A.I.C.S.: 325998

Nalco Libya (3)
Shara Ben Ashur, Tripoli, Libya
Tel.: (218) 213606427
Chemical Product & Preparation Mfr
N.A.I.C.S.: 325998
Mohammed Shelmani (Branch Mgr)

Nalco Limited (3)
Winnington Avenue, PO Box 11, Winnington, Northwich, CW8 4DX, Cheshire, United Kingdom
Tel.: (44) 16 067 4488
Web Site: http://www.nalco.com
Waste Treatment Services
N.A.I.C.S.: 221310

Nalco Netherlands BV (3)
Oude Rhijnhofweg 17, 2342 BB, Oegst-

geest, Netherlands
Tel.: (31) 71 524 1100
Web Site: http://www.nalco.com
Emp.: 120
Waste Treatment Services
N.A.I.C.S.: 221310

Nalco Norge AS (3)
Stokkamyrveien 13, PO Box 1064, 4391, Sandnes, Norway
Tel.: (47) 51963600
Emp.: 32
Waste Treatment Services
N.A.I.C.S.: 221310
David Marlow (Mgr)

Nalco Osterreich Ges m.b.H. (3)
Rivergate D1/4OG Handelskai 92, 1200, Vienna, Austria
Tel.: (43) 17152550
Waste Treatment Services
N.A.I.C.S.: 221310

Nalco Pakistan (Private) Limited (3)
D-15/1 Block-3 KDA Scheme-5, Clifton, Karachi, Pakistan
Tel.: (92) 21534861
Waste Treatment Services
N.A.I.C.S.: 221310

Nalco Philippines Inc. (3)
21F Tower I II Corporate Centre Filinvest Corporate City, Metro Manila, 1770, Muntinlupa, Philippines
Tel.: (63) 27728888
Emp.: 60
Chemical Product Whslr
N.A.I.C.S.: 424690

Nalco Polska Sp. z o. o (3)
ul Przemyslowa 55, 43-110, Tychy, Poland
Tel.: (48) 32 326 2750
Web Site: https://pl-pl.ecolab.com
Emp.: 35
Waste Treatment Services
N.A.I.C.S.: 221310

Nalco Portuguesa (Quimica Industrial) Ltd. (3)
Estrada Outeiro Polima Lote 11 3 A/C, Sao Domingos de Rana, 2785-518, Abobada, Portugal
Tel.: (351) 962405685
Waste Treatment Services
N.A.I.C.S.: 221310

Nalco Saudi Co. Ltd. (3)
First Industrial City Dammam - 11th Street, PO Box 7372, Dammam, 31462, Saudi Arabia
Tel.: (966) 13 824 9100
Web Site: http://www.en-ph.ecolab.com
Mfr & Sale of Chemicals & Services for Water Treatment
N.A.I.C.S.: 325998

Nalco Schweiz GmbH (3)
Kagenstrasse 10, 4153, Reinach, Switzerland
Tel.: (41) 417602220
Web Site: http://www.nalco.com
Waste Treatment Services
N.A.I.C.S.: 221310

Nalco Taiwan Co., Ltd. (3)
10 F No 172 Sec 4 Cheng De Rd Shih Lin Dist, Shih Lin Dist, Taipei, Taiwan
Tel.: (886) 289781234
Waste Treatment Services
N.A.I.C.S.: 221310

Nalco Venezuela S. C. A. (3)
Av Ppal La Castellana Edif Banco de Lara Piso 9, Dtto Capital, Caracas, Venezuela
Tel.: (58) 2129567300
Waste Treatment Services
N.A.I.C.S.: 221310

Nalco Water India Limited (3)
238/239 Quadra 1 2nd Floor Panchshil Magarpatta City Road, Sade Satra Nali, Pune, 411 028, India
Tel.: (91) 2066594000
Web Site: https://en-in.ecolab.com
Chemical Product & Preparation Mfr
N.A.I.C.S.: 325998
Christophe Beck (CEO)
Darrell Brown (Pres)

Nalco Italiana SrL (1)
Viale dell Esperanto 71, 00144, Rome, Italy

Tel.: (39) 0654565000
Waste Treatment Services
N.A.I.C.S.: 221310

Subsidiary (Domestic):

Nalco Italiana Manufacturing S.R.L. (2)
Via Ninfina II, 04012, Cisterna di Latina, Italy
Tel.: (39) 069 644 9400
Web Site: http://it-it.ecolab.com
Chemical Product & Preparation Mfr
N.A.I.C.S.: 325998

Nalco Japan G.K. (1)
Harumi Triton Square Tower Y 1-8-11 Harumi, Chuo-ku, Tokyo, 104-6131, Japan
Tel.: (81) 342366900
Water Infection Prevention Services
N.A.I.C.S.: 562910

Nuova Farmec S.r.l. (1)
Via W Flemming 7, Zona Industriale Settimo di, 37026, Pescantina, VR, Italy
Tel.: (39) 045 676 7672
Web Site: https://www.farmec.it
Pharmaceutical Product Mfr & Distr
N.A.I.C.S.: 325412

OWT Oil-Water Treatment Services B.V. (1)
Centraleweg 11E, 4931 NA, Geertruidenberg, Netherlands
Tel.: (31) 162519395
Web Site: http://www.oil-water-treatment.com
Waste Treatment Services
N.A.I.C.S.: 221310

Oksa Kimya Sanayi A.S. (1)
Tepeoren Mah Akdeniz Cad 21 Tuzla, Istanbul, Turkiye
Tel.: (90) 2165601600
Cleaning Service
N.A.I.C.S.: 561720

Ondeo Nalco Energy Services (1)
29 Ul Nikolaya Ershova, Kazan, Russia
Tel.: (7) 8432750894
Waste Treatment Services
N.A.I.C.S.: 221310

Oy Ecolab AB (1)
Palkkatilanportti 1, PO Box 123, 00241, Helsinki, Finland
Tel.: (358) 207561400
Food Product Machinery Mfr
N.A.I.C.S.: 333241
Anu Kuronen (Mgr-HR)

P.T. Champion Kurnia Djaja Technologies (1)
Menara Bank Danamon Suite 1203 Jl Prof DR Satrio Kav EIV/6 Mega, Jakarta Selatan, 12950, Indonesia
Tel.: (62) 215760533
Chemical Product Whslr
N.A.I.C.S.: 424690

P.T. Ecolab Indonesia (1)
Jl Jababeka 12-B Kawasan Industri Jababeka BI V/3, Cibitung, Bekasi, 17520, Indonesia
Tel.: (62) 21 8934668
Hospitality Cleaning Services
N.A.I.C.S.: 561720

P.T. Ecolab International Indonesia (1)
Pondok Indah Office Tower 5 5th Floor, Jln Sultan Iskander Muda Kav V-Ta, South Jakarta, Indonesia
Tel.: (62) 2139702320
Chemical Products Distr
N.A.I.C.S.: 424690

P.T. Nalco Indonesia (1)
Jl Pahlawan Desa Karangasem Timur Citeureup, Bogor, West Java, Indonesia
Tel.: (62) 218753175
Web Site: http://www.ecolab.com
Emp.: 100
Chemical Products Distr
N.A.I.C.S.: 424690

Purolite Corporation (1)
2201 Renaissance Blvd, King of Prussia, PA 19406
Tel.: (610) 549-4106
Web Site: http://www.purolite.com

Sales Range: $50-74.9 Million
Emp.: 130
Plastics Materials & Resins
N.A.I.C.S.: 325211

Quantum Technical Services, LLC (1)
16834 Titan Dr, Houston, TX 77058
Tel.: (281) 461-7200
Web Site: https://www.quantumtec.net
Emp.: 30
Environmental Consulting Services
N.A.I.C.S.: 541620
Chuck Winfield (Pres)

Quimiproductos, S. de R.L. de C.V. (1)
Via A Matamoros 540 Col Garza Cantu, San Nicolas, 66480, NL, Mexico
Tel.: (52) 8183056500
Web Site: http://www.quimiproductos.com.mx
Chemical Product Whslr
N.A.I.C.S.: 424690

R P Adam Limited (1)
North Riverside Industrial Park Riverside Road, Selkirk, TD7 5DU, United Kingdom
Tel.: (44) 175023780
Web Site: http://www.rpadam.co.uk
Chemical Product Mfr & Distr
N.A.I.C.S.: 325199
Geoffrey Forbes Adam (Chm)

RES-KEM LLC (1)
2 New Rd, Aston, PA 19014
Tel.: (610) 358-0717
Web Site: http://www.reskem.com
Emp.: 25
Water Treatment Equipment Mfr
N.A.I.C.S.: 333310

Royal Pest Solutions Inc. (1)
981 S Bolmar St Unit B, West Chester, PA 19382
Tel.: (610) 436-5579
Web Site: http://www.royalpest.com
Pest Control Services
N.A.I.C.S.: 561710

SWSH Daley Mfg, Inc. (1)
4100 W 6 76th St Unit L, Chicago, IL 60652
Tel.: (773) 583-3500
Emp.: 4
Soap & Detergent Mfr
N.A.I.C.S.: 325611

Soluscope International Trading (Shanghai) Co., Ltd. (1)
Room 10G Liang Feng Mansion N 8 Dongfang Road Pudong District, Shanghai, 200120, China
Tel.: (86) 2158812856
Modioal Equipment Diotr
N.A.I.C.S.: 423450

Soluscope SAS (1)
100 Rue Du Fauge ZI Les Paluds, 13400, Aubagne, France
Tel.: (33) 49 183 2122
Web Site: https://www.soluscope.com
Medical Equipment Mfr & Distr
N.A.I.C.S.: 334510

Swisher Hygiene Franchise Corp. (1)
4725 Piedmont Row Dr Ste 400, Charlotte, NC 28210-4270
Tel.: (704) 364-7707
Emp.: 2,100
Housekeeping Services
N.A.I.C.S.: 561720

Swisher Hygiene USA Operations, Inc. (1)
16750 Hedgecroft Dr Ste 512, Houston, TX 77060
Tel.: (281) 260-8003
Building Maintenance Services
N.A.I.C.S.: 561790

TIORCO LLC (1)
2452 S Trenton Way Ste M, Denver, CO 80231
Tel.: (303) 923-6440
Web Site: http://www.tiorco.com
Oil Recovery Services
N.A.I.C.S.: 213112

Technical Textile Services Limited (1)

Units 7 and 8 Rhodes Business Park Silburn Way, Middleton, Manchester, M24 4NE, United Kingdom
Tel.: (44) 1616433000
Web Site: https://www.techtex.co.uk
Emp.: 100
Medical Fabric & Filtration Product Mfr & Distr
N.A.I.C.S.: 339113

USF Healthcare SA (1)
Rue Francois Perreard 18, Chene Bourg, 1225, Geneva, Switzerland
Tel.: (41) 228397900
Web Site: https://www.usfhealthcare.com
Pharmaceuticals Product Mfr
N.A.I.C.S.: 325412

Zohar Dalia (1)
Kibbutz Dalia, Dalia, 1923900, Israel
Tel.: (972) 49897234
Web Site: http://www.zohardalia.com
Commercial Cleaning & Sanitizing Products
N.A.I.C.S.: 325611

ECOLOCAP SOLUTIONS INC.
1250 S Grove Ave Ste 308, Barrington, IL 60010
Tel.: (866) 479-7041   NV
Web Site: http://www.ecolocap.com
Year Founded: 2004
ECOS—(OTCIQ)
Renewable Energy & Carbon Reduction Solutions
N.A.I.C.S.: 221118
Michel St-Pierre (Acting CFO)
Jeung Kwak (Chm)
Michael Siegel (Pres & CEO)
James Kwak (COO)

ECOLOGIX RESOURCES GROUP, INC.
9903 Santa Monica Blvd Ste 918, Beverly Hills, CA 90212
Tel.: (90-) 12-3851
Web Site: http://www.ecologixrg.com
Year Founded: 2007
EXRG—(OTCEM)
Sales Range: Less than $1 Million
Emp.: 35
Lumber Mfr
N.A.I.C.S.: 321999
Jason Fine (Chm & CEO)
Yaffa Zwebner (Bd of Dirs & Sec)
Juan Avila (Bd of Dirs & Dir-Corp Svcs)
Robert Radoff (Pres)
Michael Handelman (CFO)

ECOM PRODUCTS GROUP CORPORATION
3419 Gray Ct, Tampa, FL 33609
Tel.: (805) 220-3955   FL
Web Site:
    http://www.ecomproductsgroup.com
Year Founded: 2010
EPGC—(OTCIQ)
Sales Range: Less than $1 Million
Internet Marketing Services
N.A.I.C.S.: 541890
Andrew Waters (Chm, CEO, COO & Treas)

ECOPLUS, INC.
120 Washington Street STE 202, Salem, MA 1970
Tel.: (978) 515-2273
Web Site:
    https://www.ecopluscorporate.com
Year Founded: 2004
ECPL—(OTCIQ)
Electric Power Distribution Services
N.A.I.C.S.: 221118
William H. Dougherty (Chm)

ECOSCIENCES, INC.
420 Jericho Tpke Ste 110, Jericho, NY 11753
Tel.: (516) 465-3964   NV

Web Site:
    https://www.ecosciences.company
Year Founded: 2010
ECEZ—(OTCIQ)
Sales Range: Less than $1 Million
Other Management Consulting Services
N.A.I.C.S.: 541618
Joel Falitz (Chm, CEO, Pres, Sec & Treas)

ECOVYST INC.
300 Lindenwood Dr, Malvern, PA 19355-1740
Tel.: (484) 617-1200   DE
Web Site: https://www.ecovyst.com
Year Founded: 2015
ECVT—(NYSE)
Rev.: $691,118,000
Assets: $1,837,751,000
Liabilities: $1,132,287,000
Net Worth: $705,464,000
Earnings: $71,154,000
Emp.: 911
Fiscal Year-end: 12/31/23
Speciality Chemical Supplier
N.A.I.C.S.: 424690
Raymond Kolberg (Pres-Catalysts)
Kurt J. Bitting (CEO)
George Vann (Pres)
Sean Dineen (VP)
Chris Hall (Controller)
Colleen Grace Donofrio (VP-Environment & Sustainability)
Joseph S. Sichko Jr. (Gen Counsel, Sec & VP)

Subsidiaries:

Ecovyst Catalyst Technologies UK Ltd.   (1)
4 Liverpool Road, Warrington, WA5 1AQ, United Kingdom
Tel.: (44) 192 598 5500
Chemical Product Mfr & Distr
N.A.I.C.S.: 325998

National Silicates Partnership   (1)
429 Kipling Avenue, Toronto, M8Z 5C7, ON, Canada
Tel.: (416) 255-7771
Specialty Chemical Whslr
N.A.I.C.S.: 424690

PQ Corporation   (1)
Linden Wood Corporate Ctr 300 Lindenwood Dr, Malvern, PA 19355-1740
Tel.: (610) 651-4200
Web Site: https://www.pqcorp.com
Emp.: 1,500
Chemical Mfr & Whslr
N.A.I.C.S.: 325998
Raymond Kolberg (Pres-Catalysts Grp)
Kurt J. Bitting (Pres-Refining Svcs)
Kurt Bitting (Pres-Refining Svcs)
Albert F. Beninati Jr. (Pres-Performance Chemicals)

Subsidiary (Domestic):

Eco Services Operations Corp.   (2)
2002 Timberloch Pl Ste 300, The Woodlands, TX 77380
Tel.: (844) 812-1812
Specialty Chemical Whslr
N.A.I.C.S.: 424690

Subsidiary (Domestic):

Chem32 LLC   (3)
3007 Burnet St, Orange, TX 77630-7115
Tel.: (409) 883-8500
Web Site: http://www.c32llc.com
Chemical & Allied Products Merchant Whslr
N.A.I.C.S.: 424690

Subsidiary (Non-US):

PQ Silicas Holdings South Africa Pty Ltd.   (2)
169 Tedstone Road Germiston, 1428, Wadeville, Gauteng, South Africa
Tel.: (27) 118207101
Specialty Chemical Whslr
N.A.I.C.S.: 424690

Subsidiary (Domestic):

PQ Silicas South Africa Pty Ltd.   (3)
188 Lansdowne Rd, Durban, 4052, Kwa-Zulu Natal, South Africa
Tel.: (27) 314608111
Specialty Chemical Whslr
N.A.I.C.S.: 424690

PQ Holdings Australia Pty Limited   (1)
9-13 Rhur Street, PO Box 4389, Dandenong, 3164, VIC, Australia
Tel.: (61) 397089200
Specialty Chemical Whslr
N.A.I.C.S.: 424690

PQ International Cooperatie U.A.   (1)
De Brand 24, 3823 LJ, Amersfoort, Netherlands
Tel.: (31) 334509030
Specialty Chemical Whslr
N.A.I.C.S.: 424690

PQ Silicas UK Limited   (1)
Bank Quay, PO Box 26, Warrington, WA5 1AB, United Kingdom
Tel.: (44) 1925416100
Specialty Chemical Whslr
N.A.I.C.S.: 424690

Potters Ballotini Ltd.   (1)
Pontefract Road, Barnsley, S71 1HJ, United Kingdom
Tel.: (44) 1226704500
Specialty Chemical Whslr
N.A.I.C.S.: 424690

Potters Ballotini S.A.S.   (1)
Zone Industrielle Du Pont Panay, Saint-Brice-sous-Foret, 03500, France
Tel.: (33) 470457045
Chemical Mfr & Whslr
N.A.I.C.S.: 325998

Potters Industrial Limitada   (1)
Av Prefeito Sa Lessa 381, Rio de Janeiro, 21530-040, Brazil
Tel.: (55) 2124725050
Web Site: http://www.potters.com.br
Road Safety Product Mfr
N.A.I.C.S.: 334290

ECP ENVIRONMENTAL GROWTH OPPORTUNITIES CORP.
40 Beechwood Rd, Summit, NJ 07901
Tel.: (973) 671-6100   DE
Year Founded: 2020
ENNV—(NASDAQ)
Investment Services
N.A.I.C.S.: 523999
Tyler Reeder (Pres & CEO)
Andrew Brown (CFO & Exec VP)
Chris Leininger (Sec, Exec VP & Gen Counsel)
Tyler Kopp (Exec VP-Corp Dev)

ECRID, INC.
1320 SE Federal Hwy, Stuart, FL 34994   NV
Web Site: https://www.ecrid.com
ECDD—(OTCIQ)
Assets: $10,019
Liabilities: $22,496
Net Worth: ($12,477)
Earnings: ($1,718,575)
Emp.: 1
Fiscal Year-end: 03/31/22
Miscellaneous Financial Investment Activities
N.A.I.C.S.: 523999
Cleveland E. Gary (Pres)

EDD HELMS GROUP, INC.
740 International Pkwy, Sunrise, FL 33325
(954) 406-3858   FL
Web Site: https://www.eddhelms.com
Year Founded: 1975
EDHD—(OTCIQ)
Sales Range: $10-24.9 Million

Electrical Contractors & Other Wiring Installation Contractors
N.A.I.C.S.: 238210
Dean Goodson (CFO)
Wade Helms (Pres & CEO)
Joni Alonso (Mgr-Trade Shows)
Michael Larabee (Mgr-Project)
Scott Doria (Mgr-HVAC Sls)
Ed Duran (Mgr-Building Automation)
John Garzia (Supvr-Electrical Field Svc)
Linda Klawans (Mgr-Westin Diplomat Events)
Roger Prendergast (Mgr-HVAC Svc)

Subsidiaries:

Edd Helms Electrical, Inc.   (1)
17850 NE 5th Ave, Miami, FL 33162
Tel.: (305) 653-2520
Web Site: http://www.eddhelms.com
Sales Range: $10-24.9 Million
Electrical Services for Residential & Commercial
N.A.I.C.S.: 238210
W. Edd Helms Jr. (CEO)

Edd Helms McDonald Air Conditioning, Inc.   (1)
17850 NE 5 Ave, Miami, FL 33162-1008   (100%)
Tel.: (305) 653-2520
Web Site: http://www.eddhelms.com
Electrical Contracting; Air Conditioning
N.A.I.C.S.: 238220

EDGE DATA SOLUTIONS, INC.
3550 Lenox Rd NE 21st Fl, Atlanta, GA 30326   DE
Web Site:
    http://www.edgedatasolutions.io
EDGS—(OTCIQ)
Rev.: $1,566,617
Assets: $3,095,177
Liabilities: $4,627,335
Net Worth: ($1,532,158)
Earnings: ($929,075)
Emp.: 10
Fiscal Year-end: 12/31/21
Information Technology Services
N.A.I.C.S.: 513210
Delray Wannemacher (Chm, Pres, CEO & Treas)
Nancy Madland (Controller)

EDGEMODE, INC.
110 E Broward Blvd Ste 1700, Fort Lauderdale, FL 33301
Tel.: (707) 687-9093   NV
Web Site: https://www.edgemode.io
Year Founded: 2011
EDGM—(OTCIQ)
Rev.: $438,042
Assets: $1,189,399
Liabilities: $2,783,071
Net Worth: ($1,593,672)
Earnings: ($32,245,997)
Emp.: 2
Fiscal Year-end: 12/31/22
Women Healthcare Services
N.A.I.C.S.: 621610
Simon Wajcenberg (Chm & CFO)

EDGEWELL PERSONAL CARE COMPANY
6 Research Dr, Shelton, CT 06484
Tel.: (203) 944-5500   MO
Web Site: https://www.edgewell.com
Year Founded: 1999
EPC—(NYSE)
Rev.: $2,251,600,000
Assets: $3,740,700,000
Liabilities: $2,200,200,000
Net Worth: $1,540,500,000
Earnings: $114,700,000
Emp.: 6,800
Fiscal Year-end: 09/30/23

Edgewell Personal Care Company—(Continued)

Holding Company; Shaving Systems,
Latex Gloves, Lotions, Feminine &
Infant Care Products Mfr
N.A.I.C.S.: 551112
Rod R. Little *(Pres & CEO)*
Eric O'Toole *(Pres-North America)*
Paul Hibbert *(Chief Supply Chain Officer)*
Nick Powell *(Pres-Intl)*
Karen Anderson *(Dir-Diversity, Equity & Inclusion)*
Chris Gough *(VP-IR)*
LaTanya Langley *(Chief People Officer & Sec)*
Ricardo de Oliveira *(Sr VP)*
Amy Knight *(VP)*
Camilla Medeiros *(VP)*
Lauren Medina *(Dir)*
Daniel J. Sullivan *(COO)*

Subsidiaries:

Billie, Inc. **(1)**
100 Crosby St Ste 301, New York, NY
10012
Web Site: https://mybillie.com
Cosmetic Product Retailer
N.A.I.C.S.: 456120

Edgewell Personal Care - Ormond
Beach **(1)**
1190 N US Hwy 1, Ormond Beach, FL
32174
Tel.: (386) 677-9559
Web Site: http://edgewell.com
Skin Care Product Mfr
N.A.I.C.S.: 325620

Edgewell Personal Care Italy
S.p.A. **(1)**
Strada 1 Palazzo E5, 20090, Assago, Italy
Tel.: (39) 02892331
Storage Battery Mfr
N.A.I.C.S.: 335910
Iacopo Biondi *(Reg Mgr-Mktg-Southern Europe)*

Edgewell Personal Care, LLC **(1)**
1350 Timberlake Manor Pkwy, Saint Louis,
MO 63017
Tel.: (314) 594-1900
Personal Care Services
N.A.I.C.S.: 812199

Energizer Group Austria Handels
GmbH **(1)**
Seidlgasse 21/113-114, Vienna, 1030, Austria
Tel.: (43) 158766160
Web Site: http://www.energizer.eu
Sales Range: $10-24.9 Million
Emp.: 9
Primary Batteries & Portable Lighting Products Mfr & Distr
N.A.I.C.S.: 335910

Energizer Group France SAS **(1)**
6 Rue Emile Pathe, 78400, Chatou, France
Tel.: (33) 114802800
Industrial Machinery Mfr
N.A.I.C.S.: 333998

Energizer Group Holland B.V. **(1)**
Papendorpseweg 53 59, Utrecht, 3528 BJ,
Netherlands
Tel.: (31) 307991103
Web Site: http://www.energizer.eu
Shaving Product Distr
N.A.I.C.S.: 424210

Energizer Group Portugal Unipessoal,
Lda. **(1)**
Avenida Forte 3, 2790, Carnaxide, Portugal
Tel.: (351) 214164700
Batteries & Dry Cell Mfr
N.A.I.C.S.: 334515

Energizer Group Venezuela C.A. **(1)**
Avenida 8, Maracaibo, Zulia, Venezuela
Tel.: (58) 2617982978
Web Site: http://www.energizer.com.ve
Batteries & Dry Cell Mfr
N.A.I.C.S.: 334515

Energizer Hong Kong Limited **(1)**
Room 1701-1708 17/F Kwong Sang Hong

Centre 151-153 Hoi Bun Road, Kwun Tong,
Kowloon, China (Hong Kong)
Tel.: (852) 29562333
Primary Batteries & Portable Lighting Products Mfr & Distr
N.A.I.C.S.: 335910

Energizer LLC **(1)**
Prospekt Mira 26 Building 5, Moscow,
129090, Russia
Tel.: (7) 959378820
Web Site: http://www.energizer.eu
Storage Battery Mfr
N.A.I.C.S.: 334515

Energizer Personal Care, LLC **(1)**
1 Razor Blade Ln, Verona, VA 24482-0979
Tel.: (540) 248-8000
Personal Care Products Mfr & Distr
N.A.I.C.S.: 325620

Energizer Puerto Rico, Inc. **(1)**
544 Aldebaran Altamira, San Juan, PR
00915
Tel.: (787) 792-8162
Primary Batteries & Portable Lighting Products Mfr & Distr
N.A.I.C.S.: 335910

Energizer-Schick Taiwan Ltd. **(1)**
18 Floor No 65 2 Tun Hwa South, Taipei,
106, Taiwan
Tel.: (886) 227552700
Primary Batteries & Portable Lighting Products Mfr & Distr
N.A.I.C.S.: 335910

Jack Black, L.L.C. **(1)**
551 Southwestern Blvd Ste 100, Coppell,
TX 75019
Tel.: (469) 341-2700
Web Site: https://www.getjackblack.com
Toilet Preparation Mfr
N.A.I.C.S.: 325620
Emily Dalton *(Co-Founder & Exec VP)*

Mintology Limited **(1)**
Unit 4 07 Grand Union Studios 332 Ladbroke Grove, London, W10 5AD, United
Kingdom
Tel.: (44) 2072888420
Web Site: https://wakencare.com
Mouth Care Product Distr
N.A.I.C.S.: 424210

Personna American Safety Razor
Company **(1)**
240 Cedar Knolls Rd, Cedar Knolls, NJ
07927
Tel.: (973) 753-3000
Web Site: http://www.personna.com
Sales Range: $300-349.9 Million
Emp.: 1,800
Shaving, Industrial & Surgical Blades,
Knives, Soap & Shampoo Mfr
N.A.I.C.S.: 339113

Personna International Israel Ltd. **(1)**
Hayotzer No 3, PO Box 813, Nazareth Illit,
17501, Israel
Tel.: (972) 46413300
Personal Care Products Mfr & Distr
N.A.I.C.S.: 325620

Personna International UK
Limited **(1)**
Ratcher Way Crown Farm Industrial Park,
Forest Town, Mansfield, NG19 0FS, United
Kingdom
Tel.: (44) 1623638627
Web Site: http://www.personna-uk.co.uk
Razor Mfr
N.A.I.C.S.: 332215

Personna International de Mexico,
S.A. de C.V. **(1)**
Calle de Diana 41A Col Nueva Industrial
Vallejo, Mexico, 53100, Mexico
Tel.: (52) 5557524719
Razor Mfr
N.A.I.C.S.: 332215

Playtex Marketing Corp. **(1)**
800 Silver Lk Blvd Ste 103, Dover, DE
19904
Tel.: (302) 678-6000
Investment Management Service
N.A.I.C.S.: 551112

Playtex Products, LLC **(1)**

5901 W Side Ave Ste 400, North Bergen,
NJ 07047
Web Site: http://www.playtexproducts.com
Baby Product Distr
N.A.I.C.S.: 424350

REBA Organizacja Odzysku S.A. **(1)**
Kubickiego 19/16, Warsaw, Poland
Tel.: (48) 225506108
Web Site: http://www.reba.com.pl
Batteries & Dry Cell Mfr
N.A.I.C.S.: 334515

Schick (Guangzhou) Company
Ltd. **(1)**
No 3 Xiayuan Road Dongji Industrial Zone
Economic Technology, Guangzhou, 510730,
Guangdong, China
Tel.: (86) 2082211162345
Razor Mfr
N.A.I.C.S.: 332215

Schick Asia Limited **(1)**
20/F Landmark East Axa Twr, Kwun Tong,
Kowloon, China (Hong Kong)
Tel.: (852) 28737600
Web Site: http://www.schick.com.hk
Razor Mfr
N.A.I.C.S.: 332215

Schick Japan K.K. **(1)**
2-24-9 Kamiosaki, Shinagawa-ku, Tokyo,
141-8671, Japan
Tel.: (81) 354876801
Web Site: http://www.schick.jp
Emp.: 99
Personal Care Products Mfr & Distr
N.A.I.C.S.: 325620

Schick Manufacturing Inc. **(1)**
10 Leighton Rd, Milford, CT 06460
Tel.: (203) 882-2100
Web Site: http://www.schick.com
Sales Range: $350-399.9 Million
Emp.: 800
Warehousing Services
N.A.I.C.S.: 493110

Schick-Wilkinson Sword **(1)**
10 Leighton Rd, Milford, CT 06460
Tel.: (203) 882-2100
Web Site: http://www.shaving.com
Sales Range: $1-4.9 Billion
Emp.: 4,000
Shaving Products Mfr
N.A.I.C.S.: 325412

Shavekit Limited **(1)**
PO Box 375, Wallington, SM6 6DN, United
Kingdom
Tel.: (44) 3031231113
Web Site: https://www.shavekit.com
Shaving Product Distr
N.A.I.C.S.: 424210

Tanning Research Laboratories,
LLC **(1)**
1190 US Hwy 1 N, Ormond Beach, FL
32174
Tel.: (386) 677-9559
Web Site: http://www.hawaiiantropic.com
Skin Care Product Mfr
N.A.I.C.S.: 325412

Tropria Holding B.V. **(1)**
Dr Willem Dreesweg 2 Suite 43b, Amstelveen, 1185 VB, Noord-Holland, Netherlands
Tel.: (31) 206402803
Holding Company
N.A.I.C.S.: 551112

Wilkinson Sword GmbH **(1)**
Schutzenstrasse 110, 42659, Solingen, Germany
Tel.: (49) 2124050
Web Site: http://www.wilkinsonsword.com
Sales Range: $150-199.9 Million
Emp.: 800
Razors & Shaving Products Mfr
N.A.I.C.S.: 332215
W. Althaus *(Mng Dir)*

Wilkinson Sword Limited **(1)**
Sword House Totteridge Road, High Wycombe, HP13 6DG, Buckinghamshire,
United Kingdom
Tel.: (44) 1494216894
Web Site: https://www.wilkinsonsword.com
Razor Blade Mfr
N.A.I.C.S.: 332215

**EDGEWISE THERAPEUTICS,
INC.**
1715 38 th St, Boulder, CO 80301
Tel.: (720) 262-7002 DE
Web Site:
    https://www.edgewisetx.com
Year Founded: 2017
EWTX—(NASDAQ)
Rev.: $14,194,000
Assets: $340,035,000
Liabilities: $21,205,000
Net Worth: $318,830,000
Earnings: ($100,163,000)
Emp.: 88
Fiscal Year-end: 12/31/23
Biotechnology Research & Development Services
N.A.I.C.S.: 541714
Kevin Koch *(Pres & CEO)*
Alan Russell *(Co-Founder & Chief Scientific Officer)*
R. Michael Carruthers *(CFO)*
Behrad Derakhshan *(Chief Bus Officer)*
John Moore *(Gen Counsel)*
Joanne M. Donovan *(Chief Medical Officer)*
Abby Bronson *(VP-Patient Advocacy & External Innovation)*
Peter Thompson *(Co-Founder & Chm)*
Badreddin Edris *(Co-Founder)*

EDGIO, INC.
11811 N Tatum Blvd Ste 3031, Phoenix, AZ 85028
Tel.: (602) 850-5000 DE
Web Site: https://www.edg.io
Year Founded: 2001
EGIO—(NASDAQ)
Rev.: $338,598,000
Assets: $542,380,000
Liabilities: $303,057,000
Net Worth: $239,323,000
Earnings: ($136,519,000)
Emp.: 980
Fiscal Year-end: 12/31/22
Custom Computer Programming Services
N.A.I.C.S.: 541511
Todd Hinders *(CEO)*
Sandra Brisentine *(VP-HR)*
Nigel Burmeister *(VP-Product Mktg)*
Dan Carney *(Sr VP-Dev & Ops-Global)*
Ersin Galloglu *(VP-Strategic Initiatives)*
Thomas Marth *(Sr VP-Sls)*
Daniel R. Boncel *(CFO)*
Christine Cross *(CMO & Sr VP)*
Kenneth H. Traub *(Chm)*
Michael D. DiSanto *(Chief Admin & Legal Officer & Sec)*

Subsidiaries:

Limelight Networks (UK) Limited **(1)**
Aviation House 7th Floor 125 Kingsway,
London, WC2B 6NH, United Kingdom
Tel.: (44) 203 923 0481
Sales Range: $100-124.9 Million
Internet Services
N.A.I.C.S.: 517131

Limelight Networks France SARL **(1)**
129 Avenue Charles de Gaulle, 92200,
Neuilly-sur-Seine, France
Tel.: (33) 14 637 0833
Web Site: https://www.limelight.com
Content Delivery & Management Network
Provider
N.A.I.C.S.: 541511

Limelight Networks Germany
GmbH **(1)**
Konrad-Zuse-Platz 1, Munich, 81829, Germany
Tel.: (49) 8989058480

Emp.: 6
Content Delivery & Management Network Provider
N.A.I.C.S.: 517111
Bob Lento *(CEO)*

Limelight Networks Inc. (1)
37th Floor 50 Raffles Place, Singapore, 48623, Singapore
Tel.: (65) 68297168
Web Site: http://www.limelight.com
Sales Range: $10-24.9 Million
Emp.: 20
Video, Music, Games & Downloads Content Delivery Internet Distr
N.A.I.C.S.: 516210

Limelight Networks India Private Limited (1)
WeWork Enam Sambhav C-20 G Block, Bandra-Kurla Complex, Mumbai, 400051, Maharashtra, India
Tel.: (91) 9833923191
Web Site: http://www.limelight.com
Content Delivery & Management Network Provider
N.A.I.C.S.: 517111

Limelight Networks Japan (1)
14F Tokyo Square Garden 3-1-1, Kyobashi Chuo-ku, Tokyo, 104-0031, Japan
Tel.: (81) 5036281545
Web Site: http://www.limelightnetworks.com
Sales Range: $100-124.9 Million
Internet Services
N.A.I.C.S.: 517121

Limelight Networks Korea Ltd. (1)
50 Jong-ro 1-gil, Jongno-gu, Seoul, 110-714, Korea (South)
Tel.: (82) 2 723 8844
Web Site: http://www.limelight.com
Applications Software Programming Services
N.A.I.C.S.: 541511

Limelight Networks Netherlands B.V. (1)
Binderij 7-R, 1185 ZH, Amstelveen, Netherlands
Tel.: (31) 206408513
Content Delivery & Management Network Provider
N.A.I.C.S.: 517111

Limelight Networks Singapore PTE LTD. (1)
37th Floor 50 Raffles Place, Singapore, 048623, Singapore
Tel.: (65) 68297168
Web Site: http://www.limelight.com
Content Delivery & Management Network Provider
N.A.I.C.S.: 517111

Limelight Web Technologies (IL) Ltd. (1)
13 Tuval Street, Ramat Gan, 5252228, Israel
Tel.: (972) 36227831
Broadcasting & Network Publishing Services
N.A.I.C.S.: 516210

**EDIBLE GARDEN AG INCOR-
PORATED**
283 County Rd 519, Belvidere, NJ 07823
Tel.: (908) 750-3953   DE
Web Site: https://ediblegardenag.com
Year Founded: 2020
EDBL—(NASDAQ)
Rev.: $11,552,000
Assets: $6,965,000
Liabilities: $9,145,000
Net Worth: ($2,180,000)
Earnings: ($12,453,000)
Emp.: 77
Fiscal Year-end: 12/31/22
Organic Product Mfr
N.A.I.C.S.: 325199
James E. Kras *(Co-Founder, Pres & CEO)*
David Ross *(VP-Sales & Marketing)*
John Kissel *(Dir-Horticulture)*

Chanida Curnutt *(Sr VP-Business Development & Compliance)*
Chris Wiersma *(Engr-Grow Sys)*
Emily Morel *(Dir-Production & Personnel)*
Jan-Tia Kern *(Dir-Food Safety)*
Amanda Caton *(Head-Grower, Belvidere, and NJ)*
Kelly Jimenez *(Assoc Dir-Creative)*
Mathew McConnell *(Dir)*
Ryan Rogers *(Dir)*
Pamela DonAroma *(Dir)*
Michael C. James *(Co-Founder)*

EDIFY ACQUISITION CORP.
888 7th Ave 29th Fl, New York, NY 10106
Tel.: (212) 603-2800   DE
Year Founded: 2020
EAC—(NASDAQ)
Rev.: $13,045,823
Assets: $20,290,369
Liabilities: $31,390,340
Net Worth: ($11,099,971)
Earnings: $11,124,257
Emp.: 2
Fiscal Year-end: 12/31/22
Investment Services
N.A.I.C.S.: 523999
Morris Beyda *(CFO)*
Susan Wolford *(Chm)*
Ronald H. Schlosser *(CEO)*

EDISON INTERNATIONAL
2244 Walnut Grove Ave, Rosemead, CA 91770
Tel.: (626) 302-2222   CA
Web Site: https://www.edison.com
Year Founded: 1987
EIX—(NYSE)
Rev.: $16,338,000,000
Assets: $81,758,000,000
Liabilities: $63,814,000,000
Net Worth: $17,944,000,000
Earnings: $1,197,000,000
Emp.: 14,316
Fiscal Year-end: 12/31/23
Holding Company; Electric Utilities Owner
N.A.I.C.S.: 221111
Pedro J. Pizarro *(Pres & CEO)*
Maria C. Rigatti *(CFO, Principal Acctg Officer & Exec VP)*
Adam S. Umanoff *(Gen Counsel & Exec VP)*
J. Andrew Murphy *(Sr VP-Strategy & Corp Dev)*
Caroline Choi *(Sr VP-Corp Affairs)*
Alisa Do *(Sec & VP)*
Beth M. Foley *(VP-Corp Comm)*
Kara Gostenhofer Ryan *(Chief Acctg Officer, VP & Controller)*
Brendan Bond *(Treas)*
Marta I. Carreira-Slabe *(VP)*
Drew Murphy *(Sr VP)*
Amy Ford Pressler *(VP)*
Natalie Schilling *(Chief HR Officer)*
Nicole Neeman Brady *(Founder)*

Subsidiaries:

Altamont Hotel Associates LP (1)
3048 16th St Apt 414, San Francisco, CA 94103-3499
Tel.: (415) 861-7099
Motor & Generator Mfr
N.A.I.C.S.: 335312

Apollo Development Associates LP (1)
422 Valencia St, San Francisco, CA 94103
Tel.: (415) 437-2868
Electric Power Distr
N.A.I.C.S.: 221122
Jeffrey Kirk *(Sr Dir-Market Res)*

Auburn Manor Apartments LP (1)
6821 Riverdale Rd, Riverdale, MD 20737
Tel.: (301) 577-7733

Web Site:
https://www.auburnmanorapts.com
Emp.: 3
Construction Services
N.A.I.C.S.: 531110

Boulder Creek Apartments LP (1)
4425 Issaquah Pine Lk Rd SE, Sammamish, WA 98075-6215
Tel.: (425) 336-0736
Web Site:
https://www.simpsonpropertygroup.com
Motor & Generator Mfr
N.A.I.C.S.: 335312

Casa Rampart LP (1)
401 S Rampart Blvd, Los Angeles, CA 90057-1717
Tel.: (213) 383-3525
Power Generation & Transmission Services
N.A.I.C.S.: 221118

Coolidge Station Apartments LLC (1)
8300 N Hayden Rd Ste A-113, Scottsdale, AZ 85258
Tel.: (520) 723-3361
Electric Power Distribution Services
N.A.I.C.S.: 221122

Cypress Cove Associates (1)
11110 Atlantic Blvd, Jacksonville, FL 32225
Tel.: (904) 641-2103
Web Site: http://www.benchmarkgrp.com
Emp.: 4
Motor & Generator Mfr
N.A.I.C.S.: 335312

Edison Capital (1)
18101 Von Karman Ave Ste 1700, Irvine, CA 92612-1012   **(100%)**
Tel.: (949) 757-2400
Web Site: http://www.edison.com
Capital & Financial Services for Energy, Infrastructure & Affordable Housing Provider
N.A.I.C.S.: 523999

Edison Mission Group Inc. (1)
18101 Von Karman Ave Ste 1700, Irvine, CA 92612-1012   **(100%)**
Tel.: (949) 757-2400
Web Site: http://www.edison.com
Sales Range: $50-74.9 Million
Emp.: 180
Development of Power Plants
N.A.I.C.S.: 237110

Edison O&M Services (1)
955 Overland Ct, San Dimas, CA 91773
Tel.: (626) 302-2284
Web Site:
http://www.edisoninternational.com
Sales Range: $25-49.9 Million
Emp.: 147
Provider of Project Management Services to Thermo & Hydro Electric Installations, Refineries, Tank & Pipeline Projects
N.A.I.C.S.: 561621

Eneractive Solutions, LLC. (1)
613 Bangs Ave, Asbury Park, NJ 07712
Tel.: (732) 988-8850
Web Site:
http://www.eneractivesolutions.com
Energy Consulting Services
N.A.I.C.S.: 541690

Midway-Sunset Cogeneration Company (1)
3466 W Crocker Springs Rd, Fellows, CA 93242
Tel.: (661) 768-3000
Sales Range: $25-49.9 Million
Emp.: 30
Electric Power Distr
N.A.I.C.S.: 221122
Dave Faiella *(Exec Dir)*

Rittenhouse School LP (1)
1705 Locust St, Norristown, PA 19401-3071
Tel.: (610) 275-5872
Motor & Generator Mfr
N.A.I.C.S.: 335312

Silver City Housing LP (1)
5815 SW 29th St Ste 200, Topeka, KS 66614
Tel.: (913) 362-4986
Lessors Residential Buildings & Dwellings Services
N.A.I.C.S.: 531110

Southern California Edison Company (1)
2244 Walnut Grove Ave, Rosemead, CA 91770
Tel.: (626) 302-1212
Web Site: http://www.sce.com
Rev.: $17,172,000,000
Assets: $77,807,000,000
Liabilities: $57,018,000,000
Net Worth: $20,789,000,000
Earnings: $954,000,000
Emp.: 12,831
Fiscal Year-end: 12/31/2022
Electric Utility Services
N.A.I.C.S.: 221122
Kevin M. Payne *(Pres & CEO)*
Kara Gostenhofer Ryan *(Chief Acctg Officer, VP & Controller)*
Michael D. Montoya *(Chief Compliance & Ethics Officer & VP)*
Jill C. Anderson *(Sr VP-Customer Svcs)*
Andrew R. Baldonado *(VP)*
Marta I. Carreira-Slabe *(VP)*

Subsidiary (Domestic):

EDISON RENEWABLE ENERGY, INC. (2)
2244 Walnut Grove Ave, Rosemead, CA 91770-3714
Tel.: (626) 302-2662
Oil & Gas Extraction Services
N.A.I.C.S.: 211120

Sunrise View Wind Farm, LLC (1)
49106 100th Ave, Albert City, IA 50510-8512
Tel.: (712) 843-5806
Motor & Generator Mfr
N.A.I.C.S.: 335312
Phil Sundblad *(Pres)*

Tioga Gardens LP (1)
1 Liberty Pl 1650 Market St Ste 3810, Philadelphia, PA 19103
Tel.: (215) 227-7708
Motor & Generator Mfr
N.A.I.C.S.: 335312

Union Meadows Associates LLC (1)
49 Union Square Blvd, North Chili, NY 14514
Tel.: (585) 293-9150
Lessors of Residential Buildings & Dwellings
N.A.I.C.S.: 531110

Vista Properties LLC (1)
256 Mammoth Rd, Lowell, MA 01854-2249
Tel.: (978) 970-0088
Motor & Generator Mfr
N.A.I.C.S.: 335312

EDITAS MEDICINE INC
11 Hurley St, Cambridge, MA 02141
Tel.: (617) 401-9000
Web Site:
https://www.editasmedicine.com
EDIT—(NASDAQ)
Rev.: $19,712,000
Assets: $514,321,000
Liabilities: $153,641,000
Net Worth: $360,680,000
Earnings: ($220,432,000)
Emp.: 226
Fiscal Year-end: 12/31/22
Genome Editing for Human Therapeutics
N.A.I.C.S.: 541715
Caren Deardorf *(Chief Strategy Officer)*
Erick J. Lucera *(CEO, CFO & Exec VP)*
Harry Gill *(Sr VP-Ops)*
James Mullen *(Chm)*
Linda C. Burkly *(Chief Scientific Officer & Exec VP)*
Linea Aspesi *(Chief People Officer)*
Chi Li *(Chief Regulatory Officer)*
Gilmore O'Neill *(Pres)*

EDUCATIONAL DEVELOP-

EDUCATIONAL DEVELOP—(CONTINUED)

MENT CORPORATION
5402 S 122nd East Ave, Tulsa, OK 74146
Tel.: (918) 622-4522   DE
Web Site: https://www.edcpub.com
Year Founded: 1965
EDUC—(NASDAQ)
Rev.: $75,583,600
Assets: $90,105,000
Liabilities: $44,654,300
Net Worth: $45,450,700
Earnings: $546,400
Emp.: 101
Fiscal Year-end: 02/29/24
Children's Books Publisher & Distr
N.A.I.C.S.: 424920
Randall W. White *(Chm)*
Craig M. White *(Pres & CEO)*
Dan E. O'Keefe *(CFO & Sec)*
Subsidiaries:

Demibooks Inc.   (1)
9299 E Falling Water Dr, Burr Ridge, IL 60527
Tel.: (312) 834-3364
Web Site: http://www.demibooks.com
Interactive Learning Software Publisher
N.A.I.C.S.: 513210

Educational Development Corporation - Home Business Division   (1)
5402 S 122 East Ave, Tulsa, OK 74146-6507
Tel.: (918) 622-4522
Web Site: http://www.edcpub.com
Sales Range: $75-99.9 Million
Emp.: 100
Children's Books Distr
N.A.I.C.S.: 424920
Randall W. White *(Pres & CEO)*

Educational Development Corporation - Publishing Division   (1)
10302 E 55th Pl, Tulsa, OK 74146-6515
Tel.: (918) 622-4522
Web Site: http://www.edcpub.com
Sales Range: $1-9.9 Million
Marketer of Books
N.A.I.C.S.: 459210
Randall W. White *(Chm, Chm, Pres & Pres)*
Jeanie Crone *(VP)*

EDWARDS LIFESCIENCES CORPORATION
1 Edwards Way, Irvine, CA 92614
Tel.: (949) 250-2500   DE
Web Site: https://www.edwards.com
Year Founded: 1958
EW—(NYSE)
Rev.: $6,004,800,000
Assets: $9,363,200,000
Liabilities: $2,643,800,000
Net Worth: $6,719,400,000
Earnings: $1,402,400,000
Emp.: 19,800
Fiscal Year-end: 12/31/23
Medical Devices for Treatment of Cardiovascular Diseases Mfr
N.A.I.C.S.: 541715
Scott B. Ullem *(CFO & VP)*
Dirksen J. Lehman *(VP-Pub Affairs)*
Arnold A. Pinkston *(Gen Counsel & VP)*
Catherine M. Szyman *(VP-Critical Care)*
Todd J. Brinton *(Chief Scientific Officer & VP-Advanced Tech)*
Daveen Chopra *(VP-Transcatheter Mitral & Tricuspid Therapies)*
Bernard J. Zovighian *(CEO)*
Arnold A. Pinkston Jr. *(Gen Counsel & VP)*
Subsidiaries:

BMEYE B.V.   (1)
Hoogoorddreef 60, 1101 BE, Amsterdam, Netherlands
Tel.: (31) 207533033

Web Site: http://www.edwards.com
Emp.: 15
Medical Equipment Distr
N.A.I.C.S.: 423450

CAS Medical Systems, Inc.   (1)
44 E Industrial Rd, Branford, CT 06405
Medical Equipment & Supplies Mfr
N.A.I.C.S.: 339113

CardiAQ Valve Technologies, Inc.   (1)
2 Jenner Ste 100, Irvine, CA 92618
Tel.: (949) 387-2615
Web Site: http://www.cardiaq.com
Electromedical & Electrotherapeutic Apparatus Mfr
N.A.I.C.S.: 334510
J. Brent Ratz *(Co-Founder, Pres & COO)*
Arshad Quadri *(Co-Founder)*

Edwards (Shanghai) Medical Products Co., Ltd.   (1)
Unit 2602-2608 2 Grand Gateway 3 Hong Qiao Road, Xu Hui District, Shanghai, 200030, China
Tel.: (86) 2153891888
Electromedical Equipment Distr
N.A.I.C.S.: 423450

Edwards Lifesciences   (1)
12050 Lone Peak Pkwy., Draper, UT 84020
Tel.: (801) 565-5200
Web Site: http://www.edwards.com
Sales Range: $75-99.9 Million
Emp.: 750
Development, Manufacture & Sale of Hospital Disposable Products for Cardiovascular & Vascular Surgery; Specialty Pharmaceuticals Mfr
N.A.I.C.S.: 339112

Edwards Lifesciences (Asia) Pte., Ltd.   (1)
35 Changi North Crescent, Singapore, 499641, Singapore   **(100%)**
Tel.: (65) 68836734
Medical Equipment Whslr
N.A.I.C.S.: 423450

Edwards Lifesciences (Canada) Inc.   (1)
6750 Century Ave Suite 303, Mississauga, L5N 2V8, ON, Canada   **(100%)**
Tel.: (905) 819-6900
Sales Range: $25-49.9 Million
Emp.: 25
Medical Devices for Treatment of Cardiovascular Diseases Distr
N.A.I.C.S.: 423450

Edwards Lifesciences (India) Private Limited   (1)
4th Floor Commerz II International Business Park Oberoi Garden City, Off Western Express Highway Goregaon East, Mumbai, 400063, India
Tel.: (91) 2266935701
Web Site: http://www.edwards.com
Medical Devices for Treatment of Cardiovascular Diseases Distr
N.A.I.C.S.: 423450

Edwards Lifesciences (Israel) Ltd   (1)
17 Hatokhen St Granit Campus - Ofek 13, Northern Industrial Park, Caesarea, 30889, Israel   **(100%)**
Tel.: (972) 46186100
Emp.: 60
Medical Devices for Treatment of Cardiovascular Diseases Distr
N.A.I.C.S.: 423450
Assaf Bash *(Gen Mgr)*

Edwards Lifesciences (Japan) Limited   (1)
Nittochi Nishi-Shinjuku Bldg 6-10-1 Nishi-Shinjuku, Shinjuku-ku, Tokyo, 160-0023, Japan   **(100%)**
Tel.: (81) 368940500
Medical Devices for Treatment of Cardiovascular Diseases Distr
N.A.I.C.S.: 423450

Edwards Lifesciences (Malaysia) Sdn. Bhd.   (1)
B03-A-15-01 Menara 3A No 3 Jalan Bangsar, KL Eco City, 59200, Kuala Lumpur, Selangor, Malaysia
Tel.: (60) 322893788

Medical Equipment Mfr
N.A.I.C.S.: 339112
Tang Chee Kong *(Mgr-Sls-SMB)*

Edwards Lifesciences (Poland) Ltd.   (1)
Aleje Jerozolimskie 100, 00-807, Warsaw, Poland   **(100%)**
Tel.: (48) 222563880
Medical Devices for Treatment of Cardiovascular Diseases Distr
N.A.I.C.S.: 423450

Edwards Lifesciences (Portugal) Comercio e Distribuicao de Dispositivos Medicos, Lda.   (1)
Lagoas Park Rua Das Lagoas Pequenas Edificio 5A - 5 Piso, Edificio 5A 5 Piso, 2744-017, Porto Salvo, Portugal
Tel.: (351) 214544460
Web Site: http://www.edwards.com
Medical Devices for Treatment of Cardiovascular Diseases Distr
N.A.I.C.S.: 423450

Edwards Lifesciences (Proprietary) Ltd   (1)
Route 21 Corporate Park, Irene X30 Tshwane, Pretoria, 0062, South Africa   **(100%)**
Tel.: (27) 123452482
Web Site: http://www.edwards.com
Emp.: 15
Medical Devices for Treatment of Cardiovascular Diseases Distr
N.A.I.C.S.: 423450

Edwards Lifesciences (Shanghai) Medical Products Co., Ltd.   (1)
Room 310 3F Tower B 21st Century Building No 40A Liangmaqiao Road, Chao Yang District, Beijing, 100125, China
Tel.: (86) 1056410888
Medical Equipment Distr
N.A.I.C.S.: 423450

Edwards Lifesciences (Singapore) Pte Ltd   (1)
35 Changi North Crescent, Singapore, 499641, Singapore
Tel.: (65) 68836789
Surgical Appliance & Supplies Mfr
N.A.I.C.S.: 339113

Edwards Lifesciences (Taiwan) Corporation   (1)
5F-7 No 51 Hengyang Road, Taipei, 100, Taiwan   **(100%)**
Tel.: (886) 2 2313 1610
Medical Devices for Treatment of Cardiovascular Diseases Distr
N.A.I.C.S.: 423450

Edwards Lifesciences (Thailand) Ltd.   (1)
191 Silom Complex Building 15th Floor Unit C Silom Road Silom, Rama 9 Road Huaykwang, Bangkok, 10500, Thailand   **(100%)**
Tel.: (66) 24948080
Medical Devices for Treatment of Cardiovascular Diseases Distr
N.A.I.C.S.: 423450

Edwards Lifesciences A/S   (1)
Arne Jackobsens Alle 7 5th Fl, PO Box 159, 2300, Copenhagen, Denmark   **(100%)**
Tel.: (45) 70223438
Medical Devices for Treatment of Cardiovascular Diseases Distr
N.A.I.C.S.: 423450

Edwards Lifesciences AG   (1)
Route de l Etraz 70, 1260, Nyon, Switzerland   **(100%)**
Tel.: (41) 227874300
Web Site: http://www.edwards.com
Medical Devices for Treatment of Cardiovascular Diseases Mfr
N.A.I.C.S.: 339112
Patrick Verguet *(CEO)*

Edwards Lifesciences Asset Management Corporation   (1)
1 Edwards Way, Irvine, CA 92614-5688
Tel.: (949) 250-2500
Web Site: http://www.edwardslifesciences.com
Surgical Appliance & Supplies Mfr
N.A.I.C.S.: 339113

Edwards Lifesciences Austria GmbH   (1)

Vorgartenstrasse 206 C, 1020, Vienna, Austria   **(100%)**
Tel.: (43) 1242200
Web Site: http://www.edwards.com
Medical Devices Distr; Heart Valves, Catheters & Pericardial Patches
N.A.I.C.S.: 423450

Edwards Lifesciences Comercio e Industria de Produtos Medico-Cirurgicos Ltda.   (1)
Rua Verbo Divino 1547 - 1 Andar Chacara Santo Antonio, Chacara Santo Antonio, Sao Paulo, 04794-000, SP, Brazil   **(100%)**
Tel.: (55) 1155675200
Medical Devices for Treatment of Cardiovascular Diseases Distr
N.A.I.C.S.: 423450

Edwards Lifesciences Corporation of Puerto Rico   (1)
State Rd 402 N Km 1 4 Industrial Park, Anasco, PR 00610-1577
Tel.: (787) 229-5699
Medical Devices for Treatment of Cardiovascular Diseases Mfr
N.A.I.C.S.: 339112

Edwards Lifesciences Costa Rica, S.R.L.   (1)
Del Pequeno Mundo 100 Este Y 200 Surzona Franca La Lima, 200 Mts Sur, Cartago, 30106, Costa Rica
Tel.: (506) 21037710
Electromedical Equipment Mfr
N.A.I.C.S.: 334510

Edwards Lifesciences Czech Republic s.r.o.   (1)
Pernerova 697/35 Prague 8 -Karlin, 186 00, Prague, Czech Republic
Tel.: (420) 221703344
Medical Equipment Distr
N.A.I.C.S.: 423450

Edwards Lifesciences DR   (1)
Parque Industrial de Itabo Carr Sanchez Km 18 5 Zona Franca, Industrial de Haina, San Cristobal, Dominican Republic
Tel.: (809) 3752200
Web Site: http://www.edwards.com
Medical Devices Mfr; Cardiovascular & Vascular Surgery Products
N.A.I.C.S.: 339112

Edwards Lifesciences Hellas, EPE   (1)
10 Kifissias Av, Neo Iraklio, 151 25, Maroussi, Greece   **(100%)**
Tel.: (30) 2102854640
Medical Devices for Treatment of Cardiovascular Diseases Distr
N.A.I.C.S.: 423450

Edwards Lifesciences Ireland, Limited   (1)
Beaux Lane House Mercer Street Lower, Dublin, 2, Ireland
Tel.: (353) 18211012
Electromedical Equipment Distr
N.A.I.C.S.: 423450
Ethna Gallagher *(Head-Supply Chain)*

Edwards Lifesciences Italia SpA   (1)
Centro Leoni Building A Via G Spadolini N 5, 20141, Milan, Italy   **(100%)**
Tel.: (39) 02568061
Medical Devices for Treatment of Cardiovascular Diseases Distr
N.A.I.C.S.: 423450

Edwards Lifesciences Korea Co., Ltd.   (1)
13 F City Air Tower 36 Teheran-ro 87-gil, Gangnam-gu, Seoul, Korea (South)   **(100%)**
Tel.: (82) 25599400
Medical Devices for Treatment of Cardiovascular Diseases Distr
N.A.I.C.S.: 423450

Edwards Lifesciences Limited   (1)
3 The Sector Newbury Business Park, 78-84 London Road, Newbury, RG14 2PZ, Berkshire, United Kingdom   **(100%)**
Tel.: (44) 1635277300
Medical Devices for Treatment of Cardiovascular Diseases Distr
N.A.I.C.S.: 423450

Edwards Lifesciences Mexico, S.A. de C.V. (1)
Av Insurgentes Sur 1431 15th Floor - Office 1502, Col Insurgentes Mixcoac, 03920, Mexico, 03920, Mexico **(100%)**
Tel.: (52) 5552927923
Web Site: http://www.edwards.com
Emp.: 1
Medical Devices for Treatment of Cardiovascular Diseases Distr
N.A.I.C.S.: 423450

Edwards Lifesciences Nordic AB (1)
Sodra Langgatan 25, 211 44, Malmo, Sweden **(100%)**
Tel.: (46) 40204850
Medical Devices for Treatment of Cardiovascular Diseases Distr
N.A.I.C.S.: 423450

Edwards Lifesciences Pty. Limited (1)
40 Talavera Road, PO Box 980, North Ryde, 2113, NSW, Australia **(100%)**
Tel.: (61) 288996300
Web Site: https://www.edwards.com
Medical Devices for Treatment of Cardiovascular Diseases Distr
N.A.I.C.S.: 423450

Edwards Lifesciences S.L. (1)
Ronda Narciso Monturiol 11 Bloque A, Parque Tecnologico de Valencia, 46980, Paterna, Valencia, Spain **(100%)**
Tel.: (34) 963053700
Medical Devices for Treatment of Cardiovascular Diseases Distr
N.A.I.C.S.: 423450
Carlos Baviera *(Mgr)*

Edwards Lifesciences S.P.R.L. (1)
Pontbeekstraat 4, 1702, Dilbeek, Belgium **(100%)**
Tel.: (32) 24813050
Medical Devices for Treatment of Cardiovascular Diseases Distr
N.A.I.C.S.: 423450

Edwards Lifesciences SAS (1)
Immeuble Gershwin 1 Rue Arnold Schoenberg, 78280, Guyancourt, 78280, France **(100%)**
Tel.: (33) 130052929
Medical Devices for Treatment of Cardiovascular Diseases Distr
N.A.I.C.S.: 423450

Edwards Lifesciences Sales (Israel) Ltd. (1)
Electra Tower 42nd Floor 98 Yigal Alon Street, Tel Aviv, 6789141, Israel
Tel.: (972) 776935029
Medical Equipment Distr
N.A.I.C.S.: 423450

Edwards Lifesciences Sales Corporation (1)
100 Gran Blvd Paseos Ste 112 MSC 181, San Juan, PR 00926
Tel.: (787) 826-8305
Medical Devices for Treatment of Cardiovascular Diseases Distr
N.A.I.C.S.: 423450

Edwards Lifesciences Services GmbH (1)
Edisonstrasse 6, 85716, Unterschleissheim, Germany **(100%)**
Tel.: (49) 89954750
Medical Devices for Treatment of Cardiovascular Diseases Distr
N.A.I.C.S.: 423450

Edwards Lifesciences World Trade (Shanghai) Co., Ltd. (1)
3/F B Baoqing Mansion, No 8 Taojiang Road, Shanghai, 200031, China **(100%)**
Tel.: (86) 21 6431 4887
Medical Devices for Treatment of Cardiovascular Diseases Distr
N.A.I.C.S.: 423450

Harpoon Medical, Inc. (1)
351 W Camden St Ste 801, Baltimore, MD 21201
Tel.: (410) 346-5687
Electromedical Equipment Mfr & Distr
N.A.I.C.S.: 334510

Valtech Cardio, Ltd. (1)

3 Ariel Sharon Ave, Or Yehuda, 60376, Israel
Tel.: (972) 35335959
Electromedical Equipment Distr
N.A.I.C.S.: 423450

EF HUTTON AMERICA, INC.
590 Madison Ave 39th Fl, New York, NY 10022
Tel.: (212) 970-5150   CO
Web Site: https://www.efhutton.com
Year Founded: 2007
HUTN—(OTCIQ)
Financial Information Services
N.A.I.C.S.: 519290
Christopher Daniels *(Co-Chm)*
Stanley Hutton Rumbough *(Co-Chm)*
Blair Friedensohn *(Mng Dir-Capital Markets)*
Joseph T. Rallo *(CEO)*
David W. Boral *(Pres)*
Nicolas de Alejo *(Mng Dir-ESG Investment Banking)*

EGAIN CORPORATION
1252 Borregas Ave, Sunnyvale, CA 94089
Tel.: (408) 636-4500   DE
Web Site: https://www.egain.com
Year Founded: 1997
EGAN—(NASDAQ)
Rev.: $92,803,000
Assets: $127,852,000
Liabilities: $69,356,000
Net Worth: $58,496,000
Earnings: $7,780,000
Emp.: 539
Fiscal Year-end: 06/30/24
Customer Communications Solutions for E-Commerce
N.A.I.C.S.: 334610
Rex Dorricott *(VP & Gen Mgr-EMEA)*
Gunjan Sinha *(Executives)*
Anand Subramaniam *(Sr VP-Marketing)*
Ashutosh Roy *(Founder, Chm & CEO)*
Eric N. Smit *(CFO)*
J. C. Rao *(VP-Svc, Support, and Operations)*

Subsidiaries:

Exony Ltd. (1)
St Catherines House Oxford Square, Oxford Street, Newbury, RG14 1JQ, Berks, United Kingdom
Tel.: (44) 1635271555
Web Site: http://www.exony.com
Sales Range: $10-24.9 Million
Software Solutions
N.A.I.C.S.: 513210

Subsidiary (US):

Exony Inc. (2)
60 State St Ste 700, Boston, MA 02109
Tel.: (617) 854-7486
Web Site: http://www.exony.com
Emp.: 50
Software Publisher
N.A.I.C.S.: 513210

eGain Communications BV (1)
Zekeringstraat 17 A, 1014 BM, Amsterdam, Netherlands
Tel.: (31) 205708934
Web Site: http://www.egain.com
Sales Range: $100-124.9 Million
Online Customer Service Solutions
N.A.I.C.S.: 541511

eGain Communications Ltd. (1)
St Catherines House Oxford Street, Newbury, RG14 1JQ, Berkshire, United Kingdom **(100%)**
Tel.: (44) 1635800087
Sales Range: $10-24.9 Million
Emp.: 40
Software Development Services
N.A.I.C.S.: 513210

eGain Communications Ltd. (1)

Bushfield House, 57 Philipsburgh Ave, Fairview, Dublin, 3, Ireland
Tel.: (353) 18373085
Sales Range: $100-124.9 Million
Online Customer Service Solutions
N.A.I.C.S.: 541511

eGain Communications Pvt. Ltd. (1)
Office number 702 7th Floor B-1 The Cerebrum IT Park, Vadgaon Sheri Kalyani Nagar, Pune, 411014, Maharashtra, India
Tel.: (91) 2066089200
Emp.: 250
Business Management Software Publisher
N.A.I.C.S.: 513210
Manish Sitania *(Gen Mgr)*

eGain Communications SrL (1)
Via Vicenzo Monti 8, 20123, Milan, Italy
Tel.: (39) 0246712239
Sales Range: $1-9.9 Million
Emp.: 2
Provider of Online Customer Service Solutions
N.A.I.C.S.: 541511

eGain France S.A.R.L. (1)
13 rue Camille Desmoulins, Issy les Moulineaux, 92441, Paris, Cedex, France
Tel.: (33) 158042434
Web Site: http://www.egain.com
Contact Center & Customer Services
N.A.I.C.S.: 561422

EHAVE, INC.
100 SE 2nd St Ste 2000, Miami, FL 33131
Tel.: (954) 233-3511   Ca
Web Site: https://www.ehave.com
Year Founded: 2011
EHVVF—(OTCIQ)
Assets: $2,972,925
Liabilities: $8,641,188
Net Worth: ($5,668,263)
Earnings: ($2,409,396)
Emp.: 1
Fiscal Year-end: 12/31/23
Healthcare Software Development Services
N.A.I.C.S.: 541511
Binyomin Posen *(Chm)*

Subsidiaries:

Mycotopia Therapies Inc. (1)
18851 NE 29th Ave Ste 700, Aventura, FL 33180 **(65.9%)**
Tel.: (954) 233-3511
Assets: $2,219,413
Liabilities: $4,247,723
Net Worth: ($2,028,310)
Earnings: ($1,181,347)
Emp.: 1
Fiscal Year-end: 12/31/2023
Therapeutic Services
N.A.I.C.S.: 621399
Benjamin Kaplan *(Chm & CEO)*

EHEALTH, INC.
13620 Ranch Rd 620 N Ste A250, Austin, TX 78717
Tel.: (737) 248-2340   DE
Web Site:
   https://www.ehealthinsurance.com
Year Founded: 1997
EHTH—(NASDAQ)
Rev.: $405,356,000
Assets: $1,112,611,000
Liabilities: $461,656,000
Net Worth: $650,955,000
Earnings: ($119,414,000)
Emp.: 1,515
Fiscal Year-end: 12/31/22
Holding Company; Internet-Based Marketer & Retailer of Health Insurance Products & Services
N.A.I.C.S.: 551112
John Dolan *(Chief Acctg Officer)*

Subsidiaries:

PlanPrescriber, Inc. (1)
8 Clock Tower Pl Ste 400, Maynard, MA 01754

Tel.: (888) 312-5447
Web Site: http://www.planprescriber.com
Sales Range: $1-9.9 Million
Emp.: 20
Educational Medical Material Services
N.A.I.C.S.: 541511

eHealthInsurance Services, Inc. (1)
440 E Middlefield Rd, Mountain View, CA 94043
Tel.: (650) 584-2700
Web Site: http://www.ehealthinsurance.com
Sales Range: $150-199.9 Million
Emp.: 300
On-Line Health Insurance Agency; Marketer of Health Insurance Products & Services
N.A.I.C.S.: 524210

EIGER BIOPHARMACEUTICALS, INC.
2155 Park Blvd, Palo Alto, CA 94306
Tel.: (650) 272-6138   DE
Web Site: https://www.eigerbio.com
Year Founded: 2000
EIGR—(NASDAQ)
Rev.: $13,484,000
Assets: $120,139,000
Liabilities: $64,829,000
Net Worth: $55,310,000
Earnings: ($96,776,000)
Emp.: 56
Fiscal Year-end: 12/31/22
Holding Company; Biopharmaceutical Developer & Mfr
N.A.I.C.S.: 551112
Thomas J. Dietz *(Chm)*
Ingrid Choong *(Sr VP-Clinical Dev)*
Colin Hislop *(Sr VP-Clinical & Dev Ops)*
Michelle Maynard *(Sr VP)*
Christopher Kurtz *(Chief Technical Officer)*
Colleen Craig *(VP)*

Subsidiaries:

EB Pharma, LLC (1)
350 Cambridge Ave Ste 350, Palo Alto, CA 94306
Tel.: (650) 272-6138
Web Site: http://www.eigerbio.com
Biopharmaceutical Developer & Mfr
N.A.I.C.S.: 325412

EIGHTCO HOLDINGS INC.
200 9th Ave N Ste 220, Safety Harbor, FL 34695   DE
Web Site: https://www.8co.holdings
Year Founded: 2021
OCTO—(NASDAQ)
Rev.: $31,820,779
Assets: $58,600,599
Liabilities: $52,789,375
Net Worth: $5,811,224
Earnings: ($47,446,060)
Emp.: 33
Fiscal Year-end: 12/31/22
Holding Company
N.A.I.C.S.: 551112
Brett Vroman *(CFO)*
Brian McFadden *(Pres)*

EJF ACQUISITION CORP.
2107 Wilson Blvd Ste 410, Arlington, VA 22201
Tel.: (703) 879-3292   Ky
Web Site:
   http://www.ejfacquisition.com
Year Founded: 2020
EJFA—(NASDAQ)
Investment Services
N.A.I.C.S.: 523999
Emanuel J. Friedman *(Chm)*
Neal Wilson *(Vice Chm)*
Kevin Stein *(CEO)*
Thomas Mayrhofer *(CFO)*
Erika Gray *(Chief Acctg Officer)*

EKO INTERNATIONAL CORP.

EKO International Corp.—(Continued)

269 S Beverly Dr, Beverly Hills, CA
90212
Tel.: (310) 440-2778
EKNL—(OTCIQ)
Holding Company
N.A.I.C.S.: 551112

EKSO BIONICS HOLDINGS, INC.

101 Glacier Point Ste A, San Rafael,
CA 94901
Tel.: (510) 984-1761 **NV**
Web Site:
https://www.eksobionics.com
Year Founded: 2005
EKSO—(NASDAQ)
Rev.: $18,279,000
Assets: $28,918,000
Liabilities: $16,312,000
Net Worth: $12,606,000
Earnings: ($15,198,000)
Emp.: 70
Fiscal Year-end: 12/31/23
Wearable Exoskeleton Apparatus Mfr
& Distr for Paralyzed Individuals
N.A.I.C.S.: 339112
Steven A. Sherman *(Chm)*
Chwee Foon Lim *(Pres-APAC)*
Stephan Aderhold *(VP-EMEA Sls & Mktg)*
Scott G. Davis *(Pres & CEO)*

Subsidiaries:

Ekso Bionics (EMEA) **(1)**
29th Floor One Canada Square Canary
Wharf, London, E14 5DY, United
Kingdom **(100%)**
Tel.: (44) 20 7060 3568
Web Site: http://www.eksobionics.com
Wearable Exoskeleton Apparatus Mfr &
Distr for Paralyzed Individuals
N.A.I.C.S.: 339112

EL CAPITAN PRECIOUS METALS INC.

5871 Honeysuckle Rd, Prescott, AZ
86305
Tel.: (928) 515-1942 **NV**
Web Site:
https://www.elcapitanpmi.com
ECPN—(OTCIQ)
Sales Range: Less than $1 Million
Emp.: 2
Gold, Silver & Platinum Mining Exploration & Development Services
N.A.I.C.S.: 213114
John F. Stapleton *(Chm, Pres, CEO & Sec)*

ELAH HOLDINGS, INC.

15301 Ventura Blvd Ste 400, Sherman Oaks, CA 91403
Tel.: (805) 435-1255 **DE**
Web Site:
http://www.realindustryinc.com
Year Founded: 1972
ELLH—(NASDAQ)
Sales Range: $1-4.9 Billion
Emp.: 1,800
Investment Holding Company
N.A.I.C.S.: 551112
John Miller *(Exec VP-Ops)*
Michael Hobey *(CFO)*
Kelly G. Howard *(Gen Counsel, Sec & Exec VP)*
Jeff Crusinberry *(Treas & Sr VP)*

Subsidiaries:

SGGH, LLC **(1)**
15301 Ventura Blvd Ste 400, Sherman
Oaks, CA 91403
Tel.: (805) 435-1255
Investment Management Service
N.A.I.C.S.: 523940
Craig T. Bouchard *(Chm & CEO)*
Kyle Ross *(CFO & Exec VP)*

Holding (Domestic):

Cosmed, Inc. **(2)**
6342 Grand Hickory Dr Ste 102, Braselton,
GA 30517
Tel.: (770) 965-1022
Web Site: http://www.clinicianscomplex.com
Skin Care Products Developer, Mfr & Distr
N.A.I.C.S.: 325620

Real Alloy Holding, Inc. **(2)**
3700 Park E Dr Ste 300, Cleveland, OH
44122
Tel.: (844) 732-5087
Web Site: http://www.realalloy.com
Holding Company; Aluminum Recycling &
Alloying Facilities Operator
N.A.I.C.S.: 551112

Subsidiary (Non-US):

Real Alloy Canada Ltd. **(3)**
7496 Torbam Road, Mississauga, L4T 1G9,
ON, Canada
Tel.: (905) 672-5569
Web Site: http://www.realalloy.com
Rolled Aluminum & Molten Metal Products
Mfr
N.A.I.C.S.: 331315

Plant (Domestic):

Real Alloy Recycling, Inc. -
Morgantown **(3)**
805 Gardener Ln, Morgantown, KY 42261
Tel.: (270) 526-5688
Web Site: http://www.realalloy.com
Aluminum Recycling
N.A.I.C.S.: 331314

Real Alloy Recycling, Inc. -
Sapulpa **(3)**
1508 N 8th St Hwy 97 N, Sapulpa, OK
74066-2200
Tel.: (918) 224-4746
Web Site: http://www.realalloy.com
Nonferrous Metals Smelting & Alloying Services
N.A.I.C.S.: 331314
James Bloomer *(Plant Mgr)*

Subsidiary (Domestic):

Real Alloy Specification, Inc. **(3)**
4525 W Old 24 PO Box 466, Wabash, IN
46992
Tel.: (260) 563-7461
Web Site: http://www.realalloy.com
Aluminum Alloy Mfr
N.A.I.C.S.: 331314

ELANCO ANIMAL HEALTH INCORPORATED

2500 Innovation Way, Greenfield, IN
46140
Web Site: https://www.elanco.com
Year Founded: 1954
ELAN—(NYSE)
Rev.: $4,417,000,000
Assets: $14,362,000,000
Liabilities: $8,139,000,000
Net Worth: $6,223,000,000
Earnings: ($1,231,000,000)
Emp.: 9,300
Fiscal Year-end: 12/31/23
Development of Products & Services
for Animal Health
N.A.I.C.S.: 325412
Todd S. Young *(CFO & Exec VP)*
David Urbanek *(Exec VP Mfg & Quality)*
Marcela A. Kirberger *(Gen Counsel & Sec)*
Ellen de Brabander *(Exec VP-Innovation & Regulatory Affairs)*
Bobby Modi *(Exec VP)*
Jose Manuel Correia de Simas *(Exec VP)*
Jeffrey N. Simmons *(Pres & CEO)*

Subsidiaries:

Aratana Therapeutics, Inc. **(1)**
11400 Tomahawk Creek Pkwy Ste 340,
Leawood, KS 66211
Tel.: (913) 353-1000

Web Site: http://www.aratana.com
Rev.: $35,412,000
Assets: $106,436,000
Liabilities: $5,614,000
Net Worth: $100,822,000
Earnings: ($14,722,000)
Fiscal Year-end: 12/31/2018
Pet Pharmaceutical Mfr
N.A.I.C.S.: 325412
Ernst Heinen *(Chief Dev Officer)*
John C. Ayres *(Gen Counsel, Sec & VP-Corp Dev & Admin)*
Debbie Walls *(VP-HR)*
Rhonda L. Hellums *(CFO, Chief Acctg Officer & Treas)*
Chris Ready *(VP-Sls & Mktg)*

Subsidiary (Domestic):

Vet Therapeutics, Inc. **(2)**
2683 Via De La Valle Ste G-335, Del Mar,
CA 92014
Tel.: (858) 361-0393
Biotechnology Research & Development
Services
N.A.I.C.S.: 541714

Bayer Animal Health GmbH **(1)**
Global Communications New Media Management Building 6210, 51368, Leverkusen,
Germany
Tel.: (49) 2173 38 2177
Web Site:
http://www.animalhealth.bayerhealth
care.com
Rev.: $132,139,000
Pest Control Products Research & Development Services
N.A.I.C.S.: 541715
Dirk Ehle *(Mng Dir)*
Marijn E. Dekkers *(Chm)*

Unit (US):

Bayer Animal Health - USA **(2)**
12707 Shawnee Mission Pkwy, Shawnee
Mission, KS 66216
Tel.: (913) 268-2000
Sales Range: $125-149.9 Million
Emp.: 400
Animal Health Products & Services
N.A.I.C.S.: 325412

Plant (Domestic):

Bayer Animal Health **(3)**
3915 S 48th St Ter, Saint Joseph, MO
64503
Tel.: (816) 364-3777
Sales Range: $50-74.9 Million
Emp.: 300
Veterinary Pharmaceutical Preparations
N.A.I.C.S.: 325412

ChemGen Corp. **(1)**
211 Perry Pkwy, Gaithersburg, MD 20877-
2144
Tel.: (301) 330-4101
Web Site: http://www.chemgen.com
Pharmaceutical Product Whslr
N.A.I.C.S.: 424210

Subsidiary (Non-US):

Aratana Therapeutics NV **(2)**
Ambachtenlaan 1, 3001, Heverlee, Belgium
Tel.: (32) 16299726
Web Site: http://www.aratana.com
Emp.: 2
Physical & Life Sciences Research Services
N.A.I.C.S.: 541715

Elanco - Augusta Technology
Center **(1)**
1788 Lovers Ln, Augusta, GA 30901-1869
Tel.: (706) 303-6300
Web Site: http://www.elanco.com
Sales Range: $50-74.9 Million
Emp.: 210
Dairy Cow Nutritional Supplement Mfr
N.A.I.C.S.: 311119

Elanco AH Portugal, Unipessoal
Lda **(1)**
Edificio Amoreiras Plaza Rua Carlos Alberto
da Mota Pinto n 9 4A2, 1070-374, Lisbon,
Portugal
Tel.: (351) 210204333
Web Site: https://omeuanimal.elanco.com
Pharmaceutical Preparation Mfr
N.A.I.C.S.: 325412

Elanco Animal Health, Korea,
Ltd. **(1)**
Tel.: (82) 25530304
Web Site: https://campaign.elanco.com
Pet Care Services
N.A.I.C.S.: 812910

Elanco Argentina S.R.L. **(1)**
Colectora Este Ramal Pilar Manuel Alberti
Suite 316-318, Buenos Aires, Argentina
Tel.: (54) 91145464112
Pharmaceuticals Product Mfr
N.A.I.C.S.: 325412
Juan Pablo Zingoni *(Gen Mgr-Southern Cone)*

Elanco Belgium BVBA **(1)**
Plantin en Moretuslei 1A, 2018, Antwerp,
Belgium
Tel.: (32) 33343000
Pharmaceuticals Product Mfr
N.A.I.C.S.: 325412
David Cappe *(Sls Mgr)*

Elanco Chile SpA **(1)**
Rosário Norte 615 Oficina 1502, Las Condes, Santiago, Chile
Tel.: (56) 226119220
Pharmaceuticals Product Mfr
N.A.I.C.S.: 325412
Claudio Linzmayer *(Mgr-Territory)*

Elanco Colombia S.A.S. **(1)**
LaCalle98No9A-41Calle98No9B-07Calle98,
No9B-25BuildingABProjectsOffice601, Bogota, Colombia
Tel.: (57) 16024258
Pharmaceuticals Product Mfr
N.A.I.C.S.: 325412
Oscar Jaime Betancur *(Mgr-Regulatory)*

Elanco Denmark ApS **(1)**
Lautrupvang 12 1 th, 2750, Ballerup, Denmark
Tel.: (45) 45266060
Web Site: https://www.elanco.dk
Pharmaceuticals Product Mfr
N.A.I.C.S.: 325412
Lise Lotte Dalgaard Skov *(Acct Mgr)*
Rie From Heldtberg *(Acct Mgr)*
Lillian Rasmussen *(Acct Mgr)*

Elanco Gesellschaft m.b.H. **(1)**
Koelblgasse 8-10, 1030, Vienna,
Austria **(100%)**
Tel.: (43) 1711780
Web Site: http://www.lilly.at
Sales Range: $50-74.9 Million
Emp.: 35
Sales of Veterinary Pharmaceuticals
N.A.I.C.S.: 424210
Simone Thompsen *(Mng Dir)*

Elanco Hayvan Sagligi Limited
Sirketi **(1)**
Kucukbakkalkoy Kayisdagi Cad No 1 K 5,
Atasehir, 34752, Istanbul, Turkiye
Tel.: (90) 2165540000
Pharmaceuticals Product Mfr
N.A.I.C.S.: 325412

Elanco Hungary Kft. **(1)**
Oktober Huszonharmadika utca 8-10 Allee
Corner Ep 4 em, 1117, Budapest, Hungary
Tel.: (36) 680201399
Web Site:
https://www.kedvencemesen.elanco.com
Animal Health Care Services
N.A.I.C.S.: 541940

Elanco Malaysia Sdn. Bhd. **(1)**
Unit 5 04 Level 5 & 6 Tower Block The
Bousteador 10 Jalan PJU 7/6, Mutiara Damansara, 47800, Petaling Jaya, Selangor,
Malaysia
Tel.: (60) 374966363
Web Site: https://my-elanco.com
Pharmaceuticals Product Mfr
N.A.I.C.S.: 325412
Cindy Khoo *(Mgr-HR)*

Elanco New Zealand **(1)**
Level 1 123 Ormiston Road Botany Junction, Auckland, 2016, New Zealand
Tel.: (64) 800266221
Web Site: https://www.elanco.co.nz
Pharmaceuticals Product Mfr

N.A.I.C.S.: 325412
Hendrik Van Der Walt *(Gen Mgr)*

Elanco Philippines Inc. (1)
Podium West Tower 12 ADB Ave Oritas Center 12th floor Unit 1202, Mandaluyong, 1604, Philippines
Tel.: (63) 92725420
Pharmaceuticals Product Mfr
N.A.I.C.S.: 325412

Elanco Products Limited (1)
Lilly House Priestley Road, Basingstoke, RG24 9NL, Hants, United Kingdom
Tel.: (44) 1256353131
Web Site: http://www.elanco.com
Sales Range: $25-49.9 Million
Emp.: 25
Animal Health Products
N.A.I.C.S.: 424210

Elanco S.R.L. (1)
Colectora Este Ramal Pilar Manuel Alberti Suite 317, Buenos Aires, Argentina
Tel.: (54) 91145464112
Pharmaceutical Preparation Mfr
N.A.I.C.S.: 325412

Elanco Valquimica S.A. (1)
Avda Industria 30, 28108, Alcobendas, Spain
Tel.: (34) 916635000
Web Site: http://www.elanco.com
Sales Range: $300-349.9 Million
Emp.: 660
Products for Pharmaceutical & Veterinary Industries
N.A.I.C.S.: 325412

Elanco Vietnam Company Limited (1)
15th Floor LIM III Tower 29A Nguyen Dinh Chieu, Da Kao Ward District 1, Ho Chi Minh City, Vietnam
Tel.: (84) 838166266
Pharmaceutical Preparation Mfr
N.A.I.C.S.: 325412

Kindred Biosciences, Inc. (1)
1555 Bayshore Hwy Ste 200, Burlingame, CA 94010
Tel.: (650) 701-7901
Web Site: http://www.kindredbio.com
Rev.: $42,164,000
Assets: $95,814,000
Liabilities: $28,332,000
Net Worth: $67,482,000
Earnings: ($21,796,000)
Emp.: 63
Fiscal Year-end: 12/31/2020
Veterinary Pharmaceutical Mfr
N.A.I.C.S.: 325412

ELASTIC N.V.
800 W El Camino Real Ste 350, Mountain View, CA 94040
Tel.: (650) 458-2620 NL
Web Site: http://www.elastic.co
Year Founded: 2012
ESTC—(NYSE)
Rev.: $1,267,321,000
Assets: $2,242,566,000
Liabilities: $1,504,381,000
Net Worth: $738,185,000
Earnings: $61,720,000
Emp.: 3,187
Fiscal Year-end: 04/30/24
Application Software Development Services
N.A.I.C.S.: 541511
Barrie Sheers *(VP-Asia-Pacific & Japan)*
Janesh Moorjani *(CFO & COO)*
Shay Banon *(CTO)*
Uri Boness *(Co-Founder)*
Simon Willnauer *(Co-Founder)*
Leah Sutton *(Sr VP-HR-Global)*
Chetan Puttagunta *(Chm)*
Ashutosh Kulkarni *(CEO)*
Ken Exner *(Chief Product Officer)*
Michael Cremen *(Chief Sls Officer)*
Mathew Donoghue *(CMO)*

Subsidiaries:

Elasticsearch (Beijing) Information Technology Co., Ltd. (1)

2A Worker Stadium North Road Pacific Century Place 5/F Chaoyang, Beijing, 100001, China
Tel.: (86) 4000011205
Application Software Development Services
N.A.I.C.S.: 541511

Elasticsearch KK (1)
WeWork Ginza Six Ginza Six 13F 6-10-1 Ginza, Chuo-ku, Tokyo, 104-0061, Japan
Tel.: (81) 363326966
Application Software Development Services
N.A.I.C.S.: 541511

Elasticsearch Korea Limited (1)
Wework Gangnam Station2 7 Teheran-ro 5-gil, Gangnam-gu, Seoul, 06134, Korea (South)
Tel.: (82) 269542311
Application Software Development Services
N.A.I.C.S.: 541511

Elasticsearch Pty. Ltd. (1)
Level 36 60 Margaret Street, Sydney, 2000, NSW, Australia
Tel.: (61) 280743149
Application Software Development Services
N.A.I.C.S.: 541511

Prelert Inc. (1)
20 Speen St Ste 200, Framingham, MA 01701-4733
Tel.: (508) 319-5300
Web Site: http://www.prelert.com
Computer Related Services
N.A.I.C.S.: 541519

elasticsearch B.V. (1)
Keizersgracht 281, 1016 ED, Amsterdam, Netherlands
Tel.: (31) 207947300
Application Software Development Services
N.A.I.C.S.: 541511

ELECTRIQ POWER HOLDINGS, INC.
625 N Flagler Dr Ste 1003, West Palm Beach, FL 33401
Tel.: (561) 945-8340 DE
Web Site:
https://www.tlgacquisitions.com
Year Founded: 2020
ELIQ—(NYSE)
Rev.: $5,683,750
Assets: $81,073,148
Liabilities: $102,675,064
Net Worth: ($21,601,916)
Earnings: $10,441,388
Emp.: 3
Fiscal Year-end: 12/31/22
Energy Storage, Home Energy Management System & Renewable Energy Semiconductor Mfr
N.A.I.C.S.: 334413
John Michael Lawrie *(Chm & CEO)*
David Johnson *(CFO)*

ELECTRO-SENSORS, INC.
6111 Blue Cir Dr, Minnetonka, MN 55343
Tel.: (952) 930-0100 MN
Web Site: https://www.electro-sensors.com
Year Founded: 1968
ELSE—(NASDAQ)
Rev.: $9,029,000
Assets: $14,044,000
Liabilities: $630,000
Net Worth: $13,414,000
Earnings: $100,000
Emp.: 34
Fiscal Year-end: 12/31/22
Motion Monitoring & Speed Control Systems Mfr
N.A.I.C.S.: 334513
David L. Klenk *(Pres, CEO & CFO)*
Gloria M. Grundhoefer *(Controller)*

Subsidiaries:

ESI Investment Co. (1)
6111 Blue Cir Dr, Minnetonka, MN 55343 (100%)
Tel.: (952) 930-0100

Sales Range: $650-699.9 Million
Investment Holdings
N.A.I.C.S.: 523999

ELECTROCORE, INC.
200 Forge Way Ste 205, Rockaway, NJ 07866
Tel.: (973) 290-0097 DE
Web Site:
https://www.electrocore.com
Year Founded: 2005
ECOR—(NASDAQ)
Rev.: $8,592,000
Assets: $24,756,000
Liabilities: $7,670,000
Net Worth: $17,086,000
Earnings: ($22,162,000)
Emp.: 62
Fiscal Year-end: 12/31/22
Bioelectronic Product Mfr & Distr
N.A.I.C.S.: 325411
Peter S. Staats *(Founder & Chief Medical Officer)*
Mike Romaniw *(Exec VP-Ops & Sys)*
Thomas J. Errico *(Executives, Bd of Dirs)*
Daniel S. Goldberger *(CEO)*
Peter Cuneo *(Chm)*
Carrie Kochek *(Sr Dir-HR)*
Mitch DeShon *(VP)*
Joshua S. Lev *(CFO & Chief Strategy Officer)*

ELECTROMED, INC.
500 6th Ave NW, New Prague, MN 56071
Tel.: (952) 758-9299 MN
Web Site: https://www.smartvest.com
Year Founded: 1992
ELMD—(NYSEAMEX)
Rev.: $54,716,000
Assets: $52,234,000
Liabilities: $7,689,000
Net Worth: $44,545,000
Earnings: $5,150,000
Emp.: 174
Fiscal Year-end: 06/30/24
Airway Clearance Healthcare Products Mfr
N.A.I.C.S.: 339112
James L. Cunniff *(Pres & CEO)*
Kathleen S. Skarvan *(Chm)*
Kristine Owata *(VP-Reimbursement & Payer Rels)*
Michelle C. Wirtz *(Controller)*
Bradley M. Nagel *(CFO, Treas & Sec)*
Stan K. Erickson *(Vice Chm)*

ELECTROMEDICAL TECHNOLOGIES, INC.
16413 N 91st St Unit C140, Scottsdale, AZ 85260
Tel.: (480) 292-8976 DE
Web Site: https://electromedtech.com
Year Founded: 2004
EMED—(OTCQB)
Rev.: $1,149,844
Assets: $1,353,271
Liabilities: $3,574,116
Net Worth: ($2,220,845)
Earnings: ($3,576,388)
Emp.: 8
Fiscal Year-end: 12/31/22
Pharmaceutical & Medical Product Mfr
N.A.I.C.S.: 325412
Matthew Wolfson *(Founder, Chm, Pres, CEO, CFO, Treas & Sec)*
Petar Gajic *(Dir-Tech)*

ELECTRONIC ARTS INC.
209 Redwood Shores Pkwy, Redwood City, CA 94065
Tel.: (650) 628-1500 CA
Web Site: https://www.ea.com

Year Founded: 1982
EA—(NASDAQ)
Rev.: $7,562,000,000
Assets: $13,420,000,000
Liabilities: $5,907,000,000
Net Worth: $7,513,000,000
Earnings: $1,273,000,000
Emp.: 13,700
Fiscal Year-end: 03/31/24
Interactive Entertainment Software Developer, Publisher & Distr
N.A.I.C.S.: 541511
Joel Linzner *(Exec VP-Worldwide Bus Affairs)*
Jacob J. Schatz *(Gen Counsel, Sec & Exec VP)*
Laura Miele *(Pres-Entertainment, Tech, and Central Dev)*
Mala Singh *(Chief People Officer)*
Chris Evenden *(VP-Investor Relations)*
Rachel Rubin Franklin *(Sr VP-Positive Play)*
Marija Radulovic-Nastic *(CTO-Creative-Development)*
Matt Thomlinson *(CTO-Enterprise)*
Stuart Canfield *(CFO & Exec VP)*
Andrew Wilson *(Chm & CEO)*

Subsidiaries:

ABC Distribution and Retail Solutions GmbH (1)
Lagerstrasse 24, Buchs, 9471, Saint Gallen, Switzerland
Tel.: (41) 817581400
Web Site: http://www.abcdistribution.ch
Video Game Developer & Publisher
N.A.I.C.S.: 513210

ABC Software GmbH (1)
Langaulistrasse 64, Buchs, 9471, Switzerland
Tel.: (41) 817581400
Web Site: http://www.abcsoftware.ch
Application Games Software Provider
N.A.I.C.S.: 513210

BioWare ULC (1)
1800-10423 101 St NW, Edmonton, T5H 0E7, AB, Canada
Tel.: (780) 430-0164
Web Site: https://www.bioware.com
Sales Range: $10-24.9 Million
Emp.: 350
Video Game Developer
N.A.I.C.S.: 513210

Bioware Austin LLC (1)
7700 W Parmer Ln Ste 250 Bldg C, Austin, TX 78729
Tel.: (512) 592-5293
Application Games Software Provider
N.A.I.C.S.: 513210

Chillingo Limited (1)
Beechfield House Winterton Way, Lyme Green Business Park, Macclesfield, SK11 0LP, United Kingdom
Tel.: (44) 1625509175
Web Site: http://www.chillingo.com
Application Games Software Provider
N.A.I.C.S.: 513210

Codemasters Group Holdings PLC (1)
Stoneythorpe, Southam, CV47 2DL, Warwickshire, United Kingdom
Tel.: (44) 1926816000
Web Site: http://www.codemasters.com
Rev.: $90,378,335
Assets: $97,738,651
Liabilities: $34,625,211
Net Worth: $63,113,441
Earnings: $4,661,110
Emp.: 504
Fiscal Year-end: 03/31/2019
Software Publisher
N.A.I.C.S.: 541511
Frank Sagnier *(CEO)*
Rashid Varachia *(CFO)*

Subsidiary (Domestic):

Slightly Mad Studios Limited (2)
Stoneythorpe, Southam, CV47 2DL, War-

Electronic Arts Inc.—(Continued)

wickshire, United Kingdom
Tel.: (44) 2072521843
Web Site:
     http://www.slightlymadstudios.com
Emp.: 175
Computer Gaming Services
N.A.I.C.S.: 513210
Ian Bell *(CEO)*
Andy Garton *(VP & Dir-Dev)*
Steve Dunn *(Sr Dir-Technical)*

Codemasters Limited (1)
Stoneythorpe, Southam, CV47 2DL, War-
wickshire, United Kingdom
Tel.: (44) 1926816000
Web Site: http://www.codemasters.com
Software Development Services
N.A.I.C.S.: 541511

Digital Illusions CE AB (1)
Sodermalmsallen 36, 118 28, Stockholm,
Sweden
Tel.: (46) 86587800
Web Site: http://www.dice.se
Emp.: 680
Developer, Publisher & Distr of Interactive
Entertainment Software
N.A.I.C.S.: 513210
Mikael Hellberg *(Mgr-Content Craft)*
Johan Husén *(Mgr-Design Craft)*
Roger Collum *(Head-Studio Dev)*
Bjorn Hedberg *(Dir-Tech Craft)*

EA Digital Illusions CE AB (1)
Sodermalmsallen 36, 118 28, Stockholm,
Sweden
Tel.: (46) 86587800
Web Site: http://www.dice.se
Sales Range: $75-99.9 Million
Emp.: 400
Application Games Software Provider
N.A.I.C.S.: 513210
Lars Gustavsson *(Creative Dir)*

EA Swiss Sarl (1)
Place du Molard 8, 1204, Geneva, Switzer-
land
Tel.: (41) 223161200
Web Site: http://www.ea.com
Sales Range: $25-49.9 Million
Emp.: 100
Developer, Publisher & Distr of Interactive
Entertainment Software
N.A.I.C.S.: 513210

EA.com (1)
209 Redwood Shores Pkwy, Redwood City,
CA 94065
Tel.: (650) 628-1500
Web Site: http://www.ea.com
Sales Range: $100-124.9 Million
Online Entertainment
N.A.I.C.S.: 541511

Division (Domestic):

Pogo.com (2)
209 Redwood Shores Pkwy, Redwood City,
CA 94065
Tel.: (650) 628-1500
Web Site: http://www.pogo.com
Sales Range: $25-49.9 Million
Emp.: 95
Online Games & Entertainment
N.A.I.C.S.: 513210

Electronic Arts (Canada), Inc. (1)
4330 Sanderson Way, Burnaby, V5G4X1,
BC, Canada (100%)
Tel.: (604) 456-3600
Web Site: http://www.electronicarts.ca
Sales Range: $500-549.9 Million
Emp.: 2,000
Developer, Publisher & Distr of Interactive
Entertainment Software
N.A.I.C.S.: 334610

Electronic Arts Belgium (1)
Avenue Reine Astrid 92, 1310, La Hulpe,
Belgium
Tel.: (32) 26346100
Application Games Software Provider
N.A.I.C.S.: 513210

Electronic Arts Czech Republic
s.r.o. (1)
Na Strzi 65, 140 00, Prague, 4, Czech Republic
Tel.: (420) 225 344 111

Web Site: http://www.electronicarts.cz
Publisher & Distr of Interactive Entertain-
ment Software
N.A.I.C.S.: 423430

Electronic Arts GmbH (1)
Im Zollhafen 15-17 NRW, 50678, Cologne,
Germany
Tel.: (49) 221975820
Web Site: http://www.electronicarts.de.com
Sales Range: $25-49.9 Million
Emp.: 150
Developer, Publisher & Distr of Interactive
Entertainment Software
N.A.I.C.S.: 334610
Olof Coenen *(Mng Dir)*

Division (Domestic):

EA Phenomic (2)
Binger Strasse 38 Am Rhein, 55218, Ingel-
heim, Germany
Tel.: (49) 613278350
Web Site: http://www.phenomic.de
Sales Range: $25-49.9 Million
Emp.: 50
Video Game Development Studio
N.A.I.C.S.: 713990

Electronic Arts HK Limited (1)
1 Matheson Street Rm 2510-11, 25/F Shell
Tower Time Square, Causeway Bay, China
(Hong Kong)
Tel.: (852) 2112 9988
Developer, Publisher & Distr of Interactive
Entertainment Software
N.A.I.C.S.: 423430

Electronic Arts Italia s.r.l. (1)
Tel.: (39) 028790931
Web Site: http://www.ea.com
Emp.: 15
Publisher & Distr of Interactive Entertain-
ment Software
N.A.I.C.S.: 423430

Electronic Arts Norway AS (1)
Nydalsveien 30B, 0484, Oslo, Norway
Tel.: (47) 22028090
Web Site: http://www.eanorge.com
Application Games Software Provider
N.A.I.C.S.: 513210

Electronic Arts Polska Sp.Z.O.O. (1)
ul Ilzecka 26, 02-135, Warsaw, Poland
Tel.: (48) 225757400
Web Site: http://www.ea.com
Publisher & Distr of Interactive Entertain-
ment Software
N.A.I.C.S.: 423430

Electronic Arts Proprietary
Limited (1)
L8 42 Marine Pde, PO Box 432, Southport,
4215, QLD, Australia
Tel.: (61) 755612828
Web Site: http://www.ea.com
Sales Range: $25-49.9 Million
Emp.: 60
Developer & Distr of Interactive Entertain-
ment Software
N.A.I.C.S.: 423430

Electronic Arts Publishing SARL (1)
Tel.: (33) 426232000
Web Site: http://www.ea.com
Sales Range: $25-49.9 Million
Emp.: 72
Developer & Distr of Interactive Entertain-
ment Software
N.A.I.C.S.: 513210

Electronic Arts Romania SRL (1)
Tel.: (40) 727346367
Sales Range: $50-74.9 Million
Emp.: 300
Developer & Distr of Interactive Entertain-
ment Software
N.A.I.C.S.: 513210

Electronic Arts Software S.L. (1)
Via De Los Poblados 3 Edificio 3, 28033,
Madrid, Spain (100%)
Tel.: (34) 913047091
Web Site: https://www.ea.com
Developer, Publisher & Distr of Interactive
Entertainment Software
N.A.I.C.S.: 334610

Electronic Arts Sweden AB (1)

Sodermalmsallen 36, 118 28, Stockholm,
Sweden
Tel.: (46) 86587800
Web Site: http://www.ea.com
Sales Range: $50-74.9 Million
Emp.: 670
Developer, Publisher & Distr of Interactive
Entertainment Software
N.A.I.C.S.: 513210

Electronic Arts UK Ltd. (1)
Onslow House Onslow Street, Guildford,
GU1 4TN, Surrey, United Kingdom (100%)
Tel.: (44) 1483463500
Web Site: http://www.ea.com
Sales Range: $200-249.9 Million
Emp.: 500
Interactive Entertainment Software Devel-
oper, Publisher & Distr
N.A.I.C.S.: 334610

Subsidiary (Domestic):

Criterion Software Ltd. (2)
Onslow House, Onslow Street, Guildford,
GU1 4TN, Surrey, United Kingdom
Tel.: (44) 1483406200
Web Site: http://www.criteriongames.com
Sales Range: $25-49.9 Million
Emp.: 170
Computer Games Mfr; Software Designer
N.A.I.C.S.: 334610

Glu Mobile Inc. (1)
875 Howard St Ste 100, San Francisco, CA
94105
Tel.: (415) 800-6100
Web Site: https://www.glu.com
Rev.: $540,522,000
Assets: $653,855,000
Liabilities: $236,761,000
Net Worth: $417,094,000
Earnings: $20,447,000
Emp.: 802
Fiscal Year-end: 12/31/2020
Mobile Games Publisher
N.A.I.C.S.: 541511
Mike Olsen *(Sr VP-Studios)*
Jerome Collin *(VP & Gen Mgr-Glu Sports)*
Mark van Ryswyk *(Exec VP)*
Eric R. Ludwig *(CFO, COO & Exec VP)*
Chris Akhavan *(Sr VP-Bus Dev, Corp Dev &
Adv)*
Scott J. Leichtner *(Gen Counsel, Sec & VP)*
Becky Ann Hughes *(Sr VP-Growth)*
Dominic Martinelli *(VP-Technical Ops &
Customer-Global)*
Harman Singh *(VP-Fin & IR)*
Puneet Kedia *(VP-Acctg)*
Sarah Fuchs *(VP & Gen Mgr-Covet Fash-
ion)*
Jakub Fiedorowicz *(VP-Product & Gen Mgr-
Crowdstar Studio)*
Eddie Garabedian *(VP-Mktg)*
Richard Au *(VP-Tech)*
Jon David *(VP & Gen Mgr)*
Carlos Calonge *(Pres)*
Jacob J. Schatz *(VP & Sec)*

Subsidiary (Domestic):

CrowdStar, Inc. (2)
330 Primrose Rd, Burlingame, CA 94010
Tel.: (650) 347-4166
Software Development Services
N.A.I.C.S.: 513210

Subsidiary (Non-US):

Glu EMEA-Glu Mobile Ltd. (2)
Beaumont House Kensington Village, Avon-
more Rd, London, W14 8TS, United
Kingdom (100%)
Tel.: (44) 2031001122
Web Site: http://www.glu.com
Sales Range: $100-124.9 Million
Emp.: 27
Global Publisher of Mobile Games
N.A.I.C.S.: 513210

Glu Mobile Technology (Beijing) Co.
Ltd. (2)
RM 906 China Life Building 16 Chaoyang-
menwai St, Chaoyang District, Beijing,
110020, China (Hong Kong) (100%)
Tel.: (852) 59632888
Web Site: http://www.glu.com
Sales Range: $100-124.9 Million
Global Publisher of Mobile Games
N.A.I.C.S.: 513210

Maxis Studio (1)
6121 Hollis St, Emeryville, CA 94608-2068
Tel.: (510) 428-4600
Web Site: http://www.maxis.com
Sales Range: $25-49.9 Million
Emp.: 140
Developer, Publisher & Distr of Interactive
Entertainment Software
N.A.I.C.S.: 513210

Playfish, Inc. (1)
2 Harrison St Ste 350, San Francisco, CA
94105
Tel.: (650) 628-1500
Web Site: http://www.playfish.com
Emp.: 203
Online Social Network Games Developer
N.A.I.C.S.: 513210

PopCap Games, LLC (1)
2401 4th Ave Ste 300, Seattle, WA 98121
Tel.: (206) 256-4200
Web Site: http://www.popcap.com
Sales Range: $100-124.9 Million
Emp.: 400
Video Game Developer
N.A.I.C.S.: 513210

S.C. Electronic Arts Romania
SRL (1)
AFI Park 2 4F General Paul Teodorescu
Boulevard, 061344, Bucharest, Romania
Tel.: (40) 317810100
Emp.: 2,000
Video Game Developer & Publisher
N.A.I.C.S.: 513210
Viorel Alex Marinescu *(COO)*

ELECTRONIC CONTROL SE-CURITY INC.
65 Kingsland Ave, Clifton, NJ 07014
Tel.: (973) 574-8555   NJ
Year Founded: 1976
EKCS—(OTCIQ)
Security Systems Services (except
Locksmiths)
N.A.I.C.S.: 561621
Arthur Barchenko *(Pres, CEO & Sec)*
Daryl K. Holcomb *(CFO)*

ELECTRONIC SERVITOR PUB-LICATION NETWORK, INC.
400 1st Ave N Ste 100, Minneapolis,
MN 55401
Tel.: (760) 990-3091   DE
Web Site: https://www.xespn.com
Year Founded: 2017
XESP—(OTCQB)
Assets: $17,139
Liabilities: $152,578
Net Worth: ($135,439)
Earnings: ($447,250)
Emp.: 3
Fiscal Year-end: 12/31/22
Investment Services
N.A.I.C.S.: 523999
Marla Palumbo *(Pres)*
Peter Hager *(CEO)*
Thomas Spruce *(COO & Sec)*

ELECTRONIC SYSTEMS TECHNOLOGY, INC.
415 N Roosevelt St Ste B, Kenne-
wick, WA 99336
Tel.: (509) 735-9092   WA
Web Site: https://www.esteem.com
Year Founded: 1982
ELST—(OTCIQ)
Rev.: $1,910,061
Assets: $2,046,457
Liabilities: $259,109
Net Worth: $1,787,348
Earnings: $146,531
Emp.: 8
Fiscal Year-end: 12/31/22
Other Communications Equipment
Manufacturing
N.A.I.C.S.: 334290

Thomas L. Kirchner *(Founder)*
Michael W. Eller *(CFO & Principal Acctg Officer)*
Daniel M. Tolley *(Pres & CEO)*

ELECTRONIC TELE-COMMUNICATIONS, INC.
1915 MacArthur Rd, Waukesha, WI 53188
Tel.: (262) 542-5600   WI
Web Site: https://www.etcia.com
Year Founded: 1980
ETCIA—(OTCIQ)
Sales Range: $1-9.9 Million
Emp.: 15
Designs, Manufactures, Programs, Markets & Leases Digital Voice Response Systems, Call Processing Systems & Related Computer Software Services
N.A.I.C.S.: 334210
Steve Thompson *(Mgr-Data Processing & Weather Center)*
Debbie Scott *(Mgr-Customer Svc)*
Jeff Hunholz *(Mgr-Technical Svcs)*
Elizabeth M. Danner *(Sec, Controller & Dir-HR)*
Liz Danner *(Pres & CEO)*
Bonita M. Danner *(Treas & VP-Engrg)*
Joseph A. Voight Jr. *(VP-Sls & Mktg)*

ELEDON PHARMACEUTICALS, INC.
19800 MacArthur Blvd Ste 250, Irvine, CA 92612
Tel.: (949) 238-8090   DE
Web Site: https://www.eledon.com
Year Founded: 2004
ELDN—(NASDAQ)
Rev.: $2,674,000
Assets: $89,266,000
Liabilities: $5,847,000
Net Worth: $83,419,000
Earnings: ($40,326,000)
Emp.: 20
Fiscal Year-end: 12/31/23
Pharmaceuticals Mfr
N.A.I.C.S.: 325412
John S. McBride *(VP-Comml Dev)*
Keith A. Katkin *(Chm)*
David-Alexandre C. Gros *(CEO)*
Steven Perrin *(Pres & Chief Scientific Officer)*
David Hovland *(Chief Regulatory Officer)*
Paul Little *(CFO & Principal Acctg Officer)*
Bryan Smith *(Chief Compliance Officer, Gen Counsel & Sec)*

ELEMENT GLOBAL, INC.
6555 Barton Ave 2nd Fl, Los Angeles, CA 90038
Tel.: (757) 306-6090
Web Site:
    https://www.elementglobal.com
ELGL—(OTCIQ)
Offices of Other Holding Companies
N.A.I.C.S.: 551112
Merle Ferguson *(Chm)*
Steven Gagnon *(Co-CEO & COO)*
John LaViolette *(Co-CEO)*
Sasha Shapiro *(Pres)*

ELEMENT SOLUTIONS INC.
500 E Broward Blvd Ste 1860, Fort Lauderdale, FL 33394
Tel.: (561) 207-9600   VG
Web Site:
    https://www.elementsolutions inc.com
Year Founded: 2013
ESI—(NYSE)
Rev.: $2,333,200,000
Assets: $4,974,100,000

Liabilities: $2,629,800,000
Net Worth: $2,344,300,000
Earnings: $118,100,000
Emp.: 5,300
Fiscal Year-end: 12/31/23
Holding Company; High Technology Specialty Chemicals Mfr; Technical Support Services
N.A.I.C.S.: 551112
Benjamin H. Gliklich *(Pres & CEO)*
John E. Capps *(Gen Counsel, Sec & Exec VP)*
Carey J. Dorman *(CFO & Exec VP)*
Michael Russnok *(Chief Acctg Officer)*
Martin Ellis Franklin *(Founder & Exec Chm)*

Subsidiaries:

Agrifocus Limitada   (1)
Av 25 Setembro Edificio Time Square Bloco 2 1 Andar-Apartado 3678, Maputo, Mozambique
Tel.: (258) 21303668
Web Site: http://www.agrifocus.co.mz
Agricultural Implement Product Distr
N.A.I.C.S.: 423820

Agriphar Hellas SA   (1)
16 Rizareiou, Halandri, Greece
Tel.: (30) 2105578777
Chemical Products Mfr
N.A.I.C.S.: 541330

Agriphar Italia Srl   (1)
6 Via Bixio Nino, 44042, Cento, FE, Italy
Tel.: (39) 0516835484
Web Site: http://www.agripharitalia.it
Chemical Products Mfr
N.A.I.C.S.: 325320

Agriphar Sarl   (1)
Route De L etraz 20, 1260, Nyon, Switzerland
Tel.: (41) 223656100
Health Care Srvices
N.A.I.C.S.: 621610

Agriphar de Colombia SAS   (1)
Avenida 82 10 62 P 5, Bogota, Colombia
Tel.: (57) 16341500
Chemical Products Mfr
N.A.I.C.S.: 541330

Agriphar de Costa Rica SA   (1)
Building 2 Centro Corporativo El Cedral, Trejos Montealegre Excazu, San Jose, Costa Rica
Tel.: (506) 25057000
Banking Services
N.A.I.C.S.: 522110

Agronomic (Pty) Ltd   (1)
Bosbok Street 16 Jordaan Park, 1441, Heidelberg, Gauteng, South Africa
Tel.: (27) 117307509
Chemical Products Distr
N.A.I.C.S.: 424690

Agroquimicos y Semillas SA de CV   (1)
15 Pte 3723 Col Belisario Dominguez, 72180, Puebla, Mexico
Tel.: (52) 12222490521
Web Site: https://www.agropue.com
Agricultural Product Mfr & Distr
N.A.I.C.S.: 325311

Alpha Assembly Solutions Belgium NV   (1)
R Rio Jaguarao 1540, Manaus, Amazonas, Brazil
Tel.: (55) 9236147400
Web Site: http://www.alent.com.br
Electronic Components Mfr
N.A.I.C.S.: 334413

Amza Limited   (1)
37 Nachshon St Industrial Area, PO Box 3068, Sgula, Petach Tikva, 4900614, Israel
Tel.: (972) 37212777
Web Site: https://www.amza-ltd.com
Emp.: 80
Metal Coating & Allied Services
N.A.I.C.S.: 332812

Anion Quimica Industrial S.A.   (1)

Rua Eli Valter Cesar 110, Jandira, Sao Paulo, 06612-130, Brazil
Tel.: (55) 1147898585
Web Site: https://www.anion.com.br
Chemical Products Mfr
N.A.I.C.S.: 541330

Aqua Plus Wasser- und Recycling-systeme GmbH   (1)
Am Barnberg 14, 73560, Bobingen, Germany
Tel.: (49) 71737144180
Web Site: https://aqua-plus.de
Water Purification Equipment Mfr & Distr
N.A.I.C.S.: 333310

Autotype Holdings (USA), Inc.   (1)
701 Industrial Rd, Middletown, DE 19709
Tel.: (302) 378-3100
Consumer Electronics Whslr
N.A.I.C.S.: 423620

Calli Ghana Ltd   (1)
Main Harbour Area Commercial Warehouse Road, PO Box TT 503, Tema, Ghana
Tel.: (233) 3032103478
Web Site: http://www.callighana.com
Chemical & Allied Product Whslr
N.A.I.C.S.: 424690

Callivoire SGFD SA   (1)
Rue Clement Ader - Marcory Zone 4A, PO Box 896, 01, Abidjan, Cote d'Ivoire
Tel.: (225) 21357504
Web Site: https://www.upl-ltd.com
Crop Planting & Protection Services
N.A.I.C.S.: 115112

Canning Gumm LLC   (1)
245 Freight St, Waterbury, CT 06702
Tel.: (800) 223-4866
Chemical Products Mfr
N.A.I.C.S.: 541330

Chemtura Chemicals India Private Limited   (1)
5th Floor, Near Thakur Polytech College, Poisor Kandivali (E), Noida, 201301, UP, India
Tel.: (91) 1204508600
Oil & Petroleum Lubricants Mfr
N.A.I.C.S.: 324191

Chemtura Columbia Ltda   (1)
Cr11A NRO 94A 56 OF501, Bogota, Colombia
Tel.: (57) 16401318
Chemical Products Mfr
N.A.I.C.S.: 541330

Chemtura Netherlands B.V.   (1)
The Corridor 5c, 3621 ZA, Breukelen, Netherlands   (100%)
Tel.: (31) 205871871
Web Site: http://www.chemtura.com
Industrial Inorganic Chemical Mfr
N.A.I.C.S.: 325180

Chemtura Pty Limited   (1)
16 Kelly Rd, PO Box 2089, Kempton Park, 1620, South Africa
Tel.: (27) 113974336
Web Site: http://www.chemtura.com
Emp.: 9
Pesticide & Agricultural Chemical Mfr
N.A.I.C.S.: 325320

Chimac S.A   (1)
Rue de Renory 26/1, Ougree, 4102, Belgium
Tel.: (32) 43859742
Plant Production Services
N.A.I.C.S.: 111219

Compugraphics International Ltd. (1)
Eastfield Business Park, Glenrothes, KY7 4NT, Fife, United Kingdom
Tel.: (44) 1592772557
Web Site: https://www.compugraphics-photomasks.com
Photomasks Mfr
N.A.I.C.S.: 334413
Dave Muir *(Sls Dir)*
Ingo Frommeyer *(Mgr-Customer Solutions)*
Dawn Cruz *(Supvr-Customer Svc)*
Laurie Sullivan *(Sr Acct Mgr)*
Peter Hunter *(Acct Mgr)*
Craig Durgy *(Sls Mgr-Eastern Reg)*
Brian Gibson *(Gen Mgr)*
Michael Grant *(Mgr-Customer Solutions)*

Subsidiary (Non-US):

Compugraphics Jena GmbH   (2)
Im Steinfeld 5, 07751, Jena, Germany
Tel.: (49) 217384900
Web Site: https://www.compugraphics-photomasks.com
Photomasks Mfr
N.A.I.C.S.: 334413

Subsidiary (US):

Compugraphics U.S.A. Inc.   (2)
43455 Osgood Rd, Fremont, CA 94539
Tel.: (510) 249-2600
Web Site: http://www.compugraphics-photomasks.com
Photomasks Mfr
N.A.I.C.S.: 334413

Branch (Domestic):

Compugraphics U.S.A. Inc. -Austin   (3)
4150 Freidrich Ln, Austin, TX 78744-1052
Tel.: (512) 416-3600
Web Site: http://www.compugraphics-photomasks.com
Photomasks Mfr
N.A.I.C.S.: 334413

Coventya AB   (1)
Odegardsgatan 3, 504 64, Boras, Sweden
Tel.: (46) 3 320 2840
Chemical Product Mfr & Distr
N.A.I.C.S.: 325998

Coventya Environmental Plating Technology (JiangSu) Co., Ltd.   (1)
1 XuHua Road, Xushuguan Town SND, Suzhou, 215151, China
Tel.: (86) 51267082628
Chemical Products Mfr
N.A.I.C.S.: 325998

Coventya GmbH   (1)
Stadtring Nordhorn 116, 33334, Gutersloh, Germany
Tel.: (49) 524193620
Web Site: https://www.coventya.com
Chemical Product Mfr & Distr
N.A.I.C.S.: 325998

Coventya Kimya Sanayi ve Ticaret Anonim Sirketi   (1)
Tuzla Chemical Industrialists Organize San Region Kristal Cad No 2, Tuzla, Istanbul, Turkiye
Tel.: (90) 2165040275
Web Site: https://www.coventya.com
Chemical Product Mfr & Distr
N.A.I.C.S.: 325998

Coventya Korea Co., Limited   (1)
77-8 5 Sandan 3ro Seongnam-myeon, Dongnam-gu, Cheonan, 31245, Chungcheongnam, Korea (South)
Tel.: (82) 415582921
Chemical Products Mfr
N.A.I.C.S.: 325998

Coventya Limited   (1)
Enterprise Drive Station Road, Four Ashes, Wolverhampton, WV10 7DF, United Kingdom
Tel.: (44) 190 279 7990
Chemical Products Mfr
N.A.I.C.S.: 325998

Coventya Malaysia Sdn. Bhd.   (1)
No 9 Jalan Padu Tampoi Industrial Estate, 80350, Johor Bahru, Johor, Malaysia
Tel.: (60) 72395757
Chemical Products Mfr
N.A.I.C.S.: 325998

Coventya Quimica Ltda   (1)
Av Deputado Oswaldo Moraes e Silva 55 - Predio 02 Bairro, Conceicao, Diadema, 09991-190, Sao Paulo, Brazil
Tel.: (55) 1140556600
Chemicals Mfr
N.A.I.C.S.: 325998

Coventya Technologies S.L.   (1)
C/ Romani 2 P I Castellbisbal Sud, Castellbisbal, 08755, Barcelona, Spain
Tel.: (34) 937733770
Chemical Products Mfr
N.A.I.C.S.: 325998

DMP Corporation   (1)
400 Bryant Blvd, Rock Hill, SC 29732
Tel.: (803) 324-2401

Element Solutions Inc.—(Continued)

Web Site: http://www.dmpcorp.com
Sales Range: $1-9.9 Million
Emp.: 55
Service Industry Machinery, Nec, Nsk
N.A.I.C.S.: 333310

Electrolube Limited (1)
Ashby Park Coalfield Way, Ashby de la
Zouch, LE65 1JR, Leicestershire, United
Kingdom
Tel.: (44) 153 041 9600
Web Site: https://electrolube.com
Chemical Product Mfr & Distr
N.A.I.C.S.: 325998

Enthone Inc. (1)
350 Frontage Rd, West Haven, CT
06516 (100%)
Tel.: (203) 934-8611
Web Site: http://www.enthone.com
Sales Range: $400-449.9 Million
Emp.: 1,210
High-Performance Specialty Chemicals &
Coatings
N.A.I.C.S.: 325998

Subsidiary (Non-US):

**Cookson Enthone Chemistry Trading
(Shanghai) Co Ltd** (2)
Building 9 Tanglang Xili, Tongfuyu Industrial
Town Nanshan District, Shenzhen, 518055,
China
Tel.: (86) 755 3690 5288
Specialty Chemicals Mfr
N.A.I.C.S.: 325199

**Cookson India Private Limited - En-
thone India Division** (2)
Developed Plot No 16 North Phase SIDCO
Industrial Estate, Ambattur, Chennai, 600
098, India
Tel.: (91) 989 2537633
Chemical Coating Product Mfr
N.A.I.C.S.: 325199

**Enthone Galvanoplasti Sanayi Ticaret
A.S.** (2)
Birlik Organize Sanayi Bolgesi Aydinli Ma-
hallesi TEM Yanyol 1 Nolu, Cad No 7 Tuzla,
34953, Istanbul, Türkiye
Tel.: (90) 2165813600
Chemical & Coating Product Whslr
N.A.I.C.S.: 424690

Enthone GmbH (2)
Quartier Belvedere Central Gertrude -
Frohlich - Sandner - Strasse 3, 1100, Vi-
enna, Austria
Tel.: (43) 19771875
Chemical Mfr & Distr
N.A.I.C.S.: 325180

Enthone Iberica S.A. (2)
Avinguda De La Riera 36 Sant Just Des-
vern, Sant Just Desvern, Barcelona, 08960,
Spain
Tel.: (34) 934803388
Chemical & Coating Product Whslr
N.A.I.C.S.: 424690
Antonio Graells (Mgr-Product)

Enthone SAS (2)
Parc d'Activites De Paris-Est Rue Leon
Jouhaux-BP no 71, PO Box 30605, Croissy-
Beaubourg, Marne-la-Vallee, 77312, France
Tel.: (33) 160059360
Chemical & Allied Product Whslr
N.A.I.C.S.: 424690

Enthone Sdn Bhd (2)
Lot 34 & 36 Lorong IKS Juru 7 Taman Per-
industrian Ringan Juru, Seberang Perai Se-
latan, 14100, Simpang Empat, Malaysia
Tel.: (60) 45077787
Chemical Products Distr
N.A.I.C.S.: 424690
Lim Thing (Mgr-Fin & Admin)

Enthone Sp. Z.o.o. (2)
Al Marszalka J Pilsudskiego 76, 90-330,
Lodz, Poland
Tel.: (48) 422521573
Electroplating Services
N.A.I.C.S.: 332813

Enthone s.r.o. (2)
Vrbovska cesta 2511/19, Piestany, 92101,
Slovakia

Tel.: (421) 337729777
Emp.: 5
Chemical & Coating Product Whslr
N.A.I.C.S.: 424690

**Enthone-OMI de Mexico S.A. de
C.V.** (2)
Norte 59 No 896 Industrial Vallejo Azcapot-
zalco, Mexico, 02300, Mexico
Tel.: (52) 5550783904
Inorganic Chemical Mfr
N.A.I.C.S.: 325180
Fernando Martinez (Mgr-Reg Sls)

Fernox Limited (1)
Unit 2 Genesis Business Park Albert Drive,
Sheerwater, Woking, GU21 5RW, Surrey,
United Kingdom
Tel.: (44) 3301007750
Web Site: https://www.fernox.com
Chemical Products Mfr
N.A.I.C.S.: 325998

**H.K. Wentworth (India) Private
Limited** (1)
No 73 6th Main 3rd Phase, Peenya Indus-
trial Area, Bengaluru, 560058, India
Tel.: (91) 8041235533
Chemical Products Mfr
N.A.I.C.S.: 325998

H.K. Wentworth Limited (1)
Ashby Park Coalfield Way, Ashby de la
Zouch, LE65 1JR, Leicestershire, United
Kingdom
Tel.: (44) 1530448950
Web Site: https://hakko.co.uk
Electronic Component Mfr & Distr
N.A.I.C.S.: 423690
Ron Jakeman (Mng Dir)

H.K. Wentworth Pty Limited (1)
Unit 3/98 Old Pittwater Road, Brookvale,
2100, NSW, Australia
Tel.: (61) 299381566
Web Site: https://www.hakko.com.au
Electronic Component Mfr & Distr
N.A.I.C.S.: 423690

**Industrial Specialty Chemicals,
Inc.** (1)
410 W 169th St, South Holland, IL 60473
Tel.: (708) 339-1313
Web Site: http://www.iscrail.com
Rev.: $6,589,000
Emp.: 15
Industrial Chemical Component Mfr
N.A.I.C.S.: 325998

Kester, Inc. (1)
800 W Thorndale Ave, Itasca, IL 60143
Tel.: (630) 616-4048
Web Site: https://www.kester.com
Solder & Solder Derivative Products Mfr
N.A.I.C.S.: 331410

MacDermid Group, Inc. (1)
1401 Blake St, Denver, CO 80202
Tel.: (720) 479-3060
Web Site: http://www.macdermid.com
Emp.: 5,000
Holding Company
N.A.I.C.S.: 551112

Subsidiary (Domestic):

MacDermid, Incorporated (2)
245 Freight St, Waterbury, CT 06702
Tel.: (203) 575-5700
Web Site: https://www.macdermid.com
Sales Range: $650-699.9 Million
Emp.: 5,000
Specialty Chemicals Mfr & Distr
N.A.I.C.S.: 325998

Subsidiary (Non-US):

Enthone GmbH (3)
Elisabeth-Selbert-Str 4, 40764, Langenfeld,
Germany
Tel.: (49) 217384900
Web Site: http://enthone.com
Chemical Coating Product Mfr
N.A.I.C.S.: 325199

Subsidiary (Domestic):

MacDermid Acumen Inc. (3)
701 Industrial Rd, Middletown, DE 19709
Tel.: (302) 376-6363
Business Management Consulting Services

N.A.I.C.S.: 541611

**MacDermid Alpha Electronics Solu-
tions, Inc.** (3)
109 Corporate Blvd, South Plainfield, NJ
07080
Tel.: (908) 791-3000
Web Site: https://www.macdermidalpha.com
Electronic Assembly Material & Equipment
Mfr
N.A.I.C.S.: 333992
Rick Fricke (VP & Gen Mgr)

Subsidiary (Non-US):

**Alent Alpha Metals (Shanghai) Trad-
ing Co. Ltd** (4)
Building 3 No 1151 Lianxi Road, Pudong
New Area, Shanghai, 201204, China
Tel.: (86) 2163900600
Metal Merchant Whslr
N.A.I.C.S.: 423510

**Alent Alpha Metals (Shenzen) Co.
Ltd** (4)
No 266 Guangtian Road Tangxiayong Com-
munity Songgang Street, Baoan District,
Shenzhen, 518105, China
Tel.: (86) 75527051100
Soldering Material Mfr
N.A.I.C.S.: 331491
Alan Hsu (Mgr-Pur)

**Alent Assembly Solutions Brasil Sol-
das Ltda.** (4)
R Rio Jaguarao, 01540-000, Manaus, Ama-
zonas, Brazil
Tel.: (55) 92 3614 7400
Web Site: http://www.alent.com.br
Soldering Products Mfr
N.A.I.C.S.: 333992

**Alent Enthone Chemistry (Shanghai)
Co. Ltd.** (4)
No 29 of Chuhua North Road, Fengxian
District, Shanghai, 201417, China
Tel.: (86) 2137585000
Chemical Products Distr
N.A.I.C.S.: 424690

Alent Hong Kong Ltd (4)
1/F Block A 21 Tung Yuen Street Yau Tong
Bay, Kowloon, China (Hong Kong)
Tel.: (852) 31903100
Chemical Products Distr
N.A.I.C.S.: 424690
Candy Chan (Sr Mgr-HR-Asia)

Alent Italia Srl (4)
Via Vigevano 61, San Martino di Trecate,
28069, Trecate, Novara, Italy
Tel.: (39) 024533921
Chemical Products Distr
N.A.I.C.S.: 421600
Dominique Willemsen (Dir-Fin & Logistics-
Germany)

Alent Japan Company (4)
Higashitoyoda 480 28, Yubinbango, Hirat-
suka, 254-0082, Kanagawa, Japan
Tel.: (81) 463533333
Web Site: http://www.alpha-alent.jp
Electrical Component Mfr & Distr
N.A.I.C.S.: 335999

**Alpha Assembly Solutions (Shenzen)
Co. Ltd** (4)
No 266 Guangtian Road Tangxiayong Com-
munity Songgang Street, Baoan District,
Shenzhen, 518105, China
Tel.: (86) 75527051100
Electronic Components Mfr
N.A.I.C.S.: 334413

**Alpha Assembly Solutions (Taiwan)
Limited** (4)
No 20 Lane 12 Sec 2 Nan-Shan Road Lu-
zhu District, Taoyuan, 33860, Taiwan
Tel.: (886) 33222721
Electronic Components Mfr
N.A.I.C.S.: 334413

**Alpha Assembly Solutions Belgium
NV** (4)
Hoge Mauw 1050, 2370, Arendonk, Bel-
gium
Tel.: (32) 14445000
Chemical Products Distr
N.A.I.C.S.: 423490
Leo Mertens (Ops Mgr)

**Alpha Assembly Solutions Brasil Sol-
das Ltda** (4)
Rio Jaguarao 1540 - Vila Buriti, Manaus,
69072-055, Amazonas, Brazil
Tel.: (55) 8000102011
Web Site: https://www.alent.com.br
Electronic Components Mfr
N.A.I.C.S.: 334413

**Alpha Assembly Solutions France
SAS** (4)
Rue Gustave Eiffel Zone Industrielle La
Bergerie, 49280, La Seguiniere, France
Tel.: (33) 241490011
Chemical Products Distr
N.A.I.C.S.: 423490

**Alpha Assembly Solutions Korea
Ltd** (4)
8-209 International complex 555-9 Hokye-
dong Dongan-gu, Anyang, Korea (South)
Tel.: (82) 314791485
Electronic Components Mfr
N.A.I.C.S.: 334413

**Alpha Assembly Solutions Nether-
lands B.V.** (4)
Energiestraat 21, 1410 AA, Naarden, 1410
AA, Netherlands
Tel.: (31) 356955411
Electronic Components Mfr
N.A.I.C.S.: 334413

Subsidiary (Domestic):

Alpha Metals, Inc. (4)
4100 6th Ave, Altoona, PA 16602 (100%)
Tel.: (814) 946-1611
Web Site: http://alphaassembly.com
Electronic Assembly Material & Equipment
Mfr
N.A.I.C.S.: 333992
Cathy Horvers (Mgr-Inside Sls Support)

Subsidiary (Non-US):

**Alpha Assembly Solutions Korea
Ltd.** (5)
1RA 310 Sihwa Industrial Complex 40
Okgucheonseo-Ro 131 Beongil, Siheung,
15007, Gyeonggi-do, Korea (South)
Tel.: (82) 314991451
Web Site: http://www.alphaassembly.com
Electronic Components Distr
N.A.I.C.S.: 423610

**Alpha Assembly Solutions Singapore
Pte Ltd** (5)
14 Tuas Avenue 10, Singapore, 639138,
Singapore
Tel.: (65) 68611977
Web Site: http://www.alphaassembly.com
Electronic Products Mfr
N.A.I.C.S.: 334419

Alpha France SAS (5)
1 Rue de Neuf Brisach, 68600, Vol-
gelsheim, France
Tel.: (33) 241490011
Web Site: http://www.alphaassembly.com
Plastic Product Mfr & Distr
N.A.I.C.S.: 326199

Alpha Metals (Taiwan) Inc (5)
No 20 Lane 100 Sec 2 Nan Shan Road, Lu
Chu Hsiang, Taoyuan, 33860, Taiwan
Tel.: (886) 3322 2721
Electronic & Chemical Product Distr
N.A.I.C.S.: 423690

Alpha Netherlands B.V. (5)
Energy street 21, PO Box 5018, 1411 AR,
Naarden, Netherlands
Tel.: (01) 356055411
Web Site: http://www.alphaassembly.com
Emp.: 75
Electronic & Chemical Product Distr
N.A.I.C.S.: 423690

**MacDermid Performance Hong Kong
Ltd.** (5)
8/f 51 Hung To Rd, Kwun Tong, China
(Hong Kong)
Tel.: (852) 31903100
Web Site: http://www.alphaassembly.com
Semifinish Metal Product Whslr
N.A.I.C.S.: 423510

Subsidiary (Non-US):

**MacDermid Autotype (Asia) Pte
Ltd** (3)

26 Tuas West Road, Singapore, 638382,
Singapore
Tel.: (65) 64300701
Printing Services
N.A.I.C.S.: 323120

Subsidiary (Domestic):

MacDermid Autotype Inc (3)
1675 Winnetka Cir, Rolling Meadows, IL
60008
Web Site:
https://www.autotype.macdermid.com
Printing Services
N.A.I.C.S.: 323120

Subsidiary (Non-US):

MacDermid Benelux B.V. (3)
Bredaseweg 185, 4872 LA, Etten-Leur,
Netherlands
Tel.: (31) 765021940
Web Site: http://www.macdermid.com
Sales Range: $25-49.9 Million
Emp.: 10
Distribution of Specialty Chemicals for the
Electronics & Metal Finishing Industries
N.A.I.C.S.: 424690

Unit (Domestic):

MacDermid Canning (3)
223 N Brockman St, Pasadena, TX 77506
Tel.: (713) 472-5081
Sales Range: $10-24.9 Million
Emp.: 50
Oils & Greases, Blending & Compounding
N.A.I.C.S.: 324191

Subsidiary (Non-US):

MacDermid Chemical Taiwan Ltd (3)
77 Kuang Fu N Rd HuKou Hsiang, Hsinchu,
Taiwan
Tel.: (886) 35981396
Chemical Preparation Mfr & Distr
N.A.I.C.S.: 325998

MacDermid Chemicals, Inc. (3)
4530 Eastgate Pkwy, Mississauga, L4W
3W6, ON, Canada
Tel.: (905) 624-1065
Web Site: http://www.macdermid.com
Sales Range: $25-49.9 Million
Emp.: 10
Specialty Chemicals Distr for the Electron-
ics & Metal Finishing Industries
N.A.I.C.S.: 424690

MacDermid Enthone GmbH (3)
Elisabeth-selbert-str 4, 40764, Langenfeld,
Germany
Tel.: (49) 217384900
Chemical Products Distr
N.A.I.C.S.: 423490

MacDermid Enthone Sp. Z.o.o. (3)
Al Marshal J Pilsudski 76, 90-330, Lodz,
Poland
Tel.: (48) 422521573
Chemical Products Distr
N.A.I.C.S.: 423490

MacDermid Espanola S.A. (3)
Avda Barcelona 6 Y 8, Santa Coloman De
Cervello, Barcelona, 08690, Spain
Tel.: (34) 936341380
Web Site: http://www.macdermid.com
Sales Range: $25-49.9 Million
Emp.: 20
Distribution of Specialty Chemicals for the
Electronics & Metal Finishing Industries
N.A.I.C.S.: 424690
Xavier Torne (Mng Dir)

MacDermid France, S.A. (3)
15 Voie Communale Porte Du Grand Ly,
Neyron, 1700, France
Tel.: (33) 472018888
Web Site: http://www.macdermid.com
Sales Range: $25-49.9 Million
Emp.: 35
Distribution of Specialty Chemicals for the
Electronics & Metal Finishing Industries
N.A.I.C.S.: 424690

MacDermid GmbH (3)
Hambrucker Strasse 80, Forst, 76694, Ger-
many
Tel.: (49) 725198170
Web Site: http://www.macdermid.com

Sales Range: $25-49.9 Million
Emp.: 50
Distribution of Specialty Chemicals for the
Electronics & Metal Finishing Industries
N.A.I.C.S.: 424690

**MacDermid Graphic Solutions Europe
SAS** (3)
15 VC-ZI Porte Du Grand Lyon, PO Box
30160, 010700, Neyron, CEDEX, France
Tel.: (33) 389384200
Metal Product Distr
N.A.I.C.S.: 423510

Subsidiary (Domestic):

**MacDermid Graphic Solutions
LLC** (3)
5210 Phillip Lee Dr, Atlanta, GA 30336
Tel.: (404) 696-4565
Web Site:
https://www.graphics.macdermid.com
Metal Product Distr
N.A.I.C.S.: 423510

Subsidiary (Non-US):

MacDermid Hong Kong Ltd. (3)
8/F Two Sky Parc 51 Hung To Road, Kwun
Tong, Kowloon, China (Hong Kong)
Tel.: (852) 225005365
Sales Range: $25-49.9 Million
Emp.: 50
Specialty Chemicals Mfr for the Electronics
& Metal Finishing Industries
N.A.I.C.S.: 424690

Subsidiary (Domestic):

MacDermid Investment Corp. (3)
245 Freight St, Waterbury, CT 06702
Tel.: (203) 575-5700
Chemical Products Mfr
N.A.I.C.S.: 541330

Subsidiary (Non-US):

MacDermid Italiana srl (3)
Via Vigevano 61 San Martino Di, San Mar-
tino di Trecate, Trecate, 28069, NO, Italy
Tel.: (39) 0321789610
Web Site: http://www.macdermid.com
Sales Range: $25-49.9 Million
Emp.: 150
Chemicals for the Electronics & Metal Fin-
ishing Industries Distr
N.A.I.C.S.: 424690

MacDermid Kft (3)
Jedlik Anyos Utca 2, Dunaharaszti, 2330,
Hungary
Tel.: (36) 24460720
Chemical Products Distr
N.A.I.C.S.: 423490

MacDermid Korea Ltd. (3)
Pan Ocean Tower 8 FL, Sungnam-City,
Seongnam, 463-440, Kyungki-Do, Korea
(South)
Tel.: (82) 317196146
Web Site: http://www.macdermid.com
Sales Range: $25-49.9 Million
Emp.: 50
Distribution of Specialty Chemicals for the
Electronics & Metal Finishing Industries
N.A.I.C.S.: 424690

MacDermid Ltd (3)
198 Golden Hillock Road, Birmingham, B11
2PN, West Midlands, United Kingdom
Tel.: (44) 1216068100
Web Site: http://www.macdermid.com
Sales Range: $25-49.9 Million
Emp.: 100
Chemicals Distrfor the Electronics & Metal
Finishing Industries
N.A.I.C.S.: 424690
Paul Bray (Mng Dir)

Subsidiary (Domestic):

MacDermid UK Ltd (4)
198 Golden Hillock Road, Birmingham, B11
2PN, United Kingdom
Tel.: (44) 1216068100
Web Site:
http://industrial.macdermidenthone.com
Holding Company
N.A.I.C.S.: 551112

Subsidiary (Domestic):

MacDermid Autotype Ltd (5)
Grove Road, Wantage, OX12 7BZ, United
Kingdom
Tel.: (44) 1235771111
Web Site:
https://www.autotype.macdermid.com
Printing Services
N.A.I.C.S.: 323120

MacDermid Canning Ltd (5)
Cale Lane New Springs, Hylo House,
Wigan, WN2 1JT, United Kingdom
Tel.: (44) 1942501000
Chemical Products Mfr
N.A.I.C.S.: 541330

Subsidiary (Non-US):

MacDermid Mexico SA de CV (3)
Boulevard Manuel Avila Camacho 1994, Col
Centro Industrial Tlalnepantla, 54050, Tlal-
nepantla, Mexico
Tel.: (52) 5552363145
Chemical Product Whslr
N.A.I.C.S.: 424690
Veronica Castillo (Controller)

**MacDermid Netherlands Cooperatief
W.A.** (3)
Bredaseweg 185, 4872 LA, Etten-Leur,
Netherlands
Tel.: (31) 765021940
Web Site: https://www.macdermid.com
Emp.: 4
Financial Management Services
N.A.I.C.S.: 541611

Subsidiary (Domestic):

**MacDermid Offshore Solutions
LLC** (3)
223 N Brockman, Pasadena, TX 77506
Tel.: (713) 472-5081
Web Site: https://offshore.macdermid.com
Sales Range: $1-9.9 Million
Emp.: 39
Chemical Products Mfr
N.A.I.C.S.: 325998

Subsidiary (Non-US):

MacDermid Overseas Asia Ltd (3)
10 York Road, Ingleburn, 2565, NSW, Aus-
tralia
Tel.: (61) 296052233
Chemical Products Mfr
N.A.I.C.S.: 541330

**MacDermid Performance Solutions
Espanola SA** (3)
Avda de la Riera 36, 08960, Sant Just Des-
vern, Spain
Tel.: (34) 936341380
Chemical Products Distr
N.A.I.C.S.: 423490

**MacDermid Performance Solutions
France S.A.S** (3)
15 Porte du Grand Lyon, 01700, Neyron,
France
Tel.: (33) 472018888
Chemical Products Distr
N.A.I.C.S.: 423490

**MacDermid Performance Solutions
Japan K.K.** (3)
480-28 Higashitoyoda, Hiratsuka, 254-0082,
Japan
Tel.: (81) 463737737
Web Site: https://www.macdermid.co.jp
Emp.: 68
Chemical Products Distr
N.A.I.C.S.: 423490

**MacDermid Performance Solutions
Kimyasal Sanayi ve Ticaret A.S.** (3)
Birlik Osb 1 Nolu Cad No 7/a Tuzla, 34953,
Istanbul, Turkiye
Tel.: (90) 2165813600
Chemical Products Distr
N.A.I.C.S.: 423490

Subsidiary (Domestic):

**MacDermid Printing Solutions,
LLC** (3)
5210 Phillip Lee Dr, Atlanta, GA 30336
Tel.: (404) 696-4565

Web Site: https://graphics.macdermid.com
Sales Range: $125-149.9 Million
Emp.: 1,100
General Printing Products & Packaging
Systems
N.A.I.C.S.: 333248
Scott Benson (Pres)

Unit (Non-US):

**MacDermid Printing Solutions
Europe** (4)
3 Rue de l Industrie, BP 30160, 68702,
Cernay, Cedex, France
Tel.: (33) 3 8938 4200
Web Site:
http://www.printing.macdermid.com
Sales Range: $50-74.9 Million
Emp.: 350
Chemical Preparations Mfr
N.A.I.C.S.: 325998

Branch (Domestic):

**MacDermid Printing Solutions, LLC -
San Marcos** (4)
260 S Pacific St, San Marcos, CA 92078
Tel.: (760) 510-6277
Sales Range: $25-49.9 Million
Emp.: 100
Manufacture & Sale of Specialty Chemicals
for Electronics & Metal Finishing Markets &
Polymer Resins & Compounds
N.A.I.C.S.: 325992

Subsidiary (Non-US):

MacDermid Scandinavia AB (3)
Massingsgatan 1, PO Box 83, Norrkoping,
60102, Sweden
Tel.: (46) 11367470
Web Site: http://www.macdermid.com
Sales Range: $25-49.9 Million
Emp.: 10
Chemical Products Distr
N.A.I.C.S.: 325998

MacDermid Singapore Pte. Ltd. (3)
No 26 Tuas West Road, Singapore,
638382, Singapore
Tel.: (65) 68611773
Sales Range: $25-49.9 Million
Emp.: 35
Distribution of Specialty Chemicals for the
Electronics & Metal Finishing Industries
N.A.I.C.S.: 424690

MacDermid Suisse Sarl (3)
Rue du Marche 20, Mevrin, 1204, Geneva,
Switzerland
Tel.: (41) 614130750
Chemical Preparations Mfr
N.A.I.C.S.: 325998

MacDermid Taiwan Ltd. (3)
77 Kuang Fu N Road Hsin-Chu Enlarged
Industrial Park, Hsinchu, 303, Taiwan
Tel.: (886) 35981396
Web Site: http://www.macdermid.com
Sales Range: $25-49.9 Million
Emp.: 97
Distribution of Specialty Chemicals for the
Metal Finishing & Electronics Industries
N.A.I.C.S.: 424690

MacDermid do Brasil Ltda. (3)
Rua Eli Walter Cesar No 110 Bairro Jd Al-
vorada, Jandira, 06612-130, Sao Paulo,
Brazil
Tel.: (55) 1147898585
Chemical Preparation Mfr & Distr
N.A.I.C.S.: 325998
Gustavo Yepez Mantilla (Coord-Admin &
Fin)

Branch (Domestic):

MacDermid, Inc. - Connecticut (3)
245 Freight St, Waterbury, CT 06702
Tel.: (203) 575-5700
Web Site: https://www.macdermid.com
Specialty Chemicals Mfr for Electronics &
Metal Finishing Markets & Polymer Resins
& Compounds
N.A.I.C.S.: 325612

Subsidiary (Non-US):

**Macdermid Panyu Specialty Chemi-
cals Co Ltd** (3)
Xin An Village, Wanqingsha Town Nansha

Element Solutions Inc.—(Continued)
Distric, Guangdong, China
Tel.: (86) 2084948083
Chemical Products Mfr
N.A.I.C.S.: 332813

Nippon MacDermid Co., Ltd. (3)
KSP C 7 3-2-1 Sakado, Takatsu-ku, Kawasaki, 213-0012, Kanagawa, Japan
Tel.: (81) 448201180
Web Site: http://www.macd.co.jp
Sales Range: $25-49.9 Million
Emp.: 75
Specialty Chemicals Mfr for the Electronics
& Metal Finishing Industries
N.A.I.C.S.: 424690

MacDermid do Brazil Ltda (1)
Rua Eli Valter Cesar 110, Jandira, 06612-130, SP, Brazil
Tel.: (55) 1147898585
Web Site: https://macdermid.com.br
Photopolymer Sheet Mfr
N.A.I.C.S.: 325992

**Mali Protection Des Cultures (MPC)
SA** (1)
Uinzanbougou Route De Sotuba Rue 499
Porte N 1892, PO Box 603, Bamako, Mali
Tel.: (223) 20 21 33 55
Crop Planting & Protection Services
N.A.I.C.S.: 115112

**Microgleit Spezialschmierstoffe,
GmbH** (1)
Blutenstrasse 62 - 64, Hohenwart, 86558,
Offenbach, Germany
Tel.: (49) 844 391 7570
Web Site: https://www.microgleit.de
Lubricant Product Mfr
N.A.I.C.S.: 324191

Nexus AG (Pty) Ltd (1)
3 & 5 Van der Lingen Street, Paarl, 7646,
South Africa
Tel.: (27) 218608040
Web Site: https://www.nexusag.net
Agrochemical Distr
N.A.I.C.S.: 424910
Jacques du Preez (CEO)
Janneman van Zyl (Mgr-Crop Protection)
Kevin Snyman (Head-Technical Dept)
Lizelle Schwarte (Mgr-Ops & Customer
Rels)
Renier Lourens (Mgr-Procurement-Crop
Protection)
Pieter Peacock (Mgr-Technical-Plant & Soil
Nutrition)
Wouter Vorster (Mgr-Procurement-Plant, Soil
Nutrition)
Fanus Komen (Mgr-Technical-Plant & Soil
Nutrition)
Jacques Fouche (Mgr-Technical-Crop Protection)
Johan Smit (Fin Mgr)
Trix Quixley (Mgr)
Chantel Visser (Mgr-Human Resources)
Japie Wiese (Mgr-Northern Cape)
Wiesie Burger (Mgr)
Wessel Cloete (Mgr-Commercial-Nutrition)
Trix Quixley (Mgr)
Chantel Visser (Mgr-Human Resources)
Japie Wiese (Mgr-Northern Cape)
Wiesie Burger (Mgr)
Wessel Cloete (Mgr-Commercial-Nutrition)

Novon Protecta (Pty) Ltd (1)
32 Malan St, Bethlehem, 9701, South Africa
Tel.: (27) 583033785
Agricultural Chemical Product Mfr & Distr
N.A.I.C.S.: 325320
Johan Klayn (CFO)

**OMG (Asia) Electronic Chemicals Co.
Ltd.** (1)
No 16 - 1 Songjiang North Road Jhongli
City, Taoyuan, 320, Taiwan
Tel.: (886) 34621928
Chemical Products Mfr
N.A.I.C.S.: 325320
Jeffrey Lin (Controller-PCB)

Platform Delaware Holdings, Inc (1)
5200 Blue Lagoon Dr Ste 855, Miami, FL
33126
Tel.: (561) 447-2509
Chemical Products Mfr
N.A.I.C.S.: 325199

SA Veto-Pharma (1)

12 - 14 rue de la Croix Martre, 91120, Palaiseau, France
Tel.: (33) 169188480
Web Site: https://www.veto-pharma.fr
Emp.: 80
Pharmaceutical Product Mfr & Distr
N.A.I.C.S.: 325412

Santamix Iberica SL (1)
Avenida Matapinonera N 11 Bloque 1 Oficina 105, San Sebastian De Los Reyes,
Madrid, 28703, Spain
Tel.: (34) 916638578
Web Site: http://www.santamix.es
Veterinary Services
N.A.I.C.S.: 541940
Juan Manuel Garcia (Gen Dir)

Saphyto SA (1)
1937 Avenue du General Sangoule Lamizana, BP 1390, Bobo-Dioulasso, Burkina
Faso
Tel.: (226) 20972018
Web Site: http://www.saphyto.com
Crop Protection Product Mfr & Whslr
N.A.I.C.S.: 311119

W. Canning International B.V. (1)
Bredaseweg 185, 4872 LA, Etten-Leur,
Netherlands
Tel.: (31) 765021940
Fruit & Vegetable Preserving Services
N.A.I.C.S.: 311421

ELEV8 BRANDS, INC.

5585 Schenck Ave Ste 5, Rockledge,
FL 32955
Tel.: (619) 558-9133
VATE—(OTCIQ)
Coffee Product Mfr
N.A.I.C.S.: 311920
Isaac Nichelson (COO)

ELEVANCE HEALTH, INC.

220 Virginia Ave, Indianapolis, IN
46204
Tel.: (317) 488-6000   IN
Web Site:
     https://www.elevancehealth.com
Year Founded: 1944
ELV—(NYSE)
Rev.: $171,340,000,000
Assets: $108,928,000,000
Liabilities: $69,523,000,000
Net Worth: $39,405,000,000
Earnings: $5,987,000,000
Emp.: 104,900
Fiscal Year-end: 12/31/23
Holding Company; Health Insurance
Products & Services
N.A.I.C.S.: 551112
Gloria M. McCarthy (Chief Admin Officer & Exec VP)
Shantanu Agrawal (Chief Health Officer)
Mark Kaye (CFO & Exec VP)
Blair Todt (Chief Legal Officer & Exec
VP)
cer)
Felicia F. Norwood (Pres-Govt Bus
Dev & Exec VP)
Bill Beck (CMO)
Darrell Gray II (Chief Health Equity
Officer)
Hakon Mattson (Chief Sustainability
Officer)
Kyle Weber (Chief Strategy Officer)
Gail Koziara Boudreaux (Pres &
CEO)

Subsidiaries:

AHI-HealthLink (1)
11200 Westheimer, Houston, TX 77056
Tel.: (713) 782-4555
Web Site: http://www.ahi-healthlink.com
Sales Range: $10-24.9 Million
Emp.: 40
Healtcare Services
N.A.I.C.S.: 524114

AMERIGROUP Corporation (1)

4425 Corporation Ln, Virginia Beach, VA
23462
Tel.: (757) 490-6900
Web Site: https://www.amerigroup.com
Public Managed Healthcare
N.A.I.C.S.: 524114
Felicia F. Norwood (Pres)
Elena McFann (Pres)
Aimee Dailey (Pres)
Barsam Kasravi (Pres)
Kristen Metzger (Pres)

Subsidiary (Domestic):

**AMERIGROUP Community Care of
New Mexico, Inc.** (2)
Two Park Sq 6565 Americas Pky NE Ste
200, Albuquerque, NM 87110
Tel.: (505) 875-4320
Healthcare Insurance
N.A.I.C.S.: 524114

AMERIGROUP Louisiana, Inc. (2)
10000 Perkins Rowe Ste G510, Baton
Rouge, LA 70810
Tel.: (225) 819-4893
Web Site: http://www.myamerigroup.com
Health Insurance Services
N.A.I.C.S.: 524114
Aaron A. Lambert (Pres)

AMERIGROUP Maryland, Inc. (2)
7550 Teague Rd Ste 500, Hanover, MD
21076
Tel.: (410) 859-5800
Web Site: http://www.amerigroup.com
Sales Range: $75-99.9 Million
Emp.: 200
Public Managed Healthcare
N.A.I.C.S.: 524114
Vincent Ancona (Pres)

AMERIGROUP New Jersey, Inc. (2)
101 Wood Ave S 501, Iselin, NJ 08830
Tel.: (732) 452-6000
Web Site: http://www.amerigroupcorp.com
Sales Range: $50-74.9 Million
Emp.: 15
Public Managed Healthcare
N.A.I.C.S.: 524114

AMERIGROUP New York, LLC (2)
9 Pine St, New York, NY 10006
Tel.: (212) 563-5570
Web Site: http://www.myamerigroup.com
Public Managed Healthcare
N.A.I.C.S.: 524114

AMERIGROUP Tennessee, Inc. (2)
22 Century Blvd Ste 220, Nashville, TN
37214
Tel.: (615) 231-6065
Web Site: https://www.amerigroupcorp.com
Sales Range: $75-99.9 Million
Emp.: 350
Public Managed Healthcare
N.A.I.C.S.: 524114
C. Brian Shipp (Pres-Medicaid-South)
Robert Garnett (COO)
Edna Willingham (Pres)

AMERIGROUP Texas, Inc. (2)
823 Congress Ave Ste 400, Austin, TX
78701
Tel.: (512) 382-4970
Web Site: http://providers.amerigroup.com
Sales Range: $10-24.9 Million
Emp.: 20
Public Managed Healthcare
N.A.I.C.S.: 524114

AMERIGROUP Washington, Inc. (2)
705 5th Ave 3 Ste 300, Seattle, WA 98104
Tel.: (206) 695-7081
Emp.: 75
Health Insurance Services
N.A.I.C.S.: 524114
McCormick Aileen (Pres & CEO)

AMGP Georgia Managed Care Company, Inc. (2)
4170 Ashford Dunwoody Rd Ste 100, Atlanta, GA 30319
Tel.: (678) 587-4840
Sales Range: $50-74.9 Million
Emp.: 100
Public Managed Healthcare
N.A.I.C.S.: 524114
Melvin W. Lindsey (Pres-Medicaid Health
Plan)

APPLIED PATHWAYS LLC (1)
1821 Walden Office Sq Ste 215, Schaumburg, IL 60173
Web Site: http://appliedpathways.com
Healtcare Services
N.A.I.C.S.: 621491
John Feldman (Founder)

Advantage Medical Group, LLC (1)
9153 2nd Notch Rd, Columbia, SC 29223
Tel.: (803) 223-9193
Web Site:
     https://advantagemedicalgroup.org
Healthcare & Pharmacy Services
N.A.I.C.S.: 621610

America's 1st Choice of South Carolina, Inc. (1)
250 BerryHill Rd Ste 311, Columbia, SC
29210
Web Site:
     http://www.americas1stchoice.com
Insurance Services
N.A.I.C.S.: 524210

**American Imaging Management,
Inc.** (1)
540 Lake Cook Rd Ste 300, Deerfield, IL
60015-5289
Tel.: (847) 564-8500
Web Site: http://www.americanimaging.net
Diagnostic Imaging Services
N.A.I.C.S.: 621512
Brandon William Cady (Pres & CEO)
Robert Mandel (Chief Medical Officer & Sr
VP)
Nancy Armatas (Chief Admin Officer & Gen
Counsel)
Michael Backus (Sr VP-Solution Innovation
& Partnerships)
Joel Cesario (Sr VP-Bus Admin)
Steven J. Fox (Sr VP-Client Partnerships)
Fred Karutz (Sr VP-Growth & Mktg)
Julie Thiel (Sr VP-Clinical Programs)
Varsha Chandramouli (Natl Dir-Medical-
Clinical Program Implementation, Performance)
George Gjermano (Sr VP)
Sam George (Sr VP)
Lisa Hu (Sr VP-Analytics & Reporting)
Richard Valdesuso (Natl Dir-Medical-
Musculoskeletal)
Thomas P. Power (Sr Dir-Medical-
Cardiology & Sleep Medicine)
Chris Buckle (Dir-Radiology, Guideline Dev)
Kerrie Reed (Dir-Medical-Rehabilitation)
Robert P. Zimmerman (Dir-Medical-
Radiation Oncology)
Stacey Ban (Dir-Medical-Oncology & VP-
Oncology)
Michael J. Fisch (Dir-Medical-Medical Oncology Programs & Genetics)
Robert Furno (Natl Dir-Medical-Govt Programs)
Darin K. McDonald (CIO)

**Amerigroup District of Columbia,
Inc.** (1)
609 H St NE Ste 200, Washington, DC
20002
Health Care Srvices
N.A.I.C.S.: 621999
Jennifer Jarrell (COO)

Amerigroup Iowa, Inc. (1)
PO Box 61010, Virginia Beach, VA 23466-
1010
Health Care Srvices
N.A.I.C.S.: 621999
Jeffrey Jones (Pres)

Anthem Behavioral Health (1)
120 Monument Cir, Indianapolis, IN 46204
Tel.: (317) 488-6000
Web Site: http://www.anthem.com
Sales Range: $75-99.9 Million
Behavioral & Mental Health Insurance Services
N.A.I.C.S.: 524298

**Anthem Benefit Administrators
Inc.** (1)
1801 Watermark Dr Ste 300, Columbus,
OH 43215-7011
Tel.: (614) 880-3500
Web Site: http://www.anthem.com
Sales Range: $10-24.9 Million
Emp.: 200
Medical Insurance Claim Processing

N.A.I.C.S.: 524292

Anthem Blue Cross & Blue Shield of Missouri (1)
1831 Chestnut St, Saint Louis, MO 63103
Tel.: (314) 923-4444
Web Site: http://www.bcbsmo.com
Sales Range: $650-699.9 Million
Emp.: 1,800
Health Care Srvices
N.A.I.C.S.: 524210
Todd Kuehl (Dir)
Amadou Yattassaye (Pres)

Anthem Blue Cross Life and Health Insurance Company (1)
21555 Oxnard St, Woodland Hills, CA 91367
Tel.: (818) 234-2700
Web Site: https://www.anthem.com
Life Insurance & Medical Plans Services
N.A.I.C.S.: 524114

Anthem Credentialing Services, Inc. (1)
200 Brickstone Sq Ste 101, Andover, MA 01810-0034
Tel.: (866) 760-7550
Web Site: http://www.anthem.com
Health Professionals Credentials Verification Service
N.A.I.C.S.: 524114

Anthem Dental (1)
120 Monument Cir, Indianapolis, IN 46204
Tel.: (317) 488-6000
Web Site: http://www.anthem.com
Sales Range: $75-99.9 Million
Dental Health Insurance Services
N.A.I.C.S.: 524298

Anthem Health Plans of Kentucky (1)
9901 Linn Station Rd, Louisville, KY 40223-3803
Tel.: (502) 423-2011
Web Site: https://www.anthem.com
Sales Range: $650-699.9 Million
Emp.: 1,800
Health Insurance Products & Services
N.A.I.C.S.: 524298

Anthem Health Plans of Maine, Inc. (1)
2 Gannett Dr, South Portland, ME 04106-6913
Tel.: (207) 822-7000
Sales Range: $25-49.9 Million
Emp.: 1,000
Health & Medical Insurance
N.A.I.C.S.: 524114

Anthem Health Plans of New Hampshire (1)
43 Constitution Dr Ste 202, Bedford, NH 03110
Tel.: (603) 695-7000
Web Site: https://www.ahpnhmedicare.com
Sales Range: $75-99.9 Million
Health Insurance for Individuals & Families & Medicare Contractor
N.A.I.C.S.: 524298

Anthem Health Plans of Virginia (1)
2015 Staples Mill Rd Ste 1, Richmond, VA 23279-3119
Tel.: (804) 354-7000
Web Site: https://www.anthem.com
Sales Range: $1-4.9 Billion
Emp.: 3,112
Managed Healthcare
N.A.I.C.S.: 524114

Subsidiary (Domestic):

HealthKeepers, Inc. (2)
2220 Edward Holland Dr, Richmond, VA 23230 (100%)
Tel.: (804) 342-0010
Sales Range: $350-399.9 Million
Emp.: 105
Health Insurance
N.A.I.C.S.: 524114

Anthem Health Plans, Inc. (1)
370 Basset Rd, North Haven, CT 06473
Tel.: (203) 239-4911
Web Site: https://www.anthem.com
Sales Range: $700-749.9 Million
Emp.: 1,864

Health Insurance for Students, Individuals & Self-Employed
N.A.I.C.S.: 524298

Anthem Holding Corp. (1)
220 Virginia Ave, Indianapolis, IN 46204
Tel.: (833) 401-1577
Holding Company
N.A.I.C.S.: 551112

Anthem Insurance Companies, Inc. (1)
120 Monument Cir, Indianapolis, IN 46204 (100%)
Tel.: (317) 488-6000
Sales Range: $500-549.9 Million
Emp.: 14,800
Health Insurance & Benefits
N.A.I.C.S.: 524114

Anthem Vision (1)
120 Monument Cir, Indianapolis, IN 46204
Tel.: (317) 488-6000
Web Site: http://www.anthem.com
Employee Vision Care Benefits
N.A.I.C.S.: 524298

Aspire Health, Inc. (1)
22 Century Blvd Ste 220, Nashville, TN 37214
Tel.: (615) 454-9850
Web Site: https://www.aspirehealthcare.com
Health Care Srvices
N.A.I.C.S.: 621610
Catherine Campbell (Pres)
Paul Mikulecky (Chief Medical Officer)
Jared Sullivan (COO)
Allen Yang (CFO)
Angela Brice (VP)

Beacon Health Options of Pennsylvania, Inc. (1)
PO Box 1840, Cranberry Township, PA 16066-1840
Web Site:
    https://pa.beaconhealthoptions.com
Health Care Srvices
N.A.I.C.S.: 621610
Sue Klaus (Mgr-Prevention, Education & Outreach)
Jonathan Edmonds (COO)

Behavioral Health Network, Inc. (1)
417 Liberty St, Springfield, MA 01104
Tel.: (413) 301-9355
Web Site: https://www.bhninc.org
Behavioral Healthcare Services
N.A.I.C.S.: 621610
Katherine B. Wilson (Pres)
Michael Kelliher (VP)
Richard Follett (VP)
Rose Evans (Sr VP)
Steven Winn (Pres & COO)
Jessica DeFlumer-Trapp (Exec VP)
Sara Brewer (Dir-Medical)
Jennifer Moore (Dir-Clinical)
Stewart Joslin (CFO)
Katherine Mague (Sr VP)
Matthew Snow (CIO-Interim)
Katherine Cook (Sr VP)
Joy Ifill (VP)
Jose Rosado-Medina (VP)
Brian Ross (VP)

Blue Cross Blue Shield Healthcare Plan of Georgia, Inc. (1)
3350 Peachtree Rd NE, Atlanta, GA 30326
Tel.: (404) 842-8000
Web Site: https://www.bcbsga.com
Sales Range: $10-24.9 Million
Emp.: 28
Hospital & Medical Service Plans
N.A.I.C.S.: 524114

Blue Cross Blue Shield of Wisconsin (1)
N17 W24340 Riverwood Dr, Waukesha, WI 53118
Tel.: (414) 459-5000
Web Site: https://www.anthem.com
Sales Range: $1-4.9 Billion
Emp.: 2,200
Group Life & Disability Insurance
N.A.I.C.S.: 524114
Paul Nobile (Pres)

Subsidiary (Domestic):

Claim Management Services, Inc. (2)

975 Hansen Rd, Green Bay, WI 54304
Tel.: (920) 497-1589
Sales Range: $10-24.9 Million
Emp.: 280
Claim Management Services & Third Party Administrative Services
N.A.I.C.S.: 524291

Blue Cross of California (1)
1 Wellpoint Way, Thousand Oaks, CA 91362
Tel.: (805) 557-6655
Sales Range: $1-4.9 Billion
Emp.: 10,900
Health Insurance Products & Related Services
N.A.I.C.S.: 524298

Affiliate (Domestic):

Blue Cross Life & Health Insurance Company (2)
1 Wellpoint Way, Thousand Oaks, CA 91362
Tel.: (805) 557-6990
Web Site: http://www.wellpoint.com
Sales Range: $10-24.9 Million
Emp.: 25
Life & Health Insurance Services
N.A.I.C.S.: 524114

CareMore Health Group, Inc. (1)
12900 Park Plaza Dr Ste 150, Cerritos, CA 90703
Tel.: (562) 741-4300
Web Site: http://www.caremore.com
Holding Company; Senior Citizen Healthcare Plans & Medical Management Services
N.A.I.C.S.: 551112
Shaden Marzouk (Pres)
Andrew Aronson (Chief Medical Officer)
Alexis Megeath (VP-Ops)
David Hsieh (VP-Fin Strategy & Plan)

Division (Domestic):

CareMore Health Plan (2)
12900 Park Plz Dr Ste 150 MS-6150, Cerritos, CA 90703
Tel.: (562) 622-2800
Web Site: https://www.caremore.com
Senior Citizen Healthcare Plans
N.A.I.C.S.: 524114

CareMore Medical Enterprises (2)
12900 Park Plz Dr Ste 150 MS 6150, Cerritos, CA 90703
Tel.: (562) 622-2800
Web Site: http://www.caremore.com
Sales Range: $300-349.9 Million
Emp.: 1,200
Senior Citizen Medical Management & Services
N.A.I.C.S.: 812990

CareMore Health System (1)
141 W Foothill Blvd, Upland, CA 91786
Tel.: (909) 296-8800
Web Site: https://www.caremore.com
Health Insurance Services
N.A.I.C.S.: 524114
Shaden Marzouk (Pres)
Andrew Aronson (Chief Medical Officer)
Alexis Megeath (VP-Ops)
David Hsieh (VP-Fin Strategy & Plan)

CareMore Holdings, Inc. (1)
10000 Lakewood Blvd, Downey, CA 90240-4020
Tel.: (562) 862-3684
Web Site: http://www.caremore.com
Holding Company
N.A.I.C.S.: 551112

CareMore Medical Management Company (1)
12900 Park Plaza Dr, Cerritos, CA 90703
Tel.: (562) 622-2900
Web Site: http://www.caremore.com
Emp.: 1,200
Management & Administrative Services
N.A.I.C.S.: 561110

Carelon Global Solutions India LLP (1)
Xenon South Tower Plot Number 39 & 40, Bagmane Solarium City Doddanakkundi, Bengaluru, 560037, India
Tel.: (91) 8069558400

Web Site: https://www.carelonglobal.in
Information Technology & Consulting Services
N.A.I.C.S.: 541519

Carelon Global Solutions Ireland Limited (1)
Clive House National Technology Park, Plassey, Limerick, V94 HN4N, Ireland
Tel.: (353) 61332581
Web Site: https://www.carelonglobal.ie
Information Technology & Consulting Services
N.A.I.C.S.: 541519

Carelon Research, Inc. (1)
123 Justison St Ste 200, Wilmington, DE 19801
Tel.: (302) 230-2000
Web Site: https://www.carelonresearch.com
Healthcare & Research Services
N.A.I.C.S.: 541720

CarelonRx, Inc. (1)
450 Headquarters Plz 7th Fl E Tower, Morristown, NJ 07960
Tel.: (833) 419-0530
Web Site: https://www.carelonrx.com
Hospitals & Health Care Services
N.A.I.C.S.: 622110

Castellana Physician Services, LLC (1)
Centro Internacional de Mercadeo Torre II Ste 505 Carr 165, Guaynabo, PR 00968
Tel.: (787) 282-6990
Web Site: https://www.castellana-ipa.com
Emp.: 500
Administrative Management Services
N.A.I.C.S.: 541611
Raul Montalvo Orsini (Pres)
Eyminel Viel (Sec)

Cerulean Companies, Inc. (1)
3350 Peachtree Rd NE, Atlanta, GA 30326
Tel.: (404) 842-8000
Emp.: 2,635
Health Insurance Services
N.A.I.C.S.: 524114

Community Insurance Company (1)
4361 Irwin Simpson Rd, Mason, OH 45040
Tel.: (513) 872-8100
Sales Range: $650-699.9 Million
Emp.: 1,700
Health & Medical Insurance Plans
N.A.I.C.S.: 524298
Steve Martenet (Pres)

DeCare Dental Insurance Ireland, Ltd. (1)
Ida Business Park, Co Mayo, Claremorris, F12 KD85, Ireland
Tel.: (353) 949378608
Web Site: https://decare.ie
Dental Care Insurance Services
N.A.I.C.S.: 524298

DeCare Operations Ireland, Limited (1)
Ida Business Park, Claremorris, Ireland
Tel.: (353) 949372250
Web Site: https://www.ddii.ie
Sales Range: $25-49.9 Million
Emp.: 100
Dental Care Insurance Services
N.A.I.C.S.: 339116

DeCare Systems Ireland, Limited (1)
Building 1 University Technology Centre
Curraheen Road, Cork, Ireland
Tel.: (353) 214925100
Web Site: http://www.decaresystems.ie
Software Development Services
N.A.I.C.S.: 541511

EasyScripts Cutler Bay, LLC (1)
7235 NW 19th St Bay E, Miami, FL 33126
Tel.: (305) 663-5400
Web Site: https://easyscripts.com
Health Care Srvices
N.A.I.C.S.: 621610

EasyScripts Hialeah LLC (1)
7235 NW 19th St Bay E, Miami, FL 33126
Tel.: (305) 663-5400
Web Site: https://easyscripts.com
Health Care Srvices
N.A.I.C.S.: 621610

EasyScripts Westchester, LLC (1)

Elevance Health, Inc.—(Continued)

7235 NW 19th St Bay E, Miami, FL 33126
Tel.: (305) 663-5400
Web Site: https://easyscripts.com
Health Care Srvices
N.A.I.C.S.: 621610

EasyScripts, LLC (1)
7235 NW 19th St Bay E, Miami, FL 33126
Tel.: (305) 663-5400
Web Site: https://easyscripts.com
Drug & Medicine Retailer
N.A.I.C.S.: 456110

Empire Blue Cross & Blue Shield (1)
1 Liberty Plz Ste 1300, New York, NY 10006
Tel.: (212) 476-1000
Web Site: http://www.empireblue.com
Sales Range: $150-199.9 Million
Health Insurance Services to Individuals & Employers
N.A.I.C.S.: 524114
Jason N. Gorevic (CMO, Chief Sls Officer & Sr VP)

Subsidiary (Domestic):

Empire HealthChoice Assurance, Inc. (2)
11 W 42nd St 17th FL, New York, NY 10036
Tel.: (212) 476-1000
Web Site: http://www.empireblue.com
Health Care & Travel Protection Insurance Services
N.A.I.C.S.: 524114

Empire HealthChoice HMO, Inc. (1)
One Liberty Plz, New York, NY 10006
Tel.: (212) 476-1000
Web Site: http://www.empireblue.com
Health Insurance Coverage Service
N.A.I.C.S.: 524114

Golden West Dental & Vision Health Plans, Inc. (1)
PO Box 5347, Oxnard, CA 93031-5347
Tel.: (805) 934-3100
Web Site:
https://www.goldenwestdental.com
Sales Range: $1-9.9 Million
Emp.: 71
Vision & Dental Insurance
N.A.I.C.S.: 524210

Golden West Health Plan, Inc. (1)
Po Box 5347, Oxnard, CA 93031
Tel.: (805) 934-3100
Insurance Agency Services
N.A.I.C.S.: 524210

Government Health Services, L.L.C. (1)
401 W Michigan St, Milwaukee, WI 53203
Tel.: (414) 226-6203
Health Insurance Services
N.A.I.C.S.: 524114

HMO Missouri, Inc. (1)
1831 Chestnut, Saint Louis, MO 63103
Tel.: (314) 923-4767
Emp.: 93
Health Care Srvices
N.A.I.C.S.: 621999

Health Core, Inc. (1)
123 Justison St Ste 200, Wilmington, DE 19801-5134
Tel.: (302) 230-2000
Web Site: https://www.healthcore.com
Sales Range: $1-9.9 Million
Emp.: 150
Healthcare Management Consulting Services
N.A.I.C.S.: 541720
Mark Cziraky (Co-Pres & Co-Founder)
Marcus D. Wilson (Co-Founder & Co-Chief Analytics Officer)
Andrea DeVries (VP-Translational Res)
Julie Miller (VP-Res Ops,Resourcing)
Crystal Holick (VP-Res Ops)
Ralph Quimbo (VP-Health Economics,Outcomes Res)
Lisa Marceau (VP-Digital Res Solutions Bus Ops)
Mary Flanigan (Chief Bus Ops Officer)
Devon H. Taylor (Dir-Planning)
Craig Waltz (Exec Dir)

Marc Overhage (Chief Medical Informatics Officer)
Daniel C. Beachler (Dir-Safety)
David Q. Jones (Assoc Gen Counsel)
Devon H. Taylor (Dir-Planning)
Craig Waltz (Exec Dir)
Marc Overhage (Chief Medical Informatics Officer)
Daniel C. Beachler (Dir-Safety)
David Q. Jones (Assoc Gen Counsel)

Health Management Corporation (1)
6800 Paragon Pl Ste 300, Richmond, VA 23230 (100%)
Web Site: http://www.choosehmc.com
Sales Range: $150-199.9 Million
Emp.: 413
Cost Containment Strategies For Employers & Managed Care Organizations
N.A.I.C.S.: 524114

HealthLink, Inc. (1)
1831 Chestnut, Saint Louis, MO 63103
Tel.: (800) 624-2356
Web Site: https://www.healthlink.com
Sales Range: $250-299.9 Million
Emp.: 650
Network Rental & Administrative Services to Employers, Unions, Governmental Subdivisions, Schools & Insurance Companies
N.A.I.C.S.: 561499

Subsidiary (Domestic):

Healthlink HMO, Inc. (2)
18731 Chestnut St, Saint Louis, MO 63103
Tel.: (800) 624-2356
Web Site: http://www.healthlink.com
Sales Range: $250-299.9 Million
Health Insurance
N.A.I.C.S.: 524298

HealthSun Health Plans, Inc. (1)
11430 NW 20th St Ste 300, Miami, FL 33172
Tel.: (305) 234-9292
Web Site: https://healthsun.com
Health Care Srvices
N.A.I.C.S.: 621610

IEC Group, Inc. (1)
2888 W Excursion Ln, Meridian, ID 83642
Tel.: (208) 344-7900
Web Site: https://ameriben.com
Emp.: 1,200
Health Care Srvices
N.A.I.C.S.: 621610

Lumenos (1)
1801 N Beauregard St Ste 10, Alexandria, VA 22311
Tel.: (703) 236-6300
Sales Range: $10-24.9 Million
Emp.: 125
Health Care Plans
N.A.I.C.S.: 524114
Reena Sood (Mgr-Mktg Programs)

MMM Healthcare, LLC (1)
PO Box 71114, San Juan, PR 00936-8014
Web Site: https://www.mmm-pr.com
Health Care Srvices
N.A.I.C.S.: 621610

MMM Multi Health, LLC (1)
Central Offices Fundacion Angel Ramos Anexo 2do piso Ave Chardon, Hato Rey, PR 00918
Tel.: (787) 999-4411
Web Site: https://www.multihealth-vital.com
Health Insurance Services
N.A.I.C.S.: 524114

MSO of Puerto Rico, LLC (1)
350 Chardon Ave Ste 500 Chardon Tower, San Juan, PR 00918
Tel.: (787) 993-2317
Web Site: https://www.mso-pr.com
Health Insurance Services
N.A.I.C.S.: 524114
Raul F. Montalvo-Orsini (Pres)
Waldemar C. Rios Alvarez (Chief Medical Officer)
Gonzalo Salinas Mulder (COO)
Jamie E. Rivera Pesante (CFO)
Rafael Perez Nieves (VP)

Massachusetts Behavioral Health Partnership, LLP (1)
200 State St Ste 305, Boston, MA 02109
Tel.: (617) 790-4000

Web Site: https://www.masspartnership.com
Healtcare Services
N.A.I.C.S.: 621610
Nancy E. Norman (Dir-Medical)
Sharon Hanson (CEO)
David J. Wolfe (Mng Dir)

Matthew Thornton Health Plan, Inc. (1)
1155 Elm St Ste 200, Manchester, NH 03101 (100%)
Web Site: https://www.antheminc.com
Health Plan Services
N.A.I.C.S.: 524114

Meridian Resource Company, LLC (1)
20725 Watertown Rd, Waukesha, WI 53186
Tel.: (262) 312-8000
Web Site:
https://www.meridianresource.com
Sales Range: $1-9.9 Million
Healthcare Auditing Services
N.A.I.C.S.: 541219

National Government Services, Inc. (1)
8115 Knue Rd Bldg 48, Indianapolis, IN 46250
Tel.: (317) 841-4400
Web Site: https://www.ngsmedicare.com
Sales Range: $150-199.9 Million
Medicare Processing Services
N.A.I.C.S.: 524292

New England Research Institutes, Inc. (1)
220 Virginia Ave, Indianapolis, IN 46204
Tel.: (211) 8334011577
Clinical & Epidemiological Research Services
N.A.I.C.S.: 541720

PHM MultiDisciplinary Clinic Arecibo LLC (1)
Barrio San Daniel Carretera 2 Km 81 2, Arecibo, PR 00612
Tel.: (787) 650-2732
Primary Care Services
N.A.I.C.S.: 621111

PHM MultiDisciplinary Clinic Cabo Rojo LLC (1)
Centro Comercial Galeria 100 Km 6 6 Carr Ste 100 Bo Miradero, Cabo Rojo, PR 00623
Tel.: (787) 808-5200
Primary Care Services
N.A.I.C.S.: 621111

PHM MultiSalud, LLC (1)
1551 Alda St Ste 201 Caribbean Urb, San Juan, PR 00926-2709
Tel.: (787) 625-2500
Web Site: https://www.pnmmultisalud.com
Primary Care Services
N.A.I.C.S.: 621111

Paragon Healthcare, Inc. (1)
7324 W Cheyenne Ave, Las Vegas, NV 89129
Tel.: (702) 214-6665
Web Site: http://www.paragonnv.com
Healtcare Services
N.A.I.C.S.: 621498

Pasteur Medical Center, LLC (1)
8000 Governors Sq Blvd Ste 201, Miami Lakes, FL 33016
Tel.: (305) 727-8387
Web Site: https://pasteurmedical.com
Healtcare Services
N.A.I.C.S.: 621491
Emelis Sanchez (Mgr)

RightCHOICE Benefit AdministratorsSM (1)
1831 Chestnut St, Saint Louis, MO 63103 (100%)
Tel.: (314) 821-3957
Web Site: http://www.secure.healthx.com
Sales Range: $75-99.9 Million
Emp.: 200
Self-Funded Medical Benefits Plans Administrators
N.A.I.C.S.: 524292

Santa Barbara Specialty Pharmacy, LLC (1)
4690 Carpinteria Ave Ste B, Carpinteria, CA 93013

Healthcare & Pharmacy Services
N.A.I.C.S.: 621610

Simply Healthcare Plans, Inc. (1)
11430 NW 20th St Ste 300, Miami, FL 33172
Tel.: (305) 408-5700
Web Site:
https://www.simplyhealthcareplans.com
Healthcare Carrier
N.A.I.C.S.: 524114

The Anthem Companies, Inc. (1)
220 Virginia Ave, Indianapolis, IN 46204
Tel.: (317) 488-6000
Health Insurance Services
N.A.I.C.S.: 524114

UNICARE Health Plan of Kansas, Inc. (1)
825 S Kansas Ave Ste 110, Topeka, KS 66612-1233
Tel.: (785) 270-1070
Web Site: http://www.unicare.com
Health Care Srvices
N.A.I.C.S.: 524114

UNICARE Health Plan of West Virginia, Inc. (1)
200 Association Dr Ste 200, Charleston, WV 25311
Web Site: https://mss.unicare.com
Health Care Srvices
N.A.I.C.S.: 621610

United Government Services, LLC (1)
6775 W Washington St, Milwaukee, WI 53214
Tel.: (414) 226-6203
Sales Range: $100-124.9 Million
Emp.: 980
Health Care Insurance Services
N.A.I.C.S.: 524292

WPMI, LLC (1)
12/F Shanghai International Ocean Shipping Building No 720 Pudong Ave, Shanghai, 200120, China
Tel.: (86) 2138527000
Web Site: http://www.wpmillc.com
Health Plan Consulting & Services
N.A.I.C.S.: 541611
Anting Tao (Sr VP-Bus Dev)

WellPoint Behavioral Health (1)
9655 Granite Ridge Dr 600, San Diego, CA 92123
Tel.: (858) 571-8136
Sales Range: Less than $1 Million
Mental Health & Employee Assistance Services
N.A.I.C.S.: 621330

WellPoint Pharmacy Management (1)
407 Fallbrook Ave, Canoga Park, CA 91304
Tel.: (818) 313-5127
Sales Range: $25-49.9 Million
Emp.: 600
Online Access to Pharmacy Benefit Management Services
N.A.I.C.S.: 524298

Division (Domestic):

PrecisionRx (2)
8407 Fallbrook Ave, West Hills, CA 91304
Tel.: (800) 451-0433
Mail-Order Pharmacy Fulfillment Facility
N.A.I.C.S.: 456110

Wellpoint Federal Corporation (1)
220 Virginia Ave, Indianapolis, IN 46204
Web Site: https://www.wellpointfederal.com
Health Care Srvices
N.A.I.C.S.: 621610

Wellpoint Iowa, Inc. (1)
PO Box 61010, Virginia Beach, VA 23466-1010
Health Education Services
N.A.I.C.S.: 624190

Wellpoint Tennessee, Inc. (1)
22 Century Blvd Ste 310, Nashville, TN 37214
Healthcare & Pharmacy Services
N.A.I.C.S.: 621610

Zip Drug Inc. (1)

30 Montgomery St Ste 1410, Jersey City,
NJ 07302
Web Site: http://www.zipdrug.com
Pharmacy Retailer
N.A.I.C.S.: 456110
Stu Libby *(Founder & CEO)*
Kyle E. Dolbow *(COO)*

myNEXUS, Inc. (1)
105 Westwood Pl Ste 400, Brentwood, TN
37027
Web Site: https://www.mynexuscare.com
Health Care Srvices
N.A.I.C.S.: 621610

ELEVATION ONCOLOGY, INC.

888 7th Ave 12th Fl, New York, NY
10106
Tel.: (716) 371-1125   DE
Web Site:
   https://www.elevationoncology.com
Year Founded: 2019
ELEV—(NASDAQ)
Assets: $94,161,000
Liabilities: $45,129,000
Net Worth: $49,032,000
Earnings: ($95,080,000)
Emp.: 33
Fiscal Year-end: 12/31/22
Biotechnology Research & Develop-
ment Services
N.A.I.C.S.: 541714
Joseph J. Ferra Jr. *(Pres & CEO)*
Shawn M. Leland *(Founder)*
Joseph Ferra *(CTO)*
Amy C. Cavers *(VP-Medical Affairs)*
Tammy Furlong *(CFO & Principal
Acctg Officer)*
Valerie Malyvanh Jansen *(Chief
Medical Officer)*
Sheila Magil *(VP-CMC & Quality)*
Brian Sullivan *(VP-Corp Dev)*
Siera Talbott *(VP-Program Mgmt &
Stratagic Alliances)*

ELI LILLY & COMPANY

Lilly Corporate Ctr, Indianapolis, IN
46285
Tel.: (317) 276-2000   IN
Web Site: https://www.lilly.com
Year Founded: 1876
LLY—(NYSE)
Rev.: $34,124,100,000
Assets: $64,006,300,000
Liabilities: $53,142,600,000
Net Worth: $10,863,700,000
Earnings: $5,240,400,000
Emp.: 43,000
Fiscal Year-end: 12/31/23
Pharmaceutical Products Mfr, Devel-
oper & Marketer
N.A.I.C.S.: 325412
David A. Ricks *(Chm, Pres & CEO)*
Eric Dozier *(Exec VP-Human Re-
sources & Diversity)*
Daniel M. Skovronsky *(Chief Scien-
tific Officer, Pres-Lilly Research Labo-
ratories & Exec VP)*
Diogo Rau *(CIO, Chief Digital Officer
& Sr VP)*
Alonzo Weems *(Chief Compliance
Officer, Chief Ethics Officer & Exec
VP/Sr VP-Enterprise Risk Mgmt)*
Patrik Jonsson *(Pres-Lilly USA & Lilly
Cardiometabolic Health, Exec VP &
Sr VP)*
Melissa S. Seymour *(Exec VP-Global
Quality)*
Jacob Van Naarden *(Pres-Lilly Oncol-
ogy & Exec VP)*
Lucas Montarce *(CFO & Exec VP)*

Subsidiaries:

ARMO BioSciences, Inc. (1)
575 Chesapeake Dr, Redwood City, CA
94063
Tel.: (650) 779-5075
Web Site: http://www.armobio.com

Biotechnology Research & Development
Services
N.A.I.C.S.: 541714

Agri Stats, Inc. (1)
6510 Mutual Dr, Fort Wayne, IN 46825
Tel.: (260) 407-2700
Web Site: https://www.agristats.com
Emp.: 100
Accounting Services
N.A.I.C.S.: 541219
Michael Snyder *(Dir-HR)*

Akouos, Inc. (1)
645 Summer St Ste 200, Boston, MA 02210
Tel.: (857) 410-1818
Web Site: http://www.akouos.com
Rev.: $1,872,000
Assets: $278,755,000
Liabilities: $45,105,000
Net Worth: $233,650,000
Earnings: ($86,671,000)
Emp.: 103
Fiscal Year-end: 12/31/2021
Biotechnology Research & Development
Services
N.A.I.C.S.: 541714
Emmanuel J. Simons *(Co-Founder, Pres &
CEO)*
John Connelly *(Sr VP-Portfolio Strategy &
R&D Ops)*
Michael McKenna *(Co-Founder & Chief
Medical Officer)*
Gregory Robinson *(Chief Scientific Officer)*
Karoline Shair *(Chief Legal Officer & Sec)*
Jennifer A. Wellman *(COO)*
Sachiyo Minegishi *(CFO)*
Kathy Reape *(Chief Dev Officer)*
Chris Smith *(CEO)*

Avid Radiopharmaceuticals, Inc. (1)
3711 Market St 7th Fl, Philadelphia, PA
19104
Tel.: (215) 298-0700
Web Site: https://www.avidrp.com
Pharmaceuticals Product Mfr
N.A.I.C.S.: 325412
Daniel M. Skovronsky *(Chm)*
John Lister-James *(Sr VP-Chemical Dev &
Mfg)*
Mark A. Mintun *(Pres)*
Emily C. Collins *(VP-Research & Develop-
ment)*
Michael Devous *(VP)*
Tyler Benedum *(VP)*
Adam S. Fleisher *(Chief Medical Officer)*

DICE Therapeutics, Inc. (1)
400 E Jamie Ct Ste 300, South San Fran-
cisco, CA 94080
Tel.: (650) 566-1420
Web Site: https://www.dicetherapeutics.com
Rev.: $5,213,000
Assets: $593,978,000
Liabilities: $26,990,000
Net Worth: $566,988,000
Earnings: ($83,887,000)
Emp.: 71
Fiscal Year-end: 12/31/2022
Pharmaceuticals Product Mfr
N.A.I.C.S.: 325412
Scott Robertson *(CFO & Chief Bus Officer)*
Timothy Lu *(Chief Medical Officer)*
John Jacobsen *(Chief Scientific Officer)*
Charon Spencer *(Chief HR Officer)*
Paul Fatheree *(Sr VP-Medicinal Chemistry)*
Venkat Thalladi *(Sr VP-CMC)*
Meina Tang *(VP-Drug Dev Sciences)*
Nico Ghilardi *(VP-Immunology)*
Philip L. Johnson *(Pres)*
Michael C. Thompson *(Treas)*
Chris Anderson *(Sec)*
Jonathan Groff *(Asst Sec)*
Katie Lodato *(Asst Treas)*

Dermira, Inc. (1)
275 Middlefield Rd Ste 150, Menlo Park,
CA 94025
Tel.: (650) 421-7200
Web Site: http://www.dermira.com
Pharmaceuticals Product Mfr
N.A.I.C.S.: 325412
Delphine Imbert *(VP)*
Bill Aurora *(Chief Scientific Affairs Officer)*
Andrew Hotchkiss *(CEO)*
Virginia Finnerty-Brooks *(Chief Bus Officer
& Sr VP)*
Harp Dhaliwal *(Sr VP-Supply Chain-
Procurement-Manufacturing)*
Gary Thompson *(VP)*

Tracy VanDenberg *(VP & Head-Human Resources)*
Thomas G. Wiggans *(Founder)*

Disarm Therapeutics Inc. (1)
1 Main St 11th Fl, Cambridge, MA 02142
Tel.: (617) 752-6884
Web Site: https://www.disarmtx.com
Health Care Srvices
N.A.I.C.S.: 621610
Raul Krauss *(Founder, VP & Head-Biology)*
Tom Engber *(Sr VP & Head-
Neuropharmacology & Translational Sci-
ences)*
Robert Hughes *(VP & Head-Molecular Dis-
covery)*
Molly B. Schlagel *(Ops Mgr)*
Marco Passini *(Sr Dir-Pharmacology)*

Dista, S.A. (1)
Avenida De La Industria 30, Alcobendas,
28108, Spain
Tel.: (34) 916635000
Industrial Chemical Mfr & Distr
N.A.I.C.S.: 325998

**Elanco (Shanghai) Animal Health Co.,
Ltd.** (1)
Tel.: (86) 2123016888
Pharmaceuticals Product Mfr
N.A.I.C.S.: 325412
Pu Chen *(Mgr-Mktg)*

**Elanco (Taiwan) Animal Health Co.
Ltd.** (1)
RM 7E02 7FL 5 Sec 5 Hsin-Yi Rd, Taipei
World Trade Center Exhibition Hall, Taipei,
Taiwan
Tel.: (886) 227228797
Pharmaceuticals Product Mfr
N.A.I.C.S.: 325412
Judy Lin *(Country Dir)*

Elanco (Thailand) Ltd. (1)
689 Bhiraj Tower at EmQuartier 17th/1
9-14th Floor Sukhumvit Rd, North Klongton
Vadhana, Bangkok, 10110, Vadhana, Thai-
land
Tel.: (66) 22690500
Web Site: https://www.elanco.com
Pharmaceuticals Product Mfr
N.A.I.C.S.: 325412

Elanco Animal Health UK Limited (1)
Form 2 Bartley Way Bartley Wood Business
Park, Hook, Basingstoke, RG27 9XA,
Hampshire, United Kingdom
Tel.: (44) 1256353131
Web Site: http://www.elanco.co.uk
Pharmaceutical Product Mfr & Distr
N.A.I.C.S.: 325412

Elanco Australasia Pty. Ltd. (1)
Level 3 7 Eden Park Drive, Macquarie Park,
2113, NSW, Australia
Tel.: (61) 1800226324
Web Site: http://www.elanco.com.au
Animal Care Support Services
N.A.I.C.S.: 812910

Elanco Canada Limited (1)
1919 Minnesota Court Suite 401, Missis-
sauga, L5N 0C9, ON, Canada
Tel.: (519) 821-0727
Web Site: http://www.elanco.ca
Emp.: 40
Animal Health Care Services
N.A.I.C.S.: 813112

Elanco Deutschland GmbH (1)
Rathausplatz 12, 61348, Bad Homburg,
Germany
Tel.: (49) 8004534847
Web Site: https://www.elanco.com
Emp.: 900
Animal Care Support Services
N.A.I.C.S.: 812910

Elanco France S.A.S. (1)
Crisco Uno Building C 3-5 avenue de la
cristallerie, 92310, Sevres, Cedex, France
Tel.: (33) 155493529
Web Site: http://www.elanco.fr
Pharmaceutical Product Mfr & Distr
N.A.I.C.S.: 325412

Elanco India Private Limited (1)
Western Edge 1 Unit No 201 2nd Floor
Near Western Express Highway, Borivali
East, Mumbai, 400 066, India
Tel.: (91) 2262431200

Pharmaceuticals Product Mfr
N.A.I.C.S.: 325412

Elanco Italia S.p.A. (1)
Via dei Colatori 12, 50019, Sesto Fioren-
tino, FI, Italy
Tel.: (39) 0554640825
Web Site: https://www.elanco.com
Emp.: 9,800
Pharmaceutical Product Mfr & Distr
N.A.I.C.S.: 325412

Elanco Nederland B.V. (1)
Van Deventerlaan 31 Room 2 01 2 02,
3528 AG, Utrecht, Netherlands
Tel.: (31) 303079245
Web Site: http://www.elanco.nl
Animal Protection Services
N.A.I.C.S.: 813312
Jan Arne den Boef *(Mgr-Acct)*

Elanco Salud Animal SA de CV (1)
Av Prol Americas No 1592 Piso 1 Col
Country Club CP, 44620, Guadalajara,
Jalisco, Mexico
Tel.: (52) 3338195534
Pharmaceuticals Product Mfr
N.A.I.C.S.: 325412

Elanco Saude Animal Ltda. (1)
Avenida Morumbi 8264, Sao Paulo, 04703-
002, Brazil
Tel.: (55) 800112690
Web Site: http://www.elanco.com.br
Pharmaceutical Product Mfr & Distr
N.A.I.C.S.: 325412

Elanco Tiergesundheit AG (1)
Mattenstrasse 24 A, 4058, Basel, Switzer-
land
Tel.: (41) 615880142
Web Site: https://www.elanco.com
Pharmaceuticals Product Mfr
N.A.I.C.S.: 325412

Elanco UK AH Limited (1)
Form 2 Bartley Way Bartley Wood Business
Park, Hook, Basingstoke, RG27 9XA,
Hampshire, United Kingdom
Tel.: (44) 1256353131
Web Site: http://www.elanco.co.uk
Animal Protection Services
N.A.I.C.S.: 813312

Elanco US, Inc. (1)
2500 Innovation Way, Greenfield, IN 46140
Tel.: (317) 276-2000
Web Site: http://www.elanco.us
Animal Care Support Services
N.A.I.C.S.: 812910
Antoine Ezell *(CMO)*

**Eli Lilly & Company (India) Pvt.
Ltd.** (1)
Plot 92 Sector 32 Institutional Area, Gur-
gaon, 122 001, Haryana, India
Tel.: (91) 1244753000
Web Site: https://www.lillyindia.co.in
Pharmaceuticals Product Mfr
N.A.I.C.S.: 325412

Eli Lilly (Malaysia) Sdn. Bhd. (1)
Level 7 Menara OBYU No 4 Jalan
PJU8/8A, Damansara Perdana, 47820, Pet-
aling Jaya, Selangor Darul Ehsan, Malaysia
Tel.: (60) 377216222
Pharmaceuticals Product Mfr
N.A.I.C.S.: 325412

Eli Lilly (Malaysia) Sdn. Bhd. (1)
Level 7 Menara OBYU No 4 Jalan PJU
8/8A Damansara Perdana, Petaling Jaya,
47820, Malaysia
Tel.: (60) 377216222
Web Site: http://www.lilly.com.my
Pharmaceuticals Product Mfr
N.A.I.C.S.: 325412
Taejin Ham *(Gen Mgr)*

**Eli Lilly (Philippines),
Incorporated** (1)
Clock In Penthouse 22nd Flr 30th Corpo-
rate Center 30 Meralco Avenue, Pasig,
1604, Philippines
Tel.: (63) 277501318
Pharmaceuticals Product Mfr
N.A.I.C.S.: 325412

**Eli Lilly (Philippines),
Incorporated** (1)
Unit 401-403 Tower 1 Rockwell Business

Eli Lilly & Company—(Continued)

Center Ortigas Avenue, Pasig, 1602, Philippines
Tel.: (63) 26897900
Web Site: http://www.lilly.com.ph
Emp.: 150
Pharmaceuticals Product Mfr
N.A.I.C.S.: 325412
Reynaldo Dela Cruz *(Gen Mgr)*

Eli Lilly Asia Pacific SSC Sdn Bhd **(1)**
Level 10 Symphony House Block D-13
Pusat Dagangan Dana 1, 47301, Petaling Jaya, Selangor, Malaysia
Tel.: (60) 378449600
Chinese Medicine Mfr
N.A.I.C.S.: 325412

Eli Lilly B-H d.o.o. **(1)**
Azize sacirbegovic 1/2, 71000, Sarajevo, Bosnia & Herzegovina
Tel.: (387) 33942020
Pharmaceuticals Product Mfr
N.A.I.C.S.: 325412

Eli Lilly CR s.r.o. **(1)**
Pobrezni 394/12, 186 00, Prague, 8, Czech Republic
Tel.: (420) 234664111
Web Site: https://www.lilly.com
Pharmaceuticals Product Mfr
N.A.I.C.S.: 325412

Eli Lilly CR s.r.o. **(1)**
Pobrezni 394/12, 186 00, Prague, Czech Republic
Tel.: (420) 234664111
Web Site: http://www.lilly.cz
Pharmaceuticals Product Mfr
N.A.I.C.S.: 325412

Eli Lilly Cork Limited **(1)**
Island House Eastgate Road, Eastgate Business Park, Little Island, Co Cork, Ireland
Tel.: (353) 214232400
Pharmaceuticals Product Mfr
N.A.I.C.S.: 325412

Eli Lilly Export S.A. **(1)**
Chemin des Coquelicots 16, PO 580, CH-1214, Vernier, Switzerland
Tel.: (41) 223060333
Pharmaceuticals Product Mfr
N.A.I.C.S.: 325412

Eli Lilly Finance, S.A. **(1)**
Chemin Des Coquelicots 16 Vernier, 1214, Geneva, Switzerland
Tel.: (41) 223060401
Emp.: 20
Financial Advisory Services
N.A.I.C.S.: 523940

Eli Lilly Ges.m.b.H. **(1)**
Erdberger Lande 26A, A-1030, Vienna, Austria
Tel.: (43) 1711780
Web Site: https://www.lilly.com
Pharmaceuticals Product Mfr
N.A.I.C.S.: 325412

Eli Lilly Hrvatska d.o.o. **(1)**
Ulica grada Vukovara 269g, Zagreb, Croatia
Tel.: (385) 12350999
Pharmaceutical Products Distr
N.A.I.C.S.: 424210

Eli Lilly Interamerica Inc., y Compania Limitada **(1)**
Calle El Rosario Norte 555 Of 1903 Psio 19, Las Condes, Santiago, Chile
Tel.: (56) 226119220
Herbel Medicine Distr
N.A.I.C.S.: 424210

Eli Lilly International Corporation **(1)**
Lilly Corporate Ctr, Indianapolis, IN 46285-0001 **(100%)**
Tel.: (317) 276-2000
Web Site: https://www.lilly.com
Holding Company
N.A.I.C.S.: 551112

Subsidiary (Non-US):

Eli Lilly (S.A.) (Proprietary) Limited **(2)**
1st Floor Golden Oak House Ballyoaks Office Park 35 Ballyclare Drive, Bryanston, 2021, South Africa **(100%)**
Tel.: (27) 115109300
Web Site: https://www.lilly.co.za
Sales Range: $50-74.9 Million
Emp.: 150
Pharmaceuticals
N.A.I.C.S.: 325412

Eli Lilly (Suisse) S.A. **(2)**
Chemin des Coquelicots 16, PO Box 580, 1214, Vernier, Switzerland **(100%)**
Tel.: (41) 22 306 0401
Web Site: https://www.lilly.ch
Emp.: 150
Mfr & Sales of Pharmaceuticals
N.A.I.C.S.: 325412

Eli Lilly Asia, Inc. **(2)**
Unit 3203-06 32/F Chubb Tower Windsor House 311 Gloucester Road, Causeway Bay, China (Hong Kong) **(100%)**
Tel.: (852) 25720160
Web Site: http://www.lilly.com.hk
Sales Range: $75-99.9 Million
Pharmaceutical Product Sales & Marketing
N.A.I.C.S.: 561499

Subsidiary (Non-US):

Eli Lilly (M) Sdn. Bhd. **(3)**
Level 7 Menara OBYU No 4 Jalan PJU8/8A, Damansara Perdana, 47820, Petaling Jaya, Selangor Darul Ehsan, Malaysia **(100%)**
Tel.: (60) 377216222
Sales Range: $100-124.9 Million
Mfr of Medical Supplies
N.A.I.C.S.: 339112

Eli Lilly (Singapore) Pte. Ltd. **(3)**
The Work Project 1 Kim Seng Promenade 1101 Great World City, East Tower, Singapore, 237994, Singapore
Tel.: (65) 67367400
Pharmaceuticals Product Mfr
N.A.I.C.S.: 424210

Subsidiary (Domestic):

Eli Lilly Asian Operations, Limited **(3)**
Unit 3203-08 32/F Ace Tower Windsor House 311 Gloucester Road, Causeway Bay, China (Hong Kong)
Tel.: (852) 225720160
Pharmaceutical Preparation Mfr
N.A.I.C.S.: 325412

Subsidiary (Non-US):

Eli Lilly Suzhou Pharmaceutical Co. Ltd. **(3)**
No 6 Baiyu Road Industrial Park, Suzhou, 215021, China
Tel.: (86) 51267615459
Pharmaceutical Preparation Manufacturing
N.A.I.C.S.: 325412

Eli Lilly and Company (Taiwan), Inc. **(3)**
11th Floor No 365 Fuxing North Road, Taipei, 105, Taiwan **(100%)**
Tel.: (886) 22 715 2950
Web Site: https://www.lilly.com.tw
Sales Range: $50-74.9 Million
Pharmaceuticals Product Mfr
N.A.I.C.S.: 325412

Lilly Korea Limited **(3)**
4th Floor 98 Huamro LG Seoul Yeok Building, Jung gu, Seoul, 04637, Korea (South)
Tel.: (82) 234592600
Web Site: https://www.lilly.co.kr
Emp.: 217
Pharmaceutical Research & Preparation Manufacturing
N.A.I.C.S.: 325412

Subsidiary (Non-US):

Eli Lilly Australia Pty. Limited **(2)**
112 Wharf Road, West Ryde, 2114, NSW, Australia **(100%)**
Tel.: (61) 180 045 4559
Web Site: https://www.lilly.com.au
Emp.: 200
Mfr of Pharmaceutical & Medical Products
N.A.I.C.S.: 325412

Jeremy Morgan *(Mng Dir)*
Benjamin L. Basil *(Pres & Gen Mgr)*
Salvador Manuel Garcia De Quevedo Perez *(Dir-Medical)*
Ping Fu *(CFO)*
Gabrielle Reppen *(COO)*
Martin Hayes *(Sls Dir)*
Jamie Preston *(Sr Dir-Human Resources)*
Gabi Mittas *(CMO)*
Margaret Pereira *(Dir-Compliance)*
Anne Sinclair *(Gen Counsel)*
Peter Vermeer *(Sr Dir)*

Subsidiary (Non-US):

Eli Lilly and Company (N.Z.) Limited **(3)**
Level 27 88 Shortland Street, Auckland, 1010, New Zealand **(100%)**
Tel.: (64) 95239300
Web Site: https://www.lilly.co.nz
Sales Range: $10-24.9 Million
Emp.: 200
Mfr of Medical Products; Owned by Eli Lilly Australia Pty. Limited
N.A.I.C.S.: 325412

Subsidiary (Non-US):

Eli Lilly Benelux, S.A. **(2)**
Markiesstraat 1 - 4B, 1000, Brussels, Belgium **(100%)**
Tel.: (32) 25488484
Web Site: https://www.lilly.be
Sales Range: $125-149.9 Million
Emp.: 250
Pharmaceuticals Supplier & Marketer
N.A.I.C.S.: 424210

Eli Lilly Canada, Inc. **(2)**
Exchange Tower 130 King Street West Suite 900, PO Box 73, Toronto, M5X 1B1, ON, Canada **(100%)**
Tel.: (416) 694-3221
Web Site: https://www.lilly.ca
Sales Range: $300-349.9 Million
Emp.: 325
Mfr & Distributor of Pharmaceuticals
N.A.I.C.S.: 325412

Eli Lilly Danmark A/S **(2)**
Lyskaer 3E 2 TV, 2730, Herlev, Denmark **(100%)**
Tel.: (45) 4 526 6000
Web Site: https://www.eli-lilly.dk
Emp.: 50
Sales of Pharmaceuticals
N.A.I.C.S.: 424210

Eli Lilly De Mexico S.A. de C.V. **(2)**
Calzada de Tlapan 2024, Col Campestre Churubusco Del Coyoacan, 04200, Mexico, DF, Mexico **(100%)**
Tel.: (52) 5554843800
Sales Range: $25-49.9 Million
Emp.: 100
Mfr & Distributor of Pharmaceuticals
N.A.I.C.S.: 325412

Eli Lilly Egypt **(2)**
Scientific Office A 2 Double Wing BB007 Cairo Festival City, 3rd Floor 5th Settlement New, 11835, Cairo, Egypt
Tel.: (20) 222685300
Sales Range: $150-199.9 Million
Pharmaceuticals Product Mfr
N.A.I.C.S.: 325412

Eli Lilly Group Limited **(2)**
Lilly House Basing View, Basingstoke, RG21 4FA, Hampshire, United Kingdom **(100%)**
Tel.: (44) 1256315000
Web Site: https://www.lilly.co.uk
Sales Range: $1-4.9 Billion
Emp.: 550
Holding Company; Pharmaceutical Developer, Mfr & Distr
N.A.I.C.S.: 551112

Subsidiary (Domestic):

Eli Lilly & Company Limited **(3)**
Lilly House, Basingstoke, RG21 4FA, Hampshire, United Kingdom **(100%)**
Tel.: (44) 125 631 5000
Web Site: https://www.lilly.co.uk
Emp.: 700
Mfr of Pharmaceuticals
N.A.I.C.S.: 325412

Subsidiary (Non-US):

Eli Lilly Interamerica, Inc. **(2)**
Tronador 4890 piso 12, 1430, Buenos Aires, Argentina **(100%)**
Tel.: (54) 1145464000
Web Site: http://www.lillylatam.com
Sales Range: $25-49.9 Million
Emp.: 130
Mfr of Pharmaceuticals
N.A.I.C.S.: 325412

Eli Lilly Israel Ltd. **(2)**
11 Shenkar Arie, PO Box 2160, Herzliyya, 46725, Israel
Tel.: (972) 99606234
Pharmaceutical Product Whslr
N.A.I.C.S.: 424210
Alberto Riva *(Gen Mgr)*

Eli Lilly Italia SpA **(2)**
Via Gramsci 731/733, 50019, Sesto Fiorentino, FI, Italy **(100%)**
Tel.: (39) 05542571
Web Site: http://www.lilly.it
Pharmaceutical Mfr & Distr
N.A.I.C.S.: 325412

Eli Lilly Italia, S.p.A. **(2)**
Via Gramsci 731/733, 50019, Sesto Fiorentino, FI, Italy **(100%)**
Tel.: (39) 05542571
Web Site: https://www.lilly.it
Sales Range: $300-349.9 Million
Pharmaceuticals Mfr & Distr
N.A.I.C.S.: 325412

Eli Lilly Japan K.K. **(2)**
5-1-28 Isogami-dori Lilly Plaza One Bldg, Chuo-Ku, Kobe, 651-0086, Japan **(100%)**
Tel.: (81) 782429000
Web Site: https://www.lilly.co.jp
Sales Range: $250-299.9 Million
Distr of Medical Instruments
N.A.I.C.S.: 423450

Eli Lilly Lithuania UAB **(2)**
Gyneju str 16, 01109, Vilnius, Lithuania
Tel.: (370) 52649600
Sales Range: $150-199.9 Million
Emp.: 30
Pharmaceutical Preparation Mfr
N.A.I.C.S.: 325412

Eli Lilly Nederland B.V. **(2)**
Papendorpseweg 83, PO Box 379, 3528 BJ, Utrecht, Netherlands **(100%)**
Tel.: (31) 306025800
Web Site: http://www.lilly.nl
Sales Range: $50-74.9 Million
Pharmaceuticals Mfr
N.A.I.C.S.: 325412

Eli Lilly Pakistan (Pvt.) Ltd. **(2)**
5-A 5th Office Floor Al-Tijarah Centre 32-1-A Block 6, PECHS Main Shahrah-e-Faisal, Karachi, 75400, Pakistan
Tel.: (92) 2111 120 1301
Web Site: https://www.lillyrahnuma.com
Pharmaceutical Research & Preparation Manufacturing
N.A.I.C.S.: 325412

Eli Lilly Polska Sp. z.o.o. (Ltd.) **(2)**
Zwirki i Wigury 18 a, 02-092, Warsaw, Poland
Tel.: (48) 22 440 3300
Web Site: https://www.lilly.pl
Pharmaceuticals Product Mfr
N.A.I.C.S.: 325412

Eli Lilly Slovakia sro **(2)**
Panenska 6, 811 03, Bratislava, Slovakia
Tel.: (421) 22 066 3111
Web Site: https://www.lilly.sk
Emp.: 29
Pharmaceutical Research & Preparation Mfr
N.A.I.C.S.: 325412

Eli Lilly Spain Holding ETVE, S.L. **(2)**
Avenida De La Industria 30, Alcobendas, 28108, Spain
Tel.: (34) 916635000
Pharmaceutical Preparation Mfr
N.A.I.C.S.: 325412

Subsidiary (Domestic):

Spaly Bioquimica, S.A. **(3)**
Avenida De La Industria 30, Alcobendas,

28108, Madrid, Spain
Tel.: (34) 916 63 50 00
Pharmaceutical Product Whslr
N.A.I.C.S.: 424210

Subsidiary (Non-US):

Eli Lilly Sweden AB (2)
Gustav III Boulevard 42 Frosundavik, PO
Box 721, 169 27, Solna, Sweden (100%)
Tel.: (46) 87378800
Web Site: https://www.lilly.se
Sales Range: $25-49.9 Million
Pharmaceuticals Mfr & Sales
N.A.I.C.S.: 325412

Eli Lilly Vostok SA (2)
Krasnopresnenskaya Nab10 Block A,
123112, Moscow, Russia
Tel.: (7) 4952585001
Web Site: http://www.elilily.com
Sales Range: $10-24.9 Million
Emp.: 45
Pharmaceutical Research & Preparation
Manufacturing
N.A.I.C.S.: 325412

**Eli Lilly and Company (India) Pvt.
Ltd.** (2)
Plot 92 Sector 32 Institutional Area, Gur-
gaon, 122 001, Haryana, India
Tel.: (91) 124 475 3000
Web Site: https://www.lillyindia.co.in
Sales Range: $250-299.9 Million
Pharmaceutical Products & Services
N.A.I.C.S.: 325412
Luca Visini (Mng Dir)
Vishal Dhoot (CFO)
Rohit Arora (Dir-Medical)
Gunjan Kaul Singh (Officer-Ethics & Compli-
ance)
Rakesh Upadhyay (Dir-Diabetes Bus Unit)
Ranjeet Singh Walia (Dir-HR)
Rimmi Kakkar (Assoc Dir-Sls Ops & Digital)
Anamika Gupta (Gen Counsel & Assoc Dir-
Legal)

**Eli Lilly and Company (Ireland)
Ltd.** (2)
Hyde House 65 Adelaide Road, Dublin,
Ireland (100%)
Tel.: (353) 16614377
Web Site: https://www.lilly.ie
Sales Range: $50-74.9 Million
Emp.: 40
Marketer & Sales of Pharmaceuticals
N.A.I.C.S.: 424210

Eli Lilly do Brasil Ltda. (2)
Av Morumbi 8264 Brooklin, Sao Paulo,
04703-002, SP, Brazil (100%)
Tel.: (55) 1121446911
Web Site: http://www.lilly.com.br
Sales Range: $350-399.9 Million
Mfr of Pharmaceuticals & Packaging
N.A.I.C.S.: 325412

**Eli Lilly y Compania de Venezuela,
S.A.** (2)
Av Ernesto Blohm Edf IBM 9th floor, Edo
Miranda, Urb Chuao frente al CCCT, Cara-
cas, 1060, Venezuela
Tel.: (58) 2129508411
Web Site: https://www.lillylatam.com
Mfr of Medical Supplies
N.A.I.C.S.: 339112

Lilly France S.A. (2)
24 Boulevard Vital Bouhot, CS 50004,
92521, Neuilly-sur-Seine, Cedex,
France (100%)
Tel.: (33) 155493434
Web Site: https://www.lilly.fr
Sales Range: $1-4.9 Billion
Pharmaceuticals Mfr
N.A.I.C.S.: 325412

Lilly Hungaria Kft (2)
Madach Imre ut 13-14 VII emelet, 1075,
Budapest, Hungary
Tel.: (36) 13285100
Web Site: https://www.lilly.com
Sales Range: $25-49.9 Million
Pharmaceutical Research & Preparation
Manufacturing
N.A.I.C.S.: 325412

Lilly Ilac Ticaret Limited Sirketi (2)
Acibadem Mah Cecen Sokak Akasya Acibadem Kent Etabi, A Blok Kat 3 Uskudar,

34660, Istanbul, Türkiye
Tel.: (90) 2165540000
Web Site: https://www.lilly.com
Sales Range: $75-99.9 Million
Pharmaceutical Preparation Mfr
N.A.I.C.S.: 325412

Lilly Pharma Holding GmbH (2)
(100%)
Tel.: (49) 61722730
Web Site: http://www.lilly-pharma.de
Rev.: $500,000,000
Emp.: 500
Holding Company; Pharmaceutical Devel-
oper, Mfr & Distr
N.A.I.C.S.: 551112

Subsidiary (Non-US):

Eli Lilly GmbH (3)
Tel.: (43) 1711780
Web Site: http://www.lilly.at
Supplier of Pharmaceuticals
N.A.I.C.S.: 424210

Lilly Deutschland GmbH (3)
(100%)
Tel.: (49) 61722730
Web Site: https://www.lilly-pharma.de
Sales Range: $800-899.9 Million
Mfr of Pharmaceuticals
N.A.I.C.S.: 325412

Subsidiary (Non-US):

Lilly Research Centre Limited (2)
Erlwood Manor London Road, Windlesham,
GU2O 6PH, Surrey, United
Kingdom (100%)
Tel.: (44) 1276483000
Web Site: http://www.lilly.com
Sales Range: $75-99.9 Million
Provider of Research Services
N.A.I.C.S.: 541720

Lilly, S.A. (2)
Avenida de la Industria 30, 28108, Alcoben-
das, Madrid, Spain (50%)
Tel.: (34) 91 663 5000
Web Site: https://www.lilly.es
Emp.: 1,000
Mfr of Pharmaceutical & Medical Products
N.A.I.C.S.: 325412

Subsidiary (Non-US):

**Greenfield-Produtos Farmaceuticos,
Lda.** (3)
Rua Galileu Galilei Nr 2 Piso 7 Fraccao
A/D, 1500-000, Lisbon, Portugal
Tel.: (351) 214126600
Pharmaceuticals Product Mfr
N.A.I.C.S.: 325412

Subsidiary (Domestic):

Lilly Pharmaceuticals (3)
Avda De La Industria 30, 28108, Alcoben-
das, Spain (100%)
Tel.: (34) 916635000
Web Site: http://www.lilly.es
Sales Range: $50-74.9 Million
Emp.: 170
Mfr of Pharmaceuticals
N.A.I.C.S.: 325412

Subsidiary (Non-US):

**Lilly-Portugal Produtos Farmaceuti-
cos, Lda.** (2)
Torre Ocidente Rua Galileu Galilei N 2 Piso
7 Fraccao A/D, Queijas, 1500-392, Lisbon,
Portugal
Tel.: (351) 21 412 6600
Web Site: https://www.lilly.pt
Pharmaceuticals Product Mfr
N.A.I.C.S.: 325412

OY Eli Lilly Finland AB (2)
Laajalahdentie 23, 00330, Helsinki, Finland
Tel.: (358) 9 854 5250
Web Site: https://www.lilly.fi
Sales Range: $25-49.9 Million
Pharmaceuticals Product Mfr
N.A.I.C.S.: 325412

Pharmaserve-Lilly S.A.C.I. (2)
15th km of the Athens-Lamia National
Road, 14564, Kifissia, Greece
Tel.: (30) 2106294600
Web Site: https://www.lilly.gr

Pharmaceutical Research & Preparation
Manufacturing
N.A.I.C.S.: 325412

Eli Lilly Norge A.S. (1)
Innspurten 15, Postboks 6090, Etterstad,
0601, Oslo, Norway
Tel.: (47) 22881800
Web Site: https://www.lilly.com
Emp.: 30
Pharmaceuticals Product Mfr
N.A.I.C.S.: 325412

Eli Lilly Norge A.S. (1)
Innspurten 15, Molndal, 0663, Oslo, Norway
Tel.: (47) 22881800
Web Site: http://www.lilly.no
Pharmaceuticals Product Mfr
N.A.I.C.S.: 325412

Eli Lilly Romania SRL (1)
Str Menuetului nr 12 Bucharest Business
Park Corp D Etaj 2 Sector 1, Bucharest,
013713, Romania
Tel.: (40) 214023000
Emp.: 100
Pharmaceuticals Product Mfr
N.A.I.C.S.: 325412
Camilla Shen (Country Mgr)

Eli Lilly Saudi Arabia Limited (1)
Olaya Towers Tower B Building No 3074
16th Floor, PO Box 92120, Prince Mo-
hamed Ibn Abdulaziz Street Olaya, Riyadh,
11653, Saudi Arabia
Tel.: (966) 114617800
Web Site: https://www.lilly.com
Pharmaceuticals Product Mfr
N.A.I.C.S.: 325412

**Eli Lilly Trading (Shanghai) Company
Limited** (1)
16-19F. Tower 1 HKRI Taikoo Hui No 288
Shi Men No 1 Road, Shanghai, 200041,
China
Tel.: (86) 2123021100
Pharmaceutical Products Distr
N.A.I.C.S.: 424210

**Eli Lilly farmacevtska druzba,
d.o.o.** (1)
Dunajska 167, 1000, Ljubljana, Slovenia
Tel.: (386) 15800010
Pharmaceuticals Product Mfr
N.A.I.C.S.: 325412

**Eli Lilly farmacevtska druzba,
d.o.o.** (1)
Dunajska cesta 167, 1000, Ljubljana, Slove-
nia
Tel.: (386) 15800010
Pharmaceutical Products Distr
N.A.I.C.S.: 424210

**Eli Lilly y Compania de Mexico, S.A.
de C.V.** (1)
Calzada de Tlalpan 2024 Col Campestre
Churubusco, Del Coyoacan, 04200, Mexico,
Mexico
Tel.: (52) 5554843800
Pharmaceuticals Product Mfr
N.A.I.C.S.: 325412

Express Markets, Inc. (1)
6510 Mutual Dr, Fort Wayne, IN 46825
Tel.: (260) 407-2728
Web Site:
https://www.expressmarketsinc.com
Emp.: 10
Poultry Market Analysing Services
N.A.I.C.S.: 541613
Rob Hontz (Dir-Sls & Mktg)
Eric Scholer (Pres)
Jay Hager (VP)

GEMS Services S.A. (1)
Markiesstraat 1/4B, Brussels, 1000, Bel-
gium
Tel.: (32) 25488484
Web Site: http://www.lilly.be
Pharmaceutical Products Distr
N.A.I.C.S.: 424210

**Immuno-Vet Services (Pty) Ltd. South
Africa** (1)
11 Vervoer St Kya Sand, Randburg, 2169,
South Africa
Tel.: (27) 116996240
Web Site: https://www.immunovet.co.za
Emp.: 40

Pharmaceutical Product Mfr & Distr
N.A.I.C.S.: 424210

Lilly Holdings, LLC (1)
31212 W Thompson Ln, Hartland, WI
53029
Tel.: (262) 367-1155
Holding Company
N.A.I.C.S.: 551112
W. Perry Halquist (Principal)

Lilly Nederland Finance B.V. (1)
Papendorpseweg 83, 3528 BJ, Utrecht,
Netherlands
Tel.: (31) 306025800
Pharmaceutical Products Distr
N.A.I.C.S.: 424210

Lilly Research Laboratories (1)
Lilly Corporate Ctr, Indianapolis, IN 46285
Tel.: (317) 276-2000
Web Site: http://www.lilly.com
Pharmaceutical Research Laboratories
N.A.I.C.S.: 621511
Jan M. Lundberg (Pres)

Plant (Domestic):

Lilly Tippecanoe Laboratories (2)
1650 Lilly Rd, Lafayette, IN 47909
Tel.: (317) 276-2000
Pharmaceutical Preparation Mfr
N.A.I.C.S.: 325412

Lilly USA, LLC (1)
1500 S Harding St, Indianapolis, IN 46221
Tel.: (317) 433-1625
Sales Range: $700-749.9 Million
Emp.: 8,000
Pharmaceuticals Product Mfr
N.A.I.C.S.: 325412

Lilly Ventures Fund I LLC (1)
115 W Washington St Ste 1680 S, India-
napolis, IN 46204
Tel.: (317) 429-0140
Capital Market Investment Services
N.A.I.C.S.: 523940

Lilly del Caribe Inc. (1)
400 Calle Fabril, Carolina, PR
00987 (100%)
Tel.: (787) 257-5555
Web Site: http://www.lilly.com
Sales Range: $400-449.9 Million
Pharmaceuticals Product Mfr
N.A.I.C.S.: 325412

**Lilly-NUS Centre for Clinical
Pharmacology** (1)
3 Biopolis Drive 02-11 Synapse, Singapore,
138623, Singapore
Tel.: (65) 64139811
Web Site: http://www.lillynus.com.sg
Biotechnology Research & Development
Services
N.A.I.C.S.: 541714

**Lohmann Animal Health Beteiligungs
GmbH** (1)
Heinz-Lohmann-Str 4, 27472, Cuxhaven,
Germany
Tel.: (49) 47217470
Pharmaceutical Products Distr
N.A.I.C.S.: 424210

Lohmann Animal Health GmbH (1)
Heinz-Lohmann-Strasse 4, 27472, Cux-
haven, Germany
Tel.: (49) 47217470
Web Site: http://www.lah.de
Pharmaceutical Products Mfr & Distr
N.A.I.C.S.: 325412

**Lohmann Animal Health International,
Inc.** (1)
375 China Rd, Winslow, ME 04901-0632
Tel.: (207) 873-3989
Web Site: http://www.lahinternational.com
Pharmaceutical Product Whslr
N.A.I.C.S.: 424210

**Lohmann Taiwan Co. Ltd.,
Taiwan** (1)
Building ForYoung 6F No59 Section 3, Jian-
Guo Road FengShan, Kaohsiung, 83044,
Taiwan
Tel.: (886) 975221812
Tiles Mfr
N.A.I.C.S.: 333310

Eli Lilly & Company—(Continued)

Loxo Oncology, Inc. (1)
281 Tresser Blvd 9th Fl, Stamford, CT 06901
Tel.: (203) 653-3880
Web Site: http://www.loxooncology.com
Rev.: $21,300,000
Assets: $783,442,000
Liabilities: $405,232,000
Net Worth: $378,210,000
Earnings: ($148,876,000)
Emp.: 59
Fiscal Year-end: 12/31/2017
Pharmaceuticals Mfr
N.A.I.C.S.: 325412
Nisha Nanda (Chief Dev Officer)
Jacob S. Van Naarden (CEO)
David Hyman (Chief Medical Officer)
Steve Andrews (Sr VP)
Liz Beja (Head)
Barb Brandhuber (VP)
Kyla Driscoll (Exec Dir)
Omar Duramad (Head)
Todd Eary (VP)
Hallee Foster (Sr Dir-Business Development)
Philip Johnson (VP-Regulatory Affairs)
Sunitha Ramamurthy (Head-Compliance)
Amy Ruscavage (VP-Quality Assurance)
Joseph Scattergood (VP)
Penelope Sinanian (VP)
Anthony Sireci (VP-Medical Affairs)
Barry Taylor (VP)
Jennifer C. Burstein (CFO, Chief Acctg Officer & Sr VP-Fin)

Lylly Centre for Clinical Pharmacology Pte. Ltd. (1)
3 Biopolis Drive 02-11 Synapse, Singapore, 138623, Singapore
Tel.: (65) 64139811
Web Site: http://www.lillyclinic.com.sg
Drug Development & Research Services
N.A.I.C.S.: 541715

Morphic Holding, Inc. (1)
35 Gatehouse Dr A2, Waltham, MA 02451
Tel.: (781) 996-0955
Web Site: https://www.morphictx.com
Rev.: $521,000
Assets: $722,514,000
Liabilities: $25,492,000
Net Worth: $697,022,000
Earnings: ($152,095,000)
Emp.: 121
Fiscal Year-end: 12/31/2023
Holding Company
N.A.I.C.S.: 551112
Michael C. Thompson (Pres & Treas)
Christopher Anderson (Sec)
Katie Lodato (Asst Treas)
Jonathan Groff (Asst Sec)

POINT Biopharma Global Inc. (1)
4850 W 78th St, Indianapolis, IN 46268
Tel.: (647) 812-2417
Web Site: https://www.pointbiopharma.com
Rev.: $226,579,563
Assets: $578,322,736
Liabilities: $91,368,943
Net Worth: $486,953,793
Earnings: $98,293,213
Fiscal Year-end: 12/31/2022
Research & Development in Biotechnology
N.A.I.C.S.: 541714
Joe McCann (CEO)
Bill Demers (CFO)
Justyna Kelly (COO)
Neil Fleshner (Chief Medical Officer)
Allan Silber (Chm)

Provail Therapeutics Inc. (1)
430 E 29th St Ste 1520, New York, NY 10016
Tel.: (917) 336-9310
Web Site: http://www.prevailtherapeutics.com
Rev.: $2,615,000
Assets: $187,102,000
Liabilities: $21,760,000
Net Worth: $165,342,000
Earnings: ($63,188,000)
Emp.: 55
Fiscal Year-end: 12/31/2019
Biotechnology Research & Development Services
N.A.I.C.S.: 541714
Yong Dai (CTO)
Franz Hefti (CEO)

Emily Minkow (Chief Bus Officer)
Jeffrey Sevigny (Chief Medical Officer)
Bob Lally (COO)
Mansuo Lu Shannon (Chief Scientific Officer)
Bob Lally (COO)
Mansuo Lu Shannon (Chief Scientific Officer)

Pt. Lohmann Animal Health Indonesia (1)
Alamanda Tower Fl 17th JL TB Simatupang Kav 23-24 Cilandak Barat, Jakarta, 12430, Indonesia
Tel.: (62) 2129660069
Veterinary Services
N.A.I.C.S.: 541940
Daru Kintoko (Dir-Tech Sls)

Sigilon Therapeutics, Inc. (1)
100 Binney St Ste 600, Cambridge, MA 02142
Tel.: (617) 336-7540
Web Site: https://www.sigilon.com
Rev.: $12,944,000
Assets: $87,278,000
Liabilities: $48,136,000
Net Worth: $39,142,000
Earnings: ($43,561,000)
Emp.: 62
Fiscal Year-end: 12/31/2022
Biotechnology Research & Development Services
N.A.I.C.S.: 541714
Paul K. Wotton (Co-Founder)
Hozefa Bandukwala (VP & Head-Immunology & Metabolic Diseases Res)
Deya Corzo (Chief Medical Officer)
Susan Drapeau (Sr VP & Head-Preclinical Dev)
Melodie Henderson (VP)
Olivia G. Kelly (VP & Head-Diabetes Res)
Matthew Kowalsky (Chief Legal Officer)
Elina Makino (VP & Head-Rare Diseases Res)
Josias Fantato De Pontes (Acting CFO & Treas)
Vanya Sagar (Chief HR Officer)
Jose Oberholzer (Co-Founder)
Arturo Vegas (Co-Founder)
Omid Veiseh (Co-Founder)
Ajay Rai (Sr VP & Head-Bus Dev)
Robert Windsor (Head-IR)
Philip Ashton-Rickardt (Chief Scientific Officer)
Bernd Kullmann (VP & Head-Mfg & Supply Chain)
Jiang Wu (VP & Head-Bioanalytical & CMC Analytical Dev)
Qing Sarah Yuan (Chief Technical Ops Officer)
Philip L. Johnson (Pres)
Michael C. Thompson (Treas)
Katie Lodato (Asst Treas)
Christopher Anderson (Sec)
Jonathan Groff (Asst Sec)

Sunrise Farms, Inc. (1)
2177 Tinkling Spring Rd, Stuarts Draft, VA 24477
Tel.: (540) 337-3773
Web Site: https://sunrisefarm.net
Poultry Processing Services
N.A.I.C.S.: 311615
Christine Jones (Pres)

ELICIO THERAPEUTICS, INC
451 D St 5th Fl Ste 501, Boston, MA 02210
Tel.: (857) 209-0050   DE
Web Site: https://elicio.com
Year Founded: 1990
ELTX—(NASDAQ)
Rev.: $2,301,000
Assets: $52,790,000
Liabilities: $9,018,000
Net Worth: $43,772,000
Earnings: ($38,807,000)
Emp.: 3
Fiscal Year-end: 12/31/22
Pharmaceutical Preparation Manufacturing
N.A.I.C.S.: 325412
Thian Kheoh (Sr VP-Biometrics)
Megan Filoon (Chief Compliance Officer, Gen Counsel & Sec)
Robert Connelly (CEO)

ELIEM THERAPEUTICS, INC.
Tel.: (425) 276-2300   DE
Web Site: https://www.eliemtx.com
Year Founded: 2018
ELYM—(NASDAQ)
Rev.: $1,375,000
Assets: $134,992,000
Liabilities: $6,277,000
Net Worth: $128,715,000
Earnings: ($45,244,000)
Emp.: 30
Fiscal Year-end: 12/31/22
Biotechnology Research & Development Services
N.A.I.C.S.: 541714
Brett Kaplan (COO)
Erin Lavelle (CFO & Exec VP)
Andrew Levin (Founder, Chm & Principal Fin Officer)
Emily Pimblett (Chief Acctg Officer & VP-Acctg)
Aoife Brennan (Pres & CEO)
Brett Kaplan (COO)
Nishi Rampal (Sr VP-Clinical Dev)

ELINX CORPORATION
156 Reasor St No 522, Tahlequah, OK 74464
Tel.: (830) 484-4096   NV
Web Site: http://www.elinxcorp.com
ELNX—(OTCIQ)
Financial Management Services
N.A.I.C.S.: 523999
Gary W. Bell (Pres & CEO)
Cara Duvall (Sec)

ELIO MOTORS, INC
2942 N 24th St Ste 114-700, Phoenix, AZ 85016
Tel.: (480) 500-6800   DE
Web Site: https://www.eliomotors.com
Year Founded: 2009
ELIO—(OTCIQ)
Sales Range: Less than $1 Million
Emp.: 7
Automobile Mfr
N.A.I.C.S.: 336110
Paul Elio (Chm, Pres & CEO)

ELITE HEALTH SYSTEMS INC.
1131 W 6th St, Ontario, CA 91672
Tel.: (949) 249-1170   DE
Web Site: https://www.elitehealthsystems.com
Year Founded: 2015
USNU—(OTCIQ)
Assets: $1,321,000
Net Worth: $645,000
Earnings: ($816,000)
Emp.: 2
Fiscal Year-end: 12/31/23
Holding Company
N.A.I.C.S.: 551112
Prasad Anjaneya Jeereddi (Chm & CEO)

Subsidiaries:

Elite Health Systems Holdings Inc. (1)
1131 W 6th St, Ontario, CA 91672
Tel.: (949) 249-1170
Stereotactic Radiosurgery Center Owner & Operator
N.A.I.C.S.: 551112
Prasad Anjaneya Jeereddi (CEO)

ELITE PHARMACEUTICALS, INC.
165 Ludlow Ave, Northvale, NJ 07647
Tel.: (201) 750-2646   DE
Web Site: https://www.elitepharma.com
ELTP—(OTCQB)
Rev.: $56,625,128
Assets: $83,653,536
Liabilities: $26,070,718

Net Worth: $57,582,818
Earnings: $20,108,631
Emp.: 64
Fiscal Year-end: 03/31/24
Pharmaceutical Developer & Mfr
N.A.I.C.S.: 325412
G. Kenneth Smith (VP-Legal)
William Scott Groner (VP-Quality & Regulatory Affairs)
Carter J. Ward (CFO, Treas & Sec)
Nasrat Hakim (Chm, Pres & CEO)
Kirko Kirkov (Chief Comml Officer)
Douglas Plassche (Exec VP-Ops)
Christopher Dick (Head-Dev)

Subsidiaries:

Elite Laboratories, Inc. (1)
165 Ludlow Ave, Northvale, NJ 07647
Tel.: (201) 750-2646
Web Site: http://www.elitepharma.com
Sales Range: $75-99.9 Million
Pharmaceutical Research & Development
N.A.I.C.S.: 541715

Elite Research, Inc. (1)
165 Ludlow Ave, Northvale, NJ 07647
Tel.: (201) 750-2646
Web Site: http://www.elitepharma.com
Sales Range: $75-99.9 Million
Pharmaceutical Research & Development
N.A.I.C.S.: 541715

ELLINGTON CREDIT COMPANY MANAGEMENT LLC
53 Forest Ave, Old Greenwich, CT 06870
Tel.: (203) 409-3773   MD
Web Site: https://www.ellingtoncredit.com
Year Founded: 2012
EARN—(NYSE)
Rev.: $42,549,000
Assets: $945,690,000
Liabilities: $809,452,000
Net Worth: $136,238,000
Earnings: $4,559,000
Emp.: 170
Fiscal Year-end: 12/31/23
Real Estate Investment Services
N.A.I.C.S.: 523999
Laurence Eric Penn (Pres & CEO)
Vincent Ambrico (Controller)
Robert Barry Allardice III (Chm)
Alaael-Deen Shilleh (Sec & Assoc Gen Counsel)
J. R. Herlihy (COO)
Mark Ira Tecotzky (Co-Chief Investment Officer)
Christopher Smernoff (CFO)
Daniel Reuven Margolis (Gen Counsel)
Michael William Vranos (Co-Chief Investment Officer)

Subsidiaries:

EARN CMO LLC (1)
53 Forest Ave, Old Greenwich, CT 06870-1526
Tel.: (203) 698-1200
Residential Building Mortgage Services
N.A.I.C.S.: 525990

EARN Mortgage LLC (1)
11752 Garden Grove Blvd Ste 224, Garden Grove, CA 92843
Tel.: (714) 467-0120
Real Estate Agency
N.A.I.C.S.: 531210

ELME COMMUNITIES
7550 Wisconsin Ave Ste 900, Bethesda, MD 20814
Tel.: (202) 774-3200   MD
Web Site: https://www.elmecommunities.com
Year Founded: 1960
ELME—(NYSE)
Rev.: $227,911,000

Assets: $1,900,028,000
Liabilities: $745,678,000
Net Worth: $1,154,350,000
Earnings: ($52,977,000)
Emp.: 243
Fiscal Year-end: 12/31/23
Real Estate Investment Trust
N.A.I.C.S.: 525990
W. Drew Hammond (Chief Acctg Officer, Treas & VP)
Andrew E. Leahy (VP-Investments)
A. Grant Montgomery (VP-Res)
Amy Hopkins (VP-IR)
Steven Freishtat (VP-Fin)
Tiffany M. Butcher (COO & Exec VP)
Steven M. Freishtat (CFO)
Kelly O'Shields (VP)
Samantha Amoako-Boateng (Reg Mgr)
Eric Duncan (VP)
Emmanuel Rendon (Reg Mgr)
Lizzie Rivera (Dir)
Lalitha Suresh (Reg Mgr)
Eric Tilden (Sr Dir)
Paul T. McDermott (Chm, Pres & CEO)
Edward J. Murn IV (Mng Dir-Dev & Multifamily Div)

Subsidiaries:

Elme Alexandria LLC (1)
205 Century Pl, Alexandria, VA 22304
Web Site: https://www.elmealexandria.com
Real Estate Services
N.A.I.C.S.: 531210

Elme Conyers LLC (1)
50 Greenleaf Rd, Conyers, GA 30013
Tel.: (770) 788-1165
Web Site: https://www.elmeconyers.com
Real Estate Services
N.A.I.C.S.: 531210

Elme Druid Hills LLC (1)
2696 N Druid Hills Rd, Atlanta, GA 30329
Tel.: (404) 633-8258
Web Site: https://www.elmedruidhills.com
Real Estate Services
N.A.I.C.S.: 531210

Elme Dulles LLC (1)
13690 Legacy Cir, Herndon, VA 20171
Tel.: (703) 561-0300
Web Site: https://www.elmedulles.com
Apartment Rental Services
N.A.I.C.S.: 531110

Elme Eagles Landing 860 LLC (1)
860 Rock Quarry Rd, Stockbridge, GA 30281
Tel.: (678) 289-6644
Web Site: https://www.elmeeagleslanding.com
Apartment Rental Services
N.A.I.C.S.: 531110

Elme Germantown LLC (1)
2 Observation Ct, Germantown, MD 20876
Tel.: (301) 972-9500
Web Site: https://www.elmegermantown.com
Apartment Rental Services
N.A.I.C.S.: 531110

Elme Herndon LLC (1)
2511 Farmcrest Dr, Herndon, VA 20171
Web Site: https://www.elmeherndon.com
Apartment Rental Services
N.A.I.C.S.: 531110

Elme Kenmore LLC (1)
5415 Connecticut Ave NW, Washington, DC 20015
Tel.: (202) 919-5675
Web Site: https://www.kenmoreapts.com
Real Estate Services
N.A.I.C.S.: 531210

Elme Leesburg LLC (1)
86 Heritage Way NE, Leesburg, VA 20176
Tel.: (571) 497-5122
Web Site: https://www.elmeleesburg.com
Real Estate Services
N.A.I.C.S.: 531210

Elme Manassas LLC (1)

10519 Lariat Ln, Manassas, VA 20109
Tel.: (703) 361-1367
Web Site: https://www.elmemanassas.com
Real Estate Services
N.A.I.C.S.: 531210

Elme Marietta LLC (1)
1113 Powers Ferry Pl SE, Marietta, GA 30067
Tel.: (770) 952-1320
Web Site: https://www.elmemarietta.com
Real Estate Services
N.A.I.C.S.: 531210

Elme Paramount LLC (1)
1425 S Eads St, Arlington, VA 22202
Tel.: (571) 366-5691
Web Site: https://www.theparamountapt.com
Real Estate Services
N.A.I.C.S.: 531210

Elme Park Adams Apartments LLC (1)
2000 N Adams St, Arlington, VA 22201
Tel.: (571) 366-5657
Web Site: https://www.parkadamsapts.com
Apartment Rental Services
N.A.I.C.S.: 531110

Elme Riverside Apartments LLC (1)
5860 Cameron Run Ter, Alexandria, VA 22303
Tel.: (571) 366-5675
Web Site:
https://www.riversidealexandria.com
Real Estate Services
N.A.I.C.S.: 531210

Elme Roosevelt Towers LLC (1)
500 N Roosevelt Blvd, Falls Church, VA 22044
Tel.: (571) 635-8953
Web Site: https://www.roosevelttowers.com
Apartment Rental Services
N.A.I.C.S.: 531110

Elme Sandy Springs LLC (1)
501 N River Pky, Atlanta, GA 30350
Web Site:
https://www.elmesandysprings.com
Real Estate Services
N.A.I.C.S.: 531210

Elme Trove LLC (1)
1201 S Ross St, Arlington, VA 22204
Tel.: (571) 297-8851
Web Site: https://www.troveapts.com
Real Estate Services
N.A.I.C.S.: 531210

Elme Watkins Mill LLC (1)
180 Watkins Station Cir, Gaithersburg, MD 20879
Tel.: (301) 977-0007
Web Site: https://www.elmewatkinsmill.com
Real Estate Services
N.A.I.C.S.: 531210

Elme Wellington LLC (1)
1850 Columbia Pike, Arlington, VA 22204
Web Site: https://www.livethewellington.com
Real Estate Services
N.A.I.C.S.: 531210

Elme Yale West LLC (1)
443 New York Ave NW, Washington, DC 20001
Tel.: (202) 652-2935
Web Site: https://www.yalewestapts.com
Real Estate Services
N.A.I.C.S.: 531210

Munson Hill Towers, L.L.C. (1)
6129 Leesburg Pike, Falls Church, VA 22041-2105
Tel.: (703) 820-7333
Web Site: http://www.munsonhilltowers.com
Emp.: 10
Apartment Building Rental & Leasing Services
N.A.I.C.S.: 531110

WRIT Braddock Office LLC (1)
6110 Executive Blvd, Rockville, MD 20852
Tel.: (301) 984-9400
Real Estate Manangement Services
N.A.I.C.S.: 531390

WashREIT Alexandria LLC (1)
5860 Cameron Run Ter, Alexandria, VA 22303

Real Estate Investment Management Services
N.A.I.C.S.: 531390

WashREIT Dulles LLC (1)
13690 Legacy Cir, Herndon, VA 20171
Tel.: (703) 270-0912
Real Estate Investment Management Services
N.A.I.C.S.: 531390

WashREIT Germantown LLC (1)
2 Observation Ct, Germantown, MD 20876
Tel.: (301) 321-7597
Real Estate Investment Management Services
N.A.I.C.S.: 531390

WashREIT Landmark LLC (1)
300 Yoakum Pkwy, Alexandria, VA 22304
Tel.: (703) 461-3636
Real Estate Investment Management Services
N.A.I.C.S.: 531390

WashREIT Leesburg LLC (1)
86 Heritage Way NE, Leesburg, VA 20176
Tel.: (703) 215-2433
Real Estate Investment Management Services
N.A.I.C.S.: 531390

WashREIT Watkins Mill LLC (1)
180 Watkins Station Cir, Gaithersburg, MD 20878
Tel.: (301) 691-2840
Real Estate Investment Management Services
N.A.I.C.S.: 531390

ELMER BANCORP, INC.
10 S Main St, Elmer, NJ 08318
Tel.: (856) 358-7000
Web Site:
https://www.elmerbank.com
ELMA—(OTCIQ)
Rev.: $17,414,881
Assets: $364,582,505
Liabilities: $331,860,285
Net Worth: $32,722,220
Earnings: $3,181,383
Emp.: 76
Fiscal Year-end: 12/31/23
Bank Holding Company
N.A.I.C.S.: 551111
Brian W. Jones (Pres & CEO)

Subsidiaries:

First National Bank of Elmer (1)
PO Box 980 10 S Main St, Elmer, NJ 08318
Tel.: (856) 358-8141
Web Site: http://www.elmerbank.com
Sales Range: $10-24.9 Million
Emp.: 75
Provider of Banking Services
N.A.I.C.S.: 522110
Justin Adams (VP)
Joanna M. Penman (Chief Banking Officer & Sr VP)
Karl A. Towns (COO, Chief Risk Officer & Sr VP)
Brian W. Jones (Pres & CEO)

ELOXX PHARMACEUTICALS, INC.
950 Winter St, Waltham, MA 02451
Tel.: (781) 557-5300   DE
Web Site:
http://www.eloxxpharma.com
ELOX—(NASDAQ)
Assets: $21,123,000
Liabilities: $31,783,000
Net Worth: ($10,660,000)
Earnings: ($36,065,000)
Emp.: 18
Fiscal Year-end: 12/31/22
Genetic Research & Development Services
N.A.I.C.S.: 541715
Martie Griffin (VP-Corp Quality, Pharmacovigilance & Regulatory Affairs)
Sumit Aggarwal (Pres & CEO)

Ali Hariri (Chief Medical Officer)
Daniel E. Geffken (Interim CFO & Principal Acctg Officer)

ELRAY RESOURCES, INC.
3651 Lindell Rd Ste D131, Las Vegas, NV 89103
Tel.: (917) 775-9689   NV
Web Site:
https://www.elraygaming.com
Year Founded: 2011
ELRA—(OTCIQ)
Sales Range: Less than $1 Million
Emp.: 2
Online Gambling Services
N.A.I.C.S.: 541810
Anthony Brian Goodman (Pres, CEO, CFO, Chief Acctg Officer & Sec)

ELUTIA INC.
12510 Prosperity Dr Ste 370, Silver Spring, MD 20904
Tel.: (240) 247-1170   DE
Web Site: https://elutia.com
Year Founded: 2015
ELUT—(NASDAQ)
Rev.: $49,187,000
Assets: $68,841,000
Liabilities: $73,874,000
Net Worth: ($5,033,000)
Earnings: ($32,897,000)
Emp.: 164
Fiscal Year-end: 12/31/22
Biotechnology Research & Development Services
N.A.I.C.S.: 541714
Michelle Leroux Williams (Chief Scientific Officer)
Randy Mills (CEO)
Matthew Ferguson (CFO)
Darryl Roberts (Exec VP-Ops & Product Dev)
Jeff Hamet (VP-Fin)
Courtney Guyer (VP-Mktg)
Kevin Rakin (Chm)
Kevin L. Rakin (Co-Founder & Exec Chm)
Charles Randal Mills (Co-Founder, Pres & CEO)

ELVA INTERNATIONAL INC.
222 Lakeview Ave PMB 160-415, West Palm Beach, FL 33401
Tel.: (925) 831-0504   FL
EVAI—(OTCIQ)
System Hardware Distr
N.A.I.C.S.: 423430
Lionel Rotcage (Chm & Pres)

EM QUANTUM TECHNOLOGIES, INC.
3700 Airport Rd Ste A309, Boca Raton, FL 33431
Tel.: (561) 757-0124   FL
Web Site:
http://www.emquantech.com
EMQU—(OTCIQ)
Hardware & Software Distr
N.A.I.C.S.: 423430
Paul Michelin (Pres, CEO & CFO)

EMBASSY BANCORP, INC.
Tel.: (610) 882-8800
Web Site:
https://www.embassybank.com
Year Founded: 2001
EMYB—(OTCQX)
Rev.: $59,786,000
Assets: $1,656,496,000
Liabilities: $1,550,841,000
Net Worth: $105,655,000
Earnings: $12,656,000
Emp.: 110
Fiscal Year-end: 12/31/23
Banking Services

Embassy Bancorp, Inc.—(Continued)

N.A.I.C.S.: 522110
Judith A. Hunsicker (CFO, COO, Treas & Sec)
Diane Maria Cunningham (Officer-Branch Admin & Exec VP)
David M. Lobach Jr. (Chm, Pres & CEO)

Subsidiaries:

Embassy Bank   (1)
100 Gateway Dr, Bethlehem, PA 18017
Tel.: (610) 882-8800
Web Site: https://www.embassybank.com
Commercial Banking Services
N.A.I.C.S.: 522110

EMBECTA CORP.

Tel.: (862) 401-0000   DE
Web Site: https://www.embecta.com
EMBC—(NASDAQ)
Rev.: $1,123,100,000
Assets: $1,285,300,000
Liabilities: $2,023,600,000
Net Worth: ($738,300,000)
Earnings: $78,300,000
Emp.: 2,100
Fiscal Year-end: 09/30/24
Medical, Dental & Hospital Equipment & Supplies Merchant Wholesalers
N.A.I.C.S.: 423450
Jake Elguicze (CFO & Sr VP)
Devdatt Kurdikar (Pres & CEO)

EMBER THERAPEUTICS, INC.

135 E 57th St 24th Fl, New York, NY 10022
Tel.: (646) 612-4000   DE
Web Site: http://www.embertx.com
Year Founded: 1987
EMBT—(OTCIQ)
Biopharmaceutical Developer & Mfr
N.A.I.C.S.: 325412

EMCOR GROUP, INC.

301 Merritt 7, Norwalk, CT 06851-1092
Tel.: (203) 849-7800   DE
Web Site:
    https://www.emcorgroup.com
Year Founded: 1994
EME—(NYSE)
Rev.: $12,582,873,000
Assets: $6,609,721,000
Liabilities: $4,138,906,000
Net Worth: $2,470,815,000
Earnings: $632,994,000
Emp.: 38,300
Fiscal Year-end: 12/31/23
Holding Company; Electrical & Mechanical Construction, Energy Infrastructure & Facilities Management Services
N.A.I.C.S.: 551112
Paul Desmarais (VP-Taxation)
Steven H. Fried (VP-Compliance)
Matthew R. Pierce (VP-Safety, Quality & Productivity)
John C. Lawson (VP-Risk Mgmt)
Jason R. Nalbandian (CFO, Chief Acctg Officer & Sr VP)
Maxine Lum Mauricio (Gen Counsel, Sec & Exec VP)
Kostas Christakos (Treas)
Laura D'Entrone (Chief Information Security Officer & VP)
Daniel Fitzgibbons (Co-COO/Exec VP-Electrical Construction & Svcs)
Robert Wilson (Co-COO/Exec VP-Electrical Construction & Svcs)
Douglas R. Harrington Jr. (Pres)
Robert Lind (Controller)
Susan N. Masters (VP)
Jarrett R. Szeftel (VP)

Olivia Sutter (VP)
Thomas Hiebert (VP)
Anthony J. Guzzi (Chm, Pres & CEO)

Subsidiaries:

Air Systems, Inc.   (1)
940 Remillard Ct, San Jose, CA 95122   (100%)
Tel.: (408) 280-1666
Web Site: https://www.airsystemsinc.com
Sales Range: $150-199.9 Million
Emp.: 300
Commercial Facility Electrical, Mechanical, Sheet Metal & Automation Systems Contractor
N.A.I.C.S.: 238220
Art Williams (Pres)
Marty Cull (CFO & Exec VP)
Alan Whitman (VP-Svc)

Ardent Services, LLC   (1)
170 New Camelia Blvd Ste 200, Covington, LA 70433
Tel.: (985) 792-3000
Web Site: http://www.ardent.us
Electrical Contractor
N.A.I.C.S.: 238210
Albert Vallotton (Co-Founder, Pres & CEO)
Eric Smith (Dir-HSE & Risk Mgmt)
James Heurtin (CFO)
Larry Smith (VP-Ops)
Tim Monson (Mgr-Ops)
Cheryl Andrus (Dir-HR)
Glen Riddle (VP-Ops)

Branch (Domestic):

Ardent Services, LLC - Kenner   (2)
17 Veterans Memorial Blvd, Kenner, LA 70062
Tel.: (504) 463-8137
Web Site: http://www.ardent.us
Commercial & Institutional Building Construction
N.A.I.C.S.: 236220

Batchelor & Kimball, Inc.   (1)
2227 Plunkett Rd, Conyers, GA 30012
Tel.: (770) 482-2000
Web Site: http://www.bkimechanical.com
Plumbing, Heating & Air-Conditioning Services
N.A.I.C.S.: 238220
David Batchelor (Pres)
Brian Batchelor (CEO)
Bill Doty (Exec VP-Preconstruction & Construction Ops)
Jeff Clotfelter (VP-Svc & Controls)
Nathan Deasy (CFO)

Dallas Mechanical Group, LLC   (1)
11925 N Stemmons Fwy Ste 130, Dallas, TX 75234
Tel.: (972) 234-4822
Web Site: http://dallasmechanicalgroup.com
Mechanical Construction & Maintenance Services
N.A.I.C.S.: 811114
John Smith (Founder & Pres)

DeBra-Kuempel   (1)
3976 Southern Ave, Cincinnati, OH 45227-1035   (100%)
Tel.: (513) 527-8040
Web Site: https://www.dkemcor.com
Sales Range: $150-199.9 Million
Emp.: 450
Commercial Facility Electrical & Mechanical Contractor
N.A.I.C.S.: 238220
Joseph D. Clark (Pres)

EMCOR Construction Services, Inc.   (1)
301 Merritt 7, Norwalk, CT 06851   (100%)
Tel.: (203) 849-7800
Web Site: https://emcorconstruction.com
Sales Range: $50-74.9 Million
Emp.: 12
Holding Company; Commercial & Industrial Facility Electrical & Mechanical Contracting Services
N.A.I.C.S.: 551112
Joseph E. Burns (Pres-Mechanical Construction & Svcs)
Daniel Fitzgibbons (Pres-Electrical Construction Svcs)
Charlie Pavelec (Sr VP-Natl Pur)
Tammy M. Johnson (VP-Human Resources)
Keith Phillips (Gen Counsel)

Subsidiary (Domestic):

Central Mechanical Construction Co., Inc.   (2)
631 Pecan Cir, Manhattan, KS 66505
Tel.: (785) 537-2437
Web Site:
    https://www.centralmechanical.com
Sales Range: $10-24.9 Million
Emp.: 30
Commercial Facility Electrical & Mechanical Contractor & Support Services
N.A.I.C.S.: 238210
John Lonker (Pres)
Brad Heinisch (VP-Ops)
Mike Pearson (CFO & Controller)

Contra Costa Electric, Inc.   (2)
825 Howe Rd, Martinez, CA 94553-3441   (100%)
Tel.: (925) 229-4250
Web Site: https://www.ccelectric.com
Sales Range: $125-149.9 Million
Commercial Facility Electrical, Mechanical, Telecommunications, Fire Protection & Automation Control Systems Contractor
N.A.I.C.S.: 238210
Charlie Hadsell (Pres & CEO)
Carla Palmer (VP-Comml)
Paul White (VP)
Matt Furrer (VP)

Design Air, Ltd.   (2)
3051 E Valley Rd, Renton, WA 98057-3328   (100%)
Tel.: (253) 854-2770
Commercial Facility Lighting, Heating, Ventilation & Air-Conditioning Contractor
N.A.I.C.S.: 238220

Duffy Mechanical Corp.   (2)
15875 Commerce Ct, Upper Marlboro, MD 20774   (100%)
Tel.: (301) 390-2300
Web Site: http://www.duffymech.com
Sales Range: $25-49.9 Million
Commercial Facility Heating, Ventilation, Air-Conditioning & Plumbing Contractor
N.A.I.C.S.: 238220

Dynalectric Company   (2)
22930 Shaw Rd Ste 100, Dulles, VA 20166-9448   (100%)
Tel.: (703) 742-3500
Web Site: https://www.dynalectric-dc.com
Sales Range: $75-99.9 Million
Commercial Facility Electrical & Telecommunications Systems Contractor
N.A.I.C.S.: 238210
Paul E. Mella (CEO)
Nicholas Robey (VP & Mgr-Construction Dev)
Brian Dugan (VP & Mgr-Residential Construction)

Branch (Domestic):

Dynalectric - Florida   (3)
3300 Corporate Ave Ste 100, Weston, FL 33331   (100%)
Tel.: (954) 624-0000
Web Site: https://www.dyna-fl.com
Sales Range: $50-74.9 Million
Emp.: 30
Commercial Facility Electrical Contractor
N.A.I.C.S.: 238210
Jeff Randle (Pres & CEO)

Dynalectric - Georgia   (3)
4025 Steve Reynolds Blvd Ste 120, Norcross, GA 30093   (100%)
Tel.: (770) 885-1200
Web Site: http://www.dynalectric.net
Sales Range: $10-24.9 Million
Emp.: 35
Commercial Facility Electrical Contractor
N.A.I.C.S.: 238210

Dynalectric - Los Angeles   (3)
4462 Corporate Center Dr, Los Alamitos, CA 90720   (100%)
Tel.: (714) 828-7000
Web Site: https://kdcinc.com
Sales Range: $100-124.9 Million
Commercial Facility Electrical Construction & Control Systems Integration Services
N.A.I.C.S.: 238210
Edward Kazimierski (Mgr-KDC Sys Div)
Earnest Brown (Pres)
Ben Martin (CFO)
Charlie Spencer (VP)
Curt Reese (VP)

Unit (Domestic):

KDC Systems   (4)
4462 Corporate Ctr Dr, Los Alamitos, CA 90720   (100%)
Tel.: (714) 828-7000
Web Site: https://www.kdc-systems.com
Sales Range: $25-49.9 Million
Emp.: 75
Process & Industrial Control Systems Integration Services
N.A.I.C.S.: 238210
Earnest Brown (Pres)
Ben Martin (CFO)
Charlie Spencer (VP)
Curt Reese (VP)

Branch (Domestic):

Dynalectric - Oregon   (3)
2225 NW 20th Ave, Portland, OR 97209   (100%)
Tel.: (503) 226-6771
Web Site: https://www.dyna-oregon.com
Commercial Facility Electrical Contractor
N.A.I.C.S.: 238210
Terry Kvochak (CFO)

Dynalectric - San Diego   (3)
1111 Pioneer Way, El Cajon, CA 92020   (100%)
Tel.: (619) 328-4007
Web Site: https://www.dyna-sd.com
Sales Range: $50-74.9 Million
Emp.: 500
Commercial Facility Electrical Contractor
N.A.I.C.S.: 238210
Frank Robledo (VP-Pre-Construction Svcs)
Bill Rueckert (VP-Field Ops)
Pablo Rivero (CFO)
Seth Gill (VP)
Ted Donald (VP)

Dynalectric Company of Colorado   (3)
345 Sheridan Blvd, Lakewood, CO 80226   (100%)
Tel.: (303) 233-4488
Web Site: https://www.dyna-co.com
Commercial Facility Electrical Contractor
N.A.I.C.S.: 238210
Rob Long (Mgr-Ops-Transportation & Infrastructure)

Dynalectric Company of Nevada   (3)
4475 Quail Ave, Las Vegas, NV 89118   (100%)
Tel.: (702) 736-8577
Web Site: https://www.dyna-lv.com
Sales Range: $25-49.9 Million
Emp.: 75
Commercial Facility Electrical Contractor
N.A.I.C.S.: 238210

Dynalectric Company of Ohio   (3)
1762 Dividend Dr, Columbus, OH 43228   (100%)
Tel.: (614) 529-7500
Web Site: https://www.dyna-ohio.com
Sales Range: $25-49.9 Million
Emp.: 80
Commercial Facility Electrical Contractor
N.A.I.C.S.: 238210
Daniel Konczal (Pres)

Subsidiary (Domestic):

Forest Electric Corp.   (2)
1375 Broadway, New York, NY 10018   (100%)
Tel.: (212) 318-1500
Web Site: https://www.forestny.com
Sales Range: $75-99.9 Million
Commercial Facility Electrical, Telecommunications & Technologies Contractors
N.A.I.C.S.: 238210
Robert Richardson (Co-Pres & CEO)
Harry Sassaman (Co-Pres)
Robert Tarallo (VP)
Andrew G. Dato (Sr VP)
Frank Rapisardi (Superintendent)
Stephen Martinis (Dir-Project Acctg)
Donna M. Lucas (Dir-Admin)
Gerard Cain (VP-Estimating-Datacom Svcs)
Michael Morrone (VP)

Gibson Electric & Technology Solutions   (2)
3100 Woodcreek Dr, Downers Grove, IL 60515-5427   (100%)

Tel.: (630) 288-3800
Web Site: https://www.gibsonelec.com
Sales Range: $50-74.9 Million
Emp.: 300
Commercial Facility Electrical & Telecom-
munications Systems Contractors
N.A.I.C.S.: 238210
Scott Rowe (Sr VP-Tech)
Steve Mulligan (Pres & CEO)
Matt Kelly (Sr VP-Electrical)
Brian Hardy (CFO)

Gowan, Inc. (2)
5550 Airline Dr, Houston, TX
77076-4998 (100%)
Tel.: (713) 696-5400
Web Site: http://www.gowaninc.com
Sales Range: $50-74.9 Million
Commercial Facility Mechanical & Sheet
Metal Contractor
N.A.I.C.S.: 238220

Hansen Mechanical Contractors,
Inc. (2)
4475 W Quail, Las Vegas, NV
89118-3094 (100%)
Tel.: (702) 361-5111
Web Site:
https://www.hansenmechanical.com
Sales Range: $100-124.9 Million
Commercial Facility Mechanical Contractor
N.A.I.C.S.: 238220
Randy Lamb (Pres)

Hyre Electric Company of Indiana,
Inc. (2)
2655 Garfield Ave, Highland, IN
46322 (100%)
Tel.: (219) 923-6100
Web Site: https://www.emcorhyre.com
Sales Range: $75-99.9 Million
Commercial Facility Electrical & Mechanical
Services
N.A.I.C.S.: 238210
Thomas R. Corsiglia (Pres & CEO)
Thomas S. Gozdecki III (Exec VP)

Lowrie Electric Company, Inc. (2)
7520 Bartlett Corporate Cove E, Bartlett,
TN 38133 (100%)
Tel.: (901) 381-4300
Web Site: https://www.lowrie-electric.com
Sales Range: $10-24.9 Million
Commercial Facility Electrical Contractor
N.A.I.C.S.: 238210
Wayne Lowrie (Pres)
Suzanne Osborne (CFO)
Chuck Wells (Mgr-Project & Estimator)

Marelich Mechanical Co., Inc. (2)
24041 Amador St, Hayward, CA
94544-1201 (100%)
Tel.: (510) 785-5500
Web Site: http://www.marelich.com
Sales Range: $100-124.9 Million
Emp.: 50
Commercial Facility Plumbing, Heating,
Ventilation & Air-Conditioning Contractor
N.A.I.C.S.: 238220

Branch (Domestic):

Marelich Mechanical Co. (3)
24041 Amador St, Hayward, CA
94544-1201 (100%)
Tel.: (510) 785-5500
Web Site: https://www.marelich.com
Sales Range: $10-24.9 Million
Emp.: 30
Commercial Facility Plumbing, Heating,
Ventilation & Air-Conditioning Contractor
N.A.I.C.S.: 238220

Subsidiary (Domestic):

Performance Mechanical, Inc. (2)
701 Willow Pass Rd Ste 2, Pittsburg, CA
94565 (100%)
Tel.: (925) 432-4080
Web Site: https://www.perfmech.com
Commercial Facility Specialty Contractor
N.A.I.C.S.: 238990
Andy Hosler (Pres & CEO)
Dimitri Hrovat (CFO & VP)
Dave Sindicic (Dir-Corp Safety)
Christian Gugliemo (Mgr-Estimating)
Jonathan Hosler (Gen Mgr-North Coast)

R.S. Harritan & Company, Inc. (2)

3280 Formex Rd, Richmond, VA
23224 (100%)
Tel.: (804) 275-7821
Web Site: https://www.rsharritan.com
Sales Range: $25-49.9 Million
Emp.: 12
Commercial Facility Heating, Ventilation,
Air-Conditioning, Plumbing, Sheet Metal &
Control Systems Contractor
N.A.I.C.S.: 238220
Jazmin Davidson (CFO & VP)
Michael J. Pantele (Pres)
Tommy Johnson (VP-Mechanical Svcs)
Korey Mason (Dir-Environmental Health &
Safety)
Lonnie Harris (Dir-Pur)
Steve Putnam (Mgr-Sheet Metal & Struc-
tural Steel Svcs-Div)
Jim Averette (Sr Project Mgr-Mechanical)

S.A. Comunale Co., Inc. (2)
2900 Newpark Dr, Barberton, OH 44203
Tel.: (330) 706-3040
Web Site: https://www.sacomunale.com
Emp.: 1,200
Commercial Facility Mechanical & Fire Pro-
tection System Contractors
N.A.I.C.S.: 922160
Sean Coustillac (VP-Svc & Inspection Div)
Steve Comunale (CEO)
Michael J. Moldvay (CFO)
J. R. Fowler (VP-Engrg & Operation Svcs)
Chuck Galosi (VP-Ops)
Jeff Robinson (Dir-Fire Alarm & Suppres-
sion)
Jobina Trimmer (Dir-Inspection Sls)
Amy Hendricks (Dir-HR)
Henry Fontana (VP)

University Mechanical & Engineering
Contractors, Inc. (2)
1168 Fesler St, El Cajon, CA
92020 (100%)
Tel.: (619) 956-2500
Web Site: http://www.umec.com
Sales Range: $100-124.9 Million
Commercial Facility Heating, Ventilation,
Air-Conditioning, Plumbing & Piping Sys-
tems Contractor
N.A.I.C.S.: 238220

Unit (Domestic):

Spira-Loc (3)
1168 Fesler St, El Cajon, CA
92020 (100%)
Tel.: (619) 956-2500
Web Site: http://www.umec.com
Sales Range: $75-99.9 Million
Commercial Technical & Performance Test-
ing Services
N.A.I.C.S.: 541990

Branch (Domestic):

University Mechanical & Engineering
Contractors, Inc. (3)
1200 N Sickles Dr, Tempe, AZ
85288 (100%)
Tel.: (480) 921-0903
Web Site: https://www.umec-az.com
Sales Range: $125-149.9 Million
Emp.: 200
Commercial Facility Heating, Ventilation,
Air-Conditioning, Plumbing & Piping Sys-
tems Contractor
N.A.I.C.S.: 238220

Subsidiary (Domestic):

Wasatch Electric (2)
2455 W 1500 S Ste A, Salt Lake City, UT
84104 (100%)
Tel.: (801) 487-4511
Web Site: https://www.wasatchelectric.com
Sales Range: $50-74.9 Million
Commercial Facility Electrical & Telecom-
munications Line Contractor
N.A.I.C.S.: 238210
Ben Homer (VP)
Brent Gardner (VP)
Shannon Marchbanks (VP)

Welsbach Electric Corp. (2)
111-01 14th Ave, College Point, NY
11356 (100%)
Tel.: (718) 670-7900
Web Site: https://www.welsbachelectric.com
Electrical Contractor
N.A.I.C.S.: 238210

Mitchell E. Mailman (Gen Mgr-Electric Lines
Div)
Alan Doubert (VP-Industrial & Comml)
Real Lamour (Dir-Engrg)
Rod Santos (Dir-Procurement)
Steven Filippazzo (Treas & Controller)
Mustafa Shinwa (Asst Controller-Acctg)
Timothy P. Miller (Pres & CEO)
Carl W. Fry (Pres)
Austin Franzoni (CFO)

Welsbach Electric Corp. of Long
Island (2)
300 Newtown Rd, Plainview, NY
11803 (100%)
Tel.: (516) 454-0023
Web Site: https://www.welsbachli.com
Sales Range: $25-49.9 Million
Electrical Contractor
N.A.I.C.S.: 238210

EMCOR Facilities Services, Inc. (1)
320 23rd St S Ste 100, Arlington, VA
22202-3746 (100%)
Tel.: (703) 769-8208
Web Site: http://www.emcorgroup.com
Sales Range: $75-99.9 Million
Emp.: 26,000
Holding Company; Commercial & Industrial
Facility Management & Support Services
N.A.I.C.S.: 551112

Subsidiary (Domestic):

Betlem Service Corporation (2)
704 Clinton Ave S, Rochester, NY
14620-1402 (100%)
Tel.: (585) 271-5505
Web Site: https://www.emcorbetlem.com
Sales Range: $25-49.9 Million
Emp.: 175
Commercial & Residential Facility Heating,
Ventilation & Air-Conditioning Contractor
N.A.I.C.S.: 238220
Sean O'Brien (CFO)
Todd Streeter (VP)
William Coe (VP)

Building Technology Engineers,
Inc. (2)
304 Cambridge Rd Ste 540, Woburn, MA
01801 (100%)
Tel.: (617) 482-5455
Web Site: https://www.emcorbte.com
Sales Range: $25-49.9 Million
Emp.: 50
Commercial Facility Heating, Ventilation,
Air-Conditioning, Plumbing & Electrical Con-
tractor
N.A.I.C.S.: 238220
Michael Manning (Acct Dir)
Sergio F. Svegliati (Mgr-Acct)
Barbara Richardson (Mgr-Payroll & HR)
Thomas Coates (VP & Gen Mgr)
Ronald Arseneault (Mgr-Safety)

Combustioneer Corp. (2)
4420 Lottsford Vista Rd Ste 1, Lanham, MD
20706 (100%)
Tel.: (301) 340-2290
Web Site: https://www.combustioneer.com
Sales Range: $100-124.9 Million
Commercial Facility Electrical & Mechanical
Contractor
N.A.I.C.S.: 238220
Jeffrey Gaddy (Pres)
Vilma Dapkute (CFO)
Charles E. Shirley (Mgr-Bus Dev)

EMCOR Facilities Knowledge
Center (2)
4050 E Cotton Ctr Blvd Ste 40, Phoenix, AZ
85040 (100%)
Tel.: (602) 685-4600
Web Site: http://www.emcorgroup.com
Sales Range: $50-74.9 Million
Emp.: 170
Facilities Support Logistics Services
N.A.I.C.S.: 541614

Division (Domestic):

EMCOR Facilities Services - Site
Based Services (2)
2800 Crystal Dr Ste 600, Arlington, VA
22202 (100%)
Tel.: (571) 403-8900
Sales Range: $75-99.9 Million
Commercial & Industrial Facility Manage-
ment & Support Services

N.A.I.C.S.: 561210

Subsidiary (Domestic):

EMCOR Government Services,
Inc. (2)
6363 Walker Ln Ste 600, Alexandria, VA
22310 (100%)
Tel.: (571) 403-8900
Web Site:
https://www.emcorgovservices.com
Sales Range: $75-99.9 Million
Government Facility Management Services
N.A.I.C.S.: 561210
Michael L. Rodgers (Pres & CEO)
Manjula Master (CFO)
Patrick Baldwin (Exec Dir-Ops)
Mario Sotelo (Exec Dir-Ops)

EMCOR Services Aircond
Corporation (2)
400 Lk Rdg Dr, Smyrna, GA
30082-5236 (100%)
Tel.: (770) 444-3355
Web Site: https://www.aircond.com
Emp.: 300
Facility Heating, Ventilation & Air-
Conditioning System Design, Engineering,
Construction & Maintenance Services
N.A.I.C.S.: 238220
Bobby Green (CFO & VP)
Kenneth Torres (Pres)
Frank Cloud Jr. (Gen Mgr-Projects & Svc-
Georgia, Alabama & Florida)

Fluidics, Inc. (2)
10981 Decatur Rd Ste 1, Philadelphia, PA
19154 (100%)
Tel.: (215) 671-7900
Web Site: https://www.fluidics.com
Sales Range: $25-49.9 Million
Emp.: 400
Commercial Facility Management Services
& Mechanical Contractor
N.A.I.C.S.: 238990
Robert K. Baranowski (Pres)
Jack Dobrowolsky (Sr VP)
Michael J. Iacobucci (CFO)

Viox Services, Inc. (2)
15 W Voorhees St, Cincinnati, OH
45215 (100%)
Tel.: (513) 948-8469
Web Site: https://www.viox-services.com
Sales Range: $75-99.9 Million
Emp.: 900
Commercial Facility Support Services
N.A.I.C.S.: 561210

EMCOR Group (UK) plc (1)
1 The Crescent, Surbiton, KT6 4BN, Surrey,
United Kingdom (100%)
Tel.: (44) 3456002300
Web Site: http://www.emcoruk.com
Sales Range: $650-699.9 Million
Emp.: 70
Commercial Facility Engineering & Support
Services
N.A.I.C.S.: 541330
Keith Chanter (CEO)

EMCOR International, Inc. (1)
301 Merritt 7 6th Fl, Norwalk, CT 06851-
1052
Tel.: (203) 849-7800
Web Site: http://www.emcor.com
Emp.: 100
Electrical Engineering Services
N.A.I.C.S.: 238210

EMCOR Services New York/New
Jersey (1)
5 Dakota Dr Ste 111, Lake Success, NY
11042 (100%)
Tel.: (516) 727-4450
Web Site: http://emcorservicesnynj.com
Sales Range: $1-4.9 Billion
Emp.: 25
Commercial Facility Heating, Air-
Conditioning, Refrigeration & Climate Con-
trol Systems Contractor
N.A.I.C.S.: 238220
Tim Murphy (Pres)
Kevin Aley (CFO)
Herman van Vliet (VP-Bus Dev)
Joseph DeMaio (Mng Dir-Bus Dev)
Art Gerow (VP-Svc)

Branch (Domestic):

EMCOR Services New York/New
Jersey (2)

EMCOR Group, Inc.—(Continued)

210 W Pkwy Unit 3 1, Pompton Plains, NJ
07444   **(100%)**
Tel.: (973) 839-8339
Web Site: http://emcorservicesnynj.com
Sales Range: $50-74.9 Million
Emp.: 8
Commercial Facility Heating, Air-
Conditioning, Refrigeration & Climate Con-
trol Systems Contractor
N.A.I.C.S.: 238990
Timothy J. Murphy *(Pres)*
Kevin Aley *(CFO)*
Art Gerow *(VP-Svc)*
Herman van Vliet *(VP-Bus Dev)*
Joseph DeMaio *(Mng Dir-Bus Dev)*
Ward Strosser *(VP)*

EMCOR Services Northeast, Inc.   **(1)**
80 Hawes Way, Stoughton, MA 02072
Tel.: (781) 573-1700
Web Site: https://www.emcornortheast.com
Commercial Facility Heating, Ventilation,
Air-Conditioning, Plumbing & Fire Protection
Systems Contractor
N.A.I.C.S.: 238220
David J. Bolduc *(Pres & Engr-Sls)*
Paul Feeney *(VP-Project Ops)*
Debra Springer *(Sr Mgr-Admin & Customer
Svc)*
Terry Keigher *(VP-Sls)*

Subsidiary (Domestic):

J.C. Higgins Corp.   **(2)**
70 Hawes Way, Stoughton, MA
02072-1163   **(100%)**
Tel.: (781) 341-1500
Web Site: https://www.jchigginscorp.com
Sales Range: $125-149.9 Million
Emp.: 200
Commercial Facility Heating, Ventilation,
Air-Conditioning, Plumbing, Fire Protection
& Other Mechanical Systems Contractor
N.A.I.C.S.: 238990
Robert Gallagher *(Pres & CEO)*
Tammy Ferland *(Dir-Bus Dev)*

Labov Mechanical, Inc.   **(2)**
6754 W Washington Ave, Pleasantville, NJ
08232   **(100%)**
Tel.: (609) 383-9600
Web Site: http://www.labovmechanical.com
Sales Range: $10-24.9 Million
Emp.: 14
Commercial Facility Heating, Ventilation,
Air-Conditioning, Plumbing & Industrial
Kitchens Contractors
N.A.I.C.S.: 238220

**EMCOR Services Team Mechanical,
Inc.**   **(1)**
431 Lexington Dr, Buffalo Grove, IL
60089   **(100%)**
Tel.: (847) 229-7600
Web Site: http://www.emcortmi.com
Sales Range: $75-99.9 Million
Emp.: 35
Commercial Facility Electrical & Mechanical
Contracting & Support Services
N.A.I.C.S.: 238990
Jeffrey R. Einck *(CFO)*
Cindy Stelzer *(VP-Engrg)*

Subsidiary (Domestic):

**EMCOR Services Team Mechanical,
Inc.**   **(2)**
431 Lexington Dr, Buffalo Grove, IL 60089
Tel.: (847) 229-7600
Web Site: http://www.emcortmi.com
Sales Range: $10-24.9 Million
Emp.: 30
Mechanical Contractor
N.A.I.C.S.: 238220
Cindy Stelzer *(VP-Engrg)*
Jeffrey R. Einck *(CFO)*
Kirk Pettingill *(Pres)*
Tim Schilling *(VP-Svc Div)*
Steve Herner *(Dir-Safety & Mgr-
Productivity)*

F&G Mechanical Corporation   **(1)**
348 New County Rd, Secaucus, NJ
07094   **(100%)**
Tel.: (201) 864-3580
Web Site: https://www.fgmech.com
Sales Range: $100-124.9 Million
Emp.: 250

Commercial Facility Heating, Ventilation,
Air-Conditioning, Plumbing & Fire Protection
Contractor
N.A.I.C.S.: 238220
Salvatore Fichera *(Co-Pres & CEO)*
Salvatore P. Giardina *(Co-Pres)*
Richard Cericola *(VP-Meadowlands Fire
Protection Ops)*
Peter Stassi *(Exec VP-Plumbing)*
Robert J. Anen *(Exec VP-HVAC)*
Donna DiPietro Leanza *(VP-HR & Admin)*
Paul Bertolini *(Dir-Safety)*
Jeffrey Petro *(Sr Mgr-IT)*
Anthony Giantonio III *(Mgr-Warehouse)*

Division (Domestic):

**Meadowlands Fire Protection
Corp.**   **(2)**
348 New County Rd, Secaucus, NJ
07094   **(100%)**
Tel.: (201) 864-3580
Web Site: http://www.fgmech.com
Commercial Facility Fire Protection Contrac-
tor
N.A.I.C.S.: 922160
Richard Cericola *(VP-Meadowlands Fire
Protection)*

Gaston Electrical Co., LLC   **(1)**
960 Turnpike St, Canton, MA 02021
Tel.: (781) 821-3939
Web Site: http://www.gastonelectrical.com
Rev.: $5,940,000
Emp.: 45
Electrical Contractor
N.A.I.C.S.: 238210
Bill Weber *(Pres)*
Eli Smith *(Project Mgr)*
Paul Higgins *(Project Mgr)*
Ed Dowling *(Mgr-Registered Comm Distr
Designer & Project Engr)*
Mark DiMillio *(Mgr-Pur)*

Harry Pepper & Associates, Inc.   **(1)**
9550 Regency Sq Blvd Ste 300, Jackson-
ville, FL 32225
Tel.: (904) 721-3300
Web Site: https://www.hpepper.com
Sales Range: $100-124.9 Million
Emp.: 100
Infrastructure Projects & Industrial Buildings
Construction
N.A.I.C.S.: 541330

**Heritage Mechanical Services,
Inc.**   **(1)**
70 Schmitt Blvd, Farmingdale, NY
11735   **(100%)**
Tel.: (516) 558-2000
Web Site: http://www.heritagemech.com
Sales Range: $10-24.9 Million
Emp.: 60
Commercial Facility Heating, Ventilation &
Air-Conditioning Contractor
N.A.I.C.S.: 238220
Jeffrey A. Porrello *(Pres & CEO)*

Illingworth Corporation   **(1)**
11217 West Becher St, West Allis, WI
53227   **(100%)**
Tel.: (414) 476-5790
Web Site: http://www.illingworth-kilgust.com
Sales Range: $125-149.9 Million
Emp.: 200
Commercial Facility Heating, Ventilation,
Air-Conditioning, Plumbing, Sheet Metal &
Control Systems Contractor & Maintenance
Services
N.A.I.C.S.: 238220
Dave Heather *(Mgr-HVAC Dept)*
Dan Pfeifer *(CEO)*
John Schmitz *(Pres)*
Christine Tessenske *(CFO)*
Scott Adams *(Mgr-Svc Ops)*
Paul E. Disch *(Mgr-Plumbing Dept)*
David Bavisotto *(VP-Bus Dev)*
Tim Wipperfurth *(Branch Mgr)*
Brian Schweizer *(Mgr-Controls Div)*
Christine Chadbourn *(Mgr-HR)*

Kilgust Mechanical, Inc.   **(1)**
301 Merritt 7 Fl 6, Norwalk, CT
06851-1052   **(100%)**
Tel.: (608) 222-9196
Web Site: http://www.illingworth-kilgust.com
Sales Range: $25-49.9 Million
Emp.: 100
Commercial Facility Heating, Ventilation &
Air-Conditioning Contractor

N.A.I.C.S.: 238220

Mesa Energy Systems, Inc.   **(1)**
2 Cromwell, Irvine, CA 92618   **(100%)**
Tel.: (949) 460-0460
Web Site: https://www.mesaenergy.com
Sales Range: $50-74.9 Million
Emp.: 120
Commercial Facility Heating, Ventilation &
Air Conditioning, Building Automation & Ret-
rofit Services Contractor
N.A.I.C.S.: 238220
Robert A. Lake *(Pres)*
Tony Ghaffari *(VP-Engrg)*
Harry Archung *(Sr VP-Bus Dev)*
Brad Cox *(Sr VP-Ops-Northern California)*
Kip Bagley *(Sr VP-Svc)*
Don Griffin *(Branch Mgr-Phoenix)*
Jeff Figueroa *(VP-Applied Sciences-
Southern California)*
Juliann Lee *(VP & Controller)*
Michael Cook *(Dir-HR)*
Ron Hickey *(Exec VP-Southern California)*
Stephan Hunt *(CFO & Sr VP)*
Jasmine G. Jean *(Dir-Mktg & Bus Dev)*
Rob Fried *(Dir-Engrg-Southern California)*
Mark Collins *(Sr VP & Gen Mgr-Northern
California)*
Devin J. Ernst *(VP-Sls)*
John Lehman *(VP-Strategic Ops)*
Bryan Gilbert *(VP-Automation & Integrated
Sys-Southern California)*
Dave Johnson *(Dir-Solar PV Bus Dev-
Southern California)*
Wayner Lacher *(VP-Retrofit & Project Dev-
Southern California)*
Stephen A. Chin *(Dir-Automation-Northern
California)*
Charles G. Fletcher Jr. *(Founder & Exec
VP)*

Subsidiary (Domestic):

EMCOR Services ARC   **(2)**
4668 Sonora Ave Ste 102, Fresno, CA
93722   **(100%)**
Tel.: (559) 277-7900
Web Site: http://www.mesaenergy.com
Sales Range: $10-24.9 Million
Emp.: 25
Commercial Facility Heating, Ventilation &
Air Conditioning, Building Automation & Ret-
rofit Services Contractor
N.A.I.C.S.: 238220

**EMCOR Services Mesa Integrated
Solutions**   **(2)**
7060 Koll Ctr Pkwy 312, Pleasanton, CA
94566   **(100%)**
Tel.: (925) 931-9801
Web Site: http://www.mesaenergy.com
Sales Range: $25-49.9 Million
Emp.: 30
Commercial Facility Heating, Ventilation &
Air Conditioning, Building Automation & Ret-
rofit Services Contractor
N.A.I.C.S.: 238990

**New England Mechanical Services,
Inc.**   **(1)**
55 Gerber Rd E, South Windsor, CT
06074   **(100%)**
Tel.: (860) 871-1111
Web Site: http://www.nemsi.com
Sales Range: $25-49.9 Million
Emp.: 400
Commercial Facility Electrical & Mechanical
Design, Engineering, Installation & Mainte-
nance Services
N.A.I.C.S.: 238220
Dana Finnegan *(Pres & CEO)*

Ohmsted, Ltd.   **(1)**
895 N Main St, Beaumont, TX 77701
Tel.: (409) 833-6375
Web Site: http://www.ohmstede.com
Sales Range: $250-299.9 Million
Emp.: 150
Industrial Heat Exchanger Engineering,
Maintenance & Fabrication Services
N.A.I.C.S.: 238220

Division (Domestic):

Ohmstede Industrial Services   **(2)**
950 W Jade Ave, Port Arthur, TX 77640
Tel.: (409) 840-6644
Web Site: http://www.ohmstede.net
Sales Range: $1-9.9 Million
Emp.: 20

Industrial Heat Exchanger Maintenance
Services
N.A.I.C.S.: 811310
Norman Thornton *(Pres)*

Subsidiary (Domestic):

**Redman Equipment & Manufacturing
Co.**   **(2)**
19800 S Normandie Ave, Torrance, CA
90502-1182
Tel.: (310) 329-1134
Web Site: https://www.redmaneq.com
Sales Range: $10-24.9 Million
Emp.: 48
Industrial Heat Exchanger Engineering,
Maintenance & Fabrication Services
N.A.I.C.S.: 238220
Don Redman *(Co-Pres)*

**PACE Mechanical Services II,
Inc.**   **(1)**
25701 Commerce Dr, Madison Heights, MI
48071
Tel.: (248) 556-7200
Commercial Facility Heating, Ventilation,
Air-Conditioning, Plumbing & Automation
Systems Contractor
N.A.I.C.S.: 238220

PPM   **(1)**
1127 S Main St, Society Hill, SC 29593
Tel.: (843) 378-4700
Web Site: https://www.morppm.com
Emp.: 45
Mechanical, Electrical & Civil Construction
Services
N.A.I.C.S.: 236210
Bobby Ollis *(Pres)*
Mike Roach *(CFO & VP)*
Chip Rogers *(Dir-Environmental, Health &
Safety)*
Phillip Davis *(VP-Sls & Mktg)*
Stacy A. Bell *(Dir-HR)*
Henry Moree *(CEO)*
Henry Moree Jr. *(COO & Exec VP)*

Penguin Air Conditioning Corp.   **(1)**
5 Penn Plz 16th Fl, New York, NY
10001   **(100%)**
Tel.: (718) 706-6500
Web Site: https://www.penguinac.com
Sales Range: $50-74.9 Million
Emp.: 150
Commercial Facility Heating, Ventilation &
Air-Conditioning Contractor & Maintenance
Services
N.A.I.C.S.: 238220

Rabalais Constructors, LLC   **(1)**
11200 Up River Rd, Corpus Christi, TX
78410
Tel.: (361) 242-3121
Web Site: https://www.rabalais.com
Electrical Contractor
N.A.I.C.S.: 238210

RepconStrickland, Inc.   **(1)**
1605 S Battleground Rd, La Porte, TX
77571
Tel.: (281) 478-6200
Building Construction Services
N.A.I.C.S.: 236115

Shambaugh & Son, L.P.   **(1)**
7614 Opportunity Dr, Fort Wayne, IN
46825-3363
Tel.: (260) 487-7777
Web Site: https://www.shambaugh.com
Sales Range: $250-299.9 Million
Emp.: 1,500
Commercial Facility Electrical, Mechanical,
Fire Protection & Control Systems Contrac-
tor
N.A.I.C.S.: 238210
Mark A. Veerkamp *(CFO)*
Robert B. Vincent *(COO-Fire Protection)*
Jeffrey L. Johns *(Sr VP)*
Gary A. Perkey *(VP-Reg Mechanical)*
William J. Meyer *(Gen Counsel & Sr VP)*
Thomas L. Scare *(Sr VP-Fin)*
Charlie Pavelec *(Sr VP-Natl Pur)*
Daniel J. Ritzert *(Sr VP & Mgr-Mechanical
Process-Grp)*
Todd A. Fink *(Sr VP-Fire Protection)*
Cale Campbell *(Sr VP & Mgr-Havel, EM-
COR Construction Svcs & Precision Con-
trols)*
Doug Hearld *(Sr VP & Mgr-Electrical Grp
Div)*
Thomas O'Connor Jr. *(Dir-Corp Safety)*

Subsidiary (Domestic):

Advanced Systems Group (2)
7625 DiSalle Blvd, Fort Wayne, IN
46825 **(100%)**
Tel.: (260) 487-7814
Web Site: http://www.advsysgrp.com
Commercial Facility Lighting, Telecommunications Line, Security, Fire Protection &
Safety Systems Contractor
N.A.I.C.S.: 238990

Division (Domestic):

Havel (2)
7525 DiSalle Blvd, Fort Wayne, IN
46825 **(100%)**
Tel.: (260) 487-7900
Web Site: https://www.havelemcor.com
Sales Range: $150-199.9 Million
Emp.: 120
Commercial Facility Electrical & Mechanical
Contractor & Maintenance Services
N.A.I.C.S.: 238990
Cale Campbell *(Sr VP & Mgr-Div)*

**Shambaugh & Son - Ed Grace
Division** (2)
2600 Duncan Rd, Lafayette, IN
47904 **(100%)**
Tel.: (765) 742-7311
Web Site: http://www.shambaugh.com
Sales Range: $125-149.9 Million
Emp.: 20
Commercial Facility Electrical, Mechanical,
Fire Protection & Control Systems Contractor
N.A.I.C.S.: 238210
Davis M. Newhart *(Mgr)*

**Southern Industrial Construction
Inc.** (1)
6101 Triangle Dr, Raleigh, NC 27617
Tel.: (919) 782-4600
Web Site: http://www.southernindustrial.com
Sales Range: $75-99.9 Million
Emp.: 450
Industrial Plant Construction Services
N.A.I.C.S.: 237990
Mike Torsiello *(CFO)*
Misha Kennedy *(Dir-HR)*
Daniel Erwin *(Dir-Safety)*
Kathleen Ventura *(Mktg Mgr)*
John Spikula *(Dir-IT)*

The Fagan Company (1)
3125 Brinkerhoff Rd, Kansas City, KS
66115 **(100%)**
Tel.: (913) 621-4444
Web Site: https://www.faganco.com
Sales Range: $150-199.9 Million
Emp.: 30
Commercial Facility Heating, Ventilation &
Air-Conditioning Contractor
N.A.I.C.S.: 238220
Robert P. Roach *(COO)*
Michael Crabtree *(Pres)*

The Poole & Kent Corporation (1)
4530 Hollins Ferry Rd, Baltimore, MD
21227 **(100%)**
Tel.: (410) 247-2200
Web Site: https://www.poole-kent.com
Sales Range: $50-74.9 Million
Emp.: 200
Commercial Facility Mechanical Contractor
& Maintenance Services
N.A.I.C.S.: 238220
Adam E. Snavely *(Pres & CEO)*
Glenn Meredith *(VP-Ops)*
Thomas P. Lynott *(VP-Estimating)*

Subsidiary (Domestic):

**The Poole & Kent Company of
Florida** (2)
1781 N W N River Dr, Miami, FL
33125 **(100%)**
Tel.: (305) 325-1930
Web Site: https://www.pkflorida.com
Sales Range: $10-24.9 Million
Emp.: 100
Commercial Facility Mechanical Contractor
& Maintenance Services
N.A.I.C.S.: 238220
Patrick Carr *(Pres & CEO)*
Brian MacClugage *(Exec VP)*
David Strickland *(Sr VP & Asst Sec)*
Asif Shaikh *(Sr VP)*
Kevin Smith *(VP)*
David BuShea *(VP)*

Trautman & Shreve, Inc. (1)
4406 Race St, Denver, CO 80216 **(100%)**
Tel.: (303) 295-1414
Web Site: http://www.trautman-shreve.com
Sales Range: $50-74.9 Million
Emp.: 330
Commercial Facility Heating, Ventilation,
Air-Conditioning, Plumbing, Sheet Metal &
Automation Systems Contractor & Maintenance Services
N.A.I.C.S.: 238220

Tucker Mechanical (1)
367 Research Pkwy, Meriden, CT
06450-7148 **(100%)**
Tel.: (203) 630-7200
Web Site: http://www.tuckermech.com
Sales Range: $50-74.9 Million
Emp.: 35
Commercial Facility Heating, Ventilation,
Air-Conditioning, Plumbing, Fire Protection
& Control Systems Contractors & Maintenance Services
N.A.I.C.S.: 238220
Hillar Kivi *(CFO & Sr VP)*
John Hilf *(Mgr-Major Projects-Grp)*
Martin Waung *(Pres & CEO)*
Enza Minutillo *(Controller)*
Emory Allaire *(Mgr-Industrial & Power Grp)*
Ben Bosco *(Gen Mgr-Svc)*
Kristina Brangi *(Mgr-HR)*
Bryan Deko *(Mgr-Field Labor)*
Kristen Jaworski *(Mgr-Customer Svc &
Mktg)*
Jason Marcroft *(Dir-Safety & Risk Mgmt)*
Victor Paulo *(Mgr-Preconstruction & Estimating)*
Paul Wieloch *(Gen Mgr-Special Projects-
Grp)*

Walker-J-Walker, Inc. (1)
6045 E Shelby Dr Ste 3, Memphis, TN
38141-7600 **(100%)**
Tel.: (901) 368-1500
Web Site: http://www.walkerjwalker.com
Sales Range: $10-24.9 Million
Emp.: 115
Commercial Facility Heating, Ventilation,
Air-Conditioning, Plumbing & Sheet Metal
Contractor
N.A.I.C.S.: 238220
Brad Bartlett *(Pres)*

EMCORE CORPORATION
2015 W Chestnut St, Alhambra, CA
91803
Tel.: (626) 293-3400 NJ
Web Site: https://www.emcore.com
Year Founded: 1984
EMKR—(NASDAQ)
Rev.: $97,716,000
Assets: $143,913,000
Liabilities: $63,623,000
Net Worth: $80,290,000
Earnings: ($75,359,000)
Emp.: 350
Fiscal Year-end: 09/30/23
Compound Semiconductor Solutions
Mfr
N.A.I.C.S.: 334413
Cletus C. Glasener *(Chm)*
Jeffrey Rittichier *(Pres & CEO)*
David Wojciechowski *(VP-Sls, Mktg &
Bus Dev)*
Hank Blauvelt *(CTO)*
Marc Cavagnolo *(VP-Corp Dev)*
Ryan Hochgesang *(Gen Counsel &
VP)*
Janet Liu *(VP-Quality & Organization
Performance)*
Gyo Shinozaki *(VP & Gen Mgr-
Broadband)*
Genzao Zhang *(VP-Engrg)*
Thomas P. Minichiello *(CFO & Chief
Acctg Officer)*

Subsidiaries:

EMCORE Fiber Optics, Inc. (1)
10420 Research Rd SE, Albuquerque, NM
87123-3345
Tel.: (505) 559-2600
Web Site: http://www.emcore.com
Fiber Optic Cable Mfr

N.A.I.C.S.: 335921

**L-3 Communications Space &
Navigation** (1)
450 Clark Dr, Budd Lake, NJ 07828
Tel.: (973) 446-4000
Web Site: http://www.l-3com.com
Sales Range: $100-124.9 Million
Emp.: 50
Pointing, Guidance, Control & Positioning
Equipment for Satellites, Artillery & Launch
Vehicles
N.A.I.C.S.: 561621

Opticomm Corporation (1)
2015 Chestnut St, Alhambra, CA 91803
Tel.: (626) 293-3400
Web Site: http://www.opticomm.com
Sales Range: $1-9.9 Million
Emp.: 23
Optical Communications System Mfr & Distr
N.A.I.C.S.: 335929

Systron-Donner Corporation (1)
2700 Systron Dr, Concord, CA 94518
Tel.: (925) 979-4400
Web Site: http://www.systron.com
Inertial Sensors & Subsystems, Accelerometers, Quartz Rate Sensors & Inertial Measurement Units
N.A.I.C.S.: 334511

EMEREN GROUP LTD
149 Water St Ste 302, Norwalk, CT
06854
Tel.: (925) 425-7335 VG
Web Site: https://www.emeren.com
SOL—(NYSE)
Rev.: $105,642,000
Assets: $478,351,000
Liabilities: $115,042,000
Net Worth: $363,309,000
Earnings: ($5,431,000)
Fiscal Year-end: 12/31/23
Green Energy Products Mfr; Solar
Wafers Mfr
N.A.I.C.S.: 334413
Chen Ke *(CFO)*
Yumin Liu *(CEO)*
Enrico Bocchi *(Exec VP-Europe)*
Mac Moore *(Exec VP-North America)*
KaiKai Zhang *(Exec VP-China)*

Subsidiaries:

ReneSola Deutschland GmbH (1)
Lyoner Strasse 15, 60528, Frankfurt am
Main, Germany
Tel.: (49) 69663786900
Web Site: http://www.renesola.com
Sales Range: $25-49.9 Million
Emp.: 35
Silicon Wafers Mfr
N.A.I.C.S.: 334413

ReneSola Singapore Pte. Ltd. (1)
1 Cleantech Loop Unit 02-28, Singapore,
637141, Singapore **(100%)**
Tel.: (65) 67959512
Web Site: http://www.renesola.com
Sales Range: $25-49.9 Million
Emp.: 4
Solar Heating Equipment Mfr
N.A.I.C.S.: 333414

**Zhejiang Yuhui Solar Energy Source
Co., Ltd.** (1)
No 8 Baoqun Road Industry Park
Yaozhuang Town, Jiaxing, 314117, China
Tel.: (86) 57384773688
Silicon Wafers Mfr
N.A.I.C.S.: 334413

Subsidiary (Domestic):

Wuxi Jiacheng Solar Energy Technology Co., Ltd. (2)
QingYuan Road Economic & Technical
Zone, Yixing, 214200, China
Tel.: (86) 510 8712 8055
Solar Water Heater Mfr
N.A.I.C.S.: 333414

EMERGENT BIOSOLUTIONS
INC.

300 Professional Dr Ste 400, Gaithersburg, MD 20879
Tel.: (240) 631-3200 DE
Web Site:
https://www.emergentbiosolutions.com
EBS—(NYSE)
Rev.: $1,120,900,000
Assets: $3,166,600,000
Liabilities: $1,783,600,000
Net Worth: $1,383,000,000
Earnings: ($223,800,000)
Emp.: 2,500
Fiscal Year-end: 12/31/22
Immunobiotics Products Developer,
Marketer & Mfr
N.A.I.C.S.: 325411
Joseph C. Papa *(Pres & CEO)*
Abigail Jenkins *(Sr VP & Head-
Vaccines & Anti-Infectives Bus Unit)*
Coleen Glessner *(Exec VP-Quality,
Quality, and Quality)*
Stephanie Duatschek *(Chief Strategy
Officer, Chief Transformation Officer
& Sr VP)*
Michelle Pepin *(Chief HR Officer & Sr
VP)*
Paul Williams *(Sr VP-Products Bus)*
Bill Hartzel *(Sr Dir-Manufacturing &
Bioservices)*
Richard S. Lindahl *(CFO, Treas &
Exec VP)*

Subsidiaries:

Adapt Pharma Inc. (1)
100 Mastsonford Rd Ste 201, Radnor, PA
19087
Web Site: https://www.narcandirect.com
Pharmaceutical Products Distr
N.A.I.C.S.: 424210
Mike Kelly *(Pres-Ops)*

**Adapt Pharma Operations
Limited** (1)
45 Fitzwilliam Sq, Dublin, Ireland
Tel.: (353) 16344172
Web Site: http://www.adaptpharma.com
Pharmaceuticals Product Mfr
N.A.I.C.S.: 325412

Cangene bioPharma, Inc. (1)
1111 S Paca St, Baltimore, MD 21230
Tel.: (410) 843-5000
Emp.: 92
Pharmaceuticals Product Mfr
N.A.I.C.S.: 325412

**Emergent BioDefense Operations
Lansing LLC** (1)
3500 N Martin Luther King Jr Blvd, Lansing,
MI 48906 **(100%)**
Tel.: (517) 327-1500
Web Site:
http://www.emergentbiosolutions.com
Sales Range: $75-99.9 Million
Biopharmaceutical Development & Biodefense Operations Services
N.A.I.C.S.: 541714

**Emergent BioSolutions Canada
Inc.** (1)
155 Innovation Drive, Winnipeg, R3T 5Y3,
MB, Canada
Tel.: (204) 275-4200
Emp.: 472
Biopharmaceutical Product Distr
N.A.I.C.S.: 424210

Emergent BioSolutions UK Ltd. (1)
Building 3 Chiswick Park 566 Chiswick High
Road, London, W4 5AY, United Kingdom
Tel.: (44) 1628965545
Pharmaceutical Research & Development
Services
N.A.I.C.S.: 541714

Emergent BioSolutions, Inc. (1)
1111 S Paca St, Baltimore, MD
21230 **(100%)**
Tel.: (410) 843-5000
Web Site:
http://www.emergentcontractmanufacturing.com
Sales Range: $25-49.9 Million
Emp.: 100
Pharmaceutical Contract Manufacturing

Emergent BioSolutions Inc.—(Continued)

N.A.I.C.S.: 325412

Emergent Countermeasures Interna-
tional Ltd. **(1)**
Building 3 Chiswick Park 566 Chiswick High
Road, London, W4 5YA, Surrey, United
Kingdom
Tel.: (44) 7825580806
Biopharmaceutical Product Distr
N.A.I.C.S.: 424210

Emergent Product Development
Gaithersburg Inc. **(1)**
300 Professional Dr Ste 100, Gaithersburg,
MD 20879 **(100%)**
Tel.: (240) 631-6300
Web Site:
  http://www.emergentbiosolutions.com
Sales Range: $25-49.9 Million
Emp.: 36
Biopharmaceutical Product Development
Services
N.A.I.C.S.: 541715

Emergent Product Development Se-
attle LLC **(1)**
2401 4th Ave Ste 1050, Seattle, WA 98121
Tel.: (206) 838-0500
Web Site: http://www.trubion.com
Sales Range: $10-24.9 Million
Emp.: 73
Biopharmaceutical Mfr & Developer of
Medicines in the Treatment of Inflammatory
Diseases & Cancer
N.A.I.C.S.: 325412
Leander F. Lauffer (Sr VP-Legal Affairs &
Corp Strategy)

Emergent Protective Products USA
Inc **(1)**
305 College Rd E, Princeton, NJ 08540-
6608
Tel.: (301) 795-1800
Emp.: 11
Surgical & Medical Instrument Mfr
N.A.I.C.S.: 339112

Emergent Sales and Marketing Ger-
many GmbH **(1)**
Vichystrasse 14, 76646, Bruchsal,
Germany **(100%)**
Tel.: (49) 725132197031
Web Site:
  (https://www.emergentbiosolutions.com
Sales Range: $10-24.9 Million
Emp.: 15
Sales & Marketing of Biosolutions Products
N.A.I.C.S.: 325414

Emergent Sales and Marketing Sin-
gapore Pte. Ltd. **(1)**
809 French Road 05-152 Kitchener Com-
plex, Singapore, 200809,
Singapore **(100%)**
Tel.: (65) 68228007
Web Site:
  http://www.emergentbiosolutions.com
Sales Range: $150-199.9 Million
Emp.: 4
Biological Product Mfr
N.A.I.C.S.: 325414

EMERGENT HEALTH CORP.
1 Marine Plz Ste 305A, North Ber-
gen, NJ 07047
Tel.: (631) 806-1420 **WY**
Web Site:
  https://emergenthealthcompany.com
Year Founded: 2018
EMGE—(OTCIQ)
Pharmaceutical Product Mfr & Distr
N.A.I.C.S.: 325412
James W. Zimbler (VP-Corp Fin)
Jim Morrison (Pres & CEO)

EMERSON ELECTRIC CO.
8000 W Florissant Ave, Saint Louis,
MO 63136
Tel.: (314) 553-2000 **MO**
Web Site: https://www.emerson.com
Year Founded: 1890
EMR—(NYSE)
Rev.: $17,492,000,000
Assets: $44,246,000,000

Liabilities: $16,737,000,000
Net Worth: $27,509,000,000
Earnings: $1,955,000,000
Emp.: 73,000
Fiscal Year-end: 09/30/24
Electric Equipment Mfr
N.A.I.C.S.: 335312
Surendral Lal Karsanbhai (Pres &
CEO)
Michael H. Train (Chief Sustainability
Officer & Sr VP)
Ram R. Krishnan (COO & Exec VP)
Elizabeth M. Adefioye (Chief People
Officer)
Michael Tang (Chief Legal Officer,
Sec & Sr VP)
Michael J. Baughman (CFO, Chief
Acctg Officer & Exec VP)
Lisa A. Flavin (Chief Compliance Offi-
cer, Chief Transformation Officer & Sr
VP)
Peter Zornio (CTO & Sr VP)
Vidya Ramnath (CMO & Sr VP)
Nick Piazza (Chief People Officer &
Sr VP)
James S. Turley (Chm)

Subsidiaries:

7AC Technologies Inc. **(1)**
100 Cummings Ctr Ste 265G, Beverly, MA
01915-6143
Tel.: (781) 574-1348
Web Site: http://www.7actech.com
Plumbing, Heating & Air-Conditioning Con-
tractors
N.A.I.C.S.: 238220
Jed Swan (CEO)

ASCO Numatics (India) Private
Limited **(1)**
H/O Factory 57 Kundrathur Main Road
Gerugambakkam Porur, Chennai, 600 128,
India
Tel.: (91) 4466337300
Motor Vehicle Parts Distr
N.A.I.C.S.: 423120

ASCO Power Technologies
Limited **(1)**
Unit 2 2 Potters Place, Skelmersdale, WN8
9PW, United Kingdom
Tel.: (44) 1628403261
Web Site: http://www.ascopower.com
Sales Range: $10-24.9 Million
Emp.: 4
Electronic Components Mfr
N.A.I.C.S.: 334419

ASCO SAS **(1)**
53 rue de la Beauce, 28110, Luce, France
Tel.: (33) 237244772
Industrial Valve Mfr
N.A.I.C.S.: 332912

Subsidiary (Non-US):

Asco Numatics, S.A. **(2)**
Poligono Brazomar s/n, 39700, Castro Ur-
diales, Spain
Tel.: (34) 942876100
Pneumatic & Electronic Control System
Distr
N.A.I.C.S.: 423830

ASCO/NUMATICS GmbH **(1)**
Otto-Hahn-Str 7-11, 75248, Olbronn-Durrn,
Germany
Tel.: (49) 72379960
Web Site: http://www.asconumatics.eu
Emp.: 200
Fluid Power & Control Equipment Distr
N.A.I.C.S.: 423690

Afag Automation Technology (Shang-
hao) Co., Ltd. **(1)**
Room 102 1/F Bldg 56 City Of Elite No
1000 Jinhai Road, Pudong New District,
Shanghai, 201206, China
Tel.: (86) 2158958065
Automation Feeding Mfr & Distr
N.A.I.C.S.: 335314

Afag GmbH **(1)**
Wernher-von-Braun-Strasse 1, D-92224,
Amberg, Germany

Tel.: (49) 9621650270
Automation Product Mfr
N.A.I.C.S.: 333111

American Governor Co. **(1)**
27 Richard Rd, Ivyland, PA 18974
Tel.: (215) 354-1144
Web Site: http://www.americangovernor.com
Turbine & Turbine Generator Set Units Mfr
N.A.I.C.S.: 333611
Scott Ginesin (Founder)

Appleton Electric, S.A. de C.V. **(1)**
Av Alfredo Del Mazo No 9, Atizapan de
Zaragoza, Ciudad Lopez Mateos, 52968,
Mexico
Tel.: (52) 5550770000
Web Site: http://www.emerson.com
Emp.: 500
Electronic Product Distr
N.A.I.C.S.: 449210

Appleton Group Canada, Ltd. **(1)**
99 Union St, Elmira, N3B 3L7, ON, Canada
Tel.: (519) 669-9222
Motor & Generator Mfr
N.A.I.C.S.: 335312

Appleton Grp LLC **(1)**
9377 W Higgins Rd, Rosemont, IL
60018 **(100%)**
Tel.: (847) 268-6000
Web Site:
  https://www.appleton.emerson.com
Sales Range: $350-399.9 Million
Emp.: 1,000
Conduit Fittings, Electrical Connectors,
Bushings & Cast Boxes for Utility & Sec-
ondary Power Distribution, Hazardous Loca-
tion Fittings, Enclosures, Motor Control &
Industrial Lighting Services
N.A.I.C.S.: 334419

Subsidiary (Non-US):

ATX S.A. **(2)**
EIN 35 Rue Andre Durouchez, 80084,
Amiens, Cedex 2, France
Tel.: (33) 322542754
Electronic Components Mfr
N.A.I.C.S.: 334419

Plant (Domestic):

Appleton Group - Cherryville **(2)**
250 Karen Ct, Cherryville, NC 28021-2140
Tel.: (704) 435-8734
Sales Range: $10-24.9 Million
Emp.: 1
Junction Boxes Sales
N.A.I.C.S.: 423610

Appleton Group - Fullerton **(2)**
2330B Artesia Ave, Fullerton, CA 92833-
2557
Tel.: (714) 525-7100
Web Site: http://www.egseg.com
Sales Range: $25-49.9 Million
Emp.: 25
Electrical Apparatus & Equipment Services
N.A.I.C.S.: 444180

Appleton Group - Memphis **(2)**
5625 Challenge Dr Ste 104, Memphis, TN
38115-5013
Tel.: (901) 794-8861
Web Site: http://www.egseg.com
Sales Range: $25-49.9 Million
Emp.: 100
Electrical Equipment & Supplies
N.A.I.C.S.: 334419

Appleton Group - South
Milwaukee **(2)**
2105 5th Ave, South Milwaukee, WI 53172-
2734
Tel.: (414) 768-6980
Web Site: http://www.egseg.com
Sales Range: $50-74.9 Million
Emp.: 150
Malleable Iron Foundry Services
N.A.I.C.S.: 335932

Appleton Group - Stephenville **(2)**
2150 West S Loop, Stephenville, TX 76401-
3922
Tel.: (254) 968-6071
Web Site: http://www.egseg.com
Sales Range: $50-74.9 Million
Emp.: 179
Outlet Boxes & Electric Wiring Devices Mfr

N.A.I.C.S.: 335932

Subsidiary (Non-US):

EGS Comercializadora Mexico, S. de
R.L. de C.V. **(2)**
Electronic Product Distr
N.A.I.C.S.: 449210

EGS Electric Group Canada Ltd. **(2)**
99 Union St, Elmira, N3B 3L7, ON,
Canada **(100%)**
Tel.: (519) 669-9222
Web Site: http://www.emerson.com
Sales Range: $25-49.9 Million
Emp.: 75
Wiring & Lighting Supplies & Equipment Mfr
& Sales
N.A.I.C.S.: 335931

Unit (Domestic):

EGS Enclosures & Controls **(2)**
13639 Aldine Westfield Rd, Houston, TX
77039-3007
Tel.: (281) 449-6271
Web Site: http://www.egs-curlee.com
Sales Range: $25-49.9 Million
Emp.: 90
Cast Electrical Enclosures & Switchracks;
Joint Venture of Emerson (55%) & SPX
(45%)
N.A.I.C.S.: 331523

Subsidiary (Domestic):

Easy Heat, Inc. **(2)**
2 Connecticut S Dr, East Granby, CT 06026
Tel.: (860) 653-1600
Web Site: http://www.easyheat.com
Sales Range: $10-24.9 Million
Emp.: 38
Electrical Heating Cables Mfr
N.A.I.C.S.: 335931

Subsidiary (Non-US):

Easy Heat Europe B.V. **(3)**
Friezenstraat 1B, 5249 JT, Rosmalen, Neth-
erlands
Tel.: (31) 735222060
Web Site: http://www.easyheat.nl
Heating Cables Units
N.A.I.C.S.: 444180

Easy Heat Ltd. **(3)**
99 Union Street, Elmira, N3B 3L7, ON,
Canada
Tel.: (519) 669-2444
Web Site: http://www.easyheat.com
Wire Product Mfr
N.A.I.C.S.: 332618

Division (Domestic):

Easy Heat, Inc. **(3)**
9377 W Higgins Rd, Rosemont, IL 60018
Tel.: (847) 268-6000
Web Site: http://www.easyheat.com
Sales Range: $10-24.9 Million
Emp.: 35
Electric Heating Cables Mfr
N.A.I.C.S.: 335931

Subsidiary (Domestic):

O-Z Gedney Company LLC **(2)**
9377 W Higgins Rd, Rosemont, IL 60018
Tel.: (847) 679-7800
Web Site: http://www.o-zgedney.com
Electrical Equipment & Supplies Mfr
N.A.I.C.S.: 333992

Subsidiary (Non-US):

Ridgid Werkzeuge AG **(2)**
Gelterkinderstrasse 24, Postfach 293, 4450,
Sissach, Switzerland
Tel.: (41) 619719562
Web Site: https://www.ridgid.eu
Sales Range: $100-124.9 Million
Machine Tools Mfr
N.A.I.C.S.: 332216

Asco Numatics Sirai Srl **(1)**
Strada per Cernusco 19, Bussero, 20060,
Milan, Italy
Tel.: (39) 02950371

Web Site: http://www.sirai.com
Emp.: 180
Industrial Valve Mfr
N.A.I.C.S.: 332911

Ascomatica S.A. de C.V. (1)
Calle 10 145 Colonia San Pedro de los Pinos, Mexico, Mexico
Tel.: (52) 5558095640
Emp.: 25
Industrial Valve Mfr
N.A.I.C.S.: 332911
Francisco Morales *(Mng Dir)*

Ascomation Pty. Ltd. (1)
12/25 Frenchs Forest Road East, Frenchs Forest Road, French's Forest, 2086, NSW, Australia (100%)
Tel.: (61) 294546400
Web Site: http://www.asco.com.au
Sales Range: $10-24.9 Million
Emp.: 20
Automatic Switches Mfr
N.A.I.C.S.: 335313
Fiona Hall *(Gen Mgr)*

Subsidiary (Domestic):

Asco Joucomatic Pty. Ltd. (2)
U 12 25 Frenchs Forest Rd Est, Frenchs Forest, Sydney, 2086, NSW, Australia
Tel.: (61) 294517077
Web Site: http://www.emerson.com
Emp.: 15
Industrial Valve Mfr
N.A.I.C.S.: 332911
Avery Lee *(Sec)*

Ascotech S.A. de C.V. (1)
Parque Industrial Progreso No 27, Mexicali, 21190, BC, Mexico
Tel.: (52) 6865559900
Web Site: http://www.ascotech.com
Sales Range: $200-249.9 Million
Emp.: 700
Gas Valves Assembler
N.A.I.C.S.: 333992

Ascoval Industria e Commercio Ltda. (1)
Rod Pres Castelo Branco Km 20 Jardim Santa Cecilia, PO Box 1010, Barueri, 06465-300, SP, Brazil (100%)
Tel.: (55) 1142081700
Web Site: http://www.ascoval.com.br
Sales Range: $10-24.9 Million
Emp.: 70
Automatic Switches for Industrial Power Applications Mfr
N.A.I.C.S.: 335313

Aspen Tech (Thailand) Ltd. (1)
47th Floor Unit 4703 1 Empire Tower South Sathorn Road, Yannawa Sathorn, Bangkok, 10120, Thailand
Tel.: (66) 26863430
Software Development Services
N.A.I.C.S.: 541511

Aspen Technology, Inc. (1)
20 Crosby Dr, Bedford, MA 01730 (57%)
Tel.: (781) 221-6400
Web Site: https://www.aspentech.com
Rev.: $1,127,482,000
Assets: $14,071,707,000
Liabilities: $1,258,852,000
Net Worth: $12,812,855,000
Earnings: ($9,771,000)
Emp.: 3,937
Fiscal Year-end: 06/30/2024
Holding Company
N.A.I.C.S.: 551112
Antonio J. Pietri *(Pres & CEO)*
Christopher Cooper *(Interim Chief Legal Officer, VP & Assoc Gen Counsel)*
David Baker *(CFO & Sr VP)*
Manish Chawla *(Chief Customer Officer & Sr VP)*

Subsidiary (Domestic):

AspenTech Corporation (2)
20 Crosby Dr, Bedford, MA 01730
Tel.: (781) 221-6400
Web Site: https://www.aspentech.com
Rev.: $709,376,000
Assets: $1,454,000,000
Liabilities: $653,243,000
Net Worth: $800,757,000
Earnings: $319,803,000

Emp.: 1,897
Fiscal Year-end: 06/30/2021
Software & Services for the Pharmaceutical, Petro Chemical, Petroleum, Metal, Electric Power, Pulp & Paper Industries
N.A.I.C.S.: 541511
Antonio J. Pietri *(Pres & CEO)*
Christopher Cooper *(Sec)*
Christopher Stagno *(CFO, Treas & VP)*
Kristie Hartley *(VP)*
Noah Davis *(VP)*
Robert Denning *(VP)*

Subsidiary (Non-US):

Aspen Technology Australia Pty Ltd. (3)
11 Queens Road Level 5, Melbourne, 3004, VIC, Australia
Tel.: (61) 398697149
Pharmaceutical, Petro Chemical, Petroleum, Metal, Electric Power, Pulp & Paper Services
N.A.I.C.S.: 541511

Aspen Technology LLC (3)
Lotte Plaza Novinskiy Boulevard Building 8, 121099, Moscow, Russia
Tel.: (7) 4959954074
Web Site: http://www.aspentech.com
Sales Range: $25-49.9 Million
Pharmaceutical, Petro Chemical, Petroleum, Metal, Electric Power, Pulp & Paper Services
N.A.I.C.S.: 541511

Aspen Technology S.A.S. (3)
Tierra Firme Carrera 9 No 115-06 Piso 17, Bogota, Colombia
Tel.: (57) 16398568
Software Development Services
N.A.I.C.S.: 541511
eEduardo Agudelo *(Sr Acct Mgr-Sls)*
Carlos Alberto Millan Obando *(Engr-Electronics-Sls)*

Aspen Technology S.L. (3)
Gran Via de les Corts Catalanes 583 5a Planta, 08011, Barcelona, Spain
Tel.: (34) 935451185
Software Development Services
N.A.I.C.S.: 541511
Luigi Branca *(Acct Mgr-Sls)*

Aspen Technology S.r.l. (3)
Lungarno Pacinotti 47, 56126, Pisa, Italy
Tel.: (39) 050931300
Software Development Services
N.A.I.C.S.: 541511
Alessandro Tripiccione *(Dir-Pro Svcs)*
Luigi Aleotti *(Dir-Bus Consulting)*

Aspen Technology WLL (3)
Bahrain Financial Harbour West Tower Building 1459, PO Box 20705, Road 4626 Block 346, Manama, Bahrain
Tel.: (973) 17 50 2747
Software & Services for the Pharmaceutical, Petro Chemical, Petroleum, Metal, Electric Power, Pulp & Paper Industries
N.A.I.C.S.: 334118

AspenTech (Beijing) Co., Ltd. (3)
Rm 801 Hyundai Motor Tower No 38 Xiaoyun Road, Chao Yang District, Beijing, 100027, China
Tel.: (86) 1059241600
Web Site: http://www.aspentech.com
Sales Range: $25-49.9 Million
Pharmaceutical, Petro Chemical, Petroleum, Metal, Electric Power, Pulp & Paper Services
N.A.I.C.S.: 541511

AspenTech (Shanghai) Co., Ltd. (3)
B8 Wison No 699 Zhongke Road Zhangjiang High-Tech Zone, Pudong, Shanghai, 2012010, China
Tel.: (86) 21 5137 5000
Pharmaceutical, Petro Chemical, Petroleum, Metal, Electric Power, Pulp & Paper Services
N.A.I.C.S.: 423430

AspenTech (Thailand) Ltd. (3)
47th Floor Unit 4703 1 Empire Tower South Sathorn Road, Yannawa Sathorn, Bangkok, 10120, Thailand
Tel.: (66) 2 686 3430
Web Site: http://www.aspentech.com

Software & Services for the Pharmaceutical, Petro Chemical, Petroleum, Metal, Electric Power, Pulp & Paper Industries
N.A.I.C.S.: 423430

AspenTech Argentina S.R.L. (3)
Ing Butty 240 4 5 Piso Suite 550, C1001AFB, Buenos Aires, Argentina
Tel.: (54) 1145902255
Software Development Services
N.A.I.C.S.: 541511

AspenTech Canada Ltd. (3)
Bow Valley Square II 3300 205-5th Avenue SW, Calgary, T2P 2V7, AB, Canada
Tel.: (403) 538-4781
Web Site: http://www.aspentech.com
Software & Services for the Pharmaceutical, Petrochemical, Petroleum, Metal, Electric Power, Pulp & Paper Industries
N.A.I.C.S.: 541511

AspenTech Europe B.V. (3)
Beech Avenue 54-80, 1119 PW, Schiphol-Rijk, Netherlands
Tel.: (31) 206586332
Pharmaceutical, Petro Chemical, Petroleum, Metal, Electric Power, Pulp & Paper Services
N.A.I.C.S.: 541511

AspenTech Europe SA/NV (3)
Twin Squares Building Vendome Culliganlaan 1b, Diegem, 1831, Brussels, Belgium
Tel.: (32) 24031770
Pharmaceutical, Petro Chemical, Petroleum, Metal, Electric Power, Pulp & Paper Services
N.A.I.C.S.: 541511

AspenTech India Pvt. Ltd. (3)
Office No 519 and 520 Fifth Floor Tower 2 World Trade Center, Opposite EON Free Zone Kharadi, Pune, 411 014, India
Tel.: (91) 2066782500
Web Site: http://www.aspentech.com
Sales Range: $25-49.9 Million
Pharmaceutical, Petro Chemical, Petroleum, Metal, Electric Power, Pulp & Paper Services
N.A.I.C.S.: 541511

AspenTech Japan Co., Ltd. (3)
Kojimachi Crystal City 10F 4-8 Kojimachi, Chiyoda-ku, Tokyo, 102-0083, Japan
Tel.: (81) 332621710
Web Site: http://www.aspentech.co.jp
Sales Range: $100-124.9 Million
Software & Services for the Pharmaceutical, Petro Chemical, Petroleum, Metal, Electric Power, Pulp & Paper Industries
N.A.I.C.S.: 541511

AspenTech Ltd. (3)
C2 Reading International Business Park Basingstoke Road, Reading, RG2 6DT, Berkshire, United Kingdom
Tel.: (44) 1189226400
Web Site: http://www.aspentech.com
Sales Range: $25-49.9 Million
Pharmaceutical, Petro Chemical, Petroleum, Metal, Electric Power, Pulp & Paper Services
N.A.I.C.S.: 541511

AspenTech Pte. Ltd. (3)
04-20/23 Galaxis 1 Fusionopolis Place, Singapore, 138522, Singapore
Tel.: (65) 63953900
Web Site: http://www.aspentech.com
Sales Range: $10-24.9 Million
Software & Services for the Pharmaceutical, Petro Chemical, Petroleum, Metal, Electric Power, Pulp & Paper Industries
N.A.I.C.S.: 541511

AspenTech S.r.l. (3)
Lungarno Pacinotti 47, 56126, Pisa, Italy
Tel.: (39) 050 931300
Web Site: http://www.aspentech.com
Pharmaceutical, Petro Chemical, Petroleum, Metal, Electric Power, Pulp & Paper Services
N.A.I.C.S.: 541511

AspenTech Software Brazil Ltda. (3)
Edificio Antonio Alves Ferreira Guedes Av Brigadeiro Faria Lima, 3729-4 andar Piso Regus, Sao Paulo, 04538-905, Brazil
Tel.: (55) 1134437270
Web Site: http://www.aspentech.com

Pharmaceutical, Petro Chemical, Petroleum, Metal, Electric Power, Pulp & Paper Services
N.A.I.C.S.: 541511

AspenTech Solutions Sdn. Bhd. (3)
Etiqa Twins Tower 2 Level 25 11 Jalan Pinang, 50450, Kuala Lumpur, Malaysia
Tel.: (60) 327269992
Pharmaceutical, Petro Chemical, Petroleum, Metal, Electric Power, Pulp & Paper Services
N.A.I.C.S.: 541511

AspenTech Venezuela, C.A. (3)
Av Francisco de Miranda Centro Lido Torre D Piso 4, Oficina 7 y 19 El Rosal, Caracas, Venezuela
Tel.: (58) 212 905 63 04
Web Site: http://www.aspentech.com
Pharmaceutical, Petro Chemical, Petroleum, Metal, Electric Power, Pulp & Paper Services
N.A.I.C.S.: 541511

AspenTech de Mexico S. de R.L. de C.V. (3)
Av Paseo de la Reforma 250 esq Niza Torre A 9th Floor Suite 991A, Col Juarez 10th Fl Office 1002, Mexico, 06600, Mexico
Tel.: (52) 5536007114
Sales Range: $25-49.9 Million
Emp.: 10
Pharmaceutical, Petro Chemical, Petroleum, Metal, Electric Power, Pulp & Paper Services
N.A.I.C.S.: 541511
Armando Calderon *(Gen Mgr)*

Subsidiary (Domestic):

AspenTech, Inc. (3)
2500 City W Blvd, Houston, TX 77042
Tel.: (281) 584-1000
Web Site: http://www.aspentech.com
Sales Range: $75-99.9 Million
Emp.: 300
Software & Services for the Pharmaceutical, Petrochemical, Petroleum, Metal, Electric Power, Pulp & Paper Industries
N.A.I.C.S.: 541511

Fidelis Group LLC (3)
122 W Way St Ste 300, Lake Jackson, TX 77566-5245
Tel.: (979) 299-0055
Web Site: http://www.fidelis-group.com
Administrative Management & General Management Consulting Services
N.A.I.C.S.: 541611
Michael Strobel *(Partner)*
Christian Kelly *(Head-Claims)*
Mark Taylor *(Sr Dir-Marine Liability Claims)*
Dustin Goodwin *(Sr Dir-Hull & Machinery Claims)*

Greenlee Tools, Inc. (1)
4455 Boeing Dr, Rockford, IL 61109-2932 (100%)
Tel.: (815) 397-7070
Web Site: https://www.greenlee.com
Wire & Cable Installation Tools
N.A.I.C.S.: 332618

Subsidiary (Domestic):

Greenlee Tools, Inc. (3)
4455 Boeing Dr, Rockford, IL 61109-2932
Tel.: (815) 397-7070
Web Site: https://www.greenlee.com
Wire & Cable Installation Tools
N.A.I.C.S.: 332618

Subsidiary (Domestic):

Greenlee Plumbing Inc. (4)
5086 Marsh Creek Ct, Braselton, GA 30517-1232
Tel.: (678) 386-7513
Web Site: https://www.greenleeplumbingatlanta.com
Pipe Line Contractors
N.A.I.C.S.: 238220

Sherman + Reilly, Inc. (4)
400 W 33rd St, Chattanooga, TN 37410-1039
Tel.: (423) 756-5300
Web Site: https://www.sherman-reilly.com
Overhead & Underground Electrical Power Lines, Equipment, Tools & Hardware Mfr

Emerson Electric Co.—(Continued)

N.A.I.C.S.: 335932

Tempo Communications, Inc. (4)
1390 Aspen Way, Vista, CA 92081
Tel.: (760) 510-0558
Web Site: http://www.tempocom.com
Test & Measurement Equipment Mfr
N.A.I.C.S.: 334515

Subsidiary (Non-US):

Tempo Europe Limited (5)
Suite 8 Brecon House William Brown Close,
Cwmbran, NP44 3AB, United Kingdom
Tel.: (44) 1633927050
Electronic Products Mfr
N.A.I.C.S.: 334419

Subsidiary (Domestic):

Mtelligence Corporation (3)
1550 Hotel Circle N Ste 120, San Diego,
CA 92108
Tel.: (619) 295-0022
Web Site: http://www.mfell.com
Emp.: 50
Industrial Equipment Monitoring & Perfor-
mance Analysis Software Publisher
N.A.I.C.S.: 513210

Subsidiary (Non-US):

SolidSim Engineering GmbH (3)
Harburger Schlossstrasse 6-12, Hamburg,
21079, Germany
Tel.: (49) 40766292360
Software Development Services
N.A.I.C.S.: 541511

AspenTech Norway AS (1)
Lysaker Torg 45, Lysaker, Norway
Tel.: (47) 94169098
Software Development Services
N.A.I.C.S.: 541511

Aventics AB (1)
Glasfibergatan 6 6TR, 125 45, Alvsjo, Swe-
den
Tel.: (46) 105109200
Pneumatic & Electronic Control System
Distr
N.A.I.C.S.: 423830

Aventics AG (1)
Neuheimstrasse 36, 8853, Lachen, Switzer-
land
Tel.: (41) 554516300
Pneumatic & Electronic Control System
Distr
N.A.I.C.S.: 423830

Aventics AS (1)
Kveldroveien 7, 1407, Vinterbro, Norway
Tel.: (47) 64918040
Pneumatic & Electronic Control System
Distr
N.A.I.C.S.: 423830
Babak Tabrizi (Chm)
Mark Syer (Gen Mgr)

Aventics B.V. (1)
Mijlstraat 22, 5281 LL, Boxtel, Netherlands
Tel.: (31) 4116511538
Pneumatic & Electronic Control System
Distr
N.A.I.C.S.: 423830

Aventics GmbH (1)
Ulmer Strasse 4, 30880, Laatzen, Germany
Tel.: (49) 51121360
Web Site: http://www.aventics.com
Pneumatic & Electronic Control System Mfr
N.A.I.C.S.: 334513
Daniel Gassmann (Mng Dir)

Aventics GmbH (1)
Traunuferstrasse 110A, 4052, Ansfelden,
Austria
Tel.: (43) 722921550
Pneumatic & Electronic Control System
Distr
N.A.I.C.S.: 423830
Holger Hanau (Gen Mgr)

Aventics Hungary Kft. (1)
Banki Donat utca 3, 3300, Eger, Hungary
Tel.: (36) 36531600
Pneumatic & Electronic Control System
Distr
N.A.I.C.S.: 423830

Istvan Godr (Mng Dir)

Aventics India Private Limited (1)
Satya Nidhi SV Building No 02 Plot No 35
1st Main2nd Phase, Peenya Industrial Area,
560058, Bengaluru, Karnataka, India
Tel.: (91) 8067727818
Pneumatic & Electronic Control System
Distr
N.A.I.C.S.: 423830

**Aventics Mexico, S. de R.L. de
C.V.** (1)
Paseo de la Reforma 295 Piso 8 Interior A
Col Cuauhtemoc, Mexico, 06500, Mexico
Tel.: (52) 5543704831
Pneumatic & Electronic Control System
Distr
N.A.I.C.S.: 423830

Aventics Oy (1)
Ayritie 12 A, 01740, Vantaa, Finland
Tel.: (358) 102774051
Pneumatic & Electronic Control System
Distr
N.A.I.C.S.: 423830
Mark Syer (Chm)
Jouni Lehtoranta (Mgr-Sls)

**Aventics Pneumatics Equipment
(Changzhou) Co., Ltd.** (1)
NO 18 Xinya Road Wujin High Tech Indus-
trial Development Zone, Changzhou, Ji-
angsu, China
Tel.: (86) 51980115329
Pneumatic & Electronic Control System
Distr
N.A.I.C.S.: 423830

**Aventics Pneumatics Trading (Shang-
hai) Co., Ltd.** (1)
Room 101A-18 Floor 2 Bulding 1 No 55 Ao
Na Road, Pilot Free Trade Zone, Shanghai,
China
Tel.: (86) 2122186196
Pneumatic & Electronic Control System
Distr
N.A.I.C.S.: 423830
Yiming Wu (Mng Dir)

Aventics S.A.S. (1)
155 Avenue de Faucigny ZI Les Fourmis,
74130, Bonneville, France
Tel.: (33) 450253545
Pneumatic & Electronic Control System
Distr
N.A.I.C.S.: 423830
Etienne Piot (Pres)

Aventics S.R.L. (1)
Piazza Maestri del Lavoro 7, 20063, Cer-
nusco sul Naviglio, Italy
Tel.: (39) 0292442501
Pneumatic & Electronic Control System
Distr
N.A.I.C.S.: 423830
Jean-Louis Tenu (Chm & Pres)

Aventics Sp. z o.o. (1)
ul Ryzowa 49, 02-495, Warsaw, Poland
Tel.: (48) 223807510
Pneumatic & Electronic Control System
Distr
N.A.I.C.S.: 423830

Aventics, spol. s.r.o. (1)
Prazska 675/10, 642 00, Brno, Czech Re-
public
Tel.: (420) 530515550
Pneumatic & Electronic Control System
Distr
N.A.I.C.S.: 423830
Tomas Borll (Gen Mgr)

Avocent Japan KK (1)
New Pier Takeshiba South Tower 7F 161
Kaigan, Minato-ku, Tokyo, 105-0022, Japan
Tel.: (81) 354038060
Web Site: http://www.avocent.co.jp
Electronic Components Distr
N.A.I.C.S.: 423690

**Beijing Rosemount Far East Instru-
ment Co., Ltd.** (1)
6 Hepingli (N) Jie, Dongcheng QU, Beijing,
100013, China
Tel.: (86) 1064282233
Sales Range: $25-49.9 Million
Emp.: 130
Industrial Control Mfr

N.A.I.C.S.: 335314

Biffi Italia S.r.l. (1)
Strada Biffi 165, Fiorenzuola d Arda, 29017,
Piacenza, Italy (100%)
Tel.: (39) 0523944411
Web Site: http://www.biffi.it
Valve Actuators Mfr
N.A.I.C.S.: 333995

**Branson Ultrasonics (Shanghai) Co.,
Ltd.** (1)
No 758 Rongle East Road, Songjiang In-
dustrial Zone, Shanghai, 201613, China
Tel.: (86) 2137819600
Web Site: http://www.emerson.cn
Measuring Device Mfr & Distr
N.A.I.C.S.: 334519

Branson de Mexico, S.A. de C.V. (1)
Carretera Nacional Km 8 5 Lote No 4,
Nuevo Laredo, 88277, Mexico
Tel.: (52) 8677110810
Electronic Components Mfr
N.A.I.C.S.: 334419

CDZ.T s.r.l. (1)
Via Ramazzotti 26/B, Saronno, 21047, Va-
rese, Italy
Tel.: (39) 02961785
Web Site: http://www.cdzt.it
Emp.: 15
Energy Management Systems Mfr
N.A.I.C.S.: 334419
Carlo Gagliardi (Gen Mgr)

Cascade Technologies Limited (1)
Glendevon House Castle Business Park,
Stirling, FK9 4TZ, Scotland, United King-
dom
Tel.: (44) 1786447721
Gas Analyzers & Industrial Process Type
Mfr
N.A.I.C.S.: 334513
Richard Cooper (Dir-Comml)

Chloride Group Limited (1)
Ebury Gate 23 Lower Belgrave Street, Lon-
don, SW1W 0NR, United Kingdom
Tel.: (44) 2078811440
Emp.: 2,540
Industrial Machinery Mfr
N.A.I.C.S.: 333310

Subsidiary (Non-US):

Chloride Koexa S.A. (2)
San Nicolas 1542, Buenos Aires,
C1407DDD, Argentina
Tel.: (54) 1146394404
Web Site: http://www.koexa.com
Electronic Product Distr
N.A.I.C.S.: 449210

**Chloride Power Protection Pty.
Ltd.** (2)
15 Telawera Rd, North Ryde, 2113, NSW,
Australia
Tel.: (61) 298881266
Electronic Components Mfr
N.A.I.C.S.: 334419

Chloride Srl (2)
Tel.: (39) 0542632111
Web Site: http://www.chloridepower.com
Electric Equipment Mfr
N.A.I.C.S.: 334419

Subsidiary (Non-US):

**Emerson Network Power Italia
Srl** (3)
Tel.: (39) 0499719111
Wiring Supplies Distr
N.A.I.C.S.: 423610

Subsidiary (Non-US):

**Emerson Network Power Industrial
Systems SAS** (2)
30 Avenue des Freres Montgolfier, BP 90,
Chassieu, 69684, France
Tel.: (33) 478401356
Electronic Equipment Mfr & Distr
N.A.I.C.S.: 334419

Subsidiary (Domestic):

Emerson Network Power SAS (3)
Batiment Liege 1 place des Etats-Unis,
94518, Rungis, France

Tel.: (33) 148844090
Web Site:
http://www.emersonnetworkpower.com
Electronic Equipment Mfr & Distr
N.A.I.C.S.: 334419

**Company Financiere de Chausey,
S.A.** (1)
Parcd Activite Des Rolandi, Dol-de-
Bretagne, 35120, France
Tel.: (33) 299482068
Electronic Product Distr
N.A.I.C.S.: 449210

**Componentes Avanzados de Mexico,
S.A. de C.V.** (1)
Fernando Baeza No 501 Sur, Ciudad Deli-
cias, 33080, CHIH, Mexico
Tel.: (52) 6394745677
Electric Equipment Mfr
N.A.I.C.S.: 334419
Luis Romero (Office Mgr)

**Computational Systems,
Incorporated** (1)
835 Innovation Dr, Knoxville, TN 37932
Tel.: (865) 675-2110
Web Site: http://www.emerson.com
Electronic Component Mfr & Distr
N.A.I.C.S.: 334419
Ronald G. Canada (Chm & CEO)

Cooper-Atkins Corporation (1)
33 Reeds Gap Rd, Middlefield, CT 06455
Tel.: (860) 349-3473
Web Site: http://www.cooper-atkins.com
Time, Temperature & Humidity Instruments
Mfr
N.A.I.C.S.: 339112
Geoffrey Grosz (Dir-Food Svc-Central &
Reg Mgr-Sls-Central)
Carol Sullivan (Dir-Food Svc-NorthEast)
Jeffrey Kautz (Dir-Food Svc-SouthEast &
East NorthCentral)
Michele Raffles (Mgr-HR & Trng)
Tony Resende (Mgr-Sls-Latin America)
Jay McEvoy (Dir-Food Processing-North
America)
Chris Ashbaugh (Dir-Healthcare Sls)
Sharon Wynkoop (Reg Mgr-Sls-East)

Plant (Domestic):

**Cooper-Atkins Corporation - Gaines-
ville Florida Facility** (2)
6911 NW 22nd St Ste B, Gainesville, FL
32653
Tel.: (860) 349-3473
Humidity Instrument Mfr
N.A.I.C.S.: 334513

Copeland Canada, Ltd. (1)
145 Sherwood Dr, Brantford, N3T 5S7, ON,
Canada (100%)
Tel.: (519) 756-6157
Web Site: http://www.copeland-corp.com
Sales Range: $50-74.9 Million
Emp.: 40
Compressor Mfr
N.A.I.C.S.: 333415

**Dar Ibtikar Al Iraq for General Ser-
vices and General Trade LLC** (1)
Al Majal Business Park I Artawi Road North
Rumaila I, Basrah, Iraq
Tel.: (964) 7827834130
Web Site: http://www2.emersonprocess.com
Emp.: 48
Electronic Components Mfr
N.A.I.C.S.: 334419

EECO, Inc. (1)
850 Library Ave, Newark, DE 19711
Tel.: (302) 456-1448
Electronic Switching System Mfr
N.A.I.C.S.: 334419

Subsidiary (Domestic):

**Emerson Electric (U.S.) Holding
Corporation** (2)
850 Library Ave, Newark, DE 19711
Tel.: (302) 292-3632
Holding Company
N.A.I.C.S.: 551112

Subsidiary (Domestic):

**Emerson Electric Overseas Finance
Corp.** (3)

8000 W Florissant Ave, Saint Louis, MO
63136
Tel.: (314) 553-2000
Financial Services
N.A.I.C.S.: 541611

**EMR Emerson Holdings (Switzerland)
GmbH** (1)
Blegistrasse 23, 6341, Baar, Switzerland
Tel.: (41) 417686111
Web Site: http://www.emersonprocess.ch
Holding Company
N.A.I.C.S.: 551112

EMR US Holdings LLC (1)
201 N Front St, Camden, NJ 08102
Tel.: (856) 583-1830
Web Site: https://us.emrgroup.com
Holding Company
N.A.I.C.S.: 551112

ESO NORD EST (1)
Za 10 Muids, Marly, 59770, France
Tel.: (33) 327299898
Emp.: 15
Electrical Equipment Supplies & Mfr
N.A.I.C.S.: 335999
Julien Fontaine *(Mng Dir)*

ESO NORMANDIE (1)
182 Avenue Jean Lagarrigue, 76530, Grand
Couronne, France
Tel.: (33) 235679500
Electrical Equipment Supplies & Mfr
N.A.I.C.S.: 335999

ESO OUEST Sarl (1)
Les Hauts De Coueron Za, Bp 38, 44220,
Coueron, France
Tel.: (33) 240867888
Electronic Product Distr
N.A.I.C.S.: 449210

ESO SUD EST Sarl (1)
Chassieu, 42100, Chassieu, France
Tel.: (33) 478732936
Emp.: 28
Fabricated Metal Component Distr
N.A.I.C.S.: 423390
Pastal Chirossel *(Gen Mgr)*

ESO SUD OUEST (1)
Za La Carrere, Saint-Vincent-de-Paul,
40990, Landes, France
Tel.: (33) 558916969
Electronic Product Distr
N.A.I.C.S.: 449210

El-O-Matic GmbH (1)
Tel.: (49) 2154499660
Web Site: http://www.emerson.com
Sales Range: $25-49.9 Million
Emp.: 25
Electric Equipment Mfr
N.A.I.C.S.: 334419

El-O-Matic Limited (1)
16-17 Beeding Close Southern Cross Trad-
ing Estate, Bognor Regis, West Sussex,
PO22 9TS, United Kingdom
Tel.: (44) 1243830363
Web Site: http://www.el-o-matic.com
Electronic Product Distr
N.A.I.C.S.: 449210

**El-O-Matic Valve Actuators (F.E.) Pte.
Ltd.** (1)
9 Gul Rd Singapore 629361, Singapore,
629361, Singapore
Tel.: (65) 62624515
Web Site: http://www.emersonprocess.com
Electronic Product Distr
N.A.I.C.S.: 449210

Elevair S.A. (1)
Avda Gral Bustamante 596, Providencia,
Chile
Tel.: (56) 27530900
Web Site: http://www.elevair.cl
Electronic Product Distr
N.A.I.C.S.: 449210

**Emergency Power Systems
Limited** (1)
Suite 16 Enterprise House Southbank Busi-
ness Park, Kirkintilloch, Glasgow, G66 1XQ,
United Kingdom
Tel.: (44) 1417751815
Web Site:
   http://www.emergencypowersystems.com
Electric Equipment Mfr

N.A.I.C.S.: 334419

Emerpowsys, S. de R.L. de C.V. (1)
Av Industrial Reynosa No 12-A, Reynosa,
88780, Tamaulipas, Mexico
Tel.: (52) 8999212991
Computer Peripheral Equipment Whslr
N.A.I.C.S.: 423430

Emerson (Taiwan) Limited (1)
3F No 122 Lane 235 Pao Chiau Rd, Xin-
Dian Dist, New Taipei City, 23145, Taiwan
Tel.: (886) 289121360
Pneumatic & Electronic Control System
Distr
N.A.I.C.S.: 423830

Emerson (Thailand) Limited (1)
555 Rasa Tower II 14th Floor Unit 1401-
1402 Phaholyothin Road, Bangkok, 21150,
Thailand
Tel.: (66) 29371190
Web Site: http://www2.emersonprocess.com
Electronic Product Distr
N.A.I.C.S.: 449210

Emerson Appliance Controls (1)
1901 S St, Elgin, IL 60123-6939
Tel.: (847) 585-8300
Web Site: http://www.emersonelectric.com
Sales Range: $25-49.9 Million
Emp.: 100
Digital Appliance Controls Engineering
N.A.I.C.S.: 334512

Emerson Argentina S.A. (1)
Avenida Maipu 660, Florida Provincia, Bue-
nos Aires, B1602AAT, Argentina
Tel.: (54) 1148377000
Web Site: http://www.emerson.com
Sales Range: $25-49.9 Million
Emp.: 93
Electronic Equipment Mfr, Sales & Market-
ing
N.A.I.C.S.: 334111

**Emerson Automation Solutions -
Germany** (1)
Nobelstrasse 14, Monchengladbach, 41189,
Germany **(100%)**
Tel.: (49) 21669550
Acuators, Valves & Spares Distr
N.A.I.C.S.: 332911

**Emerson Automation Solutions -
Netherlands** (1)
(100%)
Tel.: (31) 765434100
Web Site: http://www.emerson.com
Flow Control Products
N.A.I.C.S.: 332919

**Emerson Automation Solutions
AS** (1)
Dokkvegen 8, 3920, Porsgrunn, Norway
Tel.: (47) 35575600
Electrical Appliance Mfr
N.A.I.C.S.: 335210

**Emerson Automation Solutions Final
Control Germany GmbH** (1)
Tel.: (49) 217333480
Pneumatic & Electronic Control System
Distr
N.A.I.C.S.: 423830

**Emerson Automation Solutions Final
Control Italia S.r.l.** (1)
Via Piacenza, Lugagnano Val d'Arda,
29018, Piacenza, Italy
Tel.: (39) 0523890201
Web Site:
   https://www.vanessavalves.emerson.com
Electrical Appliance Mfr
N.A.I.C.S.: 335210

**Emerson Automation Solutions Final
Control Polska Sp. z o.o.** (1)
ul Konstruktorska 13, 02-673, Warsaw, Po-
land
Tel.: (48) 224589100
Pneumatic & Electronic Control System
Distr
N.A.I.C.S.: 423830

**Emerson Automation Solutions
GmbH** (1)
Neuhofstrasse 19a, 6340, Baar, Switzerland
Tel.: (41) 417686111

Pneumatic & Electronic Control System
Distr
N.A.I.C.S.: 423830
Simone Montada *(Dir-HR)*

**Emerson Automation Solutions Ire-
land Limited** (1)
Unit 72 Dunboyne Business Park Meath
Dunboyne, Dublin, A86 AC84, Ireland
Tel.: (353) 18013261
Electrical Appliance Mfr
N.A.I.C.S.: 335210

**Emerson Automation Solutions UK
Limited** (1)
Meridian East, Meridian Business Park 7,
Leicester, LE19 1UX, United Kingdom
Tel.: (44) 8702401978
Electrical Appliance Mfr
N.A.I.C.S.: 335210

**Emerson Beijing Instrument Co.
Ltd.** (1)
No 6 North Street He Pingli, Beijing,
100013, China
Tel.: (86) 1064282233
Fluid Meters Mfr
N.A.I.C.S.: 334519

Emerson Brazil (1)
Avenida Hollingsworth 325, Iporanga Soro-
caba, Sao Paulo, 18087-105, CEP,
Brazil **(100%)**
Tel.: (55) 1534138888
Web Site: http://www.emersonelectric.com
Sales Range: $75-99.9 Million
Emp.: 200
Mfr of Hand & Power Tools
N.A.I.C.S.: 333991

**Emerson Climate Technologies (She-
nyang) Refrigeration Co., Ltd.** (1)
10-2 No 10 Road Shenyang Economic &
Technological Development Area, She-
nyang, 110141, China
Tel.: (86) 2425506000
Web Site: http://www.emersonclimate.com
Electronic Product Distr
N.A.I.C.S.: 449210

**Emerson Climate Technologies
(South Africa) (Pty) Ltd.** (1)
Corner Precision and Staal Streets Kya
Sands, Johannesburg, South Africa
Tel.: (27) 114621740
Pneumatic & Electronic Control System
Distr
N.A.I.C.S.: 423830

**Emerson Climate Technologies (Su-
zhou) Co., Ltd.** (1)
No 69 Suhong West Road, Suzhou Indus-
trial Park, Suzhou, 215021, Jiangsu, China
Tel.: (86) 51262575505
Electrical Appliance Mfr
N.A.I.C.S.: 335210

**Emerson Climate Technologies - So-
lutions (Suzhou) Co., Ltd.** (1)
No 20 Building Chuangtou Industrial Work-
shop Yanghe Road, Suzhou Industrial Park,
Suzhou, 215122, Jiangsu, China
Tel.: (86) 51285550600
Electrical Appliance Mfr
N.A.I.C.S.: 335210

**Emerson Climate Technologies -
Transportation Solutions ApS** (1)
Axel Kiers Vej 5A, Hojbjerg, 8270, Denmark
Tel.: (45) 70234444
Web Site: http://www.emersonclimate.com
Electronic Product Distr
N.A.I.C.S.: 449210

**Emerson Climate Technologies Ara-
bia Limited Co.** (1)
7th Floor Mazen Al-Saeed Business Tower,
PO Box 3911, Al Khobar, 31952, Saudi
Arabia
Tel.: (966) 38147560
Consumer Electronics Mfr
N.A.I.C.S.: 334310

**Emerson Climate Technologies Aus-
tralia Pty. Ltd.** (1)
356 Chisholm Road, Auburn, 2137, NSW,
Australia
Tel.: (61) 297952800
Emp.: 13

Air Conditioning Equipment Distr
N.A.I.C.S.: 423730

**Emerson Climate Technologies
GmbH** (1)
Holzhauser Str 180, Berlin, 13509, Ger-
many
Tel.: (49) 3041960
Electric Equipment Mfr
N.A.I.C.S.: 336320

**Emerson Climate Technologies
GmbH** (1)
Pascalstrasse 65, 52076, Aachen, Germany
Tel.: (49) 24089290
Web Site: http://climate.emerson.com
Temperature Controls & Thermostats Mfr
N.A.I.C.S.: 334512
Jean Janssen *(Pres)*

**Emerson Climate Technologies Retail
Solutions Europe S.R.L.** (1)
Via Angelo Ramazzotti 26B, PO Box 21047,
Saronno, 21047, Varese, Italy
Tel.: (39) 02961785
Air Conditioner Accessory Distr
N.A.I.C.S.: 423620
Mark Dunson *(Pres)*

**Emerson Climate Technologies
S.r.L.** (1)
Tel.: (39) 02961781
Electric Equipment Mfr
N.A.I.C.S.: 334419

**Emerson Climate Technologies,
Inc.** (1)
1675 W Campbell Rd, Sidney, OH 45365-
0669
Tel.: (937) 498-3011
Web Site: http://www.climate.emerson.com
Condensing Units & Motor-Compressors for
Air Conditioning & Refrigeration Sales & Mfr
N.A.I.C.S.: 333415
John Shively *(Gen Counsel)*

Subsidiary (Domestic):

Computer Process Controls, Inc. (2)
1065 Big Shanty NW Rd Ste 100, Kenne-
saw, GA 30144
Tel.: (770) 425-2724
Web Site: http://www.cpcus.com
Sales Range: $75-99.9 Million
Emp.: 120
Holding Company
N.A.I.C.S.: 551112
Mark D. Dunson *(CEO)*

Control Products, Inc. (2)
1724 Lake Dr W, Chanhassen, MN 55317
Tel.: (952) 448-2217
Electronic Sensing Controls Designer & Mfr
N.A.I.C.S.: 334519

Copeland Corporation LLC (2)
500 Conrad C Harcourt Way, Rushville, IN
46173 **(100%)**
Tel.: (765) 932-2956
Web Site: http://www.copeland-corp.com
Sales Range: $25-49.9 Million
Emp.: 300
Compressors for Refrigeration & Air Condi-
tioning Equipment Mfr
N.A.I.C.S.: 333415

Subsidiary (Non-US):

**Copeland de Mexico, S.A. de
C.V.** (3)
Av Ind Falcon Lote 12 Mza-4 Pl, Reynosa,
88730, Tamaulipas, Mexico
Tel.: (52) 8992912020
Electronic Components Mfr
N.A.I.C.S.: 334419

**Emerson Climate Technologies (In-
dia) Limited** (3)
Plot No 23 Rajiv Gandhi Infotech Park
Phase - II, Hinjewadi, Pune, 411 057, Ma-
harashtra, India
Tel.: (91) 2042002000
Emp.: 100
Electric Equipment Mfr
N.A.I.C.S.: 334419

Subsidiary (Non-US):

Copeland GmbH (2)
Tel.: (49) 3041960

Emerson Electric Co.—(Continued)

Web Site: http://www.emersonclimate.eu
Sales Range: $125-149.9 Million
Emp.: 500
Refrigeration & Heating Equipment Mfr &
Sales
N.A.I.C.S.: 333415

Subsidiary (Domestic):

**Emerson Retail Services Europe
GmbH** (3)
Holzhauser Strase 180, 15366, Berlin, Germany
Tel.: (49) 304196547
Web Site: http://www.erseu.com
Sales Range: $50-74.9 Million
Emp.: 30
Electronic Services
N.A.I.C.S.: 333992

Subsidiary (Non-US):

Copeland Italia S.a.r.l. (2)
Via Ramazotti 26, 21047, Saronno, Italy
Tel.: (39) 02961781
Web Site: http://www.emersonclimate.eu
Sales Range: $50-74.9 Million
Emp.: 8
Refrigeration & Heating Equipment Sales
N.A.I.C.S.: 333415
Floriano Servizi (Mng Dir)

Unit (Domestic):

Emerson Air Comfort Products (2)
8100 W Florissant Ave Bldg T2, Saint
Louis, MO 63136-1417 (100%)
Tel.: (314) 553-5000
Web Site: http://www.emerson.com
Emp.: 25
Ceiling Fans Mfr
N.A.I.C.S.: 334514

Subsidiary (Non-US):

**Emerson Climate Technologies (Suzhou) Research & Development Co.,
Ltd.** (2)
Web Site: http://www.emerson.com
Sales Range: $150-199.9 Million
Emp.: 900
Industrial Equipment Sales & Services
N.A.I.C.S.: 425120

**Emerson Climate Technologies
Mexico SA de CV** (2)
Ing Tomas Limon Gutierrez No 3270 Col
Higuerillas 1 Seccion, Guadalajara, CP
44470, Mexico
Tel.: (52) 3336685600
Web Site: http://www.emersonclimate.com
Heating & Refrigerator Equipment Mfr
N.A.I.C.S.: 333415

Subsidiary (Domestic):

**Emerson Climate Technologies Retail
Solutions, Inc.** (2)
1065 Big Shanty Rd NW Ste 100, Kennesaw, GA 30144
Tel.: (770) 425-2724
Environmental Control Equipment Mfr
N.A.I.C.S.: 334512
Chris Tully (Mgr-Ops)

Subsidiary (Non-US):

**Emerson Climate Technologies
Sarl** (2)
8 allee du Moulin Berger, 69134, Ecully,
Cedex, France
Tel.: (33) 478668570
Sales Range: $25-49.9 Million
Emp.: 14
Refrigeration & Heating Equipment Sales
N.A.I.C.S.: 425120

Emerson Electric do Brasil Ltda (2)
Avenida Hollingsworth 325, Iporanga Sorocaba, Sao Paulo, 18087-105, Brazil
Tel.: (55) 1534138888
Web Site: https://www.emerson.com
Sales Range: $550-599.9 Million
Emp.: 1,000
Holding Company
N.A.I.C.S.: 551112

Subsidiary (Domestic):

**Emerson Comercio em Tecnologia de
Climatizacao Ltda** (3)
Avenida 1160033 4th Floor, Sao Paulo,
05578-000, Brazil
Tel.: (55) 1136186600
Web Site: http://www.emersonclimate.com
Sales Range: $25-49.9 Million
Emp.: 100
Refrigerator & Air Conditioning Equipment
Mfr
N.A.I.C.S.: 333415
Fernando Francini (Pres)

Unit (Domestic):

Emerson Flow Controls (2)
11911 Adie Rd, Maryland Heights, MO
63043-3215
Tel.: (314) 569-4500
Web Site: http://www.emersonclimate.com
Sales Range: $125-149.9 Million
Emp.: 400
Air Conditioning & Refrigeration Components Mfr & Sales
N.A.I.C.S.: 335314

Subsidiary (Non-US):

Flow Controls S.A. de C.V. (2)
Ave Industrial Falcon Lote 123, Reynosa,
Tamaulipas, Mexico
Tel.: (52) 8999216900
Web Site: http://www.flowcontrols.com
Sales Range: $75-99.9 Million
Emp.: 500
Solenoid Valves Mfr
N.A.I.C.S.: 332911

Subsidiary (Domestic):

Fusite USA (2)
6000 Fernview Ave, Cincinnati, OH
45212-1312 (100%)
Tel.: (513) 731-2020
Web Site: http://www.fusite.com
Sales Range: $50-74.9 Million
Emp.: 100
Glass-to-Metal Hermetic Seals, Connectors
& Precision Metal Stampings
N.A.I.C.S.: 334220

Division (Non-US):

Fusite Japan (3)
732 Fukasawa, Gotemba-Shi, Shizuoka,
412 0023, Japan
Tel.: (81) 550831555
Web Site: http://www.fusite.com
Glass-to-Metal Hermetic Seals & Welding
Equipment Mfr
N.A.I.C.S.: 333992

Fusite, B.V. (3)
Konigweg 16, 7602 CX, Almelo,
Netherlands (100%)
Tel.: (31) 546815520
Web Site: http://www.fusite.com
Sales Range: $125-149.9 Million
Emp.: 70
Glass-to-Metal Hermetic Seals & Welding
Equipment Mfr
N.A.I.C.S.: 333992

Division (Domestic):

Thunderline Z, Inc. (3)
11 Hazel Dr, Hampstead, NH 03841
Tel.: (603) 329-4050
Web Site: http://www.thunderlinez.com
Sales Range: $25-49.9 Million
Emp.: 25
Feedthru & Hermetic Package Mfr
N.A.I.C.S.: 334419

Subsidiary (Domestic):

Scroll Compressors LLC (2)
1675 W Campzell Rd, Sidney, OH 45365-9401
Tel.: (937) 498-3011
Web Site: http://www.copeland-corp.com
Sales Range: $350-399.9 Million
Emp.: 1,200
Refrigeration Compressor Mfr
N.A.I.C.S.: 333415

Vilter Manufacturing LLC (2)
5555 S Packard Ave, Cudahy, WI 53110-2658

Tel.: (414) 744-0111
Web Site: http://climate.emerson.com
Sales Range: $150-199.9 Million
Emp.: 340
Mfr of Industrial Refrigeration, Heat Exchange & Air Conditioning Equipment
N.A.I.C.S.: 333415

Unit (Domestic):

White-Rodgers (2)
8100 W Florissant Ave, Saint Louis, MO
63136
Tel.: (314) 553-3600
Web Site: http://www.emersonclimate.com
Sales Range: $50-74.9 Million
Emp.: 150
Thermostat Mfr
N.A.I.C.S.: 334512

Emerson Egypt LLC (1)
11 Mustafa Refaat Street Sheraton, PO Box
11799, Heliopolis, Cairo, Egypt
Tel.: (20) 22265854
Electrical Appliance Mfr
N.A.I.C.S.: 335210

Emerson Electric (Asia) Limited (1)
23/F 625 Kings Road, North Point, China
(Hong Kong) (100%)
Tel.: (852) 28271323
Web Site: http://www.emerson.com
Sales Range: $25-49.9 Million
Emp.: 25
Holding Company
N.A.I.C.S.: 551112
P. K. Yam (Pres)

Subsidiary (Non-US):

**Emerson (Philippines)
Corporation** (2)
10/F SM Cyber West Building EDSA cor
West Avenue, Barangay Bungad Diliman,
Quezon City, 1105, Philippines
Tel.: (63) 286897200
Electronic Components Mfr
N.A.I.C.S.: 334419

**Emerson Electric (China) Holding
Co., Ltd.** (1)
18th Floor Building C1 Zhiyuan Xili, Nanshan District, Shenzhen, 518000, China
Tel.: (86) 75527807953
Web Site: http://www2.emerson.com
Industrial Machinery Mfr
N.A.I.C.S.: 333310

**Emerson Electric (China) Holdings
Co., Ltd.** (1)
18th Floor Building C1 Zhiyuan Xili, Nanshan District, Shenzhen, 518000, China
Tel.: (86) 75527807953
Wob Sito: http://www.omoroon.on
Sales Range: $400-449.9 Million
Emp.: 850
Electric Equipment Mfr
N.A.I.C.S.: 333992

Emerson Electric (M) Sdn Bhd (1)
Level M2 Block A Menara PKNS-PJ Jalan
Yong Shook Lin, Petaling Jaya, 46050, Selangor, Malaysia
Tel.: (60) 379546811
Web Site: http://www.emerson.com
Electric Equipment Mfr
N.A.I.C.S.: 334513

**Emerson Electric (Malaysia) Sdn.
Bhd.** (1)
Level M2 Block A, Menara PKNS-PJ, Jalan
Yong Shook Lin, 46050, Petaling Jaya, Selangor, Malaysia
Tel.: (60) 379546811
Web Site: http://www.emerson.com
Electrical Equipment Distr
N.A.I.C.S.: 333992

**Emerson Electric (Taiwan) Company
Limited** (1)
3/F No 2 Dunhua South Road Section 1,
Taipei, Taiwan
Tel.: (886) 281617666
Air Conditioning Equipment Distr
N.A.I.C.S.: 423730

**Emerson Electric (Thailand)
Limited** (1)
34F Interlink Tower 1858/133 Debaratna
Road, Bangna-Tai Sub-District Bangna Dis-

trict, Bangkok, 10260, Thailand
Tel.: (66) 27164700
Sales Range: $250-299.9 Million
Emp.: 600
Electric Equipment Mfr
N.A.I.C.S.: 333992

Emerson Electric (U.S.) Holding Corporation (Chile) Limitada (1)
Avenida Vitacura 2736 Of, Las Condes,
Santiago, Chile
Tel.: (56) 229234200
Holding Company
N.A.I.C.S.: 551114
Cristian Merino Cabrera (Head-
Occupational Safety & Health)

Subsidiary (Domestic):

**Comercializadora Emerson Network
Power Chile Limitada** (2)
Av General Bustamante 596, Santiago,
Chile
Tel.: (56) 227530900
Electrical Equipment Whslr
N.A.I.C.S.: 423830

Subsidiary (Non-US):

Emerson Process Management Morocco SARL (2)
Casablanca Nearshore Park 1100 boulevard El Qods, 20190, Casablanca, Morocco
Tel.: (212) 5 29 044 201
Web Site: http://www2.emersonprocess.com
Electronic Product Distr
N.A.I.C.S.: 449210

**Emerson Electric Canada
Limited** (1)
66 Leek Crescent, Richmond Hill, L4B 1H1,
ON, Canada (100%)
Tel.: (905) 948-3411
Web Site: http://www.emerson.com
Sales Range: $150-199.9 Million
Emp.: 700
Industrial Process Instrumentation Mfr &
Sales
N.A.I.C.S.: 334513

Division (Domestic):

Emerson Process Management Instrument & Valve Services (2)
581 Vidal St S, Sarnia, N7T 2V8, ON,
Canada
Tel.: (519) 332-3132
Web Site: http://www.emerson.com
Sales Range: $1-9.9 Million
Emp.: 3
Instrumentation & Valve Services
N.A.I.C.S.: 811210
Tom Spector (Mng Dir)

Subsidiary (Domestic):

I Solutions Inc. (2)
Suite 900 717 7th Ave SW, Calgary, T2P
0Z3, AB, Canada
Tel.: (403) 774-1392
Web Site: http://www.isolutions.com
Data Management Consulting Services
N.A.I.C.S.: 518210

Liebert Canada (2)
151 York St, London, N6A 1A8, ON,
Canada (100%)
Tel.: (519) 645-1447
Web Site: http://www.gotoemerson.com
Sales Range: $10-24.9 Million
Emp.: 20
Warm Air Heating & Air Conditioning Services
N.A.I.C.S.: 333415

**Emerson Electric Co. (India) Private
Ltd.** (1)
6th floor Delphi Building B-Wing 604 Hiranandani Business Park, Hiranandani Gardensm Powai, Mumbai, 400 076, Maharashtra, India
Tel.: (91) 2266620566
Web Site: http://www.emerson.com
Sales Range: $25-49.9 Million
Emp.: 26
Electronic Components Mfr
N.A.I.C.S.: 334419

Emerson Electric Co. - Humboldt (1)

957 W Mullins St, Humboldt, TN 38343-
1709
Tel.: (731) 784-3611
Sales Range: $50-74.9 Million
Emp.: 240
Motors, Electric
N.A.I.C.S.: 335312

**Emerson Electric Company (India)
Private Limited** **(1)**
6th Floor Delphi Building B-Wing 604, Hi-
ranandani Business Park Hiranandani Gar-
densm Powai, Mumbai, 400076, Maharash-
tra, India
Tel.: (91) 2266620566
Industrial Machinery Mfr
N.A.I.C.S.: 333248
Giovanni Zullo *(Pres)*
Shirish Adi *(Mng Dir & VP)*
Anil Bhatia *(Mng Dir & VP)*

Emerson Electric Korea Ltd. **(1)**
5Fl NIA Building 14 Cheonggyecheon-ro,
Jung-gu, Seoul, 4520, Korea (South)
Tel.: (82) 234831500
Electric Equipment Mfr
N.A.I.C.S.: 333992

Emerson Electric Nederland BV **(1)**
Energieweg 2, 45484970, Soest, Nether-
lands
Tel.: (31) 356015551
Sales Range: $100-124.9 Million
Optical Instrument Mfr
N.A.I.C.S.: 333310

Subsidiary (Non-US):

A.P.M. Automation Solutions Ltd. **(2)**
Atidim High-Tech Ind Park Building 2, PO
Box 58171, Tel Aviv, 61580, Israel
Tel.: (972) 36488891
Web Site: http://www.apm-solutions.com
Electronic Engineering Products Mfr
N.A.I.C.S.: 541330
Yossi Rahima *(CFO)*

Alco Controls spol. s.r.o. **(2)**
K Dilnam 843, CZ 28002, Kolin, Czech Re-
public
Tel.: (420) 321737812
Hvac Solutions & Mfr
N.A.I.C.S.: 333415
Robert Miklian *(Gen Mgr)*

**EMERSON CLIMATE TECHNOLO-
GIES, s.r.o.** **(2)**
K Vapence 1633/14, Mikulov na Morave,
692 01, Mikulov, Czech Republic
Tel.: (420) 519308520
Web Site: https://21prilezitosti.cz
Air Conditioning Equipment Distr
N.A.I.C.S.: 423730

Subsidiary (Domestic):

**Emerson Automation Solutions Final
Control Netherlands B.V.** **(2)**
Patrijsweg 140, Rijswijk, Netherlands
Tel.: (31) 704136666
Pneumatic & Electronic Control System
Distr
N.A.I.C.S.: 423830

Subsidiary (Non-US):

**Emerson Network Power (Vietnam)
Co., Ltd.** **(2)**
Handi Resco Tower 13th floor Tower B 521
Kim Ma Street Ba Dinh Street, Hanoi, Viet-
nam
Tel.: (84) 437628908
Electronic Product Distr
N.A.I.C.S.: 449210

**Emerson Network Power Pakistan
(Private) Limited** **(2)**
Park Lane Tower 1st Floor, Lahore, Paki-
stan
Tel.: (92) 4236622526
Web Site:
    http://www.emersonnetworkpower.com
Sales Range: $25-49.9 Million
Emp.: 15
Electronic Equipment Supplier & Whslr
N.A.I.C.S.: 423690
Asghar Laiq *(Mng Dir)*
Cecile Cooper *(Mng Dir)*

Emerson Oradea S.R.L. **(2)**

Emp.: 8
Electronic Product Distr
N.A.I.C.S.: 449210
Calin Banciu *(Gen Mgr)*

**Emerson Process Management
(South Africa) (Proprietary) Ltd.** **(2)**
24 Angus Crescent Long Meadow Bus Es-
tate E, Johannesburg, 1616, South Africa
Tel.: (27) 114513700
Web Site: http://www.emerson.com
Sales Range: $25-49.9 Million
Emp.: 4
Automation Services
N.A.I.C.S.: 326299

Emerson S.R.L. **(2)**
Str Emerson Nr 4, Parcul Industrial Tetarom
II, Cluj-Napoca, 400641, Romania
Tel.: (40) 374132000
Web Site: http://www.emerson.ro
Electrical Equipment Component Mfr
N.A.I.C.S.: 335999

Subsidiary (Domestic):

**Fisher Rosemount Temperature
B.V.** **(2)**
Patrijsweg 140, Rijswijk, 2289 EZ, Nether-
lands
Tel.: (31) 704136666
Web Site: http://www.emerson.com
Emp.: 160
Electrical Equipment Supplies & Mfr
N.A.I.C.S.: 335999

Therm-O-Disc Europe B.V. **(2)**
Gulberg 33, Nuenen, 5674 TE, Netherlands
Tel.: (31) 402595980
Emp.: 8
Electrical Equipment Supplies & Mfr
N.A.I.C.S.: 335999

**Emerson Electric Poland Sp.
z.o.o.** **(1)**
Konstruktorska Str. 11a, 02-673, Warsaw,
Poland
Tel.: (48) 225485205
Web Site: http://www2.emersonprocess.com
Sales Range: $50-74.9 Million
Emp.: 100
Electric Equipment Mfr
N.A.I.C.S.: 444180

Subsidiary (Domestic):

**Emerson Industrial Automation Po-
land Sp. z.o.o.** **(2)**
ul Batycka 6, 61-014, Poznan, Wielkopol-
skie, Poland
Tel.: (48) 618743715
Industrial Valve Mfr
N.A.I.C.S.: 332911
Akash Gosavi *(Sr Project Engr)*
Ananda Sebastian *(Mng Dir)*
Bruno Leclercq *(Mng Dir)*
Ofir Perl *(CEO)*
Yossi Zlotnick *(CTO)*
Yossi Rahima *(CFO)*
Mordi Perl *(VP-Sls & Strategic Markets)*
Avishai Bartov *(VP-R&D)*

Emerson Electric U.K. Ltd. **(1)**
2nd Floor Accurist House, 44 Baker Street,
London, W1U 7AL, United
Kingdom **(100%)**
Tel.: (44) 2074674460
Sales Range: $100-124.9 Million
Emp.: 8
Holding Company
N.A.I.C.S.: 444180

Subsidiary (Non-US):

**Emerson Climate Technologies
FZE** **(2)**
Jebel Ali Free Zone, PO Box 26382, Dubai,
United Arab Emirates
Tel.: (971) 48118100
Emp.: 700
Electric Equipment Mfr
N.A.I.C.S.: 334419

Emerson FZE **(2)**
Jebel Ali Free Zone-South 2, PO Box
17034, Dubai, United Arab Emirates
Tel.: (971) 48118100
Web Site: http://www.emerson.com
Industrial Machinery Mfr
N.A.I.C.S.: 333310

David Sarr *(Pres)*

Emerson Saudi Arabia LLC **(2)**
3620 Building 7874 Unit 1 67th Street 2nd
Industrial City, PO Box 34332, Dammam,
Saudi Arabia
Tel.: (966) 38147560
Pneumatic & Electronic Control System
Distr
N.A.I.C.S.: 423830

**Emerson Electric de Mexico S.A. de
C.V.** **(1)**
Calle 10 145 Col San Pedro de los Pinos,
Delegacion Alvaro Obregon, 1180, Mexico,
Mexico
Tel.: (52) 5558095000
Electrical Appliance Mfr
N.A.I.C.S.: 335210

**Emerson Electronic Connector and
Components, S.A. de C.V.** **(1)**
Calle 10 No 145 Piso 3 Ala Oriente San
Pedro De Los Pinos Alvaro, Obregon,
Mexico, 1180, Mexico
Tel.: (52) 5558095100
Power Distribution & Specialty Transformer
Mfr
N.A.I.C.S.: 335311
Ramon Garcia *(Pres)*

Emerson Energy Systems **(1)**
Granvagen, PO Box 516, 82627, Bollnas,
Soderhamn, Sweden
Tel.: (46) 27076100
Web Site: http://www.emersonenergy.com
Sales Range: $75-99.9 Million
Emp.: 250
Telecommunications Equipment Mfr
N.A.I.C.S.: 334418

**Emerson Energy Systems Argentina
S.A.** **(1)**
Avenida Maipu 660, Florida, B1602AAT,
Buenos Aires, Argentina
Tel.: (54) 11 4837 7000
Sales Range: $900-999.9 Million
Electrical Systems Mfr
N.A.I.C.S.: 333992

**Emerson Industrial Automation Bel-
gium NV** **(1)**
Blarenberglaan 23 Industrial Zone North,
2800, Mechelen, Belgium
Tel.: (32) 15281010
Industrial Automation Control System Mfr
N.A.I.C.S.: 334513
Marc Van Tricht *(Mgr-Bus Dev)*

**Emerson Industrial Automation Italy
SpA** **(1)**
Via Giacomo Brodolini 7, Rozzano, 20089,
Milan, Italy
Tel.: (39) 02575751
Industrial Automation Control System Mfr
N.A.I.C.S.: 334513
Daniele Carraro *(Engr-Sls)*

Emerson Japan Ltd. **(1)**
Takehiba S Tower 7th Fl, Tokyo, 105 0022,
Japan **(100%)**
Tel.: (81) 354032900
Web Site: http://www.emerson.co.jp
Sales Range: $100-124.9 Million
Emp.: 400
Hand & Power Tool Mfr
N.A.I.C.S.: 333991

Emerson Japan, Ltd. **(1)**
(100%)
Web Site: http://www.emerson.co.jp
Sales Range: $50-74.9 Million
Emp.: 400
Industrial Process Controls & Instrumenta-
tion Products Mfr
N.A.I.C.S.: 334513

Division (Domestic):

**Emerson Japan, Ltd., Fusite
Division** **(2)**
732 Fukasawa Gotemba-Shi, Shizuoka, 412
0023, Japan **(100%)**
Tel.: (81) 550831555
Web Site: http://www.emerson.co.jp
Sales Range: $25-49.9 Million
Emp.: 100
Industrial Electric & Vibratory Welding
Equipment & Ultrasonic Cleaning Equip-
ment Mfr

N.A.I.C.S.: 333992

**Emerson Junkang Enterprise (Shang-
hai) Co., Ltd.** **(1)**
No 832 Xin Zhu Road, Minhang District,
Shanghai, 200010, China
Tel.: (86) 2154386003
Web Site: http://www.junkang.com
Electronic Product Distr
N.A.I.C.S.: 449210

**Emerson Machinery & Equipment
(Shenzhen) Co., Ltd.** **(1)**
District 68 Hongliang North Second Road,
Baoheng Technology Industrial Park Baoan
District, Shenzhen, 518101, China
Tel.: (86) 75529746888
Industrial Machinery Mfr
N.A.I.C.S.: 333310

**Emerson Mexico Finance, S.A. de
C.V., SOFOM, ENR** **(1)**
Calle 10 145 Col San Pedro de los Pinos,
Mexico, Mexico
Tel.: (52) 5558095000
Web Site: http://www.emersonsofom.com
Financial Services
N.A.I.C.S.: 523940

**Emerson Network Power (Philip-
pines), Inc.** **(1)**
29/F The Orient Square Building F Ortigas
Jr Road Ortigas Center, Pasig, 1605, Philip-
pines
Tel.: (63) 27207400
Electronic Product Distr
N.A.I.C.S.: 449210

**Emerson Network Power (South Af-
rica) (Pty) Ltd** **(1)**
Sunninghill, Johannesburg, 2157, South
Africa
Tel.: (27) 112578500
Web Site: http://www.emerson.com
Sales Range: $25-49.9 Million
Emp.: 15
Industrial Machinery Mfr
N.A.I.C.S.: 333998

**Emerson Network Power - Embedded
Computing GmbH** **(1)**
Lilienthalstr 17-19, Neubiberg, 85579, Mu-
nich, Germany
Tel.: (49) 8996082430
Electronic Components Distr
N.A.I.C.S.: 423690
Kay Geldeldmacher *(Pres)*

**Emerson Network Power Co.,
Ltd.** **(1)**
Bldg 5 Vision Business Park 9th Gaoxin
Blvd South Science & Industrial, NanShan,
Shenzhen, 518057, China
Tel.: (86) 75586010808
Web Site:
    http://www.emersonnetworkpower.com
Data Network Power Conversion System
Mfr
N.A.I.C.S.: 333310

**Emerson Network Power Enterprise
Srl** **(1)**
Via Leonardo da Vinci 16/18, Piove di
Sacco, 35028, Padua, Italy
Tel.: (39) 0499719111
Electronic Components Mfr
N.A.I.C.S.: 334419

**Emerson Network Power Guc
Sistemleri Limited Sirketi** **(1)**
Serisali 3 Turcan 3, Istanbul, 34775, Turkiye
Tel.: (90) 2165867900
Eletric Power Generation Services
N.A.I.C.S.: 221118

**Emerson Network Power Sp.
z.o.o.** **(1)**
Ul Konstruktorska 11A, Warsaw, 2673, Po-
land
Tel.: (48) 224589273
Web Site:
    http://www.emersonnetworkpower.com
Electronic Product Distr
N.A.I.C.S.: 449210

**Emerson Network Power do Brasil
Ltda** **(1)**
Av Embaixador Macedo Soares 10735 5
andar Vila Anastacio, Sao Paulo, 05095-

Emerson Electric Co.—(Continued)

035, Brazil
Tel.: (55) 1136186600
Web Site:
http://www.emersonnetworkpower.com.br
Electronic Components Mfr
N.A.I.C.S.: 334419

Emerson Pacific Pte. Ltd. **(1)**
1 Pandan Crescent, Singapore, 128461,
Singapore
Tel.: (65) 636377666
Mfr & Marketing of Electric Motors
N.A.I.C.S.: 335312

Emerson Paradigm Holding LLC **(1)**
Two Memorial Plz 820 Gessner Ste 400,
Houston, TX 77024
Tel.: (713) 393-4800
Web Site: http://www.pdgm.com
Software Development Services
N.A.I.C.S.: 513210

Emerson Process Management **(1)**
8100 W Florissant Ave K- Annex, Saint
Louis, MO 63136
Tel.: (314) 553-1900
Web Site: http://www.emersonprocess.com
Rev.: $6,652,000,000
Emp.: 70
Automatic Regulating & Control Valves
N.A.I.C.S.: 541611

Subsidiary (Domestic):

El-O-Matic USA, Inc. **(2)**
9009 King Palm Dr, Tampa, FL 33619
Tel.: (813) 319-0266
Web Site: http://www.emersonprocess.com
Sales Range: $25-49.9 Million
Emp.: 15
Pneumatic & Electric Actuators & Control
Accessories
N.A.I.C.S.: 333995

Electrical Reliability Services,
Inc. **(2)**
Ste 417 6900 Koll Center Pkwy, Pleasan-
ton, CA 94566-3157 **(100%)**
Tel.: (925) 824-0330
Sales Range: $1-9.9 Million
Emp.: 6
Electrical Testing & Maintenance
N.A.I.C.S.: 811210

Division (Domestic):

Electrical Reliability Services,
Inc. **(3)**
14141 Airline Hwy Ste W, Baton Rouge, LA
70817
Tel.: (225) 755-0530
Web Site: http://www.electro-test.com
Electrical Maintenance & Service
N.A.I.C.S.: 541330

Electrical Reliability Services,
Inc. **(3)**
3412 South 1400 West Unit A, West Valley
City, UT 84119
Tel.: (801) 281-8321
Electric Power Systems Contractors
N.A.I.C.S.: 561499

Electrical Reliability Services,
Inc. **(3)**
1012 NE Jib Ct Ste B, Lees Summit, MO
64064
Tel.: (702) 597-0020
Sales Range: $1-9.9 Million
Emp.: 300
Electrical Equipment Repair Services
N.A.I.C.S.: 811210
Grege Smith (Gen Mgr)

Electrical Reliability Services,
Inc. **(3)**
8500 Washington St NE Ste A, Albuquer-
que, NM 87113-1669
Tel.: (505) 822-0237
Web Site: http://www.electricalreliability.com
Sales Range: $1-9.9 Million
Electrical Testing
N.A.I.C.S.: 811210

Electrical Reliability Services,
Inc. **(3)**
4099 SE International Way Ste 201, Portland, OR 97222-8853 **(100%)**

Tel.: (503) 653-6781
Sales Range: $1-9.9 Million
Emp.: 17
Inspection & Testing Services
N.A.I.C.S.: 811210

Electrical Reliability Services,
Inc. **(3)**
7100 Broadway Ste 7E, Denver, CO
80221-2900 **(100%)**
Tel.: (303) 427-8809
Sales Range: $1-9.9 Million
Inspection & Testing Services
N.A.I.C.S.: 811210

Subsidiary (Domestic):

Emerson Instrument & Valve
Services **(2)**
1821 Austin St, Midland, MI
48642-5964 **(100%)**
Tel.: (989) 495-9126
Web Site: http://www.emersonprocess.com
Sales Range: $1-9.9 Million
Emp.: 2
Industrial Equipment Services
N.A.I.C.S.: 811210

Emerson Machinery Health Manage-
ment Company **(2)**
835 Innovation Dr, Knoxville, TN 37932-
2563
Tel.: (865) 675-2400
Web Site: http://www.compsys.com
Sales Range: $75-99.9 Million
Reliability Based Maintenance Products &
Services for Industrial Rotating & Recipro-
cating Machinery
N.A.I.C.S.: 334519

Division (Domestic):

Emerson Process Management **(3)**
835 Innovation Dr, Knoxville, TN
37932-2563 **(100%)**
Tel.: (865) 675-2400
Web Site:
http://www.emersonprocessmanage
ment.com
Sales Range: $100-124.9 Million
Emp.: 210
Consulting & Management Training
N.A.I.C.S.: 541330

Division (Domestic):

Emerson Process Management
CSI **(4)**
370 Baldwin Tower Blvd, Eddystone, PA
19022-1329 **(100%)**
Tel.: (610) 490-3219
Web Site: http://www.compsys.com
Sales Range: $1-9.9 Million
Emp.: 7
Engineering Maintenance Services
N.A.I.C.S.: 541330

Subsidiary (Non-US):

Emerson Process Management Dis-
tribution N.V. **(3)**
Research Pk Interleuvenlaan 50, B 3001,
Leuven, Belgium **(100%)**
Tel.: (32) 16741471
Web Site: http://www.compsys.com
Sales Range: $1-9.9 Million
Emp.: 12
Product Application & Management Training
Services; Management Consulting Services;
Engineering Services
N.A.I.C.S.: 541330

Subsidiary (Non-US):

Emerson Process Management **(2)**
Aaderupvej 41, Naestved, 4700,
Denmark **(100%)**
Tel.: (45) 70253051
Web Site: http://www.emersonprocess.com
Sales Range: $1-9.9 Million
Industrial Process & Control Instrumentation
Services
N.A.I.C.S.: 334513

Emerson Process Management **(2)**
Via Montello 71 73, 20831, Seregno,
Italy **(100%)**
Tel.: (39) 036222851
Web Site: http://www.emersonprocess.com

Sales Range: $125-149.9 Million
Emp.: 200
Electrical Products Distr
N.A.I.C.S.: 444180

Emerson Process Management **(2)**
200-110 Quarry Pk Blvd SE, Calgary, T2C
3G3, AB, Canada **(100%)**
Tel.: (403) 258-6200
Web Site: http://www.emersonprocess.com
Sales Range: $75-99.9 Million
Engineering Services
N.A.I.C.S.: 541330

Subsidiary (Domestic):

Emerson Process Management **(2)**
1100 W Louis Henna Blvd Bldg 1, Round
Rock, TX 78681
Tel.: (512) 835-2190
Web Site: http://www.emersonprocess.com
Sales Range: $200-249.9 Million
Relays & Industrial Controls Research &
Development
N.A.I.C.S.: 518210

Division (Domestic):

Daniel Measurement & Control
Inc. **(3)**
11100 Brittmoore Park Dr, Houston, TX
77041
Tel.: (713) 467-6000
Custody Transfer & Flow Measurement
Products
N.A.I.C.S.: 334513

Holding (Non-US):

Daniel Canada **(4)**
Ste 114 4215 72nd Ave Southeast, Calgary,
T2C 2G5, AB, Canada **(100%)**
Tel.: (403) 279-1879
Web Site: http://www.daniel.com
Sales Range: $10-24.9 Million
Emp.: 35
Flow Measurement Products Mfr
N.A.I.C.S.: 334513

Subsidiary (Non-US):

Daniel Industries Canada Inc. **(4)**
4215 72 Ave SE Ste 114, Calgary, T2C
2G5, AB, Canada
Tel.: (403) 279-1879
Oil Well Equipment Distr
N.A.I.C.S.: 423830
Fred Knoll (Pres)

Subsidiary (Domestic):

Daniel Measurement Control **(4)**
9750 W Sam Houston Pkwy N Ste 100,
Houston, TX 77064
Tel.: (346) 509-3700
Web Site: https://www.daniel.com
Sales Range: $10-24.9 Million
Emp.: 6
Sales of Valves & Fittings
N.A.I.C.S.: 423830

Emerson Process Management **(4)**
18703 G H Cir, Waller, TX 77484-0508
Tel.: (281) 727-5300
Web Site: http://www.emersonprocess.com
Sales Range: $75-99.9 Million
Emp.: 153
Mfr & Marketer of Valve Actuators & Con-
trols
N.A.I.C.S.: 332912

Holding (Non-US):

Bettis Canada Ltd. **(5)**
4112 91 A Street, Edmonton, T6E 5V2, AB,
Canada **(100%)**
Tel.: (780) 450-3600
Web Site: http://www.emersonprocess.com
Sales Range: $50-74.9 Million
Emp.: 3
Valve Actuators Mfr & Sales
N.A.I.C.S.: 332919

Emerson Process Management-Valve
Automation **(5)**
4112 - 91A St, Edmonton, T6E 5V2, AB,
Canada **(50%)**
Tel.: (780) 450-3600
Web Site: http://www.emersonprocess.com

Sales Range: $10-24.9 Million
Emp.: 40
Valve Sales
N.A.I.C.S.: 336310

Unit (Domestic):

Emerson Process Management **(2)**
835 Innovation Dr, Knoxville, TN
37932 **(100%)**
Tel.: (865) 675-2110
Web Site: http://www.emersonprocess.com
Sales Range: $50-74.9 Million
Vibration Equipment Training & Mfr
N.A.I.C.S.: 611710

Emerson Process Management **(2)**
2500 Park Ave W, Mansfield, OH 44906
Tel.: (419) 529-4311
Web Site: http://www.emersonprocess.com
Sales Range: $50-74.9 Million
Hydraulic Valves Mfr
N.A.I.C.S.: 332912

Subsidiary (Non-US):

Emerson Process Management
AG **(2)**
Neuhofstrasse 19 A, 6340, Baar,
Switzerland **(100%)**
Tel.: (41) 417686111
Web Site: http://www.emersonprocess.com
Sales Range: $25-49.9 Million
Holding Company; Aerospace & Process
Measurement Instruments
N.A.I.C.S.: 334513

Subsidiary (Non-US):

Emerson LLC **(3)**
Bahra bld block B office 8 35 Badamdar
Highway, AZ 1023, Baku, Azerbaijan
Tel.: (994) 124982448
Web Site: http://www.emersonprocess.ru
Sales Range: $10-24.9 Million
Emp.: 14
Electronic Components Mfr
N.A.I.C.S.: 334419
Agabala Alesjerov (Gen Mgr)

Emerson Process Management
AB **(3)**
Korkarlsvagen 8, Box 1053, 651 15, Karl-
stad, Sweden
Tel.: (46) 54172700
Web Site: http://www.emerson.com
Sales Range: $25-49.9 Million
Emp.: 65
Industrial Equipment Sales & Services
N.A.I.C.S.: 425120

Subsidiary (Non-US):

Emerson Process Management
A/S **(4)**
Generatorvej 8A 2 sal, 2860, Soborg, Den-
mark
Tel.: (45) 70253051
Web Site: http://www.emerson.com
Sales Range: $25-49.9 Million
Emp.: 12
Industrial Machinery & Equipment Whslr
N.A.I.C.S.: 423830

Subsidiary (Non-US):

Emerson Process Management
AS **(3)**
Dokkvegen 8 PO Box 204 3920, 3946,
Porsgrunn, Norway
Tel.: (47) 35575600
Web Site: http://www.emersonprocess.ru
Sales Range: $10-24.9 Million
Emp.: 60
Automation Technology & Services
N.A.I.C.S.: 334512
Osgeir Knuesen (Gen Mgr)

Emerson Process Management
GmbH & Co. OHG **(3)**
Argelsrieder Feld 3, 82234, Wesseling, Ger-
many
Tel.: (49) 81539390
Web Site: http://www.emersonprocess.com
Sales Range: $25-49.9 Million
Emp.: 180
Automation Technology & Services
N.A.I.C.S.: 334512
Richard Heinkel (Mng Dir)

Emerson Process Management GmbH & Co. OHG (3)
Rheinische Strasse 2, Haan, 42781, Germany (100%)
Tel.: (49) 21295530
Web Site: http://www.emersonprocess.com
Sales Range: $1-9.9 Million
Emp.: 250
Industrial Flow Meters Mfr
N.A.I.C.S.: 334513

Emerson Process Management Kft. (3)
Hungaria krt 166-168, 1146, Budapest, Hungary
Tel.: (36) 14624000
Web Site: http://www.emersonprocess.hu
Electronic Components Mfr
N.A.I.C.S.: 334419

Emerson Process Management Romania S.R.L. (3)
2 4 Gara Herastrau Street, Bucharest, 20334, Romania
Tel.: (40) 212062500
Web Site: http://www.emerson.com
Sales Range: $25-49.9 Million
Emp.: 40
Engineeering Services
N.A.I.C.S.: 541330

Emerson Process Management Ticaret Limited Sirketi (3)
Tel.: (90) 2165739848
Electronic Product Distr
N.A.I.C.S.: 449210

Emerson Process Management sp. z.o.o. (3)
ul Konstruktorska 13, 02-673, Warsaw, Poland
Tel.: (48) 224589200
Emp.: 100
Electronic Product Distr
N.A.I.C.S.: 449210
Marek Pienkowske (Pres)

Subsidiary (Non-US):

Emerson Process Management UAB (4)
Pilies str 8, LT-91234, Klaipeda, Lithuania
Tel.: (370) 68798334
Web Site: http://www.emersonprocess.com
Electronic Product Distr
N.A.I.C.S.: 449210

Subsidiary (Non-US):

Emerson Sweden AB (3)
Layoutvagen 01, Gothenburg, 43533, Sweden
Tel.: (46) 313370000
Web Site: http://www.emerson.com
Emp.: 350
Holding Company
N.A.I.C.S.: 551112

Subsidiary (Domestic):

Emerson Network Power AB (4)
Textilgatan 29, Stockholm, 120 30, Sweden
Tel.: (46) 87216000
Web Site: http://www.emerson.com
Emp.: 60
Industrial Machinery & Equipment Whslr
N.A.I.C.S.: 423690

Emerson Process Management (4)
Layoutvagan 1, PO Box 13045, 43533, Molnlycke, Sweden
Tel.: (46) 313370000
Web Site: http://www.emersonprocess.com
Sales Range: $125-149.9 Million
Emp.: 400
Marine & Tank Gauging Mfr
N.A.I.C.S.: 332420

Subsidiary (Non-US):

Emerson Process Management Asia Pacific Pte Ltd (2)
1 Pandan Crescent, Singapore, 128461, Singapore
Tel.: (65) 67778211
Web Site:
  http://www.ap.emersonprocess.com
Sales Range: $125-149.9 Million
Emp.: 650
Process Control Instruments Mfr

N.A.I.C.S.: 334513

Subsidiary (Non-US):

Emerson Process Management Australia Pty Limited (3)
471 Mountain Highway, Bayswater, 3153, VIC, Australia
Tel.: (61) 397210200
Web Site: http://www.emerson.com
Sales Range: $25-49.9 Million
Emp.: 150
Process Control Instruments Mfr
N.A.I.C.S.: 334513

Subsidiary (Non-US):

Emerson Process Management Distribution Ltd. (2)
Meridian Business Park, Meridian East, Leicester, LE19 1UX, Leics, United Kingdom
Tel.: (44) 8702401978
Web Site: http://www.emersonprocess.co.uk
Sales Range: $50-74.9 Million
Emp.: 200
Electrical Equipment Distr
N.A.I.C.S.: 444180

Emerson Process Management Japan Ltd. (2)
Seavans N Building 17F 1-2-1 Shibaura, Minato, Tokyo, 105-0023, Japan
Tel.: (81) 345726800
Sales Range: $25-49.9 Million
Emp.: 180
Process Control Equipment Mfr
N.A.I.C.S.: 334519
Kosuki Akila (Gen Mgr)

Emerson Process Management Limited (2)
Horsfield Way, Stockport, SK6 2SU, United Kingdom
Tel.: (44) 8702401978
Web Site: http://www.emersonprocess.co.uk
Sales Range: $10-24.9 Million
Emp.: 80
Industrial Measurement & Control Instruments Mfr
N.A.I.C.S.: 334513

Division (Domestic):

Emerson Process Management Limited (3)
Meridian East, Meridian Business Park, Leicester, United Kingdom
Tel.: (44) 8702401978
Measurement & Pressure Instruments Mfr
N.A.I.C.S.: 334513

Subsidiary (Domestic):

Groveley Detection Limited (4)
Unit 18 Somerford Business Park Wilverley Road, Christchurch, BH23 3RU, Dorsetshire, United Kingdom
Tel.: (44) 1202400630
Web Site: http://www.groveley.com
Gas Detector Mfr
N.A.I.C.S.: 334519

Subsidiary (Domestic):

Emerson Process Management Shared Services Limited (3)
Health Place, Bognor Regis, PO22 9SH, United Kingdom
Tel.: (44) 1243863121
Web Site: http://www.emersonprocess.com
Measuring & Control Devices Mfr
N.A.I.C.S.: 334519

K Controls Limited (3)
Pit Hey Place West Pimbo, Skelmersdale, WN8 9PG, Lancashire, United Kingdom
Tel.: (44) 1695713684
Web Site: http://www.k-controls.co.uk
Electrical Equipment & Component Mfr
N.A.I.C.S.: 335999

Subsidiary (Domestic):

Emerson Process Management Regulator Technologies Tulsa, LLC (2)
9932 E 58th St, Tulsa, OK 74146-6411
Tel.: (918) 622-6161
Web Site: http://www.enardo.com

Safety & Environmental Vapor Control Equipment Developer & Mfr
N.A.I.C.S.: 332911

Emerson Process Management Regulator Technologies, Inc. (2)
3200 Emerson Way, McKinney, TX 75070
Tel.: (972) 548-3574
Web Site: http://www2.emersonprocess.com
Electric Equipment Mfr
N.A.I.C.S.: 334419

Emerson Process Management Rosemount Inc. (2)
8200 Market Blvd, Chanhassen, MN 55317-9685
Tel.: (952) 941-5560
Web Site: http://www.rosemount.com
Sales Range: $700-749.9 Million
Industrial Instrumentation Mfr
N.A.I.C.S.: 334513

Division (Domestic):

Dieterich Standard Inc. (3)
5601 N 71st St, Boulder, CO 80301 (100%)
Tel.: (303) 530-9600
Web Site: http://www.rosemount.com
Sales Range: $25-49.9 Million
Emp.: 100
Process Control Instruments & Flow Measuring Devices Mfr
N.A.I.C.S.: 334513

Emerson Process Management (3)
2580 E Federal Dr Ste 407, Decatur, IL 62526-2149
Tel.: (217) 877-5278
Web Site:
  http://www.emersonprocessmanagement.com
Sales Range: $1-9.9 Million
Emp.: 3
Airspeed Instrumentation
N.A.I.C.S.: 541330

Emerson Process Management (3)
300-2 Jacobson Dr, Poca, WV 25159
Tel.: (304) 746-0123
Web Site: http://www.emersonelectric.com
Sales Range: $50-74.9 Million
Emp.: 4
Process Instruments Service
N.A.I.C.S.: 236118

Emerson Process Management Power & Water Solutions (3)
200 Beta Dr, Pittsburgh, PA 15238
Tel.: (412) 963-4000
Web Site: http://www.emerson.com
Sales Range: $150-199.9 Million
Emp.: 600
Industrial Control Mfr
N.A.I.C.S.: 335314

Emerson Process Management Rosemount & Micro Motion Division (3)
17630 Perkins Rd, Baton Rouge, LA 70810-3827 (100%)
Tel.: (225) 756-7000
Web Site: http://www.emersonprocess.com
Sales Range: $25-49.9 Million
Emp.: 10
Instrumentation Mfr
N.A.I.C.S.: 449210

Subsidiary (Domestic):

Emerson Process Management Rosemount Inc (3)
103 Enterprise Dr, Royersford, PA 19468
Tel.: (610) 495-1827
Web Site: http://www.emersonprocess.com
Sales Range: $25-49.9 Million
Emp.: 15
Electrical Apparatus & Equipment Mfr & Sales
N.A.I.C.S.: 423610

Division (Domestic):

Rosemount Inc. (3)
4400 Muhlhauser Rd, Fairfield, OH 45011 (100%)
Tel.: (513) 851-5555
Web Site: http://www.emersonprocess.com
Sales Range: $10-24.9 Million
Emp.: 6
Industrial Instrumentation Services

N.A.I.C.S.: 423830

Subsidiary (Non-US):

Emerson Asia Pacific Private Limited (4)
No 1 Pandan Crescent, Singapore, 128461, Singapore
Tel.: (65) 67778211
Motor & Generator Mfr
N.A.I.C.S.: 335312

Emerson Process Management Oy (4)
Uutistie 3C, 01770, Vantaa, Finland
Tel.: (358) 201111200
Web Site: https://www.emerson.com
Industrial Machinery & Equipment Whslr
N.A.I.C.S.: 423830

Emerson Process Management, S.L. (4)
Calle De Francisco Gervas 1, Alcobendas, 28108, Madrid, Spain
Tel.: (34) 913586000
Web Site: http://www.emersonprocess.com
Emp.: 100
Non-Durable Goods Whslr
N.A.I.C.S.: 424990

Subsidiary (Domestic):

Rosemount China Inc. (4)
12001 Technology Dr, Eden Prairie, MN 55344-3620
Tel.: (952) 941-5560
Electrical Equipment Supplies & Mfr
N.A.I.C.S.: 335999

Branch (Domestic):

Rosemount Inc. (4)
6135 Lake View Rd Ste 500, Charlotte, NC 28269 (100%)
Tel.: (704) 598-5660
Web Site: http://www.rosemount.com
Sales Range: $25-49.9 Million
Emp.: 20
Instruments & Control Equipment Mfr & Sales
N.A.I.C.S.: 423830

Subsidiary (Domestic):

Rosemount Specialty Products LLC (4)
5545 Nelpar Dr, East Wenatchee, WA 98802
Tel.: (509) 881-2100
Electrical Products Mfr
N.A.I.C.S.: 334513
Gary Huntley (Mgr-Design Engrg)

Subsidiary (Domestic):

Rosemount Nuclear Instruments (3)
8200 Market Blvd, Chanhassen, MN 55317-3620
Tel.: (952) 949-5200
Web Site: http://www.rosemountnuclear.com
Sales Range: $10-24.9 Million
Emp.: 45
Nuclear Reactor Controls
N.A.I.C.S.: 334513

Division (Domestic):

Rosemount Tank Gauging North America, Inc. (3)
6005 Rogerdale Rd, Houston, TX 77072
Tel.: (281) 879-2699
Web Site: http://www.emerson.com
Electrical Equipment Supplies & Mfr
N.A.I.C.S.: 335999

Subsidiary (Domestic):

Spectrex, Inc. (3)
6021 Innovation Blvd, Shakopee, MN 55379
Tel.: (973) 239-8398
Web Site: http://www.spectrex.net
Flame & Open Path Gas Detectors Mfr
N.A.I.C.S.: 334519

Subsidiary (Non-US):

Emerson Process Management bv (2)
Patrijsweg 140, Postbus 212, 2280 AE, Rijswijk, Netherlands (100%)

Emerson Electric Co.—(Continued)

Tel.: (31) 704136666
Web Site: http://www.emerson.com
Sales Range: $50-74.9 Million
Emp.: 250
Industrial Process & Control Instrumentation Services
N.A.I.C.S.: 334513
G. Wink *(Mng Dir)*

Emerson Process Management s.r.o. (2)
Hajkova 22, Prague, Czech Republic
Tel.: (420) 271035600
Web Site: http://www.emersonprocess.com
Sales Range: $900-999.9 Million
Emp.: 52
Machinery Repair, Service & Sales
N.A.I.C.S.: 333992

Subsidiary (Domestic):

Emerson Process Management, Valve Automation Division (2)
9009 King Palm Dr, Tampa, FL 33619-8364
Tel.: (813) 630-2255
Web Site: http://www.emersonprocess.com
Sales Range: $25-49.9 Million
Emp.: 25
Electronic Parts Mfr & Sls
N.A.I.C.S.: 423690

Subsidiary (Domestic):

Emerson Process Management Valve Actuation LLC (2)
19200 NW Hwy, Houston, TX 77065-1005
Tel.: (281) 499-1561
Web Site: http://www.emerson.com
Industrial Valves & Aircraft Mfr
N.A.I.C.S.: 332911
John Drisko *(CMO)*

Subsidiary (Non-US):

Emerson Process Management-Valve Automation (2)
6 Bracken Hill Southwest Industrial Estate, Peterlee, Durham, SR8 2LS, United Kingdom
Tel.: (44) 1915180020
Web Site: http://www.emersonprocess.com
Sales Range: $25-49.9 Million
Emp.: 15
Actuators, Valve Automation Repairs, Modifications, Testing & Commissioning Mfr & Sales
N.A.I.C.S.: 332911

Subsidiary (Domestic):

Emerson Remote Automation Solutions (2)
1100 Buckingham St, Watertown, CT 06795-6602
Tel.: (860) 945-2200
Web Site: http://www.emerson.com
Sales Range: $75-99.9 Million
Electronic Industrial Process Control Equipment Mfr
N.A.I.C.S.: 334513

Subsidiary (Non-US):

Bristol Babcock AB (3)
Kokillgatan 1, 721 33, Vasteras, Sweden
Tel.: (46) 21350450
Web Site: http://www.bbsweden.com
Electronic Industrial Process Control Equipment Mfr
N.A.I.C.S.: 334513

Subsidiary (US):

Emerson Instrument & Valve Service (4)
4400 Mulhauser Rd, Fairfield, OH 45011-9708
Tel.: (513) 942-1118
Web Site: http://www.emersonprocess.com
Sales Range: $10-24.9 Million
Emp.: 13
Industrial Valve Repair Services
N.A.I.C.S.: 811210

Branch (US):

Fisher Controls International (4)

4725 Highway 75 S, Sherman, TX 75090 **(100%)**
Tel.: (903) 868-3200
Web Site: http://www.emerson.com
Sales Range: $75-99.9 Million
Emp.: 350
Hydraulic & Pneumatic Control Valves Fluid Power Mfr
N.A.I.C.S.: 332912

Subsidiary (US):

Instrument & Valve Services Company (4)
205 S Center St, Marshalltown, IA 50158-2823
Tel.: (641) 754-3011
Emp.: 300
Valve Mfr
N.A.I.C.S.: 332911

Subsidiary (Non-US):

Nippon Fisher Co., Ltd. (4)
Seavans N Building 17F 1-2-1 Shibaura, Minato, Tokyo, 105-0023, Japan
Tel.: (81) 345726800
Emp.: 200
Industrial Valve Mfr & Distr
N.A.I.C.S.: 332911

Subsidiary (Domestic):

High Voltage Maintenance Corporation (2)
5100 Energy Dr, Dayton, OH 45414
Tel.: (937) 278-0811
Web Site: http://www.hvmcorp.com
Sales Range: $10-24.9 Million
Emp.: 50
Electrical Equipment Testing & Maintenance Services
N.A.I.C.S.: 811210

Plant (Domestic):

High Voltage Maintenance - Northeast Electrical Testing (3)
150 N Plains Industrial Rd, Wallingford, CT 06492
Tel.: (203) 949-2650
Web Site: http://www.hvmcorp.com
Sales Range: $10-24.9 Million
Emp.: 20
Electrical Equipment Inspection & Testing Services
N.A.I.C.S.: 541990

High Voltage Maintenance Corp. (3)
24371 Catherine Industrial Dr Ste 207, Novi, MI 48375 **(100%)**
Tel.: (248) 305-5596
Web Site: http://www.hvmcorp.com
Sales Range: $1-9.9 Million
Emp.: 14
Testing Laboratories
N.A.I.C.S.: 541715

High Voltage Maintenance Corp. (3)
7200 Industrial Park Blvd, Mentor, OH 44060-5316 **(100%)**
Tel.: (440) 951-2706
Web Site: http://www.hvmcorp.com
Sales Range: $1-9.9 Million
Emp.: 12
Electrical Work
N.A.I.C.S.: 811210

High Voltage Maintenance Corp. (3)
3000 S Calhoun Rd, New Berlin, WI 53151-3549 **(100%)**
Tel.: (262) 784-3660
Web Site: http://www.hvmcorp.com
Sales Range: $1-9.9 Million
Emp.: 20
Electrical Testing & Maintenance Services
N.A.I.C.S.: 811210

High Voltage Maintenance Corp. (3)
8320 Brookville Rd Ste E, Indianapolis, IN 46239-8914
Tel.: (317) 322-2055
Web Site: http://www.hvmcorp.com
Sales Range: $1-9.9 Million
Emp.: 18
Electrical Work
N.A.I.C.S.: 811210

Subsidiary (Domestic):

Management Resources Group, Inc. (2)

27 Glen Rd 3rd Fl, Sandy Hook, CT 06482
Tel.: (203) 264-0500
Web Site: http://www.mrgsolutions.com
Sales Range: $10-24.9 Million
Engineering & Management Consulting Services
N.A.I.C.S.: 541330
Daniel H. Portes *(Owner & Chm)*

Subsidiary (Domestic):

Asset Data Solutions, LLC (3)
1261 Banbury Cross Rd, Santa Ana, CA 92705-3000
Tel.: (714) 731-4237
Web Site: http://www.assetdatasolutions.net
Emp.: 4
Business Management Consulting Services
N.A.I.C.S.: 541611

Subsidiary (Non-US):

Metco Services, Ltd. (2)
Web Site: http://www.emersonprocess.com
Sales Range: $50-74.9 Million
Emp.: 60
Liquid & Gas Flow Measurement & Metering Services
N.A.I.C.S.: 334519

Mobrey Measurement Ltd. (2)
158 Edinburgh Ave, Slough, SL1 4UE, Berkshire, United Kingdom
Tel.: (44) 1753 756600
Web Site: http://www.mobrey.com
Sales Range: $50-74.9 Million
Measurement & Control Equipment Mfr
N.A.I.C.S.: 334519
Tim Chettle *(Dir-Mktg)*
Joe Wilson *(Mng Dir)*

Subsidiary (Non-US):

Emerson Process Management S.A. (3)
23 rue du Petit Albi, 95803, Cergy, France
Tel.: (33) 130174080
Web Site: http://www.mobrey.fr
Sales Range: $10-24.9 Million
Emp.: 60
Measurement & Control Equipment Mfr
N.A.I.C.S.: 334513

Subsidiary (Non-US):

Emerson Process Management, Lda (4)
Rua General Ferreira Martins 8-10B, 1495-137, Alges, Portugal
Tel.: (351) 214200700
Electric Equipment Mfr
N.A.I.C.S.: 334513

Subsidiary (Non-US):

Mobrey AB (3)
16 Johanneshov, S 121 16, Stockholm, Sweden
Tel.: (46) 87250100
Web Site: http://www.emersonprocess.se
Sales Range: $1-9.9 Million
Emp.: 16
Measurement & Control Equipment Mfr
N.A.I.C.S.: 334519

Subsidiary (Non-US):

Rosemount Tank Radar AB (2)
Layout St Wagen No 1, 43533, Molnlycke, Sweden **(100%)**
Tel.: (46) 313370000
Web Site:
http://www.rosemounttankradar.com
Emp.: 400
Systems for Industrial & Marine Level Gauging, Cargo, Control & Engine Monitoring for Tankers & Radar Communication Equipment
N.A.I.C.S.: 334511

Subsidiary (Domestic):

Rosemount Tank Radar Properties AB (3)
Layoutvägen 1, 435 33, Molnlycke, Sweden
Tel.: (46) 313370000
Emp.: 400
Radar Based Tank Gauge Mfr
N.A.I.C.S.: 332420
Thomas Ortenberg *(Mng Dir)*

Emerson Process Management Co., Ltd. (1)
No 1277 Xin Jinqiao Rd, Pudong Xinqu, Shanghai, 201206, China
Tel.: (86) 2128929000
Electrical Appliance Mfr
N.A.I.C.S.: 335210

Emerson Process Management Europe GmbH (1)
Blegistrasse 23, Baar, 6341, Switzerland
Tel.: (41) 417686111
Web Site: http://www.emersonprocess.eu
Electronic Components Mfr
N.A.I.C.S.: 334419

Emerson Process Management LLLP (1)
8000 Norman Ctr Dr, Bloomington, MN 55437
Tel.: (952) 828-3500
Web Site: http://www.emersonprocess.com
Engineering & Project Management Services
N.A.I.C.S.: 541330

Emerson Process Management Ltda. (1)
Hollingsworth 325, Sorocaba, 18087-105, SP, Brazil
Tel.: (55) 1532383788
Industrial Valve Mfr
N.A.I.C.S.: 332911

Emerson Process Management Magyarorszag Kft. (1)
Berenyi Ut 100, Szekesfehervar, 8001, Hungary
Tel.: (36) 22543600
Web Site: http://www.emerson.com
Sales Range: $100-124.9 Million
Emp.: 500
Valves & Pipe Fittings Mfr
N.A.I.C.S.: 332919

Subsidiary (Domestic):

Emerson Automation Solutions Final Control Hungari Kft. (2)
Hungari korut 166-168, Budapest, 1146, Hungary
Tel.: (36) 14624000
Pneumatic & Electronic Control System Distr
N.A.I.C.S.: 423830
Gabor Blum *(Mng Dir)*

Emerson Process Management NV (1)
Bedrijvenzone Diegem Zuid - Pegasus Park De Kleetlaan 4, Diegem, Machelen, 1831, Belgium
Tel.: (32) 27167711
Web Site: http://www3.emersonprocess.com
Emp.: 80
Electronic Components Mfr
N.A.I.C.S.: 334419

Emerson Process Management Power & Water Solutions India Private Limited (1)
Windsor IT Park Tower A Ground & First Floor A-1 Sector 125, Noida, 201301, India
Tel.: (91) 1204194444
Engineering Consulting Services
N.A.I.C.S.: 541330

Emerson Process Management Power & Water Solutions Sp. z.o.o. (1)
Szturmowa 2A, 02-678, Warsaw, Poland
Tel.: (48) 224589200
Web Site: http://www.emerson.com
Control Valves & Regulator Distr
N.A.I.C.S.: 423390
Slawomir Suchomski *(Member-Mgmt Bd)*

Emerson Process Management Qatar S.S.C. (1)
15th Floor Al Wusail Tower, PO Box 32281, Doha, Qatar
Tel.: (974) 44576777
Web Site: http://www.emerson.com
Electronic Product Distr
N.A.I.C.S.: 449210

Emerson Process Management S.r.l. (1)

Via Montello 71/73, 20038, Seregno, MI,
Italy
Tel.: (39) 036222851
Web Site: http://www.emersonprocess.it
Sales Range: $25-49.9 Million
Emp.: 20
Electronic Components Mfr
N.A.I.C.S.: 334419

Emerson Process Management SAS (1)
Europarc du Chene 14 Rue Edison, PO
Box 21, 69671, Bron, Cedex, France
Tel.: (33) 472159800
Web Site: http://www3.emersonprocess.com
Consulting Services
N.A.I.C.S.: 541614

Emerson Process Management Virgo Valves, Inc. (1)
10225 Mula Rd Ste 130, Stafford, TX
77477-3346
Tel.: (281) 933-3100
Industrial Valve Mfr
N.A.I.C.S.: 332912

Emerson Process Management de Colombia SAS (1)
Edificio Mansarovar Calle 100 No 13-76
Piso 5, Bogota, Colombia
Tel.: (57) 17058000
Pneumatic & Electronic Control System
Distr
N.A.I.C.S.: 423830

Emerson Professional Tools (Shanghai) Co., Ltd. (1)
6/F Emerson Building 1582 Gu Mei Road,
Shanghai, 200233, China
Tel.: (86) 2133387000
Web Site: http://www.emerson.com
Industrial Equipment Sales, Services & Mfr
N.A.I.C.S.: 811310

Emerson Professional Tools AG (1)
Gelterkinderstrasse 24, 4450, Sissach,
Switzerland
Tel.: (41) 619764444
Web Site: https://emerson-sissach.ch
Electrical Appliance Mfr
N.A.I.C.S.: 335210

Emerson Sales (UK) Limited (1)
1 Harvest Avebue D2 Business Park, Dyce,
Aberdeen, AB21 0BQ, United
Kingdom **(100%)**
Tel.: (44) 870 240 1978
Web Site: http://www.emerson.com
Flow Control Products
N.A.I.C.S.: 332919

Emerson Technologies GmbH & Co. OHG (1)
Tel.: (49) 60744970
Web Site: http://www.emerson.com
Emp.: 8
Electrical Equipment Supplies & Mfr
N.A.I.C.S.: 335999

Emerson Tool Company (1)
8100 W Florissant Ave, Saint Louis, MO
63136-1417
Tel.: (314) 553-5000
Web Site:
http://www.emersontoolcompany.com
Sales Range: $75-99.9 Million
Emp.: 150
Portable Space Heaters, Band & Radial
Saws, Arc Welders, Industrial Tools
N.A.I.C.S.: 332216

Division (Domestic):

Ridge Tool Company (2)
400 Clark St, Elyria, OH 44035
Tel.: (440) 323-5581
Web Site: http://www.ridgid.com
Emp.: 500
Specialty Plumbing, Piping, Power & Miscellaneous Tools & Hardware Mfr
N.A.I.C.S.: 333517
Fred Pond (Pres)

Subsidiary (Domestic):

RIDGID, Inc. (3)
400 Clark St, Elyria, OH 44035-6001
Tel.: (440) 323-5581
Web Site: http://www.ridgid.com
Machine Tools Mfr

N.A.I.C.S.: 331110

Subsidiary (Non-US):

Ridge Tool Europe N.V. (3)
Ondernemerslaan 5428, 3800, Sint-Truiden,
Belgium **(100%)**
Tel.: (32) 11598620
Web Site: http://www.ridgid.eu
Sales Range: $50-74.9 Million
Emp.: 62
Hand & Power Tools Mfr & Sales
N.A.I.C.S.: 332216

Ridge Tool GmbH & Co. OHG (3)
Hasslinghauser Strasse 150, 58285, Gevelsberg, Germany **(100%)**
Tel.: (49) 8005888076
Web Site: https://www.ridgid.eu
Sales Range: $25-49.9 Million
Emp.: 40
Hand & Power Tools Mfr & Sales
N.A.I.C.S.: 333991

Division (Domestic):

Ridgid Products (3)
14100 Old Gordonsville Rd, Orange, VA
22960-2921
Tel.: (540) 672-5150
Web Site: http://www.ridgid.com
Sales Range: $100-124.9 Million
Emp.: 200
Portable Space Heaters, Band & Radial
Saws, Arc Welders & Industrial Tools Mfr
N.A.I.C.S.: 332216

Subsidiary (Non-US):

Ridgid Scandinavia A/S (3)
Web Site: http://www.ridgid.eu
Sales Range: $125-149.9 Million
Professional Tools Mfr
N.A.I.C.S.: 332216

Von Arx AG (3)
Gelterkinderstrasse 24, 4450, Sissach,
Switzerland **(100%)**
Tel.: (41) 619764444
Web Site: http://www.vonarx.com
Sales Range: $25-49.9 Million
Emp.: 65
Hand Tools & Other Industrial Machines &
Equipment Mfr
N.A.I.C.S.: 333991
John Ruese (Mng Dir)

Emerson Venezuela C.A. (1)
Av Principal de los Ruices Edif 48 Los
Ruites Edo Miranda, 1071 A, Caracas, Miranda, Venezuela **(100%)**
Tel.: (58) 2122030711
Web Site: http://www.emersonelectric-ve.com
Sales Range: $10-24.9 Million
Emp.: 70
Electric Motors, Generators & Wiring Devices Mfr
N.A.I.C.S.: 335312

Emerson d.o.o. (1)
Selska Road 93, Zagreb, 10000, Croatia
Tel.: (385) 15603611
Web Site: http://www.emersonenergy.com
Electricity Distribution & Control Apparatus
Mfr
N.A.I.C.S.: 221122
Luka Gaspar (Gen Mgr)

Emerson eResource (Xi'an) Co., Ltd. (1)
5/F R&D Building No 34 1st Jinye Road
Xi'an High-Tech Industrial Zone, Xi'an,
710065, China
Tel.: (86) 2989180001
Electronic Product Distr
N.A.I.C.S.: 449210

Energy Solutions International Ltd. (1)
Hastings House Falcon Court, Business
Park Westland Way Preston Farm Ind Est,
Stockton-on-Tees, TS18 3TS, Cleveland,
United Kingdom
Tel.: (44) 1642677755
Electrical Equipment Whslr
N.A.I.C.S.: 423830

Energy Solutions International Private Limited (1)
264A Road No 10 Jubilee Hills Banjara

Hills, Hyderabad, 500034, India
Tel.: (91) 9848029451
Software Development Services
N.A.I.C.S.: 541511
K. V. Siva Rao (VP)

Energy Solutions International SAS (1)
Carrera 7 71 52 To B P 9, Bogota, 208,
Colombia
Tel.: (57) 13137800
Electrical Equipment Whslr
N.A.I.C.S.: 423830

Energy Solutions International, Inc. (1)
7904 N Sam Houston Pkwy West Ste 100,
Houston, TX 77064
Tel.: (281) 664-8200
Electrical Equipment Whslr
N.A.I.C.S.: 423830
Timothy Burkett (CFO)
Eric Johnson (CMO & VP-Gas Mgmt Sys)
Alex de Joode (VP-Intl)
Julie Hatfield (VP-Operational Mgmt Solutions)
Marcus Patrinicola (VP-Liquids Mgmt Solutions)
Thad McLemore (VP-Global Svcs)
TengBeng Koid (CEO)

Engineered Endeavors Inc. (1)
10975 Kinsman Rd, Newbury, OH 44065-9787
Tel.: (440) 918-1101
Web Site: http://www.engend.com
Sales Range: $10-24.9 Million
Emp.: 43
Mobile Communication Equipment Sls
N.A.I.C.S.: 334220
Pat Deloney (Mgr-Sls & Utility Structures-Natl)

Eurotronics Sistemas de Seguridad S.A.U. (1)
C/ Hermes 18 Parque Industrial Meco R2,
28880, Madrid, Spain
Tel.: (34) 916762446
Web Site: http://www.euro-tronics.com
Industrial Equipment & Truck Distr
N.A.I.C.S.: 423120

F-R Tecnologias de Flujo, S.A. de C.V. (1)
Miguel De Cervantes Saavedra No. 111,
Complejo Industrial Chihuahua, Chihuahua,
31109, Mexico
Tel.: (52) 6144297000
Web Site: http://www.emerson.com
Electrical Equipment Supplies & Mfr
N.A.I.C.S.: 335999

FLEXIM Americas Corporation (1)
Paul Lemmens 250 Executive Dr, Brentwood, NY 11717
Tel.: (631) 492-2300
Measuring Device Mfr & Distr
N.A.I.C.S.: 334519

FLEXIM Australia Pty. Ltd. (1)
PO Box 368, Beaconsfield, 3807, VIC, Australia
Tel.: (61) 407457756
Measuring Device Mfr & Distr
N.A.I.C.S.: 334519

FLEXIM Flexible Industriemesstechnick GmbH (1)
Boxberger Strasse 4, 12681, Berlin, Germany
Tel.: (49) 3093667660
Measuring Device Mfr & Distr
N.A.I.C.S.: 334519

FLEXIM Flow India Pvt. Ltd. (1)
308 Crown Heights Plot No 3B1 Sector 10,
Twin District Centre Rohini, New Delhi,
110085, India
Tel.: (91) 9811449285
Measuring Device Mfr & Distr
N.A.I.C.S.: 334519

FLEXIM France S.A.S. (1)
135 Allee des Noisetiers, 69760, Limonest,
France
Tel.: (33) 427465216
Measuring Device Mfr & Distr
N.A.I.C.S.: 334519

FLEXIM Instruments Asia Pte. Ltd. (1)

10 Toh Guan Road 06-01, Singapore,
608838, Singapore
Tel.: (65) 67945325
Measuring Device Mfr & Distr
N.A.I.C.S.: 334519

FLEXIM Instruments Benelux B.V. (1)
127 Berkelse Poort, 2651 JX, Berkel en
Rodenrijs, Netherlands
Tel.: (31) 102492333
Measuring Device Mfr & Distr
N.A.I.C.S.: 334519

FLEXIM Instruments UK Ltd. (1)
Theatre Court London Road, Northwich,
CW9 5HB, United Kingdom
Tel.: (44) 1606781420
Measuring Device Mfr & Distr
N.A.I.C.S.: 334519

FLEXIM Japan Ltd. (1)
2-7-9 Fujimi, Chuo-ku, Chiba, 260-0015,
Japan
Tel.: (81) 8032747373
Measuring Device Mfr & Distr
N.A.I.C.S.: 334519

FLEXIM S.A. (1)
5420 Cerro El Plomo Of 603, Region Metropolitana, Las Condes, Chile
Tel.: (56) 232036280
Measuring Device Mfr & Distr
N.A.I.C.S.: 334519

Fisco Ltd (1)
5-13-3 Minamiaoyama, Minato-ku, Tokyo,
Japan
Tel.: (81) 357742440
Web Site: https://www.fisco.co.jp
Research & Information Services
N.A.I.C.S.: 541720

Francel S.A. (1)
ZA la Croix Saint Mathieu, Gallardon,
28320, France
Tel.: (33) 237334700
Electrical Equipment Supplies & Mfr
N.A.I.C.S.: 335999

Fromex, S.A. de C.V. (1)
Av Industrias No 6025, Parque Industrial
Finsa, Nuevo Laredo, 88275, Tamps,
Mexico
Tel.: (52) 8677115200
Electrical Equipment Supplies & Mfr
N.A.I.C.S.: 335999

GE Intelligent Platforms, Inc. (1)
2500 Austin Dr, Charlottesville, VA 22911
Tel.: (434) 978-5329
Web Site: http://www.ge-ip.com
Sales Range: $200-249.9 Million
Emp.: 650
Automation Hardware & Software Mfr
N.A.I.C.S.: 334513

Subsidiary (Non-US):

Emerson Automation Solutions Intelligent Platforms Private Limited (2)
Building No 8 Ground Floor Velankani Tech
Park No 43 Hosur Road, Electronics City
Phase I, Bengaluru, 560100, India
Tel.: (91) 6569559413
Motor & Generator Mfr
N.A.I.C.S.: 335312

Branch (Domestic):

GE Intelligent Platforms, Inc. - Huntsville (2)
12090 S Memorial Pkwy, Huntsville, AL
35803
Tel.: (256) 382-8118
Web Site: http://www.ge-ip.com
Sales Range: $100-124.9 Million
Embedded Computing & Networking Components Mfr
N.A.I.C.S.: 334111

Subsidiary (Non-US):

ICC Intelligent Platforms GmbH (2)
Memminger Str 14, 86159, Augsburg, Germany
Tel.: (49) 225379328
Motor & Generator Mfr
N.A.I.C.S.: 335312

GeoFields, Inc. (1)

Emerson Electric Co.—(Continued)

Bank of America Plz Peachtree St, Atlanta, GA 30308
Tel.: (404) 253-1000
Web Site: http://www.geofields.com
Software Development Services
N.A.I.C.S.: 513210
R. Keith Chambless *(Pres)*

Greenlee Tools, Inc. **(1)**
4455 Boeing Dr, Rockford, IL 61109
Web Site: https://www.greenlee.com
Electrical Appliance Mfr
N.A.I.C.S.: 335210

Greenlee Tools, Inc. **(1)**
4455 Boeing Dr, Rockford, IL
61109-2932 **(100%)**
Tel.: (815) 397-7070
Web Site: https://www.greenlee.com
Wire & Cable Installation Tools
N.A.I.C.S.: 332618

Subsidiary (Domestic):

Greenlee Tools, Inc. **(3)**
4455 Boeing Dr, Rockford, IL 61109-2932
Tel.: (815) 397-7070
Web Site: https://www.greenlee.com
Wire & Cable Installation Tools
N.A.I.C.S.: 332618

Subsidiary (Domestic):

Greenlee Plumbing Inc. **(4)**
5086 Marsh Creek Ct, Braselton, GA
30517-1232
Tel.: (678) 386-7513
Web Site:
https://www.greenleeplumbingatlanta.com
Pipe Line Contractors
N.A.I.C.S.: 238220

Sherman + Reilly, Inc. **(4)**
400 W 33rd St, Chattanooga, TN 37410-1039
Tel.: (423) 756-5300
Web Site: https://www.sherman-reilly.com
Overhead & Underground Electrical Power
Lines, Equipment, Tools & Hardware Mfr
N.A.I.C.S.: 335932

Tempo Communications, Inc. **(4)**
1390 Aspen Way, Vista, CA 92081
Tel.: (760) 510-0558
Web Site: http://www.tempocom.com
Test & Measurement Equipment Mfr
N.A.I.C.S.: 334515

Subsidiary (Non-US):

Tempo Europe Limited **(5)**
Suite 8 Brecon House William Brown Close,
Cwmbran, NP44 3AB, United Kingdom
Tel.: (44) 1633927050
Electronic Products Mfr
N.A.I.C.S.: 334419

Gustav Klauke GmbH **(1)**
Auf Dem Knapp 46, 42855, Remscheid,
Germany
Tel.: (49) 21919070
Web Site: http://www.klauke.com
Aircraft Manufacturing
N.A.I.C.S.: 336411
Jean-Claude Wetzels *(Mng Dir)*

Subsidiary (Non-US):

Klauke France SARL **(1)**
16 Rue Saint-Louis Actisud, BP 40, 57150,
Creutzwald, France
Tel.: (33) 387298470
Web Site: https://www.klauke.com
Electrical Appliance Mfr
N.A.I.C.S.: 335210

Klauke UK Limited **(2)**
Hillside Road East B1062, Bungay, NR35
1JX, United Kingdom
Electrical Products Mfr
N.A.I.C.S.: 335999

InterMetro Industries Corporation **(1)**
651 N Washington St, Wilkes Barre, PA
18705-1707
Tel.: (570) 825-2741
Sales Range: $50-74.9 Million
Emp.: 100
Storage Systems, Wire Shelving & Carts
Mfr

N.A.I.C.S.: 332618
John G. Nackley Sr. *(Pres & CEO)*

Subsidiary (Non-US):

InterMetro Industries B.V. **(2)**
Tel.: (31) 765877550
Web Site: http://www.metro.com
Electrical Equipment Supplies & Mfr
N.A.I.C.S.: 335999
John G. Nackley Sr. *(Pres & CEO)*

Unit (Domestic):

InterMetro Industries Corporation **(2)**
1150 State St, Fostoria, OH
44830-3007 **(100%)**
Tel.: (419) 435-5937
Web Site: http://www.metro.com
Sales Range: $50-74.9 Million
Emp.: 100
Injection Mouldings Plastics Mfr
N.A.I.C.S.: 333924

Plant (Domestic):

InterMetro Industries Corporation **(2)**
9393 Arrow Rte, Rancho Cucamonga, CA
91730-4538
Tel.: (909) 987-4731
Web Site: http://www.metro.com
Sales Range: $50-74.9 Million
Emp.: 100
Miscellaneous Fabricated Wire Products
N.A.I.C.S.: 332618

Unit (Domestic):

InterMetro Industries Corporation **(2)**
1938 Univeristy In Unit A, Lisle, IL
60532 **(100%)**
Tel.: (630) 737-0038
Web Site: http://www.metro.com
Sales Range: $25-49.9 Million
Emp.: 3
Miscellaneous Fabricated Wire Products Mfr
N.A.I.C.S.: 425120

Subsidiary (Domestic):

Metro Industries, Inc. **(2)**
1260 W Goodale Blvd, Columbus, OH
43212
Tel.: (614) 487-8200
Web Site:
https://www.metroindustriesinc.com
Sales Range: $1-9.9 Million
Emp.: 20
Electronic Equipment Mfr & Distr
N.A.I.C.S.: 334419

Intermetro de Mexico, S, de R.L. de C.V. **(1)**
Rio Conchos No 9105, Cuauhtemoc,
31540, Mexico
Tel.: (52) 6255902400
Web Site: http://www.emerson.com
Custom Architectural Woodwork Mfr
N.A.I.C.S.: 337212

Intrinsic Safety Equipment of Texas, Inc. **(1)**
3902 Magnolia St, Pearland, TX 77584-1610
Tel.: (281) 488-0788
Web Site: http://www.magtech.com
Emp.: 80
Electric Equipment Mfr
N.A.I.C.S.: 334419

M.L.S. Holice spol. s.r.o. **(1)**
Tel.: (420) 585105200
Web Site: http://www.leroy-somer.com
Sales Range: $300-349.9 Million
Emp.: 200
Electrical Equipment Supplies & Mfr
N.A.I.C.S.: 335999

Marbaise Hanlo LS GmbH **(1)**
Heslingsweg 6, 44309, Dortmund, Germany
Tel.: (49) 2319250100
Sales Range: $25-49.9 Million
Emp.: 28
Power Transmission Equipment Mfr
N.A.I.C.S.: 333613
Diete Biumann *(Mng Dir)*

Masterguard GmbH **(1)**
Schallershofer Str 141, Erlangen, 9131,
Germany
Tel.: (49) 1805323751

Electrical Equipment Supplies & Mfr
N.A.I.C.S.: 335999

Metropolitan Wire Canada, Ltd. **(1)**
3160 Orlando Dr, Mississauga, L4V 1R5,
ON, Canada
Tel.: (905) 676-9890
Web Site: http://www.metro.com
Sales Range: $900-999.9 Million
Emp.: 9
Storage & Transport Products Mfr
N.A.I.C.S.: 332618

Micro Motion Inc. **(1)**
7070 Winchester Cir, Boulder, CO
80301-3506 **(100%)**
Tel.: (303) 530-8400
Web Site: http://www.micromotion.com
Sales Range: $125-149.9 Million
Emp.: 622
Flow Instrument Systems for Process Control Applications
N.A.I.C.S.: 334514
Tom Moser *(Pres)*

Subsidiary (Non-US):

El-O-Matic Benelux BV **(2)**
Asveldweg 11, Hengelo, 7556 BR, Netherlands
Tel.: (31) 742561010
Web Site: http://www.emersonprocess.com
Sales Range: $25-49.9 Million
Emp.: 50
Industrial Valve Mfr
N.A.I.C.S.: 332911

Division (Domestic):

Micro Motion Inc. **(2)**
4850 Romeda Rd, Beaumont, TX 77705-6333
Tel.: (409) 842-6875
Web Site: http://www.emersonprocess.com
Sales Range: $100-124.9 Million
Emp.: 2
Flow Processing Instruments Sales
N.A.I.C.S.: 334519

Mobrey Limited **(1)**
158 Edinburgh Ave, Slough, SL1 4UE,
Berks, United Kingdom
Tel.: (44) 1753756600
Web Site: http://www.emerson.com
Sales Range: $50-74.9 Million
Emp.: 220
Electrical Equipment Supplies & Mfr
N.A.I.C.S.: 335999

Motoreductores U.S., S.A. de C.V. **(1)**
Blvd Parque Industrial Monterrey No 401,
Apodaca, 66600, Nuevo Leon, Mexico
Tel.: (52) 8181565000
Web Site: http://www.emerson-ept.com
Electric Equipment Mfr
N.A.I.C.S.: 334419

Muyle Electro-Machinery SA **(1)**
Tel.: (32) 71446070
Sales Range: $10-24.9 Million
Emp.: 37
Electrical Equipment Supplies & Mfr
N.A.I.C.S.: 335999

N.J. Froment & Co. Limited **(1)**
Easton-on-the-Hill, Stamford, PE9 3NP,
United Kingdom
Power Test Equipment Mfr
N.A.I.C.S.: 334519

Net Safety Monitoring Inc. **(1)**
2721 Hopewell Place NE, Calgary, T1Y
7J7, AB, Canada
Tel.: (403) 219-0688
Fire & Gas Detection Machinery Mfr
N.A.I.C.S.: 334519
Kevin Falenda *(Co-VP-Mfg Production & Ops)*
Mike Nugent *(Co-VP-Mfg Production & Ops)*
Kevin Algar *(Co-VP-Mfg Production & Ops)*

Nidec Industrial Automation USA LLC **(1)**
Tel.: (952) 995-8000
Electric Motor Mfr
N.A.I.C.S.: 335312

Subsidiary (Non-US):

ASCO Valve, Inc. **(2)**

Tel.: (973) 966-2000
Web Site: http://www.ascovalve.com
Valve Sales
N.A.I.C.S.: 332911

Branson Ultrasonics Corporation **(2)**
Tel.: (203) 796-0400
Web Site: http://www.bransonic.com
Industrial Ultrasonic Equipment
N.A.I.C.S.: 335999

Novel Environmental Technologies Ltd. **(1)**
New Industrial Zone, 80150, Sderot, Israel
Tel.: (972) 86875444
Measuring & Controlling Device Mfr
N.A.I.C.S.: 334519

Nutsteel Industria Metalurgica Ltda **(1)**
Rua Africa do Sul 66, Santo Amaro, 04730-020, Sao Paulo, Brazil
Tel.: (55) 1121225757
Web Site: http://www.nutsteel.com.br
Hazardous Electrical Equipment Mfr
N.A.I.C.S.: 334419

O.M.T OFFICINA MECCANICA TARTARINI S.R.L. **(1)**
Tel.: (39) 0514190611
Web Site: http://www.emersonprocess.com
Electrical Equipment Supplies & Mfr
N.A.I.C.S.: 335999

OSI Automation Software Systems (Beijing) Co., Ltd. **(1)**
B-603 Tian Yuan Gang Centre No C2
Dongsanhuan Beilu, Chaoyang District, Beijing, 100027, China
Tel.: (86) 1084464699
Software Development Services
N.A.I.C.S.: 541511

OSI Energy Automation India Private Limited **(1)**
Unit No 29 Lower Grd Floor, Creator Bldg
International Tech Park Bangalore ITPB
Whitefield, Bengaluru, 560 066, India
Tel.: (91) 8041265051
Software Development Services
N.A.I.C.S.: 541511

OSI du Canada Inc. **(1)**
2000 rue Mansfield suite 1100, Montreal,
H3A 3N8, QC, Canada
Tel.: (763) 551-0559
Software Development Services
N.A.I.C.S.: 541511

Open Systems International Australia Pty Ltd **(1)**
Level 2 3 Thomas Holt Drive, Macquarie
Park, 2113, NSW, Australia
Tel.: (61) 280742200
Software Development Services
N.A.I.C.S.: 541511
Dan Candotti *(Sr Dir-Australia)*

Open Systems International Europe SL **(1)**
Avenida de la Vega 1 Edificio Veganova
Edif 3 Planta 3, Oficinas 13 y 14 Alcobendas, 28108, Madrid, Spain
Tel.: (34) 918055466
Software Development Services
N.A.I.C.S.: 541511
Sergio Bajetti *(VP-Operations-Europe,Latin America)*
Javier Martin *(Sr Dir-)*

PC&E Inc. **(1)**
641 Lambert Pointe Dr, Hazelwood, MO
63042 **(100%)**
Tel.: (314) 872-9058
Sales Range: $25-49.9 Million
Emp.: 122
Electric Control Panels
N.A.I.C.S.: 541330

PT Emerson Solutions Indonesia **(1)**
BSD Taman Tekno 8 Jl Tekno Widya Blok
H10 No 2-5 South, Tangerang, 15314, Indonesia
Tel.: (62) 2129666242
Pneumatic & Electronic Control System
Distr
N.A.I.C.S.: 423830

PT. Emerson Indonesia **(1)**
Wisma 46-Kata BNI 16th Floor suite 16 01
Jl Jend Sudirman Kav 1, Jakarta, 10220,
Indonesia
Tel.: (62) 212513003
Telecommunication Equipment Distr
N.A.I.C.S.: 423690

Pactrol Controls Ltd. **(1)**
Unit 3 Three Sisters Enterprise Park Antler
Court, Ashton-in-Makerfield, Wigan, WN4
8DU, United Kingdom
Tel.: (44) 1942529240
Web Site: https://www.pactrol.com
Sales Range: $25-49.9 Million
Emp.: 22
Electronics Instrument Mfr
N.A.I.C.S.: 334220
Michael Brooks (Mng Dir)
Philip Scaldwell (Mgr-Customer Svc)

Paradigm France S.A. **(1)**
1 rue de Gramont, 75002, Paris, France
Tel.: (33) 49490510
Pneumatic & Electronic Control System
Distr
N.A.I.C.S.: 423830

Parex Industries Limited **(1)**
5 Tolich Place, Henderson, 0610, Auckland,
New Zealand
Tel.: (64) 98366566
Web Site: https://www.parex.co.nz
Plumbing Fixture Whslr
N.A.I.C.S.: 423720
Brian Glucina (Mgr-Ops)
Barnaby Thompson (Mgr-Sls & Mktg)

Pentair Valves & Controls, Inc. **(1)**
10707 Clay Rd, Houston, TX
77041   **(100%)**
Tel.: (713) 466-1176
Web Site: http://www.tycovalves.com
Sales Range: $100-124.9 Million
Emp.: 350
Valves & Actuators Mfr
N.A.I.C.S.: 332911

Subsidiary (Non-US):

Century Industries Company **(2)**
16th St NE Ste 3003, Calgary, T2E 7K8,
AB, Canada   **(100%)**
Tel.: (403) 250-9742
Web Site: http://www.centuryvalve.com
Instrumentation Valves Mfr
N.A.I.C.S.: 332919

Subsidiary (Domestic):

Crosby Valve, Inc. **(2)**
55 Cabot Blvd, Mansfield, MA 02048-1137
Tel.: (508) 384-3121
Web Site: http://www.emerson.com
Safety, Relief Valves & Check Valves Mfr
N.A.I.C.S.: 332911

Goyen Valve LLC **(2)**
1195 Airport Rd Ste 2, Lakewood, NJ
08701-5970
Tel.: (732) 364-7800
Hydraulic Equipment Mfr
N.A.I.C.S.: 333996

Subsidiary (Non-US):

Goyen Controls Co UK Limited **(3)**
Unit 3B Beechwood Lime Tree Way, Bas-
ingstoke, RG24 8WA, Hampshire, United
Kingdom
Tel.: (44) 1256 817 800
Industrial Pneumatic Valve Mfr
N.A.I.C.S.: 332912

Goyen Controls Co. Pty Limited **(3)**
15-17 Lakewood Blv, Braeside, 3195, VIC,
Australia
Tel.: (61) 1800805372
Industrial Valve Mfr
N.A.I.C.S.: 332911

Subsidiary (Non-US):

Keystone Valve (Korea) LLC **(2)**
56 Je2gongdan 1-gil Miyang-myeon,
Gyeonggi-do, Anseong, 456-843, Korea
(South)
Tel.: (82) 316702500
Web Site: http://valves.pentair.com
Emp.: 82
Flow Control Products

N.A.I.C.S.: 332919

Unit (Domestic):

Morin Actuator **(2)**
110 Commerce Dr, Pelham, AL 35124-1838
Tel.: (205) 663-0533
Web Site: http://www.morinact.com
Sales Range: $25-49.9 Million
Emp.: 75
Actuator Mfr
N.A.I.C.S.: 333995

Subsidiary (Non-US):

**Pentair Valves & Controls (France)
S.C.A.** **(2)**
4 Rue Des Oziers, 95310, Saint-Ouen,
France
Tel.: (33) 139093808
Industrial Valve Distr
N.A.I.C.S.: 423840

**Pentair Valves & Controls (M) Sdn.
Bhd.** **(2)**
No 57-3 & 59-3 Block G Jalan PJU 1/37
Dataran Prima, Petaling Jaya, 47301, Se-
langor, Malaysia
Tel.: (60) 3 7962 9000
Industrial Valve Mfr
N.A.I.C.S.: 332911

**Pentair Valves & Controls (Taiwan)
Ltd.** **(2)**
16F-1 No 59 Sec 2 Tun-Hua Nan Road,
10681, Taipei, Taiwan
Tel.: (886) 2 27546969
Industrial Valve Mfr
N.A.I.C.S.: 332911

**Pentair Valves & Controls (Thailand)
Ltd.** **(2)**
100/96 Vongvanij Complex Building B 28th
Floor Rama 9 Road, Huaykwang, Bangkok,
10310, Thailand
Tel.: (66) 31 335 58 00
Industrial Valve Mfr
N.A.I.C.S.: 332911

**Pentair Valves & Controls Brasil
Ltda.** **(2)**
Av Antonio Bardella Sorocabo N 3000, Sao
Paulo, CEP 18 085270, Brazil   **(100%)**
Tel.: (55) 15 2102 8700
Sales Range: $25-49.9 Million
Emp.: 90
Flow Control Products
N.A.I.C.S.: 332919

**Pentair Valves & Controls Canada
Inc.** **(2)**
8080-40th Street SE, Calgary, T2C 2I3, AB,
Canada
Tel.: (403) 250-9888
Web Site: http://valves.pentair.com
Emp.: 18
Valves, Actuators & Controls Mfr & Distr
N.A.I.C.S.: 333995

Branch (Domestic):

**Pentair Valves & Controls Canada
Inc. - Burlington Office** **(3)**
1080 Clay Unit 4, Burlington, L7L0A1, ON,
Canada
Tel.: (905) 319-3406
Web Site: http://www.pentairvalves.com
Sales Range: $25-49.9 Million
Emp.: 19
Flow Control Products
N.A.I.C.S.: 332919

Subsidiary (Non-US):

**Pentair Valves & Controls Distribution
Czech s.r.o.** **(2)**
Belohorska 261/37, Prague, 16900, Czech
Republic
Tel.: (420) 220 610 379
Web Site: http://www.tycovalves.cz
Emp.: 15
Industrial Valve Distr
N.A.I.C.S.: 423840

**Pentair Valves & Controls India Pvt.
Ltd.** **(2)**
Flat No 44 Deepak Building 13 Nehru
Place, New Delhi, 110019, India
Tel.: (91) 11 2628 2441
Web Site: http://in.valves.pentair.com

Emp.: 10
Industrial Valve Mfr & Distr
N.A.I.C.S.: 332911

**Pentair Valves & Controls Italia
S.r.l.** **(2)**
Via Piacenza, Lugagnano Val D'Arda,
29018, Piacenza, Italy   **(100%)**
Tel.: (39) 0523890201
Web Site: http://www.vanessavalves.it
Sales Range: $100-124.9 Million
Emp.: 260
High Technology Rotary Process Valves Mfr
N.A.I.C.S.: 332911

**Pentair Valves & Controls Polska Sp.
z o.o.** **(2)**
Al Jerozolimskie 202, 02-486, Warsaw, Po-
land
Tel.: (48) 22 874 01 86
Web Site: http://www.tyco-valves.pl
Emp.: 15
Industrial Valve Mfr
N.A.I.C.S.: 332911

**Pentair Valves & Controls Singapore
Pte. Ltd.** **(2)**
45 Tuos Ave 9, Jurong, 639189,
Singapore   **(100%)**
Tel.: (65) 68611655
Web Site: http://www.pentairvalves.com
Sales Range: $50-74.9 Million
Emp.: 110
Flow Control Products
N.A.I.C.S.: 332919

Unit (Domestic):

**Pentair Valves & Controls, Inc. - Ba-
ton Rouge** **(2)**
15785 W Old Perkins Rd, Baton Rouge, LA
70810
Tel.: (225) 751-9000
Valves & Controls
N.A.I.C.S.: 332912

**Pentair Valves & Controls, Inc. -
Bridgeport** **(2)**
4 Killdeer Ct Ste 200, Bridgeport, NJ 08014
Tel.: (856) 467-7900
Web Site: http://www.tycoflowcontrol.com
Rev.: $37,305,856
Emp.: 15
Industrial Equipment Services
N.A.I.C.S.: 811210

**Pentair Valves & Controls, Inc. -
Corona** **(2)**
252 Corporate Terrace Cir, Corona, CA
92879
Tel.: (951) 493-4227
Web Site: http://www.tycovalves.com
Valves & Fittings Mfr
N.A.I.C.S.: 332911

**Pentair Valves & Controls, Inc. -
Prophetstown** **(2)**
320 Locust St, Prophetstown, IL 61277-
1147
Tel.: (815) 537-2311
Web Site: http://www.tycovalves-na.com
Sales Range: $50-74.9 Million
Emp.: 140
Industrial Valves
N.A.I.C.S.: 332911

**Pentair Valves & Controls, Inc. -
Stafford** **(2)**
3950 Greenbriar Dr, Stafford, TX 77477-
3919
Tel.: (281) 274-4400
Emp.: 500
Pressure Relief Valves, Manifolds, Hand
Valves, Check Valves, Regulators, Nuclear
& Fossil Fuel Power Plant Valves, Rupture
Discs Mfr
N.A.I.C.S.: 332911

Subsidiary (Non-US):

Sempell GmbH **(2)**
Werner-von-Siemens Strasse 11, 41352,
Korschenbroich, Germany
Tel.: (49) 21616150
Sales Range: $100-124.9 Million
Valve Mfr
N.A.I.C.S.: 332911

Taiwan Valve Co., Ltd **(2)**
No 3 24th Road Taichung Industrial Park,

Taichung, Taiwan
Tel.: (886) 423500011
Web Site: http://www.taiwan-valve.com.tw
Industrial Valve Mfr
N.A.I.C.S.: 332911

**Tyco Valves & Controls (Sichuan)
Co., Ltd.** **(2)**
21-22/F Innovation Building No 1009 Yi
Shan Road, Shanghai, 200233, China
Tel.: (86) 21 2412 6911
Industrial Valve Mfr
N.A.I.C.S.: 332911

**Tyco Valves & Controls de Mexico,
S.A. de C.V.** **(2)**
Calle 3 Lotes 13 14 Y 15, El Salto,
CP45680, Jalisco, Mexico   **(100%)**
Tel.: (52) 3336684000
Sales Range: $50-74.9 Million
Emp.: 200
Flow Control Products
N.A.I.C.S.: 332919

Permasense Limited **(1)**
Alexandra House Newton Road Manor
Royal, Crawley, RH10 9TT, United Kingdom
Tel.: (44) 2030023672
Industrial Equipment Mfr
N.A.I.C.S.: 333415

PolyOil Ltd. **(1)**
No 1 Harvest Avenue D2 Business Park,
Aberdeen, AB21 02Q, United Kingdom
Tel.: (44) 1224799950
Web Site: http://www.polyoil.com
Emp.: 10
Electrical Equipment Supplies & Mfr
N.A.I.C.S.: 335999

ProTeam, Inc. **(1)**
12438 W Bridger St 100, Boise, ID 83713-
1580
Tel.: (208) 377-9555
Electrical Equipment Supplies & Mfr
N.A.I.C.S.: 335999

Progea S.r.l. **(1)**
Via D' Annunzio 295, 41123, Modena, Italy
Tel.: (39) 059451060
Web Site: http://www.progea.com
Emp.: 40
Software Services
N.A.I.C.S.: 541511
Paolo Fiorani (Co-Founder & Gen Mgr)
Claudio Fiorani (Co-Founder & Mgr-R&D)
Giuseppe Bettini (Partner & Mgr-Technical)
Jean-Marc Willems (Partner)

Subsidiary (Non-US):

Progea Deutschland GmbH **(2)**
Marie-Curie Str 12, 78048, Villingen, Ger-
many
Tel.: (49) 7721998380
Software Services
N.A.I.C.S.: 541511
Detlef Brenndoerfer (Sls Mgr)

Progea International, S.A. **(2)**
Via Sottobisio 28, 6828, Balerna, Switzer-
land
Tel.: (41) 919676610
Software Services
N.A.I.C.S.: 541511
Sergio Somaschini (Mgr-Export)

Subsidiary (US):

Progea North America, Corp. **(3)**
2380 State Rd 44 Ste C, Oshkosh, WI
54904
Software Services
N.A.I.C.S.: 541511
Scott Ludwing (Gen Mgr)

Quality Components, Inc. **(1)**
8825 E Ave, Mentor, OH 44060
Tel.: (440) 255-0606
Electronic Products Mfr
N.A.I.C.S.: 334419

RPP, LLC **(1)**
12 Ballard Way, Lawrence, MA 01843
Tel.: (978) 689-2800
Web Site: https://www.rppcorp.com
Electrical Appliance Mfr
N.A.I.C.S.: 335210

Ridge Tool Australia Pty., Ltd. **(1)**
127 Metrolink Circuit, Campbellfield, 3061,

Emerson Electric Co.—(Continued)

VIC, Australia **(100%)**
Tel.: (61) 1800743443
Hand & Power Tools Mfr & Sales
N.A.I.C.S.: 333991

Ridge Tool GmbH **(1)**
Waldstr 53-55, Dietzenbach, 63128, Germany
Tel.: (49) 2332709521
Electrical Equipment Supplies & Mfr
N.A.I.C.S.: 335999

Ridge Tool N.V. **(1)**
Research Park, Haasrode, 3001, Leuven,
Belgium **(100%)**
Tel.: (32) 16380211
Web Site: http://www.rigidl.com
Sales Range: $25-49.9 Million
Emp.: 50
Hand & Power Tools Mfr
N.A.I.C.S.: 333991

Rollway Bearing N.V. **(1)**
Heiveldekens 16, Kontich, 2550, Belgium
Tel.: (32) 34576870
Web Site: http://www.rollway-bearing.de
Emp.: 42
Electrical Equipment Supplies & Mfr
N.A.I.C.S.: 335999

**Rosemount Measurement
Limited** **(1)**
158 Edinburgh Avenue, Slough, SL1 4UE,
United Kingdom
Tel.: (44) 1753756600
Web Site: http://www.emersonprocess.com
Emp.: 250
Electric Equipment Mfr
N.A.I.C.S.: 334513

Roxar ASA **(1)**
Gamle Forusveien 17, PO Box 112, 4031,
Stavanger, Norway
Tel.: (47) 51818800
Web Site: http://www.roxar.com
Sales Range: $50-74.9 Million
Emp.: 30
Electrical Equipment Supplies & Mfr
N.A.I.C.S.: 335999

Roxar Software Solutions AS **(1)**
Lysaker Torg 45, Oslo, 1366, Norway
Tel.: (47) 22547800
Web Site: http://www.roxar.com
Emp.: 100
Software Devolopment
N.A.I.C.S.: 449210

SABO-Armaturen Service GmbH **(1)**
An der Hohe 21-23, Marienhagen, 51674,
Wiehl, Germany
Tel.: (49) 226170030
Web Site: http://www.sabo-armaturen.de
Pneumatic & Electronic Control System Mfr
N.A.I.C.S.: 334513
Andreas Hellmann *(Mgr-IT)*

**SSB Wind Systems GmbH & Co.
KG** **(1)**
Neuenkirchener Strasse 13, 48499, Salzbergen, Germany
Tel.: (49) 59769460
Electrical Equipment Supplies & Mfr
N.A.I.C.S.: 335999
Michael Ross *(Specialist-HR)*
Dominique Llonch *(Pres)*

Subsidiary (Domestic):

**SSB Wind Systems GmbH & Co.
KG** **(2)**
Neuenkirchener Strasse 13, 48499, Salzbergen, Germany
Tel.: (49) 59769460
Web Site: http://www.ssbwindsystems.de
Emp.: 150
Electronic Product Distr
N.A.I.C.S.: 449210
Laurent Babaud *(Pres)*

Subsidiary (Non-US):

**SSB Wind Energy Technology
(Qingdao) Co., Ltd.** **(3)**
Zhuzhou Road 91, Qingdao, 266101, China
Electronic Product Distr
N.A.I.C.S.: 449210

Semflex, Inc. **(1)**

5550 E Mcdowell Rd, Mesa, AZ 85215
Tel.: (480) 985-9000
Web Site: http://www.semflex.com
Electronic Components Mfr
N.A.I.C.S.: 334419

Sirai Deutschland Vertrieb elektromechanischer Geraete GmbH **(1)**
Muenchener Strasse 15, Berlin, 85643,
Germany
Tel.: (49) 8094180786
Web Site: http://www.sirai.de
Sales Range: $25-49.9 Million
Emp.: 4
Electric Equipment Mfr
N.A.I.C.S.: 444180

Skil Europe B.V. **(1)**
Konijnenberg 60, Postbus 3267, 4800 DG,
Breda, Netherlands **(100%)**
Tel.: (31) 765795000
Web Site: http://www.skileurope.com
Sales Range: $75-99.9 Million
Emp.: 200
Hand & Power Tools Mfr & Distr
N.A.I.C.S.: 333991

Spence Engineering Co., Inc. **(1)**
150 Coldenham Rd, Walden, NY 12586
Tel.: (845) 778-5566
Web Site:
http://www.spenceengineering.com
Sales Range: $75-99.9 Million
Emp.: 130
Mfr of Temperature Regulator
N.A.I.C.S.: 332911

Division (Domestic):

Nicholson Steam Trap **(2)**
150 Coldenham Rd, Walden, NY 12586-
2000
Tel.: (845) 778-5566
Web Site:
http://www.spenceengineering.com
Sales Range: $75-99.9 Million
Mfr of Steam Traps, Floats, Strainers, Pipe
Unions, Valves & Pipe Fittings, Compressed
Air Mufflers, Pipe Couplings, Air Traps &
Pumps
N.A.I.C.S.: 332911

Stratos International, Inc. **(1)**
3000 Lakeside Dr Ste 308n, Bannockburn,
IL 60015-1249
Tel.: (708) 867-9600
Web Site: http://www.stratosoptical.com
Sales Range: $150-199.9 Million
Emp.: 524
Electronic Connectors & Controls; Power
Distribution Systems Mfr
N.A.I.C.S.: 334413

Subsidiary (Domestic):

Rapidwerks LLC **(2)**
1257 Quarry Ln Ste 140, Pleasanton, CA
94566
Tel.: (925) 417-0124
Web Site: http://www.rapidwerks.com
Plastic Product Mfr & Distr
N.A.I.C.S.: 326199

System Plast GmbH **(1)**
Tel.: (49) 352956150
Emp.: 250
Electrical Equipment Supplies & Mfr
N.A.I.C.S.: 335999

System Plast S.r.l. **(1)**
Via Guareschi N 2, Telgate, 24060, Bergamo, Italy
Tel.: (39) 0358351301
Web Site: http://www.svstemplast.com
Electrical Equipment Supplies & Mfr
N.A.I.C.S.: 335999

System Plast, LLC **(1)**
2923 Industrial Dr, Sanford, NC 27330
Tel.: (919) 775-5716
Web Site: http://www.emersonindustrial.com
Industrial Machinery Mfr
N.A.I.C.S.: 333310

Teilsa Servicios, S.L. **(1)**
C/Bekolarra n 4 Pab 23, Alava, 01010, Vitoria, Gasteiz, Spain
Tel.: (34) 945223346
Web Site: https://www.teilsa.com
Sales Range: $10-24.9 Million
Emp.: 14
Electrical Equipment Supplies & Mfr

N.A.I.C.S.: 335999

**Termotec de Chihuahua, S.A. de
C.V.** **(1)**
Pelicano No 5500, Chihuahua, 31166,
Mexico
Tel.: (52) 6144421600
Web Site: www
Electronic Product Distr
N.A.I.C.S.: 423690

Tescom Corporation **(1)**
12616 Industrial Blvd, Elk River, MN 55330-
2491
Tel.: (763) 441-6330
Sales Range: $100-124.9 Million
Emp.: 165
Industrial Valve Mfr
N.A.I.C.S.: 332911
Joe Dillon *(CEO)*

Subsidiary (Non-US):

**Tescom Europe Management
GmbH** **(2)**
An Der Trave 23-25, 23923, Selmsdorf,
Germany
Tel.: (49) 38823310
Web Site: http://www.tescom-europe.com
Sales Range: $25-49.9 Million
Emp.: 105
Electrical Equipment Supplies & Mfr
N.A.I.C.S.: 335999
Dirk Schilling *(Gen Mgr)*

Tescom Europe GmbH & Co. KG **(1)**
An Der Trave 23-25, 23923, Selmsdorf,
Germany
Tel.: (49) 38823310
Sales Range: $25-49.9 Million
Emp.: 105
Electrical Equipment Supplies & Mfr
N.A.I.C.S.: 335999

U.S. Electrical Motors **(1)**
500 Morrow St N, Mena, AR 71953-2521
Tel.: (479) 394-1650
Web Site: http://www.emerson.com
Sales Range: $125-149.9 Million
Emp.: 400
Electric Motor Mfr
N.A.I.C.S.: 335312

**Valvulas, Accesorios Y Maquinarias
S.A.C.** **(1)**
Blarenberglaan 23, 2800, Mechelen, Belgium
Tel.: (32) 15281010
Emp.: 20
Electrical Products Mfr
N.A.I.C.S.: 334513
Bruno Leclercq *(Mng Dir)*

**Valvulas, Accesorios Y Maquinarias
S A C** **(1)**
Calle Juan Alfaro 227, Lima, 18, Peru
Tel.: (51) 12418585
Web Site: http://www.vamsac.com.pe
Industrial Automation Control System Mfr
N.A.I.C.S.: 334513
Silvia Rojas *(Mgr-Power Industry -O & G)*

**Verdant Environmental Technologies
Inc.** **(1)**
5700 Henri-Bourassa Blvd W, Saint Laurent, H4R 1V9, QC, Canada
Tel.: (514) 344-4448
Web Site: http://www.verdant.co
Renewable Energy Services
N.A.I.C.S.: 221111

Vertu Security Limited **(1)**
65 Robinson Road, Rushden, NN10 0EH,
United Kingdom
Tel.: (44) 1604961894
Web Site: https://www.vertusecurity.co.uk
Electrical Appliance Mfr
N.A.I.C.S.: 335210

**Virgo Valves & Controls Private
Limited** **(1)**
277/278 Hinjewadi Phase II Maan, Pune,
411 057, India
Tel.: (91) 2066744000
Web Site: http://www.emersion.com
Emp.: 800
Industrial Valve Mfr
N.A.I.C.S.: 332911

Subsidiary (US):

Vintrol, Inc. **(2)**

5325 SW 36th St, Oklahoma City, OK
73179
Tel.: (405) 261-0770
Web Site: http://www.vintrol.com
Sales Range: $1-9.9 Million
Emp.: 10
Industrial Valve Mfr
N.A.I.C.S.: 332911

Wiegand S.A. de C.V. **(1)**
Arizona Y Florida S/N Parque Industrial Rio
Grande, Nuevo Laredo, 88186, Tamps,
Mexico
Tel.: (52) 8677114400
Electrical Equipment Supplies & Mfr
N.A.I.C.S.: 335999

inmation BNX B.V. **(1)**
High Tech Campus 32, 5656 AE, Eindhoven, Netherlands
Tel.: (31) 624614674
Electrical Appliance Mfr
N.A.I.C.S.: 335210

inmation Software GmbH **(1)**
Hohenzollernring 72, 50672, Cologne, Germany
Tel.: (49) 22116814416
Web Site: https://www.inmation.com
Software Development Services
N.A.I.C.S.: 541511

inmation UK Ltd. **(1)**
Unit 1K Membury Business Park, Hungerford, RG17 7TU, United Kingdom
Tel.: (44) 488469987
Web Site: https://www.inmotionuk.co.uk
Civil Engineering Services
N.A.I.C.S.: 541330

EMERSON RADIO CORP.

959 Route 46 E Ste 210, Parsippany,
NJ 07054
Tel.: (973) 428-2004 **DE**
Web Site:
https://www.emersonradio.com
Year Founded: 1948
MSN—(NYSEAMEX)
Rev.: $9,070,000
Assets: $29,065,000
Liabilities: $2,840,000
Net Worth: $26,225,000
Earnings: $766,000
Emp.: 25
Fiscal Year-end: 03/31/24
Consumer Electronics Importer, Designer, Marketer & Distr
N.A.I.C.S.: 334310
Barry Smith *(Treas & Sr VP-
Operations)*
Christopher Wing-On Ho *(Chm, Pres
& CEO)*
Richard Li *(CFO)*
Michael Andrew Barclay Binney
(COO, Sec, Exec VP & Exec Dir)

EMMAUS LIFE SCIENCES,
INC.

21250 Hawthorne Blvd Ste 800, Torrance, CA 90503
Tel.: (310) 214-0065 **DE**
Web Site:
https://www.emmausmedical.com
EMMA—(OTCQB)
Rev.: $29,597,000
Assets: $35,179,000
Liabilities: $82,935,000
Net Worth: ($47,756,000)
Earnings: ($3,733,000)
Emp.: 51
Fiscal Year-end: 12/31/23
Medical Products & Services
N.A.I.C.S.: 518210
Yutaka Niihara *(Founder)*
Willis C. Lee *(Chm, Co-Pres & COO)*
George Sekulich *(Co-Pres & Chief
Comml Officer)*

Subsidiaries:

EMI Holding, Inc. **(1)**
21250 Hawthorne Blvd Ste 800, Torrance,
CA 90503

Tel.: (310) 214-0065
Web Site: http://www.emmausmedical.com
Fiscal Year-end: 12/31/2020
Pharmaceuticals Mfr
N.A.I.C.S.: 325412

EMMIS COMMUNICATIONS CORPORATION

1 Emmis Plz 40 Monument Cir Ste 700, Indianapolis, IN 46204
Tel.: (317) 266-0100   IN
Web Site: https://www.emmis.com
Year Founded: 1979
EMMS—(NASDAQ)
Rev.: $114,131,000
Assets: $237,746,000
Liabilities: $137,379,000
Net Worth: $100,367,000
Earnings: $23,352,000
Emp.: 350
Fiscal Year-end: 02/28/19
Radio & Television Broadcasting Services; Magazine Publisher
N.A.I.C.S.: 516110
Jeffrey H. Smulyan (Founder, Chm & CEO)
Greg Loewen (Chief Strategy Officer & Pres-Publ Div)
Traci L. Thomson (VP-HR)
Elizabeth M. Ellis (Corp Counsel & VP)
J. Scott Enright (Gen Counsel, Sec & Exec VP)
Patrick M. Walsh (Pres & COO)
Ryan A. Hornaday (CFO, Treas & Exec VP)
Christopher Rickenbach (VP-Fin & Asst Treas)

Subsidiaries:

Digonex Technologies, Inc.   (1)
40 Monument Cir Ste 500, Indianapolis, IN 46204
Tel.: (317) 638-4150
Web Site: http://www.digonex.com
Emp.: 15
Software Development Services
N.A.I.C.S.: 327910
Greg Loewen (CEO)
Justin Bakke (VP-Data Analysis)
Chris Broshears (VP-Product Dev)
Julie Shedd (Dir-Fin)
Harry Tomasides (Chief Revenue Officer)

Emmis Indiana Broadcasting, L.P.   (1)
40 Monument Cir Ste 400, Indianapolis, IN 46204
Tel.: (317) 266-9422
Web Site: http://www.eib.com
Sales Range: $50-74.9 Million
Emp.: 2
Broadcasting Services
N.A.I.C.S.: 516110
Jeff Smulyan (Chm-Bd)

Unit (Domestic):

WIBC-FM   (2)
40 Monument Cir Ste 400, Indianapolis, IN 46204
Tel.: (317) 266-9422
Web Site: http://www.wibc.com
Sales Range: $75-99.9 Million
Emp.: 182
Radio Broadcasting Services
N.A.I.C.S.: 516110
Eric Wunnenberg (Mgr-Sls)
David Wood (Dir-Program)
Maddie Koss (Mgr-Digital Content)
Christopher Presley (Dir-Promos)
Chris Davis (Dir-News)

WLHK-FM   (2)
40 Monument Cir Ste 600, Indianapolis, IN 46204-3011
Tel.: (317) 266-9700
Web Site: http://www.hankfm.com
FM Radio Broadcasting Services
N.A.I.C.S.: 516110
Krystal Keithley (Dir-Promos)
Jackie Kew (Mgr-Digital Content)

Ryan Wild (Dir-Program)
James Conner (Mgr-Sls)
Christy Holifield (Gen Sls Mgr-Agency)

Emmis Meadowlands
Corporation   (1)
40 Monument Cir 7th Fl, Indianapolis, IN 46204
Tel.: (317) 684-6548
Radio Broadcasting Services & Periodical Publisher
N.A.I.C.S.: 513120

Emmis Operating Company   (1)
40 Monument Cir Ste 500, Indianapolis, IN 46204
Tel.: (317) 684-6546
Web Site: http://www.emmis.com
Sales Range: $750-799.9 Million
Emp.: 2,529
Radio & Television Broadcasting Services
N.A.I.C.S.: 516110
Jeffrey H. Smulyan (Chm, Pres & CEO)

Emmis Publishing Corporation   (1)
40 Monument Cir Ste 700, Indianapolis, IN 46204-3011
Tel.: (317) 266-0100
Holding Company; Magazine Publication Services
N.A.I.C.S.: 551112

Subsidiary (Domestic):

Emmis Publishing, L.P.   (2)
40 Monument Cir 700, Indianapolis, IN 46204
Tel.: (317) 266-0100
Web Site:
    http://www.indianapolismonthly.com
Sales Range: $100-124.9 Million
Emp.: 35
Magazine Publisher
N.A.I.C.S.: 513120
Keith Phillips (Pres & Publr)
Allison Edwards (Art Dir-Special Projects)
Andrea Ratcliff (Dir-Special Sections)
Kelly Kendall (Mng Editor)
Todd Urban (Dir-Design)
Abby Broderick (Dir-Special Events)
Michael Rubino (Editor-in-Chief)
Megan Fernandez (Dir-Editorial Ops)
Julia Spalding (Editor-Dining)
Joseph Ball (Editor-Digital)
Margo Wininger (Assoc Dir-Art)
Mike Botkin (Mgr-Production)
Megan Maguire (Coord-Adv Art)
Laura Kruty (Editor-Special Projects)
Christy Moore (Office Mgr)
Melinda Marshall (VP-Fin)

Emmis Radio, L.L.C.   (1)
40 Monument Cir 1 Emmis Plz Ste 700, Indianapolis, IN 46204
Tel.: (317) 266-0100
Web Site: http://www.emmis.com
Sales Range: $450-499.9 Million
Radio Station Broadcasting Services
N.A.I.C.S.: 516110
Richard F. Cummings (Pres-Programming)
Bob Richards (VP-Programming)

Unit (Domestic):

WEPN-FM   (2)
125 W End Ave 6th Fl, New York, NY 10023
Tel.: (646) 699-6800
Web Site: http://www.espn.com
Sales Range: $75-99.9 Million
Emp.: 150
Radio Broadcasting Stations
N.A.I.C.S.: 516110

WKQX-FM   (2)
455 N Cityfront Plaza Dr 6th Fl, Chicago, IL 60611
Tel.: (312) 245-1200
Web Site: http://www.101wkqx.com
Sales Range: $10-24.9 Million
Emp.: 50
Radio Stations
N.A.I.C.S.: 516110

WQHT-FM   (2)
395 Hudson St 7th Fl, New York, NY 10014
Tel.: (212) 229-9797
Web Site: http://www.hot97.com
Sales Range: $200-249.9 Million
Emp.: 250
Radio Broadcasting Services

N.A.I.C.S.: 516110
Ebro Darden (Asst Dir-Programming)

Expres Media s.r.o.   (1)
Vrutocka 48, 821 04, Bratislava, Bratislavsky, Slovakia
Tel.: (421) 259308955
Web Site: http://www.expres.sk
Emp.: 50
Radio & Television Broadcasting Services
N.A.I.C.S.: 516110
Lenka Camborova (Dir-Sls)
Martina Vasekova (Acct Mgr)
Katarina Kourilova (Mgr-Acct & New Media)
Maria Chuda (Acct Mgr)

Expres Net a.s.   (1)
Vrutocka 48, 82104, Bratislava, Ruzinov, Slovakia
Tel.: (421) 259308971
Web Site: http://www.expresnet.sk
Emp.: 12
Radio Networking Services
N.A.I.C.S.: 516210

EMP SOLUTIONS, INC.

PO Box 21, Germantown, OH 45327-0021
Tel.: (513) 424-7777   NV
Web Site:
    http://www.preventlightning.com
EMPS—(OTCIQ)
Electrical Equipment Distr
N.A.I.C.S.: 423690
Jay Kothari (Pres & CEO)

EMPIRE DIVERSIFIED ENERGY, INC.

1400 Main St, Follansbee, WV 26037
Tel.: (304) 935-5851   DE
Web Site:
    https://www.empirediversified
    energy.com
Year Founded: 1986
MPIR—(OTCIQ)
Rev.: $2,775,942
Assets: $98,432,241
Liabilities: $138,189,712
Net Worth: ($39,757,471)
Earnings: ($20,425,202)
Fiscal Year-end: 12/31/23
Motorcycle Mfr
N.A.I.C.S.: 336991
Carl Scotty Ewusiak (Pres)
Frank J. Rosso (CEO)
Bernard Brown (COO)
Kimberly Hawley (Chief Acctg Officer)
Timothy D. Newman (Controller)
William Tuorto (Chm)

EMPIRE GLOBAL GAMING, INC.

555 Woodside Ave, Bellport, NY 11713
Tel.: (631) 769-4222   NV
Web Site:
    http://www.empireglobalgaming
    inc.com
Year Founded: 2010
EPGG—(OTCIQ)
Rev.: $32
Assets: $26,166
Liabilities: $300,855
Net Worth: ($274,689)
Earnings: ($164,432)
Fiscal Year-end: 12/31/21
Casino Gaming Products Distr
N.A.I.C.S.: 713290
Nicholas Sorge Sr. (Founder, Pres & CFO)

EMPIRE PETROLEUM CORPORATION

2200 S Utica Pl Ste 150, Tulsa, OK 74114
Tel.: (539) 444-8002   DE
Web Site:
    https://empirepetroleumcorp.com
Year Founded: 1983

EP—(NYSEAMEX)
Rev.: $52,886,874
Assets: $71,545,075
Liabilities: $48,309,194
Net Worth: $23,235,881
Earnings: $7,084,130
Emp.: 40
Fiscal Year-end: 12/31/22
Oil & Gas Exploration Services
N.A.I.C.S.: 213112
Michael Ray Morrisett (Pres & Principal Fin Officer)
William West (Sr VP-Operations)
Thomas Pritchard (CEO)
Michael Ray Morrisett (Pres)
Eugene Sweeney (COO)

EMPIRE STATE REALTY TRUST, INC.

111 W 33rd St, New York, NY 10120
Tel.: (212) 687-8700   MD
Web Site: https://www.esrtreit.com
Year Founded: 2011
ESRT—(NYSE)
Rev.: $739,572,000
Assets: $4,219,333,000
Liabilities: $2,488,288,000
Net Worth: $1,731,045,000
Earnings: $49,044,000
Emp.: 666
Fiscal Year-end: 12/31/23
Real Estate Investment Trust
N.A.I.C.S.: 525990
Anthony E. Malkin (Chm & CEO)
Thomas P. Durels (Exec VP-Real Estate)
Christina Chiu (Pres)
Stephen V. Horn (CFO, Chief Acctg Officer & Exec VP)
Jordan Berger (VP)
Albert Balady (VP)
Jeffrey Duarte (Portfolio Mgr)
Yvonne Ding (VP)
Diane Fields (VP)
Alex Chin (VP)
Marcia T. Clark (VP)
Rodney Gomes (Sr VP)
Sandy Jacolow (CTO)
Sudhir Kumar (VP)
Eric Liang (Sr VP)
Susanne J. Lieu (Sr VP)
Patricia Niscior (VP)
Laura Palombo (Portfolio Mgr)
Michael Prunty (Sr VP)
Aaron Ratner (Chief Investment Officer)
William Regan (Sr VP)
Samantha Sieka (VP)
Heather L. Houston (Sec)

Subsidiaries:

ESRT 1359 Broadway, L.L.C.   (1)
1350 Broadway Mezzanine, New York, NY 10018
Tel.: (212) 244-3125
Web Site: https://www.1359broadwayny.info
Real Estate Related Services
N.A.I.C.S.: 531390

ESRT MH Holdings, L.L.C.   (1)
60 E 42nd St Ste 48, New York, NY 10165-3003
Tel.: (212) 687-8700
Holding Company
N.A.I.C.S.: 551112

Empire State Realty OP, L.P.   (1)
111 W 33rd St 12th Fl, New York, NY 10120
Tel.: (212) 850-2600
Rev.: $727,040,999
Assets: $4,163,593,999
Liabilities: $2,480,502,999
Net Worth: $1,683,090,999
Earnings: $59,253,999
Emp.: 666
Fiscal Year-end: 12/31/2022
Real Estate Investment Services
N.A.I.C.S.: 525990
Anthony E. Malkin (Chm, Pres & CEO)

Employers Holdings, Inc.—(Continued)

EMPLOYERS HOLDINGS, INC.
Tel.: (775) 327-2700　　　　　　NV
Web Site:
　https://www.employers.com
EIG—(NYSE)
Rev.: $713,500,000
Assets: $3,716,700,000
Liabilities: $2,772,500,000
Net Worth: $944,200,000
Earnings: $48,400,000
Emp.: 676
Fiscal Year-end: 12/31/22
Holding Company; Worker's Compensation Insurance Services
N.A.I.C.S.: 551112
Michael S. Paquette (CFO & Exec VP)
Katherine H. Antonello (Pres & CEO)
John M. Mutschink (Chief Admin Officer)
Christopher W. Laws (Chief Actuary)

Subsidiaries:

Employers Compensation Insurance Co. **(1)**
500 N Brand Blvd Ste 800, Glendale, CA 91203
Tel.: (800) 700-9113
Web Site: http://www.employers.com
Sales Range: $10-24.9 Million
Emp.: 210
Insurance Services
N.A.I.C.S.: 524298

Employers Group, Inc. **(1)**
400 N Continental Blvd Ste 300, El Segundo, CA 90245
Tel.: (775) 327-6000
Web Site: https://www.employersgroup.com
Sales Range: $150-199.9 Million
Emp.: 628
Insurance Services
N.A.I.C.S.: 524298

Employers Insurance Company of Nevada **(1)**
PO Box 539003, Henderson, NV 89053-9003
Sales Range: $25-49.9 Million
Emp.: 120
Insurance Services
N.A.I.C.S.: 524298

PartnerRe Insurance Company of New York **(1)**
200 1st Stamford Pl Ste 400, Stamford, CT 06902
Tel.: (203) 485-4200
General Insurance Services
N.A.I.C.S.: 524210

EMULATE THERAPEUTICS, INC.
13810 SE Eastgate Way Ste 560, Bellevue, WA 98005
Tel.: (425) 415-3140　　　　　　WA
Web Site: https://www.emulatetx.com
Year Founded: 2002
EMTX—(NASDAQ)
Rev.: $241,000
Assets: $7,737,000
Liabilities: $54,886,000
Net Worth: ($47,149,000)
Earnings: ($22,092,000)
Emp.: 7
Fiscal Year-end: 12/31/21
Biotechnology Research & Development Services
N.A.I.C.S.: 541714
Chris E. Rivera (Pres, CEO & Chm)
Steven Pope (Sec, VP & Gen Counsel)
Bennett M. Butters (Founder & Principal)
Donna Morgan Murray (Chief Regulatory Officer)
David Matteson (VP-Investor Relations)

ENABLE HOLDINGS, INC.
1140 W Thorndale Ave, Itasca, IL 60143-1335
Tel.: (773) 272-5000　　　　　　DE
ENAB—(OTCIQ)
Sales Range: Less than $1 Million
Emp.: 41
Excess Inventory Solutions
N.A.I.C.S.: 551112
Steven Alan Sjoblad (Chm)

Subsidiaries:

uBid.com, Inc. **(1)**
8725 W Higins Rd Ste 900, Chicago, IL 60631
Tel.: (773) 272-5000
Online Auction Services
N.A.I.C.S.: 459510
Alexander Sickel (Sr Engr-Network Infrastructure)
Michael Schmahl (Exec VP & Gen Counsel)
Bob Geras (Chm)
Michael Moss (Dir-E-Commerce)

ENABLE IPC CORP.
26893 Bouquet Canyon Rd Ste C-110, Saugus, CA 91350
Tel.: (661) 347-0607　　　　　　DE
Year Founded: 2005
EIPC—(OTCIQ)
Lithium Battery Mfr
N.A.I.C.S.: 335910
David A. Walker (Chm & CEO)

ENABLING ASIA, INC.
3445 Lawrence Ave, Oceanside, NY 11572
Tel.: (646) 768-8417　　　　　　NV
EAIN—(OTCIQ)
Software Development Services
N.A.I.C.S.: 541511
David Lazar (CEO)

ENANTA PHARMACEUTICALS, INC.
4 Kingsbury Ave, Watertown, MA 02472
Tel.: (617) 607-0800　　　　　　DE
Web Site: https://www.enanta.com
Year Founded: 1995
ENTA—(NASDAQ)
Rev.: $67,635,000
Assets: $376,652,000
Liabilities: $247,838,000
Not Worth: $128,814,000
Earnings: ($116,045,000)
Emp.: 131
Fiscal Year-end: 09/30/24
Pharmaceuticals Mfr
N.A.I.C.S.: 325412
Jay R. Luly (Pres & CEO)
Yat Sun Or (Chief Scientific Officer & Sr VP-R&D)
Paul J. Mellett (CFO & Sr VP-Fin & Admin)
Tara L. Kieffer (Sr VP-New Product Strategy & Dev)
Brendan Luu (Sr VP-Bus Dev)
Scott T. Rottinghaus (Chief Medical Officer & Sr VP)

ENB FINANCIAL CORP.
31 E Main St, Ephrata, PA 17522
Tel.: (717) 733-4181
Web Site: https://www.epnb.com
Year Founded: 2008
ENBP—(OTCQX)
Rev.: $55,959,000
Assets: $1,858,716,000
Liabilities: $1,761,381,000
Net Worth: $97,335,000
Earnings: $14,631,000
Emp.: 286
Fiscal Year-end: 12/31/22
Bank Holding Company
N.A.I.C.S.: 551111

Jeffrey S. Stauffer (Chm, Pres & CEO)
Rachel G. Bitner (Treas & Principal Fin Officer)
Joselyn D. Strohm (COO & Sr Exec VP)

Subsidiaries:

Ephrata National Bank **(1)**
31 E Main St, Ephrata, PA 17522
Tel.: (717) 733-4181
Web Site: https://www.epnb.com
Sales Range: $10-24.9 Million
Emp.: 230
Banking Services
N.A.I.C.S.: 522110
Jeffrey S. Stauffer (Chm, Pres & CEO)
Rachel G. Bitner (CFO & Exec VP)
Joselyn D. Strohm (COO & Sr Exec VP)
Adrienne L. Miller (Sr VP)

ENCISION INC.
6797 Winchester Cir, Boulder, CO 80301
Tel.: (303) 444-2600
Web Site: https://www.encision.com
ECIA—(OTCIQ)
Rev.: $6,585,882
Assets: $3,810,716
Liabilities: $1,983,968
Net Worth: $1,826,748
Earnings: ($691,783)
Emp.: 22
Fiscal Year-end: 03/31/24
Surgical Instrument Developer & Mfr
N.A.I.C.S.: 339112
David W. Newton (Founder)
Mala Ray (CFO, Principal Acctg Officer, Treas, Sec & Controller)
Brian Jackman (VP-Mktg)
Gregory J. Trudel (Pres & CEO)
Peter Geary (COO & VP-Ops)

ENCOMPASS ENERGY SERVICES, INC.
410 N Walnut Ave Ste 100, Oklahoma City, OK 73104
Tel.: (405) 595-2022
Web Site:
　http://www.encompassservices.com
EESI—(OTCIQ)
Renewable Energy Consulting Services
N.A.I.C.S.: 541690
Joseph Arsee (Mgr-Ops)

ENCOMPASS HEALTH CORPORATION
9001 Liberty Pkwy, Birmingham, AL 35242
Tel.: (205) 967-7116　　　　　　DE
Web Site:
　https://www.encompasshealth.com
Year Founded: 1984
EHC—(NYSE)
Rev.: $4,801,200,000
Assets: $6,102,400,000
Liabilities: $3,847,200,000
Net Worth: $2,255,200,000
Earnings: $352,000,000
Emp.: 22,366
Fiscal Year-end: 12/31/23
Rehabilitation & Long-Term Acute Care Services
N.A.I.C.S.: 623110
April K. Anthony (Founder)
Mark J. Tarr (Pres & CEO)
Douglas E. Coltharp (CFO & Exec VP)
Edmund Fay (Treas & Sr VP)
Barbara A. Jacobsmeyer (CEO-Home Health & Hospice)
Elissa Charbonneau (Chief Medical Officer)
Patrick Darby (Gen Counsel, Sec & Exec VP)

Subsidiaries:

A & B Homecare Solutions, LLC **(1)**
446A Blake St 3rd Fl, New Haven, CT 06515
Tel.: (203) 495-1900
Web Site: https://www.abhomecare.com
Health Care Srvices
N.A.I.C.S.: 621610

Abba Home Health, L.P. **(1)**
7120 W Interstate 40 Ste 300A, Amarillo, TX 79106
Tel.: (806) 351-1700
Health Care Srvices
N.A.I.C.S.: 621610

Advanced Homecare Holdings, Inc. **(1)**
7502 Greenville Ave, Dallas, TX 75231
Tel.: (214) 378-6800
Holding Company
N.A.I.C.S.: 551112

Advanced Homecare Management, Inc. **(1)**
10300 N Central Expwy Ste 355, Dallas, TX 75231
Tel.: (214) 503-7700
Web Site: http://www.ehhi.com
Sales Range: $200-249.9 Million
Emp.: 3,500
Home Healthcare Agencies & Pediatric & Hospice Services
N.A.I.C.S.: 621610

Alacare Home Health Services, Inc. **(1)**
2400 John Hawkins Pkwy Ste 104, Birmingham, AL 35244
Tel.: (888) 252-2273
Web Site: http://www.alacare.com
Women Healthcare Services
N.A.I.C.S.: 621610

AnMed Encompass Health Rehabilitation Hospital, LLC **(1)**
1 Spring Back Way, Anderson, SC 29621
Tel.: (864) 716-2600
Health Care Srvices
N.A.I.C.S.: 621610
Denise Murray (CEO)
William Vogenitz (Dir-Medical)
Jennifer Risser (Chief Nursing Officer)

Apex Hospice LLC **(1)**
6500 W Fwy Ste 451, Fort Worth, TX 76116
Tel.: (817) 263-8808
Health Care Srvices
N.A.I.C.S.: 621610

BJC/HealthSouth Rehabilitation Center, L.L.C. **(1)**
4455 Duncan Ave, Saint Louis, MO 63110
Tel.: (314) 658-3800
Medical Rehabilitation Services
N.A.I.C.S.: 622310

Best Home Care LP **(1)**
111 E 7th St Ste C, Big Spring, TX 79720
Tel.: (432) 264-0044
Health Care Srvices
N.A.I.C.S.: 621610

CMS Rehab of WF, L.P. **(1)**
3901 Armory Rd, Wichita Falls, TX 76302-2204
Tel.: (940) 720-5700
Web Site: http://www.healthsouth.com
Emp.: 200
Medical Rehabilitation Services
N.A.I.C.S.: 622310
Jody Gregory (Chief Nursing Officer)
Paul McShan (Dir-Plant Ops)
Kathleen Pirtle (Dir-HR)
Ashvin Patel (Dir-Medical)
Christi Cook (Dir-Case Mgmt)
Britany Rhoden (Dir-Bus Dev)
Mary Walker (Controller)
Lauren Aponte (Dir-Quality & Risk Mgmt)
Leandra Madsen (Dir-Pharmacy)
Cassie Neece (Dir-Therapy Ops)
Jacob Truelove (Chief Nursing Officer)

Central Arkansas Rehabilitation Associates, L.P. **(1)**
2201 Wildwood Ave, Sherwood, AR 72120
Tel.: (501) 834-1800
Web Site:
　http://www.stvincentrehabhospital.com

Medical Rehabilitation Services
N.A.I.C.S.: 622310
Kevin Collins *(Dir-Medical)*
Sharon Cathey *(Dir-Case Mgmt)*
Kim Hibbard *(Dir-Bus Dev)*
David Rainosek *(Assoc Dir-Medical)*
Shonda McCauley *(Dir-Therapy Ops)*
Daniel Bright *(Dir-Pharmacy)*
Sherry Clements *(Dir-Quality & Risk Management)*
Lisa Simpkins *(Chief Nursing Officer)*
Terri Evans *(Controller)*
Kenny Ross *(Dir-Facilities Mgmt)*
Alicia Wilkins *(Dir-Human Resources)*

Central Louisiana Rehab Associates, L.P. **(1)**
104 N 3rd St, Alexandria, LA 71301-8581
Tel.: (318) 449-1370
Web Site:
   http://www.healthsouthalexandria.com
Sales Range: $25-49.9 Million
Emp.: 150
Medical Rehabilitation Services
N.A.I.C.S.: 622310
Vasudeva Dhulipala *(Dir-Medical)*
Joanna Williams *(Chief Nursing Officer)*

Continental Home Care, Inc. **(1)**
111 S York St, Muskogee, OK 74403
Tel.: (918) 682-6202
Health Care Srvices
N.A.I.C.S.: 621610

DRC Health Systems, L.P. **(1)**
12727 Featherwood Dr Ste 130, Houston,
TX 77034
Tel.: (281) 484-7070
Health Care Srvices
N.A.I.C.S.: 621610

DayByDay Staff Relief, Inc. **(1)**
1913 W Tacoma St Ste G-H, Broken Arrow,
OK 74012
Tel.: (918) 524-1100
Web Site: http://www.encompasshealth.com
Health Care Srvices
N.A.I.C.S.: 621610

Dosik, Inc. **(1)**
2784 US Hwy 190 W Ste 300, Livingston,
TX 77351
Tel.: (936) 247-4700
Health Care Srvices
N.A.I.C.S.: 621610

EHHI Holdings, Inc. **(1)**
6688 N Central Expy Ste 1300, Dallas, TX
75206
Health Care Srvices
N.A.I.C.S.: 621610

Encompass Health Deaconess Rehabilitation Hospital, LLC **(1)**
9355 Warrick Trl, Newburgh, IN 47630
Tel.: (812) 476-9983
Health Care Srvices
N.A.I.C.S.: 621610
Blake Bunner *(CEO)*
Mohammed Adeel *(Exec Dir-Medical)*
R. N. Lisa Goans *(Chief Nursing Officer)*

Encompass Health Rehabilitation Hospital of Albuquerque, LLC **(1)**
7000 Jefferson St NE, Albuquerque, NM
87109
Tel.: (505) 344-9478
N.A.I.C.S.: 621610
Susan Blanchard *(Chief Nursing Officer)*
J Michael Long *(Dir-Medical)*
Ladessa Forrest *(CEO)*

Encompass Health Rehabilitation Hospital of Altamonte Springs, LLC **(1)**
831 S State Rd 434, Altamonte Springs, FL
32714
Tel.: (407) 587-8600
Health Care Srvices
N.A.I.C.S.: 621610
Ashley Collier *(Dir-Health Information Mgmt)*
Matthew Dieter *(Dir-Pharmacy)*
Donna Ogilvie *(Chief Nursing Officer)*

Encompass Health Rehabilitation Hospital of Altoona, LLC **(1)**
2005 Valley View Blvd, Altoona, PA 16602
Tel.: (814) 944-3535
Web Site: https://encompasshealth.com

Nursing Care Facility Services
N.A.I.C.S.: 623110
Scott A. Filler *(CEO)*
Rebecca Y. Winkler *(Dir-Outpatient Svcs)*

Encompass Health Rehabilitation Hospital of Bakersfield, LLC **(1)**
5001 Commerce Dr, Bakersfield, CA 93309
Tel.: (661) 323-5500
Health Care Srvices
N.A.I.C.S.: 621610
Martha Samora *(CEO)*
Janette V Menchaca *(Dir-Therapy Ops)*
Karen Bezuidenhout *(Chief Nursing Officer)*

Encompass Health Rehabilitation Hospital of Bluffton, LLC **(1)**
107 Seagrass Station Rd, Bluffton, SC
29910
Tel.: (843) 836-8200
Web Site: https://encompasshealth.com
Health Care Srvices
N.A.I.C.S.: 621610

Encompass Health Rehabilitation Hospital of Braintree, LLC **(1)**
250 Pond St, Braintree, MA 02184
Tel.: (781) 348-2500
Web Site: https://encompasshealth.com
Health Care Srvices
N.A.I.C.S.: 621610
Randy Doherty *(CEO)*

Encompass Health Rehabilitation Hospital of Cardinal Hill, LLC **(1)**
2050 Versailles Rd, Lexington, KY 40504
Tel.: (859) 254-5701
Web Site: https://encompasshealth.com
Health Care Srvices
N.A.I.C.S.: 621610
Susan Mcdowell *(Dir-Medical)*
Kelli Eads *(Dir-Bus Dev)*

Encompass Health Rehabilitation Hospital of Cincinnati, LLC **(1)**
151 W Galbraith Rd, Cincinnati, OH 45216
Tel.: (513) 418-5601
Web Site: https://encompasshealth.com
Health Care Srvices
N.A.I.C.S.: 621610
Ashok Poluri *(Dir-Medical)*
Gus Bowling *(Dir-Plant Ops)*

Encompass Health Rehabilitation Hospital of Dayton, LLC **(1)**
835 S Main St, Dayton, OH 45402
Tel.: (937) 424-8200
Health Care Srvices
N.A.I.C.S.: 621610
Minu Nair *(Dir-Quality & Rick Mgmt)*

Encompass Health Rehabilitation Hospital of East Valley, LLC **(1)**
5652 E Baseline Rd, Mesa, AZ 85206
Tel.: (480) 567-0350
Web Site: https://encompasshealth.com
Health Care Srvices
N.A.I.C.S.: 621610
Samantha Jimenez *(Chief Nursing Officer)*
Kathy Lovato *(Dir-Therapy Ops)*
Shelly Minde *(Dir-HR)*

Encompass Health Rehabilitation Hospital of Erie, LLC **(1)**
143 E 2nd St, Erie, PA 16507
Tel.: (814) 878-1200
Web Site: https://encompasshealth.com
Health Care Srvices
N.A.I.C.S.: 621610
Corey Hickey *(Dir-Medical)*

Encompass Health Rehabilitation Hospital of Fort Smith, LLC **(1)**
1401 S J St, Fort Smith, AR 72901
Tel.: (479) 785-3300
Web Site: https://encompasshealth.com
Health Care Srvices
N.A.I.C.S.: 621610
Dawn Watts *(CEO)*
Bradley Short *(Dir-Medical)*

Encompass Health Rehabilitation Hospital of Franklin, LLC **(1)**
1000 Physicians Way, Franklin, TN 37067
Tel.: (615) 721-4000
Web Site: https://encompasshealth.com
Health Care Srvices
N.A.I.C.S.: 621610
Scott Peterson *(CEO)*
Scott Craig *(Dir-Medical)*
Sheila Davy *(Dir-Therapy Ops)*
Dawn Mcmaster *(Dir-HR)*

Encompass Health Rehabilitation Hospital of Fredericksburg, LLC **(1)**
300 Park Hill Dr, Fredericksburg, VA 22401
Tel.: (540) 368-7300
Web Site: https://encompasshealth.com
Nursing Care Facility Services
N.A.I.C.S.: 623110
David Cashwell *(CEO)*
Rebecca Edwards *(Dir-Therapy Ops)*
Felix Fianko *(Dir-Pharmacy)*

Encompass Health Rehabilitation Hospital of Gadsden, LLC **(1)**
801 Goodyear Ave, Gadsden, AL 35903
Tel.: (256) 439-5000
Web Site: https://encompasshealth.com
Nursing Care Facility Services
N.A.I.C.S.: 623110
Leslie Davis *(Dir-Case Mgmt)*
Liz Mahon *(CEO)*

Encompass Health Rehabilitation Hospital of Gulfport, LLC **(1)**
4500 13th St Ste 900, Gulfport, MS 39501
Tel.: (228) 822-6965
Web Site: https://encompasshealth.com
Health Care Srvices
N.A.I.C.S.: 621610
Lee Voulters *(Dir-Medical)*
Jacqueline Lipski *(Dir-Therapy)*

Encompass Health Rehabilitation Hospital of Iowa City, LLC **(1)**
2450 Coral Ct, Coralville, IA 52241
Tel.: (319) 645-3300
Healtcare Services
N.A.I.C.S.: 621999
Angela Zaremba *(CEO)*
Philip Chen *(Dir-Medical)*
Katie Hfinkey *(Dir-Pharmacy)*
Brenda Bell *(Chief Nursing Officer)*
Brenda Harvey *(Dir-Case Mgmt)*
Nic Johnson *(Controller)*
Bradley Morrison *(Dir-Business Development)*
Joshua Schultz *(Dir-Facilities Mgmt)*
Stacey Hodges *(Dir-Therapy Ops)*
Kim Lopez *(Dir-Quality & Risk)*
Beth Nissen *(Dir-Human Resources)*

Encompass Health Rehabilitation Hospital of Kingsport, LLC **(1)**
113 Cassel Dr, Kingsport, TN 37660
Tel.: (423) 246-7240
Web Site: https://encompasshealth.com
Health Care Srvices
N.A.I.C.S.: 621610
Troy Clark *(CEO)*
Stan Hunt *(Dir-Plant Ops)*
Donna Weinman *(Dir-Pharmacy)*

Encompass Health Rehabilitation Hospital of Lakeview, LLC **(1)**
134 Heartland Dr, Elizabethtown, KY 42701
Tel.: (270) 769-3100
Web Site: https://encompasshealth.com
Health Care Srvices
N.A.I.C.S.: 621610
Tony Abang *(Dir-Medical)*
Cara Hobbs *(Dir-Pharmacy)*
Valerie Matney *(Dir-Therapy Ops)*

Encompass Health Rehabilitation Hospital of Las Vegas, LLC **(1)**
1250 S Valley View Blvd, Las Vegas, NV
89102
Tel.: (702) 877-8898
Web Site: https://encompasshealth.com
Health Care Srvices
N.A.I.C.S.: 621610
Farzin Farhang *(Dir-Medical)*
Pamela M Smith *(Dir-Therapy Ops)*
Tracey Bunch *(Dir-Quality & Risk Mgmt)*

Encompass Health Rehabilitation Hospital of Miami, LLC **(1)**
20601 Old Cutler Rd, Miami, FL 33189
Tel.: (305) 251-3800
Web Site: https://encompasshealth.com
Nursing Care Facility Services
N.A.I.C.S.: 623110
Tarif Chowdhury *(CEO)*

Encompass Health Rehabilitation Hospital of Modesto, LLC **(1)**
1303 Mable Ave, Modesto, CA 95355
Tel.: (209) 857-3400
Web Site: https://encompasshealth.com
Health Care Srvices

N.A.I.C.S.: 621610
Beth Bacher *(CEO)*
Lisa Clawson *(Dir-Bus Dev)*
Denise Shackelford *(Dir-Therapy Ops)*

Encompass Health Rehabilitation Hospital of Montgomery, Inc. **(1)**
4465 Narrow Ln Rd, Montgomery, AL 36116
Tel.: (334) 284-7700
Web Site: https://encompasshealth.com
Health Care Srvices
N.A.I.C.S.: 621610
Jeffrey Eng *(Dir-Medical)*
Michelle Von Arx *(CEO)*

Encompass Health Rehabilitation Hospital of New England, LLC **(1)**
2 Rehabilitation Way, Woburn, MA 01801
Tel.: (781) 935-5050
Web Site: https://encompasshealth.com
Health Care Srvices
N.A.I.C.S.: 621610
David Coggins *(CEO)*
Daniel Lyons *(Dir-Medical)*
Nerline Destin *(Dir-Case Mgmt)*
Teresa Hayes *(Dir-Bus Dev)*

Encompass Health Rehabilitation Hospital of Northern Kentucky, LLC **(1)**
201 Medical Village Dr, Edgewood, KY
41017
Tel.: (859) 394-6700
Web Site: https://encompasshealth.com
Health Care Services
N.A.I.C.S.: 621610
Jeremy Yates *(CEO)*
Bridgette Keith *(Dir-HR)*
Mary Pfeffer *(Dir-Therapy Ops)*

Encompass Health Rehabilitation Hospital of Northern Virginia, LLC **(1)**
24430 Millstream Dr, Aldie, VA 20105
Tel.: (703) 957-2000
Web Site: https://encompasshealth.com
Nursing Care Facility Services
N.A.I.C.S.: 623110
Matthew Pearson *(CEO)*

Encompass Health Rehabilitation Hospital of Ocala, LLC **(1)**
2275 SW 22nd Ln, Ocala, FL 34471
Tel.: (352) 282-4000
Web Site: https://encompasshealth.com
Health Care Srvices
N.A.I.C.S.: 621610
Karthik Muthu *(CEO)*

Encompass Health Rehabilitation Hospital of Rock Hill, LLC **(1)**
1795 Dr Frank Gaston Blvd, Rock Hill, SC
29732
Tel.: (803) 326-3500
Web Site: https://encompasshealth.com
Health Care Srvices
N.A.I.C.S.: 621610
Shiranee Jayasooriya *(Dir-Medical)*
Tianna Miller *(Dir-Case Mgmt)*
Scott Butler *(CEO)*

Encompass Health Rehabilitation Hospital of Savannah, LLC **(1)**
6510 Seawright Dr, Savannah, GA 31406
Tel.: (912) 235-6000
Web Site: https://encompasshealth.com
Health Care Srvices
N.A.I.C.S.: 621610
Steven Novack *(Dir-Medical)*
Greg Dutton *(Dir-Quality)*
Randal Hamilton *(CEO)*

Encompass Health Rehabilitation Hospital of Shelby County, LLC **(1)**
900 Oak Mountain Commons Ln, Pelham,
AL 35124
Tel.: (205) 216-7600
Web Site: https://encompasshealth.com
Health Care Srvices
N.A.I.C.S.: 621610
Sumer Herald *(Dir-Case Mgmt)*
Michael Bartell *(CEO)*

Encompass Health Rehabilitation Hospital of Sugar Land, LLC **(1)**
1325 Hwy 6, Sugar Land, TX 77478
Tel.: (281) 276-7574
Web Site: https://encompasshealth.com
Nursing Care Facility Services

Encompass Health Corporation—(Continued)

N.A.I.C.S.: 623110
Bindu Varghese *(CEO)*
Megan Vaughn *(Dir-Pharmacy)*
Jessica Thomas *(Dir-Therapy)*

Encompass Health Rehabilitation Hospital of Sunrise, LLC (1)
4399 Nob Hill Rd, Sunrise, FL 33351
Tel.: (954) 749-0300
Web Site: https://encompasshealth.com
Health Care Srvices
N.A.I.C.S.: 621610
Scott Tannenbaum *(Dir-Medical)*
Stacy Thomashaw *(Dir-Therapy Ops)*

Encompass Health Rehabilitation Hospital of Toledo, LLC (1)
4647 Monroe St, Toledo, OH 43623
Tel.: (567) 290-3500
Healtcare Services
N.A.I.C.S.: 621610
Al Aray *(Dir-Facilities Mgmt)*
Colleen Harrell *(Dir-Pharmacy)*
Mohamed Abdel Khalek *(Dir-Medical)*
Nick Brillhart *(Controller)*
Anthony Guinn *(Dir-Therapy Ops)*
Peggy Lucio *(Dir-Human Resources)*
Matt Ritter *(Dir-Business Development)*
Marvella Foster *(Dir-Case Mgmt)*
Mark Macaleese *(Dir-Quality & Risk)*

Encompass Health Rehabilitation Hospital of Tustin, L.P. (1)
15120 Kensington Park Dr, Tustin, CA 92782
Tel.: (714) 832-9200
Health Care Srvices
N.A.I.C.S.: 621610
Ann Vasile *(Dir-Medical)*
Gretchin Bitner *(Dir-Therapy Ops)*
Maryam Jouharzadeh *(Dir-Pharmacy)*
Joann Roiz *(Dir-HR)*

Encompass Health Rehabilitation Hospital of Western Massachusetts, LLC (1)
222 State St, Ludlow, MA 01056
Tel.: (413) 308-3300
Web Site: https://encompasshealth.com
Health Care Srvices
N.A.I.C.S.: 621610
John R Hunt *(CEO)*
Adnan Dahdul *(Dir-Medical)*
Danuta Budzyna *(Dir-HR)*
Deb Carney *(Dir-Therapy Ops)*
Deborah Santos *(Dir-Quality)*

Encompass Health Rehabilitation Hospital of Westerville, LLC (1)
597 Executive Campus Dr, Westerville, OH 43082
Tel.: (614) 392-3400
Web Site: https://encompasshealth.com
Health Care Srvices
N.A.I.C.S.: 621610
Angela Bridges *(CEO)*
Polly Bailey *(Dir-Bus Dev)*
Merri Foltz *(Dir-HR)*
Camille Milligan *(Dir-Therapy Ops)*

Encompass Health Rehabilitation Hospital of York, LLC (1)
1850 Normandie Dr, York, PA 17408
Tel.: (717) 767-6941
Web Site: https://encompasshealth.com
Health Care Srvices
N.A.I.C.S.: 621610
Bruce Sicilia *(Dir-Medical)*

Encompass Home Health of Austin, LLC (1)
7901 E Riverside Dr Bldg 2, Austin, TX 78744
Tel.: (512) 326-4191
Health Care Srvices
N.A.I.C.S.: 621610

Encompass Home Health of Colorado, LLC (1)
910 Pinon Ranch View Ste 211, Colorado Springs, CO 80907
Tel.: (719) 265-6931
Health Care Srvices
N.A.I.C.S.: 621610

Encompass Home Health of DFW, LLC (1)

1501 Hughes Rd Ste 100, Grapevine, TX 76051
Tel.: (817) 329-5449
Health Care Srvices
N.A.I.C.S.: 621610

Encompass Home Health of the Mid Atlantic, LLC (1)
6701 Peters Creek Rd Ste 100, Roanoke, VA 24019
Tel.: (540) 774-4970
Health Care Srvices
N.A.I.C.S.: 621610

Encompass Home Health of the Southeast, LLC (1)
7710 NW 71st Ct Ste 200, Tamarac, FL 33321
Tel.: (954) 746-1347
Health Care Srvices
N.A.I.C.S.: 621610

Encompass Home Health of the West, LLC (1)
3686 Washington Pkwy, Idaho Falls, ID 83404
Tel.: (208) 528-8100
Health Care Srvices
N.A.I.C.S.: 621610

Encompass Hospice of the West, LLC (1)
183 Vista Dr Ste A, Pocatello, ID 83201
Tel.: (208) 637-1100
Health Care Srvices
N.A.I.C.S.: 621610

Encompass Rehabilitation Hospital The Vintage, LLC (1)
20180 Chasewood Park Dr, Houston, TX 77070
Tel.: (281) 205-5100
Health Care Srvices
N.A.I.C.S.: 621610
Krista Uselman *(CEO)*
Amy Anderson *(Chief Nursing Officer)*

Encompass Rehabilitation Hospital of Abilene, LLC (1)
6401 Directors Pkwy, Abilene, TX 79606
Tel.: (325) 691-1600
Web Site: https://encompasshealth.com
Health Care Srvices
N.A.I.C.S.: 621610
Monica H. Wichner *(Dir-Medical)*
Boyd Davis *(CEO)*

Encompass Rehabilitation Hospital of Dallas, LLC (1)
7930 Northaven Rd, Dallas, TX 75230
Tel.: (214) 706-8200
Web Site: https://encompasshealth.com
Health Care Srvices
N.A.I.C.S.: 621610
Sharon Garrett *(CEO)*

Encompass Rehabilitation Hospital of Pearland, LLC (1)
2121 Business Center Dr, Pearland, TX 77584
Tel.: (346) 907-3000
Web Site: https://encompasshealth.com
Health Care Srvices
N.A.I.C.S.: 621610
Mike Cabiro *(CEO)*
Natasha E. Rose *(Dir-Medical)*
Oscar Gonzalez *(Coord-PAS)*

Encompass Rehabilitation Hospital of Richardson, LLC (1)
3351 Waterview Pkwy, Richardson, TX 76080
Tel.: (972) 398-5700
Web Site: https://encompasshealth.com
Health Care Srvices
N.A.I.C.S.: 621610
Ieesha Cannida *(Dir-HR)*
Ted Philmon *(Dir-Pharmacy)*

Encompass Rehabilitation Hospital of Round Rock, LLC (1)
1400 Hester s Crossing, Round Rock, TX 78681
Tel.: (512) 244-4400
Web Site: https://encompasshealth.com
Health Care Srvices
N.A.I.C.S.: 621610
Octavio Vela *(Dir-Medical)*
Lisa Luedecke *(Dir-HR)*

Encompass Rehabilitation Hospital of The Woodlands, Inc. (1)
18550 I-45 S, Conroe, TX 77384
Tel.: (281) 364-2000
Health Care Srvices
N.A.I.C.S.: 621610
Stephanie Mayne *(Chief Nursing Officer)*
Valerie Wells *(Dir-HR)*

Encompass Rehabilitation Hospital of the Mid-Cities, LLC (1)
2304 State Hwy 121, Bedford, TX 76021
Tel.: (817) 684-2000
Web Site: https://encompasshealth.com
Health Care Srvices
N.A.I.C.S.: 621610
Ashley Donahoe *(CEO)*

Encompass of Fort Worth, LP (1)
6500 W Fwy Ste 451, Fort Worth, TX 76116
Tel.: (817) 737-4300
Health Care Srvices
N.A.I.C.S.: 621610

Encompass of West Texas, LP (1)
1 Village Dr Ste 200, Abilene, TX 79606
Tel.: (325) 695-3888
Health Care Srvices
N.A.I.C.S.: 621610

Excella Home Health Agency, LLC (1)
123 Park Ave, West Springfield, MA 01089-3337
Tel.: (413) 732-8700
Health Care Srvices
N.A.I.C.S.: 621610

First Choice Children's Homecare, LP (1)
2424 Wilcrest Dr Ste 110, Houston, TX 77042
Tel.: (713) 666-8287
Health Care Srvices
N.A.I.C.S.: 621610

Geisinger HealthSouth Rehabilitation Hospital (1)
64 Rehab Ln, Danville, PA 17821-8498
Tel.: (570) 271-6110
Web Site: http://www.geisingerhealthsouth.com
Vocational Rehabilitation Services
N.A.I.C.S.: 624310
Lori Dillon *(Pres)*

Guardian Home Care, Inc. (1)
3370 10th St Ste D, Baker City, OR 97814
Tel.: (541) 523-3335
Health Care Srvices
N.A.I.C.S.: 621610

HealthCare Innovations of Oklahoma, L.L.C. (1)
614 N Washington Ave Ste A & B, Durant, OK 74701
Tel.: (580) 920-0600
Health Care Srvices
N.A.I.C.S.: 621610

HealthCare Innovations of Western Oklahoma, L.L.C. (1)
1320 NW Homestead Dr Ste H, Lawton, OK 73505
Tel.: (580) 248-7400
Health Care Srvices
N.A.I.C.S.: 621610

HealthCare InnovationsTravertine Health Services, L.L.C. (1)
2318 W 7th Ave, Stillwater, OK 74074
Tel.: (405) 707 8065
Health Care Srvices
N.A.I.C.S.: 621610

HealthSouth Clinical Technologies, LLC (1)
4255 Praytor Way, Trussville, AL 35173-1811
Tel.: (205) 655-6591
Emp.: 4
Health Care Srvices
N.A.I.C.S.: 621610
Jay Grinney *(Pres)*

HealthSouth East Valley Rehabilitation Hospital, LLC (1)
5652 E Baseline Rd, Mesa, AZ 85206
Tel.: (480) 567-0350

Web Site: http://www.healthsoutheastvalley.com
Health Care Srvices
N.A.I.C.S.: 621610

HealthSouth Harmarville Rehabilitation Hospital, LLC (1)
320 Guys Run Rd, Pittsburgh, PA 15238
Tel.: (412) 828-1300
Web Site: http://www.healthsouthharmarville.com
Emp.: 450
Medical Rehabilitation Services
N.A.I.C.S.: 622310
Dan Vrana *(Controller)*
Eileen Skalski *(Chief Nursing Officer)*
Kathy Grills *(Dir-HR)*
Casey Rodak *(Dir-Therapy Ops)*
Lisa Hopkins *(Dir-Area Bus Dev)*
James Kreshon Jr. *(Dir-Medical)*

HealthSouth Littleton Rehabilitation, LLC (1)
1001 W Mineral Ave, Littleton, CO 80120
Tel.: (303) 334-1100
Web Site: http://www.healthsouthdenver.com
Health Care Srvices
N.A.I.C.S.: 621610

HealthSouth Mesa Rehabilitation Hospital, LLC (1)
5652 E Baseline Rd, Mesa, AZ 85206
Tel.: (480) 567-0350
Sales Range: $25-49.9 Million
Emp.: 200
Medical Rehabilitation Services
N.A.I.C.S.: 622310

HealthSouth Middletown Rehabilitation Hospital, LLC (1)
250 E Hampden Rd, Middletown, DE 19709
Tel.: (302) 464-3400
Web Site: http://www.healthsouthmiddletown.com
Health Care Srvices
N.A.I.C.S.: 621610

HealthSouth Plano Rehabilitation Hospital, LLC (1)
2800 W 15th St, Plano, TX 75075
Tel.: (972) 612-9000
Web Site: http://www.healthsouthplano.com
Health Care Srvices
N.A.I.C.S.: 621610

HealthSouth Rehabilitation Center of New Hampshire, Inc. (1)
254 Pleasant St, Concord, NH 03301
Tel.: (603) 226-9800
Medical Rehabilitation Services
N.A.I.C.S.: 622310

HealthSouth Rehabilitation Center, Inc. (1)
900 E Cheves St, Florence, SC 29506
Tel.: (843) 679-9000
Web Site: http://www.healthsouth.com
Medical Rehabilitation Services
N.A.I.C.S.: 622310

HealthSouth Rehabilitation Hospital The Woodlands, Inc. (1)
18550 I45 S, Conroe, TX 77384
Tel.: (281) 364-2000
Web Site: http://www.healthsouthnorthhouston.com
Health Care Srvices
N.A.I.C.S.: 621610

HealthSouth Rehabilitation Hospital of Arlington, LLC (1)
3200 Matlock Rd, Arlington, TX 76015
Tel.: (817) 468-4000
Web Site: http://www.healthsouth.com
Emp.: 250
Medical Rehabilitation Services
N.A.I.C.S.: 622310

HealthSouth Rehabilitation Hospital of Austin, Inc. (1)
330 W Ben White Blvd, Austin, TX 78704
Tel.: (512) 730-4800
Web Site: http://www.healthsouthaustin.com
Health Care Srvices
N.A.I.C.S.: 621610

HealthSouth Rehabilitation Hospital of Beaumont, LLC (1)

3340 Plaza 10 Blvd, Beaumont, TX 77707
Tel.: (409) 835-0835
Web Site:
   http://www.healthsouthbeaumont.com
Health Care Srvices
N.A.I.C.S.: 621610

HealthSouth Rehabilitation Hospital of Charleston, LLC   **(1)**
9181 Medcom St, North Charleston, SC 29406
Tel.: (843) 820-7777
Web Site:
   http://www.healthsouthcharleston.com
Health Care Srvices
N.A.I.C.S.: 621610

HealthSouth Rehabilitation Hospital of Cypress, LLC   **(1)**
13031 Wortham Ctr Dr, Houston, TX 77065
Tel.: (832) 280-2500
Web Site:
   http://www.healthsouthcypress.com
Emp.: 100
Medical Rehabilitation Services
N.A.I.C.S.: 622310
Ignazio LaChina (Dir-Medical)
Douglas Unangst (Dir-Food Svcs)
Sheila Bollier (CEO)
Ashley Haywood (Dir-Quality & Risk Mgmt)
Byron Moore (Dir-HR)
Melissa Haddox (Controller)
Maureen Myers (Dir-Pharmacy)
Jessica Ruelas (Dir-Bus Dev)
Alex Keller (Dir-Facility Mgmt)
Susha Thomas (Dir-Therapy Ops)
Roshonda Washington (Chief Nursing Officer)

HealthSouth Rehabilitation Hospital of Desert Canyon, LLC   **(1)**
9175 W Oquendo Rd, Las Vegas, NV 89148
Tel.: (702) 252-7342
Web Site: http://www.healthsouth.com
Medical Rehabilitation Services
N.A.I.C.S.: 622310
Peggy Nelson (CEO)
Ashlyn Kelley (Dir-HR)
Sharon Nash (Dir-Case Mgmt)
David Nguyen (Dir-Pharmacy)
Lupe Storck (Chief Nursing Officer)
Tyler Wild (Dir-Therapy Ops)
Caitlin Hutchison (Dir-Medical)
Wayne Blas (Dir-Facilities Mgmt)
Mary Clarke (Dir-Bus Dev)
Amy Lockyer (Dir-Case Mgmt)
Chelsea Montervino (Controller)
Shannon Way (Dir-Quality & Risk)

HealthSouth Rehabilitation Hospital of Fort Worth, LLC   **(1)**
1212 W Lancaster Ave, Fort Worth, TX 76102
Tel.: (817) 870-2336
Web Site:
   https://www.healthsouthfortworth.com
Health Care Srvices
N.A.I.C.S.: 621610

HealthSouth Rehabilitation Hospital of Henderson, LLC   **(1)**
10301 Jeffreys St, Henderson, NV 89052
Tel.: (702) 939-9400
Web Site:
   http://www.hendersonrehabhospital.com
Health Care Srvices
N.A.I.C.S.: 621610

HealthSouth Rehabilitation Hospital of Humble, LLC   **(1)**
19002 McKay Dr, Humble, TX 77338
Tel.: (281) 446-6148
Web Site:
   http://www.healthsouthhumble.com
Health Care Srvices
N.A.I.C.S.: 621610

HealthSouth Rehabilitation Hospital of Jonesboro, LLC   **(1)**
1201 Fleming Ave, Jonesboro, AR 72401
Tel.: (870) 932-0440
Web Site:
   http://www.healthsouthjonesboro.com
Health Care Srvices
N.A.I.C.S.: 621610

HealthSouth Rehabilitation Hospital of Largo, LLC   **(1)**

901 N Clearwater Largo Rd, Largo, FL 33770
Tel.: (727) 586-2999
Web Site: https://www.healthsouthlargo.com
Health Care Srvices
N.A.I.C.S.: 621610

HealthSouth Rehabilitation Hospital of Manati, Inc.   **(1)**
Carretera Ste 2 Kilometro 47 7, Manati, PR 00674
Tel.: (787) 621-3800
Medical Rehabilitation Services
N.A.I.C.S.: 622310

HealthSouth Rehabilitation Hospital of Martin County, LLC   **(1)**
5850 SE Community Dr, Stuart, FL 34997
Tel.: (772) 324-3500
Web Site: http://www.healthsouthmartin.com
Health Care Srvices
N.A.I.C.S.: 621610

HealthSouth Rehabilitation Hospital of Mechanicsburg, LLC   **(1)**
175 Lancaster Blvd, Mechanicsburg, PA 17055
Tel.: (717) 691-3700
Web Site: http://www.healthsouthpa.com
Emp.: 240
Medical Rehabilitation Services
N.A.I.C.S.: 622310
Michael F. Lupinacci (Dir-Medical)
Josette Myers (CEO)
Erin Anderson (Dir-Quality)
Karen Burket (Dir-Therapy Ops)
Laurie Dehass (Controller)
Lisa Little (Chief Nursing Officer)

HealthSouth Rehabilitation Hospital of Midland/Odessa, LLC   **(1)**
1800 Heritage Blvd, Midland, TX 79707
Tel.: (432) 520-1600
Web Site:
   http://www.healthsouthmidland.com
Health Care Srvices
N.A.I.C.S.: 621610

HealthSouth Rehabilitation Hospital of New Mexico, Inc.   **(1)**
7000 Jefferson NE, Albuquerque, NM 87109
Tel.: (505) 344-9478
Web Site:
   http://www.healthsouthnewmexico.com
Emp.: 200
Medical Rehabilitation Services
N.A.I.C.S.: 622310
Lisa Brower (Dir-Therapy Ops)
Rachelle Spencer (CEO)
J. Michael Long (Dir-Medical)
Susan Blanchard (Chief Nursing Officer)
Edward Cole (Dir-Pharmacy & Dieticians)
Janice Emerson (Dir-Quality & Risk)
Kristen Hernandez (Dir-HR)
Tony Lucero (Dir-Plant Ops)
Michelle Martinez (Controller)
Jennifer O'Brien Dambmann (Dir-Case Mgmt)
Devin Lujan (Dir-Bus Dev)

HealthSouth Rehabilitation Hospital of Newnan, LLC   **(1)**
2101 E Newnan Crossing Blvd, Newnan, GA 30265
Tel.: (678) 552-6200
Web Site:
   https://www.healthsouthnewnan.com
Health Care Srvices
N.A.I.C.S.: 621610

HealthSouth Rehabilitation Hospital of North Houston, LP   **(1)**
117 Vision Park Blvd, Shenandoah, TX 77384
Tel.: (936) 444-1700
Health Care Srvices
N.A.I.C.S.: 621610
Jennifer Brewer (CEO)
Travis Hird (Dir-Medical)
Virginia Champagne (Dir-Therapy Ops)
Kristie Tschumperlin (Chief Nursing Officer)
Valerie Wells (Dir-HR)

HealthSouth Rehabilitation Hospital of Petersburg, LLC   **(1)**
95 MedicalPark Blvd, Petersburg, VA 23805
Tel.: (804) 504-8100
Web Site:
   https://www.healthsouthpetersburg.com

Medical Rehabilitation Services
N.A.I.C.S.: 622310
Ann Norford (Controller)
Lisa Stewart Barker (Dir-HR)
Thomas Krigbaum (Dir-Plant Ops)
Tracy Turman (CEO)

HealthSouth Rehabilitation Hospital of Reading, LLC   **(1)**
1623 Morgantown Rd, Reading, PA 19607
Tel.: (610) 796-6000
Web Site:
   http://www.healthsouthreading.com
Health Care Srvices
N.A.I.C.S.: 621610
Judy Parker (CEO)
Daniel McNeil (Dir-Medical)
Mathew Gooch (CEO-Area)
Terence Lumley (Dir-Therapy Ops)
Holly Palka (Dir-Quality & Risk)
Jason Pulaski (Controller)
Kristin Zimmerman (Dir-Case Mgmt)

HealthSouth Rehabilitation Hospital of San Juan, Inc.   **(1)**
University District Hospital, San Juan, PR 00936
Tel.: (787) 274-5100
Web Site:
   http://www.healthsouthsanjuan.com
Rehabilitation Hospital
N.A.I.C.S.: 622310
Daniel Del Castillo (CEO-Area)
Edwardo Ramos (Dir-Medical)
Milagros Burgos (Dir-Bus Dev)
Jesus Corazon (Controller-Area)
Sandra E. Gonzalez (Dir-Case Mgmt)
Rafael A. Velez Roman (Dir-Therapy Ops)
Ailenid Leon (Dir-HR)
Karen Otero (Dir-Quality & Risk)
Rocio Torrens (Chief Nursing Officer)

HealthSouth Rehabilitation Hospital of Sarasota, LLC   **(1)**
6400 Edgelake Dr, Sarasota, FL 34240
Tel.: (941) 921-8600
Web Site:
   http://www.healthsouthsarasota.com
Health Care Srvices
N.A.I.C.S.: 621610

HealthSouth Rehabilitation Hospital of Seminole County, LLC   **(1)**
831 S State Rd 434, Altamonte Springs, FL 32714
Tel.: (407) 587-8600
Web Site: http://www.healthsouthaltamonte springs.com
Health Care Srvices
N.A.I.C.S.: 621610

HealthSouth Rehabilitation Hospital of Sewickley, LLC   **(1)**
351 Camp Meeting Rd, Sewickley, PA 15143-8348
Tel.: (412) 741-9500
Web Site:
   http://www.healthsouthsewickley.com
Emp.: 140
Medical Rehabilitation Services
N.A.I.C.S.: 622310
Leah Laffey (CEO)
Melissa Coleman (Dir-HR)
Melissa Kolin (Chief Nursing Officer)
Ellen Mustovic (Dir-Medical)

HealthSouth Rehabilitation Hospital of South Jersey, LLC   **(1)**
1237 W Sherman Ave, Vineland, NJ 08360
Tel.: (856) 696-7100
Web Site: http://www.healthsouth.com
Medical Rehabilitation Services
N.A.I.C.S.: 622310

HealthSouth Rehabilitation Hospital of Tallahassee, LLC   **(1)**
1675 Riggins Rd, Tallahassee, FL 32308
Tel.: (850) 656-4800
Web Site:
   http://www.healthsouthtallahassee.com
Health Care Srvices
N.A.I.C.S.: 621610

HealthSouth Rehabilitation Hospital of Texarkana, Inc.   **(1)**
515 W 12th St, Texarkana, TX 75501
Tel.: (903) 735-5000
Web Site:
   http://www.healthsouthtexarkana.com

Health Care Srvices
N.A.I.C.S.: 621610
LaSandra Smiley (Dir-Pharmacy)
Harlo McCall (CEO)
Mark Wren (Dir-Medical)
Eunice Bond (Dir-HR)
Lorri Oglesby (Chief Nursing Officer)
Scott Reid (Dir-Plant Ops)
Shayne Smith (Dir-Case Mgmt)
Teena Thornell (Dir-Quality & Risk)
Todd Wallace (Dir-Therapy Ops)
Tiffannee Watson (Dir-Bus Dev)

HealthSouth Rehabilitation Hospital of Utah, LLC   **(1)**
8074 South 1300 E, Sandy, UT 84094
Tel.: (801) 561-3400
Web Site: http://www.healthsouthutah.com
Health Care Srvices
N.A.I.C.S.: 621610

HealthSouth Rehabilitation Institute of San Antonio (RIOSA), Inc.   **(1)**
9119 Cinnamon Hill, San Antonio, TX 78240
Tel.: (210) 691-0737
Web Site: http://www.hsriosa.com
Health Care Srvices
N.A.I.C.S.: 621610

HealthSouth Rehabilitation Institute of Tucson, LLC   **(1)**
2650 N Wyatt Dr, Tucson, AZ 85712
Tel.: (520) 325-1300
Web Site:
   http://www.rehabinstituteoftucson.com
Emp.: 100
Medical Rehabilitation Services
N.A.I.C.S.: 622310
Jeff Christensen (CEO)
Mary Donovan (Controller)
Jane Rosenbaum (Dir-Pharmacy)
Donna Stuve (Dir-HR)
Marissa Aguirre (Chief Nursing Officer)
Chelsea Downs (Dir-Quality & Risk)
Scott Knox (Dir-Facilities Mgmt)
Michele Butts (Dir-Therapy Ops)
Melinda Flannery (Dir-Case Mgmt)
Salvatore Tirrito (Dir-Program Medical)
Amir Buljina (Dir-Medical)
Carol Thompson (Dir-Area Bus Dev)

HealthSouth Scottsdale Rehabilitation Hospital, LLC   **(1)**
9630 E Shea Blvd, Scottsdale, AZ 85260
Tel.: (480) 551-5400
Web Site:
   http://www.healthsouthscottsdale.com
Emp.: 100
Medical Rehabilitation Services
N.A.I.C.S.: 622310

HealthSouth Sunrise Rehabilitation Hospital, LLC   **(1)**
4399 Nob Hill Rd, Sunrise, FL 33351
Tel.: (954) 749-0300
Web Site:
   http://www.healthsouthsunrise.com
Health Care Srvices
N.A.I.C.S.: 621610

HealthSouth Valley of the Sun Rehabilitation Hospital, LLC   **(1)**
13460 N 67th Ave, Glendale, AZ 85304
Tel.: (623) 878-8800
Web Site:
   http://www.healthsouthvalleyofthesun.com
Medical Rehabilitation Services
N.A.I.C.S.: 622310
Beth Bacher (CEO)
Michael Kravetz (Dir-Medical)
Danette Garcia (Dir-HR)
Katy Haney (Controller)
Derry Hollock (Dir-Therapy Ops)
Liz Ross (Dir-Case Mgmt)
Stephanie Palmer (Chief Nursing Officer)
Diane Hendrix (Dir-Bus Dev)
Lavonn Heberling (Mgr-Wound Care)
Brenda Harris (Dir-Quality & Risk)
Stephanie Couture (Co-Chief Nursing Officer)

HealthSouth Walton Rehabilitation Hospital, LLC   **(1)**
1355 Independence Dr, Augusta, GA 30901
Tel.: (706) 724-7746
Web Site: http://www.healthsouthwalton.com
Health Care Srvices
N.A.I.C.S.: 621610

HealthSouth of Austin, Inc.   **(1)**

Encompass Health Corporation—(Continued)

330 West Benwhite Blvd, Austin, TX 78704
Tel.: (512) 474-5700
Web Site: http://www.healthsouthaustin.com
Medical Rehabilitation Services
N.A.I.C.S.: 622310
Laura Gray *(Dir-Medical)*
Brenda Harvey *(Dir-Case Mgmt)*
Kathy Bozeman *(Controller)*
Thomas Standley *(Dir-Facility Mgmt-RoundRock)*
Rabih Chahine *(Dir-Pharmacy)*
Liz Markiand *(Dir-Therapy Ops)*
Jonathan Strader *(Dir-Therapy Ops)*
Lauren Suarez *(CEO)*
Sharelle Evans *(Coord-Patient Assessment Standards)*

HealthSouth of Dothan, Inc. **(1)**
1736 E Main St, Dothan, AL 36301-3040
Tel.: (334) 712-6333
Web Site: http://www.healthsouth.com
Sales Range: $25-49.9 Million
Emp.: 200
Medical Rehabilitation Services
N.A.I.C.S.: 622310

HealthSouth of East Tennessee, LLC **(1)**
113 Cassell Dr, Kingsport, TN 37660-3775
Tel.: (423) 246-7240
Sales Range: $25-49.9 Million
Emp.: 200
Medical Rehabilitation Services
N.A.I.C.S.: 622310
Troy Clark *(CEO)*
Debra Smith *(Chief Nursing Officer)*

HealthSouth of Houston, Inc. **(1)**
18550 Interstate 45 S, Conroe, TX 77384-4119
Tel.: (281) 364-2000
Web Site: http://www.healthsouth.com
Medical Rehabilitation Services
N.A.I.C.S.: 622310

HealthSouth of Largo Limited Partnership **(1)**
901 Clearwater Largo Rd N, Largo, FL 33770-4126
Tel.: (727) 586-2999
Web Site: http://www.healthsouthlargo.com
Medical Rehabilitation Services
N.A.I.C.S.: 622310

HealthSouth of Midland, Inc. **(1)**
1800 Heritage Blvd, Midland, TX 79707-9750
Tel.: (432) 520-1600
Web Site: http://www.healthsouthmidland.com
Sales Range: $25-49.9 Million
Emp.: 200
Medical Rehabilitation Services
N.A.I.C.S.: 622310

HealthSouth of Nittany Valley, Inc. **(1)**
550 W College Ave, Pleasant Gap, PA 16823
Tel.: (814) 359-3421
Web Site: http://www.nittanyvalleyrehab.com
Nursing Care Facilities Services
N.A.I.C.S.: 623110
Richard Allatt *(Dir-Medical)*
David Pellerano *(Dir-Quality & Risk Mgmt)*
Tracy Ewing *(Chief Nursing Officer)*
Amy Adams *(CEO)*
Michelle Katz *(Dir-HR)*
Alan Phillips *(Controller)*
Tracy Stoltz *(Dir-Therapy Ops)*
Paul Kuberna *(Assoc Dir-Medical)*
Shana Mark *(Dir-Bus Dev)*

HealthSouth of Phenix City, Inc. **(1)**
3715 Highway 280/431, Phenix City, AL 36867
Tel.: (334) 732-2200
Web Site: http://www.regionalrehabhospital.com
Health Care Srvices
N.A.I.C.S.: 621610

HealthSouth of Reading, LLC **(1)**
1623 Morgantown Rd, Reading, PA 19607
Tel.: (610) 796-6000
Web Site: http://www.healthsouthreading.com
Medical Rehabilitation Services

N.A.I.C.S.: 622310
Jason Pulaski *(Controller)*
Kristin Zimmerman *(Dir-Case Mgmt)*
Mathew Gooch *(CEO)*
Terence Lumley *(Dir-Therapy Ops)*
Shanae Stanton *(Dir-HR)*
Daniel McNeil *(Dir-Medical)*
Holly Palka *(Dir-Quality & Risk)*

HealthSouth of San Antonio, Inc. **(1)**
9119 Cinnamon Hill, San Antonio, TX 78240
Tel.: (210) 691-0737
Web Site: http://www.hsrioSA.com
Emp.: 300
Medical Rehabilitation Services
N.A.I.C.S.: 622310
Larry Spriggs *(CFO)*
Sarah Pena *(Chief Nursing Officer)*
Susanna Stuart *(Dir-Case Mgmt-Almonte Springs)*
Andrew Meade *(CEO)*
Morgan Collins *(Dir-Bus Dev)*
Patricia Dillard-Devora *(Dir-Case Mgmt)*
Bonnie Mann *(Dir-Quality)*
Andrew Posey *(Dir-Therapy Ops)*
Wen-song Yue *(Dir-Pharmacy)*

HealthSouth of Sea Pines Limited Partnership **(1)**
101 E Florida Ave, Melbourne, FL 32901-8301
Tel.: (321) 984-4600
Web Site: http://www.healthsouthseapines.com
Sales Range: $25-49.9 Million
Emp.: 400
Medical Rehabilitation Services
N.A.I.C.S.: 622310
Juan Lebron *(Dir-Medical)*
Kersten Brady *(Dir-Therapy Ops)*
Karen Grant *(Dir-Case Mgmt)*
Nupur Vanderlick *(Dir-HR)*
Marc Racicot *(CEO)*

HealthSouth of South Carolina, Inc. **(1)**
2935 Colonial Dr, Columbia, SC 29203
Tel.: (803) 254-7777
Medical Rehabilitation Services
N.A.I.C.S.: 622310
Nicole Hendricks *(CEO)*
Jessica Stricklin *(Chief Nursing Officer)*

HealthSouth of Spring Hill, Inc. **(1)**
12440 Cortez Blvd, Brooksville, FL 34613
Tel.: (352) 592-4250
Web Site: http://www.healthsouthspringhill.com
Medical Rehabilitation Services
N.A.I.C.S.: 622310
Mary Salamanca *(Dir-HR)*
Michael Vargas *(Dir-Case Mgmt)*
Olan Deguzman *(Dir-Therapy Ops)*

HealthSouth of Texarkana, Inc. **(1)**
515 W 12th St, Texarkana, TX 75501-4416
Tel.: (903) 793-0088
Web Site: http://www.healthsouth.com
Sales Range: $25-49.9 Million
Emp.: 200
Medical Rehabilitation Services
N.A.I.C.S.: 622310

HealthSouth of Texas, Inc. **(1)**
19002 Mckay Blvd, Humble, TX 77338-5701
Tel.: (281) 446-6148
Medical Rehabilitation Services
N.A.I.C.S.: 622310

HealthSouth of Toms River, LLC **(1)**
14 Hospital Dr, Toms River, NJ 08755
Tel.: (732) 244-3100
Web Site: http://www.healthsouth.com
Medical Rehabilitation Services
N.A.I.C.S.: 622310

HealthSouth of Treasure Coast, Inc. **(1)**
1600 37th St, Vero Beach, FL 32960
Tel.: (772) 778-2100
Medical Rehabilitation Services
N.A.I.C.S.: 622310
Jimmy Lockhart *(Dir-Medical)*
Kevin Hardy *(CEO)*
Karrie Mutterback *(Dir-Case Mgmt)*
Donald Watts *(Dir-Plant Ops)*
Lisa Kuh *(Chief Nursing Officer)*
Michael Morrical *(CEO)*

HealthSouth of Utah, Inc. **(1)**
8074 S 1300 E, Sandy, UT 84094-0743
Tel.: (801) 561-3400
Web Site: http://www.healthsouth.com
Sales Range: $25-49.9 Million
Emp.: 150
Medical Rehabilitation Services
N.A.I.C.S.: 622310
Owen Christenson *(Dir-HR)*
Brenda Eatherton *(Dir-Case Mgmt)*
Chris Rock *(Dir-Quality & Risk Mgmt)*
Chuck Smith *(CEO)*
Jacob Egbert *(Dir-Medical)*
Rulon Hunter *(Dir-Facilities Mgmt-Plant Ops)*
Adry Oliveira *(Chief Nursing Officer)*
Matt Poss *(CFO)*

Kansas Rehabilitation Hospital, Inc. **(1)**
1504 SW 8th Ave, Topeka, KS 66606-1632
Tel.: (785) 235-6600
Medical Rehabilitation Services
N.A.I.C.S.: 622310
Joseph Sankoorikal *(Dir-Medical)*
Lisa Rundell *(Dir-Therapy Ops)*
Clare Zaboktrsky *(Chief Nursing Officer)*
Barry Muninger *(CEO)*

La Veta Surgical Center **(1)**
681 S Parker St Ste 150, Orange, CA 92868
Tel.: (714) 744-0900
Web Site: https://www.lavetasurgical.com
Sales Range: $10-24.9 Million
Emp.: 25
Surgical Center
N.A.I.C.S.: 621493

Lakeshore System Services of Florida, Inc. **(1)**
1847 Florida Ave, Panama City, FL 32405
Tel.: (850) 914-8600
Emp.: 265
Health Care Srvices
N.A.I.C.S.: 621610
Traci Powell *(Dir-HR)*
Tony Bennett *(CEO)*
Adrienne Bartle *(Dir-Case Mgmt)*
Cambridge Carruth *(Dir-Therapy Ops)*
Brad Tilghman *(Controller)*
Patricia Foster *(Dir-Quality & Risk Mgmt)*
Brett Hanson *(Dir-Plant Operation)*
Kristopher C. Flippo *(Chief Nursing Officer)*

MMC Encompass Health Rehabilitation Hospital, LLC **(1)**
2 Center Plz, Tinton Falls, NJ 07724
Tel.: (732) 460-5320
Health Care Srvices
N.A.I.C.S.: 621610
Douglas Powell *(Dir-Bus Dev)*
Maria Clohosey *(Chief Nursing Officer)*

Myrtle Beach Rehabilitation Hospital, LLC **(1)**
4070 Hwy 17 Bypass S, Murrells Inlet, SC 29576
Tel.: (843) 652-1350
Health Care Srvices
N.A.I.C.S.: 621610
Carey Swanson *(CEO)*
Linda Gilhuly *(Chief Nursing Officer)*

New England Rehabilitation Services of Central Massachusetts, Inc. **(1)**
189 May St, Worcester, MA 01602-4339 **(80%)**
Tel.: (508) 791-6351
Web Site: https://encompasshealth.com
Medical Rehabilitation Services
N.A.I.O.O.: 022010
Peter Lancette *(CEO)*
Cathleen Butenewicz *(Chief Nursing Officer)*
John Flaherty *(Controller)*
Samantha Gould *(Dir-Human Resources)*
Jessica Marinelli *(Dir-Case Mgmt)*
Charles Schleich *(Dir-Facilities Mgmt)*
Debra Twehous *(Dir-Medical)*
Corey Leblanc *(Dir-Therapy Ops)*
Samantha Gauvin *(Dir-Quality & Risk)*
Michael Kermani *(Dir-Pharmacy)*
Poonam Saraf *(Dir-Business Development)*

Northwest Arkansas Rehabilitation Associates **(1)**
153 E Monte Painter Dr, Fayetteville, AR 72703
Tel.: (479) 444-2200

Web Site: https://encompasshealth.com
Health Care Srvices
N.A.I.C.S.: 621610
Brandia Howard *(Dir-Bus Dev)*
Adam Walker *(Dir-Plant Ops)*
Janette Daniels *(CEO)*

Novant Health Rehabilitation Hospital of Winston-Salem, LLC **(1)**
2475 Hillcrest Ctr Cir, Winston Salem, NC 27103
Tel.: (336) 754-3500
Health Care Srvices
N.A.I.C.S.: 621610
Randy Harper *(Dir-Therapy Ops)*
Christopher Fuller *(CEO)*
Erica Frazier *(Chief Nursing Officer)*

Preferred Home Health, L.P. **(1)**
350 Pine St Ste 305, Beaumont, TX 77701
Tel.: (409) 813-8109
Health Care Srvices
N.A.I.C.S.: 621610

Quillen Rehabilitation Hospital of Johnson City, LLC **(1)**
2511 Wesley St, Johnson City, TN 37601
Tel.: (423) 952-1700
Health Care Srvices
N.A.I.C.S.: 621610
Douglas Usenegr *(CEO)*
Sheila Bolter *(CFO)*
Ashley Haywood *(CEO)*
Byron Moore *(Dir-HR)*
Michael Hedge *(Dir-Therapy)*
Erin Anderson *(CEO)*
Karen Burkel *(Dir-Therapy Ops)*
Claude Derossett *(Controller)*
La Cole Conger *(Dir-Medical)*

Rehabilitation Hospital Corporation Of America, LLC **(1)**
120 12th St, Princeton, WV 24740-2352
Tel.: (304) 487-8000
Web Site: http://www.healthsouth.com
Medical Rehabilitation Services
N.A.I.C.S.: 622310
Robb Williams *(CEO)*
Greg Angle *(Chief Nursing Officer)*
Amy Flowers *(Controller)*
Kyle Zhang *(Dir-Medical)*
Tammy Dalton *(Dir-Business Development)*
Greta Walker *(Dir-Case Mgmt)*

Rehabilitation Hospital of Bristol, LLC **(1)**
103 N St, Bristol, VA 24201
Tel.: (276) 642-7901
Health Care Srvices
N.A.I.C.S.: 621610
Gabbi Cooper *(Dir-Case Mgmt)*
Christy Forbis *(Dir-HR)*
Katrina Lloyd *(Chief Nursing Officer)*
Britta Milhorn *(CEO)*

Rehabilitation Hospital of Colorado Springs, Inc. **(1)**
325 S Parkside Dr, Colorado Springs, CO 80910
Tel.: (719) 630-8000
Medical Rehabilitation Services
N.A.I.C.S.: 622310

Rehabilitation Hospital of Nevada-Las Vegas, L.P. **(1)**
1250 S Vly View Blvd, Las Vegas, NV 89102
Tel.: (702) 877-8898
Medical Rehabilitation Services
N.A.I.C.S.: 622310
Farzin Farhang *(Dir-Medical)*
Lura DeVito *(Dir-Therapy Ops)*
Christine Heinze *(Dir-Health Info Mgmt Svcs)*
Ivan Lambert *(Dir-Pharmacy Svcs)*
Gina Lewis *(Dir-HR)*
Cheryl Williams *(Exec Dir-Physician Relations)*

Rehabilitation Hospital of North Alabama, LLC **(1)**
1490 Hwy 72 E, Huntsville, AL 35811
Tel.: (256) 535-2300
Nursing Care Facility Services
N.A.I.C.S.: 623110
Deb Beecham *(Dir-Case Mgmt)*
Chelsea Sowards *(Dir-Therapy Ops)*
Brent Mills *(CEO)*

Rehabilitation Hospital of Phenix City, L.L.C. **(1)**
3715 US Hwy 431 N, Phenix City, AL 36867-2363
Tel.: (334) 732-2200

Web Site:
  http://www.regionalrehabhospital.com
Medical Rehabilitation Services
N.A.I.C.S.: 622310
Lora Davis (CEO)
Tamisha Brown Davis (Dir-Human Resources)
Daniel Evans (Dir-Facilities Mgmt)
Walter L. Johnson (Dir-Therapy)
Karrie Roberts (Dir-Case Mgmt)
Jessica Walker (Dir-Pharmacy)
Dennis Harden (Dir-Medical)
Laura Curran (Controller-Area)
Stacey Hicks (Dir-Quality & Risk)
Ivy Nash (Dir-Area Bus Dev)
Annie Scott (Chief Nursing Officer)

Rusk Rehabilitation Center, LLC   (1)
315 Business Loop 70 W, Columbia, MO
65203-3248
Tel.: (573) 817-2703
Health Care Srvices
N.A.I.C.S.: 621610
Norman Davis (Controller)
David Fredericks (Dir-Therapy Ops)
Monica Gooch (Dir-Bus Dev)
Tom Tisone (CEO)
Linda Cockrell (Chief Nursing Officer)

Saint Barnabas / HealthSouth Reha-
bilitation Center LLC   (1)
2 Ctr Plz, Tinton Falls, NJ 07724
Tel.: (732) 460-5320
Web Site: http://www.rehabnjtintonfalls.com
Emp.: 250
Medical Rehabilitation Services
N.A.I.C.S.: 622310
Todd Cooperman (Dir-Medical)
Cheryl Halpin (Dir-Case Mgmt)
Douglas Powell (Dir-Bus Dev)
Beth Lynch (CEO)
Jim Bunnell (Controller)
Keith Mosley (Dir-Plant Ops)
Reeya Shah (Dir-Pharmacy)
Lori Skowrenski (Dir-HR)
Deanna Tropea (Dir-Quality)
Carol Sonatore (Dir-Medical)
Ari Carden (Dir-Case Mgmt)
Maria Clohosey (Chief Nursing Officer)
James Juliano (Dir-Therapy)

Southern Arizona Regional Rehabili-
tation Hospital, L.P.   (1)
1921 W Hospital Dr, Tucson, AZ 85704
Tel.: (520) 742-2800
Medical Rehabilitation Services
N.A.I.C.S.: 622310
Kerby Westbrook (CEO)
Jeff Christensen (Chief Nursing Officer)

St. John Encompass Health Rehabili-
tation Hospital, LLC   (1)
1200 W Albany Dr, Broken Arrow, OK
74012
Tel.: (918) 957-3000
Health Care Srvices
N.A.I.C.S.: 621610
David Nicholas (CEO)
Beth Coffman (Dir-Therapy Ops)
Susan Day (Chief Nursing Officer)

St. Joseph Encompass Health Reha-
bilitation Hospital, LLC   (1)
1600 Joseph Dr Ste 2000, Bryan, TX 77802
Tel.: (979) 213-4300
Web Site: https://encompasshealth.com
Health Care Srvices
N.A.I.C.S.: 621610
Amy Gray (CEO)
Kelly W Lobo (Dir-Medical)
Ashley Green (Chief Nursing Officer)
Alicia Hutchins (Dir-HR)

Tarrant County Rehabilitation Hospi-
tal, Inc.   (1)
6701 Oakmont Blvd, Fort Worth, TX 76132
Tel.: (817) 370-4700
Web Site: http://www.healthsouth.com
Medical Rehabilitation Services
N.A.I.C.S.: 622310

Tyler Rehabilitation Hospital, Inc.   (1)
3131 Troup Hwy, Tyler, TX 75701-8352
Tel.: (903) 510-7000
Web Site: http://www.healthsouth.com
Emp.: 300
Medical Rehabilitation Services
N.A.I.C.S.: 622310

UVA Encompass Health Rehabilitation Hospital, LLC   (1)

515 Ray C Hunt Dr, Charlottesville, VA
22903
Tel.: (434) 244-2000
Web Site: https://encompasshealth.com
Health Care Srvices
N.A.I.C.S.: 621610
Alan Alfano (Dir-Medical)
Michael Vanhoy (Dir-Quality Improvement &
Risk Mgmt)
Vivian White (CEO)

Van Matre Rehabilitation Center
LLC   (1)
950 S Mulford Rd, Rockford, IL 61108
Tel.: (815) 381-8500
Web Site: http://www.vanmatrerehab.com
Medical Rehabilitation Services
N.A.I.C.S.: 622310
Jeffrey Reese (CEO)
Angela Bergman (Dir-Quality, Risk, HIM &
HIPAA)
Eric Guile (Reg Dir-Pharmacy)
Chrisi Karcz (Chief Nursing Officer)
Tonya Markert (Dir-Bus Dev)
Stephen Talty (Dir-Medical)
Gemma Fletcher (Dir-Therapy Ops)
James Helmick (Dir-Facilities Mgmt)
Ken Snyder (Controller-Area)
Lauren Stoklosa (Dir-HR)

WellCare, Inc.   (1)
1096 Mechem Dr Ste 302-A, Ruidoso, NM
88345
Tel.: (575) 258-0028
Web Site: https://www.ehab.com
Emp.: 40
Health Care Srvices
N.A.I.C.S.: 621610
Christian P. Michalik (Chm)
Andrew L. Asher (Sr VP)
Crissy Carlisle (CFO)
Julie Jolley (Exec VP)
Jeanne Kalvaitis (Exec VP)
Bud Langham (Exec VP)
Tanya Marion (Chief HR Officer)
Dylan Black (Gen Counsel)

West Tennessee Rehabilitation Hos-
pital, LLC   (1)
616 W Forest Ave, Jackson, TN 38301
Tel.: (731) 574-3000
Web Site: https://encompasshealth.com
Health Care Srvices
N.A.I.C.S.: 621610
Julie Taylor (CEO)
Tasha Glass (Dir-HR)
Amy Lambert Kiestler (Dir-Bus Dev)
Kyle Lusby (Dir-Pharmacy)

Yuma Rehabilitation Hospital,
LLC   (1)
901 W 24th St, Yuma, AZ 85364
Tel.: (928) 726-5000
Web Site:
  http://www.yumarehabhospital.com
Medical Rehabilitation Services
N.A.I.C.S.: 622310

ENCOMPASS HOLDINGS, INC.
310 California Ave No 554, Reno, NV
89509
Tel.: (415) 259-4108   NV
Web Site:
  http://www.encompassholdings.com
Year Founded: 1987
ECMH—(OTCEM)
Investment Management Service
N.A.I.C.S.: 523999

ENCORE CAPITAL GROUP, INC.
350 Camino De La Reina Ste 100,
San Diego, CA 92108   DE
Web Site:
  https://www.encorecapital.com
ECPG—(NASDAQ)
Rev.: $1,222,680,000
Assets: $4,630,486,000
Liabilities: $3,693,948,000
Net Worth: $936,538,000
Earnings: ($206,492,000)
Emp.: 7,400
Fiscal Year-end: 12/31/23

Consumer Debt Buying & Recovery
Services
N.A.I.C.S.: 522390
Andrew Asch (Gen Counsel & Sr VP)
Jonathan C. Clark (CFO, Principal
Acctg Officer, Treas & Exec VP)
Monique Dumais-Chrisope (CIO & Sr
VP)
Tracy Ting (Chief HR Officer & Sr
VP)
Steve Carmichael (Chief Risk & Com-
pliance Officer & Sr VP)
Bruce Thomas (VP-IR)
Ashish Masih (Pres & CEO)

Subsidiaries:

ACF Medical Services, Inc.   (1)
2727 Franklin Rd SW, Roanoke, VA 24014
Tel.: (540) 772-7800
Health Care Srvices
N.A.I.C.S.: 621610

Ascension Capital Group, Inc.   (1)
1212 Corporate Dr, Irving, TX 75038
Tel.: (817) 277-2011
Web Site: http://ascensioncapitalgroup.com
Bankruptcy & Litigation Services
N.A.I.C.S.: 541199
Anthony R. Tersigni (Chm)
Anthony R. Tersigni (Chm)

Asset Acceptance Capital Corp.   (1)
28405 Van Dyke Ave, Warren, MI 48093
Tel.: (586) 939-9600
Rev.: $226,941,188
Assets: $424,738,239
Liabilities: $274,681,089
Net Worth: $150,057,150
Earnings: $10,917,581
Emp.: 882
Fiscal Year-end: 12/31/2012
Debt & Account Receivables Collection Ser-
vices
N.A.I.C.S.: 522210
Kenneth A. Vecchione (Pres & CEO)
Darin B. Herring (VP-Legal Collections &
Bus Transformation)
Paul J. Grinberg (CFO, Treas & Exec VP)
Gregory L. Call (Gen Counsel, Sec & Sr
VP)

Subsidiary (Domestic):

Asset Acceptance, LLC   (2)
PO Box 2036, Warren, MI 48090-2036
Tel.: (586) 939-9600
Web Site: https://www.assetacceptance.com
Management Services
N.A.I.C.S.: 541611

Consumer Credit, LLC   (2)
20740 Ryan Rd, Warren, MI 48091
Tel.: (586) 759-2445
Sales Range: $250-299.9 Million
Emp.: 900
Merchandise Purchase Financing Services
N.A.I.C.S.: 522220
Nathaniel F. Bradley IV (Chm)

Atlantic Credit & Finance, Inc.   (1)
111 Franklin Rd SE Ste 400, Roanoke, VA
24011
Tel.: (540) 772-7800
Web Site:
  https://www.atlanticcreditfinance.com
Sales Range: $25-49.9 Million
Collection Agency
N.A.I.C.S.: 561440
Sarah Wilson (Dir-Compliance)

Baycorp (NZ) Limited   (1)
Victoria Street West, Private Bag 92 063,
Auckland, 1142, New Zealand
Tel.: (64) 800229267
Web Site: https://www.baycorp.co.nz
Collection Services
N.A.I.C.S.: 561440

Baycorp (WA) Pty Limited   (1)
Unit 1 235 Balcatta Road, Balcatta, 6021,
WA, Australia
Tel.: (61) 861032800
Collection Services
N.A.I.C.S.: 561440

Baycorp Holdings (NZ) Limited   (1)
Level 19 191 Queen St, Auckland, 1011,
New Zealand

Tel.: (64) 93565899
Collection Services
N.A.I.C.S.: 561440

Cabot Credit Management
Limited   (1)
1 Kings Hill Avenue, Kings Hill, West Mall-
ing, ME19 4UA, Kent, United
Kingdom   (100%)
Tel.: (44) 175 372 4400
Web Site: https://www.cabotcm.com
Financial Services Holding Company; Credit
Management & Debt Collection Services
N.A.I.C.S.: 551112

Subsidiary (Domestic):

Cabot Credit Management Group
Limited   (2)
1 Kings Hill Avenue, Kings Hill, West Mall-
ing, ME19 4UA, Kent, United Kingdom
Tel.: (44) 1753724400
Financial Services Holding Company; Credit
Intermediation & Debt Collection Services
N.A.I.C.S.: 551112
Craig Buick (CEO)
Christian Burgess (Co-CFO)

Subsidiary (Domestic):

Apex Credit Management
Limited   (3)
27 Arden Street, Stratford-upon-Avon, CV37
6NW, Warwickshire, United Kingdom
Tel.: (44) 8451647513
Web Site: http://www.apexcm.co.uk
Nondepository Credit Intermediation Ser-
vices
N.A.I.C.S.: 522299

Cabot Financial (Europe) Limited   (3)
1 Kings Hill Avenue, Kings Hill, West Mall-
ing, ME19 4UA, Kent, United Kingdom
Tel.: (44) 3445560263
Web Site: https://www.cabotfinancial.co.uk
Nondepository Credit Intermediation Ser-
vices
N.A.I.C.S.: 522299

Subsidiary (Domestic):

Cabot Financial (Marlin) Limited   (4)
Marlin House 16-22 Grafton Road, West
Sussex, Worthing, BN11 1QP, United King-
dom
Tel.: (44) 3331239999
Web Site: http://www.cabotfinancial.co.uk
Financial Management Services
N.A.I.C.S.: 523999
Ken Stannard (CEO)

Cabot Financial France   (1)
5/7 Avenue de Poumeyrol, 69300, Caluire-
et-Cuire, France
Tel.: (33) 437929218
Web Site: https://www.cabotfinancial.fr
Debt Collection Services
N.A.I.C.S.: 561440
Serge Kofman (Pres)

Grove Capital Management
Limited   (1)
One Hammersmith Broadway, London, W6
9DL, United Kingdom
Tel.: (44) 2080806480
Web Site: https://www.grove-cm.com
Nondepository Credit Intermediation Ser-
vices
N.A.I.C.S.: 522299

Lucania Gestion, S.L.   (1)
Isla Del Hierro 7 2 Planta Parque Empre-
sarial La Marina, Madrid, 28703, Spain
Tel.: (34) 911847100
Web Site: http://www.lucaniagestion.com
Collection Agency Services
N.A.I.C.S.: 561440

Lucas et Degand S.a r.l.   (1)
Le Colbert 8 Rue Sainte-Barbe, 1st District,
13001, Marseille, France
Tel.: (33) 496111414
Collection Agency Services
N.A.I.C.S.: 561440

Midland Credit Management, Inc.   (1)
PO Box 939069, San Diego, CA 92193
Web Site: https://www.midlandcreditmanage
ment.com

Encore Capital Group, Inc.—(Continued)

Sales Range: $75-99.9 Million
Emp.: 200
Credit Collection Services
N.A.I.C.S.: 522390

Mortimer Clarke Solicitors
Limited **(1)**
16-22 Grafton Road, Worthing, BN11 1QP,
West Sussex, United Kingdom
Tel.: (44) 3300450779
Web Site: https://www.mortimerclarke.co.uk
Emp.: 100
Credit Intermediation Services
N.A.I.C.S.: 522390

Propel Financial Services, LLC
7990 IH-10 W Ste 200, San Antonio, TX
78230
Tel.: (210) 582-2880
Web Site:
https://www.propelfinancialservices.com
Nondepository Credit Intermediation Ser-
vices
N.A.I.C.S.: 522299
Christina Carney (COO)
John Eisinger (CEO)

RF Encore S.a.S **(1)**
Carrera 7 32, 130, Bogota, Colombia
Tel.: (57) 13790720
Nondepository Credit Intermediation Ser-
vices
N.A.I.C.S.: 522299

Refinancia S.A. **(1)**
Carrera 7 32-93, Bogota, Colombia
Tel.: (57) 6017440777
Web Site: https://refinancia.co
Nondepository Credit Intermediation Ser-
vices
N.A.I.C.S.: 522299

Virginia Credit & Finance, Inc. **(1)**
2810 N Parham Rd Ste 310, Richmond, VA
23294-4422
Tel.: (804) 346-8263
Nondepository Credit Intermediation Services
N.A.I.C.S.: 522299

Wescot Credit Services Limited **(1)**
Kyleshill House Glencairn Street, Saltcoats,
KA21 5JT, Ayrshire, United Kingdom
Tel.: (44) 1482484673
Web Site: https://wescot.co.uk
Collection Agency Services
N.A.I.C.S.: 561440

Wescot Topco Limited **(1)**
1 Kings Hill Avenue Kings Hill, West Mall-
ing, ME19 4UA, United Kingdom
Tel.: (44) 8709020562
Credit Intermediation Services
N.A.I.C.S.: 522390

**ENCOUNTER TECHNOLO-
GIES, INC.**
2818 S Van Buren St, Enid, OK
73703
Tel.: (815) 524-1650 CO
Web Site:
http://www.encountertech.com
Year Founded: 1986
ENTI—(OTCIQ)
Online Marketing Services
N.A.I.C.S.: 541870
Randolph S. Hudson (Chm, Pres,
CEO & Treas)
Dean M. Denton (Chief Admin Officer,
Sec & Sr VP)
A. F. Urbanik Jr. (VP-Corporate De-
velopment)

**ENCOUNTERCARE SOLU-
TIONS, INC.**
2401 PGA Blvd Ste 196 E, Palm
Beach Gardens, FL 33410
Tel.: (561) 776-1222
Web Site:
https://www.encountercare.com
Year Founded: 1997
CBRF—(OTCIQ)
Sales Range: Less than $1 Million

All Other Miscellaneous Ambulatory
Health Care Services
N.A.I.C.S.: 621999
Ronald W. Mills Sr. (Chm, Pres &
CEO)

ENDEXX CORPORATION
38246 N Hazlewood Cir, Cave Creek,
AZ 85331
Tel.: (480) 595-6900
Web Site: https://www.endexx.com
EDXC—(OTCIQ)
Rev.: $650,515
Assets: $1,759,913
Liabilities: $11,747,054
Net Worth: ($9,987,141)
Earnings: ($6,808,154)
Emp.: 10
Fiscal Year-end: 09/30/21
Business Development Services
N.A.I.C.S.: 561499
Todd Davis (CEO)
Steven M. Plumb (CFO)

ENDI CORP.
2400 Old Brick Rd Ste 115, Glen Al-
len, VA 23060
Tel.: (914) 496-0834 DE
Web Site: https://www.endicorp.com
Year Founded: 2021
ENDI—(OTCQB)
Miscellaneous Financial Investment
Activities
N.A.I.C.S.: 523999

Subsidiaries:

Crossingbridge Advisors LLC **(1)**
427 Bedford Rd Ste 220, Pleasantville, NY
10570
Tel.: (914) 741-1515
Web Site:
https://www.crossingbridgefunds.com
Investment Services
N.A.I.C.S.: 523999

Enterprise Diversified, Inc. **(1)**
1806 Summit Ave Ste 300, Richmond, VA
23230
Tel.: (434) 336-7737
Web Site:
http://www.enterprisediversified.com
Rev.: $5,902,243
Assets: $17,940,758
Liabilities: $834,998
Net Worth: $17,105,760
Earnings: $2,822,349
Emp.: 6
Fiscal Year-end: 12/31/2021
Asset Management , Real Estate, Internet,
& Home Services Provider
N.A.I.C.S.: 561990

Subsidiary (Domestic):

Sitestar.net, Inc. **(2)**
4026 Wards Rd Unit G-1 Ste 271, Lynch-
burg, VA 24502
Web Site: https://www.sitestar.net
Internet Provider Services
N.A.I.C.S.: 517121

**ENDONOVO THERAPEUTICS,
INC.**
6320 Canoga Ave 15th Fl, Woodland
Hills, CA 91367 DE
Web Site: https://www.endonovo.com
ENDV—(OTCQB)
Rev.: $135,355
Assets: $1,281,266
Liabilities: $33,461,585
Net Worth: ($32,180,319)
Earnings: ($18,474,835)
Emp.: 1
Fiscal Year-end: 12/31/22
Investment Services
N.A.I.C.S.: 523999
Alan Collier (Chm, CEO, Interim CFO
& Sec)

ENDRA LIFE SCIENCES INC.

3600 Green Ct Ste 350, Ann Arbor,
MI 48105-1570
Tel.: (734) 335-0468 DE
Web Site: https://www.endrainc.com
Year Founded: 2007
NDRA—(NASDAQ)
Assets: $9,274,147
Liabilities: $2,069,643
Net Worth: $7,204,504
Earnings: ($13,179,092)
Emp.: 21
Fiscal Year-end: 12/31/22
Biotechnology Research & Develop-
ment Services
N.A.I.C.S.: 541714
Michael Thornton (CTO)
Amy Sitzler (VP-Engrg & Programs)
Richard Jacroux (CFO & Head-Fin)
Alexander Tokman (Chm & Acting
CEO)

**ENDURANCE ACQUISITION
CORP.**
630 5th Ave 20th Fl, New York, NY
10111
Tel.: (646) 585-8975 Ky
Year Founded: 2021
EDNC—(NASDAQ)
Investment Services
N.A.I.C.S.: 523999
Chandra R. Patel (Chm)
Richard C. Davis (CEO)
Graeme Shaw (CTO)
Romeo A. Reyes (CFO)

**ENDURANCE EXPLORATION
GROUP, INC.**
7405 70th Ave N, Pinellas Park, FL
33781
Tel.: (727) 789-6575 NV
Web Site:
http://www.enduranceexploration
group.com
Year Founded: 2006
EXPL—(OTCIQ)
Marine Survey & Mapping Services
N.A.I.C.S.: 541370
Carl Dilley (Co-Founder, COO & VP)
Micah James Eldred (Co-Founder,
Chm, Pres & CEO)
Christine Zitman (CFO, Treas & Sec)

ENER-CORE, INC.
8965 Research Dr, Irvine, CA 92618
Tel.: (949) 616-3300 NV
Web Site: http://www.ener-core.com
Year Founded: 2010
ENCR—(OTCEM)
Emp.: 10
Gradual Oxidizer Products Mfr
N.A.I.C.S.: 333132
Alain J. Castro (CEO)
Michael J. Hammons (Chm)
Douglas Hamrin (VP-Engrg)
Mark Owen (VP-Ops & Bus Dev)

ENERGIZER HOLDINGS, INC.
Tel.: (314) 985-2000 MO
Web Site:
https://www.energizerholdings.com
ENR—(NYSE)
Rev.: $2,959,700,000
Assets: $4,509,600,000
Liabilities: $4,298,900,000
Net Worth: $210,700,000
Earnings: $140,500,000
Emp.: 5,080
Fiscal Year-end: 09/30/23
Holding Company; Batteries & Light-
ing Products Mfr & Distr
N.A.I.C.S.: 551112
Patrick J. Moore (Chm)
Mark S. LaVigne (Pres & CEO)
John J. Drabik (CFO & Exec VP)
Sara B. Hampton (Chief Acctg Offi-
cer)

Ben Angelette (Chief Admin Officer)
Tom Bendl (VP)
Kate Dugan (Corp Counsel)
David Lamb (VP)
Dan McCarthy (CIO)
Ravi Saggar (VP)
Ryan Sedlak (VP)

Subsidiaries:

AFIS, S.A. **(1)**
73 Democratias Ave, Melissia, 15127, Ath-
ens, Greece **(40%)**
Tel.: (30) 2108030355
Web Site: http://www.afis.gr
Emp.: 4
Storage Battery Mfr
N.A.I.C.S.: 334515

American Covers, Inc. **(1)**
675 W 14600 S, Bluffdale, UT
84065 **(100%)**
Tel.: (801) 727-1300
Web Site: http://www.handstands.com
Air Fresheners Mfr & Distr
N.A.I.C.S.: 339999
Rodd Steuart (CEO)

Subsidiary (Domestic):

California Scents, Inc. **(2)**
18850 Von Karman Ave Ste 200, Irvine, CA
92612
Tel.: (949) 475-1100
Web Site: http://www.californiascents.com
Air Freshener Mfr
N.A.I.C.S.: 339999
Dave Slingsby (Exec VP)

Armored AutoGroup Inc. **(1)**
44 Old Ridgebury Rd Ste 300, Danbury, CT
06810
Tel.: (203) 205-2900
Web Site:
http://www.armoredautogroup.com
Sales Range: $250-299.9 Million
Automotive Care & Maintenance Product
Mfr & Marketer
N.A.I.C.S.: 324191
Frank Judge (Gen Counsel, Sec & Sr VP-
Law)

Subsidiary (Non-US):

Armored Auto (UK) LP **(2)**
The Mille 1000 Great W Rd, Brentford, TW8
9HH, United Kingdom
Tel.: (44) 2082324800
Automobile Parts Mfr
N.A.I.C.S.: 336110
Cate Rushton (Controller-Fin)

Armored AutoGroup Australia Pty
Ltd **(2)**
115-116/25 Solent Circuit, PO Box 6205,
Baulkham Hills, 2153, NSW, Australia
Tel.: (61) 288952222
Automobile Parts Mfr
N.A.I.C.S.: 336110

Armored AutoGroup Canada
ULC **(2)**
180 Jardin Dr Unit 7, Concord, L4K 1X8,
ON, Canada
Tel.: (905) 595-8225
Automobile Parts Mfr
N.A.I.C.S.: 336110

Shanghai AAG Automotive Products
Trading Co. Ltd **(2)**
989 Changle Road, The Center Unit 509,
Shanghai, China
Tel.: (86) 2154030055
Automotive Parts & Accessory Store Opera-
tor
N.A.I.C.S.: 441330

Subsidiary (Domestic):

The Armor ALL/STP Products
Company **(2)**
1221 Broadway, Oakland, CA 94612-1888
Tel.: (510) 271-7000
Web Site: http://www.armorall.com
Automotive Parts & Accessory Store Opera-
tor
N.A.I.C.S.: 441330

COREPILE S.A. **(1)**

17 Rue Georges Bizet, 75016, Paris, France **(20%)**
Tel.: (33) 156903090
Web Site: http://www.corepile.fr
Storage Battery Mfr
N.A.I.C.S.: 334515

ECOBAT s.r.o. **(1)**
Soborska 1302/8, 160 00, Prague, Czech Republic **(16.66%)**
Tel.: (420) 233332787
Web Site: http://www.ecobat.cz
Power Battery Mfr
N.A.I.C.S.: 334515

Ecopilhas Lda. **(1)**
Rua Padre Americo 19 D-Office D, 1600-548, Lisbon, Portugal
Tel.: (351) 217252010
Web Site: http://www.ecopilhas.pt
Battery & Accumulator Product Mfr
N.A.I.C.S.: 335910

Energizer (South Africa) Ltd. **(1)**
21 Polo Crescent Woodmead Office Park, Johannesburg, 2128, Gauteng, South Africa
Tel.: (27) 118022424
Web Site: http://www.energizerholding.com
Emp.: 30
Storage Battery Mfr
N.A.I.C.S.: 334515

Energizer (Thailand) Limited **(1)**
7th Floor Manorom Building 3354/20 22 23 Rama IV Road Klongton, Klongtoey, Bangkok, 10110, Thailand
Tel.: (66) 22498542
Batteries & Dry Cell Mfr
N.A.I.C.S.: 334515

Energizer Argentina S.A. **(1)**
Tucuman 540 Floor 22, 1049, Buenos Aires, Argentina
Tel.: (54) 1147428193
Web Site: http://www.energizer.com.ar
Primary Batteries & Portable Lighting Products Mfr & Distr
N.A.I.C.S.: 335910

Energizer Australia Pty. Ltd. **(1)**
1 Figtree Drive, Sydney Olympic Park, Sydney, 2127, NSW, Australia
Tel.: (61) 297636111
Web Site:
   http://www.energizerbatteries.com.au
Power Battery Mfr
N.A.I.C.S.: 334515

Energizer Battery Manufacturing, Inc. **(1)**
25225 Detroit Rd, Westlake, OH 44145-2536
Tel.: (440) 835-7866
Primary Batteries & Portable Lighting Products Mfr & Distr
N.A.I.C.S.: 335910

Energizer Battery, Inc. **(1)**
533 Maryville University Dr, Saint Louis, MO 63141 **(100%)**
Tel.: (314) 985-2000
Web Site: http://www.energizer.com
Sales Range: $125-149.9 Million
Emp.: 450
Primary Battery Mfr
N.A.I.C.S.: 335910

Energizer Czech spol.sr.o. **(1)**
Aviatickai 12/1048, Prague, 160 08, Czech Republic
Tel.: (420) 251100111
Web Site: http://www.energizer.cz
Power Battery Mfr
N.A.I.C.S.: 334515

Energizer Group Belgium N.V. **(1)**
Bedrijvenlaan 3, 2800, Mechelen, Belgium
Tel.: (32) 15440022
Web Site: http://www.energizer.eu
Power Battery Mfr
N.A.I.C.S.: 334515

Energizer Group Polska Sp. zo.o **(1)**
Ul Postepu 21a, Warsaw, 02-676, Poland
Tel.: (48) 224300240
Web Site: http://www.energizer.eu
Emp.: 40
Batteries & Dry Cell Mfr
N.A.I.C.S.: 334515

Energizer Group Sweden AB **(1)**

Drottningholmsvagen 22 3tr, Stockholm, 11242, Sweden
Tel.: (46) 850008950
Web Site: http://www.energizer.com
Sales Range: $10-24.9 Million
Emp.: 11
Primary Batteries & Portable Lighting Products Mfr & Distr
N.A.I.C.S.: 335910

Energizer Hellas A.E. **(1)**
14 Kifissias Ave & Halepa, 15125, Maroussi, Greece
Tel.: (30) 2108774300
Web Site: http://www.energizer.com
Emp.: 5
Primary Batteries & Portable Lighting Products Mfr & Distr
N.A.I.C.S.: 335910

Energizer Ireland Limited **(1)**
2 Portobello Harbour, Dublin, Ireland
Tel.: (353) 14782161
Primary Batteries & Portable Lighting Products Mfr & Distr
N.A.I.C.S.: 335910

Energizer Italy S.R.L. **(1)**
Strada 1 Palazzo E5, Assago-Milanofori, Milan, 20090, Italy
Tel.: (39) 02 892331
Web Site: http://www.energizer.eu
Batteries & Dry Cell Mfr
N.A.I.C.S.: 334515

Energizer Korea Ltd. **(1)**
Lions Bldg 3 5th Fl 1487-7 Seocho-gu, Seocho-dong, Seoul, 137-869, Korea (South)
Tel.: (82) 221038200
Web Site: http://www.energizer.co.kr
Emp.: 60
Primary Batteries & Portable Lighting Products Mfr & Distr
N.A.I.C.S.: 335910

Energizer Malaysia Sdn. Bhd. **(1)**
Level 12 Amoda 22 Jalan Imbi, Kuala Lumpur, 55100, Malaysia **(80.24%)**
Tel.: (60) 321425233
Web Site: http://www.energizer.com.my
Emp.: 100
Primary Batteries & Portable Lighting Products Mfr & Distr
N.A.I.C.S.: 335910

Energizer Management Holding Verwaltungs GmbH **(1)**
Schutzenstrasse 110, 42659, Solingen, Germany
Tel.: (49) 2124050
Investment Management Service
N.A.I.C.S.: 551112

Energizer Middle East and Africa Limited **(1)**
144 Emarat Atrium Sh Zayed Rd, Dubai, United Arab Emirates
Tel.: (971) 43211855
Emp.: 37
Primary Batteries & Portable Lighting Products Mfr & Distr
N.A.I.C.S.: 335910

Energizer NZ Limited **(1)**
Level 4 45 O'Rorke Road Penrose, Auckland, 1061, New Zealand
Tel.: (64) 95731830
Web Site: https://energizer.asia
Emp.: 50
Primary Batteries & Portable Lighting Products Mfr & Distr
N.A.I.C.S.: 335910

Energizer Philippines, Inc. **(1)**
23rd Floor Hanston Square 17 San Miguel Avenue Ortigas Center, Pasig, 1605, Philippines
Tel.: (63) 26557800
Batteries & Dry Cell Mfr
N.A.I.C.S.: 334515

Energizer SA **(1)**
8 Impasse Colombelle, Le Grand-Saconnex, Geneva, 1218, Switzerland
Tel.: (41) 229299411
Storage Battery Mfr
N.A.I.C.S.: 334515

Energizer Singapore Pte. Ltd. **(1)**

25 Gul Way Jurong, Singapore, 629197, Singapore **(100%)**
Tel.: (65) 68611411
Web Site: https://energizer.asia
Sales Range: $150-199.9 Million
Emp.: 500
Mfr of Batteries
N.A.I.C.S.: 335910

Energizer Trading Limited **(1)**
Sword House Totteridge Road, High Wycombe, HP13 6DG, Buckinghamshire, United Kingdom
Tel.: (44) 1494533300
Web Site: http://www.energizer.com
Sales Range: $50-74.9 Million
Emp.: 135
International Trade Financing Services
N.A.I.C.S.: 522299

Energizer do Brasil Ltda. **(1)**
Av Eng Luis Carlos Berrini 550-9 A-cj 91, 04571-000, Sao Paulo, Brazil
Tel.: (55) 1155072555
Web Site: http://www.energizerbr.com.br
Power Battery Mfr
N.A.I.C.S.: 334515

Ever Ready Limited **(1)**
Sword House, High Wycombe, HP13 6DG, Buckinghamshire, United Kingdom
Tel.: (44) 1494533300
Web Site: http://www.energizer.com
Emp.: 100
Batteries & Dry Cell Mfr
N.A.I.C.S.: 334515

Eveready Battery Company, Inc. **(1)**
533 Maryville University Dr, Saint Louis, MO 63141
Tel.: (314) 985-2000
Web Site: http://www.eveready.com
Storage Battery Mfr
N.A.I.C.S.: 334515

Eveready Ecuador C.A. **(1)**
Ernesto Noboa y, Gonzalez Suarez, Quito, 13-53, Ecuador
Tel.: (593) 22506370
Web Site: http://www.energizer.com.ec
Storage Battery Mfr
N.A.I.C.S.: 334515

Eveready de Mexico S.A, de C.V. **(1)**
Jaime Balmes No 11 Torre A Piso 3, Mexico, 11510, Mexico **(100%)**
Tel.: (52) 5591382000
Web Site: http://www.energizer.com
Sales Range: $25-49.9 Million
Emp.: 100
Mfr & Marketer of Batteries & Flashlights
N.A.I.C.S.: 335910

Innovasource LLC **(1)**
11515 Vanstory Dr-Ste 110, Huntersville, NC 28078
Tel.: (704) 584-0700
Web Site: https://innovasource.com
Cleaning Equipment Mfr
N.A.I.C.S.: 335999

RE'LEM Public Benefit Company **(1)**
Tutaj u 6/A, 1133, Budapest, Hungary **(33.3%)**
Tel.: (36) 18012910
Web Site: http://www.relem.hu
Storage Battery Mfr
N.A.I.C.S.: 334515

ROV Holding, Inc. **(1)**
601 Rayovac Dr, Madison, WI 53711
Tel.: (608) 275-3340
Investment Management Service
N.A.I.C.S.: 551112

Subsidiary (Non-US):

ROV German Limited GmbH **(2)**
Am Limespark 2, 65843, Sulzbach, Hesse, Germany
Tel.: (49) 6990240
Battery Mfr & Distr
N.A.I.C.S.: 335910

Subsidiary (Domestic):

ROV International Holdings LLC **(2)**
3001 Deming Way, Middleton, WI 53562
Tel.: (608) 275-3340
Holding Company

N.A.I.C.S.: 551112

ROVCAL, INC. **(2)**
601 Rayovac Dr, Madison, WI 53711
Tel.: (800) 736-4648
Battery Mfr & Distr
N.A.I.C.S.: 335910
Sueann Paulk *(Acct Mgr)*
Ronnie Blackwell *(Pres)*

Subsidiary (Non-US):

Ray-O-Vac de Mexico, S.A. de C.V. **(2)**
Km 14.5 Carretera Puente de Vigas Col Lecheria, Tultitlan, 54900, Mexico
Tel.: (52) 5558317070
Battery Mfr & Distr
N.A.I.C.S.: 335910

Rayovac (UK) Limited **(2)**
Stephenson Estate Unit 2A District 12, Washington, NE37 3HW, United Kingdom
Tel.: (44) 622688331
Battery Mfr & Distr
N.A.I.C.S.: 335910

Rayovac Argentina SRL **(2)**
Humbolt 2495 3 Piso, Buenos Aires, 1425, Argentina **(100%)**
Tel.: (54) 11 5353 9500
Sales Range: $25-49.9 Million
Emp.: 15
Battery & Electronics Distr
N.A.I.C.S.: 423620

Rayovac Chile Sociedad Comercial Ltda **(2)**
Avda El Parque 4161 of 503, Huechuraba, Santiago, Chile **(100%)**
Tel.: (56) 562 5713701
Sales Range: $150-199.9 Million
Battery & Electronics Distr
N.A.I.C.S.: 423620

Rayovac Costa Rica, SA **(2)**
San Francisco de Dos Rios de la Bomba La Pacifica, 400 Este carretera a Curridaba, Barrio Fatima, San Jose, Costa Rica **(100%)**
Tel.: (506) 22722242
Sales Range: $25-49.9 Million
Emp.: 20
Battery & Electronics Distr
N.A.I.C.S.: 423620

Rayovac Dominican Republic, SA **(2)**
Prolongacion Ave Romulo Betancourt, Zona Industrial de Herrera, Santo Domingo, Dominican Republic **(100%)**
Tel.: (809) 5305409
Web Site: http://www.la.rayovac.com
Sales Range: $25-49.9 Million
Emp.: 50
Battery & Electronics Distr
N.A.I.C.S.: 423620

Rayovac El Salvador SA de CV **(2)**
Blvd Merliot, Jardines de la Libertad Ciudad Merliot, Apartado Postal 2079, Santa Tecla, El Salvador **(100%)**
Tel.: (503) 2789466
Sales Range: $150-199.9 Million
Emp.: 62
Battery & Electronics Distr
N.A.I.C.S.: 423620

Rayovac Honduras, SA **(2)**
Quinta Entrada Colonia Kennedy 200 Mts Adelante de Los Silos de Ihma, Tegucigalpa, Honduras **(100%)**
Tel.: (504) 2305792
Web Site: http://la.rayovac.com
Sales Range: $100-124.9 Million
Battery & Electronics Distr
N.A.I.C.S.: 449210

Sonca Products Limited **(1)**
74 Kwong Sang Hong Centre, Room 1701-1703 & 1708 Hoi Bun, Kowloon, China (Hong Kong)
Tel.: (852) 23570322
Emp.: 50
Portable Lighting Products Mfr & Distr
N.A.I.C.S.: 423610

VARTA Consumer Batteries Italia, S.r.l. **(1)**
Via Ludovico il Moro 6 Palazzo Pacinotti,

Energizer Holdings, Inc.—(Continued)

Basiglio, 20080, Milano, Italy
Tel.: (39) 0290448311
Web Site: http://www.varta-consumer.it
Consumer Battery Mfr
N.A.I.C.S.: 335910

ENERGOUS CORPORATION

3590 N 1st St Ste 210, San Jose, CA 95134
Tel.: (408) 963-0200   **DE**
Web Site: https://www.energous.com
Year Founded: 2012
WATT—(NASDAQ)
Rev.: $474,184
Assets: $16,675,333
Liabilities: $5,177,656
Net Worth: $11,497,677
Earnings: ($19,366,763)
Emp.: 37
Fiscal Year-end: 12/31/23
Wireless Charging Technology for Remote Powering of Electronic Devices
N.A.I.C.S.: 334220
Mallorie S. Burak (CFO & Interim Principal Exec Officer)
Daniel W. Fairfax (Chm)

ENERGY AND WATER DEVELOPMENT CORP.

7901 4th St N Ste 4174, Saint Petersburg, FL 33702
Tel.: (727) 677-9408   **FL**
Web Site: https://energy-water.com
Year Founded: 2000
EAWD—(OTCQB)
Assets: $1,174,295
Liabilities: $1,656,159
Net Worth: ($481,864)
Earnings: ($1,942,580)
Emp.: 4
Fiscal Year-end: 12/31/22
Water Purification & Engineering Services
N.A.I.C.S.: 221310
Ralph M. Hofmeier (Chm, Pres & CEO)
Irma Velazquez (Vice Chm & COO)

ENERGY FINDERS, INC.

12410 Milestone Ctr Dr, Germantown, MD 20876
Tel.: (301) 401-1729   **NV**
Web Site: https://energyfinders.us
Year Founded: 2004
EGYF—(OTCIQ)
Oil & Gas Exploration Services
N.A.I.C.S.: 211130
Mohammed Zulfiquar (Co-Founder & CEO)
Keith Pivonski (Co-Founder & VP)
Ramzan Mohammed (Co-Founder & CFO)

ENERGY FOCUS, INC.

32000 Aurora Rd, Solon, OH 44139
Tel.: (440) 715-1300   **DE**
Web Site:
https://www.energyfocus.com
Year Founded: 1935
EFOI—(NASDAQ)
Rev.: $5,968,000
Assets: $8,498,000
Liabilities: $8,975,000
Net Worth: ($477,000)
Earnings: ($10,279,000)
Emp.: 20
Fiscal Year-end: 12/31/22
Commercial LED Lighting Products Developer, Mfr & Distr
N.A.I.C.S.: 335132
Chiao Chieh Jay Huang (CEO)
Kin-Fu Chen (Chm)

ENERGY FUELS INC.

225 Union Blvd Ste 600, Lakewood, CO 80228
Tel.: (303) 974-2140   **ON**
Web Site:
https://www.energyfuels.com
UUUU—(NYSEAMEX)
Rev.: $12,515,000
Assets: $273,947,000
Liabilities: $29,538,000
Net Worth: $244,409,000
Earnings: ($59,944,000)
Emp.: 126
Fiscal Year-end: 12/31/22
Uranium & Vanadium Exploration & Mining Services
N.A.I.C.S.: 212290
Mark S. Chalmers (Pres & CEO)
Scott A. Bakken (VP-Regulatory Affairs)
Dee Ann Nazarenus (VP-HR & Admin)
Tom L. Brock (CFO)
Julia Hoffmeier (Sec)
Mark S. Chalmers (Pres & CEO)
David C. Frydenlund (CFO, Gen Counsel & Sec)

Subsidiaries:

Base Resources Limited   (1)
Level 3 46 Colin Street, West Perth, 6005, WA, Australia
Tel.: (61) 894137400
Web Site:
https://www.baseresources.com.au
Rev.: $198,235,000
Assets: $416,949,000
Liabilities: $97,049,000
Net Worth: $319,900,000
Earnings: $10,981,000
Emp.: 2,200
Fiscal Year-end: 06/30/2021
Iron Ore Mining
N.A.I.C.S.: 212210
Tim Carstens (Mng Dir)
Colin Bwye (Exec Dir-Ops & Dev)
Kevin Balloch (CFO)
Denham Vickers (Gen Mgr-Ops-Kwale)
Colin Forbes (Gen Mgr-Environment & Community Affairs)
Stephen Hay (Gen Mgr-Mktg)
Chadwick Poletti (Gen Counsel & Sec)
Andre Greyling (Gen Mgr-Project Dev)
James Fuller (Mgr-Comm & IR)

Subsidiary (Non-US):

Base Titanium Ltd.   (2)
Power Factor Complex Diani Beach Road, PO Box 1214, 80400, Ukunda, Kenya
Tel.: (254) 205130100
Web Site: https://basetitanium.com
Titanium Mining Services
N.A.I.C.S.: 212290
Desterio Oyatsi (Chm)
Chadwick Poletti (Chief Legal Officer)

Base Toliara SARL   (2)
Batiment MN Ex-BRGM 28 Rue Farafaty Ampandrianomby, Antananarivo, 101, Madagascar
Tel.: (261) 202426185
Web Site: https://www.toliarasands.com
Mineral & Sand Resource Services
N.A.I.C.S.: 212322

ENERGY HOLDINGS, INC

2824 Cooper Wind Ln Unit 5, Las Vegas, NV 89183
Tel.: (951) 519-6940   **NV**
Web Site:
https://www.energyholdings.us
Year Founded: 2005
MOCI—(OTCIQ)
Film & Video Production Services
N.A.I.C.S.: 512110
Chancellor Tiscareno (Pres & CEO)

ENERGY RECOVERY, INC.

2000 Chabot Ct Ste 150, Tracy, CA 95304
Tel.: (510) 483-7370   **DE**

Web Site:
https://www.energyrecovery.com
Year Founded: 1992
ERII—(NASDAQ)
Rev.: $128,349,000
Assets: $252,974,000
Liabilities: $33,166,000
Net Worth: $219,808,000
Earnings: $21,504,000
Emp.: 269
Fiscal Year-end: 12/31/23
Energy Recovery Devices & Pumps Utilized in Water Desalination Designer & Mfr
N.A.I.C.S.: 333248
Rodney Clemente (Sr VP-Water)
Nocair Bensalah (VP-Ops)
David W. Moon (Pres & CEO)
Farshad Ghasripoor (CTO)
William W. Yeung (Chief Legal Officer)
Kuo-Chiang Chen (VP)
James Siccardi (VP)
Kelley Vendeland (VP)

ENERGY REVENUE AMERICA, INC.

2800 W Pemberton Dr, Prescott, AZ 86305
Tel.: (330) 977-0033   **NV**
Year Founded: 2003
ERAO—(OTCIQ)
Energy Support Services
N.A.I.C.S.: 213112
Douglas Nelson Pritt (CEO)
Glen Alsop Billeter (Pres)
Edwin Zelaya (CFO & COO)

ENERGY SERVICES OF AMERICA CORPORATION

75 W 3rd Ave, Huntington, WV 25701
Tel.: (304) 522-3868   **DE**
Web Site:
https://www.energyservicesofamerica.com
Year Founded: 2006
ESOA—(NASDAQ)
Rev.: $351,876,861
Assets: $158,247,000
Liabilities: $99,552,856
Net Worth: $58,694,144
Earnings: $25,105,010
Emp.: 490
Fiscal Year-end: 09/30/24
Investment Services
N.A.I.C.S.: 523999
Douglas V. Reynolds (Pres & CEO)
Marshall T. Reynolds (Chm)

Subsidiaries:

C. J. Hughes Construction Company, Inc.   (1)
75 W 3rd Ave, Huntington, WV 25701
Tel.: (304) 522-3868
Web Site: https://www.cjhughes.com
Sales Range: $10-24.9 Million
Emp.: 125
Pipeline Construction
N.A.I.C.S.: 237110
Douglas V. Reynolds (Chm & Chm)
David Combs (VP & Mgr-Water & Wastewater)
Matt Hill (VP & Mgr-Gas Transmission)
Troy Taylor (VP & Mgr-Gas Transmission)
Sean Hieronimus (Dir-Safety)

Subsidiary (Domestic):

Nitro Construction Services, Inc.   (2)
4300 1st Ave, Nitro, WV 25143
Tel.: (304) 204-1500
Web Site:
https://www.nitroconstructionservices.com
Electrical Contracting Services
N.A.I.C.S.: 238210

Tri-State Paving & Sealcoating, Inc.   (1)
3384 Teays Valley Rd, Hurricane, WV 25526

Tel.: (304) 562-5002
Web Site: https://www.tristatepavingwv.com
Road Maintenance Services
N.A.I.C.S.: 237310

West Virginia Pipeline, Inc.   (1)
300 Pipeline Rd, Princeton, WV 24739
Tel.: (304) 425-4053
Web Site: http://westvirginiapipe.com
Water, Sewer, Pipeline, Communications & Power Line Construction
N.A.I.C.S.: 237110
Daniel Bolton (VP)
David Bolton (Pres)

ENERGY TRANSFER LP

8111 Westchester Dr Ste 600, Dallas, TX 75225
Tel.: (214) 981-0700   **DE**
Web Site:
https://www.energytransfer.com
Year Founded: 2005
ET—(NYSE)
Rev.: $89,876,000,000
Assets: $105,643,000,000
Liabilities: $64,984,000,000
Net Worth: $40,659,000,000
Earnings: $4,756,000,000
Emp.: 12,565
Fiscal Year-end: 12/31/22
Natural Gas Midstream, Transportation & Storage Services; Propane Retailer
N.A.I.C.S.: 457210
Kelcy L. Warren (Chm & Co-CEO)
Marshall S. McCrea III (Co-CEO)
Thomas P. Mason (Gen Counsel & Exec VP)
Thomas E. Long (Co-CEO)
Matthew S. Ramsey (COO)
Dylan A. Bramhall (Grp CFO)
James M. Wright Jr. (Chief Compliance Officer)
Greg G. Mcilwain (Exec VP-Operations)
Beth A. Hickey (Exec VP-US Gas Pipelines)
Roger B. Herrscher (Exec VP-Refined Products & Petrochemicals)
Adam Y. Arthur (Exec VP-Crude Oil)
James Beebe (Exec VP-Gas Gathering & Optimization)
Sankar Devarpiran (Sr VP-Engineering & Special Projects)
Micah Green (Sr VP-Construction & Project Execution)
Patrick S. Flavin (Sr VP-Grp Measurement)
Christopher M. Hefty (Sr VP-Grp Mergers & Acquisitions)
Vicki Anderson Granado (VP)
Steve J. Hotte (CIO & Sr VP-Grp)
Christopher R. Curia (Chief HR Officer & Exec VP)

Subsidiaries:

CDM Holdings LLC   (1)
2001 Bryan St Ste 3700, Dallas, TX 75201
Tel.: (214) 750-1771
Holding Company
N.A.I.C.S.: 551112

DAL-TEX Consulting, LLC   (1)
5760 Legacy Dr Ste B3-324, Plano, TX 75024
Tel.: (214) 407-9337
Web Site: https://daltex-consulting.com
Petroleum Product Whslr
N.A.I.C.S.: 424720

Dual Drive Technologies, Ltd.   (1)
8111 Westchester Dr Ste 600, Dallas, TX 75225
Tel.: (469) 484-5370
Web Site:
https://www.dualdrivetechnologies.com
Oil & Gas Field Machinery Mfr
N.A.I.C.S.: 333132
Jeff Lutke (Dir-Comml Ops)
Kenneth Tinkle (Dir-Ops)

ETC M-A Acquisition LLC **(1)**
8111 Westchester Dr Ste 600, Dallas, TX 75225
Tel.: (214) 981-0700
Assets: $297,000,000
Liabilities: $3,000,000
Net Worth: $294,000,000
Earnings: ($37,000,000)
Fiscal Year-end: 12/31/2018
Investment Services
N.A.I.C.S.: 523999
Kelcy L. Warren (CEO)

ETE Common Holdings, LLC **(1)**
3738 Oak Lawn Ave, Dallas, TX 75219
Tel.: (214) 981-0700
Holding Company
N.A.I.C.S.: 551112

Enable Midstream Partners, LP **(1)**
499 W Sheridan Ave Ste 1500, Oklahoma
City, OK 73102   **(53.7%)**
Tel.: (405) 525-7788
Web Site: http://www.enablemidstream.com
Rev.: $2,463,000,000
Assets: $11,729,000,000
Liabilities: $4,634,000,000
Net Worth: $7,095,000,000
Earnings: $88,000,000
Emp.: 1,706
Fiscal Year-end: 12/31/2020
Oil & Gas Operations
N.A.I.C.S.: 211120
John P. Laws (CFO, Treas & Exec VP)

Subsidiary (Domestic):

Enable Gas Gathering, LLC **(2)**
211 N Robinson Ave N950, Oklahoma City,
OK 73102
Tel.: (405) 525-7788
Emp.: 28
Natural Gas Distr
N.A.I.C.S.: 221210

Enable Gas Transmission, LLC **(2)**
525 Milam St, Shreveport, LA 71101
Tel.: (318) 429-2700
Natural Gas Distr
N.A.I.C.S.: 221210

**Enable Gathering and Processing,
LLC** **(2)**
211 N Robinson Ave N950, Oklahoma City,
OK 73102
Tel.: (405) 525-7788
Natural Gas Distr
N.A.I.C.S.: 221210

**Enable Oklahoma Intrastate Trans-
mission, LLC** **(2)**
1 Leadership Sq North Twr 211 N Robinson
Ste 950, Oklahoma City, OK 73102
Tel.: (405) 525-7788
Natural Gas Distr
N.A.I.C.S.: 221210

Enable Products, LLC **(2)**
515 Central Park Dr Ste 600, Oklahoma
City, OK 73105-1722
Tel.: (405) 525-7788
Natural Gas Distr
N.A.I.C.S.: 221210

**Energy Transfer Crude Marketing
LLC** **(1)**
PO Box 4933, Houston, TX 77210-4933
Crude Oil & Natural Gas Distr
N.A.I.C.S.: 486110

Energy Transfer Partners, L.L.C. **(1)**
8111 Westchester Dr, Dallas, TX 75225
Tel.: (214) 981-0795
Web Site: http://www.energytransfer.com
Natural Gas Distribution Services
N.A.I.C.S.: 221210
Kelcy L. Warren (Chm)
Marshall S. McCrea III (Co-CEO)
Thomas E. Long (Co-CEO)

Affiliate (Domestic):

Energy Transfer Operating, L.P. **(1)**
8111 Westchester Dr Ste 600, Dallas, TX
75225
Tel.: (214) 981-0700
Web Site: http://www.energytransfer.com
Rev.: $38,953,999,999
Assets: $96,742,000,000
Liabilities: $63,792,000,000
Net Worth: $32,950,000,000

Earnings: ($142,000,000)
Emp.: 11,420
Fiscal Year-end: 12/31/2020
Crude Oil Acquisition, Pipeline & Terminal-
ling Services
N.A.I.C.S.: 424710
Kelcy L. Warren (Chm)

Subsidiary (Domestic):

Energy Transfer, LP **(3)**
8111 Westchester Dr, Dallas, TX 75225
Tel.: (214) 981-0700
Web Site: https://www.energytransfer.com
Rev.: $78,586,000,000
Assets: $113,698,000,000
Liabilities: $69,759,000,000
Net Worth: $43,939,000,000
Earnings: $5,294,000,000
Emp.: 15,208
Fiscal Year-end: 12/31/2023
Propane & Natural Gas Marketer & Distr
N.A.I.C.S.: 457210
Mackie S. McCrea (Co-CEO)
Tom P. Mason (Pres-LNG & Exec VP)
James M. Wright (Chief Compliance Officer,
Gen Counsel & Exec VP)
Dylan A. Bramhall (Grp CFO)
Brad D. Whitehurst (Exec VP-Tax & Corp
Initiatives)
Greg G. Mcilwain (Exec VP-Operations)
Steve J. Hotte (CIO & Sr VP)
Beth A. Hickey (Exec VP-U. ., S, ., and Gas
Pipelines)
Roger B. Herrscher (Exec VP-NGLs, Re-
fined Products, and Petrochemicals)
Adam Y. Arthur (Exec VP-Crude Oil)
James Beebe (Exec VP-Gas Gathering &
Optimization)
Sankar Devarpiran (Sr VP-Engineering &
Special Projects)
Patrick S. Flavin (Sr VP-Measurement)
Christopher M. Hefty (Sr VP-Mergers & Ac-
quisitions)
Vicki Anderson Granado (VP-Public Rela-
tions & Communications)

Subsidiary (Domestic):

ET Fuel Pipeline, L.P. **(4)**
711 Louisiana St Ste 900, Houston, TX
77002
Tel.: (832) 668-1431
Natural Gas Pipeline Operator
N.A.I.C.S.: 237120

ETC Endure Energy L.L.C. **(4)**
7400 W 129th St Ste 250, Overland Park,
KS 66213
Tel.: (913) 956-4500
Web Site: https://www.endureenergy.com
Emp.: 20
Power & Crude Oil Distr
N.A.I.C.S.: 423610
Bob Bennett (Co-Founder & VP-Power
Trading)
Mike Purmort (Co-Founder & Sr Dir-Crude
Oil Bus Dev)
Gordon Wood (Co-Founder & Dir-Day
Ahead Trading)

**ETC Fayetteville Operating Company,
LLC** **(4)**
711 Louisiana St Ste 900, Houston, TX
77002-2831
Tel.: (281) 714-2000
Natural Gas Pipeline Operator
N.A.I.C.S.: 237120

ETC Hydrocarbons, LLC **(4)**
711 Louisiana St Ste 900, Houston, TX
77002
Tel.: (832) 668-1000
Crude Petroleum & Natural Gas Extraction
Services
N.A.I.C.S.: 211120

**ETC Interstate Procurement Com-
pany, LLC** **(4)**
800 E Sonterra Blvd, San Antonio, TX
78258-3940
Tel.: (210) 403-7300
Power & Crude Oil Distr
N.A.I.C.S.: 423610

**Energy Transfer Data Center,
LLC** **(4)**
5051 Westheimer Rd, Houston, TX 77056
Tel.: (713) 545-4011
Web Site: http://www.etdcportal.com

Telecommunication Management Services
N.A.I.C.S.: 541618

Energy Transfer Fuel, LP **(4)**
8801 S Yale Ave Ste 310, Tulsa, OK 74137
Tel.: (918) 492-7272
Natural Gas Pipeline Operator
N.A.I.C.S.: 237120

Energy Transfer Group, LLC **(4)**
8111 Westchester Dr, Dallas, TX 75225
Tel.: (214) 981-0700
Electric Power Generation
N.A.I.C.S.: 221118

**Energy Transfer Technologies,
Ltd.** **(4)**
8111 Westchester Dr Ste 600, Dallas, TX
75225
Tel.: (469) 484-5370
Web Site:
    https://www.dualdrivetechnologies.com
Natural Gas Compression System Mfr
N.A.I.C.S.: 237120

Affiliate (Domestic):

**Fayetteville Express Pipeline,
LLC** **(4)**
720 Golf Course Dr, Searcy, AR
72143   **(50%)**
Tel.: (501) 268-7314
Natural Gas Transportation Services
N.A.I.C.S.: 486210

Subsidiary (Domestic):

Heritage ETC GP, L.L.C. **(4)**
8801 S Yale Ave, Tulsa, OK 74137
Tel.: (918) 492-7272
Natural Gas Transmission Services
N.A.I.C.S.: 486210

**Houston Pipe Line Company,
L.P.** **(4)**
711 Louisiana St Ste 900, Houston, TX
77002
Tel.: (832) 668-1000
Web Site: http://www.houstonianlite.com
Sales Range: $50-74.9 Million
Emp.: 175
Natural Gas Pipeline Transportation & Mar-
keting
N.A.I.C.S.: 486210

Liberty Pipeline Group, LLC **(4)**
2 Allen Ctr 24rd Fl 1200 Smith St, Houston,
TX 77002
Tel.: (713) 621-9547
Natural Gas Pipeline Transportation Ser-
vices
N.A.I.C.S.: 486210

Lone Star NGL Hattiesburg LLC **(4)**
Hwy 11 N, Petal, MS 39465
Tel.: (601) 584-6471
Web Site: http://www.lonestar.com
Natural Gas Pipeline Operator
N.A.I.C.S.: 237120

**Lone Star NGL Refinery Services
LLC** **(4)**
10334 Hwy 75, Geismar, LA 70734
Tel.: (225) 677-9399
Natural Gas Pipeline Operator
N.A.I.C.S.: 237120

**Missouri Gas Energy Employees'
Association** **(4)**
PO Box 219255, Kansas City, MO 64141
Tel.: (816) 756-5252
Web Site: http://www.spireenergy.com
Natural Gas Distr
N.A.I.C.S.: 221210

**Oasis Pipe Line Company Texas
L.P.** **(4)**
2309 County Rd 101, Ozona, TX 76943
Tel.: (325) 392-2020
Natural Gas Pipeline Operator
N.A.I.C.S.: 237120

**Panhandle Eastern Pipe Line Com-
pany, LP** **(4)**
1300 Main St, Houston, TX 77002
Tel.: (713) 989-7000
Web Site:
    https://peplmessenger.energytransfer.com
Rev.: $571,000,000
Assets: $2,931,000,000
Liabilities: $927,000,000

Net Worth: $2,004,000,000
Earnings: $196,000,000
Emp.: 206
Fiscal Year-end: 12/31/2021
Natural Gas Pipeline Operator
N.A.I.C.S.: 237120
A. Troy Sturrock (VP & Controller)

Panhandle Energy **(4)**
5051 Westheimer Rd Ste 1428, Houston,
TX 77056-5720
Tel.: (713) 989-7000
Web Site: http://www.panhandleenergy.com
Sales Range: $25-49.9 Million
Emp.: 250
Pipe Line & Gas Storage Services
N.A.I.C.S.: 493190
Matthew Rancy (Pres)

Subsidiary (Domestic):

Trunkline Gas Company **(5)**
5444 Westheimer Rd, Houston, TX 77056-
5306
Tel.: (713) 989-7000
Web Site: http://www.energytransfer.com
Natural Gas Transmission
N.A.I.C.S.: 486210

Subsidiary (Domestic):

Regency Energy Partners LP **(4)**
2001 Bryan St Ste 3700, Dallas, TX 75219
Tel.: (214) 840-5477
Web Site: http://www.regencyenergy.com
Rev.: $4,951,000,000
Assets: $17,103,000,000
Liabilities: $7,518,000,000
Net Worth: $9,585,000,000
Earnings: ($142,000,000)
Emp.: 1,879
Fiscal Year-end: 12/31/2014
Natural Gas Processing & Transportation
Services
N.A.I.C.S.: 213112
Chad Lenamon (Pres & COO-Contract
Svcs)

Subsidiary (Domestic):

ELG Oil LLC **(5)**
2001 Bryan St 3700, Dallas, TX 75201
Tel.: (214) 750-1771
Oil Exploration Services
N.A.I.C.S.: 213112

Regency Field Services LLC **(5)**
1700 Pacific Ave Ste 2900, Dallas, TX
75201
Tel.: (214) 750-1771
Natural Gas Gathering Services
N.A.I.C.S.: 213112

Regency Gas Services LP **(5)**
2001 Bryan St Ste 3700, Dallas, TX 75201-
3093
Tel.: (214) 750-1771
Sales Range: $75-99.9 Million
Emp.: 100
Oil & Gas Extraction Services
N.A.I.C.S.: 213112

Subsidiary (Domestic):

**SEC Energy Products & Services,
L.P.** **(4)**
9523 Fairbanks North Houston Rd, Hous-
ton, TX 77064
Tel.: (281) 890-9977
Web Site: https://www.sec-ep.com
Petroleum Product Whslr
N.A.I.C.S.: 424720

SU Development Co., LLC **(4)**
1100 106th Ave NE 101, Bellevue, WA
98004-4325
Tel.: (425) 453-8886
Natural Gas Pipeline Operator
N.A.I.C.S.: 237120

SUG Energy, LLC **(4)**
5444 Westheimer Rd, Houston, TX 77056
Tel.: (817) 302-9401
Natural Gas Pipeline Operator
N.A.I.C.S.: 237120

Sunoco, Inc. **(4)**
3801 W Chester Pike, Newtown Square, PA
19073
Tel.: (215) 977-3000
Web Site: http://www.sunocoinc.com

Energy Transfer LP—(Continued)

Emp.: 10,500
Petroleum Refining & Marketing, Synthetic
Crude Oil Production & Natural Gas Pro-
duction
N.A.I.C.S.: 324110

Subsidiary (Domestic):

Indiana Harbor Coke Corporation (5)
3210 Watling St, East Chicago, IN 46312
Tel.: (219) 397-5769
Web Site: http://www.ihbrr.com
Sales Range: $100-124.9 Million
Emp.: 122
Coal Producer
N.A.I.C.S.: 324199

Inland Corporation (5)
4421 Bradley Rd, Cleveland, OH 44109
Tel.: (216) 351-2210
Web Site: http://www.inlandph.com
Refined Product Pipeline Transportation
Services
N.A.I.C.S.: 486910

Subsidiary (Non-US):

Japan Sun Oil Company, Ltd. (5)
Trusty Kojimachi Bldg 3-4, Kojimachi
Chiyoda-ku, Tokyo, 102-0083, Japan,
Tel.: (81) 33 238 0231
Web Site: https://www.sunoco.co.jp
Sales Range: $25-49.9 Million
Emp.: 100
Lubricant Oil Mfr
N.A.I.C.S.: 324191
Yasuhide Iguchi (Pres & CEO)
Takao Sato (Exec Dir)
Tatsuya Ueda (Exec Dir)
Hirohide Aiko (Exec Officer)
Tatsuya Odagawa (Exec Dir)
Kazuhiro Yoshida (Exec Officer)

Subsidiary (Domestic):

**Philadelphia Energy Solutions
Inc.**
1735 Market St 11th Fl, Philadelphia, PA
19103
Tel.: (215) 339-1200
Web Site: http://pes-companies.com
Sales Range: $5-14.9 Billion
Emp.: 1,118
Holding Company; Petroleum Refining &
Logistics
N.A.I.C.S.: 551112
John B. McShane (Exec VP & Gen Coun-
sel)
Mark Cox (Chm)
Mark J. Smith (CEO)
Rachel Celiberti (CFO)
Daniel Statile (VP & Gen Mgr-Refining
Complex)
Stephanie Eggert (VP-Bus Plng)
Mark Brandon (VP-Strategy & Bus Dev)
Brad Galante (VP-Supply & Trading)
John Sadlowski (Chief Comml Officer)
Paula Fischer Gressman (Dir-Supply Chain)
Karen White (Mgr-Wholesale Fuels)

Subsidiary (Domestic):

**Philadelphia Energy Solutions,
LLC (6)**
1735 Market St 11th Fl, Philadelphia, PA
19103
Tel.: (215) 339-1200
Emp.: 1,200
Oil & Gas Refining Services
N.A.I.C.S.: 324110
James T. Nens (CFO & Exec VP)
John McShane (Exec VP & Gen Counsel)
Mark Cox (Chm)
Mark J. Smith (CEO)
Rachel Celiberti (CFO)
Daniel Statile (VP & Gen Mgr-Refining
Complex)
Mark Brandon (VP-Strategy & Bus Dev)
Stephanie Eggert (VP-Bus Plng)
Brad Galante (VP-Supply & Trading)

Subsidiary (Domestic):

Sun Company, Inc. (5)
4840 Van Gordon St Unit 1000, Wheat
Ridge, CO 80033
Tel.: (303) 424-4651
Web Site: https://suncompany.com

Petroleum Product Whslr
N.A.I.C.S.: 424720

**Sun Pipe Line Company of Delaware
LLC (5)**
2549 Brown Rd, Oregon, OH 43616
Tel.: (419) 691-8950
Sales Range: $50-74.9 Million
Emp.: 10
Crude Petroleum Natural Gas Extraction
Services
N.A.I.C.S.: 211120

Sunoco Inc. (R&M) (5)
3801 W Chester Pike, Newtown Square, PA
19073 **(100%)**
Tel.: (610) 833-3555
Sales Range: $750-799.9 Million
Emp.: 500
Pipeline Management Services
N.A.I.C.S.: 213111
Arnie Dodderer (Gen Counsel)
Ed Patterson (Mgr-Safety-Transportation)
Tony Williams (Mgr-Real Estate)

Plant (Domestic):

**Sunoco Inc. - Marcus Hook
Refinery (5)**
2 Nd & Green St, Marcus Hook, PA 19061
Tel.: (215) 977-6720
Web Site: http://www.gosunoco.com
Sales Range: $1-4.9 Billion
Emp.: 750
Petroleum Refiner
N.A.I.C.S.: 324110

**Sunoco Inc. - Philadelphia
Refinery (5)**
7265 Castor Ave, Philadelphia, PA 19149
Tel.: (215) 745-1341
Web Site: https://www.sunoco.com
Petroleum Refiner
N.A.I.C.S.: 324110

Subsidiary (Domestic):

Sunoco Mascot, Inc. (5)
999 Berkshire Blvd Ste 100, Wyomissing,
PA 19610 **(100%)**
Tel.: (610) 988-2600
Sales Range: $25-49.9 Million
Emp.: 25
Petroleum Products Marketer
N.A.I.C.S.: 457120

West Shore Pipe Line Company (5)
12920 Bell Rd, Lemont, IL 60439
Tel.: (630) 257-7583
Web Site:
https://www.westshorepipeline.com
Emp.: 15
Refined Product Pipeline Transportation
Services
N.A.I.C.S.: 486910

Subsidiary (Domestic):

TETC, LLC (4)
16811 W Hwy 22, Frost, TX 76641-3708
Tel.: (903) 695-0288
Web Site: https://tetc-env.net
Petroleum Product Whslr
N.A.I.C.S.: 424720

**Transwestern Pipeline Company,
LLC (4)**
711 Louisiana St Ste 900, Houston, TX
77002
Tel.: (281) 714-2255
Web Site:
http://twtransfer.energytransfer.com
Petroleum & Natural Gas Pipeline Transpor-
tation & Distr
N.A.I.C.S.: 486210

Subsidiary (Domestic):

Mid-Valley Pipeline Company (3)
907 S Detroit Ave, Tulsa, OK 74120
Tel.: (918) 586-6729
Web Site: http://www.sunocologistics.com
Sales Range: $125-149.9 Million
Pipeline
N.A.I.C.S.: 486990

**Sunoco Logistics Partners GP
LLC (3)**
1734 Old Route 66, Delmont, PA 15626-
1020

Tel.: (724) 468-4072
Sales Range: $50-74.9 Million
Emp.: 15
Gas line & Diesel Fuel Distr
N.A.I.C.S.: 211120

Everen Limited (1)
3 Bermudiana Road 2nd Floor, Hamilton,
HM 08, Bermuda
Tel.: (441) 2950905
Web Site: https://www.everen.bm
Mutual Insurance Services
N.A.I.C.S.: 524126

Everen Specialty Ltd. (1)
3 Bermudiana Road, Hamilton, HM08, Ber-
muda
Tel.: (441) 2950905
Web Site: https://www.everenspecialty.bm
Property & Liability Insurance Services
N.A.I.C.S.: 524126

**Evergreen Remediation Services,
LLC (1)**
6064 N Government Way, Dalton Gardens,
ID 83815
Web Site:
https://www.evergreenremediation.com
Consulting Management Services
N.A.I.C.S.: 541611

**Materials Handling Solutions
LLC (1)**
106 Old Dominion Rd, Duncan, SC 29334
Tel.: (864) 848-2147
Web Site: https://www.mhs-llc.com
Petroleum Product Whslr
N.A.I.C.S.: 424720

**Midcontinent Express Pipeline
LLC (1)**
1001 Louisiana St, Houston, TX 77002-
5089
Tel.: (713) 369-9000
Oil & Gas Related Services
N.A.I.C.S.: 221210

Midstream Logistics, LLC (1)
10777 Westheimer Rd Ste 575, Houston,
TX 77042
Tel.: (435) 915-6981
Web Site: http://www.midlgx.com
Oil & Gas Field Transportation Services
N.A.I.C.S.: 484220

**Regency Desoto-Hesco Services
LLC (1)**
1415 La St Ste 2700, Houston, TX 77002
Tel.: (281) 408-1200
Emp.: 28
Oil & Gas Related Services
N.A.I.C.S.: 221210

Regency Pipeline LLC (1)
2001 Bryan St Ste 3700, Dallas, TX 75201
Tel.: (214) 840-5800
Oil & Gas Related Services
N.A.I.C.S.: 221210

**Regency Utica Gas Gathering
LLC (1)**
2001 Bryan St Ste 3700, Dallas, TX 75201
Tel.: (214) 840-5806
Oil & Gas Related Services
N.A.I.C.S.: 221210

SemGroup Corporation (1)
2 Warren Pl 6120 S Yale Ave Ste 1500,
Tulsa, OK 74136-4231
Tel.: (918) 524-8100
Web Site: http://www.semgroup.com
Rev.: $2,503,262,000
Assets: $5,210,507,000
Liabilities: $3,369,986,000
Net Worth: $1,840,321,000
Earnings: ($26,749,000)
Emp.: 880
Fiscal Year-end: 12/31/2018
Oil & Natural Gas Operations
N.A.I.C.S.: 213112
Thomas R. McDaniel (Chm)
David B. Gosse (Exec VP-Canadian Ops)

Subsidiary (Domestic):

Glass Mountain Holding, LLC (2)
6120 S Yale Ave Ste 700, Tulsa, OK 74136
Tel.: (918) 878-7200
Holding Company
N.A.I.C.S.: 551112

HFOTCO LLC (2)
15855 Jacintoport Blvd, Houston, TX
77015-6575
Tel.: (281) 452-3390
Liquefied Petroleum Product Distr
N.A.I.C.S.: 424720

**Houston Fuel Oil Terminal Company
LLC (2)**
15855 Jacintoport Blvd, Houston, TX 77015
Tel.: (281) 452-3390
Web Site: http://www.semgroup.com
Residual & Crude Oil Storage Services
N.A.I.C.S.: 493190

New Century Transportation LLC (2)
1812 136th Ave E, Sumner, WA 98390
Web Site: https://nctrans.net
Petroleum Product Whslr
N.A.I.C.S.: 424720

Rose Rock Finance Corporation (2)
2 Warren Pl 6120 S Yale Ave Ste 700,
Tulsa, OK 74136-4216
Tel.: (918) 524-7700
Natural Gas Pipeline Transportation Ser-
vices
N.A.I.C.S.: 486210

Rose Rock Midstream, L.P. (2)
6120 S Yale Ave Ste 700, Tulsa, OK
74136-4216 **(100%)**
Tel.: (918) 524-7700
Crude Oil Services
N.A.I.C.S.: 211120
Cecil Mooreland (Mgr-Terminal)

Subsidiary (Non-US):

SemCAMS ULC (2)
Suite 700 520 3rd Avenue SW, Calgary,
T2P 0R3, AB, Canada
Tel.: (403) 536-3000
Web Site: http://www.semcams.com
Sales Range: $25-49.9 Million
Emp.: 40
Natural Gas Distribution Services
N.A.I.C.S.: 221210

Subsidiary (Domestic):

SemGas, L.P. (2)
6120 S Yale Ave Ste 700, Tulsa, OK 74136
Tel.: (918) 524-8147
Sales Range: $50-74.9 Million
Emp.: 200
Ziegler
N.A.I.C.S.: 486210
Wane Ziegler (Mgr)

SemGroup Holdings, L.P. (2)
6120 S Yale Ave Ste 700, Tulsa, OK 74136
Tel.: (918) 524-8100
Web Site: http://www.semgroupcorp.com
Holding Company
N.A.I.C.S.: 551112

Wattenberg Holding, LLC (2)
6120 S Yale Ave Ste 700, Tulsa, OK 74136-
4216
Tel.: (918) 524-8100
Holding Company
N.A.I.C.S.: 551112

Sunoco Logistic Partners L.P. (1)
525 Fritztown Rd, Sinking Spring, PA 19608
Tel.: (610) 670-3200
Web Site: http://www.sunocologistics.com
Oil & Gas Related Services
N.A.I.C.S.: 221210
Peter J. Gvazdauskas (CFO & Treas)
Michael D. Galtman (Chief Accounting Offi-
cer & Controller)
David R. Chalson (Sr VP-Operations)
Michael W. Slough (Sr VP-Engineering-
Procurement)

Susser Energy Services LLC (1)
1403 East Hwy 82, Gainesville, TX 76240
Tel.: (940) 668-8518
Web Site:
http://www.sunocoenergyservices.com
Oil & Gas Related Services
N.A.I.C.S.: 221210

TND Beverage, LLC (1)
401 E Coma Ave, Hidalgo, TX 78557
Tel.: (956) 843-2582
Emp.: 9

Oil & Gas Related Services
N.A.I.C.S.: 221210

USA Compression GP, LLC (1)
111 Congress Ave Ste 2400, Austin, TX 78701
Tel.: (512) 473-2662
Web Site: https://usacompression.com
Holding Company
N.A.I.C.S.: 551112
G. Tracy Owens *(Chief Acctg Officer, Principal Fin Officer & VP-Fin)*
Eric A. Scheller *(COO & VP)*
Eric D. Long *(Pres & CEO)*
Matthew C. Liuzzi *(Treas & VP)*
Christopher W. Porter *(Gen Counsel, Sec & VP)*
Sean T. Kimble *(VP-Human Resources)*

Western Transportation, Inc. (1)
501 S U S 81 Business, Decatur, TX 76234
Tel.: (940) 627-2956
Web Site: https://www.western-transportation-inc.business.site
Truck Transportation Services
N.A.I.C.S.: 484110

ENERGY VAULT HOLDINGS, INC.
4360 Park Terrace Dr Ste 100, Westlake Village, CA 91361
Tel.: (805) 852-0000   DE
Web Site:
https://www.energyvault.com
Year Founded: 2020
NRGV—(NYSE)
Rev.: $145,877,000
Assets: $416,713,000
Liabilities: $129,000,000
Net Worth: $287,713,000
Earnings: ($78,299,000)
Emp.: 170
Fiscal Year-end: 12/31/22
Miscellaneous Financial Investment Activities
N.A.I.C.S.: 523999
Robert Piconi *(Co-Founder & CEO)*
Robert J. Laikin *(Co-Founder)*

ENERKON SOLAR INTERNATIONAL, INC.
13620 Weyburn Dr, Delray Beach, FL 33446
Tel.: (561) 431-7762   NV
Web Site:
http://www.enerkoninternational.com
Year Founded: 1986
ENKS—(OTCIQ)
Holding Company
N.A.I.C.S.: 551112
Benjamin Ballout *(Pres, CEO & CFO)*
Ibrahim Mossad El Nattar *(Sr VP-Bus Dev-Intl)*

ENERPAC TOOL GROUP CORP.
N86 W12500 Westbrook Crossing, Menomonee Falls, WI 53051
Tel.: (262) 293-1500   WI
Web Site:
https://www.enerpactoolgroup.com
Year Founded: 1910
EPAC—(NYSE)
Rev.: $589,510,000
Assets: $777,328,000
Liabilities: $385,349,000
Net Worth: $391,979,000
Earnings: $85,749,000
Emp.: 2,000
Fiscal Year-end: 08/31/24
Electrical, Industrial & Hydraulic Control Products & Supplies Mfr & Distr
N.A.I.C.S.: 333515
E. James Ferland *(Chm)*
Paul E. Sternlieb *(Pres & CEO)*
Scot Stein *(CIO)*
Richard Roman *(Treas, VP-Tax & Asst Sec)*
Bobbi Belstner *(Sr Dir-IR & Strategy)*

Jason Kunschke *(Data Protection Officer)*
James Denis *(Interim Gen Counsel)*
Ben Topercer *(Exec VP)*

Subsidiaries:

Actuant Asia Pte Ltd (1)
25 Pandan Crescent 01-03 Tic Tech Centre, Singapore, 128477, Singapore **(100%)**
Tel.: (65) 68630611
Web Site: http://www.enerpac.com
Sales Range: $25-49.9 Million
Emp.: 25
Hydraulic & Auto Service Equipment Sales
N.A.I.C.S.: 441330
Joseph Wang *(Mng Dir)*

Actuant Australia Ltd. (1)
Block V Unit 3 Regents Park Estate 391 Park Road, Regents Park, 2143, NSW, Australia **(100%)**
Tel.: (61) 287177200
Web Site: http://www.enerpac.com.au
Sales Range: $25-49.9 Million
Emp.: 22
Hydraulic & Auto Service Equipment Sales
N.A.I.C.S.: 441330

Actuant China Ltd. (1)
No 6 Nanjing East Road Taicang Economic Dep Zone, Nanjing, Jiangsu, China
Tel.: (86) 512 5328 7500
Web Site: http://www.actuant.com
Sales Range: $150-199.9 Million
Whslr of Industrial Equipment & Supplies
N.A.I.C.S.: 423840

Actuant Corporation Japan (1)
Besshocho 85-7 Kita-ku, Toda, 331-0821, Saitama, Japan **(100%)**
Tel.: (81) 486624911
Web Site: http://www.actuant.com
Sales Range: $25-49.9 Million
Emp.: 15
Hydraulic & Auto Service Equipment Sales
N.A.I.C.S.: 441330
Mike Miller *(Pres)*

Actuant GmbH (1)
Willstatterstrasse 13, 40549, Dusseldorf, Germany
Tel.: (49) 211471490
Motor Vehicle Parts Mfr
N.A.I.C.S.: 336320

Actuant India Pvt. Ltd. (1)
No 10 Bellary Road Sadashivanagar, Bengaluru, 560080, India
Tel.: (91) 8039289000
Web Site: http://www.hydratight.com
Emp.: 150
Industrial Machinery Mfr & Distr
N.A.I.C.S.: 333998
Varun Vijay Rao *(Mng Dir)*

Actuant Korea Ltd. (1)
Tel.: (82) 314344506
Web Site: http://www.actuant.com.kr
General Purpose Machinery Mfr
N.A.I.C.S.: 333998
Steven Hopps *(Pres)*

Actuant Operations UK Ltd. (1)
5 Coopies Field, Morpeth, NE61 6JR, Northumberland, United Kingdom
Tel.: (44) 1670501000
Motor Vehicle Parts Mfr
N.A.I.C.S.: 336320

Anapac (1)
Block V Unit 3 Regents Park Estate, Regents Park, 2143, NSW, Australia
Tel.: (61) 297438988
Web Site: http://www.anapac.com.au
Sales Range: $25-49.9 Million
Emp.: 20
Whslr of Industrial Supplies
N.A.I.C.S.: 423840

B.W. Elliott Manufacturing Company, LLC (1)
11 Beckwith Ave, Binghamton, NY 13901
Tel.: (607) 772-0404
Web Site: http://www.elliottmfg.com
Sales Range: $100-124.9 Million
Emp.: 220
Mfr of Power Transmission Products
N.A.I.C.S.: 333613

CPS Convertible Power Systems GmbH (1)
Willstatterstrasse 13, 40549, Dusseldorf, Germany
Tel.: (49) 23122390008
Web Site: http://www.conposys.de
Fabric Metal Mfr
N.A.I.C.S.: 332312

Cortland Company, Inc. (1)
44 River St, Cortland, NY 13045-2311
Tel.: (607) 753-8276
Web Site: http://www.cortlandcompany.com
Fluid Power Machinery Mfr
N.A.I.C.S.: 333995

Subsidiary (Non-US):

Cortland Fibron BX Limited (2)
Unit 2 RD Park Stephenson Close, Hoddesdon, EN11 0BW, United Kingdom
Tel.: (44) 1992471444
Emp.: 100
General Purpose Machinery Mfr
N.A.I.C.S.: 333998
Neil McAdam *(Mng Dir)*

CrossCo Investment AB (1)
Alfta Industricenter, Alfta, 822 98, Sweden
Tel.: (46) 27119380
Holding Company
N.A.I.C.S.: 551112

CrossControl OY (1)
Finlaysoninkuja 21, 33210, Tampere, Finland
Tel.: (358) 207699190
Web Site: http://www.crosscontrol.com
Emp.: 200
Computer Peripherals Mfr
N.A.I.C.S.: 334118

Enerpac AS (1)
Kirkegata 3, 2000, Lillestrom, Norway
Tel.: (47) 91578300
Industrial Machinery Mfr
N.A.I.C.S.: 333248

Enerpac Co. Ltd. (1)
Besshocho 85-7, Kita-ku, Saitama, 331-0821, Japan
Tel.: (81) 486624911
Motor Vehicle Parts Mfr
N.A.I.C.S.: 336320

Enerpac Co. (1)
N86 W12500 Westbrook Crossing, Menomonee Falls, WI 53051
Tel.: (262) 293-1500
Sales Range: $25-49.9 Million
Emp.: 100
Electrical, Industrial & Hydraulic Control Products & Supplies Mfr & Distr
N.A.I.C.S.: 333995
Mark Sescik *(Pres)*

Subsidiary (Non-US):

Enerpac (2)
32 avenue de la Baltique, 91140, Villebon-sur-Yvette, France **(100%)**
Tel.: (33) 0160136868
Web Site: http://www.enerpac.fr
Sales Range: $25-49.9 Million
Emp.: 15
Hydraulic Equipment Sales
N.A.I.C.S.: 423830

Enerpac BV (2)
Galvanistraat 115, 6716 AE, Ede, Netherlands **(100%)**
Tel.: (31) 318535911
Hydraulic Tools & Equipment Sales
N.A.I.C.S.: 423830

Enerpac Hydraulics (India) Pvt. Ltd. (2)
Actuant India No 10 Bellary Road Sadashivanagar, Bengaluru, 560080, India
Tel.: (91) 80 3928 9000
Web Site: http://www.enerpac.com
Mfr & Sales of Hydraulic Pump Products
N.A.I.C.S.: 333998

Enerpac Integrated Solutions B.V (2)
Opaalstraat 44, Hengelo, 7554 TS, Overijssel, Netherlands
Tel.: (31) 742422045
Web Site: http://www.enerpac.com

Sales Range: $25-49.9 Million
General Purpose Machinery Mfr
N.A.I.C.S.: 333998

Enerpac Ltd. (2)
5 Coopies Field Morpeth, PO Box 33, Northumberland, NE61 6JR, United Kingdom **(100%)**
Tel.: (44) 1527598900
Web Site: http://www.enerpac.com
Sales Range: $10-24.9 Million
Emp.: 7
Hydraulic Equipment Sales
N.A.I.C.S.: 423830

Enerpac Middle East FZE (2)
Swiss Tower Office 902 Cluster Y Jumeirah Lake Towers, Dubai, United Arab Emirates
Tel.: (971) 45270700
Web Site: http://www.enerpac.com
Sales Range: $25-49.9 Million
Emp.: 10
Distr of Electrical Equipment & Supplies
N.A.I.C.S.: 444180

Enerpac S.p.A. (2)
Via Leonardo da Vinci 97, Trezzano sul Naviglio, 20090, Milan, Italy **(100%)**
Tel.: (39) 024861111
Sales Range: $25-49.9 Million
Emp.: 17
Mfr of of Industrial Supplies
N.A.I.C.S.: 423840

Enerpac France S.A.S. (1)
6 rue du 4 septembre Immeuble Le Poversy Batiment B- 6eme etage, 92130, Issy-les-Moulineaux, France
Tel.: (33) 160136868
Hydraulic Tool Mfr & Distr
N.A.I.C.S.: 333517

Enerpac Heavy Lifting Technology BV (1)
Zuidelijke Havenweg 3, 7554 RR, Hengelo, Netherlands
Tel.: (31) 742422045
Motor Vehicle Parts Mfr
N.A.I.C.S.: 336320

Engineered Solutions L.P. (1)
N86 W12500 Westbrook Crossing, Menomonee Falls, WI 53051
Tel.: (262) 293-1500
Web Site: http://www.actuant.com
Sales Range: $10-24.9 Million
Emp.: 30
Engineered Position & Motion Control Systems Mfr
N.A.I.C.S.: 335314

Equalizer Flange Tool Innovation Co. Ltd. (1)
No 363 Lane 888 Yongchun South Rd, Nantun District, Taichung, Taiwan
Tel.: (886) 423827366
Web Site:
http://www.equalizerinternational.com
Metal Product Mfr & Distr
N.A.I.C.S.: 332919
Jay Hu *(Mng Dir)*

Equalizer International Inc. (1)
2501 Central Pkwy Ste C1, Houston, TX 77092
Tel.: (713) 485-5255
Web Site:
http://www.equalizerinternational.com
Metal Product Mfr & Distr
N.A.I.C.S.: 332919

HTL Australasia Pty. Ltd. (1)
466 Victoria Road, Malaga, 6090, WA, Australia
Tel.: (61) 892493980
Web Site: http://www.htl-australasia.com
Industrial Machinery Mfr
N.A.I.C.S.: 333248

Hayes Industries, Ltd. (1)
14030 Florence Rd, Sugar Land, TX 77498
Tel.: (281) 565-8111
Cable Mfr & Distr
N.A.I.C.S.: 335929
Clifford King *(Chm)*

Hayes Specialty Machining, Ltd. (1)
209 Hamilton St, Trenton, TX 75490
Tel.: (903) 989-2257
Emp.: 99
Machine Tools Mfr

Enerpac Tool Group Corp.—(Continued)
N.A.I.C.S.: 332721

Hydratight Ltd. (1)
Bentley Road South, Darlaston, WS10 8LQ,
United Kingdom
Tel.: (44) 121 50 50 600
Web Site: http://www.hydratight.com
Sales Range: $150-199.9 Million
Emp.: 100
Mechanical Fastening & Connecting Equipment Mfr
N.A.I.C.S.: 332999

Subsidiary (Non-US):

Hydratight BV (2)
Charles Petitweg 8, 4827 HJ, Breda, Netherlands
Tel.: (31) 76 572 45 50
Web Site: http://www.hydratight.com
Emp.: 10
Mechanical Fastening & Connecting Equipment Mfr
N.A.I.C.S.: 332999

Hydratight Equipamentos Servicos e Industria Ltda. (2)
Tel.: (55) 2135206350
Web Site: http://www.hydratight.com
Mechanical Fastening & Connecting Equipment Mfr
N.A.I.C.S.: 332999

Hydratight FZE (2)
Web Site: http://www.hydratight.com
Emp.: 5
Mechanical Fastening & Connecting Equipment Mfr
N.A.I.C.S.: 332999

Hydratight Injectaseal Deutschland GmbH (2)
Boelckestrasse 21-23, 50171, Kerpen, Germany
Tel.: (49) 22 37 92 30 10
Web Site: http://www.hydratight.com
Emp.: 59
Mechanical Fastening & Connecting Equipment Mfr
N.A.I.C.S.: 332999

Hydratight Norge AS (2)
Randabergveien 300, B 4070, Randaberg,
Norway
Tel.: (47) 51 73 35 35
Web Site: http://www.hydratight.com
Mechanical Fastening & Connecting Equipment Mfr
N.A.I.C.S.: 332999

Hydratight Operations, Inc. (2)
Tel.: (713) 860-4200
Web Site: http://www.hydratight.com
Sales Range: $10-24.9 Million
Emp.: 15
Mechanical Fastening & Connecting Equipment Mfr
N.A.I.C.S.: 332999

Hydratight Pte. Ltd. (2)
Mechanical Fastening & Connecting Equipment Mfr
N.A.I.C.S.: 332999

Jeyco (1992) Pty. Ltd. (1)
3 Orion Road, Jandakot, 6164, WA, Australia
Tel.: (61) 894187500
Web Site: http://www.jeyco.com.au
Emp.: 15
Engineering Services
N.A.I.C.S.: 541330

Larzep, S.A. (1)
Avda Urtiaga 6, 48269, Mallabia, Spain
Tel.: (34) 943171200
Web Site: https://www.larzep.com
Industrial Machinery & Equipment Mfr
N.A.I.C.S.: 333996

Maxima Technologies & Systems LLC (1)
1090 N Charlotte St Ste 101, Lancaster, PA
17603
Tel.: (717) 581-1000
Web Site: http://www.maximatech.com
Sales Range: $50-74.9 Million
Emp.: 400

Mfr of Gauges For Measurement of Temperature & Speed
N.A.I.C.S.: 334515

Milwaukee Cylinder (1)
5877 S Pennsylvania Ave, Cudahy, WI
53110-2456
Tel.: (414) 769-9700
Web Site:
https://www.milwaukeecylinder.com
Sales Range: $50-74.9 Million
Emp.: 85
Hydraulic & Pneumatic Cylinders; Fluid
Power Products
N.A.I.C.S.: 333995

New England Controls, Inc. (1)
9 Oxford Rd, Mansfield, MA 02048-1126
Tel.: (508) 339-5522
Web Site:
http://www.newenglandcontrols.com
Sales Range: $600-649.9 Million
Emp.: 100
Whslr of Industrial Supplies
N.A.I.C.S.: 425120

Nielsen Hardware Corporation (1)
Web Site: http://www.nielsenhardware.com
Sales Range: $100-124.9 Million
Mfr of Miscellaneous Fabricated Metal
Products
N.A.I.C.S.: 332510

PT Viking SeaTech Indonesia (1)
Sovereign Plaza 21st Floor Jln T B Simatupang Kav 36, Jakarta, 12340, Indonesia
Tel.: (62) 2129398745
Emp.: 20
Marine Equipment Distr
N.A.I.C.S.: 423910

Power-Packer North America, Inc. (1)
516 Hillcrest Dr, Westfield, WI 53964-9802
Tel.: (608) 296-1132
Web Site: https://www.powerpackerus.com
Sales Range: $25-49.9 Million
Emp.: 60
Machine Tools Mfr
N.A.I.C.S.: 333517

Subsidiary (Non-US):

Power Packer Do Brasil Ltda. (2)
Rua dos Inocentes 587, Soccoro, 04760
050, Sao Paulo, Brazil
Tel.: (55) 1156872211
Whslr of Industrial Supplies
N.A.I.C.S.: 423840

Power Packer Europa B.V. (2)
Edisonstraat 2, 7575 AT, Oldenzaal,
Netherlands (100%)
Tel.: (31) 541584500
Web Site: https://www.power-packer.com
Emp.: 1,000
Customized Hydraulic Products Mfr & Sales
N.A.I.C.S.: 333517
Robert Bartelink (Sls Mgr-Medical-Global)

Precision-Hayes International (1)
704 W Simonds Rd, Seagoville, TX
75159 (100%)
Tel.: (972) 287-2390
Web Site: http://www.precision-hayes.com
Anchorage Equipment Mfr
N.A.I.C.S.: 332722

TK Simplex (1)
777 Oakmont Ln, Westmont, IL 60559
Tel.: (630) 590-6990
Web Site: http://www.tksimplex.com
Sales Range: $25-49.9 Million
Emp.: 120
Mechanical & Hydraulic Jacks, Hydraulic
Cylinders & Accessories & Worm Gear Linear Actuators Mfr
N.A.I.C.S.: 332216

Turotest Medidores Ltda. (1)
Avenida Luiz Merenda 489, Campanario,
Diadema, 09931-390, Sao Paulo, Brazil
Tel.: (55) 1140927200
Web Site: https://www.turotest.com.br
Electric Equipment Mfr
N.A.I.C.S.: 335999

Weasler Engineering Inc. (1)
7801 Hwy 45 N, West Bend, WI 53090
Tel.: (262) 338-2161
Web Site: https://www.weasler.com

Sales Range: $75-99.9 Million
Emp.: 500
Drive Lines, Universal Joints, Shock Absorbing Flexible Couplings, Torque Limiting
& Over-Running Clutches Mfr
N.A.I.C.S.: 333613

Subsidiary (Non-US):

Weasler Engineering B.V. (2)
Bijsterhuizen 3013, 6604 LP, Wijchen,
Netherlands
Tel.: (31) 246489100
Web Site: http://www.weasler.com
General Purpose Machinery Mfr
N.A.I.C.S.: 333998

Weasler Engineering, Kft (2)
Istvan Kiraly krt 24, PO Box 262, 6001, Keoskemet, Hungary
Tel.: (36) 76500410
Web Site: http://www.weasler.hu
Sales Range: $25-49.9 Million
Emp.: 70
General Purpose Machinery Mfr
N.A.I.C.S.: 333998

maximatecc AB (1)
Norra Osavagen 11 B, Alfta, 822. 40, Sweden
Tel.: (46) 271757600
Web Site: http://www.maximatecc.com
Emp.: 40
Computer Peripherals Mfr
N.A.I.C.S.: 334118

ENERSYS

2366 Bernville Rd, Reading, PA
19605
Tel.: (610) 208-1991 DE
Web Site: https://www.enersys.com
Year Founded: 2000
ENS—(NYSE)
Rev.: $3,581,871,000
Assets: $3,466,006,000
Liabilities: $1,708,934,000
Net Worth: $1,757,072,000
Earnings: $269,096,000
Emp.: 10,797
Fiscal Year-end: 03/31/24
Industrial Battery Mfr, Marketer &
Distr
N.A.I.C.S.: 335910
Andrea J. Funk (CFO & Exec VP)
Shawn M. O'Connell (Pres-Energy
Sys Global)
David M. Shaffer (Pres & CEO)
Joseph G. Lewis (Chief Compliance
Officer, Chief Legal Officer, Gen
Counsel, Sec & Sr VP)
Mark Matthews (Sr VP/VP-Specialty-
Global)
Chad Uplinger (Pres-Motive Power-
Global)
Joern Tinnemeyer (CTO & Sr VP)
Philipp Michalsky (CIO)
Patrice Baumann (Chief Integrated
Supply Chain Officer)
Jamie Gebbia (VP-Corp & Business
Development)

Subsidiaries:

**Baterias Hawker de Mexico S. de
R.L. de C.V.** (1)
Tel.: (52) 15558165800
Web Site: https://www.bateriashawker.com
Storage Battery Mfr
N.A.I.C.S.: 335910

**Battery Power International Pte
Ltd.** (1)
85 Tuas Avenue 1, Singapore, 639518,
Singapore
Tel.: (65) 65587333
Primary Battery Mfr
N.A.I.C.S.: 335910
Desmond Ong (Dir-Reg)

EH Europe GmbH (1)
Tel.: (41) 442157410
Web Site: http://www.enersys-hawker.com
Sales Range: $100-124.9 Million
Emp.: 100
Battery Mfr, Marketer & Distr

N.A.I.C.S.: 335910

Subsidiary (Non-US):

**Acumuladores Industriales Enersys
SA** (2)
Avda Autonomia 2 Planta 1a - Edificio LAN,
PO Box 260, 48940, Leioa, Vizcaya, Spain
Tel.: (34) 944521522
Sales Range: $100-124.9 Million
Emp.: 38
Battery Sales & Service
N.A.I.C.S.: 335910

Subsidiary (Non-US):

**Powersafe Acumuladores Industrialis
Unipessoal, Lda.** (3)
Est de Mem Martins 253 r/c E, Sintra,
2725-391, Portugal
Tel.: (351) 219154470
Primary Battery Mfr
N.A.I.C.S.: 335910

Subsidiary (Non-US):

EnerSys A/S (2)
Tel.: (45) 72183883
Emp.: 2
Storage Battery Sales & Service
N.A.I.C.S.: 423990
Lars Jensen (Sls Mgr)
Vibeke Damtoft (CFO)

EnerSys AB (2)
Tel.: (46) 54670670
Web Site: http://www.enersys.com
Sales Range: $100-124.9 Million
Emp.: 11
Industrial Batteries Mfr, Marketer & Distr
N.A.I.C.S.: 335910
Olle Haglund (Mng Dir & Dir-Bus-Nordic)

EnerSys AD (2)
Southern Industrial Zone Tsar Osvoboditel
Blvd Shosse 4, 7700, Targovishte, Bulgaria
Tel.: (359) 60168308
Web Site: http://www.enersys-energia.com
Sales Range: $100-124.9 Million
Emp.: 500
Storage Batteries Mfr
N.A.I.C.S.: 335910

EnerSys AE (2)
12 Kapodistriou Avenue, Attica, 15123, Maroussi, Greece
Tel.: (30) 2105580301
Storage Battery Mfr
N.A.I.C.S.: 335910
Lefteris Strofyllas (Mng Dir)

EnerSys AS (2)
Professor Birkelandsvei 27B, 1081, Oslo,
Norway
Tel.: (47) 22 90 05 05
Web Site: http://www.enersys.no
Industrial Battery Sales, Installation & Service
N.A.I.C.S.: 423990
Bjorn Vidar Rodby (Sls Mgr-Motive Power)

EnerSys BV (2)
Ebweg 32-34, 2991 LT, Barendrecht, Netherlands
Tel.: (31) 850666200
Sales Range: $100-124.9 Million
Battery Mfr, Marketer & Distr
N.A.I.C.S.: 335910

EnerSys Europe Oy (2)
Ahventie 4B, 02170, Espoo, Finland
Tel.: (358) 207715500
Storage Battery Mfr
N.A.I.C.S.: 335910

EnerSys LLC (2)
18/14 Vikentia Hvoyki Str Shekou Industrial
Zone, 04080, Kiev, Ukraine
Tel.: (380) 445865377
Power Equipment Product Distr
N.A.I.C.S.: 423610

EnerSys Ltd. (2)
Tel.: (44) 1617944611
Web Site: https://www.enersys-hawker.com
Sales Range: $25-49.9 Million
Emp.: 100
Lead Acid Batteries Mfr
N.A.I.C.S.: 335910

Subsidiary (Domestic):

ABSL Power Solutions Ltd. (3)
Denchi House Thurso Business Park,
Thurso, KW14 7XW, Caithness, United
Kingdom
Tel.: (44) 1847808077
Web Site: http://www.denchipower.com
Sales Range: $25-49.9 Million
Emp.: 100
Developer & Mfr of High-Performance Bat-
teries for Medical, Aerospace & Defense
Industries
N.A.I.C.S.: 335910

Division (Domestic):

EnerSys Motive Power (3)
Oak Court Clifton Business Park Wynne
Avenue Swinton, Swinton, Manchester, M27
8SS, United Kingdom
Tel.: (44) 1617273800
Web Site: http://www.enersys-emea.com
Emp.: 200
Industrial Battery Mfr
N.A.I.C.S.: 335910

Subsidiary (Non-US):

EnerSys S.A.R.L. (2)
Rue Alexander Zleming Z I Est, CS 40962,
62033, Arras, Cedex, France
Tel.: (33) 32 160 2525
Web Site: https://www.enersys.com
Sales Range: $100-124.9 Million
Industrial Batteries Mfr, Marketer & Distr
N.A.I.C.S.: 335910

EnerSys S.r.l. (2)
Via Torri di Confine 2, Gambellara, 36053,
Vicenza, Italy
Tel.: (39) 0444607811
Sales Range: $25-49.9 Million
Emp.: 77
Power Supply Products Mfr, Sales & Ser-
vices
N.A.I.C.S.: 335910

EnerSys SPRL (2)
Houtweg 26, Brussels, 1140, Belgium
Tel.: (32) 22479457
Emp.: 45
Storage Battery Mfr & Distr
N.A.I.C.S.: 335910
Johan Bogaerts (Mgr)

EnerSys s.r.o. (2)
Gogolova 18, 851 01, Bratislava, Slovakia
Tel.: (421) 263810363
Web Site: http://www.enersys.com
Sales Range: $10-24.9 Million
Emp.: 16
Storage Batteries Mfr
N.A.I.C.S.: 335910

Hawker GmbH (2)
Dieckstrasse 42, 58089, Hagen, Germany
Tel.: (49) 23313720
Web Site: http://www.enersys-hawker.com
Emp.: 300
Industrial Batteries Marketer & Distr
N.A.I.C.S.: 335910

ENSER Corporation (1)
5430 70th Ave, Pinellas Park, FL
33781-4228 (100%)
Tel.: (727) 520-1393
Web Site: http://www.ensercorp.com
Emp.: 99
Designs, Develops, Qualifies & Manufac-
tures Thermal Batteries
N.A.I.C.S.: 335910

EnerSys Advanced Systems Inc. (1)
104 Rock Rd, Horsham, PA 19044 (100%)
Tel.: (215) 674-3800
Web Site: http://www.enersys.com
Sales Range: $25-49.9 Million
Emp.: 50
Production of Lithium Power Sources for
Aerospace & Defense Applications
N.A.I.C.S.: 335910

EnerSys BVBA (1)
Egide Walschaertsstraat 2, 2800, Mechelen,
Belgium
Tel.: (32) 475519396
Storage Battery Mfr
N.A.I.C.S.: 335910
Jef Haverans (Mgr-Svc)

EnerSys Canada Inc. (1)
Tel.: (905) 951-2228
Web Site: http://www.enersysinc.ca
Emp.: 49
Storage Batteries Mfr
N.A.I.C.S.: 335910

EnerSys Delaware Inc. (1)
7055 Ambassador Dr, Allentown, PA 18106
Tel.: (484) 244-4150
Emp.: 25
Storage Batteries Mfr
N.A.I.C.S.: 335910

EnerSys Energy Products Inc. (1)
617 N Ridgeview Dr, Warrensburg, MO
64093
Tel.: (660) 429-2165
Sales Range: $25-49.9 Million
Emp.: 627
Industrial Battery Mfr
N.A.I.C.S.: 335910

EnerSys Hungaria Kft. (1)
Gyar utca 2, 2040, Budaors, Hungary
Tel.: (36) 23886910
Web Site: https://www.enersys.hu
Storage Battery Mfr
N.A.I.C.S.: 335910

**EnerSys India Batteries Private
Ltd.** (1)
Narasimha Rao Palem, Veerulapadu,
Krishna, 521 181, Andhra Pradesh, India
Tel.: (91) 9010742223
Primary Battery Mfr
N.A.I.C.S.: 335910

EnerSys Malaysia Sdn Bhd (1)
No 10 Jalan Anggerik Mokara 31/47,
Seksyen 31 Kota Kemuning, 40460, Shah
Alam, Malaysia
Tel.: (60) 351251111
Primary Battery Mfr
N.A.I.C.S.: 335910

**EnerSys Mexico Management
LLC** (1)
2366 Bernville Rd, Reading, PA 19605-9457
Tel.: (610) 208-1991
Primary Battery Mfr
N.A.I.C.S.: 335910

**EnerSys Reserve Power Pte,
Ltd.** (1)
14A Joo Koon Circle, 11-03 Gateway East,
Singapore, 627515, Singapore
Tel.: (65) 62581997
Sales Range: $10-24.9 Million
Emp.: 13
Storage Batteries Mfr
N.A.I.C.S.: 335910

**EnerSys South East Asia Pte.
Ltd.** (1)
152 Beach Rd Gateway East Bldg 11-08,
Singapore, 189721, Singapore
Tel.: (65) 64313700
Storage Battery Mfr
N.A.I.C.S.: 335910

**EnerSys de Mexico II, S de R.L. de
CV** (1)
Ave Lopez Mateos 4210, Colonia Casa
Blanca, 66475, San Nicolas, Mexico
Tel.: (52) 81813296400
Primary Battery Mfr
N.A.I.C.S.: 335910

EnerSys de Mexico, S.A. de CV (1)
Ave Lopez Mateos 4210 Colonia Casa
Blanca, San Nicolas de los Garza, 66475,
San Nicolas, Nuevo Leon, Mexico
Tel.: (52) 8183296400
Web Site: https://www.enersys.com.mx
Emp.: 300
Storage Battery Mfr
N.A.I.C.S.: 335910

EnerSys, s.r.o. (1)
Nadrazni 555, 267 24, Hostomice, Czech
Republic
Tel.: (420) 311715111
Power Battery Mfr
N.A.I.C.S.: 335910

EnerSystem Argentina S.A. (1)
Pitagoras 3402 - El Talar, B1618BPH, Bue-
nos Aires, Argentina
Tel.: (54) 1147363000

Battery Mfr & Distr
N.A.I.C.S.: 335910

EnerSystem do Brazil Ltda. (1)
R Toufic El Khouri Saad 333 Agua Chata,
Guarulhos, Sao Paulo, Brazil
Tel.: (55) 1124627520
Web Site: http://www.enersystem.com
Sales Range: $25-49.9 Million
Emp.: 150
Storage Batteries Mfr
N.A.I.C.S.: 335910

**Energy Leader Batteries India Private
Ltd.** (1)
Plot No 1057 M 1st Floor Road 45, Jubilee
Hills, Hyderabad, 500 033, India (100%)
Tel.: (91) 4067046701
Web Site: http://www.enersys.co.in
Emp.: 30
Storage Battery Mfr
N.A.I.C.S.: 335910
Arthur Pereira (Mng Dir)

Hawker Powersource, Inc. (1)
9404 Ooltewah Industrial Dr, Ooltewah, TN
37363
Tel.: (423) 238-5700
Web Site:
https://www.hawkerpowersource.com
Sales Range: $50-74.9 Million
Emp.: 137
Industrial Battery Mfr
N.A.I.C.S.: 335910

ICS Industries Pty Ltd (1)
309 Settlement Rd, Thomastown, 3074,
VIC, Australia
Tel.: (61) 1800010027
Web Site: https://www.icsindustries.com.au
Telecommunication Equipment Distr
N.A.I.C.S.: 423690

IE Technologies Pte Ltd. (1)
152 Beach Rd Gateway East Bldg 11-08,
Singapore, 189721, Singapore
Tel.: (65) 64313700
Primary Battery Mfr
N.A.I.C.S.: 335910

NorthStar Battery DMCC (1)
Office 702 Saba 1 Tower, Jumeirah Lake
Towers, Dubai, United Arab Emirates
Tel.: (971) 44238060
Storage Battery Mfr
N.A.I.C.S.: 335910
Nadir Mebarek (Mgr-Technical MEA)

**Outback Power Technologies,
Inc.** (1)
17825 59th Ave NE Ste B, Arlington, WA
98223
Tel.: (360) 435-6030
Web Site: http://www.outbackpower.com
Power Battery Mfr
N.A.I.C.S.: 335910

Purcell Systems, Inc. (1)
16125 E Euclid Ave, Spokane Valley, WA
99216
Tel.: (509) 755-0341
Web Site: https://www.purcellsystems.com
Sales Range: $50-74.9 Million
Emp.: 138
Outdoor Power Cabinets & Enclosures &
Outside Plant Equipment Systems Mfr
N.A.I.C.S.: 333248
Dwayne Gray (Plant Mgr)

Subsidiary (Non-US):

Purcell Systems International AB (2)
Augustendalsvagen 19, PO Box 1199,
Nacka Strand, 131 27, Stockholm, Sweden
Tel.: (46) 84664650
Telecom Market Services
N.A.I.C.S.: 517810
Robert Kjelldorff (Pres)

Quallion, LLC (1)
12744 San Fernando Rd, Sylmar, CA
91342
Tel.: (818) 833-2000
Web Site: http://www.quallion.com
Emp.: 80
Surgical Appliance & Supplies Mfr
N.A.I.C.S.: 339113

SiteTel Shanghai Co. Ltd. (1)
207 Wulumuqi North Road, JingAn District,
Shanghai, 200040, China

Tel.: (86) 2162376300
Storage Battery Mfr
N.A.I.C.S.: 335910

SiteTel Sweden AB (1)
Haukadalsgatan 8A, 164 40, Kista, Sweden
Tel.: (46) 841010200
Storage Battery Mfr
N.A.I.C.S.: 335910

The Alpha Group (1)
3767 Alpha Way, Bellingham, WA 98226
Tel.: (360) 647-2360
Web Site: http://www.alpha.com
Holding Company
N.A.I.C.S.: 551112
Fred Kaiser (Founder)

Subsidiary (Domestic):

Alpha Alternative Energy Inc. (2)
1628 W Williams Dr, Phoenix, AZ 85027
Tel.: (623) 251-3000
Reserve Power Battery Mfr
N.A.I.C.S.: 335910

Subsidiary (Non-US):

**Alpha Innovations Mexico S de R.L.
de C.V.** (2)
Juan Aldama 1122 Sur Col Universidad,
50130, Toluca, Mexico
Tel.: (52) 7222127380
Web Site: http://www.alphaim.mx
Power Battery Mfr
N.A.I.C.S.: 335910

**Alpha Tech Energy Solutions India
Private Limited** (2)
Vikas Plaza Plot No 38/1A 4 Electronic City
Phase 2 Hosur Road, Bengaluru, 560100,
Karnataka, India
Tel.: (91) 8041230299
Web Site: https://www.alphaind.in
Power Battery Mfr
N.A.I.C.S.: 335910
Vidyaranya N. H. (Mng Dir)
Vijayaraghavan M. G. (Dir-R&D)
Srikanta Prasad (Gen Mgr-Firmware)
N. H. Vidyaranya (Mng Dir)
M. G. Vijayaraghavan (Dir)

Alpha Technologies Asia Ltd. (2)
Suite 1903 Tower 1 China Hong Kong City
33 Canton Road, Tsim Tsa Tsui, Kowloon,
China (Hong Kong)
Tel.: (852) 75582197878
Power Battery Mfr
N.A.I.C.S.: 335910

Alpha Technologies Ltd. (2)
7700 Riverfront Gate, Burnaby, V5J 5M4,
BC, Canada
Tel.: (604) 436-5900
Web Site: https://www.alpha.ca
Emp.: 1,300
Design, Manufacture, Service & Installation
of AC & DC Power Solutions
N.A.I.C.S.: 335311

Alpha Technologies Pty. Ltd. (2)
Level 7 91 Phillip Street, Parramatta, 2150,
NSW, Australia
Tel.: (61) 285996960
Power Battery Mfr
N.A.I.C.S.: 335910

Alpha Technologies S.A. (2)
Boulevard de l'Europe 131, B 1301, Wavre,
Belgium
Tel.: (32) 10438211
Web Site: http://www.mitra-innovations.com
Sales Range: $25-49.9 Million
Emp.: 235
Standard & Custom Power Conversion
Equipment Mfr
N.A.I.C.S.: 335999
Vilain Sara (VP-Fin)

Subsidiary (Domestic):

Alpha Technologies, Inc. (2)
3767 Alpha Way, Bellingham, WA 98226-
8302
Tel.: (360) 647-2360
Web Site: http://www.alpha.com
Sales Range: $125-149.9 Million
Emp.: 425
Powering Solutions & Power Products for
Communications Industry
N.A.I.C.S.: 335311

EnerSys—(Continued)

Michael Perica (*VP-Fin*)

Subsidiary (Domestic):

Alpha Technologies Services, Inc. (3)
3767 Alpha Way, Bellingham, WA 98226
Tel.: (360) 647-2360
Power Battery Mfr
N.A.I.C.S.: 335910

Argus Technologies, Inc. (3)
3765 Alpha Way, Bellingham, WA 98226
Tel.: (360) 671-7054
Web Site: http://www.argusdcpower.com
Sales Range: $10-24.9 Million
Emp.: 20
Electronic Parts & Equipment Whslr
N.A.I.C.S.: 423690
Grace Borsari (*Pres*)

Seldon Systems, Inc. (3)
3050 Royal Blvd S 175, Alpharetta, GA 30022
Tel.: (770) 772-9955
Web Site: http://www.seldonsystems.com
Rev.: $1,918,000
Emp.: 7
Periodical Publishers
N.A.I.C.S.: 513120

ENERTECK CORPORATION
10701 Corporate Dr, Stafford, TX 77477
Tel.: (281) 240-1787 DE
Web Site:
  https://www.enerteckchemical.com
ETCK—(OTCIQ)
Rev.: $100,302
Assets: $314,811
Liabilities: $12,103,146
Net Worth: ($11,788,335)
Earnings: ($1,202,348)
Emp.: 4
Fiscal Year-end: 12/31/22
Chemicals Mfr
N.A.I.C.S.: 325998
Gary Byron Aman (*Pres & CEO-Acting*)
Thomas F. Donino (*Chm*)
Richard B. Dicks (*CFO*)

ENFUSION, INC.
125 S Clark St Ste 750, Chicago, IL 60603
Tel.: (312) 253-9800 DE
Web Site: https://www.enfusion.com
Year Founded: 2021
ENFN—(NYSE)
Rev.: $150,349,000
Assets: $123,783,000
Liabilities: $20,339,000
Net Worth: $103,444,000
Earnings: ($7,654,000)
Emp.: 1,006
Fiscal Year-end: 12/31/22
Offices of Other Holding Companies
N.A.I.C.S.: 551112
Bradley Herring (*CFO*)
Lorelei M. Skillman (*Chief Mktg & Comm Officer*)
Dan Groman (*CTO*)
Oleg Movchan (*CEO*)
Kathleen DeRose (*Interim Chm*)
Neal Pawar (*COO*)

ENGEX, INC.
44 Wall St 2nd Fl, New York, NY 10005
Tel.: (212) 495-4200
Web Site: http://www.engexinc.com
EXGI—(OTCIQ)
Sales Range: Less than $1 Million
Investment Services
N.A.I.C.S.: 523999
J. Morton Davis (*Chm & Pres*)
Michael Siciliano (*Chief Compliance Officer & Sec*)

ENGLOBAL CORPORATION
11740 Katy Fwy Energy Tower III 11th Fl, Houston, TX 77079
Tel.: (281) 878-1000 NV
Web Site: https://www.englobal.com
Year Founded: 1985
ENG—(NASDAQ)
Rev.: $40,189,000
Assets: $30,023,000
Liabilities: $19,698,000
Net Worth: $10,325,000
Earnings: ($18,514,000)
Emp.: 302
Fiscal Year-end: 12/31/22
Holding Company; Engineering & Construction Management Services
N.A.I.C.S.: 551112
William A. Coskey (*Founder, Exec Chm & CEO*)
Mark A. Hess (*CFO, Treas & Sec*)
Scott Curd (*VP-HR*)
John L. Kratzert (*Sr VP-Govt Svcs*)

Subsidiaries:

ENGlobal U.S., Inc. (1)
11740 Katy Fwy - Energy Tower III 11th fl, Houston, TX 77079
Tel.: (281) 878-1000
Web Site: https://www.englobal.com
Engineering & Construction Management Services
N.A.I.C.S.: 541330

ENHABIT, INC.
6688 N Central Expy Ste 1300, Dallas, TX 75206
Tel.: (214) 239-6500 DE
Web Site: https://www.ehab.com
Year Founded: 2014
EHAB—(NYSE)
Rev.: $1,071,100,000
Assets: $1,526,800,000
Liabilities: $756,700,000
Net Worth: $770,100,000
Earnings: ($40,400,000)
Emp.: 11,000
Fiscal Year-end: 12/31/22
Home Health & Hospice Services
N.A.I.C.S.: 621610
Barbara A. Jacobsmeyer (*CEO*)
Crissy Carlisle (*CFO*)
Julie Jolley (*Exec VP-Home Health*)
Jeanne Kalvaiti (*Exec VP-Hospice*)
Bud Langham (*Exec VP-Clinical Excellence & Strategy*)
Tanya Marion (*Chief HR Officer*)
Dylan Black (*Gen Counsel & Sec*)
Collin McQuiddy (*Chief Acctg Officer & Sr VP*)

Subsidiaries:

Unity Health Hospice (1)
1000 Des Peres Rd, Saint Louis, MO 63131
Tel.: (314) 364-2300
Women Healthcare Services
N.A.I.C.S.: 621610
Lisa Heisserer (*Dir*)

ENHANCE SKIN PRODUCTS INC.
50 W Liberty St Ste 880, Reno, NV 89501
Tel.: (416) 306-2493 NV
Web Site: http://www.enhanceskinproducts.com
Year Founded: 2006
EHSK—(OTCIQ)
Cosmetics Mfr
N.A.I.C.S.: 325620
Samuel S. Asculai (*Chief Scientific Officer*)
Drasko Puseljic (*Gen Counsel*)
Donald Nicholson (*Pres & CEO*)

ENHERENT CORP.
6800 Jericho Tpke Ste 120W, Syosset, NY 11791

Tel.: (516) 932-9080 DE
Web Site: https://enherentcorp.com
ENHT—(OTCIQ)
Sales Range: $10-24.9 Million
Emp.: 62
Custom Computer Programming Services
N.A.I.C.S.: 541511
Pamela Fredette (*Chm, Pres & CEO*)
Douglas K. Mellinger (*Founder*)
Thomas Minerva (*Vice Chm*)
Arunava De (*VP-Fin & Controller*)

Subsidiaries:

enherent Corp. (1)
75 Charter Oak Ave Bldg 1 1-307, Hartford, CT 06106
Tel.: (860) 247-0200
Web Site: http://www.enherent.com
Sales Range: $10-24.9 Million
Emp.: 40
E-Business Answer Services
N.A.I.C.S.: 541618

ENLINK MIDSTREAM, LLC
1722 Routh St Ste 1300, Dallas, TX 75201
Tel.: (214) 953-9500 DE
Web Site: https://www.enlink.com
Year Founded: 2014
ENLC—(NYSE)
Rev.: $6,900,100,000
Assets: $8,328,600,000
Liabilities: $5,693,500,000
Net Worth: $2,635,100,000
Earnings: $206,200,000
Emp.: 1,072
Fiscal Year-end: 12/31/23
Holding Company; Petroleum & Natural Gas Processing & Transportation Services
N.A.I.C.S.: 551112
Leldon E. Echols (*Chm*)
J. Philipp Rossbach (*Chief Acctg Officer & VP*)
Brian Brungardt (*Dir-IR*)
Jesse Arenivas (*Pres & CEO*)
Adam Forman (*Gen Counsel, Sec & Exec VP*)
Dilanka Seimon (*Chief Comml Officer & Exec VP*)

Subsidiaries:

EnLink Midstream Partners, LP (1)
1722 Routh St Ste 1300, Dallas, TX 75201 (100%)
Tel.: (214) 953-9500
Web Site: http://www.enlink.com
Energy & Gas Related Services
N.A.I.C.S.: 211120
Leldon E. Echols (*Executives, Bd of Dirs*)

Subsidiary (Domestic):

EnLink Midstream, Inc. (2)
2501 Cedar Springs Ste 100, Dallas, TX 75201
Tel.: (214) 953-9500
Natural Gas Pipeline Distr
N.A.I.C.S.: 486210
Joe A. Davis (*Gen Counsel, Sec & Exec VP*)
Christopher H. Tennant (*Sr VP-Comml*)
Jill McMillan (*VP-Pub & Indus Affairs*)
Royston Lightfoot (*Sr VP-Bus Dev*)
Stan Golemon (*Sr VP-Engrg & Ops*)

Kentucky Oil Gathering, LLC (2)
9320 Black Run Rd, Nashport, OH 43830
Tel.: (740) 828-2892
Web Site: http://www.kyogc.com
Oil & Natural Gas Exploration Services
N.A.I.C.S.: 211120
Carl Ross (*Mgr-State*)

ENLIVEN THERAPEUTICS, INC
6200 Lookout Rd, Boulder, CO 80301
Tel.: (720) 647-8519 DE
Web Site:
  https://www.enliventherapeutics.com
Year Founded: 2016

ELVN—(NASDAQ)
Rev.: $846,000
Assets: $91,959,000
Liabilities: $1,830,000
Net Worth: $90,129,000
Earnings: $1,488,000
Emp.: 6
Fiscal Year-end: 12/31/22
Research & Development in Biotechnology (except Nanobiotechnology)
N.A.I.C.S.: 541714
Helen Collins (*Chief Medical Officer*)
Rahul D. Ballal (*Pres & CEO*)
Michael P. Gray (*Chief Fin & Operating Officer*)
Anish Patel (*Founder*)
Ben Hohl (*CFO*)

ENNIS, INC.
2441 Presidential Pkwy, Midlothian, TX 76065
Tel.: (972) 775-9801 TX
Web Site: https://www.ennis.com
Year Founded: 1909
EBF—(NYSE)
Rev.: $400,014,000
Assets: $368,844,000
Liabilities: $65,029,000
Net Worth: $303,815,000
Earnings: $28,982,000
Emp.: 1,997
Fiscal Year-end: 02/28/22
Business Forms & Apparel Mfr
N.A.I.C.S.: 323111
Keith S. Walters (*Chm, Pres & CEO*)
Vera Burnett (*CFO & Treas*)
Dan Gus (*Asst Sec & Gen Counsel*)
Wade Brewer (*COO*)

Subsidiaries:

Adams McClure, LP (1)
8075 E 40th Ave, Denver, CO 80207 (100%)
Tel.: (303) 777-1984
Web Site: http://www.adamsmcclure.com
Sales Range: $10-24.9 Million
Emp.: 60
Printing & Litho Services
N.A.I.C.S.: 323111

Admore, Inc. (1)
24707 Wood Ct, Macomb, MI 40042-5078 (100%)
Tel.: (586) 949-8200
Web Site: http://www.admorefolders.com
Sales Range: $25-49.9 Million
Emp.: 100
Mfr of Premium Presentation Folders & Related Products
N.A.I.C.S.: 323111
Lisa Goebel (*Mktg Mgr*)

Division (Domestic);

Admore West (2)
200 E Cerritos Ave, Anaheim, CA 92805
Web Site: http://www.admorefolders.com
Presentation Folders & Related Items Mfr
N.A.I.C.S.: 323111

AmeriPrint Corporation (1)
1401 West Diggins St, Harvard, IL 60033
Tel.: (815) 943-9410
Web Site: http://www.ameriprint.com
Manifold Business Forms Printing
N.A.I.C.S.: 323111
Mark Diedrich (*VP-Mfg*)

American Paper Converting LLC (1)
6142 American Rd, Toledo, OH 43612
Tel.: (419) 729-4780
Web Site: https://www.apconverting.com
Paper Machinery Mfr
N.A.I.C.S.: 333243

Atlas Tag & Label (1)
2361 Industrial Dr, Neenah, WI 54957-0638 (100%)
Tel.: (920) 722-1557

Web Site: http://www.atlas-tag.com
Sales Range: $50-74.9 Million
Emp.: 140
Mfr of Paper & Cloth Tags & Labels
N.A.I.C.S.: 323111

B&D Litho of Arizona, Inc. (1)
3820 N 38th Ave, Phoenix, AZ 85019
Tel.: (602) 269-2526
Sales Range: $25-49.9 Million
Emp.: 50
Offset Printing
N.A.I.C.S.: 323111
Kevin Potter (Gen Mgr)

Block Graphics, Inc. (1)
5822 NE Skyport Way, Portland, OR
97218-1248
Tel.: (503) 287-0343
Web Site: https://www.blockgraphics.com
Sales Range: $75-99.9 Million
Emp.: 230
Business Forms & Envelopes Mfr
N.A.I.C.S.: 323111

Calibrated Forms Co., Inc. (1)
537 N E Ave, Columbus, KS
66725   (100%)
Tel.: (620) 429-1120
Sales Range: $50-74.9 Million
Emp.: 200
Manifold Business Forms
N.A.I.C.S.: 323111
Steve Reifel (Gen Mgr)

**Ennis Business Forms of Kansas,
Inc.** (1)
2920 S Richards Rd, Fort Scott, KS
66701   (100%)
Tel.: (620) 223-6500
Sales Range: $25-49.9 Million
Emp.: 100
Business Form Mfr
N.A.I.C.S.: 323111

Ennis, Inc. - Chatham (1)
1 Ennis Dr, Chatham, VA 24531
Tel.: (434) 432-2121
Web Site: https://www.ennis.com
Sales Range: $50-74.9 Million
Emp.: 75
Business Form Mfr
N.A.I.C.S.: 323111

Ennis, Inc. - Coshocton (1)
24170 Hangar Ct, Coshocton, OH 43812
Tel.: (740) 622-0222
Web Site: https://www.ennis.com
Sales Range: $10-24.9 Million
Emp.: 13
Business Form Mfr
N.A.I.C.S.: 323111
Keith S. Walters (Pres & CEO)

Ennis, Inc. - DeWitt (1)
304 3rd Ave E, De Witt, IA 52742
Tel.: (563) 659-5011
Web Site: https://www.ennis.com
Sales Range: $25-49.9 Million
Emp.: 72
Business Form Mfr
N.A.I.C.S.: 323111

Ennis, Inc. - Ennis, TX (1)
114 NE Main St, Ennis, TX 75119-4045
Tel.: (972) 875-3811
Web Site: https://www.ennis.com
Sales Range: $100-124.9 Million
Emp.: 75
Business Form Mfr
N.A.I.C.S.: 323111

Ennis, Inc. - Knoxville (1)
4214 Greenway Dr, Knoxville, TN 37918
Tel.: (865) 637-9212
Web Site: http://www.ennis.com
Sales Range: $10-24.9 Million
Emp.: 30
Printing of Business Forms
N.A.I.C.S.: 323111
Keith S. Walters (Chm, Pres & CEO)

Ennis, Inc. - Moultrie (1)
108 Industrial Pkwy, Moultrie, GA 31788
Tel.: (229) 985-1221
Web Site: http://www.ennis.com
Sales Range: $25-49.9 Million
Emp.: 18
Business Form Mfr
N.A.I.C.S.: 323111

Ennis, Inc. - Paso Robles (1)
298 Sherwood Rd, Paso Robles, CA 93446
Tel.: (805) 238-1144
Web Site: http://www.ennis.com
Sales Range: $50-74.9 Million
Emp.: 140
Business Form Mfr
N.A.I.C.S.: 323111

Ennis, Inc. - Wolfe City (1)
118 W Main St, Wolfe City, TX 75496
Web Site: https://www.ennis.com
Business Form Mfr
N.A.I.C.S.: 323111

**Independent Printing Company,
Inc.** (1)
1801 Lawrence Dr, De Pere, WI 54115
Web Site: https://www.independentinc.com
Commercial Printing Services
N.A.I.C.S.: 323111

Infoseal, LLC (1)
1825 Blue Hills Cir, Roanoke, VA 24012
Tel.: (540) 981-1140
Web Site: https://www.infoseal.com
Printed Product Mfr
N.A.I.C.S.: 323111

Integrated Print & Graphics (1)
645 Stevenson Rd, South Elgin, IL 60177-
1134
Tel.: (847) 695-6777
Web Site: https://www.ennis.com
Graphic Design Services
N.A.I.C.S.: 541430
Robert Pagel (Mgr-Information Technology)

Kay Toledo Tag, Inc. (1)
6050 Benore Rd, Toledo, OH 43612
Tel.: (419) 729-5479
Web Site: https://www.kaytag.com
Sales Range: $25-49.9 Million
Emp.: 100
Commercial Printing Services
N.A.I.C.S.: 323111

Major Business Systems, Inc. (1)
1 Ennis Dr, Chatham, VA 24531
Tel.: (919) 732-2101
Web Site: https://www.ennis.com
Rev.: $6,200,000
Emp.: 60
Coated & Laminated Paper Mfr
N.A.I.C.S.: 322220

National Imprint Corporation (1)
114 Ward Dr, Claysburg, PA 16625
Tel.: (814) 239-8141
Web Site: http://www.national-imprint.com
Sales Range: $10-24.9 Million
Emp.: 150
Envelopes & Stationery Mfr
N.A.I.C.S.: 322230

Northstar Computer Forms, Inc. (1)
7130 Northland Cir N, Brooklyn Park, MN
55428   (100%)
Tel.: (763) 531-7340
Web Site: http://www.northstar-mn.net
Business Form Mfr
N.A.I.C.S.: 323111

Subsidiary (Domestic):

General Financial Supply, Inc. (2)
1235 N Ave, Nevada, IA 50201
Tel.: (515) 382-3549
Web Site:
    http://www.generalfinancialsupply.com
Emp.: 60
Manifold Business Forms Printing
N.A.I.C.S.: 323111

Unit (Domestic):

**General Financial Supply, Inc. -
Virginia** (3)
213B Dry River Rd, Bridgewater, VA 22812
Tel.: (540) 828-3892
Web Site:
    http://www.generalfinancialsupply.com
Sales Range: $10-24.9 Million
Emp.: 50
Negotiable & Non-negotiable Secure Docu-
ments, Internal Bank Forms & Secure Dis-
tribution Services
N.A.I.C.S.: 561410

PrintGraphics, LLC (1)

1170 Industrial Park Dr, Vandalia, OH
45377
Tel.: (937) 898-3008
Web Site: http://www.printgraphicsnet.com
Emp.: 45
Commercial Printing Services
N.A.I.C.S.: 323111

PrintXcel (1)
352 S Greeno Rd, Fairhope, AL 36532
Web Site: http://www.printxcel.com
Emp.: 50
Business Documents Mfr
N.A.I.C.S.: 323111

Plant (Domestic):

PrintXcel - Visalia Plant (2)
1424 E Tulare Ave, Visalia, CA 93292
Tel.: (559) 636-6290
Web Site: http://www.printxcel.com
Sales Range: $25-49.9 Million
Manifold Business Forms Printing
N.A.I.C.S.: 323111

Printegra Corporation (1)
5040 Highlands Pkwy, Smyrna, GA 30082
Tel.: (770) 319-9500
Web Site: http://www.printegra.com
Sales Range: $250-299.9 Million
Emp.: 780
Office Products, Business Forms & Soft-
ware
N.A.I.C.S.: 323111

Royal Business Forms, Inc. (1)
3301 Avenue E E, Arlington, TX
76011   (100%)
Tel.: (817) 640-5248
Web Site: https://www.royalbf.com
Sales Range: $75-99.9 Million
Emp.: 50
Commercial Printing
N.A.I.C.S.: 323111

Sovereign Business Forms Inc. (1)
Tel.: (713) 784-9899
Sales Range: $25-49.9 Million
Emp.: 230
Business Form & Card Printing
N.A.I.C.S.: 323111

Subsidiary (Non-US):

Curtis Business Forms Inc. (2)
Tel.: (413) 536-7235
Web Site: http://www.curtisbf.com
Sales Range: $10-24.9 Million
Emp.: 30
Business Forms Printing
N.A.I.C.S.: 323111

Forms Manufacturers Inc. (2)
Tel.: (620) 724-8225
Web Site:
    http://www.formsmanufacturers.com
Sales Range: $1-9.9 Million
Emp.: 80
Manifold Business Forms
N.A.I.C.S.: 323111

Tri-C Business Forms, Inc. (2)
Tel.: (713) 784-1200
Web Site: http://www.tri-
cbusinessforms.com
Sales Range: $1-9.9 Million
Emp.: 2,300
Business Form & Card Printing
N.A.I.C.S.: 323111

**Special Service Partners
Corporation** (1)
1265 Gillingham Rd, Neenah, WI 54956
Tel.: (920) 886-2000
Web Site: http://www.ssptag.com
Sales Range: $1-9.9 Million
Emp.: 60
Commercial Printing Services
N.A.I.C.S.: 323111

Specialized Printed Forms, Inc. (1)
352 Center St, Caledonia, NY 14423
Tel.: (585) 538-2381
Web Site: http://www.spforms.com
Emp.: 25
Commercial Printing Services
N.A.I.C.S.: 323111

Stylecraft Printing, Co. (1)
8472 Ronda Dr, Canton, MI 48187
Tel.: (734) 455-5500

Web Site: http://stylecraftprinting.com
Sales Range: $1-9.9 Million
Emp.: 100
Commercial Lithographic Printing
N.A.I.C.S.: 323111
Richard Pesci (Pres & Treas)

The Flesh Company (1)
2407 Jothi Ave, Parsons, KS 67357-8471
Tel.: (620) 421-6120
Web Site: https://www.fleshco.com
Continuous Forms, Office & Business
N.A.I.C.S.: 323111
Sabrina Cherry (Dir-Strategic Accounts)
Pam Spencer (Acct Mgr)

Subsidiary (Domestic):

Impressions Direct, Inc. (2)
915 Horan Dr, Fenton, MO 63026
Tel.: (314) 951-2100
Web Site: https://www.impressions-
direct.com
Envelope Product Mfr
N.A.I.C.S.: 322230

Wisco Envelope (1)
1509 N Washington St, Tullahoma, TN
37388
Web Site: http://www.wiscoenv.com
Sales Range: $10-24.9 Million
Envelope Mfr
N.A.I.C.S.: 322230

Witt Printing Company (1)
301 W Oak, El Dorado Springs, MO 64744
Tel.: (417) 876-4721
Web Site: http://www.wittprinting.com
Sales Range: $25-49.9 Million
Emp.: 100
Business Forms Printing Services
N.A.I.C.S.: 323111

ENOVA INTERNATIONAL, INC.
175 W Jackson Blvd Ste 600, Chi-
cago, IL 60604
Tel.: (312) 568-4200   DE
Web Site: https://ir.enova.com
Year Founded: 2004
ENVA—(NYSE)
Rev.: $2,117,639,000
Assets: $4,585,536,000
Liabilities: $3,345,353,000
Net Worth: $1,240,183,000
Earnings: $175,121,000
Emp.: 1,675
Fiscal Year-end: 12/31/23
Online Financial Services
N.A.I.C.S.: 525990
Steven E. Cunningham (CFO)
David A. Fisher (Chm, Pres & CEO)
Joseph DeCosmo (CTO & Chief Ana-
lytics Officer)
Sean Rahilly (Chief Compliance Offi-
cer, Gen Counsel & Sec)
Nick Drew (Mng Dir)
James J. Lee (Chief Acctg Officer)
Ranning Li (Pres)
Claudine Kourkoumelis (Chief People
Officer)
Kelly Jordan (VP)
Matt Hollender (VP)

Subsidiaries:

Cumulus Funding, Inc. (1)
30 N LaSalle St, Chicago, IL 60602
Web Site: https://www.helloalign.com
Financial Services
N.A.I.C.S.: 523999

Headway Capital, LLC (1)
175 W Jackson Blvd Ste 1000, Chicago, IL
60604
Web Site: https://www.headwaycapital.com
Financial Services
N.A.I.C.S.: 523999

On Deck Capital Inc. (1)
1400 Broadway 25th Fl, New York, NY
10018
Tel.: (212) 876-8600
Web Site: https://www.ondeck.com
Rev.: $428,423,000
Assets: $1,304,583,000
Liabilities: $1,008,337,000

Enova International, Inc.—(Continued)

Net Worth: $296,246,000
Earnings: $27,955,000
Emp.: 742
Fiscal Year-end: 12/31/2019
Online Platform for Small Business Loans
N.A.I.C.S.: 522310
Noah Breslow (CEO & Chm)

The Business Backer, LLC   **(1)**
10856 Reed Hartman Hwy Ste 100, Cincinnati, OH 45242
Web Site: https://www.businessbacker.com
Financial Services
N.A.I.C.S.: 523999

ENOVA SYSTEMS INC.

2945 Columbia St, Torrance, CA 90503
Tel.: (650) 346-4770   **CA**
Web Site:
  http://www.enovasystems.com
Year Founded: 1976
ENVS—(OTCIQ)
Transportation Management Systems
N.A.I.C.S.: 334419
Edwin O. Riddell (Chm)

ENOVIS CORPORATION

2711 Centerville Rd Ste 400, Wilmington, DE 19808
Tel.: (302) 252-9160   **DE**
Web Site: https://www.enovis.com
Year Founded: 1995
ENOV—(NYSE)
Rev.: $1,707,197,000
Assets: $4,509,334,000
Liabilities: $1,088,633,000
Net Worth: $3,420,701,000
Earnings: ($33,261,000)
Emp.: 6,550
Fiscal Year-end: 12/31/23
Pump & Power Transmission Products Mfr
N.A.I.C.S.: 333914
Matthew L. Trerotola (Chm & CEO)
Mitchell P. Rales (Co-Founder)
Shyam P. Kambeyanda (Pres/CEO-ESAB)
Terry Ross (Grp Pres-Prevention & Recovery Segment)
Shyam Kambeyanda (Pres/CEO-ESAB & Exec VP)
Patricia Lang (Chief HR Officer & Sr VP)
Bradley J. Tandy (Gen Counsel, Sec & Sr VP)
Terry Ross (Grp Pres-Prevention & Recovery Segment)
Mike Macek (VP-Fin)
Brady R. Shirley (Pres)
Larry Coble (Sr VP-Bus Sys & Supply Chain)
Louie Vogt (Grp Pres-Reconstructive Segment)
John Kleckner (Principal Acctg Officer)
Phillip Benjamin Berry (CFO)
Philip W. Knisely (Co-Founder)

Subsidiaries:

360 Med Care Pty. Ltd.   **(1)**
Unit 1 25 Frenchs Forest Rd E, French's Forest, 2086, NSW, Australia
Tel.: (61) 448299909
Web Site: https://360med.care
Orthopaedic Surgery Services
N.A.I.C.S.: 622310

Alcotec Wire Corporation   **(1)**
2750 Aero Park Dr, Traverse City, MI 49686-9263
Web Site: https://www.alcotec.com
Welding & Soldering Equipment Mfr
N.A.I.C.S.: 333992
Lance Vernam (Dir-Comml-Global)
Mike Dortch (Sls Mgr-Tech)
Brian Harrison (Sls Mgr-Tech)
Ben Hall (Sls Mgr-Tech)

Arc Machines GmbH   **(1)**
Winkelsweg 178-180, Langenfeld, 40764, Germany
Tel.: (49) 21736824817
Web Site: http://www.arcmachines.de
Welding Equipment Mfr & Distr
N.A.I.C.S.: 333992

Charter International PLC   **(1)**
Fitzwilliam Hall Fitzwilliam Place, Dublin, Ireland
Tel.: (353) 1 669 4655
Web Site: http://www.charter.ie
Sales Range: $1-4.9 Billion
Emp.: 12,313
Welding Cutting & Automation Mfr
N.A.I.C.S.: 333992

Subsidiary (Non-US):

AustCold Refrigeration Pty Ltd   **(2)**
Unit 23 38-46 South Street, Rydalmere, 2116, NSW, Australia
Tel.: (61) 288449100
Sales Range: $25-49.9 Million
Emp.: 18
Refrigeration Equipment Mfr & Whslr
N.A.I.C.S.: 333415
John Buis (Mgr-Sls-Refrigeration Gas Compression)

Charter Ltd.   **(2)**
322 High Holborn, London, WC1V 7PB, United Kingdom
Tel.: (44) 2032060800
Web Site: http://www.colfaxcorp.com
Sales Range: $1-4.9 Billion
Emp.: 20
Holding Company; Welding Equipment Mfr; Industrial Fan, Compressor & Gas Handling Equipment Mfr
N.A.I.C.S.: 551112

Subsidiary (Non-US):

ESAB AB   **(3)**
Lindholmsallen 9, Box 8004, 402 77, Gothenburg, Sweden
Tel.: (46) 31509000
Web Site: https://www.esab.se
Sales Range: $1-4.9 Billion
Mfr of Welding Products; Handwelding Electrodes; Automatic Welding Consumables; Welding Machines; Cutting Machines & Equipment; Working Environment Equipment
N.A.I.C.S.: 333992

Subsidiary (Non-US):

AS ESAB   **(4)**
Plateverkstedet Nedre Fritzoe gate 2, 3264, Larvik, Norway
Tel.: (47) 33121000
Web Site: https://www.esab.no
Sales Range: $25-49.9 Million
Emp.: 25
Welding Equipment Mfr
N.A.I.C.S.: 333992

Aktieselskabet ESAB   **(4)**
Horkaer 9, DK 2730, Herlev, Denmark
Tel.: (45) 36300111
Web Site: http://www.esab.dk
Sales Range: $25-49.9 Million
Emp.: 45
Welding Equipment Mfr
N.A.I.C.S.: 333992

ESAB (Thailand) Ltd.   **(4)**
889 Srinakarin Road Wong Wai Wit Building, Samrongnua Samutprakarn, Samut Prakan, 10270, Thailand
Tel.: (66) 23617001
Web Site: http://www.esab.com
Welding Machinery Mfr
N.A.I.C.S.: 333131

ESAB A/S   **(4)**
C F Tietgensvej 7B, 6000, Kolding, Denmark
Tel.: (45) 36300111
Web Site: https://esab.com
Sales Range: $25-49.9 Million
Emp.: 25
Welding Equipment Mfr & Distr
N.A.I.C.S.: 333992

ESAB AG   **(4)**
Silbernstrasse 18, CH 8953, Dietikon, Switzerland

Tel.: (41) 17412525
Web Site: http://www.esab.ch
Sales Range: $10-24.9 Million
Emp.: 3
Welding Equipment Mfr & Distr
N.A.I.C.S.: 333992

ESAB Africa Welding and Cutting (Proprietary) Limited   **(4)**
53 Lake Road Longmeadow Business Estate North Gate, Edenvale, 1609, Gauteng, South Africa
Tel.: (27) 219758924
Web Site: http://www.esab.co.za
Sales Range: $25-49.9 Million
Emp.: 5
Welding & Cutting Equipment Mfr
N.A.I.C.S.: 333992

ESAB Aktiengesellschaft   **(4)**
Neuhofstrasse 4, 6340, Baar, Switzerland
Tel.: (41) 5600700
Pumps Mfr
N.A.I.C.S.: 333914

ESAB ApS   **(4)**
C F Tietgensvej 7B, 6000, Kolding, Denmark
Tel.: (45) 36300111
Web Site: http://www.esab.dk
Welding Equipment Mfr
N.A.I.C.S.: 333992

ESAB Asia/Pacific Pte. Ltd.   **(4)**
38 Joo Koon Circle, Jurong, Singapore, 629063, Singapore
Tel.: (65) 65139188
Web Site: https://esab.com
Sales Range: $25-49.9 Million
Welding Equipment Distr
N.A.I.C.S.: 423830

Subsidiary (Non-US):

ESAB (Malaysia) Sdn Bhd   **(5)**
26 & 28 Jalan Industri USJ1/1, Taman Perindustrian USJ 1, 47600, Subang Jaya, Selangor, Malaysia
Tel.: (60) 80237835
Web Site: http://www.esabasia.com
Sales Range: $10-24.9 Million
Emp.: 20
Welding Equipment Mfr & Distr
N.A.I.C.S.: 333992

Subsidiary (Non-US):

ESAB Automation Ltd.   **(4)**
Stable Block Warlies Park House, Horseshoe Hill Upshire, Waltham Abbey, EN9 3SL, Essex, United Kingdom
Tel.: (44) 1264332233
Web Site: http://www.esab.co.uk
Sales Range: $10-24.9 Million
Emp.: 20
Metal Cutting Systems Mfr
N.A.I.C.S.: 333517

ESAB Cutting Systems   **(4)**
Robert-Bosch-Str 20, PO Box 1128, 61184, Karben, Germany
Tel.: (49) 6039400
Web Site: http://www.esab-cutting.de
Sales Range: $25-49.9 Million
Emp.: 200
Cutting Equipment Mfr & Distr
N.A.I.C.S.: 333517

ESAB Egypt   **(4)**
1 El Sherifein St Bab el Louk Abdeen, PO Box 11111, Cairo, Egypt
Tel.: (20) 23909669
Web Site: https://www.esabegypt.com
Sales Hange: $10-24.9 Million
Emp.: 7
Welding Equipment Mfr & Distr
N.A.I.C.S.: 333992

ESAB France SAS   **(4)**
Building Cerianthe 2 21/23 Rue du Petit Albi, 95800, Cergy, Cedex, France
Tel.: (33) 130755500
Web Site: http://www.esab.fr
Sales Range: $25-49.9 Million
Welding Equipment Mfr & Distr
N.A.I.C.S.: 333992

ESAB Group (UK) Ltd.   **(4)**
Warlies Park House Horseshoe Hill, Upshire, Waltham Abbey, EN9 3SL, Essex, United Kingdom

Tel.: (44) 1992768515
Web Site: https://www.esab.co.uk
Sales Range: $25-49.9 Million
Welding Equipment Mfr & Distr
N.A.I.C.S.: 333992

ESAB Group Canada, Inc.   **(4)**
6200 Cantay Road Unit 20, Mississauga, L5R 3Y9, ON, Canada
Tel.: (905) 670-0220
Web Site: http://www.esab.ca
Sales Range: $25-49.9 Million
Welding Equipment Merchant Whslr
N.A.I.C.S.: 423830
Mark Elender (Sr VP-Sls & Mktg)

ESAB Iberica S.A.   **(4)**
C / Marie Curie 19 Edif Autocampo II Oficina 2 1, San Fernando de Henares, 28521, Rivas-Vaciamadrid, Spain
Tel.: (34) 918783600
Web Site: https://esab.com
Sales Range: $25-49.9 Million
Welding Equipment Mfr & Distr
N.A.I.C.S.: 333992

ESAB India Ltd.   **(4)**
13 3rd Main Road, Industrial Estate Ambattur, Chennai, 600058, Ambattur, India   **(55.56%)**
Tel.: (91) 4442281100
Web Site: https://www.esabindia.com
Rev.: $131,718,722
Assets: $56,832,324
Liabilities: $25,626,761
Net Worth: $31,205,563
Earnings: $16,267,610
Emp.: 554
Fiscal Year-end: 03/31/2023
Welding Equipment Mfr & Distr
N.A.I.C.S.: 333992
B. Mohan (VP-Finance)
S. Venkatakrishnan (Compliance Officer)
Amit Kumar De (VP-Sales)
Rohit Gambhir (Mng Dir)
Jagannathan Palle (VP-Ops)
Scott Allen Grisham (Chm)
Jaimon Antony (Gen Mgr-HR)
Kevin Joseph Johnson (Chm)

Division (Domestic):

ESAB India Ltd.-Kolkata   **(5)**
P-41 Taratala Rd, Kolkata, 700 088, India
Tel.: (91) 3324012103
Web Site: https://esab.com
Sales Range: $50-74.9 Million
Emp.: 55
Welding Equipment Distr
N.A.I.C.S.: 423830
Rohit Gambhir (Mng Dir)
B. Mohan (VP-Fin)
Jagannathan Palle (VP-Ops)
Jaimon Antony (Gen Mgr-HR)

Subsidiary (Domestic):

ESAB International AB   **(4)**
Herkulesgatan 72, PO Box 8004, Gothenburg, 417 01, Sweden
Tel.: (46) 31509000
Web Site: http://www.esab.se
Sales Range: $100-124.9 Million
Emp.: 200
Welding Equipment Research & Development
N.A.I.C.S.: 333992

Subsidiary (Non-US):

ESAB KFT   **(4)**
Bukay Janos u 44-46, 1083, Budapest, Hungary
Tel.: (36) 13821200
Web Site: https://www.esab.hu
Sales Range: $10-24.9 Million
Emp.: 120
Cutting Equipment Mfr & Distr
N.A.I.C.S.: 333517

ESAB Mexico S.A. de C.V.   **(4)**
Diego Diaz de Berlanga No 130 Col Nogalar, 66480, San Nicolas, Nuevo Leon, Mexico
Tel.: (52) 8183053700
Web Site: https://www.esab.com.mx
Sales Range: $25-49.9 Million
Emp.: 100
Welding Equipment Mfr

N.A.I.C.S.: 333992

ESAB Middle East **(4)**
Jebel Ali Free Zone, PO Box 8964, Dubai,
United Arab Emirates
Tel.: (971) 48809493
Web Site: https://www.esab.ae
Sales Range: $25-49.9 Million
Welding Equipment Mfr & Distr
N.A.I.C.S.: 333992

ESAB Middle East LLC **(4)**
PO Box 29695, Abu Dhabi, United Arab
Emirates
Tel.: (971) 25547831
Web Site: http://www.esab.ae
Emp.: 8
Welding Equipment Whslr
N.A.I.C.S.: 423490

ESAB Nederland B.V. **(4)**
Amerfoortsestraat 124 D, 3769 AN,
Soesterberg, Netherlands
Tel.: (31) 8007779777
Web Site: https://esab.com
Welding Equipment Mfr & Distr
N.A.I.C.S.: 333992

ESAB Oy **(4)**
Konalantie 47 C, PO Box 74, Helsinki,
00390, Finland
Tel.: (358) 9547761
Web Site: http://www.esab.fi
Sales Range: $25-49.9 Million
Emp.: 40
Welding Equipment Mfr & Distr
N.A.I.C.S.: 333992

Subsidiary (Domestic):

ESAB Perstorp AB **(4)**
Elektrodvagen 12, Perstorp, 284 33, Swe-
den
Tel.: (46) 43539600
Web Site: http://www.esab.se
Emp.: 15
Pump & Pumping Equipment Mfr
N.A.I.C.S.: 333914

Subsidiary (Non-US):

ESAB Russia BV **(4)**
Stanislavskogo street 21 building 2, Mos-
cow, 109004, Russia
Tel.: (7) 4956632008
Web Site: https://www.esab.ru
Pump & Pumping Equipment Mfr
N.A.I.C.S.: 333914

ESAB S.A. Industria e Comercio **(4)**
Rua Zeze Camargos 117 Cidade Industrial,
Contagem, 32210-080, MG, Brazil
Tel.: (55) 3121914333
Web Site: http://www.esab.com.br
Sales Range: $125-149.9 Million
Emp.: 600
Welding Equipment Mfr & Distr
N.A.I.C.S.: 333992

ESAB Saldatura S.p.A. **(4)**
Strada Provinciale 34 n 7, Ossona, 20002,
Milan, MI, Italy
Tel.: (39) 02979681
Web Site: https://esab.com
Sales Range: $25-49.9 Million
Welding Equipment Mfr & Distr
N.A.I.C.S.: 333992

ESAB SeAH Corporation **(4)**
51 Seongju-dong, Seongsan-Gu,
Changwon, 641-120, Kyeongnam, Korea
(South)
Tel.: (82) 552898111
Web Site: https://www.eng.esab.co.kr
Welding Equipment Mfr
N.A.I.C.S.: 333992

ESAB Slovakia sro **(4)**
Rybnicna 40, PO Box 36, 830 06, Brati-
slava, Slovakia
Tel.: (421) 244880406
Web Site: https://esab.com
Welding Equipment Mfr
N.A.I.C.S.: 333992

ESAB Sp.z.o.o. **(4)**
Ul Johna Baildona 65, 40-115, Katowice,
Poland
Tel.: (48) 323589600
Web Site: https://esab.com
Welding Equipment Distr

N.A.I.C.S.: 423830

Subsidiary (Domestic):

ESAB Sverige AB **(4)**
Lindhomes Allen 9, PO Box 8004, 402 77,
Gothenburg, Sweden
Tel.: (46) 31509500
Web Site: http://www.esab.se
Sales Range: $50-74.9 Million
Emp.: 260
Welding Equipment Mfr & Distr
N.A.I.C.S.: 333992

Subsidiary (Non-US):

**ESAB Tyumen Limited Liability
Company** **(4)**
Northeastern industrial hub 6th Km
Velizhansky tract P / 2860, 625059, Tyu-
men, Russia
Tel.: (7) 3452613122
Web Site: http://www.sibeselectrod.ru
Welding Equipment Mfr
N.A.I.C.S.: 333992

ESAB VAMBERK, s.r.o. **(4)**
Smetanovo nabrezi concern 334, 517 54,
Vamberk, Czech Republic
Tel.: (420) 494501111
Web Site: https://esab.com
Welding & Cutting Equipment Distr
N.A.I.C.S.: 423830

ESAB Vamberk a.s. **(4)**
Smetanovo Nabrezi 334, 517 54, Vamberk,
Czech Republic
Tel.: (420) 494501111
Web Site: https://esab.com
Sales Range: $200-249.9 Million
Emp.: 600
Welding Equipment Distr
N.A.I.C.S.: 423830

**ESAB Welding & Cutting Products
(Shanghai) Co Limited** **(4)**
13th Floor Hung Cheung Building Huanghe
Road, Huangpu, Shanghai, 200003, China
Tel.: (86) 2123263000
Emp.: 100
Welding & Soldering Equipment Mfr
N.A.I.C.S.: 333992

Subsidiary (Domestic):

ESAB Welding Equipment AB **(4)**
Esabvagen, 695 30, Laxa, Sweden
Tel.: (46) 58481000
Web Site: http://www.esab.se
Sales Range: $100-124.9 Million
Emp.: 500
Welding Equipment Mfr
N.A.I.C.S.: 333992
Daniel Edstrom *(Mng Dir)*

Subsidiary (Non-US):

**ESAB Welding Products (Jiangsu) Co
Limited** **(4)**
No 7 Xinjing West Road Economic Devel-
opment Zone, Zhangjiagang, 215600, Ji-
angsu, China
Tel.: (86) 51258599922
Emp.: 200
Welding Equipment Mfr
N.A.I.C.S.: 333992
Leon Mao *(Gen Mgr)*

KEBE Ersatzteile GmbH **(4)**
Beinhardsweg 9, 61191, Rossbach, Ger-
many
Tel.: (49) 6007500
Web Site: https://www.kebe-gmbh.de
Sales Range: $10-24.9 Million
Emp.: 10
Cutting Equipment Mfr
N.A.I.C.S.: 333517
Wolfgang Riepe *(Mng Dir)*
Dirk Riepe *(Mng Dir)*

S.A. ESAB N.V. **(4)**
Liersesteenweg 173H, 2220, Heist-op-den-
Berg, Belgium
Tel.: (32) 15480253
Web Site: https://esab.com
Welding Equipment Mfr & Distr
N.A.I.C.S.: 333992

Subsidiary (US):

The ESAB Group, Inc. **(4)**

411 S Ebenezer Rd, Florence, SC 29501-
7916
Tel.: (843) 669-4411
Welding & Soldering Equipment Mfr
N.A.I.C.S.: 333992
Shyam P. Kambeyanda *(Pres)*
Steve Breitzka *(Interim Sr VP-Global Ops-
Americas)*
Shyam Kambeyanda *(Pres)*

Division (Domestic):

ESAB Cutting Systems **(5)**
411 S Ebenezer Rd, Florence, SC 29501-
0545
Tel.: (843) 664-4394
Web Site: http://www.esab.ca
Sales Range: $125-149.9 Million
Emp.: 600
Welding Equipment Mfr
N.A.I.C.S.: 333992

**ESAB Welding & Cutting
Products** **(5)**
256 Midway Dr, Union, SC 29379
Tel.: (864) 466-0921
Web Site: http://www.esab.com
Welding Equipment Mfr & Distr
N.A.I.C.S.: 333992

Subsidiary (Domestic):

ARC Machines Inc. **(6)**
14320 Arminta St, Panorama City, CA
91402
Tel.: (818) 896-9556
Web Site:
 https://resources.arcmachines.com
Welding Aparatus
N.A.I.C.S.: 333992

Plant (Domestic):

**ESAB Welding & Cutting
Products** **(6)**
801 Wilson Ave, Hanover, PA 17331-1058
Tel.: (717) 637-8911
Web Site: http://www.esabna.com
Rev.: $80,000,000
Emp.: 500
Welding & Metal Cutting Equipment Distr
N.A.I.C.S.: 333992

Subsidiary (Domestic):

Victor Technologies Group, Inc. **(5)**
16052 Swingley Ridge Rd Ste 300, Saint
Louis, MO 63017
Tel.: (636) 728-3000
Web Site: http://www.victortechnologies.com
Rev.: $486,796,000
Assets: $636,246,000
Liabilities: $517,319,000
Net Worth: $118,927,000
Earnings: $22,327,000
Emp.: 1,941
Fiscal Year-end: 12/31/2013
Gas & Electric Cutting & Welding Tools Mfr
N.A.I.C.S.: 333517

Subsidiary (Non-US):

Cigweld (M) Sdn Bhd **(6)**
Lot 151 Jalan Industri 3/5A Jln Batu Arang,
Rawang Integrated Industrial Park, 48000,
Rawang, Selangor, Malaysia
Tel.: (60) 360922988
Web Site: http://www.cigweld.com.au
Cutting & Welding Equipment Mfr
N.A.I.C.S.: 333992

Cigweld Pty Ltd. **(6)**
71 Gower Street, Preston, 3072, VIC, Aus-
tralia
Tel.: (61) 394747400
Web Site: https://www.cigweld.com.au
Sales Range: $50-74.9 Million
Cutting & Welding Equipment Mfr
N.A.I.C.S.: 333992

O.C.I.M. S.r.l. **(6)**
SS 87 Km 16 460 Industrial Zone ASI,
80023, Pascarola, MI, Italy
Tel.: (39) 0818349209
Web Site: https://ocima.com
Sales Range: $100-124.9 Million
Emp.: 100
Welding & Cutting Tools Mfr
N.A.I.C.S.: 333992

PT Cigweld Indonesia **(6)**

Kawasan Industri Jababeka Jl Jababeka VI
Blok P No 3, Cikarang, Bekasi, 17550, In-
donesia
Tel.: (62) 218936077
Sales Range: $125-149.9 Million
Welding & Cutting Tools Mfr
N.A.I.C.S.: 333992

PT Victor Teknologi Indonesia **(6)**
JL Angsana 2 Blok AE No 28 Delta Silicon
Selatan Jawa Barat Cikarang, Bekasi,
17550, Indonesia
Tel.: (62) 8119783357
Web Site:
 http://www.victortechnologi.asia.com
Sales Range: $125-149.9 Million
Cutting & Welding Equipment Mfr
N.A.I.C.S.: 333992

**Philippine Welding Equipment,
Inc.** **(6)**
Ground Floor PWE Building, North Road
Jagobiao, Mandaue, Cebu, 6014, Philip-
pines
Tel.: (63) 32 346 2798
Sales Range: $125-149.9 Million
Welding Equipment Mfr
N.A.I.C.S.: 333992

Subsidiary (Domestic):

Stoody Company **(6)**
3316 National Ave, San Diego, CA 92113-
2639
Tel.: (619) 234-6750
Web Site: https://www.stoodyind.com
Sales Range: $125-149.9 Million
Welding Wire & Electrodes Mfr
N.A.I.C.S.: 333992

Subsidiary (Non-US):

Thermadyne (Shanghai) Co. Ltd. **(6)**
Room 3109 2 Grand Gateway No 3
Hongqiao Road, Xuhui District, Shanghai,
200030, China
Tel.: (86) 2164072626
Web Site:
 http://www.victortechnologies.com.cn
Sales Range: $100-124.9 Million
Emp.: 13
Welding & Cutting Tools Mfr
N.A.I.C.S.: 333992

Thermadyne Japan Ltd. **(6)**
3-18-201 Zuiko 4-chome, Higashiyodogawa-
ku, Osaka, 333-0005, Japan
Tel.: (81) 648098411
Sales Range: $100-124.9 Million
Emp.: 1
Welding & Cutting Tools Mfr
N.A.I.C.S.: 333992
Koji Tsukada *(Country Mgr-Japan)*

Subsidiary (Domestic):

Victor Equipment Company **(6)**
2800 Airport Rd, Denton, TX 76207
Tel.: (817) 490-0496
Web Site: http://www.victorequip.com
Sales Range: $100-124.9 Million
Welding & Cutting Tools Mfr
N.A.I.C.S.: 333992

Subsidiary (Non-US):

**Victor Equipment de Mexico, S.A. de
C.V.** **(7)**
Col Alvaro Obregon, Hermosillo, CP 83170,
Sonora, Mexico
Tel.: (52) 6622360001
Web Site: http://www.victortechnologies.com
Sales Range: $100-124.9 Million
Emp.: 800
Welding & Cutting Tools Mfr
N.A.I.C.S.: 333992

Subsidiary (Non-US):

**Victor Technologies Asia Sdn
Bhd** **(6)**
Lot 151 Jalan Industri 3/5A, Jalan Batu
Arang, 48000, Rawang, Selangor Darul Eh-
san, Malaysia
Tel.: (60) 378904010
Sales Range: $25-49.9 Million
Emp.: 100
Welding & Cutting Tools Mfr
N.A.I.C.S.: 333992

Victor Technologies Canada Ltd. **(6)**

Enovis Corporation—(Continued)

2070 Wyecroft Road, Oakville, L6L 5V6,
ON, Canada
Tel.: (905) 827-1111
Web Site: http://www.victortechnologies.com
Sales Range: $25-49.9 Million
Emp.: 20
Welding & Cutting Tools Mfr
N.A.I.C.S.: 333992

Victor Technologies S.R.L. (6)
Via Bolsena 7, 20098, San Giuliano Mila-
nese, MI, Italy
Tel.: (39) 0236546801
Web Site: http://www.victortechnologies.com
Sales Range: $10-24.9 Million
Emp.: 4
Welding & Cutting Tools Mfr
N.A.I.C.S.: 333992

Subsidiary (Non-US):

**Conarco Alambres y Soldaduras
S.A** (2)
Calle 18 N 4079, Villa Lynch, B1672AWG,
Buenos Aires, Argentina
Tel.: (54) 1147547000
Web Site: https://esab.com
Welding Equipment Mfr & Whslr
N.A.I.C.S.: 333992

Eutectic do Brasil Ltda (2)
Av General David Sarnoff 3335, Belo Hori-
zonte, 32210-110, Brazil
Tel.: (55) 3121914988
Web Site: http://www.eutectic.com.br
Sales Range: $25-49.9 Million
Emp.: 15
Welding Equipment Repair Services
N.A.I.C.S.: 811310

Chasm Consulting Pty. Ltd. (1)
2 Loraine St Suite 14, Capalaba, 4157,
QLD, Australia
Tel.: (61) 733902663
Industrial Equipment Distr
N.A.I.C.S.: 423830

**Comercializadora de Electrodos Ven-
ezuela COMELVEN C.A.** (1)
8th Street Building 2 Floor Of Lion, Caracas, 0203, Venezuela
Tel.: (58) 2122435763
Pumps Mfr
N.A.I.C.S.: 333914

DJO Asia-Pacific Ltd. (1)
Unit 1905 19/F Tower 2 Grand Central
Plaza, 138 Shatin Rural Committee Road
Shatin, Hong Kong, China (Hong Kong)
Tel.: (852) 31051415
Surgical Reconstructive Implant Product Mfr
& Distr
N.A.I.C.S.: 339113

DJO Benelux B.V.B.A. (1)
Kleinhoefstraat 5 bus 39, 2440, Geel, Bel-
gium
Tel.: (32) 14248090
Sporting & Athletic Medical Equipment Mfr
N.A.I.C.S.: 339920

DJO Canada Inc. (1)
6485 Kennedy Road, Mississauga, L5T
2W4, ON, Canada
Web Site: https://www.djoglobal.ca
Surgical Reconstructive Implant Product Mfr
& Distr
N.A.I.C.S.: 339113

DJO Global Switzerland SARL (1)
Chemin du Devont 7 Zl Largoo Pioooo A,
1024, Ecublens, Switzerland
Tel.: (41) 216952360
Web Site: https://www.djoglobal.ch
Sporting & Athletic Medical Equipment Mfr.
N.A.I.C.S.: 339920
Julien Mottaz (Sls Mgr-Area)

DJO Global, Inc (1)
1430 Decision St, Vista, CA 92081
Tel.: (760) 727-1280
Web Site: http://www.djoglobal.com
Emp.: 5,000
Functional Bracing, Rehabilitative Post Op-
erative Bracing, Sports Medicine Bracing,
Neoprene Products & Orthopedic Soft
Goods
N.A.I.C.S.: 339113

Terry Ross (Pres-Chattanooga)
Brady R. Shirley (Pres & CEO)
Bryan S. McMillan (Pres-Regeneration)
Gordon Briscoe (Co-CFO & Co-Sr VP)
James Keller (Sr VP-HR)
Ken Konopa (Sr VP-CBS Comml)
Michael Lorelli (Sr VP-Strategy)
Mike Peters (Exec VP-Revenue Cycle
Mgmt)
Jim Pomeroy (VP-Quality Assurance &
Regulatory Affairs)
Ruba Sarris-Sawaya (VP)
Raj Subramonian (Sr VP & Gen Mgr-
FootCare Solutions)
Jason Anderson (Pres-Bracing & Supports)
Ben Berry (CFO)
Andrew Fox-Smith (Pres-Intl Bus)
Joseph G. Martinez (Gen Counsel & Sr VP)
Gary Justak (Pres & Gen Mgr)
Tony Stallings (Sr VP-Supply Chain)

Subsidiary (Domestic):

Chattanooga Group (2)
2735 Kanasita Dr, Hixson, TN 37343-4091
Tel.: (423) 870-7200
Web Site: http://www.chattgroup.com
Sales Range: $75-99.9 Million
Emp.: 280
Physical Therapy & Chiropractic Equipment
& Supplies
N.A.I.C.S.: 339113

Subsidiary (Non-US):

DJ Orthopedics Deutschland (2)
Merzhauser Strasse 112, 79100, Freiburg,
Germany
Tel.: (49) 920397350
Web Site: http://www.djoglobal.com
Sales Range: $10-24.9 Million
Emp.: 60
Surgical & Non-Surgical Apparatus
N.A.I.C.S.: 339112

**DJ Orthopedics de Mexico SA de
CV** (1)
Carretera Libre Tijuana, 20230, Tijuana, BC,
Mexico
Tel.: (52) 6646271300
Surgical & Non-Surgical Apparatus
N.A.I.C.S.: 339112

DJO France, S.A.S. (2)
European Freight Center 3 rue de Bethar,
64990, Mouguerre, France
Tel.: (33) 559528690
Web Site: https://enovis-medtech.eu
Surgical & Non-Surgical Apparatus Mfr
N.A.I.C.S.: 339112

Subsidiary (Domestic):

DJO Surgical (2)
9800 Metric Blvd, Austin, TX 78758
Tel.: (512) 832-9500
Web Site: https://www.djoglobal.com
Sales Range: $125-149.9 Million
Emp.: 400
Reconstructive Surgical Implants, Spinal
Disorder Treatment Products & Physical
Rehabilitation Devices, Products & Equip-
ment Mfr
N.A.I.C.S.: 339112

Subsidiary (Non-US):

DJO UK Ltd. (2)
1a Guildford Business Park, Guildford, GU2
8XG, Surrey, United Kingdom
Tel.: (44) 1483459659
Web Site: http://www.djoglobal.eu
Sales Range: $1-9.9 Million
Surgical Reconstructive Implant Products
N.A.I.C.S.: 339112

Subsidiary (Domestic):

Rikco International LLC (2)
10300 N Enterprise Dr, Mequon, WI 53092
Tel.: (262) 242-5300
Web Site: https://www.drcomfort.com
Footwear Mfr
N.A.I.C.S.: 316210

Trilliant Surgical, Ltd. (2)
727 N Shepherd Dr Ste 100, Houston, TX
77007
Web Site: http://www.trilliantsurgical.com
Surgical & Medical Instrument Mfr
N.A.I.C.S.: 339112

Jon Olson (CEO)

**DJO Iberica Productos Ortopedicos
S.L.** (1)
Carretera De Cornella 144 1o4a, Esplugues
de Llobregat, 08950, Barcelona, Spain
Tel.: (34) 934803202
Surgical Reconstructive Implant Product Mfr
& Distr
N.A.I.C.S.: 339113

DJO Italia SRL (1)
Via Leonardo da Vinci 97, Trezzano sul
Naviglio, 20090, Milan, MI, Italy
Tel.: (39) 0248463386
Web Site: https://enovis-medtech.eu
Surgical Reconstructive Implant Product Mfr
& Distr
N.A.I.C.S.: 339113

DJO Nordic AB (1)
Murmansgatan 126, 212 25, Malmo, Swe-
den
Tel.: (46) 40394000
Surgical Reconstructive Implant Product Mfr
& Distr
N.A.I.C.S.: 339113

**DJO Orthopaedic South Africa Pty.
Ltd.** (1)
Unit 6 2 on London 2 London Circle Brack-
engate Business Park, Brackenfell, 7560,
Cape Town, South Africa
Tel.: (27) 212762968
Web Site: https://enovis-medtech.eu
Surgical Reconstructive Implant Product Mfr
& Distr
N.A.I.C.S.: 339113

DJO, LLC (1)
2900 Lk Vista Dr Ste 200, Lewisville, TX
75067
Tel.: (760) 727-1280
Web Site: https://www.djoglobal.com
Orthopedic Devices Distr
N.A.I.C.S.: 423450
Ben Berry (CFO)

ESAB Welding & Cutting GmbH (2)
Branch Langenfeld Winkelsweg 178 - 180,
40764, Langenfeld, Germany
Tel.: (49) 21733945300
Web Site: https://esab.com
Welding & Cutting Equipment Distr
N.A.I.C.S.: 423830

Elastic Therapy, LLC (1)
718 Industrial Park Ave, Asheboro, NC
27205
Tel.: (336) 625-0529
Web Site: https://www.elastictherapy.com
Medical Product Mfr & Distr
N.A.I.C.S.: 339112

Empi, Inc. (1)
301 E Orangethorpe Ave, Anaheim, CA
92801
Tel.: (714) 446-9606
Web Site: https://www.empius.com
Automobile Product Distr
N.A.I.C.S.: 423120

Fairmount Automation, Inc. (1)
10 Clipper Rd, West Conshohocken, PA
19428
Tel.: (610) 356-9840
Web Site:
https://www.fairmountautomation.com
Pump & Pumping Equipment Mfr.
N.A.I.C.S.: 333914
Andres Lebaudy (Co-Founder)
Gary Cane (Co-Founder)

**GCE Gas Control Equipment Co.,
Ltd.** (1)
No 4 Building 318 Xiao Wan Road, Fengx-
ian District, Shanghai, 201401, China
Tel.: (86) 2137198408
Gas Control Equipment Mfr
N.A.I.C.S.: 333132

**GCE Gas Control Equipment,
Inc.** (1)
1508 Windsor Forest Trl, Keller, TX 76262
Tel.: (817) 268-9220
Gas Control Equipment Mfr
N.A.I.C.S.: 333132

GCE GmbH (1)
Weyherser Weg 8, 36043, Fulda, Germany
Tel.: (49) 66183930

Web Site:
https://www.germany.gcegroup.com
N.A.I.C.S.: 333132
Thomas Lingenberg (Mng Dir)
Christoph Albrecht (Mng Dir)
Gerhard Storch (Mgr-Customer Svc)
Martin Deuter (Mgr-Production & Strategic
Pur)
Klaus-Peter Maier (Sls Mgr-High Purity)

GCE Group AB (1)
Murmansgatan 126, 212 25, Malmo, Swe-
den
Tel.: (46) 40388300
Web Site: https://www.gcegroup.com
Medical Gas Equipment Mfr
N.A.I.C.S.: 339112
Christophe De Fitte (CEO)
Lloyd Perry (Chm)
Piyush Sheth (CEO)
Piyush Sheth (CEO)

GCE Hungaria Kft. (1)
Janos Bokay Street 44-46 Building C6 Floor
7, 1083, Budapest, Hungary
Tel.: (36) 706726142
Web Site:
https://www.hungary.gcegroup.com
Gas Control Equipment Mfr
N.A.I.C.S.: 333132
Attila Sulyok (Sls Mgr-Healthcare)

GCE India Ltd. (1)
No 59 1st Floor Millers Road, Benson
Town, Bengaluru, 560046, Karnataka, India
Tel.: (91) 8023631685
Web Site: https://www.india.gcegroup.com
Emp.: 20
Medical Gas Equipment Mfr
N.A.I.C.S.: 339112
Dinesh Kumar Gupta (Mng Dir)

GCE Latin America Ltd. (1)
Dakris pl 6408, Los Rios, Panama, Panama
Tel.: (507) 3176168
Web Site: https://latin-
america.gcegroup.com
Gas Control Equipment Mfr
N.A.I.C.S.: 333132
Etienne Masson (Reg Mgr)

GCE Mujelli S.p.A. (1)
Via Cervi Fratelli 11, 37036, San Martino
Buon Albergo, VR, Italy
Tel.: (39) 0458780525
Web Site: https://www.italy.gcegroup.com
Gas Control Equipment Mfr
N.A.I.C.S.: 333132

GCE Portugal Unipessoal LDA (1)
Avenida do Lidador n 169 4th Right Front,
Aguas Santas, 4425-116, Maia, Portugal
Tel.: (351) 916060062
Web Site: https://portugal.gcegroup.com
Gas Control Equipment Mfr
N.A.I.C.S.: 333132

GCE Romania s.r.l. (1)
Str Alexandru Puskin nr 22 Ap 1 Sector 1,
011996, Bucharest, Romania
Tel.: (40) 213167672
Web Site:
https://www.romania.gcegroup.com
Gas Control Equipment Mfr
N.A.I.C.S.: 333132

GCE S.A.S. (1)
70 rue du Puits Charles, BP N 40110, La
Charite-sur-Loire, 58403, Bourgogne,
France
Tel.: (33) 386694600
Gas Control Equipment Mfr
N.A.I.C.S.: 333132

GCE Sp. z o.o. (1)
ul Drapinska 12, 03-581, Warsaw, Poland
Tel.: (48) 6777080
Web Site: https://poland.gcegroup.com
Gas Control Equipment Mfr
N.A.I.C.S.: 333132
Adam Marcinowski (Sls Mgr)

**Gas Control Equipment Iberica
S.L.** (1)
Avda de la Democracia 7 - of 311, 28031,
Madrid, Spain
Tel.: (34) 915711470
Web Site: https://www.spain.gcegroup.com
Gas Control Equipment Mfr

N.A.I.C.S.: 333132
Sergio Valdeande *(Mng Dir)*

Gas Control Equipment S.A. de C.V. (1)
Miguel de Cervantes Saavedra 193 Ampliacion Granada Miguel Hidalgo, Distrito Federal, 11529, Mexico, Mexico
Tel.: (52) 5526261439
Gas Control Equipment Mfr
N.A.I.C.S.: 333132

Gas-Arc Group Limited (1)
Vinces Road, Diss, Norfolk, IP22 4WW, United Kingdom
Tel.: (44) 1379652263
Web Site: http://www.gas-arc.co.uk
Gas Controlling Equipment Mfr
N.A.I.C.S.: 333992

HKS-Prozesstechnik GmbH (1)
Heinrich-Damerow-Str 2, 06120, Halle, Germany
Tel.: (49) 345683090
Web Site: https://www.hks-prozesstechnik.de
Emp.: 20
Industrial Welding Measuring Equipment Mfr & Distr
N.A.I.C.S.: 333992
Olaf Hollmann *(Co-Founder)*
Michael Kiese *(Co-Founder)*
Volker Schauder *(Co-Founder)*

Inmobiliaria Tepalcapa SA de CV (1)
Km 33 5 Autopista Mexico-Queretaro, Cuautitlan Izcalli, 54760, Mexico
Tel.: (52) 5558931443
Real Estate Rental & Leasing Services
N.A.I.C.S.: 531210

Insight Medical Systems, Inc. (1)
9801 Metric Blvd Ste 200, Austin, TX 78758
Tel.: (512) 832-9500
Web Site: https://www.insightmedsys.com
Orthopaedic Surgery Services
N.A.I.C.S.: 622310

Lima Austria GmbH (1)
Seestadtstrasse 27 Top 6-7, 1220, Vienna, Austria
Tel.: (43) 12712469
Orthopaedic Surgical Instrument Mfr
N.A.I.C.S.: 339112

Lima CZ s.r.o. (1)
Do Zahrsdek I 157/5, Trebonice, 155 21, Prague, Czech Republic
Tel.: (420) 222720011
Orthopaedic Surgical Instrument Mfr
N.A.I.C.S.: 339112

Lima Deutschland GmbH (1)
Gasstrasse 18 Haus 4, 22761, Hamburg, Germany
Tel.: (49) 4023834620
Orthopaedic Surgical Instrument Mfr
N.A.I.C.S.: 339112

Lima France S.A.S. (1)
1 Allee Des Alisiers Immeuble Le Galilee, 69500, Bron, France
Tel.: (33) 487258430
Web Site: https://fr.limacorporate.com
Orthopaedic Surgery Services
N.A.I.C.S.: 622310

Lima Implantes Portugal S.U. Lda. (1)
Rua Pero Vaz De Caminha 8 E, 2660-441, Santo Antonio dos Cavaleiros, Portugal
Tel.: (351) 217272337
Orthopaedic Surgical Instrument Mfr
N.A.I.C.S.: 339112

Lima Implantes S.L.U. (1)
Francisco Sancha 4 - Piso 3, 28034, Madrid, Spain
Tel.: (34) 910885383
Web Site: https://es.limacorporate.com
Orthopaedic Surgery Services
N.A.I.C.S.: 622310

Lima Japan KK (1)
Tokyo Front Terrace 13F 2-3-14 Higashi-Shinagawa, Shinagawa, Tokyo, 140-0002, Japan
Tel.: (81) 353221115
Medical Device Mfr & Distr
N.A.I.C.S.: 339112

Lima O.I. d.o.o. Ortopedija (1)
Ante Kovacica 3, 10000, Zagreb, Croatia
Tel.: (385) 12361740
Orthopaedic Surgical Instrument Mfr
N.A.I.C.S.: 339112

Lima Orthopaedics Canada Inc. (1)
3715 Laird Road Unit 9, Mississauga, L5L 0A3, ON, Canada
Tel.: (289) 230-0645
Orthopaedic Surgery Services
N.A.I.C.S.: 622310

Lima Orthopaedics New Zealand Pty. Ltd. (1)
20 Crummer Rd Grey Lynn 1021, Auckland, 1021, New Zealand
Tel.: (64) 93606010
Orthopedic Devices Distr
N.A.I.C.S.: 423450

Lima Orthopaedics UK Ltd. (1)
Unit 1 Campus 5 Third Avenue, Letchworth, SG6 2JF, Hertfordshire, United Kingdom
Tel.: (44) 8443320661
Orthopaedic Surgical Instrument Mfr
N.A.I.C.S.: 339112

Lima Polska Sp. z o.o. (1)
Ul Ostrowite 37, 87-400, Golub-Dobrzyn, Poland
Tel.: (48) 564623143
Web Site: https://www.lima.pl
Orthopaedic Surgical Instrument Mfr
N.A.I.C.S.: 339112

Lima SK S.r.o. (1)
Cesta na Stadion 7, 974 04, Banska Bystrica, Slovakia
Tel.: (421) 484161126
Web Site: https://limacorporate.com
Health Care Equipment Mfr
N.A.I.C.S.: 339113

Lima Sweden S.r.o. (1)
Foretagsallen 14 B, 184 40, Akersberga, Sweden
Tel.: (46) 854410380
Web Site: https://linksweden.se
Surgical Instrument Mfr & Distr
N.A.I.C.S.: 339112

Lima Switzerland S.A. (1)
Birkenstrasse 49, Rotkreuz, 6343, Zug, Switzerland
Tel.: (41) 417470660
Orthopaedic Surgical Instrument Mfr
N.A.I.C.S.: 339112

LimaCorporate S.p.A. (1)
Via Nazionale 52 Villanova Di San Daniele Del Friuli, 33038, Udine, Italy
Tel.: (39) 0432945511
Web Site: https://limacorporate.com
Orthopaedic Surgical Instrument Mfr
N.A.I.C.S.: 339112

LiteCure LLC (1)
101 Lukens Dr Ste A, New Castle, DE 19720
Web Site: http://www.litecure.com
Medical Instrument Mfr
N.A.I.C.S.: 339112
Brian Pryor *(Founder & CEO)*
Luis De Taboada *(CTO)*
Brian W. Little *(Dir-Medical)*

Lubritech Argentina, S.R.L (1)
Calle 80 N 175 between 116 and 117, PO Box 1900, Villa Elvira - La Plata, Buenos Aires, Argentina
Tel.: (54) 2214212232
Fan & Compressor Mfr
N.A.I.C.S.: 333413

Lubritech Caribbean Limited (1)
235 Southern Main Road, Pointe-a-Pierre, Trinidad & Tobago
Tel.: (868) 6593420
Fan & Compressor Mfr
N.A.I.C.S.: 333413

Lubritech Peru S.A.C. (1)
Calle Las Violetas 167 Urb Jardines Viru Bellavista, Callao, Peru
Tel.: (51) 16586792
Industrial Lubrication Services
N.A.I.C.S.: 336510

Lubritech do Brasil Servicos de Lubrificacao Ltda. (1)

Av Jurua 105 Galpao 05 Alphaville Barueri, Sao Paulo, 05455-010, Brazil
Tel.: (55) 1141916946
Fan & Compressor Mfr
N.A.I.C.S.: 333413

Mathys AG (1)
Robert Mathys Strasse 5, 2544, Bettlach, Switzerland
Tel.: (41) 326441644
Web Site: https://www.mathysmedical.com
Medical Equipment Mfr
N.A.I.C.S.: 339112

Mathys Orthopadie GmbH (1)
Seilfahrt 99, 44809, Bochum, Germany
Tel.: (49) 23 458 8590
Surgical Appliance Mfr & Distr
N.A.I.C.S.: 339113
Norbert Reichel *(Gen Mgr)*

Mathys Orthopaedics BV (1)
Papendorpseweg 100, 3528 BJ, Utrecht, Netherlands
Tel.: (31) 881300500
Surgical Appliance Mfr & Distr
N.A.I.C.S.: 339113
Rob Ringelberg *(Gen Mgr)*

Mathys Orthopaedics Ltd. (1)
Unit 6 Riverway Industrial Park, Alton, GU34 2QL, United Kingdom
Tel.: (44) 8450580938
Surgical Appliance Mfr & Distr
N.A.I.C.S.: 339113

Mathys Orthopaedics Pty. Ltd. (1)
Unit 1 76 Reserve Road, Artarmon, 2064, NSW, Australia
Tel.: (61) 294179200
Surgical Appliance Mfr & Distr
N.A.I.C.S.: 339113
Rouger Baumgartner *(Country Mgr & Head-Sales-Intl)*

Mathys Orthopedie SAS (1)
Les Courlandes, 63360, Gerzat, France
Tel.: (33) 473239595
Surgical Appliance Mfr & Distr
N.A.I.C.S.: 339113
Jean Francois Bouchard *(Gen Mgr)*

Mathys Ortopedia Srl (1)
Via dei Fontanili 11 A, 20141, Milan, Italy
Tel.: (39) 024 959 8085
Surgical Appliance Mfr & Distr
N.A.I.C.S.: 339113
Giorgia Grassi *(Country Mgr)*

NovaStep SAS (1)
2 Allee Jacques Frimot, 35000, Saint-Gregoire, France
Tel.: (33) 299338650
Web Site: http://www.novastep-ortho.com
Medical Device Mfr
N.A.I.C.S.: 339112
Gregory Gledel *(Pres & CEO)*

Ormed GmbH (1)
Botzinger Strasse 90, 79111, Freiburg, Germany
Tel.: (49) 761456601
Web Site: https://www.enovis-medtech.de
Gas Control Equipment Mfr
N.A.I.C.S.: 333132

Orthomed Medizintechnik GmbH (1)
Annagasse 5/1/top 4, 1010, Vienna, Austria
Tel.: (43) 15320834
Web Site: http://www.orthomed.cc
Medical Instrument Mfr
N.A.I.C.S.: 339112

Orthopy Health GmBH (1)
Rontgenstrasse 24, 22335, Hamburg, Germany
Tel.: (49) 8000676333
Web Site: https://www.orthopy.de
Orthopaedic Surgery Services
N.A.I.C.S.: 622310

Quantum Ops, Inc. (1)
9800 Metric Blvd, Austin, TX 78758
Tel.: (423) 805-7999
Web Site: http://www.quantumops.com
Medical Instrument Mfr
N.A.I.C.S.: 339112
Joe Olsen *(Engr-Design)*

Soldacentro SA (1)
Avenida De La Industria 32, 28108, Al-

cobendas, Madrid, Spain
Tel.: (34) 916619159
Web Site: http://www.soldacentro.com
Sales Range: $10-24.9 Million
Emp.: 16
Pump & Pumping Equipment Mfr
N.A.I.C.S.: 333914

Soldaduras West Arco S.A.S. (1)
Av Cra 68 No 5-93, Bogota, 11001000, Colombia
Tel.: (57) 14176288
Welding Equipment Mfr
N.A.I.C.S.: 333992

Soldex S.A. (1)
Av Nicolas Arriola 771, La Victoria, 13, Lima, Peru
Tel.: (51) 16199600
Web Site: https://esab.com
Welding Equipment Mfr
N.A.I.C.S.: 333992

Speetec Implantate GmbH (1)
Merzhauser Str 112, 79100, Freiburg im Breisgau, Germany
Tel.: (49) 76145665112
Web Site: http://www.djosurgical.de
Surgical Prosthetic Product Mfr
N.A.I.C.S.: 339113

Surgi-Care, Inc. (1)
71 1st Ave, Waltham, MA 02451
Tel.: (781) 290-1800
Web Site: https://www.surgi-careinc.com
Orthopedic Product Distr
N.A.I.C.S.: 423450

TBI Industries GmbH (1)
Ruhberg 14, Steinbach, 35463, Fernwald, Germany
Tel.: (49) 640491710
Web Site: https://www.tbi-industries.com
Industrial Welding Equipment Mfr & Distr
N.A.I.C.S.: 333992

TBI Industries s.r.o. (1)
Grohova 979, 76901, Holesov, Czech Republic
Tel.: (420) 573334852
Web Site: http://www.tbi-cz.com
Emp.: 30
Industrial Welding Equipment Distr
N.A.I.C.S.: 423830

TLT Babcock Europe Kft. (1)
Becsi ut 3, Budapest, 1023, Hungary
Tel.: (36) 13450720
Fan & Compressor Mfr
N.A.I.C.S.: 333413

TLT Babcock India Private Limited (1)
No 207 SARJAPUR-BAGALUR Rd SEVAGANAPALI POST KRISHNAGIRI DISTRICT, Hosur, 635103, Tamil Nadu, India
Tel.: (91) 9585595615
Web Site: http://www.howden.com
Emp.: 50
Fan & Compressor Mfr
N.A.I.C.S.: 333413

Thermadyne Brazil Holdings Ltd (1)
16052 Swingley Ridge Rd Ste 300, Saint Louis, MO 63017-2079
Tel.: (636) 728-3000
Holding Company
N.A.I.C.S.: 551112

Thermadyne Victor Ltda. (1)
Av Brasil Cordoil 13629, 21012-065, Rio de Janeiro, Brazil
Tel.: (55) 9405662000
Welding Equipment Mfr
N.A.I.C.S.: 333992

Thermadyne de Mexico S.A. de C.V. (1)
Francisco del Paso y Troncoso No 869 Los Reyes, Iztapalapa, Mexico, Mexico
Tel.: (52) 5556579494
Fan & Compressor Mfr
N.A.I.C.S.: 333413

Tushaco Pumps Private Limited (1)
Lodha iThink 9th Floor A wing Off Eastern Express Highway, Chirak Nagar Thane West, Mumbai, 400 607, Maharashtra, India
Tel.: (91) 2269197347
Web Site: http://www.tushacopumps.com
Emp.: 35

Enovis Corporation—(Continued)

Pump & Pumping Equipment Mfr
N.A.I.C.S.: 333914

Victor Technologies Australia Pty Ltd. (1)
71 Gower Street, Preston, 3072, VIC, Australia
Tel.: (61) 394747400
Welding Equipment Mfr
N.A.I.C.S.: 333992
Neil Gerard Fitzpatrick (Dir-Fin)

Victor Technologies International, Inc. (1)
16052 Swingley Rdg Rd Ste 300, Saint Louis, MO 63017
Tel.: (636) 728-3000
Web Site: http://www.victortechnologies.com
Welding Equipment Mfr
N.A.I.C.S.: 333992

ENOVIX CORPORATION
3501 W Warren Ave, Fremont, CA 94538
Tel.: (510) 695-2350   DE
Web Site: https://www.enovix.com
Year Founded: 2020
ENVX—(NASDAQ)
Assets: $482,565,000
Liabilities: $156,448,000
Net Worth: $326,117,000
Earnings: ($125,874,000)
Emp.: 215
Fiscal Year-end: 01/02/22
Miscellaneous Financial Investment Activities
N.A.I.C.S.: 523999
Ralph Schmitt (Chief Comml Officer)
Thurman J. Rodgers (Chm)
Raj Talluri (CEO)

ENPHASE ENERGY, INC.
47281 Bayside Pkwy, Fremont, CA 94538
Tel.: (707) 774-7000   DE
Web Site: http://www.enphase.com
Year Founded: 2006
ENPH—(NASDAQ)
Rev.: $2,290,786,000
Assets: $3,383,012,000
Liabilities: $2,399,388,000
Net Worth: $983,624,000
Earnings: $438,936,000
Emp.: 3,157
Fiscal Year-end: 12/31/23
Solar Energy Semiconductor-Based Microinverter System Mfr; Software Publisher
N.A.I.C.S.: 334413
Mandy Yang (CFO)
Hans Van Antwerpen (CTO)
Aaron Gordon (VP)
Mehran Sedigh (VP)
Jayant Somani (VP)
Mike LaBouff (VP)
Sunil Thamaran (VP)
Lisan Hung (Sec)
Nitish Mathur (VP)
Karen Maxwell (VP)
Ron Swenson (VP)
Badrinarayanan Kothandaraman (Pres & CEO)

Subsidiaries:

Enphase Energy Australia Pty. Ltd. (1)
88 Market Street, South Melbourne, 3205, VIC, Australia
Tel.: (61) 386691679
Semiconductor Devices Mfr
N.A.I.C.S.: 334413

Enphase Energy New Zealand Limited (1)
1 Treffers Road Wigram, Middleton, Christchurch, New Zealand
Tel.: (64) 98870421
Semiconductor Devices Mfr
N.A.I.C.S.: 334413

Enphase Energy S.A.S. (1)
905 rue d Espagne, BP 128, Saint Exupery Aeroport, 69125, Lyon, France
Tel.: (33) 474982956
Semiconductor Devices Mfr
N.A.I.C.S.: 334413
Gerald Semenjuk (Dir-France & Switzerland)

Enphase Energy S.r.l. (1)
Via Volta Alessandro 94, Carate Brianza, 20832, Desio, Italy
Tel.: (39) 0800593838
Semiconductor Devices Mfr
N.A.I.C.S.: 334413
Marco Raimondi (Mgr-Technical)

Enphase Energy UK Limited (1)
Fairbourne Drive Atterbury, Buckinghamshire, Milton Keynes, MK10 9RG, United Kingdom
Tel.: (44) 1908828928
Semiconductor Devices Mfr
N.A.I.C.S.: 334413
Martyn Berry (Dir-EMEA Svc & Support)

Enphase Service Company, LLC (1)
1420 N McDowell Blvd, Petaluma, CA 94954
Semiconductor Product Mfr
N.A.I.C.S.: 334413

Enphase Solar Energy Private Limited (1)
IndiQube Golf View Homes Ward No 73 Airport, NAL Wind Tunnel Main Road Murugeshpalaya, Bengaluru, 560 017, India
Tel.: (91) 8061172500
Solar Product Mfr
N.A.I.C.S.: 334413
Sunil Thamaran (Mng Dir & VP)

SunPower Corporation (1)
2900 Esperanza Crossing 3rd Fl, Austin, TX 78758
Tel.: (512) 735-0100
Solar Panel Mfr
N.A.I.C.S.: 334413

ENPHYS ACQUISITION CORP.
100 Wall St 20th Fl, New York, NY 10005-3708
Tel.: (646) 854-6565   Ky
Web Site: https://enphyspac.com
Year Founded: 2021
NFYS—(NYSE)
Rev.: $15,732,992
Assets: $350,642,439
Liabilities: $364,851,596
Net Worth: ($14,209,157)
Earnings: $14,816,639
Emp.: 3
Fiscal Year-end: 12/31/22
Investment Services
N.A.I.C.S.: 523999
Jorge De Pablo (CEO)
Carlos Guimaraes (Chm)
Par Lindstrom (CFO)
Matias De Bujan (COO)

ENPRO INC.
5605 Carnegie Blvd Ste 500, Charlotte, NC 28209
Tel.: (704) 731-1500   NC
Web Site:
   https://www.enproindustries.com
Year Founded: 1990
NPO (NYSE)
Rev.: $1,099,200,000
Assets: $2,647,800,000
Liabilities: $1,252,700,000
Net Worth: $1,395,100,000
Earnings: $205,100,000
Emp.: 3,500
Fiscal Year-end: 12/31/22
Engineered Industrial Products Marketer & Mfr
N.A.I.C.S.: 333991
Robert S. McLean (Chief Admin Officer, Gen Counsel, Sec & Exec VP)
Steven R. Bower (Chief Acctg Officer, Sr VP & Controller)
Ronald R. Angelillo (VP-Tax)

Ian White (VP-Corp Dev)
James Gentile (VP-IR)
Eric A. Vaillancourt (Pres & CEO)
Joe Bruderek (CFO & Exec VP)
Meredith Manz (Chief HR Officer & Sr VP)
Mike Faulkner (Pres-Sealing Technologies Div)

Subsidiaries:

Advanced Micro Instruments, Inc. (1)
18269 Gothard St, Huntington Beach, CA 92648
Tel.: (714) 848-5533
Web Site: http://www.amio2.com
Sales Range: $10-24.9 Million
Emp.: 23
Measuring & Controlling Device Mfr
N.A.I.C.S.: 334519

Alluxa, Inc. (1)
3660 N Laughlin Rd, Santa Rosa, CA 95403
Web Site: https://www.alluxa.com
Optical Filter & Thin Film Coating Mfr
N.A.I.C.S.: 333310
Mike Scobey (Founder & CEO)
Peter Egerton (Chief Comml Officer)
Jason Mulliner (CFO)
Rance Fortenberry (Dir-Tech)
Bill Kastanis (VP-Ops)

Belfab, Inc. (1)
5125 rue J-A Bombardier, Saint-Hubert, J3Z 1G4, QC, Canada
Tel.: (450) 463-3344
Web Site: https://www.pyradia.com
Emp.: 100
Industrial Machinery & Equipment Merchant Whslr
N.A.I.C.S.: 423830

CPI Pacific Pty Limited (1)
Unit 7 24 Poletti Road, Cockburn Central, Perth, 6164, WA, Australia
Tel.: (61) 894178440
Web Site: http://www.cpicompression.com
Sales Range: $10-24.9 Million
Emp.: 6
Compressor Components Mfr & Services
N.A.I.C.S.: 333912

Coltec do Brasil Productos Industriais Ltda. (1)
Rua Ana Maria Martinez 455, Assuncao, Sao Bernardo do Campo, 09811-000, Brazil
Tel.: (55) 1143528181
Web Site: http://www.garlock.com
Sales Range: $25-49.9 Million
Emp.: 8
Engineered Industrial Products Marketer & Mfr
N.A.I.C.S.: 423830

Compressor Products International (1)
4410 Greenbriar Dr, Stafford, TX 77477
Tel.: (281) 207-4600
Web Site: http://www.cpicompression.com
Sales Range: $100-124.9 Million
Emp.: 800
Compressor & Industrial Engine Components Mfr
N.A.I.C.S.: 333517

Subsidiary (Domestic):

CPI Lubrication - CC Technology (2)
3201 W Wall St, Midland, TX 79701
Tel.: (432) 520-0700
Web Site: http://www.c-p-i.com
Emp.: 7
Design, Manufacture & Installation of Lubrication Systems for Reciprocating Compressors
N.A.I.C.S.: 333998

CPI Lubrication - Premier Lubrication Systems (2)
14150 Packard St, Houston, TX 77040
Tel.: (713) 462-5255
Web Site: http://www.c-p-i.com
Sales Range: $25-49.9 Million
Emp.: 36
Design & Manufacture of Lubrication Systems for Compressors
N.A.I.C.S.: 333998

Subsidiary (Non-US):

Compressor Products International Colombia S.A.S. (2)
Vereda Vuelta Grande Km 1 5, Cota, Cundinamarca, Colombia
Tel.: (57) 14780873
Industrial Machinery & Equipment Merchant Whslr
N.A.I.C.S.: 423830

Compressor Products International GmbH (2)
Robert-Bosch-Strasse 3, 64572, Buttelborn, Germany
Tel.: (49) 615293160
Web Site: http://www.cpicompression.com
Sales Range: $25-49.9 Million
Emp.: 70
Compressor Components Mfr & Services
N.A.I.C.S.: 333912

Compressor Products International Ltd. (2)
Unit 5 Smitham Bridge Road, Hungerford, RG17 0QP, Berkshire, United Kingdom
Tel.: (44) 1488684585
Web Site: http://www.cpicompression.com
Emp.: 50
Compressor Components Mfr & Services
N.A.I.C.S.: 333912
Steve Macadam (Pres & CEO)

Compressor Products International South Korea (2)
42-16 Hwachang 1-gil, Cheongnyang-eup Ulju-gun, Ulsan, Korea (South)
Tel.: (82) 522686900
Pump & Compressor Mfr
N.A.I.C.S.: 333921
Sunghoon Ahn (Reg Sls Mgr)

Corrosion Control Corporation (1)
4990 Iris St, Wheat Ridge, CO 80033
Tel.: (303) 988-1242
Web Site: http://www.gptindustries.com
Emp.: 95
Gasket Packing & Sealing Device Mfr
N.A.I.C.S.: 339991

EnPro Associates, LLC (1)
5605 Carnegie Blvd Ste 500, Charlotte, NC 28209
Tel.: (704) 731-1500
Industrial Machinery & Equipment Merchant Whslr
N.A.I.C.S.: 423830

EnPro Holdings, Inc. (1)
5605 Carnegie Blvd Ste 500, Charlotte, NC 28209
Tel.: (800) 966-1102
Engine Equipment Mfr
N.A.I.C.S.: 333618

GGB Bearing Technology (Suzhou) Co., Ltd. (1)
No 10 Xiangjie Road SND, Suzhou, 215129, China
Tel.: (86) 51262921000
Web Site: http://www.ggbearings.com
Emp.: 50
Metal Polymer & Filament Wound Plain Bearings Mfr
N.A.I.C.S.: 336310

GGB France E.U.R.L. (1)
65 Chemin de la Prairie, BP 2074, 74009, Annecy, Cedex, France
Tel.: (33) 450336688
Web Site: http://www.ggbearings.com
Sales Range: $10-24.9 Million
Emp.: 10
Self Lubricating & Prelubricated Bearings Mfr
N.A.I.C.S.: 336310

GPT Houston (1)
6455 Clara Rd, Houston, TX 77041
Tel.: (713) 747-6948
Web Site: http://www.gptindustries.com
Sales Range: $50-74.9 Million
Emp.: 200
Pipeline Seals & Insulators Mfr
N.A.I.C.S.: 326122
John Stephenson (Product Mgr)

Garlock (Great Britain) Limited (1)
Ground Floor Riverside Mills, Elland, HX5 0RY, West Yorkshire, United Kingdom

Tel.: (44) 1422313600
Web Site: http://www.garlock.com
Industrial Sealing Product Mfr & Distr
N.A.I.C.S.: 339991

Subsidiary (Domestic):

Garlock Pipeline Technologies
Limited   (2)
3-5 Chester Road Colmworth Business
Park Eaton Socon, Saint Neots, PE19 8YT,
United Kingdom
Tel.: (44) 1480404661
Industrial Machinery & Equipment Merchant
Whslr
N.A.I.C.S.: 423830

Technetics Group U.K. Ltd.   (2)
Acan Way Coventry Road, Narborough, Le-
icester, LE19 2FT, United Kingdom
Tel.: (44) 1162727411
Web Site: http://www.techneticsgroup.com
Sales Range: $25-49.9 Million
Emp.: 21
Industrial Machinery Mfr & Distr
N.A.I.C.S.: 333310

Subsidiary (Domestic):

Technetics UK Limited   (3)
Acan Way Coventry Road, Narborough,
LE19 2FT, Leicestershire, United Kingdom
Tel.: (44) 1162727411
Web Site: http://www.technetics.com
Industrial Machinery & Equipment Merchant
Whslr
N.A.I.C.S.: 423830

Garlock Do Brasil Produtos Industri-
ais Ltda.   (1)
Av Interlagos 6556 Interlagos, Sao Paulo,
04777-000, Brazil
Tel.: (55) 1156665566
Web Site: http://www.garlockdobrasil.com.br
Industrial Machinery & Equipment Merchant
Whslr
N.A.I.C.S.: 423830

Garlock GmbH   (1)
Falkenweg 1, 41468, Neuss, Germany
Tel.: (49) 21313490
Web Site: https://www.garlockeurope.com
Sales Range: $25-49.9 Million
Emp.: 140
Industrial Sealing Products Mfr & Distr
N.A.I.C.S.: 339991

Subsidiary (Domestic):

Franken Plastiks GmbH   (2)
Balbiererstrasse 11, 90763, Furth, Germany
Tel.: (49) 911787070
Web Site: http://www.frankenplastik.de
Sales Range: $25-49.9 Million
Emp.: 40
Industrial Sealing Products Mfr & Distr
N.A.I.C.S.: 339991
Andreas Walter (Co-CEO)
Herbert Nockel (Co-CEO)
Matthias Lunz (Co-CEO, Mng Dir & Sls
Mgr)
David Burnett (Co-CEO)
Julia Muller (Project Mgr-IAK-Industrial &
Plant Marking)

Garlock Hygienic Technologies,
LLC   (1)
26 Brookfield Dr, Sparta, NJ 07871
Tel.: (973) 579-2959
Web Site: https://www.rubberfab.com
Business Support Services
N.A.I.C.S.: 561499

Garlock India Private Limited   (1)
Plot No A-88/89 H Block MIDC, Pimpri,
Pune, 411 018, India
Tel.: (91) 206 712 6601
Web Site: http://www.garlock.com
Emp.: 15
Compressor Components Mfr & Services
N.A.I.C.S.: 333912
Rajesh Baviskar (Mng Dir)

Garlock Pipeline Technologies,
Inc.   (1)
4990 Iris St, Wheat Ridge, CO 80033
Tel.: (303) 988-1242
Web Site: https://www.gptindustries.com
Industrial Machinery & Equipment Merchant
Whslr

N.A.I.C.S.: 423830

Garlock Sealing Technologies   (1)
1666 Division St, Palmyra, NY
14522   (100%)
Tel.: (315) 597-4811
Web Site: http://www.garlock.com
Sales Range: $400-449.9 Million
Emp.: 500
Industrial Seals, Gaskets, Packing, Expan-
sion Joints, Metal Gaskets & Mechanical
Seals
N.A.I.C.S.: 339991
Jim Drago (Mgr-Business Development-
Integration)

Garlock Sealing Technologies
(Shanghai) Co., Ltd.   (1)
1st Floor Building 5 Hongqiao Jiahui Lane
928 Shenhong Road, Minhang district,
Shanghai, 201106, China
Tel.: (86) 2164544412
Web Site: https://www.garlock.com.cn
Industrial Sealing Products Mfr & Distr
N.A.I.C.S.: 339991

Garlock Singapore Pte. Ltd.   (1)
2 Woodland Sector 1 03-03 Spectrum 1,
Singapore, 738068, Singapore
Tel.: (65) 62859322
Web Site: http://www.garlock.com
Industrial Machinery & Equipment Merchant
Whslr
N.A.I.C.S.: 423830

Lunar Investment, LLC   (1)
5 Lan Dr, Westford, MA 01886
Tel.: (978) 392-0406
Electronic Components Mfr
N.A.I.C.S.: 334413

Subsidiary (Non-US):

LeanTeq Co., Ltd.   (2)
No 3 Ln 28 Gaoqing Rd, Yangmei Dist,
Taoyuan, 32687, Taiwan
Tel.: (886) 3 464 3838
Web Site: https://www.leanteq.com.tw
Electronic Components Mfr
N.A.I.C.S.: 334419
Ken Loo (Dir-Technical)

Subsidiary (Domestic):

LeanTeq LLC   (2)
1530 McCarthy Blvd, Milpitas, CA 95035
Tel.: (408) 439-3770
Web Site: https://www.leanteq.com
Information Technology Services
N.A.I.C.S.: 541511

PSI Products GmbH   (1)
Ulrichstrasse 25, D-72116, Mossingen,
Germany   (100%)
Tel.: (49) 747337810
Web Site: https://www.psi-products.de
Pipeline Accessories & Flange Insulation
Products Mfr & Distr
N.A.I.C.S.: 444180
Marcus Viglahn (Mng Dir)
Herbert Nockel (Mng Dir)
Robert McLean (Mng Dir)

Player & Cornish Limited   (1)
8 Yeomans Way, Bournemouth, BH8 0BQ,
West Midlands, United Kingdom
Tel.: (44) 1215011190
Web Site: http://www.player-cornish-
marine.com
Industrial Machinery & Equipment Merchant
Whslr
N.A.I.C.S.: 423830

Stemco Inc.   (1)
300 Industrial Blvd, Longview, TX
75602-4720   (100%)
Tel.: (903) 758-9981
Web Site: http://www.stemco.com
Sales Range: $150-199.9 Million
Emp.: 400
Wheel Lubrication Systems
N.A.I.C.S.: 336390

Subsidiary (Domestic):

Advanced Transit Dynamics, Inc. (2)
3150 Corporate Pl, Hayward, CA 94545
Tel.: (510) 619-8245
Web Site: http://www.atdynamics.com

Sales Range: $1-9.9 Million
Emp.: 50
Aerodynamics Technologies Solutions
N.A.I.C.S.: 336999

Division (Domestic):

Stemco Crewson, LLC   (2)
300 Industrial Dr, Longview, TX 75602
Tel.: (903) 758-9981
Web Site: https://www.stemco.com
Automobile Brake Mfr
N.A.I.C.S.: 336340
Joe Deyarmin (Mgr-Mfg)

Stemco Kaiser   (2)
4641 Industrial Dr, Millington, MI 48746
Tel.: (989) 871-4541
Web Site: http://www.stemcokaiser.com
Suspension Components Mfr
N.A.I.C.S.: 336390

Stemco LP   (1)
300 Industrial Blvd, Longview, TX 75602
Tel.: (903) 758-9981
Web Site: http://www.stemco.com
Industrial Machinery & Equipment Merchant
Whslr
N.A.I.C.S.: 423830

Stemco Products, Inc.   (1)
300 Industrial Dr, Longview, TX 75602
Tel.: (903) 758-9981
Web Site: https://www.stemco.com
Industrial Machinery & Equipment Merchant
Whslr
N.A.I.C.S.: 423830

Stemco Vehicle Technology (Shang-
hai) Co. Ltd.   (1)
Rm 936 REECO Tower No 255 WUBAO
Road, Minhang District, Shanghai, 200336,
China
Tel.: (86) 2162787250
Industrial Machinery & Equipment Merchant
Whslr
N.A.I.C.S.: 423830

Technetics Group   (1)
10633 W Little York Bldg 3 Ste 300, Hous-
ton, TX 77041
Tel.: (713) 983-4201
Web Site: http://www.technetics.com
Sales Range: $25-49.9 Million
Emp.: 125
Engineered Plastic Products & Services
N.A.I.C.S.: 325211

Unit (Domestic):

Plastomer Technologies   (2)
1600 Industry Rd, Hatfield, PA 19440
Tel.: (215) 855-9916
Web Site: http://www.fairbanksmorse.com
Sales Range: $10-24.9 Million
Emp.: 30
Mfr of Joint & Thread Sealants, Fine Pow-
der Compounds, PTFE Fiber & Specialty
Tapes
N.A.I.C.S.: 339991

Technetics Group Daytona, Inc.   (1)
305 Fentress Blvd, Daytona Beach, FL
32114
Tel.: (386) 253-0628
Emp.: 85
Gasket Packing & Sealing Device Mfr
N.A.I.C.S.: 339991

Technetics Group Japan Ltd.   (1)
News Kyobashi 801 3-10-1 Kyobashi,
Chuo-ku, Tokyo, 104-0031, Japan
Tel.: (81) 362710546
Semiconductor Equipment Mfr
N.A.I.C.S.: 334413

Technetics Group LLC   (1)
2791 The Blvd, Columbia, SC 29209
Tel.: (803) 783-1880
Web Site: https://www.technetics.com
Gasket Packing & Sealing Device Mfr
N.A.I.C.S.: 339991

Subsidiary (Domestic):

Fabrico, Inc.   (2)
10 Old Webster Rd, Oxford, MA 01540-
2706
Tel.: (508) 987-5900
Industrial Machinery & Equipment Merchant
Whslr

N.A.I.C.S.: 423830

Qualiseal Technology, LLC   (2)
7319 W Wilson Ave, Harwood Heights, IL
60706
Tel.: (708) 887-6080
Web Site: http://www.qualiseal.com
Emp.: 51
Aircraft Equipment Mfr
N.A.I.C.S.: 336413

Technetics Group Oxford, Inc.   (2)
10 Old Webster Rd, Oxford, MA 01540-
0701
Tel.: (508) 987-5900
Web Site: http://www.techneticsgroup.com
Metal Seal Mfr
N.A.I.C.S.: 332999

Technetics Group Singapore Pte.
Ltd.   (1)
30 Marsiling Industrial Estate Road 8 05-01
& 02-01, Singapore, 739193, Singapore
Tel.: (65) 67592335
Web Site: http://technetics.com
Emp.: 60
Industrial Sealing Products Mfr & Distr
N.A.I.C.S.: 339991

ENSERVCO CORPORATION
14133 County Rd 9 1/2, Longmont,
CO 80504
Tel.: (303) 333-3678   DE
Web Site: https://www.enservco.com
Year Founded: 1980
ENSV—(NYSEAMEX)
Rev.: $21,644,000
Assets: $19,838,000
Liabilities: $18,669,000
Net Worth: $1,169,000
Earnings: ($5,575,000)
Emp.: 98
Fiscal Year-end: 12/31/22
Oil, Gas & Mineral Exploration Ser-
vices
N.A.I.C.S.: 211120
Mark K. Patterson (CFO)
Richard A. Murphy (Chm)

Subsidiaries:

Dillco Fluid Service, Inc.   (1)
513 W 4th St, Hugoton, KS 67951
Tel.: (620) 544-2929
Emp.: 50
Oil & Gas Field Operating Services
N.A.I.C.S.: 238910

Heat Waves Hot Oil Service,
LLC   (1)
685 Air Links Rd, Garden City, KS 67846
Tel.: (620) 275-9177
Web Site: http://enservco.com
Support Activities for Oil & Gas Operations
N.A.I.C.S.: 213112

ENSURGE, INC.
1024 Iron Pt Rd, Folsom, CA 95630
Tel.: (920) 415-6214   NV
Web Site: http://ensurgeinc.com
ESGI—(OTCIQ)
Sales Range: Less than $1 Million
Emp.: 20
Gold Mining Services
N.A.I.C.S.: 212220
Jason Otteson (CEO)
Steven Morse (Corp Counsel)

ENSYNC, INC.
N88 W13901 Main St, Menomonee
Falls, WI 53051
Tel.: (262) 253-9800   WI
Web Site: http://www.ensync.com
Year Founded: 1998
ESNC—(OTCIQ)
Sales Range: $10-24.9 Million
Emp.: 64
Energy Storage Systems Design, De-
velopment, Manufacture & Distribu-
tion
N.A.I.C.S.: 221111

EnSync, Inc.—(Continued)

Sandeep Gupta (Chief Restructuring Officer)
Eric Apfelbach (CEO)
William Hogoboom (CFO)

Subsidiaries:

Holu Energy LLC (1)
1110 Nuuanu St, Honolulu, HI 96813 (85%)
Tel.: (808) 754-2929
Web Site: http://www.holuenergy.com
Energy Development Services
N.A.I.C.S.: 221114
Theodore Peck (Pres)
John Rei (VP)
Matthew Choy (Mgr-Ops)

ZBB Energy Pty. Ltd. (1)
240 Barrington Street, Bibra Lake, 6163, WA, Australia (100%)
Tel.: (61) 894942055
Web Site: http://www.zbbenergy.com
Sales Range: $10-24.9 Million
Emp.: 2
Marketing & Research & Development
N.A.I.C.S.: 541715
Nathan Coad (Mgr-Facility)

ENTEGRIS, INC.
129 Concord Rd, Billerica, MA 01821
Tel.: (978) 436-6500 DE
Web Site: https://www.entegris.com
Year Founded: 1966
ENTG—(NASDAQ)
Rev.: $3,523,926,000
Assets: $8,812,591,000
Liabilities: $5,403,997,000
Net Worth: $3,408,594,000
Earnings: $180,669,000
Emp.: 8,000
Fiscal Year-end: 12/31/23
Semiconductor & Disk Drive Materials Transport & Protection Services
N.A.I.C.S.: 334413
Todd Edlund (COO & Exec VP)
Bertrand Loy (Chm, Pres & CEO)
Stuart Tison (Sr VP & Gen Mgr-Specialty Chemicals & Engineered Materials)
Clint Haris (Sr VP & Gen Mgr-Microcontamination Control)
Bill Seymour (VP-IR, Treasury & Comm)
James A. O'Neill (CTO & Sr VP)
Joe Colella (Gen Counsel, Sec & Sr VP)
Olivier Blachier (Sr VP)
Connie Chandler (Sr Dir-Corp Comm)
Linda LaGorga (CFO & Sr VP)
Michael Besnard (Chief Comml Officer)
Neil Richards (Sr VP)
Bill Shaner (Pres)
Daniel D. Woodland (Pres)
Corey Rucci (Sr VP-Bus Dev)

Subsidiaries:

ATMI International Trading Co. Ltd. (1)
Unit DEF Floor 6 Building 3 No 100 Lane 1505, Zhu Chong Zhi Road Pudong New Area, Shanghai, 201203, China
Tel.: (86) 2168767670
Web Site: http://www.atmi.com
Sales Range: $125-149.9 Million
Emp.: 60
Computer Processor Component Mfr
N.A.I.C.S.: 334118

ATMI Taiwan Co. Ltd. (1)
1F No. 669 Section 4 Chung-Hsin Road Chutung Town, Hsin-chu, 30059, Taiwan
Tel.: (886) 35820858
Web Site: http://www.atmi.com
Sales Range: $25-49.9 Million
Emp.: 60
Computer Processor Component Mfr
N.A.I.C.S.: 334118

CMC Korea Co., Ltd. (1)
26-29 Yulchonsandan 4-ro Haeryong-

myeon, Suncheon, Jeollanam, Korea (South)
Tel.: (82) 617237975
Web Site: https://cmc-korea.co.kr
Plastic Materials Mfr
N.A.I.C.S.: 325211

CMC Materials, Inc. (1)
870 N Commons Dr, Aurora, IL 60504
Tel.: (630) 375-6631
Web Site: http://www.cmcmaterials.com
Rev.: $1,199,831,000
Assets: $2,150,885,000
Liabilities: $1,271,948,000
Net Worth: $878,937,000
Earnings: ($68,577,000)
Emp.: 2,200
Fiscal Year-end: 09/30/2021
Mfr of Polishing Compounds & Pads Used in Manufacture of Semiconductors
N.A.I.C.S.: 334413
H. Carol Bernstein (Gen Counsel, Sec & VP)
David H. Li (Pres & CEO)
Jeanette A. Press (Interim CFO, Principal Acctg Officer & Controller)
Daniel D. Woodland (Pres-Electronic Materials & VP)
Eleanor K. Thorp (VP-HR)
Jeffrey M. Dysard (Pres-Performance Materials & VP)
Colleen E. Mumford (VP-Comm & Mktg)

Subsidiary (Non-US):

Cabot Microelectronics Japan K.K. (2)
1287 19 Kitakoyama Geino Cho Csushi, Mie, Japan
Tel.: (81) 592660120
Web Site: http://www.cabotcmp.com
Sales Range: $25-49.9 Million
Emp.: 100
Mfr of Chemicals
N.A.I.C.S.: 325998

Subsidiary (Domestic):

Cabot Microelectronics Polishing Corporation (2)
39 W Official Rd, Addison, IL 60101-4532
Tel.: (630) 543-6682
Web Site: http://www.cabotcmp.com
Optical Lens Machinery Mfr
N.A.I.C.S.: 333310

Subsidiary (Non-US):

Cabot Microelectronics Singapore Pte. Ltd. (2)
Blk 205 01-53/54 Woodlands Ave 9 Woodlands Spectrum II, Singapore, 738957, Singapore
Tel.: (65) 65110550
Sales Range: $25-49.9 Million
Emp.: 60
Semiconductor & Related Device Mfr
N.A.I.C.S.: 334413

Epoch Material Co., Ltd. (2)
No 2 Luke 8th Road Kaohsiung Science Park, Luzhu District, Kaohsiung, 821, Taiwan
Tel.: (886) 35526666
Sales Range: $50-74.9 Million
Emp.: 13
Copper Polish Mfr
N.A.I.C.S.: 325998
Donald Wiseman (Gen Mgr)

International Test Solutions Korea Limited (1)
B 616 Queens Park 10 66 Magokjungang 6-ro, Gangseo-gu, Seoul, 07803, Korea (South)
Tel.: (82) 263460040
Semiconductor Product Mfr
N.A.I.C.S.: 334413

Subsidiary (Domestic):

International Test Solutions, LLC (2)
1595 Meadow Wood Ln, Reno, NV 89502
Tel.: (775) 284-9220
Web Site: http://www.inttest.net
Semiconductor Equipment Mfr
N.A.I.C.S.: 333242
Gene Humphrey (Co-Founder)

KMG Chemicals, Inc. (2)

300 Throckmorton St, Fort Worth, TX 76102
Tel.: (817) 761-6100
Web Site: http://www.kmgchemicals.com
Rev.: $465,556,000
Assets: $818,434,000
Liabilities: $402,367,000
Net Worth: $416,067,000
Earnings: $64,841,000
Fiscal Year-end: 07/31/2018
Specialty Chemicals Mfr & Distr
N.A.I.C.S.: 325998

Subsidiary (Domestic):

Cyantek Corporation (3)
3055 Osgood Ct, Fremont, CA 94539-5652
Tel.: (510) 651-3341
Web Site: https://cyantek.lookchem.com
Ultra Pure Semiconductor & Microelectronic Chemicals Mfr & Whslr
N.A.I.C.S.: 325998

Flowchem LLC (3)
20333 Blinka Rd, Prairie View, TX 77484
Tel.: (936) 372-5347
Web Site: https://www.flowchem-dra.com
Chemical Additive Mfr
N.A.I.C.S.: 325998

Subsidiary (Non-US):

KMG Chemicals do Brasil Ltda (3)
Manoel da Nobrega 1280 An 10, Sao Paulo, 04001-004, Brazil
Tel.: (55) 1138840111
Chemical Products Mfr
N.A.I.C.S.: 325199

KMG Singapore Pte. Ltd. (3)
14 Tuas Avenue 20, Singapore, 638826, Singapore
Tel.: (65) 31636666
Ultra Pure Semiconductor & Microelectronic Chemicals Mfr & Whslr
N.A.I.C.S.: 325199

KMG Ultra Pure Chemicals Limited (3)
Amber Business Centre, Riddings, Alfreton, DE55 4DA, Derbyshire, United Kingdom
Tel.: (44) 1773844200
Sales Range: $25-49.9 Million
Emp.: 55
Ultra Pure Semiconductor & Microelectronic Chemicals Mfr & Whslr
N.A.I.C.S.: 325998

KMG Ultra Pure Chemicals SAS (3)
Les Vieilles Hayes, 50620, Saint-Fromond, France
Tel.: (33) 233756400
Web Site: http://www.kmgchemicals.com
Sales Range: Less than $1 Million
Emp.: 80
Ultra Pure Semiconductor & Microelectronic Chemicals Mfr & Whslr
N.A.I.C.S.: 325998

KMG de Mexico, SA de CV (3)
Carretera Sendero Nacional Kilometro 8 Estacion Rosita, 87300, Matamoros, Tamaulipas, Mexico
Tel.: (52) 8 688 101192
Web Site: http://www.kmgchemicals.com
Specialty Chemicals Mfr
N.A.I.C.S.: 325180

Subsidiary (Domestic):

KMG-Bernuth, Inc. (3)
2901 3rd St, Tuscaloosa, AL 35401
Tel.: (205) 758-0448
Web Site: http://www.kmgb.com
Sales Range: $10-24.9 Million
Emp.: 40
Wood Preservatives Products Mfr
N.A.I.C.S.: 325998

Subsidiary (Domestic):

NexPlanar Corporation (2)
7175 NW Evergreen Pkwy Ste 200, Hillsboro, OR 97124
Tel.: (503) 846-1025
Web Site: http://www.nexplanar.com
Sales Range: $10-24.9 Million
Emp.: 100
Mfr of Chemical Mechanical Planarization Pads for Semiconductor Device Industry
N.A.I.C.S.: 334413

Subsidiary (Non-US):

Nihon Cabot Microelectronics K.K. (2)
1287 19 Kitakoyama, Geino Cho Age Gun, Mie, 514 2213, Japan
Tel.: (81) 592660120
Web Site: http://www.cabotcmp.com
Sales Range: $25-49.9 Million
Emp.: 100
Provider of Nondurable Goods
N.A.I.C.S.: 425120

Subsidiary (Domestic):

Sealweld (USA), Inc. (2)
15421 Vantage Pkwy W Ste 118, Houston, TX 77032
Tel.: (713) 466-7373
Web Site: https://www.sealweld.com
Valve Fitting Equipment Mfr
N.A.I.C.S.: 332911

Digital Specialty Chemicals Limited (1)
470 Coronation Drive, Toronto, M1E 4Y4, ON, Canada
Tel.: (416) 231-2991
Web Site: http://www.digitalspecialtychemicals.com
Industrial Inorganic Chemical Mfr
N.A.I.C.S.: 325180
Ravi Gukathasan (CEO)

Entegris Canada Limited (1)
470 Coronation Drive, Toronto, M1E 4Y4, ON, Canada
Tel.: (416) 231-2991
Semiconductor Product Mfr & Distr
N.A.I.C.S.: 334413

Entegris GP, Inc. (1)
4175 Santa Fe Rd, San Luis Obispo, CA 93401 (100%)
Tel.: (805) 541-9299
Gas Purification Equipment Mfr
N.A.I.C.S.: 333998

Entegris GmbH (1)
Hugo-junkers-ring 5 Gebaude 107/w, Industriegebiet Klotzsche, 01109, Dresden, Germany (100%)
Tel.: (49) 351795970
Sales Range: $100-124.9 Million
Mfr of Microelectronics & Semiconductors
N.A.I.C.S.: 334413

Entegris Japan Holding K.K. (1)
2-4736-3 Hachimanpara, Yonezawa, Yamagata, 992-1128, Japan (100%)
Tel.: (81) 238281611
Web Site: http://www.entegris.com
Sales Range: 350-74.9 Million
Emp.: 200
Holding Company; Plastic Products
N.A.I.C.S.: 551112

Entegris Korea Ltd. (1)
KANC 13F 109 Gwanggyo-ro, Yeongtong-gu, Suwon, 16229, Gyeonggi-do, Korea (South)
Tel.: (82) 3180658300
Semiconductor Component Distr
N.A.I.C.S.: 423690

Entegris Malaysia Sdn. Bhd. (1)
Lot 17 Phase 1 Kulim Hi-Tech Park, 09000, Kulim, Kedah, Malaysia (100%)
Tel.: (60) 44274200
Web Site: http://www.entegris.com
Mfr of Semi-Conductors & Technology Products
N.A.I.C.S.: 334413

Entegris SAS (1)
Parc Centr Alp Ouest 196 rue du Rocher de Lorzier, 38430, Moirans, France
Tel.: (33) 476357350
Web Site: http://www.entegris.com
Microelectronic Components Mfr
N.A.I.C.S.: 334419

Entegris Singapore Pte. Ltd. (1)
10 Ang Mo Kio St 65, 03 06 10 Techpoint, Singapore, 569059, Singapore (100%)
Tel.: (65) 67452400
Web Site: http://www.entegris.com
Plastics Products
N.A.I.C.S.: 326199

Entegris Taiwan Technologies Co., Ltd. (1)
10F 1 No 18 Puding Rd, Hsin Chu, 00300, Taipei, Taiwan **(100%)**
Tel.: (886) 35633598
Sales Range: $10-24.9 Million
Emp.: 28
Data Storage Systems Mfr
N.A.I.C.S.: 541512

Entegris-Jetalon Solutions, Inc. (1)
325 N Wiget Ln Ste 140, Walnut Creek, CA 94598
Tel.: (925) 274-1288
Semiconductor Machinery Mfr
N.A.I.C.S.: 333242

Flex Concepts Inc. (1)
355 W 1400 N, Logan, UT 84341
Tel.: (435) 755-6113
Plastics Product Mfr
N.A.I.C.S.: 326199

Hangzhou Anow Microfiltration Co., Ltd. (1)
Room 801-804 Building 2 1001 Yuhangtang Road, Xihu District, Hangzhou, 310030, China
Tel.: (86) 57128293680
Web Site: https://www.anowfilter.com
Medical Device Mfr
N.A.I.C.S.: 339112

MPD Chemicals LLC (1)
340 Mathers Rd, Ambler, PA 19002
Tel.: (215) 364-1155
Web Site: http://www.mpdchemicals.com
Organic Chemical Mfr
N.A.I.C.S.: 325199
Carrington Smith (CEO)
Rich Tyburski (Pres-Isoscienes)

Subsidiary (Domestic):

Norquay Technology, Inc. (2)
800 W Front St, Chester, PA 19016-0468
Tel.: (610) 874-4330
Web Site: http://www.norquaytech.com
All Other Basic Organic Chemical Mfr
N.A.I.C.S.: 325199
Robert Heldt (Founder, Owner & Pres)

Nihon Entegris K.K. (1)
Mita International Building 11F 1-4-28 Mita, Minato-Ku, Tokyo, 108-0073, Japan
Tel.: (81) 354429718
Web Site: http://www.entregis.com
Semiconductor & Related Device Mfr
N.A.I.C.S.: 334413

Subsidiary (Domestic):

Entegris Japan Co. Ltd. (2)
2-4736-3 Hachimanbara, Yonezawa, 992-1128, Yamagata, Japan
Tel.: (81) 238282311
Emp.: 450
Semiconductor Machinery Mfr
N.A.I.C.S.: 333242
Eiichi Kodama (Pres)

Particle Sizing Systems, LLC (1)
8203 Kristel Cir, Port Richey, FL 34668
Tel.: (727) 846-0866
Surgical & Medical Instrument Mfr
N.A.I.C.S.: 339112

Poco Graphite Inc. (1)
300 Old Greenwood Rd, Decatur, TX 76234
Tel.: (940) 627-2121
Web Site: https://poco.entegris.com
Sales Range: $50-74.9 Million
Carbon & Graphite Products
N.A.I.C.S.: 335991

Subsidiary (Non-US):

Poco Graphite SARL (2)
1 Rue Des Vergers, 69760, Limonest, France
Tel.: (33) 472520040
Web Site: http://www.poco.com
Sales Range: $25-49.9 Million
Emp.: 6
Graphite & Graphite Products Mfr
N.A.I.C.S.: 327992
Emmanuel Ambrosetto (Gen Mgr-Sls)

Val-Tex, LLC (1)
15431 Vantage Pkwy E Ste 210, Houston, TX 77032

Tel.: (281) 530-4848
Web Site: https://www.valtex.com
Industrial Lubricant Mfr & Distr
N.A.I.C.S.: 333914

ENTERGY CORPORATION
639 Loyola Ave, New Orleans, LA 70113
Tel.: (504) 576-4000 DE
Web Site: https://www.entergy.com
Year Founded: 1914
ETR—(NYSE)
Rev.: $12,147,412,000
Assets: $59,703,396,000
Liabilities: $44,960,290,000
Net Worth: $14,743,106,000
Earnings: $2,356,536,000
Emp.: 12,177
Fiscal Year-end: 12/31/23
Electric Utilities Holding Company
N.A.I.C.S.: 221122
Roderick K. West (Grp Pres-Utility Ops)
Andrew S. Marsh (Chm & CEO)
Kimberly A. Fontan (CFO & Exec VP)
Reginald T. Jackson (Chief Acctg Officer & Sr VP)
Peter S. Norgeot Jr. (COO & Exec VP)
Marcus V. Brown (Gen Counsel & Exec VP)
Kathryn Collins (Chief HR Officer & Sr VP)
Chris Bakken (Exec VP)
Kimberly Cook-Nelson (Exec VP)
Michael A. Rhymes (CIO)
A. Christopher Bakken III (Chief Nuclear Officer & Exec VP-Nuclear Ops)

Subsidiaries:

EAM Nelson Holding, LLC (1)
2001 Timberloch Pl, The Woodlands, TX 77380
Tel.: (281) 297-5445
Investment Management Service
N.A.I.C.S.: 523940
James Striedel (Pres)

EGS Holdings, LLC (1)
2001 Timberloch Pl Ste 2000, The Woodlands, TX 77380-1336
Tel.: (409) 981-2000
Electronic Services
N.A.I.C.S.: 221118
Miriam Nunez (CFO)

Entergy Arkansas, LLC (1)
425 W Capitol Ave, Little Rock, AR 72201 **(100%)**
Tel.: (501) 377-4000
Web Site: https://www.entergy.com
Rev.: $2,673,194,000
Assets: $13,006,576,000
Liabilities: $9,224,761,000
Net Worth: $3,781,815,000
Earnings: $292,887,000
Emp.: 3,084
Fiscal Year-end: 12/31/2022
Electric Power Distr
N.A.I.C.S.: 221122
Kimberly A. Fontan (CFO & Exec VP)
Reginald T. Jackson (Chief Acctg Officer & Sr VP)
Kimberly A. Fontan (Sr VP)

Entergy Louisiana, LLC (1)
4809 Jefferson Hwy, Jefferson, LA 70121
Tel.: (504) 576-4000
Web Site: https://www.entergy.com
Rev.: $6,338,768,000
Assets: $28,144,555,000
Liabilities: $18,651,107,000
Net Worth: $9,493,448,000
Earnings: $855,870,000
Emp.: 1,597
Fiscal Year-end: 12/31/2022
Electric Power Distribution & Generation Services
N.A.I.C.S.: 221122
Kimberly A. Fontan (CFO & Exec VP)
Reginald T. Jackson (Chief Acctg Officer & Sr VP)
Phillip R. May Jr. (Chm & Pres)

Entergy Mississippi, LLC (1)
308 E Pearl St, Jackson, MS 39201 **(100%)**
Tel.: (601) 368-5000
Web Site: https://www.entergy.com
Rev.: $1,624,234,000
Assets: $6,078,764,000
Liabilities: $4,038,227,000
Net Worth: $2,040,537,000
Earnings: $176,267,000
Emp.: 716
Fiscal Year-end: 12/31/2022
Energy Distr
N.A.I.C.S.: 221122
Kimberly A. Fontan (CFO & Exec VP)
Reginald T. Jackson (Chief Acctg Officer & Sr VP)
Haley R. Fisackerly (Chm, Pres & CEO)
Kimberly A. Fontan (Sr VP)

Entergy New Orleans, LLC (1)
1600 Perdido St, New Orleans, LA 70112 **(100%)**
Tel.: (504) 670-3700
Web Site: https://www.entergy.com
Rev.: $997,333,000
Assets: $2,212,401,000
Liabilities: $1,509,585,000
Net Worth: $702,816,000
Earnings: $64,101,000
Emp.: 296
Fiscal Year-end: 12/31/2022
Electricity & Natural Gas Distr
N.A.I.C.S.: 221122
Kimberly A. Fontan (CFO & Exec VP)
Reginald T. Jackson (Chief Acctg Officer & Sr VP)
Kimberly A. Fontan (Chief Acctg Officer & Sr VP)

Entergy Nuclear Fuels Company (1)
1340 Echelon Pkwy, Jackson, MS 39213-8202
Tel.: (601) 368-5750
Basic Inorganic Chemical Mfr
N.A.I.C.S.: 325180
Jeffrey S. Forbes (Chief Nuclear Officer & Exec VP-Nuclear Ops)

Entergy Nuclear Generation Company (1)
1340 Echelon Pkwy, Jackson, MS 39213-8202
Tel.: (601) 368-5000
Sales Range: $75-99.9 Million
Emp.: 300
Nuclear Power Generation Services
N.A.I.C.S.: 221113
Jeffrey S. Forbes (Sr VP-Nuclear Ops)

Entergy Power Ventures, LLC (1)
PO Box 61000, New Orleans, LA 70161
Tel.: (504) 576-6143
Eletric Power Generation Services
N.A.I.C.S.: 221118

Entergy Texas, Inc. (1)
(100%)
Tel.: (409) 981-2000
Web Site: https://www.entergy-texas.com
Rev.: $2,288,905,000
Assets: $7,043,964,000
Liabilities: $4,364,503,000
Net Worth: $2,679,461,000
Earnings: $303,327,000
Emp.: 648
Fiscal Year-end: 12/31/2022
Electric Power & Natural Gas Distribution & Generation Services
N.A.I.C.S.: 221118
Kimberly A. Fontan (CFO & Exec VP)
Reginald T. Jackson (Chief Acctg Officer & Sr VP)
Eliecer Viamontes (Chm, Pres & CEO)
Stuart Barrett (VP-Customer Svc)
Kimberly A. Fontan (Chief Acctg Officer & Sr VP)
Abby Weaver (Dir-Resource Plng & Market Ops)
Scott Hutchinson (VP)
Ryland Ramos (VP)
Melanie Taylor (VP)
Erika Garcia (Dir)
Ernest Peeples (Dir)

Entergy Wholesale Commodities (1)
440 Hamilton Ave, White Plains, NY 10601-1839 **(100%)**
Tel.: (914) 272-3205
Web Site: http://www.entergy.com

Sales Range: $50-74.9 Million
Emp.: 200
Operator of Nuclear Power Plants
N.A.I.C.S.: 221113

System Energy Resources, Inc. (1)
1340 Echelon Pkwy, Jackson, MS 39213 **(100%)**
Tel.: (601) 368-5000
Rev.: $658,812,000
Assets: $4,214,146,000
Liabilities: $3,264,379,000
Net Worth: $949,767,000
Earnings: ($276,593,000)
Fiscal Year-end: 12/31/2022
Eletric Power Generation Services
N.A.I.C.S.: 221111
Roderick K. West (Chm, Pres & CEO)
Andrew S. Marsh (CFO & Exec VP)
Reginald T. Jackson (Chief Acctg Officer)

TLG Services, Inc (1)
148 New Milford Rd E, Bridgewater, CT 06752
Tel.: (860) 355-2300
Web Site: https://www.tlgservices.com
Engineeering Services
N.A.I.C.S.: 541330

ENTERO THERAPEUTICS, INC.
777 Yamato Rd Ste 502, Boca Raton, FL 33431
Tel.: (561) 589-7020 DE
Web Site:
https://www.enterothera.com
Year Founded: 2014
ENTO—(NASDAQ)
Rev.: $8,415
Assets: $5,439,699
Liabilities: $2,697,547
Net Worth: $2,742,152
Earnings: ($14,629,642)
Emp.: 10
Fiscal Year-end: 12/31/22
Pharmaceutical Preparation Manufacturing
N.A.I.C.S.: 325412
James Sapirstein (Chm, Pres & CEO)
Martin Krusin (Sr VP-Corp Dev)
Sarah M. Romano (CFO)
James Pennington (Chief Medical Officer)
Amy Chandler (VP)

ENTERPRISE 4.0 TECHNOLOGY ACQUISITION CORP.
630 Ramona St, Palo Alto, CA 94301
Tel.: (619) 736-6855 Ky
Year Founded: 2021
ENTF—(NASDAQ)
Rev.: $4,519,538
Assets: $310,979,805
Liabilities: $328,085,803
Net Worth: ($17,105,998)
Earnings: $3,737,355
Emp.: 4
Fiscal Year-end: 12/31/22
Investment Services
N.A.I.C.S.: 523999
Alex Vieux (Co-CEO)
Eric A. Benhamou (Co-CEO)
Steven C. Fletcher (Co-CFO)
Ron Sege (COO)
Christopher B. Paisley (Co-CFO)

ENTERPRISE BANCORP, INC.
222 Merrimack St, Lowell, MA 01852
Tel.: (978) 459-9000 MA
Web Site:
https://www.enterprisebanking.com
EBTC—(NASDAQ)
Rev.: $179,375,000
Assets: $342,895,000
Liabilities: $60,628,000
Net Worth: $282,267,000
Earnings: $42,716,000
Emp.: 554
Fiscal Year-end: 12/31/22
Bank Holding Company

Enterprise Bancorp, Inc.—(Continued)

N.A.I.C.S.: 551111
George L. Duncan *(Founder & Chm)*
Richard W. Main *(Pres)*
James F. Conway III *(Vice Chm)*
John A. Koutsos *(Sec)*
Joseph R. Lussier *(CFO, Treas & Exec VP)*
Steven R. Larochelle *(CEO)*
Chester J. Szablak Jr. *(Chief Sls Officer)*

Subsidiaries:

Enterprise Bank and Trust Company **(1)**
1281 N Warson Rd, Saint Louis, MO 63132 **(100%)**
Tel.: (314) 993-6200
Web Site: https://www.enterprisebank.com
Sales Range: $125-149.9 Million
Emp.: 300
Banking Services
N.A.I.C.S.: 522110
George L. Duncan *(Exec Chm)*
James F. Conway III *(Vice Chm)*
John A. Koutsos *(Sec)*
Steven R. Larochelle *(CEO & Chief Banking Officer)*
Brian M. Collins *(COO, Chief Digital Officer & Chief Operations Officer)*

Enterprise Wealth Services LLC **(1)**
222 Merrimack St, Lowell, MA 01852
Tel.: (978) 656-5639
Web Site:
https://www.enterprisewealthservices.com
Investment Management Service
N.A.I.C.S.: 523940
Jason Bunker *(Asst VP)*
Paul J. Landry *(VP)*
Susan Gagne *(VP)*

ENTERPRISE FINANCIAL SERVICES CORP

1281 N Warson Rd, Saint Louis, MO 63132
Tel.: (314) 725-5500 DE
Web Site:
https://www.enterprisebank.com
Year Founded: 1988
EFSC—(NASDAQ)
Rev.: $574,244,000
Assets: $13,054,172,000
Liabilities: $11,531,909,000
Net Worth: $1,522,263,000
Earnings: $203,043,000
Emp.: 1,074
Fiscal Year-end: 12/31/22
Commericial Banking
N.A.I.C.S.: 522110
James Brian Lally *(Pres & CEO)*
Troy R. Dumlao *(Chief Acctg Officer)*
Scott R. Goodman *(Sr Exec VP)*
Nicole M. Iannacone *(Chief Legal Officer)*

Subsidiaries:

Enterprise Bank & Trust **(1)**
150 N Meramec Ave, Clayton, MO 63105
Tel.: (314) 725-5500
Web Site: https://www.enterprisebank.com
Commericial Banking
N.A.I.C.S.: 522110
Nicole M. Iannacone *(Chief Risk Officer, Gen Counsel & Exec VP)*

Division (Domestic):

Enterprise Home Loans **(2)**
1281 N Warson Rd, Saint Louis, MO 63132
Tel.: (314) 994-9999
Web Site: http://www.gorman-gorman.com
Sales Range: $25-49.9 Million
Home & Consumer Financing Services
N.A.I.C.S.: 522310
Mark Gorman *(Pres)*

Enterprise Trust Company **(2)**
8077 Maryland Ave Brentwood Blvd, Clayton, MO 63105
Tel.: (314) 889-2000
Emp.: 24

Trust Services
N.A.I.C.S.: 523991
Michael Kowalkowski *(Chief Investment Officer)*
John Tiffin *(Pres & Chief Fiduciary Officer)*

Unit (Domestic):

Enterprise University **(2)**
11404 Olive Blvd, Saint Louis, MO 63141
Tel.: (314) 292-6000
Business Related Courses & Other Support Services
N.A.I.C.S.: 611410
Kay Erb *(VP & Dir)*

First Choice Bancorp **(1)**
17785 Ctr Ct Dr N Ste 750, Cerritos, CA 90703
Tel.: (562) 345-9092
Web Site: http://www.firstchoicebankca.com
Rev.: $100,222,000
Assets: $2,283,115,000
Liabilities: $2,002,374,000
Net Worth: $280,741,000
Earnings: $28,951,000
Emp.: 186
Fiscal Year-end: 12/31/2020
Bank Holding Company
N.A.I.C.S.: 551111
Robert M. Franko *(Pres & CEO)*
Phillip T. Thong *(Vice Chm)*
Khoi D. Dang *(Gen Counsel & Exec VP)*
Yolanda S. Su *(Exec VP-First Choice Bank)*

Subsidiary (Domestic):

First Choice Bank **(2)**
17785 Ctr Ct Dr N Ste 750, Cerritos, CA 90703
Tel.: (562) 345-9092
Web Site: http://www.firstchoicebankca.com
Banking Services
N.A.I.C.S.: 522110
Robert M. Franko *(Pres & CEO)*
Phillip T. Thong *(Vice Chm)*
Gene May *(Chief Credit Officer & Exec VP)*
Yolanda S. Su *(Exec VP)*
Mag Wangsuwana *(CFO & Sr VP)*
Khoi D. Dang *(Gen Counsel & Exec VP)*

Trinity Capital Corporation **(1)**
1200 Trinity Dr, Los Alamos, NM 87544
Tel.: (505) 662-5171
Web Site: http://www.lanb.com
Sales Range: $1-9.9 Million
Bank Holding Company
N.A.I.C.S.: 551111
Jennifer Pearson *(Chief Acctg Officer & Sr VP)*

Subsidiary (Domestic):

Los Alamos National Bank **(2)**
1200 Trinity Dr, Los Alamos, NM 87544-3286
Tel.: (505) 662-5171
Web Site: http://www.lanb.com
Sales Range: $50-74.9 Million
Commericial Banking
N.A.I.C.S.: 522110
Sandra Snow *(VP-AML & OFAC)*
Stan Sluder *(Chief Lending Officer)*
Robert Bransford *(VP-Ops & Risk Mgmt)*
Yin Y. Ho *(COO & CIO)*

ENTERPRISE FINANCIAL SERVICES GROUP, INC.

4091 Mt Royal Blvd, Allison Park, PA 15101
Tel.: (412) 487-0048
Web Site:
https://www.enterprisebankpgh.com
EFSG—(OTCIQ)
Rev.: $20,736,457
Assets: $413,494,533
Liabilities: $377,749,314
Net Worth: $35,745,219
Earnings: $2,535,055
Emp.: 63
Fiscal Year-end: 09/30/23
Bank Holding Company
N.A.I.C.S.: 551111
Chuck Leyh *(Chm, Pres & CEO)*
Douglas W. Lockard *(Vice Chm & Sr VP)*

Raymond R. Ford *(Sr VP & Mgr-Relationship)*
David D. Miller *(Officer-Dev & Sr VP)*
Randy J. Davidson *(VP & Mgr-Relationship)*
Jay Murgi *(Asst VP & Mgr-Relationship)*
Jodi Zelenske *(Sr VP & Mgr-Relationship)*
Mason D. Lockard *(Asst VP & Mgr-Relationship)*
Travis Gonzalez *(Asst VP & Mgr-Relationship)*
Evan Hayward *(Asst VP & Mgr-Relationship)*
Lori Cestra *(COO & Exec VP)*
Joseph P. Novitski Jr. *(VP & Mgr-Relationship)*

Subsidiaries:

Enterprise Bank **(1)**
4091 Mt Royal Blvd, Allison Park, PA 15101
Tel.: (412) 487-6048
Web Site:
http://www.enterprisebankpgh.com
Banking Services
N.A.I.C.S.: 522110
George L. Duncan *(Founder & Chm)*
Chuck Leyh *(Chm, Pres & CEO)*

ENTERPRISE PRODUCTS PARTNERS L.P.

1100 Louisiana St 10th Fl, Houston, TX 77002
Tel.: (713) 381-6500 DE
Web Site:
https://www.enterpriseproducts.com
Year Founded: 1968
EPD—(NYSE)
Rev.: $58,186,000,000
Assets: $68,108,000,000
Liabilities: $40,406,000,000
Net Worth: $27,702,000,000
Earnings: $5,487,000,000
Emp.: 7,300
Fiscal Year-end: 12/31/22
Natural Gas Liquids & Petrochemical Processing, Transport & Storage
N.A.I.C.S.: 486210
A. James Teague *(Co-Chm & Co-CEO)*
Randa Duncan Williams *(Chm)*
Murray E. Brasseux *(Gen Partner)*
James P. Bany *(Sr VP)*
F. Christopher D'Anna *(Sr VP)*
Natalie K. Gayden *(Sr VP)*
Michael C. Hanley *(Sr VP)*
Penny R. Houy *(Sr VP)*
Justin M. Kleiderer *(Sr VP)*
Yvette M. Longonje *(Sr VP)*
Robert E. Moss *(Sr VP)*
Angie M. Murray *(Sr VP)*
Phu V. Phan *(Sr VP)*
Kevin M. Ramsey *(Sr VP)*
Zachary S. Strait *(Sr VP)*

Subsidiaries:

Enterprise Products Operating LLC **(1)**
1100 Louisiana St 10th Fl, Houston, TX 77002
Tel.: (713) 381-6500
Web Site: http://www.epplp.com
Sales Range: $400-449.9 Million
Emp.: 1,000
Oil & Natural Gas Refining
N.A.I.C.S.: 324110
Mike Creel *(VP)*

Subsidiary (Domestic):

Acadian Gas, LLC **(2)**
2727 N Loop W Ste 120, Houston, TX 77008 **(66%)**
Tel.: (713) 880-6500
Web Site: http://www.applp.com
Sales Range: $350-399.9 Million
Gas Pipelines
N.A.I.C.S.: 486210

Michael Creel *(Pres)*

Subsidiary (Domestic):

Acadian Gas Pipeline System **(3)**
514 Waverly Rd, Thibodaux, LA 70302
Tel.: (985) 446-2791
Natural Gas Transportation Services
N.A.I.C.S.: 486210

Subsidiary (Non-US):

Canadian Enterprise Gas Products, Ltd. **(2)**
900 6th Ave SW Ste 300, Calgary, T2P 3K2, AB, Canada
Tel.: (403) 266-7487
Sales Range: $25-49.9 Million
Emp.: 8
Natural Gas Distr
N.A.I.C.S.: 221210
Dave Mathers *(Pres)*

Subsidiary (Domestic):

Dixie Pipeline Company LLC **(2)**
1100 Louisiana St, Houston, TX 77002
Tel.: (713) 381-6500
Pipeline Transport of Natural Gas Liquids
N.A.I.C.S.: 486210

Enterprise Crude Oil LLC **(2)**
210 Park Ave Ste 1500, Oklahoma City, OK 73102-5630
Tel.: (405) 606-4500
Web Site:
http://www.enterpriseproducts.com
Sales Range: $1-9.9 Million
Emp.: 200
Pipeline Transportation of Petroleum
N.A.I.C.S.: 486910

Enterprise Crude Pipeline LLC **(2)**
210 Park Ave Ste 1500, Oklahoma City, OK 73102-5630
Tel.: (405) 606-4500
Web Site:
https://www.enterpriseproducts.com
Emp.: 100
Crude Petroleum Pipeline Services
N.A.I.C.S.: 486110

Enterprise Field Services, LLC **(2)**
1100 Louisana St, Houston, TX 77002
Tel.: (713) 381-6500
Oil Refinery Construction Services
N.A.I.C.S.: 237120

Enterprise GTM Holdings L.P. **(2)**
4 Greenway Plz, Houston, TX 77046
Tel.: (832) 676-4853
Sales Range: $1-9.9 Million
Oil & Natural Gas Pipeline Storage & Processing
N.A.I.C.S.: 486210
Mike Creel *(Pres)*

Enterprise Gathering LLC **(2)**
1100 La St Ste 1000, Houston, TX 77002
Tel.: (713) 381-6500
Emp.: 4
Transportation Support Services
N.A.I.C.S.: 488999

Enterprise Logistic Services LLC **(2)**
1100 Louisiana St, Houston, TX 77002
Tel.: (713) 381-5979
Logistics Consulting Servies
N.A.I.C.S.: 541614

Enterprise Marine Services LLC **(2)**
141 Bayou Dularge Rd, Houma, LA 70363
Tel.: (985) 858-5600
Web Site:
https://marine.enterpriseproducts.com
Marine Engineering Services
N.A.I.C.S.: 541330

Subsidiary (Domestic):

Energy Ventures, LLC **(3)**
2275 Research Blvd Ste 500, Rockville, MD 20850
Tel.: (240) 408-4000
Web Site: http://www.energyventures.net
Eletric Power Generation Services
N.A.I.C.S.: 221118

Bradley C. Jefferies *(Founder & CEO)*
Michael Downer *(VP-Construction Mgmt)*

Branch (Domestic):

Enterprise Products Operating LLC - Beatrice Office (2)
2877 E Hoyt Rd, Beatrice, NE 68310
Tel.: (402) 984-1989
Propane Equipment Rental
N.A.I.C.S.: 532490

Subsidiary (Domestic):

Mid America Pipeline Co., LLC (2)
16653 Hwy K45, Whiting, IA 51063
Tel.: (712) 458-2436
Sales Range: $10-24.9 Million
Emp.: 3
Natural Gas Transmission
N.A.I.C.S.: 486210

Mid-America Pipeline Co., LLC (2)
1507 SW Haverhill Rd, El Dorado, KS 67042
Tel.: (316) 321-0530
Sales Range: $10-24.9 Million
Emp.: 2
Natural Gas Transmission
N.A.I.C.S.: 486210

Mid-America Pipeline Co., LLC (2)
3220 Silver Ave, Sanborn, IA 51248-7484
Tel.: (712) 729-3277
Web Site:
http://www.enterpriseproducts.com
Sales Range: $10-24.9 Million
Emp.: 4
Natural Gas Transmission
N.A.I.C.S.: 486210

Mid-America Pipeline Co., LLC (2)
6133 W US Hwy 14, Janesville, WI 53548
Tel.: (608) 754-6095
Sales Range: $10-24.9 Million
Emp.: 2
Natural Gas Transmission
N.A.I.C.S.: 486210

Mid-America Pipeline Co., LLC (2)
1015 N Jefferson St, Kearney, MO 64060
Tel.: (816) 628-5080
Sales Range: $10-24.9 Million
Emp.: 2
Natural Gas Transmission
N.A.I.C.S.: 486210

Mid-America Pipeline Co., LLC (2)
5354 American Legion Rd SE, Iowa City, IA 52240-8354
Tel.: (319) 351-5460
Web Site:
http://www.enterpriseproducts.com
Sales Range: $10-24.9 Million
Emp.: 25
Natural Gas Transmission
N.A.I.C.S.: 486210

Seminole Pipeline Company LLC (2)
16311 State Hwy 249, Houston, TX 77064 **(100%)**
Tel.: (281) 897-9890
Natural Gas Pipeline Transportation Services
N.A.I.C.S.: 221210

Subsidiary (Domestic):

Seminole Pipeline Company (2)
9602 Fm 1942, Mont Belvieu, TX 77580
Tel.: (281) 576-5111
Web Site:
http://www.enterpriseproducts.com
Sales Range: $10-24.9 Million
Emp.: 2
Coal Pipeline Operation
N.A.I.C.S.: 486990

Seminole Pipeline Company (3)
9800 Oil Field Rd, Brenham, TX 77833
Tel.: (979) 836-3801
Sales Range: $10-24.9 Million
Emp.: 6
Pipelines, Natural Gas
N.A.I.C.S.: 486210

Seminole Pipeline Company (3)
8132 County Rd 226, Freeport, TX 77541
Tel.: (979) 849-6202
Sales Range: $10-24.9 Million
Emp.: 2
Natural Gas Pipelines

N.A.I.C.S.: 486210

Poseidon Oil Pipeline Company, LLC (1)
919 Milam Ste 2100, Houston, TX 77002 **(36%)**
Tel.: (832) 280-3080
Web Site: https://www.poseidonoil.com
Sales Range: $10-24.9 Million
Emp.: 2
Crude Oil Pipeline Services
N.A.I.C.S.: 486110
Ray Cordova *(Pres-Bus Dev)*
Kenneth Moore *(Mgr-Asset)*

Transport 4, L.L.C. (1)
1150 Sanctuary Pkwy Ste 440, Alpharetta, GA 30009
Web Site: https://app.transport4.com
Natural Gas Pipeline Transportation Services
N.A.I.C.S.: 486210

ENTERRA CORPORATION
244 5th Ave Ste E 201, New York, NY 10001
Tel.: (646) 688-5999   DE
Web Site:
https://www.enterracorp.com
ETER—(OTCIQ)
Financial Investment Services
N.A.I.C.S.: 523999
Peter Lachapelle *(CEO, CFO, Treas & Sec)*

ENTERTAINMENT ARTS RESEARCH, INC.
2635 Walnut St, Denver, CO 80205
Tel.: (404) 889-2322
Web Site:
https://www.earigames.com
EARI—(OTCIQ)
Sales Range: Less than $1 Million
Game Software Developer
N.A.I.C.S.: 513210
Joseph Nathan Saulter *(Chm & Pres)*
Mark Gibbs *(CEO)*
Gary Liu *(VP-Bus Dev)*
Tariq Aziz *(VP)*

ENTRADA THERAPEUTICS, INC.
1 Design Ctr Pl Ste 17- 500, Boston, MA 02210
Tel.: (857) 520-9158   DE
Web Site: https://www.entradatx.com
Year Founded: 2016
TRDA—(NASDAQ)
Rev.: $2,632,000
Assets: $252,056,000
Liabilities: $39,502,000
Net Worth: $212,554,000
Earnings: ($94,616,000)
Emp.: 130
Fiscal Year-end: 12/31/22
Biotechnology Research & Development Services
N.A.I.C.S.: 541714
Nathan J. Dowden *(Pres & COO)*
Dipal Doshi *(CEO)*
Nerissa C. Kreher *(Chief Medical Officer)*
Kush M. Parmar *(Chm)*
Kory Wentworth *(CFO)*
Karla MacDonald *(Chief Corp Affairs Officer)*
Kevin Healy *(Sr VP-Regulatory Affairs)*
Jared Cohen *(Gen Counsel)*
Kerry Robert *(Sr VP-People)*
Natarajan Sethuraman *(Chief Scientific Officer)*

ENTRAVISION COMMUNICATIONS CORPORATION
2425 Olympic Blvd Ste 6000 W, Santa Monica, CA 90404
Tel.: (310) 447-3870   DE

Web Site:
https://www.entravision.com
Year Founded: 2000
EVC—(NYSE)
Rev.: $956,209,000
Assets: $880,841,000
Liabilities: $595,472,000
Net Worth: $285,369,000
Earnings: $18,119,000
Emp.: 1,262
Fiscal Year-end: 12/31/22
Radio & Television Broadcasting Stations
N.A.I.C.S.: 516120
Jeffery A. Liberman *(Pres & COO)*
Karl Alonso Meyer *(Chief Revenue & Product Officer)*
Mark A. Boelke *(CFO & Treas)*
Michael J. Christenson *(CEO)*

Subsidiaries:

Cisneros Interactive Bolivia, S.R.L. (1)
Avenida 4to Anillo MZA0 Edificio Torre Duo Piso 23-24-25 n 4012 UV0059, Barrio Equipetrol Norte, Santa Cruz, Bolivia
Tel.: (591) 33297879
Digital Advertising Services
N.A.I.C.S.: 541810

Cisneros Interactive Ecuador Cisteractec, S.A. (1)
Avenida Coruna N27-36 y Orellana Edificio La Moraleja oficina 504, Quito, Ecuador
Tel.: (593) 22900170
Digital Advertising Services
N.A.I.C.S.: 541810

Cisneros Interactive Guatemala, S.A. (1)
A16 Calle 06-17 Zona 10 Edificio Piale Piso 7 Oficina 706, Guatemala, Guatemala
Tel.: (502) 59873422
Digital Advertising Services
N.A.I.C.S.: 541810

Cisneros Interactive Puerto Rico, S.A. (1)
48 Rd 165 Ofc 115 City View Plz, Guaynabo, PR 00968
Tel.: (787) 641-9596
Digital Advertising Services
N.A.I.C.S.: 541810

Cisneros Interactive, S.A. (1)
Av Aviadores Del Chaco 2050 WTC Torre 4 Piso 6, Asuncion, Paraguay
Tel.: (595) 212384669
Digital Advertising Services
N.A.I.C.S.: 541810

LCG, LLC (1)
6000 Executive Blvd Ste 410, Rockville, MD 20852
Tel.: (301) 984-4004
Web Site: https://www.lcginc.com
IT Consulting Services
N.A.I.C.S.: 518210

NBC Palm Springs (1)
72920 Park View Dr, Palm Desert, CA 92260
Tel.: (760) 340-1623
Web Site: https://nbcpalmsprings.com
Television Broadcasting Station
N.A.I.C.S.: 516120
Bob McCauley *(Sr VP)*

Pulpo Media, Inc. (1)
1767 Alcatraz Ave, Berkeley, CA 94703
Tel.: (510) 594-2294
Web Site: http://www.pulpomedia.com
Media Services
N.A.I.C.S.: 327910
Solange Curutchet *(Exec VP-Natl & Gen Mgr-Argentina)*

Redmas Argentina, S.A. (1)
Santos Dumont 3429 6 Piso, Palermo Ciudad Autonoma de, Buenos Aires, Argentina
Tel.: (54) 1145560700
Digital Advertising Services
N.A.I.C.S.: 541810
Javier Montanaro *(VP-Sls)*

Redmas Columbia, S.A.S. (1)

Carrera 15 No 88-64 Oficina 305, Bogota, Colombia
Tel.: (57) 15309099
Digital Advertising Services
N.A.I.C.S.: 541810
Angela Maria Camargo *(Country Mgr)*

Redmas Peru, S.A.C. (1)
Avenida Armendariz 480 Piso 2, Miraflores, Lima, Peru
Tel.: (51) 16254733
Digital Advertising Services
N.A.I.C.S.: 541810
Javier Barraza *(Comml Dir)*

TVNorte, S. de R.L. de C.V. (1)
40 No KM 47 6 Santa Rosa Ejido Valle Hermoso, Ejido Valle Hermoso, Matamoros, 87494, Tamaulipas, Mexico
Tel.: (52) 664 7000790
Media Services
N.A.I.C.S.: 541810

The Community Broadcasting Company of San Diego, Incorporated (1)
2425 Olympic Blvd Ste 600 W, Santa Monica, CA 90404
Tel.: (310) 447-3870
Media Streaming Services
N.A.I.C.S.: 518210

ENTREPRENEUR UNIVERSE BRIGHT GROUP
3609 Hammerkop Dr, North Las Vegas, NV 89084
Tel.: (617) 843-3416   NV
EUBG—(OTCIQ)
Rev.: $3,507,590
Assets: $7,773,604
Liabilities: $889,404
Net Worth: $6,884,200
Earnings: $404,618
Emp.: 25
Fiscal Year-end: 12/31/22
Healtcare Services
N.A.I.C.S.: 621610
Guolin Tao *(Pres, CEO, CFO & Treas)*

ENTREX CARBON MARKET, LLC
150 E Palmetto Park Rd 18th Fl, Boca Raton, FL 33432
Tel.: (561) 465-7454   NV
Web Site:
https://entrexcarbonmarket.com
Year Founded: 2005
RGLG—(OTCIQ)
Holding Company; Electrical Equipment Mfr
N.A.I.C.S.: 551112
Stephen H. Watkins *(Chm)*

Subsidiaries:

Entrex Carbon Market LLC (1)
150 E Palmetto Park Rd 8th Fl, Boca Raton, FL 33432
Tel.: (561) 465-7580
Web Site: https://entrexcarbonmarket.com
Carbon Offset & Future Marketplace Developoper
N.A.I.C.S.: 523160

ENVELA CORPORATION
1901 Gateway Dr, Irving, TX 75038
Tel.: (972) 587-4049   NV
Web Site: https://www.envela.com
ELA—(NYSEAMEX)
Rev.: $182,685,854
Assets: $71,277,209
Liabilities: $27,960,759
Net Worth: $43,316,450
Earnings: $15,689,133
Emp.: 257
Fiscal Year-end: 12/31/22
Jewelry, Bullion Products & Rare Coins Sls
N.A.I.C.S.: 423940
John R. Loftus *(Chm, Pres & CEO)*
Bret A. Pedersen *(CFO)*

Envela Corporation—(Continued)

Subsidiaries:

Charleston Gold & Diamond Ex-
change, Inc. (1)
648 Long Point Rd, Mount Pleasant, SC
29464
Tel.: (843) 881-1118
Web Site:
https://charlestongoldanddiamond.com
Sales Range: $25-49.9 Million
Emp.: 8
Precious Metals, Bullion & Jewelry Whslr
N.A.I.C.S.: 423940

Fairchild International (1)
11311 Reeder Rd, Dallas, TX 75229
Tel.: (972) 238-8377
Web Site: http://www.fairchildwatches.com
Sales Range: $25-49.9 Million
Emp.: 40
Vintage Watch Whslr
N.A.I.C.S.: 423940

National Pawn (1)
100 E Washington Ave, North Little Rock,
AR 72114
Tel.: (501) 375-6789
Web Site: https://www.nationalpawn.com
Sales Range: $1-9.9 Million
Emp.: 20
Jewelry Exchange
N.A.I.C.S.: 458310

ENVERIC BIOSCIENCES, INC.
4851 Tamiami Trl N Ste 200, Naples,
FL 34103
Tel.: (239) 302-1707 DE
Web Site: https://www.enveric.com
ENVB—(NASDAQ)
Rev.: $7,457,713
Assets: $19,552,925
Liabilities: $4,881,001
Net Worth: $14,671,924
Earnings: ($18,800,323)
Emp.: 25
Fiscal Year-end: 12/31/22
Holding Company; Information Tech-
nology Management Services
N.A.I.C.S.: 551112
Joseph Tucker (CEO)
Lynn Gallant (VP-Clinical Ops)
Kevin M. Coveney (CFO)

Subsidiaries:

Ameri & Partners Inc. (1)
100 Canal Pointe Blvd, Princeton, NJ 08540
Tel.: (732) 243-9250
Web Site: http://www.ameri100.com
Emp.: 10
Information Technology Management Ser-
vices
N.A.I.C.S.: 541519

Bellsoft, Inc. (1)
3545 Cruse Rd, Lawrenceville, GA 30044
Tel.: (770) 935-4152
Web Site: http://www.bellsoftinc.com
Technology Consulting & Systems Integra-
tion Company
N.A.I.C.S.: 541511

Bigtech Software Private Limited (1)
406 7th Main Road 2nd Floor 2nd Block
Jayanagar, Bengaluru, 560 011, India
Tel.: (91) 8049602900
Web Site: http://www.bigtechsoft.com
Software Development Services
N.A.I.C.S.: 541511

Virtuoso LLC (1)
4901 W 136th St, Shawnee Mission, KS
66224
Tel.: (913) 498-9777
Web Site: http://www.virtuosollc.com
Custom Computer Programming Services
N.A.I.C.S.: 541511

ENVIRI CORPORATION
100 120 N 18th St 17th Fl, Philadel-
phia, PA 19103
Tel.: (267) 857-8715 DE
Web Site: https://www.enviri.com
Year Founded: 1956

NVRI—(NYSE)
Rev.: $1,889,065,000
Assets: $2,790,854,000
Liabilities: $2,167,812,000
Net Worth: $623,042,000
Earnings: ($180,069,000)
Emp.: 12,000
Fiscal Year-end: 12/31/22
Industrial Services & Engineered
Products for Steel, Construction, Gas
& Energy & Railway Transportation
industries
N.A.I.C.S.: 325120
David S. Martin (VP-IR)
Russell C. Hochman (Chief Compli-
ance Officer, Gen Counsel, Sec & Sr
VP)
Samuel C. Fenice (Chief Acctg Offi-
cer, VP & Controller)
Tom G. Vadaketh (CFO & Sr VP)
Jay Cooney (Chief Mktg & Comm
officer)
F. Nicholas Grasberger III (Pres &
CEO)
Jennifer Kozak (Chief HR Officer)

Subsidiaries:

Clean Earth, Inc. (1)
334 S Warminster Rd, Hatboro, PA 19040
Tel.: (877) 455-3478
Web Site: http://www.cleanearthinc.com
Treatment, Disposal & Recycling of Con-
taminated Soil, Dredge & Other Non-
Hazardous Materials
N.A.I.C.S.: 541620
Steven Sands (Exec VP)
Michael Goebner (Sr VP-Facilities)
Averil Rance (Sr VP-Environmental Health
& Safety)
James Hull (VP-Sls & Mktg)
Asuquo Edem (VP-Procurement)
Stephen Dixon (VP-Natl Accounts)
Liz Peterson (Chief Comml Officer)
Jeff Beswick (Pres)

Subsidiary (Domestic):

AERC Recycling Solutions (2)
2591 Mitchell Ave, Allentown, PA 18103
Tel.: (610) 797-7608
Recycling Services
N.A.I.C.S.: 562920

American Environmental Services,
Inc. (2)
Ste 204 8055 Ritchie Hwy, Pasadena, MD
21122
Tel.: (443) 333-7226
Web Site: https://www.aaosi.com
Sales Range: $10-24.9 Million
Emp.: 9
Hazardous Waste Collection & Disposal
Services
N.A.I.C.S.: 562211
David Torrence (Pres)

Subsidiary (Domestic):

AES Environmental LLC (3)
2100 Georgetown Dr Ste 303, Sewickley,
PA 15143
Tel.: (724) 933-4100
Waste Management Services
N.A.I.C.S.: 562998
Matt Stauber (COO)

Subsidiary (Domestic):

Clean Earth Dredging Technologies,
LLC (2)
1 Fish House Rd, Kearny, NJ 07032
Tel.: (215) 734-1400
Web Site: http://www.cleanearthinc.com
Emp.: 15
Material Recycling Services
N.A.I.C.S.: 562920
Steve Sands (Pres & CEO)

Clean Earth of Alabama, Inc. (2)
402 Webster Chapel Rd, Glencoe, AL
35905-7150
Web Site: http://www.cleanearthinc.com
Hazardous & Industrial Waste Management
Services
N.A.I.C.S.: 562211
Ed Lajza (Owner)

Clean Earth of Carteret, LLC (2)
24 Middlesex Ave, Carteret, NJ 07008
Tel.: (732) 541-8909
Sales Range: $25-49.9 Million
Emp.: 15
Contaminated Soil Treatment Services
N.A.I.C.S.: 562219

Clean Earth of Georgia, LLC (2)
5864 New Peachtree Rd, Doraville, GA
30340
Tel.: (770) 457-1341
Petroleum Contaminated Soil Treatment
Services
N.A.I.C.S.: 562211

Clean Earth of Greater Washington,
LLC (2)
6250 Dower House Rd, Upper Marlboro,
MD 20772
Tel.: (301) 599-0939
Emp.: 12
Nonhazardous Soil Treatment Services
N.A.I.C.S.: 562219

Clean Earth of Maryland, LLC (2)
1469 Oak Ridge Pl, Hagerstown, MD 21740
Tel.: (301) 791-6220
Sales Range: $25-49.9 Million
Emp.: 12
Contaminated Soil & Debris Treatment Ser-
vices
N.A.I.C.S.: 562219

Clean Earth of New Castle, LLC (2)
94 J Caldwell Ln, New Castle, DE 19720
Tel.: (302) 427-6633
Sales Range: $25-49.9 Million
Emp.: 15
Waste Treatment & Disposal Services
N.A.I.C.S.: 562219

Clean Earth of New York, Inc. (2)
304 Towpath Ln, Fort Edward, NY 12828
Tel.: (516) 867-6452
Web Site: http://www.cleanearthinc.com
Sales Range: $25-49.9 Million
Emp.: 2
Waste Brokerage Services
N.A.I.C.S.: 238990

Clean Earth of North Jersey, Inc. (2)
115 Jacobus Ave, Kearny, NJ 07032
Tel.: (973) 344-4004
Hazardous & Industrial Waste Management
& Disposal Services
N.A.I.C.S.: 562219

Clean Earth of Philadelphia, LLC (2)
3201 S 61st St, Philadelphia, PA 19153
Tel.: (215) 724-5520
Sales Range: $25-49.9 Million
Emp.: 9
Waste Treatment & Disposal Services
N.A.I.C.S.: 562219

Clean Earth of Southeast Pennsylva-
nia, LLC (2)
7 Steel Rd E, Morrisville, PA 19067-3613
Tel.: (215) 428-1700
Sales Range: $10-24.9 Million
Emp.: 15
Contaminated Soil Treatment Services
N.A.I.C.S.: 562219

Clean Earth of Southern Florida,
LLC (2)
1240 Foxmoor St, Moore Haven, FL 33471
Tel.: (941) 723-2700
Emp.: 15
Hazardous Waste Collection Services
N.A.I.C.S.: 562112

Phoenix Soil, LLC (2)
58 N Washington St, Plainville, CT
06062 (100%)
Tel.: (860) 747-8886
Web Site: http://www.phoenixsoilllc.com
Sales Range: $1-9.9 Million
Environmental Services for Soil Treatment
Solutions
N.A.I.C.S.: 325314

Harsco India Services Private
Ltd. (1)
Bldg No 3 2nd Floor Unit No 18, Madhapur,
Hyderabad, 500081, India
Tel.: (91) 4066224500
Web Site: http://www.harsco.com
Emp.: 200

Software Development Services
N.A.I.C.S.: 541511

Harsco Industrial
Patterson-Kelley (1)
155 Burson St, East Stroudsburg, PA
18301-2245
Tel.: (570) 421-7500
Web Site: http://www.harscopk.com
Sales Range: $25-49.9 Million
Emp.: 100
Diversified Manufacturing, Defense, Indus-
trial Services & Building & Engineered
Products; Infrastructure, Construction &
Transportation; Process Industry Products
N.A.I.C.S.: 522130

Harsco Infrastructure B.V. (1)
Zuidplein 126 WTC Toren H, 1077 XV, Am-
sterdam, Netherlands
Tel.: (31) 104455444
Metal Products Mfr
N.A.I.C.S.: 332999

Harsco Metals & Minerals SAS (1)
1 Rue Charles Fourier, 59760, Grande-
Synthe, 59760, France
Tel.: (33) 328292410
Metal Products Mfr
N.A.I.C.S.: 332999

Harsco Metals Group Limited (1)
Harsco House Regent Park 299 Kingston
Road, Leatherhead, KT22 7SG, Surrey,
United Kingdom (100%)
Tel.: (44) 1372381400
Web Site: http://www.harscometals.com
Sales Range: $75-99.9 Million
Emp.: 130
Diversified Manufacturing, Defense, Indus-
trial Services & Building & Engineered
Products; Infrastructure, Construction &
Transportation; Process Industry Products
N.A.I.C.S.: 424130

Subsidiary (Non-US):

Harsco ASEAN (2)
Level 3 310 Crown Street, Wollongong,
2500, NSW, Australia
Tel.: (61) 242263400
Web Site: http://www.harsco-m.com
Fabricated Structural Metal Mfr
N.A.I.C.S.: 332312

Harsco Metals & Minerals (2)
PO Box 83, Velsen, Noord, Netherlands
Tel.: (31) 251262523
Web Site: http://www.harsco-m.com
Sales Range: $25-49.9 Million
Emp.: 118
Fabricated Structural Metal Mfr
N.A.I.C.S.: 332323

Harsco Metals France S.A.S. (2)
Route Vitry Sur Orne, 57270, Uckange,
France
Tel.: (33) 382574100
Fabricated Structural Metal Mfr
N.A.I.C.S.: 332312

Subsidiary (Domestic):

Harsco Metals Logistique et Services
Specialises S.A.S. (3)
1 Rue Charles Fourier, Grande-Synthe,
59760, France
Tel.: (33) 328292410
Logistics Management Consulting Services
N.A.I.C.S.: 541614

Subsidiary (Non-US):

Harsco Metals Luxembourg S.A. (2)
Bp24, L-4501, Differdange, Luxembourg
Tel.: (352) 5926891
Web Site: http://www.harsco.com
Emp.: 100
Fabricated Structural Metal Mfr
N.A.I.C.S.: 332312

Harsco Metals Sweden A.B. (2)
Svarvargatan 22, Vastmanland county, 738
33, Norberg, Sweden
Tel.: (46) 22328100
Web Site: http://www.harscometals.com
Sales Range: $25-49.9 Million
Emp.: 65
Fabricated Structural Metal Mfr

N.A.I.C.S.: 332323

Harsco Metals India (1)
8-2-684/40 Anand Banjara Colony Rd 12
Banjara Hills, Hyderabad, 500 034, India
Tel.: (91) 4023384215
Web Site: http://www.harsco-m.com
Emp.: 650
Fabricated Structural Metal Mfr
N.A.I.C.S.: 332312

Harsco Metals Middle East FZE (1)
Office 722Building 4EA, PO Box 54495,
Dubai Airport Free Zone, Dubai, United
Arab Emirates
Tel.: (971) 42991402
Metal & Mineral Distr
N.A.I.C.S.: 423520

Harsco Metals Oostelijk Staal Interna-
tional B.V. (1)
George Stephensonweg 15, 3133 KJ,
Vlaardingen, Netherlands
Tel.: (31) 102322128
Web Site: http://www.hooymeijer.nl
Emp.: 80
Container Transportation Services
N.A.I.C.S.: 484121

Harsco Minerais Limitada (1)
Rodovia BR 381 Km 195 S/N Bairro Nucleo
Industrial, Timoteo, 35180-001, Minas
Gerais, Brazil
Tel.: (55) 3138499350
Web Site: http://www.harscominerais.com.br
Sales Range: $50-74.9 Million
Emp.: 120
Abrasive Product Mfr
N.A.I.C.S.: 327910

Harsco Minerals Deutschland
GmbH (1)
Eurode-Park 1-52, 52134, Herzogenrath,
Germany
Tel.: (49) 24069993210
Abrasive Product Mfr
N.A.I.C.S.: 327910

Harsco Minerals PA LLC (1)
5000 Ritter Rd Ste 205, Mechanicsburg, PA
17055
Tel.: (717) 506-2071
Web Site:
    http://www.blackbeautyabrasives.com
Sales Range: $100-124.9 Million
Emp.: 25
Mfr Roofing Granules & Slag Abrasives
N.A.I.C.S.: 332313

Harsco Rail (1)
2401 Edmund Rd, West Columbia, SC
29171-0020
Tel.: (803) 822-9160
Web Site: https://www.harscorail.com
Sales Range: $500-549.9 Million
Emp.: 400
Railway Maintenance Equipment Mfr
N.A.I.C.S.: 336510
Jeswant Gill (Pres)

Subsidiary (Non-US):

Harsco Rail Pty. Ltd. (2)
4 Strathwyn Street, PO Box 5287, Bren-
dale, 4500, QLD, Australia
Tel.: (61) 73 205 6500
Web Site: http://www.harscorail.com
Sales Range: $25-49.9 Million
Emp.: 25
Railway Track Maintenance Equipment Mfr
N.A.I.C.S.: 332312
Rod Lang (Mng Dir)

Harsco Rail Ltda. (1)
Av Marechal Camara 160 / 1615 Centro,
Rio de Janeiro, 20020-080, RJ, Brazil
Tel.: (55) 2125105164
Rail Transportation Services
N.A.I.C.S.: 488210
Victor Loureiro Araujo (Mng Dir)

Ilserv S.r.l. (1)
Viale Brin Benedetto 218, 05100, Terni,
Italy (65%)
Tel.: (39) 0744206511
Fabricated Structural Metal Mfr
N.A.I.C.S.: 332312

MultiServ Logistics Limited (1)
Harsco House Regent Park 299 Kingston

Road, Leatherhead, KT22 7SG, Surrey,
United Kingdom
Tel.: (44) 1372381400
Freight Transportation Services
N.A.I.C.S.: 483113

Parker Scaffolding Co Limited (1)
Carlton House Regent Park 299 Kingston
Road, Leatherhead, KT22 7SG, Surrey,
United Kingdom
Tel.: (44) 1372381300
Metal Distr
N.A.I.C.S.: 423510

Rovacabin Limited (1)
Unit B Peterley Road, Oxford, OX4 2TZ,
United Kingdom
Tel.: (44) 1865337200
Real Estate Management Services
N.A.I.C.S.: 531210

Stericycle Environmental Solutions,
Inc. (1)
700 Mulberry St, Kansas City, MO 64101
Tel.: (816) 474-1391
Web Site:
    http://www.stericycleenvironmental.com
Hazardous Waste Treatment & Disposal
Services
N.A.I.C.S.: 562211

ENVIRO-SERV, INC.
3404 W Bay Vista Ave 1 Fl, Tampa,
FL 33611
Tel.: (813) 708-9910   DE
Web Site: https://www.enviro-
serv.com
EVSV—(OTCIQ)
Pest Control Services
N.A.I.C.S.: 561710
Christoph Andreas Trina (Chm, Pres,
CEO & CFO)

ENVIRONMENTAL IMPACT AC-
QUISITION CORP.
535 Madison Ave, New York, NY
10022
Tel.: (212) 389-8109   DE
Year Founded: 2020
ENVIU—(NASDAQ)
Investment Services
N.A.I.C.S.: 523999
Daniel Coyne (Pres & CEO)
Marc Marano (CFO & Treas)
Andrew Viles (Sec)

ENVIRONMENTAL PACKAG-
ING TECHNOLOGIES HOLD-
INGS, INC.
6100 W by NW Ste 110, Houston, TX
77040
Tel.: (713) 961-2795   NV
Web Site: http://www.eptpac.com
Year Founded: 2011
EPTI—(OTCEM)
Investment Services
N.A.I.C.S.: 523999
David Skriloff (CEO)

ENVIRONMENTAL SERVICE
PROFESSIONALS, INC.
Tel.: (760) 459-1044   NV
Web Site: https://www.evsp.com
EVSP—(OTCIQ)
Building Inspection Services
N.A.I.C.S.: 541350
Edward L. Torres (Chm & CEO)
Peng Lee (Chief Science Officer)

Subsidiaries:

National Professional Services,
Inc. (1)
603 W Ramsey St, Banning, CA 92220
Web Site: http://www.npservicesinc.com
Association Management Services
N.A.I.C.S.: 541611

Porter Valley Software, Inc. (1)
810 N Farrell Dr, Palm Springs, CA 92262-
5940
Web Site: http://www.pvsoftware.com

Software Development Services
N.A.I.C.S.: 541511
John Garland (Mgr-Customer Svc)

ENVIRONMENTAL SOLUTIONS
WORLDWIDE, INC.
200 Progress Dr, Montgomeryville,
PA 18936
Tel.: (215) 699-0730   FL
Web Site: https://www.eswgroup.com
Year Founded: 1987
ESWW—(OTCEM)
Sales Range: $25-49.9 Million
Emp.: 51
Environmental & Emission Technolo-
gies
N.A.I.C.S.: 333618
Praveen Nair (CFO)
Patrick Barge (CEO)
Mike Sally (VP-Operations)
Michael Streichsbier (CTO)
Adam Gross (VP-Sales & Marketing)

ENVIRONMENTAL TECTONICS
CORPORATION
125 James Way, Southampton, PA
18966
Tel.: (215) 355-9100   PA
Web Site: https://www.etcusa.com
Year Founded: 1969
ETCC—(OTCIQ)
Rev.: $40,580,000
Assets: $48,817,000
Liabilities: $40,794,000
Net Worth: $8,023,000
Earnings: ($4,018,000)
Emp.: 234
Fiscal Year-end: 02/28/20
Simulation Systems & Chamber-
Based Products Mfr & Designer
N.A.I.C.S.: 333248
George K. Anderson (Chm)
Alper Kus (Sr VP-Aircrew Training
Sys)
James D. Cashel (Chief Compliance
Officer, Gen Counsel, Sec & VP)
Robert L. Laurent Jr. (Pres & CEO)

Subsidiaries:

ETC Simulation ADMS Innovation
Center (1)
2100 N Alafaya Trl Ste 900, Orlando, FL
32826   (100%)
Tel.: (407) 282-3378
Web Site: http://www.edms.com
Sales Range: $10-24.9 Million
Emp.: 20
Simulation & Training Equipment for Military
& Commercial Use
N.A.I.C.S.: 541511
Bob Laurent (CFO)

ETC-PZL Aerospace Industries Sp z
o.o. (1)
Al Krakowska 110/114, 02-256, Warsaw,
Poland
Tel.: (48) 228465417
Web Site:
    http://www.aerospaceindustries.com
Sales Range: $25-49.9 Million
Emp.: 110
Electronic Simulator Mfr
N.A.I.C.S.: 333248
Anna Brzozowska (Pres & Dir)

ENVIROTECH VEHICLES, INC.
1425 Ohlendorf Rd, Osceola, AR
72370
Tel.: (870) 970-3355   DE
Web Site: https://www.evtvusa.com
Year Founded: 2012
EVTV—(NASDAQ)
Rev.: $4,504,621
Assets: $33,483,689
Liabilities: $1,488,709
Net Worth: $31,994,980
Earnings: ($43,804,160)
Emp.: 13
Fiscal Year-end: 12/31/22

Motor Vehicle Electrical & Electronic
Equipment Manufacturing
N.A.I.C.S.: 336320
Susan M. Emry (Exec VP)
Phillip W. Oldridge (Chm & CEO)
David Klimczak (Mgr-Stock Transfer)
Franklin Lim (CFO & Controller)

Subsidiaries:

Envirotech Drive Systems, Inc. (1)
4100 Newport Pl Ste 670, Newport Beach,
CA 92660
Tel.: (951) 407-9860
Web Site:
    http://www.envirotechvehicles.com
Motor Engine Mfr
N.A.I.C.S.: 336320
David Oldridge (Pres & CTO)

ENVIROTECHNOLOGIES IN-
TERNATIONAL, INC.
1809 W State Rd Ste B2, Pleasant
Grove, UT 84062   DE
Web Site:
    http://www.envirotechnologiesinter
national.com
Year Founded: 1996
ETII—(OTCIQ)
Oil & Gas Field Equipment Mfr
N.A.I.C.S.: 333132
Gaylord Karren (Pres)
William Shupe (Sec)
Staci Sutherland (Accountant)
James Stone (Treas)

ENVISTA HOLDINGS CORPO-
RATION
200 S Kraemer Blvd Bldg E, Brea,
CA 92821-6208
Tel.: (714) 817-7000   DE
Web Site: https://www.envistaco.com
Year Founded: 2018
NVST—(NYSE)
Rev.: $2,566,500,000
Assets: $6,605,100,000
Liabilities: $2,431,200,000
Net Worth: $4,173,900,000
Earnings: ($100,200,000)
Emp.: 12,800
Fiscal Year-end: 12/31/23
Holding Company
N.A.I.C.S.: 551112
Paul A. Keel (Pres & CEO)
Scott Huennekens (Chm)
Curt Bludworth (Chief HR Officer &
Sr VP)
Mischa Reis (Sr VP-Strategy & Corp
Dev)
Mark Nance (Gen Counsel & Sr VP)
Claudia Ortiz (Sr VP-Regulatory Af-
fairs & Quality Assurance)
Filippo Impieri (Sr VP-Special Mar-
kets)
Jean-Claude Kyrillo (Sr VP)
Jim McGillivary (Sr VP)
Faez Kaabi (Chief Acctg Officer &
VP)
Eric D. Hammes (CFO & Sr VP)
John Marotta (Sr VP-Supply Chain &
EBS)

ENVIT CAPITAL GROUP, INC.
60 State St Ctr 7th Fl, Boston, MA
02109
Tel.: (617) 542-3333   DE
Year Founded: 1979
ECGP—(OTCIQ)
Asset Management Services
N.A.I.C.S.: 523940
Edward Laborio (Chm & CEO)

ENVIVA INC.
7272 Wisconsin Ave Ste 1800,
Bethesda, MD 20814
Tel.: (301) 657-5560   DE
Web Site:
    https://www.envivabiomass.com

Enviva Inc.—(Continued)

Year Founded: 2013
EVA—(NYSE)
Rev.: $1,177,853,000
Assets: $2,530,809,000
Liabilities: $2,691,307,000
Net Worth: ($160,498,000)
Earnings: ($685,810,000)
Emp.: 1,234
Fiscal Year-end: 12/31/23
All Other Miscellaneous Wood Product Manufacturing
N.A.I.C.S.: 321999
John K. Keppler *(Founder, Chm, Pres & CEO)*
Mark Coscio *(Chief Dev Officer & Exec VP)*
Pierre F. Lapeyre Jr. *(Gen Partner)*
David M. Leuschen *(Gen Partner)*

Subsidiaries:

Enviva LP   **(1)**
7272 Wisconsin Ave Ste 1800, Bethesda, MD 20814
Tel.: (301) 657-5560
Web Site: https://www.envivabiomass.com
Sales Range: $10-24.9 Million
Renewable Energy Wood Pellet Mfr & Distr
N.A.I.C.S.: 321999
Shai Even *(CFO & Exec VP)*
Roxanne Klein *(Exec VP)*
John-Paul Taylor *(Sr VP)*
Brandi Colander *(Sr VP)*
Mark Coscio *(Exec VP)*
Craig Lorraine *(Sr VP)*
Kate Walsh *(VP)*
Jason Paral *(Sr VP)*
Wushuang Ma *(VP)*

Subsidiary (Domestic):

Enviva Pellets Amory, LLC   **(2)**
606 A Ave, Amory, MS 38821-1722
Tel.: (662) 257-2150
Web Site: http://www.envivabiomass.com
Sales Range: $10-24.9 Million
Emp.: 22
Wood Pellet Mfr
N.A.I.C.S.: 321920

Enviva Pellets Wiggins, LLC   **(2)**
81 Old Hwy 49, Perkinston, MS 39573
Tel.: (601) 928-7552
Web Site: http://www.envivabiomass.com
Emp.: 10
Renewable Energy Wood Pellet Mfr & Distr
N.A.I.C.S.: 321999

Enviva Pellets Ahoskie, LLC   **(1)**
142 N C Route 561 E, Ahoskie, NC 27910
Tel.: (252) 209-6032
Wood Pellet Mfr
N.A.I.C.S.: 321999

Enviva Pellets Northampton, LLC   **(1)**
874 Lebanon Church Rd, Garysburg, NC 27831
Tel.: (252) 541-2631
Wood Pellet Distr
N.A.I.C.S.: 423990
Joe Sikes *(Mgr-Maintenance)*

Georgia Biomass, LLC   **(1)**
3390 Industrial Blvd, Waycross, GA 31503
Tel.: (912) 490-5293
Web Site: http://www.gabiomass.com
Wood Container & Pallet Mfr
N.A.I.C.S.: 321920

ENVVENO MEDICAL CORPORATION
70 Doppler, Irvine, CA 92618
Tel.: (949) 261-2900   DE
Web Site: https://envveno.com
Year Founded: 1987
NVNO—(NASDAQ)
Rev.: $1,792,000
Emp.: 8
Biological Implant & Medical Device Developer
N.A.I.C.S.: 339113
Robert Berman *(CEO)*
Marc Glickman *(Chief Medical Officer & Sr VP)*

Craig Glynn *(CFO)*
Hamed Alavi *(CTO & Sr VP)*
Andrew Cormack *(Chief Comml Officer)*
Kevin Belteau *(VP-Clinical Ops)*
Sandy Prietto *(VP-Marketing)*

ENZO BIOCHEM INC.
21 Executive Blvd, Farmingdale, NY 11735
Tel.: (631) 755-5500   NY
Web Site: https://www.enzo.com
Year Founded: 1976
ENZ—(NYSE)
Rev.: $31,907,000
Assets: $85,764,000
Liabilities: $29,652,000
Net Worth: $56,112,000
Earnings: ($26,078,000)
Emp.: 125
Fiscal Year-end: 07/31/24
Biotechnology Research Services
N.A.I.C.S.: 621511
Kara Cannon *(CEO)*
Dieter Schapfel *(Chief Medical Officer)*
Matthew Kupferberg *(Gen Counsel)*
Patricia Eckert *(CFO)*
Steven J. Pully *(Chm)*

Subsidiaries:

Enzo Clinical Labs Inc.   **(1)**
60 Executive Blvd, Farmingdale, NY 11735-4710
Tel.: (631) 755-5500
Web Site: http://www.enzoclinicallabs.com
Sales Range: $25-49.9 Million
Emp.: 400
Provider of Biotechnology Research Services
N.A.I.C.S.: 621511

Enzo Life Sciences   **(1)**
10 Executive Blvd, Farmingdale, NY 11735-4710
Tel.: (631) 694-7070
Web Site: http://www.enzolifesciences.com
Sales Range: $10-24.9 Million
Emp.: 30
Provider of Biotechnology Research Services
N.A.I.C.S.: 325412

Subsidiary (Non-US):

Enzo Life Sciences (ELS) AG   **(2)**
Industriestrasse 17, Lausen, 4415, Basel, Switzerland
Tel.: (41) 619268989
Emp.: 30
Life Science Research & Development Services
N.A.I.C.S.: 541715

Enzo Therapeutics Inc.   **(1)**
527 Madison Ave, New York, NY 10022
Tel.: (212) 583-0100
Web Site: http://www.enzo.com
Commercial Physical Research Services
N.A.I.C.S.: 541720

ENZOLYTICS, INC.
1101 Raintree Cir Ste 130, Allen, TX 75013
Tel · (469) 803-1287   DE
Web Site: https://www.enzolytics.com
ENZC—(OTCIQ)
Immunotherapy Drug Development Services
N.A.I.C.S.: 325998

Subsidiaries:

Immunotech Laboratories, Inc.   **(1)**
120 W Pomona Ave, Monrovia, CA 91016
Tel.: (626) 538-4779
Web Site: http://www.immunotechlab.com
Chemical Mfr Including Therapeutic Molecules
N.A.I.C.S.: 325998
Harry Zhabilov *(Pres & Chief Science Officer)*

ENZON PHARMACEUTICALS, INC.
20 Commerce Dr Ste 135, Cranford, NJ 07016
Tel.: (732) 980-4500   DE
Web Site: https://www.enzon.com
Year Founded: 1981
ENZN—(OTCQX)
Rev.: $2,261,000
Assets: $47,702,000
Liabilities: $44,197,000
Net Worth: $3,505,000
Earnings: $1,373,000
Fiscal Year-end: 12/31/23
Cancer Therapeutic Products Mfr
N.A.I.C.S.: 325414
Randolph C. Read *(Chm)*
Richard L. Feinstein *(CEO, CFO & Sec)*

ENZYMES OF AMERICA HOLDING CORP.
50633 Ryan Rd, Utica, MI 48317
Tel.: (586) 739-4615   DE
ENZH—(OTCIQ)
Pharmaceuticals Product Mfr
N.A.I.C.S.: 325412
Earl A. Braxton *(Pres & CEO)*

EOG RESOURCES, INC.
1111 Bagby S Sky Lobby 2, Houston, TX 77002
Tel.: (713) 651-7000   DE
Web Site:
  https://www.eogresources.com
Year Founded: 1999
EOG—(NYSE)
Rev.: $24,186,000,000
Assets: $43,857,000,000
Liabilities: $15,767,000,000
Net Worth: $28,090,000,000
Earnings: $7,594,000,000
Emp.: 3,050
Fiscal Year-end: 12/31/23
Domestic Exploration & Production of Oil & Natural Gas
N.A.I.C.S.: 211120
Sandeep Bhakhri *(CIO, CTO & Sr VP)*
William R. Thomas *(Chm & CEO)*
Kevin S. Hanzel *(VP-Audit)*
Ann D. Janssen *(CFO & Exec VP)*
Michael P. Donaldson *(Gen Counsel, Sec & Exec VP)*
Jill R. Miller *(VP-Engrg & Acquisitions)*
D. Lance Terveen *(Sr VP-Mktg)*
John J. Boyd *(Sr VP-Ops)*
Nicholas J. Groves *(VP-Safety & Environmental)*
Jeffrey R. Leitzell *(COO & Exec VP)*
Kenneth D. Marbach *(VP & Gen Mgr-Corpus Christi)*
Philip W. Leimer *(VP-Tax)*
Pamela R. Roth *(VP-Govt Rels)*
Heath A. Work *(VP & Gen Mgr-Oklahoma City)*
Colleen Marples *(VP & Gen Mgr-Denver)*
Jamie L. Hanafy *(Controller-Land Admin)*
Lloyd W. Helms Jr. *(Pres)*
D. Seth Woodard *(Controller)*
Joseph L. Korenek Jr. *(VP-Bus Dev)*

Subsidiaries:

EOG Argentina S.R.L.   **(1)**
Calle Victoria Ocampo 360 1107, Buenos Aires, Argentina
Tel.: (54) 1145156399
Oil & Gas Exploration & Production Services
N.A.I.C.S.: 211120

EOG Resources Canada, Inc.   **(1)**
700 9th Ave SW Ste 1300, Calgary, T2P 3V4, AB, Canada   **(100%)**

Tel.: (403) 297-9100
Sales Range: $125-149.9 Million
Emp.: 150
Explores For, Produces & Develops Oil & Gas Properties
N.A.I.C.S.: 211120

EOG Resources Trinidad Limited   **(1)**
Briar Place 10-12 Sweet Briar Road, St Clair, Port of Spain, Trinidad & Tobago
Tel.: (868) 6228653
Oil & Natural Gas Extraction Services
N.A.I.C.S.: 237120

EOG Resources Trinidad Limited   **(1)**
4th Fl Briar Pl 10-12 Sweet Briar Rd St Clair, Saint Clair, Port of Spain, Trinidad & Tobago
Tel.: (868) 6228653
Natural Gas Extraction Services
N.A.I.C.S.: 211130

EOG Resources Trinidad Nitro Unlimited   **(1)**
Briar Place 10-12 Sweet Briar Road, Saint Clair, Port of Spain, Trinidad & Tobago
Tel.: (868) 6228653
Hydrocarbons Exploration Services
N.A.I.C.S.: 213112

EOG Y Resources, Inc.   **(1)**
105 S 4th St, Artesia, NM 88210
Tel.: (575) 748-1471
Web Site: http://www.eogresources.com
Natural Gas Extraction Services
N.A.I.C.S.: 211130

Subsidiary (Domestic):

Trail Mountain Inc.   **(2)**
105 S 4th St, Artesia, NM 88210
Tel.: (575) 748-1471
Web Site: http://www.eogresources.com
Oil & Gas Exploration Services
N.A.I.C.S.: 213112

Hawthorn Oil Transportation, Inc.   **(1)**
1111 Bagby Sky Lobby 2, Houston, TX 77002
Tel.: (713) 651-7000
Web Site:
  https://www.hawthornoiltransportation.com
Crude Oil Transportation Services
N.A.I.C.S.: 486110
Lance Terveen *(Sr VP-Mktg Ops)*

Pecan Pipeline (North Dakota), Inc.   **(1)**
6201 81st Ave Nw, Stanley, ND 58784
Tel.: (701) 628-1635
Web Site: http://www.eogresources.com
Natural Gas Extraction Services
N.A.I.C.S.: 211130

EOM PHARMACEUTICAL HOLDINGS, INC.
136 Summit Ave Ste 100, Montvale, NJ 07645
Tel.: (201) 351-0605   DE
Web Site:
  https://www.eompharma.com
Year Founded: 1987
IMUC—(OTCIQ)
Sales Range: Less than $1 Million
Emp.: 7
Holding Company; Pharmaceuticals Researcher, Developer & Mfr
N.A.I.C.S.: 551112
David E. Fractor *(CFO)*
Gary S. Titus *(Chm & Sec)*
Anthony J. Gringeri *(Pres & CEO)*
Steven J. Swanson *(Sr VP-Res)*

Subsidiaries:

EOM Pharmaceuticals, Inc.   **(1)**
136 Summit Ave Ste 100, Montvale, NJ 07645
Tel.: (201) 351-0605
Web Site: https://www.eompharma.com
Pharmaceutical Developer & Mfr
N.A.I.C.S.: 325412

EP3OIL INC
2713 Charleston Dr, Plant City, FL 33563

Tel.: (702) 480-3215   DE
Web Site: https://ep3oil.com
HIHI—(OTCIQ)
Real Estate Manangement Services
N.A.I.C.S.: 531390
Glenn Klinker *(COO)*
Alverico Acencio *(VP)*

EPAM SYSTEMS, INC.

41 University Dr Ste 202, Newtown,
PA 18940
Tel.: (267) 759-9000   DE
Web Site: https://www.epam.com
Year Founded: 1993
EPAM—(NYSE)
Rev.: $4,690,540,000
Assets: $4,352,365,000
Liabilities: $880,895,000
Net Worth: $3,471,470,000
Earnings: $417,083,000
Emp.: 53,150
Fiscal Year-end: 12/31/23
Software Development, E-Commerce
& Content Services
N.A.I.C.S.: 513210
Arkadiy Dobkin *(Co-Founder, Chm,
Pres & CEO)*
Elaina Shekhter *(CMO, Sr VP &
Head-Strategy)*
Leo Lozner *(Co-Founder)*
Sam Rehman *(Chief Information Se-
curity Officer & Sr VP)*
Victor Dvorkin *(Sr VP & Head-
Delivery-Global)*
Sergey Yezhkov *(Sr VP & Co-Head-
Bus-Global)*
Jason Peterson *(CFO, Treas & Sr
VP)*
Boris Shnayder *(Sr VP & Co-Head-
Bus-Global)*
Yuriy Goliyad *(Sr VP & Head-Global
Ops)*
Lawrence F. Solomon *(Chief People
Officer & Sr VP)*
Philip Storm *(Chief Compliance Offi-
cer & Sr VP)*

Subsidiaries:

Continuum Innovation LLC   (1)
21 Drydock Ave 410 W, Boston, MA 02210
Tel.: (617) 969-5400
Graphic Designing Services
N.A.I.C.S.: 541430

Continuum LLC   (1)
21 Drydock Ave 410 W, Boston, MA 02210
Tel.: (617) 969-5400
Web Site:
   https://www.continuuminnovation.com
Computer & Computer Peripheral Equip-
ment & Software Merchant Whslr
N.A.I.C.S.: 423430
Gianfranco Zaccai *(Founder)*

Continuum SRL   (1)
Via San Bernardo 137/D, Grosseto, Gavor-
rano, Italy
Tel.: (39) 0249541500
Graphic Designing Services
N.A.I.C.S.: 541430
Roberta Bianco *(Mng Dir-Milan)*

EPAM Consulting BV   (1)
Delftechpark 37j, 2628 XJ, Delft, Nether-
lands
Tel.: (31) 202416134
Digital Innovation Software Services
N.A.I.C.S.: 423430

EPAM Sistemos   (1)
Seimyniskiu Str 19 Block C 6 floor, 09312,
Vilnius, Lithuania
Tel.: (370) 852392300
Engineerig & It Consulting Services
N.A.I.C.S.: 541512

EPAM Solutions, LLC   (1)
17A Volodymyra Monomaha Street, 49000,
Dnipropetrovsk, Ukraine
Tel.: (380) 567905651
Custom Computer Programming Services
N.A.I.C.S.: 541511

EPAM Systems (Czech Republic)
s.r.o.   (1)
City Tower Building Hvezdova 2b, Prague,
1, Czech Republic
Tel.: (420) 228882823
Custom Computer Programming Services
N.A.I.C.S.: 541511

EPAM Systems (Hong Kong)
Limited   (1)
198 Wellington Street, 26F&17F The Wel-
lington Tower, Hong Kong, China (Hong
Kong)
Tel.: (852) 58086018
Custom Computer Programming Services
N.A.I.C.S.: 541511

EPAM Systems (Poland) sp. z
o.o.   (1)
Opolska str 114 31-323, 31-323, Krakow,
Poland
Tel.: (48) 128811005
Software Development Services
N.A.I.C.S.: 513210

EPAM Systems (Switzerland)
GmbH   (1)
Boulevard Lilienthal 2 Glattpark, 8152,
Opfikon, Switzerland
Tel.: (41) 435002149
Emp.: 200
Software Development Services
N.A.I.C.S.: 513210

EPAM Systems Armenia   (1)
15 Khorenatsi Street Elite Plaza Business
Center, Elite Plaza Business Center 14th
floor, Yerevan, 0010, Armenia
Tel.: (374) 60830065
Engineerig & It Consulting Services
N.A.I.C.S.: 541512

EPAM Systems Bulgaria EOOD   (1)
69 Bulgaria Blvd Tower B fl 10-11, 1404,
Sofia, Bulgaria
Tel.: (359) 70020273
Custom Computer Programming Services
N.A.I.C.S.: 541511

EPAM Systems Canada, Ltd.   (1)
5200 Yonge Street, North York, M2N 5P6,
ON, Canada
Tel.: (647) 931-6912
Web Site: https://www.thoughtcorp.com
Sales Range: $10-24.9 Million
Emp.: 150
Software Development Services
N.A.I.C.S.: 513210

EPAM Systems GmbH   (1)
Messeturm Friedrich-Ebert-Anlage 49,
60308, Frankfurt am Main, Germany
Tel.: (49) 6931019090
Web Site: https://www.epam.de
Software Publisher
N.A.I.C.S.: 513210

EPAM Systems Japan G.K.   (1)
Kamiyacho Trust Tower Wework 23F 4-1-1
Toranomon, Minato-ku, Tokyo, 105-6923,
Japan
Tel.: (81) 368809198
Information Technology Consulting Services
N.A.I.C.S.: 541519

EPAM Systems Kft   (1)
Corvin Technology Park - CORVIN 5 Bokay
Janos street 44-46, H-1083, Budapest,
Hungary
Tel.: (36) 13277400
Web Site: https://careers.epam.hu
Emp.: 1,400
Software Publisher
N.A.I.C.S.: 513210

EPAM Systems LLC   (1)
15 Khorenatsi Street Elite Plaza Business
Center, Yerevan, 0010, Armenia
Tel.: (374) 60830065
Software Development Services
N.A.I.C.S.: 513210

EPAM Systems Ltd.   (1)
40 Bank Street Level 29, London, EC2M
4YF, United Kingdom
Tel.: (44) 2035140027
Web Site: https://www.epam.com
Software Publisher
N.A.I.C.S.: 513210

EPAM Systems Netherlands B.V.   (1)
Mercuriusplein 1, Evert van de Beekstraat
104, 2132 HA, Hoofddorp, Netherlands
Tel.: (31) 207991500
Custom Computer Programming Services
N.A.I.C.S.: 541511

EPAM Systems Nordic AB   (1)
Lilla Nygatan 2, 411 09, Gothenburg, Swe-
den
Tel.: (46) 31 361 3457
Web Site: http://www.epam.com
Emp.: 26
Software Development Services
N.A.I.C.S.: 513210

EPAM Systems PLLC   (1)
206 Moskovskaya Street, 224023, Brest,
Belarus
Tel.: (375) 173890100
Custom Computer Programming Services
N.A.I.C.S.: 541511

EPAM Systems Portugal, Unipessoal
Lda.   (1)
Rua Duque de Loule 110, 1050-093, Lis-
bon, Portugal
Tel.: (351) 300600016
Information Technology Services
N.A.I.C.S.: 541511

Emakina AB   (1)
Kungsgatan 50, 111 35, Stockholm, Swe-
den
Tel.: (46) 1785048
Software Development Services
N.A.I.C.S.: 541511

Emakina.CH LABEL.ch S.A.   (1)
13 Rue le Royer, 1227, Geneva, Switzer-
land
Tel.: (41) 223426030
Software Development Services
N.A.I.C.S.: 541511

Essentia Advisory Partners, LLC   (1)
1001 Louisiana St Ste 2500, Houston, TX
77002
Tel.: (713) 588-1713
Web Site: https://www.essentiaap.com
Agricultural Commodity Consulting Services
N.A.I.C.S.: 541690

Great Fridays Inc.   (1)
154 Grand St, New York, NY 10013
Tel.: (212) 300-6492
Custom Computer Programming Services
N.A.I.C.S.: 541511

Great Fridays Limited   (1)
40 Bank Street Level 29, 3rd Floor, London,
E14 5DS, United Kingdom
Tel.: (44) 2036514260
Web Site: https://www.greatfridays.com
Software Development Services
N.A.I.C.S.: 513210
Matt Farrar *(Founder)*

LLC IT-PARK UNIVERSITY   (1)
Makhtumkuli Street 1A, Tashkent, Uzbeki-
stan
Tel.: (998) 555039999
Web Site: https://itpu.uz
Information Technology Services
N.A.I.C.S.: 541519

Naya P.A.I.Technologies Ltd.   (1)
71 Hanadiv St, Herzliya Pituach, Israel
Tel.: (972) 97465005
Web Site: http://www.naya-tech.co.il
Software Development Services
N.A.I.C.S.: 513210

Ricston Limited   (1)
33 Triq G F Agius De Soldanis, BKR 4850,
Birkirkara, Malta
Tel.: (356) 21334457
Web Site: https://www.ricston.com
Software Development Services
N.A.I.C.S.: 541511
Peter Delia *(Dir-Svcs)*
Anastasiia Linnas *(Mktg Mgr)*
Juergen Dobler *(Project Mgr)*
Erika Quinn *(Mgr-HR)*

Ricston UK Limited   (1)
03-102 131 Finsbury Pavement, London,
EC2A 1NT, United Kingdom
Tel.: (44) 2071935107
Software Development Services
N.A.I.C.S.: 541511

Shanghai EPAM Systems Co.,
Ltd.   (1)
Building 5-3F 570 Yongjia Rd, Xuhui Dis-
trict, Shanghai, 200000, China
Tel.: (86) 53080606
Software Development Services
N.A.I.C.S.: 513210

TOO Plus Micro Kazakhstan LP   (1)
8 Auezova Street Office B, Nur-Sultan,
010000, Kazakhstan
Tel.: (7) 172475970
Web Site: http://www.epam.com
Software Developement
N.A.I.C.S.: 513210

Think Limited   (1)
2 Finsbury Avenue 5th Fl, London, EC2M
2PG, United Kingdom
Tel.: (44) 2075046000
Web Site: https://www.wearethink.com
Digital Marketing Services
N.A.I.C.S.: 541613

WhiteHat Ltd.   (1)
Tel Aviv-Yafo Russlan St 1, Tel Aviv, Israel
Tel.: (972) 37431830
Web Site: https://www.white-hat.co.il
Cyber Security System Services
N.A.I.C.S.: 561621

test IO GmbH   (1)
Kurfurstendamm 194, 10707, Berlin, Ger-
many
Tel.: (49) 3091734958
Web Site: https://test.io
Information Technology Services
N.A.I.C.S.: 541511

test IO, Inc.   (1)
1111 Broadway Fl 3, Oakland, CA 94607
Tel.: (415) 921-9891
Web Site: https://www.test.io
Information Technology Services
N.A.I.C.S.: 541511
D. Alexander *(Head-Design)*
L. Alexander *(Product Mgr)*
M. Alexandra *(Mgr-Customer Success)*
K. Matt *(Acct Mgr)*

EPICQUEST EDUCATION GROUP INTERNATIONAL LIMITED

1209 N University Blvd, Middletown,
OH 45042
Tel.: (513) 835-5394   VG
Web Site: http://www.eei-global.net
Year Founded: 2017
EEIQ—(NASDAQ)
Rev.: $5,712,480
Assets: $19,209,136
Liabilities: $8,275,426
Net Worth: $10,933,710
Earnings: ($6,762,704)
Emp.: 38
Fiscal Year-end: 09/30/23
Holding Company
N.A.I.C.S.: 551112

EPIPHANY TECHNOLOGY ACQUISITION CORP.

533 Airport Blvd Ste 400, Burlingame,
CA 94010
Tel.: (619) 736-6855   DE
Web Site:
   http://www.epiphanytechacquisi
tion.com
Year Founded: 2020
EPHY—(NASDAQ)
Rev.: $8,399,839
Assets: $403,292,284
Liabilities: $428,208,293
Net Worth: ($24,916,009)
Earnings: $7,207,291
Emp.: 3
Fiscal Year-end: 12/31/21
Investment Services
N.A.I.C.S.: 523999
Arthur Coviello *(Chm)*
Peter Bell *(CEO & CFO)*
Paul F. Deninger *(Vice Chm)*

EPLUS INC.

EPLUS INC.

ePlus Inc.—(Continued)

13595 Dulles Technology Dr, Herndon, VA 20171-3413
Tel.: (703) 984-8400   DE
Web Site: https://www.eplus.com
Year Founded: 1990
PLUS—(NASDAQ)
Rev.: $1,821,019,000
Assets: $1,166,203,000
Liabilities: $505,465,000
Net Worth: $660,738,000
Earnings: $105,600,000
Emp.: 1,577
Fiscal Year-end: 03/31/22
Other Computer Related Services
N.A.I.C.S.: 541519
Mark P. Marron (Pres & CEO)
Darren S. Raiguel (COO)
Kleyton L. Parkhurst (Asst Sec & Sr VP-Corporate Development)
Kenneth G. Farber (Pres-ePlus Software LLC)
Elaine D. Marion (CFO)
Erica S. Stoecker (Chief Compliance Officer, Sec & Gen Counsel)
Dan Farrell (Sr VP-Svcs)
Chad Fredrick (Pres-ePlus Group)
Doug King (CIO)
Dawn Kerwick (VP-Marketing)
Andrew Norton (Pres-ePlus Govt)
C. Thomas Faulders III (Chm)

Subsidiaries:

Future Com Ltd.   (1)
807 Forest Ridge Dr Ste 105, Bedford, TX 76022
Tel.: (817) 510-1100
Web Site: http://www.myfuturecom.com
Rev.: $28,397,159
Emp.: 50
Security & Network Management Solutions
N.A.I.C.S.: 541512
Kevin Dutton (Founder)
Mark Williamson (CFO & VP-Ops)
Doug Hollenshead (Pres & CEO)

Subsidiary (Domestic):

Future Com Distributors Inc.   (2)
807 Forest Rdg Dr Ste105, Bedford, TX 76022
Tel.: (817) 510-1170
Web Site: http://www.futurecom.com
Rev.: $280,000
Emp.: 30
Software, Business & Non-Game
N.A.I.C.S.: 541512

Granite Business Solutions, Inc.   (1)
233 Technology Way Ste A4, Rocklin, CA 95765
Tel.: (916) 577-2180
Web Site: http://www.go-evolve.com
Sales Range: $1-9.9 Million
Emp.: 10
Computer & Computer Peripheral Equipment & Software Merchant Whslr
N.A.I.C.S.: 423430

Innovative Technology Systems & Solutions Inc.   (1)
2809 S Lynnhaven Rd, Virginia Beach, VA 23452
Tel.: (757) 418-6583
Web Site: http://www.abstechnology.com
Information Technology Consulting Services
N.A.I.C.S.: 541512
Hunter Dorroh (CEO)
Amy Knower (VP-Sls)
Bryan Campbell (CFO)

Interchange Technologies, Inc.   (1)
127 Gaither Dr Ste 127-B, Mount Laurel, NJ 08054
Tel.: (856) 780-1100
Web Site: http://www.iti-go.com
Information Technology Services
N.A.I.C.S.: 541519

ePlus   (1)
1 Penn Plz Ste 4600, New York, NY 10119
Tel.: (212) 401-5071
Web Site: http://www.eplus.com
Sales Range: $100-124.9 Million
Emp.: 25

Supply Chain Management Solutions Including Strategic Sourcing, Automated Procurement & Online Asset Management
N.A.I.C.S.: 532420

ePlus Group, inc.   (1)
13595 Dulles Technology Dr, Herndon, VA 20171
Tel.: (703) 984-8400
Emp.: 250
Computer Hardware Equipment Leasing Services
N.A.I.C.S.: 532420
Chad Fredrick (Pres)
Andrew Norton (Pres)
Dan Farrell (Sr VP)
Darren Raiguel (COO)
Dawn Kerwick (VP)
Doug King (CIO)
Elaine Marion (CFO)
Erica Stoecker (Chief Compliance Officer)
Kenneth Farber (Pres)
Kleyton Parkhurst (Sr VP)
Mark Marron (Pres)

ePlus Technology, Inc   (1)
13595 Dulles Technology Dr, Herndon, VA 20171-3413
Tel.: (703) 984-8400
Emp.: 250
Computer Programming Services
N.A.I.C.S.: 541511
Darren S. Raiguel (Pres)
Andrew Norton (Pres)
Chad Fredrick (Pres)
Dan Farrell (Sr VP)
Dawn Kerwick (VP)
Doug King (CIO)
Elaine Marion (CFO)
Erica Stoecker (Chief Compliance Officer)
Kenneth Farber (Pres)
Mark Marron (Pres)

Subsidiary (Non-US):

IGXGlobal UK, Limited   (2)
1 Fore Street Avenue, London, EC2Y 9DT, United Kingdom
Tel.: (44) 2038907387
Web Site: https://igxglobal.com
Emp.: 50
Information Technology Support Services
N.A.I.C.S.: 541512
David Robinson (Mng Dir)

Subsidiary (Domestic):

SLAIT Consulting, LLC   (2)
100 Landmark Sq, Virginia Beach, VA 23452
Tel.: (757) 313-6500
Web Site: http://www.slaitconsulting.com
Information Technology Consulting Services
N.A.I.C.S.: 541512

EPR PROPERTIES

909 Walnut St Ste 200, Kansas City, MO 64106
Tel.: (816) 472-1700   MD
Web Site: https://www.eprkc.com
Year Founded: 1997
EPR—(NYSE)
Rev.: $705,668,000
Assets: $5,700,885,000
Liabilities: $3,246,730,000
Net Worth: $2,454,155,000
Earnings: $148,901,000
Emp.: 55
Fiscal Year-end: 12/31/23
Real Estate Investment Trust
N.A.I.C.S.: 523999
Gregory K. Silvers (Chm, Pres & CEO)
Peter C. Brown (Founder)
Mark Alan Peterson (CFO, Treas & Exec VP)
Peter C. Brown (Bd of Trustees, Executives)
Brian Moriarty (VP-Corp Comm)
Tom Hudak (VP-Investments)
Robert L. Harris II (Founder)
Rebecca Beal (VP & Assoc Gen Counsel)
April Jenkins (VP & Controller)

Paul Turvey (Gen Counsel, Sec & Sr VP)
Aaron Linn (VP-Underwriting & Analysis)
Greg Zimmerman (Chief Investment Officer & Exec VP)
Mike Rusche (VP-Information Sys)
Gwen Johnson (Sr VP)
Derek Werner (VP)

Subsidiaries:

ECE I, LLC   (1)
909 Walnut Ste 200, Kansas City, MO 64106
Tel.: (816) 472-1700
Real Estate Related Services
N.A.I.C.S.: 531390

EPT Waterparks, Inc.   (1)
909 Walnut St Ste 200, Kansas City, MO 64106-2003
Tel.: (816) 472-1700
Emp.: 54
Nonresidential Building Leasing Services
N.A.I.C.S.: 531120

EPSILON ENERGY LTD.

500 Dallas St Ste 1250, Houston, TX 77002
Tel.: (281) 670-0002   AB
Web Site:
https://www.epsilonenergyltd.com
Year Founded: 2005
EPSN—(NASDAQ)
Rev.: $69,962,709
Assets: $123,862,243
Liabilities: $19,617,038
Net Worth: $104,245,205
Earnings: $35,354,679
Emp.: 9
Fiscal Year-end: 12/31/22
Crude Petroleum Extraction Services
N.A.I.C.S.: 211120
Henry N. Clanton (COO)
Shannon Lemke (VP-Exploration)
Jason Stabell (CEO)
Andrew Williamson (CFO)

Subsidiaries:

Epsilon Energy USA Inc.   (1)
Tel.: (281) 670-0002
Sales Range: $50-74.9 Million
Oil & Gas Exploration Services
N.A.I.C.S.: 211120

EQ HEALTH ACQUISITION CORP.

4611 Bee Cave Rd Ste 106, Austin, TX 78746
Tel.: (512) 329-6977   DE
Year Founded: 2020
EQHAU—(NYSE)
Rev.: $10,173,533
Assets: $220,392,326
Liabilities: $238,778,198
Net Worth: ($18,385,872)
Earnings: $6,955,943
Fiscal Year-end: 12/31/21
Investment Services
N.A.I.C.S.: 523999
Andrew Beckman (Vice Chm)
Lewis N. Little Jr. (Chm)

EQ LABS, INC.

1016 Baronet Dr, Las Vegas, NV 89138
Tel.: (702) 806-5943   FL
Web Site: http://www.eqlabs.io
EQLB—(OTCIQ)
Software Development Services
N.A.I.C.S.: 541511
Maurice W. Owens (Founder, Chm, Pres & CEO)

EQM TECHNOLOGIES & ENERGY, INC.

1800 Carillon Blvd, Cincinnati, OH 45240

Tel.: (513) 825-7500
Web Site: https://www.eqm.com
Year Founded: 1990
EQTE—(OTCIQ)
Sales Range: $75-99.9 Million
Emp.: 130
Offices of Other Holding Companies
N.A.I.C.S.: 551112
Jonny Colin (CEO)
Jack S. Greber (Sr VP-EPA Federal Programs & Bus Dev)

Subsidiaries:

Beacon Energy Corporation   (1)
186 North Ave E, Cranford, NJ 07016
Tel.: (908) 497-9990
Sales Range: $75-99.9 Million
Biofuel Developer & Mfr
N.A.I.C.S.: 457210

EQT CORPORATION

625 Liberty Ave Ste 1700, Pittsburgh, PA 15222
Tel.: (412) 553-5700   PA
Web Site: https://www.eqt.com
Year Founded: 1888
EQT—(NYSE)
Rev.: $6,908,923,000
Assets: $25,285,098,000
Liabilities: $10,504,281,000
Net Worth: $14,780,817,000
Earnings: $1,735,232,000
Emp.: 881
Fiscal Year-end: 12/31/23
Energy Management & Infrastructure Services; Natural Gas Distr
N.A.I.C.S.: 221210
Diana M. Charletta (Executives)
Toby Z. Rice (Pres & CEO)
William E. Jordan (Gen Counsel, Sec & Exec VP)
Todd M. James (Chief Acctg Officer)
Tony Duran (CIO)
Lesley Evancho (Chief HR Officer)
Andrew Breese (Dir-IR)
Bridget McNie (Dir-Communications)
Jeremy Knop (CFO & Exec VP-Corp Dev)
Cameron Horwitz (Mng Dir-IR & Strategy)

Subsidiaries:

EQT Energy, LLC   (1)
625 Liberty Ave Ste 1700, Pittsburgh, PA 15222
Tel.: (412) 553-5700
Web Site: http://www.eqt.com
Natural Gas Exploration & Production
N.A.I.C.S.: 221210

EQT Production Company   (1)
625 Liberty Ave Ste 1700, Pittsburgh, PA 15222
Tel.: (412) 553-5700
Emp.: 400
Natural Gas Extraction Services
N.A.I.C.S.: 211120

EQT RE, LLC   (1)
625 Liberty Ave Ste 1700, Pittsburgh, PA 15222
Tel.: (412) 553-5700
Holding Company
N.A.I.C.S.: 551112

Equitable Energy, LLC   (1)
625 Liberty Ave Ste 1700, Pittsburgh, PA 15222
Tel.: (412) 553-5700
Sales Range: $50-74.9 Million
Emp.: 1,890
Gas Marketing Services
N.A.I.C.S.: 213112

Equitrans Midstream Corporation   (1)
2200 Energy Dr, Canonsburg, PA 15317
Tel.: (724) 271-7600
Web Site:
https://www.equitransmidstream.com
Rev.: $1,393,929,000
Assets: $11,709,426,000
Liabilities: $10,203,151,000
Net Worth: $1,506,275,000

Earnings: $386,717,000
Emp.: 773
Fiscal Year-end: 12/31/2023
Natural Gas Pipeline Transportation Services
N.A.I.C.S.: 486210
Diana M. Charletta *(Pres & CEO)*
Kirk Oliver *(CFO & Sr VP)*
Nate Tetlow *(VP-Corp Dev & IR)*
Stephen M. Moore *(Gen Counsel & Sr VP)*

Subsidiary (Domestic):

EQGP Holdings, LP **(2)**
625 Liberty Ave Ste 2000, Pittsburgh, PA 15222
Tel.: (412) 533-5700
Rev.: $834,096,000
Assets: $3,549,625,000
Liabilities: $1,401,404,000
Net Worth: $2,148,221,000
Earnings: $261,993,000
Fiscal Year-end: 12/31/2017
Holding Company; Oil & Gas Operations
N.A.I.C.S.: 551112
Diana M. Charletta *(Gen Partner)*

EQM Midstream Partners, LP **(2)**
2200 Energy Dr, Canonsburg, PA 15317 **(100%)**
Tel.: (724) 271-7600
Web Site: http://www.eqm-
midstreampartners.com
Assets: $11,815,019,000
Liabilities: $6,156,257,000
Net Worth: $5,658,762,000
Earnings: $183,373,000
Fiscal Year-end: 12/31/2019
Oil & Gas Exploration
N.A.I.C.S.: 211120
Diana M. Charletta *(Gen Partner)*

Subsidiary (Domestic):

Equitrans, LP **(3)**
2200 Energy Dr, Canonsburg, PA 15317 **(99%)**
Tel.: (412) 553-5700
Web Site: https://equitransproject.com
Sales Range: $150-199.9 Million
Emp.: 50
Stores & Sells Natural Gas Whslr
N.A.I.C.S.: 486210

Galderma Holding S.A. **(1)**
Avenue de Gratta Paille 2, 1018, Lausanne, Switzerland
Tel.: (41) 21 642 7800
Web Site: http://www.galderma.com
Holding Company; Skin Health Products Mfr & Whslr
N.A.I.C.S.: 551112
Janusz Czernielewski *(VP-Medical Affairs)*
Cecile Dussart *(VP-Mfg & Technical Ops)*
Alain Jacot *(VP-Scientific Div)*
Alain Kirsch *(VP-HR)*
Christian Matton *(Gen Counsel & VP)*
Peter Nicholson *(VP-Bus Dev & Strategy)*
Stuart Raetzman *(CEO)*
Christian Marcoux *(Chief Comm Officer)*
Shannon Iwaniuk *(Dir-Global Comm)*

Subsidiary (US):

ALASTIN Skincare, Inc **(2)**
3129 Tiger Run Ct Ste 109, Carlsbad, CA 92010
Web Site: http://www.alastin.com
Skin Care Product Mfr
N.A.I.C.S.: 325620
Cam L. Garner *(Founder)*
Diane S. Goostree *(Pres & CEO)*
Amber Edwards *(Chief Comml Officer)*
Alan Widgerow *(Chief Medical Officer)*
Tom Christenson *(CFO)*
Wael Albader *(VP-Ops)*

Subsidiary (Domestic):

Galderma Pharma S.A. **(2)**
Avenue de Gratta Paille 2, 1018, Lausanne, Switzerland
Tel.: (41) 21 642 78 00
Web Site: http://www.galderma.com
Holding Company; Dermatology Products Developer, Mfr & Marketer
N.A.I.C.S.: 551112

Subsidiary (Non-US):

Galderma Brasil Ltda. **(3)**

Edifico E Tower Ruafunchal 418 6 Andar, 04551-060, Sao Paulo, SP, Brazil
Tel.: (55) 1135246300
Web Site: http://www.galderma.com.br
Sales Range: $25-49.9 Million
Emp.: 50
Dermatology Products Sales & Marketing
N.A.I.C.S.: 424210

Galderma Canada, Inc. **(3)**
55 Commerce Valley Dr W 400, Thornhill, L3T 7V9, ON, Canada
Tel.: (905) 762-2500
Web Site: http://www.galderma.com
Sales Range: $25-49.9 Million
Emp.: 25
Dermatology Product Mfr
N.A.I.C.S.: 325412

Galderma International SAS **(3)**
Tour Europlaza La Defense 4 20 Avenue Andre Prothin, La Defense, 92927, Paris, Cedex, France
Tel.: (33) 158864545
Web Site: http://www.galderma.com
Sales Range: $125-149.9 Million
Emp.: 300
Dermatology Products Sales & Marketing
N.A.I.C.S.: 424210

Subsidiary (US):

Galderma Laboratories, L.P. **(3)**
14501 N Fwy, Fort Worth, TX 76177-3304
Tel.: (817) 961-5000
Web Site: http://www.galdermausa.com
Sales Range: $50-74.9 Million
Emp.: 250
Dermatology Product Mfr
N.A.I.C.S.: 325412
Alisa Lask *(VP-Aesthetic & Gen Mgr-Aesthetic & Corrective Bus unit)*
Kelly Huang *(VP & Gen Mgr-Aesthetic & Corrective Bus)*
Chris Chapman *(VP/Gen Mgr-Prescription Bus)*
Miles D. Harrison *(VP-North America)*

Subsidiary (Non-US):

Galderma Laboratorium GmbH **(3)**
Toulouser Allee 23a, 40211, Dusseldorf, Germany
Tel.: (49) 2115860100
Web Site: http://www.galderma.de
Sales Range: $50-74.9 Million
Emp.: 200
Dermatology Product Mfr
N.A.I.C.S.: 325412
Marion Bock *(Mng Dir, Head-DACH & Gen Mgr)*

Galderma Production Canada Inc. **(3)**
19400 Transcanada Highway, Baie-d'Urfe, H9X 3S4, QC, Canada
Tel.: (514) 457-3366
Web Site: http://www.galderma.com
Sales Range: $50-74.9 Million
Emp.: 220
Dermatology Product Mfr
N.A.I.C.S.: 325412

Laboratoires Galderma SAS **(3)**
Zone Industrielle Touviere, 74540, Alby-sur-Cheran, France
Tel.: (33) 158864545
Sales Range: $50-74.9 Million
Emp.: 200
Dermatology Product Mfr
N.A.I.C.S.: 325412

Q-Med AB **(3)**
Seminariegatan 21, 752 28, Uppsala, 75228, Sweden
Tel.: (46) 184749000
Web Site: http://www.q-med.com
Sales Range: $200-249.9 Million
Emp.: 636
Biotechnology & Medical Devices
N.A.I.C.S.: 339112

Subsidiary (Non-US):

Q-Med (Sweden) Australia Pty Ltd. **(4)**
37 Belmore Street, Surry Hills, 2010, Sydney, NSW, Australia
Tel.: (61) 292817727

Web Site:
http://www.revitaliseyourskin.com.au
Sales Range: $25-49.9 Million
Emp.: 20
Pharmaceutical Preparation Mfr
N.A.I.C.S.: 325412

Q-Med Brasil Comercio e Importacao de Produtos Medicos Ltda **(4)**
Rua Alexandre Dumas 2100 conjunto 22, Chacara Santo Antonio, 04717-004, Sao Paulo, SP, Brazil
Tel.: (55) 1151855589
Web Site: http://www.q-med.com
Sales Range: $50-74.9 Million
Emp.: 8
Medical Dental & Hospital Equipment & Supplies Whslr
N.A.I.C.S.: 423450

Q-Med ICT S.r.l. **(4)**
Via M Borsa 11, Codogno, 26845, Lodi, Italy
Tel.: (39) 0377436091
Web Site: http://www.q-med.com
Sales Range: $25-49.9 Million
Emp.: 50
Toilet Preparation Mfr
N.A.I.C.S.: 325620

Q-Med International Ltd **(4)**
39 Healthy Street East, Kodak House II Rm 2207-08 22nd, North Point, China (Hong Kong)
Tel.: (852) 25165002
Surgical & Medical Instrument Mfr
N.A.I.C.S.: 339112

Q-Med International Trading (Shanghai) Ltd **(4)**
Room 2017 No 1 Ji Long Road, Waigaoqiao Free Trade Zone, Shanghai, 200131, China
Tel.: (86) 1085321642
Web Site: http://www.q-med.com
Drugs & Druggists Sundries Whslr
N.A.I.C.S.: 424210

Q-Med Mexico S.A de C.V. **(4)**
Lglesia 2 Torre E Despacho 503, Colonia Tizapan San Angel, 1090, Mexico, Mexico
Tel.: (52) 5556168292
Web Site: http://www.q-med.com
Sales Range: $25-49.9 Million
Emp.: 18
Surgical Appliance & Supplies Mfr
N.A.I.C.S.: 339113

Q-Med Polska SP. Z.o.o **(4)**
Nowy Swiat 47, 00-042, Warsaw, Poland
Tel.: (48) 228929120
Web Site: http://www.q-med.com
Sales Range: $25-49.9 Million
Emp.: 15
Surgical & Medical Instrument Mfr
N.A.I.C.S.: 339112

Q-Med S.a.r.l. **(4)**
49 Rue de Lisbonne, 75008, Paris, France
Tel.: (33) 156434300
Web Site: http://www.q-med.com
Drugs & Druggists Sundries Whslr
N.A.I.C.S.: 424210

Q-Med Spain S.L. **(4)**
Agustin Foxa 29 Planta Baja, Modulo 1 C-Jose Echegaray 8, 28036, Madrid, Spain
Tel.: (34) 916369205
Web Site: http://www.q-med.com
Sales Range: $25-49.9 Million
Emp.: 30
Drugs & Druggists Sundries Whslr
N.A.I.C.S.: 424210

Rager Mountain Storage Company, LLC **(1)**
625 Liberty Ave Ste 1700, Pittsburgh, PA 15222
Tel.: (412) 395-3230
Web Site:
http://www.ragermtgasstorage.com
Natural Gas Distr
N.A.I.C.S.: 221210

EQUATOR BEVERAGE COMPANY
185 Hudson St 25 Fl, Jersey City, NJ 07302
Tel.: (929) 264-7944   NV

Web Site:
https://equatorbeverage.com
Year Founded: 2007
MOJO—(OTCQB)
Rev.: $1,821,492
Assets: $441,119
Liabilities: $295,252
Net Worth: $145,867
Earnings: ($238,836)
Emp.: 2
Fiscal Year-end: 12/31/22
Organic Beverage Distr
N.A.I.C.S.: 311411
Glenn Simpson *(Chm & CEO)*

EQUIFAX INC.
1550 Peachtree St NW, Atlanta, GA 30309
Tel.: (404) 885-8000   **GA**
Web Site: https://www.equifax.com
Year Founded: 1899
EFX—(NYSE)
Rev.: $5,265,200,000
Assets: $12,280,000,000
Liabilities: $7,727,600,000
Net Worth: $4,552,400,000
Earnings: $545,300,000
Emp.: 14,900
Fiscal Year-end: 12/31/23
Credit, Financial, Public Record & Information-Based Administrative Services
N.A.I.C.S.: 561450
Chad M. Borton *(Pres-Workforce Solutions & Exec VP)*
Cecilia H. Mao *(Chief Product Officer)*
John J. Kelley III *(Chief Legal Officer & Exec VP)*
Jamil Farshchi *(CIO, CTO, Chief Security Officer & Exec VP)*
Sunil Bindal *(Chief Corp Dev Officer & Exec VP)*
Carla J. Chaney *(Chief HR Officer)*
Julia A. Houston *(CMO, Chief Strategy Officer, Chief Strategy & Mktg Officer & Exec VP)*
Lisa M. Nelson *(Pres-Intl)*
Harald Schneider *(Chief Data Office & Chief Analytics Office)*

Subsidiaries:

Austin Consolidated Holdings, Inc. **(1)**
6333 N State Hwy 161 Ste 100, Irving, TX 75038
Tel.: (972) 756-8100
Sales Range: $25-49.9 Million
Emp.: 60
Credit Bureau Services
N.A.I.C.S.: 561450

Creditworks Australia Pty Ltd **(1)**
Level 13 316 Adelaide Street, Brisbane, 4000, QLD, Australia
Tel.: (61) 290376809
Web Site: https://www.creditworks.com.au
Credit Information Services
N.A.I.C.S.: 561450
Shardae Ros *(Officer-Client Svcs)*

DataX Ltd. **(1)**
7582 Las Vegas Blvd S Ste 693, Las Vegas, NV 89119
Web Site: https://www.dataxltd.com
Credit Reporting Bureau Services
N.A.I.C.S.: 561450

EDX Australia Pty Limited **(1)**
Level 15 100 Arthur Street, Sydney, 2060, NSW, Australia
Tel.: (61) 291195065
Web Site: https://www.edxppsr.com.au
Business Analytic Services
N.A.I.C.S.: 561110

Equifax Analytics Private Limited **(1)**
150 Old Airport Road Domlur Diamond District Tower C 4th Floor, Bengaluru, 560008, Karnataka, India
Tel.: (91) 8043577500
Web Site: https://www.equifax.in
Business Analytic Services

Equifax Inc.—(Continued)
N.A.I.C.S.: 561110

Equifax Australasia Group Services Pty Limited (1)
100 Arthur StreetLevel 15, North Sydney, 2060, NSW, Australia
Tel.: (61) 292787000
Business Analytic Services
N.A.I.C.S.: 561110

Equifax Australia Commercial Services and Solutions Pty Limited (1)
GPO Box 964, North Sydney, 2059, NSW, Australia
Tel.: (61) 138332
Business Analytic Services
N.A.I.C.S.: 561110

Equifax Australia Pty. Ltd. (1)
Level 15 100 Arthur Street, PO Box 964, North Sydney, 2059, NSW, Australia
Tel.: (61) 138332
Web Site: https://www.equifax.com.au
Emp.: 811
Holding Company
N.A.I.C.S.: 551112

Equifax Canadian Holdings Co. (1)
7171 Jean-Talon Street West, Anjou, H1M 3N2, QC, Canada
Tel.: (514) 493-2470
Holding Company
N.A.I.C.S.: 551112

Subsidiary (Domestic):

Acrofin Inc. (2)
7171 Jean-Talon Street East, Anjou, H1M 3N2, QC, Canada (100%)
Tel.: (514) 493-2470
Web Site: http://www.equifax.ca
Credit & Information Reporting Services
N.A.I.C.S.: 522390

Subsidiary (Domestic):

Equifax Canada Co. (3)
7171 Jean-Talon Rue E, Anjou, H1M 3N2, QC, Canada
Tel.: (514) 493-2470
Web Site: https://www.consumer.equifax.ca
Credit Bureau Services
N.A.I.C.S.: 561450
Lisa Nelson (Pres)

Equifax Commercial Services Ltd. (1)
IDA Business and Technology Park Rosslare Rd, Drinaugh, Wexford, Ireland (100%)
Tel.: (353) 8663495191
Web Site: https://www.equifax.co.uk
Sales Range: $100-124.9 Million
Emp.: 250
Credit Bureau Services
N.A.I.C.S.: 561450

Equifax Information Services LLC (1)
1550 Peachtree St NW, Atlanta, GA 30309-2402 (100%)
Tel.: (404) 885-8000
Sales Range: $25-49.9 Million
Emp.: 50
Credit Reports, Collection Services & Credit Card Promotional Services
N.A.I.C.S.: 561450

Subsidiary (Domestic):

Equifax Special Services LLC (2)
1550 Peachtree St NW, Atlanta, GA 30309
Tel.: (404) 885-8300
Emp.: 200
Credit Report & Credit Information Services
N.A.I.C.S.: 561450

Knowledge Works, Inc. (2)
5750 Old Orchard Rd Ste 300, Skokie, IL 60077
Web Site: http://www.paynet.com
Administrative Management & General Management Consulting Services
N.A.I.C.S.: 541611
William Phelan (Founder, Sr VP & Gen Mgr)

Subsidiary (Domestic):

Ansonia Credit Data, Inc. (3)

2108 Caton Way SW, Olympia, WA 98502-1105
Tel.: (360) 612-9506
Web Site: http://www.ansoniacreditdata.com
Business Support Services
N.A.I.C.S.: 561499
Tony Kinninger (Pres)

Subsidiary (Non-US):

PayNet, Inc. (3)
2425 Matheson Blvd East 8th Floor, Mississauga, L4W 5K4, ON, Canada
Web Site: http://www.paynet.ca
Commercial Lending & Finance Services
N.A.I.C.S.: 522299

Equifax Information Services of Puerto Rico, Inc. (1)
PO Box 105788, Atlanta, GA 30348-5788
Tel.: (404) 885-8000
Credit Report & Credit Information Services
N.A.I.C.S.: 561450

Subsidiary (Non-US):

Equifax Americas B.V. (1)
Keplerstraat 34, Badhoevedorp, 1171 CD, Netherlands
Tel.: (31) 203055700
Credit Bureau Services
N.A.I.C.S.: 561450

Subsidiary (Domestic):

Equifax Workforce Solutions (2)
11432 Lackland, Saint Louis, MO 63146
Tel.: (314) 214-7000
Web Site: https://www.equifax.com
Sales Range: $250-299.9 Million
Human Resources & Payroll Services
N.A.I.C.S.: 541512

Subsidiary (Domestic):

Equifax Workforce Solutions (3)
3400 Waterview Pkwy, Richardson, TX 75080
Tel.: (972) 764-1000
Web Site: http://www.talx.com
Sales Range: $10-24.9 Million
Emp.: 15
Interactive Telecommunications Services
N.A.I.C.S.: 518210

Equifax Workforce Solutions (3)
11432 Bowling Green Dr, Saint Louis, MO 63146
Tel.: (314) 997-2100
Web Site: http://ucm.talx.com
Credit Reporting Services
N.A.I.C.S.: 522390

Equifax Workforce Solutions (3)
1583 Savannah Hwy, Charleston, SC 29407
Tel.: (843) 556-5565
Web Site: http://www.ethority.com
Strategic Information Software Solution Provider
N.A.I.C.S.: 541511

Subsidiary (Domestic):

TALX Corporation (2)
1850 Borman Ct, Saint Louis, MO 63146
Tel.: (314) 214-7000
Credit Bureau Services
N.A.I.C.S.: 561450

Equifax Ltd. (1)
Capital House 25 Chapel Street, London, NW1 5DS, United Kingdom
Tel.: (44) 84 5603 3000
Web Site: http://www.equifax.co.uk
Sales Range: $200-249.9 Million
Emp.: 370
Credit Bureaus Services
N.A.I.C.S.: 561450
Patricio Remon (Pres-Europe)
Suzanne Brown (Officer-Fin)
Tony Banks (VP-Ops)
Johanna Edwards (VP-SIs)
Steve Reeve (Chief Compliance Officer)
Steve Taylor (Gen Mgr-Consumer Solutions-Global)
Paul Heywood (Chief Data & Analytics Officer)
Jayadeep Nair (CMO & Chief Product Officer)

Subsidiary (Domestic):

Equifax Secure UK Ltd. (2)
Capital House, London, NW1 5DS, United Kingdom
Tel.: (44) 2072983000
Web Site: http://www.equifax.co.uk
Emp.: 75
Credit Report & Credit Information Services
N.A.I.C.S.: 561450

TDX Group Limited (2)
8 Fletcher Gate, Nottingham, NG1 2FS, United Kingdom
Tel.: (44) 1159531200
Web Site: https://www.tdxgroup.com
Emp.: 500
Management Consulting Services
N.A.I.C.S.: 541611
Carlos Osorio (Dir-Debt Recovery)
Jonathan Staward (Head-Compliance)
Matt Wallis (Head-Solution Design)
Beth Whelan (Head-Debt Svcs Products)

Subsidiary (Non-US):

TDX Indigo Iberia S.L.U (3)
C/Velazquez 50-5 Planta, 28001, Madrid, Spain
Tel.: (34) 914462350
Web Site: https://www.tdxindigo.com
Debt Collection Services
N.A.I.C.S.: 561440

Equifax New Zealand Information Services and Solutions Limited (1)
Level 10 48 Shortland Street, Auckland, 1010, New Zealand
Tel.: (64) 800692733
Business Analytic Services
N.A.I.C.S.: 561110

Equifax Paraguay S.A. (1)
Chap Brizuela 650 esq, Office Corporate Building, Asuncion, Paraguay
Tel.: (595) 214399000
Web Site: https://soluciones.equifax.com.py
Data Analytic & Technology Services
N.A.I.C.S.: 518210
Hernan Pariso (Mng Dir)

Equifax Property Data & Analytics (1)
1624 Market St Ste 311, Denver, CO 80202
Tel.: (303) 893-8600
Web Site: http://www.equifax.com
Real Estate Property Valuation Services
N.A.I.C.S.: 531390

Equifax Spain Holdings S.L. (1)
Paseo Castellana 259 D Torre Esp, Madrid, 28046, Spain (100%)
Tel.: (34) 917687600
Web Site: http://www.equifax.es
Sales Range: $125-149.9 Million
Credit Bureau Services
N.A.I.C.S.: 561450

Subsidiary (Non-US):

EFX de Costa Rica, S.A. (2)
C 22 Bis Y 24 Paseo Colon, San Jose, Costa Rica
Tel.: (506) 22802818
Web Site: https://www.equifax.co.cr
Credit Report & Credit Information Services
N.A.I.C.S.: 561450

Equifax Uruguay S.A. (1)
Avda Luis A de Herrera 1248 World Trade Center Torre 3 Piso 7, Avenida Building Esc 232, Montevideo, 11324, Uruguay
Tel.: (598) 26281515
Web Site: https://www.equifax.uy
Credit Bureau Services
N.A.I.C.S.: 561450

Equifax do Brasil Holdings Ltda. (1)
Rua Teixeira da Silva 217, Sao Paulo, 04002-030, Brazil
Tel.: (55) 11301 66000
Emp.: 7
Holding Company
N.A.I.C.S.: 551112
Marcelo Simotti (Mgr)

Subsidiary (Domestic):

Equifax do Brasil Ltda. (2)
Rua Teixeira da Silva 217 8 andar, Sao Paulo, 04002-905, Brazil (100%)

Tel.: (55) 1130166300
Web Site: https://www.equifax.com
Credit Bureau Services
N.A.I.C.S.: 561450

Grupo Inffinix, S.A. de C.V. (1)
Jose Ma Castorena No 283-A Col Cuajimalpa, Mexico, 05000, Mexico
Tel.: (52) 5558131325
Business Analytic Services
N.A.I.C.S.: 561110

I-9 Advantage, LLC (1)
101 W Big Beaver Rd Ste 1452, Troy, MI 48084
Web Site: http://www.i9advantage.com
Software Development Services
N.A.I.C.S.: 513210

IXI Corporation (1)
7927 Jones Branch Dr Ste 400, McLean, VA 22102
Tel.: (703) 848-3800
Web Site: https://www.ixicorp.com
Sales Range: $25-49.9 Million
Emp.: 50
Credit Bureau Services
N.A.I.C.S.: 561450

Identity Rehab Corporation (1)
PO Box 297, Denver, CO 80201-0297
Tel.: (303) 820-3333
Web Site: https://www.idwatchdog.com
Theft Detection Services
N.A.I.C.S.: 561621
Jay B. Lewis (CFO)

Inversiones Equifax de Chile Ltda. (1)
Av. Isidora Goyenechea 2800 26th - 27th Fl, Santiago, Chile (100%)
Tel.: (56) 26315000
Web Site: https://www.soluciones.equifax.cl
Credit Reporting Services
N.A.I.C.S.: 522390

JLR, Inc. (1)
1981 McGill College Avenue Office 700, Montreal, H3A 2Y1, QC, Canada
Tel.: (514) 861-5134
Web Site: https://solutions.jlr.ca
Emp.: 50
Real Estate Services
N.A.I.C.S.: 531390

Kingsway Financial Assessments Pty Ltd (1)
Level 15 100 Arthur St, North Sydney, 2060, NSW, Australia
Tel.: (61) 292787200
Web Site: http://www.kingswayassessments.com.au
Business Analytic Services
N.A.I.C.S.: 561110

Kount Inc. (1)
917 Lusk St Ste 300, Boise, ID 83706
Tel.: (208) 489-3300
Web Site: http://www.kount.com
Sales Range: $25-49.9 Million
E-Commerce Software
N.A.I.C.S.: 513210
Jack Alton (Sr VP-SIs)
Jack Alton (Sr VP-SIs)
Donald Bush (VP-Mktg)
Bradley J. Wiskirchen (CEO)
Jim Gasaway (CTO)
Rich L. Stuppy (VP-Ops)
Kate Lenz (VP-HR)
Kelly Reynolds (VP-Client Success)
Lisa Dean (Sr VP-SIs)
Jason Glass (Chm)
Kody Kraus (CFO)
Tom War (VP-SIs-Worldwide)
Vikram Dhawan (VP-Product)

LawLogix Group, Inc. (1)
3003 N Central Ave #900, 85012, Phoenix, AZ
Tel.: (602) 357-4240
Web Site: http://www.lawlogix.com
Immigration Case Management Software Publisher
N.A.I.C.S.: 513210
John Fay (Pres)
Jesus Ancheta (VP-Ops)
Jennifer Harris (VP-Tech)
Ryan Kelly (Pres)

Mapcity.com Chile S.A. (1)

San Sebastian 2952 3 piso, Las Condes, Chile
Tel.: (56) 228295000
Web Site:
https://www.corporativo.mapcity.com
Location Analysis & Mapping Services
N.A.I.C.S.: 541370

Subsidiary (Non-US):

Mapcity Peru S.A.C. (2)
Av Calle Chinchon 1018 Piso 9, San Isidro, Lima, 15046, Peru
Tel.: (51) 17111130
Web Site: http://www.mapcity.pe
Location Analysis & Mapping Services
N.A.I.C.S.: 541370

Net Positive Business Analytics Private Limited (1)
A Wing 5th Floor Maruthi Infotech Centre Amar Jyothi Layout, Koramangala Inner Ring Road, Bengaluru, 560 071, India
Tel.: (91) 8043577500
Business Management Consulting Services
N.A.I.C.S.: 541611

ReachTEL Pty Ltd (1)
Level 10 231 North Quay, Brisbane, 4000, QLD, Australia
Tel.: (61) 1800427706
Web Site: https://www.reachtel.com.au
Business Analytic Services
N.A.I.C.S.: 561110

Secure Sentinel Australia Pty Limited (1)
Locked Bag 4845, Chatswood, 2057, NSW, Australia
Tel.: (61) 294116898
Web Site:
https://www.securesentinel.com.au
Business Analytic Services
N.A.I.C.S.: 561110

Secure Sentinel New Zealand Limited (1)
Shortland Street, PO Box 2993, Auckland, 1140, New Zealand
Tel.: (64) 800445303
Business Analytic Services
N.A.I.C.S.: 561110

Servicios Integrales de Informacion S.A (1)
Calle Chinchon 1018, 1018, San Isidro, Peru
Tel.: (51) 14150300
Sales Range: $25-49.9 Million
Emp.: 200
Credit Reporting Services
N.A.I.C.S.: 522390
Amilcar Ramos (Gen Mgr)

Teletrack, LLC (1)
The Summit at Technology Park 5550-A Peach Tree Pwy Ste 600, Norcross, GA 30092
Tel.: (770) 449-8809
Web Site: http://www.teletrack.com
Consumer Credit Information Services
N.A.I.C.S.: 561450

TrustedID, Inc. (1)
101 University Ave Ste 400, Palo Alto, CA 94301
Tel.: (888) 548-7878
Web Site: http://www.trustedid.com
Credit Bureau Services
N.A.I.C.S.: 561450

VantageScore Solutions, LLC (1)
107 Elm St Ste 907, Stamford, CT 06902
Tel.: (203) 363-0269
Web Site: http://www.vantagescore.com
Sales Range: $10-24.9 Million
Emp.: 15
Consumer Credit Scoring Services
N.A.I.C.S.: 561450
Barrett Burns (Pres & CEO)
Mike Dunn (VP-Comm & Strategic Plng)
Benjamin Tagoe (Sr VP-Strategic Plng & Alliances)
Silvio Tavares (Pres & CEO)
Latonia D. Hubbs (Sr VP & Head-Capital Markets & Strategic Alliances)

Worxtime LLC (1)
360B Quality Cir Ste 220, Huntsville, AL 35806

Web Site: https://www.worxtime.com
Software Programming Services
N.A.I.C.S.: 541511

EQUILLIUM, INC.
2223 Avenida de la Playa Ste 105, La Jolla, CA 92037
Tel.: (858) 240-1200   DE
Web Site:
https://www.equilliumbio.com
Year Founded: 2017
EQ—(NASDAQ)
Rev.: $15,759,000
Assets: $78,421,000
Liabilities: $46,479,000
Net Worth: $31,942,000
Earnings: ($62,428,000)
Emp.: 36
Fiscal Year-end: 12/31/22
Biotechnology Research & Development Services
N.A.I.C.S.: 541714
Daniel M. Bradbury (Co-Founder & Exec Chm)
Bruce D. Steel (Co-Founder, Pres & CEO)
Stephen Connelly (Co-Founder & Chief Scientific Officer)
Penny Tom (Principal Acctg Officer & Sr VP-Fin)
Christine Zedelmayer (COO)
Jason Keyes (CFO)
Joel Rothman (Chief Dev Officer)
Matt Ritter (Sr VP-Corporate Development)

Subsidiaries:

Equillium AUS Pty. Ltd. (1)
Tel.: (61) 732004844
Web Site: https://equiaustralia.com.au
Pet Food Mfr
N.A.I.C.S.: 311111

EQUINIX, INC.
1 Lagoon Dr, Redwood City, CA 94065
Tel.: (650) 598-6000   DE
Web Site: https://www.equinix.com
Year Founded: 1998
EQIX—(NASDAQ)
Rev.: $8,188,136,000
Assets: $32,650,724,000
Liabilities: $20,162,225,000
Net Worth: $12,488,499,000
Earnings: $969,178,000
Emp.: 13,151
Fiscal Year-end: 12/31/23
Designs, Builds & Operates Neutral Internet Business Exchange Centers
N.A.I.C.S.: 517111
Michael F. Montoya (Chief Info Security Officer & Sr VP)
Keith D. Taylor (CFO)
Brandi Galvin Morandi (Chief Legal & HR Officer & Sec)
Michael Campbell (Chief Sls Officer)
Milind Wagle (CIO)
Raouf Abdel (Exec VP-Ops-Global)
Simon Miller (Chief Acctg Officer)
Adaire Fox-Martin (Pres & CEO)
Justin Dustzadeh (CTO)
Jon Lin (Exec VP & Gen Mgr-Data Center Svcs)
Nicole Collins (Chief Transformation Officer)
Scott Crenshaw (Exec VP & Gen Mgr-Digital Svcs)
Kurt Pletcher (Exec VP)
Charles J. Meyers (Chm)
Adam T. Berlew (CMO)

Subsidiaries:

ALOG Data Centers do Brasil S.A. (1)
Rua Voluntarios da Patria 360, Botafogo, Rio de Janeiro, 22270-010, Brazil (100%)
Tel.: (55) 2130833333

Web Site: http://www.equinix.com
Internet Business Exchange Operator
N.A.I.C.S.: 517111

Equinix (Bulgaria) Data Centers EAD (1)
5030th Str 10 Yugozapaden, 1592, Sofia, Bulgaria
Tel.: (359) 29707707
Telecommunication Servicesb
N.A.I.C.S.: 517810

Equinix (Germany) Enterprises GmbH (1)
Kleyerstrasse 88-90, 60326, Frankfurt, Germany
Tel.: (49) 69920420
Telecommunication Servicesb
N.A.I.C.S.: 517810

Equinix (Germany) GmbH (1)
Tauben str 7-9, 60313, Frankfurt am Main, Germany
Tel.: (49) 6992042555
Web Site: http://www.equinix.de
Internet Business Exchange Operator
N.A.I.C.S.: 517111

Equinix (Hong Kong) Enterprises Limited (1)
1 Austin Road West Units 6501-04A & 6507-08 65/F, International Commerce Centre, Kowloon, China (Hong Kong)
Tel.: (852) 29707788
Telecommunication Servicesb
N.A.I.C.S.: 517810

Equinix (IBX Services) GmbH (1)
Larchenstr 110, 65933, Frankfurt, Germany
Tel.: (49) 693877790
Internet Business Exchange Operator
N.A.I.C.S.: 517111

Equinix (Italy) Enterprises S.R.L. (1)
Via Savona 125, 20144, Milan, Italy
Tel.: (39) 0236679500
Telecommunication Servicesb
N.A.I.C.S.: 517810

Equinix (LD10) Limited (1)
13 Liverpool Road, Slough, SL1 4QZ, United Kingdom
Tel.: (44) 3453732999
Telecommunication Servicesb
N.A.I.C.S.: 517810

Equinix (Netherlands) Holdings BV (1)
Amstelplein 1-Rembrandt, 1096 HA, Amsterdam, Netherlands
Tel.: (31) 207537950
Holding Company
N.A.I.C.S.: 551112

Equinix (Ottawa) Government Ltd. (1)
200 Avenue Lepine, Gatineau, J8L 0B3, QC, Canada
Tel.: (408) 451-5200
Digital Infrastructure Services
N.A.I.C.S.: 518210

Equinix (Real Estate) GmbH (1)
Taubenstrasse 7-9, Frankfurt, 60313, Germany
Tel.: (49) 1805049555
Web Site: http://www.equinix.com
Sales Range: $50-74.9 Million
Emp.: 50
Real Estate Manangement Services
N.A.I.C.S.: 531210

Equinix (Sweden) AB (1)
Kvastvagen 25-29 Skondal, 128 62, Stockholm, Sweden
Tel.: (46) 87993800
Telecommunication Servicesb
N.A.I.C.S.: 517810

Equinix (Switzerland) Enterprises GmbH (1)
Hardstrasse 235, 8005, Zurich, Switzerland
Tel.: (41) 443556900
Telecommunication Servicesb
N.A.I.C.S.: 517810

Equinix (Switzerland) GmbH (1)
Josefstrasse 225, 8005, Zurich, Switzerland
Tel.: (41) 43 508 1038
Web Site: https://de.equinix.ch
Internet Business Exchange Operator

N.A.I.C.S.: 517111

Equinix Asia Pacific Pte. Ltd. (1)
79 Robinson Rd 22-01, Singapore, 068897, Singapore (100%)
Tel.: (65) 66220100
Web Site: http://www.equinix.com
Telecommunication Servicesb
N.A.I.C.S.: 517810

Subsidiary (Non-US):

Equinix Australia Pty. Limited (2)
Unit B 639 Gardeners Road Mascot, Sydney, 2020, NSW, Australia
Tel.: (61) 283372000
Sales Range: $10-24.9 Million
Emp.: 70
Network Neutral Data Centers & Internet Exchange Services
N.A.I.C.S.: 517810
Darren Mann (Sr Dir-Bus Dev)
Jeremy Deutsch (Country Mgr)

Equinix Hong Kong Limited (2)
17/F Global Gateway 168 Yeung Uk Road, Tsuen Wan, NT, China (Hong Kong)
Tel.: (852) 3 018 1786
Web Site: https://www.equinix.hk
Network Neutral Data Center & Internet Exchange Services
N.A.I.C.S.: 517810

Equinix Japan K.K. (2)
35F Tokyo Nihonbashi Tower 2-7-1 Nihonbashi, Chuo-ku, Tokyo, 103-6035, Japan
Tel.: (81) 356571400
Web Site: http://www.equinix.com
Sales Range: $75-99.9 Million
Network-Neutral Data Centers & Internet Exchange Services
N.A.I.C.S.: 517810

Subsidiary (Domestic):

AXLBIT, Inc. (3)
T Building 2-28 Higashi Shinagawa 2, Shinagawa-Ku, 140-0002, Tokyo, Japan
Tel.: (81) 345909974
Web Site: http://www.axlbit.com
Information Technology Consulting Services
N.A.I.C.S.: 541512
Akihiro Hasegawa (Pres & CEO)
Takahashi Iron (Auditor)

Subsidiary (Domestic):

Equinix Singapore Pte. Ltd. (2)
20 Ayer Rajah Crescent, Ayer Rajah Industrial Park, Singapore, 139964, Singapore
Tel.: (65) 3 158 2175
Web Site: https://www.equinix.sg
Sales Range: $75-99.9 Million
Network Neutral Data Centers & Internet Exchange Services
N.A.I.C.S.: 517810

Equinix Canada Ltd. (1)
151 Front Street West 3rd 5th 6th and 7th Floors, Toronto, M5J 2N1, ON, Canada
Tel.: (408) 451-5200
Network Telecommunication Services
N.A.I.C.S.: 517810

Equinix Europe, Inc. (1)
2 Buckingham AvenueSlough Trading Estate, London, SL14NB, United Kingdom
Tel.: (44) 3453732999
Web Site: http://www.equinix.com
Sales Range: $10-24.9 Million
Emp.: 30
Network-Neutral Data Centers & Internet Exchange Services
N.A.I.C.S.: 517810

Subsidiary (Domestic):

Equinix UK Limited (2)
11 Devonshire Square, London, EC2M 4YR, United Kingdom
Tel.: (44) 8453732900
Network Neutral Data Centers & Internet Exchange Services
N.A.I.C.S.: 517810
Russell Poole (Mng Dir)

Equinix Group Ltd (1)
51-53 Great Marlborough Street, London, W1F 7JT, United Kingdom
Tel.: (44) 8453732900
Internet Business Exchange Operator

Equinix, Inc.—(Continued)

N.A.I.C.S.: 517111

Equinix Korea LLC **(1)**
43F Three IFC 10 Gukjegeumyungro,
Yeongdeungpo-gu, Seoul, 07326, Korea
(South)
Tel.: (82) 261384511
Telecommunication Servicesb
N.A.I.C.S.: 517121

Equinix Operating Co., LLC **(1)**
1715 N W Shore Blvd, Tampa, FL 33607
Tel.: (813) 207-7700
Web Site: http://www.equinix.com
Sales Range: $200-249.9 Million
Emp.: 376
Data Communication Services
N.A.I.C.S.: 517810

Equinix Peru S.R.L. **(1)**
Calle Centauro 115 Urb, Los Granados,
Lima, Peru
Tel.: (51) 16433557
Information Technology Services
N.A.I.C.S.: 541519

Equinix Security (CU1) LLC **(1)**
18155 Technology Dr Bldg A, Culpeper, VA
22701
Information Technology Services
N.A.I.C.S.: 541519

Equinix, Inc. - Reston **(1)**
10780 Parkridge Blvd Ste 150, Reston, VA
20191
Tel.: (703) 251-3300
Web Site: http://www.equinix.com
Emp.: 30
Computer Facilities Management Services
N.A.I.C.S.: 541513

Infomart Dallas, LP **(1)**
1950 N Stemmons Fwy #1034, Dallas, TX
75207
Data Center Leasing & Support Services
N.A.I.C.S.: 531120
Erica Clausen-Lee (Chief Product Officer)
Tammy Cohen (Founder & Chief Visionary
Officer)
Amy Phillips (CFO)

Itconic Portugal, S.A. **(1)**
Av Severiano Falcao 14, 2685-378, Prior
Velho, Portugal
Tel.: (351) 219405320
Web Site: http://www.itconic.com
Telecommunication Servicesb
N.A.I.C.S.: 517810

**MainOne Cable Company Ghana
Ltd.** **(1)**
11 Patrice Lumumba Road, Airport Residen-
tial Area, Accra, Ghana
Tel.: (233) 302744030
Emp.: 600
Telecommunication Servicesb
N.A.I.C.S.: 517810

MainOne Cable Company Ltd. **(1)**
Les Cascades Building Edith Cavell Street,
Port Louis, Mauritius
Tel.: (230) 2129800
Telecommunication Servicesb
N.A.I.C.S.: 517810

**MainOne Cable Company Nigeria
Limited** **(1)**
FF Towers 13 Ligali Ayorinde Street, Victo-
ria Island, Lagos, Nigeria
Tel.: (234) 7006246663
Web Site: https://www.mainone.net
Emp.: 500
Telecommunication Servicesb
N.A.I.C.S.: 517810

**MainOne Cable Company Portugal,
S.A.** **(1)**
Rua General Humberto Delgado 30 A - Of-
fice 3, Torre da Marinha, 2840-436, Seixal,
Portugal
Tel.: (351) 212972206
Emp.: 600
Telecommunication Servicesb
N.A.I.C.S.: 517810

Nimbo Inc. **(1)**
102 W 38th St 6th Fl, New York, NY 10018
Tel.: (212) 202-5800
Web Site: http://www.nimbo.com

Emp.: 30
Enterprise Cloud Solutions
N.A.I.C.S.: 513210
John Shaw (Co-Founder)
Ira Bell (Co-Founder)

EQUITABLE FINANCIAL CORP.
113 N Locust St, Grand Island, NE
68801
Tel.: (308) 382-3136 MD
Web Site:
https://www.equitableonline.com
Year Founded: 2015
EQFN—(OTCIQ)
Rev.: $26,122,497
Assets: $481,048,723
Liabilities: $436,069,366
Net Worth: $44,979,357
Earnings: $3,587,926
Emp.: 88
Fiscal Year-end: 06/30/23
Bank Holding Company
N.A.I.C.S.: 551111
David L. Richardson (Chief Lending
Officer)
Thomas E. Gdowski (Pres & CEO)
Darcy M. Ray (CFO)
Alison M. Larson (Sr VP-Marketing &
Communications, VP, Mktg Dir &
Mgr-Investment Ops)
Jodi Lynn Maruska (CTO)
Trisha Manolidis (Sec)
Benedict P. Wassinger Jr. (Chm)

Subsidiaries:

Equitable Bank **(1)**
113 N Locust St, Grand Island, NE 68802
Tel.: (308) 382-3136
Web Site: http://www.equitableonline.com
Rev.: $8,370,000
Assets: $172,144,000
Liabilities: $153,967,000
Net Worth: $18,177,000
Earnings: $997,000
Fiscal Year-end: 12/31/2013
Banking Services
N.A.I.C.S.: 522110
Tom Gdowski (Pres & CEO)

EQUITABLE HOLDINGS, INC.
1345 Avenue of the Americas, New
York, NY 10105
Tel.: (212) 554-1234 DE
Web Site:
https://equitableholdings.com
Year Founded: 1859
FOH—(NYSE)
Rev.: $10,528,000,000
Assets: $276,814,000,000
Liabilities: $272,426,000,000
Net Worth: $4,388,000,000
Earnings: $1,222,000,000
Emp.: 8,500
Fiscal Year-end: 12/31/23
Holding Company
N.A.I.C.S.: 551112
Mark Pearson (Pres & CEO)
Robin M. Raju (CFO)
Jeffrey J. Hurd (COO)

Subsidiaries:

**200 East 87th Street Company,
LLC** **(1)**
200 E 87th St, New York, NY 10028
Tel.: (646) 849-6673
Web Site: https://www.200e87.com
Apartment Rental Services
N.A.I.C.S.: 531110

AB Bernstein Israel Ltd. **(1)**
Rothschild Boulevard 22 Suite 1119, Tel
Aviv, 6688218, Israel
Tel.: (972) 732844514
Portfolio Management Services
N.A.I.C.S.: 523940

AXA Advisors, LLC **(1)**
2 Meridian Crossings, Minneapolis, MN
55423
Tel.: (612) 243-3200
Web Site: http://www.mn.axa-advisors.com

Emp.: 8
Mortgage Bankers & Loan Correspondence
N.A.I.C.S.: 523150
Marcus A. Healey (Exec VP)

AXA Advisors, LLC **(1)**
1290 Avenue of the Americas 8th Fl, New
York, NY 10104
Tel.: (212) 314-4600
Web Site: http://www.axaonline.com
Financial Planning Services
N.A.I.C.S.: 523999
Steve Howell (Branch Mgr)
Kyle Sims (Branch Mgr)
David W. Karr (Chm)
Gregory Manto (Exec VP & Natl Dir-Mgmt
Dev)
Richard Yust (Gen Mgr)

**AXA Corp. Solutions Insurance
Company** **(1)**
125 Broad St LBBY 5, New York, NY
10004-1501
Tel.: (212) 493-9300
Web Site: http://www.axainsurance.com
Sales Range: $50-74.9 Million
Emp.: 80
Provides Commercial & Aviation/Space In-
surance & Reinsurance Services
N.A.I.C.S.: 524210

AXA Corporate Solutions **(1)**
17 State St Fl 37, New York, NY 10004-
1501
Tel.: (212) 493-9300
Sales Range: $50-74.9 Million
Emp.: 65
Insurance Agents & Brokers
N.A.I.C.S.: 524210

Subsidiary (Domestic):

**AXA Corporate Solutions
Insurance** **(2)**
17 State St 37th Fl, New York, NY 10004-
1501
Tel.: (212) 493-9300
Property & Casualty Insurance Services
N.A.I.C.S.: 524126

Subsidiary (Domestic):

**AXA Corporate Solutions Life Rein-
surance Company** **(3)**
1290 Avenue of Americas, New York, NY
10104-1501
Tel.: (212) 554-1234
Reinsurance Services
N.A.I.C.S.: 524130
Chris Conpri (Pres)

AXA Distributors, LLC. **(1)**
1290 Ave Of The Americas, New York, NY
10104-0101
Tel.: (212) 314-4600
Web Site: http://www.us.axa.com
Sales Range: $100-124.9 Million
Emp.: 200
Security & Commodity Exchanges
N.A.I.C.S.: 524113

**AXA Equitable Life Assurance
Company** **(1)**
1290 Avenue of the Americas 13th Fl, New
York, NY 10104-0101 **(100%)**
Tel.: (212) 554-1234
Web Site: http://www.axa-equitable.com
Sales Range: $1-4.9 Billion
Emp.: 5,139
Insurance Provider
N.A.I.C.S.: 524210
Robert Jones (Exec VP-Distr)
Adrienne Johnson-Guider (Sr VP & Head-
Strategic Initiatives Grp)
Tracey Gray-Walker (Chief Diversity Officer)

**AXA Global Structured Products
Inc.** **(1)**
600 5th Ave 24th Fl, New York, NY 10020
Tel.: (212) 218-2000
Life Insurance Management Services
N.A.I.C.S.: 524113

AXA Insurance **(1)**
200 Liberty St, New York, NY
10281 **(100%)**
Tel.: (212) 493-9300
Web Site: http://www.axa-ic.com
Sales Range: $100-124.9 Million
Emp.: 150
Reinsurance Carriers Accident & Health

N.A.I.C.S.: 524130

AXA Liabilities Managers Inc. **(1)**
125 Broad St, New York, NY 10004-1501
Tel.: (212) 493-9300
Web Site: http://www.axa-
liabilitiesmanagers.com
Sales Range: $100-124.9 Million
Emp.: 200
Reinsurance
N.A.I.C.S.: 524210
Helen O'Neill Reid (Head-HR)
Michele Luongo (Head-Ops)
Fran Turco (VP-Global Ops)
Sylvain Villeroy de Galhau (CEO)

AXA Multi Manager **(1)**
600 5th Ave 24th Fl, New York, NY 10020
Tel.: (212) 218-2000
Asset Management Services
N.A.I.C.S.: 523940

AXA Network, LLC **(1)**
4251 Crums Mill Rd, Harrisburg, PA 17112
Tel.: (717) 541-8164
Sales Range: $75-99.9 Million
Emp.: 180
Holding Company; Life Insurance, Annui-
ties, Disability Income, Mutual Funds & Se-
curities
N.A.I.C.S.: 524210

**AXA Rosenberg Investment Manage-
ment LLC** **(1)**
4 Orinda Way Bldg E, Orinda, CA 94563
Tel.: (925) 254-6464
Sales Range: $50-74.9 Million
Emp.: 58
Investment Management Service
N.A.I.C.S.: 523999
Will Jump (Chief Investment Officer)
Bruno Pradal (CTO & Head-Ops)

AXA Space, Inc. **(1)**
4800 Montgomery Ln 11th Fl, Bethesda,
MD 20814
Tel.: (301) 654-8585
Web Site: http://www.axaspace.com
Health Insurance Management Services
N.A.I.C.S.: 524114

**AXA Technology Services America
Inc** **(1)**
525 Washington Blvd 23rd Fl, Jersey City,
NJ 07310
Tel.: (201) 743-6029
Web Site: http://www.axa-tech.com
Information Technology Consulting Services
N.A.I.C.S.: 541512

AllianceBernstein (Chile) SpA **(1)**
Av Isidora Goyenechea 3000 Floor 23, Las
Condes, Chile
Tel.: (56) 223644449
Portfolio Management Services
N.A.I.C.S.: 523940

AllianceBernstein Holding L.P. **(1)**
501 Commerce St, Nashville, TN 37203
Tel.: (615) 622-0000
Web Site: https://www.alliancebernstein.com
Assets: $2,074,626,000
Liabilities: $1,623,000
Net Worth: $2,073,003,000
Earnings: $274,165,000
Emp.: 4,436
Fiscal Year-end: 12/31/2022
Open-End Investment Funds
N.A.I.C.S.: 525910
Karl Sprules (COO & Sr VP)
Jackie Marks (CFO-Global)
Seth P. Bernstein (Pres & CEO)
Thomas Simeone (Chief Acctg Officer &
Controller)

Subsidiary (Domestic):

AB CarVal Investors, L.P. **(2)**
9320 Excelsior Blvd 7th Fl, Minneapolis,
MN 55343
Tel.: (952) 444-4780
Web Site: http://www.carvalinvestors.com
Sales Range: $50-74.9 Million
Emp.: 165
Investment Management Service
N.A.I.C.S.: 523940
Christopher Hedberg (CFO)
Gregory Belonogoff (Principal)
Gerardo J. Bernaldez (Principal)
Lucas Detor (Mng Principal)

James Ganley *(Mng Principal)*
Jody A. Gunderson *(Mng Principal)*
Ann Folkman *(Mng Dir)*
David Fry *(Chief Risk Officer & Principal)*
John Withrow *(Principal)*
Ryan Savell *(Mng Dir)*
Mark Sorensen *(Mng Dir)*
Avery Colcord *(Mng Dir)*
Matthew Bogart *(Chief Compliance Officer & Gen Counsel)*

Subsidiary (Non-US):

ACM Bernstein GmbH **(2)**
Maximilianstrasse 21, Munich, 80539, Germany
Tel.: (49) 89255400
Sales Range: $50-74.9 Million
Emp.: 10
Investment Management Service
N.A.I.C.S.: 523940

Subsidiary (Domestic):

AllianceBernstein L.P. **(2)**
501 Commerce St, Nashville, TN 37203
Tel.: (615) 622-0000
Web Site: https://www.alliancebernstein.com
Rev.: $4,120,728,000
Assets: $11,138,931,000
Liabilities: $6,661,291,000
Net Worth: $4,477,640,000
Earnings: $831,813,000
Emp.: 4,436
Fiscal Year-end: 12/31/2022
Financial Management Services
N.A.I.C.S.: 523999
Ramon de Oliveira *(Chm)*
Jackie Marks *(CFO-Global)*
Seth P. Bernstein *(Pres & CEO)*
Ali Dibadj *(Head-Fin & Strategy)*
Onur Erzan *(Sr VP, Head-Private Wealth & Head-Global Client Grp)*
Noel Archard *(Head-ETFs & Portfolio Solutions-Global)*

Subsidiary (Non-US):

ACMBernstein GmbH **(3)**
Maximilianstrasse 21, 80539, Munich, Germany
Tel.: (49) 89 255 40 0
Emp.: 8
Financial Management Services
N.A.I.C.S.: 523999

AXA Towarzystwo Funduszy Inwestycyjnych S.A. **(3)**
Ul Chlodna 51, 00-867, Warsaw, Poland
Tel.: (48) 22 555 07 00
Web Site: http://www.axa.pl
Emp.: 60
Asset Management Services
N.A.I.C.S.: 523940

AllianceBernstein (Argentina) S.R.L **(3)**
Maipu 1210 - 8th Floor Autonomous City, 1006, Buenos Aires, Argentina
Tel.: (54) 1148728251
Investment Management Service
N.A.I.C.S.: 523999
James Gingrich *(COO)*

AllianceBernstein (France) S.A.S. **(3)**
90 Avenue des Champs Elysees, 75008, Paris, France
Tel.: (33) 156435046
Emp.: 2
Investment Management Service
N.A.I.C.S.: 523999

AllianceBernstein (Luxembourg) S.A. **(3)**
2-4 rue Eugene Ruppert, 2453, Luxembourg, Luxembourg
Tel.: (352) 463936151
Web Site: http://www.alliancebernstein.com
Emp.: 48
Financial Management Services
N.A.I.C.S.: 523999
Simon Thelen *(Mng Dir)*

AllianceBernstein (Singapore) Limited **(3)**
One Raffles Quay 27-11 South Tower, Singapore, 048583, Singapore
Tel.: (65) 62304600
Web Site: https://www.abfunds.com.sg

Emp.: 45
Investment Management Service
N.A.I.C.S.: 523999
Ajai Kaul *(CEO)*

AllianceBernstein Asset Management (Korea) Ltd. **(3)**
Seoul Finance Center 14th Floor 136 Sejong-daero, Jung-gu, Seoul, 04520, Korea (South)
Tel.: (82) 237073400
Web Site: http://www.alliancebernstein.com
Financial Management Services
N.A.I.C.S.: 523999
Seok Jae Lee *(Mng Dir)*

AllianceBernstein Australia Limited **(3)**
Level 32 Aurora Place 88 Phillip Street, Sydney, 2000, NSW, Australia
Tel.: (61) 292551200
Web Site: http://web.alliancebernstein.com
Financial Management Services
N.A.I.C.S.: 523999

AllianceBernstein Canada, Inc **(3)**
Brookfield Place 161 Bay Street 27th Floor, Toronto, M5J 2S1, ON, Canada
Tel.: (416) 572-2534
Web Site: http://www.alliancebernstein.com
Sales Range: $50-74.9 Million
Financial Management Services
N.A.I.C.S.: 523999
Wendy Brodkin *(Mng Dir)*

Subsidiary (Domestic):

AllianceBernstein Global Derivatives Corporation **(3)**
1345 Avenue of The Americas, New York, NY 10105
Tel.: (212) 969-1000
Web Site: http://www.alliancebernstein.com
Investment Management Service
N.A.I.C.S.: 523940

AllianceBernstein Global Wealth Management **(3)**
1345 Avenue of the Americas, New York, NY 10105
Tel.: (212) 486-5800
Web Site: http://www.alliancebernstein.com
Financial Management Services
N.A.I.C.S.: 523999
Peter S. Kraus *(Chm & CEO)*

Subsidiary (Non-US):

AllianceBernstein Hong Kong Limited **(3)**
One Island East Taikoo Place 39th Floor 18 Westlands Road, Suite 3401 34th Floor, Quarry Bay, China (Hong Kong)
Tel.: (852) 29187888
Web Site: https://www.abfunds.com.hk
Emp.: 10
Investment Management Service
N.A.I.C.S.: 523999

Subsidiary (Domestic):

AllianceBernstein Institutional Investments **(3)**
1345 Ave of the Americas, New York, NY 10105
Tel.: (212) 969-1000
Web Site: http://www.alliancebernstein.com
Investment Management Service
N.A.I.C.S.: 523999

Subsidiary (Non-US):

AllianceBernstein Investment Management Australia Limited **(3)**
Level 32 Aurora Place 88 Phillip Street, Sydney, 2000, NSW, Australia
Tel.: (61) 292551200
Financial Investment Services
N.A.I.C.S.: 523999

AllianceBernstein Investments Taiwan Limited **(3)**
101 Tower 81F/81F-1 7 Xin Yi Road SEC 5, Taipei, 110, Taiwan
Tel.: (886) 287583888
Web Site: http://www.alliancebernstein.com
Financial Investment Services
N.A.I.C.S.: 523999

Subsidiary (Domestic):

AllianceBernstein Investments, Inc. **(3)**
1345 Ave of the Americas, New York, NY 10105
Tel.: (212) 969-1000
Web Site: http://www.alliancebernstein.com
Investment Management Service
N.A.I.C.S.: 523940
Thomas S. Hexner *(Pres)*

AllianceBernstein Investor Services, Inc. **(3)**
8000 IH 10 W, San Antonio, TX 78230
Tel.: (210) 384-6000
Web Site: http://www.alliancebernstein.com
Investment Management Service
N.A.I.C.S.: 523940

Subsidiary (Non-US):

AllianceBernstein Japan Ltd **(3)**
14F Hibiya Park Front 2-1-6 Uchisaiwai-cho, Chiyoda-ku, Tokyo, 100-0011, Japan
Tel.: (81) 359629000
Web Site: https://www.alliancebernstein.co.jp
Emp.: 106
Financial Investment Services
N.A.I.C.S.: 523999

AllianceBernstein Limited **(3)**
BMB Center 6th Floor Diplomatic Area, PO Box 10515, Manama, Bahrain
Tel.: (973) 17530510
Web Site: http://www.alliancebernstein.com
Sales Range: $50-74.9 Million
Emp.: 2
Financial Investment Services
N.A.I.C.S.: 523999
Chris H. Cheesman *(Sr VP & Chief Audit Officer)*

AllianceBernstein Limited **(3)**
60 London Wall, London, EC2M 5SJ, United Kingdom
Tel.: (44) 2074700100
Web Site: http://www.alliancebernstein.com
Emp.: 500
Financial Management Services
N.A.I.C.S.: 523999

Subsidiary (Domestic):

AllianceBernstein Holdings Limited **(4)**
60 London Wall, London, EC2M 5SJ, United Kingdom
Tel.: (44) 2074700100
Web Site: http://www.alliancebernstein.com
Emp.: 500
Investment Management Service
N.A.I.C.S.: 523940

Sanford C. Bernstein Limited **(4)**
60 London Wall, London, EC2M 5SJ, United Kingdom
Tel.: (44) 2071705000
Web Site: http://www.alliancebernstein.com
Financial Investment Services
N.A.I.C.S.: 523999
Csuren Chellippah *(CEO)*

Subsidiary (Non-US):

AllianceBernstein Taiwan Limited **(3)**
25F-7 No 3 Ziqiang 3rd Rd, Lingya Dist, Kaohsiung, Taiwan
Tel.: (886) 75668811
Web Site: http://www.alliancebernstein.com
Investment Management Service
N.A.I.C.S.: 523999

Subsidiary (Domestic):

W.P. Stewart & Co., Ltd. **(3)**
527 Madison Ave 20th Fl, New York, NY 10022
Tel.: (212) 750-8585
Web Site: http://www.wpstewart.com
Sales Range: $10-24.9 Million
Emp.: 48
Global Investment Advisor
N.A.I.C.S.: 523150
Mark I. Phelps *(Pres & Mng Dir-Global Investments)*

Subsidiary (Non-US):

W.P. Stewart Asset Management (Curacao) N.V. **(4)**

Penstraat 35, Willemstad, Curacao
Tel.: (599) 94650658
Sales Range: $25-49.9 Million
Emp.: 3
Asset Management & Fund Management Services
N.A.I.C.S.: 523940

Subsidiary (Domestic):

W.P. Stewart Asset Management (NA), Inc. **(4)**
527 Madison Ave 20th Fl, New York, NY 10022
Tel.: (212) 750-8585
Asset Management Services
N.A.I.C.S.: 523940
Kevin F. Crook *(Exec VP & Dir-Distr)*

W.P. Stewart Asset Management Ltd. **(4)**
527 Madison Ave 20th Fl, New York, NY 10022
Tel.: (212) 750-8585
Asset Management Services
N.A.I.C.S.: 523940

WPS Advisors, Inc. **(4)**
527 Madison Ave 20th Fl, New York, NY 10022-4362
Tel.: (212) 750-8585
Web Site: http://www.wpstewart.com
Investment Management Service
N.A.I.C.S.: 523999

Subsidiary (Non-US):

AllianceBernstein Services Limited **(2)**
60 London Wall, London, EC2M 5SJ, United Kingdom
Tel.: (44) 2074700100
Web Site: http://www.alliancebernstein.com
Emp.: 300
Investment Management Service
N.A.I.C.S.: 523940

Unit (Domestic):

Sanford C. Bernstein & Co., LLP **(2)**
1345 Avenue of the Americas, New York, NY 10105 **(55%)**
Tel.: (212) 969-1000
Web Site: http://www.alliancebernstein.com
Sales Range: $1-4.9 Billion
Emp.: 4,000
Investment Services
N.A.I.C.S.: 523940
Robert P. van Brugge *(Chm & CEO)*

Subsidiary (Non-US):

Sanford C. Bernstein (CREST Nominees) Limited **(2)**
60 London Wall, London, EC2M 5SH, United Kingdom
Tel.: (44) 2071705000
Trade Financing Services
N.A.I.C.S.: 522299

Bernstein Autonomous LLP **(1)**
60 London Wall, London, EC2M 5SH, United Kingdom
Tel.: (44) 2071705000
Portfolio Management Services
N.A.I.C.S.: 523940

CPH Capital Fondsmaeglerselskab A/S **(1)**
Lautrupsgade 7 6 Sal, 2100, Copenhagen, Denmark
Tel.: (45) 69148181
Portfolio Management Services
N.A.I.C.S.: 523940

EVSA, Inc. **(1)**
116 Tazewell Ave, Cape Charles, VA 23310
Web Site: https://www.esvainc.com
Software Development Services
N.A.I.C.S.: 541511

Equitable Advisors, LLC **(1)**
300 Lighting Way Ste 702, Secaucus, NJ 07094
Tel.: (201) 777-7325
Web Site: https://www.equitableadvisorssecaucus nj.com
Financial Planning Services
N.A.I.C.S.: 523940

Equitable Holdings, Inc.—(Continued)

Equitable Financial Life Insurance Company of America (1)
525 Washington Blvd, Jersey City, NJ 07310
Tel.: (212) 554-1234
Rev.: $627,000,000
Assets: $8,331,000,000
Liabilities: $7,960,000,000
Net Worth: $371,000,000
Earnings: ($38,000,000)
Fiscal Year-end: 12/31/2022
Fire Insurance Services
N.A.I.C.S.: 524113
Mark Pearson (CEO)
Robin M. Raju (CFO)
William Eckert (Chief Acctg Officer)

MATRIX RISK CONSULTANTS, INC. (1)
7887 Washington Vlg Dr Ste 150, Dayton, OH 45459
Tel.: (937) 432-2071
Web Site: http://www.axa-matrixrc.com
Sales Range: $25-49.9 Million
Emp.: 30
Business Management Consulting Services
N.A.I.C.S.: 541618

MONY Life Insurance Company of the Americas, Ltd. (1)
23 Palm Tree Ave Bldg 4 2nd Floor, Georgetown, KY1-1102, Grand Cayman, Cayman Islands
Tel.: (345) 949 8704
Web Site: http://www.axa-equitable.com
Sales Range: $50-74.9 Million
Emp.: 2
Life Insurance & Annuities
N.A.I.C.S.: 524130
Victor Ugolyn (Chm)

PlanConnect, LLC (1)
100 Madison Ste, Syracuse, NY 13202
Tel.:
Web Site: https://www.planconnect.com
Financial Planning Services
N.A.I.C.S.: 523940

Sanford C. Bernstein (India) Private Limited (1)
Level 6 4 North Avenue Maker Maxity Bandra Kurla Complex, Bandra East, Mumbai, 400 051, Maharashtra, India
Tel.: (91) 2268421401
Portfolio Management Services
N.A.I.C.S.: 523940

Sanford C. Bernstein (Schwiez) GmbH (1)
Talstrasse 83, 8001, Zurich, Switzerland
Tel.: (41) 433117711
Portfolio Management Services
N.A.I.C.S.: 523940

The Advest Group, Inc. (1)
Tel.: (860) 509-1000
Sales Range: $700-749.9 Million
Emp.: 1,700
Financial Services
N.A.I.C.S.: 523150

Subsidiary (Non-US):

Boston Advisors LLC (2)
Tel.: (617) 348-3180
Web Site: https://www.bostonadvisors.com
Sales Range: $50-74.9 Million
Emp.: 19
Registered Investment Advisors
N.A.I.C.S.: 523940

EQUITY BANCSHARES, INC.
7701 E Kellogg Dr Ste 300, Wichita, KS 67207
Tel.: (316) 681-1776 KS
Web Site:
https://www.equitybank.com
Year Founded: 2002
EQBK—(NASDAQ)
Rev.: $224,205,000
Assets: $4,981,651,000
Liabilities: $4,571,593,000
Net Worth: $410,058,000
Earnings: $57,688,000
Emp.: 732
Fiscal Year-end: 12/31/22

Bank Holding Company
N.A.I.C.S.: 551111
Brad S. Elliott (Founder, Chm & CEO)
John J. Hanley (CMO)
Krzysztof P. Slupkowski (Chief Credit Officer)
Julie A. Huber (Exec VP-Strategic Initiatives)
Brett A. Reber (Gen Counsel & Exec VP)
Hetai A. Desai (Chief Risk Officer)
Brian Katzfey (VP & Dir-Corp Dev & IR)
Chris Navratil (Sr VP)

Subsidiaries:

Equity Bank (1)
345 N Andover Rd, Andover, KS 67002
Tel.: (316) 733-5041
Web Site: https://www.equitybank.com
Emp.: 5
Commericial Banking
N.A.I.C.S.: 522110
Brad S. Elliott (Chm & CEO)
Krzysztof P. Slupkowski (Chief Credit Officer & Exec VP)
Julie A. Huber (COO & Exec VP)
Mark Parman (Pres/Pres-Kansas City, CEO-Metro Markets & Sr VP)
Brad Daniel (Chief Deposit Strategy Officer, Chief Deposit Strategy Officer, CEO-Community West & Chief Deposit Strategy Officer)

EQUITY COMMONWEALTH
2 N Riverside Plz Ste 2100, Chicago, IL 60606
Tel.: (312) 646-2800 MD
Web Site: https://www.ecqre.com
Year Founded: 1986
EQC—(NYSE)
Rev.: $60,524,000
Assets: $2,425,041,000
Liabilities: $34,928,000
Net Worth: $2,390,113,000
Earnings: $83,176,000
Emp.: 22
Fiscal Year-end: 12/31/23
Real Estate Investment Trust
N.A.I.C.S.: 525990
David A. Helfand (Chm, Pres & CEO)
William H. Griffiths (CFO, Treas & Exec VP)
David S. Weinberg (COO & Exec VP)
Orrin S. Shifrin (Gen Counsel, Sec & Exec VP)

Subsidiaries:

Blue Dog LLC (1)
11939 Manchester Rd Ste 153, Des Peres, MO 63131
Tel.: (314) 610-4262
Web Site: http://www.bluedogllc.com
Property Management Services
N.A.I.C.S.: 531210

Equity Commonwealth EQC (1)
2 N Riverside Plz Ste 2100, Chicago, IL 60606
Tel.: (312) 646-2800
Web Site: http://www.eqcre.com
Residential Building & Dwelling Leasing Services
N.A.I.C.S.: 531110
Adam S. Markman (CFO, Treas & Exec VP)
David A. Helfand (Pres & CEO)
Orrin S. Shifrin (Gen Counsel, Sec & Exec VP)
David Weinberg (COO & Exec VP)

First Associates LLC (1)
25 S Charles St Ste 1002A, Baltimore, MD 21201
Tel.: (410) 576-8898
Sales Range: $25-49.9 Million
Emp.: 15
Property Management Services
N.A.I.C.S.: 531210
Colleen Hall (Office Mgr)

Higgins Properties LLC (1)

120 Meadows Dr, Rutherfordton, NC 28139-7527
Tel.: (828) 287-5131
Property Management Services
N.A.I.C.S.: 531210

Hub Acquisition Trust (1)
255 Washington St, Newton, MA 02458-1637
Tel.: (617) 332-3990
Property Management Services
N.A.I.C.S.: 531210

EQUITY DISTRIBUTION ACQUISITION CORP.
2 N Riverside Plz Ste 600, Chicago, IL 60606
Tel.: (312) 454-0100 DE
Year Founded: 2020
EQD—(NYSE)
Rev.: $21,832,705
Assets: $414,837,992
Liabilities: $445,655,626
Net Worth: ($30,817,634)
Earnings: $19,597,699
Emp.: 3
Fiscal Year-end: 12/31/21
Investment Services
N.A.I.C.S.: 523999
Bill Galvin (CEO)
Philip Tinkler (CFO)
Joseph Miron (Sec)

EQUITY LIFESTYLE PROPERTIES, INC.
2 N Riverside Plz Ste 800, Chicago, IL 60606
Tel.: (312) 279-1400 MD
Web Site:
https://www.equitylifestyleproperties.com
Year Founded: 1992
ELS—(NYSE)
Rev.: $1,489,423,000
Assets: $5,613,733,000
Liabilities: $4,115,112,000
Net Worth: $1,498,621,000
Earnings: $314,191,000
Emp.: 4,000
Fiscal Year-end: 12/31/23
High Quality Resort Communities Owner & Operator
N.A.I.C.S.: 721199
Paul Seavey (CFO & Exec VP)
Patrick Waite (COO & Exec VP)
Larisa J. Drake (CMO & Exec VP)
Marguerite M. Nader (Pres & CEO)
David Eldersveld (Chief Legal Officer, Sec & Exec VP)

Subsidiaries:

Realty Systems, Inc. (1)
3165 Old Kings Rd S, Flagler Beach, FL 32136
Tel.: (386) 439-0460
Web Site: https://www.equitylifestyle.com
Sales Range: $50-74.9 Million
Emp.: 10
Real Estate Investment Trust Services
N.A.I.C.S.: 525990

Thousand Trails LP (1)
2325 Hwy 90, Gautier, MS 39553
Tel.: (214) 618-7200
Web Site: https://www.thousandtrails.com
Sales Range: $100-124.9 Million
Emp.: 900
RV Resorts & Campgrounds Operator
N.A.I.C.S.: 721214

Subsidiary (Domestic):

CB Resort Corporation (2)
2012 Hwy 90, Gautier, MS 39553
Tel.: (228) 497-4100
Web Site: http://www.1000trail.com
Rev.: $4,200,000
Emp.: 30
Subdividers & Developers
N.A.I.C.S.: 237210

Carolina Landing Corporation (2)

120 Carolina Landing Dr, Fair Play, SC 29643-2703
Tel.: (864) 972-9527
Web Site: http://www.rancho-oso.com
Sales Range: Less than $1 Million
Emp.: 7
Management Services
N.A.I.C.S.: 531210

Cherokee Landing Corporation (2)
PO Box 37, Middleton, TN 38052
Tel.: (731) 376-0935
Web Site: http://www.thousandtrails.com
Sales Range: $25-49.9 Million
Emp.: 6
Management Services
N.A.I.C.S.: 561110

Indian Lakes Wilderness Preserve Corporation (2)
7234 E State Rd 46, Batesville, IN 47006
Tel.: (812) 934-5693
Web Site: http://www.thousandtrails.com
Sales Range: Less than $1 Million
Emp.: 5
Trailer Parks & Campsites
N.A.I.C.S.: 721214

Lake Minden Resort (2)
1256 Marcum Rd, Nicolaus, CA 95659
Tel.: (530) 656-2700
Web Site: http://www.thousandtrails.com
Sales Range: $10-24.9 Million
Emp.: 20
Management Services
N.A.I.C.S.: 721214

Lake Tansi Village Inc. (2)
5050 Shoshone Loop, Crossville, TN 38572
Tel.: (931) 788-6721
Web Site: https://laketansi-poa.com
Sales Range: $1-9.9 Million
Emp.: 12
Subdividers & Developers
N.A.I.C.S.: 531390

Little Diamond RV Resort (2)
1002 McGowen Rd, Newport, WA 99156
Tel.: (509) 447-4813
Web Site: http://www.thousandtrails.com
Sales Range: Less than $1 Million
Emp.: 2
Management Services
N.A.I.C.S.: 721214

Naco Corp. (2)
3801 Parkwood Blvd Ste 100, Frisco, TX 75034
Tel.: (214) 618-7200
Sales Range: $10-24.9 Million
Emp.: 5
Management Services
N.A.I.C.S.: 721211

Turtle Beach Preserve (2)
703 Eastwilliamson Rd, Manteca, CA 95337
Tel.: (209) 239-0991
Rev.: $810,000
Emp.: 6
Management Services
N.A.I.C.S.: 721214

Virginia Landing Corporation (2)
40226 Upshur Neck Rd, Quinby, VA 23423
Tel.: (757) 442-5489
Web Site: http://www.1000trails.com
Sales Range: $10-24.9 Million
Emp.: 7
Campgrounds
N.A.I.C.S.: 721211

Wilderness Lakes (2)
30605 Briggs Rd, Sun City, CA 92584
Tel.: (951) 672-4831
Rev.: $1,800,000
Emp.: 100
Management Services
N.A.I.C.S.: 721214

EQUITY RESIDENTIAL
2 N Riverside Plz Ste 400, Chicago, IL 60606
Tel.: (312) 474-1300 MD
Web Site:
https://www.equityapartments.com
Year Founded: 1993
EQR—(NYSE)
Rev.: $2,873,964,000
Assets: $20,034,564,000

Liabilities: $8,745,436,000
Net Worth: $11,289,128,000
Earnings: $832,348,000
Emp.: 2,400
Fiscal Year-end: 12/31/23
Apartment Real Estate Investment
Trust
N.A.I.C.S.: 525990
David J. Neithercut (Chm)
Ian S. Kaufman (Chief Acctg Officer
& Sr VP)
Mark J. Parrell (Pres & CEO)
Robert A. Garechana (CFO & Exec
VP)
Catherine M. Carraway (Chief HR
Officer)

Subsidiaries:

API Fox Plaza LLC   (1)
9200 E Panorama Cir 400, Englewood, CO
80112
Tel.: (303) 708-5959
Emp.: 6
Real Estate Development Services
N.A.I.C.S.: 531210

ASN Technologies, Inc.   (1)
10291 S 1300 E Ste 118, Sandy, UT 84094
Tel.: (385) 444-0767
Software Development Services
N.A.I.C.S.: 541511

Archstone B.V.   (1)
Vondelstraat 73, Amsterdam, 1054, Nether-
lands
Tel.: (31) 206750028
Real Estate Investment Services
N.A.I.C.S.: 531210
Iwan Oude Roelink (Controller)

Archstone Cronin's Landing LLC (1)
25 Crescent St, Waltham, MA 02453
Tel.: (781) 209-2900
Real Estate Investment Services
N.A.I.C.S.: 531110

Archstone Redwood Shores LLC (1)
850 Davit Ln, Redwood City, CA 94065
Tel.: (650) 591-8906
Building & Dwelling Leasing Services
N.A.I.C.S.: 531110
Eva Sharp (Mgr)

Canterbury Apartments, L.L.C.   (1)
20015 Sweetgum Cir, Germantown, MD
20874
Tel.: (301) 804-9961
Web Site:
   http://www.livecanterburyapartments.com
Emp.: 10
Residential Building Rental & Leasing Ser-
vices
N.A.I.C.S.: 531110

Country Club Condominium,
L.L.C.   (1)
25561 Country Club Blvd, North Olmsted,
OH 44070
Tel.: (440) 779-7800
Emp.: 9
Residential Building Rental & Leasing Ser-
vices
N.A.I.C.S.: 531110

DeWAG 1. Objektgesellschaft
mbH   (1)
Kleiner Schlossplatz 13, Stuttgart, 70173,
Germany
Tel.: (49) 71149075204
Web Site: http://www.dewag.de
Emp.: 20
Real Estate Development Services
N.A.I.C.S.: 531210
Helmut Beyl (Founder, CEO & Mng Dir)
Michael Herzog (Mng Dir)
Joachim von Klitzing (Mng Dir)

DeWAG Management GmbH   (1)
Kleiner Schlossplatz 13, 70173, Stuttgart,
Germany
Tel.: (49) 711490750
Web Site: http://www.dewag.de
Real Estate Development Services
N.A.I.C.S.: 531210

EC-Mission Verde, LLC   (1)
5310 Wong Ct, San Jose, CA 95123

Tel.: (408) 578-2520
Residential Building Rental & Leasing Ser-
vices
N.A.I.C.S.: 531110

EQR-1500 Mass, LLC   (1)
1500 Massachusetts Ave NW, Washington,
DC 20005
Tel.: (202) 908-6222
Residential Building Rental & Leasing Ser-
vices
N.A.I.C.S.: 531110

EQR-175 Kent Avenue A, LLC (1)
175 Kent Ave, Brooklyn, NY 11249
Tel.: (347) 834-8053
Web Site: http://www.equityapartments.com
Residential Building Rental & Leasing Ser-
vices
N.A.I.C.S.: 531110
A. Fortesa (Mgr-Community)

EQR-228 West 71st, LLC   (1)
228 W 71st St, New York, NY 10023
Tel.: (646) 989-8688
Residential Building Rental & Leasing Ser-
vices
N.A.I.C.S.: 531110

EQR-425 Massachusetts, LLC (1)
425 Massachusetts Ave NW, Washington,
DC 20001
Tel.: (202) 908-6283
Web Site:
   http://www.425massapartments.com
Emp.: 20
Residential Building Rental & Leasing Ser-
vices
N.A.I.C.S.: 531110

EQR-600 Washington, L.L.C.   (1)
600 Washington St, New York, NY 10014
Tel.: (646) 989-8485
Residential Building Rental & Leasing Ser-
vices
N.A.I.C.S.: 531110

EQR-71 Broadway, LLC   (1)
71 Broadway, New York, NY 10006
Tel.: (646) 989-8506
Web Site: http://www.equityapartments.com
Real Estate Agencies & Brokerage Services
N.A.I.C.S.: 531210

EQR-77 Park Avenue LLC   (1)
77 Park Ave, Hoboken, NJ 07030
Tel.: (201) 942-5550
Apartment Rental Services
N.A.I.C.S.: 531110

EQR-Academy Village, L.L.C. (1)
5225 Blakeslee Ave, North Hollywood, CA
91601
Tel.: (818) 287-0297
Web Site: http://www.equityapartments.com
Residential Building Rental & Leasing Ser-
vices
N.A.I.C.S.: 531110

EQR-Cape House I, LP   (1)
2 N Riverside Plz Ste 400, Chicago, IL
60606-2624
Tel.: (312) 474-1300
Residential Building Rental & Leasing Services
N.A.I.C.S.: 531110

EQR-GLO Apartments, LLC   (1)
1050 Wilshire Blvd, Los Angeles, CA 90017
Tel.: (213) 335-6593
Web Site: http://www.equityapartments.com
Residential Building Rental & Leasing Ser-
vices
N.A.I.C.S.: 531110
S. Robb (Mgr-Community)

EQR-Gallery Apartments Limited
Partnership   (1)
414 2nd St, Hermosa Beach, CA 90254
Tel.: (424) 400-5761
Web Site: http://www.equityapartments.com
Residential Building Rental & Leasing Ser-
vices
N.A.I.C.S.: 531110

EQR-Gateway at Malden Center,
LLC   (1)
14 Summer St, Malden, MA 02148
Tel.: (617) 648-4970
Web Site: http://www.equityapartments.com

Residential Building Rental & Leasing Services
N.A.I.C.S.: 531110

EQR-Heights on Capitol Hill LLC (1)
130 Harvard Ave E, Seattle, WA 98102
Tel.: (206) 347-3594
Apartment Rental Services
N.A.I.C.S.: 531110

EQR-Heritage Ridge, L.L.C.   (1)
16619 Larch Way, Lynnwood, WA 98037
Tel.: (425) 361-0776
Residential Building Rental & Leasing Ser-
vices
N.A.I.C.S.: 531110

EQR-Hudson Crossing, LLC   (1)
400 W 37th St, New York, NY 10018
Tel.: (646) 989-8586
Web Site: http://www.equityapartments.com
Residential Building Rental & Leasing Ser-
vices
N.A.I.C.S.: 531110

EQR-Hudson Pointe, L.L.C.   (1)
131 Dudley St, Jersey City, NJ 07302
Tel.: (201) 942-5860
Residential Building Rental & Leasing Ser-
vices
N.A.I.C.S.: 531110

EQR-Ivory Wood, L.L.C.   (1)
8700 NE Bothell Way, Bothell, WA 98011
Tel.: (425) 318-8359
Web Site: http://www.equityresidential.com
Emp.: 4
Residential Building Rental & Leasing Ser-
vices
N.A.I.C.S.: 531110

EQR-Kelvin Court, LLC   (1)
2552 Kelvin Ave, Irvine, CA 92614
Tel.: (949) 774-2605
Web Site: http://www.equityapartments.com
Residential Building Rental & Leasing Ser-
vices
N.A.I.C.S.: 531110

EQR-Kings Colony, L.L.C.   (1)
8961 SW 142nd Ave, Miami, FL 33186
Tel.: (239) 579-9509
Web Site: http://www.kingscolony-living.com
Residential Building Rental & Leasing Ser-
vices
N.A.I.C.S.: 531110

EQR-Lexington Farm, L.L.C.   (1)
1000 Lexington Farm Dr, Alpharetta, GA
30004
Tel.: (866) 915-1047
Residential Building Rental & Leasing Services
N.A.I.C.S.: 531110

EQR-Liberty Tower, LLC   (1)
818 N Quincy St, Arlington, VA 22203
Tel.: (703) 664-1429
Residential Building Rental & Leasing Ser-
vices
N.A.I.C.S.: 531110

EQR-Lindley, LLC   (1)
5536 Lindley Ave, Encino, CA 91316
Tel.: (818) 528-5313
Web Site: http://www.equityapartments.com
Emp.: 4
Residential Building Rental & Leasing Ser-
vices
N.A.I.C.S.: 531110

EQR-Luna Upper Westside LLC (1)
2265 Marietta Blvd NW, Atlanta, GA 30318
Web Site:
   https://www.lunaupperwestside.com
Apartment Rental Services
N.A.I.C.S.: 531110

EQR-Mark on 8th LLC   (1)
285 8th Ave N, Seattle, WA 98109
Tel.: (206) 452-0041
Apartment Rental Services
N.A.I.C.S.: 531110

EQR-Metro on First LLC   (1)
215 1st Ave W, Seattle, WA 98119
Tel.: (206) 347-3670
Apartment Rental Services
N.A.I.C.S.: 531110

EQR-Midtown 24, LLC   (1)
700 SW 78 Ave, Plantation, FL 33324

Tel.: (954) 476-5656
Web Site: http://www.midtown24-living.com
Sales Range: $25-49.9 Million
Emp.: 6
Residential Building Rental & Leasing Ser-
vices
N.A.I.C.S.: 531110

EQR-Mill Creek, L.L.C.   (1)
14420 N Creek Dr, Mill Creek, WA 98012
Tel.: (425) 599-2383
Web Site: http://www.equityapartments.com
Sales Range: $25-49.9 Million
Emp.: 5
Residential Building Rental & Leasing Ser-
vices
N.A.I.C.S.: 531110

EQR-Miramar Lakes, L.L.C.   (1)
10160 Miromar Lakes Blvd, Miramar, FL
33913
Tel.: (239) 425-2340
Web Site: https://www.miromarlakes.com
Emp.: 6
Residential Building Rental & Leasing Ser-
vices
N.A.I.C.S.: 531110

EQR-Northpark, LLC   (1)
1080 Carolan Ave, Burlingame, CA 94010
Tel.: (650) 227-4612
Residential Building Rental & Leasing Ser-
vices
N.A.I.C.S.: 531110

EQR-Notch LLC   (1)
13800 Newcastle Golf Club Rd, Newcastle,
WA 98059
Tel.: (425) 256-4690
Apartment Development Services
N.A.I.C.S.: 624229
B. Lia (Mgr-Community)

EQR-Oak Mill, L.L.C.   (1)
20010 Frederick Rd, Germantown, MD
20876
Tel.: (866) 915-2399
Web Site: http://www.liveoakmill.com
Emp.: 7
Residential Building Rental & Leasing Ser-
vices
N.A.I.C.S.: 531110

EQR-Oaks at Falls Church, LLC (1)
2158 Evans Ct, Falls Church, VA 22043
Tel.: (866) 915-6970
Web Site:
   http://www.theoaksatfallschurch.com
Emp.: 4
Residential Building Rental & Leasing Ser-
vices
N.A.I.C.S.: 531110

EQR-Palm Trace Landing, L.L.C. (1)
6351 Palm Trace Landings Dr, Fort Lauder-
dale, FL 33314
Tel.: (954) 327-7256
Sales Range: $25-49.9 Million
Emp.: 15
Residential Building Rental & Leasing Ser-
vices
N.A.I.C.S.: 531110
Bridgitte Gearceau (Gen Mgr)

EQR-Pegasus, LLC   (1)
612 S Flower St, Los Angeles, CA 90017
Tel.: (213) 430-9112
Web Site: http://www.eqityappatement.com
Emp.: 11
Residential Building Rental & Leasing Ser-
vices
N.A.I.C.S.: 531110
L. Daniel (Gen Mgr)

EQR-Reserve at Eisenhower
LLC   (1)
5000 Eisenhower Ave, Alexandria, VA
22304
Tel.: (703) 664-1722
Apartment Development Services
N.A.I.C.S.: 624229
C. Elena (Mgr-Community)

EQR-Rivertower, LLC   (1)
420 E 54th St, New York, NY 10022
Tel.: (866) 364-5308
Web Site: http://www.eqr.com
Emp.: 30
Residential Building Rental & Leasing Ser-
vices

Equity Residential—(Continued)

N.A.I.C.S.: 531110

EQR-Siena Terrace, L.L.C. (1)
20041 Osterman Rd, Lake Forest, CA
92630
Tel.: (866) 915-5180
Web Site:
http://www.equityapartments.com
Sales Range: $25-49.9 Million
Emp.: 8
Residential Building Rental & Leasing Services
N.A.I.C.S.: 531110
G. Eric (Mgr-Community)

**EQR-Skyline Terrace Limited
Partnership** (1)
3133 Frontera Way, Burlingame, CA 94010
Tel.: (866) 614-8286
Web Site: http://www.equityapartments.com
Emp.: 4
Residential Building Rental & Leasing Services
N.A.I.C.S.: 531110
D. Sherwin (Mgr-Community)

**EQR-Southwood Limited
Partnership** (1)
2850 Middlefield Rd, Palo Alto, CA 94306
Tel.: (866) 915-5218
Web Site: http://www.equityapartments.com
Residential Building Rental & Leasing Services
N.A.I.C.S.: 531110

EQR-Uwajimaya Village, L.L.C. (1)
521 S Weller, Seattle, WA 98104
Tel.: (206) 347-3797
Web Site: http://www.equityapartments.com
Sales Range: $25-49.9 Million
Emp.: 5
Residential Building Rental & Leasing Services
N.A.I.C.S.: 531110

EQR-Vantage Pointe, LLC (1)
1281 9th Ave, San Diego, CA 92101
Web Site:
https://rent.brookfieldproperties.com
Real Estate Agencies & Brokerage Services
N.A.I.C.S.: 531210

EQR-Virginia Square LLC (1)
901 N Nelson St, Arlington, VA 22203
Tel.: (703) 664-1791
Apartment Rental Services
N.A.I.C.S.: 531110

EQR-Waterford Place, L.L.C. (1)
2801 E 120th Ave, Thornton, CO 80233
Tel.: (866) 915-8468
Residential Building Rental & Leasing Services
N.A.I.C.S.: 531110

EQR-Wellington Green, L.L.C. (1)
2301 Wellington Green Dr, Wellington, FL
33414
Tel.: (561) 791-7368
Emp.: 9
Residential Building Rental & Leasing Services
N.A.I.C.S.: 531110
Michelle Davila (Gen Mgr)

**ERP Operating Limited
Partnership** (1)
2 N Riverside Plz, Chicago, IL 60606
Tel.: (312) 474-1300
Web Site:
https://www.equityapartments.com
Rev.: $2,735,179,999
Assets: $20,218,261,999
Liabilities: $8,835,582,999
Net Worth: $11,382,678,999
Earnings: $806,994,999
Emp.: 2,399
Fiscal Year-end: 12/31/2022
Real Estate Investment Trust
N.A.I.C.S.: 525990
Mark J. Parrell (Pres & CEO)

**Equity Apartment Management,
LLC** (1)
101 E New Hampshire Ave Ste 3E, Deland,
FL 32724
Tel.: (386) 738-2280
Residential Building Rental & Leasing Services

N.A.I.C.S.: 531110

**Equity Residential Management,
L.L.C.** (1)
230 W 41st St 12th Fl, New York, NY
10036
Tel.: (646) 833-3960
Web Site: http://www.equityapartments.com
Emp.: 7
Residential Building Rental & Leasing Services
N.A.I.C.S.: 531110
Vedzaida Clemente (Mgr-Community-Manhattan)

GPT-Webster Green, LLC (1)
757 Highland Ave Apt 103S, Needham, MA
02494
Tel.: (781) 444-5800
Nursing Care Facilities Services
N.A.I.C.S.: 623110
Nicole Fitzgerald (Mgr-Property)

GR-Highland Glen, L.P. (1)
1055 Highland Glen Rd, Westwood, MA
02090
Tel.: (781) 214-8999
Web Site:
https://www.highlandglenapartments
bc.com
Residential Building Rental & Leasing Services
N.A.I.C.S.: 531110

**Lewis-McChord Communities,
LLC** (1)
Waller Hall Bldg 2150, Fort Lewis, WA
98433
Tel.: (253) 912-2150
Web Site:
http://www.mcchordcommunities.com
Residential Building Rental & Leasing Services
N.A.I.C.S.: 531110

Longview Place, LLC (1)
70 Hope Ave, Waltham, MA 02453
Tel.: (857) 263-2147
Web Site: http://www.equityapartments.com
Residential Building Rental & Leasing Services
N.A.I.C.S.: 531110

Pointe East Condominium, LLC (1)
3801 S Atlantic Ave, New Smyrna Beach,
FL 32169
Tel.: (386) 427-3894
Web Site: http://www.pointeastcondo.com
Residential Building Rental & Leasing Services
N.A.I.C.S.: 531110

**Redwood Shores Owners
Association** (1)
1820 Gateway Dr Ste 100, San Mateo, CA
94404
Tel.: (650) 637-1616
Web Site: https://www.rsoa.info
Administrative Management Consulting Services
N.A.I.C.S.: 541611
David Valkenaar (Pres)
Paul Delzio (VP)
Kathryn Massa (CFO)
Anish Srivastava (Sec)

**Residential Insurance Agency,
LLC** (1)
1209 Orange St, Wilmington, DE 19801
Tel.: (312) 928-8453
Residential Building Rental & Leasing Services
N.A.I.C.S.: 531110

Woodbine Properties (1)
227 New Centerville Rd, Somerset, PA
15501
Tel.: (814) 443-4688
Residential Building Rental & Leasing Services
N.A.I.C.S.: 531110

EQUUS TOTAL RETURN, INC.
700 Louisiana St 48th Fl, Houston,
TX 77002
Tel.: (713) 529-0900 DE
Web Site: https://www.equuscap.com
Year Founded: 1991
EQS—(NYSE)

Assets: $41,664,000
Liabilities: $6,427,000
Net Worth: $35,237,000
Earnings: ($3,629,000)
Fiscal Year-end: 12/31/22
Investment Holding Company
N.A.I.C.S.: 551112
Robert L. Knauss (Chm)
L'Sheryl D. Hudson (CFO, Treas & Sr VP)
John A. Hardy (CEO)
Kenneth I. Denos (Chief Compliance
Officer & Sec)

ERASCA, INC.
3115 Merryfield Row Ste 300, San
Diego, CA 92121
Tel.: (858) 465-6511 DE
Web Site: https://www.erasca.com
Year Founded: 2018
ERAS—(NASDAQ)
Rev.: $4,645,000
Assets: $514,909,000
Liabilities: $103,056,000
Net Worth: $411,853,000
Earnings: ($242,805,000)
Emp.: 129
Fiscal Year-end: 12/31/22
Research & Development in Biotechnology (except Nanobiotechnology)
N.A.I.C.S.: 541714
Shannon R. Morris (Chief Medical
Officer)
David Chacko (CFO)
Amanda Albert (VP-Portfolio & Program Leadership)
Brian Baker (Sr VP-Fin)
Les Brail (VP-Clinical Dev)
Rachel Cervantes (VP-Bus Dev)
Nik Chetwyn (Sr VP-Ops)
Chandra Lovejoy (Chief Regulatory
Affairs Officer)
David Luo (VP-Clinical Research &
Ops)
Robert Shoemaker (VP-Biology)
Bao Truong (VP-Program)
Jean-Michel Vernier (VP-Chemistry)
Minli Xie (VP-Pharmaceutical Dev &
Ops)
Dawei Xuan (VP-Clinical Pharmacology)
Jing Yi (VP-Data Science)
Ebun Garner (Gen Counsel & Sec)
Shannon R. Morris (Chief Medical
Officer)
Jonathan E. Lim (Founder, Chm &
CEO)
Michael D. Varney (Chm-R&D)

Subsidiaries:

Asana BioSciences, LLC (1)
400 Crossing Blvd 7th Fl, Bridgewater, NJ
08807
Tel.: (908) 698-0988
Web Site:
https://www.asanabiosciences.com
Biopharmaceutical Product Mfr
N.A.I.C.S.: 325412
Chintu Patel (Co-Founder)

ERHC ENERGY, INC.
5444 Westheimer Rd Ste 1000,
Houston, TX 77056
Tel.: (713) 626-4700 CO
Web Site: https://www.erhc.com
Year Founded: 1986
ERHE—(OTCIQ)
Sales Range: Less than $1 Million
Emp.: 9
Oil & Gas Exploration Services
N.A.I.C.S.: 211120
Andrew C. Uzoigwe (Dir)
Peter C. Ntephe (Pres & CEO)
Sylvan Odobulu (VP-Admin & Controller)
Ken Seymour (Sr Engr-Petroleum)

Howard F. Jeter (Dir)
Friday Oviawe (Dir)
Reginald J. D. Sewell (Corp Counsel)

ERIE INDEMNITY COMPANY
100 Erie Insurance Pl, Erie, PA
16530-1104
Tel.: (814) 451-5000 PA
Web Site:
https://www.erieinsurance.com
Year Founded: 1925
ERIE—(NASDAQ)
Rev.: $3,268,940,000
Assets: $2,471,964,000
Liabilities: $809,129,000
Net Worth: $1,662,835,000
Earnings: $446,061,000
Emp.: 6,481
Fiscal Year-end: 12/31/23
Holding Company; Insurance Services
N.A.I.C.S.: 551112
Sean Dugan (Exec VP-HR & Corp
Svcs)
Timothy G. NeCastro (Pres & CEO)
Parthasarathy Srinivasa (CIO & Exec
VP)
Julie Marie Pelkowski (CFO & Exec
VP)
Brian W. Bolash (Gen Counsel, Sec
& Exec VP)
Jorie L. Novacek (Sr VP & Controller)

Subsidiaries:

**Erie Family Life Insurance
Company** (1)
100 Erie Insurance Pl, Erie, PA 16530
Tel.: (814) 870-2000
Web Site: http://www.erieinsurance.com
Sales Range: $125-149.9 Million
Emp.: 4,000
Life Insurance
N.A.I.C.S.: 524113
Louis Colaizzo (Sr VP)

Erie Insurance Company (1)
100 Erie Insurance Pl, Erie, PA
16530-0001 (100%)
Tel.: (814) 870-2000
Web Site: http://www.erieinsurance.com
Sales Range: Less than $1 Million
Emp.: 2,500
Property Casualty Insurance
N.A.I.C.S.: 524113
Sean Dugan (Exec VP-HR & Corp Svcs)
Chris Marsh (Chief Diversity & Community
Dev Officer)
Sean Dugan (Exec VP-HR & Corp Svcs)
Tim NeCastro (Pres & CEO)

Subsidiary (Domestic):

**Erie Insurance Company of New
York** (2)
120 Corporate Woods Ste 150, Rochester,
NY 14623-1452 (100%)
Tel.: (585) 214-5800
Web Site: http://www.erieinsurance.com
Sales Range: $75-99.9 Million
Emp.: 100
Property Casualty Insurance
N.A.I.C.S.: 524210

**Erie Insurance Property & Casualty
Company** (1)
100 Erie Insurance Pl, Erie, PA
16530-0001 (100%)
Tel.: (814) 870-2000
Web Site: http://www.erieinsurance.com
Rev.: $491,000
Property Casualty Insurance
N.A.I.C.S.: 524113

**Flagship City Insurance
Company** (1)
100 Erie Insurance Pl, Erie, PA 16530-0001
Tel.: (814) 870-2000
Web Site: http://www.erieinsurance.com
Sales Range: $150-199.9 Million
Assigned Risk Insurance
N.A.I.C.S.: 524113

ES BANCSHARES, INC.

1441 S Ave Ste 705, Staten Island, NY 10314
Tel.: (347) 592-1956   MD
Web Site: https://www.esbna.com
ESBS—(OTCIQ)
Rev.: $19,573,000
Assets: $515,774,000
Liabilities: $481,069,000
Net Worth: $34,705,000
Earnings: $1,205,000
Emp.: 63
Fiscal Year-end: 12/31/20
Bank Holding Company
N.A.I.C.S.: 551111
Philip A. Guarnieri *(CEO)*
Thomas P. Sperzel *(Pres & COO)*
Walter Daszkowski *(Vice Chm)*
Andrew G. Finkelstein *(Chm)*

Subsidiaries:

Empire State Bank   **(1)**
1441 S Ave, Staten Island, NY 10314
Tel.: (845) 561-0003
Web Site: http://www.esbna.com
Federal Savings Bank
N.A.I.C.S.: 522180
Philip A. Guarnieri *(CEO)*
Peggy Edwards *(VP & Dir-HR)*
Thomas P. Sperzel *(Pres & COO)*
Raffaele M. Branca *(Chief Credit Officer & Exec VP)*
Erik Terpstra *(CFO & Sr VP)*

ESAB CORPORATION

909 Rose Ave N, Bethesda, MD 20852
Tel.: (301) 323-9099   DE
Web Site:
    https://www.esabcorporation.com
Year Founded: 1904
ESAB—(NYSE)
Rev.: $2,774,766,000
Assets: $3,828,629,000
Liabilities: $2,180,972,000
Net Worth: $1,647,657,000
Earnings: $205,285,000
Emp.: 9,000
Fiscal Year-end: 12/31/23
Fabrication Product Mfr
N.A.I.C.S.: 332312
Shyam P. Kambeyanda *(Pres & CEO)*
Renato Negro *(Chief Acctg Officer)*

ESCALADE, INCORPORATED

817 Maxwell Ave, Evansville, IN 47711
Tel.: (812) 467-1358   IN
Web Site:
    https://www.escaladeinc.com
Year Founded: 1927
ESCA—(NASDAQ)
Rev.: $313,612,000
Assets: $251,798,000
Liabilities: $105,183,000
Net Worth: $146,615,000
Earnings: $24,405,000
Emp.: 670
Fiscal Year-end: 12/25/21
Recreational Items Mfr
N.A.I.C.S.: 339920
Patrick J. Griffin *(VP-Corp Dev & IR)*
Walter P. Glazer Jr. *(Chm, Pres & CEO)*

Subsidiaries:

Bear Archery, Inc.   **(1)**
817 Maxwell Ave, Evansville, IN 47711
Tel.: (812) 467-1200
Web Site: https://www.beararchery.com
Emp.: 50
Archery Equipment Mfr
N.A.I.C.S.: 339920
Dave Fetherman *(CEO)*

Subsidiary (Domestic):

Jim Fletcher Archery Aids, Inc.   **(2)**

2200 Stringtown Rd, Evansville, IN 47711
Tel.: (800) 694-9494
Web Site: http://www.fletcherarchery.com
Precision Archery Equipment Mfr
N.A.I.C.S.: 459110

Escalade Sports Playground, Inc.   **(1)**
Escalade Sports 817 Maxwell Ave, Evansville, IN 47711
Web Site: https://www.escaladesports.com
Sporting & Athletic Goods Mfr
N.A.I.C.S.: 339920

Indian Industries, Inc.   **(1)**
817 Maxwell Ave, Evansville, IN 47711
Web Site: https://www.escaladesports.com
Sporting & Athletic Goods Mfr
N.A.I.C.S.: 339920

Subsidiary (Domestic):

American Heritage Billiards, LLC   **(2)**
630 Mondial Pkwy, Streetsboro, OH 44241-5211
Tel.: (330) 626-3710
Web Site:
    http://www.americanheritagebilliards.com
Sales Range: $10-24.9 Million
Emp.: 25
Game Room Furniture Mfr
N.A.I.C.S.: 339920

Goalsetter Systems, Inc.   **(2)**
1041 Cordova Ave, Lynnville, IA 50153
Web Site: https://www.goalsetter.com
Sales Range: $1-9.9 Million
Emp.: 30
Sporting & Athletic Goods Mfr
N.A.I.C.S.: 339920

Stiga Sports AB   **(2)**
Tang Lindstroms VAG 7 9, PO Box 642, 633 46, Eskilstuna, Sweden   **(50%)**
Tel.: (46) 16162600
Web Site: https://www.stigasports.com
Sales Range: $10-24.9 Million
Emp.: 40
Mfr & Sell Sporting Goods, Office & Graphic Art Products
N.A.I.C.S.: 339920

Victory Tailgate, LLC   **(1)**
8673 Transport Dr, Orlando, FL 32832
Tel.: (407) 704-8775
Web Site: https://www.victorytailgate.com
Sports Accessory Mfr
N.A.I.C.S.: 339920
Scott Sims *(Founder & CEO)*

Wedcor Holdings, Inc.   **(1)**
251 Wedcor Ave, Wabash, IN 46992
Tel.: (260) 563-0641
Web Site: https://www.martinyale.com
Sales Range: $25-49.9 Million
Emp.: 30
Sporting & Athletic Goods Mfr
N.A.I.C.S.: 339920

Subsidiary (Domestic):

Martin Yale Industries, LLC   **(2)**
251 Wedcor Ave, Wabash, IN 46992
Tel.: (260) 563-0641
Web Site: https://www.martinyale.com
Office & Mailroom Equipment Mfr
N.A.I.C.S.: 339940

ESCALON MEDICAL CORP.

435 Devon Park Dr Ste 824, Wayne, PA 19087
Tel.: (610) 688-6830   PA
Web Site:
    https://www.escalonmedical.com
Year Founded: 1987
ESMC—(OTCQB)
Rev.: $11,981,509
Assets: $4,757,925
Liabilities: $2,948,343
Net Worth: $1,809,582
Earnings: ($125,261)
Emp.: 40
Fiscal Year-end: 06/30/24
Ophthalmic Medical Devices Mfr & Distr
N.A.I.C.S.: 334510

Mark G. Wallace *(CFO, COO & Chief Acctg Officer)*
Richard J. DePiano Jr. *(Chm, Pres, CEO & Gen Counsel)*

Subsidiaries:

Escalon Medical Imaging   **(1)**
2440 S 179th St, New Berlin, WI 53146   **(100%)**
Tel.: (262) 821-9182
Sales Range: $50-74.9 Million
Emp.: 5
Medical Equipment
N.A.I.C.S.: 424210
Cathy Kocherer *(Office Mgr)*

Escalon Pennsylvania, Inc.   **(1)**
435 Devon Park Dr Bldg 100, Wayne, PA 19087   **(100%)**
Tel.: (610) 688-6830
Web Site: http://www.escalonmed.com
Sales Range: $1-9.9 Million
Emp.: 15
Medical Equipment
N.A.I.C.S.: 334510

Sonomed, Inc.   **(1)**
1979 Marcus Ave C105, Lake Success, NY 11042-1012
Tel.: (516) 354-0900
Web Site: https://www.sonomedescalon.com
Sales Range: $10-24.9 Million
Emp.: 28
Mfr of Pharmaceutical & Vascular Access Products
N.A.I.C.S.: 339112

ESCO TECHNOLOGIES, INC.

9900A Clayton Rd, Saint Louis, MO 63124-1186
Tel.: (314) 213-7200   MO
Web Site:
    https://www.escotechnologies.com
Year Founded: 1990
ESE—(NYSE)
Rev.: $1,026,759,000
Assets: $1,838,620,000
Liabilities: $601,270,000
Net Worth: $1,237,350,000
Earnings: $101,881,000
Emp.: 3,242
Fiscal Year-end: 09/30/24
Engineered Filtration Products & Systems for Industrial & Commercial Applications Mfr
N.A.I.C.S.: 334290
Christopher L. Tucker *(CFO & Sr VP)*
Bryan H. Sayler *(Pres & CEO)*
David M. Schatz *(Gen Counsel, Sec & Sr VP)*

Subsidiaries:

Advanced Technology Machining, Inc.   **(1)**
28210 Ave Crocker Ste 301, Valencia, CA 91355
Tel.: (661) 257-2313
Web Site: http://www.atmach.com
Machine Shops
N.A.I.C.S.: 332710
Joe Howton *(Founder & VP)*

ESCO Technologies Holding Inc.   **(1)**
9900A Clayton Rd, Saint Louis, MO 63124-1186   **(100%)**
Tel.: (314) 213-7200
Web Site: http://www.escotechnologies.com
Sales Range: $25-49.9 Million
Emp.: 35
Holding Company
N.A.I.C.S.: 551112

Subsidiary (Domestic):

Canyon Engineering Products, Inc.   **(2)**
28909 Avenue Williams, Valencia, CA 91355
Tel.: (661) 294-0084
Web Site:
    http://www.canyonengineering.com
Sales Range: $10-24.9 Million
Emp.: 62

Designer, Mfr & Assembly & Test of Fluid Control Devices for Aerospace Industry
N.A.I.C.S.: 336413

Crissair, Inc.   **(2)**
28909 Ave Williams, Valencia, CA 91355
Tel.: (661) 367-3300
Web Site: http://www.crissair.com
Aircraft Fluid Control Components Mfr
N.A.I.C.S.: 332912
Colleen Schultz *(Sr Dir-Quality)*
Eric Grupp *(VP-Bus Dev)*
Patrick LaCanfora *(VP-Engrg)*
Michael Alfred *(Pres)*
Mark Hughes *(CFO & VP-Fin & Admin)*
Beverly Malin *(Sr Dir-HR)*
Nicolas Eguiguren *(Sr Dir-Ops)*

Distribution Control Systems Caribe, Inc.   **(2)**
9900A Clayton Rd, Saint Louis, MO 63124   **(100%)**
Tel.: (314) 213-7200
Products & Systems for Industrial & Commercial Applications
N.A.I.C.S.: 336992

Doble Engineering Company   **(2)**
123 Felton St, Marlborough, MA 01752
Tel.: (617) 926-4900
Web Site: http://www.doble.com
Diagnostic Test Instruments Mfr & Consulting Services
N.A.I.C.S.: 334515
Bryan H. Sayler *(Pres)*
Paul Griffin *(VP-Professional Svcs)*
Bryan Sayler *(Pres)*
Don Angell *(VP-Global Strategy & Solutions)*
Julie Crisafulli Brown *(VP-Global HR & Admin)*
Ernie Grella *(VP-Global Engrg)*
Joseph McCadden *(VP-Fin)*
Jerry Olechiw *(VP-Global Sls)*

Subsidiary (Non-US):

Doble Lemke GmbH   **(3)**
Zschoner Ring 9, Kesselsdorf, 01723, Wilsdruff, Germany
Tel.: (49) 3520439000
Web Site: http://www.doble-lemke.eu
Dielectric Diagnostics & Monitoring Instruments Mfr
N.A.I.C.S.: 333994

Doble PowerTest Limited   **(3)**
5 Weyvern Park Peasmarsh, Guildford, GU3 1NA, Surrey, United Kingdom
Tel.: (44) 1483514120
Web Site: http://www.doble.com
Sales Range: $10-24.9 Million
Emp.: 20
Electrical Engineering Solutions Provider
N.A.I.C.S.: 335999

Doble TransiNor AS   **(3)**
Sorgenfriveien 9, N-7037, Trondheim, Norway
Tel.: (47) 73825350
Emp.: 10
Engineeering Services
N.A.I.C.S.: 541330
Frederik Karlsen *(Gen Mgr)*

Subsidiary (Domestic):

Vanguard Instruments Co., Inc.   **(3)**
1520 S Hellman Ave, Ontario, CA 91761
Tel.: (909) 923-9390
Web Site: http://www.doble.com
Switchgear And Switchboard Apparatus
N.A.I.C.S.: 335313
Hai Nguyen *(Pres)*

Subsidiary (Domestic):

ETS-Lindgren, L.P.   **(2)**
1301 Arrow Point Dr, Cedar Park, TX 78613-6936   **(100%)**
Tel.: (512) 531-6400
Web Site: http://www.ets-lindgren.com
Sales Range: $50-74.9 Million
Electromagnetic Compatibility Products Including Antennas, Masts, Turntables & The GTEM Cell
N.A.I.C.S.: 334519
Bruce E. Butler *(Pres)*

Subsidiary (Non-US):

ETS Lindgren Engineering India Private Limited   **(3)**

ESCO Technologies, Inc.—(Continued)

No 73 Service Road West of Chord Road, Mahalakshmipuram, Bengaluru, 560 086, Karnataka, India
Tel.: (91) 8043418600
Web Site: http://www.ets-lindgren.com
Sales Range: $25-49.9 Million
Emp.: 25
Electromagnetic & Acoustic Energy Detection Systems & Components Mfr
N.A.I.C.S.: 334513
Mark Mawdsley (Mng Dir-Asia Ops)

ETS Lindgren Japan, Inc. (3)
Kohinata 4-2-6, Bunkyo-ku, Tokyo, 112-0006, Japan
Tel.: (81) 338137100
Web Site: http://www.ets-lindgren.com
Emp.: 12
Electromagnetic & Testing Electronic Device Mfr
N.A.I.C.S.: 334510

ETS-Lindgren GmbH (3)
Wallbergstrasse 7, 82024, Taufkirchen, Germany
Tel.: (49) 896141710
Web Site: http://www.emvgmbh.de
Medical Measuring Equipment Mfr
N.A.I.C.S.: 339112
Bruce Butler (Pres)

ETS-Lindgren Limited (3)
Unit 4 Eastman Way, Pin Green Industrial Area, Stevenage, SG1 4UH, Herts, United Kingdom (100%)
Tel.: (44) 1438730700
Web Site: http://www.ets-lindgren.com
Sales Range: $10-24.9 Million
Emp.: 18
Electromagnetic Enclosures
N.A.I.C.S.: 334419

ETS-Lindgren OY (3)
Mekaanikontie 1 Fl, 27510, Eura, Finland (100%)
Tel.: (358) 28383300
Web Site: http://www.ets-lindgren.com
Sales Range: $25-49.9 Million
Emp.: 68
Light Construction
N.A.I.C.S.: 333120

Subsidiary (Domestic):

Lindgren R.F. Enclosures, Inc. (3)
400 High Grove Blvd, Glendale Heights, IL 60139 (100%)
Tel.: (630) 307-7200
Web Site: http://www.ets-lindgren.com
Sales Range: $25-49.9 Million
Emp.: 100
Devices that Measure, Shield & Control Electromagnetic Energy
N.A.I.C.S.: 333998

Subsidiary (Domestic):

Enoserv, LLC (2)
7780 E 106th St, Tulsa, OK 74133
Tel.: (918) 622-4530
Web Site: http://www.enoserv.com
Scientific & Technical Consulting Services
N.A.I.C.S.: 541690

Mayday Manufacturing Co. (2)
3100 Jim Christal Rd, Denton, TX 76207-2402
Tel.: (940) 898-8301
Web Site: http://www.maydaymfg.com
Sales Range: $25-49.9 Million
Precision Hardware Mfr
N.A.I.C.S.: 332511
Tom Shaw (Pres)
Douglas Wulf (VP-Mfg)
Amelia Fielder (Mgr-Customer Svc)

Subsidiary (Domestic):

Hi-Tech Metals, Inc. (3)
59-20 56th Ave, Maspeth, NY 11378
Tel.: (718) 894-1212
Web Site: http://www.hi-techmetals.com
Sales Range: $1-9.9 Million
Emp.: 40
Metal Finishing Services
N.A.I.C.S.: 332813

Subsidiary (Domestic):

NRG Systems, Inc. (2)

110 Riggs Rd, Hinesburg, VT 05461
Tel.: (802) 482-2255
Web Site: http://www.nrgsystems.com
Sales Range: $1-9.9 Million
Renewable Energy Support Tools Mfr
N.A.I.C.S.: 221115
Anna Grady (VP-HR)
Julia Austin (VP-Ops)
Greg Erdmann (VP-Sls-Global)
Ann Greenamyre (VP-Fin)
David Hurwitt (VP-Global Mktg & Product Mgmt)
Evan Vogel (Pres)

PTI Technologies Inc. (2)
501 Del Norte Blvd, Oxnard, CA 93030-7983 (100%)
Tel.: (805) 604-3700
Web Site: http://www.ptitechnologies.com
Sales Range: $10-24.9 Million
Emp.: 100
Mfr of Filtration Products for Aerospace, Industrial Fluid Power & Chemical Processing
N.A.I.C.S.: 336413
Rowland Ellis (Sr VP & Gen Mgr)
Beth Kozlowski (Sr VP)
Kanwar Suri (Sr VP-Engrg)
William Hoctor (VP-Contracts & Subcontracts)

VACCO Industries Inc. (2)
10350 Vacco St, South El Monte, CA 91733-3399 (100%)
Tel.: (626) 443-7121
Web Site: http://www.vacco.com
Sales Range: $125-149.9 Million
Emp.: 300
Mfr Of Specialized Flow Control Valves Filters & Filtration Systems & Photochemical Machining
N.A.I.C.S.: 332919
Andrew Baldwin (Sls Mgr-Aircraft, Defense, and Navy Products)
Cleve Samson (Sls Mgr-Space Products-West Coast)
Manan Parikh (Sls Mgr-Filtration & Space Products-East Coast)
Greg Brobston (Mgr-Sls-Precision Etched Parts Products)
Fred Willuhn (Mgr-Bus Dev-Space Products)
John A. Habis (VP-Bus Dev & Strategy-Space Products Intl)

Westland Technologies Inc. (2)
107 S Riverside Dr, Modesto, CA 95354 (100%)
Tel.: (209) 571-6400
Web Site: http://www.westlandtech.com
Sales Range: $25-49.9 Million
Emp.: 100
Manufacturer & Distributor Custom Molded Rubber Products
N.A.I.C.S.: 326299

Xtensible Solutions, Inc. (2)
6312 S Fiddlers Green Cir Ste 210E, Greenwood Village, CO 80111
Tel.: (720) 240-0500
Web Site: http://www.xtensible.net
Sales Range: $1-9.9 Million
Emp.: 15
Business Consulting Services
N.A.I.C.S.: 541618
Gregory M. Robinson (Founder & Gen Mgr)
Phillip Jones (VP-Solution Dev)
Harry Garton (VP-Professional Svcs)
Michael Covarrubias (Dir-Market Strategy & Solutions)

ETS-Lindgren Inc. (1)
1360 N Wood Dale Rd Ste G, Wood Dale, IL 60191
Tel.: (630) 307-7200
Web Site: http://www.ets-lindgren.com
Emp.: 750
Electromagnetic & Acoustic Energy Component Mfr
N.A.I.C.S.: 334515

Globe Composite Solutions, LLC (1)
200 Shuman Ave, Stoughton, MA 02072
Web Site: http://www.globecomposite.com
Mfr of Industrial Rubber, Marine & Vibration Control Products
N.A.I.C.S.: 326199
William F. Clement (CFO)
Scott Hruzd (VP-Ops)

Jim Rothwell (VP-Engrg)
Mike Logan (Mgr-Ops)
Michael Archibald (CFO)

Morgan Schaffer Ltd. (1)
225 rue Lafleur Bureau 150, La Salle, H8R 3H2, QC, Canada
Tel.: (514) 739-1967
Web Site: http://www.morganschaffer.com
Dissolved Gas Analysis Services
N.A.I.C.S.: 541380
May L. Scally (COO-Canadian Ops)

Phenix Technology, Inc. (1)
12391 Sampson St Ste H, Riverside, CA 92503-4816
Web Site: http://www.phenixfirehelmets.com
General Purpose Machinery Mfr
N.A.I.C.S.: 333998
Ray Russell (Owner)

ESH ACQUISITION CORP.
228 Park Ave S Ste 89898, New York, NY 10003-1502
Tel.: (212) 287-5022 — DE
Web Site: https://www.eshacquisition.com
Year Founded: 2021
ESHU—(NASDAQ)
Emp.: 2
Investment Services
N.A.I.C.S.: 523999
James Francis (CEO)
Jonathan Morris (CFO)
Allen Weiss (Chm)
Christopher Ackerley (Dir)
Christina Francis (Dir)
Jonathan Gordon (Dir)
Thomas Wolber (Dir)

ESM ACQUISITION CORPORATION
2229 San Felipe Ste 1300, Houston, TX 77019
Tel.: (713) 579-5000 — Ky
Web Site: http://www.esmcorporation.com
Year Founded: 2021
ESM—(NYSE)
Investment Services
N.A.I.C.S.: 523999
John T. Raymond (Chm)
John G. Calvert (Vice Chm)
Michael Davis (CEO)
Jeffrey A. Ball (CFO)

ESPERION THERAPEUTICS, INC.
3891 Ranchero Dr Ste 150, Ann Arbor, MI 48108
Tel.: (734) 887-3903 — DE
Web Site: https://www.esperion.com
Year Founded: 2008
ESPR—(NASDAQ)
Rev.: $75,475,000
Assets: $247,939,000
Liabilities: $571,717,000
Net Worth: ($323,778,000)
Earnings: ($233,659,000)
Emp.: 199
Fiscal Year-end: 12/31/22
Pharmaceuticals Mfr
N.A.I.C.S.: 325412
Sheldon L. Koenig (Pres & CEO)
Benjamin Halladay (CFO)
Glenn Brame (Chief Technical Ops Officer)
Eric Warren (Chief Comml Officer)
Benjamin O. Looker (Gen Counsel)
Betty Jean Swartz (Chief Bus Officer)

ESPEY MFG. & ELECTRONICS CORP.
233 Ballston Ave, Saratoga Springs, NY 12866-4755
Tel.: (518) 584-4100 — NY
Web Site: https://www.espey.com
Year Founded: 1928

ESP—(NYSEAMEX)
Rev.: $38,736,319
Assets: $56,542,931
Liabilities: $15,268,959
Net Worth: $41,273,972
Earnings: $5,815,140
Emp.: 148
Fiscal Year-end: 06/30/24
Other Electronic Component Manufacturing
N.A.I.C.S.: 334419
Carl Helmetag (Chm)
David A. O'Neil (Pres & CEO)

Subsidiaries:

Saratoga Industries Division (1)
233 Ballston Ave, Saratoga Springs, NY 12866-4755 (100%)
Tel.: (518) 245-4400
Web Site: http://www.espey.com
Sales Range: $75-99.9 Million
Mfr of Electronic Components
N.A.I.C.S.: 334419

ESQUIRE FINANCIAL HOLDINGS, INC.
100 Jericho Quadrangle Ste 105, Jericho, NY 11753
Tel.: (516) 535-2002 — MD
Web Site: https://www.esquirebank.com
Year Founded: 2006
ESQ—(NASDAQ)
Rev.: $85,918,000
Assets: $1,395,639,000
Liabilities: $1,237,481,000
Net Worth: $158,158,000
Earnings: $28,518,000
Emp.: 116
Fiscal Year-end: 12/31/22
Bank Holding Company
N.A.I.C.S.: 551111
Andrew C. Sagliocca (Pres & CEO)
Eric S. Bader (COO, Sec & Exec VP)
Ari P. Kornhaber (Exec VP & Head-Corp Dev)
Michael Lacapria (CFO & Sr VP)

Subsidiaries:

Esquire Bank, National Association (1)
100 Jericho Quadrangle Ste 105, Jericho, NY 11753
Tel.: (516) 214-9779
Web Site: https://www.esquirebank.com
Banking Services
N.A.I.C.S.: 522110
Andrew C. Sagliocca (Pres & CEO)
Ari P. Kornhaber (Exec VP & Dir-Sls)

ESS TECH, INC.
26440 SW Pkwy Ave Bldg 83, Wilsonville, OR 97070
Tel.: (855) 423-9920 — DE
Web Site: https://essinc.com
GWH—(NYSE)
Rev.: $894,000
Assets: $173,553,000
Liabilities: $36,579,000
Net Worth: $136,974,000
Earnings: $77,969,000
Emp.: 271
Fiscal Year-end: 12/31/22
Semiconductor & Related Device Manufacturing
N.A.I.C.S.: 334413
Michael R. Niggli Jr. (Founder)
Eric P. Dresselhuys (CEO)
Anthony Rabb (CFO)
Jeff Loebbaka (Chief Comml Officer)

ESSA BANCORP, INC.
200 Palmer St, Stroudsburg, PA 18360-0160
Tel.: (570) 421-0531 — PA
Web Site: https://www.essabank.com
Year Founded: 2006

ESSA—(NASDAQ)
Rev.: $93,405,000
Assets: $2,293,246,000
Liabilities: $2,073,538,000
Net Worth: $219,708,000
Earnings: $18,576,000
Emp.: 232
Fiscal Year-end: 09/30/23
Bank Holding Company
N.A.I.C.S.: 551111
Gary S. Olson *(Pres & CEO)*
Allan A. Muto *(CFO)*
Robert C. Selig Jr. *(Chm)*
Charles D. Hangen *(COO & Exec VP)*
Thomas J. Grayuski *(Sr VP-HR Svcs Div)*
Peter A. Gray *(Chief Banking Officer & Exec VP)*

Subsidiaries:

ESSA Bank & Trust **(1)**
200 Palmer St, Stroudsburg, PA 18360
Tel.: (570) 421-0531
Web Site: http://www.essabank.com
Sales Range: $600-649.9 Million
Emp.: 169
Commericial Banking
N.A.I.C.S.: 522110
Gary S. Olson *(Pres & CEO)*
Allan A. Muto *(CFO & Exec VP)*
Robert C. Selig Jr. *(Chm)*
Diane K. Reimer *(Sr VP-Admin & Ops Div)*
Thomas J. Grayuski *(Sr VP-HR Div)*
Charles D. Hangen *(COO & Exec VP)*
Peter A. Gray *(Chief Banking Officer & Exec VP)*
William L. Vitalos *(Sr VP & Dir-Consumer Lending)*
Stephanie Lefferson *(Sec)*
Roger Anderson *(Officer-Comml Loan)*
Barry Reifinger *(Officer-Comml Loan & VP)*
John Serafin *(Officer-Comml Loan & VP)*
W. Tyler McCann *(Officer-Comml Loan & VP)*
William E. Evans *(Mgr-Trust & Estate)*
Mary Ann Zubris *(Officer-Trust)*
David Lilly *(Sr VP)*
William Harrison *(Sr VP)*
Lisa A. Hutchins *(Officer-Comml Credit & Ops & Sr VP)*
Robert D. Kane III *(Officer-Comml Loan)*

Subsidiary (Domestic):

ESSA Advisory Services, LLC **(2)**
200 Palmer St, Stroudsburg, PA 18360
Tel.: (570) 421-0531
Investment Management Service
N.A.I.C.S.: 523940

**ESSENTIAL PROPERTIES RE-
ALTY TRUST, INC.**
902 Carnegie Ctr Blvd Ste 520,
Princeton, NJ 08540
Tel.: (609) 436-0619   MD
Web Site:
  https://www.essentialproperties.com
Year Founded: 2016
EPRT—(NYSE)
Rev.: $359,595,000
Assets: $4,768,261,000
Liabilities: $1,781,259,000
Net Worth: $2,987,002,000
Earnings: $190,707,000
Emp.: 40
Fiscal Year-end: 12/31/23
Real Estate Manangement Services
N.A.I.C.S.: 531210
Peter M. Mavoides *(Pres & CEO)*
A. J. Peil *(Sr VP & Head-Asset Mgmt)*
Timothy J. Earnshaw *(Chief Acctg Officer & Sr VP)*
Mark E. Patten *(CFO, Treas & Exec VP)*
Max Jenkins *(Sr VP)*
Kristin M. Walker *(Sr VP-Real Estate Counsel)*
Robert W. Salisbury *(Sr VP-Capital Markets)*

ESSENTIAL UTILITIES INC.
762 W Lancaster Ave, Bryn Mawr, PA
19010-3489
Tel.: (610) 527-8000   PA
Web Site: https://www.essential.co
Year Founded: 1968
WTRG—(NYSE)
Rev.: $2,053,824,000
Assets: $16,841,459,000
Liabilities: $10,945,276,000
Net Worth: $5,896,183,000
Earnings: $498,226,000
Emp.: 3,258
Fiscal Year-end: 12/31/23
Holding Company; Water & Waste
Water Services
N.A.I.C.S.: 221310
Michael Huwar *(Pres-Peoples)*
Robert A. Rubin *(Chief Acctg Officer, Sr VP & Controller)*
Kimberly Joyce *(Sec & VP-Regulatory & Govt Affairs)*
Christopher P. Luning *(Gen Counsel, Sec & Exec VP)*
Brian Dingerdissen *(Treas & VP-IR)*
Daniel J. Schuller *(CFO & Exec VP)*
Susan F. Haindl *(Chief Admin Officer & Sr VP)*
Christina Kelly *(Chief HR Officer & Sr VP)*
Jim Barbato *(VP-Fin Plng & Analysis)*
Donna Alston *(Mgr-Comm)*
Jeanne Russo *(VP-Comm)*
Sumit Nair *(CIO & VP)*
Whitney Kellett *(Sr VP-Bus Transfor-mation)*
Ron King *(VP-Peoples Gas Ops)*
James Barbato *(VP)*
Christine Saball *(VP)*
Mark McKoy *(VP)*
Christopher H. Franklin *(Chm & CEO)*

Subsidiaries:

Aqua Illinois, Inc. **(1)**
1000 S Schuyler Ave, Kankakee, IL
60901-5026   **(100%)**
Tel.: (877) 987-2782
Sales Range: $10-24.9 Million
Emp.: 30
Public Water Utility
N.A.I.C.S.: 221310
Nicholas DeBenedictis *(Chm)*
Robert Ervin *(Pres-Indiana)*
Melissa Kahoun *(Area Mgr-Kankakee & Will)*
Beth Penesis *(Area Mgr-Northern)*
Bobby Estep *(Controller)*
David Carter *(Pres-Illinois)*

Division (Domestic):

Aqua Illinois **(2)**
2026 Candlewick Dr SE, Poplar Grove, IL
61065   **(100%)**
Tel.: (815) 765-2239
Sales Range: $10-24.9 Million
Emp.: 3
Public Water Utility
N.A.I.C.S.: 221310

Aqua Illinois - Vermilion County
Division **(2)**
322 N Gilbert St, Danville, IL
61834-1130   **(100%)**
Tel.: (217) 442-0142
Public Water Utility Services
N.A.I.C.S.: 923120

Aqua Indiana, Inc. **(1)**
111 W Hamilton Rd S, Fort Wayne, IN
46814
Tel.: (260) 625-4700
Web Site: http://www.aquaindiana.com
Emp.: 30
Water & Wastewater Utility Services
N.A.I.C.S.: 221310
Kieran Tansy *(Mgr-Central & Southern Indi-ana)*
Jeffery Gard *(Mgr-Ops)*
Jim Shields *(Engr-State)*
Kari Bennett *(Pres)*
Sarah Baker *(Coord-North Indiana Con-struction)*

Aqua New Jersey, Inc. **(1)**
10 Black Forest Rd, Hamilton, NJ
08691   **(100%)**
Tel.: (609) 587-8222
Web Site: http://www.aquanewjersey.com
Sales Range: $10-24.9 Million
Emp.: 50
Water Utility
N.A.I.C.S.: 221310
John Hildabrant *(Pres)*

Division (Domestic):

Aqua New Jersey **(2)**
1099 River Rd, Phillipsburg, NJ
08865   **(100%)**
Tel.: (908) 859-4800
Web Site: http://www.aquaamerica.com
Sales Range: $10-24.9 Million
Emp.: 15
Water Utility
N.A.I.C.S.: 221310

Aqua Ohio, Inc. **(1)**
6650 S Ave, Boardman, OH 44512 **(100%)**
Tel.: (330) 726-8151
Web Site: http://www.aquaohio.com
Sales Range: $10-24.9 Million
Emp.: 23
Water Utility Services
N.A.I.C.S.: 221310

Division (Domestic):

Aqua Ohio - Lake Shore Division **(2)**
8644 Station St, Mentor, OH
44060   **(100%)**
Tel.: (440) 255-3421
Web Site: http://www.aquaamerica.com
Sales Range: $10-24.9 Million
Emp.: 9
Water Utility
N.A.I.C.S.: 221310

Aqua Ohio - Marion Division **(2)**
365 E Center St, Marion, OH 43302
Tel.: (740) 383-0935
Web Site: http://www.aquaamerica.com
Emp.: 25
Water Utility
N.A.I.C.S.: 221310
Scott Ballenger *(Mgr)*

Aqua Ohio, Inc. **(2)**
6650 S Ave, Boardman, OH 44512 **(100%)**
Tel.: (330) 726-8151
Water Utility Services
N.A.I.C.S.: 221310
Edmund Kolodziej *(Pres & CEO)*

Aqua Pennsylvania, Inc. **(1)**
762 W Lancaster Ave, Bryn Mawr, PA
19010
Tel.: (610) 527-8000
Web Site: http://www.aquaamerica.com
Sales Range: $200-249.9 Million
Water Utility & Waste Water Services
N.A.I.C.S.: 221310
Marc Lucca *(Pres)*
Krista Weeks *(Mgr-Bus Dev)*

Division (Domestic):

Aqua Pennsylvania - Roaring Creek
Division **(2)**
204 E Sunbury St, Shamokin, PA
17872-4826   **(100%)**
Tel.: (570) 648-5783
Web Site: http://www.aquaamerica.com
Sales Range: $10-24.9 Million
Emp.: 24
Water Supply Systems
N.A.I.C.S.: 221310

Aqua Pennsylvania - Shenango Val-
ley Division **(2)**
665 S Dock St, Sharon, PA 16146 **(100%)**
Tel.: (724) 981-1200
Web Site: http://www.aquaamerica.com
Sales Range: $25-49.9 Million
Emp.: 35
Public Water Utility Services
N.A.I.C.S.: 221310

Aqua Texas, Inc. **(1)**
1106 Clayton Ln Ste 400W, Austin, TX
78723-2476
Tel.: (512) 990-4400
Web Site: http://www.aquaamerica.com
Water & Waste Water Utility Services

N.A.I.C.S.: 221310
Chris Garcia *(Mgr-Southeast)*
Robert Laughman *(Pres)*
Dan Rimann *(VP-Ops & Engrg)*
Brent Reeh *(Mgr-Southwest)*
Darryl Waldock *(Mgr-North)*

Peoples Natural Gas Co. LLC **(1)**
375 N Shore Dr Ste 600, Pittsburgh, PA
15212
Tel.: (800) 764-0111
Web Site: http://www.peoples-gas.com
Gas Utility & Distribution Services
N.A.I.C.S.: 221210

Subsidiary (Domestic):

Delta Natural Gas Company, Inc. **(2)**
3617 Lexington Rd, Winchester, KY 40391
Tel.: (859) 744-6171
Web Site: http://www.deltagas.com
Sales Range: $50-74.9 Million
Emp.: 148
Natural Gas Distr
N.A.I.C.S.: 221210

Subsidiary (Domestic):

Delgasco, LLC **(3)**
3617 Lexington Rd, Winchester, KY 40391
Tel.: (859) 744-6171
Natural Gas Distr
N.A.I.C.S.: 221210
Glenn R. Jennings *(Dir)*

Delta Resources, LLC **(3)**
3617 Lexington Rd, Winchester, KY 40391
Tel.: (859) 744-6171
Buying & Reselling of Gas
N.A.I.C.S.: 221210
Glenn R. Jennings *(Dir)*

Enpro, LLC **(3)**
3617 Lexington Rd, Winchester, KY 40391
Tel.: (859) 744-6171
Gas Production Properties Operator; Gas
Purchasing & Sales
N.A.I.C.S.: 221210
Glenn R. Jennings *(Dir)*

**ESSEX PROPERTY TRUST,
INC.**
1100 Park Pl Ste 200, San Mateo,
CA 94403
Tel.: (650) 655-7800   MD
Web Site:
  https://www.essexapartment
  homes.com
Year Founded: 1994
ESS—(NYSE)
Rev.: $1,669,395,000
Assets: $12,361,427,000
Liabilities: $6,767,449,000
Net Worth: $5,593,978,000
Earnings: $405,825,000
Emp.: 1,750
Fiscal Year-end: 12/31/23
Real Estate Investment Trust
N.A.I.C.S.: 525990
Keith R. Guericke *(Vice Chm)*
George M. Marcus *(Founder & Chm)*
Barb Pak *(CFO & Exec VP)*
Rylan Burns *(Sr VP-Investment Strat-egy)*
Anne Morrison *(Chief Compliance Officer)*

Subsidiaries:

360 Residences, L.P. **(1)**
360 S Market St, San Jose, CA 95113
Tel.: (669) 201-8750
Building Construction Services
N.A.I.C.S.: 236220

BRE Properties, Inc. **(1)**
525 Market St 4th Fl, San Francisco, CA
94105
Tel.: (415) 445-6530
Web Site: http://www.breproperties.com
Residential Property Management & Leas-
ing Services
N.A.I.C.S.: 531311

City View **(1)**
25200 Carlos Bee Blvd, Hayward, CA
94542
Tel.: (866) 799-3615

Essex Property Trust, Inc.—(Continued)
Web Site:
http://www.essexapartmenthomes.com
Apartment Building Rental & Leasing Services
N.A.I.C.S.: 531110

Courtyards at 65th, L.P. (1)
1465 65th St, Emeryville, CA 94608
Tel.: (510) 319-6446
Apartment Home Leasing Services
N.A.I.C.S.: 531110

Essex Anavia, L.P. (1)
2045 S State College Blvd, Anaheim, CA 92806
Tel.: (714) 266-3692
Web Site:
http://www.essexapartmenthomes.com
Apartment Building Rental & Leasing Services
N.A.I.C.S.: 531110

Essex Bella Villagio, L.P. (1)
383 Vista Roma Way, San Jose, CA 95136
Tel.: (669) 257-6010
Building Rental & Leasing Services
N.A.I.C.S.: 531110

Essex Bellerive, L.P. (1)
1929 Beloit Ave, Los Angeles, CA 90025
Tel.: (661) 766-4300
Apartment Building Rental & Leasing Services
N.A.I.C.S.: 531110

Essex Bernard, L.P. (1)
115 Warren Ave N, Seattle, WA 98109
Tel.: (206) 539-5927
Apartment Building Rental & Leasing Services
N.A.I.C.S.: 531110

Essex Briarwood, L.P. (1)
4200 Bay St, Fremont, CA 94538
Tel.: (510) 455-8874
Apartment Building Rental & Leasing Services
N.A.I.C.S.: 531110

Essex Bridle Trails, L.P. (1)
6600 130th Ave NE, Kirkland, WA 98033
Tel.: (425) 954-3937
Web Site:
http://www.essexpropertytrust.com
Emp.: 4
Apartment Building Rental & Leasing Services
N.A.I.C.S.: 531110

Essex Brighton Ridge, L.P. (1)
2307 NE 4th St, Renton, WA 98056
Tel.: (425) 336-2799
Web Site: http://www.hrighton.com
Emp.: 5
Apartment Building Rental & Leasing Services
N.A.I.C.S.: 531110

Essex Canyon Oaks Apartments, L.P. (1)
1 Amberstone Ln, San Ramon, CA 94582
Tel.: (925) 241-5544
Web Site: http://www.canyonoaksapts.com
Emp.: 6
Apartment Building Rental & Leasing Services
N.A.I.C.S.: 531110

Essex Canyon Pointe, L.P. (1)
1630 228th St SE, Bothell, WA 98021
Tel.: (425) 329-7851
Apartment Building Rental & Leasing Services
N.A.I.C.S.: 531110

Essex Carlyle, L.P. (1)
2909 Nieman Blvd, San Jose, CA 95148
Tel.: (408) 837-7312
Apartment Building Rental & Leasing Services
N.A.I.C.S.: 531110

Essex Catalina Gardens, LLC (1)
333 S Catalina St, Los Angeles, CA 90020
Tel.: (213) 370-1763
Real Estate Investment Services
N.A.I.C.S.: 525920

Essex Davey Glen Apartments, L.P. (1)

200 Davey Glen Rd, Belmont, CA 94002
Tel.: (650) 276-4686
Apartment Building Rental & Leasing Services
N.A.I.C.S.: 531110

Essex Esplanade, L.P. (1)
350 E Taylor St, San Jose, CA 95112
Tel.: (408) 335-7725
Web Site: http://www.essex.com
Sales Range: $25-49.9 Million
Emp.: 6
Apartment Building Rental & Leasing Services
N.A.I.C.S.: 531110

Essex Fairwood Pond, L.P. (1)
14700 S E Petrovitsky Rd, Renton, WA 98058
Tel.: (425) 434-5196
Emp.: 4
Apartment Building Rental & Leasing Services
N.A.I.C.S.: 531110
Allegra Sanchez (Mgr-Property)

Essex Fountain Park Apartments, L.P. (1)
13141 Fountain Park Dr, Playa Vista, CA 90094
Tel.: (323) 508-1960
Web Site: http://www.fountainparkapts.com
Emp.: 20
Apartment Building Rental & Leasing Services
N.A.I.C.S.: 531110

Essex Fox Plaza, L.P. (1)
1390 Market St Ste 262, San Francisco, CA 94102
Tel.: (415) 626-6900
Real Estate Investment Services
N.A.I.C.S.: 531210
Michael J. Schall (Pres)

Essex Haver Hill, L.P. (1)
3100 Yorba Linda Blvd, Fullerton, CA 92831
Tel.: (714) 524-9141
Real Estate Investment Services
N.A.I.C.S.: 531210

Essex Huntington Breakers, L.P. (1)
21270 Beach Blvd, Huntington Beach, CA 92648
Tel.: (714) 786-5984
Web Site:
http://www.huntingtonbreakers.com
Emp.: 9
Apartment Building Rental & Leasing Services
N.A.I.C.S.: 531110

Essex Inglenook Court, LLC (1)
14220 Juanita Dr NE, Kirkland, WA 98034-4903
Tel.: (425) 434-5192
Building Rental & Leasing Services
N.A.I.C.S.: 531110

Essex Kings Road, L.P. (1)
733 N Kings Rd, Los Angeles, CA 90069
Tel.: (323) 546-3064
Apartment Building Rental & Leasing Services
N.A.I.C.S.: 531110

Essex Management Corporation (1)
925 E Meadow Dr, Palo Alto, CA 94303
Tel.: (650) 494-3700
Web Site:
http://www.essexpropertytrust.com
Sales Range: $125-149.9 Million
Emp.: 60
Title Insurance Services
N.A.I.C.S.: 524127
Keith R. Guericke (Vice Chm)

Essex Marbrisa Long Beach, L.P. (1)
1809 Termino Ave, Long Beach, CA 90815
Tel.: (562) 330-1288
Web Site:
http://www.essexapartmenthomes.com
Apartment Building Rental & Leasing Services
N.A.I.C.S.: 531110

Essex Marina City Club, L.P. (1)
4333 Admiralty Way, Marina Del Rey, CA 90292
Tel.: (310) 822-0611

Web Site: https://www.marinacityclub.net
Apartment Building Rental & Leasing Services
N.A.I.C.S.: 531110

Essex Monterey Villas, L.P. (1)
1018 Kelp Ln, Oxnard, CA 93035
Tel.: (805) 465-7369
Apartment Building Rental & Leasing Services
N.A.I.C.S.: 531110

Essex Parcwood Apartments, L.P. (1)
1700 Via Pacifica, Corona, CA 92882
Tel.: (951) 734-2020
Apartment Building Rental & Leasing Services
N.A.I.C.S.: 531110

Essex Portfolio, L.P. (1)
1100 Park Pl Ste 200, San Mateo, CA 94403
Tel.: (650) 655-7800
Web Site: https://www.exxes.com
Rev.: $1,606,813,999
Assets: $12,372,904,999
Liabilities: $6,477,788,999
Net Worth: $5,895,115,999
Earnings: $432,984,999
Emp.: 1,771
Fiscal Year-end: 12/31/2022
Financial Investment Services
N.A.I.C.S.: 525990
Michael J. Schall (Pres & CEO)

Essex Regency Escuela, L.P. (1)
925 E Meadow Dr, Palo Alto, CA 94303
Tel.: (650) 494-3700
Real Estate Management Services
N.A.I.C.S.: 531210

Essex Regency Tower Apartments, L.P. (1)
1130 3rd Ave, Oakland, CA 94606
Tel.: (510) 992-6234
Sales Range: $25-49.9 Million
Emp.: 5
Apartment Building Rental & Leasing Services
N.A.I.C.S.: 531110

Essex Rexford, LLC (1)
3400 Country Dr, Fremont, CA 94536
Tel.: (510) 573-7474
Real Estate Investment Services
N.A.I.C.S.: 525920

Essex Sammamish View, L.P. (1)
16160 SE Eastgate Way, Bellevue, WA 98008
Tel.: (425) 967-8809
Apartment Building Rental & Leasing Services
N.A.I.C.S.: 531110

Essex Santee Court, L.P. (1)
716 S Los Angeles St Ste B, Los Angeles, CA 90014
Tel.: (213) 761-1712
Property & Motor Vehicle Rental Services
N.A.I.C.S.: 531110

Essex Stonehedge Village, L.P. (1)
14610 93rd Blvd NE, Bothell, WA 98011
Tel.: (425) 434-5177
Apartment Building Rental & Leasing Services
N.A.I.C.S.: 531110

Essex Summerhill Park, L.P. (1)
972 Corte Madera Ave, Sunnyvale, CA 94085
Tel.: (408) 837-9134
Building Rental & Leasing Services
N.A.I.C.S.: 531110

Essex The Commons, L.P. (1)
275 Union Ave, Campbell, CA 95008
Tel.: (408) 796-4544
Web Site:
http://www.essexapartmenthomes.com
Emp.: 7
Apartment Building Rental & Leasing Services
N.A.I.C.S.: 531110

Essex The Pointe, L.P. (1)
19920 Olivewood St, Cupertino, CA 95014
Tel.: (408) 457-8106

Apartment Building Rental & Leasing Services
N.A.I.C.S.: 531110

Essex Tierra Vista, L.P. (1)
1750 Montevina Cir, Oxnard, CA 93030
Tel.: (805) 465-7367
Apartment Building Rental & Leasing Services
N.A.I.C.S.: 531110

Essex Township, L.P. (1)
333 Main St, Redwood City, CA 94063
Tel.: (650) 383-1818
Apartment Home Leasing Services
N.A.I.C.S.: 531110

Essex Velo Ray, L.P. (1)
3636 Stone Way N, Seattle, WA 98103
Tel.: (509) 215-1619
Apartment Home Leasing Services
N.A.I.C.S.: 531110

Essex Vista Belvedere, L.P. (1)
65 Red Hill Cir, Tiburon, CA 94920
Tel.: (415) 569-6963
Building Rental & Leasing Services
N.A.I.C.S.: 531110

Essex Wandering Creek, LLC (1)
12910 SE 240th St, Kent, WA 98031
Tel.: (253) 880-1313
Apartment Building Rental & Leasing Services
N.A.I.C.S.: 531110

Essex Waterford, L.P. (1)
1700 N 1st St, San Jose, CA 95112
Tel.: (408) 596-5025
Apartment Building Rental & Leasing Services
N.A.I.C.S.: 531110

Essex Wharfside Pointe, L.P. (1)
3827 14th Ave W, Seattle, WA 98119
Tel.: (206) 673-3719
Apartment Building Rental & Leasing Services
N.A.I.C.S.: 531110

Jackson School Village, L.P. (1)
300 NE Autumn Rose Way, Hillsboro, OR 97124
Tel.: (503) 854-0437
Web Site:
https://www.jacksonschoolvillage.com
Apartment Building Rental & Leasing Services
N.A.I.C.S.: 531110

Pacific Western Insurance, LLC (1)
1748 Nw 56th St, Seattle, WA 98107
Tel.: (206) 783-1624
Insurance Agency & Brokerage Services
N.A.I.C.S.: 524210

Villa Angelina Apartment Fund, LTD (1)
201 E Chapman Ave, Placentia, CA 92870
Tel.: (714) 701-6120
Apartment Building Rental & Leasing Services
N.A.I.C.S.: 531110

ESTRELLA IMMUNOPHARMA, INC.
5858 Horton St, Ste 370, Emeryville, CA 94608
Tel.: (510) 318-9098   DE
Web Site:
https://www.estrellabio.com
Year Founded: 2021
ESLA—(AIM)
Rev.: $654,071
Assets: $9,723,802
Liabilities: $11,979,487
Net Worth: ($2,255,685)
Earnings: ($996,104)
Emp.: 3
Fiscal Year-end: 12/31/22
Biopharmaceutical Company
N.A.I.C.S.: 541714

ETAO INTERNATIONAL CO., LTD.
1460 Broadway 14th Fl, New York, NY 10036

Tel.: (347) 306-5134   **Ky**
Web Site: https://www.etao.world
Year Founded: 2020
ETAO—(NASDAQ)
Rev.: $58,060,025
Assets: $52,989,821
Liabilities: $58,970,157
Net Worth: ($5,980,336)
Earnings: ($896,677,759)
Emp.: 3,600
Fiscal Year-end: 12/31/22
Health Care Srvices
N.A.I.C.S.: 621610
Hui Wang (CFO)
Wensheng Liu (Founder)

ETERNA THERAPEUTICS INC.

1035 Cambridge St Ste 18A, Cambridge, MA 92121
Tel.: (212) 582-1199   **DE**
Web Site: https://www.eternatx.com
Year Founded: 1983
ERNA—(NASDAQ)
Rev.: $8,683,000
Assets: $22,279,000
Liabilities: $10,172,000
Net Worth: $12,107,000
Earnings: ($24,595,000)
Emp.: 9
Fiscal Year-end: 12/31/22
Biotechnology Company; Cytokine-based Therapy
N.A.I.C.S.: 541714
Sandra Gurrola (Principal Fin Officer)
Dorothy Clarke (Gen Counsel)
Robert Pierce (Chief Scientific Officer)
Sanjeev Luther (Pres & CEO)

Subsidiaries:

Buzztime Entertainment, Inc   **(1)**
6965 El Camino Real Ste 105 517, Carlsbad, CA 92009
Tel.: (760) 476-1976
Web Site: https://www.buzztime.com
Sales Range: $25-49.9 Million
Emp.: 100
Interactive Gaming Developer
N.A.I.C.S.: 339930

ETHAN ALLEN INTERIORS INC.

25 Lake Ave Ext, Danbury, CT 06811-5286
Tel.: (203) 743-8500   **DE**
Web Site:
  https://www.ethanallen.com
Year Founded: 1932
ETD—(NYSE)
Rev.: $646,221,000
Assets: $744,917,000
Liabilities: $262,001,000
Net Worth: $482,916,000
Earnings: $63,816,000
Emp.: 3,404
Fiscal Year-end: 06/30/24
Holding Company; Furniture Mft & Sales
N.A.I.C.S.: 337122
M. Farooq Kathwari (Chm, Pres & CEO)
Amy Franks (Sr VP-Retail)

Subsidiaries:

Ethan Allen Global, Inc.   **(1)**
25 Lake Avenue Ext, Danbury, CT 06811   **(100%)**
Tel.: (203) 743-8500
Home Furnishings Mfr & Interior Design Services
N.A.I.C.S.: 337121

Subsidiary (Domestic):

Ethan Allen Operations, Inc.   **(2)**
Ethan Allen Dr, Danbury, CT 06811   **(100%)**
Tel.: (203) 743-8000
Furniture Distr

N.A.I.C.S.: 423210
Jack Moll (Sr Dir & Gen Mgr)

Ethan Allen Retail, Inc.   **(2)**
25 Lake Avenue Ext, Danbury, CT 06811
Tel.: (203) 743-8500
Web Site: http://www.ethanallen.com
Furniture Retailer
N.A.I.C.S.: 337121

Subsidiary (Non-US):

Ethan Allen (Canada) Inc.   **(3)**
8134 Yonge St, Thornhill, L4J 1W4, ON, Canada
Tel.: (905) 889-7761
Web Site: https://www.ethanallen.ca
Sales Range: $10-24.9 Million
Emp.: 108
Furniture Retailer
N.A.I.C.S.: 449110

Ethan Allen International, BVBA   **(1)**
Lange Gasthuisstraat 12-14, 2000, Antwerp, Belgium
Tel.: (32) 28406500
Web Site: http://www.ethanallen.be
Furniture Mfr & Distr
N.A.I.C.S.: 337121

ETHEMA HEALTH CORPORATION

950 Evernia St, West Palm Beach, FL 33401
Tel.: (516) 290-0239   **CO**
Web Site:
  http://www.ethemahealth.com
Year Founded: 1993
GRST—(OTCIQ)
Rev.: $4,820,747
Assets: $6,563,294
Liabilities: $15,795,837
Net Worth: ($9,232,543)
Earnings: $247,880
Emp.: 46
Fiscal Year-end: 12/31/22
Medical Clinic Operator
N.A.I.C.S.: 622110
Shawn E. Leon (Pres, CEO & CFO)

ETON PHARMACEUTICALS, INC.

21925 W Field Pkwy Ste 235, Deer Park, IL 60010
Tel.: (847) 787-7361   **DE**
Web Site:
  https://www.etonpharma.com
Year Founded: 2017
ETON—(NASDAQ)
Rev.: $21,251,000
Assets: $25,030,000
Liabilities: $11,952,000
Net Worth: $13,078,000
Earnings: ($9,021,000)
Emp.: 28
Fiscal Year-end: 12/31/22
Biotechnology Research & Development Services
N.A.I.C.S.: 541714
Norbert G. Riedel (Chm)
Sean E. Brynjelsen (Pres & CEO)
Bharathi Devarakonda (Sr VP-Regulatory Affairs & Technical Svcs)
Scott Grossenbach (VP-Sls Ops)
David Krempa (Chief Bus Officer)
Ingrid Hoos (Sr VP-Regulatory Affairs)
Paul Stickler (Sr VP-Comml)
Danka Radosavljevic (VP-Quality)
James Gruber (CFO, Treas & Sec)

ETSY, INC.

117 Adams St, Brooklyn, NY 11201
Tel.: (718) 880-3660   **DE**
Web Site: https://www.etsy.com
Year Founded: 2005
ETSY—(NASDAQ)
Rev.: $2,748,377,000
Assets: $2,685,400,000
Liabilities: $3,229,115,000

Net Worth: ($543,715,000)
Earnings: $307,568,000
Emp.: 2,420
Fiscal Year-end: 12/31/23
Electronic Commerce Services
N.A.I.C.S.: 423940
Joshua Silverman (CEO)
Raina Moskowitz (Chief Operating & Mktg Officer)
Kimaria Seymour (Chief HR Officer)
Deb Wasser (VP-IR & ESG Engagement)
Patricia Cruz (Mgr-IR)
Nicholas Daniel (Chief Product Officer)
Sarah Marx (Dir-Corp Comm)
Rachana Kumar (CTO)
Colin Stretch (Chief Legal Officer)
Jill Simeone (Sec)

Subsidiaries:

Reverb, Inc.   **(1)**
386 Fore St, Portland, ME 04101
Tel.: (207) 221-6553
Web Site: http://reverb.com
Rev.: $1,605,279
Assets: $1,056,434
Liabilities: $1,465
Net Worth: $1,054,969
Earnings: $331,495
Emp.: 11
Fiscal Year-end: 12/31/2013
Musical Artist Welfare Services
N.A.I.C.S.: 711130
Lauren Sullivan (Co-Founder & Co-Dir)
Adam Gardner (Co-Founder & Co-Dir)

EUCRATES BIOMEDICAL ACQUISITION CORP.

250 W 55th St Ste 13D, New York, NY 10019
Tel.: (212) 710-5220   **VG**
Year Founded: 2020
EUCR—(NASDAQ)
Rev.: $3,118,183
Assets: $12,485,358
Liabilities: $16,202,954
Net Worth: ($3,717,596)
Earnings: $2,419,605
Emp.: 4
Fiscal Year-end: 12/31/22
Investment Services
N.A.I.C.S.: 523999
Stelios Papadopoulos (Chm)
Parag Saxena (CEO)
Evangelos Vergetis (Pres & COO)
Gonzalo Cordova (CFO)
Shrikant Sathe (Sr VP)
Atanuu Agarrwal (VP)

EUREKA HOMESTEAD BANCORP, INC.

1922 Veterans Memorial Blvd, Metairie, LA 70005-2640
Tel.: (504) 834-0242   **MD**
Web Site:
  https://www.eurekahomestead.com
Year Founded: 1884
ERKH—(OTCIQ)
Rev.: $3,856,000
Assets: $103,595,000
Liabilities: $81,749,000
Net Worth: $21,846,000
Earnings: $146,000
Emp.: 13
Fiscal Year-end: 12/31/21
Offices of Bank Holding Companies
N.A.I.C.S.: 551111
Alan T. Heintzen (Chm & CEO)
Cecil A. Haskins Jr. (Pres & CFO)

EURONET WORLDWIDE, INC.

11400 Tomahawk Creek Pkwy Ste 300, Leawood, KS 66211
Tel.: (913) 327-4200   **DE**
Web Site:
  https://www.euronetworldwide.com

Year Founded: 1994
EEFT—(NASDAQ)
Rev.: $3,688,000,000
Assets: $5,894,400,000
Liabilities: $4,644,700,000
Net Worth: $1,249,700,000
Earnings: $279,700,000
Emp.: 10,000
Fiscal Year-end: 12/31/23
Electronic Financial Transactions
N.A.I.C.S.: 522320
Juan C. Bianchi (CEO-Money Transfer Segment & Exec VP)
Rick L. Weller (CFO, Chief Acctg Officer & Exec VP)
Kevin J. Caponecchi (CEO-Epay, Software & EFT-Asia Pacific Div & Exec VP)
Nikos Fountas (CEO-EFT-Europe, Middle East & Africa Div & Exec VP)
Martin L. Bruckner (CTO & Sr VP)
Michael J. Brown (Founder, Chm, Pres & CEO)
Scott D. Claassen (Gen Counsel & Sec)

Subsidiaries:

Brodos Romania SRL   **(1)**
73-81 Bucuresti - Ploiesti Road Victoria Park 2nd Building, 3rd Floor Sector 1, Bucharest, 013697, Romania
Tel.: (40) 213140672
Electronic Financial Transaction Services
N.A.I.C.S.: 522320

Continental Exchange Solutions, Inc.   **(1)**
6565 Knott Ave, Buena Park, CA 90620
Tel.: (562) 345-2100
Web Site: http://www.riafinancial.com
Sales Range: $100-124.9 Million
Emp.: 400
Financial Transaction Processing Services
N.A.I.C.S.: 522320

Delta Euronet GmbH   **(1)**
Friedrichstr 200, 10117, Berlin, 10117, Germany
Tel.: (49) 3020396800
Sales Range: $25-49.9 Million
Emp.: 20
Electronic Transaction Services
N.A.I.C.S.: 522320
Alfred Stettberger (Mng Dir)

Dolphin Debit Access, LLC   **(1)**
1340 Rayford Park Rd, Spring, TX 77386
Tel.: (504) 456-1154
Web Site: https://www.dolphindebit.com
ATM Services
N.A.I.C.S.: 423420
Joe Woods (Sr VP & Dir-Sls)
Gary Walston (CEO)
Toby Salsman (CTO)
Dea Lukac (COO)
Jenni Ayres (Controller)

EFT-Usluge d.o.o   **(100%)**
I Pile 1 / II, 10000, Zagreb, Croatia
Tel.: (385) 16326777
Web Site: https://www.euronetatms.hr
Sales Range: $1-9.9 Million
Emp.: 12
N.A.I.C.S.: 522210

Euronet Banktechnikai Szolgaltato Kft.   **(1)**
Alkotas Utca 50 Alkotas Point, 1123, Budapest, Hungary
Tel.: (36) 12244600
Emp.: 200
Electronic Financial Transaction Services
N.A.I.C.S.: 522320

Euronet Card Services, S.A.   **(1)**
1 Sachtouri Street and 2 Poseidonos Av, Kallithea, 176 74, Athens, Greece
Tel.: (30) 210 947 8478
Web Site: http://www.eeft.com
Sales Range: $50-74.9 Million
Emp.: 78
Electronic Financial Transaction Services
N.A.I.C.S.: 522320

Euronet Middle East W.L.L.   **(1)**

Euronet Worldwide, Inc.—(Continued)

Office -181/182 18th Floor Nordic Tower, PO Box no 5054, Building - 79 Road - 2802 Block - 428 Al Seef District, Manama, Bahrain
Tel.: (973) 17312888
Financial Transaction Processing Services
N.A.I.C.S.: 522320
Mohamed Mousa *(Mng Dir & VP-Middle East, Africa & Pakistan)*

Euronet Polska Sp. Z.o.o.   (1)
ul Inflancka 4C 5th floor, 00-189, Warsaw, Poland   (100%)
Tel.: (48) 225197771,
Web Site: https://euronet.pl
Sales Range: $50-74.9 Million
Emp.: 100
Electronic Payment & Transaction Processing Solutions
N.A.I.C.S.: 522320

Euronet Polska Spolka z o.o.   (1)
GBC Building D 4C Inflancka street, 00-189, Warsaw, Poland
Tel.: (48) 223835100
Electronic Financial Transaction Processing Services
N.A.I.C.S.: 522320
Marek Szafirski *(Mng Dir)*

Euronet Services GmbH   (1)
Philipp-Johnson-Haus Friedrichstrasse 200, 10117, Berlin, Germany   (100%)
Tel.: (49) 3020396800
Web Site: http://www.euronetworldwide.com
Sales Range: $25-49.9 Million
Emp.: 20
Financial Services
N.A.I.C.S.: 522210

Euronet Services Kft.   (1)
Tel.: (36) 12244600
Emp.: 180
Electronic Transaction Services
N.A.I.C.S.: 522320

Euronet Services SAS   (1)
1-3 Rue du 19 Mars 1962, 92230, Gennevilliers, France
Tel.: (33) 141327980
Financial Technology Services
N.A.I.C.S.: 522320

Euronet Services SRL   (1)
                                                          (100%)
Tel.: (40) 213166326
Sales Range: $25-49.9 Million
Emp.: 27
N.A.I.C.S.: 522210

Euronet Services d.o.o.   (1)
Spanskih Boraca 3 Zgrada B Sprat IV, Novi Beograd, 11070, Belgrade, Serbia
Tel.: (381) 113082300
Electronic Financial Transaction Processing Services
N.A.I.C.S.: 522320
Dragan Spanovic *(Country Mgr)*

Euronet Services, Spol. s.r.o.   (1)
IBC - Pobrezni 3, 186 00, Prague, 8, Czech Republic
Tel.: (420) 22 483 2252
Web Site:
    https://www.euronetworldwide.com
Credit Card Issuing Services
N.A.I.C.S.: 522210

Euronet TeleRecarga, S.L.   (1)
Edificio Amura Calle Cantabria n 2 Planta 2 Puerta A1, 28108, Alcobendas, Madrid, Spain
Tel.: (34) 910588957
Web Site: https://www.telerecarga.es
Sales Range: $125-149.9 Million
Electronic Financial Transactions
N.A.I.C.S.: 522320

Euronet USA Inc.   (1)
17300 Chenal Pkwy Ste 200, Little Rock, AR 72223-3909
Tel.: (501) 218-7300
Sales Range: $10-24.9 Million
Emp.: 51
Software Solutions for Electronic Financial Transactions
N.A.I.C.S.: 541512

Division (Domestic):

Euronet Services   (2)

3029 NE 188 St Ste 1014, Aventura, FL 33180
Tel.: (786) 207-2668
Web Site: http://www.euronetworldwide.com
Electronic Financial Transactions Software Sales
N.A.I.C.S.: 423430

Euronet Ukraine LLC   (1)
103 Stolychne Highway Europe Business Center, Kiev, 03026, Ukraine
Tel.: (380) 44 495 7700
Web Site: http://www.com
Sales Range: $25-49.9 Million
Emp.: 12
Financial Transaction Processing Services
N.A.I.C.S.: 522320

Euronet Worldwide Greece   (1)
Sachtouri 1 & Posidonos Ave 2 Kallithea, 17674, Athens, Greece   (100%)
Tel.: (30) 2109478478
Web Site: http://www.euronetworldwide.com
Sales Range: $25-49.9 Million
Emp.: 15
N.A.I.C.S.: 522210
George Athineos *(Fin Mgr)*

Gescoro Inc.   (1)
5065 Rue Saint-Denis, Montreal, H2J 2L9, QC, Canada
Tel.: (514) 908-2274
Web Site: http://www.riafinancial.com
Emp.: 7
Financial Transaction Processing Services
N.A.I.C.S.: 522320

HiFX Europe Limited   (1)
Maxis 1 Western Road, Madeira Walk, Bracknell, RG12 1RT, Berkshire, United Kingdom
Tel.: (44) 175 385 9170
Web Site: http://www.hifx.co.uk
Sales Range: $25-49.9 Billion
Emp.: 251
Foreign Currency Trading Services
N.A.I.C.S.: 523160

Subsidiary (Domestic):

HiFM Limited   (2)
Morgan House Madeira Walk, Madeira Walk, Windsor, SL4 1EP, Berkshire, United Kingdom   (100%)
Tel.: (44) 1753752752
Web Site: https://www.hifm.co.uk
Sales Range: $200-249.9 Million
Credit Intermediation Services
N.A.I.C.S.: 522390

Subsidiary (Non-US):

HiFX Limited   (2)
32 Mahuhu Crescent Level 4, Auckland, 1010, New Zealand
Tel.: (64) 93063700
Foreign Currency Trading Services
N.A.I.C.S.: 561499

Subsidiary (Non-US):

HiFX Australia Pty Ltd   (3)
Level 1 75 Castlereagh Street, Sydney, 2000, NSW, Australia
Tel.: (61) 282704500
Foreign Currency Trading Services
N.A.I.C.S.: 561499

Subsidiary (Non-US):

HiFX Spain S.L.   (2)
Avda De Manolete Centro Plaza Local 12-13, Nueva Andalucia, 29660, Marbella, Malaga, Spain   (100%)
Tel.: (34) 951203986
Web Site: http://www.hifx.co.uk
Emp.: 7
Foreign Currency Trading Services
N.A.I.C.S.: 561499

Innova Tax Free (UK) Limited   (1)
42 Upper Berkeley Street, London, W1H 5PW, United Kingdom
Tel.: (44) 2072349020
Tax Refunding Services
N.A.I.C.S.: 561440

Innova Tax Free France SAS   (1)
1-7 Rue du 19 Mars 1962, 92230, Gennevilliers, France
Tel.: (33) 181224165

Tax Refunding Services
N.A.I.C.S.: 561440

Innova Taxfree Belgium SPRL   (1)
4 Rue de la Presse, 1000, Brussels, Belgium
Tel.: (32) 26810342
Tax Refunding Services
N.A.I.C.S.: 561440

Innova Taxfree Ireland Limited   (1)
Suite 6 - 41 Dominick Court, D01 YX44, Dublin, 1, Ireland
Tel.: (353) 19015243
Tax Refunding Services
N.A.I.C.S.: 561440

Innova Taxfree Italy S.R.L.   (1)
Via Santo Stefano 50, 40124, Bologna, Italy
Tel.: (39) 0519525652
Tax Refunding Services
N.A.I.C.S.: 561440

Innova Taxfree Netherlands B.V.   (1)
Joop Geesinkweg 901, 1114 AB, Amsterdam, Netherlands
Tel.: (31) 203690782
Tax Refunding Services
N.A.I.C.S.: 561440

Innova Taxfree Portugal Unipessoal Lda.   (1)
Av D Joao II 44 C - 2 2, Parque das Nacoes, 1990-095, Lisbon, Portugal
Tel.: (351) 214139169
Tax Refunding Services
N.A.I.C.S.: 561440

Innova Taxfree Spain S.L.   (1)
Edificio Amura C/ Cantabria 2 3 planta, Alcobendas, 28108, Madrid, Spain
Tel.: (34) 915237004
Web Site: https://www.innovataxfree.com
Tax Refunding Services
N.A.I.C.S.: 561440

PaySpot, LLC   (1)
11400 Tomahawk Creek Pkwy Ste 300, Leawood, KS 66211-2672
Tel.: (913) 327-4200
Web Site: http://www.epayworldwide.com
Prepaid Electronic Payment Processor
N.A.I.C.S.: 522320

Pure Commerce (S) Pte. Ltd.   (1)
152 Beach Rd the Gateway E 18-01, Singapore, 189721, Singapore
Tel.: (65) 63910932
Web Site: http://www.pure-commerce.com
Electronic Financial Transaction Processing Services
N.A.I.C.S.: 522320

Pure Commerce Korea YH   (1)
4 I/F Star Tower 737 Yoeksam-dong, Gangnam-gu, Seoul, 135-984, Korea (South)
Tel.: (82) 220084960
Web Site: http://www.pure-commerce.com
Electronic Financial Transaction Processing Services
N.A.I.C.S.: 522320

Pure Commerce Pty Limited   (1)
Level 11 20 Martin Place, Sydney, 2000, NSW, Australia
Tel.: (61) 282160888
Web Site: https://www.pure-commerce.com
Electronic Financial Transaction Processing Services
N.A.I.C.S.: 522320

RIA Deutschland GmbH   (1)
Philipp-Johnson Haus Friedrichstrasse 200, 10117, Berlin, Germany
Tel.: (49) 3022 152 150
Web Site: http://de.riafinancial.com
Electronic Financial Transaction Services
N.A.I.C.S.: 522320

RIA Envia, Inc.   (1)
6565 Knott Ave, Buena Park, CA 90620
Tel.: (562) 345-2100
Web Site: http://www.riafinancial.com
Sales Range: $25-49.9 Million
Emp.: 500
Money Transfer Services
N.A.I.C.S.: 522320

RIA Financial Services Norway AS   (1)

Skippergata 33, 0154, Oslo, Norway
Tel.: (47) 23960260
Electronic Financial Transaction Services
N.A.I.C.S.: 522320

RIA Financial Services Sweden AB   (1)
Armegatan 40, 171 71, Solna, Sweden
Tel.: (46) 8 679 7509
Web Site: http://www.riafinancial.com
Sales Range: $25-49.9 Million
Emp.: 13
Electronic Financial Transaction Services
N.A.I.C.S.: 522320

RIA Payment Institution EP, S.A.   (1)
Calle Cantabria 2 Planta 2, Alcobendas, 28120, Madrid, Spain
Tel.: (34) 900494631
Financial Transaction Processing Services
N.A.I.C.S.: 522320

RIA Telecommunications of New York, Inc.   (1)
214 E 170th St, Bronx, NY 10456
Tel.: (718) 588-4634
Web Site:
    https://www.riatelecommunications.com
Financial Transaction Processing Services
N.A.I.C.S.: 522320

RIA de Centroamerica, S.A. de C.V.   (1)
Boulevard Vijosa 18 Edificio Ria Zona Industrial Merliot, Antiguo Cuscatlan, La Libertad, El Salvador
Tel.: (503) 2 507 2222
Web Site: http://www.riafinancial.com
Electronic Financial Transaction Services
N.A.I.C.S.: 522320

Transact Elektronische Zahlungssysteme GmbH   (1)
Fraunhoferstr 10, 82152, Martinsried, Germany
Tel.: (49) 898996430
Web Site: https://www.epay.de
Sales Range: $10-24.9 Million
Emp.: 60
Electronic Payment Processing
N.A.I.C.S.: 522320
Marc Ehler *(Mng Dir)*
Markus Landrock *(Mng Dir)*
Martin Croot *(Mng Dir)*

Yamando GmbH   (1)
Osterbekstrasse 90b, Hamburg, 22083, Germany
Tel.: (49) 40271482741
Web Site: http://www.yamando.de
Sales Range: $25-49.9 Million
Emp.: 10
Online Gift Retailer
N.A.I.C.S.: 459420

YourCash Limited   (1)
Willow House Linford Wood, Woodlands Business Park, Milton Keynes, MK14 6EU, Buckinghamshire, United Kingdom
Tel.: (44) 1908574100
Web Site: https://www.yourcash.com
Tax Refunding Services
N.A.I.C.S.: 561440

cadooz Gmbh   (1)
Osterbekstrasse 90b, 22083, Hamburg, Germany
Tel.: (49) 402714820
Web Site: https://www.cadooz.com
Emp.: 100
Management Consulting Services
N.A.I.C.S.: 541618
Stefan Grimm *(Mng Dir)*
Michael Lemmel *(Dir-Category Mgmt & Pur Cadooz Rewards)*
Robert Schneider *(Dir-Sls & Ops-Cadooz Rewards)*
Paul Riedel *(Dir-Sls & Mktg)*
Simon Schunk *(Dir-HR)*
Marcel Tahmouresinia *(Dir-Product Mgmt & Bus Dev)*

cadooz rewards GmbH   (1)
Franziska-Bilek-Weg 9, 80339, Munich, Germany
Tel.: (49) 40271482109
Web Site: http://www.cadooz.com
Marketing Consulting Services
N.A.I.C.S.: 541613

e-pay Australia Pty Ltd. (1)
Level 1 75 Castlereagh Street, Sydney, 2000, NSW, Australia
Tel.: (61) 1300301408
Web Site:
https://www.epayworldwide.com.au
Sales Range: $10-24.9 Million
Emp.: 50
Prepaid Financial Transactions Services
N.A.I.C.S.: 522320

epay Australia Pty Ltd (1)
Level 1 75 Castlereagh Street, Sydney, 2000, NSW, Australia
Tel.: (61) 1300301408
Web Site:
https://www.epayworldwide.com.au
Electronic Financial Transaction Processing Services
N.A.I.C.S.: 522320

epay Netherlands B.V. (1)
Flight Forum 40 Ground Floor, 5657 DB, Eindhoven, Netherlands
Tel.: (31) 618688611
Web Site: https://www.epay.co.nl
Payment Processing Services
N.A.I.C.S.: 522320
Amin Mahini *(Chm)*

EUROPEAN SUSTAINABLE GROWTH ACQUISITION CORP.
73 Arch St, Greenwich, CT 06830
Tel.: (203) 983-4400   Ky
Year Founded: 2020
EUSG—(NASDAQ)
Investment Services
N.A.I.C.S.: 523999
Lars Thunell *(Chm)*
Pieter Taselaar *(Co-CEO)*
Matheus Hovers *(Co-CEO)*
Karan Trehan *(Pres)*
Patrick Moroney *(CFO)*

EUROPEAN WAX CENTER INC.
5830 Granite Pkwy Ste 300, Plano, TX 75024
Tel.: (469) 264-8123
Web Site: https://www.waxcenter.com
Year Founded: 2005
EWCZ—(NASDAQ)
Rev.: $207,351,000
Assets: $716,032,000
Liabilities: $585,728,000
Net Worth: $130,304,000
Earnings: $7,277,000
Emp.: 117
Fiscal Year-end: 12/31/22
Beauty Salons
N.A.I.C.S.: 812112
Stacie R. Shirley *(CFO)*
David Coba *(Co-Founder)*
Joshua Coba *(Co-Founder)*
David P. Berg *(Chm & CEO)*
David L. Willis *(Pres & COO)*
Gavin M. O'Connor *(Chief Legal Officer, Chief Admin Officer, Chief HR Officer & Sec)*
Cindy Thomassee *(Chief Acctg Officer)*
Julie A. Hauser-Blanner *(Chief Franchise Officer)*
Joel Larkin *(Chief Dev Officer)*
Andrew Wasserman *(Chief Comml Officer)*
Mike Breeze *(CIO)*
Damyon Claar-Pressley *(VP)*
Aura De Biase *(VP)*
Doug LeMaster *(VP)*
Addison Niesman *(VP)*
Jo Gittins *(VP)*
Deanna Sieg *(VP)*

Subsidiaries:

EWC Aventura, LLC (1)
18723 Biscayne Blvd, Aventura, FL 33180
Tel.: (786) 320-5530
Wax Salon Centre Services
N.A.I.C.S.: 812112

EVANS BANCORP, INC.
6460 Main St, Williamsville, NY 14221
Tel.: (716) 926-2000   NY
Web Site:
https://www.evansbank.com
Year Founded: 1988
EVBN—(NYSEAMEX)
Rev.: $98,753,000
Assets: $2,178,510,000
Liabilities: $2,024,517,000
Net Worth: $153,993,000
Earnings: $22,389,000
Emp.: 379
Fiscal Year-end: 12/31/22
Bank Holding Company
N.A.I.C.S.: 551111
David John Nasca *(Pres & CEO)*
Lee Charles Wortham *(Chm)*

Subsidiaries:

Evans Bank, N.A. (1)
6460 Main St, Williamsville, NY 14221
Tel.: (716) 926-3313
Web Site: https://www.evansbank.com
Sales Range: $50-74.9 Million
Emp.: 244
Savings Bank
N.A.I.C.S.: 522180
David John Nasca *(Pres & CEO)*

Evans National Financial Services, LLC (1)
6460 Main St Corporate Finance, Williamsville, NY 14221   **(100%)**
Tel.: (716) 549-1120
Sales Range: $1-4.9 Billion
Emp.: 50
Holding Company; Investment & Insurance Products & Services
N.A.I.C.S.: 551112
Robert G. Miller Jr. *(Pres)*
Evan D. Malone *(Asst VP & Mgr-Customer Rels)*

Evans National Holding Corp. (1)
6460 Main St Corporate Finance, Williamsville, NY 14221
Tel.: (716) 965-2701
Commercial Banking Services
N.A.I.C.S.: 522110

Frontier Claims Services, Inc. (1)
6834 Erie Rd, Derby, NY 14047
Tel.: (716) 926-3301
Web Site: http://www.frontierclaims.com
Sales Range: $25-49.9 Million
Emp.: 5
Insurance Claims Processing Services
N.A.I.C.S.: 524292
Christopher A. Weber *(Pres & CEO)*
Kim Sexton *(Supvr-Claim Svcs)*

EVE HOLDING, INC.
1400 General Aviation Dr, Melbourne, FL 32935
Tel.: (321) 751-5050   DE
Web Site: https://eveairmobility.com
Year Founded: 2020
EVEX—(NYSE)
Assets: $312,875,428
Liabilities: $25,953,085
Net Worth: $286,922,343
Earnings: ($174,030,358)
Emp.: 149
Aviation Services
N.A.I.C.S.: 488190
Johann Christian Jean Charles Bordais *(CEO)*
Eduardo Couto *(CFO)*
Lucio Aldworth *(Dir-IR)*
Alice Altissimo *(VP-Program Mgmt & Ops)*
Larissa Maraccini *(VP-HR, HR, HR, and HR)*
Luiz Mauad *(VP-Svcs, Ops Solutions, Strategic Design, and Ecosystem)*
David Rottblatt *(VP-Sls & Sls)*
Luiz Valentini *(CTO & VP-Engineering & Technology)*

Simone Galvao De Oliveira *(Chief Compliance Officer, Gen Counsel & VP-Legal, Procurement, and Compliance)*
Antonio Carmesini *(VP-Industrialization)*

EVE MOBILITY ACQUISITION CORP.
4001 Kennet Pike Ste 302, Wilmington, DE 19807
Tel.: (302) 273-0014   Ky
Web Site:
https://www.evemobility.com
Year Founded: 2021
EVE—(NYSE)
Rev.: $3,678,066
Assets: $259,151,606
Liabilities: $268,531,328
Net Worth: ($9,379,722)
Earnings: $2,626,104
Emp.: 4
Fiscal Year-end: 12/31/22
Investment Services
N.A.I.C.S.: 523999
Osman H. Ahmed *(Pres)*

EVELO BIOSCIENCES, INC.
620 Memorial Dr, Cambridge, MA 02139
Tel.: (617) 577-0300   DE
Web Site: https://www.evelobio.com
Year Founded: 2014
EVLO—(NASDAQ)
Rev.: $61,000
Assets: $64,441,000
Liabilities: $69,433,000
Net Worth: ($4,992,000)
Earnings: ($114,527,000)
Emp.: 66
Fiscal Year-end: 12/31/22
Biotechnology Development Services
N.A.I.C.S.: 541714
Craig R. Jalbert *(Pres, Principal Exec Officer, Principal Fin Officer, Principal Acctg Officer & Sec)*
Mark Bodmer *(Chief Scientific Officer & Pres-R&D)*
Duncan McHale *(Chief Medical Officer)*
Mark Plinio *(Chief Comml Officer)*
Balkrishnan Gill *(Pres & CEO)*
Lord Ara Darzi *(Chm)*

EVENTBRITE, INC.
95 3rd St 2nd Fl, San Francisco, CA 94103
Tel.: (415) 692-7779   DE
Web Site: https://www.eventbrite.com
Year Founded: 2006
EB—(NYSE)
Rev.: $260,927,000
Assets: $895,379,000
Liabilities: $728,824,000
Net Worth: $166,555,000
Earnings: ($55,384,000,000)
Emp.: 881
Fiscal Year-end: 12/31/22
Online Ticketing Services; Event Planning & Management Software Solutions
N.A.I.C.S.: 513210
Xiaojing Fan *(Chief Acctg Officer)*
Kevin E. Hartz *(Co-Founder)*
Tamara Mendelsohn *(CMO)*
Julia Taylor *(Gen Counsel)*
Vivek Sagi *(CTO)*
John Adcock *(Chief People Officer)*
Charles C. Baker *(CFO & COO)*
Ted Dworkin *(Chief Product Officer)*
Julia Hartz *(Co-Founder, Chm & CEO)*

Subsidiaries:

Ticketfly, LLC (1)
111 Townsend St, San Francisco, CA 94107

Tel.: (877) 435-9848
Web Site: http://www.ticketfly.com
Web Based Ticketing & Marketing Services
N.A.I.C.S.: 541519

EVERCOMMERCE INC.
3601 Walnut St Ste 400, Denver, CO 80205
Tel.: (720) 647-4948   DE
Web Site:
https://www.evercommerce.com
Year Founded: 2016
EVCM—(NASDAQ)
Rev.: $620,746,000
Assets: $1,591,728,000
Liabilities: $685,035,000
Net Worth: $906,693,000
Earnings: ($59,816,000)
Emp.: 2,300
Fiscal Year-end: 12/31/22
Custom Computer Programming Services
N.A.I.C.S.: 541511
Eric Remer *(Founder, Chm & CEO)*
Matthew Feierstein *(Pres)*
Sarah Jordan *(CMO)*
Chris Alaimo *(CTO)*
Lisa M. Sterling *(Chief Admin & HR Officer)*
Elissa Beckman *(Chief People Officer)*
Stone de Souza *(COO)*
Lisa Storey *(Gen Counsel)*
Jeanne Trogan *(VP-Comm)*
Brad Korch *(Sr VP & Head-IR)*
Evan Berlin *(COO & Exec VP)*
Ryan H. Siurek *(CFO & Chief Acctg Officer)*

EVERCORE, INC.
55 E 52nd St, New York, NY 10055
Tel.: (212) 857-3100   DE
Web Site: https://www.evercore.com
Year Founded: 1995
EVR—(NYSE)
Rev.: $2,442,666,000
Assets: $3,703,298,000
Liabilities: $1,920,808,000
Net Worth: $1,782,490,000
Earnings: $255,479,000
Emp.: 2,195
Fiscal Year-end: 12/31/23
Investment Banking, Advisory & Portfolio Management Services
N.A.I.C.S.: 523150
John S. Weinberg *(Chm & CEO)*
Roger C. Altman *(Founder & Co-Chm)*
Mayer Bick *(Mng Dir-Mergers & Acquisitions-Los Angeles)*
Timothy G. Lalonde *(Sr Mng Dir & CFO)*
Paul Pensa *(Sr Mng Dir, Chief Acctg Officer & Co-Dir-Fin-Global)*
Andrew W. Sibbald *(Chm-Investment Banking-Europe & Sr Mng Dir-Investment Banking-Europe)*
Jarrett Vitulli *(Sr Mng Dir-Private Capital Advisory)*
Bill Anderson *(Sr Mng Dir/Global Head-Strategic Shareholder Advisory Practice)*
Masuo Fukuda *(Sr Mng Dir-Mergers & Acquisitions-Tokyo)*
Michael J. Paliotta *(CEO-Evercore ISI)*
Elsa Ferreira *(Mng Dir-IT & Chief Information Security Officer)*
Marc Harris *(Dir-Res-Evercore ISI)*
Matthew Lindsey-Clark *(CEO-Advisory-Europe, Middle East & Africa)*
Katy Haber *(Head-IR & ESG)*
Jamie Easton *(Head-Comm & External Affairs)*

Evercore, Inc.—(Continued)

Joy Savchenko (*Sr Mng Dir-Private Capital Advisory Grp*)
Nigel Dawn (*Head-Private Capital Advisory Grp*)
Michael Binetti (*Sr Mng Dir-Evercore ISI*)
John Kimm (*Mng Dir-Mergers & Acquisitions*)
William O. Hiltz (*Sr Mng Dir-Mergers & Acquisitions*)

Subsidiaries:

Administradora Evercore, S.C. (1)
Boulevard Presidente Manuel Avila Camacho, Miguel Hidalgo, Mexico, 11000, Mexico
Tel.: (52) 5552494300
Financial Advisory Services
N.A.I.C.S.: 523940

Evercore (Japan) Ltd. (1)
Shin Marunouchi Center 21F 1-6-2
Marunouchi, Chiyoda-ku, Tokyo, 100-0005, Japan
Tel.: (81) 332167391
Investment Advisory Services
N.A.I.C.S.: 523940
Masuo Fukuda (*Sr Mng Dir*)

Evercore Advisory (Middle East) Limited (1)
unit 1606 Level 16 Index Tower DIFC, 507204, Dubai, United Arab Emirates
Tel.: (971) 42473800
Investment Advisory Services
N.A.I.C.S.: 523940
Elias Mouawad (*Mng Dir & Head-Middle East*)

Evercore Consulting (Beijing) Co. Ltd. (1)
China World Tower 3 1 Jianguomenwai Avenue, Beijing, China
Tel.: (86) 1057372630
Investment Advisory Services
N.A.I.C.S.: 523940

Evercore GmbH (1)
Grosse Gallusstrasse 18, 60312, Frankfurt, Germany
Tel.: (49) 697079990
Financial Advisory Services
N.A.I.C.S.: 523940
Eduard Kostadinov (*Sr Mng Dir-Advisory Practice-Investment Banking*)

Evercore Group LLC (1)
55 E 52nd St, New York, NY 10055
Tel.: (212) 857-3100
Web Site: https://www.evercore.com
Holding Company
N.A.I.C.S.: 551112

Subsidiary (Domestic):

Evercore Advisors L.L.C. (2)
55 E 52nd St, New York, NY 10055
Tel.: (212) 857-3100
Web Site: https://www.evercore.com
Investment Advisory Services
N.A.I.C.S.: 523940

Subsidiary (Non-US):

Evercore Asia (Singapore) Pte. Ltd. (2)
12 Marina Boulevard 33-01 MBFC Tower 3, Singapore, 018982, Singapore
Tel.: (65) 62907000
Emp.: 20
Investment Management Service
N.A.I.C.S.: 523940

Evercore Asia Limited (2)
Two Exchange Square Suite 1405-1407, Central, China (Hong Kong)
Tel.: (852) 39832600
Investment Management Service
N.A.I.C.S.: 523940

Unit (Domestic):

Evercore Capital Partners (2)
55 E 52nd 3rd Fl, New York, NY 10055
Tel.: (212) 857-3100
Sales Range: $650-699.9 Million
Private Equity Investments
N.A.I.C.S.: 523999

Kathleen G. Reiland (*Sr Mng Dir-Corp Advisory*)
Mayer Bick (*Mng Dir-Corp Advisory*)
Kristen Grippi (*Sr Mng Dir & Head-Equity Capital Markets*)
John Weinberg (*Co-Chm & Co-CEO*)
Ralph Schlosstein (*Co-Chm & Co-CEO*)
Tim LaLonde (*COO-Investment Banking*)
Hallie Elsner Miller (*Head-IR*)

Subsidiary (Non-US):

Evercore Casa de Bolsa, S.A. de C.V. (2)
Torre Virreyes Pedregal 24 15nd Floor Col Molino del Rey, Del Miguel Hidalgo, 11040, Mexico, Mexico
Tel.: (52) 5552494490
Web Site: http://www.evercorecb.com
Investment Management Service
N.A.I.C.S.: 523940
Pedro Aspe (*Founder*)

Evercore Group Services Limited (2)
15 Stanhope Gate, London, W1K 1LN, United Kingdom
Tel.: (44) 2076536000
Investment Management Service
N.A.I.C.S.: 523940
Bruce Weir (*CFO*)

Evercore Partners Canada Ltd. (2)
181 Bay Street, Toronto, M5J 2T3, ON, Canada
Tel.: (416) 304-8100
Web Site: https://www.evercore.com
Emp.: 20
Investment Management Service
N.A.I.C.S.: 523940

Evercore Partners Limited (2)
15 Stanhope Gate, London, W1K 1LN, United Kingdom
Tel.: (44) 2076536000
Emp.: 15
Investment Management & Banking Services
N.A.I.C.S.: 523150

Evercore Partners Mexico, S. de R.L. (2)
Torre Virreyes Pedregal No 24 Col Molino del Rey, Delegacion Miguel Hidalgo Distrito Federal, 11040, Mexico, Mexico
Tel.: (52) 5552494300
Web Site: http://www.evercore.com.mx
Emp.: 200
Investment Banking & Advisory Services
N.A.I.C.S.: 523150

Subsidiary (Domestic):

Evercore Partners Services East L.L.C. (2)
55 E 52nd St, New York, NY 10055
Tel.: (212) 857-3100
Web Site: https://www.evercore.com
Investment Advisory Services
N.A.I.C.S.: 523940

Evercore Trust Company, N.A. (2)
300 Delaware Ave Ste 1225, Wilmington, DE 19801
Tel.: (302) 304-7360
Web Site: https://www.evercoretrustcompany.com
Investment Management Service
N.A.I.C.S.: 523940

Evercore Wealth Management L.L.C. (2)
55 E 52nd St, New York, NY 10055
Tel.: (212) 822 7620
Web Site: https://www.evercorewealthmanagement.com
Investment Management Service
N.A.I.C.S.: 523940
Jonathan Bergner (*Partner & Portfolio Mgr*)
Nancy Shavel Gabel (*Partner*)
Iain Silverthorne (*Partner*)
Helena Jonassen (*Partner*)
Stephanie Hackett (*Partner & Portfolio Mgr*)
Brian Pollak (*Partner & Portfolio Mgr*)
Arthur Noderer (*Partner & Portfolio Mgr-Florida*)
Thomas Mahowald (*Mng Dir & Portfolio Mgr*)
John Apruzzese (*Partner & Chief Investment Officer*)

Timothy Barrett (*Partner & Portfolio Mgr*)
Julio Castro (*Partner*)
Michael Cozene (*Partner*)
Tim Evnin (*Partner & Portfolio Mgr-Equity*)
Karen Francois (*Partner*)
James Holihan (*Partner & Portfolio Mgr*)
Judith McDonald Moses (*Partner & Portfolio Mgr-San Francisco*)
Kate Mulvany (*Partner*)
Martha Pomerantz (*Partner & Mgr-Minneapolis*)
Stacie Price (*Partner*)
Charles Ryan (*Partner & Portfolio Mgr*)
Daniel Stolfa (*Mng Dir-Minneapolis*)
Thomas Olchon (*Mng Dir*)
Steven Chung (*Mng Dir & Portfolio Mgr*)
Ross Saia (*Partner*)
Mike Seppelt (*Partner & Portfolio Mgr*)
William Vaughn (*Partner & Portfolio Mgr*)

International Strategy & Investment Group L.L.C. (2)
666 5th Ave 11th Fl, New York, NY 10103
Tel.: (212) 446-5600
Financial Advisory Services
N.A.I.C.S.: 523940
Kevin Casey (*Chief Compliance Officer*)

Subsidiary (Non-US):

Evercore ISI International Limited (3)
16 New Burlington Place, London, W1S 2HX, United Kingdom
Tel.: (44) 2078473500
Web Site: https://www.evercore.com
Investment Management Service
N.A.I.C.S.: 523940

Evercore Partners International L.L.P (1)
15 Stanhope Gate, London, W1K 1LN, United Kingdom
Tel.: (44) 2076536000
Investment Advisory Services
N.A.I.C.S.: 523940

Evercore Trust Company of Delaware (1)
300 Delaware Ave Ste 1225, Wilmington, DE 19801
Tel.: (302) 304-7360
Web Site: https://evercorewealthandtrust.com
Financial Advisory Services
N.A.I.C.S.: 523940

EVEREST CONSOLIDATOR ACQUISITION CORPORATION
4041 MacArthur Blvd 4th Fl, Newport Beach, CA 92660
Tel.: (949) 610-0035 DE
Web Site:
https://www.belayoneverest.com
Year Founded: 2021
MNTN—(NYSE)
Rev.: $2,536,113
Assets: $178,655,328
Liabilities: $185,004,612
Net Worth: ($6,349,284)
Earnings: $158,386
Emp.: 2
Fiscal Year-end: 12/31/22
Miscellaneous Financial Investment Activities
N.A.I.C.S.: 523999
Adam Dooley (*Pres, CEO, Chm, Sec & Tres*)
Jacqueline S. Shoback (*COO*)

EVERGREEN SUSTAINABLE ENTERPRISES, INC.
Tel.: (469) 209-6154 CO
Web Site:
https://www.genhempinc.com
Year Founded: 2008
EGSE—(OTCQB)
Rev.: $90,000
Assets: $3,918,994
Liabilities: $6,883,929
Net Worth: ($2,964,935)
Earnings: ($1,498,669)
Emp.: 1

Fiscal Year-end: 12/31/20
Real Estate Services
N.A.I.C.S.: 531390
Gary C. Evans (*Chm & CEO*)
Melissa M. Pagen (*Sr VP-Corp Dev*)
Rob Sanders (*Dir-Advisory*)
Watt Stephens (*Mng Dir, Chief Branding Officer & Exec VP-Corp Dev*)
Jack Sibley (*Exec VP-Ops & VP-Corp Dev*)
Brada Wilson (*Controller-Acctg*)

EVERGREEN-AGRA, INC.
19800 MacArthur Ste 300, Irvine, CA 92612 NV
Tel.: (604) 764-7646
Web Site:
http://www.evergreenagra.com
Year Founded: 2008
EGRN—(OTCIQ)
Emp.: 4
Agricultural Investment Services
N.A.I.C.S.: 523999
Rene Hamouth (*Chm, Pres & Sec*)
Todd Hazlewood (*CFO*)
Paolo Galido (*CIO*)
Matthew Rhoden (*CEO*)
Randy R. Rhoden (*COO*)

EVERGY, INC.
1200 Main St, Kansas City, MO 64105 MO
Tel.: (816) 556-2200
Web Site: https://www.evergy.com
Year Founded: 2017
EVRG—(NASDAQ)
Rev.: $5,508,200,000
Assets: $30,976,100,000
Liabilities: $21,291,100,000
Net Worth: $9,685,000,000
Earnings: $731,300,000
Emp.: 4,658
Fiscal Year-end: 12/31/23
Holding Company; Electric Power Plant Operator
N.A.I.C.S.: 551112
David A. Campbell (*Chm, Pres & CEO*)
Anthony D. Somma (*CFO & Exec VP*)
Gregory A. Greenwood (*Chief Strategy Officer & Exec VP*)
Kevin E. Bryant (*COO & Exec VP*)
Steven P. Busser (*VP-Risk Mgmt & Controller*)
Jerl L. Banning (*Chief People Officer & Sr VP*)
Heather A. Humphrey (*Gen Counsel, Sec & Sr VP*)
Charles A. Caisley (*Chief Customer Officer & Sr VP-Mktg & Pub Affairs*)
Charles King (*CTO & Sr VP*)
Bruce Akin (*VP-Transmission & Distr*)
Jeff Beasley (*VP-Customer Ops*)
John Bridson (*VP-Generation*)
Ellen Fairchild (*Chief Compliance Officer & VP*)
Deb Grunst (*VP-IT*)
Darrin Ives (*VP-Regulatory Affairs*)
Jeff Martin (*VP-Customer & Community Ops*)
Kevin Noblet (*VP-Safety & Ops Plng*)
Lori Wright (*Treas & VP-Corp Plng & IR*)
Gina Penzig (*Mgr-External Comm*)
Cody VandeVelde (*Dir-IR*)
Cleve Reasoner (*Chief Nuclear Officer & VP*)

Subsidiaries:

Evergy Kansas Central, Inc. (1)
818 S Kansas Ave, Topeka, KS 66612
Tel.: (785) 575-6300
Web Site: https://www.evergy.com
Rev.: $3,055,900,000
Assets: $13,368,300,000

Liabilities: $8,860,900,000
Net Worth: $4,507,400,000
Earnings: $408,600,000
Emp.: 4,511
Fiscal Year-end: 12/31/2022
Electric Generation & Transmission Services
N.A.I.C.S.: 221122
David A. Campbell (Pres & CEO)
Mark A. Ruelle (Chm)
Anthony D. Somma (CFO & Exec VP)

Subsidiary (Domestic):

Westar Industries, Inc. (2)
818 S Kansas Ave, Topeka, KS
66612-1203 (100%)
Tel.: (785) 575-6507
Web Site: http://www.westarenergy.com
Sales Range: $50-74.9 Million
Emp.: 475
Utility Services
N.A.I.C.S.: 561621
Mark A. Ruelle (Pres & CEO)

Evergy Metro, Inc. (1)
1200 Main St, Kansas City, MO 64105
Tel.: (816) 556-2200
Web Site: https://www.evergy.com
Rev.: $1,970,600,000
Assets: $9,249,200,000
Liabilities: $6,062,900,000
Net Worth: $3,186,300,000
Earnings: $355,400,000
Emp.: 4,512
Fiscal Year-end: 12/31/2022
Electric Utility Mfr
N.A.I.C.S.: 332911
David A. Campbell (Pres & CEO)
Mark A. Ruelle (Chm)
Gregory A. Greenwood (Chief Admin Officer & Exec VP-Strategy)
Kevin E. Bryant (COO & Exec VP)
Charles A. Caisley (Chief Customer Officer & Sr VP-Mktg & Pub Affairs)
Heather A. Humphrey (Gen Counsel)
Charles L. King (CTO)
Lesley L. Elwell (Chief HR Officer)
Steven P. Busser (Chief Acctg Officer, VP-Risk Mgmt & Controller)
Steven P. Busser (Chief Acctg Officer, VP-Risk Mgmt & Controller)

Subsidiary (Domestic):

KCP&L Greater Missouri Operations Company (2)
1200 Main St, Kansas City, MO 64105
Tel.: (816) 556-2200
Web Site: http://www.kcpl.com
Emp.: 2,213
Electric Power Distribution Services
N.A.I.C.S.: 221122

Wolf Creek Nuclear Operating Corporation (2)
1550 Oxen Ln, Burlington, KS 66839
Tel.: (620) 364-8831
Web Site: http://www.wcnoc.com
Sales Range: $1-4.9 Billion
Emp.: 1,030
Nuclear Power Plant Operator
N.A.I.C.S.: 221113

Evergy Services, Inc. (1)
1200 Main St, Kansas City, MO
64105 (100%)
Tel.: (816) 556-2200
Web Site: http://www.evergy.com
Customer Support Services
N.A.I.C.S.: 541990

EVERI HOLDINGS INC.
7250 S Tenaya Way Ste 100, Las
Vegas, NV 89113
Tel.: (702) 855-3000 DE
Web Site: https://www.everi.com
Year Founded: 1998
EVRI—(NYSE)
Rev.: $782,519,000
Assets: $1,918,243,000
Liabilities: $1,700,602,000
Net Worth: $217,641,000
Earnings: $120,489,000
Emp.: 2,000
Fiscal Year-end: 12/31/22
Offices of Other Holding Companies

N.A.I.C.S.: 551112
Michael David Rumbolz (Chm)
Richard P. Hallman (CIO & Exec VP)
Darren D. A. Simmons (Exec VP)
William Pfund (Sr VP-IR)
Mark F. Labay (CFO, Treas & Exec VP)
Dona Cassese (VP-Mktg)
Kate C. Lowenhar-Fisher (Chief Legal Officer, Gen Counsel, Corp Sec & Exec VP)
Timothy B. Richards (Chief Strategy Officer & Exec VP)
Dan Ciccarelli (CIO)
A. Ehrlich (Exec VP)
Randy L. Taylor (Pres & CEO)

Subsidiaries:

GCA (Macau) S.A. (1)
Alameda Drive Carlos D'Assumpcao No
335, Centro Hotline 21st Fl Unit X, Macau,
China (Macau)
Tel.: (853) 66407770
Web Site: http://www.globalcashaccess.com
Sales Range: $100-124.9 Million
Cash Advance Services for the Gaming Industry
N.A.I.C.S.: 561499

Multimedia Games Holding Company, Inc. (1)
206 Wild Basin Rd S Bldg B, Austin, TX
78746
Tel.: (512) 334-7500
Web Site: http://www.multimediagames.com
Rev.: $218,129,000
Assets: $315,012,000
Liabilities: $70,654,000
Net Worth: $244,358,000
Earnings: $31,929,000
Emp.: 524
Fiscal Year-end: 09/30/2014
Holding Company; Interactive Bingo, Video
Lottery & Related Electronic Games Designer, Publisher & Marketer
N.A.I.C.S.: 551112

Subsidiary (Domestic):

Multimedia Games, Inc. (2)
206 Wild Basin Rd S, Austin, TX 78746
Tel.: (512) 334-7500
Web Site: http://www.multimediagames.com
Sales Range: $100-124.9 Million
Emp.: 500
Interactive Bingo, Video Lottery & Related
Electronic Games Designer, Publisher &
Marketer
N.A.I.C.S.: 713290

EVERQUOTE, INC.
210 Broadway, Cambridge, MA
02139 DE
Web Site: https://www.everquote.com
Year Founded: 2011
EVER—(NASDAQ)
Rev.: $404,127,000
Assets: $156,519,000
Liabilities: $49,033,000
Net Worth: $107,486,000
Earnings: ($24,416,000)
Emp.: 612
Fiscal Year-end: 12/31/22
Risk Managemeng Srvices
N.A.I.C.S.: 524292
Jesse Wolf (Exec VP-Product)
Joseph Sanborn (CFO)
David Brainard (CTO)
Garett Kitch (Sr VP-Sls-Health & Life Agency)
Julia Brncic (Gen Counsel & Sec)
Jon Ayotte (Chief Acctg Officer)
David Blundin (Founder)
Jayme Mendal (Pres & CEO)

EVERSIDE HEALTH GROUP, INC.
1400 Wewatta St Ste 350, Denver,
CO 80202
Tel.: (303) 566-7161 DE

Web Site:
http://www.eversidehealth.com
Year Founded: 2018
EVSD—(NYSE)
Rev.: $113,375,000
Assets: $335,203,000
Liabilities: $73,800,000
Net Worth: $261,403,000
Earnings: ($2,901,000)
Emp.: 1,166
Fiscal Year-end: 12/31/20
Health Care Srvices
N.A.I.C.S.: 621610
Christopher T. Miller (CEO)
Gaurov Dayal (Pres & COO)
Tobias Barker (Chief Medical Officer)
Adam Johnson (Chief Growth & Strategy Officer)
Wesley Donohoe (Chief Product Officer)
Allison Velez (Chief People Officer)
Sampath Narayanan (CIO)
Courtney Harwood (CMO)
Ben Stapleton (Sr VP-Ops)

EVERSOURCE ENERGY
300 Cadwell Dr, Springfield, MA
01104
Tel.: (413) 785-5871 MA
Web Site:
https://www.eversource.com
Year Founded: 1966
ES—(NYSE)
Rev.: $11,910,705,000
Assets: $55,612,245,000
Liabilities: $41,438,353,000
Net Worth: $14,173,892,000
Earnings: ($442,240,000)
Emp.: 10,171
Fiscal Year-end: 12/31/23
Electric & Gas Utilities Services
N.A.I.C.S.: 221121
Joseph R. Nolan Jr. (Chm, Pres & CEO)
Paul Chodak III (COO & Exec VP)
Gregory B. Butler (Gen Counsel & Exec VP)
Jay S. Buth (Chief Acctg Officer)
John M. Moreira (CFO, Treas & Exec VP)
James W. Hunt III (Exec VP-Corp Rels & Sustainability)

Subsidiaries:

Aquarion Water Company (1)
200 Monroe Tpke, Monroe, CT 06468
Web Site: https://www.aquarionwater.com
Water Supply & Irrigation Systems
N.A.I.C.S.: 221310

Aquarion Water Company of Massachusetts, Inc. (1)
900 Main St, Hingham, MA 02043
Tel.: (781) 740-6693
Web Site: http://www.aquarionwater.com
Water Distribution Services
N.A.I.C.S.: 221310

Aquarion Water Company of New Hampshire, Inc. (1)
7 Scott Rd, Hampton, NH 03842
Tel.: (603) 926-3319
Web Site: https://www.aquarionwater.com
Water Distribution Services
N.A.I.C.S.: 221310

Bay State Gas Company (1)
4 Technology Dr, Westborough, MA
01581-3900 (100%)
Tel.: (508) 836-7000
Web Site: http://www.columbiagasma.com
Sales Range: $25-49.9 Million
Emp.: 45
Natural Gas Distribution
N.A.I.C.S.: 221210
Mark Kempic (Pres & COO)

NSTAR LLC (1)
800 Boylston St, Boston, MA 02199
Tel.: (617) 424-2000
Web Site: http://www.nstar.com

Emp.: 3,000
Holding Company; Electric & Natural Gas
Distr
N.A.I.C.S.: 551112

Subsidiary (Domestic):

EversourceEnergy (2)
800 Boylston St, Boston, MA 02199
Tel.: (617) 424-2000
Web Site: http://www.nstar.com
Rev.: $3,583,070,000
Assets: $15,095,620,000
Liabilities: $9,394,950,000
Net Worth: $5,700,670,000
Earnings: $492,428,000
Emp.: 1,648
Fiscal Year-end: 12/31/2022
Electric Power Distr
N.A.I.C.S.: 221122
Gregory B. Butler (Gen Counsel & Exec VP)

Subsidiary (Domestic):

Harbor Electric Energy Company (3)
800 Boylston St, Boston, MA 02199
Tel.: (617) 424-2000
Power Distribution Services
N.A.I.C.S.: 221122

Subsidiary (Domestic):

NSTAR Electric & Gas Corporation (2)
800 Boylston St Ste 1700, Boston, MA
02199 (100%)
Tel.: (617) 424-2000
Web Site: http://www.nstar.com
Rev.: $371,870,000
Emp.: 3,000
Electronic Services
N.A.I.C.S.: 221122

NSTAR Gas Company (2)
800 Boylston St, Boston, MA
02199 (100%)
Tel.: (617) 424-2000
Web Site: http://www.nstar.com
Sales Range: $50-74.9 Million
Emp.: 200
Natural Gas Distribution
N.A.I.C.S.: 221210
Paul Chodak III (CEO)
Russell D. Wright (Pres & COO)

NU Enterprises, Inc. (1)
107 Selden St, Berlin, CT 06037 (100%)
Tel.: (860) 665-2944
Web Site: http://www.nu.com
Sales Range: $200-249.9 Million
Holding Company
N.A.I.C.S.: 221118

Subsidiary (Domestic):

IP Strategy LLC (2)
3 Glen Valley Dr, Penfield, NY 14526
Tel.: (585) 787-3341
Web Site: http://www.ipstrategyllc.com
Asset Management Services
N.A.I.C.S.: 531390

North Atlantic Energy Service Corporation (2)
383 Middle St Ste 101, Bristol, CT 06011-0158
Tel.: (860) 506-2000
Emp.: 250
Mechanical & Electrical Contracting, Preventive Maintenance & Energy Management Control Services
N.A.I.C.S.: 811490

Northeast Generation Services Company (2)
301 Hammer Mill Rd, Rocky Hill, CT 06067
Tel.: (860) 810-1715
Eletric Power Generation Services
N.A.I.C.S.: 221118

Northeast Nuclear Energy Company (1)
107 Selden St, Berlin, CT 06037
Tel.: (860) 665-5000
Web Site: http://www.nu.com
Sales Range: $50-74.9 Million
Emp.: 200
Nuclear Power Mfr
N.A.I.C.S.: 221113

Eversource Energy—(Continued)

Northeast Utilities Service Company (1)
107 Selden St, Berlin, CT 06037 **(100%)**
Tel.: (860) 665-5000
Web Site: http://www.nu.com
Sales Range: $450-499.9 Million
Emp.: 2,300
Centralized Accounting, Administrative, Data Processing, Engineering, Financial, Legal, Operational, Planning, Purchasing & Other Services to the NU System Companies
N.A.I.C.S.: 541611

Public Service Company of New Hampshire (1)
780 N Commercial St, Manchester, NH 03101-1134 **(100%)**
Web Site: https://www.eversource.com
Rev.: $1,447,873,000
Assets: $5,993,451,000
Liabilities: $3,639,532,000
Net Worth: $2,353,919,000
Earnings: $195,659,000
Emp.: 830
Fiscal Year-end: 12/31/2023
Electric Power Distribution & Generation Services
N.A.I.C.S.: 221118
James J. Judge (Chm)
Paul Chodak III (CEO)
Gregory B. Butler (Gen Counsel & Exec VP)
John M. Moreira (Treas & Sr VP-Fin & Regulatory)
Werner J. Schweiger (CEO)
Jay S. Buth (Chief Acctg Officer, VP & Controller)
Philip J. Lembo (CFO & Exec VP)

Renewable Properties, Inc. (1)
1340 East Blue Lick Road Apartment 3, Shepherdsville, KY 40165
Tel.: (502) 664-8006
Emp.: 3
Roof Installation Services
N.A.I.C.S.: 238160
Aaron Halimi (Founder & Pres)
Brian Von Moos (Chief Dev Officer)

The Connecticut Light and Power Company (1)
107 Selden St, Berlin, CT 06037-1616 **(100%)**
Tel.: (860) 665-5000
Web Site: https://www.eversource.com
Rev.: $4,578,804,000
Assets: $15,849,624,000
Liabilities: $9,758,954,000
Net Worth: $6,090,670,000
Earnings: $518,733,000
Emp.: 1,529
Fiscal Year-end: 12/31/2023
Electric Power Distribution & Generation Services
N.A.I.C.S.: 221122
Paul Chodak III (CEO)
John M. Moreira (Treas & Sr VP-Fin & Regulatory)
Philip J. Lembo (CFO & Exec VP)
Gregory B. Butler (Gen Counsel & Exec VP)
Jay S. Buth (Chief Acctg Officer, VP & Controller)
Stephen T. Sullivan (Pres)

The Rocky River Realty Company (1)
107 Selden St, Berlin, CT 06037
Tel.: (800) 286-2000
Web Site: http://www.cl-p.com
Sales Range: $300-349.9 Million
Real Estate Trust Services
N.A.I.C.S.: 531190

Torrington Water Company (1)
277 Norfolk Rd, Torrington, CT 06790
Tel.: (860) 489-4149
Web Site: http://www.torringtonwater.com
Rev.: $7,480,222
Assets: $61,040,953
Liabilities: $38,716,669
Net Worth: $22,324,284
Earnings: $1,725,338
Fiscal Year-end: 12/31/2019
Water Supply Services
N.A.I.C.S.: 221310

Susan Suhanovsky (Pres)

Yankee Energy Financial Services Company (1)
107 Selden St, Berlin, CT 06037 **(100%)**
Web Site: http://www.helploan.com
Sales Range: $125-149.9 Million
Financing Programs for Residential, Industrial & Commercial Customers
N.A.I.C.S.: 522220

Yankee Energy Services Company (1)
270 Farmington Ave Ste 344, Farmington, CT 06032
Tel.: (860) 677-1618
Air Conditioning Equipment Installation Services
N.A.I.C.S.: 238220

Yankee Gas Services Company (1)
107 Selden St, Berlin, CT 06037
Tel.: (860) 665-5000
Natural Gas Distribution Services
N.A.I.C.S.: 221210
Paul Chodak III (CEO)
John M. Moreira (Treas & Sr VP-Fin & Regulatory)

EVERSPIN TECHNOLOGIES, INC
5670 W Chandler Blvd Ste 130, Chandler, AZ 85226
Tel.: (480) 347-1111   DE
Web Site: https://www.everspin.com
Year Founded: 2008
MRAM—(NASDAQ)
Rev.: $59,985,000
Assets: $55,333,000
Liabilities: $16,669,000
Net Worth: $38,664,000
Earnings: $6,129,000
Emp.: 74
Fiscal Year-end: 12/31/22
Semiconductor & Related Device Manufacturing
N.A.I.C.S.: 334413
Sanjeev Aggarwal (Pres & CEO)
Norm Armour (VP-Ops)
Yong Kim (VP-Engrg)
Khaldoun Barakat (VP)
Kerry Nagel (VP)
David Schrenk (VP)
Amit Shah (VP)
Matthew Tenorio (Interim CFO)

EVERTEC, INC.
Cupey Center Bldg Rd 176 Kilometer 1 3, San Juan, PR 00926
Tel.: (787) 759-9999   PR
Web Site:
https://www.evertecinc.com
Year Founded: 2012
EVTC—(NYSE)
Rev.: $694,709,000
Assets: $2,060,263,000
Liabilities: $1,461,855,000
Net Worth: $598,408,000
Earnings: $79,722,000
Emp.: 5,000
Fiscal Year-end: 12/31/23
Holding Company; Business Management Services
N.A.I.C.S.: 551112
Morgan M. Schuessler Jr. (Pres & CEO)
Guillermo Rospigliosi (Chief Product Officer, Chief Innovation Officer & Exec VP)
Luis A. Rodriguez (Chief Legal Officer, Chief Admin Officer, Gen Counsel, Sec & Exec VP)
Joaquin A. Castrillo-Salgado (CFO & Exec VP)
Diego Viglianco (COO & Exec VP)
Alexandra Lopez-Soler (CMO)
Alberto Lopez-Gaffney (Exec VP)

Subsidiaries:

EVERTEC Group, LLC (1)

Cupey Center Bldg Rd 176 Kilometer 1 3, San Juan, PR 00926 **(100%)**
Tel.: (787) 759-9999
Web Site: https://www.evertecinc.com
Merchant Acquiring, Payment Processing & Business Process Management Services
N.A.I.C.S.: 518210

Subsidiary (Non-US):

EVERTEC Costa Rica, S.A. (2)
Tel.: (506) 22114500
Business Management Services
N.A.I.C.S.: 561110
Luis Alvarado (Sr VP)

EVERTEC Dominicana, SAS (2)
Av Gustavo Mejia Ricart No 102 Edificio Corporativo 2010 Suite 802-B, Piantini Distrito Nacional, Santo Domingo, Dominican Republic
Tel.: (809) 6833125
Business Management Services
N.A.I.C.S.: 561110
Leila Heinsen (Sr Mgr-Card Issuing Processing Svcs)

EVERTEC Guatemala, S.A. (2)
Avenida Reforma 7-62 Oficina 404 Edificio Aristos Reforma Zona 9, Guatemala, Guatemala
Tel.: (502) 22114500
Business Management Services
N.A.I.C.S.: 561110
Werner Obando (Mgr-Comml)

EVERTEC Mexico Servicios de Procesamiento, S.A. de C.V. (2)
Jaime Balmes N 11 Torre C Mezzanine N4, Col Los Morales Polanco Miguel Hidalgo, 11510, Mexico, Mexico
Tel.: (52) 5556690603
Business Management Services
N.A.I.C.S.: 561110
Jorge Alvarez Tostado (Country Mgr)

EVERTEC Panama, S.A. (2)
Torres de las Americas Torre B Piso 2, Oficina 202 Entre Calle Darien y Boulevard Punta Pacifica, Panama, Panama
Tel.: (507) 3071500
Business Management Services
N.A.I.C.S.: 561110
Ivan A. Espinosa V (Country Mgr)

Evertec Brasil Solutions Informatica Ltda. (2)
Paygroup - Al Lorena 638 3 Andar cj 31, Jardim Paulista, Sao Paulo, 01424-000, Brazil
Tel.: (55) 1130520696
Electronic Payment Processing Services
N.A.I.C.S.: 522320
Pablo Sucari (Dir-New Bus Dev)

Evertec Chile SpA (2)
Av Apoquindo 3650 piso 3, Las Condes, Santiago, Chile
Tel.: (56) 227120680
Electronic Payment Processing Services
N.A.I.C.S.: 522320
Jose Luis Godoy (Mgr-Ops & Tech)

Evertec Colombia, SAS (2)
Calle 11 No 68-39, Bogota, Colombia
Tel.: (57) 6013278000
Electronic Payment Processing Services
N.A.I.C.S.: 522320
Patricia Parrado (Mgr-Ops & Tech)

Processa, S.A.S (2)
Calle 11 No 68-39, Bogota, Colombia
Tel.: (57) 3278000
Web Site: http://www.processa.com
Payment Processing Services
N.A.I.C.S.: 522320

Sinqia S.A. (2)
Bela Cintra Street 755 7th floor Consolacao, Sao Paulo, 01415-003, SP, Brazil
Tel.: (55) 1144504404
Web Site: https://sinqia.com.br
Rev.: $110,200,387
Assets: $278,027,379
Liabilities: $158,191,662
Net Worth: $119,835,717
Earnings: $3,138,306
Fiscal Year-end: 12/31/2022
Software Development Services
N.A.I.C.S.: 541511

Subsidiary (Domestic):

Stock & Info Ltda. (3)
Rua Conego Bernardo 57 2 Andar - Sala 201, Trindade, 88036-570, Florianopolis, SC, Brazil
Tel.: (55) 4832337139
Web Site: http://www.stockinfo.com.br
Software Services
N.A.I.C.S.: 541511
Alexandre Ferrari Souza (CEO)

EVERYTHING BLOCKCHAIN, INC.
12574 Flagler Ctr Blvd Ste 101, Jacksonville, FL 32258
Tel.: (904) 454-2111   DE
Web Site:
https://everythingblockchain.io
Year Founded: 2017
EBZT—(OTCIQ)
Rev.: $267,000
Assets: $22,200,000
Liabilities: $3,594,000
Net Worth: $18,606,000
Earnings: ($7,851,000)
Emp.: 7
Fiscal Year-end: 01/31/24
Marketing & Advertising Services
N.A.I.C.S.: 541613
Robert E. Adams (CTO)
Toney Jennings (CEO)
Bill Regan (CFO)
Brandon Hart (COO)
Lars Nyman (CMO)
Cody Margaretten (CIO)
Anthony Bolan (Chief Security Officer)

Subsidiaries:

EBI International, Inc. (1)
15244 NW Greenbrier Pkwy, Beaverton, OR 97006
Tel.: (503) 644-2290
Web Site: https://e-bi.com
Engineering Design Services
N.A.I.C.S.: 541330

EVGO INC.
11835 W Olympic Blvd Ste 900E, Los Angeles, CA 90064
Tel.: (310) 954-2900   DE
Web Site: https://www.evgo.com
Year Founded: 2020
EVGO—(NASDAQ)
Rev.: $54,588,000
Assets: $729,724,000
Liabilities: $1,087,824,000
Net Worth: ($358,100,000)
Earnings: ($106,240,000)
Emp.: 292
Fiscal Year-end: 12/31/22
Financial Services
N.A.I.C.S.: 523999
Badar Khan (CEO)
Dennis Kish (Pres)
Francine Sullivan (Chief Legal Officer & Gen Counsel)
Keith Hutchison (Chief People Officer)
Sandeep Jayaram (Exec VP-Operations)
Sara Rafalson (Exec VP-Policy & External Affairs)
Martin Sukup (Exec VP-Engineering)
Marcy Bauer (Sr VP-Deployment)
Alex Keros (Sr VP-Product)
Chris O'Toole (Sr VP-Strategy & Analytics)
Pavlos Politopoulos (Sr VP-Customer Experience)
Paul Dobson (CFO & Principal Acctg Officer)

Subsidiaries:

EVgo Recargo, LLC (1)
2231 Campus Dr, El Segundo, CA 90245
Tel.: (252) 227-7013

Web Site: https://company.plugshare.com
Software Publisher
N.A.I.C.S.: 513210

EVI INDUSTRIES, INC.
4500 Biscayne Blvd Ste 340, Miami, FL 33137
Tel.: (305) 402-9300   DE
Web Site: https://www.evi-ind.com
Year Founded: 1959
EVI—(NYSEAMEX)
Rev.: $353,563,000
Assets: $230,659,000
Liabilities: $94,053,000
Net Worth: $136,606,000
Earnings: $5,646,000
Emp.: 750
Fiscal Year-end: 06/30/24
Drycleaning & Laundry Services;
Coin-Operated Laundry Machines Whslr
N.A.I.C.S.: 812320
Henry M. Nahmad (Pres, CEO & Chm)
Robert H. Lazar (CFO, Chief Acctg Officer & VP-Fin)
Dennis Mack (Exec VP & Exec VP-Corporate Strategy)
Tom Marks (Exec VP-Bus Dev)

Subsidiaries:

ALVF, Inc.   (1)
1243 W State St, New Castle, PA 16101-1242
Tel.: (724) 658-8808
Web Site: http://www.alcowasher.com
Commercial Laundry Products Distr
N.A.I.C.S.: 423850

Aldrich Clean-Tech Equipment Corp.   (1)
59 Webster Pl, Worcester, MA 01603
Tel.: (508) 792-1007
Web Site: http://www.aldrichcleantech.com
Rev.: $2,300,000
Emp.: 13
Commercial Laundry Products Distr
N.A.I.C.S.: 812320
Kimberlee A. Aldrich (Owner)
Robert C. Aldrich (Pres)

Commercial Laundry Equipment Company, LLC   (1)
2507 Jefferson Davis Hwy, Richmond, VA 23234
Tel.: (804) 231-9668
Laundry Equipment Distr
N.A.I.C.S.: 423850

Commercial Laundry Products, Inc.   (1)
169 Commack Rd Ste H 288, Commack, NY 11725
Tel.: (631) 242-0020
Web Site: http://www.plslaundry.com
Commercial Laundry Equipment Distr
N.A.I.C.S.: 423440

Consolidated Laundry Equipment, Inc.   (1)
530 Maywood Ave, Raleigh, NC 27603
Tel.: (919) 832-4624
Web Site:
    http://www.consolidatedlaundry.com
Rev.: $2,200,000
Emp.: 50
Service Establishment Equipment & Supplies Merchant Whslr
N.A.I.C.S.: 423850
Billy Kincaid (Pres)
Russell Willard (Territory Mgr)

Dryclean USA Development Corp   (1)
290 NE 68th St, Miami, FL 33138-5520
Tel.: (305) 754-4551
Dry Cleaning & Laundry Services
N.A.I.C.S.: 812320

Dryclean USA License Corp   (1)
290 NE 68th St, Miami, FL 33138
Tel.: (305) 754-9966
Web Site: http://www.drycleanusa.com
Dry Cleaning & Laundry Services
N.A.I.C.S.: 812320

Michael Steiner (Pres & CEO)

Ed Brown Distributors   (1)
2705 Hawes Ave, Dallas, TX 75235
Tel.: (214) 352-9494
Web Site: https://edbrowndistributors.com
Rev.: $3,460,000
Emp.: 10
Cosmetics, Beauty Supplies & Perfume Stores
N.A.I.C.S.: 456120
John Koenig (Mgr-Svc)

Industrial Laundry Services, LLC   (1)
2302 Mercator Dr Ste 102, Orlando, FL 32807
Tel.: (407) 679-0040
Web Site: http://www.ilsorlando.com
Laundry Machinery & Equipment Mfr
N.A.I.C.S.: 333310

Laundry Pro of Florida, Inc.   (1)
3920 Holden Rd, Lakeland, FL 33811
Tel.: (863) 701-7714
Web Site:
    https://www.laundryprooflorida.com
Sales Range: $1-9.9 Million
Emp.: 16
Service Establish Equipment Whslr
N.A.I.C.S.: 423850

Laundry Systems of Tennessee, LLC   (1)
1506 W Meadow Ct, Sevierville, TN 37862-9359
Tel.: (865) 453-9972
Web Site: http://www.tnozone.com
Drycleaning & Laundry Services (except Coin-Operated)
N.A.I.C.S.: 812320
Jeff Large (Pres)
Tonya Large (VP)

Martin-Ray Laundry Systems, Inc.   (1)
756 S Jason St Unit Ste 12, Denver, CO 80223
Tel.: (720) 359-8000
Web Site: https://www.martinray.com
Service Establishment Equipment & Supplies Whslr
N.A.I.C.S.: 423850
William Martin Mann (Co-Owner)
Jim Ray Hohnstein (Co-Owner)

PAC Industries, LLC   (1)
5341 Jaycee Ave, Harrisburg, PA 17112
Tel.: (717) 657-0407
Web Site: https://www.pacindustries.com
Commercial Laundry Equipment Distr
N.A.I.C.S.: 812310
Joe Leo (Gen Mgr)
Scott Benjamin (Sls Mgr)
Tom Schwarz (Dir-Multi-Housing)
Jennifer Knouse (Controller)

Scott Equipment, LLC   (1)
5612 Mitchelldale St, Houston, TX 77092
Tel.: (713) 686-7268
Web Site: https://www.scott-equipment.com
Emp.: 60
Commercial Laundry Equipment Mfr & Distr
N.A.I.C.S.: 812310

Skyline Equipment, LLC   (1)
5612A Mitchelldale St, Houston, TX 77092
Tel.: (281) 445-9907
Web Site:
    https://www.skylineequipmentco.com
Commercial Laundry Equipment Distr & Support Services
N.A.I.C.S.: 423850
Russell Williams (Sls Mgr-Multi Housing)
Chris Chapman (Sls Mgr-Houston, Galveston, Bryan)
Quintin Weaver (Sls Mgr-Austin, San Antonio, RGV)

Steiner-Atlantic Corp   (1)
1714 NW 215th St, Miami Gardens, FL 33056
Tel.: (305) 754-4551
Web Site: https://www.steineratlantic.com
Sales Range: $10-24.9 Million
Emp.: 20
Laundry Equipment & Supplies
N.A.I.C.S.: 423850
Michael S. Steiner (Co-Pres)
Bill Bell (Reg VP-Sls)
Diane Nino (Controller)

Jimmy Goulet (Reg VP-Sls)
Ozzie Rubio (Reg VP-Sls)
Ralph Tuccillo (Reg VP-Sls)
Rich McKevitt (Reg Sls Mgr)
Rick O'Connell (VP-Parts Svcs)
Zach Mangones (Exec VP)
Patrick Frawley (Co-Pres)
Diego Morales (Mgr-Pur)
Cinthia Guillen (Mgr-Traffic)
Gipsy Hernandez (Coord-Svc)
Jose Arrieta (Mgr-Svc)
Robert Gonzalez (Reg VP-Sls)

Tri-State Technical Services, Inc.   (1)
1560 Old Clyattville Rd, Valdosta, GA 31601-1218
Web Site: https://www.tlctristate.com
Commercial Laundry Equipment & Services
N.A.I.C.S.: 423850
Matt Stephenson (Pres & CEO)
Brett Nolan (Dir-Coin Laundry Sys)
Janice Ayers Davis (VP-Strategic Plng)
Keith Quarles (VP-Sls & Mktg)
Rex Williamson (CFO & VP-Ops)

Washington Automated, LLC   (1)
5801 - 23rd Dr W Ste 103, Everett, WA 98203
Tel.: (425) 743-7388
Web Site:
    https://www.washingtonautomated.com
Commercial Laundry Equipment Distr & Support Services
N.A.I.C.S.: 423850

Western State Design Inc.   (1)
2331 Tripaldi Way, Hayward, CA 94545   (100%)
Tel.: (510) 786-9271
Web Site:
    https://www.westernstatedesign.com
Laundry Equipment & Supplies
N.A.I.C.S.: 423850
Dennis Mack (Pres)
Tom Marks (Co-Founder)

Wholesale Commercial Laundry Equipment SE, LLC   (1)
2950 Hwy 77, Southside, AL 35907-7601
Web Site: http://www.alaundryman.com
Service Establishment Equipment & Supplies Merchant Whslr
N.A.I.C.S.: 423850
Russ Arbuckle (Pres)

Worldwide Laundry, Inc.   (1)
1714 NW 215th St, Miami Gardens, FL 33056
Tel.: (305) 418-4030
Web Site:
    https://www.worldwidelaundry.com
Commercial Laundry Equipment Distr & Support Services
N.A.I.C.S.: 423850

Yankee Equipment Systems, Inc.   (1)
15 Glass Ln, Barrington, NH 03825
Tel.: (603) 868-6691
Web Site: http://www.yankeeequipment.com
Sales Range: $1-9.9 Million
Emp.: 35
Commercial Laundry Products Distr
N.A.I.C.S.: 423850
Joshua Jones (Project Mgr-Special)
Peter Limoncelli (Pres)
Brendan Ristaino (Sls Mgr)
Shane Horvath (Mgr-Parts)
Ted Ristaino (COO)

Zuf Acquisitions I LLC   (1)
2510 National Dr, Garland, TX 75041
Tel.: (972) 278-2138
Web Site:
    http://www.aadvantagelaundry.com
Laundry Products Distr, Installation & Services
N.A.I.C.S.: 325611
Ryan Smith (Pres)
Gregg Sumrow (VP)

EVIL EMPIRE DESIGNS, INC.
441 Egate Rd Ste A, Henderson, NV 89011
Tel.: (725) 666-3700   NV
Web Site:
    https://www.evilempiredesigns.com
Year Founded: 2009

EVVL—(OTCIQ)
Rev.: $48,997
Assets: $314,906
Liabilities: $721,059
Net Worth: ($406,153)
Earnings: ($50,970)
Emp.: 1
Fiscal Year-end: 12/31/22
Automobile Parts Distr
N.A.I.C.S.: 441330
Sheila Cunningham (Pres, CEO, Treas & Sec)

EVIO, INC.
2654 W Horizon Ridge Pkwy Ste B5-208, Henderson, NV 89052
Tel.: (702) 748-9944   CO
Web Site: http://www.eviolabs.com
Year Founded: 1977
EVIO—(OTCIQ)
Rev.: $2,363,000
Assets: $5,287,000
Liabilities: $19,491,000
Net Worth: ($14,204,000)
Earnings: ($965,000)
Fiscal Year-end: 09/30/21
Research & Advisory Services
N.A.I.C.S.: 541611
William H. Waldrop (Co-Founder)
Lori Glauser (Chm, Interim Pres, Interim CEO & COO)

EVMO, INC.
2301 N Sepulveda Blvd, Manhattan Beach, CA 90266
Tel.: (310) 926-2643   DE
Web Site: https://www.evmo.com
Year Founded: 2016
YAYO—(OTCIQ)
Rev.: $12,558,427
Assets: $25,932,197
Liabilities: $23,488,842
Net Worth: $2,443,355
Earnings: ($7,142,227)
Emp.: 27
Fiscal Year-end: 12/31/22
Application Software Development Services
N.A.I.C.S.: 541511
Terren S. Peizer (Chm)
Stephen M. Sanchez (CEO)

Subsidiaries:

Rideshare Car Rentals LLC   (1)
195 S Robertson Blvd, Beverly Hills, CA 90211
Tel.: (310) 651-4203
Web Site: https://www.ridesharerental.com
Car Rental Services
N.A.I.C.S.: 532111

EVO ACQUISITION CORP.
10 Stateline Rd, Crystal Bay, NV 89402
Tel.: (775) 624-9360   DE
Web Site: https://www.evospac.com
Year Founded: 2020
EVOJ—(NASDAQ)
Rev.: $2,530,910
Assets: $10,310,121
Liabilities: $16,469,883
Net Worth: ($6,159,762)
Earnings: $3,971,796
Emp.: 3
Fiscal Year-end: 12/31/22
Investment Services
N.A.I.C.S.: 523999
Michael Lerch (Chm)
Richard Chisholm (CEO)
Adrian Brindle (CFO)
Jason Sausto (Mng Dir)

EVO TRANSPORTATION & ENERGY SERVICES, INC.
20860 N Tatum Blvd Ste 300, Phoenix, AZ 85050
Tel.: (480) 485-5862   DE

EVO Transportation & Energy Services, Inc.—(Continued)

Web Site:
https://www.evotransinc.com
EVOA—(OTCEM)
Rev.: $309,763,000
Assets: $125,721,000
Liabilities: $141,402,000
Net Worth: ($15,681,000)
Earnings: ($18,226,000)
Emp.: 1,200
Fiscal Year-end: 12/31/22
Transportation Services
N.A.I.C.S.: 484101
Michael Bayles (CEO)
Kris Kohls (Pres & COO)
Jamie Finkle (Exec VP)
Melinda Wang (Gen Counsel & Exec VP)
Trey Peck (Exec VP-Bus Dev)

Subsidiaries:

EVO CNG, LLC (1)
PO Box 5309, Peoria, AZ 85385
Web Site: https://evocng.com
Natural Gas Distr
N.A.I.C.S.: 221210
Damon Cuzick (COO)

EVO Logistics, LLC (1)
780 S Alameda St Unit 1, Los Angeles, CA 90021
Tel.: (323) 484-4000
Web Site: http://www.evologistics.com
Logistics Transportation Services
N.A.I.C.S.: 488510
Tony Flores (Pres)

Finkle Transport, Inc. (1)
2945 S Military Trl, West Palm Beach, FL 33415
Tel.: (732) 493-1500
Web Site: http://finkletrucking.com
Local Messengers & Local Delivery
N.A.I.C.S.: 492210
Clifford Finkle (Pres)

Ritter Transport, Inc. (1)
8271 Brock Bridge Rd, Laurel, MD 20724
Web Site:
http://www.therittercompanies.com
Truckload Transportation Services
N.A.I.C.S.: 484121
Matt Ritter (Co-Owner)
Michael Ritter (Co-Owner)

Sheehy Mail Contractors, Inc. (1)
127 Central Ave, Waterloo, WI 53594
Tel.: (877) 563-4239
Specialized Freight Trucking Services
N.A.I.C.S.: 484220
John Sheehy (CEO)
Ryan Buss (Mgr-Terminal)

Thunder Ridge Transport, Inc. (1)
319 N Main Ave, Springfield, MO 65806
Tel.: (417) 833-8456
Freight Trucking Services
N.A.I.C.S.: 484220

W.E. Graham, Inc. (1)
3906 Homewood Rd, Memphis, TN 38118
Tel.: (901) 366-1546
General Freight Trucking, Long-Distance, Truckload
N.A.I.C.S.: 484121

EVOFEM BIOSCIENCES, INC.
7770 Regents Rd Ste 113-618, San Diego, CA 92122
Tel.: (858) 550-1900   DE
Web Site: https://www.evofem.com
Year Founded: 2007
EVFM—(OTCQB)
Rev.: $18,218,000
Assets: $10,554,000
Liabilities: $77,064,000
Net Worth: ($66,510,000)
Earnings: $49,995,000
Emp.: 37
Fiscal Year-end: 12/31/23
Pharmaceuticals Product Mfr
N.A.I.C.S.: 325412

Saundra Pelletier (Interim Chm, Pres & CEO)
Jay J. File (CFO)
Rachael Hildebrandt (Head-HR)
Katherine Mercier (VP-Technical Ops)
Brenda Buechler (Dir-Brand Mktg)
Danielle McNulty (Assoc Dir-Promotional Review & Compliance)
Amy Raskopf (VP-IR)
Ellen Harris (Sr Mgr-Clinical Ops)
Nick Rueb (Sr Mgr-SEC Reporting & SOX Compliance)
Keith Hinkle (Sr Mgr-Enterprise Applications)
Gaelle Saint-Louis (Sr Mgr-Technical Ops)
Harry Jordan (VP-Market Access & Distr)
Lalitha Aiyer (VP-Clinical Affairs & Pharmacovigilance)
Ivy Zhang (CFO & Sec)
John Altenberg (Sr Dir-Supply Chain Logistics)
Alex Ross (Sr Dir-Trade & Distr)
Nate LiaBraaten (Sr Dir-Strategic Plng & Analysis)
Erin Reily (Dir-Sls Ops & Analytics)
DeeDee Asuamah (Dir-Medical Information)
Nick Balistreri (Dir-Bus-East)
Bill Elixman (Dir-Bus-West)
Tom Letizia (Dir-Strategic Pricing Govt Accounts)
Damian Frantz (Dir-Strategic Markets-West)
Joe Sclafani (Dir-Process Engrg)
Brian Murphy (Dir-Sls Trng)

Subsidiaries:

Evofem, Inc (1)
7770 Regents Rd Ste 113-618, San Diego, CA 92122
Tel.: (858) 550-1900
Web Site: https://www.evofem.com
Offices of Physical, Occupational & Speech Therapists & Audiologists
N.A.I.C.S.: 621340

EVOKE PHARMA, INC.
420 Stevens Ave Ste 230, Solana Beach, CA 92075
Tel.: (858) 345-1494   DE
Web Site:
https://www.evokepharma.com
Year Founded: 2007
EVOK—(NASDAQ)
Rev.: $2,508,645
Assets: $11,851,488
Liabilities: $7,766,839
Net Worth: $4,084,649
Earnings: ($8,224,130)
Emp.: 4
Fiscal Year-end: 12/31/22
Pharmaceuticals Mfr
N.A.I.C.S.: 325412
Cam L. Garner (Co-Founder)
Mark A. Kowieski (CFO)
David A. Gonyer (Co-Founder)
Matthew J. D'Onofrio (Co-Founder & CEO)
Marilyn R. Carlson (Chief Medical Officer)
Chris Quesenberry (Chief Comml Officer)

EVOLENT HEALTH, INC.
1812 N Moore St Ste 1705, Arlington, VA 22209
Tel.: (571) 389-6000   DE
Web Site: https://www.evolent.com
Year Founded: 2011
EVH—(NYSE)
Rev.: $1,352,013,000
Assets: $1,817,293,000
Liabilities: $957,876,000
Net Worth: $859,417,000
Earnings: ($19,164,000)

Emp.: 5,100
Fiscal Year-end: 12/31/22
Healthcare Software
N.A.I.C.S.: 513210
Jonathan Weinberg (Chief Legal Officer & Gen Counsel)
Steve Tutewohl (CEO-Evolent Health Svcs)
Emily Rafferty (COO)
Seth Blackley (Founder & CEO)
Dan McCarthy (Pres)
John Johnson (CFO)
Aammaad Shams (Chief Acctg Officer, Principal Acctg Officer & Controller)

Subsidiaries:

NCH Management Systems, Inc. (1)
915 W Imperial Hwy Ste 200, Brea, CA 92821
Web Site:
https://www.newcenturyhealth.com
Women Healthcare Services
N.A.I.C.S.: 621610
Dan McCarthy (CEO)
Scott Pritchard (Pres)
Andrew Hertler (Chief Medical Officer)
Jessica Somers (CFO)
Paige Fretwell (Founder)
Giselle Habeych (Sr VP)
Geoff McHugh (Chief Growth Officer)
Jordan Silvergleid (Chief Product Officer)
John Tam (Chief Strategy Officer)

NCH Management Systmes, Inc. (1)
80 William St Ste 270, Wellesley, MA 02481
Tel.: (888) 999-7713
Web Site: http://www.newcenturyhealth.com
Healthcare Benefit Management Services
N.A.I.C.S.: 541611
Andrew Hertler (Chief Medical Officer)
Scott Pritchard (Pres)
Giselle Habeych (Sr VP-Natl Provider Solutions)
Dan McCarthy (CEO)
Michelle Engel (Chief Talent Officer)
Monica Soni (Sr Dir-Medical, Medicaid & Exchange Solutions)
Geoff McHugh (Sr VP-Strategic Accounts)
John Davis (Sr VP-Bus Dev)
Jordan Silvergleid (Sr VP-Product & Strategy)

The Accountable Care Organization Ltd. (1)
3410 Belle Chase Way Ste 600, Lansing, MI 48911
Software Development Services
N.A.I.C.S.: 513210

Valence Health, LLC (1)
800 N Glebe Rd Ste 500, Arlington, VA 22203
Tel.: (571) 389-6000
Web Site: https://www.evolenthealth.com
Health Care Consulting Services
N.A.I.C.S.: 541611

EVOLUTION PETROLEUM CORPORATION
1155 Dairy Ashford Rd Ste 425, Houston, TX 77079
Tel.: (713) 935-0122   NV
Web Site:
https://www.evolutionpetroleum.com
EPM—(NYSEAMEX)
Rev.: $85,877,000
Assets: $162,877,000
Liabilities: $81,750,000
Net Worth: $81,127,000
Earnings: $4,080,000
Emp.: 11
Fiscal Year-end: 06/30/24
Redevelopment of Mature Oil & Gas Resources into More Profitable Entities
N.A.I.C.S.: 221210
Robert Stevens Herlin (Chm)
Kelly W. Loyd (Pres & CEO)
Ryan Stash (CFO, Treas & Sr VP)
J. Mark Bunch (COO)

EVOLUTIONARY GENOMICS, INC.

4220 Morning Star Dr, Castle Rock, CO 80108
Tel.: (720) 900-8666   NV
Web Site: https://www.evolgen.com
Year Founded: 1990
FNAM—(OTCQB)
Rev.: $79,335
Assets: $2,353,710
Liabilities: $7,945,585
Net Worth: ($5,591,875)
Earnings: ($2,248,260)
Emp.: 2
Fiscal Year-end: 12/31/22
Investment Services
N.A.I.C.S.: 523999
Steve B. Warnecke (Chm, Pres, CEO & CFO)
Walter Messier (Co-Founder, CTO, Treas & Sec)
Virginia Orndorff (Co-Founder)

EVOLV TECHNOLOGIES HOLDINGS INC.
500 Totten Pond Rd 4th Fl, Waltham, MA 02451
Tel.: (781) 374-8100   DE
Web Site: https://evolv.com
Year Founded: 2020
EVLV—(NASDAQ)
Rev.: $55,195,000
Assets: $348,115,000
Liabilities: $121,130,000
Net Worth: $226,985,000
Earnings: ($86,406,000)
Emp.: 223
Fiscal Year-end: 12/31/22
Investment Services
N.A.I.C.S.: 523999
Michael Philip Ellenbogen (Founder & Chief Innovation Officer)
Jay Muelhoefer (Chief Comml Officer)
Mark Donohue (CFO)
Charlie Baynes-Reid (COO)
Adam Deutsch (CFO)
Courtney Cunnane (CMO)
Brian Norris (Sr VP-Fin & IR)
Alexandra Smith Ozerkis (VP-Corp Comm)
Peter G. George (Pres & CEO)

EVOLVE TRANSITION INFRA-STRUCTURE LP
1360 Post Oak Blvd Ste 2400, Houston, TX 77050
Tel.: (713) 783-8000   DE
Web Site:
https://www.evolvetransition.com
Year Founded: 1983
SNMP—(NYSEAMEX)
Rev.: $36,109,000
Assets: $231,674,000
Liabilities: $453,783,000
Net Worth: ($222,109,000)
Earnings: ($53,137,000)
Emp.: 12
Fiscal Year-end: 12/31/22
Holding Company; Oil & Natural Gas Extraction
N.A.I.C.S.: 551112

Subsidiaries:

CEP Mid-Continent LLC (1)
15 W 6th St Ste 1100, Tulsa, OK 74119
Tel.: (918) 877-2912
Oil & Natural Gas Extraction
N.A.I.C.S.: 211120

CEP Services Company, Inc. (1)
1801 Main St Ste 1300, Houston, TX 77002
Tel.: (832) 308-3700
Office Administrative Services
N.A.I.C.S.: 561110
Anne Lynn (Mgr-HR)

EVOME MEDICAL TECHNOLO-GIES INC.

49 Natcon Dr, Shirley, NY 11967-4704
Web Site:
https://www.salonaglobal.com
EVMT—(TSXV)
Emp.: 100
Medical Device Mfr
N.A.I.C.S.: 339112
Michael J. Plunkett *(Pres-South Dakota Partners & Gen Mgr)*
Dennis Nelson *(CFO)*
Michael Seckler *(CEO)*
Melissa Polesky-Meyrowitz *(VP-Fin & Acctg)*
Lana Newishy *(Vice Chm)*

Subsidiaries:

Arrowhead Medical, LLC **(1)**
30 County Rd 63, Grand Rapids, MN 55744
Tel.: (218) 328-0016
Web Site: http://www.arrowheadmed.com
Rev.: $1,000,000
Emp.: 5
Medical, Dental & Hospital Equipment & Supplies Merchant Whslr
N.A.I.C.S.: 423450
Dave Lutz *(Pres & CEO)*

Damar Plastics Manufacturing, Inc. **(1)**
4720 Mission Gorge Pl A, San Diego, CA 92120
Tel.: (619) 283-2300
Web Site: http://www.damarplastics.com
Rev.: $8,200,000
Emp.: 50
All Other Plastics Product Mfr
N.A.I.C.S.: 326199
Sal Acampora *(VP)*

EWELLNESS HEALTHCARE CORPORATION
1125 S Federal Hwy Ste 464, Fort Lauderdale, FL 33316
Tel.: (310) 915-9700 NV
Year Founded: 2011
EWLL—(OTCEM)
Assets: $13,564
Liabilities: $4,371,301
Net Worth: ($4,357,737)
Earnings: ($451,707)
Emp.: 2
Fiscal Year-end: 12/31/21
Medical Device Mfr
N.A.I.C.S.: 339112

EXACT SCIENCES CORPORATION
5505 Endeavor Ln, Madison, WI 53719
Tel.: (608) 284-5700 DE
Web Site:
https://www.exactsciences.com
Year Founded: 1995
EXAS—(NASDAQ)
Rev.: $2,499,766,000
Assets: $6,471,334,000
Liabilities: $3,326,029,000
Net Worth: $3,145,305,000
Earnings: ($204,149,000)
Emp.: 6,600
Fiscal Year-end: 12/31/23
Cancer Screening Technology Research & Development Services
N.A.I.C.S.: 541715
Ana Hooker *(Sr VP)*
Kevin T. Conroy *(Chm, Pres & CEO)*
G. Bradley Cole *(Gen Mgr-Precision Oncology)*
Everett Cunningham *(Chief Comml Officer)*
Dirk Zimmermann *(Gen Mgr)*
James Herriott *(Gen Counsel)*
Jorge Garces *(Chief Science Officer)*
Morry Smulevitz *(Sr VP)*
D. Scott Coward *(Chief Admin Officer, Sec & Sr VP)*

Subsidiaries:

Biomatrica, Inc. **(1)**
5627 Oberlin Dr Ste 120, San Diego, CA 92121
Tel.: (858) 550-0308
Web Site: https://www.exactsciences.com
Biotechnology Research & Development Services
N.A.I.C.S.: 541714
Gina Costa *(Sr Dir)*

Exact Sciences Deutschland GmbH **(1)**
Erna-Scheffler-Strasse 1a, 51103, Cologne, Germany
Tel.: (49) 6989914253
Web Site: https://www.exactsciences.com
Clinical Laboratory Services
N.A.I.C.S.: 621511
Erwin Morawski *(Mng Dir)*

Exact Sciences Laboratories LLC **(1)**
145 E Badger Rd Ste 100, Madison, WI 53713-2723
Tel.: (608) 284-5700
Web Site: https://www.exactlabs.com
Medical Laboratory
N.A.I.C.S.: 621511
Ana Hooker *(Sr VP-Clinical Laboratory Ops)*
Barry M. Berger *(Chief Medical Officer)*

Exact Sciences UK, Ltd. **(1)**
Scott House - The Concourse Waterloo Station, London, SE1 7LY, United Kingdom
Tel.: (44) 2030318087
Web Site: https://www.exactsciences.com
Clinical Laboratory Services
N.A.I.C.S.: 621511
Stephen Ogram *(Head-Northern Europe & Dir)*

Genomic Health, Inc. **(1)**
101 Galveston Dr, Redwood City, CA 94063
Tel.: (650) 556-9300
Genetic Research Services
N.A.I.C.S.: 541715

Subsidiary (Non-US):

Genomic Health Italia S.R.L **(2)**
Piazza Filippo Meda 3, 20121, Milan, Italy
Tel.: (39) 0689970196
Web Site: http://www.genomichealth.it
Clinical Laboratory Services
N.A.I.C.S.: 621511
Luca Barra *(Mgr-Acct-North Italy & Sardinia)*

Preventiongenetics LLC **(1)**
3700 Downwind Dr, Marshfield, WI 54449-8625
Tel.: (715) 387-0484
Web Site:
http://www.preventiongenetics.com
Medical Laboratories
N.A.I.C.S.: 621511

EXAGEN INC.
1261 Liberty Way, Vista, CA 92081
Tel.: (760) 560-1501 DE
Web Site: https://www.exagen.com
Year Founded: 2002
XGN—(NASDAQ)
Rev.: $52,548,000
Assets: $56,944,000
Liabilities: $34,250,000
Net Worth: $22,694,000
Earnings: ($23,689,000)
Emp.: 174
Fiscal Year-end: 12/31/23
Biotechnology Research & Development Services
N.A.I.C.S.: 541714
John Wegener *(Sr VP-Sls & Mktg)*
Andrew L. Concoff *(Chief Innovation Officer)*
Mike Nerenberg *(Chief Medical Officer)*
Jeffrey G. Black *(CFO)*
John Aballi *(Pres & CEO)*

EXCEL CORPORATION
6363 President George Bush Turn-

pike N State Hwy 161 Ste 310, Irving, TX 75038
Tel.: (972) 476-1000 DE
Web Site:
https://www.excelcorpusa.com
Year Founded: 2010
EXCC—(OTCIQ)
Sales Range: $10-24.9 Million
Emp.: 31
Licensing Services
N.A.I.C.S.: 561499
Joni R. Floyd *(Pres & CEO)*
Craig Jessen *(COO)*
Patrick Smith *(VP)*
Peter V. Mazeika *(Fin Dir)*

EXCELFIN ACQUISITION CORP.
100 Kingsley Park Dr, Fort Mill, SC 29715
Tel.: (917) 209-8581 DE
Web Site:
https://excelfinacquisitioncorp.com
Year Founded: 2021
XFIN—(NASDAQ)
Rev.: $3,288,133
Assets: $238,544,571
Liabilities: $247,350,532
Net Worth: ($8,805,961)
Earnings: $623,118
Emp.: 4
Fiscal Year-end: 12/31/22
Investment Services
N.A.I.C.S.: 523999
Brian Sun *(COO & Exec VP)*
Joe Ragan *(CFO)*
Joe Ragan III *(CEO)*
Goh Lin Piao *(Dir)*
Gary Meltzer *(Dir)*
Neil Wolfson *(Dir)*
Jennifer Hill *(Chm)*

EXCHANGE BANK
545 4th St, Santa Rosa, CA 95401
Tel.: (707) 524-3151
Web Site:
https://www.exchangebank.com
Year Founded: 1890
EXSR—(OTCIQ)
Sales Range: $75-99.9 Million
Emp.: 490
Trust, Investment & Banking Services
N.A.I.C.S.: 522180
William R. Schrader *(Chm)*
Rolf Nelson *(Sr VP & Mgr-Retail Delivery Grp)*
Steve Herron *(Sr VP-Comml Banking Grp)*
Ed Gomez *(Officer-Credit-Comml Lending & Sr VP)*
Marlene K. Soiland *(Sec)*
Howard Daulton *(Sr VP & Mgr-Corp Bus Dev)*
Bradley Abel *(VP-Small Bus Admin Bus Dev)*
Douglas Angelo *(Officer-Real Estate Loan & VP)*
Michael Arendt *(VP)*
Patty Brookins *(Officer-Cosumer Loan & Asst VP)*
Kenn Cunningham *(Officer-Sls & Asst VP)*
Sarah Davies *(Officer-Comml Loan & VP)*
Lori DeCosta *(VP & Mgr-Retail Lending & Loan Support)*
Terrance Flynn *(Sr VP & Mgr-Comml Real Estate Banking)*
Geofry Fong *(Officer-Comml Loan & VP)*
Brian Kilkenny *(Reg Officer-Bus Dev & VP)*
Ron Malnati *(VP-Bus Dev)*
John Matli *(VP & Branch Mgr)*
John Meislahn *(VP & Mgr-Sls & Bus Dev)*

Colleen Oller *(VP & Mgr-Retail Loan)*
Beth Ryan *(VP & Mgr-Customer Experience)*
Sherrill J. Stockton *(Sr VP & Mgr-Small Bus Admin)*
Denise Tait *(Officer-Cosumer Loan)*
Kenneth G. Taylor *(VP & Gen Mgr-Leasing)*
Timothy Taylor *(Asst Mgr-Leasing)*
Andrew T. Ware *(Sr VP & Reg Mgr-Comml Banking)*
Byron D. Webb *(VP & Mgr-Electronic Banking)*
Lori Tanenbaum Zaret *(Chief HR Officer & Sr VP)*
Ann Hudson *(Sr VP-Retail Banking)*
Jenna Brackett *(Asst VP)*
Maryanne Harris *(Asst VP)*
Charlotte Radmilovic *(CFO & Sr VP)*
Jared Cooley *(VP-Comml Banking Grp)*
Alan Aranha *(VP-Sls)*
Craig Bainbridge *(Sr VP-Product Innovation & Mgr-Delivery)*
John Mackey *(Mng Dir-Investment & Fiduciary Svcs & Sr VP)*
Cherie Chipman *(VP & Mgr-Rohnert Park)*
Rick Mossi *(Sr VP-Retail Delivery)*
Chris Ann Bachtel *(VP-Trust & Investment Mgmt Office-Roseville)*
Alysia Corell *(VP)*
Carolyn Cole-Schweizer *(Mktg Mgr-Svcs)*
Lori Crechriou *(VP & Mgr-Special Assets)*
Michael Sullivan *(Chief Credit Officer & Exec VP)*
Troy Sanderson *(Pres & CEO)*
Shari J. DeMaris *(COO & Exec VP)*
Brian Rober *(CIO & Sr VP)*
Thomas Sands *(VP & Reg Sls Mgr-South)*
Tom Duryea *(Chief Banking Officer & Exec VP)*
A. J. Vazquez *(VP/Branch Mgr-St Francis)*

EXCO RESOURCES, INC.
12377 Merit Dr Ste 1700, Dallas, TX 75251
Tel.: (214) 368-2084 TX
Web Site:
https://www.excoresources.com
EXCE—(OTCIQ)
Sales Range: $350-399.9 Million
Emp.: 153
Crude Petroleum Extraction Services
N.A.I.C.S.: 211120
Harold L. Hickey *(Pres & CEO)*
William L. Boeing *(VP-Law & Asst Sec)*
Harold H. Jameson *(COO & VP)*
Tyler Farquharson *(CFO, Treas & VP)*

Subsidiaries:

EXCO Holding MLP, Inc. **(1)**
12377 Merit Dr Ste 1700, Dallas, TX 75251
Tel.: (214) 368-2084
Holding Company
N.A.I.C.S.: 551114

North Coast Energy, Inc. **(1)**
3000 Ericsson Dr Ste 200, Warrendale, PA 15086-6501
Tel.: (330) 425-2330
Sales Range: $125-149.9 Million
Emp.: 150
Oil & Gas Producers
N.A.I.C.S.: 213111

Subsidiary (Domestic):

EXCO Resources-Ravenswood **(2)**
State Rte 2 Pleasantview Rdg, Ravenswood, WV 26164
Tel.: (304) 273-5371
Web Site: http://www.excoresources.com

EXCO Resources, Inc.—(Continued)

Sales Range: $25-49.9 Million
Emp.: 35
Oil & Gas Exploration
N.A.I.C.S.: 213111

EXECUTIVE NETWORK PART-NERING CORPORATION

137 Newbury St 7th Fl, Boston, MA 02116
Tel.: (857) 362-9205　　　　DE
Year Founded: 2020
ENPC—(NYSE)
Investment Services
N.A.I.C.S.: 523999
Paul D. Ryan *(Chm)*
Alex J. Dunn *(CEO & CFO)*

EXELA TECHNOLOGIES, INC.

2701 E Grauwyler Rd, Irving, TX 75061　　　　DE
Web Site: https://www.exelatech.com
Year Founded: 2014
XELA—(NASDAQ)
Rev.: $1,077,157,000
Assets: $721,912,000
Liabilities: $1,529,501,000
Net Worth: ($807,589,000)
Earnings: ($422,834,000)
Emp.: 15,542
Fiscal Year-end: 12/31/22
Enterprise Information Management,
Transaction Processing Solutions &
Digital Business Process Services
N.A.I.C.S.: 518210
Parvinder S. Chadha *(Chm)*

Subsidiaries:

ASTERION International GmbH　(1)
Heidelberger Strasse 59, 68519, Viernheim, Germany
Tel.: (49) 62049686860
Document Management Outsourcing Services
N.A.I.C.S.: 561499

Subsidiary (Non-US):

ASTERION Belgium, NV　(2)
Wayenborgstraat 27, 2800, Mechelen, Belgium
Tel.: (32) 15294611
Document Management Outsourcing Services
N.A.I.C.S.: 561499

ASTERION Denmark A/S　(2)
Brondby Stadion 20, DK-2605, Brondby, Denmark
Tel.: (45) 43262063
Document Management Outsourcing Services
N.A.I.C.S.: 561499

ASTERION France S.A.S.　(2)
101 Rue Charles Michels, 93200, Saint Denis, France
Tel.: (33) 155844040
Document Management Outsourcing Services
N.A.I.C.S.: 561499

Asterion DM Finland A.B.　(1)
Flygfaltsv 10, PO Box 2006, AX-22111, Mariehamn, Finland
Tel.: (358) 401916810
Business Development & Management Services
N.A.I.C.S.: 561110

Drescher Full-Service Versand GmbH　(1)
Riedwiesenstrasse 1, 71229, Leonberg, Germany
Tel.: (49) 7152505243
Web Site: https://drescherdirekt.de
Label Mfr & Distr
N.A.I.C.S.: 323111

Economic Research Services Inc.　(1)
4901 Tower Ct, Tallahassee, FL 32303
Tel.: (850) 562-1211
Web Site: http://www.ersgroup.com

Economic Research & Development Services
N.A.I.C.S.: 541720

Exela Technologies BV　(1)
Herengracht 576b, 1017 CJ, Amsterdam, Netherlands
Tel.: (31) 306023900
Software Development Services
N.A.I.C.S.: 541511

Exela Technologies GmbH　(1)
Monzastrasse 4 c, 63225, Langen, Germany
Tel.: (49) 610350710
Software Development Services
N.A.I.C.S.: 541511

Exela Technologies Ibercia S.A.　(1)
C/ Julian Camarillo 26, Madrid, 28037, Spain
Tel.: (34) 914900600
Software Development Services
N.A.I.C.S.: 541511

Exela Technologies Limited　(1)
Baronsmede 20 The Avenue, Egham, TW20 9AB, Surrey, United Kingdom
Tel.: (44) 1753778888
Software Development Services
N.A.I.C.S.: 541511

Exela Technologies S.A.　(1)
1 rue de la Mare Blanche ZI de Noisiel 1, Noisiel, 77448, Marne-la-Vallee, Cedex, France
Tel.: (33) 164762000
Data Processing & Digital Transformation Services
N.A.I.C.S.: 518210

Exela Technologies s.p. z o.o.　(1)
Ul Grudziadzka 46-48, 87-100, Torun, Poland
Tel.: (48) 571245151
Software Development Services
N.A.I.C.S.: 541511

HOVG, LLC　(1)
4145 Shackleford Rd Ste 330B, Norcross, GA 30093
Tel.: (678) 229-5010
Web Site: https://www.bayareacredit.com
Insurance Management Services
N.A.I.C.S.: 524210

Kinsella Media, LLC　(1)
2101 L St NW Ste 800, Washington, DC 20037
Tel.: (202) 686-4111
Web Site: https://kinsellamedia.com
Legal Management Services
N.A.I.C.S.: 541199
Katherine Kinsella *(Founder)*
Kristen Stallings *(Dir-Bus Dev)*

Novitex Enterprise Solutions, Inc.　(1)
300 1st Stamford Pl 2nd Fl W, Stamford, CT 06902
Tel.: (203) 351-7103
Web Site: http://www.novitex.com
Emp.: 7,500
Document Management Outsourcing Services
N.A.I.C.S.: 561499

Subsidiary (Non-US):

Novitex Enterprise Solutions Canada, Inc.　(2)
2225 Sheppard Avenue East Suite 1008, Toronto, M2J 5C2, ON, Canada
Tel.: (437) 886-2540
Web Site: http://www.novitex.com
Management Consulting Services
N.A.I.C.S.: 541611

Novitex Government Solutions, LLC　(1)
8401 Corporate Dr Ste 420, Landover, MD 20785
Tel.: (240) 770-0233
Document Management Services
N.A.I.C.S.: 561410

O.T. Drescher AG　(1)
Milan - Strasse 31, PO Box 83, 4018, Basel, Switzerland
Tel.: (41) 612728131
Web Site: https://www.drescherdruck.ch
Label Mfr & Distr

N.A.I.C.S.: 323111

TransCentra FTS Private Ltd.　(1)
3rd Floor Sharda Arcade Pune - Satara Road Bibwewadi, 411037, Pune, Maharashtra, India
Tel.: (91) 2024231612
Software Development Services
N.A.I.C.S.: 541511

EXELIXIS, INC.

1851 Harbor Bay Pkwy, Alameda, CA 94502
Tel.: (650) 837-7000　　　　DE
Web Site: https://www.exelixis.com
Year Founded: 1994
EXEL—(NASDAQ)
Rev.: $1,830,208,000
Assets: $2,942,357,000
Liabilities: $678,445,000
Net Worth: $2,263,912,000
Earnings: $207,765,000
Emp.: 1,310
Fiscal Year-end: 12/29/23
Pharmaceutical Mfr & Researcher for Cancer & Other Serious Diseases
N.A.I.C.S.: 325412
Stelios Papadopoulos *(Co-Founder & Chm)*
Michael M. Morrissey *(Pres & CEO)*
Peter Lamb *(Exec VP-Scientific Strategy)*
Amy C. Peterson *(Chief Medical Officer & Exec VP-Product Dev & Medical Affairs)*
Susan T. Hubbard *(Exec VP-Pub Affairs & IR)*
Dana T. Aftab *(Chief Scientific Officer & Exec VP-Discovery & Translational Res)*
Laura Dillard *(Exec VP-HR)*
Patrick J. Haley *(Exec VP-Comml)*
Christopher J. Senner *(CFO & Exec VP)*

EXELON CORPORATION

10 S Dearborn St 54th Fl, Chicago, IL 60680-5379　　　　PA
Web Site:
https://www.exeloncorp.com
Year Founded: 2000
EXC—(NASDAQ)
Rev.: $21,727,000,000
Assets: $101,546,000,000
Liabilities: $75,791,000,000
Net Worth: $25,755,000,000
Earnings: $2,328,000,000
Emp.: 19,962
Fiscal Year-end: 12/31/23
Holding Company; Electric Power & Natural Gas Distr
N.A.I.C.S.: 551112
Calvin G. Butler Jr. *(Pres & CEO)*
David M. Velazquez *(Exec VP)*
Cynthia McCabe *(Chief Comm Officer & Sr VP)*
Michael Innocenzo *(COO & Exec VP)*
Colette D. Honorable *(Chief External Affairs Officer & Exec VP)*
Denise Galambos *(Chief People Officer, Chief Equity Officer & Sr VP)*
John Frederick Young *(Chm)*

Subsidiaries:

Baltimore Gas and Electric Company　(1)
2 Center Plz 110 W Fayette St, Baltimore, MD 21201-3708　(100%)
Tel.: (410) 234-5000
Web Site: http://www.bge.com
Rev.: $4,027,000,000
Assets: $14,184,000,000
Liabilities: $8,694,000,000
Net Worth: $5,490,000,000
Earnings: $485,000,000
Emp.: 3,295
Fiscal Year-end: 12/31/2023
Electric Power Generation; Electricity & Natural Gas Distr

N.A.I.C.S.: 221112
Mark D. Case *(VP-Strategy & Regulatory Policy)*
Carol A. Dodson *(VP-Substations & Transmission)*
Carim V. Khouzami *(CEO)*
David M. Vahos *(CFO, Treas & Sr VP)*
Jen Herwig *(VP-HR)*
Mike Cloyd *(VP)*
Frank J. Moffa IV *(VP)*
Stacey Ullrich *(VP)*
David Ralph *(Corp Counsel)*
Steven Singh *(VP)*
Charles Washington *(VP)*
Dawn White *(VP)*
Laura A. Wright *(VP)*

CPower Holdings, LLC　(1)
111 Market Pl Ste 201, Baltimore, MD 21202-4035
Tel.: (203) 262-9444
Web Site: http://www.cpowercorp.com
Holding Company
N.A.I.C.S.: 551112
John Horton *(Pres & CEO)*
Carl Almeter *(VP & Gen Mgr-New York)*
Glenn Bogarde *(Sr VP-Sls)*
Constantine Damaskos *(Sr VP-Market Dev)*
Jason Babik *(Sr VP-Strategic Plng & Bus Dev)*
Joe Gatto *(VP & Gen Mgr-Sls-NE-Natl)*
Kyle Harbaugh *(Sr VP-IT & Product Mgmt)*
Kyle Wiggins *(CFO)*
Peter Dotson-Westphalen *(Officer-Compliance)*
Shelley Schopp *(Sr VP-Ops)*
Mathew Sachs *(Sr VP-Strategic Planning & Bus Dev)*

Commonwealth Edison Company　(1)
10 S Dearborn St, Chicago, IL 60603-2300
Tel.: (312) 394-4321
Web Site: http://www.comed.com
Rev.: $7,844,000,000
Assets: $42,827,000,000
Liabilities: $28,464,000,000
Net Worth: $14,363,000,000
Earnings: $1,090,000,000
Emp.: 6,674
Fiscal Year-end: 12/31/2023
Power Generation Services
N.A.I.C.S.: 221111
Michael A. Innocenzo *(COO & Exec VP)*
Joshua Levin *(CFO, Treas & Sr VP)*
David R. Perez *(COO & Exec VP)*
Cheryl Maletich *(Sr VP-Transmission & Substation)*
Lewis Binswanger *(Sr VP)*
Gil G. Quiniones *(CEO)*
Jenniffer Matsumura *(VP-)*
Mark Baranek *(Sr VP-Technical Services)*
Valorio Collotti *(Sr VP)*
Jaclyn Trovato-Wickersham *(VP-)*

Cool Planet Energy Systems, Inc.　(1)
6400 S Fiddlers Green Cir Ste 1300, Greenwood Village, CO 80111
Tel.: (303) 221-2029
Web Site: http://www.coolplanet.com
Biotechnology Research & Development Services
N.A.I.C.S.: 541714
James Loar *(Pres & CEO)*
Rik Miller *(Chm)*
Drew Jackson *(CFO & Exec VP-Strategy)*
Juliette MacKay *(VP-Tech & Innovation)*
Jake Quicksall *(VP-Ops)*

Essess Inc.　(1)
25 Thomson Pl Ste 460, Boston, MA 02210
Tel.: (415) 361-5488
Web Site: http://www.essess.com
Emp.: 10
Energy Management Services
N.A.I.C.S.: 541690
Sanjay Sarma *(Chm)*
Tom Scaramellino *(Pres & CEO)*
Jan Falkowski *(CTO & VP-Engrg)*
Navi Singh *(VP-Solutions Delivery)*
Bill Morris *(VP-Hardware Res & Dev)*
Erica Tennyson *(Gen Counsel)*
Rebecca Craft *(Chief Customer Officer)*

Exelon Energy Delivery Company, LLC　(1)
10 S Dearborn St 49th Fl, Chicago, IL 60603

Tel.: (312) 394-7399
Electric Power Distribution Services
N.A.I.C.S.: 221122

Exelon Transmission Company, LLC (1)
200 Exelon Way, Kennett Square, PA 19348
Tel.: (610) 765-6601
Web Site:
http://www.exelontransmission.com
Electric Power Distribution Services
N.A.I.C.S.: 221122

Grande Prairie Generation, Inc. (1)
9613b 83 Township Rd 720, Wembley, T0H3S0, AB, Canada
Tel.: (780) 766-2015
Eletric Power Generation Services
N.A.I.C.S.: 221118

JExel Nuclear Company (1)
5-2-1 Ueno, Taito-ku, Tokyo, 110-0005, Japan
Tel.: (81) 363717950
Web Site: https://www.jexelnuclear.com
Electric Power Distribution Services
N.A.I.C.S.: 221122

Ogin Inc. (1)
221 Crescent St Ste 103A, Waltham, MA 02453
Tel.: (781) 609-4700
Web Site: http://www.oginenergy.com
Wind Turbine Mfr
N.A.I.C.S.: 333611
Lars Andersen (CEO)
Alan E. Salzman (Mng Partner)
Geneva Johnson (Dir-Talent Mgmt)

PECO Energy Company (1)
2301 Market St, Philadelphia, PA 19101-8699
Tel.: (215) 841-4000
Web Site: http://www.peco.com
Rev.: $3,903,000,000
Assets: $14,502,000,000
Liabilities: $8,939,000,000
Net Worth: $5,563,000,000
Earnings: $576,000,000
Emp.: 2,886
Fiscal Year-end: 12/31/2022
Electric & Gas Utility
N.A.I.C.S.: 221122
Richard G. Webster (VP-Regulatory Policy & Strategy)
Kelly S. Lyman (VP-IT)
David M. Velazquez (CEO)
Marissa E. Humphrey (Treas)
Carolina DiGiorgia (VP- &)
Ben Armstrong (VP-Communications & Marketing)

PHI Service Company (1)
800 King St 5th Fl, Wilmington, DE 19899-0231 (100%)
Tel.: (302) 429-3105
Eletric Power Generation Services
N.A.I.C.S.: 221111

Pepco Holdings LLC (1)
701 9th St NW, Washington, DC 20068-0001
Tel.: (202) 872-2000
Web Site: http://www.pepco.com
Rev.: $5,565,000,000
Assets: $26,082,000,000
Liabilities: $14,852,000,000
Net Worth: $11,230,000,000
Earnings: $608,000,000
Emp.: 1,350
Fiscal Year-end: 12/31/2022
Holding Company; Electric Power Generator & Distr
N.A.I.C.S.: 551112
Calvin G. Butler Jr. (COO-Exelon & Sr Exec VP)
Phillip S. Barnett (CFO, Treas & Sr VP)
J. Tyler Anthony (Pres & CEO)
Anne Lindner (VP-Covt & External Affairs)
Amber Young (VP-Technical Svcs)
Gayle E. Littleton (Chief Legal Officer-)
Valencia McClure (VP)
Mayra Bergman (VP-Communications & Marketing)

Subsidiary (Domestic):

Atlantic City Electric Company (2)
500 N Wakefield Dr, Newark, DE 19702-5440

Tel.: (202) 872-2000
Web Site: http://www.atlanticcityelectric.com
Rev.: $1,522,000,000
Assets: $5,157,000,000
Liabilities: $3,345,000,000
Net Worth: $1,812,000,000
Earnings: $120,000,000
Emp.: 621
Fiscal Year-end: 12/31/2023
Electric Power Distr
N.A.I.C.S.: 221122
Doug Mokoid (Pres)

Brilliant Light Power, Inc. (2)
493 Old Trenton Rd, Cranbury, NJ 08512
Tel.: (609) 490-1090
Web Site: http://www.brilliantlightpower.com
Electric Power Distribution Services
N.A.I.C.S.: 221122
Randell L. Mills (Chm, Pres & CEO)

Delmarva Power & Light Company (2)
500 N Wakefield Dr, Newark, DE 19702-5440 (100%)
Tel.: (202) 872-2000
Web Site: http://www.delmarva.com
Rev.: $1,688,000,000
Assets: $5,966,000,000
Liabilities: $3,873,000,000
Net Worth: $2,093,000,000
Earnings: $177,000,000
Emp.: 918
Fiscal Year-end: 12/31/2023
Electric & Gas Utilities Distr
N.A.I.C.S.: 221118
Doug Mokoid (Pres)

Millennium Account Services, LLC (2)
2 Regulus Dr Ste B 2, Turnersville, NJ 08012
Tel.: (856) 256-9130
Web Site: http://www.millenniumaccountservices.com
Customer Account Services
N.A.I.C.S.: 541219
Scott Depew (Sr Supvr-Ops)
Tracy Talarico (Sr Mgr-Mgmt-Ops)
Lamar Jackson (Sr Mgr)
Lisa Vallaster (VP)
Sherrie Caudill (Sr Supvr-Operating)
Allan Bernard (Supvr-Operating)
Jarrett Monaghan (Supvr-Operating)

Potomac Electric Power Company (2)
701 9th St NW, Washington, DC 20068-0001
Tel.: (202) 872-2000
Web Site: http://www.pepco.com
Rev.: $2,824,000,000
Assets: $11,194,000,000
Liabilities: $7,050,000,000
Net Worth: $4,144,000,000
Earnings: $306,000,000
Emp.: 1,354
Fiscal Year-end: 12/31/2023
Electric & Natural Gas Distr
N.A.I.C.S.: 221122
Phillip S. Barnett (CFO, Treas & Sr VP)

RSB BondCo LLC (1)
103 Foulk Rd, Wilmington, DE 19803
Tel.: (302) 691-6409
Electric Power Distribution Services
N.A.I.C.S.: 221122

eCurv Inc. (1)
480 Pleasant St Ste B110, Watertown, MA 02472
Tel.: (617) 401-2165
Web Site: http://www.ecurv.com
Electric Power Distr
N.A.I.C.S.: 221122

EXEO ENTERTAINMENT, INC.
4478 Wagon Trail Ave, Las Vegas, NV 89118
Tel.: (702) 361-3188   NV
Web Site: https://www.exeoent.com
Year Founded: 2011
EXEO—(NASDAQ)
Rev.: $24,745
Assets: $501,160
Liabilities: $4,574,715
Net Worth: ($4,073,555)
Earnings: ($1,810,767)

Emp.: 2
Fiscal Year-end: 11/30/20
Video Gaming & Smart TV Electronics Mfr
N.A.I.C.S.: 334310
Jeffrey A. Weiland (Pres)
Robert Scott Amaral (CEO, Treas & Sec)

EXICURE, INC.
2430 N Halsted St, Chicago, IL 60614
Tel.: (847) 673-1700   DE
Web Site: https://www.exicuretx.com
Year Founded: 2017
XCUR—(NASDAQ)
Rev.: $84,000
Assets: $11,580,000
Liabilities: $8,549,000
Net Worth: $3,031,000
Earnings: ($16,914,000)
Emp.: 6
Fiscal Year-end: 12/31/23
Biotechnology Development Services
N.A.I.C.S.: 541714
Paul Kang (Pres & CEO)
Jiyoung Hwang (CFO & Sec)
Joshua Miller (Chief Acctg Officer)

EXLITES HOLDINGS INTERNATIONAL, INC.
8403 Benjamin Rd, Tampa, FL 33634
Tel.: (813) 321-9551   OK
Web Site: https://exlitesholdings.us
Year Founded: 2023
EXHI—(OTCIQ)
Medical Product Distr
N.A.I.C.S.: 423450
Mark Julian (Pres & Sec)

EXLSERVICE HOLDINGS, INC.
320 Park Ave 29th Fl, New York, NY 10022
Tel.: (212) 277-7100   DE
Web Site: https://www.exlservice.com
Year Founded: 1999
EXLS—(NASDAQ)
Rev.: $1,412,044,000
Assets: $1,346,119,000
Liabilities: $587,940,000
Net Worth: $758,179,000
Earnings: $142,968,000
Emp.: 45,400
Fiscal Year-end: 12/31/22
Business Process Outsourcing Solutions
N.A.I.C.S.: 561499
Vikas Bhalla (Co-Pres & Head-Insurance Bus)
Baljinder Singh (CIO, Sr VP & Head-Digital Transformation-Global)
Rohit Kapoor (Co-Founder, Chm & CEO)
Rohit Kapoor (Vice Chm)
Sonila Pokharia (Chief Compliance & Ethics Officer)
Anita M. Mahon (Chief Growth & Strategy Officer & Exec VP)
Maurizio Nicolelli (CFO & Exec VP)
Vivek Jetley (Co-Pres & Head-Analytics Bus)
Amy Lupinski (Sr VP)
Raghav Jaggi (Sr VP)
Jim Arslan (Sr VP)
Kurt Anderson (Sr VP)
Rowan McGrath (Sr VP)
Joel Katz (Chief Compliance Officer)

Subsidiaries:

Blue Slate Solutions, LLC (1)
39 Columbia St Fifth Fl, Albany, NY 12207
Tel.: (518) 810-0400
Web Site: http://www.blueslate.net
Sales Range: $1-9.9 Million
Emp.: 35
Management Consulting Services
N.A.I.C.S.: 541618

Datasource Consulting, LLC (1)
2399 Blake St Ste 170, Denver, CO 80205 (100%)
Web Site:
http://www.datasourceconsulting.com
Emp.: 200
Business Intelligence & Enterprise Data Management Consulting Solutions
N.A.I.C.S.: 561499
David Crolene (VP-Delivery)
Steve Dine (Founder & Mng Partner)
Ryan Baca (COO)
Asif Ghatala (Head-Enterprise Data Mgmt-BFS & Retail Verticals)
Avdhesh Singh (Sr Dir-EXL Datasource)
Sally McCormack (Sr Dir-Enterprise Data Mgmt, Credit Unions, Industry & Travel)
Chun Wu (Sr Dir-Competency-Solution Architecture)
Jerry Perez (Dir-Competency-Data Integration)
DeVon Doman (Dir-Competency-Data Architecture)
Solomon Williams (Dir-EDM Solutions)
Paul Aasmundstad (Dir-Competency-Data Governance)
Chuck Warne (Dir-Competency-Big Data)
Matt Caton (Dir-Competency-Bus Intelligence)
Bryson Dunn (Dir-Competency-MDM)
Eric Linneman (Dir-Competency-Cloud, Project Mgr-IT & Engr-Database)
Catherine Gibson (Dir-Competency-Programs & Projects)

ExlService Colombia, S.A.S. (1)
Tel.: (57) 14100400
Business Process Outsourcing Services
N.A.I.C.S.: 561499
Marcela Velasco Urdinola (Mgr-HR)

ExlService Czech Republic S.R.O. (1)
989/8 Kosmonautu 6th floor, 779 00, Olomouc, Czech Republic
Tel.: (420) 585577111
Web Site: http://www.exlservice.com
Business Support Services
N.A.I.C.S.: 561499

ExlService Philippines, Inc. (1)
6th Flr OneE-com Harbor Drive Mall of Asia Complex, Pasay, 1308, Philippines
Tel.: (63) 29769000
Web Site: http://www.exlservice.com
Business Support Services
N.A.I.C.S.: 561499

ExlService Romania Private Limited S.R.L. (1)
3rd 4th Floor Alpha Business Center 12-14 Croitorilor Street, 400162, Cluj-Napoca, Romania
Tel.: (40) 264296000
Web Site: http://www.exlservice.com
Business Support Services
N.A.I.C.S.: 561499

ExlService Technology Solutions, LLC (1)
500 Orient St Ste 110, Chico, CA 95928-5672
Tel.: (530) 891-0853
Business Process Outsourcing Services
N.A.I.C.S.: 561499

ExlService.com, Inc. (1)
280 Park Ave, New York, NY 10017
Tel.: (212) 277-7100
Web Site: http://www.exlservice.com
Sales Range: $25-49.9 Million
Emp.: 150
Outsourcing Services
N.A.I.C.S.: 561499

Subsidiary (Non-US):

ExlService.com (India) Private Limited (2)
A-48 Sector 58, Noida, 201 301, UP, India
Tel.: (91) 1202445900
Web Site: http://www.exlservice.com
Business Support Services
N.A.I.C.S.: 561499

Health Integrated, Inc. (1)
2917 St Andrews Blvd, Tarpon Springs, FL 34688
Tel.: (813) 264-7577

ExlService Holdings, Inc.—(Continued)

Clinical Outcomes, Quality Measures & Cost Containment
N.A.I.C.S.: 541611
Preston Kavaugh (CFO)

IQR Consulting, Inc. (1)
12020 Sunrise Vly Dr, Reston, VA 20191 (100%)
Tel.: (571) 969-4772
Web Site: http://www.iqrdataanalytics.com
Emp.: 200
Data Analytics & Strategic Consulting Services
N.A.I.C.S.: 541614
Rahul Nawab (Founder)

Landacorp, Inc. (1)
500 Orient St Ste 110, Chico, CA 95928
Tel.: (530) 891-0853
Web Site: http://www.landacorp.com
Sales Range: $25-49.9 Million
Emp.: 150
Health Care Management Software
N.A.I.C.S.: 513210

Outsource Partners International SDN BHD (1)
Level 3 Tower 3 Avenue 3 Bangsar South No 8 Jalan Kerinchi, Kuala Lumpur, 59200, Malaysia
Tel.: (60) 322460831
Business Process Outsourcing Solutions
N.A.I.C.S.: 561499

SCIO Health Analytics (UK) Limited (1)
Regal Court 42-44 High Street, Slough, SL1 1EL, Berkshire, United Kingdom
Tel.: (44) 1753245503
Web Site: http://www.sciohealthanalytics.com
Health Care Data Processing Services
N.A.I.C.S.: 541513

EXP WORLD HOLDINGS, INC.
2219 Rimland Dr Ste 301, Bellingham, WA 98226
Tel.: (360) 685-4206 DE
Web Site: https://www.expworldholdings.com
Year Founded: 2008
EXPI—(NASDAQ)
Rev.: $4,281,105,000
Assets: $385,668,000
Liabilities: $141,660,000
Net Worth: $244,008,000
Earnings: ($8,973,000)
Emp.: 2,114
Fiscal Year-end: 12/31/23
Real Estate Information Services
N.A.I.C.S.: 531390
Jason Gesing (Chief Industry Rels Officer & Dir)
Glenn Sanford (Founder, Chm & CEO)
Randall Miles (Vice Chm)
Kent Cheng (Chief Acctg Officer)
Alex Howland (Pres)

Subsidiaries:

Grupo eXp Realtors Mexico, S de R.L. de C.V. (1)
Av Angel Urraza 314 Col Del Valle Benito Juarez, Ciudad de Mexico, 03100, Mexico, Mexico
Tel.: (52) 6691583418
Web Site: http://www.expmexico.mx
Real Estate Services
N.A.I.C.S.: 531390

Zoocasa Realty Inc. (1)
52 Church St Suite 464, Toronto, M5C 2B5, ON, Canada
Web Site: https://www.zoocasa.ca
Real Estate Manangement Services
N.A.I.C.S.: 531320

eXp Australia Pty. Ltd. (1)
Level 13 50 Cavill Avenue, Surfers Paradise, 4217, QLD, Australia
Tel.: (61) 130 039 7777
Web Site: https://www.expaustralia.com.au
Real Estate Services

N.A.I.C.S.: 531210
Donna Wallace (Fin Mgr)
Michelle Christie (Partner-Real Estate)

eXp Global India (1)
American Plaza S-2 Eros Hotel Nehru Place, Patparganj, New Delhi, Delhi, India
Tel.: (91) 9990416363
Web Site: http://www.expglobalindia.co.in
Real Estate Services
N.A.I.C.S.: 531390
Mansi Mehta (Fin Mgr)

eXp Realty Associates, LLC (1)
1230 Peachtree St NE Ste 1900, Atlanta, GA 30309
Tel.: (770) 855-3515
Web Site: https://www.exprealty.com
Real Estate Agency & Brokerage Services
N.A.I.C.S.: 531210

eXp Realty of Canada, Inc. (1)
8214 11500 - 35th St SE, Calgary, T2Z 3W4, AB, Canada
Tel.: (403) 262-7653
Web Site: https://www.exprealty.ca
Real Estate Agency & Brokerage Services
N.A.I.C.S.: 531210
Michael Valdes (Chief Growth Officer)

eXp World UK Limited (1)
68 West Hill, Hitchin, SG5 2HY, Herts, United Kingdom
Tel.: (44) 3301330989
Web Site: http://www.exp-uk.co.uk
Real Estate Services
N.A.I.C.S.: 531210

EXPAND ENERGY CORPORATION
6100 N Western Ave, Oklahoma City, OK 73118
Tel.: (405) 848-8000 OK
Web Site: https://www.chk.com
Year Founded: 1989
EXE—(NASDAQ)
Rev.: $8,721,000,000
Assets: $14,376,000,000
Liabilities: $3,647,000,000
Net Worth: $10,729,000,000
Earnings: $2,419,000,000
Emp.: 1,000
Fiscal Year-end: 12/31/23
Natural Gas & Crude Oil Exploration, Development & Production
N.A.I.C.S.: 211120
Domenic J. Dell'Osso Jr. (Pres & CEO)
Nick Dell'Osso (Pres & CEO)
Benjamin E. Russ (Gen Counsel)
Chris Ayres (Treas)
Tim Beard (VP)
Sheldon Burleson (VP)
John Christ (CIO)
David Eudey (VP)
Matt Garner (VP)
Jim Grant (VP)
Kajsa Greenhoward (VP)
Jason Kurtz (VP)
Greg Larson (VP)
Dan Lopata (VP)
Toni Parks-Payne (VP)
Usha Turner (Chief Sustainability Officer)
Michael A. Wichterich (Chm)
Mohit Singh (CFO & Exec VP)
Josh J. Viets (COO & Exec VP)

Subsidiaries:

Brazos Valley Longhorn, L.L.C. (1)
6100 N Western Ave, Oklahoma City, OK 73118
Tel.: (405) 848-8000
Rev.: $947,386,000
Assets: $3,255,030,000
Liabilities: $1,963,622,000
Net Worth: $1,291,408,000
Earnings: $146,508,000
Emp.: 197
Fiscal Year-end: 12/31/2018
Oil & Natural Gas Exploration, Development & Production
N.A.I.C.S.: 211120

William M. Buergler (Chief Acctg Officer & Sr VP)
Robert D. Lawler (Pres & CEO)
Domenic J. Dell'Osso Jr. (CFO & Exec VP)

Chesapeake Appalachia, LLC (1)
414 Summer St, Charleston, WV 25301
Tel.: (304) 353-5000
Oil & Gas Exploration Services
N.A.I.C.S.: 213112
Matt Casto (Atty)

Chesapeake Energy Marketing, LLC (1)
6100 N Western Ave, Oklahoma City, OK 73154
Tel.: (405) 935-8878
Web Site: http://www.chk.com
Oil & Gas Marketing Services
N.A.I.C.S.: 424720

Chesapeake Lousiana, L.P (1)
6100 N Western Ave, Oklahoma City, OK 73154
Tel.: (405) 848-8000
Holding Company; Natural Gas Distr
N.A.I.C.S.: 551112

Chesapeake Mid-Continent Corp. (1)
6100 N Western Ave, Oklahoma City, OK 73118 (100%)
Tel.: (405) 879-9212
Web Site: http://www.chk.com
Sales Range: $75-99.9 Million
Crude Petroleum & Natural Gas
N.A.I.C.S.: 211120

Chesapeake Oilfield Services, Inc. (1)
6100 N Western Ave, Oklahoma City, OK 73118
Tel.: (405) 848-8000
Sales Range: $1-4.9 Billion
Oil Field Services
N.A.I.C.S.: 213111
Jerry L. Winchester (CEO)
Karl Blanchard (COO)

Chesapeake Operating, LLC (1)
6100 N Western Ave, Oklahoma City, OK 73154-0496
Tel.: (405) 848-8000
Web Site: http://www.chk.com
Sales Range: $250-299.9 Million
Emp.: 5,000
Crude Petroleum & Natural Gas Exploration
N.A.I.C.S.: 211120

Empress Louisiana Properties, L.P. (1)
9821 Katy Fwy Ste 910, Houston, TX 77024
Tel.: (713) 468-0121
Emp.: 3
Nonresidential Real Estate Services
N.A.I.C.S.: 531312

Southwestern Energy Company (1)
10000 Energy Dr, Spring, TX 77389
Tel.: (832) 796-1000
Web Site: https://www.swn.com
Rev.: $6,522,000,000
Assets: $11,991,000,000
Liabilities: $6,103,000,000
Net Worth: $5,888,000,000
Earnings: $1,557,000,000
Emp.: 1,165
Fiscal Year-end: 12/31/2023
Natural Gas Exploration & Production Services
N.A.I.C.C.: £11100
Gregory D. Kerley (CFO & Exec VP)
Catherine A. Kehr (Chm)
William J. Way (Pres & CEO)
Clayton A. Carrell (COO & Exec VP)
Chris Lacy (Gen Counsel, Sec & VP)
Quentin Dyson (Sr VP-Ops Svcs)
Carina Gillenwater (VP-HR)
Derek W. Cutright (Sr VP)
John P. Kelly (Sr VP)
Carl Fredrick Giesler Jr. (CFO & Exec VP)

Subsidiary (Domestic):

Montage Resources Corp. (2)
122 W John Carpenter Fwy Ste 300, Irving, TX 75039
Tel.: (469) 444-1647

Web Site: http://www.montageresources.com
Rev.: $634,441,000
Assets: $1,951,177,000
Liabilities: $954,091,000
Net Worth: $997,086,000
Earnings: $31,762,000
Emp.: 236
Fiscal Year-end: 12/31/2019
Oil & Gas Exploration & Production
N.A.I.C.S.: 211120
Marty L. Byrd (Sr VP-Land)
Paul Johnston (Gen Counsel & Exec VP)
Timothy J. Loos (Sr VP-Acctg & Fin)

Subsidiary (Domestic):

Blue Ridge Mountain Resources, Inc. (3)
122 W John Carpenter Fwy Ste 300, Irving, TX 75039
Tel.: (469) 444-1647
Holding Company; Oil & Natural Gas Exploration & Production Services
N.A.I.C.S.: 551112
Michael C. Jennings (Chm)
Paul M. Johnston (Gen Counsel & Sr VP)
Michael R. Koy (CFO & Exec VP)
Chris J. Hutchison (Mgr-Mktg & Midstream)
Nicole Thurmond (VP-HR)
Darrel Overgaard (Dir-Drilling & Completions Ops)

Subsidiary (Domestic):

Alpha Hunter Drilling, LLC (4)
27724 State Rte 7, Marietta, OH 45750
Tel.: (740) 374-2940
Oil & Gas Extraction Services
N.A.I.C.S.: 211120

Bakken Hunter, LLC (4)
777 Post Oak Blvd Ste 650, Houston, TX 77056
Tel.: (832) 369-6986
Oil Exploration Services
N.A.I.C.S.: 213112

MHR Management, LLC (4)
909 Lake Carolyn Pkwy Ste 600, Irving, TX 75039
Tel.: (832) 369-6986
Oil Exploration Services
N.A.I.C.S.: 213112

TransTex Hunter, LLC (4)
1442 US Highway 90A E, Hallettsville, TX 77964
Tel.: (713) 654-4440
Web Site: https://transtextreating.com
Oil Exploration Services
N.A.I.C.S.: 213112
Stephen Morgan (Pres & CEO)
Robert Shimek (VP-Ops)
Josh Smith (Dir-Construction)

Subsidiary (Domestic):

Eclipse Resources - Ohio, LLC (3)
4900 Boggs Rd, Zanesville, OH 43701
Tel.: (740) 452-4503
Emp.: 42
Oil & Gas Extraction Services
N.A.I.C.S.: 213112
Ben Hulburt (Owner & Pres)

Subsidiary (Domestic):

SEECO, Inc. (2)
2350 N Sam Houston Pkwy E Ste 125, Houston, TX 77032 (100%)
Tel.: (281) 618-4700
Sales Range: $800-899.9 Million
Emp.: 725
Providers of Natural Gas & Energy Exploration Services
N.A.I.C.S.: 213112
Gregory D. Kerley (CFO)
Harold M. Korell (Pres & CEO)
William J. Way (Exec VP)
Jennifer N. McCauley (Dir-HR)

Subsidiary (Non-US):

SWN Resources Canada, Inc. (2)
633 Main St, Moncton, E1C 9X9, NB, Canada
Tel.: (506) 382-2603
Web Site: https://www.swnb.ca
Oil & Gas Operation Services
N.A.I.C.S.: 213112

Subsidiary (Domestic):

SWN Well Services, LLC **(2)**
2350 Sam Houston Pkwy E Ste 125, Houston, TX 77032
Tel.: (281) 618-7322
Oil & Gas Well Drilling Services
N.A.I.C.S.: 213111
Steve Thomson *(Gen Mgr)*

Southwestern Energy Pipeline Services **(2)**
1083 E Sain St, Fayetteville, AR 72703-1004 **(100%)**
Tel.: (479) 521-1141
Web Site: http://www.swn.com
Sales Range: $25-49.9 Million
Emp.: 50
Natural Gas Transmission Services
N.A.I.C.S.: 486210

Southwestern Energy Production Co. **(2)**
10000 Energy Dr, Spring, TX 77389 **(100%)**
Tel.: (281) 618-4700
Web Site: http://www.swn.com
Sales Range: $125-149.9 Million
Emp.: 150
Exploration & Production of Natural Gas, Crude Oil & Petroleum Condensates
N.A.I.C.S.: 213112
Harold M. Korell *(Chm)*

Southwestern Energy Services Company **(2)**
10000 Energy Dr, Spring, TX 77389
Tel.: (832) 796-1000
Web Site: https://www.swn.com
Oil & Gas Support Services
N.A.I.C.S.: 213112
Craig Elias *(Pres)*

Southwestern Midstream Services Company **(2)**
1000 Energy Dr, Spring, TX 77389
Tel.: (281) 618-4762
Web Site: http://www.swn.com
Natural Gas Distribution Services
N.A.I.C.S.: 221210

Vine Energy Inc. **(1)**
5800 Granite Pkwy Ste 550, Plano, TX 75024
Tel.: (469) 606-0540
Web Site: http://www.vineenergy.com
Emp.: 113
Holding Company
N.A.I.C.S.: 551112
Jonathan C. Curth *(Gen Counsel, Sec & Exec VP)*
Randy Blurton *(Exec VP-Commercial & M&A)*
Brian Dutton *(Chief Acctg Officer & VP)*
David Erdman *(Dir-IR)*
Phuong Le *(Exec VP-Reserves & Reservoir Engrg)*
Jeff Smith *(Mgr-Health, Safety & Environmental)*
Beth Truelove *(Exec VP-Reservoir Dev & Strategy)*
Rachel Zavala *(Sr VP-HR & Admin)*

EXPEDIA GROUP, INC.

1111 Expedia Group Way W, Seattle, WA 98119
Tel.: (206) 481-7200   DE
Web Site:
    https://www.expediagroup.com
Year Founded: 1994
EXPE—(NASDAQ)
Rev.: $12,839,000,000
Assets: $21,642,000,000
Liabilities: $18,856,000,000
Net Worth: $2,786,000,000
Earnings: $797,000,000
Emp.: 17,100
Fiscal Year-end: 12/31/23
Holding Company; Online Travel, Hotel & Automobile Rental Arrangement Services
N.A.I.C.S.: 551112
Lance A. Soliday *(Chief Acctg Officer, Sr VP & Controller)*
Julie P. Whalen *(CFO & Exec VP)*

Robert J. Dzielak *(Chief Legal Officer & Sec)*
Ariane Gorin *(CEO)*
Cyril Ranque *(Pres-Travel Partners Grp)*
Jon T. Gieselman *(Pres-Expedia Brands)*

Subsidiaries:

A.C.N. 079 010 772 Pty Ltd **(1)**
Level 1 76-80 Clarence Street, Sydney, 2000, NSW, Australia
Tel.: (61) 292495444
Online Travel Ticketing Services
N.A.I.C.S.: 561599

Asia Web Direct (HK) Limited **(1)**
Level 43 AIA Tower 183 Electric Road, North Point, China (Hong Kong)
Tel.: (852) 39751036
Online Travel Ticketing Services
N.A.I.C.S.: 561599

Auto Escape Group **(1)**
137 Rue Jean Marie Jacquard, Pertuis, 84120, France
Tel.: (33) 490092828
Online Travel Ticketing Services
N.A.I.C.S.: 561599

Auto Escape SA **(1)**
137 rue Jacquard, Pertuis, 84120, France
Tel.: (33) 892464610
Web Site: http://www.autoescape.com
Sales Range: $25-49.9 Million
Emp.: 48
Car Rental Services
N.A.I.C.S.: 532111

Representative Office (Non-US):

Auto Escape UK **(2)**
Wilberforce House Station Road, London, NW4 4QE, United Kingdom
Tel.: (44) 844 369 0109
Web Site: http://www.autoescape.co.uk
Car Rental Services
N.A.I.C.S.: 532111

CSC Travel Group Inc. **(1)**
1055 Hastings St W Suite 400, Vancouver, V6E 2E9, BC, Canada
Tel.: (604) 685-1221
Emp.: 5
Online Travel Ticketing Services
N.A.I.C.S.: 561599
Matthew Eichhorst *(Pres)*

Car Del Mar Ferienautovermietung GmbH **(1)**
Spaldingstr 77, Hamburg, 20097, Germany
Tel.: (49) 4018048360
Web Site: http://www.cardelmar.de
Online Travel Ticketing Services
N.A.I.C.S.: 561599

Classic Vacations, LLC **(1)**
5669 Snell Ave Ste 343, San Jose, CA 95138 **(100%)**
Tel.: (408) 287-4550
Web Site: https://www.classicvacations.com
Sales Range: $125-149.9 Million
Emp.: 200
Travel Services
N.A.I.C.S.: 561520
Melissa Krueger *(CEO)*
Lori Smith *(VP-Mktg)*
Bonty Escallon *(Mng Dir)*
Darren Polino *(Sr Dir-Contact Center)*
Marilyn Cairo *(VP-Sls)*

CruiseShipCenters International Inc. **(1)**
1055 West Hastings Street Suite 400, Vancouver, V6E 2E9, BC, Canada
Tel.: (604) 685-1445
Web Site: http://www.cruiseshipcenters.com
Emp.: 90
Cruise Travel Agencies Franchisor & Operator
N.A.I.C.S.: 533110

Subsidiary (US):

CruiseShipCenters USA Inc. **(2)**
333 108th Ave NE, Bellevue, WA 98004
Tel.: (425) 679-3751
Web Site: http://www.cruiseshipcenters.com

Cruise Travel Agencies Franchisor & Operator
N.A.I.C.S.: 533110

Egencia Australia Pty. Ltd. **(1)**
Level 2 77 King Street, Sydney, 2000, NSW, Australia
Tel.: (61) 1300363696
Web Site: http://www.egencia.com.au
Tour & Travel Agency Operator
N.A.I.C.S.: 561510
Cecilia Routledge *(Mng Dir)*

Egencia GmbH **(1)**
Schellingstrasse 1, 10785, Berlin, Germany
Tel.: (49) 892020880
Web Site: https://www.egencia.de
Sales Range: $25-49.9 Million
Emp.: 60
Travel Agency
N.A.I.C.S.: 561510

Egencia UK Ltd. **(1)**
39 Piccadilly, Manchester, M1 3BN, United Kingdom
Tel.: (44) 2030772635
Web Site: https://www.egencia.co.uk
Travel Agency Operator
N.A.I.C.S.: 561510

Expedia France S.A.S. **(1)**
60 Rue Prony, 75017, Paris, France
Tel.: (33) 170718523
Web Site: http://www.expedia.fr
Travel Agency
N.A.I.C.S.: 561510

Expedia Lodging Partner Services Sarl **(1)**
Rue Du Lac 12, 1207, Geneva, Switzerland
Tel.: (41) 225801800
Online Travel Ticketing Services
N.A.I.C.S.: 561599

Expedia Online Travel Services India Private Limited **(1)**
3rd Floor Vatika Atrium Sector-53, Gurgaon, 122001, Haryana, India
Tel.: (91) 1244311115
Web Site: http://www.expedia.co.in
Travel Agency
N.A.I.C.S.: 561510

Expedia Partner Services Group SARL **(1)**
Rue du 31 Decembre 40-46, 1207, Geneva, Switzerland
Tel.: (41) 225801800
Web Site: http://www.expedia.com
Travel Agency
N.A.I.C.S.: 327910

Expedia Spain, S.L. **(1)**
Plaza de Callao 5 Planta 10, Madrid, 28013, Spain
Tel.: (34) 912757401
Web Site: http://www.expedia.es
Sales Range: $25-49.9 Million
Emp.: 53
Travel Agency
N.A.I.C.S.: 561510

Expedia Sweden AB **(1)**
Smalandsgatan 20, 111 46, Stockholm, Sweden
Tel.: (46) 200810341
Web Site: http://www.expedia.se
Travel Agency
N.A.I.C.S.: 561510

Expedia US, Inc. **(1)**
333 108th Ave NE, Bellevue, WA 98004
Tel.: (404) 728-8787
Web Site: http://www.expedia.com
Online Travel, Hotel & Automobile Rental Arrangement Services
N.A.I.C.S.: 561599

Expedia.nl B.V. **(1)**
Herengracht 469, 1017 BS, Amsterdam, Netherlands
Tel.: (31) 207094800
Web Site: http://www.expedia.nl
Travel Agency
N.A.I.C.S.: 561510

HomeAway, Inc. **(1)**
1011 W Fifth St Ste 300, Austin, TX 78703
Tel.: (512) 684-1100
Web Site: http://www.homeaway.com
Online Vacation Rental Sites Operator

N.A.I.C.S.: 561599
John Kim *(Pres)*

Subsidiary (Non-US):

HomeAway Pty Ltd **(2)**
100 William Street, Sydney, Woolloomooloo, 2011, NSW, Australia
Tel.: (61) 398672640
Web Site: http://www.homeaway.com.au
Holiday Property Rental Services
N.A.I.C.S.: 531110
John J. Ostlund *(CTO)*
Tina Weyand *(Chief Product Officer)*
Steve Davis *(Chief Digital & Cloud Officer)*
Jeff Hurst *(Chief Comml Officer)*
Trent York *(CFO)*

Hotels.com GP, LLC **(1)**
5400 LBJ Fwy Ste 500, Dallas, TX 75240-1019
Web Site: http://www.hotels.com
Home Management Services
N.A.I.C.S.: 561110

Subsidiary (Domestic):

Hotels.com, L.P. **(2)**
5400 LBJ Fwy Ste 500, Dallas, TX 75240
Tel.: (860) 500-4141
Web Site: https://www.hotels.com
Sales Range: $900-999.9 Million
Emp.: 1,150
Discount Travel Arrangement
N.A.I.C.S.: 561599

Subsidiary (Non-US):

Asia Web Direct Co., Ltd. **(3)**
4th Floor Muang Mai Building 9/17 Moo 6 Thepkasattri Road, T Rasda A Muang, Phuket, 83000, Thailand
Tel.: (66) 76236550
Web Site: http://www.asiaweb-direct.com
Sales Range: $25-49.9 Million
Emp.: 80
Online Travel Reservation Services
N.A.I.C.S.: 561599

Hotwire, Inc. **(1)**
114 Sansome St Ste 400, San Francisco, CA 94104 **(100%)**
Tel.: (417) 520-1680
Web Site: https://www.hotwire.com
Sales Range: $25-49.9 Million
Emp.: 35
Discount Travel & Airfare Products & Services Online
N.A.I.C.S.: 561510
Spencer M. Rascoff *(Co-Founder)*
Lindsay Riddell *(Sr VP-Corp & Exec Comm)*
Karl I. Peterson *(Co-Founder)*

Liberty Expedia Holdings, Inc. **(1)**
12300 Liberty Blvd, Englewood, CO 80112
Tel.: (720) 875-5800
Web Site: http://www.libertyexpedia.com
Sales Range: $5-14.9 Billion
Online Travel Services
N.A.I.C.S.: 551112
Christopher W. Shean *(Pres & CEO)*

Lodging Partner Services Denmark ApS **(1)**
Havneholmen 29, 1561, Copenhagen, Denmark
Tel.: (45) 20996543
Online Travel Ticketing Services
N.A.I.C.S.: 561599

Orbitz Worldwide, LLC **(1)**
500 W Madison St Ste 1000, Chicago, IL 60661
Tel.: (312) 894-5000
Web Site: http://www.orbitz.com
Emp.: 1,530
Online Travel Services
N.A.I.C.S.: 551112
Alex Zoghlin *(Founder)*

Subsidiary (Non-US):

Oy ebookers Finland Ltd **(2)**
Kalevankatu 6, 00100, Helsinki, Finland
Tel.: (358) 9681440
Web Site: http://www.ebookers.fi
Travel Arrangement & Reservation Services
N.A.I.C.S.: 561599

Subsidiary (Domestic):

Trip Network, Inc. **(2)**

Expedia Group, Inc.—(Continued)

500 W Madison St Ste 1000, Chicago, IL
60661
Tel.: (312) 279-7778
Web Site: https://www.cheaptickets.com
Discount Travel Agent & Airline Ticket Whslr
N.A.I.C.S.: 561599

Subsidiary (Non-US):

ebookers Limited　　　　　　　　　(2)
5th Floor 140 Aldersgate Street, London,
EC1A 4HY, United Kingdom
Tel.: (44) 2074892222
Web Site: http://www.ebookers.com
Emp.: 1,822
Travel Services
N.A.I.C.S.: 481111

SilverRail Technologies, Inc.　　　(1)
300 Trade Ctr Ste 4700, Woburn, MA
01801
Tel.: (617) 934-6786
Web Site: http://www.silverrailtech.com
Technology Solutions for Distribution of Rail
Tickets & Rail Related Products
N.A.I.C.S.: 541519
William Phillipson (Co-Founder & COO)
Aaron Gowell (Co-Founder & CEO)
Francis Lee (Head-Search)
Sarah McDonald (Head-Agency)

Subsidiary (Non-US):

**SilverRail Technologies UK
Limited**　　　　　　　　　　　　　　　(2)
The Heals Building 22 Torrington Place,
London, WC1E 7HJ, United Kingdom
Tel.: (44) 8458341069
Web Site: http://www.silverrailtech.com
Technology Solutions for Distribution of
Train Tickets & Other Rail Related Products
N.A.I.C.S.: 541519
Aaron Gowell (Co-Founder & CEO)
William Phillipson (Co-Founder & Pres)

Standby Holdings Pty Ltd　　　　　(1)
L 1 9 St Pauls Tce, Spring Hill, 4000, QLD,
Australia
Tel.: (61) 732369520
Holding Company
N.A.I.C.S.: 551112

Traveldoo SAS　　　　　　　　　　　(1)
130-136 Rue Victor Hugo, 92300, Levallois-
Perret, France
Tel.: (33) 155469530
Web Site: http://www.traveldoo.com
Emp.: 65
Travel Agency
N.A.I.C.S.: 561510
Stephane Donders (CEO)
Daniel Fitzgerald (Chief Product Officer)
L. Loic (Project Mgr)
Benoit De Lavaissiere (Head-Fin)
Jeremy Brown (CTO)
Jean-Sebastien Irigoyen (Chief Comml Offi-
cer)

Travelscape, LLC　　　　　　　　　(1)
10190 Covington Cross Dr, Las Vegas, NV
89144-7043
Tel.: (702) 792-3811
Sales Range: $100-124.9 Million
Emp.: 475
Travel Services
N.A.I.C.S.: 561510
Erik C. Blachford (Pres & CEO)

Trivago Spain, S.L.　　　　　　　　(1)
C/ Rita Levi Edifici SM2, ParcBit, 07121,
Palma de Mallorca, Majorca, Spain
Tel.: (34) 871552415
Online Travel Ticketing Services
N.A.I.C.S.: 561599

VIA Egencia AS　　　　　　　　　　(1)
Cort Adelers Gate 30, Vika, 0254, Oslo,
Norway
Tel.: (47) 23151600
Web Site: http://www.viatravelgroup.com
Online Travel Ticketing Services
N.A.I.C.S.: 561599
Rune Feltman (CEO, Mng Dir & VP)

VIA Egencia Denmark A/S　　　　　(1)
Meldahlsgade 5 3, 1613, Copenhagen,
Denmark
Tel.: (45) 70708000
Web Site: http://www.viatravel.dk

Online Travel Ticketing Services
N.A.I.C.S.: 561599

Wotif.com Holdings Pty. Ltd.　　　(1)
7 Baroona Road, Milton, 4064, QLD, Aus-
tralia
Tel.: (61) 2 8228 1670
Web Site: http://www.wotif.com
Sales Range: $150-199.9 Million
Emp.: 100
Holding Company; Online Travel Reserva-
tion Services
N.A.I.C.S.: 551112

Subsidiary (Domestic):

Lastminute.com.au Pty. Limited　(2)
Se 1002 11-17 York St, Sydney, 2000,
NSW, Australia
Tel.: (61) 292496070
Web Site: http://www.lastminute.com.au
Sales Range: $75-99.9 Million
Online Travel Reservation Services
N.A.I.C.S.: 561599

Wotif.com Pty. Ltd.　　　　　　　　(2)
13 Railway Ter, Milton, 4064, QLD, Austra-
lia
Tel.: (61) 282281670
Web Site: http://www.wotif.com
Sales Range: $50-74.9 Million
Emp.: 80
Online Travel Reservation Services
N.A.I.C.S.: 561599

Subsidiary (Non-US):

Wotif.com (NZ) Ltd.　　　　　　　　(3)
35A Scanlan St, Grey Lynn, Auckland,
1021, New Zealand
Tel.: (64) 508053284
Web Site: http://www.wotif.co.nz
Online Travel Reservation Services
N.A.I.C.S.: 561599

EXPEDITORS INTERNATIONAL
OF WASHINGTON, INC.

1015 3rd Ave, Seattle, WA 98104
Tel.: (206) 674-3400　　　　　　**WA**
Web Site:
　　https://www.expeditors.com
Year Founded: 1979
EXPD—(NYSE)
Rev.: $9,300,110,000
Assets: $4,523,809,000
Liabilities: $2,132,396,000
Net Worth: $2,391,413,000
Earnings: $752,883,000
Emp.: 18,100
Fiscal Year-end: 12/31/23
International Freight Forwarders &
Customs Broker
N.A.I.C.S.: 481212
Timothy C. Barber (Exec VP-Europe)
Daniel R. Wall (Pres-Global Geogra-
phies & Ops)
Jeffrey S. Musser (Pres & CEO)
Jose Antonio Ubeda (Sr VP-Digital
Solutions)
Bruce J. Krebs (Sr VP-Distr-Global)
Karl C. Francisco (Sr VP-Ocean-
Global)
Christopher J. McClincy (CIO & Sr
VP)
Steven J. Grimmer (Sr VP-Acct
Mgmt)
Glenn M. Alger (Founder)
Benjamin G. Clark (Chief Strategy
Officer & Sr VP)
Craig L. Wilwerding (Sr VP-Bus Ops-
Global)
J. Jonathan Song (Sr VP-Global Sls
& Mktg)
Dana L. Lorenze (Sr VP-Customs-
Global)
Blake R. Bell (Pres-Global Svcs)
Michelle D. Weaver (Sr VP-Order
Mgmt-Global)
Murali Krishnamurthy (Sr VP-Middle
East, Africa & Indian Subcontinent)
Allen Wang (Sr VP-North Asia)
Khoon Ling Lim (Sr VP-South Asia)

Jeffrey F. Dickerman (Gen Counsel,
Sec & Sr VP)
Kelly Blacker (Pres-Global Products)
William A. Romberger III (Sr VP-
America)
Bradley S. Powell (CFO & Sr VP)

Subsidiaries:

Cargo Signal Solutions, LLC　　　(1)
1015 3rd Ave, Seattle, WA 98104
Tel.: (206) 558-3500
Web Site: https://www.cargosignal.com
Cargo Tracking Services
N.A.I.C.S.: 484220
Derek Moulton (Ops Mgr)
Jose Ubeda (Sr VP)

Certuspact, LLC　　　　　　　　　　(1)
1015 Third Ave 12th Floor, Seattle, WA
98104
Tel.: (206) 393-5751
Freight Transportation Arrangement Automation
N.A.I.C.S.: 488510

ECI Taiwan Co., Ltd.　　　　　　　　(1)
11th Floor Central Finance Building No 181
Fu-Hsing North Road, Taipei, 10596, Tai-
wan
Tel.: (886) 227132145
Sales Range: $50-74.9 Million
Emp.: 150
Freight Transportation Services
N.A.I.C.S.: 488510
David Chong (Branch Mgr)

EIF SDN. BHD.　　　　　　　　　　　(1)
Crown House Suite 13 08 13th Floor No
217 Persiaran Raja Muda Musa, 42000,
Port Klang, Selangor, Malaysia
Tel.: (60) 331673704
Logistics & Freight Forwarding Services
N.A.I.C.S.: 541614

Expeditors (Bangladesh), Ltd.　　(1)
South Breeze Square Level-4 52 Gulshan
Avenue, Dhaka, 1212, Bangladesh
Tel.: (880) 29890594
Logistics & Freight Forwarding Services
N.A.I.C.S.: 541614

Expeditors (Malaysia) Sdn. Bhd.　(1)
Level 11 Tower 2 Wisma AmFirst Jalan SS
7/15, Kelena Jaya Petaling Jaya, 47301,
Kuala Lumpur, Selangor, Malaysia
Tel.: (60) 387873888
Logistics & Freight Forwarding Services
N.A.I.C.S.: 541614

**Expeditors (Portugal) Transitarios In-
ternacionais Lda.**　　　　　　　　　(1)
Rua C Edificio 124 Piso 1 Gabinete 4 Aero-
porto de Lisboa, Lisbon, 1700-008, Portugal
Tel.: (351) 21 000 3800
Web Site: http://www.expeditors.com
Sales Range: $25-49.9 Million
Emp.: 14
Logistic Services
N.A.I.C.S.: 488510

**Expeditors (Singapore) Private
Limited**　　　　　　　　　　　　　　(1)
Gedung Dana Graha Lt 2 No 209A Jl Imam
Bonjol, Nagoya Kota Batam, Singapore,
Singapore
Tel.: (65) 778432296
Logistics & Freight Forwarding Services
N.A.I.C.S.: 541614

Expeditors (Thailand) Ltd.　　　　(1)
44th Floor Empire Tower Park Wing No 1
South Sathorn Road, Yannawa Sathorn,
Bangkok, 10120, Thailand
Tel.: (66) 6701028
Logistics & Freight Forwarding Services
N.A.I.C.S.: 541614

Expeditors Cambodia Ltd.　　　　(1)
LSI Building 03 6th Floor St 1019, Sangkat
Phnom Penh Thmey Khan Sensok, Phnom
Penh, 12101, Cambodia
Tel.: (855) 2 323 1144
Web Site: http://www.expeditors.com
Sales Range: $25-49.9 Million
Emp.: 23
Logistic Services
N.A.I.C.S.: 488510

Expeditors Canada, Inc.　　　　　(1)

---

55 Standish Crt 11 Fl, Mississauga, L5R
4A1, ON, Canada
Tel.: (905) 290-6000
Freight Transportation Arrangement Ser-
vices
N.A.I.C.S.: 488510

**Expeditors Cargo Insurance Brokers
B.V.**　　　　　　　　　　　　　　　　(1)
Ganderweg 2, Schiphol, 1118 LH, Nether-
lands
Tel.: (31) 206556100
Cargo Insurance Brokerage Services
N.A.I.C.S.: 524210

**Expeditors Chile Transportes Interna-
cionales Limitada**　　　　　　　　　(1)
Avenida Apoquindo 4001 Office 601 Las
Condes, Santiago, Chile
Tel.: (56) 224822000
Logistics & Freight Forwarding Services
N.A.I.C.S.: 541614

Expeditors Denmark ApS　　　　　(1)
Arne Jacobsens Alle 7 4th floor, Copenha-
gen, 2300, Denmark
Tel.: (45) 3 840 8100
Web Site: http://www.expeditors.com
Logistic & Warehousing Services
N.A.I.C.S.: 541614

Expeditors Dominicana SAS　　　(1)
Avenida Sarasota No 39 Torre Sarasota
Center Suite 1301, Santo Domingo, 11999,
Dominican Republic
Tel.: (809) 8295954444
Logistic & Warehousing Services
N.A.I.C.S.: 541614
Vileissy Rodriguez (Controller-Country)

Expeditors Egypt S.A.E.　　　　　(1)
Area 10&11 Block 12015, Industrial Zone El
Obour, Cairo, Egypt
Tel.: (20) 244891098
Logistics & Freight Forwarding Services
N.A.I.C.S.: 541614

Expeditors Finland Oy　　　　　　(1)
Ayritie 8 D, 01510, Vantaa, Finland
Tel.: (358) 98700880
Logistics & Freight Forwarding Services
N.A.I.C.S.: 541614

Expeditors Guatemala S.A.　　　　(1)
5a Ave 5-55 Zona 14 Europlaza Torre 1 Ofi-
cina 1804, Guatemala, 01014, Guatemala
Tel.: (502) 2 381 9600
Web Site: http://www.expeditors.com
Sales Range: $25-49.9 Million
Emp.: 30
Transportation Arrangement Services
N.A.I.C.S.: 488510

Expeditors Hong Kong Limited　　(1)
Alameda Dr Carlos D' Assumpcao No 398
Edificio CNAC 9 Andar C, Macau, China,
(Macau)
Tel.: (853) 28755116
Logistics & Freight Forwarding Services
N.A.I.C.S.: 541614

**Expeditors International (Hellas)
S.A.**　　　　　　　　　　　　　　　　(1)
Tel.: (30) 2109242359
Web Site: http://www.expeditors.com
Emp.: 100
Freight Transportation Arrangement Ser-
vices
N.A.I.C.S.: 488510

**Expeditors International (India) Pvt.
Ltd.**　　　　　　　　　　　　　　　　(1)
8th Floor Prestige Centre Court No 183
NSK Salai Vadapalani, Chennai, 600 026,
India
Tel.: (91) 4466070300
Logistics & Freight Forwarding Services
N.A.I.C.S.: 541614

**Expeditors International (Kuwait)
W.L.L.**　　　　　　　　　　　　　　　(1)
Office 49 & 50 Ground Floor Plot 67 Waha
Mall Dajeej, Al Farwaniyah, Kuwait
Tel.: (965) 24341208
Logistics & Freight Forwarding Services
N.A.I.C.S.: 541614

Expeditors International (NZ) Ltd.　(1)
21 Airpark Drive Auckland Airport, Auckland,

2022, New Zealand
Tel.: (64) 9 915 6200
Web Site: http://www.expeditors.com
Sales Range: $25-49.9 Million
Emp.: 1
Logistic Services
N.A.I.C.S.: 488510

Expeditors International (Puerto Rico) Inc. (1)
Calle A Final Ave San Marcos El Comandante Industrial Park, Carolina, PR 00982
Tel.: (787) 750-7500
Web Site: http://www.expeditors.com
Emp.: 25
Logistic Services
N.A.I.C.S.: 488510

Expeditors International (Switzerland) Sagl (1)
Via Serfontana 10, 6834, Morbio Inferiore, Switzerland
Tel.: (41) 91 695 7170
Freight Transportation Arrangement Services
N.A.I.C.S.: 488510

Expeditors International (UK) Ltd. (1)
Unit 4 Shine Innovation & Tech Plant St Marks Street, Hull, HU8 7FB, North Humberside, United Kingdom
Tel.: (44) 148 260 6656
Web Site: http://www.expeditors.com
Freight Transportation Services
N.A.I.C.S.: 488510

Expeditors International - Lebanon (s.a.l.) (1)
Sodeco Square Damascus Road Block A 1st Floor, Beirut, Lebanon
Tel.: (961) 1612999
Freight Transportation Arrangement Services
N.A.I.C.S.: 488510
Samir Ghaoui (Gen Mgr)

Expeditors International B.V. (1)
Naritaweg 1, 1437 EL, Rozenburg, Netherlands
Tel.: (31) 88 397 3000
Web Site: http://www.expeditors.com
Freight Transportation Arrangement Services
N.A.I.C.S.: 488510

Expeditors International Bahrain (SPC) (1)
Office No 111 Gate No 23 Avenue No 20 Area No 224 GLS Compound, Muharraq, 75865, Bahrain
Tel.: (973) 1 753 2288
Web Site: http://www.expeditors.com
Emp.: 12
Logistic Services
N.A.I.C.S.: 488510

Expeditors International CR s.r.o. (1)
Aviaticka 12 Prague 6 Ruzyne, 160 08, Prague, Czech Republic
Tel.: (420) 233090300
Logistics & Freight Forwarding Services
N.A.I.C.S.: 541614

Expeditors International Cargo Co. Ltd. (1)
Bldg 484 Ibn Jabbara St Dobbat Dist, PO Box 92788, Al Malaz, Riyadh, 11663, Saudi Arabia
Tel.: (966) 114777726
Freight Transportation Arrangement Services
N.A.I.C.S.: 488510

Expeditors International E.I. (Switzerland) Sagl (1)
Viale Serfontana 10, 6834, Morbio Inferiore, Ticino, Switzerland
Tel.: (41) 91 695 7170
Web Site: http://www.expeditors.com
Logistics & Warehousing Services
N.A.I.C.S.: 541614

Expeditors International Espana, S.A. (1)
Tel.: (34) 917480707
Sales Range: $25-49.9 Million
Emp.: 20
Transportation Arrangement Services

N.A.I.C.S.: 488510
Diego Diaz (Branch Mgr)

Expeditors International Forwarding and Clearing (Abu Dhabi) LLC (1)
Salam / Electra Street Intersection Al Salmeen Golden Tower Suite 803, PO Box 51473, Abu Dhabi, United Arab Emirates
Tel.: (971) 26723003
Logistics & Freight Forwarding Services
N.A.I.C.S.: 541614

Expeditors International Forwarding and Clearing, LLC (1)
5096 - 5098 Cargo Meg Terminal Building, PO Box 60844, Cargo Village, Dubai, United Arab Emirates
Tel.: (971) 47034800
Web Site: http://www.expeditors.com
Emp.: 100
Freight Transportation Arrangement
N.A.I.C.S.: 488510

Expeditors International France, SAS (1)
Tel.: (33) 149195050
Freight Transportation Arrangement Services
N.A.I.C.S.: 488510
Mussel Tess (Pres)

Expeditors International GmbH (1)
Monchhofallee 10, 65479, Raunheim, Germany
Tel.: (49) 614283510
Web Site: http://www.expeditors.com
Freight Transportation Arrangement Services
N.A.I.C.S.: 488510

Expeditors International Hellas A.E. (1)
162-166 Sygrou Avenue, 17671, Athens, Greece
Tel.: (30) 2109242359
Logistics & Freight Forwarding Services
N.A.I.C.S.: 541614

Expeditors International Hungary Kft. (1)
Tel.: (36) 29552600
Sales Range: $25-49.9 Million
Emp.: 50
Freight Transportation Arrangement Services
N.A.I.C.S.: 488510

Expeditors International Italia S.r.l. (1)
Via Gorizia 1/B, Seggiano di, 20096, Pioltello, MI, Italy
Tel.: (39) 02006301
Emp.: 80
Freight Transportation Services
N.A.I.C.S.: 488510
Franco Zasserri (Deputy Mgr)

Expeditors International N.V. (1)
Bedrijvenzone Machelen-Cargo 834, 1830, Machelen, Belgium
Tel.: (32) 2 447 5400
Web Site: http://www.expeditors.com
Sales Range: $25-49.9 Million
Emp.: 35
Freight Transportation Arrangement Services
N.A.I.C.S.: 488510

Expeditors International Norway AS (1)
Brages Veg 8 Gardermoen, 2060, Jessheim, Akershus, Norway
Tel.: (47) 63928300
Web Site: http://www.expeditors.com
Sales Range: $25-49.9 Million
Emp.: 17
Freight Transportation Arrangement Services
N.A.I.C.S.: 488510

Expeditors International Ocean, Inc. (1)
5200 W Century Blvd Fl 6, Los Angeles, CA 90045
Tel.: (310) 343-6200
Logistic Services
N.A.I.C.S.: 541614

Expeditors International Pty. Limited (1)

Grange Business Park Units 3 & 4 8 Tomlinson Road, Welshpool, 6106, WA, Australia
Tel.: (61) 89 361 6661
Web Site: http://www.expeditors.com
Sales Range: $25-49.9 Million
Emp.: 15
Freight Transportation Arrangement Services
N.A.I.C.S.: 488510

Expeditors International Romania S.R.L. (1)
172-176 Bucuresti-Ploiesti Street B2 Building 3rd Floor, Bucharest, 015016, Romania
Tel.: (40) 21 206 2681
Web Site: http://www.expeditors.com
Emp.: 60
Freight Transportation Arrangement
N.A.I.C.S.: 488510

Expeditors International SA (Proprietary) Limited (1)
892 Umgeni Road Lion Match Office Park 4th Floor Unit 30, Durban, 4001, South Africa
Tel.: (27) 314760987
Logistics & Freight Forwarding Services
N.A.I.C.S.: 541614

Expeditors International Sverige AB (1)
Kanalvagen 12 6th Floor, 194 61, Upplands Vasby, Sweden
Tel.: (46) 859125000
Web Site: http://www.expeditors.com
Emp.: 30
Logistic Services
N.A.I.C.S.: 488510

Expeditors International Tasimacilik ve Ticaret As (1)
Logistic Services
N.A.I.C.S.: 541614

Expeditors International Trading (Shanghai) Co., Ltd (1)
No 1 Lane 128 Linhong Rd, Changning District, Shanghai, 200335, China
Tel.: (86) 2152574698
Transportation Arrangement Services
N.A.I.C.S.: 488510

Expeditors International de Mexico, S.A. de C.V. (1)
Avenida Isidoro Sepulveda 535, 66633, Apodaca, Mexico
Tel.: (52) 8150006700
Web Site: http://www.expeditors.com
Freight Transportation Arrangement Services
N.A.I.C.S.: 488510

Expeditors International de Uruguay S.A. (1)
Plaza Independencia 831 Office 811, Montevideo, 11100, Uruguay
Tel.: (598) 29024194
Logistic & Warehousing Services
N.A.I.C.S.: 541614
Claudia Richieri (Mgr-District)

Expeditors International do Brasil Ltda. (1)
Edificio 575 Norte Sul Rua Gustavo Armbrust 36 6th Floor Campinas, Sao Paulo, 13092-106, Brazil
Tel.: (55) 192 101 0707
Web Site: http://www.expeditors.com
Emp.: 100
Freight Transportation Arrangement Services
N.A.I.C.S.: 488510

Expeditors International-Jordan (1)
Zahran Street between the 5th and 6th circle Building 190 2nd floor, Amman, 11180, Jordan
Tel.: (962) 6 552 2521
Web Site: http://www.expeditors.com
Sales Range: $25-49.9 Million
Emp.: 24
Freight Transportation Arrangement Services
N.A.I.C.S.: 488510

Expeditors Ireland Limited (1)
Unit 6 Horizon Logistics Park, Harristown, Dublin, Ireland

Tel.: (353) 1 856 8800
Web Site: http://www.expeditors.com
Freight Transportation Arrangement Services
N.A.I.C.S.: 488510

Expeditors Japan KK (1)
KDX Hamamatsucho Place 5F 1-7-6 Shibakoen, Minato-Ku, Tokyo, 105-0011, Japan
Tel.: (81) 35 776 1151
Web Site: http://www.expeditors.com
Emp.: 80
Freight Transportation Arrangement Services
N.A.I.C.S.: 488510

Expeditors Korea Ltd. (1)
2F E&C Venture Dream Tower 2-cha 55 Digital-ro 33-gil, Guro-gu, Seoul, 08376, Korea (South)
Tel.: (82) 234755900
Logistics & Freight Forwarding Services
N.A.I.C.S.: 541614

Expeditors LLC (1)
Office No 81 8th Floor Super Plaza Way No 4805 Building No 340 Azaiba, Muscat, Oman
Tel.: (968) 24131100
Logistics & Freight Forwarding Services
N.A.I.C.S.: 541614

Expeditors Lithuania, UAB (1)
Dariaus ir Gireno 81, 02189, Vilnius, Lithuania
Tel.: (370) 52075802
Logistic Services
N.A.I.C.S.: 541614

Expeditors Mar y Tierra S.A. (1)
Edificio 200 Sobre la Radial Siquiares-Coyol, Alajuela, Costa Rica
Tel.: (506) 2 437 4747
Web Site: http://www.expeditors.com
Emp.: 98
Logistic Services
N.A.I.C.S.: 488510

Expeditors Panama Logistics Services, Inc. (1)
PH Prime Time Tower Oficina 25-A Calle La Rotonda, Costa del Este, Panama, Panama
Tel.: (507) 3215200
Web Site: http://www.expeditors.com
Emp.: 15
Logistic Services
N.A.I.C.S.: 541614

Expeditors Peru S.A.C. (1)
Avenue Javier Prado Oeste 203 Oficina 701, San Isidro, Lima, 27, Peru
Tel.: (51) 1 615 0707
Emp.: 50
Freight Transportation Arrangement Services
N.A.I.C.S.: 488510
Antonio Ramos (Gen Mgr)

Expeditors Philippines, Inc. (1)
Pascor Building III Pascor Drive Santo Nino, Paranaque, 1704, Metro Manila, Philippines
Tel.: (63) 28583800
Logistics & Freight Forwarding Services
N.A.I.C.S.: 541614

Expeditors Polska Sp. z o. o. (1)
Tel.: (48) 224682050
Sales Range: $25-49.9 Million
Emp.: 50
Freight Transportation Arrangement Services
N.A.I.C.S.: 488510

Expeditors Qatar LLC (1)
Salwa Road Al Waab Building C Office 1, PO Box 24522, Doha, Qatar
Tel.: (974) 44692257
Logistics & Freight Forwarding Services
N.A.I.C.S.: 541614

Expeditors Speditions GmbH (1)
Tel.: (43) 170169111
Web Site: http://www.expeditors.com
Emp.: 20
Freight Transportation Arrangement Services
N.A.I.C.S.: 488510

Expeditors Speditionsges.m.b.H. (1)
Concorde Business Park 1/B3, 2320,

Expeditors International of Washington,
Inc.—(Continued)

Schwechat, Austria
Tel.: (43) 170189111
Logistics & Freight Forwarding Services
N.A.I.C.S.: 541614

Expeditors Taiwan Co., Ltd. **(1)**
11th Floor No 181 Fu-Hsing North Road,
Taipei, Taiwan
Tel.: (886) 227132145
Logistics & Freight Forwarding Services
N.A.I.C.S.: 541614

**Expeditors Vietnam Company
Limited** **(1)**
Level 3 Savico Office Building 66 Vo Van
Tan Street Chinh Gian Ward, Thanh Khe
District, Da Nang, 511000, Vietnam
Tel.: (84) 5113749125
Logistics Management Services
N.A.I.C.S.: 541614

Expeditors de Colombia Ltda. **(1)**
Carrera 11 84A-09 Entrada Norte Oficina
401, Bogota, 110221, Colombia
Tel.: (57) 1 313 0098
Web Site: http://www.expeditors.com
Emp.: 32
Freight Transportation Arrangement Ser-
vices
N.A.I.C.S.: 488510

P.T. Expeditors Indonesia **(1)**
Jl Raya Juanda No 3, Surabaya, 61253,
Indonesia
Tel.: (62) 318666706
Logistics & Freight Forwarding Services
N.A.I.C.S.: 541614

EXPENSIFY, INC.

401 SW 5th Ave, Portland, OR 97204
Tel.: (971) 365-3939 **DE**
Web Site: https://use.expensify.com
Year Founded: 2009
EXFY—(NASDAQ)
Rev.: $169,495,000
Assets: $210,241,000
Liabilities: $113,000,000
Net Worth: $97,241,000
Earnings: ($27,009,000)
Emp.: 138
Fiscal Year-end: 12/31/22
Software Development Services
N.A.I.C.S.: 541511
Ryan Schaffer (CFO)
Anuradha Muralidharan (COO)
Jason Mills (Chief Product Officer)
Daniel Vidal (Chief Strategy Officer)
David Barrett (Founder & CEO)

EXPION360 INC.

2025 SW Deerhound Ave, Redmond,
OR 97756
Tel.: (541) 797-6714 **NV**
Web Site: https://expion360.com
Year Founded: 2016
XPON—(NASDAQ)
Rev.: $7,162,837
Assets: $16,698,931
Liabilities: $5,091,966
Net Worth: $11,606,965
Earnings: ($7,536,540)
Emp.: 25
Fiscal Year-end: 12/31/22
Lithium Battery Mtr
N.A.I.C.S.: 335910
Paul Shoun (Co-Founder, Chm, Pres
& COO)
John Yozamp (Co-Founder)
Greg Aydelott (CFO)
Brian Schaffner (CEO, Chief Bus Dev
Officer & Dir)

EXPONENT, INC.

149 Commonwealth Dr, Menlo Park,
CA 94025
Tel.: (650) 326-9400 **DE**
Web Site: https://www.exponent.com
Year Founded: 1967

EXPO—(NASDAQ)
Rev.: $513,293,000
Assets: $586,662,000
Liabilities: $265,910,000
Net Worth: $320,752,000
Earnings: $102,330,000
Emp.: 1,313
Fiscal Year-end: 12/31/22
Engineering & Scientific Consulting
Services
N.A.I.C.S.: 541614
Catherine Ford Corrigan (Pres &
CEO)
John D. Pye (Grp VP, Dir-Office &
Chief Engr-Transportation)
Brian Kundert (Chief HR Officer)
Ellen Donovan (VP-Business Devel-
opment)
Skip Ross (Founder)
Subbaiah Malladi (CTO & Principal-
Engineering)
Brad James (Principal-Engineering &
Grp VP)
Eric Anderson (VP-Finance & Ac-
counting)
Robert Caligiuri (Principal-
Engineering & VP-Corp)
Erica Lively (Principal-Engineering,
VP-Corp & Dir-Practice)
Gina Flynn (Gen Counsel & VP)
Joe Rakow (Principal-Engineering,
Grp VP & VP)
Brian McDonald (Principal-
Engineering & VP-Corp)
Fionna Mowat (Principal, VP-Corp &
Scientist)
George H. Brown (Principal-
Engineering & VP-Corp)
Richard L. Schlenker Jr. (CFO, Sec &
Exec VP)

Subsidiaries:

Exponent **(1)**
4101 SW 71st Ave, Miami, FL 33155
Tel.: (305) 661-1000
Web Site: https://www.exponent.com
Sales Range: $1-9.9 Million
Emp.: 7
Engineering Consulting
N.A.I.C.S.: 541330
Lee Swanger (Principal)

Exponent Environmental Group **(1)**
15375 SE 30th Pl Ste 250, Bellevue, WA
98007 **(100%)**
Tel.: (425) 519-8700
Web Site: http://www.exponent.com
Sales Range: $75-99.9 Million
Environmental Engineers
N.A.I.C.S.: 541690

**Exponent Failure Analysis
Associates** **(1)**
Kanzlerstrasse 4, Dusseldorf, 40472, NRW,
Germany **(100%)**
Tel.: (49) 211965890
Web Site: http://www.exponent.de
Sales Range: $10-24.9 Million
Emp.: 30
Computer Systems Design
N.A.I.C.S.: 541512

Exponent GmbH **(1)**
Kanzlerstr 4, 40472, Dusseldorf, Germany
Tel.: (49) 211965890
Web Site: http://www.exponent.de
Engineering & Scientific Consulting Ser-
vices
N.A.I.C.S.: 541330

Exponent Inc **(1)**
10850 Richmond Ave Ste 175, Houston, TX
77042
Tel.: (832) 325-5700
Web Site: https://www.exponent.com
Sales Range: $10-24.9 Million
Emp.: 8
N.A.I.C.S.: 541512

Exponent Inc. **(1)**
15615 Alton Pkwy Ste 350, Irvine, CA
92618
Tel.: (949) 242-6000

Web Site: https://www.exponent.com
Sales Range: $10-24.9 Million
Emp.: 23
Engineering Consulting
N.A.I.C.S.: 541330
Ali Reza (Office Dir-Los Angeles)

Exponent International Ltd. **(1)**
The Lenz 1st Floor Hornbeam Park, Harro-
gate, HG2 8RE, North Yorkshire, United
Kingdom
Tel.: (44) 1423853200
Web Site: http://eu.exponent.com
Sales Range: $25-49.9 Million
Emp.: 42
Engineering & Scientific Consulting Ser-
vices
N.A.I.C.S.: 541614

Exponent Limited **(1)**
Building 12W Unit 802-3 12 Science Park
West Avenue, Sha Tin, China (Hong Kong)
Tel.: (852) 52875091
Semiconductor Devices Mfr
N.A.I.C.S.: 334413

**Exponent Science and Technology
Consulting (Shanghai) Co., Ltd.** **(1)**
Suite 101 Building 1 No 1387 Zhangdong
Road, Pilot Free Trade Zone, Shanghai,
201203, China
Tel.: (86) 2131157850
Web Site: http://www.exponentchina.com
Engineering & Scientific Consulting Ser-
vices
N.A.I.C.S.: 541690

Exponent, Inc - Menlo Park **(1)**
149 Commonwealth Dr, Menlo Park, CA
94025
Tel.: (650) 326-9400
Web Site: http://www.exponent.com
Engineering & Scientific Consulting Ser-
vices
N.A.I.C.S.: 541618

Exponent, Inc., Philadelphia **(1)**
3440 Market St Ste 600, Philadelphia, PA
19104 **(100%)**
Tel.: (215) 594-8800
Web Site: https://www.exponent.com
Sales Range: $10-24.9 Million
Emp.: 55
Engineering & Scientific Consulting
N.A.I.C.S.: 541330
Lauren Ciccarelli (Mgr-Biomedical Engrg
Svcs)
Christie Bergerson (Mgr-Biomedical Engrg
& Sciences)
Derek Holyoak (Mgr-Biomedical Engrg &
Sciences)
Joseph Sala (VP)
John Struble (Principal)
Marta Villarraga (Principal)

**Exponent, Inc.- Alexandria,
Virginia** **(1)**
1800 Diagonal Rd Ste 500, Alexandria, VA
22314-2840
Tel.: (571) 227-7200
Web Site: https://www.exponent.com
Sales Range: $10-24.9 Million
Emp.: 35
N.A.I.C.S.: 541512
William L. Goodfellow (Dir-Practice)
Robert M. Freas (Principal)
Chris A. Ball (Sr Mgr)
Daniel O. Stewart (Sr Mgr)
Alec Amaralikit (Mgr)
Robert Hardison (Mgr)
Adam S. Lackey (Mgr)
Gayathri Shetty (Sr Mgr)
Mark Anderson (Principal)
Rick Reiss (VP)

Exponent, Inc.-Boston Area **(1)**
1075 Worcester St, Natick, MA
01760 **(100%)**
Tel.: (508) 652-8500
Web Site: https://www.exponent.com
Sales Range: $10-24.9 Million
Emp.: 50
Diary Research
N.A.I.C.S.: 541330
Steven B. MacLean (Dir-Practice)
Eugenia L. Kennedy (Principal)
Timothy J. Myers (Office Dir-Natick)
Jeffrey J. Croteau (Dir-Practice)
Jericho Moll (Principal)
Harri Kytomaa (VP)
Maureen Reitman (VP)

Exponent, Inc.-Chicago **(1)**
185 Hansen Ct Ste 100, Wood Dale, IL
60191 **(100%)**
Tel.: (630) 274-3200
Web Site: http://www.exponent.com
Sales Range: $10-24.9 Million
Emp.: 35
N.A.I.C.S.: 541512
John D. Martens (Office Dir-Chicago)
Atif Yardimci (Sr Mgr)
Falak Shah (Sr Engr)

Exponent, Inc.-Denver Area **(1)**
149 Commonwealth Dr, Menlo Park, CA
94025
Tel.: (650) 326-9400
Web Site: http://www.exponent.com
Sales Range: $100-124.9 Million
Emp.: 350
N.A.I.C.S.: 541512

Exponent, Inc.-Detroit Area **(1)**
39100 Country Club Dr, Farmington Hills,
MI 48331 **(100%)**
Tel.: (248) 324-9100
Web Site: https://www.exponent.com
Sales Range: $10-24.9 Million
Emp.: 25
Engineering & Scientific Consulting
N.A.I.C.S.: 541330
Bruce E. Ketcham (Sr Mgr-Vehicle Engrg)

Exponent, Inc.-Los Angeles **(1)**
5401 McConnell Ave, Los Angeles, CA
90066 **(100%)**
Tel.: (310) 754-2700
Web Site: https://www.exponent.com
Sales Range: $75-99.9 Million
Emp.: 40
Engineering Consulting
N.A.I.C.S.: 541330
Ali Reza (Dir-Office)

Exponent, Inc.-New York **(1)**
420 Lexington Ave Ste 1740, New York, NY
10170
Tel.: (212) 895-8100
Web Site: https://www.exponent.com
Sales Range: $75-99.9 Million
Emp.: 15
Scientific & Engineering Company
N.A.I.C.S.: 541330

Exponent, Inc.-Phoenix **(1)**
23445 N 19th Ave, Phoenix, AZ 85027
Tel.: (623) 582-6949
Web Site: https://www.exponent.com
Sales Range: $25-49.9 Million
Emp.: 100
N.A.I.C.S.: 541512
Sridhar Natarajan (Principal)
Jan Swart (Principal)
Zdravko Salipur (Mgr)
Brian J. Smyth (Mgr)
John Pye (Grp VP)
Michael Carhart (Principal)
Christine Raasch (Principal)
Sarah Sharpe (Principal)

EXTRA SPACE STORAGE,
INC.

2795 E Cottonwood Pkwy Ste 300,
Salt Lake City, UT 84121
Tel.: (801) 365-4600 **MD**
Web Site:
https://www.extraspace.com
Year Founded: 1977
EXR—(NYSE)
Rev.: $2,560,244,000
Assets: $27,456,262,000
Liabilities: $12,042,313,000
Net Worth: $15,413,949,000
Earnings: $803,198,000
Emp.: 7,618
Fiscal Year-end: 12/31/23
Real Estate Management Services
N.A.I.C.S.: 531390
Kenneth M. Woolley (Founder)
P. Scott Stubbs (CFO & Exec VP)
Joseph D. Margolis (CEO)
Grace Kunde (Sr VP-Acctg & Fin)
Gwyn Goodson McNeal (Chief Legal
Officer & Exec VP)
Samrat Sondhi (CMO & Exec VP)

Matthew Herrington *(COO & Exec VP)*
Zachary Dickens *(Chief Investment Officer & Exec VP)*

Subsidiaries:

Extra Space Storage LP (1)
2795 E Cottonwood Pkwy Ste 400, Salt Lake City, UT 84121
Tel.: (801) 562-5556
Real Estate Services
N.A.I.C.S.: 525990
Joe Margolis *(CEO)*

Life Storage, Inc. (1)
6467 Main St, Williamsville, NY 14221
Tel.: (716) 633-1850
Web Site: https://www.lifestorage.com
Rev.: $1,038,166,000
Assets: $7,387,730,000
Liabilities: $3,760,363,000
Net Worth: $3,627,367,000
Earnings: $358,128,000
Emp.: 2,508
Fiscal Year-end: 12/31/2022
Real Estate Investment Trust that Owns, Acquires, Develops & Manages Self-Storage Facilities
N.A.I.C.S.: 523999
David Dodman *(CFO, COO, Principal Acctg Officer & Sec)*
Kate White *(Sr VP)*

Subsidiary (Domestic):

Life Storage LP (2)
6467 Main St, Williamsville, NY 14221
Tel.: (716) 633-1850
Web Site: https://www.lifestorage.com
Rev.: $1,038,165,999
Assets: $7,387,729,999
Liabilities: $3,760,362,999
Net Worth: $3,627,366,999
Earnings: $358,127,999
Emp.: 2,508
Fiscal Year-end: 12/31/2022
Real Estate Manangement Services
N.A.I.C.S.: 531210
Joseph V. Saffire *(CEO)*

Storage Express Management, LLC (1)
227 W Dodds St, Bloomington, IN 47403
Tel.: (812) 339-6339
Web Site: http://www.storageexpress.com
Rev.: $5,000,000
Emp.: 35
General Warehousing & Storage Services
N.A.I.C.S.: 493110
Jefferson S. Shreve *(Founder)*

EXTRACTED OIL & DERIVA-TIVES CO.

713 Maryland Ave NE, Washington, DC 20002
Tel.: (123) 123-1234
Web Site:
https://www.extractedoils.com
Year Founded: 1959
ZEOT.CA—(EGX)
Sales Range: Less than $1 Million
Oil Products Mfr
N.A.I.C.S.: 311224
Hesham Mahmoud Gadalla *(Chm)*
Mohammed Refaat Hegab *(CEO & Mng Dir)*

EXTREME BIODIESEL, INC.

41593 Winchester Rd, Temecula, CA 92590
Tel.: (855) 774-4150 NV
Web Site:
http://www.extremebiodiesel.com
Year Founded: 2008
XTRM—(OTCIQ)
Biodiesel Mfr & Whslr
N.A.I.C.S.: 325414
Joseph Jay Spadafore *(Pres, Treas & Sec)*

EXTREME NETWORKS, INC.

2121 RDU Center Dr Ste 300, Morrisville, NC 27560

Tel.: (408) 579-2800 DE
Web Site:
https://www.extremenetworks.com
Year Founded: 1996
EXTR—(NASDAQ)
Rev.: $1,117,203,000
Assets: $1,042,594,000
Liabilities: $1,017,312,000
Net Worth: $25,282,000
Earnings: ($85,964,000)
Emp.: 2,656
Fiscal Year-end: 06/30/24
Broadband Network Solutions
N.A.I.C.S.: 334220
John C. Shoemaker *(Chm)*
Edward B. Meyercord III *(Pres & CEO)*
Kevin R. Rhodes *(CFO & Exec VP)*
Norman J. Rice III *(Chief Comml Officer)*
Nabil Bukhari *(CTO, Chief Product Officer & Gen Mgr-Subscription Bus)*
Stan Kovler *(VP-IR & Strategy)*
Kimberley Basnight *(VP-Talent & Head-Diversity & Inclusion)*
Kevin R. Rhodes *(CFO & Exec VP)*
Monica Kumar *(CMO & Exec VP)*
Katy Motiey *(Chief Admin Officer & Chief Sustainability Officer)*

Subsidiaries:

Aerohive Networks, Inc. (1)
1011 McCarthy Blvd, Milpitas, CA 95035 (81.14%)
Tel.: (408) 510-6100
Web Site: http://www.aerohive.com
Rev.: $154,909,000
Assets: $141,517,000
Liabilities: $123,909,000
Net Worth: $17,608,000
Earnings: ($18,337,000)
Emp.: 460
Fiscal Year-end: 12/31/2018
Computer Networking Services
N.A.I.C.S.: 518210
Alan Cuellar Amrod *(Sr VP & Gen Mgr-Product & Sls)*
Ben Moebes *(VP-Channel Sls)*

Subsidiary (Non-US):

Aerohive Networks Europe Ltd (2)
The Courtyard 16-18 West Street, Farnham, GU9 7DR, Surrey, United Kingdom
Tel.: (44) 1252736590
Software Development Services
N.A.I.C.S.: 541511

Extreme Networks Australia PTE, Ltd. (1)
Level 11 100 Walker Street, North Sydney, 2060, NSW, Australia
Tel.: (61) 290606438
Web Site: https://au.extremenetworks.com
Sales Range: $100-124.9 Million
Developer of Infrastructure Systems
N.A.I.C.S.: 561499

Extreme Networks B.V. (1)
Kernkade 2 Lage Weide, Utrecht, 3542, Netherlands
Tel.: (31) 308005100
Web Site: http://www.extremenetworks.com
Sales Range: $100-124.9 Million
Emp.: 30
Developer of Network Infrastructure Systems
N.A.I.C.S.: 541512

Extreme Networks Canada, Inc. (1)
6205 Airport Rd, Mississauga, L4V 1E1, ON, Canada
Tel.: (905) 672-0999
Network Infrastructure Equipment & Services
N.A.I.C.S.: 334220
Stephen Patak *(VP-Sls)*

Extreme Networks China Ltd. (1)
Floor 31 Jiamei Center No 16 Room 3115 Guangshun South Avenue, Chaoyang District, Beijing, 100013, China
Tel.: (86) 1065393900
Sales Range: $100-124.9 Million
Emp.: 10

Development of Network Infrastructure Systems
N.A.I.C.S.: 541512
Gary Newbold *(Sr VP-Asia Pacific)*

Extreme Networks GmbH (1)
Tel.: (49) 69478600
Web Site: https://de.extremenetworks.com
Sales Range: $10-24.9 Million
Emp.: 15
Developer of Network Infrastructure Services
N.A.I.C.S.: 541512

Extreme Networks Hong Kong Ltd. (1)
5/F 77 Hoi Bun Road, The Quayside, Kowloon, China (Hong Kong)
Tel.: (852) 25171123
Sales Range: $100-124.9 Million
Emp.: 5
Developer of Infrastructure Systems
N.A.I.C.S.: 561499

Extreme Networks Japan, K.K. (1)
Daido Life Kasumigaseki Building 11F 1-4-2 Kasumigaseki, Chiyoda-ku, Tokyo, 100-0013, Japan
Tel.: (81) 358424011
Web Site: https://jp.extremenetworks.com
Sales Range: $100-124.9 Million
Developer of Infrastructure Systems
N.A.I.C.S.: 561499

Extreme Networks Mexico, SA de CV (1)
Calz Gral Mariano Escobedo 526 Office 1042 Floor 10, Col Anzures Miguel Hidalgo, 11590, Mexico, Mexico
Tel.: (52) 5588974964
Software Development Services
N.A.I.C.S.: 541511

Extreme Networks Netherlands BV (1)
Kernkade 2 2nd floor Lage Weide, Utrecht, 3542 CH, Netherlands
Tel.: (31) 308005100
Communication Equipment Mfr
N.A.I.C.S.: 334210

Extreme Networks SARL (1)
120 Avenue Charles de Gaulle, 92200, Neuilly-sur-Seine, France
Tel.: (33) 141922230
Web Site: http://fr.extremenetworks.com
Wireless Internet Providing Services
N.A.I.C.S.: 517112

Extreme Networks Spain, SL (1)
Calle Acanto 22 8th floor, 28045, Madrid, Spain
Tel.: (34) 914057110
Web Site: https://es.extremenetworks.com
Wireless Internet Providing Services
N.A.I.C.S.: 517112

Extreme Networks Technology Co. (Beijing) Ltd. (1)
Unit 1507 Tower B Beijing Global Trade Center, No 36 North Third Ring Road East Dongcheng District, Beijing, 100013, China
Tel.: (86) 1065393900
Web Site: http://uk.extremenetworks.com
Communication Equipment Mfr
N.A.I.C.S.: 334210

Extreme Networks UK Limited (1)
250 Longwater Avenue Green Park, Furlong Road, Reading, RG2 6GB, Buckinghamshire, United Kingdom
Tel.: (44) 1189291200
Web Site: https://uk.extremenetworks.com
Sales Range: $25-49.9 Million
Emp.: 15
Computer Networking & Cables Sales & Service
N.A.I.C.S.: 423690

EXXE GROUP, INC.

1345 Ave of the Americas 2nd Fl, New York, NY 10105
Tel.: (416) 419-0596
Web Site:
https://www.exxegroup.com
AXXA—(OTCIQ)
Rev.: $15,341,000
Assets: $192,763,000

Liabilities: $162,479,000
Net Worth: $30,284,000
Earnings: $3,556,000
Emp.: 25
Fiscal Year-end: 03/31/20
All Other Telecommunications
N.A.I.C.S.: 517810
Paul Phillips *(Pres & CEO)*
Dave Fenwick *(VP-Ops & Customer Svc)*
Jose Fernandez *(Sec)*
Jason Cataldo *(Pres & CEO)*

EXXON MOBIL CORPORATION

22777 Springwoods Village Pkwy, Spring, TX 77389-1425
Tel.: (972) 940-6000 NJ
Web Site:
https://corporate.exxonmobil.com
Year Founded: 1859
XOM—(NYSE)
Rev.: $344,582,000,000
Assets: $376,317,000,000
Liabilities: $163,779,000,000
Net Worth: $212,538,000,000
Earnings: $36,010,000,000
Emp.: 61,500
Fiscal Year-end: 12/31/23
Holding Company; Petroleum & Natural Gas Products & Operations
N.A.I.C.S.: 551112
Kathryn A. Mikells *(CFO & Sr VP)*
Darren W. Woods *(Chm, Pres & CEO)*
Len M. Fox *(VP & Controller)*
Robert P. Williams *(Sr VP)*

Subsidiaries:

Castle Peak Power Company Limited (1)
147 Argyle St, Kowloon, China (Hong Kong)
Tel.: (852) 26788111
Power Transmission Services
N.A.I.C.S.: 221121

Cross Timbers Energy Services, Inc. (1)
810 Houston St Ste 2000, Fort Worth, TX 76102
Tel.: (817) 870-2800
Web Site: http://www.xtoenergy.com
Petrochemical Mfr
N.A.I.C.S.: 325110

Denbury Inc. (1)
5851 Legacy Cir, Plano, TX 75024
Tel.: (972) 673-2000
Web Site: https://www.denbury.com
Rev.: $1,714,659,000
Assets: $2,327,499,000
Liabilities: $794,882,000
Net Worth: $1,532,617,000
Earnings: $480,160,000
Emp.: 765
Fiscal Year-end: 12/31/2022
Holding Company; Oil & Natural Gas Exploration, Development, Drilling & Extraction
N.A.I.C.S.: 551112
Mark C. Allen *(CFO, Treas, Exec VP & Asst Sec)*
Dan E. Cole *(VP-Comml Dev & Govt Rels)*
Alan Rhoades *(Chief Acctg Officer & VP)*
James S. Matthews *(Chief Admin Officer, Gen Counsel, Sec & Exec VP)*
John Filiatrault *(Sr VP-Ops Svcs)*
Steve McLaurin *(CIO & VP)*
Matthew Dahan *(Sr VP-Bus Dev & Tech)*
David Sheppard *(Sr VP-Ops)*
Jenny Cochran *(Sr VP-HR)*
Chris Hibbetts *(VP-Fin)*
Nicole H. Jennings *(VP-Plng)*
Randy J. Robichaux *(VP-Health, Safety & Environmental)*
Nikulas J. Wood *(VP-North Reg)*

Subsidiary (Domestic):

Denbury Green Pipeline - Texas, LLC (2)
5320 Legacy Dr, Plano, TX 75024-3127
Tel.: (972) 673-2000
Crude Petroleum & Natural Gas Production Services

Exxon Mobil Corporation—(Continued)

Denbury Operating Company (2)
5320 Legacy Dr, Plano, TX 75024-4932
Tel.: (972) 673-2000
Web Site: http://www.denbury.com
Sales Range: $1-4.9 Billion
Emp.: 500
Oil & Natural Gas Exploration, Development, Drilling & Extraction
N.A.I.C.S.: 211120

EMA Lubricants Co. Ltd. (1)
PO Box 22316, Sharjah, United Arab Emirates
Tel.: (971) 65062600
Web Site: https://www.mobiluae.com
Sales Range: $75-99.9 Million
Lubricant Marketer & Distr
N.A.I.C.S.: 213112
Samy El Ansary (Gen Mgr)

ESSO Deutschland GmbH (1)
Caffamacherreihe 5, 20355, Hamburg, Germany (100%)
Tel.: (49) 6950071428
Web Site: https://www.esso.de
Sales Range: $75-99.9 Million
Emp.: 300
Building & Maintenace of Gas Pump Stations
N.A.I.C.S.: 213112

Ellora Energy Inc. (1)
4410 Arapahoe Ave Ste 100, Boulder, CO 80303
Tel.: (303) 444-8881
Oil & Gas Exploration Services
N.A.I.C.S.: 211120

Esso Australia Pty Ltd (1)
Level 9 664 Collins Street, Docklands, 3008, VIC, Australia
Tel.: (61) 392703511
Web Site: http://www.exxonmobil.com.au
Sales Range: $650-699.9 Million
Emp.: 1,275
Oil & Gas Operation Services
N.A.I.C.S.: 213112

Esso Erdgas Beteiligungsgesellschaft mbH (1)
Caffamacherreihe 5, Hamburg, 20355, Germany
Tel.: (49) 4063930
Web Site: http://www.exxonmobil.com.de
Oil & Gas Field Operating Services
N.A.I.C.S.: 213112

Esso Exploration and Production Guyana Limited (1)
00 New Market Street North Cummingsburg, Georgetown, Guyana
Tel.: (592) 2312866
Web Site: https://corporate.exxonmobil.com
Oil & Gas Exploration Services
N.A.I.C.S.: 213112

Esso Italiana S.r.l. (1)
Viale Castello della Magliana 25, 00148, Rome, Italy
Tel.: (39) 0660 2921
Web Site: https://www.exxonmobil.it
Marketing, Refining & Pipeline Transportation of Oil & Gas in Italy & Marine Transportation
N.A.I.C.S.: 486990

Esso Nederland B.V. (1)
PO Box 1, 4803 AA, Breda, Netherlands
Tel.: (31) 765291200
Web Site: http://www.esso.nl
Fuel Transport services
N.A.I.C.S.: 457210

Esso Norge AS (1)
Essovn 100, PB 2001, Tonsberg, 3103, Norway (100%)
Tel.: (47) 33377300
Web Site: http://www.esso.com
Sales Range: $150-199.9 Million
Refining, Supply & Distr of Petroleum Products
N.A.I.C.S.: 424720

Esso Norge a.s. (1)
Essoveien 100, Tolvsrod, 3153, Tonsberg, Norway (100%)

Sales Range: $600-649.9 Million
Exploration, Production, Marketing & Refining in Norway
N.A.I.C.S.: 211120
Morten Mauritzen (Mng Dir-Esso Norge & Country Mgr-ExxonMobil Co)

Esso Societe Anonyme Francaise (1)
20 rue Paul Heroult, La Defense, 92000, Nanterre, Cedex, France (100%)
Tel.: (33) 14 967 9000
Web Site: https://corporate.esso.fr
Sales Range: $100-124.9 Million
Emp.: 200
Marketing & Sales of Esso Products Throughout France
N.A.I.C.S.: 324110

Exxon Azerbaijan Limited (1)
Nizami St 96, Sabail District, Baku, AZ1000, Azerbaijan
Tel.: (994) 124982460
Oil & Gas Operation Services
N.A.I.C.S.: 213112

Exxon International Finance Company (1)
25 Ferry Road, Saint Georges, Bermuda
Tel.: (441) 4412945246
Financial Support Services
N.A.I.C.S.: 522291

Exxon Mobil Corp. - Downstream Operations (1)
3225 Gallows Rd, Fairfax, VA 22037
Tel.: (703) 846-3000
Web Site: http://www2.exxonmobil.com
Sales Range: $150-199.9 Million
Modular Homes
N.A.I.C.S.: 211120

Exxon Mobil Exploration & Production Malaysia Inc. (1)
Menara Exxonmobil Kuala Lumpur City Centre, Kuala Lumpur, 50088, Malaysia
Tel.: (60) 320533000
Web Site: http://www.exxonmobil.com
Sales Range: $650-699.9 Million
Emp.: 1,000
Petroleum Exploration & Production
N.A.I.C.S.: 211120

Exxon Mobil Global Services (1)
800 Bell St, Houston, TX 77002-7497
Tel.: (713) 656-3636
Web Site:
    http://www.exxonmobilchemical.com
Sales Range: $250-299.9 Million
Petroleum Refiner
N.A.I.C.S.: 211120

Exxon Mobil Petroleum Chemical (1)
Hermeslaan 2, 1831, Machelen, Belgium (100%)
Tel.: (32) 22393111
Web Site: http://www.exxonmobil.be
Sales Range: $650-699.9 Million
Emp.: 1,300
Chemical, Petrochemical Products & Hydrocarbons Mfr & Refiner
N.A.I.C.S.: 324110

Exxon Neftegas Limited (1)
28 Sakhalinskaya St, Yuzhno-Sakhalinsk, 693000, Russia
Tel.: (7) 4242677000
Web Site: http://www.sakhalin-1.com
Oil & Gas Operation Services
N.A.I.C.S.: 213112

ExxonMobil (China) Investment Co., Ltd. (1)
Room 801 8/F China World Tower 1, No.1 Jianguomenwai Avenue, Beijing, 100004, China
Tel.: (86) 10 5965 7385
Oil & Gas Operation Services
N.A.I.C.S.: 213112
Paul Arthur Theys (Chm & Sr VP)

ExxonMobil Aircraft Operations (1)
44760 Cockpit Ct, Dulles, VA 20166-7710 (100%)
Tel.: (703) 661-3850
Sales Range: $25-49.9 Million
Emp.: 10
Scheduled Air Transportation
N.A.I.C.S.: 457120

ExxonMobil Asia Pacific Pte Ltd. (1)
1 HarbourFront Place HarbourFront Tower One 06-00, Singapore, 098633, Singapore
Tel.: (65) 68858000
Web Site: https://www.exxonmobil.com.sg
Sales Range: $1-4.9 Billion
Emp.: 4,000
Refining & Marketing of Petroleum & Petroleum Products for Export & for Singapore Market
N.A.I.C.S.: 324110

ExxonMobil Australia Pty Ltd (1)
Level 9 664 Collins Street, Docklands, 3008, VIC, Australia
Tel.: (61) 392610000
Web Site: http://www.exxonmobil.com.au
Petroleum Product Distr
N.A.I.C.S.: 424720

ExxonMobil Canada Ltd. (1)
237 4 Avenue Southwest, Calgary, T2P 3M9, AB, Canada
Tel.: (403) 260-7910
Web Site:
    http://www.corporate.exxonmobil.com
Oil & Gas Operation Services
N.A.I.C.S.: 213112

ExxonMobil Canada Properties (1)
237 4 Ave Sw Suite 4063, Calgary, T2P 0H6, AB, Canada
Tel.: (403) 232-5300
Oil Gas Exploration
N.A.I.C.S.: 213111

ExxonMobil Central Europe Holding GmbH (1)
Caffamacherreihe 5, 20355, Hamburg, Germany (100%)
Tel.: (49) 406 3930
Web Site: https://corporate.exxonmobil.de
Sales Range: $800-899.9 Million
Emp.: 400
Holding Company; Refining, Marketing & Pipeline Transportation of Petroleum Products in Germany; Exploration & Production through BRIGITTA & Elwerath
N.A.I.C.S.: 551112

Holding (Domestic):

Mobil Oil A.G. (2)
Caffamacherreihe 5, 20355, Hamburg, Germany (100%)
Tel.: (49) 4063930
Web Site: http://www.esso.de
Petroleum Refining
N.A.I.C.S.: 324110

ExxonMobil Chemical Company (1)
22777 Springwoods Village Pkwy, Spring, TX 77389-1425
Tel.: (281) 870 6000
Web Site:
    http://www.exxonmobilchemical.com
Sales Range: $25-49.9 Billion
Emp.: 14,000
Petrochemicals
N.A.I.C.S.: 325110
Karen McKee (Pres)

Subsidiary (Domestic):

ExxonMobil Chemical Company (2)
388 S Main St, Akron, OH 44311
Tel.: (330) 849-5750
Web Site:
    http://www.exxonmobilchemical.com
Sales Range: $125-149.9 Million
Emp.: 100
Thermoplastic Elastomer Mfr
N.A.I.C.S.: 326199

ExxonMobil Chemical Company - Film Div. (2)
111 Pegasus Pkwy, LaGrange, GA 30240-5824 (100%)
Tel.: (706) 883-1908
Web Site: http://www.exxonmobil.com
Sales Range: $75-99.9 Million
Emp.: 150
Mfr Of Plastics & Polymers
N.A.I.C.S.: 326113

ExxonMobil Chemical Company - Mont Belvieu Plastics Plant (2)
13330 Hatcherville Rd, Mont Belvieu, TX 77580
Tel.: (281) 834-9400

Web Site: http://www.exxonmobil.com
Sales Range: $75-99.9 Million
Emp.: 250
Plastics Materials And Resins
N.A.I.C.S.: 325211

Branch (Domestic):

ExxonMobil Chemical Company Inc. (2)
4999 Scenic Hwy, Baton Rouge, LA 70805-3359
Tel.: (225) 977-7711
Sales Range: $900-999.9 Million
Emp.: 1,500
Chemical Products Mfr; Petroleum Refining
N.A.I.C.S.: 325998

ExxonMobil Chemical Company Inc. (2)
37567 Interchange Dr, Farmington Hills, MI 48335
Tel.: (248) 350-6500
Sales Range: $50-74.9 Million
Emp.: 50
Automotive Lubricants
N.A.I.C.S.: 211120

ExxonMobil Chemical Company Inc. (2)
11440 Hwy 90, Beaumont, TX 77713-3486
Tel.: (409) 866-3711
Web Site: http://www.exxonmobil.com
Sales Range: $150-199.9 Million
Emp.: 325
Chemical Preparations
N.A.I.C.S.: 325998

ExxonMobil Chemical Company Inc. (2)
9822 La Porte Fwy, Houston, TX 77017 (100%)
Tel.: (281) 870-6050
Web Site: http://www.exxonmobil.com
Sales Range: $75-99.9 Million
Emp.: 150
Mfr of Plastics Materials & Resins
N.A.I.C.S.: 325211

Joint Venture (Non-US):

Infineum International Ltd. (2)
Milton Hill Business and Technology Centre, PO Box 1, Abingdon, OX13 6BB, Oxfordshire, United Kingdom
Tel.: (44) 1235549500
Web Site: http://www.infineum.com
Sales Range: $150-199.9 Million
Lubricant Additives Mfr; Owned 50% by ExxonMobil Chemical Company & 50% by The Shell Petroleum Co. Ltd.
N.A.I.C.S.: 324191

ExxonMobil Chemical Films Canada, Ltd. (1)
321 University Avenue, Belleville, K8N 5t7, ON, Canada (100%)
Tel.: (613) 966-5533
Web Site: http://www.exxonmobil.com
Sales Range: $50-74.9 Million
Emp.: 180
Mfr of Polypropylene Films
N.A.I.C.S.: 326113

ExxonMobil Chemical Holland B.V. (1)
Merwedeweg 21 havennummer 5625, PO Box 5625, Europoort, 3198 LH, Rotterdam, Netherlands
Tel.: (31) 104933600
Web Site: http://www.exxonmobil.be
Emp.: 140
Chemical Products Mfr
N.A.I.C.S.: 325199

ExxonMobil Chemical Limited (1)
Marsh Lane Fawley, Southampton, SO45 1TX, Hampshire, United Kingdom (100%)
Tel.: (44) 2380892511
Web Site: http://www.exxonmobil.com
Sales Range: $1-4.9 Billion
Emp.: 3,000
Sale & Marketing of Light Polyolefins & Intermediate Chemicals
N.A.I.C.S.: 424690

ExxonMobil Chemical Operations Private Limited (1)
1 HarbourFront Place HarbourFront Tower

One 06-00, Singapore, 098633,
Singapore   **(100%)**
Tel.: (65) 68858000
Web Site: http://www.exxonmobil.com
Rev.: $60,000,000
Emp.: 3,500
Fuels & Lubricants Refiner & Supplier
N.A.I.C.S.: 324110

**ExxonMobil Coal and Minerals
Company**   **(1)**
3803 S Gessner Rd, Houston, TX 77063-
2005
Tel.: (281) 870-6050
Web Site: http://www.exxonipa.com
Sales Range: $150-199.9 Million
Emp.: 300
Coordinator & Provider of Operational Re-
sponsibilities for Coal & Nonhydrocarbon
Minerals Activities Except for Uranium Ox-
ide Marketing & Fabrication
N.A.I.C.S.: 445131

ExxonMobil Corporation   **(1)**
1795 Bert St, Beaumont, TX
77702   **(100%)**
Tel.: (409) 833-9411
Sales Range: $1-4.9 Billion
Emp.: 1,500
Crude Petroleum Production
N.A.I.C.S.: 211120

ExxonMobil Corporation   **(1)**
25230 Front Rdg Rd, Kaplan, LA 70548
Tel.: (337) 737-2505
Web Site: http://www.exxon.com
Sales Range: $10-24.9 Million
Emp.: 8
Production of Crude Petroleum & Natural
Gas
N.A.I.C.S.: 211120

ExxonMobil Corporation   **(1)**
9700 Ctr Point Dr Ste 600, Anchorage, AK
99503-3958   **(100%)**
Tel.: (907) 561-5331
Web Site: http://www.exxonmobil.com
Sales Range: $25-49.9 Million
Emp.: 30
Oil Field Services
N.A.I.C.S.: 213112

ExxonMobil Corporation   **(1)**
1513 Farm Rd, New London, TX 75682
Tel.: (903) 895-4433
Web Site: http://www.exxonmobil.com
Sales Range: $10-24.9 Million
Emp.: 4
Crude Petroleum Production
N.A.I.C.S.: 211120

ExxonMobil Corporation   **(1)**
3525 Decker Dr, Baytown, TX 77520-1646
Tel.: (281) 834-6161
Web Site: http://www.exxonmobil.com
Sales Range: $50-74.9 Million
Emp.: 210
Chemical Laboratory, Except Testing
N.A.I.C.S.: 541715

ExxonMobil Corporation   **(1)**
1301 Fannin St, Houston, TX 77002-7014
Tel.: (713) 656-3636
Sales Range: $100-124.9 Million
Emp.: 450
Computer Processing Services
N.A.I.C.S.: 518210

ExxonMobil Corporation   **(1)**
2001 Pennsylvania Ave NW, Washington,
DC 20006   **(100%)**
Tel.: (202) 862-0200
Web Site: http://www.exxonmobil.com
Sales Range: $10-24.9 Million
Emp.: 25
Public Relations & Publicity
N.A.I.C.S.: 541820

ExxonMobil Corporation   **(1)**
33 Mi NE Of Kemmerer, Kemmerer, WY
83101
Tel.: (307) 276-6200
Web Site: http://www.exxonmobil.com
Sales Range: $50-74.9 Million
Emp.: 180
Petroleum Production Plant
N.A.I.C.S.: 221210

ExxonMobil Corporation   **(1)**
17 Miles NW Of Labarge Rd, La Barge, WY
83123

Tel.: (307) 276-6300
Web Site: http://www.exxon.com
Sales Range: $25-49.9 Million
Emp.: 30
Gas Producers, Generators & other Gas
Related Equipment
N.A.I.C.S.: 333998

ExxonMobil Corporation   **(1)**
1470 Hwy 317, Franklin, LA 70538-7426
Tel.: (337) 836-5637
Web Site: http://www.exxonmobil.com
Sales Range: $25-49.9 Million
Emp.: 5
Provider of Liquefied Petroleum & Natural
Gases Production
N.A.I.C.S.: 211130

ExxonMobil Corporation   **(1)**
1601 Safe Energy Dr, Port Allen, LA 70767
Tel.: (225) 344-2901
Sales Range: $10-24.9 Million
Emp.: 5
Natural Gas Production
N.A.I.C.S.: 211130

ExxonMobil Corporation   **(1)**
14 Mile West of Kingsville, Kingsville, TX
78364   **(100%)**
Tel.: (361) 595-9212
Web Site: http://www.exxonmobil.com
Sales Range: $50-74.9 Million
Emp.: 72
Crude Petroleum Production
N.A.I.C.S.: 211120

ExxonMobil Corporation   **(1)**
12 Hampton Ct, Skillman, NJ
08558-1808   **(100%)**
Tel.: (908) 874-3535
Sales Range: $25-49.9 Million
Emp.: 1
Chemical & Allied Products
N.A.I.C.S.: 424690
Dan Collins *(Mgr)*

ExxonMobil Corporation   **(1)**
Hwy 90 A W, Hallettsville, TX 77964
Tel.: (361) 798-9700
Web Site: http://www.exxonmobil.com
Sales Range: $25-49.9 Million
Emp.: 12
Natural Gasoline Production
N.A.I.C.S.: 211130

ExxonMobil Corporation   **(1)**
End of Sycamore St, Beaumont, TX 77701
Tel.: (409) 757-3763
Web Site: http://www.exxonmobil.com
Sales Range: $75-99.9 Million
Emp.: 160
Industrial Packaging
N.A.I.C.S.: 423840

ExxonMobil Corporation   **(1)**
5201 Rock Rd, Coden, AL 36523 **(100%)**
Tel.: (251) 873-2200
Web Site: http://www.exxonmobil.com
Sales Range: $50-74.9 Million
Emp.: 65
Produce & Distribute Crude Petroleum &
Natural Gas
N.A.I.C.S.: 211120

ExxonMobil Egypt (S.A.E.)   **(1)**
PO Box 182, Magless El Shaab, Cairo,
Egypt   **(99.28%)**
Tel.: (20) 2 791 6200
Web Site: https://egypt.exxonmobil.com
Sales Range: $150-199.9 Million
Marketing of Petroleum Products
N.A.I.C.S.: 424720

ExxonMobil Exploration   **(1)**
233 Benmar, Houston, TX 77060
Tel.: (281) 654-7473
Web Site: http://www.exxonipa.com
Sales Range: $300-349.9 Million
Exploration of Petroleum & Natural Gas
N.A.I.C.S.: 211120

**ExxonMobil Exploration & Production
Malaysia Inc.**   **(1)**
Menara Exxonmobil Kuala Lumpur City
Centre, 50088, Kuala Lumpur, 50088, Ma-
laysia
Tel.: (60) 320533000
Oil & Gas Field Operating Services
N.A.I.C.S.: 213112

**ExxonMobil Exploration and Produc-
tion Norway AS**   **(1)**

Essoveien 100, Tolvsrod, 3153, Tonsberg,
Norway
Tel.: (47) 51638100
Web Site: http://www.exxonmobil.no
Oil & Gas Operation Services
N.A.I.C.S.: 213112

**ExxonMobil Finance Company
Limited**   **(1)**
Ermyn House Ermyn Way, Leatherhead,
KT22 8UX, United Kingdom
Tel.: (44) 1372222162
Financial Services
N.A.I.C.S.: 541611

ExxonMobil Finland Oy A.B.   **(1)**
Satamatie 10, 21100, Naantali, Finland
Tel.: (358) 10408500
Web Site: https://corporate.exxonmobil.com
Sales Range: $150-199.9 Million
Oil & Gas Field Services
N.A.I.C.S.: 213112

ExxonMobil Fuels & Marketing   **(1)**
3225 Gallows Rd, Fairfax, VA
22037   **(100%)**
Tel.: (703) 846-2827
Web Site: http://www.exxonmobil.com
Sales Range: $450-499.9 Million
Marketing & Refining
N.A.I.C.S.: 424720

**ExxonMobil Gas Marketing
Deutschland GmbH**   **(1)**
Caffamacherreihe 5, 20355, Hamburg, Ger-
many
Tel.: (49) 5116416202
Web Site: http://www.exxonmobil.com
Oil & Gas Exploration Services
N.A.I.C.S.: 213112

**ExxonMobil Gas Marketing Europe
Limited**   **(1)**
Ermyn House Ermyn Way, Leatherhead,
KT22 8UX, Surrey, United Kingdom
Tel.: (44) 1372222000
Web Site: http://www.exxonmobil.co.uk
Emp.: 600
Oil & Gas Operation Services
N.A.I.C.S.: 213112

**ExxonMobil Global Services
Company**   **(1)**
800 Bell St Ste 2441, Houston, TX 77002
Tel.: (713) 656-3636
Professional Scientific & Technical Services
N.A.I.C.S.: 541990

ExxonMobil Hong Kong Limited   **(1)**
Central Plaza 18 Harbour Road, Wanchai,
China (Hong Kong)
Tel.: (852) 21728300
Web Site: http://www.exxonmobil.com.hk
Petroleum Product Distr
N.A.I.C.S.: 424720

**ExxonMobil International Holdings
Inc.**   **(1)**
5959 Las Colinas Blvd, Irving, TX 75039
Tel.: (972) 444-1000
Holding Company
N.A.I.C.S.: 551112

ExxonMobil International Limited   **(1)**
Tel.: (44) 2071361798
Web Site: http://www.exxonmobil.co.uk
Sales Range: $150-199.9 Million
Emp.: 800
Gas Exploration, Production & Marketing
Services
N.A.I.C.S.: 211120

ExxonMobil Italiana Gas S.r.l.   **(1)**
Viale Castello della Magliana 25, Rome,
00148, Italy
Tel.: (39) 06659661
Web Site: http://www.exxonmobil.it
Gas Fuel Station Operating Services
N.A.I.C.S.: 457120

**ExxonMobil Lubricants & Petroleum
Specialties**   **(1)**
3225 Gallows Rd, Fairfax, VA 22037-0001
Tel.: (703) 846-3000
Web Site: http://www.exxonmobil.com
Sales Range: $150-199.9 Million
Lubricants & Petroleum Specialties
N.A.I.C.S.: 424720

ExxonMobil Marine Limited   **(1)**

Mailpoint 29 Ermyn House Ermyn Way,
Leatherhead, KT22 8UX, Surrey, United
Kingdom
Tel.: (44) 1372222000
Lubricant Distr
N.A.I.C.S.: 457210

ExxonMobil Mexico S.A. de C.V.   **(1)**
Poniente 146 Colonia Industrial Vallejo,
02300, Mexico, DF, Mexico
Tel.: (52) 5553540500
Web Site: https://corporate.exxonmobil.com
Lubricants Oils & Greases Mfr
N.A.I.C.S.: 324191

ExxonMobil Oil Corporation   **(1)**
1741 Ed Temple Blvd, Nashville, TN 37208-
1811
Tel.: (615) 244-7671
Sales Range: $10-24.9 Million
Emp.: 4
Mixed Natural & Manufactured Gas Except
Petroleum
N.A.I.C.S.: 221210

ExxonMobil Oil Corporation   **(1)**
I55 Arsenal Rd PO Box 874, Channahon, IL
60434
Tel.: (815) 521-5571
Web Site: http://www.exxonmobil.com
Sales Range: $1-4.9 Billion
Emp.: 630
Petroleum Refining
N.A.I.C.S.: 324110

ExxonMobil Oil Corporation   **(1)**
3033 Irving Blvd, Dallas, TX 75247-6204
Tel.: (214) 951-2000
Web Site: http://www.exxonmobil.com
Sales Range: $1-4.9 Billion
Emp.: 2,000
Data Processing Services
N.A.I.C.S.: 493110

ExxonMobil Oil Corporation   **(1)**
1150 Spangler Blvd, Fort Lauderdale, FL
33316
Tel.: (954) 713-3300
Web Site: http://www.exxonmobil.com
Sales Range: $25-49.9 Million
Emp.: 7
Distribution of Gasoline
N.A.I.C.S.: 425120

ExxonMobil Oil Corporation   **(1)**
605 Burnside Ave, Inwood, NY 11096-1362
Tel.: (516) 371-5775
Sales Range: $25-49.9 Million
Emp.: 6
Fuel Oil Dealers
N.A.I.C.S.: 457210
Ravinder Singh *(Owner & Gen Mgr)*

ExxonMobil Oil Corporation   **(1)**
Mobil Rd, Hull, TX 77564
Tel.: (936) 536-3108
Web Site: http://www.exxonmobil.com
Sales Range: $10-24.9 Million
Emp.: 30
Transportation of Chemicals
N.A.I.C.S.: 486910

ExxonMobil Oil Corporation   **(1)**
67040 Sargent Rd, San Ardo, CA 93450
Tel.: (831) 627-2343
Web Site: http://www.exxonmobil.com
Sales Range: $25-49.9 Million
Emp.: 1
Crude Petroleum Pipelines
N.A.I.C.S.: 457120

ExxonMobil Oil Corporation   **(1)**
1795 Burt St, Beaumont, TX 77701
Tel.: (409) 833-9411
Sales Range: $500-549.9 Million
Emp.: 1,700
Petroleum Refining
N.A.I.C.S.: 561499

**ExxonMobil Oil Corporation Research
and Engineering**   **(1)**
600 Billingsport Rd, Paulsboro, NJ 08066-
1033
Tel.: (856) 224-0200
Web Site: http://www.exxonmobil.com
Sales Range: $75-99.9 Million
Emp.: 500
Commercial Research Laboratory
N.A.I.C.S.: 541715

ExxonMobil Oil Indonesia, Inc.   **(1)**

Exxon Mobil Corporation—(Continued)

Wisma GKB1 27th Floor Jalan Jendral
Sudirman 28, Jakarta, 10210, Indonesia
Tel.: (62) 215740707
Web Site: http://www.exxonmobil.com
Sales Range: $750-799.9 Million
Emp.: 500
Explorer & Producer of Natural Gas & Oil
N.A.I.C.S.: 211120
Muhammad Nurdin *(Sr VP-Production)*
Florentina Hatmi *(VP-Fin & Support Svcs)*
Syah Reza *(Pres-ExxonMobil Lubricants)*
Bomantara Dewa Pranoedjoe *(Mgr-Facilities)*
Tania Irani Amir Hasan *(VP-Surface Engrg)*
Intan Wirya *(VP-Subsurface Engrg)*
Kamal Singh *(Mktg Dir-Fuels)*
Egon van der Hoeven *(Sr VP-Bus Dev)*
Irtiza H. Sayyed *(Pres)*
Azi N. Alam *(VP-Pub & Govt Affairs)*
Tino Voigt *(Mgr-Asset)*
Teguh H. Susanto *(Mgr-Safety, Security, Health & Environment)*
Anung Prabawa *(Mgr-Wells Execution)*

ExxonMobil PNG Limited **(1)**
Jacksons Parade, PO Box 118, NCD, Port
Moresby, Papua New Guinea
Tel.: (675) 309 7111
Web Site: https://www.pnglng.com
Development of Gas Production & Processing Facilities
N.A.I.C.S.: 213112

ExxonMobil Pensions-
Verwaltungsgesellschaft mbH **(1)**
Caffamacherreihe 5, 20355, Hamburg,
20355, Germany
Tel.: (49) 4063930
Employee Pension Services
N.A.I.C.S.: 525110

ExxonMobil Petroleum & Chemical
BVBA **(1)**
Hermeslaan 2, Machelen, 1831, Brussels,
Belgium
Tel.: (32) 221456130
Petroleum & Chemical Mfr
N.A.I.C.S.: 325194

ExxonMobil Pipeline Company
LLC **(1)**
800 Bell St, Houston, TX 77002-7497
Tel.: (713) 656-3636
Web Site:
https://www.exxonmobilpipeline.com
Pipeline Transportation of Petroleum Products
N.A.I.C.S.: 486910
Steve Yatauro *(Pres & Ops Mgr-Americas Fuels)*

Unit (Domestic):

ExxonMobil Pipeline Company **(2)**
20004 Old Galveston Hwy, Webster, TX
77598
Tel.: (281) 332-1414
Sales Range: $10-24.9 Million
Emp.: 20
Crude Petroleum Pipelines
N.A.I.C.S.: 486110

ExxonMobil Pipeline Company **(2)**
3151 Humble Rd, Grand Isle, LA 70358
Tel.: (985) 787-2141
Web Site:
http://www.exxonmobilpipeline.com
Sales Range: $25-49.9 Million
Emp.: 15
Crude Petroleum Pipelines
N.A.I.C.S.: 486110

ExxonMobil Pipeline Company **(2)**
1460 Lafiton Ln, Port Allen, LA 70767
Tel.: (225) 383-0711
Web Site: http://www.exxonmobil.com
Sales Range: $10-24.9 Million
Emp.: 11
Crude Petroleum Pipelines
N.A.I.C.S.: 486110

ExxonMobil Pipeline Company **(2)**
110 Cemetery Rd, Bridger, MT 59014
Tel.: (832) 624-7903
Web Site:
https://www.exxonmobilpipeline.com
Sales Range: $10-24.9 Million
Emp.: 6
Crude Petroleum Transportation Services

N.A.I.C.S.: 486110

ExxonMobil Pipeline Company **(2)**
1202 Morgan St, Longview, TX 75602-2148
Tel.: (903) 236-8100
Sales Range: $1-9.9 Million
Emp.: 20
Oil & Gas Transportation
N.A.I.C.S.: 486110

ExxonMobil Pipeline Company **(2)**
10915 183rd St, Mokena, IL 60448-8973
Tel.: (708) 479-2677
Web Site: http://www.exxonmobil.com
Sales Range: $10-24.9 Million
Emp.: 2
Crude Petroleum Pipelines
N.A.I.C.S.: 486110

ExxonMobil Pipeline Company **(2)**
2975 Keller Hicks Rd, Keller, TX 76248-
9542
Tel.: (817) 431-1181
Sales Range: $10-24.9 Million
Emp.: 3
Crude Petroleum Pipelines
N.A.I.C.S.: 486110

ExxonMobil Pipeline Company **(2)**
RR 2 Box 1528, Doniphan, MO 63935-9610
Tel.: (573) 996-2516
Web Site: http://www.exxonmobil.com
Sales Range: $10-24.9 Million
Emp.: 1
Crude Petroleum Pipelines
N.A.I.C.S.: 486110

ExxonMobil Pipeline Company **(2)**
1001 Ash St, Taft, CA 93268
Tel.: (661) 763-7600
Sales Range: $25-49.9 Million
Emp.: 30
Oil & Gas Pipeline Transportation Services
N.A.I.C.S.: 486910

ExxonMobil Pipeline Company **(2)**
1942 N FM 565 Rd, Mont Belvieu, TX
77580
Web Site:
http://www.exxonmobilpipeline.com
Pipeline Transportation of Crude Oil
N.A.I.C.S.: 486110
Penny Van Der Sluys *(Gen Mgr)*

ExxonMobil Producing Netherlands
B.V. **(1)**
Graaf Engelbertlaan 75, 4837 DS, Breda,
4837 DS, Netherlands
Tel.: (31) 765291000
Oil & Gas Field Operating Services
N.A.I.C.S.: 213112

ExxonMobil Refining & Supply **(1)**
700 Exxon Mobil Rd, Billings, MT 59101
Tel.: (406) 657-5380
Web Site: http://www.exxon.com
Sales Range: $150-199.9 Million
Emp.: 250
Petroleum Refining
N.A.I.C.S.: 324110
D. G. Wascom *(Pres)*

ExxonMobil Refining & Supply
Company **(1)**
4045 Scenic Hwy, Baton Rouge, LA 70805
Tel.: (225) 977-8393
Web Site:
http://www.corporate.exxonmobil.com
Petroleum Refining
N.A.I.C.S.: 324110

ExxonMobil Research &
Engineering **(1)**
3225 Gallows Rd, Fairfax, VA 22037
Tel.: (703) 846-2568
Web Site: http://www.exxonmobil.com
Sales Range: $150-199.9 Million
Research & Engineering Services
N.A.I.C.S.: 211120

Branch (Domestic):

ExxonMobil Research &
Engineering **(2)**
1545 Route 22 E Ste 1, Annandale, NJ
08801
Tel.: (908) 730-0100
Web Site: http://www.exxonmobil.com
Sales Range: $200-249.9 Million
Emp.: 1,500
Industrial Laboratory Except Testing

N.A.I.C.S.: 541715

ExxonMobil Sales & Supply LLC **(1)**
22777 Springwoods Vlg Pkwy, Spring, TX
77389
Tel.: (703) 846-7100
Sales Range: $1-9.9 Million
Emp.: 11
Lubricant Distr
N.A.I.C.S.: 457210

ExxonMobil UK Limited **(1)**
Ermyn House Ermyn Way, Leatherhead,
KT22 8UX, Surrey, United
Kingdom **(100%)**
Tel.: (44) 1372222000
Web Site: https://www.exxonmobil.co.uk
Sales Range: $150-199.9 Million
Exploration & Production of Petroleum &
Chemical Compounds
N.A.I.C.S.: 324110

Imperial Oil Limited **(1)**
505 Quarry Park Boulevard S E, Calgary,
T2C 5N1, AB, Canada **(69.6%)**
Tel.: (403) 237-2710
Web Site: http://www.imperialoil.ca
Rev.: $46,678,647,600
Assets: $34,047,954,720
Liabilities: $16,514,713,080
Net Worth: $17,533,241,640
Earnings: $5,741,935,200
Emp.: 5,300
Fiscal Year-end: 12/31/2022
Exploration, Producing, Refining, Marketing
of Petroleum Products, Petrochemicals &
Minerals
N.A.I.C.S.: 325180
Bradley W. Corson *(Chm, Pres & CEO)*
Daniel E. Lyons *(Sr VP-Fin & Admin & Controller)*
Jonathan R. Wetmore *(VP-Downstream)*
Sherri L. Evers *(Sr VP-Sustainability, Comml Dev & Product Solutions)*
Kitty Lee *(Treas)*
Kristi L. Desjardins *(VP-HR)*
Constance D. Gemmell *(Dir-Corp Tax)*
Ian R. Laing *(Gen Counsel, Sec & VP)*

Subsidiary (Domestic):

Esso Tower **(2)**
7100 Jean Talon St East, Anjou, H1M 3R8,
QC, Canada **(100%)**
Tel.: (514) 493-7275
Web Site: http://www.imperialoil.ca
Sales Range: $125-149.9 Million
Emp.: 300
Oil Royalty Traders
N.A.I.C.S.: 523910

Branch (Domestic):

Imperial Oil Limited **(2)**
1961 Merivale Rd, Ottawa, K2G 1G1, ON,
Canada **(100%)**
Tel.: (613) 226-1660
Web Site: http://www.imperialoil.ca
Sales Range: $25-49.9 Million
Emp.: 3
Petroleum Products
N.A.I.C.S.: 424720

Imperial Oil Limited **(2)**
225 Concession 2, Nanticoke, N0A 1L0,
ON, Canada **(40%)**
Tel.: (519) 587-4992
Web Site: http://www.imperialoil.com
Sales Range: $150-199.9 Million
Emp.: 250
Petroleum Refining
N.A.I.C.S.: 324110

Imperial Oil Limited **(2)**
1160 Kelley Lk Rd, Sudbury, P3E 5P4, ON,
Canada
Tel.: (705) 673-1148
Web Site: http://www.imperialoil.ca
Petroleum Product Whslr
N.A.I.C.S.: 424720

Imperial Oil Limited **(2)**
505 Quarry Park Boulevard SE, Calgary,
T2C 5N1, AB, Canada **(69.6%)**
Web Site: https://www.imperialoil.ca
Petroleum Products & Services
N.A.I.C.S.: 424720
Theresa Redburn *(Sr VP-Commercial-Corporate Development)*
John Whelan *(Sr VP)*

Glenn Peterson *(Treas)*
Daniel Lyons *(Sr VP-Finance-Administration)*
Simon Younger *(Sr VP)*
Sherri Evers *(VP-Commercial-Corporate Development)*
Jon Wetmore *(VP)*
Ian Laing *(Sec, VP & Gen Counsel)*
Kitty Lee *(Treas)*

Imperial Oil Limited **(2)**
225 Concession 2, PO Box 500, Nanticoke,
N0A 1L0, ON, Canada **(100%)**
Tel.: (519) 587-4992
Web Site: http://www.imperialoil.ca
Sales Range: $200-249.9 Million
Emp.: 300
Petroleum Refining
N.A.I.C.S.: 324110

Imperial Oil Limited **(2)**
453 Christina St S, Sarnia, N7T 5W3, ON,
Canada **(100%)**
Tel.: (519) 339-2712
Web Site: http://www.imperialoil.ca
Sales Range: $200-249.9 Million
Emp.: 1,500
Commercial Physical Research
N.A.I.C.S.: 541715

Imperial Oil Limited **(2)**
52 Black Rd, Sault Sainte Marie, P6A 6J8,
ON, Canada **(100%)**
Tel.: (705) 256-6252
Web Site: http://sault.ontario.ovh
Sales Range: $25-49.9 Million
Emp.: 2
Distribution of Gasoline & Petroleum
N.A.I.C.S.: 424720

Imperial Oil Limited **(2)**
PO Box 90, Rainbow Lake, T0H 2Y0, AB,
Canada **(100%)**
Tel.: (780) 956-8500
Sales Range: $25-49.9 Million
Emp.: 40
Oil & Gas Field Services
N.A.I.C.S.: 213112

Division (Domestic):

Imperial Oil Limited Products &
Chemicals Division **(2)**
34th St Hwy 16 A, Edmonton, T5J 2M1, AB,
Canada **(100%)**
Tel.: (780) 449-8110
Web Site: http://www.imperialoil.ca
Sales Range: $1-4.9 Billion
Emp.: 600
Petroleum Refining
N.A.I.C.S.: 324110

Joint Venture (Domestic):

Montreal Pipe Line Limited **(2)**
10803 rue Sherbrooke Est, Montreal, H1B
1B3, QC, Canada
Tel.: (514) 645-8797
Web Site: https://www.pmpl.com
Sales Range: $10-24.9 Million
Crude Petroleum Pipelines
N.A.I.C.S.: 486110
Thomas A. Hardison *(Pres)*

Unit (Domestic):

Montreal Pipe Line Limited **(0)**
148 Rang De La Pipeline, Saint Cesaire,
J0L 1T0, QC, Canada
Tel.: (450) 469-2394
Web Site: http://www.pmpl.com
Sales Range: $10-24.9 Million
Crude Oil Transportation
N.A.I.C.S.: 486990

Subsidiary (US):

Portland Pipe Line Corporation **(3)**
30 Hill St, South Portland, ME 04106-4201
Tel.: (207) 767-0421
Web Site: http://www.pmpl.com
Sales Range: $10-24.9 Million
Crude Petroleum Pipelines
N.A.I.C.S.: 486110

J. Chris Gillies *(Treas & Sec)*

Subsidiary (Domestic):

Sky Service FBO Inc. (2)
575 Palmer Road NE, Calgary, T2E 7G4,
AB, Canada (100%)
Tel.: (403) 592-3700
Web Site: https://www.skyservice.com
Sales Range: $50-74.9 Million
Business Aviation Services
N.A.I.C.S.: 481111

Mobil Oil Australia Pty Ltd (1)
12 Riverside Quay, Southbank, 3006, VIC,
Australia (100%)
Tel.: (61) 392610000
Web Site: http://www.mobil.com.au
Sales Range: $400-449.9 Million
Emp.: 500
Marketing of Petroleum
N.A.I.C.S.: 424720

Mobil Oil Corporation (1)
1001 Billingsport Rd, Paulsboro, NJ 08066
Tel.: (856) 224-5000
Sales Range: $75-99.9 Million
Emp.: 150
Lubricant Plant
N.A.I.C.S.: 457110

Mobil Oil Corporation (1)
1795 Burt St, Beaumont, TX 77701
Tel.: (409) 833-9411
Web Site: http://www.exxonmobil.com
Sales Range: $10-24.9 Million
Emp.: 15
Purchasing Service
N.A.I.C.S.: 561499

Mobil Oil Del Peru S A R L (1)
Avenida Camino Real 456 Torre Real Piso
14 San Isidro, Lima, 27, Peru (100%)
Tel.: (51) 12212520
Sales Range: $350-399.9 Million
Emp.: 120
Petroleum Marketer
N.A.I.C.S.: 424720

Mobil Oil New Zealand Limited (1)
Building B Level 2 8 Nugent Street, Grafton,
Auckland, 1023, New Zealand
Tel.: (64) 93024700
Web Site: https://www.mobil.co.nz
Petroleum & Chemical Mfr
N.A.I.C.S.: 325194

Mobil Oil New Zealand Ltd. (1)
Building B Level 2 8 Nugent Street, Grafton,
Auckland, 1023, New Zealand (100%)
Tel.: (64) 93024700
Web Site: https://www.mobil.co.nz
Sales Range: $150-199.9 Million
Petroleum Products Marketer
N.A.I.C.S.: 424720

Mobil Oil Turk AS (1)
Pakpen Plaza Sahraycedid Mah Halk Sok,
40 44 Kozyatagi 34734th Inst, Istanbul,
34888, Turkiye (100%)
Tel.: (90) 2164689700
Web Site: http://www.mobiloil.com.tr
Petroleum Products Marketer; Oil & Gas
Field Services
N.A.I.C.S.: 424720

Mobil Refining Australia Pty Ltd (1)
Level 9 664 Collins Street, Docklands,
3008, VIC, Australia
Tel.: (61) 61392865666
Oil Refining
N.A.I.C.S.: 311225

Neches River Treatment Corp. (1)
End of Burt St, Beaumont, TX
77704 (100%)
Tel.: (409) 833-9411
Sales Range: $10-24.9 Million
Emp.: 14
Refuse System
N.A.I.C.S.: 562219

PT Federal Karyatama (1)
The Prominence Office Tower Jl Jalur
Sutera Barat Kav 15, Lantai 29 Unit A-G
Kota Tangerang, Banten, 15143, Indonesia
Tel.: (62) 2130030688
Web Site: https://www.federaloil.co.id
Motor Oil & Lubricant Mfr
N.A.I.C.S.: 324191

**Saudi Aramco Lubricating Oil Refin-
ing Company** (1)
PO Box 5518, Jeddah, 21432, Saudi Arabia
Tel.: (966) 22296611
Web Site: http://www.luberef.com
Sales Range: $25-49.9 Million
Emp.: 45
Joint Venture of Saudi Arabian Oil Company
(70%) & Exxon Mobil Corporation (30%)
N.A.I.C.S.: 324110

**Saudi Aramco Mobil Refinery Com-
pany Ltd.** (1)
PO Box 30078, Yanbu Al-Sinaiyah, Yanbu,
Saudi Arabia
Tel.: (966) 143964000
Web Site: https://www.samref.com.sa
Sales Range: $100-124.9 Million
Joint Venture of Saudi Arabian Oil Company
& Exxon Mobil Corporation
N.A.I.C.S.: 324110

Terminale GNL Adriatico S.r.l (1)
Via Santa Radegonda 8, 20121, Milan,
Italy (70.68%)
Tel.: (39) 0263 6981
Web Site: https://www.adriaticlng.it
Emp.: 100
Operations of LNG Terminal
N.A.I.C.S.: 213112
Timothy J. Kelly *(Mng Dir)*
Sebastien Bumbolo *(Sec)*
Mohammed Ibrahim A. Al Sada *(Chm)*

TriState Petroleum (1)
2022 Washington Pike Greentree Rd, Carn-
egie, PA 15106
Tel.: (412) 276-8155
Sales Range: $25-49.9 Million
Emp.: 10
Gas Station
N.A.I.C.S.: 457120

**Upstream Technical Computing
Company** (1)
3120 Buffalo Speedway, Houston, TX
77098
Tel.: (713) 431-4222
Sales Range: $400-449.9 Million
Emp.: 750
Computing & Computer-Related Services to
Exxon Organizations
N.A.I.C.S.: 457120

XTO Energy Inc. (1)
22777 Springwoods Village Pkwy, Spring,
TX 77389 (100%)
Tel.: (817) 870-2800
Web Site: http://www.xtoenergy.com
Sales Range: $5-14.9 Billion
Emp.: 3,335
Oil & Natural Gas Production
N.A.I.C.S.: 211120
Timothy B. McIlwain *(Sr VP-Operations)*
T. Glenn Scott *(VP)*
Bob Simpson *(Founder)*

EYECITY.COM, INC.
17863 Hunting Bow Cr Ste 102, Lutz,
FL 33558
Tel.: (407) 455-4226   DE
Year Founded: 1999
ICTY—(OTCIQ)
Optical Product Mfr & Distr
N.A.I.C.S.: 333310
Brad Wilson *(CEO)*

EYENOVIA, INC.
295 Madison Ave Ste 2400, New
York, NY 10017
Tel.: (917) 289-1117   DE
Web Site: https://www.eyenovia.com
Year Founded: 2014
EYEN—(NASDAQ)
Rev.: $83,326
Assets: $31,036,413
Liabilities: $13,801,848
Net Worth: $17,234,565
Earnings: ($28,011,157)
Emp.: 41
Fiscal Year-end: 12/31/22
Biotechnology Research & Develop-
ment Services
N.A.I.C.S.: 541714

Sean Ianchulev *(Chm)*
Jennifer Clasby *(VP-Clinical & Regu-
latory Affairs)*
Luke Clauson *(VP-R&D, Mfg & En-
grg)*
Michael M. Rowe *(CEO)*
Norbert Lowe *(VP-Comml Ops)*
Bren Kern *(COO & VP)*
Andrew D. Jones *(CFO, Treas & Sec)*

EYEPOINT PHARMACEUTI-
CALS, INC.
480 Pleasant St Ste A 210, Water-
town, MA 02472
Tel.: (617) 926-5000   DE
Web Site:
  https://www.eyepointpharma.com
Year Founded: 2008
EYPT—(NASDAQ)
Rev.: $41,404,000
Assets: $180,356,000
Liabilities: $83,988,000
Net Worth: $96,368,000
Earnings: ($102,254,000)
Emp.: 144
Fiscal Year-end: 12/31/22
Bio-Nanotech Drug Delivery Products
& Services
N.A.I.C.S.: 325412
Goran A. Ando *(Chm)*
George O. Elston *(CFO & Exec VP)*
Jay S. Duker *(Pres & CEO)*
Dario A. Paggiarino *(Chief Medical
Officer & Sr VP)*
Nancy S. Lurker *(Vice Chm)*
Ron Honig *(Chief Legal Officer &
Sec)*
Scott Jones *(Chief Comml Officer)*
Michael C. Pine *(Chief Corp Dev &
Strategy Officer)*
Isabelle Lefebvre *(Chief Regulatory
Officer)*

Subsidiaries:

**EyePoint Pharmaceuticals US,
Inc.** (1)
480 Pleasant St Ste A-210, Watertown, MA
02472 (100%)
Tel.: (617) 926-5000
Web Site: https://www.eyepointpharma.com
Bio-Nanotech Drug Delivery Products &
Services
N.A.I.C.S.: 325412

Icon Bioscience Inc. (1)
480 Pleasant St Ste A210, Watertown, MA
02472
Tel.: (650) 369-4049
Research & Development in the Physical,
Engineering & Life Sciences
N.A.I.C.S.: 541715

pSivida Securities Corporation (1)
400 Pleasant St, Watertown, MA 02472
Tel.: (617) 926-5000
Analytical Laboratory Instrument Mfr
N.A.I.C.S.: 334516

EZCORP, INC.
2500 Bee Cave Rd Bldg 1 Ste 200,
Rollingwood, TX 78746
Tel.: (512) 314-3400   DE
Web Site: https://www.ezcorp.com
Year Founded: 1989
EZPW—(NASDAQ)
Rev.: $1,161,602,000
Assets: $1,493,237,000
Liabilities: $688,666,000
Net Worth: $804,571,000
Earnings: $83,095,000
Emp.: 7,500
Fiscal Year-end: 09/30/24
Pawnshops & Payday Loan Stores
Operator
N.A.I.C.S.: 459999
Timothy K. Jugmans *(CFO)*
John Blair Powell Jr. *(COO)*
Nikki Swies *(Chief Revenue Officer)*
Phillip E. Cohen *(Chm)*

Lachlan P. Given *(CEO)*
Keith Robertson *(CIO)*
Lisa VanRoekel *(Chief HR Officer)*
Robert J. Hicks *(Chief Acctg Officer)*
Nicole Swies *(Chief Revenue Officer)*
Thomas H. Welch Jr. *(Chief Legal
Officer & Sec)*

Subsidiaries:

Artiste Holding Limited (1)
2 Reavell Place, Ipswich, IP2 0ET, Suffolk,
United Kingdom
Tel.: (44) 8459569848
Web Site: http://www.cashgenieloans.co.uk
Financial Support & Loan Services
N.A.I.C.S.: 522291

C-N-P Northwest, Ltd. (1)
12475 Riverdale Blvd , Coon Rapids, MN
55433
Tel.: (612) 455-1083
Pawn Shop
N.A.I.C.S.: 522299

CCV Virginia, Inc. (1)
1901 Capital Pkwy, Austin, TX 78746
Tel.: (512) 314-3465
Web Site: http://www.ezcorp.com
Mortgage & Non-Mortgage Loan Brokers
N.A.I.C.S.: 522310

Cash-N-Pawn International, Ltd. (1)
2726 E Lake St, Minneapolis, MN 55406
Tel.: (612) 722-8232
Web Site: http://www.cashnpawn.com
Pawn Shop
N.A.I.C.S.: 522299

Cash-N-Pawn of Minnesota, Ltd. (1)
815 Cedar Ave S, Minneapolis, MN 55404
Tel.: (612) 206-3010
Web Site: http://www.maxid.com
Emp.: 10
Pawn Shop
N.A.I.C.S.: 522299
Matthew Little *(Gen Mgr)*

EZ ONLINE Oklahoma, LLC (1)
1901 Capital Pkwy, Austin, TX 78746
Tel.: (512) 314-3465
Pawn Shop
N.A.I.C.S.: 522299

EZMONEY Alabama, Inc. (1)
350 Mcfarland Ste A, Northport, AL 35476-
0000
Tel.: (205) 345-5474
Mortgage & Non-Mortgage Loan Brokers
N.A.I.C.S.: 522310

EZMONEY Idaho, Inc. (1)
551 S Woodruff Ave, Idaho Falls, ID 83401
Tel.: (208) 522-8833
Web Site: http://www.ezcorp.com
Mortgage & Non-Mortgage Loan Brokers
N.A.I.C.S.: 522310

EZMONEY South Dakota, Inc. (1)
1217 E Wells Ave, Pierre, SD 57501-3962
Tel.: (605) 224-6500
Mortgage & Non-Mortgage Loan Brokers
N.A.I.C.S.: 522310

EZPAWN Holdings, Inc. (1)
100 Texoma Pkwy, Sherman, TX 75090
Tel.: (903) 893-7903
Web Site: http://www.ezpawn.com
Mortgage & Non-Mortgage Loan Brokers
N.A.I.C.S.: 522310

EZPAWN Indiana, Inc. (1)
5227 W Washington St, Indianapolis, IN
46241
Tel.: (317) 244-1333
Mortgage & Non-Mortgage Loan Brokers
N.A.I.C.S.: 522310

**EZPAWN Management Mexico, SRL
de CV (Ltd., Inc.)** (1)
Fray Luis de Leon 8002 , Colinas del Ci-
matario, Mexico, 76090, Mexico
Tel.: (52) 44222116200
Web Site: http://empenofacil.com
Pawn Shop
N.A.I.C.S.: 522299

EZPAWN Nevada, Inc. (1)
10075 S Eastern Ave, Henderson, NV
89052

EZCORP, Inc.—(Continued)

Tel.: (702) 384-7296
Mortgage & Non-Mortgage Loan Brokers
N.A.I.C.S.: 522310

Fondo ACH, S.A. de C.V. SOFOM, E.N.R (1)
Prado Norte 550 Col Lomas de Chapultepec, Miguel Hidalgo, Mexico, 11000, Mexico
Tel.: (52) 41602100
Web Site: http://www.fondoh.com
Pawn Shop
N.A.I.C.S.: 522299

Red Dog Holdings, LLC (1)
8820 Lyndale Ave S, Minneapolis, MN 55420
Tel.: (612) 455-1083
Holding Company
N.A.I.C.S.: 551112

Renueva Comercial SAPI de CV (1)
Av Jalisco No 180, Delegacion Miguel Hidalgo, Mexico, 11870, Mexico
Tel.: (52) 52733500
Web Site: http://www.lomioestuyo.com
Electronic Products Whlsr
N.A.I.C.S.: 449210

USA Pawn & Jewelry CO IV, LLC (1)
4760 S Hwy 95Â, Fort Mohave, AZ 86426
Tel.: (702) 851-8155
Pawn Shop
N.A.I.C.S.: 522299

Value Financial Services, Inc. (1)
1901 Capital Pkwy, Austin, TX 78746-7613
Tel.: (512) 314-3400
Web Site: http://www.vfservices.com
Sales Range: $75-99.9 Million
Emp.: 530
Small, Secured, Non-Recourse Consumer Loans (Pawn Loans) & Related Services
N.A.I.C.S.: 522299

EZENIA! INC.
14 Celina Ave Ste 17-18, Nashua, NH 03063
Tel.: (603) 589-7600 DE
Web Site: http://www.ezenia.com
Year Founded: 1991
EZEN—(OTCIQ)
Sales Range: Less than $1 Million
Emp.: 13
Networking Equipment & Associated Software for Conferencing
N.A.I.C.S.: 334118
Larry Snyder (Pres)
Samuel A. Kidston (Chm)
Cecilia Moreno (CFO)

EZFILL HOLDINGS INC.
2999 NE 199th St, Aventura, FL 33180
Tel.: (305) 791-1169 DE
Web Site: https://www.ezfl.com
Year Founded: 2019
EZFL—(NASDAQ)
Rev.: $15,044,721
Assets: $10,597,844
Liabilities: $4,812,397
Net Worth: $5,785,447
Earnings: ($17,505,765)
Emp.: 53
Fiscal Year-end: 12/31/22
Holding Company
N.A.I.C.S.: 551112
Michael D. Handelman (CFO)
Avishai Vaknin (CTO)
Yehuda Levy (Founder & Interim CEO)

EZRAIDER CO.
1303 Central Ave S, Kent, WA 98032
Web Site: https://www.ezraider.com FL
Year Founded: 2012
EZRG—(OTCEM)
Assets: $127,239
Liabilities: $410,228
Net Worth: ($282,989)

Earnings: ($111,548)
Fiscal Year-end: 02/28/21
Offices of Other Holding Companies
N.A.I.C.S.: 551112
Elliot Mermel (Pres, Treas & Sec)

Subsidiaries:

EZ Raider, LLC (1)
1303 Central Ave S, Kent, WA 98032
Tel.: (833) 724-3378
Web Site: https://www.ezraider.com
ATV Dealer
N.A.I.C.S.: 441227

F&M BANCORP
41 S 1st St, Miamisburg, OH 45342
Tel.: (937) 866-2455 OH
Web Site:
https://www.bankwithfm.com
FMOO—(OTCIQ)
Bank Holding Company
N.A.I.C.S.: 551111
Clint G. Morton (Chief Lending Officer & Sr VP)
Cindy Spencer (Sr VP)
Gregory G. Eagan (CFO & Sr VP)
Shon B. Myers (Pres & CEO)

F&M BANK CORP.
205 S Main St, Timberville, VA 22853
Tel.: (540) 896-8941 VA
Web Site: https://www.fmbankva.com
Year Founded: 1983
FMBM—(OTCQX)
Rev.: $51,818,000
Assets: $1,245,902,000
Liabilities: $1,175,110,000
Net Worth: $70,792,000
Earnings: $8,318,000
Emp.: 143
Fiscal Year-end: 12/31/22
Bank Holding Company
N.A.I.C.S.: 551111
Dean W. Withers (Vice Chm)
Barton E. Black (Pres)
Lisa F. Campbell (CFO & Exec VP)
Charles Driest (Chief Experience Officer)
Jason Withers (Chief Credit Officer)
Melody Emswiler (Chief HR Officer & Exec VP)
Carolyn J. Dove (VP & Branch Mgr-F&M Bank)
Paul Eberly (Chief Dev Officer & Exec VP)
Aubrey Michael Wilkerson (CEO)

Subsidiaries:

Farmers & Merchants Bank (1)
205 S Main St, Timberville, VA 22853
Tel.: (540) 896-8941
Web Site: https://www.fmbankva.com
Sales Range: $125-149.9 Million
Emp.: 50
Commercial Banking Services
N.A.I.C.S.: 522110
Dean W. Withers (Vice Chm)
Larry A. Caplinger (Bd of Dirs, Executives)
Melody Emswiler (Sr VP & Dir-HR)

Subsidiary (Domestic):

Farmers & Merchants Financial Services (2)
210 W Madison St, Waterloo, WI 53594
Tel.: (920) 478-7019
Web Site:
https://www.fandmfinancialservices.com
Commercial Banking Services
N.A.I.C.S.: 551111

VBS Mortgage, LLC (2)
161 S Main St, Woodstock, VA 22664
Tel.: (540) 459-3707
Commercial Banking Services
N.A.I.C.S.: 551111

VSTitle, LLC (1)
2040 Deyerle Ave, Harrisonburg, VA 22801
Tel.: (540) 434-8571
Web Site: https://www.vstitle.com

Home Loan Mortgage Services
N.A.I.C.S.: 522299

F.N.B. CORPORATION
1 N Shore Ctr 12 Federal St, Pittsburgh, PA 15212
Tel.: (724) 981-6000 PA
Web Site: http://www.fnb-online.com
Year Founded: 1974
FNB—(NYSE)
Rev.: $1,973,000,000
Assets: $46,158,000,000
Liabilities: $40,108,000,000
Net Worth: $6,050,000,000
Earnings: $485,000,000
Emp.: 4,008
Fiscal Year-end: 12/31/23
Bank Holding Company
N.A.I.C.S.: 551111
William B. Campbell (Founder)
Vincent J. Delie Jr. (Chm, Pres & CEO)
James G. Orie (Chief Legal Officer & Sec)
Gary L. Guerrieri (Chief Credit Officer)
Thomas M. Whitesel (Chief Risk Officer)
Barbara R. Cottrell (Dir-Corp Compliance)
Jennifer M. Reel (Dir-Corp Comm)
Barry C. Robinson (Chief Consumer Banking Officer-FNBPA)
Cassandra Cooper (Mgr-Diversity & Inclusion)
Brent Semachko (Dir-Corp Responsibility)
Vincent J. Calabrese Jr. (CFO)

Subsidiaries:

First National Bank of Pennsylvania (1)
1 N Shore Ctr 12, Pittsburgh, PA 15212 (100%)
Tel.: (800) 555-5455
Web Site: http://www.fnb-online.com
Sales Range: $500-549.9 Million
Emp.: 2,632
Commercial Banking Services
N.A.I.C.S.: 522110
Vincent J. Delie Jr. (Chm, Pres & CEO)
Bryant Mitchell (Chief Wholesale Banking Officer)
Cassandra Cooper (Mgr-Diversity & Inclusion)
Brent Semachko (Dir-Corp Responsibility)
Brian P. Wozniak (Exec VP & Exec Dir-Small Bus Banking)
Barry Robinson (Chief Consumer Banking Officer)
Vincent J. Calabrese Jr. (CFO)

Subsidiary (Domestic):

First National Trust Company (2)
532 Main St Ste 6, Johnstown, PA 15901
Tel.: (814) 532-3518
Web Site:
http://www.fnbwealthmanagement.com
Sales Range: $250-299.9 Million
Emp.: 75
Investment Management, Estate Planning & Trust Services
N.A.I.C.S.: 523991

First National Insurance Agency, LLC (1)
12 Federal St Ste 405, Pittsburgh, PA 15212
Tel.: (412) 446-1010
Web Site: http://www.fn-ins.com
Sales Range: $75-99.9 Million
Emp.: 20
Commercial Banking Services
N.A.I.C.S.: 522110

Howard Bancorp, Inc. (1)
3301 Boston St, Baltimore, MD 21224
Tel.: (410) 750-0020
Web Site: http://www.howardbank.com
Rev.: $98,722,000
Assets: $2,537,991,000
Liabilities: $2,243,359,000

Net Worth: $294,632,000
Earnings: ($16,991,000)
Emp.: 235
Fiscal Year-end: 12/31/2020
Bank Holding Company
N.A.I.C.S.: 551111

Subsidiary (Domestic):

Compass Properties, LLC (2)
44 E Mifflin St Ste 304, Madison, WI 53703
Tel.: (608) 294-9400
Web Site:
http://www.compassproperties.com
Real Estate Development Services
N.A.I.C.S.: 531390
Tyler Noel (Pres)
Todd Greenwald (VP-Real Estate Ops)
Kim Kindler (Controller)
Mark Craig (Gen Mgr)
Patty Noel (Founder)

Howard Bank (2)
3301 Boston St, Baltimore, MD 21224
Tel.: (410) 750-0020
Web Site: http://www.howardbank.com
Commercial Banking
N.A.I.C.S.: 522110
Mary Ann Scully (Chm & CEO)
Charles E. Schwabe (Chief Risk Officer, Sec & Exec VP)
Robert Dietrich Kunisch Jr. (Pres & COO)
Drew McKone (Chief Deposit Officer & Exec VP)
Thomas Jones (Chief Credit Officer & Exec VP)
Steven M. Poynot (CIO & Exec VP)
Matt Reidy (VP-Comml Banking)
Robert Crismond (Sr VP-Comml Banking)
Joseph Howard (Gen Counsel & Exec VP)
Frank K. Turner Jr. (Chief Comml Banking Officer & Exec VP)

F5, INC.
801 5th Ave, Seattle, WA 98104
Tel.: (206) 272-5555 WA
Web Site: https://www.f5.com
Year Founded: 1996
FFIV—(NASDAQ)
Rev.: $2,816,120,000
Assets: $5,613,004,000
Liabilities: $2,483,626,000
Net Worth: $3,129,378,000
Earnings: $566,778,000
Emp.: 6,557
Fiscal Year-end: 09/30/24
Network Traffic Routing & Management Software
N.A.I.C.S.: 513210
Alan J. Higginson (Chm)
Scot Frazier Rogers (Gen Counsel & Exec VP)
Francois Locoh-Donou (Pres & CEO)
Chad Whalen (Exec VP-Sls-Worldwide)
Kara Sprague (Chief Product Officer & Exec VP)
Ana M. White (Chief People Officer & Exec VP)
Tom Fountain (Chief Strategy Officer & Exec VP-Global Svcs)
Sumit Agarwal (VP-Analytic Products)
Mika Yamamoto (Chief Mktg & Customer Experience Officer & Exec VP)
Suzanne DuLong (VP-IR)
Derek Smith (Sr VP-Security)
Rob Gruening (Dir-Corp Comm)
Haiyan Song (Exec VP & Gen Mgr-Security & Distributed Cloud)
Yvette H. Smith (CIO & Sr VP-Customer Success & Bus Transformation)
Francis J. Pelzer V (CFO & Exec VP)
Thomas D. Fountain (COO)
Chad Whalen (Exec VP-Sls-Worldwide)
Chad Whalen (Chief Revenue Officer)
Geng Lin (Exec VP)
Kunal Anand (CTO, Chief AI Officer, Chief Innovation Officer & Exec VP)

Subsidiaries:

F5 Networks (Israel) Ltd. **(1)**
2229 Street Building 8 Floor 30, Kiryat Atidim, Tel Aviv, 61581, Israel
Tel.: (972) 773604400
Software Development Services
N.A.I.C.S.: 541511

F5 Networks Australia Pty.
Limited **(1)**
140 Arthur Street Level 6, Sydney, 2060, NSW, Australia
Tel.: (61) 299781555
Web Site: http://www.f5networks.com.au
Sales Range: $10-24.9 Million
Emp.: 20
Network Traffic Routing & Management Software
N.A.I.C.S.: 541511
Jason Baden *(VP-Australia & New Zealand)*

F5 Networks Benelux B.V. **(1)**
World Trade Center Schiphol Schiphol Boulevard 127 Tower 3A, 1118 BG, Schiphol, Netherlands
Tel.: (31) 202014950
Web Site: http://www.f5networks.nl
Router Traffic Monitoring Software Publisher
N.A.I.C.S.: 513210
John McAdam *(CEO)*
Andy Reinland *(CFO & Exec VP)*
Ryan Kearny *(CTO & Exec VP-Product Dev)*

F5 Networks China **(1)**
Unit 07-09 17th Floor Building Tower 1 China Central Place 79, Jianguo Road Chaoyang District, Beijing, 100025, China
Tel.: (86) 1059234000
Web Site: http://www.f5.com.cn
Sales Range: $25-49.9 Million
Emp.: 60
Router Traffic Monitoring Software Publisher
N.A.I.C.S.: 513210
John McAdam *(Pres & CEO)*
Adam Judd *(Sr VP-Asia PAcific, China & Japan)*

F5 Networks Colombia S.A.S. **(1)**
Cra 10 Ste 97A-13 Of 202 Torre B, Bogota, 110221, Colombia
Tel.: (57) 3125889311
Software Development Services
N.A.I.C.S.: 541511

F5 Networks Hong Kong Limited **(1)**
Rooms 905-06 9th Floor Harbour Centre, 25 Harbour Road, Wanchai, China (Hong Kong)
Tel.: (852) 28271818
Web Site: http://www.f5.com
Sales Range: $100-124.9 Million
Emp.: 20
Network Traffic Routing & Management Software
N.A.I.C.S.: 541511

F5 Networks Iberia SL **(1)**
Tower Glass Floor 259C 18 Paseo de la Castellana, Madrid, 28046, Spain
Tel.: (34) 911190500
Web Site: http://www.f5networks.es
Emp.: 11
Router Traffic Monitoring Software Publisher
N.A.I.C.S.: 513210

F5 Networks Japan K.K. **(1)**
Akasaka Garden City 19th Floor 4-15-1 Akasaka, Minato-ku, Tokyo, 107-0052, Japan
Tel.: (81) 351143200
Web Site: http://www.f5networks.co.jp
Sales Range: $100-124.9 Million
Network Traffic Routing & Management Software
N.A.I.C.S.: 541511

F5 Networks Korea Ltd. **(1)**
Trade Tower 38th Floor Room 3801 159-1 Samsung-dong, Kangnam-ku, Seoul, 135-729, Korea (South)
Tel.: (82) 60006770
Web Site: http://www.f5networks.co.kr
Sales Range: $100-124.9 Million
Network Traffic Routing & Management Software
N.A.I.C.S.: 541511

F5 Networks LLC **(1)**

Smolensky Passage Smolenskaya Square 3 7th floor, 121099, Moscow, Russia
Tel.: (7) 4959378266
Software Development Services
N.A.I.C.S.: 541511

F5 Networks Limited **(1)**
Chertsey Gate W, 43-47 London St, Chertsey, KT16 8AP, Surrey, United Kingdom
Tel.: (44) 1932582000
Web Site: http://www.f5networks.co.uk
Sales Range: $100-124.9 Million
Emp.: 90
Computer Integrated Systems Design
N.A.I.C.S.: 541512
John McAdam *(Pres & CEO)*

Subsidiary (Non-US):

F5 Networks GmbH **(2)**
Lehrer Wirth Strasse 2, 85609, Munich, Germany **(100%)**
Tel.: (49) 8994383100
Web Site: http://www.f5.com
Sales Range: $25-49.9 Million
Computer Integrated Systems Design
N.A.I.C.S.: 541512

F5 Networks SARL **(2)**
28 rue Pages, 92150, Suresnes, France
Tel.: (33) 141448950
Web Site: http://www.f5.com
Sales Range: $1-9.9 Million
Emp.: 7
Computer Integrated Systems Design
N.A.I.C.S.: 541512

F5 Networks New Zealand Ltd. **(1)**
Level 1 Stanbeth House 22-28 Customs Street East, Auckland, 1010, New Zealand
Tel.: (64) 99505305
Software Development Services
N.A.I.C.S.: 541511

F5 Networks Poland sp z.o.o **(1)**
14th floor Skylight Tower ul Zlota 59, Warsaw, 00-120, Poland
Tel.: (48) 224577651
Database Management Software Development Services
N.A.I.C.S.: 541511
Andrzej Kroczek *(Engr-Field Sys)*

F5 Networks Singapore Pte Ltd. **(1)**
5 Temasek Boulevard 08-01/02, Suntec Tower Five, Singapore, 038985, Singapore
Tel.: (65) 65336103
Web Site: http://www.f5apac.com
Sales Range: $100-124.9 Million
Network Traffic Routing & Management Software
N.A.I.C.S.: 541511

F5 Networks, Inc. - Lowell **(1)**
41 Wellman St, Lowell, MA 01851-5134
Tel.: (978) 513-2900
Web Site: http://www.f5.com
Sales Range: $25-49.9 Million
Emp.: 100
Computer Data Storage & Networking Services
N.A.I.C.S.: 334112

Shape Security, Inc. **(1)**
2755 Augustine Dr 8th Fl, Santa Clara, CA 95054
Tel.: (650) 399-0400
Web Site: http://www.shapesecurity.com
Software Development Services
N.A.I.C.S.: 541511

Threat Stack, Inc. **(1)**
219 Buchanan St, Alexandria, VA 22314-2103
Tel.: (913) 375-2798
Web Site: http://www.threatstack.com
Software Publisher
N.A.I.C.S.: 513210
Jen Andre *(Co-Founder & CTO)*
Brian M. Ahern *(Chm & CEO)*
Jim Crowley *(VP-Enterprise & Channel Sls)*
Venkat Pothamsetty *(VP-Products & Customer Advocacy)*
Leigh Merrigan Moore *(VP-Mktg)*
Kevin Durkin *(CFO)*
Matthew Godoff *(Dir-Synergy Investments)*
Jim McDonough *(VP-Inside Sls)*
Mimi Alperovich *(Dir-Bus Dev)*
Jonaki Egenolf *(CMO)*
Chris Ford *(VP-Product)*
Aditya Joshi *(Exec VP-Products & Tech)*

FACEKEY CORPORATION
900 NE Loop 410 Ste D401, San Antonio, TX 78209
Tel.: (210) 826-8811   TX
Web Site: http://www.facekey.com
Year Founded: 1999
FAKC—(OTCIQ)
Security & Access Control Services
N.A.I.C.S.: 561621
Yevgeny B. Levitov *(Co-Founder & Pres)*
Annette H. Starkweather *(Co-Founder & VP-Ops & Bus Dev)*
Richard J. Prince *(Mgr-Customer Svc)*

FACTSET RESEARCH SYSTEMS INC.
45 Glover Ave, Norwalk, CT 06850
Tel.: (203) 810-1000   DE
Web Site: https://www.factset.com
Year Founded: 1978
FDS—(NYSE)
Rev.: $2,203,056,000
Assets: $4,055,040,000
Liabilities: $2,142,580,000
Net Worth: $1,912,460,000
Earnings: $537,126,000
Emp.: 12,398
Fiscal Year-end: 08/31/24
Online Integrated Financial Information & Analytical Applications Development, Sales & Services
N.A.I.C.S.: 518210
Helen L. Shan *(CFO & Exec VP)*
Christopher Ellis *(Sr VP & Head-Strategic Initiatives)*
Goran Skoko *(Mng Dir-EMEA & Asia Pacific, Exec VP & Head-Res)*
Rachel R. Stern *(Chief Legal Officer, Sec, Exec VP & Head-Strategic Resources)*
Robert J. Robie *(Exec VP & Head-Analytics & Trading Solutions)*
Kristina W. Karnovsky *(Chief Product Officer & Exec VP)*
Gregory T. Moskoff *(Chief Acctg Officer, Sr VP & Controller)*
Jonathan Reeve *(Exec VP & Head-Content & Tech Solutions)*
John Costigan *(Chief Content Officer)*
Linda S. Huber *(CFO & Exec VP)*
Lisa Knoll *(Sr VP & Head-Mktg)*
Kendra Brown *(Sr VP-IR)*
Kate Stepp *(CTO)*
Catrina Harding *(Chief HR Officer & Exec VP)*
Frederick Philip Snow *(CEO)*

Subsidiaries:

BTU Analytics, LLC **(1)**
165 S Union Blvd Ste 410, Lakewood, CO 80228
Tel.: (720) 552-8040
Marketing Consulting Services
N.A.I.C.S.: 541613

Cabot Investment Technology,
Inc. **(1)**
45 Glover Ave 7th Fl, Norwalk, CT 06850
Tel.: (203) 810-1000
Web Site: https://cabot.factset.com
Portfolio Management Services
N.A.I.C.S.: 541890

FactSet Data Systems, Inc. **(1)**
45 Glover Ave 7th Fl, Norwalk, CT 06850
Tel.: (203) 810-1000
Web Site: https://www.factset.com
Online Integrated Database Services
N.A.I.C.S.: 518210
Helen L. Shan *(Chief Revenue Officer)*
Linda S. Huber *(CFO & Exec VP)*
Linda S. Huber *(CFO)*
Phil Snow *(CEO)*
Helen Shan *(Chief Revenue Officer)*

FactSet Digital Solutions AG **(1)**
Loewenstrasse 2, Zurich, 8001, Switzerland
Tel.: (41) 442764611

Software Development Services
N.A.I.C.S.: 513210

FactSet Digital Solutions, LLC **(1)**
100 S Washington Ave Ste 1515, Minneapolis, MN 55401
Tel.: (952) 486-5710
Software Development Services
N.A.I.C.S.: 513210

FactSet Europe Limited **(1)**
Broadgate Quarter One Snowden Street, London, EC2A 2DQ, United Kingdom
Tel.: (44) 2030097000
Sales Range: $25-49.9 Million
Emp.: 300
Online Integrated Financial Information & Analytical Application Service Sales & Consulting; Regional Managing Office
N.A.I.C.S.: 518210

Subsidiary (Non-US):

FactSet Benelux B.V. **(2)**
Beethovenstraat 506 Beethoven 500, ITO Toren, 1082 PR, Amsterdam, Netherlands
Tel.: (31) 207085700
Online Financial Data
N.A.I.C.S.: 518210

FactSet France S.a.r.l. **(2)**
12 Rue Du Havre, 75009, Paris, France
Tel.: (33) 176711000
Sales Range: $125-149.9 Million
Provider of Online Financial Data
N.A.I.C.S.: 522320

Subsidiary (Domestic):

FactSet JCF S.A.S. **(3)**
43 rue Lafayette, 75009, Paris, France
Tel.: (33) 144532323
Sales Range: $10-24.9 Million
Emp.: 20
Online Financial Data
N.A.I.C.S.: 518210

Subsidiary (Non-US):

FactSet GmbH **(2)**
An der Welle 3, 60322, Frankfurt am Main, Germany **(100%)**
Tel.: (49) 6977061600
Sales Range: $50-74.9 Million
Emp.: 25
Online Financial Data
N.A.I.C.S.: 518210

FactSet Italia S.r.l. **(2)**
REGUS Via Broletto 46, 20121, Milan, Italy
Tel.: (39) 0200663710
Sales Range: $25-49.9 Million
Emp.: 20
Online Integrated Financial Information & Analytical Applications for Investment Professionals
N.A.I.C.S.: 518210

FactSet France SAS **(1)**
32 Rue Blanche 2nd Floor, 75009, Paris, France
Tel.: (33) 170060100
Portfolio Management & Investment Research Services
N.A.I.C.S.: 523940

FactSet Pacific, Inc. **(1)**
Otemachi One Tower 6th floor 1-2-1, Otemachi Chiyoda-ku, Tokyo, 100-0004, Japan
Tel.: (81) 362685100
Online Integrated Financial Information & Analytical Application Service Development, Sales & Consulting; Regional Managing Office
N.A.I.C.S.: 518210

Subsidiary (Non-US):

FactSet Hong Kong Limited **(2)**
20F 9 Queens Road, 15 Queens Road, Central, China (Hong Kong)
Tel.: (852) 37106100
Online Integrated Financial Information & Analytical Application Service Sales & Consulting
N.A.I.C.S.: 541990

FactSet Philippines, Inc. **(2)**
10-18 floors One LeGrand Tower McKinley West, South Bonifacio District, Taguig,

FactSet Research Systems Inc.—(Continued)

1630, Metro Manila, Philippines
Tel.: (63) 279082600
Online Integrated Financial Information &
Analytical Application Service Product De-
velopment Services
N.A.I.C.S.: 541511

**FactSet Systems India Private
Limited** (2)
7th Floor Block-4 Divyasree NSL Infrastruc-
ture Pvt Ltd SEZ, Survey No 66/1 Raidurg
Village Serilingampally Mandal, Hyderabad,
500032, Telangana, India
Tel.: (91) 4044557000
Emp.: 4,000
Online Integrated Financial Information &
Analytical Application Service Development,
Sales & Consulting
N.A.I.C.S.: 541511

FactSet Pacific, Inc. (1)
Level 15 25 Bligh Street, Sydney, 2000,
NSW, Australia
Tel.: (61) 282230400
Software Development Services
N.A.I.C.S.: 513210

FactSet Research Limited (1)
90 Park Ave 10th Fl, New York, NY 10016
Tel.: (212) 476-4300
Online Integrated Financial Information &
Analytical Application Service Sales & Con-
sulting
N.A.I.C.S.: 541990

**FactSet Research Systems Inc.
Content Collection** (1)
2002 McFarland Blvd E Ste 205, Tusca-
loosa, AL 35404
Tel.: (205) 247-4200
Web Site: http://www.factset.com
Sales Range: $1-9.9 Million
Emp.: 25
Marketing Research & Public Opinion Poll-
ing
N.A.I.C.S.: 541910

FactSet Singapore PTE LTD (1)
08-03 Guoco Tower 1 Wallich Street, 10
Collyer Quay, Singapore, 078881, Singa-
pore
Tel.: (65) 68083050
Software Publishing Services
N.A.I.C.S.: 513210

FactSet Switzerland AG (1)
Loewenstrasse 2, 8001, Zurich, Switzerland
Tel.: (41) 442764611
Software Development Services
N.A.I.C.S.: 541511

FactSet UK Limited (1)
Broadgate Quarter One Snowden Street,
London, EC2A 2DQ, United Kingdom
Tel.: (44) 2030097000
Software Development Services
N.A.I.C.S.: 513210

Market Metrics, LLC (1)
53 State St 6th Fl, Boston, MA 02109
Tel.: (617) 376-0550
Web Site: http://www.marketmetrics.com
Sales Range: $10-24.9 Million
Emp.: 25
Corporate Investment & Insurance Products
Market Research & Consulting Services
N.A.I.C.S.: 541618

Matrix Data Ltd (1)
55 New Oxford Street, London, WC1A 1BS,
United Kingdom
Tel.: (44) 2070741200
Web Site: http://www.matrixsolutions.co.uk
Administrative Management & General
Management Consulting Services
N.A.I.C.S.: 541611
Jon Abbott (Officer-Data Protection)
Scott Hawes (Head-Compliance)
Clair Lester (Head-Res)

Portware, LLC (1)
99 Park Ave 16th Fl, New York, NY 10016
Tel.: (212) 425-5233
Web Site: http://www.portware.com
Emp.: 100
Software Developer
N.A.I.C.S.: 513210
Ary Khatchikian (Owner)

Revere Data, LLC (1)
1 California St Ste 1900, San Francisco, CA
94111
Tel.: (415) 782-0454
Web Site: http://www.reveredata.com
Sales Range: $25-49.9 Million
Emp.: 50
Data, Analytics & Index Services
N.A.I.C.S.: 561499
Steven M. Shum (Founder)
Michael W. Engmann (Chm)

StreetAccount LLC (1)
1135 Maple Way 2nd Fl, Jackson, WY
83001
Tel.: (617) 261-5200
Web Site: https://www.streetaccount.com
Real Time Equity Market Intelligence Ser-
vices
N.A.I.C.S.: 541519

Vermilion Software Inc. (1)
50 Congress St, Boston, MA 02109
Tel.: (617) 279-0799
Software Development Services
N.A.I.C.S.: 513210

FAHEY BANKING COMPANY
Tel.: (740) 382-8231
Web Site:
  https://www.faheybank.bank
Year Founded: 1865
FAHE—(NASDAQ)
Sales Range: $10-24.9 Million
Emp.: 50
State Commercial Banks
N.A.I.C.S.: 522110
Carl Hughes (Chm, Pres & CEO)
Sherry Goodman (Branch Mgr)
Chris Woodard (Mgr-Info Sys & Bus
Resumption)
Krista Biederman (Branch Mgr)
Daniel Jurcich (Asst VP)
Travis Sanders (Chief Lending Offi-
cer)

FAIR ISAAC CORPORATION
5 W Mendenhall Ste 105, Bozeman,
MT 59715
Tel.: (406) 982-7276   DE
Web Site: https://www.fico.com
Year Founded: 1956
FICO—(NYSE)
Rev.: $1,513,557,000
Assets: $1,575,281,000
Liabilities: $2,263,271,000
Net Worth: ($687,990,000)
Earnings: $429,375,000
Emp.: 3,455
Fiscal Year-end: 09/30/23
Decision Management Solutions, Se-
curity Software & Credit Scoring Ser-
vices
N.A.I.C.S.: 541715
Richard S. Deal (Chief HR Officer &
Exec VP)
Mark R. Scadina (Gen Counsel, Sec
& Exec VP)
James M. Wehmann (Exec VP-
Scores)
Michael S. Leonard (Chief Acctg Offi-
cer & VP)
Steven P. Weber (CFO & Exec VP)
Braden R. Kelly (Chm)
Thomas A. Bowers (Exec VP-Corp
Strategy)
Ben Nelson (Chief Information Secu-
rity Officer)
Subsidiaries:

Adeptra Limited (1)
200 Brook Drive, Green Park, Reading,
RG2 6UB, United Kingdom
Tel.: (44) 1189231000
Consumer Credit & Risk Management Ser-
vices
N.A.I.C.S.: 541611

Adeptra Pty. Ltd. (1)
Level 11 257 Clarence Street, Sydney,
2000, NSW, Australia

Tel.: (61) 294639900
Credit Information Product Distr
N.A.I.C.S.: 522320

CR Software LLC (1)
4035 Ridge Top Rd Ste 600, Fairfax, VA
22030
Tel.: (703) 934-9060
Web Site: http://www.crsoftwarellc.com
Sales Range: $1-9.9 Million
Emp.: 98
Computer System Design Services
N.A.I.C.S.: 541512

Entiera, Inc. (1)
181 Metro Dr Ste 700, San Jose, CA 95110
Tel.: (408) 535-1500
Credit Information Product Distr
N.A.I.C.S.: 522320

Subsidiary (Non-US):

**Entiera Solutions Company
Limited** (2)
219/20 Asoke Tower Soi 21 Sukhumvit
Khwang Khlongtoey Nuea Khet, Watthana
District, Bangkok, 10110, Thailand
Tel.: (66) 26642215
Credit Information Product Distr
N.A.I.C.S.: 522320

Fair Isaac (Australia) Pty Ltd (1)
Level 11 257 Clarence Street, Sydney,
2000, NSW, Australia
Tel.: (61) 294639900
Software Development Services
N.A.I.C.S.: 541511

Fair Isaac Adeptra, Inc. (1)
181 Metro Dr Ste 700, San Jose, CA 95110
Tel.: (408) 535-1500
Sales Range: $10-24.9 Million
Emp.: 25
Customer Communication Software Devel-
oper
N.A.I.C.S.: 513210

Fair Isaac Asia Pacific Corp. (1)
10 Kishimoto Building 2-1-1 Marunouchi,
Chiyoda, Tokyo, 100-0005, Japan
Tel.: (81) 362122733
Web Site: http://www.sico.com
Emp.: 10
Credit Information Product Distr
N.A.I.C.S.: 522320

**Fair Isaac Chile Software & Services
Ltda.** (1)
Tel.: (56) 800914312
Software Development Services
N.A.I.C.S.: 513210

Fair Isaac Deutschland GmbH (1)
Berlin Branch c/o Zuse Institute Berlin,
Takustrasse 7, 14195, Berlin, Germany
Tel.: (49) 2079408718
Data & Software Support Services
N.A.I.C.S.: 518210

**Fair Isaac Information Technology
(Beijing) Co., Ltd.** (1)
Unit F2-1 A 1101-1206B Level 11 No 6
Wudinghou Street, Xi Cheng District, Bei-
jing, 100033, China
Tel.: (86) 13810388535
Decision Management Solutions, Security
Software & Credit Scoring Services
N.A.I.C.S.: 522390

Fair Isaac International Limited (1)
5th Floor Cottons Centre, Hays Lane, Lon-
don, SE1 2QP, United Kingdom
Tel.: (44) 2074031333
Credit Information Product Distr
N.A.I.C.S.: 522320

Subsidiary (Non-US):

Fair Isaac Services Limited (2)
Tel.: (44) 1217814500
Credit Information Product Distr
N.A.I.C.S.: 522320

Subsidiary (Non-US):

Fair Isaac Germany GmbH (3)
Stubenwald-Allee 19, 64625, Bensheim,
Germany
Tel.: (49) 62518263383
Web Site: http://www.fico.com
Software Publishing Services

N.A.I.C.S.: 513210

Fair Isaac South Africa (Pty) Ltd. (1)
25 Rudd Road Illovo, Sandton, 2196, South
Africa
Tel.: (27) 101408350
Software Development Services
N.A.I.C.S.: 513210

Fair Isaac UK Group Limited (1)
Fair Isaac House International Square, Star-
ley Way, Birmingham, B37 7GN, West Mid-
lands, United Kingdom
Tel.: (44) 2079408718
Emp.: 400
Software Development Services
N.A.I.C.S.: 541511

Subsidiary (Domestic):

**Fair Isaac UK International Holdings
Ltd.** (2)
5th Floor Cottons Centre, Hays Lane, Lon-
don, SE1 2QP, United Kingdom (100%)
Tel.: (44) 2079408718
Web Site: http://www.fico.com
Credit Information Product Distr
N.A.I.C.S.: 522320

Fair, Isaac do Brasil Ltda. (1)
Avenida Roque Petroni Junior No 999 Floor
12 Ste 121 / 122, Sao Paulo, 04707-000,
SP, Brazil
Tel.: (55) 1151898267
Web Site: http://www.fico.com
Credit Information Product Distr
N.A.I.C.S.: 522320

Infoglide Software Corporation (1)
6500 River Place Blvd Bldg 2 Ste 450, Aus-
tin, TX 78730
Tel.: (512) 532-3500
Web Site: http://www.infoglide.com
Sales Range: $1-9.9 Million
Emp.: 30
Database Scanning Software Developer
N.A.I.C.S.: 513210

FALCON TECHNOLOGIES,
INC.
2631 Metro Blvd, Maryland Heights,
MO 63043
Tel.: (314) 994-9066   OR
Web Site:
  https://www.falcontech.com
Year Founded: 1990
ECGS—(OTCIQ)
Other Computer Related Services
N.A.I.C.S.: 541519
William J. Delgado (Pres & CEO)

FALCON'S BEYOND GLOBAL,
INC.
1768 Park Center Dr, Orlando, FL
32835
Tel.: (407) 909-9350   DE
Web Site:
  https://www.falconsbeyond.com
Year Founded: 2000
FBYD—(NASDAQ)
Rev.: $18,244,000
Assets: $63,359,000
Liabilities: $552,353,000
Net Worth: ($488,994,000)
Earnings: ($430,930,000)
Emp.: 116
Fiscal Year end: 12/31/20
Resort Operator
N.A.I.C.S.: 721120
Scott Demerau (Chm)
Cecil D. Magpuri (CEO)
Simon Philips (Pres)
Yvette Whittaker (Chief Corp Officer)
David Schaefer (Chief Dev Officer)
Jo Merrill (CFO)
Bruce A. Brown (Chief Legal Officer
& Sec)
Simon Hirst (Chief Parks Officer-
Operations & Expansion)
Jennifer Smeresky (Exec VP-
Finance)
Jason Ambler (Pres-Digital Media)

Tori Eurton *(VP-Stakeholder Engagement)*
Eric Calderon *(Exec VP-Creative Dev)*
Daryl White *(Exec VP-Global Licensing & Business Development)*
Saham Ali *(Exec VP-Technology)*
Toni Caracciolo *(Exec VP-Marketing & Branding)*
Juan Lorenzo *(VP-Finance)*
Crystal Fahmie *(VP-Operations & Human Capital)*

FALCONSTOR SOFTWARE, INC.
111 Congress Ave Ste 500, Austin, TX 78701
Tel.: (631) 777-5188   DE
Web Site: https://www.falconstor.com
Year Founded: 2000
FALC—(OTCQB)
Rev.: $10,052,248
Assets: $10,170,112
Liabilities: $26,577,554
Net Worth: ($16,407,442)
Earnings: ($3,342,585)
Emp.: 53
Fiscal Year-end: 12/31/22
Network Storage Management Software
N.A.I.C.S.: 513210
Todd Brooks *(Pres & CEO)*
Abdul Hashmi *(VP-Customer Success)*
Clark Liddell *(VP-Strategic Ops)*
Vincent Sita *(CFO, Principal Acctg Officer & Treas)*
Rich Spring *(Chief Revenue Officer)*
Ron Morita *(VP)*
Victoria Grey *(Head)*

Subsidiaries:

FalconStor Asia Pacific   (1)
6F-1 No 521 Sec 1 Wunsin Rd, Taichung, 40848, Taiwan   (100%)
Tel.: (886) 345679555
Sales Range: $10-24.9 Million
Emp.: 50
Mfr of High Performance Networking Solutions
N.A.I.C.S.: 541512

Subsidiary (Non-US):

FalconStor China   (2)
Room 1571 NCI Tower 12A Jianguomenwai Ave, Chaoyang District, Beijing, 100022, China   (100%)
Tel.: (86) 345679555
Mfr of High Performance Networking Solutions
N.A.I.C.S.: 541512

FalconStor Japan   (2)
Chiyoda Platform Square 1007 3-21 Kanda Nishikicho, Chiyoda Ku, Tokyo, 101-0054, Japan   (100%)
Tel.: (81) 335560211
Web Site: http://www.falconstor.co.jp
Mfr of High Performance Networking Solutions
N.A.I.C.S.: 541512

FalconStor France   (1)
58 Rue Pottier, 78150, Le Chesnay, France
Tel.: (33) 1 39 23 9550
Web Site: http://www.falconstor.com
Sales Range: $1-9.9 Million
Emp.: 10
Mfr of High Performance Networking Solutions
N.A.I.C.S.: 541512

FalconStor Software (Korea), Inc.   (1)
403 Ace Bldg Secho-daero 41-gil-19, Seocho-gu, Seoul, 06595, Korea (South)
Tel.: (82) 345679555
Web Site: http://www.falconstor.co.kr
Network Storage Management Software
N.A.I.C.S.: 513210

FAME PRODUCTIONS, INC.
33 Indian Rd Ste 3k, New York, NY 10034
Tel.: (646) 504-3263   LA
Web Site:
   https://www.fameproinc.com
Year Founded: 1982
FMPR—(OTCIQ)
Rev.: $284,000
Assets: $51,000
Liabilities: $661,000
Net Worth: ($610,000)
Earnings: ($262,000)
Emp.: 4
Fiscal Year-end: 12/31/19
Media Advertising Services
N.A.I.C.S.: 541840
Brett Wright *(Chm)*
Jason Claiborne *(Treas & Sec)*

FAMILY ROOM ENTERTAINMENT CORPORATION
22600 C Lambert St Ste 902, Lake Forest, CA 92630
Tel.: (818) 802-0060   NM
Web Site: https://www.fmlyroom.com
Year Founded: 1969
FMYR—(OTCIQ)
Sales Range: Less than $1 Million
Emp.: 5
Motion Picture & Video Production
N.A.I.C.S.: 512110
Justin R. Wall *(Pres)*

FANSFRENZY CORP.
10040 W Cheyenne Ave Ste 170-162, Las Vegas, NV 89129
Tel.: (514) 773-7017   NV
Web Site: http://www.fansfrenzy.com
Year Founded: 1995
FFZY—(OTCIQ)
Web Portal Services
N.A.I.C.S.: 519290
Bernie Nicholls *(Pres & Sec)*

FANTASY ACES DAILY FANTASY SPORTS CORP.
120 Vantis Ste 300, Aliso Viejo, CA 92656
Tel.: (403) 531-1710   Ca
Web Site: http://fantasyaces.com
FASDF—(TSXV)
Sales Range: $1-9.9 Million
Online Gambling Services
N.A.I.C.S.: 541511

FAR PEAK ACQUISITION CORPORATION
511 6th Ave Ste 7342, New York, NY 10011
Tel.: (917) 737-1541   Ky
Year Founded: 2020
FPAC—(NYSE)
Investment Services
N.A.I.C.S.: 523999
Thomas W. Farley *(Chm, Pres & CEO)*
David W. Bonanno *(CFO & Sec)*

FAR POINT ACQUISITION CORPORATION
18 W 18th St, New York, NY 10011
Tel.: (212) 715-3880   DE
Web Site:
   http://www.farpoint.ventures
Year Founded: 2018
FPAC—(NYSE)
Rev.: $14,377,603
Assets: $650,629,812
Liabilities: $645,629,809
Net Worth: $5,000,003
Earnings: $9,047,005
Emp.: 3
Fiscal Year-end: 12/31/19
Investment Services
N.A.I.C.S.: 523999

Thomas W. Farley *(Chm, Pres & CEO)*
David W. Bonanno *(CFO)*

FARADAY FUTURE INTELLIGENT ELECTRIC INC.
18455 S Figueroa St, Gardena, CA 90248
Tel.: (310) 956-6488   DE
Web Site: https://www.ff.com
Year Founded: 2020
FFIE—(NASDAQ)
Assets: $510,288,000
Liabilities: $327,535,000
Net Worth: $182,753,000
Earnings: ($552,069,000)
Emp.: 586
Fiscal Year-end: 12/31/22
Holding Company; Electric Motor Vehicle Developer
N.A.I.C.S.: 551112
Matthias Aydt *(CEO-Global & Global CEO)*
Xiao Ma *(Acting Head-Corporate Strategy)*
Yt Jia *(Founder, Partner & Chief Product Officer)*
Scott Graziano *(Gen Counsel-Global)*

FARMER BROTHERS CO.
1912 Farmer Brothers Dr, Northlake, TX 76262
Tel.: (682) 549-6600   DE
Web Site:
   https://www.farmerbros.com
Year Founded: 1912
FARM—(NASDAQ)
Rev.: $341,094,000
Assets: $185,213,000
Liabilities: $139,664,000
Net Worth: $45,549,000
Earnings: ($3,875,000)
Emp.: 1,003
Fiscal Year-end: 06/30/24
Coffee, Spices & Restaurant Supplies Distr
N.A.I.C.S.: 311920
John E. Moore III *(Pres & CEO)*
Brandi Wessel *(Dir-Comm)*
Jared Vitemb *(Chief Compliance Officer, Gen Counsel, Sec & VP)*
Vance Fisher *(CFO)*
Tom Bauer *(Chief Comml Officer & VP)*

Subsidiaries:

Boyd Coffee Company   (1)
19730 NE Sandy Blvd, Portland, OR 97230-7310
Tel.: (800) 545-4077
Web Site: http://www.boydscoffeestore.com
Coffee & Tea Products; Brewing Equipment
N.A.I.C.S.: 311920

China Mist Brands, Inc.   (1)
1912 Farmer Brothers Dr, Northlake, TX 76262
Tel.: (480) 998-8807
Web Site: https://www.chinamist.com
Whol Groceries
N.A.I.C.S.: 424490

FBC Finance Co.   (1)
20333 S Normandie Ave, Torrance, CA 90502-1215   (100%)
Tel.: (310) 787-5200
Web Site: http://www.farmerbroscousa.com
Sales Range: $400-449.9 Million
Emp.: 1,000
Financial Services
N.A.I.C.S.: 522299

Farmer Bros. Co.   (1)
20333 S Normandie Ave, Torrance, CA 90502
Tel.: (310) 787-5200
Web Site: http://www.farmerbros.com
Sales Range: $350-399.9 Million
Coffee & Tea Mfr
N.A.I.C.S.: 311920
John E. Moore III *(Interim CEO)*

West Coast Coffee Company Inc.   (1)
8010 NE Mauzey Ct, Hillsboro, OR 97124
Tel.: (800) 541-1307
Web Site: http://www.westcoastcoffee.com
Coffee & Tea Mfr
N.A.I.C.S.: 311920

FARMERS & MERCHANTS BANCORP
121 W Pine St, Lodi, CA 95240
Tel.: (209) 367-2300   DE
Web Site: https://www.fmbonline.com
Year Founded: 1999
FMCB—(OTCQX)
Rev.: $204,591,000
Assets: $5,327,399,000
Liabilities: $4,842,091,000
Net Worth: $485,308,000
Earnings: $75,090,000
Emp.: 374
Fiscal Year-end: 12/31/22
Bank Holding Company
N.A.I.C.S.: 551111
Kent A. Steinwert *(Chm, Pres & CEO)*
Jay J. Colombini *(Exec VP-Wholesale Banking Div-F&M Bank)*
Ryan J. Misasi *(Exec VP-Retail Banking Div-F&M Bank)*
David M. Zitterow *(Exec VP-Wholesale Banking Div-F&M Bank)*
John W. Weubbe *(Chief Credit Officer)*
Bart R. Olson *(CFO)*
Kyle E. Koelbel *(Officer)*

Subsidiaries:

Farmers & Merchants Bank of Central California   (1)
121 W Pine St, Lodi, CA 95240-2184   (100%)
Tel.: (209) 367-2300
Web Site: http://www.fmbonline.com
Sales Range: $100-124.9 Million
Commericial Banking
N.A.I.C.S.: 522110
Kent A. Steinwert *(Chm, Pres & CEO)*
Deborah E. Skinner *(Chief Admin Officer & Exec VP)*
Kenneth W. Smith *(Officer- & Exec VP)*
Ryan J. Misasi *(Exec VP & Mgr-Retail Banking Div)*
Jay J. Colombini *(Exec VP & Dir-Banking)*
Susan Clark *(Asst VP)*
Mark K. Olson *(CFO & Exec VP)*

FARMERS & MERCHANTS BANCORP, INC.
307 No Defiance St, Archbold, OH 43502
Tel.: (419) 446-2501   OH
Web Site: https://www.fm.bank
FMAO—(NASDAQ)
Rev.: $116,686,000
Assets: $3,015,351,000
Liabilities: $2,717,211,000
Net Worth: $298,140,000
Earnings: $32,515,000
Emp.: 431
Fiscal Year-end: 12/31/22
Bank Holding Company
N.A.I.C.S.: 551111
Lars B. Eller *(Pres & CEO)*
Amy L. Cover *(CMO & Sr VP)*
David Gerken *(Chief Lending Officer & Exec VP)*
Alexis Smith *(Chief People Officer & Sr VP)*
Kevin J. Sauder *(Vice Chm)*
Barbara J. Britenriker *(CFO & Exec VP)*
Shalini Singhal *(CIO & Sr VP)*
Benet Rupp *(Chief People Officer & Sr VP)*
Phillip Lucas *(Reg Pres & Sr VP)*
Brett Baumeister *(Reg Pres)*

Farmers & Merchants Bancorp, Inc.—(Continued)

Subsidiaries:

Farmers & Merchants State
Bank (1)
Tel.: (419) 446-2501
Web Site: https://www.fm-bank.com
Sales Range: $1-4.9 Billion
Commercial Banking Services
N.A.I.C.S.: 522110
Lars B. Eller (Pres & CEO)
Amy L. Cover (CMO & Sr VP)
David Gerken (Chief Lending Officer &
Exec VP)
Alexis Smith (Chief People Officer & Sr VP)

Subsidiary (Domestic):

Perpetual Federal Savings Bank,
Inc. (2)
120 N Main St, Urbana, OH 43078
Tel.: (937) 653-1700
Web Site: http://www.pfsb-urbana.com
Sales Range: $10-24.9 Million
Emp.: 21
Savings Bank
N.A.I.C.S.: 522180
Michael R. Melvin (Pres & CEO)
Christine A. Phelps (Sec & Sr VP)
Mary E. Heaston (VP)
Jared E. Riblet (Treas)
John M. Harrigan (VP)
Jennifer J. Miller (Asst Sec)

Ossian Financial Services, Inc. (1)
102 N Jefferson St, Ossian, IN 46777
Tel.: (260) 622-4141
Web Site: http://www.ossianstatebank.com
Bank Holding Company
N.A.I.C.S.: 551111
David Morrison (Pres & CEO)

Peoples-Sidney Financial
Corporation
101 E Court St, Sidney, OH 45365-0727
Tel.: (937) 492-6129
Web Site:
http://www.peoplesfederalsandl.com
Rev.: $4,837,653
Assets: $114,488,851
Liabilities: $99,250,977
Net Worth: $15,237,874
Earnings: $799,901
Emp.: 32
Fiscal Year-end: 06/30/2019
Bank Holding Company
N.A.I.C.S.: 551111
Debra A. Geuy (Pres & CEO)

Subsidiary (Domestic):

Peoples Federal Savings & Loan As-
sociation of Sidney (2)
101 E Ct St, Sidney, OH
45365-0727 (100%)
Tel.: (937) 492-6129
Web Site:
http://www.peoplesfederalsandl.com
Sales Range: $25-49.9 Million
Emp.: 20
Provider of Banking Services
N.A.I.C.S.: 551111
Debra A. Geuy (Pres & CEO)

FARMERS AND MERCHANTS
BANCSHARES, INC.
4510 Lower Beckleysville Rd Ste H,
Hampstead, MD 21074
Tel.: (410) 374-1510 MD
Web Site: https://www.fmb1919.bank
Year Founded: 2016
FMFG—(OTCIQ)
Rev.: $28,563,591
Assets: $718,210,672
Liabilities: $670,435,709
Net Worth: $47,774,963
Earnings: $8,090,127
Emp.: 87
Fiscal Year-end: 12/31/22
Bank Holding Company
N.A.I.C.S.: 551111
Ronald W. Hux (Vice Chm)
Gary A. Harris (Pres & CEO)
Mark C. Krebs (CFO & Sr VP)

Subsidiaries:

Farmers and Merchants Bank (1)
15226 Hanover Pike, Upperco, MD 21155
Tel.: (410) 833-6600
Web Site: https://www.fmb1919.bank
Sales Range: $10-24.9 Million
Commercial Banking
N.A.I.C.S.: 522110
Bruce L. Schindler (Chm)
Gary A. Harris (Pres & CEO)
Mark C. Krebs (CFO & Sr VP)
Christopher T. Oswald (COO & Sr VP)

FARMERS BANCORP INC.
9 E Clinton St, Frankfort, IN 46041
Tel.: (765) 654-8731
Web Site:
https://www.thefarmersbank.com
FABP—(OTCIQ)
Offices of Bank Holding Companies
N.A.I.C.S.: 551111
R. Kent Ryan (Chm)
Karen Gregerson (Pres & CEO)
Bradley S. Cunningham (VP & Sec)
Chad Kozuch (Treas)
Thomas D. Crawford (Vice Chm)

FARMERS MERCHANTS BANK
LONG BEACH
302 Pine Ave, Long Beach, CA
90802
Tel.: (562) 437-0011
Web Site: http://www.fmb.com
Year Founded: 1907
FMBL—(OTCQX)
Rev.: $137,476,000
Emp.: 600
State Commercial Banks
N.A.I.C.S.: 522110
Elodia Reyes (Coord-Credit)

FARMERS NATIONAL BANC
CORP.
20 S Broad St, Canfield, OH 44406
Tel.: (330) 702-8429 OH
Web Site:
https://www.farmersbankgroup.com
FMNB—(NASDAQ)
Rev.: $186,288,000
Assets: $4,082,200,000
Liabilities: $3,789,905,000
Net Worth: $292,295,000
Earnings: $60,597,000
Emp.: 546
Fiscal Year-end: 12/31/22
Bank Holding Company
N.A.I.C.S.: 551111
Kevin J. Helmick (Pres & CEO)
Joseph W. Sabat (Controller)
David Z. Paull (Vice Chm)
Timothy Shaffer (Chief Credit Officer
& Exec VP)
Amber B. Wallace (Chief Retail &
Mktg Officer & Exec VP)
Mark J. Wenick (Chief Wealth Mgmt
Officer & Sr VP-Farmers Bank)

Subsidiaries:

Cortland Bancorp, Inc. (1)
194 W Main St, Cortland, OH 44410
Tel.: (330) 637-8040
Web Site: http://www.cortlandbank.com
Rev.: $34,592,000
Assets: $821,305,000
Liabilities: $740,300,000
Net Worth: $81,005,000
Earnings: $8,263,000
Fiscal Year-end: 12/31/2020
Bank Holding Company
N.A.I.C.S.: 551111
Stanley P. Feret (Chief Lending Officer & Sr
VP)
David J. Lucido (CFO & Sr VP)

Subsidiary (Domestic):

Cortland Savings & Banking Co. (2)
325 S High St, Cortland, OH 44410
Tel.: (330) 282-4104

Web Site: http://www.cortlandbank.com
Sales Range: $50-74.9 Million
Emp.: 169
State Commercial Banking Services
N.A.I.C.S.: 522110
James M. Gasior (Pres & CEO)

Subsidiary (Domestic):

CSB Mortgage Company, Inc. (3)
194 W Main St, Cortland, OH 44410
Tel.: (330) 637-8040
Mortgage & Non-Mortgage Loan Brokers
N.A.I.C.S.: 522310

Donald C. Bowers Insurance,
Inc. (1)
1380 Dual Hwy, Hagerstown, MD 21740
Tel.: (301) 791-7910
Web Site: https://www.bowersinsurance.com
Emp.: 15
Insurance Agencies & Brokerages
N.A.I.C.S.: 524210
Jeff Bowers (VP)
John Bowers (Pres)
Crystal Eby (Acct Mgr-Comml Lines)
Janice Fisher (Acct Mgr-Personal Lines)
Beth Schoen (Acct Mgr-Comml Lines)
Heidi Hendershot (Mgr-Fin)
Bobi Jerome (Acct Mgr-Comml Lines)
Carol Smothers (Acct Mgr-Personal Lines)
Virginia Holder (Acct Mgr-Personal Lines)
Kelly Baranowski (Acct Mgr-Comml Lines)
Alexis Bush (Mgr-Relationship)

Emclaire Financial Corp (1)
612 Main St, Emlenton, PA 16373
Web Site: http://www.emclairefinancial.com
Rev.: $41,171,000
Assets: $1,059,508,000
Liabilities: $962,549,000
Net Worth: $96,959,000
Earnings: $10,171,000
Emp.: 148
Fiscal Year-end: 12/31/2021
Bank Holding Company
N.A.I.C.S.: 551111

Subsidiary (Domestic):

The Farmers National Bank of
Emlenton (2)
612 Main St, Emlenton, PA 16373
Tel.: (724) 867-2311
Web Site: http://www.farmersnb.com
Sales Range: $10-24.9 Million
Commercial Banking
N.A.I.C.S.: 522110
William C. Marsh (Chm)
Robert W. Foust (Sr VP-Corp Banking)
Randall Labrie (VP-Corp Banking)
Drew Nedzinski (VP-Corp Banking)
Nicole Figura (Officer-Comml Loan & VP)
Richard Grejda (VP & Sr Portfolio Mgr-
Comml)

Farmers National Insurance LLC (1)
339 N High St, Cortland, OH 44410-1022
Tel.: (330) 638-6146
Banking Services
N.A.I.C.S.: 522110
Gene Francisco (VP & Dir-Bus Dev)

Farmers Trust Company (1)
42 McClurg Rd, Youngstown, OH 44512
Tel.: (330) 743-7000
Web Site: https://www.farmerstrustco.com
Sales Range: $25-49.9 Million
Emp.: 18
Investment Management Service
N.A.I.C.S.: 523940
William I Ianshaw (COO & Exec VP)
David A. Dastoli (Pres)
Jill A. Pegg (VP-Admin)
Mark Wenick (Chief Wealth Mgmt Officer)
Kirsty Courson (Officer-Trust)
Deborah L. Grinstein (Officer-Trust & Bus
Dev)
George P. Millich (Chief Fiduciary Officer &
Sr VP)
Linda A. Russell (Officer-Trust)
Anthony M. Yacapraro (VP)
John Stewart (Chief Investment Officer & Sr
VP)
John Adzema (Sr VP-Retirement Svcs)
David Culp (Officer-Trust & Mgr-Trust In-
vestment Mgmt)
Todd Finn (Officer-Trust Investment & Asst
VP)

Amy L. Jones (Officer-Trust & Trust Compli-
ance & Asst VP)
Thomas Rumbaugh (Officer-Trust & Trust
Investment III & VP)
Dale Standley (Officer-Trust & Trust Invest-
ment IV)
Michelle M. Schenker (VP)
Barbara L. Repasky (VP & Dir-Tax)
Rebecca Eberle (Asst VP)
Shannon Greene-Day (Asst VP)
Jennifer Harrington (VP & Supvr-Trust Ops)

MDH Investment Management,
Inc. (1)
1216 Forsyth Pl, East Liverpool, OH 43920
Tel.: (330) 386-4452
Web Site: https://www.mdhinv.com
Emp.: 3
Investment Management Service
N.A.I.C.S.: 523940
Marc D. Hoffrichter (Founder, Chm & CEO)
David Bickerton (Pres)
Stephanie Grey (Office Mgr)

National Associates, Inc. (1)
22720 Fairview Ctr Dr Ste 100, Fairview
Park, OH 44126
Tel.: (440) 333-0222
Web Site:
https://www.nationalassociates.biz
Sales Range: $1-9.9 Million
Emp.: 17
Management Consulting Services
N.A.I.C.S.: 541611

The Farmers National Bank of
Canfield (1)
20 S Broad St, Canfield, OH 44406
Tel.: (330) 702-8429
Web Site:
http://www.farmersbankgroup.com
Sales Range: $50-74.9 Million
Emp.: 466
Commercial Banking
N.A.I.C.S.: 522110
Kevin J. Helmick (Pres & CEO)
Joseph W. Sabat (Chief Acctg Officer & VP)
Timothy Shaffer (Chief Credit Officer)
Amber B. Wallace (CMO, Chief Retail Offi-
cer & Exec VP)
Brian E. Jackson (CIO & Sr VP)
Mark A. Nicastro (Chief HR Officer & Sr VP)
Mark J. Wenick (Chief Wealth Mgmt Officer
& Exec VP)
Troy Adair (CFO & Exec VP)
Michael Oberhaus (Chief Risk Officer & Sr
VP)

FARMHOUSE, INC.
113 Cherry St Ste 90355, Seattle,
WA 98104 NV
Web Site: https://www.weedclub.com
FMHS—(OTCQB)
Rev.: $15,227
Assets: $8,160
Liabilities: $1,986,441
Net Worth: ($1,978,281)
Earnings: ($560,789)
Emp.: 3
Fiscal Year-end: 12/31/23
Cannabis Product Mfr
N.A.I.C.S.: 325411

FARMLAND PARTNERS INC.
4600 S Syracuse St Ste 1450, Den-
ver, CO 80237
Tel.: (720) 452-3100 MD
Web Site:
https://www.farmlandpartners.com
Year Founded: 2013
FPI—(NYSE)
Rev.: $61,210,000
Assets: $1,160,149,000
Liabilities: $566,145,000
Net Worth: $594,004,000
Earnings: $11,674,000
Emp.: 30
Fiscal Year-end: 12/31/22
Real Estate Investment Services
N.A.I.C.S.: 523999
Paul A. Pittman (Exec Chm)
Luca Fabbri (Pres & CEO)

Subsidiaries:

Farmland Partners Operating Partnership, L.P. (1)

4600 S Syracuse St Ste 1450, Denver, CO 80237
Tel.: (720) 452-3100
Real Estate Development Services
N.A.I.C.S.: 531390

Murray Wise Associates LLC (1)
1605 S State St Ste 110, Champaign, IL 61820
Tel.: (239) 430-6240
Web Site:
http://www.murraywiseassociates.com
Financial Advice Services
N.A.I.C.S.: 525990
Jamie Knight (Mgr)
Murray R. Wise (CEO)

FARO TECHNOLOGIES, INC.
125 Technology Park, Lake Mary, FL 32746
Tel.: (407) 333-9911   FL
Web Site: https://www.faro.com
Year Founded: 1982
FARO—(NASDAQ)
Rev.: $345,765,000
Assets: $473,347,000
Liabilities: $162,298,000
Net Worth: $311,049,000
Earnings: ($26,756,000)
Emp.: 1,490
Fiscal Year-end: 12/31/22
Designs, Develops, Markets & Supports Portable, Software Driven, Three-Dimensional Measurement Systems Used in a Broad Range of Manufacturing & Industrial Applications
N.A.I.C.S.: 334519
Yuval Wasserman (Chm)
Peter J. Lau (Pres & CEO)
Matthew Horwath (CFO & Sr VP)
Shelley Gretlein (Sr VP-Building Insights)
Roger Isern (Chief Digital Officer)
Malvika Jhangiani (Chief HR Officer & Sr VP)
David Wilson (Gen Counsel & Sr VP)

Subsidiaries:

Advanced Technical Solutions in Scandinavia AB (1)
Krokslattsgatan 7, 431 67, Molndal, Sweden
Tel.: (46) 31209616
Web Site: https://www.ats.se
Distance Laser Measurement Instrument Mfr
N.A.I.C.S.: 334511

Antares-Desenvolvimento de Software, Lda. (1)
Edificio Tower Plaza Rotunda Eng Edgar Cardoso 23 - 9 D, Vila Nova de Gaia, 4400-676, Portugal
Tel.: (351) 221208810
Design Software Development Services
N.A.I.C.S.: 541512

Cam2 SRL (1)
Via Giacomo Matteotti 161 163/A, Rezzato, Brescia, Italy
Tel.: (39) 0117549200
Web Site: http://www.faro.com
Computer Aided Coordinate & Measurement Software Provider
N.A.I.C.S.: 513210

FARO Benelux B.V. (1)
                 (100%)
Tel.: (31) 407981000
Web Site: https://www.faro.com
Sales Range: $10-24.9 Million
Portable Measurement Device Mfr
N.A.I.C.S.: 334413

FARO Deutschland Holding GmbH (1)
Lingwiesenstr 11/2, 70825, Korntal-Munchingen, Germany
Tel.: (49) 715097970
Web Site: http://www.faro.com
Sales Range: $25-49.9 Million
Emp.: 200
Measuring & Imaging Device Equipment Mfr

N.A.I.C.S.: 334519

FARO Europe GmbH & Co. KG (1)
Lingwiesenstr 11/2, 70825, Korntal-Munchingen, Germany   (100%)
Tel.: (49) 715097970
Sales Range: $100-124.9 Million
Design, Develop & Market Portable Computerized Measurement Devices & Software Applications
N.A.I.C.S.: 334413

FARO International (Shanghai) Co., Ltd (1)
1/F Building No 2 Juxin Park 188 Pingfu Road Xuhui District, Shanghai, 200231, China
Tel.: (86) 2161917600
Design Software Development Services
N.A.I.C.S.: 541512

FARO Shanghai Co, Ltd (1)
1/F Building No 2 Juxin Information Technology Park 188 Pingfu Road, Xuhui District, Shanghai, 200231, China
Tel.: (86) 2161917600
Measuring & Imaging Device Equipment Mfr
N.A.I.C.S.: 334519

FARO Singapore Pte. Ltd. (1)
                 (100%)
Tel.: (65) 31654200
Sales Range: $10-24.9 Million
Emp.: 70
Developer & Marketer of Portable Computerized Measurement Devices
N.A.I.C.S.: 334413

FARO Spain S.L.U. (1)
Automotive Intelligence Center Edificio Fase 2, Planta Baja Poligono Boroa Parcela 2A-4, 48340, Amorebieta-Etxano, Bizkaia, Spain
Tel.: (34) 946662140
3D Measurement Technology Mfr
N.A.I.C.S.: 334112

FARO Tech Polska (1)
Ul Powstancow Slaskich 50, 53-350, Wroclaw, Poland
Tel.: (48) 713393276
Web Site: http://www.faro.com
Software Development Services
N.A.I.C.S.: 541511

FARO Technologies UK Ltd. (1)
Great Central Way Butlers Leap, Rugby, CV21 3XH, Warwickshire, United Kingdom
Tel.: (44) 2476973000
Design Software Development Services
N.A.I.C.S.: 541512

FARO Technologies do Brasil Ltda (1)
Rua San Jose 360 - Pq Ind, Cotia, Sao Paulo, 06715-862, SP, Brazil
Tel.: (55) 1135004600
Software Development Services
N.A.I.C.S.: 541511
Simon Raab (Chm)

FARO Technology Polska Sp. z o.o. (1)
Ul Powstancow Slaskich 50 15, 53-350, Wroclaw, Poland
Tel.: (48) 713393276
Counting Device Mfr
N.A.I.C.S.: 334514

FARO UK (1)
The Technocentre Coventry University Technology Pk Puma Way, Coventry, CV1 2TT, United Kingdom
Tel.: (44) 2476236151
Web Site: http://www.faro.com
Sales Range: $10-24.9 Million
Emp.: 15
Measuring & Imaging Device Equipment Mfr
N.A.I.C.S.: 334519
Joseph Arezone (Sr VP & Mng Dir-Europe, Middle East & Africa)

Faro Technologies, Inc. - Laser Division (1)
222 Gale Ln, Kennett Square, PA 19348
Tel.: (610) 444-2300
Sales Range: $25-49.9 Million
Emp.: 55
Laser Apparatus Mfr
N.A.I.C.S.: 333310

Holobuilder, Inc. (1)
250 Technology Park, Lake Mary, FL 32746
Tel.: (415) 843-5552
Web Site: https://www.holobuilder.com
Institutional Building Construction Services
N.A.I.C.S.: 236220

Laser Control Systems Limited. (1)
Unit 3B The Granary Building, Millow, Biggleswade, SG18 8RH, Bedfordshire, United Kingdom
Tel.: (44) 2038686225
Web Site: http://www.lasercontrols.com
Electromedical Product Mfr
N.A.I.C.S.: 334510

Laser Projection Technologies, Inc. (1)
8 Delta Dr, Londonderry, NH 03053   (100%)
Tel.: (603) 421-0209
Web Site: http://www.lptcorp.com
Sales Range: $1-9.9 Million
Emp.: 50
Mfr of Laser Projection & Measurement Systems
N.A.I.C.S.: 334515

Nutfield Technology, Inc. (1)
34B Londonderry Road, Londonderry, NH 03053
Tel.: (603) 893-6200
Web Site: http://www.nutfieldtech.com
Sales Range: $1-9.9 Million
Emp.: 18
Computer Peripheral Equipment Mfr
N.A.I.C.S.: 334118

Open Technologies SRL (1)
Via Giacomo Matteotti 161 163/A, 25086, Rezzato, Brescia, Italy
Tel.: (39) 0117549200
Web Site: http://www.opentechnologies.it
Software Development Services
N.A.I.C.S.: 513210

Opto-Tech SRL (1)
Via Romolo Murri 22/28, 20013, Magenta, MI, Italy
Tel.: (39) 0252804085
Optical Equipment Distr
N.A.I.C.S.: 423460
Matteo Marchini (Gen Mgr)

FAST ACQUISITION CORP.
3 Minetta St, New York, NY 10012
Tel.: (917) 921-0285   DE
Year Founded: 2020
FST—(NYSE)
Assets: $205,366,240
Liabilities: $280,083,837
Net Worth: ($74,717,597)
Earnings: ($40,556,629)
Emp.: 4
Fiscal Year-end: 12/31/21
Investment Services
N.A.I.C.S.: 523999
Kimberly S. Grant (Chief Strategy Officer)
Sandy Beall (CEO)
Garrett Schreiber (CFO)
Todd Higgins (COO)
Kevin Reddy (Chm)

FASTENAL COMPANY
2001 Theurer Blvd, Winona, MN 55987-1500
Tel.: (507) 454-5374   MN
Web Site: https://www.fastenal.com
Year Founded: 1967
FAST—(NASDAQ)
Rev.: $7,346,700,000
Assets: $4,462,900,000
Liabilities: $1,114,100,000
Net Worth: $3,348,800,000
Earnings: $1,155,000,000
Emp.: 23,201
Fiscal Year-end: 12/31/23
Industrial & Construction Products Whslr & Distr
N.A.I.C.S.: 332722
Robert A. Kierlin (Co-Founder)
Stephen M. Slaggie (Co-Founder)

Henry K. McConnon (Co-Founder)
John D. Remick (Co-Founder)
Nicholas J. Lundquist (Bd of Dirs, Executives)
James C. Jansen (Exec VP-Mfg)
Michael M. Gostomski (Co-Founder)
Sheryl A. Lisowski (Chief Acctg Officer, Treas & Exec VP)
John Lewis Soderberg (Sr Exec VP-IT)
Charles S. Miller (Sr Exec VP-Sls)
William Joseph Drazkowski (Exec VP-Sls)
Noelle J. Oas (Exec VP-HR)
Taylor Ranta Oborski (Mgr-Fin Reporting & Regulatory Compliance)
Troy Parkos (VP)
Jeffery M. Watts (Pres & Chief Sls Officer)
Daniel L. Florness (CEO)

Subsidiaries:

Fastco (Shanghai) Trading Co., Ltd. (1)
No 7 Jinxi Park Lane 180 Jinxi Road, Shanghai, 201613, China
Tel.: (86) 2133528288
Sales Range: $150-199.9 Million
Construction Fastener Sale Distr
N.A.I.C.S.: 423710
Jianfang Chen (Mgr-Sls)

Fastenal (Shanghai) International Trading Co. Ltd. (1)
Plant C8 No 7 Lane 180 Jinxi Road, Songjiang, Shanghai, 201613, China
Tel.: (86) 213 352 8288
Web Site: https://www.fastenal.cn
Emp.: 20
Industrial Supply Merchant Whslr
N.A.I.C.S.: 423840

Fastenal (Thailand) Ltd. (1)
289/27 Moo 13 KingKaew Road, Samut Prakan, 10540, Thailand
Tel.: (66) 21837847
Construction Materials Whslr
N.A.I.C.S.: 423320

Fastenal (Tianjin) International Trading Co. Ltd. (1)
8 Xingwang Rd, Wuqing Development, Tianjin, China
Tel.: (86) 2282166770
Construction Materials Whslr
N.A.I.C.S.: 423320

Fastenal Brasil Importacao, Exportacao e Distribuicao Ltda. (1)
Av Quinze De Agosto 5260 Quandra 59, Jardim Leocadia, Sorocaba, 18085-290, Brazil
Tel.: (55) 153 238 3399
Web Site: https://www.fastenal.com
Industrial & Construction Supplies Whslr
N.A.I.C.S.: 444140

Fastenal Canada, Ltd. (1)
209 Advance Blvd Unit 1, Brampton, L6T 4V9, ON, Canada
Tel.: (905) 790-8387
Web Site: http://www.fastenal.com
Industrial & Construction Supplies Whslr
N.A.I.C.S.: 444140

Fastenal Colombia S.A.S. (1)
Autopista Medellin KM 3 5 Siberia, Cota, Cundinamarca, Colombia
Tel.: (57) 18415282
Emp.: 6
Construction Materials Whslr
N.A.I.C.S.: 423320
Oscar Paez (Gen Mgr)

Fastenal Company Purchasing (1)
2001 Theurer Blvd, Winona, MN 55987-1500
Tel.: (507) 454-5374
Industrial & Construction Supplies Whslr
N.A.I.C.S.: 444140

Fastenal Europe AB (1)
Godsmottagning C Esabvagen, 695 81, Laxa, Sweden

Fastenal Company—(Continued)

Tel.: (46) 58410505
Emp.: 2
Cement Material Distr
N.A.I.C.S.: 423320
Douglas Alagna (Gen Mgr)

Fastenal Europe GmbH (1)
Waidplatzstrasse 12a, 79331, Teningen, Germany
Tel.: (49) 7663603870
Web Site: http://www.fastenal.com
Industrial & Construction Supplies Whslr
N.A.I.C.S.: 444140

Fastenal Europe RO S.r.l. (1)
1A Vidului Street, Floresti, Cluj-Napoca, 400221; Romania
Tel.: (40) 264232986
Web Site: http://www.fastenal.com
Construction Materials Whslr
N.A.I.C.S.: 423320
Ciprian Morutan (Pres)

Fastenal Europe S.r.l. (1)
Via Le Prata 114 Interno 1, 50041, Calenzano, Italy
Tel.: (39) 0550601374
Web Site: http://www.fastenal.com
Industrial & Construction Supplies Whslr
N.A.I.C.S.: 444140

Fastenal Europe, Kft. (1)
Farkasvermi utca 87, 8000, Szekesfehervar, Hungary
Tel.: (36) 22502065
Web Site: http://www.fastenal.com
Sales Range: $25-49.9 Million
Industrial & Construction Supplie Whslr
N.A.I.C.S.: 444140

Fastenal Europe, Ltd. (1)
Unit 17 Henley Industrial Estate Henley Road, Coventry, CV2 1ST, West Midlands, United Kingdom
Tel.: (44) 2476666332
Sales Range: $25-49.9 Million
Emp.: 7
Industrial & Construction Supplie Whslr
N.A.I.C.S.: 444140

Fastenal Europe, s.r.o. (1)
Trnkova 3130/119b, Lisen, 628 00, Brno, Czech Republic
Tel.: (420) 547425461
Web Site: http://www.fastenal.com
Industrial & Construction Supplie Whslr
N.A.I.C.S.: 444140

Fastenal Malaysia SDN BHD (1)
No 12 14 16 Jalan Mega1/7 Taman Perindustriang Nusa Cermerlang, 79200, Iskandar Puteri, Malaysia
Tel.: (60) 75579592
Web Site: http://www.fastenal.com
Sales Range: $25-49.9 Million
Hardware Product Retailer
N.A.I.C.S.: 444140

Fastenal Mexico Services S. de R.L. de C.V. (1)
Julian Trevino Elizondo 930 Bodega 12 Col Regio Parque, 66633, Apodaca, NL, Mexico
Tel.: (52) 8110860608
Web Site: http://www.fastenel.com
Sales Range: $25-49.9 Million
Industrial & Construction Tools Distr
N.A.I.C.S.: 444140

Fastenal Panama S.A. (1)
PH Zona Uno Terminal Industr Bodega 403 Corrodor Sur Don Bosco, Corrogimiento do Ancon, Panama, Panama
Tel.: (507) 2326584
Sales Range: $25-49.9 Million
Emp.: 8
Industrial & Construction Supplies Whslr
N.A.I.C.S.: 444140

Fastenal Services S. de R.L. de C.V. (1)
Carretera Miguel Aleman 14.2Km, Bega No 4, Apodaca, 66633, NL, Mexico
Tel.: (52) 8110860608
Web Site: http://www.fastenal.com
Sales Range: $10-24.9 Million
Emp.: 4
Construction Fastener Sales
N.A.I.C.S.: 423710

Fastenal Singapore P.T.E. Ltd. (1)
10 Pandan Crescent 05-02, Singapore, 128466, Singapore
Tel.: (65) 6 272 2524
Web Site: http://www.fastenal.com
Sales Range: $150-199.9 Million
Construction Fastener Sales
N.A.I.C.S.: 423710
Michele Yong (Mng Dir)

Holo-Krome Company (1)
61 Barnes Industrial Park N, Wallingford, CT 06492
Tel.: (203) 894-7770
Web Site: http://www.holo-krome.com
Sales Range: $25-49.9 Million
Emp.: 100
Screw & Industrial Fastener Mfr & Whslr
N.A.I.C.S.: 332722

River Surplus and Supply, LLC (1)
4905 MN Hwy 16 W, Hokah, MN 55941
Tel.: (507) 894-7770
Web Site: http://www.7riverssurplus.com
Online Marketing Services
N.A.I.C.S.: 541613

FASTLY, INC.

475 Brannan St Ste 300, San Francisco, CA 94107   DE
Web Site: https://www.fastly.com
Year Founded: 2011
FSLY—(NYSE)
Rev.: $505,988,000
Assets: $1,525,191,000
Liabilities: $545,703,000
Net Worth: $979,488,000
Earnings: ($133,088,000)
Emp.: 1,207
Fiscal Year-end: 12/31/23
Software Development Services
N.A.I.C.S.: 541511
Tyler McMullen (CTO)
Peter Alexander (CMO)
Kip Compton (Chief Product Officer)
Ronald W. Kisling (CFO)
Todd Nightingale (CEO)
Puja Jaspal (Chief People Officer)
Marshall Erwin (Chief Info Security Officer)
Karen Greenstein (Gen Counsel)
Artur Bergman (Founder)

Subsidiaries:

Signal Sciences, LLC (1)
600 Corporate Pointe Ste 1200, Culver City, CA 90230
Tel.: (424) 319-7257
Web Site: http://www.signalsciences.com
Cloud Computing Services
N.A.I.C.S.: 541512

FATE THERAPEUTICS, INC.

12278 Scripps Summit Dr, San Diego, CA 92131   DE
Tel.: (858) 875-1800
Web Site:
https://www.fatetherapeutics.com
Year Founded: 2007
FATE—(NASDAQ)
Rev.: $96,300,000
Assets: $705,561,000
Liabilities: $221,622,000
Net Worth: $483,939,000
Earnings: ($281,721,000)
Emp.: 551
Fiscal Year-end: 12/31/22
Biopharmaceutical Mfr
N.A.I.C.S.: 325412
David T. Scadden (Founder)
John D. Mendlein (Vice Chm)
William H. Rastetter (Chm)
J. Scott Wolchko (Pres & CEO)
Cindy R. Tahl (Gen Counsel)
Jim Beitel (Sr VP-Corp Dev)
Sarah Cooley (Sr VP-Clinical Translation)
Jerome Bressi (Sr VP)

FATHOM HOLDINGS INC.

2000 Regency Pkwy Ste 300, Cary, NC 27518   NC
Web Site: https://www.fathominc.com
Year Founded: 2017
FTHM—(NASDAQ)
Rev.: $412,964,000
Assets: $80,187,000
Liabilities: $18,166,000
Net Worth: $62,021,000
Earnings: ($27,626,000)
Emp.: 279
Fiscal Year-end: 12/31/22
Holding Company
N.A.I.C.S.: 551112
Scott N. Flanders (Chm)
Joshua Harley (Founder)
Marco Fregenal (Pres, CEO & CFO)
Samantha Giuggio (Chief Broker Ops Officer)
Wendy Forsythe (Chief Brand Officer)
Scott Loftin (CTO)
Veronica Salmon (Sr VP-Fin)

Subsidiaries:

Encompass Lending Group, LP (1)
23108 Seven Meadows Pkwy Ste 100, Katy, TX 77494
Tel.: (281) 693-5363
Web Site: https://encompasslending.com
Sales Range: $1-9.9 Million
Mortgage Loan Lending Services
N.A.I.C.S.: 522310
Wayne King (Pres)

Subsidiary (Domestic):

Cornerstone First Financial
2300 Wisconsin Ave NW Ste 400B, Washington, DC 20007-1885
Tel.: (202) 625-1221
Web Site: http://www.cornerstonefirst.com
Vocational Rehabilitation Services
N.A.I.C.S.: 624310
Emily Cook (Coord-Loan)
Joe Rogers (Dir-Ops)

Elite Financing Group, LLC (2)
301 Denali Pass Unit #1, Cedar Park, TX 78613
Tel.: (512) 279-0505
Web Site:
http://www.elitefinancinggroup.com
Rev.: $2,786,000
Emp.: 14
Real Estate Credit
N.A.I.C.S.: 522292
Joshua W Bibler (Founder)

Verus Title Inc. (1)
2000 Regency Pkwy Ste 368, Cary, NC 27518
Tel.: (919) 355-9090
Web Site: https://www.verustitle.com
Insurance Services
N.A.I.C.S.: 524113
Paul Yurashevich (Founder & CEO)
Angela Gurtsishvili (Dir-Ops)

FB FINANCIAL CORPORATION

1221 Broadway Ste 1300, Nashville, TN 37203
Tel.: (615) 564-1212   TN
Web Site:
https://www.firstbankonline.com
Year Founded: 1906
FBK—(NYSE)
Rev.: $606,080,000
Assets: $12,847,756,000
Liabilities: $11,522,238,000
Net Worth: $1,325,518,000
Earnings: $124,571,000
Emp.: 1,757
Fiscal Year-end: 12/31/22
Holding Company
N.A.I.C.S.: 551111
Christopher T. Holmes (Pres & CEO)
Jonathan W. Pennington (Chief Acctg Officer)
Keith Rainwater (Chief Acctg Officer)

Subsidiaries:

Franklin Financial Network, Inc. (1)

---

722 Columbia Ave, Franklin, TN 37064
Tel.: (615) 236-2265
Web Site:
http://www.franklinsynergybank.com
Rev.: $202,467,000
Assets: $3,896,162,000
Liabilities: $3,485,736,000
Net Worth: $410,426,000
Earnings: $14,822,000
Emp.: 339
Fiscal Year-end: 12/31/2019
Bank Holding Company
N.A.I.C.S.: 551111
Terry R. Howell (Officer-Corp Risk & Exec VP)
J. Myers Jones III (CEO)
Christopher J. Black (CFO & Exec VP)
Steven E. Groom (Chief HR Officer, Gen Counsel & Exec VP)
David J. McDaniel (Chief Lending Officer & Exec VP)
Eddie A. Maynard Jr. (Chief Credit Officer & Exec VP)

Subsidiary (Domestic):

Franklin Synergy Bank (2)
722 Columbia Ave, Franklin, TN 37064
Tel.: (615) 236-2963
Web Site:
http://www.franklinsynergybank.com
Sales Range: $25-49.9 Million
Commercial Banking
N.A.I.C.S.: 522110
Carl Haynes (Officer-Comml Banking-Carothers Parkway & Sr VP)
Clint McCain (Officer-Comml Banking & VP-Spring Hill)
Terry Walker (Sr VP)
Chad Randall (Officer-Comml Banking & Sr VP-Berry Farms)
Philip Feemster (Officer-Comml Banking & Sr VP-Brentwood)
Bob Goodall (Officer-Comml Banking & Sr VP-Sam Ridley Parkway)
Melinda Bailey (Officer-Comml Banking & Sr VP-Brentwood)
Greg Wiel (Officer-Comml Banking & Sr VP-Cool Springs)
Matthew Cole Hodges (Officer-Comml Banking & Sr VP-Cool Springs)

Investors Title Company (1)
219 S Central Ave, Clayton, MO 63105
Tel.: (314) 862-0303
Commercial Financial Banking Services
N.A.I.C.S.: 551111

FBEC WORLDWIDE, INC.

5104 N Orange Blossom Trl Ste 202, Orlando, FL 32810
Tel.: (402) 580-7162   NV
Web Site:
http://www.fbecworldwide.com
Year Founded: 2002
FBEC—(OTCIQ)
Sales Range: Less than $1 Million
Emp.: 1
Beverages Mfr
N.A.I.C.S.: 311999
James D. Dang (CEO)

FCCC, INC.

725 5th Ave Fl 14 Unit 3, New York, NY 10022
Tel.: (812) 933-8888   CT
Year Founded: 1960
FCIC—(OTCIQ)
Rev.: $100,000
Assets: $53,000
Liabilities: $703,000
Net Worth: ($650,000)
Earnings: ($342,000)
Emp.: 3
Fiscal Year-end: 03/31/24
Investment Services
N.A.I.C.S.: 523999
Fnu Oudom (Chm & Pres)
David He (CEO)

FCG, INC.

14239 W Bell Rd 104, Surprise, AZ 85374

Tel.: (602) 944-3901 PA
Web Site: http://www.fcgservices.com
Year Founded: 1992
FCGN—(OTCIQ)
Information Technology Services
N.A.I.C.S.: 541511
Jason Fields (Pres)

FDCTECH, INC.
200 Spectrum Dr Ste 300, Irvine, CA
92618 DE
Web Site: https://www.fdctech.com
Year Founded: 2016
FDCT—(OTCEM)
Rev.: $12,754,900
Assets: $47,543,066
Liabilities: $34,493,289
Net Worth: $13,049,777
Earnings: $1,567,827
Fiscal Year-end: 12/31/23
Online Trading Services
N.A.I.C.S.: 522299
Mitchell Eaglstein (Co-Founder, Pres & CEO)
Peggy S. Reed (COO)
Imran Firoz (Co-Founder, CFO & Sec)
Brian D. Platt (CTO)
Warwick Kerridge (Chm)

Subsidiaries:

Genesis Financial, Inc. (1)
3773 W 5th St Ste 301, Post Falls, ID
83854
Tel.: (208) 457-9442
Web Site: http://www.genesisfinance.com
Sales Range: Less than $1 Million
Emp.: 3
Real Estate Mortgage Loan Brokerage Services
N.A.I.C.S.: 522310
Mark Attinger (Pres & COO)

NSFX Ltd. (1)
168 St Christopher Street, Valletta, VLT
1467, Malta
Tel.: (356) 27781919
Web Site: https://nsfx.com
Online Trading Services
N.A.I.C.S.: 522299

FEDERAL AGRICULTURAL MORTGAGE CORPORATION
2100 Pennsylvania Ave NW Ste
450N, Washington, DC 20037
Tel.: (202) 872-7700
Web Site:
  https://www.farmermac.com
Year Founded: 1988
AGM—(NYSE)
Rev.: $755,536,000
Assets: $27,333,110,000
Liabilities: $26,061,152,000
Net Worth: $1,271,958,000
Earnings: $150,979,000
Emp.: 158
Fiscal Year-end: 12/31/22
Mortgage & Nonmortgage Loan Brokers
N.A.I.C.S.: 522310
Gregory N. Ramsey (Chief Acctg Officer, VP & Controller)
Lowell L. Junkins (Chm)
Stephen P. Mullery (Gen Counsel, Sec & Exec VP)
Patrick J. Kerrigan (VP-Bus Dev)
Bradford Todd Nordholm (Pres & CEO)
Joe Munsell (Dir-Financial Reporting & Asst Controller)
Megan Murray-Pelaez (Dir-Mktg & Comm)
Christy Prendergast (VP & Deputy Gen Counsel)
Aparna Ramesh (CFO, Treas & Exec VP)
LaJuana S. Wilcher (Vice Chm)

Zachary N. Carpenter (Chief Bus Officer & Exec VP)
Toyin Adams (Dir-Internal Audit)
Jalpa Nazareth (Dir-IR & Fin Strategy)
Marc J. Crady (Chief Credit Officer & Sr VP)
Michelle Nichols (Dir-Compliance)
Robert J. Maines (Sr VP)
Kerry T. Willie (Chief HR Officer)
Todd A. Batta (VP)
Sean T. Datcher (CIO)
Julie Bustad (Dir)
Jonathan Cohen (Gen Counsel)
Monica Coley (Dir)
Tina Johnson (Dir)
Jack Keil (Dir)
Dimitar Kolev (Head)
Brad Pierce (Dir)
Chip Schmalz (Dir)
Evan Thayer (VP)
Amy Van Meeteren (Sr Dir)

Subsidiaries:

Farmer Mac II LLC (1)
1999 K St NW 4th Fl, Washington, DC
20006
Tel.: (202) 872-7700
Web Site: https://www.farmermac2.com
Nondepository Credit Intermediation Services
N.A.I.C.S.: 522299

FEDERAL HOME LOAN MORTGAGE CORPORATION
8200 Jones Branch Dr, McLean, VA
22102-3110
Tel.: (703) 903-2000 NY
Web Site:
  https://www.freddiemac.com
Year Founded: 1970
FMCC—(OTCQB)
Rev.: $108,050,000,000
Assets: $3,280,976,000,000
Liabilities: $3,233,254,000,000
Net Worth: $47,722,000,000
Earnings: $10,538,000,000
Emp.: 8,004
Fiscal Year-end: 12/31/23
Federally Sponsored Home Mortgage Credit Services
N.A.I.C.S.: 522310
Deborah Jenkins (Exec VP & Head)
Jerry Weiss (Chief Admin Officer & Exec VP)
Anil D. Hinduja (Chief Risk Officer & Exec VP)
Frank Nazzaro (Exec VP-Technology)
Angela Locke (Chief Diversity Officer & Interim Head-HR)
John Glessner (Sr VP & Head-Investments & Capital Markets)
Jerry Mauricio (Chief Compliance Officer & Sr VP)
Donald F. Kish (Principal Acctg Officer, Sr VP & Controller)
Laura Lee (Sr VP)
Dionne Wallace Oakley (Chief HR Officer, Chief Diversity Officer & Sr VP)
Dennis Hermonstyne Jr. (Chief Compliance Officer & Sr VP)
Heidi Mason (Gen Counsel & Exec VP)
Wendell Chambliss (Sr VP)
Kevin Palmer (Sr VP)
Ravi Shankar (Sr VP)
Michael T. Hutchins (Pres)
Diana W. Reid (CEO)

FEDERAL LIFE GROUP, INC.
3750 W Deerfield Rd, Riverwoods, IL
60015
Tel.: (847) 520-1900 DE
Year Founded: 1899
FLFG—(OTCIQ)

Financial Investment Services
N.A.I.C.S.: 523999
William S. Austin (Pres & CEO)
Knut Olson (CEO)
John Horbal (CFO)
Anders Raaum (Sr VP)
David Walbrun (Chief Comml Officer)
Thomas Marra (Chm)

FEDERAL NATIONAL MORTGAGE ASSOCIATION
Midtown Ctr 1100 15th St NW, Washington, DC 20005 DC
Web Site:
  https://www.fanniemae.com
Year Founded: 1938
FNMA—(OTCQB)
Rev.: $141,240,000,000
Assets: $4,325,437,000,000
Liabilities: $4,247,755,000,000
Net Worth: $77,682,000,000
Earnings: $17,408,000,000
Emp.: 8,100
Fiscal Year-end: 12/31/23
Home Mortgage Financing Services
N.A.I.C.S.: 522310
Stergios Theologides (Chief Admin Officer & Exec VP)
Michele M. Evans (Exec VP & Head-Multifamily)
Nancy Jardini (Chief Compliance & Ethics Officer & Sr VP)
Sheila Colleen Bair (Chm)
Steve James (CMO & Sr VP)
Stergios Theologides (Gen Counsel, Sec & Exec VP)
Malloy Evans (Exec VP & Head-Single-Family)
Sharifa A. Anderson (Chief Diversity & Inclusion Officer & Sr VP)
James L. Holmberg (Sr VP & Controller)
Anthony Moon (Chief Risk Officer)
Katie O'Connell Jones (Chief HR Officer)
Ramon Richards (CIO)
Cissy Yang (Sr VP)

FEDERAL REALTY INVESTMENT TRUST
909 Rose Ave Ste 200, Rockville, MD
20852
Tel.: (301) 998-8100 MD
Web Site:
  https://www.federalrealty.com
Year Founded: 1962
FRT—(NYSE)
Rev.: $1,132,154,000
Assets: $8,436,512,000
Liabilities: $5,394,353,000
Net Worth: $3,042,159,000
Earnings: $236,985,000
Emp.: 297
Fiscal Year-end: 12/31/23
Real Estate Investment Trust
N.A.I.C.S.: 525990
Porter Bellew (CIO & VP)
Donald C. Wood (CEO)
Jan Sweetnam (Pres-Western Reg & Exec VP)
John R. Tschiderer (Sr VP-Dev)
Dawn M. Becker (Gen Counsel, Sec & Exec VP)
Jeffrey S. Berkes (Pres & COO)
Wendy Seher (Pres-Eastern Reg & Exec VP)
Barry Carty (Sr VP-Acquisitions-East Coast)
Patrick Inaba (VP)
Jeff Kreshek (Sr VP-Leasing-West Coast)
Michael Kelleher (VP-Specialty Leasing)
Jeffrey Fischer (VP-Reg Leasing)
Joseph Byrnes (VP-Reg Leasing)

Michael Ennes (Sr VP-Mixed-Use Initiatives & Corp Comm)
Ramsey D. Meiser (Sr VP-Dev)
Daniel Guglielmone (CFO, Treas & Exec VP)
Craig Klimisch (VP & Controller)
Stuart Biel (Sr VP-Reg Leasing)
Patrick Dillon (VP-Construction)
Chris Fleming (VP-Asset Mgmt)
Baris Ipeker (VP-Investments & Legal Counsel)
Patrick McMahon (Sr VP-Reg Dev)
James Milam (Sr VP)
Liz Ryan (VP-Reg Leasing)
Stuart MacDonald (VP-Reg Dev)
Angela Lee (VP-Reg Fin)
Brad Dutton (VP-Reg Construction)
Mark T. Brennan (VP-Reg Dev)
Lance Billingsley (Sr VP-Anchor Leasing)
Richard Abruscato (VP-Reg Leasing)
Jay Brinson (VP-Dev)
Kari L. Glinski (VP-Asset Mgmt)
Geoff Sharpe (VP-Creative Plng & Dev)
Deborah A. Colson (Sr VP)
Christian Melgard (VP)

Subsidiaries:

Assembly Row Condominium, Inc. (1)
275 Foley St, Somerville, MA 02145
Tel.: (617) 623-1400
Web Site: http://www.alloyatassembly.com
Real Estate Investment Services
N.A.I.C.S.: 525990

FR Mercer Mall, LLC (1)
3345 US Highway 1, Lawrence, NJ 08648
Tel.: (484) 419-1205
Nonresidential Building Leasing Services
N.A.I.C.S.: 531120

FR San Antonio Center, LLC (1)
696 Showers Dr, Mountain View, CA 94040
Tel.: (408) 234-6471
Web Site: https://sanantoniocenter.com
Nonresidential Building Leasing Services
N.A.I.C.S.: 531120

FRIT Cocowalk Owner, LLC (1)
3015 Grand Ave, Miami, FL 33133
Tel.: (305) 444-0777
Web Site: http://www.cocowalk.com
Real Estate Manangement Services
N.A.I.C.S.: 531312
William Rivas (Gen Mgr)
Brittany Castro (Mgr-Mktg)

FRIT Shops at Sunset Place, LLC (1)
5701 Sunset Dr Ste 350, South Miami, FL 33143
Tel.: (305) 663-0482
Web Site: http://www.shopsunsetplace.com
Residential Building Rental & Leasing Services
N.A.I.C.S.: 531110

FRIT Solar, Inc. (1)
1626 E Jefferson St, Rockville, MD 20852
Tel.: (301) 998-8270
Residential Building Leasing Services
N.A.I.C.S.: 531110
Norma Selman (Gen Mgr)

FRLP, Inc. (1)
State Pier 1 Water St, Fall River, MA 02724-1007
Tel.: (508) 674-5707
Web Site: http://www.fallriverlinepier.com
Social Advocacy Services
N.A.I.C.S.: 813319

Primestor Jordan Downs, LLC (1)
9901 S Alameda St, Los Angeles, CA 90002
Web Site: http://www.primestor.com
Commercial Real Estate Sale & Leasing Services
N.A.I.C.S.: 531210

SRI San Antonio, Inc. (1)
1626 E Jefferson St, Rockville, MD 20852
Tel.: (301) 998-8335

Federal Realty Investment Trust—(Continued)

Real Estate Services
N.A.I.C.S.: 531312

Street Retail West 6, L.P. **(1)**
166 W Colorado Blvd, Pasadena, CA 91105
Tel.: (626) 449-4087
Real Estate Services
N.A.I.C.S.: 531312

Street Retail, Inc. **(1)**
1626 E Jefferson St, Rockville, MD 20852
Tel.: (301) 998-8100
Web Site: http://www.federalrealty.com
Sales Range: $50-74.9 Million
Emp.: 120
N.A.I.C.S.: 525990

**The Avenue at White Marsh Business
Trust** **(1)**
8125 Honeygo Blvd, Baltimore, MD 21236
Tel.: (443) 219-1820
Web Site:
http://www.theavenueatwhitemarsh.com
Nonresidential Building Leasing Services
N.A.I.C.S.: 531120

White Marsh Plaza, LLC **(1)**
8200 Perry Hall Blvd, Baltimore, MD 21236
Tel.: (410) 931-7101
Web Site: http://www.whitemarshmall.com
Nonresidential Building Leasing Services
N.A.I.C.S.: 531120

FEDERAL SCREW WORKS
34846 Goddard Rd, Romulus, MI
48174
Tel.: (734) 941-4211 **MI**
Web Site:
https://federalscrewworks.com
Year Founded: 1917
FSCR—(OTCIQ)
Rev.: $60,010,000
Assets: $65,025,000
Liabilities: $48,379,000
Net Worth: $16,646,000
Earnings: ($2,031,000)
Emp.: 184
Fiscal Year-end: 06/30/20
Screws, Bolts, Screw Machine Parts
& Locknuts Mfr
N.A.I.C.S.: 332722

Subsidiaries:

**Federal Screw Works Romulus
Division** **(1)**
34846 Goddard Rd, Romulus, MI 48174-
3406
Tel.: (734) 941-4211
Web Site:
http://www.federalscrewworks.com
Sales Range: $10-24.9 Million
Emp.: 19
Mfr of Locknuts
N.A.I.C.S.: 335929
Scott Rozema (Engr-Sls)

**Federal Screw Works-Big Rapids
Div.** **(1)**
400 N Dekraft Ave, Big Rapids, MI
49307-2001 **(100%)**
Tel.: (231) 796-7664
Web Site:
http://www.federalscrewworks.com
Sales Range: $50-74.9 Million
Emp.: 100
Mfr of Metal Products
N.A.I.C.S.: 332722

FEDERAL SIGNAL CORPORA-
TION
1333 Butterfield Rd Ste 500, Down-
ers Grove, IL 60515
Tel.: (630) 954-2000 **DE**
Web Site:
https://www.federalsignal.com
Year Founded: 1901
FSS—(NYSE)
Rev.: $1,434,800,000
Assets: $1,524,300,000
Liabilities: $663,400,000
Net Worth: $860,900,000
Earnings: $120,400,000

Emp.: 4,100
Fiscal Year-end: 12/31/22
Other Communications Equipment
Manufacturing
N.A.I.C.S.: 334290
Mark D. Weber (COO & Sr VP)
Dennis J. Martin (Chm)
Ian A. Hudson (CFO & Sr VP)
Jennifer L. Sherman (Pres & CEO)
Diane Bonina (Gen Counsel, Sec &
VP)
Diane I. Bonina (Gen Counsel)

Subsidiaries:

Blasters, Inc. **(1)**
7813 Professional Pl, Tampa, FL 33637
Tel.: (813) 985-4500
Web Site: https://blasters.net
Specialty Trade Contractors
N.A.I.C.S.: 238990
Scott F. Boos (Pres)
Frederick A. Boos (CEO)

Deist Industries, Inc. **(1)**
3547 Perry Hwy, Hadley, PA 16130
Tel.: (724) 253-3322
Web Site: http://www.deistindustries.com
Rev.: $5,700,000
Emp.: 40
Plate Work Mfr
N.A.I.C.S.: 332313
Keith Bailey (Production Mgr)
Dennis Racine (Pres)

FS Depot, Inc. **(1)**
2645 Federal Signal Dr, University Park, IL
60484-3167
Tel.: (847) 468-2350
Web Site: http://www.fsdepot.com
Sales Range: $50-74.9 Million
Emp.: 500
Security System Monitoring Services
N.A.I.C.S.: 561621

FST Canada Inc. **(1)**
2521 Bowman St, Innisfil, L9S 3V6, ON,
Canada
Tel.: (705) 733-7700
Web Site: https://www.jjei.com
Employment Placement Services
N.A.I.C.S.: 561311

**Federal Signal Credit
Corporation** **(1)**
1415 W 22nd St Ste 1100, Oak Brook, IL
60523
Tel.: (630) 954-2000
Web Site: http://www.federalsignal.com
Sales Range: $25-49.9 Million
Emp.: 40
Public Safety Signaling & Communications
Equipment Mfr
N.A.I.C.S.: 334290

**Federal Signal Environmental Solu-
tions Group** **(1)**
1300 W Bartlett Rd, Elgin, IL 60120
Tel.: (847) 741-5370
Web Site: http://www.fsepg.com
Sales Range: $100-124.9 Million
Emp.: 330
Environmental Cleaning Products Mfr
N.A.I.C.S.: 562211

Subsidiary (Domestic):

Elgin Sweeper Company **(2)**
1300 W Bartlett Rd, Elgin, IL
60120-7528 **(100%)**
Tel.: (847) 741-5370
Web Site: https://www.elginsweeper.com
Sales Range: $125-149.9 Million
Emp.: 330
Street Sweepers Mfr
N.A.I.C.S.: 336120

Guzzler Manufacturing Inc. **(2)**
1621 S Illinois St, Streator, IL 61364
Tel.: (815) 672-3171
Web Site: https://www.guzzler.com
Emp.: 500
Environmental Cleanup Products Mfr
N.A.I.C.S.: 562998

Jetstream of Houston, LLP **(2)**
5905 Thomas Rd, Houston, TX 77041
Tel.: (832) 590-1300
Web Site: https://www.waterblast.com

Sales Range: $25-49.9 Million
Emp.: 100
Service Industry Machinery Mfr
N.A.I.C.S.: 333310

Subsidiary (Non-US):

Ravo B.V. **(2)**
Otterkoog 1, 1822 BW, Alkmaar,
Netherlands **(100%)**
Tel.: (31) 725673232
Web Site: http://ravo.fayat.com
Sales Range: $50-74.9 Million
Emp.: 140
Street Sweepers, Catch Basin & Refuse
Trucks Mfr
N.A.I.C.S.: 336120

Subsidiary (Domestic):

Vactor Manufacturing, Inc. **(2)**
1621 S Illinois St, Streator, IL
61364 **(100%)**
Tel.: (815) 672-3171
Web Site: http://www.vactor.com
Sales Range: $100-124.9 Million
Emp.: 100
Vacuum Trucks Mfr
N.A.I.C.S.: 333924

**Federal Signal Safety & Security Sys-
tems Group** **(1)**
2645 Federal Signal Dr, University Park, IL
60484 **(100%)**
Tel.: (708) 534-3400
Web Site: http://www.federalsignal.com
Sales Range: $75-99.9 Million
Emp.: 250
Emergency Equipment Mfr
N.A.I.C.S.: 335931

Subsidiary (Domestic):

Codespear, LLC **(2)**
370 E Maple Rd Ste 350, Birmingham, MI
48009
Tel.: (248) 644-1090
Sales Range: $100-124.9 Million
Interoperable Communication & Instant Alert
Notification Software
N.A.I.C.S.: 513210

Subsidiary (Non-US):

Victor Products Limited **(2)**
Unit 3A Tyne Dock East Side Port of Tyne,
South Shields, NE33 5SQ, Tyne & Wear,
United Kingdom
Tel.: (44) 191 280 8000
Web Site: https://www.victor.co.uk
Sales Range: $100-124.9 Million
Emp.: 30
Mine Safety Products Mfr
N.A.I.C.S.: 335132

Subsidiary (Non-US):

**Victor Industrial Equipment (Pty)
Ltd.** **(3)**
245 Power Street, PO Box 6698, Boksburg
East Industrial Sites, Dunswart, 1508, Gau-
teng, South Africa
Tel.: (27) 11 914 1340
Web Site: https://www.victor-ind.co.za
Sales Range: $10-24.9 Million
Mine Safety Equipment Mfr
N.A.I.C.S.: 335139

Subsidiary (US):

**Victor Products USA
Incorporated** **(3)**
322 Commerce Park Dr, Cranberry, PA
16066
Tel.: (724) 776-4900
Web Site: http://www.victorproductsusa.com
Sales Range: $10-24.9 Million
Emp.: 12
Communication Equipment Mfr
N.A.I.C.S.: 334290

Federal Signal VAMA, S.A. **(1)**
Doctor Ferran 7, Vilassar de Dalt, 08339,
Barcelona, Spain
Tel.: (34) 937417900
Web Site: https://www.fedsigvama.com
Emergency Lighting & Related Product Mfr
N.A.I.C.S.: 334290

HighMark Traffic Services, Inc. **(1)**
745 Parkway Ln, Billings, MT 59101

Tel.: (406) 373-9042
Safety & Security Services
N.A.I.C.S.: 561621

Jetstream of Houston, Inc. **(1)**
5905 Thomas Rd, Houston, TX 77041
Tel.: (832) 590-1300
Web Site: https://www.waterblast.com
Emp.: 100
Communication Equipment Mfr
N.A.I.C.S.: 334290

Joe Johnson Equipment LLC **(1)**
62 LaGrange Ave, Rochester, NY 14613
Tel.: (585) 254-7700
Construction Equipment Rental Services
N.A.I.C.S.: 532412

**Mark Rite Lines Equipment Co,
Inc.** **(1)**
5379 Southgate Dr, 59101, Billings, MT
Tel.: (406) 869-9900
Web Site: http://www.markritelines.com
General Purpose Machinery Mfr
N.A.I.C.S.: 333998
Jonathan Gonitzke (Exec VP)
Michael Schwartz (Dir-Sls-Natl)

OSW Equipment & Repair, LLC **(1)**
20812 Broadway Ave, Snohomish, WA
98296
Tel.: (425) 483-9863
Web Site: https://www.oswequipment.com
Welding Repair
N.A.I.C.S.: 811490

Subsidiary (Domestic):

Northend Truck Equipment, LLC **(2)**
14919 40th Ave NE, Marysville, WA 98271
Tel.: (360) 653-6066
Web Site: http://www.northendtruck.com
Motor Vehicle Body Mfr
N.A.I.C.S.: 336211
Chad Little (Mgr-Sls)

**Public Works Equipment & Supply,
Inc.** **(1)**
4519 Old Charlotte Hwy, Monroe, NC
28110
Tel.: (704) 289-6488
Web Site: http://www.pweasi.com
Waste Management Services
N.A.I.C.S.: 562998

Tishomingo Acquisition, LLC **(1)**
1 Independence Plz Ste 820, Homewood,
AL 35209
Tel.: (662) 438-7800
Automobile Parts Mfr
N.A.I.C.S.: 336110

Travis Body and Trailer, Inc. **(1)**
10955 FM 529, Houston, TX 77041
Web Site: https://www.travistrailers.com
Trailer Mfr
N.A.I.C.S.: 336212

**Truck Bodies & Equipment Interna-
tional, Inc.** **(1)**
1 Independence Plz Ste 820, Homewood,
AL 35209
Tel.: (205) 900-7100
Web Site: https://www.tbei.com
Holding Company; Dump Truck Bodies,
Hoists & Equipment Mfr
N.A.I.C.S.: 551112
Tina Albright (Dir-HR)
Randall Schwabacher (Controller-Grp)
Brett Hart (VP-Sales & Marketing)

Subsidiary (Domestic):

Crysteel Manufacturing, Inc. **(2)**
52182 Ember Rd, Lake Crystal, MN 56055
Tel.: (507) 726-2728
Web Site: https://www.crysteel.com
Dump Truck Bodies, Hoists & Platforms Mfr
N.A.I.C.S.: 336211
Sandy Elkins (Mgr-Customer Svc)

Ox Bodies, Inc. **(2)**
719 Columbus St E, Fayette, AL 35555
Tel.: (205) 932-5720
Web Site: https://www.oxbodies.com
Sales Range: $50-74.9 Million
Motor Vehicle Body Mfr
N.A.I.C.S.: 336211

Rugby Manufacturing Company **(2)**

515 1st St NE Industrial Park, Rugby, ND
58368
Tel.: (701) 776-5722
Web Site: https://www.rugbymfg.com
Dump Truck Bodies, Hoists & Platforms Mfr
N.A.I.C.S.: 336211

FEDERATED HERMES PREMIER MUNICIPAL INCOME FUND

4000 Ericsson Dr, Warrendale, PA
15086-7561
Tel.: (412) 288-1900   **DE**
FMN—(NYSE)
Investment Management Service
N.A.I.C.S.: 525990

FEDERATED HERMES, INC.

1001 Liberty Ave, Pittsburgh, PA
15222-3779
Tel.: (412) 288-1900   **PA**
Web Site:
  https://www.federatedhermes.com
Year Founded: 1955
FHI—(NYSE)
Rev.: $1,609,574,000
Assets: $2,101,844,000
Liabilities: $973,592,000
Net Worth: $1,128,252,000
Earnings: $298,980,000
Emp.: 2,025
Fiscal Year-end: 12/31/23
Investment Management Service
N.A.I.C.S.: 523940
Thomas R. Donahue (CFO, Treas &
VP)
Richard A. Novak (Chief Acctg Officer, VP & Asst Treas)
Diana Glassman (Executives)
John Christopher Donahue (Chm,
Pres & CEO)
Stephen P. Van Meter (Chief Compliance Officer & VP)
Peter J. Germain (Chief Legal Officer,
Gen Counsel, Sec & Exec VP)
Paul A. Uhlman (VP)
Dolores D. Dudiak (VP-HR)

Subsidiaries:

Federated Equity Management Company of Pennsylvania   **(1)**
1001 Liberty Ave, Pittsburgh, PA 15222-3779
Tel.: (412) 288-1900
Emp.: 2,000
Investment Advisory Services
N.A.I.C.S.: 523940

Federated Hermes (UK) LLP   **(1)**
150 Cheapside, London, EC2V 6ET, United Kingdom
Tel.: (44) 2072928620
Web Site:
  https://www.federatedinvestors.co.uk
Investment Management & Fund Services
N.A.I.C.S.: 523999

Subsidiary (Domestic):

Hermes Fund Managers Limited   **(2)**
150 Cheapside, London, EC2V 6ET, United
Kingdom   **(60%)**
Tel.: (44) 2077020888
Web Site: https://www.hermes-investment.com
Pension & Investment Fund Management
Services
N.A.I.C.S.: 524292

Subsidiary (Non-US):

Hermes GPE (Singapore) Pte.
Limited   **(3)**
9 Raffles Place 51-01 Republic Plaza, Singapore, 048619, Singapore
Tel.: (65) 68500677
Web Site: https://www.hermes-investment.com
Investment Management Service
N.A.I.C.S.: 523940

Division (Domestic):

Hermes Real Estate Investment Management Ltd.   **(3)**
6th Floor 150 Cheapside, London, EC2V
6ET, United Kingdom   **(100%)**
Tel.: (44) 2077020888
Web Site: https://www.hermes.co.uk
Real Estate & Property Management Services
N.A.I.C.S.: 531312

Subsidiary (Domestic):

MEPC Ltd.   **(4)**
Bee House 140 Eastern Avenue, Milton,
OX14 4SB, Oxfordshire, United
Kingdom   **(100%)**
Tel.: (44) 1235865555
Web Site: https://www.mepc.com
Commercial Property Investment, Development & Management
N.A.I.C.S.: 531312

Federated Hermes Limited   **(1)**
150 Cheapside, London, EC2V 6ET, United
Kingdom
Tel.: (44) 2077020888
Web Site: https://www.hermes-investment.com
Investment Management Service
N.A.I.C.S.: 523940

Federated MDTA LLC   **(1)**
125 High St Oliver St Tower 21st Fl, Boston, MA 02110
Tel.: (617) 235-7100
Emp.: 30
Investment Advisory Services
N.A.I.C.S.: 523940
John Basil Fisher (Pres)

Federated Securities Corp.   **(1)**
680 Park Ave, Huntington, NY 11743-3977
Tel.: (631) 421-4499
Web Site:
  https://www.federatedsecurities.com
Emp.: 2
Securities Brokerage Services
N.A.I.C.S.: 523150
Carl Lanzisera (Pres)

Hermes Equity Ownership Services
Limited   **(1)**
Sixth Floor 150 Cheapside, London, EC2V
6ET, United Kingdom
Tel.: (44) 2077020888
Investment Management Service
N.A.I.C.S.: 523940

Hermes GPE (USA) Inc.   **(1)**
55 5th Ave Ste 1306, New York, NY 10003
Tel.: (212) 292-1047
Fund Management Services
N.A.I.C.S.: 523940
Stephen Reynard (Partner-Portfolio Solutions)
Brooks Harrington (Principal)
Ryan Hayes (Principal)
Walker Guffey (VP)
Zalina Hussain (Office Mgr)

Hermes GPE LLP   **(1)**
Forum St Paul's 33 Gutter Lane, London,
EC2V 8AS, United Kingdom
Tel.: (44) 2076803880
Web Site: https://www.hermesgpe.com
Fund Management Services
N.A.I.C.S.: 523940
Peter Gale (Head-Hermes GPE Private Equity)
Tom Hillmann (Head-Portfolio Analytics)
Elias Korosis (Partner-Strategy & Growth
Investing)

Hermes Investment Management
Ltd.   **(1)**
150 Cheapside, London, EC2V 6ET, United
Kingdom
Tel.: (44) 2077020888
Web Site: https://www.hermes-investment.com
Investment Management Service
N.A.I.C.S.: 523940

FEDEX CORPORATION

3875 Airways Module H3 Dept 4634,
Memphis, TN 38116
Tel.: (901) 818-7500   **DE**

Web Site: https://www.fedex.com
Year Founded: 1997
FDX—(NYSE)
Rev.: $87,693,000,000
Assets: $87,007,000,000
Liabilities: $59,425,000,000
Net Worth: $27,582,000,000
Earnings: $4,331,000,000
Emp.: 241,000
Fiscal Year-end: 05/31/24
Logistic Services
N.A.I.C.S.: 551112
Rajesh Subramaniam (Pres & CEO)
Frederick W. Smith (Chm)
Robert B. Carter (CIO & Exec VP)
Claude F. Russ (VP-Fin Transformation)
John W. Dietrich (CFO & Exec VP)
Mark R. Allen (Gen Counsel, Sec &
Exec VP)
Jill C. Brannon (Chief Sls Officer &
Exec VP)
Brie A. Carere (Chief Customer Officer)
John A. Smith (Pres/CEO-FedEx
Ground)
Lance D. Moll (Pres/CEO-FedEx
Freight)
Rebecca Yeung (VP-Ops Science &
Advanced Tech)
Rose J. Flenorl (Mgr-Citizenship-
Global)

Subsidiaries:

FedEx Brasil Logistica e Transporte
S.A.   **(1)**
R Cel Phidias Tavora Bl 2 Arm 01a 14 360-
261 RH Pine, Pavuna, Rio de Janeiro,
21535-510, Brazil
Tel.: (55) 2120247958
Logistics Management Consulting Services
N.A.I.C.S.: 541614

FedEx Corporate Services, Inc.   **(1)**
942 S Shady Grove Rd, Memphis, TN
38120
Tel.: (901) 369-3600
Web Site: http://ir.fedex.com
Sales Range: $250-299.9 Million
Emp.: 900
Sales, Marketing & Technology Support
Services
N.A.I.C.S.: 561499
Robert B. Carter (Co-Pres & Co-CEO)
Robert B. Carter (Co-Pres & Co-CEO)
Brie A. Carere (Co-Pres & Co-CEO)

Subsidiary (Domestic):

FedEx Customer Information Services, Inc.   **(2)**
942 S Shady Grove Rd, Memphis, TN
38120
Tel.: (901) 369-3600
Web Site: http://about.fedex.designcdt.com
Sales Range: $75-99.9 Million
Management Services
N.A.I.C.S.: 541611
Frederick W. Smith (Chm, Pres & CEO)

FedEx Office & Print Services,
Inc.   **(2)**
3 Galleria Twr 13155 Noel Rd Ste 1600,
Dallas, TX 75240
Tel.: (214) 550-7000
Web Site: http://www.fedex.com
Photocopying, Duplicating & Printing Services, Ground & Express Shipping Services,
High-Speed Internet Access & Computer
Usage, WiFi Services, Videoconferencing,
Signs, Graphics & Photo Services
N.A.I.C.S.: 323111
Brian D. Philips (Pres & CEO)

Subsidiary (Non-US):

Colour Limited   **(3)**
1 Curzon St, London, W1J 5HD, United
Kingdom
Tel.: (44) 2077174900
Web Site: http://www.colourcompany.com
Sales Range: $25-49.9 Million
Emp.: 150
Express Shipping & Office Services

N.A.I.C.S.: 561499

FedEx Kinko's Canada Limited   **(3)**
357 Bay St, Toronto, M58 2T7, Canada
Tel.: (416) 323-3305
Web Site: http://www.fedexoffice.ca
Sales Range: $10-24.9 Million
Emp.: 20
Copy & Print Services
N.A.I.C.S.: 323111

FedEx Cross Border   **(1)**
10040 18th St N Ste 6, Saint Petersburg,
FL 33716
Tel.: (203) 683-4894
Web Site: http://www.bongous.com
Package & Mail Forwarding Services
N.A.I.C.S.: 481112
Gregory Unger (Mng Dir-Sls)
Mike Rude (VP)
Jay Bauder (Mng Dir-Ops)
Patrick Maier (Mng Dir-Customer Acquisition & Support)

FedEx Cross Border Technologies,
Inc.   **(1)**
10040 18th St N Ste 6, Saint Petersburg,
FL 33716
Tel.: (203) 683-4894
Web Site: http://crossborder.fedex.com
Courier Delivery Services
N.A.I.C.S.: 492110

FedEx Express Germany GmbH   **(1)**
Am Forsthaus Gravenbruch 9-11, 63263,
Neu-Isenburg, Germany
Tel.: (49) 1806111800
Web Site: https://www.fedex.com
Courier Delivery Services
N.A.I.C.S.: 492110

FedEx Express Greece Single Member L.L.C.   **(1)**
Fleming Rd, Industrial Park of Markopoulo
Mesogaia, 190 03, Athens, Greece
Tel.: (30) 2108905900
Web Site: https://www.fedex.com
General Freight Trucking Services
N.A.I.C.S.: 484111

FedEx Express Sverige AB   **(1)**
Kantyxegatan 25, 21376, Malmo, Sweden
Tel.: (46) 200252252
Logistics & Courier Services
N.A.I.C.S.: 492110

FedEx Express Transportation & Supply Chain Services (India) Pvt.
Ltd.   **(1)**
Boomerang Unit No 801 Wings A & B1 8th
Floor Chandivali Farm Road, Near Chandivali Studio Andheri, Mumbai, 400 072, India
Tel.: (91) 2261897777
Freight Transportation & Logistics Services
N.A.I.C.S.: 541614
Sudhir Bhalinge (Mgr-Ops Support-
Warehouse)

FedEx Freight Corporation   **(1)**
1715 Aaron Brenner Dr Ste 600, Memphis,
TN 38120-1444   **(100%)**
Tel.: (901) 346-4400
Web Site: http://www.fedexfreight.fedex.com
Sales Range: $1-4.9 Billion
Emp.: 33,000
Less-Than-Truckload Freight Transportation
Services
N.A.I.C.S.: 484121
John A. Smith (Pres & CEO)

Subsidiary (Domestic):

FedEx Custom Critical, Inc.   **(2)**
4205 Highlander Pkwy, Richfield, OH 44286
Tel.: (234) 310-4090
Web Site:
  http://www.customcritical.fedex.com
Sales Range: $100-124.9 Million
Surface-Expedited Freight Delivery Services
N.A.I.C.S.: 488510
Ramona T. Hood (Pres & CEO)

Subsidiary (Non-US):

FedEx Freight Canada Corp.   **(2)**
1011 Wilson Avenue, Toronto, M3K 1G4,
ON, Canada
Web Site: http://www.fedexfreight.fedex.com
Less-Than-Truckload Freight Transportation
Services

FedEx Corporation—(Continued)

N.A.I.C.S.: 484122

Subsidiary (Domestic):

FedEx Freight, Inc. (2)
2200 Forward Dr, Harrison, AR 72601-2004
Tel.: (870) 741-9000
Web Site: http://www.fedexfreight.com
Sales Range: $900-999.9 Million
Emp.: 13,200
Less-Than-Truckload Freight Transportation
Services
N.A.I.C.S.: 484122
Matt Rittenhour (CFO & Sr VP-Fin)

FedEx Ground Package System,
Inc. (1)
1000 FedEx Dr, Coraopolis, PA
15108-9373 (100%)
Tel.: (412) 269-1000
Web Site: http://www.fedex.com
Sales Range: $1-4.9 Billion
Emp.: 3,000
Ground Delivery Services for Small Pack-
ages
N.A.I.C.S.: 492110
Ward B. Strang (COO & Exec VP)
Robert D. Henning (CFO & Exec VP)

Subsidiary (Domestic):

FedEx SmartPost, Inc. (2)
16555 W Rogers Dr, New Berlin, WI 53151
Tel.: (262) 796-6800
Web Site: http://www.fedex.com
Sales Range: $200-249.9 Million
Emp.: 450
Parcel Delivery Expediting Services
N.A.I.C.S.: 492110

FedEx Supply Chain Distribution Sys-
tem, Inc. (1)
700 Cranberry Woods Dr, Cranberry Town-
ship, PA 16066
Web Site: http://supplychain.fedex.com
Courier Delivery Services
N.A.I.C.S.: 492110
Andy Smith (COO & Sr VP)
Bradley R. Peacock (Gen Counsel & First
VP)
Ryan Kelly (Sr VP-Sls, Strategy & Comm)
Stacey Heitzenrater (VP-HR)

FedEx SupplyChain Systems,
Inc. (1)
2378 Spottswood Ave, Memphis, TN 38114-
2250
Tel.: (901) 323-3686
Web Site: http://www.fedex.com
Sales Range: $200-249.9 Million
Emp.: 1,300
Supply Chain Management Services
N.A.I.C.S.: 541618

FedEx Trade Networks Trade Ser-
vices, Inc. (1)
6075 Poplar Ave Ste 300 3rd Fl, Memphis,
TN 38119
Tel.: (901) 684-4800
Trade & Customs Advisory Services
N.A.I.C.S.: 488510

FedEx Trade Networks Transport &
Brokerage (Hong Kong) Limited (1)
Unit 801 Tower 1 Metroplaza 223 Hing
Fong Rd, Kwai Fong, China (Hong Kong)
Tel.: (852) 39000700
General Freight Trucking Services
N.A.I.C.S.: 484121

FedEx UK Limited (1)
Parkhouse East Industrial Estate,
Newcastle-under-Lyme, ST5 7RB, Stafford-
shire, United Kingdom
Tel.: (44) 1782563322
Web Site: http://www.fedex.com
Sales Range: $450-499.9 Million
Emp.: 1,000
Freight Delivery Services
N.A.I.C.S.: 488510

Federal Express Canada
Corporation (1)
5985 Explorer Drive, Mississauga, L4W
5K6, ON, Canada
Tel.: (905) 212-5000
Courier Delivery Services
N.A.I.C.S.: 492110

Federal Express Corporation (1)
3610 Hacks Cross Rd, Memphis, TN 38125
Tel.: (901) 369-3600
Rev.: $26,094,000,000
Assets: $20,260,000,000
Liabilities: $10,046,000,000
Net Worth: $10,214,000,000
Earnings: $144,000,000
Fiscal Year-end: 05/31/2015
Express Mail Shipping Services
N.A.I.C.S.: 561431
Frederick W. Smith (Chm)

Subsidiary (Domestic):

FedEx Trade Networks, Inc. (2)
3800 Forest Hill Irene Rd, Memphis, TN
38125 (100%)
Tel.: (901) 752-3000
Web Site: http://www.ftn.fedex.com
Sales Range: $550-599.9 Million
Emp.: 3,500
International Express Air Freight Forwarding
& Customs Brokerage Services
N.A.I.C.S.: 488510

Branch (Domestic):

FedEx Trade Networks (3)
1 Clay Pl, Atlanta, GA 30354-1957
Tel.: (404) 761-2929
Web Site: http://www.ftn.fedex.com
Sales Range: $25-49.9 Million
Emp.: 50
Customs Brokerage
N.A.I.C.S.: 488510

Subsidiary (Non-US):

FedEx Trade Networks Transport &
Brokerage (Canada), Inc (3)
13777 Commerce Parkway Suite 240, Rich-
mond, V6V 2X3, BC, Canada
Tel.: (604) 278-7785
Web Site: http://www.fedex.ca
Sales Range: $25-49.9 Million
Emp.: 30
International Air & Ocean Freight Forward-
ing & Customs Brokerage Services
N.A.I.C.S.: 488510

Subsidiary (Domestic):

FedEx Trade Networks Transport &
Brokerage, Inc. (3)
128 Dearborn St, Buffalo, NY
14207-3122 (100%)
Tel.: (716) 879-1075
Web Site: http://www.ftn.fedex.com
Sales Range: $300-349.9 Million
Emp.: 200
International Air & Ocean Freight Forward-
ing & Customs Brokerage Services
N.A.I.C.S.: 488510

Subsidiary (Non-US):

Federal Express Canada Ltd. (2)
5985 Explorer Drive, Mississauga, L4W
5K6, ON, Canada
Tel.: (905) 212-5000
Web Site: http://www.fedex.ca
Sales Range: $100-124.9 Million
Emp.: 600
Express Shipping Services
N.A.I.C.S.: 561431

Subsidiary (Domestic):

Federal Express International,
Inc. (2)
3610 Hacks Cross Rd, Memphis, TN 38125
Tel.: (901) 369-3600
Web Site: http://www.fedex.com
Sales Range: $250-299.9 Million
Holding Company; Express Mail Shipping
Services
N.A.I.C.S.: 551112

Branch (Non-US):

Federal Express Asia Pacific (3)
11th Floor Core E Cyberport 3, 100 Cyber-
port Road, Pok Fu Lam, China
Tel.: (86) 25140800
Sales Range: $50-74.9 Million
Emp.: 100
Express Shipping Services
N.A.I.C.S.: 484220
Kawal Preet (Pres)

Federal Express Europe, Middle East
& Africa (3)
Kantersteen 47, Brussels, 1000, Belgium
Tel.: (32) 25158800
Web Site: http://www.fedex.com
Sales Range: $25-49.9 Million
Emp.: 120
Express Shipping Services
N.A.I.C.S.: 561431

Branch (Domestic):

Federal Express Latin
America-Caribbean (3)
701 Waterford Way Ste 1000, Miami, FL
33126
Tel.: (786) 388-2600
Web Site: http://www.fedex.com
Sales Range: $25-49.9 Million
Emp.: 200
Express Shipping Services
N.A.I.C.S.: 561431
Juan N. Cento (Pres)

Federal Express Europe, Inc. (1)
3610 Hacks Cross Rd, Memphis, TN 38125
Tel.: (901) 818-7500
Courier Service
N.A.I.C.S.: 492110
Karen Reddington (Pres)

Federal Express Japan G.K. (1)
2-6-1 Nakase, Mihama-ku, Chiba, 135-
0063, Japan
Tel.: (81) 120003200
Courier Delivery Services
N.A.I.C.S.: 492110

Federal Express Korea LLC (1)
I 5-6F Hapjeong Office Bldg 19, Mapo-gu,
Seoul, Korea (South)
Tel.: (82) 15880588
Courier Delivery Services
N.A.I.C.S.: 492110

Federal Express Pacific, Inc. (1)
3610 Hacks Cross Rd, Memphis, TN 38125
Tel.: (901) 818-7167
Courier Service
N.A.I.C.S.: 492110

GENCO Distribution System, Inc. (1)
100 Papercraft Park, Pittsburgh, PA 15238-
3200
Tel.: (412) 820-3700
Emp.: 10,000
Product Lifecycle & Reverse Logistics Solu-
tions
N.A.I.C.S.: 493110

GENCO Marketplace, Inc. (1)
700 Cranberry Woods Dr, Cranberry, PA
16066
Web Site:
https://www.gencomarketplace.com
Logistic Integrated Supply Chain Services
N.A.I.C.S.: 541614

ShopRunner, Inc. (1)
350 N LaSalle 6th Fl, Chicago, IL 60654
Web Site: http://www.shoprunner.com
Sales Range: $10-24.9 Million
Emp.: 30
Subscription-Based Online Shopping Ser-
vices
N.A.I.C.S.: 459999
Claude F. Russ (CEO)
Sam Yagan (CEO)
Christopher Ladd (Chief Comml Officer)

TNT Australia Pty. Limited (1)
201 Coward Street, Mascot, Sydney, 2020,
NSW, Australia
Tel.: (61) 283048000
Web Site: http://www.tnt.com.au
Emp.: 4,168
Freight Transportation & Logistics Services
N.A.I.C.S.: 484110

TNT Express GmbH (1)
Haberstrasse 2, 53842, Troisdorf, Germany
Tel.: (49) 22414970
Web Site: http://www.tnt.com
Logistics Consulting Servies
N.A.I.C.S.: 541614

TNT Express N.V. (1)
Taurusavenue 111, 2132 LS, Hoofddorp,
Netherlands (99%)
Tel.: (31) 88 393 9000
Web Site: http://www.tnt.com

Parcel, Document & Freight Delivery Ser-
vices
N.A.I.C.S.: 491110
David J. Bronczek (Chm-Supervisory Bd)

Subsidiary (Domestic):

TNT Express Nederland B.V. (2)
Bellsingel 51, 1119NT, Schiphol-Rijk, Neth-
erlands
Tel.: (31) 883939000
Parcel Delivery Services
N.A.I.C.S.: 492110

TNT Express Road Network B.V. (2)
Express 1, Duiven, 6921 RB, Gelderland,
Netherlands
Tel.: (31) 263197319
Web Site: http://www.tnt.com
Emp.: 2,000
Parcel Delivery Services
N.A.I.C.S.: 492110

TNT Nederland B.V. (1)
Taurusavenue 111, 2132 LS, Hoofddorp,
Netherlands
Tel.: (31) 883939000
Freight Transportation & Logistics Services
N.A.I.C.S.: 484110
Liesbeth Steenvoorde (Mgr-HR)

TNT UK Limited (1)
TNT Express House Holly Lane, Ather-
stone, CV9 2RY, United Kingdom
Tel.: (44) 1827303030
Freight Transportation & Logistics Services
N.A.I.C.S.: 484110
Justin Clarke (Gen Counsel & Sec)

World Tariff, Limited (1)
220 Montgomery St Ste 448, San Fran-
cisco, CA 94104-3536
Tel.: (415) 591-6666
Web Site: http://www.worldtariff.com
Duty & Tax Information Services
N.A.I.C.S.: 519290

FEDNAT HOLDING COMPANY
14050 NW 14th St Ste 180, Sunrise,
FL 33323
Tel.: (954) 308-1200 FL
Web Site: http://www.fednat.com
Year Founded: 1992
FNHC—(NASDAQ)
Rev.: $245,549,000
Assets: $1,412,670,000
Liabilities: $1,353,284,000
Net Worth: $59,386,000
Earnings: ($103,100,000)
Emp.: 341
Fiscal Year-end: 12/31/21
Insurance Holding Company
N.A.I.C.S.: 551112
Bruce F. Simberg (Chm)
Erick A. Fernandez (Chief Acctg Offi-
cer)
Richard B. Gaudet (Interim CFO)
Katie S. Goodman (Chief Restructur-
ing Officer)

Subsidiaries:

ClaimCor, LLC (1)
7861 Woodlands Center Blvd, Tampa, FL
33614
Tel.: (813) 579-6226
Web Site: http://www.claimcorsolutions.com
Property Insurance Services
N.A.I.C.S.: 524126
William Thomas (VP)

FedNat Underwriters, Inc. (1)
14050 NW 14 St Ste 180, Sunrise, FL
33323
Tel.: (954) 581-9993
Web Site: http://www.fednat.com
Insurance Related Services
N.A.I.C.S.: 524298

Federated National Insurance
Company (1)
14050 NW 14th St Ste 180, Sunrise, FL
33323
Tel.: (954) 581-9993
Sales Range: $10-24.9 Million
Emp.: 100

Automobile Insurance & Mobile Home Property/Casualty Coverage
N.A.I.C.S.: 524210
Annette Maleki *(Mgr-Mktg)*

Maison Insurance Company (1)
9100 Bluebonnet Centre Blvd Ste 502, Baton Rouge, LA 70809
Web Site: http://www.maisonins.com
Insurance Services
N.A.I.C.S.: 524210
Douglas N. Raucy *(Founder, Pres & CEO)*
Dean E. Stroud *(Chief Underwriting Officer & VP-Ops)*
Ellen Craft *(Mktg Dir)*

FELICIANA BANK & TRUST COMPANY
10926 Plank Rd, Clinton, LA 70722
Tel.: (225) 683-8565   **LA**
Web Site:
http://www.felicianabank.com
FLOL—(OTCIQ)
Commercial Banking Services
N.A.I.C.S.: 522110
John Irwin Stewart *(CEO)*
Tracye Browning *(CFO)*
Matthew Knight *(COO)*
Kyla Walker *(Branch Mgr)*
Jaye M. Bunch *(Pres & Chief Lending Officer)*

FEMASYS INC.
3950 Johns Creek Ct Ste 100, Suwanee, GA 30024-6608
Tel.: (770) 500-3910
Web Site: https://www.femasys.com
Year Founded: 2004
FEMY—(NASDAQ)
Surgical Appliance & Supplies Mfr
N.A.I.C.S.: 339113
Kathy Lee-Sepsick *(Founder, Pres & CEO)*
Dov Elefant *(CFO)*
Michael Meier *(VP-Sls & Mktg)*
Daniel Currie *(COO)*
James H. Liu *(Chief Medical Officer)*
Richard Spector *(Chief Comml Officer)*
Christine Thomas *(Sr VP-Regulatory & Clinical Affairs)*
Mary An Merchant *(VP-Counsel & Intellectual Property)*
Sue Owens *(VP-Sales)*
Andrew Young *(VP-Education & Global Training)*
Jeremy Sipos *(VP-Res, Development, and Engineering)*
Mike Hemann *(VP-Manufacturing)*
Ron Schardong *(VP-Quality Assurance)*

FENNEC PHARMACEUTICALS, INC.
68 TW Alexander Dr, Research Triangle Park, NC 27709
Tel.: (919) 636-4530   **Ca**
Web Site:
https://www.fennecpharma.com
FENC—(NASDAQ)
Rev.: $1,535,000
Assets: $26,939,000
Liabilities: $29,508,000
Net Worth: ($2,569,000)
Earnings: ($23,714,000)
Emp.: 36
Fiscal Year-end: 12/31/22
Cancer Treatment Products Developer
N.A.I.C.S.: 325412
Khalid Islam *(Chm)*
Mark Gowland *(Controller)*
Jeffrey S. Hackman *(CEO)*

FENTURA FINANCIAL, INC.
175 N Leroy St, Fenton, MI 48430-3805
Tel.: (810) 629-2263   **MI**

Web Site: https://www.fentura.com
Year Founded: 1987
FETM—(OTCQX)
Rev.: $65,619,000
Assets: $1,251,446,000
Liabilities: $1,135,578,000
Net Worth: $115,868,000
Earnings: $15,464,000
Emp.: 186
Fiscal Year-end: 12/31/20
Bank Holding Company
N.A.I.C.S.: 551111
Ronald L. Justice *(Pres & CEO)*

Subsidiaries:

The State Bank (1)
175 N Leroy St, Fenton, MI 48430
Tel.: (810) 629-2263
Web Site: http://www.thestatebank.com
Sales Range: $25-49.9 Million
Commericial Banking
N.A.I.C.S.: 522110
Ronald L. Justice *(Pres & CEO)*
David Scott *(VP-Residential Lending Div)*
Craig L. Johnson *(Sr VP)*
Kristy Schaffer *(Sr VP-HR & Mktg)*

FERNHILL CORP.
3773 Howard Hughes Pkwy Ste 500s, Las Vegas, NV 89169
Tel.: (775) 400-1180   **NV**
Web Site:
https://www.fernhillcorp.com
FERN—(OTCIQ)
Metal Mining Services
N.A.I.C.S.: 212290
Marc Lasky *(Pres, CFO & Dir)*
Jim DiPrima *(Mgr-Accounting)*
Nathanael Coonrod *(Exec VP-Engineering)*
Chris Kern *(Chm & CEO)*

FERRELLGAS PARTNERS, L.P.
2837 Roe Ln, Kansas City, KS 66103 1542
Tel.: (913) 236-5656   **DE**
Web Site: https://www.ferrellgas.com
Year Founded: 1939
FGPR—(OTCIQ)
Rev.: $1,837,116,000
Assets: $1,458,750,000
Liabilities: $1,757,089,000
Net Worth: ($298,339,000)
Earnings: $110,677,000
Emp.: 3,926
Fiscal Year-end: 07/31/24
Propane Gas Retailer
N.A.I.C.S.: 457210
James E. Ferrell *(Chm)*
Tamria A. Zertuche *(Pres & CEO)*

Subsidiaries:

Diamond Propane, Inc. (1)
6748 US Highway 11 Potsdam, New York, NY 13676
Tel.: (315) 265-1957
Web Site: http://www.diamond-propane.com
Petroleum & Petroleum Products Merchant Whslr
N.A.I.C.S.: 424720
Randy Hart *(Mgr)*

Eastern Sierra Propane
104 Sunland Reservation Rd, Bishop, CA 75063-6076
Tel.: (760) 872-2955
Web Site: http://www.premarkhs.com
Petroleum & Petroleum Products Merchant Whslr
N.A.I.C.S.: 424720

Ferrellgas Partners Finance Corp. (1)
7500 College Blvd Ste 1000, Overland Park, KS 66210   **(100%)**
Tel.: (913) 661-1500
Web Site: http://www.ferrellgas.com
Assets: $1,000
Net Worth: $1,000
Earnings: ($2,490)
Fiscal Year-end: 07/31/2021

Financial Services
N.A.I.C.S.: 525990
James E. Ferrell *(Chm, Pres & CEO)*
Dhiraj Cherian *(CFO & Treas)*
Tamria A. Zertuche *(COO)*
Jordan B. Burns *(Corp Counsel)*

Ferrellgas, L.P. (1)
1 Liberty Plz, Liberty, MO 64068
Tel.: (816) 792-1600
Web Site: https://www.ferrellgas.com
Rev.: $1,837,115,000
Assets: $1,458,302,000
Liabilities: $1,756,964,000
Net Worth: ($298,662,000)
Earnings: $110,418,000
Fiscal Year-end: 07/31/2024
Propane Retailer
N.A.I.C.S.: 551112
James E. Ferrell *(Chm, Pres & CEO)*

Unit (Domestic):

Barrow Propane Gas (2)
23 N Poplar St, Butler, GA 31006
Tel.: (478) 862-5431
Sales Range: $50-74.9 Million
Emp.: 40
Distr of Propane Gas
N.A.I.C.S.: 457210

Subsidiary (Domestic):

Blue Rhino Global Sourcing, Inc. (2)
5650 University Pkwy Ste 400, Winston Salem, NC 27105
Tel.: (336) 659-6900
Web Site: http://www.bluerhino.com
Sales Range: $150-199.9 Million
Propane Tank Exchange Retailer; Outdoor Propane Appliances Designer & Marketer
N.A.I.C.S.: 457210

Cass County Butane Co., Inc. (2)
613 E Main St, Atlanta, TX 75551
Tel.: (903) 796-2893
Web Site: http://www.welchpropane.com
Sales Range: $1-9.9 Million
Emp.: 16
Liquefied Petroleum Gas (Bottled Gas) Dealers
N.A.I.C.S.: 457210

Federal Petroleum Co., Inc. (2)
300 N Milano Rd, Weslaco, TX 78599
Tel.: (956) 464-2961
Web Site:
http://www.federalpetroleumco.com
Sales Range: $1-9.9 Million
Emp.: 12
Propane, Natural Gas & Petroleum Products Whslr
N.A.I.C.S.: 457210

Division (Domestic):

Ferrell North America (2)
7500 College Blvd Ste 1000, Overland Park, KS 66210
Tel.: (913) 661-1500
Web Site: http://www.fna.com
Propane Trader & Distr
N.A.I.C.S.: 425120
Travis Ochs *(VP-Supply, Wholesale & Transportation)*
Ryan Avila *(Dir-Supply)*
Brian Numrich *(VP-Trading & Distr)*
Jonathan Wasson *(Dir-Supply)*
Laura Hawkinson *(Sr Acct Mgr-Wholesale)*
Taylor Marolis *(Sr Acct Mgr-Wholesale)*
Lauren Vernon *(Sr Acct Mgr-Wholesale)*
Kristi Kurtz *(Mgr-Distr)*
Dustin Kuhlman *(Dir-Transportation)*
Sonny Catlett II *(Exec VP)*

Subsidiary (Domestic):

Ferrellgas Finance Corp. (2)
7500 College Blvd Ste 1000, Overland Park, KS 66210
Tel.: (913) 661-1500
Web Site: http://www.ferrellgas.com
Assets: $1,100
Net Worth: $1,100
Earnings: ($19,941)
Emp.: 75
Fiscal Year-end: 07/31/2024
Co-Issuer & Co-Obligor for Debt Securities Issued by Ferrellgas LP
N.A.I.C.S.: 561499

James E. Ferrell *(Chm, Pres & CEO)*
Dhiraj Cherian *(CFO & Treas)*

Unit (Domestic):

Ferrellgas, Inc. - Bossier City (2)
4000 Benton Rd, Bossier City, LA 71111
Web Site: http://www.ferrellgas.com
Sales Range: $25-49.9 Million
Emp.: 20
Propane Dealer
N.A.I.C.S.: 457210

Ferrellgas, Inc. - Hillsboro (2)
1190 SW Walnut St, Hillsboro, OR 97123
Tel.: (503) 648-4422
Web Site: http://www.ferrellgas.com
Sales Range: $25-49.9 Million
Emp.: 10
Propane Dealer
N.A.I.C.S.: 457210
Jon Boyer *(District Mgr)*

Ferrellgas, Inc. - Houston (2)
99 Holmes Rd, Houston, TX 77045
Tel.: (713) 667-1122
Web Site: http://www.ferrellgas.com
Sales Range: $75-99.9 Million
Emp.: 70
Propane Dealer
N.A.I.C.S.: 457210

Ferrellgas, Inc. - Roosevelt Propane Terminal (2)
244 W Hwy 40, Roosevelt, UT 84066
Tel.: (435) 722-5171
Sales Range: $25-49.9 Million
Emp.: 32
Bulk Propane Terminal
N.A.I.C.S.: 424710

Subsidiary (Domestic):

Gasco Energy Supply, LLC (2)
1603 E North St, Eldon, MO 65026-2653
Tel.: (573) 392-4275
Web Site: http://www.gascopropane.com
Natural Gas & Propane Distr
N.A.I.C.S.: 221210

Motor Propane Service, Inc. (2)
W2059 Garton Rd, Howards Grove, WI 53083
Tel.: (920) 758-2479
Web Site: http://www.motorpropane.com
Propane Gas Systems Installation & Maintenance Services
N.A.I.C.S.: 811310

Sable Environmental, LLC (2)
711 N Carancahua St Ste 1130, Corpus Christi, TX 78401
Tel.: (361) 806-2121
Web Site: http://www.sableco.com
Crude Petroleum & Natural Gas Extraction Services
N.A.I.C.S.: 211120

Reliable Propane, Inc. (1)
126 Larcel Dr, Sikeston, MO 63801-9352
Tel.: (573) 471-4541
Web Site: http://www.santiemidwest.com
Petroleum & Petroleum Products Merchant Whslr
N.A.I.C.S.: 424720

FFBW, INC.
Tel.: (262) 542-4448
Web Site:
https://www.firstfederalwisconsin.com
Year Founded: 2017
FFBW—(NASDAQ)
Rev.: $12,600,000
Assets: $357,077,000
Liabilities: $263,105,000
Net Worth: $93,972,000
Earnings: $1,983,000
Emp.: 53
Fiscal Year-end: 12/31/21
Banking Services
N.A.I.C.S.: 522110
Kathryn Sawyer Gutenkunst *(Sec)*
Edward H. Schaefer *(Pres & CEO)*
James A. Tarantino *(Chm)*
Steven L. Wierschem *(CFO)*
Leann Eddingsaas *(Principal Acctg Officer & Controller)*

FFD Financial Corporation—(Continued)

FFD FINANCIAL CORPORATION

141 W Ohio Ave, Dover, OH 44622-0038
Tel.: (330) 364-7777   **OH**
Web Site: https://www.firstfed.com
Year Founded: 1996
FFDF—(OTCIQ)
Rev.: $60,010,000
Assets: $65,025,000
Liabilities: $48,379,000
Net Worth: $16,646,000
Earnings: ($2,031,000)
Emp.: 72
Fiscal Year-end: 06/30/20
Bank Holding Company
N.A.I.C.S.: 551111
Trent B. Troyer (Pres & CEO)
Stephen G. Clinton (Chm)
Angie Delong (VP-Compliance)
Gregory W. Dorris (CFO, Treas & Sr VP)
Scott C. Finnell (Chief Credit Officer & Exec VP)
Kelly Fortney (CIO & Sr VP)
Kris Kreinbihl (VP)
Kenny Miller (Officer-Comml Loan & VP)
Matt Miller (Chief Lending Officer & Sr VP)
Suzanne Moore (VP)
Michele L. Larkin (Sr VP-Loan Admin & Mortgage Banking)

Subsidiaries:

First Federal Community Bank, N.A.   (1)
321 N Wooster Ave, Dover, OH 44622
Tel.: (330) 364-7777
Web Site: http://www.onlinefirstfed.com
Sales Range: $10-24.9 Million
Banking Services
N.A.I.C.S.: 522110
Trent B. Troyer (Pres & CEO)
Scott C. Finnell (Exec VP)
Sally K. O'Donnell (Sec & Sr VP)
Michele L. Larkin (Sr VP)
Stephanie M. Wilson (VP-HR)
Christopher Kreinbihl (VP)
Greg Dorries (CFO, Treas & Sr VP)
Karli Wengerd (Mgr-Berlin)

FFW CORPORATION

1205 N Cass St, Wabash, IN 46992
Tel.: (260) 563-3185   **DE**
Web Site:
http://www.crossroadsbanking.com
Year Founded: 1993
FFWC—(OTCIQ)
Sales Range: Less than $1 Million
Bank Holding Company
N.A.I.C.S.: 551111
Roger K. Cromer (Pres & CEO)
Daniel H. Ford (Chm)

Subsidiaries:

Crossroads Bank   (1)
1205 N Cass St, Wabash, IN 46992
Tel.: (260) 563-3185
Web Site:
http://www.crossroadsbanking.com
Emp.: 60
Banking Services
N.A.I.C.S.: 522110
Roger K. Cromer (Pres & CEO)
Daniel H. Ford (Chm)
Cynthia M. Riemersma (Dir)
Bethany Madding (Branch Mgr-Warsaw)

FG FITNESS & MEDIA GROUP, INC.

5996 S Edmond St, Las Vegas, NV 89118
Year Founded: 1947
FGFT—(OTCEM)
Magazine Publishing Services
N.A.I.C.S.: 513120

Jason Miller (CEO)

FGI INDUSTRIES LTD.

906 Murray Rd, East Hanover, NJ 07936
Tel.: (219) 940-6140   **Ky**
Web Site: https://www.fgi-industries.com
Year Founded: 2021
FGI—(NASDAQ)
Rev.: $161,718,543
Assets: $60,366,930
Liabilities: $37,622,520
Net Worth: $22,744,410
Earnings: $3,679,920
Emp.: 145
Fiscal Year-end: 12/31/22
Kitchen Product Mfr & Distr
N.A.I.C.S.: 332215
David Bruce (Pres & CEO)
John Chen (Chm)
Perry Lin (CFO)

FIBROBIOLOGICS, INC.

455 E Medical Center Blvd Ste 300, Houston, TX 77598
Tel.: (281) 651-5150   **DE**
Web Site:
https://www.fibrobiologics.com
Year Founded: 2021
FBLG—(NASDAQ)
Rev.: $2,368,000
Assets: $11,821,000
Liabilities: $10,568,000
Net Worth: $1,253,000
Earnings: ($16,485,000)
Emp.: 10
Fiscal Year-end: 12/31/23
Biotechnology Research & Development Services
N.A.I.C.S.: 541714

FIBROGEN, INC.

409 Illinois St, San Francisco, CA 94158
Tel.: (415) 978-1200   **DE**
Web Site: https://www.fibrogen.com
Year Founded: 1993
FGEN—(NASDAQ)
Rev.: $140,734,000
Assets: $610,087,000
Liabilities: $611,567,000
Net Worth: ($1,480,000)
Earnings: ($293,654,000)
Emp.: 592
Fiscal Year-end: 12/31/22
Biopharmaceutical Mfr
N.A.I.C.S.: 325412
Thane Wettig (CEO)
Michael D. Lowenstein (Chief Legal Officer)
Leanne C. Price (Chief Intellectual Property Officer)
Christine L. Chung (Sr VP-Ops-China)
Kirk Christoffersen (Chief Bus Officer)
Tricia Stewart (Chief People Officer)
John Hunter (Chief Scientific Officer)
Rahul Rajan Kaushik (Sr VP)

Subsidiaries:

Skin Sciences, Inc.   (1)
Suite 418 1011 Glenmore Trail SW, Calgary, T2V 4R6, AB, Canada
Tel.: (403) 287-1477
Web Site: https://www.skinscience.md
Skin Care Services
N.A.I.C.S.: 812112

FIDELITY D & D BANCORP, INC.

101 N Blakely St, Dunmore, PA 18512
Tel.: (570) 342-8281   **PA**
Web Site:
https://www.bankatfidelity.com
Year Founded: 1999

FDBC—(NASDAQ)
Rev.: $78,672,000
Assets: $2,378,372,000
Liabilities: $2,215,422,000
Net Worth: $162,950,000
Earnings: $30,021,000
Emp.: 291
Fiscal Year-end: 12/31/22
Bank Holding Company
N.A.I.C.S.: 551111
Daniel J. Santaniello (Pres & CEO)
Michael J. McDonald (Vice Chm)
John T. Cognetti (Sec)
Timothy P. O'Brien (Chief Lending Officer & Sr Exec VP)
Eugene J. Walsh (COO & Exec VP)
Salvatore R. Defrancesco Jr. (Treas)
Michael J. Pacyna Jr. (Chief Bus Dev Officer & Exec VP)

Subsidiaries:

The Fidelity Deposit & Discount Bank   (1)
101 N Blakely St, Dunmore, PA 18512-2201
Tel.: (570) 342-8281
Web Site: https://www.bankatfidelity.com
Sales Range: $25-49.9 Million
Commericial Banking
N.A.I.C.S.: 522110
Daniel J. Santaniello (Pres & CEO)
Michael J. McDonald (Executives, Bd of Dirs)
John T. Cognetti (Sec)
Brian J. Cali (Chm)
Timothy P. O'Brien (Chief Bus Dev Officer & Sr Exec VP)
Eugene J. Walsh (COO)
Salvatore R. Defrancesco Jr. (CFO, Treas & Exec VP)
Michael J. Pacyna Jr. (Chief Lending Officer & Exec VP)
Kerry Lobel (CIO & Sr VP)
Joann Marsili (Sr VP & Dir-Mktg & Digital Sls)
Mary T. McNichols (Sr VP & Dir-HR)
William P. McAndrew (Sr VP & Advisor-LPL Fin)

FIDELITY FEDERAL BANCORP

18 NW 4th St, Evansville, IN 47708
Tel.: (812) 424-0921   **IN**
Web Site:
http://www.unitedfidelity.com
Year Founded: 1993
FDLB—(OTCEM)
Bank Holding Company
N.A.I.C.S.: 551111
Donald N. Neel (Pres & CEO)

Subsidiaries:

United Fidelity Bank, FSB   (1)
18 NW 4th St, Evansville, IN 47708-1778
Tel.: (812) 424-0921
Web Site: http://www.unitedfidelity.com
Sales Range: $10-24.9 Million
Emp.: 32
Federal Savings Bank
N.A.I.C.S.: 522180
Donald R. Neel (Pres & CEO)
Keith A. Knipstein (CFO & Treas)

FIDELITY NATIONAL FINANCIAL, INC.

601 Riverside Ave Bldg 5, Jacksonville, FL 32204
Tel.: (904) 854-8100   **DE**
Web Site: https://www.fnf.com
Year Founded: 1847
FNF—(NYSE)
Rev.: $11,752,000,000
Assets: $80,614,000,000
Liabilities: $73,154,000,000
Net Worth: $7,460,000,000
Earnings: $517,000,000
Emp.: 22,293
Fiscal Year-end: 12/31/23
Real Estate Manangement Services
N.A.I.C.S.: 531390
William P. Foley II (Founder & Chm)
Michael J. Nolan (CEO)

Raymond R. Quirk (Vice Chm)
Paul I. Perez (Chief Compliance Officer & Deputy Chief Legal Officer)
Patrick S. Rhodin (Chief Risk Officer)
Katie G. Schmidt (Chief Regulatory Officer)
Tara B. Van Rooy (Gen Counsel)
Ray Marine (Co-Pres-Western Ops)
Don Dubois (Co-Pres-Western Ops)
Brian Maughan (CMO & Chief Innovation Officer)
Peter Sadowski (Chief Legal Officer)
Tiffany Green (Chief Audit Officer)
Liz Reilly (Chief Privacy Officer)
John Crowley (CIO)
Melissa Circelli (Chief HR Officer)
Jason Nadeau (Chief Digital Officer)
Michael L. Gravelle (Gen Counsel & Sec)
Randy Quirk (Vice Chm)

Subsidiaries:

American Blue Ribbon Holdings, LLC   (1)
400 W 48th Ave, Denver, CO 80216   (55%)
Tel.: (303) 296-2121
Web Site: http://www.bakerssquare.com
Sales Range: $450-499.9 Million
Emp.: 12,789
Holding Company; Restaurant Chains Owner & Operator
N.A.I.C.S.: 551112
Gregory A. Hayes (Chief Admin Officer)

Subsidiary (Domestic):

99 Restaurants, LLC   (2)
Four Corners 194 Cambridge Rd, Woburn, MA 01801
Tel.: (781) 938-8999
Web Site: https://www.99restaurants.com
Sales Range: $400-449.9 Million
Emp.: 7,000
Restaurant Operators
N.A.I.C.S.: 722511

Division (Domestic):

Bakers Square   (2)
400 W 48th Ave, Denver, CO 80216-1806
Tel.: (303) 296-2121
Web Site:
http://www.bakerssquarerestaurants.com
Sales Range: $200-249.9 Million
Emp.: 130
Restaurant
N.A.I.C.S.: 722511

Subsidiary (Domestic):

O'Charley's Inc.   (2)
110 Coley Davis Ct, Nashville, TN 37221
Tel.: (615) 662-4026
Web Site: https://www.ocharleys.com
Sales Range: $1-4.9 Billion
Restaurant Operators
N.A.I.C.S.: 722511
William E. Hall (Pres-Restaurant Grp)

Division (Domestic):

Village Inn Restaurants   (2)
7051 Tower Rd, Denver, CO 80249
Tel.: (303) 574-1915
Web Site:
http://www.villageinnrestaurants.com
Sales Range: $125-149.9 Million
Restaurant
N.A.I.C.S.: 722511

Ceridian Corporation   (1)
3311 E Old Shakopee Rd, Minneapolis, MN 55425-1640   (32%)
Tel.: (952) 853-8100
Web Site: https://www.ceridian.com
Sales Range: $1-4.9 Billion
Emp.: 100,000
Payroll Processing & Human Resource Services
N.A.I.C.S.: 541214
Lisa Sterling (Chief People & Culture Officer)
Eric Glass (Exec VP)
Noemie Heuland (Exec VP)

Steve Holdridge *(Pres)*
Joe Korngiebel *(Exec VP)*
Bill McDonald *(Exec VP)*
Stephen Moore *(Mng Dir)*
Wendy Muirhead *(Mng Dir)*
Carrie Rasmussen *(CIO)*
Susan Tohyama *(Exec VP)*
Erik Zimmer *(Exec VP)*
David Ossip *(CEO)*

Unit (Domestic):

Ceridian Benefits Services **(2)**
3201 34th St S, Saint Petersburg, FL 33711
Tel.: (952) 853-8100
Web Site: http://www.ceridian.com
Sales Range: $200-249.9 Million
Benefits Services
N.A.I.C.S.: 541214

Chicago Title and Trust
Company **(1)**
10 S La Salle St, Chicago, IL 60603
Tel.: (312) 223-4110
Web Site:
   https://chicagotitleandtrust.ctic.com
Real Estate & Title Insurance Services
N.A.I.C.S.: 524127

F&G Annuities & Life, Inc. **(1)**
801 Grand Ave Ste 2600, Des Moines, IA
50309 **(83.9%)**
Tel.: (515) 330-3340
Web Site: https://www.fglife.com
Holding Company; Life Insurance & Annuity
Products & Services
N.A.I.C.S.: 551112
Christopher O. Blunt *(CEO)*
John D. Currier Jr. *(Pres)*
Matt Christensen *(Exec VP)*
Mike Gravelle *(Gen Counsel)*
Wendy J. B. Young *(CFO & Exec VP)*
Leena Punjabi *(Chief Investment Officer &
Exec VP)*
Marie Norcia Gravelle *(Sec & Exec VP)*

Subsidiary (Domestic):

Fidelity & Guaranty Life Insurance
Company **(2)**
801 Grand Ave Ste 2600, Des Moines, IA
50309
Web Site: https://www.fglife.com
Life Insurance Products & Services
N.A.I.C.S.: 524113
Chris Blunt *(Pres & CEO)*
Matt Christensen *(COO)*
Scott Cochran *(Pres)*
John Currier *(Pres)*
Renee Hamlen *(Chief Human Capital Offi-
cer)*
Jodi Ahlman *(Gen Counsel)*
Dave Martin *(Chief Risk Officer)*
Leena Punjabi *(Chief Investment Officer)*
Wendy J. B. Young *(CFO)*
Ron Barrett *(Sr VP)*
Paul Conner *(Sr VP)*
Dave Czerwonka *(Sr VP)*
Lisa Foxworthy-Parker *(Sr VP)*
Ted Hughes *(Sr VP)*
Catherine James *(Sr VP)*
Sean O'Connell *(Sr VP)*
Glen Reineke *(Sr VP)*
Steve Sanders *(Sr VP)*
Micki Wildin *(Sr VP)*
Mark Wiltse *(Sr VP)*
Tamra VanAllen *(Sr VP)*

FGL Holdings **(1)**
4th Floor Boundary Hall Cricket Square,
Georgetown, KY 1-1102, Cayman
Islands **(100%)**
Tel.: (345) 9475614
Web Site: http://www.fglife.bm
Rev.: $2,113,000,000
Assets: $36,714,000,000
Liabilities: $33,971,000,000
Net Worth: $2,743,000,000
Earnings: $507,000,000
Emp.: 352
Fiscal Year-end: 12/31/2019
Investment Holding Company
N.A.I.C.S.: 551112
Christopher O. Blunt *(Pres & CEO)*
Eric Marhoun *(Gen Counsel & Sec)*
Wendy J. B. Young *(Chief Risk Officer &
Exec VP)*
Jon Bayer *(Exec VP & Head-Corp Dev &
Strategy)*
John Thomas Fleurant *(CFO)*

Fidelity National Insurance
Company **(1)**
6800 Southpoint Pkwy Ste 700, Jacksonville,
FL 32216
Tel.: (904) 854-8100
Web Site: http://www.fnf.com
Sales Range: $50-74.9 Million
Emp.: 100
Insurance Services
N.A.I.C.S.: 524126

Fidelity National Title Group, Inc. **(1)**
601 Riverside Ave, Jacksonville, FL 32204
Tel.: (904) 854-8100
Web Site: https://www.fntg.com
Sales Range: $150-199.9 Million
Title Insurance
N.A.I.C.S.: 524127
Donald Cole *(Sr VP)*
Gary P. Urquhart *(Gen Counsel & Exec VP)*

Subsidiary (Domestic):

Charter Title Company Inc. **(2)**
1717 W Loop S 12th Fl, Houston, TX
77027 **(100%)**
Tel.: (713) 871-9700
Web Site: https://www.chartertitle.com
Sales Range: $25-49.9 Million
Emp.: 50
Real Estate Title Insurance Services
N.A.I.C.S.: 524127
James A. Johnson *(Pres)*
Carol Dube *(Office Mgr)*
Becky Houssiere *(Officer-Escrow & Mgr-
Escrow)*
Cameron Franz *(Sr VP)*

Chicago Title Insurance
Company **(2)**
171 N Clark St, Chicago, IL 60601
Tel.: (312) 223-2000
Web Site: http://www.ctic.com
Sales Range: $150-199.9 Million
Title Insurance & Related Services
N.A.I.C.S.: 524127
Mike Cusack *(Sr VP & Reg Mgr)*

Subsidiary (Domestic):

Commonwealth Land Title Insurance
Company **(3)**
601 Riverside Ave, Jacksonville, FL 32204
Web Site: https://www.cltic.com
Sales Range: $750-799.9 Million
Emp.: 2,581
Land Title Insurance Services
N.A.I.C.S.: 524127
Pam K. Saylors *(Sr VP & Mgr)*

Commonwealth Title of Dallas,
Inc. **(3)**
2651 N Harwood St Ste 260, Dallas, TX
75201
Tel.: (972) 770-2121
Web Site: http://www.cltic.com
Sales Range: $10-24.9 Million
Emp.: 12
Real Estate Title Insurance Services
N.A.I.C.S.: 524127
Sharon Cooper *(Sr VP & Mgr)*

Subsidiary (Domestic):

Fidelity National Title Insurance Com-
pany of New York **(2)**
485 Lexington Ave Fl 18, New York, NY
10017
Tel.: (212) 481-5858
Web Site: https://www.newyorkncs.fntic.com
Sales Range: $50-74.9 Million
Emp.: 70
Title Insurance
N.A.I.C.S.: 541191
Joanna Patilis *(Sr VP & Reg Mgr)*
Terence Mullin *(VP-Comml Sls)*
Edward L. Heim *(VP)*
Neil Clark *(Sr VP-Comml Sls)*
John C. Maddie *(Asst VP-Comml Sls)*
Kevin Danca *(VP)*

Lawyers Title Insurance
Corporation **(2)**
601 Riverside Ave, Jacksonville, FL 32204
Web Site: https://www.ltic.com
Sales Range: $150-199.9 Million
Emp.: 60
Real Estate Title Insurance Services
N.A.I.C.S.: 524127

Subsidiary (Domestic):

Fidelity Title Insurance
Corporation **(3)**
4111 Executive Pkwy Ste 304, Columbus,
OH 43215
Tel.: (614) 221-4523
Web Site: http://www.ltic.com
Sales Range: $25-49.9 Million
Emp.: 50
Real Estate Title Insurance Services
N.A.I.C.S.: 524127

LPS Field Services, Inc. **(3)**
601 Riverside Ave, Jacksonville, FL 32204
Tel.: (904) 854-5100
Web Site: http://www.lpsfs.com
Mortgage Banking Services
N.A.I.C.S.: 522292

LPS Valuation Solutions, LLC **(3)**
9339 Carroll Park Dr Ste 100, San Diego,
CA 92121
Tel.: (858) 909-4300
Real Estate Appraisal Services
N.A.I.C.S.: 531320

LRT Record Services, Inc. **(3)**
1945 W Walnut Hill Ln, Irving, TX 75038-
4408
Tel.: (972) 580-8575
Insurance Brokerage Services
N.A.I.C.S.: 524210

Lawyers Title of Arizona **(3)**
3900 E Camelback Rd Ste 150, Phoenix,
AZ 85018
Tel.: (602) 257-2600
Web Site:
   https://www.lawyerstitlearizona.com
Real Estate Title Insurance Services
N.A.I.C.S.: 524127
Vince Beemiller *(Pres & Country Mgr)*

Lawyers Title of El Paso, Inc. **(3)**
301 East Yandell Dr, El Paso, TX 79902
Tel.: (915) 543-7600
Sales Range: $1-9.9 Million
Real Estate Title Insurance Services
N.A.I.C.S.: 524127

McDash Analytics, LLC **(3)**
814 A1A N Ste 100, Ponte Vedra Beach, FL
32082
Tel.: (904) 285-6220
Web Site: http://www.mcdash.com
Sales Range: $1-9.9 Million
Emp.: 10
Information Retrieval Services
N.A.I.C.S.: 561499

OnePointCity, LLC **(3)**
1521 N Cooper St 4th Fl, Arlington, TX
76011
Web Site: https://www.onepointcity.com
Data Processing Hosting & Related Services
N.A.I.C.S.: 518210

Property Tax Direct, Inc **(3)**
3100 New York Dr Ste 100, Pasadena, CA
91107
Tel.: (866) 457-4112
Web Site: http://www.lpstax.com
Real Estate Tax Information Services
N.A.I.C.S.: 513199

Subsidiary (Domestic):

National TaxNet **(4)**
3021 Gateway Dr Ste 240, Irving, TX 75063
Tel.: (972) 812-6950
Web Site: https://www.nationaltaxnet.com
Emp.: 10
Property Tax Information Services
N.A.I.C.S.: 513199

Subsidiary (Domestic):

RealEC Technologies, Inc. **(3)**
20 E Greenway Plaza Ste 500, Houston,
TX 77044
Tel.: (877) 273-2532
Web Site: http://www.bkfs.com
Management Software Solutions
N.A.I.C.S.: 541511

RealInfo, L.L.C. **(3)**
16W347 83rd St Ste D, Burr Ridge, IL
60527
Tel.: (630) 789-4900

Web Site: https://targetproperty.us
Online Business Directory Publisher
N.A.I.C.S.: 513140

Subsidiary (Domestic):

Service Link LP **(2)**
1400 Cherrington Pkwy, Moon Township,
PA 15108
Tel.: (724) 857-5890
Web Site: http://www.svclnk.com
Sales Range: $1-4.9 Billion
Emp.: 700
Centralized Mortgage & Residential Real
Estate Title & Closing Services
N.A.I.C.S.: 531390

ServiceLink IP Holding Company,
LLC. **(2)**
1355 Cherrington Pkwy, Coraopolis, PA
15108-4315
Web Site: https://www.svclnk.com
Property Valuation, Title & Closing Services
N.A.I.C.S.: 531320
Chris Azur *(CEO)*
David Holland *(CFO)*
Miriam Moore *(Pres-Default Svcs Div)*
Kiran Vattem *(CTO, Chief Digital Officer &
Exec VP)*
Dave Howard *(Exec VP-Origination Svcs
Sls)*
Barry Coffin *(Mng Dir-Home Equity Title &
Close)*
Susan Falsetti *(Mng Dir-Origination Title &
Close)*
Jim Gladden *(Sr VP-Origination Strategy)*
Mark Reedy *(Sr VP-Svc Link Natl Flood)*
Marco Brenes *(Sr VP-Default Svcs Sls)*
Steve Crocker *(Sr VP-Loan Modifications &
Pre-Foreclosure Title)*
Amy Daniel *(Sr VP-REO Title & Close)*
Yvette Gilmore *(Sr VP-Servicing Product
Strategy)*
Tim Guertin *(Sr VP-Field Svcs)*
Eric Murphy *(Sr VP-Process Solutions)*
Eva Tapia *(Sr VP-Svc Link Auction)*
Jeff Mills *(Exec VP)*

Division (Domestic):

ServiceLink **(3)**
10385 Westmoor Dr Ste 100, Westminster,
CO 80021
Tel.: (720) 566-8000
Web Site: http://www.svclnk.com
Emp.: 350
Real Estate Services
N.A.I.C.S.: 531390

Subsidiary (Domestic):

ServiceLink National Flood, LLC **(3)**
500 E Border St 3rd Fl, Arlington, TX 76010
Web Site:
   https://www.servicelinknationalflood.com
Flood Certification Vendor
N.A.I.C.S.: 561410

Subsidiary (Domestic):

Ticor Title Insurance Company **(2)**
1500 Quail St, Newport Beach, CA 92660
Tel.: (714) 289-3300
Web Site: http://www.ticortitle.com
Sales Range: $50-74.9 Million
Emp.: 75
Insurance
N.A.I.C.S.: 524210
Roger Jewkes *(Pres & Mgr-Ticor Div)*

Gary G. Oetgen, Inc. **(1)**
Park S Office Ctr Ste C-1 7505 Waters Ave,
Savannah, GA 31406
Tel.: (859) 283-8400
Web Site: http://www.ggoagency.com
Insurance Agency & Broker
N.A.I.C.S.: 524210
Gary G. Oetgen *(Pres)*

T-System, Inc. **(1)**
6509 Windcrest Dr Ste 165, Plano, TX
75024
Tel.: (972) 503-8899
Web Site: https://www.tsystem.com
Management Consulting Services; Clinical
Documentation & Facility Coding Software
& Services
N.A.I.C.S.: 541618

FIDELITY NATIONAL INFOR-

FIDELITY NATIONAL INFOR—(CONTINUED)

MATION SERVICES, INC.
347 Riverside Ave, Jacksonville, FL
32202
Tel.: (904) 438-6000
Web Site: https://www.fisglobal.com
Year Founded: 1968
FIS—(NYSE)
Rev.: $9,821,000,000
Assets: $55,105,000,000
Liabilities: $36,006,000,000
Net Worth: $19,099,000,000
Earnings: ($6,654,000,000)
Emp.: 60,000
Fiscal Year-end: 12/31/23
Chemical Products Mfr
N.A.I.C.S.: 325998
Ellyn Raftery *(Chief Mktg & Comm Officer)*
James Kehoe *(CFO)*
John Durrant *(Pres-Banking Solutions)*
Kelly Beatty *(Chief Performance Officer)*
Rafic Naja *(Chief Strategy Officer)*
Stephanie L. Ferris *(Pres, CEO, COO, Chief Admin Officer & VP)*
Robert A. Toohey *(Chief People Officer & Exec VP)*

Subsidiaries:

Alphakinetic Ltd.
35 New Broad Street, London, EC2M 1NH,
United Kingdom
Tel.: (44) 2038160295
Web Site: http://www.alphakinetic.com
Financial Investment Services
N.A.I.C.S.: 523999

Armed Forces Financial Network,
LLC   **(1)**
11601 Roosevelt Blvd TA-94, Saint Petersburg, FL 33716
Tel.: (727) 227-2880
Web Site: https://www.affn.org
Financial Institution Services
N.A.I.C.S.: 522320
John M. Broda *(Pres & CEO)*
Ann Morsch *(VP-Member Svcs & Ops)*
Rhonda Wilson *(Sr Dir-Member Svcs & Ops)*
Christopher Kelly *(VP)*
Karmelita Sewell *(VP)*

Asset Exchange, Inc.   **(1)**
601 Riverside Ave, Jacksonville, FL 32204
Tel.: (503) 220-0007
Credit Card Services
N.A.I.C.S.: 522210
Gary A. Norcross *(Pres)*
Michael P. Oates *(Sec)*

Capco Consulting Singapore Pte.
Ltd.   **(1)**
1 George Street 15-06, One George Street,
Singapore, 049145, Singapore
Tel.: (65) 64071220
Web Site: http://www.capco.com
Electronic Payment Services
N.A.I.C.S.: 522320

Certegy France   **(1)**
11 Ave Gubonnet Bldg Le Goublon B,
Courbevoie, 92400, France
Tel.: (33) 170734000
Web Site: http://www.fisglobal.com
Sales Range: $10-24.9 Million
Emp.: 50
Provides Credit, Debt & Merchant Processing, E-Banking, Check Risk Management &
Check Cashing Services to Financial Institutions & Merchants
N.A.I.C.S.: 522390
Yung Benn *(Pres)*

Certegy SNC   **(1)**
11 Avenue dubonnet, Courbevoie, 92400,
France
Tel.: (33) 1 70 73 40 00
Emp.: 10
Financial Services
N.A.I.C.S.: 523999

Chex Systems Inc.   **(1)**

7805 Hudson Rd Ste 100, Woodbury, MN
55125
Web Site: https://www.chexsystems.com
Financial Services
N.A.I.C.S.: 921130

Clear2Pay APAC Pty Ltd.   **(1)**
L 9 132 Arthur St, North Sydney, 2060,
NSW, Australia
Tel.: (61) 290260000
Emp.: 30
Application Software Development Services
N.A.I.C.S.: 541511
John Weiss *(Project Mgr)*

Clear2Pay Americas, Inc.   **(1)**
25 Braintree Hill Ofc Park Ste 307, Boston,
MA 02184
Tel.: (781) 908-0100
Electronic Payment Services
N.A.I.C.S.: 522320

Clear2Pay Belgium NV   **(1)**
De Kleetlaan 6A, 1831, Machelen, Belgium
Tel.: (32) 27176900
Software Development Services
N.A.I.C.S.: 541511

Clear2Pay Scotland Holdings
Limited   **(1)**
Clear2Pay House Pitreavie Court, Dunferm-
line, KY11 8UU, Fife, United Kingdom
Tel.: (44) 1383720118
Web Site: http://www.levelfour.com
Holding Company
N.A.I.C.S.: 551112

Clear2Pay Services NV   **(1)**
Maenhoutstraat 77B, 9830, Sint-Martens-
Latem, Vlaams Brabant, Belgium
Tel.: (32) 24025200
Software Development Services
N.A.I.C.S.: 541511

ClearCommerce Corporation   **(1)**
11921 N MoPac Expy Ste 400, Austin, TX
78759
Tel.: (512) 832-0132
Web Site: http://www.clearcommerce.com
Emp.: 107
Computer Related Services
N.A.I.C.S.: 541519

Endpoint Exchange, LLC   **(1)**
1105 Cornell Pkwy, Oklahoma City, OK
73108
Tel.: (405) 942-0373
Web Site:
     http://www.endpointexchange.com
Electronic Check Image Software Services
N.A.I.C.S.: 541511

FIRM II, LLC   **(1)**
601 Riverside Ave, Jacksonville, FL 32204
Tel.: (904) 438-6000
Software Development Services
N.A.I.C.S.: 541511

FIS Brokerage & Securities Services
LLC   **(1)**
2100 Enterprise Ave, Geneva, IL 60134
Tel.: (630) 482-7300
Financial Transaction Processing Services
N.A.I.C.S.: 521110

FIS Card Processing Services (Chile)
S.A.   **(1)**
Calle Marchant Pereira 10 Piso 18-19,
Providencia, Santiago, Chile
Tel.: (56) 22230600
Credit Card Services
N.A.I.C.S.: 522210

FIS Data Systems Inc.   **(1)**
Tel.: (904) 438-6000
Integrated IT Solutions & e-Processing Ser-
vices for Financial Industry
N.A.I.C.S.: 518210

Subsidiary (Non-US):

FIS Business Systems LLC   **(2)**
Tel.: (704) 561-8260
Trust Accounting Systems & Related Ser-
vices
N.A.I.C.S.: 541512

FIS Financial Systems LLC   **(2)**
Tel.: (781) 275-7444
Software Services
N.A.I.C.S.: 513210

GL Trade S.A.   **(2)**
Tel.: (33) 153400000
Sales Range: $250-299.9 Million
Emp.: 1,408
Trading & Order Management Software;
Network & Market Data Services
N.A.I.C.S.: 541512

Unit (Non-US):

Wall Street Concepts   **(2)**
                                        (100%)
Tel.: (646) 445-1099
Web Site: https://www.wsc.com
Emp.: 50
Tax Information Reporting Solutions for RE-
ITs, REMICs, WHFITs, Master Limited Part-
nerships, Mutual Funds & Long-Term OID
Bonds
N.A.I.C.S.: 541213

FIS Energy Solutions Limited   **(1)**
C/O F I S Corporate Governance The Wal-
brook Building 25, London, EC4N 8AF,
United Kingdom
Tel.: (44) 2080812000
Financial Transaction Processing Services
N.A.I.C.S.: 521110

FIS Financial Systems (France)
SAS   **(1)**
42 rue Notre Dame Des Victoires, 75002,
Paris, France
Tel.: (33) 153400000
Financial Transaction Processing Services
N.A.I.C.S.: 521110

FIS Global Trading (Iberica) S.L.
Unipersonal   **(1)**
Calle Maudes 51 - Plt 8, Madrid, 28003,
Spain
Tel.: (34) 913956330
Financial Transaction Processing Services
N.A.I.C.S.: 521110

FIS Investment Systems LLC   **(1)**
377 E Butterfield Rd Ste 800, Lombard, IL
60148
Tel.: (630) 920-3100
Financial Transaction Processing Services
N.A.I.C.S.: 521110

FIS Payments (UK) Limited   **(1)**
Tricorn House 51/53 Hagley Road Edgbas-
ton, Birmingham, B16 8TU, United Kingdom
Tel.: (44) 1214104100
Financial Transaction Processing Services
N.A.I.C.S.: 521110

FIS Systeme GmbH   **(1)**
Solmsstrasse 2 - 22, 60486, Frankfurt am
Main, 60486, Germany
Tel.: (49) 69707680
Financial Transaction Processing Services
N.A.I.C.S.: 521110

FIS Technology Services (Poland)
Sp. z.o.o.   **(1)**
Ul Sienna 73, 00-833, Warsaw, Poland
Tel.: (48) 914624900
Software Services
N.A.I.C.S.: 541511

FIS Technology Services Singapore
Pte. Ltd.   **(1)**
8 Marina View 31-01 Asia Square Tower 1,
Singapore, 018960, Singapore
Tel.: (65) 62255926
Software Development Services
N.A.I.C.S.: 541511

FIS Vietnam LLC   **(1)**
5th Floor Sentinel Place 41A Ly Thai To
Street, Hanoi, Vietnam
Tel.: (84) 439388795
Software Development Services
N.A.I.C.S.: 541511
Duong Van Thuy *(Mgr-PMO)*

FIS Wealth Management Services,
Inc.   **(1)**
601 Riverside Ave, Jacksonville, FL 32204
Tel.: (904) 854-5000
Web Site: http://www.fisglobal.com
Emp.: 310
Wealth Management Services
N.A.I.C.S.: 523940
Gary A. Norcross *(Pres & CEO)*

Subsidiary (Domestic):

Reliance Financial Corporation   **(2)**

1100 Abernathy Rd NE Ste 400, Atlanta,
GA 30328
Tel.: (404) 266-0663
Web Site: http://www.reliance-trust.com
Holding Company
N.A.I.C.S.: 551112

Subsidiary (Domestic):

Reliance Trust Company   **(3)**
1100 Abernathy Rd NE Ste 400, Atlanta,
GA 30328-5634
Tel.: (404) 266-0663
Web Site: http://www.reliance-trust.com
Sales Range: $150-199.9 Million
Emp.: 300
Trust Services
N.A.I.C.S.: 523991
William C. Harlow *(Pres)*

Subsidiary (Domestic):

Reliance Integrated Solutions
LLC   **(4)**
1100 Abernathy Rd Ste 400, Atlanta, GA
30328
Tel.: (404) 266-0663
Web Site: http://www.reliance-trust.com
Emp.: 300
Back-Office Securities Processing & Ac-
counting Services
N.A.I.C.S.: 522320
Trey Carter *(Pres)*

Reliance Operations Services
LLC   **(4)**
1100 Abernathy Rd Ste 400 NE, Atlanta,
GA 30328
Tel.: (404) 266-0663
Trust Management Services
N.A.I.C.S.: 523991
Eric Anderson *(Pres)*
Kevin Kenely *(Sr VP & Mgr-Trust Fund
Acctg)*

FIS Workflow Solutions LLC   **(1)**
104 Inverness Center Pl, Birmingham, AL
35242
Tel.: (205) 437-7500
Financial Transaction Processing Services
N.A.I.C.S.: 521110

Fidelity Information Services
GmbH   **(1)**
Barthstrasse 18, 80339, Munich, Germany
Tel.: (49) 8966065000
Web Site: http://www.fis-germany.de
Software Consulting Services
N.A.I.C.S.: 541512

Fidelity Information Services KOR-
DOBA GmbH   **(1)**
Barthstrasse 18, 80339, Munich, Germany
Tel.: (49) 8966065000
Web Site: http://www.fis-germany.de
Emp.: 12
Software Services
N.A.I.C.S.: 513210
Oliver Kurz *(Mgr-Supply Chain)*

Fidelity National Information Services,
Inc. - Herndon   **(1)**
13454 Sunrise Valley Dr 4th Fl, Herndon,
VA 20171
Tel.: (703) 478-2260
Web Site: http://www.fisglobal.com
Rev.: $47,600,000
Emp.: 140
Browser-Based Document & Report Man-
agement Software Services
N.A.I.C.S.: 423430

Fidelity National Information Services,
Inc. - Norcross   **(1)**
3150 Holcomb Bridge Rd, Norcross, GA
30071
Tel.: (770) 797-2460
Sales Range: $450-499.9 Million
Emp.: 3,000
Information Technology Solutions Services
N.A.I.C.S.: 518210

Fidelity National Information Services,
Inc. - Orlando   **(1)**
2001 Summit Park Dr Ste 100, Orlando, FL
32810
Tel.: (407) 217-0217
Web Site: http://www.fisglobal.com
Sales Range: $75-99.9 Million
Emp.: 410
Information Technology Solutions Services

N.A.I.C.S.: 541519
Gary A. Norcross *(Pres & CEO)*

Fidelity Processadora S.A. (1)
Av Antonio Frederico Ozanan 1440 Blocks
XI XII XIV, XVI - Vila Santana II, Jundiai,
13219-001, SP, Brazil
Tel.: (55) 1121363515
Web Site: http://www.fnis.com.br
Financial & Commercial Institutions Services
N.A.I.C.S.: 522320
Luiz Compagno *(CEO)*

GIFTS Software, Inc. (1)
360 Lexington Ave Rm 601, New York, NY
10017
Tel.: (646) 865-1301
Web Site: http://www.giftssoft.com
Sales Range: $10-24.9 Million
Emp.: 35
Software Developer
N.A.I.C.S.: 513210

Lexcel Solutions, Inc. (1)
4110 N Scottsdale Rd Ste 310, Scottsdale,
AZ 85251-3920
Tel.: (480) 874-0443
Electronic Payment Services
N.A.I.C.S.: 522320

Link2Gov Corp. (1)
113 Seaboard Ln Ste A-250, Franklin, TN
37067
Web Site: http://www.pay1040.com
Internet & Interactive Voice Transactions
(Government-to-citizen & Government- to-
business)
N.A.I.C.S.: 541690

NYCE Payments Network, LLC (1)
400 Plz Dr 2nd Fl, Secaucus, NJ 07094
Tel.: (904) 438-6000
Web Site: http://www.nyce.net
Sales Range: $100-124.9 Million
Emp.: 450
Electronic Payment Process Services
N.A.I.C.S.: 522320

Platform Securities LLP (1)
25 Canada Square, London, E14 5LQ,
United Kingdom
Tel.: (44) 121 233 0336
Web Site: https://empower1.fisglobal.com
Electronic Payment Services
N.A.I.C.S.: 522320

Prime Associates, Inc. (1)
63 San Miguel Dr 250, Newport Beach, CA
92660
Tel.: (949) 219-0088
Web Site:
https://www.primeassociatesinc.com
Real Estate Services
N.A.I.C.S.: 531210
Jack Siada *(Pres)*

**Sanchez Computer Associates,
LLC** (1)
2 W Liberty Ste 300, Malvern, PA 19355
Tel.: (610) 296-8877
Web Site: http://www.fisglobal.com
Sales Range: $75-99.9 Million
Emp.: 500
Financial Software Development & Services
N.A.I.C.S.: 541511

**Valuecentric Marketing Group,
Inc.** (1)
49 Court St, Binghamton, NY 13901
Tel.: (607) 584-9248
Transaction-based Marketing Services
N.A.I.C.S.: 541613

Zenmonics Inc. (1)
125 Floyd Smith Office Park Dr Ste 220,
Charlotte, NC 28262
Tel.: (704) 971-7315
Web Site: http://www.zenmonics.com
Sales Range: $10-24.9 Million
Emp.: 75
Information Technology Consulting Services
N.A.I.C.S.: 541512
Riaz Syed *(Founder & CEO)*
Beth Abernathy *(Pres)*

mFoundry, Inc. (1)
60 E Sir Francis Drake Ste 200, Larkspur,
CA 94939
Tel.: (415) 925-8550

Mobile Banking & Mobile Commerce Solutions Services
N.A.I.C.S.: 513210
Drew Sievers *(Co-Founder)*

FIDUS INVESTMENT CORPO-
RATION
1603 Orrington Ave Ste 1005, Evan-
ston, IL 60201
Tel.: (847) 859-3940   MD
Web Site: https://www.fdus.com
Year Founded: 2007
FDUS—(NASDAQ)
Rev.: $94,137,000
Assets: $935,960,000
Liabilities: $455,617,000
Net Worth: $480,343,000
Earnings: $46,549,000
Fiscal Year-end: 12/31/22
Investment Services
N.A.I.C.S.: 523999
Edward H. Ross *(Chm & CEO)*
Thomas C. Lauer *(Pres)*
Shelby E. Sherard *(CFO, Chief Com-
pliance Officer & Sec)*

Subsidiaries:

Fidus Mezzanine Capital II, L.P. (1)
1603 Orrington Ave, Evanston, IL 60201
Tel.: (847) 859-3941
Financial Investment Services
N.A.I.C.S.: 523999
Edward Ross *(CEO)*

FIELDWOOD ENERGY LLC
2000 W Sam Houston Pkwy S Ste
1200, Houston, TX 77042
Tel.: (713) 969-1000   DE
Web Site:
    http://www.fieldwoodenergy.com
Year Founded: 2013
FWDE—(OTCIQ)
Natural Gas Extraction Services
N.A.I.C.S.: 211120
John Seeger *(Sr VP-Ops)*
Mike Dane *(Sr VP & CFO)*
Thomas R. Lamme *(Sr VP, Gen
Counsel & Sec)*
John Deck *(VP-IT)*

FIFTH THIRD BANCORP
38 Fountain Square Plz, Cincinnati,
OH 45263
Tel.: (513) 579-5300   OH
Web Site: https://www.53.com
Year Founded: 1975
FITB—(NASDAQ)
Rev.: $9,760,000,000
Assets: $214,574,000,000
Liabilities: $195,402,000,000
Net Worth: $19,172,000,000
Earnings: $2,212,000,000
Emp.: 18,724
Fiscal Year-end: 12/31/23
Bank Holding Company
N.A.I.C.S.: 551111
James C. Leonard *(COO & Exec VP)*
Timothy N. Spence *(Chm, Pres &
CEO)*
Robert P. Shaffer *(Chief Risk Officer
& Exec VP)*
Kevin P. Lavender *(Exec VP & Head-
Comml Banking)*
Susan B. Zaunbrecher *(Chief Legal
Officer & Exec VP)*
Jude A. Schramm *(CIO & Exec VP)*
Bryan D. Preston *(CFO & Exec VP)*
Nancy C. Pinckney *(Chief HR Officer
& Exec VP)*
Liz Osborne *(Exec VP)*
Kris Garrett *(Grp Pres-Reg, Exec VP
& Head-Wealth & Asset Mgmt)*

Subsidiaries:

Big Data Healthcare LLC (1)
2921 Landmark Pl Ste 215-314, Madison,
WI 53713

Web Site: https://bigdatahc.com
Healthcare Payment & Remittance Services
N.A.I.C.S.: 522110

**Fifth Third Bank, National
Association** (1)
5th 3rd Ctr 38 Fountain Sq Plz, Cincinnati,
OH 45263   **(100%)**
Tel.: (513) 579-5353
Web Site: http://www.53.com
Sales Range: $125-149.9 Million
Savings Bank
N.A.I.C.S.: 522180
Timothy N. Spence *(Chm, Pres & CEO)*
Lars C. Anderson *(Vice Chm-Comml Bank-
ing Strategic Growth Initiatives & Exec VP)*
Joseph Yurosek *(Pres-Market-California)*
Richard Arendale *(Sr VP-Corp Banking &
Head-Entertainment, Lodging & Leisure)*
Richard C. Butler *(Sr VP-Corp Banking &
Head-Energy)*
Pete Foley *(Sr VP-Corp Banking & Co-
Head-Tech, Media & Telecom)*
Kevin Khanna *(Sr VP-Corp Banking & Co-
Head-Tech, Media & Telecom)*
Joshua H. Landau *(Sr VP-Corp Banking &
Head-Fin Institutions Grp)*
Zewditu Tizu Menelik *(Sr VP-Corp Banking
& Head-Intl)*
Michael Ryan *(Mng Dir-Corp Banking &
Head-Healthcare)*
Craig Wolf *(Sr VP-Corp Banking & Head-
Consumer & Retail)*
Bob Marcus *(Exec VP & Head-Capital Mar-
kets)*
Bridgit Chayt *(Sr VP & Dir-Comml Pay-
ments & Treasury Mgmt)*
Tom Partridge *(Exec VP & Head-Comml
Specialty Products)*
Dave Drury *(Head-Equipment Fin)*
Ernie Tsorvas *(Head-Direct Sls)*
Greg Eck *(Sr VP & Co-Head-Asset-Based
Lending Grp)*
William Stapel *(Sr VP & Co-Head-Asset-
Based Lending Grp)*
Kristine Garrett *(Reg Pres-Grp & Head-
Wealth-Asset Mgmt)*
Kala Gibson *(Chief Enterprise Corp Re-
sponsibility Officer & Exec VP)*
Howard Hammond *(Exec VP & Head-
Consumer Banking)*
Melissa Stevens *(Chief Digital Officer &
Exec VP)*
Timothy Tom *(VP & Mgr-Comml Relation-
ship)*
Will Hortsman *(Sr VP & Mgr-Comml Rela-
tionship)*
Stephanie Green *(Pres-South Florida)*
Kristine Garrett *(Reg Pres-Grp)*

Subsidiary (Domestic):

ClearArc Capital, Inc. (2)
580 Walnut St, Cincinnati, OH 45263
Tel.: (513) 534-7452
Web Site: http://www.cleararccapital.com
Financial Planning Consultation Services
N.A.I.C.S.: 523940
Stephen G. Mullins *(Dir-ESG Strategies)*
Mitchell L. Stapley *(Chief Investment Offi-
cer)*
John P. Hoeting *(Dir-Liquidity Mgmt)*
Peter M. Kwiatkowski *(Dir-Growth & Income
Strategies)*
David L. Withrow *(Pres)*
Robert P. Banks *(Dir-Relationship Mgmt)*
Dimitrios Contis *(Natl Dir-Distr & Sls)*
Richard Floyd *(Dir-Client Admin)*
Stephen Hedger *(Dir-Trading & Investment
Ops)*
Diane J. Hulls *(Chief Compliance Officer)*

**Epic Insurance Solutions Agency
LLC** (2)
9700 Ormsby Sta Rd Ste 200, Louisville,
KY 40223
Tel.: (502) 805-3742
Web Site:
    http://www.epicinsurancesolutions.com
Insurance Agents
N.A.I.C.S.: 524210

Fifth Third Securities, Inc. (2)
38 Fountain Sq Plz, Cincinnati, OH 45202
Tel.: (513) 699-5486
Web Site: https://www.53.com
Bond Dealers & Brokerage Services
N.A.I.C.S.: 523150
Xiao Ou Yuan *(Principal-Pub Fin)*

**Fountain Square Management
Co.** (2)
38 Fountain Sq Plz, Cincinnati, OH 45263-
0001
Tel.: (513) 579-5300
Sales Range: $25-49.9 Million
Emp.: 7
Property Management
N.A.I.C.S.: 459999

Figtree Company, LLC (1)
429 Ocean Frnt Walk, Venice, CA 90291
Tel.: (310) 392-4937
Web Site: https://www.figtreevenice.com
Food & Cocktail Restaurant Services
N.A.I.C.S.: 722513

Franklin Street Advisors, Inc. (1)
1450 Raleigh Rd Ste 300, Chapel Hill, NC
27517
Tel.: (919) 489-2600
Web Site: https://franklin-street.com
Real Estate Management Advisory Services
N.A.I.C.S.: 531390

Franklin Street Partners, Inc. (1)
1450 Raleigh Rd Ste 300, Chapel Hill, NC
27517
Tel.: (919) 489-2600
Web Site: https://www.franklin-street.com
Private Equity
N.A.I.C.S.: 523999
Carol E. Manzon *(Mng Dir)*
Jason T. Guthrie *(Dir-Ops)*
Cindy Stroik *(Chief Compliance Officer)*

Hammond Hanlon Camp LLC (1)
4655 Executive Dr Ste 280, San Diego, CA
92121
Tel.: (858) 242-4800
Web Site: http://www.h2c.com
Portfolio Management Services
N.A.I.C.S.: 523940
Philip J. Camp *(Mng Dir)*
Michael B. Hammond *(Mng Dir)*
Victoria S. Poindexter *(Mng Dir)*
C. Richard Bayman *(Mng Dir)*
William B. Hanlon III *(Mng Dir & Principal)*

Integrity HR Inc. (1)
11167 Town Country Dr, Riverside, CA
92505-3692
Tel.: (951) 833-8372
Web Site: http://www.integrityhrinc.com
Human Resources & Consulting Services
N.A.I.C.S.: 541612
Lynn Hounsley *(Owner, Pres & CEO)*

MB Financial, Inc. (1)
800 W Madison St, Chicago, IL 60607
Tel.: (847) 653-4800
Web Site: https://www.mbfinancial.com
Rev.: $1,092,235,000
Assets: $20,207,026,000
Liabilities: $17,172,178,000
Net Worth: $3,034,848,000
Earnings: $213,915,000
Emp.: 2,661
Fiscal Year-end: 12/31/2018
Bank Holding Company
N.A.I.C.S.: 551111
James N. Hallene *(Vice Chm)*

Subsidiary (Non-US):

**MB Business Capital Canada
Inc.** (2)
1155 North Service Road West 11, Oakville,
L6M 3E3, ON, Canada
Tel.: (289) 291-3898
Commercial Banking Services
N.A.I.C.S.: 522110

Subsidiary (Domestic):

MB Financial Bank, N.A. (2)
50 E WA St Ste 400, Chicago, IL
60602   **(100%)**
Tel.: (312) 494-4513
Web Site: http://www.mbfinancial.com
Emp.: 75
Federal Savings Bank
N.A.I.C.S.: 522180

Subsidiary (Domestic):

**Ashland Management Agency,
LLC** (3)
800 W Madison St, Chicago, IL 60607-2630
Real Estate Manangement Services

Fifth Third Bancorp—(Continued)

N.A.I.C.S.: 531390

Celtic Leasing Corp.   (3)
4 Park Plz Ste 300, Irvine, CA 92614
Tel.: (949) 263-3880
Web Site: http://www.celticfinance.com
Equipment Finance Leasing Services
N.A.I.C.S.: 522220

Subsidiary (Domestic):

MainStreet Investment Advisors, LLC   (2)
Strawbridge Professional Ctr 212 W Route 38 Ste 600, Moorestown, NJ 08057
Tel.: (856) 234-3550
Web Site: http://www.mainstreetia.com
Financial Investment Advisory Services
N.A.I.C.S.: 523940

R.G. McGraw Insurance Agency, Inc.   (1)
324 E 4th St, Cincinnati, OH 45202
Tel.: (513) 381-7881
Insurance Services
N.A.I.C.S.: 524210
Mike McGraw (Pres & CEO)

FIGS, INC.
2834 Colorado Ave Ste 100, Santa Monica, CA 90404
Tel.: (424) 300-8330   DE
Web Site: https://www.wearfigs.com
Year Founded: 2013
FIGS—(NYSE)
Rev.: $419,591,000
Assets: $311,751,000
Liabilities: $66,178,000
Net Worth: $245,573,000
Earnings: ($9,556,000)
Emp.: 264
Fiscal Year-end: 12/31/21
Health Care Srvices
N.A.I.C.S.: 621610
Steve Berube (COO)
Devon Duff Gago (Chief Bus Dev Officer)
Catherine Spear (Co-Founder & CEO)
Heather Hasson (Co-Founder & Exec Chm)

FINANCE OF AMERICA COMPANIES INC.
5830 Granite Pkwy Ste 400, Plano, TX 75024
Tel.: (972) 865-8114   DE
Web Site:
https://www.financeofamerica.com
Year Founded: 2013
FOA—(NYSE)
Rev.: $573,241,000
Assets: $20,872,655,000
Liabilities: $20,467,814,000
Net Worth: $404,841,000
Earnings: ($715,528,000)
Emp.: 2,312
Fiscal Year-end: 12/31/22
Lending Products & Services
N.A.I.C.S.: 522291
Matthew A. Engel (CFO)
Graham A. Fleming (CEO)
Jeremy Prahm (Chief Investment Officer)
Ben Hill (CIO)
Carolyn Frank (Chief HR Officer)
Lauren E. Richmond (Chief Legal Officer, Gen Counsel & Sec)

FINANCIAL GRAVITY COMPANIES, INC.
2501 Ranch Rd 620 S Ste 110, Lakeway, TX 78734
Tel.: (469) 342-9100   NV
Web Site:
https://www.financialgravity.com
Year Founded: 2005

FGCO—(OTCQB)
Rev.: $6,672,793
Assets: $4,349,282
Liabilities: $2,197,588
Net Worth: $2,151,694
Earnings: ($7,423,081)
Emp.: 27
Fiscal Year-end: 09/30/21
Investment Services
N.A.I.C.S.: 523999
John Pollock (Co-Chm & Exec VP-Sls)
Scott Winters (Co-Chm & CEO)
Jennifer Winters (COO & Sec)
Mark Williams (Exec VP-Ops)
Bryce Hamilton (Exec VP-Distr)

Subsidiaries:

Forta Financial Group, Inc.   (1)
5445 DTC Pkwy Ste 1100, Greenwood Village, CO 80111
Tel.: (303) 824-1600
Financial Services
N.A.I.C.S.: 524210
Tony Campen (CEO)

Subsidiary (Domestic):

NCW Group Inc.   (2)
26364 Carmel Rancho Ln Ste 200, Carmel, CA 93923
Tel.: (831) 656-1771
Web Site: http://www.ncwgroup.com
Investment Banking & Securities Dealing
N.A.I.C.S.: 523150

FINANCIAL INSTITUTIONS, INC.
220 Liberty St, Warsaw, NY 14569-1465
Tel.: (585) 786-1100   NY
Web Site: https://financialinstitutions inc.q4ir.com
Year Founded: 1931
FISI—(NASDAQ)
Rev.: $242,378,000
Assets: $5,797,272,000
Liabilities: $5,391,667,000
Net Worth: $405,605,000
Earnings: $56,573,000
Emp.: 672
Fiscal Year-end: 12/31/22
Bank Holding Company
N.A.I.C.S.: 551111
Martin K. Birmingham (Pres & CEO)
W. Jack Plants II (Exec VP)
Kevin Q. Quinn (Chief Comml Officer & Sr VP)
Laurie R. Collins (Chief HR Officer)
Gary A. Pacos (Chief Risk Officer)
Kate Croft (Dir-Investor & External Rels)
Blake G. Jones (CMO & Sr VP)
Samuel J. Burruano Jr. (Chief Legal Officer, Sec & Exec VP)

Subsidiaries:

Courier Capital, LLC   (1)
1114 Delaware Ave, Buffalo, NY 14209
Tel.: (716) 883-9595
Web Site: https://www.couriercapital.com
Sales Range: $1-9.9 Million
Investment Management & Consulting Services
N.A.I.C.S.: 523940
Thomas J. Hanlon (Co-Chief Investment Officer & Exec VP-Wealth Mgmt)
William H. Gurney (Exec VP & Sr Portfolio Mgr)
Steven A. Gattuso (Co-Chief Investment Officer & Sr Portfolio Mgr)
Stephen R. Robshaw (Exec VP, Sr VP & Sr Portfolio Mgr)
James E. Iglewski (Pres)
Jason M. Stronz (Sr Mng Dir-Institutional Svcs)
Kate Croft (Dir-Investor & External Rels)
Heather L. Wisinski (Sr Dir-Ops)
Rebecca L. Westervelt (Sr Mng Dir-Retirement Svcs)
Nicholas T. Norvell (Sr VP)
Thomas B. Reading (Sr VP)

Branch (Domestic):

Courier Capital Corporation - Jamestown Office   (2)
214 W 5th St, Jamestown, NY 14701
Tel.: (716) 484-2402
Web Site: https://www.couriercapital.com
Investment Management & Consulting Services
N.A.I.C.S.: 523940

Five Star Bank   (1)
55 N Main St, Warsaw, NY 14569
Tel.: (585) 786-4335
Web Site: https://www.five-starbank.com
Sales Range: $100-124.9 Million
Emp.: 100
Commercial Banking Services
N.A.I.C.S.: 522110
Martin K. Birmingham (Pres & CEO)
W. Jack Plants II (CFO, Treas & Sr VP)
Sean M. Willett (Chief Admin Officer)
Kevin B. Quinn (Sr VP)
Timothy Perrotta (Sr VP & Dir-HR)
Laurie Wisniewski (Dir-Plng & Facilities)
Laurie R. Collins (Chief HR Officer)
Samuel J. Burruano Jr. (Chief Legal Officer, Sec & Exec VP)

HNP Capital, LLC   (1)
100 Chestnut St 15th Fl, Rochester, NY 14604
Tel.: (585) 461-6085
Web Site: http://www.hnpcapital.com
Financial Services
N.A.I.C.S.: 523910
John P. Piccirilli (Founder & Pres)
Rebecca Westervelt (COO)
R. Christopher Hobaica (Exec VP)
Nicholas T. Norvell (Exec VP)
David C. Robbins (VP)

FINANCIAL STRATEGIES ACQUISITION CORP.
2626 Cole Ave Ste 300, Dallas, TX 75204
Tel.: (972) 560-4815   DE
Year Founded: 2020
FXCOU—(NASDAQ)
Investment Services
N.A.I.C.S.: 523999
Horst Rzepka (CFO & Dir)
Jamie Khurshid (CEO)
Jeffrey Peel (Chm)

FINCH THERAPEUTICS GROUP, INC.
Tel.: (617) 229-6499   DE
Web Site:
https://www.finchtherapeutics.com
Year Founded: 2014
FNCH—(NASDAQ)
Rev.: $861,000
Assets: $162,939,000
Liabilities: $67,228,000
Net Worth: $95,711,000
Earnings: ($114,646,000)
Emp.: 18
Fiscal Year-end: 12/31/22
Biotechnology Research & Development Services
N.A.I.C.S.: 541714
Lance Thibault (CTO)
Zain Kassam (Co-Founder & Chief Medical Officer)
Mark Smith (Co-Founder)
Gregory D. Perry (CFO)
Michelle Rose (Chief Regulatory Officer)
Andrew Noh (Co-Founder & Chief Admin Officer)
Jim Sigler (Exec VP-CMC)
Sonia Timberlake (Sr VP-Res)
James Burgess (Co-Founder & VP-Innovation)
Martina Schinke (VP-Program Mgmt)
Irina Koroleva (VP-Translational Medicine)
David Rhodes (VP-Technical Dev)
Anne Marie Conway (VP-Clinical Ops)

Rozanna Yaing (VP-Quality)
David Pugatch (VP-Clinical Dev)
Matthew P. Blischak (CEO)

FINDEX.COM, INC.
1313 S Killian Dr, Lake Park, FL 33403
Tel.: (561) 328-6488   NV
Web Site:
http://www.ecosmartsurfaces.com
Year Founded: 1997
FIND—(OTCIQ)
Sales Range: Less than $1 Million
Emp.: 6
Software Developer, Publisher, Retailer, Distr & Internet Sales; Coatings Mfr
N.A.I.C.S.: 513210
Steven Malone (Chm, Pres, CEO & CFO)

FINEMARK HOLDINGS, INC.
8695 College Pkwy Ste 100, Fort Myers, FL 33919
Tel.: (239) 461-3850
Web Site:
http://www.finemarkbank.com
Year Founded: 2007
FNBT—(OTCQX)
Emp.: 100
Bank Holding Company
N.A.I.C.S.: 551111
Brian J. Eagleston (CFO & Exec VP)

Subsidiaries:

FineMark National Bank & Trust   (1)
12681 Creekside Ln, Fort Myers, FL 33919
Tel.: (239) 461-5900
Web Site: http://www.finemarkbank.com
Rev.: $19,858,000
Assets: $717,990,000
Liabilities: $660,735,000
Net Worth: $57,255,000
Earnings: $2,109,000
Emp.: 60
Fiscal Year-end: 12/31/2013
Commercial Banking
N.A.I.C.S.: 522110
Joseph R. Catti (Co-Pres & Co-CEO)
Jeffrey B. Moes (Chief Fiduciary Officer & Exec VP)
Robert M. Arnall (Officer-Lending & Exec VP)
Brian J. Eagleston (CFO & Exec VP)
David H. Lucas (Chm)
Robert A. Parimore (Chief Risk Officer, Chief Compliance Officer & Exec VP)
Jason Manwell (VP-IT)
Jim Frisinger (VP & Controller)
David A. Highmark (Co-Pres & Co-CEO)
Malinda L. Schneider (Sr VP & Mgr-Loan Admin)
Jennifer L. Stevens (Exec VP & Dir-HR)
Christopher Battifarano (Chief Investment Officer & Exec VP)

FINGERMOTION, INC.
1460 Broadway, New York, NY 10036
Tel.: (347) 349-5339   DE
Web Site:
https://www.fingermotion.com
Year Founded: 2014
FNGR—(NASDAQ)
Rev.: $22,927,415
Assets: $10,366,905
Liabilities: $5,278,655
Net Worth: $5,088,250
Earnings: ($4,943,444)
Emp.: 68
Fiscal Year-end: 02/28/22
Game Software Developer
N.A.I.C.S.: 513210
Li Li (Sr VP)
Yew Hon Lee (CFO)
Eng Ho Ng (Chm)

FINNOVATE ACQUISITION CORP.

1007 N Orange St 10th Fl, Wilmington, DE 19801
Tel.: (424) 253-0908   Ky
Web Site:
https://www.finnovateacquisition.com
Year Founded: 2021
FNVT—(NASDAQ)
Rev.: $2,583,038
Assets: $179,089,740
Liabilities: $179,545,089
Net Worth: ($455,349)
Earnings: $1,110,622
Emp.: 3
Fiscal Year-end: 12/31/22
Investment Services
N.A.I.C.S.: 523999
Calvin Kung *(Chm & CEO)*
Tommy Wang Chiu Wong *(CFO)*

FINSERV ACQUISITION CORP.

1345 Avenue of the Americas, New York, NY 10105
Tel.: (646) 965-8218   DE
Web Site:
http://finservacquisition.com
Year Founded: 2019
FSRVU—(NASDAQ)
Rev.: $1,145,908
Assets: $252,375,272
Liabilities: $247,375,270
Net Worth: $5,000,002
Earnings: $154,152
Emp.: 2
Fiscal Year-end: 12/31/20
Investment Services
N.A.I.C.S.: 523999
Lee Einbinder *(CEO)*
Howard Kurz *(Pres & CFO)*

FINTECH ECOSYSTEM DEVELOPMENT CORP.

100 Springhouse Dr Ste 204, Collegeville, PA 19426
Tel.: (610) 226-8101   DE
Web Site:
https://www.fintechecosys.com
Year Founded: 2021
FEXD—(NASDAQ)
Rev.: $6,154,856
Assets: $119,034,334
Liabilities: $124,979,774
Net Worth: ($5,945,440)
Earnings: $3,837,124
Emp.: 2
Fiscal Year-end: 12/31/22
Investment Services
N.A.I.C.S.: 523999
Saiful Khandaker *(CEO)*
Jenny Junkeer *(CFO)*

FINTECH EVOLUTION ACQUISITION GROUP

1345 Ave of the Americas, New York, NY 10105
Tel.: (650) 739-6741   Ky
Year Founded: 2020
FTEV—(NYSE)
Rev.: $6,177,155
Assets: $275,072,368
Liabilities: $293,313,164
Net Worth: ($18,240,796)
Earnings: $4,508,323
Fiscal Year-end: 12/31/21
Investment Services
N.A.I.C.S.: 523999
Rohit Bhagat *(CEO)*
Michael Latham *(COO)*

FINWARD BANCORP

9204 Columbia Ave, Munster, IN 46321
Tel.: (219) 836-4400
Web Site:
https://www.ibankpeoples.com

FNWD—(NASDAQ)
Rev.: $83,544,000
Assets: $2,070,339,000
Liabilities: $1,933,946,000
Net Worth: $136,393,000
Earnings: $15,080,000
Emp.: 281
Fiscal Year-end: 12/31/22
Offices of Bank Holding Companies
N.A.I.C.S.: 551111
Robert T. Lowry *(COO & Exec VP)*
Anthony M. Puntillo *(Vice Chm)*
Benjamin J. Bochnowski *(Pres & CEO)*
Todd M. Scheub *(Chief Revenue Officer & Exec VP)*
Benjamin J. Bochnowski *(CEO)*

FINWISE BANCORP

756 E Winchester Ste 100, Murray, UT 84107
Tel.: (801) 501-7200   UT
Web Site:
https://www.finwisebancorp.com
Year Founded: 1999
FINW—(NASDAQ)
Rev.: $89,740,000
Assets: $400,780,000
Liabilities: $260,321,000
Net Worth: $140,459,000
Earnings: $25,115,000
Emp.: 140
Fiscal Year-end: 12/31/22
Bank Holding Company
N.A.I.C.S.: 551111
Robert E. Wahlman *(CFO, CFO/Exec VP-FinWise Bank & Exec VP)*
Kent Landvatter *(Chm, CEO & CEO-FinWise Bank)*
Simon Darchis *(VP & Dir-Specialty Lending)*
Meg Taylor *(Chief Acctg Officer-FinWise Bank & Sr VP-FinWise Bank)*
James Noone *(Pres & Pres-FinWise Bank)*
Robert Keil *(Chief Fintech Officer & Sr VP)*
Howard I. Reynolds *(Vice Chm)*
Russell F. Healey Jr. *(Chm)*

FIREMANS CONTRACTORS, INC.

2313 E Loop 820 N, Fort Worth, TX 76118
Tel.: (817) 576-1219   NV
Web Site: http://www.firemans-contractors.com
Year Founded: 2009
FRCN—(OTCIQ)
Full Service Painting Contractor
N.A.I.C.S.: 238320
Aaron Gilmore *(COO)*
Renee Gilmore *(Chm & CEO)*
Nikolay Frolov *(CFO & Treas)*

FIRMA HOLDINGS CORP.

2635 Walnut St, Denver, CO 80205
Tel.:   NV
Web Site:
https://www.taraminerals.com
FRMA—(OTCIQ)
Sales Range: Less than $1 Million
Emp.: 7
Holding Company; Mineral Exploration Services
N.A.I.C.S.: 551112
Sebastien C. Dufort *(Chm & CEO)*

FIRST ACCEPTANCE CORPORATION

7711 Ctr Ave Ste 200, Huntington Beach, CA 92647
Tel.: (615) 844-2885   DE

Web Site:
https://www.acceptanceinsurance.com
Year Founded: 1969
FACO—(OTCIQ)
Rev.: $269,580,000
Assets: $340,954,000
Liabilities: $229,268,000
Net Worth: $111,686,000
Earnings: $10,418,000
Emp.: 1,225
Fiscal Year-end: 12/31/20
Art Insurance Services
N.A.I.C.S.: 524128
Jeremy B. Ford *(Chm)*
Brian Dickman *(CFO)*
Jenna Bragg *(Accountant)*
Michael J. Bodayle *(Treas & Sec-IR)*

Subsidiaries:

First Acceptance Insurance Company, Inc.   **(1)**
1717 Church St B, Nashville, TN 37203
Tel.: (615) 327-4324
Web Site:
http://www.acceptanceinsurance.com
Insurance Agencies & Brokerages Services
N.A.I.C.S.: 524210
Joe Borbely *(Pres)*
Chris Elledge *(Sr VP-Tech)*
Jansen Schroeder *(Mgr-Mktg Comm)*
Brent Gay *(CFO)*

First Acceptance Services, Inc.   **(1)**
1842 Markley St, Norristown, PA 19401
Tel.: (610) 278-5032
Insurance Agency & Brokerage Services
N.A.I.C.S.: 524210

FIRST AMERICA RESOURCES CORPORATION

1000 E Armstrong St, Morris, IL 60450
Tel.: (815) 941-9888   NV
Year Founded: 2010
FSTJ—(OTCIQ)
Rev.: $3,920
Assets: $59,807
Liabilities: $232,445
Net Worth: ($172,638)
Earnings: ($40,831)
Fiscal Year-end: 06/30/24
Investment Services
N.A.I.C.S.: 523999
Jian Li *(Chm, Pres, CEO, CFO & Principal Acctg Officer)*

FIRST AMERICAN FINANCIAL CORPORATION

1 First American Way, Santa Ana, CA 92707-5913
Tel.: (714) 250-3000
Web Site: https://www.firstam.com
Year Founded: 1889
FAF—(NYSE)
Rev.: $6,003,500,000
Assets: $16,802,800,000
Liabilities: $11,940,000,000
Net Worth: $4,862,800,000
Earnings: $216,800,000
Emp.: 19,210
Fiscal Year-end: 12/31/23
Title Insurance & Settlement Services
N.A.I.C.S.: 524127
Dennis J. Gilmore *(Chm)*
Mark Edward Seaton *(CFO & Exec VP)*
Tanya M. Ceperley *(VP-Mergers & Acquisitions)*
Shabnam F. Jalakian *(Chief Information Security Officer & VP)*
David A. Hancock *(VP-Finance)*
Paul S. Hurst *(Chief Innovation Officer & VP)*
Ramon R. Machado *(Chief Risk Officer & VP)*
Marcus K. Reese *(Chief Comm Officer & VP)*

James H. Rogers *(VP-Investments)*
Valerie H. Royston *(VP-Internal Audit)*
Chelsea Sumrow *(CMO & VP)*
Stanley M. Tarbell *(VP-Tax)*
Sharon Wingfelder *(Chief HR Officer & VP)*
William J. Aulbert *(Asst Sec)*
Stephen R. Shultz *(Asst VP-Marketing & Communications)*
Lisa W. Cornehl *(Chief Legal Officer, Sec & Sr VP)*
Kenneth D. DeGiorgio *(CEO)*

Subsidiaries:

1031 Solutions, LLC   **(1)**
4450 Arapahoe Ave Ste 100, Boulder, CO 80303-9102
Tel.: (303) 413-1031
Web Site: http://www.1031service.com
Law firm
N.A.I.C.S.: 541110
Richard L. Levy *(Owner)*

Abstracters' Information Service, Inc.   **(1)**
3000 Marcus Ave Ste 2W02, Lake Success, NY 11042
Tel.: (516) 918-4600
Web Site: http://www.nydata.com
Sales Range: $25-49.9 Million
Emp.: 80
Municipal Tax Recording & Title Research Services
N.A.I.C.S.: 541191
Kathy Roper *(Sr Dir-Operations-Northeast)*
Charles Mauro *(VP)*
Patrick T. Roe *(Gen Mgr)*

American Escrow Company   **(1)**
2626 Howell St Fl 10, Dallas, TX 75204-4099
Tel.: (214) 855-8888
Emp.: 10
Real Estate Brokerage Services
N.A.I.C.S.: 531210

Corea Title Company   **(1)**
Mapo Tower 14th Fl 41 Mapo Daero 4 Da-gir, Mapo-Gu, Seoul, 04177, Korea (South)
Tel.: (82) 231442470
Web Site: http://www.firstam.co.kr
Emp.: 1
Title Abstract & Settlement Services
N.A.I.C.S.: 541191

Data Trace Information Services LLC   **(1)**
200 Commerce, Irvine, CA 92602
Web Site: http://www.datatracetitle.com
Title & Tax Information Services
N.A.I.C.S.: 519290
Mark Johnson *(VP-Sales-Sls Ops)*
Matt Key *(VP-Sales)*
Ben Bellomo *(Sls Dir)*

Dona Ana Title Company, Inc.   **(1)**
425 S Telshor Blvd Ste B, Las Cruces, NM 88011
Tel.: (575) 521-5800
Web Site: http://www.donaanatitle.com
Title Abstract & Settlement Services
N.A.I.C.S.: 541191
Sylvia Lauer *(VP)*
Shawna Blount *(Pres)*
Ron Coldren *(Officer-Escrow)*
Stella Meraz *(Officer-Escrow)*
Jiovanni Padilla *(Officer-Escrow)*
Annette Romero-Salas *(Officer-Escrow)*

FAF International Sigorta Aracilik Hizmetieri Anonim Sirketi   **(1)**
Hurriyet Mahallesi Dr Cemil Bengu Caddesi Hak is Merkezi, No 2 Kat 3-B Cagle Kagithane, Istanbul, 34403, Turkiye
Tel.: (90) 2122246999
Web Site: http://www.fafint.com.tr
Emp.: 3
Property & Mortgage Insurance Services
N.A.I.C.S.: 522310
Mustafa Ozdemir *(Chm)*

FATCO Holdings, LLC   **(1)**
1 1st American Way, Santa Ana, CA 92707-5913
Tel.: (714) 250-3000
Investment Management Service
N.A.I.C.S.: 523999

First American Financial Corporation—(Continued)

Faxxon Legal Information Services, Inc. (1)
901 S 2nd St Ste 201, Springfield, IL 62704
Tel.: (217) 698-8710
Sales Range: $25-49.9 Million
Emp.: 6
Management Consulting Services
N.A.I.C.S.: 541618

First American Abstract Company (1)
2001 Airport Rd, Flowood, MS 39232
Tel.: (601) 366-1222
Web Site: http://www.firstamabstract.com
Title Abstract & Settlement Services
N.A.I.C.S.: 541191

First American Data Tree LLC (1)
4 First American Way, Santa Ana, CA 92707-5913 (100%)
Tel.: (714) 250-6594
Web Site: https://dna.firstam.com
Sales Range: $10-24.9 Million
Real Estate Information Services
N.A.I.C.S.: 519290

First American Exchange Company, LLC (1)
215 S State St Ste 280, Salt Lake City, UT 84111
Tel.: (801) 944-1031
Web Site: https://www.firstexchange.com
Investment Advisory Services
N.A.I.C.S.: 523940

First American Mortgage Solutions, LLC (1)
3 1st American Way, Santa Ana, CA 92707
Web Site: https://www.firstam.com
Risk Assessment Solutions
N.A.I.C.S.: 524298

First American Professional Real Estate Services, Inc (1)
200 Commerce, Irvine, CA 92602
Tel.: (714) 250-1400
Emp.: 2,000
Real Estate Manangement Services
N.A.I.C.S.: 531210

First American SMS, LLC (1)
200 Commerce Ste, Irvine, CA 92602 (100%)
Tel.: (714) 250-1400
Web Site: http://www.smscorp.com
Sales Range: $200-249.9 Million
Emp.: 150
Escrow & Loan Settlement Service
N.A.I.C.S.: 541191
Larry Davidson (Pres)
Paul Bandiera (COO)

First American Title Insurance Company (1)
4 1st American Way, Santa Ana, CA 92707-5913 (100%)
Tel.: (714) 250-3000
Web Site: https://www.firstam.com
Title Insurance & Escrow Services
N.A.I.C.S.: 524127
Janette Waller (Pres)
Sarah Tallman (Pres)
Carroll Hyndman (Mgr)

Subsidiary (Non-US):

First American (India) Private Limited (2)
Aveda Meta No 184 Old Madras Road, Indiranagar, Bengaluru, 560038, Karnataka, India
Tel.: (91) 8046206000
Web Site: http://www.firstam.co.in
Emp.: 300
Title Insurance & Settlement Information Support Services
N.A.I.C.S.: 519290

Subsidiary (Domestic):

First American Home Buyers Protection Corporation (2)
1244 Apollo Way, Santa Rosa, CA 95407 (92.12%)
Tel.: (818) 781-5050
Web Site:
https://www.homewarranty.firstam.com

Sales Range: $100-124.9 Million
Emp.: 200
Home Warranty Services
N.A.I.C.S.: 524128

First American Lenders Advantage (2)
3 1st American Way, Santa Ana, CA 92707-5913
Tel.: (714) 481-3940
Web Site: http://www.lendersadvantage.com
Sales Range: $50-74.9 Million
Emp.: 500
Loans
N.A.I.C.S.: 921130

First American National Default Title Services (2)
3 First American Way, Santa Ana, CA 92707 (100%)
Tel.: (714) 250-4210
Sales Range: $250-299.9 Million
Emp.: 450
Title Services
N.A.I.C.S.: 524127

First American Property & Casualty Insurance Company (2)
4 First American Way, Santa Ana, CA 92707
Tel.: (714) 560-7856
Web Site: https://www.fapcig.com
Sales Range: $50-74.9 Million
Property & Casualty Insurance Brokers
N.A.I.C.S.: 524210

Branch (Domestic):

First American Property & Casualty Insurance (3)
4 First American Way, Santa Ana, CA 92707
Web Site: http://www.fapcig.com
Insurance Carrier
N.A.I.C.S.: 524126

Subsidiary (Domestic):

First American Shoshone Title (2)
1002 13th St, Cody, WY 82414 (51.69%)
Tel.: (307) 587-2261
Sales Range: $10-24.9 Million
Emp.: 8
Title Insurance Services
N.A.I.C.S.: 524127
Teresa Eicher (Mgr-Sls)

First American Specialty Insurance Company (2)
4 First American Way, Santa Ana, CA 92707
Tel.: (714) 560-7800
Specialty Insurance
N.A.I.O.O.: 524127

Unit (Domestic):

First American Title (2)
133 NW 8th St, Oklahoma City, OK 73102-5804 (100%)
Tel.: (405) 236-2861
Sales Range: $10-24.9 Million
Title Insurance Services
N.A.I.C.S.: 524127

Subsidiary (Domestic):

First American Title & Abstract Co. (2)
619 S Detroit Ave, Tulsa, OK 74120 (100%)
Tel.: (918) 584-2331
Web Site: http://www.firstamerican.com
Sales Range: $10-24.9 Million
Emp.: 42
Title Insurance & Escrow Services
N.A.I.C.S.: 541191
Kimes Branning (Pres)
Lisa Riggs (Officer)
Nita Caywood (Branch Mgr & Officer)
Lisa Riggs (Officer)
Nita Caywood (Branch Mgr & Officer)

First American Title & Trust Company (2)
133 NW 8th St, Oklahoma City, OK 73102-5804
Tel.: (405) 236-2861
Title Insurance Services
N.A.I.C.S.: 524127

Don Neilen (Dir-State Mktg)

First American Title Co. of Spokane-Escrow Opers (2)
40 E Spokane Falls Blvd, Spokane, WA 99202 (100%)
Tel.: (509) 456-0550
Rev.: $1,753,000
Emp.: 34
Title Insurance & Escrow Services
N.A.I.C.S.: 524127

First American Title Company (2)
330 N Brand Blvd Ste 1150, Glendale, CA 91203 (100%)
Tel.: (818) 242-5800
Sales Range: $25-49.9 Million
Title Insurance & Escrow Services
N.A.I.C.S.: 524127

First American Title Company Inc. (2)
1177 Kapiolani Blvd, Honolulu, HI 96814 (100%)
Tel.: (808) 536-3866
Sales Range: $25-49.9 Million
Title Insurance & Escrow Services
N.A.I.C.S.: 524127

First American Title Company of Bellingham (2)
11 Bellwether Way Ste 301, Bellingham, WA 98225 (99.98%)
Tel.: (360) 733-5320
Web Site: http://www.firstamerican.com
Sales Range: $1-9.9 Million
Emp.: 16
Title Insurance & Escrow Services
N.A.I.C.S.: 524210

First American Title Company of Hot Springs County (2)
534 Big Horn St, Thermopolis, WY 82443 (79.92%)
Tel.: (307) 864-3436
Sales Range: $10-24.9 Million
Emp.: 2
Title Insurance Services
N.A.I.C.S.: 524127

First American Title Company of Idaho, Inc. (2)
1161 W River St Ste 150, Boise, ID 83702 (100%)
Tel.: (208) 501-7664
Web Site: https://local.firstam.com
Sales Range: $25-49.9 Million
Emp.: 35
Title Insurance & Escrow Services
N.A.I.C.S.: 524127
Kurt Galitz (Mgr-Operations-Ada,Canyon County)
Gwen Main (Mgr-Sales-Ada Canyon County)
Mark Adams (Coord-Operations)

First American Title Company of Laramie County (2)
511 W 19th St, Cheyenne, WY 82001 (92.61%)
Tel.: (307) 635-1181
Sales Range: $10-24.9 Million
Emp.: 30
Title Insurance Services
N.A.I.C.S.: 541191
Paula Poythress (Mgr-)
Pamela Schliske (Mgr)
Shandi Vasquez (Mgr-Escrow)
Jennifer Page (Mgr-)

First American Title Company of Nevada (2)
701 N Green Valley Pkwy Ste 120, Henderson, NV 89074 (100%)
Tel.: (702) 731-4131
Rev.: $6,352,000
Emp.: 74
Title Insurance & Escrow Services
N.A.I.C.S.: 524127

First American Title Company of Nevada (Reno) (2)
5310 Kietzke Ln Ste 100, Reno, NV 89511 (100%)
Tel.: (775) 823-6200
Web Site: http://www.firstam.net
Sales Range: $25-49.9 Million
Emp.: 20
Title Insurance & Escrow Services

N.A.I.C.S.: 524127
Vickie Taylor (Sr Officer)
Kirsten Schroeder (Officer)
Tova McGilvray (Officer)

First American Title Company of Oregon (2)
121 SW Morrison St Ste 300, Portland, OR 97204 (100%)
Tel.: (503) 222-3651
Sales Range: $100-124.9 Million
Emp.: 100
Title Insurance & Escrow Services
N.A.I.C.S.: 524127
Shawna Mixon (VP & Mgr)
Drake Butsch (Mgr-Builder Svcs)
Chris Young (VP & Mgr-)
Dana Eller (VP & Mgr-)
Jill Shiels (VP & Sls Mgr)
Mike Brusco (Ops Mgr--County)

Division (Domestic):

First American Title Company of Oregon (3)
1225 Crater Lake Ave Ste 101, Medford, OR 97504
Tel.: (541) 779-7250
Web Site: http://www.firstam.com
Title Insurance Services
N.A.I.C.S.: 524127

Subsidiary (Domestic):

First American Title Company-National Vacation Ownership (2)
1540 International Pkwy, Lake Mary, FL 32746
Tel.: (407) 362-2105
Web Site:
http://www.vacationfirst.firstam.com
Sales Range: $10-24.9 Million
Emp.: 35
Title Insurance Services
N.A.I.C.S.: 524127

First American Title Insurance Agency of Pinal (2)
421 E Cottonwood Ln, Casa Grande, AZ 85122 (98%)
Tel.: (520) 836-1500
Web Site: http://www.thinkfirstamerican.com
Sales Range: Less than $1 Million
Emp.: 20
Title Insurance Services
N.A.I.C.S.: 541191

Unit (Domestic):

First American Title Insurance Company (2)
185 Darkmus St 5th Fl, Boston, MA 02116
Tel.: (617) 345-0088
Web Site: http://www.firstamne.com
Sales Range: $1-9.9 Million
Emp.: 75
Title & Escrow Services
N.A.I.C.S.: 524127

First American Title Insurance Company (2)
620 Freedom Business Ctr Dr Fl 4, King of Prussia, PA 19406 (100%)
Tel.: (610) 265-8440
Web Site: http://www.firstameri.com
Sales Range: $25-49.9 Million
Emp.: 50
Title Insurance
N.A.I.C.S.: 524127
Parker S. Kennedy (Chm)

First American Title Insurance Company (2)
2750 Chancellorsville Dr, Tallahassee, FL 32312 (100%)
Tel.: (850) 402-4101
Sales Range: $50-74.9 Million
Emp.: 125
Direct Title Insurance
N.A.I.C.S.: 524127

First American Title Insurance Company (2)
1271 N 15th St, Laramie, WY 82072 (100%)
Tel.: (307) 745-3480
Emp.: 5
Title Insurance Services
N.A.I.C.S.: 541191

Alexia Jones *(Branch Mgr)*

First American Title Insurance Company (2)
PO Box 566, Lusk, WY 82225 **(100%)**
Tel.: (307) 334-3692
Sales Range: $125-149.9 Million
Title Insurance Services
N.A.I.C.S.: 524127

First American Title Insurance Company (2)
1560 Johnston Ave Ste E, Wheatland, WY 82201
Tel.: (307) 322-2133
Sales Range: $150-199.9 Million
Title Insurance Services
N.A.I.C.S.: 524127

First American Title Insurance Company (2)
159 N Wolcott St 250, Casper, WY 82601 **(100%)**
Tel.: (307) 237-8486
Sales Range: $1-9.9 Million
Emp.: 20
Title Insurance Services
N.A.I.C.S.: 541191
Kevin Huber *(Mgr)*

First American Title Insurance Company (2)
9000 E Pima Ctr Pkwy, Scottsdale, AZ 85258
Tel.: (602) 685-7000
Web Site: http://www.firstm.com
Sales Range: $200-249.9 Million
Emp.: 435
Title Insurance Services
N.A.I.C.S.: 524127
Don Kennedy *(Reg VP)*

First American Title Insurance Company (2)
1880 E River Rd Ste 120, Tucson, AZ 85718
Tel.: (520) 577-8707
Sales Range: $25-49.9 Million
Emp.: 25
Title Insurance Services
N.A.I.C.S.: 524127

First American Title Insurance Company (2)
818 Stewart St, Seattle, WA 98101 **(100%)**
Tel.: (206) 728-0400
Sales Range: $25-49.9 Million
Emp.: 70
Title Insurance Services
N.A.I.C.S.: 524127
Joseph T. Perna *(VP & Dir-Community Svcs-Northwest Reg)*
Rhonda Miller *(Mgr-Escrow)*
Thomas Hartman *(Reg VP)*
Donna St. George *(Mng Dir-Northwest & VP)*

First American Title Insurance Company (2)
1100 Superior Ave Ste 200, Cleveland, OH 44114-2518
Tel.: (216) 802-3400
Web Site: http://www.ohio.firstam.com
Sales Range: $25-49.9 Million
Emp.: 75
Title Insurance Services
N.A.I.C.S.: 541191

First American Title Insurance Company (2)
27775 Diehl Rd, Warrenville, IL 60555
Tel.: (630) 799-7000
Web Site: http://www.il.firstam.com
Sales Range: $100-124.9 Million
Emp.: 130
Title Insurance Services
N.A.I.C.S.: 524127

First American Title Insurance Company (2)
935 Gravier St Ste 2100, New Orleans, LA 70112 **(100%)**
Tel.: (504) 588-9252
Sales Range: $50-74.9 Million
Emp.: 85
Title Insurance Services
N.A.I.C.S.: 524127

First American Title Insurance Company (2)

First American Title Insurance Company (2)
1653 Larkin Williams Rd, Fenton, MO 63026 **(100%)**
Tel.: (314) 336-1200
Web Site: http://www.firstaid.com
Sales Range: $25-49.9 Million
Emp.: 20
Title Insurance Services
N.A.I.C.S.: 524127

First American Title Insurance Company (2)
121 S 8th St, Minneapolis, MN 55402
Tel.: (612) 305-2000
Sales Range: $25-49.9 Million
Emp.: 50
Title Insurance Services
N.A.I.C.S.: 524127

First American Title Insurance Company (2)
1500 S Dairy Ashford Ste 300, Houston, TX 77077
Tel.: (281) 588-2200
Sales Range: $25-49.9 Million
Emp.: 50
Title Insurance Services
N.A.I.C.S.: 524127

Subsidiary (Non-US):

First American Title Insurance Company (2)
6th Floor Hanil Building 162-5 Donggyo-Dong Mapo-Gu, Seoul, 121-817, Korea (South) **(100%)**
Tel.: (82) 231442460
Web Site: http://www.firstam.co.kr
Sales Range: $10-24.9 Million
Emp.: 14
Title Insurance Services
N.A.I.C.S.: 524127

Unit (Domestic):

First American Title Insurance Company (2)
1860 SW Fountainview Blvd Ste 100, Port Saint Lucie, FL 34986 **(100%)**
Tel.: (772) 286-0850
Title Insurance & Escrow Services
N.A.I.C.S.: 541191

First American Title Insurance Company (2)
9400 Holly Ave NE Bldg 1, Albuquerque, NM 87122 **(100%)**
Tel.: (505) 881-3300
Rev.: $2,095,000
Emp.: 56
Title Insurance & Escrow Services
N.A.I.C.S.: 541191

First American Title Insurance Company (2)
7710 NE Greenwood Dr Ste 160, Vancouver, WA 98662 **(100%)**
Tel.: (360) 891-0548
Sales Range: $25-49.9 Million
Emp.: 25
Title Insurance & Escrow Services
N.A.I.C.S.: 524127

First American Title Insurance Company (2)
902 11th St, Lander, WY 82520
Tel.: (307) 332-4069
Title Insurance Services
N.A.I.C.S.: 541191

First American Title Insurance Company (2)
6077 Primacy Pkwy Ste 100, Memphis, TN 38119-5742 **(100%)**
Tel.: (901) 821-6500
Web Site: http://www.firstam.com
Sales Range: $10-24.9 Million
Emp.: 20
Title Insurance Services
N.A.I.C.S.: 524127

Subsidiary (Domestic):

First American Title Insurance Company - Wyoming (2)
25 N Main St, Buffalo, WY 82834
Tel.: (307) 684-5517
Title Insurance Services
N.A.I.C.S.: 541191

First American Title Insurance Company Lenders Advantage (2)
3409 Executive Center Dr Ste 113, Austin, TX 78731 **(100%)**
Tel.: (512) 795-9755
Sales Range: $150-199.9 Million
Emp.: 125
Loan Services
N.A.I.C.S.: 522310

First American Title Insurance Company of New York (2)
666 3rd Ave 5th Fl, New York, NY 10017 **(100%)**
Tel.: (212) 381-6600
Web Site: http://www.firstamny.com
Rev.: $47,418,000
Emp.: 114
Title Insurance & Escrow Services
N.A.I.C.S.: 524127

First American Title Insurance Company of Texas (2)
1500 S Dairy Ashford Ste 300, Houston, TX 77077-6841 **(100%)**
Tel.: (281) 588-2200
Rev.: $25,042,000
Emp.: 189
Title Insurance & Escrow Services
N.A.I.C.S.: 524127

First American Title Insurance Company of The Caribbean & Latin America (2)
13450 W Sunrise Blvd Ste 300, Sunrise, FL 33323
Tel.: (954) 839-2900
Sales Range: $25-49.9 Million
Emp.: 40
Title Insurance Services
N.A.I.C.S.: 524127

First American Trust, F.S.B. (2)
5 First American Way, Santa Ana, CA 92707 **(100%)**
Tel.: (714) 250-8277
Web Site: https://www.firstamtrust.com
Sales Range: $10-24.9 Million
Emp.: 80
Trust Services
N.A.I.C.S.: 523991
Teri L. Pierce *(CFO & Exec VP)*
Robert Krick *(Officer-Real Estate & VP)*
Cathie Panis *(Officer-Real Estate & VP)*
Jody Hudson *(VP & Sr Mgr-Relationship)*
Scott K. Laudeman *(VP & Portfolio Mgr)*
Nicholas W. Henry *(VP & Mgr-Relationship)*
Daniel Ast *(Sr VP & Sr Portfolio Mgr)*
Kevin M. Wilcox *(Sr VP & Sr Portfolio Mgr)*
Jamie Kim *(Sr VP & Sr Mgr-)*
Beth Vasquez *(Chief Fiduciary Officer)*
Stephen C. Minana *(Sr VP)*
Jerry Braakman *(Pres & Chief Investment Officer)*
Rodney Ondatje *(Chief Compliance Officer & Sr VP)*
Matt McCreadie *(CEO)*
John Metzger *(Sr VP)*
Ryan Clive-Smith *(VP)*
Michael Zagurski *(VP)*
Scott N. Sacchi *(Sr VP)*
Colin Slote *(VP)*
Angela Taylor *(VP)*
Krista Yonkers *(VP)*
Scott Dudgeon *(Dir)*
Michael L. Serrano *(VP & Portfolio Mgr)*
Jay Robinson-Duff III *(VP)*
Kenneth E. Petersen Jr. *(Sr VP)*

First American Vehicle Title Insurance (2)
510 Bienville St, New Orleans, LA 70130
Tel.: (504) 588-9252
Sales Range: $200-249.9 Million
Emp.: 400
Automobile Insurance
N.A.I.C.S.: 524128

Subsidiary (Non-US):

First Canadian Title Insurance Company Ltd. (2)
2235 Sheridan Garden Drive, Oakville, L6J 7Y5, ON, Canada **(100%)**
Tel.: (905) 287-1000
Web Site: https://www.fct.ca
Sales Range: $100-124.9 Million
Emp.: 300
Commercial Insurance Services

N.A.I.C.S.: 524298

First Hong Kong Title Ltd. (2)
Wilson House Ste 901 19 27 Wyndham St, Central, China (Hong Kong) **(100%)**
Tel.: (852) 26232388
Sales Range: $150-199.9 Million
Title Insurance Services
N.A.I.C.S.: 524127

First Title plc (2)
E C A Court 24-26 South Park, Sevenoaks, TN1 31DU, Kent, United Kingdom **(100%)**
Tel.: (44) 2071608100
Web Site: http://www.first-title.co.uk
Sales Range: $350-399.9 Million
Emp.: 600
Title Insurance Services
N.A.I.C.S.: 524127

Subsidiary (Domestic):

Goshen County Abstract & Title Company (2)
2029 Main St, Torrington, WY 82240-2708 **(76.43%)**
Tel.: (307) 532-5642
Sales Range: $10-24.9 Million
Emp.: 4
Title Insurance Services
N.A.I.C.S.: 541191

Mid-Valley Title and Escrow Company (2)
601 Main St, Chico, CA 95928 **(58.5%)**
Tel.: (530) 893-5644
Web Site: http://www.midvalleytitle.com
Sales Range: $10-24.9 Million
Emp.: 30
Title Insurance & Escrow Services
N.A.I.C.S.: 541191

Mortgage Guarantee & Title Company (2)
450 Veterans Memorial Pkwy Ste 700, East Providence, RI 02914 **(100%)**
Tel.: (401) 434-1000
Web Site: http://directory.firstam.com
Sales Range: $10-24.9 Million
Emp.: 25
Title Insurance
N.A.I.C.S.: 524127
Anthony Montalbano *(Pres)*

Pioneer Title Company (2)
500 S 20th Ave A, Thatcher, AZ 85552
Tel.: (928) 428-0180
Web Site: http://www.pioneertitleagency.com
Sales Range: Less than $1 Million
Emp.: 5
Title Insurance Services
N.A.I.C.S.: 524210
Keith Newlon *(Pres & CEO)*

TitleVest Agency, Inc. (2)
110 E 42nd St 10th Fl, New York, NY 10017
Tel.: (212) 757-5800
Web Site: http://www.titlevest.com
Sales Range: $1-9.9 Million
Emp.: 40
Title Insurance Services
N.A.I.C.S.: 524127
Brian D. Tormey *(Pres)*

Uinta Title and Insurance, Inc. (2)
1048 Main St, Evanston, WY 82930
Tel.: (307) 789-1777
Sales Range: Less than $1 Million
Emp.: 5
Title Insurance Services
N.A.I.C.S.: 541191
Georgia Harvey *(Pres)*

Wilcox Abstract & Title Guaranty Agency (2)
307 W Burkitt, Sheridan, WY 82801
Tel.: (307) 672-0768
Web Site: http://www.wilcoxabstract.com
Sales Range: Less than $1 Million
Emp.: 6
Title Insurance Services
N.A.I.C.S.: 541191
Brian Kinnison *(Dir & Pres)*
Kelly Camino *(Coord-Customer Svc & Officer)*
Casey Koltiska *(Coord)*
Brittany Lewis *(Coord)*
Casey Koltiska *(Coord)*
Brittany Lewis *(Coord)*

First American Financial Corporation—(Continued)

First American Title Insurance Company of Australia Pty Limited (1)
Level 1 799 Pacific Highway, PO Box
Q1465, Chatswood, 2067, NSW, Australia
Tel.: (61) 1300362178
Web Site: https://www.firsttitle.com.au
Title Insurance Services
N.A.I.C.S.: 524127

First American Title Insurance Company of Louisiana (1)
935 Gravier St Ste 2100, New Orleans, LA
70112
Tel.: (504) 588-9252
Property Insurance Services
N.A.I.C.S.: 524126

First American Title Insurance de Mexico, S.A. de C.V. (1)
Paseo De La Reforma No 505 Torre Mayor
Piso 36 Suite D, Colonia Cuauhtemoc,
Mexico, 6500, Mexico
Tel.: (52) 5526242314
Web Site: http://www.firstam.com.mx
Sales Range: $25-49.9 Million
Emp.: 13
Insurance & Consultancy Services
N.A.I.C.S.: 524210

First American Trustee Servicing Solutions, LLC (1)
6 Campus Cir Fl 2, Westlake, TX 76262
Tel.: (817) 699-6035
Web Site: http://www.loanstartrustee.com
Sales Range: $25-49.9 Million
Emp.: 40
Trust Administration & Investment Management Services
N.A.I.C.S.: 523991
DeeAnn Gregory (Sr Mgr)

First American Vacation Ownership Services, LLC (1)
400 S Rampart Blvd Ste 290, Las Vegas,
NV 89145
Tel.: (702) 792-6863
Title Insurance Services
N.A.I.C.S.: 524127

First Title CEE (Biztositaskozvetito Korlatolt Felelossegu Tarsasag) (1)
Szent Istvan ter 11/B, Budapest, 1051, Hungary
Tel.: (36) 13010835
Web Site: http://www.firsttitle.eu
Sales Range: $25-49.9 Million
Emp.: 3
Insurance Brokerage Services
N.A.I.C.S.: 524210

First Title Insurance plc (1)
ECA Court 24-26 South Park, Sevenoaks,
TN13 1DU, Kent, United Kingdom
Tel.: (44) 2071608100
Web Site: https://www.firsttitle.co.uk
Title Insurance Services
N.A.I.C.S.: 524127

First Title Real Estate Guaranty Co., Ltd. (1)
Suite 808 Tower 2 China Central Place No
79 Jianguo Road, Chaoyang District, Beijing, 100025, China
Tel.: (86) 1059085188
Web Site: http://www.firstam.com.cn
Real Estate Brokerage Services
N.A.I.C.S.: 531210

Hexter-Fair / First American Title Company, LLC (1)
8333 Douglas Ave Ste 130, Dallas, TX
75225
Tel.: (214) 373-9999
Emp.: 25
Title Insurance Services
N.A.I.C.S.: 524127

Live Letting Exchange Limited (1)
PO Box HK3, Leeds, LS11 5QJ, West Yorkshire, United Kingdom
Tel.: (44) 3442440283
Web Site: http://www.live-lx.com
Emp.: 400
Title Insurance Services
N.A.I.C.S.: 524127
Amy Hemingway (Mgr-Team)

Mother Lode Holding Company (1)

189 Fulweiler Ave, Auburn, CA 95603-4507
Tel.: (530) 887-2410
Web Site: http://www.placertitle.com
Sales Range: $100-124.9 Million
Emp.: 511
Provider of Title Insurance & Escrow Services
N.A.I.C.S.: 524127
Marsha A. Spence (Chm)
Dave Trimble (Mgr-Pur)
Kristi Rose (Mgr-Payroll)

Subsidiary (Domestic):

Montana Title And Escrow Company (2)
1925 N 22nd Ave Ste 102, Bozeman, MT
59718
Tel.: (406) 587-7702
Web Site: http://www.montanatitle.com
Emp.: 9
Escrow Services
N.A.I.C.S.: 523991
Darryl Seymour (Pres)

National Closing Solutions, Inc. (2)
9087 Foothills Blvd Ste 700, Roseville, CA
95747
Web Site: http://www.ncslenders.com
Real Estate Management Services
N.A.I.C.S.: 531390
Chris L. Scott (Sr VP-Natl Acct)
Judy Harp (Pres & CEO)
Randy Bradley (Exec VP & Mgr-Natl Sls)
Sean Tucker (Sr VP-Accts-Natl)

Division (Domestic):

National Closing Solutions, Inc. - Texas Division (3)
12808 W Airport Blvd Ste 330, Sugar Land,
TX 77478
Tel.: (866) 231-3873
Real Estate Management Services
N.A.I.C.S.: 531390

National Closing Solutions, Inc. - Utah Division (3)
7070 S Union Park Ste 338, Cottonwood,
UT 84047
Tel.: (801) 264-6725
Real Estate Management Services
N.A.I.C.S.: 531390

Subsidiary (Domestic):

North Idaho Title Company (2)
601 E Front Ave Ste 204, Coeur D'Alene,
ID 83814
Tel.: (208) 765-3333
Web Site: http://www.northidahotitle.com
Real Estate Management Services
N.A.I.C.S.: 531390
Marsha A. Emmett (Chm & CEO)
Rick Brown (Reg Pres)
Jim Johnston (Pres)
Darrick Blatnick (Exec VP)
Lisa Steele (Exec VP)
Randy Bradley (Exec VP)
David Philipp (CFO)
Darrell Martin (Gen Counsel, Sec & Exec VP)
Beverly Gagner (Officer-Escrow)
Dorothy Prophet (Officer-Escrow)
Julie Hjelvik (Officer-Escrow)
Kristin Linnemeyer (Officer-Escrow)
Wendy Wenger (Officer-Escrow)

Placer Title Co. Inc. (2)
9087 Foothill Blvd St 700, Roseville, CA
95747
Tel.: (916) 405-0400
Web Site: http://www.placertitle.com
Sales Range: $50-74.9 Million
Emp.: 54
Provider of Title Insurance
N.A.I.C.S.: 524127
Marsha A. Emmett (Chm & CEO)
David Philipp (CFO)
Patricia Laffin-Miko (Gen Counsel, Sec & Exec VP)
Jim Johnston (Pres)

Placer Title Insurance Agency of Utah, Inc. (2)
1086 S Main St, Saint George, UT 84770
Tel.: (435) 673-5845
General Insurance Services
N.A.I.C.S.: 524210

Division (Domestic):

Premier Reverse Closings (2)
5828 Lonetree Blvd, Rocklin, CA 95765
Tel.: (916) 542-4113
Web Site: http://www.prclosings.com
Real Estate Management Services
N.A.I.C.S.: 531390
Ben White (Mgr-Special Projects)
Christian Fisher (VP)
Mark King (Mgr-Client Svc)
Rob Awalt (Pres)
Anneta Pope (VP-Sls)
Adan Gutierrez (Coord-Bus Dev)
Natalia Herbert (Coord-Bus Dev)

Subsidiary (Domestic):

Wisconsin Title Service Company, Inc. (2)
1716 Paramount Dr, Waukesha, WI 53186
Tel.: (262) 542-1700
Web Site: http://www.wititle.com
Sales Range: $1-9.9 Million
Emp.: 71
Title Insurance
N.A.I.C.S.: 524127
Nic Hoyer (Pres)

Wyoming Title & Escrow Company, Inc. (2)
211 E Broadway, Jackson, WY 83001
Tel.: (307) 732-2983
Web Site: http://www.wyomingtitle.com
Emp.: 7
Real Estate Management Services
N.A.I.C.S.: 531390
Christina Feuz (VP & Reg Mgr)
Liz Jorgenson (VP & Reg Mgr)
Rick Brown (Reg Pres)
Hallie Lane (Officer-Escrow)
Wendy McDearman (Officer-Escrow)

Mt. Shasta Title & Escrow Company (1)
1252 S Main St, Yreka, CA 96097
Tel.: (530) 842-4333
Web Site: http://www.mtshastatitle.com
Emp.: 10
Title Insurance Services
N.A.I.C.S.: 524127
Sheila Judkins (Officer & Mgr-Title)

Ohio Bar Title Insurance Company (1)
8740 Orion Pl Ste 310, Columbus, OH
43240
Tel.: (614) 310-8098
Web Site: https://www.ohiobartitle.com
Emp.: 12
Title Insurance Services
N.A.I.C.S.: 524127
Carol Wise (Mgr-Area Sls-Central Ohio)
Maria Lukinac (Mgr-Area Sls-North Ohio)

Promeric Technologies Inc. (1)
275 Dundas Street, London, N6B 3L1, ON,
Canada
Tel.: (905) 948-1777
Web Site: http://www.promeric.com
Industrial Technology Services
N.A.I.C.S.: 541715

Regency Escrow Corporation (1)
44145 20th St W, Lancaster, CA 93534-
4058
Tel.: (661) 948-1828
Web Site: http://www.regencyescrow.net
Emp.: 2
Title Insurance Services
N.A.I.C.S.: 524127

Republic Title of Texas, Inc. (1)
2701 W Plano Pkwy Ste 100, Plano, TX
75075
Tel.: (972) 578-8611
Web Site: https://www.republictitle.com
Title Insurance Services
N.A.I.C.S.: 524127
Sheri Groom (Exec VP-Residential Ops)
Mark Roden (Sr VP & Asst Gen Counsel)
Joe Leatherwood (Sr VP-Underwriting)
Kim Brummitt (Sr VP-Residential Ops)
Lindsey Carroll (Sr VP-Comm & Mktg)
Dennis Pospisil (Sr VP-Signing Svcs & Digital Settlement)
Cory Atchley (Sr VP-Bus Tech)
Jeff Montgomery (Sr VP-Bus Dev)
Chase Evans (COO)

Matt Visinsky (Sr VP)
Steve Holley (Sr VP)
Jay Turner (Sr VP)
Jon Hooper (Sr VP)
Clay Arnold (Sr VP)
Jeff Porter (Officer-Escrow, VP & Atty)
Peter Graf (Gen Counsel & Exec VP)
Felicia Farnsworth (Exec VP-HR)
David Kramer (Exec VP)
David Shuttee (Co-Chm)
Aaron Miller (CIO)
Lisa Murray (CFO & Exec VP)
Wade Bogdon (Asst VP)
Bo Feagin (Pres)
Amy Jones (Sr VP)
Janet Allen (Sr VP-)
Bill Kramer (Co-Chm)
Sarah Mann (Sr VP)
Ward Williford (Vice Chm)

Team Conveyancing Limited (1)
Frances Way Grove Park, Enderby, LE19
1SH, Leicester, United Kingdom
Tel.: (44) 8450172222
Web Site:
　　http://www.teamconveyancing.co.uk
Title Insurance Services
N.A.I.C.S.: 524127

Texas Escrow Company, Inc. (1)
2626 Howell St 10th Fl, Dallas, TX 75204
Tel.: (214) 855-8888
Title Insurance Services
N.A.I.C.S.: 524127
Carl Janousek (Mgr)

The Heritage Escrow Company (1)
2855 Michelle Dr Ste 270, Irvine, CA 92606
Tel.: (949) 651-9000
Web Site:
　　http://www.theheritageescrow.com
Sales Range: $25-49.9 Million
Emp.: 15
Real Estate Brokerage Services
N.A.I.C.S.: 531210
Janet Tilbury (Officer)
Terra Vo (Branch Mgr & Officer)
Kris Kartozian (Pres)
Kimberly Ray (Ops Mgr)
Sharla Dabney (Sls Mgr)

The Title Security Group, Inc. (1)
33 Calle Resolucion Ste 302, San Juan, PR
00920
Tel.: (787) 782-6500
Web Site: http://www.titlesecuritygroup.com
Sales Range: $25-49.9 Million
Emp.: 15
Title Insurance Services
N.A.I.C.S.: 524127

Title Security Agency of Pinal County, LLC (1)
6390 E Tanque Verde Rd, Tucson, AZ
85715
Tel.: (520) 885-1600
Web Site: http://www.titlesecurity.com
Direct Title Insurance Carriers
N.A.I.C.S.: 524127
Tricia Hooper (Acct Mgr-Business Development)

enact Conveyancing Limited (1)
9 Manor Road, Leeds, LS11 9AH, United
Kingdom
Tel.: (44) 3442442000
Web Site: https://www.enact.co.uk
Sales Range: $100-124.9 Million
Emp.: 300
Title Insurance Services
N.A.I.C.S.: 524127
Alex Clark (Dir-Legal)
Adam Middlemass (Dir-Information Technology)
Richard Morris (Dir-Compliance)
Ben Carroll (Mng Dir)
Kelly Yates-Cuthbert (Dir-Remortgage Ops)
Amy Allen (Dir-Fin)

FIRST BANCORP
300 SW Broad St, Southern Pines,
NC 28387
Tel.: (910) 246-2500　　　　　　　　**NC**
Web Site:
　　https://investor.localfirstbank.com
Year Founded: 1983

FBNC—(NASDAQ)
Rev.: $408,942,000
Assets: $10,625,049,000
Liabilities: $9,593,453,000
Net Worth: $1,031,596,000
Earnings: $146,936,000
Emp.: 1,244
Fiscal Year-end: 12/31/22
Bank Holding Company
N.A.I.C.S.: 551111
Roberto R. Herencia *(Chm)*
Aurelio Aleman-Bermudez *(Pres & CEO)*
Juan Carlos Pavia *(Chief Credit Officer & Exec VP)*
Nayda Rivera-Batista *(Chief Risk Officer & Exec VP)*
Orlando Berges-Gonzalez *(CFO & Exec VP)*
Carlos Power Pietrantoni *(Exec VP-Consumer Lending Bus)*
Ginoris Lopez-Lay *(Exec VP-Strategic Mgmt Grp)*
Jose M. Lacasa *(Exec VP & Dir-Florida Bus)*
Lilian Diaz Bento *(Exec VP & Dir-Bus Grp)*
Sara Alvarez-Cabrero *(Gen Counsel Exec VP)*

Subsidiaries:

First Bank   **(1)**
205 SE Broad St, Southern Pines, NC 28387   **(100%)**
Tel.: (910) 692-6222
Web Site: https://www.localfirstbank.com
Sales Range: $200-249.9 Million
Savings, Loans & Commercial Banking Services
N.A.I.C.S.: 522180
Elizabeth B. Bostian *(CFO, Gen Counsel & Exec VP)*
Richard Hancock Moore *(Chm)*
Michael G. Mayer *(CEO)*
Blaise Buczkowski *(Chief Admin Officer)*
Adam Currie *(Pres)*

Subsidiary (Domestic):

First Bank Insurance Services, Inc.   **(2)**
300 SW Broad St, Southern Pines, NC 27371   **(100%)**
Tel.: (910) 572-3761
Web Site: http://secure.firstbancorp.com
Insurance Brokerage Services
N.A.I.C.S.: 524210

Subsidiary (Domestic):

Bear Insurance Service   **(3)**
173 N 2nd St, Albemarle, NC 28001
Tel.: (704) 982-1156
Web Site: http://www.bearinsurance.com
Insurance Agencies & Brokerages
N.A.I.C.S.: 524210
Paul Childress *(Owner)*

GrandSouth Bancorporation   **(1)**
381 Halton Rd, Greenville, SC 29607
Tel.: (864) 770-1000
Rev.: $58,817,000
Assets: $1,203,722,000
Liabilities: $1,106,317,000
Net Worth: $97,405,000
Earnings: $16,114,000
Emp.: 196
Fiscal Year-end: 12/31/2021
Banking Holding Company
N.A.I.C.S.: 551111
Mason Y. Garrett *(Co-Founder)*
JB Schwiers *(Pres & CEO)*

Subsidiary (Domestic):

Grandsouth Bank   **(2)**
381 Halton Rd, Greenville, SC 29607
Tel.: (864) 770-1000
Web Site: https://localfirstbank.com
Rev.: $4,486,600
Emp.: 24
Commericial Banking
N.A.I.C.S.: 522110
Mason Y. Garrett *(Co-Founder)*
Mason Garrett *(Chm)*

Select Bancorp, Inc.   **(1)**
700 W Cumberland St, Dunn, NC 28334
Tel.: (910) 892-7080
Web Site: http://www.selectbank.com
Rev.: $69,328,000
Assets: $1,730,045,000
Liabilities: $1,514,677,000
Net Worth: $215,368,000
Earnings: $8,163,000
Emp.: 246
Fiscal Year-end: 12/31/2020
Bank Holding Company
N.A.I.C.S.: 551111
Mark A. Jeffries *(CFO & Exec VP)*
Lynn H. Johnson *(COO & Exec VP)*
W. Keith Betts *(Chief Banking Officer & Exec VP)*
David Richard Tobin Jr. *(Chief Credit Officer & Exec VP)*

Subsidiary (Domestic):

Select Bank & Trust Company   **(2)**
700 W Cumberland St, Dunn, NC 28334
Tel.: (910) 892-7080
Web Site: http://www.selectbank.com
Sales Range: $25-49.9 Million
Commericial Banking
N.A.I.C.S.: 522110
J. Gary Ciccone *(Chm)*
William L. Hedgepeth II *(Pres & CEO)*

FIRST BANCORP

1519 Ponce de Leon Ave Stop 23, San Juan, PR 00908-0146
Tel.: (787) 729-8200   **PR**
Web Site: https://www.1firstbank.com
Year Founded: 1998
FBP—(NYSE)
Rev.: $929,804,000
Assets: $18,909,549,000
Liabilities: $17,411,940,000
Net Worth: $1,497,609,000
Earnings: $302,864,000
Emp.: 3,168
Fiscal Year-end: 12/31/23
Bank Holding Company
N.A.I.C.S.: 551111
Aurelio Aleman-Bermudez *(Pres & CEO)*
Elizabeth Bostian *(CFO)*
Lilian Diaz Bento *(Exec VP & Bus Dir-Grp)*
Sara Alvarez-Cabrero *(Gen Counsel & Exec VP)*

Subsidiaries:

FirstBank Insurance Agency, Inc.   **(1)**
Ave Ponce De Leon 1519 Parada 23 Esq Calle del Parque, San Juan, PR 00908-0146
Tel.: (787) 292-4380
Web Site: http://www.firstbankpr.com
Sales Range: $1-9.9 Million
Emp.: 32
Insurance Services
N.A.I.C.S.: 524210
Aurelio Aleman-Bermudez *(Chm & CEO)*

FirstBank Puerto Rico   **(1)**
1519 Ave Ponce de Leon Piso 9 Pda 23 Santurce, San Juan, PR 00908
Tel.: (787) 292-4380
Web Site: http://www.firstbankpr.com
Commercial Banking; Commercial Loans; Consumer Loans; Mortgages
N.A.I.C.S.: 522110

Subsidiary (Domestic):

First Federal Finance Corporation   **(2)**
1519 Ave Ponce De Leon Ave 2nd Fl Stop 23 Cornor, San Juan, PR 00908-1732
Tel.: (787) 729-8200
Web Site: http://www.firstbankpr.com
Sales Range: $150-199.9 Million
Emp.: 700
Financial Services
N.A.I.C.S.: 525990
Aurelio Aleman-Bermudez *(Chm & CEO)*

Division (Domestic):

FirstBank Florida   **(2)**

---

701 Waterford Way Ste 800, Miami, FL 33126   **(100%)**
Tel.: (305) 577-6000
Web Site: http://www.firstbankfla.com
Sales Range: $75-99.9 Million
Emp.: 120
Savings, Loans & Commercial Banking Services
N.A.I.C.S.: 522110

Subsidiary (Domestic):

FirstBank Overseas Corp.   **(2)**
1519 Ave Ponce de Leon Piso 16, San Juan, PR 00908
Tel.: (787) 729-8200
Web Site: http://www.firstbankpr.com
Sales Range: $125-149.9 Million
Commercial Banking Services
N.A.I.C.S.: 522110

Santander BanCorp   **(2)**
B7 Tabonuco St 18th Fl San Patricio, Guaynabo, PR 00968-3028
Tel.: (787) 281-2000
Web Site: http://www.santander.pr
Sales Range: $600-649.9 Million
Emp.: 1,764
Bank Holding Company
N.A.I.C.S.: 551111

Subsidiary (Domestic):

Banco Santander International   **(3)**
1401 Brickell Ave Ste 1500, Miami, FL 33131-3506
Tel.: (305) 530-2900
Sales Range: $200-249.9 Million
Emp.: 500
Banking Services
N.A.I.C.S.: 522110
Gabriela A. Urbina *(Asst VP & Assoc Gen Counsel)*
Clara de Castro *(Asst VP-Gen Svcs & Facilities)*
Marcos Galigarcia *(Dir-Risk & Security Ops)*
Alfredo Di Lucente *(Head-Wealth Plng)*
Borja Martinez-Pardo *(Sr VP)*
Jose Luis Marroquin *(Sr VP)*
Rafael Moreno *(Sr VP)*
Luis H. Navas *(Sr VP & Dir-Comml-Central America & Caribbean)*
Roger Jimenez *(VP)*
Ricardo J. Avila *(VP & Mgr-Relationship)*
Paulo Prado *(Sr VP & Dir-Compliance)*
Lilian Pipkin-Galdo *(Acct Mgr-Payable & Payroll)*

Island Finance, Inc.   **(3)**
Verizon Bldg Rd 1 Km 15.1, Rio Piedras, PR 00926
Tel.: (787) 759-7044
Rev.: $93,700,000
Emp.: 100
Consumer Lending Services
N.A.I.C.S.: 522291

Santander Securities Corporation   **(3)**
207 ave 4th, Guaynabo, PR 00917   **(88.63%)**
Tel.: (787) 759-5330
Web Site: http://www.santandersecurities.com
Sales Range: $100-124.9 Million
Emp.: 80
Investment Banking & Asset Management
N.A.I.C.S.: 523150

FIRST BANCORP OF INDIANA, INC.

5001 Davis Lant Dr, Evansville, IN 47715
Tel.: (812) 492-8100   **IN**
Web Site: http://www.firstfedevansville.com
Year Founded: 1904
FBPI—(OTCIQ)
Bank Holding Company
N.A.I.C.S.: 551111
George Jeffrey Smith *(Exec VP & CFO)*
Michael H. Head *(Pres & CEO)*
Christy McBride *(Exec VP & COO)*
E. Harvey Seaman *(Chm)*

Subsidiaries:

First Federal Savings Bank   **(1)**

2200 W Franklin St, Evansville, IN 47712   **(100%)**
Tel.: (812) 423-3196
Web Site: http://www.firstfedevansville.com
Sales Range: $25-49.9 Million
Emp.: 100
Banking Services
N.A.I.C.S.: 522180
George Jeffrey Smith *(CFO, Treas & Exec VP)*
Michael H. Head *(Pres & CEO)*
Dale Holt *(Sr VP-Consumer Lending)*
Monica Stinchfield *(Sr VP-Mortgage Lending)*

FIRST BANCSHARES, INC.

120 North St, Bellevue, OH 44811-0210
Tel.: (419) 483-7340   **OH**
Web Site: https://www.fnblifetime.com
Year Founded: 1982
FIBH—(OTCIQ)
Sales Range: $10-24.9 Million
Emp.: 58
Bank Holding Company
N.A.I.C.S.: 551111
Dean J. Miller *(Pres & CEO)*
Edmund Schafer *(CFO & Sr VP)*
Deb Hawkins *(Sec & Sr VP)*

Subsidiaries:

First National Bank   **(1)**
120 N St, Bellevue, OH 44811
Tel.: (419) 483-7340
Web Site: http://www.fnblifetime.com
Emp.: 30
Banking Services
N.A.I.C.S.: 522110
Dean J. Miller *(Pres & CEO)*

FIRST BANCSHARES, INC.

25 N Cascade Ave Ste 100, Colorado Springs, CO 80903
Tel.: (719) 955-2800   **MO**
Web Site: https://www.fhsb.com
Year Founded: 1993
FBSI—(OTCIQ)
Sales Range: $1-9.9 Million
Emp.: 67
Bank Holding Company
N.A.I.C.S.: 551111
Shannon Peterson *(Sec)*
Robert M. Alexander *(Chm & CEO)*
Jeffrey C. Palmer *(CFO & Exec VP)*

Subsidiaries:

First Home Bank   **(1)**
207 W 3rd St, Mountain Grove, MO 65711
Tel.: (417) 926-5151
Web Site: http://www.fhsb.com
Sales Range: $1-9.9 Million
Commericial Banking
N.A.I.C.S.: 522110
R. Bradley Weaver *(Pres)*
Shannon Peterson *(Sec)*
Abby Rinehart *(Asst VP & Mgr-Gainesville)*
Jeffrey C. Palmer *(CFO & Exec VP)*
Missy Pellham *(Mgr-Ops-Sparta)*
Joseph E. James *(Exec VP & Sr Lending Officer)*

FIRST BANK

1395 YardvilleHamilton Sq Rd, Hamilton, NJ 08691
Tel.: (609) 528-4400
Web Site: https://www.firstbanknj.com
Year Founded: 2007
FRBA—(NASDAQ)
Rev.: $95,553,000
Assets: $2,346,270,000
Liabilities: $2,108,162,000
Net Worth: $238,108,000
Earnings: $19,448,000
Emp.: 196
Fiscal Year-end: 12/31/20
Commericial Banking
N.A.I.C.S.: 522110

First Bank—(Continued)

Patrick L. Ryan (Pres & CEO)
Leslie E. Goodman (Vice Chm)
Patrick M. Ryan (Chm)
Stephen F. Carman (Officer-Acctg)
Marianne De Simone (Mgr-Lending-Grp)
Andrew L. Hibshman (CFO & Exec VP)
Gabriel K. Dragos (CTO)
Maria E. Mayshura (Chief Risk Officer & Exec VP)
Arlene Pedovitch (Officer-Credit)
Donald Theobald (Sr VP & Controller)
Casi Smith Tiernan (Sr VP & Head-Cash Mgmt)
Karen Conway (VP)
Ryan Earley (VP)
Michelle Mack (Compliance Officer & VP)
Frank Puleio (Officer-Bus Dev & VP)
Brendan Ryan (Officer-BSA & VP)
Paula Huergo (Officer-Strategic Plng & Ops & Sr VP)
Sarah Pearson (Officer-CRA & VP)
Parwinder Virk (Chief Acctg Officer)
Gregory Weckel (Sr VP & Dir-IT Ops)
Scott Bachman (Sr VP)
Belinda Blazic (Sr VP & Mgr-Loan Admin)
Michael B. Cook (Sr VP)
Sriramulu Krishnamurthy (Sr VP & Mgr-SBA)
Larry Lee (Sr VP & Mgr-Loan Workout)
Richard Tocci (Sr VP & Mgr-PA Investor Real Estate)
Arnaldo Galassi (VP & Project Mgr-Lending)
Michele Green (VP & Portfolio Mgr)
Kyle Johnson (VP, Head-Trng & Project Mgr-Retail Analytics)
John Thompson (VP-Treasury Mgmt Sls)

Subsidiaries:

Malvern Bancorp, Inc.   **(1)**
42 E Lancaster Ave, Paoli, PA 19301
Tel.: (610) 644-9400
Web Site: http://www.malvernfederal.com
Rev.: $38,416,000
Assets: $1,209,143,000
Liabilities: $1,066,975,000
Net Worth: $142,168,000
Earnings: ($92,000)
Emp.: 81
Fiscal Year-end: 09/30/2021
Bank Holding Company
N.A.I.C.S.: 551111

Subsidiary (Domestic):

Malvern Bank, National Association   **(2)**
42 E Lancaster Ave, Paoli, PA 19301
Tel.: (610) 644-9400
Web Site: https://www.mymalvernbank.com
Sales Range: $125-149.9 Million
Emp.: 100
Banking Services
N.A.I.C.S.: 522110
Joseph D. Gangemi (CFO & Sr VP)
William J. Boylan (Chief Lending Officer & Exec VP)
Cynthia Felzer Leitzell (Bd of Dirs, Executives)
Alexander Opiela III (COO)
Jeffrey Steigerwalt (Exec VP)
Sandra Selzer (Exec VP)
Renee A. Chico (Chief Risk Officer)
Susan Marshall (Sr VP)

Malvern Insurance Associates LLC   **(2)**
1000 Ridge Rd Ste 101, Pottstown, PA 19465
Tel.: (610) 695-3651
Commercial Banking Services
N.A.I.C.S.: 522110

FIRST BANK OF OHIO

175 S Washington St, Tiffin, OH 44883
Tel.: (419) 448-9740   OH
Web Site:
   http://www.firstbankofohio.com
Year Founded: 1873
FBOO—(OTCIQ)
Commercial Banking Services
N.A.I.C.S.: 522110
A. Patrick Tonti (CEO)

FIRST BANKERS TRUST-SHARES INC.

1201 Broadway, Quincy, IL 62301
Tel.: (217) 228-8000   IL
Web Site:
   https://www.fbti.firstbankers.com
Year Founded: 1988
FBTT—(OTCIQ)
Rev.: $31,037,000
Assets: $1,117,675,000
Liabilities: $1,008,600,000
Net Worth: $109,075,000
Earnings: $7,843,000
Emp.: 174
Fiscal Year-end: 12/31/20
Bank Holding Company
N.A.I.C.S.: 551111
William D. Daniels (Chm)
Steven E. Siebers (Sec)
Allen W. Shafer (Pres & CEO)

Subsidiaries:

First Bankers Trust Company   **(1)**
12th & Broadway, Quincy, IL 62301
Tel.: (217) 228-8000
Web Site: http://www.firstbankers.com
Sales Range: $50-74.9 Million
Emp.: 150
Commercial Banking
N.A.I.C.S.: 522110
Allen Shafer (Pres & CEO)
Christopher Tobe (VP)

FIRST BUSEY CORPORATION

100 W University Ave, Champaign, IL 61820
Tel.: (217) 365-4544   NV
Web Site: https://www.busey.com
Year Founded: 1980
BUSE—(NASDAQ)
Rev.: $486,789,000
Assets: $12,336,677,000
Liabilities: $11,190,700,000
Net Worth: $1,145,977,000
Earnings: $128,311,000
Emp.: 1,450
Fiscal Year-end: 12/31/22
Financial Holding Company
N.A.I.C.S.: 551111
Van A. Dukeman (Chm, Pres & CEO)
Amy L. Randolph (COO & Exec VP)
Gregory B. Lykins (Vice Chm)
John Joseph Powers (Gen Counsel & Exec VP)
Jeffrey D. Jones (CFO & Exec VP)
Lynette M. Strode (Principal Acctg Officer)
Monica L. Bowe (Chief Risk Officer & Exec VP)

Subsidiaries:

Busey Bank   **(1)**
100 W University Ave, Champaign, IL 61820
Tel.: (217) 351-6500
Web Site: http://www.busey.com
Commercial Banking Services
N.A.I.C.S.: 522110
Van A. Dukeman (Chm, Pres & CEO)
Gregory B. Lykins (Vice Chm)

Subsidiary (Domestic):

FirsTech, Inc.   **(2)**
1 N Brentwood Blvd Ste 500, Saint Louis, MO 63105
Web Site: https://www.firstechpayments.com
Emp.: 40

Payment Processing Services
N.A.I.C.S.: 522320
Amy L. Randolph (Chm)
Christen McLeod (VP-Bus Dev)

Priority Property Holdings, LLC   **(2)**
12300 Olive Blvd, Saint Louis, MO 63141
Tel.: (314) 878-2210
Web Site:
   http://www.prioritypropertyholdings.com
Emp.: 3
Commercial Banking Services
N.A.I.C.S.: 522110

Busey Wealth Management, Inc.   **(1)**
100 W University Ave, Champaign, IL 61820
Tel.: (217) 351-6500
Web Site: http://www.busey.com
Sales Range: $200-249.9 Million
Emp.: 100
Commercial Banking Services
N.A.I.C.S.: 522110

Subsidiary (Domestic):

Busey Capital Management, Inc.   **(2)**
100 W University Ave, Champaign, IL 61820-8800
Tel.: (217) 365-4800
Investment Advisory Services
N.A.I.C.S.: 523940

Investors' Security Trust Company   **(2)**
5246 Red Cedar Dr Ste 101, Fort Myers, FL 33907
Tel.: (239) 267-6655
Web Site: http://www.allabouttrust.com
Investment, Trust & Estate Management Services
N.A.I.C.S.: 525920
John A. Noland (Chm)

Millenium Properties, Inc.   **(1)**
225 W Illinois Ste 350, Chicago, IL 60606
Tel.: (312) 338-3000
Web Site: https://www.mpirealestate.com
Real Estate Brokerage Services
N.A.I.C.S.: 531210
Daniel J. Hyman (Chm & CEO)

FIRST BUSINESS FINANCIAL SERVICES, INC.

401 Charmany Dr, Madison, WI 53719
Tel.: (608) 238-8008
Web Site:
   https://www.firstbusiness.bank
FBIZ—(NASDAQ)
Rev.: $150,799,000
Assets: $2,976,611,000
Liabilities: $2,715,971,000
Net Worth: $260,640,000
Earnings: $40,858,000
Emp.: 337
Fiscal Year-end: 12/31/22
Commercial Banking, Asset-Based Lending, Equipment Leasing, Retirement Plans, Investment Management & Trustee Services
N.A.I.C.S.: 522210
Mark J. Meloy (Exec VP)
Corey A. Chambas (CEO)
Brian D. Spielmann (CFO, Chief Acctg Officer & Treas)
Barbara McCarty Conley (Gen Counsel)
Jodi A. Chandler (Chief HR Officer)
Daniel S. Ovokaitys (CIO)

Subsidiaries:

Alterra Bank   **(1)**
11120 W 135th St, Overland Park, KS 66221
Tel.: (913) 681-2223
Web Site: http://www.alterrabank.com
Commercial Banking Services
N.A.I.C.S.: 522110

First Business Bank   **(1)**
401 Charmany Dr, Madison, WI 53719
Tel.: (608) 238-8008
Web Site: http://www.firstbusiness.com
Rev.: $21,720,000

Emp.: 100
State Commercial Banks
N.A.I.C.S.: 522110
Brian D. Spielmann (CFO, Chief Acctg Officer & Treas)
James Hartlieb (Pres & CEO)
Beth Korth (Dir & Sr VP)
Chris Doering (Sr VP-Comml Banking)
Lisa Allen (Officer-Client Relationship)
Charlene Breunig (VP)
Tom Dott (Sr VP-Comml Banking)
Kari Fritz (Sr Mgr-Client Svcs)
Brian Hagen (Sr VP & Dir-)
Ryan Hughes (VP-Comml Real Estate)
Matthew Karnick (VP-Commercial Banking)
Eric Schremp (Asst VP-Commercial Banking)
Jill Thomas (VP-Comml Banking)
Tim Valentyn (Sr VP-Commercial Banking)
David Sook (Sr VP/Sls Mgr-Equipment Fin-First Bus Specialty Fin)
Marlee Jorgensen (Asst VP-Treasury Mgmt)
Brian D. Spielmann (Chief Acctg Officer & Deputy CFO)
Melissa Fellows (Sr VP)
Brendan Freeman (Pres)
Jodie Johnson (Sr Dir-Marketing-Communications)
Alan McAfee (Chief Banking Ops Officer)
Dan Ovokaitys (CIO)
Monica Schlicht (Dir-Client Services)
Theresa Wiese (Mng Dir-Compliance-Risk Management)
Emily Bradley (Sr Dir)
Lynn Ann Arians (Dir & Sec)
Melissa Fellows (Sr VP)
Jodie Johnson (Sr Dir-Marketing-Communications)
Alan McAfee (Chief Banking Ops Officer)
Dan Ovokaitys (CIO)
Monica Schlicht (Dir-Client Services)
Theresa Wiese (Mng Dir-Compliance-Risk Management)
Emily Bradley (Sr Dir)
Lynn Ann Arians (Dir & Sec)
Brian McClendon (VP-SBA Lending)
Brandon Prather (VP-SBA Lending)
DeAngelou Stevenson (VP-SBA Lending)
Marty Ferguson (Mng Dir-SBA Lending)

Subsidiary (Domestic):

First Business Capital Corp.   **(2)**
401 Charmany Dr, Madison, WI 53719
Tel.: (608) 238-8008
Web Site: http://www.firstbusiness.com
Rev.: $1,600,000
Emp.: 27
Asset-Based Lending Services
N.A.I.C.S.: 522310
Chris McCarty (VP)
Ryan Jahns (VP)
Peter Lowney (Pres)
Tyler Parker (Auditor)
John Kloss (Sr VP)
Brian Benz (VP)
Kevin McGraw (VP)
Brian Banning (VP-Business Development)

First Business Leasing LLC   **(2)**
401 Charmany Dr 100, Madison, WI 53719
Tel.: (608) 238-8008
Web Site: http://www.firstbusiness.com
Rev.: $220,000
Emp.: 4
Rental Agent, Real Estate
N.A.I.C.S.: 531210

First Business Bank-Milwaukee   **(1)**
18500 W Corporate Dr, Brookfield, WI 53045
Tel.: (202) 792-1400
Web Site: http://www.firstbusiness.com
Sales Range: $1-9.9 Million
Emp.: 20
Commercial Bank
N.A.I.C.S.: 522110
Kim Preston (Sr VP)
Bob Bell (Dir & Sr VP)
Jim Flanagan (Sr VP-Comml Banking)
Kyle Haug (VP-Commercial Banking)
Brendan Freeman (Pres)
Kevin Kane (Pres)
Matt Krutza (Dir & VP)
Mark Meloy (CEO)
David Sook (Sls Mgr & Sr VP)
Alicia Anderson (Asst VP-II)
Greg Block (VP-Commercial Banking)
Ryan Black (VP-II)

Doug Brodzik *(Sr VP)*
Jay Cashmore *(VP-Commercial Banking)*
Travis Frazier *(Portfolio Mgr-II)*
Mike Groth *(Portfolio Mgr-II)*
Bill Harrigan *(VP)*
Nancy Johnshoy *(Sr VP & Portfolio Mgr)*
Terry Kotsakis *(VP)*
Chase Kostichka *(VP-II)*
Becky Rosenow *(Portfolio Mgr)*
Aaron Osten *(VP)*
David Schade *(VP)*
Amy Schneider *(VP)*
Peggy Stoop *(VP)*
Jennifer Verbrigghe *(VP)*
Yvette Zizzo *(Office Mgr)*
Brendan Freeman *(Pres)*
Kevin Kane *(Pres)*
Matt Krutza *(Dir & VP)*
Mark Meloy *(CEO)*
David Sook *(Sls Mgr & Sr VP)*
Alicia Anderson *(Asst VP-II)*
Greg Block *(VP-Commercial Banking)*
Ryan Black *(VP-II)*
Doug Brodzik *(Sr VP)*
Jay Cashmore *(VP-Commercial Banking)*
Travis Frazier *(Portfolio Mgr-II)*
Mike Groth *(Portfolio Mgr-II)*
Bill Harrigan *(VP)*
Nancy Johnshoy *(Sr VP & Portfolio Mgr)*
Terry Kotsakis *(VP)*
Chase Kostichka *(VP-II)*
Becky Rosenow *(Portfolio Mgr)*
Aaron Osten *(VP)*
David Schade *(VP)*
Amy Schneider *(VP)*
Peggy Stoop *(VP)*
Jennifer Verbrigghe *(VP)*
Yvette Zizzo *(Office Mgr)*

FIRST CAPITAL BANCSHARES INC

304 Meeting Str 1st Fl, Charleston, SC 29401
Tel.: (843) 990-7770   SC
Web Site:
   https://www.fcbcarolinas.com
Year Founded: 1999
FCPB—(OTCIQ)
Bank Holding Company
N.A.I.C.S.: 551111

FIRST CAPITAL, INC.

Tel.: (812) 738-2198   IN
Web Site:
   https://www.firstharrison.com
Year Founded: 1998
FCAP—(NASDAQ)
Rev.: $41,867,000
Assets: $1,151,400,000
Liabilities: $1,066,130,000
Net Worth: $85,270,000
Earnings: $11,902,000
Emp.: 184
Fiscal Year-end: 12/31/22
Bank Holding Company
N.A.I.C.S.: 551111
Michael C. Frederick *(Pres & CEO)*
Joshua Stevens *(CFO)*
Jennifer Meredith *(Sec & Mgr-Human Resources)*

Subsidiaries:

First Harrison Bank   **(1)**
220 Federal Dr NW, Corydon, IN 47112
Tel.: (812) 738-2198
Web Site: https://www.firstharrison.com
Sales Range: $50-74.9 Million
Emp.: 200
Federal Savings Bank
N.A.I.C.S.: 522180
Chris Frederick *(CFO)*
Joshua Stevens *(CFO)*
Jennifer Meredith *(Dir-Human Resources)*
Angie Jett *(COO)*
Jennifer Incantalupo *(CIO)*
Joe Mahuron *(Chief Credit Officer)*
Rob Guilfoyle *(Dir)*
Bill Harrod *(Dir)*
Pam Kraft *(Dir)*
John Shireman *(Dir)*
Kathy Ernstberger *(Chm)*
Chris Byrd *(Vice Chm)*
Carolyn Wallace *(Dir)*

Dana Huber *(Dir)*
Lou Ann Moore *(Dir)*
Jill Saegesser *(Dir)*
Mark Shireman *(Dir)*

FIRST CHOICE HEALTHCARE SOLUTIONS, INC.

95 Bulldog Blvd Ste 202, Melbourne, FL 32901
Tel.: (321) 725-0090   CO
Web Site: https://www.myfchs.com
Year Founded: 2007
FCHS—(OTCIQ)
Rev.: $29,985
Assets: $3,123,232
Liabilities: $31,653,284
Net Worth: ($28,530,052)
Earnings: ($8,171,232)
Emp.: 1
Fiscal Year-end: 12/31/23
All Other Business Support Services
N.A.I.C.S.: 561499
Christian Romandetti *(Chm, Pres & CEO)*

FIRST CITIZENS BANCSHARES, INC.

1 First Citizens Pl, Dyersburg, TN 38024-4643
Tel.: (731) 285-4410   TN
Web Site: https://www.firstcnb.com
Year Founded: 1982
FIZN—(OTCIQ)
Sales Range: $1-4.9 Billion
Offices of Bank Holding Companies
N.A.I.C.S.: 551111
Laura Beth Butler *(CFO & Exec VP)*
Jeffrey Agee *(Pres & CEO)*

Subsidiaries:

First-Citizens National Bank   **(1)**
1 1st Citizens Pl, Dyersburg, TN 38024-4641
Tel.: (731) 285-4410
Web Site: http://www.firstcnb.com
Rev.: $31,657,000
Emp.: 280
National Commercial Banks
N.A.I.C.S.: 522110
Regina Moore *(VP)*
Leslie White *(Asst VP)*
Neal Headden *(Sr VP)*

FIRST CITIZENS BANCSHARES, INC.

4300 6 Forks Rd, Raleigh, NC 27609
Tel.: (919) 716-7000   DE
Web Site:
   https://www.firstcitizens.com
Year Founded: 1986
FCNCA—(NASDAQ)
Rev.: $22,466,000,000
Assets: $213,758,000,000
Liabilities: $192,503,000,000
Net Worth: $21,255,000,000
Earnings: $11,407,000,000
Emp.: 15,715
Fiscal Year-end: 12/31/23
Bank Holding Company
N.A.I.C.S.: 551111
Frank B. Holding Jr. *(Chm & CEO)*
Peter M. Bristow *(Pres)*
Hope Holding Bryant *(Vice Chm)*
Craig L. Nix *(CFO & Principal Acctg Officer)*
Gregory L. Smith *(Chief Info & Ops Officer)*

Subsidiaries:

CIT Group Inc.   **(1)**
11 W 42nd St, New York, NY 10036
Tel.: (626) 535-8964
Web Site: http://www.cit.com
Financial Holding Company; Banking, Commercial Financing, Leasing & Advisory Services
N.A.I.C.S.: 551111
Steven Solk *(Pres-Consumer Banking)*
James J. Duffy *(Chief HR Officer)*

Barbara A. Callahan *(Sr VP & Head-IR)*
Denise M. Menelly *(Exec VP & Head-Tech & Ops)*
Michael Jones *(Pres-Bus Capital)*
Gina M. Proia *(Chief Mktg & Comm Officer & Exec VP)*
John J. Fawcett *(CFO & Exec VP)*
Kenneth McPhail *(Chief Strategy Officer & Exec VP)*
Greg Bourdon *(VP-Bus Dev-Industrial,Transportation,Print,Specialty Graphics)*
Jeff Lytle *(Pres-Rail)*
Wahida Plummer *(Chief Risk Officer & Exec VP)*
Marisa Harney *(Chief Credit Officer & Exec VP)*
Aaron Kaplan *(VP-Bus Dev-Tech Sector)*
Mark Links *(Exec VP)*
Michael Edwards *(VP-Bus Dev-Industrial Sector)*
Erik Lawson *(Dir-Strategic Partnerships-Tech Sector)*
Mark Boyer *(VP-Bus Dev-Industrial,Transportation,Print,Specialty Graphics)*
James J. Gifas *(Exec VP & Head-Treasury & Payment Svcs)*
Ken Martin *(Mng Dir-Small Bus Solutions)*
Philip Robbins *(Pres-Asset Mgmt & Capital Markets)*
David Harnisch *(Pres-Comml Fin)*
James R. Hubbard *(Gen Counsel, Sec & Exec VP)*

Subsidiary (Domestic):

C.I.T. Leasing Corporation   **(2)**
1 Cit Dr Ste 3251-9, Livingston, NJ 07039
Tel.: (973) 740-5796
Commercial Banking Services
N.A.I.C.S.: 522110

Subsidiary (Non-US):

CIT (France) SA   **(2)**
5 Rue De Castiglione, Rueil Malmaison, 75001, Paris, France
Tel.: (33) 953753078
Web Site: http://www.cit-france.com
Commercial Banking Services
N.A.I.C.S.: 522110

CIT Aerospace Asia Pte Ltd.   **(2)**
30 Raffles Pl Chevron HSE 18-02 Unit, Singapore, 048622, Singapore
Tel.: (65) 63726888
Web Site: http://www.cit.com
Sales Range: $25-49.9 Million
Emp.: 10
Aircraft Leasing Services
N.A.I.C.S.: 532411

Subsidiary (Domestic):

CIT Aerospace LLC   **(2)**
11 West 42 St, New York, NY 10036   **(100%)**
Tel.: (212) 461-5200
Web Site: http://www.cit.com
Aircraft Fleets Financing & Leasing Services
N.A.I.C.S.: 522220

CIT Bank, N.A.   **(2)**
75 N Fair Oaks Ave, Pasadena, CA 91103   **(100%)**
Tel.: (626) 535-8964
Web Site: http://www.cit.com
Emp.: 3,762
Federal Savings Bank
N.A.I.C.S.: 522180

Subsidiary (Domestic):

Direct Capital Corporation   **(3)**
155 Commerce Way, Portsmouth, NH 03801
Tel.: (603) 766-9335
Web Site: http://www.directcapital.com
Sales Range: $300-349.9 Million
Emp.: 224
Leasing & Sales Financing Services
N.A.I.C.S.: 522220

Subsidiary (Non-US):

CIT Capital Finance (UK) Limited   **(2)**
Peninsular House 30-36 Monument St, London, EC3R 8LJ, United Kingdom

Tel.: (44) 2074114800
Commercial Banking Services
N.A.I.C.S.: 522110

CIT Finance & Leasing Corporation   **(2)**
18/F Chengjian International Center No 500 Fushan Rd, Pudong, Shanghai, 200122, China
Tel.: (86) 2161602288
Web Site: http://www.cit.com
Sales Range: $50-74.9 Million
Emp.: 60
Financial Lending Services
N.A.I.C.S.: 522220

Subsidiary (Domestic):

CIT Finance LLC   **(2)**
1 Cit Dr, Livingston, NJ 07039
Tel.: (973) 740-5000
Emp.: 113
Sales Financing Services
N.A.I.C.S.: 522220

Subsidiary (Non-US):

CIT Group (France) SA   **(2)**
8 Rue Eugene Et Armand Peugeot, 92500, Rueil-Malmaison, France
Tel.: (33) 899376375
Financial Services
N.A.I.C.S.: 522220

CIT Group (France) SAS   **(2)**
8 Rue Eugene Et Armand Peugeot, 92500, Rueil-Malmaison, France
Tel.: (33) 147529500
Financial Services
N.A.I.C.S.: 522220

Subsidiary (Domestic):

CIT Healthcare LLC   **(2)**
11 W 42nd St, New York, NY 10036   **(100%)**
Tel.: (212) 771-0505
Web Site: http://www.cit.com
Sales Range: $150-199.9 Million
Healthcare Industry Financing Services
N.A.I.C.S.: 525990

Subsidiary (Non-US):

CIT Leasing de Argentina S.R.L.   **(2)**
Avenida Del Libertador 7270 1429, Capital Federal, Buenos Aires, Argentina
Tel.: (54) 1147038000
Commercial Banking Services
N.A.I.C.S.: 522110

Subsidiary (Domestic):

CIT Strategic Finance, Inc.   **(2)**
1 CIT Dr Ste 3251-9, Livingston, NJ 07039
Tel.: (973) 740-5796
Financial Investment Services
N.A.I.C.S.: 523999

CRE Holdings LLC   **(2)**
4470 Chamblee Dunwoody Rd Ste 480, Atlanta, GA 30338
Tel.: (404) 358-3547
Web Site: http://www.creholdings.co
Construction Services
N.A.I.C.S.: 236220

Subsidiary (Non-US):

Capita Funding de Mexico, Sociedad Anonima de Capital Variable SOFOM ENR   **(2)**
Blvd Adolfo Lopez Mateos No 2009 Piso 9, Mexico, 1010, Mexico
Tel.: (52) 5553370000
Commercial Banking Services
N.A.I.C.S.: 522110

Subsidiary (Domestic):

Financial Freedom Acquisition LLC   **(2)**
75 N Fair Oaks Ave, Pasadena, CA 91103
Tel.: (949) 923-3800
Mortgage Brokerage Services
N.A.I.C.S.: 522310

OneWest Resources LLC   **(2)**
888 E Walnut St, Pasadena, CA 91101
Tel.: (626) 535-4870
Mortgage Brokerage Services

First Citizens BancShares, Inc.—(Continued)

N.A.I.C.S.: 522310

The CIT Group/Business Credit, Inc. (2)
11 W 42nd St Frnt 1, New York, NY 10036 **(100%)**
Tel.: (212) 771-0505
Web Site: http://www.cit.com
Emp.: 150
Offers Flexible Financing that Enables Clients to Draw on Credit Lines Only as Needed; Revolving & Term Loans
N.A.I.C.S.: 522299

The CIT Group/Capital Finance, Inc. (2)
11 W 42nd St, New York, NY 10036 **(100%)**
Tel.: (212) 771-0505
Web Site: http://www.cit.com
Sales Range: $25-49.9 Million
Emp.: 25
Financing: Automobiles Furniture Etc.
N.A.I.C.S.: 522299

Subsidiary (Non-US):

The CIT Group/Commercial Services (Asia), Limited (2)
Rm 401 4/F Fairmont Hse 8 Contton Tree Drive, Central, China (Hong Kong)
Tel.: (852) 29135300
Sales Range: $50-74.9 Million
Emp.: 160
Financial Lending Services
N.A.I.C.S.: 522220

Subsidiary (Domestic):

The CIT Group/Commercial Services, Inc. (2)
11 W 42 St, New York, NY 10036 **(100%)**
Tel.: (212) 461-5200
Web Site: http://www.cit.com
Sales Range: $250-299.9 Million
Emp.: 800
Finance Company Credit Lending Collection Accounts Receivable & Cash Advancing Services
N.A.I.C.S.: 522299
Joerg Obermueller (Mng Dir-Supply Chain Fin)
Thomas Fingleton (Chief Strategy Officer)
Michael Hudgens (Pres)
Darrin Beer (Mgr-Western Reg)
Joy Zhu (Dir-Intl)
Brian Martin (Reg Mgr-Southeast)
Marc Heller (Vice Chm)
Amna Mahmood (Reg Mgr-Northeast)
Daniel Goll (Mgr-Natl Underwriting)

Subsidiary (Domestic):

The CIT Group/Commercial Services, Inc. (Va.) (3)
134 Wooding Ave, Danville, VA 24541
Tel.: (434) 791-6200
Banking Services
N.A.I.C.S.: 522110

Subsidiary (Domestic):

The CIT Group/Consumer Finance, Inc. (2)
1 CIT Dr, Livingston, NJ 07039-5703 **(100%)**
Tel.: (973) 740-5000
Web Site: http://www.citgroup.com
Sales Range: $400-449.9 Million
Emp.: 1,300
Purchases Common Stock & Subordinated Debt in Providing Capital to Small & Mid-Sized Companies
N.A.I.C.S.: 522310

The CIT Group/Equipment Financing, Inc. (2)
1 CIT Dr Ste 3251-9, Livingston, NJ 07039
Tel.: (973) 740-5000
Financial Investment Services
N.A.I.C.S.: 523999

The CIT Group/Sales Financing, Inc. (2)
1 CIT Dr, Livingston, NJ 07039-5703 **(100%)**
Tel.: (973) 740-5000
Web Site: http://www.citgroup.com

Sales Range: $400-449.9 Million
Emp.: 1,400
Provides Financing for Manufactured Housing & Recreational Vehicles; Marine Products
N.A.I.C.S.: 522299

Entegra Financial Corp. (1)
14 One Center Ct, Franklin, NC 28734
Tel.: (828) 524-7000
Web Site: http://www.entegrabank.com
Rev.: $62,614,000
Assets: $1,636,441,000
Liabilities: $1,473,569,000
Net Worth: $162,872,000
Earnings: $13,915,000
Emp.: 269
Fiscal Year-end: 12/31/2018
Bank Holding Company
N.A.I.C.S.: 551111
Ryan M. Scaggs (COO & Exec VP)

First-Citizens Bank & Trust Company (1)
239 Fayetteville St, Raleigh, NC 27601
Tel.: (919) 716-7050
Commercial Banking
N.A.I.C.S.: 522110
Frank B. Holding Jr. (Chm & CEO)
Peter M. Bristow (Pres)
Hope Holding Bryant (Vice Chm)

Subsidiary (Domestic):

American Guarantee Insurance Company (2)
4300 Six Forks Rd, Raleigh, NC 27609
Tel.: (919) 716-7573
Sales Range: Less than $1 Million
Emp.: 10
Property & Casualty Insurance Services
N.A.I.C.S.: 524210

Entegra Bank (2)
14 One Center Ct, Franklin, NC 28734
Tel.: (828) 524-7000
Web Site: http://www.entegrabank.com
Commercial Banking
N.A.I.C.S.: 522110

First Citizens Investor Services, Inc. (2)
4300 Six Forks Rd, Raleigh, NC 27609 **(100%)**
Tel.: (919) 716-7392
Web Site: http://www.firstcitizens.com
Sales Range: $450-499.9 Million
N.A.I.C.S.: 522210

Triangle Life Insurance (2)
PO Box 45153, Jacksonville, FL 32232-5153 **(100%)**
Tel.: (800) 888-2738
Web Site: http://www.fortegrafinancial.com
Sales Range: $10-24.9 Million
Emp.: 200
Fire Insurance Services
N.A.I.C.S.: 524126

FIRST COMMERCE BANK
105 River Ave, Lakewood, NJ 08701
Tel.: (732) 364-0032
Web Site:
https://www.firstcommercebk.com
Year Founded: 2006
CMRB—(OTCIQ)
Rev.: $48,016,000
Assets: $1,007,499,000
Liabilities: $864,613,000
Net Worth: $142,886,000
Earnings: $9,180,000
Fiscal Year-end: 12/31/19
Commercial Banking Services
N.A.I.C.S.: 522110
Ira Hoberman (Chm, Pres & CEO)
Peter Cappello (Chief Lending Officer & Exec VP)
Parwinder Virk (CFO & Sr VP)
Donald Mindiak (Pres, CEO & COO)
Abraham M. Penzer (Vice Chm & Sec)
Thomas P. Bovino (Chm)
Gregory Garcia (COO & Exec VP)
Eli Rennert (Chief Lending Officer & Exec VP)
David Onderko (CFO & Sr VP)

Jill Ross (Chief Experience Officer & Sr VP)
Danny R. Beagle Jr. (Chief Risk Officer & Sr VP)
Rhiannon Williams (Chief Credit Officer & Sr VP)
LaTifa Sciscoe (CIO, CTO & Sr VP)
Tonia Thompson (Officer-OFAC & Sr VP-Compliance-BSA,AML)
Mary Kay Malec (Officer-Human Resources & Sr VP)

FIRST COMMONWEALTH FINANCIAL CORPORATION
601 Philadelphia St, Indiana, PA 15701
Tel.: (724) 349-7220 **PA**
Web Site: https://www.fcbanking.com
Year Founded: 1982
FCF—(NYSE)
Rev.: $428,661,000
Assets: $9,805,666,000
Liabilities: $8,753,592,000
Net Worth: $1,052,074,000
Earnings: $128,181,000
Emp.: 1,403
Fiscal Year-end: 12/31/22
Bank Holding Company
N.A.I.C.S.: 551111
Norman J. Montgomery (Exec VP-Bus Integration)
Leonard V. Lombardi (Exec VP)
Matthew C. Tomb (Chief Risk Officer, Gen Counsel, Sec & Exec VP)
Thomas Michael Price (Pres & CEO)
Jane Grebenc (Chief Revenue Officer & Exec VP)
James R. Reske (CFO, Treas & Exec VP)
Carrie L. Riggle (Exec VP & Mgr-Human Resources)
Jon L. Gorney (Chm)
Joe Culos (Exec VP)
Stan Foraker (Exec VP)
Vicki Fox (Officer-Diversity & Inclusion & Sr VP)
Mike McCuen (Exec VP)
Jeff Rosen (Exec VP-Consumer & Small Bus Lending)

Subsidiaries:

Centric Financial Corp. (1)
4320 Linglestown Rd, Harrisburg, PA 17112
Tel.: (717) 657-7727
Web Site: http://www.centricbank.com
Bank Holding Company
N.A.I.C.S.: 551111
Patricia A. Husic (Founder, Pres & CEO)
Sandra L. J. Schultz (CFO & Exec VP)
Jeffrey W. Myers (Chief Lending Officer & Sr Exec VP)
Terry Monteverde (Chief Credit Officer & Exec VP)
Leslie A. Meck (Sr VP & Chief Retail Officer)
Clair M. Finkenbinder III (CIO, Exec VP & Dir-Ops)
Donald E. Enders Jr. (Chm)

Subsidiary (Domestic):

Centric Bank (2)
4320 Linglestown Rd, Harrisburg, PA 17112
Tel.: (717) 657-7727
Web Site: https://www.centricbank.com
Emp.: 20
Banking Services
N.A.I.C.S.: 522110
Patricia A. Husic (Pres & CEO)
William J. Kitsch (Sr VP)

First Commonwealth Bank (1)
601 Philadelphia St, Indiana, PA 15701
Tel.: (724) 459-7027
Web Site: https://www.fcbanking.com
Commercial Banking Services
N.A.I.C.S.: 522110
Thomas Michael Price (CEO)
Jane Grebenc (Pres & Chief Revenue Officer)
Carrie Riggle (Exec VP & Mgr-HR)

Brian G. Karrip (Chief Credit Officer & Exec VP)
Jeff Rosen (Exec VP-Consumer & Small Bus Lending)
David Buckiso (Exec VP & Mgr-Wealth Svcs)
Nancy Johnson (Exec VP)
Joe Culos (Exec VP)
Stan Foraker (Exec VP)
Mike Price (CEO)

FIRST COMMUNITY BANKSHARES, INC.
Tel.: (276) 326-9000 **VA**
Web Site:
https://www.firstcommunitybank.com
Year Founded: 1989
FCBC—(NASDAQ)
Rev.: $151,501,000
Assets: $3,135,572,000
Liabilities: $2,713,587,000
Net Worth: $421,985,000
Earnings: $46,662,000
Emp.: 609
Fiscal Year-end: 12/31/22
Bank Holding Company
N.A.I.C.S.: 551111
William P. Stafford II (Chm & CEO)
Samuel L. Elmore (Vice Chm)
Gary R. Mills (Pres)
David D. Brown V (CFO)
Jason R. Belcher (COO)
Sarah W. Harmon (Chief Admin Officer)

Subsidiaries:

First Community Bank (1)
101 Sanders Ln, Bluefield, VA 24605
Tel.: (276) 322-5487
Web Site:
https://www.firstcommunitybank.com
Sales Range: $50-74.9 Million
Emp.: 200
Banking Services
N.A.I.C.S.: 522110
Gary R. Mills (Pres & CEO)
David D. Brown V (CFO)

Subsidiary (Domestic):

First Community Insurance Services, Inc. (2)
1 Stafford Cmns, Princeton, WV 24740-2567
Tel.: (304) 425-8793
Insurance Services
N.A.I.C.S.: 524210
Daniel O. Dunn (Pres)

First Community Wealth Management, Inc. (2)
1707 Jefferson St, Bluefield, WV 24701-4013
Tel.: (304) 325-7334
Emp.: 5
Commercial Banking Services
N.A.I.C.S.: 522110
Bruce Terry (Branch Mgr)

Highlands Bankshares, Inc. (1)
340 W Main St, Abingdon, VA 24210-1128
Tel.: (276) 628-9181
Web Site: http://www.hubank.com
Rev.: $28,260,000
Assets: $591,941,000
Liabilities: $535,300,000
Net Worth: $56,641,000
Earnings: $3,592,000
Emp.: 153
Fiscal Year-end: 12/31/2018
Bank Holding Company
N.A.I.C.S.: 551111
Robert W. Moser Jr. (Chm)

SURREY BANCORP (1)
145 N Renfro St, Mount Airy, NC 27030
Tel.: (336) 783-3900
Web Site: http://www.surreybank.com
Bank Holding Company
N.A.I.C.S.: 551111
Peter Pequeno (Sr VP)

FIRST COMMUNITY CORPORATION

5455 Sunset Blvd, Lexington, SC
29072
Tel.: (803) 951-2265   SC
Web Site:
   https://www.firstcommunitysc.com
FCCO—(NASDAQ)
Rev.: $62,686,000
Assets: $1,672,946,000
Liabilities: $1,554,585,000
Net Worth: $118,361,000
Earnings: $14,613,000
Emp.: 254
Fiscal Year-end: 12/31/22
Bank Holding Company
N.A.I.C.S.: 551111
Michael C. Crapps *(Pres & CEO)*
John Ted Nissen *(Chief Banking Officer & Exec VP)*
Robin D. Brown *(Chief HR & Mktg Officer)*
W. James Kitchens Jr. *(Vice Chm)*
Donald Shawn Jordan *(CFO)*
John F. Walker IV *(Chief Credit Officer)*

Subsidiaries:

First Community Bank   **(1)**
5455 Sunset Blvd, Lexington, SC 29072
Tel.: (803) 951-2265
Web Site: https://www.firstcommunitysc.com
Sales Range: $25-49.9 Million
Emp.: 250
Commericial Banking
N.A.I.C.S.: 522110
John Ted Nissen *(Pres & CEO)*
Vaughan R. Dozier Jr. *(Chief Comml & Retail Banking Officer-South Region & Exec VP)*

FIRST COMMUNITY FINANCIAL CORPORATION
2 N Main St, Mifflintown, PA 17059
Tel.: (717) 436-2144   PA
Web Site: https://pennian.bank
Year Founded: 1984
FMFP—(OTCIQ)
Rev.: $23,485,000
Assets: $608,291,000
Liabilities: $552,496,000
Net Worth: $55,795,000
Earnings: $4,065,000
Emp.: 93
Fiscal Year-end: 12/31/20
Bank Holding Company
N.A.I.C.S.: 551111
Daniel B. Brown *(Vice Chm)*
Scott E. Fritz *(Pres & CEO)*
John P. Henry III *(Chm)*
Richard R. Leitzel *(Treas)*
Kimberly A. Benner *(Exec VP & Mgr-Trust & Fin Svcs Div-Pennian Bank)*
Jennifer S. Mahoney *(Asst Sec)*
David L. Swartz *(Sec)*

Subsidiaries:

First National Bank of Mifflintown **(1)**
2 N Main St, Mifflintown, PA 17059
Tel.: (717) 436-2144
Web Site: http://www.fnbmifflintown.com
Sales Range: $50-74.9 Million
Emp.: 50
Commercial Banking Services
N.A.I.C.S.: 522110
Lowell M. Shearer *(Sec)*
Roger Shallenberger *(Vice Chm)*
Timothy P. Stayer *(COO)*
John P. Henry III *(Chm)*
Richard R. Leitzel *(CFO & VP)*
K. Lee Hopkins *(VP)*

FIRST FARMERS AND MERCHANTS CORPORATION
816 S Garden St, Columbia, TN
38401
Tel.: (931) 388-3145   TN
Web Site:
   https://www.myfirstfarmers.com
Year Founded: 1982

FFMH—(OTCIQ)
Rev.: $61,770,000
Assets: $1,802,145,000
Liabilities: $1,642,151,000
Net Worth: $159,994,000
Earnings: $14,210,000
Emp.: 250
Fiscal Year-end: 12/31/20
Bank Holding Company
N.A.I.C.S.: 551111
Brian Keith Williams *(Pres)*
Timothy E. Pettus *(Vice Chm)*
Robert E. Krimmel *(CFO & Treas)*
T. Randy Stevens *(Chm & CEO)*
Felicia Y. Brown *(CMO)*

Subsidiaries:

First Farmers & Merchants Bank **(1)**
816 S Garden St, Columbia, TN 38401-3226
Tel.: (931) 388-3145
Web Site: http://www.myfirstfarmers.com
Full Banking Services
N.A.I.C.S.: 522110
Brian Keith Williams *(Chm, Pres & CEO)*
Robert E. Krimmel *(CFO & Treas)*
Jennifer Shepard *(Pres-Brentwood)*
Emmett Webb *(Mgr-Comml Relationship)*
Tina Lilly *(Mgr-Franklin)*
Felicia Y. Brown *(Chief Mktg & Comm Officer)*
Joseph Patterson *(Mgr-Comml Relationship)*
Rory Mallard *(Chief Comml Banking Officer)*
Jennifer J. McConnell *(Chief Credit Officer)*
John P. Tomlinson III *(Chief Admin Officer & Chief Risk Officer)*

FIRST FINANCIAL BANCORP.
225 Pictoria Dr Ste 700, Cincinnati,
OH 45246   OH
Web Site:
   https://www.bankatfirst.com
Year Founded: 1982
FFBC—(NASDAQ)
Rev.: $774,647,000
Assets: $17,003,316,000
Liabilities: $14,961,943,000
Net Worth: $2,041,373,000
Earnings: $217,612,000
Emp.: 2,108
Fiscal Year-end: 12/31/22
Bank Holding Company
N.A.I.C.S.: 551111
James Michael Anderson *(CFO, COO & Exec VP)*
William R. Harrod *(Chief Credit Officer & Exec VP)*
Amanda N. Neeley *(Chief Mktg & Strategy Officer & Exec VP)*
Richard S. Dennen *(Chief Corp Banking Officer)*
Gregory A. Harris *(Pres)*
Archie M. Brown Jr. *(CEO)*

Subsidiaries:

First Financial Bank   **(1)**
225 Pictoria Dr Ste 700, Cincinnati, OH
45246   **(100%)**
Tel.: (513) 867-4744
Web Site: https://www.bankatfirst.com
Investment Banking & Security Dealing Services
N.A.I.C.S.: 523150
James Michael Anderson *(CFO)*
Bill Harrod *(Chief Credit Officer)*
Greg Harris *(Pres-Wealth Mgmt)*
Mandy Neeley *(Chief Consumer Banking & Strategy Officer)*

Division (Domestic):

Bannockburn Global Forex, LLC   **(2)**
255 East 5th St Fl 8, 45202, Cincinnati, OH
Tel.: (513) 386-7400
Web Site:
   http://www.bannockburnglobal.com
Investment Advisory Services
N.A.I.C.S.: 523940
Mark R. Wendling *(Exec Mng Dir)*
Richard K. Jones *(Sr Mng Dir)*
Alexander F. Phillips *(Mng Dir)*

Andrew C. Collins *(Mng Dir)*
Mark A. Gargano *(Mng Dir)*
Joseph M. Areddy *(Sr Mng Dir)*
Daniel P. Flanigan *(Mng Dir)*
Shari E. Kempf *(Mng Dir)*
Timothy J. Sheeran *(Mng Dir)*
Yee Kok-Eagan *(Mng Dir)*
Nicholas R. Sheridan *(Mng Dir)*
Allen D. Campbell *(Dir & CTO)*
Douglas E. Colton *(Dir)*
Jo McClanahan *(Dir)*

Subsidiary (Domestic):

First Financial Bancorp Service
Corporation   **(2)**
4400 Lewis St, Middletown, OH 45044
Tel.: (513) 705-4400
Sales Range: $75-99.9 Million
Emp.: 187
Operations Unit
N.A.I.C.S.: 522180

First Financial Equipment Finance,
LLC   **(2)**
300 High St, Hamilton, OH 45011-6078
Tel.: (513) 867-4744
Financial Services
N.A.I.C.S.: 541611

First Financial Insurance Indiana **(2)**
500 Washington St, Columbus, IN 47201
Tel.: (812) 378-4847
Property & Casualty Insurance Services
N.A.I.C.S.: 524126
Kevin Langford *(Pres-Banking Ops)*

Oak Street Funding LLC   **(2)**
8888 Keystone Crossing Ste 1700, Indianapolis, IN 46240
Tel.: (317) 854-5146
Web Site: https://www.oakstreetfunding.com
Insurance Agency Lending & Financing
Services
N.A.I.C.S.: 522299
David Christman *(CIO)*
Kathy Yeary *(Exec Dir-HR & Customer Svc)*
Barry Kehl *(Exec Dir-Underwriting)*
Alicia Chandler *(Pres)*

Subsidiary (Domestic):

Oak Street Servicing, LLC   **(3)**
8888 N Keystone Ave Ste 1700, Indianapolis, IN 46240
Web Site: https://www.oakstreetfunding.com
Mortgage Brokerage Services
N.A.I.C.S.: 522310

First Financial Preferred Capital,
Inc.   **(1)**
255 E 5th St Ste 700, Cincinnati, OH 45202
Tel.: (513) 979-5813
Financial Services
N.A.I.C.S.: 541611

First Franchise Capital
Corporation   **(1)**
8888 Keystone Crossing Ste 1700, Indianapolis, IN 46240
Web Site:
   https://www.firstfranchisecapital.com
Emp.: 51
Financial Services
N.A.I.C.S.: 541611
Kathy Yeary *(Exec Dir-HR & Customer Svc)*

FIRST FINANCIAL BANKSHARES, INC.
400 Pine St, Abilene, TX 79601
Tel.: (325) 627-7155   TX
Web Site: https://www.ffin.com
Year Founded: 1956
FFIN—(NASDAQ)
Rev.: $564,519,000
Assets: $12,974,066,000
Liabilities: $11,708,329,000
Net Worth: $1,265,737,000
Earnings: $234,475,000
Emp.: 1,400
Fiscal Year-end: 12/31/22
Bank Holding Company
N.A.I.C.S.: 551111
F. Scott Dueser *(Chm, Pres & CEO)*
Monica Houston *(Exec VP-Retail Banking & Trng)*

T. Luke Longhofer *(Chief Lending Officer & Exec VP)*
Ronald D. Butler II *(Chief Admin Officer & Exec VP)*
Michelle S. Hickox *(CFO & Exec VP)*
Randy Roewe *(Chief Risk Officer & Exec VP)*
John J. Ruzicka *(CIO & Exec VP)*
David Bailey *(Exec VP)*
Andrea Smiddy-Sclagel *(Exec VP)*
Mike Wolverton *(Exec VP)*
Mike Parker *(Chief Compliance Officer)*
Maggie Tuschinski *(Chief Digital Officer)*
Chris Cook *(Exec VP)*
Cynthia Suarez *(Chief Information Security Officer)*
Isabel Montoya *(Exec VP)*
Rett Everett *(Exec VP)*

Subsidiaries:

First Financial Bank, N.A.   **(1)**
400 Pine St, Abilene, TX
79601-5128   **(100%)**
Tel.: (325) 627-7000
Web Site: https://ffin.com
Federal Savings Bank
N.A.I.C.S.: 522180
F. Scott Dueser *(Chm)*

First Financial Insurance Agency,
Inc.   **(1)**
400 Pine St Ste 310, Abilene, TX 79601
Tel.: (325) 627-7155
Insurance Services
N.A.I.C.S.: 524210

FIRST FINANCIAL CORPORATION
1 1st Financial Plz, Terre Haute, IN
47807
Tel.: (812) 238-6000   IN
Web Site: https://www.first-online.bank
Year Founded: 1985
THFF—(NASDAQ)
Rev.: $230,017,000
Assets: $4,989,281,000
Liabilities: $4,513,988,000
Net Worth: $475,293,000
Earnings: $71,109,000
Emp.: 900
Fiscal Year-end: 12/31/22
Bank Holding Company
N.A.I.C.S.: 551111
Norman L. Lowery *(Chm)*
Norman D. Lowery *(Pres & CEO)*
Rodger A. McHargue *(CFO, Treas & Sec)*

Subsidiaries:

First Financial Bank, N.A.   **(1)**
4353 S 7th St, Terre Haute, IN
47802   **(100%)**
Tel.: (812) 238-6736
Web Site: http://www.first-online.com
Sales Range: $125-149.9 Million
Savings Bank
N.A.I.C.S.: 522180
Norman L. Lowery *(Chm)*
Norman D. Lowery *(Pres & CEO)*

FIRST FINANCIAL NORTHWEST, INC.
201 Wells Ave S, Renton, WA 98057
Tel.: (425) 255-4400   WA
Web Site: https://www.ffnwb.com
Year Founded: 2007
FFNW—(NASDAQ)
Rev.: $62,489,000
Assets: $1,502,916,000
Liabilities: $1,342,556,000
Net Worth: $160,360,000
Earnings: $13,240,000
Emp.: 151
Fiscal Year-end: 12/31/22
Bank Holding Company

First Financial Northwest, Inc.—(Continued)

N.A.I.C.S.: 551111
Simon Soh (Chief Credit Officer & Sr VP)
Joann E. Lee (Sec)
Joseph W. Kiley III (Pres & CEO)
Richard P. Jacobson (CFO, COO & Exec VP)
Dalen D. Harrison (Chief Banking Officer)
Ronnie Clariza (Chief Risk Officer)
Eva Q. Ngu (Controller)

Subsidiaries:

First Financial Diversified Corporation **(1)**
208 Williams Ave S, Renton, WA 98057-2104 **(100%)**
Tel.: (425) 255-4466
Sales Range: $10-24.9 Million
Emp.: 5
Escrow Financial Services
N.A.I.C.S.: 525990

First Financial Northwest Bank **(1)**
201 Wells Ave S, Renton, WA 98057 **(100%)**
Tel.: (425) 255-4400
Web Site: https://www.ffnwb.com
Emp.: 98
Banking Services
N.A.I.C.S.: 522110
Simon Soh (Chief Credit Officer & Sr VP)
Joann E. Lee (Executives)
Joseph W. Kiley III (Pres & CEO)
Richard P. Jacobson (CFO, COO & Exec VP)
Ralph C. Sabin (Chm)
Ronnie Clariza (Chief Risk Officer & Sr VP)
Dalen D. Harrison (Chief Banking Officer & Exec VP)

FIRST FOODS GROUP, INC.

3773 Howard Hughes Pkwy Ste 500S, Las Vegas, NV 89169-6014
Tel.: (201) 471-0988   **NV**
Web Site:
http://www.firstfoodsgroup.com
Year Founded: 2015
FIFG—(OTCQB)
Rev.: $84,795
Assets: $53,956
Liabilities: $5,219,279
Net Worth: ($5,165,323)
Earnings: ($1,696,027)
Emp.: 1
Fiscal Year-end: 12/31/22
Food Service Franchise Marketing & Consulting Services
N.A.I.C.S.: 541613
Harold Kestenbaum (Chm & CEO)
Mark J. Keeley (CFO)
Michael Kaplan (CMO)

FIRST FOUNDATION INC.

200 Crescent Ct Ste 1400, Dallas, TX 75201
Tel.: (469) 638-9636   **CA**
Web Site: https://www.ff-inc.com
Year Founded: 1990
FFWM—(NASDAQ)
Rev.: $452,112,000
Assets: $13,014,179,000
Liabilities: $11,879,801,000
Not Worth: $1,134,378,000
Earnings: $110,512,000
Emp.: 713
Fiscal Year-end: 12/31/22
Financial Holding Company
N.A.I.C.S.: 551111
Ulrich E. Keller Jr. (Chm)
Shannon Wherry (Dir-Corp Comm)
James Britton (CFO, Principal Acctg Officer & Exec VP)
Scott Farris Kavanaugh (Vice Chm, Pres & CEO)
Lisa Carlson (Chief HR Officer)
Lillian Gavin (Chief Credit Officer)
David T. Mitsuuchi (Chief Lending Officer)

Subsidiaries:

First Foundation Advisors **(1)**
18101 Von Karman Ave 7th Fl, Irvine, CA 92612 **(100%)**
Tel.: (949) 202-4100
Web Site: http://www.firstfoundationinc.com
Emp.: 511
Investment Management & Wealth Planning Services
N.A.I.C.S.: 523940
John A. Hakopian (Pres)
Eric H. Speron (Portfolio Mgr)
Ulrich E. Keller Jr. (Founder & Exec Chm)

First Foundation Bank **(1)**
18101 Von Karman Ave Ste 750, Irvine, CA 92612 **(100%)**
Tel.: (949) 202-4100
Emp.: 300
Commericial Banking
N.A.I.C.S.: 522110
Hugo J. Nuno (Chief Banking Officer & Exec VP)
Christopher M. Naghibi (COO & Exec VP)
Amy Djou (Chief Acctg Officer, Deputy CFO & Sr VP)
James Britton (CFO & Exec VP)
Scott Farris Kavanaugh (Pres & CEO)
Ulrich E. Keller Jr. (Chm)
Lisa Carlson (Chief HR Officer)
Lillian Gavin (Chief Credit Officer)
David T. Mitsuuchi (Chief Lending Officer)
Erica Dorsett (Exec VP)
Garrett Richter (Pres-Market)

FIRST GENERAL BANK

19036 Colima Rd, Rowland Heights, CA 91748
Tel.: (626) 820-1234   **CA**
Web Site: https://www.fgbusa.com
Year Founded: 2005
FGEB—(OTCIQ)
Rev.: $48,844,646
Assets: $1,098,066,506
Liabilities: $941,156,893
Net Worth: $156,909,613
Earnings: $18,505,083
Fiscal Year-end: 12/31/20
Commericial Banking
N.A.I.C.S.: 522110
Jeanette Lin (Chief Credit Officer & Exec VP)
Jackson Yang (Chm)
Tony Chan (Chief Lending Officer & Exec VP)
Wilson Mach (COO & Sr Exec VP)
Cliff J. Hsu (Pres & CEO)

FIRST GREENWICH FINANCIAL, INC.

444 E Putnam Ave, Cos Cob, CT 06807
Tel.: (203) 629-8400   **CT**
Year Founded: 2016
FGFI—(OTCIQ)
Financial Investment Services
N.A.I.C.S.: 523999
Frank J. Gaudio (Pres & CEO)
Mark L. McMillen (COO)
Ronald J. Moccio (CFO)
Bruno J. Gioffre (Chm)

FIRST GUARANTY BANCSHARES, INC.

400 E Thomas St, Hammond, LA 70401
Tel.: (985) 345-7685
Web Site: https://www.fgb.net
FGBI—(NASDAQ)
Rev.: $147,585,000
Assets: $3,151,347,000
Liabilities: $2,916,356,000
Net Worth: $234,991,000
Earnings: $28,884,000
Emp.: 465
Fiscal Year-end: 12/31/22
Bank Holding Company
N.A.I.C.S.: 551111

Eric J. Dosch (CFO, Treas & Sec)
Alton B. Lewis Jr. (Vice Chm)

Subsidiaries:

First Guaranty Bank **(1)**
400 E Thomas St, Hammond, LA 70401
Tel.: (985) 345-7685
Web Site: https://www.fgb.net
Sales Range: $50-74.9 Million
Emp.: 214
Commercial Bank
N.A.I.C.S.: 522110
Alton B. Lewis Jr. (Vice Chm)

FIRST HARTFORD CORPORATION

149 Colonial Rd, Manchester, CT 06042
Tel.: (860) 646-6555   **ME**
Web Site:
https://www.firsthartford.com
FHRT—(OTCIQ)
Rev.: $80,747,777
Assets: $248,692,462
Liabilities: $248,124,469
Net Worth: $567,993
Earnings: $2,556,452
Emp.: 111
Fiscal Year-end: 04/30/19
Other Activities Related to Real Estate
N.A.I.C.S.: 531390
Neil H. Ellis (Chm)

FIRST HORIZON CORPORATION

165 Madison Ave, Memphis, TN 38103
Tel.: (901) 523-4444   **TN**
Web Site:
https://www.firsthorizon.com
Year Founded: 1864
FHN—(NYSE)
Rev.: $4,100,000,000
Assets: $81,661,000,000
Liabilities: $72,370,000,000
Net Worth: $9,291,000,000
Earnings: $865,000,000
Emp.: 7,249
Fiscal Year-end: 12/31/22
Commercial Banking Services
N.A.I.C.S.: 551111
Anthony J. Restel (Pres-Reg Banking)
D. Bryan Jordan (Chm, Pres & CEO)
David T. Popwell (Pres-Specialty Banking)
Susan L. Springfield (Chief Credit Officer & Sr Exec VP)
Tammy S. Locascio (COO & Sr Exec VP)
Terry L. Akins (Chief Risk Officer & Sr Exec VP)
Jeff L. Fleming (Chief Acctg Officer, Exec VP & Controller)
Hope Dmuchowski (CFO & Sr Exec VP)

Subsidiaries:

FHN Financial Main Street Advisors, LLC **(1)**
10655 Park Run Dr Ste 120, Las Vegas, NV 89144
Tel.: (702) 575-6600
Investment Management Service
N.A.I.C.S.: 523940

First Tennessee Bank, N.A. **(1)**
165 Madison Ave, Memphis, TN 38103 **(100%)**
Tel.: (901) 523-4883
Web Site: http://www.firsttennessee.com
Sales Range: $700-749.9 Million
Emp.: 4,300
Savings, Loans & Commercial Banking Services
N.A.I.C.S.: 522110

Subsidiary (Domestic):

FTB Advisors, Inc. **(2)**
165 Madison Ave 14th Fl, Memphis, TN 38103
Tel.: (901) 523-4883
Web Site: https://www.firsthorizon.com
Emp.: 308
Investment Advisory Services
N.A.I.C.S.: 523940

FTN Financial Corporation **(2)**
845 Crossover Ln Ste 150, Memphis, TN 38117-4906
Tel.: (901) 435-8080
Web Site: http://www.ftnfinancial.com
Sales Range: $300-349.9 Million
Emp.: 300
Full Service Provider of Financial Service for the Investment & Banking Community
N.A.I.C.S.: 523940

FTN Financial Main Street Advisors, LLC **(2)**
10655 Park Run Dr Ste 120, Las Vegas, NV 89144
Tel.: (702) 575-6600
Web Site: http://www.ftnmainstreet.com
Investment Advisory Services
N.A.I.C.S.: 523940

FTN Financial Securities Corp. **(2)**
1000 Ridgeway Loop Rd Ste 200, Memphis, TN 38120
Tel.: (901) 435-8080
Web Site: http://www.ftnfinancial.com
Investment Management Service
N.A.I.C.S.: 523940

Subsidiary (Domestic):

Coastal Securities, Inc. **(3)**
920 Memorial City Way Cobalt Ctr 11th Fl, Houston, TX 77024
Tel.: (713) 435-4300
Web Site: http://www.coastalsecurities.com
Security Brokerage Services
N.A.I.C.S.: 523150
Brian Folk (CFO & Exec VP)

Subsidiary (Domestic):

First Tennessee Brokerage, Inc. **(2)**
165 Madison Ave, Memphis, TN 38103 **(100%)**
Tel.: (901) 523-4883
Web Site: http://www.ftb.com
Sales Range: $1-9.9 Million
Emp.: 75
National Commercial Banks
N.A.I.C.S.: 524210

North Carolina Title Center, LLC **(2)**
118 N Center St, Statesville, NC 28677
Tel.: (704) 873-6500
Web Site: https://www.nctitlecenter.com
Title Insurance Services
N.A.I.C.S.: 524127

Superior Financial Services, Inc. **(2)**
1190 E Andrew Johnson Hwy, Greeneville, TN 37745
Tel.: (423) 787-0300
Web Site: https://yoursuperiorfinance.com
Financial Services
N.A.I.C.S.: 523940

IBERIABANK Corporation **(1)**
200 W Congress St, Lafayette, LA 70501
Tel.: (337) 521-4003
Web Site: http://www.iberiabank.com
Rev.: $1,310,008,000
Assets: $31,713,450,000
Liabilities: $27,376,716,000
Net Worth: $4,336,734,000
Earnings: $384,155,000
Emp.: 3,373
Fiscal Year-end: 12/31/2019
Bank Holding Company
N.A.I.C.S.: 551111
Anthony J. Restel (Chm & CFO)
Michael S. Price (Chief Acctg Officer, Exec VP & Controller)
Jefferson G. Parker (Vice Chm & Dir-Capital Markets, Energy Lending & IR)
Elizabeth A. Ardoin (Sr Exec VP & Dir-Comm, Corp Real Estate & HR)
Terry L. Akins (Chief Risk Officer & Sr Exec VP)

J. Randolph Bryan (Exec VP & Dir-Bus Transformation)
Monica R. Sylvain (Chief Diversity Officer & Exec VP)
Peggy Dold (Sr VP & Dir-Music & Entertainment-IBERIABANK)
Alex Hernandez (Mng Dir-Sports & Entertainment Banking-IBERIABANK)
Robert B. Worley Jr. (Gen Counsel, Sec & Exec VP)

Subsidiary (Domestic):

IBERIABANK   **(2)**
200 W Congress St, Lafayette, LA 70501
Tel.: (337) 521-4886
Web Site: http://www.iberiabank.com
Commericial Banking
N.A.I.C.S.: 522110
Elizabeth A. Ardoin (Chief Comms Officer & Sr Exec VP)

Subsidiary (Domestic):

IBERIABANK Mortgage Company   **(3)**
12719 Cantrell Rd, Little Rock, AR 72223
Tel.: (501) 537-8400
Web Site:
    http://www.iberiabankmortgage.com
Mortgage Banking Services
N.A.I.C.S.: 522292

Iberia Financial Services, LLC   **(3)**
200 W Congress St, Lafayette, LA 70501   **(100%)**
Web Site: http://www.iberiabank.com
Securities & Other Financial Products & Investment Advisory Services
N.A.I.C.S.: 523940

Mercantile Capital Corporation   **(3)**
60 N Ct Ave Ste 200, Orlando, FL 32801
Tel.: (407) 786-5040
Web Site: http://www.504experts.com
Emp.: 16
Financial Lending
N.A.I.C.S.: 522310
Dawn DeTomaso (Sr VP & Mgr-Closing)

Martin & Company, Inc.   **(1)**
625 S Gay St Ste 200, Knoxville, TN 37902
Tel.: (865) 541-4747
Web Site: https://www.martin-co.com
Emp.: 11
Investment Management Service
N.A.I.C.S.: 523940

FIRST IC BANK
5593 Buford Hwy, Doraville, GA 30340
Tel.: (770) 451-7200   **GA**
Web Site: https://www.firsticbank.com
Year Founded: 2000
FIEB—(OTCIQ)
Commercial Banking Services
N.A.I.C.S.: 522110

FIRST INDUSTRIAL REALTY TRUST, INC.
1 N Wacker Dr Ste 4200, Chicago, IL 60606
Tel.: (312) 344-4300   **MD**
Web Site:
    https://www.firstindustrial.com
Year Founded: 1994
FR—(NYSE)
Rev.: $614,027,000
Assets: $5,175,765,000
Liabilities: $2,540,660,000
Net Worth: $2,635,105,000
Earnings: $274,584,000
Emp.: 156
Fiscal Year-end: 12/31/23
Real Estate Investment Trust
N.A.I.C.S.: 525990
Johannson L. Yap (Founder & Chief Investment Officer)
Christopher M. Schneider (CIO & Sr VP-Ops)
Donald Stoffle (Exec Dir-Dispositions)
Jeffrey Thomas (Sr Dir-Pennsylvania & Baltimore)
Arthur Harmon (VP-IR & Mktg)

Robert L. Denton Sr. (Co-Founder)
Peter O. Schultz (Exec VP-East)
Robert J. Walter (Sr VP-Capital Markets & Asset Mgmt)
Peter E. Baccile (Pres & CEO)
Sara E. Niemiec (Chief Acctg Officer)
Valerie Baxa (VP-Environmental)
Adam Moore (Sr Dir-Milwaukee)
John Wyeth (VP-Ops-East)
John Quinn (Dir-Northern California & Seattle)
Jennifer Matthews Rice (Gen Counsel)
Thomas Civitanova (VP-Ops-Central)
Jon Raleigh (VP-Insurance & Risk Mgmt)
Jerry Devon (Dir)
John Hanlon (Exec Dir)
Jim Schlundt (Dir)

Subsidiaries:

First Industrial Financing Partnership, L.P.   **(1)**
1 N Wacker Dr Site 4200, Chicago, IL 60606-6678
Tel.: (312) 344-4300
Property Management Services
N.A.I.C.S.: 525990

First Industrial L.P.   **(1)**
1 N Wacker Dr Site 4200, Chicago, IL 60606
Tel.: (312) 344-4300
Web Site: http://www.firstindustrial.com
Rev.: $614,026,999
Assets: $5,175,764,999
Liabilities: $2,540,659,999
Net Worth: $2,635,104,999
Earnings: $285,837,000
Emp.: 156
Fiscal Year-end: 12/31/2023
Real Estate Finance & Insurance Services
N.A.I.C.S.: 531390
Jennifer Matthews Rice (Corp Counsel)
Robert Walter (Sr VP)
Johannson Yap (Chief Investment Officer)
Peter Schultz (Exec VP)
Scott Musil (CFO)
Christopher Schneider (CIO)
Sara Niemiec (Chief Acctg Officer)
Valerie Baxa (VP)
Arthur Harmon (VP)
John Wyeth (VP)
Thomas Civitanova (VP)
Jon Raleigh (VP)

FIRST INTERNET BANCORP
8701 E 116th St, Fishers, IN 46038
Tel.: (317) 532-7900   **IN**
Web Site:
    https://www.firstinternetbancorp.com
Year Founded: 1999
INBK—(NASDAQ)
Rev.: $178,165,000
Assets: $4,543,104,000
Liabilities: $4,178,130,000
Net Worth: $364,974,000
Earnings: $35,541,000
Emp.: 314
Fiscal Year-end: 12/31/22
Bank Holding Company
N.A.I.C.S.: 551111
Kenneth J. Lovik (CFO & Exec VP)
David B. Becker (Chm & CEO)
Nicole S. Lorch (Pres & COO)
John K. Keach Jr. (Vice Chm)

Subsidiaries:

First Internet Bank of Indiana   **(1)**
8701 E 116th St, Fishers, IN 46038
Tel.: (317) 532-7900
Web Site: https://www.firstib.com
Banking Services
N.A.I.C.S.: 522110
David B. Becker (Chm & CEO)
Nicole S. Lorch (Pres & COO)
Timothy C. Dusing (Sr VP-Pub Fin)
Kevin B. Quinn (Sr VP-Retail Lending)
Tom Smith (Reg VP)
Anne Sharkey (Sr VP-Ops)

Maris J. Kancs (Dir-Single Tenant Lease Financing & First VP)
Deepu Sondhe (Asst VP & Mgr-Customer Rels)
Nick Campbell (VP & Mgr-Customer Rels)
Craig Fortner (CIO & Sr VP)
Justin Karvasky (First VP-Finance)
Nick Simulia (First VP-Mktg)
Sam Criales (VP)
Ben Woodward (VP)
Ryan Kroge (VP)
Jared Johnson (VP)
Ryan Hasher (VP-Commercial Banking)
Will Tinsley (VP-Small Bus Admin Lending)

FIRST INTERSTATE BANCSYSTEM, INC.
401 N 31st St, Billings, MT 59101
Tel.: (406) 255-5000   **MT**
Web Site: https://www.fibk.com
Year Founded: 1968
FIBK—(NASDAQ)
Rev.: $1,184,700,000
Assets: $32,287,800,000
Liabilities: $29,214,000,000
Net Worth: $3,073,800,000
Earnings: $202,200,000
Emp.: 3,783
Fiscal Year-end: 12/31/22
Bank Holding Company
N.A.I.C.S.: 551111
Lorrie L. Asker (Chief Banking Officer & Exec VP)
Kevin P. Riley (Pres & CEO)
Rachel B. Turitto (Chief HR Officer & Sr VP)
Lori A. Meyer (CIO & Exec VP)
Marcy D. Mutch (CFO & Exec VP)
Karlyn M. Knieriem (Chief Risk Officer & Exec VP)
Kirk D. Jensen (Gen Counsel, Sec & Exec VP)

Subsidiaries:

First Interstate Bank   **(1)**
2501 Central Ave, Billings, MT 59102
Tel.: (406) 255-6100
Web Site:
    https://www.firstinterstatebank.com
Commercial Banking Services
N.A.I.C.S.: 522110

FIRST KEYSTONE CORPORATION
111 W Front St, Berwick, PA 18603-0289
Tel.: (570) 752-3671   **PA**
Web Site: https://www.fkyscorp.com
Year Founded: 1983
FKYS—(OTCIQ)
Rev.: $51,744,000
Assets: $1,329,194,000
Liabilities: $1,208,808,000
Net Worth: $120,386,000
Earnings: $14,024,000
Emp.: 200
Fiscal Year-end: 12/31/22
Bank Holding Companies
N.A.I.C.S.: 551111
John E. Arndt (Vice Chm)
David R. Saracino (Sec)
Elaine A. Woodland (Pres & CEO)
Diane C. A. Rosler (CFO & Sr VP)
Christopher Zlobik (Chief Banking Officer)
Jonathan R. Littlewood (Chief Lending Officer & Sr VP)
Mark James McDonald (Chief Credit Officer & Sr VP)

Subsidiaries:

First Keystone Community Bank   **(1)**
111 W Front St, Berwick, PA 18603
Tel.: (570) 752-3671
Web Site: https://www.fkc.bank
Sales Range: $25-49.9 Million
Emp.: 131
Banking Services
N.A.I.C.S.: 522110

John E. Arndt (Vice Chm)
Robert A. Bull (Chm)
David R. Saracino (Sec)
Elaine A. Woodland (Pres & CEO)
Diane C. A. Rosler (CFO & Sr VP)
Mark McDonald (Chief Credit Officer & Sr VP)
Jeff Wozniak (Officer-Information Security, Sr VP & Mgr-IT)
Jonathan R. Littlewood (Chief Lending Officer & VP)

FIRST MERCHANTS CORPORATION
200 E Jackson St, Muncie, IN 47305
Tel.: (765) 747-1500   **IN**
Web Site:
    https://www.firstmerchants.com
Year Founded: 1982
FRME—(NASDAQ)
Rev.: $712,947,000
Assets: $17,938,306,000
Liabilities: $15,903,536,000
Net Worth: $2,034,770,000
Earnings: $222,089,000
Emp.: 2,124
Fiscal Year-end: 12/31/22
Offices of Bank Holding Companies
N.A.I.C.S.: 551111
Mark K. Hardwick (CEO)
Michael C. Rechin (Vice Chm)
Michael J. Stewart (Pres, Chief Banking Officer & Exec VP)
Stephan H. Fluhler (CIO & Sr VP)
John J. Martin (Chief Credit Officer & Exec VP)
Michele M. Kawiecki (Principal Fin & Acctg Officer & Exec VP)
Chad W. Kimball (Chief Risk Officer)

Subsidiaries:

First Merchants Bank   **(1)**
200 E Jackson St, Muncie, IN 47305-2835
Tel.: (765) 741-7278
Web Site: https://www.firstmerchants.com
Sales Range: $500-549.9 Million
Emp.: 1,887
Commericial Banking
N.A.I.C.S.: 522110
Mark K. Hardwick (CEO)
Michael C. Rechin (Vice Chm)
Michael J. Stewart (Chief Banking Officer & Exec VP)
Jadira Hoptry (Dir-Community Lending & Dev)

FIRST MID BANCSHARES, INC.
Tel.: (217) 234-7454   **DE**
Web Site: https://www.firstmid.com
Year Founded: 1981
FMBH—(NASDAQ)
Rev.: $215,891,000
Assets: $6,744,215,000
Liabilities: $6,111,060,000
Net Worth: $633,155,000
Earnings: $72,952,000
Emp.: 1,070
Fiscal Year-end: 12/31/22
Bank Holding Company
N.A.I.C.S.: 551111
Joseph R. Dively (Chm, Pres & CEO)
Clay M. Dean (CEO-First Mid Insurance Grp & Exec VP)
Michael L. Taylor (Co-COO & Sr Exec VP)
Laurel G. Allenbaugh (Co-COO & Exec VP)
Bradley L. Beesley (CEO-First Mid Wealth Mgmt & Exec VP)
Amanda D. Lewis (Chief Deposit Svcs Officer & Exec VP)
Matthew K. Smith (CFO & Exec VP)
David R. Hiden (CIO & Sr VP)

First Mid Bancshares, Inc.—(Continued)

Jason M. Crowder *(Gen Counsel & Sr VP)*
Jordan Read *(Chief Risk Officer)*
Megan McElwee *(Chief Credit Officer)*

Subsidiaries:

Blackhawk Bancorp Inc.   **(1)**
400 Broad St, Beloit, WI 53512-0719
Tel.: (608) 364-8911
Web Site: http://www.blackhawkbank.com
Sales Range: $25-49.9 Million
Emp.: 176
Bank Holding Company
N.A.I.C.S.: 551111

Subsidiary (Domestic):

Blackhawk State Bank   **(2)**
400 Broad St, Beloit, WI 53511
Tel.: (608) 364-8911
Web Site: http://www.blackhawkbank.com
Sales Range: $10-24.9 Million
Emp.: 200
State Commercial Banks
N.A.I.C.S.: 522110

Delta Bancshares Company   **(1)**
2301 Market St, Saint Louis, MO 63103-2541
Tel.: (314) 621-0100
Sales Range: $25-49.9 Million
Emp.: 65
Bank Holding Company
N.A.I.C.S.: 551111
Michael Ross *(Chm)*
Bradley A. Locke *(CFO & Sr VP)*
Dennis Ballinger *(Pres)*
Marilyn J. Oberkramer *(Sec)*
John Dulle *(VP)*

Subsidiary (Domestic):

Jefferson Bank & Trust Company   **(2)**
2301 Market St, Saint Louis, MO 63103
Tel.: (314) 621-0100
Web Site: http://www.jbt-stl.com
Sales Range: $75-99.9 Million
Emp.: 50
Retail & Commercial Banking Services
N.A.I.C.S.: 522180
Bradley A. Locke *(CFO & Exec VP)*
Richard A. Dreiling *(Compliance Officer & VP)*
Marilyn J. Oberkramer *(COO & Sr VP)*
John L. Dulle *(Pres & CEO)*
Stephen M. Bynum *(Sr VP)*
Jerry S. Von Rohr *(Sr VP)*
Patrick G. Higgins *(Sr VP-Creve Coeur)*
Mark C. Lafata *(Sr VP)*
Robert D. Joseph Jr. *(Sr VP)*

First Mid Bank & Trust, N.A.   **(1)**
1515 Charleston Ave, Mattoon, IL 61938
Tel.: (217) 258-0653
Web Site: http://www.firstmid.com
Savings Bank
N.A.I.C.S.: 522180
Joseph R. Dively *(Chm & CEO)*
Michael L. Taylor *(COO & Sr Exec VP)*
Laurel G. Allenbaugh *(Chief Ops Officer & Exec VP)*
Eric S. McRae *(Chief Credit Officer & Exec VP)*
Christopher L. Slabach *(Chief Risk Officer & Sr VP)*
Bradley L. Beesley *(CEO-First Mid Wealth Mgmt & Exec VP)*
Rhonda R. Gatons *(Chief HR Officer & Sr VP)*
Amanda D. Lewis *(Chief Deposit Svcs Officer & Exec VP)*
Matthew K. Smith *(CFO & Exec VP)*
David R. Hiden *(CIO & Sr VP)*

First Mid Insurance Group, Inc.   **(1)**
1520 Charleston Ave, Mattoon, IL 61938
Tel.: (217) 877-3344
Commercial Banking Services
N.A.I.C.S.: 522110

Subsidiary (Domestic):

Purdum Gray Ingledue Beck, Inc.   **(2)**
215 E Jackson St, Macomb, IL 61455
Tel.: (309) 833-1755

Web Site: http://www.macombinsurance.com
Insurance Related Activities
N.A.I.C.S.: 524298
Beau Ingledue *(Partner & VP)*

The Checkley Agency, Inc.   **(1)**
1520 Charleston Ave, Mattoon, IL 61938-3933
Tel.: (217) 877-3344
Web Site: http://www.firstmidinsurance.com
Commercial Banking Services
N.A.I.C.S.: 522110

FIRST NATIONAL BANK ALASKA

101 W 36th Ave, Anchorage, AK 99503-5904
Tel.: (907) 777-4362
Web Site: https://www.fnbalaska.com
FBAK—(OTCIQ)
Rev.: $174,837,000
Assets: $4,695,315,000
Liabilities: $4,108,726,000
Net Worth: $586,589,000
Earnings: $57,535,000
Emp.: 619
Fiscal Year-end: 12/31/20
National Commercial Banks
N.A.I.C.S.: 522110
Craig Thorn *(Sr VP & Reg Mgr-Branch)*
Doug Longacre *(Pres)*
Phil Griffin *(CIO & Exec VP)*
Michele M. Schuh *(CFO & Exec VP)*
Betsy Lawer *(Chm, Pres & CEO)*
Lucy Mahan *(Vice Chm)*
Cheri Gillian *(Chief Admin Officer & Exec VP)*
Ryan Strong *(Chief Banking Officer & Exec VP)*
Mike Scott *(Officer-Loan)*
Sheila Lomboy *(Officer-Loan)*
Cindi Buzitis *(Chief Compliance Officer & Exec VP)*
Darren Franz *(Chief Corp Lending Officer & Exec VP)*
Rick Flake *(Sr VP & Dir-Corp Svcs)*
Karl Heinz *(Sr VP & Dir-Branch Admin)*
Dustin Hofeling *(Sr VP & Dir-IT Sys & Support)*
Pamela Keeler *(Sr VP)*
Elaine Kroll *(Sr VP-Cash Mgmt & Dir-Anchorage Branch Admin)*
Chad Steadman *(Sr VP & Dir-Corp Lending)*
Stacy Tomuro *(Sr VP & Dir-Specialty Lending)*
Quinn Anderson *(Officer-Loan)*
Laura Asgari *(Officer-Investment Mgmt)*
Joe Donahue *(Officer-Loan)*
Ken Hanley *(Officer-Loan)*
Zac Hays *(Officer-Loan)*
Nichole Kennedy *(Officer-Investments Mgmt)*
Ligia Lutan *(Officer-Loan)*
Tinka Nasufi *(Branch Mgr-Ops)*
Jake Parrish *(Officer-Loan)*
Melissa Reiser *(Officer-Loan)*
Lydia Sobek *(Officer-Loan)*
Shin Suzuki *(Officer-Loan)*
Renne Marsjanik *(Sr VP & Dir-Wealth Mgmt)*
Steven Patin *(Sr VP & Dir-HR)*
Dunbar Anders *(Officer-Loan)*
Sean Brown *(Mgr-Treasury Mgmt)*
Darin Floyd *(Officer-Loan)*
Erica Skiff *(Sls Mgr-Treasury Mgmt)*

FIRST NATIONAL BANK OF GROTON

161 Main St, Groton, NY 13073
Tel.: (607) 898-5871   NY
Web Site: http://www.grotonbank.com
FIGR—(OTCIQ)

Commercial Banking Services
N.A.I.C.S.: 522110
Alan Christopher *(Sr VP)*
Stephen Gobel *(Pres & CEO)*
Kathleen Barnes *(Sr VP-Audit & Compliance)*
Andrew Gobel *(CFO & Sr VP)*
Karen Whatman *(Asst VP-Ops)*

FIRST NATIONAL CORPORATION

300 Ledgewood Pl Ste 101, Rockland, MA 02370
Tel.: (540) 465-9121   VA
Web Site: https://www.fncadvisor.com
FXNC—(NASDAQ)
Rev.: $62,016,000
Assets: $1,369,383,000
Liabilities: $1,261,023,000
Net Worth: $108,360,000
Earnings: $16,797,000
Emp.: 215
Fiscal Year-end: 12/31/22
Bank Holding Company
N.A.I.C.S.: 551111
Scott C. Harvard *(Pres & CEO)*
M. Shane Bell *(CFO & Exec VP)*
Gerald F. Smith Jr. *(Vice Chm & Sec)*

Subsidiaries:

First Bank   **(1)**
112 W King St, Strasburg, VA 22657
Tel.: (540) 465-9121
Web Site: https://www.fbvirginia.com
State Commercial Bank Services
N.A.I.C.S.: 522110
Elizabeth H. Cottrell *(Chm)*
Scott C. Harvard *(Executives)*

Division (Domestic):

The Bank of Fincastle   **(2)**
17 S Roanoke St, Fincastle, VA 24090
Tel.: (540) 473-2761
Web Site: http://www.bankoffincastle.bank
Commericial Banking
N.A.I.C.S.: 522110
George Edwin Holt III *(Executives, Bd of Dirs)*

FIRST NILES FINANCIAL, INC.

Tel.: (330) 652-2539   DE
Year Founded: 1998
FNFI—(OTCIQ)
Sales Range: $1-9.9 Million
Emp.: 13
Bank Holding Company
N.A.I.C.S.: 551111
P. James Kramer *(Chm)*
Mary Ann Coates *(CFO)*
Ray Calcagni *(VP-Expl)*
Raymond J. Calcagni *(VP-Exploration)*

Subsidiaries:

Home Federal Savings and Loan Association of Niles   **(1)**
55 N Main St, Niles, OH 44446   **(100%)**
Tel.: (330) 652-2539
Web Site: http://www.homefedniles.com
Sales Range: $125-149.9 Million
Emp.: 12
Commericial Banking
N.A.I.C.S.: 522110
Daniel Csontos *(Pres)*

Union Capital Mortgage Corporation   **(1)**
7676 Reynolds Rd, Mentor, OH 44060
Tel.: (440) 585-5626
Web Site: http://www.unioncapmtgs.com
Rev.: $3,500,000
Emp.: 20
Real Estate Credit
N.A.I.C.S.: 522292
Ronald M. Szuch *(Pres & CEO)*

FIRST NORTHERN COMMUNITY BANCORP

195 N 1st St, Dixon, CA 95620

Tel.: (707) 678-3041   CA
Web Site: https://www.thatsmybank.com
Year Founded: 2000
FNRN—(OTCQX)
Rev.: $62,815,000
Assets: $1,871,361,000
Liabilities: $1,746,321,000
Net Worth: $125,040,000
Earnings: $15,884,000
Emp.: 192
Fiscal Year-end: 12/31/22
Bank Holding Company
N.A.I.C.S.: 551111
Jeremiah Z. Smith *(Pres & CEO)*
Sean P. Quinn *(Vice Chm)*
Kevin M. Spink *(CFO & Exec VP)*
Amanda Connell *(Sr VP-Ops Admin)*
Libby Feyh *(Chief HR Officer, Exec VP & Sr VP)*
Brett Hamilton *(Chief Credit Officer & Exec VP)*

Subsidiaries:

First Northern Bank of Dixon   **(1)**
195 N 1st St, Dixon, CA 95620
Tel.: (707) 678-4422
Web Site: https://www.thatsmybank.com
Commercial Banking Services
N.A.I.C.S.: 522110
Jeremiah Z. Smith *(Pres & CEO)*
Sean P. Quinn *(Vice Chm)*
Kevin M. Spink *(CFO & Exec VP)*
Amanda Connell *(Sr VP-Ops Admin)*
Denise Burris *(CIO & Exec VP)*
Jeffrey Adamski *(Sr Loan Officer & Exec VP)*
Libby Feyh *(Sr Vp & Dir-HR)*
Kevin M. Spink *(CFO & Exec VP)*
Brett Hamilton *(Chief Credit Officer)*
Mike Webber *(Sr VP)*

FIRST NORTHWEST BANCORP

Tel.: (360) 457-0461   WA
Web Site: https://www.ourfirstfed.com
Year Founded: 2012
FNWB—(NASDAQ)
Rev.: $90,705,000
Assets: $2,042,070,000
Liabilities: $1,883,788,000
Net Worth: $158,282,000
Earnings: $15,645,000
Emp.: 285
Fiscal Year-end: 12/31/22
Bank Holding Company
N.A.I.C.S.: 551111
Stephen E. Oliver *(Chm)*
Christopher J. Riffle *(Chief Digital Officer & Gen Counsel)*
Matthew P. Deines *(Pres & CEO)*
Terry Anderson *(Chief Credit Officer & Exec VP)*
Geraldine L. Bullard *(CFO, COO, Treas & Exec VP)*
Derek J. Brown *(Chief HR & Mktg Officer & Exec VP)*
Sherilyn G. Anderson *(Vice Chm)*

Subsidiaries:

First Federal Savings & Loan Association of Port Angeles   **(1)**
105 W 8th St, Port Angeles, WA 98362
Tel.: (360) 417-3204
Web Site: http://www.ourfirstfed.com
Sales Range: $25-49.9 Million
Emp.: 225
Savings Bank
N.A.I.C.S.: 522180
Stephen E. Oliver *(Chm)*
Matthew P. Deines *(Pres & CEO)*
Derek Brown *(Chief HR & Mktg Officer & Exec VP)*
Jennifer Bolton *(Sr VP & Sr Dir-Digital Mktg)*

FIRST PET LIFE, INC.

2807 Allen St Ste 664, Dallas, TX 75204

Tel.: (214) 202-8580   TX
Year Founded: 2005
FPLF—(OTCIQ)
Pet Care Services
N.A.I.C.S.: 812910
Andre D. Williams *(Pres & CEO)*
Allan Conner *(VP)*

FIRST REAL ESTATE INVEST-MENT TRUST NEW JERSEY CO.

505 Main St Ste 400, Hackensack, NJ 07601
Tel.: (201) 488-6400
Web Site: https://www.freitnj.com
FREVS—(OTCIQ)
Rev.: $28,344,000
Assets: $159,115,000
Liabilities: $140,639,000
Net Worth: $18,476,000
Earnings: $760,000
Emp.: 21
Fiscal Year-end: 10/31/23
Other Financial Vehicles
N.A.I.C.S.: 525990
Ronald J. Artinian *(Chm)*
Allan Tubin *(CFO & Treas)*
John A. Aiello *(Sec)*
Robert S. Hekemian Jr. *(Pres & CEO)*

Subsidiaries:

Damascus Centre, LLC   (1)
505 Main St Ste 400, Hackensack, NJ 07601
Tel.: (201) 488-6400
Real Estate Investment Services
N.A.I.C.S.: 531210

Station Place on Monmouth, LLC (1)
145 Monmouth St, Red Bank, NJ 07701
Tel.: (201) 890-5447
Web Site:
http://www.stationplaceapartments.com
Real Estate Services
N.A.I.C.S.: 531390

FIRST RELIANCE BANCSHARES, INC.

2170 W Palmetto St, Florence, SC 29501
Tel.: (843) 656-5000   SC
Web Site:
https://www.firstreliance.com
Year Founded: 2001
FSRL—(OTCIQ)
Rev.: $50,331,145
Assets: $710,167,544
Liabilities: $641,439,691
Net Worth: $68,727,853
Earnings: $10,616,150
Emp.: 185
Fiscal Year-end: 12/31/20
Bank Holding Company
N.A.I.C.S.: 551111
Paul C. Saunders *(Co-Founder, Officer-Retail Banking & VP-First Reliance Bank)*
A. Dale Porter *(Co-Founder)*
F. Rick Saunders Jr. *(Co-Founder, CEO & CEO-First Reliance Bank)*
Jeffrey A. Paolucci *(Chief Risk Officer)*
Ben Brazell *(Chief Admin Officer & Exec VP-First Reliance Bank)*
Jack McElveen *(Exec VP-First Reliance Bank)*
Chuck Stuart *(Pres-First Reliance Mortgage)*
David Hall *(Exec VP-Dealer Svcs-First Reliance Bank)*
Robert Haile *(CFO & Sr VP)*
Brook Moore *(Chief Credit Officer & Sr VP)*
Jeremy Groom *(Exec VP-Compliance & Risk Management)*

Keith Rainwater *(Chief Acctg Officer & Exec VP)*
Leslie Chaplin *(Exec VP & Dir-Human Resources)*
John Lindley *(Sr VP & Dir-Operations)*
Robert Mayhue *(Sr VP-Information Technology)*

Subsidiaries:

First Reliance Bank   (1)
2170 W Palmetto St, Florence, SC 29501
Tel.: (843) 656-5000
Web Site: http://www.firstreliance.com
Commercial Banking
N.A.I.C.S.: 522110
Paul C. Saunders *(Co-Founder, Retail Banking Officer & VP)*
A. Dale Porter *(Co-Founder)*
F. Rick Saunders Jr. *(Co-Founder, Pres & CEO)*
Jeffrey A. Paolucci *(CFO, Sec & Exec VP)*
Jack McElveen *(Chief Credit Officer)*
Pam Anderson *(Chief Culture Officer)*
Chuck Stuart *(Exec VP-Mortgage Banking)*
David Hall *(Sr VP-Indirect Auto Fin & Consumer Lending)*
Jimmy Clarkson *(Pres-Myrtle Beach/Loris Market)*
Thomas C. Ewart *(Pres-Florence Market)*
Richard McIntyre *(Pres-Lexington Market)*
Ben Brazell *(Pres-Charleston Market)*

FIRST RESERVE SUSTAINABLE GROWTH CORP.

290 Harbor Dr 5th Fl, Stamford, CT 06902
Tel.: (713) 227-7890   DE
Web Site: http://www.frsgcorp.com
Year Founded: 2021
FRSGU—(NASDAQ)
Emp.: 3
Investment Services
N.A.I.C.S.: 523999
Alex Townsend Krueger *(Chm)*
Thomas S. Amburgey *(CFO)*
Neil A. Wizel *(CEO)*

FIRST ROBINSON FINANCIAL CORPORATION

501 E Main St, Robinson, IL 62454
Tel.: (618) 544-8621   DE
Web Site: http://www.frsb.net
FRFC—(OTCIQ)
Rev.: $16,569,000
Assets: $344,772,000
Liabilities: $314,207,000
Net Worth: $30,565,000
Earnings: $3,304,000
Emp.: 80
Fiscal Year-end: 03/31/20
Bank Holding Company
N.A.I.C.S.: 551111

Subsidiaries:

First Robinson Savings Bank
N.A.   (1)
501 E Main St, Robinson, IL 62454
Tel.: (618) 544-8621
Web Site: http://www.frsb.net
Sales Range: $25-49.9 Million
Emp.: 60
Commercial Banking
N.A.I.C.S.: 522110
Mark Hill *(Chief Lending Officer & VP)*
Tasha Briggs *(Officer-Mortgage Loan, Asst VP & Supvr-Underwriting)*
Cris Harris *(Officer-Comml & Ag Loan)*
Jamey Tingley *(Officer-Comml Loan)*
Rhonda Manship *(Officer-Mortgage Loan)*
Kylie Veach *(Officer-Mortgage Loan)*
Wesley Veach *(Officer-Mortgage Loan)*
Koert Mehler *(Officer-Comml Loan)*

FIRST SAVINGS FINANCIAL GROUP, INC.

702 N Shore Dr Ste 300, Jeffersonville, IN 47130
Tel.: (812) 283-0724   IN
Web Site: https://www.fsbbank.net

FSFG—(NASDAQ)
Rev.: $128,571,000
Assets: $2,288,854,000
Liabilities: $2,137,873,000
Net Worth: $150,981,000
Earnings: $8,172,000
Emp.: 370
Fiscal Year-end: 09/30/23
Bank Holding Company
N.A.I.C.S.: 551111
Larry W. Myers *(Pres & CEO)*
Anthony A. Schoen *(CFO)*
John E. Colin *(Chm)*
Martin A. Padgett *(Vice Chm)*
Jacqueline R. Journell *(COO)*

Subsidiaries:

First Savings Bank   (1)
501 E Lewis Clark Pkwy, Clarksville, IN 47129   (100%)
Tel.: (812) 283-0724
Web Site: http://www.fsbbank.net
Rev.: $12,850,000
Emp.: 23
Commercial Banking
N.A.I.C.S.: 522110
Larry W. Myers *(Pres & CEO)*
John E. Colin *(Chm)*
John P. Lawson Jr. *(Executives, Bd of Dirs)*
William Eric Howard *(Chief Lending Officer & Exec VP)*
Marie Haley *(Chief Retail Officer & Exec VP)*
Derrick B. Jackson *(Chief Credit Officer & Exec VP)*
Tony Schoen *(CFO)*
Jackie Journell *(COO)*
Len Basham *(CIO)*
Jim Nelson *(Chief Risk Officer)*
Jim Valete *(Chief SBA Lending Officer)*
Kent Parisien *(Pres)*

Subsidiary (Domestic):

First Savings Investments, Inc.   (2)
3993 Howard Hughes Pkwy Ste 250, Las Vegas, NV 89169-6754
Tel.: (702) 369-2875
Investment Management Service
N.A.I.C.S.: 523940

FIRST SEACOAST BANCORP, INC.

633 Central Ave, Dover, NH 03820
Tel.: (603) 742-4680   MD
Web Site:
https://www.firstseacoastbank.com
Year Founded: 2022
FSEA—(NASDAQ)
Rev.: $20,590,000
Assets: $571,035,000
Liabilities: $504,417,000
Net Worth: $66,618,000
Earnings: ($10,656,000)
Emp.: 76
Fiscal Year-end: 12/31/23
Offices of Bank Holding Companies
N.A.I.C.S.: 551111
Michael J. Bolduc *(Sec)*
James R. Brannen *(Pres & CEO)*
Paula J. Williamson-Reid *(Vice Chm)*

Subsidiaries:

First Seacoast Bank   (1)
633 Central Ave, Dover, NH 03820
Tel.: (603) 742-4680
Web Site: http://www.firstseacoastbank.com
Rev.: $15,814,000
Assets: $387,114,000
Liabilities: $354,387,000
Net Worth: $32,727,000
Earnings: $1,081,000
Emp.: 75
Fiscal Year-end: 12/31/2018
Federal Savings Bank
N.A.I.C.S.: 522180
James R. Brannen *(Pres & CEO)*
Jean Tremblay *(Officer-Retail Loan & VP)*

FIRST SOLAR, INC.

350 W Washington St Ste 600, Tempe, AZ 85281

Tel.: (419) 662-6899   DE
Web Site: https://www.firstsolar.com
Year Founded: 1999
FSLR—(NASDAQ)
Rev.: $3,318,602,000
Assets: $10,365,132,000
Liabilities: $3,677,663,000
Net Worth: $6,687,469,000
Earnings: $830,777,000
Emp.: 6,700
Fiscal Year-end: 12/31/23
Thin Film Semiconductor Solar Modules Designer & Mfr
N.A.I.C.S.: 334413
Alexander R. Bradley *(CFO)*
Caroline Stockdale *(Chief People & Comm Officer)*
Pat Buehler *(Chief Quality & Reliability Officer)*
Markus Gloeckler *(CTO)*
Jason Dymbort *(Gen Counsel & Sec)*
Georges J. Antoun *(Pres)*
Benyamin Buller *(Founder-Device Physics Team)*
Mark R. Widmar *(CEO)*

Subsidiaries:

First Solar (Australia) Pty Ltd   (1)
Level 3 16 Spring Street, Sydney, 2000, NSW, Australia
Tel.: (61) 290027700
Solar Electric Power Generation Services
N.A.I.C.S.: 221114
Jack Curtis *(Mgr-Asia Pacific)*

First Solar Asset Management, LLC   (1)
350 W Washington St Ste 600, Tempe, AZ 85281
Tel.: (602) 414-9300
Solar Electric Power Generation Services
N.A.I.C.S.: 221114
Corey Carson *(Mgr-Fin)*

First Solar Electrico (Chile) SpA   (1)
Av Apoquindo 3472, 9th floor Edificio Patio Foster Las Condes, Santiago, Chile
Tel.: (56) 225947590
Solar Electric Power Generation Services
N.A.I.C.S.: 221114

First Solar GmbH   (1)
Ludwigsstr 6, 55116, Mainz, Germany
Tel.: (49) 61318945267
Solar Panel Component Mfr
N.A.I.C.S.: 221118

First Solar Japan GK   (1)
3-2-5 Kasumigaseki, Chiyoda-ku, Tokyo, 100-6031, Japan
Tel.: (81) 355320480
Electronic Parts & Equipment Distr
N.A.I.C.S.: 423690

First Solar Malaysia Sdn. Bhd.   (1)
Lot PT 2486 First Solar Boulevard Zon Industri Fasa 3, Kulim Hi-Tech Park, 09000, Kulim, 09000, Malaysia
Tel.: (60) 44016888
Web Site: https://www.firstsolar.com
Thin Film Semiconductor Solar Modules Designer & Mfr
N.A.I.C.S.: 334413

First Solar Power India Pvt Ltd   (1)
808 8th Floor Narayan Manzil 23, Barakamba Road, New Delhi, 110001, India
Tel.: (91) 1166543730
Web Site: http://www.firstsolor.com
Solar Electric Power Generation Services
N.A.I.C.S.: 221114

FIRST SOUND BANK

925 4th Ave Ste 2350, Seattle, WA 98104
Tel.: (206) 515-2004   WA
Web Site:
http://www.firstsoundbank.com
Year Founded: 2004
FSWA—(OTCIQ)
Rev.: $5,348,000
Assets: $149,535,000

847

First Sound Bank—(Continued)

Liabilities: $136,169,000
Net Worth: $13,366,000
Earnings: ($206,000)
Emp.: 18
Fiscal Year-end: 12/31/20
Commercial Banking Services
N.A.I.C.S.: 522110
Steven J. Schwartz (Chm)
Tammy J. Hanson (COO & Exec VP)
Martin A. Steele (Pres & CEO)
Steven Evans (Chief Lending Officer & Exec VP)
Debby K. McDaniel (CFO & Exec VP)
Elliott Pierce (Chief Credit Officer & Exec VP)

FIRST TRUST ABERDEEN EMERGING OPPORTUNITY FUND
120 E Liberty Dr Ste 400, Wheaton, IL 60187
Tel.: (630) 765-8000   MA
FEO—(NYSE)
Investment Management Service
N.A.I.C.S.: 525990
Devan Kaloo (Mgr-Fund)

FIRST TRUST ENERGY INCOME & GROWTH FUND
120 E Liberty Dr Ste 400, Wheaton, IL 60187
Tel.: (630) 765-8000
FEN—(NYSEAMEX)
Fund Management Services
N.A.I.C.S.: 523940
James Jarvis Murchie (Mgr-Fund)

FIRST TRUST ENHANCED EQUITY INCOME FUND
120 E Liberty Dr Ste 400, Wheaton, IL 60187
Tel.: (630) 765-8000   MA
FFA—(NYSE)
Investment Management Service
N.A.I.C.S.: 525990

FIRST TRUST HIGH INCOME LONG/SHORT FUND
120 E Liberty Dr Ste 400, Wheaton, IL 60187
Tel.: (630) 765-8000   MA
FSD—(NYSE)
Fund Management Services
N.A.I.C.S.: 523940

FIRST TRUST INTER DUR PREF& INCOME FUND
120 E Liberty Dr Ste 400, Wheaton, IL 60187
Tel.: (630) 765-8000   MA
FPF—(NYSE)
Investment Management Service
N.A.I.C.S.: 525990

FIRST TRUST NEW OPPORTUNITIES MLP & ENERGY FUND
120 E Liberty Dr Ste 400, Wheaton, Il 60187
Tel.: (630) 765-8000
FPL—(NYSE)
Fund Management Services
N.A.I.C.S.: 523940
James Martin Dykas (Mgr-Fund)

FIRST TRUST SENIOR FLOATING RATE 2022 TARGET TERM FUND
120 E Liberty Dr Ste 400, Wheaton, IL 60187
Tel.: (630) 765-8000
FIV—(NYSE)
Investment Management Service
N.A.I.C.S.: 525990

James Allen Bowen (Chm)
Bill Housey (Mgr-Fund)

FIRST TRUST SENIOR FLOATING RATE INCOME FUND II
120 E Liberty Dr Ste 400, Wheaton, IL 60187
Tel.: (630) 765-8000   MA
FCT—(NYSE)
Fund Management Services
N.A.I.C.S.: 523940
James Allen Bowen (Chm)

FIRST TRUST SPECIALTY FINANCE & FINANCIAL OPPORTUNITIES FUND
120 E Liberty Dr Ste 400, Wheaton, IL 60187
Tel.: (630) 765-8000   MA
FGB—(NYSE)
Rev.: $10,472,965
Assets: $110,288,312
Liabilities: $25,233,837
Net Worth: $85,054,475
Earnings: $8,326,259
Fiscal Year-end: 11/30/19
Investment Management Service
N.A.I.C.S.: 525990

FIRST TRUST/ABRDN GLOBAL OPPORTUNITY INCOME FUND
120 E Liberty Dr Ste 400, Wheaton, IL 60187
Tel.: (630) 765-8000   MA
FAM—(NYSE)
Investment Management Service
N.A.I.C.S.: 525990

FIRST UNITED CORPORATION
12892 Garrett Hwy Ste 4, Oakland, MD 21550   MD
Web Site: https://www.mybank.com
FUNC—(NASDAQ)
Rev.: $62,422,000
Assets: $1,848,169,000
Liabilities: $1,696,376,000
Net Worth: $151,793,000
Earnings: $25,048,000
Emp.: 298
Fiscal Year-end: 12/31/22
Bank Holding Company
N.A.I.C.S.: 551111
Carissa L. Rodeheaver (Chm, Pres & CEO)
Jason B. Rush (COO & Sr VP)
Tonya K. Sturm (CFO, Treas, Sec & Sr VP)
Keith R. Sanders (Officer-Trust & Sr VP)
Robert L. Fisher II (Chief Revenue Officer & Sr VP)

Subsidiaries:

First United Bank & Trust   (1)
12892 Garrett Hwy Ste 4, Oakland, MD 21550
Tel.: (301) 334-9471
Web Site: https://mybank.com
Cales Range: 050-74.9 Million
Emp.: 320
Commercial Banking Services
N.A.I.C.S.: 522110
Carissa L. Rodeheaver (Chm, Pres & CEO)
Jason B. Rush (Dir-Ops & Support & Chief Risk Officer)
Tonya K. Sturm (CFO)
Paula R. Sheffield (Mgr-Community Office-Grantsville)
Phil Rodeheaver (Pres-Grantsville)
Daniel R. Ager (Mgr-Community Relationship-Riverside)
Chuck Olsson (Chief HR Officer & VP)
Denise D. Phelps (VP & Dir-Diversity & Engagement)
Kimberly R. Moyers (VP & Dir-Strategic Initiatives)

Oakfirst Life Insurance Corporation   (1)
19 S 2nd St, Oakland, MD 21550   (100%)
Tel.: (301) 334-9471
Web Site: http://www.mybank4.com
Sales Range: $300-349.9 Million
Emp.: 50
N.A.I.C.S.: 524128

FIRST US BANCSHARES, INC.
3291 US Hwy 280, Birmingham, AL 35243
Tel.: (205) 582-1200   DE
Web Site: https://www.fusb.com
Year Founded: 1983
FUSB—(NASDAQ)
Rev.: $44,648,000
Assets: $994,667,000
Liabilities: $909,532,000
Net Worth: $85,135,000
Earnings: $6,864,000
Emp.: 155
Fiscal Year-end: 12/31/22
Bank Holding Company
N.A.I.C.S.: 551111
James F. House (Vice Chm, Pres & CEO)

Subsidiaries:

Acceptance Loan Co. Inc.   (1)
121 W Church St, Jackson, AL 36545-2718
Tel.: (251) 246-1513
Web Site: http://www.acceptanceloan.com
Rev.: $190,000
Emp.: 5
Loan Broker
N.A.I.C.S.: 522110
Helen Thrash (Pres & CEO)
Candace Gealy (Asst VP & Specialist-Ops)
Sarah Kinney (Reg VP)
Chase Williams (Reg VP)
Bill Parker (Reg VP)

Acceptance Loan Company, Inc.   (1)
3976 Government Blvd Ste A, Mobile, AL 36693
Tel.: (251) 661-5776
Consumer Lending Services
N.A.I.C.S.: 522291
Chris Mitchell (Pres & CEO)
Sarah Kinney (Mgr)
Chris Goodrich (CFO & VP)

First US Bank   (1)
131 W Front St, Thomasville, AL 36784
Tel.: (334) 636-5424
Web Site: https://www.fusb.com
Banking Services
N.A.I.C.S.: 522110
James F. House (Pres & CEO)
Thomas S. Elley (CFO, Treas, Exec VP & Asst Sec)
J. Daniel Matheson (Officer-Investment & Sr VP)
Phillip Wheat (CIO, Officer-Information Security & Exec VP)
William C. Mitchell (Exec VP-Consumer Lending)
Kimberly Pretnar (Sr VP & Dir-HR)

FIRST WATCH RESTAURANT GROUP, INC.
8725 Pendery Pl Ste 201, Bradenton, FL 34201
Tel.: (941) 907-9800   DE
Web Site: https://www.firstwatch.com
Year Founded: 2017
FWRG—(NASDAQ)
Rev.: $730,162,000
Assets: $1,104,446,000
Liabilities: $581,311,000
Net Worth: $523,135,000
Earnings: $6,907,000
Emp.: 12,000
Fiscal Year-end: 12/25/22
Offices of Other Holding Companies
N.A.I.C.S.: 551112
Christopher A. Tomasso (Pres & CEO)
Mel Hope (CFO & Treas)
Jay Wolszczak (Gen Counsel & Sec)
Eric Hartman (Chief Dev Officer)

Laura Sorensen (Chief People Officer)
Calum Middleton (Chief Strategy Officer)
Rob Conti (Sr VP-Tech)
Matt Eisenacher (Sr VP-Brand Strategy & Innovation)
Brian Fisher (Sr VP-Ops)
Rania Khouri (Sr VP-Acctg & Fin Reporting)
Lilah Rippett (Sr VP-Supply Chain)
Shane Schaibly (Sr VP-Culinary Strategy)
John Zimmermann (VP-Quality Assurance & Food Safety)
Ralph Alvarez (Chm)
Edward P. Dolanski (Co-Founder)

FIRST WESTERN FINANCIAL, INC.
1900 16th St Ste 1200, Denver, CO 80202
Tel.: (303) 531-8100   CO
Web Site: https://www.myfw.gcs-web.com
Year Founded: 2002
MYFW—(NASDAQ)
Rev.: $128,886,000
Assets: $2,866,748,000
Liabilities: $2,625,884,000
Net Worth: $240,864,000
Earnings: $21,698,000
Emp.: 365
Fiscal Year-end: 12/31/22
Bank Holding Company
N.A.I.C.S.: 551111
Scott C. Wylie (Chm & CEO)
Julie A. Courkamp (COO)
David R. Weber (CFO & Treas)
Chris Pixler (Dir)
Scott Lawley (Chief Credit Officer)
Suzanne Johnson (Reg Pres)
Chuck Watts (Reg Pres)
Matt Gorr (Reg Pres)
Christine Joseph (Pres)
Mike Eden (Pres)
Tom Behr (Pres)
Charles Bantis (Pres)
Brian Weldon (Pres)
Joe O'Brien (Pres)
Todd Whittemore (Pres)
Joe Short (Pres)
Michael Glass (Pres)
Tim Morphy (Dir)
Heath Kinsland (Pres)
David Matthews (Pres)
Joe Ballestrasse (Pres)

Subsidiaries:

First Western Trust Bank   (1)
1900 16th St Mall Ste 1200, Denver, CO 80202
Tel.: (303) 531-8100
Web Site: https://www.myfw.com
Sales Range: $25-49.9 Million
Private Banking & Trust Services
N.A.I.C.S.: 523150
Scott C. Wylie (Chm & CEO)
Julie A. Courkamp (Pres & COO)
David R. Weber (CFO & Treas)
Joe O'Brien (Pres-Market)
Suzanne Johnson (Pres-Reg)

FIRSTCASH HOLDINGS, INC.
1600 W 7th St, Fort Worth, TX 76102
Tel.: (817) 335-1100   DE
Web Site: https://www.firstcash.com
Year Founded: 1988
FCFS—(NASDAQ)
Rev.: $3,151,796,000
Assets: $4,289,915,000
Liabilities: $2,293,497,000
Net Worth: $1,996,418,000
Earnings: $219,301,000
Emp.: 19,000
Fiscal Year-end: 12/31/23
Retail Based Pawn Store Operator

N.A.I.C.S.: 523999
Daniel R. Feehan *(Chm)*
Rick L. Wessel *(Vice Chm & CEO)*
R. Douglas Orr *(CFO & Exec VP)*
Thomas Brent Stuart *(Pres & COO)*

Subsidiaries:

Cash America East, Inc. **(1)**
6424 E Colonial Dr, Orlando, FL
32807 **(100%)**
Tel.: (407) 249-0555
Web Site: http://www.cashamerica.com
Financial Services
N.A.I.C.S.: 522291

Cash America Pawn L.P. **(1)**
211 E 7th St Ste 620, Austin, TX
78701 **(100%)**
Web Site: http://www.cashamerica.com
Financial Services
N.A.I.C.S.: 522291

Cash America of Missouri, Inc. **(1)**
11148 Blue Ridge Blvd, Kansas City, MO
64134 **(100%)**
Tel.: (816) 761-0203
Web Site: http://www.cashamerica.com
Consumer Lending Services
N.A.I.C.S.: 522291

Cash America, Inc. of Alaska **(1)**
1413 Gambell St, Anchorage, AK
99501 **(100%)**
Tel.: (907) 277-1229
Web Site: http://www.cashamerica.com
Financial Services
N.A.I.C.S.: 522291

Cash America, Inc. of Illinois **(1)**
3123 N Ashland Ave, Chicago, IL
60657 **(100%)**
Tel.: (773) 871-6633
Web Site: http://www.cashamerica.com
Financial Services
N.A.I.C.S.: 522291

Cash America, Inc. of North
Carolina **(1)**
2626 Glenwood Ave Ste 550, Raleigh, NC
27608 **(100%)**
Tel.: (704) 596-7810
Web Site: http://www.cashamerica.com
Financial Services
N.A.I.C.S.: 522291

Cash America, Inc. of Oklahoma **(1)**
1130 S Memorial Dr, Tulsa, OK
74112 **(100%)**
Tel.: (918) 835-0141
Web Site: http://www.cashamerica.com
Financial Services
N.A.I.C.S.: 522291

Cashland Financial Services,
Inc. **(1)**
1600 W 7th St, Fort Worth, TX
76102-2599 **(100%)**
Tel.: (800) 527-3577
Web Site: http://www.cashamerica.com
Renting Services
N.A.I.C.S.: 522390

FCFS CO, Inc. **(1)**
690 E Lamar Blvd Ste 400, Arlington, TX
76011
Tel.: (817) 505-3183
Retail Based Pawn Store Operator
N.A.I.C.S.: 523999

FCFS MO, Inc. **(1)**
3608 N Grand, Saint Louis, MO 63107
Tel.: (314) 535-6555
Nondepository Credit Intermediation Services
N.A.I.C.S.: 522299

FCFS SC, Inc. **(1)**
3235 Augusta Rd, Greenville, SC 29605-2151
Tel.: (864) 422-9660
Consumer Lending Services
N.A.I.C.S.: 522291

Famous Pawn, Inc. **(1)**
5603 Sargent Rd, Hyattsville, MD
20782 **(100%)**
Tel.: (301) 559-4000
Web Site: http://firstcash.com

Sales Range: $125-149.9 Million
Emp.: 30
Retail Based Pawn Store Operator
N.A.I.C.S.: 523999

Georgia Cash America, Inc. **(1)**
6963 Hwy 85, Riverdale, GA
30274 **(100%)**
Tel.: (770) 996-3603
Web Site: http://www.cashamerica.com
Financial Services
N.A.I.C.S.: 522291

King Pawn II, Inc. **(1)**
6824 New Hampshire Ave, Takoma Park,
MD 20912
Tel.: (301) 270-5700
Emp.: 4
Nondepository Credit Intermediation Services
N.A.I.C.S.: 522299

King Pawn, Inc. **(1)**
11000 Baltimore Ave Ste 108, Beltsville, MD
20705
Tel.: (301) 595-5333
Web Site: http://www.kingpawn.net
Nondepository Credit Intermediation Services
N.A.I.C.S.: 522299
Gary Knight *(Gen Mgr)*

LWC, LLC **(1)**
3164 S Country Club Dr Ste 12, Mesa, AZ
85210
Tel.: (480) 695-5885
Emp.: 3
Retail Based Pawn Store Operator
N.A.I.C.S.: 523999

Mr. Payroll Corporation **(1)**
1600 W 7th St, Fort Worth, TX 76102-2599
Web Site: https://www.mrpayroll.com
Renting Services
N.A.I.C.S.: 531210

FIRSTENERGY CORP.
76 S Main St, Akron, OH 44308 OH
Web Site:
  https://www.firstenergycorp.com
Year Founded: 1997
FE—(NYSE)
Rev.: $12,870,000,000
Assets: $48,767,000,000
Liabilities: $37,851,000,000
Net Worth: $10,916,000,000
Earnings: $1,102,000,000
Emp.: 12,042
Fiscal Year-end: 12/31/23
Holding Company; Electric Utility Services
N.A.I.C.S.: 551112
K. Jon Taylor *(CFO & Sr VP)*
Jason J. Lisowski *(Chief Acctg Officer, VP & Controller)*
Brian X. Tierney *(Pres & CEO)*
Christine L. Walker *(Chief HR Officer & Sr VP-FirstEnergy Service Company)*
Antonio Fernandez *(Chief Ethics & Compliance Officer & VP)*
Abigail Phillips *(Chief Risk Officer & VP)*
Amanda Mertens Campbell *(VP-External Affairs)*
Mark Mroczynski *(Acting VP-Ops)*

Subsidiaries:

FirstEnergy Foundation **(1)**
76 S Main St, Akron, OH 44308
Tel.: (330) 761-4246
Web Site: http://www.firstenergycorp.com
Eletric Power Generation Services
N.A.I.C.S.: 221118
Dee Lowery *(Pres)*

FirstEnergy Nuclear Operating
Co. **(1)**
76 S Main St 19th Fl, Akron, OH 44308-1890
Tel.: (330) 761-4055
Sales Range: $200-249.9 Million
Emp.: 2,600
Public Utility Services
N.A.I.C.S.: 221118

John Grabnar *(Gen Mgr-Beaver Valley)*
Raymond A. Lieb *(Sr VP-Fleet Engrg)*
Brian D. Boles *(VP-Nuclear Support)*
Jim Amundsen *(Supvr)*
David B. Hamilton *(VP-Perry Nuclear Power Plant)*
Frank Payne *(Gen Mgr-Plant-Perry)*
Mark B. Bezilla *(VP-Davis Besse Nuclear Power Station-Oak Harbor)*
Doug Huey *(Dir-Performance Improvement)*
Richard Bologna *(VP-Beaver Valley Power Station-Shippingport)*
Terry Brown *(VP-Fleet Oversight)*
Barry Blair *(Gen Mgr-Davis-Besse Nuclear Power Station-Oak Harbor)*

FirstEnergy Service Company **(1)**
Tel.: (234) 208-2200
Web Site: http://www.firstenergycorp.com
Electric Power Distribution Services
N.A.I.C.S.: 221122

FirstEnergy Solutions Corp. **(1)**
341 White Pond Dr Bldg B3, Akron, OH
44320 **(100%)**
Web Site: http://www.fes.com
Rev.: $3,098,000,000
Assets: $5,514,000,000
Liabilities: $5,285,000,000
Net Worth: $229,000,000
Earnings: ($2,391,000,000)
Emp.: 56
Fiscal Year-end: 12/31/2017
Energy & Energy-Related Products & Services, Including Generation & Sale of Electricity & Energy Planning & Procurement
N.A.I.C.S.: 221118
Brian Farley *(Exec VP-Retail Sls & Comml Ops)*
Donald R. Schneider *(Chm)*
Kevin T. Warvell *(CFO, Chief Risk Officer & Sec)*
Jay Bellingham *(Sr VP-Fossil Energy)*
John W. Judge *(Pres & CEO)*
Paul Harden *(Chief Nuclear Officer)*
Stephen Burnazian *(Exec VP-Corp Dev)*
Dave Griffing *(VP-Govt Affairs)*
Rick Giannantonio *(Gen Counsel)*

Jersey Central Power & Light
Company **(1)**
300 Madison Ave, Morristown, NJ
07962-1911 **(100%)**
Tel.: (973) 401-8830
Web Site: https://www.firstenergycorp.com
Rev.: $2,027,000,000
Assets: $7,138,000,000
Liabilities: $4,895,000,000
Net Worth: $2,243,000,000
Earnings: $133,000,000
Emp.: 1,410
Fiscal Year-end: 12/31/2012
Electric Power Distr
N.A.I.C.S.: 221122
James V. Fakult *(Pres)*

Metropolitan Edison Company **(1)**
76 S Main St, Akron, OH 44308 **(100%)**
Tel.: (330) 384-7939
Web Site: http://www.firstenergycorp.com
Emp.: 678
Electric Power Distribution & Generation
Services
N.A.I.C.S.: 221122

Monongahela Power Company **(1)**
5001 NASA Blvd, Fairmont, WV 26554-3526
Web Site: https://www.firstenergycorp.com
Public Electric Utility
N.A.I.C.S.: 221111

Ohio Edison Company **(1)**
76 South Main St, Akron, OH 44308
Tel.: (800) 736-3402
Electric Power Distribution & Generation
Services
N.A.I.C.S.: 221118

Pennsylvania Electric Company **(1)**
76 S Main St Basement, Akron, OH
44308 **(100%)**
Tel.: (800) 545-7741
Emp.: 896
Electric Power Distr
N.A.I.C.S.: 221122
Scott R. Wyman *(Pres-Operations)*

Pennsylvania Power Company **(1)**
76 S Main St, Akron, OH 44308

Tel.: (800) 720-3600
Web Site: http://www.firstenergycorp.com
Electric Utilities
N.A.I.C.S.: 926130

The Cleveland Electric Illuminating
Company **(1)**
76 S Main St, Akron, OH 44308
Electric Power Distr
N.A.I.C.S.: 221122
Steven R. Staub *(Treas & VP)*

The Potomac Edison Company **(1)**
10802 Bower Ave, Williamsport, MD
21795-3016 **(100%)**
Tel.: (301) 671-2017
Web Site: https://www.firstenergycorp.com
Sales Range: $900-999.9 Million
Emp.: 150
Operator of Electricity Transmission & Distribution System
N.A.I.C.S.: 221111

The Toledo Edison Company **(1)**
76 S Main St, Akron, OH 44308
Tel.: (330) 761-7837
Electric Power Distr
N.A.I.C.S.: 221122
Steven R. Staub *(Treas & VP)*

FIRSTIME DESIGN LIMITED
W237 N2889 Woodgate Rd Ste F,
Pewaukee, WI 53072
Tel.: (262) 364-5200 WI
Web Site: https://www.firstime.com
Year Founded: 1990
FTDL—(OTCIQ)
Home Decor Products Designer, Mfr
& Distr
N.A.I.C.S.: 449129
Christopher D. Bering *(Pres & CEO)*

Subsidiaries:

InnerSpace Luxury Products,
LLC **(1)**
255 Kraft Dr, Dalton, GA 30721
Tel.: (706) 428-0101
Web Site: http://www.islp.com
Customized Bedding & Home Goods Distr
N.A.I.C.S.: 449129

FIRSTMARK HORIZON ACQUISITION CORP.
100 5th Ave 3rd Fl, New York, NY
10011
Tel.: (212) 792-2200 DE
Year Founded: 2020
FMACU—(NYSE)
Investment Services
N.A.I.C.S.: 523999
Richard Heitzmann *(CEO)*
Amish Jani *(Chm & Pres)*
Eric D. Cheung *(Sec)*

FIRSTSUN CAPITAL BANCORP
1400 16th St Ste 250, Denver, CO
80202
Tel.: (303) 962-0150 DE
Web Site: https://ir.firstsuncb.com
Year Founded: 2017
FSUN—(OTCQX)
Rev.: $356,383,000
Assets: $7,430,322,000
Liabilities: $6,655,786,000
Net Worth: $774,536,000
Earnings: $59,182,000
Emp.: 1,149
Fiscal Year-end: 12/31/22
Bank Holding Company
N.A.I.C.S.: 551111
Mollie Hale Carter *(Chm, Pres & CEO)*
Neal E. Arnold *(Pres, CEO & COO)*
Laura J. Frazier *(Chief Admin Officer & Exec VP)*
Jennifer L. Norris *(Chief Credit Officer & Exec VP)*
Robert A. Cafera Jr. *(CFO)*

FirstSun Capital Bancorp—(Continued)

Subsidiaries:

Pioneer Bancshares, Inc.   **(1)**
100 Creek Rd, Dripping Springs, TX 78620
Tel.: (512) 894-0262
Web Site: http://www.pioneerbanktexas.com
Sales Range: $10-24.9 Million
Emp.: 64
Bank Holding Company
N.A.I.C.S.: 551111
Jack Seifrick (Vice Chm)
Elizabeth Blose (CFO, Sec & Exec VP)
Whit Hanks (Chm)
Ron Coben (Pres & CEO)

Sunflower Bank, National
Association   **(1)**
8117 Preston Rd Ste 220, Dallas, TX 75225
Web Site: https://www.sunflowerbank.com
Federal Savings Bank
N.A.I.C.S.: 522180
T. J. Kern (Mgr-Structured Fin Grp)
Neal Arnold (CEO)
Rob Cafera (CFO)
Laura Frazier (Chief Admin Officer)
Jennifer Norris (Chief Credit Officer)
Brian Walsh (Chief Lending Officer)
Cecil G. Edwards Jr. (Chief Banking Officer-Eastern Banking)
Chris Rude (Chief Banking Officer-Western Banking)

Division (Domestic):

Guardian Mortgage   **(2)**
2701 Dallas Pkwy Ste 180, Plano, TX 75093
Tel.: (972) 248-4663
Web Site:
https://www.guardianmortgageonline.com
Mortgage Banking
N.A.I.C.S.: 522292
Marcus McCue (Sr VP & Dir-Mortgage Strategy & Project Mgmt)
Cheryl Brown (Sr VP & Head-Ops)
Will Stokes (Sr VP-IT)

FISCALNOTE HOLDINGS, INC.
1201 Pennsylvania Ave NW 6th Fl,
Washington, DC 20004
Tel.: (202) 793-5300   **DE**
Web Site: https://fiscalnote.com
Year Founded: 2020
NOTE—(NYSE)
Rev.: $113,765,000
Assets: $433,157,000
Liabilities: $288,467,000
Net Worth: $144,690,000
Earnings: ($218,257,000)
Emp.: 720
Fiscal Year-end: 12/31/22
Software Publr
N.A.I.C.S.: 513210
Timothy Hwang (Co-Founder, Chm, CEO, Treas & Sec)
Jon Slabaugh (CFO & Chief Investment Officer)
Gerald Yao (Co-Founder)
Dakota Braun (VP-Content Strategy & Growth)
Paul Donnell (Chief Acctg Officer)
Vlad Eidelman (CTO)
Nicholas Graham (VP-Corporate Communications & Public Affairs)
Richard Henderson (Chief Revenue Officer)
Dominique Taylor (Sr VP-People & DEIBA)
Todd Aman (Gen Counsel, Sec & Sr VP)
Josh Resnik (Pres & COO)
Mike Stubbs (CIO & Sr VP)

FISERV, INC.
255 Fiserv Dr, Brookfield, WI 53045
Tel.: (262) 879-5000   **WI**
Web Site: https://www.fiserv.com
Year Founded: 1984
FI—(NYSE)
Rev.: $19,093,000,000
Assets: $90,890,000,000

Liabilities: $60,382,000,000
Net Worth: $30,508,000,000
Earnings: $3,068,000,000
Emp.: 42,000
Fiscal Year-end: 12/31/23
Financial Data Processing & Information Management Services
N.A.I.C.S.: 518210
Christopher M. Foskett (Vice Chm)
Frank J. Bisignano (Chm, Pres & CEO)
Guy Chiarello (COO)
Robert W. Hau (CFO)
Britt Zarling (VP-Corp Comm)
Jennifer A. LaClair (Head-Bus Solutions-Global)
Ann S. Cave (VP-External Comm)
Leigh Asher (CMO)
Andrew Gelb (Head-Issuer Solutions)
Tom Higgins (Head-Gen Svcs)
Jennifer M. Manchester (Chief HR Officer)
Carmen Menendez-Puerto (Chief Risk & Regulatory Compliance Officer)
Neil H. Wilcox (Head-Corp Social Responsibility)
Mark Jelfs (Mgr-PR)
Mariana Tello (Mgr-External Comm)
Chase Wallace (Dir-Comm)
Katia Karpova (Head-Europe, Middle East & Africa)
John Gibbons (Head-Banking)
Ivo Distelbrink (Head)
Gustavo Marin (Head)
Adam Rosman (Chief Legal Officer)
Joanne Sebby (Chief Risk Officer)
Torrie Miers (Mgr)
Rick Singh (Officer-Enterprise Growth)
Kim Crawford Goodman (Pres-Card Svcs)

Subsidiaries:

BillMatrix Corporation   **(1)**
8750 N Central Expy 20th Fl, Dallas, TX 75231
Tel.: (214) 750-2700
Web Site: https://www.billmatrix.com
Electronic Payment Processing Services
N.A.I.C.S.: 518210

EPSIIA Corporation   **(1)**
901 South Mo Pac Expressway Iii500, Austin, TX 78746
Tel.: (512) 329-0081
Sales Range: $100-124.9 Million
Emp.: 95
Software & Document Delivery Solutions
N.A.I.C.S.: 541511

European Merchant Services B.V.   **(1)**
Apollo Building Herikerbergweg 25, Zuidoost, 1101 CN, Amsterdam, Netherlands
Tel.: (31) 206603040
Web Site: https://www.emspay.nl
Electronic Payment Services
N.A.I.C.S.: 522320
Michael Roos (Dir-Fin & Ops)

Finxact LLC   **(1)**
1301 Riverplace Blvd Ste 2501, Jacksonville, FL 32207
Web Site: https://www.finxact.com
Financial & Investment Banking Services
N.A.I.C.S.: 523150

First Data Corporation   **(1)**
225 Liberty St 29th Fl, New York, NY 10281
Web Site: http://investor.firstdata.com
Rev.: $9,498,000,000
Assets: $38,327,000,000
Liabilities: $31,360,000,000
Net Worth: $6,967,000,000
Earnings: $1,005,000,000
Emp.: 19,000
Fiscal Year-end: 12/31/2018
Credit, Debit, Smart Card & Store-Value Card Issuing & Merchant Transaction Processing Services; Internet Commerce Solutions; Money Transfers & Money Orders; Check Processing & Verification Services

N.A.I.C.S.: 522320
Christopher M. Foskett (Exec VP, Head-Institutional Sls & Co-Head-Global Fin Solutions)
Cindy Armine-Klein (Chief Control Officer & Exec VP)
Michael K. Neborak (Chief Acctg Officer, Exec VP, Head-EMEA Reg & Controller)
Anthony S. Marino (Exec VP & Head-HR)
Dan Charron (Exec VP & Head-Global Bus Solutions)
Andrew Gelb (Exec VP & Head-Network & Security Solutions)
Thomas J. Higgins (Chief Admin Officer & Exec VP)
Christine E. Larsen (COO & Exec VP)
Himanshu A. Patel (CFO & Exec VP)
Gustavo Marin (Exec VP & Head-Latin America Reg)
Ivo Distelbrink (Exec VP & Head-Asia Pacific)

Subsidiary (Domestic):

Acculynk, Inc.   **(2)**
3225 Cumberland Blvd SE Ste 550, Atlanta, GA 30339
Tel.: (678) 894-7010
Web Site: http://www.acculynk.com
Software Publisher
N.A.I.C.S.: 513210

BluePay Processing, LLC   **(2)**
184 Shuman Blvd Ste 350, Naperville, IL 60563
Tel.: (484) 581-7690
Web Site: https://www.bluepay.com
Technology-Enabled Payment Processing Services
N.A.I.C.S.: 541519

Subsidiary (Non-US):

BluePay Canada, ULC   **(3)**
2275 Upper Middle Road E Suite 200, Oakville, L6H 0C3, ON, Canada
Payment & Financial Services
N.A.I.C.S.: 522320

Subsidiary (Domestic):

CardConnect Corporation   **(2)**
1000 Continental Dr Ste 300, King of Prussia, PA 19406
Tel.: (484) 581-2200
Web Site: http://www.cardconnect.com
Payment Processing Services
N.A.I.C.S.: 561499
Laith Yaldoo (Natl Dir-ISO Sls)

Subsidiary (Domestic):

CardConnect LLC   **(3)**
1000 Continental Dr Ste 300, King of Prussia, PA 19406
Tel.: (484) 581-2200
Web Site: https://www.cardconnect.com
Financial Card Processing Services
N.A.I.C.S.: 522390

Subsidiary (Non-US):

First Data Austria GmbH   **(2)**
Floridsdorfer Hauptstrasse 1, A- 1210, Vienna, Austria
Tel.: (43) 1260820
Web Site: https://www.telecash.at
Sales Range: $25-49.9 Million
Emp.: 30
Payment Processing Services
N.A.I.C.S.: 522320

First Data Canada Ltd.   **(2)**
2030 Skymark Ave Suite 400, Mississauga, L4W 5A4, ON, Canada
Financial Banking Services
N.A.I.C.S.: 522110
Sonal Jain (Mgr-IT)

Subsidiary (Domestic):

First Data Commercial Services Holdings, Inc.   **(2)**
6200 S Quebec St, Englewood, CO 80111
Tel.: (303) 488-8000
Web Site: http://www.fdms.com
Payment Processing Services
N.A.I.C.S.: 522320

Subsidiary (Domestic):

Cardservice International, Inc.   **(3)**

5898 Condor Dr # 220, Moorpark, CA 93021-2603
Tel.: (805) 552-8000
Web Site: http://www.cardservice.com
Sales Range: $150-199.9 Million
Emp.: 490
Credit Card Payment Processing Services
N.A.I.C.S.: 522320

First Data Merchant Services Corporation   **(3)**
1307 Walt Whitman Rd, Melville, NY 11747
Tel.: (631) 683-6000
Web Site: http://www.firstdata.com
Sales Range: $200-249.9 Million
Emp.: 700
Payment Processing Services
N.A.I.C.S.: 522320

Subsidiary (Domestic):

First Data Merchant Services Corporation   **(4)**
4000 Coral Ridge Dr, Coral Springs, FL 33065
Tel.: (954) 851-7000
Web Site: https://www.firstdata.com
Emp.: 500
Merchant Credit Card Authorization & Settlement
N.A.I.C.S.: 561499

First Data Merchant Services Corporation   **(4)**
1 Western Maryland Pkwy, Hagerstown, MD 21740
Tel.: (301) 745-7000
Web Site: http://www.firstdata.com
Sales Range: $550-599.9 Million
Credit Card Processing Services
N.A.I.C.S.: 522320

Subsidiary (Non-US):

First Data Corporation Australia (Holdings) Pty Limited   **(2)**
L 9 168 Walker St, North Sydney, 2060, NSW, Australia
Tel.: (61) 299597333
Web Site: https://www.firstdata.com
Emp.: 15
Financial Management Services
N.A.I.C.S.: 522320

Subsidiary (Domestic):

First Data Merchant Solutions Australia Pty. Ltd.   **(3)**
L 11 168 Walker St, North Sydney, 2060, NSW, Australia
Tel.: (61) 18006552
Web Site: https://www.firstdataatms.com.au
Financial Management Services
N.A.I.C.S.: 522320

First Data Resources Australia Limited   **(3)**
Level 9 168 Walker Street, Sydney, 2060, NSW, Australia
Tel.: (61) 299597333
Web Site: https://www.firstdata.com.au
Sales Range: $150-199.9 Million
Emp.: 500
Payment Processing Services
N.A.I.C.S.: 522320

Subsidiary (Non-US):

First Data Deutschland GmbH   **(2)**
Konrad Adenauer Allee 1, 61118, Bad Vilbel, Germany
Tel.: (49) 6979330
Web Site: http://www.firstdata.de
Sales Range: $50-74.9 Million
Emp.: 500
Payment Processing Services
N.A.I.C.S.: 522320

First Data Europe Limited   **(2)**
F D R House Christopher Martin Road, Basildon, SS14 9AA, Essex, United Kingdom
Tel.: (44) 17955390
Payment Processing Services
N.A.I.C.S.: 522320

Subsidiary (Domestic):

First Data Government Solutions, Inc.   **(2)**

11311 Cornell Park Dr Ste 300, Cincinnati, OH 45242-1831
Tel.: (513) 489-9599
Web Site: http://www.firstdata.com
Electronic Payment Processing Services for Government Organizations
N.A.I.C.S.: 522320

Subsidiary (Non-US):

First Data Magyarorszag Kft.   (2)
Vaci ut 135-139, Budapest, 1138, Hungary
Tel.: (36) 13017000
Web Site: http://www.firstdata.com
Emp.: 18
Payment Processing Services
N.A.I.C.S.: 522320

First Data Merchant Services Mexico, S. de R.L. de C.V.
Av Paseo de la Reforma No 505 Piso 30, Cuauhtemoc, Ciudad del Carmen, 06500, Mexico
Tel.: (52) 5511020600
Financial Management Services
N.A.I.C.S.: 523999

First Data Polska S.A.   (2)
Al Jerozolimskie 9, 00-807, Warsaw, Poland
Tel.: (48) 22 515 30 05
Web Site: http://www.firstdata.pl
Payment Processing Services
N.A.I.C.S.: 522320

Subsidiary (Domestic):

First Data Resources   (2)
1449 Kristina Way, Chesapeake, VA 23320
Tel.: (757) 413-7719
Payment Processing Services
N.A.I.C.S.: 522320

First Data Resources Inc.   (2)
72nd & Pacific St, Omaha, NE 68134
Tel.: (402) 397-0128
Sales Range: $900-999.9 Million
Emp.: 4,800
Data Processing Services
N.A.I.C.S.: 518210

FundsXpress Financial Network, Inc.   (2)
11950 Jollyville Rd, Austin, TX 78759
Tel.: (512) 493-2500
Internet Payment Processing Services
N.A.I.C.S.: 522320

Intelligent Results, Inc.   (2)
520 112th Ave NorthEast Ste 400, Bellevue, WA 98004
Tel.: (425) 455-5100
Web Site: http://www.intelligentresults.com
Sales, Risk Management & Market Analysis Services
N.A.I.C.S.: 541910

Star Networks, Inc.   (2)
495 N Keller Rd Ste 500, Maitland, FL 32751-8657
Tel.: (321) 263-3000
Sales Range: $50-74.9 Million
Emp.: 140
Financial Management Services
N.A.I.C.S.: 522320

TASQ Technology, Inc.   (2)
8875 Washington Blvd Ste A, Roseville, CA 95678-6214
Tel.: (916) 632-7600
Web Site: http://www.tasq.com
Point of Sale & Payment Processing Equipment Whslr
N.A.I.C.S.: 518210

TeleCheck Services, Inc.   (2)
5251 Westheimer Rd, Houston, TX 77056-5412
Tel.: (713) 331-7600
Web Site: http://www.telecheck.com
Sales Range: $125-149.9 Million
Emp.: 1,300
Check Guarantee & Verification Services
N.A.I.C.S.: 522320

Subsidiary (Non-US):

TeleCheck Services Canada Inc.   (3)
1100 Boul Cremazie E Ste 701, Montreal, H2P 2X2, QC, Canada

Sales Range: $25-49.9 Million
Emp.: 10
Electronic Check Verification Services
N.A.I.C.S.: 522320

Subsidiary (Domestic):

Transaction Wireless, Inc.   (2)
10180 Telesis Ct Ste 240, San Diego, CA 92121
Tel.: (858) 926-5390
Web Site:
    http://www.transactionwireless.com
Mobile Transaction & Digital Prepaid Gift Card Platform Developer & Services
N.A.I.C.S.: 541511

Subsidiary (Non-US):

Trionis SCRL   (2)
Maria Theresiastraat 11/1 Rue Marie-Therese, 1000, Brussels, Belgium
Tel.: (32) 26630211
Web Site: https://www.trionis.com
Financial Management Services
N.A.I.C.S.: 522320

Fiserv (Europe) Ltd.   (1)
First Floor The Porter Bldg 1 Brunel Way, Slough, SL1 1XL, United Kingdom (100%)
Tel.: (44) 2088333000
Web Site: https://www.fiserv.com
Custom Programming Services
N.A.I.C.S.: 541511

Fiserv ASPAC Pte. Ltd.   (1)
12 Marina Boulevard Singapore, #26-04 Marina Bay Financial Centre Tower 3, Singapore, 018982, Singapore   (100%)
Tel.: (65) 339288
Web Site: http://www.fiserv.com
Custom Programming Services
N.A.I.C.S.: 541511

Fiserv Automotive Solutions, Inc.   (1)
455 S Gulph Rd Ste 125, King of Prussia, PA 19406
Tel.: (610) 337-8686
Web Site: http://www.fiserv.com
Emp.: 200
Information Management & Electronic Commerce System Provider
N.A.I.C.S.: 518210

Fiserv Clearing, Inc.   (1)
255 Fiserv Dr, Brookfield, WI 53045
Tel.: (262) 879-5000
Web Site: http://www.fiserv.com
Sales Range: $650-699.9 Million
Securities Broker
N.A.I.C.S.: 523150

Fiserv LeMans, Inc.   (1)
455 S Gulph Rd Ste 125, King of Prussia, PA 19406
Tel.: (610) 337-8686
Web Site: http://www.lemansgroup.com
Sales Range: $75-99.9 Million
Emp.: 80
Integrated Software & Services to the Automotive Finance Industry
N.A.I.C.S.: 541511

Fiserv Polska Sp. z.o.o.   (1)
Al Jerozolimskie 100, 00-807, Warsaw, Poland   (100%)
Tel.: (48) 225153005
Web Site: https://www.polcard.pl
Financial Data Processing & Information Management Services & Products to the Financial Services Industry
N.A.I.C.S.: 518210

Fiserv Solutions, LLC   (1)
255 Fiserv Dr, Brookfield, WI 53045
Tel.: (262) 879-5000
Web Site: https://www.fiserv.com
Automotive Finance & Real Estate Lending Solution Provider
N.A.I.C.S.: 523999

Harrington Benefit Servces, Inc.   (1)
675 Brooksedge Blvd, Westerville, OH 43081
Tel.: (614) 212-7000
Sales Range: $75-99.9 Million
Emp.: 400
Health Plan Management Solutions & Services
N.A.I.C.S.: 524210

Monitise Limited   (1)
Eversheds House 70 Great Bridgewater Street, Manchester, M15ES, United Kingdom
Tel.: (44) 20 3657 1999
Mobile Banking Services
N.A.I.C.S.: 513210
Gavin James (COO)

Raddon Financial Group   (1)
701 E 22nd St Ste 400, Lombard, IL 60148
Tel.: (630) 792-8500
Web Site: http://www.raddon.com
Strategic Guidance & Tactical Solutions for the Financial Industry
N.A.I.C.S.: 541611
Louie Lambrou (Dir-Mktg & Comm)
David Irwin (Pres)
Todd Beemer (VP-Client Mgmt)
Bill Handel (VP-Res)

ReliaQuote, Inc.   (1)
1312 Vincent Pl, McLean, VA 22101
Tel.: (703) 289-0200
Web Site: http://www.reliaquote.com
Sales Range: $10-24.9 Million
Emp.: 80
Online Insurance Services
N.A.I.C.S.: 524210

Software Express Informatica Ltda   (1)
Av Paulista n 2300 8 andar, Bela Vista, 01310-300, São Paulo, Brazil
Tel.: (55) 1131705300
Web Site:
    http://www.softwareexpress.com.br
Software Services
N.A.I.C.S.: 541511

TradeStar Investments, Inc.   (1)
1900 Saint James Pl, Houston, TX 77056-4129
Tel.: (713) 993-2000
Sales Range: $650-699.9 Million
Stockbrokers
N.A.I.C.S.: 523150

USERS Incorporated   (1)
1250 Drummers Ln, Valley Forge, PA 19482
Tel.: (610) 687-9400
Technology Solutions & Services to Credit Unions
N.A.I.C.S.: 423430

XP Systems Corporation   (1)
405 Science Dr, Moorpark, CA 93021
Tel.: (805) 532-9100
Computer Integrated Systems Design
N.A.I.C.S.: 541512

ayCash GmbH   (1)
Marienbader Platz 1, v d Hohe, 61348, Bad Homburg, Germany
Tel.: (49) 8009060800
Web Site: https://www.cashforless.de
Electronic Payment Services
N.A.I.C.S.: 522320

FISION CORP

1650 W End Blvd Ste 100, Minneapolis, MN 55416
Tel.: (612) 927-3700   DE
Web Site:
    https://www.fisiononline.com
Year Founded: 2010
FSSN—(OTCIQ)
Rev.: $361,888
Assets: $52,923
Liabilities: $7,550,010
Net Worth: ($7,497,087)
Earnings: ($2,491,533)
Emp.: 11
Fiscal Year-end: 12/31/20
Computer & Computer Peripheral Equipment & Software Merchant Wholesalers
N.A.I.C.S.: 423430
Michael P. Brown (Founder, Chm & CFO)
Alistair Hancock (CTO)
William Gerhauser (CEO)
Joshua Carmona (COO & CTO)

FISKER INC.

1888 Rosecrans Ave, Manhattan Beach, CA 90266
Tel.: (310) 374-6177   DE
Web Site: https://www.fiskerinc.com
Year Founded: 2017
FSR—(NYSE)
Rev.: $342,000
Assets: $1,515,426,000
Liabilities: $1,034,921,000
Net Worth: $480,505,000
Earnings: ($547,496,000)
Emp.: 850
Fiscal Year-end: 12/31/22
E-Mobility & Technology & Automotive Company
N.A.I.C.S.: 441330
Geeta Gupta (CFO & COO)
David King (CTO)
Christian Marti (Sr VP-Marketing, Sales, and Svcs-Europe)
Alpay Uguz (Sr VP-Global Mfg)
Angel Salinas (Chief Acctg Officer)
Henrik Fisker (Chm, Pres & CEO)
Dawn Ahmed (Exec VP-Global Mktg, Sales, and Svc)
Eric Goldstein (Head-Investor Relations)
Cheryl Johnson (Sr VP-Purchasing & Supplier Quality Assurance)
Beverly Lively (VP-Internal Controls & Audit)
Corey MacGillivray (VP-Securities, Governance, and Compliance)
Dan Quirk (Exec VP-Finance & Accounting)
Kristi Katsma (Sr VP-Legal & Comml Affairs & VP)
Jennifer Kaushek (Exec VP-Human Resources & VP)
Matthew DeBord (VP-Communications & Sr Dir-Comm Strategy & Storytelling)

Subsidiaries:

Fisker Inc.   (1)
3080 Airway Ave, Costa Mesa, CA 92626-6034
Tel.: (949) 242-4904
Web Site: http://www.fiskerinc.com
New Car Dealers
N.A.I.C.S.: 441110
Henrik Fisker (Chm & CEO)

FITLIFE BRANDS, INC.

5214 S 136th St, Omaha, NE 68137
Tel.: (402) 991-5618   NV
Web Site:
    https://www.fitlifebrands.com
Year Founded: 2005
FTLF—(NASDAQ)
Rev.: $28,803,000
Assets: $25,707,000
Liabilities: $4,319,000
Net Worth: $21,388,000
Earnings: $4,429,000
Emp.: 27
Fiscal Year-end: 12/31/22
Nutraceutical Dietary Supplements
N.A.I.C.S.: 325411
Jakob York (CFO)
Dayton Robert Judd (CEO)

Subsidiaries:

Mimi's Rock Corp.   (1)
610 Chartwell Road Suite 202, Oakville, L6J 2X6, ON, Canada
Tel.: (416) 301-2949
Web Site: http://www.mimisrock.com
Rev.: $28,682,831
Assets: $31,056,011
Liabilities: $19,117,277
Net Worth: $11,938,735
Earnings: ($3,924,403)
Fiscal Year-end: 12/31/2021
Pharmaceutical Product Mfr & Distr
N.A.I.C.S.: 325412
David Kohler (CEO)
Andrew Patient (CFO)

FitLife Brands, Inc.—(Continued)

MusclePharm Corporation (1)
7380 S Eastern Ave Ste 124-287, Las Vegas, NV 89123
Tel.: (303) 396-6100
Web Site: http://www.musclepharm.com
Rev.: $50,042,000
Assets: $11,210,000
Liabilities: $43,401,000
Net Worth: ($32,191,000)
Earnings: ($12,866,000)
Emp.: 21
Fiscal Year-end: 12/31/2021
Sports Nutrition Products Mfr & Marketer
N.A.I.C.S.: 325412
Anthony Todaro (Interim CFO)

iSatori, Inc. (1)
15000 W 6th Ave Ste 202, Golden, CO 80401
Tel.: (303) 215-9174
Web Site: http://www.isatori.com
Sales Range: $1-9.9 Million
Nutritional Product Mfr
N.A.I.C.S.: 424210
Stephen Adele (Founder)

FIVE BELOW, INC.
701 Market St Ste 300, Philadelphia, PA 19106
Tel.: (215) 546-7909   PA
Web Site: https://www.fivebelow.com
Year Founded: 2002
FIVE—(NASDAQ)
Rev.: $3,559,369,000
Assets: $3,872,037,000
Liabilities: $2,287,081,000
Net Worth: $1,584,956,000
Earnings: $301,106,000
Emp.: 7,000
Fiscal Year-end: 02/03/24
Specialty Value Retailer
N.A.I.C.S.: 455219
Kristy Chipman (CFO, Principal Acctg Officer & Treas)
Joel D. Anderson (Pres & CEO)
Eric M. Specter (Chief Admin Officer)
Michael F. Romanko (Chief Mdsg Officer)
Christiane Pelz (VP-IR & Treasury)
Amit Jhunjhunwala (CIO)
Kenneth R. Bull (COO)
Thomas G. Vellios (Founder & Chm)

FIVE POINT HOLDINGS, LLC
2000 Fivepoint 4th Fl, Irvine, CA 92618
Tel.: (949) 349-1000   DE
Web Site: https://www.fivepoint.com
Year Founded: 2009
FPH—(NYSE)
Rev.: $42,694,000
Assets: $2,885,784,000
Liabilities: $1,017,737,000
Net Worth: $1,868,047,000
Earnings: ($15,403,000)
Emp.: 105
Fiscal Year-end: 12/31/22
Offices of Real Estate Agents & Brokers
N.A.I.C.S.: 531210
Stuart A. Miller (Chm)
Emile Haddad (Founder)
Michael Alvarado (COO, Chief Legal Officer, Sec & VP)
Greg McWilliams (Chief Policy Officer & VP)
Daniel Hedigan (CEO)
Leo Kij (VP-Fin Reporting)

Subsidiaries:

Five Point Operating Company, LP (1)
25 Enterprise Ste 300, Aliso Viejo, CA 92656
Tel.: (949) 349-1000
Real Estate Management Services
N.A.I.C.S.: 531210

Legacy Lands, LLC (1)

1106 W Park St Ste 20 169, Livingston, MT 59047
Tel.: (406) 848-9400
Web Site: https://legacylandsllc.com
Real Estate Services
N.A.I.C.S.: 531210
Gwen Wagner (Co-Owner)
Rick Eisen (Co-Owner)

FIVE STAR BANCORP
2240 Douglas Blvd Ste 100, Roseville, CA 95661
Tel.: (916) 626-5000   CA
Web Site: https://www.fivestarbank.com
Year Founded: 2002
FSBC—(NASDAQ)
Rev.: $174,382,000
Assets: $3,593,125,000
Liabilities: $3,307,351,000
Net Worth: $285,774,000
Earnings: $47,734,000
Emp.: 180
Fiscal Year-end: 12/31/23
Bank Holding Company
N.A.I.C.S.: 551111
Randall E. Reynoso (Vice Chm)
James E. Beckwith (Pres & CEO)
Heather Luck (CFO & Sr VP)
John W. Dalton (Chief Credit Officer & Sr VP)
Kristine M. Hyde (Chief HR & Sr VP)
Michael E. Lee (Chief Regulatory Officer & Sr VP)
Michael A. Rizzo (Chief Banking Officer & Sr VP)
Brett Wait (CIO & Sr VP)
Shelley R. Wetton (CMO & Sr VP)

FIVE9, INC.
3001 Bishop Dr Ste 350, San Ramon, CA 94583
Tel.: (925) 201-2000   DE
Web Site: https://www.five9.com
Year Founded: 2001
FIVN—(NASDAQ)
Rev.: $910,488,000
Assets: $1,494,568,000
Liabilities: $956,483,000
Net Worth: $538,085,000
Earnings: ($81,764,000)
Emp.: 2,684
Fiscal Year-end: 12/31/23
Call Center Software Developer
N.A.I.C.S.: 513210
Michael Burkland (Chm & CEO)
Barry Zwarenstein (CFO)
Daniel P. Burkland (Pres)
James Doran (Exec VP-Strategy & Ops)
David Pickering (Exec VP-Engrg)
Jonathan Rosenberg (CTO)
Anand Chandrasekaran (Exec VP-Product Mgmt)
Tricia Yankovich (Sr VP-HR)
Genefa Murphy (CMO)
Kimberly Lytikainen (Chief Compliance Officer & Gen Counsel)
Panos Kozanian (Exec VP-Cloud Ops)
Andy Dignan (COO)

Subsidiaries:

Five9 Philippines Inc. (1)
Rockwell Business Center Sheridan, 15th Floor South Tower, Sheridan Street, Mandaluyong, 1550, Metro Manila, Philippines
Tel.: (63) 6322341844
Computer System Design Services
N.A.I.C.S.: 541512

Five9, Inc. UK Limited (1)
Tricor Suite 4th Floor 50 Mark Lane, London, EC3R 7QR, United Kingdom
Tel.: (44) 2079592451
Computer System Design Services
N.A.I.C.S.: 541512

Five9.ru (1)

Nartova 6 Nizhniy, Velikiy Novgorod, Russia
Tel.: (7) 8312786090
Computer System Design Services
N.A.I.C.S.: 541512

Inference Technologies Group, Inc. (1)
2 Embarcadero Ctr 8th Fl, San Francisco, CA 94111
Web Site: http://www.inferencesolutions.com
IT Services
N.A.I.C.S.: 541519
Callan Schebella (CEO)

FLAHERTY & CRUMRINE PREFERRED & INCOME SECURITIES FUND, INC.
301 E Colorado Blvd Ste 800, Pasadena, CA 91101
Tel.: (626) 795-7300   MD
Web Site: https://flaherty-crumrine.com
Year Founded: 1983
FFC—(NYSE)
Rev.: $79,675,700
Assets: $1,357,061,980
Liabilities: $451,600,882
Net Worth: $905,461,098
Earnings: $58,029,220
Fiscal Year-end: 11/30/19
Investment Management Service
N.A.I.C.S.: 525990
Bradford S. Stone (Pres, CEO, CFO & Mgr-Fund)
R. Eric Chadwick (Chm, Mng Dir, VP & Portfolio Mgr)
Gordon Russo (Mng Dir)
Chad Conwell (Chief Compliance Officer, Chief Legal Officer & Exec VP)
Lisa Tucci (Mng Dir & VP)
Rick J. Seto (Mng Dir & VP)

FLAME SEAL PRODUCTS, INC.
9420 Knight Rd, Houston, TX 77045
Tel.: (713) 668-4291   TX
Web Site: https://www.flameseal.com
FLMP—(OTCIQ)
Commercial Product Mfr
N.A.I.C.S.: 333310
Judy Davison (Mgr-Acct)

FLANIGAN'S ENTERPRISES, INC.
5059 NE 18th Ave, Fort Lauderdale, FL 33334
Tel.: (954) 377-1961   FL
Web Site: https://www.flanigans.net
Year Founded: 1959
BDL—(NYSEAMEX)
Rev.: $174,396,000
Assets: $145,769,000
Liabilities: $70,855,000
Net Worth: $74,914,000
Earnings: $3,999,000
Emp.: 707
Fiscal Year-end: 09/30/23
Restaurant Owner & Operator
N.A.I.C.S.: 722511
James G. Flanigan II (Chm, Pres & CEO)
Jeffrey D. Kastner (CFO, Gen Counsel & Sec)
August H. Bucci (COO & Exec VP)
Christopher O'Neil (VP-Package Ops)

Subsidiaries:

Flanigan's Enterprises, Inc. (1)
1550 W 84th St, Hialeah, FL 33014-3377
Tel.: (305) 821-0993
Web Site: http://www.flanigans.net
Sales Range: $10-24.9 Million
Emp.: 60
Restaurant
N.A.I.C.S.: 722511

Flanigan's Enterprises, Inc. (1)
12790 SW 88th St, Miami, FL 33186-1746
Tel.: (305) 380-0521

Sales Range: $150-199.9 Million
N.A.I.C.S.: 445320

Flanigan's Enterprises, Inc. (1)
1479 E Commercial Blvd, Fort Lauderdale, FL 33334-5715
Tel.: (954) 493-5329
Web Site: http://www.flanigans.com
Sales Range: $50-74.9 Million
Emp.: 55
N.A.I.C.S.: 445320

Flanigan's Enterprises, Inc. (1)
4 N Federal Hwy, Hallandale, FL 33009-4339
Tel.: (954) 458-2566
Web Site: http://www.flanigans.net
Sales Range: $50-74.9 Million
Emp.: 50
Restaurant & Bar Operations
N.A.I.C.S.: 722511

Flanigan's Enterprises, Inc. (1)
2401 10th Ave N, Lake Worth, FL 33461-3128
Tel.: (561) 964-4666
Web Site: http://www.flanigans.com
Sales Range: $150-199.9 Million
Emp.: 40
N.A.I.C.S.: 445320

Flanigan's Enterprises, Inc. - Surfside (1)
9516 Harding Ave, Surfside, FL 33154
Tel.: (305) 867-0993
Web Site: http://www.flanigans.net
Restaurant Owner & Operator
N.A.I.C.S.: 722511

Flanigan's Enterprises, Inc. of Georgia (1)
6300 Powers Ferry Rd NW, Atlanta, GA 30339-2946   (100%)
Tel.: (770) 955-1638
Web Site: http://www.flanigans.net
Sales Range: $25-49.9 Million
Emp.: 200
Liquor Stores
N.A.I.C.S.: 722410

Flanigan's Restaurants (1)
5450 N State Rd 7, Fort Lauderdale, FL 33319-2922
Tel.: (954) 733-0514
Web Site: http://www.flanigan.net
Sales Range: $150-199.9 Million
Dining Restaurant
N.A.I.C.S.: 445320

FLASHZERO CORP.
5100 Westheimer St Ste 115, Houston, TX 77056
Tel.: (323) 325-8954
Year Founded: 2010
FZRO—(OTCIQ)
Software Development Services
N.A.I.C.S.: 541511
Ramiro Jordan (CEO)

FLEETWOOD BANK
E Main St & N Franklin St, Fleetwood, PA 19522
Tel.: (610) 944-8527
Web Site: https://www.fleetwoodbank.com
FLEW—(OTCIQ)
Banking Services
N.A.I.C.S.: 522110
Timothy P. Snyder (Pres & CEO)

FLEXENERGY GREEN SOLUTIONS, INC.
112 Corporate Dr Ste 3, Portsmouth, NH 03801
Tel.: (603) 430-7000   DE
Web Site: https://www.flexenergy.com
Year Founded: 2010
FLXE—(NASDAQ)
Emp.: 99
Gas Turbine Generator Mfr

N.A.I.C.S.: 336412
Mark G. Schnepel (CEO)
Wes Kimmel (CFO)
Doug Baltzer (Chief Comml Officer)
Darin Romine (Sr VP-Finance)
George Walker (Chm)

FLEXIINTERNATIONAL SOFT-WARE, INC.
2 Trap Falls Rd Ste 501, Shelton, CT
06484
Tel.: (203) 225-7000　　　DE
Web Site: https://www.flexi.com
Year Founded: 1990
FLXI—(OTCIQ)
Sales Range: $1-9.9 Million
Emp.: 41
Custom Computer Programming Ser-
vices, Enabled Financial & Account-
ing Software & Services
N.A.I.C.S.: 334610
Stefan R. Bothe (Chm & CEO)
Dmitry G. Trudov (Pres-Fin Software
Div)
John O'Connell (VP-Bus Dev)
Mary Brandon (Vp-Mktg)
Larry Jansson (Dir-Sls)

FLEXPOINT SENSOR SYS-TEMS, INC.
5718 W Dannon Way, West Jordan,
UT 84081
Tel.: (801) 568-5111　　　DE
Web Site: https://www.flexpoint.com
Year Founded: 1992
FLXT—(OTCIQ)
Rev.: $151,156
Assets: $5,194,143
Liabilities: $4,154,722
Net Worth: $1,039,421
Earnings: ($804,832)
Emp.: 3
Fiscal Year-end: 12/31/22
Other Electronic Component Manu-
facturing
N.A.I.C.S.: 334419
John A. Sindt (Chm)
Clark M. Mower (Pres, CEO & CFO)

FLEXSHOPPER, INC.
901 Yamato Rd Ste 260, Boca Raton,
FL 33431　　　DE
Web Site:
　　https://www.flexshopper.com
Year Founded: 2006
FPAY—(NASDAQ)
Rev.: $113,056,173
Assets: $148,289,510
Liabilities: $117,254,837
Net Worth: $31,034,673
Earnings: $13,631,719
Emp.: 118
Fiscal Year-end: 12/31/22
Online Lease-To-Own Consumer
Products
N.A.I.C.S.: 541611
Brad Mitchell Bernstein (Founder)
Howard S. Dvorkin (Chm)
John Davis (COO)
H. Russell Heiser Jr. (CEO & CFO)

FLEXSTEEL INDUSTRIES, INC.
385 Bell St, Dubuque, IA 52001-0877
Tel.: (563) 556-7730　　　MN
Web Site: https://www.flexsteel.com
Year Founded: 1893
FLXS—(NASDAQ)
Rev.: $412,752,000
Assets: $274,462,000
Liabilities: $124,095,000
Net Worth: $150,367,000
Earnings: $10,528,000
Emp.: 1,500
Fiscal Year-end: 06/30/24

Upholstered Furniture & Recreational
Vehicle Seating Mfr, Designer & Mar-
keter
N.A.I.C.S.: 337121
Derek P. Schmidt (Pres & CEO)
David E. Crimmins (VP-Sls)
Vic Tsai (VP-Global Strategic Sourc-
ing & Gen Mgr-Asia)
Thomas M. Levine (Chm)
Michael J. McClaflin (CIO & CTO)
Stacy M. Kammes (VP-HR)
Daniel P. Wallace (VP-Customer Ex-
perience)

Subsidiaries:

DMI Furniture, Inc.　　　(1)
9780 Ormsby Sta Rd, Louisville, KY
40223　　　(100%)
Tel.: (502) 426-4351
Web Site: http://www.dmifurniture.com
Sales Range: $75-99.9 Million
Emp.: 240
Bedroom Furniture, Residential Desks &
Office Furniture Mfr & Importer
N.A.I.C.S.: 337122

Subsidiary (Domestic):

DMI Sourcing Company, LLC　　　(2)
400 W Market St 32nd Fl, Louisville, KY
40202
Tel.: (502) 638-5708
Upholstered Furniture & Recreational Vehicle Seating Mfr & Distr
N.A.I.C.S.: 337121

Flexsteel Commercial Seating
Division　　　(1)
212 Industrial Park Rd, Starkville, MS
39759-0825　　　(100%)
Tel.: (662) 323-5481
Web Site: http://www.flexsteel.com
Sales Range: $100-124.9 Million
Emp.: 356
Upholstered & Unupholstered Wood Furni-
ture For Commercial Seating
N.A.I.C.S.: 337121

Flexsteel Dublin Division　　　(1)
701 Industrial Blvd, Dublin, GA
31021　　　(100%)
Tel.: (478) 272-6911
Web Site: http://www.flexsteel.com
Sales Range: $100-124.9 Million
Emp.: 350
Reclining Chairs & Motion Furniture
N.A.I.C.S.: 337121

Flexsteel Dubuque Division　　　(1)
3400 Jackson St, Dubuque, IA 52001
Tel.: (563) 556-7730
Web Site: http://www.flexsteel.com
Sales Range: $200-249.9 Million
Emp.: 500
Upholstered Furniture
N.A.I.C.S.: 336360

Flexsteel Lancaster Division　　　(1)
107 Pitney Rd, Lancaster, PA 17602
Tel.: (717) 392-4161
Sales Range: $50-74.9 Million
Emp.: 190
Mfr of Upholstered Furniture
N.A.I.C.S.: 337121

Flexsteel Metal Division　　　(1)
3400 Jackson St, Dubuque, IA
52001　　　(100%)
Tel.: (563) 556-7730
Web Site: http://www.flexsteel.com
Sales Range: $200-249.9 Million
Emp.: 450
Upholstered Furniture, Reclining Chairs &
Recreational Vehicle Seating Components
(Bare & Upholstered)
N.A.I.C.S.: 336360

Flexsteel New Paris Division　　　(1)
72104 County Rd 23, New Paris, IN
46553　　　(100%)
Tel.: (574) 831-4050
Sales Range: $100-124.9 Million
Emp.: 200
Office & Business Furniture
N.A.I.C.S.: 337121

Flexsteel Riverside Division　　　(1)

7227 Central Ave, Riverside, CA
92504-1432　　　(100%)
Tel.: (951) 354-2440
Web Site: http://www.flexsteel.com
Sales Range: $50-74.9 Million
Emp.: 200
Upholstered Furniture & Recreational Ve-
hicle Seating Components
N.A.I.C.S.: 624190

FLITWAYS TECHNOLOGY INC.
224 Datura St Ste 1015, West Palm
Beach, FL 33414
Tel.: (954) 837-6833　　　NV
Year Founded: 2012
FTWS—(OTCIQ)
Sales Range: $1-9.9 Million
Investment Services
N.A.I.C.S.: 523999

FLOOR & DECOR HOLDINGS, INC.
2500 Windy Rdg Pkwy SE, Atlanta,
GA 30339
Tel.: (404) 471-1634　　　DE
Web Site:
　　https://www.flooranddecor.com
Year Founded: 2000
FND—(NYSE)
Rev.: $4,413,884,000
Assets: $4,662,550,000
Liabilities: $2,731,560,000
Net Worth: $1,930,990,000
Earnings: $245,980,000
Emp.: 9,857
Fiscal Year-end: 12/31/23
Surface Flooring & Related Accesso-
ries Retailer
N.A.I.C.S.: 449121
David V. Christopherson (Chief Admin
Officer, Chief Legal Officer & Exec
VP)
David V. Christopherson (Gen Coun-
sel, Sec & Exec VP)
George Vincent West (Founder &
Vice Chm)
Steven A. Denny (Exec VP-Store
Ops)
Wayne Hood (VP-IR)
Matt McConnell (Sr Mgr-IR)
Luke Olson (Chief Acctg Officer)
Bryan H. Langley (CFO & Exec VP)
Ersan Sayman (Exec VP)
Thomas V. Taylor Jr. (CEO)

Subsidiaries:

Floor & Decor Outlets of America,
Inc.　　　(1)
2233 Lake Park Dr SE Ste 400, Smyrna,
GA 30080-8851
Tel.: (404) 471-1634
Web Site: http://www.flooranddecor.com
Emp.: 1,523
Hard Surface Flooring Retailer
N.A.I.C.S.: 449121
Lisa G. Laube (Chief Mdsg Officer & Exec
VP)
Trevor S. Lang (CFO & Exec VP)
Brian K. Robbins (Sr VP-Supply Chain)
James L. Davis (Sr VP-Store Ops)
Kevin G. Wiederhold (Sr VP-HR)
Thomas V. Taylor Jr. (CEO)

Spartan Surfaces, Inc.　　　(1)
10 S Hays St, Bel Air, MD 21014
Web Site: http://www.spartansurfaces.com
Durable Goods Merchant Whslr
N.A.I.C.S.: 423990
Tim Dormer (VP-Sls)
Kevin Jablon (Founder & CEO)

Subsidiary (Domestic):

Salesmaster Associates, Inc.　　　(2)
303 Marcus Blvd, Deer Park, NY 11729
Tel.: (631) 242-0100
Web Site:
　　http://www.salesmasterflooring.com
Sales Range: $1-9.9 Million
Emp.: 40
Home Furnishing Merchant Whslr

N.A.I.C.S.: 423220
Steven Kurtz (Pres)

FLOTEK INDUSTRIES, INC.
5775 N Sam Houston Prwy W Ste
400, Houston, TX 77086
Tel.: (713) 849-9911　　　DE
Web Site: https://www.flotekind.com
FTK—(NYSE)
Rev.: $136,092,000
Assets: $164,810,000
Liabilities: $162,214,000
Net Worth: $2,596,000
Earnings: ($42,305,000)
Emp.: 146
Fiscal Year-end: 12/31/22
Oilfield Equipment & Supplies Mfr,
Technical Services & Chemical Com-
pounds Mfr
N.A.I.C.S.: 325998
J. Bond Clement (CFO & Principal
Acctg Officer)
Shane Wise (Sr VP-Operations)
Andrea Berry (VP-People Ops)
Tom Redlinger (VP-Data Analytics)
Amy Blakeway (Gen Counsel & Sr
VP)
Leon Chad (Sr VP-Commercial)
Ryan G. Ezell (COO)

Subsidiaries:

Eclipse IOR Services, LLC　　　(1)
1670 Keller Pkwy Ste 259, Keller, TX 76248
Tel.: (817) 431-6336
Web Site: http://www.eoga.net
Oil & Gas Support Services
N.A.I.C.S.: 213112

FC Pro, LLC　　　(1)
19914 GH Cir, Waller, TX 77484
Tel.: (936) 463-4100
Web Site: http://www.fcprosolutions.com
Chemical Products Mfr
N.A.I.C.S.: 325199

Flotek Chemistry, LLC　　　(1)
1004 Plainsman Rd, Marlow, OK 73055
Tel.: (580) 658-6608
Chemical Products Mfr
N.A.I.C.S.: 325199

Petrovalve, Inc.　　　(1)
3801 Yale St Ste E, Houston, TX 77018
Tel.: (713) 676-1212
Web Site: https://petrovalve.com
Oil & Gas Field Equipment Mfr
N.A.I.C.S.: 333132

SiteLark, LLC　　　(1)
2121 W Spring Creek Pkwy Ste 106, Plano,
TX 75023
Tel.: (469) 222-5436
Web Site: http://www.sitelark.com
Chemicals Mfr
N.A.I.C.S.: 325199

FLOWERS FOODS, INC.
1919 Flowers Cir, Thomasville, GA
31757
Tel.: (229) 226-9110　　　GA
Web Site:
　　https://www.flowersfoods.com
Year Founded: 1919
FLO—(NYSE)
Rev.: $5,090,830,000
Assets: $3,426,953,000
Liabilities: $2,075,171,000
Net Worth: $1,351,782,000
Earnings: $123,416,000
Emp.: 9,300
Fiscal Year-end: 12/30/23
Holding Company; Fresh & Frozen
Bakery Foods Mfr
N.A.I.C.S.: 551112
R. Steve Kinsey (CFO & Chief Acctg
Officer)
Debo Mukherjee (CMO)
A. Ryals McMullian (Chm, Pres &
CEO)
David M. Roach (Chief Strategic Proj-
ects Officer)

Flowers Foods, Inc.—(Continued)

Heeth Varnedoe *(Pres & COO)*
Terry S. Thomas *(Chief Growth Officer)*
Mark Chaffin *(CIO)*
Stephanie B. Tillman *(Chief Legal Officer)*
Tom Winters *(Chief Supply Chain Officer)*
Cindy L. Cox *(Chief HR Officer)*
Robert L. Benton Jr. *(Exec VP-Network Optimization)*

Subsidiaries:

AVB, Inc. **(1)**
5209 SE International Way, Milwaukie, OR 97222
Tel.: (503) 335-8077
Web Site: https://www.daveskillerbread.com
Emp.: 300
Bread & Other Baked Goods Mfr & Whslr
N.A.I.C.S.: 311812
Dave Dahl *(Co-Founder)*
Shobi Dahl *(Co-Founder)*

Alpine Valley Bread Company **(1)**
300 W Southern Ave, Mesa, AZ 85210
Tel.: (480) 483-2774
Web Site: http://www.alpinevalleybread.com
Sales Range: $75-99.9 Million
Emp.: 282
Bread & Other Baked Goods Mfr & Whslr
N.A.I.C.S.: 311812

Bailey Street Bakery, LLC **(1)**
165 Bailey St SW, Atlanta, GA 30314
Tel.: (404) 588-9377
Web Site: https://www.flowerfsoods.com
Emp.: 200
Bakery Product Mfr & Distr
N.A.I.C.S.: 311812

C&G Holdings, Inc. **(1)**
701 Harger Rd Ste 190, Oak Brook, IL 60523-1490
Tel.: (630) 575-2334
Frozen Cake Mfr
N.A.I.C.S.: 311813

CK Sales Co., LLC **(1)**
1240 Cherokee Rd, Macomb, IL 61455
Tel.: (309) 836-7106
Bakery Product Mfr & Distr
N.A.I.C.S.: 311812

Canyon Bakehouse, LLC **(1)**
3600 Ronald Reagan Blvd, Johnstown, CO 80534
Tel.: (970) 461-3844
Web Site: http://www.canyonglutenfree.com
Packaged Food Product Distr
N.A.I.C.S.: 424420
Christi Skow *(Co-Founder)*

Corpus Christi Baking Co., LLC **(1)**
3717 Saratoga Blvd, Corpus Christi, TX 78415
Tel.: (361) 814-0558
Bakery Product Mfr & Distr
N.A.I.C.S.: 311812
David Brown *(Gen Mgr)*

Flowers Bakeries Brands, LLC **(1)**
1105 N Market St Ste 1300, Wilmington, DE 19801
Tel.: (302) 655-1467
Bakery Product Mfr & Distr
N.A.I.C.S.: 311812

Flowers Bakeries, LLC **(1)**
1919 Flowers Cir, Thomasville, GA 31757
Tel.: (229) 226-9110
Web Site: https://www.flowersfoods.com
Sales Range: $1-4.9 Billion
Emp.: 200
Commercial Bakeries Operator
N.A.I.C.S.: 311812

Subsidiary (Domestic):

Derst Baking Company, LLC **(2)**
1311 Mills B Ln Blvd, Savannah, GA 31405
Tel.: (912) 233-2235
Web Site: https://www.flowersfood.com
Sales Range: $250-299.9 Million
Emp.: 200
Bread, Cake & Related Products Mfr & Whslr

N.A.I.C.S.: 311812
Gary Cartee *(Pres)*

Flowers Baking Co. of Batesville, LLC **(2)**
1223 S Saint Louis St, Batesville, AR 72501
Tel.: (870) 793-6851
Rev.: $11,333,958
Emp.: 160
Breads, Rolls & Buns
N.A.I.C.S.: 311812
Michelle Parsley *(Mgr-HR)*

Lepage Bakeries, Inc. **(2)**
Country Kitchen Plz, Auburn, ME 04211
Tel.: (207) 783-9161
Web Site: http://www.lepagebakeries.com
Sales Range: $150-199.9 Million
Emp.: 525
Bakery Products Mfr & Whslr
N.A.I.C.S.: 311812
Andrew P. Barowsky *(Pres & CEO)*

Southern Bakeries, Inc. **(2)**
1919 Flowers Cir, Thomasville, GA 31757
Tel.: (863) 682-1155
Web Site: http://www.flowersfoods.com
Sales Range: $50-74.9 Million
Emp.: 200
Bread, Rolls & Related Products Mfr.
N.A.I.C.S.: 311812

Tasty Baking Company **(2)**
4300 S 26th St, Philadelphia, PA 19112
Tel.: (215) 221-8500
Web Site: https://www.tastykake.com
Sales Range: $250-299.9 Million
Cakes, Pies, Cookies & Donuts Mfr & Sales
N.A.I.C.S.: 311812

Subsidiary (Domestic):

TBC Financial Services, Inc. **(3)**
2801 W Hunting Park Ave, Philadelphia, PA 19129 **(100%)**
Tel.: (215) 221-8500
Web Site: http://www.tastykake.com
Sales Range: $200-249.9 Million
Financial Services
N.A.I.C.S.: 522299

Tasty Baking Oxford, Inc. **(3)**
700 Lincoln St, Oxford, PA 19363-1529 **(100%)**
Tel.: (610) 932-2300
Web Site: http://www.tastykake.com
Sales Range: $100-124.9 Million
Emp.: 186
Bakery
N.A.I.C.S.: 311812

Flowers Bakery of Cleveland, LLC **(1)**
1010 Flowero Cir, Thomasville, GA 31757
Tel.: (423) 472-1561
Sales Range: $75-99.9 Million
Emp.: 300
Bakery Product Mfr & Distr
N.A.I.C.S.: 311812
Kirk Gardner *(Dir-Ops)*

Flowers Bakery of Crossville, LLC **(1)**
1067 N Main St, Crossville, TN 38555
Tel.: (931) 484-6101
Web Site: https://www.flowersfoods.com
Sales Range: $75-99.9 Million
Emp.: 450
Bakery Product Mfr & Distr
N.A.I.C.S.: 311812
Frank Shipley *(Pres)*

Flowers Bakery of London, LLC **(1)**
501 E 4th St, London, KY 40741
Tel.: (606) 864-5161
Bakery Product Mfr & Distr.
N.A.I.C.S.: 311812
Kerry Phelps *(Mgr)*

Flowers Bakery of Montgomery, LLC **(1)**
140 Folmar Pkwy, Montgomery, AL 36105
Tel.: (334) 281-7030
Bakery Product Mfr & Distr
N.A.I.C.S.: 311812

Flowers Bakery of Texarkana, LLC **(1)**
7 Jim Walter Dr, Texarkana, AR 71854
Tel.: (870) 773-7523

Emp.: 100
Bakery Product Mfr & Distr
N.A.I.C.S.: 311812
Debbie Broussard *(Pres)*
Matt Phillips *(Dir-Environmental, Safety & Security)*

Flowers Bakery of Winston-Salem, LLC **(1)**
315 Cassell St, Winston Salem, NC 27108
Tel.: (336) 785-8700
Sales Range: $50-74.9 Million
Emp.: 150
Bakery Product Mfr & Distr
N.A.I.C.S.: 311812
Evan Griffin *(Pres-Plant)*

Flowers Baking Co. of Baton Rouge, LLC **(1)**
1504 Florida Blvd, Baton Rouge, LA 70802
Tel.: (225) 381-9699
Bakery Product Mfr & Distr
N.A.I.C.S.: 311812

Flowers Baking Co. of Birmingham, LLC **(1)**
900 16th St N, Birmingham, AL 35203
Tel.: (205) 263-1120
Web Site: https://www.flowersfoods.com
Emp.: 85
Bakery Product Mfr & Distr
N.A.I.C.S.: 311812

Flowers Baking Co. of Bradenton, LLC **(1)**
6490 Parkland Dr, Sarasota, FL 34203
Tel.: (941) 758-5656
Emp.: 200
Bakery Product Mfr & Distr
N.A.I.C.S.: 311812
Bo Strickland *(Pres-Plant)*
David Slozer *(Dir-Sls)*

Flowers Baking Co. of Denton, LLC **(1)**
4210 Edwards Rd, Denton, TX 76208-5964
Tel.: (940) 383-5280
Web Site: https://www.flowersfoods.com
Bakery Product Mfr & Distr
N.A.I.C.S.: 311812

Flowers Baking Co. of Denver, LLC **(1)**
80 E 62nd Ave, Denver, CO 80216
Tel.: (602) 354-7918
Frozen Cake Mfr
N.A.I.C.S.: 311813

Flowers Baking Co. of El Paso, LLC **(1)**
301 Dallas St, El Paso, TX 79901
Tel.: (915) 533-8434
Emp.: 85
Bakery Product Mfr & Distr
N.A.I.C.S.: 311812
Leonard Lcdebaca *(Dir-Distr Rels)*

Flowers Baking Co. of Florida, LLC **(1)**
1919 Flowers Cir, Thomasville, GA 31757
Tel.: (850) 478-8360
Bakery Product Mfr & Distr
N.A.I.C.S.: 311812

Flowers Baking Co. of Henderson, LLC **(1)**
501 Conestoga Way, Henderson, NV 89002
Tel.: (702) 567-6401
Emp.: 21
Frozen Cake Mfr
N.A.I.C.S.: 311813

Flowers Baking Co. of Jacksonville, LLC **(1)**
2261 W 30th St, Jacksonville, FL 32209
Tel.: (904) 354-3771
Bakery Product Mfr & Distr
N.A.I.C.S.: 311812
Jeff Perry *(Controller)*

Flowers Baking Co. of Jamestown, LLC **(1)**
801 W Main St, Jamestown, NC 27282
Tel.: (336) 841-6433
Bakery Product Mfr & Distr
N.A.I.C.S.: 311812
Tony Ufland *(VP-Sls)*

Flowers Baking Co. of Knoxville, LLC **(1)**

1919 Flowers Cir, Thomasville, GA 31757
Tel.: (865) 362-7530
Emp.: 150
Bakery Products Mfr
N.A.I.C.S.: 311812
Jess Maggard *(Pres-Plant)*

Flowers Baking Co. of Lafayette, LLC **(1)**
720 W Simcoe St, Lafayette, LA 70501
Tel.: (337) 232-1611
Web Site: https://www.flowersfoods.com
Bakery Product Mfr & Distr
N.A.I.C.S.: 311812

Flowers Baking Co. of McDonough, LLC **(1)**
715 Oak Grove Rd, McDonough, GA 30253
Tel.: (678) 583-1226
Emp.: 9
Bakery Product Mfr & Distr
N.A.I.C.S.: 311812

Flowers Baking Co. of Memphis, LLC **(1)**
1919 Flowers Cir, Thomasville, GA 31757
Tel.: (901) 213-2587
Bakery Product Mfr & Distr
N.A.I.C.S.: 311812

Flowers Baking Co. of Modesto, LLC **(1)**
736 Mariposa Rd, Modesto, CA 95354
Tel.: (209) 544-8852
Frozen Cake Mfr
N.A.I.C.S.: 311813
Paul Holshouser *(Pres)*

Flowers Baking Co. of New Orleans, LLC **(1)**
5646 Lewis Rd, New Orleans, LA 70126-2514
Tel.: (504) 241-1206
Sales Range: $25-49.9 Million
Emp.: 100
Bakery Product Mfr & Distr
N.A.I.C.S.: 311812
Rodney Beals *(Dir-Mfg)*

Flowers Baking Co. of Newton, LLC **(1)**
1633 Fisher Ct, Newton, NC 28658
Tel.: (828) 695-6000
Sales Range: $50-74.9 Million
Emp.: 200
Bakery Product Mfr & Distr
N.A.I.C.S.: 311812
Nick Webb *(Controller)*

Flowers Baking Co. of Norfolk, LLC **(1)**
1209 Corprew Ave, Norfolk, VA 23504
Tel.: (767) 622-0017
Web Site: https://www.flowersfood.com
Emp.: 145
Bakery Product Mfr & Distr
N.A.I.C.S.: 311812

Flowers Baking Co. of Ohio, LLC **(1)**
3818 Woodville Rd, Northwood, OH 43619-1844
Tel.: (419) 214-0570
Bakery Products Mfr
N.A.I.C.S.: 311812
Todd Yates *(Dir-Distr Rels)*

Flowers Baking Co. of Opelika, LLC **(1)**
101 Simmons St, Opelika, AL 36801
Tel.: (334) 749-8257
Web Site: https://www.flowersfoods.com
Sales Range: $25-49.9 Million
Emp.: 110
Bakery Product Mfr & Distr
N.A.I.C.S.: 311812

Flowers Baking Co. of Orlando, LLC **(1)**
1919 Flowers Cir, Thomasville, GA 31757-1137
Tel.: (407) 292-8227
Frozen Cake Mfr
N.A.I.C.S.: 311813

Flowers Baking Co. of San Antonio, LLC **(1)**
6000 NE Loop 410, San Antonio, TX 78218-5424
Tel.: (210) 661-2361

Bakery Product Mfr & Distr
N.A.I.C.S.: 311812
Joe Richter *(Pres)*

Flowers Baking Co. of Thomasville, LLC **(1)**
1919 Flowers Cir, Thomasville, GA 31757-1137
Tel.: (229) 226-9110
Frozen Cake Mfr
N.A.I.C.S.: 311813

Flowers Baking Co. of Tucker, LLC **(1)**
5055 S Royal Atlanta Dr, Tucker, GA 30084-3019
Tel.: (770) 723-6180
Bakery Product Mfr & Distr
N.A.I.C.S.: 311812

Flowers Baking Co. of Tuscaloosa, LLC **(1)**
641 S Lawrence St, Montgomery, AL 36104
Tel.: (205) 752-5586
Bakery Product Mfr & Distr
N.A.I.C.S.: 311812

Flowers Baking Co. of Tyler, LLC **(1)**
1200 W Erwin St, Tyler, TX 75702
Tel.: (903) 595-2421
Emp.: 150
Bakery Product Mfr & Distr
N.A.I.C.S.: 311812
Keven Moss *(Coord-Food Safety & Quality Assurance)*

Flowers Baking Co. of Villa Rica, LLC **(1)**
134 Doyle Mcclain Dr, Villa Rica, GA 30180
Tel.: (770) 459-2883
Web Site: https://www.flowersfoods.com
Bakery Product Mfr & Distr
N.A.I.C.S.: 311812

Flowers Foods Specialty Group, LLC **(1)**
5087 E S Royal Dr, Tucker, GA 30084
Tel.: (770) 723-6170
Web Site: https://www.flowersfoods.com
Bakery Product Mfr & Distr
N.A.I.C.S.: 311812

Flowers Specialty Snack Sales, Inc. **(1)**
1227 Livingston Rd, Crossville, TN 38555
Tel.: (931) 484-2192
Sales Range: $25-49.9 Million
Emp.: 20
Bakery Product Mfr & Distr
N.A.I.C.S.: 311812
Joel Norrod *(Gen Mgr)*

Franklin Baking Company, LLC **(1)**
500 W Grantham St, Goldsboro, NC 27530
Tel.: (919) 735-0344
Web Site: https://www.flowersfoods.com
Emp.: 300
Bakery Product Mfr & Distr
N.A.I.C.S.: 311812

Holsum Bakery, Inc. **(1)**
2322 W Lincoln St, Phoenix, AZ 85009-5827
Tel.: (602) 252-2351
Web Site: https://www.holsum.com
Bread, Buns & Rolls Bakery
N.A.I.C.S.: 311812

Leeland Baking Co., LLC **(1)**
4104 Leeland St, Houston, TX 77023
Tel.: (713) 220-5200
Web Site: https://www.flowersfoods.com
Emp.: 3
Bakery Product Mfr & Distr
N.A.I.C.S.: 311812

Leo's Foods, Inc. **(1)**
3200 Northern Cross Blvd, Fort Worth, TX 76137
Tel.: (817) 834-3200
Corn & Flour Tortilla Mfr
N.A.I.C.S.: 311830

FLOWERY GOLD MINES COMPANY OF NEVADA
4276 Napa Loop, Roseville, CA 95747
Tel.: (530) 394-7045   NV

Web Site:
https://www.flowerygoldmines.com
Year Founded: 1958
FLOD—(OTCIQ)
Gold Mining Services
N.A.I.C.S.: 212220
Norman A. Lamb *(Pres)*
M. Blair Ogden *(Sec)*
Katherine Ann Lamb *(Treas & VP)*

FLOWSERVE CORPORATION
5215 N O Connor Blvd Ste 700, Irving, TX 75039
Tel.: (972) 443-6500   NY
Web Site: https://www.flowserve.com
Year Founded: 1912
FLS—(NYSE)
Rev.: $4,320,577,000
Assets: $5,108,719,000
Liabilities: $3,133,668,000
Net Worth: $1,975,051,000
Earnings: $186,743,000
Emp.: 16,000
Fiscal Year-end: 12/31/23
Pumps & Precision-Engineered Flow Control Equipment Developer & Mfr
N.A.I.C.S.: 332911
Amy B. Schwetz *(CFO & Sr VP)*
R. Scott Rowe *(Pres & CEO)*
Scott K. Vopni *(Chief Acctg Officer & VP)*
Mike Mullin *(Dir-IR)*
Lamar L. Duhon *(Pres-Flowserve Pumps Div)*
Juan Carrera *(VP)*
Susan C. Hudson *(Chief Legal Officer)*
Karthik Sivaraman *(VP)*
John E. Roueche III *(Treas & VP-IR)*

Subsidiaries:

Argus GmbH & Co. K.G. **(1)**
Pforzheimer Str 126, 76275, Ettlingen, Germany **(100%)**
Tel.: (49) 724350550
Sales Range: $50-74.9 Million
Emp.: 320
Industrial Valve Mfr
N.A.I.C.S.: 332911

CALDER GMBH **(1)**
Industrie Nord, 5704, Egliswil, 5704, Switzerland
Tel.: (41) 627696060
Emp.: 7
Industrial Machinery & Equipment Distr
N.A.I.C.S.: 423830
Beat Schneider *(Mng Dir & Mgr-Global Desalination)*

Davco Equipment, Inc. **(1)**
1744 W 4th St, Freeport, TX 77541-5043 **(100%)**
Tel.: (979) 239-3300
Web Site: http://www.flowserve.com
Sales Range: $25-49.9 Million
Emp.: 7
Sales & Distribution For Valve Division Automax & Valtek Product Lines
N.A.I.C.S.: 332911

FLOWSERVE - AL MANSOORI SERVICES COMPANY LTD. **(1)**
Mussafah, PO Box 26443, Abu Dhabi, United Arab Emirates
Tel.: (971) 25542464
Web Site: http://www.almansoori.biz
Specialized Engineering Services
N.A.I.C.S.: 541330
Ibrahim Alalawi *(Deputy CEO)*
Hicham AbuChaker *(Sls Mgr)*
Nabil Alalawi *(CEO)*
Muhannad Saadeh *(COO & Pres)*
Chris Kuijken *(CTO)*
Adel Baobaid *(Pres)*
Arindam Das *(CFO)*

FLOWSERVE EMA HOLDINGS B.V. **(1)**
Parallelweg 6, 4878 AH, Etten-Leur, Netherlands
Tel.: (31) 765028200
Industrial Valve Mfr

N.A.I.C.S.: 332911

FLOWSERVE FINLAND OY **(1)**
Urakoitsijantie 12 C, 06450, Porvoo, Finland
Tel.: (358) 445758680
Industrial Machinery & Equipment Distr
N.A.I.C.S.: 423830

FLOWSERVE S. DE R.L. DE C.V. **(1)**
Av Via Morelos No 437 Santa Clara Coatitla, Ecatepec, 55540, Estado de Mexico, Mexico
Tel.: (52) 5556991000
Web Site: https://www.flowserve.com
Emp.: 900
Pump & Pumping Equipment
N.A.I.C.S.: 333914

FLOWSERVE SIHI (ITALY) S.r.L. **(1)**
Via Prealpi 30/32, Cormano, 20032, Milan, Italy
Tel.: (39) 02663251
Pumps Mfr
N.A.I.C.S.: 333914
Roberto Mario Riva *(Gen Mgr)*

FLOWSERVE SIHI (SPAIN) S.L. **(1)**
Vereda de los Zapateros s/n Pozuelo de Alarcon, 28223, Madrid, Spain
Tel.: (34) 917091310
Web Site: https://www.sterlingsihi.com
Pumps Mfr
N.A.I.C.S.: 333914
Jose Antonio Cobo *(Gen Mgr)*

FLOWSERVE SIHI CZ S.R.O. **(1)**
Zeleznicni 512/7, 779 00, Olomouc, Czech Republic
Tel.: (420) 588503041
Pumps Mfr
N.A.I.C.S.: 333914

FLOWSERVE SIHI GERMANY GMBH **(1)**
Lindenstrasse 170, 25524, Itzehoe, Germany
Tel.: (49) 4821771671
Pumps Mfr
N.A.I.C.S.: 333914

Flowserve (Austria) GmbH **(1)**
Industriestrasse B6, 2345, Brunn am Gebirge, Austria **(100%)**
Tel.: (43) 223631530
Sales Range: $125-149.9 Million
Emp.: 250
Industrial Machinery & Equipment Distr
N.A.I.C.S.: 423830

Flowserve (Belgium) BVBA **(1)**
Zone Gosset - t Hofveld 1, 1702, Groot-Bijgaarden, Belgium
Tel.: (32) 24817711
Liquid Pump & Vacuum Pump Mfr
N.A.I.C.S.: 333914

Flowserve (Thailand) Ltd. **(1)**
252/93C 17th Floor Muang Thai Phatra Complex Tower B Rachadaphisek Rd, Hauykwang, Bangkok, 10310, Thailand **(100%)**
Tel.: (66) 26934488
Web Site: https://www.flowserve.com
Sales Range: $125-149.9 Million
Flow Control Products
N.A.I.C.S.: 333914

Flowserve Ahaus GmbH **(1)**
Von-Braun-Str 19a, 48683, Ahaus, Germany **(100%)**
Tel.: (49) 2561686100
Web Site: https://www.flowserve.de
Sales Range: $75-99.9 Million
Emp.: 140
Atomic Ball Valves, Inline Strainers & Sight Glasses
N.A.I.C.S.: 332911

Flowserve Australia Pty. Ltd. **(1)**
14 Dalmore Drive, Scoresby, 3179, VIC, Australia **(100%)**
Tel.: (61) 397593300
Web Site: https://www.flowserve.com
Sales Range: $25-49.9 Million
Emp.: 118
Industrial Machinery & Equipment Distr
N.A.I.C.S.: 423830

Flowserve B.V. **(1)**

Parallelweg 6, 4878 AH, Etten-Leur, Netherlands **(100%)**
Tel.: (31) 765028200
Sales Range: $150-199.9 Million
Emp.: 400
Industrial Machinery & Equipment Distr
N.A.I.C.S.: 423830
G Snaathorst *(Mng Dir)*

Flowserve Belgium N.V. **(1)**
Excelsiorlaan 17 B3, 1930, Zaventem, Belgium **(100%)**
Tel.: (32) 27149950
Web Site: https://www.flowserve.com
Sales Range: $1-9.9 Million
Emp.: 6
Industrial Machinery & Equipment Distr
N.A.I.C.S.: 423830

Flowserve Canada Corp. **(1)**
9044 18th St, Edmonton, T6P 1K6, AB, Canada **(100%)**
Tel.: (780) 449-4850
Web Site: https://www.flowserve.com
Sales Range: $25-49.9 Million
Emp.: 50
Industrial Machinery & Equipment Distr
N.A.I.C.S.: 423830

Division (Domestic):

Flowserve Woodbridge Division **(2)**
120 Vinyl Ct, Woodbridge, L4L 4A3, ON, Canada **(100%)**
Tel.: (905) 856-1140
Web Site: http://www.flowserve.com
Sales Range: $25-49.9 Million
Emp.: 45
Pumps & Valves Whslr
N.A.I.C.S.: 423830

Flowserve Chile S.A. **(1)**
Issa Pichara 830 Sector 4-B Renca, Santiago, 8640000, Chile **(100%)**
Tel.: (56) 229799600
Web Site: https://www.flowserve.com
Sales Range: $10-24.9 Million
Emp.: 6
Industrial Machinery & Equipment Distr
N.A.I.C.S.: 423830

Flowserve Colombia, Ltda. **(1)**
Calle 13C #75-55 Casa 7, Cali, Colombia **(100%)**
Tel.: (57) 23152806
Sales Range: $125-149.9 Million
Industrial Machinery & Equipment Distr
N.A.I.C.S.: 423830

Flowserve Corp. **(1)**
2920 W Cardinal Dr, Beaumont, TX 77705-4536 **(100%)**
Tel.: (409) 842-6600
Web Site: http://www.flowserve.com
Sales Range: $10-24.9 Million
Emp.: 30
Valve & Actuator Maintenance Services to the Fossil Fuel & Processing Industries
N.A.I.C.S.: 811210

Flowserve Corp. **(1)**
7800 S 196 St, Kent, WA 98032 **(100%)**
Tel.: (253) 627-6100
Web Site: http://www.flowserve.com
Sales Range: $125-149.9 Million
Valve & Actuator Maintenance Services for the Fossil Fuel & Processing Industries
N.A.I.C.S.: 333914

Flowserve Corp. **(1)**
2300 E Vernon Ave, Los Angeles, CA 90058 **(100%)**
Tel.: (323) 587-6171
Web Site: http://www.flowserve.com
Sales Range: $450-499.9 Million
Emp.: 360
Pumps
N.A.I.C.S.: 333914

Flowserve Corp. **(1)**
2100 Factory St, Kalamazoo, MI 49001 **(100%)**
Tel.: (269) 381-2650
Web Site: http://www.flowserve.com
Sales Range: $75-99.9 Million
Emp.: 450
Rotary Mechanical Seals; Flexible Metallic Packing

Flowserve Corporation—(Continued)
N.A.I.C.S.: 339991

Flowserve Corp. (1)
1400 Cavalier Blvd, Chesapeake, VA
23323-1626 **(100%)**
Tel.: (972) 443-6500
Web Site: http://www.flowserve.com
Sales Range: $25-49.9 Million
Emp.: 30
Pumps & Pumping Equipment
N.A.I.C.S.: 333914

Flowserve Corp. (1)
5215 N O'Connor Blvd Ste 700, Irving, TX
75039 **(100%)**
Tel.: (937) 226-4000
Web Site: http://www.flowserve.com
Sales Range: $125-149.9 Million
Emp.: 280
Pumps & Valves
N.A.I.C.S.: 333914

Flowserve Corp. (1)
1978 Foreman Dr, Cookeville, TN
38501 **(100%)**
Tel.: (931) 432-4021
Web Site: http://www.flowserve.com
Sales Range: $125-149.9 Million
Emp.: 300
Process Valve Pipe Fittings
N.A.I.C.S.: 332911

Flowserve Corp. (1)
1350 Mountain Springs Pkwy, Springville,
UT 84663-3004 **(100%)**
Tel.: (801) 489-8611
Web Site: http://www.flowserve.com
Sales Range: $50-74.9 Million
Emp.: 200
Pneumatic, Electric & Hydraulic Actuators;
Pneumatic & Electronic Positioners; Limit
Switches & All Mounting Hardware
N.A.I.C.S.: 332911
Des Lowrie *(Mng Dir)*

Flowserve Corp. (1)
1341 W 2nd St, Hastings, NE
68901-4960 **(100%)**
Tel.: (402) 463-1306
Web Site: http://www.flowserve.com
Sales Range: $75-99.9 Million
Emp.: 175
Agricultural & Industrial Pumps
N.A.I.C.S.: 333914

**Flowserve Dortmund GmbH & Co.
KG** (1)
Lindentalweg 4, D-44388, Dortmund,
Germany **(100%)**
Tel.: (49) 23169640
Sales Range: $125-149.9 Million
Emp.: 200
Industrial Machinery & Equipment Distr
N.A.I.C.S.: 423830

**Flowserve Dortmund Verwaltungs
GmbH** (1)
Lindentalweg 4, 44388, Dortmund,
Germany **(100%)**
Tel.: (49) 2316964127
Sales Range: $75-99.9 Million
Emp.: 220
Pumps & Pumping Equipment
N.A.I.C.S.: 333914

Flowserve Essen GmbH (1)
Schederhofstr 71, 45145, Essen,
Germany **(100%)**
Tel.: (49) 20189195
Sales Range: $10-24.9 Million
Emp.: 8
Industrial Machinery & Equipment Distr
N.A.I.C.S.: 423830
Andreas Vandre *(Mgr-District)*

**Flowserve Flow Control Benelux
BV** (1)
Rechtzaad 17, 4703 RC, Roosendaal, 4703
RC, Netherlands **(100%)**
Tel.: (31) 165598800
Web Site: http://www.flowserve.com
Sales Range: $10-24.9 Million
Emp.: 40
Industrial Machinery & Equipment Distr
N.A.I.C.S.: 423830

Flowserve Flow Control GmbH (1)
Rudolf-Plank-Str 2, D-76275, Ettlingen,
Germany **(100%)**

Tel.: (49) 7243103480
Web Site: https://www.flowserve-argus.de
Sales Range: $125-149.9 Million
Emp.: 500
Industrial Machinery & Equipment Distr
N.A.I.C.S.: 423830

Flowserve GB Limited (1)
Euro House Abex Road, Newbury, RG14
5EY, Berkshire, United Kingdom
Tel.: (44) 163546999
Web Site: https://www.flowserve.com
Emp.: 10
Industrial Machinery & Equipment Distr
N.A.I.C.S.: 423830

Flowserve GmbH (1)
Schederhofstr 71, 45145, Essen,
Germany **(100%)**
Tel.: (49) 20189195
Web Site: http://www.flowserve.de
Sales Range: $25-49.9 Million
Emp.: 100
Special Industry Machinery
N.A.I.C.S.: 333310

Flowserve Hamburg GmbH (1)
Friedrich-Ebert-Damm 105, Hamburg,
22047, Germany **(100%)**
Tel.: (49) 40696890
Web Site: http://www.flowserve.com
Sales Range: $125-149.9 Million
Pumps & Pumping Equipment Mfr
N.A.I.C.S.: 333914

**Flowserve India Controls Pvt.
Ltd.** (1)
Plot 4 1A Road 8 ERIP, Whitefield, Benga-
luru, 560 066, Karnataka, India
Tel.: (91) 8040146200
Web Site: https://www.flowserve.com
Sales Range: $150-199.9 Million
Emp.: 500
Industrial Machinery & Equipment Distr
N.A.I.C.S.: 423830
Ajit Francis Devotta *(Dir Gen)*

Flowserve International Limited (1)
Atlas Works Station Road, Ellesmere, CH65
3EN, Cheshire, United Kingdom **(100%)**
Tel.: (44) 1513560555
Web Site: https://www.flowserve.com
Sales Range: $125-149.9 Million
Emp.: 32
Industrial Machinery & Equipment Distr
N.A.I.C.S.: 423830

Flowserve Limitorque Div. (1)
5114 Woodall Rd, Lynchburg, VA
24502-2248 **(100%)**
Tel.: (434) 528-4400
Web Site: http://www.limitorque.com
Rev.: $15,000,000
Emp.: 300
Industrial Actuators
N.A.I.C.S.: 522299

Flowserve Ltd. (1)
Harley House 94 Hare Lane, Claygate,
KT10 0RB, Esher Surrey, United
Kingdom **(100%)**
Tel.: (44) 1372463700
Web Site: http://www.flowserve.com
Sales Range: $25-49.9 Million
Emp.: 10
Sales, Assembly & Modification Center for
Durco Pumps & Valves
N.A.I.C.S.: 333914

Flowserve Ltda. (1)
Rua Tocantins 128, Sao Caetano do Sul,
09580-130, Sao Paulo, Brazil **(100%)**
Tel.: (55) 112 169 6338
Web Site: http://www.flowserve.com
Sales Range: $125-149.9 Million
Emp.: 150
Pumps & Pumping Equipment
N.A.I.C.S.: 333914

**Flowserve Niigata Worthington Com-
pany Ltd.** (1)
580 Horikawa-cho, Saiwai-ku, Kawasaki,
210-0913, Kanagawa, Japan **(100%)**
Tel.: (81) 445447461
Web Site: http://www.niigata-wor.co.jp
Sales Range: $25-49.9 Million
Emp.: 200
Pumps, Compressors & Steam Turbines Mfr
N.A.I.C.S.: 333914

Flowserve PMV USA Inc. (1)

1440 Lk Front Cir Ste 160, Spring, TX
77380-3630 **(100%)**
Tel.: (281) 292-7500
Web Site: http://www.pmvusa.com
Sales Range: $10-24.9 Million
Emp.: 8
Sales of Valves Positioners
N.A.I.C.S.: 423830

Flowserve Pompes S.A.S. (1)
Route D Angers, F-72234, Arnage,
France **(100%)**
Tel.: (33) 43405775
Sales Range: $100-124.9 Million
Emp.: 285
Industrial Machinery & Equipment Distr
N.A.I.C.S.: 423830

Flowserve Pte. Ltd. (1)
12 Tuas Ave 20, Singapore, 638824,
Singapore **(100%)**
Tel.: (65) 68798989
Web Site: https://www.flowserve.com
Industrial Machinery & Equipment Distr
N.A.I.C.S.: 423830

Flowserve Pumps Limited (1)
Hawton Lane New Balderton, PO Box 17,
Newark, NG24 3BU, Notts, United
Kingdom **(100%)**
Tel.: (44) 1636494600
Web Site: http://www.flowserve.com
Sales Range: $10-24.9 Million
Emp.: 70
Flow Control Products
N.A.I.C.S.: 333914

Flowserve S.A. (1)
S/N Pol Ind Riu Clar, 43006, Tarragona,
Spain **(100%)**
Tel.: (34) 34977554131
Web Site: https://www.flowserve.com
Sales Range: $25-49.9 Million
Emp.: 30
Pump & Pumping Equipment Mfr
N.A.I.C.S.: 333914

Flowserve S.A. de C.V. (1)
Via Morelos 537 Acatepec, Mexico, 55540,
EDO, Mexico **(100%)**
Tel.: (52) 5556991000
Sales Range: $125-149.9 Million
Emp.: 440
Pumps & Mechanical Seals Mfr
N.A.I.C.S.: 333914

Flowserve S.A.S. (1)
12 Avenue du Quebec, 91140, Villebon-sur-
Yvette, France **(100%)**
Tel.: (33) 1 69 59 24 00
Web Site: http://www.flowserve.com
Sales Range: $10-24.9 Million
Emp.: 4
Industrial Machinery & Equipment Distr
N.A.I.C.S.: 423830

Flowserve S.R.L. (1)
Chuquisaca 302 5547, Godoy Cruz, Argen-
tina
Tel.: (54) 2614053100
Flow Control Equipment Mfr
N.A.I.C.S.: 332911

Flowserve S.p.A. (1)
Via Prealpi 30/32 Cormano, 20032, Milan,
Italy **(100%)**
Tel.: (39) 02663251
Sales Range: $125-149.9 Million
Pumps & Pumping Equipment
N.A.I.C.S.: 333914

Flowserve S.r.l. (1)
Via Prealpi 30/32, Cormano, 20032, MI,
Italy
Tel.: (39) 02 663251
Web Site: http://www.flowserve.com
Sales Range: $75-99.9 Million
Emp.: 400
Industrial Machinery & Equipment Distr
N.A.I.C.S.: 423830

Flowserve Sanmar Ltd. (1)
147 Karapakkam Village, Chennai, 600 097,
Tamil Nadu, India
Tel.: (91) 4424504100
Web Site: http://www.sanmar.com
Emp.: 900
Mechanical Sealing Device Mfr; Owned by
Sanmar Holdings Ltd. & by Flowserve Cor-
poration
N.A.I.C.S.: 339991

Flowserve Sihi (France) SAS (1)
Z I Trappes-Elancourt 1-3 Avenue Georges
Politzer, 78197, Trappes, France
Tel.: (33) 134823900
Liquid Pump & Vacuum Pump Mfr
N.A.I.C.S.: 333914
Aicha Yolande Toure *(Project Mgr)*

Flowserve Sihi (Schweiz) GmbH (1)
Schweizersbildstrasse 25, 8207, Schaff-
hausen, Switzerland
Tel.: (41) 526440606
Web Site: https://www.sterlingsihi.com
Pumping Equipment Distr
N.A.I.C.S.: 423830

Flowserve Sihi Austria GmbH (1)
Gewerbestrasse 14, 2351, Wiener Neudorf,
Austria
Tel.: (43) 223631550
Liquid Pump & Vacuum Pump Mfr
N.A.I.C.S.: 333914
Michael Bauer *(Mgr-Customer Svc)*

Flowserve Sihi Bulgaria Eood (1)
75 Ilinden Blvd, 1309, Sofia, Bulgaria
Tel.: (359) 28228311
Vacuum Pump Distr
N.A.I.C.S.: 423830

Flowserve Sihi Hungary Kft (1)
Kisto Utca 11, 8200, Veszprem, Hungary
Tel.: (36) 88406633
Pumping Equipment Distr
N.A.I.C.S.: 423830

Flowserve Sweden AB (1)
Gelbgjutaregatan 2, Linkoping, 58187, Swe-
den
Tel.: (46) 13316100
Web Site: http://www.naf.se
Sales Range: $25-49.9 Million
Emp.: 80
Industrial Valve Mfr
N.A.I.C.S.: 332911

Flowserve Worthington s.r.l. (1)
Via Rossini 90 92, 20033, Desio, Milano,
Italy **(100%)**
Tel.: (39) 03626121
Web Site: http://www.flowserve.com
Sales Range: $125-149.9 Million
Emp.: 400
Pumps & Pumping Equipment
N.A.I.C.S.: 333914

Hyosung Ebara Co., Ltd. (1)
(5%)
Sales Range: $25-49.9 Million
Emp.: 40
Mfr & Sales of Pumps; Joint Venture of
Ebara Corporation & Hyosung Corporation
N.A.I.C.S.: 333914

**INGERSOLL-DRESSER PUMPS
S.R.L.** (1)
Via Gioacchino Rossini 90, 20832, Desio,
20832, Italy
Tel.: (39) 03626121
Emp.: 457
Holding Company
N.A.I.C.S.: 551112

Lawrence Pumps, Inc. (1)
371 Market St, Lawrence, MA 01843
Tel.: (978) 682-5248
Sales Range: $50-74.9 Million
Emp.: 300
Centrifugal Pumps Designer & Mfr
N.A.I.C.S.: 333914

Subsidiary (Non-US):

**Lawrence Pumps (Shanghai) Com-
pany Limited** (2)
Unit 1415D Cimic Plaza No 800 Shang
Cheng Road, Pudong, Shanghai, 200120,
China **(100%)**
Tel.: (86) 21 2215 7757
Pumps Mfr & Sales
N.A.I.C.S.: 333914

MOGAS Industries, Inc. (1)
14204 E Hardy St, Houston, TX 77039
Tel.: (281) 449-0291
Web Site: http://www.mogas.com
Sales Range: $75-99.9 Million
Emp.: 70
Mfr of Industrial Valves
N.A.I.C.S.: 332911

Matthew L. Mogas *(Pres & CEO)*
Rajan Luthra *(VP-Mktg)*
Jimmy Walker *(VP-Svc)*

Subsidiary (Non-US):

MOGAS Industries Pty Ltd **(2)**
63 Tacoma Circuit, Canning Vale, Perth,
6155, WA, Australia
Tel.: (61) 894563533
Ball Valve Sales & Repair Services
N.A.I.C.S.: 811210

MOGAS Industries, LTD **(2)**
Kingsley Business Park New Road, Market
Harborough, LE8 0LE, Leicester, United
Kingdom
Tel.: (44) 1162793367
Metal Valve & Pipe Fitting Mfr
N.A.I.C.S.: 332919

PMV AUTOMATION AB **(1)**
Korta Gatan 9, 171 54, Solna, Sweden
Tel.: (46) 855510600
Web Site: https://pmv.nu
Industrial Valve Mfr
N.A.I.C.S.: 332911
Ardeshir Anbarestani *(Mgr-QA)*

PT Flowserve
Jl Pulokambing Blok OR 5 Jakarta Industrial
Estate Pulogadung, Jakarta Timur, Jakarta,
13920, Indonesia **(75%)**
Tel.: (62) 2146830105
Web Site: https://www.flowserve.com
Sales Range: $125-149.9 Million
Emp.: 50
Industrial Machinery & Equipment Distr
N.A.I.C.S.: 332911

Palmstierna International AB **(1)**
Korta Galan 9, 171 54, Solna,
Sweden **(100%)**
Tel.: (46) 855510600
Web Site: http://www.pmv.nu
Sales Range: $125-149.9 Million
Flow Control Equipment
N.A.I.C.S.: 333914

SIHI GROUP B.V. **(1)**
Parallelweg 6, Etten-Leur, 4878 AH, Nether-
lands
Tel.: (31) 205474830
Industrial Equipment Mfr
N.A.I.C.S.: 333310

STERLING FLUID SYSTEMS (AUS-
TRIA) GMBH **(1)**
Gewerbestrasse 14, 2351, Wiener Neudorf,
Austria
Tel.: (43) 223631530
Pumps Mfr
N.A.I.C.S.: 333914

STERLING FLUID SYSTEMS
(CZECH REPUBLIC) S.R.O. **(1)**
Zeleznici 512/7, 779 00, Olomouc, Czech
Republic
Tel.: (420) 587433651
Pumping Equipment Whslr
N.A.I.C.S.: 423830
Martin Riha *(Acct Mgr-Indus Pumps)*

STERLING FLUID SYSTEMS (HUN-
GARIA) Kft. **(1)**
Radnoti ter 2/A, 8200, Veszprem, Hungary
Tel.: (36) 88406633
Industrial Machinery & Equipment Distr
N.A.I.C.S.: 332911

STERLING FLUID SYSTEMS (ITALY)
S.p.A. **(1)**
Via Pompei 15, Monza, 20052, Italy
Tel.: (39) 03928241
Air & Gas Compressor Mfr
N.A.I.C.S.: 333912
Stefano Zanardi *(Mgr-Order Processing)*

STERLING FLUID SYSTEMS (PO-
LASKA) Sp.zo.o. **(1)**
Ul Poleczki 23, 02-822, Warsaw, Poland
Tel.: (48) 223352480
Pumping Equipment Whslr
N.A.I.C.S.: 423830
Andrzej Gizicki *(Gen Mgr)*

STERLING FLUID SYSTEMS (POL-
SKA) Sp.zo.o. **(1)**
Ul Poleczki 23, 02-822, Warsaw, Poland
Tel.: (48) 223352483

Pumps Mfr
N.A.I.C.S.: 333914
Andrzej Gizicki *(Gen Mgr)*

STERLING FLUID SYSTEMS (RO-
MANIA) S.R.L. **(1)**
Strada Mihai Eminescu nr 105-107 sector 2,
020074, Bucharest, Romania
Tel.: (40) 212117678
Web Site: https://www.sterlingsihi.com
Pumping Equipment Whslr
N.A.I.C.S.: 423830
Calin Leonte *(Dir-Technic)*

STERLING SIHI (NETHERLANDS)
B.V. **(1)**
Havenstraat 22-28, 1948 NP, Beverwijk,
Netherlands
Tel.: (31) 251263232
Pumps Mfr
N.A.I.C.S.: 333914

STERLING SIHI BULGARIA
EOOD **(1)**
bul Todor Aleksandrov bl 75, 1309, Sofia,
Bulgaria
Tel.: (359) 28228311
Pumps Mfr
N.A.I.C.S.: 333914

Sterling Industry Consult GmbH **(1)**
Lindenstrasse 170, 25524, Itzehoe, Ger-
many
Tel.: (49) 4821771671
Industrial Machinery & Equipment Distr
N.A.I.C.S.: 332911

Thompsons, Kelly & Lewis Pty
Ltd **(1)**
5 Parker St, Castlemaine, 3170, VIC,
Australia **(100%)**
Tel.: (61) 300661777
Web Site: https://www.tkl.com.au
Pumping Equipment Mfr
N.A.I.C.S.: 333914

VALBART S.R.L. **(1)**
Via delle Industrie 9/5 Provincia di Monza e
della Brianza, Mezzago, 20883, Milan, Italy
Tel.: (39) 039624111
Emp.: 350
Industrial Machinery & Equipment Distr
N.A.I.C.S.: 332911

WORTHINGTON S.R.L. **(1)**
Via Rossini 90/92, PO Box 178, 20832, De-
sio, MB, Italy
Tel.: (39) 03626121
Web Site: https://www.worthington.it
Emp.: 400
Pump & Pumping Equipment
N.A.I.C.S.: 333914

Worcester Controls UK **(1)**
Burrell Rd, Haywards Heath, RH16 1TL, W
Sussex, United Kingdom **(100%)**
Tel.: (44) 1444314400
Web Site: http://www.flowserve.com
Sales Range: $75-99.9 Million
Emp.: 150
Process Ball Valves
N.A.I.C.S.: 332911

Worthington S.p.A. **(1)**
Via Rossini 90/92, PO Box 178, 20033, De-
sio, MB, Italy **(100%)**
Tel.: (39) 03626121
Web Site: http://www.flowserve.com
Sales Range: $25-49.9 Million
Emp.: 400
Pumps & Pumping Equipment
N.A.I.C.S.: 333914

FLUENCE CORPORATION LIM-
ITED

3600 Holly Ln N Ste 100, Plymouth,
MN 55447
Tel.: (763) 746-8400 **AU**
Web Site:
https://www.fluencecorp.com
Year Founded: 2008
FLC—(ASX)
Sales Range: $25-49.9 Million
Water Purification Technology Devel-
oper
N.A.I.C.S.: 221310

Ronen Shechter *(CTO)*
Yaron Bar-Tal *(VP- Global Product
Dev)*
Ilan Wilf *(VP-Global Sls)*
Richard Irving *(Chm)*
Ross Kennedy *(Sec)*
Henry Charrabe *(Mng Dir & CEO)*
Francesco Fragasso *(CFO)*
Erik Arfalk *(CMO)*
Spencer D. Smith *(Chief Legal Offi-
cer)*
Tony Hargrave *(COO)*

Subsidiaries:

Aeromix Systems, Inc. **(1)**
7135 Madison Ave W, Minneapolis, MN
55427
Tel.: (763) 746-8400
Web Site: http://www.aeromix.com
Sales Range: $1-9.9 Million
Emp.: 25
Mfg Service Industry Machinery
N.A.I.C.S.: 333310
Kevin Kernan *(Mgr-Shipping)*
Buddy Harris *(Gen Mgr)*

Emefcy Ltd. **(1)**
7 Ha'eshel Street Caesarea Industrial Park,
PO Box 3171, Caesarea, Israel
Tel.: (972) 4 6277555
Water Purification Technology Developer
N.A.I.C.S.: 221310

FLUENCE ENERGY, INC.

4601 Fairfax Dr Ste 600, Arlington,
VA 22203 **DE**
Web Site:
https://www.fluenceenergy.com
Year Founded: 2021
FLNC—(NASDAQ)
Rev.: $2,217,978,000
Assets: $1,352,149,000
Liabilities: $795,819,000
Net Worth: $556,330,000
Earnings: ($69,620,000)
Emp.: 1,112
Fiscal Year-end: 09/30/23
Offices of Other Holding Companies
N.A.I.C.S.: 551112
Herman E. Bulls *(Chm)*
Ahmed Pasha *(CFO & Sr VP)*
Tejas P. Shah *(CIO-Global)*
Michelle Philpot *(Chief Acctg Officer)*
Rebecca J. Boll *(Chief Product Offi-
cer & Sr VP)*
Carol Couch *(Chief Supply Chain &
Mfg Officer)*
Phil Goodman *(VP-Digital Ops &
Strategy)*
Roman Loosen *(Chief Bus Officer,
Transformation Officer & Sr VP)*
Shayla Ebsen *(Dir-Comm)*
Lexington May *(VP-IR)*
Brett Galura *(CTO)*
Krishna Vanka *(Chief Digital Officer)*
Larissa Cerqueira *(Chief HR Officer)*
Frank Fuselier *(Corp Counsel)*
Marek Wolek *(Sr VP)*

FLUENT, INC.

300 Vesey St 9th Fl, New York, NY
10282
Tel.: (646) 669-7272 **DE**
Web Site: https://www.fluentco.com
Year Founded: 2007
FLNT—(NASDAQ)
Rev.: $361,134,000
Assets: $183,969,000
Liabilities: $90,014,000
Net Worth: $93,955,000
Earnings: ($123,332,000)
Emp.: 272
Fiscal Year-end: 12/31/22
Holding Company; Advertising Ser-
vices
N.A.I.C.S.: 551112
Ryan Schulke *(Chm & Chief Strategy
Officer)*

Ryan Perfit *(CFO & Principal Acctg
Officer)*
Matthew Conlin *(Chief Customer Offi-
cer)*
Dan Hall *(CTO)*
Sean Cullen *(Exec VP-Product)*
Dan Barsky *(Gen Counsel)*
Jessica Batty *(Sr VP)*
Matt Koncz *(Pres)*

Subsidiaries:

Fluent, LLC **(1)**
33 Whitehall St 15th Fl, New York, NY
10004
Tel.: (646) 669-7272
Web Site: http://www.fluentco.com
Sales Range: $50-74.9 Million
Emp.: 52
Advertising & Marketing Services
N.A.I.C.S.: 541810
Ryan Schulke *(Co-Founder & CEO)*
Matt Conlin *(Co-Founder & Pres)*
Sean Cullen *(Exec VP-Product & Tech)*
Matt Koncz *(Pres-Performance Media Grp)*

FLUOR CORPORATION

6700 Las Colinas Blvd, Irving, TX
75039
Tel.: (469) 398-7000 **DE**
Web Site: https://www.fluor.com
Year Founded: 1890
FLR—(NYSE)
Rev.: $15,474,000,000
Assets: $6,973,000,000
Liabilities: $4,921,000,000
Net Worth: $2,052,000,000
Earnings: $139,000,000
Emp.: 30,187
Fiscal Year-end: 12/31/23
Holding Company; Engineering, Pro-
curement, Construction & Mainte-
nance Services
N.A.I.C.S.: 551112
John C. Regan *(Chief Acctg Officer,
Exec VP & Controller)*
James Lozier *(Mgr-Svcs)*
Dan Spinks *(Sr VP-)*
Tracey H. Cook *(VP)*
Joseph L. Brennan *(CFO & Exec VP)*
Stacy L. Dillow *(Chief HR Officer &
Exec VP)*
James R. Breuer *(Pres)*
David Edward Constable *(Chm &
CEO)*
John R. Reynolds *(Sec & Exec VP)*
James R. Breuer *(COO)*

Subsidiaries:

3Angle EPCM V.O.F. **(1)**
Taurusavenue 155, 2132 LS, Hoofddorp,
Netherlands
Tel.: (31) 237523201
Engineering Services
N.A.I.C.S.: 541330

Acqyre B.V. **(1)**
Schrevenweg 3, 8024 HB, Zwolle, Nether-
lands
Tel.: (31) 384606384
Web Site: https://www.acquire.nl
Engineering Services
N.A.I.C.S.: 541330

Agensi Pekerjaan TRS Malaysia Sdn.
Bhd. **(1)**
Suite 20-06 Integra Tower The Intermark
348 Jalan Tun Razak, 50400, Kuala Lum-
pur, Malaysia
Tel.: (60) 327227088
Web Site: https://www.trsstaffing.com
Human Resouce Services
N.A.I.C.S.: 541330

Ameco Chile S.A. **(1)**
Reyes Lavalle 3340 Oficina 501 Piso 5 Las
Condes, Santiago, Chile
Tel.: (56) 224443700
Construction Equipment Distr
N.A.I.C.S.: 423810

Choice Equipos y Servicios
S.A.C. **(1)**

Fluor Corporation—(Continued)

Avenida 28 de Julio 753 Miraflores, Villa El
Salvador, 15074, Lima, Peru
Tel.: (51) 16168400
Web Site: http://www.ameco.com
Mobile Equipment & Construction Tool Distr
N.A.I.C.S.: 423830

Denver Transit Partners, LLC **(1)**
701 W 48th Ave 5151 Fox St, Denver, CO
80216
Tel.: (720) 460-5800
Web Site: https://denvertransitpartners.com
Emp.: 35
Construction Services
N.A.I.C.S.: 237990
Nadia Garas *(Comm Mgr)*
Tina Jaquez *(Mgr-PR)*

Fluor Chile Ingenieria y Construccion
S.A. **(1)**
Reyes Lavalle 3340 Floor 7 Las Condes,
Santiago, RM, Chile
Tel.: (56) 223408000
Engineering Construction Services
N.A.I.C.S.: 541330

Fluor Chile S.A. **(1)**
Reyes Lavalle 3340 Floor 7, Las Condes,
Santiago, Chile
Tel.: (56) 223408000
Web Site: http://www.fluor.com
Engineering & Construction Services
N.A.I.C.S.: 541330

Fluor Constructors International,
Inc. **(1)**
352 Halton Rd Ste 200, Greenville, SC
29607 **(100%)**
Tel.: (864) 234-7335
Web Site: http://www.fluor.com
Sales Range: $1-4.9 Billion
Emp.: 1,700
Industrial Construction Services
N.A.I.C.S.: 236220
David Seaton *(CEO)*

Subsidiary (Non-US):

Fluor Canada Ltd **(2)**
1075 W Georgia St Suite 700, Vancouver,
V6E 4M7, BC, Canada **(100%)**
Tel.: (604) 488-2000
Web Site: https://www.fluor.com
Sales Range: $25-49.9 Million
Emp.: 900
Mining Engineering Designer
N.A.I.C.S.: 541330

Subsidiary (Domestic):

JGC Fluor BC Joint Venture **(3)**
234 City Centre, Kitimat, V8C 1T6, BC,
Canada
Tel.: (250) 632-5358
Web Site: https://www.jfjvkitimat.com
Engineering Construction Services
N.A.I.C.S.: 541330

Subsidiary (Non-US):

Fluor Canada Ltd. **(2)**
55 Sunpark Plaza SE, Calgary, T2X 3R4,
AB, Canada **(100%)**
Tel.: (403) 537-4000
Web Site: https://www.fluor.com
Sales Range: $900-999.9 Million
Emp.: 1,000
Airport Construction Management Services
N.A.I.C.S.: 236220

Fluor Constructors Canada Ltd **(2)**
00 Sunpark Plaza SE, Calgary, T2X3Y2,
AB, Canada
Tel.: (403) 537-4600
Web Site: https://www.fluorconstructors.ca
Engineeering Services
N.A.I.C.S.: 541330

Fluor Daniel India Private
Limited **(1)**
6th Floor Infinity Tower B Cyber City DLF
City Phase II, Gurgaon, 122 002, Haryana,
India
Tel.: (91) 1244570700
Web Site: http://www.fluor.com
Sales Range: $150-199.9 Million
Emp.: 700
Engineering Services
N.A.I.C.S.: 541330

Fluor Enterprises, Inc. **(1)**
3 Polaris Way, Aliso Viejo, CA 92698
Tel.: (949) 349-2000
Rev.: $15,474,000,000
Assets: $6,973,000,000
Liabilities: $4,921,000,000
Net Worth: $2,052,000,000
Earnings: $79,000,000
Emp.: 34,000
Fiscal Year-end: 12/31/2023
Engineering & Construction Services
N.A.I.C.S.: 236220

Subsidiary (Non-US):

CFPS Engenharia e Projetos,
S.A. **(2)**
Avenida Francisco Matarazzo No1400, Ed
Milano 13 Andar Agua Branca, Sao Paulo,
05001-100, SP, Brazil
Tel.: (55) 11 3050 3000
Construction Services
N.A.I.C.S.: 236220

Conops Industrial Ltd. **(2)**
205 264 Midpark Way SE, Calgary, AB T2X
1J6, AB, Canada
Tel.: (877) 722-1802
Web Site: https://www.conops.ca
Industrial Construction & Support Services
N.A.I.C.S.: 541330
Arnie Bechard *(Gen Mgr)*

Fluor Arabia Limited **(2)**
PO Box 3381, Al Khobar, 31952, Saudi
Arabia
Tel.: (966) 138829292
Web Site: http://www.fluor.com
Sales Range: $350-399.9 Million
Emp.: 930
Holding Company
N.A.I.C.S.: 551112

Fluor Australia Pty. Ltd. **(2)**
Level 2 437 St Kilda Road, Melbourne,
3004, VIC, Australia **(100%)**
Tel.: (61) 892787555
Web Site: http://www.fluor.com
Sales Range: $50-74.9 Million
Emp.: 40
Engineering & Construction Services
N.A.I.C.S.: 236220

Subsidiary (Non-US):

Fluor Brasil, Ltda. **(3)**
Av Francisco Matarazzo 1400 13 Andar Cj
132 Torre Milano Barra Funda, Sao Paulo,
05001-100, Brazil
Tel.: (55) 1130503000
Engineering Management Services
N.A.I.C.S.: 541330
Andre T. Luciano *(Mgr-Bus Dev)*

Subsidiary (Domestic):

Fluor Engenharia e Projetos S.A. **(4)**
Av Francisco Matarazzo 1400 13 Andar Cj
132 Torre Milano Barra Funda, Sao Paulo,
05001-100, Brazil
Tel.: (55) 1130503000
Engineering Construction Services
N.A.I.C.S.: 541330

Subsidiary (Domestic):

Fluor Global Services Australia Pty.
Ltd. **(3)**
Level 7 417 St Kilda Rd, Melbourne, 3004,
VIC, Australia
Tel.: (61) 390945600
Web Site: http://www.fluor.com.au
Sales Range: $50-74.9 Million
Construction & Maintenance Services
N.A.I.C.S.: 236220

Giovenco Industries (AUST) Pty
Limited **(3)**
1 Moorebank Avenue, Moorebank, 2170,
NSW, Australia
Tel.: (61) 291902100
Web Site: http://www.giovencoind.com
Industrial Contract Services
N.A.I.C.S.: 238220

Subsidiary (Domestic):

Fluor-SKM Iron Ore Joint
Venture **(4)**
Level 17 152 St Georges Terrace, PO Box

17, Perth, 6000, WA, Australia
Tel.: (61) 861044500
Web Site: http://www.fastjv.com.au
Construction Services
N.A.I.C.S.: 236116
David Cherry *(Mgr-Procurement)*

Subsidiary (Non-US):

Fluor Daniel (Japan), Inc. **(2)**
302 Moto-Akasaka 1-7-10, Minato-ku, To-
kyo, 107-0051, Japan **(100%)**
Tel.: (81) 354105531
Sales Range: $25-49.9 Million
Emp.: 10
General & Industrial Construction Services
N.A.I.C.S.: 236220

Fluor Daniel Brasil, Ltda. **(2)**
2326 5 floor Alameda Santos Jardim Pau-
lista, Sao Paulo, 01418-200, Brazil **(99%)**
Tel.: (55) 1130625590
Web Site: http://www.fluor.com
Engineering & Construction Services
N.A.I.C.S.: 236220

Subsidiary (Domestic):

Fluor Daniel Caribbean, Inc **(2)**
St 2 No 14 Metro Ofc Park Parkside Plz Ste
500, Guaynabo, PR 00969
Tel.: (787) 783-5500
Web Site: http://www.fluor.com
Engineeering Services
N.A.I.C.S.: 541330

Subsidiary (Non-US):

Fluor Daniel Chile, S.A. **(2)**
Reyes Lavalle 3340 Floor 7, Las Condes,
Santiago, Chile
Tel.: (56) 223408000
Web Site: http://www.flour.com
General & Industrial Construction
N.A.I.C.S.: 236220

Subsidiary (Domestic):

Fluor Daniel Engineers & Construc-
tors, Inc **(2)**
1 Galleria Blvd Ste 1070, Metairie, LA
70001
Tel.: (504) 834-2660
Web Site: http://www.fluor.com
Sales Range: $25-49.9 Million
Emp.: 6
Engineeering Services
N.A.I.C.S.: 541330

Subsidiary (Non-US):

Fluor (China) Engineering & Con-
struction Co. Ltd. **(3)**
3F North Podium Dawning Center No 500
Hong Bao Shi Road, Shanghai, 201103,
China
Tel.: (86) 2123250999
Web Site: http://www.fluor.com
Engineering & Construction Services
N.A.I.C.S.: 237990

Subsidiary (Non-US):

Fluor Daniel Pacific, Inc. **(2)**
7th Floor Polaris Corporate Center Spec-
trum Midway, Filinvest Corporate City Ala-
bang, Muntinlupa, 1781, Metro Manila, Phil-
ippines
Tel.: (63) 28504451
Web Site: http://www.fluor.com
Sales Range: $300-349.9 Million
Emp.: 2,000
General & Industrial Construction
N.A.I.C.S.: 236220

Subsidiary (Domestic):

Fluor Daniel, Inc. **(2)**
144 Merchant St, Cincinnati, OH
45246-3736 **(100%)**
Tel.: (513) 772-2000
Web Site: http://www.fluor.com
Sales Range: $50-74.9 Million
Emp.: 100
Industrial Building Construction
N.A.I.C.S.: 236210

Subsidiary (Non-US):

Fluor Daniel, Inc. - Philippines **(2)**

7th Floor Polaris Corporate Center Spec-
trum Midway, Filinvest Corporate City Ala-
bang Muntinlupa, Manila, 1781, Philippines
Tel.: (63) 288504451
Web Site: http://www.fluor.com
Engineering & Construction Services
N.A.I.C.S.: 237990

Fluor Europe BV **(2)**
Taurus Avenue 155, 2132 LS, Hoofddorp,
Netherlands
Tel.: (31) 235432432
Web Site: http://www.fluor.nl
Sales Range: $250-299.9 Million
Emp.: 800
Financial Holding Services
N.A.I.C.S.: 551112

Subsidiary (Domestic):

Fluor BV **(3)**
Taurusavenue 155, 2132 LS, Hoofddorp,
2132 LS, Netherlands **(100%)**
Tel.: (31) 235432432
Web Site: http://www.flour.nl
Sales Range: $350-399.9 Million
Emp.: 600
General & Industrial Construction Services
N.A.I.C.S.: 236220

Fluor Consultants BV **(3)**
Railroad 16, 4611 EL, Bergen op Zoom,
Netherlands
Tel.: (31) 235432432
Web Site: http://www.fluor.com
Sales Range: $150-199.9 Million
Emp.: 600
Construction Services
N.A.I.C.S.: 236220

Fluor Infrastructure BV **(3)**
Taurusavenue 155, 2132 LS, Hoofddorp,
Netherlands
Tel.: (31) 237523200
Web Site: http://www.fluor.com
Sales Range: $150-199.9 Million
Construction & Maintenance Services
N.A.I.C.S.: 236220

Subsidiary (Non-US):

TRS Consultants JLT **(3)**
JBC 2 Suite 1904 Jumeirah Lake Towers,
PO Box 46858, Dubai, 46858, United Arab
Emirates
Tel.: (971) 44466198
Web Site: http://www.trsstaffing.com
Emp.: 6
Human Resource Consultancy Services
N.A.I.C.S.: 561311

Subsidiary (Domestic):

TRS Staffing Solutions BV **(3)**
Taurusavenue 155, 2132 LS, Amsterdam,
Netherlands
Tel.: (31) 235433131
Web Site: https://www.trsstaffing.com
Sales Range: $100-124.9 Million
Emp.: 10
Staffing Services
N.A.I.C.S.: 541612

Subsidiary (Domestic):

Fluor Federal Services Inc. **(2)**
3160 George Washington Way, Richland,
WA 99354 **(100%)**
Tel.: (509) 392-5887
Web Site:
http://www.fluorfederalservices.com
Engineeering Services
N.A.I.C.S.: 541330

Subsidiary (Domestic):

Fluor Carlsbad, LLC **(3)**
100 Fluor Daniel Dr, Greenville, SC 29607-
2770
Tel.: (864) 281-4400
Engineering & Construction Services
N.A.I.C.S.: 237990

Fluor Portsmouth LLC **(3)**
3930 US Route 23 S, Piketon, OH 45661
Tel.: (513) 484-2205
Web Site: http://www.fbportsmouth.com
Emp.: 1,900
Demolition Services
N.A.I.C.S.: 562910

Fluor-B&W Portsmouth LLC (3)
3930 US Route 23 S, Piketon, OH 45661
Tel.: (740) 897-2331
Web Site: https://www.fbportsmouth.com
Emp.: 1,400
Decontamination & Decommissioning Services
N.A.I.C.S.: 562910
Tim Poe (Dir-Operations-Nuclear)
Greg Wilkett (Pres)

Subsidiary (Domestic):

Fluor Federal Services, LLC (2)
1101 Wilson Blvd Ste 1900, Arlington, VA 22209
Tel.: (864) 421-2167
Engineering & Construction Services
N.A.I.C.S.: 237990

Fluor Fernald Inc. (2)
7400 Willey Rd, Hamilton, OH 45013
Tel.: (513) 648-3000
Rev.: $250,000,000
Emp.: 1,700
Environmental Cleanup Services
N.A.I.C.S.: 562910

Fluor Hanford, Inc. (2)
2420 Stevens Ctr Rm 442, Richland, WA 99352   (100%)
Tel.: (509) 372-2000
Sales Range: $75-99.9 Million
Emp.: 200
Engineeering Services
N.A.I.C.S.: 325180

Fluor Heavy Civil, LLC (2)
5001 Spring Valley Rd Ste 700W, Dallas, TX 75244
Tel.: (972) 538-1906
Engineering Services
N.A.I.C.S.: 541330
Andrew Belote (Dir-Fin & Bus Svc)

Subsidiary (Non-US):

Fluor Ireland Limited (2)
Ohshima House 9 Woodford Court Woodford Business Park, Santry, Dublin, Ireland
Tel.: (353) 17979185
Engineering & Construction Services
N.A.I.C.S.: 237990

Fluor Limited (2)
Fluor Centre 140 Pinehurst Road, Farnborough, GU14 7BF, Hampshire, United Kingdom   (100%)
Tel.: (44) 1252291000
Web Site: http://www.fluorcareers.com
Emp.: 2,000
Hospital Construction & Engineering Services
N.A.I.C.S.: 236220

Subsidiary (Domestic):

Fluor Maintenance Services, Inc. (2)
316 Havenhurst Dr, Taylors, SC 29687
Tel.: (864) 281-5289
Commercial & Institutional Building Construction Services
N.A.I.C.S.: 236220

Subsidiary (Non-US):

Fluor S.A. (2)
Ul Prymasa Stefana Wyszynskiego 11, 44-101, Gliwice, 44-101, Poland
Tel.: (48) 322391500
Web Site: http://www.fluor.com
Sales Range: $25-49.9 Million
Emp.: 410
Construction & Maintenance Services
N.A.I.C.S.: 236220

Subsidiary (Domestic):

Fluor Supply Chain Solutions LLC (2)
6700 Las Colinas Blvd, Irving, TX 75039
Tel.: (469) 398-7000
Web Site: http://www.fluor.com
Engineeering Services
N.A.I.C.S.: 541330

Goar, Allison & Associates, LLC (2)
3 Polaris Way, Aliso Viejo, CA 92698
Tel.: (949) 349-3042
Web Site: http://www.goarallison.com
Emp.: 119

Sulfur Recovery & Process Engineering Services
N.A.I.C.S.: 213112

Subsidiary (Non-US):

ICA Fluor (2)
Dakota No 95 Edificio de oficinas Colonia Napoles, 03810, Mexico, Mexico
Tel.: (52) 5550617000
Web Site: https://www.icafluor.com
Emp.: 1,000
Construction Services
N.A.I.C.S.: 236220

Subsidiary (Domestic):

Pegasus Link Constructors, LLC (2)
160 Continental Ave, Dallas, TX 75207
Tel.: (214) 349-6493
Heavy & Civil Engineering Construction Services
N.A.I.C.S.: 237990

Signet Technology Inc (2)
12300 Kiln Ct Ste E, Beltsville, MD 20705
Tel.: (240) 264-3295
Web Site: http://www.signetinc.com
Emp.: 50
Engineeering Services
N.A.I.C.S.: 541330

TDF, Inc. (2)
18391 Verona Lago Dr, Miromar Lakes, FL 33913
Tel.: (239) 415-4200
Silk Screen Printing Services
N.A.I.C.S.: 313310

Subsidiary (Non-US):

TRS Staffing Solutions (Canada), Inc. (2)
Suite 105 340 Midpark Way S E, Calgary, T2X 1P1, AB, Canada
Tel.: (403) 571-4775
Web Site: https://www.trsstaffing.com
Rev.: $1,543,481
Emp.: 15
Management Consulting Services
N.A.I.C.S.: 541611

Tecnoconsult S A (2)
Av Romulo Gallegos Edf RIV, Sector Dos Caminos, Caracas, 1058, Venezuela   (100%)
Tel.: (58) 2122738000
Web Site: http://www.tecnoconsult.com
Sales Range: $75-99.9 Million
Emp.: 300
General & Industrial Contractors & Engineers
N.A.I.C.S.: 236220

Subsidiary (Domestic):

Venezco, Inc (2)
370 17th St Ste 3900, Denver, CO 80202-1370
Tel.: (303) 626-8300
Web Site: http://www.venezcoinc.com
Engineeering Services
N.A.I.C.S.: 541330
Alisa Otten (Office Mgr)

Subsidiary (Domestic):

Rock Island Integrated Services (3)
3050 Rodman Ave, Rock Island, IL 61201
Tel.: (309) 786-1650
Engineeering Services
N.A.I.C.S.: 541330

Fluor Idaho, LLC (1)
1580 Sawtelle St, Idaho Falls, ID 83402
Tel.: (208) 533-0411
Web Site: http://fluor-idaho.com
Waste Management Services
N.A.I.C.S.: 562211
Shannon McCowin Bowman (Dir-Human Resources-Labor Relations)
Ann Riedesel (Dir-Communications)
Fred Hughes (Mgr & Pres)
Bryan Breffle (Dir)
Jeff Carswell (COO)
Robert Gentry (Dir-Operations-Intec Nuclear)
Marc Jewett (Dir)
John Law (Dir-Operations-Nuclear Start,Up)
Mark Manderbach (Dir)
Kliss McNeel (Dir)

Brett Stacey (Mgr-Labor Relations)
Kim Southwick (Dir)
Thomas Williams (Dir)
Ty Blackford (Program Mgr & Pres)
Dan Coyne (Sr Dir)
Tresa Davis (Mgr)
David Hutchison (Sr Dir)
Bill Kirby (Sr Dir)
Dana Kirkham (Dir)
Ross Langseth (Dir)
Jack MacRae (Sr Dir & Officer)
Connie Simiele (Sr Dir)
Eric Trotta (Gen Counsel)
Ken Whitham (Sr Dir-Safety-Quality-Security)

Fluor Plant Engineering, S.A. (1)
Edifici 6 2 Port Tarraco Moll de Llevant 6, 43004, Tarragona, Spain
Tel.: (34) 977191700
Web Site: http://www.fluor.com
Engineeering Services
N.A.I.C.S.: 541330

Fluor-BWXT Portsmouth LLC (1)
3930 US Route 23 S, Piketon, OH 45661
Tel.: (740) 897-2331
Web Site: https://fbportsmouth.com
Emp.: 1,900
Technical Maintenance Services
N.A.I.C.S.: 811111

Gladstone Pressure Welders Pty Ltd (1)
8 Blain Dr, Gladstone, 4680, QLD, Australia
Tel.: (61) 749726379
Heavy & Civil Engineering Construction Services
N.A.I.C.S.: 237990

Istimewa Electrotechniek B.V. (1)
Frankrijkweg 3, 4389 PB, Vlissingen, Netherlands
Tel.: (31) 113612840
Web Site: http://www.istimewa-elektro.nl
Electrical System Installation Services
N.A.I.C.S.: 238210

J. Crowder Corporation (1)
13455 Sunrise Valley Dr Ste 100, Herndon, VA 20171
Tel.: (703) 793-1555
Web Site: http://www.jcc-va.com
Rev.: $7,400,000
Emp.: 60
Engineering & Construction Services
N.A.I.C.S.: 237990

NuScale Power Corporation (1)
12725 SW 66th Ave Ste 107, Portland, OR 97223   (60%)
Tel.: (971) 371-1592
Web Site: https://www.nuscalepower.com
Rev.: $11,804,000
Assets: $348,635,000
Liabilities: $71,548,000
Net Worth: $277,087,000
Earnings: ($141,573,000)
Emp.: 556
Fiscal Year-end: 12/31/2022
Investment Services
N.A.I.C.S.: 523999
Carl Fisher (COO)
John Hopkins (Pres & CEO)
Scott Kozak (Dir-IR)
Jose N. Reyes (CTO)
Robert Ramsey Hamady (CFO)
J. J. Arthur (VP-Engineering)
Eric Fischer (VP-Information Technology)
Carrie Fosaaen (VP-Regulatory Affairs)
Charles Goodnight (VP-Business Development)
Andrea Lachenmayr (Sec)
Carolyn Monaco (VP-Quality Assurance)
Karin Feldman (Sr VP-Product & Project Delivery & VP-Program Mgmt Office)

Subsidiary (Domestic):

NuScale Power, LLC (2)
6650 SW Redwood Ln Ste 210, Portland, OR 97224
Tel.: (971) 371-1592
Web Site: http://www.nuscalepower.com
Emp.: 200
Electric Light Water Reactor Mfr & Distr
N.A.I.C.S.: 335311
John L. Hopkins (Pres & CEO)
Jose N. Reyes (Founder & CTO)
Scott Bailey (VP-Supply Chain)

Tom Bergman (VP-Regulatory Affairs)
Robert Gamble (VP-Engrg)
Diane M. Hughes (VP-Mktg & Comm)
Carl Britsch (VP-HR)
Clayton Scott (Exec VP-Bus Dev)
Charles Goodnight (VP-Sls)

Sakhalinneftegasservis LLC (1)
120 B Purkaeva Street, Yuzhno-Sakhalinsk, 693006, Russia
Tel.: (7) 4242460750
Web Site: http://www.sngs.biz
Engineering & Construction Services
N.A.I.C.S.: 237990
Sergey Polyansky (Dir Gen)
Matthew Starkey (Mgr-Construction Modifications)
Irina Yan (Mgr-Admin & HR)
Sergey Didenko (Mgr-Procurement)
Elena Gremblat (Mgr-Contracts)

Savannah River Nuclear Solutions, LLC (1)
Park Ave & Laurens St, Aiken, SC 29808
Tel.: (803) 725-6211
Web Site: http://www.savannahrivernuclearsolutions.com
Emp.: 6,000
Nuclear Weapons & Materials Storage & Processing Facility Operation Management Services
N.A.I.C.S.: 493190
Jennifer T. Curtis (Gen Counsel & Sr VP)
Vahid Majidi (Dir & Exec VP)
Dave Olson (Exec VP)
Dennis Carr (Pres & CEO)
Sean Alford (Chief Admin Officer & Exec VP)
Wyatt Clark (Sr VP)
Mark Davis (Sr VP-NNSA Ops & Programs)
Chris Harkins (Officer-Nuclear Safety & Sr VP)
Sharon Marra (Deputy Dir & Sr VP)
Ted Myers (Sr VP)
Norman Powell (Sr VP-Bus Svcs)
Rick Sprague (Sr VP-Environment, Safety, Health & Quality)
Michael Swain (Sr VP-Technical Svcs)
James Toler (Exec VP)
James G. Angelos (Sr VP-Operations)
Francine Burroughs (Sr VP)
Janice Lawson (Sr VP)

Springfield Resource Recovery, Inc. (1)
6700 Las Colinas Blvd, Irving, TX 75039
Tel.: (413) 785-5120
Web Site: http://www.covanta.com
Nonhazardous Waste Disposal Services
N.A.I.C.S.: 562219

Stork Gears & Services Asia Pte. Ltd. (1)
20 Tuas Avenue 10, Singapore, 639144, Singapore
Tel.: (65) 68630878
Technical Maintenance Services
N.A.I.C.S.: 811111

Stork Holding B.V. (1)
Van Deventerlaan 121, 3528 AG, Utrecht, Netherlands   (100%)
Tel.: (31) 880891000
Web Site: http://www.stork.com
Holding Company
N.A.I.C.S.: 551112
Carla Rodenburg (VP)
Patric Jansen (Gen Counsel)
Alejandro Escalona (VP-)
Jim McQueenie (Dir-Global)
Steve Hillock (Dir-Global)
Lot Van Der Wal (CFO)
Hans Heerschop (Dir-Information Technology-Global)
Dirk-Jan Voorn (Dir-Risk Mgmt-Global)
Jorge Estrada (VP-Business Development-Strategy)
Bert Koopman (Dir--Global)
Johnno Wesseling (Dir--Global)

Subsidiary (Domestic):

Stork B.V. (2)
Van Deventerlaan 121, 3528 AG, Utrecht, Netherlands
Tel.: (31) 880891000
Web Site: https://www.stork.com
Emp.: 2,000

Fluor Corporation—(Continued)

Holding Company; Aerospace Mfr, Technical Services & Industrial Equipment Leasing Services
N.A.I.C.S.: 551112

Subsidiary (Domestic):

Stork Technical Services HOLDCO B.V. (3)
Van Deventerlaan 121, 3528 AG, Utrecht, Netherlands
Tel.: (31) 880891000
Web Site: http://www.stork.com
Holding Company; Technical & Engineering Services
N.A.I.C.S.: 551112
Igor Vermeulen (VP-HR)
Dirk-jan Voorn (Dir-Risk Mgmt-Global)

Subsidiary (Non-US):

Sinter Iberica Packaging (4)
C/La Ribera, s/n Pol Ind Gamonal Villayuda, 09007, Burgos, Spain
Tel.: (34) 947474220
Web Site: https://sinterpack.com
Food & Consumer Goods Packaging Mfr
N.A.I.C.S.: 322220
Thomas Kermorgant (Pres)

Stork - Electric Equipment Services - Regensburg (4)
Ohmstrasse 10, 93055, Regensburg, Germany
Tel.: (49) 94191030
Web Site: http://www.stork.com
Specialized Machinery Maintenance
N.A.I.C.S.: 811310

Subsidiary (Domestic):

Stork - Esloo (4)
Business Park Stein 318, 6181 MC, Elsloo, Netherlands
Tel.: (31) 880891240
Web Site: http://www.stork.com
Industrial Maintenance & Project Management
N.A.I.C.S.: 811310

Stork - Thermeq - Hengelo (4)
Ketelmakerij 2, 7553 ZP, Hengelo, Netherlands
Tel.: (31) 880891100
Web Site: http://www.stork-thermeq.com
Boiler Mfr
N.A.I.C.S.: 332410

Stork - Turbo Blading - Sneek (4)
Kamerlingh Onnesstraat 21, 8606 JN, Sneek, Netherlands
Tel.: (31) 880891290
Web Site: http://www.stork.com
Turbine Blade Mfr & Whslr
N.A.I.C.S.: 332721

Stork Gears & Services B.V. (4)
Pannerdenstraat 5-33, Postbus 5420, 3087 CH, Rotterdam, Netherlands
Tel.: (31) 880891110
Web Site: http://www.stork.com
Gearbox & Gear Technology Repair
N.A.I.C.S.: 811210

Subsidiary (Non-US):

Stork German Holding GmbH (4)
Ohmstr 10, 93055, Regensburg, Germany
Tel.: (49) 94191030
Engineeering Services
N.A.I.C.S.: 541330

Affiliate (Domestic):

Stork Plastics Machinery B.V. (4)
Alfred Marshallstraat 2, 7559 SE, Hengelo, Netherlands
Tel.: (31) 742405000
Web Site: http://www.storkimm.com
Injection Molding Machine Mfr & Whslr
N.A.I.C.S.: 333310

Subsidiary (Non-US):

Stork Power Services & Technology Beijing Limited (4)
Jiangtai Road Room 606 Lido Office Tower, Beijing, 100004, China
Tel.: (86) 1064301048

Engineering Construction Services
N.A.I.C.S.: 541330

Subsidiary (Domestic):

Stork Railway Services (4)
Pannerdenstraat 5, 3087 CH, Rotterdam, Netherlands
Tel.: (31) 880891110
Web Site: http://www.stork.com
Engineer, Manufacture & Overhaul Bogies for Railway Cars, Metro Cars & Trams
N.A.I.C.S.: 336510

Subsidiary (Non-US):

Stork Technical Services (STS) Ltd (4)
Units 21-24 Slaidburn Crescent, Southport, PR9 9YF, United Kingdom
Tel.: (44) 1704215600
Engineeering Services
N.A.I.C.S.: 541330

Stork Technical Services Belgium N.V. (4)
Oosterweelsteenweg 57, 2030, Antwerp, Belgium
Tel.: (32) 35401511
Engineeering Services
N.A.I.C.S.: 541330

Stork Technical Services Limited (4)
Norfolk House Pitmedden Road, Dyce, Aberdeen, AB21 0DP, United Kingdom
Tel.: (44) 1224722888
Web Site: http://www.stork.com
Oil & Natural Gas Production Support Services
N.A.I.C.S.: 213112

Subsidiary (Domestic):

Stork Turbo Service B.V. (4)
Damsluisweg 32, 1332 ED, Almere, Netherlands
Tel.: (31) 880891500
Engineeering Services
N.A.I.C.S.: 541330
Dirk Kuperus (Engr-Project)

Affiliate (Domestic):

hiTecs B.V. (4)
Zwedenlaan 12, 9403 DE, Assen, Netherlands
Tel.: (31) 888504175
Web Site: https://www.hitecs.nl
Internal Employment Agency
N.A.I.C.S.: 541612

Stork Turbo Blading B.V. (1)
Kamerlingh Onnesstraat 21, 8606 JN, Sneek, Netherlands
Tel.: (31) 880891290
Technical Maintenance Services
N.A.I.C.S.: 811111

Stork USA, Inc. (1)
334 Comfort Rd, Ithaca, NY 14850
Tel.: (607) 277-4968
Turbine Blade Mfr
N.A.I.C.S.: 333611

TRS Staffing Solutions Belgium B.V. (1)
Noorderlaan 147, 2030, Antwerp, Belgium
Tel.: (32) 36408721
Road & Railway Construction Product Mfr
N.A.I.C.S.: 336510

TRS Staffing Solutions GmbH (1)
Augustaanlage 67, 68165, Mannheim, Germany
Tel.: (49) 6213973155656
Road & Railway Construction Product Mfr
N.A.I.C.S.: 336510

TRS Staffing Solutions, Inc. (1)
Ste 850 3151 Briarpark Dr, Houston, TX 77042
Tel.: (832) 783-6100
Web Site: http://www.trsstaffing.com
Sales Range: $50-74.9 Million
Staffing Services
N.A.I.C.S.: 812990

Subsidiary (Non-US):

TRS Staffing Solutions (Australia) Pty Ltd (2)

225 St Georges Terrace Level 9, Perth, 6000, WA, Australia
Tel.: (61) 893477931
Web Site: https://www.trsstaffing.com
Human Resource Recruitment Services
N.A.I.C.S.: 561311

TRS Staffing Solutions (Pty) Ltd (2)
1st Floor Unit No 7 West Riding Office Park 50 West Riding Row, Sherwood, Durban, 4091, KN, South Africa
Tel.: (27) 312075145
Human Resource Recruitment Services
N.A.I.C.S.: 561311

TRS Staffing Solutions India Private Limited (2)
Unit No PSP C-04-006 4th Floor The Palm Springs Plaza, Golf Course Road, Gurgaon, 122 002, HR, India
Tel.: (91) 1244684040
Web Site: https://www.trsstaffing.com
Emp.: 14
Human Resource Recruitment Services
N.A.I.C.S.: 561311

TRS Staffing Solutions Limited (2)
8th Floor York House Kingsway, London, WC2B 6UJ, United Kingdom
Tel.: (44) 2074195800
Web Site: https://www.trsstaffing.com
Sales Range: $25-49.9 Million
Emp.: 20
Human Resource Consulting Services
N.A.I.C.S.: 541612

TRS Staffing Solutions, S. de R.L. de C.V. (2)
Avenida Insurgentes Sur No 601 Piso-12 Col Napoles Del Benito Juarez, 03810, Mexico, 03810, Mexico
Tel.: (52) 5550617741
Web Site: https://www.trsstaffing.com
Staff Recruitment Services
N.A.I.C.S.: 561330

Virta Inc. (1)
5909 Sea Lion Plc Ste B, Carlsbad, CA 92010
Tel.: (949) 349-7070
Web Site: https://www.virtainc.com
Construction Material Product Distr
N.A.I.C.S.: 423390
Grant M. Graber (Pres)

FLUOROPHARMA MEDICAL, INC.
701 S CARSON ST, Carson, NV 89701
Tel.: (973) 744-1565   NV
Web Site:
http://www.fluoropharma.com
Year Founded: 2003
FPMI—(OTCIQ)
Sales Range: Less than $1 Million
Emp.: 4
Biopharmaceutical Researcher, Developer & Mfr
N.A.I.C.S.: 325412
Walter W. Witoshkin (Interim Chm)
Thomas H. Tulip (CEO)
Ambrose O. Egbuonu (Pres, Treas & Sec)
Frank I. Igwealor (CFO & Controller)
Edward L. Lyons Jr. (VP-Mktg)

FLUSHING FINANCIAL CORPORATION
Tel.: (718) 961-5400   DE
Web Site:
https://www.flushingbank.com
Year Founded: 1994
FFIC—(NASDAQ)
Rev.: $326,635,000
Assets: $8,422,946,000
Liabilities: $7,745,789,000
Net Worth: $677,157,000
Earnings: $76,945,000
Emp.: 560
Fiscal Year-end: 12/31/22
Bank Holding Company
N.A.I.C.S.: 551111

Francis W. Korzekwinski (Chief Real Estate Lending Officer & Sr Exec VP)
Maria A. Grasso (COO, Sec & Sr Exec VP)
Susan K. Cullen (CFO, Treas & Sr Exec VP)
Thomas M. Buonaiuto (Sr Exec VP)
Michael Bingold (Sr Exec VP)
Allen M. Brewer (CIO)
Douglas McClintock (Gen Counsel)
Alfred A. DelliBovi (Chm)
John R. Buran (Pres & CEO)

Subsidiaries:

Empire Bancorp, Inc. (1)
1707 Veterans Hwy Ste 8, Islandia, NY 11749
Tel.: (631) 348-4444
Web Site: https://www.empirenb.com
Rev.: $38,254,000
Assets: $978,575,000
Liabilities: $894,385,000
Net Worth: $84,190,000
Earnings: $3,871,000
Fiscal Year-end: 12/31/2019
Bank Holding Company
N.A.I.C.S.: 551111
Douglas C. Manditch (Chm & CEO)

Subsidiary (Domestic):

Empire National Bank (2)
1707 Veterans Hwy, Islandia, NY 11749
Tel.: (631) 348-4444
Web Site: http://www.empirenb.com
Rev.: $4,600,000
Emp.: 40
Banking Services
N.A.I.C.S.: 522110
Patrick Hickey (VP)
Jeffrey Reid (VP)
Eric Rubin (VP)
Brian Handler (Sr VP)
Robert Kiraly (Chief Risk Officer & Sr VP)

Flushing Savings Bank Inc. (1)
159-18 Northern Blvd, Flushing, NY 11358
Tel.: (718) 961-7400
Web Site: http://www.flushingbank.com
Sales Range: $75-99.9 Million
Emp.: 250
Federal Savings Institutions
N.A.I.C.S.: 522180
Francis W. Korzekwinski (Chief Real Estate Lending Officer & Sr VP)
Alfred A. DelliBovi (Chm)
John R. Buran (Pres & CEO)
Alfred DelliBovi (Chm)

FLUX POWER HOLDINGS, INC.
2685 S Melrose Dr, Vista, CA 92081
Tel.: (760) 741-3589   NV
Web Site: https://www.fluxpower.com
Year Founded: 1998
FLUX—(NASDAQ)
Rev.: $42,333,000
Assets: $30,881,000
Liabilities: $16,947,000
Net Worth: $13,934,000
Earnings: ($15,609,000)
Emp.: 121
Fiscal Year-end: 06/30/22
Battery Manufacturing
N.A.I.C.S.: 335910
Kevin S. Royal (CFO & Sec)
Michael E. Johnson (Co-Founder)
Ronald F. Dutt (Chm, Pres & CEO)
Paulus Geantil (CTO)
Tim Vaughan (Dir-Engrg)
Justin Forbes (Dir-Bus Dev)
Kim Urban (Dir-HR)
Jeff Mason (Dir-Mfg)
Jim Rooney (Co-Founder, Sec, VP-Sales & VP)

FLY-E GROUP, INC.
136-40 39th Ave, Flushing, NY 11354
Tel.: (929) 410-2770   DE
Web Site: https://www.flyebike.com
Year Founded: 2018

FLYE—(NASDAQ)
Rev.: $32,205,666
Assets: $28,976,334
Liabilities: $22,194,512
Net Worth: $6,781,822
Earnings: $1,895,222
Emp.: 57
Fiscal Year-end: 03/31/24
Electric Motorcycle Distr
N.A.I.C.S.: 423110

FLYEXCLUSIVE, INC.
375 Park Ave 24th Fl, New York, NY
10152
Tel.: (212) 888-1040   DE
Year Founded: 2021
FLYX—(AIM)
Rev.: $8,345,234
Assets: $228,533,597
Liabilities: $241,766,273
Net Worth: ($13,232,676)
Earnings: $3,666,886
Emp.: 3
Fiscal Year-end: 12/31/22
Investment Services
N.A.I.C.S.: 523999
Gregg S. Hymowitz (CEO)
Gary Fegel (Chm)
Sophia Park Mullen (Pres)

Subsidiaries:

LGM Enterprises LLC   (1)
2860 Jetport Rd, Kinston, NC 28504
Tel.: (800) 544-2156
Web Site: http://www.flyexclusive.com
Oil Transportation Services
N.A.I.C.S.: 485999
Mike Guina (Pres)
Donn Yates (COO)
David Ivy (VP-Engrg)
Tommy Sowers (Pres-Private Charter Operation)

Subsidiary (Domestic):

Sky Night LLC   (2)
1110 Myers St, Greeneville, TN 37745-1824
Tel.: (423) 278-9901
Web Site: http://www.skynightllc.com
Commercial Air, Rail & Water Transportation
Equipment Rental & Leasing
N.A.I.C.S.: 532411
Scott Niswonger (Owner)

FLYWHEEL ADVANCED TECH-
NOLOGY, INC.
123 W Nye Ln Ste 455, Carson City,
NV 89706
Tel.: (646) 768-8417   NV
Web Site:
    http://www.panglobalcorp.com
Year Founded: 2010
FWFW—(OTCIQ)
Rev.: $1,448,176
Assets: $4,623,791
Liabilities: $1,769,541
Net Worth: $2,854,250
Earnings: ($1,082,789)
Fiscal Year-end: 09/30/23
Business Support Services
N.A.I.C.S.: 561499
David Lazar (Chm, Pres, CEO, CFO
& Sec)

FLYWIRE CORPORATION
141 Tremont St Ste 10, Boston, MA
02111
Tel.: (617) 329-4524   DE
Web Site: https://www.flywire.com
Year Founded: 2009
FLYW—(NASDAQ)
Rev.: $289,375,000
Assets: $674,287,000
Liabilities: $192,384,000
Net Worth: $481,903,000
Earnings: ($39,347,000)
Emp.: 1,000
Fiscal Year-end: 12/31/22
Software Development Services

N.A.I.C.S.: 541511
Phillip Riese (Chm)
Rob Orgel (Pres & COO)
Cosmin Pitigoi (CFO)
Allison MacLeod (CMO)
Peter Butterfield (Chief Compliance
Officer & Gen Counsel)
David King (CTO)
Gary Cunningham (Chief People Officer)
Barbara Cousins (CIO & Chief Info
Security Officer-Internal Audit)
Sharon Butler (Exec VP-Global Education)
John Talaga (Exec VP-Healthcare)
Ryan Frere (Exec VP & Gen Mgr-
B2B)
Colin Smyth (Sr VP/VP/Gen Mgr-
Travel)
Uday Seth (VP-Bus Ops & Corp Dev)
Mohit Kansal (Sr VP-Global Payments & Payer Svcs & VP-Global
Payments)
Eric Spear (Sr VP-Engineering)
Michael Massaro (CEO)

FMC CORPORATION
2929 Walnut St, Philadelphia, PA
19104
Tel.: (215) 299-6000   DE
Web Site: https://www.fmc.com
Year Founded: 1883
FMC—(NYSE)
Rev.: $4,486,800,000
Assets: $11,926,200,000
Liabilities: $7,492,800,000
Net Worth: $4,433,400,000
Earnings: $1,321,500,000
Emp.: 6,600
Fiscal Year-end: 12/31/23
Chemical Products Mfr
N.A.I.C.S.: 551112
Pierre R. Brondeau (Chm & CEO)
Kenneth A. Gedaka (VP-Comm &
Pub Affairs)
Barry J. Crawford (VP-Ops)
Andrew D. Sandifer (CFO & Exec
VP)
Nicholas L. Pfeiffer (Chief Acctg Officer, VP & Controller)
Karen M. Totland (Chief Sustainability
Officer & VP)
Brian P. Angeli (VP-Corp Strategy &
Precision Agriculture)
Kyle Matthews (VP-HR)
William M. Zisch (Executives)
David A. Kotch (CIO & VP)
Shawn Whitman (VP-Govt Affairs)
Pramod Thota (Pres-Asia Pacific &
VP)
Bill Chester (VP-Tax-Global)
Michael F. Reilly (Gen Counsel, Sec
& Exec VP)
Susanne Lingard (VP-Regulatory Affairs)
Brain Blair (Treas & VP)
Thaisa Hugenneyer (VP- Procurement & Global Facilities)
Seva Rostovtsev (CTO & VP)
Benedicte Flambard (VP)
Sebastia Pons (Pres)
Ronaldo Pereira (Pres)

Subsidiaries:

Cheminova A/S   (1)
Thyboronvej 78, Ronland, 7673, Harboor,
Denmark
Tel.: (45) 9 690 9690
Web Site: https://www.cheminova.asia
Emp.: 800
Agricultural Chemicals Mfr & Whslr
N.A.I.C.S.: 325320

Subsidiary (Non-US):

Cheminova Agro France S.A.S.   (2)
19 Bd Eugene Deruelle, 69003, Lyon,
France

Tel.: (33) 437236570
Web Site: http://www.cheminova.fr
Sales Range: $25-49.9 Million
Emp.: 19
Agricultural Chemical Products Whslr
N.A.I.C.S.: 424690

Cheminova Agro Italia s.r.l.   (2)
Via Fratelli Bronzetti 32/38, 24124, Bergamo, BG, Italy
Tel.: (39) 035 1990 4468
Web Site: http://www.cheminova.it
Emp.: 11
Crop Protection Chemicals Sales
N.A.I.C.S.: 424690
Francesco Liuni (Mgr-Sls-South)

Cheminova Agro de Argentina
S.A.   (2)
Aldecoa 1277, Avellaneda, B1868DTO,
Argentina
Tel.: (54) 11 4228 7047
Web Site: http://www.fmcargentina.com.ar
Agricultural Chemicals Sales
N.A.I.C.S.: 424690

Cheminova Agro de Colombia
SA   (2)
Centro empresarial Paralelo 108 Calle 108
No 45-30, Torre 2 oficinas 1004-1005, Bogota, Colombia
Tel.: (57) 1 6571900
Web Site: http://www.cheminova.co
Agricultural Chemicals Sales
N.A.I.C.S.: 424690

Cheminova Agro, S.A.   (2)
Paseo de la Castellana 257 5th Floor,
28046, Madrid, Spain
Tel.: (34) 915530104
Web Site: http://www.cheminova.es
Sales Range: $25-49.9 Million
Emp.: 44
Agricultural Chemicals Sales
N.A.I.C.S.: 424690

Cheminova Agroquimica S.A. de
C.V.   (2)
Paseo de la Reforma 265 Floor 1, Colonia
Cuauhtemoc, 06500, Mexico, DF, Mexico
Tel.: (52) 5555334280
Web Site: http://www.cheminova.com.mx
Sales Range: $25-49.9 Million
Emp.: 35
Crop Protection Product Mfr
N.A.I.C.S.: 325314

Cheminova Austria GmbH   (2)
Saint Peter Hauptstrasse 117, 8042, Graz,
Austria
Tel.: (43) 316 4602 0
Web Site: http://www.cheminova.at
Emp.: 13
Agricultural Chemicals Whslr
N.A.I.C.S.: 424690

Cheminova Bulgaria EOOD   (2)
102 Bulgaria Blvd Bellissimo Business Ctr
Office 59, Floor 5 Office 59, 1680, Sofia,
Bulgaria
Tel.: (359) 2 818 56 56
Web Site: http://www.amalgerol.com
Emp.: 6
Agricultural Chemicals Sales
N.A.I.C.S.: 424690
Ivan Rangelov (Dir)

Cheminova Deutschland GmbH &
Co. KG   (2)
Stader Elbstrasse 28, 21683, Stade, Germany
Tel.: (49) 41 41 92 04 0
Web Site: http://www.cheminova.de
Agricultural Chemicals Mfr & Distr
N.A.I.C.S.: 325320

Cheminova India Limited   (2)
Phoenix Market City Lev 4 Centrium Unit
No 2 LBS Marg, Kurla West, Mumbai, 400
070, India
Tel.: (91) 2267045504
Farm Supplies Whslr
N.A.I.C.S.: 424910
Urvish Desai (Sec)
Sandeep Singh Jawa (Sr Mgr-Plng & Logistics)

Cheminova Polska Sp. z o.o.   (2)
Aleje Jerozolimskie 212A, 02-486, Warsaw,
Poland

Tel.: (48) 225714050
Web Site: http://www.cheminova.pl
Emp.: 10
Pesticide & Agricultural Chemicals Sales
N.A.I.C.S.: 424690

Cheminova Taiwan Ltd   (2)
19th Fl-A3 No 760 Chung Ming S, Taichung, Taiwan
Tel.: (886) 51255296815
Web Site: http://www.cheminova.asia
Sales Range: $25-49.9 Million
Emp.: 1
Pesticide & Agricultural Chemicals Sales
N.A.I.C.S.: 424690

OOO Cheminova   (2)
Smolnaya Str 24D Floor 18, 125445, Moscow, Russia
Tel.: (7) 495 783 9003
Web Site: http://www.cheminova.ru
Emp.: 25
Crop Protection Chemicals Sales
N.A.I.C.S.: 424690

DuPont Agricultural Chemicals Ltd,
Shanghai   (1)
Pudong Road 3055, Shanghai, 200137,
China
Tel.: (86) 2158672488
Web Site: http://www.dupont.cn
Emp.: 6,000
Agrochemical Product Mfr
N.A.I.C.S.: 325320

Electro Quimica Mexicana S.A. de
C.V.   (1)
Av Industria No 9 Col Ind Cerro Gordo
55420 Ecatepec, Mexico, DF, Mexico
Tel.: (52) 5556990800
Hydrogen Peroxide Mfr
N.A.I.C.S.: 325180

FMC (Suzhou) Crop Care Co.,
Ltd   (1)
99 Jiepu Road Shengpu Suzhou Industrial
Park, Jiang Su, Suzhou, 215126, China
Tel.: (86) 51262863998
Web Site: http://www.fmc.com
Farm Supply Whslr
N.A.I.C.S.: 424910

FMC Agro Ltd.   (1)
Rectors Lane, Pentre, Deeside, CH5 2DH,
Flintshire, United Kingdom
Tel.: (44) 1244537370
Web Site: https://www.fmc-agro.co.uk
Pesticide & Agricultural Chemicals Mfr
N.A.I.C.S.: 325320

FMC Agroquimica de Mexico S.R.L.
de C.V.   (1)
Av Vallarta 6503 Local A1 - 6 Col Ciudad
Granja, 45040, Zapopan, Jalisco, Mexico
Tel.: (52) 8003622476
Web Site:
    http://www.fmcagroquimica.com.mx
Agricultural Chemical Mfr
N.A.I.C.S.: 325320

FMC Asia-Pacific, Inc.   (1)
18 Harbour Road Suite 2402 24/f Central
Plaza, Wanchai, China (Hong
Kong)   (100%)
Tel.: (852) 28396600
Sales Range: $10-24.9 Million
Emp.: 30
Holding Company; Regional Managing Office; Industrial Chemicals Mfr & Distr
N.A.I.C.S.: 551112
Bethwyn Todd (Pres & Dir-Agricultural
Solutions-Asia)

Subsidiary (Non-US):

FMC Australasia Pty Ltd.   (2)
12 Julius Avenue, North Ryde, 2113, NSW,
Australia   (100%)
Tel.: (61) 1800901939
Web Site: http://www.fmcaustralasia.com.au
Sales Range: $1-9.9 Million
Emp.: 20
Agricultural Chemicals Mfr & Sales
N.A.I.C.S.: 325320

FMC Philippines Inc.   (2)
Quano Compound Looc Mandaue City,
6014, Cebu, Philippines
Tel.: (63) 323460882
Web Site: http://www.fmcbiopolymer.com

FMC Corporation—(Continued)

Mfr of Industrial Chemicals & Food Additives
N.A.I.C.S.: 325998

FMC Shanghai Commercial Enterprise (2)
Room 105 Innovation Building 1009 Yi Shan Road, Shanghai, 200233, China (100%)
Tel.: (86) 21 5427 1177
Web Site: http://www.fmc.com
Sales Range: $10-24.9 Million
Emp.: 10
Mfr of Industrial Chemicals
N.A.I.C.S.: 325998

PT Bina Guna Kimia (2)
Jl HR Rasuna Said Kav B-4 Wisma Kodel Lt 10, Kuningan, 12920, Jakarta, Indonesia (51%)
Tel.: (62) 215222350
Farm Supplies Whslr
N.A.I.C.S.: 424910

FMC Chemical sprl (1)
Parc de l'Alliance Boulevard de France 9A, Braine l'Alleud, 1420, Brussels, Belgium
Tel.: (32) 26459584
Chemical & Pharmaceutical Product Mfr
N.A.I.C.S.: 325412

FMC Chemicals (Thailand) Ltd (1)
209 K Tower Bldg 15th Floor Tower A 209 Sukhumvit 21 Asoke Rd Kwang, Klongtoey Nua Khet Wattana, Bangkok, 10110, Thailand
Tel.: (66) 2402438991
Web Site: http://www.fmc.com
Emp.: 6
Chemical & Pharmaceutical Product Mfr
N.A.I.C.S.: 325412

FMC Chemicals Limited (1)
Commercial Road, Bromborough, CH62 3NL, Merseyside, United Kingdom (100%)
Tel.: (44) 1514827356
Web Site: http://www.fmclithium.com
Sales Range: $25-49.9 Million
Emp.: 70
Lithium Mfr
N.A.I.C.S.: 325199

FMC Corp. - Bangladesh Office (1)
Suite 701 Concord Tower 113 Kazil Nazrul Islam Avenue, Dhaka, 1000, Bangladesh
Tel.: (880) 29350768
Web Site: http://www.fmc.com
Sales Range: $150-199.9 Million
Emp.: 5
Agricultural Chemicals Whslr
N.A.I.C.S.: 424690

FMC Corp. - Industrial Chemicals Group (1)
2929 Walnut St, Philadelphia, PA 19104
Tel.: (215) 299-6000
Web Site: http://www.fmc.com
Sales Range: $200-249.9 Million
Emp.: 400
Mfr of Acetic Acid & Anhydride, Acetoacetarylides, Leavening Agents, Chlor-Alkalis, Solvent Chemicals
N.A.I.C.S.: 325180

Subsidiary (Non-US):

FMC Foret S.A. (2)
11 Esc B 9 Paseo de Gracia, 08007, Barcelona, 08007, Spain
Tel.: (34) 934167500
Web Site: http://www.fmc.com
Sales Range: $350-399.9 Million
Regional Managing Office; Specialty Chemicals Mfr & Distr
N.A.I.C.S.: 551114

FMC Corp. - Poland Office (1)
Ul Przasnyska 6A, 01-756, Warsaw, Poland
Tel.: (48) 228687577
Emp.: 19
Industrial Chemical Whslr
N.A.I.C.S.: 424690

FMC Corp. - Research & Technology Center (1)
701 Princeton South Corporate Ctr, Ewing, NJ 08628
Tel.: (609) 963-6200
Web Site: http://www.fmc.com

Sales Range: $1-4.9 Billion
Research & Development of Chemicals
N.A.I.C.S.: 325998

FMC Corp. - Specialty Chemicals Group, Lithium Division (1)
2801 Yorkmont Rd Ste 300, Charlotte, NC 28208
Tel.: (704) 426-5300
Web Site: http://www.fmclithium.com
Sales Range: $50-74.9 Million
Emp.: 40
Chemicals Mfr
N.A.I.C.S.: 212390

Plant (Domestic):

FMC Corp. - Lithium Division, Bessemer Plant (2)
1115 Bessemer City Kings Mtn Hwy, Bessemer City, NC 28016
Tel.: (704) 426-5300
Mfr of Lithium Chemicals, Lithium Metal & Feldspathic Sand
N.A.I.C.S.: 212390

FMC France S.A. (1)
614 Rue Benoit Mulsant, Villefranche-sur-Saone, 69400, France (100%)
Tel.: (33) 474683546
Web Site: http://www.fmc.com
Sales Range: $10-24.9 Million
Emp.: 6
Mfr & Distribution of Industrial Chemicals
N.A.I.C.S.: 325998

FMC Italy srl (1)
Via A Moro 62, 26900, Lodi, Italy
Tel.: (39) 03711841119
Web Site: http://www.fmcitalia.it
Chemical & Pharmaceutical Product Mfr
N.A.I.C.S.: 325412

FMC Korea Ltd. (1)
7F Mijin Bldg 838-11 Yeoksam 1-dong, Gangnam-gu, 135-937, Seoul, Korea (South) (100%)
Tel.: (82) 25396411
Web Site: http://www.fmc.com
Sales Range: $1-4.9 Billion
Emp.: 5
Mfr of Industrial Chemicals
N.A.I.C.S.: 325998

FMC Norway Holding AS (1)
Industriveien 33, 1337, Sandvika, Norway
Tel.: (47) 70107700
Chemical & Pharmaceutical Product Mfr
N.A.I.C.S.: 325412

FMC Quimica do Brasil Ltda (1)
Av doctor Jose, Bonifacio Coutinho Nogueira 150-1st floor, Campinas, 13091-611, Sao Paulo, Brazil (100%)
Tel.: (55) 1937354400
Sales Range: $50-74.9 Million
Emp.: 120
Farm Supplies Whslr
N.A.I.C.S.: 424910
Ronaldo Pereira (VP-Latin America)

FMC Specialty Alkali Corporation (1)
2929 Walnut St, Philadelphia, PA 19104
Tel.: (215) 299-6000
Web Site: http://www.fmc.com
Chemical & Pharmaceutical Product Mfr
N.A.I.C.S.: 325412

FMC Specialty Chemicals Research & Technology Center (1)
Avenue Mounier 83, 1200, Brussels, Belgium
Tel.: (32) 27758311
Web Site: http://www.fmc.com
Sales Range: $50-74.9 Million
Emp.: 30
Research & Technology Center for Specialty Agricultural Chemicals
N.A.I.C.S.: 424690

FMC Wyoming Corporation (1)
Highway 374, Green River, WY 82935
Tel.: (307) 875-2580
Chemical & Pharmaceutical Product Mfr
N.A.I.C.S.: 325412

FMC of Canada Limited (1)
#3 402 Ludlow St, PO Box 32033, Saskatoon, S7S 1M7, SK, Canada (100%)
Tel.: (306) 979-9225
Web Site: http://www.fmccrop.ca

Sales Range: $10-24.9 Million
Emp.: 50
Industrial Inorganic Chemicals
N.A.I.C.S.: 325180
Jeff McSymytz (Mgr-Sls-MB & South SK)
Andrew D. Sandifer (CFO)
Diane Allemang (Chief Mktg Officer)
Kathleen Shelton (CTO)
Mark A. Douglas (Pres)
Michael F. Reilly (Exec VP)

FMC-Agro Hungary Kft. (1)
Ganz u 16 2nd Floor, 1027, Budapest, Hungary
Tel.: (36) 1 336 21 20
Web Site: http://www.fmcagro.hu
Emp.: 6
Pesticide & Agricultural Chemicals Sales
N.A.I.C.S.: 424690
Tibor Racz (Engr-Szabolcs-Szatmar-Bereg County Reg)

Minera del Altiplano SA (1)
Ejercito del Norte 20, Salta, A4406BKN, Argentina
Tel.: (54) 3874322100
Emp.: 300
Farm Supplies Whslr
N.A.I.C.S.: 424910

Phytone Limited (1)
Third Avenue Centrum 100, Burton-on-Trent, DE14 2WD, United Kingdom
Tel.: (44) 1283543300
Food Color Mfr
N.A.I.C.S.: 311942

FNB, INC.
105 Grant St, Dennison, OH 44621
Tel.: (740) 922-2532   **OH**
Web Site:
   https://www.fnbdennison.com
Year Founded: 1874
FIDS—(OTCIQ)
Banking Holding Company
N.A.I.C.S.: 551111
Blair Hillyer (Board of Directors, Pres & CEO)
Nichole Zesiger (Pres)
Bob Wolf (Exec VP)
Linda Clouse (Sr VP)
Polly Clark (Sr VP)
Marty Merryman (VP)
Brian Williams (Sr VP)
Michele Grant (VP)
Taylor Wright (VP)

FNDS3000 CORP.
74-B Masters Dr, Saint Augustine, FL 32084
Tel.: (904) 273-2702   **DE**
Year Founded: 2006
FDTC—(OTCIQ)
Financial Transaction Services
N.A.I.C.S.: 522320
Raymond Goldsmith (Chm, Pres & CEO)

FOCUS IMPACT BH3 ACQUISITION COMPANY
1345 Avenue of the Americas 33rd Fl, New York, NY 10105
Tel.: (212) 213-0243   **DE**
Web Site: https://www.bh3ac.com
Year Founded: 2021
BHAC—(NASDAQ)
Rev.: $9,874,864
Assets: $51,353,729
Liabilities: $60,685,090
Net Worth: ($9,331,361)
Earnings: $7,665,862
Emp.: 3
Fiscal Year-end: 12/31/22
Investment Services
N.A.I.C.S.: 523999
Daniel Lebensohn (Co-CEO)
Carl Stanton (CEO)
Wray Thorn (Chief Investment Officer)
Ernest Lyles (CFO)

FOCUS UNIVERSAL INC.
2311 E Locust Ct, Ontario, CA 91761
Tel.: (626) 272-3883   **NV**
Web Site:
   https://www.focusuniversal.com
Year Founded: 2012
FCUV—(NASDAQ)
Rev.: $353,619
Assets: $9,323,060
Liabilities: $1,565,526
Net Worth: $7,757,534
Earnings: ($4,926,937)
Emp.: 25
Fiscal Year-end: 12/31/22
Web Marketing Services, Social & Viral Marketing Campaigns, Search Engine Optimization Consulting, Custom Web Design, Website Usability Consulting & Web Analytics Implementation
N.A.I.C.S.: 541890
Irving Kau (Co-CFO)
Desheng Wang (Founder, Founder, CEO, Sec & Sec)
Edward Lee (Chm)
Anthony Tejada (VP-Operations)

Subsidiaries:

AVX Design & Integration, Inc. (1)
10859 Venice Blvd., Los Angeles, CA 90034
Tel.: (310) 445-9989
Web Site: http://www.avxdesign.com
Electronics Stores
N.A.I.C.S.: 449210

FOGHORN THERAPEUTICS INC.
500 Technology Sq Ste 700, Cambridge, MA 02139
Tel.: (617) 586-3100   **DE**
Web Site: https://www.foghorntx.com
Year Founded: 2015
FHTX—(NASDAQ)
Rev.: $19,228,000
Assets: $404,883,000
Liabilities: $404,771,000
Net Worth: $112,000
Earnings: ($108,882,000)
Emp.: 161
Fiscal Year-end: 12/31/22
Biotechnology Research & Development Services
N.A.I.C.S.: 541714
Douglas G. Cole (Co-Founder)
Kristian F. Humer (CFO & Principal Acctg Officer)
Alfonso Quintas-Cardama (Chief Medical Officer)
Cigall Kadoch (Co-Founder)
Adrian Gottschalk (Pres & CEO)
Michael LaCascia (Chief Legal Officer)
Marina Nelen (VP-Drug Discovery)
Steven Bellon (Chief Scientific Officer)
Alena Reva (VP-Total Rewards & People Ops)
Anna Rivkin (Chief Bus Officer)
Saurabh Sewak (VP-Corporate Development)
Gromek Smolen (VP-Biology)
Kevin Wilson (VP-Chemistry)
Fanny Cavalie (Chief Strategy Officer, Chief Bus Ops Officer & Sr VP-Bus & Ops)
Carlos Costa (Chief People Officer & Sr VP-People & Organization)
Danette Daniels (VP-Protein Degrader Platform)
Dan Dinu (VP-Information Technology)
Andrew Germain (VP-Legal)
Murphy Hentemann (VP-Program Leadership)
Chong-Hui Gu (VP-CMC & QA)

Karin Hellsvik *(VP-Corp Affairs & Information Technology)*

FOMO WORLDWIDE, INC.

108 Scharberry Ln Ste 2, Mars, PA 16046
Tel.: (630) 708-0750   CA
Web Site:
   https://www.fomoworldwide.com
FOMC—(OTCIQ)
Rev.: $7,515,541
Assets: $3,584,157
Liabilities: $6,154,800
Net Worth: ($2,570,643)
Earnings: ($3,681,490)
Emp.: 11
Fiscal Year-end: 12/31/22
New Car Dealers
N.A.I.C.S.: 441110
Vikram Grover *(Chm, Pres, CEO, CFO & Sec)*

Subsidiaries:

SMARTSolution Technologies,
LP   (1)
831 W N Ave, Pittsburgh, PA 15233
Tel.: (412) 390-0803
Web Site: http://www.smarterguys.com
Rev.: $4,000,000
Emp.: 20
All Other Miscellaneous Store Retailers,
except Tobacco Stores
N.A.I.C.S.: 459999
Michel Schwartz *(Founder & CEO)*

FONAR CORPORATION

110 Marcus Dr, Melville, NY 11747
Tel.: (631) 694-2929   DE
Web Site: https://www.fonar.com
Year Founded: 1978
FONR—(NASDAQ)
Rev.: $102,884,089
Assets: $214,245,969
Liabilities: $57,457,580
Net Worth: $156,788,389
Earnings: $14,097,417
Emp.: 520
Fiscal Year-end: 06/30/24
Upright MRI Scanners & Diagnostic
Imaging Mfr
N.A.I.C.S.: 334510
Timothy V. Damadian *(Chm, Pres, CEO & Treas)*
Claudette J. V. Chan *(Sec)*
Luciano B. Bonanni *(COO & Exec VP)*

Subsidiaries:

HMCM, Inc.   (1)
110 Marcus Dr, Melville, NY 11747-4228
Tel.: (631) 694-2929
Web Site: http://www.fonar.com
Medical Diagnostic Equipment Mfr
N.A.I.C.S.: 334510

Health Management Corporation of
America   (1)
110 Marcus Dr, Melville, NY
11747-3845   (100%)
Tel.: (631) 694-2816
Web Site: https://www.hmca.com
Sales Range: $1-9.9 Million
Emp.: 400
Manages MRI Centers & Physician Practices
N.A.I.C.S.: 541380
Timothy V. Damadian *(Pres & Treas)*
Kurt Reimann *(Pres)*

Subsidiary (Domestic):

Health Diagnostics Management,
LLC   (2)
110 Marcus Dr, Melville, NY 11747
Tel.: (631) 694-2816
Laboratory Testing Services
N.A.I.C.S.: 621511
Mike Christie *(CIO)*

Raymond V. Damadian M.D. MR
Scanning Center Management

Company   (1)
110 Marcus Dr, Melville, NY 11747
Tel.: (631) 694-2929
Web Site: http://www.fonar.com
Sales Range: $150-199.9 Million
Emp.: 250
Manages MRI Centers & Physician Practices
N.A.I.C.S.: 811210
Timothy V. Damadian *(Pres)*

FOODFEST INTERNATIONAL 2000 INC.

1016 9th St, Coronado, CA 92118
Tel.: (619) 844-1279   DE
FDFT—(OTCIQ)
Assets: $9,105
Liabilities: $62,285
Net Worth: ($53,180)
Earnings: ($12,257)
Fiscal Year-end: 12/31/22
Investment Services
N.A.I.C.S.: 523999
Volha Zvalinskaya *(Pres)*

Subsidiaries:

Restore Force Inc.   (1)
106 Princewood Ln, Palm Beach Gardens,
FL 33410-1494
Tel.: (561) 951-6552
Web Site: http://www.restoreforce.com
Residential Remodeler
N.A.I.C.S.: 236118
Whitney B. Wiseman *(Pres)*

FOOT LOCKER, INC.

330 W 34th St, New York, NY 10001
Tel.: (212) 720-3700   NY
Web Site: https://www.footlocker.com
Year Founded: 1879
FL—(NYSE)
Rev.: $8,759,000,000
Assets: $7,907,000,000
Liabilities: $4,614,000,000
Net Worth: $3,293,000,000
Earnings: $342,000,000
Emp.: 15,200
Fiscal Year-end: 01/28/23
Athletic Footwear & Apparel Retailer
N.A.I.C.S.: 458210
Franklin R, Bracken *(Chief Comml Officer & Exec VP)*
Giovanna Cipriano *(Chief Acctg Officer & Sr VP)*
John A. Maurer *(Treas & VP)*
Mary N. Dillon *(Pres & CEO)*
Sheilagh M. Clarke *(Gen Counsel, Sec & Sr VP)*
James R. Lance *(VP-Fin Planning & Analysis)*
Elliott D. Rodgers *(COO & Exec VP)*
Robert Higginbotham *(Sr VP-IR, Fin Plng, and Analysis)*
Neil Bansal *(Chief Strategy & Transformation Officer & Exec VP)*
Mary Dillon *(Pres & CEO)*
Rosalind Reeves *(Chief HR Officer & Exec VP)*
Michael Baughn *(CFO & Exec VP)*

Subsidiaries:

Champs Sports   (1)
303 301 Blvd W Ste 225, Bradenton, FL
34205
Tel.: (941) 748-5392
Web Site: http://www.champssports.com
Sales Range: $125-149.9 Million
Emp.: 120
Athletic Footwear & Sporting Goods Retailer
N.A.I.C.S.: 459999

Eastbay Foot Locker.com   (1)
111 S 1st Ave, Wausau, WI 54401
Tel.: (715) 845-5538
Web Site: http://www.footlocker-inc.com
Sales Range: $350-399.9 Million
Emp.: 1,500
Private Label Athletic Footwear & Apparel
Direct Marketer

N.A.I.C.S.: 339920

Foot Locker Denmark B.V.   (1)
Tel.: (45) 70711371
Web Site: https://www.footlocker.dk
Emp.: 24
Footwear Retailer
N.A.I.C.S.: 424340

Foot Locker Europe B.V.   (1)
Stationsplein 32, 3511 ED, Utrecht,
Netherlands   (100%)
Tel.: (31) 8000200269
Web Site: http://www.footlocker.eu
Sales Range: $150-199.9 Million
Emp.: 250
Athletic Footwear & Apparel Retailer
N.A.I.C.S.: 458210

Subsidiary (Non-US):

Foot Locker Australia, Inc.   (2)
Level 1 / 16 Terrace Place, Murarrie, 4172,
QLD, Australia
Tel.: (61) 742434655
Web Site: https://www.footlocker.com.au
Sales Range: $150-199.9 Million
Emp.: 550
Athletic Footwear & Apparel Retailer
N.A.I.C.S.: 458210

Foot Locker Austria GmbH   (2)
Kaertnerstrasse 12, 1010, Vienna,
Austria   (100%)
Tel.: (43) 15129625
Web Site: http://www.footlocker.eu
Sales Range: $100-124.9 Million
Emp.: 20
Footwear Distr
N.A.I.C.S.: 424340

Foot Locker Belgium B.V.B.A.   (2)
Nieuwstraat 1, 1000, Brussels,
Belgium   (100%)
Tel.: (32) 22232479
Web Site: https://www.footlocker.be
Sales Range: $1-9.9 Million
Emp.: 10
Shoes & Sports Apparel Retailer
N.A.I.C.S.: 458210

Subsidiary (Domestic):

Foot Locker Europe.com B.V.   (2)
Stationsplein 32, 3511 ED, Utrecht, Netherlands
Tel.: (31) 3473233000
Web Site: http://www.foot-locker.co.uk
Shoes & Sport Apparel Online Retailer
N.A.I.C.S.: 458210

Subsidiary (Non-US):

Foot Locker France S.A.S.   (2)
124 rue de Verdun 2eme etage, 92800, Puteaux, France   (100%)
Tel.: (33) 142643025
Web Site: https://www.footlocker.fr
Sales Range: $75-99.9 Million
Emp.: 10
Footwear Distr
N.A.I.C.S.: 424340

Foot Locker Italy S.r.l.   (2)
Via Speronari 7, 20122, Milan, Lombardy,
Italy
Tel.: (39) 0200702354
Web Site: https://www.footlocker.it
Athletic Footwear & Apparel Retailer
N.A.I.C.S.: 458210

Subsidiary (Domestic):

Foot Locker Netherlands B.V.   (2)
Ir DS Tuijnmanweg 3-5, 4131 PN, Vianen,
Netherlands   (100%)
Tel.: (31) 347323300
Web Site: http://www.footlocker.com
Sales Range: $100-124.9 Million
Emp.: 260
Sales Of Shoes & Sport Apparel Distr
N.A.I.C.S.: 458210

Subsidiary (Non-US):

Foot Locker Spain S.L.   (2)
Tel.: (34) 932591754
Web Site: https://www.footlocker.es
Sales Range: $250-299.9 Million
Emp.: 170
Footwear Distr

N.A.I.C.S.: 424340

Subsidiary (Non-US):

Foot Locker Artigos desportivos e de
tempos livres, Lda.   (3)
Tel.: (351) 213220634
Web Site: https://www.footlocker.pt
Sales Range: $150-199.9 Million
Emp.: 5
Footwear Distr
N.A.I.C.S.: 424340

Subsidiary (Non-US):

Foot Locker Sweden Aktiebolag   (2)
Regeringsgatan 21, 111 53, Stockholm,
Sweden   (100%)
Tel.: (46) 854515480
Web Site: http://www.footlocker.com
Sales Range: $150-199.9 Million
Emp.: 35
Athletic Footwear & Apparel Retailer
N.A.I.C.S.: 458210

Freedom Sportsline Limited   (2)
1st Floor 42-48 Great Portland Street, London, W1W 7NB, United Kingdom
Tel.: (44) 1895810188
Web Site: http://www.footlocker.eu
Sales Range: $25-49.9 Million
Emp.: 15
Footwear Distr
N.A.I.C.S.: 424340

Subsidiary (Domestic):

Foot Locker U.K. Limited   (3)
Lovell House 271 Hight Street 2273, Uxbridge, UB8 1HB, Middlesex, United Kingdom
Tel.: (44) 2073181850
Web Site: http://www.foot-locker.co.uk
Sales Range: $100-124.9 Million
Emp.: 360
Athletic Footwear & Apparel Retailer
N.A.I.C.S.: 458210

Foot Locker Retail, Inc.   (1)
330 W 34th St, New York, NY
10001   (100%)
Tel.: (212) 720-3700
Web Site: http://www.footlocker-inc.com
Sales Range: $100-124.9 Million
Retail Product Distr
N.A.I.C.S.: 458210

Foot Locker Specialty, Inc.   (1)
112 W 34th St Front 2, New York, NY
10120-0101   (100%)
Tel.: (212) 760-2311
Sales Range: $100-124.9 Million
Apparel Distr
N.A.I.C.S.: 458110

Foot Locker Switzerland LLC   (1)
Aeschenvorstadt 4, 4051, Basel, Switzerland
Tel.: (41) 582113300
Footwear Retailer
N.A.I.C.S.: 424340

Footlocker.com, Inc.   (1)
111 S 1st Ave, Wausau, WI 54402-8066
Tel.: (800) 991-6815
Web Site: http://www.footlocker.com
Apparel Distr
N.A.I.C.S.: 458110

Kids Foot Locker   (1)
120 W 34th St, New York, NY 10120
Tel.: (212) 465-9041
Web Site: http://www.kidsfootlocker.com
Sales Range: $100-124.9 Million
Emp.: 500
Children's Shoes & Apparel Retailer
N.A.I.C.S.: 458110

Lady Foot Locker   (1)
112 Wt 34th St, New York, NY 10120-0101
Tel.: (212) 720-3700
Web Site: http://www.ladyfootlocker.com
Sales Range: $100-124.9 Million
Retail Athletic Shoe Store
N.A.I.C.S.: 458210

RUNNERS POINT Warenhandelsgesellschaft mbH   (1)
Tiroler Strasse 13A, Recklinghausen,
45659, Germany
Tel.: (49) 236130030

Foot Locker, Inc.—(Continued)

Web Site: http://www.runnerspoint.com
Sales Range: $250-299.9 Million
Emp.: 200
Sporting Goods Retailer
N.A.I.C.S.: 459110

Runners Point Administration GmbH (1)
Tiroler Strasse 26, 45659, Recklinghausen, Germany
Tel.: (49) 08005051660
Web Site: http://www.runnerspoint.de
Sporting Goods Retailer
N.A.I.C.S.: 459110

Team Edition Apparel, Inc. (1)
4208 19th St Ct E, Bradenton, FL 34208
Tel.: (941) 744-2011
Web Site:
https://www.teameditionapparel.com
Sales Range: $150-199.9 Million
Emp.: 300
Apparel Distr
N.A.I.C.S.: 458110

Tredex GmbH (1)
Tiroler Str 13A, 45659, Recklinghausen, Germany
Tel.: (49) 1805532533
Foot Wear Store Operator
N.A.I.C.S.: 458210

FOOTHILLS EXPLORATION, INC.
4607 Lakeview Canyon Rd Ste 235, Westlake Village, CA 91361 DE
Web Site:
https://www.foothillspetro.com
Year Founded: 2010
FTXP—(OTCIQ)
Oil & Gas Exploration & Production
N.A.I.C.S.: 213112
Kevin J. Sylla (Chm & Co-CEO)
B. P. Allaire (Co-CEO & Interim CFO)
Christopher C. Jarvis (Exec VP-Fin)

FOR THE EARTH CORP.
2375 E Camelback Rd Ste 600, Phoenix, AZ 85016
Tel.: (602) 806-9292 DE
Year Founded: 1993
FTEG—(OTCIQ)
Eco-Friendly Products Mfr
N.A.I.C.S.: 325199

Subsidiaries:

Prestige Pet Products, Inc (1)
41123 Jo Dr, Novi, MI 48375
Tel.: (248) 615-8984
Web Site: http://www.prestigepet.com
Sales Range: $10-24.9 Million
Emp.: 5
Piece Goods, Notions & Other Dry Goods Merchant Whslr
N.A.I.C.S.: 424310

FORBES ENERGY SERVICES LTD.
3000 S Business Hwy 281, Alice, TX 78332
Tel.: (361) 664-0549 BM
Web Site:
https://www.forbesenergyser
vices.com
Year Founded: 2003
FLSS—(OTCIQ)
Rev.: $188,422,000
Assets: $190,265,000
Liabilities: $166,309,000
Net Worth: $23,956,000
Earnings: ($68,399,000)
Emp.: 786
Fiscal Year-end: 12/31/19
Oil & Gas Exploration Services
N.A.I.C.S.: 211120
L. Melvin Cooper (Asst Sec)
John E. Crisp (Chm, Pres & CEO)
Steve Macek (COO & Exec VP-Well Servicing)

Subsidiaries:

C.C. Forbes, LLC (1)
3000 S Business Hwy 28, Alice, TX 78333
Tel.: (361) 396-1898
Emp.: 1,222
Oil & Gas Exploration Services
N.A.I.C.S.: 211130
Charles C. Forbes Jr. (CEO)

Superior Tubing Testers, LLC (1)
4783 S US Hwy 281, Alice, TX 78333
Tel.: (361) 396-0422
Oil & Gas Exploration Services
N.A.I.C.S.: 211130

TX Energy Services, LLC (1)
3000 S Highway 281, Alice, TX 78333
Tel.: (361) 664-5020
Oil & Gas Exploration Services
N.A.I.C.S.: 211130

FORBION EUROPEAN ACQUISITION CORP.
4001 Kennett Pike Ste 302, Wilmington, DE 19807
Tel.: (302) 273-0765 Ky
Year Founded: 2021
FRBN—(NASDAQ)
Rev.: $1,862,147
Assets: $132,043,138
Liabilities: $136,152,343
Net Worth: ($4,109,205)
Earnings: $30,726
Emp.: 2
Fiscal Year-end: 12/31/22
Investment Services
N.A.I.C.S.: 523999
Jasper Bos (CEO)
Cyril Lesser (CFO)

FORCE PROTECTION VIDEO EQUIPMENT CORP.
2629 Townsgate Rd Ste 215, Westlake Village, CA 91361
Tel.: (714) 312-6844 FL
Web Site:
http://www.forceprovideo.com
Year Founded: 2011
FPVD—(OTCIQ)
Rev.: $2,168,000
Assets: $7,570,000
Liabilities: $1,310,000
Net Worth: $6,260,000
Earnings: ($15,506,000)
Emp.: 86
Fiscal Year-end: 12/31/20
Investment Services
N.A.I.C.S.: 523999
Christopher Miglino (Chm & Interim Principal Exec Officer)
Michael Malone (CFO & Principal Acctg Officer)
George Stella (Pres & Chief Rev Officer)

FORD MOTOR COMPANY
1 American Rd, Dearborn, MI 48126
Tel.: (313) 323-2875 DE
Web Site: https://www.ford.com
Year Founded: 1919
F—(NYSE)
Rev.: $170,191,000,000
Assets: $273,310,000,000
Liabilities: $230,512,000,000
Net Worth: $42,798,000,000
Earnings: $4,347,000,000
Emp.: 177,000
Fiscal Year-end: 12/31/23
Motor Vehicles Mfr
N.A.I.C.S.: 336110
Moray S. Callum (VP)
Cathy O'Callaghan (VP)
James Duncan Farley Jr. (Pres, CEO & Pres-Ford Model e)
Elena A. Ford (Chief Customer Experience Officer-)
Lynn Antipas Tyson (Exec Dir-IR)

Stuart J. Rowley (Chief Transformation & Quality Officer-Ford of Europe)
John T. Lawler (Vice Chm & CFO)
Mark Kosman (Chief Acctg Officer)
Kumar Galhotra (Pres)
Sherry House (VP-Fin)
Lyle Alexander Watters (Gen Mgr--China)
Mark Truby (Chief Comm Officer)
David Filipe (VP-Vehicle Hardware Modules)
David McClelland (VP-Strategy & Partnerships)
Cathy O'Callaghan (VP & Controller)
Jacques Brent (Dir)
John Savona (VP-Ford Blue)
Graham Pearson (Exec Dir-Product Dev-Asia Pacific)
Joerg Beyer (Exec Dir-Engineering-Europe & Mng Dir-Product Development-Ford, Werke GmbH)
David Webb (Treas)
Mitch Bainwol (Chief Govt Rels Officer)
Nigel Brackenbury (VP-Customer Svc Div-Europe)
James A. Buczkowski (Dir-Electrical & Electronics Sys Res & Innovation)
Andrew Frick (Gen Mgr-Sales-Distribution-Ford Blue)
Peter Godsell (VP-HR-Europe)
Graham Hoare (Exec Dir-Britain & Chm)
Bob Holycross (VP-Sustainability, Environment & Safety Engrg)
Sundeep Madra (VP)
Curt Magleby (VP-Government Relations-US)
Michael S. Sheridan (VP-Intl)
Dennis Slevin (Mgr-F,Series Super Duty)
Rich Strader (VP-Mobility Platforms & Products)
Jim Baumbick (VP-Operations-Ford Blue)
Chuck Gray (VP-Ford Model e)
Mark Buzzell (Dir)
Anning Chen (Pres/CEO-China)
Jeffrey Jones (Founder-North America)
Monazza Khan (Reg Dir)
Kevin C. Legel (VP-Labor Affairs)
Werner Puetz (VP-Pur-Europe)
Beth A. Rose (Chief Compliance, Ethics & Integrity Officer)
Hans Schep (Gen Mgr-Europe)
Christian Weingaertner (Dir-Marketing-Sales-Europe & Mng Dir-Europe)
Cynthia Williams (Dir-Compliance-Global)
John F. Mellen (Gen Counsel)
Dianne Craig (Pres--Ford Blue)
Suzy Deering (CMO)
Jonathan Jennings (VP-Supply Chain-Global)
Lori Costew (Chief Diversity Officer & Dir-People Strategy)
Gil Gur Arie (Chief Data & Analytics Officer)
Alex Purdy (Dir-Bus Ops-Enterprise Connectivity)
Kieran Cahill (VP-Mfg-Europe)
Rahul Singh (Head-Autonomous Vehicle Software Dev)
Doug Field (Chief EV & Digital Sys Officer)
Martin Sander (Gen Mgr-Passenger Vehicles-Ford of Europe)
Matthew Godlewski (VP-Government Relations-US)
Steve Croley (Chief Policy Officer & Gen Counsel)
Anthony Lo (Chief Design Officer)
Franck Louis-Victor (VP)

Desi Ujkashevic (Dir-Global)
Brett Wheatley (Dir)
Pete Hockey (Dir-Supply Chain Ops-Global)
Ashwani Galhotra (Pres)
Mary Culler (CEO & VP)
Matt Jones (Dir & VP)
Mike Amend (Chief Enterprise Tech Officer)
Doug Power (VP)
Christopher Smith (Chief Govt Affairs Officer)

Subsidiaries:

American Road Services Company LLC (1)
1 American Rd, Dearborn, MI 48126-2701
Tel.: (313) 322-3000
Web Site: http://www.ford.com
Sales Range: $10-24.9 Million
Emp.: 100
Insurance Adjusters
N.A.I.C.S.: 524291

AutoAlliance International Inc. (1)
1 International Dr, Flat Rock, MI 48134-9401 (50%)
Tel.: (734) 782-0498
Automobile Manufacturing
N.A.I.C.S.: 336110
Rodney Haynes (CFO & VP-Pur & Plng)

Carey International, Inc. (1)
4530 Wisconsin Ave NW, Washington, DC 20016
Tel.: (202) 895-1200
Web Site: http://www.carey.com
Sales Range: $250-299.9 Million
Chauffeur Services & Ground Transportation Logistics Management Services
N.A.I.C.S.: 485320
Mitchell J. Lahr (CFO)
Sandy Miller (CEO)
Dan Miller (COO)

Consorcio Nacional Ford Ltda. (1)
Paulo Sergio de Souza E Silva rua Estado de Israel 975 Bairro Vila, Clementino, CEP 04-022002, Sao Paulo, SP, Brazil
Tel.: (55) 11 8696 3176
Web Site:
http://www.consorcionacionalford.com.br
Sales Range: $300-349.9 Million
Automobile Mfr
N.A.I.C.S.: 336110

Cosworth Racing Inc. (1)
3031 Fujita St, Torrance, CA 90505-4004
Tel.: (310) 534-1390
Web Site: http://www.cosworth.com
Sales Range: $10-24.9 Million
Emp.: 61
High Performance Auto Repair & Service
N.A.I.C.S.: 811198

Ford Bank GmbH (1)
Henry-Ford-Strasse 1, 50735, Cologne, Germany
Tel.: (49) 22151080
Web Site: http://www.ford.de
Automobile Mfr
N.A.I.C.S.: 336110

Ford Capital B.V. (1)
Tav CRC, Postbus 795, 1000 AT, Amsterdam, Netherlands
Tel.: (31) 205044646
Web Site: http://www.ford.nl
Insurance & Brokerage Services
N.A.I.C.S.: 524210

Subsidiary (Non-US):

Ford Romania S.A. (2)
Global City - Sos Bucuresti Nord nr 10, Voluntari Ilfov Pipera, Bucharest, 077190, Romania
Tel.: (40) 37 237 3673
Web Site: https://www.ford.ro
Automobile Mfr
N.A.I.C.S.: 336110

Ford Communications, Inc. (1)
1 American Rd, Dearborn, MI 48121 (100%)
Tel.: (313) 322-3000
Sales Range: $250-299.9 Million
Communications Division
N.A.I.C.S.: 551112

Ford Component Sales, L.L.C. **(1)**
290 Town Center Dr Ste 1000, Dearborn,
MI 48126
Tel.: (313) 390-1200
Web Site:
 http://www.fordcomponentsales.com
Motor Vehicle Supplies Mfr
N.A.I.C.S.: 423120

Ford Deutschland Holding GmbH **(1)**
Henry Ford Strasse 1, 50735, Cologne,
Germany
Tel.: (49) 2219017524
Web Site: http://www.ford.de
Automotive Distr
N.A.I.C.S.: 441110

Ford Espana S.A. **(1)**
C/ Calendula 13 Edif Miniparc IV - Soto de
la Moraleja, 28109, Alcobendas, Madrid,
Spain   **(100%)**
Tel.: (34) 917376217
Web Site: http://www.ford.es
Sales Range: $150-199.9 Million
Automobile Mfr
N.A.I.C.S.: 336110

Ford France **(1)**
1 rue du 1er Mai immeuble Axe Seine,
92000, Nanterre, France
Tel.: (33) 811022730
Web Site: http://www.ford.fr
Motor Vehicles Mfr
N.A.I.C.S.: 336110

Ford India Private Limited **(1)**
5th Floor Plot No 142 Chimes 142 Sector
44 Road Sector 44, Gurgaon, 122003,
Haryana, India
Tel.: (91) 1246133000
Web Site: https://www.india.ford.com
Automobile Mfr
N.A.I.C.S.: 336110
Anurag Mehrotra (Pres & Mng Dir)
Vinay Raina (Exec Dir-Mktg, Sls & Svc)
Rahul Gautam (VP-Mktg)
George Elisseou (Dir-HR)
David Schock (CFO)

**Ford International Capital
Corporation** **(1)**
1 American Rd, Dearborn, MI
48126   **(100%)**
Tel.: (313) 322-3000
Web Site: http://www.ford.com
Sales Range: $125-149.9 Million
Financial Management Services
N.A.I.C.S.: 522299

Subsidiary (Non-US):

Blue Oval Holdings Limited **(2)**
Rm 1 447 Eagle Way, Brentwood, CM13
3BW, United Kingdom
Tel.: (44) 04850367
Web Site: http://www.ford.co.uk
Holding Company
N.A.I.C.S.: 551112

Subsidiary (Domestic):

Ford Motor Company Limited **(3)**
Warley Central Office Room GB 1/150
Eagle Way, Warley, Brentwood, CM13
3BW, Essex, United Kingdom
Tel.: (44) 2035644444
Web Site: http://www.ford.co.uk
Mfr of Automobiles
N.A.I.C.S.: 336110

Subsidiary (Non-US):

Henry Ford & Sons Ltd **(4)**
Elm Court Boreenma na Road, Cork, T12
HHW2, Ireland   **(100%)**
Tel.: (353) 800771199
Web Site: http://www.ford.ie
Sales Range: $25-49.9 Million
Emp.: 40
Automobile Mfr
N.A.I.C.S.: 336110
Ciaran McMahon (Mng Dir)

Ford Investment Partnership **(1)**
1 American Rd, Dearborn, MI 48126
Tel.: (313) 322-3000
Web Site: http://www.ford.com
Sales Range: $650-699.9 Million
Provider of Investment Services
N.A.I.C.S.: 523999

Ford Italia S.p.A. **(1)**
Via del Serafico 89, 00142, Rome,
Italy   **(100%)**
Tel.: (39) 080 022 4433
Web Site: https://www.ford.it
Sales Range: $125-149.9 Million
Emp.: 450
Mfr & Distr of Ford Automobiles
N.A.I.C.S.: 336110

Ford Land **(1)**
17000 Rotunda Dr 1st Fl S, Dearborn, MI
48120
Tel.: (313) 323-3100
Web Site: http://www.fordland.com
Sales Range: $125-149.9 Million
Emp.: 150
Real Estate Invenstors
N.A.I.C.S.: 237210

Ford Lio Ho Motor Co., Ltd. **(1)**
705 Sec 1 Chung-Hwa Road, Chung-Li,
Taoyuan, Taiwan   **(70%)**
Tel.: (886) 034553131
Web Site: http://www.ford.com.tw
Motor Vehicles Mfr
N.A.I.C.S.: 336110

Ford Lusitana **(1)**
Avenida Defensores de Chaves N 45 - 4
andar, 1000 112, Lisbon, Portugal **(100%)**
Tel.: (351) 808200556
Web Site: http://www.ford.pt
Automobile Mfr & Distr
N.A.I.C.S.: 336110

Ford Motor Austria **(1)**
Furbergstrasse 51, Salzburg, 5020,
Austria   **(80%)**
Tel.: (43) 66265810
Web Site: http://www.ford.at
Sales Range: $25-49.9 Million
Emp.: 100
Mfr of Automobiles
N.A.I.C.S.: 336110

Ford Motor Belgium N.V. **(1)**
Hunderenveldlaan 10, 1082, Brussels,
Belgium   **(84.2%)**
Tel.: (32) 24822000
Web Site: http://www.ford.be
Sales Range: $300-349.9 Million
Emp.: 70
Mfr of Automobiles
N.A.I.C.S.: 336110

Ford Motor Co. - Lincoln Division **(1)**
16800 Executive Plaza Dr 4th Fl, Dearborn,
MI 48126
Tel.: (313) 322-3000
Web Site: http://www.lincoln.com
Sales Range: $100-124.9 Million
Emp.: 200
Marketing of Cars & Trucks
N.A.I.C.S.: 441110
Dianne C. Craig (Pres)

**Ford Motor Company (Austria)
GmbH** **(1)**
Grunbergstrasse 15 Top ME 42, 1120, Vi-
enna, Austria
Tel.: (43) 1206092424
Web Site: https://www.ford.at
Motor Vehicle Parts Mfr
N.A.I.C.S.: 336390

Ford Motor Company A/S **(1)**
Borupvang 1, 2750, Ballerup, Denmark
Tel.: (45) 43480700
Web Site: http://www.ford.dk
Sales Range: $25-49.9 Million
Emp.: 80
Distr of New Automobiles, Trucks & Parts
N.A.I.C.S.: 441330

Subsidiary (Non-US):

Ford Motor Norge A/S **(2)**
Lienga 2, PO Box 514, 1414, Trollasen,
Norway   **(100%)**
Tel.: (47) 22579099
Web Site: http://www.ford.no
Sales Range: $25-49.9 Million
Emp.: 40
Provider of Automobiles
N.A.I.C.S.: 336110
Ter Bert (Mng Dir)

Ford Motor Company AB **(1)**
Torpavallsgatan 9, PO Box 405, Gothen-

burg, 416 73, Sweden **(94.1%)**
Tel.: (46) 313259000
Web Site: http://www.ford.se
Sales Range: $75-99.9 Million
Emp.: 40
Provider of Motor Vehicle Related Financial
Services
N.A.I.C.S.: 523999

**Ford Motor Company Brasil
Ltda.** **(1)**
Av Do Taboao 899, Predio I Sala 01 Ta-
boao, Sao Bernardo do Campo, 09655-900,
Sao Paulo, Brazil
Tel.: (55) 1141748955
Web Site: http://www.ford.com.br
Automobile Merchant Whslr
N.A.I.C.S.: 423110

**Ford Motor Company Switzerland
S.A.** **(1)**
Geerenstrasse 10, 8304, Wallisellen,
Switzerland   **(100%)**
Tel.: (41) 445111445
Web Site: http://www.ford.ch
Sales Range: $25-49.9 Million
Emp.: 130
Distribution & Sales of Automobiles
N.A.I.C.S.: 561499
Paul Fratter (Mng Dir)

**Ford Motor Company of Australia
Limited** **(1)**
Private Mail Bag 5, PO Box 6, Campbell-
field, 3061, VIC, Australia **(94%)**
Tel.: (61) 133673
Web Site: http://www.ford.com.au
Sales Range: $1-4.9 Billion
Mfr of Automotive Vehicles
N.A.I.C.S.: 336110

Subsidiary (Non-US):

**Ford Motor Company of New Zealand
Ltd.** **(1)**
Level 2 The Ford Building 86 Highbrook Dr,
East Tamaki, New Zealand **(100%)**
Tel.: (64) 800367369
Web Site: http://www.ford.co.nz
Sales Range: $50-74.9 Million
Emp.: 40
Automobile Dealership
N.A.I.C.S.: 441110

**Ford Motor Company of Canada,
Limited** **(1)**
The Canadian Road, PO Box 2000, Oak-
ville, L6K 0C8, ON, Canada **(93.8%)**
Tel.: (905) 845-2511
Web Site: http://www.ford.ca
Sales Range: $5-14.9 Billion
Mfr of Cars, Trucks & Other Motor Vehicles
N.A.I.C.S.: 336120
Mark Buzzell (Pres & CEO)

Subsidiary (Domestic):

440 Ford Lincoln Laval **(2)**
2705 Boul Chomedey, Laval, H7P 0C2, QC,
Canada
Tel.: (450) 666-3673
Web Site: https://www.440ford.ca
New & Used Car Dealers
N.A.I.C.S.: 441110
Marie-Claude Guinois (Controller)
Josee Gemme (Asst Controller-Fin)
Jovite Dionne (Controller-Fin)
Sylvain Hogues (Pres)
Sylvain Judd (Mgr-Parts)
Theodore Barkoulas (Mgr-Comml Sls)
Michel Lacaille (Dir-Technical Svcs)
Martin Noel (Asst Dir-Technical Svc)

Ford Essex Engine Plant **(2)**
1 Quality Way, Windsor, N9A 6X3, ON,
Canada   **(50%)**
Tel.: (519) 944-8600
Web Site: http://www.media.ford.com
Sales Range: $350-399.9 Million
Emp.: 2,000
Automobile Mfr
N.A.I.C.S.: 336110

Parkway Ford Sales 1996 Ltd. **(2)**
455 King St N, Waterloo, N2J 2Z5, ON,
Canada   **(100%)**
Tel.: (519) 884-5110
Web Site: http://www.parkwayford.ca
Sales Range: $50-74.9 Million
Emp.: 100
New & Used Car Dealers

N.A.I.C.S.: 441110

**Ford Motor Company of Southern
Africa (Pty) Limited** **(1)**
Simon Vermooten Rd, PO Box 411, Preto-
ria, 0001, South Africa
Tel.: (27) 860011022
Web Site: https://www.ford.co.za
Sales Range: $1-4.9 Billion
Motor Vehicles Mfr
N.A.I.C.S.: 336999

Ford Motor Credit Company LLC **(1)**
1 American Rd, Dearborn, MI
48126   **(100%)**
Tel.: (313) 322-3000
Web Site: http://www.fordcredit.com
Rev.: $10,876,000,000
Assets: $149,205,000,000
Liabilities: $135,816,000,000
Net Worth: $13,389,000,000
Earnings: $1,324,000,000
Emp.: 5,000
Fiscal Year-end: 12/31/2023
Credit Services
N.A.I.C.S.: 522291
Cathy O'Callaghan (CEO)
David McClelland (Chm)
N. Joy Falotico (COO & Exec VP)
Brian E. Schaaf (CFO & Treas)
Thomas C. Schneider (Chief Risk Officer &
Exec VP)
Narpal S. Ahluwalia (Chief Risk Officer &
Exec VP)

Subsidiary (Domestic):

CAB East LLC **(2)**
1 American Rd, Dearborn, MI 48126
Tel.: (313) 845-5712
Automobile Mfr
N.A.I.C.S.: 336110

Subsidiary (Non-US):

FCE Bank plc **(2)**
Arterial Road, Laindon, SS15 6EE, Essex,
United Kingdom   **(98%)**
Tel.: (44) 8457125490
Web Site: http://www.fordcredit.co.uk
Financial Services
N.A.I.C.S.: 522210

Branch (Non-US):

FCE Bank plc - Austria **(3)**
Sterneckstrasse 31-33, 5020, Salzburg,
Austria
Tel.: (43) 6626560580
Web Site: http://www.fordbank.co.at
Sales Range: $100-124.9 Million
Emp.: 40
Provider of Financial Services
N.A.I.C.S.: 523999

FCE Bank plc - Spain **(3)**
Calendula 13 Edificio Miniparc IV, 28109,
Alcobendas, Madrid, Spain **(100%)**
Tel.: (34) 917145100
Web Site: http://www.ford.es
Sales Range: $125-149.9 Million
Financial Services
N.A.I.C.S.: 522220

Subsidiary (Non-US):

**Ford Automotive Finance (China)
Limited** **(2)**
20/F No 1155 Fangdian Rd Pudong New
Area, Shanghai, 201024, China
Tel.: (86) 2120894666
Emp.: 350
Vehicle Lending Services
N.A.I.C.S.: 522390
Jim Dorfman (Gen Mgr)

Ford Credit A/S **(2)**
Stamholmen 149 5 sal, 2650, Hvidovre,
Denmark   **(100%)**
Tel.: (45) 70219060
Web Site: http://www.fordcredit.dk
Sales Range: $25-49.9 Million
Emp.: 41
Provider of Automotive Credit Services
N.A.I.C.S.: 522210

Subsidiary (Domestic):

**Ford Credit Auto Receivables
Corporation** **(2)**
1 American Rd, Dearborn, MI 48121

Ford Motor Company—(Continued)

Tel.: (313) 322-3000
Web Site: http://www.fordcredit.com
Sales Range: $100-124.9 Million
Financial Services
N.A.I.C.S.: 561499

Subsidiary (Non-US):

Ford Credit B.V.   (2)
Marten Meesweg 97, PO Box 795, 3068
AV, Rotterdam, Netherlands
Tel.: (31) 888866969
Web Site: http://www.fordcredit.nl
Sales Range: $1-9.9 Million
Emp.: 30
Provider of Finance & Insurance Services
N.A.I.C.S.: 524298

Subsidiary (Domestic):

**Ford Credit CP Auto Receivables
LLC**   (2)
1 American Rd, Dearborn, MI 48126
Tel.: (313) 322-3000
Automobile Related Financial Services
N.A.I.C.S.: 522220

Subsidiary (Non-US):

Ford Credit Canada Company   (2)
The Canadian Road, PO Box 2000, Oak-
ville, L6J 5E4, ON, Canada   (100%)
Tel.: (905) 845-2511
Web Site: https://www.ford.ca
Automotive Credit Operation Services
N.A.I.C.S.: 522210

Subsidiary (Domestic):

Ford Credit International, Inc.   (2)
1 American Rd, Dearborn, MI 48126-2701
Tel.: (313) 322-3000
Sales Range: $1-4.9 Billion
Holding Company; Motor Vehicle Financing
Services
N.A.I.C.S.: 551112

Subsidiary (Non-US):

Ford Credit Italia SpA   (2)
Via del Serafico n 89, 00142, Rome, Italy
Tel.: (39) 0651855660
Web Site: https://www.ford.it
Motor Vehicle Parts Mfr
N.A.I.C.S.: 336390

Ford Credit Portugal   (2)
Av Liberdade 249, 1250-143, Lisbon, Portu-
gal
Tel.: (351) 213182100
Web Site: http://www.ford.pt
Sales Range: $25-49.9 Million
Emp.: 40
Mfr of Automobile Electronics
N.A.I.C.S.: 336320

Ford Credit S.A.   (2)
Geerenstrasse 10, Wallisellen, 8304,
Switzerland   (100%)
Tel.: (41) 432332401
Web Site: http://www.fordcredit.ch
Sales Range: $100-124.9 Million
Emp.: 70
Provider of Financial Services
N.A.I.C.S.: 523999

Ford Credit SpA   (2)
Via A Argoli No 54, 00143, Rome,
Italy   (100%)
Tel.: (39) 0691 806900
Web Site: http://www.fordcredit.it
Sales Range: $650-699.9 Million
Provider of Financial Services
N.A.I.C.S.: 523999

Subsidiary (Domestic):

Ford Leasing SpA   (3)
Via A Argoli No 54, 00143, Rome,
Italy   (100%)
Tel.: (39) 0651855660
Web Site: http://www.ford.it
Car Lending Services
N.A.I.C.S.: 532112

Subsidiary (Non-US):

**Ford Credit de Mexico S.A. de
C.V.**   (2)

Guillermo Gonzalez Camarena 1500, 3rd
Floor Centro De Ciudad Santa Fe Delega-
cion Alvaro Obregon, Mexico, 01210,
Mexico
Tel.: (52) 5511033000
Web Site: http://www.fordcredit.com
Sales Range: $650-699.9 Million
Emp.: 100
Financial Services
N.A.I.C.S.: 523999

Subsidiary (Domestic):

**Primus Automotive Financial Ser-
vices, Inc.**   (2)
9009 Carothers Pkwy, Franklin, TN 37067-
1634
Tel.: (615) 315-7900
Web Site: https://primusfinancial.com
Sales Range: $1-4.9 Billion
Emp.: 1,700
Financial Services
N.A.I.C.S.: 523999

Subsidiary (Non-US):

**Primus Automotive Financial Services
Limited**   (3)
Central Office Eagle Way, Brentwood,
CM13 3BW, Essex, United
Kingdom   (100%)
Tel.: (44) 1277253000
Sales Range: $1-4.9 Billion
Emp.: 1,500
Provider of Financial Services
N.A.I.C.S.: 523999

Ford Motor Japan Ltd.   (1)
19F Kamiyacho Mori Building 3-20 Tora-
nomon 4-Chome, Minato-Ku, Tokyo, 105-
6022, Japan   (100%)
Tel.: (81) 354702612
Web Site: http://www.ford.co.jp
Sales Range: $300-349.9 Million
Emp.: 60
Mfr & Sales of Motor Vehicles
N.A.I.C.S.: 336110

**Ford Motor Land Development
Corporation**   (1)
330 Town Ctr Dr Ste 1100, Dearborn, MI
48126   (100%)
Tel.: (313) 323-3100
Web Site: http://www.fordland.com
Sales Range: $75-99.9 Million
Emp.: 150
Real Estate Development Division
N.A.I.C.S.: 336110

Ford Motor Land Services Corp.   (1)
Parklane Towers E, Dearborn, MI 48120
Tel.: (313) 323-3100
Web Site: http://www.dearborn3.ford.com
Sales Range: $400-449.9 Million
Emp.: 300
Real Estate Agents & Managers
N.A.I.C.S.: 531210
Donna Inch *(Chm)*

Ford Motor Service Company   (1)
1 American Rd, Dearborn, MI 48126
Tel.: (313) 322-3000
Automobile Mfr
N.A.I.C.S.: 336110

Ford Nederland B.V.   (1)
Amsteldijk 216-217, Postbus 175, 1180 AD,
Amstelveen, Netherlands
Tel.: (31) 707703777
Web Site: https://www.ford.nl
Sales Range: $75-99.9 Million
Emp.: 200
Automotive Sales & Services
N.A.I.C.S.: 336110

Ford Otomotiv Sanayi A.S.   (1)
Akpinar Mahallesi Hasan Basri Caddesi No
2 Sancaktepe, 34885, Istanbul,
Turkiye   (41.04%)
Tel.: (90) 2165647100
Web Site: https://www.fordotosan.com.tr
Rev.: $12,722,756,189
Assets: $6,702,816,296
Liabilities: $4,447,791,818
Net Worth: $2,255,024,478
Earnings: $1,515,209,618
Emp.: 20,000
Fiscal Year-end: 12/31/2023
Automobile Mfr
N.A.I.C.S.: 336110

Ali Yildirim Koc *(Chm)*
Haydar Yenigun *(Gen Mgr)*
Guven Ozyurt *(Asst Gen Mgr-Ops)*
Ozgur Yuceturk *(Asst Gen Mgr-Mktg, Sls &
After Sls)*
Serhan Turfan *(Asst Gen Mgr-Ford Trucks)*
Stuart Rowley *(Vice Chm)*
Dave Johnston *(Deputy Gen Mgr)*
Murat Senir *(Asst Gen Mgr-Pur)*

**Ford Plastic & Trim Products Interna-
tional, Inc.**   (1)
1 American Rd, Dearborn, MI 48126-2701
Tel.: (313) 322-3000
Sales Range: $250-299.9 Million
Automotive Industry
N.A.I.C.S.: 551112

Ford Retail Group Limited   (1)
2 Charter Court Newcomen Way,
Colchester, CO4 9YA, Essex, United King-
dom
Tel.: (44) 1206754600
Web Site: http://www.fordretail.com
Sales Range: $1-4.9 Billion
Emp.: 3,000
Holding Company; Car Dealerships Opera-
tor
N.A.I.C.S.: 551112
Stuart Mustoe *(Fin Dir)*
John Leeman *(Dir-Dealer Ops)*
Sharon Ashcroft *(Dir-HR)*
Stuart Foulds *(Chm & CEO)*

Unit (Domestic):

TrustFord - Potters Bar   (2)
343 Baker Street, Hertfordshire, Potters
Bar, EN6 2DZ, Hertfordshire, United King-
dom
Tel.: (44) 1707240662
Web Site: http://www.trustford.co.uk
Emp.: 22
New & Used Car Dealer
N.A.I.C.S.: 441110

**Ford Sales & Service (Thailand) Co.,
Ltd.**   (1)
98 Sathorn Square Office Tower 11th-12th,
North Sathorn Road Silom Bangrak, Bang-
kok, 10500, Thailand
Tel.: (66) 23058592
Web Site: http://www.ford.co.th
Automobile Mfr
N.A.I.C.S.: 336110

Ford Smart Mobility LLC   (1)
40600 Ann Arbor Rd E Ste 201, Plymouth,
MI 48170
Tel.: (313) 322-3000
Mobility Services
N.A.I.C.S.: 488999
Marion Harris *(VP-Mobility Bus Grp)*
Sundeep Madra *(Co-Founder-Autonomic &
VP-Ford X)*
Rich Strader *(VP-Mobility Platforms & Prod-
ucts)*
Brett Wheatley *(VP-Mobility Mktg & Growth)*
Gavin Sherry *(Co-Founder/CEO & Auto-
nomic)*
Benjamin Black *(Co-Founder/CTO-
Autonomic)*
Amar Varma *(Co-Founder/COO & Auto-
nomic)*
Nithin Rao *(Co-Founder/VP-Product Mgmt-
Autonomic)*

Ford Vietnam Limited   (1)
6th Floor Sun Red River Building, 23 Phan
Chu Trinh Street, Hanoi, Vietnam   (75%)
Tel.: (84) 84439331282
Web Site: http://www.ford.com.vn
Sales Range: $50-74.9 Million
Emp.: 120
Mfr & Distribution of Autombiles, Trucks &
Electric Vehicles
N.A.I.C.S.: 336340

Ford-Werke GmbH   (1)
Henry-Ford-Str 1, 50735, Cologne,
Germany   (99.8%)
Tel.: (49) 22199992999
Sales Range: $5-14.9 Billion
Emp.: 30,000
Automobile Mfr
N.A.I.C.S.: 336110

**GETRAG Ford Transmissions
GmbH**   (1)
Scarletallee 2, 50735, Cologne, Germany

Tel.: (49) 22158970
Web Site: http://www.getrag.com
Emp.: 506
Transmissions Systems & Components Mfr
N.A.I.C.S.: 333613
Hans Terbrueggen *(VP-Sls & Customer
Strategy)*
Michael Weber *(Dir)*

Plant (Non-US):

**GETRAG Ford Transmissions GmbH
- Bordeaux Plant**   (2)
Zone Industrielle 65 Rue Jean Duvert, BP
123, 33294, Blanquefort, Cedex, France
Tel.: (33) 557 535 100
Web Site: http://www.getrag.com
Emp.: 1,090
Vehicle Parts Mfr
N.A.I.C.S.: 336390
Andor Paizer *(Plant Dir)*

Plant (Domestic):

**GETRAG Ford Transmissions GmbH
- Cologne-Merkenich**   (2)
Spessartstrasse, 50725, Cologne, Germany
Tel.: (49) 221 903 8202
Web Site: http://www.getrag.com
Emp.: 106
Vehicle Parts Mfr
N.A.I.C.S.: 336390
Erik Muller *(Plant Dir)*

Plant (Non-US):

**GETRAG Ford Transmissions GmbH
- Halewood Plant**   (2)
Speke Boulevard, Liverpool, L24 9LE,
United Kingdom
Tel.: (44) 151 485 6959
Web Site: http://www.getrag.com
Emp.: 639
Vehicle Parts Mfr
N.A.I.C.S.: 336390
Andy Roche *(Plant Dir)*

Subsidiary (Non-US):

**GETRAG Ford Transmissions Slova-
kia sro**   (2)
Perinska cesta 282, Kechnec, 044 58, Kos-
ice, Slovakia
Tel.: (421) 556148300
Web Site: http://www.getrag.com
Emp.: 1,009
Vehicle Parts Mfr
N.A.I.C.S.: 336390
Andy Roche *(Dir)*

Granite Management Corp.   (1)
4041 Macarthur Blvd, Newport Beach, CA
92660-2512
Tel.: (949) 440-7200
Sales Range: $25-49.9 Million
Emp.: 5
Mortgage Brokers & Loan Correspondents
N.A.I.C.S.: 522310

Greenleaf LLC   (1)
5015 Causeway Blvd, Tampa, FL 33619-
6129
Tel.: (813) 247-3171
Web Site: http://www.greenleafauto.com
Sales Range: $25-49.9 Million
Emp.: 60
Supplier of Recycled Original Automotive
Equipment & of Domestic & Foreign Ve-
hicles
N.A.I.C.S.: 325314
William Santana Li *(Founder)*

Groupe FMC France SAS   (1)
34 Rue de la Croix de Fer, 78122, Saint
Germain-en-Laye, France
Tel.: (33) 161016101
Sales Range: $50-74.9 Million
Emp.: 30
Automobile Parts Mfr
N.A.I.C.S.: 336110
Jean Luc Jerard *(Gen Dir)*

Manhattan Automobile Company   (1)
787 11th Ave, New York, NY 10019-3538
Tel.: (212) 581-7800
Web Site: http://www.manhattanauto.com
Sales Range: $150-199.9 Million
Emp.: 275
Sales of New & Used Automobiles
N.A.I.C.S.: 441110

Oy Ford Ab (1)
Ayritie 24, PL 33, 01511, Vantaa,
Finland (100%)
Tel.: (358) 985645480
Web Site: https://www.ford.fi
Sales Range: $10-24.9 Million
Emp.: 35
Sales & Marketing of Motor Vehicles
N.A.I.C.S.: 561499

Pacific Bay Homes, LLC (1)
4041 Macarthur Blvd 500, Newport Beach,
CA 92660
Tel.: (949) 440-7200
Sales Range: $1-9.9 Million
Emp.: 20
Residential Construction Services
N.A.I.C.S.: 531210

Percepta LLC (1)
290 Town Ctr Dr Fairlane Plz N Ste 610,
Dearborn, MI 48126 (45%)
Tel.: (313) 390-0157
Web Site: http://www.percepta.com
Sales Range: $10-24.9 Million
Emp.: 20
Customer Relationship Management Solu-
tions for the Automotive Industry; Joint Ven-
ture of TeleTech Holdings, Inc. (55%) &
Ford Motor Company (45%)
N.A.I.C.S.: 541618

Quantum Signal AI, LLC (1)
200 N Ann Arbor St, Saline, MI 48176
Tel.: (734) 429-9100
Web Site: http://www.quantumsignal.com
Research & Development in Biotechnology
N.A.I.C.S.: 541714
Mitchell M. Rohde (Founder & CEO)
Robert M. Lupa (CTO)
Chris Showers (CIO)
Disa Webb (CFO)

**The American Road Insurance
Company** (1)
1 American Rd, Dearborn, MI
48126 (100%)
Tel.: (313) 845-5850
Sales Range: $150-199.9 Million
Automobile Insurance
N.A.I.C.S.: 524128
Michael E. Bannister (Chm)

**Volvo Auto Bank Deutschland
GmbH** (1)
Ringstrasse 38-44, Cologne, 50996, Ger-
many
Tel.: (49) 22151081000
Sales Range: $50-74.9 Million
Emp.: 100
Financial Services
N.A.I.C.S.: 522110

FORECROSS CORPORATION

505 Montgomery St 11th Fl, San
Francisco, CA 94111
Tel.: (415) 543-1515 CA
Web Site: https://www.forecross.com
Year Founded: 1982
FRXX—(OTCIQ)
Custom Computer Programming Ser-
vices
N.A.I.C.S.: 541511
John Sherman (Dir-Bus Dev)

FORESIGHT ENERGY LP

211 N Broadway Ste 2600, Saint
Louis, MO 63102
Tel.: (314) 932-6160 DE
Web Site: http://www.foresight.com
Year Founded: 2012
FELP—(NYSE)
Thermal Coal Production & Mining
N.A.I.C.S.: 324199
Robert D. Moore (Chm, Pres & CEO)

Subsidiaries:

Foresight Energy Services LLC (1)
11351 N Thompsonville Rd, Macedonia, IL
62860
Tel.: (618) 435-2491
Coal Mining Services
N.A.I.C.S.: 213113

Macoupin Energy LLC (1)

14300 Brushy Mound Rd, Carlinville, IL
62626
Tel.: (217) 854-3291
Coal Mining Services
N.A.I.C.S.: 213113

Sitran LLC (1)
10016 Darnell School Rd, Mount Vernon, IN
47620-8415
Tel.: (812) 985-0708
Coal Mining Services
N.A.I.C.S.: 213113

Williamson Energy, LLC (1)
18624 Liberty School Rd, Marion, IL 62959
Tel.: (618) 983-3020
Emp.: 200
Coal Mining Services
N.A.I.C.S.: 213113

FORESIGHT FINANCIAL
GROUP INC.

809 Cannell-Puri Ct, Winnebago, IL
61088
Tel.: (815) 847-7500
Web Site:
https://www.foresightfg.com
Year Founded: 1986
FGFH—(OTCQX)
Sales Range: $25-49.9 Million
Emp.: 5
Bank Holding Company
N.A.I.C.S.: 551111
Robert W. Stenstrom (Chm)

Subsidiaries:

Northwest Bank of Rockford (1)
3106 N Rockton Ave, Rockford, IL 61103
Tel.: (815) 987-4550
Web Site:
http://www.northwestbankrockford.com
Rev.: $6,659,000
Emp.: 60
State Commercial Bank Services
N.A.I.C.S.: 522110
Thomas R. Walsh (Pres & CEO)
Therese Matzelle (CFO)
David Norton (Chief Credit Officer & Sr VP)
Terrance Rosenberger (Sr VP & Dir-Bus
Banking)
John J. Morrissey (Chm)

FORESTAR GROUP INC.

2221 E Lamar Blvd Ste 790, Arling-
ton, TX 76006
Tel.: (817) 769-1860 DE
Web Site: https://www.forestar.com
FOR—(NYSE)
Rev.: $1,509,400,000
Assets: $2,840,100,000
Liabilities: $1,245,000,000
Net Worth: $1,595,100,000
Earnings: $203,400,000
Emp.: 393
Fiscal Year-end: 09/30/24
Holding Company; Real Estate In-
vestment & Development Services
N.A.I.C.S.: 551112
James D. Allen (CFO, Principal Acctg
Officer & Exec VP)
Donald J. Tomnitz (Chm)
Mark S. Walker (COO & Exec VP)

Subsidiaries:

Bandera/Lantana III, LP (1)
8401 N Central Expy Ste 350, Dallas, TX
75225
Tel.: (214) 292-3410
Real Estate Related Services
N.A.I.C.S.: 531390

**Forestar (USA) Real Estate Group
Inc.** (1)
14755 Preston Rd Ste 710, Dallas, TX
75254-7898 (100%)
Tel.: (972) 341-2900
Web Site: http://www.forestargroup.com
Sales Range: $300-349.9 Million
Emp.: 14
Real Estate Services
N.A.I.C.S.: 531390

Branch (Domestic):

**Forestar (USA) Real Estate Group
Inc. - Atlanta** (2)
3330 Cumberland Blvd Ste 275, Atlanta,
GA 30339
Tel.: (770) 272-7760
Web Site: http://www.forestargroup.com
Sales Range: $300-349.9 Million
Emp.: 12
Real Estate Investment & Development
Services
N.A.I.C.S.: 531390

**Forestar (USA) Real Estate Group
Inc. - Lufkin** (2)
1607 S Chestnut Ste R, Lufkin, TX 75901
Tel.: (512) 433-5386
Real Estate Investment & Development
Services
N.A.I.C.S.: 531390

Subsidiary (Domestic):

Forestar Petroleum Corporation (2)
6300 Fm 2244 Rd Bldg 2, Austin, TX 78746
Tel.: (512) 433-5200
Sales Range: $50-74.9 Million
Emp.: 15
Natural Gas & Crude Oil Exploration & Mar-
keting Services
N.A.I.C.S.: 211120
James M. DeCosmo (Pres & CEO)
Charles D. Jehl (Chief Acctg Officer & Exec
VP)
Kenneth J. DeFehr (Mgr-Engrg-Northern
Div)
Tori A. Vandeven (Mgr-Exploration-Northern
Div)
Christopher L. Nines (CFO & Treas)
Jack Renfro (Mgr-Ops & Production-
Northern Div)

Ironstob, LLC (2)
3445 Peachtree Rd Ste 650, Atlanta, GA
30326
Tel.: (866) 934-6616
Web Site: http://www.ironstob.com
Real Estate Management Services
N.A.I.C.S.: 531210

United Oil Corporation (2)
1801 Broadway Ste 600, Denver, CO
80202
Tel.: (303) 856-6444
Sales Range: $25-49.9 Million
Emp.: 10
Crude Oil Supplier
N.A.I.C.S.: 211120

LM Land Holdings, LP (1)
1777 NE Loop 410 Ste 600A, San Antonio,
TX 78217
Tel.: (830) 386-3647
Holding Company
N.A.I.C.S.: 551112

Rayzor Ranch, LP (1)
14881 Quorum Dr, Dallas, TX 75254
Tel.: (214) 292-3410
Real Estate Related Services
N.A.I.C.S.: 531390

FOREVERGREEN WORLD-
WIDE CORPORATION

632 N 2000 W Ste 101, Lindon, UT
84042
Tel.: (801) 655-5500 NV
Web Site:
http://www.forevergreen.org
FVRG—(OTCIQ)
Sales Range: $10-24.9 Million
Emp.: 39
Whole Foods, Nutritional Supple-
ments, Personal Care Products &
Essential Oils Mfr
N.A.I.C.S.: 311999
John S. Clayton (Sec)
Jorge E. Alvarado (Pres & Chief Mktg
Officer)
Jeanette K. Foss (CFO & Treas)

Subsidiaries:

**ForeverGreen International Taiwan
LTD** (1)
Room 23 No 50-25 Sec 1 Zhongxiao W Rd,

Zhongzheng Dist, Taipei, 10041, Taiwan
Tel.: (886) 223706811
Grocery Store Operator
N.A.I.C.S.: 445110

ForeverGreen International, LLC (1)
632 N 2000 West Ste 101, Lindon, UT
84042
Tel.: (801) 655-5500
Web Site: http://www.forevergreen.org
Pharmaceuticals Product Mfr
N.A.I.C.S.: 325412
Rick Redford (CEO)

ForeverGreen Korea (1)
2F Da Sung Bldg 735-34 Yeonsam Dong,
GangNam-gu, Seoul, Korea (South)
Tel.: (82) 2 555 4411
Web Site: http://www.forevergreen.org
Emp.: 1
Whole Foods, Nutritional Supplements, Per-
sonal Care Products & Essential Oils Mfr
N.A.I.C.S.: 311999

ForeverGreen Singapore (1)
No 10 Anson Road 24-06B International
Plaza, Singapore, 079903, Singapore
Tel.: (65) 85717792
Personal Care Product Mfr & Whslr
N.A.I.C.S.: 325620

FORGE GLOBAL HOLDINGS,
INC.

4 Embarcadero Ctr Fl 15, San Fran-
cisco, CA 94111
Tel.: (415) 881-1612 Ky
Year Founded: 2020
FRGE—(NYSE)
Rev.: $69,383,000
Assets: $363,729,000
Liabilities: $38,268,000
Net Worth: $325,461,000
Earnings: ($111,859,000)
Emp.: 315
Fiscal Year-end: 12/31/22
Investment Services
N.A.I.C.S.: 523999
Jennifer Phillips (Chief Growth Officer
& Pres-Forge Markets)
Kelly Rodriques (CEO)
Johnathan H. Short (Chief Legal Offi-
cer)
Mark Lee (CFO)
Megan Hanley (CMO)
Vidya Eashwer (CTO)
Victoria Hughes (Chief People Offi-
cer)
Cathy Dondzila (Chief Acctg Officer)
Catherine Dondzila (Chief Acctg Offi-
cer)
Kelly Rodriques (CEO)

Subsidiaries:

Forge Global, Inc. (1)
415 Mission St 55th Fl, San Francisco, CA
94105
Tel.: (415) 881-1612
Web Site: http://www.forgeglobal.com
Privater Equity Firm
N.A.I.C.S.: 523999
Kelly Rodrigues (CEO)
Megan Hanley (CMO)

Forge Services, Inc. (1)
1S660 Midwest Rd Ste 140 Oakbrook, Oak-
brook Terrace, IL 60181
Tel.: (224) 877-7782
Web Site: https://forge-inc.com
Wireless Telecommunication Services
N.A.I.C.S.: 517410

FORGE INNOVATION DEVEL-
OPMENT CORP.

17800 Castleton St Ste 583, City of
Industry, CA 91748
Tel.: (626) 986-4566 NV
Web Site:
http://www.forgecorpusa.com
Year Founded: 2016
FGNV—(OTCQB)
Rev.: $122,604
Assets: $125,844

Forge Innovation Development Corp.—(Continued)

Liabilities: $217,183
Net Worth: ($91,339)
Earnings: ($34,112)
Emp.: 2
Fiscal Year-end: 12/31/22
Real Estate Manangement Services
N.A.I.C.S.: 237210
Patrick Liang (Pres, CEO, CFO & Sec)

FORIAN INC.
41 University Dr Ste 400, Newtown, PA 18940
Tel.: (267) 225-6263 DE
Web Site: https://www.forian.com
FORA—(NASDAQ)
Rev.: $28,005,857
Assets: $46,258,167
Liabilities: $33,835,691
Net Worth: $12,422,476
Earnings: ($25,971,971)
Emp.: 102
Fiscal Year-end: 12/31/22
Computing Infrastructure Providers, Data Processing, Web Hosting & Related Services
N.A.I.C.S.: 518210
Max C. Wygod (Founder, Chm, Interim Pres & Interim CEO)
Michael Vesey (CFO)
Max Wygod (Co-Founder & Chm)
Adam Dublin (Co-Founder & Chief Strategy Officer)
Andrew Douglas (Chief Analytics Officer)
Edward Spaniel Jr. (Exec VP & Gen Counsel)

Subsidiaries:

Helix Technologies, Inc.   (1)
5300 DTC Pkwy Ste 300, Greenwood Village, CO 80111
Tel.: (720) 328-5372
Web Site: http://www.helixtechnologies.com
Security & Compliance Service Provider
N.A.I.C.S.: 523999
Zachary L. Venegas (Founder & CEO)

Subsidiary (Domestic):

Security Grade Protective Services, Ltd.   (2)
10200 E Girard Ave Ste 420, Denver, CO 80231
Web Site: http://www.securitygrade.com
Security Guard Services
N.A.I.C.S.: 561612
Jonathan Wilfawn (Dir-Personnel)

Medical Outcomes Research Analytics, LLC   (1)
41 University Dr Ste 405, Newtown, PA 18940
Tel.: (267) 757-8707
Web Site: http://www.moranalytics.co
Software Development Services
N.A.I.C.S.: 513210
Max C. Wygod (Founder)
Adam Dublin (Co-Founder)
Dan Barton (CEO)

FORMATION MINERALS, INC.
203 S Church St, Jacksboro, TX 76458
Tel.: (972) 217-4080 NV
Web Site: https://www.formationminerals.com
Year Founded: 2020
FOMI—(OTCQB)
Rev.: $1,146
Assets: $14,805
Liabilities: $848,417
Net Worth: ($833,612)
Earnings: ($1,679,708)
Emp.: 3
Fiscal Year-end: 04/30/24
Holding Company; Oil & Natural Gas Exploration & Development
N.A.I.C.S.: 551112

Scott A. Cox (Pres, CEO & CFO)

Subsidiaries:

Verde Bio Holdings, Inc.   (1)
5750 Genesis Ct Ste 220B, Frisco, TX 75034
Tel.: (972) 217-4080
Rev.: $926,099
Assets: $4,160,238
Liabilities: $1,839,182
Net Worth: $2,321,056
Earnings: ($1,774,179)
Emp.: 3
Fiscal Year-end: 04/30/2023
Mobile Phone Applications Developer
N.A.I.C.S.: 551112
Scott Cox (Pres, CEO, CFO, Treas & Sec)

FORMCAP CORP.
50 W Liberty St Ste 880, Reno, NV 89501
Tel.: (775) 285-5775
Web Site: http://www.formcapcorp.com
Year Founded: 1991
FRMC—(OTCEM)
Oil & Gas Exploration Services
N.A.I.C.S.: 213112
Xianying Du (Pres)

FORMFACTOR, INC.
7005 Sfront Rd, Livermore, CA 94551
Tel.: (925) 290-4000 DE
Web Site: https://www.formfactor.com
Year Founded: 1993
FORM—(NASDAQ)
Rev.: $769,674,000
Assets: $1,020,520,000
Liabilities: $204,740,000
Net Worth: $815,780,000
Earnings: $83,924,000
Emp.: 2,293
Fiscal Year-end: 12/25/21
Semiconductor Wafer Probe Cards Mfr & Retailer
N.A.I.C.S.: 334413
Robert Selley (Sr VP-Worldwide Sls & Svc)
Michael D. Slessor (Pres & CEO)
Jarek Kister (CTO & Sr VP-Tech & R&D)
Shai Shahar (CFO)
Steven Nott (CIO)
Jens Klattenhoff (VP & Gen Mgr-Sys Bus Unit)
Christy Robertson (Gen Counsel)
Aliza Scott (Chief HH Officer)
Thomas Fries (VP)

Subsidiaries:

Astria Semiconductor Holdings, Inc   (1)
2281 Las Palmas Dr, Carlsbad, CA 92011
Tel.: (760) 603-0631
Semiconductor & Related Device Mfr
N.A.I.C.S.: 334413

Cascade Microtech, Inc.   (1)
9100 SW Gemini Dr, Beaverton, OR 97008
Tel.: (503) 601-1000
Web Site: http://www.cascademicrotech.com
Emp.: 502
Semiconductor & Related Device Mfr
N.A.I.C.S.: 334413

Subsidiary (Non-US):

Advanced Temperature Test Systems GmbH   (2)
Fraunhoferstr 11, Martinsried Planegg, 82152, Munich, Germany
Tel.: (49) 89 899 4820
Web Site: https://www.att-systems.com
Temperature Control Systems Mfr
N.A.I.C.S.: 334513
Markus Eibl (Mng Dir)
Markus Kindler (Mng Dir)

Cascade Microtech China (Shanghai) Co., Ltd.   (2)
Unit 1604 Finance Square No 333 Kiukiang Road, Shanghai, 200001, China

Tel.: (86) 2133303188
Web Site: http://www.cascademicrotech.com
Integrated Circuit & Microchip Electrical Measurement & Testing Equipment Whslr
N.A.I.C.S.: 423610

Cascade Microtech GmbH   (2)
Suss Strasse 1, Thiendorf, 01561, Meissen, Germany
Tel.: (49) 35240730
Web Site: http://www.cascademicrotech.com
Integrated Circuit & Microchip Electrical Measurement & Testing Equipment Whslr
N.A.I.C.S.: 423610

Cascade Microtech Japan, Inc.   (2)
11F/2F 134 Godo-cho, Hodogaya-ku, Yokohama, 240-0005, Kanagawa, Japan   (100%)
Tel.: (81) 453381286
Web Site: http://www.cascademicrotech.com
Integrated Circuit & Microchip Electrical Measurement & Testing Equipment Whslr
N.A.I.C.S.: 423610
Kawamata Fumihiro (CEO)

FormFactor Beaverton, Inc.   (1)
9100 SW Gemini Dr, Beaverton, OR 97008
Tel.: (503) 601-1000
Semiconductor Testing Services
N.A.I.C.S.: 541380
Donna Oakovich (Mgr-Commodity)

FormFactor Europe GmbH   (1)
Manfred-von-Ardenne-Ring 20 Haus F, 01099, Dresden, Germany   (100%)
Tel.: (49) 35188963250
Web Site: http://www.formfactor.com
Sales Range: $50-74.9 Million
Emp.: 200
Mfr & Sales of Semiconductor Wafer Probe Cards
N.A.I.C.S.: 334413

FormFactor GmbH   (1)
Suss Strasse 1, Thiendorf, 01561, Meissen, Germany
Tel.: (49) 35240730
Semiconductor Mfr & Whslr
N.A.I.C.S.: 334413
Claus Dietrich (VP & Gen Mgr)

FormFactor K.K.   (1)
Yokohama Business Park East Tower 11F / 2F 134, Godo-cho Hodogaya-ku, Yokohama, 240-0005, Kanagawa, Japan   (100%)
Tel.: (81) 45 338 1290
Web Site: https://www.formfactor.com
Sales Range: $10-24.9 Million
Emp.: 25
Mfr & Sales of Semiconductor Wafer Probe Cards
N.A.I.C.S.: 334413

FormFactor Korea, Inc.   (1)
8F Seongnam-daero 349, Bundang-Gu, Seongnam, 13558, Gyeonggi-do, Korea (South)   (100%)
Tel.: (82) 317118920
Web Site: https://formfactor.com
Sales Range: $25-49.9 Million
Emp.: 50
Mfr & Sales of Semiconductor Wafer Probe Cards
N.A.I.C.S.: 334413

High Precision Devices, Inc.   (1)
4601 Nautilus Ct S Ste 100, Boulder, CO 80301
Tel.: (303) 447-2558
Web Site: https://hpd-online.com
Cryogenic Instrument Mfr
N.A.I.C.S.: 334513

FORRESTER RESEARCH, INC.
60 Acorn Park Dr, Cambridge, MA 02140
Tel.: (617) 613-6000 DE
Web Site: https://www.forrester.com
Year Founded: 1983
FORR—(NASDAQ)
Rev.: $537,787,000
Assets: $608,438,000
Liabilities: $386,782,000
Net Worth: $221,656,000
Earnings: $21,806,000
Emp.: 2,033

Fiscal Year-end: 12/31/22
Market Research Services
N.A.I.C.S.: 541910
Scott R. Chouinard (Chief Acctg Officer & Treas)
Steven Peltzman (Chief Bus Tech Officer)
Ryan D. Darrah (Chief Legal Officer & Sec)
Mike Kasparian (CIO)
Shirley Macbeth (CMO)
Chris Finn (CFO)
Sarah Le Roy (Chief People Officer)
Sharyn Leaver (Chief Res Officer)
Lisa Riley (Sr VP)
Nate Swan (Chief Sls Officer)

Subsidiaries:

Forrester Germany GmbH   (1)
Spaces Tower One Brusseler Str 1-3, 60327, Frankfurt am Main, Germany
Tel.: (49) 699592980
Web Site: http://www.forrester.com
Research & Development Services
N.A.I.C.S.: 541720

Forrester Market Advisory (Beijing) Co., Ltd.   (1)
11/F North Tower Kerry Centre No 1 Guanghua Road, Chaoyang District, Beijing, 100020, China
Tel.: (86) 1065999161
Web Site: http://www.forrester.com
Marketing Research Service
N.A.I.C.S.: 541910

Forrester Research B.V.   (1)
Rijnsburgstraat 9 /11, 1059 AT, Amsterdam, Netherlands
Tel.: (31) 203054300
Web Site: http://www.forrester.com
Emp.: 30
Research & Development Services
N.A.I.C.S.: 541720

Forrester Research GmbH & Co. KG   (1)
Eschersheimer Landstrasse 10, 60322, Frankfurt, Germany   (100%)
Tel.: (49) 699592980
Web Site: http://www.forrester.com
Sales Range: $10-24.9 Million
Emp.: 40
Information Technology Consulting Services
N.A.I.C.S.: 541611

Forrester Research India Private Limited   (1)
Unit Nos 301 - 310 Splendor Forum Jasola, New Delhi, 110 025, Delhi, India
Tel.: (91) 1142840000
Sales Range: $25-49.9 Million
Emp.: 55
Research & Development Services
N.A.I.C.S.: 541720

Forrester Research Ltd.   (1)
61 Aldwych, London, WC2B 4AE, United Kingdom   (100%)
Tel.: (44) 207 323 7600
Web Site: http://www.forrester.com
Sales Range: $75-99.9 Million
Information Technology Consulting Services
N.A.I.C.S.: 541611

Forrester Research SAS   (1)
109-111 Rue Victor Hugo, Levallois Perret, 92300, Paris, France
Tel.: (33) 147589300
Web Site: http://www.forrester.com
Emp.: 25
Market Research & Consulting Services
N.A.I.C.S.: 541910

Forrester Research, Inc.   (1)
150 Spear St Ste 1100, San Francisco, CA 94105-1535   (100%)
Tel.: (415) 355-6000
Web Site: http://www.forrester.com
Sales Range: $10-24.9 Million
Emp.: 25
Research & Development Services
N.A.I.C.S.: 541720

Forrester Singapore Pte. Ltd.   (1)
8 Cross Street 21-01, Singapore, 048424, Singapore
Tel.: (65) 64267000

Software Development Services
N.A.I.C.S.: 541511
Hooi Chin Chow (Dir-Sls-Southeast, Asia & China)

Forrester Switzerland GmbH (1)
Dreikonigstrasse 31 A, Zurich, 8002, Switzerland
Tel.: (41) 442083835
Sales Range: $25-49.9 Million
Emp.: 10
Research & Development Services
N.A.I.C.S.: 541720

SiriusDecisions, Inc. (1)
187 Danbury Rd, Wilton, CT 06897
Tel.: (203) 665-4000
Web Site: http://www.siriusdecisions.com
Business & Marketing Consulting Services
N.A.I.C.S.: 541611

FORTE BIOSCIENCES, INC.
3060 Pegasus Park Dr Bldg 6, Dallas, TX 75247
Tel.: (310) 618-6994   DE
Web Site: https://www.fortebiorx.com
Year Founded: 2007
FBRX—(NASDAQ)
Rev.: $17,000
Assets: $41,997,000
Liabilities: $3,179,000
Net Worth: $38,818,000
Earnings: ($13,879,000)
Emp.: 6
Fiscal Year-end: 12/31/22
Clinical-stage Biopharmaceutical Company
N.A.I.C.S.: 541714
Paul A. Wagner (Chm, Pres & CEO)
Christopher Roenfeldt (COO & Head-Program Mgmt)

FORTEX, INC.
203 Redwood Shores Pkwy Ste 640, Redwood Shores, CA 94065
Tel.: (650) 591-8822   DE
Web Site: http://www.fortex.com
Year Founded: 1997
FTCX—(OTCIQ)
Software Development Services
N.A.I.C.S.: 541511
Daniel Z. Chen (Co-Founder & CEO)
Jay Zhan (Co-Founder & CTO)

FORTINET, INC.
909 Kifer Rd, Sunnyvale, CA 94086
Tel.: (408) 235-7700   DE
Web Site: https://www.fortinet.com
Year Founded: 2000
FTNT—(NASDAQ)
Rev.: $5,304,800,000
Assets: $7,258,900,000
Liabilities: $7,722,300,000
Net Worth: ($463,400,000)
Earnings: $1,147,800,000
Emp.: 13,568
Fiscal Year-end: 12/31/23
Software Development Services
N.A.I.C.S.: 541511
John Whittle (COO)
Patrice Perche (Chief Revenue Officer & Exec VP-Support)
John Maddison (Chief Mktg Officer & Exec VP-Products)
Peter Salkowski (VP-IR)
Ana Pease (VP-Talent Mgmt & Ops)
Chris Perna (VP-Talent Acquisition)
Michael Xie (Co-Founder & Pres)
Ken Xie (Co-Founder, Chm & CEO)

Subsidiaries:

AccelOps, Inc. (1)
2952 Bunker Hill Ln Ste 101, Santa Clara, CA 95054
Tel.: (408) 490-0903
Web Site: https://www.accelops.com
Software Publisher
N.A.I.C.S.: 513210

Fortinet (UK) Ltd. (1)

Gainsborough House Unit 2 Manor Park Manor Farm Road, Reading, RG2 0NA, Berkshire, United Kingdom
Tel.: (44) 118 322 4900
Web Site: http://www.fortinet.com
Network Solutions
N.A.I.C.S.: 513210

Fortinet Austria GmbH (1)
Wienerbergstrasse 11/Tower A/9th Floor, 1100, Vienna, Austria
Tel.: (43) 137600130
Networking & Software Security Development Services
N.A.I.C.S.: 541511

Fortinet BV (1)
Papendorpseweg 99, Amersfoort, 3528 BJ, Utrecht, Netherlands
Tel.: (31) 334546750
Integrated Security Services
N.A.I.C.S.: 561621

Fortinet Belgium BV (1)
Pegasuslaan 5, 1831, Diegem, Belgium
Tel.: (32) 27164927
Networking & Other Software Security Development Services
N.A.I.C.S.: 541511

Fortinet Denmark ApS (1)
Tuborg Boulevard 12, 2900, Hellerup, Denmark
Tel.: (45) 36944408
Networking & Other Software Security Development Services
N.A.I.C.S.: 541511

Fortinet Federal, Inc. (1)
12005 Sunrise Vly Dr Ste 204, Reston, VA 20191
Tel.: (408) 807-1422
Web Site: http://www.fortinetfederal.com
Emp.: 3
Network Security Solution & Services
N.A.I.C.S.: 541519

Fortinet Finland Oy (1)
Keilaranta 16B 5th Floor, 02150, Espoo, Finland
Tel.: (358) 925107117
Networking & Other Software Security Development Services
N.A.I.C.S.: 541511

Fortinet GmbH (1)
Feldbergstrasse 35, 60323, Frankfurt am Main, Germany
Tel.: (49) 693101920
Web Site: http://www.fortinet.com
Software Publishing Services
N.A.I.C.S.: 513210

Fortinet Information Technology (Beijing) Co., Ltd. (1)
Room 713 Ideal International Building, No 58 North Fourth Ring West Road Haidian District, Beijing, 100080, China
Tel.: (86) 106 296 0376
Web Site: https://www.fortinet.com
Network Security Solutions
N.A.I.C.S.: 513210

Fortinet Information Technology (Tianjin) Co., Ltd. (1)
Tianjin Economic & Technological Development Zone North Bldg, 80 4th Avenue, Tianjin, 300457, China
Tel.: (86) 22 66211149
Network Security Solutions
N.A.I.C.S.: 541519

Fortinet Japan Co. Ltd. (1)
9th Floor Tri-Seven Roppongi 7-7-7 Roppongi, Minato-ku, Tokyo, 106-0032, Japan
Tel.: (81) 8065139725
Web Site: https://www.fortinet.com
Software Publishing Services
N.A.I.C.S.: 513210
Norio Kubota (Pres & CEO)

Fortinet Malaysia SDN. BHD. (1)
Suite 33A-02/03 Level 33A Menara Keck Seng 203 Jalan Bukit Bintang, 55100, Kuala Lumpur, Malaysia
Tel.: (60) 327230300
Web Site: http://www.fortinet.com
Network Security Solutions & Technical Support Services
N.A.I.C.S.: 518210

Fortinet Mexico, S. de R.L. de C.V. (1)
Paseo De La Reforma 412 Piso 16 Col Juarez, 06600, Mexico, Mexico
Tel.: (52) 5555248428
Software Publishing Services
N.A.I.C.S.: 513210

Fortinet S.A.R.L. (1)
905 Rue Albert Einstein, Valbonne, 06560, Sophia-Antipolis, France
Tel.: (33) 489870500
Web Site: http://www.fortinet.com
Sales Range: $100-124.9 Million
Network Security Solutions
N.A.I.C.S.: 513210

Fortinet Security Israel Ltd. (1)
25 Efal Street, Petah Tiqwa, 46722, Israel
Tel.: (972) 776935670
Software Publishing Services
N.A.I.C.S.: 513210
Yossy Auslender (Engr-Sys)

Fortinet Security Korea Ltd. (1)
15th Fl Haeam Bldg 983-1 Daechi-dong Gangnam Gu, Seoul, 135-280, Korea (South)
Tel.: (82) 25599500
Software Publishing Services
N.A.I.C.S.: 513210
Peter Won Kyun Cho (Country Mgr)

Fortinet Security Network (Thailand) Ltd. (1)
Level 25 Unit ML2511 The Offices at Centralworld 999/9 Rama 1 Road, Bangkok, 10330, Thailand
Tel.: (66) 265865812
Networking & Other Software Security Development Services
N.A.I.C.S.: 541511

Fortinet Security Philippines, Inc. (1)
32nd Street One World Place, Bonifacio Global City, Taguig, 1634, Philippines
Tel.: (63) 28088798
Software Services
N.A.I.C.S.: 541511

Fortinet Security Spain S.L (1)
Avenida Europa 24- Edif B Pt 2-b, Alcobendas, 28108, Madrid, Spain
Tel.: (34) 915024874
Software Publishing Services
N.A.I.C.S.: 513210

Fortinet Singapore Private Limited (1)
8 Temasek Boulevard 12-01 Suntec Tower Three, Singapore, 038988, Singapore
Tel.: (65) 6 395 2788
Web Site: http://www.fortinet.com
Sales Range: $100-124.9 Million
Network Security Solutions
N.A.I.C.S.: 513210

Fortinet Switzerland GmbH (1)
Riedmuehlestr 8, Dietlikon, 8305, Zurich, Switzerland
Tel.: (41) 448336848
Software Services
N.A.I.C.S.: 541511

Fortinet Technologies (Canada), Inc. (1)
4190 Still Creek Drive Suite 400, Burnaby, V5C 6C6, BC, Canada
Tel.: (604) 430-1297
Web Site: http://www.fortinet.com
Sales Range: $100-124.9 Million
Software Development Services
N.A.I.C.S.: 513210

Fortinet Technologies India Private Limited (1)
C2 002 Ground Floor Tower-C The Millennia No 1 & 2 Murphy Road Ulsoor, Bengaluru, 560008, India
Tel.: (91) 37083500
Web Site: http://www.fortinet.com
Network Security Solution Services
N.A.I.C.S.: 513210
Jason Nadar (Mgr-Natl Sls-Wireless Technologies)

Fortinet Turkey Guvenlik Sistemleri Limited Sirketi (1)
Saray Mah Doktor Adnan Buyukdeniz Cad, No 4 Akkom Ofis Park 3 Blok Kat 10 Um-

raniye, Istanbul, 34768, Turkiye
Tel.: (90) 2162503259
Software Publishing Services
N.A.I.C.S.: 513210
Ozan Akdemir (Sls Mgr)

Meru Networks, Inc. (1)
894 Ross Dr, Sunnyvale, CA 94089
Tel.: (408) 215-5300
Web Site: http://www.merunetworks.com
Virtualized Wireless LAN Solutions
N.A.I.C.S.: 517112
Andrew H. Del Matto (CEO, CFO & Treas)
Gary Abad (VP-Channel Sls)

OPAQ Networks, Inc (1)
2553 Dulles View Dr Ste 100, Herndon, VA 20171
Tel.: (703) 574-2555
Web Site: http://opaq.com
Network Security & Cloud Platform
N.A.I.C.S.: 561621
Glenn C. Hazard (Chm & CEO)

Subsidiary (Domestic):

Bat Blue Corporation (2)
100 Delawanna Ave, Clifton, NJ 07014
Tel.: (212) 461-3322
Network Security
N.A.I.C.S.: 518210

PT Fortinet Indonesia Security (1)
38/F The Plaza Office Tower Jl MH Thamrin Kav 28-30, Jakarta, 10350, Indonesia
Tel.: (62) 2129922935
Networking & Other Software Security Development Services
N.A.I.C.S.: 541511

Panopta LLC (1)
412 S Wells St 9th Fl, Chicago, IL 60607
Web Site: http://www.panopta.com
Network & Security Management Services
N.A.I.C.S.: 541519

FORTISTAR SUSTAINABLE SOLUTIONS CORP.
1 N Lexington Ave, White Plains, NY 10601
Tel.: (914) 421-4900   DE
Web Site: http://www.fortistarssc.com
Year Founded: 2020
FSSI—(NASDAQ)
Rev.: $1,707,739
Assets: $259,742,007
Liabilities: $281,818,665
Net Worth: ($22,076,658)
Earnings: ($660,312)
Emp.: 4
Fiscal Year-end: 12/31/21
Investment Services
N.A.I.C.S.: 523999
Mark S. Comora (Chm)
Charles D. Bryceland (Pres)
Jonathan Maurer (Mng Dir)
Thomas J. Kelly (Sec)
Nadeem Nisar (CEO)

FORTITUDE GOLD CORPORATION
2886 Carriage Manor Pt, Colorado Springs, CO 80906
Tel.: (719) 717-9825   CO
Web Site:
  https://www.fortitudegold.com
Year Founded: 2020
FTCO—(OTCQB)
Rev.: $74,379,000
Assets: $131,156,000
Liabilities: $15,397,000
Net Worth: $115,759,000
Earnings: $14,684,000
Emp.: 60
Fiscal Year-end: 12/31/22
Gold Ore Mining Services
N.A.I.C.S.: 212220
Jason D. Reid (Pres & CEO)
Bill M. Conrad (Chm)
Greg A. Patterson (VP-Corp Dev & IR)
Allan Turner (VP-Exploration)

Fortitude Gold Corporation—(Continued)

FORTIVE CORPORATION
6920 Seaway Blvd, Everett, WA 98203
Tel.: (425) 446-5000   DE
Web Site: https://www.fortive.com
Year Founded: 2016
FTV—(NYSE)
Rev.: $6,065,300,000
Assets: $16,911,800,000
Liabilities: $6,586,500,000
Net Worth: $10,325,300,000
Earnings: $865,800,000
Emp.: 18,000
Fiscal Year-end: 12/31/23
Telecommunications Equipment Mfr
N.A.I.C.S.: 551112
James A. Lico (Pres & CEO)
Jonathan L. Schwarz (Sr VP-Corp Dev)
Edward R. Simmons (Sr VP-Strategy)
Olumide Soroye (Pres & CEO-Intelligent Operating Solutions)
Tamara S. Newcombe (Pres/CEO-Precision Technologies & Pres/CEO-Advanced Healthcare Solutions)
Peter C. Underwood (Gen Counsel, Sec & Sr VP)
Chuck McLaughlin (CFO & Sr VP)
Chris Mulhall (Chief Acctg Officer)
Stacey Walker (Chief HR Officer & Sr VP)
Alan G. Spoon (Chm)

Subsidiaries:

AKM Asia Pte Ltd   (1)
75 Tech Park Crescent, Singapore, 638070, Singapore
Tel.: (65) 68622888
Web Site: https://www.trafomaterials.com.sg
Monitoring Equipment Whslr
N.A.I.C.S.: 423490

Accruent, LLC   (1)
11500 Alterra Pkwy Ste 110, Austin, TX 78758
Tel.: (512) 861-0726
Web Site: http://www.accruent.com
Enterprise Location Management Solutions
N.A.I.C.S.: 513210
Greg Rivera (Chief Product & Strategy Officer)
James Robb (CFO)
Meg Swanson (CMO)
Andy Ruse (Pres)
Mark Van Deele (COO)
Aaron Hamilton (VP-HR)
Melissa Hammerle (Pres-Comml)
Mark Van Deele (COO)
Andrew Schafer (Sr VP & Mng Dir-Intl)
Hans de Groot (Sr VP-Channels & Partnerships)

Subsidiary (Non-US):

BlueCielo ECM Solutions B.V.   (2)
Pietersbergweg 283, Hoofddorp, 1105 BM, Amsterdam, Netherlands
Tel.: (31) 8802255700
Web Site: http://www.accruent.com
Software Development Services
N.A.I.C.S.: 541511

Subsidiary (Domestic):

VFA, Inc.   (2)
99 Bedford St Ste 300, Boston, MA 02111
Tel.: (617) 451-5100
Web Site: http://www.accruent.com
Web-based Software Products, Business Consulting & Facility Assessment Services
N.A.I.C.S.: 541618

Verisae, Inc.   (2)
730 2nd Ave S Ste 600, Minneapolis, MN 55402
Tel.: (612) 455-2300
Web Site: http://www.accruent.com
Sustainable Resource Planning & Energy Management
N.A.I.C.S.: 541618

American Precision Industries
Inc.   (1)

2480 NE Century Blvd, Hillsboro, OR 97124
Tel.: (503) 642-5611
Web Site: https://www.apiams.com
Emp.: 1,976
Metal Machine Mfr
N.A.I.C.S.: 333517

Anderson Instrument Co., Inc.   (1)
156 Auriesville Rd, Fultonville, NY 12072
Tel.: (518) 922-5315
Web Site: https://www.anderson-negele.com
Controllers & Instruments For Process Variables
N.A.I.C.S.: 334513

Censis Technologies, Inc.   (1)
4031 Aspen Grove Dr, Ste 350, Franklin, TN 37067
Tel.: (615) 468-8000
Web Site: https://censis.com
Surgical Instrument Tracking & Workflow Solutions Developer
N.A.I.C.S.: 339112

Dynapar Corporation   (1)
1675 N Delany Rd, Gurnee, IL 60031
Tel.: (847) 662-2666
Web Site: http://www.dynapar.com
Encoders Resolvers & Accessories Mfr
N.A.I.C.S.: 811310

EMS Software, LLC   (1)
6465 Greenwood Plaza Blvd Ste 600, Centennial, CO 80111
Tel.: (303) 771-0110
Web Site: http://www.emssoftware.com
Information Technology Services
N.A.I.C.S.: 541512

Fluke (Switzerland) GmbH   (1)
Hardstrasse 20, 8303, Bassersdorf, Switzerland
Tel.: (41) 445807504
Electrical & Electronic Component Mfr
N.A.I.C.S.: 335999

Fluke Corporation   (1)
6920 Seaway Blvd, Everett, WA 98203   (100%)
Tel.: (425) 347-6100
Web Site: http://www.fluke.com
Emp.: 2,400
Electronic Test Tools Mfr
N.A.I.C.S.: 334515
Anne Ensminger (VP-Human Resources)
Fred Michel (VP-Bus Ops)
Eduardo Lopez (CFO)
Neal Nowick (VP-Operations-Global)
David Swan (VP-Engineering)
Kathryn Sweers (VP & Gen Counsel-Legal)
Anil Urs (CIO)
Jason Waxman (Pres)

Subsidiary (Domestic):

Azima DLI, LLC   (2)
300 Trade Ctr, Woburn, MA 01801
Web Site: http://www.azimadli.com
General Management Consulting Services
N.A.I.C.S.: 541611
Joe Van Dyke (VP-Engrg)

Subsidiary (Non-US):

Fluke Australia Pty Ltd   (2)
Locked Bag 5004, Baulkham Hills, 2153, NSW, Australia
Tel.: (61) 1300135853
Web Site: https://www.fluke.com
Electronic Test Tools Mfr
N.A.I.C.S.: 334519

Fluke Austria GmbH   (2)
Liebermannstrasse F01, 2345, Brunn am Gebirge, Austria
Tel.: (43) 2236691355
Web Site: http://www.fluke.com
Electronic Test Tools Mfr
N.A.I.C.S.: 334519

Subsidiary (Domestic):

Fluke Biomedical   (2)
28775 Aurora Rd, Cleveland, OH 44139
Tel.: (440) 248-9300
Web Site: https://www.flukebiomedical.com
N.A.I.C.S.: 334517
Dominic Ivankovich (Pres-Fluke Portfolio)

Subsidiary (Non-US):

Fluke Deutschland GmbH   (2)

In den Engematten 14, 79286, Glottertal, Germany
Tel.: (49) 69222220200
Web Site: http://www.fluke.com
Electrical Testing Equipment Mfr & Distr
N.A.I.C.S.: 334515

Fluke Electronics Canada LP   (2)
400 Britannia Road East Unit 1, Mississauga, L4Z 1X9, ON, Canada
Tel.: (905) 890-7600
Web Site: http://www.fluke.com
Distribution Of Electronic Test, Measurement & Calibration Equipment
N.A.I.C.S.: 441330

Fluke Europe B.V.   (2)
Brainport Industries Campus 1, 5657 BX, Eindhoven, Netherlands
Tel.: (31) 402675100
Web Site: http://www.fluke.com
Electronic Test Tools & Software Distr
N.A.I.C.S.: 423430

Fluke Italia S.r.l.   (2)
Viale Lombardia 218, 20861, Brugherio, Italy
Tel.: (39) 0236002017
Web Site: http://www.fluke.com
Electronic Test Tools & Software Mfr
N.A.I.C.S.: 334419

Fluke Nederland B.V.   (2)
Science Park Eindhoven 5110, 5692 EC, Son, Netherlands
Tel.: (31) 402675100
Web Site: http://www.fluke.com
Electronic Products Mfr
N.A.I.C.S.: 334417

Subsidiary (Domestic):

Fluke Networks Inc.   (2)
6920 Seaway Blvd, Everett, WA 98203
Tel.: (425) 446-5500
Web Site: https://www.flukenetworks.com
Emp.: 700
Network Infrastructure Analysis & Testing Products Mfr
N.A.I.C.S.: 334515

Subsidiary (Non-US):

Fluke Precision Measurement Ltd.   (2)
52 Hurricane Way, Norwich, NR6 6JB, Norfolk, United Kingdom
Tel.: (44) 1603 325 6620
Web Site: http://www.fluke.com
Electronic Parts & Equipment Whslr
N.A.I.C.S.: 423690

Subsidiary (Domestic):

Ircon Inc.   (2)
1201 Shaffer Rd, Santa Cruz, CA 95060
Tel.: (831) 458-3998
Web Site: http://www.ircon.com
Industrial Thermometers Mfr
N.A.I.C.S.: 333998

Branch (Non-US):

Ircon China   (3)
SCITE Tower Room 1901, 22 Jianguomen Wai Dajie, Beijing, 100004, China
Tel.: (86) 4008103435
Web Site: http://www.ircon.com.cn
Industrial Thermometers Whslr
N.A.I.C.S.: 334513

Subsidiary (Domestic):

Lumitron Inc   (2)
9028 Evergreen Way, Everett, WA 98204-7100
Web Site: http://www.lumitron-ir.com
Imaging Systems Mfr
N.A.I.C.S.: 423830

Raytek Corporation   (2)
1201 Shaffer Rd, Santa Cruz, CA 95061-1820
Tel.: (831) 458-3900
Web Site: http://www.raytek.com
Designs, Manufactures, Markets & Services a Complete Line of Infrared, Non-contact Temperature Measurement Instruments for Industrial, Process Control & Maintenance Applications
N.A.I.C.S.: 334513

Subsidiary (Non-US):

Fluke Process Instruments GmbH   (3)
Blankenburger Strasse 135, 13127, Berlin, Germany
Tel.: (49) 30 478 0080
Web Site: http://www.flukeprocessinstruments.com
Measuring & Controlling Devices
N.A.I.C.S.: 334519

Fluke Process Instruments Japan   (3)
2-15-2 Konan Shinagawa Intercity Building B 6th Floor, Minato-ku, Tokyo, 108-6106, Japan
Tel.: (81) 367143114
Web Site: http://www.flukeprocessinstruments.com
Measuring & Controlling Devices
N.A.I.C.S.: 334519

Raytek China Company   (3)
SCITE Tower Room 1901 22 Jianguomen Wai Dajie, Beijing, 100004, China
Tel.: (86) 1064384691
Web Site: http://www.raytek.com.cn
Measuring & Controlling Devices
N.A.I.C.S.: 334519

Subsidiary (Domestic):

Solmetric Corp.   (2)
117 Morris St Ste 100, Sebastopol, CA 95472-3846
Tel.: (707) 823-4600
Web Site: http://www.solmetric.com
Solar Test & Measurement Equipment Mfr
N.A.I.C.S.: 334519
Willard McDonald (CEO)

eMaint Enterprises, LLC   (2)
438 N Elmwood Rd, Marlton, NJ 08053   (100%)
Tel.: (239) 494-8928
Web Site: http://www.emaint.com
Software Development Services
N.A.I.C.S.: 513210
Neil McGillen (Mgr-E-Learning)

Fluke Process Instruments   (1)
Lothbury House Cambridge Technopark Newmarket Rd, Cambridge, CB5 8PB, United Kingdom
Tel.: (44) 122 365 2400
Web Site: http://www.flukeprocessinstruments.com
Temperature Analysis Services
N.A.I.C.S.: 561990

Fluke South East Asia Pte. Ltd.   (1)
1 Clementi Loop 06-02/03/04, Singapore, 129808, Singapore
Tel.: (65) 67995588
Electrical & Electronic Component Mfr
N.A.I.C.S.: 335999
Mirna Maroun (Mng Dir)

Gems Sensors Inc.   (1)
1 Cowles Rd, Plainville, CT 06062-1198
Tel.: (860) 747-3000
Web Site: http://www.gemssensors.com
High Accuracy Liquid Level Monitors, Indicators & Switches Mfr
N.A.I.C.S.: 334519
Melanie Baldwin (Project Mgr)

Subsidiary (Domestic):

Setra Systems, Inc.   (2)
159 Swanson Rd, Boxboro, MA 01719
Tel.: (978) 263-1400
Web Site: http://www.setra.com
Measuring & Controlling Device Mfr
N.A.I.C.S.: 334519
S. Y. Lee (Co-Founder)

Hengstler GmbH   (1)
Uhlandstr 49, 78554, Aldingen, Germany
Tel.: (49) 742 4890
Web Site: https://www.hengstler.de
Electronic Products Mfr
N.A.I.C.S.: 334419
Jochen Feiler (Member-Mgmt Bd)
Matt Moore (Member-Mgmt Bd)

Industrial Scientific Canada ULC   (1)
Unit 140 120 Pembina Road, Sherwood Park, T8H 3I8, AB, Canada
Tel.: (780) 467-2423

Gas Detection Mfr
N.A.I.C.S.: 325120

Industrial Scientific Corporation (1)
1 Life Way, Pittsburgh, PA 15205-7500
Tel.: (412) 788-4353
Web Site: https://www.indsci.com
Measuring & Controlling Devices
N.A.I.C.S.: 334519
Clay Hughes (Gen Counsel)
Parker Burke (Pres)
Sean Harrington (VP-Fulfilment-Global)
Gavin Boorman (Mng Dir-Europe, Middle East & Africa & Gen Mgr-Europe, Middle East & Africa)
Amanda Birkhead (VP)
Himanshu Khurana (VP)
Jim Niederst (VP)
Keith Rhodes (VP)
Pronitha Shankarananda (VP)

Subsidiary (Non-US):

Industrial Scientific Asia-Pacific (2)
290 Guiqiao Rd, Pudong, Shanghai, 201206, China
Tel.: (86) 21 5899 3279
Web Site: http://www.indsci.com.cn
Gas Detection Equipment Repair, Sales & Mfr
N.A.I.C.S.: 334519

Subsidiary (Non-US):

Industrial Scientific Australia Pty Ltd (3)
Millers Junction 15 Cabot Drive, Altona, 3025, VIC, Australia
Tel.: (61) 393913344
Web Site: http://www.indsci.com
Gas Detection Equipment Distr
N.A.I.C.S.: 423690

Industrial Scientific Corporation Pte. Ltd. (3)
3 International Business Park 05-23/24 Nordic European Centre, Singapore, 609927, Singapore
Tel.: (65) 65617377
Web Site: http://www.indsci.com
Gas Detection Equipment Sales & Repair Services
N.A.I.C.S.: 423690

Industrial Scientific India PVT. LTD (3)
Unit No 102 1st Floor Kailash Commercial Complex L B S Marg, Vikhroli West, Mumbai, 400083, India
Tel.: (91) 9833575530
Web Site: http://www.indsci.com
Gas Detection Equipment Sales & Repair Services
N.A.I.C.S.: 423690
Pankaj Prajapati (Country Mgr)
Vikas Goyal (Mgr-Gujarat)

Subsidiary (Non-US):

Industrial Scientific Deutschland GmbH (2)
Grasweg 20, 32657, Lemgo, Germany
Tel.: (49) 5261189291
Web Site: http://www.indsci.com
Gas Detection Equipment Repair, Sales & Mfr
N.A.I.C.S.: 334519

Industrial Scientific FZCO (2)
LOB 7 / Suite 121 Jebel Ali Free Zone, PO Box 261086, Dubai, United Arab Emirates
Tel.: (971) 157329261
Web Site: http://www.indsci.com
Gas Detection Equipment Sales & Repair Services
N.A.I.C.S.: 423690

Industrial Scientific France SAS (2)
11D Rue Willy Brandt, CS 80097, 62000, Arras, Cedex, France
Tel.: (33) 157329261
Web Site: http://www.indsci.com
Gas Detection Equipment Sales & Repair Services
N.A.I.C.S.: 423690

Industrial Scientific Ltd (2)
Bollin House Bollin Walk, Wilmslow, SK9 1DP, Cheshire, United Kingdom
Tel.: (44) 2037882677

Web Site: http://www.indsci.com
Gas Detection Equipment Sales & Repair Services
N.A.I.C.S.: 423690

Subsidiary (Domestic):

Safer Systems LLC (2)
5141 Verdugo Way, Camarillo, CA 93012
Tel.: (805) 383-9711
Web Site: http://www.safersystem.com
Custom Computer Programming Services
N.A.I.C.S.: 541511
Eric Fishman (Pres)
Fred Humbert (VP-Sls)
Sharyar Khajehnajafi (Dir-Scientific R&D)

Infrared Integrated Systems Ltd. (1)
Park Circle Tithe Barn Way Swan Valley, Northampton, NN4 9BG, United Kingdom
Tel.: (44) 160 459 4200
Web Site: https://www.irisys.net
Analytical Instrument Mfr
N.A.I.C.S.: 334516

Intelex Technologies, ULC (1)
70 University Avenue Suite 800, Toronto, M5J 2M4, ON, Canada
Tel.: (416) 599-6009
Web Site: https://www.intelex.com
Emp.: 421
Information Technology Services
N.A.I.C.S.: 541512
Justin McElhattan (Pres)
Faith Tull (Chief People Officer)
Elie Mouzon (Chief Strategy Officer)
Roula Vrsic (Sr VP-Mktg)

Invetech Pty. Ltd. (1)
495 Blackburn Road, Mount Waverley, 3149, VIC, Australia
Tel.: (61) 39 192 6000
Web Site: https://www.invetechgroup.com
Emp.: 300
Medical Instrument Mfr
N.A.I.C.S.: 339112
Andreas Knaack (Pres)
Anthony Annibale (VP-Comml-Global)
Doug Hicks (Gen Counsel)
Paul Tsironis (Sr Dir-Hardward Engrg)
Gerald Kent (VP-Diagnostics)
David Kneen (VP-Cell Therapy)
Christian Valcke (Dir-Software Engrg-Global)
Janet O'Meara (VP-Fin)
Mark Willingham (VP & Gen Mgr-Dover Motion)
Tim Bryant (Sr Dir-HR)

Janos Technology, LLC (1)
55 Black Brook Rd, Keene, NH 03431-5044
Tel.: (603) 757-0070
Web Site: https://www.janostech.com
Optical Instrument Mfr
N.A.I.C.S.: 423460

Landauer Europe SAS (1)
9 rue Paul Dautier, CS 60731, 78457, Velizy-Villacoublay, Cedex, France
Tel.: (33) 14 095 6290
Web Site: https://www.landauer.eu
Dosimetry Services
N.A.I.C.S.: 541380

Landauer, Inc. (1)
2 Science Rd, Glenwood, IL 60425-1586
Tel.: (708) 755-7000
Web Site: http://www.landauer.com
Sales Range: $125-149.9 Million
Analytical Services to Determine Human Exposure to Radiation; Radiation Detection Monitors Mfr
N.A.I.C.S.: 334510
Michael P. Kaminski (Pres & CEO)
Michael P. Kaminski (Pres & CEO)

Subsidiary (Non-US):

Beijing Landauer Radiation Monitoring Technology Co., Ltd. (2)
Room 401 Complex Building No 2 Xinkangjie, Dewai Xicheng District, Beijing, 100088, China (70%)
Tel.: (86) 1082024357
Web Site: http://www.bjldr.com
Radiation Testing Equipment Sales & Services
N.A.I.C.S.: 541380

Joint Venture (Non-US):

Epsilon Landauer Dozimetri Teknolojileri Sanayi ve Ticaret A.S. (2)

19 Mayis Mah Dr Sevket Bey Sk No 5, Sisli, Istanbul, Turkiye (50%)
Tel.: (90) 2122476599
Web Site:
https://www.epsilonlandauer.com.tr
Radiation Dose Measurement & Tracking Equipment Mfr & Services
N.A.I.C.S.: 334519

Subsidiary (Domestic):

Global Physics Solutions, Inc. (2)
2 Science Rd, Glenwood, IL 60425-1531 (100%)
Tel.: (877) 476-8433
Medical Physics Services to Hospitals & Radiation Therapy Centers
N.A.I.C.S.: 621511
Michael Ross Kennedy (Sr VP-Strategic Mktg & Product Dev)

Subsidiary (Non-US):

Landauer Australasia Pty, Ltd. (2)
Suite 2 Level 3 67 - 69 Phillip St, Parramatta, 2150, NSW, Australia
Tel.: (61) 286514000
Web Site:
http://www.landaueraustralasia.com
Dosimeters & Radiotherapy Equipment Sales & Service
N.A.I.C.S.: 423440

Landauer Europe, Ltd. (2)
28 Bankside - Station Approach, Kidlington, OX5 1JE, Oxford, United Kingdom
Tel.: (44) 1865373008
Web Site: https://www.landauer.co.uk
Radiation Testing Equipment Sales & Service
N.A.I.C.S.: 423440

Joint Venture (Non-US):

Nagase-Landauer, Ltd. (2)
Block C22-1 Suwa, Tsukuba, 300-2686, Ibaraki, Japan (50%)
Tel.: (81) 298393322
Web Site: https://www.nagase-landauer.co.jp
Radiation Testing Services
N.A.I.C.S.: 541380

Subsidiary (Non-US):

SAPRA-Landauer, Ltda. (2)
Rua Cid Silva Cesar 600, Jordin Santa Felicia Sao Paulo, Sao Carlos, 13560-922, SP, Brazil
Tel.: (55) 1633622700
Web Site: https://www.sapralandauer.com.br
Radiation Testing Equipment Sales & Services
N.A.I.C.S.: 541380

Subsidiary (Domestic):

Yamasato, Fujiwara, Higa & Associates, Inc. (2)
8401 Washington Pl NE, Albuquerque, NM 87113
Tel.: (505) 923-3155
Web Site: https://www.aquilagroup.com
Architectural Services
N.A.I.C.S.: 541320

Subsidiary (Non-US):

ilumark GmbH (2)
Hohenlindner Str 11c, Feldkirchen, 85622, Munich, Germany
Tel.: (49) 89907795980
Web Site: https://www.ilumark.com
Health Care Equipment Mfr
N.A.I.C.S.: 456199
Holger-Claus Rossner (Bus Mgr)

Maxtek Components Corporation (1)
2905 SW Hocken Ave, Beaverton, OR 97075
Tel.: (503) 627-4521
Electrical Equipment & Component Mfr
N.A.I.C.S.: 335999
Brandon Greenley (VP & Gen Mgr)

Metron U.S., Inc. (1)
1818 Library St Ste 600, Reston, VA 20190
Tel.: (703) 787-8700
Web Site: https://www.metsci.com
Software Training Services
N.A.I.C.S.: 611420

PacSci Motion Control, Inc. (1)
211 Overlook Dr, Sewickley, PA 15143-2305
Tel.: (412) 749-0710
Electrical Equipment & Component Mfr
N.A.I.C.S.: 335999

Pacific Scientific Energetic Materials Company (Arizona) LLC (1)
7073 W Willis Rd, Chandler, AZ 85226
Tel.: (480) 763-3000
Web Site: https://psemc.com
Emp.: 1,975
Explosives Mfr
N.A.I.C.S.: 325920

Pacific Scientific Energetic Materials Company (California) LLC (1)
3601 Union Rd, Hollister, CA 95023
Tel.: (831) 637-3731
Web Site: http://www.psemc.com
Electric Equipment Mfr
N.A.I.C.S.: 335999

ProVation Medical, Inc. (1)
533 S Third St Ste 300, Minneapolis, MN 55415
Tel.: (612) 313-1500
Web Site: http://www.provationmedical.com
Health Care Publishing
N.A.I.C.S.: 513199
Tom Monteleone (CFO)
Daniel Hamburger (CEO)
Craig Moriarty (VP-Bus Dev & Corp Strategy)
Erin Surprise (Sr VP-Pro Svcs)
Daniel Manchon (VP-Mktg)
Michael McMurtry (Head-Medical Content & Informatics)
Susan Hanson (VP-HR)
Milinda Rambel-Stone (Chief Info Security Officer)
Eric Kizewski (VP-Tech Svcs)
Linda Buan (VP-Product Dev & Ops)
Srikanth Gosike (Sr VP)
Anita Santos (CMO)
Ankush Kaul (Pres)

Subsidiary (Domestic):

Infinite Software Solutions, Inc. (2)
1110 South Ave Ste 303, Staten Island, NY 10314
Tel.: (718) 982-1315
Web Site: http://www.md-reports.com
Sales Range: $1-9.9 Million
Emp.: 12
Magnetic And Optical Recording Media
N.A.I.C.S.: 334610
Srikanth Gosike (Founder, Pres & CEO)
Naina Gosike (VP)

Pruftechnik Dieter Busch GmbH (1)
Oskar-Messter-Str 19-21, 85737, Ismaning, Germany
Tel.: (49) 89996160
Web Site: http://www.pruftechnik.com
Testing Equipment Mfr
N.A.I.C.S.: 334519
Thomas Rohe (Mng Dir & COO)

Qualitrol Company LLC (1)
1385 Fairport Rd, Fairport, NY 14450
Tel.: (585) 643-3717
Web Site: https://www.qualitrolcorp.com
Qualitrol Liquid Level Gauges, Pressure Relief Devices & Indicators for Voltage Regulators Mfr
N.A.I.C.S.: 334515
Ronald N. Meyer (Pres)

Division (Non-US):

Neoptix Canada LP (2)
1415 Frank-Carrel Suite 220, Quebec, G1N 4N7, QC, Canada
Tel.: (418) 687-2500
Web Site: http://www.neoptix.com
Electric Equipment Mfr
N.A.I.C.S.: 335999

R.S. Means Company LLC (1)
30 Patewood Dr Bldg 2 Ste 350, Greenville, SC 29615
Web Site: https://www.rsmeans.com
Civil Engineering Services
N.A.I.C.S.: 541330

ServiceChannel.com, Inc. (1)

Fortive Corporation—(Continued)

6200 Stoneridge Mall Rd Ste 450, Pleasanton, CA 94588
Tel.: (800) 508-6695
Web Site: http://www.servicechannel.com
Software Developer
N.A.I.C.S.: 513210
Tom Buiocchi (CEO)
Brian Serino (Chief Revenue Officer)

Subsidiary (Domestic):

Big Sky Technologies Inc. **(2)**
9246 Lightwave Ave Ste 140, San Diego, CA 92123
Tel.: (858) 715-5000
Web Site: http://www.bigskytech.com
Sales Range: $1-9.9 Million
Emp.: 50
Software Publisher
N.A.I.C.S.: 513210
Rudolph McVicker (Dir-Engrg Svcs)
William Doll (CEO)
Thomas Krier (Pres)
Mike Roberts (Dir-Bus Dev)

Superior Electric Holding Group
LLC **(1)**
1 Cowles Rd, Plainville, CT 06062
Tel.: (800) 787-3532
Web Site:
   http://www.specialtyproducttechnologies.com
Power Control Mfr
N.A.I.C.S.: 335311

TGA Deutschland GmbH **(1)**
Greifswalder Strasse 9, 16515, Oranienburg, Germany
Tel.: (49) 15234335604
Web Site: https://www.tgadeutschland.de
Ventilation & Sanitary System Services
N.A.I.C.S.: 238220

Tektronix, Inc. **(1)**
14150 SW Karl Braun Dr, Beaverton, OR 97005-2381
Tel.: (503) 627-7111
Web Site: https://www.tek.com
Test, Measurement & Monitoring Equipment Mfr
N.A.I.C.S.: 334513
Adrian Pierce (VP-Sls-America)
Alma Jeppson (Founder)
Riley Schroder (VP)

Subsidiary (Domestic):

Keithley Instruments, LLC **(1)**
28775 Aurora Rd, Cleveland, OH 44139
Tel.: (440) 248-0400
Electrical Equipment & Component Mfr
N.A.I.C.S.: 335999

Subsidiary (Non-US):

Lade Profesional S.A. **(2)**
Av Segurola 1879, C1407AOK, Buenos Aires, Argentina
Tel.: (54) 1146398939
Web Site:
   https://www.ladeprofesional.com.ar
Test, Measurement & Monitoring Equipment
N.A.I.C.S.: 334515

Tektronix GmbH **(2)**
Heinrich Pesch Strasse 9-11, 50739, Cologne, Germany
Tel.: (49) 221 947 7400
Web Site: https://www.tek.com
Marketing & Sales of Electronic Parts & Equipment
N.A.I.C.S.: 449210
Mahboob Rashid (Mng Dir)

Tektronix India Private Limited **(2)**
16 Salarpuria Premia Opp Cessna Business Park, Sarjapur Outer Ring Road, Bengaluru, 560 103, India
Tel.: (91) 8068052891
Web Site: http://www.tek.com
Test, Measurement & Monitoring Equipment
N.A.I.C.S.: 334519

Tektronix International Sales
GmbH **(2)**
Rheingoldstrasse 50, 8212, Neuhausen am Rheinfall, Switzerland
Tel.: (41) 526753612
Web Site: http://sg.tek.com

Electronic Parts & Equipment Whslr
N.A.I.C.S.: 423690

Tektronix Japan, Ltd. **(2)**
Shinagawa Intercity Building B 6F 2-15-2 Konan, Minato-Ku, Tokyo, 108-6106, Japan
Tel.: (81) 120441046
Web Site: http://jp.tek.com
Test, Measurement & Monitoring Equipment
N.A.I.C.S.: 334519
Fuki Yoneyama (Pres)

Tektronix SAS **(2)**
3 Avenue Du Canada, 1 avenue de l Atlantique, 91941, Les Ulis, Cedex, France
Tel.: (33) 169868200
Web Site: http://sg.tek.com
Test, Measurement & Monitoring Equipment
N.A.I.C.S.: 334519

Tektronix Southeast Asia Pte Ltd **(2)**
238A Thomson Road 23-02 Novena Square Tower A, Singapore, 307684, Singapore
Tel.: (65) 63563900
Web Site: http://www.tek.com
Test, Measurement & Monitoring Equipment
N.A.I.C.S.: 334519

Tektronix UK Ltd. **(2)**
The Capitol Building, Oldbury, Bracknell, RG12 8FZ, Berkshire, United Kingdom
Tel.: (44) 1344392400
Web Site: http://www.tek.com
Test, Measurement & Monitoring Equipment
N.A.I.C.S.: 334519

The Gordian Group, Inc. **(1)**
30 Patewood Dr Ste 350, Greenville, SC 29615
Tel.: (800) 874-2291
Web Site: http://www.gordian.com
Management Consulting Services
N.A.I.C.S.: 541618
Daniel Cook (VP & Gen Mgr-SLED)
Bill Pollak (Pres)
Bryan Walter (VP/Gen Mgr-Federal Solutions Unit)
Ammon Lesher (VP)
Angie Michelini (VP)
Chris Gaudreau (CTO)
Christa Obert (VP)
Dwayne Pierre Antoine (VP)
Harshad Kharche (VP)
Jacob Johnson (VP)
Janice Nolan (VP)
Jen Marshall (VP)
Jim Streeter (VP)
Jo Medelman (VP)
John Lawler (VP)
Kathryn Hilton (VP)
Kris Gorriaran (Pres)
Lisa Cooley (VP)
Matthew Bausher (VP)
Pete Zuraw (VP)
Santosh Sreenivasan (CIO)
Scott Creekmore (VP)
Sophia Jang (VP)
Ted Kail (Chief Product Officer)

Subsidiary (Domestic):

4Clicks Solutions, LLC **(2)**
30 Patewood Dr Bldg 2 Ste 350, Greenville, SC 29615
Tel.: (719) 574-7724
Web Site: https://www.4clicks.com
Construction & Cost Estimating Software Services
N.A.I.C.S.: 513210
Katie Cassidy (Dir-Fin)

R.S. Means Company LLC **(2)**
30 Patewood Dr Bldg 2 Ste 350, Greenville, SC 29615
Tel.: (800) 874-2291
Web Site: http://www.rsmeans.com
Construction Cost Information Services
N.A.I.C.S.: 513199

Transit Solutions Proprietary
Limited **(1)**
Bruma Boulevard 20 Zulberg Close, Bruma, Johannesburg, South Africa
Tel.: (27) 118563800
Web Site: http://www.transitfms.co.za
Transportation Equipment Mfr
N.A.I.C.S.: 336360

Unfors RaySafe AB **(1)**
Uggledalsvagen 29, 427 40, Billdal, Sweden

Tel.: (46) 31 719 9700
Web Site: https://www.raysafe.com
X-ray Equipment Mfr
N.A.I.C.S.: 334517

Unifors Raysafe AB **(1)**
Uggledalsvagen 29, 427 40, Billdal, Sweden
Tel.: (46) 317199700
Web Site: https://www.raysafe.com
Medical Equipment Mfr & Distr
N.A.I.C.S.: 334517

Venture Measurement Company
LLC **(1)**
150 Venture Blvd, Spartanburg, SC 29306
Tel.: (864) 574-8960
Web Site:
   https://www.venturemeasurement.com
Measuring & Controlling Devices
N.A.I.C.S.: 334519

FORTRAN CORPORATION
3210 16th Ave SE, Conover, NC 28613
Tel.: (828) 324-4611   NC
Web Site:
   https://www.fortrancorp.com
Year Founded: 1948
FRTN—(OTCIQ)
Offices of Other Holding Companies
N.A.I.C.S.: 551112
Douglas W. Rink (Chm)
Richard W. Wilson (CFO & Controller)
F. Kent Greer (COO)
Glenn Withers (Pres & CEO)

Subsidiaries:

B&L Telephone LLC **(1)**
725 11th Ave Blvd SE, Hickory, NC 28602
Tel.: (828) 324-4611
Web Site: http://www.bltel.com
Telecommunications Installation, Integration & Related Services
N.A.I.C.S.: 541990
Douglas W. Rink (Chm, Pres & CEO)

CCI-Telecom, Inc. **(1)**
612 Signal Hill Dr Ext, Statesville, NC 28625
Tel.: (704) 873-5676
Web Site: http://www.ccitelecom.net
Emp.: 8
Telecommunications Systems Integration & Data Services
N.A.I.C.S.: 541990
Douglas W. Rink (Pres & CEO)

Fortran Communications, Inc. **(1)**
1585 Central Ave C-5 Ste 319, Summerville, SC 29483
Tel.: (843) 552-1700
Web Site: http://www.fortran-inc.com
Telecommunications Installation, Integration & Related Services
N.A.I.C.S.: 541990
Douglas W. Rink (Chm, Pres & CEO)

The New Telephone Company,
Inc **(1)**
201 E 8th St, Newton, NC 28658
Tel.: (828) 322-3412
Emp.: 10
Telecommunication Servicesb
N.A.I.C.S.: 517111
Douglas W. Rink (Pres & CEO)

WynnCom, Inc. **(1)**
911 S Talbert Blvd, Lexington, NC 27292
Tel.: (336) 249-8282
Web Site: http://www.wynncom.com
Emp.: 45
Telecommunications Equipment & Services
N.A.I.C.S.: 334220
Dough Rink (Pres)

FORTREA HOLDINGS INC.
8 Moore Dr, Durham, NC 27709
Tel.: (336) 436-5076   DE
Web Site: https://www.fortrea.com
Year Founded: 2023
FTRE—(NASDAQ)
Rev.: $3,109,000,000
Assets: $4,357,200,000
Liabilities: $2,618,400,000

Net Worth: $1,738,800,000
Earnings: ($3,400,000)
Emp.: 18,000
Fiscal Year-end: 12/31/23
Holding Company
N.A.I.C.S.: 551112
Thomas H. Pike (Chm, Pres & CEO)
Dave Cooper (Chief Admin Officer)
Tom Pike (Pres)
Robert Parks (Chief Acctg Officer)

FORTRESS BIOTECH, INC.
Tel.: (781) 652-4500   DE
Web Site:
   https://www.fortressbiotech.com
Year Founded: 2006
FBIO—(NASDAQ)
Rev.: $75,743,000
Assets: $294,301,000
Liabilities: $244,276,000
Net Worth: $50,025,000
Earnings: ($86,575,000)
Emp.: 187
Fiscal Year-end: 12/31/22
Biotechnology & Pharmaceutical Products Developer & Mfr
N.A.I.C.S.: 325412
Lindsay Allan Rosenwald (Chm, Pres & CEO)
Michael S. Weiss (Vice Chm-Strategic Dev)
George Avgerinos (Sr VP-Biologics Ops)
David Jin (CFO & VP-Corp Dev)
Eric K. Rowinsky (Vice Chm)

Subsidiaries:

Checkpoint Therapeutics, Inc. **(1)**
3 Franklin Sq Ste 4, Saratoga Springs, NY 12866
Tel.: (781) 652-4500
Web Site: https://www.checkpointtx.com
Rev.: $192,000
Assets: $13,290,000
Liabilities: $32,773,000
Net Worth: ($19,483,000)
Earnings: ($62,624,000)
Emp.: 24
Fiscal Year-end: 12/31/2022
Pharmaceutical Preparation Manufacturing
N.A.I.C.S.: 325412
Michael S. Weiss (Chm)
James F. Oliviero (Pres & CEO)
Garrett Gray (CFO)

Cyprium, Inc. **(1)**
248 Calvary Ln, Naples, ID 83847
Tel.: (208) 267-7455
Steel Foundry Operator
N.A.I.C.S.: 331513

FORTRESS CAPITAL ACQUISITION CORP.
1345 Avenue of the Americas 45th Fl, New York, NY 10105
Tel.: (212) 798-6100   KY
Year Founded: 2020
FCAXU—(NYSE)
Investment Services
N.A.I.C.S.: 523999
Daniel N. Bass (Chm, CEO & CFO)

FORTUNE BRANDS INNOVATIONS, INC.
520 Lake Cook Rd, Deerfield, IL 60015-5611
Tel.: (847) 484-4400   DE
Web Site: https://www.fbin.com
Year Founded: 2011
FBIN—(NYSE)
Rev.: $4,626,200,000
Assets: $6,565,000,000
Liabilities: $4,271,600,000
Net Worth: $2,293,400,000
Earnings: $404,500,000
Emp.: 11,700
Fiscal Year-end: 12/30/23
Home & Security Products Mfr
N.A.I.C.S.: 551112

Sheri R. Grissom *(Chief Transformation Officer & Exec VP)*
Danny Luburic *(VP & Controller)*
Martin Thomas *(Sr VP-Ops & Supply Chain Strategy)*
Cheri M. Phyfer *(Grp Pres & Exec VP)*
David Barry *(CFO & Exec VP)*
Hiranda Donoghue *(Gen Counsel, Sec & Sr VP)*
Ron Wilson *(Exec VP)*
Kristin Papesh *(Chief HR Officer & Exec VP)*
Nicholas I. Fink *(CEO)*

Subsidiaries:

Fortune Brands Doors, Inc. (1)
520 Lk Cook Rd, Deerfield, IL 60015-5611
Tel.: (847) 484-4400
Metal Window & Door Mfr
N.A.I.C.S.: 332321

Subsidiary (Domestic):

Larson Manufacturing Company, Inc. (2)
2333 Eastbrook Dr, Brookings, SD 57006-2838
Tel.: (605) 692-6115
Web Site: http://www.larsondoors.com
Sales Range: $450-499.9 Million
Emp.: 1,050
Aluminum Storm Doors Mfr
N.A.I.C.S.: 423310
Jeff Rief *(Pres & CEO)*

Fortune Brands Storage & Security LLC (1)
137 W Forest Hill Ave, Oak Creek, WI 53154
Tel.: (414) 571-5625
Hardware Mfr
N.A.I.C.S.: 332510

Master Lock Company LLC (1)
6744 S Howell Ave, Oak Creek, WI 53154 (100%)
Tel.: (414) 571-5625
Web Site: http://www.masterlock.com
Sales Range: $450-499.9 Million
Emp.: 1,300
Padlocks & Security Products Mfr
N.A.I.C.S.: 332510

Subsidiary (Non-US):

Master Lock Europe, S.A.S. (2)
131 avenue, Charles de Gaulle, 92200, France
Tel.: (33) 141437200
Web Site: http://www.master-lock.fr
Hardware Merchant Whslr
N.A.I.C.S.: 423710

Moen Incorporated (1)
25300 Al Moen Dr, North Olmsted, OH 44070-8022 (100%)
Tel.: (440) 962-2000
Web Site: http://www.moen.com
Sales Range: $100-124.9 Million
Emp.: 3,200
Bathroom & Kitchen Plumbing Fixture Mfr
N.A.I.C.S.: 332913

Subsidiary (Non-US):

Moen (Shanghai) Kitchen & Bath Products Co., Ltd. (2)
360 Pu Dian Rd. Pudong, Shanghai, 200120, China
Tel.: (86) 2163609600611
Printed Circuit Assembly (Electronic Assembly) Mfr
N.A.I.C.S.: 334418

Moen China, Limited (2)
Unit A 8th Floor Lu Jia Zui Investment Building 360 Pu Dian Rd, Pudong, Shanghai, 2020120, China
Tel.: (86) 2163609600
Web Site: http://www.moen.cn
Metal Products Mfr
N.A.I.C.S.: 332999

Moen Guangzhou Faucet Co., Ltd. (2)
Shangyuangang Shahe Tianhe Dist,

Guangzhou, 510507, Guangdong, China
Tel.: (86) 2087157100
Construction Services
N.A.I.C.S.: 236220

Moen Inc. (2)
2816 Bristol Circle, Oakville, L6H 5S7, ON, Canada (100%)
Tel.: (905) 829-3400
Web Site: http://www.moen.ca
Sales Range: $50-74.9 Million
Emp.: 125
Plumbing & Hydronic Heating Supplies
N.A.I.C.S.: 423720

Riobel LLC (1)
820 rue Nobel St, Saint-Jerome, J7Z 7A3, QC, Canada
Tel.: (450) 432-0442
Web Site: http://www.riobel.ca
Home Furnishing Distr
N.A.I.C.S.: 423220

Rohl LLC (1)
3 Parker, Irvine, CA 92618-1605
Tel.: (800) 777-9762
Web Site: http://www.rohlhome.com
Metal Products Mfr
N.A.I.C.S.: 332999
Kenneth S. Rohl *(Founder)*

Sentry Safe, Inc. (1)
900 Linden Ave, Rochester, NY 14625
Tel.: (800) 828-1438
Web Site: http://www.sentrysafe.com
Metal Products Mfr
N.A.I.C.S.: 332999

TCL Manufacturing Ltd. (1)
Unit 1 Gateway XIII Ferry Lane Rainham, London, RM13 9JY, Essex, United Kingdom
Tel.: (44) 1708526361
Web Site: https://www.perrinandrowe.co.uk
Household Metal Product Mfr
N.A.I.C.S.: 337121

TMLC Safes, S.A. de C.V. (1)
Libre Comercio 29 S/N Parque Industrial Nuevo, Nogales, Mexico
Tel.: (52) 6313111200
Cabinetry Mfr
N.A.I.C.S.: 337110

Therma-Tru Corp. (1)
1750 Indian Wood Cir, Maumee, OH 43537-4049
Tel.: (419) 891-7400
Web Site: http://www.thermatru.com
Sales Range: $400-449.9 Million
Emp.: 2,700
Exterior Door Systems, Fiberglass & Steel Frames Mfr
N.A.I.C.S.: 332321
Mark Ayers *(Sr VP-Mktg & Product Dev)*

Division (Domestic):

Therma-Tru Corp. (2)
1750 Indian Wood Cir, Maumee, OH 43537
Tel.: (540) 898-5700
Web Site: https://www.thermatru.com
Sales Range: $50-74.9 Million
Emp.: 100
Door Entry Systems Mfr
N.A.I.C.S.: 332321

Victoria & Albert Bath, LLC (1)
4269-A Crosspoint Dr, Ladson, SC 29456
Bathroom Accessory Distr
N.A.I.C.S.: 423220

Subsidiary (Non-US):

Victoria & Albert Baths Limited (2)
Unit B Hortonwood 37, Telford, TF1 7XT, Shropshire, United Kingdom
Tel.: (44) 1952221100
Web Site: https://www.vandabaths.com
Bathroom Accessory Distr
N.A.I.C.S.: 423220

Victoria & Albert Products Proprietary Limited (2)
PO Box 5055, Worcester, 6849, South Africa
Tel.: (27) 233474939
Web Site: http://www.vandabaths.com
Cabinetry Mfr
N.A.I.C.S.: 337110

Waterloo Industries, Inc. (1)

100 E Fourth St, Waterloo, IA 50703-4714 (100%)
Tel.: (319) 235-7131
Web Site: http://www.waterlooindustries.com
Sales Range: $300-349.9 Million
Emp.: 150
Storage & Organization Solutions Mfr
N.A.I.C.S.: 493110
Christopher J. Klein *(CEO)*

Subsidiary (Non-US):

Waterloo de Nogales, S.A. de C.V. (2)
Libre Comercio Nueva Nogales, Nogales, 84094, Sonora, Mexico
Tel.: (52) 6313111200
Electronic Products Mfr
N.A.I.C.S.: 334416

FORTUNE RISE ACQUISITION CORPORATION

13575 58th St N Ste 200, Clearwater, FL 33760
Tel.: (727) 440-4603   DE
Year Founded: 2021
FRLA—(NASDAQ)
Assets: $102,143,840
Liabilities: $106,475,578
Net Worth: ($4,331,738)
Earnings: ($47,609)
Emp.: 1
Fiscal Year-end: 12/31/22
Investment Services
N.A.I.C.S.: 523999
Ryan Spick *(CFO)*
Ronald J. Pollack *(Chm)*

FORU HOLDINGS, INC.

3445 Lawrence Ave, Oceanside, NY 11572
Tel.: (646) 768-8417   NV
Year Founded: 1984
FORU—(OTCIQ)
Biotechnology Research & Development Services
N.A.I.C.S.: 541714
David E. Lazar *(Chm, Pres, CEO, CFO & Sec)*
Diego Roca *(COO)*

FORUM ENERGY TECHNOLOGIES, INC.

10344 Sam Houston Park Dr, Houston, TX 77064
Tel.: (713) 351-7900   DE
Web Site: https://www.f-e-t.com
FET—(NYSE)
Rev.: $699,913,000
Assets: $834,757,000
Liabilities: $527,722,000
Net Worth: $307,035,000
Earnings: $3,712,000
Emp.: 1,500
Fiscal Year-end: 12/31/22
Offshore & Subsea Drilling Equipment, Surface Production Equipment, Process & Pipeline Equipment & Valve Products Mfr & Distr
N.A.I.C.S.: 333131
C. Christopher Gaut *(Founder)*
Neal A. Lux *(Pres & CEO)*
Michael D. Danford *(Chief HR Officer & Sr VP)*
Katherine T. Keller *(Principal Acctg Officer & VP)*
D. Lyle Williams Jr. *(CFO & Exec VP)*

Subsidiaries:

Allied Technology Inc. (1)
14800 St Mary's Ln Ste 130, Houston, TX 77079
Tel.: (281) 759-0400
Oil & Gas Production & Process Equipment Mfr
N.A.I.C.S.: 333132

Subsidiary (Domestic):

Certified Technical Services, L.P. (2)

2200 East Pasadena Frwy, Pasadena, TX 77506
Tel.: (713) 477-0404
Web Site: http://www.certifiedway.com
Petrochemical Plants & Refineries Construction Services
N.A.I.C.S.: 236210

Blohm + Voss Oil Tools GmbH (1)
Hermann-Blohm-Strasse 2, PO Box 112253, 20457, Hamburg, Germany
Tel.: (49) 40370226855
Web Site: http://www.blohmvoss-oiltools.com
Pipe Handling Tool Mfr
N.A.I.C.S.: 326122

Dynacon, Inc. (1)
831 Industrial Blvd, Bryan, TX 77803
Tel.: (979) 823-2690
Web Site: http://www.dynacon.com
Sales Range: $1-9.9 Million
Emp.: 62
Overhead Traveling Crane, Hoist & Monorail System Mfr
N.A.I.C.S.: 333923

FET Holdings LLC (1)
920 Memorial City Way, Houston, TX 77024-2649
Tel.: (281) 949-2500
Investment Management Service
N.A.I.C.S.: 551112

Forum Arabia Limited (1)
2nd Industrial City, PO Box 3544, Dammam, 34325, Saudi Arabia
Tel.: (966) 507523285
Oil & Gas Field Machinery Mfr
N.A.I.C.S.: 333132

Forum B+V Oil Tools GmbH (1)
Hermann-Blohm-Str 2, 20457, Hamburg, Germany
Tel.: (49) 40370226855
Web Site: http://www.blohmvoss-oiltools.com
Pipe Handling Tool Mfr
N.A.I.C.S.: 326122

Forum Canada ULC (1)
6623 44 St, Leduc, T9E 7E5, AB, Canada
Tel.: (780) 986-4518
Industrial Machinery & Equipment Distr
N.A.I.C.S.: 423830

Forum Energy Asia Pacific Pte. Ltd. (1)
51 Benoi Rd 06-00 Liang Huat Industrial Complex, Singapore, 629908, Singapore
Tel.: (65) 64654850
Web Site: http://www.f-e-t.com
Sales Range: $25-49.9 Million
Emp.: 58
Industrial Machinery & Equipment Distr
N.A.I.C.S.: 423830

Forum Energy Technologies, Inc. - Float Equipment (1)
2005 Garden Rd, Pearland, TX 77581
Tel.: (281) 485-8301
Web Site: http://www.f-e-t.com
Sales Range: $1-9.9 Million
Emp.: 100
Oil & Gas Field Machinery & Equipment Mfr
N.A.I.C.S.: 333132

Forum Energy Technology (Shanghai) Co., Ltd (1)
388 North Fuquan Road Changning, Shanghai, China
Tel.: (86) 2180316839
Oil & Gas Field Machinery Mfr
N.A.I.C.S.: 333132

Forum Global Tubing LLC (1)
920 Memorial City Way Ste 1000, Houston, TX 77024
Tel.: (281) 949-2500
Pipe Handling Tool Mfr
N.A.I.C.S.: 326122

Forum Valve Solutions (1)
12735 Dairy Ashford Rd, Stafford, TX 77477
Tel.: (281) 340-5400
Valves & Actuators Mfr & Distr; Gas, Petrochemical, Power, Mining & Biofuels Industries Services
N.A.I.C.S.: 332911

Forum Energy Technologies, Inc.—(Continued)

Steve Twellman *(Sr VP)*
Shirley Nicola *(Mgr-HR)*

Global Flow Technologies, Inc. **(1)**
920 Memorial City Way Ste 1000, Houston,
TX 77024
Tel.: (281) 949-2500
Web Site: http://ir.f-e-t.com
Emp.: 3,500
Industrial Valve Mfr
N.A.I.C.S.: 332911

Global Tubing, LLC **(1)**
501 County Road 493, Dayton, TX
77535-2139 **(100%)**
Tel.: (713) 265-5000
Web Site: https://www.global-tubing.com
Coiled Tubing Products for Oil & Gas Indus-
try
N.A.I.C.S.: 331210

Multilift Welltec LLC **(1)**
11050 W Little York Bldg L, Houston, TX
77041
Tel.: (855) 868-4833
Web Site: http://www.multiliftusa.com
Drilling Equipment Mfr
N.A.I.C.S.: 333131

Phoinix Global LLC **(1)**
903 Commerce Rd St, Alice, TX 78332
Tel.: (361) 664-6163
Web Site: http://www.phoinixglobal.com
Flow Control Equipment Mfr
N.A.I.C.S.: 333132

Pro-Tech Valve Sales **(1)**
9503 -12th Avenue SW, Edmonton, T6X-
0C3, AB, Canada
Tel.: (780) 980-0345
Web Site: http://www.f-e-t.com
Industrial Valve Mfr
N.A.I.C.S.: 332911

Pro-Tech Valve Sales, Inc. **(1)**
11 Cardinal Street, Barrie, L4M 6C8, ON,
Canada
Tel.: (705) 794-1600
Fitting & Valve Distr
N.A.I.C.S.: 423720
Harvey Maron *(Project Mgr-Warehouse)*

Quality Wireline & Cable Inc. **(1)**
Bay 23-7503 35 St SE, Calgary, T2C 1V3,
AB, Canada
Tel.: (403) 723-9473
Web Site: http://www.qualitywireline.com
Wireline & Cable Installation Services
N.A.I.C.S.: 213112

TGH (AP) Pte. Ltd. **(1)**
38 Loyang Drive No.01-03, Singapore,
508960, Singapore
Tel.: (65) 62140443
Sales Range: $25-49.9 Million
Emp.: 17
Oil & Gas Exploration Services
N.A.I.C.S.: 211120

Zy-Tech de Venezuela S.A. **(1)**
Avenida Principal Los Robles Con Calle
115, Edif Auto Express Sector Los Robles,
Maracaibo, 4004, Zulia, Venezuela
Tel.: (58) 2617357762
Industrial Machinery & Equipment Whslr
N.A.I.C.S.: 423830

FORWARD AIR CORPORA-
TION
1915 Snapps Ferry Rd Bldg N,
Greeneville, TN 37745
Tel.: (423) 636-7000   **TN**
Web Site: https://www.forwardair.com
Year Founded: 1990
FWRD—(NASDAQ)
Rev.: $1,973,403,000
Assets: $1,208,076,000
Liabilities: $500,832,000
Net Worth: $707,244,000
Earnings: $193,191,000
Emp.: 4,155
Fiscal Year-end: 12/31/22
Freight Transportation Arrangement
N.A.I.C.S.: 488510
James R. Faught *(Chief Acctg Offi-
cer)*

Chris C. Ruble *(Pres & COO)*
Michael L. Hance *(Chief Legal Officer
& Sec)*
Kyle R. Mitchin *(Chief People Officer)*
Jay Tomasello *(CIO)*
Nancee Ronning *(Chief Comml Offi-
cer)*
Matthew Casey *(Sr VP)*
Katie Bishop *(Head)*
Jamie G. Pierson *(CFO)*

Subsidiaries:

Central States Trucking Co. **(1)**
823 Commerce Dr, Oak Brook, IL 60523
Tel.: (630) 242-9876
Web Site: http://www.cstruck.com
Sales Range: $25-49.9 Million
Emp.: 300
General Freight Trucking & Other Supply
Chain Services
N.A.I.C.S.: 484121

FSA Network Inc. **(1)**
1545 N Park Dr, Fort Lauderdale, FL 33326
Tel.: (954) 349-2755
Web Site: http://www.fsalogistix.com
Trucking Service
N.A.I.C.S.: 484110
Charles R. Annett *(Pres & COO)*
Katherine Schwab *(Treas)*

Forward Air, Inc. **(1)**
6800 Port Rd, Groveport, OH 43215
Tel.: (614) 497-5000
Sales Range: $100-124.9 Million
Ground Transportation Services
N.A.I.C.S.: 488510

Subsidiary (Domestic):

Total Quality, Inc. **(2)**
550 3 Mile R NW Ste D, Grand Rapids, MI
49544
Tel.: (616) 785-4600
Web Site: http://shiptqi.com
Sales Range: $50-74.9 Million
Emp.: 40
Pharmaceutical & Life Science Industry
Specialized Warehousing, Transportation &
Logistics Services
N.A.I.C.S.: 488510

Unit (Domestic):

**Total Quality, Inc. - Mecosta
Terminal** **(3)**
550 3 Mile Rd NW Ste D, Grand Rapids, MI
49544
Tel.: (616) 785-4600
Web Site: http://www.shiptqi.com
Pharmaceutical & Life Science Industry
Specialized Warehousing, Transportation &
Logistics Services
N.A.I.C.S.: 493120

Omni Logistics LLC **(1)**
1755 Transcentral Ct Ste 400, Houston, TX
77032
Tel.: (281) 209-9228
Web Site: http://www.omnilogistics.com
Sales Range: $50-74.9 Million
Emp.: 20
Air Free Shipping
N.A.I.C.S.: 541614
Paul J. Gaffney *(Chief Digital Officer)*
J. J. Schickel *(CEO)*
Andy Tribble *(Sr VP-North America)*
Randy Dumas *(CFO)*
Keith Moran *(Pres-North America)*
Dill Heathcock *(VP-Ops)*
Wendy Curtis *(Chief Legal Officer & Gen
Counsel)*
Brad Stogner *(Chief Revenue Officer)*
Jennifer Dooley *(VP & Controller)*
Bobby Solis *(Pres-Asia)*
Christi Liebe *(CIO)*
Mike Painter *(VP-UK)*
Nelson Lau *(VP-North Asia)*
K. Y. Yip *(VP-South Asia)*

**Southwest Freight Distributors,
Inc.** **(1)**
8189 S Central Expy, Dallas, TX 75241-
7820
Tel.: (214) 371-1901
Web Site: http://www.southwestfreight.com
Provider of Trucking Services

N.A.I.C.S.: 484121
Richard D. Eberhart *(CEO)*

FORWARD INDUSTRIES, INC.
700 Veterans Hwy Ste 100, Haup-
pauge, NY 11788   **NY**
Web Site:
https://www.forwardindustries.com
Year Founded: 1961
FORD—(NASDAQ)
Rev.: $36,688,307
Assets: $17,386,142
Liabilities: $14,769,881
Net Worth: $2,616,261
Earnings: ($3,736,657)
Emp.: 100
Fiscal Year-end: 09/30/23
Custom Leather, Nylon & Vinyl Carry-
ing Cases Mfr & Designer for Por-
table Products
N.A.I.C.S.: 316990
Terence Bernard Wise *(Chm & CEO)*
Douglas Matthews *(COO & Sr VP)*
Kathleen Weisberg *(CFO, Treas &
Sec)*

Subsidiaries:

**Forward Industries (Switzerland)
GmbH** **(1)**
Riedstrasse 7, 6330, Cham, Switzerland
Tel.: (41) 417471102
Web Site: http://www.forwardindustries.com
Consumer Electronic Products Design &
Distr
N.A.I.C.S.: 423690
Michael D. Matte *(Gen Mgr)*

Forward Innovations GmbH **(1)**
Riedstrasse 7, Cham, 6330, Switzerland
Tel.: (41) 417471100
Web Site: http://www.forwardindustries.com
Sales Range: $1-9.9 Million
Emp.: 5
Communications Products Distr
N.A.I.C.S.: 334290

Intelligent Product Solutions, Inc. **(1)**
700 Veterans Memorial Hwy, Hauppauge,
NY 11788
Tel.: (631) 676-7744
Web Site:
https://www.intelligentproduct.solutions
Product Design & Engineering
N.A.I.C.S.: 541490
Mitchell Maiman *(Founder)*
Paul Severino *(Founder & Pres)*
June Severino Feldman *(CMO)*
Robert Wild *(COO)*

FORWARDLY, INC.
3535 Executive Terminal Dr Ste 110,
Henderson, NV 89052
Tel.: (702) 840-4433   **NV**
Web Site:
https://www.forwardlyplaced.com
Year Founded: 2005
FORW—(OTCIQ)
Security & Commodity Services
N.A.I.C.S.: 523210
George A. Sharp *(Pres, CEO & Dir)*
Leonard J. Harris *(Dir)*
Michael Pollack *(Accountant)*

FOSSIL GROUP, INC.
901 S Central Expy, Richardson, TX
75080
Tel.: (972) 234-2525   **DE**
Web Site:
https://www.fossilgroup.com
Year Founded: 1991
FOSL—(NASDAQ)
Rev.: $1,870,036,000
Assets: $1,368,719,000
Liabilities: $903,361,000
Net Worth: $465,358,000
Earnings: $25,434,000
Emp.: 6,900
Fiscal Year-end: 01/01/22

Holding Company; Watch, Jewelry &
Other Fashion Accessories Designer,
Marketer, Distr & Retailer
N.A.I.C.S.: 551112
Gregory A. McKelvey *(Chief Comml
Officer & Exec VP)*
Melissa Lowenkron *(Sr VP/Gen Mgr-
Fossil Brand)*
Holly Briedis *(Chief Digital Officer &
Exec VP)*
Franco Fogliato *(CEO)*
Jeffrey N. Boyer *(COO)*

Subsidiaries:

Fossil (East) Limited **(1)**
5/F Cdw Building 388 Castle Peak Rd,
Tsuen Wan, New Territories, China (Hong
Kong) **(100%)**
Tel.: (852) 24162710
Sales Range: $350-399.9 Million
Watches & Accessories Distr
N.A.I.C.S.: 423940

Representative Office (Non-US):

**Fossil (Asia) Holdings Ltd. - Taiwan
Office** **(2)**
5F NO 221 Zhongxiao East Rd Sec 4, Tai-
pei, Taiwan
Tel.: (886) 287739911
Web Site: http://www.fossil.com
Investment Management Service
N.A.I.C.S.: 523940

Subsidiary (Non-US):

Fossil (Australia) Pty Ltd. **(2)**
122-126 Old Pittwater Road, Brookvale,
2100, NSW, Australia
Tel.: (61) 289778086
Watches & Accessories Distr
N.A.I.C.S.: 423940

Subsidiary (Domestic):

Fossil (Hong Kong) Ltd **(2)**
Unit C&D 6/F CDW Building 388 Castle
Peak Road, Tsuen Wan, New Territories,
China (Hong Kong)
Tel.: (852) 24162710
Fashion Accessories Retailer
N.A.I.C.S.: 459420

Subsidiary (Non-US):

Fossil India Private Ltd. **(2)**
621 12th Main HAL II Stage Indiranagar,
Bengaluru, 560 008, Karnataka, India
Tel.: (91) 8009190951
Emp.: 80
Consumer Fashion Accessories Distr
N.A.I.C.S.: 459420

Fossil Singapore Pte. Ltd. **(2)**
51 Bras Basah Road 08-07 Manulife Cen-
tre, Singapore, 189554, Singapore
Tel.: (65) 64318100
Fashion Accessories Retailer
N.A.I.C.S.: 459420

Fossil Time Malaysia Sdn. Bhd. **(2)**
Service Centre Unit L2-2-7 2nd Floor
Wisma Kemajuan No 2 Jalan 19/1B, Jalan
Ampang, 46300, Petaling Jaya, Selangor,
Malaysia
Tel.: (60) 379691900
Emp.: 50
Watches & Accessories Distr
N.A.I.C.S.: 423940

Fossil Europe B.V. **(1)**
Terborgseweg 138, Doetinchem, 7005 BD,
Netherlands **(100%)**
Tel.: (31) 314799039
Web Site: http://www.fossil.com
Sales Range: $1-4.9 Billion
Emp.: 40
Watches & Accessories Distr
N.A.I.C.S.: 423940
Louis De Bruin *(Mng Dir)*

Subsidiary (Non-US):

**Fossil Accessories South Africa Pty
Ltd** **(2)**
Unit 1 48 Neptune Street, Paarden Eiland,
Cape Town, 7405, South Africa

Tel.: (27) 214180045
Web Site: https://www.watchrepublic.co.za
Jewelry & Accessory Mfr
N.A.I.C.S.: 339910
Avi Keren (Sr Mng Dir)

Fossil Europe GmbH   **(2)**
Oberwinkl 1, 83355, Grabenstatt,
Germany   **(100%)**
Tel.: (49) 86189983024
Web Site: https://www.fossil.com
Watches & Accessories Distr
N.A.I.C.S.: 423940

Fossil France SA   **(2)**
Rue du Martelberg, PO BOX 80023, Sav-
erne, 67707, Monswiller, Cedex,
France   **(100%)**
Tel.: (33) 184889325
Web Site: https://www.fossil.com
Sales Range: $50-74.9 Million
Emp.: 300
Watches, Jewelry, Sunglasses & Fashion
Accessories Whslr
N.A.I.C.S.: 423940
Dizoc Christokhe (Mng Dir)

Fossil Italia, S.r.l.   **(2)**
Via Vecchia Ferriera 4, 36100, Vicenza,
Italy
Tel.: (39) 0444955978
Web Site: https://www.fossil.com
Consumer Fashion Accessories Retailer
N.A.I.C.S.: 459420

Fossil Sweden AB   **(2)**
PO Box 5193, 402 26, Gothenburg,
Sweden   **(100%)**
Tel.: (46) 317194500
Emp.: 225
Consumer Fashion Accessories Distr
N.A.I.C.S.: 459420
Adam Eisner (Mng Dir)

Fossil Switzerland GmbH   **(2)**
                                          (100%)
Tel.: (41) 615609900
Web Site: https://www.fossil.com
Sales Range: $50-74.9 Million
Marketing of Jewelry & Precious Stones
N.A.I.C.S.: 458310
Desiree Thomann (Pres)

Fossil U.K. Holdings Ltd.   **(2)**
Featherstone House Featherstone Rd
Wolverton Mill, Milton Keynes, MK12 5TH,
Buckinghamshire, United Kingdom
Tel.: (44) 8444123277
Web Site: http://www.fossil.com
Watches & Accessories Distr
N.A.I.C.S.: 423940

Subsidiary (Domestic):

Fossil UK Ltd.   **(3)**
Featherstone House Featherstone Road
Wolverton Mill, Milton Keynes, MK12 5TH,
United Kingdom   **(100%)**
Tel.: (44) 2038685986
Web Site: https://www.fossil.com
Sales Range: $150-199.9 Million
Emp.: 100
Watches & Accessories Distr
N.A.I.C.S.: 423940
Richard Collins (Mng Dir)

Fossil Mexico, S.A. de C.V.   **(1)**
Calm Pegaso No 3692, Zapopan, 45070,
Jalisco, Mexico
Tel.: (52) 3336315940
Consumer Fashion Accessories Store
N.A.I.C.S.: 459420

Fossil Partners, L.P.   **(1)**
2280 N Greenville Ave, Richardson, TX
75082
Tel.: (972) 699-1515
Web Site: http://www.fossil.com
Emp.: 6
Watch, Jewelry & Other Fashion Accesso-
ries Designer, Marketer & Distr
N.A.I.C.S.: 423940

Skagen Designs, Ltd.
17/F CDW Building 388 Castle Peak Road,
Tsuen Wan, New Territories, China (Hong
Kong)
Tel.: (852) 24378566
Watch & Jewelry Whslr
N.A.I.C.S.: 423940

Swiss Technology Production SA **(1)**
Rue des Places 28, Glovelier, 2855, Delem-
ont, Switzerland
Tel.: (41) 324270100
Web Site: https://www.swisstp.com
Watches & Accessories Distr
N.A.I.C.S.: 423940

FOUNDERS BAY HOLDINGS
7209 Lancaster Pike Ste 1211,
Hockessin, DE 19707
Tel.: (302) 416-4816   NV
Year Founded: 1986
FDBH—(OTCIQ)
Portfolio Management Services
N.A.I.C.S.: 523940
Michael Jeremias Tomas (CEO)
Mark Herrick (Sec)

FOUR CORNERS PROPERTY TRUST, INC.
591 Redwood Hwy Ste 3215, Mill
Valley, CA 94941
Tel.: (415) 965-8030   MD
Web Site: https://www.fcpt.com
Year Founded: 2015
FCPT—(NYSE)
Rev.: $223,194,000
Assets: $2,198,587,000
Liabilities: $1,060,277,000
Net Worth: $1,138,310,000
Earnings: $97,908,000
Emp.: 543
Fiscal Year-end: 12/31/22
Property Leasing Services
N.A.I.C.S.: 531110
James L. Brat (COO)
Niccole M. Stewart (Chief Acctg Offi-
cer)
Joshua C. Zhang (Dir-Acquisitions)
Patrick L. Wernig (CFO & Treas)
Ryan C. Mesick (Coord-Legal &
Property Ops)
Baljinnyam Dashdorj (VP)
Kelly Egli (Controller)
Warren Smith (Controller)
Yesenia Lopez (Mgr)
Laura Gatti (Mgr)
Garrett Fitzgerald (Assoc Gen Coun-
sel)
Tyler Neumann (Mgr)
Logan Ferstl (Coord)
Justin Peters (Mgr)
Tammy Herndon (Coord)
Drake Nylund (Mgr)
Ena Portuguez (Mgr)
Matt Kolker (Dir)
William Howard Lenehan IV (Pres &
CEO)

Subsidiaries:

Mcalister's Deli   **(1)**
735 Addison Dr, Rock Hill, SC 29730
Tel.: (803) 329-0042
Web Site: http://www.mcalistersdeli.com
Sales Range: $1-9.9 Million
Emp.: 40
Supermarkets & Other Grocery (except
Convenience) Stores
N.A.I.C.S.: 445110

Tire Discounters, Inc.   **(1)**
7525 Wooster Pike, Cincinnati, OH 45227
Tel.: (513) 271-4422
Web Site: http://www.tirediscounters.com
Sales Range: $1-9.9 Million
Tire Dealers
N.A.I.C.S.: 441340
Jamie Ward (Pres & CEO)
Chris Yapp (CMO)
Michael Sarow (Head-Mktg)
Jonathan Burns (VP-Category Mgmt)

**Village Practice Management Com-
pany, LLC**   **(1)**
125 S Clark St Ste 900, Chicago, IL 60603
Tel.: (312) 465-7900
Web Site: https://www.villagemd.com
Healtcare Services
N.A.I.C.S.: 621610

Mark Vainisi (Chief Strategy Officer & Exec
VP)
Tim Barry (Co-Founder & CEO)
Clive Fields (Co-Founder & Chief Medical
Officer)
Paul Martino (Co-Founder & Chief Growth
Officer)
David Hatfield (Pres)
Bryan Becker (Natl Dir-Medical-Texas)

Subsidiary (Domestic):

Reliance Medical Group, LLC   **(2)**
525 Tilton Rd, Northfield, NJ 08225
Tel.: (609) 272-0655
Web Site:
    http://www.reliancemedicalgroup.net
Rev.: $1,300,000
Emp.: 15
Fiscal Year-end: 12/31/2006
Clinical Services
N.A.I.C.S.: 541618

FOUR LEAF ACQUISITION CORPORATION
4546 El Camino Real B10 Ste 715,
Los Altos, CA 94022
Tel.: (650) 720-5626   DE
Web Site:
    https://www.fourleaf.investments
Year Founded: 2022
FORL—(NASDAQ)
Rev.: $2,227,437
Assets: $58,124,201
Liabilities: $59,434,293
Net Worth: ($1,310,092)
Earnings: $834,785
Fiscal Year-end: 12/31/23
Investment Management Service
N.A.I.C.S.: 523999

FOVEA JEWELRY HOLDINGS LTD.
30 N Gould St Ste 2984, Sheridan,
WY 82801
Tel.: (702) 505-4599
Year Founded: 2006
FJHL—(OTCIQ)
Rev.: $598,486
Assets: $853,105
Liabilities: $78,120
Net Worth: $774,985
Earnings: ($70,539)
Fiscal Year-end: 12/31/21
Jewelry Mfr & Retailer
N.A.I.C.S.: 339910
Thomson Lee (Pres, CEO, Treas &
Sec)

FOX CORPORATION
1211 Ave of the Americas, New York
10036
Tel.: (212) 852-7000   DE
Web Site:
    https://www.foxcorporation.com
Year Founded: 2018
FOXA—(NASDAQ)
Rev.: $13,980,000,000
Assets: $21,972,000,000
Liabilities: $11,158,000,000
Net Worth: $10,814,000,000
Earnings: $1,554,000,000
Emp.: 10,200
Fiscal Year-end: 06/30/24
Offices of Other Holding Companies
N.A.I.C.S.: 551112
Adam G. Ciongoli (Chief Legal &
Policy Officer)
Lachlan Keith Murdoch (Chm & CEO)
John P. Nallen (COO)
Joseph Dorrego (Chief IR Officer &
Exec VP-Corp Initiatives)
Steven Tomsic (CFO)
Viet D. Dinh (Chief Legal & Policy
Officer)
Michael Biard (Pres-Ops & Distr)
Paul Cheesbrough (CTO & Pres-
Digital)
Marianne Gambelli (Pres-Adv Sls)

Kevin Lord (Exec VP-HR)
Danny O'Brien (Exec VP & Head-
Govt Rels)
Jeff A. Taylor (Gen Counsel & Exec
VP)
Claudia Teran (Gen Counsel & Exec
VP)
Inae Wilson (Exec VP-Brdcst Distr &
Mktg)
Brian Nick (Chief Comm Officer &
Exec VP)

Subsidiaries:

Bento Box Entertainment, LLC   **(1)**
5161 Lankershim Blvd Ste 120, North Holly-
wood, CA 91601-4962
Tel.: (818) 333-7700
Web Site: https://www.bentoboxent.com
Graphic Design Services
N.A.I.C.S.: 541430
Ben Jones (Creative Dir)
Scott Greenberg (Co-Founder & CEO)
Joel Kuwahara (Co-Founder & Pres-
Production)
Brett Coker (COO)
Craig Hartin (Gen Mgr-Bento Box Atlanta)
Brooke Keesling (Head-Animation Talent
Dev)
Dana Cameron (Head-Production)
Caitlin Winiarski (Dir-Dev)

Credible Labs, Inc.   **(1)**
6945 Northpark Blvd Ste L DPT Ste 6037,
Charlotte, NC 28216-0079
Tel.: (415) 570-9488
Web Site: https://www.credible.com
Rev.: $19,760,454
Assets: $51,348,351
Liabilities: $1,743,761
Net Worth: $49,604,590
Earnings: ($11,181,127)
Fiscal Year-end: 12/31/2017
Consumer Lending Services
N.A.I.C.S.: 522291
Stephen Dash (Founder & CEO)
Colin Bowman (Chief Product Officer)
Jereme Albin (COO)
Robert Humann (Chief Revenue Officer)
Justine Cutler (Sr Dir-Performance Mktg)
Karim Baki (Sr Dir-Bus Intelligence)
Jai Vijan (CTO)
Jack Osborn (VP-Partnerships)
Bob Flemma (VP-Legal & Compliance)

First Class Service, Inc.   **(1)**
9355 US 60 W, Lewisport, KY 42351
Tel.: (270) 295-3746
Web Site: http://www.firstclassservices.com
Transport Services
N.A.I.C.S.: 488999
Randy Stroup (Pres & CEO)
Randy Cutrell (VP)

Fox Baseball Holdings, Inc.   **(1)**
10201 W Pico Blvd, Los Angeles, CA 90035
Tel.: (323) 224-1500
Sports Athletes Management Services
N.A.I.C.S.: 711410

Fox Broadcasting Company, LLC **(1)**
10201 W Pico Blvd Bldg 1003220, Los An-
geles, CA 90064-2606
Tel.: (310) 369-1000
Television Broadcasting
N.A.I.C.S.: 516120
Charlie Collier (Chm & CEO)

Subsidiary (Non-US):

Fox Cable Networks, Inc.   **(2)**
Tel.: (310) 369-2362
Television Broadcasting Services
N.A.I.C.S.: 516120

Subsidiary (Non-US):

Big Ten Network, LLC   **(3)**
Tel.: (312) 665-0700
Web Site: http://www.bigtennetwork.com
Television Broadcasting Services
N.A.I.C.S.: 516120

**Fox Latin American Channels (Chile)
Limitada**   **(3)**
Tel.: (56) 27506600
Web Site: http://www.fox.com
Television Broadcasting Services
N.A.I.C.S.: 516120

Fox Corporation—(Continued)

Fox Cable Network Services, LLC (1)
10201 W Pico Blvd, Los Angeles, CA 90035
Tel.: (310) 369-7069
Cable & Pay Television Services
N.A.I.C.S.: 516210

Fox Crime Medya Hizmetleri Anonim Sirketi (1)
Kazlicesme Mah Kennedy Cad No 44,
34020, Istanbul, Turkiye
Tel.: (90) 212 414 9000
Web Site: http://www.foxchannels.com.tr
Television Broadcasting Services
N.A.I.C.S.: 516120

Fox International Channels Asia Pacific Limited (1)
13/F One Harbourfont 18 Tak Fung Street,
Hung Hom, Kowloon, China (Hong Kong)
Tel.: (852) 26218888
Television Broadcasting Services
N.A.I.C.S.: 516120

Fox International Channels Chile Ltda. (1)
Avenida Presidente Kennedy 5735 of 1601
Torre Poniente, Las Condes, Santiago,
Chile
Tel.: (56) 227506600
Television Broadcasting Services
N.A.I.C.S.: 516120

Fox International Channels Sweden AB (1)
Drottninggatan 83 2tr, 11160, Stockholm,
Sweden
Tel.: (46) 708730497
Web Site: http://www.foxtv.se
Television Broadcasting Services
N.A.I.C.S.: 516120

Fox International LLC (1)
200 Ottawa Ave NW Ste 800, Grand Rapids, MI 49503
Tel.: (616) 774-2640
Web Site: https://www.foxmotorsports.com
Automotive Parts & Accessory Distr
N.A.I.C.S.: 441330

Fox Music, Inc. (1)
4248 Dorchester Rd, North Charleston, SC 29405
Tel.: (843) 740-7200
Web Site: https://www.foxmusichouse.com
Musical Instrument & Supplies Stores
N.A.I.C.S.: 459140

Fox Net, Inc. (1)
92 Erb Street East, Waterloo, N2J 1L9, ON,
Canada
Tel.: (519) 886-8895
Web Site: http://www.foxnetsolutions.com
Convention & Show Services
N.A.I.C.S.: 561920
Bill Fox *(Founder & CEO)*

Fox Networks Group Asia Pacific Limited (1)
13/F One Harbourfont 18 Tak Fung Street,
Hung Hom, Kowloon, China (Hong Kong)
Tel.: (852) 26218888
Web Site: http://www.natgeotv.com
Discovery Channel Services
N.A.I.C.S.: 516120

Fox Networks Group Norway AS (1)
Karenslyst Alle 2, 0278, Oslo, Norway
Tel.: (47) 99540296
Web Site: http://www.foxtv.no
Television Broadcasting Services
N.A.I.C.S.: 516120

Fox Networks Group Poland Sp.zo.o. (1)
ul Prosta 68, 00-838, Warsaw, Poland
Tel.: (48) 223782782
Web Site: http://www.foxtv.pl
Television Broadcasting Services
N.A.I.C.S.: 516120

Fox Networks Group, LLC (1)
10201 W Pico Blvd, Los Angeles, CA 90035
Tel.: (310) 369-1000
Television Broadcasting Services
N.A.I.C.S.: 516120

Fox News Network, LLC (1)

1211 Avenue of the Americas, New York,
NY 10036
Tel.: (212) 301-3000
Web Site: https://www.foxnews.com
Cable News Network Operator
N.A.I.C.S.: 516120
Keith Rupert Murdoch *(Exec Chm)*
Jay Wallace *(Pres & Exec Editor)*
Kevin Lord *(Exec VP-HR)*
Suzanne Scott *(CEO)*
Meade Cooper *(Exec VP-Primetime Programming)*
John Finley *(Exec VP-Nation & Dev)*
Lauren Petterson *(Pres-FOX Bus)*
Irena Briganti *(Sr Exec VP-Corp Comm)*
Jason Ehrich *(Exec VP-Audience Dev & Strategic Partnerships)*
Jason Klarman *(Exec VP-Mktg)*
Jeff Collins *(Exec VP-Adv Sls)*
John Fiedler *(Exec VP-Digital Product & Tech-News Media)*
Warren Vandeveer *(Exec VP-Technical Ops & Engrg)*
Porter Berry *(VP & Editor-In-Chief-FOX News Digital)*
Joe Dorrego *(COO, CFO & Exec VP)*
Sharri Berg *(Exec VP-News Ops)*

Fox Production Services Pty Limited (1)
38 Driver Avenue Building 16, Moore Park,
Sydney, 2021, Australia
Tel.: (61) 293834200
Web Site:
http://www.foxstudiosaustralia.com
Motion Picture & Video Production Services
N.A.I.C.S.: 512110
Lynda Carruthers *(Head-Production Svcs)*

Fox Services, Inc. (1)
1506 Ferguson Ln Ste 102, Austin, TX 78754
Tel.: (512) 488-1120
Web Site: https://www.foxservice.com
Recycled Concrete Product Mfr
N.A.I.C.S.: 327390
James Bagby *(Gen Mgr)*

Fox Sports Digital Media, Inc. (1)
10201 W Pico Blvd, Los Angeles, CA 90064
Tel.: (310) 369-1000
Web Site: http://www.foxsports.com
Online Site Operator
N.A.I.C.S.: 541519

Fox Sports Net Ohio, LLC (1)
9200 S Hills Blvd Ste 200, Broadview
Heights, OH 44147
Tel.: (440) 746-8000
Web Site: http://www.foxsports.com
Television Broadcasting Services
N.A.I.C.S.: 516120

Fox Stations Sales, Inc. (1)
1211 Ave of the Americas, New York, NY 10036
Tel.: (212) 852-7000
Television & Radio Time Sales
N.A.I.C.S.: 541840

Fox Studio Lot LLC (1)
10201 W Pico Blvd, Los Angeles, CA 90064
Tel.: (310) 369-1000
Web Site: https://www.foxstudiolot.com
Film & Video Production Services
N.A.I.C.S.: 512120

Fox Studios Australia Pty Limited (1)
Building 16 38 Driver Avenue, Moore Park,
Sydney, 2021, NSW, Australia
Tel.: (61) 293834200
Web Site: https://disneystudiosaustralia.com
Studio Leasing Services
N.A.I.C.S.: 532490
Lynda Carruthers *(Head-Production Svcs)*
Jim Keating *(Head-Lighting)*

Fox Television Stations, LLC (1)
1211 Ave of the Americas, New York, NY 10036
Tel.: (212) 852-7000
Web Site: http://www.foxcorporation.com
Holding Company; Television Broadcasting Stations
N.A.I.C.S.: 551112
Erica Keane *(Sr VP-Comm)*

Subsidiary (Domestic):

KCOP Television, LLC (2)

1999 S Bundy Dr, Los Angeles, CA 90025
Tel.: (310) 584-2000
Web Site: https://www.foxla.com
Television Broadcasting Station
Bill Lamb *(VP & Gen Mgr)*

Unit (Domestic):

KTTV (3)
1999 S Bundy Dr, Los Angeles, CA 90025-5203
Tel.: (310) 584-2000
Web Site: http://www.myfoxla.com
Television Broadcasting Station
N.A.I.C.S.: 516120
Jill Brow-Weller *(VP-Programming & Res)*

Unit (Domestic):

KDFW-TV (2)
400 N Griffin St, Dallas, TX 75202-1901
Tel.: (214) 720-3119
Web Site: http://www.fox4news.com
Television Broadcasting Station
N.A.I.C.S.: 516120
Laurie Henderson *(Mgr-Programming)*

Subsidiary (Domestic):

KMSP-TV (2)
11358 Viking Dr, Eden Prairie, MN 55344-7238
Tel.: (952) 944-9999
Web Site: https://www.fox9.com
Television Broadcasting Station
N.A.I.C.S.: 516120
Bill Greep *(VP-Engrg)*

Unit (Domestic):

KRIV-TV (2)
4261 Southwest Fwy, Houston, TX 77027
Tel.: (713) 599-0827
Web Site: http://www.fox26houston.com
Television Broadcasting Station
N.A.I.C.S.: 516120
Ralph Rendon *(VP-Creative Svcs & Programming)*
Mark Berman *(Dir-Sports)*

KTBC-TV (2)
119 E 10th St, Austin, TX 78701-2419
Tel.: (512) 495-7701
Web Site: http://www.fox7austin.com
Television Broadcasting Station
N.A.I.C.S.: 516120
Scott Moore *(Gen Mgr-Sls)*
Carly Gill *(Sls Mgr-Local)*
David Griffiths *(Sls Mgr-Digital)*
Michael Rusinko *(Natl Sls Mgr)*

Subsidiary (Domestic):

KUTP-TV (2)
511 W Adams St, Phoenix, AZ 85003-1608
Tel.: (602) 957-7995
Web Site: http://www.fox10phoenix.com
Television Broadcasting Station
N.A.I.C.S.: 516120
Alicia Jimenez *(Coord-Community Affairs)*

Unit (Domestic):

WFLD-TV (2)
205 N Michigan Ave, Chicago, IL 60601-5927
Tel.: (312) 565-5532
Web Site: http://www.myfoxchicago.com
Television Broadcasting Station
N.A.I.C.S.: 516120

WNYW-TV (2)
205 E 67th St, New York, NY 10065-6050
Tel.: (212) 452-5500
Web Site: http://www.myfoxny.com
Sales Range: $75-99.9 Million
Television Broadcasting Station
N.A.I.C.S.: 516120

WOFL-TV (2)
35 Skyline Dr, Lake Mary, FL 32746-6202
Tel.: (407) 741-5111
Web Site: http://www.fox35orlando.com
Television Broadcasting Station
N.A.I.C.S.: 516120

WOGX-TV (2)
4727 NW 53rd Ave Ste A, Gainesville, FL 32653
Tel.: (352) 371-0051

Web Site: https://www.wogx.com
Television Broadcasting Station
N.A.I.C.S.: 516120

WTTG-TV (2)
5151 Wisconsin Ave NW, Washington, DC 20016-4124
Tel.: (202) 895-3171
Web Site: http://www.fox5dc.com
Television Broadcasting Station
N.A.I.C.S.: 516120

WTVT-TV (2)
3213 W Kennedy Blvd, Tampa, FL 33609
Tel.: (813) 870-9611
Web Site: http://www.wtvt.com
Television Broadcasting Station
N.A.I.C.S.: 516120
Monique Adams *(Mgr-Digital Sls)*
Joe Powers *(Mgr-Local Sls)*
Renee Swearingen *(Programming Coord)*

WTXF-TV (2)
330 Market St, Philadelphia, PA 19106
Tel.: (215) 982-2929
Web Site: http://www.fox29.com
Television Broadcasting Station
N.A.I.C.S.: 516120
Bruce Pelzer *(Mgr-Local Sls)*
Bjorn Henriques *(Sls Mgr-Digital)*
Tom Sredenschek *(Dir-Sports)*

Subsidiary (Domestic):

WWOR-TV (2)
205 E 67th St, New York, NY 10021
Tel.: (212) 452-5555
Web Site: http://www.my9nj.com
Television Broadcasting Station
N.A.I.C.S.: 516120
Rick Wheeler *(VP-Engrg & Ops)*

FoxTelecolombia, S.A. (1)
Carrera 50 17-77 Puente Aranda, Bogota,
Colombia
Tel.: (57) 6014174200
Web Site: https://tisproductions.com
Motion Picture & Video Production Services
N.A.I.C.S.: 512110

MyNetworkTV, Inc. (1)
2121 Ave of the Stars Ste 700, Los Angeles, CA 90067
Tel.: (310) 369-1669
Web Site: https://www.mynetworktv.com
Television Network Services
N.A.I.C.S.: 516120

NW Communications of Austin, Inc. (1)
119 E 10th St, Austin, TX 78701
Tel.: (512) 476-7777
Web Site: https://www.fox7austin.com
Television Broadcasting Services
N.A.I.C.S.: 516120
Marisa Hamvay *(Program Dir)*

NW Communications of Texas, Inc. (1)
400 N Griffin St, Dallas, TX 75202
Tel.: (214) 720-3391
Web Site: https://www.fox4news.com
Television Broadcasting Services
N.A.I.C.S.: 516120
ILaurie Henderson *(Programming Mgr)*

New World Communications of Atlanta, Inc. (1)
1551 Briarcliff Rd NE, Atlanta, GA 30306
Tel.: (404) 875-5555
Web Site: https://www.fox5atlanta.com
Television Broadcasting Services
N.A.I.C.S.: 516120
Neil Mazur *(VP-Engrg & Ops)*

New World Communications of Detroit, Inc. (1)
16550 W 9 Mile Rd, Southfield, MI 48037-2000
Tel.: (248) 552-5103
Web Site: https://www.fox2detroit.com
Television Broadcasting Services
N.A.I.C.S.: 516120
Brian Crossley *(VP-Engrg & Ops)*

New World Communications of Tampa, Inc. (1)
3213 W Kennedy Blvd, Tampa, FL 33609-3006
Tel.: (813) 870-9611

Web Site: https://www.fox13news.com
Television Broadcasting Services
N.A.I.C.S.: 516120
Renee Swearingen *(Programming Coord)*
Monique Adams *(Sls Mgr-Digital)*
Joe Powers *(Local Sls Mgr)*

FOX FACTORY HOLDING CORP.
2055 Sugarloaf Cir Ste 300, Duluth, GA 30097
Tel.: (831) 274-6500   DE
Web Site: https://www.ridefox.com
Year Founded: 2007
FOXF—(NASDAQ)
Rev.: $890,554,000
Assets: $1,286,561,000
Liabilities: $567,390,000
Net Worth: $719,171,000
Earnings: $90,674,000
Emp.: 3,000
Fiscal Year-end: 01/01/21
Motor Vehicle Steering & Suspension Components (except Spring) Manufacturing
N.A.I.C.S.: 336330
Michael C. Dennison *(CEO)*
Chris Tutton *(Pres-Specialty Sports Grp)*
Paul Stecher *(CIO)*
Toby D. Merchant *(Chief Legal Officer, Chief Compliance Officer & Sec)*
Jacqueline B. Martin *(Chief Purpose & Inclusion Officer)*
Maggie Torres *(Dir-Acctg Projects)*
Janet Wong *(Interim Chief HR Officer)*
Dennis C. Schemm *(CFO & Pres-Aftermarket Applications Grp)*

Subsidiaries:

Air Ride Technologies, Inc.   (1)
350 S St Charles St, Jasper, IN 47546
Tel.: (812) 481-4787
Web Site: https://www.ridetech.com
Automotive Part Whslr
N.A.I.C.S.: 441330

Fox Factory GmbH   (1)
Gewerbepark 6, 66989, Hohfroschen, Germany
Tel.: (49) 6334923040
Web Site: https://www.foxracingshox.de
Automotive Parts & Accessory Mfr
N.A.I.C.S.: 336330
Oliver Ernst *(Mng Dir)*

Marucci Sports, LLC   (1)
5818 McCann Dr, Baton Rouge, LA 70809
Tel.: (225) 291-2552
Web Site: https://www.maruccisports.com
Sports Equipment & Apparel Designer & Mfr
N.A.I.C.S.: 339920
James A. Burke *(Chm)*
Kurt Ainsworth *(CEO)*

Subsidiary (Domestic):

Lizard Skins, LLC   (2)
885 S Auto Mall Dr Ste C, American Fork, UT 84003
Tel.: (801) 785-7546
Web Site: http://www.lizardskins.com
Rev.: $7,380,000
Emp.: 12
Sporting Goods Retailer
N.A.I.C.S.: 459110
Brian Fruit *(Pres & CEO)*

RFE Holding (Canada) Corp.   (1)
8333 Eastlake Dr 108, Burnaby, V5A 4W2, BC, Canada
Tel.: (604) 415-2350
Motor Vehicle Services
N.A.I.C.S.: 488410

Rocky Ridge Trucks, Inc.   (1)
259 Westclock Ext, Franklin Springs, GA 30639
Tel.: (205) 655-1063
Web Site: https://www.rockyridgetrucks.com
Truck Dealer Services
N.A.I.C.S.: 441110

SCA Performance, Inc.   (1)

7769 Gadsden Hwy, Trussville, AL 35173
Tel.: (205) 655-1063
Web Site:
    https://www.blackwidowtrucks.com
Truck Dealer Services
N.A.I.C.S.: 441110

ST USA Holding Corp.   (1)
10391 Spring Arbor Rd, Spring Arbor, MI 49283-9621
Tel.: (517) 524-7121
Web Site: https://blog.sporttruckusainc.com
Motor Vehicle Steering & Suspension Components Mfr
N.A.I.C.S.: 336330

Sport Truck USA, Inc.   (1)
491 W Garfield Ave, Coldwater, MI 49036
Tel.: (517) 278-7144
Web Site: https://www.sporttruckusainc.com
Sales Range: $25-49.9 Million
Emp.: 30
Lifted Suspension & Sport Utility Vehicle Products Distr
N.A.I.C.S.: 423120

FOXO TECHNOLOGIES INC.
220 S 6th St Ste 1200, Minneapolis, MN 55402
Tel.: (612) 562-9447   DE
Web Site:
    https://foxotechnologies.com
FOXO—(NYSEAMEX)
Rev.: $145,000
Assets: $725,000
Liabilities: $14,825,000
Net Worth: ($14,100,000)
Earnings: ($26,451,000)
Emp.: 2
Fiscal Year-end: 12/31/23
Resaerch & Developement in Biotechnology
N.A.I.C.S.: 541714
Martin Ward *(CFO)*
Mark White *(CEO)*

FOXWAYNE ENTERPRISES ACQUISITION CORP.
1 Rockefeller Plz Ste 1039, New York, NY 10020
Tel.: (917) 284-8938   DE
Year Founded: 2020
FOXW—(NASDAQ)
Rev.: $5,426
Assets: $58,145,787
Liabilities: $65,035,352
Net Worth: ($6,889,565)
Earnings: ($1,045,983)
Emp.: 1
Fiscal Year-end: 12/31/21
Investment Services
N.A.I.C.S.: 523999
Robb Knie *(Chm, CEO & CFO)*

FOY-JOHNSTON INC.
7380 S Eastern Ave Ste 124, Las Vegas, NV 89123
Tel.: (917) 668-8325   DE
Year Founded: 2008
FOYJ—(OTCIQ)
Paint & Varnish Product Mfr
N.A.I.C.S.: 325510
Brian Gallant *(Pres & Sec)*
Mathew L. Richards *(Chm & CEO)*

FRAGRANCENET.COM, INC.
900 Grand Blvd, Deer Park, NY 11729-5745
Tel.: (631) 582-5204   DE
Web Site:
    http://www.fragrancenet.com
Year Founded: 1997
FGNT—(OTCIQ)
Online Fragrance Distr
N.A.I.C.S.: 456120

FRANCISCO INDUSTRIES, INC.
469 Morris Ave, Miami, FL 33256

Tel.: (908) 277-4200   NJ
FRAZ—(OTCIQ)
Food Crop Services
N.A.I.C.S.: 111419
Carlos Zarraluqui *(Pres)*

FRANKLIN BSP LENDING CORPORATION
9 W 57th St 49th Fl Ste 4920, New York, NY 10019
Tel.: (212) 588-6770   MD
Web Site: https://fbccbdc.com
Year Founded: 2010
BDVC—(NASDAQ)
Rev.: $276,411,000
Assets: $2,979,878,000
Liabilities: $1,314,421,000
Net Worth: $1,665,457,000
Earnings: $125,096,000
Fiscal Year-end: 12/31/22
Financial Investment Services
N.A.I.C.S.: 523940
Richard J. Byrne *(Chm & CEO)*
Blair Faulstich *(Pres)*
Nina Baryski *(CFO & Treas)*
Mike Frick *(Sec)*

FRANKLIN COVEY COMPANY
2200 W Parkway Blvd, Salt Lake City, UT 84119-2331
Tel.: (801) 817-1776   UT
Web Site:
    https://www.franklincovey.com
Year Founded: 1983
FC—(NYSE)
Rev.: $287,233,000
Assets: $261,539,000
Liabilities: $95,269,000
Net Worth: $166,270,000
Earnings: $23,402,000
Emp.: 1,084
Fiscal Year-end: 08/31/24
Training, Productivity Tools & Performance Solutions
N.A.I.C.S.: 541611
Robert A. Whitman *(Chm)*
Michael Sean Merrill Covey *(Pres-Education Div)*
Colleen Dom *(COO & Exec VP-Operations)*
Jennifer Colosimo *(Pres, CEO, Chief Comml Officer, Chief HR Officer, Sr VP, Sr VP & Sr VP)*
Stephen D. Young *(CFO, Sec & Exec VP-Finance)*
Adam Merrill *(Exec VP-Market & Customer Intelligence)*

Subsidiaries:

Franklin Covey   (1)
2200 W Pkwy Blvd, West Valley City, UT 84119-2331
Tel.: (801) 817-1776
Web Site: http://www.franklincovey.com
Sales Range: $75-99.9 Million
Emp.: 500
Business Services
N.A.I.C.S.: 513199

Franklin Covey (Shenzhen) Ltd.   (1)
Room D16 22th Floor Dinghe Building the Intersection of Fuhua, 3 Road and Jintian Road Futian District, Shenzhen, 518000, China
Tel.: (86) 75523373806
Management Consulting Services
N.A.I.C.S.: 541618

Franklin Covey Brasil Ltda.   (1)
Rua Florida 1568, Moncao City, Sao Paulo, 04565-001, Brazil
Tel.: (55) 1151054400
Web Site: http://www.franklincovey.com.br
Business Services
N.A.I.C.S.: 561499

Franklin Covey Canada, Ltd.   (1)
2200 W Pkwy Blvd, Salt Lake City, UT 84119
Tel.: (801) 817-1776

Web Site: http://www.franklincovey.ca
Business Consulting & Training Services
N.A.I.C.S.: 561499

Franklin Covey Catalog Sales Inc.   (1)
2200 W Pkwy Blvd, Salt Lake City, UT 84119-2331
Tel.: (801) 817-1776
Web Site: http://www.franlincovery.com
Sales Range: $100-124.9 Million
Emp.: 300
Catalog Sales
N.A.I.C.S.: 513199
Robert A. Whitman *(Chm, Pres & CEO)*

Franklin Covey Client Sales, Inc.   (1)
2200 W Pkwy Blvd, Salt Lake City, UT 84119-2331
Tel.: (801) 817-1776
Web Site: http://www.franklincovery.com
Rev.: $76,000,000
Emp.: 250
Sales Services
N.A.I.C.S.: 541612
Robert A. Whitman *(Chm, Pres & CEO)*

Franklin Covey Europe, Ltd.   (1)
Blenheim Court 19 George Street, Banbury, OX16 5BH, Oxfordshire, United Kingdom
Tel.: (44) 1295274100
Web Site: http://www.franklincovey.co.uk
Sales Range: $10-24.9 Million
Emp.: 40
Business Services
N.A.I.C.S.: 561499
Curtis A. Bateman *(Gen Mgr)*

Franklin Covey France SARL   (1)
233 rue du Faubourg Saint Honore 9 Villa Wagram, 75008, Paris, France
Tel.: (33) 155009208
Sales Range: $100-124.9 Million
Business Services
N.A.I.C.S.: 561499

Franklin Covey Germany   (1)
Friedenheimer Brucke 20, 80639, Munich, Germany
Tel.: (49) 894521480
Web Site: http://www.franklincovey.de
Sales Range: $10-24.9 Million
Emp.: 15
Business Services
N.A.I.C.S.: 561499

Franklin Covey Japan Co. Ltd.   (1)
7th Floor of Sugar Refinery Hall 5-7 Sanbancho, Chiyoda-ku, Tokyo, 102-0075, Japan
Tel.: (81) 332377711
Web Site: http://www.franklincovey.co.jp
Sales Range: $100-124.9 Million
Emp.: 44
Business Services
N.A.I.C.S.: 561499

Franklin Covey Netherlands BV   (1)
Daam Focke Malaan 10, Amersfoort, 3818 KG, Netherlands
Tel.: (31) 334530627
Web Site: http://www.franklincovey.nl
Sales Range: $1-9.9 Million
Emp.: 10
Business Services
N.A.I.C.S.: 561499

Franklin Covey Printing, Inc.   (1)
2200 W Pkwy Blvd, Salt Lake City, UT 84119
Tel.: (801) 817-1776
Web Site: http://www.franklincovey.com
Sales Range: $100-124.9 Million
Emp.: 300
Printing Services
N.A.I.C.S.: 513199
Robert A. Whitman *(Pres)*

Franklin Covey Product Sales, Inc.   (1)
2200 W Pkwy Blvd, Salt Lake City, UT 84119
Tel.: (801) 817-1776
Web Site: http://www.franklincovey.com
Sales Range: $100-124.9 Million
Emp.: 300
Sales Services
N.A.I.C.S.: 513199

Franklin Covey Company—(Continued)

Robert A. Whitman *(Chm)*

Franklin Covey Proprietary Limited (1)
Level 1 139 Coronation Dr, Milton, 4064, QLD, Australia
Tel.: (61) 733189700
Web Site: http://www.franklincovey.com.au
Sales Range: $1-9.9 Million
Emp.: 10
Business Services
N.A.I.C.S.: 561499

Franklin Covey Travel, Inc. (1)
2200 W Pkwy Blvd, Salt Lake City, UT 84119-2331
Tel.: (801) 817-1776
Sales Range: $100-124.9 Million
Emp.: 3
Travel Services
N.A.I.C.S.: 513199
James Thalman *(Gen Mgr)*

Franklin Covey de Mexico, S. de R.L. de C.V. (1)
Guillermo Gonzalez Camarena 1450 Piso 7 Centro de Ciudad Sta Fe, 01210, Mexico, Mexico
Tel.: (52) 5552796760
Business Services
N.A.I.C.S.: 561499

Franklin Development Corp. (1)
2200 W Parkway Blvd, Salt Lake City, UT 84119
Tel.: (801) 817-1776
Web Site: http://www.franklincovey.com
Sales Range: $75-99.9 Million
Emp.: 250
Business Development Services
N.A.I.C.S.: 513199

Ninety Five 5 LLC (1)
1767 Lakewood Ranch Blvd Ste 209, Bradenton, FL 34211
Tel.: (484) 323-2413
Web Site: http://www.nf5.com
Sales Range: $10-24.9 Million
Emp.: 36
Business Consulting & Sales Training Courses
N.A.I.C.S.: 541618

FRANKLIN CREDIT MANAGEMENT CORPORATION

101 Hudson St 24th Fl, Jersey City, NJ 07302
Tel.: (201) 604-1800   DE
Web Site:
    https://www.franklincredit.com
Year Founded: 1988
FCRM—(NASDAQ)
Emp.: 40
Consumer Mortgage Lender, Loan Recovery & Collection Services
N.A.I.C.S.: 522310
Glenn Murphy *(COO & Sr VP-Asset Recovery & REO)*
Bruce Grabau *(VP-Information Technology)*
Thomas J. Axon *(Chm)*

FRANKLIN ELECTRIC CO., INC.

9255 Coverdale Rd, Fort Wayne, IN 46809
Tel.: (260) 824-2900   IN
Web Site: https://www.franklin-electric.com
Year Founded: 1944
FELE—(NASDAQ)
Rev.: $2,043,711,000
Assets: $1,694,201,000
Liabilities: $624,067,000
Net Worth: $1,070,134,000
Earnings: $187,332,000
Emp.: 6,500
Fiscal Year-end: 12/31/22
Electric Motors, Drives, Controls, Submersible Water & Fueling Systems Mfr
N.A.I.C.S.: 336320

Jeffery L. Taylor *(CFO & VP)*
Gregg C. Sengstack *(Exec Chm)*
Jonathan M. Grandon *(Chief Admin Officer, Gen Counsel, Sec & VP)*
Greg Levine *(Pres-Global Water & VP)*
Jay J. Walsh *(Pres-Fueling Sys & VP)*
Brent L. Spikes *(VP)*
Kenneth Keene *(VP)*
Joseph A. Ruzynski *(CEO)*

Subsidiaries:

2M Company Inc. (1)
1215 Cordova St, Billings, MT 59101
Tel.: (406) 245-3008
Web Site: http://www.2mco.com
Emp.: 150
Pumps & Pumping Equipment Whslr
N.A.I.C.S.: 423830
Nick Kline *(Reg Mgr)*
David Hatch *(Branch Mgr)*

Action Manufacturing & Supply, Inc. (1)
2602 NE 9th Ave, Cape Coral, FL 33909
Tel.: (239) 574-3443
Web Site: http://www.actioncraft.com
Sales Range: $1-9.9 Million
Emp.: 18
Commercial & Service Industry Machinery Mfr
N.A.I.C.S.: 333310

Bombas Leao SA (1)
Via Sebastiao Fioreze 400 Distrito Industrial, Monte Azul Paulista, Sao Paulo, 14730-000, Brazil
Tel.: (55) 1733619101
Web Site: https://www.leao.com.br
Pumping Equipment Mfr
N.A.I.C.S.: 423830

Coverco S.r.l. (1)
Via Magnadola 29, Motta Di Livenza, Treviso, 31045, Italy
Tel.: (39) 04227616
Web Site: http://www.coverco.com
Sales Range: $10-24.9 Million
Emp.: 7
Electrical Apparatus & Equipment Distr
N.A.I.C.S.: 423610

Franklin Control Systems, Inc. (1)
22985 NW Evergreen Pkwy, Hillsboro, OR 97124
Tel.: (503) 646-2500
Web Site: http://www.franklin-controls.com
Emp.: 100
Control System Mfr & Distr
N.A.I.C.S.: 334513
Kate Johnson *(Acct Mgr-OEM)*
Adam Anderson *(Reg Mgr-Sls)*
Angelo Quesada *(Reg Mgr-Sls)*

Franklin Electric (Botswana) Pty Ltd (1)
Plot 42 Gaborone International Commerce Park, Gaborone, Botswana
Tel.: (267) 3974926
Web Site: http://www.franklin-electric.com
Sales Range: $25-49.9 Million
Emp.: 52
Electrical Apparatus & Equipment Distr
N.A.I.C.S.: 423610

Franklin Electric (SEA) Pty. Ltd. (1)
17 Changi Business Central 1 06-05 Honeywell Building, Singapore, 486073, Singapore
Tel.: (65) 67896865
Web Site: https://www.franklinwatersea.com
Sales Range: $10-24.9 Million
Emp.: 4
Pumping Equipment Mfr
N.A.I.C.S.: 333914

Franklin Electric (South Africa) Pty. Ltd. (1)
13 Engwena Road, Sebenza, Edenvale, 1610, South Africa
Tel.: (27) 117236500
Web Site: https://franklin-electric.co.za
Emp.: 200
Electrical Apparatus & Equipment Distr
N.A.I.C.S.: 423610

Franklin Electric (Suzhou) Co., Ltd. (1)

No 200 Su Hong Zhong Road Suzhou Industrial Park, Export Processing Zone, Suzhou, 215021, Jiangsu, China
Tel.: (86) 51262588123
Emp.: 11
Pumping Equipment Mfr
N.A.I.C.S.: 333914

Franklin Electric Canada, Inc. (1)
61 Parr Blvd Unit 7, Bolton, L7E 4E3, ON, Canada
Tel.: (905) 857-2882
Electrical Apparatus & Equipment Distr
N.A.I.C.S.: 423610

Franklin Electric Colombia SAS (1)
Autopista Medellin Km 2 7 Costado Sur Via Siberia - Bogota, Parque Industrial Los Nogales Bodega No 11 Cota, Cundinamarca, Colombia
Tel.: (57) 18237630
Pumping Equipment Mfr
N.A.I.C.S.: 423830

Franklin Electric Europa, GmbH (1)
Rudolf-Diesel-Strasse 20, 54516, Wittlich, Germany   (100%)
Tel.: (49) 6 571 1050
Web Site: https://franklinwater.eu
Sales Range: $50-74.9 Million
Emp.: 100
Motor & Generator Mfr
N.A.I.C.S.: 335312
Michael Fuka *(Engr-Field Svc)*

Franklin Electric Germany Holding GmbH (1)
Rudolf-Diesel-Strasse 20, 54516, Wittlich, Germany
Tel.: (49) 65711050
Sales Range: $25-49.9 Million
Emp.: 15
Pumping Equipment Mfr
N.A.I.C.S.: 333914

Franklin Electric Holding B.V. (1)
Herikerbergweg 238 Luna ArenA, 1101 CM, Amsterdam, Netherlands
Tel.: (31) 205405800
Electrical Apparatus & Equipment Distr
N.A.I.C.S.: 423610

Franklin Electric India Private Ltd. (1)
DBS-206 1st Floor World Trade Tower Barakhamba Avenue, Connaught Place, New Delhi, 110 001, India
Tel.: (91) 1143084697
Electrical Apparatus & Equipment Distr
N.A.I.C.S.: 423610
Anil Keswani *(Mgr)*

Franklin Electric Industria de Motobombas SA (1)
Rua Hans Dieter Schmidt, 1501 Distrito Industrial, Joinville, 89219-504, Santa Catarina, Brazil
Tel.: (55) 4732045000
Web Site: https://schneider.ind.br
Motor Pump Mfr
N.A.I.C.S.: 333996

Franklin Electric spol s.r.o. (1)
Hviezdoslavova 1271/1 Slatina, Brno, 627 00, Czech Republic   (100%)
Tel.: (420) 548424711
Web Site: http://www.franklin-electric.com
Electrical Apparatus & Equipment Distr
N.A.I.C.S.: 423610

Franklin Fueling Sistemas de Combustiveis Ltda (1)
Rua Hans Dieter Schmidt 1 501 Zona Industrial Norte, Joinville, Santa Catarina, 89219-504, Brazil
Tel.: (55) 8007100300
Web Site: http://www.ffsbrasil.com
Sales Range: $10-24.9 Million
Emp.: 5
Electrical Apparatus & Equipment Distr
N.A.I.C.S.: 423610
Moacir Arruda *(Gen Mgr)*

Franklin Fueling Systems (1)
34 Spring Hill Rd, Saco, ME 04072   (100%)
Tel.: (207) 283-0156
Web Site: http://www.franklinfueling.com
Sales Range: $50-74.9 Million
Emp.: 63
Measuring & Pumping Equipment Mfr

N.A.I.C.S.: 333914

Franklin Fueling Systems Australia Pty. Ltd. (1)
21 Aristoc Road, PO Box 47, Glen Waverley, 3150, VIC, Australia
Tel.: (61) 395501874
Web Site: http://www.franklinfueling.com
Emp.: 3
Electrical Apparatus & Equipment Distr
N.A.I.C.S.: 423610
Jim Craig *(Mng Dir)*

Franklin Fueling Systems France SARL (1)
129 Avenida du General De Gaulle Vir, Chatillon, 91170, France
Tel.: (33) 169214141
Sales Range: $10-24.9 Million
Emp.: 7
Electrical Apparatus & Equipment Distr
N.A.I.C.S.: 423610

GridSense Inc. (1)
5757 W Century Blvd Ste 815 Mail Stop 91, Los Angeles, CA 90045
Tel.: (310) 414-9830
Electric Utility Grid Monitoring Services
N.A.I.C.S.: 926130

Headwater Companies, LLC (1)
5265 S Rio Grande St Ste 201, Littleton, CO 80120
Tel.: (303) 305-5935
Web Site: https://www.headwaterco.com
Water Distribution Services
N.A.I.C.S.: 221310
Darren Mathis *(CFO)*

Subsidiary (Domestic):

Drillers Service, LLC (2)
1792 Highland Ave NE, Hickory, NC 28601
Web Site: https://www.dsidsi.com
Industrial Machinery & Equipment Mfr & Distr
N.A.I.C.S.: 423830

Milan Supply Company (2)
7125 E Pickard Rd, Mount Pleasant, MI 48804-0309
Tel.: (989) 773-5933
Web Site: http://www.milansupply.com
Sales Range: $10-24.9 Million
Emp.: 50
Water Well, Environmental, Directional Drill, Wastewater & Related Products Whslr
N.A.I.C.S.: 423810
Chad Philo *(Gen Mgr)*
Keegan Pifer *(Asst Mgr)*

Impo Motor Pompa Sanayi ve Ticaret A.S. (1)
Inonu Mah 166 Sokak No 3/1, Ayrancilar, 35870, Izmir, Turkiye
Tel.: (90) 2328548585
Web Site: https://www.impo.com.tr
Emp.: 400
Submersible Pump & Motor Mfr
N.A.I.C.S.: 333914

Industrias Rotor Pump S.A. (1)
Tacuari 537 Ciudad Autonoma de, Buenos Aires, 1071, Argentina
Tel.: (54) 43346410
Web Site: https://www.rotorpump.com
Electrical Pump Mfr
N.A.I.C.S.: 333914

Motori Sommersi Riavvolgibili S.r.l. (1)
Location Peniqola 1, Cedeqolo, 25051, Brescia, Italy
Tel.: (39) 0364625411
Web Site: http://www.franklin-electric.de
Sales Range: $25-49.9 Million
Emp.: 55
Electrical Apparatus & Equipment Distr
N.A.I.C.S.: 423610

Pioneer Pump Holdings Pty. (1)
Unit 1 67 Proximity Drive, Sunshine West, Melbourne, 3020, VIC, Australia
Tel.: (61) 399881650
Web Site: https://pioneerpump.com
Electrical Apparatus & Equipment Distr
N.A.I.C.S.: 423610

Pioneer Pump Holdings, Inc. (1)
310 S Sequoia Pkwy, Canby, OR 97013

Tel.: (503) 266-4115
Holding Company
N.A.I.C.S.: 551112
Shawn Kelly *(Mgr-Sls-South Central)*
Josh Standridge *(VP-Sls)*

Pioneer Pump Ltd.   **(1)**
Woolpit Rd, Suffolk, Rattlesden, IP30 0RZ,
Suffolk, United Kingdom
Tel.: (44) 1449736777
Web Site: http://www.pioneerpump.com
Pumps Mfr
N.A.I.C.S.: 333914

Pioneer Pump Pty. Ltd.   **(1)**
13 Engwena St Sebenza, Edenvale, 1609,
Gauteng, South Africa
Tel.: (27) 117236500
Web Site: http://www.pioneerpump.com
Emp.: 8
Centrifugal Pump Mfr
N.A.I.C.S.: 333914

Pioneer Pump Solutions Ltd.   **(1)**
21 Boss Hall Road, Ipswich, IP1 5BN,
United Kingdom
Tel.: (44) 1473553970
Web Site: https://www.pioneer-hire.co.uk
Electrical Apparatus & Equipment Distr
N.A.I.C.S.: 423610

Puronics, Inc.   **(1)**
5775 Las Positas Rd, Livermore, CA 94551
Tel.: (844) 787-6642
Web Site: http://www.puronics.com
Water Treatment Equipment Mfr
N.A.I.C.S.: 488390
Arnie D. Harmon *(VP-Sls & Mktg)*
Scott Batiste *(CEO)*
Colin Riggs *(Asst Mgr-Mfg)*

Valley Farms Supply, Inc.   **(1)**
16713 Industrial Pkwy, Lansing, MI 48906-
9176
Web Site:
    https://www.valleyfarmssupply.com
Whslr & Supplier of Water Well Products
N.A.I.C.S.: 423810

Vertical S.p.A.   **(1)**
Via Asolo 7, 36031, Dueville, Italy
Tel.: (39) 0444360366
Submersible Pump Mfr
N.A.I.C.S.: 333914

Wadcorpp Indian Private Limited   **(1)**
C-10/1 Ranjan Gaon Industrial Estate,
Pune, 412220, Maharashtra, India
Tel.: (91) 2222022106
Business Management Services
N.A.I.C.S.: 561110
Vilas Pevekar *(Mgr-Supply Chain)*

Western Hydro LLC   **(1)**
2034 Research Dr, Livermore, CA 94550
Tel.: (510) 783-9166
Web Site: http://www.westernhydro.com
Motor Mfr
N.A.I.C.S.: 335312

FRANKLIN FINANCIAL SER-VICES CORPORATION
1500 Nitterhouse Dr, Chambersburg,
PA 17201-0819
Tel.: (717) 264-6116   **PA**
Web Site: https://www.franklinfin.com
Year Founded: 1983
FRAF—(NASDAQ)
Rev.: $71,699,000
Assets: $1,699,579,000
Liabilities: $1,585,382,000
Net Worth: $114,197,000
Earnings: $14,938,000
Emp.: 298
Fiscal Year-end: 12/31/22
Bank Holding Company
N.A.I.C.S.: 551111
Timothy G. Henry *(Pres & CEO)*
G. Warren Elliott *(Chm)*
Allan E. Jennings Jr. *(Vice Chm)*

Subsidiaries:

Farmers & Merchants Trust
Chambersburg   **(1)**
20 S Main St, Chambersburg, PA 17201
Tel.: (717) 264-6116

Web Site: https://www.fmtrustonline.com
Sales Range: $25-49.9 Million
Emp.: 150
State Commercial Banks
N.A.I.C.S.: 522110
Timothy G. Henry *(Pres & CEO)*

FRANKLIN LIMITED DURA-TION INCOME TRUST
1 Franklin Pkwy, San Mateo, CA
94403-1906
Tel.: (650) 312-2000   **FL**
FTF—(NYSEAMEX)
Investment Management Service
N.A.I.C.S.: 525990

FRANKLIN RESOURCES, INC.
1 Franklin Pkwy, San Mateo, CA
94403-1906
Tel.: (650) 312-2000   **NY**
Web Site:
    https://www.franklinresources.com
Year Founded: 1947
BEN—(NYSE)
Rev.: $8,478,000,000
Assets: $32,464,500,000
Liabilities: $17,899,700,000
Net Worth: $14,564,800,000
Earnings: $607,900,000
Emp.: 10,200
Fiscal Year-end: 09/30/24
Holding Company; Investment Man-
agement Services
N.A.I.C.S.: 551112
Jennifer M. Johnson *(Pres & CEO)*
Gregory Eugene Johnson *(Chm)*
Rupert Harris Johnson Jr. *(Vice Chm)*
Alok Sethi *(Exec VP-Tech & Ops)*
Matthew Nicholls *(CFO, COO & Exec VP)*
Adam B. Spector *(Exec VP-Global Advisory Services)*
Thomas C. Merchant *(Gen Counsel, Sec & Exec VP)*
Terrence J. Murphy *(Exec VP & Head-Public Markets)*

Subsidiaries:

AdvisorEngine Inc.   **(1)**
3651 Trust Dr, Raleigh, NC 27616
Web Site: http://www.advisorengine.com
Banking Services
N.A.I.C.S.: 522110
Craig Ramsey *(COO)*
Carly De Diego *(Chief Admin Officer)*
Raj Madan *(CIO)*
Beth Haddock *(Chief Legal Officer)*

Alcentra NY LLC   **(1)**
200 Park Ave 7th Fl, New York, NY 10166
Tel.: (212) 922-8240
Web Site: http://www.alcentra.com
Emp.: 30
Commercial Banking Services
N.A.I.C.S.: 522110

Division (Domestic):

BNY Mellon-Alcentra Mezzanine
Partners   **(2)**
200 Park Ave 7th Fl, New York, NY 10166
Tel.: (212) 922-8240
Web Site: http://im.bnymellon.com
Investment Services
N.A.I.C.S.: 523999
Branko Krmpotic *(Mng Dir)*

Holding (Domestic):

Response Team 1 LLC   **(3)**
390 Holbrook Dr, Wheeling, IL 60090
Tel.: (888) 877-6766
Web Site: http://www.responseteam1.com
Emergency Recovery, Remediation & Res-
toration Services
N.A.I.C.S.: 562910
John M. Goense *(Chm)*

Subsidiary (Domestic):

Venturi Restoration - Irvine   **(4)**
15520 Rockfield Blvd Ste E-100, Irvine, CA
92618

Tel.: (949) 472-4366
Web Site: http://www.venturirestoration.com
Fire & Water Restoration
N.A.I.C.S.: 562910

Balanced Equity Management Pty.
Limited   **(1)**
Level 19 101 Collins Street, Melbourne,
3000, VIC, Australia
Tel.: (61) 396529400
Web Site: http://www.bem.com.au
Sales Range: $25-49.9 Million
Emp.: 15
Investment Advisory Services
N.A.I.C.S.: 523940

Benefit Street Partners LLC   **(1)**
9 W 57th St Ste 4920, New York, NY 10019
Tel.: (212) 588-6770
Web Site:
    http://www.benefitstreetpartners.com
Debt Investment Management Services
N.A.I.C.S.: 523940
Richard J. Byrne *(Chm, Pres & CEO)*
Michael Comparato *(Mng Dir & Head-Comml Real Estate)*
Allison B. Davi *(Mng Dir)*
Paul J. Salem *(Co-Founder)*
Matthew Winkler *(Mng Dir)*
Thomas Gahan *(CEO)*
David Manlowe *(Sr Mng Dir)*
Michael Paasche *(Sr Mng Dir)*
Jerome Baglien *(Mng Dir, CFO, COO & Portfolio Mgr-Real Estate)*
Kevin Boler *(Mng Dir)*
Michael Comparato *(Mng Dir & Head-Real Estate)*
David Elgart *(Mng Dir)*
Blair Faulstich *(Mng Dir)*
Brian Ford *(Mng Dir)*
James Hadley *(Mng Dir)*
Micah Goodman *(Mng Dir & Gen Counsel-Comml Real Estate Bus)*
Shirley Hambelton *(Mng Dir)*
David Henschke *(Head-Capital Markets)*
Matthew Jacobs *(Mng Dir & Chief Credit Officer-CRE)*
David Klein *(Mng Dir)*
Anant Kumar *(Mng Dir)*
Leon Han *(Mng Dir-Private Debt Grp)*

Affiliate (Domestic):

Benefit Street Partners BDC, Inc.   **(2)**
9 W 57th St 47th Fl, New York, NY 10019
Tel.: (212) 735-3000
Closed-End Investment Fund
N.A.I.C.S.: 525990

Franklin BSP Realty Trust, Inc.   **(2)**
1345 Avenue of the Americas Ste 32A, New
York, NY 10105
Tel.: (212) 588-6770
Web Site: https://www.fbrtreit.com
Rev.: $201,652,000
Assets: $6,203,601,000
Liabilities: $4,625,213,000
Net Worth: $1,578,388,000
Earnings: $14,431,000
Fiscal Year-end: 12/31/2022
Real Estate Investment Services
N.A.I.C.S.: 523999
Richard J. Byrne *(Chm & CEO)*
Michael Comparato *(Pres)*
Brian Buffone *(Mng Dir-Real Estate)*
Aaron Derby *(Mng Dir-Real Estate)*
David Elgart *(Mng Dir-Real Estate)*
Brain Nowakowski *(Mng Dir-Real Estate)*
Samuel Rosen *(Mng Dir-Real Estate)*
Peter Touhill *(Mng Dir-Real Estate)*
Ben Weinberger *(Mng Dir-Real Estate)*
Jacob Breinholt *(Dir-Real Estate)*
Peter Crawley *(Dir-Real Estate)*
Bradley Gladsden *(Dir-Real Estate)*
Robert Tutag *(Dir-Real Estate)*
Rochelle Estoque *(VP-Real Estate)*
Lawrence Margolis *(VP-Real Estate)*
Jared Simon *(VP-Real Estate)*
Christian Stuebe *(VP-Real Estate)*
David Henschke *(Mng Dir)*
Yuksel Dincer *(Mng Dir)*
Lain Gutierrez *(Mng Dir)*
Heidi Kormann *(Mng Dir)*
Conrad Wicker *(Mng Dir)*
Erin Beca *(Dir)*
Lindsey Crabbe *(Dir)*
Dan DeBernardi *(Dir)*
Ana May Melendez *(Dir)*
Christian Mutone *(Dir)*

Syful Nizam *(Dir)*
Daniel Cruz *(VP)*
Michael Della Cava *(VP)*
Sam Fife *(VP)*
Augusta Gahan *(VP)*
Jake Gutner *(VP)*
Alex Hagen *(VP)*
Roberto Jimenez *(VP)*
Edward Laclaustra *(VP)*
Henry Rickbeil *(VP)*

Subsidiary (Domestic):

Capstead Mortgage Corporation   **(3)**
8401 N Central Expy Ste 800, Dallas, TX
75225-4404
Tel.: (214) 874-2323
Web Site: http://www.capstead.com
Rev.: $186,735,000
Assets: $8,405,250,000
Liabilities: $7,495,087,000
Net Worth: $910,163,000
Earnings: ($129,573,000)
Emp.: 15
Fiscal Year-end: 12/31/2020
Real Estate Investment Trust
N.A.I.C.S.: 525990
Bethany L. Lee *(Asst VP)*

Subsidiary (Domestic):

Capstead, Inc.   **(4)**
8401 N Central Expy Ste 800, Dallas, TX
75225
Tel.: (214) 874-2323
Web Site: http://www.capstead.com
Sales Range: $150-199.9 Million
Mortgage Banking Services
N.A.I.C.S.: 522310

Clarion Partners (Deutschland) Eu-
rope GmbH   **(1)**
Taunusanlage 9-10, 60329, Frankfurt, Ger-
many
Tel.: (49) 695050604248
Real Estate Services
N.A.I.C.S.: 531390

Darby Asia Investors (India) Private
Limited   **(1)**
Indiabulls Finance Center Tower 2 13th
Floor Senapati Bapat Marg, Elphinstone,
Mumbai, 400013, India
Tel.: (91) 2267519100
Emp.: 5
Investment Management Service
N.A.I.C.S.: 523940
Deepa Sankarn *(Mng Dir)*

Darby Overseas Investments,
Ltd.   **(1)**
1133 Connecticut Ave NW Ste 400, Wash-
ington, DC 20036
Tel.: (202) 872-0500
Web Site: http://www.darbyoverseas.com
Sales Range: $25-49.9 Million
Emp.: 12
Privater Equity Firm
N.A.I.C.S.: 523999
Richard H. Frank *(Pres & CEO)*
Nicholas F. Brady *(Founder)*

Subsidiary (Non-US):

Franklin Templeton Austria
GmbH   **(2)**
Universitatsring 10 4th Floor, 1010, Vienna,
Austria
Tel.: (43) 1532265531
Web Site: http://www.franklintempleton.at
Sales Range: $25-49.9 Million
Emp.: 7
Privater Equity Firm
N.A.I.C.S.: 523999
Robert D. Graffam *(Sr Mng Dir-Europe)*

F S Capital Group   **(1)**
1800 Gateway Dr, San Mateo, CA 94404
Tel.: (650) 312-2000
Investment Management Service
N.A.I.C.S.: 523940

FTC Investor Services Inc.   **(1)**
350 Seventh Ave SW Ste 3000, Calgary,
T2P 3N9, AB, Canada
Tel.: (866) 204-9458
Web Site: http://www.ftcinvestorservices.ca
Sales Range: $75-99.9 Million
Emp.: 200
Investment Advisory Services

Franklin Resources, Inc.—(Continued)
N.A.I.C.S.: 523940

**Fiduciary Trust (International)
Sarl** (1)
Route De Prt-bois 29 / Case Postale 156,
Geneva, Switzerland
Tel.: (41) 227106070
Investment Management Service
N.A.I.C.S.: 523940

**Fiduciary Trust Company
International** (1)
280 Park Ave, New York, NY 10017-1216
Tel.: (212) 632-3000
Web Site: http://www.ftci.com
Sales Range: $75-99.9 Million
Emp.: 400
Investment Management & Trust Services
N.A.I.C.S.: 522110
Gail E. Cohen (Chm)
John M. Dowd (CEO)
Rebecca Radosevich (Mgr-Corp Comm)
Leslie Gillin Bohner (Chief Fiduciary Officer)

Subsidiary (Domestic):

Athena Capital Advisors LLC (2)
55 Old Bedford Rd Ste 302, Lincoln, MA
01773
Tel.: (781) 274-7812
Web Site: http://www.athenacapital.com
Emp.: 45
Portfolio Management Services
N.A.I.C.S.: 523940
Lisette Cooper (Founder)

Fiduciary International, Inc. (2)
280 Park Ave, New York, NY 10017-2302
Tel.: (212) 632-3000
Web Site: http://www.fiduciarytrust.com
Sales Range: $300-349.9 Million
Emp.: 300
Investment Services
N.A.I.C.S.: 523999
Lawrence A. Sternkopf (Pres & COO)

**Fiduciary Investment Management
International, Inc.** (2)
1133 Connecticut Ave NW Ste 410, Wash-
ington, DC 20036 (100%)
Tel.: (202) 822-2100
Web Site: http://www.fiduciarytrust.com
Sales Range: $50-74.9 Million
Emp.: 8
Investment Services
N.A.I.C.S.: 523999
C. Ware Palmer (Mng Dir-Bus Dev)

Subsidiary (Non-US):

**Fiduciary Trust International
Limited** (2)
78 Cannon St, London, EC4N 6AL, United
Kingdom (100%)
Tel.: (44) 2070738500
Web Site:
http://www.franklintempleton.co.uk
Sales Range: $125-149.9 Million
Emp.: 135
Investment Services
N.A.I.C.S.: 523999

Subsidiary (Domestic):

**Fiduciary Trust International of
California** (2)
444 S Flower St Ste 3200, Los Angeles, CA
90071-2931 (100%)
Tel.: (213) 596-8600
Web Site: http://www.fiduciarytrust.com
Sales Range: $75-99.9 Million
Emp.: 15
Investment Advice & Trust Services
N.A.I.C.S.: 523999
Kate Freeman (Mng Dir)

**Fiduciary Trust International of
Delaware** (2)
4250 Lancaster Pike Ste 210, Wilmington,
DE 19805
Tel.: (302) 429-0910
Web Site: http://www.ftci.com
Sales Range: $50-74.9 Million
Emp.: 4
Investment Services
N.A.I.C.S.: 523999

**Fiduciary Trust International of the
South** (2)

2 Alhambra Plz Ph Ste 1, Coral Gables, FL
33134 (100%)
Tel.: (305) 372-1260
Web Site: http://www.fiduciarytrust.com
Sales Range: $75-99.9 Million
Emp.: 20
Investment Advice & Trust Services
N.A.I.C.S.: 523999
Michael Cabanas (Reg Mng Dir-Coral
Gables & Fort Lauderdale)

**Fiduciary Trust Company of
Canada** (1)
200 King Street West Suite 1500, Toronto,
M5H 3T4, ON, Canada
Tel.: (403) 543-3950
Web Site: http://www.fiduciarytrust.ca
Investment Management Service
N.A.I.C.S.: 523999
Thomas E. Junkin (Sr VP-Personal Trust
Svcs)
Duane W. Green (Pres & CEO)
Manmeet Bhatia (Head-Private Wealth)
Ian Riach (Chief Investment Officer)
Clement Chan (Portfolio Mgr)

Franklin Advisers, Inc. (1)
1 Franklin Pkwy, San Mateo, CA 94403-
1906
Tel.: (650) 312-2000
General Management Consulting Services
N.A.I.C.S.: 541611

Subsidiary (Domestic):

Appvion Operations, Inc. (2)
825 E Wisconsin Ave, Appleton, WI 54912
Tel.: (920) 734-9841
Web Site: http://www.appvion.com
Specialty Paper & Packaging Products Mfr
N.A.I.C.S.: 322220
George Wurtz (Chm & Pres)
Paul Charapata (CEO)
Bob Beckwith (CFO)
Kirt Walker (Chief HR Officer)
Ryan Park (Exec VP)
Guy Leigh (Exec VP)
Beth White (Exec VP)

Franklin Advisory Services, LLC (1)
55 Challenger Rd 5th Fl, Ridgefield Park,
NJ 07660
Tel.: (201) 592-6700
Web Site: http://www.franklintempleton.com
Sales Range: $50-74.9 Million
Emp.: 17
Investment Services
N.A.I.C.S.: 523999

**Franklin Alternative Strategies Advis-
ers, LLC** (1)
1 International Pl 14th Fl, Boston, MA
02110
Tel.: (617) 310-6530
Investment Management Service
N.A.I.C.S.: 523940

Franklin Capital Corporation (1)
47 W 200 S Ste 500, Salt Lake City, UT
84101
Tel.: (801) 238-6770
Investment Advisory Services
N.A.I.C.S.: 523940

**Franklin Investment Advisory Ser-
vices, LLC** (1)
1 Franklin Pkwy 9701, San Mateo, CA
94403-1906
Tel.: (650) 312-3000
Web Site: http://www.fraklinresources.com
General Management Consulting Services
N.A.I.C.S.: 541613

Franklin Mutual Advisers, LLC (1)
101 John F Kennedy Pkwy, Short Hills, NJ
07078-2789
Tel.: (973) 912-2000
Investment Advisory & Management Services
N.A.I.C.S.: 523940

**Franklin Templeton Asset Manage-
ment (India) Private Limited** (1)
Indiabulls Finance Centre Tower 2 13th
Floor Elphinstone Road, Mumbai, 400 013,
Maharashtra, India
Tel.: (91) 2267519100
Web Site:
http://www.franklintempletonindia.com

Sales Range: $50-74.9 Million
Emp.: 7
Investment Advisory Services
N.A.I.C.S.: 523940
Pradeep Rajasekharan (Dir-Corp Comm)
Padmanaban Nair (Asst VP-Corp Comm)

**Franklin Templeton Asset Manage-
ment Mexico, S.A. de C.V.** (1)
Av Paseo de la Reforma 342 piso 8, Colo-
nea Juarez, 06600, Mexico, Mexico
Tel.: (52) 5550020650
Web Site:
http://www.franklintempleton.com.mx
Sales Range: $25-49.9 Million
Emp.: 2
Investment Advisory Services
N.A.I.C.S.: 523940

**Franklin Templeton Bank & Trust,
F.S.B.** (1)
47 W 200 S Ste 200, Salt Lake City, UT
84101-1621
Tel.: (801) 952-3300
Web Site: http://www.ftbank.com
Personal Trust & Retirement Plan Manage-
ment Services
N.A.I.C.S.: 523991
Wendy L. Harrington (Pres & CEO)

**Franklin Templeton Companies,
LLC** (1)
1 Franklin Pkwy Bldg 970, San Mateo, CA
94403-1906
Tel.: (650) 312-2000
Investment Advisory Services
N.A.I.C.S.: 523940
Mark Elliott (Head-Advisory Sls-UK)
Alex Brotherston (Dir-Retail Sls-UK)
Mark Ward (Mgr-Mktg-Nordic discretionary
& Institutional Bus-UK)

Franklin Templeton France S.A. (1)
20 Rue de la Paix, 75002, Paris, France
Tel.: (33) 140738600
Web Site: http://www.franklintempleton.fr
Emp.: 15
Investment Advisory Services
N.A.I.C.S.: 523940

**Franklin Templeton Fund Manage-
ment Limited** (1)
The Adelphi Building 1-11 John Adam
Street, London, WC2N 6HT, United King-
dom
Tel.: (44) 2070738690
Investment Management Service
N.A.I.C.S.: 523940

**Franklin Templeton Institutional,
LLC** (1)
300 SE Second St, Fort Lauderdale, FL
33394-3091
Tel.: (954) 527-7500
Web Site: http://www.franklintempleton.com
Sales Range: $1-4.9 Billion
Emp.: 500
Investment Services
N.A.I.C.S.: 523999

**Franklin Templeton Intenational Ser-
vices S.A.** (1)
88 Rue Albert borschette, 2449, Luxem-
bourg, Luxembourg
Tel.: (352) 466667212
Web Site: http://www.franklintempleton.lu
Sales Range: $125-149.9 Million
Emp.: 80
Investment Services
N.A.I.C.S.: 523999

**Franklin Temploton International Ser-
vices S.a.r.l.** (1)
8A rue Albert Borschette, 1246, Luxem-
bourg, Luxembourg
Tel.: (352) 4666671
Web Site: https://www.franklintempleton.lu
Financial Investment Services
N.A.I.C.S.: 523999

**Franklin Templeton Investimentos
(Brasil) Ltda.** (1)
Av Brigadeiro Faria Lima 3311 - 5th floor,
Sao Paulo, 04538-133, SP, Brazil
Tel.: (55) 1132060000
Web Site:
http://www.franklintempleton.com.br
Emp.: 30
General Management Consulting Services

N.A.I.C.S.: 541611

**Franklin Templeton Investment Man-
agement Limited** (1)
5 Morrison Street, Edinburgh, EH3 8BH,
United Kingdom
Tel.: (44) 01312424000
Web Site:
http://www.franklintempleton.co.uk
Sales Range: $250-299.9 Million
Emp.: 250
Investment Services
N.A.I.C.S.: 523999
Matt Philpott (Sr VP-Consultant Rels-
Global)

**Franklin Templeton Investment Ser-
vices GmbH** (1)
Mainzer Landstrasse 16, 60325, Frankfurt
am Main, Germany
Tel.: (49) 69272230
Web Site: http://www.franklintempleton.de
Sales Range: $150-199.9 Million
Emp.: 140
Investment Services
N.A.I.C.S.: 523999
Reinhard Berben (Mng Dir)

**Franklin Templeton Investment Trust
Management Co., Ltd.** (1)
3rd fl CCMM Building 12 Youido-Dong,
Youngdungpo-gu, Seoul, 150-968, Korea
(South)
Tel.: (82) 237740681
Web Site: http://www.franklintempleton.com
Sales Range: $50-74.9 Million
Emp.: 7
Financial Investment Advisory Firm
N.A.I.C.S.: 523940

**Franklin Templeton Investments
(Asia) Limited** (1)
17/F Chater House 8 Connaught Road,
Central, China (Hong Kong)
Tel.: (852) 28777733
Web Site:
http://www.franklintempleton.com.hk
Sales Range: $75-99.9 Million
Emp.: 100
Investment Services
N.A.I.C.S.: 523999
Jason Zhu Guoqing (Mng Dir & Dir-Portfolio
Mgmt-China)

**Franklin Templeton Investments (ME)
Limited** (1)
Level 2 East Wing Gate Building Dubai In-
ternational Financial Centre, PO Box
506613, Dubai, United Arab Emirates
Tel.: (971) 44284100
Web Site:
http://www.franklintempletonme.com
Emp.: 40
Investment Management Service
N.A.I.C.S.: 523940

**Franklin Templeton Investments Aus-
tralia Limited** (1)
Level 19 101 Collins Street, Melbourne,
3000, VIC, Australia
Tel.: (61) 396031200
Web Site:
http://www.franklintempleton.com.au
Investment Advisory Services
N.A.I.C.S.: 523940
Chris Siniakov (Mng Dir-Fixed Income &
Mgr-Fund)

**Franklin Templeton Investments
Corp.** (1)
200 King St W Ste 1400, Toronto, M5H
3T4, ON, Canada (100%)
Tel.: (416) 364-4672
Web Site: http://www.franklintempleton.ca
Sales Range: $1-4.9 Billion
Emp.: 300
Investment Services
N.A.I.C.S.: 523999
Jane E. Trust (Sr VP-Fund Board Mgmt)
Jenny Johnson (Co-Pres & Co-CEO)
Duane Green (Co-Pres & Co-CEO)
Manmeet Bhatia (Head-Private Wealth)
Christine Logan (Head-Mktg)
Dennis Tew (Head-Sls-Natl)
Brad Gerster (Head-Product)
Duane W. Green (Co-Pres)
Ravi Ramaswamy (VP)

**Franklin Templeton Investments Ja-
pan Limited** (1)

Ark Hills Sengokuyama Mori Tower 40F
1-9-10 Roppongi, Minato-ku, Tokyo, 106-0032, Japan
Tel.: (81) 362305600
Web Site: http://www.franklintempleton.co.jp
Emp.: 2
General Management Consulting Services
N.A.I.C.S.: 541611

Franklin Templeton Investments Poland sp. z o.o.   (1)
Nowy Rynek Przemyslowa 3, 61-579, Poznan, Poland
Tel.: (48) 616679000
Web Site: http://www.franklintempleton.com
Emp.: 25
Investment Management Service
N.A.I.C.S.: 523940

Franklin Templeton Investments South Africa (Pty) Ltd   (1)
Kildare House The Oval 1 Oakdale Road, Newlands, Cape Town, 7700, South Africa
Tel.: (27) 218317400
Web Site:
   http://www.franklintempleton.co.za
Investment Management Service
N.A.I.C.S.: 523940
Johan Meyer (Sr VP-Emerging Markets Grp)

Franklin Templeton Investor Services, LLC   (1)
1 Franklin Pkwy Bldg 970 1st Fl, San Mateo, CA 94403
Tel.: (650) 312-3200
Web Site: http://www.franklintempleton.com
Sales Range: $1-4.9 Billion
Emp.: 7,000
Stock Transfer & Shareholders Services
N.A.I.C.S.: 523999

Franklin Templeton Italia SIM S.p.A.   (1)
Cso Italia n1, 20122, Milan, Italy
Tel.: (39) 02854591
Web Site: http://www.franklintempleton.it
Asset Management Services
N.A.I.C.S.: 523940

Franklin Templeton Switzerland Ltd.   (1)
Stockerstrasse 38, 8002, Zurich, Switzerland   **(100%)**
Tel.: (41) 442178181
Web Site: http://www.franklintempleton.ch
Sales Range: $50-74.9 Million
Emp.: 2
Investment Services
N.A.I.C.S.: 523999
Robert Steiner (Dir-Sls)

Franklin/Templeton Distributors, Inc.   (1)
3355 Data Dr, Rancho Cordova, CA 95670-7313
Tel.: (916) 463-1500
Web Site: http://www.franklintempleton.com
Investment Advisory Services
N.A.I.C.S.: 523940

Franklin Templeton Travel, Inc.   (1)
777 Mariners Island Blvd, San Mateo, CA 94404-5008
Tel.: (650) 312-2000
Investment Advisory Services
N.A.I.C.S.: 523940

Goldberry Wealth GmbH   (1)
Grosse Gallusstrasse 16-18, 60312, Frankfurt am Main, Germany
Tel.: (49) 6958996450
Web Site: https://www.goldberrypro.de
Wealth Investment Services
N.A.I.C.S.: 525120

K2 Advisors L.L.C.   (1)
300 Atlantic St 12th Fl, Stamford, CT 06901   **(69%)**
Tel.: (203) 348-5252
Web Site: http://www.k2advisors.com
Rev.: $9,300,000,000
Emp.: 115
Investment Advisory Services
N.A.I.C.S.: 523940
Rob Christian (CIO)
David Manlowe (Sr Mng Dir)

K2 Advisors Limited   (1)
100 The Adelphi, 1-11 John Adam Street,

London, WC2N 6HT, United Kingdom
Tel.: (44) 2073990688
Investment Advisory Services
N.A.I.C.S.: 523940

Legg Mason Investments (Switzerland) GmbH   (1)
Stockerstrasse 38, 8002, Zurich, Switzerland
Tel.: (41) 442146681
Investment Services
N.A.I.C.S.: 523999

Legg Mason, Inc.   (1)
100 International Dr, Baltimore, MD 21202
Tel.: (410) 539-0000
Rev.: $2,922,125,000
Assets: $8,006,120,000
Liabilities: $4,184,439,000
Net Worth: $3,821,681,000
Earnings: $251,367,000
Emp.: 3,059
Fiscal Year-end: 03/31/2020
Asset Management Services
N.A.I.C.S.: 523150
Peter H. Nachtwey (CFO & Sr Exec VP)
Terence A. Johnson (Exec VP & Head-Distr-Global)
Patricia Lattin (Chief HR Officer)
Matthew Nicholls (Pres & CEO)

Subsidiary (Non-US):

Brandywine Global Investment Management (Europe) Limited   (2)
5th Floor Cannon Place 78 Cannon Street, London, EC4N 6HL, United Kingdom
Tel.: (44) 2070738620
Web Site: http://www.brandywineglobal.com
Emp.: 30
Asset Management
N.A.I.C.S.: 523940
Theodore W. Fetter (Head-Sls-Global & Client Svcs)

Subsidiary (Domestic):

Brandywine Global Investment Management, LLC   (2)
1735 Market St Ste 1800, Philadelphia, PA 19103
Tel.: (215) 609-3500
Web Site: http://www.brandywineglobal.com
Rev.: $27,000,000
Emp.: 150
Investment Advice
N.A.I.C.S.: 523940
John P. Nelson (Head-Bus Dev & Relationship Mgmt)
Theodore W. Fetter (Head-Sls & Client Svcs-Global)
Mark P. Glassman (Chief Admin Officer)
Chris Marzullo (Chief Compliance Officer & Gen Counsel)
Alison Rogers-McCoy (Chief HR Officer)
Sue Wilchusky (Dir-Bus Strategy)
Michael Arno (Assoc Portfolio Mgr)
Reina Berlien (Head-ESG)
J. Patrick Bradley (Sr VP-Investments Res)
Tracy Chen (Portfolio Mgr)
Brian L. Giuliano (Sr VP & Portfolio Mgr-Client)
Brian L. Kloss (Portfolio Mgr)
Renato Latini (Assoc Portfolio Mgr)
Richard Lawrence (Exec VP-Portfolio Mgmt-Fixed Income)
Carol Lye (Assoc Portfolio Mgr)
John McClain (Portfolio Mgr)
Jack P. McIntyre (Portfolio Mgr)
Anujeet Sareen (Portfolio Mgr)
Francis A. Scotland (Dir-Global Macro Res)
Bill Zox (Portfolio Mgr)
Justin C. Bennitt (Portfolio Mgr)
James J. Clarke (Dir-Fundamental Res & Portfolio Mgr)
Gregory P. Manley (Portfolio Mgr)
Sorin Roibu (Portfolio Mgr)

Clarion Partners, LLC   (2)
230 Park Ave, New York, NY 10169
Tel.: (212) 883-2500
Web Site: http://www.clarionpartners.com
Emp.: 280
Real Estate Investment Management Services
N.A.I.C.S.: 531390
Stephen J. Furnary (Founder, Chm & Mng Dir)
Tim Wang (Mng Dir & Head-Investment Res)

Michelle Levy (Mng Dir & COO-Client Capital Mgmt Grp)
Edward L. Carey (Mng Dir, Member-Exec Bd & Portfolio Mgr)
Gwynne M. Murphy (Mng Dir & Head-Global Consultant Rels-Client Capital Mgmt Grp)
Katie Vaz (Mng Dir & Portfolio Mgr)
Susan Boccardi (Mng Dir, Chief Compliance Officer, Member-Exec Bd & Gen Counsel)
Celia Ding (Sr VP)

Subsidiary (Non-US):

Clarion Gramercy (UK) Limited   (3)
15 Bedford Street, London, WC2E 9HE, United Kingdom
Tel.: (44) 2076477500
Web Site: http://www.gptreit.com
Financial Management Services
N.A.I.C.S.: 522320
Jon Strang (VP-Investment)
Thorben Schafer (VP-Investment)
Blair Peach (Fin Dir)
Rory Buck (Sr Dir)
Lorenzo Patrassi (CFO & COO)
Alistair Calvert (CEO)

Branch (Domestic):

Clarion Partners, LLC - Boston   (3)
101 Arch St 17th Fl, Boston, MA 02110
Tel.: (617) 482-6700
Web Site: http://www.clarionpartners.com
Emp.: 6
Real Estate Investment Management Services
N.A.I.C.S.: 531390
Hugh MacDonnell (Mng Dir, Member-Exec Bd & Head-Client Capital Mgmt)

Clarion Partners, LLC - Washington, DC   (3)
701 8th St NW Ste 800, Washington, DC 20001
Tel.: (202) 393-1957
Web Site: http://www.clarionpartners.com
Emp.: 20
Real Estate Investment Management Services
N.A.I.C.S.: 531390
Timothy W. Bright (Mng Dir & Head-Multifamily Sector)

Subsidiary (Domestic):

Gables Residential Trust   (3)
3399 Peachtree Rd NE, Atlanta, GA 30326-2832
Tel.: (404) 923-5500
Web Site: http://www.gables.com
Residential Real Estate Investment Trust
N.A.I.C.S.: 525990
Dawn H. Severt (CFO & Exec VP)
Susan Ansel (Pres & CEO)
Gigi Giannoni (Sr VP-Customer Experience)
Dennis E. Rainosek (Sr VP-Portfolio Mgmt)
Donna Summers (Pres-Gables Mgmt Company)
Matthew Bearden (Sr VP-Construction)
Jorgen Punda (Sr VP-Investments-Washington)
Philip Altschuler (Sr VP-HR)
David Reece (Sr VP-Fin & Capital Markets)
Darin Botelho (VP-Comml Real Estate & Retail Ops)
Gregory Gasior (Sr VP-Ops-East)
Michael L. Brown (Reg VP-Investments)
Mary Hollands (Sr VP-Third Party Ops)
Robert Presley (Sr VP-Facilities Mgmt & Quality Assurance)
Timothy Hutchinson (VP-REIT, JV, Third-Party Assets-Boston & Washington)
Will Gosnell (VP-Internal Audit)
Jennifer Wiebrand (VP-Investments-Austin & Texas)
Jean Anton (VP-Ops-Southeast)
Shelly Coulter (VP-Ops-Dallas & Denver)
Anna Frenzel (VP-REIT, JV, Third-Party Assets-Denver & Colorado)
James Hamrick (VP-IT)
Jennifer Harris (Sr Mgr-Community)
Lynn Riley Stokes (Reg VP-Design)
Melanie Trapnell (Sr VP-Ops-West)
Ryan Brown (Reg VP-Construction)
Teresa Meuter (VP-Third-Party Acctg)
Carrie Billiam (Sr VP-Acctg)
Brian Mosley (Sr VP-Asset Mgmt)
Rob Rector (VP-Trng & Dev)
Shane Polk (VP-Facilities Mgmt)
Julia Small (Reg Mgr)

Subsidiary (Domestic):

ClearBridge Investments, LLC   (2)
620 8th Ave 48th Fl, New York, NY 10018
Tel.: (800) 691-6960
Web Site: http://www.clearbridge.com
Investment Advisory & Asset Management Services
N.A.I.C.S.: 523940
Terrence Murphy (CEO)
Richard A. Freeman (Mng Dir & Portfolio Mgr)
Charles Harris (Mng Dir & Dir-Res)
Nicole Tarallo (Mng Dir & Head-Client Svcs)
Brian Angerame (Mng Dir & Portfolio Mgr)
Evan Bauman (Mng Dir & Portfolio Mgr)
John Baldi (Mng Dir & Portfolio Mgr)
Sean Bogda (Mng Dir & Portfolio Mgr)
Peter Bourbeau (Mng Dir & Portfolio Mgr)
Michael Clarfeld (Mng Dir & Portfolio Mgr)
Derek Deutsch (Mng Dir & Portfolio Mgr)
Chris Eades (Mng Dir & Portfolio Mgr)
Richard Elmslie (Mng Dir & Portfolio Mgr)
Robert Feitler (Mng Dir & Portfolio Mgr)
Aram Green (Mng Dir & Portfolio Mgr)
Albert Grosman (Mng Dir & Portfolio Mgr)
Charles Hamieh (Mng Dir & Portfolio Mgr)
Shane Hurst (Mng Dir & Portfolio Mgr)
George Neofytidis (Mng Dir & Portfolio Mgr-Private Client)
Elisa Mazen (Mng Dir, Head-Global Growth & Portfolio Mgr)
Richard Freeman (Mng Dir)

Subsidiary (Domestic):

ClearBridge Asset Management Inc.   (3)
620 8th Ave 48th Fl, New York, NY 10018
Tel.: (212) 805-2000
Web Site: http://www.clearbridge.com
Investment Management Service
N.A.I.C.S.: 523940

Affiliate (Domestic):

ClearBridge Energy Midstream Opportunity Fund Inc.   (4)
620 8th Ave 49th Fl, New York, NY 10018
Web Site: http://www.leggmason.com
Rev.: $12,169,127
Assets: $956,528,521
Liabilities: $328,807,000
Net Worth: $627,721,521
Earnings: ($10,048,879)
Fiscal Year-end: 11/30/2019
Closed-End Investment Fund
N.A.I.C.S.: 525990
Jane E. Trust (Chm, Pres & CEO)
Richard Freeman (Mng Dir-Portfolio Mgr)
Michael Clarfeld (Mng Dir-Portfolio Mgr)
Chris Eades (Mng Dir-Potfolio Mgr)
Peter Vanderlee (Mng Dir-Portfolio Mgr)

ClearBridge MLP & Midstream Fund Inc.   (4)
620 8th Ave 49th Fl, New York, NY 10018
Web Site: http://www.leggmason.com
Rev.: $21,046,731
Assets: $1,270,011,774
Liabilities: $471,875,128
Net Worth: $798,136,646
Earnings: ($7,297,160)
Fiscal Year-end: 11/30/2019
Closed-End Investment Fund
N.A.I.C.S.: 525990
Jane E. Trust (Chm, Pres & CEO)
Robert I. Frenkel (Chief Legal Officer & Sec)
Todd F. Kuehl (Chief Compliance Officer)

Subsidiary (Domestic):

Global Currents Investment Management, LLC   (4)
2 Righter Pkwy, Wilmington, DE 19803
Tel.: (302) 476-3800
Web Site: http://www.clearbridge.com
Sales Range: $25-49.9 Million
Emp.: 15
Investment Management Service
N.A.I.C.S.: 523940

Subsidiary (Non-US):

ClearBridge Investments Limited   (3)
Level 13 35 Clarence St, Sydney, 2000, NSW, Australia   **(100%)**
Tel.: (61) 293977300

Franklin Resources, Inc.—(Continued)

Web Site: https://www.clearbridgeinvest
ments.com.au
Investment Management Service
N.A.I.C.S.: 523940
Terrence Murphy (CEO)
Annette Golden (Mng Dir)
Matt Bushby (Mng Dir)
Jonathon Hall (COO)
Jenny Pang (VP)

Subsidiary (Domestic):

ClearBridge, LLC (2)
100 International Dr, Baltimore, MD 21202
Tel.: (410) 547-2558
Web Site: http://www.clearbridge.com
Investment Management Service
N.A.I.C.S.: 523940

Fairfield Group (2)
3415 W Chester Pike Ste 204, Newtown
Square, PA 19073-4228
Tel.: (215) 657-9400
Sales Range: $50-74.9 Million
Emp.: 8
Investment Banking & Stock Brokerage
Firm
N.A.I.C.S.: 523150

Financial Guard, LLC (2)
1952 E Fort Union Blvd Ste 200, Salt Lake
City, UT 84121
Tel.: (614) 973-6999
Web Site: http://www.financialguard.com
Investment Management Service
N.A.I.C.S.: 523940

Subsidiary (Non-US):

**Legg Mason Asset Management (Sin-
gapore) Pte Ltd.** (2)
1 George Street 23-02, Singapore, 049145,
Singapore
Tel.: (65) 65368000
Web Site: http://www.leggmason.com.sg
Investment Management Service
N.A.I.C.S.: 523940

Subsidiary (Domestic):

**Legg Mason Capital Management
Inc.** (2)
100 International Dr, Baltimore, MD 21202-
4673
Tel.: (410) 539-0000
Web Site: http://www.lmcm.com
Rev.: $3,200,000
Emp.: 131
Investment Advisor
N.A.I.C.S.: 523150
Jennifer Dukahirt (VP)
Bill Miller (Chm, Chief Investment Officer &
Portfolio Mgr)

Subsidiary (Non-US):

**Legg Mason Investments (Europe)
Limited** (2)
201 Bishopsgate, London, EC2M 3AB,
United Kingdom (100%)
Tel.: (44) 20 7070 7444
Web Site: http://www.leggmason.co.uk
Sales Range: $25-49.9 Million
Emp.: 100
Financial Investment Services
N.A.I.C.S.: 523999

**Legg Mason Investments (Luxem-
bourg) S.A.** (2)
145 Rue Du Kiem, 8030, Strassen, Luxem-
bourg
Tel.: (352) 24694121
Emp.: 6
Investment Management Service
N.A.I.C.S.: 523940

Subsidiary (Domestic):

**Legg Mason Investor Services,
LLC** (2)
100 International Dr, Baltimore, MD 21202-
1099
Web Site: http://www.leggmason.com
Emp.: 14
Investment Management Service
N.A.I.C.S.: 523940

Subsidiary (Non-US):

**Martin Currie Investment Manage-
ment Limited** (2)

Saltire Court 20 Castle Terrace, Edinburgh,
EH1 2ES, United Kingdom
Tel.: (44) 1312295252
Web Site: http://www.martincurrie.com
Investment Management Service
N.A.I.C.S.: 523940

Subsidiary (Domestic):

Martin Currie, Inc. (2)
New York Times Bldg 620 8th Ave 49th Fl,
New York, NY 10018
Tel.: (212) 805-6000
Emp.: 3
Investment Management Service
N.A.I.C.S.: 523940
Julian Ide (CEO)
Willie Watt (Chm)

Subsidiary (Non-US):

Permal Group Ltd. (2)
12 St James's Square, London, SW1Y 4LB,
United Kingdom
Tel.: (44) 20 7389 1300
Web Site: http://www.permal.com
Asset Management Firm
N.A.I.C.S.: 523999

Subsidiary (Domestic):

QS Investors, LLC (2)
880 3rd Ave 7th Fl, New York, NY 10022
Tel.: (212) 886-9200
Web Site: http://www.qsinvestors.com
Investment Management Service
N.A.I.C.S.: 523940
Janet Campagna (Chm)

Royce & Associates, LLC (2)
745 5th Ave, New York, NY 10151
Tel.: (212) 508-4500
Web Site: http://www.roycefunds.com
Sales Range: $50-74.9 Million
Emp.: 120
Investment Management Service
N.A.I.C.S.: 523940
Charles Morgan Royce (Chm & Portfolio
Mgr)
Charles R. Dreifus (Mng Dir & Portfolio
Mgr)
George Necakov (Principal & Dir-
Quantitative Strategies & Portfolio Mgr)
James J. Harvey (Principal & Portfolio Mgr)
Jay S. Kaplan (Principal & Portfolio Mgr)
Gunjan Banati (Mng Dir & Chief Risk Offi-
cer)
Francis Gannon (Mng Dir & Co-Chief In-
vestment Officer)
John Denneen (Mng Dir & Gen Counsel)
Peter Hoglund (Mng Dir, CFO & Chief Ad-
min Officer)
Christopher D. Clark (CEO & Co-Chief In-
voctment Officer)
Mark Fischer (Dir-Intl Res & Portfolio Mgr)
Brendan Hartman (Portfolio Mgr)
Miles Lewis (Principal & Portfolio Mgr)
Steven McBoyle (Principal & Portfolio Mgr)
Andrew Palen (Portfolio Mgr)
Mark Rayner (Principal & Portfolio Mgr)
Lauren Romeo (Principal & Portfolio Mgr)
Chip Skinner (Principal & Portfolio Mgr)
Jim Stoeffel (Principal & Portfolio Mgr)
Michael Connors (Asst Portfolio Mgr)
Kavitha Venkatraman (Asst Portfolio Mgr)
Steve Lipper (Mng Dir)
Jag Sriram (Dir-Strategic Res)
Dan O'Byrne (Principal, VP & Head-
Trading)
John McNulty (Mgr-Res Relationship)
Steve Clark (Head-Distr)
Lindsay Cobb (Head-Distr)
Tara Francoeur (Dir-Sls & Mktg Integration)
James A. Skinner III (Principal & Portfolio
Mgr)

Royce & Associates, LP. (2)
745 5th Ave, New York, NY 10151
Web Site: http://www.roycefunds.com
Investment Management Service
N.A.I.C.S.: 523940

Affiliate (Domestic):

**Western Asset Corporate Loan Fund,
Inc.** (2)
620 Eighth Ave, New York, NY 10018
Rev.: $9,724,836
Assets: $177,831,776
Liabilities: $69,749,716

Net Worth: $108,082,060
Earnings: $6,627,743
Fiscal Year-end: 09/30/2019
Investment Management Service
N.A.I.C.S.: 523940
Ryan Kohan (Mgr-Fund)

**Western Asset Global Corporate De-
fined Opportunity Fund, Inc.** (2)
620 Eighth Ave 49th Fl, New York, NY
10018
Tel.: (212) 601-6000
Rev.: $21,031,633
Assets: $382,502,072
Liabilities: $107,452,053
Net Worth: $275,050,019
Earnings: $14,806,272
Fiscal Year-end: 10/31/2019
Investment Management Service
N.A.I.C.S.: 525990
Jane E. Trust (Chm, Pres & CEO)
Lian Chia Liang (Mgr-Fund)

**Western Asset Global High Income
Fund, Inc.** (2)
620 Eighth Ave 49th Fl, New York, NY
10018
Tel.: (212) 601-6000
Investment Fund Management Services
N.A.I.C.S.: 523940
Jane E. Trust (Chm, Pres & CEO)
Michael C. Buchanan (Mgr-Fund)

**Western Asset High Income Fund II,
Inc.** (2)
620 Eighth Ave 49th Fl, New York, NY
10018
Tel.: (212) 601-6000
Rev.: $60,029,364
Assets: $901,187,632
Liabilities: $279,042,351
Net Worth: $622,145,281
Earnings: $4,946,190
Fiscal Year-end: 04/30/2019
Investment Management Service
N.A.I.C.S.: 525990
Jane E. Trust (Chm, Pres & CEO)
Christopher F. Kilpatrick (Mgr-Fund)

**Western Asset High Income Opportu-
nity Fund, Inc.** (2)
620 Eighth Ave 49th Fl, New York, NY
10018
Tel.: (212) 601-6000
Investment Fund Management Services
N.A.I.C.S.: 523940
Jane E. Trust (Chm, Pres & CEO)
Christopher F. Kilpatrick (Mgr-Fund)

**Western Asset High Yield Defined
Opportunity Fund Inc.** (2)
620 8th Ave 49th, Fl, New York, NY 10018
Sales Range: $25-49.9 Million
Investment Services
N.A.I.C.S.: 523999
Jane E. Trust (Chm & Pres)
Robert I. Frenkel (Chief Legal Officer &
Sec)
Steven Frank (Treas)
Ted P. Becker (Chief Compliance Officer)
Vanessa A. Williams (Identity Theft Preven-
tion Officer)
Thomas C. Mandia (Asst Sec)
Jeanne Marie Kelly (Sr VP)

**Western Asset Intermediate Muni
Fund, Inc.** (2)
620 Eighth Ave 49th Fl, New York, NY
10018
Tel.: (212) 601-6000
Rev.: $6,991,232
Assets: $192,035,690
Liabilities: $47,252,494
Net Worth: $144,783,196
Earnings: $4,483,471
Fiscal Year-end: 11/30/2019
Investment Management Service
N.A.I.C.S.: 525990
Jane E. Trust (Chm, Pres & CEO)
Robert E. Amodeo (Mgr-Fund)

**Western Asset Investment Grade De-
fined Opportunity Trust, Inc.** (2)
620 Eighth Ave 49th Fl, New York, NY
10018
Tel.: (212) 601-6000
Rev.: $11,272,088
Assets: $231,565,294
Liabilities: $2,707,092

Net Worth: $228,858,202
Earnings: $9,548,504
Fiscal Year-end: 11/30/2019
Investment Management Service
N.A.I.C.S.: 525990
Jane E. Trust (Chm, Pres & CEO)
Ryan Brist (Mgr-Fund)

**Western Asset Investment Grade In-
come Fund, Inc.** (2)
620 8th Ave 49th Fl, New York, NY 10018
Tel.: (212) 601-6000
Rev.: $7,025,334
Assets: $147,245,775
Liabilities: $126,340
Net Worth: $147,119,435
Earnings: $5,845,678
Fiscal Year-end: 12/31/2019
Investment Management Service
N.A.I.C.S.: 525990
Ryan Brist (Mgr-Fund)

**Western Asset Managed Municipals
Fund, Inc.** (2)
620 8th Ave 49th Fl, New York, NY 10018
Tel.: (212) 601-6000
Asset Management Services
N.A.I.C.S.: 523940
Jane E. Trust (Chm, Pres & CEO)

Subsidiary (Domestic):

**Western Asset Management
Company** (2)
385 E Colorado Blvd, Pasadena, CA 91101
Tel.: (626) 844-9400
Web Site: http://www.westernasset.com
Sales Range: $75-99.9 Million
Emp.: 836
Investment Advisor
N.A.I.C.S.: 525990
James William Hirschmann III (CEO)
Ahmet E. Kocagil (Chief Risk Officer)
Amit Chopra (Portfolio Mgr)
Blanton Y. Keh (Portfolio Mgr)
Jan Pieterse (Head-LDI Solutions)
Jim K. Huynh (Portfolio Mgr)
Keith A. Luna (Portfolio Mgr)
Prashant Chandran (Portfolio Mgr)
Rajiv Sachdeva (Head-Portfolio & Quantita-
tive Analysis)
Ryan K. Brist (Head-Global Investment
Grade Credit & Portfolio Mgr)
Scott M. Beatty (Portfolio Mgr)
Scott A. Spear (Mgr-Portfolio Risk)
Bonnie M. Wongtrakool (Head-ESG
Investments-Global & Portfolio Mgr)
Molly Schwartz (Portfolio Mgr)
Roy You (Mgr-Risk)

Subsidiary (Non-US):

**Western Asset Management Com-
pany Limited** (3)
10 Exchange Square Primrose Street, Lon-
don, EC2A 2EN, United Kingdom (100%)
Tel.: (44) 2074223000
Web Site: https://www.westernasset.co.uk
Pension Managers
N.A.I.C.S.: 524292
James William Hirschmann III (CEO)

**Western Asset Management Com-
pany Ltd** (3)
36F Shin-Marunouchi Building 5-1
Marunouchi 1-Chome, Chiyoda-ku, Tokyo,
100-6536, Japan
Tel.: (81) 345204300
Web Site: http://www.westernasset.co.jp
Emp.: 25
Investment Management Service
N.A.I.C.S.: 523940

**Western Asset Management Com-
pany Pte Ltd.** (3)
1 George Street 23-01, Singapore, 049145,
Singapore
Tel.: (65) 64283600
Web Site: http://www.westernasset.com.sg
Emp.: 20
Investment Management Service
N.A.I.C.S.: 523940

**Western Asset Management Com-
pany Pty Ltd** (3)
Level 48 120 Collins Street, Melbourne,
3000, VIC, Australia
Tel.: (61) 390165600
Investment Management Service

N.A.I.C.S.: 523940

Affiliate (Domestic):

Western Asset Middle Market Income Fund Inc. (2)
620 Eighth Ave 49th Fl, New York, NY 10018
Web Site: http://www.westernasset.com
Investment Services
N.A.I.C.S.: 523999
Michael Buchanan (Deputy Chief Investment Officer)
Kenneth J. Winston (Chief Risk Officer)

Western Asset Municipal Defined Opportunity Trust, Inc. (2)
620 8th Ave 49th Fl, New York, NY 10018
Tel.: (212) 601-6000
Asset Management Services
N.A.I.C.S.: 523940
Jane E. Trust (Chm, Pres & CEO)
Robert E . Amodeo (Mgr-Fund)

Western Asset Municipal High Income Fund, Inc. (2)
620 Eighth Ave 49th Fl, New York, NY 10018
Tel.: (212) 601-6000
Rev.: $7,747,570
Assets: $175,550,123
Liabilities: $1,669,039
Net Worth: $173,881,084
Earnings: $6,584,345
Fiscal Year-end: 10/31/2019
Investment Management Service
N.A.I.C.S.: 525990
Jane E. Trust (Chm, Pres & CEO)
Robert E. Amodeo (Mgr-Fund)

Western Asset Premier Bond Fund (2)
620 Eighth Ave 49th Fl, New York, NY 10018
Tel.: (212) 601-6000
Rev.: $13,304,191
Assets: $241,234,449
Liabilities: $66,669,815
Net Worth: $174,564,634
Earnings: $9,713,132
Fiscal Year-end: 12/31/2019
Investment Management Service
N.A.I.C.S.: 525990
Jane E. Trust (Pres & CEO)
Christopher F. Kilpatrick (Mgr-Fund)

Western Asset Variable Rate Strategic Fund, Inc. (2)
620 Eighth Ave 49th Fl, New York, NY 10018
Tel.: (212) 601-6000
Investment Fund Management Services
N.A.I.C.S.: 523940
Dennis J. McNamara (Mgr-Fund)

Lexington Partners Inc. (1)
660 Madison Ave Ste 23, New York, NY 10021
Tel.: (212) 754-0411
Web Site: http://www.lexingtonpartners.com
Investment Management Firm
N.A.I.C.S.: 523940
Thomas Giannetti (CFO & Partner)
Rebecca L. Weisel (VP-IR)
Rebecca S. John (Partner-IR)
Duncan A. Chapman (Partner)
Wilson Warren (Pres)
Pal Ristvedt (Partner)

Pelagos Capital Management, LLC (1)
1 International Pl 25th Fl, Boston, MA 02110
Tel.: (617) 307-5870
Web Site: http://www.pelagoscapital.com
Investment Management Service
N.A.I.C.S.: 523940
Stephen P. Burke (Co-Founder & CEO)
John C. Pickart (Co-Founder & Chief Investment Officer)

Putnam Investments, LLC (1)
100 Federal St, Boston, MA 02110
Tel.: (617) 292-1000
Web Site: http://www.putnam.com
Sales Range: $1-4.9 Billion
Investment Management Service
N.A.I.C.S.: 525910
Scott C. Sipple (Head-Putnam Retail Mgmt)
Ryan McQuilkin (Mng Dir-Fixed Income)

Robert E. Alan (Head-Global Consultant Rels-Institutional Mgmt Bus)
Kaitlin M. May (Head-Institutional Mgmt)
Robert L. Reynolds (Pres & CEO)
Jacquelyn S. VanderBrug (Head-Sustainability Strategy)

Subsidiary (Domestic):

Putnam Advisory Company, LLC (2)
30 Dan Rd, Canton, MA 02021
Tel.: (617) 292-1000
Web Site: http://www.putnam.com
Sales Range: $1-9.9 Million
Emp.: 46
Investment Advisory Services
N.A.I.C.S.: 525910

Putnam Mortgage Opportunities Fund (2)
100 Federal St, Boston, MA 02110
Tel.: (617) 292-1000
Web Site: http://www.putnam.com
Real Estate Investment Services
N.A.I.C.S.: 525990

Rensburg Fund Management Limited (1)
2nd Floor Toronto Square, Infirmary Street, Leeds, LS1 2HJ, United Kingdom
Tel.: (44) 845 609 0900
Web Site: http://www.franklintempleton.co.uk
Sales Range: $50-74.9 Million
Emp.: 100
Investment Services
N.A.I.C.S.: 523999

Templeton Asset Management Ltd. (1)
7 Temasek Boulevard 38-03 Suntec Tower One, Singapore, 038987,
Singapore (100%)
Tel.: (65) 63387177
Investment Services
N.A.I.C.S.: 523999
Mark Mopius (Mng Dir)

Templeton Global Advisors Limited (1)
Templeton Building Lyford Cay, PO Box N 7759, Nassau, Bahamas
Tel.: (242) 2423624600
Investment Management Service
N.A.I.C.S.: 523940

Templeton International, Inc. (1)
300 SE 2nd St, Fort Lauderdale, FL 33301
Tel.: (954) 527-7500
Web Site: http://www.franklintempleton.com
Sales Range: $100-124.9 Million
Emp.: 350
Investment Advisory Services
N.A.I.C.S.: 523940

Templeton Investment Counsel, LLC (1)
300 SE 2nd St, Fort Lauderdale, FL 33301
Tel.: (954) 527-7500
Web Site: http://www.franklintempleton.com
Emp.: 350
Investment Advisory Services
N.A.I.C.S.: 523940

Templeton Worldwide, Inc. (1)
300 S E 2nd St, Fort Lauderdale, FL 33301
Tel.: (954) 527-7500
Investment Advisory Services
N.A.I.C.S.: 523940

Templeton do Brasil Ltda. (1)
Rua Lauro Muller 116 Office 2404 Botafogo, Rio de Janeiro, 22290 160, Brazil
Tel.: (55) 2125432413
Web Site: http://www.franklintempleton.com
Investment Management Service
N.A.I.C.S.: 523940

Western Asset Management Company Distribuidora de Titulos e Valores Mobiliarios Limitada (1)
Av Presidente Juscelino Kubitschek n 1 455 15 andar cj 152, Sao Paulo, 04543-011, SP, Brazil
Tel.: (55) 1134785000
Web Site: https://www.westernasset.com.br
Asset Management Services
N.A.I.C.S.: 523940

FRANKLIN STREET PROPERTIES CORP.

401 Edgewater Pl, Wakefield, MA 01880
Tel.: (781) 557-1300 MD
Web Site: https://www.fspreit.com
Year Founded: 1997
FSP—(NYSEAMEX)
Rev.: $165,615,000
Assets: $1,241,666,000
Liabilities: $472,930,000
Net Worth: $768,736,000
Earnings: $1,094,000
Emp.: 28
Fiscal Year-end: 12/31/22
Real Estate Investment Trust
N.A.I.C.S.: 522292
George J. Carter (Founder, Chm & CEO)
Eriel Anchondo (COO & Exec VP)
John G. Demeritt (CFO, Treas & Exec VP)
Scott H. Carter (Gen Counsel, Sec & Exec VP)
Jeffrey B. Carter (Pres & Chief Investment Officer)
Andrew J. Klouse (Sr VP-Fin & Asst Treas)
John F. Donahue (Exec VP)
William S. Friend (Sr VP)
Matthew J. Buckley (VP & Dir-IT)
Yi-Chin Huang (VP-Financial Reporting)
Judith A. Waugh (VP/Mgr-Asset-FSP Property Management LLC)
Cynthia J. Malonson (VP-Corp Reporting)
Georgia Touma (VP & Dir-IR)
Leo H. Daley Jr. (Sr VP)

Subsidiaries:

FSP 1999 Broadway LLC (1)
1999 Broadway 510, Denver, CO 80202
Tel.: (303) 292-1999
Emp.: 8
Real Estate Development Services
N.A.I.C.S.: 531210

FSP Eldridge Green Limited Partnership (1)
401 Edgewater Pl Ste 200, Wakefield, MA 01880
Tel.: (781) 557-1339
Management Consulting Services
N.A.I.C.S.: 541618

FSP Greenwood Plaza Corp. (1)
4643 S Ulster St Ste 1210, Denver, CO 80237-4307
Tel.: (303) 779-3053
Management Consulting Services
N.A.I.C.S.: 541618

FSP Investments LLC (1)
401 Edgewater Pl 200, Wakefield, MA 01880
Tel.: (781) 246-4900
Web Site: http://www.franklinstreetproperties.com
Sales Range: $1-4.9 Billion
Real Estate Investment Services
N.A.I.C.S.: 523999
George J. Carter (Pres)

FSP Park Ten Limited Partnership (1)
16290 Katy Fwy, Houston, TX 77094
Tel.: (281) 398-0070
Property Development & Management Services
N.A.I.C.S.: 531210

FSP Property Management LLC (1)
401 Edgewater Pl Ste 200, Wakefield, MA 01880-6210
Tel.: (781) 557-1300
Web Site: http://www.franklinstreetproperties.com
Sales Range: $300-349.9 Million
Property Management Services
N.A.I.C.S.: 531312

FRANKLIN WIRELESS CORPORATION

3940 Ruffin Rd, San Diego, CA 92123
Tel.: (858) 623-0000 CA
Web Site: https://www.franklinwireless.com
FKWL—(NASDAQ)
Rev.: $30,796,690
Assets: $46,719,829
Liabilities: $10,343,831
Net Worth: $36,375,998
Earnings: ($4,166,671)
Emp.: 69
Fiscal Year-end: 06/30/24
Cell Phone Mfr
N.A.I.C.S.: 334210
Ok Chae Kim (Pres & Sec)
Gary Nelson (Chm)
David Yun J. Lee (COO & VP-Sls & Mktg-Global Carrier Bus)
Bill Bauer (Interim CFO, Gen Counsel & Dir-Strategic Plng)
John F. Parks (Dir-Human Resources-Operations)
Jeff Ward (Dir-Project Mgmt)
Mukund Halthore (Dir-IoT)

FRAZIER LIFESCIENCES ACQUISITION CORPORATION
2 Union Square 601 Union St Ste 3200, Seattle, WA 98101
Tel.: (206) 621-7200 Ky
Web Site: http://www.frazierlifesciencesacquisition.com
Year Founded: 2020
FLACU—(NASDAQ)
Investment Services
N.A.I.C.S.: 523999
James N. Topper (Chm & CEO)
David Topper (CFO)
Gordon Empey (Gen Counsel & VP)
Max M. Nowicki (VP-Acquisitions)

FRED'S INC.
4300 New Getwell Rd, Memphis, TN 38118
Tel.: (901) 365-8880 TN
Web Site: http://www.fredsinc.com
Year Founded: 1947
FRED—(NASDAQ)
Rev.: $1,271,746,000
Assets: $409,025,000
Liabilities: $243,560,000
Net Worth: $165,465,000
Earnings: ($12,967,000)
Emp.: 2,642
Fiscal Year-end: 02/02/19
Discount General Merchandise Stores
N.A.I.C.S.: 455219
Heath Bradford Freeman (Chm)
Michael H. Ladd (COO)

Subsidiaries:

C.T. Stamps, Inc. (1)
200 Marion Ave, McComb, MS 39648
Tel.: (601) 684-7621
Emp.: 25
Medical Supplies Distr
N.A.I.C.S.: 456110

Fred's Capital Management Company, Inc. (1)
4300 New Getwell Rd, Memphis, TN 38118
Tel.: (901) 365-8880
Web Site: http://www.fredsinc.com
Sales Range: $10-24.9 Million
Emp.: 50
Financial Services
N.A.I.C.S.: 561499
Michael J. Hayes (Chm)

Fred's Stores of Tennessee, Inc (1)
4300 New Getwell Rd, Memphis, TN 38118-6898
Tel.: (901) 365-8880
Web Site: http://www.fredsinc.com
Sales Range: $25-49.9 Million
Emp.: 10
Grocery Retailer

Fred's Inc.—(Continued)

N.A.I.C.S.: 455110

Reeves-Sain Drug Store, Inc. (1)
1801 Memorial Blvd, Murfreesboro, TN
37129
Tel.: (615) 896-5731
Web Site: http://www.reevessain.com
Pharmacy & Healthcare Services
N.A.I.C.S.: 621610
Jason Greene *(VP-Retail Pharmacy Ops)*

FREE FLOW, INC.
6269 Caledon Rd, King George, VA
22485
Tel.: (703) 789-3344   DE
Web Site:
  https://www.freeflowplc.com
Year Founded: 2011
FFLO—(OTCIQ)
Rev.: $195,137
Assets: $732,327
Liabilities: $2,527,182
Net Worth: ($1,794,855)
Earnings: ($2,761,312)
Emp.: 3
Fiscal Year-end: 12/31/22
Solar Pump System
N.A.I.C.S.: 333914
Sabir Saleem *(Pres, CEO, CFO,
Treas & Sec)*
Ravinder Tikoo *(Chm)*

Subsidiaries:

Accurate Auto Parts, Inc. (1)
2885 S 163rd St, New Berlin, WI 53151
Web Site:
  https://www.accurateautomaticparts.com
Screw Machine Parts Mfr
N.A.I.C.S.: 332722

FFLO - Inside Auto Parts, Inc. (1)
314 Pendleton Rd, Mineral, VA 23117
Tel.: (540) 894-4602
Web Site: https://www.insideautoparts.com
Automobile Parts Mfr
N.A.I.C.S.: 334290

FREEDOM HOLDINGS, INC.
10524 Independence Ave, Chats-
worth, CA 91311
Tel.: (818) 357-3155   MD
Web Site: https://fredomholdings.com
Year Founded: 2005
FHLD—(OTCIQ)
Assets: $588
Liabilities: $412,477
Net Worth: ($411,889)
Earnings: ($399,918)
Fiscal Year-end: 09/30/23
Heavy Oil Product Mfr
N.A.I.C.S.: 324199
Robin Wright *(CFO)*
John E. Vivian *(Pres & CEO)*

FREEDOM LEAF, INC.
3571 E Sunset Rd Ste 420, Las Ve-
gas, NV 89120
Tel.: (702) 499-6022   NV
Web Site:
  http://www.freedomleaf.com
Year Founded: 2013
FRLF—(OTCIQ)
Rev.: $2,010,749
Assets: $18,226,575
Liabilities: $9,335,585
Net Worth: $8,890,990
Earnings: ($12,730,872)
Emp.: 57
Fiscal Year-end: 06/30/19
Advocacy publishing
N.A.I.C.S.: 519290
Clifford J. Perry *(Founder)*
David Goldburg *(Chm)*
Brian D. Moon *(CFO)*
Carlos Frias *(CEO)*
Daniel Nguyen *(Chief Scientific Offi-
cer)*
Alex Frias *(VP-Fin)*

FREEPORT-MCMORAN INC.
333 N Central Ave, Phoenix, AZ
85004-2189
Tel.: (602) 366-8100   AZ
Web Site: https://www.fcx.com
Year Founded: 1913
FCX—(NYSE)
Rev.: $22,855,000,000
Assets: $52,506,000,000
Liabilities: $25,196,000,000
Net Worth: $27,310,000,000
Earnings: $1,848,000,000
Emp.: 27,200
Fiscal Year-end: 12/31/23
Copper, Gold & Molybdenum Mining
Services
N.A.I.C.S.: 212230
Kathleen L. Quirk *(Pres & CEO)*
David Joint *(VP-IR)*
Linda Hayes *(VP-Comm)*
Stephen T. Higgins *(Chief Admin Offi-
cer & Sr VP)*
William E. Cobb *(Chief Sustainability
Officer & VP)*
Pamela Q. Masson *(Chief HR Officer
& VP)*
Ellie Mikes *(Chief Acctg Officer & VP)*
Maree Robertson *(CFO)*
Douglas N. Currault II *(Gen Counsel
& Sr VP)*
Bertrand L. Odinet II *(Chief Innova-
tion Officer, CIO & VP)*

Subsidiaries:

Atlantic Copper, S.A. (1)
Edif Torre Europa Paseo De la Castellana
95, Planta 21, 28046, Madrid, Spain
Tel.: (34) 913349400
Web Site: https://www.atlantic-copper.es
Sales Range: $150-199.9 Million
Emp.: 650
Copper Processing Services
N.A.I.C.S.: 331410
Javier Targhetta *(Pres)*
Conchita Garcia *(Sr VP-Sulphuric Acid Bus)*
Heliodoro Mariscal *(Sr VP-Internal Auditing
& CSR)*
Jose Jimenez *(Sr VP-Mktg & Sls)*
Carlos Ortiz *(Sr VP-Metallurgy)*
Sol Villar *(Sr VP)*
Esther Alonso *(Sr VP)*

Atlantic Copper, S.L.U. (1)
Avda Francisco Montenegro S/N, 21001,
Huelva, Spain
Tel.: (34) 959210600
Web Site: https://atlantic-copper.es
Emp.: 1,000
Copper Product Mfr & Distr
N.A.I.C.S.: 331420

Climax Molybdenum Company (1)
333 N Central Ave, Phoenix, AZ 85004-
4415
Tel.: (602) 366-8100
Web Site:
  http://www.climaxmolybdenum.com
Sales Range: $200-249.9 Million
Molybdenum & Chemical Products Mfr
N.A.I.C.S.: 325998
Anand S. Raman *(VP-Technology-
Downstream Ops)*
Barbara J. Buck *(VP-Marketing-Sales)*
Michael J. Kendrick *(Pres)*
Timothy J. Olson *(Controller)*
Chris Gnann *(VP-Sales-Marketing)*
Barbara Buck *(VP)*

Division (Domestic):

Climax Engineered Materials (2)
800 E Pima Mine Rd, Sahuarita, AZ 85629
Tel.: (520) 806-8700
Web Site:
  http://www.climaxengineeredmateri
als.com
Sales Range: $100-124.9 Million
Specialty Metal Powders
N.A.I.C.S.: 332999

Subsidiary (Non-US):

Climax Molybdenum U.K. (2)
Limited

Needham Rd, Stowmarket, IP14 2AE, Suf-
folk, United Kingdom
Tel.: (44) 1449674431
Web Site:
  http://www.climaxmolybdenum.com
Sales Range: $1-9.9 Million
Emp.: 50
Molybdenum Processing & Mining Services
N.A.I.C.S.: 212290
David Thornton *(Pres)*

Cyprus Amax Minerals Company (1)
333 N Central Ave, Phoenix, AZ 85004
Tel.: (602) 366-8100
Mining Services
N.A.I.C.S.: 212290

Cyprus Metals Company (1)
637 W Billinis Rd S, Salt Lake City, UT
84119
Tel.: (801) 263-8188
Web Site: http://www.cypressmetals.com
Metal Distr
N.A.I.C.S.: 423510

FCX Oil & Gas Inc. (1)
21 Waterway Ave Ste 250, The Woodlands,
TX 77380
Tel.: (713) 579-6000
Web Site: http://www.fcx.com
Natural Gas Liquid Extraction Services
N.A.I.C.S.: 211130
Richard C. Adkerson *(Chm & CEO)*

FM Services Company (1)
1615 Poydras St, New Orleans, LA 70112-
1254
Tel.: (504) 582-4000
Sales Range: $10-24.9 Million
Emp.: 40
Mfr, Developer, Producer & Retailer of Engi-
neered Materials, Including Structural Fab-
rics, Used in the Commercial & Military
Aerospace Industry Market
N.A.I.C.S.: 561110
Pam Masson *(Mgr-HR)*

Freeport Minerals Corporation (1)
333 N Central Ave, Phoenix, AZ 85004
Tel.: (602) 366-8100
Emp.: 600
Copper Ore Mining Services
N.A.I.C.S.: 212230

**Freeport-McMoRan Inc. -
Bagdad** (1)
312 Minter, Bagdad, AZ 86321
Tel.: (928) 633-5986
Web Site: http://www.fce.com
Sales Range: $25-49.9 Million
Emp.: 515
Copper & Molybdenum Mining Services
N.A.I.C.S.: 212230

**Freeport-McMoRan Inc. - El
Paso** (1)
897 Hawkins Blvd, El Paso, TX 79915-2325
Tel.: (915) 778-9881
Web Site: http://www.fcx.com
Sales Range: $10-24.9 Million
Emp.: 400
Copper Refiner
N.A.I.C.S.: 212230

**Freeport-McMoRan Inc. -
Elizabeth** (1)
48-94 Bayway Ave, Elizabeth, NJ 07202
Tel.: (908) 558-4361
Web Site: http://www.fcx.com
Sales Range: $25-49.9 Million
Emp.: 63
Specialty Copper Products Mfr
N.A.I.C.S.: 331410

**Freeport-McMoRan Inc. -
Morenci** (1)
4521 N US Hwy 191, Morenci, AZ 85540
Tel.: (928) 865-4521
Sales Range: $50-74.9 Million
Emp.: 2,500
Copper Mining & Milling Services
N.A.I.C.S.: 212230
Hunter White *(Pres)*

Freeport-McMoRan Inc. - Safford (1)
8500 N Phelps Dodge, Safford, AZ 85546
Tel.: (928) 792-5801
Sales Range: $1-9.9 Million
Emp.: 35
Copper Ore Mining Services

N.A.I.C.S.: 212230

Freeport-McMoRan Inc. - Sierrita (1)
6200 W Duval Mine Rd, Green Valley, AZ
85622-0527
Tel.: (520) 648-8500
Web Site: http://www.fcx.com
Sales Range: $125-149.9 Million
Emp.: 1,000
Copper & Molybdenum Mining Services
N.A.I.C.S.: 212230

Freeport-McMoRan Morenci Inc. (1)
4521 N Us Hwy 191, Morenci, AZ 85540
Tel.: (928) 865-4521
Web Site: http://www.fcx.com
Copper Ore Mining Services
N.A.I.C.S.: 212230

**Freeport-McMoRan Oil & Gas
Inc.** (1)
Tel.: (713) 579-6000
Web Site: http://www.fcx.com
Rev.: $4,709,706,000
Assets: $20,854,002,000
Liabilities: $13,120,238,000
Net Worth: $7,733,764,000
Earnings: ($3,569,611,000)
Emp.: 1,312
Fiscal Year-end: 12/31/2014
Petroleum & Natural Gas Acquisition, Ex-
ploring, Developing & Extraction
N.A.I.C.S.: 211120

McMoRan Exploration Co. (1)
1615 Poydras St, New Orleans, LA
70112-1254   (100%)
Tel.: (504) 582-4000
Rev.: $376,888,000
Assets: $2,677,122,000
Liabilities: $1,073,911,000
Net Worth: $1,603,211,000
Earnings: ($104,294,000)
Emp.: 121
Fiscal Year-end: 12/31/2012
Exploration, Development & Production of
Oil & Gas
N.A.I.C.S.: 211120

Subsidiary (Domestic):

McMoRan Oil & Gas LLC (2)
1615 Poydras St Ste 600, New Orleans, LA
70112
Tel.: (504) 582-4000
Sales Range: $150-199.9 Million
Oil & Gas Exploration
N.A.I.C.S.: 211120

PT Freeport Indonesia (1)
Plaza 89 Lt 5 Jl HR Rasuna Said Kav X-7
No 6, Jakarta, 12940, Indonesia
Tel.: (62) 212591818
Web Site: https://ptfi.co.id
Metal Ore Mining Services
N.A.I.C.S.: 212290
Clayton Allen Wenas *(Chm)*
Jenpino Ngabdi *(Vice Chm)*

PXP Offshore LLC (1)
700 Milam St Ste 3100, Houston, TX 77002
Tel.: (713) 579-6000
Oil & Gas Exploration Services
N.A.I.C.S.: 213112
James C. Flores *(Pres)*

FREESTONE ACQUISITION
CORP.
2021 McKinney Ave Ste 1250, Dallas,
TX 75201
Tel.: (214) 269-1183   KY
Year Founded: 2021
FSTNU—(NASDAQ)
Investment Services
N.A.I.C.S.: 523999
Alan Boswell *(Co-Pres & CEO)*
John Schaufele *(Co-Pres & CFO)*
Ellen Wilkirson *(Sr VP-Fin & Bus
Dev)*

FREEZE TAG, INC.
360 E 1st St Ste 450, Tustin, CA
92780
Tel.: (714) 210-3850   DE
Web Site: https://www.freezetag.com
Year Founded: 2006

FRZT—(OTCIQ)
Rev.: $2,099,055
Assets: $1,163,189
Liabilities: $1,228,311
Net Worth: ($65,122)
Earnings: $200,701
Emp.: 12
Fiscal Year-end: 12/31/22
Internet & Mobile Device Games Developer & Publisher
N.A.I.C.S.: 513210
Craig Holland (Co-Founder, CEO & Chief Creative Officer)
Mick Donahoo (Co-Founder, CFO, COO, CTO, Chief Acctg Officer, Treas & Sec)
Dylan Derryberry (Dir-Creative)
Louise Gibson (Dir-Munzee Events-Global)
Robert D. Vardeman Jr. (Pres)

FREIGHT TECHNOLOGIES, INC.

2001 Timberloch Pl Ste 500, The Woodlands, TX 77380
Tel.: (773) 905-5076   VG
Web Site:
   https://www.fr8technologies.com
Year Founded: 2015
FRGT—(NASDAQ)
Rev.: $25,888,436
Assets: $10,415,611
Liabilities: $7,284,148
Net Worth: $3,131,463
Earnings: ($8,187,182)
Emp.: 86
Fiscal Year-end: 12/31/22
Financial Investment Advisory Services
N.A.I.C.S.: 523940
Jianxin Lin (Co-Founder)
Jinchi Xu (Co-Founder & CFO)
Warren Wang (Chm & CEO)

FREIGHTCAR AMERICA, INC.

125 S Wacker Dr Ste 1500, Chicago, IL 60606
Tel.: (312) 928-0850   DE
Web Site:
   https://www.freightcaramerica.com
Year Founded: 1901
RAIL—(NASDAQ)
Rev.: $364,754,000
Assets: $199,738,000
Liabilities: $228,322,000
Net Worth: ($28,584,000)
Earnings: ($38,847,000)
Emp.: 319
Fiscal Year-end: 12/31/22
Railroad Freight Car Design & Mfr
N.A.I.C.S.: 336510
James R. Meyer (Exec Chm)
Michael A. Riordan (Chief Acctg Officer & Corp Controller)
Jesus Salvador Gil Benavides (VP-Ops)
Matthew Tonn (Chief Comml Officer)
Greg Josephson (VP-Engrg)
Bob Cleator (Sr VP-Sls)
Michael Kelly (VP-Sls)
Juan Carlos Fuentes Sierra (Chief Acctg Officer & Controller)
Nicholas J. Randall (Pres & CEO)

Subsidiaries:

Freight Car Services, Inc.   (1)
125 S Wacker Dr Ste 1500, Chicago, IL 60606
Tel.: (312) 928-0850
Web Site:
   https://www.freightcaramerica.com
Railroad Freight Car Mfr
N.A.I.C.S.: 336510

FreightCar Roanoke, LLC   (1)
830 Campbell Ave, Roanoke, VA 24013
Tel.: (540) 853-3221
Railroad Rolling Stock Mfr

N.A.I.C.S.: 336510

JAIX Leasing Company   (1)
2 N Riverside Plz Ste 1250, Chicago, IL 60606
Tel.: (312) 928-0877
Railroad Rolling Stock Mfr
N.A.I.C.S.: 336510

Johnstown America, LLC   (1)
830 Campbell Ave SE, Roanoke, VA 24013
Tel.: (540) 853-3273
Railroad Rolling Stock Mfr
N.A.I.C.S.: 336510

Navistar, Inc.   (1)
2701 Navistar Dr, Lisle, IL 60532
Tel.: (331) 332-5000
Web Site: https://www.navistar.com
Medium & Heavy Duty Diesel Trucks, Buses, Diesel Engines & Replacement Parts Mfr & Marketer
N.A.I.C.S.: 336120
Troy A. Clarke (Chm, Pres & CEO)
Donna Dorsey (Chief People & Culture Officer & Exec VP)

Subsidiary (Domestic):

Chicago International Trucks - Chicago, LLC   (2)
2701 Navistar Dr, Lisle, IL 60532
Tel.: (331) 332-5000
Truck Dealer
N.A.I.C.S.: 441227

IC Bus, LLC   (2)
2701 Navistar Dr, Lisle, IL 60532
Tel.: (331) 332-5000
Web Site: http://www.icbus.com
Bus Bodies & Component Parts Mfr
N.A.I.C.S.: 336211

Subsidiary (Non-US):

Navistar Canada, Inc.   (2)
571 Glover Rd, Hannon, L0R 1P0, ON, Canada   (100%)
Tel.: (816) 843-7768
Web Site: http://www.navistar.com
Medium & Heavy Trucks, Diesel Engines & School Buses Marketer & Distr
N.A.I.C.S.: 423110
Roman Lewinsky (Pres & VP-Reg Sls)

Subsidiary (Non-US):

MWM International Industria de Motores da America do Sul Ltda.   (3)
Av Das Nacoes Unidas 22 002-Jurubatuba, Sao Paulo, SP, Brazil   (100%)
Tel.: (55) 11 3882 3200
Web Site: http://www.mwm.com.br
Diesel Engine Mfr
N.A.I.C.S.: 336310

Subsidiary (Domestic):

Navistar Defense, LLC   (2)
1675 E Whitcomb, Madison Heights, MI 48071   (100%)
Tel.: (248) 680-7600
Web Site: https://www.navistardefense.com
Armored & Unarmored Military Vehicles Mfr
N.A.I.C.S.: 336992
Gregory Nixon (Chm)

FRELII, INC.

2701 N Thanksgiving Way Ste 100, Lehi, UT 84043   NV
Year Founded: 2002
FRLI—(OTCEM)
Rev.: $35,945
Assets: $434,669
Liabilities: $205,284
Net Worth: $229,385
Earnings: ($5,549,678)
Fiscal Year-end: 12/31/18
Web-Based Nutrition & Fitness Programs Services
N.A.I.C.S.: 541511
Ian Jenkins (Pres, CEO & CFO)
Jayson Uffens (Bd of Dirs & CTO)

FREQUENCY ELECTRONICS, INC.

55 Charles Lindbergh Blvd, Mitchel Field, NY 11553
Tel.: (516) 794-4500   DE
Web Site:
   https://www.frequencyelectronics.com
Year Founded: 1962
FEIM—(NASDAQ)
Rev.: $55,274,000
Assets: $83,253,000
Liabilities: $43,437,000
Net Worth: $39,816,000
Earnings: $5,594,000
Emp.: 200
Fiscal Year-end: 04/30/24
Precision Time & Frequency Products for Ground, Seaborne, Airborne & Space Terminal Platforms
N.A.I.C.S.: 334419
Thomas McClelland (Pres & CEO)
Oleandro Mancini (Sr VP-Bus Dev)
Adrian Lalicata (VP-RF & Microwave Sys)
Steven Lawrence Bernstein (CFO, Treas & Sec)
Russell M. Sarachek (Chm)

Subsidiaries:

FEI Communications, Inc.   (1)
55 Charles Lindbergh Blvd, Uniondale, NY 11553
Tel.: (516) 794-4500
Web Site: http://www.freqelec.com
Sales Range: $100-124.9 Million
Emp.: 200
Precision Time & Frequency Products for Ground, Seaborne, Airborne & Space Terminal Platforms
N.A.I.C.S.: 334419

FEI Government Systems, Inc.   (1)
55 Charles Lindbergh Blvd, Uniondale, NY 11553
Tel.: (516) 794-4500
Web Site: http://www.freqelec.com
Sales Range: $25-49.9 Million
Emp.: 100
Precision Time & Frequency Products for Ground, Seaborne, Airborne & Space Terminal Platforms
N.A.I.C.S.: 334419

FEI-Elcom Tech, Inc.   (1)
260 Union St, Northvale, NJ 07647   (100%)
Tel.: (201) 767-8030
Web Site: https://fei-elcomtech.com
Sales Range: $1-9.9 Million
Emp.: 67
Radio Frequency Modules & Broadband Subsystems Designer & Mfr
N.A.I.C.S.: 334220
James J. Davis (CEO)

FEI-Zyfer, Inc.   (1)
7321 Lincoln Way, Garden Grove, CA 92841-1428
Tel.: (714) 933-4000
Web Site: https://fei-zyfer.com
Sales Range: $10-24.9 Million
Emp.: 50
Electric Equipment Mfr
N.A.I.C.S.: 334220
Steven Strang (Pres)

Gillam-FEI, s.a.   (1)
Mont Saint-Martin 58, Liege, 4000, Belgium
Tel.: (32) 42329595
Web Site: http://www.gillam-fei.be
Sales Range: $10-24.9 Million
Emp.: 50
Telecom Networks, Synchronization & Remote Control Product Mfr
N.A.I.C.S.: 334419
Daniel Leonard (Mng Dir)

Satel-FEI, s.a.   (1)
Route de Demigny, BP 254 F, 71106, Chalon-sur-Saone, Cedex, France
Tel.: (33) 3 85 97 4100
Supplier of Precision Time & Frequency (PT&F) Products for Ground, Seaborne, Airborne & Space Terminals
N.A.I.C.S.: 423690

FREQUENCY THERAPEUTICS, INC.

75 Hayden Ave Ste 300, Lexington, MA 02421
Tel.: (781) 315-4600   DE
Web Site:
   https://www.frequencytx.com
Year Founded: 2014
FREQ—(NASDAQ)
Rev.: $1,327,000
Assets: $121,238,000
Liabilities: $52,043,000
Net Worth: $69,195,000
Earnings: ($81,580,000)
Emp.: 46
Fiscal Year-end: 12/31/22
Biotechnology Research & Development Services
N.A.I.C.S.: 541714
David L. Lucchino (Co-Founder, Pres & CEO)
Christopher R. Loose (Co-Founder)
Dana Hilt (Chief Medical Officer)
Michael Bookman (Gen Counsel & Sec)
Jeff Hrkach (Sr VP-Tech Dev)
Marc A. Cohen (Chm)
Wendy Arnold (Chief People Officer)
Lisa Geller (Head-Intellectual Property)
Bill Chin (Exec VP-Translational Medicine)
Jason Glashow (Sr VP-Corp Affairs)
Will McLean (Co-Founder & VP-Biology & Regenerative Medicine)
Quentin McCubbin (Chief Mfg Officer)
Susan Stewart (Chief Regulatory Officer)
Kevin Franck (Sr VP-Strategic Mktg & New Product Plng)

FRESH DEL MONTE PRODUCE INC.

241 Sevilla Ave, Coral Gables, FL 33134
Tel.: (305) 520-8400   Ky
Web Site:
   https://www.freshdelmonte.com
Year Founded: 1892
FDP—(NYSE)
Rev.: $4,442,300,000
Assets: $3,458,900,000
Liabilities: $1,533,300,000
Net Worth: $1,925,600,000
Earnings: $98,600,000
Emp.: 6,920
Fiscal Year-end: 12/30/22
Fresh-Cut Fruit, Vegetables & Other Fresh Produce Distr & Marketer
N.A.I.C.S.: 311421
Sergio Mancilla (VP-South America)
Gianpaolo Renino (VP-Europe & Africa)
Mohammed Abbas (COO & Exec VP)
Jorge Pelaez (VP-CECAB)
Ziad Nabulsi (Sr VP-Ops)
Effie D. Silva (Gen Counsel)
Claudia Pou (VP)
Mohammad Abu-Ghazaleh (Chm & CEO)
Monica Vicente (CFO, Principal Acctg Officer, Sr VP & VP-Corp Fin)

Subsidiaries:

Del Monte (UK) Ltd.   (1)
Third Floor Mallard Court Market Square, Staines-upon-Thames, TW18 4RH, United Kingdom
Tel.: (44) 1784447400
Web Site: https://www.delmonteeurope.com
Sales Range: $50-74.9 Million
Emp.: 40
Canned Fruits & Beverages
N.A.I.C.S.: 311421

Del Monte B.V.   (1)
Klappolder 170, 2665 MP, Bleiswijk, 2665 MP, Netherlands
Tel.: (31) 105242222
Web Site: https://www.delmonteeurope.nl

Fresh Del Monte Produce Inc.—(Continued)

Emp.: 1
Fresh Fruits & Vegetables Whslr
N.A.I.C.S.: 424480
Hani El-Naffy (Principal)

Mann Packing Co., Inc. (1)
PO Box 690, Salinas, CA 93902-0690
Tel.: (831) 422-7405
Web Site:
https://www.veggiesmadeeasy.com
Grower, Shipper & Crop Preparation Services For Market
N.A.I.C.S.: 311421

FRESH FACTORY B.C. LIMITED
238 Tubeway Dr, Carol Stream, IL 60188
Web Site:
https://www.thefreshfactory.co
Year Founded: 2018
FRFAF—(OTCIQ)
Rev.: $23,688,174
Assets: $11,535,654
Liabilities: $5,827,848
Net Worth: $5,707,806
Earnings: ($3,374,524)
Fiscal Year-end: 12/31/23
Frozen Specialty Food Manufacturing
N.A.I.C.S.: 311412
Bill Besenhofer (CEO)
John Mikulich (CFO)

FRESH TRACKS THERAPEUTICS, INC.
2000 Central Ave Ste 100, Boulder, CO 80301
Tel.: (720) 505-4755 DE
Web Site: https://www.frtx.com
Year Founded: 1987
FRTX—(NASDAQ)
Rev.: $6,943,000
Assets: $10,271,000
Liabilities: $3,077,000
Net Worth: $7,194,000
Earnings: ($21,102,000)
Emp.: 13
Fiscal Year-end: 12/31/22
Developer of Gene-Based Drugs for the Treatment of Infectious Diseases
N.A.I.C.S.: 325411
Reginald L. Hardy (Chm)
Andrew D. Sklawer (Founder)
Deepak Chadha (COO & Chief R&D Officer)
David R. McAvoy (Chief Compliance Officer & Gen Counsel)
Michael P. Doyle (VP-Regulatory Affairs)
John Koleng (VP-Product Dev)
Ginger McWilliams (VP-Professional Rels & New Product Plng)
Nancy Seretta (VP & Head-Clinical Ops)
Gary Walker (CMO)
Albert N. Marchio II (CFO)
Sue Fattor (Head-HR)
Aron Aizenstat (Sr Dir-Corp Dev & Ops)
Aaron Fox-Collis (Chief Acctg Officer & VP-Finance)

FRESH VINE WINE, INC.
11500 Wayzata Blvd Ste 1147, Minnetonka, MN 55305 NV
Web Site:
https://www.freshvinewine.com
Year Founded: 2019
VINE—(NYSEAMEX)
Rev.: $2,860,001
Assets: $8,586,154
Liabilities: $2,972,548
Net Worth: $5,613,606
Earnings: ($15,202,507)
Emp.: 8
Fiscal Year-end: 12/31/22

Wine Mfr & Distr
N.A.I.C.S.: 312130
Roger Cockroft (CEO)
Keith Johnson (Sec)

FRESHPET, INC.
400 Plaza Dr 1st Fl, Secaucus, NJ 07094
Tel.: (201) 520-4000 DE
Web Site: https://www.freshpet.com
Year Founded: 2006
FRPT—(NASDAQ)
Rev.: $766,895,000
Assets: $1,464,421,000
Liabilities: $510,967,000
Net Worth: $953,454,000
Earnings: ($33,614,000)
Emp.: 1,083
Fiscal Year-end: 12/31/23
Pet Food Mfr
N.A.I.C.S.: 311111
Scott Morris (Founder, Pres & COO)
Charles A. Norris (Chm)
Stephen Macchiaverna (Treas, Sec & Exec VP)
Thomas Farina (Sr VP-Sls)
Christopher Taranto (VP-Procurement & Plng)
William B. Cyr (CEO)
Todd E. Cunfer (CFO)
Thembi Machaba (Sr VP-HR)
Ivan Garcia (VP-Fin & Controller)
Dirk K. Martin (VP-Customer Svc & Logistics)
Dirk Martin (VP-Customer Svc & Logistics)
Richard A. Kassar (Vice Chm)

FRESHWORKS INC.
2950 S Delaware St Ste 201, San Mateo, CA 94403
Tel.: (650) 513-0514 DE
Web Site:
https://www.freshworks.com
Year Founded: 2010
FRSH—(NASDAQ)
Rev.: $596,432,000
Assets: $1,456,772,000
Liabilities: $384,510,000
Net Worth: $1,072,262,000
Earnings: ($137,436,000)
Emp.: 4,900
Fiscal Year-end: 12/31/23
Custom Computer Programming Services
N.A.I.C.S.: 541511
Dennis M. Woodside (Pres & CEO)
Mika Yamamoto (Chief Customer & Mktg Officer)
Pradeep Rathinam (Chief Revenue Officer)
Johanna Jackman (Chief People Officer)
Tyler Sloat (CFO)
Shanmugam Krishnasamy (Co-Founder & CTO)
Prakash Ramamurthy (Chief Product Officer)
Suman Gopalan (Chief HR Officer)
Pam Sergeeff (Chief Legal Officer & Gen Counsel)
Pradeep Rathinam (Chief Customer Officer)
Rathna Girish Mathrubootham (Co-Founder & Chm)
Tyler Sloat (CFO & COO)

Subsidiaries:

Freshworks Australia Pty. Ltd. (1)
Level 28 161 Castlereagh Street, Sydney, 2000, NSW, Australia
Tel.: (61) 180 086 1302
Information Technology Services
N.A.I.C.S.: 541511

Freshworks GmbH (1)

Alte Jakobstrasse 85/86, 10179, Berlin, Germany
Tel.: (49) 305 884 9246
Information Technology Services
N.A.I.C.S.: 541511

Freshworks SAS (1)
WeWork 92 Av des Champs-Elysees, 75008, Paris, France
Tel.: (33) 17 585 0312
Information Technology Services
N.A.I.C.S.: 541511

Freshworks Technologies B.V. (1)
Stationsplein 32, 3511 ED, Utrecht, Netherlands
Tel.: (31) 85 001 3362
Information Technology Services
N.A.I.C.S.: 541511

Freshworks Technologies Private Limited (1)
Global Infocity Block B 40 MGR Road, Chennai, 600 096, India
Tel.: (91) 446 667 8080
Information Technology Services
N.A.I.C.S.: 541511

Freshworks Technologies UK Limited (1)
3rd Floor Johnson Building 77 Hatton Garden, London, EC1N 8JS, United Kingdom
Tel.: (44) 189 280 5040
Information Technology Services
N.A.I.C.S.: 541511

FRIEDMAN INDUSTRIES, INC.
1121 Judson Rd Ste 124, Longview, TX 75601
Tel.: (903) 758-3431 TX
Web Site:
https://www.friedmanindustries.com
Year Founded: 1939
FRD—(NYSEAMEX)
Rev.: $516,251,000
Assets: $230,019,000
Liabilities: $102,544,000
Net Worth: $127,475,000
Earnings: $17,345,000
Emp.: 268
Fiscal Year-end: 03/31/24
Semi-Finished Hot Rolled Steel, Sheets & Plates; Tubular Goods; Fastener Products
N.A.I.C.S.: 331221
Alex LaRue (CFO, Treas & Sec)
Howard Henderson (VP-Ops-Tubular Products)
Robert McCain (VP-Ops-Decatur Facility)
Steve Teeter (VP-Ops-Hickman Facility)
Michael Thompson (VP-Sls-Tubular Products)
Michael J. Taylor (Chm)
Jonathan Holcomb (VP-Sls-Coil Divisions)

Subsidiaries:

Texas Tubular Products (1)
FM 250, Lone Star, TX 75668 (100%)
Tel.: (903) 639-2511
Web Site:
http://www.friedmanindustries.com
Sales Range: $25-49.9 Million
Emp.: 50
Marketing of Structural Steel Pipes
N.A.I.C.S.: 331210
Howard Henderson (VP-Ops)
Michael Thompson (VP-Sls)

FRIENDABLE, INC.
1821 S Bascom Ave Ste 353, Campbell, CA 95008
Tel.: (855) 473-8473 NV
Web Site: https://www.friendable.com
Year Founded: 2007
FDBL—(OTCIQ)
Rev.: $6,629
Assets: $253,523
Liabilities: $5,007,005
Net Worth: ($4,753,482)

Earnings: ($2,905,180)
Emp.: 5
Fiscal Year-end: 12/31/21
Social Media Application Developer
N.A.I.C.S.: 541810
Frank Garcia (CFO)
Jeffrey M. Canouse (CEO)
Robert A. Rositano Jr. (Founder)

FRIENDLY HILLS BANK
16011 Whittier Blvd, Whittier, CA 90603
Tel.: (562) 947-1920
Web Site:
http://www.friendlyhillsbank.com
FHLB—(OTCIQ)
Sales Range: $1-9.9 Million
Emp.: 22
Commercial Banking
N.A.I.C.S.: 522110
Elizabeth M. Buckingham (COO & Exec VP)
William Chris Greenbeck (Chm)
Robert A. Marshall (Chief Credit Officer & Exec VP)
Dan McGregor (Exec VP)
James Burgess (CFO & Exec VP)
Azim Sheikh (Chief Info & Tech Officer & Exec VP)
Paulette Silva (Chief Admin Officer & Exec VP)
Nathan Rogge (Pres & CEO)

FRMO CORP.
1 N Lexington Ave Ste 12C, White Plains, NY 10601
Tel.: (646) 495-7337 DE
Web Site: https://www.frmocorp.com
Year Founded: 1993
FRMO—(OTCIQ)
Rev.: $5,081,547
Assets: $303,493,732
Liabilities: $19,379,323
Net Worth: $284,114,409
Earnings: ($31,761,772)
Emp.: 5
Fiscal Year-end: 05/31/23
Financial Management Services
N.A.I.C.S.: 541611
Therese Byars (Sec)
Peter Doyle (VP)
Jay Kesslen (Gen Counsel)
Steven Bregman (Pres & CEO)
Murray Stahl (Chm & CFO)

FRONTDOOR, INC.
3400 Players Club Pkwy, Memphis, TN 38125
Tel.: (901) 701-5000 DE
Web Site:
https://www.frontdoorhome.com
Year Founded: 2018
FTDR—(NASDAQ)
Rev.: $1,662,000,000
Assets: $1,082,000,000
Liabilities: $1,021,000,000
Net Worth: $61,000,000
Earnings: $71,000,000
Emp.: 1,712
Fiscal Year-end: 12/31/22
Appliance Repair & Maintenance
N.A.I.C.S.: 811412
William C. Cobb (Chm & CEO)
Jeffrey A. Fiarman (Gen Counsel, Sec & Sr VP)
Scott Brown (Sr VP-Customer Experience)
Raj Midha (Sr VP & Gen Mgr)
Piras Thiyagarajan (CTO & Sr VP)
Brett Worthington (Sr VP-Bus Dev)
Matt Davis (VP-IR)

Chastitie S. Brim *(Chief Accounting Officer ,VP & Controller)*
Jen Alessandra *(Chief People Officer & Sr VP)*
Kathy Collins *(CMO & Sr VP)*
Jessica P. Ross *(CFO & Sr VP)*

Subsidiaries:

American Home Shield Corporation   **(1)**
3400 Players Club Pkwy Ste 300, Memphis, TN 38125
Tel.: (901) 537-8000
Web Site: https://www.ahs.com
Home Warranty Company
N.A.I.C.S.: 524128

Subsidiary (Domestic):

Home Security of America, Inc.   **(2)**
150 Peabody Pl Ste 300, Memphis, TN 38103
Web Site: https://www.onlinehsa.com
Home Warranty Services
N.A.I.C.S.: 524128

Landmark Home Warranty, LLC   **(2)**
3400 Players Club Pkwy Ste 300, Memphis, TN 38125
Web Site: https://www.landmarkhw.com
Home Warranty Service & Coverage Plans (for Residential Properties)
N.A.I.C.S.: 522310

FRONTERA GROUP INC.
701 S Carson St Ste 200, Carson City, NV 89701
Tel.: (425) 402-1400   **NV**
Web Site: https://www.frtgtech.com
Year Founded: 2013
FRTG—(OTCIQ)
Business Development & Market Consultancy Services
N.A.I.C.S.: 541611

FRONTERA RESOURCES CORP.
3040 Post Oak Blvd Ste 1100, Houston, TX 77056
Tel.: (713) 585-3200
Web Site:
   http://www.fronteraresources.com
Year Founded: 1996
FRR—(AIM)
Drilling Oil & Gas Wells
N.A.I.C.S.: 213111
Zaza Mamulaishvili *(CEO)*
Paolo Pratelli *(VP-Ops)*
Levan Bakhutashvili *(Gen Counsel, Sec & VP)*
Giorgi Kalandarishvili *(VP-Fin & Admin)*
Reginal W. Spiller *(Exec VP-Exploration & Production)*

FRONTIER ACQUISITION CORP.
660 Madison Ave 19th Fl, New York, NY 10065
Tel.: (212) 803-9080   **Ky**
Year Founded: 2021
FRON—(NASDAQ)
Investment Services
N.A.I.C.S.: 523999
Rick Gerson *(Co-Pres)*
Christian Angermayer *(CEO)*
Ryan Khoury *(Co-Pres)*
Matthew Corey *(CFO)*
Scott Carpenter *(COO)*

FRONTIER COMMUNICATIONS PARENT, INC.
401 Merritt 7, Norwalk, CT 06851
Tel.: (203) 614-5600   **DE**
Web Site: https://www.frontier.com
Year Founded: 2021
FYBR—(NASDAQ)
Rev.: $5,751,000,000
Assets: $20,693,000,000

Liabilities: $15,414,000,000
Net Worth: $5,279,000,000
Earnings: $29,000,000
Emp.: 13,300
Fiscal Year-end: 12/31/23
Holding Company; Telecommunications Services
N.A.I.C.S.: 551112
Nick Jeffery *(Pres & CEO)*
Scott C. Beasley *(CFO & Exec VP)*
John G. Stratton *(Exec Chm)*
John Harrobin *(Exec VP-Consumer)*
William McGloin *(Chief Acctg Officer & Controller)*
M. Alan Gardner *(Chief People Officer & Exec VP)*

Subsidiaries:

Frontier Communications Corporation   **(1)**
401 Merritt 7, Norwalk, CT 06851
Tel.: (203) 614-5600
Web Site: http://www.frontier.com
Telecommunications, Internet & Satellite Television Services
N.A.I.C.S.: 517111
Nick Jeffery *(Pres & CEO)*
Melissa Pint *(Chief Digital Info Officer)*
Charlon McIntosh *(Chief Customer Ops Officer)*

Subsidiary (Domestic):

CTSI, LLC   **(2)**
3864 Courtney St Ste 240, Bethlehem, PA 18017
Tel.: (610) 317-4400
Telecommunication Servicesb
N.A.I.C.S.: 517121
David Klotz *(Mgr)*

Citizens Telecommunications Company of Minnesota, LLC   **(2)**
2378 Wilshire Blvd, Mound, MN 55364-1652
Tel.: (952) 491-5576
Web Site: http://www.frontiercorp.com
Emp.: 6
Telecommunication Servicesb
N.A.I.C.S.: 517121

Citizens Telecommunications Company of Nebraska   **(2)**
2302 1st Ave, Kearney, NE 68847
Tel.: (308) 234-6731
Telecommunication Servicesb
N.A.I.C.S.: 517121

Commonwealth Telephone Enterprises, Inc.   **(2)**
100 CTE Dr, Dallas, PA 18612-9774
Tel.: (570) 631-2700
Web Site: http://www.frontieronline.com
Sales Range: $300-349.9 Million
Emp.: 1,110
Telecommunication Servicesb
N.A.I.C.S.: 541618

Unit (Domestic):

Frontier Communications   **(2)**
8110 S Anthony Blvd, Fort Wayne, IN 46816
Tel.: (260) 428-8106
Sales Range: $10-24.9 Million
Emp.: 4
Telecommunication Servicesb
N.A.I.C.S.: 517121
Jacqueline R. Kinney *(VP-State Govt Affairs-California)*
Carl Erhart *(VP)*

Subsidiary (Domestic):

Frontier Communications Corporate Services Inc.   **(2)**
3 High Ridge Park, Stamford, CT 06905
Tel.: (203) 614-5600
Telecommunication Servicesb
N.A.I.C.S.: 517111

Frontier Communications of Breezewood, LLC   **(2)**
150 S Main St, Breezewood, PA 15533
Tel.: (814) 735-4001
Emp.: 16
Telecommunication Servicesb

N.A.I.C.S.: 517121

Frontier Communications of Delaware, Inc.   **(2)**
19 E Central Ave, Delaware, OH 43015
Tel.: (740) 369-2780
Telecommunication Servicesb
N.A.I.C.S.: 517810

Frontier Communications of Michigan, Inc.   **(2)**
109 Randolph St, Brooklyn, MI 49230
Tel.: (517) 592-0201
Emp.: 30
Telecommunication Servicesb
N.A.I.C.S.: 517121

Unit (Domestic):

Frontier Communications   **(3)**
601 N Us Hwy 131, Three Rivers, MI 49093   **(100%)**
Tel.: (269) 273-0392
Sales Range: $10-24.9 Million
Emp.: 20
Telecommunication Servicesb
N.A.I.C.S.: 517810

Subsidiary (Domestic):

Frontier Communications of Minnesota, Inc.   **(2)**
1405 W 150th St, Burnsville, MN 55306   **(100%)**
Tel.: (952) 898-6422
Web Site: http://www.frontieronline.com
Rev.: $89,449,039
Emp.: 500
Local Telephone Communication Services
N.A.I.C.S.: 517121

Frontier Communications of Mississippi LLC   **(2)**
44 Main St, Rienzi, MS 38865
Tel.: (662) 462-4000
Web Site: http://www.frontiernet.net
Rev.: $68,000
Emp.: 12
Telecommunication Servicesb
N.A.I.C.S.: 517121

Frontier Communications of Mt. Pulaski, Inc.   **(2)**
117 W Jefferson St, Mount Pulaski, IL 62548
Tel.: (309) 454-7803
Sales Range: $10-24.9 Million
Emp.: 6
Telecommunication Servicesb
N.A.I.C.S.: 517121

Frontier Communications of New York, Inc.   **(2)**
180 S Clinton Ave, Rochester, NY 14646
Tel.: (914) 783-5226
Web Site: http://www.frontier.com
Sales Range: $1-4.9 Billion
Emp.: 2,600
Telecommunication Servicesb
N.A.I.C.S.: 517121

Frontier Communications of Pennsylvania, LLC   **(2)**
37-43 Diller Ave, New Holland, PA 17557
Tel.: (717) 355-7000
Emp.: 66
Telecommunication Servicesb
N.A.I.C.S.: 517121
Elena Kilpatrick *(VP & Gen Mgr)*

Frontier Communications of Thorntown LLC   **(2)**
115 E Bow St, Thorntown, IN 46071
Tel.: (765) 436-7800
Web Site: http://www.frontier.com
Telecommunication Servicesb
N.A.I.C.S.: 517810

Frontier Communications of Wisconsin LLC   **(2)**
154 E 2nd St, New Richmond, WI 54017
Tel.: (715) 243-7004
Web Site: http://www.frontier.com
Sales Range: $10-24.9 Million
Emp.: 16
Telecommunication Servicesb
N.A.I.C.S.: 517121

Frontier North Inc.   **(2)**
400 Westwood Dr, Wausau, WI 54401

N.A.I.C.S.: 517121

Tel.: (715) 843-8827
Sales Range: $25-49.9 Million
Emp.: 50
Telecommunication Servicesb
N.A.I.C.S.: 517121

Frontier West Virginia Inc.   **(2)**
1500 MacCorkle Ave SE, Charleston, WV 25396
Tel.: (304) 343-9911
Sales Range: $1-4.9 Billion
Emp.: 3,350
Telecommunication Servicesb
N.A.I.C.S.: 517121

Subsidiary (Domestic):

Frontier West Virginia Inc.   **(3)**
120 Applanchian Dr, Beckley, WV 25801
Tel.: (304) 255-9859
Sales Range: $10-24.9 Million
Emp.: 30
Telephone Communications
N.A.I.C.S.: 517121

Frontier West Virginia Inc.   **(3)**
RR Two Box 40C, Ripley, WV 25271
Tel.: (304) 372-7900
Sales Range: $10-24.9 Million
Emp.: 15
Telephone Communications
N.A.I.C.S.: 517111

Frontier West Virginia Inc.   **(3)**
145 Fayette St, Morgantown, WV 26505
Tel.: (304) 291-9974
Sales Range: $10-24.9 Million
Emp.: 7
Telecommunication Servicesb
N.A.I.C.S.: 517121

Subsidiary (Domestic):

NCC Systems Inc.   **(2)**
664 Tom Miller Rd, Plattsburgh, NY 12901
Tel.: (518) 562-9339
Web Site: http://nccsystems.com
Sales Range: $10-24.9 Million,
Emp.: 20
Security System Services
N.A.I.C.S.: 561621

Tele-Tec Contractors, Inc.   **(2)**
1207 Severn Ridge Rd, Webster, NY 14580
Tel.: (585) 872-4915
Telecommunication Servicesb
N.A.I.C.S.: 517111

The Southern New England Telephone Company   **(2)**
227 Church St, New Haven, CT 06510
Tel.: (203) 771-5200
Telecommunication Servicesb
N.A.I.C.S.: 517121

Unit (Domestic):

AT&T   **(3)**
1175 Wood End Rd, Bridgeport, CT 06615   **(100%)**
Tel.: (203) 383-6653
Sales Range: $10-24.9 Million
Emp.: 125
Provides Construction for Telephones & Communication Systems
N.A.I.C.S.: 237130

AT&T External Affairs   **(3)**
111 Trumbull St, Hartford, CT 06103   **(100%)**
Tel.: (860) 947-7198
Sales Range: $1-9.9 Million
Emp.: 6
Provider of Local & Long Distance Telephone Communication
N.A.I.C.S.: 517121

FRONTIER GROUP HOLDINGS, INC.
4545 Airport Way, Denver, CO 80239
Tel.: (720) 374-4490   **DE**
Web Site: https://ir.flyfrontier.com
Year Founded: 2013
ULCC—(NASDAQ)
Rev.: $3,589,000,000
Assets: $4,993,000,000
Liabilities: $4,486,000,000
Net Worth: $507,000,000

Frontier Group Holdings, Inc.—(Continued)

Earnings: ($11,000,000)
Emp.: 7,235
Fiscal Year-end: 12/31/23
Low-Cost Airline Services
N.A.I.C.S.: 481111
Barry L. Biffle *(CEO)*
William A. Franke *(Chm)*
Barry L. Biffle *(Pres & CEO)*
James G. Dempsey *(CFO & Exec VP)*
Howard M. Diamond *(Gen Counsel, Sec & Sr VP)*
Mark C. Mitchell *(CFO & Sr VP)*
Daniel M. Shurz *(Sr VP-Comml)*
Jake F. Filene *(Sr VP-Customers)*
Trevor J. Stedke *(Sr VP-Ops)*
Rajat Khanna *(CIO & Sr VP)*
Matthew Saks *(Treas & VP)*
James G. Dempsey *(Pres)*

FRONTIER INVESTMENT CORP.

3411 Silverside Rd Tatnall Bldg Ste 104, Wilmington, DE 19810
Tel.: (302) 351-3367   Ky
Year Founded: 2021
FICV—(NASDAQ)
Rev.: $9,664,444
Assets: $203,561,210
Liabilities: $213,408,781
Net Worth: ($9,847,571)
Earnings: $6,513,806
Emp.: 2
Fiscal Year-end: 12/31/22
Investment Services
N.A.I.C.S.: 523999
Asar Asar *(Chm & CEO)*
Arif Mansuri *(CFO)*
Hedi Ben Mlouka *(Principal-Investment)*
Suveer Arenja *(Principal-Investment)*
Anvita Varshney *(Principal-Investment)*
Mohamed Khalifa *(Principal-Investment)*

FRP HOLDINGS, INC.

200 W Forsyth St 7th Fl, Jacksonville, FL 32202
Tel.: (904) 396-5733   FL
Web Site: https://www.frpdev.com
Year Founded: 1988
FRPH—(NASDAQ)
Rev.: $37,481,000
Assets: $701,084,000
Liabilities: $256,873,000
Net Worth: $444,211,000
Earnings: $4,565,000
Emp.: 13
Fiscal Year-end: 12/31/22
Real Estate Services
N.A.I.C.S.: 531390
David H. deVilliers Jr. *(Vice Chm & Pres)*
David H. deVilliers III *(COO)*
John D. Klopfenstein *(Chief Acctg Officer & Controller)*
Matthew C. McNulty *(CFO & Treas)*
John Daniel Baker III *(CEO)*
Todd Evans *(Dir-Acquisitions & Asset Mgmt)*
Matt Martin *(Sr Mgr-Construction)*
Suzanne Mayle *(Controller)*
Brendan White *(Mgr)*
John D. Milton Jr. *(Gen Counsel & Exec VP)*

Subsidiaries:

FRP Development Corp.   (1)
34 Loveton Cir Ste 200, Sparks, MD 21152
Tel.: (410) 771-4100
Web Site: https://www.frpdev.com
Commercial Real Estate Services
N.A.I.C.S.: 531390

David H. deVilliers Jr. *(Vice Chm & Pres)*
David H. deVilliers III *(COO & Exec VP)*
Matthew C. McNulty *(CFO)*
John D. Baker III *(CEO)*
Janet Bitzelberger *(Asst Office Mgr-Executive HR Coordinator)*
Todd Evans *(Dir-Acquisitions & Asset Mgmt)*
Matt Martin *(Sr Mgr-Construction)*
John D. Klopfenstein *(Controller)*
Suzanne Mayle *(Controller)*

FRP Transit Business Park   (1)
115 W Patrick St, Frederick, MD 21701-5513
Tel.: (301) 698-1932
Investment Management Service
N.A.I.C.S.: 523940

Florida Rock & Tank Lines, Inc.   (1)
200 W Forsyth St 7th Fl, Jacksonville, FL 32202
Tel.: (904) 396-5733
Web Site: https://www.floridarockandtanklines.com
Sales Range: $50-74.9 Million
Emp.: 80
Transportation Services
N.A.I.C.S.: 484110

FRX INNOVATIONS INC.

200 Turnpike Rd, Chelmsford, MA 01824
Tel.: (978) 244-9500
Web Site: https://www.frx-innovations.com
FRXI—(TSXV)
Miscellaneous Financial Investment Activities
N.A.I.C.S.: 523999

Subsidiaries:

FRX Polymers Inc.   (1)
200 Tpke Rd Ste 1, Chelmsford, MA 01824-4000
Tel.: (978) 244-9500
Web Site: http://www.frxpolymers.com
Testing Laboratories
N.A.I.C.S.: 541380
Marc Lebel *(CEO)*
Ina Jiang *(VP-Mktg)*
Ulrich Girrbach *(VP-Fibres & Textiles)*

FS BANCORP, INC.

6920 220th St SW, Mountlake Terrace, WA 98043
Tel.: (425) 771-5299   WA
Web Site: https://www.fsbwa.com
FSBW—(NASDAQ)
Rev.: $136,802,000
Assets: $2,632,898,000
Liabilities: $2,401,201,000
Net Worth: $231,697,000
Earnings: $29,649,000
Emp.: 537
Fiscal Year-end: 12/31/22
Bank Holding Company
N.A.I.C.S.: 551111
Joseph C. Adams *(CEO)*
Matthew D. Mullet *(CFO, Treas & Sec)*
Dennis V. O'Leary *(Chief Lending Officer & Exec VP)*
Vickie A. Jarman *(Chief HR Officer & Exec VP)*
Donn C. Costa *(Exec VP-Home Lending Production)*
Kelli B. Nielsen *(Exec VP-Retail Banking & Mktg)*
Shana Allen *(CIO)*
Jill Coates *(Sr VP)*
Ben Crowl *(Sr VP)*
Kyle Johnson *(Sr VP)*
Brian Kunkel *(Sr VP)*
Kathrine Shairrick *(Sr VP)*
May-Ling Sowell *(Officer)*
Paul Taylor *(Sr VP)*

Subsidiaries:

1st Security Bank of Washington   (1)
6920 220th St SW, Mountlake Terrace, WA 98043

Tel.: (425) 697-8124
Web Site: https://www.fsbwa.com
Sales Range: $75-99.9 Million
Commercial Banking
N.A.I.C.S.: 522110
Joseph C. Adams *(CEO)*
Matthew D. Mullet *(CFO & Exec VP)*
Donn C. Costa *(Chief Home Lending Officer, Exec VP-Home Lending & Exec VP)*
May-Ling Sowell *(Compliance Officer & Sr VP)*
Shana Allen *(CIO)*
Kathrine Shairrick *(Sr VP, Sr VP-Svc & Operations & Mgr-Svcs & Operations)*
Anita Schmucker *(VP & Mgr-Hadlock)*
Kelli B. Nielsen *(Exec VP-Retail Banking & Mktg)*
Erin M. Burr *(Chief Risk Officer & Exec VP)*
Kyle Johnson *(Sr VP-Capital Markets)*
Vickie Jarman *(Chief HR Officer & Exec VP)*
Jill Coates *(Sr VP-Home Lending Credit)*
Paul Taylor *(Sr VP-Home Lending Ops)*
Brian Kunkel *(Sr VP & Dir-Comml Lending)*
John Hill *(Sr VP & Dir-Community & Bus Banking)*
Ben Crowl *(Chief Lending Officer)*
Albert Suh *(VP)*
Casey Cronk *(VP)*
Darrell Jenkins *(VP)*
Joe Corona *(VP)*
Kevin Richards *(Sr VP)*
Kylen Stevenson *(VP, Asst VP & Asst Mgr-Comml Lending Relationship)*
Mike Charters *(VP)*
Dan Icasiano *(Sr VP & Dir-Treasury Mgmt)*
Camberly Gilmartin *(Mktg Mgr)*
Sean McCormick *(Exec VP)*
Addriane DeVito *(Officer-Cash Management)*
Matthew Mullet *(Exec VP)*
Jason Ramos *(VP)*
Torie Ramirez *(VP-Community & Bus Banking)*
Adit Nair *(Officer-Cash Management)*
Jarrett Olson *(Officer-Cash Management-CTP)*
Patrick Ryan *(VP)*
Anthony Galvan *(Asst VP)*
Blake Mittlestaedt *(Asst VP)*

FTAC ATHENA ACQUISITION CORP.

2929 Arch St Ste 1703, Philadelphia, PA 19104
Tel.: (484) 459-3476   Ky
Year Founded: 2020
FTAA—(NASDAQ)
Rev.: $1,866,139
Assets: $250,610,475
Liabilities: $268,718,864
Net Worth: ($18,108,389)
Earnings: $4,215
Emp.: 2
Fiscal Year-end: 12/31/21
Investment Services
N.A.I.C.S.: 523999
Amanda J. Abrams *(Pres & CEO)*
Douglas Listman *(CFO)*

FTAC EMERALD ACQUISITION CORP.

2929 Arch St Ste 1703, Philadelphia, PA 19104
Tel.: (215) 701-9555   DE
Year Founded: 2021
FLD—(NASDAQ)
Rev.: $3,619,061
Assets: $255,664,716
Liabilities: $264,165,533
Net Worth: ($8,500,817)
Earnings: $1,115,764
Emp.: 2
Fiscal Year-end: 12/31/22
Investment Services
N.A.I.C.S.: 523999
Betsy Cohen *(Chm)*
Bracebridge H. Young *(Pres & CEO)*
Douglas Listman *(CFO)*
Mark Tercek *(Vice Chm)*

FTAC HERA ACQUISITION CORP.

2929 Arch St Ste 1703, Philadelphia, PA 19104
Tel.: (215) 701-9555   Ky
Year Founded: 2021
HERA—(NASDAQ)
Rev.: $7,598,954
Assets: $852,897,654
Liabilities: $903,243,395
Net Worth: ($50,345,741)
Earnings: $6,105,749
Emp.: 2
Fiscal Year-end: 12/31/21
Investment Services
N.A.I.C.S.: 523999
Betsy Z. Cohen *(Chm)*
Daniel G. Cohen *(Pres & CEO)*
Douglas Listman *(CFO)*

FTAC PARNASSUS ACQUISITION CORP.

2929 Arch St Ste 1703, Philadelphia, PA 19104
Tel.: (215) 701-9555   DE
Year Founded: 2020
FTPA—(NASDAQ)
Rev.: $950,590
Assets: $251,130,673
Liabilities: $268,305,575
Net Worth: ($17,174,902)
Earnings: ($183,703)
Emp.: 2
Fiscal Year-end: 12/31/21
Investment Services
N.A.I.C.S.: 523999
Daniel G. Cohen *(Chm)*
Ryan M. Gilbert *(Pres & CEO)*
Joseph W. Pooler Jr. *(CFO)*

FTAC ZEUS ACQUISITION CORP.

2929 Arch St Ste 1703, Philadelphia, PA 19104
Tel.: (215) 701-9555   DE
Year Founded: 2020
ZING—(NASDAQ)
Rev.: $5,888,798
Assets: $420,996,415
Liabilities: $437,658,522
Net Worth: ($16,662,107)
Earnings: $1,378,408
Emp.: 2
Fiscal Year-end: 12/31/22
Investment Services
N.A.I.C.S.: 523999
Daniel G. Cohen *(Chm)*
Ryan M. Gilbert *(Pres & CEO)*
Shami Patel *(COO & Sec)*
Joseph W. Pooler Jr. *(CFO)*

FTAI INFRASTRUCTURE, INC.

1345 Avenue of the Americas 45th Fl, New York, NY 10105
Tel.: (646) 734-9414   DE
Web Site: https://www.fipinc.com
Year Founded: 2021
FIP—(NASDAQ)
Rev.: $261,966,000
Assets: $2,478,399,000
Liabilities: $1,953,605,000
Net Worth: $524,794,000
Earnings: ($187,517,000)
Emp.: 690
Fiscal Year-end: 12/31/22
Freight Transportation Arrangement
N.A.I.C.S.: 488510
Joseph P. Adams Jr. *(Chm)*
Kenneth J. Nicholson *(Pres)*
Scott Christopher *(Treas)*

FTC SOLAR, INC.

9020 N Capital of Texas Hwy Bldg 1 Ste 260, Austin, TX 78759
Tel.: (737) 787-7906   DE
Web Site: https://www.ftcsolar.com

Year Founded: 2017
FTCI—(NASDAQ)
Rev.: $123,066,000
Assets: $134,398,000
Liabilities: $67,948,000
Net Worth: $66,450,000
Earnings: ($99,613,000)
Emp.: 221
Fiscal Year-end: 12/31/22
Solar Engineering Services
N.A.I.C.S.: 541330
Thurman John Rodgers *(Chm)*
Patrick Cook *(CFO & Treas)*
Cathy Behnen *(Interim CFO & Chief Acctg Officer)*
Patrick M. Cook *(Chief Comml Officer & Sr VP-Capital Markets & Bus Dev)*
Sasan Aminpour *(COO)*
Jacob Wolf *(Gen Counsel)*
Yann Brandt *(Pres & CEO)*

FTE NETWORKS, INC.

237 W 35th St Ste 806, New York,
NY 10001   NV
Web Site: http://www.ftenetwork.com
FTNW—(NYSEAMEX)
Sales Range: $200-249.9 Million
Emp.: 223
Information Technology Systems Infrastructure Solutions
N.A.I.C.S.: 541519
Michael Palleschi *(Chm & CEO)*
John Wood *(COO & Pres-Network Svcs)*
Carlie Ancor *(CTO)*
William P. Leonard *(VP-Sls-Central & East)*

Subsidiaries:

Benchmark Builders, Inc.   (1)
237 W 35th St Ste 901, New York, NY
10001
Tel.: (212) 766-8800
Web Site: http://www.benchmark-ny.com
Construction Management Services
N.A.I.C.S.: 541330

Jus-Com Inc.   (1)
7F No 137 Datong Road Section 2 Xizhi
District, New Taipei City, 22183, Taiwan
Tel.: (886) 286926782
Web Site: http://www.juscom.com
Computer Related Services
N.A.I.C.S.: 541519

FTI CONSULTING, INC.

555 12 St NW, Washington, DC
20004
Tel.: (202) 312-9100   MD
Web Site:
    https://www.fticonsulting.com
Year Founded: 1982
FCN—(NYSE)
Rev.: $3,489,242,000
Assets: $3,325,878,000
Liabilities: $1,344,458,000
Net Worth: $1,981,420,000
Earnings: $274,892,000
Emp.: 7,990
Fiscal Year-end: 12/31/23
Financial Restructuring, Litigation Support, Performance & Compliance Consulting Services
N.A.I.C.S.: 541611
Albert S. Conly *(Sr Mng Dir & Sr Mng Dir-Dallas)*
Curtis P. Lu *(Gen Counsel)*
Sean Gumbs *(Sr Mng Dir & Sr Mng Dir-New York)*
Jason Frankl *(Founder-Activism & M&A Solutions Practice & Sr Mng Dir)*
Kathryn McCarthy *(Sr Mng Dir-Tech Practice-Washington)*
Paul Linton *(Chief Strategy & Transformation Officer)*
Joseph DeSantis *(Mng Dir-Performance Improvement Practice-Corp Fin & Restructuring)*

Anthony L. Alvizu *(Mng Dir-Forensic & Litigation Consulting-Chicago)*
Ingrid R. Noone *(Sr Mng Dir-Corp Fin-Roseland)*
J. Medlin *(Sr Mng Dir-Corp Fin-Dallas)*
Mary Ann Kaptain *(Mng Dir-Corp Fin-Los Angeles)*
Tim Renjilian *(Sr Mng Dir-Health Solutions-Atlanta)*
Todd Lester *(Sr Mng Dir-Economic Consulting-Austin)*
Brendan Keating *(Chief Acctg Officer & Controller)*
Sean Harding *(Sr Mng Dir-Corp Fin-Denver)*
William Brydges *(Mng Dir-Tech Transformation Offering-Corp Fin & Restructuring)*
Shannon Maher Banaga *(Sr Mng Dir)*
Johnathan Bridbord *(Co-Mng Dir)*
Matt Chevraux *(Co-Mng Dir)*
Kyle Cormney *(Co-Mng Dir)*
Lauren Crawford Shaver *(Sr Mng Dir)*
Patrick Creighton *(Sr Mng Dir)*
Kathryn DeVito *(Sr Mng Dir)*
Josh Drobnyk *(Co-Mng Dir)*
Edward P. Goodwin Jr. *(Co-Mng Dir)*
Steven H. Gunby *(Pres & CEO)*
Mark Dewar *(Mng Dir-Sydney)*
Mark Bezant *(Sr Mng Dir-London & Head-Economic & Fin Consulting-EMEA)*
John A. MacColl *(Sr Mng Dir-Client Engagement & Conflict Resolution)*
Wendy Dobson *(Sr Mng Dir-London-Strategic Comm Segment)*
Vincent A. Thomas *(Sr Mng Dir-Chicago)*
Tom Kerr *(Sr Dir-Philadelphia-Philadelphia)*
Scott Friedland *(Sr Mng Dir-Forensic & Litigation Consulting-New York)*
Paul Braithwaite *(Sr Mng Dir-New York)*
Nicole P. Wells *(Sr Mng Dir-Chicago-Chicago)*
Michelle D. Herman *(Sr Mng Dir-Los Angeles-Los Angeles)*
Mark Grover *(Sr Mng Dir-Boston-Boston)*
Mark Chertok *(Sr Mng Dir-Corp Fin-New York)*
Lindi Jarvis *(Sr Mng Dir)*
Larissa Gotguelt *(Mng Dir-Corp Fin-Los Angeles)*
Kenneth O'Brien *(Mng Dir-Corp Fin-Roseland)*
Joseph C. Slavis *(Sr Mng Dir, Sr Mng Dir-Forensic & Litigation Consulting-Atlanta & Head-North America Construction-Atlanta)*
Jeffrey Isler *(Sr Mng Dir-New York-New York)*
Jahn S. Brodwin *(Sr Mng Dir-Corp Fin-New York)*
Glenn Brill *(Mng Dir-Corp Fin-New York)*
David S. Turner *(Sr Mng Dir & Sr Mng Dir-Forensic & Litigation Consulting)*
Clara Chin *(Mng Dir-Forensic & Litigation Consulting-New York)*
Benton V. Fisher *(Sr Mng Dir-McLean-McLean)*
Patrick M. Beeman *(Mng Dir-Forensic & Litigation Consulting-Chicago)*
Brian M. Carl *(Sr Mng Dir-Forensic & Litigation Consulting-Chicago)*
Alan Tantleff *(Sr Mng Dir-Corp Fin-New York)*
Louie C. Wu *(Sr Mng Dir)*
Jordan Rae Kelly *(Sr Mng Dir & Head-Cybersecurity-America)*

John Stiffler *(Sr Mng Dir & Sr Mng Dir-San Francisco)*
Cristiano Rios *(Sr Mng Dir-Corp Fin & Restructuring-Brazil)*
Rick Arrowsmith *(Sr Mng Dir)*
Mark Crawshaw *(Sr Mng Dir)*
Brian G. Kushner *(Sr Mng Dir)*
Daniel Kokini *(Mng Dir & Sr Mng Dir-New York)*
John C. Crittenden *(Co-Mng Dir)*
William C. Steere III *(Co-Mng Dir)*
Matthew Bashalany *(Mng Dir & Mng Dir-Corporate Communications)*
Cory Fritz *(Sr Mng Dir & Mng Dir)*
Tina Knight *(Co-Mng Dir)*
Leslie Marlo *(Co-Mng Dir)*
John Gleba *(Co-Mng Dir)*
Ajay Sabherwal *(CFO)*
Holly Paul *(Chief HR Officer)*
Sophie Ross *(CEO-Tech-Global)*
Linda Birta-Mammet *(Treas)*
Michael Buenzow *(Sr Mng Dir, Vice Chm-Restructuring & Sr Mng Dir-Chicago)*
David R. Alfaro *(Sr Mng Dir-San Francisco)*
Greg Gotthardt *(Sr Mng Dir-Los Angeles)*
Alan J. Ruffier *(Sr Mng Dir-Forensic & Litigation Consulting-Los Angeles)*
Amir Agam *(Sr Mng Dir-Corp Fin-Los Angeles)*
Basil A. Imburgia *(Sr Mng Dir-New York)*
Brian Ong *(Sr Mng Dir-New York)*
Bryan Armstrong *(Sr Mng Dir-Strategic Comm-Chicago)*
Carlin Adrianopoli *(Sr Mng Dir-Corp Fin-Chicago)*
Chad E. Coben *(Sr Mng Dir-Corp Fin-Dallas)*
Charles Mikulka *(Sr Mng Dir-New York-New York)*
Chris Tucker *(Sr Mng Dir-Strategic Comm-Washington)*
Christie L. Corbett *(Sr Mng Dir-Atlanta-Atlanta)*
Chuck Carroll *(Sr Mng Dir-Corp Fin-Dallas)*
Cynthia A. Nelson *(Sr Mng Dir-Corp Fin-Los Angeles)*
David B. Lasater *(Sr Mng Dir-Forensic & Litigation Consulting-Houston)*
Dawn Hall *(Sr Mng Dir-Forensic & Litigation Consulting-New York)*
Drew M. Sheehan *(Sr Mng Dir & Sr Mng Dir-Forensic & Litigation Consulting)*
Glenn Tobias *(Sr Mng Dir-New York)*
Jason P. Abbott *(Sr Mng Dir-Corp Fin-Chicago)*
Jeffrey Ellis *(Sr Mng Dir-Chicago-Chicago)*
Jiva J. Jagtap *(Sr Mng Dir-Corp Fin-Denver)*
Kenneth M. Stern *(Sr Mng Dir-New York-New York)*
Kevin McCadden *(Sr Mng Dir-Boston-Boston)*
Kris Coghlan *(Sr Mng Dir-Corp Fin-Philadelphia)*
Lisa M. Collura *(Sr Mng Dir-New York-New York)*
Lou Colasuonno *(Sr Mng Dir-Strategic Comm-New York)*
Mateo Millett *(Sr Mng Dir-Strategic Comm-Boston)*
Matthew Diaz *(Sr Mng Dir-Corp Fin-New York)*
Michael R. Baranowski *(Sr Mng Dir-Economic Consulting-McLean)*
Michael Cordasco *(Sr Mng Dir-Corp Fin-New York)*

Michael Katzenstein *(Sr Mng Dir-Dallas)*
Michael Malloy *(Sr Mng Dir-New York-New York)*
Michael A. Tucker *(Sr Mng Dir-Corp Fin-Phoenix)*
Mike Kinnaman *(Sr Mng Dir-Tech-Seattle)*
Patrick K. Strong *(Sr Mng Dir-Tech-Denver)*
Peter L. Dressel *(Sr Mng Dir & Sr Mng Dir-Health Solutions)*
Robert Fraga *(Sr Mng Dir-Forensic & Litigation Consulting-Boston)*
Ronald F. Greenspan *(Sr Mng Dir-Los Angeles)*
Ronnie A. Martin *(Sr Mng Dir-Houston-Houston)*
Samuel E. Star *(Sr Mng Dir-Corp Fin-New York)*
Scott Bingham *(Sr Mng Dir-Atlanta)*
Stella M. Mendes *(Sr Mng Dir-New York-New York)*
Stephen D. Prowse *(Sr Mng Dir-Dallas-Dallas)*
Steven J. Hazel *(Sr Mng Dir-Los Angeles-Los Angeles)*
Steven J. Joffe *(Sr Mng Dir-Corp Fin-New York)*
Steven D. Simms *(Sr Mng Dir-Corp Fin-New York)*
Tanya Meerovich *(Sr Mng Dir-Corp Fin-New York)*
Tim McDonagh *(Sr Mng Dir-Corp Fin-New York)*
Timothy J. Dragelin *(Sr Mng Dir-Corp Fin-Charlotte)*
Todd J. Smith *(Sr Mng Dir-Corp Fin-Denver)*
Tom Finnegan *(Sr Mng Dir-Atlanta-Atlanta)*
William Berkowitz *(Sr Mng Dir-Great Neck-Great Neck)*
William Clogg *(Sr Mng Dir-Corp Fin-Chicago)*
William Hengemihle *(Sr Mng Dir-Wayne-Wayne)*
Miriam Wrobel *(Sr Mng Dir-San Francisco-Corp Fin,Restructuring)*
Neil Doyle *(Sr Mng Dir-London & Head-Fin Svcs Practice-Strategic Comm Segment-EMEA)*
Ellen S. Smith *(Sr Mng Dir-Boston)*
Brian Grove *(Sr Mng Dir/Mng Dir-Strategic Comm-Houston)*
Allan Kaufman *(Mng Dir-New York-New York)*
Angie Gorman *(Mng Dir-Chicago-Chicago)*
Anil Varghese *(Mng Dir-Forensic & Litigation Consulting-Chicago)*
Ben Goren *(Exec VP & Mng Dir-Corp Fin-Chicago)*
Brian Christie *(Mng Dir-Boston-Boston)*
Carter N. Davis *(Mng Dir-Economic Consulting-Houston)*
Dan Margolis *(Mng Dir-Los Angeles-Los Angeles)*
Dana H. Hayes *(Mng Dir-New York-New York)*
David Becker *(Mng Dir-Tech-Chicago)*
David A. Norkiewicz *(Mng Dir-Chicago-Chicago)*
David G. Ownby *(Mng Dir-Houston-Houston)*
Eric Houle *(Sr Mng Dir-Atlanta & Mng Dir-Corp Fin & Restructuring-Atlanta)*
James Bracken *(Mng Dir-Forensic & Litigation Consulting-New York)*
Jeff Bockus *(Mng Dir-Boston-Boston,MA)*
Joseph Myatt *(Mng Dir-Corp Fin-Chicago)*
Kate Holmes *(Mng Dir-Tech-Seattle)*

FTI Consulting, Inc.—(Continued)

Melanie Finn *(Sr Mng Dir/Mng Dir-Boston)*
Micah P. Trilling *(Mng Dir-Forensic & Litigation Consulting-San Francisco)*
Michael Flaharty *(Mng Dir-Forensic & Litigation Consulting-New York)*
Michael Garibaldi *(Mng Dir-San Francisco-San Francisco)*
Michael Linsk *(Mng Dir-Corp Fin-Los Angeles)*
Michael J. Talarico *(Mng Dir-Corp Fin-Pittsburgh)*
Mohan V. Kirtane *(Mng Dir-Corp Fin-Brentwood)*
Mollie Hawkes *(Mng Dir-IR & Comm & Head-Communications & Investor Relations)*
Nancy L. Freeman *(Mng Dir-Atlanta-Atlanta)*
Nimisha Patel *(Mng Dir-Tech-New York)*
Patrick S. Curtin *(Mng Dir-Corp Fin-Chicago)*
Richard M. Winn *(Mng Dir-New York-New York)*
Robert Stanislaro *(Mng Dir-Strategic Comm-New York)*
Sam Hill *(Mng Dir-Chicago-Chicago)*
Scott Scharlau *(Sr Mng Dir-Chicago & Mng Dir-Corp Fin & Restructuring-Chicago)*
Shawn Martinez *(Mng Dir-Los Angeles-Los Angeles)*
Stephen Belyn *(Mng Dir-Corp Fin-Chicago)*
Thomas J. Sterner *(Mng Dir-Chicago-Chicago)*
Tiko V. Shah *(Mng Dir-Forensic & Litigation Consulting-San Francisco)*
Timothy W. Eickhoff *(Mng Dir-Corp Fin-Chicago)*
Timothy J. Wondolowski *(Mng Dir-Forensic & Litigation Consulting-Boston)*
Bill Stotzer *(Mng Dir-Chicago)*
Matthew Pachman *(Chief Compliance Officer, Chief Risk Officer & VP)*
Adam Ingber *(Sr Dir-Tech-Los Angeles)*
Selvin Akkus-Clemens *(Mng Dir)*
Jose Alberro *(Sr Mng Dir)*
Michael R. Busen *(Mng Dir)*
Julie Carney *(Mng Dir)*
Gosalia Celmanbet *(Mng Dir)*
Ryan Chiang *(Mng Dir)*
Mike Rosenthall *(Sec & Assoc Gen Counsel)*
Parameswaran Toledo *(Sr Mng Dir)*
Faulkner Rowland *(Sr Mng Dir)*
Houle Pericak *(Sr Mng Dir)*
Juan M. Montanez *(Sr Mng Dir)*

Subsidiaries:

Andersch AG (1)
Taunusanlage 9-10, 60329, Frankfurt am Main, Germany
Tel.: (49) 6927229950
Web Site: https://www.fti-andersch.com
Emp.: 4,700
Restructuring Consulting Services
N.A.I.C.S.: 541611

CDG Group, LLC (1)
645 5th Ave, New York, NY 10022
Tel.: (212) 813-1300
Investment Advice
N.A.I.C.S.: 561499

Compass Lexecon LLC (1)
332 S Michigan Ave Ste 1300, Chicago, IL 60604 **(100%)**
Tel.: (312) 322-0200
Web Site: https://www.compasslexecon.com
Emp.: 850
Business Consultants
N.A.I.C.S.: 541690
Andrew M. Rosenfield *(Founder)*
Daniel R. Fischel *(Chm & Pres)*

Gustavo E. Bamberger *(Exec VP)*
Charles C. Cox *(Exec VP)*
Kevin F. Dages *(Exec VP)*
Fredrick A. Flyer *(Exec VP)*
Rajiv B. Gokhale *(Exec VP)*
David B. Gross *(Exec VP)*
Michael A. Keable *(Exec VP)*
Todd D. Kendall *(Exec VP)*
H. Neal Lenhoff *(Exec VP)*
Colleen P. Loughlin *(Exec VP)*
Gerald B. Lumer *(Exec VP)*
Jessica P. Mandel *(Exec VP)*
Bradley N. Reiff *(Exec VP)*
Rahul Sekhar *(Exec VP)*
Allan L. Shampine *(Exec VP)*
Yoad Shefi *(Exec VP)*
Hal S. Sider *(Exec VP)*
Thomas A. Stemwedel *(Exec VP)*
Paul S. Anderson *(Sr VP)*
Dzmitry Asinski *(Sr VP)*
Erica L. Benton *(Sr VP)*
Evan C. McKay *(Sr VP)*
Agustina Levy *(VP)*
Alice O'Donnell *(Sr VP)*
Amy Affelt *(Dir)*
Andrew Lin *(VP)*
Anne Marie Yale *(VP)*
Clifford S. Ang *(Exec VP)*
Constance Kelly *(Sr VP)*
Daniel W. Stone *(VP)*
David Strahlberg *(Sr VP)*
Deborah A. Healy *(VP)*
Elizabeth A. Wall *(VP)*
Erika D. Morris *(VP)*
Eugenia A. Vinogradsky *(VP)*
Gregory J. Pelnar *(Sr VP)*
Heather R. Spang *(VP)*
James R. Libby *(Dir)*
Jennifer C. Milliron *(Exec VP)*
Jonathan H. Tompkins *(VP)*
Jonathan Polonsky *(Sr VP)*
Joseph H. Goodman *(Sr VP)*
Jurgen Petersen Hans *(Sr VP)*
Kevin D. Hartt *(VP)*
Kirupakaran C. Ramaiah *(Sr VP)*
Laura R. Yergesheva *(Sr VP)*
Lynette R. Neumann *(Exec VP)*
M. Laurentius Marais *(Exec VP)*
Margaret Hlebowitsh *(VP)*
Mary J. Li *(VP)*
Nabila Lotayef *(VP)*
Narsid Golic *(Sr VP)*
Otto R. Hansen *(VP)*
Peter B. Clayburgh *(Exec VP)*
Peter Marlantes *(VP)*
Quinn P. Johnson *(Sr VP)*
Ran Wei *(Sr VP)*
Robin E. Stahl *(Sr VP)*
Ryan T. Dorow *(VP)*
V. Van Der Merwe *(Exec VP)*
Yili Wang *(VP)*

Branch (Domestic):

Compass Lexecon - Cambridge (2)
200 State St Ste 9 Fl, Boston, MA 02109
Tel.: (617) 520-0200
Web Site: http://www.compasslexecon.com
Sales Range: $10-24.9 Million
Emp.: 40
Economic Related Business Consultants
N.A.I.C.S.: 541690
Jeffrey D. Tranen *(Exec VP)*

Compass Lexecon Spain, S.L. (1)
Paseo de la Castellana 7 9th Floor, 28046, Madrid, MD, Spain
Tel.: (34) 915861000
Law Services
N.A.I.C.S.: 541110

FTI Capital Advisors, LLC (1)
900 Commerce Rd, Annapolis, MD 21401
General Management Consulting Services
N.A.I.C.S.: 541611
Carlyn R. Taylor *(Chm)*
Colin McCafferty *(Sr Mng Dir)*

FTI Commercial Consulting (Shanghai) Co. Ltd. (1)
Room 2206 LT Square 500 Chengdu N Road, Shanghai, 200003, China
Tel.: (86) 2151088002
Sales Range: $25-49.9 Million
Emp.: 70
Administrative & General Management Consulting Services
N.A.I.C.S.: 541611

FTI Consulting (Asia) Ltd (1)

Level 35 Oxford House Taikoo Place 979 King's Road, Quarry Bay, China (Hong Kong)
Tel.: (852) 37684500
Administrative & General Management Consulting Services
N.A.I.C.S.: 541611
Baron Zhao *(Mng Dir)*
Foreky Wong *(Mng Dir)*
Joanne Wong *(Sr Mng Dir)*
Alex Wong *(Mng Dir)*
Edwina Tam *(Sr Mng Dir)*
Amanda Rasmussen *(Mng Dir)*
Sally Peng *(Sr Mng Dir)*
Neha Parmar *(Mng Dir)*
William Pan *(Sr Mng Dir)*
Kyran McCarthy *(Sr Mng Dir)*
Edmund Lo *(Sr Mng Dir)*
Sean Lam *(Sr Mng Dir)*
Ben Johnson *(Sr Mng Dir)*
Sandeep Jadav *(Sr Mng Dir)*
Jason Ho *(Sr Mng Dir)*
Greg Hallahan *(Sr Mng Dir)*
Ken Fung *(Sr Mng Dir)*
Vincent Fok *(Sr Mng Dir)*
Daniel Chow *(Sr Mng Dir)*
Joe Cheng *(Mng Dir)*
Nick Adams *(Sr Mng Dir)*

FTI Consulting (China) Ltd. (1)
Level 16 Units 09-12 China World Tower A 1 Jianguomen Outer St Guomao, Chaoyang District, Beijing, 100022, China
Tel.: (86) 1050825052
Administrative & General Management Consulting Services
N.A.I.C.S.: 541611

FTI Consulting (SC) Inc. (1)
Wall Street Plz 88 Pine St 32nd Fl, New York, NY 10005
Tel.: (212) 850-5600
Web Site: http://www.fticonsulting.com
Strategic Communications
N.A.I.C.S.: 541820
Mark McCall *(Pres)*
Christa Hart *(Sr Mng Dir-Corp Fin)*
Brian Kennedy *(Sr Mng Dir & Head-Americas)*
Melissa Marlette Kresse *(Mng Dir-Corp Comm)*
Robert Skeffington *(Sr Mng Dir)*
Yvonne Gyimah *(Sr Mng Dir-Corp Fin)*

Subsidiary (Non-US):

FTI Consulting (SC) Ltda. (2)
Calle 93 11A-11 Suite 701, Bogota, Colombia
Tel.: (57) 13198400
Web Site: https://www.fticonsulting.com
Public Relations
N.A.I.C.S.: 541010

FTI Consulting SC GmbH (2)
Taunusanlage 9-10, 60329, Frankfurt am Main, Germany
Tel.: (49) 69920370
Sales Range: $10-24.9 Million
Emp.: 40
N.A.I.C.S.: 541820
Lutz Golsch *(Sr Mng Dir & Head-Strategic Comm)*

Financial Dynamics Ireland Ltd. (2)
The Academy Suites 2A 2B 42 Pearse Street, Dublin, 2, Ireland
Tel.: (353) 17650800
Web Site: http://www.fd.com
Sales Range: $10-24.9 Million
Emp.: 16
N.A.I.C.S.: 541820

Strategic Communications (2)
5 Rue Scribe, 75009, Paris, France
Tel.: (33) 147036810
Web Site: http://www.fticonsulting.com
Sales Range: $10-24.9 Million
Emp.: 20
Economic & Financial Consulting & Strategies
N.A.I.C.S.: 525990

FTI Consulting (Singapore) PTE. LTD. (1)
1 Raffles Quay 27-10 South Tower, Singapore, 048583, Singapore
Tel.: (65) 68317820
Web Site: https://www.fticonsulting.com

Administrative & General Management Consulting Services
N.A.I.C.S.: 541611
Andrew McCarthy *(Sr Mng Dir-Fin Crime Compliance-Singapore & Southeast Asia)*
Anna Bleazard *(Mng Dir-Fin Crime Compliance-Singapore & Southeast Asia)*
Brett Clapp *(Sr Mng Dir)*
Thomas R. Evrard *(Sr Mng Dir)*
Nick Gronow *(Sr Mng Dir)*
Rachel Layburn *(Sr Mng Dir)*
James Nicholson *(Sr Mng Dir)*
Martin Wong *(Sr Mng Dir)*
Oliver Watts *(Sr Mng Dir)*
Jeremy Tan *(Sr Mng Dir)*
Vincent Stevens *(Sr Mng Dir)*
Amar Singh *(Mng Dir)*
Andrew Oddie *(Mng Dir)*
Vinod Nair *(Sr Mng Dir)*
Yaoguo Lun *(Mng Dir)*
May Yee Koay *(Mng Dir)*
James Jarman *(Mng Dir)*
Benjamin Ee *(Mng Dir)*
John Collins *(Mng Dir)*
Natalie Carter *(Mng Dir)*
Lee Baker *(Sr Mng Dir)*
Gino Bello *(Sr Mng Dir)*

FTI Consulting - FD Australia Holdings Pty Ltd (1)
Level 22 Gateway 1 Macquarie Place, Sydney, 2000, NSW, Australia
Tel.: (61) 282478000
Web Site: https://www.fticonsulting.com
Sales Range: $25-49.9 Million
Emp.: 76
Investment Management Service
N.A.I.C.S.: 551112

FTI Consulting Belgium SA (1)
Avenue Marnix 23, 1000, Brussels, Belgium
Tel.: (32) 22890930
Web Site: https://www.fticonsulting.com
Emp.: 70
Administrative & General Management Consulting Services
N.A.I.C.S.: 541611
Simon Dibb *(Sr Mng Dir-Strategic Comm)*
Hans Hack *(Sr Mng Dir-Strategic Comm)*
Pablo Lopez-Alvarez *(Sr Mng Dir & Head-Trade & Litigation)*
Antoine Mialhe *(Mng Dir-Strategic Comm)*
Aled Williams *(Mng Dir-Strategic Comm)*
Julia Harrison *(Sr Mng Dir & Head-Pub Affairs & Govt Rels-Global)*

FTI Consulting Colombia S.A.S. (1)
Calle 93 11A-11 Suite 701, Bogota, Colombia
Tel.: (57) 13198400
Administrative & General Management Consulting Services
N.A.I.C.S.: 541611

FTI Consulting Denmark ApS (1)
Bredgade 6 Unit 4 21 and 4 20, Copenhagen, 1260, Denmark
Tel.: (45) 70707383
Crude Oil & Natural Gas Distr
N.A.I.C.S.: 424720

FTI Consulting Panama, SDAD. LTDA. (1)
50th Street and 55th East Street Building balboa Bank 4th floor, Panama, Panama
Tel.: (507) 2973450
Web Site: http://www.fticonsulting.com
Emp.: 16
Administrative & General Management Consulting Services
N.A.I.C.S.: 541611

FTI Consulting S.A. (1)
Bouchard 547 11th Floor, C1106ABG, Buenos Aires, C1106ABG, Argentina
Tel.: (54) 1143219700
Administrative & General Management Consulting Services
N.A.I.C.S.: 541611

FTI Consulting Services Limited (1)
200 Aldersgate Aldersgate Street, London, EC1A 4HD, United Kingdom
Tel.: (44) 2037211000
Web Site: http://www.fticonsulting.co.uk
Sales Range: $50-74.9 Million
Emp.: 800
Administrative & General Management Consulting Services

N.A.I.C.S.: 327910
Andreas Von Keitz *(Sr Mng Dir-Corp Fin)*
Mark Hunt *(Sr Mng Dir-Forensic & Litigation Consulting)*
Nigel Webb *(Sr Mng Dir-Forensic & Litigation Consulting)*
Caroline Das-Monfrais *(Sr Mng Dir & Chief Strategy Officer-EMEA)*
Simon Granger *(Sr Mng Dir & Head-Corp Fin & Restructuring-EMEA)*
Paul Inglis *(Sr Mng Dir-Client Svcs-EMEA)*
Alwin Magimay *(Chief Digital Officer-EMEA & Sr Mng Dir-Corp Fin)*
Joshua Burch *(Sr Mng Dir-Forensic & Litigation Consulting)*
Matt Callaghan *(Sr Mng Dir- Corp Fin & Restructuring)*
David Morris *(Sr Mng Dir & Head-Restructuring-UK)*

FTI Consulting Solutions Limited (1)
200 Aldersgate Aldersgate Street, London, EC1A 4HD, United Kingdom
Tel.: (44) 2073893800
Strategic Management & Commercial Consultancy Services
N.A.I.C.S.: 541611
Clare Hartnell *(Sr Mng Dir-Tax Advisory Practice-Corp Fin & Restructuring Segment)*

FTI Consulting Spain, S.R.L. (1)
Paseo de Recoletos 3 3rd Floor, 28004, Madrid, 28004, Spain
Tel.: (34) 915243840
Web Site: https://www.fticonsulting.com
Administrative & General Management Consulting Services
N.A.I.C.S.: 541611

FTI Consulting Technology (Sydney) Pty Ltd (1)
Level 21 Bourke Place 600 Bourke Street, Melbourne, 3000, VIC, Australia
Tel.: (61) 396040600
Administrative & General Management Consulting Services
N.A.I.C.S.: 541611

FTI Consultoria Ltda. (1)
Av Presidente Juscelino Kubitschek 1327- 3rd floor, Condominium Plaza Internacional Building II Itaim Bibi, Sao Paulo, SP 04543- 011, Brazil
Tel.: (55) 1131654535
Sales Range: $25-49.9 Million
Emp.: 35
Administrative & General Management Consulting Services
N.A.I.C.S.: 541611
Samuel Aguirre *(Sr Mng Dir-Corp Fin & Restructuring)*
Luciano Lindemann *(Mng Dir-Corp Fin & Restructuring)*

Madison Consulting Group, Inc. (1)
30 Montgomery St Ste 1210, Jersey City, NJ 07302
Tel.: (201) 434-5678
Web Site: http://www.madisoncg.com
Sales Range: $1-9.9 Million
Emp.: 20
Administrative Management & General Management Consulting Service
N.A.I.C.S.: 541611
Mark Crawshaw *(Pres)*
George Swetlitz *(Mng Partner)*

PT. FTI Consulting Indonesia (1)
Level 11 One Pacific Place Jl Jend Sudirman kav 52 RT 5/RW 3, Jakarta, 12190, Indonesia
Tel.: (62) 2139503500
Emp.: 6
Administrative & General Management Consulting Services
N.A.I.C.S.: 541611
Jon Rowell *(Sr Mng Dir)*

Sports Analytics LLC (1)
909 Commerce Rd, Annapolis, MD 21401
Tel.: (410) 224-8770
Crude Oil & Natural Gas Distr
N.A.I.C.S.: 424720

FUBOTV INC.
1330 6th Ave, New York, NY 10019
Tel.: (212) 672-0055   FL
Web Site: https://www.fubo.tv
Year Founded: 2009

FUBO—(NYSE)
Rev.: $1,008,696,000
Assets: $1,277,774,000
Liabilities: $876,092,000
Net Worth: $401,682,000
Earnings: ($561,919,000)
Emp.: 510
Fiscal Year-end: 12/31/22
Feature Films & Television Series Finance, Production & Distribution
N.A.I.C.S.: 512110
Alberto Horihuela *(Co-Founder & COO)*
John Janedis *(CFO)*
Gina DiGioia *(Chief Legal Officer)*
David Gandler *(Co-Founder & CEO)*
Edgar Miles Bronfman Jr. *(Chm)*

FUEGO ENTERPRISES, INC.
3250 NE 1st Ave Ste 310, Miami, FL 33137
Tel.: (305) 602-0219   NV
Web Site:
https://www.fuegoenterprises inc.com
Year Founded: 2004
FUGI—(OTCIQ)
Sales Range: Less than $1 Million
Holding Company; Video & Entertainment Media Content Production & Distribution Services
N.A.I.C.S.: 551110
Hugo A. Cancio *(Pres & CEO)*
Edward Steinback *(CFO, Principal Acctg Officer, Treas & Controller)*

Subsidiaries:

Cuba Business Development Group, Inc. (1)
15476 NW 77 Court Ste 433, Miami Lakes, FL 33016
Tel.: (305) 823-9193
Web Site: http://www.cbdg.co
Consulting, Sales Representation & Marketing Representation to the Entertainment Industry
N.A.I.C.S.: 541618

FUEL DOCTOR HOLDINGS, INC.
23961 Craftsman Rd Ste L, Calabasas, CA 91302
Tel.: (818) 224-5678   DE
Web Site:
http://www.fueldoctorusa.com
Year Founded: 2008
FDOC—(OTCIQ)
Assets: $107,064
Liabilities: $55,144
Net Worth: $51,920
Earnings: ($102,223)
Emp.: 2
Fiscal Year-end: 12/31/22
Fuel Efficiency Booster Distr
N.A.I.C.S.: 457210
Gadi Levin *(CFO)*
Amitay Weiss *(CEO)*

FUEL TECH, INC.
27601 Bella Vista Pkwy, Warrenville, IL 60555
Tel.: (630) 845-4500   DE
Web Site: https://www.ftek.com
Year Founded: 1981
FTEK—(NASDAQ)
Rev.: $27,081,000
Assets: $50,388,000
Liabilities: $6,674,000
Net Worth: $43,714,000
Earnings: ($1,538,000)
Emp.: 72
Fiscal Year-end: 12/31/23
Air Pollution Control Systems Developer, Licenser & Sales
N.A.I.C.S.: 238220
Vincent J. Arnone *(Chm, Pres & CEO)*

Ellen T. Albrecht *(CFO, Treas & VP)*
Bradley W. Johnson *(Gen Counsel, Sec & VP)*
William Decker *(VP-Water & Wastewater Treatment Tech)*
Devin Sullivan *(Mng Dir)*
William E. Cummings Jr. *(Sr VP)*

Subsidiaries:

Beijing Fuel Tech Environmental Technologies Co., Ltd. (1)
11th Floor Building 2 The World Profit Center 16 Tianze Road, Chaoyang District, Beijing, 100125, China (100%)
Tel.: (86) 10 8487 1472
Air Pollution Control Systems Developer, Licenser & Sales
N.A.I.C.S.: 238220

Cleveland Roll Forming Environmental Division, Inc. (1)
27881 Clemens Rd, Westlake, OH 44145 (100%)
Tel.: (440) 899-3888
Air Pollution Control Systems Developer, Licenser & Sales
N.A.I.C.S.: 334519

Fuel Tech Srl (1)
Centro Direzionale Le Torri Via Marsala 34/A, 21013, Gallarate, Varese, Italy (100%)
Tel.: (39) 0331701110
Web Site: https://ftek.com
Emp.: 10
Air Pollution Control Systems Developer, Licenser & Sales
N.A.I.C.S.: 238220

FUELCELL ENERGY, INC.
3 Great Pasture Rd, Danbury, CT 06810
Tel.: (203) 825-6000   DE
Web Site:
https://www.fuelcellenergy.com
Year Founded: 1969
FCEL—(NASDAQ)
Rev.: $123,394,000
Assets: $955,520,000
Liabilities: $255,072,000
Net Worth: $700,448,000
Earnings: ($107,568,000)
Emp.: 591
Fiscal Year-end: 10/31/23
Electrochemical Technologies for Electric Power Generation & Storage; Mfr of Fuel Cell & Battery Products, Generally on a Contract Basis
N.A.I.C.S.: 336320
Michael S. Bishop *(CFO, Principal Acctg Officer & Exec VP)*
Jason B. Few *(Pres & CEO)*
Michael J. Lisowski *(Exec VP-Strategic Partnerships)*
Anthony Leo *(CTO & Exec VP)*
Jill Crossman *(Sr VP & Controller-Global)*
Tom Gelston *(Sr VP-Fin & IR)*
Joshua Dolger *(Gen Counsel, Sec & Exec VP)*
Mark Feasel *(Chief Comml Officer & Exec VP)*
John Torrance *(Sr VP-Product Mgmt)*
Karen Farrell *(Chief HR Officer)*
Lilyanne McClean *(Sr VP-Global Public Policy & Government Affairs)*
Shankar Achanta *(Sr VP & Chief Engr)*

Subsidiaries:

FuelCell Energy, Inc.- Eastern Region (1)
3 Great Pasture Rd, Danbury, CT 06810 (100%)
Tel.: (203) 825-6000
Web Site: http://www.fuelcellenergy.com
Sales Range: $100-124.9 Million
Oil & Gas Services
N.A.I.C.S.: 335999

FuelCell Energy, Inc.- Manufacturing (1)
539 Technology Park Dr, Torrington, CT 06790
Tel.: (860) 496-1111
Web Site: http://www.fuelcellenergy.com
Sales Range: $100-124.9 Million
Emp.: 300
Oil & Gas Services
N.A.I.C.S.: 335999

Versa Power Systems, Inc. (1)
8392 S Continental Dv, Littleton, CO 80127
Tel.: (303) 226-0770
Storage Battery Mfr
N.A.I.C.S.: 335910

Versa Power Systems, Ltd. (1)
4852 52nd st SE, Calgary, T2B 3R2, AB, Canada
Tel.: (403) 204-6100
Web Site: http://www.fce.com
Emp.: 35
Battery Product Mfr
N.A.I.C.S.: 335910

FUELSTREAM, INC.
11650 S State St Ste 240, Draper, UT 84020
Tel.: (801) 816-2510   DE
Web Site: http://www.fuel-stream.com
FLST—(OTCEM)
Sales Range: Less than $1 Million
Emp.: 6
Holding Company Commercial Aircraft Fuel Brokerage Services
N.A.I.C.S.: 551112
Kenneth I. Denos *(Chm & CEO)*
Chene C. Gardner *(CFO)*

Subsidiaries:

Aviation Fuel International, Inc. (1)
510 Shotgun Rd Ste 110, Fort Lauderdale, FL 33326 (100%)
Tel.: (954) 423-5345
Web Site: http://www.aviationfuelintl.com
Commercial Aircraft Fuel Brokerage Services
N.A.I.C.S.: 425120

FULCRUM THERAPEUTICS, INC.
26 Landsdowne St, Cambridge, MA 02139
Tel.: (617) 651-8851   DE
Web Site: https://www.fulcrumtx.com
Year Founded: 2015
FULC—(NASDAQ)
Rev.: $6,342,000
Assets: $226,685,000
Liabilities: $27,743,000
Net Worth: $198,942,000
Earnings: ($109,871,000)
Emp.: 89
Fiscal Year-end: 12/31/22
Biotechnology Research & Development Services
N.A.I.C.S.: 541714
Christopher Moxham *(Chief Scientific Officer)*
Judith A. Dunn *(Pres/Head-R&D)*
Kim Hazen *(Sr VP-HR)*
Mark Levin *(Chm)*
Bradley E. Bernstein *(Co-Founder)*
Rudolf Jaenisch *(Co-Founder)*
Danny Reinberg *(Co-Founder)*
Michael R. Green *(Co-Founder)*
Jeannie T. Lee *(Co-Founder)*
Pamela S. Strode *(Sr VP-Regulatory Affairs & Quality Assurance)*
Nicole T. Gallagher *(Dir-Admin)*
Curtis Oltmans *(Gen Counsel)*
Gregory Tourangeau *(Principal Acctg Officer & Controller)*
Mel Hayes *(Exec VP-Patient Experience)*
Dee Smith *(Exec Dir-Corp Comm)*
Alex C. Sapir *(Pres & CEO)*
Alan A. Musso *(CFO & Treas)*

Fulgent Genetics, Inc.—(Continued)

FULGENT GENETICS, INC.

4399 Santa Anita Ave, El Monte, CA 91731
Tel.: (626) 350-0537   **DE**
Web Site:
https://www.fulgentgenetics.com
Year Founded: 2011
FLGT—(NASDAQ)
Rev.: $618,968,000
Assets: $1,386,053,000
Liabilities: $116,178,000
Net Worth: $1,269,875,000
Earnings: $143,403,000
Emp.: 1,012
Fiscal Year-end: 12/31/22
Biopharmaceutical Research & Development Service
N.A.I.C.S.: 541714
Paul Kim (CFO)
Ming Hsieh (Founder, Chm, Pres & CEO)
Hanlin Gao (Chief Scientific Officer & Dir-Lab)
Mary Jane Abalos (VP-Finance)
Mike Lacenere (VP-Sys Applications & Integration)
Doreen Ng (VP-Operations & Compliance)
Elias Nyankojo (Chief Information Security Officer)
Jakub Sram (VP-Business Development & Sales)
Ellen Tsui (VP-Human Resources)
David Yu (VP-IT Infrastructure)
Ray Yin (Pres & Chief Scientific Officer-Fulgent Pharma)
Natalie Prescott (Chief Privacy Officer & Gen Counsel)
Chris Wicker (VP & Gen Mgr)

Subsidiaries:

CSI Laboratories, Inc.   (1)
2580 Westside Pkwy Ste 400, Alpharetta, GA 30004-8948
Tel.: (678) 838-4827
Web Site: http://www.csilaboratories.com
Research & Development in Biotechnology
N.A.I.C.S.: 541714
Heather Creran (CEO)

Inform Diagnostics, Inc.   (1)
6655 N MacArthur Blvd, Irving, TX 75039
Tel.: (214) 227-8700
Web Site: http://www.informdx.com
Anatomic Pathology Services
N.A.I.C.S.: 622110
Darryl Goss (CEO)
Dana Simonds (Sr VP, Chief Compliance Officer & Ethics Officer)
Nancy Gay (Pres & COO)
David Engelberg (Sr VP & CFO)
Kevin O'Janovac (Sr Vp & Chief Comml Officer)
Anuradha Singhal (Sr VP & Chief Medical Officer)

FULL ALLIANCE GROUP, INC.

14150 McCormick Dr, Tampa, FL 33626
Tel.: (510) 330-1888
Web Site:
https://www.fullalliance.com
FAGI—(OTCIQ)
Medical Insurance Services
N.A.I.C.S.: 524114
Brian Volpp (CEO)

FULL HOUSE RESORTS, INC.

1980 Festival Plz Dr Ste 680, Las Vegas, NV 89135
Tel.: (702) 221-7800   **DE**
Web Site:
https://www.fullhouseresorts.com
FLL—(NASDAQ)
Rev.: $163,281,000
Assets: $595,329,000
Liabilities: $495,538,000

Net Worth: $99,791,000
Earnings: ($14,804,000)
Emp.: 1,281
Fiscal Year-end: 12/31/22
Destination Resorts & Entertainment, Gaming & Commercial Centers Developer
N.A.I.C.S.: 713910
Lewis A. Fanger (CFO, Treas & Sr VP)
Alex J. Stolyar (Chief Dev Officer & Sr VP)
John Ferrucci (COO)
Daniel R. Lee (Pres & CEO)

Subsidiaries:

Pioneer Group, Inc.   (1)
233 E Bennett Ave, Cripple Creek, CO 80813
Tel.: (719) 689-2142
Web Site:
http://www.broncobillyscasino.com
Casino Hotel Owner & Operator
N.A.I.C.S.: 721120

Silver Slipper Casino Venture, LLC   (1)
5000 S Beach Blvd, Bay Saint Louis, MS 39520
Tel.: (228) 469-2777
Web Site: http://www.silverslipper-ms.com
Casino Hotels
N.A.I.C.S.: 721120
Bill DesJardins (Dir-Table Games & Player Dev)
David Pisarich (Dir-Slot Ops & Keno)
Mike Creel (Dir-Surveillance)
Dave Jarvis (Dir-Support Ops)
Victoria Langlinais (Dir-Sls & Mktg)
Chuck Anger (Dir-Food & Beverage)
Rich Chase (Dir-Hotel Ops)

Stockman's Casino   (1)
1560 W Williams Ave, Fallon, NV 89406
Tel.: (775) 423-2117
Web Site:
https://www.stockmanscasino.com
Sales Range: $25-49.9 Million
Emp.: 140
Owner of Casinos
N.A.I.C.S.: 713290

FULL MOTION BEVERAGE, INC.

121-24 Dupont St, Plainview, NY 11803
Tel.: (516) 537-8237   **DE**
Year Founded: 2000
FMBV—(OTCIQ)
Alcoholic Beverage Mfr & Distr
N.A.I.C.S.: 312140
Dean Petkanas (Chm & CEO)

FULLNET COMMUNICATIONS, INC

201 Robert S Kerr Ave Ste 210, Oklahoma City, OK 73102
Tel.: (405) 236-8200   **OK**
Web Site: https://www.fullnet.net
Year Founded: 1995
FULO—(OTCIQ)
Rev.: $4,268,263
Assets: $3,176,384
Liabilities: $1,774,855
Net Worth: $1,401,529
Earnings: $672,236
Emp.: 15
Fiscal Year-end: 12/31/22
Internet & Other Telecommunications Services
N.A.I.C.S.: 517810
Timothy J. Kilkenny (Chm)
Roger P. Baresel (CEO, CFO, Chief Acctg Officer & Sec)
Jason C. Ayers (Pres)

FULTON FINANCIAL CORPORATION

1 Penn Sq, Lancaster, PA 17604-4887

Tel.: (717) 291-2411   **PA**
Web Site:
https://www.fultonbank.com
Year Founded: 1982
FULT—(NASDAQ)
Rev.: $1,091,968,000
Assets: $26,931,702,000
Liabilities: $24,351,945,000
Net Worth: $2,579,757,000
Earnings: $286,981,000
Emp.: 3,300
Fiscal Year-end: 12/31/22
Bank Holding Company
N.A.I.C.S.: 551111
Beth Ann L. Chivinski (Interim CFO & Sr Exec VP)
Curtis J. Myers (Chm & CEO)
Meg R. Mueller (Sr Exec VP & Head-Comml Banking)
Angela M. Sargent (CIO, Sr Exec VP & Mgr-IT)
Anthony L. Cossetti (Chief Acctg Officer, Exec VP & Controller)
Natasha R. Luddington (Chief Legal Officer, Sec & Sr Exec VP)
Bernadette M. Taylor (Chief HR Officer & Sr Exec VP)
Karthik Sridharan (Chief Ops & Tech Officer & Sr Exec VP)
Andy B. Fiol (Sr Exec VP & Head-Consumer & Small Bus)
Atul Malhotra (Chief Risk Officer & Exec VP)

Subsidiaries:

FFC Management, Inc.   (1)
22215 Dupont Blvd, Georgetown, DE 19947
Tel.: (302) 855-0920
Financial Services
N.A.I.C.S.: 523940

FNB Bank, N.A.   (1)
Mill & Bloom St, Danville, PA 17821
Tel.: (570) 275-3740
Web Site: http://www.fnbbank.com
Sales Range: $1-9.9 Million
Emp.: 30
Federal Savings Bank
N.A.I.C.S.: 522180

Fulton Bank of New Jersey   (1)
533 Fellowship Rd Ste 250, Mount Laurel, NJ 08054
Tel.: (855) 900-3265
Web Site: http://www.fultonbanknj.com
Sales Range: $150-199.9 Million
Emp.: 551
Commercial Banking
N.A.I.C.S.: 522110

Fulton Bank, N.A.   (1)
1 Penn Sq, Lancaster, PA 17602-2853
Tel.: (717) 291-2618
Web Site: https://www.fultonbank.com
Federal Savings Bank
N.A.I.C.S.: 522180
David B. Hanson (CEO-Fulton Private Bank)
Mark Trapnell (Chief Investment Officer)
Beth Ann L. Chivinski (Interim CFO & Sr Exec VP)
Curtis J. Myers (Chm & CEO)
Dara C. Bachman (Pres-Fulton Private Bank)

Subsidiary (Domestic):

Benefitworks, Inc.   (2)
PO Box 1209, Lebanon, PA 17042
Tel.: (717) 273-8441
Web Site: http://www.benefitworks.com
Other Financial Vehicles
N.A.I.C.S.: 525990
Brooks Trefsgar (Pres)
B. T. Trefsgar (VP)

Unit (Domestic):

Fulton Financial Advisors   (2)
1 Penn Sq, Lancaster, PA 17602-2853
Tel.: (717) 291-2590
Web Site:
http://www.fultonfinancialadvisors.com
Sales Range: $75-99.9 Million
Financial Advisory Services
N.A.I.C.S.: 523940

David B. Hanson (CEO)
Mark Trapnell (Chief Investment Officer)
P. Randolph Taylor (Exec VP & Dir-Private Banking)

Lafayette Ambassador Bank   (1)
PO Box 94, East Petersburg, PA 17520
Tel.: (800) 752-8400
Web Site: http://www.lafambank.com
Sales Range: $10-24.9 Million
Emp.: 43
Commercial Banking Services
N.A.I.C.S.: 522110

Prudential Bancorp, Inc.   (1)
1834 W Oregon Ave, Philadelphia, PA 19145
Tel.: (215) 755-1500
Web Site: http://www.psbanker.com
Rev.: $41,676,000
Assets: $1,100,468,000
Liabilities: $970,012,000
Net Worth: $130,456,000
Earnings: $7,780,000
Emp.: 88
Fiscal Year-end: 09/30/2021
Bank Holding Company
N.A.I.C.S.: 551111
Jack E. Rothkopf (CFO, Chief Acctg Officer, Treas & Sr VP)
Sharon M. Slater (Chief Risk Officer, Sec & Sr VP)
Anthony V. Migliorino (COO & Exec VP)

Subsidiary (Domestic):

Prudential Bank   (2)
1834 W Oregon Ave, Philadelphia, PA 19145
Tel.: (215) 755-1500
Web Site: http://www.psbanker.com
Federal Savings Bank
N.A.I.C.S.: 522180
Bruce E. Miller (Chm)
Jack E. Rothkopf (CFO, Treas & Sr VP)
Sharon M. Slater (Chief Risk Officer, Sec & Sr VP)
Anthony V. Migliorino (COO & Exec VP)
Nicholas A. DiGianivittorio (Officer-CRA & First VP-Credit Admin)
Nicole Canalichio (Officer-Ops, First VP & Dir-Mktg)
Dominique Vanderveer (Asst VP & Dir-HR)
Matthew Graham (Co-Chief Lending Officer & VP)

Swineford National Bank   (1)
227 E Main St, Middleburg, PA 17842
Tel.: (570) 837-1881
Web Site: http://www.swineford.com
Sales Range: $1-9.9 Million
Emp.: 12
Financial Services
N.A.I.C.S.: 523940

The Columbia Bank   (1)
7168 Columbia Gateway Dr, Columbia, MD 21044
Tel.: (410) 423-8000
Web Site: https://www.thecolumbiabank.com
Sales Range: $50-74.9 Million
Emp.: 360
Financial Services
N.A.I.C.S.: 523940

FUNKO INC.

2802 Wetmore Ave, Everett, WA 98201
Tel.: (425) 783-3616   **DE**
Web Site: https://www.funko.com
Year Founded: 2017
FNKO—(NASDAQ)
Rev.: $1,322,706,000
Assets: $1,091,145,000
Liabilities: $701,456,000
Net Worth: $389,689,000
Earnings: ($8,035,000)
Emp.: 1,466
Fiscal Year-end: 12/31/22
Toy & Hobby Goods & Supplies Merchant Whslr
N.A.I.C.S.: 423920

Tracy Daw *(Chief Legal Officer)*
Johanna Gepford *(Sr VP-Direct to Consumer)*
Charles D. Denson *(Chm)*
Andrew Oddie *(Chief Revenue Officer)*
Dolly Ahluwalia *(Sr VP)*
Derrick Baca *(Sr VP)*
Rob Cassidy *(Sr VP)*
Liz DeSilva *(Sr VP)*
Mike Hyde *(Mng Dir)*
Yves LePendeven *(Acting CFO & Principal Acctg Officer)*
Sarah Martinez *(Sr VP)*
Doug Oglesby *(Sr VP)*
Malcolm Ottley *(Sr VP)*
Dave Renke *(Sr VP)*
Husnal Shah *(Sr VP)*
Emily Sly *(VP)*
Raj Varughese *(VP)*
Cynthia Williams *(CEO)*

Subsidiaries:

A Large Evil Corporation Ltd.   **(1)**
11 Seven Dials Sawclose, Bath, BA1 1EN, United Kingdom
Tel.: (44) 1225461122
Web Site: http://www.evilcorp.tv
Toy & Hobby Goods Whslr
N.A.I.C.S.: 423920

Funko Games, LLC   **(1)**
5030 Roosevelt Way NE Ph, Seattle, WA 98105
Tel.: (206) 547-7155
Web Site: https://funkogames.com
Board Game Developer
N.A.I.C.S.: 339930

Loungefly, LLC   **(1)**
20310 Plummer St, Chatsworth, CA 91311
Tel.: (818) 718-5600
Toy & Hobby Goods Whslr
N.A.I.C.S.: 423920

Mondo Tees, LLC   **(1)**
4115 Guadalupe St, Austin, TX 78751-4222
Tel.: (512) 296-2447
Web Site: http://www.mondotees.com
Vinyl Records, Posters, Soundtracks, Toys, Apparel, Books, Games & Other Collectibles Mfr
N.A.I.C.S.: 459120
Lisa Harr *(Mgr)*

FUSE GROUP HOLDING INC.
805 W Duarte Ste 102, Arcadia, CA 91007
Tel.: (626) 210-0000   NV
Web Site:
   https://www.fuseholding.com
Year Founded: 2013
FUST—(OTCQB)
Assets: $72,205
Liabilities: $249,962
Net Worth: ($177,757)
Earnings: ($474,802)
Emp.: 2
Fiscal Year-end: 09/30/23
Mineral Mining Services
N.A.I.C.S.: 213114
Umesh Patel *(CEO & CFO)*

FUSE MEDICAL, INC.
4343 Sigma Rd Ste 500, Farmers Branch, TX 75244
Tel.: (469) 862-3030   DE
Web Site:
   https://www.fusemedical.com
Year Founded: 1968
FZMD—(OTCIQ)
Rev.: $18,644,784
Assets: $19,762,581
Liabilities: $20,073,435
Net Worth: ($310,854)
Earnings: $3,098,113
Fiscal Year-end: 12/31/22
Medical, Dental & Hospital Equipment & Supplies Merchant Wholesalers
N.A.I.C.S.: 423450

Lawrence S. Yellin *(CFO & Treas)*
Mark W. Brooks *(Chm & Pres)*
Christopher C. Reeg *(CEO & Sec)*
Renato V. Bosita Jr. *(Dir-Medical)*

FUSION INTERACTIVE CORP.
4380 NE 11th Ave 4-8B, Oakland Park, FL 33334
Tel.: (954) 280-9090   WA
Year Founded: 2000
FUIG—(OTCIQ)
Telecommunication Servicesb
N.A.I.C.S.: 517810
Andy Rouse *(CEO)*

FUSS BRANDS CORP.
80 Broad St 5th Fl, New York, NY 10004
Tel.: (917) 685-0300   NV
Web Site: http://www.renhuang.com
Year Founded: 1988
FBDS—(OTCIQ)
Assets: $139,364
Liabilities: $588,007
Net Worth: ($448,643)
Earnings: ($505,197)
Emp.: 1
Fiscal Year-end: 10/31/23
Pharmaceuticals Mfr
N.A.I.C.S.: 325412
Cheskel Meisels *(CEO)*

FUTURE HEALTH ESG CORP.
8 The Green Ste 12081, Dover, DE 19901
Tel.: (317) 590-6959   DE
Web Site: https://www.fhesg.com
Year Founded: 2021
FHLT—(NASDAQ)
Assets: $17,258,387
Liabilities: $26,646,494
Net Worth: ($9,388,107)
Earnings: $59,807
Emp.: 2
Fiscal Year-end: 12/31/22
Investment Services
N.A.I.C.S.: 523999
Bradley A. Bostic *(CEO)*
Travis A. Morgan *(CFO)*
Jesvin Kaur *(COO)*

FUTUREFUEL CORP.
2800 Gap Rd, Batesville, AR 72501
Tel.: (870) 698-3000   DE
Web Site:
   https://www.futurefuelcorporation.com
Year Founded: 2005
FF—(NYSE)
Rev.: $395,555,000
Assets: $355,969,000
Liabilities: $72,969,000
Net Worth: $283,000,000
Earnings: $15,211,000
Emp.: 472
Fiscal Year-end: 12/31/22
Bio-fuel Mfr
N.A.I.C.S.: 324199
Rose M. Sparks *(CFO, Principal Acctg Officer & Treas)*
Tom McKinlay *(CEO)*
Paul Anthony Novelly II *(Chm)*

Subsidiaries:

FutureFuel Chemical Company   **(1)**
2800 Gap Rd, Batesville, AR 72501   **(100%)**
Tel.: (870) 698-3000
Web Site: https://futurefuelcorporation.com
Chemicals Mfr
N.A.I.C.S.: 424690
Stacy Gunderman *(Dir-Admin)*

FUTURELAND, CORP.
10901 Roosevelt Blvd Ste 1000c, Saint Petersburg, FL 33716
Tel.: (720) 370-3554   CO

Year Founded: 2007
FUTL—(OTCQB)
Real Estate Development Services
N.A.I.C.S.: 531390
Cameron Cox *(Pres & CEO)*

FUTURIS COMPANY
22 Baltimore Rd, Rockville, MD 20850
Web Site:
   https://www.futuris.company
FTRS—(OTCIQ)
Gold Exploration & Mining Services
N.A.I.C.S.: 212220
Peter Price *(COO)*

Subsidiaries:

AKVARR Inc.   **(1)**
4031 University Dr Suite 100, Fairfax, VA 22030
Tel.: (240) 482-8767
Web Site: http://www.akvarr.com
Sales Range: $1-9.9 Million
Emp.: 70
Vijai Anand *(CEO)*
Amit Kekre *(Co-Founder & CTO)*

Computer Deductions, Inc.   **(1)**
8680 Greenback Ln Ste 210, Orangevale, CA 95662
Tel.: (916) 987-3600
Web Site: http://www.cdi-hq.com
Sales Range: $1-9.9 Million
Computer & Software Stores
N.A.I.C.S.: 449210
Tom Calabro *(CEO)*
Tim Oconnell *(Mgr-IT Infrastructure & Engr-Enterprise Sys & Storage)*

Futuris Technology Services, Inc.   **(1)**
43330 Junction Plz 164 150, Ashburn, VA 20147
Tel.: (703) 310-7334
Web Site: http://www.futuris.company
Human Capital Management Company
N.A.I.C.S.: 541612
Kalyan Pathuri *(Pres)*
Amit Jain *(CFO)*

Insigma Inc.   **(1)**
22 Baltimore Rd, Rockville, MD 20850
Tel.: (703) 310-6928
Web Site: http://www.insigmainc.com
Electronics Stores
N.A.I.C.S.: 449210
Chintan Patel *(Pres)*

FVCBANKCORP, INC.
11325 Random Hills Rd Ste 240, Fairfax, VA 22030
Tel.: (703) 436-3800   VA
Web Site: https://www.fvcbank.com
Year Founded: 2018
FVCB—(NASDAQ)
Rev.: $83,516,000
Assets: $2,344,322,000
Liabilities: $2,141,940,000
Net Worth: $202,382,000
Earnings: $24,984,000
Emp.: 131
Fiscal Year-end: 12/31/22
Bank Holding Company
N.A.I.C.S.: 551111
L. Burwell Gunn Jr. *(Vice Chm)*
Patricia Ann Ferrick *(Pres)*
David W. Pijor *(Chm & CEO)*
William G. Byers *(Chief Lending Officer & Exec VP-FVCbank)*
Michael G. Nassy *(Chief Credit Officer & Exec VP-FVCbank)*
Jennifer L. Deacon *(CFO & Exec VP)*
Sharon L. Jackson *(Chief Deposit Officer & Exec VP-FVCbank)*
Sharon Ricciardi *(Sr VP & Dir-Bus Dev)*

Subsidiaries:

FVCbank   **(1)**
11325 Random Hills Rd Ste 240, Fairfax, VA 22030
Tel.: (703) 436-3800
Web Site: http://www.fvcbank.com

Commercial Banking
N.A.I.C.S.: 522110
L. Burwell Gunn Jr. *(Vice Chm)*
Patricia Ann Ferrick *(Pres)*
David W. Pijor *(Chm & CEO)*
B. Todd Dempsey *(COO & Exec VP)*
Michael G. Nassy *(Chief Credit Officer & Exec VP)*
Jennifer L. Deacon *(CFO & Exec VP)*
Sharon L. Jackson *(Chief Deposit Officer & Exec VP)*
Debbie Cabala *(VP)*
Bill Byers *(Chief Lending Officer)*
Brittany Bower *(VP)*
Peggy S. Elie *(VP)*

G&P ACQUISITION CORP.
222 Bellevue Ave, Newport, RI 02840
Tel.: (212) 415-6500   DE
Web Site: http://www.gapacq.com
Year Founded: 2020
GAPA—(NYSE)
Rev.: $5,993,434
Assets: $177,674,465
Liabilities: $192,299,795
Net Worth: ($14,625,330)
Earnings: $5,018,038
Emp.: 4
Fiscal Year-end: 12/31/21
Investment Services
N.A.I.C.S.: 523999
Brendan T. O'Donnell *(CEO)*
Joseph Marnikovic *(CFO & Treas)*
Michael R. Anderson *(Gen Counsel & Sec)*
Curtis Parker *(Sr VP)*
Nicholas S. Schorsch *(Chm)*
Nicholas S. Schorsch Jr. *(Pres & CIO)*

G-III APPAREL GROUP, LTD.
512 7th Ave, New York, NY 10018
Tel.: (212) 403-0500   DE
Web Site: https://www.giii.com
Year Founded: 1974
GIII—(NASDAQ)
Rev.: $3,226,728,000
Assets: $2,712,405,000
Liabilities: $1,326,957,000
Net Worth: $1,385,448,000
Earnings: ($133,061,000)
Emp.: 3,600
Fiscal Year-end: 01/31/23
Apparel Designer, Marketer & Mfr
N.A.I.C.S.: 313310
Morris Goldfarb *(Chm & CEO)*
Neal S. Nackman *(CFO & Treas)*
Sammy Aaron *(Vice Chm & Pres)*
Jeffrey Goldfarb *(Exec VP & Dir-Strategic Plng)*

Subsidiaries:

Andrew & Suzanne Co. Inc.   **(1)**
570 Fashion Ave, New York, NY 10018
Tel.: (212) 840-1800
Web Site: http://www.andrewmarc.com
Sales Range: $50-74.9 Million
Emp.: 110
Designs, Manufactures & Distributes Clothing & Watches
N.A.I.C.S.: 424350

Donna Karan International Inc.   **(1)**
240 W 40th St, New York, NY 10018
Tel.: (212) 789-1500
Web Site: https://www.donnakaran.com
Fashion Apparel Designer, Mfr & Retailer
N.A.I.C.S.: 458110

Subsidiary (Non-US):

Donna Karan (Italy) Srl   **(2)**
Via Senato 16, 20121, Milan, Italy
Tel.: (39) 02762161
Clothing & Accessory Retailer
N.A.I.C.S.: 458110

Donna Karan Service Company BV   **(2)**
Hanzepoort 30, 7575 DA, Oldenzaal, Netherlands
Tel.: (31) 541573666

G-III Apparel Group, Ltd.—(Continued)

Apparel, Accessory & Leather Goods Retailer
N.A.I.C.S.: 458110

Subsidiary (Domestic):

The Donna Karan Company LLC   **(2)**
240 W 40th St, New York, NY 10018
Tel.: (212) 768-5957
Web Site: www.donnakaran.com
Clothing Accessory Retailer
N.A.I.C.S.: 424350

The Donna Karan Company LLC   **(2)**
1760 Military Rd, Niagara Falls, NY 14304
Tel.: (716) 297-0752
Web Site: http://www.donnakaran.com
Women Clothing & Accessory Retailer
N.A.I.C.S.: 458110

**The Donna Karan Company Store
LLC**   **(2)**
512 7th Ave 31st Fl, New York, NY 10018
Tel.: (212) 403-0619
Web Site: https://www.dkny.com
Luxury Product Retailer
N.A.I.C.S.: 459999

G-III Leather Fashions, Inc.   **(1)**
512 7th Ave, New York, NY 10018
Tel.: (212) 403-0500
Web Site: http://www.g-iii.com
Emp.: 100
Leather Apparel Mfr
N.A.I.C.S.: 316990

G.H. Bass & Co.   **(1)**
10 Farber Dr Ste 26 27, Bellport, NY
11713   **(100%)**
Tel.: (631) 286-0743
Web Site: http://www.ghbass.com
Sales Range: $100-124.9 Million
Emp.: 400
Footwear Manufacturer & Retailer
N.A.I.C.S.: 458210

Jessica Howard, Ltd.   **(1)**
1400 Broadway 19th Fl, New York, NY
10018-5300
Tel.: (212) 354-8670
Web Site: http://www.g-iii.com
Sales Range: $1-9.9 Million
Emp.: 85
Womens Dresses Designer & Marketer
N.A.I.C.S.: 315250

Kostroma Ltd.   **(1)**
Rm 1010 10/f Houston Ctr 63 Mody Rd,
Tsim Sha Tsui, Kowloon, China (Hong
Kong)
Tel.: (852) 27582989
Clothing Distr
N.A.I.C.S.: 458110

Naiman GmbH   **(1)**
Weinplatz 8, 8001, Zurich, Switzerland
Tel.: (41) 442219426
Apparel Clothing Whslr
N.A.I.C.S.: 459510

VBQ Acquisition B.V.   **(1)**
Schiphol Boulevard 231, 1118 BH, Schiphol,
Netherlands
Tel.: (31) 885609950
Men's Clothing & Furnishing Merchant
Whslr
N.A.I.C.S.: 424350

Vilebrequin International SA   **(1)**
Rue du Rhone 100, 1204, Geneva, Switzerland
Tel.: (41) 228104088
Clothing Distr
N.A.I.C.S.: 458110

Vilebrequin Saint Maarten   **(1)**
Holland House Beach Hotel Frontstreet 45,
Philipsburg, Saint Martin
Tel.: (721) 5438000
Web Site: https://www.vilebrequin.com
Family Clothing Retailer
N.A.I.C.S.: 458110

G3 VRM ACQUISITION CORP.
420 Boylston St Ste 302, Boston, MA
02116
Tel.: (617) 531-9911   DE
Year Founded: 2021

GGGVU—(NASDAQ)
Investment Services
N.A.I.C.S.: 523999
Matthew Konkle (Chm & CEO)
Don Van Der Wiel (CFO)

G6 MATERIALS CORP.
760 Koehler Ave Ste 2, Ronkonkoma,
NY 11779
Tel.: (516) 382-8649
Web Site: https://www.g6-
materials.com
GGG—(TSXV)
Rev.: $922,000
Assets: $1,165,000
Liabilities: $449,000
Net Worth: $716,000
Earnings: ($1,014,000)
Fiscal Year-end: 05/31/20
Support Activities for Printing
N.A.I.C.S.: 323120
Daniel Stolyarov (Pres & CEO)
Robert James Scott (CFO)
John Garrett Dyal (Chm)

GABELLI DIVIDEND & IN-COME TRUST
1CorporateCtr, Rye, NY 10580-1422
Tel.: (914) 921-5100
Web Site: http://www.gabelli.com
Year Founded: 1976
GDV—(NYSE)
Rev.: $52,341,717
Assets: $2,668,601,205
Liabilities: $7,698,507
Net Worth: $2,660,902,698
Earnings: $28,877,496
Fiscal Year-end: 12/31/19
Investment Management Service
N.A.I.C.S.: 525990
Mario J. Gabelli (Chm & Chief Investment Officer)
Peter Goldstein (Sec & VP)
Carter W. Austin (VP-Ombudsman)
David I. Schachter (VP)

GABELLI HEALTHCARE & WELLNESSRX TRUST
1 Corporate Ctr Rye, New York, NY
10580-1434
Tel.: (914) 921-5070
GRX—(NASDAQ)
Investment Management Service
N.A.I.C.S.: 525990

GABELLI MULTIMEDIA TRUST, INC.
One Corporate Center Rye, New
York, NY 10580-1434
Tel.: (914) 921-5070
Web Site: http://www.gabelli.com
GGT—(NYSE)
Rev.: $6,511,409
Assets: $299,493,365
Liabilities: $1,916,811
Net Worth: $297,576,554
Earnings: $3,185,626
Fiscal Year-end: 12/31/19
Investment Management Service
N.A.I.C.S.: 525990
Mario J. Gabelli (Chm & Chief Investment Officer)
Peter Goldstein (Sec & VP)
Carter W. Austin (VP-Ombudsman)
Laurissa M. Martire (VP)

GADSDEN PROPERTIES, INC.
8800 Village Dr Ste 202, San Antonio, TX 78217
Tel.: (480) 530-3495   NV
Web Site:
http://www.fcglobalrealty.com
Year Founded: 1980
GADS—(NASDAQ)
Sales Range: Less than $1 Million
Emp.: 2

Laser & Fiber-Optic Medical Equipment Mfr
N.A.I.C.S.: 334517
BJ Parrish (Interim CEO)
George Bell (COO)

Subsidiaries:

Gadsden Growth Properties, Inc.   **(1)**
15150 N Hayden Rd Ste 225, Scottsdale,
AZ 85260
Tel.: (480) 750-8700
Real Estate Investment Services
N.A.I.C.S.: 531210
John Hartman (Chm & CEO)
Keith Moser (Sr VP-Construction & Acq)
Scott Yorkison (VP-Acq)
B. J. Parrish (Sec)

LK Technology Importacao E Exportacao LTDA   **(1)**
Av Brg Faria Lima 1234 - Cj 123, Pinheiros,
Sao Paulo, 01451-001, Brazil
Tel.: (55) 1130959222
Web Site: http://www.lktechnology.com.br
Software Development Services
N.A.I.C.S.: 541511

Radiancy, Inc.   **(1)**
40 Ramland Rd S Ste 200, Orangeburg, NY
10962
Tel.: (845) 398-1647
Web Site: http://www.radiancy.com
Aesthetic & Dermatological Devices Mfr &
Distr; Skin Treatment Services
N.A.I.C.S.: 812199
Jeff Rabinowitz (Dir-Ops)

GAENSEL ENERGY GROUP, INC.
444 Somerville Ave, Somerville, MA
02143
Tel.: (212) 220-3968   NV
Year Founded: 1994
GEGR—(OTCIQ)
Installing Wind Powered Services
N.A.I.C.S.: 221115
Peter Albert Koley (CEO)
Dionysios Apostolopoulos (CFO)

GAIA, INC.
833 W S Boulder Rd, Louisville, CO
80027
Tel.: (303) 222-3600   CO
Web Site: https://www.gaia.com
Year Founded: 1988
GAIA—(NASDAQ)
Rev.: $82,035,000
Assets: $138,303,000
Liabilities: $49,319,000
Net Worth: $88,984,000
Earnings: ($3,095,000)
Emp.: 111
Fiscal Year-end: 12/31/22
Holding Company; Global Digital
Video Subscription Services
N.A.I.C.S.: 551112
Jirka Rysavy (Chm)
Brad Warkins (Head-Bus Dev & Intl)
James Colquhoun (COO)
Kiersten Medvedich (Pres)
Ned Preston (CFO)

GAIN THERAPEUTICS, INC.
4800 Montgomery Ln Ste 220,
Bethesda, MD 20814
Tel.: (301) 500-1556   DE
Web Site:
https://www.gaintherapeutics.com
Year Founded: 2020
GANX—(NASDAQ)
Rev.: $140,108
Assets: $24,099,387
Liabilities: $5,219,873
Net Worth: $18,879,514
Earnings: ($17,590,738)
Emp.: 28
Fiscal Year-end: 12/31/22
Biotechnology Research & Development Services
N.A.I.C.S.: 541714

Matthias Alder (Pres & CEO)
Manolo Bellotto (Gen Mgr)
Ana Maria Garcia-Collazo (VP-Research)
Elena Cubero-Jorda (Dir-Computational Chemistry)
Natalia Perez-Carmona (Dir-Biology)
Roberto Maj (VP-Dev)
Xavier Barril (Chief Scientific Officer)
Khalid Islam (Founder & Chm)
Stacey Jurchison (VP-IR)
Gianluca Fuggetta (Principal Acctg
Officer & VP-Fin)

GAINCLIENTS, INC.
6245 E Broadway Blvd Ste 400, Tucson, AZ 85711
Tel.: (206) 229-5515   FL
Web Site:
https://www.gainclients.com
Year Founded: 2001
GCLT—(OTCIQ)
Network Marketing Services
N.A.I.C.S.: 541613
Raymond Desmond (Founder & Pres)
Edward Laine (CEO)
Karen A. Fisher (Treas)

GALAXY DIGITAL HOLDINGS LTD.
107 Grand St, New York, NY 10013
Tel.: (416) 847-6905
Web Site: http://galaxydigital.io
BRPHF—(OTCIQ)
Rev.: $5,846,146
Assets: $81,040,806
Liabilities: $1
Net Worth: $81,040,805
Earnings: ($132,519,262)
Emp.: 2
Fiscal Year-end: 12/31/19
Developer of Cancer Treatment Products
N.A.I.C.S.: 325412
Samuel E. Englebardt (Partner)
Mike Novogratz (Founder, Chm &
CEO)
Michael Novogratz (Founder, Chm &
CEO)
Christopher Ferraro (Pres)
Luka Jankovic (Head-Res & Portfolio
Mgr)
Steve Kurz (Head-Asset Mgmt)
Andrew Siegel (Chief Compliance
Officer & Gen Counsel)
Ian Taylor (Head-Investment Banking)
Greg Wasserman (Head-Venture)
Peter Wisniewski (Head-Trading-
Global)

GALAXY GAMING INC.
6480 Cameron St Ste 305, Las Vegas, NV 89118
Tel.: (702) 939-3254   NV
Web Site:
https://www.galaxygaming.com
GLXZ—(OTCQB)
Rev.: $23,442,306
Assets: $42,010,516
Liabilities: $59,895,903
Net Worth: ($17,885,387)
Earnings: ($1,773,189)
Emp.: 42
Fiscal Year-end: 12/31/22
Casino Table Games Developer
N.A.I.C.S.: 713990
Harry C. Hagerty III (Treas & Sec)
Matt Reback (Pres & CEO)
Mark A. Lipparelli (Chm)
Chris Reynolds (Head-iGaming)

GALAXY NEXT GENERATION, INC.

285 Big A Rd, Toccoa, GA 30577
Tel.: (706) 391-5030   NV
Web Site: https://www.galaxynext.us
Year Founded: 2000
GAXY—(OTCIQ)
Rev.: $3,941,832
Assets: $4,565,392
Liabilities: $6,796,581
Net Worth: ($2,231,189)
Earnings: ($6,250,956)
Emp.: 24
Fiscal Year-end: 06/30/22
Holding Company
N.A.I.C.S.: 551112
Gary LeCroy *(Pres & CEO)*
Magen McGahee *(CFO, COO, Sec & Exec VP)*

Subsidiaries:

Classroom Technology Solutions,
Inc.   **(1)**
2604 1 Powers Ave, Jacksonville, FL 32207
Tel.: (904) 731-1006
Web Site: http://www.ctsed.com
Rev.: $2,700,000
Emp.: 6
Optical Instrument & Lens Mfr
N.A.I.C.S.: 333310
Cy Marshall *(Pres & CEO)*

GALECTIN THERAPEUTICS, INC.

4960 Peachtree Industrial Blvd Ste
240, Norcross, GA 30071
Tel.: (678) 620-3186   NV
Web Site:
   https://www.galectintherapeu
   tics.com
Year Founded: 2000
GALT—(NASDAQ)
Rev.: $52,000
Assets: $21,285,000
Liabilities: $55,202,000
Net Worth: ($33,917,000)
Earnings: ($38,776,000)
Emp.: 12
Fiscal Year-end: 12/31/22
Pharmaceutical Mfr, Developer &
Researcher
N.A.I.C.S.: 325412
Kevin D. Freeman *(Vice Chm)*
James C. Czirr *(Founder)*
Eliezer Zomer *(Exec VP-Mfg & Product Dev & VP-Discovery Res & Product Dev)*
Jack W. Callicutt *(CFO)*
Joel Lewis *(Pres & CEO)*
Richard E. Uihlein *(Chm)*
Ezra R. Lowe *(Exec Dir-Clinical & Preclinical Pharmacology)*

GALERA THERAPEUTICS, INC.

45 Liberty Blvd Ste 230, Malvern, PA
19355
Tel.: (610) 725-1500   DE
Web Site: https://www.galeratx.com
Year Founded: 2012
GRTX—(NASDAQ)
Rev.: $506,000
Assets: $44,036,000
Liabilities: $153,217,000
Net Worth: ($109,181,000)
Earnings: ($62,222,000)
Emp.: 31
Fiscal Year-end: 12/31/22
Biotechnology Research & Development Services
N.A.I.C.S.: 541714
J. Mel Sorensen *(Pres & CEO)*
Dennis P. Riley *(Co-Founder)*
Arthur J. Fratamico *(Chief Bus Officer)*
Jennifer Evans Stacey *(Chief Legal & Compliance Officer)*
Andie Collier *(Chief Regulatory Officer)*

Eugene P. Kennedy *(Chief Medical Officer)*
Judy Schnyder *(Sr VP)*
Robert A. Beardsley *(Co-Founder)*
Michael F. Powell *(Chm)*

GAMCO INVESTORS, INC.

1 Corporate Ctr, Rye, NY 10580
Tel.: (203) 629-2726   NY
Web Site: http://www.gabelli.com
Year Founded: 1977
GBL—(NYSE)
Rev.: $301,126,000
Assets: $231,672,000
Liabilities: $137,792,000
Net Worth: $93,880,000
Earnings: $73,199,000
Emp.: 168
Fiscal Year-end: 12/31/21
Asset Manager & Financial Services
N.A.I.C.S.: 551112
Jane Dinsmore O'Keeffe *(Portfolio Mgr)*
Mario J. Gabelli *(Founder, Chm, Co-CEO & Chief Investment Officer-Value Portfolios)*
Christopher J. Marangi *(Mng Dir, Co-Chief Investment Officer-Value Team & Portfolio Mgr)*
Daniel M. Miller *(Exec VP & Portfolio Mgr)*
Kevin V. Dreyer *(Mng Dir, Co-Chief Investment Officer-Value Team & Portfolio Mgr)*
Peter D. Goldstein *(Gen Counsel)*
Kieran Caterina *(CFO & Chief Acctg Officer)*
Joseph A. Gabelli *(Portfolio Mgr)*
Caesar M. P. Bryan *(Portfolio Mgr)*
Melody Bryant *(Portfolio Mgr)*
James Dinsmore *(Portfolio Mgr)*
Thomas Dinsmore *(Portfolio Mgr)*
Sergey Dluzhevskiy *(Portfolio Mgr)*
Sarah Donnelly *(Portfolio Mgr)*
Ronald S. Eaker *(Portfolio Mgr)*
Joseph Gabelli *(Portfolio Mgr)*
Vincent Hugonnard-Roche *(Dir & Portfolio Mgr)*
Jeffery J. Jones *(Portfolio Mgr)*
Ian Lapey *(Portfolio Mgr)*
Wayne C. Plewniak *(Mng Dir & Portfolio Mgr)*
Judith Raneri *(VP)*
Brain Sponheimer *(Portfolio Mgr)*
Hendi F. Ward *(CIO-Growth)*
Chris Ward *(Assoc Portfolio Mgr)*
Timothy Winter *(Portfolio Mgr)*

Subsidiaries:

GAMCO Asset Management (UK)
Limited   **(1)**
3 St James's Place, London, SW1A 1NP,
United Kingdom
Tel.: (44) 203 206 2100
Web Site: https://www.gabelli.co.uk
Emp.: 200
Asset Management & Financial Services
N.A.I.C.S.: 523940

GAMCO Asset Management Inc.   **(1)**
1 Corporate Ctr, Rye, NY 10580-1422
Tel.: (914) 921-5000
Web Site: http://www.gabelli.com
Emp.: 350
Investment Management Service
N.A.I.C.S.: 523940
Mario J. Gabelli *(Chief Investment Officer-Value Portfolios)*
Christopher J. Marangi *(Portfolio Mgr)*

Gabelli & Company, Inc.   **(1)**
1 Corporate Ctr, Rye, NY 10580
Tel.: (914) 921-3700
Business Management Services
N.A.I.C.S.: 561110
Daniel M. Miller *(Chm)*

Subsidiary (Domestic):

Gabelli & Company Investment Advisers, Inc.   **(2)**

1 Corporate Ctr, Rye, NY 10580
Tel.: (914) 921-5135
Web Site: http://www.gabelli.com
Investment Management Service
N.A.I.C.S.: 523940

Gabelli Funds, LLC   **(1)**
1 Corporate Ctr, Rye, NY 10580   **(100%)**
Tel.: (914) 921-5100
Web Site: http://www.gabelli.com
Financial Investment Services
N.A.I.C.S.: 523940
Mario J. Gabelli *(Chief Investment Officer-Value Portfolios)*
Christopher J. Marangi *(Portfolio Mgr)*

Affiliate (Domestic):

Bancroft Fund Ltd.   **(2)**
1 Corporate Ctr, Rye, NY 10580-1422
Tel.: (914) 921-5100
Web Site: http://www.gabelli.com
Rev.: $3,945,784
Assets: $167,860,736
Liabilities: $31,699,894
Net Worth: $136,160,842
Earnings: $2,254,633
Fiscal Year-end: 10/31/2019
Closed-End Investment Fund
N.A.I.C.S.: 525990
James Dinsmore *(Portfolio Mgr)*
Thomas Dinsmore *(Portfolio Mgr)*

GAMCO Natural Resources, Gold &
Income Trust   **(2)**
1 Corporate Ctr, Rye, NY 10580-1422
Tel.: (914) 921-5100
Web Site: http://www.gabelli.com
Rev.: $2,716,201
Assets: $169,224,073
Liabilities: $11,222,087
Net Worth: $158,001,986
Earnings: $563,986
Fiscal Year-end: 12/31/2019
Closed-End Investment Fund
N.A.I.C.S.: 525990
Agnes Nora Mullady *(Treas)*

Gabelli Global Utility & Income
Trust   **(2)**
1 Corporate Ctr, Rye, NY 10580-1422
Tel.: (914) 921-5100
Web Site: http://www.gabelli.com
Sales Range: $10-24.9 Million
Closed-End Investment Fund
N.A.I.C.S.: 525990
Mario J. Gabelli *(Portfolio Mgr)*
Agnes Nora Mullady *(Treas)*
Bruce N. Alpert *(Pres)*
David I. Schachter *(VP)*
Andrea R. Mango *(Sec & VP)*
Richard J. Walz *(Chief Compliance Officer)*
Adam E. Tokar *(VP)*

The Gabelli Equity Trust Inc.   **(2)**
1 Corporate Ctr, Rye, NY 10580-1422
Tel.: (914) 921-5100
Web Site: http://www.gabelli.com
Rev.: $34,684,099
Assets: $1,986,433,351
Liabilities: $20,426,642
Net Worth: $1,966,006,709
Earnings: $15,001,077
Fiscal Year-end: 12/31/2019
Non-Diversified Closed-End Investment
Fund
N.A.I.C.S.: 525990
David I. Schachter *(VP)*
Andrea R. Mango *(Sec & VP)*
Richard J. Walz *(Chief Compliance Officer)*
Carter W. Austin *(VP)*
Molly A. F. Marion *(VP)*
Jennie Tsai *(Portfolio Mgr)*
John C. Ball *(Treas)*

GAMER PAKISTAN INC.

35 E Horizon Ridge Pkwy Ste 110-
481, Henderson, NV 89002-7906
Tel.: (702) 905-1171   DE
Web Site:
   https://www.gamerpakistan.com
Year Founded: 2021
GPAK—(NASDAQ)
Rev.: $733
Assets: $3,989,567
Liabilities: $201,280
Net Worth: $3,788,287
Earnings: ($2,051,111)

Emp.: 7
Fiscal Year-end: 12/31/23
Sports Event Operator
N.A.I.C.S.: 711320
James Knopf *(Pres & CEO)*
Keith Fredriksen *(Sec)*

Subsidiaries:

K2 Gamer (PVT) Ltd.   **(1)**
H No 53 Street No 02 Block-E Asc Colony,
Nowshera, 24100, Khyber Pakhtunkhwa,
Pakistan
Tel.: (92) 3338712355
Web Site: https://k2gamerpakistan.com
Sports & Gaming Ecosystem Services
N.A.I.C.S.: 711211

GAMES & ESPORTS EXPERIENCE ACQUISITION CORP.

7381 La Tijera Blvd, Los Angeles, CA
90045
Tel.: (213) 266-7674   Ky
Web Site: https://www.geexspac.com
Year Founded: 2021
GEEX—(NASDAQ)
Rev.: $19,797,250
Assets: $208,297,153
Liabilities: $216,355,219
Net Worth: ($8,058,066)
Earnings: $17,984,720
Emp.: 2
Fiscal Year-end: 12/31/22
Investment Services
N.A.I.C.S.: 523999
Ari Segal *(Co-Founder & CEO)*
Tomi Kovanen *(Co-Founder & COO)*

GAMESTOP CORP.

625 Westport Pkwy, Grapevine, TX
76051
Tel.: (817) 424-2000   DE
Web Site: https://www.gamestop.com
Year Founded: 1983
GME—(NYSE)
Rev.: $5,272,800,000
Assets: $2,709,000,000
Liabilities: $1,370,400,000
Net Worth: $1,338,600,000
Earnings: $6,700,000
Emp.: 8,000
Fiscal Year-end: 02/03/24
Consumer Software & Video Game
Entertainment Retailer
N.A.I.C.S.: 449210
Ryan Cohen *(Chm, Pres & CEO)*
Mark H. Robinson *(Gen Counsel & Sec)*
Daniel Moore *(Principal Acctg Officer & Interim Principal Financial Officer)*

Subsidiaries:

Electronics Boutique Australia Pty.
Ltd.   **(1)**
25 Backhouse Place Trade Coast Central,
Eagle Farm, 4009, QLD, Australia
Tel.: (61) 73 860 7777
Web Site: https://www.ebgames.com.au
Video Game & Electronic Component Distr
N.A.I.C.S.: 423920

Electronics Boutique Canada
Inc.   **(1)**
8995 Airport Road, Brampton, L6T 5T2,
ON, Canada
Tel.: (705) 429-1119
Web Site: http://www.ebgame.com
Emp.: 4
Video Game & Electronic Component Distr
N.A.I.C.S.: 423920

GS Mobile, Inc.   **(1)**
625 Westport Pkwy, Grapevine, TX 76051-
6740
Tel.: (817) 424-2000
Hobby, Toy & Game Store Operator
N.A.I.C.S.: 459120

GameStop Deutschland GmbH   **(1)**
Walterstr 20, Tannheim, D-88459, Biberach,
Germany
Tel.: (49) 83958133100

GameStop Corp.—(Continued)

Web Site: https://www.gamestop.de
Emp.: 120
Video Game & Electronic Component Distr
N.A.I.C.S.: 423920
Judith Poppek (Officer-Youth Protection)
Manuel Erpenbach (Officer-Data Protection)
Karsten Jennissen (Mng Dir)

GameStop Group Limited (1)
Estuary House Swords Business Park,
Swords, 216410, Ireland
Tel.: (353) 1 813 5350
Web Site: http://www.gamestop.ie
Sales Range: $100-124.9 Million
Emp.: 400
Videogame Retailer
N.A.I.C.S.: 449210

Subsidiary (Domestic):

GameStop Ltd. (2)
12 Lower Liffey Street, Dublin, D01 W9F2,
Ireland
Tel.: (353) 8724305
Web Site: http://www.gamestop.ie
Videogame Retailer
N.A.I.C.S.: 449210

Subsidiary (Non-US):

GameStop UK Limited (2)
5 Fleet Place, London, EC4M 7RD, United
Kingdom
Tel.: (44) 13353285156
Video Game & Accessorie Retailer
N.A.I.C.S.: 459120

GameStop Iberia S.L. (1)
Plaza de l'Ermita, Xirivella, 46950, Valencia,
Spain
Tel.: (34) 961124431
Video Game & Electronic Component Distr
N.A.I.C.S.: 512199

GameStop Norway AS (1)
Ploens Gate 4, Oslo, 0181, Norway
Tel.: (47) 22177077
Web Site: http://www.gamestop.no
Video Game & Electronic Component Distr
N.A.I.C.S.: 423920

GameStop Schweiz GmbH (1)
Seefeldstrasse 69, 8008, Zurich, Switzer-
land
Tel.: (41) 4983 319 2920
Web Site: https://www.gamestop.ch
Sales Range: $25-49.9 Million
Emp.: 3
Video Game & Electronic Component Distr
N.A.I.C.S.: 423920

GameStop Sweden AB (1)
Hammarvagen 5, 202 07, Arlov, Sweden
Tel.: (46) 40 600 86 00
Web Site: http://www.gamestop.se
Sales Range: $25-49.9 Million
Emp.: 350
Video Game & Electronic Component Distr
N.A.I.C.S.: 423920

GameStop, Inc. (1)
5115 Burning Tree Rd Ste 315, Duluth, MN
55811-1883
Tel.: (218) 722-0020
Web Site: http://www.gamestop.com
Sales Range: $25-49.9 Million
Emp.: 6
Videogame Retailer
N.A.I.C.S.: 449210

Subsidiary (Domestic):

Sunrise Publications, Inc. (1)
724 N 1st St 3rd Fl, Minneapolis, MN 55401
Tel.: (612) 486-6100
Web Site: http://www.gameinformer.com
Sales Range: $10-24.9 Million
Publication Services
N.A.I.C.S.: 513110

Jolt Online Gaming Limited
(Ireland) (1)
7 St Stephen s Green, Dublin, 2, Ireland
Tel.: (353) 16729626
Web Site: http://www.joltonline.com
Sales Range: $10-24.9 Million
Emp.: 30
Online Game Development & Publishing
Services

N.A.I.C.S.: 513210

Micromania Group SAS (1)
Ecolucioles 955 Route Des Lucioles, 06901,
Sophia-Antipolis, France
Tel.: (33) 492943600
Web Site: https://www.micromania.fr
Video Game & Electronic Component Distr
N.A.I.C.S.: 423920

Spawn Labs, Inc. (1)
5813 Lookout Mountain Dr, Austin, TX 78731
Tel.: (512) 547-9974
Web Site: http://www.spawnlabs.com
Video Game Mfr
N.A.I.C.S.: 512250

ThinkGeek, Inc. (1)
11216 Waples Mill Rd Ste 100, Fairfax, VA
22030-6099
Tel.: (508) 970-2002
Web Site: http://www.thinkgeek.com
Online Novelty Retailer
N.A.I.C.S.: 459420

GAMING & HOSPITALITY AC-
QUISITION CORP.
3755 Breakthrough Way Ste 300, Las
Vegas, NV 89135   DE
Year Founded: 2020
GHAC—(NASDAQ)
Rev.: $1,957,878
Assets: $201,070,928
Liabilities: $212,466,104
Net Worth: ($11,395,176)
Earnings: ($1,676,152)
Emp.: 3
Fiscal Year-end: 12/31/21
Investment Services
N.A.I.C.S.: 523999
Mary E. Higgins (CEO)
Eric Fiocco (COO)
Andrei Scrivens (CFO)
James J. Zenni Jr. (Chm)

GAMING AND LEISURE PROP-
ERTIES, INC.
845 Berkshire Blvd Ste 200, Wyo-
missing, PA 19610
Tel.: (610) 401-2900   **PA**
Web Site: https://www.glpropinc.com
Year Founded: 2013
GLPI—(NASDAQ)
Rev.: $1,440,392,000
Assets: $11,806,658,000
Liabilities: $7,297,704,000
Net Worth: $4,508,954,000
Earnings: $734,283,000
Emp.: 18
Fiscal Year-end: 12/31/23
Real Estate Investment Services
N.A.I.C.S.: 523999
Desiree A. Burke (CFO & Treas)
Steven Ladany (Chief Dev Officer &
Sr VP)
Peter M. Carlino (Chm & CEO)

Subsidiaries:

GLP Capital, L.P. (1)
825 Berkshire Blvd, Wyomissing, PA 19610
Tel.: (610) 401-2900
Casino & Gaming Services
N.A.I.C.S.: 721120

Louisiana Casino Cruises, Inc. (1)
1717 River Rd N, Baton Rouge, LA 70802
Tel.: (225) 709-7777
Web Site: http://www.hollywoodbr.com
Sales Range: $200-249.9 Million
Owner & Operator of Riverboat Gaming
Facilities
N.A.I.C.S.: 713290

GAMING INNOVATION GROUP
INC.
8359 Stringfellow Rd, Saint James
City, FL 33956
Tel.: (239) 282-0563
Web Site: http://www.gig.com
GIGSEK—(OSL)
Rev.: $77,412,282

Assets: $114,411,784
Liabilities: $109,982,751
Net Worth: $4,429,033
Earnings: ($21,720,196)
Emp.: 460
Fiscal Year-end: 12/31/20
Online Gambling Services
N.A.I.C.S.: 713290
Richard Brown (CEO)
Richard Carter (CEO-Platform &
Sportsbook)
Justin Psaila (CFO)
Claudia Ginex (Chief People Officer)
Jonas Warrer (Mng Dir & CMO)
Claudio Caruana (Gen Counsel)
Petter Nylander (Chm)
Nicola Fitton (COO)
Marcel Elfersy (Chief Comml Officer)

GAMING TECHNOLOGIES,
INC.
2 Summerlin, Las Vegas, NV 89135
Tel.: (347) 983-1227   **DE**
Web Site: https://www.gametech.com
Year Founded: 2019
GMGT—(OTCQB)
Rev.: $102,816
Assets: $703,811
Liabilities: $5,171,143
Net Worth: ($4,467,332)
Earnings: ($4,299,860)
Emp.: 1
Fiscal Year-end: 12/31/22
Video Game Development Services
N.A.I.C.S.: 541511
Darin Oliver (Head-Corp Regulatory
Strategy)
Jason Drummond (Founder, Chm,
Pres, CEO, CFO & Sec)
Steven M. Plumb (CFO)

GAN LIMITED
400 Spectrum Center Dr Ste 1900,
Irvine, CA 92618
Tel.: (702) 964-5777   **BM**
Web Site: https://www.gan.com
Year Founded: 2019
GAN—(NASDAQ)
Rev.: $141,528,000
Assets: $103,080,000
Liabilities: $82,312,000
Net Worth: $20,768,000
Earnings: ($197,498,000)
Emp.: 701
Fiscal Year-end: 12/31/22
Holding Company
N.A.I.C.S.: 551112
Seamus McGill (Chm)
David Goldberg (Vice Chm)
Brian Chang (CFO)
Ervin Jarvlepp (CMO)
Betty Wong (Chief People Officer)
Rob Lekites (Sr VP-Sports Betting)
Sylvia Tiscareno (Chief Legal Officer)

GANNETT CO., INC.
Tel.: (703) 854-6000   **DE**
Web Site: https://www.gannett.com
Year Founded: 2013
GCI—(NYSE)
Rev.: $2,945,303,000
Assets: $2,393,555,000
Liabilities: $2,098,182,000
Net Worth: $295,373,000
Earnings: ($78,002,000)
Emp.: 11,200
Fiscal Year-end: 12/31/22
Holding Company; Digital Marketing
Services Business
N.A.I.C.S.: 551112
Michael E. Reed (Chm & CEO)
Mayur Gupta (Chief Mktg & Strategy
Officer)
Douglas E. Horne (CFO)
Samantha Howland (Chief People
Officer)

Lark-Marie Anton (Chief Comm Offi-
cer)
Kristin Roberts (Chief Content Offi-
cer)
Chris Cho (Pres-Digital Mktg Solu-
tions)
Cindy Gallagher (Chief Acctg Officer
& Controller)

Subsidiaries:

Citizen Publishing Company (1)
262 N Cedar St, Hazleton, PA 18201
Tel.: (570) 454-5911
Web Site: https://www.citpublish.com
Newspaper Publishing Services
N.A.I.C.S.: 513110

Cummings Acquisition, Inc. (1)
175 Sullys Trl Ste 3, Pittsford, NY 14534
Tel.: (585) 598-0030
Web Site: http://www.gatehousemedia.com
Investment Management Service
N.A.I.C.S.: 523940

DB Arkansas Holdings, Inc. (1)
5111 Rogers Ave Ste 471, Fort Smith, AR
72903
Tel.: (479) 785-7718
Web Site: https://www.swtimes.com
Holding Company
N.A.I.C.S.: 551112

DB Texas Holdings, Inc. (1)
603 S Sam Rayburn Fwy, Sherman, TX
75091
Tel.: (903) 893-8181
Web Site: https://www.heralddemocrat.com
Holding Company
N.A.I.C.S.: 551112

EnMotive Company LLC (1)
951 Corporate Grove Dr, Buffalo Grove, IL
60089
Tel.: (847) 243-8405
Web Site: https://info.enmotive.com
Event Management Services
N.A.I.C.S.: 561920

Enterprise NewsMedia, LLC (1)
400 Crown Colony Dr, Quincy, MA 02269-
9159
Tel.: (617) 786-7000
Web Site: https://www.patriotledger.com
Emp.: 60
Newspaper Publishing Services
N.A.I.C.S.: 513110

Gannett Media Corp. (1)
7950 Jones Branch Dr, McLean, VA 22107-
0150
Tel.: (703) 854-6000
Holding Company; Newspaper Publishing &
Multi-Platform News & Information Services
N.A.I.C.S.: 551112

Subsidiary (Domestic):

Action Advertising, Inc. (2)
N6637 Rolling Meadows Dr, Fond Du Lac,
WI 54937
Tel.: (252) 756-8655
Web Site:
  https://www.actionadvertisingnc.com
Sales Range: $50-74.9 Million
Emp.: 150
Newspaper Publisher Services
N.A.I.C.S.: 513110
Pamela Henson (Publr)

Alexandria Newspapers, Inc. (2)
1201 3rd St, Alexandria, LA 71301
Tel.: (318) 487-6397
Web Site: https://www.thetowntalk.com
Sales Range: $50-74.9 Million
Emp.: 250
Newspaper Publisher Services
N.A.I.C.S.: 513110

Subsidiary (Domestic):

The Town Talk (3)
1201 3rd St, Alexandria, LA 71306
Tel.: (318) 487-6397
Web Site: https://www.thetowntalk.com
Sales Range: $50-74.9 Million
Newspaper Publishers
N.A.I.C.S.: 513110

Unit (Domestic):

Argus Leader (2)
200 S Minnesota Ave, Sioux Falls, SD
57104 **(100%)**
Tel.: (605) 331-2200
Web Site: https://www.argusleader.com
Emp.: 250
Newspaper Publishers
N.A.I.C.S.: 513110

Asbury Park Press (2)
3601 Hwy 66, Neptune, NJ 07754
Tel.: (732) 922-6000
Web Site: https://www.app.com
Sales Range: $400-449.9 Million
Emp.: 350
Newspaper Publishers
N.A.I.C.S.: 513110

Asheville Citizen-Times (2)
14 O Henry Ave, Asheville, NC
28802 **(100%)**
Tel.: (828) 252-5611
Web Site: https://www.citizen-times.com
Sales Range: $50-74.9 Million
Emp.: 100
Newspaper Publishers
N.A.I.C.S.: 513110

Subsidiary (Domestic):

Black Mountain News (3)
111 S Richardson Blvd, Black Mountain, NC
28711 **(100%)**
Tel.: (828) 669-8727
Web Site:
  http://www.static.blackmountainnews.com
Emp.: 5
Newspaper Publishers
N.A.I.C.S.: 513110
Lyn Prince (Acct Exec-Adv)

Subsidiary (Domestic):

Baxter County Newspapers, Inc. (2)
16 W 6th St, Mountain Home, AR 72653
Tel.: (870) 508-8000
Web Site: https://www.baxterbulletin.com
Newspaper Publisher Services
N.A.I.C.S.: 513110

Unit (Domestic):

The Baxter Bulletin (3)
16 W 6th St, Mountain Home, AR
72653-3508 **(100%)**
Tel.: (870) 508-8000
Web Site: https://www.baxterbulletin.com
Sales Range: $25-49.9 Million
Emp.: 25
Newspaper Publishers
N.A.I.C.S.: 513110

Unit (Domestic):

Bucyrus Telegraph-Forum (2)
113 W Rensselaer St, Bucyrus, OH
44820-2215 **(100%)**
Tel.: (419) 562-3333
Web Site:
  https://www.bucyrustelegraphforum.com
Emp.: 5
Newspaper Publishers
N.A.I.C.S.: 513110

Chillicothe Gazette (2)
927 E Main St, Chillicothe, OH
45601-3103 **(100%)**
Tel.: (740) 349-1111
Web Site:
  https://www.chillicothegazette.com
Newspaper Publishers
N.A.I.C.S.: 513110

Subsidiary (Domestic):

Courier News (2)
201 E 2nd St, Russellville, AR
72801 **(100%)**
Tel.: (479) 968-5252
Web Site: https://www.couriernews.com
Sales Range: $125-149.9 Million
Emp.: 30
Newspaper Publishers
N.A.I.C.S.: 513110

Unit (Domestic):

Courier-Post (2)

301 Cuthbert Blvd, Cherry Hill, NJ
08002-2905 **(100%)**
Tel.: (856) 663-6000
Web Site:
  https://www.courierpostonline.com
Sales Range: $100-124.9 Million
Emp.: 700
Newspaper Publishers
N.A.I.C.S.: 513110

Daily Record (2)
100 Commons Way, Rockaway, NJ 07866
Tel.: (973) 428-6200
Web Site: https://www.dailyrecord.com
Sales Range: $25-49.9 Million
Emp.: 100
Newspaper Publishers
N.A.I.C.S.: 513110

Subsidiary (Domestic):

Daily Tribune (2)
101 W Riverview Expy Ste 131, Wisconsin
Rapids, WI 54495 **(100%)**
Tel.: (715) 423-7200
Web Site:
  https://www.wisconsinrapidtribune.com
Emp.: 25
Newspaper Publishers
N.A.I.C.S.: 513110
Mark Treinen (Dir-News)
Jamie Rokus (Editor-Community Engagement)

Daily World (2)
604 S Union St, Opelousas, LA 70570
Tel.: (337) 942-4971
Web Site: https://www.dailyworld.com
Emp.: 5
Newspaper Publishers
N.A.I.C.S.: 513110

Unit (Domestic):

Democrat & Chronicle (2)
245 E Main St, Rochester, NY
14604 **(100%)**
Tel.: (585) 232-7100
Web Site:
  https://www.democratandchronicle.com
Sales Range: $25-49.9 Million
Emp.: 400
Newspaper Publishers
N.A.I.C.S.: 513110

Subsidiary (Domestic):

**Des Moines Register and Tribune
Company** (2)
400 Locust St Ste 500, Des Moines, IA
50309
Tel.: (515) 284-8000
Web Site:
  https://www.desmoinesregister.com
Sales Range: $300-349.9 Million
Emp.: 1,000
Newspaper Publisher Services
N.A.I.C.S.: 513110
Kevin R. Johnson (Gen Mgr-GPS Des
Moines & Reg Dir)

**Detroit Newspaper Partnership,
L.P.** (2)
160 W Fort St, Detroit, MI 48226-3124
Tel.: (313) 222-6400
Web Site: https://www.michigan.com
Sales Range: $750-799.9 Million
Emp.: 2,600
Newspaper Publisher Services
N.A.I.C.S.: 513110
Aaron Velthoven (VP-Mktg)
David Davies (VP-Fin)
John Morey (Sr Dir-Ops)
Allen Jones (Pres)
Ashley Wright (VP)

Subsidiary (Domestic):

Detroit Free Press, Inc. (3)
160 W Fort St, Detroit, MI 48226
Tel.: (313) 222-6400
Web Site: https://www.freep.com
Emp.: 320
Newspaper Publishers
N.A.I.C.S.: 513110
Peter Bhatia (VP & Editor)
Kirkland Crawford (Editor-Sports)
Brian Dickerson (Editor-Editorial Page)
Jewel Gopwani (Sr Editor-Engagement &
Events)

Jim Schaefer (Sr Dir-News-Autos, Bus &
Education)
Kathy Kieliszewski (Sr Dir-News-Photo, Visual & Freep Film Fest)
Dora Robles Hernandez (Office Mgr)
Ritu Sehgal (Editor-Politics)
Maryann Struman (Editor-Freep Now)
Kayla Cockrel (Editor-Web)
Amy Huschka (Editor-Web)
Brian Todd (Editor-Web)
Tanya Wildt (Editor-Web)
Elissa Robinson (Editor-Web)
Joe Cybulski (Editor-News)

Subsidiary (Domestic):

**EXCHANGE ENTERPRISES
LIMITED** (2)
35 Stagg St, Stratford, CT 06615
Tel.: (203) 386-9466
Web Site:
  https://www.exchangeenterprises.com
Business Services
N.A.I.C.S.: 561990

Federated Publications, Inc. (2)
300 S Washington Sq Ste 300, Lansing, MI
48933
Tel.: (703) 854-6000
Web Site:
  https://www.lansingstatejournal.com
Holding Company; Newspaper Publisher
N.A.I.C.S.: 551112

Unit (Domestic):

Battle Creek Enquirer (3)
77 E Michigan Ave Ste 101, Battle Creek,
MI 49017 **(100%)**
Tel.: (269) 964-7161
Web Site:
  https://www.battlecreekenquirer.com
Sales Range: $50-74.9 Million
Emp.: 50
Newspaper Publishing
N.A.I.C.S.: 513110

Subsidiary (Domestic):

Lansing State Journal (3)
300 S Washington Sq Ste 300, Lansing, MI
48933 **(100%)**
Tel.: (517) 377-1000
Web Site:
  https://www.lansingstatejournal.com
Newspaper Publishers
N.A.I.C.S.: 513110
Stephanie Angel (Exec Editor)
Barry Kiel (Editor-Sports)

Subsidiary (Domestic):

Fort Collins Coloradoan (2)
1300 Riverside Ave, Fort Collins, CO
80524 **(100%)**
Tel.: (970) 493-6397
Web Site: https://www.coloradoan.com
Sales Range: $50-74.9 Million
Emp.: 100
Newspaper Publishers
N.A.I.C.S.: 513110
Eric Larsen (Exec Editor)
Chris Abshire (Editor-Sports & State Content Coach)
Sarah Kyle (Editor)
Rebecca Powell (Editor)

Gannett Missouri Publishing, Inc. (2)
901 E St Louis St Ste 1100, Springfield, MO
65806 **(100%)**
Tel.: (417) 836-1100
Web Site: https://www.news-leader.com
Emp.: 350
Newspaper Publishers
N.A.I.C.S.: 513110
Cheryl Whitsitt (Dir-News)
Tom Tate (Reg Dir)
Allen Vaughan (Dir-Consumer Experience)
Paul Berry (Exec Editor)

**Gannett Publishing Services,
LLC** (2)
7950 Jones Branch Dr, McLean, VA 22107
Tel.: (703) 854-3400
Web Site: https://www.gannettpublishingservices.com
Production & Circulation Operations for
Newspaper Publishing
N.A.I.C.S.: 323120

Kelly Provant (VP-Fin)
Tom Kelly (VP-Natl Distr)
Jack Saunders (VP-Publ Svcs)
Dale Carpenter (VP-Ops)
Tony Simmons (Dir-Distr Ops & Tech)
Sarah Kingsley (Dir-HR)
Bill Bolger (VP-Production)
Greg Fiorito (VP-Ops-West)
Jack Roth (VP-Ops-East)
Mike Christopher (Gen Mgr & Dir-Sls-Natl)
Mike Donohue (Reg VP-Distr)
Steve Wagenlander (Reg VP-Distr)
Joe Werlinich (Reg VP-Distr)
Chris Hansen (Dir-Sls Svcs & Dist)

Gannett Supply Corporation (2)
7950 Jones Branch Dr, McLean, VA
22107 **(100%)**
Tel.: (703) 854-6000
Sales Range: $450-499.9 Million
Emp.: 30,000
Sourcing of all Commodities Used in Publishing & Digital Services, Including Services, Equipment & Supplies
N.A.I.C.S.: 561499
Frank O'Toole (Pres)

Gannett Vermont Publishing, Inc. (2)
426 Industrial Ave Ste 160, Williston, VT
05495
Tel.: (802) 863-3441
Web Site:
  https://www.burlingtonfreepress.com
Newspaper Publisher Services
N.A.I.C.S.: 513110

Unit (Domestic):

Burlington Free Press (3)
426 Industrial Ave Ste 160, Williston, VT
05495 **(100%)**
Tel.: (802) 660-1873
Web Site:
  https://www.burlingtonfreepress.com
Sales Range: $75-99.9 Million
Emp.: 250
Newspaper Publishers
N.A.I.C.S.: 513110
Aki Soga (Editor-Engagement & Insights)

Unit (Domestic):

Great Falls Tribune (2)
205 River Dr S, Great Falls, MT 59405
Tel.: (406) 791-1444
Web Site: https://www.greatfallstribune.com
Sales Range: $50-74.9 Million
Emp.: 180
Newspaper Publishers
N.A.I.C.S.: 513110

Unit (Domestic):

Consumers Press (3)
205 River Dr S, Great Falls, MT 59405
Tel.: (406) 761-2406
Web Site:
  https://consumerspress.mt.newsmemory.com
Emp.: 75
Shopping News Publisher
N.A.I.C.S.: 513199

Unit (Domestic):

Green Bay Press-Gazette (2)
435 E Walnut St, Green Bay, WI
54305-3430 **(100%)**
Tel.: (920) 435-4411
Web Site:
  https://www.greenbaypressgazette.com
Emp.: 300
Newspaper Publishers
N.A.I.C.S.: 513110

Greenville News (2)
305 S Main St, Greenville, SC
29602 **(100%)**
Tel.: (864) 298-4100
Web Site: https://www.greenvilleonline.com
Sales Range: $75-99.9 Million
Emp.: 500
Newspaper Publishers
N.A.I.C.S.: 513110
Steve Bruss (Dir-News)

Subsidiary (Domestic):

Guam Publications, Incorporated (2)
PO Box DN, Hagatna, GU 96932 **(100%)**
Tel.: (671) 472-1736
Web Site: https://www.guampdn.com

Gannett Co., Inc.—(Continued)
Newspaper Publishers
N.A.I.C.S.: 513110

Unit (Domestic):

Pacific Daily News (3)
PO Box DN, Hagatna, GU 96932 **(100%)**
Tel.: (671) 472-1736
Web Site: http://www.guampdn.com
Emp.: 200
Newspaper Publishers
N.A.I.C.S.: 513110

Unit (Domestic):

Hattiesburg American (2)
403 Main St, Hattiesburg, MS
39401 **(100%)**
Tel.: (601) 582-4321
Web Site:
https://www.hattiesburgamerican.com
Emp.: 50
Newspaper Publishers
N.A.I.C.S.: 513110

Herald Times Reporter (2)
902 Franklin St, Manitowoc, WI
54220 **(100%)**
Tel.: (920) 684-4433
Web Site: https://www.htrnews.com
Emp.: 100
Newspaper Publishers
N.A.I.C.S.: 513110

Subsidiary (Domestic):

Home News Tribune (2)
35 Kennedy Blvd, East Brunswick, NJ
08816
Tel.: (732) 246-5500
Web Site: http://www.mycentraljersey.com
Newspaper Publishing
N.A.I.C.S.: 513110

Indiana Newspapers, LLC (2)
130 S Meridian St, Indianapolis, IN 46225
Tel.: (317) 444-4000
Web Site: https://www.indystar.com
Emp.: 1,200
Newspaper Publisher Services
N.A.I.C.S.: 513110
Patricia Miller (Pres)

Unit (Domestic):

Indianapolis Star (3)
130 S Meridian St, Indianapolis, IN 46225
Tel.: (317) 444-4000
Web Site: https://www.indystar.com
Sales Range: $450-499.9 Million
Newspaper Publishers
N.A.I.C.S.: 513110
Katrice Hardy (Exec Editor)

Unit (Domestic):

Journal & Courier (2)
300 Main St Ste 314, Lafayette, IN
47901 **(100%)**
Tel.: (765) 423-5511
Web Site: https://www.jconline.com
Sales Range: $75-99.9 Million
Emp.: 100
Newspaper Publishers
N.A.I.C.S.: 513110

Subsidiary (Domestic):

Journal Media Group, Inc. (2)
6550 Carothers Pkwy Ste 420, Franklin, TN
37067
Tel.: (414) 224-2000
Web Site: https://livabilitymedia.com
Sales Range: $400-449.9 Million
Emp.: 2,800
Holding Company; Newspaper Publisher
N.A.I.C.S.: 551112
Barbara W. Wall (VP)

Subsidiary (Domestic):

Abilene Reporter-News, LLC (3)
101 Cypress St, Abilene, TX
79601-5816 **(100%)**
Tel.: (325) 671-8318
Web Site: https://www.reporternews.com
Sales Range: $50-74.9 Million
Emp.: 220
Newspaper Publishers
N.A.I.C.S.: 513110

Greg Jaklewicz (Dir-Newsroom)

Anderson Independent Mail, LLC (3)
1000 Williamston Rd, Anderson, SC
29621-6508 **(100%)**
Tel.: (864) 224-4321
Web Site: https://www.independentmail.com
Sales Range: $50-74.9 Million
Emp.: 80
Newspaper Publishers
N.A.I.C.S.: 513110
Steve Bruss (Exec Editor)
Mike Burns (Editor-Watchdog Team)
Rick Spruill (Editor-Breaking News)
Jim Rice (Editor-Sports)

Corpus Christi Caller-Times LLC (3)
820 N Lower Broadway, Corpus Christi, TX
78401 **(100%)**
Tel.: (361) 884-2011
Web Site: https://www.caller.com
Sales Range: $75-99.9 Million
Emp.: 250
Newspaper Publishers
N.A.I.C.S.: 513110
Clay Carpenter (Editor-Plng)
Len Hayward (Editor-Sports & Reg Dir-
Sports)
Allison Ehrlich (Coord-Archive)

Evansville Courier Company, Inc. (3)
300 E Walnut, Evansville, IN
47713 **(94%)**
Tel.: (812) 424-7711
Web Site: https://www.courierpress.com
Sales Range: $50-74.9 Million
Emp.: 300
Newspaper Publisher Services
N.A.I.C.S.: 513110

**Journal Community Publishing Group,
Inc.** (3)
600 Industrial Dr, Waupaca, WI 54981
Tel.: (715) 258-8450
Newspaper Publishers
N.A.I.C.S.: 513110

Unit (Domestic):

Jefferson County Advertiser (4)
W4540 Linmar Ln, Watertown, WI 53094
Tel.: (920) 674-2672
Web Site: http://www.livinglakecountry.com
Emp.: 6
Shopping News Publishing
N.A.I.C.S.: 513110

Metroparent West Magazine (4)
810 Cardinal Ln Ste 210, Hartland, WI
53029
Tel.: (262) 367-3272
Periodical Publishing
N.A.I.C.S.: 513120
Steve Lyles (Gen Mgr)

Subsidiary (Domestic):

Journal Sentinel, Inc. (3)
PO Box 371, Milwaukee, WI
53201 **(100%)**
Tel.: (414) 224-2000
Web Site: https://www.jsonline.com
Emp.: 1,400
Newspaper Publishers
N.A.I.C.S.: 513110
Jill Williams (Sr Editor-Features)
Thomas Koetting (Editor-Enterprise)
Greg Borowski (Sr Editor-News, Bus, and
PolitiFact Wisconsin)
Mark Stewart (Editor-Prep Sports)
Paul A. Smith (Editor-Outdoors)
Rick Klauer (Editor-Packer Plus)
Louisa Boardman (Editor-Milwaukee Sports)
Angela Peterson (Editor-Photo)
Mike De Sisti (Editor-Video & Photo)
Berford Gammon (Dir-Photography)
Lainey Seyler (Editor-Social & Trending)
Rachel Piper (Sr Editor-Digital News)
Robert Zizzo (Editor-Sports-Reg)
Ray Hollnagel (Asst Dir-Night News)
Jen Steele (Editor-Digital Plng)

Kitsap Sun, LLC (3)
545 5th St, Bremerton, WA
98337-1413 **(100%)**
Tel.: (360) 377-3711
Web Site: https://www.kitsapsun.com
Emp.: 200
Newspaper Publishers

N.A.I.C.S.: 513110
David Nelson (Editor)

Knoxville News Sentinel, LLC (3)
2332 News Sentinel Dr, Knoxville, TN
37921 **(100%)**
Tel.: (865) 342-6265
Web Site: https://www.knoxnews.com
Sales Range: $50-74.9 Million
Emp.: 500
Newspaper Publishers
N.A.I.C.S.: 513110
Joel Christopher (Exec Editor)
Aaron Torres (Editor-High School Sports)

Memphis Publishing Company (3)
120 S Front St, Memphis, TN 38103
Tel.: (901) 529-2345
Web Site:
https://www.commercialappeal.com
Sales Range: $75-99.9 Million
Emp.: 840
Newspaper Publisher Services
N.A.I.C.S.: 513110
Mark Russell (Exec Editor)

Naples Daily News, LLC (3)
1185 Immokalee Rd Ste 310, Naples, FL
34110 **(100%)**
Tel.: (239) 213-6000
Web Site: https://www.naplesnews.com
Sales Range: $100-124.9 Million
Emp.: 280
Daily Newspaper Publisher
N.A.I.C.S.: 513110
Dave Osborn (Editor-Reg Features & Enter-
tainment)

Subsidiary (Domestic):

Bonita Banner (4)
9102 Bonita Beach Rd Se, Bonita Springs,
FL 34135 **(100%)**
Tel.: (239) 765-0110
Web Site: http://www.naplesnews.com
Emp.: 30
Daily Newspaper Publishing
N.A.I.C.S.: 513110

Marco Island Eagle (4)
579 E Elkam Cir, Marco Island, FL
34145 **(100%)**
Tel.: (239) 213-5365
Web Site: https://marcomagazine-
fl.newsmemory.com
Emp.: 35
Newspaper Publishers
N.A.I.C.S.: 513110

Subsidiary (Domestic):

**Redding Record Searchlight,
LLC** (3)
1320 Yuba St Ste 216, Redding, CA
96001 **(100%)**
Tel.: (530) 225-8211
Web Site: https://www.redding.com
Sales Range: $100-124.9 Million
Emp.: 200
Newspaper Publishers
N.A.I.C.S.: 513110

**San Angelo Standard-Times,
LLC** (3)
34 W Harris, San Angelo, TX
76901 **(100%)**
Tel.: (325) 659-8100
Web Site: https://www.gosanangelo.com
Sales Range: $25-49.9 Million
Emp.: 85
Newspaper Publishers
N.A.I.C.S.: 513110
Jennifer Killin-Guadarrama (Dir-News)

**Treasure Coast Newspapers,
LLC** (3)
110 S 2nd St Ste 200, Fort Pierce, FL
34950
Tel.: (772) 287-1550
Web Site: https://www.tcpalm.com
Emp.: 4
Newspaper Publishing
N.A.I.C.S.: 513110
Bob Brunjes (Pres)

Subsidiary (Domestic):

Indian River Press Journal (4)
2066 14th Ave Ste 200, Vero Beach, FL
32960 **(100%)**

Tel.: (772) 562-2315
Web Site: http://www.tcpalm.com
Emp.: 30
Newspaper Publishers
N.A.I.C.S.: 513110

Unit (Domestic):

Jupiter Courier Newsweekly (4)
1939 SE Federal Hwy, Stuart, FL
34994 **(100%)**
Tel.: (561) 745-3311
Web Site: http://www.tcpalm.com
Emp.: 21
Newspaper Publishing
N.A.I.C.S.: 513110
Kelly Rogers (Editor-Visuals)
Arnie Rosenberg (Editor-Govt, Growth &
Dev)
Cheryl Smith (Editor-Investigations, Enter-
prise, Environment & Politics)

Subsidiary (Domestic):

The Stuart News (4)
110 S 2nd St Ste 200, Fort Pierce, FL
34950 **(100%)**
Tel.: (772) 287-1550
Web Site: https://www.tcpalm.com
Emp.: 475
Newspaper Publishing
N.A.I.C.S.: 513110

Subsidiary (Domestic):

Ventura County Star, LLC (3)
771 E Daily Dr Ste 300, Camarillo, CA
93010 **(100%)**
Tel.: (805) 437-0000
Web Site: https://www.vcstar.com
Emp.: 200
Newspaper Publishing
N.A.I.C.S.: 513110
Michael Skrocki (Editor-Adv)
Jon Catalini (Editor-Plng)
Loren Ledin (Editor-Prep)

**Wichita Falls Times Record News,
LLC** (3)
1301 Lamar St, Wichita Falls, TX
76301-7032 **(100%)**
Tel.: (940) 767-8341
Web Site: https://www.timesrecordnews.com
Sales Range: $50-74.9 Million
Emp.: 100
Newspaper Publishers
N.A.I.C.S.: 513110
Claire Kowalick (Editor-News)

Subsidiary (Domestic):

KICKSERV, INC. (2)
533 Shasta Way, Mill Valley, CA 94941
Web Site: https://www.kickserv.com
Newspaper Publishers
N.A.I.C.S.: 513110

Unit (Domestic):

Mansfield News Journal (2)
70 W 4th St, Mansfield, OH
44903-1676 **(100%)**
Tel.: (419) 522-3311
Web Site:
https://www.mansfieldnewsjournal.com
Newspaper Publishing
N.A.I.C.S.: 513110
David Yonke (Editor)

Subsidiary (Non-US):

NEW FOREST POST LIMITED (2)
Newspaper House Test Lane Redbridge,
Southampton, SO16 9JX, Hampshire,
United Kingdom
Tel.: (44) 2380424966
Web Site: http://www.newforestpost.co.uk
Newspaper Publishers
N.A.I.C.S.: 513110

**NEWSQUEST (NORTH EAST)
LIMITED** (2)
PO Box 14, Priestgate, Darlington, DL1
1NF, United Kingdom
Tel.: (44) 1325381313
Newspaper Publishers
N.A.I.C.S.: 513110
Ryan Fenwick (Dir-Adv)

**NEWSQUEST SPECIALIST MEDIA
LIMITED** (2)

4th Floor Queen's House 55-56 Lincoln's Inn Fields, London, WC2A 3LJ, United Kingdom
Tel.: (44) 2089557014
Web Site: https://www.insurancetimes.co.uk
Newspaper Publishers
N.A.I.C.S.: 513110

Newsquest (Herald & Times) Limited   (2)
125 Fullarton Drive Glasgow East Investment Park, Glasgow, G32 8FG, United Kingdom
Tel.: (44) 1413027000
Advertising Agency Services
N.A.I.C.S.: 541810

Newsquest Media Group Ltd.   (2)
Loudwater Mill Station Rd, Station Road, High Wycombe, HP10 9TY, Bucks, United Kingdom
Tel.: (44) 1494 755000
Web Site: http://www.newsquest.co.uk
Sales Range: $900-999.9 Million
Emp.: 6,600
Newspaper, Magazine & Internet Publisher
N.A.I.C.S.: 513110
Julia Lancett (Mng Dir-Midlands South)
David Coates (Mng Dir-North East)
Dawn Sweeney (Mng Dir-NQRS)
Mike Harper (Reg Mng Dir-South East)
Tracey Olaleye (Dir-HR)
Vincent Boni (Mng Dir-Hampshire, Dorset & South West)
Toby Granville (Dir-Editorial Dev)
Simon Hill (Product Dir)
Nick Ashwood (Dir-DMS)
Morgan Stevenson (Dir-SME Solutions)
Alison Headley (Dir-Publ)

Subsidiary (Domestic):

North Jersey Media Group, Inc.   (2)
1 Garret Mountain Plz, Woodland Park, NJ 07424-0471
Tel.: (973) 585-5633
Web Site: http://www.northjersey.com
Emp.: 1,007
News & Marketing Services
N.A.I.C.S.: 513110
Daniel Sforza (Exec Editor)
Albina Sportelli (Editor-Assignment)
Joshua Jongsma (Editor-Breaking News)
John Connolly (Editor-Breaking News)
James M. O'Neill (Editor-Assignment)
Alex Nussbaum (Editor-Assignment)
Zach Miller (Deputy Dir-Sports)
Dave Rivera (Sr Dir-Sports)
John Flynn (Creative Dir)
Liz Johnson (Sr Dir-Features)
Sean Oates (Sr Dir-Multimedia)
Nancy Pascarella (Editor-Photo)
Ed Forbes (Sr Dir-Opinion)
Paul Wood Jr. (Coord-Multimedia)

Unit (Domestic):

Oshkosh Northwestern   (2)
224 State St, Oshkosh, WI 54901
Tel.: (920) 235-7700
Web Site: https://www.thenorthwestern.com
Sales Range: $25-49.9 Million
Emp.: 83
Newspaper Publishers
N.A.I.C.S.: 513110

Subsidiary (Non-US):

PACKET NEWSPAPERS LIMITED   (2)
Tremough Innovation Centre Tremough Campus, Cornwall, Penryn, TR10 9TA, United Kingdom
Tel.: (44) 1326213331
Newspaper Publishers
N.A.I.C.S.: 513110
Paul Armstrong (Editor)

Subsidiary (Domestic):

Palladium-Item   (2)
1200 NW N St, Richmond, IN 47374   (100%)
Tel.: (765) 962-1575
Web Site: https://www.pal-item.com
Sales Range: $50-74.9 Million
Emp.: 55
Newspaper Publishers
N.A.I.C.S.: 513110

Unit (Domestic):

Pensacola News-Journal   (2)
2 N Palafox St, Pensacola, FL 32502   (100%)
Tel.: (850) 435-8500
Web Site: https://www.pnj.com
Sales Range: $125-149.9 Million
Emp.: 250
Newspaper Publishers
N.A.I.C.S.: 513110
Lisa Nellessen Savage (Exec Editor)

Subsidiary (Domestic):

Phoenix Newspapers, Inc.   (2)
200 E Van Buren St, Phoenix, AZ 85004
Tel.: (602) 444-8000
Web Site: https://www.azcentral.com
Sales Range: $450-499.9 Million
Emp.: 3,000
Newspaper Publishers
N.A.I.C.S.: 513110

Subsidiary (Domestic):

The Arizona Republic   (3)
200 E Van Buren St, Phoenix, AZ 85004
Tel.: (602) 444-8000
Web Site: https://www.azcentral.com
Sales Range: $450-499.9 Million
Emp.: 3,000
Newspaper Publishers
N.A.I.C.S.: 513110
Mark Faller (Dir-Azcentral Sports)

Subsidiary (Domestic):

Poughkeepsie Journal   (2)
7950 Jones Branch Dr, McLean, VA 22102   (100%)
Tel.: (845) 454-2000
Web Site: https://www.poughkeepsiejournal.com
Sales Range: $50-74.9 Million
Emp.: 100
Newspaper Publishers
N.A.I.C.S.: 513110
Jim Fogler (Pres & Publr)

Press & Sun-Bulletin   (2)
33 Lewis Rd, Binghamton, NY 13905   (100%)
Tel.: (607) 798-1234
Web Site: https://www.pressconnects.com
Sales Range: $75-99.9 Million
Emp.: 200
Newspaper Publishers
N.A.I.C.S.: 513110
Kevin Hogan (Exec Editor)
Kristen Cox Roby (Editor-Reg Storytelling)

Press-Citizen Company Inc.   (2)
1725 N Dodge St, Iowa City, IA 52244-2480   (100%)
Tel.: (319) 337-3181
Web Site: http://www.press-citizen.com
Emp.: 45
Newspaper Publisher Services
N.A.I.C.S.: 513110

ReachLocal, Inc.   (2)
21700 Oxnard St Ste 1600, Woodland Hills, CA 91367   (100%)
Tel.: (818) 274-0260
Web Site: https://www.reachlocal.com
Sales Range: $300-349.9 Million
Internet Advertising Solutions & Marketing Services
N.A.I.C.S.: 541890
Kris Barton (Chief Product Officer)

Subsidiary (Domestic):

DealOn, LLC   (3)
21700 Oxnard St Ste 1600, Woodland Hills, CA 91367
Web Site: https://www.dealon.com
Advertising Agency Services
N.A.I.C.S.: 541810

Subsidiary (Non-US):

ReachLocal Australia Pty Ltd   (3)
Level 10 54 Miller Street, North Sydney, 2060, NSW, Australia
Tel.: (61) 1300655312
Internet Advertising Solutions & Marketing Services
N.A.I.C.S.: 541890

ReachLocal Europe BV   (3)
WTC D-Tower 8th Floor Strawinskylaan 865, 1077 XX, Amsterdam, Netherlands
Tel.: (31) 202583000
Web Site: http://www.reachlocal.com
Advertising Agency Consulting Services
N.A.I.C.S.: 541810

ReachLocal GmbH   (3)
Kurfurstendamm 22, 10719, Berlin, Germany
Tel.: (49) 3060985000
Web Site: http://www.reachlocal.de
Advertising Agency Consulting Services
N.A.I.C.S.: 541810

ReachLocal Japan Services G.K.   (3)
Roppongi Tokyo 1-8-7 MFPR Roppongi Azabudai building 10F, Minato-ku, Tokyo, Japan
Tel.: (81) 344058712
Web Site: http://www.reachlocal.co.jp
Internet Advertising Agency
N.A.I.C.S.: 541810

ReachLocal Services Pvt. Ltd.   (3)
5th Floor B Wing Express Zone Patel Vanika Western Express Highway, Opp Oberoi Mall Goregaon East, Mumbai, 400 097, India
Tel.: (91) 2267226666
Web Site: https://www.reachlocalindia.com
Emp.: 700
Marketing Consulting Services
N.A.I.C.S.: 541613

Subsidiary (Domestic):

Reno Newspapers, Inc.   (2)
80 W 1st St Ste C, Reno, NV 89501   (100%)
Tel.: (775) 788-6200
Web Site: https://www.rgj.com
Newspaper Publisher Services
N.A.I.C.S.: 513110
John F. Maher (Pres)

Subsidiary (Domestic):

Reno Gazette-Journal   (3)
80 W 1st St Ste C, Reno, NV 89501   (100%)
Tel.: (775) 788-6200
Web Site: https://www.rgj.com
Emp.: 280
Newspaper Publishers
N.A.I.C.S.: 513110
Brett McGinness (Editor-Opinion & Engagement)
Peggy Santoro (Exec Editor)

Subsidiary (Domestic):

Salinas Newspapers LLC   (2)
123 W Alisal St, Salinas, CA 93901   (100%)
Tel.: (831) 424-2221
Web Site: https://www.thecalifornian.com
Emp.: 50
Newspaper Publisher Services
N.A.I.C.S.: 513110

St. Cloud Times   (2)
24 8th Ave S, Saint Cloud, MN 56301   (100%)
Tel.: (320) 356-8215
Web Site: https://www.sctimes.com
Sales Range: $75-99.9 Million
Emp.: 120
Newspaper Publishers
N.A.I.C.S.: 513110

Unit (Domestic):

Star-Gazette   (2)
310 E Church St, Elmira, NY 14901   (100%)
Tel.: (607) 734-5151
Web Site: https://www.stargazette.com
Sales Range: $10-24.9 Million
Emp.: 40
Newspaper Publishers
N.A.I.C.S.: 513110

Statesman Journal   (2)
340 Vista Ave SE, Salem, OR 97302   (100%)
Tel.: (503) 399-6727
Web Site: https://www.statesmanjournal.com
Emp.: 250

Newspaper Publishers
N.A.I.C.S.: 513110
Alia Beard Rau (Sr Editor-News)

Stevens Point Journal   (2)
1200 3rd St, Stevens Point, WI 54481
Tel.: (715) 344-6100
Web Site: https://www.stevenspointjournal.com
Sales Range: $25-49.9 Million
Emp.: 25
Newspaper Publishers
N.A.I.C.S.: 513110

Joint Venture (Domestic):

TNI Partners   (2)
4850 S Park Ave, Tucson, AZ 85714
Tel.: (520) 573-4427
Web Site: https://tucson.com
Sales Range: $300-349.9 Million
Emp.: 750
Newspaper Publisher Services
N.A.I.C.S.: 513110
Mark Henschen (Pres & Publr)

Unit (Domestic):

The Arizona Daily Star   (3)
4850 S Park Ave, Tucson, AZ 85714-1637
Tel.: (520) 573-4366
Web Site: https://www.tucson.com
Sales Range: $50-74.9 Million
Emp.: 170
Newspaper Publishing
N.A.I.C.S.: 513110
John F. Lundgren (Dir-Print Ops)

Unit (Domestic):

Tallahassee Democrat   (2)
277 N Magnolia Dr, Tallahassee, FL 32301
Tel.: (850) 599-2100
Web Site: https://www.tallahassee.com
Sales Range: $25-49.9 Million
Emp.: 350
Newspaper Publishers
N.A.I.C.S.: 513110
Chet Noll (Dir-Distr)
Jim Henry (Editor-Sports)

Subsidiary (Domestic):

Texas-New Mexico Newspapers, LLC   (2)
500 W Overland Ave Ste 150, El Paso, TX 79901-1086
Tel.: (915) 546-6100
Emp.: 425
Newspaper Publisher Services
N.A.I.C.S.: 513110
Lilia Castillo Jones (Pres)

Unit (Domestic):

Alamogordo Daily News   (3)
518 24th St, Alamogordo, NM 88310
Tel.: (575) 437-7120
Web Site: https://www.alamogordonews.com
Sales Range: $10-24.9 Million
Emp.: 20
Newspaper Publishing
N.A.I.C.S.: 513110
Anthony Davis (Coord-Ops)
Ken Wright (District Mgr)
Mary Wright (Coord-Ops)
Jessica Onsurez (Dir-News)

Carlsbad Current-Argus   (3)
620 S Main St, Carlsbad, NM 88220
Tel.: (575) 628-5501
Web Site: https://www.currentargus.com
Emp.: 23
Newspaper Publishing
N.A.I.C.S.: 513110
Jessica Onsurez (Mng Editor)

El Paso Times   (3)
500 W Overland Ste 150, El Paso, TX 79901
Tel.: (915) 546-6200
Web Site: https://www.elpasotimes.com
Emp.: 400
Newspaper Publishers
N.A.I.C.S.: 513110
Tim Archuleta (Exec Editor)

Las Cruces Sun-News   (3)
256 W Las Cruces Ave, Las Cruces, NM 88004

Gannett Co., Inc.—(Continued)

Tel.: (575) 541-5400
Web Site: https://www.lcsun-news.com
Emp.: 60
Newspaper Publishing
N.A.I.C.S.: 513110
Jason Groves *(Editor-Sports)*

Unit (Domestic):

Missile Ranger **(4)**
1782 Headquarters Ave, White Sands
Missile Range, NM 88002
Tel.: (575) 678-2716
Web Site: http://www.missileranger.com
Newspaper Publishing
N.A.I.C.S.: 513110

Unit (Domestic):

Lebanon Daily News **(3)**
718 Poplar St, Lebanon, PA 17042
Tel.: (717) 272-5611
Web Site: https://www.ldnews.com
Emp.: 50
Newspaper Publishers
N.A.I.C.S.: 513110

Public Opinion **(3)**
77 N 3rd St, Chambersburg, PA 17201-1812
Tel.: (717) 264-6161
Web Site:
https://www.publicopiniononline.com
Emp.: 23
Newspaper Publishers
N.A.I.C.S.: 513110
Sara Glines *(Publr)*

Ruidoso News **(3)**
104 Park Ave, Ruidoso, NM 88345
Tel.: (575) 257-4001
Web Site: https://www.ruidosonews.com
Emp.: 6
Newspaper Publishing
N.A.I.C.S.: 513110
Jessica Onsurez *(Dir-News)*

The Daily Times **(3)**
203 W Main St, Farmington, NM 87401
Tel.: (505) 325-4545
Web Site: https://www.daily-times.com
Emp.: 100
Newspaper Publishing
N.A.I.C.S.: 513110
Mike Easterling *(Editor-A & E & Night)*

Unit (Domestic):

Four Corners Business Journal **(4)**
305 W, Farmington, NM 87402
Tel.: (505) 564-4673
Web Site: http://www.daily-times.com
Newspaper Publishing
N.A.I.C.S.: 513110

Unit (Domestic):

The Deming Headlight **(3)**
208 S Gold Ave, Deming, NM 88030
Tel.: (575) 546-2611
Web Site: https://www.demingheadlight.com
Emp.: 8
Newspaper Publishing
N.A.I.C.S.: 513110

The Evening Sun **(3)**
37 Broadway 1st 2nd Fl, Hanover, PA
17331
Tel.: (717) 633-4509
Web Site: https://www.eveningsun.com
Emp.: 12
Newspaper Publishers
N.A.I.C.S.: 513110
Kent Holmes *(Dir-Circulation)*

York Daily Record-York Sunday News
LLC **(3)**
1891 Loucks Rd, York, PA 17408
Tel.: (717) 771-2000
Web Site: https://www.ydr.com
Emp.: 200
Newspaper Publishers
N.A.I.C.S.: 513110
Randy Parker *(Exec Editor)*
Lyzz Stallings *(Editor-Sports-Eastern &
Central Reg)*

Subsidiary (Domestic):

The Advertiser Company **(2)**

---

425 Molton St, Montgomery, AL 36104
Tel.: (334) 262-1611
Web Site:
https://www.montgomeryadvertiser.com
Newspaper Publisher Services
N.A.I.C.S.: 513110

Unit (Domestic):

The Advocate **(2)**
22 N 1st St, Newark, OH 43055
Tel.: (740) 345-4053
Web Site: https://www.newarkadvocate.com
Newspaper Publishers
N.A.I.C.S.: 513110

The Cincinnati Enquirer **(2)**
312 Plum St Ste 1250, Cincinnati, OH
45202 **(100%)**
Tel.: (513) 721-2700
Web Site: https://www.cincinnati.com
Sales Range: $350-399.9 Million
Emp.: 800
Newspaper Publishers
N.A.I.C.S.: 513110
Jim Eichert *(Reg Dir-Fin)*
Jordan Kellogg *(Sr Dir-News & Digital)*
Beryl Love *(Exec Editor)*

The Clarion-Ledger **(2)**
201 S Congress St, Jackson, MS
39201 **(100%)**
Tel.: (601) 961-7000
Web Site: https://www.clarionledger.com
Sales Range: $50-74.9 Million
Emp.: 475
Newspaper Publishers
N.A.I.C.S.: 513110
Mary Irby-Jones *(Editor)*

Subsidiary (Domestic):

The Courier-Journal, Inc. **(2)**
525 W Broadway, Louisville, KY 40201-7431
Tel.: (502) 582-4011
Web Site: https://www.courier-journal.com
Emp.: 600
Newspaper Publishers
N.A.I.C.S.: 513110
Richard A. Green *(Editor)*

Unit (Domestic):

The Daily Journal **(2)**
891 E Oak Rd, Vineland, NJ
08360 **(100%)**
Tel.: (856) 691-5000
Web Site: https://www.thedailyjournal.com
Sales Range: $50-74.9 Million
Emp.: 130
Newspaper Publishers
N.A.I.C.S.: 513110
Joseph Calchi *(Pres & Publr)*

Subsidiary (Domestic):

The Daily Times **(2)**
115 S Division St, Salisbury, MD 21801
Tel.: (410) 749-7171
Web Site: https://www.delmarvanow.com
Emp.: 350
Newspaper Publishers
N.A.I.C.S.: 513110
Keith Demko *(Editor-Plng)*
Kamleshkumar Desai *(Editor-Plng)*

The Desert Sun Publishing
Company **(2)**
750 N Gene Autry Trl, Palm Springs, CA
92262
Tel.: (760) 322-8889
Web Site: https://www.desertsun.com
Newspaper Publishers
N.A.I.C.S.: 513110

Unit (Domestic):

The Desert Sun **(3)**
750 N Gene Autry Trl, Palm Springs, CA
92262 **(100%)**
Tel.: (760) 322-8889
Web Site: https://www.desertsun.com
Emp.: 300
Newspaper Publishers
N.A.I.C.S.: 513110
Al Franco *(Editor-Engagement-Opinion &
Social)*
Julie Makinen *(Exec Editor)*
Matt Solinsky *(Editor-Plng-Print & Digital)*

Unit (Domestic):

The Ithaca Journal **(2)**
123 W State Martin Luther King Jr St,
Ithaca, NY 14850 **(100%)**
Tel.: (607) 272-2321
Web Site: https://www.ithacajournal.com
Sales Range: $10-24.9 Million
Emp.: 30
Newspaper Publishers
N.A.I.C.S.: 513110

The Jackson Sun **(2)**
245 W Lafayette St, Jackson, TN
38301 **(100%)**
Tel.: (731) 427-3333
Web Site: https://www.jacksonsun.com
Sales Range: $25-49.9 Million
Emp.: 141
Newspaper Publishers
N.A.I.C.S.: 513110

Subsidiary (Domestic):

The Journal News **(2)**
2 Westchester Park Dr Lbby Ste B, West
Harrison, NY 10604 **(100%)**
Tel.: (914) 694-9300
Web Site: https://www.lohud.com
Emp.: 300
Newspaper Publishers
N.A.I.C.S.: 513110
Mary Dolan *(Editor)*

Unit (Domestic):

The Leaf-Chronicle **(2)**
200 Commerce St, Clarksville, TN
37040-5101 **(100%)**
Tel.: (931) 552-1808
Web Site: https://www.theleafchronicle.com
Sales Range: $25-49.9 Million
Emp.: 30
Newspaper Publishers
N.A.I.C.S.: 513110

The Marion Star **(2)**
3007 Harding Hwy E Unit 309, Marion, OH
43302
Tel.: (740) 387-0400
Web Site: https://www.marionstar.com
Sales Range: $10-24.9 Million
Newspaper Publishers
N.A.I.C.S.: 513110

The Montgomery Advertiser **(2)**
425 Molton St, Montgomery, AL
36104 **(100%)**
Tel.: (334) 262-1611
Web Site:
https://www.montgomeryadvertiser.com
Sales Range: $25-49.9 Million
Emp.: 240
Newspaper Publishers
N.A.I.C.S.: 513110

Subsidiary (Domestic):

The News Journal **(2)**
950 W Basin Rd, Wilmington, DE
19805 **(100%)**
Tel.: (302) 324-2679
Web Site: https://www.delawareonline.com
Newspaper Publishers
N.A.I.C.S.: 513110
Phil Freedman *(Dir-News)*
Robert Long *(Dir-Consumer Experience)*
Mike Feeley *(Exec Editor)*

Unit (Domestic):

The News Leader **(2)**
11 N Central Ave, Staunton, VA
24401 **(100%)**
Tel.: (540) 885-7281
Web Site: https://www.newsleader.com
Emp.: 100
Newspaper Publishers
N.A.I.C.S.: 513110

Subsidiary (Domestic):

The News-Messenger **(2)**
1800 E State St Ste B, Fremont, OH
43420 **(100%)**
Tel.: (419) 332-5511
Web Site: https://www.thenews-
messenger.com
Newspaper Publishers
N.A.I.C.S.: 513110
David Yonke *(Editor)*

Unit (Domestic):

The News-Press **(2)**
4415 Metro Pkwy, Fort Myers, FL
33901-3904 **(100%)**
Tel.: (239) 335-0200
Web Site: https://www.news-press.com
Sales Range: $100-124.9 Million
Emp.: 680
Newspaper Publishers
N.A.I.C.S.: 513110
Ed Reed *(Editor-Reg Sports)*
Stacey Henson *(Editor-Live News)*
Steve McQuilkin *(Editor-Reg Bus & Environ-
ment)*

The News-Star **(2)**
411 N 4th St, Monroe, LA
71201-6743 **(100%)**
Tel.: (318) 322-5161
Web Site: https://www.thenewsstar.com
Sales Range: $50-74.9 Million
Emp.: 25
Newspaper Publishers
N.A.I.C.S.: 513110

The Post-Crescent **(2)**
222 W College Ave, Appleton, WI 54911
Tel.: (920) 993-1000
Web Site: https://www.postcrescent.com
Sales Range: $75-99.9 Million
Emp.: 500
Newspaper Publishers
N.A.I.C.S.: 513110

Subsidiary (Domestic):

The Reporter **(2)**
N6637 Rolling Meadows Dr, Fond Du Lac,
WI 54936 **(100%)**
Tel.: (920) 922-4600
Web Site: https://www.fdlreporter.com
Sales Range: $50-74.9 Million
Emp.: 50
Newspaper Publishers
N.A.I.C.S.: 513110

Unit (Domestic):

The Sheboygan Press **(2)**
605 N 8th St, Sheboygan, WI 53081
Tel.: (920) 457-7711
Web Site: https://www.sheboyganpress.com
Sales Range: $25-49.9 Million
Emp.: 25
Newspaper Publishers
N.A.I.C.S.: 513110

The Spectrum **(2)**
335 E St George Blvd, Saint George, UT
84770-2954 **(100%)**
Tel.: (435) 674-6200
Web Site: https://www.thespectrum.com
Sales Range: $25-49.9 Million
Emp.: 140
Newspaper Publishers
N.A.I.C.S.: 513110

The Star Press **(2)**
345 S High St, Muncie, IN 47305-1620
Tel.: (765) 213-5700
Web Site: https://www.thestarpress.com
Sales Range: $25-49.9 Million
Emp.: 63
Newspaper Publishers
N.A.I.C.S.: 513110
Greg Fallon *(Exec Editor)*

The Tennessean **(2)**
1801 W End Ave, Nashville, TN
37203 **(100%)**
Tel.: (615) 259-8300
Web Site: https://www.tennessean.com
Sales Range: $350-399.9 Million
Emp.: 800
Newspaper Publishers
N.A.I.C.S.: 513110
David Plazas *(Editor)*
Heather Fritz Aronin *(Editor)*
Duane W. Gang *(Editor)*
Jeremy Harmon *(Editor)*
Chris Thomas *(Editor & Dir-South Reg
Sports)*

Unit (Domestic):

The News Examiner **(3)**
1 Examiner Ct, Gallatin, TN 37066
Tel.: (615) 452-2561

Web Site:
    http://www.gallatinnewsexaminer.com
Newspaper Publishers
N.A.I.C.S.: 513110

Subsidiary (Domestic):

The Times   (2)
401 Market St Ste 1500, Shreveport, LA
71101
Tel.: (318) 459-3200
Web Site: https://www.shreveporttimes.com
Sales Range: $50-74.9 Million
Emp.: 135
Newspaper Publishers
N.A.I.C.S.: 513110
Kevin Welsh (Sr Dir-Circulation)

The Times Herald Company   (2)
1411 3rd St Ste E, Port Huron, MI
48060   (100%)
Tel.: (810) 985-7171
Web Site: https://www.thetimesherald.com
Emp.: 260
Newspaper Publisher Services
N.A.I.C.S.: 513110

Unit (Domestic):

Times Recorder   (2)
34 S 4th St, Zanesville, OH 43701 (100%)
Tel.: (740) 452-4561
Web Site:
    https://www.zanesvilletimesrecorder.com
Sales Range: $10-24.9 Million
Newspaper Publishers
N.A.I.C.S.: 513110
Pam James (Editor)

USA Today   (2)
7950 Jones Branch Dr, McLean, VA
22102   (100%)
Tel.: (703) 854-3400
Web Site: https://www.usatoday.com
Sales Range: $600-649.9 Million
Emp.: 2,100
Newspaper Publishers
N.A.I.C.S.: 513110
Nicole Carroll (Editor-in-Chief)
Andrew P. Scott (Dir-Photo, Video News
    Gathering)
Javier Zarracina (Editor-Graphics)
Victoria Spigai (Office Mgr)
Shawn J. Sullivan (Editor)
Jim Sergent (Editor-Graphics)
George Petras (Editor-Graphics)
Jordan Culver (Editor-News)
Charles Ventura (Editor-Breaking News)
Joe Rayos (Editor-Plng)
Jim Reineking (Editor-NOW)
Erick Smith (Editor-College Sports)
Jesse Yomtov (Editor-MLB)
Gary Levin (Editor-TV)
Barbara Vandenburgh (Editor-Books)
Thuan Le Elston (Editor-Ops)
Ed Brackett (Editor-Audience)

Subsidiary (Domestic):

USA Today   (3)
7950 Jones Branch Dr, McLean, VA 22102
Tel.: (212) 715-5350
Web Site: https://www.usatoday.com
Sales Range: $25-49.9 Million
Emp.: 130
Newspaper Publishers
N.A.I.C.S.: 513110

Subsidiary (Domestic):

**USA Today Sports Media Group,
LLC**   (2)
1440 Broadway 40th & Broadway, New
York, NY 10018
Tel.: (646) 937-5500
Web Site: https://www.usatoday.com
Newspaper Publishing & Printing Services
N.A.I.C.S.: 513110
Chris Pirrone (Gen Mgr)

Visalia Newspapers LLC   (2)
330 N West St, Visalia, CA 93279
Tel.: (559) 735-3200
Web Site: https://www.visaliatimesdelta.com
Newspaper Publishing & Printing Services
N.A.I.C.S.: 513110
Eric Woomer (Editor-News)

Unit (Domestic):

Tulare Advance-Register   (3)

330 N W St, Visalia, CA 93279
Tel.: (559) 735-3200
Web Site:
    http://www.tulareadvanceregister.com
Emp.: 100
Newspaper Publishers
N.A.I.C.S.: 513110

Visalia Times-Delta   (3)
330 N W St, Visalia, CA 93279   (100%)
Tel.: (559) 735-3200
Web Site: https://www.visaliatimesdelta.com
Sales Range: $50-74.9 Million
Emp.: 120
Newspaper Publishers
N.A.I.C.S.: 513110
David Sutton (Mgr-Ops)

Unit (Domestic):

Wausau Daily Herald   (2)
800 Scott St, Wausau, WI
54403-4951   (100%)
Tel.: (715) 842-2101
Web Site:
    https://www.wausaudailyherald.com
Sales Range: $50-74.9 Million
Emp.: 100
Newspaper Publishers
N.A.I.C.S.: 513110

Subsidiary (Domestic):

WordStream, Inc.   (2)
101 Huntington Ave 7th Fl, Boston, MA
02199
Tel.: (617) 963-0555
Web Site: https://www.wordstream.com
Advertising & Marketing Software Develop-
ment Services
N.A.I.C.S.: 541511
Mitchell Leiman (Sr VP & Gen Mgr)

York Dispatch LLC   (2)
1891 Loucks Rd, York, PA 17408
Tel.: (717) 854-1575
Web Site: https://www.yorkdispatch.com
Emp.: 35
Newspaper Publishers
N.A.I.C.S.: 513110
Patrick DeLany (Editor)

York Newspaper Company   (2)
1891 Loucks Rd, York, PA 17408-9708
Tel.: (717) 767-6397
Web Site: https://www.inyork.com
Newspaper Publisher Services
N.A.I.C.S.: 513110

GateHouse Media, LLC   (1)
175 Sullys Trl 3rd Fl Corporate Crossings
Office Park, Pittsford, NY 14534
Tel.: (585) 598-0030
Web Site: http://www.gatehousemedia.com
Print & Online Publisher
N.A.I.C.S.: 513110
Mike Distelhorst (Publr-The Fayetteville Ob-
server)

Subsidiary (Domestic):

Aberdeen News Company   (2)
124 S 2nd St, Aberdeen, SD 57402
Tel.: (605) 225-4100
Web Site: http://www.aberdeennews.com
Sales Range: $10-24.9 Million
Emp.: 100
Newspaper Publishers
N.A.I.C.S.: 513110
Carrie Cole (Mgr-Emerging Media & Special
    Projects)
Mondell Keck (Editor-Content)
Kim Mills (Coord-Member Assistance)
Scott Waltman (Mng Editor)
Brenda VanMeter (Specialist-Recruitment)
Joe Moore (Product Mgr-Digital Sls)
Lynde Ross (Mgr-Sls)
Kristie Jacobson (Coord-Adv)
Laurel Osborne (Mgr-Distr)

**Alliance Publishing Company Inc.,
LLC**   (2)
40 S Linden Ave, Alliance, OH 44601
Tel.: (330) 453-1304
Web Site: http://www.the-review.com
Newspaper Publishers
N.A.I.C.S.: 513110

Unit (Domestic):

Amarillo Globe-News   (2)

600 S Tyler Ste 103, Amarillo, TX 79101
Tel.: (806) 376-5881
Web Site: https://www.amarillo.com
Newspaper Publishers
N.A.I.C.S.: 513110

Subsidiary (Domestic):

Ashland Publishing Co., LLC   (2)
40 E 2nd St, Ashland, OH 44805-2304
Tel.: (419) 281-0581
Web Site: http://www.times-gazette.com
Newspaper Publishers
N.A.I.C.S.: 513110
Deb Boreman (Mgr-Circulation)
Aaron Bass (Gen Mgr & Dir-Adv)
Russ Whisler (District Mgr)
Bill Albrecht (Publr)
Rick Armon (Editor)

Unit (Domestic):

Athens Banner-Herald   (2)
1 Press Pl, Athens, GA 30601
Tel.: (706) 549-0123
Web Site: https://www.onlineathens.com
Newspaper Publishers
N.A.I.C.S.: 513110

Subsidiary (Domestic):

Beaver Newspapers Inc.   (2)
400 Corporation Dr, Beaver, PA 15001
Tel.: (724) 775-3200
Web Site: https://www.timesonline.com
Newspaper Publishing
N.A.I.C.S.: 513110
Tina Bequeath (Publr & Controller)
Nick Hink (Dir-Adv-Interim)
Kaitlin McCracken (Mgr-Classified)
Dani Fitzgerald (Editor-Multimedia Copy)
Bryan Heraghty (Editor-Multimedia Copy)
Jim Pane (Editor-Multimedia Copy)
Vince Townley (Editor-Sports)

Burlington Times, Inc.   (2)
116 Burrs Rd Ste B, Willingboro, NJ 08046
Tel.: (609) 871-8000
Web Site:
    https://www.burlingtoncountytimes.com
Newspaper Publishing
N.A.I.C.S.: 513110

Courier Times, Inc.   (2)
1 Oxford Vly 2300 E Lincoln Hwy Ste 500D,
Langhorne, PA 19047
Tel.: (215) 949-4000
Web Site: https://www.phillyburbs.com
Newspaper Printing & Publishing
N.A.I.C.S.: 513110
Carol Schramm (Fin Dir)
Kathy Weber (Partner-HR Bus)
Kevin O'Malley (Dir-Adv Sls)
Shane Fitzgerald (Exec Editor-Reg)
Danielle Camilli (Dir-News)
Crissa Shoemaker Debree (Editor-
Enterprise & Investigative)
Bob Braun (Dir-Ops & Comml Printing)

Unit (Domestic):

Dodge City Daily Globe   (2)
2002 1st Ave, Dodge City, KS 67801-0820
Tel.: (620) 471-8001
Web Site: https://www.dodgeglobe.com
Sales Range: $10-24.9 Million
Emp.: 50
Daily Newspaper Publisher
N.A.I.C.S.: 513110
Shelton Burch (Editor-Sports)
Vincent Marshall (Editor)

Subsidiary (Domestic):

El Dorado Times   (2)
111 N Madison Ave, El Dorado, AR 71730
Tel.: (870) 444-4878
Web Site: https://www.eldoradonews.com
Sales Range: $10-24.9 Million
Emp.: 11
Newspaper Publishers
N.A.I.C.S.: 513110
Jennifer Wilson (Gen Mgr)

Unit (Domestic):

Flashes Publishers   (2)
595 Jenner Dr M40, Allegan, MI 49010
Tel.: (269) 673-2141
Web Site: http://www.flashespublishers.com

Sales Range: $25-49.9 Million
Emp.: 90
Shopping Guides Publisher & Commercial
Printing Services
N.A.I.C.S.: 513120

Subsidiary (Domestic):

GateHouse Live, LLC   (2)
1160 N Town Center Dr Ste 330, Las Ve-
gas, NV 89144
Tel.: (423) 551-4119
Web Site: http://gatehouselive.com
Event Management Services
N.A.I.C.S.: 711320
Jason Taylor (Pres)
Lyndsi Lane (VP)
Tanya Williamson (Dir-Events)
Sarah Bass (Dir-Ops)
Ellie Kuhn (Dir-Sls & Mktg)
Sarah Dolmovich (Coord-Event Mktg)
Steven Ratajczyk (Brand Mgr)

GateHouse Media New England   (2)
15 Pacella Park Dr, Randolph, MA 01752
Tel.: (781) 433-8200
Web Site: https://www.wickedlocal.com
Sales Range: $100-124.9 Million
Emp.: 300
Newspaper Publishers
N.A.I.C.S.: 513110
Ron Bright (Mgr-Classified Adv)

Unit (Domestic):

Abington Mariner   (3)
165 Enterprise Dr, Marshfield, MA 02050
Tel.: (781) 837-4545
Web Site: http://www.wickedlocal.com
Sales Range: $25-49.9 Million
Emp.: 40
Newspaper Publishers
N.A.I.C.S.: 513110
Mark Olivieri (Publr)
Seth Jacobson (Editor-News)
Rafal Lipowicz (Mgr-Adv)
Gregory Mathis (Reg Dir-News & Ops)
Michael Kane (Deputy Dir-Multimedia)
Beth Doyle (Editor-Special Sections & Real
    Estate)
Nicole Simmons (Dir-Digital & Teams)

Allston-Brighton TAB   (3)
254 2nd Ave, Needham, MA 02494-2811
Tel.: (617) 254-7530
Web Site: http://www.wickedlocal.com
Sales Range: $100-124.9 Million
Newspaper Publishers
N.A.I.C.S.: 513110

Amesbury News   (3)
72 Cherry Hill Dr 4, Beverly, MA 01915
Tel.: (978) 388-2406
Web Site: http://www.wickedlocal.com
Sales Range: $25-49.9 Million
Emp.: 100
Newspaper Publishers
N.A.I.C.S.: 513110
Charles Goodrich (Publr)

Ashland TAB   (3)
33 New York Ave, Framingham, MA 01701
Tel.: (508) 626-3957
Web Site: http://www.wickedlocal.com
Sales Range: $10-24.9 Million
Emp.: 2
Newspaper Publishers
N.A.I.C.S.: 513110

Subsidiary (Domestic):

Bedford Minuteman   (3)
150 Baker Ave Ext Ste 101, Concord, MA
01742
Tel.: (978) 371-5796
Web Site: http://www.wickedlocal.com
Sales Range: $10-24.9 Million
Emp.: 50
Newspaper Publishers
N.A.I.C.S.: 513110

Belmont Citizen-Herald   (3)
9 Meriam St, Lexington, MA 02420
Tel.: (781) 674-7723
Web Site: https://www.wickedlocal.com
Sales Range: $10-24.9 Million
Emp.: 40
Newspaper Publishers
N.A.I.C.S.: 513110

Gannett Co., Inc.—(Continued)

Chuck Goodrich *(Publr)*

Unit (Domestic):

Beverly Citizen (3)
75 Sylvan St C 105, Danvers, MA 01923
Tel.: (978) 927-2777
Web Site: http://www.wickedlocal.com
Sales Range: $10-24.9 Million
Emp.: 2
Newspaper Publishers
N.A.I.C.S.: 513110

Subsidiary (Domestic):

Billerica Minuteman (3)
150 Baker Ave Ext Ste 101, Concord, MA 01742
Tel.: (781) 674-7729
Web Site: http://www.wickedlocal.com
Sales Range: $10-24.9 Million
Emp.: 50
Newspaper Publishers
N.A.I.C.S.: 513110

Unit (Domestic):

Boston Homes (3)
254 2nd Ave, Needham, MA 02494
Tel.: (781) 433-6944
Web Site: http://www.homefind.com
News Media Services
N.A.I.C.S.: 424920

Braintree Forum (3)
165 Enterprise Dr, Marshfield, MA 02050
Tel.: (781) 843-2937
Web Site: http://www.wickedlocal.com
Sales Range: $100-124.9 Million
Emp.: 60
Newspaper Publishers
N.A.I.C.S.: 513110
Mark Olivieri *(Publr)*
Rafal Lipowicz *(Mgr-Adv)*
Gregory Mathis *(Reg Dir-News & Ops)*
Michael Kane *(Deputy Dir-Multimedia)*
Beth Doyle *(Editor-Special Sections & Real Estate)*

Burlington Union (3)
150 Baker Ave Ext, Concord, MA 01742
Tel.: (781) 229-0918
Web Site: http://www.wickedlocal.com
Sales Range: $10-24.9 Million
Emp.: 52
Newspaper Publishers
N.A.I.C.S.: 513110

Subsidiary (Domestic):

Cambridge Chronicle (3)
80 Central St, Somerville, MA 02143-1612
Tel.: (781) 433-8282
Web Site: https://www.wickedlocal.com
Sales Range: $100-124.9 Million
Emp.: 10
Newspaper Publishers
N.A.I.C.S.: 513110

Cape Codder (3)
5 Namskaket Rd, Orleans, MA 02653
Tel.: (508) 255-2121
Web Site: https://www.wickedlocal.com
Sales Range: $10-24.9 Million
Emp.: 40
Newspaper Publishers
N.A.I.C.S.: 513110

Cohasset Mariner (3)
165 Enterprise Dr, Marshfield, MA 02050
Tel.: (781) 383-8139
Web Site: https://www.wickedlocal.com
Sales Range: $25-49.9 Million
Emp.: 100
Newspaper Publishers
N.A.I.C.S.: 513110
Mark Olivieri *(Publr)*

Country Gazette (3)
159 S Main St, Milford, MA 01757
Tel.: (508) 528-2600
Web Site: http://www.wickedlocal.com
Sales Range: $10-24.9 Million
Emp.: 1
Newspaper Publishers
N.A.I.C.S.: 513110

Unit (Domestic):

Danvers Herald (3)
75 Sylvan St C 105, Danvers, MA 01923
Tel.: (978) 774-0505
Web Site: http://www.wickedlocal.com
Sales Range: $25-49.9 Million
Emp.: 50
Newspaper Publishers
N.A.I.C.S.: 513110

Subsidiary (Domestic):

Dover-Sherborn Press (3)
7 West St, Walpole, MA 02181
Tel.: (781) 433-6700
Web Site: http://dover.wickedlocal.com
Sales Range: $50-74.9 Million
Emp.: 150
Newspaper Publishers
N.A.I.C.S.: 513110
Maureen Sullivan *(Editor)*

Easton Journal (3)
5 Cohannet St, Taunton, MA 02767
Tel.: (508) 967-3510
Web Site: http://www.wickedlocal.com
Sales Range: $100-124.9 Million
Newspaper Publishers
N.A.I.C.S.: 513110

Subsidiary (Domestic):

Enterprise Publishing Company, LLC (3)
5 Cohannet St, Brockton, MA 02301
Tel.: (508) 586-6200
Web Site: https://www.enterprisenews.com
Sales Range: $25-49.9 Million
Publisher of Newspapers
N.A.I.C.S.: 513110
Ken Johnson *(Editor-Online)*

Fayetteville Publishing Co. (3)
458 Whitfield St, Fayetteville, NC 28302
Tel.: (910) 323-4848
Web Site: http://www.fayobserver.com
Newspaper Publishers
N.A.I.C.S.: 513110

Unit (Domestic):

Hamilton-Wenham Chronicle (3)
75 Sylvan St C 105, Danvers, MA 01923
Tel.: (978) 739-8542
Web Site: http://www.wickedlocal.com
Sales Range: $100-124.9 Million
Newspaper Publishers
N.A.I.C.S.: 513110

Hanover Mariner (3)
165 Enterprise Dr, Marshfield, MA 02050
Tel.: (781) 837-4545
Web Site: http://www.wickedlocal.com
Sales Range: $100-124.9 Million
Emp.: 100
Newspaper Publishers
N.A.I.C.S.: 513110
Mark Olivieri *(Publr)*
Gregory Mathis *(Reg Dir-News & Ops)*
Michael Kane *(Deputy Dir-Multimedia)*
Mark Burridge *(Editor-Print)*
Chris Avis *(Mgr-Adv)*
Beth Doyle *(Editor-Special Sections & Real Estate)*

Harwich Oracle (3)
5 Namskaket Rd, Orleans, MA 02653
Tel.: (978) 371-5744
Web Site: http://www.wickedlocal.com
Sales Range: $10-24.9 Million
Emp.: 8
Newspaper Publishers
N.A.I.C.S.: 513110

Subsidiary (Domestic):

Hingham Journal (3)
73 S St, Hingham, MA 02043
Tel.: (781) 749-0031
Web Site: https://www.wickedlocal.com
Sales Range: $100-124.9 Million
Emp.: 4
Newspaper Publishers
N.A.I.C.S.: 513110

Unit (Domestic):

Holbrook Sun (3)
15 Pactella Park Dr, Randolph, MA 02368
Tel.: (508) 967-3515
Web Site: http://www.wickedlocal.com
Sales Range: $25-49.9 Million
Emp.: 2
Newspaper Publishers
N.A.I.C.S.: 513110

Holliston TAB (3)
33 New York Ave, Framingham, MA 01701
Tel.: (508) 626-3800
Web Site:
  http://www.holliston.wickedlocal.com
Sales Range: $10-24.9 Million
Emp.: 5
Newspaper Publishers
N.A.I.C.S.: 513110

Hopkinton Crier (3)
1 Speen St, Framingham, MA 01701
Tel.: (508) 626-3800
Web Site:
  http://www.wickedlocalhopkinton.com
Sales Range: $100-124.9 Million
Emp.: 3
Newspaper Publishers
N.A.I.C.S.: 513110

Hudson Sun (3)
40 Mechanic St, Marlborough, MA 01752
Tel.: (978) 562-2379
Web Site: http://www.wickedlocal.com
Sales Range: $100-124.9 Million
Newspaper Publishers
N.A.I.C.S.: 513110

Ipswich Chronicle (3)
75 Sylvan St Ste C 105, Danvers, MA 01923
Tel.: (978) 739-1303
Web Site:
  http://www.ipswich.wickedlocal.com
Sales Range: $100-124.9 Million
Emp.: 70
Newspaper Publishers
N.A.I.C.S.: 513110

Subsidiary (Domestic):

Kingston Reporter (3)
182 Standish Ave, Plymouth, MA 02360
Tel.: (508) 591-6600
Web Site: http://www.wickedlocal.com
Sales Range: $10-24.9 Million
Emp.: 12
Newspaper Publishers
N.A.I.C.S.: 513110

Lexington Minuteman (3)
9 Meriam St, Lexington, MA 02420
Tel.: (781) 674-7722
Web Site: https://www.wickedlocal.com
Sales Range: $10-24.9 Million
Emp.: 10
Newspaper Publishers
N.A.I.C.S.: 513110

Unit (Domestic):

Lincoln Journal (3)
150 Baker Ave Ste 101, Concord, MA 01742
Tel.: (978) 371-5759
Web Site: http://www.wickedlocal.com
Sales Range: $10-24.9 Million
Emp.: 50
Newspaper Publishers
N.A.I.C.S.: 513110

Malden Observer (3)
75 Sylvan St C 105, Danvers, MA 01923
Tel.: (781) 393-1827
Web Site: http://www.wickedlocal.com
Sales Range: $10-24.9 Million
Emp.: 1
Newspaper Publishers
N.A.I.C.S.: 513110

Mansfield News (3)
370 Paramount Dr Unit 3, Raynham, MA 02767
Tel.: (508) 967-3510
Web Site: http://www.wickedlocal.com
Sales Range: $100-124.9 Million
Newspaper Publishers
N.A.I.C.S.: 513110

Subsidiary (Domestic):

Marblehead Reporter (3)
40 S St Ste 102, Marblehead, MA 01945
Tel.: (781) 639-4800
Web Site: https://www.wickedlocal.com
Sales Range: $10-24.9 Million
Emp.: 4
Newspaper Publishers
N.A.I.C.S.: 513110

Unit (Domestic):

Marshfield Mariner (3)

Holliston TAB (duplicate removed)

165 Enterprise Dr, Marshfield, MA 02050
Tel.: (781) 837-4545
Web Site: https://www.wickedlocal.com
Sales Range: $25-49.9 Million
Emp.: 100
Newspaper Publishers
N.A.I.C.S.: 513110

Unit (Domestic):

Melrose Free Press (3)
72 Cherry Hill Dr, Beverly, MA 01915
Tel.: (978) 739-1314
Web Site: http://www.wickedlocal.com
Sales Range: $10-24.9 Million
Emp.: 50
Newspaper Publishers
N.A.I.C.S.: 513110

MetroWest Daily News (3)
1 Speen St, Framingham, MA 01701
Tel.: (508) 626-4412
Web Site:
  https://www.metrowestdailynews.com
Sales Range: $100-124.9 Million
Emp.: 200
Newspaper Publishers
N.A.I.C.S.: 513110

Natick Bulletin & TAB (3)
1 Speen St, Framingham, MA 01701
Tel.: (508) 626-3800
Web Site: http://www.wickedlocal.com
Sales Range: $100-124.9 Million
Newspaper Publishers
N.A.I.C.S.: 513110

Subsidiary (Domestic):

Needham Times (3)
254 2nd Ave, Needham, MA 02494
Tel.: (781) 433-8366
Web Site: http://www.wickedlocal.com
Sales Range: $100-124.9 Million
Newspaper Publishers
N.A.I.C.S.: 513110

Newton TAB (3)
254 2nd Ave 1, Needham, MA 02494
Tel.: (617) 969-0340
Web Site: http://www.wickedlocal.com
Sales Range: $100-124.9 Million
Emp.: 4
Newspaper Publishers
N.A.I.C.S.: 513110

North Andover Citizen (3)
72 Cherry Hill Dr, Beverly, MA 01915
Tel.: (978) 685-5128
Web Site: http://www.wickedlocal.com
Sales Range: $100-124.9 Million
Newspaper Publishers
N.A.I.C.S.: 513110

Unit (Domestic):

North Shore Sunday (3)
75 Sylvan St C 105, Danvers, MA 01923
Tel.: (978) 739-1300
Web Site: http://www.wickedlocal.com
Sales Range: $50-74.9 Million
Emp.: 100
Newspaper Publishers
N.A.I.C.S.: 513110

Norton Mirror (3)
370 Paramont Dr Ste 3, Raynham, MA 02767
Tel.: (508) 967-3510
Web Site: http://www.wickedlocal.com
Sales Range: $100-124.9 Million
Newspaper Publishers
N.A.I.C.S.: 513110

Norwell Mariner (3)
165 Enterprise Dr, Marshfield, MA 02050
Tel.: (781) 837-4500
Web Site: http://www.wickedlocal.com
Sales Range: $100-124.9 Million
Emp.: 70
Newspaper Publishers
N.A.I.C.S.: 513110
Mark Olivieri *(Publr)*
Gregory Mathis *(Reg Dir-News & Ops)*
Michael Kane *(Deputy Dir-Multimedia)*
Chris Avis *(Mgr-Adv)*
Beth Doyle *(Editor-Special Sections & Real Estate)*
Mark Burridge *(Editor-Print)*

Unit (Domestic):

Pembroke Mariner & Reporter (3)

165 Enterprise Dr, Marshfield, MA 02050-0682
Tel.: (781) 837-4500
Web Site: http://www.wickedlocal.com
Sales Range: $100-124.9 Million
Newspaper Publishers
N.A.I.C.S.: 513110
Gregory Mathis (Reg Dir-News & Ops)
Chris Avis (Mgr-Adv)
Beth Doyle (Editor-Special Sections & Real Estate)
Michael Kane (Deputy Dir-Multimedia)

Saugus Advertiser (3)
75 Sylvan St C 105, Danvers, MA 01923
Tel.: (978) 739-1395
Web Site: http://saugus.wickedlocal.com
Newspaper Publishers
N.A.I.C.S.: 513110

Subsidiary (Domestic):

Scituate Mariner (3)
165 Enterprise Dr, Marshfield, MA 02050
Tel.: (781) 545-2978
Web Site: http://www.wickedlocal.com
Sales Range: $10-24.9 Million
Emp.: 50
Newspaper Publishers
N.A.I.C.S.: 513110
Mark Olivieri (Publr)
Gregory Mathis (Reg Dir-News & Ops)
Michael Kane (Deputy Dir-Multimedia)
Jenn Mann (Dir-Multimedia Sls)
Chris Avis (Mgr-Adv)
Beth Doyle (Editor-Special Sections & Real Estate)
Mark Burridge (Editor-Print)

Unit (Domestic):

Sharon Advocate (3)
254 2nd Ave, Needham, MA 02494
Tel.: (781) 433-8367
Web Site: http://www.wickedlocal.com
Sales Range: $10-24.9 Million
Emp.: 5
Newspaper Publishers
N.A.I.C.S.: 513110

Shrewsbury Chronicle (3)
33 New York Ave, Framingham, MA 01701
Tel.: (508) 842-8787
Web Site: http://www.wickedlocal.com
Sales Range: $25-49.9 Million
Emp.: 3
Newspaper Publishers
N.A.I.C.S.: 513110

Subsidiary (Domestic):

Somerville Journal (3)
80 Central St, Somerville, MA 02143
Tel.: (781) 433-6700
Web Site: http://www.wickedlocal.com
Sales Range: $100-124.9 Million
Emp.: 8
Newspaper Publishers
N.A.I.C.S.: 513110

Unit (Domestic):

Stoneham Sun (3)
20-40 Holland St, Somerville, MA 02144
Tel.: (781) 279-1051
Web Site: http://www.wickedlocal.com
Sales Range: $10-24.9 Million
Emp.: 3
Newspaper Publishers
N.A.I.C.S.: 513110

Stoughton Journal (3)
5 Pacella Park Dr, Randolph, MA 02368
Tel.: (508) 967-3515
Web Site: http://www.wickedlocal.com
Sales Range: $10-24.9 Million
Emp.: 1
Newspaper Publishers
N.A.I.C.S.: 513110
Stuart Green (Editor)

Tewksbury Advocate (3)
150 Baker Ave Ext Ste 101, Concord, MA 01742
Tel.: (978) 371-5744
Web Site: http://www.wickedlocal.com
Sales Range: $100-124.9 Million
Emp.: 50
Newspaper Publishers
N.A.I.C.S.: 513110

The Arlington Advocate (3)
9 Meriam St, Lexington, MA 02420
Tel.: (781) 674-7726
Web Site: http://www.wickedlocal.com
Sales Range: $10-24.9 Million
Emp.: 8
Newspaper Publishers
N.A.I.C.S.: 513110

Subsidiary (Domestic):

The Beacon (3)
150 Baker Ave Ext Ste 101, Concord, MA 01742
Tel.: (978) 371-5714
Web Site: http://www.wickedlocal.com
Sales Range: $25-49.9 Million
Emp.: 130
Newspaper Publishers
N.A.I.C.S.: 513110

The Beacon-Villager (3)
150 Baker Ave Ste 101, Concord, MA 01742
Tel.: (978) 371-5759
Web Site: http://www.wickedlocal.com
Sales Range: $100-124.9 Million
Emp.: 100
Newspaper Publishers
N.A.I.C.S.: 513110

Unit (Domestic):

The Framingham Tab (3)
1 Speen St, Framingham, MA 01701
Tel.: (508) 626-3800
Web Site: http://www.wickedlocal.com
Emp.: 120
Newspaper Publishers
N.A.I.C.S.: 513110

The Herald News (3)
207 Pocasset St, Fall River, MA 02722
Tel.: (508) 676-8211
Web Site: https://www.heraldnews.com
Sales Range: $10-24.9 Million
Emp.: 50
Newspaper Publishers
N.A.I.C.S.: 513110
Tracy R Sabala (Publr)

The Patriot Ledger (3)
2 Adams Pl, Quincy, MA 02269-9159
Tel.: (617) 786-7000
Web Site: https://www.patriotledger.com
Sales Range: $100-124.9 Million
Emp.: 103
Newspaper Publishers
N.A.I.C.S.: 513110
Dana Barbuto (Editor-Features)

Subsidiary (Domestic):

The Sudbury Town Crier (3)
1 Speen St, Framingham, MA 01701
Tel.: (508) 626-3800
Web Site: http://www.wickedlocal.com
Sales Range: $25-49.9 Million
Emp.: 120
Newspaper Publishers
N.A.I.C.S.: 513110

The Swampscott Reporter (3)
40 S St Ste 102, Marblehead, MA 01945
Tel.: (781) 639-4800
Web Site: https://www.wickedlocal.com
Sales Range: $10-24.9 Million
Emp.: 2
Newspaper Publishers
N.A.I.C.S.: 513110

Unit (Domestic):

The Taunton Gazette (3)
5 Cohannet St, Taunton, MA 02780-3903
Tel.: (508) 880-9000
Web Site: http://www.tauntongazette.com
Sales Range: $10-24.9 Million
Emp.: 50
Newspaper Publishers
N.A.I.C.S.: 513110

The Villager (3)
40 Mechanic St Ste 220, Marlborough, MA 01752
Tel.: (508) 490-7454
Web Site: http://www.wickedlocal.com
Sales Range: $100-124.9 Million
Emp.: 50
Newspaper Publishers
N.A.I.C.S.: 513110

Wakefield Observer (3)
72 Cherry Hill Dr Ste 1001, Beverly, MA 01915
Tel.: (781) 224-2546
Web Site: http://www.wickedlocal.com
Sales Range: $10-24.9 Million
Emp.: 50
Newspaper Publishers
N.A.I.C.S.: 513110

Waltham News Tribune (3)
15 Pacella Park Dr, Randolph, MA 01752
Tel.: (781) 433-8282
Web Site: https://www.wickedlocal.com
Sales Range: $10-24.9 Million
Emp.: 7
Newspaper Publishers
N.A.I.C.S.: 513110

Subsidiary (Domestic):

Wayland Town Crier (3)
1 Speen St, Framingham, MA 01701
Tel.: (508) 626-3800
Web Site: http://www.wickedlocal.com
Sales Range: $100-124.9 Million
Emp.: 80
Newspapers
N.A.I.C.S.: 513110

Unit (Domestic):

West Roxbury Transcript (3)
254 2nd Ave, Needham, MA 02494
Tel.: (781) 433-6700
Web Site: http://www.wickedlocal.com
Sales Range: $100-124.9 Million
Emp.: 125
Newspaper Publishers
N.A.I.C.S.: 513110

Westborough News (3)
40 Mechanic St Ste 220, Marlborough, MA 01752
Tel.: (508) 490-7471
Web Site: http://www.wickedlocal.com
Sales Range: $100-124.9 Million
Emp.:
Newspaper Publishers
N.A.I.C.S.: 513110

Westford Eagle (3)
150 Baker Ave Ext Ste 101, Concord, MA 01742
Tel.: (978) 371-5729
Web Site: http://www.westford.wickedlocal.com
Sales Range: $100-124.9 Million
Emp.: 40
Newspaper Publishers
N.A.I.C.S.: 513110

Westwood Press (3)
254 2nd Ave, Needham Heights, MA 02494
Tel.: (503) 432-8142
Web Site: https://www.westwoodpress.com
Sales Range: $10-24.9 Million
Emp.: 1
Newspaper Publishers
N.A.I.C.S.: 513110

Weymouth News (3)
15 Pacella Park Dr, Randolph, MA 02368
Tel.: (781) 682-4850
Web Site: http://www.wickedlocal.com
Sales Range: $10-24.9 Million
Emp.: 6
Newspaper Publishers
N.A.I.C.S.: 513110

Wilmington Advocate (3)
150 Baker Ave Ext Ste 101, Concord, MA 01742
Tel.: (978) 371-5744
Web Site: http://www.wilmington.wickedlocal.com
Sales Range: $50-74.9 Million
Emp.: 150
Newspaper Publishers
N.A.I.C.S.: 513110

Winchester Star (3)
100 N Loudoun St Ste 110, Winchester, VA 22601
Tel.: (540) 667-3200
Web Site: https://www.winchesterstar.com
Sales Range: $10-24.9 Million
Emp.: 10
Newspaper Publishers
N.A.I.C.S.: 513110

Subsidiary (Domestic):

Woburn Advocate (3)
150 Baker Ave Ext, Concord, MA 01742
Tel.: (781) 937-8000
Web Site: http://www.wickedlocal.com
Sales Range: $100-124.9 Million
Newspaper Publishers
N.A.I.C.S.: 513110

Group (Domestic):

Gatehouse Media Ohio Holdings II, Inc. (2)
605 S Front St Ste 300, Columbus, OH 43215
Tel.: (585) 598-0030
Web Site: https://www.dispatch.com
Newspaper & Magazine Publisher
N.A.I.C.S.: 513110
Alan D. Miller (Editor)

Unit (Domestic):

ThisWeek Community News (3)
7801 N Central Dr, Lewis Center, OH 43035
Tel.: (740) 888-6000
Web Site: http://www.thisweeknews.com
Community Newspapers Publisher
N.A.I.C.S.: 513110

Unit (Domestic):

Hannibal Courier-Post (2)
200 N 3rd St, Hannibal, MO 63401
Tel.: (573) 221-2800
Web Site: http://www.hannibal.net
Sales Range: $10-24.9 Million
Emp.: 50
Newspaper Publishers
N.A.I.C.S.: 513110
Forrest Gossett (Editor-Salt River Journal)

Subsidiary (Domestic):

Hawaii Tribune Herald (2)
355 Kinoole St, Hilo, HI 96720
Tel.: (808) 935-6621
Web Site: https://www.hawaiitribune-herald.com
Newspaper Publishing
N.A.I.C.S.: 513110
David Bock (Publr & Editor)

Unit (Domestic):

Hillsdale Daily News (2)
263 Industrial Dr, Hillsdale, MI 49242-0287
Tel.: (517) 437-7351
Web Site: https://www.hillsdale.net
Sales Range: $10-24.9 Million
Emp.: 27
Newspaper Publishers
N.A.I.C.S.: 513110
RoxAnne Morgret (Dir-Circulation)

Subsidiary (Domestic):

Homer News, LLC (2)
3482 Landings St, Homer, AK 99603-7999
Tel.: (907) 235-7767
Web Site: https://www.homernews.com
Newspaper Publishers
N.A.I.C.S.: 513110

Hoosier-Times, Inc. (2)
1900 S Walnut St, Bloomington, IN 47401
Tel.: (812) 332-4401
Newspaper Publishers
N.A.I.C.S.: 513110
Kristina Wood (Editor-Copy)
Cory Bollinger (Reg Publr)

Unit (Domestic):

Journal Star, Inc. (2)
1 News Plz, Peoria, IL 61643
Tel.: (309) 686-3114
Web Site: https://www.pjstar.com
Newspaper Publishers
N.A.I.C.S.: 513110
Ron Rude (Mgr-Information Sys)
Wes Huett (Editor-Sports)
Dean Muellerleile (Editor-Copy)
Romando Dixson (Exec Editor)

Juneau Empire (2)
8800 Glacier Hwy Ste 219, Juneau, AK 99801
Tel.: (907) 308-4898

Gannett Co., Inc.—(Continued)
Web Site: https://www.juneauempire.com
Newspaper Publishers
N.A.I.C.S.: 513110

Subsidiary (Domestic):

Local Media Group, Inc. (2)
90 Crystal Run Rd Ste 310, Middletown, NY 10941
Tel.: (845) 341-1100
Web Site: https://www.recordonline.com
Sales Range: $25-49.9 Million
Emp.: 1,500
Business Magazines & Newspaper Publishing
N.A.I.C.S.: 513110

Unit (Domestic):

Cape Cod Times (3)
319 Main St, Hyannis, MA 02601
Tel.: (508) 775-1200
Web Site: https://www.capecodtimes.com
Newspaper Publishers
N.A.I.C.S.: 513110
Molly Evans (Dir-Adv)

Daily Press (3)
13891 Park Ave, Victorville, CA 92392
Tel.: (760) 241-7755
Web Site: https://www.vvdailypress.com
Newspapers
N.A.I.C.S.: 513110

Desert Dispatch (3)
130 Coolwater Ln, Barstow, CA 92311
Tel.: (760) 256-2257
Web Site: http://www.desertdispatch.com
Sales Range: $10-24.9 Million
Emp.: 12
Newspapers
N.A.I.C.S.: 513110
Matthew Cabe (Editor-City)
Steve Nakutin (Gen Mgr & Dir-Adv)

Hesperia Star (3)
15550 Main St Ste C11, Hesperia, CA 92345
Tel.: (760) 956-7827
Web Site: http://www.hesperiastar.com
Sales Range: $10-24.9 Million
Emp.: 4
Newspapers
N.A.I.C.S.: 541840

Subsidiary (Domestic):

Inquirer & Mirror, Inc. (3)
1 Old S Rd, Nantucket, MA 02554-6029
Tel.: (508) 228-0001
Web Site: https://www.ack.net
Sales Range: $10-24.9 Million
Emp.: 14
Newspaper Publishers
N.A.I.C.S.: 513110

LMG Stockton, Inc. (3)
445 W Weber Ave Ste 128C, Stockton, CA 95203
Tel.: (209) 943-6397
Web Site: https://www.recordnet.com
Newspaper Publishing
N.A.I.C.S.: 513110

Subsidiary (Domestic):

The Record (4)
530 E Market St, Stockton, CA 95202-3009
Tel.: (209) 943-6397
Web Site: https://www.recordnet.com
Newspaper Publishers
N.A.I.C.S.: 513110
Claudine Dunham (Mgr-Acctg)
Dan Loffelbein (Mgr-Ad Svcs)
Paula Allard (Mgr-Support Ops)

Subsidiary (Domestic):

Seacoast Newspapers, Inc. (3)
210 Commerce Way Ste 330, Portsmouth, NH 03801
Tel.: (585) 598-0030
Web Site: https://www.seacoastonline.com
Newspaper Publishing
N.A.I.C.S.: 513110

The Nickel of Medford, Inc. (3)
111 N Fir St, Medford, OR 97501
Tel.: (541) 776-4466
Web Site: https://www.medfordnickel.com

Weekly Shopper Newspaper Publishing
N.A.I.C.S.: 513110

Unit (Domestic):

Times Herald-Record (3)
90 Crystal Run Rd Ste 310, Middletown, NY 10941
Tel.: (845) 341-1100
Web Site: https://www.recordonline.com
Sales Range: $25-49.9 Million
Emp.: 100
Newspaper Publishers
N.A.I.C.S.: 513110

Subsidiary (Domestic):

Mineral Daily News Tribune, Inc. (2)
455 S Mineral St, Keyser, WV 26726
Tel.: (304) 788-3333
Web Site: https://www.newstribune.info
Sales Range: $1-9.9 Million
Emp.: 10
Newspaper Publishing Services
N.A.I.C.S.: 513110
Liz Beavers (Editor-Sports & Mng Editor)
Carla Braithwaite (Mgr-Adv)

News Leader, Inc. (2)
716 E Napoleon St, Sulphur, LA 70663
Tel.: (318) 527-7075
Web Site:
https://www.sulphurdailynews.com
Newspaper Publishing Services
N.A.I.C.S.: 513110

Record Publishing Company (2)
1050 W Main St, Kent, OH 44240
Tel.: (330) 296-8414
Web Site: https://www.record-courier.com
Newspaper Publishers
N.A.I.C.S.: 513110

Unit (Domestic):

Rockford Register Star (2)
99 E State St, Rockford, IL 61104
Tel.: (815) 987-1200
Web Site: https://www.rrstar.com
Sales Range: $75-99.9 Million
Emp.: 250
Newspaper Publishing
N.A.I.C.S.: 513110
Bruce Heisel (Editor-Digital Assigning-Nights)
Kevin Haas (Editor-Metro)

Savannah Morning News
1375 Chatham Pkwy, Savannah, GA 31405
Tel.: (912) 236-9511
Web Site: https://www.savannahnow.com
Newspaper Publishers
N.A.I.C.S.: 513110
Zach Dennis (Editor-Multimedia Content & Do Savannah)
Nathan Dominitz (Editor-Sports Content)

Shawnee News-Star (2)
1725 N Kickapoo Ste 101, Shawnee, OK 74801
Tel.: (405) 273-4200
Web Site: https://www.news-star.com
Sales Range: $10-24.9 Million
Emp.: 54
Newspaper Publishers
N.A.I.C.S.: 513110
Kim Morava (Editor)
Brian Johnson (Editor-Sports)

Subsidiary (Domestic):

Star Courier (2)
105 E Central Blvd, Kewanee, IL 61443
Tel.: (309) 852-2181
Web Site: https://www.starcourier.com
Sales Range: $10-24.9 Million
Emp.: 7
Newspaper Publishing
N.A.I.C.S.: 513110
David Adams (Publr)

Unit (Domestic):

Sylvania Telephone (2)
208 N Main St, Sylvania, GA 30467-0010
Tel.: (912) 564-2045
Web Site: http://www.augustachronicle.com
Newspaper Publishing
N.A.I.C.S.: 513110

The Augusta Chronicle (2)

725 Broad St, Augusta, GA 30903 **(100%)**
Tel.: (706) 722-5620
Web Site: https://www.augustachronicle.com
Newspaper Publishers
N.A.I.C.S.: 513110
Tony Bernados (Pres)

Subsidiary (Domestic):

The Beacon Journal Publishing Company (2)
388 S Main St Ste 720, Akron, OH 44309
Tel.: (330) 996-3000
Web Site: http://www.beaconjournal.com
Newspaper Publishers
N.A.I.C.S.: 513110
Michael Shearer (Editor)
Cheryl Powell (Editor-Metro)

Unit (Domestic):

Akron Beacon Journal (3)
388 S Main St Ste 720, Akron, OH 44309-0640
Tel.: (330) 996-3487
Web Site: http://www.ohio.com
Sales Range: $100-124.9 Million
Emp.: 500
Newspapers
N.A.I.C.S.: 513110
Michael Shearer (Editor)
Cheryl Powell (Mng Editor)
Joe Thomas (Editor-Metro & Local)

Unit (Domestic):

The Bulletin (2)
10 Railroad Pl, Norwich, CT 06360
Tel.: (860) 887-5582
Web Site: https://www.norwichbulletin.com
Newspaper Publishers
N.A.I.C.S.: 513110

The Canton Repository (2)
500 Market Ave S, Canton, OH 44702
Tel.: (330) 580-8500
Web Site: https://www.cantonrep.com
Newspaper Publishing Services
N.A.I.C.S.: 513110
Chris Beaven (Editor-Sports)

Subsidiary (Domestic):

The Courier (2)
2201 Woodlawn Rd Ste 345, Lincoln, IL 62656
Tel.: (217) 732-2101
Web Site: https://www.lincolncourier.com
Sales Range: $25-49.9 Million
Emp.: 4
Newspapers
N.A.I.C.S.: 513110
Jean Ann Miller (Mng Editor)

Unit (Domestic):

The Daily Ardmoreite (2)
34 N Washington, Ardmore, OK 73401
Tel.: (580) 223-2200
Web Site: http://www.ardmoreite.com
Sales Range: $10-24.9 Million
Emp.: 48
Daily Newspaper Publisher
N.A.I.C.S.: 513110
Kim Benedict (Publr & Dir-Adv)

Subsidiary (Domestic):

The Daily Reporter (2)
15 W Pearl St, Coldwater, MI 49036
Tel.: (517) 278-2318
Web Site: https://www.thedailyreporter.com
Sales Range: $1-9.9 Million
Emp.: 25
Evening Newspaper, Except Sunday
N.A.I.C.S.: 513110

Unit (Domestic):

The Examiner (2)
300 N Osage St -1st fl, Independence, MO 64050
Tel.: (816) 648-1611
Web Site: https://www.examiner.net
Sales Range: $25-49.9 Million
Emp.: 75
Daily Newspaper Publisher
N.A.I.C.S.: 513110
Deneane M. Hyde (Mgr-Bus)

Subsidiary (Domestic):

The Florida Times-Union (2)
1 Independent Dr Ste 200, Jacksonville, FL 32202
Tel.: (904) 359-4255
Web Site: https://www.jacksonville.com
Newspaper Publishers
N.A.I.C.S.: 513110
William S. Morris (Owner)
Paul Runnestrand (Editor-News)
Gary Mills (Dir-Digital)
Tom Szaroleta (Editor-Lifestyle)
Anne Hammock (Editor-Homes)

The Holland Sentinel (2)
54 W 8th St, Holland, MI 49423
Tel.: (616) 546-4200
Web Site: https://www.hollandsentinel.com
Sales Range: $25-49.9 Million
Emp.: 110
Newspaper Publishers
N.A.I.C.S.: 513110
Sarah Leach (Editor-in-Chief)
Brian Vernellis (Dir-Digital)
Dan D'Addona (Editor-Sports)
Will Kennedy (Editor-Asst Sports)

Unit (Domestic):

The Independent (2)
729 Lincoln Way E, Massillon, OH 44646
Tel.: (330) 833-7554
Web Site: https://www.indeonline.com
Sales Range: $100-124.9 Million
Emp.: 20
Daily Newspaper
N.A.I.C.S.: 516210
Veronica Van Dress (Editor)

Subsidiary (Domestic):

The Jeffersonian Company, LLC (2)
831 Wheeling Ave, Cambridge, OH 43725
Tel.: (740) 439-3531
Web Site: https://www.daily-jeff.com
Newspaper Publishers
N.A.I.C.S.: 513110

The Lubbock Avalanche-Journal (2)
710 Ave J, Lubbock, TX 79401
Tel.: (806) 762-8844
Web Site: https://www.lubbockonline.com
Newspaper Publishers
N.A.I.C.S.: 513110
Shoni Wiseman (Mgr-Adv)
Robin Morse (Mgr-Classified Adv)
Jill Nevels-Haun (Exec Editor-Reg)

The Morning Sun (2)
701 N Locust St, Pittsburg, KS 66762-0570
Tel.: (620) 231-2600
Web Site: https://www.morningsun.net
Sales Range: $25-49.9 Million
Emp.: 35
Newspaper Publishers
N.A.I.C.S.: 513110

Unit (Domestic):

The Newton Kansan (2)
517 N Main St, Newton, KS 67114
Tel.: (316) 283-1500
Web Site: https://www.thekansan.com
Sales Range: $10-24.9 Million
Emp.: 35
Newspaper Publishers
N.A.I.C.S.: 513110

The Oak Ridger, LLC (2)
575 Oak Ridge Tpke Ste 100, Oak Ridge, TN 37831-3446
Tel.: (865) 482-1021
Web Site: https://www.oakridger.com
Sales Range: $10-24.9 Million
Emp.: 12
Newspaper Publishers
N.A.I.C.S.: 513110
Darrell Richardson (Publr & Editor)

Subsidiary (Domestic):

The Observer-Dispatch (2)
70 Genesee St, Utica, NY 13501
Tel.: (315) 792-5000
Web Site: https://www.uticaod.com
Sales Range: $75-99.9 Million
Emp.: 250
Newspaper Publishers
N.A.I.C.S.: 513110

Robert Booth *(Editor-Night)*
Pam Sperbeck *(Editor-Community, Scene & Accent)*
Barbara Laible *(Coord-Web)*
George Amendolare *(Mgr-Single Copy)*

Unit (Domestic):

The Peninsula Clarion (2)
150 Trading Bay Rd Ste 1, Kenai, AK 99611
Tel.: (907) 283-7551
Web Site: https://www.peninsulaclarion.com
Newspaper Publishers
N.A.I.C.S.: 513110

Subsidiary (Domestic):

The Peoria Journal Star, Inc. (2)
1 News Plz, Peoria, IL 61643-0001
Tel.: (309) 686-3000
Web Site: https://www.pjstar.com
Newspaper Publishing Services
N.A.I.C.S.: 513110
Wes Huett *(Editor-Sports)*

The Progress-Index (2)
15 Franklin St, Petersburg, VA 23803
Tel.: (804) 490-0055
Web Site: https://www.progress-index.com
Emp.: 80
Newspapers & Weekly Publications Publisher
N.A.I.C.S.: 513110

The Providence Journal Company (2)
75 Fountain St, Providence, RI 02902
Tel.: (401) 277-7000
Web Site:
    https://www.providencejournal.com
Sales Range: $100-124.9 Million
Newspaper Publishing & TV Broadcasting
N.A.I.C.S.: 513110

Subsidiary (Domestic):

Rhode Island Monthly Communications, Inc (3)
560 Mineral Spring Ave Unit 100B, Pawtucket, RI 02860
Tel.: (401) 649-4800
Web Site: http://www.rimonthly.com
Periodical Publishers
N.A.I.C.S.: 513120
Howard G. Sutton *(Publr)*

Branch (Domestic):

Rhode Island Monthly Communications, Inc. (4)
560 Mineral Spring Ave Unit 100B, Pawtucket, RI 02860
Tel.: (401) 649-4800
Web Site: http://www.rimonthly.com
Newspaper Publishers
N.A.I.C.S.: 513110
John Palumbo *(Owner)*

Unit (Domestic):

The Reading Advocate (2)
75 Sylvan St Ste C105, Danvers, MA 01923-2765
Tel.: (978) 371-5750
Web Site: http://reading.wickedlocal.com
Newspaper Publishers
N.A.I.C.S.: 513110

The Register Mail (2)
140 S Prairie St, Galesburg, IL 61401-4605
Tel.: (309) 343-7181
Web Site: https://www.galesburg.com
Sales Range: $25-49.9 Million
Emp.: 120
Newspapers
N.A.I.C.S.: 513110
Tom Martin *(Editor)*

Subsidiary (Domestic):

The Santa Cruz County Sentinel, Inc. (2)
1800 Green Hills Rd Ste 210, Scotts Valley, CA 95066
Tel.: (831) 706-3201
Web Site:
    https://www.santacruzsentinel.com
Newspaper Publishing Services
N.A.I.C.S.: 513110
Mardi Browning *(Mgr-Mktg & Circulation)*

Unit (Domestic):

The St. Augustine Record (2)
1 News Pl, Saint Augustine, FL 32086
Tel.: (904) 819-3430
Web Site: https://www.staugustine.com
Newspaper Publishers
N.A.I.C.S.: 513110
Peter Willott *(Editor-Visual)*

The State Journal-Register (2)
421 S Grand Ave W Ste 1A, Springfield, IL 62704
Tel.: (217) 788-1300
Web Site: https://www.sj-r.com
Sales Range: $50-74.9 Million
Emp.: 200
Publishing & Editing Newspapers
N.A.I.C.S.: 513110
Leisa Richardson *(Exec Editor)*

The Sun-Times (2)
107 N 4th St, Heber Springs, AR 72543-3042
Tel.: (501) 362-2425
Web Site: https://www.thesuntimes.com
Sales Range: $10-24.9 Million
Emp.: 21
Newspaper Publishers
N.A.I.C.S.: 513110
Shane Allen *(Publr)*

Subsidiary (Domestic):

The Times Reporter (2)
629 Wabash Ave NW, New Philadelphia, OH 44663
Tel.: (330) 364-8387
Web Site: https://www.timesreporter.com
Sales Range: $50-74.9 Million
Emp.: 150
Newspaper Publishers
N.A.I.C.S.: 513110

Unit (Domestic):

The Topeka Capital-Journal (2)
100 SE 9th St Ste 500, Topeka, KS 66612-1213 (100%)
Tel.: (785) 295-1111
Web Site: https://www.cjonline.com
Newspaper Publisher Services
N.A.I.C.S.: 513120

Wellsville Daily Reporter (2)
159 N Main St, Wellsville, NY 14895
Tel.: (585) 593-5300
Web Site: http://www.wellsvilledaily.com
Sales Range: $10-24.9 Million
Emp.: 12
Newspaper Publishers
N.A.I.C.S.: 513110
Heather Falkey *(Dir-Mktg)*
Abigail Wilcox *(Mgr-Circulation)*
Rick Emanuel *(Publr-Reg)*
Chris Potter *(Editor-Reg)*

Subsidiary (Domestic):

Wooster Daily Record, Inc., LLC (2)
212 E Liberty St, Wooster, OH 44691
Tel.: (330) 287-1615
Web Site: https://www.the-daily-record.com
Newspaper Publishers
N.A.I.C.S.: 513110
Veronica VanDress *(Editor)*

George W. Prescott Publishing Company, LLC (1)
2 Adams Pl, Quincy, MA 02269
Tel.: (617) 786-7026
Web Site: https://www.patriotledger.com
Newspaper Publishing Services
N.A.I.C.S.: 513110

Halifax Media Holdings, LLC (1)
2339 Beville Rd, Daytona Beach, FL 32119
Tel.: (386) 265-6700
Web Site:
    http://www.halifaxmediagroup.com
Sales Range: $250-299.9 Million
Emp.: 2,000
Holding Company; Newspaper Publisher
N.A.I.C.S.: 551112
Rick Martin *(COO)*

Subsidiary (Domestic):

Daytona Beach News-Journal Corp. (2)
901 6th St, Daytona Beach, FL 32117

Tel.: (386) 252-1511
Web Site: https://www.news-journalonline.com
Newspaper Publishers
N.A.I.C.S.: 513110
Scot Forrest *(Mgr-Adv Sls)*
Mark Shekhter *(Mgr-Adv Ops)*
Kaitlyn Stier *(Mgr-Events)*
Clayton Park *(Editor-Bus)*
Brian Bell *(Editor-Multimedia)*
Chris Bridges *(Mgr-Digital)*
Laurie Hahn *(Office Mgr-Flagler Bureau)*
Nancy Niles *(Editor-Multimedia)*
Krys Fluker *(Editor-Opinion)*
John Gallas *(Mng Editor)*
Jewel Tomazin *(Editor-Entertainment)*
Ashley Varese *(Editor-Communities)*
Dave Wersinger *(Deputy Mng Dir)*
Mark Harper *(Editor-Political)*

Unit (Domestic):

Argus-Courier (3)
1372 E N McDowell Blvd, Petaluma, CA 94954
Tel.: (707) 762-4541
Web Site: https://www.petaluma360.com
Sales Range: $100-124.9 Million
Community Newspaper
N.A.I.C.S.: 513110

Subsidiary (Domestic):

Comet-Press Newspapers, Inc. (3)
705 W 5th St, Thibodaux, LA 70301-3148 (100%)
Tel.: (985) 448-7623
Web Site: https://www.dailycomet.com
Sales Range: $10-24.9 Million
Emp.: 30
Newspapers
N.A.I.C.S.: 513110
Lawrence Knoblock *(Mgr-Circulation)*
Mike Gorman *(Editor-Opinion)*
Julie Theriot *(Dir-Fin & Reg Mgr-Acctg)*
Peyvand Maghsoud *(Mgr-Digital Sls)*
Dan Shuman *(Reg Dir-Circulation)*
Keith Magill *(Exec Editor)*
Mike Hill *(Editor-Night City)*
Kelly McElroy *(Editor-Sports)*

Gainesville Sun Publishing Company (3)
2700 SW 13th St, Gainesville, FL 32608-2015 (100%)
Tel.: (352) 378-1411
Web Site: http://www.gainesville.com
Sales Range: $50-74.9 Million
Emp.: 200
Newspaper Publishing
N.A.I.C.S.: 513110
Rusty Jacobs *(Dir-Production)*
Chuck Mason *(Dir-IT)*
Douglas Ray *(Gen Mgr & Editor)*
Ben Howell *(Mgr-Home Delivery)*
Mickie Anderson *(Editor-Local News)*
Arnold Feliciano *(Editor-Sports)*
Gerard Walen *(Editor-Copy)*
Ken Gartin *(Mgr-Imaging)*
Criag Pressnell *(Mgr-Distr)*
Cleveland Tinker *(Editor-Guardian)*
Alan Festo *(Sr Editor-Copy)*
Vickie Williams *(Coord-Circulation)*
Robert Bolone *(Dir-Circulation)*
Maddie Mottle *(Coord-Events)*
Rynni Henderson *(Publr & Dir-Adv)*

Hendersonville Newspaper Corporation (3)
106 Henderson Crossing Plz, Hendersonville, NC 28792 (100%)
Tel.: (828) 692-0505
Web Site: https://www.blueridgenow.com
Sales Range: $10-24.9 Million
Emp.: 30
Newspaper Publishing
N.A.I.C.S.: 513110
Jennifer Heaslip *(Editor-News)*
Nancy Mullinax-Hogsed *(Reg Mgr-Classified Call Center)*
Dean Hensley *(Editor-Sports)*

Herald-Tribune Company (3)
1777 Main St, Sarasota, FL 34236-7824 (100%)
Tel.: (941) 953-7755
Web Site: https://www.heraldtribune.com
Sales Range: $100-124.9 Million
Emp.: 650
Newspaper Publishers

N.A.I.C.S.: 513110
Zac Anderson *(Editor-Political)*
Danny DeJarnette *(Editor-Night News)*
Kat Dow *(Editor-Copy)*
Jay Handelman *(Editor-Arts)*
John Howell *(Editor-Multimedia)*
Victor D. Hull *(Editor-Pub Interests)*
Barbara Peters Smith *(Editor-Opinions)*
Scott B. Peterson *(Editor-Sports)*
Brian Ries *(Editor-Digital)*
M. H. Syin *(Editor-Multimedia)*
Wade Tatangelo *(Editor-Entertainment)*
Lee Williams *(Editor-Topics)*
Ashley Deets *(Product Mgr-Digital)*
C. J. Finch *(Coord-Preprint)*
Roger Brown *(Editor-Opinion)*

Lakeland Ledger Publishing Corporation (3)
300 W Lime St, Lakeland, FL 33815-4731 (100%)
Tel.: (863) 802-7000
Web Site: https://www.theledger.com
Sales Range: $25-49.9 Million
Emp.: 350
Newspaper Publishers
N.A.I.C.S.: 513110
Sharon Schackne *(Dir-HR)*
Jeff Amero *(Mgr-Home Delivery Ops)*

Subsidiary (Domestic):

News Chief (4)
300 W Lime St, Lakeland, FL 33815
Tel.: (863) 401-6900
Web Site: https://www.newschief.com
Sales Range: $25-49.9 Million
Emp.: 60
Newspaper Publishers
N.A.I.C.S.: 513110

Subsidiary (Domestic):

Spartanburg Herald-Journal (3)
189 W Main St, Spartanburg, SC 29306
Tel.: (864) 582-4511
Web Site: https://www.goupstate.com
Sales Range: $75-99.9 Million
Emp.: 250
Daily Newspaper Publishing
N.A.I.C.S.: 513110
Jose Franco *(Editor-Magazine)*
Nick Foster *(Editor-Multimedia Copy)*
Linda Conley *(Editor-Features)*

The Dispatch Publishing Company, Inc. (3)
30 E 1st Ave, Lexington, NC 27292-3302 (100%)
Tel.: (336) 249-3981
Web Site: https://www.the-dispatch.com
Sales Range: $10-24.9 Million
Emp.: 25
Newspaper Publishing
N.A.I.C.S.: 513110
Mike Duprez *(Editor-Sports)*
Donnie Fetter *(Editor-Reg)*

The Gadsden Times (3)
251 S 4th St, Gadsden, AL 35901-3737
Tel.: (256) 549-2022
Web Site: https://www.gadsdentimes.com
Sales Range: $25-49.9 Million
Emp.: 50
Daily Newspaper
N.A.I.C.S.: 513110
Richard Davis *(Dir-Fin)*
Haley Rodgers *(Mgr-Ad Plng)*

The Houma Courier Newspaper Corporation (3)
3030 Barrow St, Houma, LA 70360 (100%)
Tel.: (985) 857-2222
Web Site: https://www.houmatoday.com
Sales Range: $25-49.9 Million
Emp.: 100
Newspaper Publishers
N.A.I.C.S.: 513110
Marian Long *(Dir-Adv)*

Unit (Domestic):

The Press Democrat (3)
416 B St Ste C, Santa Rosa, CA 95401-6313
Tel.: (707) 546-2020
Web Site: https://www.pressdemocrat.com
Sales Range: $25-49.9 Million
Emp.: 400
Daily Newspaper

Gannett Co., Inc.—(Continued)

N.A.I.C.S.: 513110
Rick Green (Exec Editor)

The Tuscaloosa News (3)
315 28th Ave, Tuscaloosa, AL 35401-1724
Tel.: (205) 345-0505
Web Site: https://www.tuscaloosanews.com
Sales Range: $100-124.9 Million
Emp.: 165
Daily Newspaper
N.A.I.C.S.: 424920

Subsidiary (Domestic):

Wilmington Star-News, Inc. (3)
115 N 3rd St Ste 400, Wilmington, NC
28401 (100%)
Tel.: (910) 343-2000
Web Site: https://www.starnewsonline.com
Sales Range: $75-99.9 Million
Emp.: 120
Newspaper Publishers
N.A.I.C.S.: 513110
Cheryl Theiss (Mgr-Adv Sls)

Unit (Domestic):

Havelock News (2)
230 Stonebridge Sq, Havelock, NC 28532
Tel.: (252) 444-1999
Web Site: http://www.havenews.com
Sales Range: $10-24.9 Million
Emp.: 5
Newspapers
N.A.I.C.S.: 513110
Chris Segal (Exec Editor)
Matt Hinson (Mng Editor)

News Herald (2)
500 W 11th St, Panama City, FL
32401-1940 (100%)
Tel.: (850) 747-5000
Web Site: https://www.newsherald.com
Sales Range: $10-24.9 Million
Emp.: 150
Newspapers
N.A.I.C.S.: 513110

Northwest Florida Daily News (2)
2 Eglin Pkwy NE, Fort Walton Beach, FL
32548 (100%)
Tel.: (850) 863-1111
Web Site: https://www.nwfdailynews.com
Sales Range: $1-9.9 Million
Emp.: 125
Newspapers
N.A.I.C.S.: 513110

Sun Journal (2)
3200 Wellon Blvd, New Bern, NC
28562-5234 (100%)
Tel.: (252) 638-8101
Web Site: https://www.newbernsj.com
Sales Range: $10-24.9 Million
Emp.: 50
Newspapers
N.A.I.C.S.: 513110
John McClure (Publr)

**The Daily News - Jacksonville,
NC** (2)
724 Bell Fork Rd, Jacksonville, NC 28540-
6311
Tel.: (910) 353-1171
Web Site: https://www.jdnews.com
Sales Range: $1-9.9 Million
Emp.: 175
Newspapers
N.A.I.C.S.: 513110
John McClure (Publr)

The Destin Log (2)
2 Eglin Pkwy NE, Fort Walton Beach, FL
32548
Tel.: (850) 837-2828
Web Site: https://www.thedestinlog.com
Sales Range: $10-24.9 Million
Emp.: 15
Newspapers
N.A.I.C.S.: 513110

The Free Press (2)
2103 N Queen St, Kinston, NC 28502
Tel.: (252) 527-3191
Web Site: https://www.kinston.com
Sales Range: $1-9.9 Million
Emp.: 50
Newspapers
N.A.I.C.S.: 513110

The Gaston Gazette (2)
1893 Remount Rd, Gastonia, NC 28054
Tel.: (704) 869-1823
Web Site: https://www.gastongazette.com
Sales Range: $10-24.9 Million
Emp.: 200
Newspapers
N.A.I.C.S.: 513110
Kevin Ellis (Mng Editor)

The Star (2)
315 E Graham St, Shelby, NC
28150 (100%)
Tel.: (704) 669-3350
Web Site: https://www.shelbystar.com
Sales Range: $10-24.9 Million
Emp.: 60
Newspapers
N.A.I.C.S.: 513110

The Times-News (2)
707 S Main St, Burlington, NC 27215
Tel.: (336) 227-0131
Web Site: https://www.thetimesnews.com
Sales Range: $125-149.9 Million
Emp.: 175
Newspapers
N.A.I.C.S.: 513110

The Topsail Advertiser (2)
206A S Topsail Dr, Surf City, NC 28445
Tel.: (910) 328-3033
Web Site: http://www.topsailadvertiser.com
Sales Range: $10-24.9 Million
Emp.: 5
Newspapers
N.A.I.C.S.: 513110

The Walton Sun (2)
5597 Hwy 98 W Ste 203, Santa Rosa
Beach, FL 32459
Tel.: (850) 267-4555
Web Site: http://www.waltonsun.com
Sales Range: $10-24.9 Million
Emp.: 2
Newspapers
N.A.I.C.S.: 513110

Subsidiary (Domestic):

**Worcester Telegram & Gazette
Corporation** (2)
100 Frnt St, Worcester, MA 01615
Tel.: (508) 793-9200
Web Site: https://www.telegram.com
Emp.: 175
Newspaper Publishers
N.A.I.C.S.: 513110
David Nordman (Exec Editor)
Michael Elfland (Editor-Breaking News)
Mark Conti (Editor-News-Days)
Winston Wiley (Editor-News-Nights)
Jim Wilson (Editor Sports)
Nancy Campbell (Editor-Features)
Andy Pagan (Coord-Digital Acct)

Subsidiary (Domestic):

Coulter Press (3)
114 Tpke Rd Ste 3, Chelmsford, MA 01824
Tel.: (978) 545-1050
Web Site: https://www.clintonitem.com
Sales Range: $10-24.9 Million
Emp.: 10
Newspaper Publishing
N.A.I.C.S.: 513110

Imagn Content Services, LLC (1)
1675 Broadway 23rd Fl, New York, NY
10019
Tel.: (646) 601-7202
Web Site: https://www.imagn.com
Media Production Services
N.A.I.C.S.: 512191
Bruce Odle (Pres)
Justin Weiss (VP-Sls)
Nick Carter (Sr Dir-Tech)
Jerry Lai (Sr Dir-Editorial Content)
Kristi Guerriero (Sr Mgr-Photo Ops)

Palm Beach Newspapers, LLC (1)
2751 S Dixie Hwy, West Palm Beach, FL
33405
Tel.: (561) 820-3800
Web Site:
https://www.palmbeachdailynews.com
Newspaper Publishers
N.A.I.C.S.: 513110
Carol Rose (Editor-News)

Starline Printing Company, LLLP (1)
7777 Jefferson St NE, Albuquerque, NM
87109
Tel.: (505) 345-8900
Web Site: https://www.starlineprinting.com
Commercial Printing Services
N.A.I.C.S.: 513191

SureWest Directories (1)
1225 Pleasant Grove Ste 140, Roseville,
CA 95678
Tel.: (916) 772-4000
Web Site:
https://www.surewestdirectories.com
Newspaper Publishing Services
N.A.I.C.S.: 513110

Tap-on-it, LLC (1)
5409 Victoria Ave, Davenport, IA 52807
Web Site: https://www.taponitdeals.com
Digital Marketing Services
N.A.I.C.S.: 541613

The Daily Independent, Inc. (1)
224 17th St, Ashland, KY 41101
Tel.: (606) 326-2600
Web Site: https://www.dailyindependent.com
Emp.: 95
Newspaper Publishing Services
N.A.I.C.S.: 513110
Lee Ward (Editor-Lifestyles)
Aaron Snyder (Editor)
Kim Harper (Mgr-Adv Sls)

ThriveHive, Inc. (1)
108 Myrtle St, Quincy, MA 02171
Tel.: (617) 249-2600
Web Site: https://localiq.com
Software Development Services
N.A.I.C.S.: 513210

Times Publishing Co. (1)
205 W 12th St, Erie, PA 16501
Tel.: (814) 870-1600
Web Site: https://www.goerie.com
Sales Range: $10-24.9 Million
Emp.: 175
Newspapers, Publishing & Printing
N.A.I.C.S.: 513110

UpCurve Cloud LLC (1)
10801 National Blvd Ste 410, Los Angeles,
CA 90064
Web Site: https://www.upcurvecloud.com
Business Management Services
N.A.I.C.S.: 561110

UpCurve, Inc. (1)
108 Myrtle St 6th Fl, Quincy, MA 02171
Tel.: (617) 706-9010
Web Site: http://www.upcurve.com
Advertising Services
N.A.I.C.S.: 541810
Bill Scanlon (CFO)
Nilay Gandhi (Pres)

ViWo LLC (1)
19 Spear Rd Ste 101, Ramsey, NJ 07446
Web Site: https://www.upcurvecloud.com
Software Development Services
N.A.I.C.S.: 513210

GARDINER HEALTHCARE AC-QUISITIONS CORP.

3107 Warrington Rd, Shaker Heights,
OH 44120
Tel.: (216) 633-6708 DE
Web Site:
https://www.gardinerhealthcare.com
Year Founded: 2021
GDNR—(NASDAQ)
Rev.: $2,445,784
Assets: $20,563,541
Liabilities: $22,051,205
Net Worth: ($1,487,664)
Earnings: $442,188
Emp.: 3
Fiscal Year-end: 12/31/22
Investment Services
N.A.I.C.S.: 523999
Marc F. Pelletier (CEO & Chm)
Paul R. McGuirk (Chief Dev Officer &
Exec VP)

GARTNER, INC.

56 Top Gallant Rd, Stamford, CT
06902-7700
Tel.: (203) 964-0096 DE
Web Site: https://www.gartner.com
Year Founded: 1979
IT—(NYSE)
Rev.: $5,906,956,000
Assets: $7,835,919,000
Liabilities: $7,155,285,000
Net Worth: $680,634,000
Earnings: $882,466,000
Emp.: 20,237
Fiscal Year-end: 12/31/23
Research & Advisory Services to the
Information Technology Industry
N.A.I.C.S.: 551114
Eugene A. Hall (Chm & CEO)
Robin B. Kranich (Chief HR Officer &
Exec VP)
Craig W. Safian (CFO & Exec VP)
Joe Beck (Exec VP-Tech Sls-Global)
Michael P. Diliberto (CIO & Exec VP)
Scott Hensel (Exec VP-Delivery &
Svcs-Global)
Yvonne Genovese (Exec VP-Global
Product Mgmt)
Claire Herkes (Exec VP-Conferences)
Akhil Jain (Exec VP-Consulting)
Thomas Kim (Gen Counsel, Sec & Sr
VP)
Val Sribar (Sr VP-Res & Advisory)
Jim Wartinbee (Sr VP-Global Sls
Strategy & Ops)
Ken Allard (CMO & Exec VP)
Alwyn Dawkins (Exec VP-Global Bus
Sls)

Subsidiaries:

CEB LLC. (1)
1919 N Lynn St, Arlington, VA 22209
Tel.: (571) 303-3000
Rev.: $949,794,000
Assets: $1,412,592,000
Liabilities: $1,587,522,000
Net Worth: ($174,930,000)
Earnings: ($34,658,000)
Emp.: 4,900
Fiscal Year-end: 12/31/2016
Business Research & Analysis Services
N.A.I.C.S.: 541611

Subsidiary (Domestic):

Evanta Ventures, Inc. (2)
Koin Tower 222 SW Columbia Ste 950,
Portland, OR 97201
Tel.: (503) 445-6600
Web Site: https://www.evanta.com
Corporate Management Consulting Services
& Leadership Forum Organizer
N.A.I.C.S.: 541611
Katy Brown (VP-Global Communities)

Iconoculture, Inc. (2)
244 1st Ave N Ste 200, Minneapolis, MN
55401
Tel.: (612) 642-2222
Sales Range: $10-24.9 Million
Emp.: 95
Consumer Trend Research & Advisory Ser-
vices
N.A.I.C.S.: 541910

Capterra, Inc. (1)
1201 Wilson Blvd 9th Fl, Arlington, VA
22209
Tel.: (703) 584-1700
Web Site: http://www.capterra.com
Online Software Marketing Services
N.A.I.C.S.: 513140

Gartner Australasia Pty. Ltd. (1)
Level 18 40 Mount Street, North Sydney,
2060, NSW, Australia (100%)
Tel.: (61) 294594600
Web Site: http://www.gartner.com
Sales Range: $25-49.9 Million
Emp.: 150
Information Technology Research & Advi-
sory Services
N.A.I.C.S.: 517810

Unit (Domestic):

Gartner Australia - Brisbane (2)

Christie SpacesLevel 3240 Queen St, Brisbane, 4000, QLD, Australia
Tel.: (61) 294594600
Web Site: http://www.gartner.com
Information Technology Research & Advisory Services
N.A.I.C.S.: 519290
Elizabeth Dashwood *(Mgr)*

Gartner Australia - Canberra　(2)
Level 310 National Circuit, Barton, Canberra, 2600, ACT, Australia
Tel.: (61) 261475200
Web Site: http://www.gartner.com
Information Technology Research & Advisory Services
N.A.I.C.S.: 519290

Gartner Australia - Melbourne　(2)
Level 20357 Collins Street, Melbourne, 3000, VIC, Australia
Tel.: (61) 392222600
Web Site: http://www.gartner.com
Information Technology Research & Advisory Services
N.A.I.C.S.: 519290
Elizabeth Dashwood *(Mgr)*

Subsidiary (Domestic):

Ideas International Limited　(2)
Level 3 20 George St, Hornsby, 2077, NSW, Australia
Tel.: (61) 294727777
Web Site: http://www.ideasinternational.com
Sales Range: $25-49.9 Million
Emp.: 43
Enterprise IT, Research & Analyst Services
N.A.I.C.S.: 561499
Stephen Williams *(Sr VP & Gen Mgr-EMEA)*
Peter Cullen *(Sr VP-Product Dev & Info Svcs)*
Gary Burgess *(Sr VP)*
Stephen Bowhill *(CEO)*
Chris Ober *(Sr VP)*

Gartner Austria GmbH　(1)
Karntner Str 25, 1010, Vienna, Austria
Tel.: (43) 1 533 2350
Web Site: https://www.gartner.com
Emp.: 15
Information Technology Research & Advisory Services
N.A.I.C.S.: 541611

Gartner Beijing　(1)
F8 Building B Parkview Green FangCaoDi No 9 Dongdaqiao Road, Beijing, 100020, Chaoyang, China
Tel.: (86) 1058960888
Web Site: http://www.gartner.com
Information Technology Research & Advisory Services
N.A.I.C.S.: 541910

Gartner Belgium BVBA　(1)
Corporate Village Building Figueras L Da Vincilaan 11, 1930, Zaventem, Belgium
Tel.: (32) 27255959
Web Site: http://www.gartner.com
Emp.: 60
Information Technology Research & Advisory Services
N.A.I.C.S.: 541611

Gartner Canada Co.　(1)
5700 Yonge St 14th Floor Suite 1402, Toronto, M2M 7E9, ON, Canada
Tel.: (416) 222-7900
Information Technology Research & Advisory Services
N.A.I.C.S.: 541611

Gartner Czech Republic s.r.o.　(1)
Arbes Building Stefanikova 32, 150 00, Prague, Czech Republic
Tel.: (420) 257322524
Web Site: https://kpc-group.cz
Information Technology Consulting Services
N.A.I.C.S.: 541512

Gartner Danmark ApS　(1)
Kalvebod Brygge 45 3rd Floor, 1560, Copenhagen, Denmark
Tel.: (45) 45586400
Information Technology Services
N.A.I.C.S.: 541519

Gartner Espana, S.L.　(1)
Edificio Piramide Paseo de la Castellana 31 7th floor, 28046, Madrid, Spain
Tel.: (34) 911144700
Information Technology Research & Advisory Services
N.A.I.C.S.: 541611

Gartner Finland Oy　(1)
Keilaranta 15, 02150, Espoo, Finland
Tel.: (358) 92515500
Market Analysis & Research Services
N.A.I.C.S.: 541910

Gartner France S.A.R.L.　(1)
Tour Europlaza Defense 4 20 Avenue Andre Prothin La Def, 92737, Paris, 92737, France
Tel.: (33) 171013100
Information Technology Research & Advisory Services
N.A.I.C.S.: 541611

Gartner Hong Kong, Limited　(1)
Suite 2204-6 22/F Berkshire House 25 Westlands Road, 25 Westlands Road, Quarry Bay, China (Hong Kong)　(100%)
Tel.: (852) 3 402 0402
Web Site: https://www.gartner.com
Sales Range: $10-24.9 Million
Emp.: 20
Marketing Research & Analysis
N.A.I.C.S.: 541910

Gartner Israel Advisory Ltd.　(1)
10 Ha-Menofim St 3rd Floor, PO Box 12956, Herzliya Pituach, 4672561, Israel
Tel.: (972) 772203663
Information Technology Research & Advisory Services
N.A.I.C.S.: 541611

Gartner Italia, S.r.l.　(1)
Via Caldera 21 Edif E-Ala 2, 20153, Milan, Italy
Tel.: (39) 02482891
Sales Range: $25-49.9 Million
Emp.: 40
Information Technology Research & Advisory Services
N.A.I.C.S.: 541611

Gartner Japan Ltd.　(1)
Atago Green Hills MORI Tower 5F 2-5-1, Atago Minato-ku, Tokyo, 105-6205, Japan　(100%)
Tel.: (81) 364301800
Web Site: http://www.gartner.com
Sales Range: $25-49.9 Million
Emp.: 150
N.A.I.C.S.: 541910

Gartner Nederland B.V.　(1)
De Entree 79 - 16th Floor, 1101 BH, Amsterdam, Netherlands
Tel.: (31) 203144144
Web Site: http://www.gartner.com
Sales Range: $25-49.9 Million
Emp.: 90
Information Technology Research & Advisory Services
N.A.I.C.S.: 541611

Gartner Poland SP z.o.o　(1)
Regus Skylight XIV floor Ul Zlota 59, 00-120, Warsaw, Poland
Tel.: (48) 224577688
Market Analysis & Research Services
N.A.I.C.S.: 541910

Gartner RUS LLC　(1)
Level 6 Butyrsky Val Ulltsa 10, 125047, Moscow, Russia
Tel.: (7) 4957401266
Web Site: http://www.gartner.com
Emp.: 20
Market Analysis & Research Services
N.A.I.C.S.: 541910

Gartner Research & Advisory Korea Co., Ltd.　(1)
Suite 2407 Trade Tower 511 Yeongdong-daero, Gangnam-Gu, Seoul, 06164, Korea (South)
Tel.: (82) 234105300
Web Site: http://www.gartner.com
Leading Research & Advisory Company; Information Technology Research & Advisory Services
N.A.I.C.S.: 541611

Gartner Saudi Arabia Ltd　(1)
Laysen Valley Building 13 Level 3 Umm Al Hamam Al Gharbi, PO Box 231772, Office 404, Riyadh, 11321, Saudi Arabia
Tel.: (966) 112074130
Market Analysis & Research Services
N.A.I.C.S.: 541910

Gartner Sverige AB　(1)
Gustav Ills Boulevard 54, 169 74, Solna, Sweden
Tel.: (46) 86246300
Web Site: http://www.gartner.com
Emp.: 184
Information Technology Research & Advisory Services
N.A.I.C.S.: 541611
Anne Hanson *(CEO)*

Gartner Turkey Teknoloji Arastirma ve Danismanlik Hizmetleri Limited Sirketi　(1)
Trump Towers KustepeMah, Mecidi-yekoyYolu Cad No 12 Kule 2 Kat 18, Istanbul, 34387, Turkiye
Tel.: (90) 2123063163
Market Analysis & Research Services
N.A.I.C.S.: 541910

Gartner U.K. Limited　(1)
Tamesis The Glanty, Egham, TW20 9AH, Surrey, United Kingdom
Tel.: (44) 1784431611
Web Site: http://www.gartner.com
Market Analysis & Research Services
N.A.I.C.S.: 541910

Subsidiary (Domestic):

Wentworth Research Limited　(2)
Tamesis the Glanty, Egham, TW20 9AH, Surrey, United Kingdom
Tel.: (44) 1784431611
Web Site: http://www.gartner.com
Information Technology Research & Advisory Services
N.A.I.C.S.: 541611

Software Advice, Inc.　(1)
200 Academy Dr Ste 120, Austin, TX 78704
Tel.: (512) 539-0017
Web Site: http://www.softwareadvice.com
Sales Range: $1-9.9 Million
Emp.: 100
Computers Hardware, Software & Services
N.A.I.C.S.: 423430
Blake Clark *(Gen Mgr)*

The Research Board, Inc.　(1)
1325 Ave of the Americas 17th Fl, New York, NY 10019
Tel.: (212) 632-7600
Web Site: http://www.researchboard.com
Emp.: 56
Information Technology Research & Advisory Services
N.A.I.C.S.: 541611
Brendan J. Conway *(VP & Program Dir)*

GATEKEEPER USA, INC.
23235 Lake Dr, Lexington Park, MD 20653
Tel.: (631) 499-3684　　NV
Web Site:
　http://www.gatekeeperusainc.com
Year Founded: 2002
GTKP—(OTCIQ)
Sales Range: Less than $1 Million
Maritime Container Security Services
N.A.I.C.S.: 561601
James W. Wishart *(Chm & CEO)*
Nicholas Canakakis *(VP-Bus Dev-Europe)*
A. John Leontakianakos *(Sr VP-Fin)*
Trevor E. Holewinski *(Dir-IT)*
Michael Bilirakis *(Dir-Advisory)*
Randal Null *(Dir-Advisory)*
Sterling Mortensen *(Dir-Advisory)*
Bernard Rudnick *(Dir-Advisory)*

GATOS SILVER, INC.
8400 E Crescent Pkwy Ste 600, Greenwood Village, CO 80111
Tel.: (303) 784-5350　　DE
Web Site: http://www.gatossilver.com
Year Founded: 2011
GATO—(NYSE)
Rev.: $38,767,000

Assets: $400,904,000
Liabilities: $33,357,000
Net Worth: $367,547,000
Earnings: $12,860,000
Emp.: 901
Fiscal Year-end: 12/31/23
Metal Exploration Services
N.A.I.C.S.: 213114
Dale E. Andres *(CEO)*
Janice Alayne Stairs *(Chm)*
Andre Van Niekerk *(CFO)*
Luis Felipe Huerta *(VP-Mexico)*
Adam Dubas *(Chief Admin Officer)*
Rodrigo Monroy *(Gen Counsel)*
Nicolas Vachon *(VP-Fin)*
Tony Scott *(VP-Evaluations & Technical Svcs)*
James Woeller *(VP-Corp Dev & Bus Improvement)*

Subsidiaries:

Gatos Silver Canada Corporation　(1)
925 W Georgia Street Suite 910, Vancouver, V6C 3L2, BC, Canada
Tel.: (604) 424-0984
Web Site: https://gatossilver.com
Silver Mining Services
N.A.I.C.S.: 212220

GATX CORPORATION
233 S Wacker Dr, Chicago, IL 60606-7147
Tel.: (312) 621-6200　　NY
Web Site: https://www.gatx.com
Year Founded: 1898
GATX—(NYSE)
Rev.: $1,273,000,000
Assets: $10,072,000,000
Liabilities: $8,042,400,000
Net Worth: $2,029,600,000
Earnings: $155,900,000
Emp.: 1,904
Fiscal Year-end: 12/31/22
Holding Company; Financial Services & Management of Railroad Tank Cars & Specialized Railcars
N.A.I.C.S.: 551112
Robert A. Zmudka *(Chief Comm Officer-Rail-North America & Sr VP)*
Thomas A. Ellman *(CFO & Exec VP)*
Irma Dominguez *(Coord-IR)*
Kevin J. Hillesland *(Sr VP-Structured Fin)*
Jennifer L. Van Aken *(Chief Risk Officer, Treas & Sr VP)*
Robert C. Lyons *(Pres & CEO)*
Jennifer M. McManus *(Chief Acctg Officer, Sr VP & Controller)*
Niyi A. Adedoyin *(Sr VP)*
Jeffery R. Young *(Chief Tax Officer & Sr VP)*
Shari Hellerman *(Sr Dir-IR, ESG, and External Comm)*
Brian L. Glassberg *(Gen Counsel, Sec & Exec VP)*
M. Kim Nero *(Chief HR Officer)*
Geoffrey D. Phillips *(Sr VP-Ops)*
John M. Sbragia *(Sr VP-Engrg & Quality)*

Subsidiaries:

GATX Corporation　(1)
233 S Wacker Dr, Chicago, IL 60606　(100%)
Tel.: (312) 621-6200
Web Site: https://www.gatx.com
Rev.: $217,000,000
Emp.: 47
Owns, Leases & Finances Capital Equipment
N.A.I.C.S.: 522299

GATX Global Finance B.V.　(1)
Schiphol Boulevard 231, 1118 BH, Schiphol, Netherlands
Tel.: (31) 885609950
Web Site: http://www.vistra.com
Financial Services

GATX Corporation—(Continued)
N.A.I.C.S.: 541611

GATX Rail (1)
222 W Adam St, Chicago, IL
60606 (100%)
Tel.: (312) 621-6200
Web Site: http://www.gatx.com
Rev.: $700,000,000
Emp.: 300
Sells & Service Leases Tank Cars & Specialty Freight Cars; Sells Rail Car Management & Maintenance Services; Storage & Handling of Bulk Liquids; Refined Petroleum Pipelines
N.A.I.C.S.: 532411

GATX Rail Austria GmbH (1)
Am Europlatz 5 Building C, 1120, Vienna, Austria
Tel.: (43) 186566850
Web Site: https://www.gatx.eu
Truck Trailer Rental & Leasing Services
N.A.I.C.S.: 532411
Joerg Nowaczyk *(Chief Comml Officer)*
Christopher LaHurd *(VP)*

GATX Rail Canada (1)
1801 Avenue McGill College Bureau 1475, Montreal, H3A 2N4, QC, Canada
Tel.: (514) 931-7343
Web Site: http://www.gatx.com
Sales Range: $10-24.9 Million
Emp.: 5
Rail Services
N.A.I.C.S.: 532411

GATX Rail Germany GmbH (1)
Emporio Tower Valentinskamp 70, 20355, Hamburg, Germany
Tel.: (49) 40368040
Railcar Leasing Services
N.A.I.C.S.: 532411

GAUCHO GROUP HOLDINGS, INC.
112 NE 41st St Ste 106, Miami, FL 33137
Tel.: (212) 739-7700
Web Site: https://www.gaucho.com
Year Founded: 1999
VINO—(NASDAQ)
Rev.: $1,643,716
Assets: $18,692,985
Liabilities: $7,901,304
Net Worth: $10,791,681
Earnings: ($21,753,037)
Emp.: 80
Fiscal Year-end: 12/31/22
Other Activities Related to Real Estate
N.A.I.C.S.: 531390
Scott L. Mathis *(Chm, Pres & CEO)*
Maria I. Echevarria *(CFO, COO, Chief Acctg Officer, Officer-Compliance, Treas & Sec)*
Brian J. Stern *(Sr Mng Dir-Venture Capital)*
Eric Stear *(Dir-Mktg)*
Gregory Gassoso *(Sr Mng Dir-Real Estate Dev)*
Ignacio Goldin *(VP-Ops-Argentina)*
Keith T. Fasano *(Sr Mng Dir)*

GAXOS.AI INC.
101 Eisenhower Pkwy Ste 300, Roseland, NJ 07006
Tel.: (973) 275-7428   DE
Web Site: https://www.gaxos.ai
Year Founded: 2021
GXAI—(NASDAQ)
Rev.: $2,924
Assets: $941,427
Liabilities: $255,694
Net Worth: $685,733
Earnings: ($1,421,172)
Emp.: 3
Fiscal Year-end: 12/31/22
Software Development Services
N.A.I.C.S.: 541511
Steven A. Shorr *(CFO)*
Vadim Mats *(CEO)*

GB SCIENCES, INC.
9205 W Russell Rd Ste 240, Las Vegas, NV 89148   DE
Web Site:
  https://www.gbsciences.com
GBLX—(OTCQB)
Rev.: $100,000
Assets: $352,323
Liabilities: $4,759,706
Net Worth: ($4,407,383)
Earnings: ($4,125,194)
Emp.: 3
Fiscal Year-end: 03/31/23
Indoor Agriculture Technology for Medical Cannabis Industry
N.A.I.C.S.: 115112
Andrea Small-Howard *(Pres & Chief Scientific Officer)*
John Claybron Poss *(CEO, Interim CFO & Chm)*

GBT TECHNOLOGIES INC.
8557 N West Knoll Dr, West Hollywood, CA 90069
Tel.: (424) 257-0198   NV
Web Site: https://gbtti.com
Year Founded: 2009
GTCH—(OTCIQ)
Rev.: $1,197,555
Assets: $370,625
Liabilities: $19,201,534
Net Worth: ($18,830,909)
Earnings: $5,323,856
Emp.: 4
Fiscal Year-end: 12/31/22
Applications Software
N.A.I.C.S.: 513210
Mansour Khatib *(CEO & CFO)*
Danny Rittman *(CIO, CTO & Chief Security Officer)*

GCM GROSVENOR INC.
900 N Michigan Ave Ste 1100, Chicago, IL 60611
Tel.: (312) 506-6500   DE
Web Site:
  https://www.gcmgrosvenor.com
Year Founded: 2020
GCMG—(NASDAQ)
Rev.: $446,530,000
Assets: $488,933,000
Liabilities: $582,939,000
Net Worth: ($94,006,000)
Earnings: $19,820,000
Emp.: 529
Fiscal Year-end: 12/31/22
Holding Company
N.A.I.C.S.: 551112
Pamela L. Bentley *(CFO & Mng Dir-Fin)*
J. B. Kiley *(Mng Dir-Client Grp)*
Kevin C. Nickelberry *(Mng Dir & Co-Head-Private Equity Co-Investments)*
Michael J. Sacks *(Chm & CEO)*
Jonathan R. Levin *(Pres)*

Subsidiaries:

CF Finance Acquisition Corp. (1)
110 E 59th St, New York, NY 10022
Tel.: (212) 938-5000
Rev.: $3,007,000
Assets: $186,153,000
Liabilities: $17,386,000
Net Worth: $168,767,000
Earnings: ($65,011,000)
Emp.: 100
Fiscal Year-end: 12/31/2021
Investment Services
N.A.I.C.S.: 523999

GCM Grosvenor Holdings (Canada) ULC (1)
TD Canada Trust Tower 161 Bay Street 27th Fl, Brookfield Place, Toronto, M5J 2S1, ON, Canada
Tel.: (647) 417-7361
Asset Management Services
N.A.I.C.S.: 523940

GCM Investments Hong Kong Limited (1)
Two International Finance Centre Suites 5714-15, 57/F 8 Finance Street, Central, China (Hong Kong)
Tel.: (852) 24529400
Asset Management Services
N.A.I.C.S.: 523940

GCM Investments Japan K.K. (1)
Roppongi First Building 1-9-9, Roppongi Minato-ku, Tokyo, 106-0032, Japan
Tel.: (81) 355738110
Asset Management Services
N.A.I.C.S.: 523940

GCM Investments UK LLP (1)
33 Jermyn Street, Level Seven, London, SW1Y 6DN, United Kingdom
Tel.: (44) 2037274450
Asset Management Services
N.A.I.C.S.: 523940

GCT SEMICONDUCTOR HOLDING, INC.
477 Madison Ave, New York, NY 10022
Tel.: (212) 883-4330   DE
GCTS—(NYSE)
Emp.: 100
Investment Services
N.A.I.C.S.: 523999

Subsidiaries:

GCT Semiconductor, Inc. (1)
2121 Ringwood Ave, San Jose, CA 95131
Tel.: (408) 434-6040
Web Site: https://www.gctsemi.com
Sales Range: $50-74.9 Million
Emp.: 203
Semiconductor & Related Device Mfr
N.A.I.C.S.: 334413
Gene Kulzer *(CFO & Chief Admin Officer)*
Kyeongho H. Lee *(Founder)*
John Schlaefer *(CEO)*
Jeongmin Kim *(CTO & VP-Engrg)*

Subsidiary (Non-US):

GCT Research, Inc. (2)
Specialty Construction Center B/D 10F & 11F 395-70 Shindaebang Dong, Dongjak Gu, Seoul, 156-714, Korea (South)
Tel.: (82) 221671100
Web Site: http://www.gctsemi.com
Emp.: 200
Semiconductor Research & Development
N.A.I.C.S.: 541715

GDL FUND
1 Corporate Ctr, Rye, NY 10580-1434
Tel.: (914) 921-5100   DE
GDL—(NYSE)
Fund Management Services
N.A.I.C.S.: 523940
Mario J. Gabelli *(Chief Investment Officer)*

GE HEALTHCARE TECHNOLOGIES INC.
500 W Monroe St, Chicago, IL 60661
Tel.: (617) 443-3400   DE
Web Site:
  https://www.gehealthcare.com
Year Founded: 2022
GEHC—(NASDAQ)
Rev.: $19,552,000,000
Assets: $32,454,000,000
Liabilities: $25,309,000,000
Net Worth: $7,145,000,000
Earnings: $1,385,000,000
Emp.: 51,000
Fiscal Year-end: 12/31/23
Healtcare Services
N.A.I.C.S.: 621610
Taha Kass-Hout *(CTO)*
Peter J. Arduini *(Pres)*
Frank R. Jimenez *(CEO)*
James K. Saccaro *(CFO & VP)*

Subsidiaries:

BK Medical Australia Pty Ltd. (1)
G 01 4 Talavera Rd, Macquarie Park, 2113, NSW, Australia
Tel.: (61) 288170447
Surgical & Medical Product Distr
N.A.I.C.S.: 423450

BK Medical Austria GmbH (1)
Inkustrasse 1-7 Stiege 7 Haus G, 3400, Klosterneuburg, Austria
Tel.: (43) 224323991
Surgical & Medical Product Distr
N.A.I.C.S.: 423450

BK Medical France SAS (1)
8 Rue Joseph Nicephore Niepce, 69740, Genas, France
Tel.: (33) 437545993
Surgical & Medical Product Distr
N.A.I.C.S.: 423450

BK Medical Holding Company, Inc. (1)
25 Corporate Dr Ste 230, Burlington, MA 01803
Web Site: https://www.bkmedical.com
Surgical & Medical Product Distr
N.A.I.C.S.: 423450

BK Medical Italia S.r.l. (1)
Via R Morandi 10, Melegnano, 20077, Milan, Italy
Tel.: (39) 0290781347
Surgical & Medical Product Distr
N.A.I.C.S.: 423450

BK Medical Schweiz GmbH (1)
Charmerstrasse 172, 6300, Zug, Switzerland
Tel.: (41) 415629870
Surgical & Medical Product Distr
N.A.I.C.S.: 423450

BK Medical Sweden AB (1)
Vastberga Alle 26 3tr, Hagersten, 126 30, Stockholm, Sweden
Tel.: (46) 87440211
Surgical & Medical Product Distr
N.A.I.C.S.: 423450

BK Medical Technology Shanghai Co., Ltd. (1)
Room 602 Building 2 No 1 Alley 777 Wanrong Road, Jingan District, Shanghai, 20072, China
Tel.: (86) 8009881516
Surgical & Medical Product Distr
N.A.I.C.S.: 423450

BK Medical UK Limited (1)
Unit 2 Ground Floor Hampton Industrial Estate Wassage Way, Hampton Lovett, Droitwich, Wr9 0NX, Worcestershire, United Kingdom
Tel.: (44) 1264568686
Surgical & Medical Product Distr
N.A.I.C.S.: 423450

GE BE Private Ltd. (1)
60 Export Promotion Industrial Park Whitefield, Bengaluru, 560 066, Karnataka, India
Tel.: (91) 8040785000
Health Care Management Services
N.A.I.C.S.: 621491

GE HealthCare Korea, Inc. (1)
15th Floor Seoul Square 416 Hangangdaero, Jung-gu, Seoul, 04637, Korea (South)
Tel.: (82) 262013114
Web Site: https://www.gehealthcare.co.kr
Health Care Management Services
N.A.I.C.S.: 621491

GE Healthcare AB (1)
Vendevagen 89, 182 11, Danderyd, Sweden
Tel.: (46) 855950400
Health Care Management Services
N.A.I.C.S.: 621491

GE Healthcare Algerie SARL (1)
11 boulevard du 11 Decembre Bt 03 Val dhydra, El Biar, 16035, Hydra, Algeria
Tel.: (213) 21796363
Health Care Management Services

N.A.I.C.S.: 621491

GE Healthcare Buchler GmbH & Co. KG (1)
Oskar-Schlemmer-Str 11, 80807, Munich, Germany
Tel.: (49) 89962810
Health Care Management Services
N.A.I.C.S.: 621491

GE Healthcare Cote d'Ivoire SARL (1)
Immeuble Green Buro-Rez de Chaussee
Rue Viviane-Cocody Ambassade, Abidjan, Cote d'Ivoire
Tel.: (225) 22402541
Health Care Management Services
N.A.I.C.S.: 621491

GE Healthcare Danmark A/S (1)
Park Alle 295, 2605, Brondby, Denmark
Tel.: (45) 43295400,
Health Care Management Services
N.A.I.C.S.: 621491

GE Healthcare GmbH (1)
Beethovenstr 239, 42655, Solingen, Germany
Tel.: (49) 21228020
Health Care Management Services
N.A.I.C.S.: 621491

GE Healthcare Handels GmbH (1)
Technologiestrasse 10 Europlaza Gebaude E, A-1120, Vienna, Austria
Tel.: (43) 1972720
Health Care Management Services
N.A.I.C.S.: 621491

GE Healthcare Kenya Limited (1)
The Courtyard Building General Mathenge Drive-Westlands, PO Box 41608-00100, Nairobi, Kenya
Tel.: (254) 204215000
Health Care Management Services
N.A.I.C.S.: 621491

GE Healthcare Limited (1)
Amersham Place, Little Chalfont, HP7 9NA, Buckinghamshire, United Kingdom
Tel.: (44) 1494544000
Web Site: https://www.gehealthcare.co.uk
Sales Range: $15-24.9 Billion
Emp.: 42,500
Medical Imaging Technologies, Medical Diagnostics, Patient Monitoring Systems, Drug Discovery & Biopharmaceutical Manufacturing Technologies Developer
N.A.I.C.S.: 541714
Kieran P. Murphy (Pres & CEO)
Thomas Westrick (Chief Quality Officer & VP)
Michael Stockhammer (Mng Dir)
Helmut Zodl (CFO & VP)
Katya Kruglova (VP-HR)
Michael McAlevey (Gen Counsel & VP)
Amit Phadnis (Chief Digital Officer & VP)
Ian Dale (Chief Supply Chain Officer)
Laila Gurney (Chief Quality & Regulatory Officer)
Steve Laurent (CIO)
Greg Gibbons (Chief Comm Officer)

Subsidiary (Non-US):

GE Healthcare AS (2)
Nycoveien 1, PO Box 4220, Nydalen, 0401, Oslo, Norway
Tel.: (47) 23185050
Web Site: http://www.gehealthcare.in
Healthcare Information Technology Consulting Services
N.A.I.C.S.: 541512

Subsidiary (Domestic):

GE Healthcare Bio-Sciences (2)
Amersham Place, Little Chalfont, HP7 9NA, Buckinghamshire, United Kingdom
Tel.: (44) 1494544000
Web Site: http://www.gehealthcare.com
Sales Range: $1-4.9 Billion
Emp.: 2,000
Contrast Imaging Agents Mfr
N.A.I.C.S.: 325180
John Flannery (CEO)

Subsidiary (Non-US):

GE Healthcare Bio-Sciences AB (3)
Bjorkgatan 30, 751 25, Uppsala, Sweden

Tel.: (46) 18 6120000
Web Site: http://www.gehealthcare.com
Sales Range: $75-99.9 Million
Emp.: 1,200
Infrared Optical Lens Mfr
N.A.I.C.S.: 334516
Bo Lundstrom (Mng Dir)

GE Healthcare Bio-Sciences Europe GmbH (3)
Munzinger Str 5, 79111, Freiburg, Germany
Tel.: (49) 8009080711
Web Site: https://www.gehealthcare.de
Sales Range: $250-299.9 Million
Emp.: 550
Contrast Imaging Agents Mfr
N.A.I.C.S.: 325180

GE Healthcare Japan Corporation (3)
4-7-127 Asahigaoka, Hino, Tokyo, 191-8503, Japan
Tel.: (81) 12 018 7855
Web Site: https://www.gehealthcare.co.jp.
Emp.: 1,700
Pharmaceuticals Whslr
N.A.I.C.S.: 424210
Hiroko Watanate (Mng Dir)

Subsidiary (US):

GE Healthcare Financial Services (2)
1 Beacon St 2nd Fl, Boston, MA 02109-1803
Tel.: (866) 217-0300
Sales Range: $25-49.9 Million
Emp.: 132
Financing to Medical & Dental Practices
N.A.I.C.S.: 532283
Catherine Estrampes (CEO)

Subsidiary (Non-US):

GE Healthcare Finland Oy (2)
Kuortaneenkatu 2, 00510, Helsinki, Finland
Tel.: (358) 1039411
Web Site: https://www.gehealthcare.fi
Sales Range: $200-249.9 Million
Emp.: 1,000
Medical & Surgical Instrument Mfr
N.A.I.C.S.: 339112
Terho Hoskonen (Mng Dir)

Subsidiary (US):

GE Medical Systems Information Technologies, Inc. (2)
8200 W Tower Ave, Milwaukee, WI 53223
Tel.: (414) 355-5000
Emp.: 3,125
Medical Ultrasound Equipment Mfr
N.A.I.C.S.: 334510

GE Medical Systems, Inc. (2)
3000 Grandview Blvd, Waukesha, WI 53188
Tel.: (262) 544-3011
Custom Computer Programming Services
N.A.I.C.S.: 541511

OEC Medical Systems, Inc. (2)
640 Wright Brothers Dr, Salt Lake City, UT 84116
Tel.: (801) 536-4891
Emp.: 715
Medical & Surgical Equipment Mfr & Distr
N.A.I.C.S.: 339112

U-Systems, Inc. (2)
447 Indio Way, Sunnyvale, CA 94085
Tel.: (408) 245-1970
Web Site: http://www.u-systems.com
Sales Range: $1-9.9 Million
Emp.: 41
All Other Miscellaneous Electrical Equipment & Component Mfr
N.A.I.C.S.: 335999

Subsidiary (Domestic):

Whatman International Ltd. (2)
Springfield Mill, James Whatman Way, Maidstone, ME14 2LE, Kent, United Kingdom
Tel.: (44) 1622676670
Web Site: http://www.whatman.com
Sales Range: $300-349.9 Million
Emp.: 101

Laboratory Sample Preparation & Filtration Equipment Mfr
N.A.I.C.S.: 334516

GE Healthcare Magyarorszag Kft. (1)
Vaci Greens Building C, Bence u 3, 1138, Budapest, Hungary
Tel.: (36) 14797100
Web Site: https://www.gehealthcare.hu
Health Care Management Services
N.A.I.C.S.: 621491

GE Healthcare Pharma Limited (1)
4-10-18 Takanawa, Minato-ku, Tokyo, 108-0074, Japan
Tel.: (81) 120241454
Pharmaceutical Product Mfr & Distr
N.A.I.C.S.: 325412

GE Healthcare Sverige AB (1)
Vendevagen 89, 182 11, Danderyd, Sweden
Tel.: (46) 855950010
Health Care Management Services
N.A.I.C.S.: 621491

GE Healthcare Tunisia SARL (1)
Les Jardins du Lac / Les Bergers du Lac II, 1053, Tunis, Tunisia
Tel.: (216) 70019096
Health Care Management Services
N.A.I.C.S.: 621491

GE Medical Systems (Schweiz) AG (1)
Europastrasse 31, CH-8152, Glattbrugg, Switzerland
Tel.: (41) 448099292
Health Care Management Services
N.A.I.C.S.: 621491

GE Medical Systems Global Technology Company, LLC (1)
3000 N Grandview Blvd, Waukesha, WI 53188
Tel.: (262) 544-3011
Web Site: http://www.gehealthcare.com
Sales Range: $900-999.9 Million
Diagnostic Imaging Equipment & Accessories Mfr
N.A.I.C.S.: 334517

GE Medical Systems Limited (1)
Pollards Wood Nightingales Lane, Chalfont Saint Giles, HP8 4SP, Buckinghamshire, United Kingdom
Tel.: (44) 1494544000
Health Care Management Services
N.A.I.C.S.: 621491

GE Medical Systems Polska Sp. z o.o. (1)
Ul Woloska 9, 02-583, Warsaw, Poland
Tel.: (48) 223308300
Web Site: https://www.gehealthcare.pl
Health Care Management Services
N.A.I.C.S.: 621491

GE Vingmed Ultrasound A/S (1)
Postboks 4574, Nydalen Vitaminveien 1, 0422, Oslo, Norway
Tel.: (47) 23185050
Health Care Management Services
N.A.I.C.S.: 621491

General Electric Healthcare Portugal, Sociedade Unipessoal, Lda. (1)
Avenida Forte 6 6-AEd Ramazzotti, 2790-072, Carnaxide, Portugal
Tel.: (351) 214251300
Web Site: https://generalelectric.pai.pt
Financial Support Services
N.A.I.C.S.: 541611

MIM Software Inc. (1)
25200 Chagrin Blvd, Cleveland, OH 44122
Tel.: (216) 896-9798
Web Site: http://www.mimsoftware.com
Sales Range: $1-9.9 Million
Emp.: 13
Custom Computer Programming Services, Nsk
N.A.I.C.S.: 541511
Babajide Falae (Engr-Clinical Support)
Brad Allison (Mgr-IT)

Schleifring Medical Systems, LLC (1)
1420 Crispin Dr, Elgin, IL 60123
Tel.: (847) 741-9600

Web Site: https://www.schleifringmedical.com
Medical Equipment Mfr & Distr
N.A.I.C.S.: 339112

GE VERNOVA INC.
58 Charles Street, Cambridge, MA 02141
Tel.: (617) 674-7555   DE
Web Site: https://www.gevernova.com
Year Founded: 2023
GEV—(NYSE)
Electric Power Services
N.A.I.C.S.: 221122
Rachel A. Gonzalez (Gen Counsel)
Victor R. Abate (CEO-Wind)
Scott L. Strazik (CEO)
Daniel Garceau (Chief Supply Chain Officer)
Kenneth S. Parks (CFO)
Steven Baert (Chief People Officer)
Kristin Carvell (Chief Comm Officer)

GECKOSYSTEMS INTL. CORP.
1640B Hwy 212 SW, Conyers, GA 30094-4225
Tel.: (678) 413-9236   GA
Web Site: https://www.geckosystems.com
Year Founded: 2020
GOSY—(OTCIQ)
Sales Range: Less than $1 Million
Mobile Service Robots
N.A.I.C.S.: 335210
R. Martin Spencer (Chm, Pres & CEO)
Elaine G. Spencer (CFO, Treas & Sec)

GEE GROUP INC.
7751 Belfort Pkwy Ste 150, Jacksonville, FL 32256
Tel.: (630) 954-0400   IL
Web Site: https://www.geegroup.com
Year Founded: 1893
JOB—(NYSEAMEX)
Rev.: $116,483,000
Assets: $95,901,000
Liabilities: $11,690,000
Net Worth: $84,211,000
Earnings: ($24,102,000)
Emp.: 210
Fiscal Year-end: 09/30/24
Holding Company; Staffing Services
N.A.I.C.S.: 551102
Derek E. Dewan (Chm & CEO)
Alex Stuckey (Chief Admin Officer)
Kim Thorpe (CFO & Sr VP)

Subsidiaries:

Access Data Consulting Corporation (1)
8101 E Prentice Ave Ste 1075, Greenwood Village, CO 80111
Tel.: (303) 770-2881
Web Site: https://www.adcc.com
Systems Outsourcing & Data Consulting Services
N.A.I.C.S.: 541511
Dan Dampier (Pres & CEO)

Agile Resources, Inc. (1)
1000 Windward Concourse Ste 160, Alpharetta, GA 30005
Tel.: (678) 722-8200
Web Site: https://www.gotoagile.com
IT Staffing & Consulting Solutions
N.A.I.C.S.: 561330
Matthew Marini (Pres)
Shannon Famosi (VP-Southeast)
Leslie Stalder (Sls Mgr)
Justin Ellis (Mgr-Recruiting)
Taylor Allen (Ops Mgr)
Falcon Harbison (Acct Exec)
Jessica Carroll (Acct Exec)
Jackie Farahdel (Acct Exec)
Wendy Frank (Specialist-Onboarding)

Ashley Ellis LLC (1)

GEE Group Inc.—(Continued)

1 Tower Ln Ste 2200, Oakbrook Terrace, IL
60181
Tel.: (630) 954-0400
Web Site: http://www.ashleyellis.com
Information Technology Staffing Services
N.A.I.C.S.: 561320

Paladin Consulting, Inc.   (1)
14241 Dallas Pkwy Ste 200, Dallas, TX
75254
Tel.: (972) 783-1995
Web Site: https://www.paladininc.com
Emp.: 100
Temporary Help Service
N.A.I.C.S.: 561320
Nathan Stilwill (COO)

Pivot Companies, LLC   (1)
11225 College Blvd Ste 250, Overland
Park, KS 66220
Tel.: (800) 581-6398
Web Site: http://www.pivotcompanies.com
Software Development Services
N.A.I.C.S.: 541511
Cary T. Daniel (CEO)
James Windmiller (COO)

SNI Companies   (1)
4500 Westown Pkwy Ste 120, West Des
Moines, IA 50266
Tel.: (515) 222-6350
Web Site: http://www.snicompanies.com
Recruitment & Staffing Services
N.A.I.C.S.: 561311
Laurie Knafo (Reg VP-Florida & Tri-State)
Moe Harrison (Reg VP-Texas & Minneapo-
lis)
Chris Alex (Reg VP)

Subsidiary (Domestic):

Staffing Now, Inc.   (2)
1 Pleasure Is Rd, Wakefield, MA 01880
Tel.: (781) 295-0632
Web Site: http://www.staffingnow.com
Recruitment & Staffing Services
N.A.I.C.S.: 561311

Scribe Solutions, Inc.   (1)
Tel.: (202) 260-6342
Web Site: http://www.scribesolutions.com
All Other Support Services
N.A.I.C.S.: 561990
Mary Claire Menze (Founder & Pres)

Triad Personnel Services, Inc.   (1)
6100 Rockside Woods Blvd Ste 350, Inde-
pendence, OH 44131   (100%)
Tel.: (216) 642-1300
Web Site: http://www.triadcontract.com
Emp.: 12
Light Industrial Staffing Services
N.A.I.C.S.: 561311

GELESIS HOLDINGS, INC.
501 Boylston St Ste 6102, Boston,
MA 02116
Tel.: (617) 456-4718   DE
Web Site: https://www.gelesis.com
Year Founded: 2020
GLS—(NYSE)
Rev.: $25,767,000
Assets: $103,324,000
Liabilities: $128,380,000
Net Worth: ($25,056,000)
Earnings: ($95,062,000)
Emp.: 93
Fiscal Year-end: 12/31/22
Investment Services
N.A.I.C.S.: 523999
Yishai Zohar (Founder, Pres, CEO,
Chief Compliance Officer, Interim
Principal Fin Officer, Principal Acctg
Officer, Treas & Sec)
David Pass (COO & Chief Comml
Officer)
Harry L. Leider (Chief Medical Offi-
cer)
Elaine Chiquette (Chief Scientific
Officer)

Subsidiaries:

Gelesis, Inc.   (1)

500 Boylston St Ste 1600, Boston, MA
02116
Tel.: (617) 456-4718
Web Site: http://www.gelesis.com
Pharmaceuticals Mfr
N.A.I.C.S.: 325412
Yishai Zohar (Founder & CEO)
Eyal S. Ron (Head-Regulatory)
Hassan Heshmati (Chief Medical Officer)
David Pass (COO)
William Aschenbach (VP-Medical Affairs)
Joy Bauer (Chief Nutrition Officer)
Elaine Chiquette (Chief Scientific Officer)
John L. LaMattina (Chm)

GELSTAT CORPORATION
333 SE 2nd Ave Ste 2000, Miami, FL
33131
Tel.: (772) 212-1368
Web Site: https://www.gelstat.com
Year Founded: 1991
GSAC—(OTCIQ)
Sales Range: $1-9.9 Million
Consumer Healthcare Product Devel-
opment Services
N.A.I.C.S.: 325412
Lisa M. Bachmann (Mgr-Product Dev)
Robert Estey (CEO)
Gerald N. Kieft (CFO)
Javier G. Acosta (COO)

Subsidiaries:

Mastix Medica, LLC   (1)
10711 Gilroy Rd, Hunt Valley, MD 21031
Tel.: (410) 316-1080
Web Site: http://www.mastixmedica.com
Sales Range: $1-9.9 Million
Emp.: 13
Pharmaceutical Preparation Mfr
N.A.I.C.S.: 325412
Robert Estey (CEO)
Mary Schmidt (VP-Consumer Products)

GELTECH SOLUTIONS, INC.
1460 Park Ln S Ste 1, Jupiter, FL
33458
Tel.: (561) 427-6144   DE
Web Site:
    http://www.geltechsolutions.com
Year Founded: 2006
GLTC—(OTCIQ)
Sales Range: $1-9.9 Million
Emp.: 20
Fire Protection & Water Conservation
Products
N.A.I.C.S.: 922160
Michael R. Hull (CFO)
Peter Cordani (Founder, CEO-Acting
& CTO)
Matthew Struzziero (VP-Firelce Wild-
land & Soil2O)
Daniel P. Simon (COO)
Gerry Kaiser (Natl Sls Mgr)
Michael Reger (Chm & Pres)

**GEMINI GROUP GLOBAL
CORP.**
127 Rollingwood Dr, Mesquite, TX
75149
Web Site:
    https://www.geminivapour.com
Year Founded: 1989
GMNI—(OTCIQ)
Vapor & E-Cigarrette Mfr
N.A.I.C.S.: 312230
Christopher Cox (CEO)

GEMXX CORPORATION
2300 W Sahara Ave Ste 800, Las
Vegas, NV 89102
Tel.: (702) 930-1815   DE
Web Site: https://www.gemxx.com
Year Founded: 1999
GEMZ—(OTCIQ)
Gemstone & Gold Mining
N.A.I.C.S.: 212390
Richard Clowater (Interim CEO & In-
terim CFO)

GEMZ CORP.
2180 N Park Ave Ste 200, Winter
Park, FL 32789
Tel.: (407) 674-9444   NV
Year Founded: 1998
GMZP—(OTCIQ)
Jewelry Product Mfr & Distr
N.A.I.C.S.: 339910
Stephen Walter Carnes (Pres, CEO &
Treas)

GEN DIGITAL INC.
60 E Rio Salado Pkwy Ste 1000,
Tempe, AZ 85281
Tel.: (650) 527-8000   DE
Web Site: https://www.gendigital.com
Year Founded: 1982
GEN—(NASDAQ)
Rev.: $3,812,000,000
Assets: $15,772,000,000
Liabilities: $13,575,000,000
Net Worth: $2,197,000,002
Earnings: $616,000,000
Emp.: 3,400
Fiscal Year-end: 03/29/24
Computer Programming Services
N.A.I.C.S.: 541511
Natalie M. Derse (CFO)
Frank Emmanuel Dangeard (Chm)
Vincent Pilette (Pres & CEO)
Kara Jordan (Chief People & Culture
Officer)
Bryan Ko (Gen Counsel & Sec)

Subsidiaries:

Avast Software B.V.   (1)
Enterprise Office Center Pikrtova 1737/1A,
140 00, Prague, Czech Republic
Tel.: (420) 274005777
Web Site: http://www.avast.com
Holding Company; Information Technology
Security Software Developer, Publisher &
Whslr
N.A.I.C.S.: 551112
Gagan Singh (Sr VP & Gen Mgr-Mobile)
Ondrej Vlcek (CEO)
Eduard Kucera (Co-Founder)
Pavel Baudis (Co-Founder)
Rene-Heinrich Bienz (CFO)
Robin Selden (CMO)
Jim Holden (Sr VP & Gen Mgr-Platform)
Steven Scheers (Chief HR Officer)
Detlef Steinmetz (CIO)
Peter Turner (Sr VP-Sls & Mktg-Consumer)
Josef Hos (Sr VP-Product & Ops-
Consumer)
Phil Marshall (CFO)
Vita Santrucek (Gen Mgr-Small & Mid-size
Bus)
Michal Trs (Sr Dir-Engrg)
Tomas Motal (Dir-Quality & Technical Sup-
port)
Trudy Cooke (Gen Counsel & Sec)

Subsidiary (Domestic):

Avast Software s.r.o.   (2)
1737/1A Pikrtova, 140 00, Prague, 4, Czech
Republic
Tel.: (420) 274005777
Web Site: https://www.avast.com
Information Technology Security Software
Developer, Publisher & Whslr
N.A.I.C.S.: 513210
Ondrej Vlcek (CEO)

Subsidiary (Non-US):

AVG Technologies B.V.   (3)
Tel.: (31) 205226210
Web Site: http://www.avg.com
Security Software Developer
N.A.I.C.S.: 513210

Subsidiary (Non-US):

AVG Technologies CZ s.r.o.   (4)
Tel.: (420) 549524011
Web Site: http://www.avg.com
Security Software Developer
N.A.I.C.S.: 513210

Location Labs, Inc.   (4)
Tel.: (510) 601-7012

Web Site: http://www.locationlabs.com
Emp.: 150
Mobile Security Solutions
N.A.I.C.S.: 513210

Subsidiary (US):

Avast Software, Inc.   (3)
2625 Broadway St, Redwood City, CA
94063-1532
Tel.: (650) 581-1789
Web Site: http://www.avast.com
Information Technology Security Software
Publisher & Whslr
N.A.I.C.S.: 513210
Robin Selden (CMO)

Subsidiary (Non-US):

Piriform Ltd.   (3)
110 High Holborn, London, WC1V 6JS,
United Kingdom
Tel.: (44) 207 193 1776
Web Site: http://www.ccleaner.com
Holding Company; Computer Restoration
Software Developer & Publisher
N.A.I.C.S.: 551112
Jamie Cowan (VP-Sls)
Louise Kinane (VP-Ops)
Paul Yung (VP-Products)
Claire Chivers (Head-Mktg & Comm)

Subsidiary (Domestic):

Piriform Software Ltd.   (4)
100 New Bridge Street, London, EC4V 6JA,
United Kingdom
Tel.: (44) 2071931776
Web Site: http://www.ccleaner.com
Computer Restoration Software Developer
& Publisher
N.A.I.C.S.: 513210
Louise Kinane (VP-Ops)
Jamie Cowan (VP-Sls)

LifeLock, Inc.   (1)
60 E Rio Salado Pkwy Ste 1000, Tempe,
AZ 85281
Tel.: (480) 457-4500
Web Site: https://www.nortonlifelock.com
Sales Range: $550-599.9 Million
Identity Theft Prevention Software & Ser-
vices
N.A.I.C.S.: 513210

LiveOffice LLC   (1)
2780 Skypark Dr Ste 300, Torrance, CA
90505
Tel.: (310) 539-6980
Web Site: http://www.liveoffice.com
Sales Range: $10-24.9 Million
Emp.: 107
Email Archiving Software Mfr
N.A.I.C.S.: 513210

SwapDrive, Inc.   (1)
1313 F St NW 4th Fl, Washington, DC
20004-1102
Tel.: (202) 393-9900
Sales Range: $10-24.9 Million
Emp.: 15
Online Computer Storage Solutions
N.A.I.C.S.: 334112

Symantec   (1)
Tour Egee 17th Ave Arche, 25 Quai Gal-
lieni, 92671, Courbevoie, France   (100%)
Tel.: (33) 141385700
Web Site: http://www.symantec.fr
Sales Range: $50-74.9 Million
Emp.: 212
Mfr of Application & System Software for
Personal Computers
N.A.I.C.S.: 334610

Symantec (Switzerland) Sarl   (1)
Prime Center 3 Hotelstrasse 1 Flughafen,
8058, Zurich, Switzerland
Tel.: (41) 445676315
Software Development Services
N.A.I.C.S.: 513210

Symantec (UK) Ltd.   (1)
Hines Meadow, Saint Cloud Way, Maiden-
head, SL6 8XB, Berk Shire, United
Kingdom   (100%)
Tel.: (44) 628592222
Web Site: http://www.symantec.co.uk

Sales Range: Less than $1 Million
Emp.: 150
Application & System Software Mfr
N.A.I.C.S.: 334610

Branch (Domestic):

Symantec (UK) Ltd. - Reading   (2)
350 Brook Drive GreenPark, Reading, RG2
6UH, United Kingdom
Tel.: (44) 8702431080
Web Site: http://www.symantec.com
Sales Range: $350-399.9 Million
Software Developer
N.A.I.C.S.: 513210

Symantec Corporation - Miami   (1)
9155 S Dadeland Blvd, Miami, FL 33156
Tel.: (305) 671-2312
Web Site: http://www.symantec.com
Sales Range: $10-24.9 Million
Emp.: 30
Software Publisher
N.A.I.C.S.: 513210

Symantec Corporation - Orem   (1)
1359 N Research Way Bldg K, Orem, UT
84059
Tel.: (801) 437-8900
Web Site: http://www.symantec.com
Rev.: $64,000,000
Emp.: 309
Storage Lifecycle Automation Solutions
N.A.I.C.S.: 513210

**Symantec Corporation -
Waltham**   (1)
275 2nd Ave, Waltham, MA 02451
Tel.: (781) 530-2324
Web Site: http://www.imlogic.com
Sales Range: $1-9.9 Million
Emp.: 40
Developer of Instant Message Application
Software
N.A.I.C.S.: 513210

Symantec GmbH   (1)
Kaiserswerther Str 115, 40880, Ratingen,
Germany   **(100%)**
Tel.: (49) 210274530
Web Site: http://www.symantec.com
Sales Range: $10-24.9 Million
Emp.: 70
Mfr of Application & System Software for
Personal Computers
N.A.I.C.S.: 334610

Symantec India Private Limited   (1)
2nd 7 8 9 Floors City Tower, 17 Boat Club
Road, Pune, 411 011, India
Tel.: (91) 2066157000
Sales Range: $100-124.9 Million
Software Developer
N.A.I.C.S.: 513210
Sanjay Rohatgi (Pres-Sls-Delhi)
Shrikant Shitole (Mng Dir-Enterprise Secu-
rity Bus)

Symantec International Ltd.   (1)
Ballycoolin Business Park, Blanchardstown,
Dublin, 15, Ireland   **(100%)**
Tel.: (353) 18035400
Web Site: http://www.symantec.ie
Sales Range: $200-249.9 Million
Emp.: 800
Mfr of Application & System Software for
Personal Computers
N.A.I.C.S.: 334610

Symantec Japan, Inc.   (1)
Shibuya Infoss Tower 17F 20-1
Sakuragaoka-Cho, Shibuya-Ku, Tokyo, 150,
Japan
Tel.: (81) 354575300
Web Site: http://www.symantec.com
Sales Range: $75-99.9 Million
Emp.: 300
Mfr of Application & System Software for
Personal Computers
N.A.I.C.S.: 334610

Symantec Limited   (1)
Ballycoolin Business Park, Blanchardstown,
15, Dublin, Ireland
Tel.: (353) 18035400
Computer Programming Services
N.A.I.C.S.: 541511

Symantec Ltd.   (1)
Smolenskaya Square 3, Smolenskaya Pas-

sage 6th Floor, 121099, Moscow,
Russia   **(100%)**
Tel.: (7) 495 937 82 37
Web Site: http://www.symantec.ru
Sales Range: $1-9.9 Million
Emp.: 5
Mfr of Application & System Software for
Personal Computers
N.A.I.C.S.: 334610

Symantec SRL   (1)
Via Rivoltana 2D, Segrete, 20090, Milan,
Italy   **(100%)**
Tel.: (39) 02703321
Web Site: http://www.symantec.it
Sales Range: $10-24.9 Million
Emp.: 50
Mfr of Application & System Software for
Personal Computers
N.A.I.C.S.: 334610

Symantec Security (UK) Limited   (1)
Reading International Business Park, Read-
ing, RG2 6DH, United Kingdom
Tel.: (44) 1189204000
Software Development Services
N.A.I.C.S.: 541511

**Symantec Technologies (Ireland)
Limited**   (1)
Ballycoolin Business Park, Blanchardstown,
Dublin, 15, Ireland
Tel.: (353) 18035400
Software Development Services
N.A.I.C.S.: 513210

Vontu, Inc.   (1)
475 Sansome St Ste 2000, San Francisco,
CA 94111
Tel.: (415) 364-8100
Web Site: http://www.vontu.com
Sales Range: $25-49.9 Million
Software Solutions Developer
N.A.I.C.S.: 513210

GEN RESTAURANT GROUP,
INC.
11480 S St Ste 205, Cerritos, CA
90703
Tel.: (562) 356-9929   **DE**
Web Site:
https://investor.genkoreanbbq.com
Year Founded: 2011
GENK—(NASDAQ)
Rev.: $163,729
Assets: $138,878
Liabilities: $145,639
Net Worth: ($6,761)
Earnings: $10,281
Emp.: 2,350
Fiscal Year-end: 12/31/22
Restaurant Operators
N.A.I.C.S.: 722511
David Kim (Co-CEO)
Jae Kim (Co-CEO)
Thomas V. Croal (CFO)

GENASYS, INC.
16262 W Bernardo Dr, San Diego,
CA 92127
Tel.: (858) 676-1112   **DE**
Web Site: https://www.genasys.com
Year Founded: 1980
GNSS—(NASDAQ)
Rev.: $46,663,000
Assets: $49,905,000
Liabilities: $16,093,000
Net Worth: $33,812,000
Earnings: ($18,396,000)
Emp.: 187
Fiscal Year-end: 09/30/23
Directed Sound Solutions & Services
N.A.I.C.S.: 334310
Richard S. Danforth (CEO)
Dennis Klahn (CFO)

Subsidiaries:

Genasys II Spain, S.A.U.   (1)
Pz Sta M Soledad Torres Acosta n 2 planta
4 A, 28004, Madrid, Spain
Tel.: (34) 913649100
Web Site: http://www.genasys.com
Telecommunication Servicesb

N.A.I.C.S.: 517810

GENCO SHIPPING & TRADING
LIMITED
299 Park Ave 12th Fl, New York, NY
10171
Tel.: (646) 443-8550   **MH**
Web Site:
https://www.gencoshipping.com
GNK—(NYSE)
Rev.: $536,934,000
Assets: $1,173,866,000
Liabilities: $205,557,000
Net Worth: $968,309,000
Earnings: $158,576,000
Emp.: 970
Fiscal Year-end: 12/31/22
Deep Sea Shipping Services
N.A.I.C.S.: 483211
John C. Wobensmith (Pres & CEO)
Joseph Adamo (Chief Acctg Officer)
James G. Dolphin (Chm)
Jesper Christensen (Chief Comml
Officer)
Peter Allen (CFO)

Subsidiaries:

Baltic Trading Limited   (1)
299 Park Ave 12th Fl, New York, NY 10171
Tel.: (646) 443-8550
Dry Bulk Shipping Services
N.A.I.C.S.: 483111

Genco Holdings Limited   (1)
Caledonia House 89 Seaward Street, Glas-
gow, G41 1HJ, United Kingdom
Tel.: (44) 1413548888
Web Site: http://www.genco-solutions.co.uk
Construction Management Services
N.A.I.C.S.: 236220

Genco Shipping A/S   (1)
Orient Plads 1B, 2150, Copenhagen, Den-
mark
Tel.: (45) 32741995
Water Transportation Services
N.A.I.C.S.: 483211

Genco Shipping Pte. Limited   (1)
16 Raffles Quay 41-05A Hong Leong Build-
ing, Singapore, 048581, Singapore
Tel.: (65) 63299190
Deep Sea Shipping Services
N.A.I.C.S.: 483111

GENCOR INDUSTRIES, INC.
5201 N Orange Blossom Trl, Orlando,
FL 32810
Tel.: (407) 290-6000   **DE**
Web Site: https://www.gencor.com
Year Founded: 1968
GENC—(NYSEAMEX)
Rev.: $105,075,000
Assets: $195,748,000
Liabilities: $14,165,000
Net Worth: $181,583,000
Earnings: $14,666,000
Emp.: 314
Fiscal Year-end: 09/30/23
Construction Machinery Mfr
N.A.I.C.S.: 333120
Marc G. Elliott (Pres)
E. J. Elliott (Founder & Chm)

Subsidiaries:

Bituma Corporation   (1)
508 Hwy 18 W, Marquette, IA
52158   **(100%)**
Tel.: (563) 873-3431
Web Site: http://www.alpinecom.net
Sales Range: $25-49.9 Million
Emp.: 50
Mfr of Drum Mix & Batch Type Asphalt
Plants & Related Equipment for Highway
Construction
N.A.I.C.S.: 333120

Bituma-Stor, Inc.   (1)
PO Box 430, Marquette, IA 52158
Tel.: (563) 873-3431
Structural Steel Mfr
N.A.I.C.S.: 332312

Equipment Services Group, Inc.   (1)
5201 N Orange Blossom Trl, Orlando, FL
32810-1008
Tel.: (407) 290-6000
Construction Machinery & Equipment Mfr
N.A.I.C.S.: 333120

General Combustion Corporation   (1)
5201 N Orange Blossom Trl, Orlando, FL
32810
Tel.: (407) 290-6000
Web Site: http://www.gencor.com
Mfr of Combustion Technology, Asphalt &
Drying Industry
N.A.I.C.S.: 324121

GENE BIOTHERAPEUTICS
INC.
11230 Sorrento Valley Rd Ste 220,
San Diego, CA 92121
Tel.: (858) 414-1477   **DE**
Web Site:
https://genebiotherapeutics.com
Year Founded: 2003
CRXM—(OTCEM)
Pharmaceutical Preparation Manufac-
turing
N.A.I.C.S.: 325412
Lois A. Chandler (COO)
Christopher J. Reinhard (CEO)
Robert L. Engler (Chief Medical Advi-
sor)
James L. Grainer (Chm, CFO & Sec)
Ronald J. Shebuski (Chief Scientific
Officer)

Subsidiaries:

Tissue Repair Company   (1)
12255 El Camino Real Ste 250, San Diego,
CA 92130-4090   **(100%)**
Tel.: (858) 793-6641
Sales Range: $150-199.9 Million
Biopharmaceutical Developer of Tissue Re-
pair Products
N.A.I.C.S.: 325414

GENEDX HOLDINGS CORP.
333 Ludlow St N Tower 6th Fl, Stam-
ford, CT 06902
Tel.: (212) 474-6745   **DE**
Web Site: https://www.genedx.com
Year Founded: 2020
WGS—(NASDAQ)
Rev.: $234,694,000
Assets: $490,942,000
Liabilities: $237,237,000
Net Worth: $253,705,000
Earnings: ($548,980,000)
Emp.: 1,100
Fiscal Year-end: 12/31/22
Miscellaneous Financial Investment
Activities
N.A.I.C.S.: 523999
Katherine Stueland (Pres & CEO)
Keith Arlyn Meister (Chm)
Eric Schadt (Founder & Chief R&D
Officer)
Devin K. Schaffer (Gen Counsel)

Subsidiaries:

GeneDx, Inc.   (1)
207 Perry Pkwy, Gaithersburg, MD 20877
Tel.: (301) 519-2100
Web Site: http://www.genedx.com
Testing & Diagnostic Medical Laboratories
N.A.I.C.S.: 541380
Kevin Feeley (Head)
Sherri J. Bale (Co-Founder)
John G. Compton (Co-Founder)
Anne Maddalena (Assoc Dir-Clinical Pro-
grams)
Gabriele Richard (Dir-Medical)
Isabelle Olivos-Glander (Dir-Core Labora-
tory & Core Support Svcs)
Patricia McAndrew (Assoc Dir-Core Lab
Ops)
Rhonda Brandon (VP-Laboratory Sys)
Sean Hofherr (Exec VP & Dir-CLIA Labora-
tory)

GeneDx Holdings Corp.—(Continued)

Renkui Bai (Dir-Mitochondrial Disorder Testing Svcs)
Elizabeth Butler (Dir-Genetic Counseling Svcs)
Heather C. Hackworth (Dir-HR)
Kathleen Hruska (Dir-Hereditary Cancer)
Jane Juusola (VP-Medical Affairs & Dir-Clinical Genomics Program)
Daniela Macaya (Dir-Cardiogenetics Program)
Ludmila Matyakhina (Dir-Cytogenetics Program)
Jeanne Meck (Dir-Prenatal Diagnosis & Cytogenomics)
Sharon F. Suchy (Dir-Neurogenetics & Metabolics)
Tracy Brandt (Dir-Clinical Dev)
Amanda Lindy (Dir-Neurogenetics)
Kristin G. Monaghan (Assoc Dir-Clinical Genomics Program)
Kyle Retterer (CTO & Sr VP)
Brandi Thompson (Asst Dir-Hereditary Cancer Program)
Fanggeng Zou (Asst Dir-Neurogenetics)
Ganka Douglas (Assoc Dir-Clinical Genomics Program)
Hong Cui (Asst Dir-Mitochondrial Disorders & Cardiogenetics)
Jaimie Higgs (Asst Dir-Genetic Counseling Svcs)
Joy Adigun (Asst Dir-Next Generation Sequencing)
Julie Schultz (Asst Dir-Ops & Review Analysis)
Kelly K. Parsons (Assoc Dir-Test Dev & Integration)
Leah M. Williams (Asst Dir-Genetic Counseling Svcs)
Lindsay Henderson (Assoc Dir-Clinical Genomics Program & Asst Dir-Postgraduate)
Margaret Chen (Asst Dir-Cardiogenetic Testing Svcs)
Mitzi Li Murray (Asst Dir-Cardiogenetics)
Renee Varga (Asst Dir-Core Support Svcs)
Roshni Alva (Asst Dir-Primary Analysis)
Sabrina Buchholz (Asst Dir-Analysis)
Stephanie Warren (Asst Dir-Microarray Ops)
Tara Hart (Asst Dir-Post Graduation Education)
Rachel Klein (Sr VP)
Paul Kruszka (Chief Medical Officer & Sr VP)
Chris Sands (Sr VP-Sls)
Dean Gaalaas (Sr VP-Ops)

GENERAC HOLDINGS INC.
S45 W29290 Hwy 59, Waukesha, WI 53189
Tel.: (262) 544-4811 DE
Web Site: https://www.generac.com
Year Founded: 1959
GNRC—(NYSE)
Rev.: $4,022,667,000
Assets: $5,093,312,000
Liabilities: $2,750,242,000
Net Worth: $2,343,070,000
Earnings: $214,606,000
Emp.: 8,315
Fiscal Year-end: 12/31/23
Holding Company; Generator Mfr
N.A.I.C.S.: 551112
Aaron P. Jagdfeld (Chm & CEO)
York A. Ragen (CFO & Chief Acctg Officer)
Erik Wilde (Exec VP-Industrial Americas)
Kevin Anderson (Exec VP-Corp Strategy & Dev)
Rhonda Matschke (Exec VP-HR)
Tim Hearden (Exec VP-Ops-Global)
Steve Goran (Chief Strategy Officer)
Paolo Campinoti (Exec VP-EMEA, APAC, and South America)
Raj Kanuru (Gen Counsel, Sec & Exec VP)
Kyle Raabe (Pres-Consumer Power)
Tim Dickson (CIO)
Norman Taffe (Pres)
Amanda Teder (Exec VP)

Subsidiaries:
AF SRL (1)

Via Marco Polo 121, Bientina, 56031, Pisa, Italy
Tel.: (39) 0587757376
Web Site: https://www.af-srl.com
Industrial Machinery Mfr
N.A.I.C.S.: 333998

Captiva Energy Solutions Private Limited (1)
5th Floor Unit No 607 and 608 Plot No AH-5 Action Area-1A New Town, Dongfang Building, Kolkata, 700 163, West Bengal, India
Tel.: (91) 6292210977
Web Site: https://www.captivaenergy.co
Emp.: 150
Generator Mfr & Distr
N.A.I.C.S.: 335312

Country Home Products Inc. (1)
75 Meigs Rd, Vergennes, VT 05491
Tel.: (802) 877-1200
Web Site: http://www.chp.com
Nursery & Garden Equipment Mfr
N.A.I.C.S.: 333112

Deep Sea Electronics India Private Limited (1)
405 406 Pride Gateway Baner, Pune, 411045, Maharashtra, India
Tel.: (91) 2068195900
Web Site:
  https://www.deepseaelectronics.com
Motor Generator Mfr
N.A.I.C.S.: 335312

Deep Sea Electronics Limited (1)
Highfield House, Hunmanby Industrial Estate Hunmanby, Scarborough, YO14 0PH, North Yorkshire, United Kingdom
Tel.: (44) 1723890099
Web Site:
  https://www.deepseaelectronics.com
Generator Mfr & Distr
N.A.I.C.S.: 423610

Generac Brasil Ltda (1)
Rua Umuarama 164, Pinhais, 83325-000, Brazil
Tel.: (55) 4135252255
Web Site: http://www.generacbrasil.com.br
Generator Mfr
N.A.I.C.S.: 333611

Generac Mexico Administracion, S.A. de C.V. (1)
Av General Mariano Escobedo 555 Piso 7 Col Bosques de Chapultepec, 11580, Mexico, Mexico
Tel.: (52) 5556245600
Web Site: https://generaclatam.com
Generator Distr
N.A.I.C.S.: 423830

Generac Mobile Products S.r.l (1)
Via Stazione 3 Bis, Villanova d'Ardenghi, 27030, Pavia, Italy
Tel.: (39) 038 256 7011
Web Site: https://www.towerlight.com
Lighting Tower Mfr
N.A.I.C.S.: 335132
Alessandro Rossi (Mng Dir)
Alessandro Capone (Mgr-Bus Dev-Latin America)
Aaron Cardelino (Mgr-Business Development-Latin America)
Alessandro Carenzio (Mgr-Business Development-Europe)
Daniele Crepaldi (Mgr)

Generac Mobile Products UK Ltd (1)
Arrow South PRAMAC-GENERAC UK Pramac House James Brindley Way Tunstall, Stoke-on-Trent, ST6 54SF, United Kingdom
Tel.: (44) 441270445777
Web Site:
  http://www.generacmobileproducts.co.uk
Lighting Tower Mfr
N.A.I.C.S.: 335139
Steve Hallam (Comml Dir)
Andy Martin (Sls Mgr)

Generac Mobile Products, LLC (1)
215 Power Dr, Berlin, WI 54923
Tel.: (920) 361-4442
Web Site:
  https://www.generacmobileproducts.com
Generator Distr
N.A.I.C.S.: 423610

Generac Power Systems, Inc. (1)
S45W29290 Hwy 59, Waukesha, WI 53189
Tel.: (262) 544-4811
Web Site: https://www.generac.com
Sales Range: $125-149.9 Million
Generator Mfr
N.A.I.C.S.: 335312
William Treffert (Pres)
Gerry Ruehlow (VP)
Norman P. Taffe (Pres-Energy Tech)
Aaron Jagdfeld (Pres & CEO)

Plant (Domestic):

Generac Power Systems, Inc. - Oshkosh Plant (2)
3815 Oregon St, Oshkosh, WI 54902
Tel.: (920) 236-4200
Web Site: https://www.generac.com
Sales Range: $50-74.9 Million
Emp.: 200
Generator Mfr
N.A.I.C.S.: 335312

Generac Services, Inc. (1)
75 Meigs Rd, Vergennes, VT 05491
Tel.: (802) 877-1200
Portable Generator Mfr
N.A.I.C.S.: 335312

Lifter China Ltd Company (1)
No 29 Hongxi Road Niutang Town, Wujin District, Changzhou, 213161, Jiangsu, China
Tel.: (86) 51986396789
Web Site: http://www.lifterchina.com
Lifter Equipment Mfr
N.A.I.C.S.: 333924

Motortech Americas LLC (1)
1400 Dealers Ave Ste A, New Orleans, LA 70123
Tel.: (504) 355-4212
Gas Engine Mfr & Distr
N.A.I.C.S.: 333618
Mark Skidmore (Mgr-Svcs)

Motortech GmbH (1)
Hunaeusstrasse 5, 29227, Celle, Germany
Tel.: (49) 514193990
Web Site: https://www.motortech.de
Emp.: 250
Gas Engine Mfr & Distr
N.A.I.C.S.: 333618
Markus Kruse (Mng Dir)

Motortech Polska Sp. Z.o.o. (1)
ul Polna 25, Charzyno, 78-122, Kolobrzeg, Poland
Tel.: (48) 943514720
Web Site: https://www.motortechpolska.pl
Gas Engine Mfr & Distr
N.A.I.C.S.: 333618

Motortech Shanghai Co., Ltd. (1)
Room 1018 Enterprise Square No 228 Meiyuan Road, Jing'An Dist, Shanghai, 200070, China
Tel.: (86) 2163807338
Gas Engine Mfr & Distr
N.A.I.C.S.: 333618

Neurio Technology ULC (1)
Suite 201-43 W Hastings St, Vancouver, V6B 1G4, BC, Canada
Web Site: https://www.neur.io
Information Technology Management Services
N.A.I.C.S.: 541512

Ottomotores S.A. de C.V. (1)
Calz San Lorenzo 1150 Col Cerro de la Estrella, Delegacion Iztapalapa, Mexico, CP 09860, Mexico
Tel.: (52) 5556245600
Web Site: http://www.ottomotores.com.mx
Sales Range: $100-124.9 Million
Industrial Generator Mfr & Distr
N.A.I.C.S.: 335312

Ottomotores do Brasil Energia Ltda. (1)
Rua Umuarama 164, Pinhais, 83325-000, PR, Brazil
Tel.: (55) 41 3525 2255
Web Site: http://www.generac.com
Industrial Generator Mfr & Distr
N.A.I.C.S.: 335312

PR Australia PTY Ltd (1)
Suite 202 59 Kirby Street, Rydalmere, 2116,

NSW, Australia
Tel.: (61) 290718181
Generator Mfr & Whslr
N.A.I.C.S.: 335312

PR Industrial S.r.l. (1)
Localita II Piano snc, Casole d'Elsa, 53031, Siena, Italy
Tel.: (39) 05779651
Web Site: https://www.pramac.com
Emp.: 1,100
Generator Mfr & Whslr
N.A.I.C.S.: 335312

PR Middle East Fze (1)
1706 Jafza View 18, PO Box 262478, Jebel Ali Free Zone - South 1, Dubai, United Arab Emirates
Tel.: (971) 48865275
Generator Mfr & Whslr
N.A.I.C.S.: 335312

Pika Energy, Inc. (1)
35 Bradley Dr Ste 1, Westbrook, ME 04092
Tel.: (207) 887-9105
Turbine & Turbine Generator Set Units Mfr
N.A.I.C.S.: 333611
Ben Polito (Founder & CEO)

Pramac Asia PTE Ltd (1)
10 Bukit Batok Crescent 11-08 The Spire, Singapore, 658079, Singapore
Tel.: (65) 587888
Generator Mfr & Whslr
N.A.I.C.S.: 335312
Joseph Wu (Gen Mgr)

Pramac Caribe Srl (1)
Avda 27 De Febrero Esq Caonabo 664 Los Restauradores, 10137, Santo Domingo, Dominican Republic
Tel.: (809) 8095310067
Generator Mfr & Whslr
N.A.I.C.S.: 335312

Pramac Europe SAS (1)
2 Place Leonard de Vinci, 42190, Sainte-Luce-sur-Loire, France
Tel.: (33) 477692020
Generator Mfr
N.A.I.C.S.: 335312

Pramac Fu Lee Foshan Power Equipment Ltd (1)
No 25 Xinhui Road, Wusha Daliang Shunde, Foshan, 528333, Guangdong, China
Tel.: (86) 75722804888
Generator Mfr & Whslr
N.A.I.C.S.: 335312

Pramac GmbH (1)
Merowinger Str 7-9, Fellbach, 70736, Stuttgart, Germany
Tel.: (49) 7115174290
Generator Mfr & Whslr
N.A.I.C.S.: 335312

Pramac Iberica S.A.U. (1)
Parque Empresarial Polaris C/Mario Campinoti 1, Autovia Murcia-San Javier Km 18 Balsicas, 30591, Murcia, Spain
Tel.: (34) 968334900
Generator Mfr & Whslr
N.A.I.C.S.: 335312

Pramac RUS Ltd (1)
Neverovskogo Street 9 Office 316, Moscow, Russia
Tel.: (7) 4956516866
Generator Mfr & Whslr
N.A.I.C.S.: 335312

Pramac Sp. Z.o.o. (1)
St Krakowska 141 - 155 building F 50-428, Wroclaw, Poland
Tel.: (48) 717822690
Generator Mfr & Whslr
N.A.I.C.S.: 335312
Grzegorz Olejnik (Gen Mgr)

Pramac Storage Systems GmbH (1)
Marktstrasse 185, 72793, Pfullingen, Germany
Tel.: (49) 7121159770
Web Site: https://www.pramac-storage-systems.com
Generator & Battery Storage Mfr
N.A.I.C.S.: 335312

Pramac UK Limited   (1)
5 - 6 Orion Way, Cheshire, Crewe, CW1
6NG, United Kingdom
Tel.: (44) 1270445777
Generator Mfr & Whslr
N.A.I.C.S.: 335312

SC Pramac Generators S.r.l.   (1)
Sos Bucuresti Targoviste Nr 12A Corp A
Etaj 3, Ilfov, 077135, Mogosoaia, Romania
Tel.: (40) 314170765
Generator Mfr & Whslr
N.A.I.C.S.: 335312

Services & Gestion France Sarl   (1)
Ruche Des 2 Lys Avenue De l Europe,
74160, Armentieres, France
Tel.: (33) 890109333
Web Site: https://www.setg.fr
Real Estate Agency Services
N.A.I.C.S.: 531210

**West Coast Energy Systems
LLC**   (1)
7100 S Longe St Ste 300, Stockton, CA
95206
Tel.: (209) 870-1900
Web Site: https://energysystems.com
Power Generator Rental Services
N.A.I.C.S.: 532490

ecobee Technologies ULC   (1)
207 Queens Quay West Suite 600, Toronto,
M5J 1A7, ON, Canada
Tel.: (647) 428-2220
Web Site: https://www.ecobee.com
Electronic Computer Mfr & Distr
N.A.I.C.S.: 423690
Rob Cammalleri *(Reg Sls Mgr)*

GENERAL AMERICAN INVESTORS, INC.
530 5th Ave 26th Fl, New York, NY
10036
Tel.: (212) 916-8400
Web Site:
https://www.generalamericaninvestors.com
Year Founded: 1927
GAM—(NYSE)
Rev.: $15,206,240
Assets: $1,306,920,382
Liabilities: $28,832,144
Net Worth: $1,278,088,238
Earnings: $3,134,606
Emp.: 17
Fiscal Year-end: 12/31/20
Investment Services
N.A.I.C.S.: 523150
Sally A. Lynch *(VP)*
Jeffrey W. Priest *(Pres & CEO)*
Connie A. Santa Maria *(Mgr-HR & Asst Sec)*
Samantha X. Jin *(Officer-Acctg Ops & Treas)*
Anang A. Majmudar *(Sr VP)*
Spencer Davidson *(Chm)*
Eugene S. Stark *(Chief Compliance Officer & VP-Admin & Admin)*
Craig A. Grassi *(VP)*
Kronzon Lee *(VP)*

GENERAL CHEMICAL GROUP, INC.
Liberty Lane, Hampton, NH 03842
Tel.: (603) 929-2606   DE
GNMP—(OTCIQ)
Inorganic Chemical Mfr
N.A.I.C.S.: 325180

GENERAL DATACOMM INDUSTRIES, INC.
353 Christian St, Oxford, CT 06478
Tel.: (203) 729-0271   DE
Web Site: https://www.gdc.com
Year Founded: 1969
GNRD—(OTCIQ)
Sales Range: $1-9.9 Million
Emp.: 115
Network Access Equipment Designer,
Developer & Mfr

N.A.I.C.S.: 334210
Frank Giannone *(VP-Ops)*
Joe Autem *(CFO)*
Mark A. Johns *(COO)*
Mike Conway *(Pres & CEO)*

GENERAL DYNAMICS CORPORATION
11011 Sunset Hills Rd, Reston, VA
20190
Tel.: (703) 876-3000   DE
Web Site: https://www.gd.com
Year Founded: 1952
GD—(NYSE)
Rev.: $42,272,000,000
Assets: $54,810,000,000
Liabilities: $33,511,000,000
Net Worth: $21,299,000,000
Earnings: $3,315,000,000
Emp.: 111,600
Fiscal Year-end: 12/31/23
Military Aircraft, Submarines, Marine
Systems, Space Vehicles, Electric
Motors & Armored Vehicles Mfr
N.A.I.C.S.: 336414
Phebe N. Novakovic *(Chm & CEO)*
Christopher Marzilli *(Exec VP-Technologies)*
Ira P. Berman *(VP)*
Gregory S. Gallopoulos *(Gen Counsel, Sec & Sr VP)*
Kenneth R. Hayduk *(VP-Tax)*
Kimberly A. Kuryea *(CFO & Sr VP)*
Mark L. Burns *(VP)*
David Paddock *(Pres-General Dynamics Land Sys)*
Firat H. Gezen *(VP)*
William A. Moss *(VP & Controller)*
Howard A. Rubel *(VP-IR)*
Robert E. Smith *(Exec VP-Marine Sys)*
Christopher J. Brady *(VP)*
David J. Carver *(VP)*
David Paddock *(VP)*
Elizabeth L. Schmid *(VP-Govt Rels)*
Andy C. Chen *(Treas & VP)*
Danny Deep *(Exec VP-Combat Sys)*
Shane A. Berg *(Sr VP-HR & Admin)*
M. Amy Gilliland *(Pres-IT)*
Charles Krugh *(Pres)*
David Roberts *(VP-Real Estate & Facilities-Electric Boat)*
Jason W. Aiken *(Exec VP-Technologies)*

Subsidiaries:

Applied Physical Sciences Corp.   (1)
475 Bridge St Ste 100, Groton, CT 06340-3780
Tel.: (860) 448-3253
Web Site: https://aphysci.com
Research Development & Engineering Services
N.A.I.C.S.: 541715

Australian Avionics Pty. Ltd.   (1)
Hangar 149 Tom McDonald Drive Cairns
Airport, PO Box 1136, Aeroglen, Cairns,
4870, QLD, Australia
Tel.: (61) 740301800
Web Site: http://www.australianavionics.com
Aircraft Assembly & Parts Mfr
N.A.I.C.S.: 336413

Avion Logistics Limited   (1)
Room B 23rd Floor Excelsior Industrial
Building 68-76 Sha Tsui Road, Tsuen Wan,
China (Hong Kong)
Tel.: (852) 24089533
Web Site: http://www.avionlogistics.com.hk
Freight Trucking Logistics Services
N.A.I.C.S.: 541614

CSRA Bolivia S.R.L.   (1)
Calle Walter Khon 806 Zona Cristo Rey,
Box 13387, La Paz, Bolivia
Tel.: (591) 22415752
Web Site: http://www.csra-bolivia.org
Telecommunication Management Consulting
Services
N.A.I.C.S.: 541618

Mayra Montevilla *(Mgr-Project)*
Dardo Chavez *(Reg Dir)*
Ramiro Llanque Torrez *(Dir-Natl)*

DynPort Vaccine Company LLC   (1)
64 Thomas Johnson Dr, Frederick, MD
21702-4501
Tel.: (240) 236-9000
Web Site: http://www.gdit.com
Biotechnological & Pharmaceutical Consulting Services
N.A.I.C.S.: 541618
Zsolt P. Harsanyi *(Founder)*
Mary Kate Hart *(Chief Scientific Officer)*

Eagle Enterprise, Inc.   (1)
2610 S Sheridan St Ste A, Wichita, KS
67217
Tel.: (316) 945-8500
Web Site: http://www.eagleict.com
Graphic Design Services
N.A.I.C.S.: 541430

Electrocom, Inc.   (1)
760 W Cherry St, Palmyra, PA
17078   **(100%)**
Tel.: (717) 838-3034
Aerospace & Shipbuilding Products Mfr
N.A.I.C.S.: 336611

Fortress Technologies, Inc.   (1)
2 Technology Park Dr Ste 2000, Westford,
MA 01886-3140
Tel.: (978) 923-6400
Web Site: http://www.fortresstech.com
Sales Range: $25-49.9 Million
Emp.: 70
Custom Computer Programing
N.A.I.C.S.: 334118

GD Arabia Ltd   (1)
PO Box 3362, Riyadh, 11471, Saudi Arabia
Tel.: (966) 114605796
Web Site: http://www.gdarabia.com
Defense Products Distr & Mfr; Information
Technology Consultant
N.A.I.C.S.: 336992

**GD European Land Systems - Steyr
GmbH**   (1)
Bleibtreustrasse 2, 1110, Vienna, Austria
Tel.: (43) 1760640
Web Site: http://www.gdels.com
Motor Vehicle Components & Accessories
Mfr
N.A.I.C.S.: 336350
M. Reischer *(Mng Dir)*

**GD European Land Systems Holding
GmbH**   (1)
2 Haidequerstrasse 3, 1111, Vienna, Austria
Tel.: (43) 1760640
Holding Company
N.A.I.C.S.: 551112

GPS Source, Inc.   (1)
2121 Executive Cir, Colorado Springs, CO
80906
Tel.: (719) 421-7300
Web Site: https://www.gpssource.com
Fiscal Year-end: 12/31/2006
Signal Distribution Product Mfr & Distr
N.A.I.C.S.: 334220

**General Dynamics Aerospace
Group**   (1)
2941 Fairview Park Dr Ste 100, Falls
Church, VA 22042
Tel.: (703) 876-3000
Sales Range: $5-14.9 Billion
Jet Aircraft Engineering & Mfr
N.A.I.C.S.: 336411

Subsidiary (Domestic):

**Gulfstream Aerospace
Corporation**   (2)
500 Gulfstream Rd, Savannah, GA 31408
Tel.: (912) 965-3000
Web Site: http://www.gulfstream.com
Sales Range: $750-799.9 Million
Emp.: 13,313
Designer, Developer, Producer & Marketer
of Large-Cabin & Business Jet Aircraft
N.A.I.C.S.: 336411
Mark L. Burns *(Pres)*
Ira P. Berman *(Gen Counsel & Sr VP-Admin)*

Subsidiary (Domestic):

The Nordam Group, Inc.   (3)

6911 N Whirlpool Dr, Tulsa, OK 74117
Tel.: (918) 587-4105
Web Site: http://www.nordam.com
Sales Range: $150-199.9 Million
Emp.: 2,000
Aircraft Components Repair & Mfr
N.A.I.C.S.: 336413
Bailey J. Siegfried *(VP-Culture, Comm, IT, HR & Corp Responsibility)*
Marc Overton *(VP-Bus Dev)*
Alain Poupin *(VP-Sls-Europe, Middle East & Africa)*
William Lawless *(VP-Supply Chain)*
Barry Walters *(VP-Sls)*
Galen Deeds *(VP-NTR Engrg)*
Carlos Flores *(VP-Mfg Sls)*
Raegen Siegfried *(VP-HushWorks)*
Judy Carle *(CFO)*
Meredith Siegfried Madden *(CEO)*

Subsidiary (Non-US):

NORDAM Europe Limited   (4)
Hawtin Park Blackwood, Gwent, NP12 2EU,
South Wales, United Kingdom
Tel.: (44) 1443865400
Web Site: http://www.nordam.com
Emp.: 300
Aircraft Part Mfr
N.A.I.C.S.: 336413

NORDAM Singapore Pte Ltd   (4)
33 Changi North Crescent, Singapore,
499640, Singapore
Tel.: (65) 64967100
Emp.: 100
Aircraft Part Mfr
N.A.I.C.S.: 336413

Subsidiary (Domestic):

The Nordam Group, Inc.   (4)
7018 N Lakewood, Tulsa, OK
74117   **(100%)**
Tel.: (918) 274-2700
Sales Range: $25-49.9 Million
Emp.: 140
Aircraft Parts & Equipment Mfr
N.A.I.C.S.: 336413

Subsidiary (Non-US):

Jet Aviation Management   (2)
Zurich Airport, PO Box 229, Zurich, 8058,
Switzerland
Tel.: (41) 581588888
Web Site: http://www.jetaviation.com
Sales Range: $1-4.9 Billion
Emp.: 60
Aircraft Maintenance & Repair Services
N.A.I.C.S.: 488190
Hardy Butschi *(VP-Ops-Middle East & Gen Mgr-Dubai)*

Subsidiary (US):

Jet Aviation Group   (3)
112 Charles A Lindberg Dr, Teterboro, NJ
07608
Tel.: (201) 462-4000
Web Site: http://www.jetaviation.com
Aircraft Management & Flight Support
N.A.I.C.S.: 336412

Subsidiary (Domestic):

Jet Aviation St. Louis, Inc.   (4)
6400 Curtiss Steinberg Dr, Cahokia, IL
62206-1445
Tel.: (618) 646-8000
Web Site: http://www.jetaviation.com
Sales Range: $50-74.9 Million
Aircraft Maintenance & Modification
N.A.I.C.S.: 488190
Charles F. Krugh *(Sr VP & Gen Mgr)*

**General Dynamics Combat Systems
Group**   (1)
2941 Fairview Park Dr Ste 100, Falls
Church, VA 22042
Tel.: (703) 876-3000
Web Site: http://www.generaldynamics.com
Land & Expeditionary Combat Systems
Support & Mfr
N.A.I.C.S.: 336992
Mark C. Roualet *(Exec VP)*

Subsidiary (Domestic):

General Dynamics Armament & Technical Products   (2)

General Dynamics Corporation—(Continued)

Four LakePointe Plz 2118 Water Rdg Pkwy,
Charlotte, NC 28217-4526
Tel.: (704) 714-8000
Web Site: http://www.gd.com
Business Development, Strategic Planning,
Finance, Human Resources & Administration Services for Division
N.A.I.C.S.: 551114

Subsidiary (Non-US):

General Dynamics European Land
Systems GmbH   **(2)**
Bleibtreustrasse 2, A-1110, Vienna,
Austria   **(100%)**
Tel.: (43) 1760640
Web Site: http://www.gdels.com
Sales Range: $500-549.9 Million
Emp.: 2,200
Combat Vehicles, Artillery Systems & Light
Weapons & Munitions Mfr
N.A.I.C.S.: 336992

Subsidiary (Non-US):

General Dynamics European Land
Systems Germany GmbH   **(3)**
Barbarossastr 30, 67655, Kaiserslautern,
Germany   **(100%)**
Tel.: (49) 63136160
Web Site: http://www.gdels.com
Sales Range: $250-299.9 Million
Emp.: 300
Military Vehicle Merchant Whslr
N.A.I.C.S.: 423860

Subsidiary (Domestic):

General Dynamics European Land
Systems-Steyr   **(3)**
2 Haidequerstrasse 3, PO Box 100, Vienna,
1111, Austria   **(100%)**
Tel.: (43) 1 760 64
Web Site: http://www.steyr-ssf.com
Sales Range: $300-349.9 Million
Emp.: 150
Armored Vehicle Mfr
N.A.I.C.S.: 336992
M. Reischer (Mng Dir)

Subsidiary (Non-US):

MOWAG GmbH   **(3)**
Unterseestrasse 65, 8280, Kreuzlingen,
Switzerland   **(100%)**
Tel.: (41) 716775500
Web Site: http://www.mowag.com
Sales Range: $300-349.9 Million
Military Vehicle Mfr
N.A.I.C.S.: 336992

Santa Barbara Sistemas S.A.
PE Cristalia Edificio 7/8 C/Via de los Pobla-
dos 3, 28033, Madrid, Spain   **(100%)**
Tel.: (34) 915850110
Web Site: http://www.gdels.com
Combat Vehicles, Artillery Systems & Light
Weapons & Munitions Mfr
N.A.I.C.S.: 336992

Subsidiary (Domestic):

General Dynamics Land Systems
Inc.   **(2)**
38500 Mound Rd, Sterling Heights, MI,
48310
Tel.: (586) 825-4000
Web Site: http://www.gdls.com
Sales Range: $1-4.9 Billion
Military Vehicle Mfr
N.A.I.C.S.: 336992
Gary L. Whited (Pres)

Subsidiary (Domestic):

Force Protection, Inc.   **(3)**
1520 Old Trolley Rd, Summerville, SC
29485
Tel.: (843) 574-7001
Web Site: http://www.forceprotection.net
Sales Range: $650-699.9 Million
Emp.: 1,280
Aircraft Mfr
N.A.I.C.S.: 336411
Francis P. Kavanaugh (Founder)

General Dynamics Robotic
Systems   **(3)**

1231 Tech Ct, Westminster, MD 21157-
3029
Tel.: (410) 876-9200
Web Site: http://www.gdrs.com
Sales Range: $25-49.9 Million
Emp.: 250
Aircraft Mfr
N.A.I.C.S.: 336411

Subsidiary (Domestic):

General Dynamics Ordnance and
Tactical Systems, Inc.   **(2)**
11399 16th Ct N Ste 200, Saint Petersburg,
FL 33716   **(100%)**
Tel.: (727) 578-8100
Web Site: http://www.gd-ots.com
Sales Range: $125-149.9 Million
Emp.: 300
Large & Small Caliber Munitions Mfr
N.A.I.C.S.: 332993
Firat H. Gezen (Pres)

Subsidiary (Domestic):

General Dynamics OTS (DRI),
Inc.   **(3)**
1425 Commerce Blvd, Anniston, AL
36207   **(100%)**
Tel.: (256) 835-1660
Web Site: http://www.gd-ots.com
Sales Range: $75-99.9 Million
Emp.: 200
Armored Military Vehicle Mfr
N.A.I.C.S.: 336992

General Dynamics OTS (Versatron),
Inc.   **(3)**
511 Grove St, Healdsburg, CA 95448-4814
Tel.: (707) 473-9200
Web Site: http://www.generaldynamics.com
Sales Range: $25-49.9 Million
Emp.: 115
Developer of Aerospace Engineering
N.A.I.C.S.: 333995

General Dynamics Ordnance & Tacti-
cal Systems   **(3)**
1200 N Glenbrook Dr, Garland, TX 75040-
5029
Tel.: (972) 276-5131
Web Site: http://www.generaldynamics.com
Military Ordnance Mfr
N.A.I.C.S.: 332994

General Dynamics Ordnance and
Tactical Systems - Munition
Services   **(3)**
4174 County Rd 180, Carthage, MO
64836   **(100%)**
Tel.: (417) 624-0212
Web Site: http://www.ebveec.com
Sales Range: $1-9.9 Million
Emp.: 130
Disposal of Explosives & Explosive Wastes
N.A.I.C.S.: 562211

Subsidiary (Non-US):

General Dynamics Ordnance and
Tactical Systems-Canada Inc.   **(3)**
5 Montee Des Arsenaux, Repentigny, J5Z
2P4, QC, Canada
Tel.: (450) 581-3080
Web Site: http://www.gd-otscanada.com
Emp.: 1,200
Operational Ammunition Mfr
N.A.I.C.S.: 332993
Rene Blouin (Pres)

Subsidiary (Domestic):

St. Marks Powder, Inc.   **(3)**
7121 Coastal Hwy, Crawfordville, FL 32327-
2918
Tel.: (850) 925-6111
Web Site: http://www.generaldynamics.com
Sales Range: $100-124.9 Million
Emp.: 300
Propellant Manufacturing; Research & De-
velopment
N.A.I.C.S.: 325199

General Dynamics Commercial Cyber
Services, LLC   **(1)**
13857 McLearen Rd, Herndon, VA 20171
Tel.: (703) 268-7088
Aircraft & Submarine Mfr
N.A.I.C.S.: 336411

David Ross (Gen Mgr)

General Dynamics Corp. - Convair
Division   **(1)**
PO Box 85357, San Diego, CA 92186-5357
Tel.: (858) 573-8000
Rev.: $731,000,000
Emp.: 2,500
Mfr of Aircraft Fuselages
N.A.I.C.S.: 813920

General Dynamics European Land
Systems - Austria GmbH   **(1)**
Haidequerstrasse 3, 1110, Vienna, Austria
Tel.: (43) 1760640
Armored Military Vehicle Mfr
N.A.I.C.S.: 336992
Josef Esberger (Program Mgr)

General Dynamics European Land
Systems - Bridge Systems
GmbH   **(1)**
Barbarossastr 30, 67655, Kaiserslautern,
Germany
Tel.: (49) 63136160
Armored Wheeled Vehicle Mfr
N.A.I.C.S.: 336992
Christian Kauth (Mng Dir & VP-Bridge Sys-
tems)

General Dynamics European Land
Systems - Czech s.r.o.   **(1)**
Nachodska 469/137, Horni Pocernice, 193
00, Prague, 9, Czech Republic
Tel.: (420) 230234620
Wheeled Vehicle Mfr
N.A.I.C.S.: 336999

General Dynamics European Land
Systems - Deutschland GmbH   **(1)**
Pariser Platz 4a 1 OG, 10117, Berlin, Ger-
many
Tel.: (49) 30300145704
Armored Wheeled Vehicle Mfr
N.A.I.C.S.: 336992
Thomas Kauffmann (Mng Dir)

General Dynamics European Land
Systems - FWW GmbH   **(1)**
Krusehofer Str 22 24, Woldegk, 17036,
Neubrandenburg, Germany
Tel.: (49) 3954531100
Armored Wheeled Vehicle Mfr
N.A.I.C.S.: 336992

General Dynamics European Land
Systems - Mowag GmbH   **(1)**
Unterseestrasse 65, 8280, Kreuzlingen,
Switzerland
Tel.: (41) 716775500
Web Site: http://www.gdels.com
Motor Vehicle Components & Accessories
Mfr
N.A.I.C.S.: 336350
Oliver Duerr (Mng Dir)

General Dynamics Government Sys-
tems Corporation   **(1)**
77 A St, Needham Heights, MA 02494
Tel.: (781) 449-2000
Communication Equipment Mfr
N.A.I.C.S.: 334290

General Dynamics Information Sys-
tems & Technology Group   **(1)**
2941 Fairview Park Dr Ste 100, Falls
Church, VA 22042-4513
Tel.: (703) 876-3000
Sales Range: $5-14.9 Billion
Government & Commercial Systems Inte-
gration Expertise; Hardware & Software
Products; & Engineering, Management &
Support Services
N.A.I.C.S.: 561990

Subsidiary (Domestic):

General Dynamics Information Tech-
nology, Inc.   **(2)**
3150 Fairview Park Dr, Falls Church, VA
22042   **(100%)**
Tel.: (703) 995-8700
Web Site: http://www.gdit.com
Sales Range: $100-124.9 Million
Designer, Builder & Operator of Enterprise
& Wireless Networks
N.A.I.C.S.: 541512
Alison Harbrecht (CFO & VP-Fin)
Kelly Ferrell (Sr VP-Intelligence & Home-
land Security)

Kristine Grinnell (CIO & VP-IT & Supply
Chain)
Tammy Kness (VP-HR & Comm)
Paul Nedzbala (Sr VP-Federal Civilian)
Leigh Palmer (Sr VP-Defense)
Kyle McNamara (Gen Counsel & Sr VP)
Dave Collins (VP)
John Slota (Chief Growth Officer & VP)
Ben Gianni (CTO & VP)
M. Amy Gilliland (Pres)
Garrett Yee (VP-Army Sector & Gen Mgr-
Army Sector)
Justin DePalmo (Chief Info Security Officer)
James Hannah (CIO-Global & Sr VP-Supply
Chain)
Barbara Graham (VP-Navy & Marine Corps
Accounts & Gen Mgr-Navy & Marine Corps
Accounts)

Division (Domestic):

General Dynamics Information
Technology   **(3)**
99 Mechanic St, Pawcatuck, CT 06379-
2132
Tel.: (860) 441-2510
Web Site: http://www.gdit.com
Engineering Technologies & Technology-
Based Training Solutions
N.A.I.C.S.: 541519

General Dynamics Information
Technology   **(3)**
1545 Crossways Blvd Ste A, Chesapeake,
VA 23320
Tel.: (757) 424-6311
Web Site: http://www.gdit.com
Marine Vessel Computer Design Services
N.A.I.C.S.: 541512

General Dynamics Information
Technology   **(3)**
2450 Oakdale Blvd, Coralville, IA
52241   **(100%)**
Tel.: (319) 665-7900
Web Site: http://www.gdit.com
Sales Range: $75-99.9 Million
Emp.: 250
Information Management & Business Pro-
cess Outsourcing Services
N.A.I.C.S.: 561499

General Dynamics Information
Technology   **(3)**
3150 Fairview Park Dr, Falls Church, VA
22042
Tel.: (703) 995-8700
Web Site: https://www.gdit.com
Sales Range: $10-24.9 Million
Emp.: 50
Custom Computer Programming Services
N.A.I.C.S.: 541512

General Dynamics Information
Technology   **(3)**
77 A St, Needham, MA 02494   **(100%)**
Tel.: (781) 444-7407
Web Site: http://www.gdit.com
Developer of Computer Systems
N.A.I.C.S.: 541512
Matthew McFadden (VP-Cyber)

Subsidiary (Domestic):

ViPS Inc.   **(3)**
1 W Pennsylvania Ave, Baltimore, MD
21204
Tel.: (410) 832-8300
Web Site: http://www.vips.com
Rev.: $15,100,000
Emp.: 255
Healthcare Data Management, Analytics,
Decision Support, Process Automation &
Related Information Technology Services
N.A.I.C.S.: 541512

Subsidiary (Domestic):

General Dynamics Mission Systems,
Inc.   **(2)**
12450 Fair Lakes Cir, Fairfax, VA 22033-
3810
Tel.: (877) 449-0600
Web Site: https://gdmissionsystems.com
Emp.: 12,000

Provider of Command Information, Intelligence & Surveillance Solutions
N.A.I.C.S.: 334111

Subsidiary (Domestic):

General Dynamics Global Imaging Technologies, Inc. (3)
24 Simon St, Nashua, NH 03060
Tel.: (603) 864-6300
Web Site: http://www.gd-imaging.com
Emp.: 1,284
Aircraft Mfr
N.A.I.C.S.: 336411

Plant (Domestic):

General Dynamics Global Imaging Technologies, Inc. - Cullman (4)
6717 Alabama Hwy 157, Cullman, AL 35057
Tel.: (256) 737-5200
Web Site: http://www.gd-imaging.com
Sales Range: $75-99.9 Million
Emp.: 250
Gas Bearings, Components & Assemblies Mfr
N.A.I.C.S.: 335312

General Dynamics Global Imaging Technologies, Inc. - Rochester Hills (4)
2909 Waterview Dr, Rochester Hills, MI 48309-4600
Tel.: (248) 293-2900
Web Site: http://www.gd-imaging.com
Sales Range: $50-74.9 Million
Emp.: 100
Sensitive Optical, Scanners & Mirrors Systems Devices Mfr
N.A.I.C.S.: 333310

General Dynamics Global Imaging Technologies, Inc. - San Diego (4)
7603 Saint Andrews Ave, San Diego, CA 92154
Tel.: (619) 671-5400
Web Site: http://www.gd-imaging.com
Sales Range: $50-74.9 Million
Emp.: 180
Servo & Motors, Digital Encoders, Clutches & Brakes, Actuator Systems Mfr
N.A.I.C.S.: 335314

Plant (Domestic):

General Dynamics Mission Systems, Inc (3)
8800 Queen Ave S, Bloomington, MN 55431 **(100%)**
Tel.: (952) 921-6100
Web Site: https://gdmissionsystems.com
Software & Hardware Mfr
N.A.I.C.S.: 334290

Subsidiary (Domestic):

General Dynamics Mission Systems, Inc. (3)
5440 Mill Stream Rd, Greensboro, NC 27301 **(100%)**
Tel.: (336) 698-8000
Web Site: https://gdmissionsystems.com
Advances Systems for the Federal Government, Digital Studio System
N.A.I.C.S.: 541330

Plant (Domestic):

General Dynamics Mission Systems, Inc. (3)
12450 Fair Lakes Cir, Fairfax, VA 22030
Tel.: (877) 449-0600
Protector of Critical Information Assets & Transforming Data into Usable Knowledge for Real-Time Decision-Making
N.A.I.C.S.: 541512

Subsidiary (Non-US):

General Dynamics UK Ltd. (2)
Unit 1 & 3 Oakdale Court Oakdale Business Park, Blackwood, NP12 4AD, United Kingdom **(100%)**
Tel.: (44) 1495236300
Web Site:
   http://www.generaldynamics.uk.com
Sales Range: $350-399.9 Million
Emp.: 1,500

Military Computer Database & Communication Network Services
N.A.I.C.S.: 541512

General Dynamics Information Technology Canada, Limited (1)
30 Camelot Dr, Nepean, K2G 5X8, ON, Canada
Tel.: (613) 723-9500
Web Site: http://www.canada.gdit.com
Computer System Design Services
N.A.I.C.S.: 541512

General Dynamics Information Technology Commercial Solutions, LLC (1)
3211 Jermantown Rd, Fairfax, VA 22030
Tel.: (703) 995-8700
Information Technology Consulting Services
N.A.I.C.S.: 541511

General Dynamics Information Technology Limited (1)
South Quay Buildg 3 189 Marsh Wall Canary Wharf, London, E14 9SH, United Kingdom
Tel.: (44) 2079393600
Web Site: http://www.uk.gdit.com
Emp.: 50
Information Technology Services
N.A.I.C.S.: 541512
Assad Tabet (Mng Dir)

General Dynamics Itronix Europe Ltd. (1)
Earlplace Business Park Fletchamstead Highway, Coventry, CV4 9UR, West Midlands, United Kingdom
Tel.: (44) 2476714800
Web Site: http://www.gd-itronix.com
Computer Component Mfr
N.A.I.C.S.: 334118

General Dynamics Land Systems - Canada Corporation (1)
1991 Oxford St E, London, N5V 2Z7, ON, Canada
Tel.: (519) 964-5900
Web Site: http://www.gdlscanada.com
Emp.: 1,650
Aerospace & Motor Vehicle Parts Mfr
N.A.I.C.S.: 336411

General Dynamics Land Systems Customer Service & Support Company (1)
38500 Mound Rd, Sterling Heights, MI 48310-3260
Tel.: (586) 825-4000
Web Site: https://www.gdls.com
Shipbuilding & Repairing Services
N.A.I.C.S.: 336611

General Dynamics Marine Systems, Inc. (1)
2941 Fairview Park Dr Ste 100, Falls Church, VA 22042
Tel.: (703) 876-3000
Web Site: http://www.generaldynamics.com
Sales Range: $5-14.9 Billion
Navy Submarine & Surface Ships Mfr
N.A.I.C.S.: 336611

Subsidiary (Domestic):

American Overseas Marine Corporation (2)
100 Newport Ave Ext, Quincy, MA 02171-1759 **(100%)**
Tel.: (617) 786-8300
Web Site: http://www.gdamsea.com
Sales Range: $50-74.9 Million
Emp.: 249
Military Vehicles Mfr
N.A.I.C.S.: 336992
Thomas W. Merrell (Pres)

Bath Iron Works Corporation (2)
700 Washington St, Bath, ME 04530-2574 **(100%)**
Tel.: (207) 443-3311
Web Site: http://www.gdbiw.com
Sales Range: $800-899.9 Million
Ship Building & Repairs
N.A.I.C.S.: 336611
Dirk A. Lesko (Pres)
Brent West (VP-Supply Chain Mgmt & Quality)
Eugene Miller (VP-Ops)

Andrew Bond (VP-HR)
Christopher Waaler (VP-Engrg & IT)
Chris Ouellette (Dir-Strategic Plng)
Vincent Dickinson (Dir-Facilities)
Scott Zamer (CFO & VP-Fin)

Electric Boat Corporation (2)
75 Eastern Point Rd, Groton, CT 06340 **(100%)**
Tel.: (860) 433-3000
Web Site: http://www.gdeb.com
Sales Range: $1-4.9 Billion
Electrical Boat Mfr
N.A.I.C.S.: 336611
Sean Davies (VP-Quonset Point Ops)
T. Blair Decker (Chief Supply Officer & VP)
James P. Gildart (VP-Ops)
Matthew S. Luxton (Gen Counsel & VP)
Kevin Graney (Pres)
Kurt A. Hesch (Sr VP-Programs)
Will Lennon (VP-Quality & Radiological Controls)
Emil Casciano (VP-Engrg & Design)
Larry Runkle (VP-Virginia Program)
Andrew Bond (VP-HR)
Joe Drake (VP-Facilities Master Plan)
Mark Rayha (VP-Fin)
Ray Gabriel (VP-Plng)
Brett Cicchese (Dir-Strategic Plng)
Ken Jeanos (CIO)
Liz Power (Dir-Comm & Pub Affairs)
John V. Leonard Jr. (CFO & VP-Fin, Contracts & Strategic Plng)

NASSCO Holdings Incorporated (2)
2798 E Harbor Dr, San Diego, CA 92113 **(100%)**
Tel.: (619) 544-3400
Web Site: http://www.nassco.com
Sales Range: $650-699.9 Million
Ship Repairing Services
N.A.I.C.S.: 336611
David J. Carver (Pres)
Debora Burke (Gen Counsel & VP)
Dave Baker (VP-Repair)
Steve Davison (VP-Ops)
Steve Eckberg (VP-Programs & Bus Dev)
Tim Glinatsis (CIO & VP-Engrg)
Treavor Callum (VP-Ops Support)
Peter Brown (VP-Supply Chain)
Steve Solomon (VP-HR)

Subsidiary (Domestic):

NASSCO-Norfolk (3)
200 Ligon St, Norfolk, VA 23323
Tel.: (757) 543-6801
Web Site: http://www.nassconorfolk.com
Sales Range: $100-124.9 Million
Emp.: 400
Ship Building & Repairing Services
N.A.I.C.S.: 336611

General Dynamics Mission Systems - Canada (1)
1941 Robertson Road, Ottawa, K2H 5B7, ON, Canada
Tel.: (613) 596-7000
Web Site: http://www.gdcanada.com
Defence Technology & Systems Integration Services
N.A.I.C.S.: 541512

General Dynamics Mission Systems - Italy S.R.L. (1)
Viale Egeo 100-106, 00144, Rome, Italy
Tel.: (39) 06503951
Web Site: http://www.gd-ms.it
Telecommunication Servicesb
N.A.I.C.S.: 517810
Andrea Floris (Pres)
Pasquale Andolfo (Gen Mgr)
Marco Martorelli (Fin Dir)
Toni Partipilo (Dir-Bus Dev & Sls)

General Dynamics Mission Systems Asia-Pacific Sdn. Bhd. (1)
Unit 3 First Floor Simpang 88 Kiulap Commercial Centre, Kg Kiulap, Negara, Brunei Darussalam
Tel.: (673) 2565255
Web Site: https://gd-ms.asia
Aircraft Mfr
N.A.I.C.S.: 336411

General Dynamics Mission Systems, LLC (1)
12450 Fair Lakes Cir, Fairfax, VA 22033
Tel.: (312) 282-1048

Web Site:
   http://www.gdmissionsystems.com
Communication Management Services
N.A.I.C.S.: 517410
Bill Weiss (VP-Mfg & Logistics)
Carlo Zaffanella (VP & Gen Mgr-Maritime & Strategic Sys)
Christopher J. Brady (Pres)
David Ibbetson (VP & Gen Mgr-Mission Sys-Intl)
Devon Engel (Gen Counsel & VP)
Jerzy Piatkowski (VP-Contracts & Comml)
Jim Stockdale (Sr VP-Bus Ops)
Manny Mora (VP & Gen Mgr-Space & Intelligence Sys)
Christopher J. Hiltbrand (VP-People)
Bo Elam (CFO & VP)
Sharon Dunbar (VP-Cross-Company Bus Initiatives)
William E. Patterson (VP & Gen Mgr-Ground Sys)
Brian Morrison (VP & Gen Mgr-Cyber Sys)
Lisa Finneran (VP-Engrg)
Scott Butler (Sr VP-Program Execution)
Nadia Short (VP-Strategy & Bus Dev)
Michael McDermott (VP-Mktg)
Scott Blanchard (CTO & VP)
Scotty Miller (VP-Supply Chain Mgmt)

General Dynamics OTS (Niceville), Inc. (1)
115 Hart St, Niceville, FL 32578
Tel.: (850) 897-9700
Emp.: 125
Automobile Parts Mfr
N.A.I.C.S.: 336211

General Dynamics OTS (Pennsylvania), Inc. (1)
156 Cedar Ave, Scranton, PA 18505-1138
Tel.: (570) 340-1114
Automobile Parts Mfr
N.A.I.C.S.: 336211

General Dynamics Ordnance and Tactical Systems - Canada Valleyfield Inc. (1)
55 Rue Masson, Valleyfield, J6S 4V9, QC, Canada
Tel.: (450) 371-5520
Web Site: http://www.gd-otscanada.com
Ammunition Products Mfr
N.A.I.C.S.: 332993

General Dynamics Ordnance and Tactical Systems - Simunition Operations, Inc. (1)
PO Box 576, Avon, CT 06001-0576
Tel.: (860) 404-0162
Web Site: http://www.gd-otscanada.com
Emp.: 10
Armored Military Vehicle Parts Mfr
N.A.I.C.S.: 336992

General Dynamics Properties, Inc. (1)
2941 Farview Pk Dr, Falls Church, VA 22042 **(100%)**
Tel.: (703) 876-3631
Web Site: http://www.gd.com
Property Consulting Services
N.A.I.C.S.: 531390

General Dynamics Satcom Technologies Asia Private Limited (1)
Suite 844 Udyog Vihar Phase V Opposite Oberoi Hotel, Gurgaon, 122016, Haryana, India
Tel.: (91) 1244581900
Web Site: http://www.gdsatcom.com
Emp.: 50
Communication Equipment Merchant Whslr
N.A.I.C.S.: 423690

General Dynamics Satellite Communication Services, Inc. (1)
8201 E Mcdowell Rd, Scottsdale, AZ 85257
Tel.: (480) 441-3033
Aircraft Mfr
N.A.I.C.S.: 336411

General Dynamics Shared Resources, Inc. (1)
2044 India Rd, Charlottesville, VA 22901
Tel.: (434) 964-2595
Web Site:
   http://www.generaldynamicscareers.com
Aerospace Products Mfr
N.A.I.C.S.: 336411

General Dynamics Corporation—(Continued)

**General Dynamics United Kingdom
Limited** (1)
Unit 1 and 3 Oakdale Court Oakdale Business Park, Blackwood, South Wales, NP12
4AD, United Kingdom
Tel.: (44) 1495236300
Web Site: https://generaldynamics.uk.com
Armoured Fighting Vehicle Mfr & Distr
N.A.I.C.S.: 336211

General Dynamics Vertex RSI
1217 Digtal Dr, Richardson, TX 75081-2800
Tel.: (972) 690-8865
Web Site: http://www.vertexrsi.com
Sales Range: $25-49.9 Million
Emp.: 58
Large Satellite Earth Station Antennas Mfr
N.A.I.C.S.: 334220

General Dynamics Worldwide Holdings, Inc. (1)
2941 Frview Park Dr Ste 100, Falls Church,
VA 22042
Tel.: (703) 876-3000
Aircraft Product Mfr
N.A.I.C.S.: 336411

General Dynamics-OTS, Inc. (1)
11399 16th Ct N Ste 200, Saint Petersburg,
FL 33716
Tel.: (727) 578-8100
Web Site: http://www.gd-ots.com
Weapon & Tank Component Mfr
N.A.I.C.S.: 336992

Gulfstream - California, Inc. (1)
1501 Aviation Blvd, Lincoln, CA 95648-9388
Tel.: (916) 645-8961
Aircraft Part Mfr
N.A.I.C.S.: 336411

**Gulfstream Aerospace Corporation of
Texas** (1)
7440 Aviation Pl, Dallas, TX 75235-2804
Tel.: (214) 902-7500
Web Site: http://www.gulfstream.com
Aircraft Product Mfr
N.A.I.C.S.: 336411
Brent Monroe (Sr VP-Sls-Canada)

**Gulfstream Aerospace Services
Corporation** (1)
W6365 Discovery Dr, Appleton, WI 54914-
9190
Tel.: (920) 735-7000
Aircraft Product Mfr
N.A.I.C.S.: 336411
Mark Knall (VP & Gen Mgr)

**Hawker Pacific Airservices
Limited** (1)
Room B 23rd Floor Excelsior Industrial-
Building, 68-76 Sha Tsui Road, Tsuen Wan,
China (Hong Kong)
Tel.: (852) 66036363
Aircraft Maintenance & Heavy Transport Mfr
N.A.I.C.S.: 336411

Subsidiary (Non-US):

Jet Aviation Australia Pty Ltd (2)
112 Airport Avenue Bankstown Airport,
Bankstown, Sydney, 2200, NSW, Australia
Tel.: (61) 287131190
Emp.: 221
Aviation Services
N.A.I.C.S.: 488119

Interiores Aereos S.A. de C.V. (1)
Boulevard Lazaro Cardenas No 2385 Col
Ellas Calles, Mexicali, 21397, Mexico
Tel.: (52) 6865628600
Web Site: http://www.gulfstream.com
Emp.: 5,000
Automobile Part Merchant Whslr
N.A.I.C.S.: 423110

Itronix Corporation (1)
12825 E Mirabeau Pkwy, Spokane Valley,
WA 99216-1464
Tel.: (509) 624-6600
Web Site: http://www.itronix.com
Sales Range: $150-199.9 Million
Emp.: 400
Mfr And Selling of Ruggedized Portable
Notebook Computers for Field-Service Applications
N.A.I.C.S.: 334111

Subsidiary (Non-US):

Itronix UK (2)
Fleychamstead Business Park Fletcham-
stead Highway, Coventry, CV4 7AW, United
Kingdom
Tel.: (44) 2476714800
Web Site: http://www.gd-itronix.com
Sales Range: $75-99.9 Million
Emp.: 35
N.A.I.C.S.: 523910

Janteq Australia Pty. Limited (1)
1 Talavera Road Suite 12, Macquarie Park,
2113, NSW, Australia
Tel.: (61) 298708070
Wireless Equipment Mfr
N.A.I.C.S.: 334220

Janteq Corp. (1)
9975 Toledo Way, Irvine, CA 92618
Tel.: (949) 215-2603
Web Site: https://www.janteq.com
Wireless Equipment Mfr
N.A.I.C.S.: 334220

Jet Aviation AG (1)
Aeschengraben 6, 4051, Basel, Switzerland
Tel.: (41) 581584111
Aircraft Mfr
N.A.I.C.S.: 336411

**Jet Aviation Business Jets
Deutschland GmbH** (1)
Cologne/Bonn Airport Hangar 3, 51147, Co-
logne, Germany
Tel.: (49) 2203955555
Aviation Industry Services
N.A.I.C.S.: 481219

Jet Aviation Holding GmbH (1)
Flughafenstrasse, PO Box 214, Basel-
Airport, 4030, Basel, Switzerland
Tel.: (41) 581584111
Web Site: http://www.jetaviation.com
Emp.: 1,300
Holding Company
N.A.I.C.S.: 551112
Matthew Woollaston (VP-Completions Sls)
Stefan Benz (Sr VP-Ops-EMEA)

Jet Aviation Houston, Inc. (1)
8620 W Monroe William P Hobby Airport,
Houston, TX 77061
Tel.: (713) 358-9100
Web Site: http://www.jetaviation.com
Emp.: 50
Aviation Industry Services
N.A.I.C.S.: 481219
Brandon Davis (Dir-FBO Svcs)

Jet Aviation Services GmbH (1)
Flughafenstrasse 60, 40474, Dusseldorf,
Germany
Tel.: (49) 2114217062
Aviation Industry Services
N.A.I.C.S.: 481219

Metro Machine Corp. (1)
PO Box 1860, Norfolk, VA 23501
Tel.: (757) 543-6801
Web Site: https://www.nassconorfolk.com
Aircraft Mfr
N.A.I.C.S.: 336411

OOO Jet Aviation Vnukovo (1)
Office 229 Building 1 House 3 Airport Vnu-
kovo, Moscow, 119027, Russia
Tel.: (7) 4954366049
Web Site: http://www.jetaviation.com
Emp.: 32
Aircraft Maintenance Services
N.A.I.C.S.: 488119
Vitaly Aleksikov (Gen Dir)

Open Kernel Labs Pty Ltd (1)
Suite 3 540 Botany Road, Alexandria, Syd-
ney, 2015, NSW, Australia
Tel.: (61) 280039900
Software Programming Services
N.A.I.C.S.: 541511

Open Kernel Labs, Inc. (1)
200 S Wacker Dr 15th Fl, Chicago, IL
60606
Tel.: (312) 924-1445
Web Site: http://www.ok-labs.com
Software Programming Services
N.A.I.C.S.: 541511

SC3 LLC (1)

13857 McLearen Rd, Herndon, VA 20171
Tel.: (703) 880-2333
Web Site: http://www.sc3.com
Consulting & Technology Solution Services
N.A.I.C.S.: 921190
David Clark (CFO & COO)

Vertex RSI (1)
1004 N Martin Luther King Ave, Wortham,
TX 76693
Tel.: (254) 765-3304
Sales Range: $25-49.9 Million
Emp.: 100
Steel Communication Antennas Mfr
N.A.I.C.S.: 336611
Shawn Boyer (Mgr-Site)

**Vulnerability Research Labs,
LLC** (1)
2100 Reston Pkwy Ste 500, Reston, VA
20191-1200
Tel.: (571) 323-8200
Web Site: http://www.vrlsec.com
Custom Computer Programming Services
N.A.I.C.S.: 541511

GENERAL ELECTRIC COMPANY
1 Neumann Way, Cincinnati, OH
45215
Tel.: (407) 378-6203 NY
Web Site: https://www.ge.com
Year Founded: 1892
GE—(NYSE)
Rev.: $67,954,000,000
Assets: $163,045,000,000
Liabilities: $134,466,000,000
Net Worth: $28,579,000,000
Earnings: $9,186,000,000
Emp.: 125,000
Fiscal Year-end: 12/31/23
Holding Company
N.A.I.C.S.: 551112
Christoph Pereira (Chief Risk Officer
& VP-Strategy)
H. Lawrence Culp Jr. (Chm & CEO)
Michael J. Holston (Gen Counsel,
Sec & Sr VP)
L. Kevin Cox (Chief HR Officer & Sr
VP)
Jennifer VanBelle (Treas & Sr VP)
Rahul Ghai (CFO, CFO-GE Aero-
space & Sr VP)
Tara DiJulio (Chief Comm Officer,
Chief Corp Affairs Officer & VP)
Russell T. Stokes (Pres/CEO-
Commercial Engines & Svcs)
James C. Katzman (Sr VP-Bus Dev)
Germaine Hunter (Chief Diversity Of-
ficer)
Patrick de Castelbajac (Chief Strat-
egy Officer)
Phil Wickler (Chief Transformation
Officer)
Riccardo Procacci (Pres & CEO-
Propulsion & Additive Technologies)
Jake Phillips (Gen Counsel, Sec & Sr
VP)
Christian Meisner (Chief HR Officer)
Amy Gowder (Pres & CEO-Defense
& Sys)
David Burns (CIO)
Mohamed Ali (Sr VP-Engrg Div)
Mike Kauffman (Sr VP-Supply Chain)

Subsidiaries:

Avio, Inc. (1)
2700 Industrial Row Dr, Troy, MI 48084
Tel.: (248) 280-2200
Web Site: https://www.avioinc.com
Electrical Equipment Installation Services
N.A.I.C.S.: 238210

Bank BPH SpoBka Akcyjna (1)
ul Cypriana Kamila Norwida 1, 80-280,
Gdansk, Poland
Tel.: (48) 58 300 7500
Web Site: https://www.bph.pl
Banking Services
N.A.I.C.S.: 522110

Cardinal Cogen, Inc. (1)
288 Campus Dr, Stanford, CA 94305
Tel.: (650) 723-1790
Emp.: 30
Electronic Components Mfr
N.A.I.C.S.: 334419
Ron Dahlin (Mgr)

Concept Laser GmbH (1)
An Der Zeil 8, 96215, Lichtenfels, Germany
Tel.: (49) 957116790
Web Site: http://www.concept-laser.de
Metal Mfr & Distr
N.A.I.C.S.: 331110
Frank Herzog (Founder)

GE Albany US Holdings LLC (1)
3135 Easton Tpke, Fairfield, CT 06828
Tel.: (203) 373-3095
Holding Company
N.A.I.C.S.: 551112

GE Caledonian Limited (1)
Monument Crescent Shaw Farm Industrial
Estate, Prestwick, KA9 2RX, Ayrshire,
United Kingdom
Tel.: (44) 1292673000
Web Site:
    http://www.prestwickaerospace.com
Aircraft Gas Turbine Engine Mfr
N.A.I.C.S.: 336412
George Adam (Mng Dir)

GE Capital Global Holdings, LLC (1)
901 Main Ave, Norwalk, CT 06851
Tel.: (203) 840-6300
Emp.: 47,000
Financial Services
N.A.I.C.S.: 523940

GE Distributed Power, Inc. (1)
1101 W Saint Paul Ave, Waukesha, WI
53188
Tel.: (262) 547-3311
Emp.: 425
Eletric Power Generation Services
N.A.I.C.S.: 221115
Hinterberg Megan (Mgr-Comml)

GE Druck Holdings Limited (1)
Fir Tree Lane, Groby, LE6 0FH, Leicester,
United Kingdom
Tel.: (44) 1162317100
Web Site: http://www.ge.com
Emp.: 400
Sensor & Measurement Control Devices Mfr
N.A.I.C.S.: 334513

**GE Energy Power Conversion
GmbH** (1)
Culemeyerstrasse 1, Berlin, 12277, Ger-
many
Tel.: (49) 3076220
Wob Site:
    http://www.gepowerconversion.com
Eletric Power Generation Services
N.A.I.C.S.: 221115

**GE Energy Power Conversion UK
Holdings Limited** (1)
Boughton Road, Rugby, CV21 1BU, War-
wickshire, United Kingdom
Tel.: (44) 1788563563
Eletric Power Generation Services
N.A.I.C.S.: 221115

**GE Energy Power Conversion USA
Inc.** (1)
610 Epsilon Dr, Pittsburgh, PA 15238
Tel.: (412) 967-0765
Eletric Power Generation Services
N.A.I.C.S.: 221115

GE Energy Switzerland GmbH (1)
Brown Boveri Strasse 7, 5401, Baden, Swit-
zerland
Tel.: (41) 585057733
Eletric Power Generation Services
N.A.I.C.S.: 221115

**GE Engine Services Distribution,
LLC** (1)
1800 Donaldson Hwy, Erlanger, KY 41018-
3111
Tel.: (859) 525-3100
Engine Services
N.A.I.C.S.: 541330

GE Engine Services, LLC (1)
1 Neumann Way F118, Cincinnati, OH
45215

Tel.: (513) 552-3272
Aircraft Machinery Mfr
N.A.I.C.S.: 336413

GE Evergreen Engine Services Corporation (1)
8 Hang-Zhan S Rd, Dayan District, Taoyuan, 337, Taiwan
Tel.: (886) 33943000
Web Site: https://www.geevergreen.com
Aircraft Engine Parts Mfr
N.A.I.C.S.: 336412

GE Healthcare Limited (1)
Pollards Wood Nightingales Lane, Chalfont Saint Giles, HP8 4SP, Buckinghamshire, United Kingdom
Tel.: (44) 149 454 4000
Web Site: https://www.gehealthcare.co.uk
Medical Equipment Mfr & Distr
N.A.I.C.S.: 334510
Frank R. Jimenez *(Gen Counsel & Sec)*

GE Hungary Co. Ltd. (1)
Vaci St 77, 1044, Budapest, Hungary **(100%)**
Tel.: (36) 13991100
Web Site: http://www.ge.com
Sales Range: $600-649.9 Million
Emp.: 4,000
Electronic Products Mfr
N.A.I.C.S.: 335999

GE Hungary Kft. (1)
Kisret utca 1, 2112, Veresegyhaz, Hungary
Tel.: (36) 28587000
Electronic Components Distr
N.A.I.C.S.: 423690
Barsony Farkas *(Mng Dir)*

GE Intelligent Platforms Embedded Systems, Inc. (1)
2500 Austin Dr, Charlottesville, VA 22911
Tel.: (434) 978-5000
Hardware Mfr & Software Services
N.A.I.C.S.: 513210

GE Investments, Inc. (1)
3003 Summer St 6th Fl, Stamford, CT 06904
Tel.: (203) 326-2300
Financial Holding Company Services
N.A.I.C.S.: 551112
George Rhyne *(Pres)*

GE Jenbacher GmbH (1)
Achenseestrasse 1-3, 6200, Jenbach, Austria
Tel.: (43) 52446000
Web Site: https://www.innio.com
Gas Engine Mfr
N.A.I.C.S.: 335312

GE Oil & Gas U.K. Limited (1)
Gapton Hall Road, Great Yarmouth, NR31 0NL, Norfolkshire, United Kingdom
Tel.: (44) 1275811777
Oil & Gas Transmission Equipment Mfr
N.A.I.C.S.: 333132

GE Pacific Pte. Ltd. (1)
11 North Buona Vista Drive 09-00 the Metropolis Tower 2, Singapore, 138589, Singapore **(100%)**
Tel.: (65) 62207022
Web Site: http://www.ge.com
Sales Range: $100-124.9 Million
Emp.: 360
Appliance & Lighting Products Mfr & Repair Services
N.A.I.C.S.: 335220

GE Packaged Power, Inc. (1)
1333 W Loop S, Houston, TX 77027
Tel.: (713) 803-0900
Turbine Generator Mfr
N.A.I.C.S.: 333611

GE Packaged Power, L.P. (1)
16415 Jacintoport Blvd, Houston, TX 77015-6589
Tel.: (281) 452-3610
Turbine Generator Mfr
N.A.I.C.S.: 333611

GE Power (1)
1 River Rd, Schenectady, NY 12345
Tel.: (518) 385-2211
Web Site: http://www.gepower.com
Holding Company; Power Generation Systems & Equipment Mfr

N.A.I.C.S.: 551112

Subsidiary (Non-US):

Alstom Power Turbomachines SA (2)
3 Avenue des 3 Chenes, 90000, Belfort, 90000, France
Tel.: (33) 384551000
Web Site: https://www.alstom.com
Steam Turbines & Parts Mfr
N.A.I.C.S.: 333611

Unit (Domestic):

GE Energy (2)
13000 Jameson Rd, Tehachapi, CA 93561-8157
Tel.: (661) 823-6700
Web Site: http://www.gewindenergy.com
Rev.: $450,000,000
Emp.: 60
Electric Generating Wind Mills
N.A.I.C.S.: 333611

Subsidiary (Non-US):

GE Energy (2)
Daniel Goldbach Strasse 17-19, 40880, Ratingen, Germany
Tel.: (49) 21021080
Web Site: http://www.gepower.com
Sales Range: $10-24.9 Million
Emp.: 60
Network & Software Design
N.A.I.C.S.: 541512

GE Energy (2)
No 8 Tangi Hua Street, Auckland, 1010, New Zealand
Tel.: (64) 93631740
Web Site: http://www.ge.com
Sales Range: $100-124.9 Million
Emp.: 8
Energy & Power Production
N.A.I.C.S.: 221122

Unit (Domestic):

GE Energy (2)
5660 Greenwood Plz Blvd, Denver, CO 80111
Tel.: (303) 268-6125
Web Site: http://www.gepower.com
Sales Range: $25-49.9 Million
Emp.: 3
Designs & Manages Corporate Networks
N.A.I.C.S.: 541512

Subsidiary (Non-US):

GE Energy (2)
Engelbergerstrasse 21, 79106, Freiburg, Germany
Tel.: (49) 761368210
Web Site: http://www.gepower.com
Sales Range: $10-24.9 Million
Emp.: 50
Information Technology & Software Developer
N.A.I.C.S.: 541511

GE Energy (2)
2300 Meadowvale Blvd, Mississauga, L5N 5P9, ON, Canada
Tel.: (905) 858-5100
Web Site: http://www.ge-energy.com
Emp.: 700
Hydro Turbines & Generators Mfr
N.A.I.C.S.: 333611

Unit (Domestic):

GE Energy (2)
1990 W NASA Blvd, Melbourne, FL 32904
Tel.: (321) 435-7000
Web Site: http://www.gepower.com
Sales Range: $50-74.9 Million
Emp.: 250
Energy Management Systems
N.A.I.C.S.: 518210

GE Energy - San Jose (2)
1989 Little Orchard St, San Jose, CA 95125-1014
Tel.: (408) 925-7000
Sales Range: $50-74.9 Million
Emp.: 200
Nuclear Power Generation
N.A.I.C.S.: 221113

Subsidiary (Non-US):

GE Energy Europe BV (2)
Westervoortsedijk 73-HB, 6827 AV, Arnhem, Netherlands
Tel.: (31) 206590633
Web Site: http://www.gepowersystems.com
Sales Range: $50-74.9 Million
Emp.: 40
Used Automotive & Part Retailer
N.A.I.C.S.: 221121

GE Energy Products France SNC (2)
20 Ave Du Marechal Juin Tranfer Bldg, PO Box 379, 90000, Belfort, France
Tel.: (33) 384591000
Web Site: http://www.ge.com
Emp.: 4,000
Power Gas Turbine Mfr
N.A.I.C.S.: 336412

Joint Venture (Domestic):

GE Grid Solutions LLC (2)
7000 West Bert Kouns Industrial Loop, Shreveport, LA 71129
Tel.: (678) 844-6777
Web Site: http://www.gegridsolutions.com
Emp.: 20,000
Electricity Distribution
N.A.I.C.S.: 221122
Reinaldo Garcia *(CEO)*

Subsidiary (Non-US):

GE Hydro France (2)
82 Ave Leon Blum, 38100, Grenoble, France
Tel.: (33) 476393000
Power Generation Systems & Equipment Design, Engineering & Mfr
N.A.I.C.S.: 333611

GE Power (2)
1430 Blair Pl Ste 500, Ottawa, K1J9N2, ON, Canada
Tel.: (613) 747-5222
Power Generation Equipment & Services
N.A.I.C.S.: 221118

GE Power AG (2)
Boverstrasse 22, 68309, Mannheim, Germany
Tel.: (49) 6213290
Eletric Power Generation Services
N.A.I.C.S.: 221118

Subsidiary (Domestic):

GE Power Systems GmbH (3)
Boveristrasse 22, 68309, Mannheim, Germany
Tel.: (49) 6213290
Supplier of Maintenance & Repair Svcs for Steam, Gas & Combined Cycle Power Plants
N.A.I.C.S.: 811210

Joint Venture (Non-US):

NTPC GE Power Services Private Limited (4)
6th Floor Tower-B Indian Glycols Limited Building Plot No2B, Near Lotus Valley School Sector 126, Noida, 201304, Uttar Pradesh, India
Tel.: (91) 1206937700
Web Site: https://ngsl.co.in
Electric Power Distr
N.A.I.C.S.: 221122
Anand Mohan Awasthy *(Mng Dir)*
T. V. Morali *(CFO)*
A. K. Gupta *(Chm)*

Subsidiary (Non-US):

GE Power Conversion France SAS (2)
30 Avenue Carnot, 91345, Massy, France
Tel.: (33) 164538300
Web Site: http://www.converteam.com
Sales Range: $900-999.9 Million
Emp.: 5,500
Power Conversion Equipment Mfr
N.A.I.C.S.: 333613

Subsidiary (US):

GE Power Conversion (3)
610 Epsilon Dr, Pittsburgh, PA 15238

Tel.: (412) 967-0765
Web Site: http://www.gepowerconversions.com
Sales Range: $50-74.9 Million
Emp.: 229
Power Conversion Equipment Mfr
N.A.I.C.S.: 333613

Subsidiary (Non-US):

GE Power Conversion UK Ltd. (3)
Boughton Road, Rugby, CV211BU, Warwickshire, United Kingdom
Tel.: (44) 1788563563
Web Site: http://www.ge.com
Sales Range: $75-99.9 Million
Emp.: 400
Power Conversion Equipment Mfr
N.A.I.C.S.: 333613

Subsidiary (Non-US):

GE Power Norway AS (2)
Drammensveien 165, 0277, Oslo, Norway
Tel.: (47) 22127000
Power Generation Systems & Equipment Design, Engineering & Manufacture
N.A.I.C.S.: 333611
Mette Egli *(Mng Dir)*

GE Power Sweden AB (2)
Slottsgatan 69, Norrkoping, Sweden
Tel.: (46) 1188300
Web Site: http://www.ge.com
Hydro-Electric Generator Systems Mfr
N.A.I.C.S.: 333611

Branch (Domestic):

GE Power Sweden AB (3)
Kvrwagan 2, 352 41, Vaxjo, Sweden
Tel.: (46) 470762000
Hydro-Electric Generator Systems Mfr
N.A.I.C.S.: 333611

Subsidiary (Non-US):

GE Power Sweden AB (2)
Slottsgatan 69, 602 22, Norrkoping, Sweden
Tel.: (46) 1188300
Hydroelectric Power Generation Services
N.A.I.C.S.: 221111
Lillemor Hjalmefjord *(Head-Quality)*

GE Power s.r.o (2)
Olomoucka 3419/7, 618 00, Brno, Czech Republic
Tel.: (420) 545103103
Combined-Cycle & Hydro-Electric Power Plant Design, Manufacture & Installation
N.A.I.C.S.: 237130

GE T&D India Ltd. (2)
A-18 First Floor, Okhla Industrial Area Phase II, New Delhi, 110 020, India **(75.02%)**
Tel.: (91) 1141610660
Web Site: http://www.ge.com
Rev.: $336,568,551
Assets: $441,155,806
Liabilities: $312,541,215
Net Worth: $128,614,591
Earnings: $178,646
Emp.: 1,873
Fiscal Year-end: 03/31/2023
Power Transmission Equipment Mfr
N.A.I.C.S.: 335311
Pitamber Shivnani *(CEO & Mng Dir)*

Subsidiary (Domestic):

Alstom Projects India Ltd (3)
Axis House Plot No 1-14 Towers 5&6, Jaypee Wish Town Sector 128, Noida, 201 301, Uttar Pradesh, India **(100%)**
Tel.: (91) 1205011011
Web Site: https://www.ge.com
Power Generation Systems & Equipment Design, Engineering & Manufacture
N.A.I.C.S.: 333611

Subsidiary (Non-US):

Grid Solutions SAS (2)
51 Esplanade du General de Gaulle Immeuble le Galilee, Paris La Defense, Paris, 92907, France
Tel.: (33) 134963000
Electric Grid Mfr
N.A.I.C.S.: 335311

General Electric Company—(Continued)

Subsidiary (Non-US):

GE Grid GmbH (3)
Lilienthalstrasse 150, 34123, Kassel, Germany
Tel.: (49) 5615020
Electrical Grid Installation Services
N.A.I.C.S.: 237120

GE Grid Solutions Pte. Ltd. (3)
31 Kaki Bukit Rd 3 02-05 TechLink, Singapore, 417818, Singapore
Tel.: (65) 67490777
Web Site: http://www.geavation.com
Electric Grid Mfr
N.A.I.C.S.: 335311
Pitamber Shivnani *(Pres-South Asia)*

Grid Soltuions Oy (3)
Vehmaistenkatu 5, 33730, Tampere, Finland
Tel.: (358) 3388311
Web Site: https://www.ge.com
Electric Grid Mfr
N.A.I.C.S.: 327110
Risto Peltola *(Dir-Sls)*

Grid Solutions Enerji Endustrisi A.S (3)
Baris Mah Guney Yanyol Cad No 320, Gebze, 41400, Turkiye
Tel.: (90) 262 648 33 00
Electrical Grid Installation Services
N.A.I.C.S.: 237130

Grid Solutions S.p.A (3)
Via Mario Villa 210 Sesto San Giovanni, Milan, Italy
Tel.: (39) 0421309511
Electric Grid Mfr
N.A.I.C.S.: 335311

UK Grid Solutions Limited (3)
St Leonards Building, Redhill Business Park, Stafford, ST16 1WT, United Kingdom
Tel.: (44) 1785250070
Electric Grid Mfr
N.A.I.C.S.: 335311

Subsidiary (Domestic):

Metem Corporation (2)
700 Parsippany Rd, Parsippany, NJ 07054
Tel.: (973) 828-6300
Web Site: https://www.metem.com
Emp.: 112
Miscellaneous Fabricated Metal Product Mfr
N.A.I.C.S.: 332999

Subsidiary (Non-US):

Wuhan Boiler Company Limited (2)
Donghu New Technology Development Zone No1 Liufangyuan Road, Wuhan, 430205, HUB, China
Tel.: (86) 2781993210
Web Site: http://www.wbcl.com.cn
Development, Production & Sale of Power Station Boilers, Specialty Boilers, Desulfurizing Equipment & Other Pressure Vessels & Related Equipment
N.A.I.C.S.: 332410

GE Steam Power S & E Africa Proprietary Limited (1)
Building 8 21 Woodlands Drive, Woodmead, Johannesburg, 2191, South Africa
Tel.: (27) 11 518 8100
Industrial Machinery Distr
N.A.I.C.S.: 423840

GE Vietnam Limited (1)
V 1503-1506A Pacific Place 83B Ly Thuong Kiet Street, Hanoi, Vietnam
Tel.: (84) 471067288
Emp.: 1,300
Motor & Generator Mfr
N.A.I.C.S.: 335312

GE-Fairchild LLC (1)
200 Fairchild Ln, Glen Lyn, VA 24093
Tel.: (540) 921-8007
Web Site: http://www.fairchildint.com
Sales Range: $10-24.9 Million
Emp.: 87
Mining Machinery
N.A.I.C.S.: 333131

General Electric (Switzerland) GmbH (1)

Brown Boveri Strasse 8, 5400, Baden, Switzerland
Tel.: (41) 585057733
Motor & Generator Mfr
N.A.I.C.S.: 335312

General Electric Austria GmbH (1)
Euro Plaza E/5 Technologiestrasse 10, 1120, Vienna, Austria
Tel.: (43) 126016012
Eletric Power Generation Services
N.A.I.C.S.: 221115

General Electric Canada Company (1)
2300 Meadowvale Blvd, Mississauga, L5N 5P9, ON, Canada
Tel.: (905) 858-5100
Web Site: http://www.ge.com
Emp.: 7,000
Appliances, Lighting Products, Plastics & Engineered Materials Mfr
N.A.I.C.S.: 335220
Kim Warburton *(VP-Comm & Pub Affairs)*

Subsidiary (Domestic):

GE Multilin (2)
650 Markland St, Markham, L6C 0M1, ON, Canada
Tel.: (905) 927-7070
Web Site: http://www.gemultilin.com
Protection Relays, Control & Monitoring Equipment Mfr
N.A.I.C.S.: 335314

General Electric Capital Services, Inc. (1)
3135 Easton Tpke, Fairfield, CT 06828-0001 (100%)
Tel.: (203) 373-2211
Sales Range: $50-74.9 Billion
Emp.: 73,000
Holding Company; Consumer & Commercial Lending, Leasing & Asset Financing Services
N.A.I.C.S.: 551112
Daniel O. Colao *(VP-Fin Plng & Analysis)*
Matt LeSage *(Chief Comml Officer-Equipment Fin)*
Robert Y. Casper *(Chief Data Officer & VP)*

Division (Domestic):

GE Aviation Systems LLC (2)
1 Neumann Way, Cincinnati, OH 45215-1915
Tel.: (513) 552-3272
Web Site: http://www.geaviation.com
Sales Range: $5-14.9 Billion
Emp.: 10,000
Mfr of Commercial & Military Jet Engines & Components; Mfr of Aircraft Electrical & Mechanical Systems
N.A.I.C.S.: 336412
H. Lawrence Culp Jr. *(CEO)*
Mary E. Bradford *(CIO)*
Margaret Sidney Ashworth *(VP-Washington Operations)*

Joint Venture (Domestic):

CFAN Inc (3)
1000 Technology Way, San Marcos, TX 78666-8500
Tel.: (512) 353-2832
Web Site: https://c-fan.com
Composite Fan Blades for Aircarft Engines. Joint Venture of General Electric Company (50%) & Societe Nationale d'Etude et de Construction de Moteurs d'Aviation (50%)
N.A.I.C.S.: 336412
Benoit Graby *(VP)*

CFM International Inc. (3)
1 Neumann Way, Cincinnati, OH 45215-0514
Tel.: (513) 552-3272
Web Site: https://www.cfmaeroengines.com
Sales Range: $150-199.9 Million
Jet Engine Mfr; Owned by SAFRAN & General Electric Company
N.A.I.C.S.: 423860

Subsidiary (Domestic):

Critical Technologies, Inc. (3)
3601 S Broadway Ste 1400, Edmond, OK 73013
Tel.: (405) 478-8181

Web Site: http://www.criticaltech.com
Sales Range: $1-9.9 Million
Emp.: 30
Electronic Records Management Products & Services
N.A.I.C.S.: 561410

Joint Venture (Non-US):

Fabrications Mecaniques de l'Atlantique SA (3)
Zone Industrielle De Brais Rue Edison, PO Box 218, 44614, Saint Nazaire, France
Tel.: (33) 240172323
Web Site: http://www.famat.fr
Sales Range: $150-199.9 Million
Emp.: 470
Welded Castings & Other Components for Aircraft Engines Mfr; Owned 50% by Societe Nationale d'Etude et de Construction de Moteurs d'Aviation & 50% by General Electric
N.A.I.C.S.: 336412

Subsidiary (Non-US):

GE Aviation Czech s.r.o. (3)
Beranovych 65, 199 02, Prague, 9, Letnany, Czech Republic
Tel.: (420) 222538111
Web Site:
    https://www.geaviationturboprop.com
Motor & Generator Mfr
N.A.I.C.S.: 335312

GE Aviation Distribution Japan Co., Ltd. (3)
5-2-20 Akasaka Park Building, Yubinbango Akasaka Minato-ku, Tokyo, 107-6109, Japan
Tel.: (81) 355443905
Web Site: https://www.ge.com
Aircraft Engine & Engine Parts Distr
N.A.I.C.S.: 423860
Eriko Asai *(Pres & CEO)*

GE Aviation Service Operation LLP (3)
Level 9 the Metropolis Tower 2 11 North Buona Vista Drive, Singapore, 138589, Singapore (100%)
Sales Range: $75-99.9 Million
Emp.: 690
Aircraft Engine Component Repair Services

Subsidiary (Domestic):

Airfoil Technologies International Singapore Pte Ltd. (4)
62 Loyang Way, Singapore, 508770, Singapore
Tel.: (65) 65437818
Sales Range: $100-124.9 Million
Emp.: 535
Repair Technologies & Services for Cold Section Airfoils of Commercial Flight Turbines
N.A.I.C.S.: 336412

Unit (Domestic):

GE Aviation Systems LLC - Bohemia (3)
1000 MacArthur Memorial Hwy, Bohemia, NY 11716
Tel.: (631) 467-5500
Web Site: http://www.ge.com
Sales Range: $75-99.9 Million
Emp.: 372
Design & Manufacture of Aerospace Electronic Systems
N.A.I.C.S.: 334511

GE Aviation Systems LLC - Clearwater (3)
14200 Roosevelt Blvd, Clearwater, FL 33762
Tel.: (727) 531-7781
Web Site: http://www.geaviation.com
Sales Range: $125-149.9 Million
Emp.: 400
Mfr of Avionics Systems & Equipment for Military Aircraft
N.A.I.C.S.: 335312

GE Aviation Systems LLC - Grand Rapids (3)
3290 Patterson Ave SE, Grand Rapids, MI 49512-1991
Tel.: (616) 241-7000

Sales Range: $500-549.9 Million
Emp.: 1,600
Mfr of Instrument Systems for Aircraft Reference & Navigation, Missile Guidance, Spacecraft Control & Guidance & Weapon Systems Operations
N.A.I.C.S.: 334511

GE Aviation Systems LLC - Pompano Beach (3)
2705 Gateway Dr, Pompano Beach, FL 33069-4803
Tel.: (954) 984-7000
Sales Range: $10-24.9 Million
Emp.: 40
Engineeering Services
N.A.I.C.S.: 334419

Subsidiary (Non-US):

GE Aviation Systems Limited (3)
Cheltenham Road Bishops Cleeve, Cheltenham, GL52 8SF, Gloucestershire, United Kingdom
Tel.: (44) 1242673355
Web Site: http://www.geaviation.com
Sales Range: $450-499.9 Million
Emp.: 1,400
Provider of Aerospace Electronic Equipment
N.A.I.C.S.: 336413

Subsidiary (Domestic):

Dowty Propellers (4)
Anson Business Park Cheltenham Road East, Staverton, Gloucester, GL2 9QN, Gloucestershire, United Kingdom
Tel.: (44) 1452716000
Web Site: http://www.dowty.com
Sales Range: $75-99.9 Million
Emp.: 200
N.A.I.C.S.: 333995

Subsidiary (Non-US):

Air-Log (5)
Tel.: (44) 1252324411
Web Site: http://www.airlog.co.uk
Emp.: 75
Missile Containers, Hydro-Pneumatic Damper Systems, Protective Storage Systems & Materials Handling Equipment
N.A.I.C.S.: 332439

Subsidiary (US):

Dowty Aerospace Propellers, Repair & Overhaul (5)
114 Powers Ct, Sterling, VA 20166-9321
Tel.: (703) 421-4430
Sales Range: $25-49.9 Million
Emp.: 35
Repair & Overhaul of Propeller Systems
N.A.I.O.O.: 501100

Subsidiary (Non-US):

Kontak Manufacturing Co. Ltd. (5)
Tel.: (44) 1476591110
High Tolerance Components, Primarily for Combustion Engines Mfr
N.A.I.C.S.: 333618

Division (Domestic):

GE Aircraft Engines UK (4)
Sovereign Ct 635 Sipson Rd, London, West Drayton, UB7 OJE, Middlesex, United Kingdom
Tel.: (44) 2088974200
Web Site: http://www.ge.com
Sales Range: $10-24.9 Million
Emp.: 25
Mfr of Aircraft Parts
N.A.I.C.S.: 336412

Unit (Domestic):

GE Aviation Systems Ltd. - Eastleigh (4)
School Lane Chandlers Ford, Eastleigh, SO53 4YG, Hants, United Kingdom
Tel.: (44) 2380242000
Web Site: http://www.ge.com
Sales Range: $25-49.9 Million
Emp.: 100
Provider of Aviation Electronics
N.A.I.C.S.: 334417

GE Aviation Systems Ltd. - Southampton (4)

Kings Ave Hamble Le Rice, Southampton, SO31 4NF, Hampshire, United Kingdom
Tel.: (44) 2380453371
Web Site: http://www.ge.com
Sales Range: $350-399.9 Million
Emp.: 800
Aircraft Part Mfr
N.A.I.C.S.: 336413

Subsidiary (Non-US):

GE Avio S.r.l.   (3)
Via I Maggio 99, 10040, Rivalta di Torino, Italy
Tel.: (39) 0110082111
Web Site: http://www.avioaero.com
Sales Range: $1-4.9 Billion
Emp.: 4,700
Civil & Military Aircraft Engine & Components Mfr
N.A.I.C.S.: 336412
Piera Carra (CIO)
Homyar Madan (CFO)

Subsidiary (Domestic):

GE Engine Services, Inc.   (3)
1 Neumann Way, Cincinnati, OH 45215
Tel.: (513) 243-2000
Web Site: http://www.geae.com
Sales Range: $50-74.9 Million
Aviation Maintenance Services
N.A.I.C.S.: 811310

Subsidiary (Domestic):

Johnson Technology   (4)
2034 Latimer Dr, Muskegon, MI 49442-6232
Tel.: (231) 777-2685
Engine Turbine Components Mfr
N.A.I.C.S.: 336412

Subsidiary (Non-US):

GE Sweden Holdings AB   (3)
Vendevagen 89 Danderyd, Stockholm, 182 32, Sweden
Tel.: (46) 87303050
Aerospace Component Mfr
N.A.I.C.S.: 336999

Subsidiary (Domestic):

Arcam AB   (4)
Krokslatts Fabriker 27A, SE-431 37, Molndal, Sweden   (95%)
Tel.: (46) 317103200
Web Site: http://www.arcam.com
Sales Range: $50-74.9 Million
Mechanical or Industrial Engineering; Electron Beam Melting & 3D Printing
N.A.I.C.S.: 333992

Subsidiary (Non-US):

Milestone Aviation Group Limited   (3)
Minerva House 2nd Floor Simmonscourt Road, Ballsbridge, Dublin, Ireland
Tel.: (353) 12165700
Web Site: http://www.milestoneaviation.com
Helicopter Leasing Services
N.A.I.C.S.: 532411
Kalliopi Tzagaki (VP)
Claire Brugirard (VP)
Roberto Farnese (VP)

Subsidiary (US):

Milestone Aviation Group LLC   (4)
375 N Front St Ste 325, Columbus, OH 43215
Tel.: (614) 233-2300
Web Site: http://www.milestoneaviation.com
Helicopter Leasing Services
N.A.I.C.S.: 532411

Subsidiary (Domestic):

Naverus, Inc.   (3)
20415 72nd Ave S Ste 300, Kent, WA 98032
Tel.: (253) 867-3900
Web Site: http://www.geaviation.com
Sales Range: $25-49.9 Million
Emp.: 60
Navigational Instrument Mfr
N.A.I.C.S.: 334511

Tech Development Inc.   (3)
6800 Poe Ave, Dayton, OH 45414-2530

Tel.: (937) 898-9600
Web Site: http://www.tdi-airstarter.com
Sales Range: $75-99.9 Million
Emp.: 200
Mfr & Distributor of Air Starters & Air Motors
N.A.I.C.S.: 333611

Unison Industries, LLC   (3)
7575 Baymeadows Way, Jacksonville, FL 32256
Tel.: (904) 739-4005
Web Site: http://www.unisonindustries.com
Sales Range: $300-349.9 Million
Emp.: 700
Mfr of Aircraft Engine Electrical & Mechanical Components
N.A.I.C.S.: 336412

Subsidiary (Non-US):

Paradigm Precision Burnley Ltd   (4)
Network 65 Business Park 1 Bentley Wood Way Hapton, Burnley, BB11 5TG, Lancashire, United Kingdom
Tel.: (44) 1282831199
Web Site:
    http://www.paradigmprecision.com
Land-based Power Generation & Aircraft Engine Components Mfr
N.A.I.C.S.: 336412

Subsidiary (Domestic):

Tru-Form Inc.   (4)
1141 Hwy 315, Wilkes Barre, PA 18702-6928
Tel.: (570) 821-2750
Sales Range: $50-74.9 Million
Emp.: 60
Aircraft Engine Rings Mfr
N.A.I.C.S.: 332111

Plant (Domestic):

Unison Engine Components   (4)
701 Crestwood Rd, Mountain Top, PA 18707
Tel.: (570) 474-6371
Web Site:
    http://www.unisonenginecomponents.com
Sales Range: $50-74.9 Million
Emp.: 140
Aircraft Engine Components Mfr
N.A.I.C.S.: 336412

Subsidiary (Non-US):

Unison Engine Components   (4)
RR 1 20 Progress Dr, Orillia, L3V 6H1, ON, Canada
Tel.: (705) 326-6611
Web Site:
    http://www.paradigmprecision.com
Sales Range: $75-99.9 Million
Emp.: 180
Aircraft Engine Components Mfr
N.A.I.C.S.: 336412

Unison Industries   (4)
Industrial La Angostura Carretera Saltillo Zacatecas Km 45, Saltillo, 25315, Mexico
Tel.: (52) 8442886400
Sales Range: $200-249.9 Million
Emp.: 400
Mfr of Aircraft Signals, Control Harnesses & Panel Assemblies
N.A.I.C.S.: 336412,

Plant (Domestic):

Unison Industries LLC   (4)
7575 Baymeadows Way, Jacksonville, FL 32256
Tel.: (904) 739-4005
Web Site: http://www.unisonindustries.com
Emp.: 600
Mfr of Piston Engine Ignition & Controls
N.A.I.C.S.: 336412

Unison Industries LLC   (4)
2455 Dayton-Xenia Rd, Dayton, OH 45434
Tel.: (937) 426-0621
Web Site: http://www.unisonindustries.com
Emp.: 700
Mfr of Aircraft Engine Electrical & Mechanical Components; Aircraft Engine Repair & Technical Support Services
N.A.I.C.S.: 336412

Unison Industries, LLC   (4)

5345 State Hwy 12, Norwich, NY 13815   (100%)
Tel.: (607) 335-5179
Web Site: http://www.unisonindustries.com
Emp.: 340
Complex Gas Turbine Engine Components & Electrical & Mechanical Systems Mfr
N.A.I.C.S.: 336412

Division (Domestic):

GE Energy & Industrial Services, Inc.   (2)
4200 Wildwood Pkwy, Atlanta, GA 30339-8402
Tel.: (678) 844-6000
Web Site: http://www.gepower.com
Sales Range: $5-14.9 Billion
Emp.: 35,000
Gas, Steam, Hydro, Nuclear & Wind Turbines & Electrical Transmission Equipment Mfr
N.A.I.C.S.: 333132

Subsidiary (Domestic):

Bently Nevada, Inc.   (3)
1631 Bently Pkwy S, Minden, NV 89423-4119
Tel.: (775) 782-3611
Sales Range: $250-299.9 Million
Emp.: 800
Electronic Monitoring Equipment Mfr
N.A.I.C.S.: 335311

Holding (Non-US):

Bently Nevada Canada Ltd.   (4)
9403 17th Ave NW, Edmonton, T6N 1J1, AB, Canada
Tel.: (780) 439-4000
Web Site: http://www.bently.com
Sales Range: $10-24.9 Million
Emp.: 20
Electronic Monitoring Systems
N.A.I.C.S.: 335311

Bently Nevada Canada Ltd.   (4)
180 Riveria Dr, Markham, L3R 5M1, ON, Canada
Tel.: (905) 475-2240
Web Site: http://www.bently.com
Sales Range: $10-24.9 Million
Emp.: 10
Electronic Monitoring Systems
N.A.I.C.S.: 335311

Bently Nevada France S.A.R.L.   (4)
14 rue de la Haltiniere GE Wind GE Digital Energy GE Pgs, 44300, Nantes, France
Tel.: (33) 240729944
Web Site: http://www.ge.com
Sales Range: $10-24.9 Million
Emp.: 25
Electronic Monitoring Services
N.A.I.C.S.: 561621

Bently Nevada, Australia Pty. Ltd.   (4)
20 Healey Cct, Huntingwood, 2148, NSW, Australia
Tel.: (61) 296727447
Web Site: http://www.bently.com
Sales Range: $1-9.9 Million
Emp.: 10
Electronic Monitoring Equipment Mfr
N.A.I.C.S.: 334519

GE Energy Germany   (4)
Tel.: (49) 610273960
Web Site: http://www.bently.com
Sales Range: $10-24.9 Million
Emp.: 20
Vibration Measuring & Analyzing Machines Mfr
N.A.I.C.S.: 334519

IGE Energy Services (UK) Ltd   (4)
The Arena Downshire Way, Bracknell, RG12 1PU, Berkshire, United Kingdom
Tel.: (44) 1344460500
Web Site: http://www.ge-energy.com
Vibration Monitoring Equipment & Vibration Proximity Transducers Mfr
N.A.I.C.S.: 334519

Subsidiary (Non-US):

GE Aviation Systems Group Limited   (3)

Cheltenham Road, Cheltenham, GL52 8SF, Gloucestershire, United Kingdom
Tel.: (44) 1242673333
Emp.: 1,800
Air Transport Equipment Mfr
N.A.I.C.S.: 336413

GE Canada   (3)
107 Park St N, Peterborough, K9J 3V6, ON, Canada
Tel.: (705) 748-8486
Web Site: http://www.ge.com
Sales Range: $400-449.9 Million
Emp.: 1,200
Mfr of Large Motors
N.A.I.C.S.: 335312

Subsidiary (Domestic):

GE Drives & Controls Inc.   (3)
1501 Roanoke Blvd, Salem, VA 24153
Tel.: (540) 387-7000
Emp.: 900
Electronic Product Distr
N.A.I.C.S.: 449210

GE Energy (USA), LLC   (3)
231 Lake Dr, Newark, DE 19702
Tel.: (302) 451-7500
Engine Equipment Mfr
N.A.I.C.S.: 333618

Subsidiary (Non-US):

Hydril Private Ltd   (4)
27 Benoi Sector Jurong Town, Singapore, 629859, Singapore
Tel.: (65) 62612566
Web Site: http://www.hydril.com
Sales Range: $10-24.9 Million
Emp.: 10
Oilfield Equipment
N.A.I.C.S.: 333132

Unit (Domestic):

GE Oil & Gas Rotoflow   (3)
3300 Medalise Dr, Oshkosh, WI 54902
Tel.: (800) 577-5155
Web Site: http://www.gepower.com
Sales Range: $125-149.9 Million
Emp.: 300
Radial Expander Designer & Mfr
N.A.I.C.S.: 423830

GE Oil & Gas, Inc. - Twinsburg   (3)
8499 Darrow Rd, Twinsburg, OH 44087
Tel.: (330) 425-3755
Web Site: http://www.geoilandgas.com
Sales Range: $50-74.9 Million
Emp.: 251
Sensor & Detector Mfr
N.A.I.C.S.: 334519

Subsidiary (Non-US):

Midwest Electric Products Inc.   (3)
Tel.: (507) 345-2505
Web Site: http://www.midwestelectric.com
Sales Range: $10-24.9 Million
Electric Equipment Mfr
N.A.I.C.S.: 335932

Nuovo Pignone S.p.A.   (3)
Via Felice Matteucci 2, PO Box 6313-6314, Florence, 50127, Italy
Tel.: (39) 0554233812
Web Site: http://www.geoilandgas.com
Air Compressors, Expanders, Centrifugal Pumps & Gas Turbines Mfr
N.A.I.C.S.: 333611

Opal Software   (3)
Box Business Centre 65 Tennant Street Unit 5, Fyshwick, 2609, ACT, Australia
Tel.: (61) 262829007
Web Site: http://www.opalsoftware.com.au
Professional Engineering Services & Software Products to the Utilities Sector
N.A.I.C.S.: 541330

Subsidiary (Domestic):

PrimeStar Solar, Inc.   (3)
14401 W 65th Way Unit B, Arvada, CO 80004
Tel.: (303) 278-3180
Web Site: http://www.primestarsolar.com
Sales Range: $25-49.9 Million
Emp.: 90
Solar Energy Equipment Mfr

General Electric Company—(Continued)
N.A.I.C.S.: 334413

Subsidiary (Non-US):

Sondex Limited (3)
Bldg X107 Range Road, Cody Technology
Park, Farnborough, GU14 0FG, Hants,
United Kingdom
Tel.: (44) 1252862200
Web Site: http://www.ge-energy.com
Sales Range: $125-149.9 Million
Emp.: 513
Oil & Gas Industry Technologies Designer,
Developer & Mfr
N.A.I.C.S.: 333132

Subsidiary (US):

GE Energy Oilfield Technology (4)
1402 Fm 2854, Conroe, TX 77303-1751
Tel.: (936) 756-2331
Web Site: http://www.ge-energy.com
Sales Range: $100-124.9 Million
Oil & Gas Field Machinery & Equipment Mfr
N.A.I.C.S.: 333132

GE Energy Oilfield Technology,
Inc. (4)
208 Ida Rd, Broussard, LA 70518
Tel.: (337) 837-2016
Web Site: http://www.ge-energy.com
Sales Range: $25-49.9 Million
Emp.: 100
Oil & Gas Field Machinery & Equipment Mfr
& Sales
N.A.I.C.S.: 333132

Subsidiary (Non-US):

Wellstream Holdings Limited (3)
Wellstream House Wincomblee Road,
Walker Riverside, Newcastle upon Tyne,
NE6 3PF, United Kingdom
Sales Range: $550-599.9 Million
Emp.: 600
Holding Company

Subsidiary (Non-US):

Wellstream Australia Pty Limited (4)
Level 61 14-16 Victoria Ave, Perth, 6000,
WA, Australia
Tel.: (61) 893276888
Web Site: http://www.wellstream.com
Sales Range: $25-49.9 Million
Emp.: 10
Offshore Equipment & Supplies Distr
N.A.I.C.S.: 423440

Wellstream do Brazil Industria e Ser-
vicos Ltda (4)
Avenue Rio Branco 138 11 Andar, Rio de
Janeiro, 20040-002, Brazil
Tel.: (55) 2121076500
Sales Range: $25-49.9 Million
Emp.: 80
Flexible Pipeline Products Mfr & Distr
N.A.I.C.S.: 326122

Subsidiary (US):

Wellstream, Inc. (4)
11210 Equity Dr Ste 350, Houston, TX
77041
Tel.: (281) 249-0926
Sales Range: $25-49.9 Million
Emp.: 30
Flexible Pipeline Distr
N.A.I.C.S.: 326122
Tricia Hill (VP-Sls & Bus Dev)

Unit (Domestic):

GE Transportation Rail (2)
2901 E Lake Rd, Erie, PA 16531-0001
Tel.: (814) 875-2234
Web Site: http://www.getransportation.com
Sales Range: $750-799.9 Million
Emp.: 5,000
Diesel/Electric Locomotives, Switching &
Mining Locomotives, Transit Car Propulsion
& Electric Drive Systems Mfr
N.A.I.C.S.: 336510

Subsidiary (Domestic):

Railcar Management, LLC (3)
3475 Piedmont Rd Ste 250, Atlanta, GA
30305

Tel.: (404) 355-6734
Web Site: http://www.rmiondemand.com
Sales Range: $10-24.9 Million
Emp.: 104
Transportation Management Software &
Analytics for Railroad Industry
N.A.I.C.S.: 513210

Subsidiary (Domestic):

GECAS Asset Management
Services (2)
3860 E Holmes Rd Ste 108, Memphis, TN
38118-7710
Tel.: (901) 547-2493
Web Site: http://www.gecas.com
Sales Range: $75-99.9 Million
Emp.: 150
Wholesale Distr of Aircraft Engines & En-
gine Parts; Aircraft Equipment & Supplies
N.A.I.C.S.: 336412

General Electric Capital
Corporation (2)
901 Main Ave, Norwalk, CT
06851-1168 (100%)
Tel.: (203) 840-6300
Web Site: http://www.gecapital.com
Rev.: $42,725,000,000
Assets: $500,216,000,000
Liabilities: $409,818,000,000
Net Worth: $90,398,000,000
Earnings: $7,396,000,000
Emp.: 47,000
Fiscal Year-end: 12/31/2014
Consumer & Commercial Lending, Leasing
& Asset Financing Services
N.A.I.C.S.: 525990
Jennifer VanBelle (CEO & Sr VP)

Subsidiary (Non-US):

Bank BPH S.A. (3)
ul plk Jana Palubickiego 2, 80-175, War-
saw, Poland
Tel.: (48) 583007500
Web Site: http://www.bph.pl
Sales Range: $200-249.9 Million
Mortgage Banking Services
N.A.I.C.S.: 522292
Wieslaw Rozlucki (Chm-Supervisory Bd)
Pawel Bandurski (Pres-Mgmt Bd)
Malgorzata Romaniuk (Member-Mgmt Bd &
VP)
Monika Godzinska (Member-Mgmt Bd &
VP)
Marcin Berger (Member-Mgmt Bd & VP)

GE Artesia Bank (3)
Herengracht 539-543, Amsterdam, 1017
BW, Netherlands
Sales Range: $75-99.9 Million
Emp.: 145
Private Banking Services

Subsidiary (Domestic):

GE Capital Aviation Services
LLC (3)
901 Main Ave, Norwalk, CT 06851
Financing & Leasing Services to the Com-
mercial Aviation Industry
Alec Burger (Chm)
Declan Kelly (Chief Comml Officer-Ireland)
John Bordeaux (Chief Investment Officer)
Greg Conlon (Pres & CEO)
Diarmuid Hogan (CFO & Exec VP)
Mayank Bhatnagar (Exec VP-HR)
Virginia Connolly (Sr VP & Mgr-Mktg &
Corp Comm)
Chris Damianos (Exec VP & Mgr)

Subsidiary (Non-US):

GE Capital Bank Limited (3)
23-59 Staines Road Hounslow, Middlesex,
TW3 3HF, United Kingdom (100%)
Tel.: (44) 1932792000
Web Site: http://www.gecapital.co.uk
Sales Range: $10-24.9 Million
Emp.: 50
Financial Products & Services
N.A.I.C.S.: 525990

GE Capital Finance Australasia Pty.
Ltd. (3)
572 Swan St, Burnley, Melbourne, 3121,
VIC, Australia
Tel.: (61) 399216522
Web Site: http://www.gemoney.com.au

Sales Range: $1-4.9 Billion
Emp.: 3,000
Commercial Lending & Credit Services
N.A.I.C.S.: 522310

Unit (Domestic):

GE CreditLine (4)
PO Box 223, Parramatta, 2124, NSW, Aus-
tralia
Tel.: (61) 394254886
Web Site: http://www.gecreditline.com.au
Sales Range: $150-199.9 Million
Emp.: 500
Credit Card Services to Consumers & Re-
tailers
N.A.I.C.S.: 522210

Subsidiary (Domestic):

GE Capital Real Estate (3)
901 Main Ave, Norwalk, CT 06851
Sales Range: $1-4.9 Billion
Emp.: 5,400
Commercial Real Estate Services
Eileen Brumback (Gen Counsel & Sr VP)
Hank Zupnick (CIO-Real Estate)
Bradley J. Trotter (Pres-North America)

Subsidiary (Non-US):

GE Capital Transportation Financial
Services, ltd. (3)
Alfacs Building 1 Rafi Marg, New Delhi,
110001, India
Financial Services
Kanwarpal Singh Bindra (Chm)

Subsidiary (Domestic):

GE Energy Financial Services (3)
800 Long Ridge Rd, Stamford, CT 06927
Sales Range: $650-699.9 Million
Assets: $14,000,000,000
Energy, Pipelines & Related Infrastructures,
Project & Corporate Finances & Commer-
cial Debt & Leases
Susan T. Flanagan (Pres & CEO)
Mark Ortiz (CFO)

General Electric Company Polska Sp.
z o.o. (1)
Al Krakowska 110/114, 02-256, Warsaw,
Poland
Tel.: (48) 225205353
Web Site: https://edc.pl
Aircraft Mfr
N.A.I.C.S.: 336411

General Electric Deutschland Holding
GmbH (1)
Bleichstrasse 64-66, 60313, Frankfurt am
Main, Germany
Tel.: (49) 69450909333
Motor & Generator Mfr
N.A.I.C.S.: 335312

Global Nuclear Fuel - Japan Co.,
Ltd. (1)
2-3-1 Uchikawa, Yokosuka, 239-0836, Ka-
nagawa, Japan
Tel.: (81) 468332326
Web Site: https://www.gnfjapan.com
Petroleum Product Mfr & Distr
N.A.I.C.S.: 324199

Grid Solutions (U.S.) LLC (1)
830 W 40th St, Chicago, IL 60609
Tel.: (773) 299-6725
Electrical Engineering Services
N.A.I.C.S.: 541330

Industrea Mining Technology Pty
Ltd (1)
3 Co-Wyn Close, Fountaindale, 2258, NSW,
Australia
Tel.: (61) 2 4336 1800
Web Site: http://www.industrea.com.au
Sales Range: $25-49.9 Million
Emp.: 50
Electronic Measuring Equipment Mfr & Distr
N.A.I.C.S.: 336320

LM Wind Power (Spain) SLU (1)
C/ Anabel Segura no 11 Centro de Nego-
cios Albatros Edificio A, 4a Planta Departa-
mento C, 28108, Alcobendas, Spain
Tel.: (34) 914907200
Industrial Machinery Distr
N.A.I.C.S.: 423840

LM Wind Power A/S (1)
Jupitervej 6, 6000, Kolding, Denmark
Tel.: (45) 7 984 0000
Web Site: https://www.lmwindpower.com
Emp.: 11,492
Wind Turbine Blade Mfr
N.A.I.C.S.: 333611

LM Wind Power Blades (Poland) Sp.
z.o.o. (1)
Ul Nowa 3, Lozienica, 72-100, Goleniow,
Poland
Tel.: (48) 914699700
Web Site: https://szkolenialm.pl
Mechanical Power Transmission Equipment
Mfr
N.A.I.C.S.: 333613

Meridium, Inc. (1)
207 Bullitt Ave SE 11th Fl, Roanoke, VA
24013
Tel.: (540) 344-9205
Web Site: http://www.meridium.com
Asset Performance Management Software
Developer & Services
N.A.I.C.S.: 541511

Product Distribution Company (1)
3925 Produce Rd, Louisville, KY 40218-
3005
Tel.: (502) 968-8711
Web Site:
    http://www.productdistributionco.com
Sales Range: $25-49.9 Million
Emp.: 60
Provider of Trucking Services
N.A.I.C.S.: 484121
John Slucher (CFO)

ShipXpress, Inc. (1)
2315 Beach Blvd Ste 104, Jacksonville
Beach, FL 32250 (100%)
Tel.: (904) 241-5850
Web Site: http://www.shipxpress.net
Emp.: 200
Software Publisher
N.A.I.C.S.: 513210

Whatman Limited (1)
Springfield Mill James Whatman Way,
Maidstone, ME14 2LE, Kent, United King-
dom
Tel.: (44) 1622676670
Bio Technology Services
N.A.I.C.S.: 541714

Wipro GE Healthcare Private
Limited (1)
No 4 Kadugodi Industrial Area, Bengaluru,
560067, Karnataka, India
Tel.: (91) 8041801290
Web Site: https://www.gehealthcare.in
Beta-Ray Irradiation Equipment Mfr
N.A.I.C.S.: 334517
Jan Makela (Co-Pres & CEO-)
Peter J. Arduini (Co-Pres & CEO)
Helmut Zodl (Co-Pres & CFO)
Roland Rott (Co-Pres & CEO)

GENERAL ENTERPRISE VEN-
TURES, INC.
1740H Del Range Blvd Ste 166,
Cheyenne, WY 82009 WY
Web Site:
    https://www.generalenterpriseven
    tures.com
Year Founded: 1990
GEVI—(OTCIQ)
Rev.: $62,732
Assets: $4,409,586
Liabilities: $1,060,918
Net Worth: $3,348,668
Earnings: ($2,907,828)
Emp.: 8
Fiscal Year-end: 12/31/22
Miscellaneous Financial Investment
Activities
N.A.I.C.S.: 523999
Joshua Ralston (Chm)

GENERAL FINANCE & DEVEL-
OPMENT, INC.
1400 Van Buren St NE Ste 175, Min-
neapolis, MN 55413
Tel.: (763) 567-2208 MN
Web Site: http://www.genfd.com

GFDV—(OTCIQ)
Financial Investment Services
N.A.I.C.S.: 523999
William Kieger (Chm & CEO)

Subsidiaries:

Art Force LLC (1)
600 County Rd D W Ste 15, New Brighton,
MN 55112
Tel.: (763) 567-2200
Web Site: http://www.artforce.org
Art Work Services
N.A.I.C.S.: 459920
Zoe Bailey (Gen Mgr & Dir-Ops)
Leslie Palmer Ross (Dir-Healthcare & Art
Svcs)
Gabriel Vespasiano (Mgr-Bus Dev & Mktg)
Matthew Wiig (Mgr-Production & Installa-
tion)
Magdiel Tapias (Specialist-Order Fulfillment)

GENERAL MILLS, INC.
No 1 General Mills Blvd, Minneapolis,
MN 55426
Tel.: (763) 764-7600 DE
Web Site:
https://www.generalmills.com
Year Founded: 1928
GIS—(NYSE)
Rev.: $19,857,200,000
Assets: $31,469,900,000
Liabilities: $21,821,400,000
Net Worth: $9,648,500,000
Earnings: $2,496,600,000
Emp.: 34,000
Fiscal Year-end: 05/26/24
Flour Milling Product Mfr
N.A.I.C.S.: 311211
Kofi A. Bruce (CFO)
Jeffrey L. Harmening (Chm & CEO)
Bethany C. Quam (Pres-Morning
Foods-US)
Dana M. McNabb (Grp Pres-Retail-
North America)
Ricardo Fernandez (Pres-Intl)
Jonathon J. Nudi (Pres-Pet, Intl, and
North America Foodservice)
Richard C. Allendorf (Gen Counsel,
Sec & Sr VP)
Mark A. Pallot (Chief Acctg Officer &
VP)
Jodi Benson (Co-CTO, Chief Innova-
tion & Quality Officer & Sr VP)
Jaime Montemayor (Co-CTO & Chief
Digital Officer)
Paul J. Gallagher (Chief Supply
Chain Officer)
Sean Anderson (Sr VP)
Jacqueline R. Williams-Roll (Sr VP-
HR)
Jeff Siemon (Dir-IR)
Jerald A. Young (VP & Controller)
Jacqueline R. Williams-Roll (Chief HR
Officer & Sr VP-HR)
Jeff Siemon (VP/Dir-IR)

Subsidiaries:

AGRICOLA NOVA INDEMIL
LTDA (1)
R Sao Cristovao 70 Esq Com Av Heit,
Paranavai, 87706-000, Brazil
Tel.: (55) 4434238936
Food Products Mfr
N.A.I.C.S.: 311991

Aliments Ultima Inc (1)
2177 Fernand-Lafontaine Blvd, J4G 2V2,
Longueuil, QC, Canada
Tel.: (450) 651-3737
Web Site: http://www.ultima.ca
Sales Range: $100-124.9 Million
Emp.: 550
Dairy Products Mfr
N.A.I.C.S.: 311514

Annie's, Inc. (1)
1610 5th St, Berkeley, CA 94710
Tel.: (510) 558-7500
Web Site: http://www.annies.com
Emp.: 70

Organic Foods Mfr & Wholesaler
N.A.I.C.S.: 311999
Carla Vernon (Pres)

Subsidiary (Domestic):

ANNIE'S ENTERPRISES, INC. (2)
1610 5th St, Berkeley, CA 94710
Tel.: (802) 456-8866
Packaged Frozen Food Whslr
N.A.I.C.S.: 424420

ANNIE'S HOMEGROWN, INC. (2)
1610 5th St, Berkeley, CA 94710
Tel.: (510) 558-7500
Packaged Frozen Food Whslr
N.A.I.C.S.: 424420
John Foraker (CEO)
Amanda Steele (Sr VP-Mktg)
Bob Kaake (Chief Innovation Officer)
Shauna Sadowski (Dir-Sustainability)

BENEFICIADORA DE CEREAIS
MANI LTDA.
Avenida Eugenio Coneglian 1706-Distrito
Industrial, Marilia, Sao Paulo, Brazil
Tel.: (55) 1434251102
Agricultural Services
N.A.I.C.S.: 115112

Betty Crocker Products (1)
1 General Mills Blvd, Minneapolis, MN
55426
Tel.: (763) 764-7600
Web Site: http://www.bettycrocker.com
Sales Range: $350-399.9 Million
Food Mfr
N.A.I.C.S.: 311230

Blue Buffalo Co., Ltd. (1)
11 River Rd, Wilton, CT 06897
Tel.: (203) 762-9751
Web Site: https://www.bluebuffalo.com
Pet Food Mfr
N.A.I.C.S.: 311111
David M. Petrie (Co-Founder & VP)

Blue Buffalo Company, Ltd. (1)
PO Box 770, Wilton, CT 06897
Web Site: https://www.bluebuffalo.com
Pet Food Mfr & Distr
N.A.I.C.S.: 311119
Bill Bishop (Founder)

C.P.D. Cereal Partners Deutschland
Gmbh & Co. OHG (1)
Lyoner Strasse 23, 60523, Frankfurt am
Main, Germany
Tel.: (49) 6966718888
Consumer Food Mfr & Distr
N.A.I.C.S.: 311230

COLOMBO, INC. (1)
35 Danton Dr Ste 1, Methuen, MA 01844
Tel.: (978) 689-1300
Food Products Sales Services
N.A.I.C.S.: 445298

Cereal Partners U.K. (1)
2 Albany Place 28 Bridge Road East,
Welwyn Garden City, AL7 1RR, Hertford-
shire, United Kingdom
Tel.: (44) 1707824400
Consumer Food Mfr & Distr
N.A.I.C.S.: 311230
Jake Kirkham (Mktg Mgr)

Cereal Partners Worldwide S.A. (1)
Chemin Viaduc 1, PO Box 1000, Lausanne,
1016, Switzerland
Tel.: (41) 216225511
Web Site: http://www.cerealpartners.com
Sales Range: $50-74.9 Million
Emp.: 150
Cereal Mfr; Owned 50% by General Mills,
Inc. & 50% by Nestle S.A.
N.A.I.C.S.: 311230
David V. Clark II (Pres & CEO)

EPIC PROVISIONS, LLC (1)
PO Box 684581, Austin, TX 78768-4581
Tel.: (512) 944-8502
Web Site: http://www.epicbar.com
Meat Product Mfr & Distr
N.A.I.C.S.: 311615
Katie Forrest (Co-Founder)
Taylor Collins (Co-Founder)

GARDETTO'S BAKERY, INC. (1)
4625 S 6th St, Milwaukee, WI 53221
Tel.: (414) 483-6001

Snack Food Mfr & Distr
N.A.I.C.S.: 311919

GENERAL MILLS ARGENTINA
S.A. (1)
Uruguay 3675, San Fernando, B1644HJY,
Argentina
Tel.: (54) 11 4725 9200
Web Site: http://www.generalmills.com
Emp.: 50
Food Products Mfr
N.A.I.C.S.: 311999

GENERAL MILLS CEREALS HOLD-
ING (SOUTH AFRICA) PTY
LIMITED (1)
15E Riley Rd Ofice Pk, Bedfordview, 2144,
South Africa
Tel.: (27) 11 608 0880
Web Site: http://www.generalmills.co.za
Emp.: 100
Food Products Mfr
N.A.I.C.S.: 311999

GENERAL MILLS DE MEXICO, S.
DE R.L. DE C.V. (1)
Ave Magnocentro No 5 Piso 3, Col Centro
Urbano C P, 52760, Huixquilucan, Estado
de Mexico, Mexico
Tel.: (52) 5550890200
Web Site: http://www.generalmills.com.mx
Food Supplement Services
N.A.I.C.S.: 456191

GENERAL MILLS DIRECT MARKET-
ING, INC. (1)
1000 Boone Ave Ste 600A, Minneapolis,
MN 55427
Tel.: (763) 764-7600
Emp.: 60
Mail Order Services
N.A.I.C.S.: 424420

GENERAL MILLS FOODS, INC. (1)
10th Fl Philam Life Tower 8767 Paseo de
Roxas, Makati, 1226, Philippines
Tel.: (63) 2 885 0424
Food Products Mfr
N.A.I.C.S.: 311999

GENERAL MILLS HOLDING (AUS-
TRALIA) PTY LIMITED (1)
4 Ricketts Rd, Mount Waverley, Mount Wa-
verley, 3149, VIC, Australia
Tel.: (61) 392398777
Web Site: http://www.generalmills.com.au
Sales Range: $50-74.9 Million
Emp.: 20
Food Products Mfr
N.A.I.C.S.: 311999

GENERAL MILLS HOLDING ONE
(GERMANY) GmbH (1)
Osterbekstr 90c, 22083, Hamburg, Ger-
many
Tel.: (49) 406894140
Web Site: http://www.generalmills.com
Emp.: 80
Food Products Mfr
N.A.I.C.S.: 311999

GENERAL MILLS INTERNATIONAL
BUSINESSES, INC. (1)
1 General Mills Blvd, Minneapolis, MN
55426
Tel.: (763) 764-7600
Food Products Mfr
N.A.I.C.S.: 621999

GENERAL MILLS INTERNATIONAL
SARL (1)
Avenue Reverdil 8, 1260, Nyon, Switzerland
Tel.: (41) 223656000
Web Site: http://www.generalmills.com
Food Products Mfr
N.A.I.C.S.: 445298

GENERAL MILLS MALAYSIA SDN.
BHD. (1)
Suite 16.01, Level 16, The Gardens South
Tower, Mid Valley City,, Lingkaran Syed Pu-
tra, Kuala Lumpur, 59200, Malaysia
Tel.: (60) 3 2282 0998
Food Products Mfr
N.A.I.C.S.: 311999

GENERAL MILLS MANUFACTUR-
ING AUSTRALIA PTY LIMITED (1)
16 Kellogg Rd, Rooty Hill, 2766, NSW, Australia

Tel.: (61) 298309000
Food Products Mfr
N.A.I.C.S.: 311999

GENERAL MILLS MARKETING,
INC. (1)
1 General Mills Blvd, Minneapolis, MN
55426
Tel.: (763) 293-2157
Food Processor Mfr
N.A.I.C.S.: 333241

GENERAL MILLS MIDDLE EAST &
NORTH AFRICA FZE (1)
Jafza View 18 13th Fl Office 1-5, Jebel Ali,
262514, United Arab Emirates
Tel.: (971) 44239200
Web Site:
http://www.generalmillsmiddleeast.com
Sales Range: $25-49.9 Million
Emp.: 25
Food Products Mfr
N.A.I.C.S.: 311999

GENERAL MILLS NEW ZEALAND
LIMITED (1)
600 Great Soiurkh Road Allar Slia, East Ta-
maki, Auckland, New Zealand
Tel.: (64) 92729720
Web Site: http://www.generalmills.co.nz
Sales Range: $25-49.9 Million
Emp.: 15
Food Products Mfr
N.A.I.C.S.: 311999

GENERAL MILLS SALES SINGA-
PORE PTE. LTD. (1)
Robinson Rd Unit 26-01 Capital power, Sin-
gapore, 068912, Singapore
Tel.: (65) 67321566
Food Products Mfr
N.A.I.C.S.: 311999

GENERAL MILLS SAN ADRIAN, S.L.
UNIPERSONAL (1)
Industrial Termino Sansande Fase Iii Sn,
San Adrian, 31750, Spain
Tel.: (34) 948 67 00 00
Web Site: http://www.generalmills.com
Emp.: 800
Food Products Mfr
N.A.I.C.S.: 311999

GENERAL MILLS SCANDINAVIA
AB (1)
August Barks Gata 6a Vastra, 421 32, Frol-
unda, Sweden
Tel.: (46) 317343630
Web Site: http://www.generalmills.se
Sales Range: $25-49.9 Million
Emp.: 30
Food Products Mfr
N.A.I.C.S.: 311999

GENERAL MILLS SINGAPORE PTE.
LTD. (1)
68 Robinson Road 26-01 Capital Tower,
Singapore, 068912, Singapore
Tel.: (65) 67321566
Food & Flour Distr
N.A.I.C.S.: 424490

GIGANTE VERDE S. de R.L. de
C.V. (1)
Paseo Solidaridad No 11051, Irapuato,
36680, Baja California, Mexico
Tel.: (52) 4626238787
Agriculture Farming Services
N.A.I.C.S.: 111219

General Mills (1)
16 Kellogg Rd, Sydney, 2766,
Australia (100%)
Tel.: (61) 298309000
Web Site: http://www.generalmills.com
Sales Range: $50-74.9 Million
Emp.: 130
Holding Co
N.A.I.C.S.: 551112

General Mills (1)
Harman House 1 George St, Uxbridge, UB8
1BQ, Middlesex, United Kingdom (100%)
Tel.: (44) 895201100
Rev.: $72,688,000
Emp.: 170
Regional Headquarters
N.A.I.C.S.: 722410

General Mills (1)

General Mills, Inc.—(Continued)

707 Pillsbury Ln, New Albany, IN 47150-
2238
Tel.: (812) 944-8411
Web Site: http://www.generalmills.com
Sales Range: $150-199.9 Million
Emp.: 600
Mfr & Distributor of Refrigerated Dough
N.A.I.C.S.: 337122

General Mills   (1)
9999 Wayzata Blvd, Minnetonka, MN
55305-5513
Tel.: (763) 764-6900
Web Site: http://www.gmfcu.org
Sales Range: $150-199.9 Million
Emp.: 290
Credit Union
N.A.I.C.S.: 522130

General Mills   (1)
1 General Mills Blvd, Minneapolis, MN
55426-1347
Tel.: (763) 764-7600
Web Site: http://www.yoplaitusa.com
Sales Range: $450-499.9 Million
Refrigerated Food Items; Yogurt
N.A.I.C.S.: 424430

General Mills - Wellston Plant   (1)
2403 S Pennsylvania Ave, Wellston, OH
45692-9503
Tel.: (740) 286-2170
Sales Range: $600-649.9 Million
Emp.: 1,200
Mfr of Frozen Pizza & Pizza Snacks
N.A.I.C.S.: 493130

General Mills Australia Pty. Ltd.   (1)
Level 4 545 Blackburn Road, Mount Waver-
ley, 3149, VIC, Australia   (100%)
Tel.: (61) 392398777
Web Site: https://www.generalmills.com.au
Sales Range: $250-299.9 Million
Emp.: 500
Food Products Mfr
N.A.I.C.S.: 311999

General Mills Bakery & Foodservice
Pty Ltd   (1)
4 Ricketts Rd, Mount Waverley, Melbourne,
3149, VIC, Australia
Tel.: (61) 392398777
Web Site: http://www.generalmills.com.au
Sales Range: $75-99.9 Million
Emp.: 20
Bakery Food Products Distr
N.A.I.C.S.: 424420

General Mills Brazil Ltda.   (1)
Chucri Zaidan, 940 - 7Flr, Sao Paulo,
Brazil   (100%)
Tel.: (55) 1133231576
Web Site: https://www.generalmills.com.br
Sales Range: $250-299.9 Million
Food Products Mfr
N.A.I.C.S.: 311999

General Mills Canada Corp.   (1)
1875 Buckhorn Gate Suite 201, Missis-
sauga, L4W 5N9, ON, Canada   (100%)
Tel.: (905) 212-4000
Web Site: https://www.generalmills.com
Sales Range: $100-124.9 Million
Emp.: 300
Packaged Foods
N.A.I.C.S.: 424420

General Mills France (SAS)   (1)
2 Rue Paul Dautier, 32 avenue de l'Europe,
78941, Velizy-Villacoublay, France (100%)
Tel.: (33) 134585860
Sales Range: $250-299.9 Million
Food Products Mfr
N.A.I.C.S.: 311999
Giuseppe A. D'Angelo (Pres-Europe, Latin
America & Africa)

Subsidiary (Domestic):

SERETRAM   (2)
519 Route Royale, 40300, Labatut,
France   (100%)
Tel.: (33) 558981923
Sales Range: $50-74.9 Million
Emp.: 312
Produces Green Giant Sweet Corn
N.A.I.C.S.: 311221
Jean Payzan (Mng Dir)

General Mills GmbH   (1)
Osterbekstrasse 90c, 22083, Hamburg,
Germany   (100%)
Tel.: (49) 406894140
Web Site: http://www.generalmills.de
Sales Range: $250-299.9 Million
Food Products Mfr
N.A.I.C.S.: 311999

General Mills Hellas S.A.   (1)
6 Andrea Metaxa Street, 145 64, Athens,
Greece   (100%)
Tel.: (30) 2108198000
Sales Range: $100-124.9 Million
Emp.: 51
Food Products Mfr
N.A.I.C.S.: 311520
Dimitris Donias (Mng Dir)
Kirk Louis (Chm)

General Mills Hong Kong Limited   (1)
Level 21 Tower 1 Megabox Enterprise Sq 5
38 Weng Chiu Rd, Kowloon, China (Hong
Kong)   (100%)
Tel.: (852) 26296188
Web Site: http://www.generalmills.com
Sales Range: $250-299.9 Million
Emp.: 500
Food Products Mfr
N.A.I.C.S.: 311999

General Mills Iberica, S.A.U.   (1)
Serrano Galvache 56, 28033, Madrid,
Spain   (100%)
Tel.: (34) 913835714
Web Site: http://www.generalmills.es
Sales Range: $50-74.9 Million
Emp.: 50
Food Products Mfr
N.A.I.C.S.: 311999

General Mills India Private
Limited   (1)
902 Ventura Hiranandani Business Park,
Mumbai, 400076, Powai, India   (100%)
Tel.: (91) 2240430430
Web Site: http://www.generalmills.co.in
Sales Range: $250-299.9 Million
Emp.: 900
Branded Food Product Marketer
N.A.I.C.S.: 311999

General Mills Israel Ltd.   (1)
2 Pashosh St, PO Box 2072, Industrial
Zone, Ramla, 7212001, Israel
Tel.: (972) 89132818
Web Site: http://www.generalmills.co.il
Frozen Bakery Product Supplier & Cereal
Mfr
N.A.I.C.S.: 311813

General Mills Korea Co. Ltd.   (1)
311 Teheran-ro Yeoksam-dong Anam Tower
6th floor, Gangnam-gu, Seoul, 06151, Ko-
rea (South)
Tel.: (82) 25088500
Web Site: https://general-mills.co.kr
Food Products Mfr
N.A.I.C.S.: 311423

General Mills Operations, Inc.   (1)
1 General Mills Blvd, Minneapolis, MN
55426   (100%)
Tel.: (763) 764-7600
Sales Range: $550-599.9 Million
Emp.: 6,000
Grain & Field Beans-Buying & Marketing
N.A.I.C.S.: 493130

General Mills South Africa (Pty)
Ltd.   (1)
15E Riley Road, PO Box 76793, Bedford-
view, 2007, South Africa   (100%)
Tel.: (27) 8002487310
Web Site: https://www.generalmills.co.za
Sales Range: $50-74.9 Million
Emp.: 100
Food Service & Bakery Item Mfr
N.A.I.C.S.: 311999

General Mills Taiwan Limited   (1)
Zhongshan 8th Floor No 156 Section 1
Road, Banqiao District, New Taipei City,
22065, Taiwan
Tel.: (886) 289643599
Web Site: https://www.generalmills.com.tw
Food Products Mfr
N.A.I.C.S.: 311999

General Mills UK Ltd.   (1)

Harman House 1 George Street, Uxbridge,
UB8 1QQ, Middlesex, United
Kingdom   (100%)
Tel.: (44) 800591223
Web Site: https://www.generalmills.co.uk
Rev.: $350,000,000
Emp.: 160
Marketer & Mfr of Chilled, Canned & Frozen
Foods
N.A.I.C.S.: 311520

General Mills, Consumer Foods
Sales Division   (1)
Number 1 General Mills Blvd, Minneapolis,
MN 55426   (100%)
Tel.: (763) 764-7600
Web Site: http://www.generalmills.com
Sales Range: $1-4.9 Billion
Emp.: 12,000
National Sales Organization for Consumer
Foods Group
N.A.I.C.S.: 311230

HAAGEN-DAZS ARRAS SNC   (1)
155 Route de Cambrai, 62217, Tilloy-les-
Mofflaines, France
Tel.: (33) 321501919
Sales Range: $75-99.9 Million
Emp.: 300
Food Products Mfr
N.A.I.C.S.: 311999
Francois-Xavier Brehon (Gen Mgr)

HAAGEN-DAZS BELGIUM
(SPRL)   (1)
Place Louise 2A, Brussels, 1060, Belgium
Tel.: (32) 25122838
Emp.: 30
Food Products Mfr
N.A.I.C.S.: 311999

Haagen-Dazs Europe   (1)
2 Rue Paul Dautier, 32 avenue de l'Europe,
78941, Velizy-Villacoublay, France
Tel.: (33) 134585858
Sales Range: $250-299.9 Million
Emp.: 150
Mfr, Market & Distribute Super-Premium,
All-Natural Ice Cream & Frozen Yogurt
Products
N.A.I.C.S.: 311520

Haagen-Dazs Japan, Inc.   (1)
2-1-1 Kamimeguro, Meguro-ku, Tokyo, 153-
0051, Japan
Tel.: (81) 120190821
Web Site: https://www.haagen-dazs.co.jp
Sales Range: $50-74.9 Million
Ice Cream Producer
N.A.I.C.S.: 311520

Heartland Pet Food Manufacturing
Iowa, Inc.   (1)
PO Box 2020, Springdale, AR 72765
Web Site: http://www.truechews.com
Dog Food Mfr
N.A.I.C.S.: 311111

INO FITA GMBH   (1)
Osterbekstr90 c, 22083, Hamburg, Ger-
many
Tel.: (49) 4044405490
Web Site: http://www.generalmills.com
Sales Range: $25-49.9 Million
Emp.: 7
Frozen Food Mfr
N.A.I.C.S.: 311412

KIFISSIA PASTRIES S.A.   (1)
36 Kyriazi, Kifissia, Greece
Tel.: (30) 2106233589
Food Products Mfr
N.A.I.C.C.: 011000
Georgia Bourtsoukli (Gen Mgr)

LATICINIOS CAROLINA LTDA   (1)
Rua Benjamin Constant 840, Ribeirao
Claro, 86410-000, Parana, Brazil
Tel.: (55) 4335368100
Web Site: https://www.latcarolina.com.br
Dairy Product Whslr
N.A.I.C.S.: 424490

MOUNTAIN HIGH LLC   (1)
8320 Fauntleroy Way SW, Seattle, WA
98136
Tel.: (206) 938-3233
Recreational Trail Services
N.A.I.C.S.: 713990

Medallion Laboratories   (1)

9000 Plymouth Ave N, Minneapolis, MN
55427   (100%)
Tel.: (763) 764-8755
Web Site: https://www.medallionlabs.com
Sales Range: $25-49.9 Million
Emp.: 100
Nutritional Labeling & Analytical Testing
Services
N.A.I.C.S.: 561910

Molinos Modernos, S.A.   (1)
Km 17 5 Pacific Hwy Barcenas Crossroad
400 mts, Guatemala, Villanueva,
Guatemala   (100%)
Tel.: (502) 6313212
Web Site: http://www.molsa.com.sv
Sales Range: $250-299.9 Million
Emp.: 600
Flour Mills
N.A.I.C.S.: 311211

Molsa San Salvador   (1)
Boulevard Del Ejercito Nacional Y 50 Av
Norte, San Salvador, El Salvador   (100%)
Tel.: (503) 23457455
Web Site: https://www.molsa.com.sv
Sales Range: $25-49.9 Million
Emp.: 450
Flour Mills Production
N.A.I.C.S.: 311211

PINEDALE TRADING PTE
LIMITED   (1)
168 Robinson Road Capital Tower level 26-
01, Singapore, 068912, Singapore
Tel.: (65) 67321566
Web Site: http://www.generalmills.com
Food Products Mfr
N.A.I.C.S.: 311999

POWER HOUSE FOODS PTY
LTD   (1)
Mayfair Park McDowells Rd, Bendigo, 3550,
VIC, Australia
Tel.: (61) 3 5449 2626
Sales Range: $25-49.9 Million
Emp.: 80
Food Products Mfr
N.A.I.C.S.: 311999

SODIMA SAS   (1)
0 Route de Riom-RN 9, Cebazat, 63118,
Auvergne, France
Tel.: (33) 473248548
Furniture Whslr
N.A.I.C.S.: 423210

Seneca Food Corp.   (1)
911 Crestloch Ln, Pasco, WA 99301-9519
Tel.: (315) 926-8100
Web Site: http://consumer.senecafoods.com
Sales Range: $50-74.9 Million
Emp.: 5
Agriculture
N.A.I.C.S.: 111998

Small Planet Foods Inc.   (1)
106 Woodworth St, Sedro Woolley, WA
98284-1431
Tel.: (360) 855-0100
Web Site: http://www.smallplanetfoods.com
Sales Range: $75-99.9 Million
Emp.: 70
Organic Foods Producer
N.A.I.C.S.: 311423

Snow Brand Pillsbury, Inc.   (1)
No 13 Honshio Cho Shinjuku Ku, Tokyo,
160 8575, Japan   (13%)
Tel.: (81) 332262111
Web Site: http://www.meg-snow.com
Sales Range: $150-199.9 Million
Emp.: 400
Frozen Foods; Joint Venture with Snow
Brand Milk Products Co., Ltd.
N.A.I.C.S.: 311412

TRANSYOKI - TRANSPORTES YOKI
LTDA   (1)
Estr Do Rosario 135, Duque De Caxias, Rio
de Janeiro, 25215-365, Brazil
Tel.: (55) 2127733507
Truck Transport Services
N.A.I.C.S.: 484121

The Pillsbury Company   (1)
2533 General Mills Way, Murfreesboro, TN
37127-5524
Tel.: (615) 890-9900
Web Site: https://www.pillsbury.com

Sales Range: $500-549.9 Million
Emp.: 800
Producer of Cake Mixes
N.A.I.C.S.: 311211

Yoplait S.A.S. (1)
150 Rue Gallieni, 92657, Boulogne, Cedex,
France (51%)
Tel.: (33) 800022121
Web Site: http://www.yoplait.fr
Sales Range: $5-14.9 Billion
Dairy Product Produce Mfr
N.A.I.C.S.: 311514

Subsidiary (Non-US):

YOPLAIT CANADA CO. (2)
1875 Buckhorn Gate Suite 201, Missis-
sauga, L4W 5N9, ON, Canada
Web Site: https://www.yoplait.ca
Food Products Mfr
N.A.I.C.S.: 311412

Subsidiary (Domestic):

YOPLAIT FRANCE SAS (2)
150 rue Gallieni, 92641, Boulogne, Cedex,
France
Tel.: (33) 800022121
Web Site: http://www.yoplait.fr
Dairy Product Whslr
N.A.I.C.S.: 424430

Subsidiary (Non-US):

YOPLAIT IRELAND LIMITED (2)
Unit 16A Fonthill Industrial Park, Clondalkin,
Dublin, 22, Ireland
Tel.: (353) 818818988
Web Site: https://www.yoplait.ie
Dairy Product Whslr
N.A.I.C.S.: 424430

YOPLAIT SVERIGE AB (2)
Hollandargatan 20, 111 60, Stockholm,
Sweden
Tel.: (46) 200434345
Web Site: http://www.yoplait.se
Dairy Product Whslr
N.A.I.C.S.: 424430

Subsidiary (US):

YOPLAIT USA, INC. (2)
128 E Slosson Ave, Reed City, MI 49677
Tel.: (231) 832-3285
Web Site: http://www.yoplait.com
Fluid Milk Mfr
N.A.I.C.S.: 311511

Subsidiary (Non-US):

Yoplait UK Ltd. (2)
Harman House 1 George Street, Portsmith
Rd, Uxbridge, UB8 1QQ, Surrey, United
Kingdom
Tel.: (44) 8003580401
Web Site: https://www.yoplait.co.uk
Dairy Product Merchant Whslr
N.A.I.C.S.: 424430
Nick Wishman (Mng Dir)

GENERAL MOTORS COMPANY

300 Renaissance Ctr, Detroit, MI
48265-3000
Tel.: (313) 667-1500   DE
Web Site: https://www.gm.com
Year Founded: 1908
GM—(NYSE)
Rev.: $171,842,000,000
Assets: $273,064,000,000
Liabilities: $204,875,000,000
Net Worth: $68,189,000,000
Earnings: $10,022,000,000
Emp.: 163,000
Fiscal Year-end: 12/31/23
Automobiles, Trucks, Diesel Locomo-
tives & Engines, Aircraft Engines &
Engine Parts, Automotive, Locomo-
tive & Aircraft Components
N.A.I.C.S.: 336110
Daniel E. Berce (Pres/CEO-Financial
& Sr VP)
Mary T. Barra (Chm & CEO)
Mark L. Reuss (Pres)

Steven A. Kiefer (Pres-South America
& Intl Ops & Sr VP)
Craig B. Glidden (Gen Counsel &
Exec VP)
Paul A. Jacobson (CFO & Exec VP)
Rory Harvey (Pres-Global Markets &
Exec VP)
John Roth (VP-Global Cadillac)
Josh Tavel (Sr VP-Energy Storage,
Propulsion, R&D, and Mfg Engrg)

Subsidiaries:

**Advantage Chevrolet of Bolingbrook,
Inc.** (1)
115 W S Frontage Rd, Bolingbrook, IL
60440
Tel.: (630) 759-5600
Web Site: http://www.advantagechevbb.com
Automobile Mfr
N.A.I.C.S.: 336110
Jim Galbraith (Mgr-Internet)
Tim McDonald (Mgr-Used Car)
Mark Burbach (Mgr-Svc)
Melissa Kociuba (Mgr-Office)
Freddy Pantoja (Mgr-New Vehicle)
Tom Steinbraker (Mgr-Internet)
Joseph Striska (Gen Mgr-Sls)
John Fischer (Gen Mgr)
Marge Bardoczi (Controller)

**Alambrados Automotrices, S.A. de
C.V.** (1)
Av Las Fabricas 5838 Col Parque Industrial
Finsa Nuevo Laredo, Tamaulipas, 88275,
Mexico, DF, Mexico (100%)
Tel.: (52) 8677114999
Web Site: http://www.gm.com.mx
Assembly of Automotive Wiring Systems
N.A.I.C.S.: 335931

Antelope Valley Chevrolet, Inc. (1)
1160 Motor Ln, Lancaster, CA 93534
Tel.: (661) 235-6935
Web Site: https://www.avchevy.com
Automobile Mfr
N.A.I.C.S.: 336110
Justin Gonzales (Gen Mgr)
Jack Oh (Gen Sls Mgr)
Nina Garcia (Mgr-Sls)
Nicole McCracken (Mgr-PR)
David Ledesma (Mgr-New Car Inventory)
David Acevedo (Mgr-Fin)
Alex Cuesta (Mgr-Sls)
Erin Emard (Mgr-Customer Care)
Kevin Daeley (Mgr-Parts)
Lamel Scott (Sls Mgr)
Jay Blitzer (Dir-Fixed Ops)
Daniel Toro (Sls Mgr-Internet)
Francisco Majano (Sls Mgr-Internet)
Erik Pacheco (Sls Mgr-Internet)
Agnieszka Maslowiec (Sls Mgr-Internet)
Jorge Sauceda (Sls Dir-Internet)
Joaquin Matuz (Sls Mgr-Internet)
Carlos Castellon Chairez (Mgr-Internet)
Jason Beaini (Fin Mgr)
Richard Hertzburg (Fin Mgr)
James Gonzalez (Fin Mgr)
Roberto Chirinos (Mgr-Svc)

Astyx GmbH (1)
Caroline-Herschel-Strasse 2, 85521, Ottob-
runn, Germany
Tel.: (49) 892018040
Web Site: https://cruisemunich.de
Microchip Mfr
N.A.I.C.S.: 334413

Athens Chevrolet, Inc. (1)
4110 Atlanta Hwy, Athens, GA 30606-0810
Tel.: (706) 621-6739
Web Site: http://www.athenschevy.com
Emp.: 25
Automotive Distr
N.A.I.C.S.: 441227
Mike Burge (Gen Mgr)
Steve Motz (Mgr-Bus Dev)
Justin Octavi (Mgr-Fin)
Rick Gonzalez (Mgr-Fixed Ops)
Walter Bonds (Mgr-Detail)
Bobby Roberts (Mgr-Parts)

Bean Chevrolet Buick GMC Ltd. (1)
375 McNeely Ave, Carleton Place, K7C
0A1, ON, Canada
Tel.: (613) 257-2432
Web Site: https://www.beancars.ca
Car Dealing Services

N.A.I.C.S.: 441110
Jim Whitmarsh (Gen Mgr-Sls)
Kim Fitzgerald (Mgr-Fin Svcs)
Ross Tubman (Controller)
Monique McFaul (Mgr-Fin Svcs)
Kelsey Miriguay (Mgr-Sls)
April Bean (Gen Mgr)
Darryl Warlich (Mgr-Parts & Accessories)
Jon Harding (Mgr-Used Car)
Jami-Lea Forbes (Gen Mgr-PRO Sls &
Leasing Consultant)
Mackenzie Kennedy (Gen Mgr-PRO Sls &
Leasing Consultant)
Bill Phair (Mgr-Collision Centre)

Boden Brussels NV (1)
Gentsesteenweg 528-550, 1080, Brussels,
Belgium
Tel.: (32) 24145400
Web Site: http://www.garageboden.be
General Automotive Repair Services
N.A.I.C.S.: 811111

Bridgewater Chevrolet, Inc. (1)
1548 US Hwy Route 22 E, Bridgewater, NJ
08807
Tel.: (732) 907-1564
Web Site: http://www.bridgewaterchevy.com
Automobile Maintenance Services
N.A.I.C.S.: 811114

Britain Chevrolet, Inc. (1)
4495 I-30, Greenville, TX 75402
Tel.: (903) 450-4216
Sales Range: $25-49.9 Million
Emp.: 35
Automobile Mfr
N.A.I.C.S.: 336110
Byron Britain (CEO)

**CHEVYPLAN S.A. Sociedad Adminis-
tradora de Planes de Autofinan-
ciamiento Comercial** (1)
Cr 7 75 - 26, Bogota, Colombia
Tel.: (57) 6013769120
Web Site: http://www.chevyplan.com.co
Commercial Self-Financing Services
N.A.I.C.S.: 522320

Cadillac Europe GmbH (1)
Boulevard Lilienthal 6, Glattpark, 8152,
Opfikon, Switzerland
Tel.: (41) 448282700
Web Site: http://www.cadillac.de
Car Distr
N.A.I.C.S.: 441110

Cadillac Polanco, S.A. de C.V. (1)
Campos Eliseos 233, Col Polanco de
Miguel Hidalgo, Mexico, 11560, Mexico
Tel.: (52) 5552817999
Web Site: http://www.surmanpolanco.com
Sales Range: $25-49.9 Million
Emp.: 35
Automotive Distr
N.A.I.C.S.: 441227

Cadillac of Greenwich, Inc. (1)
144 Railroad Ave, Greenwich, CT 06830
Tel.: (203) 987-4367
Web Site:
    http://www.cadillacofgreenwich.com
Car Dealing Services
N.A.I.C.S.: 441110
Rondell Douglas (Gen Mgr-Sls)
Eric Sandstrom (VP)
Mike Phillips (Mgr-Svc)

**Champion Chevrolet, Pontiac, Buick,
Inc.** (1)
502 S 1st St, La Grange, KY 40031
Tel.: (502) 565-4571
Web Site: https://www.championcpb.com
Automobile Mfr
N.A.I.C.S.: 336110
Fred Tolsdorf (Pres)
Judy Tolsdorf (Dir-Customer Rels)
Ed Brown (Gen Mgr-Sls)
Mariah Lange (Mgr-Sls)
Melissa Sutton (Dir-Fin)
Theresa Torres (Office Mgr)
Karen Hawkins (Dir-Fixed Ops)
Ron Pike (Mgr-Parts)
Tim Alvey (Mgr-Collision Center)
Mike Daleo (Dir-Pre-Owned)
Paul Mahoney (Mgr-Pre-Owned)
Raymond Kellar (Dir-Fin)
David McNulty (Mgr-Customer Relationship)
Robby Shepherd (Mgr-Svc)
Deon Sylvester (Mgr-Detail)

**Chevrolet Otomotiv Ticaret Limited
Sirketi** (1)
Kemalpasa road, Torbali, 35860, Izmir, Tur-
kiye
Tel.: (90) 2123755261
Web Site: https://www.chevrolet.com.tr
New Car Retailer
N.A.I.C.S.: 441110

**Chevrolet Sales (Thailand)
Limited** (1)
555 Rasa Tower II 28 th Floor Phanolyothin
Rd, Chatuchak, Bangkok, 10900, Thailand
Tel.: (66) 800012083
Web Site: https://www.chevrolet.co.th
Sales Range: $25-49.9 Million
Emp.: 90
Automobile Mfr
N.A.I.C.S.: 336110

**Chevrolet Sales India Private
Ltd.** (1)
03-107-B WeWork Blue One Square Udyog
Vihar Phase 4 Rd, Panchmahals, Gurgaon,
122016, Haryana, India
Tel.: (91) 2676221000
Web Site: http://www.chevrolet.co.in
Car Distr
N.A.I.C.S.: 441110

**Chevrolet Sociedad Anonima de
Ahorro para Fines Determinados** (1)
San Martin 140 piso 14 Cuidad Autonoma
de, Buenos Aires, Argentina
Tel.: (54) 8107777526
Web Site: https://www.chevrolet.com.ar
Automobile Mfr
N.A.I.C.S.: 336110

Chevrolet of Columbus, Inc. (1)
2825 Merchant Mile, Columbus, IN 47201
Tel.: (812) 375-2900
Web Site: http://www.chevyofcolumbus.com
Emp.: 32
Car Distr
N.A.I.C.S.: 423110
Nick Crowder (Gen Mgr-Sls)
Blake Roberts (Sls Dir)
Fred Armstrong (Coord-Community Out-
reach)
Krista Slate (Mgr-Parts)
Tyler Tope (Fin Dir)
Marcelo Agudo (Dir-Special Fin)

Chevrolet of Novato, Inc. (1)
7123 Redwood Blvd, Novato, CA 94945-
4102
Tel.: (415) 897-2191
Web Site: http://www.novatochevrolet.com
Emp.: 28
Car Distr
N.A.I.C.S.: 441110

Componentes Delfa, C.A. (1)
Calle Parocotos Indust Marin II, Caracas,
106, Venezuela (49%)
Tel.: (58) 2392121514
Web Site: http://www.faaca.com
Assembly of Automotive Air Conditioning
Compressors & Controls; Supported by
Harrison Radiator Division
N.A.I.C.S.: 333415

Concorde Automobile Ltd (1)
3003 Rue Picard, Saint-Hyacinthe, J2S
1H2, QC, Canada
Tel.: (450) 774-5336
Web Site: http://www.gm.ca
Sales Range: $25-49.9 Million
Emp.: 40
New & Used Car Dealers
N.A.I.C.S.: 441110

Corporacion Proauto S.A. (1)
Av Eloy Alfaro N43-02 Y Av de Los Grana-
dos, Quito, Ecuador
Tel.: (593) 983305525
Web Site: https://corporacionproauto.com.ec
Car Dealer
N.A.I.C.S.: 441110

**Crash Avoidance Metrics
Partnerships** (1)
39255 Country Club Dr Ste B40, Farming-
ton Hills, MI 48331-3420
Tel.: (248) 848-9595
Automobile Mfr
N.A.I.C.S.: 336110

Cruise Munich GmbH (1)

General Motors Company—(Continued)

Caroline-Herschel-Strasse 2, 85521, Ottobrunn, Germany
Tel.: (49) 40554364026
Web Site: https://cruisemunich.de
Automation Equipment Mfr
N.A.I.C.S.: 335314

DHB-Componentes Automotivos, S.A. **(1)**
Avda Das Ind 864, Bairro Anchieta, 90200-290, Porto Alegre, RS, Brazil **(49%)**
Tel.: (55) 5121211244
Web Site: http://www.dhb.com.br
Emp.: 750
Mfr of Automotive & Industrial Components
N.A.I.C.S.: 336340
Luiz Carlos Mandelli *(CEO)*

Dealership Liquidations, Inc. **(1)**
2142 Austin Dr, Troy, MI 48083
Tel.: (248) 740-9590
Emp.: 5
Automotive Part Whslr
N.A.I.C.S.: 441330

Dinuba Auto Center, Inc. **(1)**
1500 W El Monte Way, Dinuba, CA 93618
Tel.: (559) 591-5000
Web Site: http://www.dinubachamber.com
Automobile Mfr
N.A.I.C.S.: 336110
Edward Dena *(Pres)*

Elasto S.A. **(1)**
Bartolome Sanchez N74-04 y Antonio Basantes, Panamericana Norte KM 6 1/2, Quito, Ecuador
Tel.: (593) 983342486
Web Site: http://www.indelasto.com
Automobile Mfr
N.A.I.C.S.: 336110

Empower Energies, Inc. **(1)**
5750 New King St Ste 330, Troy, MI 48098
Tel.: (248) 852-1300
Web Site: http://www.empowerenergies.com
Eletric Power Generation Services
N.A.I.C.S.: 221118
John Clapp *(Pres & CEO)*
Khalil Qasimi *(Sr VP & Head-Fin)*
Michael Belko *(COO)*
Pamela Maines *(Sr VP-Bus Dev)*
Joe Jazdzewski *(VP-Ops)*
Mark Molitor *(VP-Structured Fin)*
Scott Taylor *(CFO)*
Dennis Haines *(Gen Counsel, Sec & Sr VP)*
Robert Edwards Jr. *(Chief Legal Officer & Sr VP)*

Envia Systems, Inc. **(1)**
7979 Gateway Blvd Ste 101, Newark, CA 94560
Tel.: (510) 509-1367
Web Site: http://www.enviasystems.com
Automotive Electronic Product Distr
N.A.I.C.S.: 423120
Sujeet Kumar *(CTO)*
Michael Sinkula *(Founder & Dir-Bus Dev)*
Herman Lopez *(VP-R&D)*

Fox Valley Buick-GMC, Inc. **(1)**
1421 E Main St, Saint Charles, IL 60174
Tel.: (630) 338-0202
Web Site: https://www.foxvalleybuickgmc.com
Automobile Maintenance Services
N.A.I.C.S.: 811114
Emir C. Abinion *(Owner & Pres)*
Kim Ryan *(Office Mgr)*
Tracy Mulcahy *(Mgr-Svc)*
Michael Johnson *(Mgr-Sls & Fin)*
Tony Spedale *(Mgr-Parts)*
Danielle West *(Mgr-HR)*
Alex Katselis *(Gen Mgr-Sls)*
Justin Mansk *(Gen Mgr)*
Frank Butnaru *(Gen Mgr)*
Frank Rubino *(Asst Mgr-Svc)*

Fredericktown Chevrolet Co., Inc. **(1)**
109 Bollinger Dr, Fredericktown, OH 43019
Tel.: (740) 848-5999
Web Site: http://www.fredychevy.com
Automobile Mfr
N.A.I.C.S.: 336110

GM Components Holdings, LLC **(1)**
200 Upper Mountain Rd, Lockport, NY 14094-1819

Tel.: (716) 439-2011
Automobile Mfr
N.A.I.C.S.: 336110
Ed Peet *(Dir-Personnel)*
Robert Nevins *(Engr-Mfg)*
Mile Kordovski *(Mgr-Mfg Engrg)*
Ethan Koss *(Supvr-Maintenance)*
William Buchholz *(Supvr-Maintenance)*
Angela Johnson *(Supvr-Ops)*

GM Corretora de Seguros Ltda. **(1)**
Rua Safira 555-B, Prado, Belo Horizonte, 30411-127, Minas Gerais, Brazil
Tel.: (55) 3136462223
Web Site: http://www.gmcorretora.com.br
Insurance Agency & Brokerage Services
N.A.I.C.S.: 524210

GM Cruise Holdings LLC **(1)**
1201 Bryant St, San Francisco, CA 94103
Automobile Mfr
N.A.I.C.S.: 336110

GM Daewoo Auto & Technology Co. **(1)**
199 Chongchon-dong, Pupyong-ku, Incheon, Korea (South) **(51%)**
Tel.: (82) 325202114
Web Site: http://www.gmdaewoo.co.kr
Sales Range: $5-14.9 Billion
Emp.: 17,000
Mfr of Passenger Cars & Commercial Vehicles
N.A.I.C.S.: 336110

Subsidiary (Domestic):

Daewoo Automotive Components, Ltd. **(2)**
10 Tongil Ro, Jung-gu, Seoul, Korea (South)
Tel.: (82) 27592114
Web Site: http://www.daewoo.com
Sales Range: $200-249.9 Million
Emp.: 1,200
Motor Vehicle Brake System Mfr
N.A.I.C.S.: 336340

Subsidiary (Non-US):

GM Daewoo Australia Pty. Limited **(2)**
Suite 2 Level 4 621 Pacific Highway, Saint Leonards, 2065, NSW, Australia
Tel.: (61) 299067355
Metal, Machinery & Automotive Components Mfr
N.A.I.C.S.: 333120

GM Daewoo UK Limited **(2)**
Wyvern House Kimpton Road, Luton, LU2 0DW, Bedfordshire, United Kingdom
Tel.: (44) 8708748888
Car Distr
N.A.I.C.S.: 441110

GM Finance Co. Holdings LLC **(1)**
300 Renaissance Ctr Ste L1, Detroit, MI 48265-3000
Tel.: (586) 986-7799
Investment Management Service
N.A.I.C.S.: 523940

GM Global Technology Operations LLC **(1)**
300 Renaissance Ctr, Detroit, MI 48243-1402
Tel.: (313) 665-3988
Web Site: http://www.gm.com
Automobile Mfr
N.A.I.C.S.: 336110

GM Holden Ltd. **(1)**
191 Salmon Street, Port Melbourne, 3207, VIC, Australia
Tel.: (61) 396471111
Web Site: http://www.holden.com.au
Sales Range: $75-99.9 Million
Emp.: 2,000
Motor Vehicles & Parts Mfr & Distr
N.A.I.C.S.: 336110
Mark Bernhard *(Chm & Mng Dir)*

GM LAAM Holdings, LLC **(1)**
300 Renaissance Ctr, Detroit, MI 48265-3000
Tel.: (313) 556-5000
Web Site: http://www.gm.com
Automobile Mfr
N.A.I.C.S.: 551112

GM Philippines, Inc. **(1)**
RCBC Savings Bank Corporate Center 26th & 25th Streets Floor 20, Bonifacio Global City Metro Manila, Taguig, Philippines
Tel.: (63) 23177100
Motor Vehicle & Parts Distr
N.A.I.C.S.: 423120

GM Powertrain Group **(1)**
823 Joslyn Ave, Pontiac, MI 48340
Tel.: (248) 857-0932
Sales Range: $15-24.9 Billion
Emp.: 60,000
Engines, Transmissions, Casting & Components
N.A.I.C.S.: 336390

GM Preferred Finance Co. Holdings LLC **(1)**
300 Renaissance Ctr, Detroit, MI 48243-1402
Tel.: (313) 556-5000
Mortgage Services
N.A.I.C.S.: 522310

GM Singapore Pte. Limited **(1)**
7 Ubi Close, Singapore, 408604, Singapore **(100%)**
Tel.: (65) 5113033
Web Site: http://www.chevrolet.com.sg
Sales Range: $100-124.9 Million
Assembly of Electronic Automotive Components
N.A.I.C.S.: 334419

GM Technical Center Korea, Ltd. **(1)**
233 Cheongcheon-dong Bupyeong-daero, Bupyeong-gu, Incheon, Korea (South)
Tel.: (82) 8030005000
Emp.: 3,000
Vehicle Component Mfr & Distr
N.A.I.C.S.: 336110
Hyunjun Ku *(Mgr)*

GMF Leasing LLC **(1)**
801 Cherry St Ste 3500, Fort Worth, TX 76102
Tel.: (817) 302-7000
Automotive Part Whslr
N.A.I.C.S.: 441330
Chris A. Choate *(CFO & Exec VP)*

General Motors (Thailand) Limited **(1)**
555 Rasa Tower Level 21 2101-2104 Phaholyothin Road, Jatuchak, Bangkok, 10900, Thailand
Tel.: (66) 27913400
Automotive Part Whslr
N.A.I.C.S.: 441330
Amnat Saengjan *(VP-Mfg)*

General Motors Asia Pacific (Pte) Ltd. **(1)**
238a Thomson Road 17-00 Novena Square - Tower, Singapore, 307684, Singapore
Tel.: (65) 6567379588
Automobile Maintenance Services
N.A.I.C.S.: 811114
Bob Parcell *(Mgr-Mfg-International Ops)*

General Motors Asia Pacific Holdings, LLC **(1)**
300 Renaissance Ctr, Detroit, MI 48243
Tel.: (313) 556-5000
Holding Company
N.A.I.C.S.: 551112

General Motors Asset Management Corporation **(1)**
1345 Ave Of The Americas, New York, NY 10105
Tel.: (212) 418-3550
Emp.: 19
Automobile Mfr
N.A.I.C.S.: 336110

General Motors Automobiles Philippines, Inc. **(1)**
37th Floor Lkg Tower, Makati, Philippines
Tel.: (63) 23177325
Automotive Distr
N.A.I.C.S.: 441110

General Motors Chile Industria Automotriz Limitada **(1)**
Los Jardines 931, Huechuraba, Santiago, Chile
Tel.: (56) 25206100
Web Site: http://www.chevrolet.cl

Car Distr
N.A.I.C.S.: 423110

General Motors Chile S.A., Industria Automotriz **(1)**
Av Americo Vespucio 811, Santiago, 8590723, Chile **(100%)**
Tel.: (56) 25206100
Web Site: http://www.gm.cl
Sales Range: $25-49.9 Million
Emp.: 200
Vehicle Mfr
N.A.I.C.S.: 336110

General Motors Colmotores, S.A. **(1)**
avenida Boyaca Calle 56 A Sur No 33-53, Bogota, Colombia **(82.6%)**
Tel.: (57) 6014249393
Web Site: http://www.chevrolet.com.co
Sales Range: $200-249.9 Million
Plywood Products Mfr
N.A.I.C.S.: 336110

General Motors Del Ecuador S.A. **(1)**
Av Galo Plaza Lasso OE1-134 y Enrique Guerrero Portilla, Parque Industrial, Quito, Ecuador **(100%)**
Tel.: (593) 22977700
Web Site: http://www.chevrolet.com.ec
Sales Range: $250-299.9 Million
Imported Vehicle & Automotive Component Mfr
N.A.I.C.S.: 336340

General Motors Egypt S.A.E. **(1)**
4th Industrial Zone, 6th of October City, Egypt
Tel.: (20) 225299444
Web Site: http://www.gmegypt.com
Sales Range: $75-99.9 Million
Emp.: 1,400
Automobile Whslr
N.A.I.C.S.: 423110

General Motors Financial Company, Inc. **(1)**
801 Cherry St Ste 3500, Fort Worth, TX 76102
Tel.: (817) 302-7000
Web Site: http://www.gmfinancial.com
Rev.: $14,224,000,000
Assets: $132,011,000,000
Liabilities: $116,469,000,000
Net Worth: $15,542,000,000
Earnings: $2,126,000,000
Emp.: 9,000
Fiscal Year-end: 12/31/2023
Auto Loan Financing Services
N.A.I.C.S.: 522291
Daniel E. Berce *(Pres & CEO)*
Kyle R. Birch *(Pres-Ops-North America)*
Susan B. Sheffield *(CFO & Exec VP)*
James R. Vance *(Chief Pricing & Analytics Officer & Exec VP)*
Connie Coffey *(Chief Acctg Officer, Exec VP & Controller)*
Doug Johnson *(Chief Legal Officer & Exec VP)*
Lesa Powell *(Sr VP)*
Mike Kanarios *(Chief Strategy Officer & Exec VP)*
Jim Nagy *(Chief HR Oficer-Global & Exec VP)*
Richard A. Gokenbach *(Treas & Exec VP)*
Randy Hanna *(CTO-Global & Exec VP)*
Stephanie Casto *(Chief Compliance & Privacy Officer & Sr VP)*
Scott Dishman *(Exec VP-Servicing)*
Will Stacy *(Chief Mktg & Digital Officer & Exec VP)*
Bob Neaton *(Gen Counsel & Exec VP)*
Gabriela Rosende *(Exec VP-Customer Experience)*

Subsidiary (Domestic):

ACF Investment Corp. **(2)**
801 Cherry St Ste 12, Fort Worth, TX 76102-6885
Tel.: (817) 524-4022
Sales Range: $1-4.9 Billion
Emp.: 1,200
Financial Investors Services
N.A.I.C.S.: 523999

Mike Barrington *(CEO & Pres)*

AFS SenSub Corp.   **(2)**
801 Cherry St Ste 3600, Fort Worth, TX
76102-6855
Tel.: (817) 302-7000
Financial & Investment Services
N.A.I.C.S.: 523999
Chris A. Choate *(CFO & Exec VP)*

AmeriCredit Financial Services, Inc.   **(2)**
801 Cherry St Ste 3500, Fort Worth, TX
76102
Tel.: (817) 302-7000
Web Site: http://dealers.americredit.com
Financial Services
N.A.I.C.S.: 525990

Subsidiary (Non-US):

Banco GMAC S.A.   **(2)**
Avenida Indianopolis 3096, Planalto Paulista, Sao Paulo, 04062-003, Brazil
Tel.: (55) 8007226022
Web Site: http://www.chevroletsf.com.br
Emp.: 400
Commercial Banking Services
N.A.I.C.S.: 522110
David Brinkan *(Mng Dir)*

G.M.A.C. Financiera de Colombia S.A. Compania de Financiamiento Comercial   **(2)**
Calle 98 No 22-64 Piso 1, Bogota, Colombia
Tel.: (57) 6380909
Web Site: http://www.gmac.com.co
Financial Management Consulting Services
N.A.I.C.S.: 541611

GMAC Administradora de Consorcios Ltda.   **(2)**
Indianopolis 3096 Bl B An 1, Sao Paulo, 04062-003, Brazil
Tel.: (55) 1150797020
Automotive Part Whslr
N.A.I.C.S.: 441330

GMAC International Holdings B.V.   **(2)**
Hogeweg 16, Hague, 2582, Netherlands
Tel.: (31) 707503100
Holding Company
N.A.I.C.S.: 551112

Subsidiary (Non-US):

GM Financial AB   **(3)**
PO Box 44084, 100 73, Stockholm, Sweden
Tel.: (46) 84125660
Web Site: http://www.gmacfs.com
Automobile Financial Consulting Services
N.A.I.C.S.: 522220

GM Financial GmbH   **(3)**
Zeppelinstr 48a, 14471, Potsdam, Germany
Tel.: (49) 33158170100
Automobile Financial Consulting Services
N.A.I.C.S.: 522220

GMAC - Instituicao Financeira de Credito, S.A.   **(3)**
Rua Dr Antonio Loureiro Borges 9-2 Piso-Complexo, Arquiparque-Miraflores, Alges, 1495-131, Portugal
Tel.: (351) 214128100
Web Site: http://www.gmacfs.com
Automobile Financial Consulting Services
N.A.I.C.S.: 522220

GMAC Banque S.A.   **(3)**
1 Avenue du Marais BP 175, Argenteuil, 95105, France
Tel.: (33) 134262500
Web Site: http://www.gmacfs.com
Emp.: 63
Automobile Financial Consulting Services
N.A.I.C.S.: 522220

GMAC Espana de Financiacion, S.A. Unipersonal   **(3)**
Av Bruselas 20, 28108, Alcobendas, Madrid, Spain
Tel.: (34) 914170992
Emp.: 25
Automobile Financial Consulting Services
N.A.I.C.S.: 522220
Jesus Dalda *(Gen Mgr)*

GMAC Italia SpA   **(3)**
40 Piazzale Dell Industria, 00144, Rome, Italy
Tel.: (39) 0687422111
Web Site: http://www.gmacfs.it
Automobile Financial Consulting Services
N.A.I.C.S.: 522220

Subsidiary (Domestic):

GMAC Nederland N.V.   **(3)**
Lage Mosten 49-63, Postbus 981 4600 AZ
Bergen op Zoom, 4822 NK, Breda, Netherlands
Tel.: (31) 0765448900
Web Site: http://www.gmacfs.nl
Automobile Financing Services
N.A.I.C.S.: 522220

Subsidiary (Non-US):

GMAC UK plc   **(3)**
Heol Y Gamlas Parc Nantgarw Treforest, Cardiff, CF15 7QU, United Kingdom
Tel.: (44) 8448712222
Web Site: http://www.gmacfs.com
Commercial Banking Services
N.A.I.C.S.: 522110
Mark Tweed *(Mng Dir-UK & Sweden)*
Denise Buckley *(CFO-UK & Sweden)*

General Motors Financial Suisse SA   **(3)**
Sageweg 7, 2557, Studen, Switzerland
Tel.: (41) 323736616
Web Site: http://www.gmacfs.ch
Automobile Financial Consulting Services
N.A.I.C.S.: 522220

Subsidiary (Non-US):

GMAC Servicios S.A.S.   **(2)**
Calle 98 22 64 P 9, Bogota, Colombia
Tel.: (57) 16380900
Automotive Part Whslr
N.A.I.C.S.: 441330

GMAC de Venezuela, C.A.   **(2)**
Av Orinoco entre calles Perija y Copernico
Edif Oricenter Piso 3, Las Mercedes, Caracas, Venezuela
Tel.: (58) 2122129700
Web Site: http://www.gmacfs.com.ve
Automobile Financing Services
N.A.I.C.S.: 525990

General Motors Financial of Canada Limited   **(2)**
2001 Sheppard Ave East Suite 600, Toronto, M2J 4Z8, ON, Canada
Tel.: (416) 753-4000
Web Site: http://www.gmfinancial.ca
Loan Collection Services
N.A.I.C.S.: 561440
Ronald Gass *(VP-Credit & Funding)*
Robert Coulman *(VP-Fin-Canadian Dealer Svcs)*
John Paonessa *(VP-Remarketing Solutions)*
Diana Geary *(VP-Ops Support)*
Howard Cobham *(Exec VP)*

Subsidiary (Domestic):

JS Folsom Automotive, Inc.   **(2)**
12640 Auto Mall Cir, Folsom, CA 95630
Tel.: (916) 358-8963
Automobile Mfr
N.A.I.C.S.: 336110

Mangino Chevrolet, Inc.   **(2)**
4447 St Hwy 30, Amsterdam, NY 12010
Tel.: (518) 620-7756
Web Site: http://www.manginochevy.com
Emp.: 50
Automobile Parts Mfr
N.A.I.C.S.: 336390
Dave Groesbeck *(Gen Mgr)*
Brian Greene *(Mgr-Parts)*
Joseph Kulewicz *(Mgr-Internet, Digital & Inventory)*
Dick Mucilli *(Mgr-Svc)*
Paula Jackson *(Office Mgr)*
Tina Mangino-Coffey *(Pres)*
Patricia Mangino *(Treas & Sec)*
Mike Coffey *(VP)*
Rich Youngs *(Mgr-Sls)*
Shawn Bulger *(Mgr-Bus)*
Joanne Earley *(Mgr-Bus Dev & Customer Care Center)*
Ron Nichols *(Gen Mgr-Sls)*
Ralph Mangino Jr. *(Mgr-Sls)*

Saab Financial Services Corp.   **(2)**
17500 Chenal Pkwy, Little Rock, AR
72223   **(100%)**
Tel.: (501) 821-7800
Web Site: http://www.saabfinancial.com
Sales Range: $25-49.9 Million
Emp.: 7
Automobile Financing Services
N.A.I.C.S.: 522291
Sylvia Borchert *(Asst Sec)*

General Motors Global Service Operations, Inc.   **(1)**
300 Renaissance Ctr, Detroit, MI 48243-1402
Tel.: (586) 492-7333
Automobile Maintenance Services
N.A.I.C.S.: 811114

General Motors Holdings LLC   **(1)**
300 Renaissance Ctr L1, Detroit, MI 48243-1402
Tel.: (313) 556-5000
Automobile Mfr
N.A.I.C.S.: 336110

General Motors India Private Limited   **(1)**
B/201 2nd Flr Trade Ave Suren Andheri E, Mumbai, 400096, Maharashtra, India   **(91%)**
Tel.: (91) 2226823401
Web Site: http://www.chevrolet.co.in
Sales Range: $10-24.9 Million
Emp.: 16
Automobile Mfr
N.A.I.C.S.: 336110
Sanjiv Gupta *(Pres & Mng Dir)*

General Motors International Holdings, Inc.   **(1)**
300 Renaissance Ctr, Detroit, MI 48243-1402
Tel.: (313) 556-5000
Automobile Mfr
N.A.I.C.S.: 336110

General Motors Japan Limited   **(1)**
Shinagawa Seaside East Tower 8th Floor
4-12-8 Higashi-Shinagawa, Shinagawa-ku, Tokyo, 140-8687, Japan
Tel.: (81) 367115600
Web Site: http://search-careers.gm.com
Automobile Parts Distr
N.A.I.C.S.: 441110
Kaku Wakamatsu *(Pres & CEO)*

General Motors Overseas Distribution LLC   **(1)**
300 Renaissance Ctr, Detroit, MI 48243
Tel.: (313) 556-5000
Motor Vehicle Parts Distr
N.A.I.C.S.: 423120

General Motors Peru S.A.   **(1)**
Av Juan de Arona 151, San Isidro, Lima, Peru
Tel.: (51) 12010930
Web Site: http://www.chevrolet.com.pe
Automotive Distr
N.A.I.C.S.: 336110

General Motors Powertrain (Thailand) Limited   **(1)**
111/4 Moo 4 Eastern Seaboard Industrial
Estate, Pluak Daeng, Rayong, 21140, Thailand
Tel.: (66) 33047699
Automobile Mfr
N.A.I.C.S.: 336110

General Motors Trkiye Limited Sirketi   **(1)**
Kemal Pasa Yolu, Torbali, Izmir, 35860, Turkiye
Tel.: (90) 2328504000
Web Site: http://www.opel.com.tr
Automotive Distr
N.A.I.C.S.: 441110

General Motors de Argentina S.r.l.   **(1)**
Av Leandro Alem 855 2nd Floor, Buenos
Aires, C1001AAD, Argentina
Tel.: (54) 1145102700
Automobile Mfr
N.A.I.C.S.: 336110

General Motors de Mexico, S.A. de C.V.   **(1)**
Avenida Ejercito Nacional 843-B Col
Granada, Delegacion Miguel Hidalgo, 11520, Mexico, D.F., Mexico   **(100%)**
Tel.: (52) 5553290811
Web Site: http://www.gm.com.mx
Motor Vehicle Parts Mfr
N.A.I.C.S.: 336110
Francisco Garza *(Pres & CEO)*
Monica Garcia *(Dir-Global Purchasing & Supply Chain)*

General Motors do Brasil Ltda.   **(1)**
Goias 1805 Sao Caetano Do Sul, Sao
Paulo, 09501-970, SP, Brazil   **(100%)**
Tel.: (55) 1142347700
Web Site: http://www.chevrolet.com.br
Sales Range: $1-4.9 Billion
Emp.: 8,000
Automobile Assembling Services
N.A.I.C.S.: 336110
Barry Engle *(Pres-Interim)*

General Motors of Canada Company   **(1)**
500 Wentworth Street WEST, Oshawa, L1J
0C5, ON, Canada
Web Site: https://www.gm.ca
Automobile Design, Mfr & Marketer
N.A.I.C.S.: 336110
Sandor Piszar *(VP-Sls, Svc, and Mktg)*
David Paterson *(VP-Corp & Environmental Affairs)*
Marissa West *(Pres & Mng Dir)*
Faithlyn Hemmings *(VP)*
Tobias Sunner *(VP)*

Division (Domestic):

GM CAMI Assembly   **(2)**
300 Ingersoll Street, Ingersoll, N5C 4A6, ON, Canada
Tel.: (519) 485-6400
Web Site: http://www.gm.ca
Sales Range: $300-349.9 Million
Emp.: 2,550
Automobile Production & Distribution
N.A.I.C.S.: 336110

General Motors Canada Components Div.   **(2)**
570 Glendale Avenue, Saint Catharines, L2P 0B2, ON, Canada   **(100%)**
Tel.: (905) 641-6424
Web Site: https://www.gm.ca
Sales Range: $700-749.9 Million
Emp.: 3,400
Mfr of Transmission Final Drive & Differential Assemblies, Rear Axles, Front Suspensions, Brake & Drum Assemblies & Components
N.A.I.C.S.: 336330

General Motors Canada Engine Div.   **(2)**
570 Glendale Avenue, Saint Catharines, L2P 0B2, ON, Canada   **(100%)**
Tel.: (905) 641-6424
Web Site: https://www.gm.ca
Sales Range: $600-649.9 Million
Emp.: 4,000
Mfr of V-6 & V-8 Engines
N.A.I.C.S.: 336340

General Motors Canada Transmission Div.   **(2)**
1550 Kildare Road, Windsor, N8W 5M1, ON, Canada   **(100%)**
Tel.: (519) 255-4200
Web Site: http://www.gmcanada.com
Sales Range: $300-349.9 Million
Emp.: 2,000
Mfr of Front-Wheel-Drive Automatic Transmissions, Components & Stampings
N.A.I.C.S.: 336340

General Sales Company of West Chester, Inc.   **(1)**
1550 Wilmington Pike Rte 202, West Chester, PA 19382
Tel.: (610) 455-1700
Web Site: http://www.ruggericadillac.com
Automobile Mfr
N.A.I.C.S.: 336110

Georgia Automotive Group, Inc.   **(1)**
2031 Gordon Hwy, Augusta, GA 30909
Tel.: (706) 733-9411
Web Site:
http://www.malcolmcunninghamchevrolet.com

General Motors Company—(Continued)

Emp.: 7
Car Dealing Services
N.A.I.C.S.: 441110

HRL Laboratories, LLC **(1)**
3011 Malibu Canyon Rd, Malibu, CA 90265-4797
Tel.: (310) 317-5000
Web Site: http://www.hrl.com
Sales Range: $100-124.9 Million
Emp.: 300
Research & Development Labs
N.A.I.C.S.: 541330
Paul G. Kaminski (Chm)
P. C. Albright (Pres & CEO)

Holden Employees Superannuation Fund Pty Ltd **(1)**
PO Box 9946, Melbourne, 3001, VIC, Australia
Tel.: (61) 386871878
Web Site: http://www.superfacts.com
Employee Benefit & Investment Services
N.A.I.C.S.: 525110

Holden New Zealand Limited **(1)**
2/118 Savill Dr, Mangere, 2024, Auckland, New Zealand
Tel.: (64) 99783600
Web Site: http://www.holden.co.nz
Emp.: 40
New & Used Car Retailer
N.A.I.C.S.: 441110
Marc Ebolo (Mng Dir)

Infinite Velocity Automotive, Inc. **(1)**
800 Davis St, San Leandro, CA 94577
Tel.: (510) 351-5800
Car Distr
N.A.I.C.S.: 441110
Steve Song (Pres)

Isuzu Truck South Africa (Pty.) Limited **(1)**
Woodmead N Office Park 54 Maxwell Dr, Johannesburg, 2153, Gauteng, South Africa
Tel.: (27) 115634000
Web Site: http://www.isuzutruckssa.com
Emp.: 50
Automobile Mfr
N.A.I.C.S.: 336110
Masaji Shimizu (CFO)

Jim Browne Chevrolet, Inc. **(1)**
11300 N Florida Ave, Tampa, FL 33612-5666
Tel.: (813) 935-3100
Web Site: http://www.jimbrownechevy.com
New & Used Car Distr
N.A.I.C.S.: 441110
Art Yanni (Mgr-Parts)
Andrew Conrad (Gen Sls Mgr)
Scott Cannella (Gen Sls Mgr)
Clint Fortier (Dir-Used Vehicle)
Ivan Ruiz (Mgr-New Car)
Melonie Wilkerson (Mgr-Internet)
Christian Dukes (Fin Dir)
Lauren Lindhout (Fin Mgr)
Andrew Gentile (Dir-Fixed Ops)

Joe Morgan Chevrolet Cadillac, Inc. **(1)**
1901 S Main St, Stuttgart, AR 72160-6717
Tel.: (870) 673-8558
Web Site: http://www.joemorganchevrolet.com
Sales Range: $25-49.9 Million
Emp.: 18
Automotive Distr
N.A.I.C.S.: 441227

Lakeside Chevrolet Buick GMC Ltd. **(1)**
792 Broadway St, Kincardine, N2Z 2G1, ON, Canada
Tel.: (888) 741-9855
Web Site: http://www.lakesidegm.com
Emp.: 19
Car Distr
N.A.I.C.S.: 441110
Julie Gudelj (Controller)
Alecia Dunbar (Sls Mgr)
Sara Dunbar (Mgr-Fixed Ops)

Laplante Cadillac Chevrolet Buick GMC Ltd. **(1)**
640 Main Street West, Hawkesbury, K6A 2J3, ON, Canada

Tel.: (866) 357-0055
Web Site: http://www.laplantecadillac.com
Emp.: 40
Automotive Distr
N.A.I.C.S.: 441110
Michel Plouffe (Mgr-Svc)

Las Cruces Automotive Group, Inc. **(1)**
1601 S Main St, Las Cruces, NM 88005
Tel.: (575) 527-3848
Web Site: https://www.bravolascruces.com
New & Used Car Distr
N.A.I.C.S.: 423110
Mauro Holguin (Mgr-Svc)
Armando Martinez (Mgr-Used Sls)
Richard Archuleta (Mgr-Parts)
Orlando Urias (Mgr-New Sls)
Rebecca Parra (Mgr-Inventory)
Crystal Sweet (Mgr-BDC & Internet)
David Provencio (Sls Mgr-New)
Ken Zwigart (Gen Mgr)
Jose Mailander (Gen Mgr-Sls)
Raymond Palacios Jr. (Pres)

Manual Transmissions of Muncie **(1)**
1200 W 8th St, Muncie, IN 47302-2238
Tel.: (765) 281-2200
Sales Range: $200-249.9 Million
Emp.: 1,000
Motor Vehicle Transmissions, Drive Assemblies & Parts
N.A.I.C.S.: 336350

Martin Automotive, Inc. **(1)**
729 S 8th St, Sheboygan, WI 53083
Tel.: (920) 458-4631
Web Site: http://www.martinautomotiveinc.com
Automobile Maintenance Services
N.A.I.C.S.: 811114

Memorial Highway Chevrolet, Inc. **(1)**
1 Chevy Dr Rte 56, Windber, PA 15963-2529
Tel.: (814) 467-2577
Web Site: http://www.memorialchevy.com
Car Dealing Services
N.A.I.C.S.: 441110
Andrea Palmar (Mgr-Compliance)
Loretta Myers (Controller)
Andre Palmar (VP)
Jonathan Beskid (Sls Mgr)
Betty Flook (Office Mgr)
Lewis Skiles (Sls Mgr)
Eddie Palmar (Mgr-Internet Sls)
Mark Geiser (Mgr-Svc)
Alan Sterner (Mgr-Parts)
Kathi Geiser (Mgr-Body Shop)
Gustavo Palmar (Principal-Dealer)
Ashley Alwine (Mgr-Customer Rels)
Taylor Holby (Sls Mgr)

Merced Chevrolet, Inc. **(1)**
1485 W 15th St, Merced, CA 95340-5602
Tel.: (209) 383-3306
Web Site: http://www.chevroletofmerced.com
Car Distr
N.A.I.C.S.: 441110
Raelynn Lyon (Mgr-Parts)
Mayra Burciaga (Mgr-Sls)
Christian Rodriguez (Mgr-Fin)
Mike McKay (Gen Mgr-Sls)

Metal Casting Technology, Inc. **(1)**
127 Old Wilton Rd, Milford, NH 03055-3120
Tel.: (603) 673-9720
Web Site: http://www.mct-inc.com
Automobile Mfr
N.A.I.C.S.: 336110

Mike Reichenbach Chevrolet, Inc. **(1)**
10 University Pkwy, Okatie, SC 29926
Tel.: (843) 800-2760
Web Site: http://www.mrchevrolet.com
Car Distr
N.A.I.C.S.: 423110

Moran Automotive Group, Inc. **(1)**
4511 24th Ave, Fort Gratiot, MI 48059-3401
Tel.: (810) 479-4642
Web Site: http://www.moranchevyfortgratiot.com
New & Used Car Dealer
N.A.I.C.S.: 441110
Chris Aleksander (Dir-Mktg & Inventory)
Daniel Mugridge (Mgr-Svc)

Jeff Wilson (Mgr-Parts Dept-Clyde)
Dave Troy (Mgr-Body Shop)
Jeff Szostek (Bus Mgr)
Kelly Counts (Gen Mgr)
Dan Cohen (Dir-Variable Ops)
Dick Barker (Dir-Fixed Ops)
Jon Mowinski (Fin Mgr)

New Castle Chevrolet, Inc. **(1)**
174 N Dupont Hwy, New Castle, DE 19720
Tel.: (302) 327-1171
Web Site: http://www.nucarconnection.com
Car Distr
N.A.I.C.S.: 423110
Mitch Miller (Mgr-Pre-Owned Sls)
Steve Saunders (Mgr-Pre-Owned Sls)
Tracy Gell (Dir-Mktg & eCommerce)
Brian Ferrell (Mgr-Sls-Chevy)
Tony Copeman (Mgr-Fin)
Sam Odongkara (Mgr-Fin)
Ed Woodring (Mgr-Fin)
Darrin Aliberto (Mgr-Svc)
Ira Benson (Mgr-Parts)
Tony Catalano (Sls Mgr-Chevy)
Damon Snipe (Fin Mgr)

North American New Cars, Inc. **(1)**
3773 Howard Hughes Pkwy, Las Vegas, NV 89169-0949
Tel.: (702) 866-2233
Automobile Mfr
N.A.I.C.S.: 336110

Novasentis, Inc. **(1)**
2560 9th St Ste 314, Berkeley, CA 94710
Tel.: (814) 238-7400
Web Site: http://www.novasentis.com
Electromechanical Polymer Actuator Mfr
N.A.I.C.S.: 333995
Ralph Russo (Co-Founder)
Linda Ara (CFO)
John Jacobi (VP-Mfg)
Francois Jeanneau (Pres & CEO)
Michael Vestel (CTO)
Qiming Zhang (Co-Founder)

OT Mobility, Inc. **(1)**
1808 Wedemeyer St Ste 140, San Francisco, CA 94129
Tel.: (415) 727-9000
Software Development Services
N.A.I.C.S.: 541511

Omnibus BB Transportes, S. A. **(1)**
Av Galo Plaza Lasso Oe1-34 y Enrique Guerrero Portilla Norte, Quito, Pichincha, Ecuador
Tel.: (593) 22977700
Automobile Parts Distr
N.A.I.C.S.: 441110

OnStar, LLC **(1)**
400 Renaissance Ctr, Detroit, MI 48265
Tel.: (248) 588-6050
Web Site: http://www.onstar.com
Automobile Mfr
N.A.I.C.S.: 336110

Opel Group GmbH **(1)**
Bahnhofsplatz 1, 65428, Russelsheim, Germany
Tel.: (49) 61429119800
Web Site: http://www.opel-group.com
Holding Company; Regional Managing Office; Automobile Mfr & Distr
N.A.I.C.S.: 551112
Johan Willems (Executives)

Subsidiary (Non-US):

Auto Fornebu AS **(2)**
Rolfsbuktveien 4, 1364, Fornebu, Norway
Tel.: (47) 98043147
Web Site: http://www.autofornebu.no
Car Mfr
N.A.I.C.S.: 336110

Subsidiary (Domestic):

Autohaus G.V.O. GmbH **(2)**
Nurnberger Str 128, 97076, Wurzburg, Germany
Tel.: (49) 931270150
Web Site: http://www.ehrlich.de
Sales Range: $25-49.9 Million
Emp.: 4
Automotive Distr
N.A.I.C.S.: 441227

Autozentrum West Koln GmbH **(2)**

Oskar-Jager-Str 97, 50825, Cologne, Germany
Tel.: (49) 221546090
Car Distr
N.A.I.C.S.: 441110

Subsidiary (Non-US):

BS Auto Praha sro **(2)**
Za opravnou 186/1, 150 00, Prague, Czech Republic
Tel.: (420) 257215145
Web Site: http://www.bsauto.cz
Car Distr
N.A.I.C.S.: 441110

BilCirkeln Malmo AB **(2)**
Jagershillgatan 4, 213 75, Malmo, Sweden
Tel.: (46) 406428000
Web Site: http://www.bilcirkeln.se
Automotive Distr
N.A.I.C.S.: 441110

Subsidiary (Domestic):

Bochum Perspektive 2022 GmbH **(2)**
Viktoriastrasse 10, 44787, Bochum, Germany
Tel.: (49) 23461063305
Web Site: http://www.bochum2022.de
Engineering Services
N.A.I.C.S.: 541330

Subsidiary (Non-US):

Chevrolet Central and Eastern Europe **(2)**
Szabadsag Ut 117, Budaors, 2040, Hungary
Tel.: (36) 23447000
Web Site: http://www.chevrolet.hu
Sales Range: $25-49.9 Million
Emp.: 20
Automobile Mfr
N.A.I.C.S.: 336110

Subsidiary (Domestic):

Chevrolet Deutschland GmbH **(2)**
Postfach 1248, 65402, Russelsheim, Germany
Tel.: (49) 8006647446
Web Site: http://www.chevrolet.de
Automobile Mfr
N.A.I.C.S.: 336110

Subsidiary (Non-US):

Chevrolet Europe GmbH **(2)**
Stelzenstrasse 4, Glattpark, CH-8152, Opfikon, Switzerland
Tel.: (41) 844850850
Web Site: http://www.chevroleteurope.com
Holding Company; Automobile Distr
N.A.I.C.S.: 551112

Chevrolet Italia S.p.A. **(2)**
Via A Gustave Eiffel 15, Rome, 148, Italy
Tel.: (39) 0654651
Web Site: http://www.chevrolet.it
Automobile Mfr
N.A.I.C.S.: 336110

Chevrolet Suisse S.A. **(2)**
Stelzenstrasse 4, Glattpark, 8152, Opfikon, Switzerland
Tel.: (41) 844850850
Web Site: http://www.chevrolet.ch
Automotive Distr
N.A.I.C.S.: 423110

Chevrolet Sverige AB **(2)**
Arstaangsvagen 17, 117 43, Stockholm, Sweden
Tel.: (46) 86326070
Web Site: http://www.chevrolet.se
Car Distr
N.A.I.C.S.: 441110

DENICAR S.R.L. **(2)**
Via Bisceglie 92, 20152, Milan, Italy
Tel.: (39) 02483381
Car Distr
N.A.I.C.S.: 441110

Subsidiary (Domestic):

Fludicon GmbH **(2)**
Landwehrstr 55 Gebaeude 8, 64293, Darmstadt, Germany
Tel.: (49) 615127986

Web Site: http://www.fludicon.com
Automotive Parts Mfr & Distr
N.A.I.C.S.: 336390
Heinz Ulrich Hensgen *(CEO & Engr-Degreed)*
Sonke Mehrgardt *(Chm)*

Subsidiary (Non-US):

GM Global Purchasing and Supply Chain Romania Srl (2)
Str Emil Cioran 2, Sibiu, 550209, Romania
Tel.: (40) 269501353
Emp.: 40
Automotive Distr
N.A.I.C.S.: 441227
Wim Wuyts *(Gen Mgr)*

General Motors Austria GmbH (2)
Grob-Enzersdorfer Strabe 59, Vienna, 1220, Austria
Tel.: (43) 1288770
Automobile Mfr
N.A.I.C.S.: 336110

Subsidiary (Domestic):

Chevrolet Austria GmbH (3)
Grob Enzersdorfer-Strabe 59, Vienna, 1220, Austria
Tel.: (43) 13602771917
Web Site: http://www.chevrolet.at
Emp.: 2
Automobile Mfr
N.A.I.C.S.: 336110

Subsidiary (Non-US):

General Motors Benelux (2)
Lage Mosten 49-63, PO Box 8770, 4822 NK, Breda, Netherlands (100%)
Tel.: (31) 8001410
Web Site: http://www.opel.nl
Sales Range: $25-49.9 Million
Emp.: 110
Automobile Products Importer; Service Training, Modification of Automatic Transmissions
N.A.I.C.S.: 336110

Subsidiary (Domestic):

Chevrolet Euro Parts Center B.V. (3)
Hazeldonk 6520, Breda, 4836LD, Netherlands
Tel.: (31) 765937050
Web Site: http://www.chevroletepc.com
Automobile Parts Mfr
N.A.I.C.S.: 336390

Subsidiary (Non-US):

General Motors Belgium N.V. (3)
Prins Boudewijnlaan 24 B, Kontich, 2550, Belgium
Tel.: (32) 38909111
Web Site: http://www.opel.de
Sales Range: $25-49.9 Million
Emp.: 50
Automobile Mfr
N.A.I.C.S.: 336110

Subsidiary (Domestic):

Beerens O.C. NV (4)
Groenendaallaan 397, Antwerp, 2030, Belgium
Tel.: (32) 32315930
Web Site: http://www.beerens.be
Car Distr
N.A.I.C.S.: 441110

General Motors Continental (4)
401 Noorderlaan, 2030, Antwerp, Belgium (100%)
Tel.: (32) 35401600
Web Site: http://www.gmac.be
Assembly of Opel & Vauxhall Vehicles, Import of GM Products & Manufacturer of Automotive Components
N.A.I.C.S.: 336110

Subsidiary (Domestic):

Orange Motors B.V. (3)
Klompenmakerstraat 51, 2672 GA, Naaldwijk, Netherlands
Tel.: (31) 174291660
Web Site: http://www.orangemotors.nl
Emp.: 160
Car Mfr & Distr

N.A.I.C.S.: 336110
Gerald van Well *(Gen Dir)*

Stam-Terberg Autobedrijven B. V. (3)
Gemini 1, Amersfoort, 3824 MH, Utrecht, Netherlands
Tel.: (31) 334635104
Web Site: http://www.stam.nl
Automotive Distr
N.A.I.C.S.: 441110

Subsidiary (Non-US):

General Motors Espana S.L. (2)
Edificio Gorbea 4 - Avda Bruselas 20, E-28108, Alcobendas, Spain
Tel.: (34) 914569299
Web Site: http://media.opel.es
Sales Range: $1-4.9 Billion
Passenger Cars, Automotive Components; Importer of Automobiles Mfr
N.A.I.C.S.: 336110

Subsidiary (Domestic):

Betula Cars S.L. (3)
Poligono Industrial Barreiros Cn 525 S/N Km 234, San Cibrao das Vinas, 32911, Spain
Tel.: (34) 988227800
Web Site: http://www.betulacars.es
Car Distr
N.A.I.C.S.: 441110

Chevrolet Espana, S.A. (3)
Avda Bruselas 20, Madrid, 28108, Alcobendas, Spain
Tel.: (34) 902303900
Web Site: http://www.chevrolet.es
Automobile Mfr
N.A.I.C.S.: 336110

Diso Madrid S.l.r. (3)
Calle De Francisco Gervas 1, Alcobendas, 28108, Madrid, Spain
Tel.: (34) 914903684
Web Site: http://www.disomadrid.es
Car Distr
N.A.I.C.S.: 441110

Motor Repris Automocio S.L. (3)
Calle Gran Via De Les Corts Catalanes 484, Barcelona, 08015, Spain
Tel.: (34) 932894630
Web Site: http://www.motorrepris.net
Automotive Distr
N.A.I.C.S.: 441110

Subsidiary (Non-US):

General Motors Europe Holdings, S.L. (2)
Carretera Nacional 232 Km 29 Pg Entrerrios Zaragoza, Figueruelas, 50639, Spain
Tel.: (34) 976658107
Sales Range: $25-49.9 Million
Emp.: 100
Automobile Mfr
N.A.I.C.S.: 336110
Anno Tovo *(Gen Mgr)*

General Motors Finland Oy (2)
Perinto 2D, Vantaa, 01510, Finland
Tel.: (358) 9615881
Web Site: http://www.opel.fi
Sales Range: $25-49.9 Million
Emp.: 33
Automobiles, Parts & Accessories Importer
N.A.I.C.S.: 441330
Rami Kittila *(Mng Dir)*

Subsidiary (Domestic):

Chevrolet Finland Oy (3)
Perintotie 2 D, Vantaa, FI-1510, Finland
Tel.: (358) 981710147
Web Site: http://www.chevrolet.fi
Car Distr
N.A.I.C.S.: 441110

Subsidiary (Non-US):

General Motors France Automobiles S.A. (2)
1 a 9 Avenue du Marais, PO Box 84, 95100, Argenteuil, France
Tel.: (33) 134263000
Web Site: http://www.generalmotors.fr
Rev.: $2,629,000,000
Emp.: 150

Import of Opel & Other GM Products & Manufacturer of Automotive Components
N.A.I.C.S.: 336110

Subsidiary (Domestic):

Atlantic Automobiles SAS (3)
76 Rue Marietton, 69009, Lyon, France
Tel.: (33) 472850850
Web Site: http://www.atlantic-automobiles.fr
Automobile Mfr
N.A.I.C.S.: 336110

Subsidiary (Non-US):

General Motors Hellas S.A. (2)
56 Kifissias Ave & Delfon, Maroussi, 15125, Greece
Tel.: (30) 2106164600
Automobile Mfr
N.A.I.C.S.: 336110

General Motors Nederland B.V. (2)
Lage Mosten 49-63, Breda, 4822 NK, Netherlands
Tel.: (31) 206545751
Automobile Mfr
N.A.I.C.S.: 336110

General Motors Poland Spolka, z o. o. (2)
Woloska 5, Warsaw, 02-675, Poland
Tel.: (48) 222091700
Web Site: http://www.opel.pl
Sales Range: $25-49.9 Million
Emp.: 100
Automobile Mfr
N.A.I.C.S.: 336110

Subsidiary (Domestic):

General Motors Manufacturing Poland Sp. z o o. (3)
Ul Rataja Opla 1, Gliwice, Poland
Tel.: (48) 322709204
Web Site: http://www.gm.com
Automobile Mfr
N.A.I.C.S.: 336110

Subsidiary (Domestic):

General Motors Powertrain - Germany GmbH (2)
Friedrich-Lutzmann-Ring 1, Russelsheim, 65428, Germany
Tel.: (49) 6142770
Web Site: http://www.opel.de
Automobile Mfr
N.A.I.C.S.: 336110
Karl-Thomas Neumann *(CEO)*

Subsidiary (Non-US):

General Motors de Portugal, Sociedade Anonima (2)
Apartado 4427, Lisbon, Portugal (100%)
Tel.: (351) 21782815
Web Site: http://www.opel.pt
Assembly of Imported Vehicles & GM Products
N.A.I.C.S.: 336110

Subsidiary (Domestic):

Chevrolet Portugal, Lda. (3)
Quinta Da Fonte Edificio Gil Eanes Piso 3, Paco De Arcos, Oeiras, 2770-192, Portugal
Tel.: (351) 214407500
Web Site: http://www.chevrolet.pt
Automobile Mfr
N.A.I.C.S.: 336110

General Motors Portugal Lda. (3)
Quinta Da Fonte Edificio Fernao De Magalhaes Piso 2, Fernao De Magalhaes, Paco d'Arcos, 2770-190, Portugal
Tel.: (351) 214407500
Web Site: http://www.gm.com
Sales Range: $25-49.9 Million
Emp.: 80
Automobile Mfr
N.A.I.C.S.: 336110

Subsidiary (Domestic):

ISF Internationale Schule Frankfurt-Rhein-Main GmbH & Co. KG (2)
Strasse zur Internationalen Schule 33, 65931, Frankfurt, Germany
Tel.: (49) 69954319710
Web Site: http://www.isf-net.de

Education Services
N.A.I.C.S.: 611710

Subsidiary (Non-US):

Opel Leasing Austria GmbH (2)
Gross-Enzersdorfer Strasse 59, 1220, Vienna, Austria
Tel.: (43) 810300436
Web Site: http://www.opel-leasing.at
Automobile Finance Leasing Services
N.A.I.C.S.: 522220

Subsidiary (Domestic):

ProSTEP AG (2)
Dolivostrasse 11, 64293, Darmstadt, Germany
Tel.: (49) 615192870
Web Site: http://www.prostep.com
Emp.: 100
Automobile Mfr
N.A.I.C.S.: 336110

Subsidiary (Non-US):

Vauxhall Motors Limited (2)
11 Campbells Meadow, King's Lynn, PE30 4YN, United Kingdom
Tel.: (44) 1553422983
Web Site: https://www.thurlownunn.co.uk
Sales Range: $25-49.9 Million
Emp.: 3
Automobile Mfr
N.A.I.C.S.: 336110

Subsidiary (Domestic):

Aftermarket (UK) Limited (3)
Griffin House Osborne Rd, Luton, LU1 3YT, Bedfordshire, United Kingdom
Tel.: (44) 1582426240
Web Site: http://www.acdalco.eu.com
Sales Range: $10-24.9 Million
Emp.: 12
Automobile Mfr
N.A.I.C.S.: 336110
Lee Quinney *(Gen Mgr)*

Approach (UK) Limited (3)
Newbury Rd, Hampshire, Andover, SP10 1DS, Hampshire, United Kingdom
Tel.: (44) 1264324233
Web Site: http://www.approach.co.uk
Sales Range: $25-49.9 Million
Emp.: 7
Automobile Parts Mfr
N.A.I.C.S.: 336110
Louise Croft Baker *(Mng Partner)*
Edward Croft Baker *(Mng Partner)*

Autovision (Scotland) Limited (3)
40 Harbour Rd, Inverness, IV1 1LY, United Kingdom
Tel.: (44) 1463251500
Web Site: http://www.scottishvauxhall.co.uk
Emp.: 6
Automobile Mfr
N.A.I.C.S.: 336110

Baylis (Gloucester) Limited (3)
Cole Avenue, Gloucestershire, Gloucester, GL2 5ER, United Kingdom
Tel.: (44) 1452526711
Web Site: http://www.baylis.uk.com
Automotive Distr
N.A.I.C.S.: 441227

Subsidiary (Domestic):

Southern (Merthyr) Limited (4)
Citypoint 16th Floor Ropemaker Street, London, EC2Y 9AW, United Kingdom
Tel.: (44) 1685789196
Automobile Mfr
N.A.I.C.S.: 336110

Subsidiary (Domestic):

Brandish Limited (3)
2 Raglan St West Midlands, Coventry, CV1 5QB, United Kingdom
Tel.: (44) 2476225361
Web Site: http://www.brandishvauxhall.co.uk
Sales Range: $25-49.9 Million
Emp.: 80
Automobile Mfr
N.A.I.C.S.: 336110
Dan Pierce *(Mgr-Sls)*

Chevrolet UK Limited Ltd (3)

General Motors Company—(Continued)

Osborne Rd Griffin House, Cambridgeshire, Luton, CB2 9NE, Bedfordshire, United Kingdom
Tel.: (44) 800666222
Web Site: http://www.chevrolet.co.uk
Sales Range: $25-49.9 Million
Emp.: 6
Automobile Mfr
N.A.I.C.S.: 336110

Drive Motor Retail Limited (3)
Aisecome Way Avon, Weston-super-Mare, BS22 8NA, United Kingdom
Tel.: (44) 1934427700
Web Site: http://www.drivemotorretail.co.uk
Automotive Retailer
N.A.I.C.S.: 441227
Richard Broady (Gen Mgr)
Simon Strange (Sls Mgr)
Phil Grove (Sls Mgr-Svcs)
Steve Davey (Mgr-Parts)
Gary Paddock (Mgr-Bodyshop)
Stuart Heal (Bus Mgr)

Eden (GM) Limited (3)
38-40 Portman Road, Reading, RG30 1JG, United Kingdom
Tel.: (44) 8451211571
Web Site: http://www.edenvauxhall.co.uk
Car Distr
N.A.I.C.S.: 441110

GM (UK) Pension Trustees Limited (3)
Griffin House UK1-101-135 Osborne Road, Luton, LU1 3YT, Bedfordshire, United Kingdom
Tel.: (44) 8007315267
Web Site: http://www.vauxhall.co.uk
Automobile Mfr
N.A.I.C.S.: 336110
Rory Hirvey (CEO)

GM Automotive UK (3)
Griffin House MP UK1 101 135 Osborne Road, Luton, LU1 3YT, United Kingdom
Tel.: (44) 1582721122
Automotive Distr
N.A.I.C.S.: 441110

GPSC UK Limited (3)
5th Floor Dudley House 169 Piccadilly, London, W1J 9EJ, United Kingdom
Tel.: (44) 2076290970
Web Site: http://www.gpscltd.com
Project Management Consulting Services
N.A.I.C.S.: 541618
Mario Danese (Pres & CEO)

Subsidiary (Non-US):

Go Motor Retailing Limited (3)
Perry Street, Chislehurst, BR7 6HB, London, United Kingdom - England
Tel.: (44) 2083020911
Automotive Distr
N.A.I.C.S.: 441110
Robert Quirk (Mng Dir)

Subsidiary (Domestic):

Jeffery (Wandsworth) Limited (3)
80 Plough Ln, London, SW17 0BW, United Kingdom
Tel.: (44) 2086059393
Automobile Mfr
N.A.I.C.S.: 336110

Marshall of Ipswich Limited (3)
2 Augusta Close The Havens Ransomes Europark, Suffolk, Ipswich, IP3 9SJ, United Kingdom
Tel.: (44) 1473849865
Web Site: http://www.marshallweb.co.uk
Sales Range: $25-49.9 Million
Emp.: 5
Automobile Mfr
N.A.I.C.S.: 336110

Marshall of Peterborough Limited (3)
Mallory Rd, Cambridgeshire, Peterborough, PE1 5AU, United Kingdom
Tel.: (44) 1733894894
Web Site: http://www.marshallvolvopeterborough.co.uk
Automobile Mfr
N.A.I.C.S.: 336110
Ian Murray (Gen Mgr)

Motorbodies Luton Limited (3)
2-6 Bilton Way Dallow Road, Luton, LU1 1UU, Bedfordshire, United Kingdom
Tel.: (44) 1582454666
Web Site: http://www.motorbodies.com
Automobile Mfr & Sales
N.A.I.C.S.: 336110
Nigel Gray (Mng Dir)

Now Motor Retailing Limited (3)
Crockford Bridge Farm New Haw Rd, Addlestone, KT15 2BY, United Kingdom
Tel.: (44) 2031315683
Web Site: http://www.nowvauxhall.co.uk
Automobile Mfr
N.A.I.C.S.: 336110
Jon Taylor (Mng Dir)

Pearl (Crawley) Limited (3)
Flemming Way Indstl Est, Crawley, RH10 9NS, West Sussex, United Kingdom
Tel.: (44) 1293540541
Automobile Mfr
N.A.I.C.S.: 336110

Reeve (Derby) Limited (3)
Pentagon Island Nottingham Road, Derby, DE21 6HB, Derbyshire, United Kingdom
Tel.: (44) 1332362661
Automobile Mfr
N.A.I.C.S.: 336110
Dave White (Gen Mgr)

Seward (Wessex) Limited (3)
400 Poole Rd, Poole, BH12 1DD, United Kingdom
Tel.: (44) 1202545700
Web Site: http://www.edens.com
Automobile Mfr
N.A.I.C.S.: 336110
Nick Broughten (Mng Dir)

Skurrays Limited (3)
Langley Rd Hillmead West, Swindon, SN5 5QJ, United Kingdom
Tel.: (44) 8433204798
Web Site: http://www.skurrays.co.uk
Emp.: 40
Automotive Distr
N.A.I.C.S.: 441227

Sterling Motor Properties Limited (3)
Freemens Common Road, Leicester, LE2 7SL, United Kingdom
Tel.: (44) 1162557567
Emp.: 700
Real Estate Development Services
N.A.I.C.S.: 531390

Vertu Motors (Chingford) Limited (3)
Vertu House 5th Ave Business Pk, Gateshead, NE11 0XA, Tyne & Wear, United Kingdom
Tel.: (44) 1914912121
Web Site: http://www.vertumotors.com
Emp.: 70
Automotive Distr
N.A.I.C.S.: 441110

Vickers (Lakeside) Limited (3)
Lakeside Autopark West Thurrock Way, West Thurrock, Grays, RM20 3WE, Essex, United Kingdom
Tel.: (44) 1708201014
Web Site: http://www.tonylavoi.co.uk
Automobile Mfr
N.A.I.C.S.: 336110
Joy Collins (Gen Mgr)

Wheatcroft (Worksop) Limited (3)
Old Manton Wood Colliery Site Retford Rd, Worksop, S80 2RZ, United Kingdom
Tel.: (44) 1909501111
Web Site: http://www.walkersworksop.co.uk
Emp.: 30
Automobile Mfr
N.A.I.C.S.: 336110
Dean Bowden (Gen Mgr)

Whitmore's of Edenbridge Limited (3)
Mill Road, Sevenoaks, TN13 2UZ, Kent, United Kingdom
Tel.: (44) 8454214521
Web Site: http://www.whitmoresvauxhall.co.uk
Sales Range: $10-24.9 Million
Emp.: 15
Automobile Mfr

N.A.I.C.S.: 336110

Wilson & Co. (Motor Sales) Limited (3)
Moorwell Rd Bottesford North Lincolnshire, Scunthorpe, DN17 2SY, United Kingdom
Tel.: (44) 1724843284
Web Site: http://www.wilsonandco.co.uk
Sales Range: $25-49.9 Million
Emp.: 80
Automotive Retailer
N.A.I.C.S.: 441227
Robin Wilson (Mng Dir)

Subsidiary (Non-US):

Welcome S.R.L. (2)
Via Quinto Alpini 6/A, 24124, Bergamo, Italy
Tel.: (39) 03519910770
Web Site: http://www.welcomeadv.it
Emp.: 20
Advertising Services
N.A.I.C.S.: 541890
Vanessa Salomoni (Sr Acct Mgr)
Franco Armati (Dir-Art)

Packard Electric Division Mexican Operations (1)
Lago Victoria 74 Col Granada, Mexico, 11520, DF, Mexico (100%)
Tel.: (52) 52503777
Web Site: http://www.gm.com
Automotive Brake System Mfr
N.A.I.C.S.: 336340

Packard Electric Europa Ges.m.b.H. (1)
Industriestrasse 1, 7503, Grosspetersdorf, Austria
Tel.: (43) 336241000
Web Site: http://www.delphi.com
Sales Range: $50-74.9 Million
Emp.: 400
Administrative & Technical Support to European Automotive Power & Signal Distribution Systems Operations
N.A.I.C.S.: 561110

Pan Asia Technical Automotive Center Co., Ltd. (1)
No 2199 Jufeng Road, 201201, Shanghai, Pudong, China
Tel.: (86) 2150165016
Web Site: http://www.patac.com.cn
Automotive Engineering & Design Services
N.A.I.C.S.: 541490

Patriot Chevrolet, Inc. (1)
40 Auto Park Blvd, Limerick, PA 19468
Tel.: (610) 572-2297
Car Mfr & Distr
N.A.I.C.S.: 336110
Mary Ritter (Controller)
Richard Egofl (Gen Mgr)
Daniel McHugh (Gen Mgr-Sls)
Heather Kennedy (Mgr-Fin)
Estelle Holland (Mgr-Fin)
Kristen Toth (Dir-Bus Dev)
Joe Tarelia (Mgr-Svcs)
Wendy Manwiller (Dir-Customer Rels)

Performance Opportunities Fund, L.P. (1)
2 Pickwick Plz, Greenwich, CT 06830
Tel.: (203) 742-2320
Financial Services
N.A.I.C.S.: 525990

Powermat Technologies Ltd. (1)
94 Derech Shlomo Shmeltzer Ofer Park Bldg Brosh, Petach Tikva, 4970602, Israel
Tel.: (972) 29950500
Web Site: http://www.powermat.com
Wireless Mobile Charging Device Mfr
N.A.I.C.S.: 334419
Ran Poliakine (Founder)
Elad Dubzinski (CEO)
Itay Sherman (CTO & VP-Bus Dev)
Aya Kantor (VP-Product)
Kfir Avraham (CFO)
Ofer Furth (Chm)
Adiv Baruch (Chief Strategic Officer)
Guy Raveh (VP-R&D)
Ronen Diamant (VP-Sls)

Princeton Chevrolet, Inc. (1)
200 Renaissance Blvd, Lawrenceville, NJ 08648-4773
Tel.: (877) 877-7569

N.A.I.C.S.: 336110

Wilson & Co. (Motor Sales)

Web Site: http://www.chevroletprinceton.com
New & Used Car Dealer
N.A.I.C.S.: 441110
Christopher Fernandes (Mgr-Used Car)
Erin O'Rourke (Mgr-Svc Customer care)
Dave Marra (Mgr-Svc)
Brian Piccinetti (Mgr-Parts)
Brendan Boyle (Mgr-New Car)
Eric Gomez (Mgr-Fin)
Clarence Brunot (Mgr-Fin)
Matthew Biderman (Mgr-Customer Care)
James Jimenez (Gen Mgr-Sls)
Joseph Goulazian (Dir-Fin)
Shane Hoiles (Asst Mgr-Svc)
J. P. Valverde (Asst Mgr-Svc)

Princeton Chevrolet, Inc. (1)
200 Renaissance Blvd, Lawrenceville, NJ 08648
Tel.: (609) 323-2200
Web Site:
http://www.chevroletprinceton.com
Emp.: 40
Automotive Distr
N.A.I.C.S.: 441110
James Jimenez (Gen Mgr)
Christopher Fernandes (Gen Sls Mgr)
Joseph Goulazian (Mgr-New Car)
Clarence Brunot (Fin Dir)
Brian Piccinetti (Mgr-Parts)
Meghan Dornisch (Asst Mgr-Svc)
James Hogan (Mgr-Customer Care)
Erin O'Rourke (Mgr-Svc Customer Care)
Hank Kaufmann (Fin Mgr)
John De La Rosa (Fin Mgr)

Renton Cadillac Pontiac GMC, Inc. (1)
215 SW 12th St, Renton, WA 98057
Tel.: (425) 981-1000
Emp.: 45
Automobile Mfr
N.A.I.C.S.: 336110
Arun Vaidyanathan (Gen Mgr)

SAIC GM Wuling Automobile Company Limited (1)
18th Hexi Road, Liuzhou, 545007, Guangxi, China
Tel.: (86) 7722650233
Web Site: https://www.sgmw.com.cn
Automobile Mfr
N.A.I.C.S.: 336110

SAIC General Motors Sales Company Limited (1)
1/F Administration Building No 1500 Shenjiang Rd, Shanghai, 201206, China
Tel.: (86) 2128902890
Automobile Parts Distr
N.A.I.C.S.: 441110

SDC Materials, Inc. (1)
940 S Park Ln Ste 2, Tempe, AZ 85281
Tel.: (480) 966-6106
Web Site: http://www.sdcmaterials.com
Nano Enhanced Product Development & Design Services
N.A.I.C.S.: 541713
Maximilian Biberger (CEO)
William Staron (Chm)
Ken Williams (Ops Mgr)
Rene Fletcher (Controller)
Wolfgang Russeler (Mgr-Factory)

Saankhya Labs Pvt. Ltd. (1)
Third Floor Embassy Icon 3 Infantry Rd Vasanth Nagar, Kacharakanahalli, Bengaluru, 560001, Karnataka, India
Tel.: (91) 8061171000
Web Site: http://www.saankhyalabs.com
Semiconductor Equipment Mfr
N.A.I.C.S.: 334413
Anindya Saha (CTO)
Parag Naik (Co-Founder & CEO)
Vishwakumara Kayargadde (Co-Founder & COO)
Hemant Mallapur (Co-Founder & Exec VP-Engrg)
Gururaj B. Padaki (Assoc VP-Software)
Vivek Kimbahune (Exec VP-Sls & Bus Dev)
Rakesh Joshi (Mgr-Embedded Software)
Preetham Uthaiah (Exec VP-Mktg & Strategy)
Virupaxappa Karki (VP-Test Engrg & Mfg)
Susmit Datta (Assoc VP-VLSI)
Abdul Aziz (Architect-Sys)
K. S. Subrahmanya (Engr-Algorithms)

Santosh Billava *(Mgr-IC Verification)*
H. R. Sunil *(VP-Tech & Solutions)*
Balaraman Kuppuswamy *(Assoc VP-Sys Engrg)*
Shrinivas Bhat *(Principal-Engrg)*
Paresh Krishnakant Joshi *(Dir-Dev)*
V. Sudarshan *(Dir-Wireless Solutions)*
B. H. Manoj Kumar *(Sr Mgr-Fin & Ops)*
V. Soumya *(Sr Mgr-HR)*

San Fernando Valley Automotive, LLC **(1)**
700 San Fernando Rd, San Francisco, CA 91340-1309
Tel.: (818) 832-1600
Automotive Retailer
N.A.I.C.S.: 441110

Shanghai GM (Shenyang) Norsom Motors Co. Ltd **(1)**
15 Beidaying St, Dadong District, Shenyang, 110044, China
Tel.: (86) 2488345678
Automobile Mfr
N.A.I.C.S.: 336110

Shanghai General Motors Corporation Ltd. **(1)**
1500 Shejiang Road Jin Qiao, Pudong New Area, Shanghai, 201206, China
Tel.: (86) 2128902890
Web Site: http://www.shanghaigm.com
Automobile Mfr
N.A.I.C.S.: 336110

Shanghai OnStar Telematics Co. Ltd. **(1)**
yuan Rd3-4/F B Bldg Xinye No 1801 Hongmei Rd, Shanghai, 200233, China
Tel.: (86) 2133959988
Automobile Mfr
N.A.I.C.S.: 336110

Shinsung Packard Company, Ltd. **(1)**
694, Dukgye-Ri, Whoichun-Eup, Yangju-Gun, PO Box 10256, Seoul, Korea (South) **(50%)**
Tel.: (82) 4 17 580 114
Sales Range: $150-199.9 Million
Emp.: 725
Mfr of Wiring Harness
N.A.I.C.S.: 336320

Simpson Garden Grove, Inc. **(1)**
10150 Trask Ave, Garden Grove, CA 92843
Tel.: (714) 656-2803
Web Site: http://www.simpsonchevroletgardengrove.com
Automotive Distr
N.A.I.C.S.: 441110
David Simpson *(Pres)*
George Shire *(Gen Mgr)*
Mike Hughes *(Mgr-Comml)*
Jason Arvidson *(Gen Sls Mgr)*
Ray Vara *(Asst Mgr-Sls)*
Chris Sanchez *(Mgr-Internet Sls)*
Richard Brown *(Controller)*
Jonathan Menge *(Mgr-Svc)*
Brian Afdahl *(Mgr-Sls)*
Eddie Neri *(Mgr-Sls)*
Ted Eid *(Asst Mgr-Sls)*
Gerry Romero *(Mgr-Remarketing)*
Darren Frank *(Dir-Used Vehicle)*
Jose Pacheco *(Mgr-Used Vehicle)*
Sewell Gutierrez *(Asst Mgr-Svc)*
Dan Luna *(Mgr-Parts)*
Anita Vallejo *(Mgr-Fin)*
Jim Gillette *(Mgr-Fin)*
Manuel Lopez Jr. *(Mgr-Internet)*

Sung San Company, Ltd. **(1)**
436-41 Songso Industrial Complex Talso-Gu, Taegu, Korea (South) **(50%)**
Tel.: (82) 535578511
Sales Range: $50-74.9 Million
Emp.: 250
Mfr of Side Markers
N.A.I.C.S.: 339940

Tactus Technology, Inc. **(1)**
47509 Seabridge Dr, Fremont, CA 94538
Tel.: (510) 244-3968
Web Site: http://www.tactustechnology.com
Electric Equipment Mfr
N.A.I.C.S.: 334419
Perry Constantine *(CEO)*
Justin Virgili *(VP-Engrg)*

Brian Flamm *(Sr Engr-Materials)*
Adrianne Kordelos *(Sr Dir-Bus Ops)*
Curtis Takagi *(Mgr-R&D)*
Ryosuke Isobe *(Dir-Process Engrg)*
Umesh Padval *(Dir)*
Nobuyuki Kambe *(Dir)*
Tiemin Zhao *(Dir)*
Bob Pape *(CFO)*

Todd Wenzel Buick GMC of Davison, Inc. **(1)**
1146 S State Rd, Davison, MI 48423
Tel.: (810) 503-4595
Web Site: http://www.toddwenzeldavison.com
Automobile Mfr & Distr
N.A.I.C.S.: 336110
Colin Gage *(CFO)*
Brian Scott *(Mgr-Parts)*
Sandra Cole *(Office Mgr)*
Scott Kohagen *(Dir-Fixed Ops-Eastern Michigan)*
Megan Potts *(Dir-Mktg)*
Nina Van Harn *(Dir-HR)*
Geoff Bossenbroek *(Controller)*
Shawn O'Brien *(Auditor-Loss Prevention)*
Jim Peters *(Mgr-Inventory)*
Chris Johnson *(Mgr-Customer Retention)*
Will Mullins *(Exec Mgr-Acct)*
Matt Wyss *(Dir-Corp Fin)*
Drew Smith *(Reg Dir-Eastern Michigan)*
Josh Gordon *(Gen Mgr)*
Chris Bauer *(Mgr-Sls-Used Car)*
Troy Sharp *(Coord-Delivery)*
Bobby Hill *(Sls Mgr)*
Stephen Hayward *(Mgr-Fin)*
John Gring *(Mgr-Svc)*
Nick Roberts *(Mgr-Corp Asset)*
Jason Abbasspour *(Mgr-Fin)*
Anton Salsa *(Mgr-Fin)*
Crystal Sherman *(Coord-Platinum)*
Angel Hahn *(Coord-Delivery)*
Don Whitney *(Mgr-Body Shop)*
Corey Klenow *(Mgr-Quick Lube)*
Elizabeth Dailey *(Coord-Delivery)*
Brad Parker *(Fin Mgr)*

Todd Wenzel Buick GMC of Westland **(1)**
35100 Ford Rd, Westland, MI 48185
Tel.: (734) 423-1007
Web Site: https://www.toddwenzelwestland.com
Car Dealing Services
N.A.I.C.S.: 441110
Lisa Hedger *(Office Mgr)*
Barbara Gress *(Mgr-Inventory)*
Chris Johnson *(Mgr-Customer Retention)*
Matt Wyss *(Dir-Corp Fin)*
Colin Gage *(CFO)*
Geoff Bossenbroek *(Controller)*
Nick Roberts *(Mgr-Corp Asset)*
Megan Potts *(Dir-Mktg)*
Nina Van Harn *(Dir-HR)*
Nayeem Abdelnour *(Gen Mgr-Sls)*
Justin Shewchuck *(Sls Mgr)*
Bryce Collier *(Mgr-Used Car)*
Woody Blackburn *(Mgr-Body Shop)*
Paul Williams *(Mgr-Parts)*
Scott Kohagen *(Dir-Eastern Michigan Fixed Ops)*
Jordan Jessee *(Dir-Svc)*

Tooling & Equipment International Corp. **(1)**
12550 Tech Center Dr, Livonia, MI 48150
Tel.: (734) 522-1422
Web Site: http://www.teintl.com
Sales Range: $10-24.9 Million
Emp.: 120
Laundry Equipment Mfr
N.A.I.C.S.: 333248
Oliver Johnson *(Pres)*

Tradition Chevrolet Buick, Inc. **(1)**
847 Routes 5 & 20, Geneva, NY 14456-9548
Tel.: (315) 828-1701
Web Site: http://www.traditioncarsgeneva.com
Car Distr
N.A.I.C.S.: 423110
Bud Hutt *(Gen Mgr)*
Cliff Jones *(Mgr-Sls)*
Joel Haley *(Mgr-Bus)*
Phillip Guererri *(Mgr-Svc)*
Keven Keuer *(Mgr-Parts)*
Anjail Jaavaid *(Controller)*

Turo Inc. **(1)**

116 New Montgomery, San Francisco, CA 94105
Tel.: (866) 735-2901
Web Site: http://www.turo.com
Vehicle Rental & Leasing Services
N.A.I.C.S.: 532120
Shelby Clark *(Founder)*
Andre Haddad *(CEO)*
Alex Benn *(Pres)*
Tom Wang *(Chief Product Officer)*
Andrew Mok *(CMO)*
Michelle Fang *(Chief Legal Officer)*
Avinash Gangadharan *(CTO)*
Charles Fisher *(CFO)*
Lorie Boyd *(Chief People Officer)*
Brian Beaver *(VP-Design)*
Ali Keegan *(VP-Legal)*
Brent Loder *(VP-Fin)*
Albert Mangahas *(VP-Analytics & Insights)*
Roy Schaham *(VP-Product Mgmt)*
Jennifer Schultz *(VP & Controller)*
Francisco Silva *(VP-Tax)*
Steve Webb *(VP-Comm & Brand Partnerships)*
Julie Wiengardt *(VP-Ops)*

Union Motors Car Sales S.r.l. **(1)**
145 Bucharest-Ploiesti road sector 1, Bucharest, Romania
Tel.: (40) 212082727
Web Site: http://www.union-motors.ro
Automobile Mfr & Distr
N.A.I.C.S.: 336110

United States Council for Automotive Research LLC **(1)**
3000 Town Ctr Ste 35, Southfield, MI 48075
Tel.: (248) 223-9000
Web Site: http://www.uscar.org
Emp.: 12
Automobile Mfr
N.A.I.C.S.: 336110

Universal Motors Israel Ltd. **(1)**
5 Platin Naftali, PO Box 17011, Rishon le Zion, 75653, Israel
Tel.: (972) 39534444
Web Site: http://www.umi.co.il
Automobile Mfr
N.A.I.C.S.: 336110
David Any *(Owner)*

Uptown Chevrolet-Cadillac, Inc. **(1)**
1101 E Commerce Blvd, Slinger, WI 53086-9027
Tel.: (262) 297-4471
Web Site: http://www.uptownchevrolet.com
Car Dealing Services
N.A.I.C.S.: 441110
Glenn Pentler *(Pres)*
Mark Pentler *(Gen Mgr & Dir-Ops)*
Tracy Carr *(Mgr-Bus)*
Lee Markgraf *(Mgr-Used Car)*
Jessica Loos *(Office Mgr)*
Jim Vandervelt *(Mgr-Corp Sls)*
Ken Rayeske *(Mgr-Svc)*
Rob Benicke *(Mgr-Parts)*
Adam Voss *(Mgr-New Car)*
Carrie Roell *(Gen Mgr & Mgr-Certified Internet)*
Mary Sica Manders *(Bus Mgr)*

VM Motori S.p.A. **(1)**
Via Ferrarese 29, 44042, Cento, Ferrara, Italy
Tel.: (39) 0516837511
Web Site: http://www.vmmotori.it
Sales Range: $200-249.9 Million
Emp.: 1,200
Diesel Engine Mfr
N.A.I.C.S.: 336310

Woodbridge Buick GMC, Inc. **(1)**
14530 Jefferson Davis Hwy, Woodbridge, VA 22191
Tel.: (703) 297-8653
Web Site: http://www.route1buickgmc.com
Automotive Distr
N.A.I.C.S.: 441110

GENERAL PAYMENT SYSTEMS, INC.
15375 Barranca Pkwy Ste C-102, Irvine, CA 96734
Tel.: (808) 220-1509   **NV**
GPSI—(OTCIQ)
Business Support Services
N.A.I.C.S.: 561499

Ronald A. Hodge *(Pres & CEO)*

GENERATION ALPHA, INC.
1689-A Arrow Rte, Upland, CA 91786   **NV**
Web Site: http://genalphainc.com
Year Founded: 2010
GNAL—(OTCIQ)
Rev.: $1,282,000
Assets: $702,000
Liabilities: $9,438,000
Net Worth: ($8,736,000)
Earnings: ($571,000)
Emp.: 5
Fiscal Year-end: 12/31/20
Lighting & Ancillary Equipment Research, Design, Development & Mfr
N.A.I.C.S.: 335139
George G. O'Leary *(Chm)*

GENERATION BIO CO.
301 Binney St, Cambridge, MA 02142
Tel.: (617) 655-7500   **DE**
Web Site: https://www.generationbio.com
Year Founded: 2016
GBIO—(NASDAQ)
Rev.: $4,543,000
Assets: $376,264,000
Liabilities: $93,771,000
Net Worth: $282,493,000
Earnings: ($136,639,000)
Emp.: 150
Fiscal Year-end: 12/31/22
Biotechnology Research & Development Services
N.A.I.C.S.: 541714
Jason P. Rhodes *(Co-Founder)*
Phillip Samayoa *(Co-Founder & Chief Strategy Officer)*
Mark Angelino *(Co-Founder)*
Matthew Stanton *(Chief Scientific Officer)*
Sara Den Besten *(Chief People Officer)*
Antoinette Paone *(COO)*
Robert Kotin *(Co-Founder)*
Matthew Norkunas *(CFO)*
Yalonda Howze *(Chief Legal Officer & Sec)*
Zhong Zhong *(VP & Head-Gene Therapy)*
Leslie Wolfe *(Sr VP & Head-Chemistry, Mfg & Controls)*
Cameron Geoffrey McDonough *(Pres & CEO)*

GENERATION INCOME PROPERTIES, INC.
401 E Jackson St Ste 3300, Tampa, FL 33602
Tel.: (813) 448-1234   **MD**
Web Site: https://www.gipreit.com
Year Founded: 2015
GIPR—(NASDAQ)
Rev.: $5,432,462
Assets: $64,210,095
Liabilities: $53,073,322
Net Worth: $11,136,773
Earnings: ($3,237,640)
Emp.: 6
Fiscal Year-end: 12/31/22
Offices of Real Estate Agents & Brokers
N.A.I.C.S.: 531210
David Sobelman *(Chm, CEO, Pres, Treas & Sec)*
Stephen Brown *(Dir-Dev)*
Emily Cusmano *(VP-Admin)*

GENERATIONS BANCORP NY, INC.
Tel.: (315) 568-5855   **MD**
Web Site: https://www.generationsbancorpny.com

Generations Bancorp NY, Inc.—(Continued)

Year Founded: 2020
GBNY—(NASDAQ)
Rev.: $15,421,000
Assets: $386,293,000
Liabilities: $348,965,000
Net Worth: $37,328,000
Earnings: $1,087,000
Emp.: 79
Fiscal Year-end: 12/31/22
Offices of Bank Holding Companies
N.A.I.C.S.: 551111
Angela M. Krezmer (Pres, CEO & CFO)
Jose A. Acevedo (Vice Chm)
Anthony G. Cutrona (Sr VP)
Derek M. Dyson (CIO & Sr VP)
Angela M. Krezmer (CFO & Sr VP)

Subsidiaries:

Generations Bank **(1)**
19 Cayuga St, Seneca Falls, NY 13148
Tel.: (315) 568-5855
Web Site: https://www.mygenbank.com
Sales Range: $1-9.9 Million
Emp.: 18
Savings Bank
N.A.I.C.S.: 522180

Subsidiary (Domestic):

Generations Agency, Inc. **(2)**
19 Cayuga St, Seneca Falls, NY
13148 **(100%)**
Tel.: (315) 568-9476
Web Site: http://www.mygenbank.com
Sales Range: $1-9.9 Million
Emp.: 6
Insurance Agents
N.A.I.C.S.: 524210
Jerry Graziano (VP & Head-Insurance Div)
Holly Moran-Arndt (Asst VP)

GENEREX BIOTECHNOLOGY CORPORATION

10102 USA Today Way, Miramar, FL
33025
Tel.: (416) 364-2551 DE
Web Site: http://www.generex.com
Year Founded: 1997
GNBT—(OTCIQ)
Rev.: $2,661,396
Assets: $45,382,944
Liabilities: $57,341,214
Net Worth: ($11,958,270)
Earnings: ($33,335,030)
Fiscal Year-end: 07/31/20
Pharmaceutical Research & Development
N.A.I.C.S.: 325412
Joseph Moscato (Chm, Pres & CEO)
Andrew Ro (Chief Investment Officer)
Jason B. Terrell (Chief Medical Officer & Chief Scientific Officer)
Richard Purcell (Exec VP-Res & Drug Dev)
Anthony S. Crisci (Chief Admin Officer & Chief Legal Officer)
Terry Thompson (COO)

Subsidiaries:

Hema Diagnostic Systems, LLC **(1)**
10102 USA Today Way, Miramar, FL
33025 **(100%)**
Tel.: (954) 919-5123
Web Site:
    http://www.hemadiagnosticsystems.com
Measuring & Controlling Device Mfr
N.A.I.C.S.: 334519

NuGenerex Immuno-Oncology,
Inc. **(1)**
10102 USA Today Way, Miramar, FL 33025
Tel.: (416) 364-2551
Web Site: http://www.antigenexpress.com
Assets: $84
Liabilities: $5,841,307
Net Worth: ($5,841,223)
Earnings: ($1,588,810)
Emp.: 6
Fiscal Year-end: 07/31/2020

Immunotherapy Developer
N.A.I.C.S.: 325412
Eric von Hofe (Pres & Chief Scientific Officer)
Joseph Moscato (Chm & CEO)
Mark Caorrao (Interim CFO)
Richard Purcell (Exec VP-R&D)
Jason B. Terrell (Chief Medical Officer)
Anthony Crisci (Chief Legal Officer & Sec)

Olaregen Therapeutix, Inc. **(1)**
1001 Avenue of the Americas 2nd Fl, New York, NY 10018
Web Site: http://www.olaregen.com
Medical Equipment Mfr
N.A.I.C.S.: 339112
Anthony J. Dolisi (Chm, Pres & CEO)
Clifford Keeling (COO & Exec VP-Comml Ops)
Wesley Ramjeet (CFO)
John Sentman (VP-Bus Strategy)
Scott Emmens (Sr VP-Sls & Bus Dev)

Regentys Corporation **(1)**
6135 NW 167th St E15, Miami Lakes, FL 33015
Web Site: http://www.regentys.com
Healtcare Services
N.A.I.C.S.: 621999
Richard C. Bulman (Co-Founder & CEO)
Steven D. Wexner (Chief Medical Officer)
Scott Winston (VP-R&D)
John F. Howes (VP-Clinical & Regulatory Affairs)
Christine V. Sapan (Co-Founder & Chief Scientific Officer)

GENESCO INC.

535 Marriott Dr, Nashville, TN 37214
Tel.: (615) 367-7000 TN
Web Site: https://www.genesco.com
Year Founded: 1924
GCO—(NYSE)
Rev.: $2,384,888,000
Assets: $1,456,426,000
Liabilities: $849,460,000
Net Worth: $606,966,000
Earnings: $71,915,000
Emp.: 19,000
Fiscal Year-end: 01/28/23
Footwear & Men's Apparel Sales
N.A.I.C.S.: 458210
Mimi Eckel Vaughn (Chm, Pres & CEO)
Andrew I. Gray (Pres-Journeys Grp & Sr VP)
Claire S. McCall (Dir-Corp Rels)
Parag D. Desai (Chief Strategy & Digital Officer & Sr VP)
Scott E. Becker (Gen Counsel, Sec & Sr VP)
Daniel E. Ewoldsen (Sr VP)
Thomas Allen George (CFO & Sr VP-Fin)
Andy Gray (Pres-Journeys Grp)

Subsidiaries:

Genesco Brands, LLC **(1)**
1415 Murfreesboro Rd Ste 264, Nashville, TN 37217 **(100%)**
Tel.: (615) 367-7000
Sales Range: $100-124.9 Million
Branded Footwear Retailer
N.A.I.C.S.: 458210
Jonathan D. Caplan (Sr VP)
Bob Dennis (CEO)

Genesco Merger Company, Inc. **(1)**
1415 Murfreesboro Pike, Nashville, TN 37217 **(100%)**
Tel.: (615) 367-7000
Web Site: http://www.genesco.com
Sales Range: $100-124.9 Million
Emp.: 3
Business Services
N.A.I.C.S.: 458210

Hat World, Inc. **(1)**
7555 Woodland Dr, Indianapolis, IN 46278
Tel.: (317) 334-9428
Web Site: http://www.lids.com
Sales Range: $25-49.9 Million
Emp.: 900
Sports Apparels Distr

N.A.I.C.S.: 458110
Britten Maughan (Pres)

Subsidiary (Domestic):

Nashville Sporting Goods, LLC **(2)**
169 Rosa L Parks Blvd, Nashville, TN 37203
Tel.: (615) 259-4241
Web Site: http://vandevst.addr.com
Sales Range: $1-9.9 Million
Emp.: 17
Sporting Equipment Whslr
N.A.I.C.S.: 423910
Robert A. Butler Jr. (Pres)

Johnston & Murphy Co. **(1)**
1415 Murfreesboro Rd Ste 190, Nashville, TN 37217 **(100%)**
Tel.: (615) 367-8101
Web Site: http://www.johnstonmurphy.com
Sales Range: $100-124.9 Million
Men's Shoes, Apparel & Accessories Mfr & Marketer
N.A.I.C.S.: 458210

Branch (Domestic):

Johnston & Murphy Retail/Wholesale Stores **(2)**
1415 Murphysboro Pike, Nashville, TN 37217
Tel.: (615) 367-4443
Web Site: http://www.johnstonmurphy.com
Sales Range: $100-124.9 Million
Emp.: 4
Men's Shoes & Accessories
N.A.I.C.S.: 458210

Keuka Footwear, Inc. **(1)**
1415 Murfreesboro Rd Ste 388, Nashville, TN 37217
Tel.: (877) 566-7547
Web Site: http://www.keukafootwear.com
Emp.: 50
Online Footwear Retailer
N.A.I.C.S.: 316210

Schuh Limited **(1)**
1 Neilson Square, Deans Industrial Estate, Livingston, EH54 8RQ, United Kingdom
Tel.: (44) 1506460250
Web Site: https://www.schuh.co.uk
Sales Range: $200-249.9 Million
Emp.: 3,000
Footwear Distr
N.A.I.C.S.: 424340
Colin Temple (Mng Dir)

GENESIS ENERGY, L.P.

811 Louisiana St Ste 1200, Houston, TX 77002
Tel.: (713) 860-2500 DE
Web Site:
    https://www.genesisenergy.com
Year Founded: 1996
GEL—(NYSE)
Rev.: $3,176,996,000
Assets: $7,018,778,000
Liabilities: $6,121,590,000
Net Worth: $897,188,000
Earnings: $26,995,000
Emp.: 2,111
Fiscal Year-end: 12/31/23
Crude Oil Production & Marketing; Pipeline Transportation of Crude Oil & Natural Gas; Industrial Gas Marketing & Processing
N.A.I.C.S.: 424710
Louie V. Nicol (Chief Acctg Officer)
Will W. Rainsberger (Sr VP)
Jeff J. Rasmussen (VP)

Subsidiaries:

AP MARINE, LLC **(1)**
919 Milam Ste 2100, Houston, TX 77002
Tel.: (713) 860-2500
Crude Oil Pipeline Transportation Services
N.A.I.C.S.: 486110

GENESIS ALKALI WYOMING, LP **(1)**

580 Westvaco Rd, Green River, WY 82935
Tel.: (307) 875-2580
Web Site: https://alkali.genesisenergy.com
Natural Gas Transportation Services

N.A.I.C.S.: 486210

Poseidon Oil Pipeline Company,
LLC **(1)**
919 Milam Ste 2100, Houston, TX 77002 **(28%)**
Tel.: (832) 280-3080
Web Site: https://www.poseidonoil.com
Sales Range: $10-24.9 Million
Emp.: 2
Crude Oil Pipeline Services
N.A.I.C.S.: 486110
Ray Cordova (Pres-Bus Dev)
Kenneth Moore (Mgr-Asset)

Red River Terminals, L.L.C. **(1)**
10911 Hwy 1, Shreveport, LA 71115
Tel.: (713) 860-2500
Emp.: 4
Crude Petroleum & Natural Gas Extracting Services
N.A.I.C.S.: 211120

GENESIS UNICORN CAPITAL CORP.

281 Witherspoon St Ste 120, Princeton, NJ 08540
Tel.: (609) 466-0792 DE
Year Founded: 2021
GENQ—(NASDAQ)
Rev.: $1,281,044
Assets: $89,099,189
Liabilities: $92,259,565
Net Worth: ($3,160,376)
Earnings: ($519,798)
Emp.: 4
Fiscal Year-end: 12/31/22
Investment Holding Company
N.A.I.C.S.: 551112
Juan Fernandez Pascual (CEO & CFO)
Adeoye Olukotun (CTO)

GENETHERA, INC.

3051 W 105th Ave Ste 350251, Westminster, CO 80035
Tel.: (720) 587-5100 NV
Web Site: http://www.genethera.net
Year Founded: 1998
GTHR—(OTCIQ)
Assets: $11,582
Liabilities: $7,692,086
Net Worth: ($7,680,504)
Earnings: ($774,463)
Emp.: 2
Fiscal Year-end: 12/31/20
Biotechnology Research & Development Services
N.A.I.C.S.: 541714
Tannya L. Irizarry (Interim CFO & Chief Admin Officer)
Antonio Milici (Chm, Pres & CEO)

GENIE ENERGY LTD.

520 Broad St, Newark, NJ 07102
Tel.: (973) 438-3500 DE
Web Site: https://www.genie.com
Year Founded: 2011
GNE—(NYSE)
Rev.: $315,539,000
Assets: $277,615,000
Liabilities: $103,971,000
Net Worth: $173,644,000
Earnings: $87,805,000
Emp.: 125
Fiscal Year-end: 12/31/22
Oil & Gas Exploration Services & Electric Power Distr
N.A.I.C.S.: 211120
Joyce J. Mason (Sec)
Avi Goldin (CFO)
Michael M. Stein (CEO)

Subsidiaries:

American Shale Oil, LLC **(1)**
110 East 3rd St Ste 201, Rifle, CO 81650
Tel.: (970) 625-4324
Oil Extraction Services
N.A.I.C.S.: 211120

Lumo Energia Ojy (1)
Teollisuuskatu 21, 00510, Helsinki, Finland
Tel.: (358) 942720444
Web Site: http://www.lumoenergia.fi
Renewable Energy Services
N.A.I.C.S.: 221118
Otto Savasti (CEO)

**Prism Solar Technologies
Incorporated** (1)
520 Broad St, Newark, NJ 07102
Tel.: (845) 883-4200
Web Site: http://www.prismsolar.com
Semiconductor & Related Device Mfr
N.A.I.C.S.: 334413

Southern Federal Power, LLC (1)
5858 Westheimer Rd Ste 707, Houston, TX
77057
Web Site: https://www.southernfederal.com
Electric Power Distr
N.A.I.C.S.: 221122
Nazim Bhamani (Ops Mgr)

GENOCEA BIOSCIENCES, INC.
100 Acorn Park Dr, Cambridge, MA
02140
Tel.: (617) 876-8191   DE
Web Site: http://www.genocea.com
Year Founded: 2006
GNCA—(NASDAQ)
Rev.: $1,641,000
Assets: $55,967,000
Liabilities: $28,892,000
Net Worth: $27,075,000
Earnings: ($33,196,000)
Emp.: 74
Fiscal Year-end: 12/31/21
Pharmaceuticals Mfr
N.A.I.C.S.: 325412
William D. Clark (Pres & CEO)

GENOIL INC.
130 30 31st Ave Ste 512, Flushing,
NY 11354
Tel.: (212) 688-8868
Web Site: https://www.genoil.ca
GNOLF—(OTCIQ)
Assets: $240,720
Liabilities: $376,040
Net Worth: ($135,320)
Earnings: ($4,326,294)
Fiscal Year-end: 12/31/23
Crude Petroleum Extraction Services
N.A.I.C.S.: 211120
Haiming Lai (Dir-Engrg)
David K. Lifschultz (Chm, CEO &
CFO)
Bruce S. Abbott (Pres & COO)
Raushan Telyashev (VP-Genoil
Middle East)
Conan Taylor (Vice Chm)
Moktar Gaouad (Dir-Bus Dev Dept &
Comm-Global)
Hassan Al Fadli (Sr VP-Bus Dev Dept
& Media-Global)
Emile Heskey (Sr VP-Bus Dev-
Caribbean)

GENPREX, INC.
3300 Bee Cave Rd Ste 650-227,
Austin, TX 78746
Tel.: (512) 370-4081   DE
Web Site: https://www.genprex.com
Year Founded: 2009
GNPX—(NASDAQ)
Assets: $10,670,592
Liabilities: $3,254,208
Net Worth: $7,416,384
Earnings: ($30,860,461)
Emp.: 26
Fiscal Year-end: 12/31/23
Biopharmaceutical Research & De-
velopment Services
N.A.I.C.S.: 325412
J. Rodney Varner (Founder, Chm,
Pres, CEO & Sec)

Suzanne Thornton-Jones (Sr VP-
Regulatory Affairs & Regulatory Af-
fairs)
Ryan M. Confer (Pres, CEO & CFO)
Kalyn Dabbs (Sr Mgr-Comm & Mktg)
Jose A. Moreno Toscano (Chm)
Amy Patel (Mgr-Quality Assurance)
Gina Johnson (Sr Mgr-QC, Stability,
and Product Lifecycle Mgmt)
Greg Jancarik (Controller-Corp)
Jackie Opiola (Assoc Dir-Clinical Pro-
gram)
John Ayres (Assoc VP & Assoc Gen
Counsel)
Laura Tirado (Sr Mgr-CMC Project
Mgmt)
Pier-Anne Lachance (Dir-Quality Con-
trol & Product Development)
Mark Berger (Chief Medical Officer)
Thomas Gallagher (Sr VP-Intellectual
Property & Licensing)
Sarah Nguyen (Assoc Dir-Quality As-
surance)

GENTEX CORPORATION
600 N Centennial St, Zeeland, MI
49464
Tel.: (616) 772-1800   MI
Web Site: https://www.gentex.com
Year Founded: 1974
GNTX—(NASDAQ)
Rev.: $2,299,215,044
Assets: $2,611,437,552
Liabilities: $298,920,483
Net Worth: $2,312,517,069
Earnings: $428,403,272
Emp.: 6,245
Fiscal Year-end: 12/31/23
Automotive Mirrors, Smoke Detec-
tors, Fire Alarms & Signaling Devices
Mfr
N.A.I.C.S.: 336390
Paul Flynn (VP-Ops)
Steven R. Downing (Pres & CEO)
Sue Franz (VP-Chemical Technolo-
gies)
Brad Bosma (VP-Vision Sys & Dim-
mable Glass)
Kevin Nash (CFO, Treas & VP-Fin)
Neil C. Boehm (CTO & VP-Engrg)
Matt Fox (VP-Mechanical Engrg)
Angela Nadeau (VP-Comml Mgmt)
Brian Lorence (VP-Sales)
Randy Pappal (VP-Purchasing &
Supply Chain)
Cliff Burgess (Officer-Information Se-
curity & VP-Information Technology)
Seth Bushouse (VP-Human Re-
sources)
Dave Hiemstra (VP-Engineering)
Richard O. Schaum (Chm)

Subsidiaries:

Argil, Inc. (1)
309 Laurelwood Rd Ste 24, Santa Clara,
CA 95054
Tel.: (408) 216-9186
Web Site: http://www.argilinc.com
Electrochromic Device Mfr
N.A.I.C.S.: 334413

E.C. Aviation Services, Inc. (1)
600 N Centennial St, Zeeland, MI
49464   (100%)
Tel.: (616) 772-1800
Emp.: 6
Oil Transportation Services
N.A.I.C.S.: 481211

**Gentex (Shanghai) Electronic Tech-
nology Co., Inc.** (1)
Building No 6 666 Min Shen Road Song
Jiang Industrial Zone, Song Jiang Industrial
Zone, Shanghai, 201612, China
Tel.: (86) 2157685062
Web Site: http://www.gentex.com
Sales Range: $300-349.9 Million
Automotive Mirrors, Smoke Detectors, Fire
Alarms & Signaling Devices Mfr

N.A.I.C.S.: 336390

Gentex France, SAS (1)
168 Avenue Jean Jaures Batiment D,
92120, Montrouge, France   (100%)
Tel.: (33) 478381134
Automotive Machinery Sls
N.A.I.C.S.: 423830
Robert Steel (Pres)

Gentex GmbH (1)
Georg-Ohm-Strasse 6, 74235, Erlenbach,
Germany   (100%)
Tel.: (49) 71321560
Web Site: http://www.gentex.com
Sales Range: $10-24.9 Million
Emp.: 90
Provider of Automotive Accessory Sales &
Engineering Services
N.A.I.C.S.: 541330

Gentex Holdings, Inc. (1)
600 N Centennial St, Zeeland, MI
49464   (100%)
Tel.: (616) 772-1800
Web Site: http://www.gentex.com
Holding Company
N.A.I.C.S.: 327215

Gentex Mirrors Ltd. (1)
Shillingwood House Westwood Way, Cov-
entry, CV4 8JZ, West Midlands, United
Kingdom   (100%)
Tel.: (44) 2476440293
Sales Range: $10-24.9 Million
Emp.: 3
Mfr of Rear View Mirrors for Cars
N.A.I.C.S.: 336340

GENTHERM INCORPORATED
21680 Haggerty Rd, Northville, MI
48167
Tel.: (248) 504-0500   MI
Web Site: https://www.gentherm.com
Year Founded: 1991
THRM—(NASDAQ)
Rev.: $1,469,076,000
Assets: $1,234,371,000
Liabilities: $589,649,000
Net Worth: $644,722,000
Earnings: $40,343,000
Emp.: 14,504
Fiscal Year-end: 12/31/23
Automotive Components Mfr
N.A.I.C.S.: 336390
Barbara J. Runyon (Chief HR Officer
& Sr VP)
Yijing Brentano (Sr VP-Corp Dev, IR,
and Strategy)
Wayne Kauffman (Gen Counsel, Sec
& Sr VP)
Rafael Barkas (Sr VP-Ops & Supply
Chain-Global)
Aine L. Denari (Executives)
Steve Fletcher (Sr VP & Gen Mgr-
Medical)
Nicholas Breisacher (Chief Acctg Offi-
cer)
Phillip M. Eyler (Pres, CEO & Interim
CFO)

Subsidiaries:

**Etratech Asia-Pacific Electronics
(Shenzhen) Ltd.** (1)
Xiang Yuer Industrial Zone Block 9 No 8
LongSheng Road, Longgang Street Long-
gang District, Shenzhen, 518116, China
Tel.: (86) 75589905976
Electronic Control Equipment Mfr
N.A.I.C.S.: 423830

Etratech Asia-Pacific Limited (1)
Unit 708 Tower 2 Cheung Sha Wan Plaza
833 Cheung Sha Wan Road, Kowloon,
China (Hong Kong)
Tel.: (852) 27368192
Electronic Control Equipment Mfr
N.A.I.C.S.: 335314

**Gentherm Asia Pacific
Incorporated** (1)
1-7-2 Otemachi Sankei Bldg 15F, Chiyoda-
ku, Tokyo, 100-0004, Japan
Tel.: (81) 332729521

Sales Range: $125-149.9 Million
Developer of Thermoelectric Technologies
for Automotive Industry
N.A.I.C.S.: 333415

**Gentherm Automotive Systems
(China) Ltd.** (1)
Langfang Economic and Technical Develop-
ment Zone 3 Jinyuan Road, Langfang,
065001, Hebei, China
Tel.: (86) 3166071100
Thermal Product Mfr
N.A.I.C.S.: 325992
Ralph Cao (Deputy Mgr-HR)

Gentherm Enterprises GmbH (1)
Rudolf-Diesel-Strasse 12, 85235, Odel-
zhausen, 85235, Germany
Tel.: (49) 81349330
Thermal Product Mfr
N.A.I.C.S.: 325992

Gentherm Europe GmbH (1)
Rudolf-Diesel-Strasse 12, Odelzhausen,
85235, Germany
Tel.: (49) 8134 933 0
Web Site: http://www.gentherm.com
Emp.: 150
Motor Vehicle Electrical & Electronic Equip-
ment Mfr
N.A.I.C.S.: 336320

Subsidiary (Domestic):

Gentherm GmbH (2)
Rudolf-Diesel-Strasse 12, 85235, Odel-
zhausen, Germany
Tel.: (49) 81349330
Web Site: http://www.gentherm.com
Fiscal Year-end: 12/31/2017
Holding Company; Automobile Parts &
Equipment Mfr & Distr
N.A.I.C.S.: 551112

Subsidiary (Non-US):

**W.E.T. Automotive Systems (China)
Limited** (3)
Jinyuan Road Langfang Economic & Tech-
nical Development Zone, Langfang,
065001, China
Tel.: (86) 3166071100
Sales Range: $150-199.9 Million
Emp.: 490
Automobile Parts & Equipment Mfr & Distr
N.A.I.C.S.: 336390

Subsidiary (Domestic):

**Comair Rotron Shanghai Fan Co.,
Ltd.** (4)
Bldg 58 No 506 Nanhuan Road Xinqiao
Town, Songjiang District, Shanghai,
201612, China
Tel.: (86) 2167693756
Web Site: http://www.comairrotron.com
Motor Vehicle Electrical & Electronic Equip-
ment Mfr
N.A.I.C.S.: 336320

Subsidiary (Non-US):

**W.E.T. Automotive Systems (Malta)
Limited** (3)
Suite 6 Paolo Court Giuseppe Cali Street,
Ta' Xbiex, XBX 1423, Malta
Tel.: (356) 23270100
Sales Range: $25-49.9 Million
Emp.: 6
Automobile Parts & Equipment Whslr
N.A.I.C.S.: 423120

**W.E.T. Sistemas Automotrices, S.A.
de C.V.** (3)
Carr Presa La Amistad KM 7 5, Parque In-
dustrial La Paz, Acuna, Mexico
Tel.: (52) 8777730385
Sales Range: $150-199.9 Million
Emp.: 600
Automobile Parts & Equipment Mfr
N.A.I.C.S.: 336390

**Gentherm Global Power
Technologies** (1)
16 7875-57 St SE, Calgary, T2C 5K7, AB,
Canada
Tel.: (403) 236-5556
Web Site:
   http://www.genthermglobalpower.com
Emp.: 90

Gentherm Incorporated—(Continued)

Thermoelectric Power Generators Mfr
N.A.I.C.S.: 335999

Jeffery Williams *(Mgr-Intl Bus Dev)*

Gentherm Hungary Kft (1)
Banyatelep14 Pilisszentivan, 2084, Buda-
pest, 2084, Hungary
Tel.: (36) 26567510
Thermal Product Mfr
N.A.I.C.S.: 325992

Gentherm Japan Inc. (1)
Hirotake Bldg 4F 9-7 Hashimotocho,
Naka-ku Hiroshima-shi, Hiroshima, 730-
0015, Japan
Tel.: (81) 825559636
Thermal Product Mfr
N.A.I.C.S.: 325992

Gentherm Korea Inc. (1)
4 FL 28 Simin-daero 327beon-gil, Dongan-
gu, Anyang, 14055, Gyeonggi-do, Korea
(South)
Tel.: (82) 314269642
Thermal Product Mfr
N.A.I.C.S.: 325992

Gentherm Medical, LLC (1)
12011 Mosteller Rd, Cincinnati, OH 45241-
1528
Tel.: (513) 772-8810
Web Site: https://www.gentherm.com
Medical Device Product Mfr
N.A.I.C.S.: 334512

Gentherm Technologies (Shanghai)
Co. Ltd. (1)
6F Max Overseas Building A No 1033 Xiehe
Road, Changning District, Shanghai, China
Tel.: (86) 216 239 1966
Printed Circuit Assembly Mfr
N.A.I.C.S.: 334418

Gentherm U.K. Ltd. (1)
Unit 6 Oak Court Pilgrims Walk Prologis
Park, Coventry, CV6 4QH, United Kingdom
Tel.: (44) 2476937183
Thermal Product Mfr
N.A.I.C.S.: 325992

Gentherm de Mexico S.A. de
C.V (1)
Carr Presa La Amistad Km 7.5 Parque In-
dustrial La Paz, Acuna, Coahuila, Mexico
Tel.: (52) 8777730385
Automobile Component Distr
N.A.I.C.S.: 423120

K3 Works GmbH (1)
Industriestrasse 5, 91757, Treuchtlingen,
Germany
Tel.: (49) 9914220240
Web Site: https://www.k3works.de
Emp.: 35
Automotive & Fuel Pump Mfr
N.A.I.C.S.: 336320

Stihler Electronic GmbH (1)
Gaussstrasse 4, 70771, Leinfelden-
Echterdingen, Germany
Tel.: (49) 711720670
Web Site: https://www.stihlerelectronic.de
Medicinal Product Mfr
N.A.I.C.S.: 339112

**GENUFOOD ENERGY EN-
ZYMES CORP.**
1108 S Baldwin Ave Ste 107, Arca-
dia, CA 91007
Tel.: (213) 330-6770 NV
Web Site:
  http://www.geecenzymes.com
Year Founded: 2010
GFOO—(OTCIQ)
Rev.: $2
Assets: $201,562
Liabilities: $147,842
Net Worth: $53,720
Earnings: ($627,702)
Emp.: 1
Fiscal Year-end: 09/30/23
Enzyme Products Mfr & Distr
N.A.I.C.S.: 325414

David Tang *(CEO)*
John Jui Pin Lin *(Pres)*
Shao-Cheng Wang *(CFO, Treas &
Sec)*

GENUINE PARTS COMPANY
2999 Wildwood Pkwy, Atlanta, GA
30339
Tel.: (678) 934-5000 GA
Web Site: https://www.genpt.com
Year Founded: 1928
GPC—(NYSE)
Rev.: $23,090,610,000
Assets: $17,968,454,000
Liabilities: $13,551,469,000
Net Worth: $4,416,985,000
Earnings: $1,316,524,000
Emp.: 60,000
Fiscal Year-end: 12/31/23
Automotive Replacement Parts, In-
dustrial Replacement Parts, Office
Products & Electrical/Electronic Mate-
rials Distr & Whslr
N.A.I.C.S.: 441330
Herbert C. Nappier *(CFO & Exec VP)*
Paul D. Donahue *(Chm)*
Christopher T. Galla *(Gen Counsel &
Sr VP)*
Randall P. Breaux *(Grp Pres-North
America)*
William P. Stengel II *(Pres & CEO)*
Naveen Krishna *(Chief Info & Digital
Officer & Exec VP)*

Subsidiaries:

ADAMS AUTO PARTS, LLC (1)
415 Old Easley Hwy, Greenville, SC 29611
Tel.: (864) 269-3521
Web Site: http://www.adamsautoparts.com
Automotive Part Whslr
N.A.I.C.S.: 441330

ALTROM AUTO GROUP LTD (1)
3464 Gardner Court, Burnaby, V5G 3K4,
BC, Canada
Tel.: (604) 296-4981
Web Site: https://www.altrom.com
Automobile Parts Distr
N.A.I.C.S.: 441330

ALTROM CANADA CORP. (1)
4242 Phillips Ave-Unit C, Burnaby, V5A
2X2, BC, Canada
Tel.: (604) 294-2311
Web Site: http://www.altrom.com
Emp.: 100
Automotive Parts Import & Distr
N.A.I.C.S.: 423120

Subsidiary (US):

Olympus Imported Auto Parts (2)
4425 Brookfield Corporate Dr Ste 1000,
Chantilly, VA 20151
Tel.: (703) 378-6666
Web Site: https://www.forparts.com
Sales Range: $1-9.9 Million
Emp.: 24
Imported Auto Parts Distr
N.A.I.C.S.: 423120
Michael Brown *(Mgr-Store)*

EIS de MEXICO (1)
Carretera Huinala 235 Col El Milagro, Apo-
daca, 66634, Nuevo Leon, Mexico
Tel.: (52) 818 321 3388
Web Site: http://www.eis-inc.com
Emp.: 19
Automobile Parts Distr
N.A.I.C.S.: 423120

ELECTRICAL INSULATION SUPPLI-
ERS de MEXICO, S.A. de C.V. (1)
Periferico Norte Lateral Sur No 1011, Za-
popan, 45158, Jalisco, Mexico
Tel.: (52) 3331655452
Electronic Parts & Equipment Whslr
N.A.I.C.S.: 423690
Alexander Gonzalez *(VP)*

GPC ASIA PACIFIC HOLDINGS PTY
LTD (1)
22 Enterprise Drive, Rowville, 3178, VIC,
Australia

Tel.: (61) 395665444
Web Site: https://www.gpcasiapac.com
Automotive Parts & Accessory Services
N.A.I.C.S.: 551112
Rob Cimeron *(Mng Dir)*

GPC FINANCE COMPANY (1)
300 Delaware Ave, Wilmington, DE 19801-
1607
Tel.: (302) 576-2686
Automotive Parts & Accessories Distr
N.A.I.C.S.: 441330

GPIC LLC (1)
22 Marina Gardens Dr, Palm Beach Gar-
dens, FL 33410
Tel.: (917) 345-2504
Automotive Parts & Accessories Distr
N.A.I.C.S.: 441330

Genuine Parts Company - U.S. Auto-
motive Parts Group (1)
2999 Wildwood Pkwy, Atlanta, GA 30339
Tel.: (678) 934-5000
Web Site: http://www.genpt.com
Sales Range: $150-199.9 Million
Emp.: 300
Automobile Parts Distr
N.A.I.C.S.: 423120
Kevin E. Herron *(Pres & COO)*

Subsidiary (Non-US):

Auto Todo Mexicana S.A. de
C.V. (2)
Mexico Puebla Highway No 7532 Colonia,
72110, Puebla, Mexico
Tel.: (52) 2222235000
Web Site: https://www.autotodo.com
Sales Range: $75-99.9 Million
Emp.: 230
Auto Parts Distr
N.A.I.C.S.: 423120

Division (Domestic):

National Automotive Parts Association, LLC (2)
1257 Pryor Rd SW, Atlanta, GA
30315 (100%)
Tel.: (404) 622-6272
Automotive Replacement Parts Mfr & Whslr
N.A.I.C.S.: 423120

Subsidiary (Domestic):

Auto Parts of Jupiter, Inc. (3)
17905 Jupiter Farms Rd, Jupiter, FL 33478
Tel.: (561) 746-7410
Web Site: http://www.napalocator.com
Automotive Parts & Accessories Retailer
N.A.I.C.S.: 441330

Balkamp, Inc. (3)
2601 Stout Heritage Pkwy, Plainfield, IN
46168 (89.6%)
Tel.: (317) 244-7241
Web Site: https://www.balkamp.com
Sales Range: $50-74.9 Million
Automotive Parts & Accessories Distr
N.A.I.C.S.: 441330

Branch (Domestic):

Genuine Auto Parts of Fairbanks (3)
304 Gaffney Rd, Fairbanks, AK 99701
Tel.: (907) 458-6272
Sales Range: $10-24.9 Million
Emp.: 70
Retail & Wholesale Automotive Parts
N.A.I.C.S.: 423120
Gregory L. Durdik *(Pres)*

NAPA Auto Parts Genuine Parts
Company (3)
360 Riverview Ave, Logan, WV 25601
Tel.: (304) 752-4650
Web Site: http://www.napaonline.com
Automotive Parts & Accessories Stores
N.A.I.C.S.: 441330

Napa Automotive Parts Distribution
Center (3)
2665 W Dublin Granville Rd, Columbus, OH
43235-2710
Tel.: (614) 766-1142
Web Site: http://www.gpc.com
Automobile Parts Distr
N.A.I.C.S.: 441330

Division (Domestic):

Rayloc (2)
3100 Windy Hill Rd SE, Atlanta, GA
30339 (100%)
Tel.: (404) 521-5000
Automotive Parts Rebuilding Services
N.A.I.C.S.: 423120

Subsidiary (Non-US):

UAP Inc. (2)
2015 Haig Avenue, Montreal, H1N 2B3,
QC, Canada
Tel.: (514) 251-6565
Web Site: https://www.uapinc.com
Emp.: 4,000
Automotive Parts & Replacement Accesso-
ries Distr, Remanufacturer & Merchandiser
N.A.I.C.S.: 423140
Caroline Tremblay *(Sr VP-Comm & HR)*
Alain Primeau *(Exec VP)*

Subsidiary (Domestic):

MTC Suspension Inc. (3)
950 boul Simard, Chambly, J3L 4X2, QC,
Canada
Tel.: (450) 658-3893
Web Site: https://www.mtc-suspension.com
Sales Range: $25-49.9 Million
Emp.: 40
Springs & Leaf Springs Mfr
N.A.I.C.S.: 332613
Steve Paradis *(Plant Mgr)*
Lucie Rivard *(Sec)*

Division (Domestic):

Napa Auto Parts (3)
5530 C 3rd St SE, Calgary, T2H 1J9, AB,
Canada (100%)
Tel.: (403) 212-4633
Web Site: https://www.napacanada.com
Automotive Replacement Parts Distr
N.A.I.C.S.: 441330

Subsidiary (Domestic):

Optimax Engine Inc. (3)
816 Industrial Blvd Bois Des Filion J6Z 083,
Terrebonne, J6W 1Z7, QC, Canada
Tel.: (450) 471-6681
Sales Range: $10-24.9 Million
Emp.: 8
Automotive Engine Mfr, Distr & Re-builder
N.A.I.C.S.: 333618

Division (Domestic):

Traction (3)
1080 Montee de Liesse, Saint Laurent, H4S
1J4, QC, Canada (100%)
Tel.: (514) 332-1003
Web Site: http://www.traction.com
Automotive Repair Shops
N.A.I.C.S.: 811111

UAP, Inc. (Cadel Div.) (3)
1080 montee de liesse, Montreal, H4S1J4,
QC, Canada (100%)
Tel.: (514) 331-4616
Web Site: http://www.cadel.ca
Sales Range: $10-24.9 Million
Emp.: 14
Motor Vehicle Parts Mfr
N.A.I.C.S.: 336340

Genuine Parts Company Eastern
Division (1)
1260 Newfield St, Middletown, CT 06457-
1873
Tel.: (860) 632-2424
Sales Range: $10-24.9 Million
Emp.: 6
Automobile Parts Distr
N.A.I.C.S.: 423120

Genuine Parts Company Mountain &
Western Division (1)
7150 S Fulton St Ste 300, Centennial, CO
80112
Tel.: (303) 623-7373
Sales Range: $10-24.9 Million
Emp.: 10
Automobile Parts Distr
N.A.I.C.S.: 423120
Brad Shaffer *(VP-Western Div)*

Impact Products, LLC (1)
2840 Centennial Rd, Toledo, OH 43617

Tel.: (419) 841-2891
Web Site: https://www.impact-products.com
Emp.: 135
Cleaning & Maintenance Product Mfr
N.A.I.C.S.: 335220
Robb Borgen *(VP-Mktg)*

Inenco Group Pty Ltd. (1)
18 Worth Street, Chullora, 2190, NSW,
Australia   (100%)
Tel.: (61) 29947 9200
Web Site: http://www.inencogroup.com.au
Transmission, Bearing & Hydraulic Equipment & Services
N.A.I.C.S.: 423830
Roger Jowett *(CEO)*

Merles Automotive Supply, Inc. (1)
4015 S Dodge Blvd, Tucson, AZ 85714
Tel.: (520) 889-7202
Web Site: https://www.merlesauto.com
Automotive Supplies & Parts
N.A.I.C.S.: 423120

Monroe Motor Products Corp. (1)
40 Joseph Ave, Rochester, NY 14605
Tel.: (585) 546-6633
Web Site: http://www.partsplusny.com
Automotive Supplies & Parts
N.A.I.C.S.: 423120

Motion Asia Pacific Pty Ltd (1)
18 Worth Street, Chullora, 2190, NSW, Australia
Tel.: (61) 1300642722
Web Site: https://www.motionasiapac.com
Metal Parts Mfr
N.A.I.C.S.: 332119

Motion Industries, Inc. (1)
1605 Alton Rd, Birmingham, AL
35210-3770   (100%)
Tel.: (205) 956-1122
Web Site: http://www.motion.com
Bearings, Power Transmission & Fluid
Power Replacement Parts Distr
N.A.I.C.S.: 423840
Randall P. Breaux *(Pres)*
Randy Breaux *(Pres)*

Subsidiary (Domestic):

AST Bearings LLC (2)
222 New Rd Ste 1, Parsippany, NJ 07045
Tel.: (973) 335-2230
Web Site: https://www.astbearings.com
Sales Range: $25-49.9 Million
Emp.: 50
Automotive Parts & Accessories Distr
N.A.I.C.S.: 441330

Apache Inc. (2)
4805 Bowling St SW, Cedar Rapids, IA
52404-5021
Tel.: (319) 365-0471
Web Site: https://www.apache-inc.com
Hoses, Industrial Fittings & Conveyor Belts
Mfr & Distr
N.A.I.C.S.: 423840

Subsidiary (Domestic):

AG Belt, Inc. (3)
4517 SE 14th St, Des Moines, IA 50320
Web Site: https://www.agbeltinc.com
Baler Belt Mfr & Distr
N.A.I.C.S.: 326220

Seals Unlimited, Inc. (3)
6410 NE Jacobson St, Hillsboro, OR 97124
Tel.: (503) 690-6644
Web Site: https://www.sealsunlimited.com
Molded Rubber Product Mfr
N.A.I.C.S.: 326299

Subsidiary (Domestic):

**Applied Machine & Motion Control,
Inc.** (2)
1491 Dixie Hwy, Park Hills, KY 41011
Tel.: (859) 655-2222
Web Site: http://www.ammc.com
Electrical Apparatus & Related Equipment
Merchant Whslr
N.A.I.C.S.: 423610
Rob Hollman *(Acct Mgr, Fin Mgr, Product
Mgr, Partner, Fin Dir & Co-Owner)*
David Locke *(Dir, Mgr-Information Technology, Owner & VP)*
Steve Keeney *(Dir-Sales-Marketing-Information Technology)*

Dave Pflaumer *(Mgr-Customer Service)*
Trevor Pernic *(Mgr)*
Paul Striley *(VP-Sales-Business Development)*
Bob Theis *(Mgr)*
Jim Ruthemeyer *(Mgr)*
Stefan Gudry *(Mgr)*
Colin Theis *(Mgr)*
Eric Davidson *(Sr Acct Mgr)*
Sean Overmyer *(Sys Engr)*
Justin Fischesser *(Sys Engr)*
Cindy Leese *(Mgr-Accounting-Quality Assurance)*

Braas Company (2)
7350 Golden Triangle Dr, Eden Prairie, MN
55344
Tel.: (952) 937-8902
Web Site: https://www.braasco.com
Bearings & Power Transmission Equipment
Distr
N.A.I.C.S.: 423120
Joe Schwartz *(Pres)*

Colmar Belting Co., Inc. (2)
20 W 5th St, Boston, MA 02127
Tel.: (617) 269-7056
Web Site: http://colmarbelting.com
Sales Range: $1-9.9 Million
Emp.: 14
Industrial Supplies Merchant Whslr
N.A.I.C.S.: 423840
Richard Brunaccini *(Pres)*

D.P. Brown of Detroit Inc. (2)
1646 Champagn Dr, Saginaw, MI 48604
Tel.: (989) 771-0200
Sales Range: $10-24.9 Million
Emp.: 34
Power Transmission Equipment Mfr
N.A.I.C.S.: 423610

Dayton Supply & Tool Co. (2)
507 E 1st St, Dayton, OH 45401
Tel.: (937) 461-4550
Web Site: http://www.motionindustries.com
Sales Range: $25-49.9 Million
Emp.: 45
Industrial Supplies
N.A.I.C.S.: 423840
Jerry Kronenberger *(Pres)*

Drago Supply Company Inc. (2)
740 Houston Ave, Port Arthur, TX 77640
Tel.: (409) 983-4911
Web Site: http://www.dragosupply.com
Sales Range: $50-74.9 Million
Emp.: 85
Industrial Supplies Distr
N.A.I.C.S.: 423840

Epperson & Company Inc. (2)
5202 Shadowlawn Ave, Tampa, FL 33610
Tel.: (813) 626-6125
Web Site:
   https://www.miconveyancesolutions.com
Industrial Supplies
N.A.I.C.S.: 423840

F&L Industrial Solutions, Inc. (2)
12550 Stowe Dr, Poway, CA 92064-8878
Tel.: (858) 602-1500
Web Site: http://www.fandl8020.com
Industrial Machinery & Equipment Merchant
Whslr
N.A.I.C.S.: 423830
Mike Fanolla *(Co-Founder)*
Lori Lefeuvre *(Co-Founder)*

General Tool & Supply Co. Inc. (2)
1370 County St, Attleboro, MA 02703-6104
Tel.: (401) 345-8766
Web Site:
   https://www.generaltoolworldwide.com
Sales Range: $50-74.9 Million
Emp.: 163
Industrial Tools & Supplies Distr
N.A.I.C.S.: 423840
William C. Derville *(Pres)*

Hub Supply Company (2)
2546 S Leonine Rd, Wichita, KS 67217-1071
Tel.: (316) 265-9608
Web Site: http://www.motionindustries.com
Sales Range: $50-74.9 Million
Emp.: 30
Industrial Supplies Whslr
N.A.I.C.S.: 423840

**Miller Bearings Division -
Westmoreland** (2)

1 S Westmoreland Dr, Orlando, FL 32805
Tel.: (407) 849-6000
Web Site: http://www.motionindustries.com
Industrial Supplies Distr
N.A.I.C.S.: 423840

Division (Domestic):

Miller Bearings Division - Miami (3)
6661 NW 82nd Ave, Miami, FL 33166
Tel.: (305) 592-7626
Web Site: http://www.motionindustries.com
Bearing Products Mfr
N.A.I.C.S.: 333613

Division (Domestic):

**Missouri Power Transmission,
Inc.** (2)
3226 Blair Ave, Saint Louis, MO
63107   (100%)
Tel.: (314) 421-0919
Web Site: http://www.motionindustries.com
Power Transmission Equipment & Industrial
Supplies Distr
N.A.I.C.S.: 423840
Mitch Stierwalt *(CFO)*

Subsidiary (Non-US):

Motion Industries (Canada) Inc. (2)
B-5448 Timberlea Blvd, Mississauga, L4W
2T7, ON, Canada
Tel.: (289) 374-2100
Web Site: http://www.motioncanada.com
Sales Range: $75-99.9 Million
Emp.: 20
Holding Company
N.A.I.C.S.: 551112

Branch (Domestic):

Motion Industries (Canada) Inc. (3)
236 36th Street North, Lethbridge, T1H
3Z7, AB, Canada
Tel.: (403) 327-1571
Web Site: http://www.motionindustries.com
Sales Range: $10-24.9 Million
Emp.: 15
Industrial Parts & Equipment Distr
N.A.I.C.S.: 423840

Subsidiary (Domestic):

Obbco Safety & Supply, Inc. (2)
1737 S Park Ct, Chesapeake, VA 23320
Tel.: (757) 420-4000
Web Site:
   https://www.obbcosafetysupply.com
Sales Range: $1-9.9 Million
Emp.: 15
Industrial Safety Supplies Distr
N.A.I.C.S.: 811310
W. Michael Bryant *(Pres)*

Voorhies Supply Company, LLC (2)
401 W Saint Peter St, New Iberia, LA
70560
Tel.: (337) 365-0548
Web Site: http://www.motionindustries.com
Sales Range: $25-49.9 Million
Emp.: 10
Wholesale of Machinery & Hardware
N.A.I.C.S.: 423840

**REISTERSTOWN AUTO PARTS,
INC.** (1)
24 Westminster Pike, Reisterstown, MD
21136
Tel.: (908) 200-8011
Automotive Part Whslr
N.A.I.C.S.: 441330

**S. P. RICHARDS CO. CANADA
INC.** (1)
102-107 25th Ave NE, Calgary, T3N 0A4,
AB, Canada
Tel.: (403) 252-5085
Stationery & Office Supplies Whslr
N.A.I.C.S.: 424120

**SPR PROCUREMENT
COMPANY** (1)
6300 Highlands Pkwy SE, Smyrna, GA
30082-7231
Tel.: (770) 436-6881
Automotive Parts & Accessories Distr
N.A.I.C.S.: 441330

Shuster Corporation (1)

55 Samuel Barnet Blvd, New Bedford, MA
02674
Tel.: (508) 999-3261
Web Site: https://www.shusterbearings.com
Ball & Roller Bearing Mfr
N.A.I.C.S.: 332991

UAPRO INC (1)
7025 Rue Ontario E, Montreal, H1N 2B3,
QC, Canada
Tel.: (514) 256-5031
Web Site: http://www.uapinc.com
Automotive Parts & Accessories Distr
N.A.I.C.S.: 441330

**WILLIAMSPORT AUTOMOTIVE,
INC.** (1)
350 W 3rd St, Williamsport, PA 17701-6479
Tel.: (570) 326-1991
Emp.: 6
Motor Vehicle Parts Whslr
N.A.I.C.S.: 423120

GENWORTH FINANCIAL, INC.
6620 W Broad St, Richmond, VA
23230
Tel.: (804) 281-6000   DE
Web Site: https://www.genworth.com
Year Founded: 1871
GNW—(NYSE)
Rev.: $7,488,000,000
Assets: $90,817,000,000
Liabilities: $82,482,000,000
Net Worth: $8,335,000,000
Earnings: $76,000,000
Emp.: 2,700
Fiscal Year-end: 12/31/23
Fire Insurance Services
N.A.I.C.S.: 524113
Jerome Thomas Upton *(CFO & Exec
VP)*
Gregory S. Karawan *(Gen Counsel &
Exec VP)*
Melissa Hagerman *(Chief HR Officer
& Exec VP)*
Mark Blakeley Hodges *(Chief Risk
Officer & Exec VP)*
Kelly Saltzgaber *(Chief Investment
Officer)*
Joost Heideman *(Sr VP)*
Thomas J. McInerney *(Pres & CEO)*

Subsidiaries:

Enact Holdings, Inc. (1)
8325 6 Forks Rd, Raleigh, NC 27615
Tel.: (919) 846-4100
Web Site: https://www.enactmi.com
Rev.: $1,095,046,000
Assets: $5,709,149,000
Liabilities: $1,608,241,000
Net Worth: $4,100,908,000
Earnings: $704,157,000
Emp.: 496
Fiscal Year-end: 12/31/2022
Offices of Other Holding Companies
N.A.I.C.S.: 551112
Rohit Gupta *(Pres & CEO)*

Genworth Consulting Services (Beijing) Limited (1)
11/F North Tower Beijing Kerry Centre No 1
Guang Hua Road, Beijing, 10020, Chaoyang, China
Tel.: (86) 1065997951
Management Consulting Services
N.A.I.C.S.: 541611
Portia Jiang *(Dir-Comml Trng)*

**Genworth Financial Advisers
Corporation** (1)
200 W Madison St, Chicago, IL 60606
Tel.: (312) 690-9526
Web Site: http://www.genworth.com
Investment Advisory Services
N.A.I.C.S.: 523940

Genworth Financial Canada (1)
2060 Winston Park Drive Suite 300, Oakville, L6H 5R7, ON, Canada
Tel.: (905) 829-2636
Web Site: http://www.genworth.ca
Sales Range: $100-124.9 Million
Emp.: 200
Mortgage Insurance Services

Genworth Financial, Inc.—(Continued)

N.A.I.C.S.: 524128
Winsor MacDonell (Gen Counsel, Sec & Sr VP)
Philip Mayers (CFO & Sr VP)
Stuart Levings (Pres & CEO)

Genworth Financial India Private Limited (1)
1st Floor Tower A DLF Building No 9 DLF Phase III, Gurgaon, 122 002, Haryana, India
Tel.: (91) 124 465 4910
Web Site: https://www.genworth.in
Insurance Services
N.A.I.C.S.: 524210

Genworth Financial Trust Company (1)
3200 N Central Ave 7th Fl, Phoenix, AZ 85012
Tel.: (602) 285-3500
Financial Management Services
N.A.I.C.S.: 523940

Genworth Life and Annuity Insurance Company (1)
6610 W Broad St, Richmond, VA 23230
Web Site: http://www.genworth.com
Sales Range: $1-4.9 Billion
Direct Life Insurance Carriers
N.A.I.C.S.: 524113

Genworth Mortgage Insurance Corporation of North Carolina (1)
8325 6 Forks Rd, Raleigh, NC 27615
Tel.: (919) 846-4100
Web Site: http://www.genworth.com
Direct Property & Casualty Insurance Services
N.A.I.C.S.: 524126

Genworth Mortgage Services, LLC (1)
8325 6 Forks Rd, Raleigh, NC 27615-6520
Tel.: (919) 846-4100
Web Site:
http://www.mortgageinsurance.gen worth.com
Trust Management Nondeposit Trust Facility & Services
N.A.I.C.S.: 523991

Genworth Operaciones Colombia S.A.S. (1)
Cr 7 52-00 Trr A of 504, Bogota, 202, Colombia
Tel.: (57) 16467321
Insurance Services
N.A.I.C.S.: 524210

National Eldercare Referral Systems, LLC (1)
60 Hickory Dr 4th Fl, Waltham, MA 02451
Web Site: https://www.carescout.com
Emp.: 75
Direct Property & Casualty Insurance Services
N.A.I.C.S.: 524126
Brian Harrington (Chief Sls Officer)
Ed Motherway (Pres)
Karen Petruna (COO)
Rauf Zeynalov (Chief Strategy Officer)
Ted Bream (Chief Mktg Officer)
Zach Sloane (CTO)

GEO JS TECH GROUP CORP.
5177 Richmond Ave Ste 775, Houston, TX 77056
Tel.: (347) 341-0731   TX
Year Founded: 2010
GJST—(OTCIQ)
Iron Ore Mining & Trading
N.A.I.C.S.: 212210
Jimmy Yee (Chm & CFO)
Edward Mui (CEO)
Huang Yi-Lun Kao (Sec & Gen Dir-Taiwan)
Leo Kao (Sec)

GEORGE RISK INDUSTRIES, INC.
802 S Elm St, Kimball, NE 69145-1599
Tel.: (308) 235-4645   CO

Web Site: https://www.grisk.com
Year Founded: 1967
RSKIA—(OTCIQ)
Rev.: $21,767,000
Assets: $60,780,000
Liabilities: $6,143,000
Net Worth: $54,637,000
Earnings: $7,558,000
Emp.: 185
Fiscal Year-end: 04/30/24
Other Communications Equipment Manufacturing
N.A.I.C.S.: 334290
Sharon Alberta Westby (Treas & Sec)
Stephanie M. Risk-McElroy (Chm, Pres, CEO & CFO)
Scott McMurray (Dir-Sls)

Subsidiaries:

Labor Saving Devices, Inc. (1)
5678 Eudora St, Commerce City, CO 80022-3809
Tel.: (303) 287-2121
Web Site: http://www.lsdinc.com
Wire & Cable Installation Tools Mfr
N.A.I.C.S.: 333991
David Morgan (CEO)

GEOSPACE TECHNOLOGIES CORPORATION
7007 Pinemont Dr, Houston, TX 77040
Tel.: (713) 986-4444   DE
Web Site: https://www.geospace.com
GEOS—(NASDAQ)
Rev.: $124,509,000
Assets: $153,042,000
Liabilities: $20,326,000
Net Worth: $132,716,000
Earnings: $12,206,000
Emp.: 681
Fiscal Year-end: 09/30/23
Seismic Data Measuring Equipment Mfr
N.A.I.C.S.: 334519
Gary D. Owens (Chm)
Robbin B. Adams (Chief Technical Officer & Sr VP)
Walter Richard Wheeler (Pres, CEO & Engr-Design)
Robert L. Curda (CFO, Sec & VP)
David Witt (CIO)
Jorgen Skjott (VP-Oil & Gas Sls)
Ken Nesteroff (Dir-Adjacent Markets)
Loretta Bazan (Dir-Health, Safety & Environmental)
Alisha Betancourt (Dir-Supply Chain)
Nathan Gall (Dir-Mfg)
Mercy Thomas (Mgr-Corp Quality)
Caroline Kempf (CMO)

Subsidiaries:

Exile Technologies Corporation (1)
7007 Pinemont Dr, Houston, TX 77040
Tel.: (713) 343-5662
Web Site: http://www.exiletech.com
Industrial Machinery & Equipment Mfr
N.A.I.C.S.: 333998

Exile Technologies Limited (1)
F3 Bramingham Business Park Enterprise Way, Luton, LU3 4BU, United Kingdom
Tel.: (44) 1582573980
Web Site: http://www.exiletech.co.uk
Emp.: 7
Industrial Machinery Mfr
N.A.I.C.S.: 333998
Mark William Evans (Mng Dir)

Geospace Engineering Resources International, Inc. (1)
7007 Pinemont Dr, Houston, TX 77040
Tel.: (713) 986-4444
Web Site: http://www.geospace.com
Industrial Machinery & Equipment Mfr
N.A.I.C.S.: 333998

Geospace Technologies Canada, Inc. (1)
2735-37 Ave NE, Calgary, T1Y 5R8, AB, Canada

Tel.: (403) 250-9600
Web Site: http://www.geospacetech.ca
Industrial Machinery & Equipment Mfr
N.A.I.C.S.: 333998

OYO Geospace China (1)
Room 700 7th Floor Lido Office Tower, Beijing, 100004, China
Tel.: (86) 1064378768
Sales Range: $10-24.9 Million
Emp.: 55
Seismic Instrument Mfr
N.A.I.C.S.: 334516
Tao Lu (Mng Dir)

Quantum Technology Sciences, Inc. (1)
5700 N Harbor City Blvd Ste 100, Melbourne, FL 32940
Tel.: (321) 868-0288
Web Site: https://www.qtsi.com
Engineering Services
N.A.I.C.S.: 541330
Mark Tinker (CEO)

GEOVAX LABS, INC.
1900 Lake Park Dr Ste 380, Smyrna, GA 30080
Tel.: (678) 384-7220   DE
Web Site: https://www.geovax.com
Year Founded: 2001
GOVX—(NASDAQ)
Rev.: $81,526
Assets: $31,347,928
Liabilities: $4,747,894
Net Worth: $26,600,034
Earnings: ($14,021,125)
Emp.: 14
Fiscal Year-end: 12/31/22
Human Immunodeficiency Virus Vaccine Researcher, Developer & Mfr
N.A.I.C.S.: 325412
Mark W. Reynolds (CFO & Sec)
David Alan Dodd (Chm, Pres & CEO)
Kelly T. McKee Jr. (Chief Medical Officer)
J. Marc Pipas (Exec Dir-Medical Oncology)

GERMAN AMERICAN BANCORP, INC.
1600 Amphitheatre Pkwy, Mountain View, CA 94043
Tel.: (812) 482-1314   IN
Web Site:
https://www.germanamerican.com
Year Founded: 1983
GABC—(NASDAQ)
Rev.: $229,841,000
Assets: $5,608,539,000
Liabilities: $4,940,080,000
Net Worth: $668,459,000
Earnings: $84,137,000
Emp.: 894
Fiscal Year-end: 12/31/21
Bank Holding Company
N.A.I.C.S.: 551111
Bradley M. Rust (Pres, CFO & COO)
D. Neil Dauby (Chm & CEO)
Michael F. Beckwith (Chief Comml Banking Officer & Exec VP)
Vicki L. Schuler (Principal Acctg Officer, Sr VP & Controller)
Bradley C. Arnett (Chief Legal Officer, Sec & Sr VP)

Subsidiaries:

Citizens Union Bancorp of Shelbyville, Inc. (1)
1854 Midland Trl, Shelbyville, KY 40065
Tel.: (502) 633-4450
Web Site: https://www.cubbank.com
Sales Range: $25-49.9 Million
Emp.: 130
Bank Holding Company
N.A.I.C.S.: 551111
David M. Bowling (Pres)

GAB Investment Company, Inc. (1)
3993 Howard Hughes Pkwy Ste 250, Las Vegas, NV 89169-6754

Tel.: (702) 650-0239
Commercial Banking Services
N.A.I.C.S.: 522110

German American Bank (1)
711 Main St, Jasper, IN 47546
Tel.: (812) 482-1314
Web Site: https://www.germanamerican.com
Commercial Banking
N.A.I.C.S.: 522110
Bradley M. Rust (Pres, CFO, COO & Exec VP)
Keith A. Leinenbach (Chief Credit Officer & Sr VP)
D. Neil Dauby (Chm & CEO)
Amy D. Jackson (Chief Admin Officer)
Clay M. Barrett (Chief Digital Officer)
Michael F. Beckwith (Chief Comml Banking Officer)
W. Scott Powell (Chief Credit Officer)

German American Financial Advisors & Trust Company (1)
711 Main St, Jasper, IN 47546
Tel.: (812) 482-1314
Financial Advisory Services
N.A.I.C.S.: 523940
Gene Mattingly (Sr VP-Investment Svcs)
Dave Mitchell (Chief Investment Officer & Sr VP-Trust Div)

GERON CORPORATION
919 E Hillsdale Blvd Ste 250, Foster City, CA 94404
Tel.: (650) 473-7700   DE
Web Site: https://www.geron.com
Year Founded: 1992
GERN—(NASDAQ)
Rev.: $596,000
Assets: $190,575,000
Liabilities: $110,577,000
Net Worth: $79,998,000
Earnings: ($141,901,000)
Emp.: 107
Fiscal Year-end: 12/31/22
Cell & Gene Therapy Research Services
N.A.I.C.S.: 325412
Michelle J. Robertson (CFO, Principal Acctg Officer, Treas & Exec VP)
Melissa A. Kelly Behrs (Chief Alliance Officer & Exec VP-Bus Ops)
John A. Scarlett (Chm, Pres & CEO)
Stephen N. Rosenfield (Chief Legal Officer, Sec & Exec VP)
Andrew J. Grethlein (COO & Exec VP)
Anil Kapur (Chief Comm Officer & Exec VP-Corp Strategy)
Peter Avalos (VP-Trade & Channel Rels)
Nishan Sengupta (VP-Market Access & Pricing)
Lorraine Shui (VP-Mktg)
Scott Hutson (VP-Sls)
Denise Meyer (VP-Medical Affairs)
Edward E. Koval (Chief Bus Officer)
Faye Feller (Chief Medical Officer)
Aron Feingold (VP-IR & Corp Comm)
Kristen Kelleher (Sr Mgr-IR)

GERSON LEHRMAN GROUP, INC.
60 E 42nd St 3rd Fl, New York, NY 10165
Tel.: (212) 984-8500   DE
Web Site:
https://www.glginsights.com
Year Founded: 1998
GLGX—(NYSE)
Rev.: $589,139,000
Assets: $396,304,000
Liabilities: $1,010,053,000
Net Worth: ($613,749,000)
Earnings: $34,092,000
Emp.: 2,300
Fiscal Year-end: 12/31/20
Financial Information Services
N.A.I.C.S.: 519290

Paul Todd *(CEO)*
Martijn Tel *(CFO)*
Jay Chakrapani *(Chief Product Officer)*
Roger C. Freeman *(Chm)*
Jenifer S. Brooks *(CMO)*

GET YOUR FEELZ ON

PO Box 251, Balboa Island, CA 92662
Tel.: (949) 610-2804   NV
Web Site:
    http://www2.getyourfeelzon.com
DSOL—(OTCIQ)
Pharmaceuticals Product Mfr
N.A.I.C.S.: 325414
Genie O'Malley *(Founder & Co-Chm)*
Aubree Galbiso *(Chief Admin Officer)*
Brian Campbell *(Co-Chm)*

GETAROUND, INC.

55 Green St, San Francisco, CA 94111
Tel.: (415) 295-5725   DE
Web Site: https://getaround.com
GETR—(NYSE)
Rev.: $59,455,000
Assets: $205,419,000
Liabilities: $135,919,000
Net Worth: $69,500,000
Earnings: ($136,065,000)
Emp.: 283
Fiscal Year-end: 12/31/22
Car Sharing Services
N.A.I.C.S.: 532111
Jason B. Mudrick *(Chm)*
Eduardo Vazquez Iniguez *(CEO)*
Sam Zaid *(Founder)*
Patricia Huerta *(Chief Acctg Officer)*
Spencer Jackson *(Gen Counsel & Sec)*
A. J. Lee *(COO)*

GETSWIFT TECHNOLOGIES LIMITED

1185 6th Ave, New York, NY 10036
Tel.: (646) 648-1022
Web Site: http://www.getswift.co
Year Founded: 2020
GSW—(TSX)
N.A.I.C.S.: 541714
Joel Macdonald *(Founder)*
Chris Tyson *(Exec VP-MZ North America)*
Bane Hunter *(CEO)*
Rob Bardunias *(COO)*
Michael Willetts *(CFO)*
Julian Rockett *(Chm)*

Subsidiaries:

Getswift Limited   **(1)**
Level 12 225 George Street, Sydney, 2000, NSW, Australia
Tel.: (61) 280162841
Web Site: http://www.getswift.co
Rev.: $18,596,289
Assets: $53,122,212
Liabilities: $17,878,464
Net Worth: $35,243,748
Earnings: ($21,915,435)
Fiscal Year-end: 06/30/2020
Software Development Services
N.A.I.C.S.: 513210

GETTY IMAGES HOLDINGS, INC.

605 5th Ave S Ste 400, Seattle, WA 98104
Tel.: (206) 925-5000   DE
Web Site: https://www.gettyimages.in
Year Founded: 1995
GETY—(NYSE)
Rev.: $926,244,000
Assets: $2,468,183,000
Liabilities: $1,875,135,000
Net Worth: $593,048,000
Earnings: ($147,450,000)

Emp.: 1,700
Fiscal Year-end: 12/31/22
Holding Company
N.A.I.C.S.: 551112
Jennifer Leyden *(CFO)*
Nate Gandert *(CTO)*
Gene Foca *(CMO & Officer-Revenue)*
Grant Farhall *(Chief Product Officer & Sr VP)*
Kjelti Kellough *(Gen Counsel)*
Ken Mainardis *(Sr VP-Editorial)*
Peter Orlowsky *(Sr VP-Strategic Development)*
Matthew J. Richards *(VP-Customer Service)*
Rebecca Swift *(Sr VP-Creative)*
Michael Teaster *(Sr VP & Head-Staff)*
Rick Thompson *(VP-Sls Ops & Enablement)*
Lizanne Vaughan *(Chief People Officer)*
Daine Weston *(Sr VP-ECommerce)*
Mark H. Getty *(Founder)*
Craig Peters *(CEO)*

GETTY REALTY CORP.

292 Madison Ave 9th Fl, New York, NY 10017-6318
Tel.: (646) 349-6000   MD
Web Site:
    https://www.gettyrealty.com
Year Founded: 1997
GTY—(NYSE)
Rev.: $165,588,000
Assets: $1,562,295,000
Liabilities: $802,445,000
Net Worth: $759,850,000
Earnings: $90,043,000
Emp.: 32
Fiscal Year-end: 12/31/22
Property Investment & Management
N.A.I.C.S.: 551112
Joshua Dicker *(Gen Counsel, Sec & Exec VP)*
Christopher J. Constant *(Pres & CEO)*
Mark J. Olear *(COO & Exec VP)*
Brian R. Dickman *(CFO, Treas & Exec VP)*
R. J. Ryan *(Sr VP)*
Brad Fisher *(VP)*
Elena Lokis *(Gen Counsel)*
Gavin Orman *(Gen Counsel)*
Juliet Voses *(Gen Counsel)*

Subsidiaries:

AOC Transport, Inc.   **(1)**
2 Jericho Plz Wing C Ste 110, Jericho, NY 11753
Tel.: (516) 478-5400
Web Site: http://www.gettyrealty.com
Sales Range: $25-49.9 Million
Nonresidential Buildings Rental & Leasing Services
N.A.I.C.S.: 531120

Getty Properties Corp.   **(1)**
2 Jericho Plaza Suite-110, Jericho, NY 11753   **(100%)**
Tel.: (516) 478-5400
Web Site: http://www.gettyrealty.com
Sales Range: $25-49.9 Million
Emp.: 25
Real Estate Investment
N.A.I.C.S.: 525990

GEVO, INC.

345 Inverness Dr S Bldg C Ste 310, Englewood, CO 80112
Tel.: (303) 858-8358   DE
Web Site: https://www.gevo.com
Year Founded: 2005
GEVO—(NASDAQ)
Rev.: $1,175,000
Assets: $700,748,000
Liabilities: $95,271,000
Net Worth: $605,477,000
Earnings: ($98,007,000)

Emp.: 87
Fiscal Year-end: 12/31/22
Renewable Chemicals & Advanced Biofuels Mfr & Marketer
N.A.I.C.S.: 325998
Patrick R. Gruber *(CEO)*
Christopher Michael Ryan *(Pres & COO)*
Samir Kaul *(Founder)*
L. Lynn Smull *(CFO)*
Paul D. Bloom *(Chief Carbon & Innovation Officer)*
Heather Manuel *(VP-IR & Comm)*
Alisher Nurmat *(Principal Acctg Officer, VP & Controller)*
Kimberly Bowron *(Chief People Officer)*
Nancy N. Young *(Chief Sustainability Officer)*
Lindsay Fitzgerald *(VP)*
Geoffrey T. Williams Jr. *(Gen Counsel, Sec & VP)*

GEX MANAGEMENT, INC.

3662 W Camp Wisdom Rd, Dallas, TX 75237   TX
Web Site:
    https://www.gexmanagement.com
Year Founded: 2004
GXXM—(OTCIQ)
Rev.: $2,270,535
Assets: $462,814
Liabilities: $1,840,499
Net Worth: ($1,377,685)
Earnings: ($1,125,342)
Emp.: 35
Fiscal Year-end: 12/31/22
Commercial Services
N.A.I.C.S.: 561110
Srikumar Vanamali *(Chm, CEO & CFO)*
Shaheed Bailey *(Interim CIO)*

GIBRALTAR INDUSTRIES, INC.

3556 Lake Shore Rd, Buffalo, NY 14219-0228
Tel.: (716) 826-6500   DE
Web Site: https://www.gibraltar1.com
Year Founded: 1972
ROCK—(NASDAQ)
Rev.: $1,389,966,000
Assets: $1,210,613,000
Liabilities: $388,514,000
Net Worth: $822,099,000
Earnings: $82,406,000
Emp.: 2,117
Fiscal Year-end: 12/31/22
Holding Company; Infrastructure, Renewable Energy, Residential & Agricultural Technology Services
N.A.I.C.S.: 551112
William T. Bosway *(Chm & CEO)*
Lori A. Rizzo *(VP & Controller)*
Jeff Bedard *(Gen Mgr-Sunesta & Gutter Helmet)*
Katherine E. Bolanowski *(Gen Counsel, Sec & VP)*
Mark Dunson *(Grp Pres-Prospiant)*
Chris Lok *(Chief Digital Information Officer)*
Ed McKiernan *(Pres)*
Kerri Winter *(VP)*
Joseph Allen Lovechio *(CFO & VP)*

Subsidiaries:

Air Vent Inc.   **(1)**
4117 Pinnacle Point Dr Ste 400, Dallas, TX 75211   **(100%)**
Tel.: (214) 630-7377
Web Site: https://www.airvent.com
Sales Range: $75-99.9 Million
Emp.: 150
Mfr of Attic Ventilation Products & Accessories
N.A.I.C.S.: 332322

Alabama Metal Industries
Corporation   **(1)**

3245 Fayette Ave, Birmingham, AL 35208-4822
Tel.: (205) 787-2611
Web Site: http://www.amico-online.com
Sales Range: $250-299.9 Million
Emp.: 120
Mfr & Distr of Industrial Flooring, Grating & Expanded Metal Products
N.A.I.C.S.: 332323

Subsidiary (Non-US):

AMICO   **(2)**
1080 Corporate Drive, Burlington, L7L 5R6, ON, Canada
Tel.: (905) 335-4474
Web Site: http://www.amico-online.com
Sales Range: $25-49.9 Million
Emp.: 20
Mfr of Grating, Expanded Metal Products & Metal Lath
N.A.I.C.S.: 332323

AMICO Canada, Inc.   **(2)**
1080 Corporate Dr, Burlington, L7L 5R6, ON, Canada
Tel.: (905) 335-4474
Fabricated Structural Metal Distr
N.A.I.C.S.: 423390
Glenn MacKay *(VP & Gen Mgr)*

Unit (Domestic):

AMICO Fontana   **(2)**
11093 Beech Ave, Fontana, CA 92337-7268
Tel.: (909) 350-9280
Web Site: http://www.amico-online.com
Sales Range: $75-99.9 Million
Emp.: 5
Mfr of Expanded Metals
N.A.I.C.S.: 332323

AMICO Houston   **(2)**
120 N Latham, Houston, TX 77011
Tel.: (713) 921-5355
Web Site: http://www.amico-online.com
Sales Range: $25-49.9 Million
Emp.: 8
Distr of Metal Bar Grating, Expanded Metal & Metal Lath
N.A.I.C.S.: 332323

AMICO Lakeland   **(2)**
1033 Pine Chase Ave, Lakeland, FL 33801
Tel.: (863) 688-9256
Web Site: http://www.amicoglobal.com
Sales Range: $50-74.9 Million
Emp.: 7
Distr & Retailer of Metal Bar Grating, Expanded Metal & Metal Lath
N.A.I.C.S.: 332323

AMICO Orem   **(2)**
212 N 1330 W, Orem, UT 84057
Tel.: (801) 225-9350
Web Site: http://www.amico-online.com
Sales Range: $50-74.9 Million
Emp.: 110
Mfr of Metal Bar Grating, Expanded Metal & Metal Lath
N.A.I.C.S.: 332323

Subsidiary (Domestic):

Diamond Perforated Metals, Inc.   **(2)**
7300 W Sunnyview Ave, Visalia, CA 93291
Tel.: (559) 651-1889
Web Site: https://www.diamondperf.com
Sales Range: $150-199.9 Million
Mfr & Distr of Perforated & Expanded Metals
N.A.I.C.S.: 332323

Seasafe Inc.   **(2)**
209 Glaser Dr, Lafayette, LA 70508
Tel.: (337) 406-2345
Web Site: http://www.seasafe.com
Sales Range: $25-49.9 Million
Emp.: 80
Mfr of Fiberglass Bar Grating
N.A.I.C.S.: 326199
Clay Theard *(Sls Mgr-Natl)*
Scotty Prejean *(Mgr-Drafting)*

Appleton Supply Co., Inc.   **(1)**
1905 W Haskel St, Appleton, WI 54914   **(100%)**
Tel.: (920) 738-4242

Gibraltar Industries, Inc.—(Continued)

Web Site: https://www.appletonsupply.com
Sales Range: $50-74.9 Million
Emp.: 75
Mfr of Soffit Systems, Roof Trim & Flashing
N.A.I.C.S.: 444180

Florence Corporation (1)
5935 Corporate Dr, Manhattan, KS 66503
Tel.: (785) 323-4400
Web Site:
  https://www.florencemailboxes.com
Sales Range: $75-99.9 Million
Emp.: 450
Mailboxes & Mailbox Accessories Mfr
N.A.I.C.S.: 337215
Stacy Kohlmeier (VP-Sales-Marketing)
Steve Penn-Berkeley (VP-Operations)

Subsidiary (Domestic):

Florence Corporation of Kansas (2)
5935 Corporate Dr, Manhattan, KS 66503-9675
Tel.: (785) 323-4400
Web Site:
  https://www.florencemailboxes.com
Sales Range: $50-74.9 Million
Emp.: 300
Sheet Metal Work Mfg
N.A.I.C.S.: 332322
Kerri Winter (VP-Accounting-Administration)
Lori Ladouceur (Mgr-Sls-Natl)
Ted Redding (Sls Mgr-Southeast)
Taurris Baskerville (Sls Mgr)
Chris Beck (Sls Mgr-West)
Mike Travisano (Mgr-Sls-Central Reg)
Gene Laminack (Gen Mgr)

Gibraltar Steel Corporation of New York (1)
3556 Lake Shore Rd, Buffalo, NY 14219-1445 (100%)
Tel.: (716) 826-6500
Web Site: https://www.gibraltar1.com
Emp.: 30
Steel Building Products Mfr
N.A.I.C.S.: 331110

Subsidiary (Domestic):

Pacific Awards Metals, Inc. (2)
1450 Virginia Ave, Baldwin Park, CA 91706
Tel.: (626) 814-4410
Web Site:
  https://www.gibraltarbuildingproducts.com
Metal Building & Component Mfr
N.A.I.C.S.: 332311

Subsidiary (Domestic):

Construction Metals, LLC (3)
10302 Birtcher Dr, Fontana, CA 91752
Tel.: (909) 390-9880
Web Site:
  http://www.constructionmetals.com
Roofing Sheet Metal Products Mfr
N.A.I.C.S.: 238160

Noll/Norwesco, LLC (3)
3860 Grant St, Washougal, WA 98671
Tel.: (360) 835-3021
Web Site: http://www.norwesco.com
Metal Building & Component Mfr
N.A.I.C.S.: 332311

Nexus Corporation (1)
10983 Leroy Dr, Northglenn, CO 80233
Tel.: (303) 457-9199
Web Site: http://www.nexuscorp.com
Metal Greenhouses Mfr
N.A.I.C.S.: 332311

Division (Domestic):

National Greenhouse Company (2)
6 Industrial Park Dr, Pana, IL 62557
Tel.: (217) 562-9333
Web Site:
  http://www.nationalgreenhouse.com
Institutional Greenhouse Designer & Mfr
N.A.I.C.S.: 321992

Noll/Norwesco LLC (1)
1320 Performance Dr, Stockton, CA 95206
Tel.: (209) 234-1600
Sheet Metal Products Mfr
N.A.I.C.S.: 332322

Subsidiary (Domestic):

M & N Plastics, Inc. (2)
38 SE 97th Ave, Portland, OR 97216
Tel.: (503) 252-8811
Sales Range: $10-24.9 Million
Emp.: 20
Plastic Vent Mfr
N.A.I.C.S.: 326199

Noll/Norwesco LLC (2)
3556 Lake Shore Rd, Buffalo, NY 14219
Tel.: (253) 926-1600
Sheet Metal Products Mfr
N.A.I.C.S.: 332322

Package Concierge, Inc. (1)
445 Main St Ste 201, Medfield, MA 02052
Tel.: (888) 989-7225
Electronic Locker Systems Services
N.A.I.C.S.: 561621
Georgianna W. Oliver (Founder, VP & Gen Mgr)
John Doyle (COO)
Lindsey Wilker (Dir-Ops)
Regan Hartley (Dir-Sls)

Quality Aluminum Products Inc. (1)
429 S Michigan Ave, Hastings, MI 49058
Tel.: (269) 945-0376
Web Site: http://www.qualityaluminum.com
Aluminum Building Products Mfr
N.A.I.C.S.: 332322
George J. Clark (Co-Founder & Pres)
Bob Clark (Pres)

RBI Solar Brazil LTDA (1)
Rua dos Inconfidentes n 867 2 Andar -
Bairro Savassi, Belo Horizonte, 30140-120,
Minas Gerais, Brazil
Tel.: (55) 3125322446
Web Site: http://www.rbisolar.com.br
Solar Mounting System Mfr
N.A.I.C.S.: 335132
Richard Reilly (Pres)

RBI Solar KK (1)
1-5-9 Nishi-Shinbashi TS, Minato-Ku
Minami-Azabu, Tokyo, 105-0003, Japan
Tel.: (81) 362733377
Web Site: https://www.rbisolar.jp
Solar Mounting System Mfr
N.A.I.C.S.: 334413

Rough Brothers Greenhouse Manufacturing (Shanghai) Co., Ltd (1)
No A235-237 YueJie Industry Zone 11 1101
HuYi Road, Nanxiang Town Jiading District,
Shanghai, 201802, China
Tel.: (86) 2169173540
Web Site: https://www.roughbroschina.com
Greenhouse Mfr
N.A.I.C.S.: 332311

Rough Brothers Manufacturing, Inc. (1)
5513 Vine St, Cincinnati, OH 45217
Tel.: (513) 242-0310
Web Site: https://www.roughbros.com
Greenhouse Construction Services
N.A.I.C.S.: 236220

Rough Brothers, Inc. (1)
5513 Vine St, Cincinnati, OH 45217
Tel.: (513) 242-0310
Web Site: https://www.prospiant.com
Commercial & Industrial Greenhouses &
Components Design & Mfr
N.A.I.C.S.: 332311
Tom Vezdos (Gen Mgr)

Subsidiary (Domestic):

RBI Solar, Inc. (2)
6715 Steger Dr, Cincinnati, OH 45237
Tel.: (513) 242-2051
Web Site: https://www.rbisolar.com
Solar Power Mounting Equipment Mfr
N.A.I.C.S.: 334419

Subsidiary (Domestic):

SolarBOS (3)
310 Stealth Ct, Livermore, CA 94551-4551
Tel.: (925) 456-7744
Web Site: http://www.solarbos.com
Electrical Equipment Mfr & Distr
N.A.I.C.S.: 335931

Sea Safe, Inc. (1)
209 Glaser Dr, Lafayette, LA 70508

Web Site: http://www.seasafe.com
Fabricated Structural Metal Mfr
N.A.I.C.S.: 332312

Solar Group, Inc. (1)
107 Fellowship Rd, Taylorsville, MS
39168-4476 (100%)
Tel.: (601) 785-4711
Web Site: https://www.thesolargroup.com
Sales Range: $75-99.9 Million
Emp.: 400
Metal Building & Component Mfr
N.A.I.C.S.: 332311

Southeastern Metals Manufacturing Co. Inc. (1)
2737 Ignition Dr Ste 8, Jacksonville, FL 32218
Tel.: (904) 757-4200
Web Site: https://www.semetals.com
Sales Range: $100-124.9 Million
Emp.: 250
Mfr of Metal Products
N.A.I.C.S.: 332322

TerraSmart, LLC (1)
14590 Global Pkwy, Fort Myers, FL 33913
Tel.: (239) 362-0211
Web Site: http://www.terrasmart.com
Sales Range: $1-9.9 Million
Emp.: 25
Solar Ground Mount Racking Mfr & Engineering
N.A.I.C.S.: 332999
Ryan Reid (CEO)
Renee Roggow (Dir-Ops)
Michael Faraone (Dir-Engrg)
Richard van Fleet (Dir-Project Ops)
Shannon Sheets (Plant Mgr)
Randy Smith (Dir-HSEQ & Field Ops)
Anthony Lomanno (Sls Mgr)
Rob Turner (Dir-Emerging Bus)
Ashleigh Kent (Mktg Dir)
Chris Felkamp (Dir-Bus Dev)
Storm Reid (Acct Mgr-Natl)
Stephen Lafleur (Acct Mgr-Natl)
Will King (Acct Mgr-Natl)
Lance Reid (Sr Mgr-Construction)
John Kelton (Sr Mgr-Civil)
Thomas Smith (Mgr-Survey)
Chase Anderson (Sr Engr-Design)
Terrence Corsen (Engr-Design)
Joshua Brooks (Engr-Mfg)
Karl Hilaire (Coord-Testing)
Brian Martin (Engr-Project)
Toby Holden (Sr Engr-Design)
Brooks Washburn (Engr-QA & QC)
Andy Fouse (Dir-Software Dev)
Andrew Karki (Engr-Controls & Commissioning)
Huw Jones (Dir-Supply Chain)

The D.S. Brown Company (1)
300 E Cherry St N, North Baltimore, OH 45872-1227
Tel.: (419) 257-3561
Web Site: https://www.dsbrown.com
Sales Range: $50-74.9 Million
Emp.: 275
Engineered Products Designer, Mfr & Supplier for Bridge & Highway Construction
N.A.I.C.S.: 326291
Scott Jenkins (VP)
Tom Lewis (VP-Sales, Marketing, and Customer Service)

The Expanded Metal Company Limited (1)
Longhill Industrial Estate, PO Box 14,
Cleveland, Hartlepool, TS25 1PR, United Kingdom
Tel.: (44) 1429867398
Web Site:
  https://www.expandedmetalcompany.com
Metal Products Mfr
N.A.I.C.S.: 332999

Thermo Energy Solutions, Inc. (1)
2035 Spinks Drive, Kingsville, N9Y 2E5,
ON, Canada
Tel.: (519) 322-0388
Web Site: https://www.thermoenergy.ca
Heating & Cooling System Distr
N.A.I.C.S.: 423730

GIFA, INC.
1660 Hotel Circle N Ste 207, San Diego, CA 92108

Tel.: (619) 497-2555 NV
Year Founded: 2008
GIFX—(OTCIQ)
Mobile & Internet Marketing; Online Social Network for Education
N.A.I.C.S.: 541890
Harshawardhan Shetty (Founder, Pres, CEO, Treas & Sec)

GILEAD SCIENCES, INC.
333 Lakeside Dr, Foster City, CA 94404
Tel.: (650) 574-3000 DE
Web Site: https://www.gilead.com
Year Founded: 1987
GILD—(NASDAQ)
Rev.: $27,116,000,000
Assets: $62,025,000,000
Liabilities: $39,276,000,000
Net Worth: $22,749,000,000
Earnings: $5,665,000,000
Emp.: 18,000
Fiscal Year-end: 12/31/23
Biotechnology Research & Development Services
N.A.I.C.S.: 325414
Jyoti Mehra (Exec VP-HR)
Monica Tellado (Sr VP-Fin)
Daniel P. O'Day (Chm & CEO)
Andrew D. Dickinson (CFO)
Cindy Perettie (Exec VP-Kite)
Adam D. Levy (Head-Corp Strategy & Exec Dir)
Flavius Martin (Exec VP-Res)
Johanna Mercier (Chief Comml Officer)
Jyoti K. Mehra (Exec VP-HR)
Stacey Ma (Exec VP-Mfg & Pharmaceutical Dev)
Deborah Telman (Gen Counsel, Sec & Exec VP-Corp Affairs)
Robert L. Mecca (Sr VP-Fin)
Taiyin Yang (Exec VP-Mfg & Pharmaceutical Dev)
Merdad Parsey (Chief Medical Officer)

Subsidiaries:

Asegua Therapeutics, LLC (1)
333 Lakeside Dr, Foster City, CA 94404
Web Site: https://www.asegua.com
Pharmaceuticals Product Mfr
N.A.I.C.S.: 325412

CymaBay Therapeutics, Inc. (1)
7575 Gateway Blvd Ste 110, Newark, CA 94560
Tel.: (510) 293-8800
Web Site: https://www.cymabay.com
Rev.: $2,017,000
Assets: $141,852,000
Liabilities: $105,698,000
Net Worth: $36,154,000
Earnings: ($106,001,000)
Emp.: 63
Fiscal Year-end: 12/31/2022
Pharmaceutical Preparation Mfr
N.A.I.C.S.: 325412
Harish Shantharam (CFO & Principal Acctg Officer)
Robert L. Martin (Sr VP-Mfg & Nonclinical Dev)
Patrick J. O'Mara (Sr VP-Bus Dev)
Klara A. Dickinson-Eason (Chief Regulatory & Quality Assurance Officer)
Ken Boehm (Sr VP-HR)
Lewis Stuart (Chief Comml Officer)
Becki Filice (Sr VP-Portfolio)

EpiTherapeutics ApS (1)
Ole Maaloesvej 3, Copenhagen, 2200, Denmark
Tel.: (45) 20253560
Web Site:
Pharmaceutical Products Distr
N.A.I.C.S.: 424210

Forty Seven, Inc. (1)
1490 O'Brien Dr Ste A, Menlo Park, CA 94025
Tel.: (650) 352-4150
Web Site: http://www.fortyseveninc.com
Rev.: $15,678,000

Assets: $343,593,000
Liabilities: $25,665,000
Net Worth: $317,928,000
Earnings: ($87,621,000)
Emp.: 68
Fiscal Year-end: 12/31/2019
Biotechnology Research & Development Services
N.A.I.C.S.: 541714
Andrew D. Dickinson *(Pres & Treas)*
Brett A Pletcher *(Sec)*
Christina Carlson *(Asst Sec)*

Fosun Pharma Kite Biotechnology Co., Ltd. (1)
No 2277 Kangxin Road, Pudong New Area, Shanghai, 201210, China
Tel.: (86) 2153295300
Web Site: https://www.fosunkitebio.com
Pharmaceuticals Product Mfr
N.A.I.C.S.: 325412

Gilead Alberta ULC (1)
1021 Hayter Road, Edmonton, T6S 1A1, AB, Canada
Tel.: (780) 701-6400
Web Site: http://www.gilead.com
Pharmaceutical Preparation Mfr
N.A.I.C.S.: 325412
Greg Klak *(VP-Ops & Gen Mgr)*
Scott Ogonoski *(Assoc Dir-EH&S)*

Gilead Connecticut, Inc. (1)
36 E Industrial Rd, Branford, CT 06405
Tel.: (203) 315-1222
Pharmaceutical Preparation Mfr
N.A.I.C.S.: 325412

Gilead Sciences (Shanghai) Consulting Co., Ltd. (1)
Floor 31 Building 1 Century Link Office Building No 1198 Century Ave, Pudong New Area, Shanghai, 200135, China
Tel.: (86) 2138934588
Pharmaceuticals Product Mfr
N.A.I.C.S.: 325412

Gilead Sciences Canada, Inc. (1)
6711 Mississauga Rd Suite 600, Mississauga, L5N 2W3, ON, Canada
Tel.: (905) 363-8008
Web Site: https://www.gilead.ca
Emp.: 500
Active Pharmaceutical Ingredients Mfr
N.A.I.C.S.: 325412

Gilead Sciences Europe Ltd. (1)
2 Roundwood Avenue, Stockley Park, Uxbridge, UB11 1AF, Middlesex, United Kingdom
Tel.: (44) 208 587 2200
Web Site: http://www.gilead.com
Emp.: 400
Holding Company; Regional Managing Office
N.A.I.C.S.: 551112

Subsidiary (Non-US):

Gilead Sciences Belgium BVBA/SPRL (2)
Park Lane Culliganlaan 2D, 1831, Diegem, Belgium
Tel.: (32) 2 401 3550
Web Site: http://www.gilead.com
Emp.: 17
Biopharmaceutical Product Mfr
N.A.I.C.S.: 325414

Gilead Sciences Ges m.b.H. (2)
Wagramer Strasse 19, 1220, Vienna, Austria
Tel.: (43) 126 0830
Web Site: https://www.gilead.com
Biopharmaceutical Product Mfr
N.A.I.C.S.: 325414

Gilead Sciences GmbH (2)
Fraunhoferstrasse 17, Martinsried, 82152, Munich, Germany
Tel.: (49) 898998900
Web Site: http://www.gilead.com
Sales Range: $25-49.9 Million
Emp.: 80
Biopharmaceutical Product Mfr
N.A.I.C.S.: 325414

Gilead Sciences Hellas .EPE (2)
4 P. Faliro Floor 2, Helliniko, 17561, Athens, Greece

Tel.: (30) 2108930100
Biopharmaceutical Product Mfr
N.A.I.C.S.: 325414

Subsidiary (Domestic):

Gilead Sciences International Ltd. (2)
Granta Park, Abington, Cambridge, CB21 6GT, United Kingdom
Tel.: (44) 1223897300
Sales Range: $50-74.9 Million
Emp.: 160
Pharmaceuticals Product Mfr
N.A.I.C.S.: 325412
Luis Casanova *(Mgr-Regulatory Affairs)*

Subsidiary (Non-US):

Gilead Sciences Pty Ltd (3)
Level 6 417 St Kilda Road, Melbourne, 3004, VIC, Australia
Tel.: (61) 39 272 4400
Web Site: https://www.gilead.com.au
Sales Range: $25-49.9 Million
Emp.: 30
Biopharmaceutical Product Mfr
N.A.I.C.S.: 325414

Subsidiary (Non-US):

Gilead Sciences Ltd. (2)
IDA Business & Technology Park, Carraigtohill, Cork, Ireland
Tel.: (353) 21 4825500
Web Site: http://www.gilead.com
Sales Range: $50-74.9 Million
Emp.: 200
Medicinal Drugs Mfr & Distr
N.A.I.C.S.: 325412

Subsidiary (Domestic):

Gilead Sciences Ltd. (2)
280 High Holborn, London, WC1V 7EE, United Kingdom
Tel.: (44) 2036814500
Sales Range: $50-74.9 Million
Emp.: 200
Biopharmaceuticals Distr
N.A.I.C.S.: 424210

Subsidiary (Non-US):

Gilead Sciences Netherlands BV (2)
Vinoly Tower Floor 9 Claude Debussylaan 22, 1082 MD, Amsterdam, Netherlands
Tel.: (31) 20 718 3650
Web Site: http://www.gilead.com
Sales Range: $25-49.9 Million
Emp.: 30
Biopharmaceutical Product Mfr
N.A.I.C.S.: 325414

Gilead Sciences Poland (2)
Adgar Plaza 6th Floor ul Postepu 17A, 02-676, Warsaw, Poland
Tel.: (48) 222628702
Medicinal Drugs Mfr
N.A.I.C.S.: 325412

Gilead Sciences S.r.l (2)
Via Melchiorre Gioia 26, 20124, Milan, Italy
Tel.: (39) 0243 9201
Web Site: https://www.gilead.it
Emp.: 200
Biopharmaceutical Product Mfr
N.A.I.C.S.: 325414

Gilead Sciences SAS (2)
65 Quai Georges Gorse, 92100, Boulogne, France
Tel.: (33) 146094100
Web Site: https://www.gilead.fr
Medicinal Drugs Mfr
N.A.I.C.S.: 325412

Gilead Sciences Sweden AB (2)
Solna Gate Hemvarnsgatan 9, 171 54, Solna, Sweden
Tel.: (46) 85 057 1800
Web Site: http://www.gilead.com
Biopharmaceutical Product Mfr
N.A.I.C.S.: 325414

Gilead Sciences Switzerland Sarl (2)
General-Guisan-Strasse 8, 6300, Zug, Switzerland
Tel.: (41) 41 580 0200
Web Site: https://www.gilead.com

Sales Range: $25-49.9 Million
Emp.: 40
Pharmaceutical Products Distr
N.A.I.C.S.: 424210

Gilead Sciences Ilac Ltd (2)
AND Kozyatagi Icerenkoy Mahallesi Umut Sokak 10-12 Atasehir, 34752, Istanbul, Etiler, Turkiye
Tel.: (90) 2165590300
Web Site: http://www.gilead.com
Sales Range: $25-49.9 Million
Emp.: 50
Biopharmaceutical Product Mfr
N.A.I.C.S.: 325414

Gilead Sciences, Lda. (2)
Atrium Saldanha Praca Duque de Saldanha n.1 - 8 A e B, 1050-094, Lisbon, Portugal
Tel.: (351) 217928790
Web Site: https://www.gilead.com
Sales Range: $25-49.9 Million
Emp.: 30
Biopharmaceutical Product Mfr
N.A.I.C.S.: 325414

Gilead Sciences, S.L. (2)
Parque Empresarial Cristalia Edificio 7/8 planta 6a, C/ Via de los Poblados 3, 28033, Madrid, Spain
Tel.: (34) 91 378 9830
Web Site: https://www.gilead.es
Biopharmaceutical Product Mfr
N.A.I.C.S.: 325414

Gilead Sciences Farmaceutica do Brasil Ltda (1)
Avenida Doutor Chucri Zaidan 1240, Cj 1501-1502 - 15 andar Golden Tower - Morumbi Corporate, 04711-130, Sao Paulo, 04711-130, Brazil
Tel.: (55) 1130369988
Pharmaceuticals Product Mfr
N.A.I.C.S.: 325412

Gilead Sciences Finland Oy (1)
Karhumaentie 3, 01530, Vantaa, Finland
Tel.: (358) 942726918
Biopharmaceutical Product Research & Development Services
N.A.I.C.S.: 541714

Gilead Sciences Hong Kong Limited (1)
Room 2603 26th Floor Hysan Place 500 Hennessy Road, Causeway Bay, China (Hong Kong)
Tel.: (852) 31292000
Web Site: https://www.gilead.com.hk
Biopharmaceutical Product Research & Development Services
N.A.I.C.S.: 541714

Gilead Sciences Ireland UC (1)
IDA Business & Technology Park, Co Cork, Carrigtohill, Ireland
Tel.: (353) 214825500
Pharmaceutical Product Mfr & Distr
N.A.I.C.S.: 325412
Niall Barrett *(Dir-Fin)*

Gilead Sciences Israel Limited (1)
4 HaHarash, PO 6090, Hod Hasharon, 4254075, Israel
Tel.: (972) 732844540
Web Site: https://www.gileadisrael.co.il
Pharmaceutical Products Distr
N.A.I.C.S.: 424210

Gilead Sciences KK (1)
GranTokyo South Tower 16F 1-9-2, Marunouchi Chiyoda-ku, Tokyo, 100-6616, Japan
Tel.: (81) 36 837 0055
Web Site: https://www.gilead.co.jp
Emp.: 401
Biotechnology Research & Development Services
N.A.I.C.S.: 541714

Gilead Sciences Korea Limited (1)
15th Floor West Wing Center One Building 26 Eulji-ro 5-gil, Jung-gu, Seoul, 04539, Korea (South)
Tel.: (82) 260303300
Web Site: https://www.gilead.co.kr
Biotechnology Research & Development Services
N.A.I.C.S.: 541714

Gilead Sciences Mexico S. de R.L. de C.V. (1)

Av Insurgentes Sur 1431 Piso 9 Col Insurgentes Mixcoac Del, Miguel Hidalgo, 03920, Mexico, Mexico
Tel.: (52) 5553504900
Biopharmaceutical Product Research & Development Services
N.A.I.C.S.: 541714

Gilead Sciences Russia LLC (1)
White Gardens 9 Lesnaya Street, 125196, Moscow, Russia
Tel.: (7) 4951399500
Health Care Srvices
N.A.I.C.S.: 621493

Gilead Sciences Singapore Pte. Ltd. (1)
88 Market Street Suite 3906, Singapore, 048948, Singapore
Tel.: (65) 69949848
Biopharmaceutical Product Research & Development Services
N.A.I.C.S.: 541714

Gilead Sciences Slovakia s.r.o. (1)
Laurinska 18, 811 01, Bratislava, Slovakia
Tel.: (421) 232121210
Biopharmaceutical Product Research & Development Services
N.A.I.C.S.: 541714

Gilead Sciences South Africa (Pty) Ltd (1)
Ground Floor Mac Mac Building Maxwell Office Park Magwa Crescent, Waterfall, Johannesburg, 2090, South Africa
Tel.: (27) 103461920
Biopharmaceutical Product Research & Development Services
N.A.I.C.S.: 541714

Gilead Sciences s.r.o. (1)
Pujmanove 1753 10a 2nd floor, Prague 4, 140 00, Prague, Czech Republic
Tel.: (420) 910871986
Health Care Srvices
N.A.I.C.S.: 621493

Gilead Sciences, Inc. - Seattle (1)
199 E Blaine St, Seattle, WA 98102
Tel.: (206) 728-5090
Web Site: https://www.gilead.com
Sales Range: Less than $1 Million
Emp.: 130
Developer of Biopharmaceutical Products for the Treatment of Respiratory & Infectious Diseases
N.A.I.C.S.: 541714

Gilead YM ULC (1)
5045 Orbitor Drive Building 11 Suite 400, Mississauga, L4W 4Y4, ON, Canada
Tel.: (650) 574-3000
Pharmaceuticals Product Mfr
N.A.I.C.S.: 325412

Immunomedics, Inc. (1)
300 The American Rd, Morris Plains, NJ 07950
Tel.: (973) 605-8200
Web Site: http://www.immunomedics.com
Sales Range: Less than $1 Million
Emp.: 366
Cancer Diagnostics & Drug Therapies Developer & Mfr
N.A.I.C.S.: 325412
Usama Malik *(CFO & Chief Bus Officer)*
William Fricker *(Chief Acctg Officer & Controller)*
Jared Freedberg *(Gen Counsel & Gen Counsel)*
Kurt J. W. Andrews *(Chief HR Officer)*
Bryan Ball *(Chief Quality Officer)*
Andrew D. Dickinson *(Pres & Treas)*
Brett A. Pletcher *(Sec)*
Christina Carlson *(Asst Sec)*
Loretta M. Itri *(Chief Medical Officer)*

Subsidiary (Domestic):

IBC Pharmaceuticals, Inc. (2)
300 The American Rd, Morris Plains, NJ 07950
Tel.: (973) 605-8200
Sales Range: $10-24.9 Million
Emp.: 200
Joint Venture of Immunomedics, Inc. & Beckman Coulter Pharmaceuticals
N.A.I.C.S.: 325412
Cynthia L. Sullivan *(Pres)*

Gilead Sciences, Inc.—(Continued)

Subsidiary (Non-US):

Immunomedics GmbH (2)
Paul-Ehrlich-Str 22 / D1, 63322, Roder-
mark, Germany   (100%)
Tel.: (49) 60742153600
Web Site: http://www.immunomedics.com
Sales Range: $1-9.9 Million
Emp.: 2
Mfr & Developer of Cancer Diagnostics &
Drug Therapies
N.A.I.C.S.: 325413

Immunomedics, B.V. (2)
Haarlemmerstraat 30, 2181 HC, Hillegom,
Netherlands   (100%)
Tel.: (31) 252 531 800
Web Site: http://www.immunomedics.com
Cancer Diagnostics & Drug Therapies Mfr &
Developer
N.A.I.C.S.: 325413

Kite Pharma EU B.V. (1)
Tufsteen 1, 2132 NT, Hoofddorp, Nether-
lands
Tel.: (31) 237117400
Biopharmaceutical Product Research & De-
velopment Services
N.A.I.C.S.: 541714

Kite Pharma UK, Ltd (1)
2 Roundwood Avenue Stockley Park,
Middlesex, Uxbridge, UB11 1AF, United
Kingdom
Tel.: (44) 2085872200
Biopharmaceutical Product Research & De-
velopment Services
N.A.I.C.S.: 541714

Kite Pharma, Inc. (1)
2400 Broadway, Santa Monica, CA 90404
Tel.: (310) 824-9999
Web Site: https://www.kitepharma.com
Pharmaceuticals Mfr
N.A.I.C.S.: 325412

GILLA INC.
475 Fentress Blvd Unit L, Daytona
Beach, FL 32114
Tel.: (416) 843-2881   NV
Web Site: http://gillainc.com
Year Founded: 1995
GLLA—(OTCIQ)
Sales Range: $1-9.9 Million
Emp.: 36
E-Cigarettes, Vaporizers, E-Liquids &
Related Accessories Marketer & Distr
N.A.I.C.S.: 424940
Ashish Kapoor (CFO & Sec)
Daniel Yuranyi (Chief Procurement
Officer)
John Graham Simmonds Jr. (Chm &
CEO)

Subsidiaries:

Vape Brands International Inc. (1)
2525 Tedlo Street Unit A, Mississauga, L5A
4A8, ON, Canada
E-liquid & Related Accessories Distr
N.A.I.C.S.: 424940

**GINKGO BIOWORKS HOLD-
INGS, INC.**
27 Drydock Ave 8th Fl, Boston, MA
02210
Tel.: (310) 209-7280   Ky
Web Site:
    https://www.ginkgobioworks.com
Year Founded: 2020
DNA—(NYSE)
Rev.: $251,455,000
Assets: $1,665,342,000
Liabilities: $568,190,000
Net Worth: $1,097,152,000
Earnings: ($892,869,000)
Emp.: 1,218
Fiscal Year-end: 12/31/23
Investment Services
N.A.I.C.S.: 523999
Eli Baker (Pres, CFO & Sec)
Jason Kelly (CEO)

Reshma Shetty (Pres & COO)
Mark Dmytruk (CFO)
Steven P. Coen (Chief Acctg Officer)

Subsidiaries:

Ginkgo Bioworks, Inc. (1)
27 Drydock Ave 8th Fl, Boston, MA 02210
Web Site: https://www.ginkgobioworks.com
Biotechnology Research & Development
N.A.I.C.S.: 541714
Austin Che (Co-Founder)
Reshma Shetty (Co-Founder)
Barry Canton (Co-Founder)
Tom Knight (Co-Founder)

Subsidiary (Domestic):

Novogy, Inc. (2)
85 Bolton St, Cambridge, MA 02140
Tel.: (617) 674-5800
Web Site: http://www.novogyinc.com
Biotechnology Research Services
N.A.I.C.S.: 541714
Greg Stephanopoulos (Chief Security Offi-
cer)
Ginja R. Tavares da Silva (VP-Fin)
A. Joe Shaw (Sr Dir-R&D)

Zymergen, Inc. (1)
5980 Horton St Ste 105, Emeryville, CA
94608
Tel.: (415) 801-8073
Web Site: http://www.zymergen.com
Rev.: $16,743,000
Assets: $522,396,000
Liabilities: $113,910,000
Net Worth: $408,486,000
Earnings: ($361,785,000)
Emp.: 507
Fiscal Year-end: 12/31/2021
Bio Technology Services
N.A.I.C.S.: 541714
Joshua Hoffmann (Co-Founder)
Mina Kim (Chief Security Officer)
Jed Dean (Co-Founder & VP-Ops & Engrg)
Judy Gilbert (Chief People Officer)
Mina Kim (Chief Legal Officer)
Enakshi Singh (CFO)
Aindrea Campbell (Chief Mfg Officer)

Subsidiary (Domestic):

enEvolv, Inc. (2)
200 Boston Ave Ste 2975, Medford, MA
02155
Tel.: (617) 209-6120
Web Site: https://www.enevolv.com
Research & Development in Biotechnology
N.A.I.C.S.: 541714
Colin South (CEO)
Farren Isaacs (Co-Founder)
George Church (Co-Founder)
Jay Konieczka (Co-Founder)

GITLAB INC.
268 Bush St Ste 350, San Francisco,
CA 94104
Tel.: (650) 474-5175   DE
Web Site: https://about.gitlab.com
Year Founded: 2014
GTLB—(NASDAQ)
Rev.: $579,906,000
Assets: $1,317,861,000
Liabilities: $699,927,000
Net Worth: $617,934,000
Earnings: ($424,174,000)
Emp.: 2,130
Fiscal Year-end: 01/31/24
Software Development Services
N.A.I.C.S.: 541511
Erin Mannix (Chief Acctg Officer)
Sytse Sijbrandij (Founder, Chm &
CEO)
Brian Robins (CFO)
Robin J. Schulman (Chief Legal Offi-
cer & Sec)
Ashley Kramer (Chief Mktg & Strat-
egy Officer)
Ashley Kramer (CMO, Chief Strategy
Officer & Interim Chief Revenue Offi-
cer)

GLACIER BANCORP, INC.

49 Commons Loop, Kalispell, MT
59901
Tel.: (406) 756-4200   MT
Web Site:
    https://www.glacierbancorp.com
Year Founded: 1990
GBCI—(NYSE)
Rev.: $950,372,000
Assets: $26,635,375,000
Liabilities: $23,792,070,000
Net Worth: $2,843,305,000
Earnings: $303,202,000
Emp.: 3,235
Fiscal Year-end: 12/31/22
Bank Holding Company
N.A.I.C.S.: 551111
Randall M. Chesler (Pres & CEO)
Ronald J. Copher (CFO & Exec VP)

Subsidiaries:

Altabancorp (1)
1 E Main St, American Fork, UT 84003
Tel.: (801) 642-3998
Web Site: http://www.altabancorp.com
Rev.: $133,171,000
Assets: $3,366,228,000
Liabilities: $2,995,090,000
Net Worth: $371,138,000
Earnings: $43,502,000
Emp.: 471
Fiscal Year-end: 12/31/2020
Bank Holding Company
N.A.I.C.S.: 551111
Judd J. Austin (Chief Banking Officer &
Exec VP-AltaBank)
Judd P. Kirkham (Chief Credit Officer &
Exec VP-AltaBank)

Subsidiary (Domestic):

Altabank (2)
33 E Main St, American Fork, UT 84003
Tel.: (801) 642-3456
Web Site: http://altabank.com
Financial Banking Services
N.A.I.C.S.: 522110
Len E. Williams (CEO)
Becky Ivins (Officer)
Chefin Carson (Officer-Loan)
Jordan Ivins (Officer)
Steve Winters (Officer-Loan)
Terry Grant (Pres)
Judd Austin (Chief Banking Officer)
Jeremy Despain (CFO)
Ryan Jones (Chief Loan Officer)
Judd Kirkham (Chief Credit Officer)
Shana Savage (Sr VP)
Stan Sorensen (CMO)
Will Hickox (Sr VP)

Bank of American Fork (2)
33 E Main St, American Fork, UT 84003
Tel.: (801) 756-7681
Web Site: http://www.bankaf.com
Emp.: 520
Commericial Banking
N.A.I.C.S.: 522110
Paul R. Gunther (Chm)

Lewiston State Bank (2)
17 E Ctr, Lewiston, UT 84320
Tel.: (435) 258-2456
Web Site: http://www.ls-bank.com
Sales Range: $10-24.9 Million
Emp.: 60
Commericial Banking
N.A.I.C.S.: 522110
Dale M. Buxton (Pres)

Community Financial Group, Inc. (1)
222 N Wall St Ste 308, Spokane, WA
99201
Tel.: (509) 242-5626
Banking Services
N.A.I.C.S.: 522110
Susan Horton (Pres & CEO)

Subsidiary (Domestic):

Wheatland Bank (2)
1442 S Pioneer Way, Moses Lake, WA
98837-2484
Tel.: (509) 764-4602
Web Site: https://wheatland.bank
Commericial Banking
N.A.I.C.S.: 522110
Terri Brown (Mgr)

Glacier Bank (1)
202 Main St, Kalispell, MT 59901-4454
Tel.: (406) 756-4200
Web Site: https://www.glacierbank.com
Sales Range: $450-499.9 Million
Commercial Banking
N.A.I.C.S.: 522110
Randall M. Chesler (CEO)

Division (Domestic):

1st Bank (2)
245 E 1st St, Powell, WY 82435
Tel.: (307) 789-3864
Web Site: http://www.1stbank-online.com
Sales Range: $10-24.9 Million
Emp.: 60
Savings, Loans, Commercial & Investment
Banking Services
N.A.I.C.S.: 522110
Kelli Furniss (Chief Deposit Officer & Exec
VP)

Bank of the San Juans (2)
144 E 8th St, Durango, CO 81301
Tel.: (970) 247-1818
Web Site: https://www.banksanjuans.com
Sales Range: $1-9.9 Million
Emp.: 30
State Commercial Banks
N.A.I.C.S.: 522110
Arthur C. Chase (Pres & CEO)
Brett Armour (Sls Mgr)

Big Sky Western Bank (2)
4150 Valley Commons Dr, Bozeman, MT
59718
Tel.: (406) 587-2922
Web Site: http://www.bigskybank.com
Sales Range: $10-24.9 Million
Emp.: 78
Savings, Loans, Commercial & Investment
Banking Services
N.A.I.C.S.: 522110

Citizens Community Bank (2)
201 S Main, Pocatello, ID 83204
Tel.: (208) 232-5373
Web Site: https://www.ccb-idaho.com
Sales Range: $10-24.9 Million
Emp.: 25
Savings & Commercial Banking Services
N.A.I.C.S.: 522110

First Bank of Montana (2)
224 W Main St, Lewistown, MT 59457
Tel.: (406) 538-7471
Web Site: https://www.1stbmt.com
Rev.: $7,000,000
Emp.: 27
Commericial Banking
N.A.I.C.S.: 522110
Dean Comes (Pres)

First Bank of Wyoming (2)
245 E 1st St, Powell, WY 82435
Tel.: (307) 754-2201
Web Site:
    http://www.firstbankofwyoming.com
Sales Range: $25-49.9 Million
Emp.: 85
Retail & Commercial Banking & Lending
Services
N.A.I.C.S.: 522180
Bob Golden (COO)

Subsidiary (Domestic):

First National Bank of Layton (2)
12 S Main St, Layton, UT 84041
Tel.: (801) 544-4241
Web Site: http://www.fnbutah.com
Sales Range: $50-74.9 Million
Emp.: 160
Banking Services
N.A.I.C.S.: 522110
Lynn Schofield (Branch Mgr)
Zack Brown (CIO & Sr VP)

Division (Domestic):

First Security Bank (2)
208 E Main St, Bozeman, MT
59715   (100%)
Tel.: (406) 585-3800
Web Site: https://www.ourbank.com
Commericial Banking
N.A.I.C.S.: 522110

First Security Bank of Missoula (2)
1704 Dearborn, Missoula, MT 59801

Tel.: (406) 728-3115
Web Site: https://www.fsbmsla.com
Sales Range: $25-49.9 Million
Emp.: 162
Savings, Loans, Commercial & Investment Banking Services
N.A.I.C.S.: 522110

First State Bank (2)
1405 16th St, Wheatland, WY 82201
Tel.: (307) 322-5222
Web Site: https://www.fsbwy.com
Emp.: 25
Commericial Banking
N.A.I.C.S.: 522110

Mountain West Bank (2)
125 Ironwood Dr, Coeur D'Alene, ID 83814
Tel.: (208) 765-0284
Web Site:
https://www.mountainwestbank.com
Sales Range: $50-74.9 Million
Emp.: 304
Savings, Loans & Commercial Banking Services
N.A.I.C.S.: 522110
Michael B. Hormaechea (Chm)
Scott Anderson (Pres & CEO)

North Cascades Bank (2)
220 Johnson Ave, Chelan, WA 98816
Tel.: (509) 682-4502
Web Site:
https://www.northcascadesbank.com
Sales Range: $10-24.9 Million
Emp.: 60
Commericial Banking
N.A.I.C.S.: 522110
Charles Guildner (Pres & CEO)
Beth Stipe (Chm)

The Foothills Bank (2)
11689 S Foothills Blvd, Yuma, AZ 85367
Tel.: (928) 305-5000
Web Site: https://www.foothillsbank.com
Retail & Commercial Banking
N.A.I.C.S.: 522110
Scott Fagin (Dir-Commercial Banking)
Susana Aguilar (Asst Mgr)

Valley Bank of Helena (2)
3030 N Montana Ave, Helena, MT 59601
Tel.: (406) 495-2400
Web Site:
https://www.valleybankhelena.com
Sales Range: $10-24.9 Million
Emp.: 93
Savings, Loans, Commercial & Investment Banking Services
N.A.I.C.S.: 522110
Gail Whitney (Exec VP & Mgr-Retail Banking)

Western Security Bank (2)
2812 1st Ave N, Billings, MT 59101
Tel.: (406) 238-8820
Web Site:
https://www.westernsecuritybank.com
Sales Range: $10-24.9 Million
Emp.: 115
Savings, Loans, Commercial & Investment Banking Services
N.A.I.C.S.: 522110
Ryan Combs (Mgr-eBanking)

GLASS HOUSE BRANDS INC.
3645 Long Beach Blvd, Long Beach, CA 90807
Tel.: (212) 299-7670   BC
Web Site:
https://www.glasshousebrands.com
Year Founded: 2019
GLASF—(OTCQX)
Rev.: $160,835,847
Assets: $303,774,997
Liabilities: $158,539,082
Net Worth: $145,235,915
Earnings: ($98,269,418)
Emp.: 362
Fiscal Year-end: 12/31/23
Cannabis Product Distr
N.A.I.C.S.: 424590
Benjamin Vega (Gen Counsel)
Hilal Tabsh (Chief Revenue Officer)
Kyle Kazan (CEO)
Mark Vendetti (CFO)
Graham Farrar (Pres)

GLASS HOUSES ACQUISITION CORP.
3811 Turtle Creek Blvd Ste 1100, Dallas, TX 75219
Tel.: (972) 850-7474   DE
Year Founded: 2021
GLHAU—(NASDAQ)
Emp.: 2
Investment Services
N.A.I.C.S.: 523999
Quincy Fennebresque (CEO)
Tonya Clark (CFO)

GLASSBRIDGE ENTERPRISES, INC.
18 E 50th St, New York, NY 10022
Tel.: (212) 220-3300   DE
Web Site:
https://www.glassbridge.com
Year Founded: 1996
GLAE—(OTCIQ)
Rev.: $100,000
Assets: $14,600,000
Liabilities: $5,500,000
Net Worth: $9,100,000
Earnings: ($3,000,000)
Emp.: 5
Fiscal Year-end: 12/31/22
Investment Holding Company
N.A.I.C.S.: 551111
Alex Spiro (Chm)
Daniel A. Strauss (CEO)
Francis A. Ruchalski (CFO)

Subsidiaries:

GlassBridge Asset Management, LLC (1)
1099 Helmo Ave N Ste 250, Oakdale, MN 55128
Tel.: (651) 704-4000
Web Site: http://www.glassbridge.com
Investment Asset Management Services
N.A.I.C.S.: 523940
Danny Zheng (CEO-Interim & CFO)

TME GmbH (1)
Humboldtstrasse 2, 4105, Hamburg, Germany
Tel.: (49) 3412120340
Web Site: http://www.tme.eu
Electronic Parts Distr
N.A.I.C.S.: 423690

GLATFELTER CORPORATION
4350 Congress St Ste 600, Charlotte, NC 28209
Tel.: (704) 885-2555   PA
Web Site: https://www.glatfelter.com
Year Founded: 1864
GLT—(NYSE)
Rev.: $1,491,326,000
Assets: $1,647,353,000
Liabilities: $1,329,349,000
Net Worth: $318,004,000
Earnings: ($194,208,000)
Emp.: 3,250
Fiscal Year-end: 12/31/22
Printing Papers & Other Specialty Papers Mfr
N.A.I.C.S.: 322120
David C. Elder (Chief Acctg Officer & VP-Fin)
Thomas M. Fahnemann (Pres & CEO)
Ramesh Shettigar (CFO, Treas & Sr VP)
Thomas M. Fahnemann (Pres & CEO)
Boris Illetschko (COO & Sr VP)

Subsidiaries:

Glatfelter Caerphilly Ltd. (1)
Pontygwindy Industrial Estate, Caerphilly, CF83 3HU, Mid Glamorgan, United Kingdom
Tel.: (44) 292 088 5988
Web Site: http://www.glatfelter.com
Emp.: 120

Paper & Engineered Products Mfr
N.A.I.C.S.: 322120

Glatfelter Canada, Inc. (1)
1680 Rue Atmec, Gatineau, J8P 7G7, QC, Canada
Tel.: (819) 669-8100
Web Site: http://www.glatfelter.com
Sales Range: $75-99.9 Million
Emp.: 300
Holding Company; Paper Products Mfr
N.A.I.C.S.: 551112

Subsidiary (Domestic):

Glatfelter Gatineau, Ltee. (2)
1680 rue Atmec, Gatineau, J8R 7G7, QC, Canada
Tel.: (819) 669-8100
Web Site: http://www.glatfelter.com
Sales Range: $75-99.9 Million
Emp.: 300
Paper Products Mfr
N.A.I.C.S.: 322299

Glatfelter Costa Rica, S.r.l. (1)
Autopista 27 Camino a Multiplaza, Oficentro Trilogia Edificio 1 Oficina 111-A San Rafael, 10203, San Jose, Costa Rica
Tel.: (506) 22282596
Paper & Engineered Product Mfr & Distr
N.A.I.C.S.: 322299

Glatfelter Dresden GmbH (1)
Pirnaer Str 31-33, 01809, Heidenau, Germany
Tel.: (49) 35295540
Wallpaper Mfr
N.A.I.C.S.: 322220

Glatfelter Falkenhagen Holdings GmbH (1)
Rolf-Hovelmann-Strasse 10, Pritzwalk, 16928, Brandenburg, Germany
Tel.: (49) 3 3986 69 0
Web Site: http://www.glatfelter.com
Emp.: 400
Holding Company
N.A.I.C.S.: 551112

Subsidiary (Domestic):

Glatfelter Falkenhagen GmbH (2)
Rolf-Hovelmann-Strasse 10, Business Park Prignitz Falkenhagen Pritzwalk, 16928, Brandenburg, Germany
Tel.: (49) 33986690
Emp.: 400
Paper & Engineered Products Mfr
N.A.I.C.S.: 322299
Torten Gherter (Mgr)

Glatfelter France SARL (1)
PO Box 2, 29390, Scaer, France
Tel.: (33) 298664200
Paper Product Distr
N.A.I.C.S.: 424130

Glatfelter Gernsbach GmbH (1)
Hordener Strasse 5, 76593, Gernsbach, Germany (100%)
Tel.: (49) 7224660
Web Site: http://www.glatfelter.com
Sales Range: $350-399.9 Million
Emp.: 550
Engineered Papers & Specialized Printing Papers Mfr
N.A.I.C.S.: 322120

Glatfelter Lydney, Ltd. (1)
Church Road, Lydney, GL15 5EJ, Gloucestershire, United Kingdom
Tel.: (44) 1594842235
Web Site: http://www.glatfelter.com
Sales Range: $75-99.9 Million
Emp.: 282
Paper & Engineered Products Mfr
N.A.I.C.S.: 322120

Glatfelter Oberschmitten GmbH (1)
Rhonstrasse 13, Ober-Schmitten, 63667, Nidda, Germany
Tel.: (49) 604380801
Wallpaper Mfr
N.A.I.C.S.: 322220

Glatfelter Scaer SAS (1)
Foret de Cascadec, BP2, 29390, Scaer, France (100%)
Tel.: (33) 298664200
Web Site: http://www.glatfelter.com

Sales Range: $10-24.9 Million
Emp.: 130
Engineered Papers & Specialized Printing Papers Mfr
N.A.I.C.S.: 322120

Glatfelter Steinfurt GmbH (1)
Dieselstrasse 16, 48565, Steinfurt, Germany
Tel.: (49) 25511400
Paper Product Distr
N.A.I.C.S.: 424130
Kaisa Lumme (Mgr-Sls)

Newtech Pulp Inc. (1)
Barrio Maria Cristina, Iligan, 9217, Philippines
Tel.: (63) 28937640
Web Site: http://www.glatfelter.com
Sales Range: $25-49.9 Million
Emp.: 85
Mfr of Engineered Papers & Specialized Printing Papers
N.A.I.C.S.: 322120

P. H. Glatfelter Company (1)
781 Far Hills Dr Ste 450, New Freedom, PA 17349
Tel.: (717) 225-4711
Web Site: https://www.glatfelter.com
Pulp & Paper Mill Operator
N.A.I.C.S.: 322110

The Glatfelter Pulp Wood Company (1)
96 S George St Ste 520, York, PA 17401
Tel.: (717) 850-0170
Web Site: http://www.glatfelter.com
Emp.: 800
Forest Management Plans Preparation Services
N.A.I.C.S.: 115310

GLAUKOS CORPORATION
1 Glaukos Way, Aliso Viejo, CA 92656
Tel.: (949) 367-9600   DE
Web Site: https://www.glaukos.com
Year Founded: 1998
GKOS—(NYSE)
Rev.: $314,711,000
Assets: $940,414,000
Liabilities: $478,648,000
Net Worth: $461,766,000
Earnings: ($134,661,000)
Emp.: 907
Fiscal Year-end: 12/31/23
Ophthalmic Medical Equipment Mfr
N.A.I.C.S.: 339112
Thomas W. Burns (Chm & CEO)
Chris M. Calcaterra (Exec VP-Global Comml Ops)
Joseph E. Gilliam (Pres & COO)
Jane E. Rady (Sr VP-Corp Strategy & Bus Dev)
Gabriella Szekely (VP-R&D & Combination Pharmaceutical Products)
Tomas Navratil (Chief Dev Officer)
Diane W. Biagianti (Gen Counsel & Sr VP)
Tomas Navratil (Sr VP-R&D)
Alex R. Thurman (CFO & Sr VP)
Jay L. Katz (Chief Medical Officer)
Matt Young (Sr VP)
Michele M. Allegretto (Sr VP-HR)
Diane W. Biagianti (Gen Counsel & Sr VP)

Subsidiaries:

Avedro, Inc. (1)
201 Jones Rd, Waltham, MA 02451
Tel.: (781) 768-3400
Web Site: http://www.avedro.com
Rev.: $27,672,000
Assets: $25,867,000
Liabilities: $31,032,000
Net Worth: ($5,165,000)
Earnings: ($25,122,000)
Emp.: 122
Fiscal Year-end: 12/31/2018
Medical Device Distr
N.A.I.C.S.: 423450
Edmond R. Coletta (Co-Founder)

Glaukos Corporation—(Continued)

Glaukos Australia Pty Ltd   **(1)**
Suite 109/12 Corporate Drive, Heatherton,
3202, VIC, Australia
Tel.: (61) 288824900
Web Site: https://glaukos.net.au
Medical Instrument Distr
N.A.I.C.S.: 423450
Glenn Fawcett *(Gen Mgr)*

Glaukos Canada Inc.   **(1)**
95 Mural Street 6th Floor, Richmond Hill,
L4B 3G2, ON, Canada
Tel.: (905) 695-3555
Medical Instrument Distr
N.A.I.C.S.: 423450
Kevin Shearer *(Gen Mgr)*

Glaukos Europe GmbH   **(1)**
Gustav-Stresemann-Ring 1, 65189, Wies-
baden, Germany
Tel.: (49) 61197774403
Medical Instrument Distr
N.A.I.C.S.: 423450
Lutz Temme *(Mng Dir)*

Glaukos Germany GmbH   **(1)**
Gustav-Stresemann-Ring 1, 65189, Wies-
baden, Germany
Tel.: (49) 603692295
Surgical Device Mfr
N.A.I.C.S.: 339112
Lutz Temme *(Mng Dir)*

Glaukos Japan GK   **(1)**
9F Shinagawa Grand Central Tower 2-16-4
Konan, Minato-ku, Tokyo, 108-0075, Japan
Tel.: (81) 367123292
Medical Instrument Distr
N.A.I.C.S.: 423450
Narimitsu Yamaguchi *(Gen Mgr)*

Glaukos Produtos Medicos Ltda.   **(1)**
Av Queiroz Filho 1560 salas 216/217-Edif
Gaivota VI Hamburguesa, Sao Paulo,
05319-000, SP, Brazil
Tel.: (55) 1130216090
Web Site: https://www.glaukos.com
Hospital Surgical Equipment Whslr
N.A.I.C.S.: 423450

GLEN BURNIE BANCORP

101 Crain Hwy SE, Glen Burnie, MD
21061
Tel.: (410) 766-3300   **MD**
Web Site:
https://www.thebankofglenbur
nie.com
Year Founded: 1949
GLBZ—(NASDAQ)
Rev.: $14,086,000
Assets: $381,436,000
Liabilities: $365,382,000
Net Worth: $16,054,000
Earnings: $1,745,000
Emp.: 89
Fiscal Year-end: 12/31/22
Bank Holding Company
N.A.I.C.S.: 551111
Mark C. Hanna *(Pres & CEO)*
Jeffrey D. Harris *(CFO, Treas & Sr VP)*
Frederick W. Kuethe III *(VP)*
Michelle R. Stambaugh *(Sec, Sr VP & Dir-HR)*
Andrew J. Hines *(Chief Lending Officer & Exec VP)*
Janet Kim *(Dir-Mktg & PH)*

Subsidiaries:

The Bank of Glen Burnie   **(1)**
101 Crain Hwy SE, Glen Burnie, MD
21061   **(100%)**
Tel.: (410) 768-8852
Web Site:
https://www.thebankofglenburnie.com
Sales Range: $125-149.9 Million
Commericial Banking
N.A.I.C.S.: 522110
Mark C. Hanna *(Pres & CEO)*
Jeffrey D. Harris *(CFO & Sr VP)*
Jan Meinster *(Sr VP-IT)*
Andrew J. Hines *(Chief Lending Officer, Chief Lending Officer & Exec VP)*

Donna Smith *(Sr VP)*
Michelle Stambaugh *(Sr VP)*
Michael Morse *(VP-Commercial Lending)*
Youn Choe *(VP-Commercial Lending)*
Christina Kopchinski *(VP)*
Jo Ann Pyles *(Asst VP)*
Beth Redolf *(Branch Mgr)*

GLENFARNE MERGER CORP.

292 Madison Ave 19th Fl, New York,
NY 10017
Tel.: (212) 500-5454   **DE**
Web Site:
http://www.glenfarnemerger.com
Year Founded: 2020
GGMC—(NASDAQ)
Investment Services
N.A.I.C.S.: 523999
Brendan Duval *(Chm & CEO)*
Bryan Murphy *(COO & Gen Counsel)*
Vlad Bluzer *(Chief Strategy Officer)*
Enrique Reus Jimeno *(CFO)*
Carl Strickler *(Chief Technical Officer)*

GLENVILLE BANK HOLDING CO., INC.

201 Mohawk Ave, Scotia, NY 12302
Tel.: (518) 370-7200   **NY**
GLNV—(OTCIQ)
Commercial Banking Services
N.A.I.C.S.: 522110
John Buhrmaster *(Pres & CEO)*
Bob Dieterich *(CFO)*
Louis Buhrmaster *(Chm)*

GLOBAL ACQUISITIONS CORPORATION

6730 S Las Vegas Blvd, Las Vegas,
NV 89119
Tel.: (702) 317-7302   **NV**
Web Site:
http://www.taylormadegolfexperi
ence.com
Year Founded: 1984
AASP—(OTCIQ)
Assets: $38
Liabilities: $540,412
Net Worth: ($540,374)
Earnings: ($57,428)
Fiscal Year-end: 12/31/22
Golf Course
N.A.I.C.S.: 713910
Kirk Hartle *(CFO)*

GLOBAL AI, INC.

110 Front St Ste 300, Jupiter, FL
33477
Tel.: (561) 240-0333   **NV**
Web Site:
http://wallstreetmediaco.com
Year Founded: 2009
WSCOD—(OTCQB)
Rev.: $49,000
Assets: $1,097
Liabilities: $29,080
Net Worth: ($27,983)
Earnings: ($116,108)
Emp.: 1
Fiscal Year-end: 09/30/23
Ecommerce Services
N.A.I.C.S.: 513140

GLOBAL ARENA HOLDING, INC.

208 E 51 St Ste 112, New York, NY
10022
Tel.: (646) 801-5524   **DE**
Web Site: https://gahc.info
Year Founded: 2000
GAHC—(OTCIQ)
Rev.: $826,700
Assets: $587,742
Liabilities: $9,691,929
Net Worth: ($9,104,187)
Earnings: ($1,192,260)
Fiscal Year-end: 12/31/23

Holding Company; Investment Services
N.A.I.C.S.: 551112
John S. Matthews *(Chm, CFO & Controller)*

GLOBAL BLOCKCHAIN ACQUISITION CORP.

6555 Sanger Rd Ste 200, Orlando,
FL 32827
Tel.: (407) 720-9250   **DE**
Year Founded: 2021
GBBK—(NASDAQ)
Rev.: $2,476,888
Assets: $178,880,786
Liabilities: $177,645,211
Net Worth: $1,235,575
Earnings: $1,231,665
Emp.: 2
Fiscal Year-end: 12/31/22
Investment Services
N.A.I.C.S.: 523999
Max Hooper *(Pres & CEO)*
Jonathan Morris *(CFO)*

GLOBAL BROKERAGE, INC.

55 Water St Fl 50, New York, NY
10041
Tel.: (212) 897-7660   **DE**
Web Site: http://www.fxcm.com
Year Founded: 2010
GLBR—(OTCIQ)
Sales Range: $250-299.9 Million
Emp.: 787
Holding Company; Securities Broker-
age & Dealing Services
N.A.I.C.S.: 551112
David Sakhai *(COO)*
Kenneth Grossman *(CEO & Mng Dir)*
Robert N. Lande *(CFO)*

Subsidiaries:

FXCM Bullion Limited   **(1)**
1/F 100 Queen's Road Central, Hong Kong,
China (Hong Kong)
Tel.: (852) 34709038
Web Site: http://www.fxcmbullion.com
International Trade Financing Services
N.A.I.C.S.: 522299

FXCM Holdings, LLC   **(1)**
55 Water St 50th Fl, New York, NY 10041
Tel.: (212) 897-7660
Holding Company
N.A.I.C.S.: 551112

Subsidiary (Non-US):

FXCM Australia Limited   **(2)**
Suite 2 Level 18 420 George Street, Syd-
ney, 2000, NSW, Australia
Tel.: (61) 1800109751
Web Site: http://www.forextrading.com.au
Financial Advisory Services
N.A.I.C.S.: 523940

Subsidiary (Domestic):

Forex Capital Markets LLC   **(2)**
Financial Sq 32 Old Slip Fl 10, New York,
NY 10005
Tel.: (212) 897-7660
Web Site: http://www.fxcm.com
Online Foreign Exchange Trading
N.A.I.C.S.: 522299

Subsidiary (Domestic):

FXCM Pro LLC   **(3)**
55 Water St 50th Fl, New York, NY 10041
Tel.: (212) 201-7319
Web Site: http://www.fxcmpro.com
Financial Advisory Services
N.A.I.C.S.: 523940
Andreas Putz *(Pres)*
Paul Gyles *(CMO)*
Brendan Callan *(CEO)*

Forex Trading LLC   **(3)**
11345 N Point Dr, Hollywood, FL 33026-
3734
Tel.: (954) 430-9830
Emp.: 1
Investment Banking & Security Services

N.A.I.C.S.: 523150
Michael Hartmann *(Principal)*

Subsidiary (Non-US):

Forex Capital Markets Limited   **(2)**
Northern and Shell Building 10 Lower
Thames Street 8th Floor, London, EC3R
6AD, United Kingdom
Tel.: (44) 2073984050
Web Site: http://www.fxcm.co.uk
Securities Brokerage Services
N.A.I.C.S.: 523150

V3 Markets, LLC   **(1)**
141 W Jackson Blvd Ste 210, Chicago, IL
60604
Tel.: (312) 809-0439
International Trade Financing Services
N.A.I.C.S.: 522299

GLOBAL BUSINESS TRAVEL GROUP, INC.

666 3rd Ave 4th Fl, New York, NY
10172
Tel.: (646) 344-1290   **DE**
Web Site:
https://www.amexglobalbusinesstra
vel.com
GBTG—(NYSE)
Rev.: $1,851,000,000
Assets: $3,728,000,000
Liabilities: $2,357,000,000
Net Worth: $1,371,000,000
Earnings: ($229,000,000)
Emp.: 19,000
Fiscal Year-end: 12/31/22
Travel Management Services
N.A.I.C.S.: 561599
Andrew Crawley *(Pres)*
Eric J. Bock *(Chief Legal Officer, Sec & Head-Merger & Acq-Global)*
Patricia Huska *(Chief People Officer)*
Boriana Tchobanova *(Chief Transformation Officer & Sr VP)*
Karen Williams *(CFO)*
David Thompson *(CIO, CTO & Chief IT Officer)*
Evan Konwiser *(CMO, Chief Strategy Officer & Chief Product Officer)*
Mark Hollyhead *(Chief Product Officer)*
Paul Abbott *(CEO)*

Subsidiaries:

**30 SecondsToFly (Thailand) Co.,
Ltd.**   **(1)**
T-One Building 15th Floor Room 15-104 8
Soi Sukhumvit 40, Khwaeng Phra Khanong
Khet Khlong Toei, Bangkok, 10110, Thai-
land
Tel.: (66) 28215063
Web Site: https://www.30secondstofly.com
Travel Arrangement Services
N.A.I.C.S.: 561599
Riccardo Vittoria *(CEO)*
Felicia Schneiderhan *(Chief People Officer)*

Chartwell Travel Ltd.   **(1)**
15 Little Portland Street, London, W1W
8BW, United Kingdom
Tel.: (44) 2076364423
Web Site: https://www.ovationtravel.com
Travel Arrangement Services
N.A.I.C.S.: 561599

DFB-Reisebuero GmbH   **(1)**
Otto-Fleck-Schneise 6a, 60528, Frankfurt
am Main, Germany
Tel.: (49) 6967720720
Web Site: https://www.dfb-reisebuero.de
Travel Agency Services
N.A.I.C.S.: 561510

FC Bayern Tours GmbH   **(1)**
Sabener Strasse 57, 81547, Munich, Ger-
many
Tel.: (49) 89219090933
Web Site: https://www.fcbayerntours.de
Travel Management Services
N.A.I.C.S.: 561599

GBT III B.V.   **(1)**
Tel.: (31) 203469411

Travel Management Services
N.A.I.C.S.: 561510

Subsidiary (Non-US):

American Express Business Travel AB   (2)
Magnus Ladulsgatan 5, Stockholm, 118 65, Sweden
Tel.: (46) 84292000
Web Site:
  http://www.businesstravel.americanexpress.com
Travel Management Services
N.A.I.C.S.: 561510
Jason Geall *(VP & Gen Mgr-UK)*
Elyes Mrad *(Mng Dir-EMEA)*

American Express Business Travel AS   (2)
Tordenskiolds gate 8-10, 0160, Oslo, Norway
Tel.: (47) 22983500
Travel Management Services
N.A.I.C.S.: 561510

American Express Business Travel ApS   (2)
Nansensgade 19, 1366, Copenhagen, Denmark
Tel.: (45) 70230460
Emp.: 150
Travel Agency Services
N.A.I.C.S.: 561520

American Express Corporate Travel BVBA   (2)
Kunstlaan 19 A-D, 1000, Brussels, Vlaams Brabant, Belgium
Tel.: (32) 27272222
Emp.: 150
Travel Management Services
N.A.I.C.S.: 561599
Thomas Avella Shaw *(Gen Mgr)*

GBT Finland Oy   (2)
Tietotie 9 3rd floor, 01530, Vantaa, Finland
Tel.: (358) 108261
Web Site:
  http://www.amexglobalbusinesstravel.fi
Travel Management Services
N.A.I.C.S.: 481111
Jutta Vatanen *(Dir)*

Affiliate (Non-US):

GBT Travel Services UK Ltd.   (2)
5 Churchill Place, Canary Wharf, London, E14 5HU, United Kingdom   **(50%)**
Tel.: (44) 1273521268
Web Site:
  http://www.amexglobalbusinesstravel.com
Travel Services
N.A.I.C.S.: 561599
Paul Abbott *(CEO)*

Subsidiary (US):

Ovation Travel Group, Inc.   (3)
666 3rd Ave, New York, NY 10017
Tel.: (212) 679-1600
Web Site: http://www.ovationtravel.com
Corporate Travel Services
N.A.I.C.S.: 561510
Paul A. Metselaar *(Chm & CEO)*
Sunil Mahtani *(Exec VP)*
Lisa Lundquist *(VP & Gen Mgr)*
Jenn Smukler *(Dir-Sls, Meetings & Events)*

Subsidiary (Non-US):

Hogg Robinson Group Limited   (2)
Spectrum Point 279 Farnborough Road, Farnborough, GU14 7NJ, Hants, United Kingdom
Tel.: (44) 1252 881000
Web Site: http://www.hrgworldwide.com
Sales Range: $400-449.9 Million
Emp.: 14,000
Holding Company; Travel Services
N.A.I.C.S.: 551112

Subsidiary (Domestic):

Farnborough Limited   (3)
279 Farnborough Rd, Farnborough, GU14 7NJ, Hampshire, United Kingdom
Tel.: (44) 252881000
Holding Company
N.A.I.C.S.: 551112

HRG Debtco Limited   (3)
Global House Victoria Street, Basingstoke, RG21 3BT, Hampshire, United Kingdom
Tel.: (44) 1256312600
Administrative Support Services
N.A.I.C.S.: 541611
Nigel Northridge *(Chm)*

Subsidiary (Non-US):

Hogg Robinson Limited   (3)
5 Churchill Place, Canary Wharf, E14 5HU, London, United Kingdom - England
Tel.: (44) 1256312600
Web Site:
  https://www.amexglobalbusinesstravel.com
Holding Company; Corporate Travel Management, Expense Management & Consulting Services
N.A.I.C.S.: 551112
Kevin Ruffles *(COO)*

Subsidiary (US):

Executive Travel Associates LLC   (4)
1333 New Hampshire Ave NW Ste 701, Washington, DC 20036
Tel.: (202) 828-3501
Web Site: http://www.exectravel.com
Travel Ticket Booking Services
N.A.I.C.S.: 561599

Subsidiary (Non-US):

GBT CR, s.r.o.   (4)
Plynarni 1617/10, Holesovice, Praque, 17000 Contact Details: Purc, Czech Republic
Tel.: (420) 234096111
Travel Management & Consulting Services
N.A.I.C.S.: 561599

HRG Belgium NV   (4)
Hovenierstr 37, Antwerp, 2018, Belgium
Tel.: (32) 32211212
Web Site:
  https://www.amexglobalbusinesstravel.com
Travel Management & Consulting Services
N.A.I.C.S.: 561599

Hogg Robinson (Travel) Limited   (4)
5 Churchill Place, Canary Wharf, London, E14 5HU, United Kingdom
Tel.: (44) 1252881000
Web Site:
  https://www.amexglobalbusinesstravel.com
Travel Management & Consulting Services
N.A.I.C.S.: 561599

Hogg Robinson Australia Pty Limited   (4)
Level 22 360 Collins Street, Melbourne, 3000, VIC, Australia
Tel.: (61) 396043400
Web Site: http://www.hrgworldwide.com
Travel Management & Consulting Services
N.A.I.C.S.: 561510

Hogg Robinson Germany GmbH & Co. KG   (4)
Agrippastr 87-93, Cologne, 50676, Germany
Tel.: (49) 22120280
Web Site:
  https://www.amexglobalbusinesstravel.com
Travel Services
N.A.I.C.S.: 561510
Wolfgang Strasser *(Mng Dir)*

Hogg Robinson Group Poland   (4)
Cybernetyki 7 A, 02-231, Warsaw, Poland
Tel.: (48) 224402900
Web Site:
  https://www.amexglobalbusinesstravel.com
Travel Management & Consulting Services
N.A.I.C.S.: 561599

Hogg Robinson Magyarorszag Kft.   (4)
Rakoczi ut 42, Budapest, 1072, Hungary
Tel.: (36) 14862910
Web Site:
  https://www.amexglobalbusinesstravel.com
Travel Agency

N.A.I.C.S.: 561510
Ralph Doerig *(Mng Dir)*

Hogg Robinson Nordic AB   (4)
St Eriksgatan 117, 113 43, Stockholm, Sweden
Tel.: (46) 850885000
Web Site: http://www.hrgworldwide.com
Sales Range: $25-49.9 Million
Travel Management & Consulting Services
N.A.I.C.S.: 561599

Hogg Robinson Nordic OY   (4)
Elimaenkatu 28 A 6th Floor, 00520, Helsinki, Finland
Tel.: (358) 9685850
Web Site: http://www.hrgworldwide.com
Travel Management & Consulting Services
N.A.I.C.S.: 561599

Hogg Robinson Singapore Pte Limited   (4)
3 Harbourfront Place No 06-02 Harbourfront Tower 2, Singapore, 99254, Singapore
Tel.: (65) 68857540
Web Site: http://www.hrgworldwide.com
Sales Range: $25-49.9 Million
Travel Management & Consulting Services
N.A.I.C.S.: 561510

ZAO BTI Russia   (4)
Bolshoi Kharitonievskiy Per 24, Moscow, 107078, Russia
Tel.: (7) 4959613434
Web Site: http://www.hrgworldwide.com
Sales Range: $25-49.9 Million
Travel Management & Consulting Services
N.A.I.C.S.: 561599

GBT India Private Limited   (1)
G-21 Ground Floor Salcon Rasvilas Plot No D-1, Saket District Centre Saket, New Delhi, 110017, Haryana, India
Tel.: (91) 1246284940
Travel Arrangement Services
N.A.I.C.S.: 561599

Hanseat Reiseburo GmbH   (1)
Langenstrasse 20, 28195, Bremen, Germany
Tel.: (49) 421160568787
Web Site: https://www.hanseatreisen.de
Travel Agency Services
N.A.I.C.S.: 561510

OFB Reisen GmbH   (1)
Meiereistrasse 7, 1020, Vienna, Austria
Tel.: (43) 1727180
Web Site: https://www.oefb.at
Sports Product Distr
N.A.I.C.S.: 423910

Ovation Travel Group UK Limited   (1)
5 Churchill Place, Canary Wharf, London, E14 5HU, United Kingdom
Tel.: (44) 8004311112
Travel Services
N.A.I.C.S.: 561510

Ovation Travel, LLC   (1)
666 3rd Ave, New York, NY 10017
Travel Services
N.A.I.C.S.: 561510

GLOBAL CAPITAL PARTNERS, INC.
6000 Fairview Rd Ste 1410, Charlotte, NC 28210
Tel.: (704) 643-8220   DE
GCPL—(OTCIQ)
Financial Investment Services
N.A.I.C.S.: 523999
Sameer Lakhani *(Mng Dir)*

GLOBAL CLEAN ENERGY HOLDINGS, INC.
Tel.: (661) 742-4600   DE
Web Site:
  https://www.gceholdings.com
GCEH—(OTCQB)
Rev.: $2,591,054
Assets: $708,068,296
Liabilities: $736,276,292
Net Worth: ($28,207,996)
Earnings: ($54,108,708)
Emp.: 134
Fiscal Year-end: 12/31/22

Agriculture & Biofuel Development Services
N.A.I.C.S.: 111191
Richard Palmer *(Founder)*
David R. Walker *(Chm)*
Wade Adkins *(CFO, Chief Acctg Officer & Sr VP)*
Ralph J. Goehring *(Treas & Sr VP)*
Noah Verleun *(Pres & Interim CEO)*

GLOBAL CLEAN ENERGY INC.
6040 Upshaw Ste 105, Humble, TX 77396
Tel.: (713) 566-0046
Web Site:
  https://www.globalcleanenergy.net
GCEI—(OTCIQ)
Support Activities for Oil & Gas Operations
N.A.I.C.S.: 213112
Steven R. Mann *(Pres & CEO)*
Hakim Zahar *(CTO)*

GLOBAL CONSORTIUM, INC.
6810 N State Rd 7, Coconut Creek, FL 33073
Tel.: (954) 905-9896   NV
Web Site: http://www.gcgx.org
GCGX—(OTCIQ)
Pharmaceuticals Product Mfr
N.A.I.C.S.: 325412
Matthew P. Dwyer *(CEO)*

GLOBAL CROSSING AIRLINES GROUP INC.
4th Fl 4200 NW 36th St, Miami, FL 33166
Tel.: (786) 751-8550   DE
Web Site: https://globalxair.com
Year Founded: 1966
JETBF—(OTCIQ)
Offices of Other Holding Companies
N.A.I.C.S.: 551112
Christopher W. Jamroz *(Chm)*
Ryan Goepel *(Pres & CFO)*
Dix Lawson *(VP-Strategic Plng & Cost Control)*
Olen Aasen *(VP-Legal)*
Jennifer Paterson *(Dir-Corp Dev)*
Lara Wilson *(Sec)*
Jordi Porcel *(Chief Sls , Mktg & Customer Experience Officer)*
Brad Warren *(COO & VP-Maintenance)*
Eddy Doyle *(CEO)*

Subsidiaries:

Global Crossing Airlines, Inc.   (1)
4200 NW 36th St Bldg 5A, Miami International Airport, Miami, FL 33166
Tel.: (786) 751-8550
Web Site: https://www.globalxair.com
Charter Passenger & Cargo Airline Operator
N.A.I.C.S.: 481211

Subsidiary (Domestic):

Global Crossing Airlines Operations LLC   (2)
4200 NW 36th St Bldg 5A, Miami International Airport, Miami, FL 33166
Tel.: (786) 751-8550
Charter Passenger & Cargo Airline
N.A.I.C.S.: 481211

GLOBAL DEVELOPMENTS, INC.
300 Delaware Ave Ste 210, Wilmington, DE 19801
Tel.: (732) 523-1180   DE
Year Founded: 2004
GDVM—(OTCIQ)
Financial Services
N.A.I.C.S.: 522220
Melvin Ejiogu *(Pres & CEO)*

Global Digital Solutions, Inc.—(Continued)

GLOBAL DIGITAL SOLUTIONS, INC.
777 S Flagler Dr Ste 800 W Tower,
West Palm Beach, FL 33401
Tel.: (561) 515-6198   NJ
Web Site: https://www.gdsi.co
Year Founded: 1995
GDSI—(OTCIQ)
Assets: $1,043
Liabilities: $16,076,425
Net Worth: ($16,075,382)
Earnings: ($5,761,061)
Emp.: 2
Fiscal Year-end: 12/31/22
Small Arms Mfr, Consulting, Technology & Security Services
N.A.I.C.S.: 332994
William J. Delgado (Chm, CEO & Exec VP)
Jerome J. Gomolski (CFO)
Ross L. Trevino (VP-Bus Dev)

GLOBAL ECOLOGY CORPORATION
1333 N Buffalo Dr Ste 210, Las Vegas, NV 89128
Tel.: (973) 655-9001
Web Site: https://www.geco.us
GLEC—(OTCEM)
Sales Range: Less than $1 Million
Emp.: 4
Mineral Ionization Services
N.A.I.C.S.: 213115
Peter D. Ubaldi (Pres & CEO)
Joseph Battiato (Chm & Mng Dir)

GLOBAL ENTERTAINMENT HOLDINGS, INC.
4915 E Hunter Ave, Anaheim, CA 92807
Tel.: (702) 516-9684   NV
Web Site: http://www.global-gbhl.com
Year Founded: 1996
GBHL—(OTCIQ)
Motion Picture Production & Distribution Services
N.A.I.C.S.: 512110
Gary Rasmussen (CEO)
Alan Bailey (CFO)
Terry Gabby (Controller)

GLOBAL GAS CORPORATION
99 Wall St Ste 436, New York, NY 10005
Tel.: (917) 327-0437   DE
Year Founded: 2020
HGAS—(NASDAQ)
Rev.: $407,976
Assets: $1,183,911
Liabilities: $1,918,581
Net Worth: $734,670
Earnings: $300,176
Emp.: 2
Fiscal Year-end: 12/31/23
Industrial Gas Mfr
N.A.I.C.S.: 325120
Shachi Shah (CFO & COO)

GLOBAL GOLD CORPORATION
555 Theodore Fremd Ave Ste C208, Rye, NY 10580
Tel.: (914) 925-0020   DE
Web Site:
   https://www.globalgoldcorp.com
Year Founded: 1980
GBGD—(OTCIQ)
Emp.: 25
Gold Ore & Silver Ore Mining
N.A.I.C.S.: 212220
Jan E. Dulman (CFO)
Van Z. Krikorian (Chm, CEO & Gen Counsel)
Drury J. Gallagher (Treas & Sec)

GLOBAL HEALTHCARE & EDUCATION MANAGEMENT, INC.
6901 Jericho Tpke Ste 215, New York, NY 11791
Tel.: (519) 656-9250
GHEU—(OTCIQ)
Educational Support Services
N.A.I.C.S.: 611710
Michael I. Knopf (CEO)

GLOBAL INDUSTRIAL COMPANY
11 Harbor Park Dr, Port Washington, NY 11050
Tel.: (516) 608-7000   DE
Web Site:
   https://www.globalindustrial.com
Year Founded: 1951
GIC—(NYSE)
Rev.: $1,166,100,000
Assets: $455,200,000
Liabilities: $244,800,000
Net Worth: $210,400,000
Earnings: $78,800,000
Emp.: 1,650
Fiscal Year-end: 12/31/22
Computers, Peripherals & Software
N.A.I.C.S.: 334118
Thomas W. Axmacher (VP & Controller)
Manoj Shetty (CIO & Sr VP)
Adina G. Storch (Gen Counsel, Sec & Sr VP)
Donna Fielding (Chief HR Officer & Sr VP)
Claudia Hughes (Chief Sls Officer & Sr VP)
Chris Longhito (Chief Supply Chain Officer)
Alex Tomey (Chief Mdsg Officer)
Bruce Leeds (Co-Vice Chm)
Robert Leeds (Co-Vice Chm)
Richard B. Leeds (Chm & CEO)

Subsidiaries:

Global Directmail B.V.   (1)
Kalkbranderij 2, 1185 ZX, Amstelveen, Netherlands
Tel.: (31) 205470606
Information Technology Services
N.A.I.C.S.: 519290

Global Equipment Company Inc.   (1)
11 Harbor Park Dr, Port Washington, NY 11050
Tel.: (516) 625-4300
Web Site: https://www.globalindustrial.com
Emp.: 200
Industrial Machinery & Equipment Supply Distr
N.A.I.C.S.: 423830

Global Industrial Canada Inc.   (1)
Unit 1 10 35 Staples Ave, Richmond Hill, L4B 4W6, Canada
Tel.: (888) 645-2986
Web Site: http://www.globalindustrial.ca
Electronic Shopping & Mail Order Services
N.A.I.C.S.: 811198

Global Industrial Services Inc.   (1)
6800 Jericho Tpke Ste 120 W, Syosset, NY 11791
Tel.: (516) 802-4855
Web Site: https://global-industrialservices.com
Information Technology Services
N.A.I.C.S.: 519290

I-Com Software   (1)
Batiment Aquitaine Centre d'Affaires la Boursidiere, 92357, Le Plessis-Robinson, France   (100%)
Tel.: (33) 155719467
Web Site: http://www.i-comsoftware.com
Emp.: 50
Software Development Services
N.A.I.C.S.: 513210

Indoff Inc.   (1)

11816 Lackland Rd, Saint Louis, MO 63146-2908
Tel.: (314) 997-1122
Web Site: https://www.indoff.com
Sales Range: $100-124.9 Million
Emp.: 450
Distr of Material Handling Equipment & Contract Office Furniture
N.A.I.C.S.: 423830
John S. Ross (Co-Founder & Chm)
Jim Malkus (CEO)
John Shamblin (Partner)

Nexel Industries, Inc.   (1)
11 Harbor Park Dr, Port Washington, NY 11050   (100%)
Tel.: (516) 625-0084
Web Site: http://www.nexelwire.com
Sales Range: $1-9.9 Million
Emp.: 12
Conveyors & Conveying Equipment
N.A.I.C.S.: 333922

Systemax Business Services K.F.T.   (1)
11 Harbor Park Dr, Port Washington, NY 11050
Tel.: (516) 608-7000
Information Technology Services
N.A.I.C.S.: 519290

Systemax Manufacturing Co.   (1)
6990 Us Route 36, Fletcher, OH 45326
Tel.: (937) 368-2300
Sales Range: $200-249.9 Million
Emp.: 300
Catalog & Mail-Order Computers
N.A.I.C.S.: 423430

Worldwide Rebates Inc.   (1)
600 W Hillsboro Blvd Ste 450, Deerfield Beach, FL 33441
Tel.: (954) 573-6781
Sales Range: $25-49.9 Million
Emp.: 50
Computer Peripheral Equipment Whslr
N.A.I.C.S.: 423430

GLOBAL INNOVATIVE PLATFORMS INC.
149 James Pl, Orlando, FL 32751
Tel.: (321) 230-3739   DE
Year Founded: 2020
GIPL—(OTCIQ)
Assets: $15
Liabilities: $33,153
Net Worth: ($33,138)
Earnings: ($136,197)
Emp.: 1
Fiscal Year-end: 09/30/24
Asset Management Services
N.A.I.C.S.: 523999

GLOBAL LINKS CORP.
3571 E Sunset Rd Ste 102, Las Vegas, NV 89120
Tel.: (702) 430-9250   NV
Web Site:
   http://www.globallinkscorp.com
Year Founded: 1952
GLCO—(OTCIQ)
Sales Range: Less than $1 Million
Housing Construction Services
N.A.I.C.S.: 236117
Frank J. Dobrucki (Pres & CEO)

GLOBAL MEDICAL REIT INC.
7373 Wisconsin Ave Ste 800, Bethesda, MD 20814
Tel.: (202) 524-6851   NV
Web Site:
   https://www.globalmedicalreit.com
Year Founded: 2011
GMRE—(NYSE)
Rev.: $137,283,000
Assets: $1,393,261,000
Liabilities: $744,196,000
Net Worth: $649,065,000
Earnings: $13,320,000
Emp.: 29
Fiscal Year-end: 12/31/22

Other Activities Related to Real Estate
N.A.I.C.S.: 531390
Jeffrey M. Busch (Chm, Pres & CEO)
Alfonzo Leon (Chief Investment Officer)
Jamie Barber (Gen Counsel & Sec)
Danica C. Holley (COO)

GLOBAL PARTNERS LP
800 S St Ste 500, Waltham, MA 02454-9161
Tel.: (781) 894-8800   DE
Web Site: https://www.globalp.com
GLP—(NYSE)
Rev.: $16,492,174,000
Assets: $3,446,011,000
Liabilities: $2,645,351,000
Net Worth: $800,660,000
Earnings: $152,506,000
Emp.: 3,485
Fiscal Year-end: 12/31/23
Petroleum Whslr & Distr
N.A.I.C.S.: 457210
Richard Slifka (Chm)
Gregory B. Hanson (CFO)
Sean T. Geary (Chief Legal Officer)

Subsidiaries:

Alliance Energy LLC   (1)
800 S St Ste 500, Waltham, MA 02454
Tel.: (781) 674-7780
Web Site: http://www.allianceenergy.com
Fuel Dealers Services
N.A.I.C.S.: 457210

Basin Transload, LLC   (1)
6550 County Rd 20, Zap, ND 58580
Tel.: (701) 948-2262
Fuel Dealers Services
N.A.I.C.S.: 457210

Cascade Kelly Holdings LLC   (1)
81200 Kallunki Rd, Clatskanie, OR 97016
Tel.: (503) 728-7000
Holding Company
N.A.I.C.S.: 551112

Chelsea Sandwich LLC   (1)
11 Broadway, Chelsea, MA 02150
Tel.: (617) 660-1100
Web Site: http://www.globalp.com
Emp.: 25
Petroleum Product Mfr
N.A.I.C.S.: 324199

Global Companies LLC   (1)
800 S Ste 500, Waltham, MA 02454-9161   (100%)
Tel.: (781) 894-8800
Web Site: https://www.globalp.com
Sales Range: $150-199.9 Million
Emp.: 175
Storage, Distribution & Marketing of Gasoline
N.A.I.C.S.: 213112

Global Energy Marketing II LLC   (1)
2800 Bruckner Blvd Ste 304, Bronx, NY 10465
Tel.: (781) 894-8800
Natural Gas Distr
N.A.I.C.S.: 221210

Global Montello Group Corporation   (1)
800 S St Ste 200, Waltham, MA 02454-9161   (100%)
Tel.: (781) 894-8800
Web Site: https://www.globalp.com
Sales Range: $150-199.9 Million
Emp.: 270
Fuel Dealers Services
N.A.I.C.S.: 457210
William G. Davidson (Sr VP-Terminals & Ops)

GLOBAL PAYMENT TECHNOLOGIES, INC.

170 Wilbur Pl, Bohemia, NY 11716
Tel.: (631) 563-2500　　　　DE
Web Site: https://www.gpta.com.au
Year Founded: 1988
GPTX—(OTCIQ)
Sales Range: $10-24.9 Million
Emp.: 30
Commercial & Service Industry Machinery Manufacturing
N.A.I.C.S.: 333310

Subsidiaries:

Global Payment Technologies (Europe) Limited　　　　**(1)**
29 Park Royal Metro Ctr, Britannia Way, London, NW10 7PA, United
Kingdom　　　　**(100%)**
Tel.: (44) 2089616116
Web Site: http://www.gpt.com
Sales Range: $10-24.9 Million
Emp.: 2
Mfr & Retailer of Paper Currency Validators & Related Stackers
N.A.I.C.S.: 333310

GLOBAL PAYMENTS INC.

3550 Lenox Rd, Atlanta, GA 30326
Tel.: (770) 829-8000　　　　GA
Web Site:
　　https://www.globalpayments.com
Year Founded: 2000
GPN—(NYSE)
Rev.: $9,654,419,000
Assets: $50,570,186,000
Liabilities: $27,290,636,000
Net Worth: $23,279,550,000
Earnings: $986,233,000
Emp.: 27,000
Fiscal Year-end: 12/31/23
Electronic Payment Processing Solutions & Money Transfers
N.A.I.C.S.: 522320
Cameron M. Bready *(CEO)*
David Lawrence Green *(Gen Counsel, Sec & Sr Exec VP)*
David M. Sheffield *(Chief Acctg Officer & Exec VP)*
Joshua J. Whipple *(CFO & Sr Exec VP)*
Andrea Carter *(Chief HR Officer & Sr Exec VP)*
Kelley Knutson *(Pres)*
David Rumph *(Exec VP)*
Maureen Schumacher *(CMO)*
Gaylon Jowers Jr. *(Pres-TSYS Issuer Solutions & Sr Exec VP)*

Subsidiaries:

Active Network, LLC　　　　**(1)**
717 N Harwood St Ste 2500, Dallas, TX 75201
Tel.: (858) 964-3800
Web Site: https://www.activenetwork.com
Activity & Participant Management Software Solutions
N.A.I.C.S.: 513210

Subsidiary (Domestic):

Active Network IPICO (US) Inc.　　**(2)**
717 N Harwood St Ste 2500, Dallas, TX 75201
Tel.: (214) 996-7301
Web Site: http://www.ipicosports.com
Sports Timing & Tracking System Developer
N.A.I.C.S.: 334220

JumpForward LLC　　　　**(2)**
112 S Sangamon St, Chicago, IL 60607
Tel.: (773) 355-9552
Web Site: http://www.jumpforward.com
Collegiate Recruiting & Compliance Software Publisher
N.A.I.C.S.: 541511

Maximum Solutions, LLC　　　**(2)**
4570 W 77th St Ste 365, Edina, MN 55435
Tel.: (763) 541-9116
Web Site: http://www.maxsolutions.com
Recreation Management Software Publisher
N.A.I.C.S.: 513210

AdvancedMD, Inc.　　　　**(1)**
10876 S River Front Pkwy Ste 400, South Jordan, UT 84095
Tel.: (801) 984-9500
Web Site: http://www.advancedmd.com
Physician Office & Billing Management Software Mfr
N.A.I.C.S.: 513210
Jim Elliot *(CMO)*

Subsidiary (Domestic):

Nuesoft Technologies, Inc.　　**(2)**
1685 Terrell Mill Road, Marietta, GA 30067
Tel.: (678) 303-1140
Web Site: http://www.nuemd.com
Software Publisher
N.A.I.C.S.: 513210

EVO Payments, Inc.　　　　**(1)**
10 Glenlake Pkwy S Tower Ste 950, Atlanta, GA 30328
Tel.: (770) 336-8463
Web Site: https://www.evopayments.com
Rev.: $543,082,000
Assets: $2,490,815,000
Liabilities: $3,621,568,000
Net Worth: ($1,130,753,000)
Earnings: $5,279,000
Emp.: 2,400
Fiscal Year-end: 12/31/2022
Electronic Fund Transfer Services
N.A.I.C.S.: 522320
Kelli Sterrett *(Gen Counsel)*

Subsidiary (Non-US):

Anderson Zaks Limited　　　**(2)**
Lily Hill House Lily Hill Rd, Bracknell, RG12 2SJ, United Kingdom
Tel.: (44) 134 431 7910
Web Site: https://www.andersonzaks.com
Financial Transaction Processing Services
N.A.I.C.S.: 522320

Centrum Elektronicznych Uslug Platniczych eService Sp. z o.o.　**(2)**
Ul Jan Olbracht 94, 01-102, Warsaw, Poland
Tel.: (48) 225332222
Electronic Payment Services
N.A.I.C.S.: 522320
Agnieszka Grzyb *(Dir-HR)*

Clear One, S.L.　　　　**(2)**
Avda de la Industria 4 NATEA Business Park Alcobendas, 28108, Madrid, Spain
Tel.: (34) 914900150
Web Site: http://www.clearone.es
Electronic Payment Services
N.A.I.C.S.: 522320
Paul Zander *(Founder & CEO)*

Delego Software ULC　　　　**(2)**
305 King Street West Suite 302, Kitchener, N2G 1B9, ON, Canada
Tel.: (226) 785-1920
Web Site: https://www.delegopayments.com
Data Security Services
N.A.I.C.S.: 561621

EVO Merchant Services Canada Co.　　　　**(2)**
505 de Maisonneuve Boulevard West Suite 500, Montreal, H3A 3C2, QC, Canada
Tel.: (514) 315-2935
Web Site: http://www.evotrac.com
Electronic Payment Services
N.A.I.C.S.: 522320
Antonio Romano *(VP-Ops)*

EVO Payments International Corp.　　　　**(2)**
2075 Boul Robert-Bourasssa Suite 1500, Montreal, H3A 2L1, QC, Canada
Web Site: http://www.evopayments.ca
Financial Services
N.A.I.C.S.: 522110
Tony Buffone *(Sr Mgr-Sales)*

EVO Payments International Sp. z o.o.　　　　**(2)**
Jana Olbrachta Street 94, 01-102, Warsaw, Poland
Tel.: (48) 223823855
Web Site: https://www.revopayments.pl
Secure & Reliable Payment Services
N.A.I.C.S.: 522320

EVO Payments UK Ltd.　　　　**(2)**

Scottish Provident Building Ste 330 7 Donegall Square West, County Antrim, Belfast, BT1 6JH, United Kingdom
Tel.: (44) 121 827 9100
Web Site: https://www.evopayments.co.uk
Financial Transaction Processing Services
N.A.I.C.S.: 522320
Andy White *(Head-Sales-Intl & Gen Mgr)*
Darren Wilson *(Pres-International)*
Barry Gray *(Mktg Dir)*

Federated Payment Canada Corporation　　　　**(2)**
440 Laurier Ave West-Suite 200, Ottawa, K1R 7X6, ON, Canada
Web Site: http://www.federatedcanada.com
Electronic & Credit Card Processing Services
N.A.I.C.S.: 522320
Jon Levitt *(CEO)*
John Guirguis *(Pres)*
Evan Schweitzer *(CFO)*
Scott Avery *(Sr VP-Sls)*
Jim Perri *(VP-Ops)*
Gunter Whetstone *(Dir-Corp Trng)*
Jeff Zervos *(Mgr-Product Support & Technical Svcs)*
Darrell Peppers *(Mgr-Customer Care)*
Richard Placa *(Mgr-Underwriting & Risk Mgmt)*
Joanne Vassallo *(Dir-New Accounts & Mgr-Bus Office)*
Joanne D'Aprile *(Dir-Sls Support)*
Greg Slote *(VP-Mktg & Corp Comm)*

Subsidiary (Domestic):

Federated Payment Systems LLC　　　　**(2)**
One Huntington Quadrangle 4th Fl Ctr Bldg, Melville, NY 11747
Tel.: (800) 217-8711
Web Site:
　　http://www.federatedpayments.com
Electronic Payment Services
N.A.I.C.S.: 561499
Jon Levitt *(CEO)*
Evan Schweitzer *(CFO)*
John Guirguis *(Pres)*
Jim Perri *(VP-Ops)*
Gregory Slote *(VP-Mktg & Corporate Comm)*
Joanne DAprile *(Dir-Sls Support)*
Richard Placa *(Mgr-Underwriting & Risk Mgmt)*
Jeff Zervos *(Mgr-Product Support & Technical Svcs)*
Gunter Whetstone *(Dir-Corp Trng)*

Subsidiary (Non-US):

Intelligent Payments Group Limited　　　　**(2)**
Suite 4 2 International House Bell Lane, Gibraltar, GX11 1AA, Gibraltar
Tel.: (350) 20010800
Web Site:
　　http://www.intelligentpayments.co.uk
Mobile Payment & Payment Processing Services
N.A.I.C.S.: 522320

Subsidiary (Domestic):

Nodus Technologies, Inc.　　**(2)**
1900 S State College Blvd Ste 525, Anaheim, CA 92806
Tel.: (909) 482-4701
Web Site: https://www.nodus.com
Software Development Services
N.A.I.C.S.: 541511

Pineapple Payments, LLC　　**(2)**
11 Stanwix St Ste 1202, Pittsburgh, PA 15222
Tel.: (412) 235-7235
Web Site:
　　https://www.pineapplepayments.com
Emp.: 60
Payment Processing Services
N.A.I.C.S.: 522320
Brian Shanahan *(CEO)*

Subsidiary (Non-US):

Universalpay, Entidad De Pago, S.L.　　　　**(2)**
Calle Condesa de Venadito 1, 28027, Madrid, Spain

Tel.: (34) 917407363
Web Site: https://www.universalpay.es
Business Payment Services
N.A.I.C.S.: 522320

Subsidiary (Domestic):

Vision Payment Solutions, LLC　　**(2)**
320 Cumberland Ave, Portland, ME 04101
Software Development Services
N.A.I.C.S.: 513210

e-Onlinedata, LLC　　　　**(2)**
515 Broadhollow Rd, Melville, NY 11747
Electronic Payment Services
N.A.I.C.S.: 522320
Robert Castora *(Mgr-Product)*

EZ HK, Ltd.　　　　**(1)**
27/F Manhattan Place 23 Wang Tai Road Kowloon Bay, Kowloon, China (Hong Kong)
Tel.: (852) 29699888
Management Consulting Services
N.A.I.C.S.: 541611

Ezi Management Pty Ltd.　　　**(1)**
Level 5 12 Commercial Road, Newstead, 4006, QLD, Australia
Tel.: (61) 1300763256
Management Consulting Services
N.A.I.C.S.: 541611

Ezidebit Pty Ltd.　　　　**(1)**
L 5 12 Commercial Rd, Newstead, 4006, QLD, Australia
Tel.: (61) 1300763256
Web Site: https://www.ezidebit.com
Emp.: 40
Management Consulting Services
N.A.I.C.S.: 541611

GP Finance, Inc.　　　　**(1)**
Corporation Trust Center 1209 Orange St, Wilmington, DE 19801
Tel.: (302) 576-2888
Financial Transaction Processing Services
N.A.I.C.S.: 522320

Global Payment Systems Asia-Pacific (Malaysia) Sdn. Bhd.　　**(1)**
Upper Penthouse B-22-2 Northpoint Offices No 1 Medan Syed Putra Utara, 59200, Kuala Lumpur, Malaysia
Tel.: (60) 377236818
Electronic Financial Payment Services
N.A.I.C.S.: 522320

Global Payments Asia Pacific Limited　　　　**(1)**
27/F Manhattan Pl 23 Wang Tai Rd, Kowloon Bay, Kowloon, China (Hong
Kong)　　　　**(100%)**
Tel.: (852) 29699888
Electronic Payment Processing Solutions
N.A.I.C.S.: 522320
Ian Courtnage *(Pres-Global Payments)*

Global Payments Asia-Pacific (Singapore) Private Limited　　**(1)**
Tanjong Pagar Post Office, PO Box 151, Singapore, 910806, Singapore
Tel.: (65) 66221168
Electronic Financial Payment Services
N.A.I.C.S.: 522320

Global Payments Asia-Pacific Lanka (Private) Limited　　　**(1)**
Advantage Building Complex 4th Floor 74A, Dharmapala Mawatha, Colombo, 00700, Sri Lanka
Tel.: (94) 112377666
Electronic Financial Payment Services
N.A.I.C.S.: 522320

Global Payments Asia-Pacific Philippines Incorporated　　　**(1)**
11th Floor Robinsons Cybergate Plaza Pioneer Corner EDSA, Mandaluyong, 1550, Philippines
Tel.: (63) 25816363
Electronic Financial Payment Services
N.A.I.C.S.: 522320

Global Payments Canada Inc.　**(1)**
3381 Steeles Ave East Ste 200, Toronto, M2H 3S7, ON, Canada
Tel.: (800) 263-2970
Web Site:
　　http://www.globalpaymentsinc.com
Electronic Payment Processing Solutions
N.A.I.C.S.: 522320

Global Payments Inc.—(Continued)

Global Payments Direct, Inc. (1)
10705 Red Run Blvd, Owings Mills, MD
21117-5134
Financial Transaction Processing Services
N.A.I.C.S.: 522320

Global Payments Europe, s.r.o. (1)
V Olsinach 626/80 Strasnice, 100 00,
Prague, Czech Republic
Tel.: (420) 26 719 7197
Web Site:
　　https://www.globalpaymentsinc.com
Servicer of ATMs & Electronic Terminals &
Administrator of Payment & Identity Cards
N.A.I.C.S.: 522320

Global Payments Gaming Services,
Inc. (1)
7201 W Lake Mead Ste 501, Las Vegas,
NV 89128
Tel.: (702) 822-7200
Web Site:
　　https://www.globalpaymentsgaming.com
Financial Transaction Processing Services
N.A.I.C.S.: 522320

Global Payments Limited (1)
Ground Floor Continental Business Centre
Old Railway Track, Santa Vennera, SVR
9018, Malta
Tel.: (356) 22265656
Ecommerce Transaction Services
N.A.I.C.S.: 522320
Jon Bayliss *(CEO)*

Greater Giving
2035 NW Front Ave Ste 205, Portland, OR
97209
Tel.: (503) 597-0378
Web Site: https://www.greatergiving.com
Sales Range: $1-9.9 Million
Emp.: 60
Auction Event Organization, Software &
Payment Processing Services
N.A.I.C.S.: 561499
James Balazs *(VP-Bus Analysis & Support)*
Matthew Craven *(VP-Sls & Mktg)*
David Hagland *(Dir-Infrastructure)*
Jill Boyer *(Mktg Dir)*
Tyson Prescott *(VP)*

Heartland Payment Systems,
LLC (1)
3550 Lenox Rd NE Ste 3000, Atlanta, GA
30326
Web Site: https://www.heartland.us
Bankcard Payment Processing Services &
Payroll Services
N.A.I.C.S.: 522320

Subsidiary (Domestic):

Debitek, Inc. (2)
2115 Chapman Rd Ste 159, Chattanooga,
TN 37421
Tel.: (423) 894-6177
Web Site:
　　http://www.heartlandmicropayments.com
Electronic Payment Systems Mfr
N.A.I.C.S.: 334118
Ron Farmer *(Pres-Campus Solutions)*

Heartland Payroll Solutions, Inc. (2)
90 Linden Oaks Dr Ste 110, Rochester, NY
14625
Tel.: (866) 341-3510
Web Site: http://www.ovationpayroll.com
Payroll Processing Services
N.A.I.C.S.: 541214

Division (Domestic):

Heartland School Solutions (2)
765 Jefferson Rd Ste 400, Rochester, NY
14623
Tel.: (585) 227-6740
Web Site:
　　https://www.heartlandschoolsolutions.com
Emp.: 230
Custom Computer Programming Services
N.A.I.C.S.: 541511
Rich Miceli *(VP-Client Svcs)*

Subsidiary (Domestic):

Payroll 1, Inc. (2)
34100 Woodward Ave Ste 250, Birmingham, MI 48009
Tel.: (888) 999-7291

Payroll Processing & Accounting Services
N.A.I.C.S.: 541214

TouchNet Information Systems,
Inc. (2)
9801 Renner Blvd Ste 150, Lenexa, KS
66219
Tel.: (913) 599-6699
Web Site: https://www.touchnet.com
Commerce Management Software Devel-
oper
N.A.I.C.S.: 513210
Heather Richmond *(VP-Mktg)*
Adam McDonald *(Pres)*
Keith Grabill *(VP & Controller-Div)*
David Kelley *(VP-Product Dev)*
Jeff Allen *(VP-Sls)*
Ryan Audus *(Sr Dir-Product Strategy)*
Anthony McKelvy *(Dir-Fin)*
Chris Setcos *(Sr Dir-Bus Dev)*
Mike Quinn *(Dir-Onecard Ops)*
Lisa Sawyer *(Dir-HR)*

pcAmerica, LLC (2)
One Blue Hill Plz Fl 16, Pearl River, NY
10965
Tel.: (845) 920-0800
Web Site: http://www.pcamerica.com
Software Development Services
N.A.I.C.S.: 541511

OpenEdge Payments LLC (1)
8200 Central Ave, Newark, CA 94560
Tel.: (510) 795-2290
Web Site:
　　http://www.openedgepayment.com
Emp.: 200
Payment Solutions
N.A.I.C.S.: 513210

Branch (Domestic):

OpenEdge - Pleasant Grove (2)
2436 W 700 S, Pleasant Grove, UT 84062
Tel.: (888) 427-2260
Payment Solutions
N.A.I.C.S.: 513210
Frans Nelson *(Dir- Boarding & Risk)*

PayLease LLC (1)
9330 Scranton Rd Ste 450, San Diego, CA
92121
Tel.: (866) 729-5327
Web Site: http://www.gozego.com
Online Residential Payment Services
N.A.I.C.S.: 522320
Ty Kalklosch *(Founder)*
Matt Amoia *(Chief Customer Officer)*
Kristin Runyan *(Sr VP)*
Stephen Baker *(Pres & Gen Mgr)*
Jason Day *(VP-Sales)*
Brent Glover *(VP-Engineering)*
Yolanda Muchnik *(VP-Marketing)*
Cheryl O'Malley *(VP)*
Mark Peters *(VP-Finance)*
Dan Snyder *(VP)*
Laura Trussell *(VP)*

PayPros LLC (1)
8200 Central Ave, Newark, CA 94560-3448
Tel.: (866) 795-2290
Application Software Development Services
N.A.I.C.S.: 541511

Secure Payment Solutions Pty
Ltd. (1)
PO Box 190, Melbourne, 8009, VIC, Austra-
lia
Tel.: (61) 1300786756
Web Site: http://www.securepay.com.au
Ecommerce Transaction Services
N.A.I.C.S.: 522320

Sicom Systems, Inc. (1)
1684 S Broad St Ste 300, Lansdale, PA
19446
Tel.: (215) 489-2500
Web Site: https://www.sicom.com
Computer & Computer Peripheral Equip-
ment & Software Merchant Whslr
N.A.I.C.S.: 423430

Storman Software Limited (1)
Level 4 AMI House 63 Albert Street, Auck-
land Airport, Auckland, 1010, New Zealand
Tel.: (64) 92803393
Web Site: http://www.storman.co.nz
Software Development Services
N.A.I.C.S.: 513210

Storman Software Pty Ltd. (1)
Level 9/480 St Pauls Terrace, Fortitude Val-
ley, 4006, QLD, Australia
Tel.: (61) 1300669020
Web Site: http://www.storman.com
Software Development Services
N.A.I.C.S.: 513210

Storman Software, Inc. (1)
3410 La Sierra Ave Ste F488, Riverside,
CA 92503
Tel.: (951) 900-3149
Web Site: http://www.storman.com
Software Development Services
N.A.I.C.S.: 513210

Total System Services, Inc. (1)
1 TSYS Way, Columbus, GA 31901
Web Site: http://www.tsys.com
Rev.: $4,028,211,000
Assets: $7,468,709,000
Liabilities: $4,882,803,000
Net Worth: $2,585,906,000
Earnings: $576,656,000
Emp.: 12,820
Fiscal Year-end: 12/31/2018
Electronic Payment Processing Services
N.A.I.C.S.: 522320
Paul Michael Todd *(CFO)*

Subsidiary (Domestic):

Cayan LLC (2)
1 Federal St 2nd Fl, Boston, MA 02110
Tel.: (617) 896-5590
Web Site: http://www.tsys.com
Credit Card Processing Equipment & Ser-
vices
N.A.I.C.S.: 522320

Subsidiary (Domestic):

Card Payment Services Inc. (3)
866 97th Ave N, Naples, FL 34108
Tel.: (972) 731-9624
Web Site: https://cpspayments.com
Payment Services
N.A.I.C.S.: 522320

Subsidiary (Domestic):

Columbus Productions, Inc. (3)
4580 Cargo Dr, Columbus, GA 31907-1958
Tel.: (706) 644-1595
Web Site:
　　http://www.columbusproductionsinc.com
Sales Range: $25-49.9 Million
Emp.: 30
Digital Printing Services
N.A.I.C.S.: 323113

NetSpend Holdings, Inc. (2)
701 Brazos St Ste 1300, Austin, TX 78701-
2582
Tel.: (512) 532-8200
Web Site: http://www.netspend.com
Sales Range: $350-399.9 Million
Emp.: 500
Holding Company
N.A.I.C.S.: 551112

ProPay Inc. (2)
2675 W 600 N, Lehi, UT 84042
Tel.: (801) 341-5300
Web Site: https://www.propay.com
Sales Range: $10-24.9 Million
Emp.: 100
Credit Card Processing & Electronic Pay-
ment Services
N.A.I.C.S.: 522390
Mark Johnson *(CIO)*

TSYS Acquiring Solutions LLC (2)
8320 S Hardy Dr, Tempe, AZ 85284
Tel.: (480) 333-7600
Web Site: http://www.vitalps.com
Sales Range: $250-299.9 Million
Emp.: 575
Merchant Acquiring Services
N.A.I.C.S.: 522320

Subsidiary (Non-US):

TSYS International Management
Limited (2)
Fulford Moor House Fulford Road, York,
YO10 4EY, United Kingdom
Tel.: (44) 1904562000
Data Processing, Hosting & Related Ser-
vices
N.A.I.C.S.: 518210

TSYS Managed Services Canada,
Inc. (2)
1993 Regent St, Sudbury, P3E 5R2, ON,
Canada
Tel.: (705) 522-6636
Electronic Payment Processing Services
N.A.I.C.S.: 522320

Subsidiary (Domestic):

TSYS Merchant Solutions, LLC (2)
1620 Dodge St, Omaha, NE 68197
Tel.: (800) 354-3988
Web Site:
　　http://www.tsysmerchantsolutions.com
N.A.I.C.S.: 327910

Division (Domestic):

TSYS Merchant Solutions -
Atlanta (3)
2 W Paces Ferry Rd NW 16002727, At-
lanta, GA 30339
Tel.: (770) 431-3022
Web Site: http://www.tsysmerchantsolutions-
atl.com
Sales Range: $50-74.9 Million
Emp.: 100
Electronic Credit Card Processing, Back
Office Processing, Financial Institution Rela-
tions & Development
N.A.I.C.S.: 522320

TransFirst, LLC (3)
12202 Airport Way Ste 100, Broomfield, CO
80021 (100%)
Tel.: (303) 625-8000
Web Site: http://www.transfirst.com
Electronic Payment Processing Services
N.A.I.C.S.: 522320
Stephen Cadden *(COO)*
Jeff Baer *(Chief Info Sys Officer & VP)*
Nathalie Worley *(VP-Ops)*

Subsidiary (Non-US):

Total System Services Holding Eu-
rope LP (2)
Fulford Moor House Fulford Road, York,
YO10 4EY, North Yorkshire, United King-
dom
Tel.: (44) 1904562000
Web Site: http://www.tsys.com
Bankcard Data Processing & Payment Ser-
vices
N.A.I.C.S.: 518210

Subsidiary (Domestic):

TSYS Card Tech Limited (3)
Fulford Moor House Fulford Rd, York, YO10
4EY, United Kingdom
Tel.: (44) 1904562000
Bankcard Data Processing & Payment Ser-
vices
N.A.I.C.S.: 518210
Kelly Knutson *(Exec VP-Intl Svcs)*

Subsidiary (Non-US):

TSYS Card Tech Services
Limited (3)
90 Arch Makariou III Ave, Nicosia, 1077,
Cyprus
Tel.: (357) 22882600
Electronic Payment Processing Services
N.A.I.C.S.: 522320

Subsidiary (Domestic):

TSYS Managed Services EMEA
Limited (3)
Burystead Court 120 Caldecotte Lake Drive,
Milton Keynes, MK7 8LE, Buckinghamshire,
United Kingdom (100%)
Tel.: (44) 1908681820
Sales Range: $75-99.9 Million
Emp.: 200
Electronic Payment Processing Services
N.A.I.C.S.: 522320

Subsidiary (Non-US):

TSYS Managed Services EMEA
(Netherlands) B.V. (4)
Thorbeckelaan 91-93, 3771 ED, Barneveld,
Netherlands
Tel.: (31) 342459600
Emp.: 125
Electronic Payment Processing Services

N.A.I.C.S.: 522320

Subsidiary (Domestic):

Total System Services Processing
Europe Limited (3)
Fulford Moor House, Fulford Road, York,
YO10 4EY, United Kingdom
Tel.: (44) 1904562000
Web Site:
http://www.totalsystemservices.com
Sales Range: $10-24.9 Million
Emp.: 300
Bankcard Data Processing & Payment Ser-
vices
N.A.I.C.S.: 518210

Total System Services Sales Europe
Limited (3)
Fulford Moor House, Fulford Road, York,
YO10 4EY, United Kingdom
Tel.: (44) 1904562004
Web Site:
http://www.tsysinternationalcareers.com
Sales Range: $100-124.9 Million
Bankcard Data Processing & Payment Ser-
vices
N.A.I.C.S.: 518210

GLOBAL PAYMENTS, INC.
3550 Lenox Rd, Atlanta, GA 30326
Tel.: (770) 829-8755
Web Site:
https://www.globalpayments.com
Year Founded: 2004
GPN—(NYSE)
Sales Range: $1-9.9 Million
Emp.: 17
Management Consulting Services
N.A.I.C.S.: 541611
Joseph H. Osnoss (Dir)
Jeffrey S. Sloan (CEO & Dir)
Joshua J. Whipple (CFO & Sr Exec
VP)
David M. Sheffield (Chief Acctg Offi-
cer & Exec VP)
M. Troy Woods (Chm)
F. Thaddeus Arroyo (Dir)
Robert H. B. Baldwin Jr. (Dir)
John G. Bruno (Dir)
Joia M. Johnson (Dir)
Ruth Ann Marshall (Dir)
Connie D. McDaniel (Dir)
Joseph Osnoss (Dir)
William B. Plummer (Dir)
John T. Turner (Dir)

GLOBAL POLE TRUSION
GROUP CORP.
4320 S Corbett Ave Ste 214, Port-
land, OR 97239
Tel.: (503) 660-9790 FL
Web Site: https://www.novacab.ca
Year Founded: 1995
GPGC—(OTCIQ)
Rev.: $202,316
Liabilities: $223,231
Net Worth: ($223,231)
Earnings: $192,656
Fiscal Year-end: 12/31/23
Automotive Thermal Energy Storage
Systems Mfr
N.A.I.C.S.: 336320
Samat Sultanovych Nurmakhanov
(Pres & CEO)
Zbigniew Lambo (Sec)

GLOBAL PROFIT TECHNOLO-
GIES, INC.
9393 N 90th St Ste 102-344, Scotts-
dale, AZ 85258
Tel.: (480) 327-6001
Web Site: http://www.glpt.io
GLPT—(OTCIQ)
Rev.: $37,571
Assets: $9,800,837
Liabilities: $566,782
Net Worth: $9,234,055
Earnings: ($1,085,490)
Fiscal Year-end: 12/31/19

Financial Software
N.A.I.C.S.: 513210

GLOBAL ROUNDTABLE COR-
PORATION
7535 East Ave Ste 400, Denver, CO
80231
Tel.: (845) 390-0673 CO
Web Site: http://www.gcbdinc.com
Year Founded: 1986
GRCU—(OTCIQ)
Medical Marijuana & Botanical Medi-
cal Products Mfr & Distr
N.A.I.C.S.: 325411
Joe Tragesser (CEO)
Robert Keith Tanko (CEO)
Paul W. Nelson (Exec VP)

GLOBAL SELF STORAGE,
INC.
3814 Route 44, Millbrook, NY 12545
Tel.: (212) 785-0900 MD
Web Site:
https://www.globalselfstorage.us
Year Founded: 1996
SELF—(NASDAQ)
Rev.: $11,944,850
Assets: $67,382,752
Liabilities: $19,043,638
Net Worth: $48,339,114
Earnings: $2,057,723
Emp.: 31
Fiscal Year-end: 12/31/22
Real Estate Investment Services
N.A.I.C.S.: 531210
Angelito Sarabia (Controller)
Thomas O'Malley (CFO, Treas, Sr VP
& VP)
Russell Kamerman (VP, Asst Sec &
Asst Gen Counsel)
Robert J. Mathers (VP-Property Ops)
Donald Klimoski II (Chief Compliance
Officer, Gen Counsel, Sec, Sr VP-
Operations & VP)
Mark Campbell Winmill (Chm, Pres &
CEO)

GLOBAL STAR ACQUISITION
INC.
1641 International Dr Unit 208,
McLean, VA 22102
Tel.: (703) 790-0717 DE
Web Site:
https://www.globalstarspac.com
Year Founded: 2019
GLST—(NASDAQ)
Rev.: $852,003
Assets: $96,293,292
Liabilities: $98,621,390
Net Worth: ($2,328,098)
Earnings: $168,814
Fiscal Year-end: 12/31/22
Investment Management Service
N.A.I.C.S.: 523999
Shan Cui (CFO)
Anthony Ang (Chm & CEO)
Nicholas Khoo (COO)

GLOBAL SYNERGY ACQUISI-
TION CORP.
540 Madison Ave 17th Fl, New York,
NY 10022
Tel.: (929) 251-0688 Ky
Year Founded: 2020
GSAQU—(NASDAQ)
Emp.: 3
Investment Services
N.A.I.C.S.: 523999
Alok Vaswani (Pres & Co-CEO)
Suresh Vaswani (Co-CEO)
Hank Uberoi (Chm)
Murtaza MoochhalaCF (CFO & COO)

GLOBAL SYSTEMS DYNAMIC,
INC.

815 Walker St Ste 1155, Houston, TX
77002
Tel.: (740) 229-0829 DE
Web Site: https://www.gsd.xyz.com
Year Founded: 2021
GSD—(NASDAQ)
Investment Services
N.A.I.C.S.: 523999
David J. Gladstone (Pres, CEO &
Chief Investment Officer)
Michael J. Malesardi (CFO)
Terry L. Brubaker (COO)
Michael LiCalsi (Gen Counsel & Sec)
Bill Frisbie (Exec VP-East Coast Ops)
Bill Reiman (Exec VP-West Coast
Ops)

GLOBAL TECH INDUSTRIES
GROUP, INC.
511 6th Ave Ste 800, New York, NY
10011
Tel.: (212) 204-7926 NV
Web Site: https://www.gtii-us.com
Year Founded: 1980
GTII—(OTCQB)
Assets: $1,276,198
Liabilities: $8,333,132
Net Worth: ($7,056,934)
Earnings: ($97,882,781)
Emp.: 2
Fiscal Year-end: 12/31/23
Investment Services
N.A.I.C.S.: 523999
David I. Reichman (CEO, CFO, Prin-
cipal Acctg Officer & Chm)
Kathy M. Griffin (Pres)

GLOBAL TECHNOLOGIES,
LTD.
8 Campus Dr Ste 105, Parsippany,
NJ 07054
Tel.: (973) 223-5151 DE
Web Site:
https://www.globaltechnologies
ltd.info
GTLL—(OTCIQ)
Rev.: $1,057,685
Assets: $8,362,682
Liabilities: $6,830,211
Net Worth: $1,532,471
Earnings: $812,081
Emp.: 2
Fiscal Year-end: 06/30/24
Information Technology Services
N.A.I.C.S.: 541511
Jimmy Wayne Anderson (Chm, Pres,
CEO, CFO, Treas & Sec)

Subsidiaries:

911 Help Now, LLC (1)
35246 US Hwy 19 N Ste 270, Palm Harbor,
FL 34684
Web Site: http://www.911helpnow.com
Electronic Product Distr
N.A.I.C.S.: 423690

GLOBAL WARMING SOLU-
TIONS, INC.
28751 Rancho California Rd Ste 100,
Temecula, CA 92590
Tel.: (951) 528-2102
Web Site:
https://www.gwsogroup.com
GWSO—(OTCIQ)
Assets: $237,563
Liabilities: $352,902
Net Worth: ($115,339)
Earnings: ($516,266)
Emp.: 1
Fiscal Year-end: 12/31/23
Solar Energy Equipment Mfr
N.A.I.C.S.: 333414
Vladimir Vasilenko (Co-Pres, CEO &
Treas)
Michael Pollastro (Chm, Co-Pres &
Sec)

Artem Madatov (Chief Scientific Offi-
cer)
Erin McQueeny (Sls Dir)
Brooke Pollastro (Dir-Ops)

GLOBAL WATER RE-
SOURCES, INC.
21410 N 19th Ave Ste 220, Phoenix,
AZ 85027
Tel.: (480) 360-7775 DE
Web Site:
https://www.gwresources.com
Year Founded: 2003
GWRS—(NASDAQ)
Rev.: $44,728,000
Assets: $323,086,000
Liabilities: $278,692,000
Net Worth: $44,394,000
Earnings: $5,506,000
Emp.: 94
Fiscal Year-end: 12/31/22
Holding Company; Water, Wastewa-
ter & Recycled Water Utilities Opera-
tor
N.A.I.C.S.: 551112
Ron L. Fleming (Chm, Pres & CEO)
Michael J. Liebman (CFO, Sec & Sr
VP)
Jason Thuneman (VP-Project Mgmt
Office)
Jon Corwin (VP & Gen Mgr)
Christopher D. Krygier (COO)
Steven Brill (VP)
Shelley Kitts (VP)

Subsidiaries:

Global Water Management, Inc. (1)
21410 N 19th Ave Ste 201, Phoenix, AZ
85027 (48.1%)
Tel.: (623) 518-4000
Web Site: http://www.gwresources.com
Water, Wastewater & Recycled Water Utili-
ties Operator
N.A.I.C.S.: 221310

GLOBAL WATER TECHNOLO-
GIES, INC.
125 W S St Ste 702, Indianapolis, IN
46206
Tel.: (317) 452-4488 DE
Web Site: https://www.gwtr.com
GWTR—(OTCIQ)
Environmental Consulting Services
N.A.I.C.S.: 541620
Erik Hromadka (Chm & CEO)

Subsidiaries:

Electric H2O, Inc. (1)
7160 Irving St, Westminster, CO 80030
Tel.: (303) 215-5298
Web Site: http://www.electrich2o.com
Water Treatment Equipment Mfr & Distr
N.A.I.C.S.: 333310

GLOBAL WHOLEHEALTH
PARTNERS CORPORATION
8025 Summer Pl St, Fontana, CA
92336
Tel.: (714) 392-9752 NV
Web Site: https://www.gwhpcorp.com
Year Founded: 2013
GWHP—(OTCIQ)
Rev.: $40,196
Assets: $411,553
Liabilities: $508,649
Net Worth: ($97,096)
Earnings: ($9,034,123)
Emp.: 1
Fiscal Year-end: 06/30/21
Crude Petroleum Extraction Services
N.A.I.C.S.: 211120
Shuijie Cui (Chief Science Officer)
F. Rene Alvarez Jr. (Pres, CEO,
COO, Treas, Sec & Exec VP)
Wolfgang Groeters (Dir-Bus Control)
Edgar B. Gonzalez (Exec VP)

Globalink Investment Inc.—(Continued)

GLOBALINK INVESTMENT INC.

200 Continental Dr Ste 401, Newark, DE 19713
Tel.: (212) 382-4605 DE
Year Founded: 2021
GLLI—(NASDAQ)
Rev.: $3,090,407
Assets: $28,872,916
Liabilities: $36,136,661
Net Worth: ($7,263,745)
Earnings: $1,320,324
Emp.: 2
Fiscal Year-end: 12/31/23
Investment Services
N.A.I.C.S.: 523999

GLOBALSTAR, INC.

1351 Holiday Sq Blvd, Covington, LA 70433
Tel.: (985) 335-1500 DE
Web Site: https://www.globalstar.com
Year Founded: 1991
GSAT—(NYSEAMEX)
Rev.: $148,504,000
Assets: $833,395,000
Liabilities: $518,624,000
Net Worth: $314,771,000
Earnings: ($258,252,000)
Emp.: 332
Fiscal Year-end: 12/31/22
Voice & Data Communication Services
N.A.I.C.S.: 517112
Paul E. Jacobs (CEO)
James Monroe III (Chm)
Matthew S. Grob (CTO)
Rebecca S. Clary (CFO & VP)
Timothy E. Taylor (VP-Fin, Strategy, and Bus Ops)
Jake Rembert (VP-Sls-Africa, Central & South America)
Matt Grob (CTO)
Mersad Cavcic (CMO)
Wen Doong (Sr VP-Engrg & Ops)
Kyle Pickens (VP-Strategy & Comm)
James Kilfeather (VP-Emerging Technologies)
Tim Calamari (VP-Network, IT, and Applications)
Mark Witsaman (VP-Product Engrg)
L. Barbee Ponder IV (Gen Counsel & VP-Regulatory Affairs)

Subsidiaries:

Globalstar Argentina S.R.L. (1)
25 de Mayo 704 - 4 P, Buenos Aires, Argentina
Tel.: (54) 1155547000
Web Site: http://www.sintectur.com.ar
Tour Agency Operator
N.A.I.C.S.: 561520

Globalstar Canada Satellite Co. (1)
115 Matheson Blvd W, Mississauga, L5R 3L1, ON, Canada (100%)
Tel.: (905) 890-1377
Wireless Telecommunication Services
N.A.I.C.S.: 517410

Globalstar Japan, Inc. (1)
6th floor Hamamatsucho Rise Square 1-3-3, Shibaura Minato-ku, Tokyo, 105-0023, Japan
Tel.: (81) 5031732846
Web Site: https://www.globalstar.co.jp
Communication Equipment Mfr
N.A.I.C.S.: 334290

Globalstar Slovakia, S.R.O. (1)
Opatovska cesta 14, 040 01, Kosice, Slovakia
Tel.: (421) 917204060
Travel Management Services
N.A.I.C.S.: 561510

GLOBALTECH CORPORATION

3550 Barron Way Ste 13a, Reno, NV 89511
Tel.: (775) 624-4817 NV
Web Site:
https://www.globaltechcorporation.com
Year Founded: 2017
GLTK—(NASDAQ)
Rev.: $11,620,515
Assets: $90,745,709
Liabilities: $48,796,041
Net Worth: $41,949,668
Earnings: ($12,422,808)
Emp.: 397
Fiscal Year-end: 12/31/22
Electronic Components Mfr
N.A.I.C.S.: 334419
Dean Christensen (Sec)

GLOBALTECH HOLDINGS, INC.

116 Lakewood Dr, Thomasville, GA 31792
Tel.: (347) 878-5388 WY
Year Founded: 1995
GLBH—(OTCIQ)
Sales Range: Less than $1 Million
Management & Holding Company for Real & Intellectual Properties
N.A.I.C.S.: 551112
Gerald Barber (CEO)
David Bosko (CFO)
John E. Lux (Corp Counsel)
Ormand Hunter Jr. (Vice Chm & Pres)

GLOBE LIFE INC.

3700 S Stonebridge Dr, McKinney, TX 75070
Tel.: (972) 569-4000 DE
Web Site:
https://home.globelifeinsurance.com
Year Founded: 1900
GL—(NYSE)
Rev.: $5,447,533,000
Assets: $28,051,499,000
Liabilities: $23,564,696,000
Net Worth: $4,486,803,000
Earnings: $970,755,000
Emp.: 3,636
Fiscal Year-end: 12/31/23
Investment Management Service
N.A.I.C.S.: 551112
Robert Brian Mitchell (Chief Risk Officer, Gen Council & Exec VP)
J. Matthew Darden (Co-Chm & Co-CEO)
Frank M. Svoboda (Co-Chm & Co-CEO)
Christopher T. Moore (Sec & Sr VP)
Joel P. Scarborough (Sr VP-Legal & Compliance)
Michael Shane Henrie (Chief Acctg Officer & Sr VP)
Pamela I. Ramirez (Sr VP-Enterprise Transformation)
Robert E. Hensley (Chief Investment Officer)
Christopher K. Tyler (CIO)
Jeffrey S. Morris (Chief Actuary)

Subsidiaries:

American Income Holding, Inc. (1)
1200 Wooded Acre Dr, Waco, TX 76710
Tel.: (254) 761-6400
Web Site: http://www.ailife.com
Sales Range: $300-349.9 Million
Emp.: 400
Insurance Holding Company; Markets, Underwrites & Issues Individual Supplemental Life & Fixed-Benefit Accident & Health Insurance
N.A.I.C.S.: 524128

Family Heritage Life Insurance Company of America (1)
6001 E Royalton Rd Ste 200, Cleveland, OH 44147

Tel.: (440) 922-5222
Web Site: http://www.familyheritagelife.com
Sales Range: $150-199.9 Million
Emp.: 107
Life Insurance Products & Services
N.A.I.C.S.: 524113

Globe Life & Accident Insurance Company (1)
Globe Life Ctr 204 N Robinson, Oklahoma City, OK 73102 (100%)
Tel.: (972) 540-6542
Web Site: http://www.globeontheweb.com
Sales Range: $250-299.9 Million
Emp.: 400
Life & Health Insurance Services
N.A.I.C.S.: 524113

Subsidiary (Domestic):

American Income Life Insurance Company (2)
1200 Wooded Acres Dr, Waco, TX 76710-4436
Tel.: (254) 761-6400
Web Site: https://www.ailife.com
Sales Range: $250-299.9 Million
Emp.: 320
Insurance
N.A.I.C.S.: 524128

American Life & Accident Insurance Company (2)
3700 S Stonebridge Dr, McKinney, TX 75070-5934
Tel.: (972) 540-6516
Web Site: http://www.unitedamerican.com
Sales Range: $200-249.9 Million
Life & Accident Insurance
N.A.I.C.S.: 524210

Liberty National Life Insurance Co. (1)
100 Concourse Pkwy Ste 350, Hoover, AL 35244 (100%)
Tel.: (205) 325-2722
Web Site: http://www.libnat.com
Sales Range: $900-999.9 Million
Emp.: 150
Fire Insurance Services
N.A.I.C.S.: 524113

Subsidiary (Domestic):

Brown-Service Funeral Homes Co. Inc. (2)
1340 26th Ave N, Birmingham, AL 35204-1118 (100%)
Tel.: (205) 251-2965
Web Site: http://www.libnat.com
Sales Range: $10-24.9 Million
Emp.: 50
Furnish Merchandise & Contracts with Funeral Directors for Services Under Insurance Policies
N.A.I.C.S.: 339995

Liberty National Insurance Co (2)
2001 3rd Ave S, Birmingham, AL 35233-2115 (100%)
Tel.: (205) 325-2722
Web Site: http://www.libnat.com
Sales Range: $350-399.9 Million
Trustee for Fully Insured Group Insurance Issued to Multiple Employeers
N.A.I.C.S.: 524113

United American Insurance Company (1)
3700 S Stonebridge Dr, McKinney, TX 75070-5934 (100%)
Tel.: (972) 529-5085
Web Site: https://www2.unitedamerican.com
Sales Range: $400-449.9 Million
Emp.: 630
Medicare Supplement Insurance
N.A.I.C.S.: 524113

Subsidiary (Domestic):

Globe Life Insurance Company of New York (2)
PO Box 8080, McKinney, TX 75070 (100%)
Tel.: (972) 529-5085
Web Site:
https://www.globelifeofnewyork.com
Sales Range: $1-9.9 Million
Life Insurance & Medical Supplement
N.A.I.C.S.: 524113

GLOBE PHOTOST, INC.

6445 S Tenaya Way B-130, Las Vegas, NV 89113
Tel.: (702) 722-6113 DE
Web Site:
http://www.globephotos.com
Year Founded: 2004
GBPT—(OTCIQ)
Sales Range: $1-9.9 Million
Emp.: 48
Classic, Contemporary & Limited Edition Photographic Images Distr
N.A.I.C.S.: 459920
Stuart Scheinman (Pres & CEO)

GLOBESTAR THERAPEUTICS CORPORATION

719 Jadwin Ave, Richland, WA 99352
Tel.: (206) 451-1970 NV
Web Site: http://globestarthera.com
Year Founded: 2010
GSTC—(OTCIQ)
Liabilities: $1,433,861
Net Worth: ($1,433,861)
Earnings: ($1,949,249)
Fiscal Year-end: 09/30/23
Biotechnology Research & Development Services
N.A.I.C.S.: 541714
James C. Katzaroff (Pres & CEO)
Robert Chicoski (CFO, Principal Acctg Officer, Treas & Sec)

Subsidiaries:

SomaCeuticals, Inc. (1)
2500 Wilcrest Dr 3rd Fl, Houston, TX 77042
Tel.: (832) 781-8521
Web Site: http://www.soma-ceuticals.com
Pharmaceutical Products Distr
N.A.I.C.S.: 424210
James C. Katzaroff (Pres)

GLOBIS ACQUISITION CORP.

805 3rd Ave 15th Fl, New York, NY 10022
Tel.: (212) 847-3248 DE
Year Founded: 2020
GLAQ—(NASDAQ)
Rev.: $7,838
Assets: $117,426,679
Liabilities: $120,827,582
Net Worth: ($3,400,903)
Earnings: ($2,670,676)
Fiscal Year-end: 12/31/21
Investment Services
N.A.I.C.S.: 523999
Paul Packer (CEO & CFO)

GLOBUS MEDICAL, INC.

2560 General Armistead Ave, Audubon, PA 19403
Tel.: (610) 930-1800 DE
Web Site:
https://www.globusmedical.com
Year Founded: 2003
GMED—(NYSE)
Rev.: $1,568,476,000
Assets: $5,086,083,000
Liabilities: $1,088,124,000
Net Worth: $3,997,959,000
Earnings: $122,873,000
Emp.: 5,000
Fiscal Year-end: 12/31/23
Spine Related Medical Device Mfr
N.A.I.C.S.: 339112
Daniel T. Scavilla (Pres & CEO)
Keith W. Pfeil (CFO, COO, Chief Acctg Officer & Sr VP)
Kelly G. Huller (Gen Counsel, Sec & Sr VP)
David C. Paul (Chm)

Subsidiaries:

Globus Medical Australia Pty Limited (1)
Baulkham Hills Business Centre, PO Box 8151, Baulkham Hills, 2153, NSW, Australia
Tel.: (61) 288244830
Surgical & Medical Instrument Mfr
N.A.I.C.S.: 339112

Globus Medical Austria GmbH (1)
Campus 21 Liebermannstrasse A01/503-2, 2345, Brunn am Gebirge, Austria
Tel.: (43) 2236320347
Surgical & Medical Instrument Mfr
N.A.I.C.S.: 339112

Globus Medical Brasil Ltda. (1)
Rua Otavio Carneiro 143 Sales 901-905, Icarai, Niteroi, 24230-190, Brazil
Tel.: (55) 2127148054
Medical Device Mfr
N.A.I.C.S.: 339112

Globus Medical Brazil Ldta. (1)
Rua Otavio Carneiro 143 Salas 901-905, Icarai, Niteroi, Rio de Janeiro, 24230-190, Brazil
Tel.: (55) 2127148054
Medical Device Mfr & Distr
N.A.I.C.S.: 339113

Globus Medical Italy S.r.l. (1)
Via Giuseppe Ripamonte 89, Milan, Italy
Tel.: (39) 02 266 0041
Medical Equipment Whslr
N.A.I.C.S.: 423450

Globus Medical Japan, Inc. (1)
6F Ichibancho M Building 10-2 Ichibancho, Chiyoda-Ku, Tokyo, 102-0082, Japan
Tel.: (81) 335115185
Web Site: http://www.alphatecjp.com
Medical Equipment Distr & Sales
N.A.I.C.S.: 423450
Mitsuo Asai *(Pres & CEO)*

Globus Medical South Africa Pty Limited (1)
5 Yellow Wood Place Woodmead Business Park 145 Western Service Road, Kya Sands Industrial Village Kya Sand, Johannesburg, 2191, South Africa
Tel.: (27) 117082840
Web Site: https://www.globusmedical.com
Surgical & Medical Instrument Mfr
N.A.I.C.S.: 339112

Globus Medical Sweden AB (1)
Lille Langenv 4, 441 63, Alingsas, Sweden
Tel.: (46) 701460017
Pharmaceutical Goods Whslr
N.A.I.C.S.: 424210

Globus Medical UK Limited (1)
Heathrow Boulevard 2 284 Bath Road, Sipson, West Drayton, UB7 0DQ, United Kingdom
Tel.: (44) 204 516 2854
Web Site:
http://international.globusmedical.com
Medical Supplies Whslr
N.A.I.C.S.: 423450
Ian Griffith *(Mng Dir)*

Nemaris, Inc. (1)
475 Park Ave S 11th Fl, New York, NY 10016
Tel.: (646) 794-8650
Web Site: https://www.surgimap.com
Surgical Appliance Mfr
N.A.I.C.S.: 339113
Carlos Calderon *(Sr Engr-Software QA)*
Conner Adams *(Engr-Machine Learning)*
Xavi Paez *(Engr-Software)*

NuVasive Italia S.r.l. (1)
Via Giacomo Watt 32, 20143, Milan, Italy
Tel.: (39) 0236725611
Medical Device Mfr & Distr
N.A.I.C.S.: 339113

NuVasive, Inc. (1)
12101 Airport Way, Broomfield, CO 80021
Tel.: (858) 909-1800
Web Site: https://www.nuvasive.com
Emp.: 3,000
Fiscal Year-end: 12/31/2022
Surgical Appliance & Supplies Manufacturing
N.A.I.C.S.: 339113

Daniel T. Scavilla *(CEO)*
Keith W. Pfeil *(Sec)*
Kelly G. Huller *(CFO)*

Subsidiary (Domestic):

Impulse Monitoring, Inc. (2)
10420 Little Patuxent Pkwy Ste 250, Columbia, MD 21044
Tel.: (410) 740-2370
Web Site:
http://www.impulsemonitoring.com
Sales Range: $10-24.9 Million
Emp.: 25
Health Care Srvices
N.A.I.C.S.: 622110

Subsidiary (Non-US):

NuVasive (AUS/NZ) Pty. Ltd. (2)
620 High Street Ground Floor, Kew, 3101, VIC, Australia
Tel.: (61) 398167200
Medical Equipment Whslr
N.A.I.C.S.: 423450

Subsidiary (Domestic):

NuVasive Clinical Services Monitoring, Inc. (2)
10420 Little Patuxent Pkwy Ste 250, Columbia, MD 21044-3638
Tel.: (410) 740-2370
Surgical & Medical Instrument Mfr
N.A.I.C.S.: 339112

Subsidiary (Non-US):

NuVasive Germany, GmbH (2)
Flughafenallee 11, 28199, Bremen, Germany
Tel.: (49) 42198538340
Web Site: https://www.nuvasive.de
Emp.: 50
Medical Equipment Whslr
N.A.I.C.S.: 423450

NuVasive Netherlands B.V. (2)
Grutterij 14, 1185ZV, Amstelveen, Netherlands
Tel.: (31) 207233012
Medical Equipment Whslr
N.A.I.C.S.: 423450
Adri van der Werff *(Office Mgr)*

Subsidiary (Domestic):

NuVasive Specialized Orthopedics, Inc. (2)
101 Enterprise Ste 100, Aliso Viejo, CA 92656
Tel.: (949) 837-3600
Web Site: http://www.nuvasive.com
Surgical & Medical Instrument Mfr
N.A.I.C.S.: 339112
Arthur ONeal *(Sr Dir-Marketing)*

Subsidiary (Non-US):

NuVasive UK Limited (2)
Suite B Ground Floor Caspian House the Waterfront, Elstree, WD6 3BS, Hertfordshire, United Kingdom
Tel.: (44) 2082387850
Web Site: http://www.nuvasive.com
Sales Range: $10-24.9 Million
Emp.: 11
Medical Instrument Mfr
N.A.I.C.S.: 339112

Subsidiary (Domestic):

Safe Passage Neuromonitoring (2)
915 Broadway Ste 1200, New York, NY 10010
Web Site: http://www.safepassagenm.com
Health Care Srvices
N.A.I.C.S.: 621491
Adam T. Doan *(Dir-Clinical Svcs)*

GLORI ENERGY INC.
957 Nasa Pkwy Ste 571, Houston, TX 77058
Tel.: (713) 237-8880 DE
Web Site: http://www.glorienergy.com
GLRI—(OTCIQ)
Sales Range: $1-9.9 Million
Emp.: 35

Oil & Gas Exploration Utilizing Biotechnology
N.A.I.C.S.: 211120
Victor M. Perez *(CFO)*
Kenneth Nimitz *(Sr VP-Ops)*

GLORYWIN ENTERTAINMENT GROUP, INC.
2313 Hollyhill Ln, Denton, TX 76205
Tel.: (626) 429-2780 NV
Year Founded: 2010
GWIN—(OTCIQ)
Biomass Fuel Services
N.A.I.C.S.: 221117
Sorphea Rath *(CEO)*
Solin Hoem *(CFO)*
Jiami Cheng *(VP)*

GLUCOSE HEALTH, INC.
609 SW 8th St 6th Fl, Bentonville, AR 72712
Tel.: (479) 802-3827 NV
Web Site:
https://glucosehealthinc.com
Year Founded: 2007
GLUC—(OTCIQ)
Rev.: $480,000
Assets: $344,000
Liabilities: $303,000
Net Worth: $41,000
Earnings: ($581,000)
Emp.: 4
Fiscal Year-end: 12/31/20
Dietary Supplements Mfr
N.A.I.C.S.: 325412
Murray S. Fleming *(CEO & CFO)*

GLYCOMIMETICS, INC.
9708 Medical Ctr Dr, Rockville, MD 20850
Tel.: (240) 243-1201 DE
Web Site:
https://www.glycomimetics.com
Year Founded: 2003
GLYC—(NASDAQ)
Rev.: $75,000
Assets: $51,810,589
Liabilities: $8,880,752
Net Worth: $42,929,837
Earnings: ($46,688,802)
Emp.: 38
Fiscal Year-end: 12/31/22
Pharmaceuticals Mfr
N.A.I.C.S.: 325412
Rachel K. King *(Co-Founder)*
John L. Magnani *(Co-Founder)*
Brian M. Hahn *(CFO & Sr VP)*
Harout Semerjian *(Pres & CEO)*
Stephanie Irish *(VP-Acctg)*
John M. Peterson *(VP-Medicinal Chemistry)*

GMS INC.
100 Crescent Centre Pkwy Ste 800, Tucker, GA 30084
Tel.: (770) 939-1711 DE
Web Site: https://www.gms.com
Year Founded: 1971
GMS—(NYSE)
Rev.: $5,329,252,000
Assets: $3,267,008,000
Liabilities: $1,992,251,000
Net Worth: $1,274,757,000
Earnings: $332,991,000
Emp.: 7,007
Fiscal Year-end: 04/30/23
Holding Company; Wallboard, Suspended Ceiling Systems & Interior Construction Products Distr
N.A.I.C.S.: 551112
John J. Gavin Jr. *(Chm)*
Craig D. Apolinsky *(Gen Counsel, Sec & VP)*
Thomas L. Dumay *(Dir-Risk Mgmt)*
Eric Sundby *(CIO & VP)*
Scott M. Deakin *(CFO & VP)*

William Forrest Bell *(Chief Acctg Officer)*
Darryl Little *(VP-Ops & Procurement)*
George Travis Hendren *(COO)*
John C. Turner Jr. *(Pres & CEO)*

Subsidiaries:

Blair Building Materials Inc. (1)
10445 Keele Street, PO Box 730, Maple, L6A 1S7, ON, Canada
Tel.: (416) 798-4996
Web Site:
https://www.blairbuildingmaterials.com
Building Material Products Distr
N.A.I.C.S.: 444180
Martin Lieberman *(CEO)*
Dante DiGiovanni *(Pres)*

D.L. Building Materials Inc. (1)
760 rue de Vernon, Gatineau, J9J 3K5, QC, Canada
Tel.: (819) 770-9974
Web Site:
https://www.dlbuildingmaterials.com
Building Materials Distr
N.A.I.C.S.: 423390

Engler, Meier & Justus, Inc. (1)
1030 Vandustrial Dr, Westmont, IL 60559
Tel.: (630) 852-4600
Web Site: https://www.emjcompanies.com
Sales Range: $10-24.9 Million
Emp.: 30
Building Materials
N.A.I.C.S.: 423390
Gary Wietecha *(VP-Ops)*

Subsidiary (Domestic):

Westmont Interior Supply House (2)
1030 Vandustrial Dr, Westmont, IL 60559
Tel.: (630) 852-4600
Web Site: http://www.naiacoustics.com
Rev.: $13,500,000
Emp.: 10
Ceiling Systems & Products
N.A.I.C.S.: 423390

Gypsum Management & Supply, Inc. (1)
100 Crescent Ctr Pkwy Ste 800, Tucker, GA 30084
Tel.: (770) 939-1711
Web Site: https://www.gms.com
Wallboard, Suspended Ceilings Systems & Interior Construction Products Distr
N.A.I.C.S.: 423390

Subsidiary (Domestic):

Badgerland Supply, Inc. (2)
809 Watson Ave, Madison, WI 53725
Tel.: (608) 274-6630
Web Site:
https://www.badgerlandsupply.com
Building Materials Distr
N.A.I.C.S.: 423320
James Downing *(Pres)*

Capitol Building Supply, Inc. (2)
431 Mill St NE, Vienna, VA 22180
Tel.: (703) 281-5151
Web Site: http://www.cbsi.net
Sales Range: $10-24.9 Million
Emp.: 50
Industrial Chemical, Maintenance & Cleaning Products & Janitorial Supplies Distr
N.A.I.C.S.: 424690
Rob Harwood *(Pres)*

Branch (Domestic):

Capitol Building Supply (3)
6813 Quad Ave, Baltimore, MD 21237
Tel.: (410) 284-2800
Web Site: https://cbsi.net
Sales Range: $10-24.9 Million
Emp.: 50
Commercial & Residential Construction Supplies Whslr
N.A.I.C.S.: 423390
Bill Naehle *(Mgr)*

Subsidiary (Domestic):

Capitol Interior Products, Inc. (2)
240 E 5th St, Bayonne, NJ 07032
Tel.: (201) 998-2400
Web Site: http://www.cip-gms.com

GMS Inc.—(Continued)

Building Material Distribution Services
N.A.I.C.S.: 444180

Capitol Materials Coastal, Inc. (2)
103 Spaulding Ct, Brunswick, GA 31525
Tel.: (912) 264-5770
Web Site: https://cmcoastal.com
Emp.: 275
Building Material Distribution Services
N.A.I.C.S.: 444180
Glenn Whiteman *(Gen Mgr)*
Parfait Konan *(Mgr-Yard)*

Capitol Materials, Incorporated (2)
1466 White Rd Ct, Marietta, GA 30060
Tel.: (404) 352-4640
Web Site: https://www.capmat.com
Emp.: 275
Construction Equipment Distr
N.A.I.C.S.: 423810

Chaparral Materials, Inc. (2)
4220 Stanley Dr NE, Rio Rancho, NM 87144
Tel.: (505) 771-7755
Web Site:
https://www.chaparralmaterials.com
Supplier of Brick, Stone & Related Material
N.A.I.C.S.: 423320

Charles G. Hardy, Inc. (2)
15723 Vermont Ave, Paramount, CA 90723-4228
Tel.: (562) 634-6560
Web Site: http://charlesghardy.com
Interior Building Products Distr
N.A.I.C.S.: 423710
Joe Barloon *(Pres)*

Cherokee Building Materials Inc. (2)
12222 E 60th St, Tulsa, OK 74146-6901
Tel.: (918) 252-1666
Web Site: https://www.cherbmi.com
Sales Range: $10-24.9 Million
Emp.: 25
Retail & Wholesale of Sheetrock
N.A.I.C.S.: 423310

Subsidiary (Domestic):

Cherokee Building Materials of OKC, Inc. (3)
100 NE 31st St, Oklahoma City, OK 73105-2606
Tel.: (405) 525-5710
Web Site:
http://www.gypsummanagement.com
Sales Range: $10-24.9 Million
Emp.: 22
Supplier of Plywood & Millwork
N.A.I.C.S.: 423310

Subsidiary (Domestic):

Colonial Materials Inc. (2)
4602 Rozzelles Ferry Rd, Charlotte, NC 28216-3857
Tel.: (704) 392-0100
Web Site: http://www.colonialmaterials.com
Sales Range: $10-24.9 Million
Emp.: 32
Drywall Services
N.A.I.C.S.: 423320

Subsidiary (Domestic):

Colonial Materials of Fayetteville, Inc. (3)
570 Belt Blvd, Fayetteville, NC 28301-6332
Tel.: (910) 405-5099
Web Site: https://www.colonialmaterials.com
Sales Range: $10-24.9 Million
Emp.: 50
Supplier of Brick, Stone & Related Material
N.A.I.C.S.: 423320
Kevin Coble *(Mgr-Ops)*

Subsidiary (Domestic):

Commercial Builders Group LLC (2)
235 Jaubert Ln, La Place, LA 70068
Tel.: (985) 565-7818
Web Site:
http://www.commercialbuildersgroup.com
Construction & Mining Machinery
N.A.I.C.S.: 423810
David Lastrap *(Pres)*

Commonwealth Building Materials, Inc. (2)
11066-A Washington Hwy, Glen Allen, VA 23059
Tel.: (804) 752-0110
Web Site: https://www.cbmi-va.com
Building Supplies Distr
N.A.I.C.S.: 423310

Cowtown Materials, Inc. (2)
401 Garden Acres Dr, Fort Worth, TX 76140-5522
Tel.: (817) 551-1805
Web Site:
https://www.cowtownmaterials.com
Sales Range: $10-24.9 Million.
Emp.: 25
Retail of Drywall Materials
N.A.I.C.S.: 423320

GMS Strategic Solutions, Inc. (2)
1817 Fellowship Rd, Tucker, GA 30084
Tel.: (770) 939-1711
Building Product Mfr & Distr
N.A.I.C.S.: 327420

GTS Drywall Supply Company (2)
10819 120th Ave NE, Kirkland, WA 98033
Tel.: (425) 828-6761
Web Site: https://www.gtsinteriorsupply.com
Construction Materials Mfr
N.A.I.C.S.: 423390

Gator Gypsum Inc. (2)
3904 E Adamo Dr, Tampa, FL 33605-5902
Tel.: (813) 248-6393
Web Site: https://www.gatorgypsum.com
Distr of Lumber, Plywood & Millwork
N.A.I.C.S.: 423310

Gypsum Supply Company (2)
859 74th St SW, Byron Center, MI 49315
Tel.: (616) 583-9300
Web Site: https://www.gypsum-supply.com
Drywall & Other Related Building Materials Distr
N.A.I.C.S.: 423320

Hathaway & Sons, Inc. (2)
77-920 Varner Rd, Palm Desert, CA 92211
Tel.: (760) 772-2630
Web Site:
http://hathawaybuildingmaterial.com
Drywall & Other Building Materials Distr
N.A.I.C.S.: 444180

J&B Materials, Inc. (2)
10819 120th Ave NE, Kirkland, WA 98033
Tel.: (425) 828-0608
Web Site: http://www.jbmaterials.com
Emp.: 120
Construction & Mining, except Oil Well, Machinery & Equipment Merchant Whslr
N.A.I.C.S.: 423810
Brian Carrriere *(Mgr)*

Lone Star Materials, Inc. (2)
11111 Bluff Bend Dr, Austin, TX 78753-3221 (100%)
Tel.: (512) 834-8611
Web Site:
https://www.lonestarmaterials.com
Sales Range: Less than $1 Million
Emp.: 27
Distr of Drywall Metal Studs & Acoustics Celings
N.A.I.C.S.: 423320

Missouri Drywall Supply, Inc. (2)
314 McDonnell Blvd, Hazelwood, MO 63042
Tel.: (314) 731-2282
Web Site: https://modrywall.com
Building Material Distribution Services
N.A.I.C.S.: 444180

New England Gypsum Supply, Inc. (2)
3250 Main St, Hartford, CT 06120
Tel.: (860) 541-5911
Web Site: https://www.negypsum.com
Building Product Mfr
N.A.I.C.S.: 327420

Ohio Valley Supply, Inc. (2)
2700 Commerce Cir, Trafford, PA 15085
Tel.: (412) 646-1936
Web Site: http://www.ovdrywall.com
Construction Equipment Distr
N.A.I.C.S.: 423810

Olympia Building Supplies, LLC (2)
1405 SW 8th St, Pompano Beach, FL 33069
Tel.: (954) 782-7782
Web Site: http://www.gms.com
Building Material Supplier
N.A.I.C.S.: 444180

Pioneer Materials West, Inc. (2)
7271 S Eagle St, Centennial, CO 80112-4203
Tel.: (303) 693-7900
Web Site:
https://www.pioneermaterialswest.com
Sales Range: $10-24.9 Million
Emp.: 40
Drywall Distr
N.A.I.C.S.: 423320

Pioneer Materials, Inc. (2)
1916 S Kessler St, Wichita, KS 67213-1227
Tel.: (316) 943-2281
Web Site: https://pioneerks.com
Sales Range: $10-24.9 Million
Emp.: 23
Supplier of Lumber, Plywood & Millwork
N.A.I.C.S.: 423310
Michael Hamel *(Gen Mgr)*

River Bend Materials Inc. (2)
4300 Amnicola Hwy, Chattanooga, TN 37406-1013
Tel.: (423) 622-3060
Web Site:
http://www.riverbendmaterials.com
Sales Range: $10-24.9 Million
Emp.: 16
Supplier Of Drywall And Plaster Ceilings
N.A.I.C.S.: 532490

Subsidiary (Domestic):

Windsor Rock Products, Inc. (3)
8425 Windsor Is Rd, Keizer, OR 97303
Tel.: (503) 393-8920
Web Site:
http://www.windsorrockproducts.com
Mining
N.A.I.C.S.: 212321
Bill McCall *(Pres)*

Subsidiary (Domestic):

Robert N. Karpp Co. Inc. (2)
480 E 1st St, Boston, MA 02127
Tel.: (617) 269-5880
Web Site: http://www.karpp.com
Building Supply Whlsr & Services
N.A.I.C.S.: 423310

Rocky Top Materials, Inc. (2)
2707 John Deere Dr, Knoxville, TN 37917-4848 (100%)
Tel.: (865) 522-0060
Web Site: http://www.rockytopmat.com
Sales Range: $10-24.9 Million
Emp.: 32
Supplier of Lumber, Plywood & Millwork
N.A.I.C.S.: 423310

Southern Wall Products Inc. (2)
1825 Fellowship Rd, Tucker, GA 30084-6560
Tel.: (770) 621-3065
Web Site: https://www.ruco.com
Sales Range: $10-24.9 Million
Supplier of Gypsum Products
N.A.I.C.S.: 327420

Southwest Building Materials, LLC (2)
5330 N 16th St, Phoenix, AZ 85043
Tel.: (623) 466-6800
Web Site:
http://southwestbuildingproducts.vendecommerce.com
Brick, Stone & Related Construction Material Merchant Whslr
N.A.I.C.S.: 423320

State Line Building Supply Inc. (2)
RR 113, Selbyville, DE 19975
Tel.: (302) 436-8624
Sales Range: $10-24.9 Million
Emp.: 20
Distr of Day Wall
N.A.I.C.S.: 423310
Charlie Gibson *(Office Mgr)*

Tamarack Materials, Inc. (2)
9300 James Ave S, Bloomington, MN 55431-2317
Tel.: (952) 888-5556
Web Site:
https://www.tamarackmaterials.com
Sales Range: $10-24.9 Million
Emp.: 175
Dry Wall & Stucco Material
N.A.I.C.S.: 423320
Jeremy Lablanc *(Mgr)*

Tejas Materials, Inc. (2)
1902 Weber St, Houston, TX 77007-2809
Tel.: (713) 868-5711
Web Site: https://www.tejasmaterials.com
Sales Range: $10-24.9 Million
Emp.: 52
Sheet Rock & Related Material Distr
N.A.I.C.S.: 423320

Subsidiary (Non-US):

Tool Source Warehouse, Inc. (2)
Tel.: (770) 242-8100
Web Site: https://www.tswfast.com
Sales Range: $10-24.9 Million
Emp.: 25
Supplier Of Industrial Machinery & Equipment
N.A.I.C.S.: 423830

Subsidiary (Domestic):

Tucker Acoustical Products, Inc. (2)
2014 Steel Dr, Tucker, GA 30084-5832
Tel.: (770) 447-0890
Web Site: https://www.tuckeracoustical.com
Sales Range: $1-9.9 Million
Emp.: 15
Supplier of Brick, Stone & Related Material
N.A.I.C.S.: 423320

Tucker Materials, Inc. (2)
709 N Belair Rd, Evans, GA 30809
Tel.: (706) 826-4848
Web Site: http://tuckermaterialsinc.com
Building Material Distribution Services
N.A.I.C.S.: 444180
Scott Brown *(Gen Mgr)*

United Building Materials, Inc. (2)
1509 Stanley Ave, Dayton, OH 45404
Tel.: (937) 222-4444
Web Site:
http://www.unitedbuildingmaterials.com
Sales Range: $1-9.9 Million
Emp.: 20
Lumber & Building Materials Retailer
N.A.I.C.S.: 444180

Subsidiary (Domestic):

United Construction Products, Inc. (3)
4140 Fisher Rd Ste B, Columbus, OH 43228
Tel.: (614) 351-3511
Web Site:
http://www.unitedbuildingmaterials.com
Sales Range: $1-9.9 Million
Emp.: 15
Building Material Retailer
N.A.I.C.S.: 444180

Subsidiary (Non-US):

WSB Titan Inc. (2)
50 Royal Group Crescent Unit 2, Vaughan, L4H 1X9, ON, Canada
Web Site: http://www.wsbtitan.com
Roofing Sheet Metal Mfr
N.A.I.C.S.: 332322

Subsidiary (Domestic):

Washington Builders Supply Co. (2)
313 Country Club Rd, Meadow Lands, PA 15347
Tel.: (724) 222-8079
Web Site: https://www.washbldrs.com
Construction Supply Mfr
N.A.I.C.S.: 212321

Wildcat Materials, Inc. (2)
2235 W Catalpa St, Springfield, MO 65807-1119
Tel.: (417) 864-4800
Web Site: http://www.wildcatinc.net
Sales Range: $10-24.9 Million
Emp.: 54
Distr of Brick, Stone & Related Material
N.A.I.C.S.: 423320

Kamco Supply Corporation (1)
301 Robbins Ln, Syosset, NY 11791
Tel.: (516) 935-8660
Web Site: http://www.kamconewyork.com
Lumber, Plywood, Millwork & Wood Panel
Merchant Whslr
N.A.I.C.S.: 423310
Allen B. Swerdlick (CEO)

Trowel Trades Supply, Inc. (1)
206 Hegeman Ave, Colchester, VT 05446-3136
Tel.: (802) 655-3166
Web Site:
   http://www.troweltradessupply.com
Fireplace Mason, Drywall Supplies & Land-
scaping Product Distr
N.A.I.C.S.: 423320
Bernie Metivier (Ops Mgr)

Westside Building Material Corp. (1)
1111 E Howell Ave, Anaheim, CA 92805
Tel.: (714) 385-1644
Web Site: http://www.westsidebmc.com
Sales Range: $25-49.9 Million
Emp.: 50
Plastering Materials
N.A.I.C.S.: 423320
Arlynn Avendano (Dir-HR)

GNCC CAPITAL, INC.
848 N Rainbow Blvd Ste 4870, Las
Vegas, NV 89107
Tel.: (702) 990-0156   WY
Web Site: https://www.gncc-
   capital.com
Year Founded: 2014
GNCP—(OTCIQ)
Holding Company
N.A.I.C.S.: 551112
Nicolaas Edward Blom (Pres)
Ronald Yadin Lowenthal (Treas &
Sec)

GO ACQUISITION CORP.
450 W 14th St, New York, NY 10014
Tel.: (212) 524-7300   DE
Year Founded: 2020
GOACU—(NYSE)
Investment Services
N.A.I.C.S.: 523999
Noam Gottesman (Co-CEO)
M. Gregory O'Hara (Founder & Co-
CEO)
Guy Weltsch (Pres & CFO)
Spencer Marsden (VP)
Alejandro San Miguel (Sec & VP)

**GO GREEN GLOBAL TECH-
NOLOGIES CORP.**
5 Production Dr, Brookfield, CT
06804   NV
Web Site: https://gogreen-tech.org
Year Founded: 2006
GOGR—(OTCQB)
Water Treatment & Fuel Combustion
Technology
N.A.I.C.S.: 339999
Danny G. Bishop (Pres & CEO)
John Eric D'Alessandro (Sls Dir-
Manufacturing)
Corrine Couch (COO)

GO-PAGE CORPORATION
500 N Rainbow Rd Ste 300, Las Ve-
gas, NV 89107
Tel.: (702) 448-8179   NV
Web Site: http://www.gopage.com
GOPG—(OTCIQ)
Emp.: 3
Software Developer
N.A.I.C.S.: 513210
Peter Schulhof (Pres & CEO)
Anthony Jackson (CFO)

GOAL ACQUISITIONS CORP.
12600 Hill Country Blvd Bldg R Ste
275, Bee Cave, TX 78738   DE
Web Site:
   https://www.goalacquisitions.com

Year Founded: 2020
PUCK—(NASDAQ)
Rev.: $4,069,175
Assets: $262,288,567
Liabilities: $266,193,095
Net Worth: ($3,904,528)
Earnings: ($296,853)
Emp.: 2
Fiscal Year-end: 12/31/22
Investment Services
N.A.I.C.S.: 523999
William T. Duffy (CFO & COO)
Harvey Schiller (CEO)
Alex Greystoke (Founder)

GOGO INC.
105 Edgeview Dr Ste 300, Broom-
field, CO 80021
Tel.: (303) 301-3271   DE
Web Site: https://www.gogoair.com
GOGO—(NASDAQ)
Rev.: $397,577,000
Assets: $781,539,000
Liabilities: $740,814,000
Net Worth: $40,725,000
Earnings: $145,678,000
Emp.: 457
Fiscal Year-end: 12/31/23
In-Flight Connectivity & Wireless In-
Cabin Digital Entertainment Solutions
N.A.I.C.S.: 513210
Will Davis (VP-IR)
Jessica Betjemann (CFO & Exec VP)
Leigh Goldfine (Chief Acctg Officer,
VP & Controller)
Oakleigh B. Thorne (Chm, Pres &
CEO)
Marguerite M. Elias (Gen Counsel,
Sec & VP)

Subsidiaries:

**Aircell Business Aviation Services
LLC** (1)
105 Edgeview Dr Ste 300, Broomfield, CO
80021
Tel.: (303) 301-3278
Sales Range: $1-9.9 Million
Emp.: 150
In-Flight Internet Connectivity & Wireless
In-Cabin Digital Entertainment Solutions
N.A.I.C.S.: 517810
Dennis Hildreth (Mgr-Sls-OEM)
Shuaib Shahid (Mgr-Svc Sls)

Subsidiary (Domestic):

LiveTV Airfone, LLC (2)
2809 Butterfield Rd, Oak Brook, IL
60522   (100%)
Tel.: (630) 572-1800
Airborne Voice & Data Communications
Services
N.A.I.C.S.: 517112

Gogo Air International Sarl (1)
Chemin Des Graviers 8, 2016, Cortaillod,
Switzerland
Tel.: (41) 328412838
Game Development Services
N.A.I.C.S.: 513210

Gogo Business Aviation LLC (1)
105 Edgeview Dr Ste 300, Broomfield, CO
80021
Tel.: (303) 301-3278
Web Site: https://www.gogoair.com
Other Aircraft Parts & Auxiliary Equipment
Mfr
N.A.I.C.S.: 336413
Dave Glenn (VP-Customer Ops)
Crystal Gordon (Chief Admin Officer, Corp
Counsel, Gen Counsel & Exec VP)
Andy Geist (Sr VP)
Gustavo Nader (Chief Strategy Officer)
Jessi Betjemann (CFO, Chief Acctg Officer
& Exec VP)
Mark Sander (Sr VP)
Melissa Hale (Sr VP)
Mike Begler (Sr VP)
Oakleigh Thorne (CEO)

Gogo LLC (1)

111 N Canal St Ste 1500, Chicago, IL
60606
Tel.: (630) 647-1074
Web Site: http://www.gogoair.com
Game Development Services
N.A.I.C.S.: 513210

**GOGREEN INVESTMENTS
CORP.**
1 City Ctr 1021 Main St Ste 1960,
Houston, TX 77002
Tel.: (713) 337-4075   Ky
Web Site: https://www.gogreeninvest-
   ments.com
Year Founded: 2021,
GOGN—(NYSE)
Rev.: $4,126,342
Assets: $285,957,989
Liabilities: $290,841,206
Net Worth: ($4,883,217)
Earnings: ($1,271,060)
Emp.: 6
Fiscal Year-end: 12/31/22
Investment Services
N.A.I.C.S.: 523999
John Dowd (Chm & CEO)
Vikas Anand (Chief Dev Officr)
Dan Foley (CTO)
Govind Friedland (COO)
Sergei Pokrovsky (Chief Decarbon-
ization Officer)
Michael Sedoy (CFO)

GOHEALTH, INC.
222 W Merchandise Mart Plz Ste
1750, Chicago, IL 60654
Tel.: (312) 386-8200   DE
Web Site: https://www.gohealth.com
Year Founded: 2020
GOCO—(NASDAQ)
Rev.: $631,675,000
Assets: $1,659,290,000
Liabilities: $1,116,891,000
Net Worth: $542,399,000
Earnings: ($148,706,000)
Emp.: 2,467
Fiscal Year-end: 12/31/22
Holding Company
N.A.I.C.S.: 551112
Katherine Hayes O'Halloran (Interim
CFO & Chief Acctg Officer)
Vijay Kotte (CEO)
Clinton P. Jones (Chm)
Alison Moriarty (Chief People Officer)
Michael Hargis (Chief Customer En-
gagement Officer)
Michael Kelley (Sr VP)
Jay Sreedharan (CTO)
Steve Moffat (CMO)

**GOLD AND GEMSTONE MIN-
ING INC.**
4020 N MacArthur Blvd Ste 122, Ir-
ving, TX 75038
Tel.: (646) 405-4805   NV
Year Founded: 2007
GGSM—(OTCIQ)
Gold & Diamond Mining
N.A.I.C.S.: 212220
Rafael A. Pinedo (Pres, CEO, Sec &
Treas)
Ivan Mondragon (VP-Exploration &
Dir-Ops)

GOLD FLORA CORP.
3165 Red Hill Ave, Costa Mesa, CA
92626
Tel.: (949) 252-1908   BC
Web Site: https://www.goldflora.com
Year Founded: 2019
GRAM—(OTCIQ)
Rev.: $173,414,881
Assets: $571,454,989
Liabilities: $168,923,416
Net Worth: $402,531,573
Earnings: ($587,060,124)
Emp.: 432

Fiscal Year-end: 12/31/21
Holding Company
N.A.I.C.S.: 551112
Laurie Holcomb (Founder & CEO)
Rozlyn Lipsey (COO)
Marshall Minor (CFO)
Greg Gamet (Chief Compliance Offi-
cer)
Mark Russ (Chief Revenue Officer)
Phillip Hague (Chief Cultivation Offi-
cer)
Judith Schvimmer (Chief Legal Offi-
cer)
Chris Lane (CMO)

GOLD LAKES CORP.
3401 Enterprise Pkwy Ste 340,
Beachwood, OH 42122
Tel.: (216) 916-9393   NV
Year Founded: 2007
GLLK—(OTCIQ)
Gold & Other Metal Mining Services
N.A.I.C.S.: 212220
Christopher P. Vallos (Pres, CEO &
CFO)

GOLD RESERVE INC.
999 W Riverside Ave Ste 401, Spo-
kane, WA 99201
Tel.: (509) 623-1500   AB
Web Site:
   https://www.goldreserveinc.com
Year Founded: 1956
GDRZF—(OTCQX)
Rev.: $582,523
Assets: $52,943,925
Liabilities: $1,351,341
Net Worth: $51,592,584
Earnings: ($8,596,516)
Emp.: 5
Fiscal Year-end: 12/31/22
Gold Ore & Silver Ore Mining
N.A.I.C.S.: 212220
James Hayward Coleman (Pres)
Robert A. Cohen (Chm)
David P. Onzay (CFO)

**GOLD RESOURCE CORPORA-
TION**
7900 E Union Ave Ste 320, Denver,
CO 80237
Tel.: (303) 320-7708   CO
Web Site:
   https://www.goldresourcecorp.com
Year Founded: 1998
GORO—(NYSEAMEX)
Rev.: $138,724,000
Assets: $204,171,000
Liabilities: $92,407,000
Net Worth: $111,764,000
Earnings: ($6,321,000)
Emp.: 587
Fiscal Year-end: 12/31/22
Gold & Silver Mining Services
N.A.I.C.S.: 212220
Allen J. Palmiere (Pres & CEO)
Alberto Reyes (COO)
Chet Holyoak (Interim CFO & Con-
troller)

Subsidiaries:

Aquila Resources Inc. (1)
141 Adelaide St West Suite 520, Toronto,
M5H 3L5, ON, Canada
Tel.: (647) 943-5672
Web Site: http://www.aquilaresources.com
Assets: $30,290,305
Liabilities: $39,844,199
Net Worth: ($9,553,894)
Earnings: ($7,530,530)

Gold Resource Corporation—(Continued)

Emp.: 19
Fiscal Year-end: 12/31/2019
Zinc Mining Services
N.A.I.C.S.: 212230
Andrew Boushy (Sr VP-Projects)
Stephanie Malec (CFO)
David Carew (Dir-Corp Dev & IR)
David Anderson (Gen Mgr)
Bob Mahin (Dir-Exploration)
Michael Foley (Dir-Environment & Infrastructure)

GOLD ROCK HOLDINGS INC.

2020 General Booth Blvd Unit 230,
Virginia Beach, VA 23454
Tel.: (757) 306-6090   **NV**
Web Site:
   https://www.goldrockholdings.us
Year Founded: 1993
GRHI—(OTCIQ)
Offices of Other Holding Companies
N.A.I.C.S.: 551112
Merle Ferguson (Chm)
Richard Kaiser (CFO)

GOLDEN ALLY LIFETECH GROUP, INC.

901 S Mopac Exp Bldg 1 Ste 300,
Austin, TX 78746
Tel.: (512) 430-1553   **DE**
Web Site: https://goldenaltg.com
Year Founded: 2005
AQPW—(OTCIQ)
Assets: $1,720,816
Liabilities: $129,323
Net Worth: $1,591,493
Earnings: ($6,071,587)
Emp.: 10
Fiscal Year-end: 12/31/22
Medical Device Mfr
N.A.I.C.S.: 339112
Oliver K. Ban (CEO)
Wen Li (CTO)
Carter Yeung (Officer-Marketing)

GOLDEN ARROW MERGER CORP.

10 E 53rd St 13th Fl, New York, NY
10022
Tel.: (212) 430-2214   **DE**
Web Site:
   https://www.goldenarrowspac.com
Year Founded: 2020
GAMC—(NASDAQ)
Rev.: $11,950,157
Assets: $291,067,513
Liabilities: $301,153,089
Net Worth: ($10,085,576)
Earnings: $9,846,711
Emp.: 1
Fiscal Year-end: 12/31/22
Investment Services
N.A.I.C.S.: 523999
Jacob Doft (Chm)
Timothy Babich (CEO & CFO)

GOLDEN DEVELOPING SOLUTIONS, INC.

PO Box 400573, Fort Lauderdale, FL
33346
Tel.: (623) 826-5206
Web Site:
   https://www.goldendeveloping.com
Year Founded: 1998
DVLP—(OTCIQ)
Assets: $8,713,325
Liabilities: $6,672,735
Net Worth: $2,040,590
Earnings: ($1,410,505)
Fiscal Year-end: 12/31/22
Health Care Srvices
N.A.I.C.S.: 621999
Stavros A. Triant (Chm, Pres, CEO, CFO, Treas & Sec)

GOLDEN ENTERTAINMENT, INC.

6595 S Jones Blvd, Las Vegas, NV
89118
Tel.: (702) 893-7777   **MN**
Web Site: https://www.goldenent.com
GDEN—(NASDAQ)
Rev.: $1,121,719,000
Assets: $1,508,670,000
Liabilities: $1,155,750,000
Net Worth: $352,920,000
Earnings: $82,346,000
Emp.: 6,400
Fiscal Year-end: 12/31/22
Offices of Other Holding Companies
N.A.I.C.S.: 551112
Thomas E. Haas (Sr VP-Acctg)
Stephen A. Arcana (Chief Dev Officer)
Blake L. Sartini II (COO & Exec VP)
Blake L. Sartini (Chm & CEO)
Charles H. Protell (Pres & CFO)

Subsidiaries:

American Casino & Entertainment
Properties LLC   (1)
2000 Las Vegas Blvd S, Las Vegas, NV
89104
Tel.: (702) 383-5242
Web Site: http://www.aceplllc.com
Emp.: 4,300
Holding Company; Casino Hotel Owner &
Operator
N.A.I.C.S.: 551112

Subsidiary (Domestic):

Stratosphere LLC   (2)
2000 Las Vegas Blvd S, Las Vegas, NV
89104
Tel.: (702) 380-7777
Web Site: https://thestrat.com
Hotel & Casino Operator
N.A.I.C.S.: 721120

Subsidiary (Domestic):

Stratosphere Gaming LLC   (3)
2000 Las Vegas Blvd S, Las Vegas, NV
89104
Tel.: (702) 380-7777
Web Site: https://thestrat.com
Casino Operator
N.A.I.C.S.: 721120

Subsidiary (Domestic):

Vacation Village, Inc.   (2)
1900 S Casino Dr, Laughlin, NV 89029
Tol.: (702) 208 5111
Web Site:
   http://www.aquariuscasinoresort.com
Hotel & Casino Operator
N.A.I.C.S.: 721120

Golden Gaming, LLC   (1)
6595 S Jones Blvd, Las Vegas, NV 89118-
1725
Tel.: (702) 893-7777
Casino Operator
N.A.I.C.S.: 721120
Kim Ast (Dir-Adv & Creative Mktg)

Golden Pahrump Nugget, LLC   (1)
681 S Hwy 160, Pahrump, NV 89048
Tel.: (775) 751-7770
Web Site:
   https://www.goldencasinogroup.com
Casino Operator
N.A.I.C.S.: 721120

Golden Pahrump Town, LLC   (1)
771 S Frontage Rd, Pahrump, NV 89048
Tel.: (775) 751-7700
Web Site: http://www.gtowncasino.com
Casino Operator
N.A.I.C.S.: 721120

Golden Route Operations LLC   (1)
6595 S Jones Blvd, Las Vegas, NV 89118
Tel.: (702) 597-9000
Web Site: https://www.gronevada.com
Gambling Services
N.A.I.C.S.: 721120
Blake Sartini II (Exec VP)

Lakes Gaming & Resorts, LLC   (1)

130 Cheshire Ln Ste 101, Minnetonka, MN
55305-1052
Tel.: (952) 449-9092
Emp.: 30
Casinos, Hotels & Resorts Management
Services
N.A.I.C.S.: 713210
Timothy J. Cope (Pres, CFO & Treas)

Unit (Domestic):

Rocky Gap Casino Resort   (2)
16701 Lakeview Rd, Flintstone, MD 21530-
1055
Tel.: (301) 784-8400
Web Site: http://www.rockygapcasino.com
Sales Range: $1-9.9 Million
Emp.: 125
Casino & Resort Operator
N.A.I.C.S.: 721110

GOLDEN FALCON ACQUISITION CORP.

850 Library Ave Ste 204, Newark, DE
19711
Tel.: (970) 315-2644   **DE**
Web Site:
   https://www.goldenfalconcorp.com
Year Founded: 2020
GFX—(NYSE)
Rev.: $17,634,587
Assets: $42,678,519
Liabilities: $54,813,414
Net Worth: ($12,134,895)
Earnings: $13,802,503
Emp.: 3
Fiscal Year-end: 12/31/22
Investment Services
N.A.I.C.S.: 523999
Scott J. Freidheim (Chm)
Makram Azar (CEO)
Eli Muraidekh (CFO)
John M. Basnage de Beauval (Gen
Counsel & Sec)

GOLDEN GRAIL TECHNOLOGY CORP.

4548 N Federal Hwy, Fort Lauderdale, FL 33308
Tel.: (561) 800-3891   **NV**
Year Founded: 1985
GOGY—(OTCIQ)
Online Marketing Services
N.A.I.C.S.: 541810
Russ Kaffenberger (Chief Revenue
Officer)
Steven Hoffman (CEO)

GOLDEN GROWERS COOPERATIVE

1002 Main Ave W Ste 5, West Fargo,
ND 58078
Tel.: (701) 281-0468
Web Site:
   https://www.goldengrowers.com
Year Founded: 1994
GGROU—(OTCIQ)
Rev.: $107,409,000
Assets: $27,859,000
Liabilities: $205,000
Net Worth: $27,654,000
Earnings: $6,680,000
Emp.: 1
Fiscal Year-end: 12/31/22
Corn Production Services
N.A.I.C.S.: 111150
Leslie O. Nesvig (Treas)
Mark Leon Harless (Chm)
Matthew Hasbargen (Sec)
Scott Stofferahn (CEO, CFO & Exec
VP)
Nicolas Pyle (Vice Chm)

GOLDEN MATRIX GROUP, INC.

3651 Lindell Rd Ste D131, Las Vegas, NV 89103-1200
Tel.: (702) 318-7548   **NV**

Web Site:
   https://www.goldenmatrix.com
Year Founded: 2008
GMGI—(NASDAQ)
Rev.: $43,511,520
Assets: $35,582,817
Liabilities: $4,479,423
Net Worth: $31,103,394
Earnings: ($1,172,750)
Emp.: 30
Fiscal Year-end: 10/31/23
Online Game Development Services
N.A.I.C.S.: 541511
Anthony Brian Goodman (CEO)
Henry Zhang (CTO)
Weiting Feng (COO)
Brett Goodman (Sr VP & VP)
Zoran Milosevic (CEO-Meridianbet
Grp)
Omar Jimenez (CFO, Chief Compliance Officer & Principal Acctg Officer)

Subsidiaries:

Global Technology Group Pty Ltd   (1)
90 Bluestone Circuit, Seventeen Mile
Rocks, Brisbane, 4073, QLD, Australia
Tel.: (61) 733744038
Web Site:
   http://www.globaltechgroup.com.au
Information Technology Development Services
N.A.I.C.S.: 541511

GOLDEN MINERALS COMPANY

350 Indiana St Ste 650, Golden, CO
80401
Tel.: (303) 839-5060   **CO**
Web Site:
   https://www.goldenminerals.com
Year Founded: 1993
AUMN—(NYSEAMEX)
Rev.: $23,285,000
Assets: $14,944,000
Liabilities: $8,464,000
Net Worth: $6,480,000
Earnings: ($9,906,000)
Emp.: 238
Fiscal Year-end: 12/31/22
Gold Mining & Exploration Services
N.A.I.C.S.: 212220
Karen L. Winkler (Dir-IR & Asst Sec)
Pablo Castanos (Pres & CEO)

Subsidiaries:

Ingelec S.A.   (1)
Av Hernando Siles N 5593 Tunupa Building
3rd Floor - Office 303, 1198, La Paz, Bolivia
Tel.: (591) 22784242
Web Site: https://www.ingelec.com.bo
Sales Range: $250-299.9 Million
Emp.: 15
Water & Sewer Line & Related Structures
Construction
N.A.I.C.S.: 237110

GOLDEN PACIFIC BANCORP, INC.

1409 28th St, Sacramento, CA 95816
Tel.: (916) 288-1069
Web Site:
   http://www.goldenpacificbank.com
GPBI—(OTCIQ)
Bank Holding Company
N.A.I.C.S.: 551111
Virginia Varela (Pres & CEO)

Subsidiaries:

Golden Pacific Bank, N.A.   (1)
1409 28th St, Sacramento, CA 95814
Tel.: (916) 444-2450
Web Site: http://www.goldenpacificbank.com
Commericial Banking
N.A.I.C.S.: 522110
Virginia Varela (CEO)

GOLDEN STAR ACQUISITION CORP.

99 Hudson St 5th Fl, New York, NY 10013
Tel.: (646) 706-5365   Ky
Year Founded: 2021
GODN—(NASDAQ)
Rev.: $2,357,323
Assets: $72,086,698
Liabilities: $74,315,425
Net Worth: ($2,228,727)
Earnings: $1,499,586
Emp.: 2
Fiscal Year-end: 12/31/23
Investment Management Service
N.A.I.C.S.: 523999

GOLDEN STAR RESOURCE CORP.

Ste 300-500 N Rainbow Blvd, Las Vegas, NV 89107
Tel.: (760) 464-9869   NV
Web Site: https://www.gsr.com
Year Founded: 2006
GLNS—(OTCQB)
Assets: $2,813
Liabilities: $821,854
Net Worth: ($819,041)
Earnings: ($47,628)
Fiscal Year-end: 06/30/24
Mineral Exploration Services
N.A.I.C.S.: 212290
Marilyn Miller *(Pres, CEO, CFO, Principal Acctg Officer, Treas & Sec)*

GOLDEN STATE BANCORP

500 N Brand Blvd 23rd Fl, Glendale, CA 91203
Tel.: (818) 254-1052   Ca
Web Site:
   https://www.goldenstatebank.com
GSBX—(OTCIQ)
Rev.: $18,405,606
Assets: $352,163,174
Liabilities: $320,781,237
Net Worth: $31,381,937
Earnings: $1,402,644
Fiscal Year-end: 12/31/19
Offices of Bank Holding Companies
N.A.I.C.S.: 551111
Robert H. Setrakian *(Chm & CEO)*
Tom Vertin *(COO & Exec VP)*
Yvonne Chen *(CFO & Exec VP)*

GOLDEN TIME NETWORK MARKETING LTD.

801 W Big Beaver Ste 650, Troy, MI 48084
Tel.: (248) 430-4300
Web Site:
   http://www.supportsave.com
Year Founded: 2007
GTNM—(OTCIQ)
Sales Range: $1-9.9 Million
Emp.: 290
Offshore Business Process Outsourcing Services
N.A.I.C.S.: 561499
Beatrice Pia White *(VP)*
Christopher S. Johns *(Pres, CEO & CFO)*

GOLDEN TRIANGLE VENTURES, INC.

3305 E Patrick Ln Ste 15, Las Vegas, NV 89120
Web Site:
   https://www.goldentriangleinc.com
GTVH—(OTCIQ)
Holding Company
N.A.I.C.S.: 551112
Steffan Dalsgaard *(Chm)*

Subsidiaries:

Napa Wine Co. LLC   **(1)**

7830-40 St Helena Hwy, Oakville, CA 94562
Tel.: (707) 944-8669
Web Site: http://www.napawineco.com
Sales Range: $1-9.9 Million
Emp.: 35
Wines, Brandy, And Brandy Spirits, Nsk
N.A.I.C.S.: 312130
Andy Hoxsey *(Principal)*

GOLDEN VALLEY BANK

190 Cohasset Rd Ste 170, Chico, CA 95926
Tel.: (530) 894-1000   CA
Web Site:
   https://www.goldenvalley.bank
Year Founded: 2006
GVYB—(OTCIQ)
Commercial Banking Services
N.A.I.C.S.: 522110
Mark Francis *(Pres & CEO)*
James Doss *(Chief Credit Officer)*
Barbara Crouse *(CFO)*
Dayle Quiroga *(Officer-Rels Banking)*
Ashley Hilton *(Officer-Rels Banking)*

GOLDEN VALLEY DEVELOPMENT, INC.

30 N Gould St Ste R, Sheridan, WY 82801
Tel.: (404) 301-3979   NV
Web Site:
   http://www.goldenvalleydev.com
Year Founded: 2004
GVDI—(OTCIQ)
Sales Range: Less than $1 Million
Emp.: 2
Farming Commodities Broker
N.A.I.C.S.: 213115
M. Kevin Sorrels *(Chm & Co-CEO)*
Nikolaos M. Balomenos *(Co-CEO)*
Carter Ransom *(COO & VP)*

GOLDENSTONE ACQUISITION LTD.

37-02 Prince St 2nd Fl, Flushing, NY 11354
Tel.: (330) 352-7788   DE
Year Founded: 2020
GDST—(NASDAQ)
Rev.: $1,483,785
Assets: $60,448,458
Liabilities: $62,545,647
Net Worth: ($2,097,189)
Earnings: $145,511
Fiscal Year-end: 03/31/23
Investment Services
N.A.I.C.S.: 523999
Eddie Ni *(Pres, CEO & CFO)*

GOLDENWELL BIOTECH, INC.

581 Boston Mills Rd Ste 300, Hudson, OH 44087
Tel.: (440) 666-7999   NV
Web Site:
   http://www.goldenwellbiotech.com
Year Founded: 2019
GWLL—(OTCQB)
Rev.: $47,800
Assets: $248,400
Liabilities: $46,782
Net Worth: $201,618
Earnings: ($985,097)
Emp.: 3
Fiscal Year-end: 12/31/22
Pharmaceutical Products Distr
N.A.I.C.S.: 424210
Shuang Liu *(Pres & CEO)*
Li Yang *(Treas)*
Xie Hua *(Sec)*

GOLDKEY CORPORATION

10220 N Ambassador Dr, Kansas City, MO 64153
Tel.: (816) 220-3000   NV
Web Site: https://www.goldkey.com
ZWBC—(OTCIQ)

Other Computer Related Services
N.A.I.C.S.: 541519
Roger E. Billings *(Chm & CEO)*

GOLDMAN SACHS MLP & ENERGY RENAISSANCE FUND

200 W St, New York, NY 10282
Web Site:
   http://www.goldmansachs.com
GER—(NYSE)
Rev.: $5,742,472
Assets: $538,048,647
Liabilities: $210,365,089
Net Worth: $327,683,558
Earnings: ($9,211,177)
Fiscal Year-end: 11/30/19
Investment Management Service
N.A.I.C.S.: 525990
Cheryl K. Beebe *(Chm)*
James A. McNamara *(Pres)*

GOLDRICH MINING COMPANY

2525 E 29th Ave Ste 10B 160, Spokane, WA 99223
Tel.: (509) 535-7367   AK
Web Site:
   https://www.goldrichmining.com
Year Founded: 1959
GRMC—(OTCIQ)
Assets: $761,924
Liabilities: $11,976,360
Net Worth: ($11,214,436)
Earnings: ($1,055,630)
Emp.: 2
Fiscal Year-end: 12/31/22
Gold Mining & Exploration Services
N.A.I.C.S.: 212220
William Orchow *(Chm)*
Stephen M. Vincent *(Interim CEO)*
Ted R. Sharp *(CFO, Principal Acctg Officer, Treas & Sec)*

GOLIATH FILM & MEDIA HOLDINGS, INC.

4640 Admiralty Way Ste 500, Marina Del Rey, CA 90292
Tel.: (909) 612-1708   NV
Web Site:
   https://www.goliathfilmandmediain
   ternational.com
GFMH—(OTCIQ)
Rev.: $47,674
Assets: $437
Liabilities: $101,039
Net Worth: ($100,602)
Earnings: ($396)
Fiscal Year-end: 04/30/24
Video Content Developer & Distr
N.A.I.C.S.: 512120
Lamont K. Roberts *(Pres, CEO & Acting CFO)*
Michael Criscione *(Dir-Marketing & COO)*

GOLOGIQ, INC.

85 Broad St 16-079, New York, NY 10004
Tel.: (659) 366-2322   NV
Web Site: https://gologiq.com
Year Founded: 2018
GOLQ—(OTCIQ)
Rev.: $5,454,119
Assets: $11,835,254
Liabilities: $2,109,528
Net Worth: $9,725,726
Earnings: ($24,254,322)
Emp.: 1
Fiscal Year-end: 12/31/22
Application Software Development Services
N.A.I.C.S.: 541511
Brent Y. Suen *(Chm)*
Granger Whitelaw *(CEO)*
Eddie Foong *(Chief Product Officer)*

GOOD TIMES RESTAURANTS, INC.

651 Corporate Cir No 200, Golden, CO 80401
Tel.: (303) 384-1400   NV
Year Founded: 1987
GTIM—(NASDAQ)
Rev.: $142,315,000
Assets: $87,118,000
Liabilities: $54,030,000
Net Worth: $33,088,000
Earnings: $1,879,000
Emp.: 2,110
Fiscal Year-end: 09/24/24
Fast Food Restaurants Owner & Operater
N.A.I.C.S.: 722513
Boyd E. Hoback *(Founder)*
Ryan M. Zink *(Pres & CEO)*
Donald L. Stack *(Sr VP-Ops)*

Subsidiaries:

Bad Daddy's International, LLC   **(1)**
504 Hanes Mall Blvd, Winston Salem, NC 27103
Tel.: (336) 893-6456
Web Site:
   http://www.baddaddysburgerbar.com
Limited-Service Restaurants
N.A.I.C.S.: 722513

Good Times Drive-Thru, Inc.   **(1)**
141 Union Blvd Ste 400, Lakewood, CO 80228
Tel.: (303) 384-1400
Full-Service Restaurants
N.A.I.C.S.: 722511

GOOD VIBRATIONS SHOES INC.

3535 Executive Terminal Dr Ste 110, Henderson, NV 89052
Tel.: (321) 735-4653
Web Site:
   http://www.goodvibrationsshoes.com
GVSI—(OTCIQ)
Sales Range: Less than $1 Million
Shoe Mfr
N.A.I.C.S.: 316210
Richard Koenig *(CEO)*

GOOD WORKS ACQUISITION CORP.

4265 San Felipe Ste 603, Houston, TX 77027
Tel.: (713) 468-2717   DE
Year Founded: 2020
GWII—(NASDAQ)
Rev.: $36,932
Assets: $232,193,317
Liabilities: $230,150,719
Net Worth: $2,042,598
Earnings: ($501,609)
Emp.: 2
Fiscal Year-end: 12/31/21
Investment Services
N.A.I.C.S.: 523999
Frederick Schwartz Zeidman *(Chm & CEO)*
Cary Grossman *(Pres)*

GOODRX HOLDINGS, INC.

2701 Olympic Blvd W Building Ste 200, Santa Monica, CA 90404   DE
Web Site: https://www.goodrx.com
Year Founded: 2015
GDRX—(NASDAQ)
Rev.: $766,554,000
Assets: $1,604,631,000
Liabilities: $789,804,000
Net Worth: $814,827,000
Earnings: ($32,828,000)
Emp.: 952
Fiscal Year-end: 12/31/22
Holding Company
N.A.I.C.S.: 551112
Scott W. Wagner *(Interim CEO & Principal Operating Officer)*

GoodRx Holdings, Inc.—(Continued)

Dorothy Gemmell *(Chief Comml Officer)*
Karsten Voermann *(CFO)*
Romin Nabiey *(Chief Acctg Officer)*
Mike Walsh *(Pres & Exec VP-Prescription Marketplace)*
Nitin Shingate *(CTO)*
Vina Leite *(Chief People Officer)*
Gracye Cheng *(Gen Counsel)*
Douglas Hirsch *(Co-Founder & Chief Mission Officer)*
Trevor Bezdek *(Co-Founder & Chm)*
Vina Leite *(Chief People Officer)*

Subsidiaries:

VitaCare Prescription Services, Inc. **(1)**
6800 Broken Sound Pkwy NW, Boca Raton, FL 33487
Tel.: (561) 961-1902
Web Site: http://www.vitamedmdrx.com
Pharmaceutical Product Mfr & Distr
N.A.I.C.S.: 325412
John C. K. Milligan IV *(CEO)*

GOOI GLOBAL

317 6th Ave Ste 400, Des Moines, IA 50309 **DE**
Web Site: http://www.gooiglobal.com
Year Founded: 1986
GOOI—(OTCIQ)
Investment Holding Company Services
N.A.I.C.S.: 551112
Mike Kemery *(CEO)*
John W. Pim *(CFO & Controller)*
Jill Stookesberry *(Sec)*
Brian Baltutat *(Chief Product Officer)*

GOOOGREEN, INC.

3160 NW 1st Ave, Pompano Beach, FL 33064
Tel.: (954) 908-3366
Year Founded: 2007
GOOO—(OTCIQ)
Health Care Srvices
N.A.I.C.S.: 621999
Thomas Terwilliger *(Pres)*

GOOSEHEAD INSURANCE, INC.

1500 Solana Blvd Ste 4500, Westlake, TX 76262
Tel.: (214) 838-5500 **DE**
Web Site:
https://www.gooseheadinsurance.com
Year Founded: 2017
GSHD—(NASDAQ)
Rev.: $261,276,000
Assets: $354,892,000
Liabilities: $338,106,000
Net Worth: $16,786,000
Earnings: $14,140,000
Emp.: 1,415
Fiscal Year-end: 12/31/23
Insurance Agencies & Brokerages
N.A.I.C.S.: 524210
Mark E. Jones *(Co-Founder, Exec Chm & CFO)*
Robyn Jones *(Co-Founder & Vice Chm)*
P. Ryan Langston *(Chief Legal Officer & Sec)*
Mark K. Miller *(Pres, CEO & COO)*
Brian Pattillo *(VP)*
Dan Farrell *(VP-Capital Markets)*
Justin Ricketts *(Exec VP-Tech & Partnerships)*
Mark E. Jones Jr. *(CFO)*
John O'Connor *(Gen Counsel)*
Ann Challis *(CMO)*
Matthew Hunt *(VP)*
Craig Lauck *(VP)*
Ted Olsen *(VP)*

Lauren Menuey *(Mng Dir)*
Nathan Roberts *(Mng Dir)*
Sally Dahlstrom *(Mng Dir)*
Brim Basom *(Mng Dir)*
Brad Giannini *(Mng Dir)*
Matt Walker *(Mng Dir)*
Julia Jordan *(Mng Dir)*
Jared Sinclair *(Mng Dir)*
Shana Bibbs *(Mng Dir)*
Anthony Roland *(Mng Dir)*
Marissa Brumbeloe *(Mng Dir)*
Erin Baima *(Mng Dir)*
Gregory Lappo *(Mng Dir)*
Jacob Cravens *(Mng Dir)*
William Prassas *(Mng Dir)*
Jackie May *(Mng Dir)*
Marisa Wagner *(Mng Dir)*
Mitchell Stella *(Mng Dir)*
Kaely Ferguson *(Mng Dir)*
Ethan Warren *(Mng Dir)*
Dericka Marshall-Dillon *(Mng Dir)*

GOPRO, INC.

3025 Clearview Way, San Mateo, CA 94402
Tel.: (650) 332-7600 **DE**
Web Site: https://www.gopro.com
GPRO—(NASDAQ)
Rev.: $1,005,459,000
Assets: $967,951,000
Liabilities: $412,105,000
Net Worth: $555,846,000
Earnings: ($53,183,000)
Emp.: 930
Fiscal Year-end: 12/31/23
Photographic Equipment Mfr
N.A.I.C.S.: 333310
Christopher Clark *(VP-Corp Comm)*
Cedri Fernandes *(VP-Software Engrg)*
Brian McGee *(CFO, COO & Exec VP)*
Vincent Nakayama *(Sr VP-Engrg)*
Pablo Lema *(Sr VP/VP-Product Mgmt)*
Tim Betry *(Sr VP/VP-People & Places)*
Kacey Sharrett *(VP-Direct to Customer)*
Nicholas Woodman *(Founder, Chm & CEO)*

Subsidiaries:

GoPro GmbH **(1)**
Flubergasse 2, 81369, Munich, Germany
Tel.: (49) 8921093535
Software & Hardware Developing Services
N.A.I.C.S.: 541512

GORES GUGGENHEIM, INC.

6260 Lookout Rd, Boulder, CO 80301
Tel.: (303) 531-3100 **DE**
Year Founded: 2020
GGPI—(NASDAQ)
Assets: $801,836,231
Liabilities: $932,929,383
Net Worth: ($131,093,152)
Earnings: ($81,941,027)
Emp.: 3
Fiscal Year-end: 12/31/21
Investment Services
N.A.I.C.S.: 523999
Alec Gores *(Chm)*
Mark Stone *(CEO)*
Andrew M. Rosenfield *(Pres)*
Andrew McBride *(CFO & Sec)*

GORES TECHNOLOGY PARTNERS, INC.

6260 Lookout Rd, Boulder, CO 80301
Tel.: (303) 531-3100 **DE**
Year Founded: 2020
GTPA—(NASDAQ)
Rev.: $21,852
Assets: $276,315,457
Liabilities: $298,816,953

Net Worth: ($22,501,496)
Earnings: ($5,124,924)
Emp.: 3
Fiscal Year-end: 12/31/21
Investment Services
N.A.I.C.S.: 523999
Alec Gores *(Chm)*
Ted Fike *(CEO)*
Andrew McBride *(CFO & Sec)*

GOSSAMER BIO, INC.

3013 Science Park Rd Ste 200, San Diego, CA 92121
Tel.: (858) 684-1300 **DE**
Web Site:
https://www.gossamerbio.com
Year Founded: 2015
GOSS—(NASDAQ)
Rev.: $1,583,000
Assets: $272,450,000
Liabilities: $260,373,000
Net Worth: $12,077,000
Earnings: ($229,378,000)
Emp.: 178
Fiscal Year-end: 12/31/22
Pharmaceutical Product Mfr & Distr
N.A.I.C.S.: 325412
Deanna Weber *(Sr VP-HR)*
Richard Aranda *(Chief Medical Officer)*
Matt Cravets *(Sr VP)*
Lisa Nolan *(Pres)*
Mario Orlando *(Sr VP)*
Caryn Peterson *(Exec VP)*
Colin Rowlings *(Sr VP)*
Faheem Hasnain *(Founder, Chm & CEO)*
Bryan Giraudo *(CFO & COO)*

GOULD INVESTORS, L.P.

60 Cuttermill Rd Ste 303, Great Neck, NY 11021
Tel.: (516) 466-3100 **MA**
Web Site: https://www.gouldlp.com
Year Founded: 1960
GDVTZ—(OTCIQ)
Sales Range: $350-399.9 Million
Emp.: 25
Real Estate Investment Trust & Property Lessor
N.A.I.C.S.: 525990

GPO PLUS, INC.

3571 E Sunset Rd Ste 300, Las Vegas, NV 89120
Tel.: (852) -238-9111 **NV**
Web Site: https://www.gpoplus.com
Year Founded: 2016
GPOX—(OTCQB)
Rev.: $4,356,303
Assets: $909,997
Liabilities: $4,455,669
Net Worth: ($3,545,672)
Earnings: ($4,937,934)
Emp.: 19
Fiscal Year-end: 04/30/24
Support Services
N.A.I.C.S.: 561990
Brett H. Pojunis *(CEO, Chm, Treas & Sec)*
Laurence Ruhe *(CFO)*
Wayne Smeal *(COO)*

GQG PARTNERS INC.

450 E Las Olas Blvd Ste 750, Fort Lauderdale, FL 33301
Tel.: (754) 218-5500 **DE**
Web Site: https://gqg.com
Year Founded: 2016
GQG—(ASX)
Rev.: $517,585,000
Assets: $389,502,000
Liabilities: $39,963,000
Net Worth: $349,539,000
Earnings: $282,518,000
Emp.: 189

Fiscal Year-end: 12/31/23
Asset Management Services
N.A.I.C.S.: 523999
Bobby Sokolich *(CTO)*
Charles Falck *(COO)*
Rajiv Jain *(Chm)*
Tim Carver *(CEO)*

Subsidiaries:

GQG Partners (Australia) Pty Ltd. **(1)**
Level 15 03 Chifley Tower 2 Chifley Square, Sydney, 2000, NSW, Australia
Tel.: (61) 272558313
Financial Management Services
N.A.I.C.S.: 551112

GRACO, INC.

88 11th Ave NE, Minneapolis, MN 55413
Tel.: (612) 623-6000 **MN**
Web Site: https://www.graco.com
Year Founded: 1926
GGG—(NYSE)
Rev.: $2,195,606,000
Assets: $2,722,007,000
Liabilities: $497,782,000
Net Worth: $2,224,225,000
Earnings: $506,511,000
Emp.: 4,000
Fiscal Year-end: 12/29/23
Lubricating & Fluid Material Handling Equipment, Paint Circulating & Application Equipment, Atomizing Devices, Control Hardware & Software & Specialized Pumps, Regulators & Dispensing Valves Mfr
N.A.I.C.S.: 333914
Mark W. Sheahan *(Pres & CEO)*
David M. Lowe *(CFO & Treas)*
Caroline M. Chambers *(Pres-EMEA & Exec VP-Information Sys)*
Kathryn L. Schoenrock *(CTO & Exec VP)*
Christopher D. Knutson *(Principal Acctg Officer, Exec VP & Controller)*
Inge Grasdal *(Exec VP-Corp Dev)*
Laura L. Evanson *(Exec VP-Mktg)*
Ronita Banerjee *(Chief HR Officer & Exec VP)*
Chris Knutson *(Dir)*
Joseph J. Humke *(Gen Counsel, Sec & Exec VP)*
Karen Park Gallivan *(Gen Counsel, Sec & Exec VP)*

Subsidiaries:

Alco Valves Group Limited **(1)**
Armytage Road, Brighouse, HD6 1PT, West Yorkshire, United Kingdom
Tel.: (44) 1484710511
Web Site: https://www.alco-valves.com
Industrial Valve Mfr
N.A.I.C.S.: 332911

Subsidiary (US):

Alco Valves (US), Inc. **(2)**
11275 W Sam Houston Pkwy S Ste 175, Houston, TX 77031
Tel.: (281) 564-2526
Web Site: http://www.alco-valves.com
Emp.: 5
Industrial Valve Mfr
N.A.I.C.S.: 332911

Subsidiary (Non-US):

Alco Valves Inc. **(2)**
27 Monarch Road Unit 1, Guelph, N1K 1N4, ON, Canada
Tel.: (519) 767-6655
Emp.: 9
Industrial Valve Mfr
N.A.I.C.S.: 332911

COROB S.p.A. **(1)**
Via Agricoltura 103, 41038, San Felice sul Panaro, MO, Italy
Tel.: (39) 0535663111

Web Site: http://www.corob.com
Paint & Coating Industry Mixing & Point-of-Sale Equipment Mfr & Whslr
N.A.I.C.S.: 333310
Valentina Franceschini (Chm)

Subsidiary (Non-US):

Automation Techniques Pty. Ltd. (2)
52 Hannah Road, PO Box 17257, Congella, Durban, 4013, South Africa
Tel.: (27) 86 11 000 55
Web Site: http://www.automation.co.za
Integrated Tinting Solutions
N.A.I.C.S.: 423440

COROB Brasil (2)
Condominio Sao Bento Modulo 05 Av Leonil Cre Bortolosso 88, Osasco, 06186-260, Sao Paulo, Brazil
Tel.: (55) 11 3607 3553
Web Site: http://corob.com
Paint & Coating Industry Mixing & Point-of-Sale Equipment Whslr
N.A.I.C.S.: 423440

COROB GmbH (2)
Rheinstrasse 7, D-41836, Huckelhoven, Germany
Tel.: (49) 2433 45804 70
Web Site: http://corob.com
Paint & Coating Industry Mixing & Point-of-Sale Equipment Whslr
N.A.I.C.S.: 423440

COROB India Pvt. Ltd. (2)
SF A 01 Art Guild House-Phoenix MArket City Complex Kanami Junction, LBS MArg Kurka W, 400070, Mumbai, India
Tel.: (91) 22 664 97 777
Web Site: http://corob.com
Paint & Coating Industry Mixing & Dispensing Equipment Mfr & Whslr
N.A.I.C.S.: 333310

Subsidiary (US):

COROB North America, Inc. (2)
4901-A Gibbon Rd, Charlotte, NC 28269
Tel.: (704) 588-8408
Web Site: http://corob.com
Paint & Coating Industry Mixing & Point-of-Sale Equipment Whslr
N.A.I.C.S.: 423440
Bill Rotner (VP-Sls)

Subsidiary (Non-US):

COROB Oy (2)
Paivolantie 5, 28400, Ulvila, Finland
Tel.: (358) 20 1710 400
Web Site: http://corob.com
Paint & Coating Industry Mixing & Point-of-Sale Equipment Mfr & Whslr
N.A.I.C.S.: 333310

COROB Pte. Ltd. (2)
No 8 Boon Lay Way 09-06/07 8 Tradehub21, Singapore, 609964, Singapore
Tel.: (65) 6665 1301
Web Site: http://www.corob.com
Paint & Coating Industry Mixing & Point-of-Sale Equipment Whslr
N.A.I.C.S.: 423440

COROB Rus (2)
14/3 Krzhizhanovskogo Str BC Ferro-Plaza Offices 345-351, 117218, Moscow, Russia
Tel.: (7) 4957874352
Web Site: https://www.corob.com
Paint & Coating Industry Mixing & Point-of-Sale Equipment Whslr
N.A.I.C.S.: 423440

COROB S.A. (2)
Edificio NEXUS Dpto 003, Ruta 8 km 17500-Zonamerica, Montevideo, Uruguay
Tel.: (598) 25185500
Web Site: http://corob.com
Paint & Coating Industry Mixing & Point-of-Sale Equipment Whslr
N.A.I.C.S.: 423440
Reubens Da Cunha (Mng Dir, VP & Head-Sls)

COROB Scandinavia AB (2)
Knipplekullen 3B, S-417 49, Gothenburg, Sweden
Tel.: (46) 317 481 850
Web Site: http://corob.com

Paint & Coating Industry Mixing & Point-of-Sale Equipment Whslr
N.A.I.C.S.: 423440

COROB Trading (Shenzhen) Limited (2)
Room 1440 14F-Times Financial Centre 6011-4001 Shennan Avenue, Futian District, Shenzhen, 518046, Guandong, China
Tel.: (86) 755 82520432
Web Site: http://corob.com
Paint & Coating Industry Mixing & Point-of-Sale Equipment Whslr
N.A.I.C.S.: 423440

Electric Torque Machines, Inc. (1)
1409 E Butler Ave, Flagstaff, AZ 86001
Tel.: (928) 779-3169
Web Site: https://www.etmpower.com
Motor Mfr
N.A.I.C.S.: 335312

Finishing Brands (Shanghai) Co., Ltd. (1)
1st Floor No 201 Minyi Road Songji Ang, Shanghai, 201612, China
Tel.: (86) 2133730108
Industrial Valve Mfr
N.A.I.C.S.: 332911
David Chen (Dir-Mktg & Sls)

Finishing Brands Germany GmbH (1)
Justus-von-liebig Strasse 31, 63128, Dietzenbach, Germany
Tel.: (49) 60744031
Industrial Valve Mfr
N.A.I.C.S.: 332911

GG Manufacturing s.r.l. (1)
Street Stefan Cel Mare nr 193, Siblu, 550321, Romania
Tel.: (40) 269253299
Web Site: http://www.denmarkpowderpcoatings.com
Emp.: 65
Industrial Valve Mfr
N.A.I.C.S.: 332911
Ovidiu Lus (Plant Mgr)

Gema Mexico Powder Finishing, S. de R.L. de C.V. (1)
Avenida Presidente Juarez No 125 B Col San Jeronimo Tepetlacalco, 54090, Tlalnepantla, Mexico
Tel.: (52) 5553668130
Powder Coating Equipment Distr
N.A.I.C.S.: 424690

Gema Switzerland AG (1)
Moevenstrasse 17, 9015, Saint Gallen, Switzerland **(100%)**
Tel.: (41) 713138300
Web Site: https://www.gemapowdercoating.com
Sales Range: $50-74.9 Million
Pumps Mfr
N.A.I.C.S.: 333914

Subsidiary (Non-US):

Gema (Shanghai) Co., Ltd. (2)
Suide Road 628 B1 Building, Shanghai, 200331, China
Tel.: (86) 216 627 5566
Web Site: http://www.itwgema.com.cn
Powder Coating Equipment Mfr & Whslr
N.A.I.C.S.: 423830

Gema Europe s.r.l. (2)
Via Carlo Goldoni 29, 20090, Trezzano sul Naviglio, MI, Italy
Tel.: (39) 024 840 0486
Web Site: https://www.gemapowdercoating.com
Powder Coating Equipment Sales
N.A.I.C.S.: 423830

Subsidiary (US):

Gema USA Inc. (2)
4141 W 54th St, Indianapolis, IN 46254
Tel.: (317) 298-5000
Web Site: https://www.gemapowdercoating.com
Sales Range: $25-49.9 Million
Valve Mfr
N.A.I.C.S.: 332911

Geotechnical Instruments (U.K.) Limited (1)

Cyan Park Unit 3 Jimmy Hill Way, Coventry, CV2 4QP, United Kingdom
Tel.: (44) 3338000088
Web Site: http://www.geotechuk.com
Pump Mfr & Distr
N.A.I.C.S.: 333914
Dean Kavanagh (Mng Dir)
Carl Harris De Melo (Mgr)
Craig Millar (Project Mgr)
Mike Holton (Coord-Quality)
Anthony Li (Sys Engr)
Paul Gooch (Dir-Marketing)
Piotr Slonina (Mgr)
Jesse Yu (Mgr-APAC)
Mike White (Mgr-UK,Ireland)
Paul Gooch (Dir-Marketing)
Piotr Slonina (Mgr)
Jesse Yu (Mgr-APAC)
Mike White (Mgr-UK,Ireland)

Glas-Craft, Inc. (1)
5845 W 82nd St, Indianapolis, IN 46278-1388
Tel.: (317) 875-5592
Web Site: http://www.glascraft.com
Sales Range: $75-99.9 Million
Emp.: 65
Fiberglass, Polyurethane & Industrial Protective Coating Application Equipment Mfr
N.A.I.C.S.: 423830

Graco Australia Pty Ltd (1)
Suite 17 2 Enterprise Drive, Bundoora, Melbourne, 3083, VIC, Australia
Tel.: (61) 39 468 8500
Web Site: http://www.graco-australia.business.site
Fluid Power Pump & Motor Mfr & Distr
N.A.I.C.S.: 333996

Graco Automotive Technology Center (1)
47800 Halyard Dr, Plymouth, MI 48170-2454 **(100%)**
Tel.: (734) 416-3400
Web Site: http://www.graco.com
Sales Range: $450-499.9 Million
Emp.: 40
Paint Finishing Equipment
N.A.I.C.S.: 333996

Graco BVBA (1)
Industrieterrein Oude Bunders, Slakweidestraat 31, 3630, Maasmechelen, Belgium
Tel.: (32) 89770700
Web Site: https://www.graco.com
Emp.: 150
Industrial Valve Mfr
N.A.I.C.S.: 332911

Graco Distribution BVBA (1)
Industrieterrein Oude Bunders Slakweidestraat 31, 3630, Maasmechelen, Belgium
Tel.: (32) 89770700
Web Site: https://www.graco.com
Pump Distr
N.A.I.C.S.: 423830

Graco High Pressure Equipment Inc. (1)
2955 W 17th St, Erie, PA 16505
Tel.: (814) 838-2028
Web Site: https://www.highpressure.com
Pressure Equipment Mfr & Distr
N.A.I.C.S.: 332911

Graco India Private Limited (1)
Plot No 295 Udyog Vihar Phase-IV, Gurgaon, 122 015, Haryana, India
Tel.: (91) 1246610200
Web Site: https://www.graco.com
Pump Distr
N.A.I.C.S.: 423830

Graco KK (1)
1-27-12 Hayabuchi, Tsuzuki-ku, Yokohama, 224-0025, Japan **(100%)**
Tel.: (81) 455937300
Web Site: https://www.graco.co.jp
Sales Range: $10-24.9 Million
Marketing of Service Industry Machinery
N.A.I.C.S.: 333310

Graco Korea, Inc. (1)
38 Samsung 1-ro 1-gil, Hwaseong, 1849, Gyeonggi, Korea (South) **(100%)**
Tel.: (82) 3180150961
Web Site: https://www.graco.com

Sales Range: $10-24.9 Million
N.A.I.C.S.: 333996

Graco Minnesota Inc. (1)
20500 David A Koch Ave, Rogers, MN 55374
Tel.: (612) 623-6000
Web Site: https://www.graco.com
Sales Range: $200-249.9 Million
Valve Mfr
N.A.I.C.S.: 332911

Subsidiary (Non-US):

Graco Fluid Equipment (Suzhou) Co., Ltd. (2)
No 36 Qiming Road Integrated Free Trade Zone SIP, Suzhou, 215021, China
Tel.: (86) 51262603288
Web Site: https://www.gww.graco.com
Fluid Power Pump & Motor Distr
N.A.I.C.S.: 423830

Graco N.V. (1)
Industreiterrein Oude Bunders Slakweidestraat 31, Maasmechelen, 3630, Limburg, Belgium **(100%)**
Tel.: (32) 89770700
Web Site: http://www.graco.be
Sales Range: $100-124.9 Million
Emp.: 220
Marketing of Service Industry Machinery
N.A.I.C.S.: 333310

Graco Ohio Inc. (1)
8400 Port Jackson Ave NW, North Canton, OH 44720-5464
Tel.: (330) 494-1313
Web Site: https://www.graco.com
Emp.: 3,700
Paint, Lubricant & Sealant Application Equipment Mfr
N.A.I.C.S.: 334514

Graco Shanghai Office (1)
Building 7 1029 Zhongshan Road South, Huangpu District, Shanghai, 200011, China **(100%)**
Tel.: (86) 2164950088
Web Site: http://www.graco.com
Sales Range: $10-24.9 Million
Emp.: 50
N.A.I.C.S.: 333996

Graco South Dakota Inc. (1)
3501 N 4th Ave, Sioux Falls, SD 57104-0785 **(100%)**
Tel.: (605) 333-6760
Web Site: https://www.graco.com
Sales Range: $75-99.9 Million
Emp.: 160
Mfr of Paint Spray Guns & Other Accessories
N.A.I.C.S.: 333996

Gusmer Sudamerica S.A. (1)
Av Velez Sarsfield 195, C1282AFB, Buenos Aires, Argentina
Tel.: (54) 1143055080
Web Site: http://www.gragus.com.ar
Pump & Pumping Equipment Mfr
N.A.I.C.S.: 333914

Gusmer-Europe (1)
Rambla Torre De Onclet 7 Pol Industrial Masia Den Barreres, Vilanova I La Geltru, 08800, Barcelona, Spain
Tel.: (34) 938115300
Web Site: http://www.gusmer-europe.com
Sales Range: $25-49.9 Million
Emp.: 49
Supplier of Equipment for Spraying, Pouring & Injection of Polyurethane Foams & Elastomeric Coatings
N.A.I.C.S.: 326140

Hi-Tech Spray Equipment, S.A. (1)
Cami Pla 31 - Pol Ind Mas Alba, Sitges, 08870, Barcelona, Spain
Tel.: (34) 938114000
Web Site: https://hitechspray.com
Industrial Machinery & Equipment Whslr
N.A.I.C.S.: 423830

High Pressure Equipment Company (1)
2955 W 17th St, Erie, PA 16505
Tel.: (814) 838-2028
Web Site: https://www.highpressure.com
Sales Range: $10-24.9 Million
Emp.: 75
High Pressure Equipment Mfr

Graco, Inc.—(Continued)
N.A.I.C.S.: 332996
Larry Loper *(Pres)*

International Polymer Solutions Inc. (1)
5 Studebaker, Irvine, CA 92618
Tel.: (435) 783-6040
Web Site: https://www.ipolymer.com
Valve Mfr & Distr
N.A.I.C.S.: 332912

Landtec North America, Inc. (1)
2355 Bishop Cir W, Dexter, MI 48130
Tel.: (734) 995-2547
Web Site: https://www.landtecna.com
Electrical Instrument Mfr & Distr
N.A.I.C.S.: 334515

MULTIMAQ - Pistolas e Equipamentos para Pintura Ltda (1)
Av Bernardino Silveira Amorim 1056,
91140-410, Porto Alegre, Brazil
Tel.: (55) 5133645757
Web Site: http://www.multimaq.com.br
Valve Mfr
N.A.I.C.S.: 332911
Enio Rossi *(Mgr-Supplies & Logistics)*

Q.E.D. Environmental Systems Limited (1)
Cyan Park Unit 3 Jimmy Hill Way, Coventry, CV2 4QP, United Kingdom
Tel.: (44) 3338000088
Environmental System Distr
N.A.I.C.S.: 423830

QED Environmental Systems, Inc. (1)
2355 Bishop Cir W, Dexter, MI 48130
Tel.: (734) 995-2547
Web Site: https://www.qedenv.com
Sales Range: $10-24.9 Million
Groundwater Sampling & Remediation Pumping Equipment Mfr
N.A.I.C.S.: 333914

SAT (Surface Aluminium Technologies) S.r.l. (1)
Via Meucci 4, 37135, Verona, Italy
Tel.: (39) 0458280601
Web Site: https://www.sataluminium.com
Engineering Consulting Services
N.A.I.C.S.: 541330

Smith Surface Preparation Systems Inc. (1)
2504 NW 19 St Bldg O, Pompano Beach, FL 33069
Tel.: (954) 941-9744
Web Site: https://www.smithmfg.com
Surface Equipment Mfr
N.A.I.C.S.: 000120

Staffordshire Hydraulic Services Limited (1)
Mount Road Kidsgrove, Stoke-on-Trent, ST7 4AZ, Staffordshire, United Kingdom
Tel.: (44) 17827711225
Web Site: https://www.staffshydraulics.co.uk
Pumping Equipment Mfr & Distr
N.A.I.C.S.: 333996

Surfaces & Finitions S.A.S. (1)
163-171 Avenue des Aureats BP 1453, Valence, 26014, France
Tel.: (33) 475752700
Industrial Valve Mfr
N.A.I.C.S.: 332911

White Knight Fluid Handling, Inc. (1)
187 E 670 S, Kamas, UT 84036
Tel.: (435) 783-6040
Web Site: https://www.wkfluidhandling.com
Sales Range: $1-9.9 Million
Fluid Handling Equipment Mfr
N.A.I.C.S.: 333996
Courtney Parsons *(Dir-Engrg)*

GRAHAM CORPORATION
20 Florence Ave, Batavia, NY 14020
Tel.: (585) 343-2216   DE
Web Site:
https://www.grahamcorp.com
Year Founded: 1936
GHM—(NYSE)
Rev.: $185,533,000
Assets: $233,879,000

Liabilities: $128,313,000
Net Worth: $105,566,000
Earnings: $4,556,000
Emp.: 595
Fiscal Year-end: 03/31/24
Holding Company; Vacuum System & Heat Transfer Engineering Services
N.A.I.C.S.: 551112
Jonathan W. Painter *(Chm)*
Alan E. Smith *(VP & Gen Mgr)*
Christopher J. Thome *(CFO, Chief Acctg Officer & VP-Fin)*
Daniel J. Thoren *(Pres & CEO)*

Subsidiaries:

Barber-Nichols Inc. (1)
6325 W 55 Ave, Arvada, CO 80002
Tel.: (303) 421-8111
Web Site: http://www.barber-nichols.com
Emp.: 64
Industrial Turbo Machinery Mfr
N.A.I.C.S.: 333310
Bob Barber *(Co-Founder)*
Ken Nichols *(Co-Founder)*
Jeff Shull *(VP-Sls & Mktg)*
Matt Johnson *(Dir-Ops)*

Graham Vacuum and Heat Transfer Technology Co., Ltd. (1)
Suite 601 23-B Harmony Times Square
Huachi Street, Suzhou Industrial Park, Suzhou, 215028, China   **(100%)**
Tel.: (86) 51262887530
Web Site: http://www.graham-mfg.com
Sales Range: $150-199.9 Million
Emp.: 7
Vacuum & Heat Exchange Equipment Mfr
N.A.I.C.S.: 423730

GRAHAM HOLDINGS COMPANY
1300 N 17th St 17th Fl, Arlington, VA 22209
Tel.: (703) 345-6300   DE
Web Site: https://www.ghco.com
Year Founded: 1947
GHC—(NYSE)
Rev.: $3,924,493,000
Assets: $6,582,215,000
Liabilities: $2,829,554,000
Net Worth: $3,752,661,000
Earnings: $67,079,000
Emp.: 19,527
Fiscal Year-end: 12/31/22
Holding Company; Magazines, Broadcasting, Cable, Educational & Career Service Centers, Database Publishing & Electronic Information Services
N.A.I.C.S.: 551112
Wallace R. Cooney *(CFO & Sr VP-Fin)*
Andrew S. Rosen *(Exec VP)*
Anne M. Mulcahy *(Chm)*
Jacob M. Maas *(Exec VP)*
Jarvis Obispo *(VP-Corp Audit Svcs)*
Michael Baker *(VP-Risk Management)*
Timothy J. O'Shaughnessy *(Pres & CEO)*
Marcel A. Snyman *(Chief Acctg Officer & VP)*
Sandra M. Stonesifer *(Chief HR Officer & VP)*
Nicole M. Maddrey *(Gen Counsel, Sec & Sr VP)*
Matthew R. Greisler *(Treas & VP)*
Stacey Halota *(VP-Information Security & Privacy)*
Elaine Wolff *(VP, Asst Sec & Deputy Gen Counsel)*
Cherie Kummer *(VP-Tax)*
Emily D. Firippis *(Asst Treas)*
Scott McClure *(VP-Information Technology)*
Pinkie Dent Mayfield *(Chief Comm Officer & VP-Corp Affairs)*

Subsidiaries:

Alpadia S.A. (1)

Grand-Rue 42, PO Box 1206, 1820, Montreux, Switzerland
Tel.: (41) 216218888
Web Site: https://www.alpadia.com
Language School Operator
N.A.I.C.S.: 611630

BEO UK Limited (1)
Clarendon House 52 Cornmarket Street, Oxford, OX1 3HJ, United Kingdom
Tel.: (44) 1865522669
Web Site: http://www.beo-study.com
Educational Support Services
N.A.I.C.S.: 611710

CGRH, LLC (1)
3236 M St NW, Washington, DC 20007
Tel.: (202) 849-4499
Web Site: https://www.clydescares.com
Holding Company; Restaurant Operator
N.A.I.C.S.: 551112

Subsidiary (Domestic):

Clyde's at Mark Center, LLC (2)
1700 N Beauregard St, Alexandria, VA 22311
Tel.: (703) 820-8300
Web Site: https://www.clydes.com
Restaurant Services
N.A.I.C.S.: 722511

Clyde's of Chevy Chase, LLC (2)
5441 Wisconsin Ave, Chevy Chase, MD 20815
Tel.: (301) 951-9600
Restaurant Operators
N.A.I.C.S.: 722511

Subsidiary (Domestic):

Clyde's Tower Oaks Lodge, LLC (3)
707 7th St NW, Washington, DC 20001
Tel.: (202) 349-3700
Restaurant Services
N.A.I.C.S.: 722511

Cybervista LLC (1)
1300 17th St N 16th Fl, Arlington, VA 22209
Web Site: https://www.cybervista.net
Cybersecurity Tarining, Education & Workforce Development
N.A.I.C.S.: 611699
Simone Petrella *(Co-Founder & CEO)*
Jung Lee *(Chief Product Officer)*
Brian McNulty *(CFO)*
Patrick Mullan *(VP-Sls & Mktg)*

Eagle Education & Training Limited (1)
Unit 2 The Business Centre Molly Millars Lane, Wokingham, RG41 2QZ, Berkshire, United Kingdom
Tel.: (44) 1978722511
Web Site: https://www.eagle-education.co.uk
Professional & Reliable Services
N.A.I.C.S.: 611430

Forney Corporation (1)
16479 N Dallas Pkwy Ste 213, Addison, TX 75001
Tel.: (972) 458-6100
Web Site: https://www.forneycorp.com
Sales Range: $25-49.9 Million
Emp.: 70
Industrial Combustion, Burner Management & Flame Detection Equipment Mfr & Distr
N.A.I.C.S.: 333414

Subsidiary (Domestic):

Forney Maquila, LLC (2)
16479 Dallas Pkwy, Addison, TX 75001
Tel.: (972) 458-6100
Newspaper Publishing Services
N.A.I.C.S.: 513110

Subsidiary (Non-US):

FMMX S. de R.L. de C.V. (3)
Av Salinas Garza No 301, Santa Catarina Centro, Santa Catarina, 66350, NL, Mexico
Tel.: (52) 8182884300
Newspaper Publishing Services
N.A.I.C.S.: 513110

Franklyn Scholar Pty Ltd. (1)
Level 1 600 Glenferrie Rd, Hawthorn, 3122, VIC, Australia
Tel.: (61) 399121000

Web Site: http://www.franklynscholar.edu.au
Educational Support Services
N.A.I.C.S.: 611710

Graham Automotive LLC (1)
801 W 41st St, Sioux Falls, SD 57105
Tel.: (605) 336-3655
Web Site: https://www.grahamauto.com
New & Old Car Dealing Services
N.A.I.C.S.: 441110

Graham Healthcare Group, Inc. (1)
5440 Corporate Dr Ste 400, Troy, MI 48098
Web Site:
https://www.grahamhealthcaregroup.com
Homecare & Hospice Services
N.A.I.C.S.: 621610
David Curtis *(CEO-Home Health)*
Justin Dewitte *(CEO-Hospice)*
Jason Pierce *(CFO & Sr VP-Fin & Acctg)*
Tara O'Daniel *(Officer-Privacy & Mgr-Internal Controls)*
LeeAnn Lang *(Sr VP-Admin)*
Wendy Bongero *(Sr VP-Operations &)*
Natalie Hagyari *(Sr VP-)*

Subsidiary (Domestic):

Celtic Healthcare, Inc. (2)
150 Scharberry Lane, Mars, PA 16046
Tel.: (724) 742-4360
Web Site: https://www.celtichealthcare.com
Sales Range: $25-49.9 Million
Hospice & Home Health Care Services
N.A.I.C.S.: 621610

Subsidiary (Domestic):

Celtic Community Services of NE Ohio, Inc. (3)
3530 Belmont Ave Ste 7, Youngstown, OH 44505-1400
Tel.: (724) 742-4360
Health Care Services
N.A.I.C.S.: 621610

Celtic Healthcare of Carlisle, Inc. (3)
220 Wilson St Ste 100, Carlisle, PA 17013
Tel.: (717) 245-5600
Health Care Srvices
N.A.I.C.S.: 621610

Celtic Healthcare of E. MO, LLC (3)
1653 Larkin Williams Rd, Fenton, MO 63026
Tel.: (724) 720-1232
Health Care Srvices
N.A.I.C.S.: 621610

Celtic Healthcare of NC PA, LLC (3)
427 Hetburn st, Williamsport, PA 17701
Tel.: (570) 327-3060
Health Care Srvices
N.A.I.C.S.: 621610

Celtic Healthcare of NE Ohio, Inc. (3)
3530 Belmont Ave Ste 7, Youngstown, OH 44505
Tel.: (330) 884-2500
Health Care Srvices
N.A.I.C.S.: 621610

Celtic Rehabilitation, Inc. (3)
231 Crowe Ave, Mars, PA 16046
Tel.: (724) 625-4280
Health Care Srvices
N.A.I.C.S.: 621610

Subsidiary (Domestic):

Graham Healthcare Capital, LLC (2)
4017 Hillsboro Pike Ste 418, Nashville, TN 37215
Tel.: (615) 800-6207
Web Site:
https://www.grahamhealthcarecapital.com
Homecare & Hospice Services
N.A.I.C.S.: 621610
David Curtis *(Mng Dir)*
Justin Dewitte *(Mng Dir)*
Ed O'Bryan *(Chief Medical Officer)*
Jon L'Heureux *(VP-Business Development)*
Tiffany Smiley *(Sr VP-Finance)*
Quinn Nunes *(VP-Marketing &)*

Graham Media Group, Inc. (1)
161 N Clark St Ste 2900, Chicago, IL 60601
Tel.: (312) 917-6240
Web Site: http://www.grahammedia.com

Television Broadcasting Stations Operator
N.A.I.C.S.: 516120
Julie Dreixler *(Chief HR Officer & VP)*
Katherine Fuller *(VP-Res)*
Kim Parker *(CFO & VP)*
Anthony Plosz *(VP)*
Stephanie Slagle *(Chief Innovation Officer)*
Jane Marshall *(VP)*
Sean McLaughlin *(VP-)*
Aaron King *(VP)*

Subsidiary (Domestic):

**Graham Media Group, Florida,
Inc.**   **(2)**
4 Broadcast Pl, Jacksonville, FL
32207   **(100%)**
Tel.: (904) 399-4000
Sales Range: $50-74.9 Million
Emp.: 188
Television Broadcasting Station
N.A.I.C.S.: 516120

**Graham Media Group, Houston,
Inc.**   **(2)**
8181 Southwest Fwy, Houston, TX
77074   **(100%)**
Tel.: (713) 222-2222
Web Site: https://www.click2houston.com
Sales Range: $25-49.9 Million
Emp.: 140
Television Broadcasting Station
N.A.I.C.S.: 516120
Phil Lane *(VP)*

**Graham Media Group, Michigan,
Inc.**   **(2)**
550 W Lafayette Blvd, Detroit, MI 48226-
3140
Tel.: (313) 222-0444
Web Site: https://www.clickondetroit.com
Sales Range: $50-74.9 Million
Emp.: 200
Television Broadcasting Station
N.A.I.C.S.: 516120
Bob Ellis *(VP)*

**Graham Media Group, Orlando,
Inc.**   **(2)**
4466 John Young Pkwy, Orlando, FL 32804
Tel.: (407) 521-1200
Sales Range: $25-49.9 Million
Emp.: 150
Television Broadcasting Station
N.A.I.C.S.: 516120

**Graham Media Group, San Antonio,
Inc.**   **(2)**
1408 N St Mary's St, San Antonio, TX
78215
Tel.: (210) 351-1200
Web Site: https://www.ksat.com
Sales Range: $25-49.9 Million
Emp.: 150
Television Broadcasting Station
N.A.I.C.S.: 516120
Ashley Parker *(VP)*

Unit (Domestic):

WCWJ-TV   **(2)**
4 Broadcast Pl, Jacksonville, FL 32207
Tel.: (904) 393-9844
Web Site: http://www.news4jax.com
Television Broadcasting Station
N.A.I.C.S.: 516120
Bob Ellis *(VP & Gen Mgr)*
Kathryn Bonfield *(Dir-News)*

WSLS-TV   **(2)**
401 3rd St SW, Roanoke, VA 24011
Tel.: (540) 342-3036
Web Site: https://www.wsls.com
Television Station
N.A.I.C.S.: 516120
Jaimie Leon *(Gen Mgr)*
Margaret Ashburn *(Dir-News)*
John Appicello *(Dir-Sports)*

Group Dekko, Inc.   **(1)**
2505 Dekko Dr, Garrett, IN 46738
Tel.: (260) 357-3621
Web Site: https://www.dekko.com
Engineered Electrical Components & As-
semblies Mfr & Contractor
N.A.I.C.S.: 335999

Unit (Domestic):

Dekko Technical Center   **(2)**

11913 E 450 S, Laotto, IN 46763-9750
Tel.: (260) 637-3964
Web Site: http://www.dekko.com
Sales Range: $10-24.9 Million
Emp.: 20
Analytical Lab
N.A.I.C.S.: 335931

Subsidiary (Domestic):

Electri-Cable Assemblies, Inc.   **(2)**
10 Mtn View Dr, Shelton, CT 06484
Tel.: (203) 924-6617
Web Site: http://www.electri-cable.com
Electrical Apparatus & Related Equipment
Merchant Whslr
N.A.I.C.S.: 423610

Unit (Domestic):

Group Dekko - Avilla   **(2)**
300 Dekko Dr, Avilla, IN 46710
Tel.: (260) 897-3459
Web Site: http://www.dekko.com
Sales Range: $25-49.9 Million
Emp.: 150
Mfr of Molded Plastic Products
N.A.I.C.S.: 326199

Group Dekko - Merriam   **(2)**
0071 E 400 S, Albion, IN 46701-9636
Tel.: (260) 636-2551
Web Site: http://www.dekko.com
Sales Range: $10-24.9 Million
Emp.: 100
Wire Harnesses Power Cords & Insert
Molded Connectors
N.A.I.C.S.: 334419

Group Dekko - North Webster   **(2)**
8701 E Backwater Rd, North Webster, IN
46555
Tel.: (574) 834-2818
Web Site: http://www.dekko.com
Sales Range: $25-49.9 Million
Emp.: 300
Mfr of Heating Units, Epoxy Sealers & Re-
sistor Units
N.A.I.C.S.: 335931

**Hoover Treated Wood Products,
Inc.**   **(1)**
154 Wire Rd, Thomson, GA 30824
Tel.: (706) 595-9855
Web Site: https://www.frtw.com
Wood Products Mfr
N.A.I.C.S.: 321114

Joyce/Dayton Corp.   **(1)**
3300 S Dixie Dr, Dayton, OH 45439
Tel.: (937) 294-6261
Web Site: http://www.joycedayton.com
Sales Range: $10-24.9 Million
Emp.: 50
Heavy Duty Lifting & Positioning Equipment
Mfr
N.A.I.C.S.: 333248

Subsidiary (Domestic):

EDrive Actuators, Inc.   **(2)**
120 Vanderbilt Ave, West Hartford, CT
06110
Tel.: (860) 953-0588
Web Site: http://www.edriveactuators.com
Fluid Power Cylinder & Actuator Mfr
N.A.I.C.S.: 333995

Justin Craig Education Limited   **(1)**
Tyttenhanger House Coursers Road, Saint
Albans, AL4 0PG, Hertfordshire, United
Kingdom
Tel.: (44) 1727744340
Web Site: https://www.justincraig.ac.uk
Academic Tutoring Services
N.A.I.C.S.: 611691

Kaplan, Inc.   **(1)**
6301 Kaplan University Ave, Fort Lauder-
dale, FL 33309   **(100%)**
Web Site: https://www.kaplan.com
Educational & Career Services
N.A.I.C.S.: 611710
Andrew S. Rosen *(Chm & CEO)*
Melissa Mack *(Chm & Chief Comm & HR
Officer)*
Yael Aufgang *(Gen Counsel)*
Brandon Busteed *(Chief Partnership Officer
& Head-Global)*
Matthew Seelye *(CFO)*

Subsidiary (Non-US):

Aspect Education Limited   **(2)**
2F Warwick Building Kensington Village
Avonmore Road, London, W14 8HQ, United
Kingdom
Tel.: (44) 2070455000
Web Site:
  https://www.kaplaninternational.com
Educational Institution Operator
N.A.I.C.S.: 611310

Subsidiary (Non-US):

**Aspect Internationale Sprachschule
GmbH**   **(3)**
Zeil 65-69, Frankfurt am Main, 60313, Ger-
many
Tel.: (49) 69244500500
Web Site:
  http://www.kaplaninternational.com
Emp.: 30
Education Services
N.A.I.C.S.: 611710

**Kaplan International Colleges,
C.A.**   **(3)**
Avenida Principal Del Cafetal Chuao, Cara-
cas, Venezuela
Tel.: (58) 2129938778
Educational Support Services
N.A.I.C.S.: 611710

**Kaplan International English (Austra-
lia) Pty Limited**   **(3)**
98-104 Goulburn Street, Sydney, 2000,
NSW, Australia
Tel.: (61) 92838055
Web Site: https://www.kicaustralia.com.au
Educational Support Services
N.A.I.C.S.: 611710

Pacific Language Institute, Inc.   **(3)**
755 Burrard Street Suite 300, Vancouver,
V6Z 1X6, BC, Canada
Tel.: (604) 688-8330
Web Site:
  https://www.kaplaninternational.com
Educational Institution Services
N.A.I.C.S.: 611710

Pro Linguis   **(3)**
Nuschelerstrasse 35, Zurich, 8001, Switzer-
land
Tel.: (41) 449241111
Web Site: http://www.prolinguis.ch
Emp.: 35
Education Services
N.A.I.C.S.: 611710

Subsidiary (Domestic):

Bootcamp Education, Inc.   **(2)**
633 Folsom St 6th Fl, San Francisco, CA
94107
Tel.: (415) 800-6579
Educational Support Services
N.A.I.C.S.: 611710

Subsidiary (Non-US):

**Hands On Education Consultants
Co., Ltd.**   **(2)**
317 Kamolsukosol Building 15th Floor Silom
Road, Silom Bangrak, Bangkok, 10500,
Thailand
Tel.: (66) 26355230
Web Site: https://www.hands-on.co.th
Educational Support Services
N.A.I.C.S.: 611710

Hawksmere Limited   **(2)**
4th Floor Block 3 Angel Square, London,
EC1V 1NY, United Kingdom
Tel.: (44) 8455646104
Web Site:
  https://www.hawksmere.kaplan.co.uk
Sales Range: $10-24.9 Million
Emp.: 36
Educational Institution Services
N.A.I.C.S.: 611710

Holborn College Limited   **(2)**
Woolwich Road, London, SE7 8LN, United
Kingdom
Tel.: (44) 2083176000
Web Site: https://www.holborncollege.ac.uk
Educational Institution Services
N.A.I.C.S.: 611310

ILA South Pacific Limited   **(2)**
10 Titoki Street Parnell, Auckland, 1052,
New Zealand
Tel.: (64) 93076507
Web Site:
  http://www.kaplaninternational.com
Sales Range: $10-24.9 Million
Emp.: 16
Educational Support Services
N.A.I.C.S.: 611710

Kaplan (India) Private Limited   **(2)**
Plot No-15 PH-III Industrial Estate, Okhla
Industrial Area, Delhi, 110020, India
Tel.: (91) 1130880513
Software Development Services
N.A.I.C.S.: 513210

**Kaplan Business School Australia Pty
Ltd**   **(2)**
Level 1 68 Grenfell Street, Adelaide, 5000,
SA, Australia
Tel.: (61) 8 8215 4100
Web Site: http://www.kbs.edu.au
Emp.: 2
Educational Institution
N.A.I.C.S.: 611710

Kaplan Business School Pty Ltd.   **(2)**
Level 1 68 Grenfell Street, Adelaide, 5000,
SA, Australia
Tel.: (61) 882154100
Web Site: https://www.kbs.edu.au
Educational Institution Services
N.A.I.C.S.: 611710

Kaplan Canada Inc.   **(2)**
180 Bloor St W, Toronto, M5S 2V6, ON,
Canada   **(100%)**
Tel.: (416) 967-4733
Web Site: https://www.kaptest.com
Rev.: $512,533
Emp.: 36
Test Preparation
N.A.I.C.S.: 611710

Kaplan Education Pty. Limited   **(2)**
Level 4 45 Clarence Street, Sydney, 2000,
NSW, Australia
Tel.: (61) 2 9908 0200
Web Site:
  http://www.kaplanprofessional.edu.au
Sales Range: $10-24.9 Million
Emp.: 122
Educational & Professional Development
Services for Financial Companies
N.A.I.C.S.: 561499
Brian Knight *(CEO)*
Jennifer Hornsey *(Head-CPD)*
Julie Harrison *(Head-Student Experience)*
Lucia Stejer *(Head-Teaching & Learning)*
Luke Knight *(Head-Corp Sls)*
Marnie Diamataris *(Head-Comml Ops)*
Nicole Jarouge *(Head-Ops)*
Tom Le *(Mgr-Bus Sys)*
Vicky Labroski *(Head-Mktg)*

Kaplan Financial Limited   **(2)**
179-191 Borough High St, London, SE1
1HR, United Kingdom
Tel.: (44) 1612597400
Web Site: https://kaplan.co.uk
Emp.: 150
Financial, Accounting & Business Profes-
sional Training Services
N.A.I.C.S.: 611430

Subsidiary (Domestic):

Kaplan Global Solutions, LLC   **(2)**
3333 S Congress Ave 100, Delray Beach,
FL 33445
Tel.: (561) 381-6379
Emp.: 75
Educational Support Services
N.A.I.C.S.: 611710

Division (Domestic):

Kaplan Higher Education, LLC   **(2)**
6301 Kaplan University Ave, Fort Lauder-
dale, FL 33309   **(100%)**
Tel.: (954) 515-3993
Sales Range: $25-49.9 Million
Emp.: 125
Postsecondary Education
N.A.I.C.S.: 611710
Andrew S. Rosen *(Chm-Kaplan University)*

Subsidiary (Non-US):

**Kaplan Higher Education Academy
Pte. Ltd.**   **(3)**

Graham Holdings Company—(Continued)

1 Selegie Road 09-01, Singapore, 188306, Singapore
Tel.: (65) 67331877
Web Site: https://www.kaplan.com.sg
Professional Training Services
N.A.I.C.S.: 611430

Subsidiary (Non-US):

Kaplan Institute Limited (2)
G/F to 3/F E-Tech Centre Nos 402-406, Hennessy Road, Causeway Bay MTR Exit A, Wanchai, China (Hong Kong)
Tel.: (852) 25263686
Web Site: https://www.kaplan.com.hk
Emp.: 100
Educational Support Services
N.A.I.C.S.: 611710
Wen Lu (Mng Dir)
Dickson Ma (VP-Fin)
Rebecca Lui (VP-Ops & Academics)
Rowena Li (Dir-Bus Dev)

Kaplan International (Manly) Pty Limited (2)
30-32 South Steyne, Manly, 2095, NSW, Australia
Tel.: (61) 299762422
Web Site:
http://www.kaplaninternational.com
Educational Institution Services
N.A.I.C.S.: 611710

Kaplan International Colleges U.K. Limited (2)
Palace House 3 Cathedral Street, London, SE1 9DE, United Kingdom
Tel.: (44) 2070455000
Web Site:
https://www.kaplaninternational.com
Emp.: 300
Educational Institution Services
N.A.I.C.S.: 611710

Subsidiary (Domestic):

Kaplan International College London Limited (3)
Palace House 3 Cathedral Street, London, SE1 9DE, United Kingdom
Tel.: (44) 2087273500
Web Site: https://www.kiclondon.org.uk
Educational Support Services
N.A.I.C.S.: 611710

Mander Portman Woodward Limited (3)
90-92 Queen's Gate, London, SW7 5AB, United Kingdom
Tel.: (44) 2078351355
Web Site: https://www.mpw.ac.uk
Colleges Universities & Professional Schools
N.A.I.C.S.: 611310
Mat Carmody (Head-Faculty)
Phillip Carr (Dir-Studies)
Erica Stillwell (Dir-Studies)
Peter Zhao (Dir-Studies)
Duncan Chamberlain (Head-Faculty)
Anna Ardizzon (Dir-Studies)
Eoin Rafferty (Dir-Studies)
Oliver Stimpson (Dir-Studies)

Subsidiary (Non-US):

Kaplan Law School Limited (2)
179-191 Borough High Street, London, SE11HR, United Kingdom
Tel.: (44) 2073676400
Web Site: http://www.kaplan.com
Education Services
N.A.I.C.S.: 611710

Kaplan Open Learning (Essex) Limited (2)
Palace House 3 Cathedral Street, London, SE1 9DE, United Kingdom
Tel.: (44) 2070454925
Web Site: https://www.kaplanpathways.com
Educational Institution
N.A.I.C.S.: 611710

Division (Domestic):

Kaplan Professional (2)
332 Front St S Fl 5, La Crosse, WI 54601
Tel.: (702) 893-0059

Web Site:
http://www.kaplanprofessional.com
Licensing & Continuing Education Training
N.A.I.C.S.: 611710

Subsidiary (Domestic):

Kaplan Financial (3)
1905 Palace St, La Crosse, WI 54603
Tel.: (608) 779-8301
Web Site: http://www.kseducation.com
Real Estate & Financial Services Licensing Programs & Continuing Education
N.A.I.C.S.: 611710

Kaplan Professional Schools, Inc. (3)
1295 Bandana Blvd N Ste 245, Saint Paul, MN 55108 (100%)
Tel.: (651) 641-1000
Web Site: http://www.prosource.com
Real Estate & Insurance School Programs
N.A.I.C.S.: 611519

The College for Financial Planning Institutes Corporation (3)
9000 East Nichols Avenue Ste 200, Greenwood Village, CO 80112
Tel.: (303) 220-1200
Web Site: http://www.cffp.edu
Financial Planning Services
N.A.I.C.S.: 611310

Subsidiary (Non-US):

Kaplan Publishing Limited (2)
Unit 2 The Business Centre Molly Millars Lane, Wokingham, RG41 2QZ, Berkshire, United Kingdom
Tel.: (44) 1189123000
Web Site: https://kaplanpublishing.co.uk
Emp.: 30
Educational Institution Services
N.A.I.C.S.: 611710

Kensington Student Services Limited (2)
Kensington Student Services First Floor 52A Cromwell Road, London, SW7 5BE, United Kingdom
Tel.: (44) 2072441960
Web Site: https://www.kss.co.uk
Student Accommodation Provider
N.A.I.C.S.: 721310

Subsidiary (Domestic):

Professional Publications, Inc. (2)
1250 Fifth Ave, Belmont, CA 94002
Tel.: (650) 593-9119
Web Site: http://www.ppi2pass.com
Prepress Services
N.A.I.C.S.: 323120

SmartPros Ltd. (2)
12 Skyline Dr, Hawthorne, NY 10532
Tel.: (914) 345-2620
Web Site: https://sp.smartpros.com
Sales Range: $10-24.9 Million
Emp.: 20
Continuing Education Products & Services
N.A.I.C.S.: 541910

Subsidiary (Domestic):

Loscalzo Associates, Ltd. (3)
1151 Broad St 214, Shrewsbury, NJ 07702 (100%)
Tel.: (732) 741-1600
Web Site: http://www.loscalzo.com
Professional Education & Corporate Training Services
N.A.I.C.S.: 611710

SMM, Ltd. (3)
203 Mn St 328, Flemington, NJ 08822 (100%)
Tel.: (908) 429-0099
Web Site: http://www.skyemm.com
E-Learning & Mobile Development Services
N.A.I.C.S.: 334610

Subsidiary (Non-US):

The Dublin Business School Limited (2)
13/14 Aungier Street, Dublin, Ireland
Tel.: (353) 14177500
Web Site: http://www.dbs.ie
Educational Institution Services
N.A.I.C.S.: 611710

Gerry Muldowney (CEO)
Cliona O'Beirne (Dir-Admissions)

Subsidiary (Domestic):

i-Human Patients, Inc. (2)
4675 Stevens Creek Blvd, Santa Clara, CA 95051
Tel.: (877) 656-5539
Web Site: http://www.i-human.com
Cloud-based Multimedia & E-Learning
N.A.I.C.S.: 513210

Leaf Group Ltd. (1)
1655 26th St, Santa Monica, CA 90404
Tel.: (310) 656-6253
Web Site: http://www.leafgroup.com
Rev.: $212,061,000
Assets: $140,927,000
Liabilities: $62,624,000
Net Worth: $78,303,000
Earnings: ($8,860,000)
Emp.: 360
Fiscal Year-end: 12/31/2020
Social Media Content Development & Distribution Services
N.A.I.C.S.: 541511
Brian Pike (COO & CTO)
Adam Wergeles (Chief Admin Officer)
Alan Waldman (Exec VP-Product & Tech)
Jeanne Anderson (Sr VP & Gen Mgr-Saatchi Art)
Scott Messer (Sr VP & Gen Mgr-Media)
Ilona Jurkiewicz (Sr VP-People)
Susan Turner (Dir-PR)
Ross Landsbaum (CFO)
Sean Moriarty (CEO)
Lindsey Abramo (Chief Revenue Officer-Media)

Subsidiary (Non-US):

Other Art Fairs Australia Pty Ltd (2)
21/94 Oxford Street, Darlinghurst, 2010, NSW, Australia
Tel.: (61) 293319255
Contemporary Painting Services
N.A.I.C.S.: 238320

Other Art Fairs Ltd (2)
4th Floor15 D'Arblay Street, London, W1F 8DZ, United Kingdom
Tel.: (44) 8056670
Web Site: https://www.theotherartfair.com
Hand Art Publishing Services
N.A.I.C.S.: 711510
Ryan Stanier (Founder & Gen Mgr)

Subsidiary (Domestic):

Society6, LLC (2)
1655 26th St, Santa Monica, CA 90404
Tel.: (310) 910-1781
Web Site: https://society6.com
Online Art Gallery
N.A.I.C.S.: 459920

Marketplace Strategy, LLC (1)
3615 Superior Ave Ste 4407A, Cleveland, OH 44114
Tel.: (216) 716-2510
Web Site:
https://www.marketplacestrategy.com
Customer Service Management Consulting Services
N.A.I.C.S.: 541613
Curtis Rummel (Co-Founder)
Jeff Walcoff (VP-Sls & Mktg)
Dina Podnar (Mgr-Mktg)
Aaron Price (Mgr-Bus Dev)
Alexa Guarino (Coord-Client)

Osborne Books Limited (1)
Unit 2 The Business Centre Molly Millars Lane, Wokingham, RG41 2QZ, United Kingdom
Tel.: (44) 1905748071
Web Site: https://www.osbornebooks.co.uk
Market-Leading Publisher
N.A.I.C.S.: 513130

Residential Hospice, LLC (1)
5440 Corporate Dr Ste 400, Troy, MI 48098
Tel.: (248) 524-6400
Web Site:
https://www.residentialhospice.com
Health Care Srvices
N.A.I.C.S.: 621610

SAI Rockville L, LLC (1)
15501 Frederick Rd, Derwood, MD 20855

Tel.: (866) 297-7000
Web Site: http://www.lexusofrockville.com
New Car Dealers
N.A.I.C.S.: 441110

SAI Tysons Corner H, LLC (1)
1580 Sprinh Hill Rd, Vienna, VA 22182
Tel.: (888) 699-6048
Web Site:
http://www.ourismanhondaoftysonscorner.com
Car Dealer
N.A.I.C.S.: 423110

Slate Magazine (1)
95 Morton St 4th Fl, New York, NY 10014
Tel.: (212) 445-5330
Web Site: http://www.slate.com
Sales Range: $100-124.9 Million
Online Magazine Publisher
N.A.I.C.S.: 513120
Jared Hohlt (Editor-in-Chief)
Dan Check (CEO)
Charlie Kammerer (Pres)

Sociedad de Capacitacion Structuralia Chile Limitada (1)
Cerro el Plomo 5931 Oficina 805 Las Condes, Santiago, 13114, Chile
Tel.: (56) 228110187
Educational Support Services
N.A.I.C.S.: 611710

The Slate Group LLC (1)
15 MetroTech Ctr 8th Fl, Brooklyn, NY 11201
Tel.: (806) 794-7752
Web Site: https://slate.com
Online Publishing Services
N.A.I.C.S.: 513110

Tribeca Learning Pty Limited (1)
Level 4 45 Clarence Street, Sydney, 2000, NSW, Australia
Tel.: (61) 299080200
Educational Support Services
N.A.I.C.S.: 611710

GRAND BANK CORPORATION
Tel.: (781) 631-6000
Web Site: http://www.ngbank.com
GABK—(OTCEM)
Sales Range: $10-24.9 Million
Emp.: 44
Bank Holding Company
N.A.I.C.S.: 551111
Rae Weed (Controller)
Michael Spencer (CFO & VP)
James Nye (Pres)

Subsidiaries:

The National Grand Bank of Marblehead (1)
91 Pleasant St, Marblehead, MA 01945
Tel.: (781) 631-6000
Web Site: http://www.ngbank.com
Sales Range: $10-24.9 Million
National Commercial Banks
N.A.I.C.S.: 522110
James Nye (Pres)
Carl Edwards (Chief Lending Officer & Exec VP)
Charles Ball (Sr VP)

GRAND CANYON EDUCATION, INC.
2600 W Camelback Rd, Phoenix, AZ 85017
Tel.: (602) 247-4400   DE
Web Site: https://www.gce.com
Year Founded: 2003
LOPE—(NASDAQ)
Rev.: $960,899,000
Assets: $930,463,000
Liabilities: $212,449,000
Net Worth: $718,014,000
Earnings: $204,985,000
Emp.: 5,800
Fiscal Year-end: 12/31/23
Online & Traditional Post-Secondary Education Services
N.A.I.C.S.: 611699
Brian E. Mueller (Chm, Pres & CEO)
William Stan Meyer (COO)
Daniel E. Bachus (CFO)

Dilek Marsh (CTO)
Lori Browning (Chief Acctg Officer, Sr VP & Controller)
Kathy J. Claypatch (CIO)

Subsidiaries:

Grand Canyon University   (1)
3300 W Camelback Rd, Phoenix, AZ 85017
Tel.: (602) 639-7500
Web Site: https://www.gcu.edu
Colleges & Universities
N.A.I.C.S.: 611310
Brian E. Mueller (Pres)
Tim Griffin (VP-Student Affairs & Dean-Students)
Brian M. Roberts (Chief Admin Officer, Sec & Gen Counsel)
Jennifer Lech (Officer-Accreditation Liaison & Exec VP-Academic Affairs)
Joe Veres (VP-Student Success)
Shanna Milonas (Asst VP-Academic Compliance & Coord-Title IX & 504)
Junette C. West (VP-Bus & Fin)
Jamie Boggs (Dir-Athletic-Interim)
Will Gonzalez (Chm)
Michael Berger (Dean-)
Kimberly LaPrade (Dean)
Claude Pensis (Dean-)
Sherman Elliott (Dean-)
Lisa Smith (Dean-)
Mark Wooden (Dean-Engineering-Technology)
Jason Hiles (Dean-)
Christel Mosby (Exec VP-Marketing)
Trish Leonard (VP-Student Fin & Aid Compliance)
Hank Radda (Provost)
Greg Rogers (VP)
Ray Kaselonis (Chief Admin Officer & Gen Counsel)
T. Kale Gober (VP)
Hank Radda (Provost)
Greg Rogers (VP)
Ray Kaselonis (Chief Admin Officer & Gen Counsel)
T. Kale Gober (VP)
Hank Radda (Provost)
Greg Rogers (VP)
Ray Kaselonis (Chief Admin Officer & Gen Counsel)
T. Kale Gober (VP)
James Kossler (VP)

Orbis Education Services, LLC   (1)
301 Pennsylvania Pkwy Ste 400, Indianapolis, IN 46280
Tel.: (317) 663-0260
Web Site: http://www.orbiseducation.com
Sales Range: $1-9.9 Million
Educational Support Services
N.A.I.C.S.: 611710
Daniel J. Briggs (Founder & Chief Growth Officer)
Scott McCormick (COO)
Craig Huke (CFO)
Dave Palmisano (VP-Strategic Partnerships & Solutions)
Matt Merino (Chief Experience Officer)
Deborah Highfill (Sr VP-Nursing Academics)
Jack Lewandowski (VP-Partnerships)
Walter Desocio (Chief Compliance Officer)
Andrea Mount (VP-Partnerships)
Steve Khederian (VP-Partnerships)
Matt Jakircevic (VP-Partnerships)
Caitlin Masterson (VP-Allied Health Academic Ops)
Mike Pote (Chief Admin Officer)
Angi Becerra (VP-Enrollment Mgmt)
Dale Scalise-Smith (VP-Allied Health Academic Svcs)
Stephen Cramer (VP-Partnerships)
George Dickert (VP-Partnerships)

GRAND HAVANA INC.
761 NW 23rd St, Miami, FL 33127 TX
Web Site:
  http://www.grandhavanacoffee.com
Year Founded: 2009
ESKYF—(OTCQX)
Emp.: 7
Online Clothing & Related Products Retailer
N.A.I.C.S.: 445298
Robert Rico (CEO & CFO)
Tanya Bredemeier (Pres)
Luis Bustelo (COO)

GRAND RIVER COMMERCE, INC.
4471 Wilson Ave SW, Grandville, MI 49418
Tel.: (616) 929-1600   MI
Web Site:
  https://grcommerce.q4ir.com
Year Founded: 2006
GNRV—(OTCQX)
Rev.: $26,615,000
Assets: $549,076,000
Liabilities: $513,448,000
Net Worth: $35,628,000
Earnings: ($1,213,000)
Fiscal Year-end: 12/31/23
Bank Holding Company
N.A.I.C.S.: 551111

GRANITE CONSTRUCTION INCORPORATED
585 W Beach St, Watsonville, CA 95076
Tel.: (831) 724-1011   DE
Web Site:
  https://www.graniteconstruction.com
Year Founded: 1990
GVA—(NYSE)
Rev.: $3,301,256,000
Assets: $2,167,933,000
Liabilities: $1,182,788,000
Net Worth: $985,145,000
Earnings: $83,302,000
Emp.: 2,000
Fiscal Year-end: 12/31/22
Holding Company; Heavy Civil Construction Contractor Services
N.A.I.C.S.: 551112
Kyle T. Larkin (Pres & CEO)
Craig Hall (Compliance Officer, Gen Counsel, Sec & Sr VP)
Staci M. Woolsey (CFO, Chief Acctg Officer & Exec VP)
James A. Radich (COO & Exec VP)
Brian A. Dowd (Sr VP & Mgr-California Grp)
Tim Gruber (Sr VP-HR)
Tracy Coppinger (VP-Continuous Improvement, Strategy & Construction Tech)
Jim Grogan (VP)
Ken Olson (Treas)
Brad Williams (Sr VP)

Subsidiaries:

Dickerson & Bowen, Inc.   (1)
669 Industrial Park Dr NE, Brookhaven, MS 39601-2064
Tel.: (601) 833-4291
Web Site:
  http://www.dickersonandbowen.com
Sales Range: $10-24.9 Million
Emp.: 150
Asphalt Mfr
N.A.I.C.S.: 324121
Lester Williams (Pres)
Cecil Estess (Treas & Sec)

GILC Incorporated   (1)
585 W Beach St, Watsonville, CA 95076-5123
Tel.: (831) 724-1011
Web Site:
  http://www.graniteconstruction.com
Emp.: 300
Residential Building Construction Services
N.A.I.C.S.: 236115

Granite Construction Company   (1)
585 W Beach St, Watsonville, CA 95076   (100%)
Tel.: (831) 724-1011
Sales Range: $800-899.9 Million
Emp.: 250
Heavy Civil Construction Contractor Services
N.A.I.C.S.: 237990
Kyle T. Larkin (Pres & Principal Exec Officer)

Branch (Domestic):

Granite Construction - Washington Region   (2)

1525 E Marine View Dr, Everett, WA 98201
Tel.: (425) 551-3100
Web Site:
  http://www.graniteconstruction.com
Loading Dock Equipment Sales & Installation Services
N.A.I.C.S.: 237310

Granite Construction Co. - Arizona   (2)
4115 E Illinois St, Tucson, AZ 85714
Tel.: (520) 748-8000
Sales Range: $50-74.9 Million
Emp.: 70
Building & Construction Materials
N.A.I.C.S.: 236210
Dave Richard (Branch Mgr)

Granite Construction Co. - Bakersfield Branch   (2)
3005 James Rd, Bakersfield, CA 93308
Tel.: (661) 399-3361
Web Site: http://www.granite.com
Sales Range: $1-9.9 Million
Emp.: 40
Building & Construction Materials
N.A.I.C.S.: 237310

Granite Construction Co. - Bay Area Branch   (2)
715 Comstock St, Santa Clara, CA 95054
Tel.: (408) 327-7000
Web Site:
  http://www.graniteconstruction.com
Sales Range: $50-74.9 Million
Emp.: 150
Building & Construction Materials
N.A.I.C.S.: 236115

Granite Construction Co. - Central Valley Branch   (2)
2716 Granite Ct, Fresno, CA 93706
Tel.: (559) 441-5700
Web Site:
  http://www.graniteconstruction.com
Sales Range: $1-9.9 Million
Emp.: 45
Distr of Building & Construction Materials
N.A.I.C.S.: 237310

Granite Construction Co. - Monterey Bay Branch   (2)
580 W Beach St, Watsonville, CA 95076-5085
Tel.: (831) 763-6100
Web Site:
  http://www.graniteconstruction.com
Sales Range: $1-9.9 Million
Emp.: 40
Building & Construction Materials
N.A.I.C.S.: 237310

Granite Construction Co. - Nevada   (2)
1900 Glendale Ave, Sparks, NV 89431
Tel.: (775) 358-8792
Web Site: http://www.gcinc.com
Sales Range: $250-299.9 Million
Building & Construction Materials
N.A.I.C.S.: 237310

Granite Construction Co. - Sacramento Valley Branch   (2)
4001 Bradshaw Rd, Sacramento, CA 95827
Tel.: (916) 855-4400
Web Site: http://www.gcinc.com
Sales Range: $200-249.9 Million
Emp.: 300
Building & Construction Materials
N.A.I.C.S.: 236210
Jeff Pasquetti (Mgr-Equipment)

Granite Construction Co. - Santa Barbara Branch   (2)
5335 Debbie Rd, Santa Barbara, CA 93111
Tel.: (805) 964-9951
Web Site:
  http://www.graniteconstruction.com
Sales Range: $1-9.9 Million
Emp.: 45
Distr of Building & Construction Materials
N.A.I.C.S.: 237310

Granite Construction Co. - Southern California Branch   (2)
38000 Monroe St, Indio, CA 92203
Tel.: (760) 775-7500
Web Site:
  http://www.graniteconstruction.com

Sales Range: $200-249.9 Million
Emp.: 400
Building & Construction Materials
N.A.I.C.S.: 237310

Granite Construction Co. - Stockton Branch   (2)
10500 S Harlan Rd, French Camp, CA 95231
Tel.: (209) 982-4750
Web Site: http://www.gcinc.com
Sales Range: $25-49.9 Million
Emp.: 260
Building & Construction Materials
N.A.I.C.S.: 237310
Steve Bridge (Mgr-Large Project)

Granite Construction Co. - Utah   (2)
1000 N Warm Springs Rd, Salt Lake City, UT 84116
Tel.: (801) 526-6000
Sales Range: $25-49.9 Million
Emp.: 200
Building & Construction Materials
N.A.I.C.S.: 237310

Granite Construction Co. - Yakima   (2)
80 Pond Rd, Yakima, WA 98901
Tel.: (509) 248-8376
Web Site:
  http://www.graniteconstruction.com
Sales Range: $25-49.9 Million
Emp.: 50
Highway & Street Construction
N.A.I.C.S.: 237310

Granite Construction Northeast, Inc.   (1)
120 White Plains Rd Ste 310, Tarrytown, NY 10591
Tel.: (914) 606-3600
Web Site:
  http://www.graniteconstruction.com
Sales Range: $50-74.9 Million
Emp.: 200
Industrial Building Construction Services
N.A.I.C.S.: 236210

Layne Christensen Company   (1)
9303 New Trails Dr Ste 200, The Woodlands, TX 77381
Tel.: (281) 475-2600
Web Site:
  https://www.graniteconstruction.com
Sales Range: $450-499.9 Million
Holding Company; Water Management, Construction & Drilling Services
N.A.I.C.S.: 551112

Subsidiary (Domestic):

Granite Inliner, LLC   (2)
4520 N State Rd 37, Orleans, IN 47452
Tel.: (812) 865-3232
Water & Sewer Line Construction Services
N.A.I.C.S.: 237110
Larry D. Purlee (Pres)

Subsidiary (Domestic):

Liner Products, LLC   (3)
1468 W Hospital Rd, Paoli, IN 47454
Tel.: (812) 723-0244
Web Site: https://www.linerproducts.com
Emp.: 100
Pipe & Pipeline Fitting Mfr
N.A.I.C.S.: 333998
Justin Hardesty (Mgr-Ops)
Brent Buckalew (VP)
Keith Oxner (Mgr-Quality)

Subsidiary (Non-US):

International Directional Services of Canada, Ltd.   (2)
582 Falconbridge Rd Unit 1, Sudbury, P3A 4S4, ON, Canada   (100%)
Tel.: (705) 560-6460
Web Site: http://www.idsdrill.com
Drilling & Borehole Survey Services
N.A.I.C.S.: 213115

Subsidiary (Domestic):

International Directional Services, L.L.C.   (2)
12030 E Riggs Rd, Chandler, AZ 85249
Tel.: (480) 824-7100
Web Site: http://www.idsdrill.com

Granite Construction Incorporated—(Continued)

Drilling Equipment Rental & Sales Services
N.A.I.C.S.: 532412

Subsidiary (Non-US):

Layne Drilling Zambia **(2)**
Plot 1746 Nakambala Road Industrial Area,
PO Box 1667, Ndola, 10101, Zambia
Tel.: (260) 212651309
Water & Sewer Line Construction Services
N.A.I.C.S.: 237110

Subsidiary (Domestic):

Layne Energy, Inc. **(2)**
1900 Shawnee Mission Pkwy, Mission
Woods, KS 66205 **(100%)**
Tel.: (913) 677-6800
Water & Sewer Line Construction Services
N.A.I.C.S.: 237110

Layne GeoConstruction **(2)**
27002 Vista Ter, Lake Forest, CA 92630
Tel.: (949) 955-1122
Sales Range: $25-49.9 Million
Emp.: 15
Engineeering Services
N.A.I.C.S.: 541330
Mauro Chinchelli *(Pres)*

Layne Texas, Incorporated **(2)**
5931 Brittmoore Rd, Houston, TX 77041
Tel.: (978) 937-2252
Sales Range: $50-74.9 Million
Emp.: 25
Water & Sewer Line Construction Services
N.A.I.C.S.: 237110
Rich Ducote *(Mng Dir)*

Layne-Western Co., Inc. **(2)**
620 S 38th St, Kansas City, KS
66106 **(100%)**
Tel.: (913) 321-5000
Web Site: http://www.laynechristensen.com
Sales Range: $1-9.9 Million
Emp.: 30
Drilling Services
N.A.I.C.S.: 237110
Russell Redding *(Mgr-Bus Dev)*

Subsidiary (Non-US):

Tecniwell S.r.l. **(2)**
Via I Maggio 61, 29027, Podenzano, PC,
Italy
Tel.: (39) 0523524086
Web Site: https://www.tecniwell.it
Drilling Machines Mfr
N.A.I.C.S.: 333131

Subsidiary (Domestic):

Vibration Technology, Inc. **(2)**
122 Dalton St, Shreveport, LA 71135
Tel.: (318) 686-0001
Web Site:
http://www.vibrationtechnology.com
Drilling Contracting Services
N.A.I.C.S.: 213111

GRANITE POINT MORTGAGE TRUST INC.

3 Bryant Park 24th Fl, New York, NY
10036
Tel.: (212) 364-5500 **MD**
Web Site: https://www.gpmtreit.com
Year Founded: 2017
GPMT—(NYSE)
Rev.: $210,854,000
Assets: $3,454,101,000
Liabilities: $2,470,431,000
Net Worth: $983,670,000
Earnings: ($55,327,000)
Emp.: 35
Fiscal Year-end: 12/31/22
Offices of Real Estate Agents & Brokers
N.A.I.C.S.: 531210
Stephen Alpart *(Chief Investment Officer, VP & Co-Head-Orginations)*
Steven Plust *(COO & VP)*
Peter Morral *(Chief Dev Officer, VP & Co-Head-Orginations)*

Michael J. Karber *(Gen Counsel, Sec & VP)*
John A. Taylor *(Pres & CEO)*

GRANITE RIDGE RESOURCES INC.

5217 McKinney Ave Ste 400, Dallas,
TX 75205
Tel.: (214) 396-2850 **DE**
Web Site:
https://www.graniteridge.com
Year Founded: 2022
GRNT—(NYSE)
Rev.: $497,417,000
Assets: $794,777,000
Liabilities: $172,373,000
Net Worth: $622,404,000
Earnings: $262,344,000
Emp.: 2
Fiscal Year-end: 12/31/22
Support Activities for Oil & Gas Operations
N.A.I.C.S.: 213112
Luke C. Brandenberg *(CEO)*
Tyler S. Farquharson *(CFO)*

GRAPEFRUIT USA, INC.

1000 Northwest St Mid-Town Brandy
Wine Ste1200-3094, Wilmington, DE
19801
Tel.: (310) 575-1175
Web Site: http://www.imaging3.com
Year Founded: 1993
IGNG—(OTCIQ)
Rev.: $3,672,353
Assets: $3,048,987
Liabilities: $7,728,734
Net Worth: ($4,679,747)
Earnings: ($4,056,996)
Emp.: 14
Fiscal Year-end: 12/31/20
Diagnostic Imaging Product Mfr
N.A.I.C.S.: 339999
Kenneth Joe Biehl *(CFO & Exec VP)*
Daniel J. Yourist *(COO & Sec)*
Bradley J. Yourist *(Chm & CEO)*

GRAPHENE & SOLAR TECHNOLOGIES LTD

11201 N Tatum Blvd Ste 300, Phoenix, AZ 85028
Tel.: (602) 388-8335 **CO**
Web Site: https://www.gstx.ltd
Year Founded: 2010
GSTX—(OTCIQ)
Rev.: $31,455
Assets: $18,130
Liabilities: $4,997,159
Net Worth: ($4,979,029)
Earnings: ($1,305,062)
Fiscal Year-end: 09/30/23
High-end Electronics-Grade High Purity Quartz Sand Mfr
N.A.I.C.S.: 335999
Jason Roger May *(CEO)*
Paul Saffron *(COO)*
Kristine Roberta Woo *(Sr VP)*

GRAPHIC PACKAGING HOLDING COMPANY

1500 Riveredge Pkwy Ste 100, Atlanta, GA 30328
Tel.: (770) 240-7200 **DE**
Web Site:
https://www.graphicpkg.com
Year Founded: 1991
GPK—(NYSE)
Rev.: $9,428,000,000
Assets: $11,175,000,000
Liabilities: $8,393,000,000
Net Worth: $2,782,000,000
Earnings: $723,000,000
Emp.: 23,500
Fiscal Year-end: 12/31/23
Holding Company; Packaging Mfr
N.A.I.C.S.: 551112

Michael P. Doss *(Pres & CEO)*
Joseph P. Yost *(Pres-Intl Bus & Exec VP)*
Stephen R. Scherger *(CFO & Exec VP)*
Michael J. Farrell *(Exec VP-Mills Div)*
Stacey Valy Panayiotou *(Exec VP-HR)*
Lauren S. Tashma *(Gen Counsel, Sec & Exec VP)*
Charles D. Lischer *(Chief Acctg Officer & Sr VP)*
Melanie Skijus *(VP-IR)*

Subsidiaries:

Brandpack Consulting GmbH **(1)**
Leverkusenstr 54, 22761, Hamburg, Germany
Tel.: (49) 4085507580
Web Site: https://www.brandpack.de
Graphic Design Services
N.A.I.C.S.: 541430

G-BOX SA de CV. **(1)**
FFCC Via Tampico No 1021 Col Valle Soleado, Guadalupe, 67114, Mexico
Tel.: (52) 8182625000
Web Site: http://www.g-box.com.mx
Paper Packaging Product Mfr & Distr
N.A.I.C.S.: 322220
Marcelo Belden *(CEO)*

GPI Krakow Sp. z o.o. **(1)**
Stanislawice 360, Gm Bochnia, 32-015,
Klaj, Poland
Tel.: (48) 122797300
Web Site: https://gpi-krakow.pl
Emp.: 225
Tobacco Product Mfr & Distr
N.A.I.C.S.: 312230

Graphic Packaging International
Canada, ULC **(1)**
531 Golspie St, Winnipeg, R2K 2T9, MB,
Canada
Tel.: (204) 667-6600
Emp.: 150
Paper Packaging Product Distr
N.A.I.C.S.: 424130
Christine Barrett *(Mgr-HR)*

Graphic Packaging International
Gateshead Limited **(1)**
Dukesway South Team Valley Trading Estate Tyne & Wear, Gateshead, NE11 0BF,
United Kingdom
Tel.: (44) 1914916080
Web Site:
https://www.graphicpkgeurope.com
Paper Packaging Product Distr
N.A.I.C.S.: 424130

Graphic Packaging International Partners, LLC **(1)**
1500 Riveredge Pkwy Ste 100, Atlanta, GA
30328 **(79.5%)**
Tel.: (770) 240-7200
Holding Company
N.A.I.C.S.: 551112

Subsidiary (Domestic):

Graphic Packaging International,
LLC **(2)**
1500 Riveredge Pkwy Ste 100, Atlanta, GA
30328
Tel.: (770) 240-7200
Web Site: http://www.graphicpkg.com
Rev.: $6,559,899,999
Assets: $7,794,700,000
Liabilities: $5,420,900,000
Net Worth: $2,373,800,000
Earnings: $232,900,000
Emp.: 18,774
Fiscal Year-end: 12/31/2020
Paperboard Packaging Mfr
N.A.I.C.S.: 322220
Michael P. Doss *(Pres & CEO)*
Stephen R. Scherger *(CFO & Exec VP)*
Michael J. Farrell *(Exec VP-Mills Div)*
Lauren S. Tashma *(Gen Counsel, Sec & Exec VP)*
Joseph P. Yost *(Pres-Americas & Exec VP)*
Charles D. Lischer *(Chief Acctg Officer & Sr VP)*
Jean-François Roche *(Pres-Europe, Middle East & Africa & Sr VP)*

Subsidiary (Domestic):

Artistic Carton Company **(3)**
1975 Big Timber Rd, Elgin, IL 60123
Tel.: (847) 741-0247
Web Site: http://www.artisticcarton.com
Emp.: 150
Paperboard Boxes Mfr
N.A.I.C.S.: 322130
Mark R. Hopkinson *(CFO)*

Division (Domestic):

Artistic Carton Company - Auburn
Division **(4)**
1201 Grandstaff Dr, Auburn, IN 46706
Tel.: (260) 925-6060
Folding Cartons Mfr
N.A.I.C.S.: 322212

Subsidiary (Domestic):

White Pigeon Paper Company **(4)**
15781 River St, White Pigeon, MI
49099-9410 **(100%)**
Tel.: (269) 483-7601
Web Site: http://www.whitepigeonpaper.com
Rev.: $22,000,000
Emp.: 100
Boxboard & Related Product Mfr
N.A.I.C.S.: 322130

Subsidiary (Domestic):

Carton Craft Corporation **(3)**
2549 Charlestown Rd, New Albany, IN
47150-2554
Tel.: (812) 949-4393
Web Site: http://www.cartonpkg.com
Sales Range: $1-9.9 Million
Corrugated & Solid Fiber Folding Carton &
Box Mfr
N.A.I.C.S.: 322211
John Reiss *(Pres)*

Field Container Queretaro (USA),
L.L.C. **(3)**
814 Livingston Ct, Marietta, GA 30067
Tel.: (770) 644-3000
Paperboard Mfr
N.A.I.C.S.: 322130

Golden Equities, Inc. **(3)**
4455 Table Mountain Dr, Golden, CO 80403
Tel.: (303) 215-4600
Financial Services
N.A.I.C.S.: 523999

Subsidiary (Non-US):

Graphic Packaging International Australia Pty Limited **(3)**
U 4 21 Huntingdale Rd, Burwood, 3125,
Australia
Tel.: (61) 398080777
Web Site:
https://www.graphicpackaging.com
Industrial Machinery Mfr
N.A.I.C.S.: 334519

Graphic Packaging International Box
Holdings Limited **(3)**
Interlink Way South Bardon Hill, Coalville,
LE67 1PE, Leicestershire, United Kingdom
Tel.: (44) 1530518200
Holding Company
N.A.I.C.S.: 551112

Graphic Packaging International
Bremen GmbH **(3)**
Funkschneise 19, 28309, Bremen, Germany
Tel.: (49) 4214108829
Packaging Materials Mfr
N.A.I.C.S.: 326199

Graphic Packaging International
Canada Corporation **(3)**
1355 Aerowood Dr, Mississauga, L4W 1C2,
ON, Canada
Tel.: (905) 602-7877
Emp.: 50
Food Products Mfr
N.A.I.C.S.: 311991

Graphic Packaging International Europe Cartons B.V. (3)
Kooiweg 12, 4631 SZ, Hoogerheide, Netherlands
Tel.: (31) 16 461 1500
Web Site: https://www.graphicpkg.com
Packaging Materials Mfr
N.A.I.C.S.: 326199

Graphic Packaging International France (3)
2 Allee Des Chenes, Hauts-de-France, 59241, Masnieres, France
Tel.: (33) 32 775 7578
Web Site: https://www.graphicpkg.com
Packaging Materials Mfr
N.A.I.C.S.: 326199

Graphic Packaging International Holding Sweden AB (3)
PO Box 1, 601 02, Norrkoping, Sweden
Tel.: (46) 11155700
Holding Company
N.A.I.C.S.: 551112

Graphic Packaging International Japan Ltd. (3)
5F Shintora South bldg 20-4 Shinbashi 5-chome, Minato-ku, Tokyo, 105-0004, Japan
Tel.: (81) 35 401 1225
Web Site: https://www.graphicpkg.jp
Packaging Material Mfr & Distr
N.A.I.C.S.: 326199
Kaeko Gondo (Pres)

Subsidiary (Domestic):

Rengo Riverwood Packaging, Ltd. (4)
1-270 Konan Shinagawa Season Terrace 7th Floor, Minato-ku, Tokyo, 108-0075, Japan
Tel.: (81) 35 715 8833
Web Site: https://www.rrp.co.jp
Emp.: 20
Packaging Material Distr
N.A.I.C.S.: 423840
Kaeko Gonto (Chm)
Sadanori Inoue (Pres)
Yasuhiro Yuda (VP)
Hiroyuki Oba (Mng Dir)

Subsidiary (Non-US):

Graphic Packaging International Limited (3)
Filwood Road, Fishponds, Bristol, BS16 3SB, Avon, United Kingdom
Tel.: (44) 117 988 2429
Web Site: https://www.graphicpkg.com
Packaging Materials Mfr
N.A.I.C.S.: 326199

Graphic Packaging International Mexicana, S. de R.L. de C.V. (3)
Camino Campo Militar Km 1 Col San Antonio de la Punta, 76135, Queretaro, Mexico
Tel.: (52) 442 153 5600
Web Site: http://www.graphicphc.com
Packaging Materials Mfr
N.A.I.C.S.: 326199
Almac Squeza (Mgr-HR)

Graphic Packaging International S.p.A. (3)
Via Le Rimembranze 21/13, 20020, Lainate, Italy
Tel.: (39) 029375311
Packaging Material Distr
N.A.I.C.S.: 423840

Graphic Packaging International Spain, S.A. (3)
Crta N-IIa Km 557 Odena, 8711, Igualada, Spain
Tel.: (34) 938017337
Packaging Materials Mfr
N.A.I.C.S.: 326199

Graphic Packaging International do Brasil - Embalagens Ltda. (3)
Rua Arquimedes 350 Avenidas Arquimedes, Jundiai, Sao Paulo, 13211-840, Brazil
Tel.: (55) 114 589 4536
Web Site: http://www.graphicpkg.com.br
Packaging Materials Mfr
N.A.I.C.S.: 326199

Plant (Domestic):

Graphic Packaging International, Inc. - Carol Stream (3)
400 E N Ave, Carol Stream, IL 60188
Tel.: (630) 260-6500
Emp.: 300
Consumer Packaging Products Mfr
N.A.I.C.S.: 322211

Graphic Packaging International, Inc. - Crosby (3)
975 3rd St SW, Crosby, MN 56441
Tel.: (218) 546-2100
Sales Range: $50-74.9 Million
Emp.: 130
Packaging Machinery Mfr
N.A.I.C.S.: 333248

Graphic Packaging International, Inc. - Elk Grove Village (3)
1500 Nicholas Blvd, Elk Grove Village, IL 60007
Tel.: (847) 437-1700
Sales Range: $100-124.9 Million
Emp.: 300
Paperboard & Plastic Packaging Mfr
N.A.I.C.S.: 322220

Graphic Packaging International, Inc. - Salt Lake City (3)
2357 S 900 W, Salt Lake City, UT 84119
Tel.: (801) 972-3005
Web Site: http://www.graphicpkg.com
Sales Range: $100-124.9 Million
Multiwall Bag Mfr
N.A.I.C.S.: 322220

Graphic Packaging International, Inc. - West Monroe (3)
1000 Jonesboro Rd, West Monroe, LA 71294
Tel.: (318) 362-2000
Sales Range: $50-74.9 Million
Packaging Mfr
N.A.I.C.S.: 322120

Graphic Packaging International, LLC - Clarksville (3)
2593 Old Russellville Pike, Clarksville, TN 37040
Tel.: (931) 648-3600
Food Packaging Container Mfr
N.A.I.C.S.: 326199

Graphic Packaging International, LLC - Pittston (3)
20 Commerce Rd, Pittston, PA 18640
Tel.: (570) 883-0299
Food Packaging Container Mfr
N.A.I.C.S.: 326199

Subsidiary (Domestic):

Lithocraft, Inc. (3)
1502 Beeler St, New Albany, IN 47150
Tel.: (812) 948-1608
Web Site: http://www.lithocraftinc.com
Sales Range: $1-9.9 Million
Commercial Lithographic Printing
N.A.I.C.S.: 323111
Robert Brewer (Pres)
William Brewer (VP)

Walter G. Anderson Inc. (3)
4535 Willow Dr, Hamel, MN 55340
Tel.: (763) 478-2133
Web Site: http://www.graphicpkg.com
Folding Cartons Mfr
N.A.I.C.S.: 322212

GRAY TELEVISION, INC.

4370 Peachtree Rd NE, Atlanta, GA 30319
Tel.: (404) 504-9828   GA
Web Site: https://www.gray.tv
Year Founded: 1897
GTN—(NYSE)
Rev.: $3,676,000,000
Assets: $11,152,000,000
Liabilities: $9,036,000,000
Net Worth: $2,116,000,000
Earnings: $403,000,000
Emp.: 8,942
Fiscal Year-end: 12/31/22
Holding Company; Television Broadcasting Stations & Digital Media Platforms Owner & Operator

N.A.I.C.S.: 551112
Donald Pat LaPlatney (Pres & Co-CEO)
Sandra Breland (COO & Exec VP)
Hilton H. Howell Jr. (Exec Chm & Co-CEO)
Kevin P. Latek (Chief Legal & Dev Officer & Exec VP)
Gregory Conklin (VP-Corp Programming)
Sabra Cowart (Sr VP-Fin Reporting)
Robert Folliard (Sr VP-Govt Rels & Distr)
Vance Luke (Sr VP & Controller)
Becky Meyer (Sr VP-Natl Sls)
David Burke (CTO & Sr VP)
Jan Goldstein (Sr VP-HR)
Matt Jaquint (Chief Revenue Officer & Sr VP)
Mike King (CMO & Sr VP)
Ellenann Yelverton (Sr VP & Deputy Gen Counsel)
Sharel Bend (Dir-Employee Rels)
Robin Collins (VP-Tax)
Brittany Cook (VP-Internal Reporting)
David Evans (VP-Broadcast Engrg)
Ronna Corrente (Sr VP)
Colin Gaston (Sr VP)
Ted Fortenberry (VP)
Kym Grinnage (VP)
Corey Hanson (VP)
Jasmine Hardin (VP)
Brent McClure (VP)
Matt Moran (VP)
Dana Neves (VP)
Thom Pritz (VP)
Matt Pumo (VP)
Sue Ramsett (VP)
Joe Sciortino (VP)
Holly Steuart (VP)
Don Vesely (VP)
Lisa Allen (VP)
Lori Brock (VP)
Brandon Omohundro (VP)
Justin Campbell (VP)
Tom Casey (VP)
Jennifer Dale (VP)
Brad Eaton (VP)
Blanca Esparza Pap (VP)
Claire Ferguson (Sec)
James Finch (VP)
Maurice Gibson (VP)
Garrett Pope (Sr VP-Sls Ops)
Jason Hall (VP-Spanish Media Sls-Telemundo Station Grp)
Susan Sim Oh (VP-Ops & Strategy-Telemundo Station Grp)
Jackson S. Cowart IV (Chief Acctg Officer & Sr VP)

Subsidiaries:

Gray Media Group, Inc. (1)
201 Monroe St 20th Fl, Montgomery, AL 36104
Tel.: (334) 206-1400
Television Broadcasting Station
N.A.I.C.S.: 516120

Subsidiary (Domestic):

KAIT, LLC (2)
472 CR 766, Jonesboro, AR 72401
Tel.: (870) 931-8888
Web Site: https://www.kait8.com
Television Broadcasting Station
N.A.I.C.S.: 516120
Hatton Weeks (VP & Gen Mgr)

KOLD, LLC (2)
7831 N Business Park Dr, Tucson, AZ 85743-9622
Tel.: (520) 744-1313
Web Site: https://www.kold.com
Television Broadcasting Station
N.A.I.C.S.: 516120
Damien Alameda (Dir-Sports)

KPLC, LLC (2)
320 Division St, Lake Charles, LA 70601-7060

Tel.: (337) 439-9071
Web Site: https://www.kplctv.com
Television Broadcasting Station
N.A.I.C.S.: 516120
Dianna Mayo (Sls Mgr)
John Ware (Gen Mgr)

KSLA, LLC (2)
1812 Fairfield Ave, Shreveport, LA 71101-4461
Tel.: (318) 222-1212
Web Site: https://www.ksla.com
Television Broadcasting Station
N.A.I.C.S.: 516120

Tupelo-Honey Raycom, LLC (2)
5200 E 64th St, Indianapolis, IN 46220
Tel.: (317) 759-9900
Web Site: https://www.tupelohoney.net
Post Production Services
N.A.I.C.S.: 512191
Cary Glotzer (Co-Founder & CEO)
Stephen Wallen (Sr VP-Production & Special Projects)
Douglas Cowen (Dir-Fin)
Greg Weitekamp (COO)
John Servizzi (Co-Founder & CTO)
Greg Ambrose (Dir)
Adam Coppinger (VP-Remote Production)
Sandra Doerr (Dir-Remote Productions & Ops)
Steven Towle (Dir-Remote Production)
Tom Cavanaugh (VP-Remote Production)
Kyle Cleaver (Dir-HR & Bus Affairs)
Angelica Locsin (Dir-Ops)
Peter Loomis (Dir-Production)
Nick Young (Dir-Production)
Jacob Matthews (Engr-Engrg & Ops)
John Fritz (Sr Dir-Remote Production)
David Harris (Dir-Remote Production)
Breanna Manley (Assoc Dir-Production)
Braden Pretzsch (Assoc Dir-Production)
Charlie Volz (Engr-Engrg & Ops)
Curtis Varju (Sr Engr-Engrg & Ops)
Jake Thorn (Engr-Engrg & Ops)
Donna Mack (Mgr-Crewing & Travel)
Kyle Clore (Engr-Engrg & Ops)

WALB, LLC (2)
1709 Stuart Ave, Albany, GA 31707
Tel.: (229) 446-1010
Web Site: https://www.walb.com
Television Broadcasting Station
N.A.I.C.S.: 516120
Bruce Austin (Gen Mgr)
Paul Serio (Chief Engr)
Richard Shepherd (Ops Mgr-News)
Jerry Nolan (Dir-Mktg)
Jordan Barela (Mgr-Digital Content)
Liz Knight (Gen Mgr-Sls)
Kelli Roberts (Sls Mgr-Local)
Kristi Bratcher (Sls Mgr-Local)

WAVE Holdings, LLC (2)
725 S Floyd St, Louisville, KY 40203-2337
Tel.: (502) 585-2201
Web Site: https://www.wave3.com
Television Broadcasting Station
N.A.I.C.S.: 516120

WBRC, LLC (2)
1720 Valley View Dr, Birmingham, AL 35209
Tel.: (205) 583-4343
Web Site: https://www.wbrc.com
Television Broadcasting Station
N.A.I.C.S.: 516120
Theresa Cottrell (Natl Sls Mgr)
Shannon Isbell (Dir-News)
Jenna Wood (Mgr-Digital Mktg)
Lori McNamara (Mgr-Local Sls)
Micah McAfee (Dir-Res)
Jason Mathews (Gen Mgr)

WBTV, LLC (2)
1 Julian Price Pl, Charlotte, NC 28208-5211
Tel.: (704) 374-3500
Web Site: https://www.wbtv.com
Television Broadcasting Station
N.A.I.C.S.: 516120
Mike Gurthie (Dir-Tech)
Michal Campbell (Mgr-Local Sls)
Bob Nemenz (Mgr-Local Sls)
Patti Goodnight (Mgr-Natl Sls)
Amiya Lilly (Sls Mgr-Digital)

WCSC, LLC (2)
2126 Charlie Hall Blvd, Charleston, SC 29414
Tel.: (843) 402-5555

Gray Television, Inc.—(Continued)
Web Site: https://www.live5news.com
Television Broadcasting Station
N.A.I.C.S.: 516120
Kevin Bilodeau (Dir-Sports)
A. Daniel Cates (VP & Gen Mgr)
Amanda Curry (Mktg Dir)

WFIE, LLC (2)
1115 Mount Auburn Rd, Evansville, IN 47720
Tel.: (812) 426-1414
Web Site: https://www.14news.com
Television Broadcasting Station
N.A.I.C.S.: 516120
Bobby Barnett (Dir-Tech)
Jill Lyman (Mgr-Digital Content)
Joe Schlaerth (Dir-News)
Beth Sweeney (Asst Dir-News)

WIS, LLC (2)
1111 Bull St, Columbia, SC 29201
Tel.: (803) 799-1010
Web Site: https://www.wistv.com
Television Broadcasting Station
N.A.I.C.S.: 516120
Andrea Starr (Gen Sls Mgr)

WLBT, LLC (2)
715 S Jefferson St, Jackson, MS 39201
Tel.: (601) 948-3333
Web Site: https://www.wlbt.com
Television Broadcasting Station
N.A.I.C.S.: 516120
Ted Fortenberry (VP & Gen Mgr)

WLOX, LLC (2)
208 DeBuys Rd 39531, Biloxi, MS 39531-4596
Tel.: (228) 896-1313
Web Site: http://www.wlox.com
Television Broadcasting Station
N.A.I.C.S.: 516120
Rick Williams (Gen Mgr)
Dannah Dobson (Gen Sls Mgr)

WSFA, LLC (2)
445 Dexter Ave Ste 7000, Montgomery, AL 36104
Tel.: (334) 288-1212
Web Site: https://www.wsfa.com
Television Broadcasting Station
N.A.I.C.S.: 516120
Scott Duff (Dir-News)
Mark Bunting (Gen Mgr)
Stephen Gunter (Dir-Sports)
Morris Pollock (Dir-News)
Morgan Carlson (Mgr-Digital Content)
Bill Poplin (Gen Sls Mgr)
Kerry Johnson (Sls Mgr)
Travis Dent (Mktg Dir)

WTOC, LLC (2)
11 The News Pl, Savannah, GA 31405
Tel.: (912) 234-1111
Web Site: https://www.wtoc.com
Television Broadcasting Station
N.A.I.C.S.: 516120
Matt Nixon (Mgr-Natl Sls)
Kevin Orloff (Mgr-Digital Sls)

WWBT, LLC (2)
5710 Midlothian Tpke, Richmond, VA 23225
Tel.: (804) 230-1212
Web Site: https://www.nbc12.com
Television Broadcasting Station
N.A.I.C.S.: 516120
Kym Grinnage (Gen Mgr)
Rodney Bryant (Dir-Sls)
Gina Honeycutt (Mgr-Sls-Local)
Frank Jones (Dir-News)
J. W. Barnes (Asst Dir-News)
Ben Milewczik (Dir-Tech)
David Hayes (Natl Sls Mgr-Political)

Gray Media Group, Inc. (1)
1 Walnut St, Boston, MA 02108
Tel.: (617) 305-4160
Web Site: https://www.graymediagroup.com
Public Relations Services
N.A.I.C.S.: 541820
Rob Gray (Founder & Pres)

Gray Television Group, Inc. (1)
4370 Peachtree Rd NE, Atlanta, GA 30319
Tel.: (404) 504-9828
Web Site: http://www.gray.tv
Television Broadcasting Stations & Digital Media Platforms Operator
N.A.I.C.S.: 516120

Hilton H. Howell Jr. (Chm & Co-CEO)

Unit (Domestic):

KALB-TV News Channel 5 (2)
605 Washington St, Alexandria, LA 71301-8028
Tel.: (318) 445-2456
Web Site: http://www.kalb.com
Television Station
N.A.I.C.S.: 516120
Phillip Taylor (Mgr-Engrg)
Vernilla Brooks (Mgr-Programming)
Herbert Bruce (Gen Mgr-Sls)
Allie Purser (Mgr-News Production)

KCRG-TV (2)
501 2nd Ave SE, Cedar Rapids, IA 52401
Tel.: (319) 399-5900
Web Site: http://www.kcrg.com
Sales Range: $1-9.9 Million
Emp.: 150
Television Broadcasting Station
N.A.I.C.S.: 516120

KEVN-TV (2)
2001 Skyline Dr, Rapid City, SD 57701
Tel.: (605) 394-7777
Web Site: https://www.blackhillsfox.com
Television Broadcasting Station
N.A.I.C.S.: 516120
Jack Caudill (Asst Dir-News)
Timothy Knapp (Supvr-Videography)
Chris Gross (Gen Mgr)

KFYR-TV (2)
200 N 4th St, Bismarck, ND 58501
Tel.: (701) 255-5757
Web Site: http://www.kfyrtv.com
Emp.: 60
Television Broadcasting Station
N.A.I.C.S.: 516120
Barry Schumaier (Gen Mgr)
J. R. Havens (Dir-News)
Timmerman Lee (Dir-Sports)
Randy Hoffman (Dir-Digital Solutions)

KKTV-TV (2)
520 E Colorado, Colorado Springs, CO 80903
Tel.: (719) 634-2844
Web Site: http://www.kktv.com
Emp.: 1,500
Television Broadcasting Station
N.A.I.C.S.: 516120

KMOT-TV (2)
1800 SW 16th St, Minot, ND 58701
Tel.: (701) 852-4101
Web Site: http://www.kmot.com
Television Broadcasting Station
N.A.I.C.S.: 516120
Aaron Dietrich (Dir-Sports)
Randy Minter (Gen Mgr-Sls)

KNOE-TV (2)
1400 Oliver Rd, Monroe, LA 71201
Tel.: (318) 388-8888
Web Site: http://www.knoe.com
Emp.: 35
Television Broadcasting Station
N.A.I.C.S.: 516120

KNOP-TV (2)
8020 N Hwy 83, North Platte, NE 69101
Tel.: (308) 532-2222
Web Site: http://www.knopnews2.com
Television Broadcasting Station
N.A.I.C.S.: 516120

KOSA-TV CBS 7 (2)
4101 E 42nd St Ste J7, Odessa, TX 79762
Tel.: (432) 580-5672
Web Site: http://www.cbs7.com
Television Broadcasting Station
N.A.I.C.S.: 516120
Jim McKinnon (Chief Engr)
Toni Frady (Office Mgr)
Don Davis (VP & Gen Mgr)
Craig Stewart (Dir-Weather)
Shelby Landgraf (Dir-Interim News)
Andrea Storm (Asst Dir-Interim)

KSFY-TV (2)
325 S 1st Ave Ste 100, Sioux Falls, SD 57104
Tel.: (605) 336-1300
Web Site: http://www.ksfy.com
Emp.: 75
Television Broadcasting Station
N.A.I.C.S.: 516120

KUMV-TV (2)
602 Main St, Williston, ND 58801
Tel.: (701) 572-4676
Web Site: http://www.kumv.com
Emp.: 11
Television Broadcasting Station
N.A.I.C.S.: 516120
Jon Cole (Dir-Sports)

KVLY-TV (2)
1350 21st Ave S, Fargo, ND 58103
Tel.: (701) 237-5211
Web Site: http://www.valleynewslive.com
Emp.: 90
Television Broadcasting Station
N.A.I.C.S.: 516120

KWCH-TV (2)
2815 E 37th St N, Wichita, KS 67219
Tel.: (316) 838-1212
Web Site: http://www.kwch.com
Television Station
N.A.I.C.S.: 516120
Shawn Hilferty (Dir-Digital Media & Ops)
Dominic Gauna (Dir-Creative Svcs & Programming)
Kim Wilhelm (Dir-News)
Steve Reiter (Chief Engr)

Affiliate (Domestic):

KBSD-TV (3)
2815 E 37th St N, Wichita, KS 67219
Tel.: (316) 838-1212
Television Station
N.A.I.C.S.: 516120

KBSH-TV (3)
2815 E 37th St N, Wichita, KS 67219
Tel.: (316) 838-1212
Emp.: 6
Television Station
N.A.I.C.S.: 516120
Dominic Gauna (Dir-Mktg)

KBSL-TV (3)
3023 W 31st St, Goodland, KS 67735
Tel.: (785) 899-2321
Television Station
N.A.I.C.S.: 516120

Unit (Domestic):

WABI-TV (2)
35 Hildreth St, Bangor, ME 04401
Tel.: (207) 947-8321
Web Site: https://www.wabi.tv
Television Broadcasting Station
N.A.I.C.S.: 516120
Jon Small (Dir-News)

WCJB-TV (2)
6220 NW 43rd St, Gainesville, FL 32653
Tel.: (352) 377-2020
Web Site: https://www.wcjb.com
Television Broadcasting Services
N.A.I.C.S.: 516120
Jon Levy (Dir-News)
Kevin Walls (Dir-Sports)

WCTV-TV (2)
1801 Halstead Blvd, Tallahassee, FL 32309
Tel.: (850) 893-6666
Web Site: https://www.wctv.tv
Television Broadcasting Station
N.A.I.C.S.: 516120

WDTV-TV (2)
5 Television Dr, Bridgeport, WV 26330
Tel.: (304) 848-5000
Web Site: https://www.wdtv.com
Television Broadcasting Station
N.A.I.C.S.: 516120
Timothy DeFazio (Gen Mgr)
Timothy Knapp (Supvr-Videography)
Eric Wilson (Sls Mgr-Local)

WIFR-TV (2)
2523 N Meridian Rd, Rockford, IL 61101 (100%)
Tel.: (815) 987-5300
Web Site: http://www.wifr.com
Emp.: 60
Television Broadcasting Station
N.A.I.C.S.: 516120

WITN-TV (2)
203 W Main St, Washington, NC 27889 (100%)
Tel.: (252) 439-7777
Web Site: http://www.witn.com

Television Broadcasting Station
N.A.I.C.S.: 516120
Billy Weaver (Dir-Sports)

WJHG-TV (2)
8195 Front Beach Rd, Panama City Beach, FL 32407 (100%)
Tel.: (850) 234-7777
Web Site: https://www.wjhg.com
Television Broadcasting Station
N.A.I.C.S.: 516120
Sean Dixon (Dir-Creative Svcs)
Ulysses Carlini (Gen Mgr)
Lesley Smith (Editor)
Kristen White (Gen Mgr-Sls)

WKYT-TV (2)
2851 Winchester Rd, Lexington, KY 40509-9581 (100%)
Tel.: (859) 299-0411
Web Site: http://www.wkyt.com
Television Broadcasting Station
N.A.I.C.S.: 516120

WOWT-TV (2)
3501 Farnam St, Omaha, NE 68131
Tel.: (402) 346-6666
Web Site: http://www.wowt.com
Television Broadcasting Station
N.A.I.C.S.: 516120
Chris Ahrens (Mgr-Digital Sls)
Mary Beth Keating (Sls Mgr-Natl)
Joe Nugent (Dir-Sports)
Gina Dvorak (Dir-Digital)

WRDW-TV (2)
1301 Georgia Ave, North Augusta, SC 29841-3019
Tel.: (803) 278-1212
Web Site: http://www.wrdw.com
Television Broadcasting Station
N.A.I.C.S.: 516120

WSAZ-TV (2)
645 5th Ave, Huntington, WV 25701
Tel.: (304) 697-4780
Web Site: http://www.wsaz.com
Television Broadcasting Station
N.A.I.C.S.: 516120
Aaron Withrow (Chief Engr)
Anna Baxter (Dir-News)
Melanie Oliver (Natl Sls Mgr)
Matt Moran (VP & Gen Mgr)
Timothy Knapp (Supvr-Videography)
Kristen Bentley (Asst Dir-News)
Vince Wardell (Natl Mgr-Reg)
Joel Swisher (Mgr-Local Sls-Charleston)
Jeff Perry (Mgr-Ops)
Markie Owens (Mgr-Assignment)

Subsidiary (Domestic):

WVLT-TV, Inc. (2)
6450 Papermill Dr, Knoxville, TN 37919
Tel.: (865) 450-8888
Web Site: http://www.wvlt.tv
Television Broadcasting Station
N.A.I.C.S.: 516120
Jasmine Hatcher Hardin (Gen Mgr)
Marybeth Jacoby (Dir-News)
Sara Foster (Gen Mgr-Sls)
Doug Stallard (Chief Engr)
Chad Kennedy (Dir-Mktg & Ops)
Sheree White (Mgr-Bus)
Justin Daugherty (Reg Mgr & Natl Sls Mgr)
Tara Carr (Sls Mgr-Local)
Rick Russo (Dir-Sports)
Kristin Reed (Sls Mgr-Digital)

Unit (Domestic):

WYMT-TV (2)
199 Black Gold Blvd, Hazard, KY 41701 (100%)
Tel.: (606) 436-5757
Web Site: http://www.wymt.com
Emp.: 54
Television Broadcasting Station
N.A.I.C.S.: 516120
Neil Middleton (VP & Gen Mgr)
Steve Hensley (Dir-News)
Kyle Collier (Asst Dir-News)
Willie Hope III (Dir-Sports)

Subsidiary (Domestic):

Young Broadcasting of Davenport, Inc. (2)
805 Brady St, Davenport, IA 52803
Tel.: (563) 383-7000

Web Site: https://www.kwqc.com
Television Broadcasting Station
N.A.I.C.S.: 516120
Doug Bierman *(Chief Engr)*
Todd Grady *(Gen Sls Mgr)*
Tim Stinson *(Sls Mgr-Local)*
Joey Donia *(Dir-Sports)*
Sue Ramsett *(Gen Mgr)*
Annette Trefz *(Bus Mgr)*
Stephanie Hedrick *(Dir-News)*
Kerry Johnson *(Sls Mgr-Digital)*
Marcia Teel *(Mgr-Programming & Creative Svcs)*

Young Broadcasting of Green Bay, Inc. (2)
115 S Jefferson St, Green Bay, WI 54301
Tel.: (920) 432-3331
Web Site: https://www.wbay.com
Television Broadcasting Station
N.A.I.C.S.: 516120
Steve Lavin *(Gen Mgr)*
Matt Kummer *(Dir-News)*
Dale Mitchell *(Chief Engr)*
Brian Teeters *(Gen Sls Mgr)*
Pam Jessen *(Dir-Ops & Programming)*
Pat Mayo *(Mgr-Mktg & Promo)*
Ted Miller *(Mgr-Digital Media)*
Kelly Grambow *(Sls Mgr-Digital)*
Lori Meyers *(Supvr-Traffic)*
Kelly Coonen *(Office Mgr)*

Quincy Media, Inc. (1)
130 S 5th St, Quincy, IL 62306
Tel.: (217) 223-5100
Web Site: http://www.careersatquincy.com
Television & Radio Broadcasting; Newspaper Publishing
N.A.I.C.S.: 516120
Ralph M. Oakley *(Pres & CEO)*
Brady Dreasler *(Dir-Capital, Engrg & Facilities)*
Jena Schulz *(Dir-HR)*
Mary Oakley Winters *(VP-Interactive)*
Ron Wallace *(VP-Newspapers)*
Tom Allen *(Reg VP)*
Jerry Watson *(Reg VP)*
Kelly Hibbard *(Dir-Broadcast Svcs)*
Brad Eaton *(Dir-Fin)*
Mike McGrath *(Mgr-Acctg)*
Mike Funk *(Dir-IT)*
Dennis Kendall *(Dir-Broadcast News)*
Dan Batchelor *(Dir-Broadcast & Interactive Sls)*
Chuck Roth *(Dir-Bus Administration)*

Unit (Domestic):

KTIV-TV (2)
3135 Floyd Blvd, Sioux City, IA 51108
Tel.: (712) 239-4100
Web Site: http://www.ktiv.com
Sales Range: $10-24.9 Million
Emp.: 50
Television Broadcasting Station
N.A.I.C.S.: 516120
Richard Herr *(Engr)*
Adrian Wisner *(Mgr-Gen Sls)*
Bridget Breen *(Mgr-Station)*
Tom Stock *(Mgr-Production)*
Brad Pautsch *(Dir-Sports)*

KTTC-TV (2)
6301 Bandel Rd NW, Rochester, MN 55901-3478 (100%)
Tel.: (507) 288-4444
Web Site: http://www.kttc.com
Sales Range: $10-24.9 Million
Emp.: 60
Television Broadcasting Station
N.A.I.C.S.: 516120
Jerry Watson *(VP & Gen Mgr)*
Vickie Broughton *(Mgr-Traffic & Programming)*
Brendan Ford *(Mgr-Production)*

Subsidiary (Domestic):

KVOA Communications, Inc. (2)
209 W Elm St, Tucson, AZ 85705-6538
Tel.: (520) 792-2270
Web Site: http://www.kvoa.com
Sales Range: $10-24.9 Million
Emp.: 110
Television Broadcasting Station
N.A.I.C.S.: 516120
Jeff Green *(Gen Mgr-Sls)*
Bill Shaw *(Pres & Gen Mgr)*
Cathie Batbie *(Dir-News)*
Linda Tremelling *(Mgr-Bus)*
Randall K. Smith *(Dir-Ops)*

Unit (Domestic):

KWWL-TV (2)
500 E 4th St, Waterloo, IA 50703-5798
Tel.: (319) 291-1240
Web Site: http://www.kwwl.com
Sales Range: $10-24.9 Million
Emp.: 100
Television Station
N.A.I.C.S.: 516120
Don Morehead *(Mgr-Sls-Natl)*

Subsidiary (Domestic):

New Jersey Herald Inc. (2)
2 Spring St, Newton, NJ 07860-2077
Tel.: (973) 383-1500
Web Site: http://www.njherald.com
Sales Range: $10-24.9 Million
Emp.: 120
Newspapers
N.A.I.C.S.: 513110
Bruce Tomlinson *(Exec Editor)*

Unit (Domestic):

WGEM-TV (2)
513 Hampshire St, Quincy, IL 62301-2928 (100%)
Tel.: (217) 228-6600
Web Site: http://www.wgem.com
Sales Range: $10-24.9 Million
Emp.: 75
Television Broadcasting Station
N.A.I.C.S.: 516120
Jim Lawrence *(Dir-Ops & Engrg)*
Shawn Dickerman *(Dir-Mktg)*
Amy Carothers *(Acct Mgr)*

WKOW-TV (2)
5727 Tokay Blvd, Madison, WI 53719
Tel.: (608) 274-1234
Web Site: http://www.wkow.com
Television Broadcasting Station
N.A.I.C.S.: 516120
Tom Allen *(VP & Gen Mgr)*
Bruce Briney *(Gen Sls Mgr)*
Bob Goessling *(Dir-Programming & Ops)*
Ed Reams *(Dir-News)*
Jill Genter *(Mgr-Mktg & Community Rels)*
Kerry Maki *(Chief Engr)*

WPTA-TV (2)
3401 Butler Rd, Fort Wayne, IN 46808
Tel.: (260) 483-0584
Web Site: http://www.wpta21.com
Television Broadcasting Station
N.A.I.C.S.: 516120
Doug Barrow *(Gen Sls Mgr)*
Jackie Giammara *(Local Sls Mgr)*
Jennifer McCloskey *(Acct Exec-Adv)*
Richard Ash *(Acct Exec)*

WSJV-TV (2)
58096 County Rd 7, Elkhart, IN 46517-9223
Tel.: (574) 679-9758
Web Site: http://www.fox28.com
Sales Range: $10-24.9 Million
Emp.: 80
Television Broadcasting Station
N.A.I.C.S.: 516120
Dean Huppert *(Dir-Sports)*

WVVA-TV (2)
3052 Big Laurel Hwy, Bluefield, WV 24701
Tel.: (304) 325-5487
Web Site: http://www.wvva.com
Sales Range: $10-24.9 Million
Emp.: 45
Television Broadcasting Station
N.A.I.C.S.: 516120
Tom Moses *(Mgr-Production)*
Frank Brady *(Gen Mgr)*
Yvonne Moses *(Reg Mgr-Sls)*
Charity Holman *(Mgr-Sls)*
Audrey Sluss *(Bus Mgr)*
A. J. Good *(Dir-Sports)*
Lisa Grimm *(Acct Exec)*
Carmen Hendrick *(Acct Exec)*
Nathan Hendrick *(Acct Exec)*
Paul Hess *(Dir-Internet)*
Steve Korioth *(Dir-News)*
Keith Von Scio *(Acct Exec)*

GRAYSCALE BITCOIN TRUST
290 Harbor Dr 4th Fl, Stamford, CT 06902
Tel.: (212) 668-1427 DE
Web Site: https://www.grayscale.co

Year Founded: 2013
GBTC—(OTCQX)
Assets: $10,464,263,000
Net Worth: $10,464,263,000
Earnings: ($360,683,000)
Fiscal Year-end: 12/31/22
Investment Trust Services
N.A.I.C.S.: 523991
Simcha Wurtzel *(VP-Fin)*
Michael Sonnenshein *(CEO)*

GRAYSCALE LITECOIN TRUST
290 Harbor Dr 4th Fl, Stamford, CT 06902
Tel.: (212) 668-1427 DE
Web Site: https://www.grayscale.com
LTCN—(OTCQX)
Assets: $158,667,000
Net Worth: $158,667,000
Earnings: $2,816,000)
Fiscal Year-end: 06/30/23
Financial Investment Services
N.A.I.C.S.: 523999

GREAT AJAX CORP.
799 Broadway 8th Fl, New York, NY 10003
Tel.: (646) 868-5483 MD
Web Site: https://www.greatajax.com
Year Founded: 2014
AJX—(NYSE)
Rev.: $35,636,000
Assets: $1,484,426,000
Liabilities: $1,146,961,000
Net Worth: $337,465,000
Earnings: ($28,679,000)
Fiscal Year-end: 12/31/22
Real Estate Investment Services
N.A.I.C.S.: 525990
Russell A. Schaub *(Pres)*
Mary B. Doyle *(CFO & Principal Acctg Officer)*

GREAT AMERICAN BANCORP, INC.
Tel.: (217) 356-2265 DE
Web Site:
  https://www.greatamericanbancorp.com
GTPS—(OTCIQ)
Sales Range: $1-9.9 Million
Emp.: 67
Bank Holding Company
N.A.I.C.S.: 551111
George R. Rouse *(Pres & CEO)*
Ronald E. Guenther *(Chm)*
Patrick J. McWilliams *(CFO, Treas & Sec)*

Subsidiaries:

First Federal Savings Bank of Champaign-Urbana (1)
1311 S Neil St, Champaign, IL 61820 (100%)
Tel.: (217) 356-2265
Web Site: http://www.356bank.com
Savings Bank
N.A.I.C.S.: 522180
George R. Rouse *(Pres & CEO)*
Jane F. Adams *(Treas, Sec & Sr VP-Fin)*
Atka M. Durukan *(Sr VP-HR & Mktg)*
Mark D. Piper *(Sr VP-Ops)*
Paul D. Wilson *(Sr VP-Lending)*

Park Avenue Service Corporation (1)
13011 S Neil St, Champaign, IL 61820-6558
Tel.: (217) 356-2265
Web Site: http://www.356bank.com
Sales Range: $50-74.9 Million
Emp.: 53
Securities & Annuities Brokerage Services
N.A.I.C.S.: 236117
George R. Rouse *(Pres)*
Jane F. Adams *(Treas & Sec)*

GREAT AMERICAN FOOD CHAIN, INC.

400 N Saint Paul St Ste 720, Dallas, TX 75201
Tel.: (214) 507-9984 NV
Year Founded: 1997
GAMN—(OTCIQ)
Restaurant Operators
N.A.I.C.S.: 722511
Edward Sigmond *(Chm, Pres, CEO, Treas & Sec)*

GREAT BASIN ENERGIES, INC.
999 W Riverside Ave Ste 401, Spokane, WA 99201
Tel.: (509) 623-1500 WA
Year Founded: 1981
GBEI—(OTCIQ)
Mining Exploration Services
N.A.I.C.S.: 213114
Douglas Belanger *(VP)*
David P. Onzay *(CFO)*
Debra Van Driel *(Controller)*

GREAT ELM GROUP, INC.
3801 PGA Blvd Ste 603, Palm Beach Gardens, FL 33410
Tel.: (617) 375-3006 DE
Web Site:
  https://www.greatelmgroup.com
GEG—(NASDAQ)
Rev.: $17,834,000
Assets: $140,446,000
Liabilities: $70,251,000
Net Worth: $70,195,000
Earnings: ($926,000)
Emp.: 31
Fiscal Year-end: 06/30/24
Asset Management Services
N.A.I.C.S.: 523999
Jason W. Reese *(Chm & CEO)*
Keri A. Davis *(CFO & Chief Acctg Officer)*

GREAT LAKES AVIATION, LTD.
1022 Airport Pkwy, Cheyenne, WY 82001
Tel.: (307) 432-7000 IA
Year Founded: 1977
GLUX—(OTCEM)
Regional Airline Services
N.A.I.C.S.: 481111
Charles R. Howell IV *(Pres)*

GREAT LAKES DREDGE & DOCK CORPORATION
9811 Katy Fwy Ste 1200, Houston, TX 77024
Tel.: (346) 359-1010 DE
Web Site: https://www.gldd.com
Year Founded: 1890
GLDD—(NASDAQ)
Rev.: $589,625,000
Assets: $1,110,840,000
Liabilities: $725,292,000
Net Worth: $385,548,000
Earnings: $13,906,000
Emp.: 364
Fiscal Year-end: 12/31/23
Dredging & Other Port Services
N.A.I.C.S.: 237990
David J. Johanson *(Sr VP-Ops & Project Acquisition)*
Christopher G. Gunsten *(Sr VP-Project Svcs & Fleet Engrg)*
Steven W. Becker *(Sr VP-Fleet Engrg)*
Scott L. Kornblau *(CFO, Treas & Sr VP)*
Steven R. Auernhamer *(VP-Comml Clinets)*
Lasse J. Petterson *(Pres & CEO)*
Jason W. Campbell *(VP-Health, Safety, and Environment)*
Mark Reid *(VP-Northeast Reg)*
Eleni Beyko *(Sr VP)*
Lynn Nietfeld *(Sr VP)*

Great Lakes Dredge & Dock
Corporation—(Continued)

Garrett L. Gibson *(VP)*
Stan Ekren *(VP)*
Trond Ellefsen *(VP)*
Armand F. Riehl *(VP)*
Dave Allen *(VP)*
Ryan Bayer *(Chief Acctg Officer &
VP)*

Subsidiaries:

Great Lakes Dredge & Dock Com-
pany, LLC **(1)**
1 Parkview Plz Ste 800, Oakbrook Terrace,
IL 60181
Tel.: (630) 574-3000
Web Site: http://www.gldd.com
Sales Range: $25-49.9 Million
Emp.: 125
Heavy & Civil Engineering Construction
Services
N.A.I.C.S.: 237990
Kyle D. Johnson *(COO & Exec VP)*
David J. Johanson *(Sr VP--Gulf Reg)*
Christopher G. Gunsten *(Sr VP-Intl)*
William H. Hanson *(Sr VP-Government
Relations-Business Development)*
Steven L. Lane *(Mgr & VP)*
Christopher G. Gunsten *(Sr VP-Intl)*
David Johanson *(Sr VP-Gulf Reg)*
Kathleen Hayes O'Halloran *(VP & Control-
ler)*
Scott Kornblau *(CFO, Treas & Sr VP)*
Eleni Beyko *(Sr VP-)*
Lynn Nietfeld *(Sr VP)*
Garrett L. Gibson *(VP)*
Stan Ekren *(VP & Mgr-)*
T. Christopher Roberts *(VP & Mgr-)*
Armand F. Riehl *(VP)*

North American Site Developers,
Inc. **(1)**
39 Olympia Ave, Woburn, MA 01801
Tel.: (781) 250-6600
Web Site: http://www.nasdidemo.com
Demolition & Environmental Remediation
Services
N.A.I.C.S.: 562910
Chris Berardi *(Pres)*

Terra Contracting Services, LLC **(1)**
2222 W Cheyenne Ave Ste C, Las Vegas,
NV 89032
Tel.: (702) 651-8100
Web Site: http://www.terracontracting.com
Environmental Contracting Services
N.A.I.C.S.: 562910
Ed McSwain *(Founder & CEO)*

Terra Fluid Management, LLC **(1)**
1507 Enterprise Dr, Kalkaska, MI 49040
Tel.: (231) 258-7082
Freight Transportation Services
N.A.I.C.S.: 484121

GREAT SOUTHERN BAN-
CORP, INC.

218 S Glenstone, Springfield, MO
65802
Tel.: (417) 887-4400 **MD**
Web Site:
https://www.greatsouthernbank.com
Year Founded: 1989
GSBC—(NASDAQ)
Rev.: $261,118,000
Assets: $5,680,702,000
Liabilities: $5,147,615,000
Net Worth: $533,087,000
Earnings: $75,948,000
Emp.: 914
Fiscal Year-end: 12/31/22
Bank Holding Company
N.A.I.C.S.: 551111
Joseph William Turner *(Pres & CEO)*
Kelly Polonus *(VP)*

Subsidiaries:

Great Southern Bank **(1)**
218 S Glenstone, Springfield, MO 65802
Tel.: (417) 225-7020
Web Site:
https://www.greatsouthernbank.com

Sales Range: $125-149.9 Million
Emp.: 500
National Commercial Banks
N.A.I.C.S.: 522180
William V. Turner *(Chm)*
Joseph William Turner *(Pres & CEO)*

GREAT WESTERN BANCORP,
INC.

225 S Main Ave, Sioux Falls, SD
57104
Tel.: (605) 334-2548 **DE**
Web Site:
http://www.greatwesternbank.com
GWB—(NYSE)
Rev.: $491,708,000
Assets: $12,911,468,000
Liabilities: $11,709,989,000
Net Worth: $1,201,479,000
Earnings: $203,258,000
Emp.: 1,607
Fiscal Year-end: 09/30/21
Bank Holding Company
N.A.I.C.S.: 551111
Karlyn M. Knieriem *(Chief Risk Offi-
cer & Exec VP)*
Mark Borrecco *(Pres & CEO)*
Stephen W. Yose *(Chief Credit Officer
& Exec VP)*

Subsidiaries:

Great Western Bank **(1)**
35 1st Ave NE, Watertown, SD 57201
Tel.: (605) 886-8401
Web Site: http://www.greatwesternbank.com
Sales Range: $350-399.9 Million
Commercial Banking
N.A.I.C.S.: 522110
Douglas Bass *(COO)*
Tim Kintner *(Pres-Mkg)*
Cheryl Olson *(Head-Mktg)*
Ryan Boschee *(Grp Pres-Sioux Falls)*
Dan Gomez *(Mgr-Bus Banking)*
Tom Kueter *(Pres-Agri Bus)*
Kristi Benningsdorf *(Mgr-Private Banking)*
Michael Adams *(Mgr-Bus Banking)*
Gary Buehner *(Pres-Market)*
Jeff Burright *(Officer-Mortgage Loan)*
Dave Carlson *(Mgr-Retirement Plan Solu-
tions)*
Delmar Cryer *(Officer-Mortgage Loan)*
Machelle Dale *(Mgr-Treasury Mgmt)*
Amy Dang *(Officer-Mortgage Loan)*
Kevin Dejong *(Pres-Market)*
Jeremy Douglas *(Pres-Market)*
Matt Dutcher *(Pres-Market)*
Bart Floyd *(Pres-Reg)*
Lori Fods *(Portfolio Mqr)*
Lee Fritson *(Pres-Market)*
Joaquin Gallegos *(Pres-Agribusiness Mar-
ket)*
Aaron Gehling *(Pres-Market)*
Gary Geis *(Pres-Reg)*
Gail Grant *(Pres-Reg)*
Doug Green *(Pres-Market)*
Bryan Guest *(Pres-Northern Colorado Grp)*
Renee Gullickson *(Officer-Mortgage Loan)*
Daryl Halvorson *(Officer-Mortgage Loan)*
Carl Hamilton *(Officer-Mortgage Loan)*
Amy Johnson *(Dir-Treasury Mgmt)*

Subsidiary (Domestic):

Hometown Investment Services,
Inc. **(2)**
225 S Main Ave, Sioux Falls, SD 57104
Tel.: (605) 333-7696
Investment Management Service
N.A.I.C.S.: 523940

GREEN BRICK PARTNERS,
INC.

5501 Headquarters Dr Ste 300W,
Plano, TX 75024
Tel.: (469) 573-6755 **DE**
Web Site:
https://www.greenbrickpartners.com
Year Founded: 2006
GRBK—(NYSE)
Rev.: $1,757,793,000
Assets: $1,655,675,000
Liabilities: $572,860,000

Net Worth: $1,082,815,000
Earnings: $291,900,000
Emp.: 550
Fiscal Year-end: 12/31/22
Land Developer & Homebuilder
N.A.I.C.S.: 237210
Jed Dolson *(Pres & COO)*
James R. Brickman *(Co-Founder &
CEO)*
Richard A. Costello *(CFO)*
Neal Suit *(Chief Compliance Officer,
Chief Risk Officer & Gen Counsel)*
David Michael Einhorn *(Co-Founder
& Chm)*

Subsidiaries:

BHome Mortgage, LLC **(1)**
2805 N Dallas Pkwy Ste 120, Plano, TX
75093
Tel.: (214) 880-4894
Web Site: https://www.applywithbhome.com
Mortgage Investment Services
N.A.I.C.S.: 525990

CB JENI Apples Crossing, LLC **(1)**
4859 Ellie Ln, Fairview, TX 75069
Tel.: (469) 418-1037
New Housing & Construction Services
N.A.I.C.S.: 236116
Janet Martin *(Mgr-Community Sls)*

CB JENI Iron Horse, LLC **(1)**
6625 Iron Horse Blvd, North Richland Hills,
TX 76180
Tel.: (972) 955-4083
New Housing & Construction Services
N.A.I.C.S.: 236116
Clayton Cook *(Mgr-Community Sls)*

CB JENI Majestic Gardens, LLC **(1)**
7392 Sideoats Gama St, Frisco, TX 75034
Tel.: (214) 662-5370
Land Development & Home Building Ser-
vices
N.A.I.C.S.: 236117
Tammie Phillips *(Sls Mgr-Community)*
Clayton Cook *(Sls Mgr-Community)*

CB JENI Management, LLC **(1)**
2805 Dallas Pkwy Ste 690, Plano, TX
75093-8722
Tel.: (469) 298-3319
New Single Family Housing Construction
Services
N.A.I.C.S.: 236115

CB JENI Meridian at Southgate,
LLC **(1)**
Stewart Rd, McKinney, TX 75069
Tel.: (972) 891-9703
Land Development & Home Building Ser-
vices
N.A.I.C.S.: 236117

CB JENI Pecan Square, LLC **(1)**
2764 N Market Sq, Denton, TX 76247
Tel.: (972) 404-0624
Land Development & Home Building Ser-
vices
N.A.I.C.S.: 236117
Jenn Wilde *(Sls Mgr-Community)*

CB JENI Ridge View Villas, LLC **(1)**
3966 Sukay Dr, McKinney, TX 75070
Tel.: (214) 531-8435
New Housing & Construction Services
N.A.I.C.S.: 236116
Xuan Le *(Mgr-Community Sls)*

CB JENI Riverset, LLC **(1)**
2663 High Cotton Ln, Garland, TX 75042
Tel.: (972) 891-9703
Land Development & Home Building Ser-
vices
N.A.I.C.S.: 236117
Monica Watkins-Calderon *(Sls Mgr-
Community)*

CB JENI Terraces at Las Colinas,
LLC **(1)**
566 Cobblestone Ln, Irving, TX 75039
Tel.: (972) 891-9703
New Housing & Construction Services
N.A.I.C.S.: 236116
Bill Skiles *(Mgr-Community Sls)*

CB JENI Trophy Club, LLC **(1)**
100 Claire Dr, Trophy Club, TX 76262

Tel.: (214) 251-4366
Land Development & Home Building Ser-
vices
N.A.I.C.S.: 236117
Rich Gonzalez *(Sls Mgr-Community)*

CB JENI Twin Creeks, LLC **(1)**
1002 Switchgrass Ln, Allen, TX 75013
Tel.: (469) 382-1160
Land Development & Home Building Ser-
vices
N.A.I.C.S.: 236117
Diamond Richardson *(Sls Mgr-Community)*

CB JENI Vista Del Lago, LLC **(1)**
SB Hwy 121 Service Rd and Lk Vista Dr,
Lewisville, TX 75067
Tel.: (972) 891-9703
New Housing & Construction Services
N.A.I.C.S.: 236116

Centre Living Homes, LLC **(1)**
4300 MacArthur Ave Ste 165, Dallas, TX
75209
Tel.: (469) 567-3518
Web Site: https://centrelivinghomes.com
Residential Construction
N.A.I.C.S.: 236115

Green Brick Title, LLC **(1)**
5501 Headquarters Dr Ste 200W, Plano, TX
75024
Tel.: (469) 573-6757
Web Site: https://www.greenbricktitle.com
Real Estate Services
N.A.I.C.S.: 531210
Sheila Dunn *(Pres)*

Normandy Homes Apples Crossing,
LLC **(1)**
4854 Connor Pl, Fairview, TX 75069
Tel.: (469) 418-2385
New Housing & Construction Services
N.A.I.C.S.: 236116
Wendi Leigh *(Mgr-Community Sls)*

Normandy Homes Cypress Meadows,
LLC **(1)**
2033 Temperate Dr, Allen, TX 75013
Tel.: (469) 418-2385
New Single Family Housing Construction
Services
N.A.I.C.S.: 236115

Normandy Homes Edgewood,
LLC **(1)**
12800 Shepherds Hill Ln, Frisco, TX 75035
Tel.: (469) 785-5574
New Housing & Construction Services
N.A.I.C.S.: 236116
Todd Maxwell *(Mgr-Community Sls)*

Normandy Homes Essex Park,
LLC **(1)**
4812 Zilker Ave, Carrollton, TX 75010
Tel.: (469) 405-1412
Land Development & Home Building Ser-
vices
N.A.I.C.S.: 236117
Niki Grogan *(Sls Mgr-Community)*

Normandy Homes Frisco Springs,
LLC **(1)**
7414 Zachery Dr, Frisco, TX 75033
Tel.: (469) 369-0949
Land Development & Home Building Ser-
vices
N.A.I.C.S.: 236117

Normandy Homes Lakeside, LLC **(1)**
609 Sandy Ln, Flower Mound, TX 75022
Tel.: (972) 691-2696
Residential Construction
N.A.I.C.S.: 236115

Normandy Homes Legends at Twin
Creeks, LLC **(1)**
1018 Ocean Breeze Dr, Allen, TX 75013
Tel.: (469) 369-1709
Land Development & Home Building Ser-
vices
N.A.I.C.S.: 236117

Normandy Homes Liberty Hills,
LLC **(1)**
5825 Stonewall Dr, McKinney, TX 75070
Tel.: (972) 795-4686
New Housing & Construction Services
N.A.I.C.S.: 236116
Kris Weir *(Mgr-Community Sls)*

Providence Luxury Homes, L.L.C. (1)
671 Main St 100A, Suwanee, GA 30024
Tel.: (800) 343-5097
Emp.: 40
Residential Construction
N.A.I.C.S.: 236115

Southgate Homes - Suburban Living, LLC (1)
2805 Dallas Pkwy Ste 400, Plano, TX 75093
Tel.: (469) 573-6700
Web Site: https://www.southgatehomes.com
Emp.: 20
New Single Family Housing Construction Services
N.A.I.C.S.: 236115

The Providence Group of Georgia, L.L.C. (1)
11340 Lakefield Dr, Johns Creek, GA 30097
Tel.: (678) 475-9400
Web Site:
http://www.theprovidencegroup.com
New Single Family Housing Construction Services
N.A.I.C.S.: 236115
Warren S. Jolly (Pres)
Mike Smith (VP)
Nathan Borghi (CFO)
Troy Caldwell (COO)

Trophy Signature Homes, LLC (1)
2805 Dallas Pkwy Ste 450, Plano, TX 75093
Tel.: (214) 550-5733
Web Site:
https://www.trophysignaturehomes.com
New Housing & Construction Services
N.A.I.C.S.: 236116
Angelo Vitale (Mgr-Community Sls)

GREEN DOT CORPORATION
114 W 7th St Ste 240, Austin, TX 78701
Tel.: (626) 765-2000   DE
Web Site: https://www.greendot.com
Year Founded: 1999
GDOT—(NYSE)
Rev.: $1,449,566,000
Assets: $4,789,176,000
Liabilities: $4,007,695,000
Net Worth: $781,481,000
Earnings: $64,212,000
Emp.: 1,200
Fiscal Year-end: 12/31/22
Prepaid Credit Card Issuer
N.A.I.C.S.: 522210
Steven W. Streit (Founder)
Jess Unruh (CFO)
George W. Gresham (Pres, CEO & Interim Chief Fin & Operating Officer)
Jason Bibelheimer (Chief HR Officer)
Teresa Watkins (COO)
Chris Ruppel (Chief Revenue Officer)
Abhijit Chaudhary (Chief Product Officer)
Alex Bartels (Gen Mgr)
Alison Lubert (VP)
Amit Parikh (Exec VP)
Amy Pugh (Gen Counsel)
Jamison Jaworski (Sr VP)
Jaclyn Kleiner (Head)
Mike Tekulve (Sr VP)
Philip Lerma (Chief Risk Officer)
Shaun Rowan-Popoff (Sr VP)
Timothy Willi (Sr VP)
Dave Harden (CTO)
William I. Jacobs (Chm)

Subsidiaries:

Green Dot Bank (1)
1675 N Freedom Blvd 200 W, Provo, UT 84604
Tel.: (801) 374-9500
Web Site: https://www.bonnevillebank.com
Credit Card Issuing Services
N.A.I.C.S.: 522210

Ready Financial Group, Inc. (1)
PO Box 7554, Boise, ID 83707-7554
Tel.: (866) 465-1645

Web Site: http://www.readyfinancial.com
Credit Card Issuing Services
N.A.I.C.S.: 522210
Will Tumulty (Pres)

GREEN ENVIROTECH HOLDINGS CORP.
241 S Lander St Ste 203, Seattle, WA 98134
Tel.: (209) 605-1180   DE
Web Site:
http://www.greenenvirotech.com
Year Founded: 2007
GETH—(OTCIQ)
Sales Range: Less than $1 Million
Emp.: 5
Plastics Recovery, Separation, Cleaning & Recycling Services
N.A.I.C.S.: 562119
Gary Martin DeLaurentiis (Founder)
Christopher Richard Smith (Chm)
Mark Gantar (Pres)
Burak Erten (Fin Dir)

GREEN FOR ENERGY, INC.
910 Pierremont Rd Ste 410, Shreveport, LA 71106
Tel.: (318) 861-8687
GRGG—(OTCIQ)
Eletric Power Generation Services
N.A.I.C.S.: 221117
Leland Jamison (CFO)

GREEN HYGIENICS HOLDINGS INC.
13795 Blaisdell Pl Ste 202, Poway, CA 92064   NV
Web Site:
http://www.greenhygienics.com
Year Founded: 2008
GRYN—(OTCIQ)
Rev.: $40,954
Assets: $6,054,838
Liabilities: $12,898,367
Net Worth: ($6,843,529)
Earnings: ($8,391,343)
Emp.: 20
Fiscal Year-end: 07/31/21
Holding Company
N.A.I.C.S.: 551112
Jerry Halamuda (Sr VP-Bus Dev-Agriculture Div)
Todd Mueller (CEO)
Kyle MacKinnon (COO)
Jeff Palumbo (CTO)
Scott Slyker (Chief Product Officer & Chief Technical Officer)
David Racz (Sr VP-Global Sls & Bus Dev & VP-Sales & Marketing)
Greg Stinson (Gen Mgr & Mgr-Project & Ops)
Ronald W. Loudoun (CFO, Treas & Sec)

GREEN LEAF INNOVATIONS, INC.
15800 Pines Blvd Ste 3200, Pembroke Pines, FL 33027
Web Site:
https://www.greenleafinnovation.com
GRLF—(NASDAQ)
Assets: $3,705,000
Liabilities: $5,784,000
Net Worth: ($2,079,000)
Earnings: $105,000
Emp.: 10
Fiscal Year-end: 12/31/22
Tobacco Product Mfr & Distr
N.A.I.C.S.: 312230

GREEN MOUNTAIN DEVELOPMENT CORP.
6965 El Camino Real Ste 105-279, Carlsbad, CA 92009
Tel.: (619) 488-3744   DE

Year Founded: 2001
GMND—(OTCIQ)
Engineering & Construction Services
N.A.I.C.S.: 541330
Robert A. Brehm (CEO)

GREEN MOUNTAIN MERGER, INC.
2681 E Parleys Way Ste 204, Salt Lake City, UT 84109
Tel.: (801) 322-3401
Year Founded: 2004
GMTU—(OTCIQ)
Metal & Mining Services
N.A.I.C.S.: 213114
Geoffrey Williams (Pres)

GREEN PLAINS INC.
1811 Aksarben Dr, Omaha, NE 68106
Tel.: (402) 884-8700   IA
Web Site: https://www.gpreinc.com
GPRE—(NASDAQ)
Rev.: $3,295,743,000
Assets: $1,939,322,000
Liabilities: $949,266,000
Net Worth: $990,056,000
Earnings: ($93,384,000)
Emp.: 921
Fiscal Year-end: 12/31/23
Ethanol Plants Construction & Operation Services
N.A.I.C.S.: 325193
Todd A. Becker (Pres & CEO)
George Patrich Simpkins Jr. (Chief Transformation Officer)
Michelle S. Mapes (Chief Admin & Legal Officer)
Alain Treuer (Vice Chm)
Phil Boggs (Exec VP-IR)
Lisa Gibson (Comm Mgr)
Chris Osowski (Exec VP-Ops & Tech)
Jamie Herbert (Chief HR Officer)
James Stark (CFO)

Subsidiaries:

Green Plains Atkinson LLC (1)
87590 Hillcrest Rd, Atkinson, NE 68713
Tel.: (402) 925-5570
Emp.: 40
Ethyl Alcohol Mfr
N.A.I.C.S.: 325193
Todd A. Becker (Pres & CEO)

Green Plains Central City LLC (1)
214 20th St, Central City, NE 68826
Tel.: (308) 946-9700
Web Site: http://gpreinc.com
Emp.: 49
Methanol Mfr
N.A.I.C.S.: 325193

Green Plains Commodities LLC (1)
450 Regency Pkwy Ste 400, Omaha, NE 68114
Tel.: (402) 884-8700
Web Site: http://www.gpreinc.com
Emp.: 150
Ethanol Production Marketing & Commodity Services
N.A.I.C.S.: 325193

Green Plains Essex Inc. (1)
411 N St, Essex, IA 51638
Tel.: (712) 379-3155
Web Site: http://www.gpreinc.com
Sales Range: $150-199.9 Million
Emp.: 4
Grain Elevators
N.A.I.C.S.: 493130

Green Plains Fairmont LLC (1)
1125 Bixby Rd, Fairmont, MN 56031
Tel.: (507) 238-3600
Web Site: http://www.gpreinc.com
Emp.: 59
Methanol Mfr
N.A.I.C.S.: 325193

Green Plains Grain Company TN LLC (1)
1811 Ak-Sar-Ben Dr, Omaha, NE 68106
Tel.: (402) 884-8700

Web Site: http://www.gpreinc.com
Emp.: 130
Grain Elevators Operations
N.A.I.C.S.: 493130

Division (Domestic):

Como Grain (2)
10870 Hwy 54, Paris, TN 38242   (100%)
Tel.: (731) 885-9226
Web Site: http://www.andersonsgrain.com
Sales Range: $25-49.9 Million
Emp.: 10
Grain Elevators
N.A.I.C.S.: 493130

Dyer Grain (2)
347 S Main St, Dyer, TN 38330
Tel.: (731) 692-3677
Web Site: http://www.gpreinc.com
Sales Range: $25-49.9 Million
Emp.: 11
Grain Elevators
N.A.I.C.S.: 493130

Green Plains Hereford LLC (1)
4300 County Rd 8, Hereford, TX 79045
Tel.: (806) 258-7800
Web Site: http://www.gpreinc.com
Emp.: 55
Methanol Mfr
N.A.I.C.S.: 325193

Green Plains Madison LLC (1)
395 Bissell St, Madison, IL 62060
Tel.: (618) 451-8195
Emp.: 52
Ethanol Distr
N.A.I.C.S.: 424820

Green Plains Mount Vernon LLC (1)
8999 W Franklin Rd, Mount Vernon, IN 47620
Tel.: (812) 985-7480
Emp.: 52
Ethanol Distr
N.A.I.C.S.: 424820

Green Plains Ord LLC (1)
48267 Val-E Rd, Ord, NE 68862
Tel.: (308) 496-4800
Web Site: http://www.gpreinc.com
Emp.: 40
Methanol Mfr
N.A.I.C.S.: 325193

Green Plains Otter Tail LLC (1)
24096 170th Ave, Fergus Falls, MN 56537
Tel.: (218) 998-4301
Web Site: http://www.gpreinc.com
Emp.: 42
Methanol Mfr
N.A.I.C.S.: 325193

Green Plains Partners LP (1)
1811 Aksarben Dr, Omaha, NE 68106   (100%)
Tel.: (402) 884-8700
Web Site:
https://www.greenplainspartners.com
Rev.: $79,767,000
Assets: $121,422,000
Liabilities: $120,672,000
Net Worth: $750,000
Earnings: $40,650,000
Emp.: 32
Fiscal Year-end: 12/31/2022
Ethanol & Fuel Storage Tanks, Terminals & Transportation Operations
N.A.I.C.S.: 213112
Todd A. Becker (Pres & CEO)
James E. Stark (CFO & Principal Acctg Officer)
George Patrich Simpkins Jr. (Chief Transformation Officer)
Jim Stark (CFO)
Jamie Herbert (Chief HR Officer)
Paul Kolomaya (Chief Acctg Officer)

Green Plains Shenandoah LLC (1)
4124 Airport Rd, Shenandoah, IA 51601
Tel.: (712) 246-2932
Web Site: http://www.gpreinc.com
Sales Range: $25-49.9 Million
Emp.: 41
Methanol Mfr
N.A.I.C.S.: 325193

Green Plains Trade Group LLC (1)
1811 Aksarben Dr, Omaha, NE 68106
Tel.: (402) 884-8700

Green Plains Inc.—(Continued)

Web Site: http://www.gpre.com
Emp.: 180
Ethanol & Distillers Grains Whslr & Distr
N.A.I.C.S.: 424820

Green Plains Wood River LLC (1)
7874 S 140th Rd, Wood River, NE 68883
Tel.: (308) 392-3133
Web Site: http://www.gpreinc.com
Emp.: 60
Methanol Mfr
N.A.I.C.S.: 325193

Green Plains York LLC (1)
1414 Rd O, York, NE 68467
Tel.: (402) 362-0088
Ethanol Distr
N.A.I.C.S.: 424820

GREEN PLANET BIOENGI-NEERING CO., LTD.
20807 Biscayne Blvd Ste 203, Aventura, FL 33180
Tel.: (786) 279-2900   DE
Year Founded: 2006
GPLB—(OTCIQ)
Liabilities: $381,920
Net Worth: ($381,920)
Earnings: ($32,533)
Fiscal Year-end: 12/31/22
Holding Company
N.A.I.C.S.: 551112
Jordan Weingarten (Pres)

GREEN PLANET GROUP, INC.
2410 W 14th St, Tempe, AZ 85281
Tel.: (602) 616-0014   NV
Web Site:
   https://greenplanetgroup.com
Year Founded: 1978
GNPG—(OTCEM)
Rev.: $109,061
Assets: $1,359,605
Liabilities: $1,847,617
Net Worth: ($488,012)
Earnings: ($435,764)
Emp.: 5
Fiscal Year-end: 03/31/22
Petroleum Lubricating Oil & Grease
Manufacturing
N.A.I.C.S.: 324191

GREEN POLKADOT BOX INC.
1450 So Blackhawk Blvd, Mount Pleasant, UT 84647
Tel.: (801) 478 2500   NV
Year Founded: 2010
GPDB—(OTCIQ)
Online Natural & Organic Foods Retailer
N.A.I.C.S.: 424490
Rod A. Smith (Chm, Pres & CEO)
Andrew W. Smith (Sec)

GREEN STAR PRODUCTS, INC.
7735 Sand St, Fort Worth, TX 76118
Tel.: (817) 591-4577   UT
Web Site: http://www.gspi.com
Year Founded: 1984
GSPI—(OTCIQ)
Sales Range: Less than $1 Million
Lubrication & Cleaning Products Mfr
N.A.I.C.S.: 324191
Dennis Hopkins (Pres & CEO)
Gina Brosenne (Treas)

GREEN STREAM HOLDINGS INC.
201 E 5th St Ste 100, Sheridan, CA 82801
Tel.: (310) 228-8897   WY
Year Founded: 2004
GSFI—(OTCIQ)
Rev.: $4,138
Assets: $781,865
Liabilities: $831,033

Net Worth: ($49,168)
Earnings: ($186,650)
Emp.: 2
Fiscal Year-end: 04/30/23
Holding Company
N.A.I.C.S.: 551112
James C. DiPrima (Chm, CEO, CFO & Sec)

GREEN STREET CAPITAL CORP.
425 Madison Ave 19th Fl, New York, NY 10017
Tel.: (212) 453-6703   MN
Web Site:
   https://www.greenestreetcapital.com
JAGR—(OTCIQ)
Miscellaneous Financial Investment Activities
N.A.I.C.S.: 523999
Ari Bernstein (Founder & Partner)
Todd E. Benson (Partner)

GREEN THUMB INDUSTRIES, INC.
325 W Huron St, Chicago, IL 60654
Tel.: (312) 471-6720   BC
Web Site: https://www.gtigrows.com
Year Founded: 2002
GTBIF—(OTCQX)
Rev.: $1,017,375,000
Assets: $2,433,528,000
Liabilities: $768,096,000
Net Worth: $1,665,432,000
Earnings: $11,978,000
Emp.: 3,800
Fiscal Year-end: 12/31/22
Pharmaceutical Preparation Manufacturing
N.A.I.C.S.: 325412
Anthony Georgiadis (CFO)
Benjamin Kovler (Founder, Chm & CEO)
Rachel Albert (Chief Admin Officer)
Josh Barrington (Sr VP)
Rebecca Brown (VP)
Kelly Dean (Sr VP)
Matt Ingram (Sr VP)
Jai Kensey (Dir)
Bret Kravitz (Gen Counsel)
Ryan Marek (Sr VP)
Matt Navarro (Sr VP)
Dominic O'Brien (Sr VP)
Shannon Weaver (VP)

Subsidiaries:

GTI Nevada, LLC (1)
1220 S Commerce Ste 120, Las Vegas, NV 89102
Tel.: (702) 220-5621
Web Site: http://www.gtinevada.com
Commercial Landscaping Services
N.A.I.C.S.: 561730

GREENBELT RESOURCES CORP.
3500 Dry Creek Rd Ste 6, Paso Robles, CA 93446
Web Site:
   https://www.greenbeltresources.com
GRCO—(OTCIQ)
Sales Range: Less than $1 Million
All Other Industrial Machinery Manufacturing
N.A.I.C.S.: 333248
Darren Eng (Pres & CEO)
Floyd S. Butterfield (Treas & Sec)
Joseph Pivinski (CFO)

GREENE COUNTY BANCORP, INC.
302 Main St, Catskill, NY 12414
Tel.: (518) 943-2600
Web Site:
   https://www.thebankofgreene
   county.com

GCBC—(NASDAQ)
Rev.: $117,572,000
Assets: $2,825,788,000
Liabilities: $2,619,788,000
Net Worth: $206,000,000
Earnings: $24,769,000
Emp.: 189
Fiscal Year-end: 06/30/24
Bank Holding Company
N.A.I.C.S.: 551111
Donald E. Gibson (Pres & CEO)
Jay P. Cahalan (Chm)
Perry M. Lasher (Chief Lending Officer & Exec VP)

Subsidiaries:

The Bank of Greene County (1)
100 Catskill Commons, Catskill, NY 12414
Tel.: (518) 943-2600
Web Site:
   https://www.thebankofgreenecounty.com
Sales Range: $125-149.9 Million
Commericial Banking
N.A.I.C.S.: 522110
Charles H. Schaefer (Bd of Dirs, Executives)
Donald E. Gibson (Pres & CEO)
Sean DuBois (VP-Comml Lending & Bus Dev)
Trish Lamb (VP & Dir-Residential & Consumer Lending)
Gregory Spampinato (CIO & VP)
Mary Seely (VP & Dir-HR)
Allen Austin (Officer-Admin & Dir-Corp Cash Mgmt)
Allison Eldred (Officer-Portfolio Investment)
Andrea DiPace (Asst VP)
Carmela Hendricks (Asst VP-Ops)
Cheryl Rothkranz (Mgr-Credit)
Cynthia DuPilka (VP-BSA, Compliance & Operational Support)
Dan Lamarre (Officer-Security & Dir-Facilities)
Donald MacCormack (VP-Municipal Banking)
Jackie Stiffler (Mgr-Consumer & Residential Lending)
Jennifer Beers (Officer-Comml & Residential Loan Servicing)
John Antalek (VP-Comml Lending & Bus Dev)
John Dudek (Officer-Fin & Asst Controller)
John Olivett (VP-Ops)
Justin Goldman (Officer-Bus Dev & Lending)
Kathryn Nelson (Officer-HR)
Margaret Tobiassen (Asst VP-IT Application Support)
Martha Keeler (VP & Dir-Mktg)
Martin Smith (Chm)
Susan Timan (Sec & Asst VP-e-Comm)
Susan Wren (Asst VP-e-Svcs)
Timothy Bartholomew (VP-Investment Svcs)
Christa Bush (Reg Mgr-Branch)
Robert Agostinoni (Asst VP-Comml Lending & Bus Dev)

GREENGRO TECHNOLOGIES INC.
68374 Kieley Rd, Cathedral City, CA 92234
Tel.: (714) 367-6538   NV
Web Site:
   http://www.greengrotech.com
Year Founded: 1996
GRNH—(OTCIQ)
Sales Range: $1-9.9 Million
Aquaponic & Hydroponic Systems
N.A.I.C.S.: 333111

GREENHOUSE SOLUTIONS INC.
8400 E Crescent Pkwy Ste 600, Greenwood Village, CO 80111
Tel.: (970) 439-1905   NV
Web Site:
   http://www.ghsolutionsinc.com
Year Founded: 2009
GRSU—(OTCIQ)
Urban Gardening Products & Greenhouses Importer, Distr & Sales
N.A.I.C.S.: 423820

Ted Tinsman (VP-Architecture)
Loren Priest (VP-Engrg)
Rik J. Deitsch (Chm & CEO)
John George Michak III (COO)

GREENIDGE GENERATION HOLDINGS INC.
590 Plant Rd, Dresden, NY 14441
Tel.: (315) 536-2359   DE
Web Site: http://greenidgellc.com
Year Founded: 1937
GREE—(NASDAQ)
Rev.: $89,979,000
Assets: $163,767,000
Liabilities: $210,814,000
Net Worth: ($47,047,000)
Earnings: ($271,068,000)
Emp.: 347
Fiscal Year-end: 12/31/22
Holding Company
N.A.I.C.S.: 551112
David Anderson (Chm & CEO)
Jordan Kovler (COO)
Christian Mulvihill (CFO)
George Rogers (Vice Chm)

Subsidiaries:

Greenidge Generation LLC (1)
590 Plant Rd, Dresden, NY 14441
Tel.: (585) 703-7213
Bitcoin Mining & Power Generation
N.A.I.C.S.: 221118
Jeff Kirt (CEO)

GREENKRAFT, INC.
2530 S Birch St, Santa Ana, CA 92707
Tel.: (714) 545-7777   NV
Web Site:
   https://www.greenkraftinc.com
GKIT—(OTCIQ)
Sales Range: Less than $1 Million
Emp.: 6
Industrial Truck, Tractor, Trailer & Stacker Machinery Manufacturing
N.A.I.C.S.: 333924
George Gemayel (Chm, Pres & Sec)

GREENLANE HOLDINGS, INC.
1095 Broken Sound Pkwy NW Ste 100, Boca Raton, FL 33487
Tel.: (561) 443-0122   DE
Web Site: https://www.gnln.com
Year Founded: 2018
GNLN—(NASDAQ)
Rev.: $65,373,000
Assets: $38,093,000
Liabilities: $27,101,000
Net Worth: $10,992,000
Earnings: ($32,175,000)
Emp.: 66
Fiscal Year-end: 12/31/23
Holding Company
N.A.I.C.S.: 551112
Nicholas Kovacevich (Chief Corp Dev Officer)
Ryan Selewicz (VP-E-Commerce)
Aaron LoCascio (Co-Founder)
Lana Reeve (CFO & Chief Legal Officer)
Adam Schoenfeld (Co-Founder)
Douglas Fischer (Gen Counsel)
Richard Finlow (Mng Dir-Europe)
Nick Kovacevich (CEO)

Subsidiaries:

KushCo Holdings, Inc. (1)
6261 Katella Ave Ste 250, Cypress, CA 90630
Tel.: (714) 462-4603
Web Site: http://www.kushco.com
Rev.: $113,837,000
Assets: $127,656,000

Liabilities: $40,927,000
Net Worth: $86,729,000
Earnings: ($77,656,000)
Emp.: 108
Fiscal Year-end: 08/31/2020
Packaging Services
N.A.I.C.S.: 561910
Peter Kadens (Executives)
Dallas Imbimbo (Executives)
Carmen Lam (Sr VP-Bus Dev)
Stephen Christoffersen (CFO)
Brian Stewart (Sr VP-Product)
Rhiana Barr (Chief People Officer)
Amir Sadr (Gen Counsel)

Subsidiary (Domestic):

KIM International Corporation **(2)**
6261 Katella Ave Ste 250, Cypress, CA
90630
Web Site: http://www.kimintcorp.com
Pharmacy Products Distr
N.A.I.C.S.: 424210

Kush Supply Co. LLC **(2)**
6261 Katella Ave Ste 250, Cypress, CA
90630
Web Site: http://www.kushsupplyco.com
Glass Container Mfr
N.A.I.C.S.: 327213
Rey Glazier (Mgr-Shipping)

The Hybrid Creative LLC **(2)**
751 4th St, Santa Rosa, CA 95404
Tel.: (707) 596-5100
Web Site: http://www.thehybridcreative.com
Cannabis Product Design & Packaging Mfr
N.A.I.C.S.: 325411
Alistair Campbell (Pres)
Zack Winter (Mng Dir)
Laurel Gregory (Creative Dir)
Jeff Nagy (Project Mgr)
Colby Whitted (Mgr-Tech)

Zack Darling Creative Associates,
LLC **(2)**
751 4th St, Santa Rosa, CA 95404
Web Site:
    http://www.zdca.thehybridcreative.com
Cannabis Product Design & Packaging Mfr
N.A.I.C.S.: 325411

Pollen Gear LLC **(1)**
23650 Brodiaea Ave, Moreno Valley, CA
92553
Web Site: https://www.pollengear.com
Packaging Products Mfr
N.A.I.C.S.: 326199

Warehouse Goods LLC **(1)**
1095 Broken Sound Pkwy NW Ste 100,
Boca Raton, FL 33487
Tel.: (561) 443-0122
Web Site:
    https://www.warehousegoods.com
Products Distr
N.A.I.C.S.: 423990
Brad Dulin (Reg Dir-Southeast)

GREENLINK INTERNATIONAL, INC.
711 Ct A Ste 204, Tacoma, WA 98402
Tel.: (833) 587-4669   CO
Web Site:
    http://www.greenlinkholdings.com
Year Founded: 1998
WSHE—(OTCIQ)
Real Estate & Financing Services
N.A.I.C.S.: 531390
Jake George (Pres & CEO)
Richard Schmidtke (Treas)

GREENROSE HOLDING CO INC.
111 Broadway Ste No 212, Amityville,
NY 11701
Tel.: (516) 346-5270   DE
Year Founded: 2019
GNRSQ—(NASDAQ)
Rev.: $1,156,603
Assets: $174,011,548
Liabilities: $169,011,541
Net Worth: $5,000,007
Earnings: ($441,978)
Emp.: 5

Fiscal Year-end: 12/31/20
Investment Services
N.A.I.C.S.: 523999

GREENVILLE FEDERAL FINANCIAL CORPORATION
690 Wagner Ave, Greenville, OH
45331
Tel.: (937) 548-4158
Web Site:
    https://www.greenvillefederal.com
Year Founded: 2006
GVFF—(OTCIQ)
Bank Holding Company
N.A.I.C.S.: 551111
Jeff D. Kniese (Pres & CEO)

Subsidiaries:

Greenville Federal **(1)**
690 Wagner Ave, Greenville, OH 45331
Tel.: (937) 548-4158
Web Site: http://www.greenvillefederal.com
Sales Range: $1-9.9 Million
Emp.: 40
Savings Bank
N.A.I.C.S.: 522180
Annette Ryan (VP & Mgr)
Brian Beam (Mgr-Mktg)
Jeff D. Kniese (Pres & CEO)
Nick Good (Mgr-Sls)

GREENWAVE TECHNOLOGY SOLUTIONS, INC.
4016RaintreeRdSte300, Chesapeake,
VA 23321
Tel.: (303) 816-8070   DE
Web Site: https://www.gwav.com
Year Founded: 2013
GWAV—(NASDAQ)
Rev.: $35,667,982
Assets: $46,411,849
Liabilities: $50,865,997
Net Worth: ($4,454,148)
Earnings: ($26,935,990)
Emp.: 131
Fiscal Year-end: 12/31/23
Mobile Network For the Cannabis
Community
N.A.I.C.S.: 513210
Danny Meeks (Chm & CEO)
Isaac Dietrich (CFO)

Subsidiaries:

Empire Services, Inc. **(1)**
277 Suburban Dr, Suffolk, VA 23434
Tel.: (757) 925-1115
Rev.: $2,500,000
Emp.: 20
Recyclable Material Merchant Whslr
N.A.I.C.S.: 423930

GREENWAY BANK
Tel.: (419) 238-9662   MD
Web Site: https://greenwaybank.com
Year Founded: 2022
VWFB—(OTCQX)
Rev.: $12,254,575
Assets: $311,254,121
Liabilities: $274,706,289
Net Worth: $36,547,832
Earnings: ($2,019,533)
Emp.: 43
Fiscal Year-end: 06/30/24
Bank Holding Company
N.A.I.C.S.: 551111
Michael D. Cahill (Pres & CEO)
Rich Brackin (CFO & Treas)
Gary L. Clay (Chm)
Brian Collentine (CIO)
Andrew D. Holy (Chief Risk Officer)
Johanna Quarles (Branch Mgr)

GREENWAY TECHNOLOGIES, INC.
1521 N Cooper St Ste 205, Arlington,
TX 76011
Tel.: (972) 342-4051   TX
Web Site: https://www.gwtechinc.com

Year Founded: 2002
GWTI—(OTCIQ)
Assets: $1,132
Liabilities: $12,030,443
Net Worth: ($12,029,311)
Earnings: ($1,580,735)
Emp.: 2
Fiscal Year-end: 12/31/23
Holding Company; Energy, Oil, Gas,
Aerospace, Food, Beverage & Mining
N.A.I.C.S.: 551112
Ransom Bert Jones (CFO, Principal
Acctg Officer, Treas & Sec)
Raymond Wright (Chm)

GREENWICH LIFESCIENCES, INC.
3992 Bluebonnet Dr Bldg 14,
Stafford, TX 77477
Tel.: (832) 819-3232   DE
Web Site:
    https://www.greenwichlifescien
    ces.com
Year Founded: 2006
GLSI—(NASDAQ)
Rev.: $215,017
Assets: $13,477,029
Liabilities: $262,905
Net Worth: $13,214,124
Earnings: ($7,825,237)
Emp.: 3
Fiscal Year-end: 12/31/22
Biotechnology Research & Development Services
N.A.I.C.S.: 541714
Eric Rothe (Founder)
David B. McWilliams (Chm)
Snehal S. Patel (CEO & CFO)
F. Joseph Daugherty (Chief Medical
Officer)
Jaye Thompson (VP-Clinical & Regulatory Affairs)
Christine T. Fischette (VP-Bus Dev)

GREETEAT CORPORATION
50 W Liberty St Ste 880, Reno, NV
89501
Tel.: (236) 471-6618   NV
Web Site: https://greeteat.com
Year Founded: 2010
REPO—(OTCIQ)
Data Processing Services
N.A.I.C.S.: 518210
Victor Sima (Co-Founder & CTO)
Vishal Patel (Co-Founder & CEO)
Kenny Koichi Shimokura (Co-Founder
& COO)

GREIF INC.
425 Winter Rd, Delaware, OH 43015
Tel.: (740) 549-6000   DE
Web Site: https://www.greif.com
Year Founded: 1877
GEF—(NYSE)
Rev.: $5,448,100,000
Assets: $6,647,600,000
Liabilities: $4,400,200,000
Net Worth: $2,247,400,000
Earnings: $295,500,000
Emp.: 14,000
Fiscal Year-end: 10/31/24
Industrial Packaging Products Mfr
N.A.I.C.S.: 322219
Ole G. Rosgaard (Pres & CEO)
Tim Bergwall (Pres-Paper Pkg & Soterra LLC & Sr VP)
Bala V. Sathyanarayanan (Chief HR
Officer & Sr VP)
Kim Kellermann (Sr VP-Global Ops
Grp)
Bruce A. Edwards (Chm)
Paddy Mullaney (Pres, Grp Pres-Global Industrial Packaging & Sr VP)
Vivian Bouet (CIO & Chief Digital Officer)

Bill D'Onofrio (VP-Corporate Development & Investor Relations)
Tina Schoner (Chief Supply Chain
Officer & Sr VP)
Gary R. Martz (Gen Counsel, Sec &
Exec VP)
Lawrence A. Hilsheimer (CFO & Exec
VP)

Subsidiaries:

American Flange & Manufacturing
Co., Inc. **(1)**
290 E Fullerton Ave, Carol Stream, IL
60188-1826
Tel.: (630) 665-7900
Web Site: http://www.tri-sure.com
Sales Range: $25-49.9 Million
Emp.: 40
Mfr of Metal & Plastic Nozzles, Spouts &
Container Closures, Drum Closures, Pail &
Can Fittings & Bottle Caps
N.A.I.C.S.: 326199
Kees Van De Klippe (Pres)

Box Board Products, Inc. **(1)**
8313 Triad Dr, Greensboro, NC 27409-9621
Tel.: (336) 668-3347
Web Site:
    https://www.boxboardproducts.com
Custom Corrugated Containers Mfr
N.A.I.C.S.: 332439
Gray Ingram (Chm)

Caraustar Industries, Inc. **(1)**
5000 Austell-Powder Springs Rd Ste 300,
Austell, GA 30106-3227
Tel.: (770) 948-3101
Web Site: http://www.caraustar.com
Sales Range: $150-199.9 Million
Paper Products Recycling & Paper Board
Mfr
N.A.I.C.S.: 322130

Subsidiary (Non-US):

Caraustar Industrial Canada, Inc. **(2)**
55 Progress Ave, Toronto, M1P 2Y7, ON,
Canada   **(100%)**
Tel.: (416) 298-6551
Web Site: http://www.caraustar.com
Sales Range: $10-24.9 Million
Emp.: 45
Mfr of Spiral & Convolute Wound Tubes
N.A.I.C.S.: 322219

Plant (Domestic):

Caraustar Industries **(2)**
8800 Crump Rd, Pineville, NC
28134   **(100%)**
Tel.: (704) 552-9211
Web Site: http://www.caraustar.com
Sales Range: $25-49.9 Million
Emp.: 125
Folding Cartons & Packaging Services
N.A.I.C.S.: 322130

Caraustar Industries, Inc. - Arlington
Tube Plant **(2)**
3700 New York Ave Ste 100, Arlington, TX
76014
Tel.: (817) 467-3805
Web Site: http://www.caraustar.com
Spiral Wound Tube Mfr
N.A.I.C.S.: 322299

Caraustar Industries, Inc. - Austell
Boxboard Mill **(2)**
3300 Joe Jerkins Blvd, Austell, GA 30106-
3227
Tel.: (770) 948-3100
Folding Paperboard Box Mfr
N.A.I.C.S.: 322212

Caraustar Industries, Inc. - Austell
Tube Plant **(2)**
3082 Humphries Hill Rd, Austell, GA 30106
Tel.: (770) 948-6100
Recycled & Converted Paperboard Product
Mfr
N.A.I.C.S.: 322299

Caraustar Industries, Inc. - Beardstown Tube Plant **(2)**
100 Forest Ln, Beardstown, IL 62618
Tel.: (217) 323-5225
Web Site: http://www.caraustar.com
Sales Range: $25-49.9 Million
Emp.: 41
Spiral Wound Tube Mfr

Greif Inc.—(Continued)
N.A.I.C.S.: 322299

Caraustar Industries, Inc. - Bucyrus Contract Packaging Plant (2)
1375 Isaac Beal Rd, Bucyrus, OH 44820-9604
Tel.: (419) 562-8866
Paperboard Packaging Products Mfr
N.A.I.C.S.: 322130

Caraustar Industries, Inc. - Burlington Rigid Box Plant (2)
322 Fonville St, Burlington, NC 27217
Tel.: (336) 226-1616
Web Site: http://www.caraustar.com
Sales Range: $25-49.9 Million
Emp.: 30
Gift Box Mfr
N.A.I.C.S.: 322130

Caraustar Industries, Inc. - Cantonment Tube Plant (2)
410 Washington St, Cantonment, FL 32533
Tel.: (850) 968-9534
Box Board Products Mfr
N.A.I.C.S.: 322299

Caraustar Industries, Inc. - Charlotte Recycling Plant (2)
4915 Hovis Rd, Charlotte, NC 28208
Tel.: (704) 333-5488
Web Site: http://www.caraustar.com
Emp.: 45
Fiber Recovery Services
N.A.I.C.S.: 562920

Caraustar Industries, Inc. - Chattanooga Recycling Plant (2)
1845 Central Ave, Chattanooga, TN 37408
Tel.: (423) 267-3801
Fiber Recycling Services
N.A.I.C.S.: 562920

Caraustar Industries, Inc. - Chicago Carton Plant (2)
555 N Tripp Ave, Chicago, IL 60624
Tel.: (773) 722-0555
Web Site: http://www.caraustar.com
Folding Cartons Mfr
N.A.I.C.S.: 322299

Caraustar Industries, Inc. - Chicago Packaging Plant (2)
555 N Tripp Ave, Chicago, IL 60624-1000
Tel.: (773) 722-0555
Web Site: http://www.caraustar.com
Sales Range: $50-74.9 Million
Emp.: 150
Mfr of Folding Paperboard Boxes
N.A.I.C.S.: 322212

Caraustar Industries, Inc. - Cleveland Recycling Plant (2)
3400 Vega Ave, Cleveland, OH 44113
Tel.: (216) 961-5060
Waste Recycling Services
N.A.I.C.S.: 562211

Caraustar Industries, Inc. - Corinth Tube Plant (2)
1504 S Fulton Dr, Corinth, MS 38834
Tel.: (662) 287-2492
Web Site: http://www.caraustar.com
Sales Range: $25-49.9 Million
Emp.: 17
Spiral Wound Tube Mfr
N.A.I.C.S.: 322299

Caraustar Industries, Inc. - Dalton Tube Plant (2)
121 Callahan Rd SE, Dalton, GA 30721
Tel.: (706) 277-3931
Spiral Wound Tube Mfr
N.A.I.C.S.: 322299

Caraustar Industries, Inc. - Denver Carton Plant (2)
1377 S Jason St, Denver, CO 80223-3407
Tel.: (303) 777-3300
Recycled & Converted Paperboard Product Mfr
N.A.I.C.S.: 322212

Caraustar Industries, Inc. - Franklin, KY Tube Plant (2)
115 Quail Ridge Rd, Franklin, KY 42134
Tel.: (270) 586-9565
Web Site: http://www.caraustar.com

Sales Range: $25-49.9 Million
Emp.: 35
Spiral Wound Tube Mfr
N.A.I.C.S.: 322299

Caraustar Industries, Inc. - Grand Rapids Carton Plant (2)
1957 Beverly Ave SW, Wyoming, MI 49519
Tel.: (616) 247-0330
Folding Cartons Mfr
N.A.I.C.S.: 322212

Caraustar Industries, Inc. - Hardeeville Recycling Plant (2)
Hwy 17 & Hwy 321, Hardeeville, SC 29927
Tel.: (843) 784-3437
Sales Range: $25-49.9 Million
Emp.: 30
Recycled Paperboard Mfr
N.A.I.C.S.: 322130

Caraustar Industries, Inc. - Kernersville Adhesives Plant (2)
1485 Plz South Dr, Kernersville, NC 27284
Tel.: (336) 993-6565
Adhesive Mfr
N.A.I.C.S.: 325520

Caraustar Industries, Inc. - Kernersville Tube Plant (2)
1045 Industrial Park Dr, Kernersville, NC 27284
Tel.: (336) 996-4165
Spiral Wound Tube Mfr
N.A.I.C.S.: 322299

Caraustar Industries, Inc. - Kingston Springs Carton Plant (2)
167 Luyben Hills Rd, Kingston Springs, TN 37082
Tel.: (615) 952-4300
Web Site: http://www.caraustar.com
Emp.: 100
Folding Cartons Mfr
N.A.I.C.S.: 322299

Plant (Non-US):

Caraustar Industries, Inc. - Kingston Tube Plant (2)
309 Dalton Avenue, Kingston, K7K6Z1, ON, Canada
Tel.: (613) 548-3120
Recycled & Converted Paperboard Product Mfr
N.A.I.C.S.: 322299

Plant (Domestic):

Caraustar Industries, Inc. - Lancaster Tube Plant (2)
1820 Olde Homestead Ln, Lancaster, PA 17601
Tel.: (717) 295-0047
Spiral Wound Tube Mfr
N.A.I.C.S.: 322299

Caraustar Industries, Inc. - Minerva Tube Plant (2)
460 Knox Ct, Minerva, OH 44657
Tel.: (330) 868-4111
Spiral Wound Tube Mfr
N.A.I.C.S.: 322299

Caraustar Industries, Inc. - Phoenix Tube Plant (2)
22 N 47th Ave, Phoenix, AZ 85043
Tel.: (602) 269-0223
Spiral Wound Tube Mfr
N.A.I.C.S.: 322299

Caraustar Industries, Inc. - Rock Hill Plant (2)
1379 McDow Dr, Rock Hill, SC 29732-2442
Tel.: (803) 329-2131
Web Site: http://www.caraustar.com
Sales Range: $25-49.9 Million
Emp.: 100
Paper Tube Plant
N.A.I.C.S.: 322130

Caraustar Industries, Inc. - Saginaw Tube Plant (2)
3265 Commerce Centre Dr, Saginaw, MI 48601
Tel.: (989) 793-4820
Spiral Wound Tube Mfr
N.A.I.C.S.: 322299

Caraustar Industries, Inc. - Salt Lake City Tube Plant (2)
2585 S 2570 W, Salt Lake City, UT 84119
Tel.: (801) 972-1476
Spiral Wound & Construction Tube Mfr
N.A.I.C.S.: 322299

Caraustar Industries, Inc. - Silsbee Tube Plant (2)
932 John Hare Rd, Silsbee, TX 77656
Tel.: (409) 898-6600
Emp.: 15
Spiral Wound Tube Mfr
N.A.I.C.S.: 322299
David Leblanc *(Gen Mgr)*

Caraustar Industries, Inc. - Tacoma Tube Plant (2)
902 E 11th St, Tacoma, WA 98421
Tel.: (253) 272-1648
Web Site: http://www.caraustar.com
Spiral Wound Mfr
N.A.I.C.S.: 322299

Caraustar Industries, Inc. - Taylors Tube Plant (2)
1001 Alexander Rd, Taylors, SC 29687
Tel.: (864) 244-8151
Spiral Wound Tube Mfr
N.A.I.C.S.: 332996

Caraustar Industries, Inc. - Texarkana Recycling Plant (2)
112 Lelia St, Texarkana, TX 75501
Tel.: (903) 793-6231
Paperboard Recycling Services
N.A.I.C.S.: 322130

Caraustar Industries, Inc. - Texarkana Tube Plant (2)
4201 Waco St, Texarkana, TX 75501
Tel.: (903) 832-4543
Spiral Wound & Construction Tube Mfr
N.A.I.C.S.: 322299

Caraustar Industries, Inc. - Toledo Tube Plant (2)
4031 Spartan Dr, Oregon, OH 43616
Tel.: (419) 690-0524
Web Site: http://www.caraustar.com
Sales Range: $25-49.9 Million
Emp.: 25
Spiral Wound Tube Mfr
N.A.I.C.S.: 322299

Plant (Non-US):

Caraustar Industries, Inc. - Toronto Tube Plant (2)
55 Progress Avenue, Scarborough, M1P 2Y7, ON, Canada
Tel.: (416) 298-6551
Spiral Wound Tube Mfr
N.A.I.C.S.: 322299

Plant (Domestic):

Caraustar Industries, Inc. - West Monroe Tube Plant (2)
612 Grantham Ave, West Monroe, LA 71292
Tel.: (318) 323-5511
Spiral Wound Tube Mfr
N.A.I.C.S.: 322299

Caraustar Industries, Inc. - Weyers Cave Tube Plant (2)
780 Keezletown Rd, Weyers Cave, VA 24486
Tel.: (540) 234-0431
Web Site: http://www.caraustar.com
Emp.: 13
Core Pre-Cutting Tube Mfr
N.A.I.C.S.: 322299

Plant (Non-US):

Caraustar Industries, Inc. - Winnipeg Tube Plant (2)
1707 Dugald Rd, Winnipeg, R2J 0H3, MB, Canada
Tel.: (204) 661-8333
Spiral Wound Tube Mfr
N.A.I.C.S.: 322299

Subsidiary (Domestic):

Caraustar Mill Group, Inc. (2)
5000 Austell-Powder Springs Rd Ste 300, Austell, GA 30106-3227 **(100%)**

Tel.: (770) 948-3101
Web Site: http://www.caraustar.com
Sales Range: $50-74.9 Million
Mfr of Recycled Paperboard & Converted Paperboard Products
N.A.I.C.S.: 321918

Subsidiary (Domestic):

Cincinnati Paperboard (3)
5500 Wooster Rd, Cincinnati, OH 45226-2227
Tel.: (513) 871-0982
Web Site: http://www.caraustar.com
Sales Range: $50-74.9 Million
Emp.: 100
Folding Box Mfr
N.A.I.C.S.: 322130

Los Angeles Paper Box, LLC (3)
6027 S Eastern Ave, Commerce, CA 90040
Tel.: (323) 685-8900
Web Site: http://www.lapb.com
Rev.: $4,609,000
Emp.: 20
Corrugated & Solid Fiber Box Mfr
N.A.I.C.S.: 322211

Subsidiary (Domestic):

Caraustar Recovered Fiber Group, Inc. (2)
5000 Austell Powder Spring Rd, Austell, GA 30106 **(100%)**
Tel.: (770) 745-3760
Web Site: http://www.caraustar.com
Sales Range: $10-24.9 Million
Emp.: 25
Paperboard Mfr
N.A.I.C.S.: 322130

Plant (Domestic):

Caraustar Converted Products Group (3)
167 Luyben Hills Rd, Kingston Springs, TN 37082-8905
Tel.: (615) 952-4300
Web Site: http://www.caraustar.com
Mfr of Folding Carton & Other Converted Recyclable Products
N.A.I.C.S.: 322212

Caraustar Recycling Plant (3)
145 Phelps Rd SE, Dalton, GA 30720-7614
Tel.: (706) 259-8591
Web Site: http://www.caraustar.com
Paper Recycler
N.A.I.C.S.: 322130

Columbus Recycling Plant (3)
756 Lindsay Dr, Columbus, GA 31906-3485
Tel.: (706) 323-6306
Web Site: http://www.caraustar.com
Recycling Plant
N.A.I.C.S.: 322130

Doraville Recycling Plant (3)
4069 Winters Chapel Rd, Doraville, GA 30360
Tel.: (770) 451-1334
Web Site: http://www.caraustar.com
Mfr of Paper
N.A.I.C.S.: 562920

Subsidiary (Domestic):

Federal Transport, Inc. (2)
702 East Main St, Saint Paris, OH 43072
Tel.: (937) 663-4142
Sales Range: $25-49.9 Million
Emp.: 200
Long Distance Trucking Services
N.A.I.C.S.: 484121

Orrville Composite Container Plant (2)
425 Collins Blvd, Orrville, OH 44667-9752
Tel.: (330) 683-6015
Web Site: http://www.sonoco.com
Sales Range: $10-24.9 Million
Emp.: 110
Composite Can Mfr
N.A.I.C.S.: 332431

Centurion Container LLC (1)
15555 La Salle St, South Holland, IL 60473
Web Site: https://centurionibc.com
Industrial Packaging Product Distr
N.A.I.C.S.: 423840

Cimplast Embalagens Importacao, Exportacao E. Comercio S.A. (1)
av Mauro Monteiro Lindenberg Dr s n Sn, Osasco, 06278-010, Brazil
Tel.: (55) 1136012004
Web Site: http://www.cimplast.com.br
Container Packing Systems Services
N.A.I.C.S.: 561910
Marcelo Magaz *(Bus Mgr)*

Colepak, Inc. (1)
1138 Phoenix Dr, Urbana, OH 43078 (51%)
Tel.: (937) 652-3910
Web Site: http://www.colepak.com
Sales Range: $1-9.9 Million
Emp.: 44
Corrugated & Solid Fiber Box Mfr
N.A.I.C.S.: 322211
Patrick Maurice *(Office Mgr)*

Container Life Cycle Management LLC (1)
1 Louise Ct, Ludlow, KY 41016-1590
Tel.: (708) 293-5601
Industrial Packaging Product & Services
N.A.I.C.S.: 332439

CorrChoice, Inc. (1)
846 3rd St NW, Massillon, OH 44647-4206 (100%)
Tel.: (330) 833-5705
Web Site: http://www.ferguson.com
Sales Range: $75-99.9 Million
Emp.: 260
Mfr of Corrugated Sheets
N.A.I.C.S.: 322299

Subsidiary (Domestic):

Michigan Packaging Co. (2)
700 Eden Rd, Mason, MI 48854-0070
Tel.: (517) 676-8700
Sales Range: $25-49.9 Million
Emp.: 100
Mfr of Corrugated Sheets
N.A.I.C.S.: 322211
John Klein *(VP & Gen Mgr)*

Ohio Packaging Co. (2)
777 3rd St NW, Massillon, OH 44647
Tel.: (330) 833-2884
Web Site: http://www.grief.com
Sales Range: $10-24.9 Million
Emp.: 80
Mfr of Corrugated Sheets
N.A.I.C.S.: 322299

Division (Domestic):

Southeastern Packaging Co. (2)
2200 Mulberry Rd, Concord, NC 28025
Tel.: (704) 455-3000
Sales Range: $25-49.9 Million
Emp.: 130
Mfr of Corrugated Boxes
N.A.I.C.S.: 322211
Don Mullinex *(Coord-Continuous Improvement)*

Delta Companies Group (1)
334 Tidal Rd, Deer Park, TX 77536 (100%)
Tel.: (281) 479-7288
Web Site: http://www.deltacogroup.com
Global Packaging & Supply Chain Services
N.A.I.C.S.: 541614

Earth Minded LLC (1)
142 Technology Dr, Arkadelphia, AR 71923
Tel.: (870) 230-8800
Web Site: http://www.earthminded.com
Reuse & Recycling Services
N.A.I.C.S.: 325991

EarthMinded Benelux NV (1)
Schaapbruggestraat 37, Rumbeke, 8800, Roeselare, Belgium
Tel.: (32) 51226464
Web Site: http://www.earthminded.com
Emp.: 100
Plastic Product Recycling Services
N.A.I.C.S.: 325991

EarthMinded France S.A.S. (1)
270 Avenue de Berlin ZI Artois Flandres Secteur C, PO Box 50526, Billy Berclau, 62092, Haisnes, Cedex, France
Tel.: (33) 321742742
Plastic Product Recycling Services

N.A.I.C.S.: 325991

EarthMinded Germany GmbH (1)
Ernst-Abbe-Str 5, 56743, Mendig, Germany
Tel.: (49) 265258090
Web Site: http://www.earthminded.com
Plastic Product Recycling Services
N.A.I.C.S.: 325991

EarthMinded Netherlands B.V. (1)
Marsweg 3, 8013 PD, Zwolle, Netherlands
Tel.: (31) 384218991
Plastic Product Recycling Services
N.A.I.C.S.: 325991

Fustiplast do Brasil Ltda (1)
Rua Joao Batista Nogueira 520 - Vila Nova Cumbica, Guarulhos, 07230-451, Brazil
Tel.: (55) 1124820579
Packaging Services
N.A.I.C.S.: 561910

Greif - Chile (1)
Camino Melipilla 11000, Santiago, Chile (100%)
Tel.: (56) 23510320
Web Site: http://www.dreis.cl
Sales Range: $25-49.9 Million
Emp.: 30
Provider of Food Packaging Services
N.A.I.C.S.: 327213

Greif - Massillon (1)
PO Box 675, Massillon, OH 44648-0675 (100%)
Tel.: (330) 879-2101
Web Site: http://www.greis.com
Sales Range: $25-49.9 Million
Emp.: 95
N.A.I.C.S.: 322219

Greif Argentina S.A. (1)
(100%)
Tel.: (54) 1151694700
Web Site: http://www.greif.com.ar
Sales Range: $150-199.9 Million
Packaging Products Manufacturing & Services
N.A.I.C.S.: 326199

Greif Belgium B.V.B.A. (1)
Bollaarstraat 6, 2500, Lier, Belgium (100%)
Tel.: (32) 294238201
Web Site: http://www.greif.be
Sales Range: $25-49.9 Million
Mfr of Miscellaneous Metal Work
N.A.I.C.S.: 332439

Greif Brothers Canada, Inc. (1)
2555 Dollard ave, La Salle, H8N 3A9, QC, Canada (100%)
Tel.: (514) 363-0721
Web Site: http://www.grief.com
Sales Range: $10-24.9 Million
Emp.: 4
Mfr of Fiber Drums
N.A.I.C.S.: 322219

Greif Colombia S.A. (1)
Calle 20 No 68 B 35, Bogota, Colombia (100%)
Tel.: (57) 4232240
Web Site: http://www.greif.com.co
Rev.: $130,000,000
Emp.: 96
Production of Metal Containers for Solid, Powdery or Liquid Substances
N.A.I.C.S.: 332439

Greif Containers, Inc. (1)
4300 W 130th St, Alsip, IL 60803-2003 (100%)
Tel.: (708) 371-4777
Web Site: http://www.greif.com
Sales Range: $100-124.9 Million
Mfr of Steel Drums & Pails
N.A.I.C.S.: 332439

Greif Corrugated Products (1)
PO Box 3068, Huntington, WV 25702-0068 (100%)
Tel.: (304) 525-0342
Web Site: http://www.greif.com
Sales Range: $100-124.9 Million
Emp.: 36
Mfr of Bulk Shipping Containers
N.A.I.C.S.: 322211

Greif Costa Rica S.A. (1)

Zona Industrial Las Brisa, San Jose, 10104, Costa Rica
Tel.: (506) 22511195
Web Site: http://www.greif.co.cr
Sales Range: $25-49.9 Million
Emp.: 16
Mfr of Steel Drums
N.A.I.C.S.: 332439

Greif Czech Republic A/S (1)
Konecna 252, 400 01, Usti nad Labem, Czech Republic (100%)
Tel.: (420) 475668911
Web Site: http://www.greif-cz.com
Sales Range: $50-74.9 Million
Emp.: 60
Production of Metal Containers for Solid, Powdery or Liquid Substances
N.A.I.C.S.: 332439

Greif Denmark A/S (1)
Lpalderseuen 8, Hedehusene, 2640, Denmark
Tel.: (45) 46740681
Web Site: http://www.greif.dk
Sales Range: $10-24.9 Million
Emp.: 30
Mfr of Fiber Drums
N.A.I.C.S.: 322219

Greif Embalagens Industriais do Brasil Ltda. (1)
Av das Nacoes Unidas 21102, Sao Paulo, 04795-910, Brazil
Tel.: (55) 1156949800
Web Site: http://www.greif.com.br
Sales Range: $75-99.9 Million
Mfr & Wholesale of Metal Barrels & Drums
N.A.I.C.S.: 332439

Greif Flexibles Benelux B.V. (1)
Jupiterweg 1, 4761 RW, Moerdijk, North Brabant, Netherlands
Tel.: (31) 168359999
Plastic Drum Product Mfr
N.A.I.C.S.: 326199

Greif Flexibles Changzhou Co. Ltd (1)
8 Tenglong Road, Changzhou, 213149, Jiangsu, China
Tel.: (86) 51986362592
Web Site: http://www.greif.com
Packaging Services
N.A.I.C.S.: 561910

Greif Flexibles Finland Oy (1)
Vasarakuja 19, PO Box 548, FIN 67101, Kokkola, Finland (100%)
Tel.: (358) 68245100
Web Site: http://www.greif.com
Sales Range: $1-9.9 Million
Emp.: 45
Packaging & Flexible Intermediate Bulk Containers Mfr
N.A.I.C.S.: 327213

Greif Flexibles France SARL (1)
Scrigno France zone artisanale Sainte Elisabeth, 71300, Montceau-les-Mines, France
Tel.: (33) 38 569 0069
Web Site: https://www.greif-flexibles-france.fr
Steel Drum Product Distr
N.A.I.C.S.: 424130

Greif Flexibles Germany GmbH & Co. (1)
Werner Heisenberger St No 7, 68519, Viernheim, Germany
Tel.: (49) 620496640
Web Site: http://www.greif.com
Sales Range: $200-249.9 Million
Emp.: 10
Packaging & Flexible Intermediate Bulk Containers Mfr
N.A.I.C.S.: 326112

Subsidiary (Non-US):

Chongqing Storsack Jianfeng (2)
Plastic Industry Co., Fuling District, Chongqing, 408601, China
Tel.: (86) 2372597635
Web Site: http://www.storsack.com
Sales Range: $75-99.9 Million
Packaging & Flexible Intermediate Bulk Containers Mfr
N.A.I.C.S.: 327213

Zhang Guoyou *(Mgr)*

Greif Flexible Products & Services (2)
1154 Rua Vale do Salgueiro Raso do Salgueiro Z1 EN1 Norte, 3750-753, Travasso, Agueda, Portugal (100%)
Tel.: (351) 234612260
Web Site: http://www.greif-flexibles.com
Sales Range: $25-49.9 Million
Emp.: 35
Intermediate Bulk Containers, Plastic Sacks & Plastic & Paper Carrier Bags Mfr
N.A.I.C.S.: 322220

Greif Flexibles Belgium N.V. (2)
Industrieterrein Mandeldal Lodewijk De Raetlaan 31, B 8870, Izegem, Belgium
Tel.: (32) 51331414
Web Site: http://www.greif.com
Sales Range: $25-49.9 Million
Emp.: 50
Packaging & Flexible Intermediate Bulk Containers Mfr
N.A.I.C.S.: 327213

India FIBC Customer Service Center (2)
103 10th Floor Atlanta Nariman Point, Mumbai, 4000 21, India
Tel.: (91) 22 6739 6401
Web Site: http://www.blvlindia.com
Sales Range: $25-49.9 Million
Emp.: 400
Packaging & Flexible Intermediate Bulk Containers Mfr
N.A.I.C.S.: 322219

Mulox de Mexico C. V. (2)
Carretera Central KM 612 Colonia Olivar de Las Animas, 78790, Matehuala, Mexico
Tel.: (52) 4888824032
Web Site: http://www.greif.com
Emp.: 300
Packaging & Flexible Intermediate Bulk Containers Mfr
N.A.I.C.S.: 327213

Pacific Containerbag Co. Ltd. (2)
662 51-52 Rama 3 Road JSP Pharam III Trade Center, Bangpongpang, Bangkok, Thailand
Tel.: (66) 2 682 4730
Packaging & Flexible Intermediate Bulk Containers Mfr
N.A.I.C.S.: 327213

Storsack PVT Ltd. (2)
501 Business Avenue, Karachi, Pakistan
Tel.: (92) 21 4545495
Web Site: http://www.storsack.com.pk
Sales Range: $25-49.9 Million
Packaging & Flexible Intermediate Bulk Containers Mfr
N.A.I.C.S.: 327213
Tanveer Ahmed *(Dir-Fin)*

Storsack Shenzen Co., Ltd. (2)
No 4 Yulong Street Jinshuiqiao Industrial Zone, Shenzhen, China
Tel.: (86) 755 84072261
Web Site: http://www.storsack.com
Packaging & Flexible Intermediate Bulk Containers Mfr
N.A.I.C.S.: 327213

Storsack Vietnam Ltd. (2)
Honai Industrial Zone Lot IV-4B, Bien Hoa, Vietnam
Tel.: (84) 613986698
Sales Range: $50-74.9 Million
Packaging & Flexible Intermediate Bulk Containers Mfr
N.A.I.C.S.: 327213
Bruce Alan Boyd *(Gen Mgr)*

Greif Flexibles Germany GmbH & Co. KG (1)
Industriestrasse 55-57, 48432, Rheine, Germany
Tel.: (49) 59753030
Web Site: http://www.greif-flexibles.com
Flexible Industrial Packaging Services
N.A.I.C.S.: 561910

Greif Flexibles Romania SRL (1)
Calea Nationala 1F, Botosani, 710001, Romania
Tel.: (40) 736107298
Web Site: http://www.greif.com

Greif Inc.—(Continued)

Sales Range: $50-74.9 Million
Plastic Drum Product Mfr
N.A.I.C.S.: 326199

Greif Flexibles Trading Holding B.V. (1)
Schipholweg 101-N, Leiden, 2316 XC, South Holland, Netherlands
Tel.: (31) 717110781
Web Site: http://www.greif.com
Emp.: 12
Investment Management Service
N.A.I.C.S.: 551112

Greif Flexibles UK Ltd. (1)
Dalton Airfield Industrial Estate, Thirsk, YO7 3HE, N Yorkshire, United Kingdom
Tel.: (44) 1845577464
Web Site: http://www.grief-flexibles.com
Plastic Drum Product Mfr
N.A.I.C.S.: 326199

Greif Flexibles USA Inc. (1)
14200 Hollister Rd Ste 100, Houston, TX 77066
Tel.: (713) 461-0840
Web Site: http://www.greif.com
Sales Range: $25-49.9 Million
Paper Bag & Treated Paper Mfr
N.A.I.C.S.: 322220

Greif France Holdings SAS (1)
Chemin Du Gord, 76120, Le Grand-Quevilly, France
Tel.: (33) 235182000
Web Site: http://www.greif.com
Sales Range: $75-99.9 Million
Emp.: 250
Holding Company
N.A.I.C.S.: 551112
Stephane Serrano (Sls Dir)
Michael Vvedenskiy (Sls Dir-Western Europe)

Greif France S.A.S. (1)
Chemin Du Gord, Le Grand-Quevilly, 76121, Rouen, France
Tel.: (33) 235182000
Web Site: http://www.greif.com
Sales Range: $75-99.9 Million
Mfr of Metal Cans
N.A.I.C.S.: 332431

Greif Germany GmbH (1)
Dieselstrasse 4-6, D-50859, Cologne, Germany
Tel.: (49) 223470150
Web Site: http://www.greif-germany.de
Mfr of Bulk Shipping Containers Including Fibre, Plastic & Steel Drums
N.A.I.C.S.: 332439

Greif Hellas (1)
Local Rd Mandra Magoula, 196 00, Mandra-Attikis, Greece (100%)
Tel.: (30) 2105555527
Web Site: http://www.greif.gr
Sales Range: $25-49.9 Million
Emp.: 20
Mfr of Steel Containers
N.A.I.C.S.: 332439

Greif Hua I Taiwan Co., Ltd. (1)
No 309 Dasi Road, Ping-tung, 90093, Taiwan
Tel.: (886) 87559161
Sales Range: $25-49.9 Million
Emp.: 80
Metal Tank Mfr
N.A.I.C.S.: 332431

Greif Hungary Kft (1)
Fo ut 21, Almasfuzito, 2931, Komarom-Esztergom, Hungary
Tel.: (36) 34548200
Web Site: http://www.greif.hu
Emp.: 60
Steel Drum Product Mfr
N.A.I.C.S.: 332439

Greif International Holding Supra II C.V. (1)
Asterweg 25, 1031 HL, Amsterdam, Netherlands
Tel.: (31) 206347700
Investment Management Service
N.A.I.C.S.: 551112

Greif Italia SpA (1)

Via Vespucci 1, 20066, Melzo, Italy (100%)
Tel.: (39) 0295124267
Sales Range: $50-74.9 Million
Emp.: 90
Mfr of Metal Containers
N.A.I.C.S.: 332439
Bomenico Rinalvini (Mng Dir)

Greif Jamaica Ltd. (1)
279 Spanish Town Rd, Box 367, Kingston, 11, Jamaica
Tel.: (876) 757 5205
Web Site: http://www.greif.com
Sales Range: $100-124.9 Million
Steel Drums Mfr
N.A.I.C.S.: 332439

Greif Malaysia Sdn Bhd (1)
No 10 Jalan Kilang, 46050, Petaling Jaya, Malaysia
Tel.: (60) 377876800
Container Product Mfr
N.A.I.C.S.: 332439

Greif Mexico, S.A. de C.V. (1)
Cristaleta No 50 Col Bugambilias, Cuenavaca, 62577, Jiutepec, Morelos, Mexico
Tel.: (52) 5554038756
Web Site: http://www.greif.com.mx
Sales Range: $25-49.9 Million
Container Product Mfr
N.A.I.C.S.: 332439

Greif Mimaysan Ambalaj Sanayi AS (1)
Gebze Organize Sanayi Bolgesi Ihsan Dede Caddesi 800 Sokak No 808, 41480, Gebze, Kocaeli, Turkiye
Tel.: (90) 2626737700
Web Site: https://www.greif.com.tr
Emp.: 40
Steel Drums Mfr
N.A.I.C.S.: 332431

Greif Nederland B.V. (1)
Bergseweg 6, 3633 AK, Vreeland, Netherlands
Tel.: (31) 294238911
Web Site: http://www.greif.com
Sales Range: $75-99.9 Million
Emp.: 150
Mfr of Packaging Materials; Drums; Closures; Film; Moulded Fibre Products; Consumer Packaging Products; Food Service Products; Rigid Food Packaging; Flexible Food Packaging
N.A.I.C.S.: 332439

Unit (Domestic):

Tri-Sure Closures Netherlands (2)
Asterweg 25, 1031 HL, Amsterdam, Netherlands (100%)
Tel.: (31) 206347700
Web Site: http://www.tri-sure.com
Sales Range: $75-99.9 Million
Emp.: 130
N.A.I.C.S.: 326199
Daniela Bergamaschi (Sls Mgr)

Greif Norway AS (1)
Titangata 11, 1630, Fredrikstad, Norway
Tel.: (47) 69320036
Web Site: http://www.greif.no
Industrial Container Product Mfr
N.A.I.C.S.: 332439

Greif Packaging France Investments SAS (1)
Chemin Du Gord, Le Grand-Quevilly, 76120, France
Tel.: (33) 235182050
Web Site: http://www.greif.com
Emp.: 150
Financial Investment Services
N.A.I.C.S.: 523999
Frederic Leroy (Gen Dir)

Greif Packaging LLC (1)
366 Greif Pkwy, Delaware, OH 43015-8260
Tel.: (740) 549-6000
Web Site: http://www.greif.com
Industrial Packaging Product & Services
N.A.I.C.S.: 322219

Greif Packaging Morocco S.A. (1)
Allee Des Cactus Ain Sebaa, Casablanca, Morocco
Tel.: (212) 522359097

Packaging Services
N.A.I.C.S.: 561910

Greif Packaging Spain SA (1)
Calle Marie Curie Pol Industrial La Torre 2 Y 4, Martorell, 08760, Barcelona, Spain
Tel.: (34) 937766900
Metal Tank Mfr
N.A.I.C.S.: 332431

Greif Plastics Italy Packaging Service (1)
Viale Industria 29, 24040, Bottanuco, Bergamo, Italy
Tel.: (39) 0354994611
Web Site: http://www.fustiplast.it
Recycling of Used Metal Packaging Containers
N.A.I.C.S.: 423930

Greif Plastics Italy SRL (1)
Viale Industria 29, Bottanuco, Bergamo, Italy
Tel.: (39) 0354994611
Web Site: http://www.fustiplast.it
Drum Mfr
N.A.I.C.S.: 326199

Greif Poland Sp. z.o.o. (1)
Przemyslowa 3, 44-203, Rybnik, Poland (100%)
Tel.: (48) 324295040
Web Site: http://www.greif.com.pl
Sales Range: $25-49.9 Million
Plastic Product Manufacturing
N.A.I.C.S.: 326199
Krzysztof Glinianowicz (Mng Dir)

Greif Portugal Ltda. (1)
Rua da Leziria 1, 2625-114, Povoa de Santa Iria, Portugal
Tel.: (351) 219533000
Sales Range: $25-49.9 Million
Emp.: 30
Provider of Food Packaging Services
N.A.I.C.S.: 327213

Greif Riverville Mill (1)
861 Fibre Plant Rd, Gladstone, VA 24553
Tel.: (434) 933-4100
Web Site: http://www.greif.com
Sales Range: $100-124.9 Million
Emp.: 305
Industrial Packaging Systems Mfr
N.A.I.C.S.: 322219

Greif S.A. (Pty) Ltd. (1)
Martin Blvd, PO Box 271, Vanderbijlpark, 1900, South Africa (100%)
Tel.: (27) 169301100
Web Site: http://www.greif.co.za
Sales Range: $100-124.9 Million
Emp.: 150
N.A.I.C.S.: 326199

Greif Singapore Pte Ltd (1)
5 Pioneer Sector 3, Singapore, 628344, Singapore
Tel.: (65) 686 353 00
Web Site: http://www.greif.com
Metal & Plastic Containers Mfr
N.A.I.C.S.: 332439

Greif South Africa (Pty) Ltd. (1)
Martin Blvd Vanderbijlpark N E 3, PO Box 271, Vanderbijlpark, 1900, South Africa (100%)
Tel.: (27) 169301100
Web Site: http://www.greif.co.za
Sales Range: $1-4.9 Billion
Mfr of Plastic & Steel Drums
N.A.I.C.S.: 331221

Greif Sweden AB (1)
Kvekatorpsvagen 25, PO Box 203, 311 32, Falkenberg, Halland, Sweden
Tel.: (46) 346714666
Web Site: http://www.greif.se
Plastic Drum Product Mfr
N.A.I.C.S.: 326199

Greif Tholu B.V. (1)
Francis Baconstraat 2, 6718 XA, Ede, Netherlands
Tel.: (31) 318452277
Web Site: https://www.tholu.com
Industrial Packaging Services
N.A.I.C.S.: 561910

Greif UK Ltd. (1)
Merseyside Works Oil Sites Road, Elles-

mere Port, CH65 4EZ, Cheshire, United Kingdom
Tel.: (44) 1513732000
Web Site: http://www.greif.co.uk
Steel Drum Product Mfr
N.A.I.C.S.: 332439

Greif Venezuela, C.A. (1)
2nd cross section Paraparal Industrial Zone Los Guayos Valencia, Edo Carabobo, Valencia, Venezuela
Tel.: (58) 2455712915
Web Site: http://www.greif.com.ve
Mfr of Steel Drums, Plastic Drums, Water Bottles & Blow-molded Plastic Containers
N.A.I.C.S.: 326199

Greif Zimbabwe Private Ltd. (1)
47 High Field Rd Southerton, Harare, ST193, Zimbabwe (100%)
Tel.: (263) 4620661
Sales Range: $25-49.9 Million
Emp.: 100
Mfr of Steel Drums, Plastic Drums, Plastic Films, Molded Fiber Egg Packaging & Sacks
N.A.I.C.S.: 326199
Tichafa Ndoro (Plant Mgr)

Lee Container Corporation, Inc. (1)
PO Box 575, Homerville, GA 31634
Tel.: (912) 487-3631
Web Site: http://www.leecontainer.com
Plastic Mfr
N.A.I.C.S.: 326130
Robert Varnedoe (Pres)

Pachmas Packaging Ltd (1)
M P Hefer, Ein HaHoresh, 3898000, Israel
Tel.: (972) 4 625 0204
Web Site: https://www.pachmas.com
Sales Range: $50-74.9 Million
Emp.: 120
Fiber Metal & Plastic Drum Product Mfr
N.A.I.C.S.: 326199
Tal Segev (CEO)
Haim Shwartz (COO)
Orna Bachrach (CFO)
Udi Tadmor (Mgr-Sls & Mktg)
Tomer Golan (CTO)
Hadar Shaked (Mgr-HR)
Yoav Schnitzer (Engr-Plant)

Reliance Products, Ltd. (1)
1093 Sherwin Road, Winnipeg, R3H 1A4, MB, Canada
Tel.: (204) 633-4403
Web Site: http://www.relianceproducts.com
Rev.: $24,230,670
Emp.: 130
Plastic Consumer Products Mfr
N.A.I.C.S.: 326199
Charles Schiele (Pres)

Soterra LLC (1)
439 Katherine Dr A, Flowood, MS 39232-0018
Tel.: (601) 933-0088
Web Site: https://soterrallc.com
Sales Range: $10-24.9 Million
Emp.: 22
Land Management Services
N.A.I.C.S.: 113110
David Johns (VP & Gen Mgr)
Andy Callahan (Mgr-Sls & Svc)
Bill White (Mgr-Land Admin)
Russell Brunson (Mgr-Consulting Svcs)

Southline Metal Products Company (1)
3777 W 12th St, Houston, TX 77055
Tel.: (713) 869-4343
Sales Range: $25-49.9 Million
Emp.: 99
Metal Container Mfr
N.A.I.C.S.: 332439

Unsa Ambalaj Sanayi Ve Ticaret Anonim Sirketi (1)
Fabrika Sok No 8 Samandira, Kartal, 81430, Istanbul, Turkiye
Tel.: (90) 2163115000
Metal Tank Mfr
N.A.I.C.S.: 332431

Van Leer Containers (Nigeria) Plc (1)
Olukunle Obadina, Apapa, Nigeria (51%)
Tel.: (234) 15870866
Sales Range: $700-749.9 Million
Production of Metal Containers for Solid, Powdery or Liquid Substances

N.A.I.C.S.: 332439

Vulsay Industries, Ltd. (1)
35 Regan Road, Brampton, L7A 1B2, ON, Canada
Tel.: (905) 846-2200
Web Site: https://www.vulsay.com
Automotive & Household Liquid Packaging Services
N.A.I.C.S.: 561910

pack2pack Group N.V. (1)
Schaapbruggestraat 48, 8800, Rumbeke, Belgium
Tel.: (32) 51261470
Web Site: http://www.pack2pack.com
Sales Range: $150-199.9 Million
Emp.: 650
Packaging Products Mfr & Services
N.A.I.C.S.: 488991

Subsidiary (Non-US):

EarthMinded France (2)
270 Avenue de Berlin ZI Artois Flandres Secteur C, 62092, Haisnes, Cedex, France
Tel.: (33) 321742742
Web Site: http://www.earthminded.com
Plastics Product Mfr
N.A.I.C.S.: 326199

pack2pack Zwolle B.V. (1)
Marsweg 3, 8013 PD, Zwolle, Overijssel, Netherlands
Tel.: (31) 384218991
Plastic Drum Product Mfr
N.A.I.C.S.: 326199

GREYSON INTERNATIONAL, INC.
Tel.: (754) 229-6858 DE
Web Site: http://www.greysonintl.com
GYSN—(OTCIQ)
Beauty Product Distr
N.A.I.C.S.: 456120
C. Mukesh Prasad *(Pres)*

GREYSTONE LOGISTICS, INC.
1613 E 15th, Tulsa, OK 74120
Tel.: (918) 583-7441 OK
Web Site:
https://greystonepallets.com
Year Founded: 1969
GLGI—(OTCQB)
Rev.: $61,780,715
Assets: $52,256,309
Liabilities: $28,275,560
Net Worth: $23,980,749
Earnings: $5,027,491
Emp.: 190
Fiscal Year-end: 05/31/24
Recycled Plastic Pallets Mfr & Sales
N.A.I.C.S.: 326199
Warren F. Kruger *(Chm)*
Ron Schelhaas *(Plant Mgr)*
Ce Ce Des Marais *(Coord-Sustainability)*

GRI BIO, INC.
2223 Avenida de la Playa Ste 208, La Jolla, CA 92037
Tel.: (619) 940-0117 DE
Web Site: https://gribio.com
Year Founded: 2018
GRI—(NASDAQ)
Rev.: $26,000
Assets: $4,152,000
Liabilities: $1,810,000
Net Worth: $2,342,000
Earnings: $7,024,000
Emp.: 2
Fiscal Year-end: 12/31/22
Research & Development in Biotechnology (except Nanobiotechnology)
N.A.I.C.S.: 541714
Marc Hertz *(Pres & CEO)*
Vipin Kumar Chaturvedi *(Chief Scientific Officer)*
Albert Agro *(Chief Medical Officer)*
Leanne Kelly *(CFO)*

GRID DYNAMICS HOLDINGS, INC.
5000 Executive Pkwy Ste 520, San Ramon, CA 94583
Tel.: (650) 523-5000 DE
Web Site:
https://www.griddynamics.com
Year Founded: 2018
GDYN—(NASDAQ)
Rev.: $310,482,000
Assets: $411,146,000
Liabilities: $48,102,000
Net Worth: $363,044,000
Earnings: ($29,214,000)
Emp.: 3,798
Fiscal Year-end: 12/31/22
Investment Services
N.A.I.C.S.: 523999
Eric A. Benhamou *(Executives, Bd of Dirs)*
Lloyd A. Carney *(Chm)*
Leonard Livschitz *(CEO)*
Anil Doradla *(CFO)*
Yury Gryzlov *(COO)*
Vadim Kozyrkov *(Sr VP-Engrg)*
Rahul Bindlish *(VP-Sls & Mktg)*
Ilya Katsov *(VP-Tech)*

Subsidiaries:

Tacit Knowledge Ltd. (1)
10 Midford Place, London, W1T 5AG, United Kingdom
Tel.: (44) 2074048040
Software Development Services
N.A.I.C.S.: 513210

Subsidiary (US):

Tacit Knowledge, Inc. (2)
27 Maiden Ln 4th Fl, San Francisco, CA 94108
Tel.: (415) 694-4322
Web Site: http://www.tacitknowledge.com
Computer Software Consulting Services
N.A.I.C.S.: 541512

GRIFFON CORPORATION
712 5th Ave 18th Fl, New York, NY 10019
Tel.: (212) 957-5000 DE
Web Site: https://www.griffon.com
Year Founded: 1970
GFF—(NYSE)
Rev.: $2,623,520,000
Assets: $2,370,954,000
Liabilities: $2,146,066,000
Net Worth: $224,888,000
Earnings: $209,897,000
Emp.: 5,300
Fiscal Year-end: 09/30/24
Plastics Product Mfr
N.A.I.C.S.: 326199
Ronald J. Kramer *(Chm & CEO)*
Michael A. Sarrica *(Sr VP)*
Brian G. Harris *(CFO & Sr VP)*
Robert F. Mehmel *(Pres & COO)*
Seth L. Kaplan *(Gen Counsel, Sec & Sr VP)*
W. Christopher Durborow *(Chief Acctg Officer & VP)*

Subsidiaries:

ATT Holding Company (1)
465 Railroad Ave, Camp Hill, PA 17011-5611
Tel.: (717) 737-1500
Holding Company
N.A.I.C.S.: 551112

Clopay Corporation (1)
8585 Duke Blvd, Mason, OH 45040-3101 **(100%)**
Tel.: (513) 770-4800
Web Site: http://www.clopay.com
Garage Door Mfr; Supplies & Installs Commercial Doors & Self-Storage Systems; Distributes & Installs Building Products; Plastic Films Mfr & Supplier
N.A.I.C.S.: 423390

Subsidiary (Domestic):

Clopay Building Products Company, Inc. (2)
8585 Duke Blvd, Mason, OH 45040 **(100%)**
Tel.: (513) 770-4800
Web Site: http://www.clopaydoor.com
Garage Doors Mfr, Sells Building Materials
N.A.I.C.S.: 321911

Subsidiary (Domestic):

CornellCookson, Inc. (3)
24 Elmwood Ave, Mountain Top, PA 18707
Tel.: (570) 474-6773
Web Site: http://www.cornellcookson.com
Rolling Metal Door Grilles & Shutters Mfr
N.A.I.C.S.: 332321
Sean Smith *(Chief Comml Officer)*

Subsidiary (Non-US):

Clopay Dombuhl GmbH (2)
Verpackungsfolien Johannes-Bohme-Str 1-5, Ansbach, 91601, Bavaria, Germany
Tel.: (49) 986898100
Web Site: http://www.clopayplastics.com
Emp.: 100
Polyolefin Resin & Filler Product Mfr
N.A.I.C.S.: 325211

Clopay Europe GmbH (2)
Am Limespark 2, Sulzbach, 65843, Germany
Tel.: (49) 61968838320
Web Site: http://www.clopay.de
Emp.: 5
Chemical Products Distr
N.A.I.C.S.: 325199

ClosetMaid LLC (1)
13485 Veterans Way, Orlando, FL 32827
Tel.: (352) 401-6000
Vinyl-Coated Steel Rod Shelving & Storage Mfr
N.A.I.C.S.: 332618

Cornell Storefront Systems, Inc. (1)
140 Maffet St, Wilkes Barre, PA 18705
Web Site: https://storefronts.cornelliron.com
Emp.: 700
Storefront System Services
N.A.I.C.S.: 238190

Garant GP (1)
375 Chemin Saint Francois Ouest, Laval, G0R 3A0, QC, Canada
Tel.: (418) 259-7711
Web Site: http://www.garant.com
Snow Removal & Gardening Tools Mfr
N.A.I.C.S.: 333111

Hunter Ventiladores de Mexico S.A. de C.V. (1)
Torre WorkSpace 109 28 Suite 603 Ave Eugenio Garza Laguera, 4001 Col Del Paseo Residencial, 64909, Monterrey, Mexico
Tel.: (52) 8125572026
Web Site: https://www.hunterfan.com.mx
Ceiling Fan Parts Distr
N.A.I.C.S.: 423620

La Hacienda Limited (1)
Hangar 27 Site C Aston Down Airfield Nr, Stroud, GL6 8HR, United Kingdom
Tel.: (44) 1285762060
Web Site: https://www.lahacienda.co.uk
Farm Product Distr
N.A.I.C.S.: 424910

Systems Engineering Group, Inc. (1)
9861 Broken Land Pkwy Ste 350, Columbia, MD 21046
Tel.: (410) 381-8740
Web Site: http://www.telephonics.com
Telecommunication Engineering Product Services
N.A.I.C.S.: 541330

The Ames Companies UK Ltd. (1)
Units 7-8 Acorn Park Vernon Road Blackheath, Birmingham, B62 8EG, United Kingdom
Tel.: (44) 3304041195
Web Site: http://www.amesgroup.co.uk
Waste Collection Services
N.A.I.C.S.: 562111

The Ames Companies, Inc. (1)
465 Railroad Ave, Camp Hill, PA 17011

Tel.: (717) 737-1500
Web Site: http://www.ames.com
Lawn & Garden Equipment Mfr & Distr
N.A.I.C.S.: 332216
Mark R. Traylor *(Pres)*

Branch (Domestic):

Ames True Temper - Bernie (2)
206 E Hunts Ave, Bernie, MO 63822-9516
Tel.: (573) 293-5341
Web Site: http://www.amestruetemper.com
Sales Range: $25-49.9 Million
Emp.: 50
Wood Tool Handles Mfr
N.A.I.C.S.: 321999

Subsidiary (Domestic):

Harper Brush Works Incorporated (2)
400 N 2nd St, Fairfield, IA 52556
Tel.: (641) 472-5186
Web Site: http://www.harperbrush.com
Brooms & Brushes Mfr
N.A.I.C.S.: 339994

Hunter Fan Company (2)
7130 Goodlett Farm Pkwy Ste 400, Cordova, TN 38016
Tel.: (901) 743-1360
Web Site: http://www.hunterfan.com
Sales Range: $350-399.9 Million
Ceiling Fans Mfr
N.A.I.C.S.: 335210

Subsidiary (Domestic):

Casablanca Fan Company (3)
7130 Goodlett Farms Pkwy Ste 400, Memphis, TN 38016
Tel.: (909) 629-1477
Web Site: http://www.casablancafanco.com
Ceiling Fan Mfr
N.A.I.C.S.: 335210

GRIID INFRASTRUCTURE INC.
2577 Duck Creek Rd, Cincinnati, OH 45212
Tel.: (513) 268-6185
Web Site: https://griid.com
Year Founded: 2019
GRDI—(NYSE)
Bitcoin Mining
N.A.I.C.S.: 921130
Trey Kelly *(Founder, Chm & CEO)*
Jerry King *(COO)*
Al Wallander *(CFO)*

Subsidiaries:

Adit EdTech Acquisition Corp. (1)
1345 Avenue of the Americas 33rd Fl, New York, NY 10105
Tel.: (646) 291-6930
Web Site: http://www.aditedtech.com
Rev.: $8,569,290
Assets: $27,204,553
Liabilities: $39,629,871
Net Worth: ($12,425,318)
Earnings: $4,832,848
Emp.: 3
Fiscal Year-end: 12/31/2022
Investment Services
N.A.I.C.S.: 523999
David L. Shrier *(Pres & CEO)*
John J. D'Agostino *(CFO & Treas)*
Elizabeth B. Porter *(CTO & Sec)*

GRILLIT, INC.
8795 SW Tualatin-Sherwood Rd 1006, Tualatin, OR 97062
Tel.: (541) 651-8800 NV
Year Founded: 2002
GRLT—(OTCIQ)
Restaurant Operators
N.A.I.C.S.: 722511
Gregory P. Mitchell *(Chm, Treas & Sec)*

GRINDR INC.
Tel.: (310) 776-6680 Ky
Web Site: https://www.grindr.com
Year Founded: 2020

Grindr Inc.—(Continued)

GRND—(NYSE)
Rev.: $195,015,000
Assets: $438,828,000
Liabilities: $434,776,000
Net Worth: $4,052,000
Earnings: $852,000
Emp.: 202
Fiscal Year-end: 12/31/22
Social Networking
N.A.I.C.S.: 513210
G. Raymond Zage III *(Chm & CEO)*

GRITSTONE BIO, INC.
5959 Horton St Ste 300, Emeryville,
CA 94608
Tel.: (510) 871-6100   DE
Web Site:
  https://www.gritstonebio.com
Year Founded: 2015
GRTS—(NASDAQ)
Rev.: $19,945,000
Assets: $240,754,000
Liabilities: $69,973,000
Net Worth: $170,781,000
Earnings: ($119,687,000)
Emp.: 233
Fiscal Year-end: 12/31/22
Medical Research & Development
Services
N.A.I.C.S.: 541715
Andrew R. Allen *(Pres & CEO)*
Matthew J. Hawryluk *(Chief Bus Officer & Exec VP)*
Timothy Chan *(Co-Founder)*
Naiyer Rizvi *(Co-Founder)*
Karin Jooss *(Head-R&D)*
Vijay Yabannavar *(Chief Mfg & Technical Ops Officer & Exec VP)*
Celia Economides *(CFO & Exec VP)*
James Cho *(Chief Acctg Officer)*
Stacy Proctor *(Chief People Officer)*

GRIZZLY ENERGY, LLC
5847 San Felipe Ste 3000, Houston,
TX 77057
Tel.: (832) 327-2255   DE
Web Site: https://grizzlyenergyllc.com
Year Founded: 2009
GRZZU—(OTCEM)
Holding Company; Oil & Natural Gas
Investment, Development & Production
N.A.I.C.S.: 551112
Jonathan C. Curth *(Interim Pres, Interim CEO, Gen Counsel, Corp Sec & VP-Land)*
Ryan Midgett *(CFO)*

Subsidiaries:

Encore Energy Partners LP   (1)
5847 San Felipe Ste 3000, Houston, TX
77057
Tel.: (832) 327-2255
Web Site: http://www.encoreenp.com
Sales Range: $150-199.9 Million
Oil & Natural Gas Exploration Services
N.A.I.C.S.: 211120
Scott W. Smith *(Pres & CEO)*
Richard A. Robert *(CFO, Sec & Exec VP)*

LRR Energy, L.P.   (1)
Heritage Plz 1111 Bagby St Ste 4600,
Houston, TX 77002
Tel.: (713) 292-9510
Web Site: http://www.lrrenergy.com
Rev.: $187,905,000
Assets: $558,954,000
Liabilities: $340,317,000
Net Worth: $218,637,000
Earnings: $52,742,000
Fiscal Year-end: 12/31/2014
Oil & Natural Gas Exploration Services
N.A.I.C.S.: 211120

Vanguard Operating, LLC   (1)
5847 San Felipe Ste 3000, Houston, TX
77056
Tel.: (832) 377-2206
Oil & Gas Field Services

N.A.I.C.S.: 213112

GROCERY OUTLET HOLDING CORP.
5650 Hollis St, Emeryville, CA 94608
Tel.: (510) 845-1999   DE
Web Site:
  https://www.groceryoutlet.com
Year Founded: 2014
GO—(NASDAQ)
Rev.: $3,969,453,000
Assets: $2,969,586,000
Liabilities: $1,750,247,000
Net Worth: $1,219,339,000
Earnings: $79,437,000
Emp.: 901
Fiscal Year-end: 12/30/23
Holding Company
N.A.I.C.S.: 551112
Ramesh Chikkala *(COO & Exec VP)*
Lindsay E. Gray *(Interim CFO & Principal Acctg Officer)*
Andrea R. Bortner *(Chief HR Officer & Exec VP)*
Pamela B. Burke *(Chief Stores Officer)*
Heather L. Mayo *(Chief Sls & Mdsg Officer-East & Exec VP)*
Brian T. McAndrews *(Chief New Store Dev Officer & Sr VP)*
Thomas H. McMahon *(Chief Sls & Mdsg Officer-West & Exec VP)*
Steven K. Wilson *(Chief Pur Officer & Sr VP)*
Jon Decker *(VP-Sls & Mdsg-West)*
Christian Janzen *(VP-Fin)*
Layla Kasha *(CMO & Sr VP)*
Jeff Phillips *(VP-Operator Recruiting & Trng)*
Michael Thomas *(VP-Supply Chain)*
Steve Tuscher *(VP-IT)*
Harrison Lewis *(CIO & Sr VP)*
Joseph Pelland *(VP-IR)*
Eric J. Lindberg Jr. *(Chm)*
Robert Joseph Sheedy Jr. *(Pres & CEO)*

Subsidiaries:

Amelia's, LLC   (1)
17 State St 14th Fl, New York, NY 10004
Tel.: (212) 708-5500
Web Site: http://www.amelia.com
Information Technology Services
N.A.I.C.S.: 541511
Chetan Dube *(Founder & CEO)*
Jonathan Crane *(Chief Comml Officer)*
Eray Ekici *(VP)*
Anne Meisner *(CFO)*
Mike Ghicas *(VP-Svc Design)*

GROGENESIS, INC.
101 S Reid St Ste 307, Sioux Falls,
SD 57103
Tel.: (605) 836-3100   NV
Web Site: http://www.grogenesis.com
Year Founded: 2010
GROG—(OTCIQ)
Sales Range: Less than $1 Million
Emp.: 1
Plant Surfactant Producer
N.A.I.C.S.: 325998
Grant B. Walsh *(Chm)*
Sadru Habib *(Mng Dir-Southeast Asia)*
Peter Woodhouse *(CEO, CFO, Treas & Sec)*

GROM SOCIAL ENTERPRISES, INC.
2060 NW Boca Raton Blvd Ste 6,
Boca Raton, FL 33431
Tel.: (561) 287-5776   FL
Web Site:
  https://www.gromsocialenterprises.com
Year Founded: 2012

GROM—(NASDAQ)
Rev.: $5,426,501
Assets: $24,644,897
Liabilities: $4,297,049
Net Worth: $20,347,848
Earnings: ($16,332,636)
Emp.: 90
Fiscal Year-end: 12/31/22
Online Entertainment Services
N.A.I.C.S.: 516210
Jason A. Williams *(CFO, Chief Acctg Officer, Treas & Sec)*
Zachary Marks *(Founder)*
Darren Marks *(Chm, Pres & CEO)*
Wayne Dearing *(Mng Dir-Top Draw Animation)*

GROOVE BOTANICALS INC.
310 4th Ave S Ste 7000, Minneapolis,
MN 55415
Tel.: (612) 315-5068   NV
Year Founded: 1991
GRVE—(OTCIQ)
Rev.: $64,492
Assets: $2,142
Liabilities: $762,699
Net Worth: ($760,557)
Earnings: ($202,089)
Emp.: 1
Fiscal Year-end: 03/31/24
Oil & Natural Gas Extraction Services
N.A.I.C.S.: 213112
Kent A. Rodriguez *(Pres, CEO, CFO & Sec)*

GROUP 1 AUTOMOTIVE, INC.
800 Gessner Ste 500, Houston, TX
77024
Tel.: (713) 647-5700   DE
Web Site:
  https://www.group1auto.com
Year Founded: 1995
GPI—(NYSE)
Rev.: $17,873,700,000
Assets: $7,774,100,000
Liabilities: $5,099,700,000
Net Worth: $2,674,400,000
Earnings: $601,600,000
Emp.: 16,011
Fiscal Year-end: 12/31/23
New & Used Car Dealer
N.A.I.C.S.: 441110
Peter C. DeLongchamps *(Sr VP-Mfr Rels, Fin Svcs & PR)*
Daniel J. McHenry *(CFO & Sr VP)*
Jamie Albertine *(VP-Corp Dev)*
Terry Bratton *(Mgr-IR)*
Gillian Hobson *(Chief Legal Officer)*
Edward McKissic *(Chief HR Officer)*
Kimberly Barta *(CMO)*
Daryl A. Kenningham *(Pres & CEO)*

Subsidiaries:

Advantage BMW Clear Lake   (1)
400 Gulf Fwy S, League City, TX
77573   **(100%)**
Tel.: (281) 557-7000
Web Site:
  http://www.advantagebmwclearlake.com
Sales Range: $50-74.9 Million
Emp.: 100
New Car Dealership
N.A.I.C.S.: 441227

Advantage BMW Midtown   (1)
1305 Gray St, Houston, TX 77002   **(100%)**
Tel.: (713) 289-1200
Web Site:
  https://www.advantagebmwhouston.com
Sales Range: $50-74.9 Million
Emp.: 70
Car Dealership Operator
N.A.I.C.S.: 441110
Garrett Burleson *(Mgr-Sls-New Car)*
Russell Graves *(Mgr-Sls-Pre-Owned)*
Yvonne Guerra *(Mgr-Inventory)*
Sal Guerra *(Mgr-Fin)*
Younus Nadeem *(Mgr-Fin)*

Eric Sanchez *(Dir-After Sls)*
Wilson Martinez *(Dir-Parts)*
Moe Hamadneh *(Sls Mgr-Pre-Owned)*
Ana Mejia *(Mgr-Svc)*

Advantagecars.com, Inc.   (1)
10505 Southwest Freeway, Houston, TX
77074
Tel.: (713) 981-3990
Web Site: http://www.advantagecars.com
New Car Dealers
N.A.I.C.S.: 441110

BMW of El Paso   (1)
6318 Montana Ave, El Paso, TX 79925
Tel.: (915) 778-9381
Web Site: https://www.bmwofelpaso.com
Sales Range: $50-74.9 Million
Emp.: 100
Motor Vehicle Retailers
N.A.I.C.S.: 441110
Russell Stover *(Gen Mgr)*
Christian Ugarte *(Dir-Svc)*
Armando Gomez *(Mgr-F&I)*
Ismael Rodriguez *(Mgr-F&I)*
Alex Navarro *(Dir-Sls-BMW)*

BMW of Stratham   (1)
71 Portsmouth Ave, Stratham, NH 03885
Tel.: (603) 395-2727
Web Site: https://www.bmwofstratham.com
General Automotive Repair Services
N.A.I.C.S.: 811111
Mike Coco *(Gen Mgr)*

Baron BMW   (1)
9010 Shawnee Mission Pkwy, Merriam, KS
66202
Tel.: (913) 722-5100
Web Site: https://www.baronbmw.com
General Automotive Repair Services
N.A.I.C.S.: 811111

Baron MINI   (1)
9000 Shawnee Mission Pkwy, Merriam, KS
66202
Tel.: (913) 671-4954
Web Site: https://www.baronmini.com
General Automotive Repair Services
N.A.I.C.S.: 811111
Samer Saba *(Sls Mgr-Mini)*
Clay Shafer *(Gen Mgr)*
Aaron Cass *(Mgr-Collision)*

Barons Automotive Limited   (1)
Clifton Parc Caxton Road, Bedford, MK41
0GL, Bedfordshire, United Kingdom
Tel.: (44) 1234438253
New Car Whslr
N.A.I.C.S.: 441110

Barons Autostar Limited   (1)
Northern Way, Bury Saint Edmunds, IP32
6NH, Suffolk, United Kingdom
Tel.: (44) 1284545318
New Car Whslr
N.A.I.C.S.: 441110

Beadles Coulsdon Limited   (1)
Gateway Business Park, Coulsdon, CR5
2AR, Surrey, United Kingdom
Tel.: (44) 2081316472
New Car Whslr
N.A.I.C.S.: 441110

Beadles Dartford Limited   (1)
Bromley Hill, Bromley, BR1 4JS, Kent,
United Kingdom
Tel.: (44) 2081315609
New Car Whslr
N.A.I.C.S.: 441110

Beadles Maidstone Limited   (1)
Wood Close Quarry Wood Retail Park, Aylesford, Maidstone, ME20 7UB, Kent,
United Kingdom
Tel.: (44) 1622393385
New Car Whslr
N.A.I.C.S.: 441110

Beadles Medway Limited   (1)
Wood Close Aylesford Retail Park, Aylesford, Maidstone, ME20 7UB, Kent, United
Kingdom
Tel.: (44) 1622790222
Web Site:
  http://www.beadlesmaidstone.toyota.co.uk
New Car Whslr
N.A.I.C.S.: 441110
Jason Millen *(Mgr-Sls)*
Tim Ford *(Mgr-Bus Centre)*

Russell Turner *(Gen Mgr)*
Craig Coyle *(Mgr-Aftersales)*
Andrew Gumley *(Mgr-Transaction)*
Robert Pearson *(Controller-Workshop)*

Beadles Sidcup Limited (1)
143-145 Main Road, Sidcup, DA14 6PB,
Kent, United Kingdom
Tel.: (44) 2083092220
New Car Whslr
N.A.I.C.S.: 441110

Beck & Masten Automotive Group, Inc. (1)
25503 State Hwy, Tomball, TX 77375-7711
Tel.: (281) 617-1165
Web Site: http://www.beckmastenkia.com
New Car Dealers
N.A.I.C.S.: 441110
Kevin Hoge *(Gen Mgr)*

Bob Howard Motors, Inc. (1)
12929 N Kelley Ave, Oklahoma City, OK
73131
Tel.: (405) 936-8600
Web Site:
https://www.bobhowardtoyota.com
Car Dealer
N.A.I.C.S.: 441110

Subsidiary (Domestic):

Bob Howard Automotive-East, Inc. (2)
9146 S Memorial Dr, Tulsa, OK 74133
Tel.: (918) 481-8000
Web Site:
https://www.southpointechevrolet.com
Automotive Services
N.A.I.C.S.: 811198

Bob Howard Chevrolet, Inc. (2)
13130 N Broadway Ext, Oklahoma City, OK
73114-2292
Tel.: (405) 463-9779
Web Site:
https://www.bobhowardchevrolet.com
Emp.: 30
Car Dealer
N.A.I.C.S.: 441110
Peyton McGarraugh *(Mgr-New Car)*
Paul Kaveh *(Dir-Bus)*
Chris Olson *(Dir-Svc)*
Tim Branch *(Gen Mgr)*
Terry Williamson *(Mgr-New Car)*
Scott Bowman *(Mgr-Pre-Owned)*
Gilbert Wester *(Asst Mgr-Parts)*

Bob Howard Dodge, Inc. (2)
13252 Broadway Ext, Oklahoma City, OK
73114
Tel.: (405) 775-9576
Web Site: https://www.bobhowardcjd.com
Car Dealer
N.A.I.C.S.: 441110

Bob Howard Nissan, Inc. (2)
13200 Bdwy Ext, Oklahoma City, OK 73114
Tel.: (405) 302-0947
Web Site:
https://www.bobhowardnissan.com
New Car Dealers
N.A.I.C.S.: 441110

Cadillac of Arlington (1)
2001 N Collins St, Arlington, TX 76011-
8844
Tel.: (817) 461-2222
Web Site: http://www.cadillacofarlington.com
Sales Range: $50-74.9 Million
Emp.: 170
Retailer of New & Used Automobiles
N.A.I.C.S.: 441110

Chandlers (Hailsham) Limited (1)
Gleneagles Drive, Hailsham, BN27 3UA,
East Sussex, United Kingdom
Tel.: (44) 1323407590
Web Site:
http://www.chandlershailshambmw.co.uk
General Automotive Repair Services
N.A.I.C.S.: 811111

Chandlers Garage (Brighton) Limited (1)
Victoria Road Portslade, Brighton, BN41
1YH, East Sussex, United Kingdom
Tel.: (44) 1273974498
Web Site:
http://www.chandlersbrightonbmw.co.uk

New Car Dealers
N.A.I.C.S.: 441110
Will Hopkinson *(Mgr-Retail)*
Ben Prout *(Mgr-Retail)*
Greg Lindley *(Mgr-Retail)*
Chris Ledger *(Mgr)*
Ryan O'Neill *(Mgr)*
Chris Rooney *(Gen Mgr-Sls)*
Niki Whitchurch *(Sls Mgr-)*
Mark Phelps *(Bus Mgr)*
Callum Denega *(Mgr-)*

Chandlers Garage Worthing Limited (1)
Manor Retail Park, Rustington, BN16 3FH,
West Sussex, United Kingdom
Tel.: (44) 903334218
Web Site:
http://www.chandlersworthingmini.co.uk
Sales Range: $25-49.9 Million
Emp.: 8
New Car Dealers
N.A.I.C.S.: 441110

Elms Stansted Limited (1)
Stansted Road, Bishop's Stortford, CM23
2BT, Hertfordshire, United Kingdom
Tel.: (44) 8443267244
Web Site:
http://www.elmsstanstedbmw.co.uk
General Automotive Repair Services
N.A.I.C.S.: 811111

Estero Bay Chevrolet, Inc (1)
10640 Chevrolet Way, Estero, FL 33928-
4420
Tel.: (239) 908-2600
New Car Dealers
N.A.I.C.S.: 441110
Pat Denson *(Owner)*

Freedom Chevrolet - San Antonio (1)
13483 IH 10 W, San Antonio, TX 78260
Tel.: (210) 551-0934
Web Site: https://www.freedomchevy.com
Car Dealership
N.A.I.C.S.: 441110
Paul Patina III *(Mgr-Svc Drive)*

G1R Mass, LLC (1)
800 Gessner Rd Ste 500, Houston, TX
77024
Tel.: (713) 647-5700
General Automotive Repair Services
N.A.I.C.S.: 811111

GPI FL-H, LLC (1)
3601 E 15th St, Panama City, FL 32404
Tel.: (850) 763-5495
Web Site:
https://www.hondaofbaycounty.com
Emp.: 40
General Automotive Repair Services
N.A.I.C.S.: 811111

GPI GA-CGM, LLC (1)
1661 Whittlesey Rd, Columbus, GA 31904
Tel.: (706) 940-3891
Web Site:
https://www.rivertownbuickgmc.com
General Automotive Repair Services
N.A.I.C.S.: 811111
Michael Holland *(Gen Mgr)*
Stacey Day *(Gen Sls Mgr)*
Mark Cunnea *(Dir-Internet)*
Thelma West *(Office Mgr)*

GPI LA-H, LLC (1)
510 E Howze Beach Rd, Slidell, LA 70461
Tel.: (985) 243-9057
Web Site: https://www.hondaofslidell.com
New Car Whslr
N.A.I.C.S.: 441110

GPI NM-J, Inc. (1)
5010 Alameda Blvd NE, Albuquerque, NM
87113
Tel.: (505) 797-3600
Web Site:
https://www.landroveralbuquerque.com
New Car Whslr
N.A.I.C.S.: 441110

GPI NM-LRII, Inc. (1)
2582 Camino Entrada, Santa Fe, NM
87507
Tel.: (505) 474-0888
Web Site: https://www.landroversantafe.com
Car Distr

GPI TX-AII, Inc. (1)
7330 Hawkins Center Dr, Benbrook, TX
76126
Tel.: (817) 632-6710
Web Site: https://www.audifortworth.com
New Car Whslr
N.A.I.C.S.: 441110
Veronica Zamora *(Dir-Svc)*
Alex Bagherloo *(Gen Mgr)*
Bill Whitlock *(Dir-New Car Sls)*
Ivan Martinez *(Dir-Used Car)*
Steven Stallcup *(Mgr-Parts)*
David Carpenter *(Fin Mgr)*
Marc McWhorter *(Fin Mgr)*

GPI TX-DMIV, Inc. (1)
7401 S Interstate 35, Georgetown, TX
78626
Tel.: (512) 930-6161
Web Site: https://www.mbofgeorgetown.com
New Car Whslr
N.A.I.C.S.: 441110

GPI TX-EPGM, Inc. (1)
955 Crockett St, El Paso, TX 79922-1363
Tel.: (915) 519-1116
Web Site:
https://www.shamaleybuickgmc.com
Emp.: 80
General Automotive Repair Services
N.A.I.C.S.: 811111

GPI TX-HIII, Inc. (1)
8015 Interstate 35 Access Rd, San Antonio,
TX 78224
Tel.: (210) 928-1500
Web Site: https://www.fernandezhonda.com
New Car Whslr
N.A.I.C.S.: 441110
Don Keoviva *(Dir-Bus Office)*
Gilbert Martinez *(Mgr-Fin)*
John Ridings *(Gen Mgr)*
Ray Barrera *(Dir-New Car)*
Jason Rhoads *(Sls Mgr)*
Paul Poole *(Mgr-Used Car)*
Jeanne Mann *(Mgr-BDC)*
Joe Ramirez *(Mgr-Internet)*
Mauricio Figueroa *(Dir-Svc)*
Elias Marroquin *(Mgr-Svc Drive)*
Jesus Acebedo *(Dir-Parts)*
Akaki Tsutskiridze *(Fin Mgr)*

GPI TX-SKII, Inc. (1)
5306 S IH 35 Frontage Rd, Austin, TX
78745-3233
Tel.: (512) 444-6635
Web Site: https://www.kiaofsouthaustin.com
General Automotive Repair Services
N.A.I.C.S.: 811111

GPI TX-SVIII Inc. (1)
1402 NE Interstate 410 Loop, San Antonio,
TX 78209
Tel.: (210) 904-1846
General Automotive Repair Services
N.A.I.C.S.: 811111
John Brown *(Gen Mgr)*

Harvey GM, LLC (1)
3815 Lapalco Blvd, Harvey, LA 70058
Tel.: (504) 708-4011
Web Site: http://www.bohngmc.com
New Car Dealers
N.A.I.C.S.: 441110

Hassel Motors Inc. (1)
291 W Sunrise Hwy, Freeport, NY 11520
Tel.: (516) 223-6160
Web Site: http://www.hasselbmw.com
Sales Range: $25-49.9 Million
Emp.: 30
Car Dealership
N.A.I.C.S.: 441110

Hodgson Automotive Limited (1)
Start Hill, Bishop's Stortford, CM22 7DW,
Hertfordshire, United Kingdom
Tel.: (44) 1279467777
Emp.: 280
General Automotive Repair Services
N.A.I.C.S.: 811111

Jay Automotive Group Inc. (1)
1661 Whittlesey Rd, Columbus, GA 31904
Tel.: (706) 324-1234
Web Site: http://www.rivertownautomall.com
Sales Range: $125-149.9 Million
Emp.: 250
Car Dealership

Jim Tidwell Ford, Inc. (1)
2205 Barret Lakes Blvd, Kennesaw, GA
30144
Tel.: (770) 427-5531
Web Site: https://www.jimtidwellford.com
New & Used Car Dealer
N.A.I.C.S.: 441110

Lubbock Motors-T, Inc. (1)
6102 19th St, Lubbock, TX 79407
Tel.: (806) 748-4800
Web Site:
https://www.genemessertoyota.com
Emp.: 60
Car Dealer
N.A.I.C.S.: 441110
Brady Keys *(Gen Mgr)*
Jordan Pointon *(Mgr-New Car)*
Robert Fullerton *(Dir-Fin)*
Lane Sullivan *(Mgr-Used Car)*

Maxwell Ford, Inc. (1)
5000 S IH-35, Austin, TX 78745
Tel.: (512) 443-5000
Web Site: https://www.maxwellford.com
Emp.: 60
New Car Dealers
N.A.I.C.S.: 441110
Ed Sevillano *(Mgr-New Car)*
Ike Haines *(Mgr-Used Car-GSM)*
Aaron Camargo *(Mgr-Used Car)*
Fernando Duran II *(Mgr-Internet)*

Maxwell-NII, Inc. (1)
3050 N Interstate Hwy 35, Round Rock, TX
78681
Tel.: (512) 244-8500
Web Site: https://www.roundrocknissan.com
New & Pre-Owned Car Dealer & Mainte-
nance Services
N.A.I.C.S.: 441110

McCall-F, Inc. (1)
6445 SW Fwy, Houston, TX 77074
Tel.: (281) 588-5000
Web Site:
https://www.sterlingmccallford.com
Rev.: $60,000,000
Emp.: 131
Car Dealership Operator
N.A.I.C.S.: 441110

McCall-TII, Inc. (1)
20465 SW Fwy, Richmond, TX 77469
Tel.: (281) 341-5900
Web Site:
https://www.sterlingmccalltoyotafort
bend.com
New & Used Car Dealer
N.A.I.C.S.: 441110
Martin Morcho *(Gen Mgr)*
Jerry Dismuke *(Dir-Internet)*
Eric Johnson *(Mgr-Fin)*
Ryan O'Neil *(Mgr-Fin)*
Bibin Thomas *(Mgr-Internet Sls)*
David Pham *(Mgr-New Car Sls)*
Kevin Schutt *(Mgr-Svc)*
Alex Luengas *(Mgr-Fin)*
Angus Adam *(Mgr-New Car Sls)*
Eduardo Rivera *(Dir-Svc)*

Mike Smith Autoplex Dodge, Inc. (1)
1945 Interstate 10 S, Beaumont, TX 77701
Tel.: (409) 840-3550
Web Site: https://www.mikesmithcjd.com
New Car Dealers
N.A.I.C.S.: 441110

Miller-DM, Inc. (1)
9250 Beverly Blvd, Beverly Hills, CA 90210-
3710
Tel.: (310) 860-4401
Web Site: https://www.bhbenz.com
Sales Range: $150-199.9 Million
Emp.: 300
Automotive Sales & Service
N.A.I.C.S.: 441110
Mark Barsoomian *(Mgr)*
Frank Murphy *(Gen Mgr)*
Robert Burt *(Mgr-Owned)*
Neil Perlmuter *(Sls Mgr-)*
Aria Nasseri *(Mgr)*
Evonne Ghoul *(Mgr-Public Relations)*
Alex Kraenkel *(Mgr-)*
Hans Ang *(Mgr-)*
David Handley *(Sls Mgr)*
Farhad Nasiri *(Sls Mgr)*
Alison Burdt *(Dir-)*
Helen Benderskiy *(Fin Mgr)*

Group 1 Automotive, Inc.—(Continued)

Kamran Malik (Fin Mgr)
Farshad Pirshirazi (Fin Mgr)
Steven Bobak (Mgr-Owned)
Andres Antelo (Mgr-)
Luis Chavarria (Mgr-)
William Rodriguez (Asst Mgr)

Modern Classic Motors Inc. (1)
161 Fording Island Rd, Bluffton, SC 29910-5115
Tel.: (843) 681-8500
Web Site:
http://www.modernclassicmotors.com
Rev.: $40,000,000
Emp.: 65
Dealer of Automobiles, New & Used
N.A.I.C.S.: 441110
Gordon Faulkner (Pres)
Peggy Rapp (Controller)

Munday Mazda (1)
555 FM 1960 W, Houston, TX 77090
Tel.: (281) 583-3400
Web Site: http://www.mundaymazda.com
Sales Range: $10-24.9 Million
Emp.: 40
New & Used Car Dealer
N.A.I.C.S.: 441110

Spire Automotive Limited (1)
Shenley Lane London Colney, Saint Albans, AL2 1DG, Hertfordshire, United Kingdom
Tel.: (44) 1727823146
Car Distr
N.A.I.C.S.: 441110

Sterling McCall Cadillac (1)
10150 Southwest Fwy, Houston, TX 77074
Tel.: (713) 777-7151
Web Site:
https://baywaycadillacsouthwest.com
New & Used Automobiles
N.A.I.C.S.: 441110
Dee Brooks (Sls Mgr)

Sterling McCall Honda (1)
22575 US-59, Kingwood, TX 77339
Tel.: (281) 358-8880
Web Site:
https://www.sterlingmccallhonda.com
General Automotive Repair Services
N.A.I.C.S.: 811111
Mike Collins (Gen Mgr)

Sterling McCall Toyota Group (1)
9400 SW Fwy, Houston, TX 77074-1408
Tel.: (713) 270-3900
Web Site:
https://www.sterlingmccalltoyota.com
Sales Range: $125-149.9 Million
Emp.: 200
Automobile Dealers
N.A.I.C.S.: 441110

World Ford - Stone Mountain (1)
3800 Hwy 78, Snellville, GA 30039
Tel.: (678) 344-3300
Sales Range: $25-49.9 Million
Emp.: 100
Automobiles, New & Used
N.A.I.C.S.: 441110

World Toyota (1)
5800 Peachtree Blvd, Atlanta, GA 30341 (100%)
Tel.: (678) 547-9030
Web Site: https://www.worldtoyota.com
Sales Range: $25-49.9 Million
Emp.: 100
Car Dealership
N.A.I.C.S.: 441227
George Ofori (Mgr-Fin)

GROUP NINE ACQUISITION CORP.
568 Broadway Fl 10, New York, NY 10012
Tel.: (212) 966-2263 DE
Year Founded: 2020
GNACU—(NASDAQ)
Rev.: $8,699,184
Assets: $231,111,513
Liabilities: $247,290,711
Net Worth: ($16,179,198)
Earnings: $6,619,992
Emp.: 3

Fiscal Year-end: 12/31/21
Investment Services
N.A.I.C.S.: 523999
Ben Lerer (Chm & CEO)
Brian Sugar (Pres)
Sean Macnew (CFO)

GROUPON INC.
35 W Wacker Dr 25th Fl, Chicago, IL 60601
Tel.: (773) 945-6801 DE
Web Site: https://www.groupon.com
Year Founded: 2008
GRPN—(NASDAQ)
Rev.: $599,085,000
Assets: $793,117,000
Liabilities: $784,259,000
Net Worth: $8,858,000
Earnings: ($237,609,000)
Emp.: 2,904
Fiscal Year-end: 12/31/22
Online Coupon Website Operator
N.A.I.C.S.: 541890
Dusan Senkypl (CEO)
Vojtech Rysanek (Interim CTO)
Branislav Majorsky (Sr VP-Revenue)
Rana Kashyap (Sr VP-Corporate Development & Investor Relations)
Jiri Ponrt (CFO)
Filip Popovic (COO & Sr VP)
Zdenek Linc (CMO)
Marie Havlickova (Sr VP-Strategy)
Emma Coleman (VP-Communications, Engagement, and Inclusion)
Dane Drobny (Chief Admin Officer, Gen Counsel & Sec)

Subsidiaries:

Groupon France SAS (1)
6 Place de la Madeleine, 75008, Paris, France
Tel.: (33) 970732000
Web Site: https://www.groupon.fr
Online Shopping Website Operator
N.A.I.C.S.: 541810

Groupon GmbH (1)
WeWork Alexanderplatz Dircksenstrasse 3, 10178, Berlin, Germany
Tel.: (49) 1806000133
Web Site: https://www.groupon.de
Sales Range: $125-149.9 Million
Emp.: 60
Online Coupon Website Operator
N.A.I.C.S.: 513199

Groupon Spain, SLU (1)
Calle del Pintor Juan Gris 4 1a Planta, 28020, Madrid, Spain
Tel.: (34) 902050668
Web Site: https://www.groupon.es
Online Shopping Website Operator
N.A.I.C.S.: 519290

LivingSocial, LLC (1)
600 W Chicago Ave, Chicago, IL 60654
Tel.: (888) 808-6676
Web Site: https://privacy.livingsocial.com
Online Coupon Website Operator
N.A.I.C.S.: 513140

Subsidiary (Non-US):

LivingSocial Ltd. (2)
12-27 Swan Yard, London, N1 1SD, United Kingdom
Tel.: (44) 8000148431
Online Coupon Website Operator
N.A.I.C.S.: 513199

ideeli Inc. (1)
620 Eighth Ave 45th Fl, New York, NY 10018
Tel.: (646) 745-1000
Web Site: http://www.ideeli.com
Sales Range: $75-99.9 Million
Emp.: 145
Fashion Apparels Mfr
N.A.I.C.S.: 424350
Stefan Pepe (CEO)

GROVE COLLABORATIVE

HOLDINGS, INC.
1301 Sansome St, San Francisco, CA 94111
Tel.: (212) 497-9050 Ky
Web Site: https://www.grove.co
GROV—(NYSE)
Rev.: $321,527,000
Assets: $174,045,000
Liabilities: $147,512,000
Net Worth: $26,533,000
Earnings: ($87,715,000)
Emp.: 550
Fiscal Year-end: 12/31/22
Special Purpose Acquisition Company
N.A.I.C.S.: 523999
Jeffrey Yurcisin (Pres & CEO)
Richard Branson (Founder)

Subsidiaries:

Grove Collaborative, Inc. (1)
1301 Sansome St, San Francisco, CA 94111
Tel.: (650) 667-7418
Web Site: http://www.grove.co
Sales Range: $1-9.9 Million
Household Product Distr
N.A.I.C.S.: 449210
John B. Replogle (Chm)
Stuart Landesberg (Founder & CEO)
Jennie Perry (CMO)

GROW CAPITAL, INC.
2485 Village View Dr Ste 180, Henderson, NV 89074
Tel.: (702) 830-7919 NV
Web Site: https://growcapitalinc.com
Year Founded: 1999
GRWC—(OTCIQ)
Rev.: $2,368,504
Assets: $1,913,258
Liabilities: $1,921,303
Net Worth: ($8,045)
Earnings: ($2,346,753)
Fiscal Year-end: 06/30/20
Holding Company; Software, Technology & Financial Services
N.A.I.C.S.: 551112
Carl S. Sanko (Treas & Sec)
Jonathan Bonnette (CTO)
James Olson (Chm)
Terry Kennedy (Pres & CEO)
Trevor K. Hall (CFO)
Angela Lafrance (Accountant)

GROW SOLUTIONS HOLDINGS, INC.
1111 Broadway Ste 406, Denver, CO 80203
Tel.: (646) 863-6341 NV
Web Site:
http://www.growsolutionsinc.com
Year Founded: 2014
GRSO—(OTCIQ)
Sales Range: $1-9.9 Million
Emp.: 15
Garden Equipments Distr
N.A.I.C.S.: 423820
Chad Fischl (CEO)
Wayne Hansen (CFO)

GROWGENERATION CORP.
5619 DTC Pkwy Ste 900, Greenwood Village, CO 80111 CO
Web Site:
https://www.growgeneration.com
Year Founded: 2008
GRWG—(NASDAQ)
Rev.: $278,166,000
Assets: $293,442,000
Liabilities: $77,046,000
Net Worth: $216,396,000
Earnings: $163,747,000
Emp.: 429
Fiscal Year-end: 12/31/22
Hydroponic & Organic Gardening Retail Store Operator

N.A.I.C.S.: 444240
Gregory Sanders (CFO, VP & Controller)
Stephen Kozey (Gen Counsel)
Clifton Tomasini (VP-Ops)
Son Nguyen (CIO)
Rebecca Haluska (Sr VP)
Keith Harrington (Sr VP)
Darren Lampert (Co-Founder, Chm & CEO)
Michael Salaman (Co-Founder & Pres)

Subsidiaries:

GrowGeneration Oklahoma Corp. (1)
20 NE 46th St, Oklahoma City, OK 73105
Tel.: (405) 400-7701
Farm Machinery & Equipment Distr
N.A.I.C.S.: 423820

H2o Hydroponics, LLC (1)
5210 W Saginaw Hwy, Lansing, MI 48917-1913
Tel.: (517) 203-5222
Web Site: http://www.h2ohydroponics.com
All Other Specialty Food Stores
N.A.I.C.S.: 445298
Bryan Havens Lee (Owner)

Indoor Garden & Lighting Inc. (1)
3839 6th Ave, Tacoma, WA 98406
Tel.: (253) 761-7478
Web Site: http://www.indoorgarden.com
Nursery & Garden Centers
N.A.I.C.S.: 444240
Mike Long (Founder)

San Diego Hydroponics & Organics, Inc. (1)
4122 Napier St, San Diego, CA 92110
Tel.: (760) 510-1444
Web Site: http://www.sdhydroponics.com
Florists
N.A.I.C.S.: 459310

GROWLIFE, INC.
11335 NE 122nd Way Ste 105, Kirkland, WA 98034 DE
Web Site:
https://www.growlifeinc.com
Year Founded: 2001
PHOT—(OTCIQ)
Assets: $254,208
Liabilities: $8,664,942
Net Worth: ($8,410,734)
Earnings: ($4,482,877)
Emp.: 2
Fiscal Year-end: 12/31/22
Mini-Hydroponic Greenhouses, Horticultural Seeds, Mineral Nutrient Solutions, Growing Mediums & Germination Kits Mfr & Distr
N.A.I.C.S.: 333111
Thom Kozik (Interim Sec)
David Dohrmann (Pres, CEO & CFO)

Subsidiaries:

EZ Clone Enterprises Inc. (1)
10170 Croydon Way Ste G, Sacramento, CA 95827-2104 (51%)
Tel.: (916) 626-3000
Web Site: http://www.ezclone.com
Hydroponic & Indoor Gardening Services & Machinery Mfr
N.A.I.C.S.: 423820

Evergreen Garden Center, LLC (1)
17395 E Main St, Louisville, MS 39339-2764
Tel.: (662) 803-6358
Hydroponic Equipment Product Distr
N.A.I.C.S.: 424910

GRUPO INTERNATIONAL, INC.
1909 Palm Ave, San Diego, CA 92154
Tel.: (619) 308-7943
Web Site:
http://www.gruponainternacional.com

GRPI—(OTCIQ)
Pharmaceuticals Product Mfr
N.A.I.C.S.: 325412
Ramon Richard Mora *(Pres & CEO)*

GRYPHON DIGITAL MINING, INC.

1180 N Town Center Dr Ste 100, Las Vegas, NV 89144
Tel.: (877) 646-3374   DE
GRYP—(NASDAQ)
Rev.: $13,645,030
Assets: $19,468,492
Liabilities: $24,294,020
Net Worth: ($4,825,528)
Earnings: ($80,013,110)
Emp.: 112
Fiscal Year-end: 12/31/22
Technology Software & Financial Intermediation Services
N.A.I.C.S.: 551112
Simeon Salzman *(Sec)*
Steve Gutterman *(CEO)*

Subsidiaries:

MJ Freeway LLC   **(1)**
1601 Arapahoe St Ste 900, Denver, CO 80202
Tel.: (888) 932-6537
Web Site: http://www.mjfreeway.com
Sales Range: $1-9.9 Million
Data Management Services
N.A.I.C.S.: 518210
Jessica Billingsley *(Co-Founder, Chm & CEO)*
Amy Poinsett *(Co-Founder)*
Ray Thompson *(COO)*

MTech Acquisition Corp.   **(1)**
10124 Foxhurst Ct, Orlando, FL 32836
Tel.: (407) 345-8332
Rev.: $959,645
Assets: $58,474,545
Liabilities: $53,474,542
Net Worth: $5,000,003
Earnings: ($29,957)
Emp.: 2
Fiscal Year-end: 12/31/2018
Investment Holding Company
N.A.I.C.S.: 551112
Scott Sozio *(CEO)*
Tahira Rehmatullah *(CFO)*

GSE SYSTEMS, INC.

6940 Columbia Gateway Dr Ste 470, Columbia, MD 21046
Tel.: (410) 970-7800   DE
Web Site: https://www.gses.com
GVP—(NASDAQ)
Rev.: $47,734,000
Assets: $26,496,000
Liabilities: $16,265,000
Net Worth: $10,231,000
Earnings: ($15,343,000)
Emp.: 222
Fiscal Year-end: 12/31/22
Real-Time, High Fidelity Training Simulators Mfr
N.A.I.C.S.: 334610
Gill R. Grady *(Sr VP-Corp Bus Dev & Acquisition Integration)*
Bahram Meyssami *(CTO)*
Daniel W. Pugh *(Chief Legal & Risk Officer & Sec)*
Emmett A. Pepe *(CFO)*
Ravi Khanna *(Pres & CEO)*
Kathryn O'Connor Gardner *(Chm)*
Don Horn *(Pres-Engrg Svcs)*
Greg Hietpas *(Pres-DP Engrg)*
Brian Greene *(VP-Nuclear Industry Trng & Consulting Bus)*

Subsidiaries:

Absolute Consulting, Inc.   **(1)**
7552 Navarre Pkwy Ste 63, Navarre, FL 32566
Tel.: (850) 939-8965
Web Site: http://www.absoluteconsulting.com
Human Resource Consulting Services

N.A.I.C.S.: 541612

GSE Power Systems AB   **(1)**
Repslagaregatan 43 A, PO Box 62, Nykoping, 61122, Sweden   **(100%)**
Tel.: (46) 0015578700
Web Site: http://www.gses.com
Sales Range: Less than $1 Million
Emp.: 30
N.A.I.C.S.: 541512

Hyperspring, LLC   **(1)**
400 Meridian St Ste 105, Huntsville, AL 35801   **(100%)**
Tel.: (256) 772-3636
Web Site: http://www.hyperspring.com
Sales Range: $10-24.9 Million
Staff Augmentation, Training & Development & Plant Operations Support Services
N.A.I.C.S.: 561499

True North Consulting LLC   **(1)**
150 Merchant Dr, Montrose, CO 81401
Tel.: (970) 252-1832
Web Site: http://www.gses.com
Engineeering Services
N.A.I.C.S.: 541330

GSI TECHNOLOGY, INC.

1213 Elko Dr, Sunnyvale, CA 94089
Tel.: (408) 331-8800   DE
Web Site:
   https://www.gsitechnology.com
Year Founded: 1995
GSIT—(NASDAQ)
Rev.: $21,765,000
Assets: $42,464,000
Liabilities: $6,494,000
Net Worth: $35,970,000
Earnings: ($20,087,000)
Emp.: 148
Fiscal Year-end: 03/31/24
Static Random Access Memory Products Designer, Developer & Marketer
N.A.I.C.S.: 334413
Lee-Lean Shu *(Co-Founder, Chm, Pres & CEO)*
Didier Lasserre *(VP-Sls)*
Douglas M. Schirle *(CFO)*
Robert Yau *(Co-Founder, Sec & VP-Engrg)*

GSV, INC.

191 Post Rd, Westport, CT 06880
Tel.: (203) 221-2690   DE
GSVI—(OTCIQ)
Oil & Gas Exploration Services
N.A.I.C.S.: 213112
Gilad Gat *(Pres & CEO)*
Sagi Matza *(Chm)*

GT BIOPHARMA, INC.

315 Montgomery St 10th Fl, San Francisco, CA 94104
Tel.: (415) 919-4040   DE
Web Site:
   https://www.gtbiopharma.com
Year Founded: 1993
GTBP—(NASDAQ)
Rev.: $292,000
Assets: $16,736,000
Liabilities: $5,002,000
Net Worth: $11,734,000
Earnings: ($20,884,000)
Emp.: 2
Fiscal Year-end: 12/31/22
Pharmaceutical Preparation Manufacturing
N.A.I.C.S.: 325412
Manu Ohri *(CFO)*
Bruce Wendel *(Vice Chm)*
Martin Schroeder *(CTO)*
Anthony J. Cataldo *(Founder & Pres)*

GUARANTY BANCSHARES, INC.

16475 Dallas Pkwy Ste 600, Addison, TX 75001
Tel.: (972) 447-0800   TX
Web Site: https://www.gnty.com

Year Founded: 1980
GNTY—(NYSE)
Rev.: $146,694,000
Assets: $3,351,495,000
Liabilities: $3,055,937,000
Net Worth: $295,558,000
Earnings: $40,447,000
Emp.: 494
Fiscal Year-end: 12/31/22
Bank Holding Company
N.A.I.C.S.: 551111
Tyson T. Abston *(Chm & CEO)*
Kirk L. Lee *(Pres)*
Sondra Cunningham *(Sec)*
Shalene A. Jacobson *(CFO, Chief Risk Officer, Principal Acctg Officer & Exec VP)*
Cappy Payne *(Sr Exec VP)*
Shalene A. Jacobson *(CFO)*
Lisa Gallerano *(Exec VP)*
Travis Brown *(Exec Officer)*
Robert P. Sharp *(Chief Risk Officer & Exec VP)*
Harold E. Lower II *(Sr Exec VP)*

Subsidiaries:

Guaranty Bank & Trust, N.A.   **(1)**
100 W Arkansas St, Mount Pleasant, TX 75455-4420   **(100%)**
Tel.: (903) 572-9881
Web Site: https://www.gnty.com
Sales Range: $50-74.9 Million
Emp.: 265
Federal Savings Bank
N.A.I.C.S.: 522180
Tyson T. Abston *(Chm, CEO & Sr VP)*
Kirk L. Lee *(Vice Chm & Chief Credit Officer)*
Sondra Cunningham *(Chief Culture Officer, Sec & Sr VP)*
Shalene A. Jacobson *(CFO & Exec VP)*
John F. Griesemer *(Executives)*
Lacy McMillen *(Sr VP-Trust Admin)*
Marco Valencia *(Officer)*
Meredith Biery *(Officer)*
Nate Walton *(Sr VP)*
Zac Jordan *(VP)*

GUARANTY CORPORATION

929 Government St, Baton Rouge, LA 70802-6089
Tel.: (225) 383-0355   LA
Year Founded: 1926
GRTYA—(OTCEM)
Sales Range: $150-199.9 Million
Emp.: 140
Holding Company
N.A.I.C.S.: 551112
John Lancaster *(Pres)*
G. A. Foster Jr. *(Chm)*

Subsidiaries:

Guaranty Broadcasting Company, LLC   **(1)**
929 Government St, Baton Rouge, LA 70802-6034   **(100%)**
Tel.: (225) 388-9898
Sales Range: $10-24.9 Million
Emp.: 100
Radio Broadcasting Stations
N.A.I.C.S.: 516110
Gordy Rush *(VP & Mgr-Mktg)*
T. J. Solis *(Dir-Sls)*

Guaranty Real Estate Management Company, LLC   **(1)**
929 Government St, Baton Rouge, LA 70802-6034   **(100%)**
Tel.: (225) 383-0355
Sales Range: $1-9.9 Million
Real Estate Management
N.A.I.C.S.: 524113
John Lancaster *(Pres & CEO-GILICO)*

GUARANTY FINANCIAL CORP.

4000 W Brown Deer Rd, Brown Deer, WI 53209
Tel.: (414) 362-4000
Web Site:
   http://www.guarantybank.com

Year Founded: 2002
GFCJ—(OTCIQ)
Bank Holding Company
N.A.I.C.S.: 551111
Gerald J. Levy *(Chm)*

GUARDANT HEALTH, INC.

3100 Hanover St, Palo Alto, CA 94304   DE
Web Site:
   https://www.guardanthealth.com
Year Founded: 2011
GH—(NASDAQ)
Rev.: $563,948,000
Assets: $1,786,421,000
Liabilities: $1,627,737,000
Net Worth: $158,684,000
Earnings: ($479,449,000)
Emp.: 1,768
Fiscal Year-end: 12/31/23
Biotechnology Research & Development Services
N.A.I.C.S.: 541714
Terilyn Juarez Monroe *(Chief People Officer)*
Kumud Kalia *(CIO)*
Darya Chudova *(CTO)*
Daniel Simon *(Sr VP-Biopharma Bus Dev)*
Andy Ament *(Sr VP-Ops)*
Steven Collora *(VP-Sls)*
Bill Getty *(VP-Comml)*
Michael Bell *(CFO)*
John Saia *(Gen Counsel, Sec & Sr VP)*
Craig Eagle *(Chief Medical Officer)*
Chris Freeman *(Chief Comml Officer)*
Helmy Eltoukhy *(Co-Founder, Chm & Co-CEO)*
AmirAli Talasaz *(Co-Founder & Co-CEO)*

GUARDION HEALTH SCIENCES, INC.

2925 Richmond Ave Ste 1200, Houston, TX 77098
Tel.: (858) 605-9055   DE
Web Site:
   https://www.guardionhealth.com
Year Founded: 2009
GHSI—(NASDAQ)
Rev.: $11,049,772
Assets: $21,686,068
Liabilities: $13,768,146
Net Worth: $7,917,922
Earnings: ($14,922,228)
Emp.: 12
Fiscal Year-end: 12/31/22
Medical Product Mfr & Distr
N.A.I.C.S.: 325412
Katherine Cox *(Chief Acctg Officer)*

Subsidiaries:

VectorVision Ocular Health, Inc.   **(1)**
1850 Livingston Rd Ste E, Greenville, OH 45331
Tel.: (937) 548-7970
Web Site: https://www.vectorvision.com
Ophthalmic Goods Whslr
N.A.I.C.S.: 423460
David W. Evans *(Founder)*
Tamara Evans *(Co-Founder & VP-Mktg)*
Brian E. Wilson *(VP-Ops)*

GUERRILLA RF, INC.

2000 Pisgah Church Rd, Greensboro, NC 27455
Tel.: (336) 510-7840   DE
Web Site: https://www.guerrilla-rf.com
Year Founded: 2020
GUER—(OTCIQ)
Rev.: $11,600,904
Assets: $16,664,216
Liabilities: $14,309,323
Net Worth: $2,354,893
Earnings: ($12,026,766)
Emp.: 68

Guerrilla RF, Inc.—(Continued)

Fiscal Year-end: 12/31/22
Miscellaneous Financial Investment
Activities
N.A.I.C.S.: 523999
Ryan Pratt *(Founder, Chm & CEO)*
Mark Mason *(COO)*
John Berg *(CFO)*
Jeff Broxson *(VP-Sales)*
Samuel Funchess Sr. *(VP-IR)*

Subsidiaries:

Guerrilla RF Operating
Corporation   **(1)**
1196 Pleasant Ridge Rd, Greensboro, NC
27409   **(100%)**
Tel.: (336) 510-7840
Web Site: https://www.guerrilla-rf.com
Computer Hardware Product Distr
N.A.I.C.S.: 444140
Ryan Pratt *(Founder & CEO)*
Mark Mason *(COO)*
John Berg *(CFO)*
Jeff Broxson *(VP-Sls)*
Kellie Chong *(Chief Bus Officer)*

GUESS? INC.

1444 S Alameda St, Los Angeles, CA
90021
Tel.: (213) 765-5578   **DE**
Web Site:
  https://investors.guess.com
Year Founded: 1981
GES—(NYSE)
Rev.: $2,687,350,000
Assets: $2,425,448,000
Liabilities: $1,852,697,000
Net Worth: $572,751,000
Earnings: $149,610,000
Emp.: 12,500
Fiscal Year-end: 01/28/23
Holding Company; Men's, Women's
& Children's Clothing Designer, Mar-
keter, Distr, Online Retailer & Licen-
sor
N.A.I.C.S.: 551112
Carlos E. Alberini *(CEO)*
Alex Yemenidjian *(Chm)*
Fabrice Benarouche *(Chief Acctg Of-
ficer & Sr VP-Finance & Investor Re-
lations)*
Dennis R. Secor *(Interim CFO &
Exec VP-Fin)*

Subsidiaries:

Beziers Polygone Sarl   **(1)**
3 carrefour de l Hours, 34500, Beziers,
France
Tel.: (33) 467097550
Web Site: http://www.polygone-beziers.com
Fashion Apparels Retailer
N.A.I.C.S.: 458110

G-LABS SAGL   **(1)**
Via Luigi Lavizzari 12, 6830, Chiasso, Swit-
zerland
Tel.: (41) 916827878
Web Site: https://www.glab.ch
Software Development Services
N.A.I.C.S.: 513210

Guess? Europe Sagl   **(1)**
Strada Regina 44, 6934, Bioggio, Switzer-
land
Tel.: (41) 918095000
Web Site: https://www.guess.eu
Emp.: 640
Fashion Apparel Designer & Distr
N.A.I.C.S.: 458110

Guess? Italia, Srl   **(1)**
Via Por Santa Maria 38, Florence, Italy
Tel.: (39) 0552657972
Web Site: http://www.ripe.net
Sales Range: $100-124.9 Million
Clothing Accessory Distr
N.A.I.C.S.: 458110
Nello Rocchetti *(Pres)*

Guess? Portugal, LDA   **(1)**
R Miguel Serrano n 9 - 6, Miraflores Alges,
1495-173, Lisbon, Portugal

Tel.: (351) 210004500
Family Clothing Store Operator
N.A.I.C.S.: 458110

Guess.com, Inc.   **(1)**
1444 S Alameda St, Los Angeles, CA
90021-2433
Tel.: (213) 765-3100
Web Site: http://www.guess.com
Sales Range: $125-149.9 Million
Emp.: 80
Online Apparel Retailer
N.A.I.C.S.: 458110

Guess? Asia Limited   **(1)**
Shop 2607 Level 2 Gateway Arcade, Har-
bour City, Tsim Tsa Tsui, 2630 3373, China
(Hong Kong)
Tel.: (852) 22680099
Web Site: https://www.guess.hk
Sales Range: $100-124.9 Million
Clothing Accessory Distr
N.A.I.C.S.: 458110

Guess? Canada Corporation   **(1)**
12225 Boul Industriel Suite 14, Pointe Aux
Trembles, Quebec, H1B 5M7, QC,
Canada   **(100%)**
Tel.: (781) 575-2879
Clothing Accessory Distr
N.A.I.C.S.: 458110

Guess? Deutschland GmbH   **(1)**
Heegbarg 31, Kaufmannshaus, 22391,
Hamburg, Germany   **(100%)**
Tel.: (49) 4069796278
Web Site: http://www.guess.eu
Clothing Accessory Distr
N.A.I.C.S.: 458110

GUGGENHEIM CREDIT ALLO-
CATION FUND

227 W Monroe St, Chicago, IL
60606
GGM—(NYSE)
Rev.: $18,533,024
Assets: $207,745,989
Liabilities: $61,316,122
Net Worth: $146,429,867
Earnings: $14,041,526
Fiscal Year-end: 05/31/19
Investment Management Service
N.A.I.C.S.: 525990
Byron Scott Minerd *(Mgr-Fund)*

GUGGENHEIM ENHANCED
EQUITY INCOME FUND

227 W Monroe St, Chicago, IL
60606
GPM—(NYSE)
Hev.: $10,179,992
Assets: $568,650,149
Liabilities: $182,990,923
Net Worth: $385,659,226
Earnings: ($86,751)
Fiscal Year-end: 12/31/19
Investment Management Service
N.A.I.C.S.: 525990
Amy J. Lee *(Chief Legal Officer)*
Ronald E. Toupin Jr. *(Chm)*
Scott Barker *(Mgr-Fund)*

GUGGENHEIM STRATEGIC
OPPORTUNITIES FUND

227 W Monroe St, Chicago, IL 60606
Tel.: (312) 827-0100   **DE**
GOF—(NY3E)
Fund Management Services
N.A.I.C.S.: 523940

GUIDED THERAPEUTICS, INC.

5835 Peachtree Corners E Ste B,
Peachtree Corners, GA 30092
Tel.: (770) 242-8723
Web Site: https://www.guidedinc.com
GTHP—(OTCQB)
Rev.: $13,000
Assets: $3,366,000
Liabilities: $6,249,000
Net Worth: ($2,883,000)
Earnings: ($4,972,000)
Emp.: 6

Fiscal Year-end: 12/31/22
Surgical & Medical Instrument Manu-
facturing
N.A.I.C.S.: 339112
Mark L. Faupel *(Founder, Pres &
CEO)*
Michael C. James *(CFO)*

GUIDEWIRE SOFTWARE, INC.

970 Park Pl Ste 200, San Mateo, CA
94403
Tel.: (650) 357-9100   **DE**
Web Site: https://www.guidewire.com
Year Founded: 2001
GWRE—(NYSE)
Rev.: $980,497,000
Assets: $2,226,294,000
Liabilities: $883,562,000
Net Worth: $1,342,732,000
Earnings: ($6,103,000)
Emp.: 3,469
Fiscal Year-end: 07/31/24
Insurance Software Publisher
N.A.I.C.S.: 513210
Marcus S. Ryu *(Chm)*
Brian Desmond *(CMO)*
Mike Polelle *(Chief Delivery Officer)*
James Winston King *(Chief Admin
Officer, Gen Counsel & Sec)*
Paul Mang *(Chief Innovation Officer)*
Diego Devalle *(Chief Product Dev
Officer)*
Christina Colby *(Chief Customer Offi-
cer)*
Sinead Condon *(Sr VP-People)*
John Mullen *(Pres & Chief Revenue
Officer)*
David Laker *(CFO & Chief Sls Offi-
cer)*
Michael Howe *(Chief Product Officer)*
Diana Stott *(Dir-Comm)*
John Raguin *(Founder)*
Michael Rosenbaum *(CEO)*

Subsidiaries:

FirstBest Systems, Inc.   **(1)**
213 Burlington Rd, Bedford, MA 01730
Tel.: (781) 863-6000
Web Site: http://www.firstbest.com
Computer Technology Development Ser-
vices
N.A.I.C.S.: 541511
John O'Brien *(VP-Fin)*
Ellenmarie Rhone *(VP-HR)*
Julian Pelenur *(Co-Founder & CTO)*
John Belizaire *(Co-Founder & CEO)*

Guidewire Canada Ltd.   **(1)**
5050 Satellite Drive Suite 200, Mississauga,
L4W 0G1, ON, Canada
Tel.: (905) 267-3809
Web Site: https://www.guidewire.com
Software Development Services
N.A.I.C.S.: 541511

Guidewire Software (Beijing) Co.
Ltd.   **(1)**
14th Floor A Tower Pacific Century Place,
2A Workers Stadium Road North, Beijing,
100027, China
Tel.: (86) 1065876445
Web Site: http://www.guidewire.pl
Emp.: 6
Software Development Services
N.A.I.C.S.: 541511

Guidewire Software (Ireland)
Limited   **(1)**
No 1 Stemple Exchange, Blanchardstown
Corporate Park Ballycoolin, Dublin, D15,
K66D, Ireland
Tel.: (353) 19072024
Insurance Software Publisher
N.A.I.C.S.: 513210

Guidewire Software (Malaysia) Sdn.
BHD   **(1)**
Suite 29-2 Level 29 Tower B The Vertical
Corporate Towers, Avenue 10 Bangsar
South No 8 Jalan Kerinchi, 59200, Kuala
Lumpur, Malaysia
Tel.: (60) 327718660

Software Development Services
N.A.I.C.S.: 513210

Guidewire Software (Switzerland)
GmbH   **(1)**
4th Floor Bahnhofstrasse 100, Zurich, 8001,
Switzerland
Tel.: (41) 445627147
Web Site: http://www.guidewire.pl
Software Development Services
N.A.I.C.S.: 541511

Guidewire Software Asia Ltd.   **(1)**
1901 19th Fl lee Garden One 33 Hysan
Avenue Causeway, Hong Kong, China
(Hong Kong)
Tel.: (852) 9700 6761
Web Site: http://www.guidewire.com
Emp.: 9
Insurance Software Publisher
N.A.I.C.S.: 513210

Guidewire Software Canada Ltd.   **(1)**
5050 Satellite Drive Suite 200, Mississauga,
L4W 0G1, ON, Canada
Tel.: (905) 267-3809
Insurance Software Publisher
N.A.I.C.S.: 513210

Guidewire Software Denmark
ApS   **(1)**
Flaesketorvet 28, 1711, Copenhagen, Den-
mark
Tel.: (45) 53537892
Software Development Services
N.A.I.C.S.: 513210

Guidewire Software France SAS   **(1)**
Regus Opera 27 avenue de l Opera,
75001, Paris, France
Tel.: (33) 170385100
Web Site: https://www.guidewire.com
Insurance Software Publisher
N.A.I.C.S.: 513210

Guidewire Software GmbH   **(1)**
Hopfenstrasse 8, 80335, Munich, Germany
Tel.: (49) 89206054210
Web Site: https://www.guidewire.com
Emp.: 1
Insurance Software Publisher
N.A.I.C.S.: 513210

Guidewire Software Japan K.K.   **(1)**
19th Floor Kabukiza Tower 4-12-15 Ginza,
Chuo-ku, Tokyo, 104-0061, Japan
Tel.: (81) 345904500
Web Site: http://www.guidewire.jp
Insurance Software Publisher
N.A.I.C.S.: 513210

Guidewire Software Ltd.   **(1)**
4th Floor 9 Cloak Lane, London, EC4R
2RU, United Kingdom
Tel.: (44) 2070427750
Emp.: 100
Insurance Software Publisher
N.A.I.C.S.: 513210

Guidewire Software Pty. Ltd.   **(1)**
Suite 1 - L2 345 George Stree, Sydney,
2000, NSW, Australia
Tel.: (61) 284884800
Insurance Software Publisher
N.A.I.C.S.: 513210

Millbrook, Inc.   **(1)**
191 Sheree Blvd, Exton, PA 19341
Tel.: (484) 816-0196
Web Site: http://www.millbrookinc.com
Sales Range: $1-9.9 Million
Emp.: 20
Data Processing, Hosting & Related Ser-
vices
N.A.I.C.S.: 518210

GULF COAST ULTRA DEEP
ROYALTY TRUST

601 Travis St 16th Fl, Houston, TX
77002
Tel.: (512) 236-6555   **DE**
Web Site:
  https://www.gultu.q4web.com
Year Founded: 2012
GULTU—(OTCIQ)
Rev.: $2,472,908
Assets: $2,310,845
Liabilities: $1,065,351

Net Worth: $1,245,494
Earnings: $1,842,816
Fiscal Year-end: 12/31/22
Oil & Gas Investment Services
N.A.I.C.S.: 213112
Sarah C. Newell *(VP)*

GULF ISLAND FABRICATION, INC.
2170 Buckthorne Pl Ste 420, The Woodlands, TX 77380
Tel.: (713) 714-6100   LA
Web Site: https://www.gulfisland.com
Year Founded: 1985
GIFI—(NASDAQ)
Rev.: $142,320,000
Assets: $134,866,000
Liabilities: $32,242,000
Net Worth: $102,624,000
Earnings: ($3,352,000)
Emp.: 874
Fiscal Year-end: 12/31/22
Oil & Gas Pipeline & Related Structures Construction
N.A.I.C.S.: 237120
Michael A. Flick *(Chm)*
Westley S. Stockton *(CFO, Principal Acctg Officer, Treas, Sec & Exec VP)*
Richard W. Heo *(Pres & CEO)*
Thomas M. Smouse *(Chief HR Officer & VP)*

Subsidiaries:

Dolphin Services, LLC   (1)
400 Thompson Rd, Houma, LA 70363
Tel.: (985) 851-5130
Web Site: http://www.gulfisland.com
Sales Range: $25-49.9 Million
Emp.: 100
Inshore & Offshore Drilling Platform Construction
N.A.I.C.S.: 238120

Gulf Island Shipyards, LLC   (1)
301 Gulf Island Rd, Houma, LA 70361
Tel.: (985) 872-2305
Ship Building & Repair Services
N.A.I.C.S.: 336611
Jay Hebert *(VP)*
Cliff Long *(Gen Mgr-Houma)*

Gulf Island, LLC   (1)
583 Thompson Rd, Houma, LA 70363
Tel.: (985) 872-2100
Web Site: http://www.gulfisland.com
Sales Range: $10-24.9 Million
Emp.: 100
Offshore Drilling & Production Platform Structural Steel Fabrication
N.A.I.C.S.: 238120

Gulf Marine Fabricators, L.P.   (1)
1982 FM 2725, Aransas Pass, TX 78336
Tel.: (361) 775-4600
Web Site: http://www.gulfisland.com
Sales Range: $100-124.9 Million
Emp.: 1,000
Offshore Drilling Platform Construction & Service
N.A.I.C.S.: 238120

GULF WEST SECUTIRY NETWORK, INC.
2851 Johnson St Unit Ste 194, Lafayette, LA 70503
Tel.: (337) 210-8790   NV
Web Site:
http://www.gulfwestsecurity.com
Year Founded: 2013
GWSN—(OTCIQ)
Rev.: $9,980
Assets: $47,475
Liabilities: $3,056,344
Net Worth: ($3,008,869)
Earnings: ($291,471)
Emp.: 1
Fiscal Year-end: 12/31/21
Security Services
N.A.I.C.S.: 561621
Louis J. Resweber *(Chm, Pres, CEO, CFO & Sec)*

GULFPORT ENERGY CORPORATION
713 Market Dr, Oklahoma City, OK 73114
Tel.: (405) 252-4600   DE
Web Site:
https://www.gulfportenergy.com
Year Founded: 1997
GPOR—(NYSE)
Rev.: $1,791,702,000
Assets: $3,267,613,000
Liabilities: $1,105,933,000
Net Worth: $2,161,680,000
Earnings: $1,253,716,000
Emp.: 226
Fiscal Year-end: 12/31/23
Oil & Natural Gas Exploration & Production Services
N.A.I.C.S.: 211120
Lester Zitkus *(Sr VP-Land)*
Michael L. Hodges *(CFO & Exec VP)*
Jessica Antle *(Dir-IR)*
Matthew Rucker *(Sr VP-Ops)*
Michael J. Sluiter *(Sr VP)*
Patrick K. Craine *(Chief Legal Officer)*
John K. Reinhart *(Pres & CEO)*

Subsidiaries:

GRUS, LLC   (1)
401 N Industrial Blvd, Lindsay, OK 73052
Tel.: (405) 756-0060
Oil & Gas Exploration Services
N.A.I.C.S.: 213112

GULFSLOPE ENERGY, INC.
1000 Main St Ste 2300, Houston, TX 77002
Tel.: (281) 918-4100   DE
Web Site: https://www.gulfslope.com
Year Founded: 2003
GSPE—(OTCIQ)
Rev.: $1,085
Assets: $13,698,485
Liabilities: $13,638,650
Net Worth: $59,835
Earnings: ($2,226,319)
Emp.: 7
Fiscal Year-end: 09/30/21
Crude Oil & Natural Gas Extraction Services
N.A.I.C.S.: 211120
John N. Seitz *(Chm, Interim Pres, CEO & COO)*
Charles G. Hughes *(VP-Land)*
John H. Malanga *(CFO & VP)*
Felix Acree *(VP-Engrg & Bus Dev)*

GUNTHER GRANT, INC.
509 Brightwater St, Henderson, NV 89014
Tel.: (631) 413-5813   DE
Web Site:
https://www.gunthergrant.com
Year Founded: 2004
GNGR—(OTCIQ)
Silver & Gold Jewelry Casting Product Mfr
N.A.I.C.S.: 339910
Grant Newsteder *(CEO)*

GUOZI ZHONGYU CAPITAL HOLDINGS COMPANY
18818 Teller Ave Ste 115, Irvine, CA 92612
Tel.: (310) 890-2209   NV
Year Founded: 2003
GZCC—(OTCIQ)
Rev.: $1,674
Assets: $6,000
Liabilities: $38,838
Net Worth: ($32,838)
Earnings: ($68,562)
Emp.: 1
Fiscal Year-end: 12/31/19
Investment Services
N.A.I.C.S.: 523999

Long Chen *(CEO)*
Qiulin Shi *(CFO)*
Lichen Guo *(Sec)*
Zhicheng Rao *(Co-Chm)*
Shifei Wang *(Co-Chm)*

GUSHEN, INC.
3445 Lawrence Ave, Oceanside, NY 11572
Tel.: (646) 768-8417   NV
Year Founded: 2015
GSHN—(OTCIQ)
Liabilities: $17,524
Net Worth: ($17,524)
Earnings: ($28,705)
Fiscal Year-end: 04/30/21
Managerial & IT Support Services
N.A.I.C.S.: 561499
Pengfei Zhou *(Chm, Pres, CEO, CFO, Treas & Sec)*

GUSKIN GOLD CORP.
Tel.: (408) 766-1511   NV
Web Site:
https://www.guskingold.com
Year Founded: 2010
GKIN—(OTCQB)
Rev.: $2,359,373
Assets: $167,913
Liabilities: $2,737,351
Net Worth: ($2,569,438)
Earnings: $1,985,803
Fiscal Year-end: 09/30/23
Junior Mining Company
N.A.I.C.S.: 213114
Francis Lovebridge Agezo *(Dir-Exploration)*
Naana Asante *(Founder, Pres, CEO & Sec)*
Samuel Jojo Andrews *(Gen Counsel)*

GUYANA GOLD CORP.
220 Bowen Way, Covington, GA 30016
Tel.: (404) 661-2389   NV
Year Founded: 2004
GYGC—(OTCIQ)
Gold Mining Services
N.A.I.C.S.: 212220
Simon Okeke *(Pres & COO)*
Frank Lkechukwu Igwealor *(Chm & Controller)*

GWG HOLDINGS, INC.
325 N St Paul St Ste 2650, Dallas, TX 75201
Tel.: (612) 746-1944   DE
Web Site: http://www.gwgh.com
Year Founded: 2006
GWGH—(NASDAQ)
Rev.: $124,371,000
Assets: $3,564,957,000
Liabilities: $3,124,143,000
Net Worth: $440,814,000
Earnings: ($168,545,000)
Emp.: 160
Fiscal Year-end: 12/31/20
Fire Insurance Services
N.A.I.C.S.: 524113
Dan Callahan *(Dir-Comm)*
Merriah Harkins *(Exec VP-Retail Capital Markets)*
Jenniffer Daigle *(Sr VP-Accounts-Natl)*
Christina Granada *(VP-Due Diligence)*
Peter Anderson *(VP-Sls & Bus Dev)*
Matthew Paine *(Sr VP-Sls & Trng)*
Michele Drummond *(VP-Accounts-Natl)*
Kyla Hoppe *(Asst VP-Accounts-Natl)*
Michael A. Tucker *(CFO)*

Subsidiaries:

Beneficient   (1)

325 N Saint Paul St Ste 4850, Dallas, TX 75201
Tel.: (214) 445-4700
Web Site: https://www.trustben.com
Rev.: $4,791,000
Assets: $368,501,000
Liabilities: $309,567,000
Net Worth: $58,934,000
Earnings: ($2,658,180,000)
Emp.: 80
Fiscal Year-end: 03/31/2024
Asset Management Services
N.A.I.C.S.: 523940
Brad K. Heppnar *(Chm & CEO)*
Derek Fletcher *(Pres, Chief Fiduciary Officer & Dir-Wealth Strategies)*
Greg Ezell *(CFO)*
Scott Wilson *(Chief Underwriting Officer)*
Maria Rutledge *(CTO)*

Subsidiary (Domestic):

Avalon Acquisition Inc.   (2)
2 Embarcadero Ctr 8th Fl, San Francisco, CA 94111
Tel.: (415) 423-0010
Web Site: https://www.avalonspac.com
Rev.: $4,087
Assets: $211,668,654
Liabilities: $226,823,590
Net Worth: ($15,154,936)
Earnings: $3,813,684
Emp.: 3
Fiscal Year-end: 12/31/2021
Investment Services
N.A.I.C.S.: 523999
S. Craig Cognetti *(CEO)*
John Griff *(Pres)*
R. Rachel Hsu *(CFO)*

GXO LOGISTICS, INC.
2 American Ln, Greenwich, CT 06831
Tel.: (203) 489-1287   DE
GXO—(NYSE)
Rev.: $9,778,000,000
Assets: $9,507,000,000
Liabilities: $6,561,000,000
Net Worth: $2,945,999,999
Earnings: $229,000,000
Emp.: 87,000
Fiscal Year-end: 12/31/23
Logistics & Warehousing Services
N.A.I.C.S.: 541614
Marlene M. Colucci *(Vice Chm)*
Malcolm Wilson *(CEO)*

Subsidiaries:

PFSweb, Inc.   (1)
9250 N Royal Ln Ste 100, Irving, TX 75063
Tel.: (972) 881-2900
Web Site: https://www.pfscommerce.com
Rev.: $295,122,000
Assets: $204,662,000
Liabilities: $118,438,000
Net Worth: $86,224,000
Earnings: ($16,558,000)
Emp.: 1,352
Fiscal Year-end: 12/31/2022
E-Commerce & Logistics Solutions Company
N.A.I.C.S.: 541512
Zeeshan Naqvi *(Pres & Treas)*
Karlis Kirsis *(Sec & VP)*

Subsidiary (Domestic):

CrossView, Inc.   (2)
505 Millennium Dr, Allen, TX 75013
Tel.: (972) 881-2900
Web Site: http://www.crossview.com
Administrative Management Consulting Services
N.A.I.C.S.: 541611

LiveAreaLabs,   (2)
3131 Western Ave Ste 515, Seattle, WA 98121
Tel.: (206) 659-5227
Web Site: http://www.livearealabs.com
E-Commerce Website Designing Services
N.A.I.C.S.: 541511

REV Solutions Inc.   (2)
10400 Viking Dr Ste 500, Eden Prairie, MN 55344
Tel.: (952) 746-6005
Emp.: 135

GXO Logistics, Inc.—(Continued)

Software Development Services
N.A.I.C.S.: 541511
Steve Stephan (Pres)

Subsidiary (Non-US):

REVTECH Solutions India Private Limited (2)
8th floor Block 1 Bhartiya City Milestone Buildcon SEZ, Chokkanahalli Village, Bengaluru, 560 064, India
Tel.: (91) 8067430000
Web Site: http://www.pfsweb.com
Emp.: 93
Software Development Services
N.A.I.C.S.: 541511

Supplies Distributors S.A. (2)
Rue Louis Bleriot no 5 Zoning Industriel Liege Logistics, 4460, Grace-Hollogne, Liege, Belgium
Tel.: (32) 43644111
Web Site: http://www.pfsweb.com
Sales Range: $25-49.9 Million
Emp.: 600
Printing Equipment & Supplies Distr
N.A.I.C.S.: 333248

Wincanton plc (1)
Methuen Park, Chippenham, SN14 0WT, Wiltshire, United Kingdom
Tel.: (44) 1249710000
Web Site: http://www.wincanton.co.uk
Rev.: $1,929,863,208
Assets: $925,014,636
Liabilities: $838,663,644
Net Worth: $86,350,992
Earnings: $65,034,788
Emp.: 20,152
Fiscal Year-end: 03/31/2022
Holding Company; Integrated Supply Chain Services
N.A.I.C.S.: 551112
Adrian Colman (Co-CEO)
Martin Read (Chm)
James Wroath (Co-CEO)
Sally Austin (Chief HR Officer)
Lyn Colloff (Sec)
Daniel Porte (Mng Dir)

Subsidiary (Domestic):

Wincanton Group Limited (2)
Methuen Park, Chippenham, SN14 0WT, Wilts, United Kingdom
Tel.: (44) 1249710000
Web Site: http://www.wincanton.co.uk
Emp.: 100
Integrated Supply Chain Services
N.A.I.C.S.: 484110
Richard Bell (Gen Mgr)

Subsidiary (Domestic):

Wincanton Holdings Limited (3)
Methuen Park, Chippenham, SN14 0WT, Wilts, United Kingdom
Tel.: (44) 1249710000
Emp.: 500
Holding Company
N.A.I.C.S.: 551112

Wincanton International Limited (3)
Methuen Park, Chippenham, SN14 0WT, Wilts, United Kingdom
Tel.: (44) 1249710000
Holding Company
N.A.I.C.S.: 551112
Adrian Colman (Mng Dir)

Wincanton UK Limited (3)
Methuen Park, Chippenham, SN14 0WT, Wilts, United Kingdom
Tel.: (44) 1249710000
Web Site: http://www.wincanton.co.uk
Integrated Supply Chain Services
N.A.I.C.S.: 484110

GYRODYNE, LLC
1 Flowerfield Ste 24, Saint James, NY 11780
Tel.: (631) 584-5400   NY
Web Site: https://www.gyrodyne.com
GYRO—(NASDAQ)
Assets: $40,907,831,000
Liabilities: $18,419,887,000
Net Worth: $22,487,944,000

Emp.: 4
Fiscal Year-end: 12/31/20
Real Estate Investment Services
N.A.I.C.S.: 523999
Peter Pitsiokos (COO, Chief Compliance Officer, Sec & Exec VP)
Gary J. Fitlin (Pres, CEO, CFO & Treas)
Paul L. Lamb (Chm)

GZ6G TECHNOLOGIES CORP.
1 Technology Dr Bldg B Ste no B123, Irvine, CA 92618
Tel.: (949) 872-1965   NV
Web Site: https://www.gz6g.com
GZIC—(OTCQB)
Rev.: $221,946
Assets: $1,372,732
Liabilities: $10,064,615
Net Worth: ($8,691,883)
Earnings: ($6,871,020)
Emp.: 14
Fiscal Year-end: 12/31/22
Information Technology Services
N.A.I.C.S.: 541519

H&E EQUIPMENT SERVICES, INC.
7500 Pecue Ln, Baton Rouge, LA 70809
Tel.: (225) 298-5200   DE
Web Site: https://www.he-equipment.com
Year Founded: 1971
HEES—(NASDAQ)
Rev.: $1,244,518,000
Assets: $2,291,699,000
Liabilities: $1,890,657,000
Net Worth: $401,042,000
Earnings: $132,170,000
Emp.: 2,375
Fiscal Year-end: 12/31/22
Equipment Distr; Rentals, Sales, Parts & Service of Construction, Mining & Industrial Equipment
N.A.I.C.S.: 236210
John Martindale Engquist (Chm)
Bradley W. Barber (CEO)
Jeffrey L. Chastain (VP-IR)
John McDowell Engquist (Pres & COO)
Leslie S. Magee (CFO & Sec)

Subsidiaries:

H&E Equipment Services (California), LLC (1)
6006 Miramar Rd, San Diego, CA 92121
Tel.: (619) 938-1966
Construction Machinery Equipment Whslr
N.A.I.C.S.: 423810

H&E Equipment Services (Mid-Atlantic), Inc. (1)
10409 Success St, Ashland, VA 23005
Tel.: (804) 798-9740
Heavy Machinery & Equipment Rental Services
N.A.I.C.S.: 532412

H&E Equipment Services (Midwest), Inc. (1)
H&E Rentals 5520 W 96th St, Zionsville, IN 46077
Tel.: (317) 733-8010
Heavy Construction Equipment Distr
N.A.I.C.S.: 423840

H&E Equipment Services Inc. - Phoenix (1)
4010 S 22nd St, Phoenix, AZ 85040
Tel.: (602) 232-0600
Web Site: http://www.he-equipment.com
Heavy Equipment Rentals & Sales Services
N.A.I.C.S.: 532412
Matt Phelps (Mgr-Rental)
Neil Dauphinais (Mgr-Parts)
Tom Dunlap (Coord-Parts)
Dan Keck (Asst Mgr-Fire Truck Svc)
Scott DeLay (Branch Mgr)
Chris Douglas (Coord-Parts)
David Heinz (Mgr-Svc)

H&E Equipment Services LLC (1)
1301 Rockland Ave NW, Roanoke, VA 24012
Tel.: (540) 362-3600
Web Site: http://www.heequipment.com
Sales Range: $150-199.9 Million
Emp.: 33
Construction Equipment Distr
N.A.I.C.S.: 423810

H&R BLOCK, INC.
1 H&R Block Way, Kansas City, MO 64105
Tel.: (816) 854-3000   MO
Web Site: https://www.hrblock.com
Year Founded: 1955
HRB—(NYSE)
Rev.: $3,610,347,000
Assets: $3,218,810,000
Liabilities: $3,128,216,000
Net Worth: $90,594,000
Earnings: $595,317,000
Emp.: 4,200
Fiscal Year-end: 06/30/24
Holding Company; Income Tax Preparation, Temporary Help, Computer Information & Communications Services
N.A.I.C.S.: 551112
Robert A. Gerard (Chm)
Tiffany Scalzitti Monroe (Chief People & Culture Officer)
Kellie J. Logerwell (Chief Acctg Officer)
Alan Lowden (CIO & Sr VP)
Heather Watts (Sr VP-Consumer Tax Products & Support)
Jeffrey J. Jones II (Pres & CEO)
Jamil Khan (Chief Strategy & Dev Officer)
Roxane Harris (VP-Franchise Ops-US)
Bob Moretti (Sr VP-Retail Ops-US)
Les Whiting (Chief Financial Svcs Officer)
Tom Gannon (Chief Govt Rels Officer & VP)
Nicki Cole (VP-Tech, Small Bus & Fin Svcs)
Dara S. Redler (Chief Legal Officer)
Jill Cress (Chief Mktg & Experience Officer)
Amy Labroo (VP-Growth Mktg & Engagement)
Chris Linderwell (VP-Consumer Tax Products)
Mike Halvorsen (VP-Client Experience)
Tony Bisbiglia (VP--Central Market)
Jason Mann (VP-Retail Sls-Svc-West Market)
Wendy Fitch (VP-Brand-Content-Insights)
Shilpi Pathak (VP-Go-to-Market Strategy)
Tiffany L. Mason (CFO & Exec VP-Fin)

Subsidiaries:

Emerald Financial Services, LLC (1)
8870 N Himes Ave, Tampa, Fl 33614
Tel.: (813) 408-9133
Investment Advisory Services
N.A.I.C.S.: 523940

H&R Block (India) Private Limited (1)
3rd floor Plot No 461 No 36 Odyssey Mall, Jubilee Hills, Hyderabad, 500 033, Telangana, India
Tel.: (91) 4061656622
Web Site: http://www.hrblock.in
Tax Preparation Services
N.A.I.C.S.: 541213

H&R Block Group, Inc. (1)
4400 Main St, Kansas City, MO 64111-1812
Tel.: (816) 753-6900
Tax Preparation Services

N.A.I.C.S.: 541213

H&R Block Tax Resolution Services, Inc. (1)
445 Dolley Madison Rd 200, Greensboro, NC 27410
Tel.: (336) 601-3001
Software Development Services
N.A.I.C.S.: 541511

H&R Block Tax Services LLC (1)
4400 Main St, Kansas City, MO 64111-1812
Tel.: (816) 753-6900
Web Site: http://www.hrblock.com
Sales Range: $250-299.9 Million
Emp.: 1,200
Tax Return Preparation Services
N.A.I.C.S.: 541213

Subsidiary (Domestic):

H&R Block Company of Utah (2)
3865 Wasatch Blvd, Salt Lake City, UT 84109
Tel.: (801) 277-7566
Web Site: http://www.hrblock.com
Rev.: $14,500,000
Emp.: 4
Tax Return Preparation Services
N.A.I.C.S.: 541213

H&R Block Eastern Enterprises, Inc. (2)
7541 Wornall, Kansas City, MO 64114
Tel.: (816) 361-3900
Web Site: http://www.hrblock.com
Sales Range: $50-74.9 Million
Tax Return Preparation Services
N.A.I.C.S.: 541213

H&R Block Tax and Business Services, Inc. (1)
1331 N Wilmot Rd Ste 100, Tucson, AZ 85712
Tel.: (520) 327-6647
Web Site: http://www.hrblock.com
Emp.: 7
Tax Preparation & Related Services
N.A.I.C.S.: 541213

HRB Corporate Services LLC (1)
1 H & R Block Way, Kansas City, MO 64105
Tel.: (816) 854-4345
Tax Preparation & Related Services
N.A.I.C.S.: 541213

HRB Digital LLC (1)
1 H & R Block Way, Kansas City, MO 64105-1905
Tel.: (816) 854-5500
Tax Preparation & Related Services
N.A.I.C.S.: 541213

HRB Resources LLC (1)
Eastway Plz, Erie, PA 16510
Tel.: (816) 854-3000
Taxation Services
N.A.I.C.S.: 921130

H-D INTERNATIONAL HOLDINGS GROUP COMPANY
848 N Rainbow Blvd Ste 225, Las Vegas, NV 89107
Tel.: (214) 361-8812   NV
Year Founded: 2004
HDIH—(OTCIQ)
Data Processing Services
N.A.I.C.S.: 518210
Mike Roberts (Controller)

H.B. FULLER COMPANY
1200 Willow Lake Blvd, Saint Paul, MN 55110-5101
Tel.: (651) 236-5900   MN
Web Site: https://www.hbfuller.com
Year Founded: 1887
FUL—(NYSE)
Rev.: $3,510,934,000
Assets: $4,723,575,000
Liabilities: $2,967,662,000
Net Worth: $1,755,913,000
Earnings: $144,906,000

Emp.: 7,200
Fiscal Year-end: 12/02/23
Adhesives, Sealants, Coatings,
Paints & Other Chemical Products
Mfr & Sales
N.A.I.C.S.: 325520
Celeste Beeks Mastin *(Pres & CEO)*
Traci L. Jensen *(Chief Admin Officer & Exec VP)*
Robert J. Martsching *(VP & Controller)*
Zhiwei Cai *(Exec VP-Engrg Adhesives)*
Heidi Weiler *(Treas & VP)*
John J. Corkrean *(CFO & Exec VP)*
M. Shahbaz Malik *(Sr VP-Construction Adhesives-Global)*
Nathanial D. Weaver *(VP-Human Resources)*
Kirstin Hedin *(VP-Marketing-Hygiene,Health,Consumables Adhesives)*
James J. East *(Sr VP)*
Boz Malik *(Sr VP)*
Gregory Ogunsanya *(Gen Counsel, Sec & Sr VP)*

Subsidiaries:

Adecol Industria Quimica Ltda. (1)
Rua Supercor 87 Agua Chata Guarulhos,
Sao Paulo, 07251-450, Brazil
Tel.: (55) 1146100800
Web Site: http://www.hbfuller.com
Adhesive Product Mfr
N.A.I.C.S.: 325520

Adhezion Biomedical, LLC (1)
1 Meridian Blvd Ste 1B02, Wyomissing, PA 19610
Tel.: (484) 334-2929
Web Site: http://www.adhezion.com
Professional Equipment & Supplies Merchant Whslr
N.A.I.C.S.: 423490
Richard G. Jones *(Sr VP-Clinical)*

Apollo Chemicals Limited (1)
Sandy Way, Amington Industrial Estate,
Tamworth, B77 4DS, Staffordshire, United Kingdom
Tel.: (44) 182754281
Web Site: https://www.apollo.co.uk
Coating Product Mfr & Distr
N.A.I.C.S.: 325510

Apollo Roofing Solutions Limited (1)
Sandy Way, Amington Industrial Estate,
Tamworth, B77 4DS, United Kingdom
Tel.: (44) 182754281
Web Site:
    https://www.apolloroofingsolutions.co.uk
Roofing Material Mfr & Distr
N.A.I.C.S.: 332322

Beardow Adams A.B. (1)
Gasverksgatan 3, SE-261 35, Landskrona,
Sweden
Tel.: (46) 418395100
Packaging Adhesive Mfr & Distr
N.A.I.C.S.: 325520

Beardow Adams GmbH (1)
Vilbeler Landstr 20, D-60386, Frankfurt am
Main, Germany
Tel.: (49) 69401040
Packaging Adhesive Mfr & Distr
N.A.I.C.S.: 325520

**Beardow Adams Hot Melt Werk
GmbH** (1)
Kilianstadter Strasse 8, D-60386, Frankfurt
am Main, Germany
Tel.: (49) 69401040
Packaging Adhesive Mfr & Distr
N.A.I.C.S.: 325520

Beardow Adams OY (1)
Itamerenkatu 5, 00180, Helsinki, Finland
Tel.: (358) 447711440
Packaging Adhesive Mfr & Distr
N.A.I.C.S.: 325520

Beardow Adams S.A.S. (1)
CRA 13 38-65, OF 1003, Bogota, Colombia
Tel.: (57) 14660419
Packaging Adhesive Mfr & Distr

N.A.I.C.S.: 325520

**Beardow Adams do Brasil Adhesives
Ltda.** (1)
Av das Nacoes Unidas 14 171 - Marble
Tower 15 andar Salas 1561-1563, Chacara
Santo Antonio, Sao Paulo, CEP 04794-000,
Brazil
Tel.: (55) 11945560568
Packaging Adhesive Mfr & Distr
N.A.I.C.S.: 325520

**Beardow and Adams (Adhesives)
Limited** (1)
32 Blundells Road, Bradville England, Milton Keynes, MK13 7HF, United Kingdom
Tel.: (44) 1908574000
Packaging Adhesive Mfr & Distr
N.A.I.C.S.: 325520

BeardowAdams, Inc. (1)
3034 Horseshoe Ln, Charlotte, NC 28208
Tel.: (704) 359-8443
Packaging Adhesive Mfr & Distr
N.A.I.C.S.: 325520

Cyberbond, LLC (1)
9001 W Fey Dr, Frankfort, IL 60423
Tel.: (866) 525-6122
Web Site: http://www.cyberbond1.com
Adhesive Mfr & Sales
N.A.I.C.S.: 325520

Subsidiary (Non-US):

Cyberbond CS s.r.o. (2)
ul Generala Svobody 49/15, 460 01, Liberec, Nove Pavlovice, Czech Republic
Tel.: (420) 416 59 18 02
Web Site: http://www.cyberbond1.com
Adhesive Product Mfr
N.A.I.C.S.: 325520

Cyberbond Europe GmbH (2)
Werner-von-Siemens-Str 2, D-31515, Wunstorf, Germany
Tel.: (49) 503195660
Web Site: http://www.cyberbond.de
Adhesive Products Mfr & Sales
N.A.I.C.S.: 325520

Cyberbond France S.A.R.L. (2)
15 A Grand-rue, BP 30 213, 57282, Hauconcourt, France
Tel.: (33) 3 87 61 76 90
Web Site: http://www.cyberbond.eu.com
Adhesive Product Mfr
N.A.I.C.S.: 325520

Cyberbond Iberica S.L. (2)
Rambla Catalunya 49 Pral 2 a, 08007, Barcelona, Spain
Tel.: (34) 93 452 16 14
Web Site: http://www.cyberbond.eu.com
Adhesive Product Mfr
N.A.I.C.S.: 325520

Cyberbond UK Ltd (2)
Unit B1 TY Verlon Ind Est Cardiff Road,
Barry, CF63 2BG, United Kingdom
Tel.: (44) 29 20 59 58 18
Web Site: http://www.cyberbond1.com
Adhesive Product Mfr
N.A.I.C.S.: 325520

Engent, Inc. (1)
3140 Northwoods Pkwy Ste 300A, Norcross, GA 30071
Tel.: (678) 990-3320
Web Site: http://www.engentaat.com
Sales Range: $10-24.9 Million
Emp.: 45
Electronics Mfr
N.A.I.C.S.: 811210
Matt Perry *(Founder & Mng Dir)*
Giorgos Hatzilias *(Dir-Ops)*

Eternabond, LLC (1)
175 N Archer Ave, Mundelein, IL 60060-2310
Tel.: (517) 841-7106
Web Site: http://www.eternabond.com
Adhesive Tape Product Mfr
N.A.I.C.S.: 322220

Extreme Adhesives, LLC (1)
Tel.: (603) 895-4028
Web Site: https://www.pvctrimwelder.com
Adhesive Product Distr
N.A.I.C.S.: 424690
Ann Pecola *(Gen Mgr)*

Fourny NV (1)
Hoeikensstraat 1, 2830, Willebroek, Belgium
Tel.: (32) 38862770
Web Site: https://fourny.be
Adhesive Mfr & Distr
N.A.I.C.S.: 325520

**H.B. Fuller (China) Adhesives,
Ltd.** (1)
No 88 Hefeng Road, YongHe Industrial
Zone, Guangzhou, 510730, China
Tel.: (86) 2032106201
Web Site: http://www.hbfuller.com
Adhesive Mfr
N.A.I.C.S.: 325520

**H.B. Fuller (Guangzhou) Adhesives
Co., Ltd** (1)
No 88 Hefeng Road, YongHe Industrial
Zone, Guangzhou, 510730, China
Tel.: (86) 2032106201
Adhesive Product Mfr
N.A.I.C.S.: 325520

H.B. Fuller (Philippines), Inc. (1)
11 Gyro St LISP 1 Bo Diezmo, Cabuyao,
4025, Philippines   (100%)
Tel.: (63) 495548840
Web Site: http://www.na.hbfuller.com
Sales Range: $1-9.9 Million
Adhesives
N.A.I.C.S.: 325520

H.B. Fuller (Shanghai) Co. Ltd. (1)
Room 1002 Building C No 3 Lane 227
Dongyu Road, Pudong, Shanghai, 200126,
China
Tel.: (86) 2160363288
Adhesive Product Mfr
N.A.I.C.S.: 325520
Julia Feng *(Mgr-Fin Integration)*

H.B. Fuller (Thailand) Co., Ltd. (1)
8th Floor 615 Jit Uthai Building Ramkhamhaeng Road Huamark, Bangkok, Thailand
Tel.: (66) 23757442
Web Site: http://www.hbfuller.com
Adhesive Mfr
N.A.I.C.S.: 325520

**H.B. Fuller Adhesives France
SAS** (1)
56 Rue du General de Gaulle, 67250, Surbourg, France   (100%)
Tel.: (33) 80 091 7537
Web Site: http://www.hbfuller.com
Sales Range: $25-49.9 Million
Emp.: 66
Coatings & Adhesives Mfr
N.A.I.C.S.: 325520

**H.B. Fuller Adhesives Hong Kong
Limited** (1)
Unit 802B 8/F Fourseas Building 208-212
Nathan Road, Kowloon, China (Hong Kong)
Tel.: (852) 28329622
Adhesive Product Mfr
N.A.I.C.S.: 325520

**H.B. Fuller Adhesives Italia
S.p.A.** (1)
Via dell'Industria 8 San Lorenzo VI, 36060,
Pianezze, Italy
Tel.: (39) 0800985778
Adhesive & Sealant Mfr
N.A.I.C.S.: 325520

**H.B. Fuller Adhesives Netherlands
B.V.** (1)
Hoofdstraat 46, Genderen, 4265HL,
Netherlands   (100%)
Tel.: (31) 41 635 8200
Sales Range: $1-9.9 Million
Emp.: 15
Sales of Adhesives
N.A.I.C.S.: 424690

**H.B. Fuller Adhesives Romania
SRL** (1)
Sos Borsului Nr 40, 410605, Oradea, Romania
Tel.: (40) 259476807
Web Site: http://www.hbfuller.com
Adhesive & Sealant Distr
N.A.I.C.S.: 424690

H.B. Fuller Argentina, S.A.I.C (1)
Ruta 8 Km 60 Calle 3 No 1783 Parque Industrial Pilar, B1629MXA, Pilar, Buenos Ai-

res, Argentina   (2%)
Tel.: (54) 2304536650
Web Site: http://www.hbfuller.com.ar
Adhesive Mfr
N.A.I.C.S.: 325520

H.B. Fuller Belgie BVBA (1)
Avenue Louise 475, 1050, Brussels, Belgium
Tel.: (32) 25126798
Adhesive & Sealant Mfr & Distr
N.A.I.C.S.: 325520

H.B. Fuller Canada (partnership) (1)
21 Four Seasons Pl Ste 101, Toronto, M9B
6J8, ON, Canada
Tel.: (416) 641-4970
Adhesive & Sealant Mfr & Distr
N.A.I.C.S.: 325520

H.B. Fuller Centroamerica, S.A. (1)
Terracampus Office Center Third Floor, PO
Box 170-2250, Tres Rios, Cartago, Costa
Rica
Tel.: (506) 2 518 7500
Web Site: http://www.hbfuller.com
Industrial Adhesives Mfr
N.A.I.C.S.: 325520

H.B. Fuller Chile, S.A. (1)
Camino Lo Espejo 1350, Comuna de
Maipu, 925000, Santiago, Chile   (100%)
Tel.: (56) 225304600
Polymers Mfr
N.A.I.C.S.: 325520

H.B. Fuller Colombia S.A.S. (1)
300 mts Autopista Medellin - Bogota Centro
Ciudad Karga Fase II, Bodega 140 Antioquia, Rionegro, Colombia
Tel.: (57) 43788200
Web Site: http://www.hbfuller.com
Adhesive Product Mfr
N.A.I.C.S.: 325520

**H.B. Fuller Company Australia Pty.
Ltd.** (1)
16-22 Redgum Drive, Dandenong, 3175,
VIC, Australia   (100%)
Tel.: (61) 397976222
Web Site: https://www.hbfuller.com.au
Sales Range: $25-49.9 Million
Emp.: 110
Mfr of Adhesives
N.A.I.C.S.: 325520

Subsidiary (Non-US):

**H.B. Fuller (New Zealand)
Limited** (2)
49-51 Grayson Avenue, Papatoetoe, Auckland, 2241, New Zealand
Tel.: (64) 92779116
Adhesive Product Distr
N.A.I.C.S.: 424690

**H.B. Fuller Construction Products
Inc.** (1)
1105 S Frontenac, Aurora, IL 60504
Tel.: (630) 978-7766
Web Site: http://www.hbfuller-cp.com
Construction Machinery & Equipment Mfr &
Whslr
N.A.I.C.S.: 423810

Division (Domestic):

**H.B. Fuller Construction Products Inc.
- La Mirada** (2)
16421 Phoebe Ave, La Mirada, CA
90638-5615   (100%)
Tel.: (714) 523-5007
Web Site: http://www.hbfuller-cp.com
Sales Range: $25-49.9 Million
Emp.: 1
Powder Coatings
N.A.I.C.S.: 332117

**H.B. Fuller Deutschland Holding
GmbH** (1)
An der Roten Bleiche 2-4, 21335,
Luneburg, Germany
Tel.: (49) 41317050
Holding Company
N.A.I.C.S.: 551112

Subsidiary (Domestic):

**H.B. Fuller Adhesives Deutschland
GmbH** (2)

H.B. Fuller Company—(Continued)

Mallaustrasse 74, 68219, Mannheim, Germany **(100%)**
Tel.: (49) 80080150801
Sales Range: $25-49.9 Million
Emp.: 150
Mfr & Sales of Surface Materials, Coatings & Adhesives
N.A.I.C.S.: 325520

H.B. Fuller Deutschland GmbH **(2)**
An Der Roten Bleiche 2-3, 21335, Luneburg, Germany **(100%)**
Tel.: (49) 4 131 7050
Web Site: http://www.hbfuller.com
Sales Range: $50-74.9 Million
Mfr of Casein Cold Glue, Vegetable Glue, Dextrin, Synthetic Glues, Hotmelts, Packing Compounds
N.A.I.C.S.: 325520

H.B. Fuller Deutschland Produktions GmbH **(1)**
Henriettenstrasse 32, 31582, Nienburg, Germany
Tel.: (49) 80080150801
Emp.: 300
Investment Management Service
N.A.I.C.S.: 523940

H.B. Fuller Espana, S.A. **(1)**
Calle Rafael Altamira, 3002, Alicante, Spain **(100%)**
Tel.: (34) 80 009 9493
Specialty Chemicals Distr
N.A.I.C.S.: 424690

H.B. Fuller Greece S.A.I.C. **(1)**
51-53 Agamemnonos Street, Athens, 17675, Kallithea, Greece
Tel.: (30) 2109522981
Emp.: 26
Adhesive & Sealant Mfr
N.A.I.C.S.: 325520

H.B. Fuller Group Limited **(1)**
Globe Lane Industrial Estate Outram Road, Dukinfield, SK16 4XE, Cheshire, United Kingdom
Tel.: (44) 1616660666
Web Site: http://www.hbfuller.com
Emp.: 62
Chemical & Allied Products Mfr
N.A.I.C.S.: 325520

H.B. Fuller Hungary Kft. **(1)**
Gubacsi ut 6/c, 1097, Budapest, Hungary
Tel.: (36) 12190597
Adhesive Product Distr
N.A.I.C.S.: 424690
Andras Madi (Acct Mgr-Converting & Graphic Arts & Tobacco)

H.B. Fuller International, Inc. **(1)**
Unit 802B 8 F Fourseas Building Nos 2082 212 Nathan Road, Kowloon, China (Hong Kong) **(100%)**
Tel.: (852) 28329622
Web Site: http://www.hbfuller.com.hk
Sales Range: $10-24.9 Million
Emp.: 2
Area Office
N.A.I.C.S.: 325520
Marie Mak (Mgr-Fin)

H.B. Fuller Pension Trustees Limited **(1)**
Globe Lane Industrial Estate Outram Road, Dukinfield, SK16 4XE, Cheshire, United Kingdom
Tel.: (44) 1616660666
Financial Intermediation Services
N.A.I.O.O.: 520910

H.B. Fuller Poland Sp.Z.o.o. **(1)**
Ul Minska 63a, 03-828, Warsaw, Poland
Tel.: (48) 223308116
Emp.: 5
Industrial Supplies Whslr
N.A.I.C.S.: 423840

H.B. Fuller Rus Ltd. **(1)**
Building 1 Office 306 Elektrozavodskaya Street 24, 107023, Moscow, Russia
Tel.: (7) 4952210489
Web Site: http://www.hbfuller.com
Adhesive Product Mfr
N.A.I.C.S.: 325520

H.B. Fuller South Africa (Pty) Ltd. **(1)**

Yvonne House Office 5 Cnr Lucas and Scott Road, Bedfordview, 2008, Gauteng, South Africa
Tel.: (27) 11 792 6556
Chemical Products Mfr
N.A.I.C.S.: 325998

H.B. Fuller Taiwan Co., Ltd. **(1)**
3F No 250 Zhongshan Rd, Linkou Dist, New Taipei City, 24446, Taiwan **(100%)**
Tel.: (886) 226033385
Web Site: http://www.hpfuller.com
Sales Range: $10-24.9 Million
Mfr of Adhesives
N.A.I.C.S.: 325520
Jeff Huang (Gen Mgr)

Lemtapes OY **(1)**
Tikinmaantie 66, 37630, Valkeakoski, Finland
Tel.: (358) 35433888
Web Site: https://lemtapes.fi
Packaging Adhesive Mfr & Distr
N.A.I.C.S.: 325520

ND Industries Inc. **(1)**
1000 N Crooks Rd, Clawson, MI 48017
Tel.: (248) 288-0000
Web Site: http://www.ndindustries.com
Sales Range: $25-49.9 Million
Emp.: 80
Coating Of Metals & Formed Products
N.A.I.C.S.: 332812
Richard M. Wallace (Chm)
David Zess (Supvr-Production Div)
Matt Hurd (Mgr-IT)

Division (Domestic):

ND Adhesives & Sealants Division **(2)**
1675 Providence Blvd Ste A, Deltona, FL 32725
Tel.: (386) 860-4522
Web Site: https://www.ndindustries.com
Sales Range: $10-24.9 Million
Emp.: 5
Metal Plating Services
N.A.I.C.S.: 325520

ND Compound Blending Division/Michigan **(2)**
1893 Barrett Rd, Troy, MI 48084
Tel.: (248) 655-2580
Web Site: https://www.ndindustries.com
Emp.: 20
Coating of Metals & Formed Products
N.A.I.C.S.: 332812
Mike Tohlman (Gen Mgr)

ND Compound Blending Division/Texas **(2)**
3615 Dalworth St, Arlington, TX 76011
Tel.: (817) 633-6301
Web Site: https://www.ndindustries.com
Coating of Metals & Formed Products
N.A.I.C.S.: 541715

Subsidiary (Non-US):

ND Electronics (Kunshan) Co., Ltd. **(2)**
395 Central Yu Cheng Road, Cheng Bei District, Kunshan, 215300, China
Tel.: (86) 51257765335
Web Site: https://www.ndindustries.com
Emp.: 40
Fastener Whslr
N.A.I.C.S.: 423710
Eddie Davis (Mgr-Sls)

Division (Domestic):

ND Fluoropolymer Coatings Division **(2)**
1819 Thunderbird St, Troy, MI 48084
Tel.: (248) 288-0000
Web Site: https://www.ndindustries.com
Sales Range: $25-49.9 Million
Emp.: 10
Coating of Metals & Formed Products
N.A.I.C.S.: 449110

Subsidiary (Non-US):

ND INDUSTRIES A.S. **(2)**
Ikitelli Osb Metal-Is S S 4 Blok No1 Basaksehir, Istanbul, Turkiye
Tel.: (90) 2125490545
Web Site: https://www.ndindustries.com

Hardware Product Whslr
N.A.I.C.S.: 423710

Division (Domestic):

ND Industries **(2)**
1893 Barrett Rd, Troy, MI 48084
Tel.: (248) 288-0000
Web Site: https://www.ndindustries.com
Sales Range: $10-24.9 Million
Emp.: 20
Coating Of Metals & Formed Products
N.A.I.C.S.: 332812
Jim Counts (Plant Mgr)

ND Industries Inc. - Eastern Fastener Processing Division **(2)**
128-2 Bauer Dr, Oakland, NJ 07436
Tel.: (201) 651-1500
Fastener Mfr
N.A.I.C.S.: 339993

ND Industries Inc. - Midwestern Fastener Processing Division **(2)**
3954 S Central, Rockford, IL 61102
Tel.: (815) 963-3600
Web Site: https://www.ndindustries.com
Fastener Mfr
N.A.I.C.S.: 332722

ND Industries Inc. - Southeastern Fastener Processing Division **(2)**
2220-C Center Park Dr, Charlotte, NC 28217
Tel.: (704) 329-0033
Fastener Mfr
N.A.I.C.S.: 339993

ND Industries Inc. - Southwestern Fastener Processing Division **(2)**
3611 Dalworth St, Arlington, TX 76011
Tel.: (817) 633-2788
Fastener Mfr
N.A.I.C.S.: 339993

ND Industries Inc. - Western Fastener Processing Division **(2)**
13929 Dinard Ave, Santa Fe Springs, CA 90670
Tel.: (562) 926-3321
Fastener Mfr
N.A.I.C.S.: 332722

ND Manufacturing Engineering Group **(2)**
1819 Thunderbird St, Troy, MI 48084
Tel.: (248) 288-0000
Web Site: https://www.ndindustries.com
Sales Range: $10-24.9 Million
Emp.: 10
Coating Of Metals & Formed Products
N.A.I.C.S.: 333519

Oy H.B. Fuller Nordic AB **(1)**
Mankimiehentie 10, 02780, Espoo, Finland
Tel.: (358) 96156700
Adhesive Product Mfr
N.A.I.C.S.: 325520

Plexbond Quimica S/A **(1)**
Rua Antonio Lacerda Braga 680 - CIC, Curitiba, 81170-240, PR, Brazil
Tel.: (55) 4121088800
Chemical Products Distr
N.A.I.C.S.: 424690

Royal Adhesives & Sealants, LLC **(1)**
2001 W Washington St, South Bend, IN 46628-2032
Tel.: (574) 246-5000
Web Site: http://www.royaladhesives.com
Industrial Adhesives & Sealants, Commercial Roofing Adhesives & Mirror Mastics Mfr & Marketer
N.A.I.C.S.: 325520

Unit (Domestic):

Advanced Polymers International **(2)**
3584 Walters Rd, Syracuse, NY 13209
Tel.: (315) 451-1755
Web Site: http://www.geltac.com
Adhesive Mfr
N.A.I.C.S.: 325520

Subsidiary (Domestic):

Bacon Industries, Inc. **(2)**
16731 Hale Ave, Irvine, CA 92606
Tel.: (949) 863-1499

Web Site: http://www.baconadhesives.com
Adhesive Mfr
N.A.I.C.S.: 325520

Subsidiary (Non-US):

Kommerling Chemische Fabrik GMBH **(2)**
Zweibrucker Str 200, 66954, Pirmasens, Germany
Tel.: (49) 6331562000
Web Site: https://www.koe-chemie.de
Sealants, Adhesives & Bonding Products Mfr
N.A.I.C.S.: 325520

Plant (Domestic):

Royal Adhesives & Sealants, LLC - Wayne **(2)**
48 Burgess Pl, Wayne, NJ 07470
Tel.: (973) 694-0845
Web Site: http://www.royaladhesives.com
Adhesives, Sealants & Coatings Mfr
N.A.I.C.S.: 325520

Sekisui Fuller Co. Ltd. **(1)**
Taiyo Life Shinagawa Building 5F 2-16-2 Konan, Minato-ku, Tokyo, 108-0075, Japan **(100%)**
Tel.: (81) 354950661
Web Site: http://www.sekisui-fuller.co.jp
Sales Range: $50-74.9 Million
Mfr of Adhesives
N.A.I.C.S.: 325520
Takeshi Maruyama (Pres)
Tatsuo Hayasaki (Exec VP)

Specialty Construction Brands, Inc. **(1)**
1105 S Frontenac St, Aurora, IL 60504 **(100%)**
Tel.: (630) 851-0782
Sales Range: $10-24.9 Million
Emp.: 20
Coating Mfr
N.A.I.C.S.: 325510

Plant (Domestic):

Specialty Construction Brands - Palatine **(2)**
315 S Hicks Rd, Palatine, IL 60067
Tel.: (847) 358-9500
Specialty Chemicals Mfr
N.A.I.C.S.: 325520

Tonsan Adhesive, Inc. **(1)**
5 Shuangyuan Rd, Badachu High-Tech Zone, Beijing, 100041, China
Tel.: (86) 1088795588
Web Site: http://www.tonsan.com
Adhesive Mfr
N.A.I.C.S.: 325520

Subsidiary (Domestic):

Suzhou Tonsan Adhesive Co., Ltd. **(2)**
40 Youxiang Rd, Wuzhong Economic Development Zone, Suzhou, 215000, China
Tel.: (86) 51287775588
Web Site: http://www.tonsan.com
Adhesive Mfr
N.A.I.C.S.: 325520

Subsidiary (US):

Tonsan Adhesive U.S., Inc. **(2)**
401 Coral Way, Coral Gables, FL 33134
Tel.: (786) 360-6885
Sealant Merchant Whslr
N.A.I.C.S.: 424690

XChem International LLC **(1)**
Industrial Plot A-03 RAK Investment Authority, PO Box 32635, Ras al Khaimah, United Arab Emirates
Tel.: (971) 72445105
Web Site: https://xchem.ae
Packaging Adhesive Mfr & Distr
N.A.I.C.S.: 325520

H.C.B. FINANCIAL CORP.
150 W Court St, Hastings, MI 49058
Tel.: (269) 945-2401 MI
Web Site:
https://www.highpointcommunity bank.com
Year Founded: 1886

HCBN—(OTCIQ)
Rev.: $21,668,252
Assets: $561,431,846
Liabilities: $524,204,917
Net Worth: $37,226,929
Earnings: $5,014,831
Fiscal Year-end: 12/31/23
Bank Holding Company
N.A.I.C.S.: 551111
Mark A. Kolanowski *(Pres & CEO)*

H.I.G. ACQUISITION CORP.
1450 Brickell Ave 31st Fl, Miami, FL
33131
Tel.: (305) 379-2322   Ky
Year Founded: 2020
HIGAU—(NYSE)
Investment Services
N.A.I.C.S.: 523999
Brian Schwartz *(CEO)*
Rob Wolfson *(Pres)*
Timur Akazhanov *(CFO)*
Richard Siegel *(Gen Counsel & VP)*

HAEMONETICS CORPORA-TION
125 Summer St, Boston, MA 02110
Tel.: (781) 848-7100   MA
Web Site:
   https://www.haemonetics.com
Year Founded: 1971
HAE—(NYSE)
Rev.: $1,309,055,000
Assets: $2,195,591,000
Liabilities: $1,235,632,000
Net Worth: $959,959,000
Earnings: $117,558,000
Emp.: 3,657
Fiscal Year-end: 03/30/24
Blood Processing Equipment & Dis-
posables Mfr
N.A.I.C.S.: 339112
Michelle L. Basil *(Exec VP & Gen
Counsel)*
Josep Lluis Llorens *(Sr VP-Supply
Chain & Mfg-Global)*
Stewart W. Strong *(Pres-Global Hos-
pital)*
Olga Guyette *(Dir-IR)*
James C. D'Arecca *(CFO & Exec VP)*
Maryanne Farris *(Chief Acctg Officer
& VP)*
Ellen M. Zane *(Chm)*
Christopher A. Simon *(Pres & CEO)*

Subsidiaries:

Advanced Cooling Therapy, Inc.   (1)
3440 S Dearborn St Ste 21, Chicago, IL
60616-5149
Tel.: (508) 266-5338
Web Site: https://www.attune-medical.com
Surgical & Medical Instrument Mfr
N.A.I.C.S.: 339112
Erik Kulstad *(Founder)*
Robin Drassler *(VP-Sls-North America)*
Maria Gray *(Dir-Clinical Svcs)*
Alan Elphick *(Mgr-Key Sls)*
Ruben Trevino *(Mgr-Key Sls)*
Bill Benson *(Mgr-Key Sls)*
Dalton Akkerman *(Mgr-Key Sls)*

Arryx, Inc.   (1)
316 N Michigan Ave Ste 400, Chicago, IL
60601
Tel.: (312) 726-6675
Web Site: http://www.arryx.com
Nanophotonic Component Mfr
N.A.I.C.S.: 334419

Cardiva Medical, Inc.   (1)
1615 Wyatt Dr, Santa Clara, CA 95054
Tel.: (408) 470-7170
Web Site: http://www.cardivamedical.com
Medical Device Mfr & Distr
N.A.I.C.S.: 339112

Enicor GmbH   (1)
Hanauer Strasse 85 85a, 80993, Munich,
Germany
Tel.: (49) 89997428100
Web Site: http://www.clot.pro

Medical Device Mfr
N.A.I.C.S.: 339112
Andreas Calatzis *(Founder & Gen Mgr)*

Haemonetics (Shanghai) Manage-
ment Co. Ltd.   (1)
The Center 2501-03 2510-11 Room 989
Chang le Road, Xu Hui District, Shanghai,
200031, China
Tel.: (86) 51236690794
Medical Equipment Distr
N.A.I.C.S.: 456199

Haemonetics Asia, Inc.   (1)
26F-1 NO 102 Roosevelt Rd Sec 2, Taipei,
100, Taiwan
Tel.: (886) 223690722
Web Site: http://www.haemonet.com
Sales Range: $1-9.9 Million
Emp.: 14
Mfr of Blood Processing Equipment & Dis-
posables
N.A.I.C.S.: 334516
James Wu *(Gen Mgr)*

Haemonetics Belgium N.V.   (1)
Parc d Alliance 9 Boulevard De France Ba-
timent A, Braine-l'Alleud, B-1420, Belgium
Tel.: (32) 80075480
Web Site: http://www.haemonetics.com
Emp.: 1
Blood Processing Equipment & Disposable
Mfr
N.A.I.C.S.: 339112

Haemonetics CZ, Spol.s.r.o   (1)
Ptasinskeho 311/8, 602 00, Brno, Czech
Republic   (100%)
Tel.: (420) 800143243
Web Site: http://www.haemonetics.com
Blood Processing Equipment & Disposables
Mfr
N.A.I.C.S.: 334516

Haemonetics Canada, Ltd.   (1)
Software Solutions Suite 500 10025 102A
Avenue, Edmonton, T5J 2Z2, AB, Canada
Tel.: (780) 425-6560
Blood Processing Equipment & Disposable
Mfr
N.A.I.C.S.: 339112

Haemonetics France S.A.R.L.   (1)
Building K-Ouest 53 rue de l'Etang, 69760,
Limonest, France   (100%)
Tel.: (33) 800901158
Web Site: http://www.haemonetics.fr
Blood Processing Equipment & Disposables
Mfr
N.A.I.C.S.: 334516

Haemonetics Hong Kong Ltd.   (1)
Unit 1615-20 16/F Tower II Grand Century
Place, 193 Prince Edward Road West Mong
Kok, Kowloon, China (Hong Kong)
Tel.: (852) 28689218
Web Site: http://www.haemonetics.com
Medical Device Mfr
N.A.I.C.S.: 339112

Haemonetics Hospitalar EIRELI   (1)
Rua Gomes de Carvalho No 911, Vila Olim-
pia, 04547-003, Sao Paulo, Brazil
Tel.: (55) 1135981878
Medical Device Mfr
N.A.I.C.S.: 339112

Haemonetics Italia, S.R.L.   (1)
Via Alberto Falck 16, Sesto San Giovanni,
20099, Milan, Italy
Tel.: (39) 0800870200
Web Site: http://www.haemonetics.it
Mfr of Blood Processing Equipment & Dis-
posables
N.A.I.C.S.: 334516

Haemonetics Japan Co., Ltd.   (1)
Tokyo Club Building 3-2-6 Kasumigaseki,
Chiyoda-Ku, Tokyo, 100-0013, Japan
Tel.: (81) 332377310
Web Site: http://www.haemonetics.co.jp
Sales Range: $10-24.9 Million
Emp.: 70
Mfr of Blood Processing Equipment & Dis-
posables
N.A.I.C.S.: 334516

Haemonetics Japan GK   (1)
Tokyo Club Building 3-2-6, Kasumigaseki
Chiyoda-ku, Tokyo, 100-013, Japan
Tel.: (81) 120010835

Medical Equipment Mfr
N.A.I.C.S.: 335999

Haemonetics Ltd.   (1)
3MB Middlemarch Office Park Siskin Drive,
Coventry, CV3 4FJ, United
Kingdom   (100%)
Tel.: (44) 8082344817
Web Site: http://www.haemonetics.com
Sales Range: $1-9.9 Million
Emp.: 12
Mfr of Blood Processing Equipment & Dis-
posables
N.A.I.C.S.: 334516

Haemonetics Manufacturing, Inc.   (1)
1630 Industrial Park St, Covina, CA 91722
Tel.: (626) 339-7388
Sales Range: $50-74.9 Million
Emp.: 250
Blood Collection, Filtration & Processing
Products Mfr
N.A.I.C.S.: 339112

Haemonetics Medical Devices
(Shanghai) Trading Co., Ltd.   (1)
Room 1103-06 Evergo Mansion No 1325
Middle Huaihai Road, Shanghai, 200031,
China   (100%)
Tel.: (86) 2153895200
Sales Range: $10-24.9 Million
Emp.: 20
Blood Processing Equipment & Disposables
Mfr
N.A.I.C.S.: 334516

Haemonetics Puerto Rico, LLC   (1)
Carr 194 Pall Blvd Ste 98, Fajardo, PR
00738
Tel.: (787) 355-4100
Sales Range: $50-74.9 Million
Emp.: 350
Biomedical Filtration Products Mfr
N.A.I.C.S.: 339113
Francisco Garcia *(Gen Mgr)*
Edwin Santos *(Mgr-HR)*

Haemonetics Scandinavia AB   (1)
Scheelev 17, 223 63, Lund, Sweden
Tel.: (46) 462862320
Web Site: http://www.haemonetics.com
Blood Processing Equipment & Disposables
Mfr
N.A.I.C.S.: 334516

Haemonetics Singapore Pte. Ltd.   (1)
9 Temasek Boulevard No 09-01 Suntec
Tower Two, Singapore, 38989, Singapore
Tel.: (65) 64071500
Medical Equipment Mfr
N.A.I.C.S.: 335999

Haemonetics, GmbH   (1)
Kistlerhofstrasse 75, 81379, Munich,
Germany   (100%)
Tel.: (49) 8001808890
Web Site: http://www.haemonetics.de
Sales Range: $10-24.9 Million
Emp.: 40
Mfr of Blood Processing Equipment & Dis-
posables
N.A.I.C.S.: 334516

Inlog   (1)
235 rue de l Etang, Limonest, 69760,
France
Tel.: (33) 478665353
Sales Range: $25-49.9 Million
Emp.: 50
Medico Technical Software Development
Services & Publisher
N.A.I.C.S.: 513210
Audrey Roy *(Office Mgr)*

Opsens Inc.   (1)
750 Boul du Parc Technologique, Quebec,
G1P 4S3, QC, Canada
Tel.: (418) 781-0333
Web Site: https://www.opsens.com
Rev.: $26,960,357
Assets: $45,773,084
Liabilities: $12,659,176
Net Worth: $33,113,908
Earnings: ($899,957)
Emp.: 163
Fiscal Year-end: 08/31/2021
Scientific Instrument Mfr
N.A.I.C.S.: 334513

Subsidiary (Domestic):

Opsens Solutions Inc.   (2)

319 Franquet Street Suite 110, Quebec,
G1P 4R4, QC, Canada
Tel.: (418) 682-9996
Web Site: https://opsens-solutions.com
Sales Range: $25-49.9 Million
Emp.: 2
Offshore Engineering Services
N.A.I.C.S.: 541330

HAGERTY, INC.   DE
Web Site:
   https://investor.hagerty.com
Year Founded: 2020
HGTY—(NYSE)
Rev.: $787,588,000
Assets: $1,312,518,000
Liabilities: $945,149,000
Net Worth: $367,369,000
Earnings: $2,403,000
Emp.: 1,874
Fiscal Year-end: 12/31/22
Holding Company; Insurance Broker-
age Services
N.A.I.C.S.: 551112
Collette Champagne *(COO)*
McKeel Hagerty *(Chm & CEO)*
Patrick S. McClymont *(CFO)*
Jay Koval *(Sr VP-IR)*

Subsidiaries:

The Hagerty Group, LLC   (1)
121 Drivers Edge, Traverse City, MI 49684-
4203
Web Site: https://www.hagerty.com
Holding Company; Motor Vehicle Insurance
Brokerage Services
N.A.I.C.S.: 551112
Collette Champagne *(COO)*
McKeel Hagerty *(CEO)*
Russell Page *(CIO)*
Patrick S. McClymont *(CFO)*

Subsidiary (Domestic):

Hagerty Insurance Agency, LLC   (2)
121 Drivers Edge, Traverse City, MI 49684-
4203
Tel.: (231) 947-6868
Web Site: https://www.hagerty.com
Sales Range: $10-24.9 Million
Emp.: 520
Insurance Agencies & Brokerages
N.A.I.C.S.: 524210
Collette Champagne *(COO)*
McKeel Hagerty *(CEO)*
Belynda Poupard *(Mgr-IT Infrastructure)*
Michelle Ayers *(Asst Mgr-Claims)*

Subsidiary (Non-US):

Hagerty International Limited   (2)
The Arch Barn Pury Hill Farm, Towcester,
NN12 7TB, Northamptonshire, United King-
dom
Tel.: (44) 8448241134
Web Site:
   http://www.hagertyinsurance.co.uk
Insurance Brokerage
N.A.I.C.S.: 524210
Angus Forsyth *(Mng Dir)*
Marcus Atkinson *(Dir-Mktg)*
Robin Harman *(Mgr-Ops)*

HALITRON, INC.
3 Simms Ln Ste 2F, Newtown, CT
06470
Tel.: (203) 565-8707
Web Site: http://www.halitroninc.com
Year Founded: 2003
HAON—(OTCIQ)
Asset Management Services
N.A.I.C.S.: 523940
Bernard Findley *(Chm & CEO)*

HALL OF FAME BEVERAGES, INC.
263 W Olive Ave, Burbank, CA 91502
Tel.: (480) 316-1712
HFBG—(OTCIQ)
Beverage Product Mfr
N.A.I.C.S.: 312111
Greg Thrasher *(CEO)*

Hall of Fame Resort & Entertainment
Company—(Continued)

HALL OF FAME RESORT & ENTERTAINMENT COMPANY
2014 Champions Gateway Ste 100,
Canton, OH 44708
Tel.: (330) 458-9176   DE
Web Site: https://www.hofreco.com
Year Founded: 2019
HOFV—(NASDAQ)
Rev.: $15,979,372
Assets: $456,296,961
Liabilities: $265,038,849
Net Worth: $191,258,112
Earnings: ($46,946,504)
Emp.: 114
Fiscal Year-end: 12/31/22
Investment Services
N.A.I.C.S.: 523999
Valerie McGee (Sr VP-Revenue)
Michael A. Crawford (Chm, Pres,
CEO, Interim Principal Fin Officer &
Chm/Pres/CEO-Hall of Fame Village)
Mike Levy (Pres-Ops)
Anne Graffice (Exec VP-Pub Affairs)
Lisa Gould (VP-HR)
Scott Langerman (Exec VP-Media
Bus Dev)
John Van Buiten (Interim Principal
Acctg Officer, VP-Acctg & Controller)
Karl L. Holz (Vice Chm)

HALLADOR ENERGY COMPANY
1183 E Canvasback Dr, Terre Haute,
IN 47802
Tel.: (303) 839-5504
Web Site:
    https://www.halladorenergy.com
Year Founded: 1949
HNRG—(NASDAQ)
Rev.: $361,991,000
Assets: $630,554,000
Liabilities: $415,530,000
Net Worth: $215,024,000
Earnings: $18,105,000
Emp.: 980
Fiscal Year-end: 12/31/22
Coal Exploration & Production Ser-
vices
N.A.I.C.S.: 212115
Brent K. Bilsland (Chm, Pres & CEO)
Marjorie A. Hargrave (CFO)
Elliott Batson (Chief Comm Officer)
Jamalyn Sarver (Dir-Govt Affairs)
Roy Dressler (Mgr-Land)
Heath Lovell (Pres-Hallador Power
Co)

Subsidiaries:

Summit Terminal, LLC   (1)
2483 E State Rd 66, Rockport, IN 47635
Tel.: (812) 649-8980
Web Site: http://www.summitterminal.com
Marine Cargo Handling Services
N.A.I.C.S.: 488320

Sunrise Coal LLC   (1)
1183 E Canvasback Dr, Terre Haute, IN
47802-5304
Tel.: (812) 299-2800
Web Site: http://sunrisecoal.com
Emp.: 500
Coal Mining Services
N.A.I.C.S.: 212114
Lawrence D. Martin (Pres)

Sunrise Energy, LLC   (1)
151 Evandale Dr, Pittsburgh, PA 15220
Tel.: (412) 921-2758
Web Site: https://www.sunrise-energy.net
Solar Power Generation Services
N.A.I.C.S.: 221118

Sunrise Land Company, LLC   (1)
162 Mike Lounge Dr, Burlington, CO 80807
Tel.: (719) 342-1500
Web Site: https://www.slc.land
Dry Pea & Bean Farming Services
N.A.I.C.S.: 111130

HALLIBURTON COMPANY
3000 N Sam Houston Pkwy E, Hous-
ton, TX 77032
Tel.: (281) 871-2699   DE
Web Site:
    https://www.halliburton.com
Year Founded: 1919
HAL—(NYSE)
Rev.: $23,018,000,000
Assets: $24,683,000,000
Liabilities: $15,250,000,000
Net Worth: $9,433,000,000
Earnings: $2,638,000,000
Emp.: 48,000
Fiscal Year-end: 12/31/23
Holding Company; Oil Field Services
& Products; Engineering & Construc-
tion Services
N.A.I.C.S.: 551112
Lawrence J. Pope (Chief HR Officer
& Exec VP-Admin)
Bruce A. Metzinger (Asst Sec & VP)
Myrtle L. Jones (Sr VP-Tax)
Eric J. Carre (CFO & Exec VP)
Jeffery S. Spalding (Sr VP & Deputy
Gen Counsel)
Mark J. Richard (Pres-Western Hemi-
sphere)
Van H. Beckwith (Chief Legal Officer,
Sec & Exec VP)
Abu Zeya (Sr Dir-IR)
Marina Matselinskaya (Dir-IR)
David Coleman (Sr Dir-IR)
Shannon Slocum (Pres-Eastern
Hemisphere)
Jill D. Sharp (Sr VP)
Charles E. Geer Jr. (Chief Acctg Offi-
cer & Sr VP)
Jeffrey Allen Miller (Chm, Pres &
CEO)

Subsidiaries:

Halliburton Canada Corp.   (1)
645 7 Ave Sw 1600, Calgary, T2P 4G8, AB,
Canada
Tel.: (403) 231-9416
Emp.: 1,800
Oil & Gas Operation Support Services
N.A.I.C.S.: 213112
John Gorman (VP)

Halliburton Drilling & Evaluation   (1)
3000 N Sam Houston Pkwy E, Houston, TX
77032
Tel.: (281) 871-4000
Web Site: http://www.halliburton.com
Field & Reservoir Modeling, Drilling, Evalua-
tion & Well-Bore Placement Solutions
N.A.I.C.S.: 213111

Unit (Domestic):

Halliburton Energy Services, Inc.   (2)
10200 Bellaire Blvd, Houston, TX
77072   (100%)
Tel.: (281) 575-3000
Web Site: http://www.halliburton.com
Sales Range: $5-14.9 Billion
Emp.: 30,000
Oil Field Services & Products Whslr; Engi-
neering & Construction Services
N.A.I.C.S.: 213112

Division (Domestic):

Barold Drilling Fluids Division   (3)
3000 N Sam Houston Pkwy E, Houston, TX
77032   (100%)
Tel.: (281) 871-4000
Web Site: http://www.halliburton.com
Sales Range: $1-4.9 Billion
Emp.: 3,000
Drilling Fluid Systems, Performance Addi-
tives, Solids Control & Waste Management
Services for Oil & Gas Drilling, Completion
& Workover Operations
N.A.I.C.S.: 423830

Subsidiary (Non-US):

Halliburton AS   (3)
Eldfiskveien 1, 4065, Tananger,
Norway   (100%)

Tel.: (47) 51837000
Web Site: http://www.halliburton.com
Sales Range: $250-299.9 Million
Emp.: 50,000
Engineering, Construction & Oilfield Ser-
vices
N.A.I.C.S.: 541330
Jorunn Saetre (Chm)

Halliburton Argentina S.A.   (3)
Maipu 942 14 1006, Buenos Aires,
Argentina   (100%)
Tel.: (54) 1143074514
Web Site: http://www.halliburton.com
Sales Range: $600-649.9 Million
Emp.: 400
Oil & Gas Field Services
N.A.I.C.S.: 213112

Halliburton Company Germany
GmbH   (3)
Hans Heinrich Warnke, Str 12, Celle,
29227, Germany
Tel.: (49) 51419990
Web Site: http://www.halliburton.com
Sales Range: $100-124.9 Million
Emp.: 60
Oil & Gas Drilling Services
N.A.I.C.S.: 213111
Christian Kiesl (Mng Dir)

Division (Domestic):

Halliburton Energy Services, Inc.   (3)
3000 N Sam Houston Pkwy E, Houston, TX
77032   (100%)
Tel.: (281) 871-4000
Web Site: http://www.halliburton.com
Sales Range: $125-149.9 Million
Oil Field Services
N.A.I.C.S.: 213112

Subsidiary (Non-US):

Halliburton Group Canada Inc.   (3)
645 7 Ave Sw Suite 1600, Calgary, T2P
4G8, AB, Canada   (100%)
Tel.: (403) 231-9300
Web Site: http://www.halliburton.com
Sales Range: $200-249.9 Million
Emp.: 1,800
Oil Field Services & Products Mfr
N.A.I.C.S.: 237120

Halliburton Limited   (3)
14th Floor CitiBank Tower Al-Qutayat
Street, PO Box 3111, Dubai, United Arab
Emirates
Tel.: (971) 43036666
Web Site: http://www.halliburton.com
Sales Range: $600-649.9 Million
Emp.: 420
Oil & Gas Field Services
N.A.I.C.S.: 213112

Halliburton Manufacturing & Services
Limited   (3)
Elliot Industrial Estate Angus, Arbroath,
DD11 2NJ, Scotland, United
Kingdom   (100%)
Tel.: (44) 1241432000
Web Site: http://www.halliburton.com
Sales Range: $75-99.9 Million
Emp.: 170
Oil & Gas Field Machinery Equipment Mfr
N.A.I.C.S.: 333132

Halliburton Nigeria Limited   (3)
Plot 90 Ajose Adeogun Street, Victoria Is-
land, Lagos, Nigeria   (100%)
Tel.: (234) 12715020
Web Site: http://www.halliburton.com
Sales Range: $125-149.9 Million
Emp.: 225
Oil & Gas Field Services
N.A.I.C.S.: 213112

Division (Domestic):

Halliburton Security DBS   (3)
105 Jordan Plz Blvd, Tyler, TX
75704-2050   (100%)
Tel.: (903) 533-1555
Web Site: http://www.halliburton.com
Sales Range: $125-149.9 Million
Emp.: 12
Drill Bits Mfr
N.A.I.C.S.: 333132

Subsidiary (Non-US):

Halliburton Trinidad Limited   (3)

Coconut Drive, PO Box 57, Cross Crossing,
San Fernando, Trinidad & Tobago
Tel.: (868) 2990985
Web Site: http://www.halliburton.com
Sales Range: $75-99.9 Million
Emp.: 110
Oil & Gas Field Services
N.A.I.C.S.: 213112

Halliburton de Mexico S.A. de
C.V.   (3)
Av Paseo La Choca 5 A Fracc La Choca
Col Tabasco 2000, Villahermosa, 86035,
Tabasco, Mexico   (100%)
Tel.: (52) 9933101100
Web Site: http://www.halliburton.com
Sales Range: $250-299.9 Million
Emp.: 300
Oil & Gas Field Services
N.A.I.C.S.: 213112

Subsidiary (Domestic):

Landmark Graphics Corporation   (3)
3000 N Sam Houston Pkwy E, Houston, TX
77032-3219
Tel.: (713) 839-2000
Web Site: http://www.lgc.com
Sales Range: $1-4.9 Billion
Emp.: 1,022
Oil & Gas Industry Software & Technical
Services
N.A.I.C.S.: 513210
Sherri Moore (Coord-Export Traffic)

Subsidiary (Domestic):

Petris Technology, Inc.   (4)
1900 Saint James Pl Ste 700, Houston, TX
77056
Tel.: (713) 956-2165
Web Site: http://www.petris.com
Sales Range: $10-24.9 Million
Emp.: 147
Software Developer
N.A.I.C.S.: 541511

Joint Venture (Non-US):

PetroData AS   (4)
Eldfiskvegen 1, 4056, Tananger, Norway
Tel.: (47) 51838250
Sales Range: $25-49.9 Million
Emp.: 100
Data Management & Storage Services;
Owned 66% by Landmark Graphics Corpo-
ration & 33% by International Business Ma-
chines Corporation
N.A.I.C.S.: 513140

Subsidiary (Domestic):

Multi-Chem Group, LLC   (3)
2905 SW Blvd, San Angelo, TX 76904
Tel.: (325) 223-6200
Web Site: http://www.multichem.com
Sales Range: $1-9.9 Million
Emp.: 50
Chemicals & Allied Products Mfr
N.A.I.C.S.: 424690

Halliburton Energy Services
Limited   (1)
Halliburton House Howe Moss Crescent,
Aberdeen, AB21 0GN, United Kingdom
Tel.: (44) 1224777000
Web Site: http://www.halliburton.com
Holding Company
N.A.I.C.S.: 551112

Halliburton Global Affiliates Holdings
B.V.   (1)
Verrijn Stuartlaan 1 C, 2288 EK, Rijswijk,
Netherlands
Tel.: (31) 703071500
Holding Company
N.A.I.C.S.: 551112

Halliburton International, Inc.   (1)
3855 Jurupa St, Ontario, CA 91761
Tel.: (909) 428-8520
Web Site: http://www.haliburton.net
Emp.: 170

Frozen Specialty Food Mfr
N.A.I.C.S.: 311412

Halliburton Netherlands Holdings B.V. (1)
Verrijn Stuartlaan 1 C, 2288 EK, Rijswijk, Netherlands
Tel.: (31) 703071500
Web Site: http://www.halliburton.com
Mining Machinery & Equipment Mfr
N.A.I.C.S.: 333131

Halliburton Worldwide GmbH (1)
Baarerstrasse 96, 6300, Zug, Switzerland
Tel.: (41) 417286600
Patent Agency Services
N.A.I.C.S.: 541199
Scott Wendorf (Dir-Global Intellectual Asset Mgmt)

Halliburton/WellDynamics (1)
445 Woodline Dr, Spring, TX 77386
Tel.: (281) 297-1200
Web Site: http://www.halliburton.com
Sales Range: $250-299.9 Million
Emp.: 165
Developer of Oil Well Monitoring & Analysis Systems
N.A.I.C.S.: 213112

Ingrain, Inc. (1)
3733 Westheimer Rd 2nd Fl, Houston, TX 77027
Tel.: (713) 993-9795
Web Site: http://www.ingrainrocks.com
Laboratory Operating & Testing Services
N.A.I.C.S.: 541380
Marcus Ganz (CEO)

HALLMARK FINANCIAL SERVICES, INC.
Two Lincoln Centre 5420 Lyndon B Johnson Fwy Ste 1100, Dallas, TX 75240-2345
Tel.: (817) 348-1600   NV
Web Site:
https://www.hallmarkgrp.com
HALL—(NASDAQ)
Rev.: $159,918,000
Assets: $1,536,702,000
Liabilities: $1,476,408,000
Net Worth: $60,294,000
Earnings: ($108,110,000)
Emp.: 257
Fiscal Year-end: 12/31/22
Property & Casualty Insurance Services
N.A.I.C.S.: 524128
Christopher J. Kenney (Pres, CEO & CFO)
Debra Fontenot (Sr VP-Information Technology Services)
Chuck Mitzel (VP-Sr Actuary)
Pavinee Hat (Chief HR Officer)
Mark E. Schwarz (Chm)

Subsidiaries:

Aerospace Holdings, LLC (1)
330 Madison Ave Fl 28, New York, NY 10017   (100%)
Tel.: (949) 455-0665
Web Site: http://www.aerospaceim.com
Emp.: 60
Aircraft Components Mfr
N.A.I.C.S.: 332510
James Dimonte (Pres)

Subsidiary (Domestic):

Aerospace Claims Management Group, Inc. (2)
13727 Noel Rd, Dallas, TX 75240   (100%)
Tel.: (972) 852-1200
Web Site: http://www.aerospaceim.com
Emp.: 33
Aviation Insurance Services
N.A.I.C.S.: 524291

Aerospace Insurance Managers, Inc. (2)
15280 Addison Rd Ste 250, Addison, TX 75001   (100%)
Tel.: (972) 852-1200
Web Site: http://www.aerospaceim.com
Aviation Insurance

N.A.I.C.S.: 524128

Aerospace Special Risk, Inc. (2)
15280 Addison Rd Ste 250, Addison, TX 75001   (100%)
Tel.: (972) 852-1200
Aviation Insurance Services
N.A.I.C.S.: 524128

American Hallmark Insurance Company of Texas (1)
777 Main St Ste 1000, Fort Worth, TX 76102
Tel.: (817) 348-1600
Web Site: http://www.hallmarkgrp.com
Sales Range: $75-99.9 Million
Fire & Casualty Insurance
N.A.I.C.S.: 524126

Subsidiary (Domestic):

Texas Builders Insurance Company (2)
11612 RM2244 Ste 1-200, Austin, TX 78738
Tel.: (512) 708-0148
Web Site: http://www.tbic.com
Sales Range: $1-9.9 Million
Emp.: 24
Direct Property & Casualty Insurance Carriers
N.A.I.C.S.: 524126
Andrew J. Reynolds (Exec VP & Treas)

American Hallmark Insurance Services, Inc. (1)
777 Main St Ste 1000, Fort Worth, TX 76102
Tel.: (817) 348-1600
Web Site: http://www.hallmarkgrp.com
Sales Range: $50-74.9 Million
Emp.: 100
Property & Casualty Insurance Services
N.A.I.C.S.: 524128

Hallmark Claims Service Inc. (1)
6500 Pinecrest Dr Ste 100, Plano, TX 75024
Tel.: (469) 298-5700
Rev.: $982,662
Emp.: 40
Insurance Claims Services
N.A.I.C.S.: 524298

Hallmark Insurance Company (1)
6500 Pinecrest Dr Ste 100, Plano, TX 75024
Tel.: (972) 934-2400
Web Site: http://www.hallmarkinsco.com
Sales Range: $25-49.9 Million
Emp.: 100
Insurance Services
N.A.I.C.S.: 524126

Hallmark Specialty Insurance Company (1)
7550 W Interstate 10 Ste 1400& 970, San Antonio, TX 78229
Tel.: (210) 949-9100
Web Site: http://www.hallmarksu.com
Insurance Services
N.A.I.C.S.: 524298

Heath XS, LLC (1)
59 S Finley Ave, Basking Ridge, NJ 07920   (80%)
Tel.: (908) 766-7140
Web Site: http://www.heathxs.com
Insurance Underwriting Services
N.A.I.C.S.: 524298
Katherine Rible (VP-Underwriting)

HALLMARK VENTURE GROUP, INC.
5112 W Taft Rd Ste M, Liverpool, NY 13088
Tel.: (760) 294-9858   NV
Year Founded: 2006
HLLK—(OTCIQ)
Liabilities: $898,348
Net Worth: ($898,348)
Earnings: ($288,546)
Fiscal Year-end: 12/31/22
Building Construction Services
N.A.I.C.S.: 236220
John D. Murphy Jr. (Pres & CEO)
Paul Strickland (Sec)

HALO COMPANIES, INC.
7800 N Dallas Pkwy Ste 320, Plano, TX 75024
Tel.: (214) 644-0065   DE
Web Site: http://www.haloco.com
Year Founded: 2004
HALN—(OTCIQ)
Sales Range: $1-9.9 Million
Emp.: 11
Portfolio Advisory Services
N.A.I.C.S.: 523940
Brandon Cade Thompson (Chm & CEO)
Paul O. Williams (Vice Chm- & Asst Sec)
T. Craig Friesland (Sec)

Subsidiaries:

Halo Group, Inc. (1)
5550 Granite Pkwy Ste 175, Plano, TX 75024
Tel.: (972) 342-9695
Web Site: http://www.halogroup.us
Information Technology Support Services
N.A.I.C.S.: 541519
Valerie Niemiec (Dir-Bus Dev)
Denise Doepker (Dir-Natl Acct)
Jeff Miller (VP-Detroit)
Toni Beaubien (CFO)
Ted Strauss (VP)

Halo Portfolio Advisors, LLC (1)
7800 Dallas Pkwy, Plano, TX 75024
Tel.: (214) 644-0065
Financial Advisory Services
N.A.I.C.S.: 523940
Michael Barry (Pres)

HALOZYME THERAPEUTICS, INC.
12390 El Camino Real, San Diego, CA 92130
Tel.: (858) 794-8889   NV
Web Site: https://www.halozyme.com
Year Founded: 1998
HALO—(NASDAQ)
Rev.: $829,253,000
Assets: $1,733,270,000
Liabilities: $1,649,462,000
Net Worth: $83,808,000
Earnings: $281,594,000
Emp.: 373
Fiscal Year-end: 12/31/23
Recombinant Human Enzyme Mfr, Developer & Marketer
N.A.I.C.S.: 325412
Michael J. LaBarre (Chief Technical Officer & Sr VP)
Helen I. Torley (Pres & CEO)
Tram Bui (Head-Investor Relations & Corporate Communications)
Nicole LaBrosse (CFO & Sr VP)
Mark Snyder (Chief Compliance Officer, Chief Legal Officer, Gen Counsel, Sec & Sr VP)
Chris Wahl (Chief Bus Officer)
Cortney Caudill (Chief Ops Officer)
Gary Grote (Chief Comml Officer)

Subsidiaries:

Antares Pharma AG (1)
Gewerbestrasse 18, 4123, Allschwil, Switzerland
Tel.: (41) 614864141
Sales Range: $150-199.9 Million
Emp.: 3
Pharmaceuticals Product Mfr
N.A.I.C.S.: 325412

Antares Pharma, Inc. (1)
100 Princeton S Ste 300, Ewing, NJ 08628
Tel.: (609) 359-3020
Web Site: http://www.antarespharma.com
Rev.: $183,982,000
Assets: $257,505,000
Liabilities: $81,747,000
Net Worth: $175,758,000
Earnings: $46,289,000
Emp.: 201
Fiscal Year-end: 12/31/2021
Pharmaceuticals Product Mfr

N.A.I.C.S.: 339112

HAMILTON BEACH BRANDS HOLDING COMPANY
4421 Waterfront Dr, Glen Allen, VA 23060
Tel.: (804) 273-9777   DE
Web Site: https://www.hamiltonbeach brands.com
Year Founded: 1988
HBB—(NYSE)
Rev.: $640,949,000
Assets: $388,950,000
Liabilities: $264,416,000
Net Worth: $124,534,000
Earnings: $25,267,000
Emp.: 700
Fiscal Year-end: 12/31/22
Holding Company
N.A.I.C.S.: 551112
Gregory H. Trepp (Pres & CEO)
Linda Woermer (Interim Principal Fin Officer & Interim Principal Acctg Officer)
R. Scott Tidey (Pres & CEO)
Sally M. Cunningham (CFO)
Lawrence K. Workman Jr. (Gen Counsel)

Subsidiaries:

Hamilton Beach Brands Canada, Inc. (1)
50 Greenleaf Court, PO Box 1630, Belleville, K8N 5T5, ON, Canada   (100%)
Web Site: https://www.hamiltonbeach.ca
Small Kitchen Appliances Whslr & Retailer
N.A.I.C.S.: 423620

Hamilton Beach Brands, Inc. (1)
4421 Waterfront Dr, Glen Allen, VA 23060   (100%)
Tel.: (804) 527-7168
Web Site: https://www.hamiltonbeach.com
Small Appliances Mfr
N.A.I.C.S.: 335210
R. Scott Tidey (Pres & CEO)

Subsidiary (Domestic):

Hamilton Beach, Inc. (2)
4421 Waterfront Dr, Glen Allen, VA 23060-3375
Tel.: (804) 527-7168
Web Site: http://www.hamiltonbeach.com
Kitchen Product Mfr
N.A.I.C.S.: 332215

Plant (Domestic):

Hamilton Beach/Proctor Silex, Inc. (2)
360 Page Rd, Washington, NC 27889
Tel.: (252) 975-7800
Web Site: http://www.hamiltonbeach.com
Sales Range: $10-24.9 Million
Emp.: 30
Electric Home Appliances Mfr & Distr
N.A.I.C.S.: 335210

The Kitchen Collection, LLC (1)
2675 Skypark Dr Ste 305, Torrance, CA 90505   (100%)
Tel.: (310) 540-4090
Web Site: https://thekitchencollection.com
Kitchen Product Online Retailer
N.A.I.C.S.: 445298

Weston Brands, LLC (1)
261 Yadkin Rd, Southern Pines, NC 28387   (100%)
Tel.: (216) 901-6801
Web Site: https://westonbrands.com
Food Product Equipment Mfr
N.A.I.C.S.: 333241

HAMILTON LANE INCORPORATED
110 Washington St Ste 1300, Conshohocken, PA 19428
Tel.: (610) 934-2222   DE
Web Site:
https://www.hamiltonlane.com
Year Founded: 2007

Hamilton Lane Incorporated—(Continued)

HLNE—(NASDAQ)
Rev.: $367,919,000
Assets: $1,294,946,000
Liabilities: $557,460,000
Net Worth: $737,486,000
Earnings: $145,986,000
Emp.: 540
Fiscal Year-end: 03/31/22
Financial Investment Advisory Services
N.A.I.C.S.: 523940
Andrea Anigati Kramer (COO)
Jeffrey B. Armbrister (CFO & Treas)
Hartley Raymond Rogers (Chm)
Mario L. Giannini (Co-Chm)
Erik R. Hirsch (Co-CEO)
Juan Delgado-Moreira (Co-CEO)
Lydia A. Gavalis (Gen Counsel)
Mingchen Xia (Co-Head-Investment-Asia)
Collwyn Tan (Co-Head-Investment-Asia)
Kerrine Koh (Mng Dir-Client Solutions Grp-Southeast Asia)
Juan Delgado-Moreira (Vice Chm-Asia & Head-Asia)
Victor Jung (Head-Digital Assets)
Kristin Brandt (Chief HR Officer)
Drew Carl (Principal Acctg Officer)
Leslie A. Brun (Founder)

Subsidiaries:

361 Capital LLC　　　　　　　　(1)
4600 S Syracuse St, Denver, CO 80237
Tel.: (303) 224-3914
Web Site: http://www.361capital.com
Financial Investment Activities
N.A.I.C.S.: 523999
Andrea Coleman (Principal)
David Rueth (Principal)
Kelsey Sokoloski (VP)
Patrick Morelli (Principal)

Hamilton Lane (Australia) Pty Limited　　　　　　　　　　　(1)
Level 33 Aurora Place 88 Phillip Street, Sydney, 2000, NSW, Australia
Tel.: (61) 292937950
Investment Management Service
N.A.I.C.S.: 523940

Hamilton Lane (Japan) GK　　(1)
13F Marunouchi Bldg 2-4-1, Marunouchi Chiyoda-ku, Tokyo, 100-6313, Japan
Tel.: (81) 358603940
Investment Management Service
N.A.I.C.S.: 541611

Hamilton Lane Alliance Holdings I, Inc.　　　　　　　　　　　(1)
1 Presidential Blvd, Bala Cynwyd, PA 19004
Tel.: (610) 617-6026
Web Site: http://www.hlallianceholdings.com
Rev.: $3,266,185
Assets: $276,864,436
Liabilities: $294,808,568
Net Worth: ($17,944,132)
Earnings: $2,019,255
Emp.: 3
Fiscal Year-end: 12/31/2021
Investment Management Service
N.A.I.C.S.: 523940
Andrea Anigati Kramer (CEO & Mng Dir)
Andrea Kramer (CEO & Mng Dir)
Atul varma (CFO & Treas)
Hartley Rogers (Chm)
Jay Rosenberger (Principal)

Hamilton Lane Investimentos Ltda.　　　　　　　　　　　(1)
Av Niemeyer 2 Loja 102 Leblon, Rio de Janeiro, 22450-220, Brazil
Tel.: (55) 2121136722
Investment Management Service
N.A.I.C.S.: 523940

HAMLIN BANK & TRUST COMPANY
333 W Main St, Smethport, PA 16749
Tel.: (814) 887-5555

Web Site:
https://www.hamlinbank.com
Year Founded: 1863
HMLN—(OTCIQ)
Sales Range: $10-24.9 Million
Emp.: 80
Commercial Banking
N.A.I.C.S.: 522110

HAMMER TECHNOLOGY HOLDINGS
6151 Lk Osprey Dr, Sarasota, FL 34240
Tel.: (941) 306-3019　　　NV
Web Site: https://www.hmmrgroup.com
Year Founded: 2010
HMMR—(OTCEM)
Rev.: $3,256,611
Assets: $7,828,038
Liabilities: $3,669,858
Net Worth: $4,158,180
Earnings: ($1,920,242)
Emp.: 15
Fiscal Year-end: 12/31/23
Investment Holding Company
N.A.I.C.S.: 551112
Erik B. Levitt (Principal Fin Officer)
Michael P. Cothill (Chm)
Kristen Vasicek (COO & Sec)

HAN TANG TECHNOLOGY, INC.
531 Airport N Office Park Fort, Fort Wayne, IN 46825
Tel.: (260) 490-9990
HTTI—(OTCIQ)
Assets: $1,000
Liabilities: $220,000
Net Worth: ($219,000)
Earnings: ($39,000)
Fiscal Year-end: 06/30/19
Management Consulting Services
N.A.I.C.S.: 541611
Brian K. Kistler (CEO)

HANCOCK WHITNEY CORPORATION
1 Hancock Plz 2510 14th St, Gulfport, MS 39501
Tel.: (228) 868-4727　　　MS
Web Site:
https://www.hancockwhitney.com
Year Founded: 1984
HWC—(NASDAQ)
Rev.: $1,908,077,000
Assets: $35,578,573,000
Liabilities: $31,774,912,000
Net Worth: $3,803,661,000
Earnings: $392,602,000
Emp.: 3,591
Fiscal Year-end: 12/31/23
Bank Holding Company
N.A.I.C.S.: 551111
John M. Hairston (Pres & CEO)
D. Shane Loper (COO & Sr Exec VP)
Joy Lambert Phillips (Gen Counsel, Sec & Sr Exec VP)
Cindy S. Collins (Chief Compliance Officer)
Alan M. Ganucheau (Treas)
Christopher S. Ziluca (Chief Credit Officer & Exec VP)
Cecil W. Knight Jr. (Chief Banking Officer)

Subsidiaries:

Hancock Whitney Bank　　　　(1)
1 Hancock Plz, Gulfport, MS 39501　　　　　　　　　　(100%)
Tel.: (228) 822-4300
Web Site: http://www.hancockwhitney.com
Sales Range: $1-4.9 Billion
Emp.: 4,052
Commercial Bank
N.A.I.C.S.: 522110
John M. Hairston (CEO)
D. Shane Loper (COO & Exec VP)

Chip Knight (Chief Banking Officer)
Miles S. Milton (Chief Wealth Mgmt Officer)
Rudi Hall Wetzel (Chief HR Officer)
Christopher S. Ziluca (Chief Credit Officer)
Laura Sullivan Ethridge (CMO & Exec VP)

Hancock Whitney Investment Services, Inc.　　　　　　　　(1)
Hancock Whitney Plz 2510 14th St, Gulfport, MS 39501
Tel.: (228) 822-4300
Web Site: http://www.hancockwhitney.com
Investment & Wealth Management Services
N.A.I.C.S.: 523150
James H. Fujinaga (Pres & CEO)

HANESBRANDS INC.
1000 E Hanes Mill Rd, Winston Salem, NC 27105
Tel.: (336) 519-8080　　　MD
Web Site: https://www.hanes.com
Year Founded: 1901
HBI—(NYSE)
Rev.: $6,801,240,000
Assets: $7,071,436,000
Liabilities: $6,368,943,000
Net Worth: $702,493,000
Earnings: $77,224,000
Emp.: 59,000
Fiscal Year-end: 01/01/22
Underwear, Legwear & Activewear Mfr
N.A.I.C.S.: 315250
Stephen B. Bratspies (CEO)
Kristin L. Oliver (Chief HR Officer)
Joseph W. Cavaliere (Pres-Innerwear & Global)

Subsidiaries:

Alternative Apparel, Inc.　　（1）
1650 Indian Brook Way Bldg 200, Norcross, GA 30093
Tel.: (770) 209-2902
Web Site: http://www.alternativeapparel.com
Clothing Retail Stores
N.A.I.C.S.: 458110

Belfein Slovakia A.S.　　　　(1)
A Hlinku, 022 01, Cadca, Slovakia
Tel.: (421) 414302111
Web Site: http://belfein.webnode.sk
Clothing Store Operator
N.A.I.C.S.: 458110

Bellinda Ceska republika, s.r.o.　(1)
K Tresnovce 247, Dolni Redice, 533 75, Pardubice, Czech Republic
Tel.: (420) 466005101
Web Site: https://www.bellinda.cz
Clothing Store Operator
N.A.I.C.S.: 458110

Bellinda Hungaria Kft.　　　　(1)
Baross Utca 165, 2040, Budaors, Hungary
Tel.: (36) 309018693
Web Site: http://www.bellinda.hu
Clothing Store Operator
N.A.I.C.S.: 458110

Bellinda Slovensko s.r.o.　　(1)
Kollarova 12, 902 01, Pezinok, Slovakia
Tel.: (421) 336452426
Web Site: https://www.bellinda.sk
Clothing Store Operator
N.A.I.C.S.: 458110
Michal Bucka (Mgr-Traditional Trade)

Bras N Things Pty. Limited　　(1)
391 Park Rd Building T, Regents Park Industrial Estate Off Commercial Drive, Regents Park, 2143, NSW, Australia (100%)
Tel.: (61) 800810031
Web Site: http://www.brasnthings.com
Sales Range: $125-149.9 Million
Women's Lingerie, Sleepwear & Swimwear Retailer
N.A.I.C.S.: 458110
George Wahby (CEO)

Canadelle L.P.　　　　　　　(1)
4405 Metropolitan Blvd E, Saint Leonard, H1R 1Z4, QC, Canada
Tel.: (514) 376-6240
Sales Range: $150-199.9 Million
Emp.: 400
Womens Apparel Mfr

N.A.I.C.S.: 315210

Champion Athleticwear Inc.　（1）
1000 E Hanes Mill Rd, Winston Salem, NC 27105-1384
Tel.: (336) 519-8080
Web Site: http://www.championusa.com
Sales Range: $100-124.9 Million
Emp.: 1,200
Athletic, Casual Knitwear & Apparel Mfr & Whslr
N.A.I.C.S.: 315250

Champion Europe S.r.l.　　　（1）
Via dellAgricoltura 51, 41012, Carpi, MO, Italy
Tel.: (39) 0596259001
Web Site: http://www.championstore.com
Sports Footwear & Apparel Whslr
N.A.I.C.S.: 423910

DBA Bodywear Germany GmbH　(1)
Birkenallee 110-134, 48432, Rheine, Germany
Tel.: (49) 59719930
Web Site: http://www.elbeo.de
Clothing Store Operator
N.A.I.C.S.: 458110

DBApparel Italia Srl　　　　　(1)
Via Della Liberazione 8 Peschiera, Grassobbio, Bergamo, 20068, Italy
Tel.: (39) 025471580
Clothing Store Operator
N.A.I.C.S.: 458110
Valentina Carpani (Mgr-Category)

DBApparel S.A.S.　　　　　　(1)
2 rue des Martinets, 92500, Rueil-Malmaison, France
Tel.: (33) 147591515
Web Site: http://www.dbapparel.com
Sales Range: $800-899.9 Million
Emp.: 6,200
Holding Company; Women's & Men's Intimate Apparel Mfr & Distr
N.A.I.C.S.: 551112

Subsidiary (Non-US):

DBA Deutschland GmbH　　　(2)
Birkenallee 110 - 134, 48432, Rheine, Germany
Tel.: (49) 59719930
Web Site: https://www.nurdie.de
Sales Range: $125-149.9 Million
Emp.: 400
Women's Intimate Apparel Mfr & Distr
N.A.I.C.S.: 315250

Subsidiary (Domestic):

Hanes France S.A.S.　　　　　(2)
2 rue des Martinets, 92500, Rueil-Malmaison, France
Tel.: (33) 14 759 1515
Web Site: https://www.dim.fr
Jean Apparel Mfr
N.A.I.C.S.: 315250
Francois Riston (Mng Dir & Dir-Publ)

DBApparel South Africa (PTY) Limited　　　　　　　　　　（1）
101 Lawley Street Jacobs, Durban, 4052, South Africa
Tel.: (27) 314608611
Clothing Store Operator
N.A.I.C.S.: 458110

DBApparel UK Ltd　　　　　　(1)
Britannia Wharf Monument Road, Woking, GU21 5LW, United Kingdom
Tel.: (44) 2036081700
Clothing Store Operator
N.A.I.C.S.: 458110
Ed Clyne (Dir-Sls)

DBApparel UK Trading Ltd　　(1)
Britannia Wharf, Woking, GU21 5LW, United Kingdom
Tel.: (44) 1483291450
Emp.: 40
Jean Apparel Mfr
N.A.I.C.S.: 315250

DIM Portugal - Importacao e Comercializacao, Lda.　　　（1）
Estrada de Tires Manique, Sao Domingos de Rana, 2776-953, Portugal
Tel.: (351) 214457100
Clothing Store Operator

N.A.I.C.S.: 458110

GFSI, Inc. (1)
9700 Commerce Pkwy, Lenexa, KS 66219
Tel.: (913) 693-3200
Web Site: http://www.gearforsports.com
Sportswear & Accessories Mfr
N.A.I.C.S.: 315250
James R. Malseed (Pres-Campus Div)

Subsidiary (Domestic):

GearCo, Inc. (2)
9700 Commerce Pkwy, Lenexa, KS 66219
Tel.: (913) 693-3200
Web Site: http://www.gearforsports.com
Sales Range: $200-249.9 Million
Emp.: 700
Sports Apparel Retailer
N.A.I.C.S.: 315250
Jim Malseed (Exec VP-Sales)

Game 7 Athletics S.r.l. (1)
Via Ferrari 2, 41011, Campogalliano, MO, Italy
Tel.: (39) 0419690094
Web Site: http://www.game7athletics.com
Sports Footwear & Apparel Whslr
N.A.I.C.S.: 423910

HBI Receivables LLC (1)
1000 E Hanes Mill Rd, Winston Salem, NC 27105
Tel.: (336) 519-2700
Sportswear, Underwear & Casual Wear Mfr
N.A.I.C.S.: 315250

Hanes Australasia Pty Ltd (1)
115 Cotham Road, Kew, 3101, VIC, Australia
Tel.: (61) 388621400
Web Site: https://www.hanesaustralasia.com
Sales Range: $500-549.9 Million
Emp.: 6,500
Underwear, Hosiery, Footwear, Outerwear & Bedding Mfr
N.A.I.C.S.: 315250
David Ellis (Gen Mgr-Sourcing & Supply)
Joanne Higham (Gen Mgr-Bus Dev)

Subsidiary (Domestic):

Sheridan Australia Pty. Limited (2)
Shop 5018 Level 5 Westfield Centre 500 Oxford St, Bondi Junction, 2022, NSW, Australia
Tel.: (61) 29 386 0112
Web Site: https://www.sheridan.com.au
Broadwoven Fabric Mfr
N.A.I.C.S.: 313210
Paul Gould (Gen Mgr-Grp)
Claudio Alcorso (Founder)

Hanes Austria GmbH (1)
Lastenstrasse 38, 4020, Linz, Austria
Tel.: (43) 7326606500
Web Site: http://www.edoo.at
Men & Women Apparel Mfr
N.A.I.C.S.: 315250

Hanes Bodywear Germany GmbH (1)
Kundenservice Birkenallee 110-134, 48432, Rheine, Germany
Tel.: (49) 8000998899
Textile Products Mfr
N.A.I.C.S.: 313310

Hanes Germany GmbH (1)
Birkenallee 110-134, 48432, Rheine, Germany
Tel.: (49) 5 971 9930
Web Site: https://www.hanes-germany-karriere.de
Emp.: 390
Cloth & Fabric Mfr
N.A.I.C.S.: 315990

Hanes Italy Srl (1)
Via Boschetti 53/55, 24050, Grassobbio, BG, Italy
Tel.: (39) 035678111
Web Site: http://www.lovable.it
Sports Footwear & Apparel Whslr
N.A.I.C.S.: 423910

Hanes Poland Sp. z o.o. (1)
ul Legionow 93/95, 91-072, Lodz, Poland
Tel.: (48) 69 341 4225
Web Site: https://www.bellinda.pl
Clothing Store Operator

N.A.I.C.S.: 458110

Hanes South Africa (PTY) Limited (1)
101 Lawley Street, Jacobs, Durban, 4026, South Africa
Tel.: (27) 314608611
Web Site: http://www.she-bear.co.za
Cloth & Fabric Mfr
N.A.I.C.S.: 315990
Clayton Carter (Dir-Fin)

HanesBrands Brazil Textil Ltda. (1)
Travessa Macapa 120, Cotia, 06703-580, SP, Brazil
Tel.: (55) 1146154800
Web Site: https://www.hanesbrands.com.br
Clothing Retailer
N.A.I.C.S.: 458110

Hanesbrands Direct, LLC (1)
450 W Hanes Mill Rd, Morganton, NC 28655
Tel.: (336) 519-8080
Emp.: 10,001
Women & Infant Apparel Accessory Whslr
N.A.I.C.S.: 424350
Kim Hahn (Sr Mgr-Category Mgmt)
Wanda Hauser (Mgr-Ops Svcs)
Jennifer Leonard (Sr Mgr-Product PR & Events)

Hanesbrands Philippines Inc. (1)
C Dona Irenea st Metro Manila, Ireneville 1 Sucat, Paranaque, 1719, Metro Manila, Philippines
Tel.: (63) 28260095
Web Site: http://www.hanes.com
Emp.: 19
Women & Infant Apparel Accessory Whslr
N.A.I.C.S.: 424350

Hanesbrands ROH Asia Ltd. (1)
Exchange Tower Unit 2801-2804 No 388 Sukhumvit Rd Klong Toey, Klong Toey, Bangkok, 10110, Thailand
Tel.: (66) 26275700
Women & Infant Apparel Accessory Whslr
N.A.I.C.S.: 424350

It's Greek To Me, Inc. (1)
520 McCall Rd, Manhattan, KS 66502
Web Site: https://championteamwear.com
Emp.: 900
Garment Mfr & Distr
N.A.I.C.S.: 315250

Knights Apparel, Inc. (1)
5475 N Blackstock Rd, Spartanburg, SC 29303-4702
Tel.: (864) 587-9690
Web Site: http://www.knightsapparel.com
Emp.: 36
Licensed Sports Apparel Distr
N.A.I.C.S.: 423910
Joseph Bozich (Founder)

Knights Apperal LLC (1)
1545 B US Hwy 19 S, Leesburg, GA 31763
Tel.: (229) 483-0501
Web Site: https://knightsappareldandgifts.com
Clothing Retailer
N.A.I.C.S.: 458110

Lovable Italiana International Limited (1)
Britannia Wharf, Woking, GU21 5LW, United Kingdom
Tel.: (44) 1475504040
Emp.: 3
Trading Stamp Promotion & Redemption Services
N.A.I.C.S.: 561990

Maidenform Brands, LLC (1)
485F US Hwy 1 S, Iselin, NJ 08830
Tel.: (732) 621-2500
Web Site: http://www.maidenform.com
Rev.: $600,277,000
Assets: $435,951,000
Liabilities: $181,667,000
Net Worth: $254,284,000
Earnings: $33,459,000
Emp.: 1,250
Fiscal Year-end: 12/29/2012
Jean Apparel Mfr
N.A.I.C.S.: 315250

Maidenform LLC (1)

1000 E Hanes Mill Rd, Winston Salem, NC 27105
Tel.: (336) 519-8080
Web Site: https://www.maidenform.com
Jean Apparel Mfr
N.A.I.C.S.: 315250
Lucille DeHart (CMO & Sr VP)

National Textiles, LLC (1)
480 Hanes Mill Rd, Winston Salem, NC 27105
Tel.: (336) 714-8400
Sales Range: $300-349.9 Million
Emp.: 5,000
Open-End & Ring-Spun Cotton, Cotton-Polyester Blend Yarns, Knit Fabrics & Cut Parts Mfr
N.A.I.C.S.: 313110

Playtex Apparel, Inc. (1)
1000 E Haines Mill Rd, Winston Salem, NC 27105
Tel.: (336) 519-8080
Sales Range: $200-249.9 Million
Emp.: 1,900
Intimate Apparel Mfr
N.A.I.C.S.: 315250
Vicki Seawright (Dir-Mktg-Intimate Apparel)

Seamless Puerto Rico, Inc. (1)
273 Calle Munoz Rivera, Camuy, PR 00627
Tel.: (787) 262-3610
Web Site: http://www.hanesbrands.com
Emp.: 150
Casual Wear Mfr
N.A.I.C.S.: 315250

Seamless Textiles, LLC (1)
Km 86 3 RR 3, Humacao, PR 00791
Tel.: (787) 850-3440
Web Site: http://www.hanesbrands.com
Emp.: 189
Women & Infant Apparel Accessory Whslr
N.A.I.C.S.: 424350

Sheridan U.K. Limited (1)
Unit 3D Warrington South Distribution Park, Warrington, WA4 4SN, Cheshire, United Kingdom
Tel.: (44) 192 545 3410
Web Site:
https://www.sheridanaustralia.co.uk
Home Appliance Distr
N.A.I.C.S.: 449129

Shock Absorber US Inc (1)
29475 McCabe Rd, Selbyville, DE 19975
Tel.: (302) 436-1844
Emp.: 4
Automotive Parts & Accessory Store Operator
N.A.I.C.S.: 441330

HANMI FINANCIAL CORPORATION

3660 Wilshire Blvd PH A, Los Angeles, CA 90010
Tel.: (213) 382-2200   DE
Web Site: https://www.hanmi.com
Year Founded: 2000
HAFC—(NASDAQ)
Rev.: $308,013,000
Assets: $7,378,262,000
Liabilities: $6,740,747,000
Net Worth: $637,515,000
Earnings: $101,394,000
Emp.: 626
Fiscal Year-end: 12/31/22
Bank Holding Company
N.A.I.C.S.: 551111
Bonita I. Lee (Pres & CEO)
David L. Rosenblum (Vice Chm)
Romolo C. Santarosa (CFO & Sr Exec VP)

Subsidiaries:

Hanmi Bank (1)
950 S Los Angeles St, Los Angeles, CA 90015-1717
Tel.: (213) 347-6051
Web Site: https://www.hanmi.com
Sales Range: $150-199.9 Million
Commercial Banking Services
N.A.I.C.S.: 522110

HANNON ARMSTRONG SUS-

TAINABLE INFRASTRUCTURE CAPITAL, INC.

1 Park Pl Ste 200, Annapolis, MD 21401
Tel.: (410) 571-9860   MD
Web Site: https://www.hasi.com
Year Founded: 2012
HASI—(NYSE)
Rev.: $319,871,000
Assets: $6,552,350,000
Liabilities: $4,410,725,000
Net Worth: $2,141,625,000
Earnings: $148,836,000
Emp.: 139
Fiscal Year-end: 12/31/23
Real Estate Investment Services
N.A.I.C.S.: 523999
Jeffrey W. Eckel (Exec Chm)
Susan Nickey (Chief Client Officer & Exec VP)
Jeffrey A. Lipson (Pres & CEO)
Marc T. Pangburn (CFO)
Amanuel Haile-Mariam (Sr Mng Dir & Mng Dir)
Annmarie Reynolds (Sr Mng Dir & Mng Dir)
Daniela Shapiro (Sr Mng Dir & Mng Dir)
Steven L. Chuslo (Chief Legal Officer & Exec VP)
Charles W. Melko (Chief Acctg Officer, Treas & Sr VP)
Katherine McGregor Dent (Chief HR Officer & Sr VP)
Viral Amin (Chief Risk Officer, Exec VP & Head-Portfolio Mgmt)

Subsidiaries:

HA Howard Services LLC (1)
1800 Saint James Pl, Houston, TX 77056
Tel.: (713) 781-7300
Investment Advisory Services
N.A.I.C.S.: 523940

Hannon Armstrong Securities, LLC (1)
1 Pk Pl Ste 200, Annapolis, MD 21401
Tel.: (410) 571-9860
Web Site: https://www.hasi.com
Financial Management Services
N.A.I.C.S.: 541611

HANOVER BANCORP INC.

80 E Jericho Tpke, Mineola, NY 11501
Tel.: (516) 548-8500
Web Site:
https://www.hanoverbank.com
Year Founded: 2016
HNVR—(NASDAQ)
Rev.: $113,891,000
Assets: $2,149,535,000
Liabilities: $1,963,628,000
Net Worth: $185,907,000
Earnings: $15,164,000
Emp.: 176
Fiscal Year-end: 09/30/23
Bank Holding Company
N.A.I.C.S.: 551111
Brian K. Finneran (Pres)
Michael P. Puorro (Chm & CEO)
Lance P. Burke (CFO & Exec VP)
Denise Chardavoyne (CIO, Chief Retail Officer & Exec VP)
Kenneth Sapanski (Chief Credit Officer & Exec VP)
Robert Marrali (Chief Lending Officer & Sr VP)
Lisa A. DiIorio (Chief Acctg Officer & Sr VP)
Alice T. Rouse (Chief Risk Officer & Sr VP)
James H. Carter (Sr VP-Ops)
Mac Wilcox (Chief Comm Officer, Chm, Chm, Sr Exec VP & Sr Exec VP)

Hanover Bancorp Inc.—(Continued)

Kevin Corbett (*Chief Comm Officer, Chief Credit Officer, Chm, Chm, Sr Exec VP & Sr Exec VP*)
Michael P. Locorriere (*Chief Comm Officer, Chief Credit Officer, Chm, Chm, Sr Exec VP, Sr Exec VP, Exec VP & Exec VP*)

Subsidiaries:

Hanover Community Bank (1)
80 E Jericho Tpke, Mineola, NY 11501.
Tel.: (516) 548-8500
Commericial Banking
N.A.I.C.S.: 522110
Michael P. Puorro (*Chm & CEO*)
Lance P. Burke (*CFO & Exec VP*)
Michael P. Puorro (*Chm & CEO*)
Denise Chardavoyne (*CIO, Chief Retail Officer & Exec VP*)
Kenneth Sapanski (*Chief Credit Officer & Exec VP*)
Robert Marrali (*Chief Lending Officer & Sr VP*)
Lisa A. DiIorio (*Chief Acctg Officer & Sr VP*)
Alice T. Rouse (*Chief Risk Officer & Sr VP*)
James H. Carter (*Sr VP-Ops*)
Michelle Socias (*First VP & Mgr-Mortgage Ops*)
Michael Locorriere (*Chief Municipal Officer & Exec VP*)
McClelland Wilcox (*Pres*)
Joseph Burns (*Chief Lending Officer & Exec VP*)

HANOVER FOODS CORPORATION
1125 Wilson Ave, Hanover, PA 17331
Tel.: (717) 632-6000 PA
Web Site:
https://www.hanoverfoods.com
Year Founded: 1924
HNFSA—(OTCIQ)
Sales Range: Less than $1 Million
Emp.: 2,200
Fruit & Vegetable Canning
N.A.I.C.S.: 311421
Jeff Salo (*Sr VP-Pur*)

Subsidiaries:

Aunt Kitty's Foods, Inc (1)
270 N Mill Rd, Vineland, NJ 08360
Tel.: (856) 691-2100
Web Site: http://www.auntkittys.com
Sales Range: $250-299.9 Million
Food Products Mfr
N.A.I.C.S.: 311900

Bickel's Snack Foods, Inc. (1)
1120 Zinns Quarry Rd, York, PA 17404-3533
Tel.: (717) 843-0738
Web Site: http://www.bickelssnacks.com
Sales Range: $100-124.9 Million
Emp.: 180
Snack Food Mfr
N.A.I.C.S.: 311999

Subsidiary (Domestic):

Troyer Potato Products, Inc. (2)
821 Rte 97 S PO Box 676, Waterford, PA 16441
Tel.: (814) 796-2611
Web Site: http://www.troyerfarms.com
Sales Range: $75-99.9 Million
Potato Chips, Pretzels & Corn Snack Products Mfr
N.A.I.C.S.: 311919

Hanover Foods (1)
PO Box 193, Centre Hall, PA 16828-0193
Tel.: (814) 364-1482
Web Site: http://www.hanoverfoods.com
Sales Range: $75-99.9 Million
Emp.: 180
Frozen Food & Food Processor
N.A.I.C.S.: 311411
Carl Anderson (*Plant Mgr*)

Hanover Foods Corp. (1)
Rte 6 & Duck Creek Rd, Clayton, DE 19938 (100%)
Tel.: (302) 653-9281

Web Site: http://www.hanoverfoods.com
Sales Range: $100-124.9 Million
Emp.: 200
Processor of Canned & Frozen Foods
N.A.I.C.S.: 311421
Bruce Dubuc (*Gen Mgr*)
Justin Prystajko (*Mgr-Field*)
Perry Boulter (*Mgr-Production-USDA*)
Dale Elford (*Mgr-QC*)

HARBOR BANKSHARES CORPORATION
25 W Fayette St, Baltimore, MD 21201
Tel.: (410) 528-1800 MD
Web Site:
https://www.theharborbank.com
Year Founded: 1992
HRBK—(OTCIQ)
Offices of Bank Holding Companies
N.A.I.C.S.: 551111
Joseph Haskins Jr. (*Chm & CEO*)
John G. McLean (*CFO & Sr VP*)
John Lewis (*Exec VP-Chief Admin Officer*)
Stanley Arnold (*Sr VP-Sr Lending Officer*)
Angela Cook (*Sr VP-Chief Credit Officer*)
Tiana Wells-Lawson (*Sr VP-Bus & Economic Dev Officer*)
Tony Thomas (*Mng Dir & Head-Fin Advisory & Asset Mgmt Practice*)

Subsidiaries:

The Harbor Bank of Maryland (1)
25 W Fayette St, Baltimore, MD 21201
Tel.: (410) 528-1800
Web Site: http://www.theharborbank.com
Rev.: $260,000
Emp.: 3
Investment Certificate Sales
N.A.I.C.S.: 523999
Joseph Haskins Jr. (*Pres & CEO*)
Angela Cook (*Mgr-Loan Admin*)
Tammy Walker (*Supvr-Ops*)

HARBOR CUSTOM DEVELOPMENT, INC.
11505 Burnham Dr Ste 301, Gig Harbor, WA 98332
Tel.: (253) 649-0636 WA
Web Site: http://www.harborcustomhomes.com
Year Founded: 2014
HCDI—(NASDAQ)
Rev.: $55,414,300
Assets: $236,166,400
Liabilities: $160,610,500
Net Worth: $75,555,900
Earnings: ($24,681,600)
Emp.: 41
Fiscal Year-end: 12/31/22
Building Construction Services
N.A.I.C.S.: 236116
Sterling Griffin (*Founder*)
Jeffrey B. Habersetzer (*Interim Pres, Interim CEO & COO*)
Yoshi Niino (*Chief Acctg Officer*)
James Burton (*Sec*)

HARBOR DIVERSIFIED, INC.
W6390 Challenger Dr Ste 203, Appleton, WI 54914-9120
Tel.: (920) 749-4188 DE
Web Site: https://www.harbortx.com
HRBR—(OTCIQ)
Rev.: $199,205,000
Assets: $236,304,000
Liabilities: $59,660,000
Net Worth: $176,644,000
Earnings: ($15,985,000)
Emp.: 1,008
Fiscal Year-end: 12/31/23
Pharmaceuticals Mfr
N.A.I.C.S.: 325412
Christine R. Deister (*CEO & Sec*)

Subsidiaries:

Harbor Therapeutics, Inc. (1)
919 Towne Centre Dr Ste 409, San Diego, CA 92122
Tel.: (858) 587-9333
Web Site: http://www.harbortx.com
Pharmaceuticals Mfr
N.A.I.C.S.: 325412

HARBORONE BANCORP, INC.
Tel.: (508) 895-1000 MA
Web Site:
https://www.harborone.com
Year Founded: 2016
HONE—(NASDAQ)
Rev.: $229,239,000
Assets: $5,359,545,000
Liabilities: $4,742,569,000
Net Worth: $616,976,000
Earnings: $45,589,000
Emp.: 609
Fiscal Year-end: 12/31/22
Bank Holding Company
N.A.I.C.S.: 551111
Joseph F. Casey (*Pres & CEO*)
Jean Levesque (*Interim CFO*)
Paul Roukey (*Interim Principal Acctg Officer*)

Subsidiaries:

HarborOne Bank (1)
68 Legion Pkwy, Brockton, MA 02301
Tel.: (508) 895-1000
Web Site: https://www.harborone.com
Banking Services
N.A.I.C.S.: 522110
Joseph F. Casey (*Pres & CEO*)
Scott Sanborn (*Chief Lending Officer & Exec VP*)
David Tryder (*CMO & Sr VP*)
Brenda Diepold (*Exec VP*)
Inez H. Friedman-Boyce (*Chief Legal Officer, Gen Counsel, Sec, Sec & Exec VP*)
H. Scott Sanborn (*Exec VP*)
Brenda K. Diepold (*Exec VP*)
Brent W. Grable (*Sr VP*)
Susan B. Stewart (*Sr VP*)
Stephen W. Finocchio (*Exec VP*)

Subsidiary (Domestic):

HarborOne Mortgage, LLC (2)
650 Elm St Ste 600, Manchester, NH 03101
Tel.: (603) 606-3703
Web Site:
https://www.harboronemortgage.com
Emp.: 250
Mortgage Lending Services
N.A.I.C.S.: 522292
Timothy Boyle (*CFO & Exec VP*)
Camille Madden (*Pres*)
David Gravelle (*Sr VP*)
Anne Desmond (*Sr VP*)
Jason Swanson (*Chief Risk Officer, Chief Risk Officer & Sr VP*)
Laura Beavis (*Sr VP*)
Robert Kostraba (*Sr VP*)

HARFORD BANK
8 W Bel Air Ave, Aberdeen, MD 21001
Tel.: (410) 272-5000
Web Site:
https://www.harfordbank.com
HFBK—(OTCIQ)
Rev.: $19,526,717
Assets: $485,948,582
Liabilities: $440,752,085
Net Worth: $45,196,497
Earnings: $3,197,406
Emp.: 75
Fiscal Year-end: 12/31/20
Commericial Banking
N.A.I.C.S.: 522110
John S. Karas (*Chm*)
Michael F. Allen (*Pres & Principal Exec Officer*)
Lorrie Schenning (*Chief Lending Officer & Exec VP*)
Scott Elliott (*Officer-Bus Dev & Sr VP*)

Danielle Carroll (*Officer-Bus Banking & Asst VP*)
Jamie Bennett (*Officer-Bus Banking & VP*)
Lisa Bair (*Portfolio Mgr*)

HARLEY-DAVIDSON, INC.
3700 W Juneau Ave, Milwaukee, WI 53208
Tel.: (414) 342-4680 WI
Web Site: https://www.harley-davidson.com
Year Founded: 1903
HOG—(NYSE)
Rev.: $5,836,478,000
Assets: $12,140,554,000
Liabilities: $8,888,259,000
Net Worth: $3,252,295,000
Earnings: $695,046,000
Emp.: 6,400
Fiscal Year-end: 12/31/23
Motorcycles, Parts & Accessories Mfr & Distr
N.A.I.C.S.: 336991
Jonathan Root (*CFO*)
Edel O'Sullivan Coyne (*Chief Comml Officer*)
Jochen Zeitz (*Chm & Pres*)
Mark R. Kornetzke (*Chief Acctg Officer*)
David Viney (*Treas & VP*)
Tori Termaat (*Chief HR Officer*)
Theo Keetell (*VP*)
Andy Benka (*CEO*)
David Viney (*Treas & VP*)

Subsidiaries:

H-D Group LLC (1)
3700 W Juneau Ave, Milwaukee, WI 53208
Tel.: (414) 343-4680
Web Site: http://www.harley-davidson.com
Sales Range: $300-349.9 Million
Motorcycle Mfr
N.A.I.C.S.: 336991

H-D U.S.A., LLC (1)
3700 W Juneau Ave, Milwaukee, WI 53208
Tel.: (414) 343-4056
Web Site: http://www.harley-davidson.com
Motorcycle Parts Mfr
N.A.I.C.S.: 336991

Harley-Davidson Australia Pty. Limited (1)
1 Sirius Rd, PO Box 133, North Ryde, 1670, NSW, Australia
Tel.: (61) 298860600
Web Site: https://www.harley-davidson.com
Emp.: 48
Automobile & Motor Whslr
N.A.I.C.S.: 423110

Harley-Davidson Canada LP (1)
100 New Park Place Suite 330, Vaughan, L4K 0H9, ON, Canada
Tel.: (905) 660-3500
Motor Cycle Distr
N.A.I.C.S.: 423110

Harley-Davidson Dealer Systems, Inc. (1)
9885 Rockside Rd Ste 100, Valley View, OH 44125
Web Site: http://www.hdds.com
Automobile & Motor Vehicle Whslr
N.A.I.C.S.: 423110

Harley-Davidson Europe Limited (1)
Globe House 1 Chertsey Rd, Twickenham, TW1 1LR, United Kingdom
Tel.: (44) 8709041450
Web Site: http://www.harley-davidson.co.uk
Sales Range: $75-99.9 Million
Emp.: 150
Holding Company
N.A.I.C.S.: 551112

Subsidiary (Non-US):

Harley-Davidson Benelux B.V. (2)
Postbus 75, NL-2280 AH, Rijswijk, Netherlands
Tel.: (31) 707574909
Web Site: http://www.harley-davidson.com

Motorcycle Dealers
N.A.I.C.S.: 336991

Harley-Davidson Espana S.L. (2)
Av De las Cortes Catalanas 9-11 edificio 3,
08173, Sant Cugat del Valles, Barcelona,
Spain
Tel.: (34) 932022800
Web Site: https://www.harley-davidson.com
Sales Range: $10-24.9 Million
Emp.: 14
Motorcycle Mfr
N.A.I.C.S.: 336991

Subsidiary (Domestic):

**Harley-Davidson Financial Services
Europe Ltd.** (2)
115 Colmore Row, PO Box 3627, Birming-
ham, B3 3AL, Wokingham, United Kingdom
Tel.: (44) 1865 719068
Web Site: http://www.harley-davidson.com
Sales Range: $25-49.9 Million
Emp.: 45
Motorcycle Mfr
N.A.I.C.S.: 336991

Subsidiary (Non-US):

Harley-Davidson GmbH (2)
Konrad - Adenauer Str 3, Neu-Isenburg,
63263, Germany
Tel.: (49) 49 06105 284 0
Web Site: http://www.harley-davidson.com
Emp.: 45
Motorcycle Mfr
N.A.I.C.S.: 336991

Harley-Davidson Italia S.r.l. (2)
Via Privata Bastia 5, 20139, Milan, MI, Italy
Tel.: (39) 0286886811
Web Site: https://www.harley-davidson.com
Motorcycle Mfr
N.A.I.C.S.: 336991

**Harley-Davidson Switzerland
GmbH** (2)
Buckhauserstrasse 26, 8048, Zurich, Swit-
zerland
Tel.: (41) 844427539
Web Site: http://www.harley-davidson.com
Sales Range: $10-24.9 Million
Emp.: 7
Motorcycles
N.A.I.C.S.: 336991

**Harley-Davidson Financial Services,
Inc.** (1)
PO Box 22048, Carson City, NV 89721-
2048
Tel.: (414) 343-4056
Web Site: https://www.myhdfs.com
Sales Range: $125-149.9 Million
Motorcycle Mfr
N.A.I.C.S.: 336991

Subsidiary (Domestic):

**Harley-Davidson Financial Services
International, Inc.** (2)
8272 Gateway Blvd E, El Paso, TX 79907
Tel.: (915) 592-5804
Web Site: http://www.harley-davidson.com
Emp.: 100
Financial Services
N.A.I.C.S.: 522390

Subsidiary (Non-US):

**Harley-Davidson Financial Services
Canada, Inc.** (3)
100 New Park Place Ste 330, Vaughan,
L4K 0H9, ON, Canada
Tel.: (905) 660-3500
Automobile & Motor Parts Whslr
N.A.I.C.S.: 423110

Subsidiary (Domestic):

**Harley-Davidson Insurance Services
of Illinois, Inc.** (2)
3700 W Juneau Ave, Milwaukee, WI 53208
Tel.: (414) 342-4680
Insurance Services
N.A.I.C.S.: 524126

Harley-Davidson France SAS (1)
Europarc 12 rue Eugene Dupuis, 94043,
Creteil, Cedex, France
Tel.: (33) 158431200

Web Site: https://www.harley-davidson.com
Sales Range: $25-49.9 Million
Emp.: 25
Automobile & Motor Vehicle Whlsr
N.A.I.C.S.: 423110

**Harley-Davidson Holding Co.,
Inc.** (1)
3700 W Juneau Ave, Milwaukee, WI 53208-
2818
Tel.: (414) 343-4782
Web Site: http://www.harley-davidson.com
Motorcycle Mfr & Whlsr
N.A.I.C.S.: 336991

Subsidiary (Non-US):

**Harley-Davidson (Thailand) Company
Limited** (2)
388 Rama IX Road, Bangkapi Huaikhwang
District, Bangkok, 10310, Thailand
Tel.: (66) 23188488
Web Site: https://www.harley-
davidsonbangkok.com
Motor Vehicle Distr
N.A.I.C.S.: 423110

**Harley-Davidson Canada GP
Inc.** (2)
100 New Park Place Suite 330, Vaughan,
L4K 0H9, ON, Canada
Tel.: (905) 660-3500
Motor Vehicle Distr
N.A.I.C.S.: 423110

**Harley-Davidson Central and Eastern
Europe s.r.o.** (2)
Bucharova 1281/2, 158 00, Prague, Czech
Republic
Tel.: (420) 245001180
Motorcycle Mfr
N.A.I.C.S.: 336991
Michal Fric *(Mgr-Mktg)*

**Harley-Davidson Insurance Services,
Inc.** (1)
222 W Adams St, Chicago, IL 60606
Tel.: (312) 368-9501
Web Site: https://www.insurance.harley-
davidson.com
Sales Range: $50-74.9 Million
Emp.: 1,000
Insurance Services
N.A.I.C.S.: 524298

**Harley-Davidson Motor Company Op-
erations, Inc.** (1)
1425 Eden Rd, York, PA 17402
Tel.: (717) 505-7093
Automobile & Motor Vehicle Whlsr
N.A.I.C.S.: 423110

Subsidiary (Domestic):

**H-D Tomahawk Industrial Park,
LLC** (2)
426 E Somo Ave & 611 Kaphaem Rd,
Tomahawk, WI 54487
Tel.: (715) 453-2191
Web Site: http://www.harley-davidson.com
Automobile & Motorcycle Whslr
N.A.I.C.S.: 423110

**Harley-Davidson Motor Company,
Inc.** (1)
3700 W Juneau Ave, Milwaukee, WI
53208 **(100%)**
Tel.: (414) 343-4056
Web Site: https://www.harley-davidson.com
Sales Range: $450-499.9 Million
Emp.: 1,500
Motorcycles, Motorcycle Clothing & Acces-
sories
N.A.I.C.S.: 336991
Luke Mansfield *(Chief Comml Officer)*
Bryan Niketh *(Sr VP-Product & Ops)*
Jagdish Krishnan *(Chief Digital Officer)*

Subsidiary (Domestic):

HASC, LLC (2)
3993 Jurupa Ave Ste 105, Riverside, CA
92506
Tel.: (951) 222-2284
Web Site: http://www.hasc.org
Motorcycles Bicycles & Parts Mfr
N.A.I.C.S.: 336991
Dimitrios Alexiou *(Co-Pres & CEO)*
Julia Slininger *(VP-Reg Quality Network)*
Ana Reza *(VP-Patient Access Svcs)*

Patricia Wall *(VP-Membership & Education
Svcs)*
Teri Hollingsworth *(VP-HR Svcs)*
Soraya Peters *(VP-Health Care Comm
Tech)*
Adam Blackstone *(VP-External Affairs &
Strategic Comm)*
Gustavo Valdespino *(Treas)*
Paul Young *(Sr VP-Pub Policy & Reim-
bursement)*
Scott Twomey *(Sr VP)*
Joe Avelino *(Sec)*
Lisa Mitchell *(Mgr-Program & Workforce
Dev)*
Susan Harrington *(Exec Dir-Communities
Lifting Communities)*
Erik Skindrud *(Dir-Program-Electronic &
Print Publications)*
Jamila Mayers *(Dir-Program-Education)*
Katrina Quinto *(Dir-Membership Svcs)*
Darryl Sanford *(Dir-Member Rels & Assoc
Svcs)*
Tom Soto *(Dir-IT)*
Robert Vlach *(Dir-HR)*
George W. Greene *(Co-Pres)*
Kristina Tran *(Controller)*
Bernard Klein *(Chm)*

Harley-Davidson Retail, Inc. (2)
3700 W Juneau Ave, Milwaukee, WI 53208
Tel.: (887) 437-8625
Motorcycle Mfr
N.A.I.C.S.: 336991

**Harley-Davidson Motorcycle Trust
2013-1** (1)
c/o Wilmington Trust Company National As-
sociation 1100 N Market St, Wilmington, DE
19801-1605
Tel.: (302) 636-6000
Trust Management Services
N.A.I.C.S.: 523991
James Darrell Thomas *(Treas, VP & Asst
Sec)*
James Darrell Thomas *(Treas, VP & Asst
Sec)*

StaCyc, Inc. (1)
6861 Corporation Pkwy Ste 100, Fort
Worth, TX 76126
Tel.: (951) 813-2084
Web Site: http://www.stacyc.com
Motorcycle Mfr
N.A.I.C.S.: 336991

HARLEYSVILLE FINANCIAL
CORPORATION
271 Main St, Harleysville, PA 19438
Tel.: (215) 256-8828 **PA**
Web Site:
   https://www.harleysvillebank.com
Year Founded: 1915
HARL—(OTCIQ)
Rev.: $29,620,000
Assets: $854,876,000
Liabilities: $776,245,000
Net Worth: $78,631,000
Earnings: $7,111,000
Fiscal Year-end: 09/30/20
Bank Holding Company
N.A.I.C.S.: 551111
Ronald B. Geib *(Chm)*
Adrian D. Gordon *(CIO, Sec & Sr VP)*
Sheri L. Strouse *(Chief Retail Officer
& Sr VP)*
Stephen J. Kopenhaver *(Chief Lend-
ing Officer & Sr VP)*
M. Shane Michalak *(CFO & Sr VP)*
Brendan J. McGill *(Pres & CEO)*
Joe Bergquist *(Officer-Comml Loan &
VP)*
Suzette Gardner *(Controller & Asst
VP)*
Sarah Dandridge *(Asst VP)*
Diane Heisler *(Asst VP)*
Christopher Jennings *(Officer-Comml
Loan & Asst VP)*
Scott Little *(Officer-Comml Loan &
VP)*
Craig M. Munson *(Officer-Credit &
VP)*
Brian R. Murphy *(Asst VP)*
Ryan Schuck *(Officer-Comml Loan &
VP)*

L. Shollenberger *(Officer-Comml Loan
& VP)*
Jo Wanamaker *(Asst VP)*

Subsidiaries:

Harleysville Savings Bank (1)
271 Main St, Harleysville, PA 19438-2495
Tel.: (215) 256-8828
Web Site: http://www.harleysvillebank.com
Sales Range: $100-124.9 Million
Emp.: 130
Banking Services
N.A.I.C.S.: 522110
Ronald B. Geib *(Pres & CEO)*
Sarah Kelsh *(Asst VP & Mgr-Sumneytown)*

HARMONIC, INC.
2590 Orchard Pkwy, San Jose, CA
95131
Tel.: (408) 542-2500 **DE**
Web Site:
   https://www.harmonicinc.com
Year Founded: 1988
HLIT—(NASDAQ)
Rev.: $607,907,000
Assets: $768,206,000
Liabilities: $331,332,000
Net Worth: $436,874,000
Earnings: $83,994,000
Emp.: 1,359
Fiscal Year-end: 12/31/23
Fiber Optic & Wireless Network
Transmission Products to Enable
Video-on-Demand Services
N.A.I.C.S.: 334220
Neven Haltmayer *(Sr VP-R&D &
Video Bus)*
Nimrod Ben-Natan *(Pres & CEO)*
Walter F. Jankovic *(CFO & Principal
Acctg Officer)*
Timothy C. Chu *(Gen Counsel, Sec &
Sr VP-HR)*
Jeremy Rosenberg *(Sr VP-Bus Dev)*
Jean-Marc Guiot *(Sr VP-Ops & IT)*
Crystele Trevisan *(Sr VP-Corp Mktg
& Comm)*
Walter Jankovic *(CFO)*
Gil Rudge *(Sr VP)*

Subsidiaries:

Harmonic (UK) Limited (1)
IQ Farnborough Ground Floor 250 Fowler
Avenue, Farnborough, GU14 7JP, Hamp-
shire, United Kingdom
Tel.: (44) 125 255 5400
Web Site: http://www.harmonicinc.com
Emp.: 30
Video Processing Equipment Mfr
N.A.I.C.S.: 334220

Harmonic Europe S.A.S. (1)
50 rue Camille Desmoulins, 1st floor,
92130, Moulineaux, France
Tel.: (33) 149195770
Sales Range: $10-24.9 Million
Emp.: 2
Video Infrastructure Products Mfr
N.A.I.C.S.: 334310
Ian Graham *(VP-Sls-EMEA)*

Harmonic France SAS (1)
12 rue Rouget de I Isle 1st Floor, 92130,
Issy-les-Moulineaux, France
Tel.: (33) 299285000
Video Streaming & Broadband Access Ser-
vices
N.A.I.C.S.: 518210

**Harmonic International Australia Pty.
Ltd.** (1)
Unit 1/ Level 1 706 Mowbray Rd, Lane
Cove, 2066, NSW, Australia
Tel.: (61) 294278839
Telecommunication Products Mfr
N.A.I.C.S.: 334220

Harmonic International Limited (1)
Unit 01 - 02 12/F C-Bons International Cen-
ter 108 Wai Yip Street, Kowloon, Kwun
Tong, China (Hong Kong)
Tel.: (852) 25268382
Web Site: https://www.harmonic-intl.com.hk

Harmonic, Inc.—(Continued)

Broadcast & Wireless Communications
Equipment Mfr
N.A.I.C.S.: 334220

Harmonic Technologies (Beijing) Co.
Ltd. **(1)**
Rm 1108 Office Tower B Global Trade Center No 36, North 3rd Ring Rd East, Beijing,
100013, China
Tel.: (86) 1057982600
Telecommunication Products Mfr
N.A.I.C.S.: 334220

Harmonic Technologies (HK)
Limited **(1)**
Level 23 Office Tower Langham Place 8
Argyle Street, Mongkok, Kowloon, China
(Hong Kong)
Tel.: (852) 3 713 9300
Web Site: http://www.harmonicinc.com
Digital Video Equipment Mfr
N.A.I.C.S.: 334310

Harmonic Video Systems Ltd. **(1)**
Industrial Pk Pardes Hana 19 Alon Hatavor
St, PO Box 3600, Caesarea, 38900,
Israel **(100%)**
Tel.: (972) 46230150
Sales Range: $25-49.9 Million
Emp.: 70
Manufactures Fiber-Optic & Digital Systems
for Delivering Video, Voice & Data Services
N.A.I.C.S.: 334310

Omneon, Inc. **(1)**
4300 N 1st St, San Jose, CA 95134
Tel.: (408) 542-2500
Web Site: http://www.harmonic.com
Sales Range: $75-99.9 Million
Emp.: 219
Networked Media Storage & Servers for
Production & Broadcast
N.A.I.C.S.: 541519

**HARMONY BIOSCIENCES
HOLDINGS, INC.**
630 W Germantown Pike Ste 215,
Plymouth Meeting, PA 19462
Tel.: (484) 539-9800 DE
Web Site:
https://www.harmonybiosciences.com
Year Founded: 2017
HRMY—(NASDAQ)
Rev.: $582,022,000
Assets: $811,448,000
Liabilities: $344,456,000
Net Worth: $466,992,000
Earnings: $128,853,000
Emp.: 246
Fiscal Year-end: 12/31/23
Holding Company
N.A.I.C.S.: 551112
Christian Ulrich (Gen Counsel)
Sandip Kapadia (CFO)
Jeffrey S. Aronin (Founder)
Jeffrey M. Dayno (Pres & CEO)
Andrew Serafin (Chief Strategy Officer)
Jeffrey Dierks (Chief Comml Officer &
Exec VP)
Nancy Leone (Head-Corp Comm)
David Bradshaw (Head-Technical
Ops)
Cate McCanless (Head-Corp Affairs
& Pub Policy)
Lisa Caperelli (Head-IR)
Tricia Glover (Chief Compliance Officer)
Sharon Goldbach (Head-Facilities
Ops & Exec Admin)
Audrey Murphy (Head-HR)

Subsidiaries:

Zynerba Pharmaceuticals, Inc. **(1)**
80 W Lancaster Ave Ste 300, Devon, PA
19333
Tel.: (484) 581-7505
Web Site: https://www.zynerba.com
Rev.: $846,860
Assets: $55,520,894

Liabilities: $9,292,137
Net Worth: $46,228,757
Earnings: ($35,035,806)
Emp.: 25
Fiscal Year-end: 12/31/2022
Pharmaceuticals Mfr
N.A.I.C.S.: 325412
Christian Ulrich (Sec)
Sandip Kapadia (CEO)

HARRIS EXPLORATION, INC.
19 Scheckler Cutoff, Fallon, NV
89406
Tel.: (775) 867-4004
Web Site:
https://www.harrisexploration.com
HXPN—(OTCIQ)
Commercial Banking Services
N.A.I.C.S.: 522110
Pat Harris (Pres & Mgr-Business Development)
Ray Gordon (Mgr-Coring Ops)
Jason Hazlett (Mgr-Reverse Circulation)
Mike Wasylyshen (Mgr-Health,
Safety, and Environment)

HARTE HANKS, INC.
1 Executive Dr Ste 303, Chelmsford,
MA 01824
Tel.: (512) 434-1100 DE
Web Site:
https://www.hartehanks.com
Year Founded: 1920
HHS—(NASDAQ)
Rev.: $206,278,000
Assets: $119,984,000
Liabilities: $101,176,000
Net Worth: $18,808,000
Earnings: $36,776,000
Emp.: 1,881
Fiscal Year-end: 12/31/22
Business Publications, Direct Response Marketing, Direct-to-
Consumer
N.A.I.C.S.: 541860
David A. Garrison (CFO)
Ben Chacko (Mng Dir-Customer
Care)
Nina Hall (VP-People & HR)
Pat O'Brien (Mng Dir-Fulfillment &
Logistics)
Bob Wyman (Corp Counsel)
Elliott Peterson (CTO)

Subsidiaries:

Harte Hanks Consulting **(1)**
1404 Larimer St, Denver, CO 80202-1714
Tel.: (720) 035-4136
Web Site: http://www.aleutianconsulting.com
Management Consulting Services
N.A.I.C.S.: 541618

Harte Hanks Direct
Marketing/Cincinnati, Inc. **(1)**
2950 Robertson Ave, Cincinnati, OH 45209-
1266
Tel.: (513) 458-7610
Sales Range: $50-74.9 Million
Emp.: 125
Direct Marketing Services
N.A.I.C.S.: 541870

Subsidiary (Domestic):

Harte-Hanks Direct
Marketing/Jacksonville, LLC **(2)**
1 Executive Dr Ste303, Chelmsford, MA
01824 **(100%)**
Tel.: (410) 636-6660
Web Site: http://www.harte-hanks.com
Sales Range: $25-49.9 Million
Emp.: 400
Direct Marketing Services
N.A.I.C.S.: 541870

Harte-Hanks Belgium NV **(1)**
Ekkelgaarden 6B, 3500, Hasselt, Belgium
Tel.: (32) 11300300
Direct Marketing Services
N.A.I.C.S.: 327910

Harte-Hanks CRM Services Belgium
N.V. **(1)**
Ekkelgaarden 6B, 3500, Hasselt, Belgium
Tel.: (32) 11300300
Web Site: http://www.hartehanks.com
Sales Range: $50-74.9 Million
Emp.: 40
Management Consulting Services
N.A.I.C.S.: 541611

Harte-Hanks Data Technologies,
Inc. **(1)**
25 Linneli Cir, Billerica, MA 01821
Tel.: (978) 663-9955
Web Site: http://www.hartehanks.com
Sales Range: $50-74.9 Million
Emp.: 200
Computer Information Systems & Services
N.A.I.C.S.: 518210

Harte-Hanks Direct
Marketing/Baltimore, Inc. **(1)**
4545 Annapolis Rd, Baltimore, MD 21227
Tel.: (410) 636-6660
Web Site: http://www.harte-hanks.com
Sales Range: $75-99.9 Million
Emp.: 249
Direct Marketing Services
N.A.I.C.S.: 541870

Harte-Hanks Direct Marketing/Dallas,
L.P. **(1)**
2750 114th St Ste 100, Grand Prairie, TX
75050 **(100%)**
Tel.: (972) 660-4242
Web Site: http://www.harte-hanks.com
Sales Range: $25-49.9 Million
Emp.: 100
Direct Marketing Services
N.A.I.C.S.: 541860

Branch (Domestic):

Harte-Hanks Direct Marketing **(2)**
2800 Wells Branch Pkwy, Austin, TX
78728-6762 **(100%)**
Tel.: (512) 434-1100
Marketing Consulting Services
N.A.I.C.S.: 541611

Harte-Hanks Direct
Marketing/Fullerton, Inc. **(1)**
2337 W Commonwealth Ave, Fullerton, CA
92833 **(100%)**
Tel.: (714) 738-5478
Web Site: http://www.pennysaverusa.com
Sales Range: $25-49.9 Million
Emp.: 85
Direct Marketing Services
N.A.I.C.S.: 541870

Harte-Hanks Direct Marketing/Kansas
City, LLC **(1)**
6700 Orville Ave Ste100, Kansas City, KS
66102-3126
Tel.: (913) 312-8100
Web Site: http://www.harte-hanks.com
Sales Range: $75-99.9 Million
Emp.: 499
Direct Marketing Services
N.A.I.C.S.: 541870

Harte-Hanks Direct, Inc. **(1)**
2050 Cabot Blvd W, Langhorne, PA 19047
Tel.: (215) 750-6600
Web Site: http://www.harte-hanks.com
Sales Range: $50-74.9 Million
Emp.: 180
Direct Marketing Services
N.A.I.C.S.: 541870

Harte-Hanks Florida, Inc. **(1)**
201 Kelsey Ln, Tampa, FL 33619-4300
Tel.: (813) 626-9430
Direct Marketing Services
N.A.I.C.S.: 541870
Anne Matthews (Sr Acct Mgr)

Subsidiary (Domestic):

Harte Hanks Logistics, LLC **(2)**
1400 E Newport Center Dr Ste 200, Deerfield Beach, FL 33442
Tel.: (954) 429-3771
Web Site: http://hhl1.harte-hanks.com
Freight Trucking Transportation Services
N.A.I.C.S.: 484121

Harte-Hanks Flyer, Inc. **(1)**
201 Kelsey Ln, Tampa, FL 33619

Tel.: (813) 626-9430
Emp.: 200
Direct Mail Advertising Services
N.A.I.C.S.: 541860
James Tucker (CFO)

Harte-Hanks Market Intelligence Europe B.V. **(1)**
Martinus Nijhofflaan 2, 2624 ES, Delft, Zuid-
Holland, Netherlands
Tel.: (31) 152569251
Direct Mail Advertising Services
N.A.I.C.S.: 541860

Harte-Hanks Response
Management/Boston, Inc. **(1)**
600 N Bedford St, East Bridgewater, MA
02333 **(100%)**
Tel.: (508) 894-1500
Web Site: http://www.hartehanks.com
Sales Range: $75-99.9 Million
Emp.: 224
Direct Marketing Services
N.A.I.C.S.: 541870

Harte-Hanks Shoppers Inc. **(1)**
2830 Orbiter St, Brea, CA 92821
Tel.: (714) 996-8900
Marketing Consulting Services
N.A.I.C.S.: 541613
Al Chappell (Mgr)

Harte-Hanks Stock Plan, Inc. **(1)**
Tel.: (210) 829-9000
Stock Exchange Services
N.A.I.C.S.: 523999

Subsidiary (Non-US):

Harte-Hanks Direct Marketing/Dallas,
Inc. **(2)**
Tel.: (972) 660-4242
Direct Mail Advertising Services
N.A.I.C.S.: 541860

Harte-Hanks Tampa Flyer Inc. **(1)**
201 Kelsey Ln, Tampa, FL 33619 **(100%)**
Tel.: (813) 626-9430
Web Site: http://www.theflyer.com
Sales Range: $50-74.9 Million
Emp.: 250
Shopper Guide Publisher
N.A.I.C.S.: 513199

Harte-Hanks, Inc. **(1)**
1525 NW 3rd St Ste 21, Deerfield Beach,
FL 33442-1667
Tel.: (954) 429-3771
Web Site: http://www.hhlogistics.com
Sales Range: $25-49.9 Million
Emp.: 130
Direct Marketing Services
N.A.I.C.S.: 541860

Harte-Hanks, Inc. **(1)**
165 New Commerce Blvd, Wilkes Barre, PA
18706
Tel.: (570) 826-0414
Web Site: http://www.hartehanks.com
Direct Marketing Services
N.A.I.C.S.: 541860

Trillium Software, Inc. **(1)**
17 New England Executive Park Ste 300,
Burlington, MA 01803
Tel.: (978) 901-0000
Web Site: http://www.trilliumsoftware.com
Software Publisher
N.A.I.C.S.: 513210

**HARTFORD GREAT HEALTH
CORP.**
8832 Glendon Way, Rosemead, CA
91770
Tel.: (626) 321-1915 NV
Web Site:
https://www.hfuscreative.com
Year Founded: 2008
HFUS—(OTCIQ)
Rev.: $1,399,945
Assets: $3,688,968
Liabilities: $7,042,442
Net Worth: ($3,353,474)
Earnings: $1,092,874
Emp.: 19
Fiscal Year-end: 07/31/24
Medical Equipment Mfr

N.A.I.C.S.: 339112
Sheng-Yih Chang (CEO)

HARVARD APPARATUS REGENERATIVE TECHNOLOGY, INC.

Hill Rd Ste 11, Holliston, MA 01746
Tel.: (774) 233-7300   DE
Web Site: https://hregen.com
Year Founded: 2009
HRGN—(OTCQB)
Rev.: $103,000
Assets: $2,614,000
Liabilities: $968,000
Net Worth: $1,646,000
Earnings: ($8,945,000)
Emp.: 18
Fiscal Year-end: 12/31/23
Regenerated Organ Biotechnological Device Mfr
N.A.I.C.S.: 339113
David Green (Founder)
William Fodor (Chief Scientific Officer)
Shunfu Hu (VP-Bus Dev & Ops)
Hong Yu (Pres)
Linghui Meng (Dir-Product Dev)
Jerry Junli He (CEO)
Joseph L. Damasio Jr. (CFO)

HARVARD BIOSCIENCE, INC.

84 October Hill Rd, Holliston, MA 01746
Tel.: (508) 893-8999   DE
Web Site:
   https://www.harvardbioscience.com
Year Founded: 1901
HBIO—(NASDAQ)
Rev.: $113,335,000
Assets: $145,360,000
Liabilities: $73,140,000
Net Worth: $72,220,000
Earnings: ($9,516,000)
Emp.: 436
Fiscal Year-end: 12/31/22
Life Science Analytical Instrument Developer, Mfr & Marketer
N.A.I.C.S.: 334516
James W. Green (Chm, Pres & CEO)
Ryan Wallace (VP-Sls-Global & Preclinical Sys)
Jennifer Cote (CFO, Principal Acctg Officer & Treas)
David Balcom (Sr VP)
John Fry (Sec)
Lori Packer (VP)
Diane Houston (VP)
Nitya Shetty (VP)

Subsidiaries:

AHN Biotechnologie GmbH   (1)
Uthleber Weg 14, 99734, Nordhausen, Germany
Tel.: (49) 3631652420
Web Site: https://www.ahn-bio.de
Analytical Laboratory Instrument Mfr
N.A.I.C.S.: 334516

BTX   (1)
84 October Hill Rd, Holliston, MA 01746
Tel.: (508) 893-8999
Web Site: https://www.btxonline.com
Sales Range: $1-9.9 Million
Emp.: 10
Electroporation & Electrofusion Equipment Mfr
N.A.I.C.S.: 334516

Biochrom Ltd.   (1)
Building 1020 Cambourne Business Park, Cambourne, Cambridge, CB23 6DW, United Kingdom   (100%)
Tel.: (44) 1223423723
Web Site: http://www.biochrom.co.uk
Sales Range: $10-24.9 Million
Emp.: 60
Developer of Drug Discovery Research Tools for Pharmaceutical & Biotechnology Companies
N.A.I.C.S.: 325412

Biochrom US, Inc.   (1)
84 October Hill Rd, Holliston, MA 01746-1388
Web Site: http://www.harvardbiochrom.com
Emp.: 100
Medical Research Tools & Equipment Mfr
N.A.I.C.S.: 334516

Coulbourn Instruments, LLC   (1)
5583 Roosevelt St, Whitehall, PA 18052
Tel.: (610) 395-3771
Web Site: https://www.coulbourn.com
Sales Range: $10-24.9 Million
Emp.: 11
Life Science Laboratory Instrument Developer Mfr
N.A.I.C.S.: 334516

Data Sciences International   (1)
119 14th St NW Ste 100, Saint Paul, MN 55112
Tel.: (651) 481-7404
Web Site: https://www.datasci.com
Implantable Telemetric Physiologic Monitors Mfr
N.A.I.C.S.: 339112
Lori Packer (Head-HR-Global)
Dave Franz (Dir-Fin)
Mark Hodge (VP-Ops)
Ryan Wallace (VP-Sls-Global)

Denville Scientific, Inc.   (1)
3005 Hadley Rd, South Plainfield, NJ 07080
Tel.: (908) 757-7577
Web Site: http://www.denvillescientific.com
Emp.: 100
Research Equipment & Plastic Products Mfr
N.A.I.C.S.: 334516

FKA GSI US, Inc.   (1)
84 October Hill Rd, Holliston, MA 01746
Tel.: (508) 893-8999
Genomic & Proteomic Instrumentation, Software, Consumables & Services Mfr, Designer, Developer & Marketer
N.A.I.C.S.: 334516

FKAUBI, Inc.   (1)
84 October Hill Rd, Holliston, MA 01746
Tel.: (508) 893-3115
Application Software Development Services
N.A.I.C.S.: 513210

HEKA Electronik Dr. Schulze GmbH   (1)
Wiesenstrasse 55, 67466, Lambrecht, Germany
Tel.: (49) 632595530
Web Site: https://www.heka.com
Scientific Measuring Instrument Mfr
N.A.I.C.S.: 423490

HEKA Instruments Incorporated   (1)
84 October Hill Rd, Holliston, MA 01746
Tel.: (516) 882-1155
Scientific Measuring Instrument Mfr
N.A.I.C.S.: 423490

Harvard Apparatus Limited   (1)
Fircroft Way, Edenbridge, TN8 6HE, Kent, United Kingdom
Tel.: (44) 1732864001
Web Site:
   http://www.harvardapparatus.co.uk
Sales Range: $10-24.9 Million
Emp.: 20
Developer of Drug Discovery Research Tools for Pharmaceutical & Biotechnology Companies
N.A.I.C.S.: 325412

Harvard Apparatus S.A.R.L.   (1)
6 Ave des Andes Miniparc - Bat 8, 91952, Les Ulis, Cedex, France   (100%)
Tel.: (33) 164460085
Web Site: http://www.harvardapparatus.fr
Sales Range: $10-24.9 Million
Emp.: 2
Developer of Drug Discovery Research Tools for Pharmaceutical & Biotechnology Companies
N.A.I.C.S.: 325412

Harvard Bioscience (Shanghai) Co. Ltd.   (1)
Room 8C Zhongxi Tower 121 Jiangsu Road, Changning District, Shanghai, 200050, China
Tel.: (86) 2162260239
Pharmaceutical Research Instrument & Equipment Mfr

N.A.I.C.S.: 339112
Dewen Deng (Gen Mgr & Dir-Asia Bus)

Hugo Sachs Elektronik-Harvard Apparatus GmbH   (1)
Gruenstrasse 1, Hugstetten, 79232, March, Germany
Tel.: (49) 766592000
Web Site: https://www.hugo-sachs.de
Sales Range: $10-24.9 Million
Emp.: 16
Laboratory Equipment Mfr
N.A.I.C.S.: 334516

KD Scientific, Inc.   (1)
84 October Hill Rd, Holliston, MA 01746
Tel.: (508) 429-6809
Web Site: https://www.kdscientific.com
Sales Range: $25-49.9 Million
Emp.: 21
Life Science Analytical Instrument Mfr
N.A.I.C.S.: 339112

Multi Channel Systems MCS GmbH   (1)
Aspenhaustrasse 21, 72770, Reutlingen, Germany
Tel.: (49) 7121909250
Web Site:
   https://www.multichannelsystems.com
Scientific Measuring Instrument Mfr
N.A.I.C.S.: 423490
Karl-Heinz Boven (Co-Founder)
Andreas Moller (Co-Founder)
Joe Eyles (CEO)
Benjamin Haase (Controller-Fin)
Florian Ludwig (Mgr-Pur)
Georg Schmidt (Head-HR-EMEA)
Karla Bellack (Mgr-Mktg)
Horst Strobel (Head-Production Dept)
Dieter Patzwahl (Head-Software Dept)
Jannis Meents (Head-Res Projects & Predevelopment)

Panlab s.l.   (1)
C/ Energia112, 08940, Cornella, Barcelona, Spain
Tel.: (34) 934750697
Web Site: https://www.panlab.com
Sales Range: $10-24.9 Million
Emp.: 35
Life Science Research Software Publisher
N.A.I.C.S.: 513210

Scie-Plas Ltd.   (1)
East Wing Building 1020 Cambourne Business Park, Cambourne, Cambridge, CB23 6DW, United Kingdom
Tel.: (44) 1223427888
Web Site: http://www.scie-plas.com
Gel Electrophoresis Equipment Mfr
N.A.I.C.S.: 327910

Triangle Biosystems Inc.   (1)
2224 Page Rd Ste 108, Durham, NC 27703-3908
Tel.: (919) 361-2663
Electromedical & Electrotherapeutic Apparatus Mfr
N.A.I.C.S.: 334510

Warner Instruments LLC   (1)
84 October Hill Rd, Holliston, MA 01746
Tel.: (508) 893-8999
Web Site: https://www.warneronline.com
Medical Research Tools & Equipment Mfr
N.A.I.C.S.: 334510
Ralph Abate (Gen Mgr)

HARVEST CAPITAL CREDIT CORPORATION

767 3rd Ave 29th Fl, New York, NY 10017
Tel.: (212) 906-3589
Web Site:
   http://www.harvestcapitalcredit.com
Year Founded: 2011
HCAP—(NASDAQ)
Rev.: $11,547,816
Assets: $129,944,513
Liabilities: $67,727,992
Net Worth: $62,216,521
Earnings: $1,664,179
Fiscal Year-end: 12/31/20
Investment Services
N.A.I.C.S.: 523999

Joseph Andrew Jolson (Chm & Co-CEO)
James J. Fowler (Co-Chief Investment Officer)
Ted Goldthorpe (Co-CEO)
Jason Roos (Co-CFO, Treas & Co-Sec)
Patrick Schafer (Co-Chief Investment Officer)
Andrew Devine (Co-Chief Compliance Officer)
William E. Alvarez Jr. (Co-CFO, Co-Chief Compliance Officer & Co-Sec)
Richard P. Buckanavage (Pres)

HASBRO, INC.

1027 Newport Ave, Pawtucket, RI 02861
Tel.: (401) 431-8697   RI
Web Site: https://www.hasbro.com
Year Founded: 1923
HAS—(NASDAQ)
Rev.: $5,003,300,000
Assets: $6,540,900,000
Liabilities: $5,453,900,000
Net Worth: $1,087,000,000
Earnings: ($1,489,300,000)
Emp.: 5,502
Fiscal Year-end: 12/31/23
Toys, Games, Puzzles & Dolls, Preschool & Infant Items Mfr & Retailer
N.A.I.C.S.: 339930
Christian P. Cocks (CEO)
Tarrant Sibley (Chief Legal Officer, Sec & Exec VP)
Christian P. Cocks (CEO)

Subsidiaries:

Boulder Media Limited   (1)
14 Hawkins Street, Dublin, 2, Ireland
Tel.: (353) 16779775
Web Site: https://www.bouldermedia.tv
Emp.: 150
Animation Video Production Services
N.A.I.C.S.: 512110

Cap Candy, Inc.   (1)
1027 Newport Ave, Pawtucket, RI 02861-2539   (100%)
Tel.: (707) 251-9321
Sales Range: $50-74.9 Million
Emp.: 50
Toys & Candy Whslr
N.A.I.C.S.: 459120

Cranium, Inc.   (1)
1027 Newport Ave, Pawtucket, RI 02861
Tel.: (401) 431-8697
Web Site: http://www.cranium.com
Sales Range: $25-49.9 Million
Board Game Developer & Marketer
N.A.I.C.S.: 423920

Hasbro Australia   (1)
Level 4 67-71 Epping Road, Macquarie Park, 2113, NSW, Australia   (100%)
Tel.: (61) 298740999
Sales Range: $10-24.9 Million
Emp.: 80
Consumer Care Product Mfr
N.A.I.C.S.: 339930

Hasbro Australia Pty Ltd   (1)
Level 4 67-71 Epping Road, Macquarie Park, 2113, NSW, Australia
Tel.: (61) 1300138697
Web Site: http://www.hasbro.com
Toys Whslr
N.A.I.C.S.: 423920

Hasbro B.V.   (1)
Antwoordnummer 15611, 4780 VS, Moerdijk, Netherlands
Tel.: (31) 208004649
Web Site: http://products.hasbro.com
Sales Range: $25-49.9 Million
Emp.: 15
Toy & Hobby Goods Distr
N.A.I.C.S.: 423920

Hasbro Bradley Far East Ltd.   (1)
Rm 1308 World Commerce Havart City 11 Canton Rd Tfim Shaw 17 Hankow Rd, Kow-

Hasbro, Inc.—(Continued)

Ioon, China (Hong Kong)
Tel.: (852) 27368373
Web Site: http://www.hasbro.com
Rev.: $40,944,000
Emp.: 450
Infant Toys Mfr
N.A.I.C.S.: 339930

Hasbro Canada Corporation **(1)**
2350 Rue De La Province, Longueuil, J4G
1G2, QC, Canada **(100%)**
Tel.: (450) 670-9820
Web Site: http://www.hasbro.com
Sales Range: $10-24.9 Million
Emp.: 80
Toy & Game Mfr
N.A.I.C.S.: 339930

Hasbro France **(1)**
Savoie Technolac, 73370, Le Bourget du
Lac, France **(100%)**
Tel.: (33) 479964848
Web Site: https://products.hasbro.com
Toy Mfr
N.A.I.C.S.: 339930

Subsidiary (Non-US):

Hasbro Deutschland GmbH **(2)**
Overweg 29, D-59494, Soest, Germany
Tel.: (49) 2921965343
Web Site: https://products.hasbro.com
Emp.: 100
Toy & Hobby Goods Distr
N.A.I.C.S.: 423920

Hasbro Hellas Industrial & Commer-
cial Company S.A. **(1)**
Eucalyptus 2 & Pentelis 43, Marousi, Ath-
ens, 15126, Greece
Tel.: (30) 2106141480
Web Site: http://www.hasbro.com
Toy & Hobby Goods Distr
N.A.I.C.S.: 423920

Hasbro Hong Kong Limited **(1)**
Levels L18-L20 Hang Seng Tower Telford
Plaza 33 Wai Yip Street, Tsim Sha Tsui,
Kowloon Bay, China (Hong Kong)
Tel.: (852) 27388300
Web Site: https://www.hasbro.com
Toy & Hobby Goods Whslr
N.A.I.C.S.: 423920

Hasbro International Holdings,
B.V. **(1)**
De entree 240, 1101 EE, Amsterdam, Neth-
erlands
Tel.: (31) 207072920
Investment Management Service
N.A.I.C.S.: 523940

Subsidiary (Non-US):

Cartamundi Ireland Ltd. **(2)**
Cork Road, Waterford, X91 Y235, Ireland
Tel.: (353) 51331100
Web Site: https://cartamundi.ie
Game Toy & Childrens Vehicle Mfr
N.A.I.C.S.: 423920
Terry Power *(Mng Dir)*

Subsidiary (Domestic):

Hasbro Netherlands Holdings,
B.V. **(2)**
De Entree 240, 1101 EE, Amsterdam, Neth-
erlands
Tel.: (31) 207072920
Financial Holding Services
N.A.I.C.S.: 551112

Hasbro Managerial Services LLC **(1)**
1027 Newport Ave, Pawtucket, RI 02861
Tel.: (401) 431-8697
Sales Range: $400-449.9 Million
Emp.: 1,000
Toy & Hobby Goods Distr
N.A.I.C.S.: 423920
Barbara Finigan *(Gen Counsel & Exec VP)*

Hasbro S.A. **(1)**
Rue Emile-Boechat 31, Delemont, 2800,
Switzerland
Tel.: (41) 324210800
Web Site: http://www.hasbro.ch
Sales Range: $25-49.9 Million
Emp.: 27
Toy & Hobby Goods Distr

N.A.I.C.S.: 423920

Hasbro Toys & Games Holdings,
S.L. **(1)**
28 Dels Gremis Pg Ind Oliveral, Riba-roja
de Turia, 46190, Spain
Tel.: (34) 962719400
Sales Range: $50-74.9 Million
Emp.: 100
Toy & Hobby Goods Mfr
N.A.I.C.S.: 423920
Alan G. Hassenfeld *(Chm & CEO)*
Jose Savall *(Gen Mgr)*

Hasbro UK Ltd **(1)**
4 The Square Stockley Park, Uxbridge,
UB11 1ET, Middlesex, United Kingdom
Tel.: (44) 2085691234
Web Site: https://products.hasbro.com
Sales Range: $150-199.9 Million
Emp.: 400
Toys & Board Game Product Mfr
N.A.I.C.S.: 336991
Jonathan Evan *(Mng Dir)*

Hasbro de Mexico S.R.L. de
C.V. **(1)**
Boulevard Manuel Avila Camacho No 32
Piso 3, Col Lomas de Chapultepec I Sec-
tion, 11000, Mexico, Mexico
Tel.: (52) 58762998
Web Site: http://products.hasbro.com
Toy & Hobby Goods Mfr
N.A.I.C.S.: 339930

S.A. Hasbro N.V. **(1)**
Industrialaan 1 bus A, 1702, Groot-
Bijgaarden, Belgium
Tel.: (32) 24673360
Web Site: http://www.hasbro.be
Sales Range: $25-49.9 Million
Emp.: 40
Toy & Hobby Goods Distr
N.A.I.C.S.: 423920

Wizards of the Coast, LLC **(1)**
1600 Lind Ave Ste 400, Renton, WA 98057-
4068
Tel.: (425) 226-6500
Web Site:
https://www.company.wizards.com
Game Mfr & Distr
N.A.I.C.S.: 339930

HASHICORP, INC.
101 2nd St Ste 700, San Francisco,
CA 94105
Tel.: (415) 301-3227 DE
Year Founded: 2013
HCP—(NASDAQ)
Rev.: $583,137,000
Assets: $1,691,947,000
Liabilities: $478,954,000
Net Worth: $1,212,993,000
Earnings: ($190,668,000)
Emp.: 2,200
Fiscal Year-end: 01/31/24
Software Development Services
N.A.I.C.S.: 541511
David McJannet *(Chm & CEO)*
Armon Dadgar *(Co-Founder & CTO)*
Mitchell Hashimoto *(Co-Founder)*
Marc Holmes *(CMO)*
Michael Weingartner *(Chief Product
Officer)*
Talha Tariq *(CIO & Chief Security Of-
ficer)*
Alex Kurtz *(VP-IR)*
Kate Lehman *(Dir-Corp Comm)*
Susan St. Ledger *(Pres-Worldwide
Field Ops)*

HAUPPAUGE DIGITAL, INC.
909 Motor Pkwy, Hauppauge, NY
11788
Tel.: (631) 434-1600 DE
Web Site:
https://www.hauppauge.com
Year Founded: 1985
HAUP—(OTCIQ)
Sales Range: $25-49.9 Million
Emp.: 99

Computer Terminal & Other Com-
puter Peripheral Equipment Manufac-
turing
N.A.I.C.S.: 334118
Kenneth H. Plotkin *(Pres & CEO)*
Gerald Tucciarone *(CFO)*

Subsidiaries:

HCW Distributing Corp. **(1)**
91 Cabot Ct, Hauppauge, NY 11788-3717
Tel.: (631) 434-1600
Web Site: http://www.ampelectric.com
Sales Range: $50-74.9 Million
Emp.: 65
Distr of Computer Components
N.A.I.C.S.: 424990
Kenneth H. Plotkin *(Pres)*
Cheryl Willins *(Controller)*

Hauppauge Computer Works
GmbH **(1)**
Ohlerkamp 14, Monchengladbach, 41069,
Germany **(100%)**
Tel.: (49) 2161694880
Web Site: http://www.hauppauge.de
Sales Range: $10-24.9 Million
Emp.: 10
Mfr & Developer of Analog & Digital Video,
TV & Data Broadcast Receiver Products for
Personal Computers
N.A.I.C.S.: 334118
Vana Steffen *(Mgr-Fin)*

Hauppauge Computer Works
Inc. **(1)**
91 Cabot Ct, Hauppauge, NY 11788-3717
Tel.: (631) 434-1600
Web Site: http://www.hauppage.com
Sales Range: $50-74.9 Million
Emp.: 25
Mfr & Developer of Analog & Digital Video,
TV & Data Broadcast Receiver Products for
Personal Computers
N.A.I.C.S.: 334118

Hauppauge Computer Works
Sarl **(1)**
15 Edward Station, Luxembourg, 2636,
Luxembourg
Tel.: (352) 26431073
Sales Range: $125-149.9 Million
Mfr & Developer of Analog & Digital Video,
TV & Data Broadcast Receiver Products for
Personal Computers
N.A.I.C.S.: 334118

Hauppauge Computer Works
Sarl **(1)**
48 rue du Claire, 725002, Paris,
France **(99%)**
Tel.: (33) 156265121
Web Site: http://www.hauppauge.fr
Sales Range: $10-24.9 Million
Emp.: 6
Mfr & Developer of Analog & Digital Video,
TV & Data Broadcast Receiver Products for
Personal Computers
N.A.I.C.S.: 334118

Hauppauge Computer Works UK
Ltd. **(1)**
Bank Chambers, 6-10 Borough High St,
London, SE1 9QQ, United Kingdom
Tel.: (44) 2034051717
Web Site: http://www.hauppauge.co.uk
Sales Range: $10-24.9 Million
Emp.: 15
Mfr & Developer of Analog & Digital Video,
TV & Data Broadcast Receiver Products for
Personal Computers
N.A.I.C.S.: 334118

Hauppauge Digital Asia Pte Ltd. **(1)**
1093 Lowr Delta Rd No 04-05, Singapore,
169204, Singapore
Tel.: (65) 62769163
Web Site: http://www.hauppage.com.sg
Sales Range: $10-24.9 Million
Emp.: 9
Mfr & Developer of Analog & Digital Video,
TV & Data Broadcast Receiver Products for
Personal Computers
N.A.I.C.S.: 334118
Gopal Krishnan *(Mng Dir)*

Hauppauge Digital Inc. **(1)**
9F-1 No 413 Ruiguang Rd, Neihu District,
Taipei, 11492, Taiwan

Tel.: (886) 226562187
Sales Range: $10-24.9 Million
Emp.: 5
Computer Peripheral Equipment Mfr
N.A.I.C.S.: 334118

PCTV Systems **(1)**
Frankfurter Strasse 3c, D 38122, Braun-
schweig, Germany **(100%)**
Tel.: (49) 53121830
Web Site: http://www.pctvsystems.com
Designer, Mfr & Marketer of Digital Video
Post Production Tools
N.A.I.C.S.: 334310

HAVERTY FURNITURE COM-
PANIES, INC.
780 Johnson Ferry Rd Ste 800, At-
lanta, GA 30342
Tel.: (404) 443-2900 MD
Web Site: https://www.havertys.com
Year Founded: 1885
HVT—(NYSE)
Rev.: $1,047,215,000
Assets: $649,049,000
Liabilities: $359,650,000
Net Worth: $289,399,000
Earnings: $89,358,000
Emp.: 2,831
Fiscal Year-end: 12/31/22
Residential Furniture & Accessories
Retailer
N.A.I.C.S.: 449110
Richard B. Hare *(CFO & Exec VP)*
Clarence H. Smith *(Chm & CEO)*
Steven G. Burdette *(Pres)*
Kelly A. Fladger *(Chief HR Officer &
Sr VP)*
Janet E. Taylor *(Gen Counsel & Sr
VP)*
Jenny Hill Parker *(Sec & Sr VP-Fin)*
John L. Gill *(Exec VP-Mdsg)*
Helen B. Bautista *(Sr VP-Mktg)*

Subsidiaries:

Havertys Credit Services, Inc. **(1)**
1501 Riverside Dr, Chattanooga, TN 37406-
4309
Tel.: (423) 624-1969
Consumer Financial Services
N.A.I.C.S.: 522390

HAWAII VINTAGE CHOCOLATE
CO.
1050 Bishop St Ste 162, Honolulu, HI
96813
Tel.: (808) 735-8494 HI
HWVI—(OTCIQ)
Chocolate Product Mfr
N.A.I.C.S.: 311351
James Walsh *(CEO & CFO)*

HAWAIIAN ELECTRIC INDUS-
TRIES, INC.
1001 Bishop St Ste 2900, Honolulu,
HI 96813
Tel.: (808) 543-5662 HI
Web Site: https://www.hei.com
Year Founded: 1981
HE—(NYSE)
Rev.: $3,682,166,000
Assets: $17,243,821,000
Liabilities: $14,898,980,000
Net Worth: $2,344,841,000
Earnings: $199,238,000
Emp.: 3,597
Fiscal Year-end: 12/31/23
Holding Company; Electric Power
Generation & Distribution; Banking
Services
N.A.I.C.S.: 551112
Scott W. H. Seu *(Pres & CEO)*
Scott DeGhetto *(CFO, Treas & Exec
VP)*
Kurt K. Murao *(Chief Admin Officer,
Gen Counsel, Sec & Exec VP)*
Christine Ohashi *(VP-Internal Audit)*

AJ Halagao (*VP-Corp & Community Advancement*)
Avelino J. Halagao (*VP*)

Subsidiaries:

ASB Hawaii, Inc.   **(1)**
1001 Bishop St Ste 2900, Honolulu, HI 96814   **(100%)**
Tel.: (808) 543-5662
Web Site: https://www.asbhawaii.com
Bank Holding Company
N.A.I.C.S.: 551111
Ann C. Teranishi (*Pres & CEO*)

Subsidiary (Domestic):

American Savings Bank, F.S.B.   **(2)**
1001 Bishop St, Honolulu, HI 96813   **(100%)**
Tel.: (808) 627-6900
Web Site: https://www.asbhawaii.com
Sales Range: $250-299.9 Million
Emp.: 1,159
Federal Savings Bank
N.A.I.C.S.: 522180
Richard J. Dahl (*Pres*)
Ann C. Teranishi (*Pres & CEO*)
Gabriel S. H. Lee (*Exec VP-Comml Markets*)
Natalie Taniguchi (*Exec VP-Enterprise Risk & Regulatory Rels*)
Beth Whitehead (*Chief Admin Officer & Exec VP*)
Alan Miyasaki (*Exec Officer-Residential Loan & First VP*)
Dani Aiu (*Exec VP-Consumer Banking*)
Jason Williams (*VP*)
Alan Fentriss (*Sr VP & Dir-Home Loans*)
Alex Truong (*Exec Officer-Residential Loan & Asst VP*)
Debbie Goto (*Exec Officer-Residential Loan, VP & Mgr-Projects*)
Dane Teruya (*CFO & Exec VP*)
John Ward (*Chief Experience Officer & Exec VP*)
Brian Yoshii (*CIO & Exec VP*)
Eric Miyajima (*Exec Officer-Residential Loan & First VP*)
Pom Luxton (*First VP & Mgr-Residential Loan-Private Lending Grp*)
Yvonne Ako (*First VP & Mgr-Residential Loan*)
Lisa Carillo (*Exec Officer-Residential Loan & VP*)
Ann Sakamoto (*First VP & Mgr-Residential Loan*)
Vianne Tabata (*Exec Officer-Residential Loan & VP*)
Larry Lau (*Exec Officer-Residential Loan & Asst VP*)
Betty Yada (*VP*)
Swee Wah (*Exec Officer-Residential Loan & VP*)
Glenn Tarumoto (*Exec Officer-Residential Loan & VP*)
Bryce Tani (*First VP & Mgr-Residential Loan*)
Paul Santos (*Exec Officer-Residential Loan & VP*)
Misha Myung Pak (*Exec Officer-Residential Loan & Asst VP*)
Lita Manuel (*Exec Officer-Residential Loan & VP*)
Michelle Luxton (*Exec Officer-Residential Loan-Private Lending Grp & VP*)
Alan Magno (*Exec Officer-Residential Loan & VP*)
Derek Cheng (*Officer-Residential Loan & VP*)
Carolyn Johiro (*Exec Officer-Residential Loan & VP*)
Mark James (*Exec Officer-Residential Loan & VP*)
Patti Kino (*Sr VP & Dir-Strategic Growth & Bus Dev*)
Steven Nakahara (*Chief Credit Officer & Exec VP*)
Stefan Kant Jr. (*Exec Officer-Residential & VP*)

Hawaiian Electric Company, Inc.   **(1)**
1099 Alakea St Ste 2200, Honolulu, HI 96813   **(100%)**
Tel.: (808) 543-7771
Web Site: https://www.hei.com
Rev.: $3,408,587,000
Assets: $6,597,467,000
Liabilities: $2,634,150,000

Net Worth: $3,963,317,000
Earnings: $190,009,000
Emp.: 2,511
Fiscal Year-end: 12/31/2022
Electric Power Distribution Services
N.A.I.C.S.: 221122
Shelee M.T. Kimura (*Pres & CEO*)
Paul K. Ito (*CFO, Treas & Sr VP*)
Shelee M. T. Kimura (*Sr VP-Customer Svc & Pub Affairs*)
Brendan Bailey (*VP*)
Rebecca Dayhuff Matsushima (*VP*)
Mike Decaprio (*VP*)
Jackie Ingamells (*VP*)

Subsidiary (Domestic):

Hawaii Electric Light Company, Inc.   **(2)**
1200 Kilauea Ave, Hilo, HI 96720-4206   **(100%)**
Tel.: (808) 969-6999
Web Site:
  https://www.hawaiielectriclight.com
Electric Utility
N.A.I.C.S.: 221118

Maui Electric Company, Limited   **(2)**
210 W Kamehameha Ave, Kahului, HI 96732
Tel.: (808) 871-8461
Web Site: https://www.hawaiianelectric.com
Electric Power Distribution Services
N.A.I.C.S.: 221122

HAWAIIAN HOSPITALITY GROUP, INC.

58-057 Kamehameha Hwy, Haleiwa, HI 96712
Tel.: (808) 744-7211   **WY**
Year Founded: 1993
HHGI—(OTCIQ)
Real Estate Manangement Services
N.A.I.C.S.: 531210
Linda Kress (*CEO*)

HAWKEYE SYSTEMS, INC.

6605 Abercorn St Ste 204, Savannah, GA 31405
Tel.: (912) 253-0375   **NV**
Web Site:
  https://www.hawkeyesystems
  inc.com
Year Founded: 2018
HWKE—(OTCQB)
Rev.: $103,556
Assets: $2,500
Liabilities: $2,606,527
Net Worth: ($2,604,027)
Earnings: ($578,717)
Emp.: 2
Fiscal Year-end: 06/30/24
Information Technology Services
N.A.I.C.S.: 518210
Corby Marshall (*Founder & CEO*)

HAWKINS, INC.

2381 Rosegate, Roseville, MN 55113
Tel.: (612) 331-6910   **MN**
Web Site:
  https://www.hawkinsinc.com
Year Founded: 1938
HWKN—(NASDAQ)
Rev.: $919,162,000
Assets: $657,934,000
Liabilities: $251,908,000
Net Worth: $406,026,000
Earnings: $75,363,000
Emp.: 928
Fiscal Year-end: 03/31/24
Bulk Specialty Chemicals Processor & Distr
N.A.I.C.S.: 424690
Richard G. Erstad (*Gen Counsel, Sec & VP*)
James Theodore Thompson (*Chm*)
Patrick H. Hawkins (*Pres & CEO*)
Jeffrey P. Oldenkamp (*CFO, Treas & Exec VP*)
Drew M. Grahek (*VP-Ops*)

Shirley A. Rozeboom (*VP-Health & Nutrition*)
Douglas A. Lange (*VP-Water Treatment Grp*)

Subsidiaries:

C & L Aqua Professionals, Inc.   **(1)**
3301 Carbide Dr, Sulphur, LA 70665-8662
Tel.: (337) 882-1580
Web Site: http://www.claquapro.com
Chemical & Allied Products Merchant Whslr
N.A.I.C.S.: 424690

Ecotech Enterprises Inc.   **(1)**
Colonel Maynard Rd, Scott, AR 72142
Tel.: (501) 821-1181
Water Treatment Chemicals Mfr & Distr
N.A.I.C.S.: 424690

Hawkins Terminal I   **(1)**
1125 Childs Rd, Saint Paul, MN 55106
Tel.: (612) 617-8500
Web Site: http://www.hawkinsinc.com
Sales Range: $50-74.9 Million
Emp.: 12
Stores & Distributes Various Chemicals
N.A.I.C.S.: 424690

Stauber Performance Ingredients, Inc.   **(1)**
4120 N Palm St, Fullerton, CA 92835-1026
Tel.: (714) 441-3900
Web Site: https://www.stauberusa.com
Chemical Ingredient Distr
N.A.I.C.S.: 424690
Monica Mitchell (*VP-Strategic Brand Sls & Mktg*)
Becki Schwietz (*Dir-Strategic Sls & Bus Dev*)
Katie Laughlin (*Dir-Sls*)
Robert Arakelian (*VP-Strategic Global Sourcing*)
Pat Stano (*Brand Mgr*)
Shirley Rozeboom Sr. (*VP-Health & Nutrition*)

Subsidiary (Domestic):

Stauber California, Inc.   **(2)**
4120 N Palm St, Fullerton, CA 92835
Tel.: (714) 441-3900
Emp.: 95
Pharmaceutical Product Mfr & Distr
N.A.I.C.S.: 325412
Olivier Guiot (*Pres*)
Steve Graham (*CFO & COO*)
Shirley Rozeboom (*Sr VP-Sls & Mktg*)
Dan Stauber (*Chief Brand Officer*)
Pat Wratschko (*VP-Quality Assurance*)

Stauber New York, Inc.   **(2)**
41 Bridge St, Florida, NY 10921
Tel.: (845) 615-7133
Web Site: http://www.stauberusa.com
Chemical Ingredient Distr
N.A.I.C.S.: 424690

Vertex Chemical Corporation   **(1)**
11685 Manchester Rd, Saint Louis, MO 63131
Tel.: (314) 471-0500
Web Site: http://www.vertexchemical.com
Inorganic Chemical Mfr & Distr
N.A.I.C.S.: 325180
Dave Hertel (*Acct Mgr*)
Tom Magrecki (*VP-Fin*)

Water Solutions Unlimited, Inc.   **(1)**
295 Industrial Dr, Franklin, IN 46131
Tel.: (317) 736-6868
Web Site: http://www.getwsu.com
Rev.: $3,536,000
Emp.: 14
Other Chemical & Allied Products Merchant Whslr
N.A.I.C.S.: 424690

HAWKS ACQUISITION CORP.

600 Lexington Ave 9th Fl, New York, NY 10022
Tel.: (212) 542-4540   **DE**
Web Site:
  https://www.hawksacquisition
  corp.com
Year Founded: 2021
HWKZ—(NYSE)
Rev.: $3,313,492

Assets: $233,587,141
Liabilities: $242,125,831
Net Worth: ($8,538,690)
Earnings: $1,109,552
Emp.: 3
Fiscal Year-end: 12/31/22
Investment Services
N.A.I.C.S.: 523999
J. Carney Hawks (*Chm & CEO*)
John Maher (*COO*)
Lois A. Mannon (*CFO & Treas*)

HAWTHORN BANCSHARES, INC.

Tel.: (573) 761-6100   **MO**
Web Site: https://www.hawthornbanc
  shares.com
Year Founded: 1992
HWBK—(NASDAQ)
Rev.: $83,234,000
Assets: $1,923,540,000
Liabilities: $1,796,129,000
Net Worth: $127,411,000
Earnings: $20,751,000
Emp.: 299
Fiscal Year-end: 12/31/22
Bank Holding Company
N.A.I.C.S.: 551111
Christopher Hafner (*CFO, Principal Acctg Officer & Sr VP*)
Brent M. Giles (*CEO*)
David T. Turner (*Chm*)
Kathleen L. Bruegenhemke (*Chief Risk Officer, Sec & Sr VP*)
Gregg A. Bexten (*Pres*)

Subsidiaries:

Hawthorn Bank   **(1)**
132 E High St, Jefferson City, MO 65101   **(100%)**
Tel.: (573) 761-6100
Web Site: https://www.hawthornbank.com
Sales Range: $125-149.9 Million
Retail & Commercial Banking Services
N.A.I.C.S.: 522110
Christopher Hafner (*CFO & Sr VP*)
Brent M. Giles (*CEO*)
David T. Turner (*Chm*)
Kathleen L. Bruegenhemke (*Chief Risk Officer & Chief Operating Officer*)
David Turner (*Chm*)
Brent Giles (*CEO*)
Chris E. Hafner (*CFO*)
Kathleen Bruegenhemke (*Exec VP*)
Gregg Bexten (*Pres*)
Chris Bracht (*Asst VP*)
Doug Hagenhoff (*VP*)
Dan Renfrow (*Officer-Senior Trust*)
Chris Schrimpf (*Co-Pres-Market*)
Jason Schwartz (*Sr VP*)
Kevin Schwarzer (*Co-Pres-Mortgage Loan*)
Crystal Tellman (*Asst VP-Comml Banker*)
Sherry Waddill (*Sr VP*)
Amie Wheeler (*Sr VP-Comml Banker*)
Keith Asel (*Co-Pres-Market*)
Jay Dorst (*Sr VP-Comml Banker*)
Holly Schroer (*Officer-Trust*)
Becky Wood (*Branch Mgr*)
Lynn Ivie (*Branch Mgr*)
Andy Engelhart (*Asst VP*)
Heather Fowler (*Asst VP*)
Dave Garnett (*Co-Pres-Market*)
Julie Hilliard (*VP*)
Doug Wheeler (*VP-Comml Banker*)
Max Buchheim (*Branch Mgr*)
Ryan Clifton (*Sr VP-Comml Banker*)
David Clithero (*VP-Treasury Sls & Private Banking*)
Brandon Kalista (*Asst VP-Comml Banker*)
Mike Moran (*VP-Comml Banker*)
Rob Patrick (*VP-Comml Banker*)
Bill Gray (*Sr VP-Comml Banker*)
Kristie Fisher (*Sr VP-Comml Banker*)
Ashley Franklin (*Branch Mgr*)
Shawna D. Croucher (*Sr VP*)
Juliana Totta (*Sr VP*)
Jeff Carr (*Officer-Comml Loan*)
Kyla Schrimpf (*Branch Mgr*)
Jana Lehman (*VP*)
Chris Champ (*VP-Treasury Services*)
Katie Collobert (*Officer-Consumer Loan*)
Kent Peterson (*Co-Pres-Market*)
Elan Adams (*Asst VP-Mortgage Loan*)

Hawthorn Bancshares, Inc.—(Continued)

Timothy Brockhaus (Sr VP)
Jon Brown (VP)
Kayla Davis (VP)
Tom Lay (Sr VP-Comml Banker)
Chuck Allcorn (Sr VP-Comml Banker)
Carmen Mantonya (Asst VP)

HAYWARD HOLDINGS, INC.
1415 Vantage Park Dr Ste 400, Charlotte, NC 28203
Tel.: (704) 285-5445   DE
Web Site:
   https://www.global.hayward.com
Year Founded: 2017
HAYW—(NYSE)
Rev.: $992,452,000
Assets: $2,946,284,000
Liabilities: $1,634,826,000
Net Worth: $1,311,458,000
Earnings: $80,687,000
Emp.: 1,875
Fiscal Year-end: 12/31/23
Holding Company
N.A.I.C.S.: 551112
Kevin P. Holleran (Pres & CEO)
Eifion Jones (CFO & Sr VP)
Rick Roetken (Pres-North America)
Kevin Maczka (VP-IR)
Billy Emory (Principal Acctg Officer)

Subsidiaries:

ChlorKing, LLC   (1)
6767 Peachtree Indl G, Norcross, GA 30092
Tel.: (770) 452-0330
Web Site: https://www.chlorking.com
Rev.: $4,000,000
Emp.: 15
Pharmaceutical Preparation Mfr
N.A.I.C.S.: 325412
David Von Broembsen (Co-Founder, Pres, Office Mgr & Engr-Chemical)
Steven Pearce (CFO)

HAZ HOLDINGS, INC.
PO Box 1609, Silverdale, WA 98383
Tel.: (206) 941-4485   TX
Web Site:
   https://www.hazholdings.com
Year Founded: 1998
HAZH—(OTCIQ)
Building Construction Services
N.A.I.C.S.: 236220
Alkarim Bhanji (Chm & CEO)
Diallah Bhanji (VP & Counsel)

HBANCORPORATION INC.
2201 James St, Lawrenceville, IL 62439
Tel.: (618) 943-1038
Web Site: http://www.heritagesb.com
HBIN—(OTCIQ)
Bank Holding Company
N.A.I.C.S.: 551111
Cleora Gillespie (Sec)

Subsidiaries:

Heritage State Bank   (1)
2201 James St, Lawrenceville, IL 62439
Tel.: (618) 943-1038
Web Site: http://www.heritagesb.com
Rev.: $4,250,000
Assets: $73,335,000
Liabilities: $65,399,000
Net Worth: $7,936,000
Earnings: $1,687,000
Emp.: 22
Fiscal Year-end: 12/31/2013
Savings Institutions
N.A.I.C.S.: 522180
Kevin J. Kavanaugh (Pres & CEO)

HBT FINANCIAL, INC.
401 N Hershey Rd, Bloomington, IL 61704
Tel.: (309) 662-4444   DE
Web Site: https://ir.hbtfinancial.com

HBT—(NASDAQ)
Rev.: $187,771,000
Assets: $4,286,734,000
Liabilities: $3,913,102,000
Net Worth: $373,632,000
Earnings: $56,456,000
Emp.: 711
Fiscal Year-end: 12/31/22
Bank Holding Company
N.A.I.C.S.: 551111
Peter R. Chapman (CFO & Exec VP)
Fred L. Drake (Chm)
J. Lance Carter (Pres & CEO)
Lawrence J. Horvath (Chief Lending Officer & Exec VP)
Mark W. Scheirer (Chief Credit Officer & Exec VP)
Andrea E. Zurkamer (Chief Risk Officer & Exec VP)
Diane H. Lanier (Chief Retail Officer & Exec VP)

Subsidiaries:

Heartland Bank & Trust
Company   (1)
401 N Hershey Rd, Bloomington, IL 61702-0067   (100%)
Tel.: (309) 662-4444
Web Site: https://www.hbtbank.com
Sales Range: $125-149.9 Million
Commericial Banking
N.A.I.C.S.: 522110
Peter R. Chapman (CFO & Exec VP)
Fred L. Drake (Chm)
Patrick F. Busch (Vice Chm)
J. Lance Carter (Pres & CEO)
Lawrence J. Horvath (Chief Lending Officer & Exec VP)
Jay Riippi (Mgr-Retail-Sycamore)

HCA HEALTHCARE, INC.
1 Park Plz, Nashville, TN 37203
Tel.: (615) 344-9551   DE
Web Site:
   https://www.hcahealthcare.com
Year Founded: 1968
HCA—(NYSE)
Rev.: $64,968,000,000
Assets: $56,211,000,000
Liabilities: $55,151,000,000
Net Worth: $1,060,000,000
Earnings: $5,242,000,000
Emp.: 220,000
Fiscal Year-end: 12/31/23
Holding Company; Hospital & Medical Facility Operator
N.A.I.C.S.: 551112
Samuel N. Hazen (CEO)
Kathleen M. Whalen (Chief Ethics & Compliance Officer & Sr VP)
Timothy A. McManus (Pres-Natl Grp)
Kathryn A. Torres (Sr VP-Payer Contracting & Alignment)
Deborah M. Reiner (Sr VP-Mktg & Mktg)
Christopher F. Wyatt (Principal Acctg Officer, Sr VP & Controller)
Phillip G. Billington (Sr VP-Internal Audit Svcs)
Jennifer Berres (Chief HR Officer & Sr VP)
Jeff E. Cohen (Sr VP-Govt Rels)
Frank Morgan (VP-IR)
Michael A. Marks (CFO & Exec VP)
Sammie Mosier (Sr VP)
Jon M. Foster (COO & Exec VP)
Chad Wasserman (CIO & Sr VP)
Michael R. McAlevey (Chief Legal Officer, Chief Legal & Admin Officer & Exec VP)
Michael S. Cuffe (Chief Clinical Officer & Exec VP)
Erol R. Akdamar (Pres-American Grp)
Richard A. Hammett (Pres-Atlantic Grp)
Harlow Sumerford (Dir-Media Rels)
Thomas F. Frist III (Chm)
Joseph A. Sowell III (Chief Dev Officer & Sr VP)

Subsidiaries:

52 Alderley Road LLP   (1)
52-54 Alderley Road, Wilmslow, SK9 1NY, Cheshire, United Kingdom
Tel.: (44) 1625836302
General Medical & Surgical Services
N.A.I.C.S.: 622110

Subsidiary (Domestic):

The Wilmslow Hospital   (2)
52-54 Alderley Road, Wilmslow, SK9 1NY, Cheshire, United Kingdom
Tel.: (44) 1617688102
Web Site:
   http://www.thewilmslowhospital.co.uk
Health Care Srvices
N.A.I.C.S.: 621610

ADC Surgicenter, LLC   (1)
7600 N Capital Of Texas Hwy, Austin, TX 78731
Tel.: (512) 901-4029
Health Care Srvices
N.A.I.C.S.: 621491

AOI Surgicenter, LLC   (1)
3200 Downwood Cir NW Ste 400, Atlanta, GA 30327
Tel.: (404) 390-3294
Web Site: https://www.aoisurgerycenter.com
Orthopaedic Surgical Services
N.A.I.C.S.: 621111

Access 2 Health Care Physicians, LLC   (1)
14690 Spring Hill Dr, Spring Hill, FL 34609
Tel.: (352) 799-0046
Web Site: https://www.a2hcp.com
Health Care Srvices
N.A.I.C.S.: 621399
Carlos Arias (COO)

Access Health Care Physicians, LLC   (1)
14690 Spring Hill Dr, Spring Hill, FL 34609
Tel.: (352) 688-8116
Web Site: https://theaccesshealthcare.com
General Medical & Surgical Services
N.A.I.C.S.: 622110

Acute Kids Urgent Care of Medical City Children's Hospital, PLLC   (1)
6565 N Macarthur Blvd Ste 350, Irving, TX 75039-2490
Tel.: (972) 401-8720
General Medical & Surgical Services
N.A.I.C.S.: 622110

Alaska Regional Hospital   (1)
2801 Debarr Rd, Anchorage, AK 99508
Tel.: (907) 276-1131
Web Site: https://www.alaskaregional.com
Sales Range: $75-99.9 Million
Emp.: 1,000
Hospital
N.A.I.C.S.: 622110
Ali Miller (VP-HR)
Jennifer Opsut (CEO)
Rob Stantus (COO)
Timothy Ballard (Chief Medical Officer)
Ashlyn Hall (Chief Nursing Officer)
Jeff Chilson (CFO)

Alaska Regional Medical Group, LLC   (1)
11260 Old Seward Hwy Ste 107, Anchorage, AK 99515
Tel.: (907) 433-5100
Web Site:
   http://www.alaskaregionalcenter.com
Emp.: 20
General Medical & Surgical services
N.A.I.C.S.: 622110

Alaska Spine Center, LLC   (1)
4100 Lake Otis Pkwy Ste 212, Anchorage, AK 99508
Tel.: (907) 389-7246
Web Site:
   https://www.alaskaspinecenter.com
Spine Care Services
N.A.I.C.S.: 621111
Kevin Barry (CEO)
Brion Beerle (Dir-Medical)

Alaska Surgery Center Limited Partnership   (1)
1230 Northway Dr, Anchorage, AK 99508

Tel.: (907) 550-6100
Web Site: https://aksurgery.com
Surgical Equipment Mfr
N.A.I.C.S.: 339112

Albany Family Practice, LLC   (1)
901 N Maddison St, Albany, GA 31701
Tel.: (229) 446-2322
General Medical & Surgical Services
N.A.I.C.S.: 622110

All About Staffing, Inc.   (1)
10020 N Rodney Parham Rd Ste B, Little Rock, AR 72227
Tel.: (501) 221-1555
Web Site: http://www.allaboutstaffinginc.com
Medical Office Management Services
N.A.I.C.S.: 561110

Alleghany Hospitalists, LLC   (1)
One ARP Ln Ste 300, Low Moor, VA 24457
Tel.: (540) 862-6357
General Medical Care Services
N.A.I.C.S.: 622110

Ambulatory Endoscopy Clinic of Dallas, Ltd.   (1)
6390 Lyndon B Johnson Fwy Ste 200, Dallas, TX 75240
Tel.: (972) 934-3691
Web Site: http://www.aecdallas.com
Fiscal Year-end: 12/31/2006
Surgical Care Services
N.A.I.C.S.: 621493

Ambulatory Surgery Center Group, Ltd.   (1)
4500 E Fletcher Ave, Tampa, FL 33613
Tel.: (813) 977-8550
Web Site: http://www.tampaambulatory.com
Outpatient Care Centers
N.A.I.C.S.: 621498

Anchorage Surgicenter, LLC   (1)
4001 Laurel St Ste A, Anchorage, AK 99508-5300
Tel.: (907) 563-1800
Web Site:
   https://www.surgerycenterofanchor
   age.com
Emp.: 50
General Medical & Surgical services
N.A.I.C.S.: 622110

Appledore Medical Group, Inc.   (1)
155 Borthwick Ave Ste 101 E, Portsmouth, NH 03801
Web Site:
   https://appledoremedicalgroup.com
General Medical & Surgical Services
N.A.I.C.S.: 622110

Appledore Medical Group, Inc.   (1)
155 Borthwick Ave Ste 101 E, Portsmouth, NH 03801
Tel.: (603) 294-1231
Web Site:
   http://www.appledoremedicalgroup.com
General Medical & Surgical Services
N.A.I.C.S.: 622110

Appomattox Imaging, LLC   (1)
930 South Ave Ste 1, Colonial Heights, VA 23834-3621
Tel.: (804) 524-2340
Web Site: http://www.hcavaopimaging.com
Emp.: 12
Medical & Surgical Hospital Services
N.A.I.C.S.: 622110
Donald Bodenhamer (Dir-)

Arapahoe Surgicenter, LLC   (1)
1001 Southpark Dr, Littleton, CO 80120
Tel.: (303) 722-8987
Web Site: https://arapahoe-endoscopy.com
General Medical & Surgical services
N.A.I.C.S.: 622110

Arthritis Specialists of Nashville, Inc.   (1)
3443 Dickerson Pike Ste 520, Nashville, TN 37207
Tel.: (615) 340-4611
General Medical & Surgical Services
N.A.I.C.S.: 622110

Atlanta Outpatient Surgery Center   (1)
5730 Glenridge Dr Ste 400, Sandy Springs, GA 30328
Tel.: (404) 252-3074

Web Site:
https://atlantaoutpatientsurgerycenter.com
General Medical & Surgical Services
N.A.I.C.S.: 622110

Atlanta Surgery Center, Ltd. (1)
5730 Glenridge Dr Ste 400, Sandy Springs,
GA 30328
Tel.: (404) 252-3074
Web Site:
http://www.atlantaoutpatientsurgerycen
ter.com
Emp.: 100
General Medical & Surgical Services
N.A.I.C.S.: 622110

Atlantis Outpatient Center (1)
5645 S Military Trl, Lake Worth, FL 33463
Tel.: (561) 964-3966
Web Site:
https://www.atlantissurgerycenter.com
Emp.: 30
Outpatient Health Care Services
N.A.I.C.S.: 621399

Atlantis Outpatient Center (1)
5645 S Military Trl, Lake Worth, FL 33463
Tel.: (561) 964-3966
Web Site: https://atlantissurgerycenter.com
General Medical & Surgical Services
N.A.I.C.S.: 622110

Augusta CyberKnife, LLC (1)
1 Park Plz, Nashville, TN 37203
Tel.: (615) 524-4036
Health Care Srvices
N.A.I.C.S.: 621610

**Augusta Primary Care Services,
LLC** (1)
3624 J Dewey Gray Cir Ste 308, Augusta,
GA 30909-6584
Tel.: (706) 855-5650
Health Care & Allied Services
N.A.I.C.S.: 621999

Augusta Surgical Center (1)
915 Russell St, Augusta, GA 30904
Tel.: (706) 738-4925
Web Site:
https://www.augustasurgicalcenter.com
Health Care Srvices
N.A.I.C.S.: 621399

Austin Heart, PLLC (1)
3801 N Lamar Ste 300, Austin, TX 78756
Tel.: (512) 206-3600
Web Site: http://www.austinheart.com
Hospital Management Services
N.A.I.C.S.: 621493
Cindi Becker (Mgr-Practice-Round Rock)

Austin Urogynecology, PLLC (1)
12319 N Mopac Expy Bldg C Ste 200, Aus-
tin, TX 78758
Tel.: (512) 973-8276
Web Site: https://austinurogynecology.com
General Medical & Surgical Services
N.A.I.C.S.: 622110

**Aventura Healthcare Specialists
LLC** (1)
20950 NE 27th Ct Ste 300, Aventura, FL
33180
Tel.: (786) 428-0303
Web Site:
http://www.aventuraoncollegies.com
General Medical & Surgical Services
N.A.I.C.S.: 622110

**Aventura Hospital & Medical
Center** (1)
20900 Biscayne Blvd, Aventura, FL 33180
Tel.: (305) 682-7000
Web Site: http://www.aventurahospital.com
Health Care & Allied Services
N.A.I.C.S.: 621999
Jeffrey Scheck (Chm)
David Was (COO)
David Lemonte (CEO & Sec)
Jalima Hernandez (CFO)
Jesse Gabuat (Chief Nursing Officer)
Trish Stephens (Chief Medical Officer)
Alejandro Andreu (Treas & Sec)
Michael Decker (Dir)
Allan Stewart (Dir)
Ali Bazzi (Dir)
Howard Estrin (Dir)
Haim Sahalon (Dir)
Karen Toronczyk (Dir)

Jean Holewinski (Dir)
Nisha Mani (Dir)
Juan Premoli (Dir)
Mark Mitchell (Chm)
Michelle Lister (Chm)
Eric Schiffman (Chm)
Samuel Neuhut (Chm)
Gerardo Kahane (Chm)
Hoan Bui (Chm)
Jalima Hernandez (CFO)
Jesse Gabuat (Chief Nursing Officer)
Trish Stephens (Chief Medical Officer)
Alejandro Andreu (Treas & Sec)
Michael Decker (Dir)
Allan Stewart (Dir)
Ali Bazzi (Dir)
Howard Estrin (Dir)
Haim Sahalon (Dir)
Karen Toronczyk (Dir)
Jean Holewinski (Dir)
Nisha Mani (Dir)
Juan Premoli (Dir)
Mark Mitchell (Chm)
Michelle Lister (Chm)
Eric Schiffman (Chm)
Samuel Neuhut (Chm)
Gerardo Kahane (Chm)
Hoan Bui (Chm)
Jalima Hernandez (CFO)
Jesse Gabuat (Chief Nursing Officer)
Trish Stephens (Chief Medical Officer)
Alejandro Andreu (Treas & Sec)
Michael Decker (Dir)
Allan Stewart (Dir)
Ali Bazzi (Dir)
Howard Estrin (Dir)
Haim Sahalon (Dir)
Karen Toronczyk (Dir)
Jean Holewinski (Dir)
Nisha Mani (Dir)
Juan Premoli (Dir)
Mark Mitchell (Chm)
Michelle Lister (Chm)
Eric Schiffman (Chm)
Samuel Neuhut (Chm)
Gerardo Kahane (Chm)
Hoan Bui (Chm)

Backlogs Limited (1)
Silvaco Technology Centre Compass Point,
Saint Ives, PE27 5JL, Cambridgeshire,
United Kingdom
Tel.: (44) 148 049 8250
Web Site: http://www.backlogs.co.uk
Diagnostic Equipment Distr
N.A.I.C.S.: 423450

**Bailey Square Ambulatory Surgical
Center, Ltd.** (1)
1111 W 34th St, Austin, TX 78705-1900
Tel.: (512) 454-6753
General Medical & Surgical Services
N.A.I.C.S.: 622110

Bailey Square Surgery Center (1)
1111 W 34th St, Austin, TX 78705
Tel.: (512) 454-6753
Web Site:
https://baileysquaresurgerycenter.com
General Medical & Surgical Services
N.A.I.C.S.: 622110

Basil Street Practice Limited (1)
3 Basil Street, London, SW3 1AU, United
Kingdom
Tel.: (44) 207 235 6642
Web Site: https://www.3bsp.com
Health Care Srvices
N.A.I.C.S.: 621111

Bay Area Healthcare Group, Ltd. (1)
3315 S Alameda St, Corpus Christi, TX
78411-1820
Tel.: (361) 761-1501
Hospital Management Services
N.A.I.C.S.: 622110
Jay Woodall (CEO)

**Bay Area Houston Endoscopy
Center** (1)
1015 W Medical Center Blvd Ste 1200,
Webster, TX 77598
Tel.: (281) 554-3494
Web Site: https://bahewebster.com
General Medical & Surgical Services
N.A.I.C.S.: 622110

Bay Area Surgicare Center, Inc. (1)
502 W Medical Center Blvd, Webster, TX
77598

Tel.: (281) 332-2433
Web Site:
https://www.bayareasurgicare.com
Emp.: 50
Surgical & Health Care Servcies
N.A.I.C.S.: 622110
Stephanie Walker (Officer-Ethics & Compli-
ance)
Johan Trautman (Dir-Medical)
Lisa Wolf (Supvr-Bus Office)
Roberta Stewart (Mgr)
Gina Taylor (Mgr-Quality-Risk)
Erin Flanagan (Mgr)
Priscilla Archer (Mgr-Risk-Op,PACU)

Bay Hospital, Inc. (1)
449 W 23rd St, Panama City, FL 32405-
4507
Tel.: (850) 769-8341
Web Site:
https://www.hcafloridahealthcare.com
Sales Range: $75-99.9 Million
Emp.: 1,200
Hospital
N.A.I.C.S.: 622110
Holly Dean (COO)
Neil Kooy (Chief Medical Officer)
Amber Goodpaster (CFO)
Brittany Durr (Chief Nursing Officer)
Marla Peak (VP)
Tracy Mcglon (VP-Human Resources)
Kim Gleason (VP)
Edy Rivard (VP-Administrative Services)
Sam Wolf (Treas & Sec)
Holly Dean (COO)
Neil Kooy (Chief Medical Officer)
Amber Goodpaster (CFO)
Brittany Durr (Chief Nursing Officer)
Marla Peak (VP)
Tracy Mcglon (VP-Human Resources)
Kim Gleason (VP)
Edy Rivard (VP-Administrative Services)
Sam Wolf (Treas & Sec)
Chase Christianson (Pres)
Joel Leone (COO)

**Bayonet Point Surgery & Endoscopy
Center** (1)
14104 Yosemite Dr, Hudson, FL 34667
Tel.: (727) 869-5040
Web Site: https://www.bayonetsurgery.com
Health Care Srvices
N.A.I.C.S.: 621399

**Bayonet Point Surgery and Endos-
copy Center** (1)
14104 Yosemite Dr, Hudson, FL 34667
Tel.: (727) 869-5040
Web Site: https://bayonetsurgery.com
General Medical & Surgical Services
N.A.I.C.S.: 622110

**Behavioral Health Wellness Center,
LLC** (1)
37 Bollingbrook St, Petersburg, VA 23803
Tel.: (804) 861-6188
Web Site: http://www.bhwc-va.com
Health Care Srvices
N.A.I.C.S.: 621610
Marrlin Metters (Pres)

Belleair Surgery Center, Ltd. (1)
1130 Ponce De Leon Blvd, Clearwater, FL
33756
Tel.: (727) 581-4800
Web Site:
https://www.belleairsurgerycenter.com
Outpatient Care Centers
N.A.I.C.S.: 621498

**Belton Family Practice Clinic,
LLC** (1)
204 E N Ave, Belton, MO 64012
Tel.: (816) 331-7744
Healthcare Support Services
N.A.I.C.S.: 621111

Belton Regional Medical Center (1)
17065 S 71 Hwy, Belton, MO 64012
Tel.: (816) 348-1200
Web Site: https://careers.hcahealthcare.com
Emp.: 300
Health Care Srvices
N.A.I.C.S.: 621399

Blake Medical Center (1)
2020 59th St W, Bradenton, FL 34209
Tel.: (941) 792-6611
Web Site:
http://www.blakemedicalcenter.com

Sales Range: $50-74.9 Million
Emp.: 1,471
Hospital
N.A.I.C.S.: 622110
Randy Currin (Pres, CEO & Sec)
Trudy Moon (Chm)
John K. Lourie (Treas & Sec)
Marc Kallins (Vice Pres)
Steve Nierman (Co-Sec)
Guruswamy Ramamurthy (Treas & Co-Sec)
Iftekhar Baig (Chm)
Michael Van Vliet (Chm)
Ralph Barker (Dir)
Steve Nierman (Co-Sec)
Guruswamy Ramamurthy (Treas & Co-Sec)
Iftekhar Baig (Chm)
Michael Van Vliet (Chm)
Ralph Barker (Dir)

Blossoms Healthcare LLP (1)
21 Garlick Hill, London, EC4V 2AU, United
Kingdom
Tel.: (44) 345 437 0364
Web Site:
http://www.blossomshealthcare.co.uk
Health Care Srvices
N.A.I.C.S.: 621111

**Boulders Ambulatory Surgery
Center** (1)
1115 Boulders Pkwy Ste 210, Richmond,
VA 23225
Tel.: (804) 672-4040
Web Site: https://www.bouldersasc.com
Ambulatory Health Care Services
N.A.I.C.S.: 621493

Bountiful Surgery Center, LLC (1)
620 Medical Dr Ste 200, Bountiful, UT
84010
Tel.: (801) 296-2122
Web Site:
http://www.lakeviewendoscopy.com
Emp.: 5
Health Care Srvices
N.A.I.C.S.: 621111

Subsidiary (Domestic):

**Mountain West Endoscopy
Center** (2)
6360 S 3000 E Ste 320, Salt Lake City, UT
84121
Tel.: (801) 944-3166
Web Site: https://mtwestendo.com
Health Care Srvices
N.A.I.C.S.: 621610

**Boynton Beach EFL Imaging Center,
LLC** (1)
2300 S Congress Ave Ste 105, Boynton
Beach, FL 33426
Tel.: (561) 733-5001
Healthcare Support Services
N.A.I.C.S.: 621111

**Bradenton Outpatient Services,
LLC** (1)
2020 59th St W, Bradenton, FL 34209
Tel.: (615) 344-5228
Clinic Care Services
N.A.I.C.S.: 621399

Brandon Regional Hospital (1)
119 Oakfield Dr, Brandon, FL 33511
Tel.: (813) 681-5551
Web Site: http://www.brandonhospital.com
Sales Range: $75-99.9 Million
Emp.: 2,361
Hospital
N.A.I.C.S.: 622110
Bland Eng (CEO)
Gary Searls (CFO)
Kyle Thrift (Chief Nursing Officer)
Melissa Snively (Chm)
Michael Miranda (Vice Chm)

**Brigham City Community Hospital,
Inc.** (1)
950 S Medical Dr, Brigham City, UT 84302
Tel.: (435) 734-9471
Web Site:
http://www.brighamcityhospital.com
Sales Range: $25-49.9 Million
Hospital
N.A.I.C.S.: 622110

Brighton Surgicenter, LLC (1)
980 Westfall Rd, Rochester, NY 14618
Tel.: (585) 295-8500

HCA Healthcare, Inc.—(Continued)

Web Site: https://www.brightonsurgery.com
Surgical Product Distr
N.A.I.C.S.: 423450
Tom Weibel (COO)
Scott Berry (Dir-Medical)

Broward Neurosurgeons, LLC (1)
8251 W Broward Blvd Ste 300, Plantation,
FL 33324
Tel.: (954) 475-9244
Web Site:
http://neurosurgicalspecialistsofsouth
florida.com
Health Care Srvices
N.A.I.C.S.: 621399

Brownsville Surgical Specialists,
PLLC (1)
100 E Alton Gloor Blvd Bldg B Ste 260,
Brownsville, TX 78526
Tel.: (956) 350-3901
Web Site:
https://www.brownsvillesurgicalspecial
ists.com
General Medical & Surgical Services
N.A.I.C.S.: 622110

Buford Road Imaging, L.L.C. (1)
2612 Buford Rd, Richmond, VA 23235
Tel.: (804) 639-5489
General Medical & Surgical Services
N.A.I.C.S.: 622110

CCBH Psychiatric Hospitalists,
LLC (1)
340 Hospital Dr, Macon, GA 31217
Tel.: (478) 765-7000
Web Site:
http://www.coliseumhealthsystem.com
Emp.: 1,400
Health Care & Allied Services
N.A.I.C.S.: 621999

CHCA West Houston, L.P. (1)
12141 Richmond Ave, Houston, TX 77082
Tel.: (281) 558-3444
Web Site: http://hcahoustonhealthcare.com
Medical Center
N.A.I.C.S.: 621112

CJW Infectious Disease, LLC (1)
7101 Jahnke Rd, Richmond, VA 23225
Tel.: (804) 320-3911
Health Care Srvices
N.A.I.C.S.: 621111

CJW Medical Center (1)
7101 Jahnke Rd, Richmond, VA 23225
Tel.: (804) 483-0000
Web Site: http://www.cjwmedical.com
Sales Range: $50-74.9 Million
Emp.: 1,000
Hospital
N.A.I.C.S.: 622110
William Lunn (CEO)
Kristin Dyer (CFO)
Sheldon Barr (COO)
Raymond Makhoul (Chief Medical Officer)
Ann Winn (Chief Nursing Officer)

CP Surgery Center, LLC (1)
900 W 38th St 200, Austin, TX 78705
Tel.: (512) 323-2061
Web Site: https://centralparksurgery.com
Surgical Care Services
N.A.I.C.S.: 621493

Subsidiary (Domestic):

Central Park Surgery Center (2)
411 Central Park Dr, Arlington, TX 76014
Tel.: (817) 784-8300
Web Site: http://www.centralparkasc.net
Surgical Care Services
N.A.I.C.S.: 621493

Calder Immediate Care, PLLC (1)
1108 Gulf Fwy S Ste 220, League City, TX
77573
Tel.: (281) 557-4404
Web Site: http://www.calderurgent.com
Health Care Srvices
N.A.I.C.S.: 621610

Calder Urgent Care, PLLC (1)
1108 S Gulf Frwy Ste 230, League City, TX
77573
Tel.: (281) 557-4404
Web Site: http://www.calderurgent.com

Health Care Srvices
N.A.I.C.S.: 327910

Calloway Creek Surgery Center,
L.P. (1)
4300 City Point Dr Ste 100, North Richland
Hills, TX 76180
Tel.: (817) 548-4000
Web Site:
https://www.callowaycreeksurgerycen
ter.com
Health Care Srvices
N.A.I.C.S.: 621999
Teresa Tumbale (Mgr-Nurse)
Danielle Karabinis (Office Mgr)
Anastasia Schuman (Dir-Medical)

Cape Coral Surgery Center, Inc. (1)
2721 Del Prado Blvd, Cape Coral, FL
33904
Tel.: (239) 242-8010
Web Site:
https://www.capecoralsurgerycenter.com
Health Care Srvices
N.A.I.C.S.: 621399

Cape Coral Surgery Center, Inc. (1)
2721 Del Prado Blvd, Cape Coral, FL
33904
Tel.: (239) 242-8010
Web Site:
https://www.capecoralsurgerycenter.com
General Medical & Surgical Services
N.A.I.C.S.: 622110

Capital Area Primary Care
Providers (1)
7200 Wyoming Springs Dr, Round Rock,
TX 78681
Tel.: (512) 218-8696
General Medical & Surgical Services
N.A.I.C.S.: 622110

Capital Area Providers (1)
4007 James Casey St Ste B220, Austin, TX
78745
Tel.: (512) 440-1113
Surgical Care Services
N.A.I.C.S.: 621493

Capital Regional Heart Associates
LLC (1)
2770 Capital Medical Blvd Ste 109 C, Talla-
hassee, FL 32308
Tel.: (850) 877-0320
Web Site: http://www.capitalregionalca.com
Miscellaneous Health Practitioner Services
N.A.I.C.S.: 621399

Capital Regional Medical Center (1)
2626 Capital Medical Blvd, Tallahassee, FL
32308
Tel.: (850) 325-5000
Web Site:
https://www.hcafloridahealthcare.com
Sales Range: $50-74.9 Million
Emp.: 1,597
Hospital
N.A.I.C.S.: 622110
Alan B. Keesee (Co-Pres, CEO & Co-Sec)
Robert Jack Atwater (Chm)
Myrna Hoover (Vice Chm)
Tom Eisel (CFO-North Florida Div)
Ann C. Smith (Chief Nursing Officer-North
Florida Div)
Rachel Bray-Stiles (Dir-Comm & Commu-
nity Engagement)
Trey Blake (Chief Medical Officer)
Christopher Wilhoit (Pres-Medical)
Elizabeth Paine (COO)
Marino Martinez Vargas (Treas & Co-Sec)
Tara Beth Anderson (Chief Nursing Officer)
Jason Washington (VP-Operations)
Tamara Tatum (Dir)
Tanesh Sadarangani (Co-Pres)

Capital Regional Psychiatry Associates, LLC (1)
2626 Capital Medical Blvd, Tallahassee, FL
32308
Tel.: (850) 219-2369
Health Care Srvices
N.A.I.C.S.: 621491

Cardiac Surgical Associates,
LLC (1)
7101 Jahnke Rd Ste 500, Richmond, VA
23225
Tel.: (804) 320-2751
Web Site: http://www.heartsurgeryva.com

Emp.: 15
Medical & Surgical Hospital Services
N.A.I.C.S.: 622110

Cardio Vascular Surgeons of North
Texas, PLLC (1)
3900 W 15th St Ste 208, Plano, TX 75075-
7751
Tel.: (972) 519-8300
General Medical & Surgical Services
N.A.I.C.S.: 622110

Cardiology Clinic of San Antonio,
PLLC (1)
4411 Medical Dr Ste 300, San Antonio, TX
78229
Tel.: (210) 614-5400
Web Site:
http://www.methodistphysicianpracti
ces.com
Cardio Care Services
N.A.I.C.S.: 621111

Cardiology Specialists of North
Texas, PLLC (1)
777 Forest Ln Ste C339, Dallas, TX 75230-
2501
Tel.: (972) 566-8855
Emp.: 3
Healthcare Training Services
N.A.I.C.S.: 621111

CareSpot of Overland Park (W. 151st
Street), LLC (1)
7935 W 151st St, Overland Park, KS 66223
Tel.: (913) 440-0834
Web Site: http://www.carespot.com
Health Care Srvices
N.A.I.C.S.: 621999

Carolina Forest Imaging Center,
LLC (1)
199 Village Ct Blvd Ste 110, Myrtle Beach,
SC 29579
Tel.: (843) 236-7878
Emp.: 10
Medical Laboratory Services
N.A.I.C.S.: 621511
Mark Sims (CEO)

Cartersville Medical Center, LLC (1)
960 Joe Frank Harris Pkwy, Cartersville,
GA 30120
Tel.: (470) 490-1000
Web Site:
http://www.cartersvillemedical.com
Sales Range: $75-99.9 Million
Hospital
N.A.I.C.S.: 622110
J. Christopher Mosley (CEO)
Mark Senger (Chief Medical Officer)
Benny McDonald (CFO)
Lori Rakes (OOO)
Jan Tidwell (Chief Nursing Officer)

Cartersville Occupational Medicine
Center, LLC (1)
960 Joe Frank Harris Pkwy, Cartersville,
GA 30120
Tel.: (770) 382-1530
Web Site:
http://www.cartersvillemedical.com
Health Care & Allied Services
N.A.I.C.S.: 621999

Catalog360 Limited (1)
19 George Road, Birmingham, B15 1NU,
United Kingdom
Tel.: (44) 845 887 5000
Web Site: https://catalog360.com
Online Publishing Services
N.A.I.C.S.: 513199

Cedar Creek Medical Group,
LLC (1)
100 NW Mock Ave, Blue Springs, MO
64014-2500
Tel.: (816) 463-6001
Health Care Srvices
N.A.I.C.S.: 621399

Cedarcare, Inc. (1)
15685 Sw 116th Ave Ste141, Portland, OR
97224-2651
Tel.: (503) 307-9062
Emp.: 2
Health Care Management Services
N.A.I.C.S.: 621999
Kevin Dartlett (Partner)

Cedars Healthcare Group, Ltd. (1)
1400 NW 12th Ave, Miami, FL 33136
Tel.: (305) 325-5511
Health Care Srvices
N.A.I.C.S.: 621399

Centennial Heart, LLC (1)
2400 Patterson St Ste 502, Nashville, TN
37203
Tel.: (615) 515-1900
Web Site: http://www.centennialheart.com
Health Care Srvices
N.A.I.C.S.: 621610

Centennial Medical Center (1)
2300 Patterson St, Nashville, TN 37203
Tel.: (615) 342-1000
Sales Range: $100-124.9 Million
Emp.: 3,163
Hospital
N.A.I.C.S.: 622110

Subsidiary (Domestic):

Parthenon Pavilion Inc. (2)
2401 Parman Pl, Nashville, TN 37203
Tel.: (615) 342-1450
Sales Range: $25-49.9 Million
Emp.: 350
Psychiatric Hospitals
N.A.I.C.S.: 622210

Centennial Neuroscience, LLC (1)
330 23rd Ave N Ste 140, Nashville, TN
37203
Tel.: (615) 342-6840
Web Site: http://tristarmedgroup.com
Health Care Srvices
N.A.I.C.S.: 621610

Centennial Primary Care, LLC (1)
14000 E Arapahoe Rd Ste 380, Centennial,
CO 80112
Tel.: (303) 226-6180
Web Site:
https://healthonephysiciangroup.com
Emp.: 11
Health Care Srvices
N.A.I.C.S.: 621999
Annette Mell (Gen Mgr)

Centennial Psychiatric Associates,
LLC (1)
310 25th Ave N Ste 307, Nashville, TN
37203
Tel.: (615) 320-8887
Health Care Srvices
N.A.I.C.S.: 621999

Centennial Surgery Center, L.P. (1)
502 Centennial Blvd Ste 1, Voorhees, NJ
08043
Tel.: (856) 874-0790
Web Site:
http://www.centennialsurgerycenter.com
Health Care Srvices
N.A.I.C.S.: 621999

Centennial Surgical Associates,
LLC (1)
1600 N Grand Ave Ste 510, Pueblo, CO
81003
Tel.: (719) 566-3535
Emp.: 7
Healtcare Services
N.A.I.C.S.: 621999
Bruce Johnson (Partner)

Centennial Surgical Clinic, LLC (1)
2400 Patterson St Ste 215, Nashville, TN
37203-6501
Tel.: (615) 342-7345
General Medical & Surgical Services
N.A.I.C.S.: 622110

Center for Advanced Diagnostics
LLC (1)
8101 E Lowry Blvd Ste 120, Denver, CO
80230
Tel.: (303) 340-8439
Health Care Srvices
N.A.I.C.S.: 621999

Center for Occupational Medicine,
LLC (1)
635 Ronald Reagan Dr, Evans, GA 30809
Tel.: (706) 922-5056
Web Site: http://www.occmedaugusta.com
Emp.: 7
Health Care Services

N.A.I.C.S.: 621610

Center for Special Surgery (1)
350 23rd Ave E Ste 201, West Fargo, ND 58078
Tel.: (701) 356-4770
Web Site: https://www.specialsurg.com
General Medical & Surgical Services
N.A.I.C.S.: 622110

Centerpoint Ambulatory Surgery Center (1)
19550 E 39th St, Independence, MO 64057
Tel.: (816) 478-2600
Web Site: http://www.centerpointasc.com
Health Care Srvices
N.A.I.C.S.: 621399

Centerpoint Cardiology Services, LLC (1)
19550 E 39th St S Ste 225, Independence, MO 64057-2303
Tel.: (816) 228-2060
Health Care Srvices
N.A.I.C.S.: 621399

Centerpoint Clinic of Blue Springs, LLC (1)
725 NW State Route 7 Ste B, Blue Springs, MO 64014
Tel.: (816) 229-8187
Health Care & Allied Services
N.A.I.C.S.: 621999

Centerpoint Hospital Based Physicians, LLC (1)
19600 E 39th St S 3rd Fl OB, Independence, MO 64057-2301
Tel.: (816) 698-7189
Health Care Srvices
N.A.I.C.S.: 621399

Centerpoint Medical Center of Independence, LLC (1)
19600 E 39th St S, Independence, MO 64057
Tel.: (816) 698-7000
Web Site: http://www.centerpointmedical.com
Medical Support Services
N.A.I.C.S.: 621111

Centerpoint Orthopedics, LLC (1)
19550 E 39th St Ste 230, Independence, MO 64057
Tel.: (816) 795-6630
Web Site: https://mymidwestphysician.com
Health Care & Allied Services
N.A.I.C.S.: 621999

Centerpoint Physicians Group, LLC (1)
19550 E 39th St Ste 245, Independence, MO 64057
Tel.: (816) 373-0655
Web Site: https://mymidwestphysician.com
Health Care Srvices
N.A.I.C.S.: 621399

Central Florida Regional Hospital (1)
1401 W Seminole Blvd, Sanford, FL 32771
Tel.: (407) 321-4500
General Medical & Surgical Services
N.A.I.C.S.: 622110

Central Florida Regional Hospital, Inc. (1)
1401 W Seminole Blvd, Sanford, FL 32771
Tel.: (407) 321-4500
Web Site: http://www.centralfloridaregional.com
Health Care Management Services
N.A.I.C.S.: 621999
Trey Abshier (CEO)

Central Shared Services, LLC (1)
12610 W Airport Blvd Ste 180, Sugar Land, TX 77478
Tel.: (281) 295-5187
Surgical Hospital Services
N.A.I.C.S.: 622110

Centrum Surgery Center, Ltd. (1)
8200 E Belleview Ste 300 E Tower, Englewood, CO 80111
Tel.: (303) 290-0600
Web Site: http://www.centrumsurgicalcenter.com
Health Care Srvices
N.A.I.C.S.: 621999

Michael Culliton (Dir-Medical)
Rehanna Curtis (Dir-Clinical)

Subsidiary (Domestic):

Centrum Surgical Center (2)
8200 E Belleview Ave Ste 300 E, Greenwood Village, CO 80111
Tel.: (303) 290-0600
Web Site:
    https://www.centrumsurgicalcenter.com
General Medical & Surgical services
N.A.I.C.S.: 622110

Chattanooga Diagnostic Associates, LLC (1)
2205 McCallie Ave Ste 300, Chattanooga, TN 37404
Tel.: (423) 622-6848
Web Site:
    http://www.parkridgemedicalgroup.com
Diagnostic Services
N.A.I.C.S.: 621512

Chelsea Outpatient Centre LLP (1)
280 Kings Road, London, SW3 5AW, United Kingdom
Tel.: (44) 207 881 4114
Web Site:
    http://www.chelseaoutpatientcentre.com
Diagnostic Imaging Services
N.A.I.C.S.: 621512

Chesterfield Imaging, LLC (1)
13636 Hull St Rd, Midlothian, VA 23112-2108
Tel.: (804) 639-5489
General Medical & Surgical Services
N.A.I.C.S.: 622110

Chesterfield Imaging, LLC (1)
13636 Hull Street Rd, Midlothian, VA 23112
Tel.: (804) 639-5489
General Medical & Surgical Services
N.A.I.C.S.: 622110

Chippenham & Johnston-Willis Hospitals, Inc. (1)
1401 Johnston Willis Dr, North Chesterfield, VA 23235
Tel.: (804) 330-2000
Web Site: http://www.cjwmedical.com
General Medical Care Services
N.A.I.C.S.: 622110

Chippenham & Johnston-Willis Sports Medicine, LLC (1)
1115 Boulders Pkwy Ste 110, Richmond, VA 23225
Tel.: (804) 560-6500
Web Site: http://hcavirginiaphysicians.com
Health Care Srvices
N.A.I.C.S.: 621111

Chippenham Pediatric Specialists, LLC (1)
101 Cowardin Ave Ste 207, Richmond, VA 23224
Tel.: (804) 237-7761
Web Site: http://www.cjwpediatrics.com
Emp.: 3
General Medical & Surgical Services
N.A.I.C.S.: 622110

Chiswick Outpatient Centre LLP (1)
347-352 Chiswick High Road Bond House, London, W4 4HS, United Kingdom
Tel.: (44) 2031314734
Health Care Srvices
N.A.I.C.S.: 621491

Christiansburg Internal Medicine, LLC (1)
10 Hickok St Ste 101, Christiansburg, VA 24060
Tel.: (540) 381-1882
Health Care Srvices
N.A.I.C.S.: 621111

Citrus HomeHealth, Inc. (1)
1 Park Plz, Nashville, TN 37203-6527
Tel.: (615) 344-2994
Health Care Srvices
N.A.I.C.S.: 621610

Citrus Memorial Hospital, Inc. (1)
502 W Highland Blvd, Inverness, FL 34452
Tel.: (352) 726-1551
Web Site: http://citrusmh.com
Emp.: 1,028
General Medical & Surgical services

N.A.I.C.S.: 622110
George Mavros (COO)
Ralph Aleman (CEO)
Caroline Stewart (Chief Nursing Officer)
Raylene Platel (Chief Medical Officer)
Ghulam Anwar (Treas & Sec)
Lisa Nummi (CEO)
Ginger Carroll (CEO)
Joshua Moore (COO)
Zach Riggins (CFO)
Sue DeLeon (Chief Nursing Officer)
Ginger Carroll (CEO)
Joshua Moore (COO)
Zach Riggins (CFO)
Sue DeLeon (Chief Nursing Officer)

Citrus Primary Care, Inc. (1)
450 W Roosevelt Blvd, Inverness, FL 34465
Tel.: (352) 527-6646
Medical Center Services
N.A.I.C.S.: 621112
Jessica West (Office Mgr)

Clarksville Surgicenter, LLC (1)
121 Hillcrest Dr, Clarksville, TN 37043
Tel.: (931) 552-9992
Web Site:
    https://surgerycenterofclarksville.com
Health Care Srvices
N.A.I.C.S.: 621491

Clear Creek Surgery Center, LLC (1)
7809 W 38th Ave Ste 100, Wheat Ridge, CO 80033
Tel.: (303) 422-5555
Web Site:
    https://www.clearcreeksurgery.com
Medical & Surgical Hospital Services
N.A.I.C.S.: 622110

Clear Lake Family Physicians, PLLC (1)
1045 Gemini St Ste 200B, Houston, TX 77058
Tel.: (281) 486-7900
Web Site: http://clearlakemed.com
General Medical & Surgical Services
N.A.I.C.S.: 622110

Clear Lake Regional Medical Center, Inc. (1)
500 Medical Centre Blvd, Webster, TX 77598
Tel.: (281) 332-2511
Web Site: http://www.clearlakermc.com
Sales Range: $75-99.9 Million
Hospital
N.A.I.C.S.: 622110
Todd Caliva (CEO)
John O. Armour (CFO)
Jim Russell (COO)
Sherry Camacho (Chief Nursing Officer)
Richard Gornto (Chm)
Nadir Ali (Vice Chm)
William Killinger (Chief Medical Officer)
Elias Armendariz (COO)
William Killinger (Chief Medical Officer)
Elias Armendariz (COO)

Clipper Cardiovascular Associates, Inc. (1)
7 Henry Graf Jr Rd, Newburyport, MA 01950
Tel.: (978) 462-1110
Web Site: https://clippercardiovascular.com
General Medical & Surgical Services
N.A.I.C.S.: 622110

Clipper Cardiovascular Associates, Inc. (1)
7 Henry Graf Jr Rd, Newburyport, MA 01950
Tel.: (978) 462-1110
Web Site:
    https://www.clippercardiovascular.com
Emp.: 20
Health Care Srvices
N.A.I.C.S.: 621999
Salman Ghiasuddin (Dir-Medical)

Coastal Healthcare Services, Inc. (1)
3801 Connecticut Ave NW Ste 100, Washington, DC 20008
Tel.: (202) 525-1641
Web Site: https://www.moveplayspeak.com
Healthcare Support Services
N.A.I.C.S.: 622110

Coastal Inpatient Physicians, LLC (1)
295 Midland Pkwy, Summerville, SC 29483
Tel.: (843) 824-3225
General Medical & Surgical Services
N.A.I.C.S.: 622110

Coliseum Health Group, LLC (1)
3200 Riverside Dr, Macon, GA 31210-2550
Tel.: (478) 757-1500
General Medical & Surgical Services
N.A.I.C.S.: 622110

Coliseum Health System (1)
350 Hospital Dr, Macon, GA 31217
Tel.: (478) 765-7000
Web Site:
    http://www.coliseumhealthsystem.com
Sales Range: $75-99.9 Million
Emp.: 1,500
Hospital System
N.A.I.C.S.: 622110
Scott Anderton (CFO)
Stephen J. Daugherty (CEO)
Richard Rubio (Chief Medical Officer)
David Threatt (Chief Nursing Officer)
Louise Truitt (VP-Human Resources)
Robin Parker (VP-Marketing)
Angie Walker (Exec Dir-Human Resources)
Gary Bernstein (Chief Medical Officer)
Alisha Neal (CFO)
Scott Strong (COO)
Angie Walker (Exec Dir-Human Resources)
Gary Bernstein (Chief Medical Officer)
Alisha Neal (CFO)
Scott Strong (COO)

Subsidiary (Domestic):

Coliseum Northside Hospital, LLC (2)
400 Charter Blvd, Macon, GA 31210
Tel.: (478) 757-8200
Web Site: http://coliseumhealthsystem.com
Hospital Operations
N.A.I.C.S.: 622110

Coliseum Medical Center, LLC (1)
350 Hospital Dr, Macon, GA 31217
Tel.: (478) 765-7000
Web Site: https://www.piedmont.org
Health Care Srvices
N.A.I.C.S.: 621491
Bridget Denzik (Chief Nursing Officer)

College Park Endoscopy Center, LLC (1)
10787 Nall Ave Ste 100, Overland Park, KS 66211
Tel.: (913) 385-4400
Web Site:
    https://collegeparkendoscopycenter.com
Health Care Srvices
N.A.I.C.S.: 621491

Colleton Ambulatory Surgery Center (1)
304 Medical Park Dr, Walterboro, SC 29488
Tel.: (843) 782-2700
Web Site: https://www.colletonsurgery.com
Health Care Srvices
N.A.I.C.S.: 621399

Colleton Diagnostic Center, LLC (1)
304 Medical Park Dr, Walterboro, SC 29488
Tel.: (843) 782-2717
Women Healthcare Services
N.A.I.C.S.: 621610

Colleton Medical Center (1)
501 Robertson Blvd, Walterboro, SC 29488
Tel.: (843) 782-2000
Web Site: https://www.colletonmedical.com
Sales Range: $25-49.9 Million
Emp.: 450
Hospital
N.A.I.C.S.: 622110
Jimmy Hiott (CEO & Sec)
Vonda Calcutt (Chm)
Barnwell Fishburne (VP)
Moultrie Plowden (Chm)
Hugh Tappan (Pres)
Tiffany Norton-Cornette (Dir-Public Relations)
Cassie Ball (CFO)
Missy Feather (Chief Nursing Officer)
Dayton Strader (VP-Operations)
Debi Drew (VP-Risk Management)
Missy Ragland (VP-Human Resources)

HCA Healthcare, Inc.—(Continued)

Tiffany Norton-Cornette (Dir-Public Relations)
Cassie Ball (CFO)
Missy Feather (Chief Nursing Officer)
Dayton Strader (VP-Operations)
Debi Drew (VP-Risk Management)
Missy Ragland (VP-Human Resources)

Collin County Diagnostic Associates, PLLC (1)
8080 State Hwy 121 Ste 360, McKinney, TX 75070-2901
Tel.: (214) 383-6676
Healtcare Services
N.A.I.C.S.: 621999

Colonial Heights Surgery Center (1)
930 South Ave Ste 2, Colonial Heights, VA 23834
Tel.: (804) 520-8272
Web Site: https://www.hcavirginia.com
Emp.: 25
Surgical Care Services
N.A.I.C.S.: 621493

Columbia Hospital (Palm Beaches) Limited Partnership (1)
2201 45th St, West Palm Beach, FL 33407
Tel.: (561) 842-6141
Health Care Services
N.A.I.C.S.: 621999

Columbia Hospital Corporation of Corpus Christi (1)
3315 S Alameda St 3rd Fl Conference Room 3W, Corpus Christi, TX 78410
Tel.: (361) 761-1227
Web Site: http://www.ccmedicalcenter.com
Orthopedic Hospital Operating Services
N.A.I.C.S.: 622310

Columbia Hospital Corporation of South Broward (1)
8201 W Broward Blvd, Plantation, FL 33324-2701
Tel.: (954) 473-6600
Web Site: http://www.westsideregional.com
Hospital Management Services
N.A.I.C.S.: 622110
Barbara Simmons (CEO)

Columbia Hospital at Medical City Dallas Subsidiary, L.P. (1)
7777 Forest Ln, Dallas, TX 75230
Tel.: (972) 566-7000
Web Site: https://medicalcityhealthcare.com
Health Care Services
N.A.I.C.S.: 621399
Chris Mowan (Pres & CEO)
Barbara Watkins (Chm)
Joseph Carlos (Vice Chm)

Columbia Medical Center of Arlington Subsidiary, L.P. (1)
3301 Matlock Rd, Arlington, TX 76015
Tel.: (682) 509-6200
Web Site: https://medicalcityhealthcare.com
Health Care Services
N.A.I.C.S.: 621999
Sharn Barbarin (Sec)
Eric Benink (Chief Medical Officer)
Jim Allard (Chief Nursing Officer)
Dillon Rai (COO)
Nathan Tindall (CFO)
Elizabeth Merwin (Chm)
Miguel Reyes (Vice Chm)

Columbia Medical Center of Denton Subsidiary, L.P. (1)
3535 S Interstate 35, Denton, TX 76210-6850
Tel.: (940) 384-3535
Web Site: https://medicalcityhealthcare.com
Emp.: 900
General Medical & Surgical Services
N.A.I.C.S.: 622110

Columbia Medical Center of Las Colinas, Inc. (1)
6800 N MacArthur Blvd, Irving, TX 75039
Tel.: (972) 969-2000
Surgical Hospital Services
N.A.I.C.S.: 622110
Daniela Decell (CEO)

Columbia Medical Center of Lewisville Subsidiary, L.P. (1)
500 W Main St, Lewisville, TX 75057

Tel.: (469) 370-2000
Web Site: http://www.lewisvillemedical.com
Health Care Srvices
N.A.I.C.S.: 621399
John Walker (Sec)
Ken Stevens (COO)
Whitney Bendel (CFO)
Emily Sneed (Chief Nursing Officer)
Stephanie MacVeigh (VP)
Gary Lewis (Chm)
Moiz Shafiq (Vice Chm)
Megan Gallegos (Chief Nursing Officer)

Columbia Medical Center of McKinney Subsidiary, L.P. (1)
4500 Medical Center Dr, McKinney, TX 75069
Tel.: (972) 547-8000
Web Site: http://www.medicalcitymckinney.com
Health Care Srvices
N.A.I.C.S.: 621399
Manjula Julka (Chief Medical Officer)
Allen Marsh (COO)
Renee Sturgeon (CFO)
Megan Gallegos (Chief Nursing Officer)
Dan Brooks (Chm)
Ray Eckenrode (Vice Chm)
C. Lynch III (CEO)

Columbia Medical Center of Plano Subsidiary, L.P. (1)
3901 W 15th St, Plano, TX 75075
Tel.: (972) 596-6800
Web Site: http://medicalcityplano.com
Emp.: 1,600
Health Care Srvices
N.A.I.C.S.: 621399
Ben Coogan (Sec)
Jordan Allred (Chief Dev Officer)
Jonathan Clarke (Chief Medical Officer)
Thomas Heffernan (Chm)

Columbia Medical Group - Centennial, Inc. (1)
2400 Parman Pl, Nashville, TN 37203
Tel.: (615) 342-5626
Health Care Srvices
N.A.I.C.S.: 621399

Columbia North Hills Hospital Subsidiary, L.P. (1)
4401 Booth Calloway Rd, North Richland Hills, TX 76180
Tel.: (817) 255-1000
Web Site: http://www.medicalcitynorthhills.com
Medical & Surgical Hospital Services
N.A.I.C.S.: 622110
Mark Deno (Sec)
Kevin Inderhees (Chief Nursing Officer)
Teddy Jones (CFO)
Patrick I. Allen II (Chm)
Curtis Johnson (Vice Chm)

Columbia Plaza Medical Center of Fort Worth Subsidiary, L.P. (1)
900 8th Ave, Fort Worth, TX 76104
Tel.: (817) 877-5292
Healthcare Support Services
N.A.I.C.S.: 621111
Jyric Sims (CEO)

Columbia Polk General Hospital, Inc. (1)
2360 Rockmart Hwy, Cedartown, GA 30125-2644
Tel.: (770) 748-2500
Web Site: http://www.polkhospital.org
Health Care Srvices
N.A.I.C.S.: 621399

Columbia Primary Care, LLC (1)
4700 N Congress Ave Ste 201, West Palm Beach, FL 33407
Tel.: (561) 881-2640
General Medical & Surgical Services
N.A.I.C.S.: 327910

Columbia/Alleghany Regional Hospital, Incorporated (1)
1 ARH Ln, Low Moor, VA 24457
Tel.: (540) 862-6879
General Medical & Surgical Services
N.A.I.C.S.: 622110

Columbia/HCA Retreat Hospital, Inc. (1)
2621 Grove Ave, Richmond, VA 23220-4308

Tel.: (804) 254-5100
Web Site: http://www.retreathospital.com
Sales Range: $25-49.9 Million
Emp.: 420
Hospital
N.A.I.C.S.: 622110

Columbia/HCA of North Texas, Inc. (1)
6565 N MacArthur Blvd Ste 350, Irving, TX 75039
Tel.: (972) 401-8750
Web Site: http://www.hcanorthtexas.com
Medical Support Services
N.A.I.C.S.: 621111

Commonwealth Perinatal Services, LLC (1)
7601 Forest Ave Ste 336, Richmond, VA 23229
Tel.: (804) 289-4972
Web Site: http://hcavirginiaphysicians.com
Health Care Srvices
N.A.I.C.S.: 621111

Commonwealth Specialists of Kentucky, LLC (1)
279 Kings Daughters Dr Ste 308, Frankfort, KY 40601
Tel.: (502) 875-7000
Web Site: http://frankfortregionalhealth.com
Health Care Srvices
N.A.I.C.S.: 621399

Commure, Inc (1)
1300 Terra Bella Ave, Ste 200, Mountain View, CA 94043
Tel.: (424) 375-7095
Web Site: https://www.commure.com
IT Services
N.A.I.C.S.: 513210

Subsidiary (Domestic):
Augmedix, Inc. (2)
111 Sutter St Ste 1300, San Francisco, CA 94104
Web Site: https://www.augmedix.com
Rev.: $30,933,000
Assets: $33,641,000
Liabilities: $32,175,000
Net Worth: $1,466,000
Earnings: ($24,449,000)
Emp.: 1,040
Fiscal Year-end: 12/31/2022
Remote Medical Documentation & Live Clinical Support Services
N.A.I.C.S.: 621610
Manny Krakaris (CEO)
Sandra Breber (COO)
Paul Ginocchio (CFO)
Saurav Chatterjee (CTO)
Ian Shakil (Founder & Chief Strategy Officer)
Davin Lundquist (Chief Medical Officer)
Jonathan Hawkins (Chief Revenue Officer)

Comprehensive Radiology Management Services, Ltd. (1)
8019 Fredericksburg Rd, San Antonio, TX 78229
Tel.: (210) 617-9300
Emp.: 260
General Medical & Surgical Services
N.A.I.C.S.: 622110

Concept EFL Imaging Center, LLC (1)
2290 10th Ave N Ste 101, Lake Worth, FL 33461
Tel.: (561) 540-8100
Web Site: http://www.floridaopenimaging.com
Emp.: 50
Health Care Srvices
N.A.I.C.S.: 621999

Congenital Heart Surgery Center, PLLC (1)
7777 Forest Ln Ste B-120, Dallas, TX 75230
Tel.: (972) 566-2525
Web Site: http://medicalcitychildrensheart.com
Medical Support Services
N.A.I.C.S.: 621111

Conroe Regional Medical Center (1)
504 Medical Ctr Blvd, Conroe, TX 77304
Tel.: (936) 539-1111

Web Site: https://hcahoustonhealthcare.com
Sales Range: $50-74.9 Million
Emp.: 1,200
Hospital
N.A.I.C.S.: 622110
Matt Davis (CEO)
Lawrence Verfurth (Chief Medical Officer)
Chase Redden (CFO)
Diana Howell (VP-Human Resources)
Jerrica George (COO)
A. J. Foster (Dir)
Alice D. Woods (Dir)
Barbara Laing (Dir)
Christy Anderson (Dir)
Darren DeSimone (Dir)
David Davidson (Dir)
Elizabeth Byerman (Dir)
Janet Gammon (Dir)
Joan Kelly (Dir)
Kelly Mohan (Dir)
Laura Littlejohn (Dir-Public Relations)
Laurie Philips (Dir)
Le'Qunna Johnson (Dir)
Mary Berczy (Dir-Surgical,Trauma)
Michelle Jackson (Dir)
Mike Horger (Dir & Officer-Safety)
Minnie Washington (Dir)
Monica Sanders (Dir)
O'Keefe Allen (Dir-Supply Chain)
Sharla Shumaker (Dir-Administration)
Steve Herring (Dir-Information Technology)
Robert Sabina (COO)
Angelo Carambas (Chief Nursing Officer)
Robert Sabina (COO)
Angelo Carambas (Chief Nursing Officer)
Brandon Frazier (CFO)

Coral Springs Surgi-Center, Ltd. (1)
967 University Dr, Coral Springs, FL 33071
Tel.: (954) 341-5553
Web Site: http://surgerycentercoralsprings.com
Outpatient Care Services
N.A.I.C.S.: 621498

Corpus Christi Heart Clinic, PLLC (1)
1202 3rd St, Corpus Christi, TX 78404
Tel.: (361) 883-3962
Web Site: https://corpuschristiheartclinic.com
Health Care Srvices
N.A.I.C.S.: 621491

Corpus Christi Medical Center (1)
7101 S Padre Island Dr, Corpus Christi, TX 78412
Tel.: (361) 761-1000
Web Site: https://ccmedicalcenter.com
Sales Range: $75-99.9 Million
Emp.: 1,500
Hospital
N.A.I.C.S.: 622110
Chris Nicosia (CFO)
Kathleen Rubano (Chief Nursing Officer)
Eric Evans (CEO)
Yasmene McDaniel (COO)
Deppert Eric (Chief Medical Officer)
Mary Lou Roper (Pres)
Troy Villarreal (Gen Partner)
Mark Roberts (COO)
Dean H. Hommer (Chief Medical Officer)
Mark Roberts (COO)
Dean H. Hommer (Chief Medical Officer)

Corpus Christi Radiation Oncology, PLLC (1)
1625 Rodd Field Rd Ste 200, Corpus Christi, TX 78412
Tel.: (361) 985-2273
Web Site: http://www.ccradiationoncology.com
Cancer Treatment Services
N.A.I.C.S.: 622310

Countryside Surgery Center (1)
3291 N McMullen Booth Rd, Clearwater, FL 33761
Tel.: (727) 725-5800
Web Site: https://countrysidesurgerycenter.com
General Medical & Surgical Services
N.A.I.C.S.: 622110

Countryside Surgery Center, Ltd. (1)
3291 N McMullen Booth Rd, Clearwater, FL 33761
Tel.: (727) 725-5800
Web Site: https://countrysidesurgerycenter.com

Outpatient Care Centers
N.A.I.C.S.: 621498

Crewe Outpatient Imaging, LLC (1)
12522 W Colonial Trl Hwy Ste 1, Crewe, VA
23930-3329
Tel.: (434) 538-0028
General Medical & Surgical Services
N.A.I.C.S.: 622110

Cumberland Medical Center, Inc. (1)
421 S Main St, Crossville, TN 38555
Tel.: (931) 484-9511
Web Site: http://www.cmchealthcare.org
Health Care Srvices
N.A.I.C.S.: 621610
David Bunch *(Chief Admin Officer)*

**Cy-Fair Medical Center Hospital,
LLC** (1)
10655 Steepletop Dr, Houston, TX 77065
Tel.: (281) 890-4285
Health Care Srvices
N.A.I.C.S.: 621491

Dallas Medical Specialists, PLLC (1)
7777 Forest Ln Ste C-300, Dallas, TX
75230
Tel.: (972) 566-6000
Web Site: https://dallasmedical.com
General Medical & Surgical Services
N.A.I.C.S.: 622110

Dauterive Hospital (1)
600 N Lewis St, New Iberia, LA 70563
Tel.: (337) 374-4136
Web Site: http://www.dauterivehospital.com
Sales Range: $25-49.9 Million
Emp.: 420
Hospital
N.A.I.C.S.: 622110

Davie Medical Center, LLC (1)
329 NC Hwy 801 N, Bermuda Run, NC
27006
Tel.: (336) 998-1300
Web Site: https://www.wakehealth.edu
Orthopaedics Physical Therapy & Medical
Center Services
N.A.I.C.S.: 622310

**Day Surgery Center at Denton Re-
gional Medical Center** (1)
3316 Colorado Blvd, Denton, TX 76210
Tel.: (940) 349-5500
Web Site:
    http://www.medicalcitysurgerydenton.com
Surgical Care Services
N.A.I.C.S.: 621493

**Denver Mid-Town Surgery Center,
Ltd.** (1)
1919 E 18th Ave, Denver, CO 80206
Tel.: (303) 322-3993
Web Site:
    http://www.midtownsurgicalcenter.com
Medical & Surgical Services
N.A.I.C.S.: 622110
Jack Johnson *(Dir-Medical)*
Scott Harkey *(Dir-Bus Dev)*

Denver Surgicenter, LLC (1)
8155 E 1st Ave, Denver, CO 80230-7163
Tel.: (303) 344-4844
Web Site: https://denver-endocenter.com
General Medical & Surgical services
N.A.I.C.S.: 622110

**Devonshire Diagnostic Centre
Limited** (1)
16 Devonshire Street, Marylebone, London,
W1G 7AF, United Kingdom
Tel.: (44) 2039939772
Diagnostic Center Operator
N.A.I.C.S.: 621512

Doctors Hospital (Conroe), Inc. (1)
504 Medical Center Blvd, Conroe, TX
77304
Tel.: (409) 539-1111
Health Care Srvices
N.A.I.C.S.: 621399

**Doctors Hospital North Augusta Imag-
ing Center, LLC** (1)
105 Hugh St Ste A, North Augusta, SC
29841
Tel.: (803) 426-2000
Health Care Srvices
N.A.I.C.S.: 621610

**Doctors Hospital of Augusta Neurol-
ogy, LLC** (1)
3651 Wheeler Rd, Augusta, GA 30909-6521
Tel.: (706) 651-3232
Web Site: http://www.doctors-hospital.net
Health Care Srvices
N.A.I.C.S.: 621399

**Doctors Hospital of Augusta,
LLC** (1)
3651 Wheeler Rd, Augusta, GA 30909
Tel.: (706) 651-3232
Web Site: https://www.doctors-hospital.net
Sales Range: $50-74.9 Million
General Medical And Surgical Hospitals
N.A.I.C.S.: 622110

Doctors Hospital of Sarasota (1)
5731 Bee Rdg Rd, Sarasota, FL 34233
Tel.: (941) 342-1100
Web Site: http://www.doctorsofsarasota.com
Sales Range: $50-74.9 Million
Emp.: 792
Hospital
N.A.I.C.S.: 622110
Robert C. Meade *(CEO & Sec)*
Ravi Chari *(Pres-West Florida Div)*
Mireya Eavey *(Vice Chm)*
Michael H. Jaquith *(Chm)*
Allyssa Tobitt *(COO)*

**Doctors Same Day Surgery Center,
Inc.** (1)
5741 Bee Ridge Rd Ste 100, Sarasota, FL
34233
Tel.: (941) 342-1303
Web Site:
    https://www.doctorssamedaysurgery.com
Outpatient Care Centers
N.A.I.C.S.: 621498

**Doctors Same Day Surgery Center,
Ltd.** (1)
5741 Bee Ridge Rd Ste 100, Sarasota, FL
34233
Tel.: (941) 342-1303
Web Site:
    http://www.doctorssamedaysurgery.com
Health Care Management Services
N.A.I.C.S.: 327910

Dominion Hospital (1)
2960 Sleepy Hollow Rd, Falls Church, VA
22044
Tel.: (703) 538-2872
General Medical & Surgical Services
N.A.I.C.S.: 622110

Dominion Hospital (1)
2960 Sleepy Hollow Rd, Falls Church, VA
22044
Tel.: (703) 536-2000
Web Site: https://www.hcavirginia.com
General Medical Care Services
N.A.I.C.S.: 622110

Dura Medical, Inc. (1)
608 Buchanan Dr, Burnet, TX 78611
Tel.: (512) 756-8550
Emp.: 4
Hospital Equipment Distr
N.A.I.C.S.: 423450
Cresta Tate *(Gen Mgr)*

EASTSIDE URGENT CARE LLC (1)
14 Mitylene Park Ln, Montgomery, AL
36117
Tel.: (334) 213-4433
Web Site: https://www.eastside-
    urgentcare.com
Health Care Srvices
N.A.I.C.S.: 621491

EPIC Development, Inc. (1)
430 Plasters Ave NE Ste 100, Atlanta, GA
30324
Tel.: (770) 228-2000
Web Site: https://epicdevelopment.com
General Medical & Surgical Services
N.A.I.C.S.: 622110

EPIC Properties, Inc. (1)
12402 Slide Rd Ste 201, Lubbock, TX
79424
Tel.: (806) 543-0667
Web Site: https://epicproperties.com
General Medical & Surgical Services
N.A.I.C.S.: 622110

EPIC Surgery Centers, Inc. (1)

11261 Nall Ave Ste 200, Leawood, KS
66211
Tel.: (913) 671-3290
Web Site: https://epicsurgerycenter.com
General Medical & Surgical Services
N.A.I.C.S.: 622110

East Falls Family Medicine, LLC (1)
3200 Channing Way Ste 304, Idaho Falls,
ID 83404
Tel.: (208) 535-4567
Web Site: https://eastfallsclinics.com
Emp.: 8
Health Care Srvices
N.A.I.C.S.: 621399

**East Florida CareNow Urgent Care,
LLC** (1)
1900 SE Port St Lucie Blvd, Port Saint Lu-
cie, FL 34952
Tel.: (772) 398-1588
Health Care Srvices
N.A.I.C.S.: 621491

**East Florida Emergency Physician
Group, LLC** (1)
2201 45th St, West Palm Beach, FL 33407
Tel.: (561) 863-3900
Health Care Srvices
N.A.I.C.S.: 621399

East Florida Hospitalists, LLC (1)
2801 N State Rd 7, Margate, FL 33063-
5727
Tel.: (954) 974-0400
Health Care Srvices
N.A.I.C.S.: 621399

East Florida Primary Care, LLC (1)
8395 W Oakland Park Blvd Ste E, Sunrise,
FL 33351-7301
Tel.: (954) 741-7500
Healtcare Services
N.A.I.C.S.: 621999

East Pointe Hospital, Inc. (1)
1500 Lee Blvd, Lehigh Acres, FL 33936
Tel.: (239) 369-2101
Healtcare Services
N.A.I.C.S.: 621999
Joanie Jeanette *(Gen Mgr)*

**Eastern Idaho Regional Medical
Center** (1)
3100 Channing Way, Idaho Falls, ID 83404
Tel.: (208) 529-6111
Web Site: https://www.eirmc.com
Health Care Srvices
N.A.I.C.S.: 621399
Ann Kjosa *(Chief Nursing Officer)*
Jami Lieber *(Asst Chief Nursing Officer)*
Tami Frost *(Chief Nursing Officer)*
Timothy Ballard *(Chief Medical Officer)*
Jeff Sollis *(CEO)*
Nick Manning *(COO)*
Aaron Martin *(CFO)*
Patty Howell *(Chief Medical Officer)*
Wendy Mcclain *(VP-Operations)*
Betsy Hunsicker *(CEO)*
Brandi Allred *(Chief Nursing Officer)*

**Eastside Heart and Vascular,
LLC** (1)
1700 Tree Ln Ste 190, Snellville, GA 30078
Tel.: (770) 736-6300
Health Care Srvices
N.A.I.C.S.: 621491

Edmond General Surgery, LLC (1)
105 S Bryant Ave Ste 104, Edmond, OK
73034
Tel.: (405) 216-0956
Healtcare Services
N.A.I.C.S.: 621999

**Edmond Physician Services,
LLC** (1)
105 S Bryant Ave Ste 104, Edmond, OK
73034-6330
Tel.: (405) 715-2022
Health Care Srvices
N.A.I.C.S.: 621999

**Edmond Podiatry Associates,
LLC** (1)
4900 S Monaco St Ste 210, Denver, CO
80237-3486
Tel.: (303) 584-8000
Health Care Srvices
N.A.I.C.S.: 621399

El Paso Healthcare System, Ltd. (1)
6044 Gateway Blvd E Ste 700, El Paso, TX
79905-2023
Tel.: (915) 521-1200
Web Site:
    http://www.laspalmasdelsolhealthcare.com
Emp.: 800
General Medical & Surgical Services
N.A.I.C.S.: 622110
Don Karl *(Co-CEO)*
Art Garza *(Co-CEO)*
Jacob Stercula *(Co-COO)*
Alejandro Romero *(Co-COO)*
Oscar Vega Jr. *(Chief Medical Officer)*
Malik Merchant *(Chief Medical Officer)*
Christine Walker *(Chief Nursing Officer)*
Annie Garcia *(Chief Nursing Officer)*

Unit (Domestic):

Del Sol Medical Center (2)
10301 Gateway Blvd W, El Paso, TX 79925
Tel.: (915) 595-9000
Web Site:
    https://laspalmasdelsolhealthcare.com
Sales Range: $50-74.9 Million
Emp.: 1,100
Hospital
N.A.I.C.S.: 622110
David Shimp *(CEO)*
Annie Garcia *(Chief Nursing Officer)*
Gary Purushotham *(COO)*
Art Garza *(CEO)*
Brian Allen *(COO)*

El Paso Surgery Centers, L.P. (1)
1815 N Stanton, El Paso, TX 79902
Tel.: (915) 533-8412
Web Site:
    http://www.elpasosurgerycenters.com
Surgical Care Services
N.A.I.C.S.: 621493

**Elite Orthopaedics of El Paso,
PLLC** (1)
10201 Gateway Blvd W Ste 201, El Paso,
TX 79925-7652
Tel.: (915) 595-2701
Healtcare Services
N.A.I.C.S.: 621999

**Elite Orthopaedics of Irving,
PLLC** (1)
6750 N Macarthur Blvd Ste 270, Irving, TX
75039
Tel.: (214) 496-9700
Health Care Srvices
N.A.I.C.S.: 621999

**Emergency Psychiatric Medicine,
PLLC** (1)
7808 Clodus Fields Dr, Dallas, TX 75251
Tel.: (972) 770-1032
Web Site:
    http://www.emergencypsychmed.com
Emp.: 10
Health Care Srvices
N.A.I.C.S.: 621999

Emory Johns Creek Hospital (1)
6325 Hospital Pkwy, Johns Creek, GA
30097
Tel.: (678) 474-7000
Web Site: http://www.emoryjohnscreek.com
Sales Range: $50-74.9 Million
Emp.: 550
Hospital
N.A.I.C.S.: 622110
Marilyn Margolis *(CEO)*
Lynne Riley *(Chm)*
Alex Almanza *(VP-Human Resources)*
Hasan Shabbir *(Chief Quality Officer)*
Heather Redrick *(Chief Nursing Officer)*
JoAnn Manning *(CFO)*
Shawn Tritt *(Chief Medical Officer)*
Laurie Hansen *(VP-Operations)*
Hannah Henry *(VP-Operations)*
Hannah Lampron *(VP-Operations)*
Arthur Holst *(Vice Chm)*

Endoscopy of Plano, L.P. (1)
1600 Coit Rd Ste 401A, Plano, TX 75075
Tel.: (972) 612-9771

HCA Healthcare, Inc.—(Continued)

Web Site:
https://www.endoscopyofplano.com
Emp.: 15
Health Care Srvices
N.A.I.C.S.: 621999

Englewood Community Hospital (1)
700 Medical Blvd, Englewood, FL 34223
Tel.: (941) 475-6571
General Medical & Surgical Services
N.A.I.C.S.: 622110

Englewood Community Hospital, Inc. (1)
700 Medical Blvd, Englewood, FL 34223
Tel.: (941) 475-6571
Web Site:
http://www.englewoodcommhospital.com
Medical & Surgical Services
N.A.I.C.S.: 622110
Kathleen Pace (COO & Chief Nursing Officer)
Steve Young (CEO)

Enhancecorp Limited (1)
53 Beta Road, Cove, Farnborough, GU14 8PH, Hampshire, United Kingdom
Tel.: (44) 1252680323
Web Site: https://www.enhance-corporation.com
General Medical & Surgical Services
N.A.I.C.S.: 622110

Evans Surgery Center (1)
635 Ronald Reagan Dr, Evans, GA 30809
Tel.: (706) 868-3110
Web Site:
https://www.evanssurgerycenter.com
Health Care & Allied Services
N.A.I.C.S.: 621999

FMH Health Services, LLC (1)
11 Whitehall Rd, Rochester, NH 03867
Tel.: (603) 332-5211
Web Site: https://www.frisbiehospital.com
Health Care Hospital Services
N.A.I.C.S.: 622110
Tim Jones (CEO)
Megan Gray (Chief Nursing Officer)
Kira Riley (VP-Human Resources)

Fairfax Surgical Center (1)
10730 Main St, Fairfax, VA 22030
Tel.: (703) 691-0670
Web Site: https://fairfaxsurgicalcenter.com
General Medical & Surgical Services
N.A.I.C.S.: 622110

Fairfax Surgical Center, L.P. (1)
10730 Main St, Fairfax, VA 22030
Tel.: (703) 691-0670
Web Site:
https://www.fairfaxsurgicalcenter.com
Surgical Care Services
N.A.I.C.S.: 621493

Fairview Park Hospital (1)
200 Industrial Blvd, Dublin, GA 31021-2981
Tel.: (478) 275-2000
Web Site:
https://www.fairviewparkhospital.com
Sales Range: $50-74.9 Million
Emp.: 700
Hospital
N.A.I.C.S.: 622110
Donald R. Avery (Pres & CEO)
Stacey Howard (COO)
Lindsay Thetford Black (Dir-Mktg & Comm)
Jeff Bruton (VP-HR)
Donna Trickey (Chief Nursing Officer)
George E. Harrison (Chief Medical Officer)
Cindie Nobles (CFO)
Karen Carswell (Dir-Physician & Provider Rels)
Kofi A. Cash (VP-Ops)
Debra Huddleston (Dir)
Sherry Robbins (Dir)
Pam Manders (Chief Nursing Officer)

Family Care Partners, LLC (1)
6520 Ft Caroline Rd, Jacksonville, FL 32277
Tel.: (904) 726-1600
Web Site:
https://www.familycarepartners.com
Health Care Srvices
N.A.I.C.S.: 622110

Family Care at Arbor Walk, LLC (1)

1301 Arbor Walk Blvd Ste A, Lees Summit, MO 64082
Tel.: (816) 537-6232
Web Site: https://mymidwestphysician.com
Emp.: 8
Physicians Health Services
N.A.I.C.S.: 621111

Family Care of E. Jackson County, LLC (1)
725 NW Hwy 7 Ste A, Blue Springs, MO 64014-3096
Tel.: (816) 229-8187
Web Site: https://mymidwestphysician.com
General Medical & Surgical Services
N.A.I.C.S.: 622110

Family Health Medical Group of Overland Park, LLC (1)
7381 W 133rd St Ste 100, Overland Park, KS 66213
Tel.: (913) 491-1616
General Medical & Surgical Services
N.A.I.C.S.: 622110

Family Health Medical Group of Overland Park, LLC (1)
7381 W 133rd St Ste 100, Overland Park, KS 66213
Tel.: (913) 491-1616
Web Site: http://mymidwestphysician.com
Health Care Srvices
N.A.I.C.S.: 621399

Family Health Specialists of Lee's Summit, LLC (1)
2000 SE Blue Pkwy Ste 270B, Lees Summit, MO 64063
Tel.: (816) 524-8488
General Medical & Surgical Services
N.A.I.C.S.: 622110

Family Medicine Associates of Edmond, LLC (1)
3824 S Blvd, Edmond, OK 73013-5778
Tel.: (405) 348-2424
Health Care Srvices
N.A.I.C.S.: 621610

Family Medicine of Blacksburg, LLC (1)
1645 N Main St, Blacksburg, VA 24060
Tel.: (540) 552-1246
General Medical & Surgical Services
N.A.I.C.S.: 622110

Family Medicine of Terre Haute, LLC (1)
3903 S 7th St Ste 2F, Terre Haute, IN 47802
Tel.: (812) 234-5400
Health Care Srvices
N.A.I.C.S.: 621399

Fannin Surgicare (1)
7700 Fannin St, Houston, TX 77054
Tel.: (713) 796-3800
Web Site: https://fanninsurgicare.com
General Medical & Surgical Services
N.A.I.C.S.: 622110

Fannin Surgicare (1)
7700 Fannin St, Houston, TX 77054
Tel.: (713) 796-3800
Web Site: https://www.fanninsurgicare.com
Emp.: 25
Surgical Care Services
N.A.I.C.S.: 621493
Howard Miller (Dir-Medical)

Fawcett Memorial Hospital (1)
21298 Olean Blvd, Port Charlotte, FL 33952
Tel.: (941) 629-1181
General Medical & Surgical Services
N.A.I.C.S.: 622110

Fawcett Memorial Hospital, Inc. (1)
21298 Olean Blvd, Port Charlotte, FL 33952
Tel.: (941) 629-1181
Web Site: http://www.fawcetthospital.com
Sales Range: $50-74.9 Million
Hospital
N.A.I.C.S.: 622110

Flamingo Surgery Center (1)
2565 E Flamingo Rd, Las Vegas, NV 89121
Tel.: (702) 697-7900
Web Site:
https://www.flamingosurgerycenter.com
Health Care Srvices

N.A.I.C.S.: 621399

Focus Hand Surgicenter, Llc (1)
601 E Hampden Ave Ste 500, Englewood, CO 80113
Tel.: (720) 570-3304
Web Site: https://focus-handsurgery.com
Health Care Srvices
N.A.I.C.S.: 621491

Fort Pierce Orthopaedics, LLC (1)
2402 Frist Blvd Ste 102, Fort Pierce, FL 34950
Tel.: (772) 465-4651
Web Site:
http://www.ftpierceorthopedics.com
Health Care Srvices
N.A.I.C.S.: 621399

Fort Walton Beach Medical Center, Inc. (1)
1000 Mar-Walt Dr, Fort Walton Beach, FL 32547
Tel.: (850) 862-1111
Web Site: http://www.fwbmc.com
Sales Range: $75-99.9 Million
Emp.: 1,331
Hospital
N.A.I.C.S.: 622110
Mitch Mongell (CEO)

Frankfort Regional Medical Center (1)
299 Kings Daughters Dr, Frankfort, KY 40601
Tel.: (502) 875-5240
Web Site: https://www.frankfortregional.com
Sales Range: $50-74.9 Million
Emp.: 587
Hospital
N.A.I.C.S.: 622110
Reed Hammond (CEO)
Ashley Hickel (COO)
Stephanie Stratton (Chief Nursing Officer)
Spencer Hankins (CFO)

Ft. Walton Beach Anesthesia Services, LLC (1)
1000 Marwalt Dr, Fort Walton Beach, FL 32547
Tel.: (850) 375-2395
Health Care Srvices
N.A.I.C.S.: 621399

G. Rowe, M.D. , PLLC (1)
7580 Fannin Ste 335-A, Houston, TX 77054
Tel.: (713) 795-4800
Web Site:
http://drrowe.womanshealthgroup.com
General Medical & Surgical Services
N.A.I.C.S.: 622110

G. Schnider, M.D., PLLC (1)
7580 Fannin St Ste 310, Houston, TX 77054-1900
Tel.: (713) 797-9701
Health Care Srvices
N.A.I.C.S.: 621399

GI Associates of Lewisville, PLLC (1)
475 W Elm St Ste 100, Lewisville, TX 75057
Tel.: (214) 222-3571
Web Site:
http://www.giassociatesoflewisville.com
General Medical & Surgical Services
N.A.I.C.S.: 622110

Gainesville Family Physicians (1)
6900 NW 9th Blvd, Gainesville, FL 32605
Tel.: (352) 333-6680
Web Site:
http://gainesvillefamilyphysicians.com
Allopathic & Osteopathic Physicians Services
N.A.I.C.S.: 622110

Galen Health Institutes, Inc. (1)
1031 Zorn Ave, Louisville, KY 40207
Tel.: (502) 410-6200
Web Site: http://www.galencollege.edu
Nursing College Services
N.A.I.C.S.: 623110
Mark A. Vogt (CEO)
David Ray (Chief Strategy Officer & VP)
Thomas Dwyer (VP-Fin)
Carter Smith (VP-Enrollment Mgmt)
Joan L. Frey (Pres)
Steve Hyndman (Exec VP & Provost)

Allyson Wolfe (Chief Cultural Officer & VP-Human Resources)
Kathleen A. Dwyer (VP-Operations-Regulatory Affairs)
Anna Kitson (VP-Marketing-Communications)
Cathryn J. Rolfe (COO)
Jim Lepianka (VP-Information Technology)
Jane Englebright (Chm)

Galen Hospital Alaska, Inc. (1)
2801 Debarr Rd, Anchorage, AK 99508-2932
Tel.: (907) 276-1131
Web Site: http://www.alaskaregional.com
Health Care Srvices
N.A.I.C.S.: 621999

Galichia Heart Hospital (1)
550 N Hillside, Wichita, KS 67214
Tel.: (316) 962-2000
Web Site: https://wesleymc.com
Emp.: 3,000
Health Care Srvices
N.A.I.C.S.: 621399
Allen Poston (VP-Mktg & PR)

Garden Park Community Hospital Limited Partnership (1)
15200 Community Rd, Gulfport, MS 39503
Tel.: (228) 575-7000
General Medical & Surgical Services
N.A.I.C.S.: 622110

Garden Park Hospitalist Program, LLC (1)
15200 Community Rd 4th Fl, Gulfport, MS 39503-3085
Tel.: (228) 575-7243
Health Care Srvices
N.A.I.C.S.: 621399

Garden Park Medical Center (1)
15200 Community Rd, Gulfport, MS 39503
Tel.: (228) 575-7000
Web Site: http://www.gpmedical.com
Sales Range: $25-49.9 Million
Emp.: 250
Hospital
N.A.I.C.S.: 622110
Michael Matthews (Chm)
Michael Pocchiari (VP-HR)
Randy Rogers (CEO)
Robert Stringer (VP-Clinical Ops)
Stacey O'Connell (CFO)
Tim West (VP-Ops)

Garden Park Physician Group, Inc. (1)
15190 Community Rd Ste 200, Gulfport, MS 39503
Tel.: (228) 328-1401
Web Site:
http://www.gardenparkdoctors.com
General Medical & Surgical Services
N.A.I.C.S.: 622110

Gardens EFL Imaging Center, LLC (1)
3335 Burns Rd Ste 101, Palm Beach Gardens, FL 33410
Tel.: (561) 627-6227
Emp.: 30
General Medical & Surgical Services
N.A.I.C.S.: 622110
Tabitha Tarpley (Mgr)

Gastroenterology Specialists of Middle Tennessee, LLC (1)
397 Wallace Rd Ste 203 Bldg C, Nashville, TN 37211
Tel.: (615) 831-5422
Web Site: https://www.tristarmedgroup.com
Emp.: 10
Medical & Surgical Hospital Services
N.A.I.C.S.: 622110
Sharon Garr (Office Mgr)

General Medical Clinics Limited (1)
2-3 Salisbury Court, London, EC4Y 8AA, United Kingdom
Tel.: (44) 2074270606
Web Site: http://www.genmed.org.uk
Emp.: 83
General Medical & Surgical Services
N.A.I.C.S.: 622110

General Surgeons of Pasadena, PLLC (1)

3801 Vista Rd Ste 450, Pasadena, TX 77504
Tel.: (713) 944-2240
Web Site:
http://www.generalsurgeonsofpasadena.com
Medical Support Services
N.A.I.C.S.: 621111

Genospace, Llc   (1)
27 School St, Boston, MA 02108
Tel.: (617) 714-3420
Web Site: https://www.genospace.com
Emp.: 4
Health Care Srvices
N.A.I.C.S.: 621491

Good Samaritan Hospital, L.P.   (1)
2425 Samaritan Dr, San Jose, CA 95124
Tel.: (408) 559-2011
Web Site: http://www.goodsamsanjose.com
Sales Range: $100-124.9 Million
Hospital
N.A.I.C.S.: 622110
Rich Briones (Chief Medical Officer)
Patrick Rohan (CEO)
Kelli Wray (Chief Nursing Officer)
P. J. Thrasher (CFO)

Good Samaritan Hospital, LLC   (1)
2425 Samaritan Dr, San Jose, CA 95124
Tel.: (408) 559-2011
Web Site: https://www.goodsamsanjose.com
General Medical & Surgical Services
N.A.I.C.S.: 622110

Goppert-Trinity Family Care, LLC   (1)
6675 Holmes Rd 360, Kansas City, MO 64131
Tel.: (816) 276-7600
Web Site: http://www.goppert-trinity.com
Healthcare Support Services
N.A.I.C.S.: 621111

Grace Family Practice, LLC   (1)
440 Charter Blvd Ste 3303, Macon, GA 31210
Tel.: (478) 405-0280
Web Site:
http://www.gracefamilypractise.com
Emp.: 3
Gynecology Services
N.A.I.C.S.: 621111

Gramercy Outpatient Surgery Center   (1)
2727 Gramercy St, Houston, TX 77025
Tel.: (713) 660-6900
Web Site:
https://www.gramercyoutpatientsurgery.com
General Medical & Surgical Services
N.A.I.C.S.: 622110

Grand Strand Regional Medical Center   (1)
809 82nd Pkwy, Myrtle Beach, SC 29572
Tel.: (843) 692-1000
Web Site:
https://www.mygrandstrandhealth.com
Sales Range: $50-74.9 Million
Hospital
N.A.I.C.S.: 622110

Grand Strand Senior Health Center, LLC   (1)
4237 River Hills Dr Ste 150, Little River, SC 29566
Tel.: (843) 281-2778
Health Care Srvices
N.A.I.C.S.: 621999

Grand Strand Specialty Associates, LLC   (1)
920 Doug White Dr Ste 460, Myrtle Beach, SC 29572
Tel.: (843) 449-2336
Web Site:
http://www.spineandneurocare.com
Health Care Srvices
N.A.I.C.S.: 621999

Grand Strand Surgical Specialists, LLC   (1)
920 Doug White Dr Ste 210, Myrtle Beach, SC 29572
Tel.: (843) 497-6348
Web Site: http://grandstrandsurgical.com
Health Care Srvices
N.A.I.C.S.: 621610

Grande Dunes Surgery Center   (1)
1021 Cipriana Dr Ste 100, Myrtle Beach, SC 29572
Tel.: (843) 449-7885
Web Site:
https://www.grandedunessurgerycenter.com
Health Care Srvices
N.A.I.C.S.: 621399

Grandview Health Care Clinic, LLC   (1)
900 Main St, Grandview, MO 64030
Tel.: (816) 765-8900
Clinic Care Services
N.A.I.C.S.: 621399

Grant Center Hospital of Ocala, Inc.   (1)
1910 Hillbrook Trail Ste 2, Tallahassee, FL 32311
Tel.: (850) 878-2637
General Medical & Surgical Services
N.A.I.C.S.: 622110

Grayson Primary Care, LLC   (1)
3435 Hwy 81 Ste 100, Grayson, GA 30052
Tel.: (678) 225-4999
Web Site:
http://www.graysonprimarycare.com
Emp.: 10
Health Care Srvices
N.A.I.C.S.: 621399

Greater Gwinnett Internal Medicine Associates, LLC   (1)
1608 Tree Ln Bldg C, Snellville, GA 30078
Tel.: (678) 344-4472
Web Site:
http://www.greatergwinnettmedicine.com
Emp.: 20
Health Care & Allied Services
N.A.I.C.S.: 621999

Greater Tampa Bay Physician Network, LLC   (1)
3614 W Kennedy Blvd Ste B, Tampa, FL 33609-2852
Tel.: (813) 870-2528
General Medical & Surgical Services
N.A.I.C.S.: 622110

Greater Tampa Bay Physician Specialists, LLC   (1)
602 S Audubon Ave Ste A, Tampa, FL 33609-4217
Tel.: (813) 877-1415
General Medical & Surgical Services
N.A.I.C.S.: 622110

Greater Tampa Bay Physicians - Pinellas, LLC   (1)
1100 62nd Ave S, Saint Petersburg, FL 33705-5620
Tel.: (727) 866-3166
General Medical & Surgical Services
N.A.I.C.S.: 622110

Green Oaks Hospital   (1)
7808 Clodus Fields Dr, Dallas, TX 75251
Tel.: (972) 991-9504
Web Site: http://www.greenoakspsych.com
Psychiatric Medical Services
N.A.I.C.S.: 621420

Greenview Regional Hospital   (1)
1801 Ashley Cir, Bowling Green, KY 42104
Tel.: (270) 793-1000
Web Site: https://www.tristarhealth.com
Health Care Srvices
N.A.I.C.S.: 621399

Greenview Specialty Associates, LLC   (1)
1325 Andrea St Ste 201, Bowling Green, KY 42104
Tel.: (270) 843-7557
Web Site:
https://www.greenviewspecialty.com
Emp.: 4
Health Care Srvices
N.A.I.C.S.: 621399

Gulf Coast Division, Inc.   (1)
3737 Buffalo Speedway Ste 1400, Houston, TX 77098
Tel.: (713) 852-1500
Web Site: https://www.hcagulfcoast.com
Healthcare Support Services
N.A.I.C.S.: 621111

Troy A. Villarreal (Pres)
Jeffery Sliwinski (CFO)
Andrew Moore (Chief Medical Officer)

Gulf Coast Medical Center Primary Care, LLC   (1)
229 Southwood Dr, Panama City, FL 32405
Tel.: (850) 769-1462
Web Site:
http://www.gulfcoastprimarycare.com
Health Care & Allied Services
N.A.I.C.S.: 621999

Gulf Coast Physician Administrators, Inc.   (1)
211 Highland Cross Ste 275, Houston, TX 77073-1733
Tel.: (281) 784-1500
Emp.: 23
General Medical & Surgical Services
N.A.I.C.S.: 622110

Gulf Coast Surgery Center   (1)
411 2nd St E, Bradenton, FL 34208
Tel.: (941) 746-1121
Web Site: https://www.gulfcoastsurgery.com
General Medical & Surgical Services
N.A.I.C.S.: 622110

Gulf Pointe Surgery Center   (1)
21260 Olean Blvd Ste 100, Port Charlotte, FL 33952
Tel.: (941) 235-5800
Web Site:
https://www.gulfpointesurgerycenter.com
General Medical & Surgical Services
N.A.I.C.S.: 622110

H2U Wellness Centers - Conroe Regional Medical Center, PLLC   (1)
504 Medical Ctr Blvd, Conroe, TX 77304
Tel.: (936) 539-1111
Web Site: http://hcahoustonhealthcare.com
Health Care Srvices
N.A.I.C.S.: 621399

H2U Wellness Centers - Del Sol Medical Center, PLLC   (1)
10301 Gateway Blvd W, El Paso, TX 79925
Tel.: (915) 595-9000
Web Site: http://www.laspalmasdelsolhealthcare.com
Health Care Srvices
N.A.I.C.S.: 621399

H2U Wellness Centers, LLC   (1)
3322 W End Ave Ste 400, Nashville, TN 37203
Tel.: (615) 344-4401
Web Site: http://www.h2u.com
Sales Range: $25-49.9 Million
Emp.: 85
Medical & Surgical Hospital Services
N.A.I.C.S.: 622110

HCA - Raleigh Community Hospital, Inc.   (1)
3400 Wake Forest Rd, Raleigh, NC 27609-7317
Tel.: (919) 954-3616
General Medical & Surgical Services
N.A.I.C.S.: 622110

HCA Florida West Tampa Hospital   (1)
6001 Webb Rd, Tampa, FL 33615
Tel.: (813) 888-7060
Web Site:
https://www.hcafloridahealthcare.com
General Medical & Surgical Services
N.A.I.C.S.: 622110

HCA Gulf Coast Division   (1)
3737 Buffalo Speedway Ste 1400, Houston, TX 77098
Tel.: (713) 852-1500
Web Site: http://hcagulfcoast.com
Hospitals & Outpatient Surgery Centers
N.A.I.C.S.: 622110
Jeffery L. Sliwinski (CFO)
Troy A. Villarreal (Pres)
Mauricio Camargo (Sr VP-Plng & Bus Intelligence)
Evan Ray (Chief Admin Officer & Exec VP)
Mujtaba Ali-Khan (Chief Medical Officer)
Jose A. Perez Jr. (VP-Graduate Medical Education)

HCA Health Services of Oklahoma, Inc.   (1)

700 NE 13th St, Oklahoma City, OK 73104
Tel.: (405) 271-8132
Health Care & Allied Services
N.A.I.C.S.: 621999

HCA Health Services of Tennessee, Inc.   (1)
1 Park Plz, Nashville, TN 37203
Tel.: (615) 344-9551
General Medical & Surgical Services
N.A.I.C.S.: 622110

Subsidiary (Domestic):

TriStar Ashland City Medical Center   (2)
313 N Main St, Ashland City, TN 37015
Tel.: (615) 792-3030
Web Site: https://www.tristarhealth.com
Health Care Srvices
N.A.I.C.S.: 621399

TriStar Centennial Medical Center   (2)
2300 Patterson St, Nashville, TN 37203
Tel.: (615) 342-1000
Web Site: https://careers.hcahealthcare.com
Health Care Srvices
N.A.I.C.S.: 621399

TriStar Southern Hills Medical Center   (2)
391 Wallace Rd, Nashville, TN 37211
Tel.: (615) 781-4000
Web Site: https://careers.hcahealthcare.com
Health Care Srvices
N.A.I.C.S.: 621399

TriStar StoneCrest Medical Center   (2)
200 StoneCrest Blvd, Smyrna, TN 37167
Tel.: (615) 768-2000
Web Site: https://careers.hcahealthcare.com
Health Care Srvices
N.A.I.C.S.: 621399

TriStar Summit Medical Center   (2)
5655 Frist Blvd, Hermitage, TN 37076
Tel.: (615) 316-3000
Web Site: https://careers.hcahealthcare.com
Health Care Srvices
N.A.I.C.S.: 621399
Brian Marger (CEO)

HCA Health Services of Virginia   (1)
1602 Skipwith Rd, Richmond, VA 23229
Tel.: (804) 289-4500
Web Site: http://www.henricodoctors.com
Sales Range: $50-74.9 Million
Emp.: 3,000
Hospital Operator
N.A.I.C.S.: 622110

Subsidiary (Domestic):

Henrico Doctors' Hospital   (2)
1602 Skipwith Rd, Richmond, VA 23229
Tel.: (804) 289-4500
Web Site: https://www.hcavirginia.com
Sales Range: $50-74.9 Million
Emp.: 700
Acute-Care Full-Range Emergency, Medical, Surgical & Rehabilitative Hospital Services
N.A.I.C.S.: 622110

Division (Domestic):

Parham Doctors' Hospital   (3)
7700 E Parham Rd, Richmond, VA 23294
Tel.: (804) 747-5600
Web Site: http://www.henricodoctors.com
Acute Care Hospital
N.A.I.C.S.: 622110

Retreat Doctors' Hospital   (3)
2621 Grove Ave, Richmond, VA 23220   (100%)
Tel.: (804) 254-5100
Web Site: http://www.henricodoctors.com
Traditional Acute-Care & Private Room Hospital Services
N.A.I.C.S.: 622110
Patrick Farrell (Pres)

HCA Healthcare Mission Fund, LLC   (1)
12 Ardmore St, Asheville, NC 28803
Tel.: (828) 412-6045
Web Site: https://www.hcahealthcaremissionfund.com
General Medical & Surgical Services
N.A.I.C.S.: 622110

HCA Healthcare, Inc.—(Continued)

HCA Houston ER 24/7 - Cypress Fairbanks (1)
10655 Steepletop Dr, Houston, TX 77065
Tel.: (281) 890-4285
Web Site:
https://www.hcahoustonhealthcare.com
Freestanding Emergency Room
N.A.I.C.S.: 621493
Hannah Gelbs (COO)

HCA Houston Healthcare - Southeast (1)
4000 Spencer Hwy, Pasadena, TX 77504
Tel.: (713) 359-2000
Web Site:
https://www.hcahoustonhealthcare.com
Hospital Services
N.A.I.C.S.: 622110

HCA Houston Healthcare Tomball (1)
605 Holderrieth Blvd, Tomball, TX 77375
Tel.: (281) 401-7500
Web Site: https://hcahoustonhealthcare.com
Hospital Operator & Medical Care Services
N.A.I.C.S.: 622110
Richard Ervin (CFO)
Robert Marmerstein (CEO)
Angelle Rhemann (Chief Nursing Officer)
Adrian Moreno (COO)

HCA Houston Healthcare West (1)
12141 Richmond Ave, Houston, TX 77082
Tel.: (281) 558-3444
Web Site: https://www.hcahoustonhealthcare.com
General Medical Care Services
N.A.I.C.S.: 622110
Megan Marietta (CEO)
Kenny Russo (CFO)
Emily Sedgwick (Chief Medical Officer)
Tashauna McCray (Chief Nursing Officer)
Justin Brewer (COO)
Ernest Mendoza (Chief Medical Officer)

HCA Houston Healthcare-Mainland (1)
6801 Emmett F Lowry Expwy, Texas City, TX 77591
Tel.: (409) 938-5000
Web Site: https://hcahoustonhealthcare.com
Hospital
N.A.I.C.S.: 622110
Troy Villarreal (Pres-Gulf Coast Div)
Evan Ray (Chief Admin Officer)
Andrew Moore (Chief Medical Officer)

HCA International Holdings Limited (1)
New Oxford Street, London, WC1A 1HB, United Kingdom
Tel.: (44) 2077593700
General Medical & Surgical Services
N.A.I.C.S.: 622110

HCA International Limited (1)
242 Marylebone Road, London, NW1 6JL, United Kingdom
Tel.: (44) 2081315184
Web Site: http://www.hcahealthcare.co.uk
Sales Range: $450-499.9 Million
Emp.: 3,800
Health Care Service Company Services
N.A.I.C.S.: 622110

Subsidiary (Domestic):

The Harley Street Clinic (2)
35 Weymouth Street, London, W1G 8BJ, United Kingdom
Tel.: (44) 39930715
Web Site:
http://www.theharleystreetclinic.com
Emp.: 600
General Medical Care Services
N.A.I.C.S.: 622110

HCA Richmond Cardiac Clinical Co-Management Company, LLC (1)
9930 Independence Park Dr, Richmond, VA 23233
Tel.: (804) 229-0540
General Medical & Surgical Services
N.A.I.C.S.: 622110

HCA Switzerland Finance GmbH (1)
Klausstrasse 33, 8008, Zurich, Switzerland
Tel.: (41) 227196111
Financial Management Services

N.A.I.C.S.: 541611

HCA-HealthONE, LLC (1)
4900 S Monaco St Ste 380, Denver, CO 80237
Tel.: (303) 575-0055
Web Site: http://healthonecares.com
Emp.: 11,000
Healtcare Services
N.A.I.C.S.: 622110
Greg D'Argonne (CFO)
Leonard Kalm (Sr VP-Strategic Pricing & Analytics)
Lindy Garvin (VP-Quality & Patient Safety)
Sylvia Young (Pres & CEO)
Sara Smith (Sr VP-Strategy & Bus Dev)
Dan Davidson (VP-Mktg & PR)
Kevin Kucera (VP-Real Estate)
Bob Vasil (VP-Reimbursement)

Subsidiary (Domestic):

Presbyterian/St. Luke's Medical Center (2)
1719 E 19th Ave, Denver, CO 80218
Tel.: (720) 754-6000
Web Site: https://healthonecares.com
Sales Range: $25-49.9 Million
Emp.: 1,310
Hospital Services
N.A.I.C.S.: 622110
Maureen Tarrant (Pres & CEO)
Brett Matens (COO)
David Leslie (Chief Nursing Officer)
Phillip Sensing (CFO)

Swedish Medical Center (2)
501 E Hampden Ave, Englewood, CO 80113
Tel.: (303) 788-5000
Web Site: http://www.swedishhospital.com
Health Care Srvices
N.A.I.C.S.: 621999
Ryan Tobin (Pres & CEO)
Monique Butler (Chief Medical Officer)
Ryan Thornton (Chief Nursing Officer)
Karl Leistikow (COO)
Regina Ramazani (CFO)

HDH Thoracic Surgeons, LLC (1)
2004 Bremo Rd 103, Richmond, VA 23226
Tel.: (804) 565-0383
Web Site:
http://www.richmondthoracicsurgeons.com
Emp.: 3
General Medical & Surgical Services
N.A.I.C.S.: 622110

HPG Solutions, LLC (1)
124 Ellington Blvd Ste 231, Gaithersburg, MD 20850
Tel.: (202) 550-9980
Web Site: https://hpgss.com
General Medical & Surgical Services
N.A.I.C.S.: 622110

HSS Systems, LLC (1)
PO Box 422, South Park, PA 15129
Tel.: (412) 212-1400
Web Site: https://www.hss-systems.com
General Medical & Surgical Services
N.A.I.C.S.: 622110

HWCA, PLLC (1)
7400 Fannin St Ste 1050, Houston, TX 77054-1920
Tel.: (713) 795-1000
Surgical Hospital Services
N.A.I.C.S.: 622110

Hamilton Memorial Hospital, Inc. (1)
506 4th St NW, Jasper, FL 32052
Tel.: (904) 792-2101
Surgical Care Services
N.A.I.C.S.: 622110

Harley Street Clinic @ The Groves LLP (1)
242 Marylebone Road, London, NW1 6JQ, United Kingdom
Tel.: (44) 2076164848
Web Site:
http://www.harleystreetatthegroves.co.uk
Health Care Srvices
N.A.I.C.S.: 621111

Hca Healthcare Uk Limited (1)
2 Cavendish Square, London, W1G 0PU, United Kingdom
Tel.: (44) 2039937940

Web Site: https://www.hcahealthcare.co.uk
General Medical & Surgical Services
N.A.I.C.S.: 622110

Health Partners of Kansas, Inc. (1)
550 N Lorraine, Wichita, KS 67214
Tel.: (316) 652-1327
Web Site: https://www.hpkansas.com
Health Care Srvices
N.A.I.C.S.: 621399

HealthONE Clinic Services - Cancer Specialties, LLC (1)
4900 S Monaco St 210, Denver, CO 80237-3486
Tel.: (303) 584-8000
Healthcare Support Services
N.A.I.C.S.: 621111

HealthONE Clinic Services - Primary Care, LLC (1)
720 S Colorado Blvd, Glendale, CO 80246
Tel.: (303) 584-8000
Health Care Srvices
N.A.I.C.S.: 621999

HealthONE Colorado Care Partners ACO LLC (1)
4900 S Monaco St Ste 240, Denver, CO 80237
Tel.: (303) 320-2073
Web Site: https://h1ccp.com
Health Care Srvices
N.A.I.C.S.: 621610

HealthONE Mental Health Therapy Center, LLC (1)
6169 S Balsam Way Ste 380, Littleton, CO 80123
Tel.: (303) 749-3070
Mental Health & Wellness Center Services
N.A.I.C.S.: 621420

HealthONE Ridge View Endoscopy Center, LLC (1)
10103 Ridgegate Pkwy Ste 312, Lone Tree, CO 80124
Tel.: (303) 406-4281
Web Site: https://ridgeviewendoscopy.com
Emp.: 35
General Medical & Surgical Services
N.A.I.C.S.: 622110
Pam Franklin (Mgr-Admin)

HealthONE of Denver, Inc. (1)
1801 High St, Denver, CO 80218
Tel.: (303) 869-2443
General Medical & Surgical Services
N.A.I.C.S.: 622110

HealthOne Heart Care LLC (1)
1444 S Potomac St Ste 300, Aurora, CO 80012
Tel.: (303) 645-0090
Health Care Srvices
N.A.I.C.S.: 621999

HealthTrust - Europe LLP (1)
19 George Road, Edgbaston, Birmingham, B15 1NU, United Kingdom
Tel.: (44) 845 887 5000
Web Site: http://www.healthtrusteurope.com
Emp.: 80
Medical Consulting Management Services
N.A.I.C.S.: 541611
Gary Welch (CEO)
Emma James (Chief Comml Officer)

HealthTrust Europe Company Limited (1)
19 George Road, Birmingham, B15 1NU, United Kingdom
Tel.: (44) 8458875000
Web Site:
https://www.healthtrusteurope.com
General Medical & Surgical Services
N.A.I.C.S.: 622110

HealthTrust Workforce Solutions, LLC (1)
1000 Sawgrass Corporate Pkwy 6th Fl, Sunrise, FL 33323
Tel.: (954) 858-1833
Web Site: https://healthtrustjobs.com
Hospitality Recruitment Services
N.A.I.C.S.: 561311
Jim Davis (Chief Revenue Officer)
Brendan Courtney (Pres & CEO)

Healthcare Support Services, LLC (1)

101 Southhall Lane Ste 100, Maitland, FL 32751
Tel.: (407) 606-5923
Web Site: https://healthcaresupport.com
Health Care Services
N.A.I.C.S.: 621610

Healthy State, Inc. (1)
1940 Hendersonville Rd, Asheville, NC 28803
Web Site: http://www.healthystate.us
Health Care Insurance Services
N.A.I.C.S.: 524114

Heart Hospital of Austin, a Campus of St. Davids Medical Center (1)
3801 N Lamar Blvd, Austin, TX 78756
Tel.: (512) 407-7000
Web Site:
http://www.hearthospitalofaustin.com
General Medical Care Services
N.A.I.C.S.: 622110
Melissa Johnson (VP-Operations)
Megan Drake (COO)
Michael Lopez (Chief Nursing Officer)
Seth Herrick (CFO)
Charles McCoy (Chief Nursing Officer)

Heart of America ASC, LLC (1)
8935 State Ave, Kansas City, KS 66112
Tel.: (913) 334-8935
Web Site: http://www.hoasc1.com
Emp.: 20
Health Care Services
N.A.I.C.S.: 621399

Heathrow Internal Medicine, LLC (1)
4106 W Lk Mary Blvd Ste 100, Lake Mary, FL 32746-3315
Tel.: (407) 333-2273
General Medical & Surgical Services
N.A.I.C.S.: 622110

Hendersonville Hospital Corporation (1)
355 New Shackle Island Rd, Hendersonville, TN 37075-2300
Tel.: (615) 338-1000
Web Site: https://www.tristarhealth.com
Healtcare Services
N.A.I.C.S.: 621999

Hendersonville Medical Center (1)
355 New Shackle Island Rd, Hendersonville, TN 37075
Tel.: (615) 338-1000
Web Site:
http://www.hendersonvillemedicalcenter.com
Sales Range: $25-49.9 Million
Emp.: 375
Hospital
N.A.I.C.S.: 622110

Hendersonville OB/GYN, LLC (1)
353 New Shackle Island Rd Ste 221B, Hendersonville, TN 37075
Tel.: (615) 822-3880
Web Site:
http://www.hendersonvilleobgyn.com
Health Care Srvices
N.A.I.C.S.: 621999

Henrico Radiation Oncology, LLC (1)
1602 Skipwith Rd, Richmond, VA 23229
Tel.: (804) 289-4500
Web Site: http://www.henricodoctors.com
Health Care Srvices
N.A.I.C.S.: 621111

Hermitage Primary Care, LLC (1)
5653 Frist Blvd Ste 236, Hermitage, TN 37076
Tel.: (615) 232-8812
Web Site: http://www.hermitageprimary.com
Health Care Srvices
N.A.I.C.S.: 621999

Hip & Joint Specialists of North Texas, PLLC (1)
7777 Forest Ln Ste C135, Dallas, TX 75230-2571
Tel.: (972) 566-5051
Health Care Services
N.A.I.C.S.: 621610

Hospitalists at Fairview Park, LLC (1)
200 Industrial Blvd, Dublin, GA 31021-2981
Tel.: (478) 275-2000

Web Site:
http://www.fairviewparkhospital.com
Health Care Srvices
N.A.I.C.S.: 621399
Donald R. Avery (Pres & CEO)
Cindie Nobles (CFO)
Jeff Bruton (VP-HR)
Karen Carswell (Dir-Provider Rels & Physician)
Pam Manders (Chief Nursing Officer)
Ross Kemp (COO)

Hospitalists at StoneCrest, LLC (1)
200 StoneCrest Blvd, Smyrna, TN 37167
Tel.: (615) 768-2507
General Medical & Surgical Services
N.A.I.C.S.: 622110

Houston Heart, PLLC (1)
1200 Binz St Ste 900, Houston, TX 77004
Tel.: (713) 522-0220
Web Site:
https://houstonheartmedcenter.com
Health Care Srvices
N.A.I.C.S.: 621610

Houston Northwest Medical Center, Inc. (1)
710 Cypress Creek Pkwy, Houston, TX 77090
Tel.: (281) 440-1000
Web Site: https://hcahoustonhealthcare.com
Emp.: 600
Medical Devices
N.A.I.C.S.: 622110
Scott Davis (CEO)
Ahmad Maarouf (Chief Medical Officer)
Tricia McGusty (COO)
Thomas Holt (CFO)
Jeffrey Mills Jr. (Chief Nursing Officer)

Subsidiary (Domestic):

Houston Northwest Operating Company, L.L.C. (2)
710 Cypress Creek Pkwy, Houston, TX 77090-3402
Tel.: (281) 440-2105
Web Site: http://www.hnmc.com
Medical Devices
N.A.I.C.S.: 622110
Scott Davis (CEO)
Troy A. Villarreal (Pres)
Evan Ray (Chief Admin Officer & Exec VP)
Jeffery L. Sliwinski (CFO)
Mujtaba Ali-Khan (CMO)
Mauricio Camargo (Sr VP-Planning)
Jose A. Perez Jr. (VP)

Houston Pediatric Specialty Group, PLLC (1)
7900 Fannin Ste 3200, Houston, TX 77054
Web Site: https://houstondocs4kidz.com
General Medical & Surgical Services
N.A.I.C.S.: 622110

Houston Urologic Surgicenter, LLC (1)
4219 Richmond Ave, Houston, TX 77027-6893
Tel.: (713) 634-4433
Web Site: https://hmusc.com
Hospital Management Services
N.A.I.C.S.: 622110

ICC Healthcare, LLC (1)
1 Park Plz, Nashville, TN 37203
Tel.: (561) 997-0821
Web Site: https://www.icchealthcare.com
Health Care Srvices
N.A.I.C.S.: 621399

IMX Holdings, LLC (1)
333 E City Ave Ste 600, Bala Cynwyd, PA 19004
Tel.: (610) 667-4463
Holding Company Services
N.A.I.C.S.: 551112

Imaging Services of Louisiana, LLC (1)
5000 Ambassador Caffery Pkwy Bldg 10, Lafayette, LA 70508
Tel.: (337) 993-8300
Web Site:
http://www.womensimagingservices.com
General Medical & Surgical Services
N.A.I.C.S.: 622110

InVivoLink, Inc. (1)

2204 Charlotte Ave, Nashville, TN 37203
Web Site: https://www.invivolink.com
General Medical & Surgical Services
N.A.I.C.S.: 622110
Cody King (CTO)
Dani Depoy (Owner)
Elizabeth Worley (Assoc Mgr-Product)
Kelly Dennen (Assoc Mgr-Product)
Lewis Walker (Project Mgr)
Rob Crowell (Mgr-Infrastructure-Privacy)
Sam Peters (Coord-Client Services)
Adam Underwood (Sys Engr)
Brandon Law (Sys Engr)
Jacob Mccoy (Sys Engr)
John Batte (Sys Engr)
Nelson Wells (Sys Engr)
Phillip Morrow (Sys Engr-II)
Pio Molina (Sys Engr)
Riley Ellis (Dir)
Rocky Rosche (Sys Engr)
Seth Riedel (Sys Engr)
Stephen Anthony (Sys Engr)
Steve Strickland (Dir-Engineering)
Tanner Evins (Sys Engr)
Vic Dutra (Sys Engr)
Kent Moreland (Sys Engr)
Kyle Marcum (Sys Engr)

Independence Regional Medical Group, LLC (1)
2825 Albert Pike Rd, Hot Springs National Park, AR 71913-2619
Tel.: (501) 321-2546
Emp.: 200
General Medical & Surgical Services
N.A.I.C.S.: 622110
Jessica Robertson (Gen Mgr)

Indian Path Hospital, Inc. (1)
2000 Brookside Dr, Kingsport, TN 37660-4682
Tel.: (423) 857-7000
Emp.: 640
General Medical & Surgical Services
N.A.I.C.S.: 622110

Institute for Women's Health and Body, LLC (1)
1395 S State Rd 7 Ste 450, Wellington, FL 33414
Tel.: (561) 798-1233
Web Site: http://www.iwhbpalmbeach.com
Health Care Srvices
N.A.I.C.S.: 621610

Institute of Advanced ENT Surgery, LLC (1)
2200 Pump Rd Ste 240, Richmond, VA 23233
Tel.: (804) 433-1400
Web Site:
http://www.advancedentsurgery.com
General Medical & Surgical Services
N.A.I.C.S.: 622110

Integrated Regional Lab, LLC (1)
3201 SW 15th St, Deerfield Beach, FL 33442
Web Site: https://irlfl.com
General Medical & Surgical Services
N.A.I.C.S.: 622110

Integrated Regional Laboratories Pathology Services, LLC (1)
5361 NW 33rd Ave, Fort Lauderdale, FL 33309-6313
Tel.: (954) 777-0018
Web Site: http://irlfl.com
General Medical & Surgical Services
N.A.I.C.S.: 622110

Internal Medicine Associates of Southern Hills, LLC (1)
393 Wallace Rd Ste A-104, Nashville, TN 37211
Tel.: (615) 331-4104
Web Site: http://tristarmedgroup.com
Medical & Surgical Hospital Services
N.A.I.C.S.: 622110

Internal Medicine of Blacksburg, LLC (1)
3698 S Main St, Blacksburg, VA 24060
Tel.: (540) 951-6070
Emp.: 10
General Medical & Surgical Services
N.A.I.C.S.: 622110

Internal Medicine of Pasadena, PLLC (1)

3326 Watters Rd Bldg B, Pasadena, TX 77504-2020
Tel.: (713) 947-9508
Web Site:
https://internalmedicinepasadena.com
Hospital Management Services
N.A.I.C.S.: 622110

Internist Associates of Houston, PLLC (1)
7580 Fannin St Ste 205, Houston, TX 77054-1900
Tel.: (713) 797-9933
Health Care Srvices
N.A.I.C.S.: 621112

JFK Medical Center (1)
5301 S Congress Ave, Atlantis, FL 33462
Tel.: (561) 965-7300
Web Site: http://www.jfkmc.com
Sales Range: $300-349.9 Million
Hospital
N.A.I.C.S.: 622110
Gina Melby (CEO & Co-Sec)
Tom Schlemmer (CFO)
Tina Miller (COO)
Jane Forsythe (Chief Nursing Officer)
Jack Zeltzer (Chm)
Kleper De Almeida (Treas & Co-Sec)
David Husted (Chm)
Alex Paya (Chief Medical Officer)
Suzanne Bertsch-Gibson (Chief Nursing Officer)
Roberta Fowler (VP-Quality)
Jay Maizes (Chm)
Heidi Bahna (Chm)
Shaun Isaac (Dir-Medical)
Mazyar Rouhanie (Dir-Medical-Emergency Medicine)
Mehdi Bathaii (Dir-Medical-Radiology)
Gabriel Camilo (Dir-Medical-Anesthesiology)
Lewis Starasoler (Dir-Medical-Pathology)
Kleper De Almeida (Treas & Co-Sec)
David Husted (Chm)
Alex Paya (Chief Medical Officer)
Suzanne Bertsch-Gibson (Chief Nursing Officer)
Roberta Fowler (VP-Quality)
Jay Maizes (Chm)
Heidi Bahna (Chm)
Shaun Isaac (Dir-Medical)
Mazyar Rouhanie (Dir-Medical-Emergency Medicine)
Mehdi Bathaii (Dir-Medical-Radiology)
Gabriel Camilo (Dir-Medical-Anesthesiology)
Lewis Starasoler (Dir-Medical-Pathology)

JFK North Surgicenter, LLC (1)
2201 45th St, West Palm Beach, FL 33407
Tel.: (561) 842-6141
General Surgical Services
N.A.I.C.S.: 622110

Jackson County Pulmonary Medical Group, LLC (1)
19550 E 39th St Ste 310, Independence, MO 64057
Tel.: (816) 478-8113
Web Site: https://mymidwestphysician.com
Health Care Srvices
N.A.I.C.S.: 621399

Jacksonville CareNow Urgent Care, LLC (1)
4888 Town Ctr Pkwy Ste 107, Jacksonville, FL 32246-8437
Tel.: (904) 800-1735
Hospital Management Services
N.A.I.C.S.: 622110

Jacksonville Multispecialty Services, LLC (1)
1679 Eagle Harbor Pkwy Ste B, Orange Park, FL 32003-4815
Tel.: (904) 399-6109
General Medical & Surgical Services
N.A.I.C.S.: 622110

Jacksonville Specialists, LLC (1)
3625 University Blvd S, Jacksonville, FL 32216-4207
Tel.: (904) 702-6111
Health Care Srvices
N.A.I.C.S.: 621399

Jacksonville Surgery Center, Ltd. (1)
7021 A C Skinner Pkwy, Jacksonville, FL 32256
Tel.: (904) 281-0021

Web Site: https://jaxsurgerycenter.com
General Medical & Surgical Services
N.A.I.C.S.: 622110

James River Internists, LLC (1)
13440 Tredegar Lake Pkwy Bldg 2, Midlothian, VA 23112
Tel.: (804) 745-2200
General Medical & Surgical Services
N.A.I.C.S.: 622110

James River Internists, LLC (1)
13440 Tredegar Lake Pkwy Bldg 2, Midlothian, VA 23112
Tel.: (804) 745-2200
Web Site: http://hcavirginiaphysicians.com
Health Care Srvices
N.A.I.C.S.: 621111

John Randolph Medical Center (1)
411 W Randolph Rd, Hopewell, VA 23860
Tel.: (804) 541-1600
Web Site: http://www.johnrandolphmed.com
Sales Range: $75-99.9 Million
Emp.: 800
Hospital
N.A.I.C.S.: 622110
Joe Mazzo (CEO)

John Randolph OB/GYN, LLC (1)
12801 Iron Bridge Rd Ste 100, Chester, VA 23831
Tel.: (804) 706-5827
Emp.: 3
General Medical & Surgical Services
N.A.I.C.S.: 622110

Johnson County Neurology, LLC (1)
12140 Nall Ave 230, Overland Park, KS 66209
Tel.: (913) 661-9448
Web Site: http://mymidwestphysician.com
Health Care Srvices
N.A.I.C.S.: 621399

Johnson County Neurology, LLC (1)
12140 Nall Ave Ste 230, Overland Park, KS 66209
Tel.: (913) 661-9448
General Medical & Surgical Services
N.A.I.C.S.: 622110

Jordan Family Health, L.L.C. (1)
8846 S Redwood Rd Ste E-121, West Jordan, UT 84088
Tel.: (801) 569-1999
Web Site:
http://www.jordanfamilyhealth.com
Health Care Srvices
N.A.I.C.S.: 621111

Jupiter EFL Imaging Center, LLC (1)
875 Military Trl Ste 101, Jupiter, FL 33458-5700
Tel.: (561) 748-9828
General Medical & Surgical Services
N.A.I.C.S.: 622110

KPH-Consolidation, Inc. (1)
22999 US Hwy 59 N, Kingwood, TX 77339
Tel.: (281) 348-8000
Web Site: http://www.kingwoodmedical.com
Emp.: 1,300
Health Care Srvices
N.A.I.C.S.: 621399
Darren DeSimone (Chief Nursing Officer)
Virgil Winslow (CFO)
Joel North (COO)
Ahmad Maarouf (Chief Medical Officer)
John Corbeil (CEO)

Kansas City Gastroenterology & Hepatology Physicians Group, LLC (1)
6675 Holmes Rd Ste 430, Kansas City, MO 64131
Tel.: (913) 234-7600
Web Site: https://mymidwestphysician.com
General Medical & Surgical Services
N.A.I.C.S.: 622110

Kansas City Neurology Associates, LLC (1)
1980 SE Blue Pkwy Ste 2130, Lees Summit, MO 64063
Tel.: (816) 524-1700

HCA Healthcare, Inc.—(Continued)

General Medical & Surgical Services
N.A.I.C.S.: 622110

**Kansas City Pulmonology Practice,
LLC** (1)
2330 E Meyer Blvd Ste 303, Kansas City,
MO 64132
Tel.: (816) 333-1919
Web Site: https://mymidwestphysician.com
Women Healthcare Services
N.A.I.C.S.: 621610

**Kansas City Vascular & General Sur-
gery Group, LLC** (1)
5100 W 110th St Ste 300, Overland Park,
KS 66211
Tel.: (913) 754-2800
Web Site:
http://www.kcvascularandgeneralsur
gery.com
Emp.: 35
Healtcare Services
N.A.I.C.S.: 621999

**Kansas City Women's Clinic Group,
LLC** (1)
10600 Quivira Rd 200, Overland Park, KS
66215
Tel.: (913) 541-0990
Web Site:
http://www.womenshealthcaregroup
kc.com
Obstetric & Gynecology Services
N.A.I.C.S.: 622310

**Kansas Pulmonary & Sleep Special-
ists, LLC** (1)
10550 Quivira Rd Ste 335, Overland Park,
KS 66215-2306
Tel.: (913) 599-3800
Health Care Srvices
N.A.I.C.S.: 621399

**Kansas Pulmonary and Sleep Spe-
cialists, LLC** (1)
10550 Quivira Rd Ste 335, Overland Park,
KS 66215
Tel.: (913) 599-3800
General Medical & Surgical Services
N.A.I.C.S.: 622110

**Kansas Trauma & Critical Care Spe-
cialists, LLC** (1)
550 N Hillside St, Wichita, KS 67214
Tel.: (316) 962-2000
Health Care Srvices
N.A.I.C.S.: 621399

Kathy L. Summers, M.D., PLLC (1)
7400 Fannin St Ste 1150, Houston, TX
77054
Tel.: (713) 795-5054
Web Site:
http://www.womanshealthgroup.com
General Medical & Surgical Services
N.A.I.C.S.: 622110

**Kendall Regional Medical Center,
LLC** (1)
11750 SW 40th St, Miami, FL 33175-3530
Tel.: (305) 223-3000
Web Site: http://www.kendallmed.com
Sales Range: $50-74.9 Million
Emp.: 2,091
Medical Center
N.A.I.C.S.: 622110

**Kendall Regional Urgent Care,
LLC** (1)
10725 NW 58th St, Doral, FL 33178-2801
Tel.: (305) 629-9644
General Medical & Surgical Services
N.A.I.C.S.: 622110

Kennedale Primary Care PLLC (1)
201 W Kennedale Pkwy, Kennedale, TX
76060
Tel.: (817) 563-2300
General Medical & Surgical Services
N.A.I.C.S.: 622110

Kingwood Medical Center (1)
22999 US Hwy 59 N, Kingwood, TX 77339
Tel.: (281) 348-8000
Web Site: https://hcahoustonhealthcare.com
Sales Range: $50-74.9 Million
Emp.: 550
Medical Center

N.A.I.C.S.: 622110
John Corbeil (CEO)
Robert A. Marmerstein (CTO)
Virgil Winslow (CFO)
Joel North (COO)
Darren DeSimone (Chief Nursing Officer)
Sterling Ray III (Chief Medical Officer)

Kingwood Surgery Center, LLC (1)
19502 McKay Dr Ste 101, Humble, TX
77338
Tel.: (281) 312-6900
Web Site: http://www.humblekingwoodendos
copy.com
Medical Support Services
N.A.I.C.S.: 621111

Subsidiary (Domestic):

**Humble Kingwood Endoscopy
Center** (2)
19502 McKay Dr Ste 101, Humble, TX
77338
Tel.: (281) 312-6900
Web Site:
https://humblekingwoodendoscopy.com
Surgical Care Services
N.A.I.C.S.: 621493

LAD Imaging, LLC (1)
1555 Saxon Blvd Ste 401, Deltona, FL
32725
Tel.: (386) 860-9336
Web Site: http://akumin.com
Health Care Srvices
N.A.I.C.S.: 621399

LOC at Chelsea LLP (1)
102 Sydney Street Chelsea, London, SW3
6NJ, United Kingdom
Tel.: (44) 2039053700
Cancer Treatment Services
N.A.I.C.S.: 622310

**LOC at The Harborne Hospital
Limited** (1)
Mindelsohn Way, Birmingham, B15 2FQ,
United Kingdom
Tel.: (44) 1214688967
Diagnostic Center Operator
N.A.I.C.S.: 621512

Lafayette OB Hospitalists, LLC (1)
4600 Ambassador Caffery Pkwy, Lafayette,
LA 70508
Tel.: (337) 521-9103
General Medical & Surgical Services
N.A.I.C.S.: 622110

**Lafayette Regional Health
Center** (1)
1500 State St, Lexington, MO 64067
Tel.: (660) 259-2203
General Medical & Surgical Services
N.A.I.C.S.: 622110

**Lafayette Surgery Center Limited
Partnership** (1)
4630 Ambassador Caffery Pkwy Ste 101,
Lafayette, LA 70508-6949
Tel.: (337) 993-1193
Web Site: http://www.lafayettesurgicare.com
Health Care Srvices
N.A.I.C.S.: 621399

Lafayette Surgicare, Inc. (1)
4630 Ambassador Caffery Pkwy, Lafayette,
LA 70508
Tel.: (337) 993-1193
Web Site: https://lafayettesurgicare.com
General Medical & Surgical Services
N.A.I.C.S.: 622110

Lake City Imaging, LLC (1)
3140 NW Medical Ctr Ln Ste 100, Lake
City, FL 32055-4717
Tel.: (386) 755-2020
General Medical & Surgical Services
N.A.I.C.S.: 622110

Lake City Medical Center (1)
340 NW Commerce Dr, Lake City, FL
32055
Tel.: (386) 719-9000
Web Site: http://www.lakecitymedical.com
Sales Range: $25-49.9 Million
Emp.: 350
Hospital
N.A.I.C.S.: 622110
Rick Naegler (CEO)

**Lake City Regional Medical Group,
LLC** (1)
4225 NW American LN, Lake City, FL
32055
Tel.: (386) 758-6141
Emp.: 20
Health Care Srvices
N.A.I.C.S.: 622110
Janet Tuttle (Gen Mgr)

**Lake Nona Emergency Physicians,
LLC** (1)
PO Box 80294, Philadelphia, PA 19101-
1294
Health Care & Surgical Services
N.A.I.C.S.: 622110

**Lake Nona Inpatient Services,
LLC** (1)
PO Box 80295, Philadelphia, PA 19101-
1295
Health Care & Surgical Services
N.A.I.C.S.: 622110

Lakeview Endoscopy Center (1)
620 E Medical Dr Ste 200, Bountiful, UT
84010
Tel.: (801) 299-6760
Web Site: https://lakeviewendoscopy.com
General Medical & Surgical Services
N.A.I.C.S.: 622110

Lakeview Hospital (1)
630 E Medical Dr, Bountiful, UT 84010
Tel.: (801) 299-2200
Web Site: https://mountainstar.com
Sales Range: $25-49.9 Million
Emp.: 597
Hospital
N.A.I.C.S.: 622110
Audrey Glasby (Dir-PR-Mountain View Hos-
pital)

**Lakeview Hospital Physician Ser-
vices, LLC** (1)
630 E Medical Dr, Bountiful, UT 84010
Tel.: (801) 299-2200
Emp.: 597
Gynecology Services
N.A.I.C.S.: 621111
Kane J. David (VP)

Lakeview Internal Medicine, LLC (1)
444 W Bourne Cir Ste 101, Farmington, UT
84025
Tel.: (801) 294-9333
Web Site:
http://mountainstarmedicalgroup.com
Pulmonary Services
N.A.I.C.S.: 621111

Lakeview Medical Center, LLC (1)
95 Judge Tanner Blvd, Covington, LA
70433-7500
Tel.: (985) 867-3800
Web Site: http://www.lakeviewregional.com
Sales Range: $50-74.9 Million
Hospital
N.A.I.C.S.: 622110

**Lakeview Neurosurgery Clinic,
LLC** (1)
620 Medical Dr Ste 300, Bountiful, UT
84010
Tel.: (801) 299-3871
Health Care Srvices
N.A.I.C.S.: 621111

**Lakeview Regional Physician Group,
LLC** (1)
95 Judge Tanner Blvd, Covington, LA 70433
Tel.: (985) 867-3900
Web Site:
https://www.lakeviewphysiciangroup.com
General Medical & Surgical Services
N.A.I.C.S.: 622110

Largo Physician Group, LLC (1)
7655 38th Ave N, Saint Petersburg, FL
33710
Tel.: (727) 347-9000
General Medical & Surgical Services
N.A.I.C.S.: 622110

Las Colinas Surgery Center, Ltd. (1)
4255 N MacArthur Blvd, Irving, TX 75038
Tel.: (972) 257-0144
Web Site:
http://www.medicalcitysurgerylascoli
nas.com

Health Care Srvices
N.A.I.C.S.: 621999
Michael Hicks (Dir-Medical)

Las Encinas Hospital (1)
2900 E Del Mar Blvd, Pasadena, CA 91107
Tel.: (626) 795-9901
Web Site:
https://www.lasencinashospital.com
General Medical & Surgical Services
N.A.I.C.S.: 622110

Las Encinas Hospital (1)
2900 E Del Mar Blvd, Pasadena, CA 91107
Tel.: (626) 795-9901
Web Site:
http://www.lasencinashospital.com
Health Care Srvices
N.A.I.C.S.: 621999
Veronica Herrera (Dir-HR)
Trevor Asmus (CEO)
Michael Fink (Dir-Business Development)
Jim Cussio (Dir-Plant Ops)
Ligaya Fontanilla (Dir)
Melissa Mitchell (Chief Nursing Officer)
Amanda Kirkner (Dir)
Julie Crenshaw (Dir)
Ariane Loera (Dir-Medical Staff Svcs)
Daniel Suzuki (Dir-Medical)
Amir Alikhan (Asst Dir-Medical)
Marvin Cajina (Dir-HIM)
Adam Waddell (Dir-Nutritional Svcs)
Jennifer Tuck (Dir)
Margaret Andricos (Dir)
Caroline Anyadike (Dir-Risk Management)
Peter Ma (Dir)

Las Palmas Del Sol Healthcare (1)
1801 N Oregon St, El Paso, TX 79902
Tel.: (915) 521-1200
Web Site:
https://laspalmasdelsolhealthcare.com
General Medical & Surgical Services
N.A.I.C.S.: 622110

**Las Palmas Del Sol Urgent Care,
PLLC** (1)
13650 Eastlake Dr Bldg A Ste 104, El Paso,
TX 79928
Tel.: (915) 852-5086
Web Site: https://lpdsurgentcare.com
Health Care Srvices
N.A.I.C.S.: 524114

Las Vegas Surgery Center (1)
870 S Rancho Dr, Las Vegas, NV 89106
Tel.: (702) 870-2090
Web Site: https://www.lvdaysurgery.com
Health Care & Allied Services
N.A.I.C.S.: 621999

**Lawnwood Cardiovascular Surgery,
LLC** (1)
2401 Frist Blvd Ste 5, Fort Pierce, FL
34950
Tel.: (772) 465-8100
Web Site: http://www.fhvcare.com
Health Care & Allied Services
N.A.I.C.S.: 621999

**Lawnwood Pavilion Physician Ser-
vices, LLC** (1)
1860 N Lawnwood Cir, Fort Pierce, FL
34950-4828
Tel.: (772) 467-3906
Health Care & Allied Services
N.A.I.C.S.: 621999

**Lawnwood Regional Medical
Center** (1)
1700 S 23rd St, Fort Pierce, FL 34950
Tel.: (772) 461-4000
Web Site: http://www.lawnwoodmed.com
Sales Range: $50-74.9 Million
Emp.: 1,662
Medical Center
N.A.I.C.S.: 622110

Layton Family Practice, LLC (1)
2950 Church St Ste200, Layton, UT 84040
Tel.: (801) 771-7700
Web Site:
http://www.laytonfamilymedicine.com
Medical Support Services
N.A.I.C.S.: 621111

**Leaders in Oncology Care
Limited** (1)
95-97 Harley Street, London, W1G 6AF,
United Kingdom
Tel.: (44) 207 317 2504

Web Site: http://www.theloc.com
General Medical Care Services
N.A.I.C.S.: 622110

Lee's Summit Medical Center (1)
2100 SE Blue Pkwy, Lees Summit, MO 64063
Tel.: (816) 282-5000
Web Site: https://careers.hcahealthcare.com
Emp.: 500
Health Care Srvices
N.A.I.C.S.: 621399

Lewis-Gale Hospital, Incorporated (1)
1900 Electric Rd 200, Salem, VA 24153
Tel.: (540) 776-4704
Web Site: http://www.lewisgale.com
Emp.: 1,300
Medical & Surgical Hospital Services
N.A.I.C.S.: 622110

Lewis-Gale Medical Center, LLC (1)
1900 Electric Rd, Salem, VA 24153
Tel.: (540) 776-4000
Web Site: http://www.lewisgale.com
Sales Range: $75-99.9 Million
Hospital
N.A.I.C.S.: 622110

Lewis-Gale Physicians, LLC (1)
1802 Braeburn Dr, Salem, VA 24153
Tel.: (540) 772-3400
Web Site: http://www.lgphysicians.com
Health Care Srvices
N.A.I.C.S.: 621111

LewisGale Hospital Alleghany (1)
1 ARH Ln, Low Moor, VA 24457
Tel.: (540) 862-6011
Web Site: http://www.lewisgale.com
Sales Range: $25-49.9 Million
Emp.: 400
Hospital
N.A.I.C.S.: 622110
Sean Pressman (CEO)
Angela Reynolds (CFO)
Lee Higginbotham (COO)
Jim Ballou (Pres)

LewisGale Hospital Alleghany (1)
1 Arh Ln, Low Moor, VA 24457
Tel.: (540) 862-6879
General Medical & Surgical Services
N.A.I.C.S.: 622110

LewisGale Hospital Montgomery (1)
3700 S Main St, Blacksburg, VA 24060
Tel.: (540) 951-1111
General Medical & Surgical Services
N.A.I.C.S.: 622110

LewisGale Hospital-Pulaski (1)
2400 Lee Hwy, Pulaski, VA 24301
Tel.: (540) 994-8100
Web Site: https://www.hcavirginia.com
Emp.: 400
Hospital
N.A.I.C.S.: 622110

Lincoln Surgery Center, LLC (1)
11960 Lioness Way Ste 120, Parker, CO 80134
Tel.: (720) 542-6700
Web Site:
  https://www.lincolnsurgerycenter.com
Medical & Surgical Hospital Services
N.A.I.C.S.: 622110

Lister Fertility at Portland Hospital Limited (1)
First Floor 215 Great Portland Street, London, W1W 5PN, United Kingdom
Tel.: (44) 2039934027
Women Fertility Care Services
N.A.I.C.S.: 621410

Lister Hospital (1)
Chelsea Bridge Rd, London, SW1W 8RH, United Kingdom
Tel.: (44) 2077307733
General Medical & Surgical Services
N.A.I.C.S.: 622110

Live Oak Immediate Care Center, LLC (1)
1150 US Hwy 41 NW, Jasper, FL 32052-5888
Tel.: (615) 373-7600
General Medical & Surgical Services
N.A.I.C.S.: 622110

London Bridge Hospital (1)
27 Tooley St, London, SE1 2PR, United Kingdom
Tel.: (44) 2074073100
General Medical & Surgical Services
N.A.I.C.S.: 622110

London Bridge Hospital (1)
27 Tooley Street, London, SE1 2PR, United Kingdom
Tel.: (44) 39936849
Web Site:
  http://www.londonbridgehospital.com
General Medical Care Services
N.A.I.C.S.: 622110
Kamal Ahmed (Dir-Medical)
Victoria Goodacre (Chief HR Officer)
Stephen Maxwell (CFO)
Janene Madden (CEO)
Kathryn Hornby (Chief Nursing Officer)
Gregory Bale (COO)

London Radiotherapy Centre Ltd. (1)
Borough Wing Lower Ground Floor Guys Hospital Great Maze Pond, London, SE1 9RT, United Kingdom
Tel.: (44) 2037137505
Radiotherapy Treatment Services
N.A.I.C.S.: 621512

Lone Peak Hospital, Inc. (1)
11925 S State St, Draper, UT 84020-7735
Tel.: (801) 545-8000
Web Site: http://www.lonepeakhospital.com
General Medical Care Services
N.A.I.C.S.: 622110

Lonestar Provider Network (1)
7777 Forest Ln Ste C300, Dallas, TX 75230-2505
Tel.: (972) 566-6000
Web Site: https://dallasmedical.com
Health Care Srvices
N.A.I.C.S.: 621112

Los Robles Regional Medical Center (1)
215 W Janss Rd, Thousand Oaks, CA 91360
Tel.: (805) 497-2727
Web Site: http://www.losrobleshospital.com
Sales Range: $75-99.9 Million
Hospital
N.A.I.C.S.: 622110
Natalie Mussi (Pres)
Kyle Himsl (Vice Chm)
Michael Wildermuth (Chm)
Phil Buttell (CEO)

Los Robles SurgiCenter, LLC (1)
2190 Lynn Rd Ste 100, Thousand Oaks, CA 91360
Tel.: (805) 497-3737
Web Site: https://losroblessurgicenter.com
General Medical & Surgical Services
N.A.I.C.S.: 622110

Lowry Surgery Center, LLC (1)
8101 E Lowry Blvd Ste 100, Denver, CO 80230
Tel.: (303) 366-5656
Web Site: http://www.lowrysurgery.com
Emp.: 30
Medical & Surgical Hospital Services
N.A.I.C.S.: 622110

MH Angel Medical Center, LLLP (1)
124 1 Cntr Ct, Franklin, NC 28734
Tel.: (828) 524-8411
Web Site: https://missionhealth.org
Hospital Management Services
N.A.I.C.S.: 621111

MH Eckerd Living Center, LLLP (1)
250 Hospital Dr, Highlands, NC 28741
Tel.: (828) 526-1315
Web Site:
  https://www.eckerdlivingcenter.com
Hospital Management Services
N.A.I.C.S.: 621111
Emily Bowers (Dir-Nursing)

MH Highlands-Cashiers Medical Center, LLLP (1)
190 Hospital Dr, Highlands, NC 28741
Tel.: (828) 526-1200
Web Site: https://missionhealth.org
Hospital Management Services
N.A.I.C.S.: 621111

Greg Lowe (Pres)
Tom Neal (CEO)

MH Mission Hospital McDowell, LLLP (1)
430 Rankin Dr, Marion, NC 28752
Tel.: (828) 659-5000
Web Site: https://missionhealth.org
Hospital Management Services
N.A.I.C.S.: 621111
Bobbi Young (Vice Chm)
Greg Lowe (Pres)

MH Mission Hospital, LLLP (1)
509 Biltmore Ave, Asheville, NC 28801
Tel.: (828) 213-1111
Web Site: https://missionhealth.org
Hospital Management Services
N.A.I.C.S.: 621111
Chad Patrick (CEO)
Wyatt Chocklett (COO)
Laurie Haynes (CFO)

MH Transylvania Regional Hospital, LLLP (1)
260 Hospital Dr, Brevard, NC 28712
Tel.: (828) 884-9111
Web Site: https://missionhealth.org
Hospital Management Services
N.A.I.C.S.: 621111
Frank Porter (Vice Chm)

MVH Professional Services, LLC (1)
1000 E 100 N, Payson, UT 84651-1600
Tel.: (801) 465-7045
Health Care Srvices
N.A.I.C.S.: 621111

Macon Psychiatric Hospitalists, LLC (1)
340 Hospital Dr Bldg E, Macon, GA 31217-3838
Tel.: (478) 474-4343
General Medical & Surgical Services
N.A.I.C.S.: 622110
Lan Jones (CEO)

Madison Behavioral Health, LLC (1)
600 Medical Park Dr Ste 204, Madison, TN 37115
Tel.: (615) 889-9902
Mental Health Care Services
N.A.I.C.S.: 622110

Madison Internal Medicine, LLC (1)
95 Madison Ave Ste 405, Morristown, NJ 07960
Tel.: (973) 829-9998
Web Site:
  http://madisoninternalmedicine.atlantic
  health.org
Health Care Srvices
N.A.I.C.S.: 621999

Mainland Primary Care Physicians, PLLC (1)
6807 Emmett F Lowry Expy Ste 103, Texas City, TX 77591
Tel.: (409) 938-1770
Surgical Hospital Services
N.A.I.C.S.: 622110

Manatee Surgicare, Ltd. (1)
411 2nd St E, Bradenton, FL 34208
Tel.: (941) 746-1121
Emp.: 3
General Medical & Surgical Services
N.A.I.C.S.: 622110

Marietta Outpatient Surgery, Ltd. (1)
5730 Glendrivge Dr, Atlanta, GA 30342
Tel.: (404) 252-3074
Health Care Srvices
N.A.I.C.S.: 621399

Marietta Surgical Center, Inc. (1)
780 Canton Rd Ste 100, Marietta, GA 30060
Tel.: (770) 422-1579
Web Site: https://mariettasurgicalcenter.com
General Medical & Surgical Services
N.A.I.C.S.: 622110

Marshland Emergency Physicians, LLC (1)
18167 Us Hwy Ste 19 N, Clearwater, FL 33765
Surgery & Orthopaedic Care Services
N.A.I.C.S.: 621493

Martin Fletcher Associates Holdings, Inc. (1)

400 E Las Colinas Blvd Ste 300, Irving, TX 75039
Tel.: (972) 443-5500
Holding Company
N.A.I.C.S.: 551112

McKinney Surgeons, PLLC (1)
4510 Medical Ctr Dr Ste 214, McKinney, TX 75069-1650
Tel.: (214) 592-9200
General Medical & Surgical Services
N.A.I.C.S.: 622110

MediCredit, Inc. (1)
3620 Interstate 70 Dr SE, Columbia, MO 65201-6582
Tel.: (573) 874-1182
General Medical & Surgical Services
N.A.I.C.S.: 622110

MediVision, Inc. (1)
4883 E La Palma Ave Ste 503, Anaheim, CA 92807
Tel.: (714) 563-2772
Web Site: https://medivisionusa.com
General Medical & Surgical Services
N.A.I.C.S.: 622110

Medical Center of Arlington (1)
3301 Matlock Rd, Arlington, TX 76015
Tel.: (682) 509-6200
Web Site:
  http://www.medicalcityarlington.com
Sales Range: $50-74.9 Million
Emp.: 1,583
Hospital
N.A.I.C.S.: 622110
Jeff M. Ardemagni (CFO)
Keith V. Zimmerman (CEO)
Eric Benink (Chief Medical Officer)
Cathleen McLaughlin (Chief Nursing Officer)
Ben Coogan (Co-COO)
Mary Beth Short (VP-HR)
Marcus Jackson (VP-Ops)
Jamie Gibbs (VP-Fin)
Skyler Reed (Co-COO)

Medical Center of Baton Rouge, Inc. (1)
17000 Medical Ctr Dr, Baton Rouge, LA 70816
Tel.: (225) 752-2470
General Medical & Surgical Services
N.A.I.C.S.: 622110

Medical Center of Lewisville (1)
500 W Main St, Lewisville, TX 75057
Tel.: (469) 370-2000
Web Site:
  http://www.medicalcitylewisville.com
Sales Range: $25-49.9 Million
Emp.: 750
Hospital
N.A.I.C.S.: 622110
Sue Cobb (VP-Quality)
Renee Sturgeon (CFO)
Megan Gallegos (Chief Nursing Officer)
Dara Biegert (VP-HR)
Gary Fullerton (Asst VP-Ops)
Sharn Barbarin (CEO)
Allen Marsh (COO)
Stephanie MacVeigh (VP-Quality)
Misty Ricard (VP-Human Resources)
Michelle Wildman (Dir-Administration-Nursing Ops)
Ginger Eads (Chm)
Jacquelyn Delin (Vice Chm)
LaSharndra Barbarin (Sec)

Medical Center of McKinney (1)
4500 Medical Ctr Dr, McKinney, TX 75069
Tel.: (972) 547-8000
Web Site:
  http://www.medicalcenterofmckinney.com
Sales Range: $50-74.9 Million
Emp.: 1,149
Hospital
N.A.I.C.S.: 622110

Medical Center of Plano (1)
3901 W 15th St, Plano, TX 75075
Tel.: (972) 596-6800
Sales Range: $75-99.9 Million
Emp.: 2,271
Hospital
N.A.I.C.S.: 622110
Khang N. Tran (Chief Medical Officer)
Charles Gressle (CEO)
Melissa McLeroy (CFO)

Medical Center of Santa Rosa, Inc. (1)

HCA Healthcare, Inc.—(Continued)

6002 Berryhill Rd, Milton, FL 32570
Tel.: (850) 626-7762
Web Site: https://www.srmcfl.com
General Medical & Surgical Services
N.A.I.C.S.: 622110

Medical Center of Trinity (1)
9330 SR-54 E, Trinity, FL 34655
Tel.: (727) 834-4000
Web Site:
    http://www.medicalcentertrinity.com
Health Care Srvices
N.A.I.C.S.: 621399
Leigh Massengill (Co-CEO & Co-Sec)
William Killinger (Chief Medical Officer)
Tripp Owings (Co-CEO & Co-Sec)
Richard A. Miller (Chm)
Peter DiMartino (Treas)

Medical City Dallas Ambulatory Surgery Center (1)
7777 Forest Ln Ste C-150, Dallas, TX 75230
Tel.: (972) 566-6171
Web Site:
    https://medicalcitysurgerydallas.com
Surgical Care Services
N.A.I.C.S.: 621493

Medical City Hospital (1)
7777 Forest Ln, Dallas, TX 75230-2505
Tel.: (972) 566-7000
Web Site:
    http://www.medicalcityhospital.com
Sales Range: $300-349.9 Million
Emp.: 2,600
Hospital
N.A.I.C.S.: 622110

Medical City Surgery Center Southlake, LLC (1)
2815 W Southlake Blvd Ste 100, Southlake, TX 76092
Tel.: (817) 431-3200
Web Site:
    https://medicalcitysurgerysouthlake.com
Surgical Equipment Mfr
N.A.I.C.S.: 339112

Medical City Surgery Center of Allen, LLC (1)
1125 Raintree Cir Ste 200, Allen, TX 75013
Tel.: (469) 898-8400
Web Site:
    https://medicalcitysurgeryallen.com
Surgery Center Services
N.A.I.C.S.: 621493

Medical City Surgery Center of Alliance, LLC (1)
8900 Medical City Way, Fort Worth, TX 70177
Tel.: (817) 898-6610
Web Site:
    https://medicalcitysurgeryalliance.com
General Medical & Surgical Services
N.A.I.C.S.: 622110

Medical City Surgery Center of Frisco, LLC (1)
5575 Frisco Square Blvd Ste 100, Frisco, TX 75034
Tel.: (972) 324-0200
Web Site:
    https://medicalcitysurgeryfrisco.com
General Medical & Surgical Services
N.A.I.C.S.: 622110

Medical Group - Southern Hills of Brentwood, LLC (1)
317 Seven Springs Way Ste 104, Brentwood, TN 37027
Tel.: (615) 377-4999
General Medical & Surgical Services
N.A.I.C.S.: 622110
Brook Peck (Office Mgr)

Medical Group - StoneCrest, Inc. (1)
300 Stonecrest Blvd Ste 110, Smyrna, TN 37167
Tel.: (615) 223-9233
Web Site: http://www.stonecrestim.com
Emp.: 18
Medical & Surgical Hospital Services
N.A.I.C.S.: 622110

Medical Oncology Associates, LLC (1)

1348 Walton Way Ste 6700, Augusta, GA 30901
Tel.: (706) 722-4245
Health Care Srvices
N.A.I.C.S.: 621610

Medical Park Diagnostic Center (1)
9090 SW 87th Ct, Miami, FL 33176-2305
Tel.: (305) 279-7275
Web Site: http://medicalparkgroup.us
Sales Range: $25-49.9 Million
Emp.: 100
Medical Center
N.A.I.C.S.: 622110

Medical Specialties, Inc. (1)
4600 Lebanon Rd, Charlotte, NC 28227-8252
Tel.: (704) 573-4040
Web Site: https://www.medspec.com
Medical Support Services
N.A.I.C.S.: 621111

Memorial Endoscopy Center (1)
1233 Campbell Rd, Houston, TX 77055
Tel.: (713) 468-9200
Web Site:
    https://www.memorialendoscopy.com
Medicare Services
N.A.I.C.S.: 923130

Memorial Healthcare Group, Inc. (1)
3625 University Blvd S, Jacksonville, FL 32216
Tel.: (904) 702-6111
Web Site:
    http://www.memorialhospitaljax.com
Emp.: 1,800
Health Care Srvices
N.A.I.C.S.: 621399
Ray Gyarmathy (Chm)
Eleanor Lynch (Sr VP-Ops)
Stuart Thompson (VP-HR)
Tammy Razmic (COO)
Kevin McKeown (CFO)
Albert E. Holt (Chief Medical Officer)
Odette Struys (Assoc VP-Comm & PR)
Reed Hammond (CEO)
David Threatt (Chief Nursing Officer)

Memorial Hospital (1)
3625 Univ Blvd S, Jacksonville, FL 32216
Tel.: (904) 702-6111
Web Site:
    http://www.memorialhospitaljax.com
Sales Range: $75-99.9 Million
Emp.: 1,800
Hospital
N.A.I.C.S.: 622110
Bradley S. Talbert (Pres & CEO)
Odette Struys (Assoc VP-Comm & PR)
Ray Gyarmathy (Chm)
Mary Reval (Chief Nursing Officer)
Eleanor Lynch (Sr VP-Ops)
Stuart Thompson (VP-HR)
Chris Belmont (CIO & VP)
Tammy L. Razmic (COO)
Kevin McKeown (CFO)
Albert E. Holt (Chief Medical Officer)

Memorial Hospital of Tampa (1)
2901 W Swann Ave, Tampa, FL 33609
Tel.: (813) 873-6400
Web Site:
    http://www.memorialhospitaltampa.com
Emp.: 862
Health Care Srvices
N.A.I.C.S.: 621399
Sonia Wellman (CEO)
Mari Elliott (COO)
Christine Van Cott (Chief Medical Officer)
Michelle Harvey (CFO)
Pariss Clark (Chief Nursing Officer)
Paige Niehaus (Vice Chm)

Memorial Neurosurgery Group, LLC (1)
3627 University Blvd S, Jacksonville, FL 32216
Tel.: (904) 296-2522
Neurology Services
N.A.I.C.S.: 621111

Memorial Satilla Specialists, LLC (1)
1908 Alice St, Waycross, GA 31501
Tel.: (912) 338-6010
Web Site:
    https://memorialsatillaspecialists.com
General Medical & Surgical Services
N.A.I.C.S.: 622110

Menorah Medical Group, LLC (1)
5701 W 119th St Ste 150, Overland Park, KS 66209
Tel.: (913) 491-3724
Health Care Srvices
N.A.I.C.S.: 621399

Merritt Island Surgery Center (1)
220 N Sykes Creek Pkwy Ste 101, Merritt Island, FL 32953
Tel.: (321) 459-0015
Web Site:
    https://merrittislandsurgerycenter.com
General Medical & Surgical Services
N.A.I.C.S.: 622110

Methodist Ambulatory Surgery Center of Boerne, LLC (1)
110 Menger Springs Rd, Boerne, TX 78006
Tel.: (830) 331-6006
Web Site: https://methodistascboerne.com
Health Care Srvices
N.A.I.C.S.: 524114

Methodist Ambulatory Surgery Center of Landmark, LLC (1)
5510B Presidio Pkwy Ste 100, San Antonio, TX 78249
Tel.: (210) 583-7500
Web Site:
    https://methodistsurgerycenterlandmark.com
General Medical & Surgical Services
N.A.I.C.S.: 622110

Methodist CareNow Urgent Care, PLLC (1)
5755 Nw Loop 410, San Antonio, TX 78238-2502
Tel.: (972) 906-8107
Health Care Srvices
N.A.I.C.S.: 524114

Methodist Healthcare System of San Antonio, Ltd. (1)
15727 Anthem Pkwy Ste 600, San Antonio, TX 78249
Tel.: (210) 575-0355
Web Site: http://www.sahealth.com
Sales Range: $800-899.9 Million
Emp.: 5,400
Hospital Operator
N.A.I.C.S.: 622110
Jaime Wesolowski (Pres & CEO)

Subsidiary (Domestic):

MHS Surgery Centers, L.P. (2)
8109 Fredericksburg Rd Ste 2, San Antonio, TX 78229
Tel.: (210) 242-7169
Emp.: 3
Healthcare Training Services
N.A.I.C.S.: 621111

Methodist Ambulatory Surgery Hospital - Northwest (2)
15727 Anthem Pkwy Ste 600, San Antonio, TX 78249
Tel.: (210) 575-0355
Web Site:
    http://www.methodisthealthcare.com
Surgical Care Services
N.A.I.C.S.: 621493

Methodist Hospital Hill Country (2)
1020 S State Hwy 16, Fredericksburg, TX 78624
Tel.: (830) 997-4353
Web Site: https://sahealth.com.
Sales Range: $50-74.9 Million
Emp.: 797
Health Care Srvices
N.A.I.C.S.: 622110
Clinton Kotal (CEO)

Methodist Hospital South (2)
1905 Hwy 97 E, Jourdanton, TX 78026
Tel.: (830) 769-3515
Web Site: https://www.sahealth.com
Hospital Operator
N.A.I.C.S.: 622110

Methodist Inpatient Management Group (2)
8109 Fredericksburg Rd, San Antonio, TX 78229-3311
Tel.: (210) 575-8505
Health Care Srvices
N.A.I.C.S.: 621610

Methodist Medical Center ASC, L.P. (2)
4411 Medical Dr, San Antonio, TX 78229
Tel.: (210) 575-4521
Health Care Srvices
N.A.I.C.S.: 621399

Methodist Physician Alliance (2)
8109 Fredericksburg Rd, San Antonio, TX 78229
Tel.: (210) 575-0252
Web Site: http://www.methodistphysicianalliance.com
Health Care Srvices
N.A.I.C.S.: 621399

Methodist Stone Oak Hospital (2)
1139 E Sonterra Blvd, San Antonio, TX 78258
Tel.: (210) 638-2000
Web Site: https://sahealth.com
Health Care Srvices
N.A.I.C.S.: 621399
Marc Strode (CEO)

Metropolitan Methodist Hospital (2)
1310 McCullough Ave, San Antonio, TX 78212
Tel.: (210) 757-2200
Web Site: https://www.joinmethodist.com
Health Care Srvices
N.A.I.C.S.: 621399

Metropolitan Methodist Hospital, a Methodist Hospital facility (2)
1310 McCullough Ave, San Antonio, TX 78212
Tel.: (210) 757-2200
Web Site: https://sahealth.com
Health Care Srvices
N.A.I.C.S.: 621610
Tamara Peavy (Chief Nursing Officer)

Northeast Methodist Hospital (2)
12412 Judson Rd, Live Oak, TX 78233
Tel.: (210) 757-7000
Web Site: https://www.joinmethodist.com
Health Care Srvices
N.A.I.C.S.: 621399

Methodist Hospital (1)
7700 Floyd Curl Dr, San Antonio, TX 78229
Tel.: (210) 575-4000
General Medical & Surgical Services
N.A.I.C.S.: 622110

Methodist Physician Practices, PLLC (1)
1139 E Sonterra Blvd Ste 240A, San Antonio, TX 78258-4349
Tel.: (210) 404-9950
Web Site:
    https://methodistphysicianpractices.com
General Medical & Surgical Services
N.A.I.C.S.: 622110

Miami Lakes Surgery Center, Ltd. (1)
15501 NW 67th Ave Ste 200, Miami Lakes, FL 33014
Tel.: (305) 820-2900
Web Site:
    https://www.miamilakessurgerycenter.com
Health Care Srvices
N.A.I.C.S.: 621399

Miami-Dade Cardiology Consultants, LLC (1)
3801 Biscayne Blvd Ste 300, Miami, FL 33137
Tel.: (305) 571-0620
Web Site: http://www.micc.com
Health Care Srvices
N.A.I.C.S.: 621399

Mid-America Surgery Center, LLC (1)
5525 W 119th St, Leawood, KS 66209
Tel.: (913) 906-0855
Health Care & Allied Services
N.A.I.C.S.: 621999

Mid-America Surgery Institute, LLC (1)
5525 W 119th St Ste 100, Overland Park, KS 66209
Tel.: (913) 906-0855

Web Site: https://midamericasurgery.com
General Medical & Surgical Services
N.A.I.C.S.: 622110

MidAmerica Division, Inc. (1)
903 E 104th St Ste 500, Kansas City, MO
64131
Tel.: (816) 508-4000
Web Site: http://www.hcamidamerica.com
Emp.: 5,000
Health Care Srvices
N.A.I.C.S.: 621399

MidAmerica Oncology, LLC (1)
1100 Dr Martin L King Jr Blvd Ste 800,
Nashville, TN 37203
Tel.: (615) 329-7274
Web Site: https://sarahcannon.com
General Medical & Surgical Services
N.A.I.C.S.: 622110

MidAmerica Oncology, LLC (1)
250 25th Ave N, Nashville, TN 37203-1632
Tel.: (615) 846-1107
General Medical & Surgical Services
N.A.I.C.S.: 622110

**Middle Tennessee Neurology
LLC** (1)
300 StoneCrest Blvd Ste 365, Smyrna, TN
37167
Tel.: (615) 768-4300
Web Site: http://tristarmedgroup.com
Neurological Hospital Operating Services
N.A.I.C.S.: 622310

**Midwest Cardiovascular & Thoracic
Surgeons of Kansas, LLC** (1)
5701 W 119th St Ste 430, Overland Park,
KS 66209
Tel.: (913) 906-0833
Health Care & Allied Services
N.A.I.C.S.: 621999
Amanda Carwford (Gen Mgr)

**Midwest Cardiovascular & Thoracic
Surgery, LLC** (1)
1515 W Truman Rd, Independence, MO
64050
Tel.: (816) 523-7088
Health Care & Allied Services
N.A.I.C.S.: 621999

**Midwest Cardiovascular & Thoracic
Surgery, LLC** (1)
6400 Prospect Ave Ste 382, Kansas City,
MO 64132-4144
Tel.: (816) 333-7135
Physicians Health Services
N.A.I.C.S.: 621111

Midwest Division - ACH, LLC (1)
3066 N Kentucky St, Iola, KS 66749-3505
Tel.: (620) 365-1000
Web Site:
     http://www.allencountyregional.com
Emp.: 165
Health Care Srvices
N.A.I.C.S.: 621399

Midwest Division - OPRMC, LLC (1)
10500 Quivira Rd, Overland Park, KS
66215
Tel.: (913) 541-5000
Web Site: http://hcamidwest.com
Health Care Srvices
N.A.I.C.S.: 621399
John Heurtin (CFO)
Nan Rick (Chief Nursing Officer)
Larry Watts (Chief Medical Officer)
Patrick Rafferty (COO)
Matt Sogard (CEO)

Subsidiary (Domestic):

**Overland Park Regional Medical
Center** (2)
10500 Quivira Rd, Overland Park, KS
66215
Tel.: (913) 541-5000
Web Site: https://careers.hcahealthcare.com
Emp.: 500
Health Care Srvices
N.A.I.C.S.: 621399

Affiliate (Domestic):

Surgicenter of Johnson County (3)
8800 Ballentine, Overland Park, KS 66214
Tel.: (913) 894-4050

Web Site: https://www.surgicenterjc.com
General Medical & Surgical Hospitals
N.A.I.C.S.: 622110

**Midwest Heart & Vascular Specialists,
LLC** (1)
5100 W 110th St 2nd Fl, Overland Park, KS
66211
Tel.: (913) 253-3000
Web Site:
     https://midwestheartandvascular.com
Health Care Srvices
N.A.I.C.S.: 621399

Midwest Holdings, Inc. (1)
2900 S 70th St Ste 400, Lincoln, NE 68506
Tel.: (402) 817-5701
Web Site: https://www.midwestholding.com
General Medical & Surgical Services
N.A.I.C.S.: 622110

**Midwest Infectious Disease Special-
ists, LLC** (1)
19550 E 39th St Ste 205, Independence,
MO 64057
Tel.: (816) 254-2552
Emp.: 6
Healthcare Support Services
N.A.I.C.S.: 621111
Kimberly Teen (Mgr)

**Midwest Metropolitan Physicians
Group, LLC** (1)
2340 E Mayer Bld 2 Ste 640, Kansas City,
MO 64132
Tel.: (816) 523-7000
Emp.: 15
General Medical & Surgical Services
N.A.I.C.S.: 622110
Jamie Cox (Office Mgr)

**Midwest Oncology Associates,
LLC** (1)
2316 E Meyer Blvd 1 Cancer W, Kansas
City, MO 64132-1136
Tel.: (816) 276-4700
General Medical & Surgical Services
N.A.I.C.S.: 622110

Mission Health Partners, Inc. (1)
1940 Hendersonville Rd, Asheville, NC
28803
Tel.: (828) 213-3250
Web Site:
     http://www.missionhealthpartners.org
Healtcare Services
N.A.I.C.S.: 621999

Mobile Heartbeat, Llc (1)
51 Sawyer Rd Ste 320, Waltham, MA
02453
Tel.: (781) 238-0000
Web Site: https://www.mobileheartbeat.com
Health Care Srvices
N.A.I.C.S.: 621491
Ron Remy (CEO)
Mike Detjen (COO)
Saji Aravind (CTO)
Annabaker Garber (Chief Clinical Officer)

Montgomery Cancer Center, LLC (1)
4145 Carmichael Rd, Montgomery, AL
36106
Tel.: (334) 273-7000
Web Site:
     http://www.montgomerycancercenter.com
Health Care Srvices
N.A.I.C.S.: 621111

**Montgomery Regional Hospital,
Inc.** (1)
3700 S Main St, Blacksburg, VA 24060
Tel.: (540) 776-4000
Web Site: http://lewisgale.com
Sales Range: $25-49.9 Million
Emp.: 500
Hospital
N.A.I.C.S.: 622110
Carol Ballard (Vice Chm)
Rachael Stanton (CFO)
Sarah Tavenner (COO)
Devin LaPuasa (Chief Nursing Officer)
Kelly Oaks (Vice Chm)

Subsidiary (Domestic):

LewisGale Hospital Montgomery (2)
3700 S Main St, Blacksburg, VA 24060
Tel.: (540) 951-1111
Web Site: https://www.hcavirginia.com

General Medical Care Services
N.A.I.C.S.: 622110

**Montgomery Surgery Associates,
LLC** (1)
809 Davis St, Blacksburg, VA 24060
Tel.: (540) 961-1590
Emp.: 5
Health Care Srvices
N.A.I.C.S.: 621111
Destiny Coneley (Gen Mgr)

Mountain Division - CVH, LLC (1)
2380 N 400 E Ste 100, Logan, UT 84341
Tel.: (435) 713-9700
Web Site:
     http://www.cachevalleyhospital.com
Emp.: 250
Health Care Srvices
N.A.I.C.S.: 621610
Jamie Andrus (Chm)
Marion Bishop (Vice Chm)

Mountain View Hospital, Inc. (1)
1000 E 100 N, Payson, UT 84651
Tel.: (801) 465-7000
Web Site: http://mountainstar.com
General Medical Care Services
N.A.I.C.S.: 622110

Subsidiary (Domestic):

Mountain View Hospital (2)
3100 N Tenaya Way, Las Vegas, NV 89128
Tel.: (702) 962-5000
Web Site: https://www.mountainview-
     hospital.com
Health Care Srvices
N.A.I.C.S.: 621610
Jeremy Bradshaw (CEO)
Matthew Cova (COO)
Carl H. James (CFO)
Harsha Dave (VP-Quality-Risk)
Chris Marlin (VP-Human Resources)
Jennifer McDonnell (Dir-Public Relations-
Communications)

**Mountain West Surgery Center,
LLC** (1)
1551 S Renaissance Towne Dr Ste 200,
Bountiful, UT 84010
Tel.: (801) 383-1111
Web Site:
     http://www.mountainwestsurgicalcen
     ter.com
Medical Support Services
N.A.I.C.S.: 621111

**MountainStar Behavioral Health,
LLC** (1)
630 Medical Dr, Bountiful, UT 84010-4908
Tel.: (801) 299-2186
Health Care Srvices
N.A.I.C.S.: 621111

**MountainStar Cardiology St. Marks,
LLC** (1)
1160 E 3900 S Ste 2000, Salt Lake City,
UT 84124
Tel.: (801) 266-3418
General Medical & Surgical Services
N.A.I.C.S.: 622110

**MountainStar Care Partners ACO,
LLC** (1)
60 E S Temple St 1900, Salt Lake City, UT
84111
Tel.: (801) 568-5982
Health Care Srvices
N.A.I.C.S.: 621610

**MountainStar Care Partners,
LLC** (1)
60 E S Temple St Ste 1900, Salt Lake City,
UT 84111
Tel.: (801) 715-4152
Web Site: https://www.mountainstar.com
Health Care Srvices
N.A.I.C.S.: 621610

**MountainStar Intensivist Services,
LLC** (1)
750 W 800 N, Orem, UT 84057
Tel.: (801) 714-6387
General Medical & Surgical Services
N.A.I.C.S.: 622110

**MountainStar Medical Group - Cache
Valley, LLC** (1)
2380 N 400 E Ste A, Logan, UT 84341

Tel.: (435) 713-1300
Web Site:
     https://mountainstarmedicalgroup.com
General Medical & Surgical services
N.A.I.C.S.: 622110

**MountainStar Medical Group Neuro-
surgery - St. Marks, LLC** (1)
1200 E 3900 S Ste 4-E, Salt Lake City, UT
84124-1377
Tel.: (801) 261-8507
General Medical & Surgical Services
N.A.I.C.S.: 622110

**MountainStar Specialty Services,
LLC** (1)
6985 S Union Park Ctr Ste 500, Cotton-
wood Heights, UT 84047
Tel.: (801) 568-5999
Web Site: http://mountainstar.com
Health Care Srvices
N.A.I.C.S.: 621610

MountainStar Urgent Care, LLC (1)
8846 S Redwood Rd Ste E-121, West Jor-
dan, UT 84088
Tel.: (801) 569-1999
Web Site: http://www.jordanfamily.com
General Medical & Surgical Services
N.A.I.C.S.: 622110

**Mountainstar Cardiovascular Ser-
vices, LLC** (1)
5405 S 500 E Ste 200, Ogden, UT 84405
Tel.: (801) 476-6900
Web Site: http://heartsurgeryutah.com
Emp.: 5
Medical Support Services
N.A.I.C.S.: 621111

**Mountainstar Medical Group Timpa-
nogos Specialty Care, Llc** (1)
3340 N Center St, Lehi, UT 84043
Tel.: (801) 653-2757
Health Care Srvices
N.A.I.C.S.: 621491

**Mountainstar Ogden Pediatrics,
LLC** (1)
5405 S 500 E Ste 205, Ogden, UT 84405
Tel.: (801) 479-0174
Web Site:
     http://www.mountainstarpediatrics.com
Emp.: 10
Medical Support Services
N.A.I.C.S.: 621111

Mountainview Hospital (1)
3100 N Tenaya Way, Las Vegas, NV 89128
Tel.: (702) 962-5000
Web Site: https://www.mountainview-
     hospital.com
Sales Range: $50-74.9 Million
Emp.: 2,150
Hospital
N.A.I.C.S.: 622110
Jeremy S. Bradshaw (CEO)
Matthew Cova (COO)
Carl H. James (CFO)
Harsha Dave (VP-Quality-Risk)
Chris Marlin (VP-Human Resources)
Jennifer McDonnell (Dir-Public Relations-
Communications)

**Mountainview Hospital (Payson
UT)** (1)
1000 E 100 N, Payson, UT 84651
Tel.: (801) 465-7000
Web Site: https://mountainstar.com
Sales Range: $25-49.9 Million
Emp.: 450
General Medical & Surgical Hospitals
N.A.I.C.S.: 622110
Kevin R. Johnson (CEO)
Nathan Black (Dir-Communications)
Audrey Glasby (Dir-Public Relations)
Brittany Glas (Dir-Communications)

Mt. Ogden Surgical Center (1)
4364 Washington Blvd, Ogden, UT 84403
Tel.: (801) 479-4470
Web Site: https://www.mtogdensurgery.com
Surgical Care Services
N.A.I.C.S.: 621493

**Mt. Ogden Utah Surgical Center,
LLC** (1)
4364 Washington Blvd, Ogden, UT 84403
Tel.: (801) 479-4470
Web Site: https://mtogdensurgery.com

HCA Healthcare, Inc.—(Continued)

General Medical & Surgical Services
N.A.I.C.S.: 622110

**National Patient Account Services,
Inc.** (1)
3600 Harwood Rd Ste B, Bedford, TX
76021
Tel.: (817) 358-8000
Web Site: http://www.npasweb.com
General Medical & Surgical Services
N.A.I.C.S.: 622110

Navarre Family Care, LLC (1)
1905 Andorra St, Navarre, FL 32566
Tel.: (850) 936-8048
General Medical & Surgical Hospitals
N.A.I.C.S.: 622110

Neuro Texas, PLLC (1)
5625 Eiger Rd Ste 150, Austin, TX 78735
Tel.: (512) 654-4550
Web Site: https://www.neurotexas.net
Emp.: 10
Neurological Hospital Operating Services
N.A.I.C.S.: 622310

**Neurological Specialists of McKinney,
PLLC** (1)
4510 Medical Ctr Dr Ste 300, McKinney, TX
75069-1650
Tel.: (214) 544-1300
Neurological Hospital Operating Services
N.A.I.C.S.: 622310

**Neuroscience Associates of Kansas
City, LLC** (1)
10550 Quivira Rd Ste 400, Overland Park,
KS 66215
Tel.: (913) 340-7980
Web Site: https://mymidwestphysician.com
Health Care Srvices
N.A.I.C.S.: 621399

Neurosurgery Atlanta, Llc (1)
1700 Tree Ln Ste 470, Snellville, GA 30078
Tel.: (770) 809-3291
Health Care Srvices
N.A.I.C.S.: 621491

Neurosurgery Of Kingwood, Pllc (1)
22999 Hwy 59 N Ste 220, Kingwood, TX
77339
Tel.: (281) 312-6457
Health Care Srvices
N.A.I.C.S.: 621491

**Neurosurgical Associates of North
Texas, PLLC** (1)
909 9th Ave Ste 201, Fort Worth, TX 76104
Tel.: (817) 870-5094
Web Site:
http://www.neurosurgicalassociatesof
ntx.com
Neurological Hospital Operating Services
N.A.I.C.S.: 622310

**Neurosurgical Specialists of El Paso,
PLLC** (1)
1700 N Oregon Ste 710, El Paso, TX
79902
Tel.: (915) 351-1444
Web Site:
https://neurosurgicalspecialistsofel
paso.com
Emp.: 15
Neurological Hospital Operating Services
N.A.I.C.S.: 622310

**Neurosurgical Specialists of North
Texas, PLLC** (1)
7777 Forest Ln Ste A337, Dallas, TX
75230-2584
Tel.: (972) 566-5200
Web Site:
http://www.dallasbrainandspine.com
Emp.: 15
Neurological Hospital Operating Services
N.A.I.C.S.: 622310

**New Port Richey Surgery Center at
Trinity** (1)
9332 SR 54 Ste 100, Trinity, FL 34655
Tel.: (727) 848-0446
Web Site: https://www.nprsurgerycenter.com
General Medical & Surgical services
N.A.I.C.S.: 622110

Niceville Family Practice, LLC (1)

4400 State Hwy 20 E Ste 201, Niceville, FL
32578
Tel.: (850) 897-3678
Web Site:
http://www.nicevillefamilypractice.com
Health Care Srvices
N.A.I.C.S.: 621399

North Austin Surgery Center (1)
12201 Renfert Way Ste 120, Austin, TX
78758
Tel.: (512) 832-9088
Web Site:
http://www.stdavidssurgerycenters.com
Emp.: 50
General Medical & Surgical services
N.A.I.C.S.: 622110

**North Central Methodist ASC,
L.P.** (1)
19010 Stone Oak Pkwy, San Antonio, TX
78258
Tel.: (210) 575-5200
Web Site:
http://www.methodistambulatorysurgery
centers.com
Health Care Srvices
N.A.I.C.S.: 621399

North County Surgicenter (1)
4000 Burns Rd, Palm Beach Gardens, FL
33410
Tel.: (561) 626-6446
Web Site:
https://www.northcountysurgicenter.com
Health Care Srvices
N.A.I.C.S.: 621399
Lucas Buchholz (Bus Mgr)

**North Florida Cancer Center Lake
City, LLC** (1)
795 State Rd 47, Lake City, FL 32025
Tel.: (386) 758-7822
Web Site:
http://www.cancercenterlakecity.com
Emp.: 8
Medical & Surgical Hospital Services
N.A.I.C.S.: 622110

North Florida Endoscopy Center (1)
6500 W Newberry Rd, Gainesville, FL
32605
Tel.: (352) 333-5900
Web Site:
http://www.northfloridaendoscopycen
ter.com
Health Care Srvices
N.A.I.C.S.: 621399

North Florida Endoscopy Center (1)
6400 W Newberry Rd Ste 201, Gainesville,
FL 32605
Tel.: (352) 333-5900
Web Site:
https://northfloridaendoscopycenter.com
General Medical & Surgical Services
N.A.I.C.S.: 622110

**North Florida Outpatient Imaging
Center, Ltd.** (1)
6605 NW 9th Blvd, Gainesville, FL 32605
Tel.: (352) 333-4703
General Medical & Surgical Services
N.A.I.C.S.: 622110

**North Florida Radiation Oncology,
LLC** (1)
6420 W Newberry Rd, Gainesville, FL
32605
Tel.: (352) 333-5840
Web Site: http://www.cancergainesville.com
Emp.: 30
Medical & Surgical Hospital Services
N.A.I.C.S.: 622110

**North Florida Regional Medical Cen-
ter, Inc.** (1)
6500 W Newberry Rd, Gainesville, FL
32605-4309
Tel.: (352) 333-4000
Web Site: http://www.nfrmc.com
Acute Care Hospital
N.A.I.C.S.: 622110

**North Florida Regional Otolaryngol-
ogy, LLC** (1)
6500 W Newberry Rd, Gainesville, FL
32605-6605
Tel.: (352) 333-4000
Web Site: http://www.nfrmc.com

Health Care Srvices
N.A.I.C.S.: 621399

**North Florida Surgical Associates,
LLC** (1)
1121 NW 64th Ter Ste B, Gainesville, FL
32605
Tel.: (352) 331-2010
General Medical & Surgical Services
N.A.I.C.S.: 622110

**North Florida Surgical Associates,
LLC** (1)
1121 NW 64th Ter Ste A, Gainesville, FL
32605-4243
Tel.: (352) 331-3583
Emp.: 13
General Medical & Surgical Services
N.A.I.C.S.: 622110
Mickey Pickler (VP)
Jen Hall (Gen Mgr)

North Hills Surgicare, L.P. (1)
4375 Booth Calloway Rd St 100, North
Richland Hills, TX 76180-8359
Tel.: (817) 255-1010
Web Site: http://www.texaspedi.com
Surgical Care Services
N.A.I.C.S.: 621493

**North Miami Beach Surgery Center
Limited Partnership** (1)
120 NE 167th St, North Miami Beach, FL
33162
Tel.: (305) 952-2000
Web Site:
http://www.northmiamibeachsurgical.com
Medical & Surgical Hospital Services
N.A.I.C.S.: 622110

**North Miami Beach Surgical Center,
LLC** (1)
120 NE 167th St, North Miami Beach, FL
33162
Tel.: (305) 952-2000
Web Site:
https://northmiamibeachsurgical.com
General Medical & Surgical Services
N.A.I.C.S.: 622110

North Suburban Medical Center (1)
9191 Grant St, Thornton, CO 80229
Tel.: (303) 451-7800
Web Site: https://healthonecares.com
Sales Range: $50-74.9 Million
Emp.: 843
Hospital
N.A.I.C.S.: 622110

North Texas - MCA, LLC (1)
3101 N Tarrant Pkwy, Fort Worth, TX 76177
Tel.: (817) 639-1000
Web Site:
http://www.medicalcityalliance.com
Emp.: 230
Health Care Srvices
N.A.I.C.S.: 621399

Subsidiary (Domestic):

Medical Center Alliance (2)
3101 N Tarrant Pkwy, Fort Worth, TX 76177
Tel.: (817) 639-1000
Emp.: 492
Health Care Srvices
N.A.I.C.S.: 621610

**North Texas Heart Surgery Center,
PLLC** (1)
7777 Forest Ln Ste A307, Dallas, TX
75230-2505
Tel.: (972) 566-4866
Web Site:
http://www.southwestcardiotherapicsur
geon.com
Emp.: 15
General Medical & Surgical Services
N.A.I.C.S.: 622110

**North Texas Internal Medicine Spe-
cialists, PLLC** (1)
3105 W 15th St Ste B, Plano, TX 75075
Tel.: (214) 216-6921
Web Site: https://www.ntims.net
General Medical & Surgical Services
N.A.I.C.S.: 622110

North Texas Medical Center, Inc. (1)
1900 Hospital Blvd, Gainesville, TX 76240
Tel.: (940) 665-1751

Web Site: https://ntmconline.net
General Medical & Surgical Services
N.A.I.C.S.: 622110

**North Texas Pulmonary Critical Care,
PLLC** (1)
475 W Elm St Ste 100, Lewisville, TX
75057
Tel.: (214) 222-3571
Web Site:
https://www.ntxpulmonarycriticalcare.com
Surgical Hospital Services
N.A.I.C.S.: 622110

**North Texas Stroke Center,
PLLC** (1)
7777 Forrest Ln Ste C-300, Dallas, TX
75230-2505
Tel.: (972) 566-5146
Health Insurance Services
N.A.I.C.S.: 524114

North Transfer Center, LLC (1)
3625 University Blvd S, Jacksonville, FL
32216
Tel.: (904) 390-6000
Health Care Srvices
N.A.I.C.S.: 621399

**Northeast Methodist Surgicare,
Ltd.** (1)
12702 IH 35 N, Live Oak, TX 78233-2609
Tel.: (210) 575-5700
General Medical & Surgical Services
N.A.I.C.S.: 622110

Northeast PHO, Inc. (1)
1 Park Plz, Nashville, TN 37203
Tel.: (615) 344-9551
Medical & Surgical Hospital Services
N.A.I.C.S.: 622110

**Northern Utah Healthcare
Corporation** (1)
1200 E 3900 S, Salt Lake City, UT 84124
Tel.: (801) 268-7111
General Medical Care Services
N.A.I.C.S.: 622110

Northern Utah Imaging, LLC (1)
3738 S 900 E, Salt Lake City, UT 84106-
1913
Tel.: (801) 313-1955
General Medical & Surgical Services
N.A.I.C.S.: 622110

**Northside Hospital and Heart
Institute** (1)
6000 49th St N, Saint Petersburg, FL 33709
Tel.: (727) 521-4411
Web Site: http://www.northsidehospital.com
Sales Range: $75-99.9 Million
Emp.: 014
Hospital Operator
N.A.I.C.S.: 622110
Valerie Powell-Stafford (CEO)
Peter Kennedy (COO)
Helena Walo (Chief Nursing Officer)
Kristy Redd-Hachey (CFO)
Danny Cox (VP-Quality-Patient Safety)
Tiffani Smith (VP-Human Resources)
Janice K. Wittman (Chm)
Ravi Chari (Pres)
Tom Zweng (Chief Medical Officer)

**Northwest Florida Multispecialty Phy-
sicians, LLC** (1)
1032 Mar Walt Dr Ste 250, Fort Walton
Beach, FL 32547-6661
Tel.: (850) 863-3463
General Medical & Surgical Services
N.A.I.C.S.: 622110

**Northwest Florida Primary Care,
LLC** (1)
4418 Commons Dr E, Destin, FL 32541-
8405
Tel.: (850) 650-3148
Emp.: 4
General Medical & Surgical Services
N.A.I.C.S.: 622110
Christin Chandler (Office Mgr)

Notami Hospitals of Florida, Inc. (1)
340 NW Commerce Dr, Lake City, FL
32055
Tel.: (386) 719-9000
General Medical & Surgical Services
N.A.I.C.S.: 622110

Notami, LLC (1)
1 Park Plz, Nashville, TN 37203
Tel.: (615) 344-2000
Emp.: 55
General Medical & Surgical Services
N.A.I.C.S.: 622110

Nuclear Diagnosis, Inc. (1)
3003 E Chestnut Expressway Ste 2007,
Springfield, MO 65802
Tel.: (417) 831-6520
Emp.: 10
Medical Laboratory Services
N.A.I.C.S.: 621511

OU Medical Center (1)
1200 Everett Dr Rm 8305, Oklahoma City,
OK 73104
Tel.: (405) 271-5211
Web Site: http://www.oumedicine.com
Sales Range: $10-24.9 Million
Emp.: 15
Respiratory Hospital
N.A.I.C.S.: 622110

OU Medical Center Edmond (1)
1 S Bryant Ave, Edmond, OK 73034
Tel.: (405) 341-6100
Web Site: https://www.ouhealth.com
Sales Range: $25-49.9 Million
Emp.: 400
Hospital
N.A.I.C.S.: 622110

Oak Hill Hospital (1)
11375 Cortez Blvd, Brooksville, FL 34613
Tel.: (352) 596-6632
Web Site: http://www.oakhillhospital.com
Emp.: 1,696
Hospital
N.A.I.C.S.: 622110
Mickey Smith (CEO)
Leanne Salazar (Chief Nursing Officer)
Edward P. Nast (Chief Medical Officer)
Jeremy Gallman (COO)
Chris Green (CFO)
David Slovut (Chief Medical Officer)
Austin Brown (VP-Operations)
Rob Foreman (VP)
Lacey Rains (VP-Quality)
Deborah H. Tracy (Chm)
Randy Woodruff (Vice Chm)
Ali Vaziri (Chm)
Jennifer Ward (Treas & Sec)

**Oakwood Surgery Center, Ltd.,
LLP** (1)
16030 Park Valley Dr 100, Round Rock, TX
78681-4018
Tel.: (512) 246-8777
Web Site:
   http://www.oakwoodsurgerycenter.com
Emp.: 50
Offices of Physician Services
N.A.I.C.S.: 621111

**Ocala Health Imaging Services,
LLC** (1)
2300 SE 17th St Bldg 800, Ocala, FL
34471
Tel.: (352) 867-9606
Emp.: 50
Health Care Srvices
N.A.I.C.S.: 622110
Randy Mcvay (CEO)

**Ocala Health Surgical Group,
LLC** (1)
4600 SW 46th Ct Ste 340, Ocala, FL 34474
Tel.: (352) 291-0239
Web Site:
   http://ocalahealthsurgicalgroup.com
General Medical & Surgical Services
N.A.I.C.S.: 622110

Ocala Health Trauma, LLC (1)
1431 SW 1st Ave, Ocala, FL 34471
Tel.: (352) 401-1000
Web Site:
   http://www.ocalahealthsystem.com
Health Care Srvices
N.A.I.C.S.: 621399

Ocala Regional Medical Center (1)
1431 SW 1st Ave, Ocala, FL 34471-4000
Tel.: (352) 401-1000
Web Site:
   http://www.ocalahealthsystem.com
Sales Range: $75-99.9 Million
Emp.: 2,583
Hospital

N.A.I.C.S.: 622110

**Occupational and Family Medicine of
South Texas** (1)
4001 Preston Ave, Pasadena, TX 77505-
2019
Tel.: (281) 249-2273
Emp.: 1,200
General Medical & Surgical Services
N.A.I.C.S.: 622110

**Ogden Internal Medicine & Urology,
LLC** (1)
5405 S 500 E Ste 203, Ogden, UT 84405
Tel.: (801) 475-8600
Web Site:
   http://mountainstarmedicalgroup.com
Medical Support Services
N.A.I.C.S.: 621111

Ogden Regional Medical Center (1)
5475 S 500 E, Ogden, UT 84405
Tel.: (801) 479-2111
Web Site: https://mountainstar.com
Sales Range: $50-74.9 Million
Emp.: 1,000
Hospital
N.A.I.C.S.: 622110

Okaloosa Hospital, Inc. (1)
2190 Hwy 85 N, Niceville, FL 32578
Tel.: (850) 678-4131
Web Site: http://www.tchospital.com
Emp.: 330
Health Care Srvices
N.A.I.C.S.: 621399

Oklahoma Surgicare, Inc. (1)
4317 W Memorial Rd, Oklahoma City, OK
73134
Tel.: (405) 755-6240
Web Site: https://www.oksurgicare.com
Health Care Srvices
N.A.I.C.S.: 621610

**Orange Park Medical Center,
Inc.** (1)
2001 Kingsley Ave, Orange Park, FL 32073
Tel.: (904) 639-8500
Web Site: http://www.opmedical.com
Sales Range: $75-99.9 Million
Hospital
N.A.I.C.S.: 622110
Lisa Valentine (Pres & CEO)
Michael Nordness (COO)
Bradley Shumaker (Chief Medical Officer)
Chris Glenn (CFO)
Joseph Warburton (VP-Operations)
Brad Coburn (VP-Human Resources)
Carrie Turansky (Dir-Public Relations-
Communications)
Pete Long-Innes (COO)
Emily Lloyd (CFO)
Kathy Neely (Chief Nursing Officer)

Orange Park Surgery Center (1)
2050 Professional Ctr Dr, Orange Park, FL
32073-4461
Tel.: (904) 272-2550
Web Site:
   http://www.orangeparksurgerycenter.com
Health Care Srvices
N.A.I.C.S.: 621399

**Orlando Outpatient Surgical Center,
Inc.** (1)
1736 33rd St, Orlando, FL 32839
Tel.: (407) 385-1555
Web Site:
   https://www.orlandooutpatientasc.com
General Medical & Surgical Services
N.A.I.C.S.: 622110

Orthopedics Specialists, LLC (1)
110 N Robinson St Ste 103, Richmond, VA
23220
Tel.: (804) 254-9751
Medical & Surgical Hospital Services
N.A.I.C.S.: 622110

**Osceola Regional Medical
Center** (1)
700 W Oak St, Kissimmee, FL 34741
Tel.: (407) 846-2266
Web Site: http://www.osceolaregional.com
Sales Range: $50-74.9 Million
Emp.: 2,163
Hospital
N.A.I.C.S.: 622110

Carrie Biggar (CFO)
Davide Carbone (CEO)
Steve Gordon (COO)
Barbara Watson (Chief Nursing Officer)
Ross Taylor (Chief Medical Officer)

**Osceola Surgical Associates,
LLC** (1)
320 W Bass St Ste 320, Kissimmee, FL
34741
Tel.: (407) 846-3166
General Medical & Surgical Services
N.A.I.C.S.: 622110

**Osceola Surgical Associates,
LLC** (1)
320 W Bass St Ste 320, Kissimmee, FL
34741
Tel.: (407) 846-3166
Web Site:
   https://www.hcafloridaphysicians.com
Health Care Srvices
N.A.I.C.S.: 621399

**Our Lady of Lourdes Women's &
Children's Hospital** (1)
4600 Ambassador Caffrey Pkwy, Lafayette,
LA 70508
Tel.: (337) 470-5500
Web Site: https://lourdesrmc.com
Hospital Services
N.A.I.C.S.: 622310
Bryan Lee (CEO)
Christa V. Billeaud (Vice Chm)
Matthew B. Boudreaux (Pres)
Bryan J. Hanks (Chm)
Edward J. Krampe (Treas & Sec)
Bradley Dowden (VP)
Christopher Lagraize (Chm)
Thad Bourque (Vice Chm-Surgery)
Eric Thomassee (Chm)
Michael Liu (Vice Chm-Medicine)
Deiadra Garrett (Chm)
Derek Baumbouree (Vice Chm-Pediatrics)
Francis Cardinale (Chm)
Russell Phelps (Vice Chm-
Obstetrics,Gynecology)
Paul Billeaud (Dir)
Justin Bordelon (Dir)
R. Bruce Williams (Dir)

**Outpatient Surgical Services,
Ltd.** (1)
301 NW 82nd Ave, Plantation, FL 33324
Tel.: (954) 693-8600
Web Site: https://ossplantation.com
General Medical & Surgical Services
N.A.I.C.S.: 622110

**Overland Park Medical Specialists,
LLC** (1)
10500 Quivira Rd, Overland Park, KS
66215
Tel.: (913) 541-5000
Web Site: http://www.oprmc.com
Health Care Srvices
N.A.I.C.S.: 621399
Matt Sogard (CEO)
Patrick Rafferty (COO)
Larry Watts (CMO)
Nan Rick (Chief Nursing Officer)
John Heurtin (CFO)

Overland Park Orthopedics, LLC (1)
12200 W 106th St Ste 400, Overland Park,
KS 66215
Tel.: (913) 541-5000
Web Site:
   https://www.overlandparkorthopedics.com
Health Care Srvices
N.A.I.C.S.: 621399

Overland Park Surgery Center (1)
10601 Quivira Rd, Overland Park, KS
66215
Tel.: (913) 894-7260
Web Site: https://www.opsurgerycenter.com
Emp.: 60
Health Care Srvices
N.A.I.C.S.: 621399

**Overland Park Surgical Specialties,
LLC** (1)
10550 Quivira Rd, Overland Park, KS
66215
Tel.: (913) 227-0501
General Medical & Surgical Services
N.A.I.C.S.: 622110

Oviedo Medical Center, LLC (1)

8300 Red Bug Lake Rd, Oviedo, FL 32765
Tel.: (407) 890-2273
Web Site:
   https://www.hcafloridahealthcare.com
Health Care Srvices
N.A.I.C.S.: 621399

PMM, Inc. (1)
25811 Frederick Rd, Clarksburg, MD 20871
Tel.: (301) 770-1516
Surgical Hospital Services
N.A.I.C.S.: 622110

**Pacific Partners Management Ser-
vices, Inc.** (1)
1051 E Hillsdale Blvd Ste 750, Foster City,
CA 94404
Tel.: (650) 358-5800
Web Site: https://www.ppmsi.com
Health Care Srvices
N.A.I.C.S.: 621491
Kersten Kraft (Chief Medical Officer)
Marsha Bluto (VP-)
Don Thompson (CFO)

Palace Gate Practice Limited (1)
The Universal Building 364 Kensington High
Street, London, W14 8NS, United Kingdom
Tel.: (44) 2072445800
Web Site:
   https://www.palacegatepractice.com
Medical Practice Services
N.A.I.C.S.: 621399

**Palm Beach Hospitalists Program,
LLC** (1)
5301 S Congress Ave, Atlantis, FL 33462-
1149
Tel.: (561) 588-4844
General Medical & Surgical Services
N.A.I.C.S.: 622110

Palms West Hospital (1)
13001 Southern Blvd, Loxahatchee, FL
33470
Tel.: (561) 798-3300
Web Site:
   http://www.palmswesthospital.com
Sales Range: $75-99.9 Million
Emp.: 900
Hospital
N.A.I.C.S.: 622110

Palms West Surgicenter (1)
12961 Palms West Dr, Loxahatchee, FL
33470
Tel.: (561) 793-0437
Web Site:
   https://www.palmswestsurgicenter.com
Emp.: 40
Health Care & Allied Services
N.A.I.C.S.: 621999

Palms of Pasadena Hospital (1)
1501 Pasadena Ave, Saint Petersburg, FL
33707
Tel.: (727) 381-1000
Web Site: http://www.palmspasadena.com
Emp.: 530
Health Care Srvices
N.A.I.C.S.: 621399
Jake Fisher (CEO)
Mike Irvin (CFO)

**Paragon Surgery Centers of Texas,
Inc.** (1)
1101 Matlock Rd, Mansfield, TX 76063
Tel.: (817) 473-2120
Web Site: https://paragonsurgerycenter.com
General Medical & Surgical Services
N.A.I.C.S.: 622110

**Parallon Business Solutions,
LLC** (1)
6640 Carothers Pkwy, Franklin, TN 37067
Tel.: (615) 807-8000
Web Site: http://www.parallon.net
Sales Range: $1-4.9 Billion
Emp.: 600
General Medical & Surgical Services
N.A.I.C.S.: 622110

Subsidiary (Domestic):

**HealthTrust Purchasing Group,
L.P.** (2)
155 Franklin Rd Ste 400, Brentwood, TN
37027
Tel.: (615) 344-3000
Web Site: http://www.healthtrustpg.com

HCA Healthcare, Inc.—(Continued)

General Medical & Surgical Services
N.A.I.C.S.: 622110
John Young (Chief Medical Officer)
Michael Seestedt (CIO)
Rob Arreola (Chief Legal Officer)
Jocelyn Bradshaw (Sr VP-Supply Chain &)
Allen Wright (Sr VP-)
David Osborn (Sr VP-Account Management & Sales)
Lisa Garman (VP-Marketing & Communications)
Jennie Hanson (VP-Human Resources)
Cody King (Chief Product Officer)
Rich Philbrick (CEO)
Ron Powell (CFO)

Parallon Workforce Management Solutions, LLC (2)
6640 Carothers Pkwy, Franklin, TN 37067
Tel.: (615) 807-8000
Web Site: http://www.parallon.com
Emp.: 800
Healthcare Staffing & Labor Management Services
N.A.I.C.S.: 541612

The Outsource Group, Inc. (2)
3 City Pl Dr Ste 690, Saint Louis, MO 63141
Tel.: (314) 692-6500
Web Site:
   http://www.theoutsourcegroup.com
Emp.: 1,420
Medical Business Outsourcing & Billing Services
N.A.I.C.S.: 561499

Parallon Technology Solutions, LLC (1)
1100 Dr Martin L King Jr Blvd Ste 1700, Nashville, TN 37203
Web Site: https://cerecore.net
Information Services
N.A.I.C.S.: 519290

Park Central Surgical Center, Ltd. (1)
12200 Park Central Dr 3rd Fl, Dallas, TX 75251
Tel.: (972) 661-0505
Web Site:
   http://www.parkcentralsurgicalcenter.com
Surgical Care Services
N.A.I.C.S.: 621493

Park Plaza Hospital Billing Center, L.L.C. (1)
1313 Hermann Dr, Houston, TX 77004-7005
Tel.: (713) 527-5000
Health Care Srvices
N.A.I.C.S.: 621000

Park Ridge Surgery Center, LLC (1)
10450 Park Meadows Dr Ste 200, Lone Tree, CO 80124
Tel.: (303) 792-2422
Web Site:
   https://parkridgesurgerycenter.com
General Medical & Surgical Services
N.A.I.C.S.: 621493

Parkland Medical Center (1)
1 Parkland Dr, Derry, NH 03038
Tel.: (603) 432-1500
Web Site:
   https://www.parklandmedicalcenter.com
Sales Range: $25-49.9 Million
Emp.: 500
Hospital
N.A.I.C.S.: 622110
Zachary Spigelman (Dir-Medical)
John Skevington (CEO)
Jacob Wiesmann (CFO)
Eileen Mary Keefe (Chief Nursing Officer)
Mark Bolen (VP-Operations)
Jennifer Charles (VP-Human Resources)
Randall DeLee (VP-Operations)

Parkland Oncology, LLC (1)
1 Parkland Dr, Derry, NH 03038
Tel.: (603) 432-1500
Web Site:
   http://www.parklandmedicalcenter.com
Health Care Srvices
N.A.I.C.S.: 621399

Parkland Physician Services, Inc. (1)

31 Stiles Rd Ste 2100, Salem, NH 03079
Tel.: (603) 894-0500
Web Site:
   http://www.parklandphysiciansalem.com
General Medical & Surgical Services
N.A.I.C.S.: 622110

Parkside Surgery Center, Inc. (1)
2731 Park St, Jacksonville, FL 32205
Tel.: (904) 389-1077
Web Site:
   https://www.parksidesurgerycenter.com
Emp.: 35
Outpatient Care Centers
N.A.I.C.S.: 621498

PatientKeeper, Inc. (1)
2261 Market St Ste 4072, San Francisco, CA 94114
Tel.: (781) 373-6126
Web Site: https://www.commure.com
Surgical & Medical Equipment Mfr
N.A.I.C.S.: 339112
Cathy Donohue (VP-Product Mgmt-QA)
Phil Gaudette (VP-Svcs)
Jim Melanson (CFO)
Michael Southern (VP-Human Resources)
Philip Meer (CEO)
Sally Buta (Founder & VP-Strategy)
Barry Gutwillig (VP-Sales-Marketing)
Christopher Maiona (Chief Medical Officer)
John M. Kelly (CTO)

Pediatric Cardiac Intensivists of North Texas, PLLC (1)
7777 Forest Ln Ste C-300J, Dallas, TX 75230
Tel.: (972) 566-7730
Web Site: https://www.pcintx.com
Health Care Srvices
N.A.I.C.S.: 621111

Pediatric Hospitalists of Conroe, PLLC (1)
500 Medical Ctr Blvd Ste 300, Conroe, TX 77304
Tel.: (936) 538-2400
Web Site: http://www.conroeregional.com
Emp.: 1,500
Health Care Srvices
N.A.I.C.S.: 621111

Pediatric Intensivist Group, LLC (1)
111 Jfk Dr Ste A, Atlantis, FL 33462-6634
Tel.: (954) 767-5716
General Medical & Surgical Services
N.A.I.C.S.: 622110

Pediatric Specialists of Clear Lake, PLLC (1)
450 Medical Ctr Blvd Ste 600, Webster, TX 77598
Tel.: (281) 554-4300
Health Care Srvices
N.A.I.C.S.: 621111

Pediatric Specialty Clinic LLC (1)
12200 W 106th St Ste 400, Overland Park, KS 66215
Tel.: (913) 214-8060
Web Site: https://mymidwestphysician.com
Health Care Srvices
N.A.I.C.S.: 621399

Pediatrics of Greater Houston, PLLC (1)
7900 Fannin St Ste 3300, Houston, TX 77054
Tel.: (713) 630-0660
Web Site:
   https://www.pediatricsofgreaterhouston.com
Health Care Srvices
N.A.I.C.S.: 621610

Physicians Endoscopy Center (1)
3030 S Gessner Ste 150, Houston, TX 77063
Tel.: (713) 587-0909
Web Site: https://www.pec-tx.com
Diagnostic Imaging Services
N.A.I.C.S.: 621512

Physicians Endoscopy Center (1)
3030 S Gessner Ste 150, Houston, TX 77063
Tel.: (713) 587-0909
Web Site: https://pec-tx.com
General Medical & Surgical Services
N.A.I.C.S.: 622110

Pinnacle Physician Network, LLC (1)
315 75th St W, Bradenton, FL 34209-3201
Tel.: (941) 761-1998
General Medical & Surgical Services
N.A.I.C.S.: 622110

Plantation General Hospital (1)
401 NW 42nd Ave, Plantation, FL 33317
Tel.: (954) 587-5010
Web Site: http://www.plantationgeneral.com
Sales Range: $50-74.9 Million
Emp.: 874
Hospital
N.A.I.C.S.: 622110
Madeline Nava (CEO)
Rolando J. De Leon (Chm)

Subsidiary (Domestic):

Mercy Hospital, a campus of Plantation General Hospital (2)
3663 S Miami Ave, Miami, FL 33133
Tel.: (305) 854-4400
Web Site: http://www.mercymiami.com
Health Care Srvices
N.A.I.C.S.: 621399
Joseph D. Melchiode (CEO)
Rolando De Leon (Chm)
David Donaldson (CIO)
Ryan LeMasters (COO)
Lauren Cutter (Chief Nursing Officer)
Mark Multach (CMO)
Hunter Adams (CFO)

Plaza Medical Center of Fort Worth (1)
900 8th Ave, Fort Worth, TX 76104
Tel.: (817) 336-2100
General Medical & Surgical Services
N.A.I.C.S.: 622110

Plaza Medical Specialists, PLLC (1)
301 Clifford Ctr Dr Ste 115, Fort Worth, TX 76108-4443
Tel.: (817) 737-6552
General Medical & Surgical Services
N.A.I.C.S.: 622110

Plaza Specialty Hospital, LLC (1)
1300 Binz, Houston, TX 77004
Tel.: (713) 285-1000
Web Site: http://plazaspecialtyhospital.com
Hospital Specialty Services
N.A.I.C.S.: 524114
Rick Pletz (CEO)

Plaza Surgery Center II (1)
6138 Kennerly Rd Ste 201, Jacksonville, FL 32216-4395
Tel.: (904) 208-4120
Web Site:
   http://www.memorialhospitaljax.com
General Medical & Surgical services
N.A.I.C.S.: 622110

Plaza Transplant Center, PLLC (1)
909 9th Ave, Fort Worth, TX 76104-3903
Tel.: (817) 885-7575
General Medical & Surgical Services
N.A.I.C.S.: 622110

Polk Medical Center (1)
424 N Main St, Cedartown, GA 30125
Tel.: (770) 748-2500
Sales Range: $25-49.9 Million
Emp.: 112
Hospital
N.A.I.C.S.: 622110
Kim Seoggins (CEO)

Port St. Lucie Surgery Center, Ltd. (1)
1310 SE W Star Ave, Port Saint Lucie, FL 34952
Tel.: (772) 337-5200
Web Site:
   http://www.stluciesurgerycenter.com
Health Care Srvices
N.A.I.C.S.: 621399

Portsmouth Regional Ambulatory Surgery Center, LLC (1)
333 Borthwick Ave Ste 200, Portsmouth, NH 03801
Tel.: (603) 433-0941
Web Site: https://prasc.com
General Medical & Surgical Services
N.A.I.C.S.: 622110

Portsmouth Regional Hospital (1)

333 Borthwick Ave, Portsmouth, NH 03801
Tel.: (603) 436-5110
Web Site: https://portsmouthhospital.com
Sales Range: $50-74.9 Million
Emp.: 1,000
Hospital
N.A.I.C.S.: 622110
Dean M. Carucci (CEO)

Premier Orthopaedic Surgery Center (1)
394 Harding Pl Ste 100, Nashville, TN 37211
Tel.: (615) 332-3600
Web Site: https://www.posc-nashville.com
Surgical Care Services
N.A.I.C.S.: 621493

Primary Care of West End, LLC (1)
2004 Bremo Rd Ste 201, Richmond, VA 23226
Tel.: (804) 239-1640
General Medical & Surgical Services
N.A.I.C.S.: 622110

Primary Health Group, Inc. (1)
12254 Branders Creek Dr, Chester, VA 23831
Tel.: (804) 271-8990
Web Site: http://phg-ironbridge.com
Health Care Srvices
N.A.I.C.S.: 621111

Primary Health, Inc. (1)
10482 W Carlton Bay Dr, Garden City, ID 83714
Tel.: (208) 955-6500
Web Site: https://www.primaryhealth.com
Health Care Srvices
N.A.I.C.S.: 621610
Tim Miller (Pres)

Princess Grace Hospital (1)
42-52 Nottingham Place, London, W1U 5NY, United Kingdom
Tel.: (44) 2037330661
General Medical & Surgical Services
N.A.I.C.S.: 622110

Psychiatry Services of Osceola, LLC (1)
720 W Oak St, Kissimmee, FL 34741-4924
Tel.: (407) 847-0113
Web Site: http://www.osceolaregional.com
Emp.: 1,100
Health Care Srvices
N.A.I.C.S.: 621610

Pulaski Community Hospital, Inc. (1)
2400 Lee Hwy N, Pulaski, VA 24301
Tel.: (540) 994-8100
Emp.: 400
Hospital Management Services
N.A.I.C.S.: 622110

Purchase Clinic, LLC (1)
10221 River Rd 60053, Potomac, MD 20854
Web Site: https://www.purchaseclinic.com
Health Care Srvices
N.A.I.C.S.: 621610

Putnam Hospital, Inc. (1)
611 Zeagler Dr, Palatka, FL 32177
Tel.: (386) 328-5711
Web Site: http://www.pcmcfl.com
Health Care Srvices
N.A.I.C.S.: 621399

Putnam Radiation Oncology, LLC (1)
600 Zeagler Dr, Palatka, FL 32177
Tel.: (386) 326-7900
Web Site: https://cancercenterputnam.com
Hospital Management Services
N.A.I.C.S.: 622110

Putnam Surgical Group, LLC (1)
414 Zeagler Dr, Palatka, FL 32177
Tel.: (386) 328-4123
Web Site: http://www.putnamsurgical.com
General Medical & Surgical services
N.A.I.C.S.: 622110

Quivira Internal Medicine, Inc. (1)
10601 Quivira Rd Ste 200, Overland Park, KS 66215
Tel.: (913) 541-3340
General Medical & Surgical Services
N.A.I.C.S.: 622110

Quivira Internal Medicine, Inc. (1)
10601 Quivira Rd Ste 200, Overland Park, KS 66215
Tel.: (913) 541-3340
Web Site: https://mymidwestphysician.com
Health Care Srvices
N.A.I.C.S.: 621399

RMCA Professionals Mgmt, LLC (1)
2810 Ambassador Caffery Pkwy, Lafayette, LA 70506-5906
Tel.: (337) 706-1500
General Medical & Surgical Services
N.A.I.C.S.: 622110

Radford Family Medicine, LLC (1)
600 E Main St Ste D, Radford, VA 24141-1826
Tel.: (540) 633-3980
General Medical & Surgical Services
N.A.I.C.S.: 622110

Rapides After Hours Clinic, L.L.C. (1)
2389 Hwy 28 E, Pineville, LA 71360
Tel.: (318) 487-1925
Web Site: http://rapidesurgentcare.com
Health Care Srvices
N.A.I.C.S.: 621399

Rapides Regional Medical Center (1)
211 4th St, Alexandria, LA 71301
Tel.: (318) 769-3000
Web Site: https://rapidesregional.com
Sales Range: $100-124.9 Million
Emp.: 2,000
Hospital
N.A.I.C.S.: 622110

Rapides Regional Physician Group Primary Care, LLC (1)
301 4th St Ste 4C, Alexandria, LA 71301
Tel.: (318) 769-7650
Web Site:
    http://www.rapidesregionalphysician
    group.com
Emp.: 8
Health Care Srvices
N.A.I.C.S.: 621399

Rapides Regional Physician Group Specialty Care, LLC (1)
301 4th St Ste 4C, Alexandria, LA 71301-8421
Tel.: (318) 769-3000
Web Site:
    http://www.rapidesregionalphysician
    group.com
Health Care Srvices
N.A.I.C.S.: 621399

Rapides Regional Physician Group, LLC (1)
301 4th St Ste 4C, Alexandria, LA 71301
Tel.: (318) 769-7650
Web Site:
    https://www.rapidesregionalphysician
    group.com
Health Care Srvices
N.A.I.C.S.: 621399

Rapides Regional Physician Group, LLC (1)
301 4th St Ste 4C, Alexandria, LA 71301
Tel.: (318) 769-7650
Web Site:
    https://rapidesregionalphysiciangroup.com
General Medical & Surgical Services
N.A.I.C.S.: 622110

Raulerson GYN, LLC (1)
1713 Hwy 441 N Ste F, Okeechobee, FL 34972
Tel.: (863) 763-8000
Web Site: http://www.raulersongyn.com
Health Care & Allied Services
N.A.I.C.S.: 621999

Raulerson Hospital (1)
1796 Hwy 441 N, Okeechobee, FL 34972
Tel.: (863) 763-2151
Web Site: http://www.raulersonhospital.com
Sales Range: $10-24.9 Million
Emp.: 478
Hospital
N.A.I.C.S.: 622110

Raymore Medical Group, LLC (1)

1118 Remington Plz Ste B, Raymore, MO 64083
Tel.: (816) 318-1725
Women Healthcare Services
N.A.I.C.S.: 621610

Red Rock at Smoke Ranch, LLC (1)
11011 W Charleston Blvd, Las Vegas, NV 89128
Tel.: (702) 797-7777
Web Site: www.redrock.sclv.com
Medical & Surgical Hospital Services
N.A.I.C.S.: 622110

Red Rocks Radiation & Oncology, LLC (1)
400 Indiana St Ste 220, Golden, CO 80401
Tel.: (720) 420-3300
Emp.: 10
Health Care Srvices
N.A.I.C.S.: 621999
Todd Grigereit *(Office Mgr)*

Red Rocks Surgery Center, LLC (1)
400 Indiana St Ste 100, Golden, CO 80401
Tel.: (720) 420-3000
Web Site: https://redrockssurgery.com
General Medical & Surgical Services
N.A.I.C.S.: 622110

Redmond Anesthesia Services, LLC (1)
501 Redmond Rd, Rome, GA 30165
Tel.: (706) 291-0291
Web Site: http://www.redmondregional.com
Health Care Srvices
N.A.I.C.S.: 621399

Redmond Regional Medical Center (1)
501 Redmond Rd, Rome, GA 30165-1415
Tel.: (706) 291-0291
Web Site: http://www.redmondregional.com
Sales Range: $50-74.9 Million
Emp.: 1,200
Hospital
N.A.I.C.S.: 622110
John Quinlivan *(CEO)*

Regional Medical Center Bayonet Point (1)
14000 Fivay Rd, Hudson, FL 34667
Tel.: (727) 819-2929
Web Site: http://www.rmchealth.com
Sales Range: $75-99.9 Million
Emp.: 1,436
Hospital
N.A.I.C.S.: 622110
Melanie Wetmore *(Chief Nursing Officer)*
Rao Musunuru *(Chm)*
Jorge Ayub *(Vice Chm)*
Tom Lawhorne *(CFO)*
Regina Temple *(CEO & Co-Sec)*
Christine Behan *(Chm)*
Paige Laughlin *(COO)*
Erika van Doorn *(Dir-Trauma)*
Michael Trevisani *(Chief Medical Officer)*
John Marker *(Chief Nursing Officer)*
Sherry Pressner *(VP-Human Resources)*
Julie Lallanilla *(VP)*
Linda Budzilek *(VP-Quality)*
Rick McNamara *(Dir-Communications)*
Mrunal Shah *(Chm)*
Rami Mufleh Akel *(Vice Chm-Medicine Dept)*
Adam Lazarus *(Dir-Medical-Div of Emergency Medicine)*
Gaurav Kumar *(Dir-Medical-Div of Radiology)*
Shaival Thakore *(Program Dir & Dir-Medical-Hospitalists)*
Steven Austin Visnaw *(Chm)*
Scott Jarmer *(Dir-Medical-Div of Pathology)*
Chirag Patel *(Treas & Co-Sec)*

Regional Medical Center of San Jose (1)
225 N Jackson Ave, San Jose, CA 95116
Tel.: (408) 259-5000
Web Site:
    https://regionalmedicalsanjose.com
Sales Range: $75-99.9 Million
Emp.: 1,670
Hospital
N.A.I.C.S.: 622110
Kenneth M. West *(Pres & CEO)*
Lori Katterhagen *(Co-Chief Nursing Officer)*
Tarannum Guller *(Chief Medical Officer)*
Carl H. James *(CFO)*

Nanette Logan *(Co-Chief Nursing Officer)*
P. J. Thrasher *(CTO)*
Mark Amox *(COO)*

Research Medical Center (1)
2316 E Meyer Blvd, Kansas City, MO 64132
Tel.: (816) 276-4000
Web Site: https://careers.hcahealthcare.com
Health Care Srvices
N.A.I.C.S.: 621399

Resource Optimization & Innovation, L.L.C. (1)
645 Maryville Centre Dr Ste 200, Saint Louis, MO 63141
Web Site: https://roiscs.com
General Medical & Surgical Services
N.A.I.C.S.: 622110

Reston Hospital Center (1)
1850 Town Center Pkwy, Reston, VA 20190
Tel.: (703) 689-9000
Web Site: http://www.restonhospital.com
Sales Range: $75-99.9 Million
Surgical Hospital Services
N.A.I.C.S.: 622110
John Deardorff *(Pres)*
Dustin Fosness *(CFO)*
Nathan Vooys *(CEO)*
Alice Tang *(Chief Medical Officer)*
Laura-Anne Cleveland *(Chief Nursing Officer)*
Whitney Fenyak *(COO)*

Reston Surgery Center (1)
1860 Town Ctr Dr G100, Reston, VA 20190
Tel.: (703) 639-3100
Web Site:
    https://www.restonsurgerycenter.com
Emp.: 70
Health Care Srvices
N.A.I.C.S.: 621610

Reston Surgery Center, L.P. (1)
1860 Town Center Dr G100, Reston, VA 20190
Tel.: (703) 639-3100
Web Site: https://restonsurgerycenter.com
General Medical & Surgical Services
N.A.I.C.S.: 622110

Retreat Internal Medicine, LLC (1)
110 N Robinson St Ste 400, Richmond, VA 23220
Tel.: (804) 822-3480
Web Site: http://hcavirginiaphysicians.com
Health Care Srvices
N.A.I.C.S.: 621111

Richmond Pediatric Surgeons, LLC (1)
7119 Jahnke Rd, Richmond, VA 23225
Tel.: (804) 323-2847
Emp.: 7
Healthcare Support Services
N.A.I.C.S.: 621999
Rochelle Murtaza *(Office Mgr)*

Ridgeline Endoscopy Center (1)
6028 S Ridgeline Dr Ste 100, Ogden, UT 84405
Tel.: (801) 475-4900
Web Site: https://www.ridgelinesurgical.com
Ambulatory Health Care Services
N.A.I.C.S.: 621493

Rio Grande Regional Hospital, Inc. (1)
101 E Ridge Rd, McAllen, TX 78503
Tel.: (956) 632-6000
Web Site: https://riohealth.com
General Medical & Surgical Services
N.A.I.C.S.: 622110

Rio Grande Valley Cardiology, PLLC (1)
100 E Ridge Rd Ste A, McAllen, TX 78503
Tel.: (956) 682-5665
Web Site: http://www.rgvcardiology.com
Emp.: 300
Health Care Srvices
N.A.I.C.S.: 621111

Riverside Community Hospital (1)
4445 Magnolia Ave, Riverside, CA 92501
Tel.: (951) 788-3000
Web Site:
    https://www.riversidecommunityhospi
    tal.com

Sales Range: $75-99.9 Million
Emp.: 1,600
Hospital
N.A.I.C.S.: 622110

Riverside Hospital, Inc. (1)
500 J Clyde Morris Blvd, Newport News, VA 23601
Tel.: (757) 594-2000
Web Site: http://www.riversideonline.com
Medical & Surgical Hospital Services
N.A.I.C.S.: 622110

Riverwalk ASC, LLC (1)
200 3rd Ave W Ste 170, Bradenton, FL 34205
Tel.: (941) 782-5439
Web Site: https://www.riverwalkasc.com
General Medical & Surgical Services
N.A.I.C.S.: 622110

Riverwalk Surgery Center (1)
8350 Riverwalk Park Blvd, Fort Myers, FL 33919
Tel.: (239) 489-4909
Web Site:
    https://www.riverwalksurgerycenter.com
General Medical & Surgical services
N.A.I.C.S.: 622110

Roanoke Surgery Center, L.P. (1)
1802 Braeburn Dr, Salem, VA 24153-7357
Tel.: (540) 725-4533
General Medical & Surgical Services
N.A.I.C.S.: 622110

Subsidiary (Domestic):

Blue Ridge Surgery Center (2)
2308 Wesvill Ct, Raleigh, NC 27607
Tel.: (919) 781-4311
Web Site:
    http://www.blueridgesurgerycenter.com
Surgical Care Services
N.A.I.C.S.: 621493
Robert Alphin *(Dir-Medical)*
Angela Evans *(CEO)*
Melanie Pressley *(Dir-Nursing)*
Gloria Otero *(Mgr)*
Alex Ratterree *(Mgr-Op,PACU)*
Tricia Winner *(Mgr-OR)*
Kathryn Lennert *(Coord-Bus Office)*
Nicole Cox *(Mgr-Op,PACU)*

Rocky Mountain Pediatric Hematology Oncology, LLC (1)
2055 N High St Ste 340, Denver, CO 80205
Tel.: (303) 832-2344
Web Site:
    http://www.rockymountainkidscancer
    care.com
Health Care Srvices
N.A.I.C.S.: 621999

Rocky Mountain Surgery Center, LLC (1)
401 W Hampden Pl Ste 100, Englewood, CO 80111
Tel.: (303) 789-4000
Web Site: https://rockymountainsurgery.com
General Medical & Surgical Services
N.A.I.C.S.: 622110

Rocky Mountain Surgery Center, LLC (1)
401 W Hampden Pl Ste 100, Englewood, CO 80111
Tel.: (303) 789-4000
Web Site: https://rockymountainsurgery.com
General Medical & Surgical Services
N.A.I.C.S.: 622110
Alex Slucky *(Dir-Medical)*
Kate Randolph *(Dir-Nursing)*

Roodlane Medical Limited (1)
58 New Broad Street, London, EC2M 1JJ, United Kingdom
Tel.: (44) 1745775894
Web Site: http://www.roodlane.co.uk
Health Care Srvices
N.A.I.C.S.: 621111
Gill MacLeod *(CEO)*
Harry Trakoshis *(Co-COO)*
John Reay *(Dir)*
Catherine Vickery *(VP-Legal Svcs)*
Stuart King *(VP-Strategy)*
Jennifer Hirst *(Mgr)*
Niaz Khan *(Chief Clinical Officer)*
Zahoor Khan *(Dir)*

HCA Healthcare, Inc.—(Continued)

Eric Neethling *(CFO)*
Paul Sanford *(CEO)*
Paul Bowes *(Co-COO)*
Robyn Knott *(Head)*

Rose Medical Center Inc. (1)
4567 E 9th Ave, Denver, CO 80220
Tel.: (303) 320-2121
Web Site: https://healthonecares.com
Sales Range: $75-99.9 Million
Emp.: 1,125
Hospital
N.A.I.C.S.: 622110
Hollie Seeley *(CEO & Interim & COO)*
Linda Gray *(Chief Nursing Officer)*
Julie Hogan *(Mktg Dir)*
Jeff Lewis *(Pres)*
Dave Theil *(Chm)*
Andrew Ziller *(Chm)*
John Hammer *(Chm)*
Shalini Chahal *(Chm)*
James Banks *(Chm)*
Vijay Subbarao *(Pres)*
Galo Garces *(Chm)*
Michael Hull *(Chm)*
Lacy-Ann Harari *(Chm)*
Vijay Subbarao *(Pres)*
Galo Garces *(Chm)*
Michael Hull *(Chm)*
Lacy-Ann Harari *(Chm)*

Rose Surgical Center (1)
4700 E Hale Pkwy Ste 200, Denver, CO 80220
Tel.: (303) 758-1175
Web Site: https://rosesurgicalcenter.com
General Medical & Surgical Services
N.A.I.C.S.: 622110

Rose Surgical Center (1)
4700 E Hale Pkwy Ste 200, Denver, CO 80220
Tel.: (303) 758-1175
Web Site:
https://www.rosesurgical.com
Health Care Srvices
N.A.I.C.S.: 621999

Round Rock Hospital, Inc. (1)
2400 Round Rock Ave, Round Rock, TX 78681
Tel.: (512) 341-1000
Surgical Hospital Services
N.A.I.C.S.: 622110

Round Rock Medical Center (1)
2400 Round Rock Ave, Round Rock, TX 78681
Tel.: (512) 341-1000
Web Site: http://stdavids.com
Sales Range: $75-99.9 Million
Emp.: 000
Hospital Services
N.A.I.C.S.: 622110
Jeremy Barclay *(CEO)*
Laura Wiess *(CFO)*
Katie Lattanzi Perkins *(COO)*
Michael Craun *(Chief Medical Officer)*
Tami Taylor *(Chief Nursing Officer)*

Round Rock Trauma Surgeons, PLLC (1)
2300 Round Rock Ave Ste 201, Round Rock, TX 78681-4006
Tel.: (512) 482-4107
General Medical & Surgical services
N.A.I.C.S.: 622110

Sahara Surgery Center (1)
2401 Paseo Del Prado, Las Vegas, NV 89102
Tel.: (702) 362-7874
Web Site: https://www.saharasurgery.com
General Medical & Surgical Services
N.A.I.C.S.: 622110

Salem Surgery Center, Limited Partnership (1)
32 Stiles Rd Ste 103, Salem, NH 03079
Tel.: (603) 685-0001
Web Site: http://www.sasnh.com
Emp.: 10
Women Healthcare Services
N.A.I.C.S.: 621610

San Antonio Surgicenter, LLC (1)
21 Spurs Ln Ste SL-100, San Antonio, TX 78240-1669

Tel.: (210) 614-0187
General Medical & Surgical Services
N.A.I.C.S.: 622110

Subsidiary (Domestic):

The Center for Special Surgery at TCA (2)
21 Spurs Ln Ste SL-1, San Antonio, TX 78240
Tel.: (210) 575-5700
Web Site:
https://www.tcaspecialsurgery.com
General Medical & Surgical services
N.A.I.C.S.: 622110

San Jose Healthcare System, LP (1)
225 N Jackson Ave, San Jose, CA 95116-1603
Tel.: (408) 259-5000
Web Site:
http://www.regionalmedicalsanjose.com
Emp.: 1,670
Health Care Srvices
N.A.I.C.S.: 621399
Tarannum Guller *(Chief Medical Officer)*
Nanette Logan *(COO)*
Jina Canson *(Chief Nursing Officer)*

San Marcos ASC, LLC (1)
1891 Medical Pkwy, San Marcos, TX 78666-7559
Tel.: (512) 754-7999
Web Site:
https://sanmarcossurgerycenter.com
Emp.: 30
General Medical & Surgical Services
N.A.I.C.S.: 622110

San Marcos Surgery Center (1)
1891 Medical Pkwy, San Marcos, TX 78666
Tel.: (512) 754-7999
Web Site:
https://sanmarcossurgerycenter.com
Emp.: 25
Health Care Srvices
N.A.I.C.S.: 621399
Trisha Camacho *(Principal)*
Phil Neeoly *(Exec Dir)*

Sarah Cannon Development Innovations, LLC (1)
1100 Dr Martin L King Jr Blvd Ste 800, Nashville, TN 37203
Tel.: (615) 329-7274
Web Site: https://sarahcannon.com
Cancer Care Institute Services
N.A.I.C.S.: 622310
Ian W. Flinn *(Dir-Lymphoma Res)*
Ian W. Flinn *(Dir-Lymphoma Res)*
Dee Anna Smith *(CEO)*
Fred LeMaistre *(Sr VP)*
Andy Corts *(CIO)*
Amber Woodward-Smith *(CFO)*
Aashish Shah *(Sr VP-Development)*
David Spigel *(Chief Scientific Officer)*
Nick Lane *(VP-Human Resources)*
Hendrik-Tobias Arkenau *(Exec Dir-Medical-Drug Dev)*
Carlos Bachier *(Dir-Cellular Therapy Res)*
Minoo Battiwalla *(Dir-Outcomes Res)*
Johanna C. Bendell *(Dir & Chief Dev Officer)*
Jesus G. Berdeja *(Dir-Myeloma Res)*
Todd Bauer *(Assoc Dir)*
Amanda Bilbrey *(Assoc VP)*
Rocky Billups *(VP-Operations)*
Jennifer Cole *(VP)*
Tonya Cox *(Asst VP-Operations)*
Therese Dodd *(Dir-Quality Improvement)*
Gerald S. Falchook *(Dir-Drug Dev)*
F. Anthony Greco *(Co-Founder)*
John D. Hainsworth *(Co-Founder)*
Debbie Haynes *(VP)*
Sybil Hyatt *(Sr Dir-Cardiovascular Ops)*
Marcy Vallone *(VP-Strategic Development)*
Lindsay Sears *(Sr Dir)*
Howard A. Burris III *(Chief Medical Officer & Pres-Clinical Ops)*

Sarah Cannon Research Institute UK Limited (1)
93 Harley Street, London, W1G 6AD, United Kingdom
Tel.: (44) 2032195200
Cancer Treatment Services
N.A.I.C.S.: 622310

Sarah Cannon Research Institute, LLC (1)
1100 Charlotte Ave Ste 800, Nashville, TN 37203
Tel.: (615) 298-3180
Web Site:
http://www.sarahcannonresearch.com
Medical & Surgical Hospital Services
N.A.I.C.S.: 622110
Ian W. Flinn *(Dir-Lymphoma Res)*
Ian W. Flinn *(Dir-Lymphoma Res)*
Dee Anna Smith *(CEO)*
John D. Hainsworth *(Co-Founder)*
Margaret C. Mazzone *(Officer-Ethics & Compliance & VP)*
Jennifer Cole *(VP-Clinical Ops)*
Rocky Billups *(VP-Ops)*
Debbie Haynes *(VP-Bus Innovation)*
Fred LeMaistre *(Sr VP-Market Ops)*
David Spigel *(Chief Scientific Officer)*
Nick Lane *(VP-HR)*
Amy Abbott *(VP-North Florida Div)*
Carlos Bachier *(Dir-Cellular Therapy Res)*
Minoo Battiwalla *(Dir-Outcomes Res)*
Johanna C. Bendell *(Chief Dev Officer & Dir-GI Cancer Res Program)*
Jesus G. Berdeja *(Dir-Myeloma Res)*
Amanda Bilbrey *(Sr Dir-Clinical Ops)*
Barrett K. Blackmon *(Reg VP-Gulf Coast Div)*
Tonya Cox *(Asst VP-Ops)*
Therese Dodd *(Dir-Quality Improvement)*
Gerald S. Falchook *(Dir-Drug Dev)*
F. Anthony Greco *(Co-Founder)*
Marcy Vallone *(VP-Strategic Dev)*
Lindsay Sears *(Sr Dir-Health Outcomes Res)*
Melissa Threlkeld *(Reg VP-HCA North Texas)*
Samantha Kirby *(Reg VP-TriStar Div)*
Erika P. Hamilton *(Dir-Breast Cancer & Gynecologic Cancer Res Program)*
Sybil Hyatt *(Dir-Ops-Cardiovascular Res)*
Melissa Johnson *(Dir)*
Denise Jones *(Asst VP)*
Suzanne Jones *(Sr Dir & Dir-Scientific-Strategic Dev)*
Andrew Kennedy *(Dir-Radiation Oncology Res)*
Dax Kurbegov *(VP)*
Lisa Morrissey *(Assoc VP-Corp Affairs)*
Zahra Raki *(Reg VP-Cancer Svcs-Continental Div)*
Jonathan Tinker *(VP-Capital Div)*
Aashish Shah *(Sr VP-Development)*
Hendrik-Tobias Arkenau *(Exec Dir-Medical-Drug Dev Program)*
Amber Woodward-Smith *(CFO)*
Stephanie Graff *(Assoc Dir)*
Angela Fletcher *(Reg VP-North Carolina Div)*
Gregg Fromell *(VP)*
Ryan Hallenbeck *(Reg VP-Cancer Svcs)*
Raymond Jackson *(Reg VP-San Antonio Div)*
Meredith McKen *(Assoc Dir-Melanoma & Skin Cancer Res)*
Frances M. Palmieri *(Dir-Oncology Strategic Sites)*
Michelle Rowe *(Asst VP-Clinical Ops)*
Anita Sexton *(Head-Sarah Cannon Res)*
Haydar Frangoul *(Dir-Medical-Hematology,Oncology,Pediatric Transplant-,Cellular)*
Keith Gregory *(Assoc VP)*
Shekeab Jauhari *(Assoc VP)*
Andrew McKenzie *(Dir)*
Denise A. Yardley *(Asst Dir)*
Ishwaria Subbiah *(Exec Dir-Cancer Care Equity & Professional Wellness)*
Howard A. Burris III *(Pres)*

Sarah Cannon Research UK Limited (1)
93 Harley Street, London, W1G 6AD, United Kingdom
Tel.: (44) 2032195200
Web Site:
http://www.sarahcannonresearch.co.uk
Medical Research & Development Services
N.A.I.C.S.: 541715
Dee Anna Smith *(CEO)*

Sarasota Doctors Hospital, Inc. (1)
5731 Bee Ridge Rd, Sarasota, FL 34233
Tel.: (941) 342-1100
Web Site:
http://www.doctorshospitalofsarasota.com

Emp.: 765
Hospital
N.A.I.C.S.: 622110
Robert C. Meade *(Sec)*
Jeffrey Silverstein *(Chm)*
Bill English *(CFO)*
Todd Cruz *(Chief Nursing Officer)*
Jennifer Bocker *(Chief Medical Officer)*
Charles Schwaner *(CFO)*
Kelly Malloy *(COO)*
Kathleen Boswell-Gregg *(VP-Quality &)*
Theresa Levering *(VP-Human Resources)*
Erin McLeod *(Chm)*
Michael Schandorf Lartey *(Vice Chm)*
Jyric Sims *(Pres-)*
John Averyt *(Pres-Medical Staff)*

Sebring Hospital Management Associates, LLC (1)
3600 S Highlands Ave, Sebring, FL 33870
Tel.: (863) 385-6101
Web Site: http://www.highlandsregional.com
Emp.: 430
Hospital Operator
N.A.I.C.S.: 622110
Brenda Dane *(VP-HR)*

Senior Health Associates, LLC (1)
600 NW Murray Rd, Lees Summit, MO 64081
Tel.: (816) 347-1532
General Medical & Surgical Services
N.A.I.C.S.: 622110

Silicon Valley Surgery Center, L.P. (1)
14601 S Bascom Ave Ste 100, Los Gatos, CA 95032
Tel.: (408) 402-0663
Web Site: https://siliconvalleysurgery.com
Healthcare Surgical Services
N.A.I.C.S.: 621493

Sky Ridge Medical Center (1)
10101 Ridgegate Pkwy, Lone Tree, CO 80124
Tel.: (720) 225-1000
General Medical & Surgical Services
N.A.I.C.S.: 622110

Sky Ridge Surgery Center, L.P. (1)
10099 Ridge Gate Pkwy Conifer Bldg Ste 100, Lone Tree, CO 80124
Tel.: (720) 225-5000
Web Site:
http://www.skyridgesurgicalcenter.com
Medical Support Services
N.A.I.C.S.: 621111

Subsidiary (Domestic):

Sky Ridge Surgical Center (2)
10099 Ridge Gate Pkwy Conifer Bldg Ste 100, Lone Tree, CO 80124
Tel.: (720) 225-5000
Web Site:
https://www.skyridgesurgicalcenter.com
Ambulatory Surgical Center
N.A.I.C.S.: 621493

Skyline Medical Center (1)
3441 Dickerson Pike, Nashville, TN 37207
Tel.: (615) 769-2000
Web Site:
http://www.skylinemedicalcenter.com
Sales Range: $75-99.9 Million
Emp.: 800
Hospital
N.A.I.C.S.: 622110

Skyline Medical Group, LLC (1)
3443 Dickerson Pike Ste G30, Nashville, TN 37207
Tel.: (615) 234-6390
Web Site:
http://www.skylinemedicalgroup.com
Outpatient Care Services
N.A.I.C.S.: 621498

Skyline Neuroscience Associates, LLC (1)
3443 Dickerson Pike Ste 580, Nashville, TN 37207
Tel.: (615) 860-1040
Web Site: http://skylineneuroscience.com
Outpatient Care Centers
N.A.I.C.S.: 621498

Solis Mammography at Clear Lake Regional Medical Center, LLC (1)

400 Medical Ctr Blvd Ste 100, Webster, TX 77598
Tel.: (281) 526-6840
Medical Devices
N.A.I.C.S.: 621512
DaWanda Nelson (VP-Ops)

Solis Mammography at Conroe Regional Medical Center, LLC **(1)**
500 Medical Center Blvd Ste 175, Conroe, TX 77304
Tel.: (936) 539-7100
Mammography & Imaging Centre Operator
N.A.I.C.S.: 621512
Deanna Flahart (Dir-Center)
Melissa Harris (Dir-Market-North Houston)
Dawanda Nelson (VP-Ops-South Central)

Solis Mammography at Denton Regional Medical Center, LLC **(1)**
3537 S I-35E Ste 211, Denton, TX 76210
Tel.: (940) 382-5400
Web Site: https://www.solismammo.com
Medical Devices
N.A.I.C.S.: 621512
Cathy Wilson (VP-Ops-Arizona & North Texas)
Mattie Hartman (Dir-Denton)

Solis Mammography at HCA Houston Tomball, LLC **(1)**
13426 Medical Complex Dr Ste 100, Tomball, TX 77375
Tel.: (281) 401-7034
Web Site: https://www.solismammo.com
Mammography & Imaging Centre Operator
N.A.I.C.S.: 621512
Ashley Connell (Dir-Center)
Denise Bacon (Dir-Market-South Central)
DaWanda Nelson (VP)

Solis Mammography at Kingwood Medical Center, LLC **(1)**
22999 US Hwy 59 N Ste 240, Kingwood, TX 77339
Tel.: (281) 348-8091
Mammography & Imaging Centre Operator
N.A.I.C.S.: 621512
Lorre Yeary (Dir-Center)

Solis Mammography at Las Colinas Medical Center, LLC **(1)**
6750 N MacArthur Ste 153, Irving, TX 75039
Tel.: (469) 677-3174
Web Site: https://www.solismammo.com
Diagnostic Center Operator
N.A.I.C.S.: 621512
Cathy Wilson (VP-New Markets & Implementation)
Grant Davies (CEO)
Paige Terra (CFO)
Candace Baer (Sr VP-Ops-West & Central)
Timothy Mueller (Gen Counsel)
Dawanda Nelson (VP-Ops-South Central)
Elizabeth Prom (VP-Bus Dev)
Ferl Howard (VP-Infrastructure & Svc Delivery)
Mary Simmons (Chief People & Culture Officer)

Solis Mammography at Medical Center Alliance, LLC **(1)**
3025 N Tarrant Pkwy Ste 250, Fort Worth, TX 76177
Tel.: (817) 509-6137
Web Site: https://www.solismammo.com
Medical Devices
N.A.I.C.S.: 621512
Kim Lunsford (Dir-Alliance)
Cathy Wilson (VP-Ops-Arizona & North Texas)

Solis Mammography at Medical Center Arlington, LLC **(1)**
3201 Matlock Rd Ste 110, Arlington, TX 76015
Tel.: (817) 375-9357
Web Site: https://www.solismammo.com
Medical Devices
N.A.I.C.S.: 621512
Elizabeth McDuff (Dir-Arlington)
Stephanie Swanson (VP)

Solis Mammography at Medical Center of Lewisville, LLC **(1)**
500 W Main St Ste 300, Lewisville, TX 75057
Tel.: (972) 350-0078

Web Site: https://www.solismammo.com
Cancer Treatment Services
N.A.I.C.S.: 622310

Solis Mammography at Medical Center of McKinney, LLC **(1)**
4201 medical Ctr Dr Ste 100A, McKinney, TX 75069
Tel.: (214) 620-2346
Web Site: https://www.solismammo.com
Medical Center Operator
N.A.I.C.S.: 621491

Solis Mammography at Medical Center of Plano, LLC **(1)**
3801 W 15th St Bldg C Ste 150A, Plano, TX 75075
Tel.: (972) 596-4033
Web Site: https://www.solismammo.com
Hospital Management Services
N.A.I.C.S.: 622110

Solis Mammography at Medical City Dallas, LLC **(1)**
7777 Forest Ln Ste C-236, Dallas, TX 75230
Tel.: (214) 294-9051
Web Site: https://www.solismammo.com
Diagnostic Breast Mammography & Imaging Services
N.A.I.C.S.: 621512
Stephanie Swanson (VP)

Solis Mammography at Ogden Regional Medical Center, LLC **(1)**
5475 S 500 E, Ogden, UT 84405
Tel.: (385) 244-0527
Mammography Center Services
N.A.I.C.S.: 621512

Solis Mammography at Pearland Medical Center, LLC **(1)**
10970 Shadow Creek Pkwy Ste 190, Pearland, TX 77584
Tel.: (713) 770-7767
Diagnostic Breast Mammography & Imaging Services
N.A.I.C.S.: 621512

Solis Mammography at Rose Medical Center, LLC **(1)**
4700 E Hale Pkwy Ste 450, Denver, CO 80220
Tel.: (303) 320-7127
Web Site: https://www.solismammo.com
Mammography & Imaging Centre Operator
N.A.I.C.S.: 621512
Tina Baxter (Dir-Market-Midwest)
Cathy Wilson (VP-Ops & New Markets)

Solis Mammography at Skyline Medical Center, LLC **(1)**
3443 Dickerson Pike Ste 260, Nashville, TN 37207
Tel.: (615) 760-0511
Mammography & Imaging Centre Operator
N.A.I.C.S.: 621512

Solis Mammography at St. David's Medical Center, LLC **(1)**
1015 E 32nd St 3rd Fl Ste 308, Austin, TX 78705
Tel.: (512) 427-2500
Screening Mammogram Treatment Services
N.A.I.C.S.: 621512

Solis Mammography at St. David's Round Rock Medical Center, LLC **(1)**
1015 E 32nd St 3rd Fl Ste 308, Austin, TX 78705
Tel.: (512) 427-2500
Health Care Srvices
N.A.I.C.S.: 621610

Solis Mammography at St. Mark's Hospital, LLC **(1)**
1140 E 3900 S 1st Fl, Salt Lake City, UT 84124
Tel.: (385) 215-8704
Screening Mammogram Treatment Services
N.A.I.C.S.: 621512

Solis Mammography at StoneCrest Medical Center, LLC **(1)**
537 Stonecrest Pkwy Ste 202, Smyrna, TN 37167
Tel.: (615) 768-2368
Mammography & Imaging Centre Operator

N.A.I.C.S.: 621512

Solis Mammography at Timpanogos Regional Hospital, LLC **(1)**
750 W 800 N, Orem, UT 84057
Tel.: (801) 850-9544
Mammography Center Services
N.A.I.C.S.: 621512

Solis Mammography at West Houston Medical Center, LLC **(1)**
12606 W Houston Center Blvd Ste 330, Houston, TX 77082
Tel.: (281) 588-8675
Diagnostic Breast Mammography & Imaging Services
N.A.I.C.S.: 621512

Solis Mammography at Womans Hospital of Texas, LLC **(1)**
7400 Fannin St Ste 100, Houston, TX 77054
Tel.: (713) 791-7176
Web Site: https://www.solismammo.com
Medical Devices
N.A.I.C.S.: 621512
DaWanda Nelson (VP)

Solis Mammography of Cedar Hill, LLC **(1)**
617 Uptown Blvd Ste 103, Cedar Hill, TX 75104
Tel.: (214) 294-9070
Web Site: https://www.solismammo.com
Diagnostic Breast Mammography & Imaging Services
N.A.I.C.S.: 621512

Solis Mammography of CyFair, LLC **(1)**
11307 FM 1960 Rd W Ste 340, Houston, TX 77065
Tel.: (281) 336-8277
Web Site: https://www.solismammo.com
Mammography & Imaging Centre Operator
N.A.I.C.S.: 621512

Solis Mammography of Flower Mound, LLC **(1)**
4001 Long Prairie Ste 115, Flower Mound, TX 75028
Tel.: (214) 313-9361
Web Site: https://www.solismammo.com
Medical Devices
N.A.I.C.S.: 621512
Joanna Collich (Dir-Flower Mound)

Solis Mammography of Frisco, LLC **(1)**
5757 Main St Ste 102, Frisco, TX 75034
Tel.: (972) 941-4800
Web Site: https://www.solismammo.com
Diagnostic Breast Mammography & Imaging Services
N.A.I.C.S.: 621512

Solis Mammography of Garland, LLC **(1)**
4430 Lavon Dr Ste 326, Garland, TX 75040
Tel.: (214) 703-9201
Web Site: https://www.solismammo.com
Medical Devices
N.A.I.C.S.: 621512

Solis Mammography of Grand Prairie, LLC **(1)**
4927 Lake Ridge Pkwy Ste 150, Grand Prairie, TX 75052
Tel.: (972) 941-4820
Web Site: https://www.solismammo.com
Mammography & Imaging Centre Operator
N.A.I.C.S.: 621512
Elizabeth Mcduff (Dir-Center)
Amy Peterson (Dir-Market-North Texas)
Stephanie Swanson (VP)

Solis Mammography of Houston NW, LLC **(1)**
800 Peakwood Dr Ste 1F, Houston, TX 77090
Tel.: (281) 440-2678
Web Site: https://www.solismammo.com
Mammography & Imaging Centre Operator
N.A.I.C.S.: 621512

Solis Mammography of Katy, LLC **(1)**
1331 W Grand Pkwy N Ste 240, Katy, TX 77493

Tel.: (281) 769-0437
Web Site: https://www.solismammo.com
Medical Devices
N.A.I.C.S.: 621512

Solis Mammography of Mainland, LLC **(1)**
6807 Emmett F Lowry Expwy Ste 308, Texas City, TX 77591
Tel.: (409) 938-5554
Medical Devices
N.A.I.C.S.: 621512

Solis Mammography of Mansfield, LLC **(1)**
3141 E Broad St Ste 331, Mansfield, TX 76063
Tel.: (972) 941-4830
Web Site: https://www.solismammo.com
Mammography & Imaging Centre Operator
N.A.I.C.S.: 621512
Stephanie Swanson (VP)

Solis Mammography of Mesquite, LLC **(1)**
1515 Town East Blvd Ste 141, Mesquite, TX 75150
Tel.: (214) 294-9060
Web Site: https://www.solismammo.com
Mammography & Imaging Centre Operator
N.A.I.C.S.: 621512
Stephanie Swanson (VP)

Solis Mammography of Montgomery, LLC **(1)**
20042 Eva St Ste 104, Montgomery, TX 77356
Tel.: (936) 538-2984
Web Site: https://www.solismammo.com
Diagnostic Breast Mammography & Imaging Services
N.A.I.C.S.: 621512

Solis Mammography of North Cypress, LLC **(1)**
21216 Northwest Fwy Ste 220, Cypress, TX 77429
Tel.: (832) 912-3600
Web Site: https://www.solismammo.com
Mammography & Imaging Centre Operator
N.A.I.C.S.: 621512
Beth Phelps (Dir-Center)
DaWanda Nelson (VP)

Solis Mammography of Red Oak, LLC **(1)**
317 E Ovilla Rd Ste 300, Red Oak, TX 75154
Tel.: (469) 240-8592
Web Site: https://www.solismammo.com
Mammography Imaging Services
N.A.I.C.S.: 621512

Solis Mammography of River Oaks, LLC **(1)**
2415 W Alabama St Ste 214, Houston, TX 77098
Tel.: (713) 300-9370
Diagnostic Imaging Services
N.A.I.C.S.: 621512
Jamie Prinster (Dir-)
Melissa Harris (Dir-North Houston)
DaWanda Nelson (VP-Operations-South Central)

Solis Mammography of Rowlett, LLC **(1)**
5601 Liberty Grove Rd Ste 300, Rowlett, TX 75089
Tel.: (214) 440-1030
Mammography Center Services
N.A.I.C.S.: 621512

Solis Mammography of Southwest Fort Worth, LLC **(1)**
3700 Vision Dr Ste 120, Fort Worth, TX 76109
Tel.: (817) 200-3135
Mammography Center Services
N.A.I.C.S.: 621512

Solis Mammography of Sugar Land, LLC **(1)**
1111 Hwy 6 S Ste 260, Sugar Land, TX 77478
Tel.: (281) 204-2439
Web Site: https://www.solismammo.com
Medical Devices
N.A.I.C.S.: 621512

HCA Healthcare, Inc.—(Continued)
DaWanda Nelson (VP)

Solis Mammography of Towne Lake, LLC (1)
9818 Fry Rd Ste 100, Cypress, TX 77433
Tel.: (832) 334-0202
Diagnostic Imaging Services
N.A.I.C.S.: 621512
Vanessa Smith (Dir-)
DaWanda Nelson (VP-Operations-South Central)

Solis Mammography of West Plano, LLC (1)
5920 W Parker Rd Ste 200, Plano, TX 75093
Tel.: (972) 781-0444
Web Site: https://www.solismammo.com
Medical Devices
N.A.I.C.S.: 621512
Tonia Tindell (Dir-Plano West)

Solis Mammography of Womans Place, LLC (1)
10223 Broadway Ste E, Pearland, TX 77584
Tel.: (866) 841-2335
Medical Devices
N.A.I.C.S.: 621512

South Austin Surgery Center, Ltd. (1)
4207 James Casey St Ste 203, Austin, TX 78745-3365
Tel.: (512) 440-7894
Web Site:
https://southaustinsurgerycenter.com
Ambulatory Health Care Services
N.A.I.C.S.: 621493
David Huffstutler (CEO)

South Bay Hospital (1)
4016 Sun City Ctr Blvd, Sun City Center, FL 33573
Tel.: (813) 634-3301
Web Site: http://www.southbayhospital.com
Sales Range: $25-49.9 Million
Emp.: 507
Hospital
N.A.I.C.S.: 622110
Daniel Bender (Co-CEO)
Ahmad Ghasson Ksaibati (Vice Chm)
Jennifer Wells (Chm)
Kimberly Giffard (Vice Chm)
Sheldon Barr (Co-CEO)
Anthony Infante (Chm)
Jill Zyrek (Chm)
Yeshitila Agzew (Chm)

South Bay Imaging, LLC (1)
4051 Upper Creek Dr Ste 103, Sun City Center, FL 33570
Tel.: (813) 634-8329
Medical Imaging Services
N.A.I.C.S.: 621512

South Lakes Surgicenter, LLC (1)
521 W Southlake Blvd Ste 175, Southlake, TX 76092
Tel.: (817) 328-2100
Web Site:
https://www.southlakesurgerycenter.com
Cosmetic Surgery Services
N.A.I.C.S.: 622110

Southern Hills Medical Center (1)
391 Wallace Rd, Nashville, TN 37211
Tel.: (615) 781-4000
Web Site:
http://www.tristarsouthernhills.com
Sales Range: $25-49.9 Million
Emp.: 650
Hospital Operator
N.A.I.C.S.: 622110

Subsidiary (Domestic):

Southern Hills Hospital & Medical Center (2)
9300 W Sunset Rd, Las Vegas, NV 89148
Tel.: (702) 916-5000
Web Site:
https://www.southernhillshospital.com
Emp.: 911
Health Care & Allied Services
N.A.I.C.S.: 621999

Southern Hills Neurology Consultants, LLC (1)

397 Wallace Rd Ste C-305, Nashville, TN 37211
Tel.: (615) 333-3115
N.A.I.C.S.: 621999

Southern Kentucky Medicine Associates, LLC (1)
990 Wilkinson Trace Ste 100, Bowling Green, KY 42103
Tel.: (270) 781-4043
Emp.: 3
General Medical & Surgical Services
N.A.I.C.S.: 622110

Southwest Medical Center Surgical Group, LLC (1)
4212 W Congress St, Lafayette, LA 70506-6765
Tel.: (337) 981-1695
General Medical & Surgical Services
N.A.I.C.S.: 622110

Space Coast Surgical Center, Ltd. (1)
595 N Courtenay Pkwy Ste 103, Merritt Island, FL 32953
Tel.: (321) 890-1800
Web Site:
http://www.spacecoastsurgerycenter.com
Health Care & Allied Services
N.A.I.C.S.: 621999

Spalding Rehabilitation L.L.C. (1)
900 Potomac St, Aurora, CO 80011
Tel.: (303) 367-1166
Web Site: http://www.spaldingrehab.com
Medical Support Services
N.A.I.C.S.: 621111

Specialty Associates of West Houston, PLLC (1)
15200 SW Freeway Ste 290, Sugar Land, TX 77478-3845
Tel.: (281) 980-2010
General Medical & Surgical Services
N.A.I.C.S.: 622110

Specialty Surgery Center (1)
7250 Cathedral Rock Dr, Las Vegas, NV 89128
Tel.: (702) 933-3999
Web Site: http://www.specialtysclv.com
Health Care & Allied Services
N.A.I.C.S.: 621999

Spotsylvania Multi-Specialty Group, LLC (1)
4604 Spotsylvania Pkwy Ste 200, Fredericksburg, VA 22408
Tel.: (540) 423-6600
Web Site: http://hcavirginiaphysicians.com
General Medical Care Services
N.A.I.C.S.: 622110

Spotsylvania Regional Medical Center (1)
4600 Spotsylvania Pkwy, Fredericksburg, VA 22408
Tel.: (540) 498-4000
General Medical & Surgical Services
N.A.I.C.S.: 622110

Spotsylvania Regional Medical Center (1)
4604 Spotsylvania Pkwy, Fredericksburg, VA 22408
Tel.: (540) 498-4000
Web Site: https://www.hcavirginia.com
Emp.: 450
General Medical Care Services
N.A.I.C.S.: 622110

Spring Hill Imaging, LLC (1)
12037 Cortez Blvd, Brooksville, FL 34613-7349
Tel.: (352) 597-9008
General Medical & Surgical Services
N.A.I.C.S.: 622110
Agnes Augeloo (Gen Mgr)

Spring Hill Physicians, LLC (1)
3001 Reserve Blvd Ste 200, Spring Hill, TN 37174
Tel.: (931) 499-7244
Web Site: http://tristarmedgroup.com
Health Care Srvices
N.A.I.C.S.: 621399

St. David's Cardiology, PLLC (1)
1015 E 32nd St Ste 508, Austin, TX 78705

Tel.: (512) 807-3140
Web Site: https://www.cardiotexas.com
Cardio Care Services
N.A.I.C.S.: 621111

St. David's Georgetown Hospital (1)
2000 Scenic Dr, Georgetown, TX 78626
Tel.: (512) 943-3000
General Medical & Surgical Services
N.A.I.C.S.: 622110

St. David's Medical Center (1)
919 E 32nd St, Austin, TX 78704
Tel.: (512) 476-7111
General Medical & Surgical Services
N.A.I.C.S.: 622110

St. David's North Austin Medical Center (1)
12221 N Mopac Expwy, Austin, TX 78758
Tel.: (512) 901-1000
Web Site: https://stdavids.com
Health Care Srvices
N.A.I.C.S.: 621111
Cynthia Nicholas (Chief Nursing Officer)
Tom Jackson (CEO)
Becky Barnes (COO)
Jill Leone (CFO)

St. David's Round Rock Medical Center (1)
2400 Round Rock Ave, Round Rock, TX 78681
Tel.: (512) 341-1000
Web Site: https://stdavids.com
Health Care Srvices
N.A.I.C.S.: 621111
Tami Taylor (Chief Nursing Officer)
Katie Lattanzi Perkins (COO)
Jeremy Barclay (CEO)
Laura Wiess (CFO)
Emily Marcus (Officer)

St. David's South Austin Medical Center (1)
901 W Ben White Blvd, Austin, TX 78704
Tel.: (512) 447-2211
General Medical & Surgical Services
N.A.I.C.S.: 622110

St. David's Specialized Womens Services, PLLC (1)
12221 Renfert Way Ste 220, Austin, TX 78758
Tel.: (512) 719-5224
Web Site: http://www.stdavidssws.com
Health Care Srvices
N.A.I.C.S.: 621111

St. Davis's South Austin Medical Center (1)
901 W Ben White Blvd, Austin, TX 78704
Tel.: (512) 447-2211
Web Site: https://stdavids.com
Hospital Services
N.A.I.C.S.: 622110
C. David Huffstutler (Pres & CEO)
Shari Collier (CFO & VP)
Kenneth White Mitchell (Chief Medical Officer)
Robert Nagel (Sr VP-Bus Dev)
Marian J. Wu (Chief Legal Officer & VP)
William H. Rice (Sr VP)
Julie Hajek (Sr VP-Human Resources)
Mike Blom (CIO)
Jon Treadon (VP)
Denise Bradley (VP-Communications-Community Affairs)
Kelli Shifflett (VP)
Amanda Gibson (VP-Marketing)
Diana Kraus (Asst VP)
Caroline Murphy (Officer)
Hamel Patel (VP-Operations)
Susan Sample (VP)
Marisa Strumeyer (VP-Planning)
Mark Worsham (VP)
Janet Smith (VP)
Jane Jordan (Asst VP)

St. Lucie Hospitalists, LLC (1)
1800 SE Tiffany Ave, Port Saint Lucie, FL 34952-7521
Tel.: (772) 335-9000
Web Site: http://www.stluciemed.com
Emp.: 7
Health Care Srvices
N.A.I.C.S.: 621399

St. Lucie Medical Center (1)

1800 SE Tiffany Ave, Port Saint Lucie, FL 34952
Tel.: (772) 335-4000
Web Site: http://www.stluciemed.com
Sales Range: $75-99.9 Million
Emp.: 1,195
Hospital
N.A.I.C.S.: 622110

St. Lucie Medical Specialists, LLC (1)
1700 SE Hillmoor Dr Ste 406 - 407, Port Saint Lucie, FL 34952-7521
Tel.: (772) 335-9600
General Medical & Surgical Services
N.A.I.C.S.: 622110

St. Mark's Hospital (1)
1200 E 3900 S, Salt Lake City, UT 84124-1300
Tel.: (801) 268-7111
Web Site: https://mountainstar.com
Hospital Services
N.A.I.C.S.: 622110

St. Marks Physician Billing, LLC (1)
1160 E 3900 S Ste G200, Salt Lake City, UT 84124-1202
Tel.: (801) 268-7766
Ambulatory Health Care Services
N.A.I.C.S.: 621493

St. Petersburg General Hospital (1)
6500 38th Ave N, Saint Petersburg, FL 33710
Tel.: (727) 384-1414
Web Site: http://www.stpetegeneral.com
Sales Range: $50-74.9 Million
Emp.: 587
Hospital
N.A.I.C.S.: 622110
Janice Balzano (Pre)
Frank P. Marsalisi (Vice Chm)
Kenneth Wicker (Pres, CEO & Sec)
Ron Rasmussen (Chief Medical Officer)
Mary Tabor (Chief Nursing Officer)
Shawn Gregory (CFO)
Liz Rigney (VP-Quality)
Danielle McIntyre (VP-Human Resources)
Jennifer Garbowicz (Vice Chm)
Romeo Acosta Jr. (Chm)

Statland Medical Group, LLC (1)
12140 Nall Ave Ste 100, Overland Park, KS 66209
Tel.: (913) 345-8500
Web Site: https://mymidwestphysician.com
Health Care Srvices
N.A.I.C.S.: 621399

Statland Medical Group, LLC (1)
12140 Nall Ave Ste 100, Overland Park, KS 66209
Tel.: (913) 345-8500
General Medical & Surgical Services
N.A.I.C.S.: 622110

Stephenson Laser Center, L.L.C. (1)
1000 N Lincoln Blvd Ste 190, Oklahoma City, OK 73104
Tel.: (405) 271-2500
Health Care Srvices
N.A.I.C.S.: 621399

Sterling Primary Care Associates, LLC (1)
2400 Patterson St Ste 500, Nashville, TN 37203
Tel.: (615) 327-7400
Web Site: http://tristarmedgroup.com
Health Care Srvices
N.A.I.C.S.: 621999

Stiles Road Imaging LLC (1)
31 Stiles Rd Ste 1200, Salem, NH 03079
Tel.: (603) 893-4352
Emp.: 28
Health Care Srvices
N.A.I.C.S.: 621399
Beveley Dudois (Office Mgr)

Stone Oak Surgicenter, LLC (1)
123 N Loop 1604 E Ste 107, San Antonio, TX 78232
Tel.: (210) 267-1374
Web Site: https://www.stoneoaksc.com
Surgical Care Services
N.A.I.C.S.: 621493

Stonecrest Medical Group - Family Practice of Murfreesboro, LLC (1)

2706 Old Fort Pkwy Suite E, Murfreesboro,
TN 37128
Tel.: (615) 893-1230
General Medical & Surgical Services
N.A.I.C.S.: 622110

Sugar Land Surgery Center, Ltd. (1)
15300 Southwest Fwy Ste 100, Sugar
Land, TX 77478
Tel.: (281) 274-6670
Web Site: https://sugarlandsurgery.com
General Medical & Surgical Services
N.A.I.C.S.: 622110

Summit Surgery Center, L.P. (1)
231 W Pueblo St, Santa Barbara, CA
93105
Tel.: (805) 898-2797
Web Site:
 https://www.summitsurgerycenter.com
Surgical Hospital Services
N.A.I.C.S.: 622110

Summit Walk-in Clinic, LLC (1)
669 S Mt Juliet Rd, Mount Juliet, TN 37122
Tel.: (615) 758-2929
Web Site: http://www.summitwalk-in.com
Women Healthcare Services
N.A.I.C.S.: 621610

Sun-Med, LLC (1)
2710 Northridge Dr NW, Grand Rapids, MI
49544
Tel.: (616) 259-8400
Web Site: https://www.sun-med.com
Medical Equipment Distr
N.A.I.C.S.: 423450

Subsidiary (Domestic):

Westmed, Inc. (2)
5580 S Nogales Hwy, Tucson, AZ 85706-
5706
Web Site: http://www.westmedinc.com
Surgical Appliance & Supplies Mfr
N.A.I.C.S.: 339113
Jon McKinnon (CEO)

**Sunrise Hospital & Medical
Center** (1)
3186 S Maryland Pkwy, Las Vegas, NV
89109
Tel.: (702) 961-5000
Web Site: http://www.sunrisehospital.com
Medical Devices
N.A.I.C.S.: 622110

**Sunrise Hospital and Medical Center,
LLC** (1)
3186 S Maryland Pkwy, Las Vegas, NV
89109
Tel.: (702) 961-5000
Web Site: https://sunrisehospital.com
General Medical & Surgical Services
N.A.I.C.S.: 622110

Sunrise Trauma Services, LLC (1)
3196 S Maryland Pkwy Ste 101, Las Ve-
gas, NV 89109
Tel.: (702) 731-8099
General Medical & Surgical Services
N.A.I.C.S.: 622110

**Surgery Associates of NTX,
PLLC** (1)
8865 Synergy Dr 100, McKinney, TX 75070
Tel.: (972) 562-1119
Web Site:
 https://www.surgicalassociatesofnorth
 texas.com
General Medical & Surgical services
N.A.I.C.S.: 622110
Gina Moffat (Mgr-Scheduling)

Surgery Center at St. Andrews (1)
1350 E Venice Ave, Venice, FL 34285
Tel.: (941) 488-2030
Web Site:
 https://www.saintandrewssurgery.com
Emp.: 25
Health Care Srvices
N.A.I.C.S.: 621399

Surgery Center of Aventura, Ltd. (1)
20601 E Dixie Hwy Ste 400, Aventura, FL
33180
Tel.: (305) 792-0323
Web Site: https://scaventura.com
General Medical & Surgical Services
N.A.I.C.S.: 622110

**Surgery Center of Chattanooga,
L.P.** (1)
400 N Holtzclaw Ave, Chattanooga, TN
37404
Tel.: (423) 698-6871
Web Site: http://www.csmosurgery.com
Health Care Srvices
N.A.I.C.S.: 621999

**Surgery Center of Port Charlotte,
Ltd.** (1)
21260 Olean Blvd Ste 105, Port Charlotte,
FL 33952
Tel.: (941) 629-1181
General Medical & Surgical Services
N.A.I.C.S.: 622110

Surgery Center of Rome, L.P. (1)
16 John Maddox Dr, Rome, GA 30165
Tel.: (706) 802-3727
Web Site:
 http://www.surgerycenterofrome.com
Health Care Srvices
N.A.I.C.S.: 621399

**Surgery Center of the Rockies,
LLC** (1)
1300 S Potomac St Ste 122, Aurora, CO
80012
Tel.: (303) 369-1600
Web Site:
 http://www.surgerycenteroftherockies.com
Health Care Srvices
N.A.I.C.S.: 621999
Suzanne Boulter (Dir-Nursing)

**Surgical Associates of the New River
Valley, LLC** (1)
830 Hospital Dr, Blacksburg, VA 24060-
7023
Tel.: (540) 382-6613
Health Care Srvices
N.A.I.C.S.: 621999

Surgical Center of El Paso (1)
1815 N Stanton, El Paso, TX 79902
Tel.: (915) 533-8412
Web Site: https://elpasosurgerycenters.com
General Medical & Surgical Services
N.A.I.C.S.: 622110

Surgical Park Center, Ltd. (1)
9065 Dadeland Blvd, Miami, FL 33156
Tel.: (305) 271-9100
Web Site: https://surgicalparkcenter.com
General Medical & Surgical Services
N.A.I.C.S.: 622110

**Surgical Specialists of Clear Lake,
PLLC** (1)
450 Medical Ctr Blvd Ste 600, Webster, TX
77598
Tel.: (281) 332-4596
Web Site:
 https://www.clearlakesurgeons.com
Medical & Surgical Hospital Services
N.A.I.C.S.: 622110
Melissa Ashmus (Office Mgr)

**Surgicare of Central Park Surgery
Center, LLC** (1)
900 W 38th St Ste 200, Austin, TX 78705
Tel.: (512) 323-2061
Web Site:
 http://www.stdavidssurgerycenters.com
Ambulatory & Health Care Services
N.A.I.C.S.: 621493

Surgicare of Clarksville, LLC (1)
121 Hillcrest Dr, Clarksville, TN 37043
Tel.: (931) 552-9992
Web Site:
 http://www.surgerycenterofclarksville.com
Health Care Srvices
N.A.I.C.S.: 621498

Surgicare of Corpus Christi, LLC (1)
718 Elizabeth St, Corpus Christi, TX 78404
Tel.: (361) 882-3204
Web Site: https://www.corpuschristi-sc.com
General Medical & Surgical Services
N.A.I.C.S.: 622110

Surgicare of Countryside, Inc. (1)
3291 N Mcmullen Booth Rd, Clearwater, FL
33761
Tel.: (727) 725-5800
General Medical & Surgical Services
N.A.I.C.S.: 622110

**Surgicare of Denver Mid-Town,
Inc.** (1)
1919 E 18th Ave, Denver, CO 80206-1107
Tel.: (303) 322-3993
Emp.: 24
Medical Support Services
N.A.I.C.S.: 621111
Sofi Angeles (Gen Mgr)

Surgicare of Salem, LLC (1)
32 Stiles Rd, Salem, NH 03079
Tel.: (603) 898-7910
Emp.: 4
General Medical & Surgical Services
N.A.I.C.S.: 622110

Surgicare of South Austin (1)
4307 James Casey, Austin, TX 78745
Tel.: (512) 416-6006
Web Site:
 https://www.surgicareofsouthaustin.com
General Medical & Surgical Services
N.A.I.C.S.: 622110

Surgicare of South Austin, Inc. (1)
4307 James Casey, Austin, TX 78745
Tel.: (512) 416-6006
Web Site:
 http://www.stdavidssurgerycenters.com
Medical & Surgical Hospital Services
N.A.I.C.S.: 622110

Surgicare of Southern Hills, Inc. (1)
1001 Health Park Dr Ste 101, Brentwood,
TN 37027
Tel.: (615) 750-8777
Web Site:
 https://www.brentwoodsurgerycenter.com
General Medical & Surgical Services
N.A.I.C.S.: 622110

Surgicare of Wasatch Front, LLC (1)
3715 W 4100 S, West Valley City, UT
84120-5537
Tel.: (801) 417-1010
General Medical & Surgical Services
N.A.I.C.S.: 622110

Surgicare of Wichita, LLC (1)
2818 N Greenwich Rd, Wichita, KS 67226
Tel.: (316) 685-2207
Web Site: https://surgicareofwichita.com
Outpatient Surgical Services
N.A.I.C.S.: 622110

**Surgicenter of Johnson County,
Ltd.** (1)
8800 Ballentine, Overland Park, KS 66214
Tel.: (913) 894-4050
Web Site: https://surgicenterjc.com
General Medical & Surgical Services
N.A.I.C.S.: 622110

**Surgicenter of Kansas City,
L.L.C.** (1)
701 E 101st Ter, Kansas City, MO 64131
Tel.: (816) 523-0100
Web Site: https://www.sckcmo.com
Ambulatory Surgical Centers
N.A.I.C.S.: 621493

Sycamore Shoals Hospital, Inc. (1)
1501 W Elk Ave, Elizabethton, TN 37643-
2854
Tel.: (423) 542-1300
Hospital Management Services
N.A.I.C.S.: 622110
Marie Cole (Supvr-Nursing)

**TUHC Anesthesiology Group,
LLC** (1)
4700 I-10 Service Rd, Metairie, LA 70001
Tel.: (504) 780-8282
Healthcare Support Services
N.A.I.C.S.: 621111

TUHC Physician Group, LLC (1)
4700 S I 10 Service Rd W, Metairie, LA
70001-1241
Tel.: (504) 780-8282
Web Site: http://www.tulanelakeside.com
Health Care Srvices
N.A.I.C.S.: 621399

Tallahassee Medical Center, Inc. (1)
2626 Capital Medical Blvd, Tallahassee, FL
32308
Tel.: (850) 325-5000
Health Care Srvices
N.A.I.C.S.: 621399

**Tallahassee Outpatient Surgery
Center** (1)
3334 Capital Medical Blvd Ste 500, Talla-
hassee, FL 32308
Tel.: (850) 877-4688
Web Site: https://tallahasseeoutpatient.com
General Medical & Surgical Services
N.A.I.C.S.: 622110

**Tampa Eye & Specialty Surgery
Center** (1)
4302 N Gomez Ave, Tampa, FL 33607
Tel.: (813) 870-6330
Web Site: https://tampaeyesurgery.com
General Medical & Surgical Services
N.A.I.C.S.: 622110

**Tarrant County Surgery Center,
L.P.** (1)
3501 Matlock Rd, Arlington, TX 76015
Tel.: (817) 375-9370
Web Site:
 http://www.trinityparksugerycenter.com
Medical & Surgical Hospital Services
N.A.I.C.S.: 622110
Stephen Ellis (Dir-Medical)

**Tennessee Healthcare Management,
Inc.** (1)
3 Maryland Farms Ste 250, Armuchee, GA
30105
Tel.: (615) 373-7600
Emp.: 100
General Medical & Surgical Services
N.A.I.C.S.: 622110

Terre Haute Regional Hospital (1)
3901 S 7th St, Terre Haute, IN 47802-5709
Tel.: (812) 232-0021
Web Site: https://www.regionalhospital.com
Sales Range: $75-99.9 Million
Hospital
N.A.I.C.S.: 622110
Bart Colwell (Pres)
Mark Casanova (CEO)
Korenna Power (CFO)
Anthony Roberts (COO)

**Texas Institute of Medicine &
Surgery** (1)
7711 Louis Pasteur Dr Ste707, San Anto-
nio, TX 78229
Tel.: (210) 575-8501
Emp.: 42
General Medical & Surgical Services
N.A.I.C.S.: 622110

**Texas Institute of Pediatrics,
PLLC** (1)
4410 Medical Dr Ste 540, San Antonio, TX
78229-3755
Tel.: (210) 575-6240
Web Site:
 https://methodistphysicianpractices.com
Health Care Srvices
N.A.I.C.S.: 621610

Texas Joint Institute, PLLC (1)
7777 Forest Ln Ste C-106, Dallas, TX
75230
Tel.: (972) 566-5255
Web Site: https://www.txjointinstitute.com
Orthopedic Clinic Services
N.A.I.C.S.: 621340

Texas Orthopedic Hospital (1)
7401 S Main St, Houston, TX 77030
Tel.: (713) 799-8600
Web Site: https://www.texasorthopedic.com
Orthopedic Hospital Operating Services
N.A.I.C.S.: 622310
Hussein Elkousy (Chm)
Eric Becker (CEO)

Texas Orthopedic Hospital (1)
7401 S Main St, Houston, TX 77030
Tel.: (713) 799-8600
Web Site: https://texasorthopedic.com
General Medical & Surgical Services
N.A.I.C.S.: 622110

**The Austin Diagnostic Clinic,
PLLC** (1)
2400 Cedar Bend Dr, Austin, TX 78758
Tel.: (512) 901-1111
Web Site: https://adclinic.com
General Medical & Surgical Services
N.A.I.C.S.: 622110

The Birth Company Limited (1)
137 Harley Street, London, W1G 6BF,
United Kingdom

HCA Healthcare, Inc.—(Continued)

Tel.: (44) 207 725 0528
Web Site:
https://www.thebirthcompany.co.uk
Diagnostic Imaging Services
N.A.I.C.S.: 621512
Kate Richardson (Mng Dir)

The Cancer Care Center of North Florida, LLC (1)
289 Stonegate Ter Ste 103, Lake City, FL 32024
Tel.: (386) 755-1655
Web Site: http://ccofnf.com
Cancer Treatment Services
N.A.I.C.S.: 622310

The Christie Clinic LLP (1)
Wilmslow Road, Manchester, M20 4BX, United Kingdom
Tel.: (44) 1619187538
Web Site: http://www.thechristieclinic.co.uk
General Medical Care Services
N.A.I.C.S.: 622110

The Harley Street Clinic (1)
35 Weymouth Street, London, W1G 8BJ, United Kingdom
Tel.: (44) 2039930651
General Medical & Surgical Services
N.A.I.C.S.: 622110

The London Breast Institute UK Ltd (1)
The Princess Grace Hospital 42-52 Nottingham Place, London, W1U 5NY, United Kingdom
Tel.: (44) 2079082029
Web Site:
http://www.londonbreastinstitute.co.uk
Diagnostic Imaging Services
N.A.I.C.S.: 621512
Ewa O'Brien (Sec)

The London Gamma Knife Centre LLP (1)
Platinum Medical Centre 15 - 17 Lodge Road St Johns Wood, London, NW8 7JA, United Kingdom
Tel.: (44) 2035532432
Brain Tumour Surgical Services
N.A.I.C.S.: 622310

The London General Practice Limited (1)
114a Harley Street, London, W1G 7JL, United Kingdom
Tel.: (44) 2079351000
Web Site:
https://www.thelondongeneralpractice.com
Emp.: 30
Medical Consulting & Health Care Services
N.A.I.C.S.: 541611

The Medical Center of Aurora (1)
1501 S Potomac St, Aurora, CO 80012
Tel.: (303) 695-2600
Web Site: https://healthonecares.com
Sales Range: $50-74.9 Million
Emp.: 2,075
Hospital
N.A.I.C.S.: 622110
Bryce Dehaven (CFO)
Ryan Simpson (Pres & CEO)
Cindy Meyer (COO-Behavioral Health Svcs)
Hallie Woods (COO)
Katie Weihe (VP-HR)
Alexandra Hoffman (VP-Business Development)
Phil Stahel (Chief Medical Officer)
Tyler Hood (Chief Admin Officer)

The Medical Group of Kansas City, LLC (1)
5701 W 119th St Ste 345, Leawood, KS 66209
Tel.: (913) 339-9046
General Medical & Surgical Services
N.A.I.C.S.: 622110

The Neurohealth Sciences Center, LLC (1)
450 E Las Olas Blvd, Fort Lauderdale, FL 33301
Tel.: (407) 833-7505
General Medical & Surgical Services
N.A.I.C.S.: 622110

The Physicians Clinic Limited (1)

13-14 Devonshire Street, London, W1G 7AE, United Kingdom
Tel.: (44) 2070348164
Web Site:
http://www.thephysiciansclinic.co.uk
Physician Clinic Services
N.A.I.C.S.: 621111
Paul Glynne (Co-Founder)
Tim Strawbridge (CEO)
Huw Beynon (Co-Founder)

The Platinum Medical Centre (1)
Platinum Medical Centre 15-17 Lodge, London, NW8 7JA, United Kingdom
Tel.: (44) 39939085
Web Site:
http://www.theplatinummedicalcentre.com
Health Care Srvices
N.A.I.C.S.: 621610

The Prostate Centre Limited (1)
18 Devonshire Street, London, W1G 7AQ, United Kingdom
Tel.: (44) 207 935 9720
Web Site: http://www.theprostatecentre.com
Diagnostic Imaging Services
N.A.I.C.S.: 621512

The Wasatch Endoscopy Center, Ltd. (1)
1220 E 3900 S Ste 1B, Salt Lake City, UT 84124
Tel.: (801) 281-3657
Web Site:
https://wasatchendoscopycenter.com
General Medical & Surgical Services
N.A.I.C.S.: 622110

The Wellington Hospital (1)
Wellington Place St John's Wood, London, NW8 9LE, United Kingdom
Tel.: (44) 2039931055
General Medical & Surgical Services
N.A.I.C.S.: 622110

The Woman's Hospital of Texas (1)
7600 Fannin, Houston, TX 77054
Tel.: (713) 790-1234
Web Site: https://www.womanshospital.com
Sales Range: $50-74.9 Million
Hospital
N.A.I.C.S.: 622110
Blair Callaway (CFO)
Cindy Celnik (Chief Medical Officer)
Jeanna Bamburg (CEO)

Timpanogos Regional Hospital (1)
750 W 800 N, Orem, UT 84057
Tel.: (801) 714-6000
Web Site: https://mountainstar.com
Sales Range: $25-49.9 Million
Emp.: 500
Hospital
N.A.I.C.S.: 622110
Kimball Anderson (CEO)

Total Imaging - Parsons, LLC (1)
2700 University Sq Dr, Tampa, FL 33612
Tel.: (813) 874-3177
Web Site: http://towerradiologycenters.com
General Medical & Surgical Services
N.A.I.C.S.: 622110

Town Plaza Family Practice, LLC (1)
5701 W 119th St Ste 330, Overland Park, KS 66209
Tel.: (913) 345-3650
General Medical & Surgical Services
N.A.I.C.S.: 622110

Town Plaza Family Practice, LLC (1)
5701 W 119th St Ste 330, Overland Park, KS 66209
Tel.: (913) 345-3650
General Medical & Surgical Services
N.A.I.C.S.: 622110
Wendy Stillwyl (Mgr)

Trauma Medicine Services of TN, LLC (1)
2300 Patterson St, Nashville, TN 37203-1538
General Health Care Services
N.A.I.C.S.: 621491

Tri-County Surgical Specialists, LLC (1)
9313 Medical Pl Ste 204, North Charleston, SC 29406
Tel.: (843) 797-5151

Web Site: http://tricountysurgical.com
Health Care Srvices
N.A.I.C.S.: 621399

TriStar Bone Marrow Transplant, LLC (1)
250 25th Ave N Ste 316, Nashville, TN 37203
Tel.: (615) 342-7440
Hospital Management Services
N.A.I.C.S.: 622110

TriStar Cardiovascular Surgery, LLC (1)
2400 Patterson St Ste 307, Nashville, TN 37203
Tel.: (615) 342-6900
Web Site:
http://www.tristarcardiovascularsurgery.com
Emp.: 12
Surgical Care Services
N.A.I.C.S.: 621493

TriStar Family Care, LLC (1)
313 N Main St, Ashland City, TN 37015
Tel.: (615) 792-1911
Web Site: http://www.tristarfamilycare.com
Family Health Care Services
N.A.I.C.S.: 621111

TriStar Greenview Regional Hospital (1)
1801 Ashley Cir, Bowling Green, KY 42104
Tel.: (270) 793-1000
Web Site: https://www.tristarhealth.com
General Medical & Surgical services
N.A.I.C.S.: 622110

TriStar Gynecology Oncology, LLC (1)
330 23rd Ave N ste 600, Nashville, TN 37203
Tel.: (615) 340-4640
Emp.: 30
Health Care Srvices
N.A.I.C.S.: 621399
Farah White (Mgr-Practice)

TriStar Health System (1)
1000 Health Park Dr Ste 500, Brentwood, TN 37027
Tel.: (615) 886-5000
Web Site: https://www.tristarhealth.com
Sales Range: $25-49.9 Million
Emp.: 400
Healtcare Services
N.A.I.C.S.: 621410

Subsidiary (Domestic):

Eastside Medical Center (2)
1700 Medical Way, Snellville, GA 30078
Tel.: (770) 979-0200
Web Site: http://www.eastsidemedical.com
Hospital
N.A.I.C.S.: 622110
Scottly Schmid (CEO)

Parkridge Medical Center, Inc. (2)
2333 McCallie Ave, Chattanooga, TN 37404
Tel.: (423) 698-6061
Web Site:
http://www.parkridgemedicalcenter.com
Sales Range: $50-74.9 Million
Hospital
N.A.I.C.S.: 622110

Subsidiary (Domestic):

Parkridge East Hospital (3)
941 Spring Creek Rd, Chattanooga, TN 37412
Tel.: (423) 894-7870
Web Site: https://parkridgehealth.com
Emp.: 382
Health Care Srvices
N.A.I.C.S.: 621399

Parkridge Valley Hospital (3)
1000 Tennessee 28, Jasper, TN 37347
Tel.: (423) 837-3350
Web Site: https://parkridgehealth.com
Health Care Services
N.A.I.C.S.: 621399

Parkridge West Hospital (3)
1000 Tennessee 28, Jasper, TN 37347
Tel.: (423) 837-9500
Web Site: https://parkridgehealth.com

Sales Range: $25-49.9 Million
Emp.: 150
Hospital
N.A.I.C.S.: 622110

Subsidiary (Domestic):

Summit Medical Center (2)
5655 Frist Blvd, Hermitage, TN 37076
Tel.: (615) 316-3000
Web Site: https://www.tristarhealth.com
General Medical & Surgical Hospitals
N.A.I.C.S.: 622110

TriStar Hendersonville Medical Center (1)
355 New Shackle Island Rd, Hendersonville, TN 37075
Tel.: (615) 338-1000
Web Site: https://www.tristarhealth.com
Health Care Srvices
N.A.I.C.S.: 621399

TriStar Horizon Medical Center (1)
111 Hwy 70 E, Dickson, TN 37055
Tel.: (615) 446-0446
Web Site: https://www.tristarhealth.com
Health Care Srvices
N.A.I.C.S.: 621399

TriStar Joint Replacement Institute, LLC (1)
2400 Patterson St Ste 100, Nashville, TN 37203-1562
Tel.: (615) 342-0038
Web Site: https://sjri.com
Health Care Services
N.A.I.C.S.: 621610

TriStar Medical Group - Legacy Health, LLC (1)
2400 Patterson St ste 418, Nashville, TN 37203
Tel.: (615) 342-6000
Web Site:
http://www.tristarlegacyhealth.com
Medicine Practice Services
N.A.I.C.S.: 621111

TriStar Radiation Oncology, LLC (1)
2410 Patterson St, Nashville, TN 37203-1551
Tel.: (615) 342-4850
Emp.: 23
General Medical & Surgical Services
N.A.I.C.S.: 622110
Dr. Hunt (Mng Dir)

TriStar Skyline Madison Campus (1)
500 Hospital Dr, Madison, TN 37115
Tel.: (615) 769-5000
Web Site: https://www.tristarhealth.com
Health Care Srvices
N.A.I.C.S.: 621399

TriStar Skyline Medical Center (1)
3441 Dickerson Pike, Nashville, TN 37207
Tel.: (615) 769-2000
Web Site: https://www.tristarhealth.com
Emp.: 900
Health Care Srvices
N.A.I.C.S.: 621399

TriStar Tennessee Heart and Vascular, LLC (1)
353 New Shackle Rd Bldg C Ste 300, Hendersonville, TN 37075
Tel.: (615) 824-0043
Cardiovascular Surgical Services
N.A.I.C.S.: 622110

Trident Behavioral Health Services, LLC (1)
9330 Medical Plaza Dr, Charleston, SC 29406-9104
Tel.: (843) 797-7000
Web Site:
http://www.tridenthealthsystem.com
Health Care Srvices
N.A.I.C.S.: 621399

Trident Health System (1)
9330 Medical Plz Dr, Charleston, SC 29406
Tel.: (843) 797-7000
Web Site:
https://www.tridenthealthsystem.com
Sales Range: $100-124.9 Million
Emp.: 2,000
Hospital Network
N.A.I.C.S.: 622110

Todd Gallati *(Pres)*
Christina Oh *(CEO)*

Subsidiary (Domestic):

Trident Medical Center, LLC (2)
9330 Medical Plaza Dr, Charleston, SC 29406
Tel.: (843) 797-7000
Web Site:
http://www.tridenthealthsystem.com
Hospital Management Services
N.A.I.C.S.: 622110

Trident Neonatology Services, LLC (1)
9330 Medical Plz Dr, Charleston, SC 29406-9104
Tel.: (843) 797-4272
Web Site: http://www.healthcare.com
Health Care Srvices
N.A.I.C.S.: 621399

Trinity Park Surgery Center (1)
3501 Matlock Rd, Arlington, TX 76015
Tel.: (817) 375-9370
Web Site:
https://trinityparksurgerycenter.com
General Medical & Surgical Services
N.A.I.C.S.: 622110

Tulane Medical Center (1)
1415 Tulane Ave, New Orleans, LA 70112
Tel.: (504) 988-5263
Web Site: http://www.tulanehealthcare.com
Health Care Srvices
N.A.I.C.S.: 621399

Twin Cities Hospital (1)
2190 Hwy 85 N, Niceville, FL 32578
Tel.: (850) 678-4131
Web Site: http://www.tchospital.com
Sales Range: $25-49.9 Million
Emp.: 330
Hospital
N.A.I.C.S.: 622110
David Whalen *(CEO)*
Shaun Lampron *(Chief Nursing Officer)*

U.S. Collections, Inc. (1)
3 City Pl Dr Ste 690, Saint Louis, MO 63141
Tel.: (314) 692-6500
Business Management Services
N.A.I.C.S.: 561110

University Hospital & Medical Center (1)
7201 N University Dr, Tamarac, FL 33321-2913
Tel.: (954) 721-2200
Web Site: http://www.uhmchealth.com
Sales Range: $25-49.9 Million
Emp.: 712
Hospital
N.A.I.C.S.: 622110

University Hospital, Ltd. (1)
7201 N University Dr, Tamarac, FL 33321
Tel.: (954) 721-2200
Web Site: http://www.uhmchealth.com
Hospital Management Services
N.A.I.C.S.: 622110

University Surgicenter, LLC (1)
561 Cranbury Rd, East Brunswick, NJ 08816
Tel.: (732) 390-4300
Web Site: https://universitysurgicenter.com
Health Care & Surgical Services
N.A.I.C.S.: 622110

Urology Specialists of Kingwood, PLLC (1)
22751 Professional Dr Ste 270, Kingwood, TX 77339-6028
Tel.: (281) 358-0171
Hospital Management Services
N.A.I.C.S.: 622110

Urology Specialists of Richmond, LLC (1)
8720 Stony Point Pkwy Ste 120, Richmond, VA 23235
Tel.: (804) 323-0226
Web Site: http://www.urospecva.com
Emp.: 10
Health Care Srvices
N.A.I.C.S.: 621111

Urology Surgery Center of Colorado, LLC (1)
2777 Mile High Stadium Cir, Denver, CO 80211
Tel.: (303) 825-3888
Web Site:
http://www.urologysurgerycenter.com
Emp.: 150
Medical Support Services
N.A.I.C.S.: 621111

Utah Surgical Center (1)
3715 W 4100 S Ste 100, West Valley City, UT 84120
Tel.: (801) 957-0200
Web Site: https://utahsurgicalcenter.com
General Medical & Surgical Services
N.A.I.C.S.: 622110

Valify, Inc. (1)
3001 Dallas Pkwy Ste 100, Frisco, TX 75034
Tel.: (972) 963-5130
Web Site: https://www.getvalify.com
Cost Management Services
N.A.I.C.S.: 541611
Les Popiolek *(CEO)*
Jay McCullough *(Chief Customer Officer)*

Valley Regional Medical Center (1)
100 A Alton Gloor Blvd, Brownsville, TX 78526
Tel.: (956) 350-7000
Web Site:
https://valleyregionalmedicalcenter.com
Sales Range: $25-49.9 Million
Emp.: 710
Hospital Operator
N.A.I.C.S.: 622110

Vidant Edgecombe Hospital (1)
111 Hospital Dr, Tarboro, NC 27886-2011
Tel.: (252) 641-7700
Web Site: http://www.vidanthealth.com
Health Care & Allied Services
N.A.I.C.S.: 621999

Virginia Gynecologic Oncology, LLC (1)
7607 Forest Ave Ste 200, Richmond, VA 23229
Tel.: (804) 200-7062
Web Site: http://vagynonc.com
Emp.: 11
General Medical Care Services
N.A.I.C.S.: 622110
Will Wagnan *(CEO)*

Virginia Gynecologic Oncology, LLC (1)
7607 Forest Ave Ste 410, Richmond, VA 23229
Tel.: (804) 200-7062
General Medical & Surgical Services
N.A.I.C.S.: 622110

Virginia Hematology & Oncology Associates, Inc. (1)
4501 Empire Ct, Fredericksburg, VA 22408
Tel.: (540) 371-0079
Web Site:
https://www.hoafredericksburg.com
General Medical Care Services
N.A.I.C.S.: 622110

Virginia Hospitalists, Inc. (1)
7155 Jahnke Rd, Richmond, VA 23225
Tel.: (804) 327-4046
General Medical Care Services
N.A.I.C.S.: 622110

Vision Consulting Group LLC (1)
6605 78th Pl NE Ste A, Marysville, WA 98270
Tel.: (425) 298-9600
General Medical & Surgical Services
N.A.I.C.S.: 622110

Walterboro Community Hospital, Inc. (1)
501 Robertson Blvd, Walterboro, SC 29488
Tel.: (843) 782-2000
Web Site: https://www.colletonmedical.com
Emp.: 400
Health Care Srvices
N.A.I.C.S.: 621399

Wasatch Endoscopy Center (1)
1220 E 3900 S Ste 1B, Salt Lake City, UT 84124
Tel.: (801) 281-3657
Web Site:
https://www.wasatchendoscopycenter.com
Diagnostic Imaging Services
N.A.I.C.S.: 621512

Wasatch Front Surgery Center, LLC (1)
3715 W 4100 S Ste 100, West Valley City, UT 84120
Tel.: (801) 957-0200
Web Site:
http://www.utahsurgicalcenter.com
Emp.: 30
Ambulatory Health Care Services
N.A.I.C.S.: 621493

Waterway Primary Care, LLC (1)
3600 Sea Mountain Hwy, Little River, SC 29566
Tel.: (843) 399-4848
Health Care & Allied Services
N.A.I.C.S.: 621999

Weatherford Texas Hospital Company, LLC (1)
713 E Anderson St, Weatherford, TX 76086-5705
Tel.: (682) 582-1000
Web Site:
http://www.weatherfordregional.com
General Medical & Surgical Hospitals
N.A.I.C.S.: 622110

Wellington Diagnostic Services LLP (1)
Roman House 296 Golders Green Road, London, NW11 9PY, United Kingdom
Tel.: (44) 2039932682
Web Site:
http://www.wellingtondiagnosticscentre.com
Diagnostic Imaging Services
N.A.I.C.S.: 621512
Eric Reichle *(CEO)*
Nikesh Davda *(CFO)*
Claire Dunsterville *(COO)*
Janice Stevens *(Chief Nursing Officer)*
Stephen Edmondson *(Head)*
Adrian Steele *(Chm-Clinical Governance)*
Huw Beynon *(Dir-Medical)*
Stephanie Grainger *(Chief HR Officer)*
Chris Rogerson *(CIO)*

Wesley Medical Center, LLC (1)
550 N Hillside St, Wichita, KS 67214
Tel.: (316) 962-2000
Web Site: http://www.wesleymc.com
Hospital
N.A.I.C.S.: 622110

West Boynton Beach Open Imaging Center, LLC (1)
10151 Enterprise Ctr Blvd Ste 109, Boynton Beach, FL 33437-3759
Tel.: (561) 752-5050
Web Site:
http://www.floridaopenimaging.com
General Medical & Surgical Services
N.A.I.C.S.: 622110

West Florida Behavioral Health, Inc. (1)
2191 E Johnson Ave, Pensacola, FL 32514
Tel.: (850) 494-3917
General Medical & Surgical Services
N.A.I.C.S.: 622110

West Florida Cardiology Network, LLC (1)
6006 49th St N Ste 200, Saint Petersburg, FL 33709-2148
Tel.: (727) 490-2100
General Medical & Surgical Services
N.A.I.C.S.: 622110
Julie Klean *(Mgr-Practice)*

West Florida Division, Inc. (1)
3031 N Rocky Point Dr W Ste 400, Tampa, FL 33607
Tel.: (813) 402-9400
Web Site: http://www.hcawestflorida.com
Emp.: 120
General Medical & Surgical Services
N.A.I.C.S.: 622110

West Florida Internal Medicine, LLC (1)
2120 E Johnson Ave Ste 100, Pensacola, FL 32514
Tel.: (850) 494-4600
Web Site:
http://www.westfloridamedicalgroup.com
Health Care & Allied Services
N.A.I.C.S.: 621999

West Florida Physician Network, LLC (1)
3501 Cortez Rd W, Bradenton, FL 34210-3104
Tel.: (941) 752-2700
Web Site: http://www.hcahealthcare.com
General Medical & Surgical Services
N.A.I.C.S.: 622110

West Florida Regional Medical Center (1)
8333 N Davis Hwy, Pensacola, FL 32514
Tel.: (850) 494-4000
Web Site:
http://www.westfloridahospital.com
Sales Range: $75-99.9 Million
Emp.: 1,600
Medical Center
N.A.I.C.S.: 622110

West Hills Hospital & Medical Center (1)
7300 Medical Ctr Dr, West Hills, CA 91307
Tel.: (818) 676-4000
Web Site: https://www.westhillshospital.com
Emp.: 900
Hospital Services
N.A.I.C.S.: 622110
Roshan Ghaznavi *(Chm)*

West Hills Surgical Center, Ltd. (1)
7240 Medical Center Dr, West Hills, CA 91307
Tel.: (818) 226-9151
Web Site: https://westhillssurgicalcenter.com
General Medical & Surgical Services
N.A.I.C.S.: 622110

West Hills Surgical Center, Ltd. (1)
7240 Medical Center Dr, West Hills, CA 91307
Tel.: (818) 226-9151
Web Site:
https://www.westhillssurgicalcenter.com
Health Care Srvices
N.A.I.C.S.: 621999
David M. Fung *(Dir-Medical)*
Mark Boyajian *(Dir-Medical)*
Victoria Hannah *(Dir-Clinical-CNOR)*
Monica O'Hayer *(Mgr-OR)*
Allison Anderson *(Coord-Bus Office)*

West Houston Surgicare, Inc. (1)
970 Campbell Rd, Houston, TX 77024
Tel.: (713) 461-3547
Web Site:
https://www.westhoustonsurgicare.com
General Medical & Surgical Services
N.A.I.C.S.: 622110

West Houston Surgicare, Inc. (1)
970 Campbell Rd, Houston, TX 77024
Tel.: (817) 410-4300
Web Site:
http://www.westhoustonsurgicare.com
General Medical & Surgical Services
N.A.I.C.S.: 622110

West LPN Fort Worth Oncology, PLLC (1)
1001 12th Ave Ste 200, Fort Worth, TX 76104-7400
Tel.: (817) 338-9291
Cancer Treatment Services
N.A.I.C.S.: 622310

West Valley Imaging, LLC (1)
3715 W 4100 S, West Valley City, UT 84120-5537
Tel.: (801) 924-0029
Web Site:
Medical Support Services
N.A.I.C.S.: 621111

West Valley Medical Center (1)
1717 Arlington Ave, Caldwell, ID 83605-4802
Tel.: (208) 459-4641
Web Site:
https://www.westvalleymedctr.com
Sales Range: $25-49.9 Million
Emp.: 800
Hospital
N.A.I.C.S.: 622110
Kaycee Emery *(Dir-Mktg & PR)*

HCA Healthcare, Inc.—(Continued)

West Valley Medical Group, LLC (1)
315 E Elm St Ste 350, Caldwell, ID 83605
Tel.: (208) 459-0028
Web Site: https://westvalleymedgroup.com
General Medical & Surgical Services
N.A.I.C.S.: 622110

Western Plains Capital, Inc. (1)
1011 Ctr Rd, Wilmington, DE 19805
Tel.: (302) 573-3850
Heathcare Services
N.A.I.C.S.: 621999

Westside Surgery Center, Ltd. (1)
2731 Park St, Jacksonville, FL 32205-7607
Tel.: (904) 389-1077
Web Site:
  http://www.parksidesurgerycenter.com
Health Care Srvices
N.A.I.C.S.: 621399

Woman's Health Group, PLLC (1)
7600 Fannin, Houston, TX 77054
Tel.: (713) 795-5450
Web Site:
  http://www.womanshealthgroup.com
Health Care Srvices
N.A.I.C.S.: 621111

**Women Specialists of Clear Lake,
PLLC** (1)
400 Medical Ctr Blvd Ste 300, Webster, TX
77598-4244
Tel.: (281) 557-0300
Web Site: https://womensclearlake.com
Health Care Srvices
N.A.I.C.S.: 621610

**Women Specialists of Mainland,
PLLC** (1)
3828 Hughes Ct Ste 207, Dickinson, TX
77539-6244
Tel.: (281) 799-2422
General Medical & Surgical Services
N.A.I.C.S.: 622110

**Women's Center at Brookside,
LLC** (1)
6675 Holmes Rd Ste 300, Kansas City, MO
64131-1150
Tel.: (816) 333-5005
Healthcare Support Services
N.A.I.C.S.: 621111

**Women's and Children's Professional
Management, L.L.C.** (1)
4600 Ambassador Caffery Pkwy, Lafayette,
LA 70508
Tel.: (337) 470-2000
Web Site: http://lourdesrmc.com
Healthcare Support Services
N.A.I.C.S.: 621111

**Women's and Children's Specialists,
LLC** (1)
330 23rd Ave N, Nashville, TN 37203
Tel.: (615) 342-7339
Surgical Care Services
N.A.I.C.S.: 621493

**WomensLink Center of Wylie - A
Medical Center of Plano Facility,
LLC** (1)
3901 W 15th St, Plano, TX 75075
Tel.: (972) 596-6800
Web Site: http://medicalcityplano.com
Health Care Srvices
N.A.I.C.S.: 621111

HCI GROUP, INC.
3802 Coconut Palm Dr, Tampa, FL
33619
Tel.: (813) 849-9500   FL
Web Site: https://www.hcigroup.com
Year Founded: 2006
HCI—(NYSE)
Rev.: $499,563,000
Assets: $1,803,328,000
Liabilities: $1,642,074,000
Net Worth: $161,254,000
Earnings: ($54,603,000)
Emp.: 578
Fiscal Year-end: 12/31/22
Property & Casualty Insurance Services

N.A.I.C.S.: 524126
Sanjay Madhu (VP-Mktg)
Gregory Politis (Executives)
Karin Coleman (COO)
Andrew L. Graham (Gen Counsel,
Sec & VP)
Martin A. Traber (Founder)
James Mark Harmsworth (CFO)
Paresh Patel (Chm & CEO)

Subsidiaries:

Exzeo Software Private Limited (1)
42/6 A 42 Block A Sector 62, Noida,
201309, Uttar Pradesh, India
Tel.: (91) 1204668200
Web Site: https://www.exzeo.com
Emp.: 100
Insurance Services
N.A.I.C.S.: 524298

Exzeo USA, Inc. (1)
1000 Century Park Dr, Tampa, FL 33607
Tel.: (813) 289-2914
Insurance Services
N.A.I.C.S.: 524298

Greenleaf Capital LLC (1)
1000 Century Park Dr, Tampa, FL 33607
Tel.: (813) 405-3260
Web Site: https://www.gleafcapital.com
Construction Engineering Services
N.A.I.C.S.: 541330
Anthony Saravanos (Pres)
Jeromy Houser (Mgr-Facilities)
Gil Siman (Controller)
Michelle Clark (Coord-Office)

**Homeowners Choice Property & Ca-
sualty Insurance Company, Inc.** (1)
3802 Coconut Palm Dr, Tampa, FL 33619
Tel.: (813) 405-3600
Web Site: https://www.hcpci.com
Sales Range: $50-74.9 Million
Emp.: 150
Property & Casualty Insurance Services
N.A.I.C.S.: 524126
Paresh Patel (Chm)

Omega Insurance Agency, Inc. (1)
1000 Century Park Dr, Tampa, FL 33607
Tel.: (813) 341-1530
Web Site: https://omega-ins.com
Insurance Services
N.A.I.C.S.: 524298
Jamie Kendig (Principal-Agency)

Tierre Verde Marina (1)
100 Pinellas Bayway S, Tierra Verde, FL
33715-1700
Tel.: (727) 866-0255
Web Site: https://www.tvmarina.com
Marinas
N.A.I.C.S.: 713930

TypTap Insurance Company (1)
3001 S E Maricamp Rd, Ocala, FL 34471
Tel.: (352) 509-9008
Web Site: https://www.typtap.com
Casualty Insurance Carrier Services
N.A.I.C.S.: 524126

**United Property & Casualty Insurance
Company** (1)
800 2nd Avenue S, Saint Petersburg, FL
33701
Tel.: (727) 895-7737
Web Site: http://www.upcinsurance.com
Sales Range: $50-74.9 Million
Emp.: 200
Property & Casualty Insurance Products &
Services
N.A.I.C.S.: 524126

HCM ACQUISITION CORP.
100 1st Stamford Pl Ste 330, Stam-
ford, CT 06902
Tel.: (203) 930-2200   Ky
Web Site:
  https://www.hcmacquisition.com
Year Founded: 2021
HCMA—(NASDAQ)
Rev.: $16,699,403
Assets: $298,599,516
Liabilities: $314,575,508
Net Worth: ($15,975,992)
Earnings: $14,783,303

Emp.: 2
Fiscal Year-end: 12/31/22
Investment Services
N.A.I.C.S.: 523999
Shawn Matthews (Chm & CEO)
James Bond (Pres & CFO)

HCW BIOLOGICS INC.
2929 N Commerce Pkwy, Miramar,
FL 33025
Tel.: (954) 842-2024   DE
Web Site:
  https://www.hcwbiologics.com
Year Founded: 2018
HCWB—(NASDAQ)
Rev.: $2,586,378
Assets: $46,809,155
Liabilities: $9,380,649
Net Worth: $37,428,506
Earnings: ($14,900,703)
Emp.: 44
Fiscal Year-end: 12/31/22
Research & Development in Biotech-
nology (except Nanobiotechnology)
N.A.I.C.S.: 541714
Hing C. Wong (Founder & CEO)
Peter Rhode (Chief Scientific Officer
& VP-Clinical Ops)
Jin-an Jiao (VP-Dev)
Rebecca Byam (CFO)
Lee Flowers (Sr VP-Bus Dev)
Nicole Valdivieso (Dir-Legal Affairs)
Raquel Diaz (Dir-HR)
Hing C. Wong (Founder & CEO)
Scott T. Garrett (Chm)

HEALIXA INC.
51 Elm St, Huntington, NY 11743
Tel.: (646) 558-8656
Web Site: https://healixa.com
Year Founded: 1977
EMOR—(OTCIQ)
Health & Wellness Organic Product
Mfr
N.A.I.C.S.: 325411
Ian Parker (Chm & CEO)

HEALTH ADVANCE INC.
685 Citadel Dr E Ste 290, Colorado
Springs, CO 80909
Tel.: (719) 466-6699   WY
Web Site:
  http://www.healthadvanceinc.com
Year Founded: 2010
IIADV—(OTCIQ)
Healthcare Products Online Retailer
N.A.I.C.S.: 456110
Gregory Shusterman (Chm & Pres)
Muhammad Mukhtar (Interim CEO)
Christian Diesveld (Sec & VP-IR)

HEALTH ASSURANCE ACQUI-
SITION CORP.
20 University Rd, Cambridge, MA
02138
Tel.: (617) 234-7000   DE
Year Founded: 2020
HAACU—(NASDAQ)
Investment Services
N.A.I.C.S.: 523999
Homant Tanoja (Chm & CEO)
Mark Allen (CFO)

HEALTH CATALYST, INC.
10897 S River Front Pkwy Ste 300,
South Jordan, UT 84095
Tel.: (801) 708-6800   DE
Web Site:
  https://www.healthcatalyst.com
Year Founded: 2008
HCAT—(NASDAQ)
Rev.: $295,938,000
Assets: $701,814,000
Liabilities: $334,895,000
Net Worth: $366,919,000
Earnings: ($118,147,000)

Emp.: 1,300
Fiscal Year-end: 12/31/23
Healthcare Software Development
Services
N.A.I.C.S.: 541511
Daniel Burton (CEO)
Steven C. Barlow (Co-Founder)
Thomas D. Burton (Co-Founder)
John A. Kane (Chm)
Trudy Sullivan (Chief Comm & Diver-
sity, Equity & Inclusion Officer)
Linda Llewelyn (Chief People Officer)
Bryan Hinton (CTO)
Jason Jones (Chief Analytics & Data
Science Officer)
Daniel LeSueur (COO)
Jason Alger (CFO & Chief Acctg Offi-
cer)
Jill Terry (Chief Learning Officer)
Darian Allen (Sr VP & Gen Mgr-
Population Health)
Melissa Welch (Chief Medical Officer)
Edward Sheen (Chief Population
Health Officer & Sr VP)
Dave Ross (CTO)
Benjamin Landry (Corp Counsel &
Sec)
Maxine Liu (Sr VP)

Subsidiaries:

Able Health LLC (1)
1516 Folsom St Unit C, San Francisco, CA
94103
Tel.: (805) 288-0240
Web Site: https://www.ablehealth.com
Women Healthcare Services
N.A.I.C.S.: 621610

Electronic Registry Systems, Inc. (1)
155 Tricounty Pkwy Ste 110, Cincinnati, OH
45246
Tel.: (513) 771-7330
Rev.: $2,100,000
Emp.: 25
Fiscal Year-end: 12/31/2009
Custom Computer Programming Services
N.A.I.C.S.: 541511
Ashok Ramaswamy (Pres)
Todd Carter (Mgr-Support Svcs)

Healthfinch, Inc. (1)
8517 Excelsior Dr Ste 403, Madison, WI
53717
Tel.: (608) 561-1844
Web Site: http://www.healthfinch.com
Information Technology Services
N.A.I.C.S.: 541511
Curtis Winn (Pres)
Jonathan Baran (Co-Founder & Chief Strat-
egy Officer)
Lyle Berkowitz (Co-Founder & Chief Medi-
cal Officer)
Chris Tyne (COO)
Matt Schwartz (VP-Sls & Mktg)

Medicity, Inc. (1)
257 E 200 S Ste 1300, Salt Lake City, UT
84111
Tel.: (801) 322-4444
Hospital & Medical Office Technology Solutions
N.A.I.C.S.: 518210

Vitalware, LLC (1)
1200 Chesterley Dr Ste 260, Yakima, WA
98902
Web Site: http://www.vitalware.com
Sales Range: $1-9.9 Million
Emp.: 51
Healthcare Software Development Services
N.A.I.C.S.: 541511
Kerry Martin (CEO)

HEALTH DISCOVERY CORPO-
RATION
2002 Summit Blvd Ste 300, Atlanta,
GA 30319
Tel.: (404) 566-4865   GA
Web Site:
  http://www.healthdiscoverycorp.com
Year Founded: 2001
HDVY—(OTCEM)
Rev.: $983,000

Assets: $932,000
Liabilities: $557,000
Net Worth: $375,000
Earnings: ($759,000)
Emp.: 3
Fiscal Year-end: 12/31/20
Molecular Diagnostics Analyzer
N.A.I.C.S.: 325413
Hong Zhang (Chief Science Officer)

HEALTH REVENUE ASSURANCE HOLDINGS, INC.
1185 Ave of the Americas 3rd Fl, New York, NY 10036
Tel.: (646) 768-8417   NV
Web Site:
  http://www.healthrevenue.com
HRAA—(OTCIQ)
Liabilities: $25,640
Net Worth: ($25,640)
Earnings: ($745,640)
Fiscal Year-end: 12/31/20
Medical Contract Coding, Billing, Coding Audits, Education Services & Courses
N.A.I.C.S.: 561499
David Lazar (Chm, Pres, CEO, CFO, Treas & Sec)

HEALTH SCIENCES GROUP, INC.
14331 Euclid St Ste 207, Garden Grove, CA 92843   DE
Year Founded: 2000
HESG—(OTCIQ)
Industrial Organic Chemicals Mfr
N.A.I.C.S.: 325199
Nhue Le (Pres, Treas & Sec)

HEALTH-CHEM CORP.
101 Sinking Springs Ln, Emigsville, PA 17318
Tel.: (717) 764-1191   DE
HCLC—(OTCIQ)
Pharmaceuticals Product Mfr
N.A.I.C.S.: 325412
Andy Yurowitz (Chm & CEO)
Ron Berghauser (CFO)

HEALTHCARE CAPITAL CORP.
1250 Prospect St Ste 200, La Jolla, CA 92037
Tel.: (650) 396-7700   DE
Year Founded: 2020
HCCCU—(NASDAQ)
Investment Services
N.A.I.C.S.: 523999
William Johns (CEO)
Philip A. Baseil (CFO)
David Milch (Chm)

HEALTHCARE CORPORATION OF AMERICA
66 Ford Rd, Denville, NJ 07834
Tel.: (973) 983-6300   DE
HCCA—(OTCIQ)
Healtcare Services
N.A.I.C.S.: 621610

HEALTHCARE INTEGRATED TECHNOLOGIES INC.
311 S Weisgarber Rd, Knoxville, TN 37919
Tel.: (865) 237-4448   NV
Web Site: https://www.gethitc.com
Year Founded: 2013
HITC—(OTCIQ)
Rev.: $322,000
Assets: $729,327
Liabilities: $1,022,522
Net Worth: ($293,195)
Earnings: ($702,486)
Emp.: 4
Fiscal Year-end: 07/31/24

Miscellaneous Financial Investment Activities
N.A.I.C.S.: 523999
Scott M. Boruff (Founder, Pres & CEO)
Kenneth M. Greenwood (CTO)
Susan A. Reyes (Chief Medical Officer)

HEALTHCARE REALTY TRUST INCORPORATED
3310 West End Ave Ste 700, Nashville, TN 37203
Tel.: (480) 998-3478   MD
Web Site:
  https://www.healthcarerealty.com
Year Founded: 2006
HR—(NYSE)
Rev.: $1,343,769,000
Assets: $12,637,131,000
Liabilities: $5,718,217,000
Net Worth: $6,918,914,000
Earnings: ($278,261,000)
Emp.: 584
Fiscal Year-end: 12/31/23
Healthcare Industry Real Estate Investment Trust
N.A.I.C.S.: 525910
Todd J. Meredith (Pres & CEO)
Amanda L. Callaway (Chief Acctg Officer & Sr VP)
Amanda L. Houghton (Exec VP-Asset Mgmt)
Caroline E. Chiodo (Sr VP-Acquisitions & Dev)
Bettina Hunt (Sr VP-Leasing)
Melinda Alford (Mgr-Leasing)
Jason Cheek (VP-Leasing-West)
Julia Ehret (Sr VP-Leasing-East & Midwest)
Todd Sloan (Sr VP-Leasing-Southeast)
Andrew Nordhoff (VP-Leasing-Florida)
Al O'Connor (Dir-Facilities)
Jeff Spiller (VP-Dev)
Olivia Waalboer (Controller)
Heather Borders (Asst Controller)
Kristen Armstrong (VP-Admin & Dir-Capital Tenant Improvements)
Dave Cohen (Dir-Bus Dev)
Amy Pearce (VP-Mktg & Comm)
David Perkins (Mgr-Dev)
Jered White (Mgr-Construction-Southeast)
Noah Meyer (Mgr-Construction-Northeast)
Lindsay C'Debaca (Mgr-Tax)
Tim Ames (Mgr-Financial Reporting)
Dustin Bator (Mgr-Treasury)
Tammy Hogue (Mgr-Accounts Payable)
Kurt Goertemiller (VP-Ops-Midwest)
Leanna Komoromi (VP-Ops-East)
John Magni (Dir-IT)
Jennifer Sypien-Kent (Dir-HR)
Joyce Larscheid (Mgr-HR)
Robert E. Hull (COO & Exec VP)
Julie F. Wilson (Chief Admin Officer & Exec VP)
Ryan E. Crowley (Chief Investment Officer & Exec VP)

Subsidiaries:

Healthcare Management of America, Inc.   (1)
300 Ashville Ave, Cary, NC 27518
Tel.: (919) 977-1181
Health Care Srvices
N.A.I.C.S.: 621610

Healthcare Realty Holdings, L.P.   (1)
16435 N Scottsdale Rd Ste 320, Scottsdale, AZ 85254
Tel.: (480) 998-3478
Rev.: $767,072,999
Assets: $6,889,688,999

Liabilities: $3,545,372,999
Net Worth: $3,344,315,999
Earnings: $99,784,000
Emp.: 356
Fiscal Year-end: 12/31/2021
Holding Company
N.A.I.C.S.: 551112

Subsidiary (Domestic):

HRTI, LLC   (2)
3310 W End Ave Ste 700, Nashville, TN 37203
Tel.: (615) 269-8175
Web Site: https://www.healthcarerealty.com
Rev.: $932,637,000
Assets: $13,849,631,000
Liabilities: $6,169,813,000
Net Worth: $7,679,818,000
Earnings: $40,897,000
Emp.: 583
Fiscal Year-end: 12/31/2022
Healthcare Real Estate Investment Trust
N.A.I.C.S.: 525990
Stephen E. Cox (Sr VP & Asst Gen Counsel)
Anne C. Barbour (First VP-Leasing)
Matthew J. Lederer (VP-Dev)
Revell Michael (VP-Mktg)
Greg Smith (VP-Design & Construction)
Burney Dawkins (First VP-Investments)
Joe Fogarty (VP-Dev)
Erika Frye (Assoc VP & Dir-Real Estate)
Nyssa Rogers (Assoc VP & Asst Controller)
Kris Douglas (CFO)
Laura Carson (VP)
Tony Diganci (VP)
Chris Donovan (Treas)
Jack Moore (Assoc VP)
Lindsay C'Debaca (Assoc VP)
Andy Baxter (CTO)
Chris Pribyl (VP)
Ron Hubbard (VP)
John M. Bryant Jr. (Gen Counsel & Exec VP)

Subsidiary (Domestic):

Healthcare Realty Services Incorporated   (3)
3310 W End Ave Ste 700, Nashville, TN 37203
Tel.: (615) 269-8175
Web Site: http://www.healthcarerealty.com
Residential Building & Dwelling Services
N.A.I.C.S.: 531110

HEALTHCARE ROYALTY, INC.
300 Atlantic St Ste 600, Stamford, CT 06901
Tel.: (203) 487-8300   DE
Web Site:
  http://www.healthcareroyalty.com
Year Founded: 2006
HCRX—(NASDAQ)
Emp.: 25
Health Care Srvices
N.A.I.C.S.: 621610
Clarke B. Futch (Chm & CEO)
Christopher A. White (Pres & CFO)
Timothy R.M. Bryant (Gen Counsel)
Thomas K. Conner (Chief Acctg Officer & Treas)
Carlos M. Almodovar (Chief Bus Officer)
Matthew H. Bullard (Mng Dir)
Warren D. Cooper (Chief Medical Officer)
Robert W. Czesak (Controller)
Paul J. Hadden (Sr Mng Dir)
Shin W. Kang (Chief Scientific Officer)
Sean S. Mansoory (VP)
Anthony G. Rapsomanikis (Mng Dir)
Andrew T. Reardon (Chief Legal Officer)
Michele D. Romaniello (VP)
Spencer H. Schneider (Chief Compliance Officer)
Amogh Sivarapatna (VP)
John A. Urquhart (Sr Mng Dir)

HEALTHCARE SERVICES AC-

QUISITION CORPORATION
7809 Woodmont Ave Ste 200, Bethesda, MD 20814
Tel.: (301) 605-1309   DE
Year Founded: 2020
HCARU—(NASDAQ)
Investment Services
N.A.I.C.S.: 523999
David T. Blair (Chm & CEO)
Martin J. Payne (Pres)
Joshua B. Lynn (CFO)
Tao Tan (COO)

HEALTHCARE SERVICES GROUP, INC.
3220 Tillman Dr Ste 300, Bensalem, PA 19020
Tel.: (215) 639-4274   PA
Web Site: https://www.hcsgcorp.com
Year Founded: 1977
HCSG—(NASDAQ)
Rev.: $1,671,389,000
Assets: $790,652,000
Liabilities: $334,036,000
Net Worth: $456,616,000
Earnings: $38,386,000
Emp.: 33,400
Fiscal Year-end: 12/31/23
Support Services to Healthcare Industry
N.A.I.C.S.: 621999
John Christopher Shea (Chief Admin Officer)
Jason J. Bundick (Chief Compliance Officer & Gen Counsel)
Matthew J. McKee (Chief Comm Officer)
Andrew W. Kush (COO)
Theodore Wahl (Pres & CEO)
Andrew M. Brophy (Principal Acctg Officer, Sr VP & Controller)

Subsidiaries:

ELuminate, LLC   (1)
756 Lotus Blossom St, Encinitas, CA 92024
Tel.: (760) 458-5583
Web Site: https://www.eluminate.net
Consulting Management Services
N.A.I.C.S.: 541618

HEALTHCARE TRIANGLE, INC.
7901 Stoneridge Dr Ste 220, Pleasanton, CA 94588
Tel.: (925) 270-4812   DE
Web Site:
  https://www.healthcaretriangle.com
Year Founded: 2019
HCTI—(NASDAQ)
Rev.: $45,886,000
Assets: $20,763,000
Liabilities: $8,375,000
Net Worth: $12,388,000
Earnings: ($9,610,000)
Emp.: 51
Fiscal Year-end: 12/31/22
Health Care Srvices
N.A.I.C.S.: 621610
Lakshmanan Kannappan (Head-Strategic Partnership)
Anand Kumar (CEO & Chief Revenue Officer)
David A. Rosa (Chm)
Shibu Kizhakevilayil (Head-Merger & Acq)
Thyagarajan Ramachandran (CFO)
Mike Preston (VP-Solutions)
Ronald Beteta (VP-Customer Success)
Chris Paalman (Dir-Engineering & Operations)
Laurie Isaacson (Dir-Practice)
Jason Mudrick (Dir-Epic Practice)
Lena Kannappan (Founder & Head)

HEALTHEQUITY, INC.
Tel.: (801) 727-1000   DE

HealthEquity, Inc.—(Continued)

Web Site:
https://www.healthequity.com
Year Founded: 2002
HQY—(NASDAQ)
Rev.: $861,748,000
Assets: $3,088,900,000
Liabilities: $1,193,260,000
Net Worth: $1,895,640,000
Earnings: ($26,143,000)
Emp.: 3,170
Fiscal Year-end: 01/31/23
Health Planning Services
N.A.I.C.S.: 923120
Jon Kessler (Pres & CEO)
Robert W. Selander (Chm)
Stephen D. Neeleman (Founder & Vice Chm)
Steve Lindsay (Sr VP-Relationship Mgmt)
Brad Bennion (Sr VP-Corp Dev)
James Lucania (CFO & Exec VP)
Eli Rosner (CTO & Exec VP)
Cheryl King (Chief People Officer & Exec VP)
Tia Padia (CMO & Exec VP)
Michael Fiore (Chief Comm Officer & Exec VP)
Kamesh Tumsi (Sr VP-Product)

Subsidiaries:

WageWorks, Inc. (1)
1100 Park Pl 4th Fl, San Mateo, CA 94403
Tel.: (650) 577-5200
Web Site: http://www.wageworks.com
Rev.: $472,184,000
Assets: $1,785,153,000
Liabilities: $1,120,012,000
Net Worth: $665,141,000
Earnings: $25,970,000
Emp.: 1,955
Fiscal Year-end: 12/31/2018
Tax-Advantaged Spending Accounts Management
N.A.I.C.S.: 561499

HEALTHIER CHOICES MANAGEMENT CORP.
3800 N 28th Way Ste 1, Hollywood, FL 33020
Tel.: (305) 600-5004   DE
Web Site:
https://www.healthiercmc.com
HCMC—(OTCIQ)
Rev.: $29,267,003
Assets: $55,255,030
Liabilities: $35,049,006
Net Worth: $20,206,024
Earnings: ($7,217,611)
Fiscal Year-end: 12/31/22
Holding Company; Vaporizers & Electronic Devices Mfr & Distr
N.A.I.C.S.: 551112
Christopher Santi (Pres & COO)
Jeffrey Elliot Holman (Chm & CEO)
John A. Ollet (CFO)

Subsidiaries:

The Vape Store, Inc. (1)
1110 Del Prado Blvd S Unit D, Cape Coral, FL 33990
Tel.: (239) 673-6650
Web Site: https://thevapestoreinc.com
Electronic Cigarettes & Liquids Whslr
N.A.I.C.S.: 459991

The Vitamin Store, LLC (1)
3800 N 28th Way Bay 1, Hollywood, FL 33020
Web Site: http://www.thevitaminstore.com
Nutrition Product Distr
N.A.I.C.S.: 456191

HEALTHLYNKED CORP.
1265 Creekside Pkwy Ste 302, Naples, FL 34108
Tel.: (239) 513-1992   NV
Web Site:
https://www.healthlynked.com

Year Founded: 2014
HLYK—(OTCQB)
Rev.: $5,858,202
Assets: $4,580,716
Liabilities: $4,266,266
Net Worth: $314,450
Earnings: ($8,815,744)
Emp.: 53
Fiscal Year-end: 12/31/22
Personal Health Information Management Services
N.A.I.C.S.: 518210
Michael T. Dent (Founder, Chm & CEO)
George G. O'Leary (CFO)
William Crupi (COO)

Subsidiaries:

ACO Health Partners LLC (1)
9822 Tapestry Park Cir Ste 208, Jacksonville, FL 32246
Web Site:
https://www.acohealthpartners.com
Health Care Srvices
N.A.I.C.S.: 621999
Maria Connor (Mgr-Practice)
Ruth Harris (Chief Transformation Officer)
Marsha Boggess (Co-Founder & Mng Partner)
Nicole Bradberry (Co-Founder & Chief Growth & Innovation Officer)
Mark Armatige (Dir-Medical)

Bridging the Gap Physical Therapy LLC (1)
28410 Bonita Crossings Blvd Bldg B Ste 110, Bonita Springs, FL 34135
Tel.: (239) 676-0546
Web Site: https://www.bridgingthegappt.com
Physiotherapy Services
N.A.I.C.S.: 621340
Elizabeth Feins (Mgr)

Naples Womens Center (1)
1726 Medical Blvd Ste 101, Naples, FL 34110
Tel.: (239) 513-1992
Web Site:
http://www.napleswomenscenter.com
Health Care Srvices
N.A.I.C.S.: 621498

HEALTHPEAK PROPERTIES, INC.
4600 S Syracuse St Ste 500, Denver, CO 80237
Tel.: (720) 428-5050   MD
Web Site:
https://www.healthpeak.com
Year Founded: 2022
PEAK—(NYSE)
Rev.: $2,181,003,000
Assets: $15,698,850,000
Liabilities: $8,773,980,000
Net Worth: $6,924,870,000
Earnings: $306,009,000
Emp.: 193
Fiscal Year-end: 12/31/23
Real Estate Investment Trust
N.A.I.C.S.: 525990
Thomas M. Klaritch (Vice Chm & COO)
Peter A. Scott (CFO)
Shawn G. Johnston (Chief Acctg Officer & Exec VP)
Antonio Acevedo (Sr VP-Medical Office)
James A. Croy (Sr VP-Brokerage)
Scott M. Brinker (Pres & CEO)
Lisa A. Alonso (Chief HR Officer & Exec VP)
Adam G. Mabry (Chief Investment Officer)
Jeffrey H. Miller (Gen Counsel)
Scott R. Bohn (Chief Dev Officer & Head-Lab)
Ankit B. Patadia (Treas-Corp Fin & Exec VP)
Tracy A. Porter (Sr VP & Deputy Gen Counsel)

Frank Russo (Sr VP-Risk Mgmt)
Michelle Wood (CFO, Sr VP & Controller-Senior Housing)
Michael Dorris (Sr VP-Life Sciences)
Kelvin Moses (Sr VP-Investments)
Andrew Johns (Sr VP)

Subsidiaries:

Healthpeak OP, LLC (1)
4600 S Syracuse St Ste 500, Denver, CO 80237   (100%)
Tel.: (720) 428-5050
Web Site: https://www.healthpeak.com
Rev.: $2,061,178,000
Assets: $15,771,229,000
Liabilities: $8,588,631,000
Net Worth: $7,182,598,000
Earnings: $500,449,000
Emp.: 199
Fiscal Year-end: 12/31/2022
Healthcare Real Estate Investment Trust Management Services
N.A.I.C.S.: 531390
Scott M. Brinker (Pres & CEO)

Subsidiary (Domestic):

HCP Life Science Estates, Inc. (2)
400 Oyster Point Blvd Ste 409, South San Francisco, CA 94110
Tel.: (650) 875-1002
Healthcare Real Estate Investment Services
N.A.I.C.S.: 531120

HCP MOB Scottsdale LLC (2)
10200 N 92nd St, Scottsdale, AZ 85258
Tel.: (480) 525-8440
Emp.: 6
Healthcare Real Estate Investment Services
N.A.I.C.S.: 531120
Mercedes Marquez (Gen Mgr)

MHI Investments, LLC (2)
3800 Grandlake Blvd, Kenner, LA 70065
Tel.: (504) 305-5420
Healthcare Real Estate Investment Services
N.A.I.C.S.: 531120

Oakmont of Camarillo OpCo, LLC (2)
305 Davenport St, Camarillo, CA 93012
Tel.: (805) 920-8615
Web Site:
http://www.oakmontofcamarillo.com
Assisted Living & Memory Care Services
N.A.I.C.S.: 623312
Lea Bogoyevac (Exec Dir)
Don Saunders (Mktg Dir)
Angelica Claudio (Dir-Activities)
James Christensen (Dir-Memory Care)
Tomas Vasquez (Dir-Maintenance)

Oakmont of Concord LLC (2)
1401 Civic Ct, Concord, CA 94520
Tel.: (925) 301-9179
Web Site:
http://www.oakmontofconcord.com
Assisted Living & Memory Care Services
N.A.I.C.S.: 623312
Angeles Sticka (Exec Dir)
Evelyn Stinebaugh (Dir-Health Svcs)
Pam Campbell (Mktg Dir)
Jose Zurita (Dir-Maintenance)
May Tate (Office Dir)

Oakmont of Fair Oaks LLC (2)
8484 Madison Ave, Fair Oaks, CA 95628
Tel.: (916) 621-5995
Web Site:
http://www.oakmontoffairoaks.com
Assisted Living & Memory Care Services
N.A.I.C.S.: 623312
Kawana Anthony (Exec Dir)
DeDe Bryant (Office Dir)
Nekia Xavier (Dir-Health Svcs)
Edwin Gonzalez (Dir-Maintenance)
Chelsea Xiong (Dir-Activities)

Oakmont of Mariner Point LLC (2)
2400 Mariner Square Dr, Alameda, CA 94501
Tel.: (510) 344-6302
Web Site:
http://www.oakmontofmarinerpoint.com
Assisted Living & Memory Care Services
N.A.I.C.S.: 623312
Elaine Wong (Exec Dir)
Angelica Gonzalez (Dir-Health Svc)

Vanessa Gonzalez (Office Dir)
Cayia Peevy (Dir-Traditions)
Adalberto Lazo Jr. (Dir-Maintenance)

Oakmont of Pacific Beach OpCo, LLC (2)
955 Grand Ave, San Diego, CA 92109
Tel.: (858) 914-4338
Web Site:
http://www.oakmontofpacificbeach.com
Assisted Living & Memory Care Services
N.A.I.C.S.: 623312
Shawn Amirhoushmand (Exec Dir)
Rachel Farias (Office Dir)
Sandra Ritchey (Mktg Dir)
Nicole-Jane Alfaro (Dir-Health Svcs)
Martin Sanchez (Dir-Maintenance)

Oakmont of Riverpark OpCo, LLC (2)
901 Town Center Dr, Oxnard, CA 93036
Tel.: (805) 429-0550
Web Site:
http://www.oakmontofriverpark.com
Assisted Living & Memory Care Services
N.A.I.C.S.: 623312
Eric Terrill (Exec Dir)
Amanda Zamudio (Mktg Dir)
Christina Ruiz (Mktg Dir)
Juan Garcia (Dir-Activities)
Gustavo Munguia (Dir-Maintenance)

Pikesville Assisted Living, LLC (2)
3800 Old Court Rd, Pikesville, MD 21208-3810
Tel.: (410) 602-0033
Web Site:
https://www.sunriseseniorliving.com
Healthcare Real Estate Investment Services
N.A.I.C.S.: 531120

S-H Forty-Nine PropCo Ventures, LLC (2)
737 Magnolia Ave, Corona, CA 92879
Tel.: (949) 407-0700
Real Estate Services
N.A.I.C.S.: 531390

Seminole Shores Living Center, LLC (2)
850 Seminole Rd, Norton Shores, MI 49441
Tel.: (231) 780-2944
Healthcare Real Estate Investment Services
N.A.I.C.S.: 531120

Physicians Realty Trust (1)
309 N Water St Ste 500, Milwaukee, WI 53202
Tel.: (414) 367-5600
Web Site: https://www.docreit.com
Rev.: $526,635,000
Assets: $5,096,877,000
Liabilities: $2,103,026,000
Net Worth: $2,993,851,000
Earnings: $104,366,000
Emp.: 101
Fiscal Year-end: 12/31/2022
Real Estate Investment Services
N.A.I.C.S.: 523999
John T. Thomas (Pres & CEO)
John W. Lucey (Chief Admin Officer & Chief Acctg Officer)
Jeffrey N. Theiler (CFO & Exec VP)
Del Mar Deeni Taylor (Chief Investment Officer & Exec VP)
Daniel M. Klein (Sr VP)
John W. Sweet Jr. (Founder)
Amy Miranda Hall (Sr VP-Leasing & Physician Strategy)
Mark D. Theine (Exec VP-Asset Mgmt)
Bradley D. Page (Gen Counsel & Sr VP)
Laurie P. Becker (Sr VP & Controller)
David G. Domres (VP-Construction & Project Mgmt)
Jennifer A. D. Manna (VP & Assoc Gen Counsel)
Tony Bradt (VP & Controller-Property)
Michael H. Farinawicz (VP)

HEALTHSTREAM, INC.
500 11th Ave N Ste 1000, Nashville, TN 37203
Tel.: (615) 301-3100   TN
Web Site:
https://www.healthstream.com
HSTM—(NASDAQ)
Rev.: $266,826,000
Assets: $497,741,000

Liabilities: $163,677,000
Net Worth: $334,064,000
Earnings: $12,091,000
Emp.: 1,135
Fiscal Year-end: 12/31/22
Education & Training for Health Care
Professionals
N.A.I.C.S.: 541512
Jeffrey L. McLaren (Co-Founder)
J. Edward Pearson (Pres & COO)
Jeffrey Cunningham (CTO & Sr VP)
Scott A. Roberts (CFO & Sr VP-Acctg
& Fin)
Robert A. Frist Jr. (Co-Founder, Chm
& CEO)

Subsidiaries:

Echo   (1)
17085 Camino San Bernardo, San Diego,
CA 92127
Tel.: (858) 673-1700
Web Site: http://www.echo-solutions.com
Healthcare Software Publisher
N.A.I.C.S.: 513210

HCT2 Co.   (1)
500 11th Ave N Ste 1000, Nashville, TN
37203
Web Site: https://www.nursegrid.com
Information Technology Services
N.A.I.C.S.: 541511

Health Care Compliance Strategies,
Inc.   (1)
30 Jericho Executive Plz Ste 400C, Jericho,
NY 11753
Tel.: (516) 478-4100
Web Site: http://www.hccs.com
Sales Range: $1-9.9 Million
Emp.: 33
Healthcare Compliance & Training Solutions
N.A.I.C.S.: 611430
Ben Diamond (VP-Compliance Solutions)
David Rosenthal (VP-Bus Dev)
Debbie Newsholme (Sr Dir-Content Ops)
Greg Hackbart (Sr Dir-Sls & Compliance)

HealthStream Research   (1)
7710 Montpelier Rd, Laurel, MD 20723
Tel.: (301) 575-9300
Web Site: http://www.healthstream.com
Sales Range: $75-99.9 Million
Healthcare Market Research Firm
N.A.I.C.S.: 541910

HealthStream Research   (1)
209 10th Ave S Ste 536, Nashville, TN
37203-7110
Tel.: (615) 224-1550
Web Site:
   http://www.healthstreamresearch.com
Sales Range: $10-24.9 Million
Emp.: 250
Healthcare Quality Surveyor
N.A.I.C.S.: 541910

Providigm, LLC   (1)
8055 E Tufts Ave Ste 1200, Denver, CO
80237
Web Site: http://www.providigm.com
Senior Care Information & Resource Providers
N.A.I.C.S.: 621999

ShiftWizard, Inc.   (1)
500 11th Ave N Ste 1000, Nashville, TN
37203
Web Site: https://www.shiftwizard.com
Emp.: 1,000
Software Development Services
N.A.I.C.S.: 541511

Sy.Med Development, Inc.   (1)
101 Westpark Dr Ste 140, Brentwood, TN
37027
Tel.: (615) 370-0078
Web Site: http://www.symed.com
Sales Range: $1-9.9 Million
Emp.: 20
Computer Programming Services
N.A.I.C.S.: 541511

VerityStream, Inc.   (1)
500 11th Ave N Ste 1000, Nashville, TN
37203
Healthcare Organization Services
N.A.I.C.S.: 622110

Wendy Nixx (Mgr-Mktg & Events)

HEALTHTECH SOLUTIONS, INC.
181 Dante Ave, Tuckahoe, NY
10707   UT
Web Site: http://www.xnyhonline.com
HLTT—(OTCIQ)
Rev.: $1,687,691
Assets: $2,752,387
Liabilities: $5,827,256
Net Worth: ($3,074,869)
Earnings: ($3,457,306)
Emp.: 18
Fiscal Year-end: 12/31/22
Holding Company; Printing
N.A.I.C.S.: 551112
Manuel E. Iglesias (Pres)
Robert Brantl (Sec)
Jelena Olmstead (CEO)
James Pesoli (Sr VP)

Subsidiaries:

World Reach Health, LLC   (1)
3501 W Algonquin Rd Ste 135, Rolling
Meadows, IL 60008
Tel.: (847) 220-4664
Web Site:
   https://www.worldreachhealth.com
Medical Device Distr
N.A.I.C.S.: 423450

HEALTHWAREHOUSE.COM, INC.
7107 Industrial Rd, Florence, KY
41042   DE
Web Site:
   https://www.healthwarehouse.com
Year Founded: 1982
HEWA—(OTCIQ)
Rev.: $17,178,000
Assets: $3,341,000
Liabilities: $5,096,000
Net Worth: ($1,755,000)
Earnings: $641,000
Emp.: 102
Fiscal Year-end: 12/31/20
Online Pharmaceuticals Retailer
N.A.I.C.S.: 456110
Joseph Peters (Pres & CEO)
Tim Reilly (Chm)

Subsidiaries:

Hocks.com, Inc.   (1)
7107 Industrial Rd, Florence, KY 41042-
2979
Tel.: (513) 618-0913
Pharmaceutical Preparation Distr
N.A.I.C.S.: 424210
Jeff Holmister (Mng Dir)

HEALTHY EXTRACTS INC.
6445 S Tenaya Way, Las Vegas, NV
89113
Tel.: (702) 201-6450   NV
Web Site:
   http://www.greycloaktech.com
Year Founded: 2014
HYEX—(OTCQB)
Rev.: $2,251,469
Assets: $2,781,118
Liabilities: $902,788
Net Worth: $1,878,330
Earnings: ($983,121)
Emp.: 2
Fiscal Year-end: 12/31/22
Software Publishing Services
N.A.I.C.S.: 513210
Fred Covely (CTO)
Kevin Pitts (Pres & COO)
Robert Madden (CFO & Sec)

HEART TEST LABORATORIES, INC.
550 Reserve St Ste 360, Southlake,
TX 76092

Tel.: (682) 244-2578   TX
Web Site: https://heartsciences.com
Year Founded: 2007
HSCS—(NASDAQ)
Rev.: $18,600
Assets: $9,503,113
Liabilities: $2,185,812
Net Worth: $7,317,301
Earnings: ($6,605,208)
Emp.: 15
Fiscal Year-end: 04/30/24
Professional Equipment & Supplies
Merchant Whslr
N.A.I.C.S.: 423490
Andrew Simpson (Chm & CEO)
Danielle Watson (CFO)
Aaron Peterson (VP-R&D)
Mark T. Hilz (COO)
Isabella Schmitt (VP-Clinical & Regu-
latory Affairs)

HEARTBEAM, INC.
2118 Walsh Ave Ste 210, Santa
Clara, CA 95050
Tel.: (408) 899-4443   DE
Web Site:
   https://www.heartbeam.com
Year Founded: 2015
BEAT—(NASDAQ)
Rev.: $69,000
Assets: $4,039,000
Liabilities: $1,665,000
Net Worth: $2,374,000
Earnings: ($12,962,000)
Emp.: 15
Fiscal Year-end: 12/31/22
Medical Device Mfr
N.A.I.C.S.: 334510
Richard M. Ferrari (Chm)
Branislav Vajdic (Founder & CEO)
Robert P. Eno (Pres)
Ken Persen (CTO)
Peter J. Fitzgerald (Chief Medical Of-
ficer)
Richa Gujarati (Sr VP-Product)
Deborah Castillo (VP-Regulatory Af-
fairs)
Pooja Chatterjee (VP-Clinical)
Timothy Cruickshank (CFO)

HEARTLAND BANCCORP
430 N Hamilton Rd, Whitehall, OH
43213
Tel.: (614) 337-4600
Web Site: https://www.heartland.bank
Year Founded: 1911
HLAN—(OTCQX)
Rev.: $70,136,000
Assets: $1,547,080,000
Liabilities: $1,406,184,000
Net Worth: $140,896,000
Earnings: $14,767,000
Emp.: 282
Fiscal Year-end: 12/31/20
Bank Holding Company
N.A.I.C.S.: 551111
Gregory Scott McComb (Chm, Pres &
CEO)
Jay B. Eggspuehler (Vice Chm)
Carrie L. Almendinger (CFO & Exec
VP)
Jennifer Eckert (Sec)

Subsidiaries:

Heartland Bank   (1)
850 N Hamilton Rd, Gahanna, OH 43230
Tel.: (614) 337-4600
Web Site: http://www.heartlandbank.com
Sales Range: $75-99.9 Million
Emp.: 150
Savings, Loans, Retirement Products & In-
vestment Banking Services
N.A.I.C.S.: 522110
Gregory Scott McComb (Chm, Pres & CEO)
Robert F. Halley (Sr VP & Mgr-Comml Rela-
tionships)
David P. Curby (VP-Mortgage Grp)
Mark A. Matthews (VP-Credit Review)

Jennifer Eckert (Sec, VP & Compliance Of-
ficer)
Kemper Allison (Mgr-Comml Relationship)
Alyssa Booms (Mgr-Retail Sls)
Bennett Musselman (Asst VP)
Joe Gottron (Chief Admin Officer & Exec
VP)
Jessica McNamee (Dir-Fin Plng)
James Duckro (Mgr-Ops)
Tame Tassniyom (Dir-Tech & Info Security)
Sara Hudson (Mgr-Retail)
Matthew Booms (Dir-Mortgage Banking)
Brian Brockhoff (Pres-Cincinnati)

TransCounty Title Agency LLC   (1)
850 N. Hamilton Rd. 2nd Flooranna, OH
43230, Gahanna, OH 43230
Tel.: (614) 799-2464
Web Site: http://www.tcountytitle.com
Commercial & Residential Title Insurance,
Underwriting & Real Estate Property Clos-
ing Services
N.A.I.C.S.: 524127
Rob Febes (Exec VP & Branch Mgr-
Circleville OH)
Tica Kotarba (Ops Mgr)

HEARTLAND EXPRESS, INC.
901 Heartland Way, North Liberty, IA
52317
Tel.: (319) 645-7060   NV
Web Site:
   https://www.heartlandexpress.com
Year Founded: 1978
HTLD—(NASDAQ)
Rev.: $967,996,000
Assets: $1,669,488,000
Liabilities: $814,011,000
Net Worth: $855,477,000
Earnings: $133,584,000
Emp.: 6,500
Fiscal Year-end: 12/31/22
General Freight Trucking, Local
N.A.I.C.S.: 484110
David P. Millis (Pres-Millis Transfer)
Michael J. Gerdin (Chm & CEO)
Christopher Alan Strain (CFO, Treas,
Sec & VP-Fin)
Russell Gerdin (Founder)

Subsidiaries:

Heartland Express, Inc., of Iowa   (1)
901 Heartland Way, North Liberty, IA 52317
Tel.: (319) 626-3600
Sales Range: $25-49.9 Million
Emp.: 100
Interstate Carrier
N.A.I.C.S.: 561499

Millis Transfer Inc.   (1)
Tel.: (715) 284-4384
Web Site: https://www.millistransfer.com
Rev.: $74,786,112
Emp.: 700
Contract Haulers
N.A.I.C.S.: 484121
David P. Millis (Pres & CEO)

Smith Transport, Inc.   (1)
153 Smith Transport Rd, Roaring Spring,
PA 16673-2237
Tel.: (814) 224-5155
Web Site: https://www.smithtransport.com
Sales Range: $75-99.9 Million
Emp.: 1,000
Trucking
N.A.I.C.S.: 484121
Barry F. Smith (Founder)
Michael Donovan (COO)
Nichole Musselman (Coord-Log)
Chip Castello (Dir-Safety-Well Svcs Div)
Jeffrey Musselman (VP-Well Svcs)
Todd Smith (Pres)

HEARTLAND FINANCIAL USA, INC.
1800 Larimer St Ste 1800, Denver,
CO 80202
Tel.: (303) 285-9200   DE
Web Site: https://www.htlf.com
Year Founded: 1981
HTLF—(NASDAQ)
Rev.: $802,920,000
Assets: $20,244,228,000

Heartland Financial USA, Inc.—(Continued)

Liabilities: $18,509,173,000
Net Worth: $1,735,055,000
Earnings: $212,180,000
Emp.: 2,002
Fiscal Year-end: 12/31/22
Offices of Bank Holding Companies
N.A.I.C.S.: 551111
Kevin G. Quinn *(Chief Banking Offi-
cer & Exec VP)*
Thomas L. Flynn *(Vice Chm)*
Janet M. Quick *(Chief Acctg Officer,
Deputy CFO & Exec VP)*
Laura J. Hughes *(Chief Mktg Officer
& Exec VP)*
Deborah K. Deters *(Chief HR Officer
& Exec VP)*
Kevin G. Quinn *(Chief Banking Offi-
cer & Exec VP)*
Tamina O'Neill *(Chief Risk Officer &
Exec VP)*
Kevin L. Thompson *(CFO & Exec
VP)*
Wendy Reynolds *(Chief Diversity, Eq-
uity & Inclusion Officer)*
Mark A. Frank *(COO & Exec VP)*
Nathan R. Jones *(Chief Credit Offi-
cer)*

Subsidiaries:

Arizona Bank & Trust **(1)**
2036 E Camelback Rd, Phoenix, AZ 85016
Tel.: (602) 381-2090
Web Site: https://www.arizbank.com
Emp.: 25
Commercial & Retail Banking Services
N.A.I.C.S.: 522110
Kenneth B. Gabel *(Sr VP & Mgr-Retail
Banking)*
William Callahan *(Pres & CEO)*
John Benton *(Chm)*
Frank E. Walter *(Vice Chm)*
Justin Bretag *(VP)*
Joy Graham *(VP)*
Holley Stacy *(VP)*

Blue Valley Ban Corp. **(1)**
11935 Riley St, Overland Park, KS 66213
Tel.: (913) 338-1000
Web Site: http://www.bankbv.com
Sales Range: $10-24.9 Million
Bank Holding Company
N.A.I.C.S.: 551111

Subsidiary (Domestic):

Bank of Blue Valley **(2)**
11935 Riley St, Overland Park, KS 66210
Tel.: (913) 338-1000
Web Site: http://www.bvmortgage.com
Sales Range: $50-74.9 Million
Emp.: 350
National Commercial Banks
N.A.I.C.S.: 522110
Robert D. Regnier *(Co-Chm & CEO)*
Nick Harling *(VP)*
Deborah Perkins *(VP)*
Kurt M. Saylor *(Co-Chm)*
Jack Tate *(VP)*
Aladdin Ashkar *(Sr VP)*
Brandon Brown *(VP)*
Brent Giles *(Pres)*
Cathy Ford *(VP)*
David LaBeaume *(VP)*
Jim Kleikamp *(VP)*
Lisa Siebert *(VP)*
Shane Deal *(VP)*
Will Fox *(Exec VP)*

Citizens Finance Co. **(1)**
2200 John F Kennedy Rd Ste 104,
Dubuque, IA 52002
Tel.: (563) 589-0925
Web Site: http://www.citizensfinance.com
Sales Range: $25-49.9 Million
Emp.: 10
Personal Credit Services
N.A.I.C.S.: 522291
Al Green *(Pres)*

Citizens Finance of Illinois Co. **(1)**
262 S Randall Rd, Elgin, IL 60123
Tel.: (224) 276-5222
Commercial Banking Services

N.A.I.C.S.: 522110
Chris Phillips *(Branch Mgr)*

Citywide Banks **(1)**
1800 Larimer St Ste 100, Denver, CO
80202 **(100%)**
Tel.: (303) 365-3800
Web Site: https://www.citywidebanks.com
Commercial Banking
N.A.I.C.S.: 522110
Marcus Meston *(Sr VP-Cherry Creek Bank-
ing Center)*
Joanne C. Sherwood *(Pres & CEO)*

Dubuque Bank & Trust Company **(1)**
500 N Grandview Ave, Dubuque, IA 52001
Tel.: (563) 589-2160
Web Site: http://www.dubuquebank.com
Sales Range: $75-99.9 Million
Emp.: 373
Commercial Banking
N.A.I.C.S.: 522110
Lynn Butch Fuller *(Pres & CEO)*
Mark C. Falb *(Chm)*
Thomas L. Flynn *(Vice Chm)*

Subsidiary (Domestic):

DB&T Insurance, Inc. **(2)**
309 1st St S, Farley, IA 52046-9583
Tel.: (563) 744-3354
Web Site: https://www.dubuquebank.com
Property & Casualty Insurance Services
N.A.I.C.S.: 524126

First Bank & Trust **(1)**
9816 Slide Rd, Lubbock, TX 79424
Tel.: (806) 788-0800
Web Site: http://www.firstbanklubbock.com
Sales Range: $50-74.9 Million
Commercial Banking
N.A.I.C.S.: 522110
Barry H. Orr *(Chm & CEO)*

Illinois Bank & Trust **(1)**
6855 E Riverside Blvd, Rockford, IL 61114
Tel.: (815) 637-7000
Web Site: https://www.illinoisbank.com
Sales Range: $10-24.9 Million
Emp.: 75
Commercial Banking
N.A.I.C.S.: 522110
Gina Caruana *(Sr VP & Mgr-Retail)*
Jeffrey S. Hultman *(CEO)*
Sarilyn Neiber *(VP)*
Barry Kramer *(VP-Wealth Advisor)*
Thomas D. Budd *(Pres)*
Joseph Mattingley *(Pres-Market)*
Tamera Netsell *(Partner-HR Bus)*
Frank E. Walter *(Chm)*
Chris Paige *(Pres-Chicagoland Market)*

Minnesota Bank & Trust **(1)**
7701 France Ave 3, Edina, MN 55435
Tel.: (952) 841-9300
Web Site: http://www.mnbankandtrust.com
Commercial & Retail Banking Services
N.A.I.C.S.: 522110
Lynn Butch Fuller *(Vice Chm)*
Duane E. White *(Dir)*
Stephen Bishop *(Pres & CEO)*

New Mexico Bank & Trust **(1)**
320 Gold Ave SW Ste 100, Albuquerque,
NM 87102
Tel.: (505) 830-8169
Web Site: http://www.nmb-t.com
Sales Range: $25-49.9 Million
Emp.: 140
Commercial Banking
N.A.I.C.S.: 522110
R. Greg Leyendecker *(Pres & CEO)*
Nadyne Bicknell *(Chm)*

Premier Valley Bank **(1)**
255 E River Park Cir Dr Ste 180, Fresno,
CA 93720
Tel.: (559) 438-2002
Web Site:
https://www.premiervalleybank.com
Sales Range: $10-24.9 Million
Emp.: 95
Commercial Banking
N.A.I.C.S.: 522110
Thomas G. Richards *(Chm)*
Lo B. Nestman *(Pres & CEO)*
Brad Fischer *(Sr VP & Mgr-Area-Ops)*
Arianne Hall *(Officer)*
Blake Rowan *(Sr VP)*
Charlie Synold *(Sr VP)*

David Triplitt *(Exec VP)*
Denny Rudd *(Sr VP)*
Douglas E. Weber *(Sr VP)*
Garrett B. Yacopetti *(Sr VP)*
Hakan Erdinc *(Exec VP)*
Jason Miller *(Officer)*
Jennifer Abney Acevedo *(VP)*
Justin Bell *(VP)*
Justin Rodgers *(Sr VP)*
Laura Cellini *(Officer)*
Maribeth Velasco *(Sr VP)*
Michael Mierau *(Sr VP)*
Mike Hazelrigg *(Officer)*
Patrick Bishop *(Sr VP)*
Scott Bess *(VP)*
Travis Moncada *(Sr VP)*
Tyler Jewell *(VP)*
Wesley Deen *(VP)*

**PrimeWest Mortgage
Corporation** **(1)**
7806 Indiana Ave, Lubbock, TX 79423
Tel.: (806) 788-1090
Web Site:
https://www.primewestmortgage.com
Mortgage Lending Services
N.A.I.C.S.: 522292
Casey Taylor *(Officer-Mortgage Loan & VP)*
Jack Bibb *(Reg Pres-New Mexico)*
Leanna Harris *(Officer-Mortgage Loan &
VP)*
Meagan Hood *(Officer-Mortgage Loan &
VP)*
Jeff Sicking *(Officer-Mortgage Loan & Sr
VP)*
Nate Melvin *(Officer-Mortgage Loan & VP)*
Rosa Erculiani *(VP)*

Rocky Mountain Bank **(1)**
2615 King Ave W, Billings, MT 59108
Tel.: (406) 656-3140
Web Site: https://www.rmbank.com
Sales Range: $75-99.9 Million
Assets: $360,000,000
Emp.: 26
State Commercial Banks
N.A.I.C.S.: 523150
Lynn Butch Fuller *(Vice Chm)*
Tod Petersen *(Pres & CEO)*
Dan Bettencourt *(Sr VP)*
Dennis Nolan *(Pres)*
Jason Miller *(Officer)*
Joel Nieskens *(Sr VP)*

**The Morrill & Janes Bank & Trust
Company** **(1)**
6740 Antioch Rd, Merriam, KS 66204
Tel.: (913) 677-4500
Web Site: http://www.mjbtrc.com
Rev.: $23,679,000
Assets: $754,575,000
Liabilities: $672,890,000
Net Worth: $81,685,000
Earnings: $6,728,000
Emp.: 50
Fiscal Year-end: 12/31/2012
Commercial Banking
N.A.I.C.S.: 522110

Wisconsin Bank & Trust **(1)**
119 Jct Rd, Madison, WI 53717
Tel.: (608) 203-1200
Web Site:
https://www.wisconsinbankandtrust.com
Sales Range: $25-49.9 Million
Emp.: 140
Commercial Banking
N.A.I.C.S.: 522110
Lynn Butch Fuller *(Vice Chm)*
Ronald M. Markham *(Pres-Market & Sr VP)*
Craig D. Aderhold *(Pres-Market & Sr VP)*

**HEARTLAND MEDIA ACQUISI-
TION CORP.**
3282 Northside Pkwy Ste 275, At-
lanta, GA 30327
Tel.: (470) 355-1944 DE
Year Founded: 2021
HMA—(NYSE)
Rev.: $12,532,337
Assets: $200,720,710
Liabilities: $207,757,811
Net Worth: ($7,037,101)
Earnings: $10,676,120
Emp.: 2
Fiscal Year-end: 12/31/22

Investment Services
N.A.I.C.S.: 523999
Robert S. Prather Jr. *(CEO)*
Shawn Pack *(CFO)*

HEARTSOFT, INC.
3101 N Hemlock Cir, Broken Arrow,
OK 74012
Tel.: (918) 362-3600
HTSF—(OTCIQ)
Software Development Services
N.A.I.C.S.: 541511
Rodger Graham *(CFO)*

HECLA MINING COMPANY
6500 N Mineral Dr Ste 200, Coeur
D'Alene, ID 83815-9408
Tel.: (208) 769-4100 DE
Web Site: https://www.hecla.com
Year Founded: 1891
HL—(NYSE)
Rev.: $718,905,000
Assets: $2,927,172,000
Liabilities: $948,205,000
Net Worth: $1,978,967,000
Earnings: ($37,348,000)
Emp.: 1,850
Fiscal Year-end: 12/31/22
Precious Metal Ore Mining & Pro-
cessing
N.A.I.C.S.: 212220
Theodore Crumley *(Chm)*
David C. Sienko *(Gen Counsel & VP)*
Robert D. Brown *(VP-Corp Dev &
Sustainability)*
Michael L. Clary *(Chief Admin Officer
& Sr VP)*
Kurt D. Allen *(VP-Exploration)*
Anvita Mishra Patil *(VP)*
Catherine Jean Boggs *(Chm, Interim
Pres & Interim CEO)*

Subsidiaries:

ATAC Resources Ltd. **(1)**
1016-510 West Hastings Street, Vancouver,
V6B 1L8, BC, Canada
Tel.: (604) 687-2522
Web Site: http://www.atacresources.com
Rev.: $120,564
Assets: $5,883,418
Liabilities: $177,105
Net Worth: $5,706,313
Earnings: ($80,316,881)
Fiscal Year-end: 12/31/2020
Metal Exploration Services
N.A.I.C.S.: 213114
Graham N. Downs *(Pres & CEO)*
Ian J. Talbot *(COO)*
Larry B. Donaldson *(CFO)*
Glenn R. Yeadon *(Sec)*
Douglas O. Goss *(Chm)*
Adam Coulter *(VP-Exploration)*
Andrew Carne *(VP-Corp & Project Dev)*

Alexco Resource Corp. **(1)**
Suite 1225 Two Bentall Centre 555 Burrard
Street, PO Box 216, Vancouver, V7X 1M9,
BC, Canada
Tel.: (604) 633-4888
Web Site: http://www.alexcoresource.com
Rev.: $21,502,000
Assets: $210,362,000
Liabilities: $24,260,000
Net Worth: $186,102,000
Earnings: ($3,146,000)
Emp.: 187
Fiscal Year-end: 12/31/2021
Metal Mining & Processing Services
N.A.I.C.S.: 212290
Bradley A. Thrall *(Pres)*
Alan McOnie *(VP-Exploration)*
Gordon Wong *(VP-Fin)*
Wayne Zigarlick *(VP-Ops & Gen Mgr)*
Paul Jones *(Sr VP-Corp Dev)*

Subsidiary (Domestic):

Alexco Keno Hill Mining Corp. **(2)**
PO Box 7, Elsa, YT, Canada
Tel.: (867) 995-3113
Emp.: 100
Mineral Exploration Services

N.A.I.C.S.: 213115

Subsidiary (US):

Alexco Resource US Corp (2)
12150 E Briarwood Ave Ste 135, Centennial, CO 80112-5304
Tel.: (303) 862-3929
Sales Range: $50-74.9 Million
Emp.: 100
Mineral Exploration Services
N.A.I.C.S.: 213115
Joe Harrington (VP-Tech & Strategic Dev)

Burke Trading, Inc. (1)
6500 N Mineral Dr Ste 200, Coeur D'Alene, ID 83815
Tel.: (208) 769-4100
Silver Mining Services
N.A.I.C.S.: 212220
Dean W. A. McDonald (Pres)

Subsidiary (Non-US):

Mineral Hecla, S.A. de C.V. (2)
20 De Noviembre 519 Colonia Centro, Durango, Mexico
Tel.: (52) 6188184131
Ore Distr
N.A.I.C.S.: 423520

Greens Creek Mining Co. (1)
Admiralty Is, Juneau, AK 99801
Tel.: (907) 789-8100
Sales Range: $25-49.9 Million
Gold, Silver, Lead & Zinc Mining
N.A.I.C.S.: 212230
Greg Pegues (Project Coord-Underground)

Hecla Canada Ltd. (1)
800 W Pender St 970, Vancouver, V6C 2V6, BC, Canada
Tel.: (604) 682-6201
Silver Mining
N.A.I.C.S.: 212220

Hecla Greens Creek Mining Company (1)
PO Box 32199, Juneau, AK 99803
Tel.: (907) 789-8100
Ore Distr
N.A.I.C.S.: 423520
Whit Adam (Mgr-Mine)

Hecla Limited - Lucky Friday Mine (1)
PO Box 31, Mullan, ID 83846
Tel.: (208) 744-1751
Web Site: http://www.hecla-mining.com
Precious Metals Mining
N.A.I.C.S.: 212221
Clayr Alexander (VP & Gen Mgr)

Montanore Minerals Corp. (1)
34524 US Hwy 2, Libby, MT 59923
Tel.: (406) 293-8888
Web Site: http://www.hecla-mining.com
Silver & Copper Mining Services
N.A.I.C.S.: 212220

Revett Silver Company (1)
Hwy 56 South Mine Rd PO Box 1660, Troy, MT 59935 (100%)
Tel.: (406) 295-5882
Silver Mining
N.A.I.C.S.: 212220

Subsidiary (Domestic):

RC Resources, Inc. (2)
17 Main St, Kalispell, MT 59853 (100%)
Tel.: (406) 257-9220
Web Site: http://flatheadbeacon.com
Silver Mining
N.A.I.C.S.: 212220
Douglas Miller (VP-Ops)

Rio Grande Silver, Inc. (1)
625 USS Rd 504 1 A, Creede, CO 81130
Tel.: (719) 658-1080
Web Site: http://www.heclamining.com
Sales Range: $50-74.9 Million
Emp.: 3
Silver Mining
N.A.I.C.S.: 212220

HEICO CORPORATION

3000 Taft St, Hollywood, FL 33021
Tel.: (954) 987-4000   FL
Web Site: https://www.heico.com

Year Founded: 1957
HEI—(NYSE)
Rev.: $3,857,669,000
Assets: $7,592,822,000
Liabilities: $3,529,260,000
Net Worth: $4,063,562,000
Earnings: $559,086,000
Emp.: 10,000
Fiscal Year-end: 10/31/24
Holding Company; Aircraft Components & Electronic Equipment Mfr
N.A.I.C.S.: 551112
Eric A. Mendelson (Co-Pres)
Victor H. Mendelson (Co-Pres)
Laurans A. Mendelson (Chm & CEO)
Carlos L. Macau Jr. (Treas)

Subsidiaries:

A2C Air Cost Control SAS (1)
11 Rue Commandant Cousteau Ste 100, 32600, L'Isle-Jourdain, France
Tel.: (33) 562070200
Transportation Equipment Distr
N.A.I.C.S.: 423860
Laurent Parelle (CEO)
Laure Parelle (Mng Dir)

Aeroworks (Asia) Ltd. (1)
Laem Chabang Ind Estate 49/39 Moo 5 Tungsukhla, Si Racha, 20230, Chonburi, Thailand
Tel.: (66) 384914224
Aircraft Engine & Engine Parts Mfr
N.A.I.C.S.: 336412

Aeroworks Europe B.V. (1)
Hoornseweg 25, 1775 RB, Middenmeer, Netherlands
Tel.: (31) 227503800
Web Site: https://www.aeroworks.nl
Holding Company
N.A.I.C.S.: 551112

Air Cost Control Germany GmbH (1)
Sudportal 1, 122848, Hamburg, Germany
Tel.: (49) 40709756400
Web Site: https://www.aircostcontrol.com
Transportation Equipment Distr
N.A.I.C.S.: 423860
Armelle Meyer-Burgdorf (Mgr-Acct)

Air Cost Control Pte. Ltd. (1)
690 West Camp Rd, Singapore, 797523, Singapore
Tel.: (65) 66944195
Web Site: https://www.aircostcontrol.com
Aircraft Parts & Auxiliary Equipment Mfr
N.A.I.C.S.: 336413

Air Cost Control US, LLC (1)
13800 NW 2nd St Ste 100, Sunrise, FL 33325
Tel.: (954) 991-4667
Aircraft Parts & Auxiliary Equipment Mfr
N.A.I.C.S.: 336413
Laurent Parelle (CEO)
Laure Parelle (Mng Dir)
Tifanny Vincent (Asst Mng Dir)
Thaismara Fonseca (Mgr-Acct)
Cindy Montalvo (Sr Mgr-Acct)

Alcon Electronics Pvt. Ltd. (1)
34-B MIDC Industrial Estate, Satpur, Nashik, 422007, Maharashtra, India
Tel.: (91) 2532350533
Web Site: https://alconelectronics.com
Aluminum Electrolytic Capacitor Mfr & Distr
N.A.I.C.S.: 334416

Bay Equipment Corp. (1)
395 Roost Ave, Holland, MI 49424
Tel.: (616) 392-1811
Web Site: http://www.bayequipmentco.com
Material Handling Equipment Mfr
N.A.I.C.S.: 333922

Carbon by Design, L.P. (1)
1491 Poinsettia Ave Ste 136, Vista, CA 92081
Tel.: (760) 643-1300
Web Site: http://www.carbonbydesign.com
Aeronautic Supplies & Parts Mfr
N.A.I.C.S.: 336411
Dominick Consalvi (Pres)

Connect Tech Inc. (1)
489 Clair Rd W, Guelph, N1L 0H7, ON, Canada

Tel.: (519) 836-1291
Web Site: https://www.connecttech.com
Hardware Product Mfr
N.A.I.C.S.: 332510
Patrick Dietrich (CTO)

Exxelia SAS (1)
93 Rue Oberkampf, 75011, Paris, France
Tel.: (33) 149231000
Web Site: https://exxelia.com
Emp.: 2,100
Capacitor Spare Parts Mfr & Distr
N.A.I.C.S.: 334416

HEICO Aerospace Holdings Corp. (1)
3000 Taft St, Hollywood, FL 33021-4441
Tel.: (954) 987-4000
Web Site: http://www.heico.com
Holding Company
N.A.I.C.S.: 551112
Eric A. Mendelson (Pres & CEO)
Thomas S. Irwin (CFO & Exec VP)

Subsidiary (Domestic):

Aero Design, Inc. (2)
101 Clemmons Rd, Mount Juliet, TN 37122-2974
Tel.: (615) 754-7700
Web Site: https://www.batteryshop.com
Sales Range: $10-24.9 Million
Emp.: 18
Storage Batteries Mfr
N.A.I.C.S.: 335999

Astroseal Products Mfg Corporation (2)
85 Airport Industrial Park Rd, Chester, CT 06412
Tel.: (860) 526-8605
Web Site: https://www.astrosealproducts.com
Sales Range: $1-9.9 Million
Emp.: 25
Gasket, Packing & Sealing Device Mfr
N.A.I.C.S.: 339991

Battery Shop, LLC (2)
101 Clemmons Rd, Mount Juliet, TN 37122
Tel.: (615) 754-7700
Web Site: https://www.batteryshop.com
Emp.: 35
Aircraft Equipment Mfr
N.A.I.C.S.: 336413

CSI Aerospace, Inc. (2)
2020 W Detroit, Broken Arrow, OK 74012
Tel.: (918) 258-1290
Web Site: https://www.heico.com
Sales Range: $25-49.9 Million
Aircraft Component Maintenance & Repair Services
N.A.I.C.S.: 336413

DEC Technologies, Inc. (2)
136 Industrial Park Rd, Piney Flats, TN 37686
Tel.: (423) 538-0919
Aircraft Equipment Mfr
N.A.I.C.S.: 336413

Decavo LLC (2)
489 N 8th St Ste 205, Hood River, OR 97031-3104
Tel.: (541) 716-0100
Web Site: https://www.decavo.com
Carbon Composite Components & Assemblies Designer & Mfr
N.A.I.C.S.: 335991
Phil Nies (Founder & Pres)

Future Aviation, Inc. (2)
14111 Jetport Loop, Fort Myers, FL 33913-7705
Tel.: (239) 225-0101
Web Site: http://www.futureaviation.com
Sales Range: $25-49.9 Million
Emp.: 100
Aircraft Parts Whslr
N.A.I.C.S.: 811310

HEICO Aerospace Corporation (2)
3000 Taft St, Hollywood, FL 33021-4441 (100%)
Tel.: (954) 987-4000
Web Site: http://www.heico.com
Sales Range: $125-149.9 Million
Emp.: 300
Aerospace Operations

N.A.I.C.S.: 336412
Eric A. Mendelson (Pres & CEO)

Subsidiary (Domestic):

Aircraft Technology, Inc. (3)
3000 Taft St, Hollywood, FL 33021-4449
Tel.: (954) 744-7726
Web Site: https://www.heico.com
Sales Range: $125-149.9 Million
Emp.: 60
Jet Engine & Aircraft Components Repair Services
N.A.I.C.S.: 811310
Larry Medosan (CEO)

Jet Avion Corporation (3)
3000 Taft St, Hollywood, FL 33021-4441 (100%)
Tel.: (954) 987-6101
Web Site: https://www.heico.com
Sales Range: $100-124.9 Million
Emp.: 250
Jet Engine Parts Mfr
N.A.I.C.S.: 336412

LPI Corporation (3)
3000 Taft St, Hollywood, FL 33021-4441
Tel.: (954) 987-4000
Web Site: http://www.heico.com
Sales Range: $75-99.9 Million
Emp.: 300
Aviation Components Mfr
N.A.I.C.S.: 336412

Parts Advantage, LLC (3)
3000 Taft St, Hollywood, FL 33021
Tel.: (954) 987-6101
Web Site: http://www.heico.com
Sales Range: $125-149.9 Million
Emp.: 300
Jet Engine & Aircraft Components Repair Services
N.A.I.C.S.: 811310
Laurans A. Mendelson (Chm & CEO)

Subsidiary (Domestic):

HEICO Aerospace Parts Corp. (2)
3000 Taft St, Hollywood, FL 33021-4441
Tel.: (954) 987-4000
Web Site: https://www.heico.com
Sales Range: $125-149.9 Million
Emp.: 300
Aircraft Part Mfr
N.A.I.C.S.: 336413

Group (Domestic):

HEICO Component Repair Group (2)
7875 NW 64th St, Miami, FL 33166-2719
Tel.: (305) 463-0455
Web Site: http://www.heico.com
Sales Range: $150-199.9 Million
Emp.: 310
Aircraft Components Repair Services
N.A.I.C.S.: 811210

Subsidiary (Domestic):

HEICO Parts Group, Inc. (2)
3000 Taft St, Hollywood, FL 33021-4441
Tel.: (954) 987-4000
Web Site: http://www.heico.com
Emp.: 300
Aircraft Equipment Mfr
N.A.I.C.S.: 336413

Group (Domestic):

HEICO Wire Group (2)
5555 Irwindale Ave, Irwindale, CA 91706
Tel.: (626) 969-7651
Web Site: http://www.heicowiregroup.com
Sales Range: $75-99.9 Million
Galvanized Wire Mfr
N.A.I.C.S.: 331222
Laurans A. Mendelson (Chm & CEO)

Subsidiary (Domestic):

Davis Wire Corporation (3)
5555 Irwindale Ave, Irwindale, CA 91706-2070
Tel.: (626) 969-7651
Web Site: http://www.daviswire.com
Sales Range: $75-99.9 Million
Emp.: 230
Mfr of Wire & Wire Products
N.A.I.C.S.: 331222

HEICO Corporation—(Continued)

Subsidiary (Domestic):

Harter Aerospace, LLC (2)
401 W Gemini Dr, Tempe, AZ 85283-1709
Tel.: (480) 345-9595
Aircraft Repair & Maintenance Services
N.A.I.C.S.: 811310
Indra Hall (Asst Controller)
William J. Hinski (Mng Dir & VP)
Charles R. Kollett (Chief Engr)
Bradley K. Smith (Gen Mgr)
David Sandoval (Mgr-Customer Support)
Danielle Kim (Mgr-Sls Support)
Dallin Pear (Acct Mgr)
Kyle Hinski (Sls Dir)
Brian Francis (Acct Mgr)
Jordan Rogers (Acct Mgr)
Dean Boeckholt (Controller)
Brett Matthews (Mgr-Quality Assurance)
Darin Houle (Mgr-Capability Dev & Pricing)
William J. Hinski Jr. (Sls Dir-Customer Svcs)

McClain International, Inc. (2)
4785 Roosevelt Hwy, College Park, GA
30349-2417
Tel.: (770) 964-3361
Web Site: http://www.heico.com
Sales Range: $10-24.9 Million
Emp.: 50
Jet Engine & Aircraft Components Repair
Services
N.A.I.C.S.: 811310

Niacc-Avitech Technologies Inc. (2)
245 W Dakota Ave, Clovis, CA 93612
Tel.: (559) 291-2500
Sales Range: $25-49.9 Million
Emp.: 80
Aircraft Accessories Repair Services
N.A.I.C.S.: 811310

Optical Display Engineering LLC (2)
375 Alpha Park, Highland Heights, OH
44143
Tel.: (440) 995-6555
Web Site: https://www.heico.com
Aircraft Part & Auxiliary Equipment Mfr
N.A.I.C.S.: 336413

Prime Air, LLC (2)
230 NE 70 St, Miami, FL 33138
Tel.: (786) 923-1000
Web Site: http://www.heico.com
Aircraft Equipment Distr
N.A.I.C.S.: 423830

Subsidiary (Non-US):

Prime Air Europe Limited (3)
3 Hall Road, Maylands Wood Estate, Hemel
Hempstead, HP2 7BH, United Kingdom
Tel.: (44) 1442262698
Web Site: http://www.primeair.com
Aircraft Equipment Distr
N.A.I.C.S.: 423860

Subsidiary (Domestic):

Sunshine Avionics LLC (2)
9974 Premier Pkwy, Miramar, FL 33025
Tel.: (954) 517-1294
Web Site: http://www.heico.com
Emp.: 30
Aircraft Equipment Distr
N.A.I.C.S.: 423860

Turbine Kinetics, Inc. (2)
60 Sequin Dr, Glastonbury, CT 06033-2443
Tel.: (860) 633-8520
Web Site: https://www.heico.com
Sales Range: $10-24.0 Million
Emp.: 40
Aircraft Part Mfr
N.A.I.C.S.: 336412

**HEICO Electronic Technologies
Corp.** (1)
3000 Taft St, Hollywood, FL 33021
Tel.: (954) 987-4000
Web Site: https://www.heico.com
Emp.: 10
Holding Company; Electronic Components
& Systems Mfr
N.A.I.C.S.: 551112
Victor H. Mendelson (Pres & CEO)

Subsidiary (Non-US):

3D Plus SAS (2)

408 rue Helene Boucher - ZI, 78532, Buc,
France
Tel.: (33) 13 083 2650
Web Site: https://www.3d-plus.com
Emp.: 200
Electronic Components Mfr
N.A.I.C.S.: 334419

Subsidiary (Domestic):

Bernier Connect SAS (3)
2 Rue du Languedoc, 91220, Bretigny-sur-
Orge, France
Tel.: (33) 160842140
Web Site: https://www.bernier.tm.fr
Electromechanical Component Mfr
N.A.I.C.S.: 334419

Subsidiary (Domestic):

**Moulages Plastiques Industriels de
L'essonne SARL** (4)
8 rue du Languedoc, 91220, Bretigny-sur-
Orge, France
Tel.: (33) 16 085 1233
Web Site: https://www.mpide.com
Emp.: 13
Technical Part Mfr
N.A.I.C.S.: 336390

Subsidiary (Domestic):

3D Plus U.S.A., Inc. (2)
151 Callan Ave Ste 310, San Leandro, CA
94577
Tel.: (510) 824-5591
Web Site: https://www.3d-plus.com
Emp.: 200
Electronic Components Mfr
N.A.I.C.S.: 334419

Aeroantenna Technology, Inc. (2)
20732 Lassen St, Chatsworth, CA 91311
Tel.: (818) 993-3842
Web Site: https://www.aeroantenna.com
Sales Range: $1-9.9 Million
Emp.: 140
Search & Navigation Equipment Mfr
N.A.I.C.S.: 334511

Analog Modules, Inc. (2)
126 Baywood Ave, Longwood, FL 32750-
3426
Tel.: (407) 339-4355
Web Site: https://www.analogmodules.com
Sales Range: $10-24.9 Million
Emp.: 65
Electrical Component Mfr
N.A.I.C.S.: 334419
Ian Crawford (Founder)
Bruce Soileau (Mgr-Product & Mktg)
Tim Cable (Mgr-Product)

Apex Microtechnology, Corp. (2)
5980 N Shannon Rd, Tucson, AZ
85741 (93%)
Tel.: (520) 690-8600
Web Site: https://www.apexanalog.com
Precision High Power Analog Device Mfr
N.A.I.C.S.: 334413

Connectronics Corp. (2)
2745 Avondale Ave, Toledo, OH 43607-
3232
Tel.: (419) 537-0020
Web Site:
https://www.connectronicscorp.com
Electronic Connector Mfr
N.A.I.C.S.: 334417
Michael Hands (Mgr-Sls-Midwest)

Dielectric Sciences, Inc. (2)
88 Tpke Rd, Chelmsford, MA 01824-3526
Tel.: (978) 250-1507
Web Site:
https://www.dielectricsciences.com
High Voltage Cable Connector Mfr
N.A.I.C.S.: 334417
Jerry Goldlust (Pres)

Dukane Seacom, Inc. (2)
7135 16th St E Ste 101, Sarasota, FL
34243
Tel.: (941) 739-3200
Web Site: https://www.dukaneseacom.com
Sales Range: $10-24.9 Million
Underwater Locator Beacons Mfr
N.A.I.C.S.: 334511

Subsidiary (Non-US):

EMD Technologies Incorporated (2)

400 du Parc, Saint-Eustache, J7R 0A1, QC,
Canada
Tel.: (450) 491-2100
Web Site: https://emd-technologies.com
High Voltage Power Electronic Product Mfr
N.A.I.C.S.: 335999

Subsidiary (Domestic):

Engineering Design Team, Inc. (2)
3423 NE John Olsen Ave, Hillsboro, OR
97124
Tel.: (503) 690-1234
Web Site: https://edt.com
Sales Range: $25-49.9 Million
Video Interface Card Mfr
N.A.I.C.S.: 334419

Subsidiary (Non-US):

**Essex X-Ray & Medical Equipment
LTD** (2)
Unit 18 Flitch Industrial Estate Chelmsford
Road, Great Dunmow, CM6 1XJ, United
Kingdom
Tel.: (44) 137 187 5661
Web Site: https://www.essexxray.com
Emp.: 142
Electronic Components Distr
N.A.I.C.S.: 423690

High Voltage Technology Limited (2)
18 Flitch Industrial Estate Chelmsford Road,
Great Dunmow, CM6 1XJ, Essex, United
Kingdom
Tel.: (44) 1371875661
Web Site: http://www.essex-x-ray.com
Electronic Components Mfr
N.A.I.C.S.: 334419

Subsidiary (Domestic):

Inertial Aerospace Services (2)
375 Alpha Park, Highland Heights, OH
44143-2237
Tel.: (440) 995-6555
Web Site: http://www.heico.com
Emp.: 50
Navigation Equipment Repair Services
N.A.I.C.S.: 811310

Ironwood Electronics Inc. (2)
11351 Rupp Dr, Burnsville, MN
55337 (80%)
Tel.: (952) 229-8200
Web Site:
http://www.ironwoodelectronics.com
Rev.: $3,200,000
Emp.: 26
Radio & Television Broadcasting & Wireless
Communications Equipment Mfr
N.A.I.C.S.: 334220
Betty Fedde (CFO)
Mickiel Fedde (Pres)

Leader Tech, Inc. (2)
12420 Race Track Rd, Tampa, FL 33626-
3018
Tel.: (813) 855-6921
Web Site: https://www.leadertechinc.com
Sales Range: $50-74.9 Million
Emp.: 160
Precision Stamping, Machining & Metal
Fabrication Services
N.A.I.C.S.: 332999
Sheila Jackson (Mgr-Customer Svc & Mktg)

Lucix Corp. (2)
3883 Via Pescador, Camarillo, CA 93012
Tel.: (805) 987-6645
Web Site: https://www.lucix.com
Sales Range: $10-24.9 Million
Emp.: 140
Designer & Mfr of Microwave & Millimeter
Devices & Subsytems
N.A.I.C.S.: 334419

Lumina Power, Inc. (2)
26 Ward Hill Ave, Bradford, MA 01835
Tel.: (978) 241-8260
Web Site: https://luminapower.com
Laser Product Mfr
N.A.I.C.S.: 334413

**Midwest Microwave Solutions,
Inc.** (2)
2000 Progress Dr, Hiawatha, IA 52233
Tel.: (319) 393-4055
Web Site: https://mms-rf.com
Electronic Components Mfr
N.A.I.C.S.: 334419

Pyramid Semiconductor Corp. (2)
1249 Reamwood Ave, Sunnyvale, CA
94089-2226
Tel.: (408) 734-8200
Web Site:
https://www.pyramidsemiconductor.com
Semiconductors And Related Devices, Nsk
N.A.I.C.S.: 334413
Douglas Beaubien (Co-Founder & VP-Ops)
Joe Rothstein (Co-Founder, Pres & CEO)

Quell Corp. (2)
5639 Jefferson NE, Albuquerque, NM
87109
Tel.: (505) 243-1423
Web Site: https://eeseal.com
Electronic Connectors
N.A.I.C.S.: 334417

Radiant Power Corp. (2)
7135 16th St E Ste 101, Sarasota, FL
34243
Tel.: (941) 739-3200
Web Site: https://www.rpcaero.com
Aerospace Power Control Systems Mfr
N.A.I.C.S.: 336413

Ramona Research, Inc. (2)
13741 Danielson St Ste J, Poway, CA
92064-6895
Tel.: (858) 679-0717
Web Site: https://www.ramonaresearch.com
Sales Range: $10-24.9 Million
Microwave Amplifier & Transmitter Design &
Mfr
N.A.I.C.S.: 334220

**Research Electronics International,
LLC** (2)
455 Security Dr, Cookeville, TN
38506 (75%)
Tel.: (931) 537-6032
Web Site: https://www.reiusa.net
Search, Detection, Navigation, Guidance,
Aeronautical & Nautical System & Instru-
ment Mfr
N.A.I.C.S.: 334511
Bruce Barsumian (Founder)

Robertson Fuel Systems, LLC (2)
800 W Carver Rd Ste 101, Tempe, AZ
85284
Tel.: (480) 337-7050
Web Site:
http://www.robertsonfuelsystems.com
Measuring & Controlling Device Mfr
N.A.I.C.S.: 334519

Santa Barbara Infrared, Inc. (2)
30 S Calle Cesar Chavez Ste D, Santa Bar-
bara, CA 93103-5652
Tel.: (805) 965-3669
Web Site: https://www.sbir.com
Sales Range: $25-49.9 Million
Infrared Test Equipment Mfr
N.A.I.C.S.: 334516

Subsidiary (Domestic):

IRCameras LLC (3)
30 S Calle Cesar Chavez Ste D, Santa Bar-
bara, CA 93103
Tel.: (805) 965-9650
Web Site: https://ircameras.com
Emp.: 70
Infrared Imaging System Provider
N.A.I.C.S.: 334419

Subsidiary (Domestic):

**Sensor Technology Engineering,
LLC** (2)
70 S Kellogg Ave Ste 1, Goleta, CA 93117-
6408
Tel.: (805) 964-9507
Web Site: http://www.radiationpager.com
Engineering Services
N.A.I.C.S.: 541330

**Sierra Microwave Technology,
LLC** (2)
1 Sierra Way, Georgetown, TX 78626-7578
Tel.: (512) 869-5007
Web Site: https://www.sierramicrowave.com
Sales Range: $10-24.9 Million
Communications Equipment
N.A.I.C.S.: 334290
Troy Rodriguez (Pres & CEO)

Switchcraft Inc. (2)

5555 N Elston Ave, Chicago, IL 60630
Tel.: (773) 792-2700
Web Site: https://www.switchcraft.com
Sales Range: $100-124.9 Million
Electronic Switch Mfr & Distr
N.A.I.C.S.: 334419

Subsidiary (Domestic):

Conxall Corporation   (3)
601 E Wildwood, Villa Park, IL 60181-2762
Tel.: (630) 834-7504
Electronic Components Mfr
N.A.I.C.S.: 334419

Subsidiary (Non-US):

**Switchcraft Far East Company,
Ltd.**   (3)
543-1 Gajoa-Dong, Seo-Ku, Incheon, 404-250, Korea (South)
Tel.: (82) 325781201
Web Site: https://www.switchcraft.co.kr
Electronic Components Mfr
N.A.I.C.S.: 334419

Subsidiary (Domestic):

TTT-Cubed, Inc.   (2)
48531 Warm Springs Blvd Ste 417, Fremont, CA 94539
Tel.: (510) 657-8995
Web Site: http://www.ttt-cubedinc.com
Electronic Measurement Instrument Mfr
N.A.I.C.S.: 334515

Transformational Security, LLC   (2)
9101 Guilford Rd, Columbia, MD 21046-1802
Tel.: (301) 490-0112
Web Site: http://www.powerfulsecurity.com
Chemicals Mfr
N.A.I.C.S.: 325998
Jon Whittingham *(Founder & Pres)*
Scott Erik Norrholm *(Mng Dir & Exec VP)*
Shane Clark *(COO)*
Wanda Forrest *(CFO)*

VPT, Inc.   (2)
1971 Kraft Dr, Blacksburg, VA 24060
Tel.: (540) 552-5000
Web Site: https://www.vptpower.com
Sales Range: $25-49.9 Million
Power Conversion Component Mfr
N.A.I.C.S.: 335999
Dan Sable *(Founder & CEO)*
John Hodock *(Pres)*
Shawn Graham *(Exec Mgr-Product Assurance)*
Leonard Leslie *(VP-Engrg)*
Ben Savage *(CFO)*
Malcolm Campbell *(Exec Dir-Intl Sls & Mktg)*
Clay Rogers *(Dir-Ops)*
Jeremy Ferrell *(Dir-Engrg)*
Emily Miller *(Controller)*
Todd Ullman *(Mgr-Product & Program Assurance)*
Kevin Seaton *(Mgr-Comml Space Product Dev)*
Bryan Christian *(Mgr-IT Sys)*
Debbie Martilla *(Mgr-Logistics)*
Katie Bouchard *(Mgr-Mktg Comm)*

Subsidiary (Domestic):

**Freebird Semiconductor
Corporation**   (3)
17 Parkridge Rd, Haverhill, MA 01835
Tel.: (978) 208-1334
Web Site: http://www.freebirdsemi.com
Electronic Components Mfr
N.A.I.C.S.: 334419

Subsidiary (Domestic):

dB Control Corp.   (2)
1120 Auburn St, Fremont, CA 94538-7328
Tel.: (510) 656-2325
Web Site: https://www.dbcontrol.com
Emp.: 90
Amplifier Product Design & Mfr
N.A.I.C.S.: 335999
Joe Hajduk *(Founder)*

Subsidiary (Domestic):

Charter Engineering, Inc.   (3)
6729 55th St, Pinellas Park, FL 33781
Tel.: (727) 525-1025
Web Site: http://www.ceiswitches.com

Sales Range: $1-9.9 Million
Emp.: 15
Engineeering Services
N.A.I.C.S.: 541330
Keith Charti *(Pres)*

HEICO Flight Support Corp.   (1)
3000 Taft St, Hollywood, FL 33021
Tel.: (954) 987-4000
Web Site: https://www.heico.com
Emp.: 280
Holding Company; Aircraft OEM Parts Mfr, Parts Distr & Repair Services
N.A.I.C.S.: 551112
Eric A. Mendelson *(Pres & CEO)*

Subsidiary (Domestic):

Accurate Metal Machining, Inc.   (2)
882 Callendar Blvd, Painesville, OH 44077
Tel.: (440) 350-8225
Web Site:
   https://www.accuratemetalmachining.com
Sales Range: $10-24.9 Million
Emp.: 175
Machine Shop Operator
N.A.I.C.S.: 332710
John Racic *(Pres)*
Gabriel Loiczly *(VP)*
Thomas Loiczly *(VP)*
Chuck Polizzi *(Mgr-Quality Assurance)*

Action Research Corporation   (2)
34A Freedom Ct, Greer, SC 29650
Tel.: (864) 848-1244
Web Site: https://arc-labs.com
Aircraft Equipment Repair & Assembly Services
N.A.I.C.S.: 488190

Aerospace & Commercial Technologies, LLC   (2)
970 FM2871, Fort Worth, TX 76126
Tel.: (817) 560-6600
Web Site: https://aero-com-tech.com
Emp.: 50
Military Aircraft Replacement Parts Mfr, Maintenance, Repair & Overhaul Services
N.A.I.C.S.: 811310
Ross M. Smith *(Owner & VP-Bus Mgmt)*
Dave R. Smith *(Pres)*
Gary D. Fort *(Chief Engr-Project)*
Deborah A. Brown *(Gen Mgr)*

Blue Aerospace LLC   (2)
6211 Nob Hill Rd, Tamarac, FL 33321
Tel.: (954) 718-4404
Web Site: https://blueaero.com
Emp.: 40
Spares Acquisition & Repair Management Services
N.A.I.C.S.: 488190
Michael Navon *(Pres)*

Jetseal, Inc.   (2)
10310 E Buckeye Ln, Spokane Valley, WA 99206
Tel.: (509) 467-9133
Web Site: https://www.jetseal.com
Emp.: 65
Gaskets & Seals Mfr
N.A.I.C.S.: 339991
Steve Hudlet *(Mgr-Engrg)*
Keith Adams *(Engr-Applications & Test)*

Reinhold Industries Inc.   (2)
12827 E Imperial Hwy, Santa Fe Springs, CA 90670-4713
Tel.: (562) 944-3281
Web Site: https://reinhold-ind.com
Structural Composites; Ablative Composites; Reinforced Plastics
N.A.I.C.S.: 336413

Seal Dynamics LLC   (2)
2 Adams Ave, Hauppauge, NY 11788
Tel.: (631) 667-4000
Web Site: https://www.sealdynamics.com
Sales Range: $10-24.9 Million
Emp.: 80
Industrial Parts Mfr
N.A.I.C.S.: 423840
David Susser *(Pres & CEO)*

Subsidiary (Domestic):

Seal Dynamics LLC   (3)
13780 McCormick Dr, Tampa, FL 33626
Tel.: (813) 920-7898
Web Site: http://www.sealdynamics.com

Industrial Parts Mfr & Whslr
N.A.I.C.S.: 423840

Subsidiary (Domestic):

Thermal Structures, Inc.   (2)
2362 Railroad St, Corona, CA 92878
Tel.: (951) 736-9911
Web Site:
   https://www.thermalstructures.com
Emp.: 300
Insulation & Composite Products Mfr
N.A.I.C.S.: 327999

Intelligent Devices, LLC   (1)
9101 Guilford Rd Ste 112, Columbia, MD 21046
Tel.: (301) 498-7590
Web Site: https://www.intdevices.com
Software Development Services
N.A.I.C.S.: 541511

Marway Power Systems Inc.   (1)
1721 S Grand Ave, Santa Ana, CA 92705   **(92.5%)**
Tel.: (714) 917-6200
Web Site: http://www.marway.com
Rev.: $14,200,000
Emp.: 45
Computer Peripheral Equipment
N.A.I.C.S.: 334118
Dan Richter *(Pres & CEO)*

R H Laboratories, Inc.   (1)
1 Tanguay Ave, Nashua, NH 03063
Tel.: (603) 459-5900
Web Site: http://www.rh-labs.com
Sales Range: $1-9.9 Million
Emp.: 45
Electronic Components, Nec, Nsk
N.A.I.C.S.: 334419
Benjamin Robinson *(CEO)*

Reinhold Holdings, Inc.   (1)
12827 Imperial Hwy, Santa Fe Springs, CA 90670
Tel.: (562) 944-3281
Plastics Product Mfr
N.A.I.C.S.: 326199

Subsidiary (Non-US):

Seal Dynamics Limited   (2)
Unit 3A Beechwood Lime Tree Way, Chineham Business Park, Basingstoke, RG24 8WA, United Kingdom
Tel.: (44) 1256300747
Web Site: https://www.sealdynamics.com
Sales Range: $10-24.9 Million
Emp.: 6
Aircraft Equipment Distr
N.A.I.C.S.: 336413

**Rocky Mountain Hydrostatics,
LLC**   (1)
25400 E 152nd St, Brighton, CO 80603
Tel.: (303) 637-0500
Web Site: https://new.rmhydro.com
Hydraulic Pump & Motor Mfr & Distr
N.A.I.C.S.: 333996
Therese Zuercher *(Co-Owner & Mgr)*
Terrence Moore *(Dir-Sls & Mktg)*
Brad Zuercher *(Co-Owner)*

Sensor Systems Inc.   (1)
8929 Fullbright Ave, Chatsworth, CA 91311
Tel.: (818) 341-5366
Web Site: https://www.sensorantennas.com
Rev.: $20,800,000
Emp.: 250
Antennas, Transmitting & Communications
N.A.I.C.S.: 334220

Silver Wings Aerospace, Inc.   (1)
25400 SW 140th Ave, Princeton, FL 33032
Tel.: (305) 258-5950
Airframe Component Mfr & Distr
N.A.I.C.S.: 336413

Solid Sealing Technology, Inc.   (1)
44 Dalliba Ave, Watervliet, NY 12189   **(85%)**
Tel.: (518) 874-3600
Web Site: https://www.solidsealing.com
Electronic Connector Mfr
N.A.I.C.S.: 334417
Alan Fuierer *(Pres)*
Don Walzer *(Sls Mgr)*
Tom Forbes *(Mgr-Mfg)*
Don French *(Mgr-Facilities)*
Christopher Blanchard *(Mgr-Acctg)*

Heath Johnson *(Mgr-Engrg)*
Adam Bush *(Mktg Mgr)*
Scott Hill *(Mgr-Quality)*
Juliana Spath *(Mgr-HR)*
Amy LeBlanc *(Mgr-Customer Svc)*
Mathieu Morissette *(Engr-Sls)*

Specialty Silicone Products, Inc.   (1)
Corporate Technology Park 3 McCrea Hill Rd, Ballston Spa, NY 12020
Tel.: (518) 885-8826
Web Site: http://www.sspinc.com
Emp.: 70
Industrial Organic Chemicals, Nec
N.A.I.C.S.: 325199

Thermal Energy Products, Inc.   (1)
2702 7th Ave S, Fargo, ND 58103
Tel.: (701) 237-0071
Web Site: https://www.tepinc.com
Building Material Merchant Whslr
N.A.I.C.S.: 444180
Mark Walstead *(Owner & Pres)*

Wencor Group, LLC   (1)
416 Dividend Dr, Peachtree, GA 30269
Tel.: (801) 489-2000
Web Site: http://www.wencorgroup.com
Emp.: 200
Holding Company; Aircraft Parts Mfr & Distr
N.A.I.C.S.: 551112
Keith Hicks *(CIO)*
Rob Frese *(CFO)*
Eric Vernon *(Gen Counsel & Exec VP)*
Shawn Trogdon *(CEO)*
Josh Abelson *(Chief Comml Officer-PMA & Distr & Pres-PMA)*
Scott Herndon *(Pres-Defense)*

Subsidiary (Domestic):

Absolute Aviation Services, LLC   (2)
8122 W Pilot Dr, Spokane, WA 99224
Tel.: (509) 747-2904
Web Site: http://www.absoluteaviation.com
Commercial & Military Aircraft Electronics, Electrical Systems & Instrumentation Repair Services
N.A.I.C.S.: 488190
Timothy Todd Slater *(Dir-Bus Dev)*

**Accessory Technologies
Corporation**   (2)
219 Central Ave, Farmingdale, NY 11735
Tel.: (631) 753-2282
Web Site: http://www.atcny.com
Aviation Equipment Repair Services
N.A.I.C.S.: 811310

Aero-Glen International, LLC   (2)
13751 Independence Pkwy, Fort Worth, TX 76177
Tel.: (817) 328-6600
Web Site: http://www.aeroglen.com
Hardware Merchant Whslr
N.A.I.C.S.: 423710
Tyson Kay *(VP & Gen Mgr)*
Tyson Kay *(VP & Gen Mgr)*

Soundair Aviation Services, LLC   (2)
1826 Bickford Ave, Snohomish, WA 98290
Tel.: (360) 453-2300
Web Site: http://www.soundair.com
Emp.: 65
Aircraft Component Repair Services
N.A.I.C.S.: 488190
Greg Harwood *(Pres & CEO)*
Travis Dykstra *(Dir-Sls & Mktg)*

Subsidiary (Domestic):

PHS/MWA   (3)
42374 Avenida Alvarado, Temecula, CA 92590
Tel.: (951) 695-1008
Web Site: http://www.phsmwa.com
Sales Range: $10-24.9 Million
Aircraft Component Repair Services
N.A.I.C.S.: 488190
Gerg Harwood *(Pres)*

Subsidiary (Domestic):

Wencor, LLC   (2)
1625 N 1100 W, Springville, UT 84663
Tel.: (801) 489-2000
Web Site: http://www.wencor.com
Emp.: 150
Aircraft Parts Mfr & Distr
N.A.I.C.S.: 336413
Andy Shields *(VP-PMA)*

HEICO Corporation—(Continued)

HEIDRICK & STRUGGLES INTERNATIONAL, INC.
233 S Wacker Dr Willis Tower Ste 4900, Chicago, IL 60606-6303
Tel.: (312) 496-1200 **DE**
Web Site: https://www.heidrick.com
Year Founded: 1953
HSII—(NASDAQ)
Rev.: $1,083,586,000
Assets: $1,175,638,000
Liabilities: $764,992,000
Net Worth: $410,646,000
Earnings: $79,486,000
Emp.: 2,141
Fiscal Year-end: 12/31/22
Holding Company; Executive Search Consulting & Placement Services
N.A.I.C.S.: 551112
Thomas L. Monahan III *(CEO)*
Todd R. Monti *(Mng Partner-Financial Svcs & Private Equity-Global & New York)*
Alyse D. Bodine *(Mng Partner-Global-Healthcare & Life Sciences-Philadelphia)*
Julian Ha *(Partner-Private Equity-Washington)*
Stephen Schwanhausser *(Mng Partner-Consumer Market-Global & Stamford)*
Samantha Carey *(Partner-Healthcare & Life Sciences-Washington)*
Lisa B. Baird *(Partner-Bus & Professional Svcs-New York & Stamford)*
John Mitchell *(Partner-Healthcare & Life Sciences-New York)*
Stephen A. Bondi *(VP & Controller)*
Sarah Payne *(Chief HR Officer)*
Markus Kaiser *(Mng Partner-Automotive Practice-Munich & Global)*
Peter Behncke *(Partner-Industrial-Frankfurt)*
Paul W. Benson *(Partner-Energy-New York & Stamford)*
Rebekah Bill *(Partner-Industrial-Houston)*
Jenni Hibbert *(Mng Partner-Financial Svcs-Global & London)*
Jonathan M. Graham *(Mng Partner-Global-Energy, Industrial & Private Equity)*
Mary MacDonald *(Partner)*
Gustavo Alba *(Partner-Bus & Professional Svcs-New York City & Miami Beach)*
Tracey Heaton *(Chief Legal Officer & Sec)*

Subsidiaries:

Beijing Heidrick & Struggles International Management Consulting Company Limited **(1)**
Suite 718 South Tower Kerry Center, Beijing, 100020, China
Tel.: (86) 1065988288
Human Resource & Consulting Services
N.A.I.C.S.: 541612
Helen Chen *(Principal)*
Ming Luo *(Principal)*

Business Talent Group, LLC **(1)**
15332 Antioch St Ste 20, Pacific Palisades, CA 90272 **(100%)**
Tel.: (646) 513-4770
Web Site:
https://www.businesstalentgroup.com
Sales Range: $25-49.9 Million
Business Consulting Services
N.A.I.C.S.: 541611
Elizabeth Adeoye *(Principal-Client Svcs)*
Jennifer Barnes *(Principal-Client Svcs)*
Dak Gilinsky *(Dir-Client Dev)*
Robin Goolsbee *(Principal-Client Svcs)*
Laura Klein *(Principal & Head-Specialist Program)*
Brian Lafer *(Sr Dir-Client Dev)*
Linda Lavine *(Principal-Client Svcs)*

Ryan Leventhal *(Sr Dir-Client Dev)*
Stephanie Lo *(Principal-Client Svcs)*
Michelle Madden *(Head-Mktg & Comm)*
Julie Nelson *(Principal-Client Svcs)*
Chris Panagakos *(Principal-Client Svcs)*
Kristin Patrick *(Principal-Client Svcs)*
Richard Perez *(Sr VP-Client Dev & Sls Ops)*
Jill Perrin *(Sr VP-Talent Dev)*
Patricia Petersen *(Chief Admin Officer & Gen Counsel)*
Letitia Peypoch *(Sr VP-Client Svcs)*
Sandra Pinnavaia *(Chief Knowledge & Innovation Officer & Exec VP)*
Kathy Ranek *(Principal-Client Svcs & Head-People)*
Kim Roffey *(Principal-Client Svcs)*
Jennifer Schiff *(Principal-Client Svcs)*
Tania Suster *(Principal-Client Svcs & Digital Products)*
Paul Tufaro *(Dir-Client Dev)*
Amelia Tyagi *(Co-Founder & Co-CEO)*
Ysette Witteveen *(Principal-Client Svcs)*
Adam Zellner *(Dir-Client Dev)*
Laurie Zorn *(Principal-Client Svcs)*
Jody Greenstone Miller *(Co-Founder)*

HEIDRICK & STRUGGLES (INDIA) PRIVATE LIMITED **(1)**
Floor No 10 Building No 9B DLF Cyber City Phase III, Gurgaon, 122002, Haryana, India
Tel.: (91) 1244655300
Web Site: http://www.heidrick.com
Emp.: 20
Executive Search Consultants Services
N.A.I.C.S.: 541612
Gauri Padmanabhan *(Partner)*
Ankit Goyal *(Partner)*
Charul Madan *(Partner)*
Amardeep Rana *(Partner)*

HEIDRICK & STRUGGLES (MIDDLE EAST) LLC **(1)**
ICD Brookfield Place Level 7 Dubai International Financial Centre, PO Box 482075, Dubai, United Arab Emirates
Tel.: (971) 4 376 4600
Web Site: http://www.heidrick.com
Sales Range: $25-49.9 Million
Emp.: 23
Executive Search Consulting Services
N.A.I.C.S.: 541612
Ali Alhadithi *(Principal)*
Suhas Anand *(Principal)*
Niels Bentzen *(Partner)*
Tom Clarke *(Principal)*
Nick Cunningham *(Partner)*
Alain Deniau *(Partner)*
Shadi El Farr *(Mng Partner-Reg)*
Simon Fletcher *(Principal)*
Tanja Ivkovic *(Principal)*
Maliha Jilani *(Partner)*
Ralph Maonon *(Partner)*
Markus Wiesner *(Partner)*
James Raley *(Partner)*
Neha Mohunta *(Principal)*

HEIDRICK & STRUGGLES (SHP) LIMITED **(1)**
40 Argyll Street, London, W1F 7EB, United Kingdom
Tel.: (44) 2070754000
Web Site:
http://www.heidrickandstruggles.com
Sales Range: $25-49.9 Million
Emp.: 100
Executive Search Consultants Services
N.A.I.C.S.: 541612
Susie Clements *(Mng Partner)*
Marcus de Luca *(Partner)*
Mariam Abbott *(Principal)*
Sam Bell *(Principal)*
Chris Bray *(Mng Partner-Reg)*
Alice Breeden *(Partner)*
Lucy Bull *(Principal)*
Clare Buxton *(Partner)*
Chantal Clavier *(Partner)*
George Corbett *(Partner)*
Tom Cunningham *(Partner)*
Helen Dingwall *(Partner)*
Priya Dixit Vyas *(Partner)*
Sarah Driscoll *(Principal)*
Rachel Farley *(Principal)*
Adam Howe *(Principal)*
Mark Jackson *(Partner)*
Sherree Kendall *(Principal)*
Shaloo Kulkarni *(Partner)*
Emma Penny *(Principal)*
Adam Vaughan *(Partner)*

Duncan Wardley *(Partner)*
Linda Wegelius *(Partner)*

HEIDRICK & STRUGGLES INTERIM EXECUTIVE GMBH **(1)**
Keplerstrasse 20, Munich, 81679, Germany
Tel.: (49) 89998110
Web Site: http://www.heidrick.com
Emp.: 70
Executive Search Consulting Services
N.A.I.C.S.: 541612
Michael Oberwegner *(Partner)*
Christine Stimpel *(Partner)*

HEIDRICK & STRUGGLES UNTERNEHMENSBERATUNG VERWALTUNG- GMBH **(1)**
Sky Office Kennedydamm 24, Dusseldorf, 40476, Germany
Tel.: (49) 21182820
Web Site: http://www.heidrick.com
Sales Range: $25-49.9 Million
Emp.: 12
Executive Search Consulting Services
N.A.I.C.S.: 541612
Werner Knips *(Partner)*
Christine Stimpel *(Partner)*
Nicolas van Rosty *(Partner)*
Sebastian Walter *(Partner)*

Heidrick & Struggles (NZ) Limited **(1)**
Level 13 DLA Phillips Fox Tower, PO Box 7446, 209 Queen Street, Auckland, 1010, New Zealand
Tel.: (64) 93066630
Web Site: http://www.heidrick.com
Sales Range: $1-9.9 Million
Emp.: 9
Executive Search Consultants
N.A.I.C.S.: 541612

Heidrick & Struggles A/S **(1)**
Amaliegade 10 4th Floor, 1256, Copenhagen, Denmark
Tel.: (45) 33377600
Emp.: 50
Human Resource & Consulting Services
N.A.I.C.S.: 541612

Heidrick & Struggles AB **(1)**
Norrlandsgatan 16 1tr, Stockholm, 11143, Sweden
Tel.: (46) 84067100
Web Site: http://www.heidrick.com
Sales Range: $100-124.9 Million
Emp.: 10
Executive Search Consultants
N.A.I.C.S.: 541612
Peter Christiansen *(Partner)*

Heidrick & Struggles AG **(1)**
Holbeinstrasse 22, Zurich, 8008, Switzerland
Tel.: (41) 444881313
Web Site: http://www.heidrick.com
Sales Range: $10-24.9 Million
Emp.: 20
Executive Search Consultants
N.A.I.C.S.: 541612

Heidrick & Struggles Australia, Ltd. **(1)**
Level 28 Chifley Tower 2 Chifley Square, Sydney, 2000, NSW, Australia
Tel.: (61) 28 205 2000
Web Site: http://www.heidrick.com
Sales Range: $25-49.9 Million
Emp.: 100
Executive Search Consultants
N.A.I.C.S.: 541612

Heidrick & Struggles BV **(1)**
Rembrandt Tower, Amstelplein 1, 1096 HA, Amsterdam, Netherlands
Tel.: (31) 204627777
Web Site: http://www.heidrick.com
Sales Range: $100-124.9 Million
Emp.: 7
Executive Search Consultants
N.A.I.C.S.: 541612
Roger Muys *(Partner)*
Camilla Reventlow *(Principal)*
Claire Babel *(Partner)*
Daniel Filet *(Partner)*
Thorsten Kocherscheidt *(Principal)*

Heidrick & Struggles Canada, Inc. **(1)**

100 King Street West Suite 4630, Toronto, M5X 1E3, ON, Canada
Tel.: (416) 361-4700
Web Site: http://www.heidrick.com
Sales Range: $10-24.9 Million
Emp.: 15
Executive Search Consultants
N.A.I.C.S.: 541612
Jonathan MacKey *(Partner)*
Dominique Fortier *(Partner)*
Tim Jensen *(Principal)*
Nancie Lataille *(Partner)*
Nicole Northwood *(Principal)*

Heidrick & Struggles Espana, Inc. **(1)**
Edificio Piramide, Paseo de la Castellana 31 3 A, 28046, Madrid, Spain
Tel.: (34) 913915256
Web Site: http://www.heidrick.com
Sales Range: $10-24.9 Million
Emp.: 70
Executive Search Consultants
N.A.I.C.S.: 541612
Pilar Santiago *(Partner)*

Heidrick & Struggles Hong Kong Ltd. **(1)**
Suite 3005 One Pacific Place 88 Queensway, 88 Queensway Admiralty, Hong Kong, China (Hong Kong)
Tel.: (852) 21039300
Web Site: http://www.heidrick.com
Sales Range: $10-24.9 Million
Emp.: 40
Executive Search Consultants
N.A.I.C.S.: 541612
Harry J. O'Neill III *(Partner)*

Heidrick & Struggles International SRL **(1)**
Palazzo Serbelloni Corso Venezia 16, Corso Venezia 16, 20121, Milan, Italy
Tel.: (39) 02762521
Web Site: http://www.heidrick.com
Sales Range: $10-24.9 Million
Emp.: 20
Executive Search Consultants
N.A.I.C.S.: 541612

Heidrick & Struggles Ireland, Limited **(1)**
26 Fitzwilliam Square, D02 RR80, Dublin, 2, Ireland
Tel.: (353) 12597500
Human Resource & Consulting Services
N.A.I.C.S.: 541612

Heidrick & Struggles Japan, Ltd. **(1)**
Atago Green Hills MORI Tower 25f 2-5-1 Atago, Minato-ku, Tokyo, 105-6225, Japan
Tel.: (81) 345207800
Web Site: http://www.heidrick.com
Sales Range: $100-124.9 Million
Emp.: 30
Executive Search Consultants
N.A.I.C.S.: 541612
Yuki Handa *(Principal)*
Noriko Watanabe *(Partner)*
Aya Iinuma *(Partner)*
Ken Suzuki *(Partner)*
Yoshihira Terashima *(Principal)*

Heidrick & Struggles Korea, Inc. **(1)**
5th Floor Gangnam Finance Centre 152 Teheran-ro, Gangnam-gu, Seoul, 06236, Korea (South)
Tel.: (82) 23 430 6000
Web Site: http://www.heidrick.com
Sales Range: $10-24.9 Million
Emp.: 13
Executive Search Consultants
N.A.I.C.S.: 541612
Mark Sungrae Kim *(Partner)*
Eunyoung Choi *(Principal)*
Kiwook Kim *(Partner)*
Yeonho Kim *(Partner)*
ChaKyoon Koo *(Principal)*

Heidrick & Struggles Recruitment Thailand Co., Ltd. **(1)**
57 Park Ventures Ecoplex 11/F Unit 1105 Wireless Road, Bangkok, 10330, Thailand
Tel.: (66) 26318500
Web Site: http://www.heidrick.com
Sales Range: $25-49.9 Million
Emp.: 10
Executive Search Consultants
N.A.I.C.S.: 541612

Heidrick & Struggles Russia LLC (1)
Business Park Vivaldi Summer Letnikovs-
kaya Street 2, Building 1 Block D 4th Floor,
115114, Moscow, Russia
Tel.: (7) 4956461818
Web Site: http://www.heidrick.com
Sales Range: $100-124.9 Million
Emp.: 7
Executive Search Consultants
N.A.I.C.S.: 541612

Heidrick & Struggles S.A. de C.V. (1)
Torre Chapultepec Ruben Dario No 281 Ofi-
cina 700, Mexico, DF, Mexico
Tel.: (52) 559 138 0370
Web Site: http://www.heidrick.com
Sales Range: $10-24.9 Million
Emp.: 19
Executive Search Consultants
N.A.I.C.S.: 541612

Heidrick & Struggles Singapore Pte Ltd. (1)
5 Temasek Boulevard 15-03 Suntec Tower
Five, Singapore, 038985, Singapore
Tel.: (65) 63325001
Web Site: http://www.heidrick.com
Sales Range: $10-24.9 Million
Emp.: 50
Executive Search Consultants
N.A.I.C.S.: 541612

Heidrick & Struggles Sp. z o.o. (1)
Chmielna 19 Nowy Dom Jablkowskich 5th
Floor, 00-021, Warsaw, Poland
Tel.: (48) 225849898
Web Site: http://www.heidrick.com
Sales Range: $100-124.9 Million
Executive Search Consultants
N.A.I.C.S.: 541612

Heidrick & Struggles UK Ltd. (1)
40 Argyll Street, London, W1F 7EB, United
Kingdom
Tel.: (44) 207 075 4000
Web Site: http://www.heidrick.com
Sales Range: $10-24.9 Million
Emp.: 120
Executive Search Consultants
N.A.I.C.S.: 541612
Alice Breeden (Partner)
Shaloo Kakkar Kulkarni (Partner)
Sam Bell (Principal)
Louis Besland (Partner)
Chris Bray (Mng Partner-Reg)
Sam Burman (Mng Partner-Global)
Clare Buxton (Partner)
Chantal Clavier (Partner)
Susie Clements (Mng Partner-Reg)
George Corbett (Partner)
David Crawford (Partner)
Tom Cunningham (Partner)
Marcus De Luca (Partner)
Helen Dingwall (Partner)
Priya Dixit Vyas (Partner)
Sarah Driscoll (Principal)
Adam Howe (Principal)
Mark Jackson (Partner)
Sherree Kendall (Principal)
Will Moynahan (Mng Partner)
Lucy Bull (Principal)
Rachel Farley (Principal)
T. A. Mitchell (Principal)
David Molen (Principal)
Emma Penny (Principal)
Cathy Powell (Partner)
Audrey Rassam (Principal)
Alistair Reily (Principal)
Anna Rex (Principal)
Dominique Robertson (Principal)
Alex Ross (Partner)
Adrian Samms (Principal)
Sharon Sands (Partner)
Sophie Scholes (Partner)
Jane Schroeder (Principal)
Malcolm Sclanders (Principal)
Guy Shaul (Principal)
Harry Simons (Principal)
Claire Skinner (Mng Partner-Reg)
Andy Smith (Partner)
Richard Sumner (Partner)
Adam Vaughan (Partner)
Duncan Wardley (Partner)
Mariam Abbott (Principal)
Jorge Gouveia de Oliveira (Partner)
Andrew Macleod (Mng Partner-Reg)
Gordon McCree (Principal)
Amanda Milsom (Principal)

Nick Parfitt (Partner)
Dustin Seale (Partner)
Ian Tomlinson-Roe (Partner)
Amy Turner (Partner)
Jacqueline Wrotniak (Principal)

Heidrick & Struggles Unternehmensberatung GmbH (1)
Kohlmartt 1, 1010, Vienna, Austria
Tel.: (43) 153310070
Web Site: http://www.heidrick.com
Sales Range: $1-9.9 Million
Emp.: 10
Executive Search Consultants
N.A.I.C.S.: 541612

Heidrick & Struggles de Chile Limitada (1)
Avenida Andres Bello 2777 Oficina 903, Las
Condes, Santiago, Chile
Tel.: (56) 27535300
Web Site: http://www.heidrick.com
Sales Range: $100-124.9 Million
Emp.: 6
Executive Search Consultants
N.A.I.C.S.: 541612

Heidrick & Struggles do Brasil Ltda. (1)
Bolsa de Imoveis Building Av das Nacoes
Unidas No 11 541 9th Floor, Brooklin Novo,
Sao Paulo, SP, Brazil
Tel.: (55) 115 504 4000
Web Site: http://www.heidrick.com
Sales Range: $10-24.9 Million
Emp.: 17
Executive Search Consultants
N.A.I.C.S.: 541612

Heidrick & Struggles, Inc. (1)
233 S Wacker Dr Ste 4900, Chicago, IL
60606-6303
Tel.: (312) 496-1200
Web Site: http://www.heidrick.com
Emp.: 200
Executive Search Consulting & Placement
Services
N.A.I.C.S.: 561311

Unit (Domestic):

Philosophy IB, LLP (2)
25A Vreeland Rd #306, Florham Park, NJ
07932
Tel.: (973) 443-9202
Web Site: http://www.philosophyib.com
Administrative Management & General
Management Consulting Services
N.A.I.C.S.: 541611
Paul Black (Dir-Leadership Dev)
Kristin Luckenbill (Principal)

Senn-Delaney Leadership Consulting Group, LLC (1)
7755 Ctr Ave Ste 900, Huntington Beach,
CA 92647
Tel.: (562) 426-5400
Web Site: http://www.senndelaney.com
Sales Range: $10-24.9 Million
Emp.: 130
Leadership Consulting Services
N.A.I.C.S.: 541612
Amy Turner (Partner)
Adrian Samms (VP)
Allie Dulaney (Mgr-Resource)
Brian Lowenthal (VP)
Brian Reger (Sr VP-Measurement)
Sharon Dogra (Mgr-Client Svcs-London)
Senn Delaney (Founder)
Larry E. Senn (Founder & Chm)
Regina Salvucci (Partner)
Ian Johnston (Mng Partner-Culture
Shaping-EMEA)
Bill Parsons (Partner & Exec VP)
John McKay (Partner)
Rose Gailey (Partner)
Jaclyn Eiler (Dir-Bus Dev)
Julia Stone (Sr Dir-Bus Dev)
Michael Williams (Dir-Bus Dev)
Christine Rivera (Mgr-Client Svcs)
Denise Montgomery-Harley (Mgr-Client
Svcs)
Linda Ellison (Mgr-Product)
Margee Infante (Dir-Consultant Dev)
Mike Dyakon (Dir-Client Svcs)
Rich Crafton (Mgr-Client Ops)
Sheldon White (Mgr-Client Svcs)
Bill Bradley (VP)
Brian Klapper (Principal)

Chad Carr (Principal)
Christina D'Onofrio (Principal)
Dennis Alimena (VP)
Edward Cass (VP)
Holly McLeod (VP)
Jane E. Black (Principal)
Sebastien Terral (VP)
Scott Tempel (Principal)
Priya Dixit Vyas (VP)
Tania Hotmer (VP)
Teresa Garza (VP)
Jon Graziano (Principal)
Kurt Kamph (Principal)
Matt Herzberg (Partner)

HELIOGEN, INC.
130 W Union St, Pasadena, CA
91103
Tel.: (626) 720-4530   DE
Web Site: https://www.heliogen.com
HLGN—(OTCQX)
Rev.: $13,751,000
Assets: $191,619,000
Liabilities: $66,295,000
Net Worth: $125,324,000
Earnings: ($142,000,000)
Emp.: 220
Fiscal Year-end: 12/31/22
Solar Electric Power Generation
N.A.I.C.S.: 551112
Robert Phelps Morris (CFO)
Julie M. Kane (Chm)
Christie Obiaya (CEO)
Tom Doyle (Chief Comml Officer)

HELIOS AND MATHESON ANALYTICS INC.
Empire State Bldg 350 5th Ave, New
York, NY 10118
Tel.: (212) 979-8228   NY
Web Site: http://www.hmny.com
Year Founded: 1983
HMNY—(OTCIQ)
Sales Range: $10-24.9 Million
Emp.: 71
Computer Related Consulting Ser-
vices
N.A.I.C.S.: 541511
Parthasarathy Krishnan (Interim CEO
& Chief Innovation Officer)

HELIOS TECHNOLOGIES, INC.
7456 16th St E, Sarasota, FL 34243
Tel.: (941) 362-1200   FL
Web Site:
    https://www.heliostechnologies.com
Year Founded: 1970
HLIO—(NYSE)
Rev.: $869,185,000
Assets: $1,415,346,000
Liabilities: $706,383,000
Net Worth: $708,963,000
Earnings: $104,596,000
Emp.: 2,350
Fiscal Year-end: 01/01/22
Mfr & Designer of High-Performance,
Screw-In, Hydraulic Cartridge Valves
& Manifolds that Control Force,
Speed & Motion as Integral Compo-
nents in Fluid Power Systems
N.A.I.C.S.: 333112
Wichlacz F. Lee (Pres-Electronics)
Rick Martich (Pres-Hydraulics-
Americas & Sr VP-Global Ops & Sys
Sls)
Tania Almond (VP-IR & Corp Comm)
Billy Aldridge (Mng Dir, Sr VP & Mng
Dir-Enovation Controls)
Jean-Pierre Parent (Mng Dir & Sr VP)
Sean P. Bagan (Interim Pres, CEO &
CFO)
Marc Greenberg (Gen Counsel &
Sec)
Philippe J. Lemaitre (Exec Chm)

Subsidiaries:

Custom Fluidpower Pty. Ltd. (1)
36 Huntington Place, Banyo, Brisbane,

4014, QLD, Australia
Tel.: (61) 733078200
Web Site: https://www.custom.com.au
Fluid Power Equipment Mfr & Distr
N.A.I.C.S.: 333995

Custom Fluidpower Vietnam Company Ltd. (1)
3rd Floor Smart View Building 161A-163-
165 Tran Hung Dao Street, Co Giang Ward
District 1, Ho Chi Minh City, Vietnam
Tel.: (84) 2839208079
Hydraulic Fluid Pump Mfr
N.A.I.C.S.: 333996
Mark Wood (Dir-Dev-South East Asia)

Daman Products Company, Inc. (1)
1811 N Home St, Mishawaka, IN 46545-
7267
Tel.: (574) 259-7841
Web Site: https://www.daman.com
Sales Range: $10-24.9 Million
Emp.: 128
Hydraulic Valves Mfr
N.A.I.C.S.: 332912
Gordon Weiler (Mgr-Natl Sls)
Matt Giloth (Mgr-Distr Svcs)
Krysten Shoulders (Dir-HR)
Larry Davis (Pres)
Dave Mischler (VP)

Enovation Controls, Ltd. (1)
Swichgage House Church Road, Laver-
stock, Salisbury, SP1 1QZ, United Kingdom
Tel.: (44) 1722410055
Web Site:
    https://www.enovationcontrols.com
Emp.: 300
Engine Equipment Mfr
N.A.I.C.S.: 333618

Faster Germany GmbH (1)
Ursulaweg 39, 40764, Langenfeld, Ger-
many
Tel.: (49) 217383924
Fitting Material Distr
N.A.I.C.S.: 423840

Faster Hydraulics Pvt. Ltd. (1)
Plot n 10 Gate N 108 Ambethan Taluka
Khed, Pune, 410501, Maharastra, India
Tel.: (91) 2135678006
Fitting Material Distr
N.A.I.C.S.: 423840

Faster Hydraulics Shanghai Co. Ltd. (1)
1st floor Bld 4 No 333 Wanfang Rd, Min-
hang District, Shanghai, 201114, China
Tel.: (86) 2162213086
Web Site: https://www.fastercouplings.cn
Fitting Material Distr
N.A.I.C.S.: 423840

Faster Inc. (1)
6560 Weatherfield Ct, Maumee, OH 43537
Tel.: (419) 868-8197
Couplings Mfr
N.A.I.C.S.: 331511

Faster S.P.A. (1)
via Ludovico Ariosto 7, Rivolta d'Adda,
26027, Cremona, Italy
Tel.: (39) 0363377211
Web Site: https://www.fastercouplings.com
Fitting Material Mfr
N.A.I.C.S.: 332912

Faster do Brasil Ltda. (1)
Tel.: (55) 1230269699
Fitting Material Distr
N.A.I.C.S.: 423840
Alexandre Kuster (Gen Mgr)

Schultes Precision Manufacturing, Inc. (1)
1250 Busch Pkwy, Buffalo Grove, IL 60089
Tel.: (847) 465-0300
Web Site: http://www.schultes.com
General Purpose Machinery Manufacturing
N.A.I.C.S.: 333998
Rick Ruppert (Gen Mgr)

Sun Hydraulics China Co., Ltd. (1)
Hong Kong New World Tower 47th Floor
300 Huaihai Zhong Road, Shanghai,
200021, China
Tel.: (86) 2162375885
Web Site: http://www.sunhydraulics.com
Sales Range: $1-9.9 Million
Emp.: 30
Hydraulic Manifold Systems Mfr

Helios Technologies, Inc.—(Continued)
N.A.I.C.S.: 332912

Sun Hydraulics Korea Corporation (1)
51 Bukhang-ro 193beon-gil, Seo-gu, Incheon, 22856, Korea (South)
Tel.: (82) 328131350
Web Site: http://www.sunhydraulics.com
Fluid Power Valve & Hose Fitting Mfr
N.A.I.C.S.: 332912

Sun Hydraulics Limited (1)
Tel.: (44) 2476217400
Web Site: http://www.sunhydraulics.com
Emp.: 80
Fluid Power Valve Fitting Mfr
N.A.I.C.S.: 332912

Sun Hydraulik GmbH (1)
Brusseler Allee 2, 41812, Erkelenz, Germany
Tel.: (49) 243180910
Web Site: https://www.sunhydraulics.com
Emp.: 38
Fluid Power Valve & Hose Fitting Mfr
N.A.I.C.S.: 332912

Sun Murphy International Trading (Shanghai) Co., Ltd (1)
B15 Room 6 Building 351 Sizhuan Road Songjiang District, Shanghai, 201601, China
Tel.: (86) 2162375885
Engine Equipment Mfr
N.A.I.C.S.: 333618

HELIUS MEDICAL TECHNOLOGIES, INC.
642 Newtown Yardley Rd Ste 100, Newtown, PA 18940
Tel.: (215) 944-6100　　　WY
Web Site:
　　https://www.heliusmedical.com
Year Founded: 2014
HSDT—(NASDAQ)
Rev.: $644,000
Assets: $7,692,000
Liabilities: $5,342,000
Net Worth: $2,350,000
Earnings: ($8,850,000)
Emp.: 22
Fiscal Year-end: 12/31/23
Medical Device Mfr
N.A.I.C.S.: 339112
Jeffrey S. Mathiesen *(CFO, Treas & Sec)*
R. Blane Walter *(Chm)*
Antonella Favit-Van Pelt *(Chief Medical Officer)*
Lawrence Picciano *(Sr VP)*

HELIX BIOMEDIX, INC.
19125 Ncreek Pkwy Ste 120, Bothell, WA 98011
Tel.: (425) 402-8400　　　DE
Web Site:
　　https://www.helixbiomedix.com
HXBM—(OTCIQ)
Sales Range: Less than $1 Million
Emp.: 8
Pharmaceutical Preparation Manufacturing
N.A.I.C.S.: 325412
R. Stephen Beatty *(Chm)*
Robin L. Carmichael *(Pres & CEO)*
Lijuan Zhang *(Sr Dir-R&D Innovation)*
Kelly Forsythe *(Assoc Dir-Mktg)*

HELIX ENERGY SOLUTIONS GROUP, INC.
3505 W Sam Houston Pkwy N Ste 400, Houston, TX 77043
Tel.: (281) 848-6747　　　MN
Web Site: https://helixenergysolutions
　　groupinc.gcs-web.com
Year Founded: 1997
HLX—(NYSE)
Rev.: $873,100,000
Assets: $2,389,338,000
Liabilities: $872,629,000

Net Worth: $1,516,709,000
Earnings: ($87,784,000)
Emp.: 2,280
Fiscal Year-end: 12/31/22
Marine Contractor & Operator of Offshore Oil & Gas Properties & Production Facilities
N.A.I.C.S.: 211120
Owen E. Kratz *(Pres & CEO)*
Erik Heymann *(Asst Sec & Deputy Gen Counsel)*
Scotty Sparks *(COO & Exec VP)*
Erik Staffeldt *(CFO & Exec VP)*
Kimberly Seitz *(VP-Internal Audit)*
Brent Arriaga *(Chief Acctg Officer & Controller-Corp)*

Subsidiaries:

Canyon Offshore Limited (1)
Kirkton Drive Pitmedden Road Industrial Estate, Dyce, Aberdeen, AB21 0BG, Aberdeenshire, United Kingdom
Tel.: (44) 1224351800
Web Site: http://www.helixesg.com
Sales Range: $75-99.9 Million
Emp.: 15
Oil & Gas Well Drilling Services
N.A.I.C.S.: 213111

Canyon Offshore, Inc. (1)
10801 Hammerly Ste 200, Houston, TX 77043
Tel.: (713) 467-1133
Oil & Gas Well Drilling Services
N.A.I.C.S.: 213111

Helix Offshore International Holdings S.a r.l. (1)
12C Rue Guillaume Kroll R C S, 1882, Luxembourg, Luxembourg
Tel.: (352) 28669206
Holding Company
N.A.I.C.S.: 551112

Subsea Technologies Limited (1)
Helix House Kirkton Drive Dyce, Aberdeen, AB21 0BG, United Kingdom
Tel.: (44) 1224392200
Web Site: https://www.subseatek.com
Oil & Gas Equipment Mfr
N.A.I.C.S.: 333132
Drummond Lawson *(Mng Dir)*

HELMERICH & PAYNE, INC.
222 N Detroit Ave, Tulsa, OK 74120
Tel.: (918) 742-5531　　　DE
Web Site:
　　https://www.helmerichpayne.com
Year Founded: 1920
HP—(NYSE)
Rev.: $2,756,607,000
Assets: $5,781,898,000
Liabilities: $2,864,746,000
Net Worth: $2,917,152,000
Earnings: $344,165,000
Emp.: 6,200
Fiscal Year-end: 09/30/24
Oil, Gas Drilling & Real Estate Services
N.A.I.C.S.: 213111
John W. Lindsay *(CEO)*
Mark W. Smith *(CFO & Sr VP)*
Sara M. Momper *(Chief Acctg Officer & VP)*
Dave Wilson *(VP-IR)*
Michael Lennox *(Sr VP)*
Trey Adams III *(Sr VP)*
Chay Chinsethagid *(Sr VP)*
Raymond John Adams III *(VP-Digital Ops, Sls & Mktg)*

Subsidiaries:

DrillScan Europe SAS (1)
24 rue Johannes Kepler Zone Europa, 64000, Pau, France
Tel.: (33) 559987590
Oil & Energy Services
N.A.I.C.S.: 213112
Regis Studer *(Dir-Engrg)*

DrillScan SAS (1)
Pole Pixel - Bat C2 26 rue Emile Decorps,

69100, Villeurbanne, France
Tel.: (33) 482900150
Web Site: http://www.drillscan.com
Oil & Energy Services
N.A.I.C.S.: 213112

DrillScan US, Inc. (1)
2000 S Dairy Ashford Rd Ste 470, Houston, TX 77077
Tel.: (281) 679-6370
Web Site: https://store.drillscan.com
Oil & Energy Services
N.A.I.C.S.: 213112
Guy Le Breton *(Mgr-Bus Dev)*

HP Middle East Holdings Limited Company (1)
Floor 14 King Fahad Highway, Olaya District, Riyadh, Saudi Arabia
Tel.: (966) 112803990
Computer Peripheral Equipment Distr
N.A.I.C.S.: 423430

Helmerich & Payne (Colombia) Drilling Co. (1)
Calle 100 9 A-45 Torre II 7th Floor 100 Street Building, PO Box 410, Bogota, Colombia (100%)
Tel.: (57) 16182399
Web Site: http://www.hpidc.com
Sales Range: $1-9.9 Million
Emp.: 300
Drilling Contractor
N.A.I.C.S.: 213111

Helmerich & Payne Inc (1)
1437 S Boulder Ave, Tulsa, OK 74119 (100%)
Tel.: (918) 742-5531
Sales Range: $150-199.9 Million
Emp.: 300
Drilling Contractor & Rental & Supply Company for Drilling Equipment
N.A.I.C.S.: 213111

Helmerich & Payne International Drilling Co. (1)
1437 S Boulder Ave, Tulsa, OK 74119 (100%)
Tel.: (918) 742-5531
Web Site: http://www.hpinc.com
Sales Range: $150-199.9 Million
Emp.: 500
Contract Drilling
N.A.I.C.S.: 213111
John R. Bell *(VP-Intl & Offshore Ops)*
John R. Bell *(VP-Intl & Offshore Ops)*
Michael Lennox *(VP-Land)*
Wade Clark *(VP-Land)*

Helmerich & Payne Properties, Inc. (1)
1437 S Boulder Ave, Tulsa, OK 74119 (100%)
Tel.: (918) 742-5531
Web Site: http://www.hpinc.com
Sales Range: $150-199.9 Million
Emp.: 200
Real Estate Management & Development
N.A.I.C.S.: 213111

Helmerich & Payne Rasco, Inc. (1)
1437 S Boulder Ave Ste 1400, Tulsa, OK 74119
Tel.: (918) 742-5531
Web Site: http://www.hpinc.com
Sales Range: $150-199.9 Million
Emp.: 300
Oil & Gas Drilling Services
N.A.I.C.S.: 213111

Helmerich & Payne de Venezuela C.A. (1)
CA Apartado 16 Carretera Negra, Km 98 Detras Club Molino, Anaco, 0212, Edo Anzoategui, Venezuela (100%)
Tel.: (58) 2824247754
Web Site: http://www.hpidc.com
Sales Range: $250-299.9 Million
Emp.: 300
Drilling Contractor
N.A.I.C.S.: 213111

Helmerich & Payne del Ecuador, Inc. (1)
Luis Cordero y Andalucia Edificio Cyede Quinto Piso, Quito, Ecuador (100%)
Tel.: (593) 24006700
Sales Range: $75-99.9 Million
Emp.: 100
Drilling Contractor

N.A.I.C.S.: 213111

Helmerich and Payne Mexico Drilling, S. De R.L. de C.V. (1)
Honduras No 149 Local B, Matamoros, 87360, Tamaulipas, Mexico
Tel.: (52) 8999211864
Oil & Gas Drilling Services
N.A.I.C.S.: 213111

Magnetic Variation Services, LLC (1)
1050 17th St Ste 1700 Independence Plz, Denver, CO 80265
Tel.: (303) 539-5339
Web Site: https://www.magvar.com
Software Development Services
N.A.I.C.S.: 513210
Kay Yang *(Mgr-HR)*

Motive Drilling Technologies, Inc. (1)
1807 Ross Ave Ste 250, Dallas, TX 75201
Tel.: (469) 729-6470
Web Site: http://www.motivedrilling.com
Drilling Services
N.A.I.C.S.: 213111
Todd Benson *(CEO)*
Bill Chmela *(VP-Mktg & Bus Dev)*
Richard Kulavik *(Sr VP-Engrg)*

Space Center, Inc. (1)
1437 S Boulder Ste 1400, Tulsa, OK 74119 (100%)
Tel.: (918) 742-5531
Sales Range: $10-24.9 Million
Emp.: 5
Rental of Warehouse Space
N.A.I.C.S.: 531110
David Merrill *(Mgr-Property)*

Surcon, Ltd. (1)
1050 17th St Ste 1700 Independence Plz, Denver, CO 80265
Tel.: (303) 539-5339
Web Site: http://www.surcon.net
Management Consulting Services
N.A.I.C.S.: 541618

TerraVici Drilling Solutions, Inc. (1)
4000 Greenbriar Dr 400, Stafford, TX 77477
Tel.: (281) 329-4200
Web Site: http://www.terravici.com
Oil & Gas Drilling Services
N.A.I.C.S.: 213111

Utica Square Shopping Center, Inc. (1)
1437 S Boulder Ave Ste 1400, Tulsa, OK 74119 (100%)
Tel.: (918) 742-5531
Web Site: https://www.uticasquare.com
Sales Range: $200-249.9 Million
Emp.: 30
Regional Shopping Center
N.A.I.C.S.: 531120

White Eagle Assurance Company (1)
100 Bank St Ste 610, Burlington, VT 05401
Tel.: (802) 864-5599
Insurance Brokerage Services
N.A.I.C.S.: 524128

HELO CORP.
180 Steuart St Ste 192750, San Francisco, CA 94119
Tel.: (650) 646-2193　　　NV
Web Site: http://www.worldcorp.com
Year Founded: 2010
HLOC—(OTCIQ)
Rev.: $1,991,982
Assets: $738,017
Liabilities: $3,978,302
Net Worth: ($3,240,285)
Earnings: ($1,555,204)
Fiscal Year-end: 12/31/19
Electric Equipment Mfr
N.A.I.C.S.: 334111
Fabio Galdi *(Chm, CTO & Chief Visionary Officer)*
Sean McVeigh *(Pres & CEO)*
David Ufheil *(CFO)*
Kevin Fuller *(CMO)*
Clayton A. Jones *(Gen Counsel & Sec)*

HEMAGEN DIAGNOSTICS, INC.

9033 Red Branch Rd, Columbia, MD 21045
Tel.: (443) 367-5500   DE
Web Site: https://www.hemagen.com
HMGN—(OTCIQ)
Sales Range: $1-9.9 Million
Medical Laboratories
N.A.I.C.S.: 621511

HEMP NATURALS, INC.

7441 Rte 9, Plattsburgh, NY 12901
Tel.: (347) 301-8431   DE
Web Site: http://www.ir-
hempnaturals.com
Year Founded: 2015
HPMM—(OTCIQ)
Assets: $1,271,000
Liabilities: $1,003,000
Net Worth: $268,000
Earnings: ($1,654,000)
Emp.: 1
Fiscal Year-end: 11/30/20
Beauty & Personal Care Product
Distr
N.A.I.C.S.: 424210
Levi Jacobson (CEO, CFO, COO,
Chief Acctg Officer & Sec)

HEMP, INC.

2400 S Cimarron Ave #120, Las Vegas, NV 89117
Tel.: (720) 220-0037   CO
Web Site: https://www.hempinc.com
Year Founded: 2008
HEMP—(OTCIQ)
Sales Range: Less than $1 Million
Industrial Hemp
N.A.I.C.S.: 325411
Bruce Perlowin (CEO)
Craig Perlowin (Co-Sec)

HEMPACCO CO., INC.

9925 Airway Rd, San Diego, CA 92154
Tel.: (619) 779-0715   NV
Web Site: https://www.hempaccoinc.com
Year Founded: 2019
HPCO—(NASDAQ)
Rev.: $4,045,637
Assets: $18,043,080
Liabilities: $18,822,405
Net Worth: ($779,325)
Earnings: ($13,442,221)
Fiscal Year-end: 12/31/23
Hemp Product Mfr
N.A.I.C.S.: 325411
Sandro Piancone (Pres, CEO, Co-Founder, Treas & Sec)
Neville Pearson (CFO)
Jorge Olson (Co-Founder, CMO & Exec VP)

HEMPLIFE TODAY

3570 E 12th Ave, Denver, CO 80206
Web Site:
http://www.ubiquitechsoftware.com
Year Founded: 2007
UBQU—(OTCIQ)
Sales Range: $1-9.9 Million
Software Publisher
N.A.I.C.S.: 513210

HENLEY PARK ACQUISITION CORP.

1900 M St NW Ste 300, Washington, DC 20036
Tel.: (202) 765-3077   DE
Year Founded: 2020
HPAC—(NYSE)
Investment Services
N.A.I.C.S.: 523999
Miguel Payan (CEO)
Robert Haywood (Pres & CFO)

HENNESSY ADVISORS, INC.

7250 Redwood Blvd Ste 200, Novato, CA 94945
Tel.: (415) 899-1555   CA
Web Site:
https://www.hennessyadvisors.com
Year Founded: 1989
HNNA—(NASDAQ)
Rev.: $29,646,000
Assets: $152,099,000
Liabilities: $60,788,000
Net Worth: $91,311,000
Earnings: $7,097,000
Emp.: 17
Fiscal Year-end: 09/30/24
Investment Management Service
N.A.I.C.S.: 523940
Neil Joseph Hennessy (Chm & CEO)
Teresa Mariani Nilsen (Pres, COO & Sec)
Kathryn R. Fahy (CFO & Sr VP)
Brian C. Carlson (Chief Compliance Officer & Sr VP)

HENRY SCHEIN, INC.

135 Duryea Rd, Melville, NY 11747
Tel.: (631) 843-5500   DE
Web Site:
https://www.henryschein.com
Year Founded: 1932
HSIC—(NASDAQ)
Rev.: $12,339,000,000
Assets: $10,573,000,000
Liabilities: $6,284,000,000
Net Worth: $4,289,000,000
Earnings: $416,000,000
Emp.: 25,000
Fiscal Year-end: 12/30/23
Healtcare Services
N.A.I.C.S.: 423450
Stanley M. Bergman (Chm & CEO)
James P. Breslawski (Vice Chm & Pres)
Mark E. Mlotek (Chief Strategic Officer & Exec VP)
Michael Racioppi (Chief Mdsg Officer & Sr VP)
Walter Siegel (Chief Legal Officer & Sr VP)
Michael S. Ettinger (COO & Exec VP)
Lorelei McGlynn (Chief HR Officer & Sr VP)
Ann Marie Gothard (VP-Global Corp Media Rels)
Brad Connett (CEO-North America Distr Grp)
Christopher Pendergast (CTO & Sr VP)
James Mullins (Sr VP-Global Supply Chain)
Dirk Benson (Chief Comml Officer-North America Distr Grp & VP-North America Distr Grp)
Dave Steck (VP-US Dental Grp & Gen Mgr-US Dental Grp)
Ty Ford (VP-U.S. Medical Sls & Gen Mgr-U.S. Medical Sls)
Ronald N. South (CFO & Sr VP)
Shirley Taylor (Chief Security & Safety Officer-Global & VP)
Trinh Clark (Chief Global Customer Experience Officer & Sr VP)
Leigh Benowitz (Chief Global Digital Transformation Officer & Sr VP)
Lonnie Shoff (Pres-Global Healthcare Specialty Grp & CEO-Global Animal Health & Strategic Partnership Grp)
Kelly Murphy (Gen Counsel)

Subsidiaries:

ACE Surgical Supply Co., Inc.   (1)
1034 Pearl St, Brockton, MA 02301
Web Site: http://www.acesurgical.com
Surgical Applicance Distr
N.A.I.C.S.: 423450

Baynon International Corporation (1)

266 Cedar St, Cedar Grove, NJ 07009
Tel.: (973) 239-2952
Rev.: $8
Assets: $5,349
Liabilities: $155,841
Net Worth: ($150,492)
Earnings: ($28,129)
Fiscal Year-end: 12/31/2019
Investment Services
N.A.I.C.S.: 523999
Pasquale Catizone (Pres)
Daniel Generelli (Treas & Sec)

BioHorizons Camlog Italia SRL   (1)
Via Ettore Cristoni 88, 40033, Casalecchio di Reno, BO, Italy
Tel.: (39) 051590700
Web Site: https://www.biohorizonscamlog.it
Dental Product Distr
N.A.I.C.S.: 423450

BioHorizons, Inc.   (1)
2300 Riverchase Ctr, Birmingham, AL 35244   (60%)
Tel.: (205) 967-7880
Web Site: https://www.biohorizons.com
Sales Range: $100-124.9 Million
Dental Implant Products Mfr & Marketer
N.A.I.C.S.: 339114
R. Steven Boggan (Pres & CEO)
J. Todd Strong (COO & Exec VP)
David P. Dutil (Gen Counsel & Sr VP)
Barry S. Thornton (Sr VP-Quality Assurance & Regulatory Affairs)
Juan Jaramillo (VP-Global Bus Support)
Mike Mills (CFO & Exec VP)
Andrew Baroody (VP-Sls Ops)
Bill Rosene (VP-Ops)
Boyd Peters (VP-Marketing)
Craig Estes (VP-Mfg)
Mark LoPresti (Sr VP-Sls-US)
Mike Walters (VP-Quality Assurance)
Winston Greer (VP-Regulatory Affairs)
Patricio Nilo (VP-Intl Sls-Latin & South America)
Kathy Bessiere (Dir-Human Resources)
Fred J. Molz IV (VP-R&D)
Elbert Jenkins Jr. (VP-Information Technology)

Caligor Pharmacy   (1)
1226 Lexington Ave, New York, NY 10028
Tel.: (212) 369-6000
Web Site: https://www.caligorpharmacy.com
Sales Range: $25-49.9 Million
Emp.: 9
Retailer Pharmaceutical Preparations
N.A.I.C.S.: 456110
Gary Halpern (Supvr-Pharmacists)

Cliniclands AB   (1)
Hansagatan 4A, 231 42, Trelleborg, Sweden
Tel.: (46) 410741220
Web Site: https://www.cliniclands.se
Dental Equipment Product Whslr
N.A.I.C.S.: 423450

Dentrix Dental Systems, Inc.-PMT   (1)
727 E Utah Vly Dr Ste 500, American Fork, UT 84003-3346
Tel.: (801) 763-9300
Web Site: http://www.dentrix.com
Sales Range: $200-249.9 Million
Emp.: 400
N.A.I.C.S.: 456199

Exan Enterprises Inc.   (1)
1930 Vlg Ctr Cir Ste 3-1305, Las Vegas, NV 89134
Software Development Services
N.A.I.C.S.: 513210

Handpiece Headquarters Corp.   (1)
620 S Placentia Ave, Placentia, CA 92870-6300
Tel.: (714) 579-0175
Web Site:
https://www.handpieceheadquarters.com
Rev.: $2,600,000
Emp.: 15
Dental Instrument Repair
N.A.I.C.S.: 811210
Scott Mathott (Pres)

Henry Schein Arcona, Inc.   (1)
3403 Griffith Street, Saint Laurent, H4T 1W5, QC, Canada   (100%)
Tel.: (514) 337-3368

Web Site: https://www.henryschein.ca
Sales Range: $10-24.9 Million
Emp.: 150
Medical & Hospital Equipment
N.A.I.C.S.: 423450

Henry Schein Canada, Inc.   (1)
345 Townline Road, PO Box 6000, Niagara-on-the-Lake, L0S 1J0, ON, Canada
Tel.: (905) 646-1711
Web Site: http://www.henryschein.ca
Veterinarian Equipment Distr
N.A.I.C.S.: 423450

Henry Schein Dental Warehouse (Pty) Ltd.   (1)
Building 2 106 16th Road, Midrand, 1686, South Africa
Tel.: (27) 117199111
Web Site: https://www.henryschein.co.za
Dental Product Distr
N.A.I.C.S.: 423450

Henry Schein Espana, S.L.   (1)
Av Albufera 153 8th Floor, 28038, Madrid, Spain
Tel.: (34) 913606000
Web Site: http://www.henryschein.es
Dental Product Distr
N.A.I.C.S.: 423450

Henry Schein Hemao Guangzhou-Medical Device Co., Ltd.   (1)
Room 504 505 506 Guangdong Navigation Building No 48 Baqi Er Ma Road, Yuexiu District, Guangzhou, 510111, Guangdong, China
Tel.: (86) 4001508686
Medical Device Distr
N.A.I.C.S.: 423450

Henry Schein Holding GmbH   (1)
Monzastr 2a, 63225, Langen, Hessen, Germany
Tel.: (49) 61037575000
Web Site: http://www.henryschein-mag.de
Subsidiary Management Services
N.A.I.C.S.: 551114
Seldmer Achim (CEO)

Henry Schein Hong Kong Limited   (1)
Unit B 21/F 78 Hung To Road, kwun Tong, Kowloon, China (Hong Kong)
Tel.: (852) 25412290
Web Site: https://www.henryschein.com.hk
Dental Product Distr
N.A.I.C.S.: 423450

Henry Schein Inc.-Indiana   (1)
5315 W 74th St, Indianapolis, IN 46268   (100%)
Tel.: (317) 876-7800
Web Site: http://www.henryschein.com
Sales Range: $125-149.9 Million
Emp.: 250
N.A.I.C.S.: 456199

Henry Schein Medical   (1)
80 Summit View Ln, Bastian, VA 24314
Tel.: (276) 688-4121
Web Site: http://www.giv.com
Sales Range: $125-149.9 Million
Emp.: 200
Pharmaceuticals Distr
N.A.I.C.S.: 424210

Henry Schein Medical   (1)
5315 W 74th St Ste 100, Indianapolis, IN 46268
Tel.: (317) 824-0900
Web Site: http://www.henryschein.com
Sales Range: $50-74.9 Million
Emp.: 100
Supply Stores for Medical & Dental Companies
N.A.I.C.S.: 423450

Henry Schein One Australia   (1)
3/39 Railway Road, Blackburn, 3130, VIC, Australia
Tel.: (61) 1300889668
Web Site:
https://www.henryscheinone.com.au
Software Development Services
N.A.I.C.S.: 541511

Henry Schein One, LLC   (1)
1220 S 630 E Ste 100, American Fork, UT 84003

Henry Schein, Inc.—(Continued)

Web Site: https://www.henryscheinone.com
Software Development Services
N.A.I.C.S.: 541511

Henry Schein Practice Solutions
Inc. **(1)**
1220 S 630 E Ste 100, American Fork, UT
84003
Tel.: (801) 763-9300
Software Development Services
N.A.I.C.S.: 541512

Henry Schein Regional Limited **(1)**
243-249 Bush Road, Rosedale, Auckland,
0632, New Zealand
Tel.: (64) 94140040
Web Site: https://www.henryschein.co.nz
Dental Product Distr
N.A.I.C.S.: 423450

Henry Schein Regional Pty Ltd **(1)**
Building 3 Level 6 189 O'Riordan Street,
Mascot, 2020, NSW, Australia
Tel.: (61) 1300658822
Web Site: https://www.henryschein.com.au
Dental Product Distr
N.A.I.C.S.: 423450

Henry Schein Sunshine (Beijing)
Medical Device Co., Ltd. **(1)**
F-601 QiFa Building Sheng Gu Zhong Lu 2,
Chao Yang District, Beijing, 100029, China
Tel.: (86) 1064442178
Medical Device Distr
N.A.I.C.S.: 423450

Henry Schein Trading (Shanghai)
Co., Ltd. **(1)**
Suite 4B Ying Long Building 1358 Yan An
West Road, Shanghai, China
Tel.: (86) 13585825218
Dental Product Distr
N.A.I.C.S.: 423450

Henry Schein UK Holdings
Limited **(1)**
Medcare House Centurion Close, Gilling-
ham Business Park, Gillingham, ME8 0SB,
Kent, United Kingdom
Tel.: (44) 1634878750
Web Site: http://www.henryschein.co.uk
Sales Range: $700-749.9 Million
Emp.: 960
Holding Company; Healthcare Products
Whslr
N.A.I.C.S.: 551112
Patrick Thompson Allen *(Mng Dir)*

Henry Schein, Inc. **(1)**
101 N Plains Industrial Rd Bldg 3, Walling-
ford, CT 06492
Tel.: (203) 265-2836
Web Site: http://www.henryschein.com
Sales Range: $25-49.9 Million
Emp.: 30
Providers of Dental And Medical Supplies
N.A.I.C.S.: 423450

Henry Schein, Inc. **(1)**
8591 Prairie Trl Dr Ste 300, Englewood, CO
80112 **(100%)**
Tel.: (303) 790-7745
Web Site: http://www.henryschein.com
Sales Range: $25-49.9 Million
Emp.: 25
Sales & Service of Dental Equipment
N.A.I.C.S.: 423450

Henry Schein, Inc. - Atlanta, GA **(1)**
1225 Old Alpharetta Rd Ste 280, Alpharetta,
GA 30005
Tel.: (678) 291-0374
Web Site: http://www.henryschein.com
Sales Range: $25-49.9 Million
Emp.: 25
Sales of Dental Products
N.A.I.C.S.: 423450

Henry Schein, Inc. - Birmingham,
AL **(1)**
511 Mineral Trace Ste 100, Birmingham, AL
35244
Tel.: (205) 987-8397
Sales Range: $25-49.9 Million
Emp.: 30
Dental Sales
N.A.I.C.S.: 423450

Henry Schein, Inc. - Boise, ID **(1)**

2404 S Orchard St Ste 1000, Boise, ID
83705-6726
Tel.: (208) 433-1852
Web Site: http://www.henryschein.com
Sales Range: $25-49.9 Million
Emp.: 15
Distr of Products & Services to Healthcare
Practitioners
N.A.I.C.S.: 423450

Henry Schein, Inc. - Boston, MA **(1)**
140 Gould St, Needham, MA 02494
Tel.: (781) 453-1194
Web Site: http://www.henryschein.com
Sales Range: $25-49.9 Million
Emp.: 75
Dental Supplies Mfr
N.A.I.C.S.: 423450

Henry Schein, Inc. - Buffalo, NY **(1)**
135 Duryea Rd, Melville, NY 11747
Tel.: (631) 843-5500
Web Site: http://www.henryschein.com
Sales Range: $650-699.9 Million
Emp.: 1,000
Dental Laboratory
N.A.I.C.S.: 339116

Henry Schein, Inc. - Chicago, IL **(1)**
1000 Oak Creek Dr Ste 1010, Chicago, IL
60148
Tel.: (630) 516-3481
Web Site: http://www.henryschein.com
Sales Range: $25-49.9 Million
Emp.: 12
Dental Supplies
N.A.I.C.S.: 423450

Henry Schein, Inc. - Cincinnati,
OH **(1)**
9472 Meridian Way, West Chester, OH
45069-6527
Tel.: (513) 870-9635
Web Site: http://www.henryschein.com
Sales Range: $25-49.9 Million
Emp.: 18
Sales of Dental Equipment
N.A.I.C.S.: 423450

Henry Schein, Inc. - Columbus,
OH **(1)**
6185 Huntley Rd Ste J, Columbus, OH
43229-1094
Tel.: (614) 781-5481
Web Site: http://www.henryschein.com
Sales Range: $25-49.9 Million
Emp.: 20
Dental Services
N.A.I.C.S.: 456199

Henry Schein, Inc. - Detroit, MI **(1)**
46943 Enterprise Ct Ste 100, Wixom, MI
48393
Tel.: (248) 277-9100
Web Site: http://www.henryschein.com
Sales Range: $25-49.9 Million
Emp.: 15
Dental Sales
N.A.I.C.S.: 423450

Henry Schein, Inc. - Grand Rapids,
MI **(1)**
265 Leonard St NW, Grand Rapids, MI
49504-4221
Tel.: (616) 454-1223
Web Site: http://www.henryschein.com
Sales Range: $25-49.9 Million
Emp.: 20
Dental Laboratory
N.A.I.C.S.: 423450

Henry Schein, Inc. - Grapevine,
TX **(1)**
1001 Nolan Dr Ste 400, Grapevine, TX
76051 **(100%)**
Tel.: (817) 416-9770
Web Site: http://www.henryschein.com
Sales Range: $75-99.9 Million
Emp.: 140
N.A.I.C.S.: 456199

Henry Schein, Inc. - Greenville,
SC **(1)**
526 Congaree Rd, Greenville, SC 29607-
3516
Tel.: (864) 297-3680
Sales Range: $50-74.9 Million
Emp.: 150
Provider Of Health Sevices
N.A.I.C.S.: 423450

Bruce Campbell *(VP)*

Henry Schein, Inc. - Jackson,
MS **(1)**
834 Wilson Dr Ste D, Ridgeland, MS
39157-4510
Tel.: (601) 956-4260
Web Site: http://www.henryschein.com
Sales Range: $25-49.9 Million
Emp.: 15
Dental Accessories Supplier
N.A.I.C.S.: 423450

Henry Schein, Inc. - Las Vegas,
NV **(1)**
7140 Dean Martin Dr Ste 300, Las Vegas,
NV 89118-4522
Tel.: (702) 895-9921
Web Site: http://www.henryschein.com
Sales Range: $25-49.9 Million
Emp.: 15
Medical Supplies
N.A.I.C.S.: 423450

Henry Schein, Inc. - Livermore,
CA **(1)**
7667 Longard Rd, Livermore, CA 94551
Tel.: (925) 961-9052
Web Site: http://www.henryschein.com
Sales Range: $150-199.9 Million
Dental Equipment Supplies
N.A.I.C.S.: 339114

Henry Schein, Inc. - Memphis,
TN **(1)**
8370 Wolf Lake Dr Ste 105, Bartlett, TN
38133-4189
Tel.: (901) 373-2572
Web Site: http://www.henryschein.com
Sales Range: $25-49.9 Million
Emp.: 15
N.A.I.C.S.: 456199

Henry Schein, Inc. - Milwaukee,
WI **(1)**
16515 W Beloit Rd, New Berlin, WI 53151
Tel.: (262) 782-0772
Web Site: http://www.henryschein.com
N.A.I.C.S.: 456199
Timothy Sullivan *(Pres)*

Henry Schein, Inc. - Minneapolis/St.
Paul, MN **(1)**
875 Blue Gentian Rd Ste 1100, Eagan, MN
55121
Tel.: (651) 905-3973
Web Site: http://www.henryschein.com
Sales Range: $25-49.9 Million
Emp.: 32
Dental Services
N.A.I.C.S.: 423450

Honry Sohoin, Ino. - Nashville,
TN **(1)**
2525 Perimeter Pl Ste 115, Nashville, TN
37217
Tel.: (615) 884-6421
Web Site: http://www.henryschein.com
Sales Range: $10-24.9 Million
Emp.: 14
Supply Of Dental Products
N.A.I.C.S.: 238990

Henry Schein, Inc. - Omaha, NE **(1)**
10184 L St, Omaha, NE 68127-1120
Tel.: (402) 592-0934
Web Site: http://www.henryschein.com
Sales Range: $1-4.9 Billion
Dental Equipment Servicer & Distr
N.A.I.C.S.: 423450

Henry Schein, Inc. - Orange, CA **(1)**
307 W Taft Ave Ste N, Orange, CA 92865-
4248
Tel.: (714) 279-1660
Web Site: http://www.henry-schein.com
Sales Range: $25-49.9 Million
Emp.: 26
Sales of Dental Products
N.A.I.C.S.: 423450

Henry Schein, Inc. - Philadelphia,
PA **(1)**
3060 Plz Dr Ste 102-103, Garnet Valley, PA
19061
Tel.: (610) 358-1905
Sales Range: $10-24.9 Million
Emp.: 10
N.A.I.C.S.: 456199

Chris Wickham *(Gen Mgr)*

Henry Schein, Inc. - Richmond,
VA **(1)**
452-454 Southlake Blvd, Richmond, VA
84003
Tel.: (804) 379-6467
Web Site: http://www.henryschein.com
Sales Range: $25-49.9 Million
Emp.: 15
Dental Supply Company
N.A.I.C.S.: 423450

Henry Schein, Inc. - San Antonio,
TX **(1)**
12007 Starcrest Dr, San Antonio, TX 78247
Tel.: (210) 545-3147
Web Site: http://www.henryschein.com
Sales Range: $25-49.9 Million
Emp.: 30
Sales of Dental Equipment Supplies
N.A.I.C.S.: 423450

Henry Schein, Inc. - San
Francisco **(1)**
510 Myrtle Ave Ste 101, South San Fran-
cisco, CA 94080
Tel.: (650) 794-0417
Sales Range: $25-49.9 Million
Emp.: 3
N.A.I.C.S.: 456199

Henry Schein, Inc. - San Jose,
CA **(1)**
5595 Winfield Blvd Ste 107, San Jose, CA
95123-1220
Tel.: (408) 227-0566
Web Site: http://www.henryschein.com
Sales Range: $25-49.9 Million
Emp.: 25
N.A.I.C.S.: 456199

Henry Schein, Inc. - Solon, **(1)**
30600 Aurora Rd Ste 110, Solon, OH 44139
Tel.: (440) 349-0891
Web Site: http://www.henryschein.com
Sales Range: $150-199.9 Million
Dental Supplies
N.A.I.C.S.: 339114

Henry Schein, Inc. - Tampa, FL **(1)**
4710 Eisenhower Blvd Ste B-1, Tampa, FL
33634-6334
Tel.: (813) 888-8107
Web Site: http://www.henryschein.com
Sales Range: $150-199.9 Million
Emp.: 40
Dental & Laboratory Services
N.A.I.C.S.: 339116

Henry Schein, Inc. - Tulsa, OK **(1)**
10203B E 61st St, Tulsa, OK 74133
Tel.: (918) 250-1419
Web Site: http://www.henryschein.com
Sales Range: $25-49.9 Million
Emp.: 20
Dental Equipment Supplies
N.A.I.C.S.: 423450

Henry Schein, Inc. - Wisconsin **(1)**
1004 Quinn Dr Ste 1, Madison, WI 53719
Tel.: (608) 850-6830
Web Site: http://www.henryschein.com
Providers of Dental Supplies
N.A.I.C.S.: 423450

Henry Schein, Inc.-Denver,
Pennsylvania **(1)**
Distribution Ctr 41 Weaver Rd, Denver, PA
17517
Tel.: (717) 335-7230
Web Site: http://www.henryschein.com
Sales Range: $150-199.9 Million
Emp.: 320
Distribution Of Medicines
N.A.I.C.S.: 423450

Henry Schein, Inc.-Florida **(1)**
5450 NW 33rd Ave Ste 100-102, Fort Lau-
derdale, FL 33309 **(100%)**
Tel.: (954) 733-9426
Web Site: http://www.henryschein.com
Sales Range: $1-9.9 Million
Emp.: 3
Distr Of Dental Equipments & Supplies
N.A.I.C.S.: 621111

Henry Schein, Inc.-Florida **(1)**
1600 SW Archer Rd Rm D2 31, Gainesville,
FL 32610 **(100%)**

Tel.: (352) 378-5750
Web Site: http://www.henryschein.com
Sales Range: $10-24.9 Million
Emp.: 3
Dental Supply Distributor
N.A.I.C.S.: 423450

Henry Schein, Inc.-Florida South (1)
1912 NW 84th Ave Bldg 10, Doral, FL
33126
Tel.: (305) 418-4101
Sales Range: $25-49.9 Million
Emp.: 10
N.A.I.C.S.: 456199

Henry Schein, Inc.-Ft. Wayne, Indiana (1)
6011 Highview Dr Ste C, Fort Wayne, IN
46818
Tel.: (260) 489-3399
Sales Range: $25-49.9 Million
Emp.: 20
N.A.I.C.S.: 456199

Henry Schein, Inc.-Kansas (1)
7938 Marshall Dr, Lenexa, KS
66214-1482 **(100%)**
Tel.: (913) 894-1735
Web Site: http://www.henryschein.com
Sales Range: $25-49.9 Million
Emp.: 16
N.A.I.C.S.: 456199

Henry Schein, Inc.-Louisville, Kentucky (1)
2600 Stanley Gault Pkwy Ste 300, Louisville, KY 40223
Tel.: (502) 253-0814
Web Site: http://www.henryschein.com
Sales Range: $150-199.9 Million
Emp.: 25
General Distribution Company
N.A.I.C.S.: 456199

Henry Schein, Inc.-Murray, Utah (1)
4414 Century Dr, Murray, UT
84123 **(100%)**
Tel.: (801) 269-9753
Web Site: http://www.henryschien.com
Sales Range: $150-199.9 Million
Distr of Health Care Products
N.A.I.C.S.: 423450

Henry Schein, Inc.-Nevada Reno (1)
520 S Rock Blvd, Reno, NV 89502
Tel.: (775) 327-3344
Web Site: http://www.henryschein.com
Sales Range: $50-74.9 Million
Emp.: 270
Medical, Dental & Veterinary Services
N.A.I.C.S.: 423450

Henry Schein, Inc.-Nevada Sparks (1)
Distribution Ctr 255 Vista Blvd, Sparks, NV
89434
Tel.: (775) 352-3700
Web Site: http://www.henryschein.com
Sales Range: $150-199.9 Million
Emp.: 300
N.A.I.C.S.: 456199

Henry Schein, Inc.-New Mexico (1)
9019 Washington St NE Ste B2, Albuquerque, NM 87113-2705
Tel.: (505) 856-3384
Web Site: http://www.henryschein.com
Sales Range: $25-49.9 Million
Emp.: 10
N.A.I.C.S.: 456199

Henry Schein, Inc.-New York (1)
135 Duryea Rd, Melville, NY
11747 **(100%)**
Tel.: (631) 843-5500
Web Site: https://www.henryschein.com
Sales Range: $150-199.9 Million
Emp.: 22,000
N.A.I.C.S.: 456199

Henry Schein, Inc.-New York (1)
135 Duryea Rd, Melville, NY
11747 **(100%)**
Tel.: (631) 843-5500
Web Site: http://www.henryschein.com
Sales Range: $650-699.9 Million
Emp.: 1,000
Medical Supplies Mfr
N.A.I.C.S.: 456199

Henry Schein, Inc.-North Carolina (1)

625-102 Hutton St, Raleigh, NC 27606-
6321
Tel.: (919) 832-8962
Web Site: http://www.henryschein.com
Sales Range: $25-49.9 Million
Emp.: 40
Sales Dental Equipment & Supply
N.A.I.C.S.: 423450

Henry Schein, Inc.-North Carolina (1)
1020 Crews Rd Bldg P, Matthews, NC
28105
Tel.: (704) 814-4782
Web Site: http://www.henryschein.com
Sales Range: $25-49.9 Million
Emp.: 30
Dental Supplies
N.A.I.C.S.: 423450

Henry Schein, Inc.-Pennsylvania (1)
3223 N Broad St Rm 472, Philadelphia, PA
19140 **(100%)**
Tel.: (215) 707-3617
Web Site: http://www.henryschein.com
Sales Range: $25-49.9 Million
Emp.: 1
N.A.I.C.S.: 456199

Henry Schein, Inc.-Pennsylvania (1)
765 Commonwealth Dr Ste 108, Warrendale, PA 15086
Tel.: (724) 778-8000
Web Site: http://www.henryschein.com
Sales Range: $75-99.9 Million
Emp.: 50
Dental Services
N.A.I.C.S.: 541921

Henry Schein, Inc.-Texas (1)
4333 W Sam Houston Pkwy N Ste 120,
Houston, TX 77043
Tel.: (713) 856-8620
Web Site: http://www.henryschein.com
Dental Services
N.A.I.C.S.: 423450

Henry Schein, Inc.-Toledo, Ohio (1)
1225 Corporate Dr, Holland, OH 43528
Tel.: (419) 867-8455
Web Site: http://www.henryschein.com
Sales Range: $10-24.9 Million
Emp.: 5
Selling Dental Supplies
N.A.I.C.S.: 423450

Henry Schein, Inc.-Wilsonville, Oregon (1)
25589 SW Canyon Creek Rd Ste 600, Wilsonville, OR 97070
Tel.: (503) 682-2609
Web Site: http://www.henryschein.com
Sales Range: $150-199.9 Million
Dental/Medical Supplies Distr
N.A.I.C.S.: 456199

Infomed Software, S.L. (1)
Via Augusta 158 4 planta, 08006, Barcelona, Spain
Tel.: (34) 934144340
Web Site: https://www.grupoinfomed.es
Software Development Services
N.A.I.C.S.: 541511

Kopfwerk Datensysteme GmbH (1)
Schonngasse 15-17, 1020, Vienna, Austria
Tel.: (43) 12162802
Web Site: https://www.kopfwerk.at
Software Development Services
N.A.I.C.S.: 541511

Medentis Medical GmbH (1)
Walporzheimer Str 48-52, 53474, Bad
Neuenahr-Ahrweiler, Germany
Tel.: (49) 264191100
Web Site: https://medentis.com
Medical Equipment Mfr
N.A.I.C.S.: 339112

Midway Dental Supply, Inc. (1)
701 N Michigan St, Lakeville, IN 46536-
9768
Web Site: http://www.midwaydental.com
Dental Equipment & Supplies Mfr
N.A.I.C.S.: 339114
Roberto Lopez (Mgr-Midway Detroit Equipment)

NAR Training, LLC (1)
7055 Speedway Blvd Ste E104, Las Vegas,
NV 89115

Web Site: https://www.nartraining.com
Online Training Services
N.A.I.C.S.: 611430

North American Rescue, LLC (1)
35 Tedwall Ct, Greer, SC
29650-4791 **(93%)**
Tel.: (864) 675-9800
Web Site: http://www.narescue.com
Military Medical Product Mfr
N.A.I.C.S.: 339113
Robert Castellani (Founder & CEO)
Teresa Valentine (Mgr-Customer Svcs)
Jun Magpayo (VP-Bus Dev)
Brent Bronson (VP)
Chuck Bolin (Dir-State,Fed Govt Dept)
Anthony Horton (Dir-Fire, EMS & Tactical
EMS)
Brandon Brown (Dir-Law Enforcement &
Tactical Law Enforcement)
Shannon Seidel (Dir)
Chris Hoyne (Dir-Community Preparedness)
Mario Colon (Dir-Intl & Military Program Sls)
Matt Westra (Sr Dir-Military Programs-DOD
Distr)
Corina Bilger (Dir)

Orisline Espana S.L. (1)
Madrid Transport Center Ctra Villaverde-
Vallecas Km 3 5, 28053, Madrid, Spain
Tel.: (34) 915396316
Information Technology Services
N.A.I.C.S.: 541511

Ortho Technology, Inc. (1)
1 Southern Ct, West Columbia, SC 29169
Tel.: (813) 501-1650
Web Site: https://www.orthotechnology.com
Dental Supplies
N.A.I.C.S.: 423450
Maria White (Mgr-Global Customer Svc)
Anne Oliver (Mgr-Product)
Mary Cay Werner (Mgr-Human Resources)
Brian Kuess (Dir-Regulatory Affairs & Quality Assurance)
Geoff Parsley (Sls Mgr-North American)
Shirley Stanley (Exec Dir)

Prism Medical Products, L.L.C. (1)
112 Church St Ste 101, Elkin, NC 28621
Web Site: https://www.prism-medical.com
Medical Equipment Distr
N.A.I.C.S.: 423450
Chris Cartwright (CEO & Founder)

Schein Ernst Mishra Eye, P.C. (1)
10 Capital Dr Ste 300, Harrisburg, PA
17110
Tel.: (717) 233-3937
Web Site: https://www.seegreat.net
Emp.: 30
Dental Equipment Mfr
N.A.I.C.S.: 621111

Servimed Tecnicos, S.L.U. (1)
Trail of anthill 118 3rd Floor, Vallecas,
28032, Madrid, Spain
Tel.: (34) 915096505
Web Site: http://www.servimed.org
Dental Equipment Mfr
N.A.I.C.S.: 339114

Software of Excellence United Kingdom Limited (1)
Medcare South Bailey Drive Gillingham
Business Park, Gillingham, ME8 0PZ, Kent,
United Kingdom
Tel.: (44) 1634266800
Web Site:
https://www.softwareofexcellence.com
Software Development Services
N.A.I.C.S.: 541511

Spain Dental Express S.A.U. (1)
C/ Doctor Esquerdo 105, 28007, Madrid,
Spain
Tel.: (34) 915009183
Web Site: https://www.dentalexpress.es
Dental Product Distr
N.A.I.C.S.: 423450

TDSC, Inc. (1)
135 Duryea Rd, Melville, NY 11747
Web Site: https://www.tdsc.com
Dental Equipment Retailer
N.A.I.C.S.: 423450

HEPION PHARMACEUTICALS, INC.

399 Thornall St 1st Fl, Edison, NJ
08837
Tel.: (732) 902-4000   DE
Web Site: https://hepionpharma.com
Year Founded: 2013
HEPA—(NASDAQ)
Assets: $18,094,397
Liabilities: $10,813,590
Net Worth: $7,280,807
Earnings: ($48,926,042)
Emp.: 22
Fiscal Year-end: 12/31/23
Pharmaceuticals Mfr
N.A.I.C.S.: 325412
James Sapirstein (Executives)
John Cavan (CFO)
Daren Ure (Chief Scientific Officer)
Daniel J. Trepanier (Sr VP-Drug Dev)
Patrick R. Mayo (Sr VP-Clinical Pharmacology)
Launa J. Aspeslet (COO)
John P. Brancaccio (Exec Chm, Interim CEO & Interim CFO)

HER IMPORTS

8861 W Sahara Ave Ste 210, Las
Vegas, NV 89117
Tel.: (702) 544-0195   NV
Web Site: http://herimportsusa.com
Year Founded: 2005
HHER—(OTCIQ)
Sales Range: $10-24.9 Million
Emp.: 27
Human Hair Hairweaves & Extensions Importer
N.A.I.C.S.: 812990
Barry W. Hall (Chm, CEO & CFO)

HERBORIUM GROUP, INC.

4306 Kenston Pl, Missouri City, TX
77459
Tel.: (201) 849-4431
Web Site: https://www.herborium.com
HBRM—(OTCIQ)
Rev.: $875,000
Assets: $173,000
Liabilities: $678,000
Net Worth: ($505,000)
Earnings: ($76,000)
Fiscal Year-end: 11/30/19
Medicinal Product Mfr
N.A.I.C.S.: 325412
Agnes P. Olszewski (Founder &
CEO)

HERC HOLDINGS INC.

27500 Riverview Ctr Blvd, Bonita
Springs, FL 34134
Tel.: (239) 301-1000   DE
Web Site:
     https://www.hercrentals.com
HRI—(NYSE)
Rev.: $2,738,800,000
Assets: $5,956,800,000
Liabilities: $4,848,100,000
Net Worth: $1,108,700,000
Earnings: $329,900,000
Emp.: 6,600
Fiscal Year-end: 12/31/22
Holding Company; Equipment Rental
Services
N.A.I.C.S.: 551112
Lawrence H. Silber (Pres & CEO)
Aaron Birnbaum (COO & Sr VP)
Christian J. Cunningham (Chief HR
Officer & Sr VP)
Tamir Peres (CIO & Sr VP)
S. Wade Sheek (Chief Legal Officer,
Sec & Sr VP)
W. Mark Humphrey (CFO & Sr VP)

Subsidiaries:

Herc Rentals Inc. (1)
27500 Riverview Center Blvd Ste 100, Bonita Springs, FL 34134
Tel.: (239) 301-1032
Web Site: https://www.hercrentals.com

Herc Holdings Inc.—(Continued)

Equipment Rental Services
N.A.I.C.S.: 532412
Lawrence H. Silber (Pres & CEO)
Paul Dickard (VP-Comm)
Mark Humphrey (CFO)
Tamir Peres (CIO)
Wade Sheek (Chief Legal Officer)

Subsidiary (Domestic):

Aerial Work Platforms, Inc. (2)
W230N 6080 Hi Tech Dr, Sussex, WI 53089
Tel.: (262) 246-9300
Web Site: http://www.awpdelivers.com
Sales Range: $1-9.9 Million
Emp.: 17
Construction, Mining & Forestry Machinery
& Equipment Rental & Leasing
N.A.I.C.S.: 532412
Patrick Barney (Pres)

Cinelease, Inc. (2)
5375 W San Fernando Rd, Los Angeles,
CA 90039
Tel.: (818) 841-8282
Web Site: https://cinelease.com
Sales Range: $10-24.9 Million
Motion Picture Equipment Rental Services
N.A.I.C.S.: 532490

Subsidiary (Domestic):

Cinelease, LLC (3)
4729 River Road, New Orleans, LA 70121
Tel.: (504) 267-9075
Web Site: http://www.cinelease.com
Equipment Rental Companies Services
N.A.I.C.S.: 238910

Subsidiary (Domestic):

MAC Equipment, LLC (2)
246 1st St, Troy, NY 12180-4642
Tel.: (518) 272-2700
Web Site: http://www.macequipmentllc.com
Consumer Electronics & Appliances Rental
N.A.I.C.S.: 532210
Rob Miller (Mgr)

Temp-Power, Inc. (1)
229 Southgate Ave, Virginia Beach, VA
23462
Tel.: (757) 932-8463
Web Site: https://www.temp-power.net
Generator Rental Services
N.A.I.C.S.: 532420

HERCULES CAPITAL, INC.
1 N B St Ste 2000, San Mateo, CA
94401
Tel.: (650) 289-3060 MD
Web Site: https://www.htgc.com
Year Founded: 2003
HTGC—(NYSE)
Rev.: $321,688,000
Assets: $3,028,855,000
Liabilities: $1,627,396,000
Net Worth: $1,401,459,000
Earnings: $188,068,000
Emp.: 100
Fiscal Year-end: 12/31/22
Closed-End Investment Services
N.A.I.C.S.: 523999
Janice Bourque (Mng Dir-Life Sciences Grp)
Kristen Kosofsky (Sr Mng Dir-Bus Dev-Life Sciences & Broader Healthcare Market)
Charlie Vandis (Chief Credit Officer)
Michael Hara (Mng Dir-IR & Corp Comm)
Lake McGuire (Mng Dir-Bus Dev-Life Science & Broader Healthcare Market)
Seth H. Meyer (CFO & Chief Acctg Officer)
Kiersten Zaza Botelho (Chief Compliance Officer & Gen Counsel)
Scott Bluestein (Pres, CEO & Chief Investment Officer)

Subsidiaries:

Hercules Funding I LLC (1)

400 Hamilton Ave Ste 310, Palo Alto, CA
94301
Tel.: (303) 410-4417
Sales Range: $250-299.9 Million
Emp.: 50
Investment Firm
N.A.I.C.S.: 525910

Hercules Technology SBIC Management, LLC (1)
400 Hamilton Ave Ste 310, Palo Alto, CA
94301
Tel.: (650) 289-3060
Web Site: http://www.htgc.com
Sales Range: $650-699.9 Million
Investment Firm
N.A.I.C.S.: 523999

Solar Spectrum Holdings LLC (1)
150 Linden St, Oakland, CA 94607
Tel.: (844) 777-6527
Web Site: http://www.solarspectrum.com
Holding Company
N.A.I.C.S.: 551112
William B. Nettles Jr. (Pres & COO)

Subsidiary (Domestic):

Solar Spectrum LLC (2)
150 Linden St, Oakland, CA 94607
Tel.: (844) 777-6527
Web Site: http://www.solarspectrum.com
Solar Technology Services
N.A.I.C.S.: 221114
William B. Nettles Jr. (Pres & COO)
Patrick McGivern (CEO)

Sungevity, Inc. (2)
66 Franklin St Ste 310, Oakland, CA 94607
Tel.: (510) 496-5500
Web Site: https://www.sungevity.com
Solar Technology Services
N.A.I.C.S.: 221114
David White (CFO)

Subsidiary (Domestic):

Hawaii Energy Connection (3)
99-1350 Koaha Placa, Aiea, HI 96701
Tel.: (808) 524-7336
Web Site: https://www.kumukit.com
Commercial & Residential Sustainable Energy Services Including Grid-Tied Photovoltaic Systems
N.A.I.C.S.: 221114

Spa Chakra, Inc. (1)
730 5th Ave Fl 9, New York, NY 10019
Tel.: (212) 659-7783
Sales Range: $75-99.9 Million
Emp.: 250
Spa Operator
N.A.I.C.S.: 713940

HERE TO SERVE HOLDING CORP.
12540 Broadwell Rd Ste 1203, Milton, GA 30004
Tel.: (678) 871-7457 DE
Year Founded: 2002
HTSC—(OTCIQ)
Holding Company
N.A.I.C.S.: 551112
Jeffrey S. Cosman (Chm & CEO)

HERITAGE COMMERCE CORP
224 Airport Pkwy, San Jose, CA
95110
Tel.: (408) 947-6900 CA
Web Site:
https://www.heritagecommerce
corp.com
Year Founded: 1997
HTBK—(NASDAQ)
Rev.: $198,939,000
Assets: $5,157,580,000
Liabilities: $4,525,124,000
Net Worth: $632,456,000
Earnings: $66,555,000
Emp.: 340
Fiscal Year-end: 12/31/22
Bank Holding Company
N.A.I.C.S.: 551111

Robertson Jones Jr. (Pres & CEO)
Lawrence D. McGovern (CFO & Exec VP)
Deborah K. Reuter (Sec & Exec VP)
Julianne M. Biagini-Komas (Vice Chm)
May K. Y. Wong (Exec VP & Controller)

Subsidiaries:

Heritage Bank of Commerce (1)
224 Airport Pkwy, San Jose, CA
95110 (100%)
Tel.: (408) 947-6900
Web Site: https://www.heritagebankofcommerce.com
Sales Range: $100-124.9 Million
Commericial Banking
N.A.I.C.S.: 522110
Robertson Jones Jr. (Pres & CEO)
Dustin Warford (Pres-Community Bus Banking, Exec VP, Exec VP & Mgr-Bus Banking)
Christopher D. Edmonds-Waters (Chief People Officer, Chief Culture Officer & Exec VP)
Susan Just (Chief Credit Officer & Exec VP)
Larry McGovern (CFO)
Clay Jones (Pres)
Debbie Reuter (Chief Risk Officer)
Sachin Vaidya (CIO)
Karol Watson (Exec VP)
Suzanne Zierman (Exec VP-Audit Liason)
Chris Edmonds-Waters (Chief People Officer)

Subsidiary (Domestic):

CSNK Working Capital Finance Corp. (2)
224 Airport Pkwy Ste 200, San Jose, CA
95110
Tel.: (650) 294-6600
Web Site: https://www.bayviewfunding.com
Sales Range: $1-9.9 Million
Emp.: 30
Invoice Factoring Services
N.A.I.C.S.: 522299
Glen Shu (Pres)
Andrew Aquino (Exec VP)
Seth Herman (Exec VP & Mgr-Sls-Natl)
Magaly Alfaro (VP & Portfolio Mgr)
Morgan Hansen (VP)
Ryan Altick (VP)

HERITAGE FINANCIAL CORPORATION
201 5th Ave SW, Olympia, WA 98507
Tel.: (360) 943-1500 WA
Web Site: https://www.hf-wa.com
Year Founded: 1997
HFWA—(NASDAQ)
Rev.: $257,048,000
Assets: $6,980,100,000
Liabilities: $6,182,207,000
Net Worth: $797,893,000
Earnings: $81,875,000
Emp.: 793
Fiscal Year-end: 12/31/22
Bank Holding Company
N.A.I.C.S.: 551111
Bryan D. McDonald (COO & Exec VP)
Donald J. Hinson (CFO & Exec VP)
Jeffrey J. Deuel (Pres & CEO)
Tony Chalfant (Chief Credit Officer & Exec VP)
Kaylene M. Lahn (Sec & Sr VP)

Subsidiaries:

Heritage Bank (1)
201 5th Ave SW, Olympia, WA 98501
Tel.: (360) 943-1500
Web Site: https://www.heritagebanknw.com
Sales Range: $75-99.9 Million
Commercial Banking Services
N.A.I.C.S.: 522110
Bryan D. McDonald (Pres & COO)
Donald J. Hinson (CFO & Exec VP)
Austin Patjens (Officer)

Division (Domestic):

Whidbey Island Bank (2)

450 SW Bayshore Dr, Oak Harbor, WA
98277-7003
Tel.: (360) 675-5968
Web Site: https://local.heritagebanknw.com
Sales Range: $75-99.9 Million
Commericial Banking
N.A.I.C.S.: 522110

HERITAGE INSURANCE HOLDINGS, INC.
1401 N Wshore Blvd, Tampa, FL
33607
Tel.: (727) 362-7200 DE
Web Site:
https://www.heritagepci.com
Year Founded: 2012
HRTG—(NYSE)
Rev.: $662,460,000
Assets: $2,392,600,000
Liabilities: $2,261,561,000
Net Worth: $131,039,000
Earnings: ($154,363,000)
Emp.: 612
Fiscal Year-end: 12/31/22
Offices of Other Holding Companies
N.A.I.C.S.: 551112
Ernesto J. Garateix (CEO)
Kirk H. Lusk (CFO & Treas)

Subsidiaries:

Heritage Property & Casualty Insurance Company (1)
Property & Casualty Insurance Product Services
N.A.I.C.S.: 524126
Richard Widdicombe (Pres)
Steven Martindale (Pres)
Ernesto J. Garateix (COO)

Naragansett Bay Insurance Company (1)
PO Box 820, Pawtucket, RI 02860-0820
Tel.: (401) 495-6007
Web Site: https://www.nbic.com
Insurance Services
N.A.I.C.S.: 524210
Timothy Moura (Pres)
Kirk Lusk (CFO)
Glen Tiziani (Sr VP-Sls & Distr)

Zephyr Acquisition Company (1)
1001 Bishop St Ste 2750, Honolulu, HI
96813
Tel.: (808) 440-5400
Emp.: 13
Property & Casualty Insurance Services
N.A.I.C.S.: 524126

Zephyr Insurance Company, Inc. (1)
1001 Bishop St Ste 2750, Honolulu, HI
96813
Tel.: (808) 440-5400
Web Site: https://www.zephyrins.com
Property & Casualty Insurance Products & Services
N.A.I.C.S.: 524126

HERITAGE NOLA BANCORP, INC.
205 N Columbia St, Covington, LA
70433
Tel.: (985) 892-4565 MD
Web Site:
https://www.heritagebank.org
Year Founded: 2017
HRGG—(OTCIQ)
Rev.: $7,259,000
Assets: $174,025,000
Liabilities: $153,752,000
Net Worth: $20,273,000
Earnings: ($1,535,000)
Emp.: 28
Fiscal Year-end: 12/31/23
Bank Holding Company
N.A.I.C.S.: 551111
W. David Crumhorn (Chm, Pres & CEO)
Lisa B. Hughes (CFO & Sr VP)

Subsidiaries:

Heritage Bank of St. Tammany (1)
205 N Columbia St, Covington, LA 70433
Tel.: (985) 892-4565
Web Site: http://www.heritagebank.org

Banking Services
N.A.I.C.S.: 522110

HERO INTERNATIONAL USA HOLDING CORP.

923 E Valley Blvd Ste 203, San Gabriel, CA 91776
Tel.: (626) 343-6668   NV
HIUH—(OTCIQ)
Pharmaceuticals Product Mfr
N.A.I.C.S.: 325412
Yong Kang Zhou (CEO)

HERO TECHNOLOGIES INC.

8 The Green Ste 4000, Dover, DE 19901
Tel.: (302) 538-4165   NV
Web Site:
  https://herotechnologiesinc.com
Year Founded: 2004
HENC—(OTCQB)
Rev.: $183
Assets: $645,217
Liabilities: $835,540
Net Worth: ($190,323)
Earnings: ($541,583)
Emp.: 1
Fiscal Year-end: 12/31/22
Oil & Gas Exploration Services
N.A.I.C.S.: 211120
Eric Prim (COO)
Gina Serkasevich (CFO)
Destiny Aigbe (Co-CEO)
Timothy E. Dunleavy (VP-Finance)
Ali Tabassi (CTO)
Dan Centeno (Project Mgr)
Thandi Ncube (Corp Mgr-Development)
Saveez Irfan (Project Mgr-Development)
Maxi PonDevida (Mgr-Social Media)
Shazia Khan (Atty)
Marinelle Nazario (Mgr-Public Relations)

HERON THERAPEUTICS, INC.

4242 Campus Point Ct Ste 200, San Diego, CA 92121
Tel.: (858) 251-4400   DE
Web Site: https://www.herontx.com
Year Founded: 1983
HRTX—(NASDAQ)
Rev.: $107,672,000
Assets: $250,951,000
Liabilities: $237,379,000
Net Worth: $13,572,000
Earnings: ($182,024,000)
Emp.: 203
Fiscal Year-end: 12/31/22
Biochronomer Polymer-Based Pharmaceutical Developer & Mfr
N.A.I.C.S.: 325412
Thomas B. Ottoboni (Chief Scientific Officer & Sr VP-Pharmaceutical Translational Sci)
David Szekeres (COO & Exec VP)
John C. Arthur (VP-Mfg & Supply)
William P. Forbes (Chief Dev Officer & Exec VP)
Chris Storgard (Chief Medical Officer)
Adam Morgan (Chm)
Jason Grillot (VP-Sales-Marketing-Acute Care)
Ira Duarte (CFO, Principal Acctg Officer & Exec VP)
Craig Alexander Collard (CEO)

HERSHEY CREAMERY COMPANY

301 S Cameron St, Harrisburg, PA 17101-2815
Tel.: (717) 238-8134   DE
Web Site:
  https://www.hersheyicecream.com
Year Founded: 1894
HRCR—(OTCEM)

Sales Range: $500-549.9 Million
Emp.: 530
Ice Cream Mfr
N.A.I.C.S.: 311520
George H. Holder Sr. (Chm)

HERTZ GLOBAL HOLDINGS, INC.

8501 Williams Rd, Estero, FL 33928
Tel.: (239) 301-7000   DE
Web Site: https://www.hertz.com
Year Founded: 2015
HTZ—(NASDAQ)
Rev.: $9,371,000,000
Assets: $24,605,000,000
Liabilities: $21,513,000,000
Net Worth: $3,092,000,000
Earnings: $616,000,000
Emp.: 27,000
Fiscal Year-end: 12/31/23
Holding Company; Passenger Vehicle Rental Services
N.A.I.C.S.: 551112
Alexandra D. Brooks (CFO & Exec VP)
Wayne Gilbert West (CEO)
Angela Brav (Pres-Intl)
Wayne Davis (CMO & Exec VP)
Thomas Wagner (Vice Chm)
Greg O'Hara (Founder)
Darren Arrington (Exec VP)
Liz Bowyer (Exec VP)
Tim Langley-Hawthorne (CIO)
Eric Leef (Chief HR Officer)
Ned Ryan (Chief Product Dev Officer)
Kelly Galloway (Chief Acctg Officer, Sr VP & Controller)
Justin Keppy (COO & Exec VP)

Subsidiaries:

The Hertz Corporation   (1)
8501 Williams Rd, Estero, FL 33928
Tel.: (239) 301-7000
Rev.: $8,684,999,999
Assets: $22,496,000,000
Liabilities: $19,217,000,000
Net Worth: $3,279,000,000
Earnings: $1,355,000,000
Emp.: 24,999
Fiscal Year-end: 12/31/2022
Automobiles, Trucks & Equipment Renting & Leasing
N.A.I.C.S.: 532490
Colleen R. Batcheler (Gen Counsel)
Alexandra D. Brooks (Chief Acctg Officer & Sr VP)
Wayne Gilbert West (CEO)
Alexandra D. Brooks (Chief Acctg Officer & Sr VP)
Eric Leef (Chief HR Officer & Exec VP)
Stephen Scherr (CEO)
Liz Bowyer (Exec VP-Corp Affairs)
Colleen Batcheler (Corp Counsel)
Wayne Davis (CMO)
Tim Langley-Hawthorne (CIO)

Subsidiary (Domestic):

Dollar Thrifty Automotive Group, Inc.   (2)
5310 E 31st St, Tulsa, OK 74135
Tel.: (918) 669-2219
Web Site: http://www.dollar.com
Sales Range: $1-4.9 Billion
Emp.: 6,000
Vehicle Rental Services
N.A.I.C.S.: 532111

Subsidiary (Domestic):

DTG Operations, Inc.   (3)
7777 E Apache, Tulsa, OK 74115
Tel.: (918) 838-5236
Daily Auto Rentals Services
N.A.I.C.S.: 532111

DTG Supply, LLC   (3)
5330 E 31st St 100, Tulsa, OK 74135
Tel.: (918) 669-2503
Emp.: 5
Car Rental Services
N.A.I.C.S.: 532111

Subsidiary (Non-US):

Dollar Thrifty Automotive Group Canada Inc.   (3)
6050 Indian Line, Mississauga, L4V 1G5, ON, Canada
Tel.: (905) 671-7814
Sales Range: $25-49.9 Million
Emp.: 120
Automobile Rentals Leasing Parking
N.A.I.C.S.: 532111

Subsidiary (Domestic):

Thrifty, LLC   (3)
5330 E 31st St, Tulsa, OK 74135
Tel.: (918) 665-3930
Web Site: http://www.thriftycars4rent.com
Automobile Rentals, Leasing & Parking Services
N.A.I.C.S.: 532111

Subsidiary (Domestic):

Rental Car Finance LLC   (4)
5330 E 31st St Ste 100, Tulsa, OK 74153
Tel.: (918) 665-3930
Car Rental Services
N.A.I.C.S.: 532111

Thrifty Car Sales Inc.   (4)
5330 E 31st St, Tulsa, OK 74135-5073
Tel.: (918) 669-2048
Web Site: http://www.thrifty.com
Rev.: $2,600,000
Emp.: 30
Car Sales
N.A.I.C.S.: 532111

Subsidiary (Domestic):

Donlen FSHCO Company   (2)
3000 Lakeside Dr 2nd Fl, Bannockburn, IL 60015
Tel.: (847) 714-1400
Web Site: http://www.donlen.com
Passenger Car Leasing Services
N.A.I.C.S.: 532112

Subsidiary (Non-US):

Hertz Asia Pacific Pte. Ltd.   (2)
Shaw House 350 Orchard Road Suite 14-08, Singapore, 238868, Singapore
Tel.: (65) 67357566
Automobile Rental Services
N.A.I.C.S.: 532111
Jocelyn Chu (Mgr-Admin)

Hertz Australia Pty. Limited   (2)
124 Thistlewaite Street, South Melbourne, 3205, VIC, Australia
Tel.: (61) 392766690
Car Rental Management Services
N.A.I.C.S.: 532111

Subsidiary (Domestic):

HA Fleet Pty Ltd.   (3)
Level 6 10-16 Dorcas Street, South Melbourne, 3205, VIC, Australia
Tel.: (61) 396982444
Passenger Car Rental Services
N.A.I.C.S.: 532111

Subsidiary (Non-US):

Hertz Autovermietung GmbH   (2)
Ludwig-Erhard-Str 12, 65760, Eschborn, Germany
Tel.: (49) 61969370
Automobile Rental Services
N.A.I.C.S.: 532111
Yvonne Bremer (Mgr-Inbound Logistik)

Hertz Belgium b.v.b.a.   (2)
Excelsiorlaan 20, 1930, Zaventem, Belgium
Tel.: (32) 70695695
Web Site: https://www.hertz.be
Automobile Rental Services
N.A.I.C.S.: 532111

Subsidiary (Domestic):

Hertz Car Sales LLC   (2)
2025 W Main St, Mesa, AZ 85201-6801
Tel.: (480) 668-1300
Web Site: http://www.hertzcarsales.com
Car Rental Services
N.A.I.C.S.: 532111

Subsidiary (Non-US):

Hertz Claim Management B.V.   (2)
Siriusdreef 62, PO Box 270, Hoofddorp, 2132 WT, Netherlands
Tel.: (31) 235670718
Insurance Holding Company Services
N.A.I.C.S.: 551112

Hertz Claim Management GmbH   (2)
Ginnheimer Strasse 4, 65760, Eschborn, Germany
Tel.: (49) 6196937431
Insurance Holding Company Services
N.A.I.C.S.: 551112

Hertz Do Brasil Ltda.   (2)
Estrada para Nova Lima 385 conjunto 903 Belvedere, Belo Horizonte, 30320-760, Minas Gerais, Brazil
Tel.: (55) 3132861425
Web Site: https://www.hertzdobrasil.com.br
Passenger Car Rental Services
N.A.I.C.S.: 532111

Hertz Holdings Netherlands B.V.   (2)
Siriusdreef 62, 2132 WT, Hoofddorp, Netherlands
Tel.: (31) 235670747
Web Site: http://www.hertz.com
Emp.: 45
Car Rental Services
N.A.I.C.S.: 532111

Subsidiary (Domestic):

Stuurgroep Fleet (Netherlands) B.V.   (3)
62 Siriusdreef, 2132 WT, Hoofddorp, Netherlands
Tel.: (31) 206444558
Car Rental Services
N.A.I.C.S.: 532111

Subsidiary (Domestic):

Hertz Local Edition Corp.   (2)
3205 Virginia Beach Blvd, Virginia Beach, VA 23452-5725
Tel.: (757) 456-0170
Automobile Rental Services
N.A.I.C.S.: 532111

Navigation Solutions LLC   (2)
3314 N Central Expy Ste 210, Plano, TX 75074
Tel.: (972) 633-2301
Web Site:
  http://www.navigationsolutions.com
Car Rental Services
N.A.I.C.S.: 532111

Subsidiary (Non-US):

Probus Insurance Company Europe DAC   (2)
Hertz Europe Service Centre, Swords Business Park Co Dublin, Swords, Ireland
Tel.: (353) 18291293
Web Site: https://probusinsurance.ie
Car Rental Services
N.A.I.C.S.: 532111
Martin Scullion (Gen Mgr)
Charlotte Torr (Head-Fin)
Andrew Oja (Head-Compliance)

HERZFELD CARIBBEAN BASIN FUND, INC.

119 Washington Ave Ste 504, Miami, FL 33139
Tel.: (305) 777-1660   MD
CUBA—(NASDAQ)
Rev.: $800,409
Assets: $46,697,300
Liabilities: $155,757
Net Worth: $46,541,543
Earnings: ($148,649)
Fiscal Year-end: 06/30/19
Investment Management Service
N.A.I.C.S.: 525990
Thomas J. Herzfeld (Chm & Portfolio Mgr)
Alice H. Tham (Sec)
Zachary P. Richmond (Treas)
Ryan M. Paylor (Portfolio Mgr)

Herzfeld Caribbean Basin Fund, Inc.—(Continued)

Erik M. Herzfeld *(Pres & Portfolio Mgr)*
Thomas K. Morgan *(Chief Compliance Officer & Asst Sec)*

HESS CORPORATION

1185 Avenue of the Americas 40th Fl,
New York, NY 10036
Tel.: (212) 997-8500   **NV**
Web Site: https://www.hess.com
Year Founded: 1933
HES—(NYSE)
Rev.: $10,645,000,000
Assets: $24,007,000,000
Liabilities: $14,405,000,000
Net Worth: $9,602,000,000
Earnings: $1,382,000,000
Emp.: 1,756
Fiscal Year-end: 12/31/23
Oil & Gas Exploration Services
N.A.I.C.S.: 213112
Timothy B. Goodell *(Chief Compliance Officer, Gen Counsel, Sec & Exec VP)*
John B. Hess *(CEO)*
Gregory P. Hill *(Pres & COO)*
Jay R. Wilson *(VP-IR)*
John P. Rielly *(CFO & Exec VP)*
Jonathan C. Stein *(Chief Risk Officer & Sr VP-Strategy & Plng)*
Eric Fishman *(Treas)*
Richard Lynch *(Sr VP-Tech & Svcs)*
Barbara J. Lowery-Yilmaz *(Chief Exploration Officer & Sr VP)*
Alex Sagebien *(VP-Environment, Health & Safety)*
Andrew P. Slentz *(Sr VP-HR & Office Mgmt)*
Lorrie Hecker *(VP-Comm)*
Alex Mistri *(VP-Govt & External Affairs)*
Michael B. Chadwick *(Controller)*

Subsidiaries:

Hess Bakken Investments II
L.L.C.   **(1)**
1501 McKinney St, Houston, TX 77010
Tel.: (713) 496-4000
Web Site: http://www.hess.com
Crude Petroleum & Natural Gas Extraction
Services
N.A.I.C.S.: 211120

Hess Corp. Houston Regional
Office   **(1)**
1501 McKinney St, Houston, TX 77010
Tel.: (713) 496-4000
Web Site: http://www.hess.com
Sales Range: $700-749.9 Million
Emp.: 1,500
Oil & Natural Gas Exploration & Production
N.A.I.C.S.: 211120

Hess Corp. - Port Reading Refinery &
Terminal   **(1)**
420 Hook Rd, Bayonne, NJ 07002
Tel.: (201) 437-1017
Petroleum Refinery & Bulk Storage Facility
N.A.I.C.S.: 424710

Hess Exploration Australia PTY
Limited   **(1)**
Level 18 77 St Georges Terrace, Perth,
6000, WA, Australia
Tel.: (61) 894263000
Emp.: 8
Oil & Gas Exploration Services
N.A.I.C.S.: 213112
George Lumsden *(Gen Mgr)*

Hess Ltd.   **(1)**
Level 9 the Adelphi Buld 1 11 John Adam
St, London, WC2N 6AG, United
Kingdom   **(100%)**
Tel.: (44) 2073313000
Web Site: http://www.hess.com
Sales Range: $200-249.9 Million
Emp.: 250
Exploration & Production
N.A.I.C.S.: 211120

Hess Malaysia Sdn. Bhd.   **(1)**
   (100%)
Tel.: (60) 320509000
Sales Range: $50-74.9 Million
Emp.: 60
International Oil & Gas Exploration
N.A.I.C.S.: 211120

Hess Midstream Partners LP   **(1)**
1501 McKinney St, Houston, TX 77010
Tel.: (713) 496-4200
Web Site: http://www.hessmidstream.com
Rev.: $662,400,000
Assets: $2,819,700,000
Liabilities: $108,800,000
Net Worth: $2,710,900,000
Earnings: $70,800,000
Fiscal Year-end: 12/31/2018
Oil & Gas Exploration Services
N.A.I.C.S.: 211120
John B. Hess *(Chm & CEO)*

Hess Trading Corporation   **(1)**
Hess Tower 1501 McKinney St, Houston,
TX 77010
Tel.: (713) 496-4000
Oil & Gas Field Drilling Services
N.A.I.C.S.: 213111

HESS MIDSTREAM LP

1501 McKinney St, Houston, TX
77010
Tel.: (713) 496-4200   **DE**
Web Site:
   https://www.hessmidstream.com
Year Founded: 2019
HESM—(NYSE)
Rev.: $1,275,200,000
Assets: $3,588,200,000
Liabilities: $3,059,200,000
Net Worth: $529,000,000
Earnings: $83,900,000
Emp.: 199
Fiscal Year-end: 12/31/22
Crude Oil & Natural Gas Distr
N.A.I.C.S.: 486210
John B. Hess *(Chm & CEO)*
Michael Frailey *(Chief Comml Officer & VP)*
Charles Tack *(VP-Midstream Ops)*
Dan Farler II *(VP-Engrg Project)*

HESTIA INSIGHT, INC.

400 S 4th St Ste 500, Las Vegas, NV
89101
Tel.: (702) 793-4028   **NV**
Web Site:
   https://www.hestiainsight.com
HSTA—(OTCQB)
Rev.: $15,000
Assets: $712,635
Liabilities: $34,106
Net Worth: $678,529
Earnings: ($1,713,921)
Emp.: 3
Fiscal Year-end: 11/30/22
Financial Investment Services
N.A.I.C.S.: 523999
John Z. Lin *(VP-Bus Dev)*
Loretta Lee *(Dir-Corp Affairs)*
Edward C. Lee *(Chm, Pres, CEO, CFO, Treas & Sec)*
Robin Hult *(VP-Fin)*

HEWLETT PACKARD ENTERPRISE COMPANY

1701 E Mossy Oaks Rd, Spring, TX
77389
Tel.: (678) 259-9860   **DE**
Web Site: https://www.hpe.com
Year Founded: 1939
HPE—(NYSE)
Rev.: $30,127,000,000
Assets: $71,262,000,000
Liabilities: $46,382,000,000
Net Worth: $24,880,000,000
Earnings: $2,579,000,000
Emp.: 61,000
Fiscal Year-end: 10/31/24
Computer System Design Services

N.A.I.C.S.: 541512
John F. Schultz *(Chief Operating & Legal Officer & Exec VP)*
Marie E. Myers *(CFO & Exec VP)*
Kumar Sreekanti *(CTO & Head-Software)*
Kirt Paul Karros *(Treas & Sr VP-Fin)*
Andrew Simanek *(Head-IR)*
Jim Jackson *(CMO)*
Jennifer Temple *(Chief Comm Officer)*
Aziz Megji *(VP-Corp Dev)*
Hemant Hebbar *(Sr Dir-Corp Dev)*
Ram Venkatachalam *(Sr Dir-Corp Dev)*
Sanjot Khurana *(Dir-IR)*
Nancy Lee *(Dir-IR)*
Fidelma Russo *(CTO & Sr VP)*
Sandile Dube *(Mgr-Sls & Channel-South Africa)*
Tumi Kgonare *(Mgr-Distr-South Africa)*
David Hughes *(Sr VP)*
Heiko Meyer *(Chief Sls Officer)*
Mark Bakker *(Gen Mgr-Global Ops)*
Neil MacDonald *(Exec VP & Gen Mgr-Compute, HPC, and AI Bus)*
Tom Black *(Sr VP & Gen Mgr-Storage)*
Jeremy K. Cox *(Principal Acctg Officer, Chief Tax Officer, Sr VP & Controller)*
Justin Hotard *(Exec VP)*
Pradeep Kumar *(Sr VP)*
Phil Mottram *(Exec VP)*
Keith White *(Exec VP)*
Seth Kindley *(CTO)*
Jaspreet Sood *(VP-Sls-North America & Gen Mgr-Infrastructure & Svcs)*
Antonio Fabio Neri *(Pres & CEO)*

Subsidiaries:

3PAR Inc.   **(1)**
3000 Hanover St, Palo Alto, CA 94304-1185
Tel.: (650) 687-5817
Web Site: http://www.hpe.com
Utility Storage Systems Mfr
N.A.I.C.S.: 334112

Cloud Technology Partners, Inc.   **(1)**
321 Summer St 5th Fl, Boston, MA 02210
Tel.: (617) 674-0874
Web Site: http://www.cloudtp.com
Software Developer & IT Solutions
N.A.I.C.S.: 513210
Bruce Coughlin *(CEO)*
Robert Christiansen *(VP)*
Bill Peluzus *(VP-Tech Cloud Solutions)*
Brian Ott *(VP & Gen Mgr-Managed Cloud Controls)*
Jonathan Bumba *(VP-Global Bus Dev)*
Dave Clark *(VP-Delivery)*
Holly Lynch *(Sr VP-People & Culture)*
Paul Morris *(VP-Sls)*
Alexey Gerasimov *(VP-Global Cloud Delivery)*
Debbie Mounts *(Dir-Portfolio & Product Mgmt)*
Brad Young *(Dir-Mktg)*
Alan Zall *(VP-Global Engrg & Technical Svcs)*

CloudPhysics, Inc.   **(1)**
3979 Freedom Cir Ste 540, Santa Clara,
CA 95054
Tel.: (650) 646-4616
Web Site: http://www.cloudphysics.com
Virtualization & Cloud Infrastructure Solutions
N.A.I.C.S.: 513210
John Blumenthal *(Co-Founder & VP)*
Irfan Ahmad *(Co-Founder & CTO)*
Jim Kleckner *(Co-Founder & VP-Analytics)*
Xiaojun Liu *(Co-Founder)*
Jeffrey Hausman *(CEO)*
Carl Waldspurger *(Dir-Res)*
Chris Schin *(VP-Product Mgmt)*

Cray Inc.   **(1)**
901 5th Ave Ste 1000, Seattle, WA 98164
Tel.: (206) 701-2000
Web Site: http://www.cray.com
Supercomputers Mfr
N.A.I.C.S.: 334111

Subsidiary (Domestic):

Appro International, Inc.   **(2)**
901 5th Ave Ste 1000, Seattle, WA 98164
Tel.: (206) 701-2000
Web Site: http://www.cray.com
Computer Storage Device Mfr
N.A.I.C.S.: 334112

Subsidiary (Non-US):

Cray Australia Pty. Limited   **(2)**
Building 3 Suite 17 Level 2 195 Wellington
Road Clayton, Melbourne, 3168, VIC,
Australia   **(100%)**
Tel.: (61) 392981800
Web Site: http://www.cray.com
Sales Range: $150-199.9 Million
Emp.: 22
Regional Center; Marketing, Support & Software Development
N.A.I.C.S.: 423430

Cray Canada ULC   **(2)**
602-1420 Blair Place, Ottawa, K1J 9L8,
ON, Canada
Tel.: (613) 263-3315
Computer Software Store Operator
N.A.I.C.S.: 449210

Cray Computer Deutschland
GmbH   **(2)**
Waldhofer Strasse 102, 69123, Heidelberg,
Germany   **(100%)**
Tel.: (49) 6221825692
Web Site: http://www.cray.de
Sales Range: $25-49.9 Million
Emp.: 50
Regional Center; Marketing, Support & Software Development
N.A.I.C.S.: 423430

Cray Computer GmbH   **(2)**
Hochbergerstrasse 60C, 4057, Basel, Switzerland
Tel.: (41) 616332244
Web Site: http://www.cray.com
Computer Hardware & Software Whslr
N.A.I.C.S.: 423430

Cray Computer SAS   **(2)**
15 Rue De Norvege Courtaboeuf, PO Box
116, 91140, Villebon-sur-Yvette,
France   **(100%)**
Tel.: (33) 169285686
Web Site: http://www.cray.com
Sales Range: $25-49.9 Million
Emp.: 10
Regional Center; Marketing, Support & Software Development
N.A.I.C.S.: 423430

Division (Domestic):

Cray Inc.   **(2)**
2131 Lindau Ln Ste1000, Bloomington, MN
55425
Tel.: (651) 605-9000
Web Site: http://www.cray.com
Sales Range: $75-99.9 Million
Emp.: 200
Mfr of Large Scale Computers
N.A.I.C.S.: 334111
Krishna Chaitanya Kandalla *(Engr-Software)*

Subsidiary (Non-US):

Cray Japan, Inc.   **(2)**
15F Hibiya Daibiru 1-2-2 Uchisaiwai-Cho,
Chiyoda-ku, Tokyo, 100-0011,
Japan   **(100%)**
Tel.: (81) 335030901
Web Site: http://www.cray.com
Sales Range: $150-199.9 Million
Computer Sales & Support Services
N.A.I.C.S.: 423430
Mamoru Nakano *(Pres)*

Cray Korea, Inc.   **(2)**
No 317 G5 Central Plaza 1685-8 Seocho-
Dong, Seocho-Gu, Seoul, 137-070, Korea
(South)
Tel.: (82) 25320344
Sales Range: $10-24.9 Million
Emp.: 18
Computer Peripheral Equipment Mfr
N.A.I.C.S.: 334111

Cray Supercomputers (India) Private Limited (2)
Regus Business Centre Level-2 Elegance Tower Mathura Road Jasola, New Delhi, 110 025, India
Tel.: (91) 1166351211
Web Site: http://www.cray.com
Sales Range: $150-199.9 Million
Emp.: 5
Supercomputers Sales & Sales Support
N.A.I.C.S.: 423430

Cray Taiwan, Inc. (2)
4F 200 Sec 1 Keelung Road, Taipei, 11071, Taiwan
Tel.: (886) 277253661
Web Site: http://www.cray.com
Computer Hardware & Software Whslr
N.A.I.C.S.: 423430

Cray U.K. Limited (2)
Broad Quay House Prince Street, High Street, Bristol, BS1 4DJ, Berkshire, United Kingdom (100%)
Tel.: (44) 1179926790
Web Site: http://www.cray.com
Sales Range: $150-199.9 Million
Regional Center; Marketing, Support & Software Development
N.A.I.C.S.: 423430

Subsidiary (Domestic):

YarcData LLC (2)
901 5th Ave 1000, Seattle, WA 98164
Tel.: (206) 701-2000
Emp.: 50
Bail Bonding Services
N.A.I.C.S.: 812990

EYP Mission Critical Facilities, Inc. (1)
500 Summit Lake Dr Ste 180, Valhalla, NY 10595
Tel.: (315) 956-6100
Web Site: https://www.eypmcfinc.com
Information Technology Services
N.A.I.C.S.: 541512

Hewlett Packard Enterprise BV (1)
Startbaan 16, 1187 XR, Amstelveen, Netherlands
Tel.: (31) 205476911
Web Site: http://www.hpe.com
Computer Peripheral Equipment Mfr
N.A.I.C.S.: 334118

Hewlett Packard Enterprise Canada Co. (1)
5150 Spectrum Way Ste 400, Mississauga, L4W 5G2, ON, Canada
Tel.: (905) 206-4725
Web Site: https://www.hpe.com
Computer Products Related Services
N.A.I.C.S.: 541519

Hewlett Packard Taiwan Ltd. (1)
NanKang Software Park III 10F-1 No 66 Jing Mao 2 Road, Taipei, 11568, Taiwan
Tel.: (886) 801857086
Information Technology Management Services
N.A.I.C.S.: 541512

Hewlett-Packard Asia Pacific Pte. Ltd.
1 Depot Close 11-01, Singapore, 109841, Singapore
Tel.: (65) 6 670 9524
Web Site: https://www.hpe.com
Holding Company; Regional Managing Office
N.A.I.C.S.: 551112

Subsidiary (Non-US):

Hewlett Packard Enterprise (China) Co., Ltd. (2)
Building A LSH Center No 8 Guangshun Avenue South, Chaoyang District, Beijing, 100102, China
Tel.: (86) 105 983 6366
Web Site: https://www.hpe.com
Computer Products Marketer
N.A.I.C.S.: 423430

Subsidiary (Domestic):

Shanghai Hewlett-Packard Co. Ltd. (3)

3F Block A 2727 Jinke Road, Zhangjiang Hi-tech Park, Shanghai, 201203, China
Tel.: (86) 10 6990 5888
Web Site: http://www.hpe.com
Computer Product Mfr
N.A.I.C.S.: 334111

Subsidiary (Non-US):

Hewlett Packard Enterprise Global-Soft Private Limited (2)
G 3 4 Fl 24 Salapuria Arena Hosur Main Road, Bengaluru, 560030, Karnataka, India
Tel.: (91) 80 6703 7209
Web Site: http://www.hpe.com
Software Development & Call Center Services
N.A.I.C.S.: 513210

Hewlett-Packard (M) Sdn. Bhd. (2)
Ground Floor Block A No 12 Jalan Gelenggang HPE Towers, Bukit Damansara, Kuala Lumpur, 50490, Malaysia
Tel.: (60) 3 6207 4533
Web Site: http://www.hpe.com
Computer Product Mfr
N.A.I.C.S.: 334118

Hewlett-Packard Australia Pty. Ltd. (2)
353 Burwood Hwy L3, Forest Hill, Melbourne, 3131, VIC, Australia
Tel.: (61) 131347
Web Site: http://www.hpe.com
Computer Products Distr
N.A.I.C.S.: 423430

Branch (Domestic):

Hewlett-Packard Australia Pty. Ltd. (3)
410 Concord Road, Rhodes, Sydney, 2138, NSW, Australia
Tel.: (61) 131347
Web Site: http://www.hpe.com
Computer Products Distr
N.A.I.C.S.: 423430

Subsidiary (Non-US):

Hewlett-Packard HK SAR Limited (2)
18/F Cityplaza One 1111 King's Road, Taikoo Shing, Hong Kong, China (Hong Kong)
Tel.: (852) 3 009 5155
Web Site: https://www.hpe.com
Computer Peripheral Distr
N.A.I.C.S.: 423430

Hewlett-Packard Japan, Ltd. (2)
2-2-1 Ojima, Koto-ku, Tokyo, 136-8711, Japan
Tel.: (81) 36 743 6382
Web Site: https://www.hpe.com
Computer Products Marketer, Developer, Mfr & Importer; IT Services
N.A.I.C.S.: 423430

Hewlett-Packard Korea Ltd. (2)
14F SK Securities Building 31 Gukjegeumyung-ro 8-gil, Yeongdeungpo-gu, Seoul, 150-724, Korea (South)
Tel.: (82) 707 488 3090
Web Site: https://www.hpe.com
Computer Related Services
N.A.I.C.S.: 541519

Hewlett-Packard New Zealand (2)
22 Viaduct Harbour, Auckland, 1010, New Zealand
Tel.: (64) 68806177
Web Site: http://www.hpe.com
Computer Products Distr; Consulting & IT Services
N.A.I.C.S.: 423430

Subsidiary (Domestic):

Hewlett-Packard Singapore (Sales) Pte. Ltd. (2)
2nd Floor 452 Alexandra Road, Singapore, 119961, Singapore
Tel.: (65) 62753888
Web Site: http://www.hpe.com
Computer Peripheral Distr
N.A.I.C.S.: 423430

Affiliate (Non-US):

Mushko Electronics (Pvt) Limited (2)
Victoria Chambers Abdullah Haroon Road,

Karachi, 74400, Pakistan
Tel.: (92) 21 3566 0770 3
Web Site: http://www.mushko.com
Emp.: 166
Computers & Related Products Sales & Services
N.A.I.C.S.: 423430
Faisal A. Ali *(Mng Dir)*
Maliha Shoaib *(Asst Mgr-HR)*
Haris Ahmed *(Exec Dir)*
Moinuddin Ahmed *(Exec Dir-Admin)*
Kaleem Uddin *(Gen Mgr)*
Mohammad Farhan Abdullah *(Sr Mgr-Accts, Fin & Ops)*
Imtiaz A. Gilani *(Product Mgr)*
Imran Ahmed Siddiqui *(Product Mgr)*
Sajid A. Muneer *(Product Mgr-IPG)*
Danish Khan *(Mgr-Customer Care & Comml Support)*
Muhammad Kamran Ansari *(Mgr-Enterprise Solution & Support)*
Muhammad Ehtesham Uddin *(Mgr-Inventory & Logistics)*

Hewlett-Packard Financial Services (India) Private Limited (1)
G 3 4 Fl 24 Salapuria Arena Hosur Main Road, Bengaluru, 560030, Karnataka, India
Tel.: (91) 8033829000
Web Site: http://www.hpe.com
Leasing & Financial Services
N.A.I.C.S.: 532420

Hewlett-Packard Financial Services Canada Company (1)
5150 Spectrum Way Ste 400, Mississauga, L4W 5G2, ON, Canada
Tel.: (905) 206-4725
Web Site: http://www.hpe.com
Office Machinery & Equipment Rental Services
N.A.I.C.S.: 532420

Hewlett-Packard International Sarl (1)
150 Route du Nant D'Avril, 1217, Meyrin, Geneva, Switzerland
Tel.: (41) 584 448 111
Web Site: http://www.hpe.com
Holding Company; Regional Managing Office
N.A.I.C.S.: 551112

Subsidiary (Non-US):

Hewlett-Packard (Israel) Ltd. (2)
Dafna Street 9, Ra'anana, 43662, Israel
Tel.: (972) 97623300
Web Site: http://www.hpe.com
Computer Products Distr
N.A.I.C.S.: 423430

Hewlett-Packard (Nigeria) Limited (2)
5th Floor Mulliner Towers 39 Alfred Rewane Road, Ikoyi, 101233, Lagos, Nigeria
Tel.: (234) 1903 3711
Web Site: http://www.hpe.com
Computer Peripherals Mfr
N.A.I.C.S.: 334111

Subsidiary (Domestic):

Hewlett-Packard (Schweiz) GmbH (2)
Ueberlandstrasse 1, Duebendorf, 8600, Zurich, Switzerland
Tel.: (41) 58 444 55 55
Web Site: http://www.hpe.com
Computer Products Distr
N.A.I.C.S.: 423430
Marcel Borgo *(Mng Dir)*

Branch (Domestic):

Hewlett Packard (Schweiz) GmbH (3)
150 Route du Nant D'Avril, Meyrin, 1217, Geneva, Switzerland
Tel.: (41) 58 444 55 55
Web Site: http://www.hpe.com
Computer Products Distr
N.A.I.C.S.: 423430

Hewlett-Packard (Schweiz) GmbH (3)
Schwarzenburgstrasse 160, Liebefeld, 3097, Bern, Switzerland
Tel.: (41) 31 666 50 00

Web Site: http://www.hpe.com
Computer Products Distr
N.A.I.C.S.: 423430

Subsidiary (Non-US):

Hewlett-Packard ApS (2)
Engholm Parkvej 8, 3450, Allerod, Denmark
Tel.: (45) 7 875 5887
Web Site: https://www.hpe.com
Computer Products Distr
N.A.I.C.S.: 423430

Hewlett-Packard Belgium SPRL/BVBA (2)
Hermeslaan 1A Building A, 1831, Diegem, Belgium
Tel.: (32) 28979367
Web Site: http://www.hpe.com
Computer Products Distr
N.A.I.C.S.: 423430

Hewlett-Packard France SAS (2)
4 rue Paul Lafargue, 92800, Puteaux, Cedex, France
Tel.: (33) 17 301 8471
Web Site: https://www.hpe.com
Computer Peripheral Distr
N.A.I.C.S.: 423430

Branch (Domestic):

Hewlett-Packard France (3)
Bldg GRE03 5 Raymond Chanas, 38053, Grenoble, France
Tel.: (33) 173 430 215
Web Site: http://www.hpe.com
Computer Products Distr
N.A.I.C.S.: 423430

Subsidiary (Non-US):

Hewlett-Packard Gesellschaft mbH (2)
Canettistrasse 5, 1100, Vienna, Austria
Tel.: (43) 81 000 2000
Web Site: https://www.hpe.com
Computer Products Distr
N.A.I.C.S.: 423430

Hewlett-Packard GmbH (2)
Lutzowplatz 15, 10785, Berlin, Germany
Tel.: (49) 69 6680 5506
Web Site: http://www.hpe.com
Computer Products Distr
N.A.I.C.S.: 423430

Branch (Domestic):

Hewlett-Packard GmbH (3)
Baumschulenallee 20-22, 30625, Hannover, Germany
Tel.: (49) 69 6680 5506
Web Site: http://www.hpe.com
Computer Products Distr
N.A.I.C.S.: 423430

Hewlett-Packard GmbH (3)
Herrenberger Strasse 140, 71034, Boblingen, Germany
Tel.: (49) 6938 078 9143
Web Site: https://www.hpe.com
Computer Products Distr
N.A.I.C.S.: 423430

Hewlett-Packard GmbH (3)
Hugo-Junkers-Strasse 15-17, 90411, Nuremberg, Germany
Tel.: (49) 69 6680 5506
Web Site: http://www.hpe.com
Computer Products Distr
N.A.I.C.S.: 423430

Hewlett-Packard GmbH (3)
Hewlett-Packard Strasse 1, 61352, Bad Homburg, Germany
Tel.: (49) 69 6680 5506
Web Site: http://www.hpe.com
Computer Products Distr
N.A.I.C.S.: 423430

Hewlett-Packard GmbH (3)
Berliner Strasse 111, 40880, Ratingen, Germany
Tel.: (49) 69 6680 5506
Web Site: http://www.hpe.com
Computer Products Distr
N.A.I.C.S.: 423430

Subsidiary (Non-US):

Hewlett-Packard Italiana S.r.l. (2)

Hewlett Packard Enterprise Company—(Continued)

Via Giuseppe Di Vittorio 9, Cernusco sul
Naviglio, 20063, Milan, Italy
Tel.: (39) 024 527 9050
Web Site: https://www.hpe.com
Computer Products Distr
N.A.I.C.S.: 423430

Hewlett-Packard Limited (2)
Cain Road Amen Corner, Bracknell, London, RG12 1HN, Berks, United Kingdom
Tel.: (44) 845 605 6095
Web Site: http://www.hpe.com
Computer Products Distr
N.A.I.C.S.: 423430

Branch (Domestic):

Hewlett-Packard Limited (3)
210 Wharfedale Road, Winnersh, RG41
5TP, Berkshire, United Kingdom
Tel.: (44) 808 164 4441
Web Site: https://www.hpe.com
Computer Related Services
N.A.I.C.S.: 541519

Subsidiary (Non-US):

**Hewlett-Packard Middle East
FZ-LLC** (2)
Building 13 3rd Floor Dubai Internet City,
17295, Dubai, United Arab Emirates
Tel.: (971) 4391 6000
Web Site: http://www.hpe.com
Computer Peripheral Distr
N.A.I.C.S.: 423430

Hewlett-Packard Nederland B.V. (2)
Stroombaan 16, 1181 VX, Amstelveen,
Netherlands
Tel.: (31) 20 225 1030
Web Site: https://www.hpe.com
Computer Products Distr
N.A.I.C.S.: 423430

Hewlett-Packard Norge A/S (2)
Rolfsbuktveien 4B, Fornebu, 1364, Oslo,
Norway
Tel.: (47) 8 005 6044
Web Site: https://www.hpe.com
Computer Products Distr
N.A.I.C.S.: 423430

Hewlett-Packard OY (2)
Keilaniementie 1, 02150, Espoo, Finland
Tel.: (358) 94 255 0607
Web Site: https://www.hpe.com
Computer Products Distr
N.A.I.C.S.: 423430

Hewlett-Packard Portugal Lda. (2)
Quinta da Fonte, Paco de Arcos, 2774-528,
Lisbon, Portugal
Tel.: (351) 213 164 164
Web Site: http://www.hpe.com
Computer Peripheral Distr
N.A.I.C.S.: 423430

Hewlett-Packard S.A.R.L. (2)
1100 Bld Al Qods Shore 14-3e Etage,
Casablanca, Morocco
Tel.: (212) 522 24 8770
Web Site: http://www.hpe.com
Computer Products Distr
N.A.I.C.S.: 423430

Hewlett-Packard South Africa (Proprietary) Limited (2)
12 Autumn Street, Rivonia Sandton, Johannesburg, 2128, South Africa
Tel.: (27) 860001020
Web Site: http://www.hpe.com
Computer Products Distr
N.A.I.C.S.: 423430

Hewlett-Packard Sverige AB (2)
Gustav III Boulevard 36 A-Building, Solna,
169 85, Stockholm, Sweden
Tel.: (46) 406887527
Web Site: http://www.hpe.com
Computer Products Distr
N.A.I.C.S.: 423430

Hewlett-Packard s.r.o. (2)
Za Brumlovkou 1559/5, 140 00, Prague,
Czech Republic
Tel.: (420) 228883531
Web Site: http://www.hpe.com
Computer Products Distr
N.A.I.C.S.: 423430

Hewlett-Packard Latin America (1)
3000 Hanover St, Palo Alto, CA 94304-1112
Tel.: (650) 687-5817
Web Site: http://www.hpe.com
Regional Managing Office: Computers &
Software & Services
N.A.I.C.S.: 551114
Alfredo Yepez (Mng Dir-Sls-Latin America)

Subsidiary (Non-US):

Hewlett-Packard Brasil Ltda. (2)
Av. das Nacoes Unidas 12 901, Sao Paulo,
04578-000, SP, Brazil   **(100%)**
Tel.: (55) 1155025000
Web Site: http://www.hpe.com
Sales & Marketing of Computer Products
N.A.I.C.S.: 449210

**Hewlett-Packard Mexico S. de R.L.
de C.V.** (2)
Prolongacion Reforma #700, Santa Fe,
01210, Mexico, Mexico
Tel.: (52) 55 1500 3155
Web Site: http://www.hpe.com
Computer Product Mfr
N.A.I.C.S.: 334111

Branch (Domestic):

**Hewlett-Packard Mexico -
Monterrey/Nuevo Leon** (3)
Calzada del Valle n 116 B, 66260, Monterrey, Nuevo Leon, Mexico
Tel.: (52) 55 1500 3155
Web Site: http://www.hpe.com
Computer Product Mfr
N.A.I.C.S.: 334111

Subsidiary (Domestic):

**Hewlett-Packard Operations Mexico,
S. de R.L. de C.V.** (3)
Prolongacion Reforma #700, Santa Fe,
01210, Mexico, Mexico
Tel.: (52) 55 1500 3155
Web Site: http://www.hpe.com
Electronic Computer Mfr
N.A.I.C.S.: 334111

Subsidiary (Non-US):

IS Costa Rica, S.A. (2)
Calle 25 Avs 6 & 8 Edificio #648, 1047-
1000, San Jose, Costa Rica
Tel.: (506) 25234300
Web Site: http://www.iscr.com
Information Technology Services
N.A.I.C.S.: 518210
Jose Soto (Pres)

Ipesa de Guatemala (2)
17 Avenida 19-70 Edificio Torino Oficina
1111 Nivel 11 Zona 10, Guatemala, Guatemala
Tel.: (502) 2444 5700
Web Site: http://www.ipesa.com
Information Technology Services
N.A.I.C.S.: 518210
Luis Gutierrez (Pres)

Unisistemas Panama, SA (2)
Av Ricardo J Alfaro Entrada a Dos Mares,
Panama, Panama
Tel.: (507) 236 1005
Web Site: http://www.unisistemas.com.pa
Computer Sales
N.A.I.C.S.: 423430

Zerto Ltd. (2)
Abba Eban 10 Po Box 12292, Herzliya, Tel
Aviv, Israel
Tel.: (072) 70 700 £100
Web Site: http://www.zerto.com
Emp.: 70
Data Replication & Recovery Software Developer
N.A.I.C.S.: 513210
Ziv Kedem (Co-Founder & CEO)
Oded Kedem (Co-Founder & CTO)
Ian Perez Ponce (VP-Product Mgmt &
Strategy)
Gil Levonai (CMO)
Paul Zeiter (Pres)
Coley Burke (Chief Revenue Officer)
Steve Lobisser (Dir-Technical Support-
Global)
Avi Raichel (CIO)
Emily Weeks (Dir-Sls-East Americas)
Eric Barnhart (Dir-Channel Sls-Americas)

Jim Ortbals (VP-Worldwide Channel &
Cloud Sls)
Amber Johanson (VP-Global Pre-Sls Engrg)
Chris Nelson (VP-Sls-Americas)

**Hewlett-Packard Manufacturing
Ltd.** (1)
1 George Square, Glasgow, G2 1AL,
United Kingdom
Tel.: (44) 845 605 6095
Web Site: http://www.hpe.com
Electronic Computer Mfr
N.A.I.C.S.: 334111

**Hewlett-Packard Philippines
Corporation** (1)
25th Floor Twenty-Five Seven McKinley
25th Street corner 7th Avenue, Bonifacio
Global City, Taguig, 1630, Metro Manila,
Philippines
Tel.: (63) 80089086404
Information Technology Management Services
N.A.I.C.S.: 541512

**Hewlett-Packard Servicios Espana
S.L** (1)
Calle Vicente Aleixandre 1, Las Rozas de
Madrid, 28232, Madrid, Spain
Tel.: (34) 90 201 2969
Web Site: https://www.hpe.com
Data Management Services
N.A.I.C.S.: 518210

**Hewlett-Packard Teknoloji Cozumleri
Limited Sirketi** (1)
   (100%)
Information Technology Management Services
N.A.I.C.S.: 541512

MapR Technologies, Inc. (1)
4555 Great America Pkwy 201, Santa
Clara, CA 95054
Tel.: (408) 914-2390
Web Site: http://www.mapr.com
Software Developer
N.A.I.C.S.: 513210
John Schroeder (Co-Founder)
M. C. Srivas (Co-Founder)
Jack Norris (Sr VP-WW Alliances & Channels)
Pinaki Mukerji (Exec VP-Engrg)
Anil P. Gadre (Chief Product Officer & Exec
VP)
Cindy Arthur (VP-HR)
Wayne Cappas (VP-Professional Svcs)
Ted Dunning (CTO)
Suzanne Ferry (VP-Education Svcs)
David H. Greenberg (VP-Legal)
Narsi Subramanian (VP-Customer Success
& Support)

Nimble Storage, Inc. (1)
211 River Oaks Pkwy, San Jose, CA 95134
Tel.: (408) 432-9600
Web Site: http://www.nimblestorage.com
Computer Storage Device Mfr
N.A.I.C.S.: 334112

Silver Peak Systems, Inc. (1)
2860 De La Cruz Blvd Ste 100, Santa
Clara, CA 95050
Tel.: (408) 935-1800
Web Site: http://www.silver-peak.com
Network Appliances Developer for Re-
Centralization of Branch Office Infrastructure
N.A.I.C.S.: 517810
David Hughes (Founder, Chm & CEO)
Ian Whiting (Pres-Global Field Ops)
Lisa McGill (Chief HR Officer)

Zerto, Inc. (1)
27-43 Wormwood St Ste 530, Boston, MA
02210
Tel.: (617) 993-6331
Web Site: https://www.zerto.com
Data Backup & Recovery Services
N.A.I.C.S.: 518210

HEXCEL CORPORATION

281 Tresser Blvd 16th Fl, Stamford,
CT 06901   DE
Tel.: (203) 969-0666
Web Site: https://www.hexcel.com
Year Founded: 1946

HXL—(NYSE)
Rev.: $1,789,000,000
Assets: $2,918,500,000
Liabilities: $1,202,000,000
Net Worth: $1,716,500,000
Earnings: $105,700,000
Emp.: 5,590
Fiscal Year-end: 12/31/23
Advanced Composites Company;
Structural Materials Developer, Mfr &
Retailer
N.A.I.C.S.: 325211
Thomas C. Gentile III (Pres & CEO)
Nick L. Stanage (Exec Chm)
Patrick Joseph Winterlich (CFO &
Exec VP)
Gail E. Lehman (Gen Counsel, Sec &
Exec VP)
Don Morrison (CIO & Sr VP)
Paul Dominic Mackenzie (CTO & Sr
VP)
Marilyn L. Minus (CTO & Sr VP)
David P. DiBoyan (VP-Environmental,
Safety & Health)
Amy S. Evans (Chief Acctg Officer &
Sr VP)
Robert G. Hennemuth (Exec VP)

Subsidiaries:

ARC Technologies, Inc. (1)
37 S Hunt Rd, Amesbury, MA 01913
Tel.: (978) 388-2993
Data Processing, Hosting & Related Services
N.A.I.C.S.: 518210

Hexcel Composites GmbH (1)
Sophie-Scholl-Weg 22, 21684, Stade, Germany
Tel.: (49) 4141787900
Web Site: http://www.hexcel.com
Emp.: 150
Carbon Fiber Reinforcement Aircraft Products Mfr
N.A.I.C.S.: 336413

**Hexcel Composites GmbH & Co.
KG** (1)
Industriegelaende 2, 4720, Neumarkt, Austria
Tel.: (43) 773366510
Web Site: http://www.hexcel.com
Sales Range: $50-74.9 Million
Engineered Materials, Including Structural
Fabrics, Used in the Commercial & Military
Aerospace Industry Market Mfr, Developer,
Producer & Retailer
N.A.I.C.S.: 541330

Hexcel Composites Limited (1)
Ickleton Road, Duxford, Cambridge, CB22
4QB, United Kingdom
Tel.: (44) 1223833141
Web Site: http://www.hexcel.com
Sales Range: $75-99.9 Million
Engineered Materials, Including Structural
Fabrics, Used in the Commercial & Military
Aerospace Industry Market Retailer
N.A.I.C.S.: 541330

Hexcel Composites S.A. (1)
45 rue de la Plaine CS 01126, BP 27, Dagneux, 01121, Dagneux, France
Tel.: (33) 472252627
Sales Range: $75-99.9 Million
Emp.: 300
Mfr, Developer, Producer & Retailer of Engineered Materials, Including Structural Fabrics, Used in the Commercial & Military
Aerospace Industry Market
N.A.I.C.S.: 541330

Hexcel Composites S.P.R.L. (1)
Parc Industriel Rue 3 Bourdons 54, 4840,
Welkenraedt, Belgium
Tel.: (32) 87307411
Web Site: http://www.hexcel.com
Sales Range: $75-99.9 Million
Engineered Materials, Including Structural
Fabrics, Used in the Commercial & Military
Aerospace Industry Market Whslr
N.A.I.C.S.: 541330

Hexcel Composites SASU (1)
45 rue de la Plaine CS 10027, 01126, Dag-

neux, Cedex, France
Tel.: (33) 472252627
Industrial Fiber Product Mfr & Distr
N.A.I.C.S.: 335991

Hexcel Corp. - Dublin   (1)
11711 Dublin Blvd, Dublin, CA
94568-2832   (100%)
Tel.: (925) 551-4900
Web Site: http://www.hexcel.com
Sales Range: $25-49.9 Million
Emp.: 130
Research & Development Services
N.A.I.C.S.: 541715

Hexcel Europe Limited   (1)
Ickleton Rd Duxford, Cambridge, CB22
4QB, Cambridgeshire, United Kingdom
Tel.: (44) 1223833141
Web Site: http://www.hexcel.com
Aircraft Merchant Whslr
N.A.I.C.S.: 423860

Hexcel Fibers Inc.   (1)
6700 W 5400 S, Salt Lake City, UT 84118
Tel.: (801) 508-8000
Sales Range: $250-299.9 Million
Emp.: 600
Polyacrylonitrile-Based Carbon Fibers Mfr
N.A.I.C.S.: 325220

Hexcel Holding GmbH   (1)
Schardinger Strasse 1, 4061, Pasching,
Austria
Tel.: (43) 72297720
Web Site: http://www.hexcel.com
Sales Range: $25-49.9 Million
Carbon Fiber Mfr
N.A.I.C.S.: 335991

Hexcel Pottsville Corporation   (1)
172 Industrial Park Rd, Saint Clair, PA
17970
Tel.: (570) 429-1741
Sales Range: $50-74.9 Million
Emp.: 300
Advanced Structural Materials Mfr
N.A.I.C.S.: 333998

Hexcel Reinforcements   (1)
Route des Nappes CS 20027, Les Ave-
nieres, 38630, France
Tel.: (33) 474339933
Web Site: http://www.hexcel.com
Sales Range: $125-149.9 Million
Emp.: 350
Carbon Fiber Reinforcements Mfr
N.A.I.C.S.: 541330

Hexcel Reinforcements Corp.   (1)
1913 N King St, Seguin, TX 78155-2115
Tel.: (830) 379-1580
Web Site: http://www.hexcel.com
Emp.: 280
Aircraft Merchant Whslr
N.A.I.C.S.: 423860

Hexcel Reinforcements SASU   (1)
Route des Nappes CS 20027, 38630, Les
Avenieres, France
Tel.: (33) 474339933
Industrial Fiber Product Mfr & Distr
N.A.I.C.S.: 335991

**Hexcel Reinforcements UK
Limited**   (1)
Unit 4 Cutters Close, Narborough, Leices-
ter, LE19 2FZ, United Kingdom
Tel.: (44) 1162752200
Web Site: http://www.formax.co.uk
Reinforcing Fabric Mfr
N.A.I.C.S.: 314994

**Hexcel Reinforcements UK
Limited**   (1)
Cutters Close, Narborough, Leicester, LE19
2FZ, United Kingdom
Tel.: (44) 1162752200
Industrial Fiber Product Mfr & Distr
N.A.I.C.S.: 335991
Rob Frost *(Mgr-Technical)*

Hexcel-China Holdings Corp.
B707 Yin Hai Building 250 Cao Xi Road,
Shanghai, 200233, China
Tel.: (86) 2164836741
Sales Range: $25-49.9 Million
Emp.: 8
Holding Company
N.A.I.C.S.: 551112
X. P. Au *(Mng Dir)*

Structil SASU   (1)
18 Rue Lavoisier, 91710, Vert-le-Petit,
France
Tel.: (33) 169908989
Web Site: http://www.hexcel.com
Adhesive & Resin Mfr; High-performance
Composites Mfr
N.A.I.C.S.: 325520

HF FOODS GROUP INC.
17700 Castleton St Ste 469, City of
Industry, CA 91748
Tel.: (336) 268-2080   DE
Web Site:
   https://www.hffoodsgroup.com
Year Founded: 2016
HFFG—(NASDAQ)
Rev.: $1,170,467,000
Assets: $637,529,000
Liabilities: $341,280,000
Net Worth: $296,249,000
Earnings: $460,000
Emp.: 890
Fiscal Year-end: 12/31/22
All Other Specialty Food Retailers
N.A.I.C.S.: 445298
Christine Chang *(Chief Compliance
Officer & Gen Counsel)*
Peter Zhang *(CEO)*
Xi Lin *(Pres, Interim CFO & COO)*

Subsidiaries:

Great Wall Seafood LA, LLC   (1)
15854 Ornelas St, Irwindale, CA 91706
Tel.: (626) 452-0908
Web Site:
   https://www.greatwallseafoodla.com
Seafood Distr
N.A.I.C.S.: 424460

Han Feng, Inc.   (1)
6001-A W Market St, Greensboro, NC
27409
Tel.: (336) 268-2080
Web Site: https://www.hanfenginc.com
Food Products Distr
N.A.I.C.S.: 424420

R & C Trading L.L.C.   (1)
3401 W Buckeye Rd, Phoenix, AZ 85009
Tel.: (602) 278-0131
Web Site: http://www.rnctrading.com
Food & Beverage Product Retailer
N.A.I.C.S.: 445298

HF SINCLAIR CORPORATION
2828 N. Harwood, Ste 1300, Dallas,
TX 75201
Tel.: (214) 871-3555   DE
Web Site: https://www.hfsinclair.com
DINO—(NYSE)
Rev.: $31,964,395,000
Assets: $17,716,265,000
Liabilities: $7,478,967,000
Net Worth: $10,237,298,000
Earnings: $1,589,666,000
Emp.: 5,218
Fiscal Year-end: 12/31/23
Holding Company; Oil Marketing &
Distr
N.A.I.C.S.: 551112
Timothy Go *(Pres & CEO)*
Atanas H. Atanasov *(CFO, Principal
Acctg Officer & Exec VP)*
Atanas H. Atanasov *(CFO & Exec
VP)*

Subsidiaries:

HF Sinclair Casper Refining LLC (1)
5700 E Hwy 20-26, Casper, WY 82609
Tel.: (307) 232-2400
Oil Extraction Services
N.A.I.C.S.: 213112

**HF Sinclair El Dorado Refining
LLC**   (1)
1401 Douglas Rd, El Dorado, KS 67042-
3698
Tel.: (316) 321-2200
Oil Extraction Services
N.A.I.C.S.: 213112

HF Sinclair Parco Refining LLC   (1)
100 E Lincoln Hwy, Sinclair, WY 82334
Tel.: (307) 324-3404
Oil Extraction Services
N.A.I.C.S.: 213112

**HF Sinclair Puget Sound Refining
LLC**   (1)
8505 S Texas Rd, Anacortes, WA 98221-
0622
Tel.: (360) 293-0800
Oil Extraction Services
N.A.I.C.S.: 213112

Holly Energy Partners, L.P.   (1)
2828 N Harwood Ste 1300, Dallas, TX
75201-1507
Tel.: (214) 871-3555
Web Site: https://www.hollyenergy.com
Rev.: $547,480,000
Assets: $2,747,502,000
Liabilities: $1,820,622,000
Net Worth: $926,880,000
Earnings: $216,783,000
Emp.: 404
Fiscal Year-end: 12/31/2022
Petroleum Transportation Services
N.A.I.C.S.: 486110
Michael C. Jennings *(Chm)*
Rob Jamieson *(COO)*
Vaishali S. Bhatia *(Gen Counsel)*

Subsidiary (Domestic):

Cheyenne Logistics LLC   (2)
11701 Missouri Bottom Rd, Hazelwood, MO
63042
Tel.: (314) 551-0007
Web Site: http://www.cheyennelogistics.com
Packing Crating & Logistics Services
N.A.I.C.S.: 541614

HollyFrontier Corporation   (1)
2828 N Harwood Ste 1300, Dallas, TX
75201-1507
Tel.: (214) 871-3555
Web Site: http://www.hollyfrontier.com
Rev.: $18,389,142,000
Assets: $12,916,613,000
Liabilities: $6,622,148,000
Net Worth: $6,294,465,000
Earnings: $558,324,000
Emp.: 4,208
Fiscal Year-end: 12/31/2021
Holding Company; Petroleum Refiner &
Whslr
N.A.I.C.S.: 551112
Richard Lawrence Voliva III *(CFO & Exec
VP)*
Vaishali S. Bhatia *(Gen Counsel, Sec & Sr
VP)*
Timothy Go *(Pres & COO)*

Subsidiary (Domestic):

Black Eagle LLC   (2)
5835 Avenida Encinas 114, Carlsbad, CA
92008
Tel.: (760) 438-2808
Emp.: 3
Petroleum Refinery Services
N.A.I.C.S.: 324110

**Ethanol Management Company
LLC**   (2)
8501 E 96th Ave, Henderson, CO 80640
Tel.: (303) 286-8978
Warehousing & Storage Services
N.A.I.C.S.: 493190

**Frontier El Dorado Refinery
Company**   (2)
1401 S Douglas Rd, El Dorado, KS 67042
Tel.: (316) 321-2200
Web Site: http://www.frontieroil.com
Sales Range: $1-4.9 Billion
Emp.: 390
Refiner & Marketer of Gasoline & Diesel;
Petroleum Refinery
N.A.I.C.S.: 324110
Skipp Kistler *(VP & Mgr-Refinery-Tulsa)*
Darin Rains *(VP & Mgr-Refinery)*

Frontier Pipeline LLC   (2)
2828 N Harwood Ste 1300, Dallas, TX
75201
Tel.: (214) 871-3555
Pipeline Transportation Services
N.A.I.C.S.: 486110

Frontier Refining, Inc.   (2)
300 Morrie Ave, Cheyenne, WY
82007-1734   (100%)
Tel.: (307) 634-3551
Web Site: http://www.frontieroil.com
Sales Range: $1-4.9 Billion
Emp.: 262
Gas & Oil Refinery
N.A.I.C.S.: 324110

HEP El Dorado LLC   (2)
2828 N Harwood Ste 1300, Dallas, TX
75201
Tel.: (214) 871-3555
Petroleum Refining Services
N.A.I.C.S.: 324110

Holly Logistic Services, L.L.C. (2)
2828 N Harwood Ste 1300, Dallas, TX
75201   (100%)
Tel.: (214) 871-3555
Sales Range: $50-74.9 Million
Emp.: 80
Oil & Gas Refining
N.A.I.C.S.: 324110

Holly Petroleum, Inc.   (2)
2828 N Harwood Ste 1300, Dallas, TX
75201   (100%)
Tel.: (214) 871-3555
Sales Range: $25-49.9 Million
Emp.: 52
Petroleum Refining
N.A.I.C.S.: 324110

**Holly Refining & Marketing
Company**   (2)
100 Crescent Ct Ste 1600, Dallas, TX
75201-6927   (100%)
Tel.: (214) 871-3555
Sales Range: $1-4.9 Billion
Oil & Gas Refining
N.A.I.C.S.: 324110

**Holly Refining & Marketing Company
- Woods Cross LLC**   (2)
393 S 800 W, Woods Cross, UT 84087-
1435
Tel.: (801) 299-6600
Petroleum Refining Services
N.A.I.C.S.: 324110

**Holly Refining & Marketing-Tulsa
LLC**   (2)
1700 S Union Ave, Tulsa, OK 74107
Tel.: (918) 594-6600
Web Site: http://www.hollyfrontier.com
Sales Range: $200-249.9 Million
Emp.: 400
Refinery
N.A.I.C.S.: 457120

**Holly Refining Communications,
Inc.**   (2)
100 Crescent Ct Ste 1600, Dallas, TX
75201-6927   (100%)
Tel.: (214) 871-3555
Sales Range: $1-4.9 Billion
Oil & Gas Refining
N.A.I.C.S.: 324110

**HollyFrontier Asphalt Company
LLC**   (2)
2411 N Freeman Ave, Artesia, NM 88210-
9606
Tel.: (575) 748-1368
Petroleum Refining Services
N.A.I.C.S.: 324110

**HollyFrontier El Dorado Refining
LLC**   (2)
1401 Douglas Rd, El Dorado, KS 67042
Tel.: (316) 321-2200
Emp.: 400
Petroleum Refining Services
N.A.I.C.S.: 324110
Kane Hittle *(Project Mgr)*

**HollyFrontier Navajo Refining
LLC**   (2)
501 E Main St, Artesia, NM 88210
Tel.: (575) 748-3311
Petroleum Refining Services
N.A.I.C.S.: 324110

**HollyFrontier Refining & Marketing
LLC**   (2)
2828 N Harwood Ste 1300, Dallas, TX
75201
Tel.: (214) 954-6560

HF Sinclair Corporation—(Continued)

Construction Material Mfr & Whslr
N.A.I.C.S.: 324122
Pat Gribbin *(VP-Lubricants, Specialty Products & Asphalt)*

Hollycorp Aviation, LLC (2)
100 Crescent Ct Ste 1600, Dallas, TX
75201-6915 **(100%)**
Tel.: (214) 871-3555
Sales Range: $1-4.9 Billion
Oil & Gas Refining
N.A.I.C.S.: 324110

Subsidiary (Non-US):

**Jia Shi Lubricants Trading (Shanghai)
Co. Ltd.** (2)
1908 World Trade Tower 500 Guangdong
Road, Huangpu, Shanghai, 200001, China
Tel.: (86) 2163620066
Petroleum Refinery Services
N.A.I.C.S.: 324110
Tobey Chen *(Mgr-Technical Svcs)*

Subsidiary (Domestic):

Lorefco, Inc. (2)
100 Crescent Ct Ste 1600, Dallas, TX
75201-6915 **(100%)**
Tel.: (214) 871-3555
Sales Range: $100-124.9 Million
Oil & Gas Refining
N.A.I.C.S.: 324110

NK Asphalt Partners (2)
4949 Edith Blvd Ne, Albuquerque, NM
87107
Tel.: (505) 344-3526
Petroleum Refining Services
N.A.I.C.S.: 324110

Navajo Holdings, Inc. (2)
100 Crescent Ct Ste 1600, Dallas, TX
75201-6915 **(100%)**
Tel.: (214) 871-3555
Sales Range: $25-49.9 Million
Emp.: 52
Crude Oil Sales
N.A.I.C.S.: 324110

Navajo Pipeline Co., L.P. (2)
1602 W Main St, Artesia, NM
88210 **(100%)**
Tel.: (575) 748-4000
Sales Range: $10-24.9 Million
Emp.: 100
Petroleum Pipeline
N.A.I.C.S.: 486110

Subsidiary (Domestic):

Navajo Pipeline GP, LLC (3)
100 Crescent Ct Ste 1600, Dallas, TX
75201-6927 **(100%)**
Tel.: (214) 871-3885
Oil & Gas Refining
N.A.I.C.S.: 533110

Navajo Pipeline LP, LLC (3)
100 Crescent Ct Ste 1600, Dallas, TX
75201-6915 **(100%)**
Tel.: (214) 871-3885
Web Site: https://www.hollycorp.com
Oil & Gas Refining
N.A.I.C.S.: 533110

Subsidiary (Domestic):

Navajo Refining LP, L.L.C. (2)
501 E Main, Artesia, NM 88210
Tel.: (575) 748-3311
Petroleum Refining Services
N.A.I.C.S.: 324110

Navajo South, Inc. (2)
100 Crescent Ct Ste 100, Dallas, TX
75201-6962 **(100%)**
Tel.: (575) 748-3555
Sales Range: $250-299.9 Million
Oil & Gas Refining
N.A.I.C.S.: 533110

Subsidiary (Non-US):

**Petro-Canada Europe Lubricants
Limited** (2)
Wellington House Starley Way Birmingham
International Park, Solihull, B37 7HB,
United Kingdom
Tel.: (44) 1217817401

Petroleum Product Distr
N.A.I.C.S.: 424720

Petro-Canada Lubricants Inc. (2)
2310 Lakeshore Road West, Mississauga,
L5J 1K2, ON, Canada
Web Site: https://petrocanadalubricants.com
Petroleum Product Mfr
N.A.I.C.S.: 324110

Subsidiary (Domestic):

Red Giant Oil Company (2)
1701 S 3rd St, Council Bluffs, IA 51503-
6873
Tel.: (712) 323-2441
Web Site: https://www.redgiantoil.com
Petroleum Products Merchant Whslr
N.A.I.C.S.: 424720

Sinclair Oil LLC (2)
550 E South Temple St, Salt Lake City, UT
84102-1005
Tel.: (801) 524-2700
Web Site: http://www.sinclairoil.com
Sales Range: $1-4.9 Billion
Emp.: 7,000
Petroleum Refiner; Service Stations, Conve-
nience Stores, Ski Resorts & Hotels Owner
& Operator
N.A.I.C.S.: 324110
Diane Wheeler *(Mgr-Income Tax)*
Ray Hansen *(Mgr-Ops)*
Carleen Walker *(Mgr-Customer Svc)*
Andrea Carey *(Dir-Medical Plans)*
David Crittenden *(VP & Controller)*
Craig Anderson *(Mgr-Indus Sls & Fuels
Quality)*
Diana McCashland *(Mgr-Accts Payable)*
James Branch *(Project Mgr)*
Jay Mick *(VP)*
Lynn Hart *(Gen Counsel & VP)*
Mike Remy *(Mgr-Renewable Fuels)*
Stephanie Coleman *(Mgr-Adv)*
Juel Iverson *(Coord-Sinclair Lubricants)*
Dan Pankowski *(Mgr-IT Ops)*
Kayla Cowley *(Supvr-Payroll)*
Trent Allen *(Brand Mgr-License)*
Ron Mrocek *(Brand Mgr-Support)*
Nathan Larsen *(Mgr-IT Network)*

Holding (Domestic):

Grand America Hotels & Resorts (3)
555 S Main St, Salt Lake City, UT 84111
Tel.: (801) 258-6000
Web Site: http://www.grandamerica.com
Emp.: 1,000
Hotel
N.A.I.C.S.: 721110
Bruce Fery *(Pres)*
Susanne Maitzen *(Exec Dir-Hospitality
Comm)*
Kelly Andersen *(Dir-Beverage)*
Carl Sokia *(Dir-HR)*
David Hirasawa *(VP & Controller)*

Subsidiary (Domestic):

Little America Hotels (4)
500 S Main St, Salt Lake City, UT
84101-2405 **(100%)**
Tel.: (801) 596-5700
Web Site:
http://www.saltlake.littleamerica.com
Sales Range: $100-124.9 Million
Hotel
N.A.I.C.S.: 721110
Ed Box *(Gen Mgr)*
Laurie Cannon *(Sr Mgr-Sls)*

Sun Valley Company (4)
1 Sun Vly Rd, Sun Valley, ID 83353
Tel.: (208) 622-4111
Web Site: http://www.sunvalley.com
Hotels & Resorts
N.A.I.C.S.: 721110
Dick Andersen *(Dir-Hotel Ops)*
Jack Sibbach *(Dir-Mktg & PR)*
Brent Gillette *(Dir-Sls)*
Jennifer Uhrig *(Mgr-Ticket Sls)*
Mike Federko *(Mgr-Mountain)*
Fernando M. Murga *(Mgr-Credit)*
Rob Prew *(Dir-IT)*
Doug Horn *(Mgr-Catering)*
Tim Silva *(Gen Mgr)*
Jim Snyder *(Dir-Food & Beverage)*

The Westgate Hotel (4)
1055 2nd Ave, San Diego, CA 92101

Tel.: (619) 238-1818
Web Site: http://www.westgatehotel.com
Sales Range: $25-49.9 Million
Emp.: 150
Hotel
N.A.I.C.S.: 721110
Richard Cox *(Gen Mgr)*
Margaret Klatt *(Mgr-Catering Sls)*
Jennifer Emereiann *(Mgr-Catering Sls)*
Mark Nakanishi *(Dir-PR)*
Andrew Hottenstein *(Dir-Sls & Catering)*
Audrey Nimura *(Mgr-Sls)*
Ronaldo Santiago *(Mgr-Sls)*

Holding (Domestic):

Sinclair Casper Refinery (3)
PO Box 510, Evansville, WY 82636-0510
Tel.: (307) 265-2800
Sales Range: $25-49.9 Million
Emp.: 110
Gasoline, Fuel Oils
N.A.I.C.S.: 484110

Subsidiary (Domestic):

Snowbasin Resort Company (3)
3925 E Snowbasin Rd, Huntsville, UT
84317
Tel.: (801) 620-1000
Web Site: http://www.snowbasin.com
Hotel Operating Services
N.A.I.C.S.: 721110

Subsidiary (Domestic):

**Woods Cross Refining Company,
LLC** (2)
393 S 800 W, Woods Cross, UT
84087-1435 **(100%)**
Tel.: (801) 299-6600
Web Site: http://www.hollyfrontier.com
Sales Range: $100-124.9 Million
Emp.: 300
Oil & Gas Refining
N.A.I.C.S.: 324110

HFACTOR, INC.
244 Madison Ave Ste 1249, New
York, NY 10016
Tel.: (516) 647-5171 DE
Web Site: https://hfactorwater.com
HWTR—(OTCIQ)
Rev.: $1,886,666
Assets: $1,675,884
Liabilities: $6,225,343
Net Worth: ($4,549,459)
Earnings: ($2,421,493)
Fiscal Year-end: 12/31/22
Biopharmaceutical Research & De-
velopment Services
N.A.I.C.S.: 541713
Gail Levy *(Pres & CEO)*
Mike Lee *(COO)*

HFB FINANCIAL CORPORA-
TION
1602 Cumberland Ave, Middlesboro,
KY 40965
Tel.: (606) 248-1095 TN
Web Site:
https://www.hearthsidebank.com
Year Founded: 1992
HFBA—(OTCIQ)
Bank Holding Company
N.A.I.C.S.: 551111
Stephen Cambron *(Sr VP)*
Charlotte Vaughn *(VP & Mgr-Branch
Ops)*
Joyce Rucker *(VP)*
Rhonda Gilliam *(Sr VP)*

Subsidiaries:

Home Federal Bank Corporation (1)
1602 E Cumberland Ave, Middlesboro, KY
40965
Tel.: (606) 248-1095
Web Site: http://www.homefederalbank.com
Commericial Banking
N.A.I.C.S.: 522110
D. Alex Cook *(Pres & CEO)*
Diana Miracle *(Chief Admin Officer & Exec
VP)*
Stephen Cambron *(VP & Mgr-Middlesboro
Market)*

HG HOLDINGS, INC.
2115 E 7th St Ste 101, Charlotte, NC
28204
Tel.: (850) 772-0698 DE
Web Site:
https://www.hgholdingsinc.net
Year Founded: 1924
STLY—(OTCQB)
Rev.: $14,482,000
Assets: $41,103,000
Liabilities: $7,677,000
Net Worth: $33,426,000
Earnings: $3,659,000
Emp.: 76
Fiscal Year-end: 12/31/22
Holding Company; Residential Furni-
ture Mfr
N.A.I.C.S.: 551112
Ben Carter *(Gen Counsel)*
Anna Lieb *(Principal Fin & Acctg Offi-
cer & Sec)*
Steven A. Hale II *(Chm & CEO)*

HHGREGG, INC.
160 W Carmel Dr Ste 263, Carmel,
IN 46032
Tel.: (317) 848-8710 DE
Year Founded: 1955
HGGG—(OTCEM)
Sales Range: $1-4.9 Billion
Emp.: 5,100
Home Appliances & Consumer Elec-
tronics Retailer
N.A.I.C.S.: 449210
Kevin J. Kovacs *(Pres, CEO, CFO,
Principal Acctg Officer & Sr VP)*

Subsidiaries:

Gregg Appliances, Inc. (1)
4151 E 96th St, Indianapolis, IN 46240-
1442
Tel.: (317) 848-8710
Web Site: http://www.hhgreg.com
Sales Range: $125-149.9 Million
Home Appliances & Consumer Electronics
Retailer
N.A.I.C.S.: 449210

Subsidiary (Domestic):

HHG Distributing LLC (2)
4141 E 96th St, Indianapolis, IN 46240-
1442
Tel.: (317) 848-8710
Web Site: http://www.hhgregg.com
Sales Range: $125-149.9 Million
Home Appliances & Consumer Electronics
Retailer
N.A.I.C.S.: 449210

HI-GREAT GROUP HOLDING
CO.
621 S Virgil Ave Ste 460, Los Ange-
les, CA 90005
Tel.: (213) 219-7746 NV
Web Site: https://www.higreat.com
HIGR—(OTCIQ)
Rev.: $109,491
Assets: $84,138
Liabilities: $193,551
Net Worth: ($109,413)
Earnings: ($121,758)
Fiscal Year-end: 12/31/23
Wellness Supplement & Oil Distr
N.A.I.C.S.: 456191

HIGH COUNTRY BANCORP,
INC.
7360 W Hwy 50, Salida, CO 81201
Tel.: (719) 539-2516 CO
Web Site:
https://www.highcountrybank.net
Year Founded: 1997
HCBC—(OTCQX)
Rev.: $15,840,000
Assets: $331,751,000
Liabilities: $296,884,000
Net Worth: $34,867,000
Earnings: $4,332,000

Emp.: 89
Fiscal Year-end: 06/30/20
Bank Holding Company
N.A.I.C.S.: 551111
Larry D. Smith *(Pres & CEO)*
Dennis M. Weber *(CFO)*
Sylvia Veltri *(COO)*

Subsidiaries:

High Country Bank (1)
7360 W US Hwy 50, Salida, CO 81201
Tel.: (719) 539-2516
Web Site: http://www.highcountrybank.net
Sales Range: $50-74.9 Million
Emp.: 60
Retail & Commercial Banking Services
N.A.I.C.S.: 522180
Glynis Laub *(Officer-Loan)*
Rich Mancuso *(Officer-Comml Loan)*
Ron Fore *(Officer-Comml Loan)*
Avery Bechtel *(Officer-Comml Loan)*

HIGH SIERRA TECHNOLO-GIES, INC.
1495 Ridgeview Dr Ste 230A, Reno,
NV 89519
Tel.: (775) 410-4100 CO
Web Site: https://high-sierra.com
Year Founded: 1996
HSTI—(OTCQB)
Assets: $101,502
Liabilities: $611,785
Net Worth: ($510,283)
Earnings: ($323,952)
Fiscal Year-end: 12/31/22
Investment Services
N.A.I.C.S.: 523999
Vincent C. Lombardi *(Founder, Pres & CEO)*
Gregg W. Koechlein *(CFO, COO, Gen Counsel, Treas & Sec)*
Glenn C. Miller *(Chief Scientific Officer)*

HIGH WIRE NETWORKS INC.
30 N Lincoln St, Batavia, IL 60510
Tel.: (952) 974-4000 BC
Web Site:
https://www.highwirenetworks.com
Year Founded: 2007
HWNI—(OTCQB)
Rev.: $55,049,441
Assets: $32,594,971
Liabilities: $26,846,534
Net Worth: $5,748,437
Earnings: ($19,035,088)
Emp.: 342
Fiscal Year-end: 12/31/22
Holding Company; Oil & Gas Services; Marketing & Graphic Design Services
N.A.I.C.S.: 551112
Roger M. Ponder *(Chm)*
Mark W. Porter *(CEO)*
Michael Obi *(Executives)*
Stephen W. LaMarche *(COO)*
John J.P. Peterson *(Chief Product Officer)*
Susanna Song *(CMO)*

Subsidiaries:

ADEX Corporation (1)
980 N Federal Hwy, Boca Raton, FL 33432
Tel.: (678) 393-7900
Web Site: https://www.adextelecom.com
Telecommunications Network Engineering & Support Services
N.A.I.C.S.: 517810

TNS, Inc. (1)
1225 Rand Rd, Des Plaines, IL
60016 (100%)
Tel.: (847) 759-2001
Web Site: http://www.tnscabling.com
Design, Installation & Maintenance of Structured Cabling Systems
N.A.I.C.S.: 238990

Tropical Communications, Inc. (1)
6937 NW 82nd Ave, Miami, FL 33166

Tel.: (305) 599-2114
Web Site: https://www.tropicalcom.com
Emp.: 10
Electrical & Underground Utility Contractor
N.A.I.C.S.: 238210

HIGHLAND SURPRISE CON-SOLIDATED MINING CO.
PO Box 469, Wallace, ID 83873
Tel.: (208) 752-1131 ID
HSCM—(OTCIQ)
Exploration & Mining Services
N.A.I.C.S.: 213114
H. F. MacPhea *(Sec)*

HIGHLAND TRANSCEND PARTNERS I CORP.
777 Arthur Godfrey Rd #202, Miami,
FL 33140
Tel.: (617) 401-4015 Ky
Web Site:
http://www.highlandtranscend.com
HTPA—(NYSE)
Rev.: $109,007
Assets: $301,079,588
Liabilities: $339,101,903
Net Worth: ($38,022,315)
Earnings: ($11,745,088)
Emp.: 3
Fiscal Year-end: 12/31/21
Special Purpose Acquisition Company
N.A.I.C.S.: 523999
Ian Friedman *(CEO)*
Dan Nova *(Chief Investment Officer)*
Ian Friedman *(CEO)*

HIGHPEAK ENERGY, INC.
421 W 3rd St Ste 1000, Fort Worth,
TX 76102
Tel.: (817) 850-9200 DE
Web Site:
https://www.highpeakenergy.com
Year Founded: 2019
HPK—(NASDAQ)
Natural Gas Extraction
N.A.I.C.S.: 211130
Jack D. Hightower *(Chm & CEO)*

Subsidiaries:

HighPeak Energy Acquisition
Corp. (1)
421 W 3rd St Ste 1000, Forth Worth, TX
76102
Tel.: (817) 850-9200
Crude Oil & Natural Gas Extraction
N.A.I.C.S.: 211130

HIGHWOODS PROPERTIES, INC.
150 Fayetteville St Ste 1400, Raleigh,
NC 27601
Tel.: (919) 872-4924 MD
Web Site:
https://www.highwoods.com
Year Founded: 1978
HIW—(NYSE)
Rev.: $833,997,000
Assets: $6,002,928,000
Liabilities: $3,564,906,000
Net Worth: $2,438,022,000
Earnings: $146,230,000
Emp.: 349
Fiscal Year-end: 12/31/23
Real Estate Investment Trust
N.A.I.C.S.: 525990
Daniel L. Clemmens *(Chief Acctg Officer & VP)*
Theodore J. Klinck *(Pres & CEO)*
Carman J. Liuzzo *(Sr VP-Investments)*
Jeffrey D. Miller *(Gen Counsel, Sec & Exec VP)*
Michael D. Starchville *(Sr VP-Asset Mgmt)*
L. Randy Roberson *(Sr VP-Dev)*
Steven J. Garrity *(VP-Orlando)*

James V. Bacchetta *(VP-Atlanta)*
Brendan C. Maiorana *(CFO & Exec VP)*
Jane DuFrane *(VP-Richmond)*
Brian M. Leary *(COO & Exec VP)*
Ryan Hunt *(CIO & VP)*
Tripp Merchant *(Sr VP)*
Chris Urban *(Sr Gen Mgr)*
Betsy Bullard *(Sr Dir)*
Alex Chambers *(Sr VP)*
Dan Woodward *(Sr VP)*

Subsidiaries:

HIW-KC Orlando, LLC (1)
201 E Pine St, Orlando, FL 32801
Tel.: (407) 849-2275
Web Site: https://www.highwoods.com
Nonresidential Building Operators
N.A.I.C.S.: 531312

Highwoods Realty Limited
Partnership (1)
150 Fayetteville St Ste 1400, Raleigh, NC
27601
Tel.: (919) 872-4924
Web Site: https://www.highwoods.com
Rev.: $833,996,999
Assets: $6,002,927,999
Liabilities: $3,593,716,999
Net Worth: $2,409,211,000
Earnings: $149,394,000
Emp.: 348
Fiscal Year-end: 12/31/2023
Real Estate Services
N.A.I.C.S.: 531190
Carlos E. Evans *(Chm)*

HILLENBRAND, INC.
1 Batesville Blvd, Batesville, IN
47006
Tel.: (812) 931-5000
Web Site:
https://www.hillenbrand.com
HI—(NYSE)
Rev.: $2,826,000,000
Assets: $5,547,700,000
Liabilities: $3,884,800,000
Net Worth: $1,662,900,000
Earnings: $569,700,000
Emp.: 10,400
Fiscal Year-end: 09/30/23
Caskets & Industrial Products Mfr
N.A.I.C.S.: 339995
Kimberly K. Ryan-Dennis *(Pres, CEO & Exec VP)*
Nicholas R. Farrell *(Chief Compliance Officer, Gen Counsel, Sec & Sr VP)*
Robert M. VanHimbergen *(CFO & Sr VP)*
Megan A. Walke *(Chief Acctg Officer & VP)*
J. Michael Whitted *(Sr VP-Strategy & Corp Dev)*
Bhavik N. Soni *(CIO & VP)*
Ling An-Heid *(Pres-Mold-Masters & Sr VP)*
Michael M. Jones *(Pres-Milacron Injection Molding & Extrusion & Sr VP)*
Christopher H. Trainor *(Pres-Batesville Casket Company & Sr VP)*
Michael D. Prado *(Chief Procurement Officer & VP-Supply Mgmt-Global)*
Tory Flynn *(Chief Sustainability Officer)*
Ulrich Bartel *(Pres-Coperion & Sr VP)*
Aneesha Arora *(Chief HR Officer)*
Carole Phillips *(Chief Procurement Officer)*
Leo J. Kulmaczewski Jr. *(Sr VP-Ops Center of Excellence & HOM)*
Helen W. Cornell *(Chm)*

Subsidiaries:

Batesville Services, Inc. (1)
1 Batesville Blvd, Batesville, IN 47006
Tel.: (812) 934-7500
Web Site: http://www.batesville.com
Funeral Services
N.A.I.C.S.: 812210

Subsidiary (Non-US):

Batesville Canada Ltd. (2)
8782 51 Ave Nw, Edmonton, T6E 5E8, AB,
Canada
Tel.: (780) 469-2311
Web Site: http://www.batesville.com
Emp.: 4
Burial Casket Mfr & Distr
N.A.I.C.S.: 423850

Batesville Casket de Mexico, S.A. de
C.V. (2)
Poniente No 116 No 713, Mexico, 02300,
Mexico
Tel.: (52) 5555673622
Funeral Services
N.A.I.C.S.: 812210

Subsidiary (Domestic):

Industrias Arga, S.A. de C.V. (3)
Camino a Huitzila No 29 Col Zona Industrial, Tizayuca, 43804, Mexico, Hidalgo,
Mexico
Tel.: (52) 7791002554
Web Site: http://www.industriasarga.com
Industrial Fabricated Machinery Mfr
N.A.I.C.S.: 332999

Subsidiary (Non-US):

Batesville Holding UK, Limited (2)
The Old Vicarage, Derby, DE74 2JB,
Derbyshire, United Kingdom
Tel.: (44) 1332856372
Holding Company
N.A.I.C.S.: 551112
Emily Arnett *(Gen Mgr)*

Subsidiary (Domestic):

Batesville Casket UK Limited (3)
The Old Vicarage Market Street, Castle
Donington, DE74 2JB, Derbyshire, United
Kingdom
Tel.: (44) 1332856372
Web Site: http://www.batesville.co.uk
Burial Casket & Cases Mfr
N.A.I.C.S.: 339995

Subsidiary (Domestic):

Batesville Manufacturing, Inc. (2)
1 Batesville Blvd, Batesville, IN 47006-7756
Tel.: (812) 934-7000
Funeral Services
N.A.I.C.S.: 812210

HMIS, Inc. (2)
10 Al Paul Ln Ste 102, Merrimack, NH
03054
Tel.: (603) 883-5692
Web Site: http://www.hmisinc.com
Emp.: 30
Software Developer
N.A.I.C.S.: 513210
Frank Hanlon *(Founder & CEO)*
Mike Hanlon *(Pres)*

MCP, Inc. (2)
2333 Lake Shore Dr, Pekin, IL 61554
Tel.: (309) 346-8342
Web Site: http://www.mcpincorporated.com
Janitorial Services
N.A.I.C.S.: 561720

Coperion GmbH (1)
Theodorstrasse 10, 70469, Stuttgart, Germany
Tel.: (49) 7118970
Web Site: http://www.coperion.com
Emp.: 800
Compounding Systems Mfr & Marketer
N.A.I.C.S.: 331513
Kimberly K. Ryan-Dennis *(Chm-Exec Bd & Mng Dir)*
Kimberly K. Ryan *(Chm-Exec Bd & Mng Dir)*
Markus Parzer *(Pres)*
Klaus Beulker *(VP)*
Falk Kohler *(Chief Procurement Officer)*

Subsidiary (Domestic):

Abel GmbH (2)
Abel-Twiete 1, D-21514, Buchen, Germany
Tel.: (49) 41558180
Web Site: https://www.abelpumps.com
Displacement Pumps Design & Mfr
N.A.I.C.S.: 333914

Hillenbrand, Inc.—(Continued)

Sally Powell *(Principal)*

Subsidiary (Non-US):

Abel Equipos, S.A. (3)
Tel.: (34) 917154848
Web Site: https://www.abelpumps.com
Displacement Pumps Design & Mfr
N.A.I.C.S.: 333914

Subsidiary (Non-US):

Coperion (Nanjing) Machinery Co., Ltd. (2)
No 1296 Jiyin Avenue, Jiangning Economic & Technology Development Zone, Nanjing, 211106, China
Tel.: (86) 2552783922
Web Site: http://www.coperion.com
Industry Equipment Mfr
N.A.I.C.S.: 332510

Coperion AB (2)
Linnegatan 81, PO Box 1191, 11460, Huddinge, Sweden
Tel.: (46) 86081818
Web Site: http://www.cooperion.com
Sales Range: $25-49.9 Million
Emp.: 4
Plastics & Rubber Compound Mfr
N.A.I.C.S.: 326199

Subsidiary (US):

Coperion Corporation (2)
590 Woodbury Glassboro Rd, Sewell, NJ 08080
Tel.: (856) 256-3175
Compounding Equipment Mfr
N.A.I.C.S.: 333248

Branch (Domestic):

Coperion Corp. (3)
10424 Torrelle Dr, Charlotte, NC 28277
Tel.: (704) 759-9991
Web Site: http://www.coperion.com
Rev.: $1,804,000
Emp.: 11
All Other Plastics Product Mfr
N.A.I.C.S.: 326199

Branch (Domestic):

Coperion GmbH (2)
Niederbieger Strasse 9, Weingarten, 88250, Germany
Tel.: (49) 7514080
Web Site: http://www.coperion.com
Sales Range: $100-124.9 Million
Emp.: 300
Bulk Plastics Mfr
N.A.I.C.S.: 326199
Kimberly K. Ryan-Dennis *(Chm-Exec Bd, Pres & Mng Dir)*
Ulrich Bartel *(Pres & Mng Dir)*
Kimberly K. Ryan *(Chm-Exec Bd & Mng Dir)*

Affiliate (Non-US):

Coperion Ideal Pvt Ltd. (2)
Ideal House A-35 Sector 64, Noida, 201 307, Uttar Pradesh, India
Tel.: (91) 1204299333
Web Site: http://www.coperion.com
Emp.: 250
Plastics Product Mfr
N.A.I.C.S.: 326199

Subsidiary (Non US):

Coperion International Trading (Shanghai) Co. Ltd. (2)
Bldg No A2 6000 Shenzhuan Road, Dongjing Town Songjiang District, Shanghai, 201619, China
Tel.: (86) 2167679505
Web Site: http://www.coperion.com
Material Handling Services
N.A.I.C.S.: 811310

Subsidiary (Domestic):

Coperion K.K. (2)
4F Leaf Square Shin-Yokohama Bldg 3-7-3, Shin-Yokohama Kohoku-ku, Yokohama, 222-0033, Kanagawa, Japan
Tel.: (81) 455959801
Web Site: http://www.coperion.com

Sales Range: $25-49.9 Million
Emp.: 11
Plants & Equipment for the Chemical & Plastics Industries
N.A.I.C.S.: 326199

Coperion Ltd. (2)
Unit 4 Acorn Business Park Heaton Lane, Stockport, SK4 1AS, Cheshire, United Kingdom (100%)
Tel.: (44) 1612094810
Web Site: http://www.coperion.com
Sales Range: $25-49.9 Million
Emp.: 12
Materials Handling & Compounding & Extrusion Services
N.A.I.C.S.: 326199

Coperion Ltda. (2)
R Dona Germaine Buchard 418, 05002-062, Sao Paulo, Brazil
Tel.: (55) 1138742740
Compounding & Extrusion Services
N.A.I.C.S.: 331318

Coperion Machinery & Systems (Shanghai) Co. Ltd. (2)
Bldg No A2 6000 Shenzhuan Road, Dongjing Town Songjiang District, Shanghai, 201619, China
Tel.: (86) 2167679505
Web Site: http://www.coperion.com
Material Handling Services
N.A.I.C.S.: 811310

Affiliate (Non-US):

Coperion Middle East Co. Ltd. (2)
PO Box 821, Al Jubayl, 31951, Saudi Arabia
Tel.: (966) 33411368
Compounding & Extrusion Material Handling Services
N.A.I.C.S.: 331318

Subsidiary (Non-US):

Coperion N.V. (2)
Industrieweg 2, 2845, Niel, Belgium
Tel.: (32) 38705100
Web Site: http://www.coperion.com
Emp.: 14
Compounding & Extrusion Material Handling Services
N.A.I.C.S.: 331318
Johan Gogne *(Mng Dir)*

Subsidiary (Domestic):

Coperion Pelletizing Technology GmbH (2)
Heinrich-Krumm-Str 6, 63073, Offenbach, Germany
Tel.: (49) 6998932380
Web Site: http://www.pell-tec.de
Industrial Machinery Mfr
N.A.I.C.S.: 333248

Subsidiary (Non-US):

Coperion Pte Ltd. (2)
8 Jurong Town Hall Road 28-01/02/03 The JTC Summit, Singapore, 609434, Singapore
Tel.: (65) 64188200
Web Site: http://www.coperion.com
Sales Range: $25-49.9 Million
Emp.: 43
Plastic & Rubber Compound Mfr
N.A.I.C.S.: 326199

Coperion S.L. (2)
Balmes 73 pral, 08007, Barcelona, Spain
Tel.: (34) 934517337
Web Site: http://www.coperion.com
Emp.: 6
Compounding & Extrusion Material Handling Services
N.A.I.C.S.: 331318
Carles Sola *(Mng Dir)*

Coperion S.a.r.l. (2)
56 boulevard de Courcerin, 77183, Croissy-Beaubourg, France
Tel.: (33) 164801600
Web Site: http://www.coperion.com
Sales Range: $25-49.9 Million
Emp.: 3
Plastic & Rubber Compound Mfr
N.A.I.C.S.: 326199

Coperion S.r.l. (2)

Via E da Rotterdam 25, 44122, Ferrara, Italy
Tel.: (39) 0532779911
Web Site: http://www.coperion.com
Material Handling Services
N.A.I.C.S.: 532490

Subsidiary (Domestic):

Weicom S.r.l. (3)
Via Erasmo Da Rotterdam 25, 44122, Ferrara, Italy
Tel.: (39) 0532779911
Emp.: 80
Weighing & Bagging System Mfr
N.A.I.C.S.: 332999
Giampaolo Dotto *(Gen Mgr)*

Subsidiary (Non-US):

OOO "Coperion" (2)
Proezd Serebryakova 14 Bld 15 Office 219, 129343, Moscow, Russia
Tel.: (7) 4992584206
Web Site: http://www.coperion.com
Emp.: 9
Compounding & Extrusion Material Handling Services
N.A.I.C.S.: 331318

D-M-E (China) Limited (1)
Room 708 Shui Hing Centre 13 Sheung Yuet Road, Kowloon Bay, China (Hong Kong)
Tel.: (852) 27951035
Mold Component Mfr
N.A.I.C.S.: 333511

Subsidiary (Non-US):

D-M-E Mold Technology (Shenzhen) Company Ltd. (2)
No 502 Building 5C Skyworth Innovation Valley Tangtou 1st RD, Shiyan Subdistrict Baoan District, Shenzhen, Guangdong, China
Tel.: (86) 75586019031
Mold Component Mfr
N.A.I.C.S.: 333511

D-M-E Normalien GmbH (1)
Neumattrig 1, 76532, Baden-Baden, Germany
Tel.: (49) 23514370
Molding Component Mfr
N.A.I.C.S.: 333511

DIOSNA Dierks & Sohne GmbH (1)
Am Tie 23, 49086, Osnabruck, Germany
Tel.: (49) 541331040
Web Site: https://www.diosna.com
Farm Equipment Mfr & Distr
N.A.I.C.S.: 333111

Diosna CS s.r.o. (1)
Prazska 992, 407 46, Ceska Lipa, Krasna Lipa, Czech Republic
Tel.: (420) 412383248
Web Site: https://diosna.cz
Farm Equipment Mfr & Distr
N.A.I.C.S.: 333111

Gabler Engineering GmbH (1)
Daimlerstrasse 20c, 76316, Malsch, Germany
Tel.: (49) 724692500
Web Site: https://www.gablermade.com
Industrial Weaving & Textile Machine Mfr
N.A.I.C.S.: 333248

Herbold Meckesheim GmbH (1)
Industriestrasse 33, 74909, Meckesheim, Germany
Tel.: (49) 62269320
Web Site: https://www.herbold.com
Plastic Scrap Distr
N.A.I.C.S.: 423930

Hillenbrand Germany Holding GmbH (1)
Theodorstr 10, Stuttgart, 70469, Baden-Wurttemberg, Germany
Tel.: (49) 7118970
Holding Company
N.A.I.C.S.: 551112

K-Tron International, Inc. (1)
590 Woodbury Glassboro Rd, Sewell, NJ 08080
Tel.: (856) 589-0500
Web Site: http://www.ktron.com

Sales Range: $150-199.9 Million
Emp.: 639
Industrial Process Control Equipment & Material Handling Equipment Mfr
N.A.I.C.S.: 334513

Subsidiary (Non-US):

Coperion K-Tron (Schweiz) GmbH (2)
Lenzhardweg 43/45, 5702, Niederlenz, Switzerland
Tel.: (41) 628857171
Web Site: http://www.coperion.com
Pneumatic Conveying Equipment Mfr
N.A.I.C.S.: 333922

Subsidiary (Non-US):

Coperion K-Tron (Shanghai) Co. Ltd. (3)
Building A2-A3 6000 Shenzhuan Road, Dongjing Town Songjiang District, Shanghai, 201619, China
Tel.: (86) 2163757925
Industrial Equipment Whsr
N.A.I.C.S.: 423830

Coperion K-Tron Asia Pte. Ltd. (3)
8 Jurong Town Hall Road 28-01/02/03 The JTC Summit, Singapore, 609434, Singapore
Tel.: (65) 64188200
Web Site: http://www.ktron.com
Sales Range: $10-24.9 Million
Emp.: 10
Feeders & Pneumatic Conveying Equipment Mfr
N.A.I.C.S.: 333922

Coperion K-Tron Deutschland GmbH (3)
Heinrich-Krumm-Strasse 6, 63073, Offenbach, Germany
Tel.: (49) 6983008990
Web Site: http://www.coperion.com
Industry Equipment Mfr
N.A.I.C.S.: 332510

Coperion K-Tron France S.a.r.l. (3)
Les Espaces du Chene, 56 boulevard de Courcerin, F-77183, Croissy-Beaubourg, France
Tel.: (33) 164801600
Web Site: http://www.ktron.com
Industrial Process Control Equipment Sales
N.A.I.C.S.: 335314

Coperion K-Tron Great Britain Limited (3)
Unit 4 Acorn Business Park Heaton Lane, Stockport, SK4 1AS, Cheshire, United Kingdom
Tel.: (44) 1612094810
Web Site: http://www.ktron.com
Sales Range: $125-149.9 Million
Emp.: 15
Industrial Machinery Mfr
N.A.I.C.S.: 333131

K-Tron (Shanghai) Co. Ltd. (3)
Building A2-A3 No 6000 Shen Zhuan Gong Road, Songjiang district, Shanghai, 401619, China
Tel.: (86) 2163757925
Web Site: http://www.ktron.com
Engineeering Services
N.A.I.C.S.: 541330

K-Tron China Ltd. (3)
Room 907 Sinotrans Mansion No 188, Fujian Road, Shanghai, 200001, China
Tel.: (86) 2163757925
Web Site: http://www.ktron.com
Sales Range: $125-149.9 Million
Emp.: 11
Industrial Machinery Mfr
N.A.I.C.S.: 333131

Rotex Europe Ltd. (3)
Aston Lane North Whitehouse Vale, Runcorn, WA7 3FA, Cheshire, United Kingdom
Tel.: (44) 1928706100
Web Site: http://www.rotex.com
Emp.: 60
Dry Material Screening Equipment Mfr
N.A.I.C.S.: 333248

Subsidiary (Domestic):

Gundlach Equipment Corporation (2)

1 Freedom Dr, Belleville, IL 62226
Tel.: (618) 233-7208
Sales Range: $1-9.9 Million
Emp.: 73
Mining & Mineral Processing Equipment Mfr
N.A.I.C.S.: 333131
Summer Chanj *(Gen Mgr)*

Division (Domestic):

K-Tron Electronics (2)
590 Woodbury Glassboro Rd, Sewell, NJ 08080
Tel.: (856) 232-2300
Web Site: http://www.ktron.com
Sales Range: $10-24.9 Million
Emp.: 100
Electronic Components Mfr
N.A.I.C.S.: 334513

K-Tron Process Group (2)
590 Woodbury-Glassboro Rd, Sewell, NJ 08080
Tel.: (856) 589-0500
Web Site: http://www.ktron.com
Sales Range: $25-49.9 Million
Emp.: 100
Conveyor Machinery Mfr
N.A.I.C.S.: 333922

K-Tron Investment Co. (1)
300 Delaware Ave Ste 900, Wilmington, DE 19801-1671
Tel.: (302) 421-7361
Investment Management Service
N.A.I.C.S.: 523940

Subsidiary (Domestic):

Coperion K-Tron Pitman, Inc. (2)
590 Woodbury Glassboro Rd, Sewell, NJ 08080
Tel.: (856) 589-0500
Web Site: http://www.coperion.com
Emp.: 200
Gravimetric & Volumetric Feeders & Auxiliary Equipment Mfr
N.A.I.C.S.: 334513

Coperion K-Tron Salina (2)
606 N Front St, Salina, KS 67401
Tel.: (785) 825-1611
Web Site: http://www.coperion.com
Industry Equipment Mfr
N.A.I.C.S.: 332510

TerraSource Global Corporation (2)
1 Freedom Dr, Belleville, IL 62226
Tel.: (618) 233-7208
Web Site: http://www.terrasource.com
Material Handling Equipment Distr
N.A.I.C.S.: 423830
Laurie Phillips *(Pres & CFO)*
Jeff Horvath *(VP-Supply Chain & Ops)*
Matt Richardson *(VP-Sls & Mktg-Global)*
David Baur *(Fin Dir)*

Subsidiary (Domestic):

TerraSource Global Corporation - Duncan (3)
215 Pkwy E Ste A, Duncan, SC 29334
Tel.: (864) 476-7523
Web Site: http://www.terrasource.com
Sales Range: $125-149.9 Million
Mining Equipment Mfr
N.A.I.C.S.: 333131

Subsidiary (Non-US):

Jeffrey Rader AB (4)
Linnegatan 81, 11460, Stockholm, Spanga, Sweden
Tel.: (46) 856475747
Web Site: http://www.terrasource.com
Emp.: 7
Wood Fiber Preparation & Material Handling Services
N.A.I.C.S.: 333248

Jeffrey Rader Canada Company (4)
135 Boulevard Brunswick, Pointe-Claire, H9R 5N2, QC, Canada
Tel.: (514) 822-2660
Web Site: http://www.jeffreyrader.com
Sales Range: $125-149.9 Million
Wood Fiber Preparation & Material Handling Systems
N.A.I.C.S.: 333248

LINXIS Group (1)

3 rue Menou, 44000, Nantes, France
Tel.: (33) 240732604
Web Site: https://www.linxisgroup.com
Emp.: 1,142
Specialized Equipment Solutions Designer & Mfr
N.A.I.C.S.: 423830
Tim Cook *(VP)*
Kevin Buchler *(Pres)*
Andreas Wobmann *(CFO)*

Subsidiary (US):

Shick Esteve (2)
4346 Clary Blvd, Kansas City, MO 64130
Tel.: (877) 744-2587
Industrial Automation Services
N.A.I.C.S.: 811310
Tim Cook *(Pres & CEO)*

Subsidiary (Domestic):

W.D. Laramore Manufacturing Inc. (3)
11763 Hwy 319 N, Thomasville, GA 31757-2448
Tel.: (229) 226-8870
Web Site: http://www.wdlaramore.com
Food Product Machinery Mfr
N.A.I.C.S.: 333241
W. D. Laramore Sr. *(Pres)*

Milacron Czech Republic Spol s.r.o. (1)
Na Vysehrade 1091, Policka, Pardubice, Czech Republic
Tel.: (420) 468002800
Injection Molding Machine Mfr
N.A.I.C.S.: 333248

Milacron Holdings Corp. (1)
10200 Alliance Rd Ste 200, Cincinnati, OH 45242
Tel.: (513) 487-5000
Web Site: http://www.milacron.com
Rev.: $1,258,200,000
Assets: $1,732,500,000
Liabilities: $1,205,700,000
Net Worth: $526,800,000
Earnings: $41,500,000
Emp.: 5,797
Fiscal Year-end: 12/31/2018
Holding Company; Plastics Mfr
N.A.I.C.S.: 551112
Bruce Chalmers *(CFO & VP-Fin)*

Subsidiary (Domestic):

CanGen Holdings, Inc. (2)
1057 Vijay Dr, Chamblee, GA 30341-3136
Tel.: (770) 458-4882
Web Site:
    http://www.canterburyengineering.com
Sales Range: $10-24.9 Million
Emp.: 65
Holding Company
N.A.I.C.S.: 551112

Milacron LLC (2)
10200 Alliance Rd Sten200, Cincinnati, OH 45242
Tel.: (513) 487-5000
Web Site: http://www.milacron.com
Sales Range: $800-899.9 Million
Emp.: 2,800
Plastics Processing Technologies & Industrial Metalworking Fluids Mfr & Distr
N.A.I.C.S.: 333248

Subsidiary (Domestic):

DME Company LLC (3)
29111 Stephenson Hwy, Madison Heights, MI 48071-2330 **(100%)**
Tel.: (248) 398-6000
Web Site: http://www.dme.net
Sales Range: $25-49.9 Million
Plastic Mold Machinery Developer, Mfr & Marketer
N.A.I.C.S.: 333248

Subsidiary (Non-US):

DME Europe C.V.B.A. (4)
Schalienhoevedreef 20-D Mechelen Campus, Industriepark Noord G1, 2800, Mechelen, Belgium **(100%)**
Tel.: (32) 15288730
Web Site: http://www.dmeeu.com

Sales Range: $10-24.9 Million
Plastic Mold Machinery Mfr
N.A.I.C.S.: 333248

DME of Canada, Ltd. (4)
6210 Northwest Dr, Mississauga, L4V 1P6, ON, Canada **(100%)**
Tel.: (905) 677-6370
Web Site: http://www.dme.net
Sales Range: $25-49.9 Million
Emp.: 12
Plastic Mold Machinery Distr
N.A.I.C.S.: 423830

Subsidiary (Non-US):

Milacron B.V. (3)
Schiedamsedijk 20, 3134 KK, Vlaardingen, Netherlands **(100%)**
Tel.: (31) 104450055
Holding Company; Plastics Processing Machinery Mfr & Distr
N.A.I.C.S.: 551112

Subsidiary (Domestic):

Milacron Plastics Technologies Group LLC (3)
4165 Half Acre Rd, Batavia, OH 45103-3247
Tel.: (513) 536-2000
Web Site: http://www.milacron.com
Sales Range: $50-74.9 Million
Emp.: 800
Plastics Injection Molding Machinery Mfr
N.A.I.C.S.: 333248

Subsidiary (Non-US):

Ferromatik Milacron GmbH (4)
Bruhlstrasse 10, 79331, Teningen, Germany **(100%)**
Tel.: (49) 7641954588000
Web Site: http://www.ferromatik.com
Sales Range: $25-49.9 Million
Emp.: 280
Plastic Injection Molding Machine Developer, Mfr & Marketer
N.A.I.C.S.: 333248
Winfried Stocklin *(Exec Officer)*

Ferromatik Milacron India Ltd. (4)
93/2 & 94/1 Phase-I GIDC, Vatva, Ahmedabad, 382 445, Gujarat, India **(90%)**
Tel.: (91) 7961341700
Web Site: https://www.milacronindia.com
Sales Range: $50-74.9 Million
Emp.: 700
Plastic Injection Molding Machinery Mfr & Marketer
N.A.I.C.S.: 333248

Subsidiary (Non-US):

Mold-Masters (2007) Limited (3)
233 Armstrong Avenue, Georgetown, L7G 4X5, ON, Canada
Tel.: (905) 877-0185
Web Site: https://www.moldmasters.com
Sales Range: $50-74.9 Million
Emp.: 800
Hot Runner Industrial Molding Machinery Mfr & Distr
N.A.I.C.S.: 333248
Oliver Lindenberg *(VP-Sls & Mktg-Global)*

Milacron Mold-Masters Sistemas de Processamento de Plasticos Ltda. (1)
R James Clerk Maxwell 280-Techno Park, Campinas, Sao Paulo, 13069-380, Brazil
Tel.: (55) 1935184040
Plastic Processing Equipment Mfr
N.A.I.C.S.: 333248

Mold-Masters (Kunshan) Co. Ltd. (1)
Zhao Tian Rd, Lu Jia Town, Kunshan, Jiangsu, China
Tel.: (86) 51286162882
Plastic Processing Equipment Mfr
N.A.I.C.S.: 333248

Mold-Masters (U.K.) Ltd. (1)
Netherwood Road, Rotherwas Ind Est, Hereford, HR2 6JU, United Kingdom
Tel.: (44) 1432265768
Plastic Processing Equipment Mfr
N.A.I.C.S.: 333248

Mold-Masters Europa GmbH (1)

Neumattring 1, 76532, Baden-Baden, Germany
Tel.: (49) 722150990
Plastic Processing Equipment Mfr
N.A.I.C.S.: 333248

Subsidiary (Non-US):

Mold-Masters Kabushiki Kaisha (2)
1-4-17 Kurikidai, Asaoku, Kawasaki, 215-0032, Kanagawa, Japan
Tel.: (81) 449862101
Plastic Processing Equipment Mfr
N.A.I.C.S.: 333248

Mold-Masters Handelsgesellschaft m.b.h. (1)
Pyhrnstrasse 16, Schlierbach, 4553, Kirchdorf am Inn, Austria
Tel.: (43) 758251877
Plastic Processing Equipment Mfr
N.A.I.C.S.: 333248

Peerless Food Equipment LLC (1)
500 S Vandemark Rd, Sidney, OH 45365-0769
Tel.: (937) 492-4158
Web Site: https://peerlessfood.com
Food Equipment Mfr & Distr
N.A.I.C.S.: 333241

Rotex Global, LLC (1)
1230 Knowlton St, Cincinnati, OH 45223
Tel.: (513) 541-1236
Web Site: http://www.rotex.com
Emp.: 200
Screening Equipment Mfr
N.A.I.C.S.: 326199
Lawrence Rentz *(Pres)*
Dan Frye *(VP)*
Will Chaparro *(CFO)*

Schenck Process (Thailand) Ltd. (1)
888/1 Moo 20 Soi Boonmeesap Bangplee Tamru Road, Bangpleeyai Bangplee, Samut Prakan, 10540, Thailand
Tel.: (66) 23825100
Plastic Food Processing Equipment Mfr & Distr
N.A.I.C.S.: 333241

Schenck Process FCP Equipamentos Industrias Ltda. (1)
Av Werner Sonnenfeld 801 Complexo Industrial Cilo 12 Agua Quente, Tremembe, Sao Paulo, 12122-720, Brazil
Tel.: (55) 1230429926
Plastic Food Processing Equipment Mfr & Distr
N.A.I.C.S.: 333241

TerraSource Global CIS Limited Liability Company (1)
14 Serebryakova Proezd Building 15 Office 219, Moscow, 129343, Russia
Tel.: (7) 4956654898
Web Site: http://www.terrasource.com
Emp.: 6
Engineeering Services
N.A.I.C.S.: 541330

Tirad s.r.o. (1)
Sasovice 62, Zeletava, 675 26, Trebic, Czech Republic
Tel.: (420) 568409211
Web Site: http://www.tirad.cz
Plastic Injection Mold Mfr
N.A.I.C.S.: 333511

Unifiller Systems UK Ltd. (1)
Unit 6 Morris Close Park Farm, Wellingborough, NN8 6XF, United Kingdom
Tel.: (44) 1933676005
Pumping & Decorating Equipment Distr
N.A.I.C.S.: 423830

HILLEVAX, INC.
321 Harrison Ave 5th Fl, Boston, MA 02118
Tel.: (617) 213-5054   DE
Web Site: https://www.hillevax.com
Year Founded: 2020
HLVX—(NASDAQ)
Rev.: $3,875,000
Assets: $317,211,000
Liabilities: $49,982,000
Net Worth: $267,229,000
Earnings: ($159,809,000)

HilleVax, Inc.—(Continued)

Emp.: 62
Fiscal Year-end: 12/31/22
Biotechnology Research & Development Services
N.A.I.C.S.: 541714
Shane Maltbie (CFO)
Rob Hershberg (Co-Founder, Chm, Pres & CEO)
Aditya Kohli (Co-Founder & Chief Bus Officer)
Astrid Borkowski (Chief Medical Officer)
Anju Chatterji (CTO)
Ozzie Berger (Sr VP-Regulatory Affairs)
Sean McLoughlin (COO)
Paul Bavier (Chief Admin Officer, Gen Counsel & Sec)
Aditya Kohli (Co-Founder & Chief Bus Officer)
Robert M. Hershberg (Co-Founder, Chm, Pres & CEO)

HILLIARD CORPORATION
100 W 4th St, Elmira, NY 14901-2148
Tel.: (607) 733-7121   **NY**
Web Site:
    https://www.hilliardcorp.com
Year Founded: 1905
HLRD—(OTCEM)
Sales Range: $150-199.9 Million
Emp.: 500
Mfr of Clutches & Purification & Dust Collection Equipment
N.A.I.C.S.: 333998

HILLMAN SOLUTIONS CORP.
1280 Kemper Meadow Dr, Forest Park, OH 45240
Tel.: (513) 851-4900
Web Site:
    https://www.hillmangroup.com
HLMN—(NASDAQ)
Rev.: $1,476,477,000
Assets: $2,331,101,000
Liabilities: $1,176,572,000
Net Worth: $1,154,529,000
Earnings: ($9,589,000)
Emp.: 3,801
Fiscal Year-end: 12/30/23
Offices of Other Holding Companies
N.A.I.C.S.: 551112
Douglas J. Cahill (Chm)
Robert O. Kraft (CFO)
Jon Michael Adinolfi (Pres & CEO)

Subsidiaries:

Koch Industries, Inc.   (1)
151 Cheshire Ln N Ste 400, Minneapolis, MN 55441
Tel.: (763) 302-5400
Web Site: https://kochmm.com
Sales Range: $1-9.9 Million
Emp.: 30
Wire Ropes, Tools & Cutters & Hardware Products Whslr
N.A.I.C.S.: 314994
Keturah Austin (Mgr-Corp Comm)

The Hillman Companies, Inc.   (1)
10590 Hamilton Ave, Cincinnati, OH 45231
Tel.: (513) 851-4900
Web Site: http://www.hillmangroup.com
Rev.: $1,368,295,000
Assets: $2,468,618,000
Liabilities: $2,104,031,000
Net Worth: $364,587,000
Earnings: ($24,499,000)
Emp.: 3,780
Fiscal Year-end: 12/26/2020
Holding Company
N.A.I.C.S.: 551112
Douglas J. Cahill (Chm, Pres & CEO)
Robert O. Kraft (CFO & Treas)
Jarrod T. Streng (Pres-Personal Protective Solutions & Corp Mktg)
Randall J. Fagundo (Pres-Divisional-Robotics & Digital Solutions)
Scott Ride (Pres)

Subsidiary (Non-US):

H. Paulin & Co., Limited   (2)
900 Passmore Avenue, Toronto, M1X 0C6, ON, Canada
Tel.: (416) 694-3351
Web Site: https://www.hpaulin.com
Sales Range: $125-149.9 Million
Emp.: 700
Fasteners, Fluid System Products, Automotive Parts & Screw Machine Components Mfr
N.A.I.C.S.: 332722

Division (Domestic):

H. Paulin & Co., Ltd. - Capital Metal Industries   (3)
55 Milne Avenue, Toronto, M1L 4L3, ON, Canada
Tel.: (416) 694-3351
Web Site: http://www.hpaulin.com
Sales Range: $75-99.9 Million
Machine Tool & Metal Cutting Types Mfr
N.A.I.C.S.: 333517
Michael Falkenstein (Mng Dir)

H. Paulin & Co., Ltd. - Dominion Fittings   (3)
380 Ambassador Drive, Mississauga, L5T2J3, ON, Canada
Tel.: (905) 362-0509
Sales Range: $50-74.9 Million
Emp.: 30
Electron Tube Mfr
N.A.I.C.S.: 334419
Mike Carter (Gen Mgr)

H. Paulin & Co., Ltd. - Jeyco Machine Products   (3)
2420 Anson Drive, L5S1G2, Mississauga, ON, Canada
Tel.: (905) 677-4474
Web Site: http://www.hpaulin.com
Sales Range: $50-74.9 Million
Emp.: 25
General Purpose Machinery Mfr
N.A.I.C.S.: 333998

H. Paulin & Co., Ltd. - Long-Lok Canada   (3)
5 Crockford Blvd, Toronto, M1L 4J9, ON, Canada
Tel.: (416) 288-6855
Web Site: http://www.hpaulin.com
Sales Range: $50-74.9 Million
Emp.: 15
Machine Tool & Metal Cutting Types Mfr
N.A.I.C.S.: 333517
Rob Tracey (Plant Mgr)

H. Paulin & Co., Ltd. - Precision Fasteners   (3)
470 Harrop Dr, Milton, L9T 3H2, ON, Canada
Tel.: (905) 826-9270
Web Site: http://www.hpaulin.com
Sales Range: $50-74.9 Million
Emp.: 40
Machine Tool & Metal Cutting Types Mfr
N.A.I.C.S.: 333517

H. Paulin & Co., Ltd. - Pro-Tip   (3)
470 Harrop Dr, Milton, L9T3H2, ON, Canada
Tel.: (905) 878-1376
Web Site: http://www.hpaulin.com
Sales Range: $50-74.9 Million
Emp.: 6
Machine Tool & Metal Cutting Types Mfr
N.A.I.C.S.: 333517
Sue Arnold (Gen Mgr)

Subsidiary (US):

Paulin Industries Inc.   (3)
12400 Plz Dr Unit 1, Cleveland, OH 44130-1057
Tel.: (216) 433-7633
Web Site: http://www.hpaulin.com
Sales Range: $125-149.9 Million
Emp.: 20
Fasteners, Fluid System Products, Automotive Parts & Screw Machine Components Mfr & Distr
N.A.I.C.S.: 339993

Subsidiary (Domestic):

The Hillman Group, Inc.   (2)

10590 Hamilton Ave, Cincinnati, OH 45231
Tel.: (513) 851-4900
Web Site: https://www.hillmangroup.com
Metal Inscription Machinery, Fastener, Tag & Key Mfr
N.A.I.C.S.: 339993
Robert O. Kraft (CFO & Treas)

Subsidiary (Domestic):

Big Time Products, LLC   (3)
2 Wilbanks Rd SE, Rome, GA 30161
Tel.: (706) 295-3770
Web Site: http://www.bigtimeproducts.net
Hand Protection Product Mfr & Distr
N.A.I.C.S.: 316110
Harry S. Pierce (Co-Founder & CEO)
Rick Chambers (Co-Founder & Pres)
Greg Benner (VP-Product Devt)

Hargis Industries Inc.   (3)
6357 Reynolds Rd, Tyler, TX 75708
Tel.: (903) 592-2826
Web Site:
    http://www.stfasteningsystems.com
Fasteners, Industrial Nuts, Bolts & Screws Mfr
N.A.I.C.S.: 423840

Branch (Domestic):

The Hillman Group - Tempe   (3)
8990 S Kyrene Rd, Tempe, AZ 85284
Tel.: (480) 731-6699
Web Site: http://www.hillmangroup.com
Sales Range: $75-99.9 Million
Emp.: 250
Supplier of Keys & Key Machines to Retailers; Manufacturer of Letters, Numbers, Signs & Markers
N.A.I.C.S.: 332510
Todd Spangler (Gen Mgr)

HILLS BANCORPORATION
131 E Main St, Hills, IA 52235
Tel.: (319) 679-2291   **IA**
Web Site: https://www.hillsbank.com
Year Founded: 1982
HBIA—(OTCIQ)
Rev.: $158,867,000
Assets: $3,980,481,000
Liabilities: $3,552,221,000
Net Worth: $428,260,000
Earnings: $47,753,000
Emp.: 477
Fiscal Year-end: 12/31/22
Bank Holding Company
N.A.I.C.S.: 551111
Dwight O. Seegmiller (Pres & CEO)
Ann Marie Rhodes (VP)
Tony Roetlin (CFO, Chief Acctg Officer, Treas & Sr VP)

Subsidiaries:

Hills Bank & Trust Company   (1)
131 E Main St, Hills, IA 52235
Tel.: (319) 679-2291
Web Site: http://www.hillsbank.com
Retail & Commercial Banking Services
N.A.I.C.S.: 522110
Dwight O. Seegmiller (CEO)
Lisa A. Shileny (Pres & COO)
Dave Hochstetler (Sr VP-Comml Banking-Kalona)
Matt Olson (Sr VP-Mortgage Lending)

HILLTOP HOLDINGS INC.
6565 Hillcrest Ave, Dallas, TX 75205
Tel.: (214) 855-2177   **MD**
Web Site: https://www.hilltop.com
HTH—(NYSE)
Rev.: $1,567,348,000
Assets: $16,466,996,000
Liabilities: $14,316,667,000
Net Worth: $2,150,329,000
Earnings: $109,646,000
Emp.: 3,800
Fiscal Year-end: 12/31/23
Financial Holding Company; Banking & Insurance Products & Services
N.A.I.C.S.: 551111
Gerald J. Ford (Chm)
Jeremy B. Ford (Pres & CEO)

Corey Prestidge (Gen Counsel & Sec)
William B. Furr (CFO)
Darren E. Parmenter (Chief Admin Officer)
Wayne Becker (Chief Investment Officer & Treas)
Keith E. Bornemann (Chief Acctg Officer, Principal Acctg Officer, Exec VP & Controller)
Dudley Strawn (Chief HR Officer)
Jim Fields (Chief Enterprise Risk Officer)
Don Foley (Chief Operational Risk & Compliance Officer)
Jennifer Sterns (Dir-Mktg & Comm)
Bill Lines (Chief Information Security Officer)

Subsidiaries:

Ariva Mortgage Services, LLC   (1)
401 E Hillside Rd Ste 101, Laredo, TX 78041
Tel.: (956) 531-6503
Web Site: https://lo.arivamortgage.com
Mortgage Services
N.A.I.C.S.: 522310
Alex Bernal (Mng Dir)

First Southwest Leasing Company   (1)
325 N Saint Paul St Ste 800, Dallas, TX 75201
Tel.: (214) 953-4000
Emp.: 10
Machinery Equipment Finance Leasing Services
N.A.I.C.S.: 522220

Grand Home Loans, LLC   (1)
5150 Keller Springs Rd Ste 200A, Dallas, TX 75248
Web Site: https://lo.grandhomeloans.com
Home Loan Services
N.A.I.C.S.: 522310

Green Brick Mortgage, LLC   (1)
18111 Preston Rd Ste 850, Dallas, TX 75252
Web Site: http://lo.greenbrickmortgage.com
Mortgage Loan Services
N.A.I.C.S.: 522310
Todd Frank (Production Mgr)

Highland HomeLoans, LLC   (1)
5700 Granite Pkwy Ste 100, Plano, TX 75024
Tel.: (214) 373-7400
Web Site: https://lo.highlandhomeloans.com
Home Loan Services
N.A.I.C.S.: 522299

Hilltop Securities Holdings LLC   (1)
717 N Harwood St Ste 3400, Dallas, TX 75201
Tel.: (214) 953-4000
Web Site: https://www.hilltopsecurities.com
Sales Range: $300-349.9 Million
Financial Holding Company; Securities Transaction Processing, Investment Banking & Asset Management Services
N.A.I.C.S.: 551111

Subsidiary (Domestic):

Hilltop Securities Inc.   (2)
717 N Harwood St Ste 3400, Dallas, TX 75201
Tel.: (214) 953-4000
Web Site: https://www.hilltopsecurities.com
Emp.: 1,225
Securities Brokerage & Investment Services
N.A.I.C.S.: 523150
Lana Calton (Sr Mng Dir & Head-Clearing)
Bradley Winges (Pres & CEO)
John R. Muschalek (Head-)
Mike Edge (CFO)
Brian Wittneben (Gen Counsel)
Reno Jones (Sr VP)
Eric Kloppers (VP)
Clare Graca (Chief Admin Officer)
David Holleran (COO)
Melinda Fleming (Dir-Human Resources)

Hilltop Securities Independent Network Inc. (2)
1201 Elm St Ste 3500, Dallas, TX 75270
Tel.: (214) 859-1800
Web Site: http://www.hilltopsecurities.com
Securities Brokerage & Investment Services
N.A.I.C.S.: 523150

Jet Homeloans, LLC (1)
95507 Orchid Blossom Trail, Fernandina Beach, FL 32034
Tel.: (904) 530-7213
Web Site: https://jethl.com
Housing Loan Providing Services
N.A.I.C.S.: 522299
Joseph Clouston (Production Mgr)
Dan Herbon (CIO & Chief Information Security Officer)
Dyron Watford (CFO)
Irene Gonzalez (VP-Human Resources)
Jim Girard (Officer & Sr VP)
Michael Dunn (Gen Counsel)
Sal Nunziata (Vice Chm)
Stephanie Simmons (Dir-Marketing)
Todd Boss (Exec VP)
Travis Rulle (COO)
Vinay Miglani (Sr VP)
Dan Herbon (CIO & Chief Information Security Officer)
Dyron Watford (CFO)
Irene Gonzalez (VP-Human Resources)
Jim Girard (Officer & Sr VP)
Michael Dunn (Gen Counsel)
Sal Nunziata (Vice Chm)
Stephanie Simmons (Dir-Marketing)
Todd Boss (Exec VP)
Travis Rulle (COO)
Vinay Miglani (Sr VP)

PlainsCapital Corporation (1)
6565 Hillcrest Ave Ste 100, Dallas, TX 75205
Tel.: (214) 525-9000
Web Site: http://www.plainscapital.com
Bank Holding Company
N.A.I.C.S.: 551111
Jeremy B. Ford (Pres & CEO)

Subsidiary (Domestic):

PlainsCapital Bank (2)
6565 Hillcrest Ave Ste 100, Dallas, TX 75205
Tel.: (214) 525-9000
Web Site: https://www.plainscapital.com
Emp.: 60
Retail, Commercial & Investment Banking, Mortgage Lending, Investment Advisory & Wealth Management Services
N.A.I.C.S.: 522110
Jeremy B. Ford (Chm)
Jerry L. Schaffner (Pres & CEO)
Jeremy B. Ford (CEO)
Brian Heflin (COO)
Pete Villarreal (Chief Admin Officer)
Steve Hambrick (Chm)
Paul Holubec (Chm-Austin Reg)
John C. Owens (Chm)
Robert C. Norman (Chm-Rio Grande Valley Reg)
Allie Bueno Abraham (Co-CFO)
Brent Raindl (Chm)
Linda Irby (Chief HR Officer)
Thomas M. Neville (Exec VP & Head-Private Banking & Wealth Mgmt)
Darrell G. Adams (Chief Credit Officer & Chief Credit Officer)
Scott Luedke (Sec, Exec VP & Gen Counsel)
Tye Barton (Exec VP & Dir-Treasury Svcs)
Will Furr (Co-CFO)
Andy Lane (Chm)
Michael Molak (Chm-San Antonio)
Frank Hastings (Chm-Coastal Bend Reg)
Mark Warren (Chm)
Derrich Rodriguez (Sr VP-Lending Grp-San Antonio)
Jamie Gutierrez (VP-San Antonio)
Danny Schroder (Chm-Houston)
Kristi Conway (Exec VP-Lending Grp-Houston)
Richard Wyatt (Chief Investment Officer & Exec VP)
Steve Thompson (Dir)
Marcus Q. Poole (Sr VP-Comml Lending)

Subsidiary (Domestic):

PrimeLending, a PlainsCapital Company (3)

18111 Preston Rd Ste 900, Dallas, TX 75252
Tel.: (469) 737-5714
Web Site: https://www.primelending.com
Sales Range: $500-549.9 Million
Emp.: 1,500
Mortgages
N.A.I.C.S.: 522310
Todd Salmans (Chm)
Eric Pretzlaff (CFO & Exec VP)
Tim Elkins (Chief Production Officer)
Steve Thompson (Pres & CEO)
Al Velasco (Exec VP & Mgr-West Div)
Chris Cordry (Exec VP & Sr Dir-Capital Markets)
Nisa Reyes Howard (Dir-Compliance & Exec VP)
Karen Blakeslee (Exec VP & Mgr-PrimeLending-Eastern)
Kristi Harris (Exec VP)
Cindy Buhr (Exec VP & Gen Counsel)
Susie Garza (Dir & Exec VP)
Gene Lugat (Exec VP)
Michael Heeb (Area Mgr-Pacific Northwest)
Kim Dybvad (VP & Area Mgr-Loan Origination Production-Mid-America)
Kelly McGuinness (Sr VP-Northeast & Reg Mgr-Northeast)

PrimeLending Ventures, LLC (1)
18111 Preston Rd Ste 900-A, Dallas, TX 75252
Tel.: (972) 713-3271
Insurance Services
N.A.I.C.S.: 524210

HILTON GRAND VACATIONS INC.

6355 MetroWest Blvd Ste 180, Orlando, FL 32835
Tel.: (407) 613-3100   DE
Web Site:
https://www.hiltongrandvacations.com
Year Founded: 2016
HGV—(NYSE)
Rev.: $3,835,000,000
Assets: $8,004,000,000
Liabilities: $5,853,000,000
Net Worth: $2,151,000,000
Earnings: $352,000,000
Emp.: 14,500
Fiscal Year-end: 12/31/22
Holding Company; Vacation Time-Share Rentals, Resort Management & Vacation Club Services
N.A.I.C.S.: 551112
Daniel J. Mathewes (Pres & CFO)
Mark D. Wang (CEO)
Charles R. Corbin Jr. (Chief Legal Officer, Gen Counsel & Exec VP)
Dusty Tonkin (CMO, Chief Sls Officer & Exec VP)
Carlos Hernandez (Chief Acctg Officer & Sr VP)
Valerie Spangler (Chief Comml Officer & Sr VP)
Kelly Olinger (Sr VP-Development)
Caterina Rovati (Sr VP-Strategy & Innovation)
Onkar Birk (CTO & Exec VP)
Derek De Salvia (Chief Customer Officer & Exec VP)
Jeff Bernier (Sr VP & Mng Dir-APAC & Hawaii)
Erin Day (Exec VP-Finance & Sr VP)
Leonard A. Potter (Chm)
Gordon Gurnik (COO & Sr Exec VP)

Subsidiaries:

Bluegreen Vacations Holding Corporation (1)
4960 Conference Way N Ste 100, Boca Raton, FL 33431
Tel.: (561) 912-8000
Web Site: https://www.bvhcorp.com
Rev.: $919,429,000
Assets: $1,398,385,000
Liabilities: $1,154,392,000
Net Worth: $243,993,000
Earnings: $64,385,000

Emp.: 5,924
Fiscal Year-end: 12/31/2022
Diversified Investment Holding Company
N.A.I.C.S.: 551112
Daniel J. Mathewes (Sr Exec VP)
Mark D. Wang (Pres)
Charles R. Corbin Jr. (Sec & Exec VP)
Gordon S. Gurnik (Sr Exec VP)
Daniel J. Mathewes (Sr Exec VP)
Carlos Hernandez (Sr VP)
Jorge de la Osa (Chief Legal Officer)
Chanse W. Rivera (CIO)
Kathy Foster (Sr VP)
Ada Grzywna (Sr VP)
Angela Blevins (Sr VP)

Subsidiary (Domestic):

BBX Capital Asset Management, LLC (2)
401 E Las Olas Blvd, Fort Lauderdale, FL 33301   (100%)
Tel.: (954) 940-5300
Web Site: http://www.bbxcapital.com
Real Estate Asset Management Services
N.A.I.C.S.: 531390

Subsidiary (Domestic):

Professional Valuation Services, LLC (3)
2812 SE 6th St, Blue Springs, MO 64014
Tel.: (816) 694-0708
Web Site: http://www.pvsappraisals.com
Real Estate Appraisal Services
N.A.I.C.S.: 531320

Subsidiary (Domestic):

BBX Sweet Holdings, LLC (2)
401 E Las Olas Blvd Ste 800, Fort Lauderdale, FL 33301
Tel.: (954) 940-4000
Holding Company
N.A.I.C.S.: 551112

Subsidiary (Domestic):

Anastasia Confections, Inc. (3)
1815 Cypress Lake Dr, Orlando, FL 32837
Tel.: (407) 816-9944
Web Site:
https://www.anastasiaconfections.com
Chocolate & Confectionery Mfr
N.A.I.C.S.: 311352

Chocolate Acquisition Sub, LLC (3)
5300 Wisconsin Ave NW, Washington, DC 20015
Tel.: (202) 966-4946
Web Site: https://www.krondc.com
Chocolate & Confectionery Mfr & Distr
N.A.I.C.S.: 311352

Droga Chocolates, LLC (3)
401 E Las Olas Blvd Ste 800, Fort Lauderdale, FL 33301
Web Site: http://www.drogachocolates.com
Chocolate Mfr
N.A.I.C.S.: 311351
Michelle Crochet (Founder)

Good Fortunes East, LLC (3)
5190 Lake Worth Rd, Greenacres City, FL 33463
Tel.: (561) 439-8813
Web Site: http://www.goodfortunes.com
Cookie Mfr & Distr
N.A.I.C.S.: 311821

Hoffmans Chocolate, LLC (3)
5190 Lake Worth Rd, Greenacres City, FL 33463
Tel.: (561) 967-2213
Web Site: https://www.hoffmans.com
Chocolate & Confectionery Mfr
N.A.I.C.S.: 311352

It'sugar LLC. (3)
3155 SW 10th St Ste A, Deerfield Beach, FL 33442   (93%)
Tel.: (561) 962-3508
Web Site: https://www.itsugar.com
Candy & Gift Item Store
N.A.I.C.S.: 445292
Jeffrey Rubin (Founder & CEO)

Sweet Acquisitions CA3, LLC (3)
2734 Loker Ave W Ste L, Carlsbad, CA 92010
Tel.: (760) 504-6904

Web Site: http://www.thetoffeebox.com
Toffee Mfr
N.A.I.C.S.: 311340

Sweet Acquisitons UT1 (3)
708 South Utah Valley Dr, American Fork, UT 84003
Tel.: (801) 756-6916
Web Site: http://www.kencraftcandy.com
Candy Mfr & Distr
N.A.I.C.S.: 311352

Subsidiary (Domestic):

Bluegreen Vacations Corporation (2)
4960 Conference Way N Ste 100, Boca Raton, FL 33431   (100%)
Tel.: (561) 912-8000
Web Site:
http://www.bluegreenvacations.com
Rev.: $521,112,000
Assets: $1,222,370,000
Liabilities: $853,658,000
Net Worth: $368,712,000
Earnings: $8,225,000
Fiscal Year-end: 12/31/2020
Residential Land & Timeshare Properties Acquisition, Development & Sales
N.A.I.C.S.: 237210
Alan B. Levan (Pres & CEO)
Raymond S. Lopez (CFO, COO, Treas & Exec VP)
John E. Abdo (Vice Chm)
Adrienne Kelley (Chief Acctg Officer & Sr VP)
Jorge de la Osa (Chief Legal & Compliance Officer)
Ada Grzywna (Sr VP-Resorts Mgmt)

Subsidiary (Domestic):

BBCV Receivables-Q 2010 LLC (3)
4950 Communication Ave Ste 900, Boca Raton, FL 33431
Tel.: (561) 912-8210
Vacation Resort Operator
N.A.I.C.S.: 721120

Bluegreen Communities, LLC (3)
100 Lake Ridge Pkwy, Cedar Hill, TX 75104-8202
Tel.: (972) 299-5253
Sales Range: $10-24.9 Million
Emp.: 50
Vacation Resort Operator
N.A.I.C.S.: 721120

Bluegreen Vacations Unlimited, Inc. (3)
4960 Conference Way N Ste 100, Boca Raton, FL 33431
Tel.: (561) 912-8000
Web Site:
https://www.bluegreenvacations.com
Sales Range: $150-199.9 Million
Vacation Resort Operator
N.A.I.C.S.: 721110
Ahmad M. Wardak (CMO & Exec VP)
Peter Menges (Sr VP-Customer Acquisition & Alliances)
Chanse W. Rivera (CIO & Exec VP)
Dusty Tonkin (Chief Sls Officer & Exec VP)
Jorge de la Osa (Chief Compliance Officer, Chief Legal Officer & Exec VP)
Justin Taylor (Chief HR Officer & Exec VP)
Kathy Foster (Sr VP-Bus Dev & Innovation)
Ada Grzywna (Sr VP-Resorts Mgmt)

Bluegreen/Big Cedar Vacations, LLC (3)
1285 Estate Dr, Ridgedale, MO 65739
Tel.: (417) 348-4085
Web Site: http://www.bluegreenonline.com
Vacation Resort Operator
N.A.I.C.S.: 721120

Jordan Lake Preserve Corporation (3)
840 The Preserve Trl, Chapel Hill, NC 27517-7600
Tel.: (919) 542-5501
Web Site:
http://www.thepreservegolfclub.com
Land Preservation Services
N.A.I.C.S.: 813312
Gene Fones (Gen Mgr)
Brian Peters (Superintendent-Golf Course-Reg)
Daniel Swomley (Dir-Golf)
Geoff Stevens (Mgr-Food & Beverage)

Hilton Grand Vacations Inc.—(Continued)

Leisure Capital Corporation (3)
650 Town Ctr Dr Ste 670, Costa Mesa, CA 92626
Tel.: (714) 384-4050
Emp.: 7
Investment Management Service
N.A.I.C.S.: 523940
Ray Robinson (Gen Mgr)

Managed Assets Corporation (3)
5001 Spring Valley Rd, Dallas, TX 75244
Tel.: (972) 702-0010
Sales Range: $25-49.9 Million
Emp.: 10
Asset Management Services
N.A.I.C.S.: 531390
Kim Holland (Gen Mgr)

New England Advertising Corporation (3)
4960 Conference Way N, Boca Raton, FL 33431-3313
Tel.: (561) 912-7987
Advertising Agency Services
N.A.I.C.S.: 541810

Outdoor Traveler Destinations, LLC (3)
4960 Conference Way N Ste 100, Boca Raton, FL 33480
Tel.: (888) 760-8188
Web Site: http://www.otdestinations.com
Travel Agencies
N.A.I.C.S.: 561510

Pinnacle Vacations, Inc. (3)
4600 Summerlin Rd Ste C-2, Fort Myers, FL 33919
Tel.: (239) 489-1995
Web Site:
　https://www.pinnaclevacations.com
Sales Range: $25-49.9 Million
Emp.: 4
Resort Resale Services
N.A.I.C.S.: 531210

Subsidiary (Domestic):

Core Commercial Group, LLC (2)
10161 Park Run Dr Ste 150, Las Vegas, NV 89145
Tel.: (702) 332-8046
Web Site:
　https://www.corecommercialgroup.com
Real Estate Services
N.A.I.C.S.: 531210
Chris Meranto (Pres & CEO)
Alfred Wendler (Partner & VP)
Daniel Malak (VP-Investment Svcs)
Peter Wellman (VP-Comml Agent)

Eden Services, Inc. (2)
Urb Eucaliptos 16021 Palm, Canovanas, PR 00729-4516
Tel.: (787) 503-3347
Website Design Services
N.A.I.C.S.: 541511
Jorge Iglesias (VP)

Holding (Domestic):

Helen Grace Chocolates, Inc. (2)
2369 E Pacifica Pl, Compton, CA 90220
Tel.: (310) 638-8400
Web Site: http://www.helengrace.com
Sales Range: $1-9.9 Million
Emp.: 120
Chocolate Mfr
N.A.I.C.S.: 311352

Subsidiary (Non-US):

Renin Canada Corporation (2)
110 Walker Dr, Brampton, L6T 4H6, ON, Canada
Tel.: (905) 791-7930
Web Site: http://www.renin.com
Door Hardware System Mfr & Distr
N.A.I.C.S.: 332510

Subsidiary (Non-US):

Renin UK Corporation (3)
Unit 45 Woolmer Way, Bordon, GU35 9QE, Hampshire, United Kingdom
Tel.: (44) 1420488022
Real Estate Management Services
N.A.I.C.S.: 531210

Subsidiary (Domestic):

Risk Management Services, LLC (2)
11404 Lk Sherwood Ave N, Baton Rouge, LA 70835-0647
Tel.: (225) 389-9944
Web Site: https://www.rmsla.com
Portfolio Management Services
N.A.I.C.S.: 523940
Jean L. Robert (Founder & Owner)
Christopher B. Kennedy (VP-Claims)
Randy P. Hava (VP-Loss Prevention)
Deidre Wilson-Creel (VP-Policy Svcs & Underwriting)
Albert E. Roevens Jr. (CFO)

The Altman Companies, Inc. (2)
201 E Las Olas Blvd Ste 1900, Fort Lauderdale, FL 33301
Tel.: (954) 890-2600
Web Site: https://www.altmancos.com
Sales Range: $150-199.9 Million
Emp.: 310
Land Subdivision, Multifamily Housing Construction & Property Management
N.A.I.C.S.: 237210
Seth M. Wise (Co-CEO)
Timothy Alan Peterson (CFO)
Joel L. Altman (Chm & Co-CEO)
T. Nat Barganier (VP-Dev)
Christina Webb (VP-Dev)
Robbie Thapa (Dir-Mktg)
Rob Gillette (Co-COO & Sr VP-Construction)
Chris Tanis (Controller)
Susan Fry (Controller)
Michael Mosher (Mgr-Dev)
Jeffery Roberts (Pres & Co-COO)
Carol Loveless (Sr VP-Midwest Div)
Derek Lubsen (VP-Asset Mgmt)
Seth Wise (Co-CEO)

Subsidiary (Domestic):

Altman Contractors, Inc. (3)
1515 S Federal Hwy Ste 300, Boca Raton, FL 33432
Tel.: (561) 997-8661
Multifamily Housing Construction
N.A.I.C.S.: 236116

Altman Development Corporation (3)
1515 S Federal Hwy Ste 300, Boca Raton, FL 33432
Tel.: (561) 997-8661
Web Site: http://www.altmancos.com
Multifamily Communities Developer
N.A.I.C.S.: 236116
Joel L. Altman (Chm)

Subsidiary (Domestic):

Tradition Hilton Head, LLC (2)
31A Mathews Dr, Hilton Head Island, SC 29926
Tel.: (843) 681-6211
Web Site: https://www.traditionshh.com
Furniture Mfr & Distr
N.A.I.C.S.: 337121

Tradition Realty, LLC (2)
1046 Riverside Ave, Jacksonville, FL 32204
Tel.: (904) 683-5230
Web Site: https://www.traditionsjax.com
Real Estate Agency Services
N.A.I.C.S.: 531210

Tradition Title Company, LLC (2)
12428 Memorial Dr, Houston, TX 77024
Tel.: (713) 973-9700
Web Site:
　https://www.traditiontitlecompany.com
Residential & Commercial Title Services
N.A.I.C.S.: 541191
Maria Meyer Oakum (Officer-Escrow-Washington Avenue)
Valerie Holladay (Officer-Escrow-Memorial Office)
Barbara Simmang (Officer-Escrow-Memorial Office)
Kathy James (Officer-Escrow & Branch Mgr)

Grand Vacations Services LLC (1)
6355 Metrowest Blvd Ste 180, Orlando, FL 32835
Tel.: (407) 722-3100
Vacation & Resort Operator
N.A.I.C.S.: 721214

Hilton Grand Vacations Company, LLC (1)
5323 Millenia Lakes Blvd Ste 400, Orlando, FL 32839
Tel.: (703) 722-3100
Web Site:
　http://www.hiltongrandvacations.com
Vacation Time-Share Rentals, Resort Management & Vacation Club Services
N.A.I.C.S.: 561599

HILTON WORLDWIDE HOLDINGS INC.

7930 Jones Branch Dr, McLean, VA 22102
Tel.: (703) 883-1000　　　　　　**TX**
Web Site: https://ir.hilton.com
Year Founded: 1925
HLT—(NYSE)
Rev.: $10,235,000,000
Assets: $15,401,000,000
Liabilities: $17,748,000,000
Net Worth: ($2,347,000,000)
Earnings: $1,141,000,000
Emp.: 178,000
Fiscal Year-end: 12/31/23
Holding Company; Hotels & Resorts Operator
N.A.I.C.S.: 551112
Simon Vincent (Pres-Europe, Middle East & Africa & Exec VP)
Christopher W. Silcock (Chief Comml Officer & Exec VP)
Danny Hughes (Pres-Americas & Exec VP)
Laura Fuentes (Chief HR Officer & Exec VP)
Kevin J. Jacobs (CFO & Pres-Global Dev)
Christopher J. Nassetta (Pres & CEO)
Jonathan D. Gray (Chm)
Katherine Lugar (Exec VP-Corp Affairs)

Subsidiaries:

Conrad International Hotels (HK) Limited (1)
Pacific Place 88 Queensway, Hong Kong, 518000, China (Hong Kong)
Tel.: (852) 2 521 3838
Web Site: https://conraddining.com
Hotel Operator
N.A.I.C.S.: 721110

DT Real Estate, LLC (1)
2824 Prince St, Conway, AR 72034
Tel.: (501) 499-6707
Web Site:
　http://www.dtrealestate.propertyware.com
Real Estate Development Services
N.A.I.C.S.: 531311

Doubletree LLC (1)
7930 Jones Branch Dr, McLean, VA 22102
Tel.: (703) 883-1000
Web Site: http://www.doubletree3.hilton.com
Hotel Developer, Franchisor & Management Services
N.A.I.C.S.: 561110

Unit (Domestic):

Doubletree Hotel Denver/Boulder (2)
8773 Yates Dr, Westminster, CO 80031-3680
Tel.: (303) 427-4000
Web Site: http://doubletree3.hilton.com
Sales Range: $1-9.9 Million
Emp.: 130
Hotel
N.A.I.C.S.: 721110

Doubletree Hotel Wilmington (2)
4727 Concord Pike, Wilmington, DE 19803
Tel.: (302) 478-6000
Web Site: http://www.doubletree3.hilton.com
Rev.: $12,000,000
Emp.: 150
Hotel
N.A.I.C.S.: 721110

Embassy Suites Management LLC (1)

755 Crossover Ln, Memphis, TN 38117
Tel.: (901) 374-5000
Web Site: http://embassysuites3.hilton.com
Home Management Services
N.A.I.C.S.: 561110
James E. Holthouser (Sr VP-Brand Mgmt)

Unit (Domestic):

Embassy Suites Casino San Juan (2)
8000 Tartak St, Carolina, PR 00979
Tel.: (787) 791-0505
Web Site: http://embassysuites3.hilton.com
Sales Range: $50-74.9 Million
Emp.: 350
Hotel
N.A.I.C.S.: 721110

GW Hotel Inc. (1)
60 S Main St, Washington, PA 15301
Tel.: (724) 225-3200
Web Site:
　https://www.thegeorgewashington.com
Hotel Operator
N.A.I.C.S.: 721110
Kyrk Pyros (Owner & Pres)
Kim Rowan (Mgr)
William Hutchinson (VP)
Robert Plutto (Gen Mgr)
Erica Isaac (Dir)
William Hutchinson (VP)
Robert Plutto (Gen Mgr)
Erica Isaac (Dir)

Hampton Inns LLC (1)
755 Crossover Ln, Memphis, TN 38117
Tel.: (901) 374-5000
Web Site:
　http://www.hamptoninn1.hilton.com
Hotel Developer, Franchisor & Management Services
N.A.I.C.S.: 561110
Phil Cordell (Sr VP)

Hilton Canada Inc. (1)
145 Richmond Street West, Toronto, M5H 2L2, ON, Canada
Tel.: (416) 869-3456
Web Site: http://www.hilton.com
Hotel
N.A.I.C.S.: 721110

Hilton Garden Inns Management LLC (1)
755 Crossover Ln, Memphis, TN 38117
Tel.: (901) 374-5000
Web Site: http://hiltongardeninn3.hilton.com
Home Management Services
N.A.I.C.S.: 561110

Hilton Honors Worldwide LLC (1)
7930 Jones Br Dr Ste 1100, McLean, VA 22102
Tel.: (703) 883-1000
Web Site: http://hiltonhonors3.hilton.com
Member Rewards Program Operator
N.A.I.C.S.: 522390

Hilton Hotels of Australia (Melbourne) Pty. Ltd. (1)
270 Flinders Street, Melbourne, 3000, VIC, Australia
Tel.: (61) 396546888
Hotel Operator
N.A.I.C.S.: 721110

Hilton Hotels of Australia Pty. Ltd. (1)
488 George Street, Sydney, 2000, NSW, Australia
Tel.: (61) 292662000
Web Site: http://www.hiltonsydney.com.au
Hotel Operations
N.A.I.C.S.: 721110

Hilton International Hotels (UK) Limited (1)
Maple Court Reeds Crescent, Watford, WD24 4QQ, Hertfordshire, United Kingdom
Tel.: (44) 2078568137
Web Site: http://www.hiltonworldwide.com
Hotel Management
N.A.I.C.S.: 721110

Subsidiary (Domestic):

Conrad Hotels & Resorts (2)
Maple Court Reeds Crescent, Watford, WD24 4QQ, Hertfordshire, United Kingdom

Tel.: (44) 2078568137
Web Site:
http://www.conradhotels3.hilton.com
Sales Range: $125-149.9 Million
Hotels & Resorts
N.A.I.C.S.: 721110

Subsidiary (Non-US):

Hilton International (Switzerland) GmbH (2)
Hohenbuehlstrasse 10, 8152, Opfikon, Switzerland
Tel.: (41) 44 828 5050
Web Site: http://www.hilton.com
Sales Range: $10-24.9 Million
Emp.: 50
Hotel Operator
N.A.I.C.S.: 721110
Heinz Buchel (CEO)

Hilton International Wien GmbH (1)
Am Stadtpark 1, Vienna, Austria
Tel.: (43) 171700
Hotel Operator
N.A.I.C.S.: 721110
Astrid Kogler (Mgr-Cluster HR)

Hilton Malta Limited (1)
Portomaso, Saint Julian's, Malta
Tel.: (356) 21383383
Hotel Operator
N.A.I.C.S.: 721110
Melanie Faure (Mgr-Mktg)

Hilton Management LLC (1)
7930 Jones Br Dr Ste 1100, McLean, VA 22102
Tel.: (703) 883-1000
Web Site: http://www.hilton.com
Home Management Services
N.A.I.C.S.: 561110
Steve Dollenbach (Pres)

Unit (Domestic):

Hilton El Conquistador Golf & Tennis Resort (2)
10000 N Oracle Rd, Tucson, AZ 85704
Tel.: (520) 544-5000
Web Site:
http://www.hiltonelconquistador.com
Rev.: $21,900,000
Emp.: 400
Resort Hotel
N.A.I.C.S.: 721110

Hilton Hawaiian Village (2)
2005 Kalia Rd, Honolulu, HI 96815
Tel.: (808) 949-4321
Web Site: http://www.hilton.com
Sales Range: $150-199.9 Million
Emp.: 1,500
Resort Hotel
N.A.I.C.S.: 721110

Hilton McLean Tysons Corner (2)
7920 Jones Branch Dr, McLean, VA 22102
Tel.: (703) 847-5000
Web Site: http://www.hiltonworldwide.com
Rev.: $10,100,000
Emp.: 250
Hotel
N.A.I.C.S.: 721110

Hilton New York (2)
1335 Avenue of the Americas, New York, NY 10019
Tel.: (212) 586-7000
Web Site:
http://www.newyorktowers.hilton.com
Sales Range: $125-149.9 Million
Emp.: 1,300
Hotel
N.A.I.C.S.: 721110

Hilton Palm Springs Hotel & Resort (2)
400 E Tahquitz Canyon Way, Palm Springs, CA 92262-6605
Tel.: (760) 320-6868
Web Site: http://www3.hilton.com
Sales Range: $10-24.9 Million
Emp.: 200
Luxury Hotel & Resort Operator
N.A.I.C.S.: 721110

Hilton Singer Island Oceanfront/Palm Beaches Resort (2)
3700 N Ocean Dr, Riviera Beach, FL 33404
Tel.: (561) 848-3888

Web Site: http://www3.hilton.com
Hotel Operator
N.A.I.C.S.: 721110

Lynnwood Inns, Inc. (2)
19324 Alderwood Mall Pkwy, Lynnwood, WA 98036
Tel.: (425) 771-1888
Web Site: http://www.hilton.com
Hotels (except Casino Hotels) & Motels
N.A.I.C.S.: 721110

Pointe Hilton Tapatio Cliffs Resort (2)
11111 N 7th St, Phoenix, AZ 85020
Tel.: (602) 866-7500
Web Site: http://www.tapatiocliffshilton.com
Sales Range: $25-49.9 Million
Emp.: 600
Resort Hotel
N.A.I.C.S.: 721110

Hilton Munich Airport Hotel Manage GmbH (1)
Terminalstrasse Mitte 20, 85356, Munich, Germany
Tel.: (49) 8997820
Hotel Operator
N.A.I.C.S.: 721110

Hilton Nairobi Limited (1)
Mama Ngina St, Nairobi, 00100, Kenya
Tel.: (254) 202288000
Hotel Operator
N.A.I.C.S.: 721110

Hilton Reservations Worldwide LLC (1)
2050 Chenault Dr, Carrollton, TX 75006
Tel.: (972) 770-6100
Web Site: http://www.hilton.com
Sales Range: $500-549.9 Million
Emp.: 300
Hotel & Motel Reservation Service
N.A.I.C.S.: 561599

Subsidiary (Domestic):

Hilton Reservations & Customer Care (2)
2050 Chenault Dr, Carrollton, TX 75006
Tel.: (972) 770-6100
Web Site: http://www.hiltonworldwide.com
Sales Range: $75-99.9 Million
Hotel Reservations
N.A.I.C.S.: 561599

Hilton San Diego LLC (1)
1 Park Blvd, San Diego, CA 92101
Tel.: (619) 564-3333
Hotel Operator
N.A.I.C.S.: 721110

Hilton Supply Management LLC (1)
7930 Jones Branch Dr, McLean, VA 22102
Web Site:
https://www.mysupplymanagement.com
Hospitality Product Distr
N.A.I.C.S.: 423850
David Depkon (VP)

Hilton Vienna Danube (1)
Handelskai 269, 1020, Vienna, Austria
Tel.: (43) 172777
Web Site: http://www3.hilton.com
Hotel
N.A.I.C.S.: 721110

Hilton Worldwide - Memphis Operations Center (1)
755 Crossover Ln, Memphis, TN 38117
Tel.: (901) 374-5000
Web Site: http://www.hiltonworldwide.com
Sales Range: $100-124.9 Million
Emp.: 1,200
Regional Managing Office; Hotel Operator
N.A.I.C.S.: 551114
Christopher J. Nassetta (Pres & CEO)

Hilton of Panama Limited (1)
Balboa Avenida Aquilino de la, Panama, Panama
Tel.: (507) 2808000
Hotel Operator
N.A.I.C.S.: 721110

Homewood Suites By Hilton (1)
1000 Perimeter Rd, Manchester, NH 03103
Tel.: (603) 668-2200
Web Site: http://www.hilton.com
Hotels (except Casino Hotels) & Motels

N.A.I.C.S.: 721110

Homewood Suites Management LLC (1)
755 Crossover Ln, Memphis, TN 38117
Tel.: (901) 374-5000
Web Site:
http://homewoodsuites3.hilton.com
Home Management Services
N.A.I.C.S.: 561110

Izmir Enternasyonal Otelcilik Anonim Sirketi (1)
Gaziosmanpasa Bulvari No 7 K 4/410, Cankaya, Izmir, Turkiye
Tel.: (90) 2324899064
Home Management Services
N.A.I.C.S.: 721110

Puckrup Hall Hotel Limited (1)
Puckrup, Tewkesbury, GL20 6EL, United Kingdom
Tel.: (44) 1684296200
Hotel Reservation Services
N.A.I.C.S.: 561599

Rahn Bahia Mar, LLC (1)
801 Seabreeze Blvd, Fort Lauderdale, FL 33316
Tel.: (954) 764-2233
Web Site: http://www.hilton.com
Hotels (except Casino Hotels) & Motels
N.A.I.C.S.: 721110

Royal Place Owner, LLC (1)
1900 Buena Vista Dr, Lake Buena Vista, FL 32830
Tel.: (407) 827-2727
Web Site: http://www.hilton.com
Hotels (except Casino Hotels) & Motels
N.A.I.C.S.: 721110

Sydell Group Ltd. (1)
30 W 26th St 12th Fl, New York, NY 10010
Tel.: (646) 307-9600
Web Site: http://www.sydellgroup.com
Sales Range: $10-24.9 Million
Emp.: 20
Hotel Development & Management
N.A.I.C.S.: 721110
Andrew Zobler (Co-Founder & CEO)
Jeremy Selman (Co-Founder & Pres)
T. Blake Danner (COO & Sr VP)
Matthew Livian (Chief Investment Officer & Sr VP)
Joshua Babbitt (Gen Counsel & VP)
Jake Lamstein (Chief Dev Officer & Sr VP)
Sean Lavelle (VP-Dev-West)
Bob Gregson (Gen Mgr)

Tapestry Management LLC (1)
2001 Killebrew Dr Ste 100, Minneapolis, MN 55425
Tel.: (952) 854-8800
Web Site:
http://www.tapestrymanagement.com
Financial Property Management Services
N.A.I.C.S.: 531311
Tom LaSalle (Principal)
Ronald E. Sellnow (VP)
Rick Berc (CFO)
Tracy Popp (Mgr-Compliance)
Lisa Loge (Office Mgr)
Jack Brandt (Pres)
Richard Bienapfl (COO)
Susan Veeder (Fin Dir)
Greg LaSalle (VP)
Tim Trimble (Exec VP)
Teresa Pawlina (Chief Clinical Officer)

Tel Aviv Hilton Limited (1)
205 Hayarkon St, Independence Park, Tel Aviv, 6340506, Israel
Tel.: (972) 35202222
Restaurant Operators
N.A.I.C.S.: 722511

The Hilton Garden Inn (1)
1959 N Alafaya Trl, Orlando, FL 32826
Tel.: (407) 992-5000
Web Site: http://www.hilton.com
Hotels (except Casino Hotels) & Motels
N.A.I.C.S.: 721110
Anil Valbh (CEO)

Tokyo Bay Hilton Co. Ltd. (1)
1-8 Maihama, Urayasu, 279-0031, Chiba, Japan
Tel.: (81) 473555000
Web Site: https://tokyobay.hiltonjapan.co.jp

Restaurant Operators
N.A.I.C.S.: 722511

Waldorf Astoria Management LLC (1)
755 Crossover Ln, Memphis, TN 38117
Tel.: (901) 374-5000
Web Site: http://waldorfastoria3.hilton.com
Home Management Services
N.A.I.C.S.: 561110

Washington Hilton, L.L.C. (1)
1919 Connecticut Ave NW, Washington, DC 20009
Tel.: (202) 483-3000
Hotel Operator
N.A.I.C.S.: 721110
Mervin Henry (Dir-Revenue Mgmt)

HIMALAYA TECHNOLOGIES, INC.
625 Stanwix St Ste 2504, Pittsburgh, PA 15222
Tel.: (630) 708-0750   NV
Web Site:
https://www.himalayatechnologies.com
Year Founded: 2003
HMLA—(NASDAQ)
Sales Range: Less than $1 Million
Emp.: 2
Oil & Gas Exploration Services
N.A.I.C.S.: 213112
Vik Grover (Pres & CEO)
John Conklin (COO)

HIMS & HERS HEALTH, INC.
2269 Chestnut St Ste 523, San Francisco, CA 94123
Tel.: (415) 851-0195   DE
Web Site: https://www.forhims.com
Year Founded: 2017
HIMS—(NYSE)
Rev.: $526,916,000
Assets: $366,341,000
Liabilities: $54,600,000
Net Worth: $311,741,000
Earnings: ($65,678,000)
Emp.: 651
Fiscal Year-end: 12/31/22
Health & Wellness Products & Services
N.A.I.C.S.: 456199
Mike Chi (Chief Comml Officer & Chief Growth Officer)
Melissa Baird (COO)
Soleil Teubner Boughton (Chief Legal Officer & Sec)
Khobi Brooklyn (Chief Comm Officer)
Dan Kenger (Chief Design Officer)
Andrew Dudum (Co-Founder, Chm & CEO)
Patrick Carroll (Chief Medical Officer)

HINES GLOBAL INCOME TRUST, INC.
845 Texas Ave Ste 3300, Houston, TX 77002-1656   MD
Web Site:
https://www.hinesglobalincome trust.com
Year Founded: 2013
ZHGIDX—(NASDAQ)
Rev.: $259,519,000
Assets: $3,679,800,000
Liabilities: $1,634,514,000
Net Worth: $2,045,286,000
Earnings: ($48,097,000)
Fiscal Year-end: 12/31/22
Real Estate Investment Services
N.A.I.C.S.: 523999
Jeffrey C. Hines (Co-Owner, Chm & CEO)
J. Shea Morgenroth (CFO)
Alfonso J. Munk (Pres & Chief Investment Officer-Americas)
Alex Knapp (Chief Investment Officer-Europe)
A. Gordon Findlay (Chief Acctg Officer, Treas & Sec)

Hines Global Income Trust, Inc.—(Continued)

Omar H. Thowfeek (COO & Mng Dir-Investment Mgmt)
Fiona Hipkiss (Chief Compliance Officer)

HINGHAM INSTITUTION FOR SAVINGS

49 Main St, Hingham, MA 02043
Tel.: (781) 749-2200
Web Site:
https://www.hinghamsavings.com
Year Founded: 1834
HIFS—(NASDAQ)
Rev.: $106,952,000
Assets: $2,590,346,000
Liabilities: $2,343,123,000
Net Worth: $247,223,000
Earnings: $38,927,000
Emp.: 86
Fiscal Year-end: 12/31/19
Banking Services
N.A.I.C.S.: 522180
Shawn T. Sullivan (VP-Comml Lending)
Alexander L. Boyd (VP-Comml Lending)
Patrick R. Gaughen (Pres & COO)
Paul Barry (VP-Comml Lending)
Mark W. Constable (Chief Compliance Officer & VP)
Sara Congdon (VP & Reg Mgr-Nantucket)
Patrick Garvey (VP-Comml Lending)
Scott Proper (VP-Comml Lending)
Janice Spiess (VP-Comml Credit Admin)
Robin Johnson (Asst VP & Mgr-Customer Rels-Boston)
Cristian Melej (CFO & VP)
Eileen Trainor (Treas & VP)
Maggie McInnis (Mktg Dir)
Kristin Casey (Officer-AML & Asst VP-BSA)
Brenda McGillicuddy (Dir-HR)
Joseph Bears (CIO & VP)
Holly Cirignano (VP-Specialized Deposit Grp)
Andrew Vebber (VP-Retail Banking)
Leigh Hemmings (VP-Digital Banking Grp)
Michael Grady (Mgr-Customer Rels-Specialized Deposit Grp)
Cindy DoLoogh (Acct VP & Mgr Customer Experience-Specialized Deposit Grp)
Tara Williams (Mgr-Customer Rels-Specialized Deposit Grp)
Denise Quirk (Asst VP-Norwell Branch)
Selam Eyassu (Mgr-Customer Rels-Specialized Deposit Grp)
Mohsin Khan (Asst VP-South End Branch)
Michael Anderson (Asst VP-Beacon Hill Branch)
Jinnie Walsh (Asst VP-Hull Branch)
Janet McNulty (Asst VP-South Hingham Branch)
Larry Corthell (Asst VP-Cohasset Branch)
Donna Bryant (Asst VP-Linden Ponds Branch)
Robert H. Gaughen Jr. (Chm & CEO)
William M. Donovan Jr. (VP-Facilities)

HIPPO HOLDINGS INC.

150 Forest Ave, Palo Alto, CA 94301
Tel.: (650) 294-8463   DE
Web Site: https://www.hippo.com
Year Founded: 2020
HIPO—(NYSE)
Rev.: $91,200,000
Assets: $1,642,700,000
Liabilities: $781,000,000

Net Worth: $861,700,000
Earnings: ($371,400,000)
Emp.: 621
Fiscal Year-end: 12/31/21
Holding Company
N.A.I.C.S.: 551112
Stewart Ellis (CFO & Chief Strategy Officer)
Jo Overline (CTO)
Assaf Wand (Co-Founder & Exec Chm)
Richard McCathron (Pres & CEO)
Richard L. McCathron (Pres & CEO)

HIREQUEST, INC.

111 Springhall Dr, Goose Creek, SC 29445
Tel.: (843) 723-7400   WA
Web Site: https://www.hirequest.com
Year Founded: 2002
HQI—(NASDAQ)
Rev.: $37,882,000
Assets: $103,826,000
Liabilities: $41,094,000
Net Worth: $62,732,000
Earnings: $6,135,000
Emp.: 103
Fiscal Year-end: 12/31/23
Temporary Staffing Services
N.A.I.C.S.: 561320
Steven G. Crane (CFO)
R. Rimmy Malhotra (Vice Chm)
Cory Smith (Chief Acctg Officer)
Richard F. Hermanns (Pres & CEO)
John McAnnar (Chief Legal Officer & VP)
Dave Gerstner (VP-Ops)
Jarrett Lindon (Natl Dir-Accounts)
David Hartley (Dir-Corp Dev)
Heidi Windmueller (Controller)
Monica Reese (Dir-HR)
C.J. Williams (VP-VetsQuest)
David S. Burnett (CFO)
Joseph Gianzanti (CIO)
Tim Neilson (VP)
R. Rimmy Malhotra (Vice Chm)

Subsidiaries:

HQ Insurance Corporation   (1)
2451 Atrium Way, Nashville, TN 37214
Tel.: (615) 884-3535
Web Site: https://www.hqinsurance.com
Insurance Services
N.A.I.C.S.: 524210

The Dubin Group, Inc.   (1)
555 City Ave Ste 430, Bala Cynwyd, PA 19004
Tel.: (610) 667-5100
Web Site: http://www.thedubingroup.com
Professional, Scientific & Technical Services
N.A.I.C.S.: 541990
Erica Otto (VP-Ops)
Kenny Dubin (Founder & CEO)

HIRU CORP.

500 S Australian Ave Ste 600, West Palm Beach, FL 33401
Tel.: (954) 228-1053   GA
Web Site: https://otchiru.com
Year Founded: 1989
HIRU—(OTCIQ)
Online Plumbing & Lighting Housewares Retailer
N.A.I.C.S.: 444140
Khalid Nasser (CEO)

HISPANIC EXPRESS, INC.

1900 S Main St, Los Angeles, CA 90007
Tel.: (213) 763-4808
HXPR—(OTCIQ)
Financial Consulting Services
N.A.I.C.S.: 523940
Gary M. Cypres (Chm, Pres & CEO)

HISTOGEN, INC.

10655 Sorrento Valley Rd Ste 200, San Diego, CA 92121
Tel.: (858) 200-9520   DE
Web Site: https://www.histogen.com
Year Founded: 2005
HSTO—(NASDAQ)
Rev.: $3,769,000
Assets: $19,073,000
Liabilities: $5,697,000
Net Worth: $13,376,000
Earnings: ($10,644,000)
Emp.: 7
Fiscal Year-end: 12/31/22
Pharmaceuticals Mfr
N.A.I.C.S.: 325412

HK BATTERY TECHNOLOGY, INC.

800 E Colorado Blvd Ste 888, Pasadena, CA 91101
Tel.: (626) 683-9120
Year Founded: 2004
HKBT—(OTCEM)
Motor Vehicle Part & Accessory Mfr
N.A.I.C.S.: 336211
Jianguo Xu (CEO)

HK GRAPHENE TECHNOLOGY CORPORATION

800 E Colorado Blvd Ste 888, Pasadena, CA 91101
Tel.: (626) 683-9120   NV
Year Founded: 2006
HKGT—(OTCIQ)
Investment Services
N.A.I.C.S.: 523999
Jianguo Xu (Pres)
Chunhua Huang (CFO & Treas)
Yung Yeung (Chm)

HKN, INC.

180 State St Ste 202, Southlake, TX 76092
Tel.: (817) 310-0240   DE
Web Site: http://www.hkninc.com
Year Founded: 1979
HKNI—(OTCIQ)
Sales Range: Less than $1 Million
Emp.: 17
Oil & Gas Exploration, Extraction, Production & Distribution
N.A.I.C.S.: 211120
Mikel D. Faulkner (Pres & CEO)

Subsidiaries:

Nautilus Marine Services Plc   (1)
3 More London Riverside, London, SE1 2AQ, United Kingdom
Tel.: (44) 2071234567
Web Site: http://www.nautilusmarineplc.com
Rev.: $526,000
Assets: $31,079,000
Liabilities: $22,142,000
Net Worth: $8,937,000
Earnings: ($9,079,000)
Emp.: 14
Fiscal Year-end: 12/31/2018
Petroleum & Gas Exploration & Production
N.A.I.C.S.: 211120

HL ACQUISITIONS CORP.

499 Park Ave 12th Fl, New York, NY 10022
Tel.: (212) 486-8100   VG
Web Site:
http://www.hlacquisitions.com
Year Founded: 2018
HCCHU—(NASDAQ)
Rev.: $825,828
Assets: $54,029,387
Liabilities: $49,029,382
Net Worth: $5,000,005
Earnings: ($201,554)
Emp.: 2
Fiscal Year-end: 06/30/20
Investment Services
N.A.I.C.S.: 523999

Jeffrey E. Schwarz (Chm & CEO)
Greg Drechsler (CFO)
Benjamin Schwarz (VP-Bus Dev)

HLK BIOTECH HOLDING GROUP, INC.

30 N Gould St Ste R, Sheridan, WY 82801
Tel.: (727) 482-1505
AMHD—(OTCIQ)
Holding Company
N.A.I.C.S.: 551112
Aziz Hirji (Chm & CEO)

HMG/COURTLAND PROPERTIES, INC.

1870 S Bayshore Dr, Coconut Grove, FL 33133
Tel.: (305) 854-6803   DE
Web Site:
http://www.hmgcourtland.com
Year Founded: 1971
HMG—(NYSEAMEX)
Rev.: $400,318
Assets: $20,891,568
Liabilities: $1,467,263
Net Worth: $19,424,305
Earnings: ($1,052,114)
Fiscal Year-end: 12/31/20
Commercial Real Estate Investment Trust
N.A.I.C.S.: 525990
Carlos Camarotti (CFO, VP-Fin & Asst Sec)
Maurice A. Wiener (Chm, Pres, CEO & Sec)

HNI CORPORATION

600 E 2nd St, Muscatine, IA 52761-0071
Tel.: (563) 272-7400   IA
Web Site: https://www.hnicorp.com
Year Founded: 1944
HNI—(NYSE)
Rev.: $2,184,408,000
Assets: $1,497,897,000
Liabilities: $907,930,000
Net Worth: $589,967,000
Earnings: $59,814,000
Emp.: 79,000
Fiscal Year-end: 01/01/22
Office Furniture & Hearth Products Mfr & Marketer
N.A.I.C.S.: 337214
Jeffrey D. Lorenger (Chm, Pres & CEO)
Marshall H. Bridges (CFO & Sr VP)
Steven M. Bradford (Gen Counsel, Sec & Sr VP)
Donna D. Meade (VP)
Cooper Evans (VP-Internal Audit)
Jack D. Herring (Treas & VP-Corp Fin)
Julie Abramowski (VP & Controller)
Vincent P. Berger (Pres-Hearth & Home Technologies & Exec VP)
Matt McCall (VP-IR & Corp Dev)
Kris Rao (Chief Information & Digital Officer & VP)

Subsidiaries:

Allsteel Inc.   (1)
2210 2nd Ave, Muscatine, IA 52761
Tel.: (563) 272-4800
Web Site: https://www.allsteeloffice.com
Sales Range: $100-124.9 Million
Emp.: 220
Steel Office Furniture Mfr
N.A.I.C.S.: 337214

BP Ergo Limited   (1)
406 Windfall C-wing Sahara Plaza Andheri - Kurla Road, J B Nagar Andheri East, Mumbai, 400 059, Maharashtra, India
Tel.: (91) 2240775555
Web Site: http://www.hni-india.com
Emp.: 400
Office Furniture Mfr

N.A.I.C.S.: 337214
Sudhir Mambully (Mng Dir)

Compass Office Solutions LLC (1)
2450 Hollywood Blvd Ste 401, Hollywood, FL 33020
Tel.: (954) 430-4590
Web Site: www.compass-office.com
Office Furniture Products Retailer
N.A.I.C.S.: 449110

Contract Resource Group LLC (1)
7108 Old Katy Rd Ste 150, Houston, TX 77024
Tel.: (713) 803-0100
Web Site: http://www.crgoffice.com
Sales Range: $25-49.9 Million
Emp.: 30
Office Furniture Products Mfr
N.A.I.C.S.: 337214

HNI Asia L.L.C. (1)
401 4F Shen Yao Bldg Ba Gua 3rd Road, Shenzhen, 518029, China
Tel.: (86) 75582055458
Sales Range: $25-49.9 Million
Emp.: 50
Office Furniture & Hearth Products Mfr & Marketer
N.A.I.C.S.: 337214

HNI Asia Technology Services (Shenzhen) Limited (1)
Shenyao Mansion Bagua San Rd Futian Dist, Shenzhen, 518029, China
Tel.: (86) 75582056478
Office Furniture & Hearth Product Mfr & Marketer
N.A.I.C.S.: 337214
Terry Yang (Gen Mgr)

HNI Office India Ltd. (1)
406 Windfall C-wing Sahara Plaza Andheri - Kurla Road, J B Nagar Andheri East, Mumbai, 400 059, Maharashtra, India
Tel.: (91) 8600039632
Web Site: http://www.hni-india.com
Office Furniture Mfr
N.A.I.C.S.: 337214

Hearth & Home Technologies, Inc. (1)
7571 215th St W, Lakeville, MN 55044 (100%)
Tel.: (952) 985-6000
Web Site: https://www.hearthnhome.com
Sales Range: $200-249.9 Million
Emp.: 180
Mfr of Fireplace Systems & Woodburning Stoves
N.A.I.C.S.: 333414

Hickory Business Furniture (1)
900 12th St Dr NW, Hickory, NC 28601-4763
Tel.: (828) 328-2064
Web Site: https://www.hbf.com
Office Furniture Mfr
N.A.I.C.S.: 337211

Kimball International, Inc. (1)
1600 Royal St, Jasper, IN 47546-2256
Tel.: (812) 482-1600
Web Site: https://www.kimballinternational.com
Rev.: $665,877,000
Assets: $461,278,000
Liabilities: $247,742,000
Net Worth: $213,536,000
Earnings: ($15,714,000)
Emp.: 2,410
Fiscal Year-end: 06/30/2022
Office & Hospitality Furniture Mfr; Contract Electronics Mfr
N.A.I.C.S.: 337211
Kourtney L. Smith (COO)
Katherine S. Sigler (Pres-Hospitality & Exec VP)
R. Gregory Kincer (Treas & Exec VP-Corp Dev)
Lonnie P. Nicholson (Chief HR Officer)
Darren S. Gress (Controller)
Phyllis M. Goetz (Pres-Health & Exec VP)
Koorosh Sharghi (Chief Strategy & Innovation Officer, Pres-eBusiness & Exec VP)
Gregory A. Meunier (Exec VP-Ops-Global)
Timothy T. J. Wolfe (CFO & Exec VP)
Michael Roch (Chief Customer Officer-Workplace & Health)
Willi Candra (Chief Digital & Info Officer)
Chris Robison (Pres-Poppin)

Group (Domestic):

Kimball Furniture Group, LLC (2)
1600 Royal St, Jasper, IN 47546 (100%)
Tel.: (812) 482-1600
Web Site: http://www.kimball.com
Sales Range: $1-4.9 Billion
Office & Hospitality Furniture Mfr & Whslr
N.A.I.C.S.: 337211

Subsidiary (Domestic):

Kimball Hospitality, Inc. (3)
1180 E 16th St, Jasper, IN 47546 (100%)
Tel.: (812) 482-8090
Web Site: http://www.kimballhospitality.com
Sales Range: $10-24.9 Million
Emp.: 60
Furniture Design & Supply for Hospitality Industry
N.A.I.C.S.: 423210
Katherine S. Sigler (Pres)

Subsidiary (Domestic):

D'Style, Inc. (4)
3451 Main St Ste 108, Chula Vista, CA 91911
Tel.: (619) 662-0560
Web Site: http://www.dstyleinc.com
Miscellaneous Fabricated Metal Product Mfr
N.A.I.C.S.: 332999
Roberto Besquin (Founder & Exec Dir)

Subsidiary (Domestic):

Kimball Office, Inc. (3)
1600 Royal St, Jasper, IN 47549-0001
Tel.: (812) 482-1600
Web Site: http://www.kimballoffice.com
Sales Range: $1-4.9 Billion
Office Furniture Whslr
N.A.I.C.S.: 449110
Allen Parker (VP-Product, Sls & Mktg)
Pedro Ayala (Dir-Architecture & Design Strategies)

Plant (Domestic):

Kimball Office, Inc. - Borden (4)
555 E Water St, Borden, IN 47106-0903
Tel.: (812) 967-2041
Web Site: http://www.kimballoffice.com
Sales Range: $100-124.9 Million
Emp.: 370
Office Furniture Mfr
N.A.I.C.S.: 337211

Kimball Office, Inc. - Jasper, 15th Street (4)
1037 E 15th St, Jasper, IN 47549-1007
Tel.: (812) 482-8517
Web Site: http://www.kimballoffice.com
Sales Range: $100-124.9 Million
Emp.: 400
Office Furniture Mfr
N.A.I.C.S.: 337211

Kimball Office, Inc. - Jasper, Cherry Street (4)
1620 Cherry St, Jasper, IN 47549-1004
Tel.: (812) 482-8401
Web Site: http://www.kimballoffice.com
Sales Range: $50-74.9 Million
Emp.: 200
Office Furniture Mfr
N.A.I.C.S.: 337211

Kimball Office, Inc. - Post Falls (4)
1881 W Seltice Way, Post Falls, ID 83854-8132
Tel.: (208) 777-8400
Web Site: http://www.kimballoffice.com
Sales Range: $150-199.9 Million
Emp.: 575
Office Furniture Mfr
N.A.I.C.S.: 337211

Kimball Office, Inc. - Salem (4)
200 Kimball Blvd, Salem, IN 47167
Tel.: (812) 883-1850
Web Site: http://www.kimballoffice.com
Sales Range: $100-124.9 Million
Emp.: 360
Office Furniture Mfr
N.A.I.C.S.: 337211

Subsidiary (Domestic):

National Office Furniture, Inc. (3)
1600 Royal St, Jasper, IN 47546 (100%)

Tel.: (812) 482-1600
Web Site: http://www.nationalofficefurniture.com
Sales Range: $150-199.9 Million
Emp.: 200
Office Furniture Whslr
N.A.I.C.S.: 423210

Plant (Domestic):

National Office Furniture, Inc. - Fordsville (4)
Hwy 69 N, Fordsville, KY 42343
Tel.: (270) 276-3606
Web Site: http://www.nationalofficefurniture.com
Sales Range: $75-99.9 Million
Office Furniture Mfr
N.A.I.C.S.: 337211

National Office Furniture, Inc. - Jasper, 11th Ave (4)
340 E 11th Ave, Jasper, IN 47549-1005
Tel.: (812) 634-3526
Web Site: http://www.nationalofficefurniture.com
Sales Range: $100-124.9 Million
Mfr of Office, Residential, Hospitality & Healthcare Seating
N.A.I.C.S.: 337211

National Office Furniture, Inc. - Santa Claus (4)
1299 W State Rd 162, Santa Claus, IN 47579-0199
Tel.: (812) 937-4581
Web Site: http://www.nationalofficefurniture.com
Sales Range: $150-199.9 Million
Emp.: 290
Office Furniture Mfr
N.A.I.C.S.: 337211

Subsidiary (Domestic):

Kimball International Transit, Inc. (2)
1001 HRJ Ln, Jasper, IN 47549-0001 (100%)
Tel.: (812) 634-3346
Web Site: http://www.kimball.com
Sales Range: $50-74.9 Million
Emp.: 130
Transportation Services
N.A.I.C.S.: 484122

Poppin, Inc. (2)
16 Madison Square W 3rd Fl, New York, NY 10010
Web Site: http://www.poppin.com
Furniture Distr
N.A.I.C.S.: 449110

Maxon Furniture, Inc (1)
200 Oak St, Muscatine, IA 52761-5662 (100%)
Tel.: (253) 872-0396
Web Site: http://www.maxonfurniture.com
Sales Range: $50-74.9 Million
Emp.: 140
Mfr of Office Panel Systems
N.A.I.C.S.: 332710

Monessen Holding Company (1)
149 Cleveland Dr, Paris, KY 40361
Tel.: (859) 987-0740
Emp.: 750
Heating Equipment Mfr
N.A.I.C.S.: 333414

OFM, LLC (1)
161 Tradition Trl, Holly Springs, NC 27540
Web Site: https://www.ofminc.com
Furniture Mfr
N.A.I.C.S.: 337214
Jake Lassiter (Mgr-Sls-Natl)
Blake Zalcberg (Pres)
Jim Needell (Dir-HR)

Omni Workspace Company (1)
1300 Washington Ave N, Minneapolis, MN 55411
Tel.: (612) 627-1600
Web Site: https://www.omniworkspace.com
Sales Range: $100-124.9 Million
Office Design Consulting & Office Furniture Installation Services
N.A.I.C.S.: 561499

Subsidiary (Domestic):

Atmosphere Commercial Interiors, LLC (2)

81 S 9th St Ste 450, Minneapolis, MN 55402 (100%)
Tel.: (612) 343-0868
Web Site: https://www.atmphereci.com
Sales Range: $50-74.9 Million
Emp.: 80
Office Furniture Distr & Interior Design Services
N.A.I.C.S.: 423210
Carlene Wilson (Pres & CEO)
Catherine Mika (VP-Client Svcs & Ops)
Myra Basar (Dir-HR)
Megan Sciera (Dir-Mktg & Digital)
Craig Holst (Reg VP-Minnesota)
Byron Wieberdink (CFO)
Abe Zanto (CIO)

Branch (Domestic):

Target Commercial Interiors, Inc. - Green Bay (3)
1365 N Rd, Green Bay, WI 54313
Tel.: (920) 884-0265
Web Site: http://www.targetcommercialinteriors.com
Sales Range: $10-24.9 Million
Emp.: 10
Office Furniture Distr
N.A.I.C.S.: 423210

Paoli LLC (1)
201 E Martin St, Orleans, IN 47452-9013
Tel.: (812) 865-1525
Web Site: http://www.paoli.com
Wood Office Furniture Mfr
N.A.I.C.S.: 337211
Sandy Horton (VP-Mktg)

The Gunlocke Company (1)
1 Gunlocke Dr, Wayland, NY 14572-9515 (100%)
Tel.: (585) 728-5111
Web Site: http://www.gunlocke.com
Sales Range: $200-249.9 Million
Emp.: 700
Mfr of High Quality Office Furniture
N.A.I.C.S.: 337211

The HON Company, LLC (1)
200 Oak St, Muscatine, IA 52761-4313
Tel.: (563) 272-7100
Web Site: http://www.hon.com
Office Furniture Including Chairs, Panel Systems, Desks & Storage Mfr
N.A.I.C.S.: 337214

Plant (Domestic):

The HON Co. (2)
200 Oak St, Muscatine, IA 52761-4313 (100%)
Tel.: (563) 272-7100
Web Site: https://www.hon.com
Sales Range: $100-124.9 Million
Emp.: 300
Metal Office Furniture Manufacturing Plant
N.A.I.C.S.: 337214

Wilson Office Interiors LLC (1)
1341 W Mockingbird Ln Ste 1100W, Dallas, TX 75247
Tel.: (972) 488-4100
Web Site: https://wilsonbauhaus.com
Emp.: 50
Office Furniture Product Mfr & Distr
N.A.I.C.S.: 337214

Young Office Solutions LLC (1)
733 Frnt St Unit 200 a, San Francisco, CA 94111-1993
Tel.: (415) 399-5300
Office Furniture Whslr
N.A.I.C.S.: 423210
Paul Stier (Principal)
Rose Young (Principal)

HNO INTERNATIONAL, INC.
41558 Eman Dr, Murrieta, CA 92562
Tel.: (951) 305-8872   NV
Web Site: https://hnointl.com
Year Founded: 2005
HNOI—(OTCIQ)
Rev.: $13,000
Assets: $1,342,634
Liabilities: $1,434,835
Net Worth: ($92,201)
Earnings: ($1,441,335)
Emp.: 2

HNO International, Inc.—(Continued)

Fiscal Year-end: 10/31/23
Holding Company; Renewable Energy Development Services
N.A.I.C.S.: 551112
James Wood (VP-Bus Dev)

Subsidiaries:

Clenergen Corporation Limited   (1)
29 Harley Street, London, W1G 9QR, United Kingdom
Tel.: (44) 207 291 1728
Renewable Energy Development Services
N.A.I.C.S.: 221118

Clenergen Ghana Limited   (1)
PO Box CT1925 Cantonments, Accra, Ghana
Tel.: (233) 243 803039
Web Site: http://www.clenergen.com
Renewable Energy Development Services
N.A.I.C.S.: 221118

Clenergen Philippines Corporation   (1)
Unit 311 The Annex #24 Gen Areneta Street, San Antnio Village, Pasig, 1600, Philippines
Tel.: (63) 2 584 3716
Web Site: http://www.clenergen.com
Renewable Energy Development Services
N.A.I.C.S.: 221118

HNR ACQUISITION CORP.
3730 Kirby Dr Ste 1200, Houston, TX 77098
Tel.: (713) 834-1145   DE
Web Site: https://www.hnra-nyse.com
Year Founded: 2020
HNRA—(NYSEAMEX)
Rev.: $1,269,331
Assets: $89,400,888
Liabilities: $92,577,077
Net Worth: ($3,176,189)
Earnings: ($750,347)
Emp.: 2
Fiscal Year-end: 12/31/22
Investment Services
N.A.I.C.S.: 523999
Jesse J. Allen (VP-Operations)
Mark H. Williams (VP-Finance & Administration)
Dante Caravaggio (CEO & Dir)
Mitchell B. Trotter (CFO & Dir)
David M. Smith (Gen Counsel, Sec & VP)

HOCKING VALLEY BANCSHARES, INC.
7 W Stimson Ave, Athens, OH 45701
Tel.: (740) 592-4441   OH
Web Site: http://www.hvbonline.com
Year Founded: 1963
HCKG—(OTCIQ)
Bank Holding Company
N.A.I.C.S.: 551111
Tammy Bobo (Pres & CEO)
Benedict Weissenrieder (Chm, Treas & VP)
Polly Sumney (Chief Compliance Officer, Sec & Exec VP)
Kimberly Kelly (Vice Chm)

Subsidiaries:

Hocking Valley Bank   (1)
7 W Stimson Ave, Athens, OH 45701
Tel.: (740) 592-4441
Web Site: http://www.hvbonline.com
Rev.: $10,593,000
Assets: $242,272,000
Liabilities: $218,502,000
Net Worth: $23,770,000
Earnings: $1,893,000
Emp.: 58
Fiscal Year-end: 12/31/2012
State Commercial Banks
N.A.I.C.S.: 522110
Benedict Weissenrieder (Chm & CEO)
Tammy Bobo (VP)

HOLDCO NUVO GROUP D.G LTD.
300 Witherspoon St Ste 201, Princeton, NJ 08542   II
Web Site:
   https://www.nuvocares.com
Year Founded: 2023
NUVO—(NASDAQ)
Surgical & Medical Instrument Mfr
N.A.I.C.S.: 339112
Amit Reches (CTO)
Orly Hirsch (VP-People)
Dotan Raviv (VP-Operations)
Noah Klein (VP-Business Development)
Keren Shalev (VP-Product)
Ryan Kraudel (VP-Marketing)
Moshe Ofry (VP-Software)
Doug Blankenship (CFO)
Chen Rubinstein (Sr Dir-Regulatory Affairs & Quality Assurance)
Rice Powell (CEO)

Subsidiaries:

LAMF Global Ventures Corp. I   (1)
9255 Sunset Blvd Ste 1100 W, Hollywood, CA 90069
Tel.: (424) 343-8760
Investment Services
N.A.I.C.S.: 523999

Nuvo Group Ltd.   (1)
Yigal Alon 94 St Alon Tower 1, Tel Aviv, 6789155, Israel
Tel.: (972) 36242266
Web Site:
   https://www.apacquisitioncorp.com
Rev.: $30,000
Assets: $2,911,000
Liabilities: $4,127,000
Net Worth: ($1,216,000)
Earnings: ($11,244,000)
Emp.: 41
Fiscal Year-end: 12/31/2020
Medical Device Mfr
N.A.I.C.S.: 339112
Kelly Londy (CEO)
Oren Oz (Chief Innovation Officer)
Eran Schindler (CFO)
Amit Reches (CTO)
Orly Hirsch (VP-People)

HOLLEY INC.
1801 Russellville Rd, Bowling Green, KY 42101
Tel.: (270) 782-2900   DE
Web Site: https://www.holley.com
Year Founded: 2021
HLLY—(NYSE)
Holding Company; Aftermarket Motor Vehicle Parts Mfr & Whslr
N.A.I.C.S.: 551112
Matthew J. Stevenson (Pres & CEO)
Matthew E. Rubel (Chm)
Jesse Weaver (CFO & Head-Information Technology)
Vinod Nimmagadda (Exec VP-Corporate Development & New Ventures)
Patrick Pierce (Chief HR Officer)
Carly Kennedy (Gen Counsel, Sec & Exec VP)
Philip Dobbs (Sr VP-Customer Experience Mktg)

Subsidiaries:

Holley Performance Products Inc.   (1)
1801 Russellville Rd, Bowling Green, KY 42101
Tel.: (270) 782-2900
Web Site: http://www.holley.com
Sales Range: $75-99.9 Million
Emp.: 350
Motor Vehicle Component Mfr
N.A.I.C.S.: 336310
Thomas W. Tomlinson (Pres & CEO)

HOLLUND INDUSTRIAL MARINE, INC.

3000 Green Mountain Dr Ste 107-413, Branson, MO 65616
Tel.: (417) 339-4553
Year Founded: 1988
HIMR—(OTCEM)
Woodworking Machinery Mfr
N.A.I.C.S.: 333243
Peter Meier (Pres)

HOLLYWALL ENTERTAINMENT INC.
3753 Howard Hughes Pkwy Ste 200, Las Vegas, NV 89169
Tel.: (202) 615-4090   NV
Web Site: http://www.hollywall.com
Year Founded: 2009
HWAL—(OTCIQ)
Rev.: $3,600,000
Assets: $59,720,000
Liabilities: $13,288,000
Net Worth: $46,432,000
Earnings: ($1,063,000)
Fiscal Year-end: 09/30/19
Music, Film & Video Distr
N.A.I.C.S.: 512120
Roxanna Lou Green (Pres, COO & Sec)

HOLOGIC, INC.
250 Campus Dr, Marlborough, MA 01752
Tel.: (508) 263-2900   DE
Web Site: https://www.hologic.com
Year Founded: 1985
HOLX—(NASDAQ)
Rev.: $4,030,300,000
Assets: $9,156,000,000
Liabilities: $4,026,000,000
Net Worth: $5,130,000,000
Earnings: $789,500,000
Emp.: 7,063
Fiscal Year-end: 09/28/24
Medical Diagnostic Product Mfr
N.A.I.C.S.: 339112
John M. Griffin (Gen Counsel)
Benjamin J. Cohn (VP & Controller)
Patrick Brady (Sr VP-Global Supply Chain, Quality & Regulatory)
Erik Anderson (Pres-Global Svcs)
Ryan Simon (VP-IR)
Francis Pruell (Dir-IR)
Lisa Hellmann (Sr VP-Corp Comm & HR-Global)
Jennifer Meade (Pres-Breast & Skeletal Health Solutions Div)
Essex D. Mitchell (COO)
Monica Aguirre Berthelot (Co-Founder)
Paul Malenchini (Co-Founder)
Karleen M. Oberton (CFO)
Stephen P. MacMillan (Chm, Pres & CEO)

Subsidiaries:

Beijing TCT Medical Technology Co., Ltd.   (1)
Room 1005 Block A Feng Lan Guo Ji Center 32 Xizhimen Bei Da Jie, Haidian District, Beijing, 100082, China
Tel.: (86) 1062290000
Medical Device Mfr
N.A.I.C.S.: 339112

Biotheranostics, Inc.   (1)
9620 Towne Centre Dr Ste 200, San Diego, CA 92121-1987
Web Site: http://www.biotheranostics.com
Medical Laboratories
N.A.I.C.S.: 621511
Miriam J. Bloch (Dir-Laboratory)
Debra Hadley (VP-Laboratory Ops)
Karla Kelly (Gen Counsel)
Debbie Ledet (VP-Market Access)
Matt Sargent (Chief Comml Officer)
Lisa Whitmyer (VP-Mktg)
Catherine Schnabel (Chief Scientific Officer)
Gail A. Sloan (CFO)
Bill Zondler (CIO)
Donnie M. Hardison (Pres & CEO)

Cynosure Portugal, Unipessoal, Limitada   (1)
Avda da Republica numero 6 7 esquerdo, 1050-191, Lisbon, Portugal
Tel.: (351) 915064946
Medical Equipment Distr
N.A.I.C.S.: 423450

Cytyc Prenatal Products Corp.   (1)
1240 Elko Dr, Sunnyvale, CA 94089
Tel.: (408) 745-0975
Emp.: 125
Medical Device Mfr
N.A.I.C.S.: 339112

Cytyc Surgical Products II, LLC   (1)
250 Campus Dr, Marlborough, MA 01752
Tel.: (508) 263-2900
Surgical Product Services
N.A.I.C.S.: 339113

Diagenode Co., Ltd.   (1)
1-1-25 Arakawa, Toyama, 930-0982, Japan
Tel.: (81) 764823110
Web Site: https://diagenode.co.jp
Medical Equipment Mfr
N.A.I.C.S.: 339112

Diagenode SA   (1)
Rue Bois Saint-Jean 3, Ougree, 4102, Seraing, Belgium
Tel.: (32) 43642050
Medical Equipment Mfr
N.A.I.C.S.: 339112

Diagenode SPA   (1)
Constanza 95, 251000, Concon, Valparaiso, Chile
Tel.: (56) 985285210
Medical Equipment Mfr
N.A.I.C.S.: 339112

Direct Radiography Corp.   (1)
600 Technology Dr, Newark, DE 19702   (100%)
Tel.: (302) 631-2700
Web Site: http://www.hology.com
Sales Range: $25-49.9 Million
Emp.: 150
Direct to Digital Radiology Systems
N.A.I.C.S.: 334517
Toni Patrick (Mgr-HR)

Emsor, Sociedad de Responsabilidad Limitada   (1)
Edificio Emsor 5 Planta Local 138, 28050, Madrid, Spain
Tel.: (34) 913446990
Web Site: http://www.emsor.es
Surgical & Medical Instrument Mfr
N.A.I.C.S.: 339112

Faxitron Bioptics, LLC   (1)
3440 E Britannia Dr Ste 150, Tucson, AZ 85706
Tel.: (520) 399-8180
Web Site: http://www.faxitron.com
Surgical & Medical Instrument Mfr
N.A.I.C.S.: 339112

Focal Therapeutics Inc.   (1)
30 Enterprise Ste 220, Aliso Viejo, CA 92656
Tel.: (650) 530-2394
Web Site: http://www.focalrx.com
All Other Support Services
N.A.I.C.S.: 561990
Gail Lebovic (Chief Medical Officer)

Gen-Probe Incorporated   (1)
10210 Genetic Center Dr, San Diego, CA 92121
Tel.: (858) 410-8000
Web Site: http://www.hologic.com
Nucleic Acid Testing Product Mfr
N.A.I.C.S.: 541715

Subsidiary (Non-US):

Gen-Probe Denmark ApS   (2)
Herlev Hovedgade 195, 2730, Herlev, Denmark
Tel.: (45) 80881378
Medical Device Mfr
N.A.I.C.S.: 339112

Subsidiary (Domestic):

Gen-Probe Prodesse, Inc.   (2)
W229 N 1870 Westwood Dr, Waukesha, WI 53186

Tel.: (262) 446-0700
Medical Device Mfr
N.A.I.C.S.: 339112

Subsidiary (Non-US):

Gen-Probe Sweden AB (2)
Torshamnsgatan 35, 164 40, Kista, Sweden
Tel.: (46) 20797943
Medical Device Mfr
N.A.I.C.S.: 339112

Hologic Asia Pacific Limited (1)
518 5 F Trade Square 681 Cheung Sha
Wan Road Cheung, Kowloon, China (Hong
Kong)
Tel.: (852) 37487700
Sales Range: $10-24.9 Million
Emp.: 25
Women's Health Product Designer & Mfr
N.A.I.C.S.: 339112

Subsidiary (Non-US):

Hologic (Australia) Pty Limited (2)
Suite 402 Level 4 2-4 Lyon Park Road Mac-
quarie Centre, PO Box 1971, Macquarie
Park, 2113, NSW, Australia
Tel.: (61) 298888000
Web Site: http://www.hologic.com
Emp.: 20
Women's Health Product Sales, Design &
Mfr
N.A.I.C.S.: 339112

Hologic Austria GmbH (1)
Weyringergasse 6, 1040, Vienna, Austria
Tel.: (43) 150466710
Medical Equipment Distr
N.A.I.C.S.: 423450

Hologic Deutschland GmbH (1)
Otto-von-Guericke-Ring 15, 65205, Wies-
baden, Germany
Tel.: (49) 612270760
Web Site: http://www.hologic.com
Women's Health Product Designer & Mfr
N.A.I.C.S.: 339112

Hologic France S.A. (1)
Paris Nord 2 11 allee des Cascades, BP
48042, 95912, Villepinte, Roissy-en-France,
France
Tel.: (33) 148178370
Medical Instrument Mfr
N.A.I.C.S.: 339112

Hologic France, SARL (1)
11 alle des Cascades, BP 48042, Roissy,
Villepinte, Cedex, France
Tel.: (33) 148178370
Web Site: http://www.novasure.com
Sales Range: $100-124.9 Million
Emp.: 20
Women's Health Product Mfr
N.A.I.C.S.: 339112

Hologic Hitec-Imaging GmbH (1)
Max- Planck-Strasse 7, 59581, Warstein,
Germany
Tel.: (49) 2902861231
Web Site: http://www.hitec-imaging.de
Emp.: 50
Medical Device Mfr
N.A.I.C.S.: 339112
Franz-Josef Schmucker (Mng Dir)

Hologic Iberia, S.L. (1)
C/Tarragona 161 Planta 12, 08014, Barce-
lona, Spain
Tel.: (34) 932925144
Web Site: http://www.hologic.com
Sales Range: $10-24.9 Million
Emp.: 10
Women's Health Product Designer & Mfr
N.A.I.C.S.: 339112

**Hologic International Holdings
B.V.** (1)
Herengracht 477, Amsterdam, 1017 BS,
Netherlands
Tel.: (31) 205215645
Holding Company
N.A.I.C.S.: 551112

Hologic Italia S.r.l. (1)
Viale Citta d'Europa 681, 00144, Rome,
Italy
Tel.: (39) 0645437534
Web Site: http://www.hologic.it

Sales Range: $1-4.9 Billion
Women's Health Product Designer & Mfr
N.A.I.C.S.: 325412

Hologic Japan, Inc. (1)
Nikkyohan Bldg 1-4-25 Koraku, Bunkyo-ku,
Tokyo, 112-0004, Japan
Tel.: (81) 358042340
Web Site: http://www.hologic.co.jp
Medical Device Mfr
N.A.I.C.S.: 339112

Hologic Medicor Suisse GmbH (1)
Gewerbestrasse 10, 6330, Cham, Switzer-
land
Tel.: (41) 417410700
Medical Equipment Distr
N.A.I.C.S.: 423450

Hologic N.V. (1)
Leuvensesteenweg 250A, Vilvoorde, 1800,
Belgium (100%)
Tel.: (32) 27114680
Web Site: http://www.hologic.com
Sales Range: $25-49.9 Million
Emp.: 100
Imaging Equipment Sales
N.A.I.C.S.: 423450
Andrew Haton (Mng Dir)

Hologic Netherlands B.V. (1)
Transistorstraat 60, Almere, 1322 CG, Neth-
erlands
Tel.: (31) 367111186
Emp.: 17
Medical Diagnostic Product Mfr
N.A.I.C.S.: 339112
Bert Boer (Mgr-HR)

Hologic SA (1)
Paris Nord 2 11 allee des Cascades Roissy
CDG CDX, PO Box 48042, Villepinte,
95912, France
Tel.: (33) 148178370
Medical Equipment Distr
N.A.I.C.S.: 423450

Hologic Suisse SA (1)
World Trade Center Av de Gratta-Paille 2,
1018, Lausanne, Switzerland
Tel.: (41) 216333900
Web Site: http://www.hologic.com
Sales Range: $25-49.9 Million
Emp.: 25
Medical Diagnostic Product Mfr
N.A.I.C.S.: 339112

**Hologic Surgical Products Costa Rica
S.A.** (1)
562 Parkway Coyol Free Zone, Alajuela,
Costa Rica
Tel.: (506) 24362600
Web Site: http://www.hologic.com
Sales Range: $100-124.9 Million
Emp.: 500
Medical Diagnostic Product Mfr
N.A.I.C.S.: 339112

Hologic Sweden AB (1)
Sollentunavagen 63, 191 40, Sollentuna,
Sweden
Tel.: (46) 858579805
Medical Instrument Mfr
N.A.I.C.S.: 339112

**Hologic, Inc. - Breast Imaging
Solutions** (1)
36 Apple Ridge Rd, Danbury, CT 06810
Tel.: (203) 207-4500
Web Site: http://www.hologic.com
Sales Range: $50-74.9 Million
Emp.: 200
Medical Equipment & Mammography Sys-
tems Mfr
N.A.I.C.S.: 621512

Mobidiag UK Ltd. (1)
Herschel House 58 Herschel Street,
Slough, SL1 1PG, Berkshire, United King-
dom
Tel.: (44) 3333057506
Medical Equipment Mfr
N.A.I.C.S.: 339112

Sentinelle Medical USA Inc. (1)
250 Campus Dr, Marlborough, MA 01752
Tel.: (508) 263-2900
Medical Device Mfr & Distr
N.A.I.C.S.: 339112

**Somatex Medical Technologies
GmbH** (1)

Hohenzollerndamm 150/151, 14199, Berlin,
Germany
Tel.: (49) 30319822500
Web Site: https://www.somatex.com
Medical Device Mfr & Distr
N.A.I.C.S.: 339112

Third Wave Agbio, Inc. (1)
502 Rosa Rd, Madison, WI 53719
Tel.: (608) 273-8933
Web Site: http://www.hologic.com
Emp.: 90
Diagnostic Test Kits Developer for Use in
Animals
N.A.I.C.S.: 325413

Third Wave Technologies, Inc. (1)
502 S Rosa Rd, Madison, WI 53719
Tel.: (608) 273-8933
Sales Range: $25-49.9 Million
Emp.: 179
Molecular Diagnostic Tests Mfr
N.A.I.C.S.: 325413

HOLOGRAPHIC STORAGE LTD.
102 NE 2nd St 265, Boca Raton, FL
33432
Tel.: (561) 542-6039
HSTG—(OTCIQ)
Media Representative Services
N.A.I.C.S.: 541840
Todd Violette (Pres)

HOMASOTE COMPANY
932 Lower Ferry Rd, West Trenton,
NJ 08628
Tel.: (609) 883-3300   NJ
Web Site: https://www.homasote.com
Year Founded: 1909
HMTC—(OTCIQ)
Sales Range: $10-24.9 Million
Emp.: 101
Reconstituted Wood Product Manu-
facturing
N.A.I.C.S.: 321219

HOME BANCORP WISCONSIN, INC.
3762 E Washington Ave, Madison, WI
53704
Tel.: (608) 282-6000   MD
Web Site: http://www.home-
savings.com
HWIS—(OTCIQ)
Sales Range: $1-9.9 Million
Emp.: 36
Bank Holding Company
N.A.I.C.S.: 551111
Mark A. Fritz (CFO & Sr VP)
James R. Bradley Jr. (Chm, Pres &
CEO)

Subsidiaries:

Home Savings Bank (1)
3762 E Washington Ave, Madison, WI
53704
Tel.: (608) 282-6000
Web Site: http://www.home-savings.com
Commericial Banking
N.A.I.C.S.: 522110

HOME BANCORP, INC.
503 Kaliste Saloom Rd, Lafayette, LA
70508
Tel.: (337) 237-1960   LA
Web Site:
https://www.home24bank.com
Year Founded: 2008
HBCP—(NASDAQ)
Rev.: $139,815,000
Assets: $3,228,280,000
Liabilities: $2,898,326,000
Net Worth: $329,954,000
Earnings: $34,072,000
Emp.: 475
Fiscal Year-end: 12/31/22
Bank Holding Company
N.A.I.C.S.: 551111

John W. Bordelon (Chm, Pres &
CEO)
Darren E. Guidry (Chief Credit Officer
& Exec VP-Home Bank)
Natalie B. Lemoine (Chief Admin Offi-
cer & Sr Exec VP)
John J. Zollinger IV (Chief Banking
Officer & Sr Exec VP)
David T. Kirkley (CFO & Exec VP)

Subsidiaries:

**Home Bank, National
Association** (1)
503 Kaliste Saloom Rd, Lafayette, LA
70508
Tel.: (337) 237-1960
Web Site: https://www.home24bank.com
Commericial Banking
N.A.I.C.S.: 522180
John W. Bordelon (Chm, Pres & CEO)
Darren E. Guidry (Chief Credit Officer &
Exec VP)
Natalie B. Lemoine (Chief Admin Officer &
Sr Exec VP)
John J. Zollinger IV (Chief Banking Officer
& Sr Exec VP)

HOME BANCSHARES, INC.
Tel.: (501) 328-4625   AR
Web Site:
https://www.homebancshares.com
Year Founded: 1998
HOMB—(NYSE)
Rev.: $1,052,877,000
Assets: $22,883,588,000
Liabilities: $19,357,226,000
Net Worth: $3,526,362,000
Earnings: $305,262,000
Emp.: 2,774
Fiscal Year-end: 12/31/22
Bank Holding Company
N.A.I.C.S.: 551111
John W. Allison (Co-Founder, Exec
Chm & CEO)
Jack E. Engelkes (Vice Chm)
Brian S. Davis (CFO & Treas)
Robert H. Adcock Jr. (Co-Founder)
Kevin D. Hester (Pres & Chief Lend-
ing Officer)
Donna J. Townsell (Sr Exec VP &
Dir-IR)
Jennifer C. Floyd (Chief Acctg Offi-
cer)
J. Stephen Tipton (COO)
Mikel Williamson (Pres)

Subsidiaries:

Centennial Bank (1)
620 Chestnut St, Conway, AR
72032 (100%)
Tel.: (501) 328-4663
Web Site: https://www.my100bank.com
Commericial Banking
N.A.I.C.S.: 522110
Kevin W. Ahern (Founder)
John W. Allison (Co-Founder)
Brian S. Davis (Treas)
Robert H. Adcock Jr. (Vice Chm)
Kevin D. Hester (Pres & Chief Lending Offi-
cer)
Donna J. Townsell (Executives, Bd of Dirs)
J. Stephen Tipton (CEO)

Happy Bancshares, Inc. (1)
701 S Taylor St, Amarillo, TX 79101
Tel.: (806) 342-2400
Web Site: http://www.happybank.com
Rev.: $7,300,000
Emp.: 63
Fiscal Year-end: 12/31/2006
Bank Holding Companies
N.A.I.C.S.: 551111
J. Pat Hickman (Founder)
J. Pat Hickman (Chm)
Mikel Williamson (CEO)

HOME BISTRO, INC.
15000 W 6th Ave Ste 400, Golden,
CO 80401
Tel.: (631) 964-1111   NV
Web Site: http://www.homebistro.com

Home Bistro, Inc.—(Continued)

Year Founded: 2009
HBISD—(OTCIQ)
Rev.: $1,335,859
Assets: $483,670
Liabilities: $2,398,664
Net Worth: ($1,914,994)
Earnings: ($1,241,661)
Emp.: 5
Fiscal Year-end: 12/31/20
Beverages Mfr
N.A.I.C.S.: 722515
Zalmi Duchman (CEO, Interim CFO & Sec)

Subsidiaries:

Vapir Inc. (1)
2212 Ringwood Ave, San Jose, CA 95131
Tel.: (408) 649-2786
Web Site: http://www.vapir.com
Vaporizer Mfr
N.A.I.C.S.: 335210

HOME FEDERAL BANCORP, INC. OF LOUISIANA

624 Market St, Shreveport, LA 71101
Tel.: (318) 222-1145 LA
Web Site: https://www.hfbla.com
HFBL—(NASDAQ)
Rev.: $33,448,000
Assets: $637,512,000
Liabilities: $584,709,000
Net Worth: $52,803,000
Earnings: $3,593,000
Emp.: 78
Fiscal Year-end: 06/30/24
Bank Holding Company
N.A.I.C.S.: 551111
James R. Barlow (Chm, Pres & CEO)

Subsidiaries:

Home Federal Bank (1)
624 Market St, Shreveport, LA 71101
Tel.: (318) 222-1145
Banking Services
N.A.I.C.S.: 522110
James R. Barlow (Chm, Pres & CEO)

HOME FINANCIAL BANCORP

279 E Morgan St PO Box 187, Spencer, IN 47460
Tel.: (812) 829-2095 IN
Web Site: http://www.owencom.com
Year Founded: 1996
HWEN—(OTCIQ)
Sales Range: $1-9.9 Million
Emp.: 19
Bank Holding Company
N.A.I.C.S.: 551111
Kurt D. Rosenberger (Pres & CEO)
Tad Wilson (Chm)
Lori Porter (VP-Lending)
Lisa Wilson (Sr Mgr-Info Sys & Support)
Tammy Randolph (VP-HR)

HOME LOAN FINANCIAL CORPORATION

413 Main St, Coshocton, OH 43812-1580
Tel.: (740) 622-0444 OH
Web Site: https://www.homeloanfinancial corp.com
Year Founded: 1997
HLFN—(OTCIQ)
Bank Holding Company
N.A.I.C.S.: 551111
Robert C. Hamilton (Chm & CEO)
Breann L. Miller (CFO, Treas, Sec & VP)

Subsidiaries:

The Home Loan Savings Bank (1)
413 Main St, Coshocton, OH 43812-1580 (100%)
Tel.: (740) 622-0444

Web Site: http://www.homeloansavingsbank.com
Sales Range: $50-74.9 Million
Emp.: 50
Savings & Loan Banking Services
N.A.I.C.S.: 522110
Thomas R. Conidi (Exec VP & Dir-Loan Admin)
Robert C. Hamilton (Chm & CEO)
Kyle R. Hamilton (Pres & COO)
Laura L. Miller (VP)
Patty Paul (Head-Ops & Asst VP)

HOME PLATE ACQUISITION CORPORATION

PO Box 1314, New York, NY 10028
Tel.: (917) 703-2312 DE
Web Site: https://www.homeplateacq.com
Year Founded: 2021
HPLT—(NASDAQ)
Rev.: $12,663,460
Assets: $204,313,446
Liabilities: $210,510,307
Net Worth: ($6,196,861)
Earnings: $10,085,667
Fiscal Year-end: 12/31/22
Investment Services
N.A.I.C.S.: 523999
Daniel Ciporin (Chm & CEO)
Jonathan Rosenzweig (CFO & Sec)

HOMELAND SECURITY CORPORATION

123 W Nye Ln Ste 129, Carson City, NV 89706
Tel.: (775) 580-5395 NV
Web Site: https://homelandsecuritycorp.us
Year Founded: 1997
HSCC—(OTCIQ)
Security System Services
N.A.I.C.S.: 561621
James Werner (CEO & Treas)
Gary Williams (Sec & VP)

HOMESTEAD GOLD & SILVER LTD.

114 W Magnolia St Ste 400, Bellingham, WA 98225-4318
Tel.: (360) 756-6538 NV
Year Founded: 2004
SNLM—(OTCIQ)
Metal Mining Services
N.A.I.C.S.: 213114
Andy Ruppanner (CEO)

HOMESTREET, INC.

601 Union St Ste 2000, Seattle, WA 98101
Tel.: (206) 623-3050 WA
Web Site: https://www.homestreet.com
Year Founded: 1921
HMST—(NASDAQ)
Rev.: $355,858,000
Assets: $9,364,760,000
Liabilities: $8,802,613,000
Net Worth: $562,147,000
Earnings: $66,540,000
Emp.: 937
Fiscal Year-end: 12/31/22
Bank Holding Company
N.A.I.C.S.: 551111
Mark K. Mason (Chm, Pres & CEO)
Jay C. Iseman (Chief Credit Officer & Exec VP)
Darrell S. van Amen (Chief Investment Officer, Treas & Exec VP)
Godfrey B. Evans (Chief Admin Officer, Gen Counsel, Sec & Exec VP)
John M. Michel (CFO & Exec VP)
Diane P. Novak (Chief Risk Officer & Exec VP)

Subsidiaries:

HomeStreet Bank (1)

1314 6th Ave, Seattle, WA 98101
Tel.: (206) 621-0100
Web Site: https://www.homestreet.com
Sales Range: $250-299.9 Million
Commercial Banking
N.A.I.C.S.: 522110
Mark K. Mason (Chm, Pres & CEO)
Jay C. Iseman (Chief Credit Officer & Exec VP)
Godfrey B. Evans (Chief Admin Officer, Gen Counsel, Sec & Exec VP)
Darrell S. van Amen (Chief Investment Officer, Treas & Exec VP)
David Parr (Exec VP & Dir-Comml Banking)
Erik D. Hand (Exec VP & Dir-Residential Lending)

Subsidiary (Domestic):

YNB Real Estate LLC (2)
8731 W Hustis St, Milwaukee, WI 53224
Tel.: (414) 364-3604
Web Site: http://www.ynbrealestate.com
Commercial Banking Services
N.A.I.C.S.: 522110

HomeStreet Capital Corporation (1)
601 Union St Ste 2000 Two Union Sq, Seattle, WA 98101-2326
Tel.: (206) 389-7750
Web Site: http://www.homestreet.com
Commercial Banking Services
N.A.I.C.S.: 522110

HOMETRUST BANCSHARES, INC.

10 Woodfin St, Asheville, NC 28801
Tel.: (828) 259-3939 MD
Web Site: https://www.htb.com
HTBI—(NASDAQ)
Rev.: $155,310,000
Assets: $3,549,204,000
Liabilities: $3,160,359,000
Net Worth: $388,845,000
Earnings: $35,653,000
Emp.: 493
Fiscal Year-end: 06/30/22
Bank Holding Company
N.A.I.C.S.: 551111
Tony J. VunCannon (CFO, Treas, Sec & Exec VP)
C. Hunter Westbrook (Vice Chm, Pres & CEO)
Marty T. Caywood (CIO & Exec VP)
R. Parrish Little (Chief Risk Officer & Exec VP)

Subsidiaries:

HomeTrust Bank (1)
10 Woodfin St, Asheville, NC 28801
Tel.: (828) 259-3939
Web Site: http://www.hometrustbanking.com
Commericial Banking
N.A.I.C.S.: 522110
Dana L. Stonestreet (Chm)
Tony J. VunCannon (CFO, Sec & Exec VP)
C. Hunter Westbrook (Pres & CEO)
Richard Tyrone Williams (Vice Chm)
Keith J. Houghton (Chief Credit Officer & Exec VP)
R. Parrish Little (Chief Risk Officer & Exec VP)
Kristin Powell (Exec VP-Mortgage Lending)
Marty T. Caywood (CIO & Exec VP)
Anna Marie Smith (Chief HR Officer & Exec VP)

HONAT BANCORP INC.

724 Main St, Honesdale, PA 18431
Tel.: (570) 253-3355
Web Site: https://www.hnbbank.bank
HONT—(OTCIQ)
Rev.: $42,721,000
Assets: $963,210,000
Liabilities: $838,380,000
Net Worth: $124,830,000
Earnings: $12,866,000
Emp.: 170
Fiscal Year-end: 12/31/23
Offices of Bank Holding Companies
N.A.I.C.S.: 551111

William Schweighofer (Chm)
John P. Burlein (Vice Chm)
David E. Raven (Pres & CEO)
Katherine M. Bryant (Treas)

Subsidiaries:

The Honesdale National Bank (1)
733 Main St, Honesdale, PA 18431
Tel.: (570) 253-3355
Web Site: http://www.hnbbank.com
Emp.: 55
Commercial Banking
N.A.I.C.S.: 522110
Luke W. Woodmansee (Chief Credit Officer & VP)

HONEST COMPANY, INC.

12130 Millennium Dr 5th Fl, Los Angeles, CA 90094
Tel.: (310) 917-9199 CA
Web Site: https://www.honest.com
Year Founded: 2011
HNST—(NASDAQ)
Rev.: $344,365,000
Assets: $201,621,000
Liabilities: $78,482,000
Net Worth: $123,139,000
Earnings: ($39,238,000)
Emp.: 176
Fiscal Year-end: 12/31/23
Online Toxin-Free Household & Personal Care Products Retailer
N.A.I.C.S.: 455219
David Loretta (CFO)
Jessica Marie Alba (Founder)
Christopher Gavigan (Co-Founder)
Steve Austenfeld (VP-IR)
Kate Barton (Chief Growth Officer)
Rick Rexing (Chief Revenue Officer)
Steve Winchell (Exec VP)
Janis Hoyt (Chief People Officer)
Brendan Sheehey (Gen Counsel)
Jennifer Kroog Rosenberg (VP)
Carla Vernon (CEO)

HONEYWELL INTERNATIONAL INC.

4D5 115 Tabor Rd, Morris Plains, NJ 07950
Tel.: (704) 627-6200 DE
Web Site: https://www.honeywell.com
Year Founded: 1885
HON—(NASDAQ)
Rev.: $36,662,000,000
Assets: $61,525,000,000
Liabilities: $45,091,000,000
Net Worth: $16,434,000,000
Earnings: $5,658,000,000
Emp.: 95,000
Fiscal Year-end: 12/31/23
Aerospace, Automotive, Engineered Materials, Automation & Control Products Mfr & Distr
N.A.I.C.S.: 334512
Karen Mattimore (Chief HR Officer & Sr VP)
Kenneth J. West (Pres/CEO-Energy & Sustainability Solutions)
Torsten Pilz (Chief Supply Chain Officer & Sr VP)
Vimal Kapur (Chm & CEO)
Gregory P. Lewis (CFO & Sr VP)
Sheila Jordan (Chief Digital Tech Officer & Sr VP)
Kevin Dehoff (Chief Strategy Officer & Pres/CEO-Honeywell Connected Enterprise)
Anne T. Madden (Gen Counsel & Sr VP)
Eric Seidel (Chief Comml Officer & Sr VP)

Subsidiaries:

ADI-Gardiner Limited (1)
61 Southwark Street, London, SE1 0HL, United Kingdom
Tel.: (44) 2079027910

Web Site: http://www.adi-gardiner.com
Electric Equipment Mfr
N.A.I.C.S.: 335999

AdvanSix's Hopewell Facility (1)
905 E Randolph Rd, Hopewell, VA 23860
Tel.: (804) 541-5000
Web Site: https://www.advansix.com
Chemical & Resin Product Mfr
N.A.I.C.S.: 325998

Ballard Unmanned Systems, Inc. (1)
153 Northboro Rd, Southborough, MA
01772-1034
Tel.: (508) 490-9960
Fuel Cell Mfr
N.A.I.C.S.: 334413
Paul Osenar *(Founder, Pres & CEO)*

**Elster American Meter Company,
LLC** (1)
2221 Industrial Rd, Nebraska City, NE
68410-6889
Tel.: (402) 873-8200
Gas Measurement Product Mfr
N.A.I.C.S.: 334513

Elster s.r.o. (1)
Nam Dr A Schweitzera 194, 916 01, Stara
Tura, Slovakia
Tel.: (421) 32 323 7260
Web Site: http://www.elster.sk
Emp.: 400
Residential Mfr
N.A.I.C.S.: 334512
Radoslav Masar *(Area Mgr)*

Hand Held Products, Inc (1)
700 Visions Dr, Skaneateles Falls, NY
13153
Tel.: (315) 685-8945
Web Site: http://www.handheld.com
Residential Electric Lighting Fixture Services
N.A.I.C.S.: 335131

Honeywell (China) Co., Ltd. (1)
No 555 Huanke Road, Zhangjiang Hi-Tech
Park Pudong New Area, Shanghai, 201203,
China
Tel.: (86) 4006396841
Web Site: http://www.honeywell.com.cn
Emp.: 1,800
Relays & Industrial Control Equipments Mfr
N.A.I.C.S.: 335314

Honeywell Aerospace (1)
1720 E Grant St, Phoenix, AZ 85034-3442
Tel.: (602) 365-3099
Web Site:
https://www.aerospace.honeywell.com
Sales Range: $1-4.9 Billion
Emp.: 59,000
Develops & Manufactures Products for Aircraft, Missile & Commercial Applications
N.A.I.C.S.: 811210
Mike Madsen *(Pres & CEO)*

Subsidiary (Non-US):

**AlliedSignal Aerospace Service
Corporation** (2)
Andrew Lloyd Honeywell House Arlington
Business Park, Bracknell, RG11EB, Berks,
United Kingdom (100%)
Tel.: (44) 14803533020
Aerospace Services
N.A.I.C.S.: 488190

Unit (Domestic):

**Honeywell Aerospace - Boyne
City** (2)
375 N Lake St, Boyne City, MI 49712-1101
Tel.: (231) 582-6526
Web Site:
http://www.honeywellinternational.com
Sales Range: $75-99.9 Million
Emp.: 268
Aircraft Components Mfr
N.A.I.C.S.: 336413

**Honeywell Aerospace - Houston, Air
Center Boulevard** (2)
16580 Air Center Blvd Ste 400, Houston,
TX 77032
Tel.: (281) 821-1021
Web Site: http://www.honeywell.com
Sales Range: $25-49.9 Million
Emp.: 100
Aerospace Systems & Components Mfr

N.A.I.C.S.: 336412
David M. Cote *(Chm)*

**Honeywell Aerospace -
Moorestown** (2)
121 Whittendale Dr A, Moorestown, NJ
08057-1373
Tel.: (856) 234-5020
Sales Range: $25-49.9 Million
Emp.: 75
Aircraft Wireless Network Product Mfr
N.A.I.C.S.: 336413

Honeywell Aerospace - Norcross (2)
660 Engineering Dr, Norcross, GA 30092
Tel.: (770) 263-9200
Sales Range: $350-399.9 Million
Emp.: 1,160
Wireless Systems; Antenna, Microwave,
Digital Command & Control, Optical &
Broadband Products Mfr
N.A.I.C.S.: 334220
Darius E. Adamczyk *(Pres)*

Honeywell Aerospace - Torrance (2)
2525 W 190th St, Torrance, CA
90504-6002 (100%)
Tel.: (310) 323-9500
Web Site: http://www.honeywell.com
Emp.: 1,500
Aerospace Equipment Mfr
N.A.I.C.S.: 336413

Honeywell Aerospace - Urbana (2)
550 State Rte 55, Urbana, OH 43078
Tel.: (937) 484-2000
Web Site: http://www.honeywellaes.com
Emp.: 800
Aircraft Lighting, Displays & Electronics Designer & Mfr
N.A.I.C.S.: 336413

Division (Domestic):

**Honeywell Aerospace Electronic
Systems** (2)
21111 N 19th Ave, Phoenix, AZ
85027 (100%)
Tel.: (602) 365-3099
Web Site: http://www.honeywell.com
Sales Range: $1-4.9 Billion
Emp.: 17,000
Aerospace & Electronic Systems
N.A.I.C.S.: 927110

Subsidiary (Non-US):

Honeywell Aerospace Yeovil (2)
Bunford Lane, Yeovil, BA20 2YD, Somerset,
United Kingdom
Tel.: (44) 1935475181
Web Site:
http://www.aerospace.honeywell.com
Aerospace Control Systems
N.A.I.C.S.: 334519

Unit (Domestic):

Honeywell Air Transport Systems (2)
21111 N 19th Ave, Phoenix, AZ 85027
Tel.: (602) 436-2311
Sales Range: $100-124.9 Million
Emp.: 2,000
Automatic Flight Control, Flight Management, Navigation, Surveillance, Warning &
Inertial Reference Systems, Cockpit Displays & Air Data Computers for Large Commercial Aircraft
N.A.I.C.S.: 334511
Patty Fiori *(Sr Mgr-Contracts)*

**Honeywell Aircraft Landing
Systems** (2)
3520 Westmoor St, South Bend, IN 46628-
1373
Tel.: (574) 231-2000
Web Site: http://www.honeywell.com
Sales Range: $350-399.9 Million
Emp.: 1,000
Aircraft Landing Components Mfr
N.A.I.C.S.: 336413

Honeywell Airport System (2)
2121 Union Pl, Simi Valley, CA 93065
Tel.: (805) 522-1624
Sales Range: $25-49.9 Million
Emp.: 3
Airport Lighting Fixtures Mfr
N.A.I.C.S.: 335132

David M. Cote *(Chm)*
Richard Muler *(Branch Mgr)*

**Honeywell Commercial Electronic
Systems** (2)
1 Technology Ctr 23500 W 105th St,
Olathe, KS 66061 (100%)
Tel.: (913) 782-0400
Web Site: http://www51.honeywell.com
Sales Range: $450-499.9 Million
Emp.: 1,300
Aircraft Electronics Mfr
N.A.I.C.S.: 336412

**Honeywell Defense Avionics
Systems** (2)
9201 San Mateo Blvd NE, Albuquerque, NM
87113
Tel.: (708) 633-1166
Web Site: http://www.honeywell.com
Sales Range: $350-399.9 Million
Emp.: 1,000
Military Aircraft Components Mfr
N.A.I.C.S.: 336413

Honeywell Defense and Space Electronic Systems (2)
1433 Ridgway Pkwy, Minneapolis, MN
55413 (100%)
Tel.: (612) 951-5365
Web Site: http://honeywell.com
Sales Range: $150-199.9 Million
Laser Inertial Navigation & Guidance System
N.A.I.C.S.: 423420

Honeywell Electronic Materials (2)
15128 E Euclid Ave, Spokane Valley, WA
99216 (100%)
Tel.: (509) 252-2200
Web Site: http://www.honeywell.com
Rev.: $63,800,000
Emp.: 350
Residential Mfr
N.A.I.C.S.: 334512

**Honeywell Engine Systems &
Services** (2)
717 N Bendix Dr, South Bend, IN
46628 (100%)
Tel.: (574) 231-3000
Web Site: http://www51.honeywell.com
Sales Range: $50-74.9 Million
Emp.: 7
Nautical Instrument Mfr
N.A.I.C.S.: 334511

**Honeywell Federal Manufacturing
Technology** (2)
14520 Botts Rd, Kansas City, MO 64147
Tel.: (816) 488-2000
Web Site: https://www.kcnsc.doe.gov
Government Equipment Mfr
N.A.I.C.S.: 334511

Subsidiary (Non-US):

Honeywell Global Tracking (2)
Miller Court Severn Drive, Tewkesbury Business Park, Tewkesbury, GL20 8DN, Gloucestershire, United Kingdom
Tel.: (44) 1684278610
Sales Range: $10-24.9 Million
Satellite Telematics, Asset Tracking & Monitoring Services
N.A.I.C.S.: 335999

Unit (Domestic):

Honeywell Space Systems (2)
13350 US Hwy 19 N, Clearwater, FL
33764 (100%)
Tel.: (727) 539-2997
Web Site: http://www.honeywell.com
Sales Range: $500-549.9 Million
Emp.: 1,800
Spacecraft Guidance, Navigation & Control
Systems Designer & Mfr
N.A.I.C.S.: 336419

Subsidiary (Domestic):

Phoenix Controls Corporation (2)
75 Discovery Way, Acton, MA
01720 (100%)
Tel.: (978) 795-1285
Web Site: http://www.phoenixcontrols.com
Sales Range: $10-24.9 Million
Emp.: 112

Air Flow, Air Conditioning & Refrigeration
Controls Mfr
N.A.I.C.S.: 334512

Honeywell Aerospace Avionics Malaysia Sdn Bhd. (1)
3057 Tingkat Perusahaan 4B Kawasan
Perisahaan, Pulau Penang, 13600, Malaysia
Tel.: (60) 4 398 9112
Aircraft Engine & Engine Part Whslr
N.A.I.C.S.: 423860

Honeywell Aerospace GmbH (1)
Frankfurter Strasse 41-65, 65479, Raunheim, Germany
Tel.: (49) 61424050
Aircraft Engine Mfr
N.A.I.C.S.: 336412

**Honeywell Aerospace de Mexico, S.
de R.L. de C.V.** (1)
Circuito Aeroespacial Lote Suite 2, Mexicali,
BC, Mexico
Tel.: (52) 6865805300
Aircraft Engine & Engine Part Whslr
N.A.I.C.S.: 423860

**Honeywell Analytics Asia Pacific Co.,
Ltd.** (1)
Sangam IT Tower 4 5 7th Floor Sangamdong 434 World Cupbuk-ro, Mapo-gu,
Seoul, 03922, Korea (South)
Tel.: (82) 279961145
Web Site: http://www.honeywell.com
Aerospace Hardware Parts Mfr
N.A.I.C.S.: 336411

**Honeywell Automation & Control
Solutions** (1)
115 Tabor Rd, Morris Plains, NJ 07950
Tel.: (973) 455-2000
Web Site: http://www.honeywell.com
Temperature, Access, Security, Fire &
Safety Control Systems Developer & Mfr
N.A.I.C.S.: 334512

Subsidiary (Non-US):

Elster Group GmbH (2)
Steinern Strasse 19-21, 55252, Mainz-
Kastel, Germany
Tel.: (49) 6 134 6050
Web Site: https://www.elster-instromet.com
Emp.: 7,000
Holding Company; Water, Gas & Electricity
Metering Equipment Mfr
N.A.I.C.S.: 551112

Subsidiary (US):

Eclipse Inc. (3)
1665 Elmwood Rd, Rockford, IL 61103
Tel.: (815) 877-3031
Web Site: http://www.eclipsenet.com
Industrial Heating & Drying Products Design
& Mfr
N.A.I.C.S.: 333414

Subsidiary (Domestic):

Algas-SDI International LLC (4)
151 S Michigan St, Seattle, WA 98108
Tel.: (206) 789-5410
Web Site: http://www.algas-sdi.com
Liquified Petroleum Gas Processing, Vaporizing & Mixing Equipment Mfr
N.A.I.C.S.: 333998
Kirsten Bellar *(Sls Dir-LP-Gas Distributed
Products & Sls Mgr-North Americas)*

Subsidiary (US):

**Elster Canadian Meter Company,
LLC** (3)
2221 Industrial Rd, Nebraska City, NE
68410
Tel.: (402) 873-8200
Web Site: http://www.elster-
americanmeter.com
Metering Device Mfr
N.A.I.C.S.: 334519

Subsidiary (Domestic):

Elster GmbH (3)
Strotheweg 1, Buren, 49504, Lotte, Germany
Tel.: (49) 54112140
Web Site: https://www.kromschroeder.de
Gas Metering Products Mfr

Honeywell International Inc.—(Continued)

N.A.I.C.S.: 334519
Martin Schroder *(Mng Dir)*
Ulrich Clasemann *(Mng Dir)*
Michael Zimmermann *(Mng Dir)*
Olga Slipetska *(Mng Dir)*
Silvester Ibes *(Chm-Supervisory Bd)*

Elster Instromet GmbH (3)
Steinern Strasse 19-21, 55252, Mainz-
Kastel, Germany
Tel.: (49) 61346050
Web Site: http://www.elster-instromet.com
Gas Metering Equipment Mfr
N.A.I.C.S.: 334519

Subsidiary (Domestic):

**Elster Instromet Production
GmbH** (4)
Steinern Str 19-21 129, 55252, Mainz, Ger-
many
Tel.: (49) 61346050
Web Site: http://www.elster.com
Gas Measuring & Regulating Devices Mfr
N.A.I.C.S.: 334519

Subsidiary (Non-US):

Elster N.V./S.A. (4)
Rue du Fourneau 28, 4030, Liege, Belgium
Tel.: (32) 43495049
Web Site: http://www.elster-cogegaz.be
Gas Regulator Mfr
N.A.I.C.S.: 334513

Elster S.r.l. (4)
Via Cava Trombetta 5, 20090, Segrate, Italy
Tel.: (39) 02 2130321
Web Site: http://www.elster.it
Gas Metering Device Mfr
N.A.I.C.S.: 334519

Elster-Instromet A/S (4)
Laesovej 3 B, 9800, Hjorring, Denmark
Tel.: (45) 98911055
Web Site: http://www.elster-instromet.dk
Gas Measuring Equipment Mfr
N.A.I.C.S.: 334519

**Elster-Instromet Vertriebsgesellschaft
m.b.H.** (4)
Heiligenstadter Str 45, 1190, Vienna, Aus-
tria
Tel.: (43) 136926550
Web Site: http://www.elster-instromet.at
Gas Measuring Equipment Mfr
N.A.I.C.S.: 334519
Thomas Linzer *(Mng Dir)*

Subsidiary (US):

Hauck Manufacturing Company (4)
1665 Elmwood Rd, Rockford, IL 61103
Tel.: (815) 877-3031
Web Site:
http://www.thermalsolutions.honeywell.com
Industrial Oil & Gas Burners & Equipment
Mfr
N.A.I.C.S.: 333414

Subsidiary (US):

Elster Solutions LLC (3)
208 S Rogers Ln, Raleigh, NC 27610-2144
Tel.: (919) 212-4800
Web Site: http://www.elstersolutions.com
Natural Gas Measurement & Controlling
Devices Mfr
N.A.I.C.S.: 334514

Subsidiary (Non-US):

**Elster Water Metering Holdings
Limited** (3)
130 Camford Way Sundon Park, Luton,
LU3 3AN, Bedfordshire, United Kingdom
Tel.: (44) 1582 846400
Web Site: http://www.elstermetering.com
Water Metering Equipment Mfr
N.A.I.C.S.: 334514

Subsidiary (US):

Elster AMCO Water, LLC (4)
10 SW 49th Ave Bldg 100, Ocala, FL 34474
Tel.: (352) 369-6500
Web Site: http://www.elsteramcowater.com
Water Metering Equipment Mfr
N.A.I.C.S.: 334514

Subsidiary (Non-US):

Elster Metering Pty Ltd. (4)
55 Northcorp Boulevard, Broadmeadows,
3047, VIC, Australia
Tel.: (61) 393552000
Web Site: http://www.elstermetering.com
Water Metering Equipment Mfr
N.A.I.C.S.: 334514

Elster Water Metering B.V. (4)
Minervum 7146, 4817 ZN, Breda, Nether-
lands
Tel.: (31) 765727333
Web Site: http://www.elster.nl
Water Metering Equipment Mfr
N.A.I.C.S.: 334514

Subsidiary (Domestic):

Elster Water Metering Ltd. (4)
130 Camford Way Sundon Park, Luton,
LU3 3AN, Bedfordshire, United Kingdom
Tel.: (44) 1582 846400
Web Site: http://www.elstermetering.com
Water Metering Equipment Mfr
N.A.I.C.S.: 334514

Subsidiary (Non-US):

EnergyICT N.V. (3)
Bedrijvencentrum Generaal Deprezstraat
2/050, 8530, Harelbeke, Belgium
Tel.: (32) 56245691
Web Site: http://www.elstersolutions.com
Energy Management Solutions Services
N.A.I.C.S.: 541690

Affiliate (Non-US):

**Sejong-AMC Corporation Co.
Ltd.** (3)
740 4 Jakjeon Dong, Incheon, Gyeyang Gu,
Korea (South)
Tel.: (82) 325402500
Web Site: http://www.sjamc.co.kr
Metering Products Mfr
N.A.I.C.S.: 334519

Division (Domestic):

Honeywell Building Solutions (2)
1985 Douglas Dr N, Golden Valley, MN
55422-3992
Tel.: (763) 954-5421
Heating, Ventilation, Air Conditioning & Se-
curity System Installation & Maintenance
Services
N.A.I.C.S.: 333415

Subsidiary (Non-US):

Trend Control Systems Limited (3)
Honeywell House Skimped Hill Lane, Brack-
nell, RG12 1EB, Berks, United Kingdom
Tel.: (44) 1403211888
Intelligent Building Controls Mfr
N.A.I.C.S.: 332510

Division (Domestic):

**Honeywell Environmental & Combus-
tion Controls** (2)
1985 Douglas Dr N, Golden Valley, MN
55422
Tel.: (763) 950-5500
Web Site: http://yourhome.honeywell.com
Heating, Ventilation, Air Purification & Lighting Control System Developer & Mfr
N.A.I.C.S.: 334512

Subsidiary (Domestic):

Inncom International Inc. (3)
277 W Main St, Niantic, CT 06357
Tel.: (860) 739-4468
Web Site: http://www.inncom.com
Sales Range: $10-24.9 Million
Emp.: 50
Developer, Manufacturer & Marketer of Ad-
vanced Guestroom Control Systems
N.A.I.C.S.: 334419

Maxon Corporation (3)
201 E 18th St, Muncie, IN 47307-0068
Tel.: (765) 284-3304
Web Site: http://www.maxoncorp.com
Sales Range: $75-99.9 Million
Emp.: 500
Industrial Combustion Equipment & Valves
Mfr

N.A.I.C.S.: 333414

Subsidiary (Non-US):

**Maxon Combustion Equipment
Shanghai Co. Ltd.** (4)
1 4f No 225 Meisheng Rd Waigaoq, Pu-
dong N Shanghai, Shanghai, 200131,
China
Tel.: (86) 2158661166
Sales Range: $100-124.9 Million
Emp.: 80
Combustion Control Instruments
N.A.I.C.S.: 334513

Maxon International B.V.B.A. (4)
Luchthavenlaan 16-18, 1800, Vilvoorde,
Belgium
Tel.: (32) 22550909
Web Site: http://www.maxoncorp.com
Sales Range: $50-74.9 Million
Emp.: 150
Mfr of Combustion Equipment & Valves
N.A.I.C.S.: 334513
Bart Geyskens *(Mng Dir)*

Subsidiary (Non-US):

Maxon B.V. (5)
Archimedesstraat 10, 3316 AB, Dordrecht,
Netherlands
Tel.: (31) 786393770
Web Site: http://www.maxoncorp.com
Sales Range: $800-899.9 Million
Emp.: 6
Industrial Combustion Equipment & Valves
Distr
N.A.I.C.S.: 333414

Maxon Combustion Systems A/S (5)
Nordager 22, 6000, Kolding, Denmark
Tel.: (45) 70270999
Web Site: http://www.maxoncorp.com
Sales Range: $100-124.9 Million
Emp.: 1
Industrial Combustion Equipment & Valves
Distr
N.A.I.C.S.: 333414

Maxon Combustion Systems AB (5)
Rotebergsvagen 13, 19278, Sollentuna,
Sweden
Tel.: (46) 87542006
Web Site: http://www.maxoncorp.com
Sales Range: $100-124.9 Million
Emp.: 2
Industrial Combustion Equipment & Valves
Distr
N.A.I.C.S.: 333414

Maxon Combustion Systems Ltd. (5)
Unit 14-15, The Courtyard, Buntsford Drive
Bromsgrove, Coleshill, B60 3DJ, United
Kingdom
Tel.: (44) 1675464334
Web Site: http://www.maxoncorp.com
Sales Range: $25-49.9 Million
Emp.: 11
Industrial Combustion Equipment & Valves
Distr
N.A.I.C.S.: 333414

Maxon GmbH (5)
Niederlassung Gottlieb Daimler Strasse 17
Kernen, 71394, Stuttgart, Germany
Tel.: (49) 7151949040
Web Site: http://www.maxoncorp.com
Sales Range: $25-49.9 Million
Emp.: 7
Industrial Combustion Equipment & Valves
Distr
N.A.I.C.S.: 333414

Maxon GmbH (5)
Schuermannstrasse 32, Essen, 45136, Ger-
many
Tel.: (49) 201851160
Web Site: http://www.maxoncorp.com
Sales Range: $1-9.9 Million
Emp.: 10
Industrial Combustion Equipment & Valves
Distr
N.A.I.C.S.: 333414

Maxon S.A.R.L. (5)
12 Chaussee Jules Cesar Osny, PO Box
G0339, Pomtoise, 95526, Cergy, Cedex,
France
Tel.: (33) 134201080
Web Site: http://www.maxoncorp.com

Sales Range: $25-49.9 Million
Emp.: 9
Industrial Combustion Equipment & Valves
Distr
N.A.I.C.S.: 333414

Division (Domestic):

Honeywell Life Safety (2)
12 Clintonville Rd, Northford, CT 06472
Tel.: (203) 484-7161
Web Site:
http://www.honeywelllifesafety.com
Mfr of Fire Systems, Smoke & Gas Detection Sensors, Personal Protective Equipment & Remote Healthcare Monitoring Devices
N.A.I.C.S.: 922160
Mark Levy *(Pres)*

Subsidiary (Non-US):

Honeywell Analytics AG (3)
Javastrasse 2, Hegnau, 8604, Switzerland
Web Site:
http://www.honeywellanalytics.com
Sales Range: $25-49.9 Million
Emp.: 120
Toxic & Flammable Gas & Fire Detection
Systems Mfr
N.A.I.C.S.: 922160

Plant (US):

Honeywell Analytics (4)
405 Barclay Blvd, Lincolnshire, IL 60069
Tel.: (847) 955-8200
Web Site:
http://www.honeywellanalytics.com
Sales Range: $10-24.9 Million
Toxic & Flammable Gas & Fire Detection
Systems Mfr
N.A.I.C.S.: 922160

Subsidiary (Non-US):

Honeywell Analytics AG (4)
Elsenheimer Strasse 43, 80687, Munich,
Germany
Tel.: (49) 897919220
Web Site:
http://www.honeywellanalytics.com
Sales Range: $1-9.9 Million
Emp.: 10
Toxic & Flammable Gas & Fire Detection
Systems Mfr
N.A.I.C.S.: 922160

Honeywell Analytics France S.A. (4)
Route De L Orme Cd 128 Parc Tech-
nologique Saint A Cd 12, PO Box 87,
91190, Saint Aubin, France **(100%)**
Tel.: (33) 810204111
Web Site:
http://www.honeywellanalytics.com
Sales Range: $1-9.9 Million
Emp.: 15
Toxic & Flammable Gas & Fire Detection
Systems Whslr
N.A.I.C.S.: 922160

Plant (US):

**Honeywell Analytics
Instrumentation** (4)
651 S Main St, Middletown, CT
06457-4252 **(100%)**
Tel.: (860) 344-1079
Web Site: http://www.sperian.com
Sales Range: $25-49.9 Million
Emp.: 100
Measuring & Controlling Device Mfr
N.A.I.C.S.: 334519

Subsidiary (Non-US):

Honeywell Analytics Limited (4)
4 Stinsford Road, Poole, BH17 0RW,
United Kingdom
Tel.: (44) 1202645544
Web Site:
http://www.honeywellanalytics.com
Toxic & Flammable Gas & Fire Detection
Systems Mfr
N.A.I.C.S.: 922160

Subsidiary (Domestic):

**Honeywell Safety Products USA,
Inc.** (3)

4090 Azalea Dr, Charleston, SC 29405
Tel.: (843) 554-0660
Web Site: http://www.honeywellsafety.com
Surgical Instrument Mfr
N.A.I.C.S.: 339112

Subsidiary (Domestic):

**Honeywell First Responder
Products** **(4)**
1 Innovation Ct, Dayton, OH 45414-3967
Tel.: (937) 264-2662
Web Site:
    http://www.honeywellfirstresponder.com
Sales Range: $200-249.9 Million
Emp.: 430
Fire & Emergency Medical Services Protec-
tive Equipment Mfr
N.A.I.C.S.: 315990

Honeywell Safety Products **(4)**
900 Douglas Pike, Smithfield, RI 02917
Tel.: (401) 943-4400
Web Site: http://www.honeywellsafety.com
Emp.: 200
Personal Protection Equipment Mfr
N.A.I.C.S.: 315990

Subsidiary (Non-US):

**Honeywell North Safety Products
Canada** **(5)**
10550 Parkway Blvd, Anjou, H1J 2K4, QC,
Canada
Tel.: (514) 351-7233
Web Site: http://www.northsafety.com
Sales Range: $125-149.9 Million
Emp.: 200
Protective Glove, Eyewear & Clothing Mfr
N.A.I.C.S.: 315990

**North Safety Products Europe
B.V.** **(5)**
Anodeweg 1, 4338 RA, Middelburg, Nether-
lands
Tel.: (31) 118656400
Web Site: http://www.northsafety.nl
Sales Range: $100-124.9 Million
Emp.: 120
Protective Apparel, Eyewear & Glove Mfr
N.A.I.C.S.: 315990

Subsidiary (Non-US):

**Honeywell Safety Products Australia
Pty Ltd** **(4)**
43 Garden Blvd, Dingley, 3172, VIC,
Australia **(100%)**
Tel.: (61) 1300139166
Web Site: http://www.honeywellsafety.com
Sales Range: $25-49.9 Million
Emp.: 50
Surgical Appliance & Supplies Mfr
N.A.I.C.S.: 339113
Heather Torrey (Sls Dir)

Subsidiary (Domestic):

**Honeywell Safety Products Emer-
gency Eyewash** **(4)**
900 Douglas Pkwy, Smithfield, RI
02917 **(100%)**
Tel.: (401) 233-0333
Web Site: http://www.sperian.com
Chemical Product & Preparation Mfr
N.A.I.C.S.: 325998

**Honeywell Safety Products Gloves
USA, LLC** **(4)**
85 Innsbruck Dr, Buffalo, NY
14201 **(100%)**
Tel.: (716) 668-2000
Web Site: http://www.honeywellsafety.com
Safety Glove Mfr
N.A.I.C.S.: 315990

**Honeywell Safety Products Hearing
Protection, LLC** **(4)**
7828 Waterville Rd, San Diego, CA
92154 **(100%)**
Tel.: (619) 661-8383
Web Site: http://www.howardleight.com
Sales Range: $25-49.9 Million
Emp.: 50
Surgical Appliance & Supplies Mfr
N.A.I.C.S.: 339113

Subsidiary (Non-US):

**Honeywell Safety Products Italia
Srl** **(4)**

Via Vittorio Veneto 142, Dorno Lombardy,
27020, Pavia, Italy **(100%)**
Tel.: (39) 0382812111
Web Site: http://www.honeywellsafety.com
Sales Range: $25-49.9 Million
Emp.: 25
Industrial Supplies Whslr
N.A.I.C.S.: 423840

Subsidiary (Domestic):

**Honeywell Safety Products Respira-
tory Protection USA, LLC** **(4)**
3001 S Susan St, Santa Ana, CA
92704 **(100%)**
Tel.: (800) 821-7236
Web Site: http://www.survivair.com
Sales Range: $25-49.9 Million
Emp.: 100
Ophthalmic Goods Mfr
N.A.I.C.S.: 339115

**Honeywell Salisbury Electrical
Safety** **(4)**
101 E Crossroads Pkwy Ste A, Bolingbrook,
IL 60440-3690
Tel.: (847) 679-6700
Web Site:
    http://www.salisburybyhoneywell.com
Sales Range: $75-99.9 Million
Emp.: 220
Electrical Safety Products Mfr
N.A.I.C.S.: 326299

Subsidiary (Non-US):

King's Safetywear Limited **(4)**
22 Defu Lane 1, Singapore, 539493, Singa-
pore
Tel.: (65) 62878787
Web Site: http://www.kingsafetywear.com
Sales Range: $125-149.9 Million
Emp.: 1,500
Holding Company; Industrial Safety Foot-
wear Mfr & Distr
N.A.I.C.S.: 551112

Subsidiary (Domestic):

**King's Shoe Manufacturing Pte.
Ltd.** **(5)**
22 Defu Lane 1, Singapore, 539493, Singa-
pore
Tel.: (65) 6383 8787
Industrial Safety Footwear Mfr
N.A.I.C.S.: 316210
Johnny Chang (Gen Mgr-Sls)

Subsidiary (Domestic):

Miller Technical Service **(4)**
1345 15th St, Franklin, PA
16323-1941 **(100%)**
Tel.: (814) 432-2118
Web Site: http://www.millerfallprotection.com
Disinfecting & Pest Control Services
N.A.I.C.S.: 561710

Subsidiary (Non-US):

Sperian Protection Apparel Ltd. **(4)**
4200 St-Laurent Blvd 6th Fl, Montreal, H2W
2R2, QC, Canada **(100%)**
Tel.: (514) 282-0503
Web Site: http://www.sperian.com
Sales Range: $25-49.9 Million
Emp.: 100
Apparel Accessories & Apparel Mfr
N.A.I.C.S.: 315990

Sperian Protection Armor SAS **(4)**
Indus Zone ZI de la Gare, Plaintel, 22940,
Rennes, France **(100%)**
Tel.: (33) 296429242
Web Site: http://www.honywell.com
Sales Range: $50-74.9 Million
Emp.: 130
Nonwoven Fabric Mills
N.A.I.C.S.: 313230

Sperian Protection Clothing S.A. **(4)**
Zac Des Pres Secs, Lozanne, Lyon,
France **(100%)**
Tel.: (33) 474267940
Web Site: http://www.honywell.com
Sales Range: $25-49.9 Million
Emp.: 100
Plastics Products
N.A.I.C.S.: 326199

Sperian Protection Workwear Srl **(4)**

Via Vittorio Veneto 142, Dorno, Pavia,
27020, Dorno, Italy **(100%)**
Tel.: (39) 0382812111
Web Site: http://www.sperianprotection.it
Waterproof Outerwear
N.A.I.C.S.: 315120
Paolo Randazzo (Mng Dir)

Subsidiary (Non-US):

MK Electric Limited **(3)**
The Arnold Centre Paycocke Rd, Basildon,
SS14 3EA, Essex, United
Kingdom **(100%)**
Tel.: (44) 1268563000
Web Site: http://www.mkelectric.co.uk
Sales Range: $125-149.9 Million
Emp.: 250
Electric & Electronic Connection Equipment
Systems Mfr
N.A.I.C.S.: 335999

Subsidiary (Domestic):

System Sensor **(3)**
3825 Ohio Ave, Saint Charles, IL
60174 **(100%)**
Tel.: (630) 377-6580
Web Site: http://www.systemsensor.com
Sales Range: $350-399.9 Million
Sensor Equipment for Fire Alarm Systems
Mfr
N.A.I.C.S.: 334290

Subsidiary (Non-US):

System Sensor Canada **(4)**
6581 Kitimat Rd Unit 6, Mississauga, L5N
3T5, ON, Canada **(100%)**
Tel.: (905) 812-0767
Web Site: http://www.systemsensor.ca
Sales Range: $25-49.9 Million
Emp.: 20
Distribution of Fire Alarm Equipment
N.A.I.C.S.: 423610

System Sensor Europe **(4)**
Unit C2 Foundry Lane, Horsham, RH13
5YZ, West Sussex, United
Kingdom **(100%)**
Tel.: (44) 1403226240
Web Site:
    http://www.systemsensoreurope.com
Sales Range: $10-24.9 Million
Emp.: 6
Distribution of Fire Alarm Equipment
N.A.I.C.S.: 423610

**Xi'an System Sensor Electronics
Ltd.** **(4)**
No 40 Zhang Ba 2nd Road, Hi-tech Devel-
opment Zone, Xi'an, 710075,
China **(60%)**
Tel.: (86) 2985387800
Web Site: http://www.systemsensor.com.cn
Sales Range: $50-74.9 Million
Emp.: 170
Fire Alarm & Related Sensory Equipment
Mfr
N.A.I.C.S.: 334511

Division (Domestic):

Honeywell Process Solutions **(2)**
1860 W Rose Garden Ln, Phoenix, AZ
85027 **(100%)**
Tel.: (610) 641-3610
Web Site: http://hpsweb.honeywell.com
Automation & Process Control Systems
Developer
N.A.I.C.S.: 334512

Subsidiary (Domestic):

Honeywell Enraf Americas, Inc. **(3)**
2000 Northfield Ct, Roswell, GA 30076
Tel.: (770) 475-1900
Web Site: http://www.honeywellenraf.com
Sales Range: $25-49.9 Million
Emp.: 36
Precision Fluid Management Services; De-
velopment, Manufacturing, Sales, Service &
Support of Precision Instrumentation & Soft-
ware Systems for Bulk Storage Manage-
ment
N.A.I.C.S.: 334513

Mercury Instruments LLC **(3)**
3940 Virginia Ave, Cincinnati, OH 45227
Tel.: (513) 272-1111

Web Site:
    http://www.mercuryinstruments.com
Sales Range: $1-9.9 Million
Emp.: 75
Measuring & Controlling Device Mfr
N.A.I.C.S.: 334519

Division (Domestic):

Honeywell Security **(2)**
2 Corporate Center Dr Ste 100, Melville, NY
11747 **(100%)**
Tel.: (516) 577-2000
Web Site:
    http://www.security.honeywell.com
Burglar & Fire Alarm Mfr
N.A.I.C.S.: 561621

Subsidiary (Domestic):

ADI **(3)**
263 Old Country Rd, Melville, NY
11747 **(100%)**
Tel.: (631) 692-1000
Web Site: http://www.adiglobal.us
Sales Range: $75-99.9 Million
Emp.: 200
Distribution of Burglar Fire Alarms, CCTV,
Intercom & Sound Systems, Telephone &
Card Access System
N.A.I.C.S.: 423610

Branch (Domestic):

ADI **(4)**
5818 W Spring Mtn Rd, Las Vegas, NV
89146
Tel.: (702) 362-8788
Web Site: http://www.adilink.com
Rev.: $460,000
Emp.: 4
Distribution of Security Devices
N.A.I.C.S.: 423710

ADI Puerto Rico **(4)**
Rexco Industrial Park, Guaynabo, PR
00968
Tel.: (787) 793-8830
Web Site: http://www.adiglobal.com
Sales Range: $10-24.9 Million
Emp.: 7
Distr of Security Alarm Systems
N.A.I.C.S.: 423610
Luis Colon (Branch Mgr)

Subsidiary (Non-US):

ADI Global Distribution **(3)**
Amperestraat 41, 1446 TR, Purmerend,
Netherlands **(100%)**
Tel.: (31) 882345400
Web Site: https://www.adiglobal.nl
Sales Range: $10-24.9 Million
Emp.: 57
Security Alarm Systems Mfr
N.A.I.C.S.: 561621
Robert Aarnes (Pres)

Subsidiary (Domestic):

Honeywell Access **(3)**
135 W Forest Hill Ave, Oak Creek, WI
53154 **(100%)**
Tel.: (414) 762-5136
Web Site: http://www.honeywellaccess.com
Sales Range: $75-99.9 Million
Emp.: 60
Electronic Access Controls Mfr
N.A.I.C.S.: 335999

Branch (Domestic):

Vindicator Security Solutions **(4)**
5307 Industrial Oaks Blvd Ste 130, Austin,
TX 78735
Tel.: (512) 301-8400
Web Site: http://www.vintec.com
Sales Range: $10-24.9 Million
Emp.: 50
Security System Mfr
N.A.I.C.S.: 561621

Subsidiary (Non-US):

Honeywell Ademco Security **(3)**
Units 01-02 11/F CDW Bldg 388 Castle
Peak Rd, Tsuen Wan, China (Hong
Kong) **(60%)**
Tel.: (852) 24052323
Web Site:
    http://www.cn.security.honeywell.com

Honeywell International Inc.—(Continued)

Sales Range: $50-74.9 Million
Emp.: 50
Security Services
N.A.I.C.S.: 561621

Subsidiary (Domestic):

Honeywell Scanning & Mobility (3)
700 Visions Dr, Skaneateles Falls, NY
13153-0208
Tel.: (315) 554-6000
Web Site: http://www.honeywellaidc.com
Sales Range: $250-299.9 Million
Automatic Identification & Data Collection
Products & Services
N.A.I.C.S.: 334111

Subsidiary (Domestic):

Intermec, Inc. (4)
6001 36th Ave W, Everett, WA 98203-1264
Tel.: (425) 348-2600
Web Site: http://www.intermec.com
Sales Range: $750-799.9 Million
Emp.: 2,214
Designs, Develops, Integrates & Sells
Wired & Wireless Automated Identification &
Data Collection Solutions
N.A.I.C.S.: 334118

Subsidiary (Non-US):

Intermec (South America) Ltda. (5)
Avenida Tambore 267 16 E 17 Andares
Torre Sul, Varginha, Barueri, 06460-000,
SP, Brazil
Tel.: (55) 1137116770
Web Site: http://www.intermec.com.br
Automated Identification & Data Capture
Equipment Mfr & Sales
N.A.I.C.S.: 334118

Division (Domestic):

Intermec Media Products (5)
9290 Le Saint Dr, Fairfield, OH
45014   (100%)
Tel.: (513) 874-0121
Web Site: http://www.intermec.com
Sales Range: $75-99.9 Million
Emp.: 200
Mfr of Labels & Tags for Bar Code Printers
N.A.I.C.S.: 323111

Subsidiary (Domestic):

**Intermec Technologies
Corporation** (5)
300 Deschutes way SW Ste 208, Tumwa-
ter, WA 98501
Tel.: (425) 348-2600
Barcode Symbology Products Mfr
N.A.I.C.S.: 334118

Subsidiary (Non-US):

**ITC Intermec Technologies Corpora-
tion AS** (6)
Karihaugveien 89, 1086, Oslo, Norway
Tel.: (47) 679 117 10
Automated Identification & Data Equipment
Sales & Service
N.A.I.C.S.: 423430

**Intermec Technologies (S) Pte
Ltd** (6)
17 Changi Business Park Central 1 Honey-
well Building, Singapore, 486073, Singa-
pore
Tel.: (65) 67146800
Web Site: http://www.intermec.com
Aircraft Engine & Engine Part Whslr
N.A.I.C.S.: 423860

Intermec Technologies AB (6)
Vendevaegen 85 B, 182 91, Danderyd,
Sweden
Tel.: (46) 86220660
Web Site: http://www.intermec.se
Automated Identification & Data Capture
Equipment Mfr
N.A.I.C.S.: 334118

**Intermec Technologies Australia Pty.
Limited** (6)
Level 3 No.2 Richardson North Ryde, Syd-
ney, 2113, Australia
Tel.: (61) 293304400
Web Site: http://www.intermec.com.au

Automated Identification & Data Capture
Equipment Mfr
N.A.I.C.S.: 334118

**Intermec Technologies Canada
ULC** (6)
7065 Tranmere Drive, Mississauga, L5S
1M2, ON, Canada
Tel.: (905) 673-9333
Web Site: http://www.intermec.com
Sales Range: $10-24.9 Million
Emp.: 25
Automated Identification & Data Capture
Equipment Sales
N.A.I.C.S.: 423430

Intermec Technologies GmbH (6)
Burgunderstrasse 31, 40549, Dusseldorf,
Germany
Tel.: (49) 211536010
Web Site: http://www.intermec.com
Emp.: 30
Automated Identification & Data Capture
Equipment Sales & Service
N.A.I.C.S.: 423430

Intermec Technologies S.A.S. (6)
22 Quai Gallieni, Suresnes, 92150, France
Tel.: (33) 1 41 44 30 50
Web Site: http://www.intermec.fr
Automated Identification & Data Capture
Equipment Sales & Service
N.A.I.C.S.: 423430

Intermec Technologies S.r.l. (6)
Via Gorky 105, Cinisello Balsamo, 20092,
Italy
Tel.: (39) 02 36 72 54 50
Web Site: http://www.intermec.it
Automated Identification & Data Capture
Equipment Sales & Service
N.A.I.C.S.: 423430

**Intermec Technologies U.K.
Limited** (6)
100 Brook Drive Green Park, Reading,
RG26UJ, Berkshire, United Kingdom
Tel.: (44) 118 923 0800
Web Site: http://www.intermec.co.uk
Automated Identification & Data Capture
Equipment Sales
N.A.I.C.S.: 423430

**Intermec Technologies de Mexico, S.
de R.L. de C.V.** (6)
Tamaulipas No 141 Primer Piso Colonia
Hipodromo Condesa, Mexico, 06140, DF,
Mexico
Tel.: (52) 55 52 41 48 00
Web Site: http://www.honeywellaedc.com
Sales Range: $25-49.9 Million
Emp.: 100
Automated Identification & Data Capture
Equipment Sales & Service
N.A.I.C.S.: 423430
Lues Olmeda (Gen Mgr)

Intermec Technologies, S.L.U. (6)
Avda De La Vega 15, 28108, Alcobendas,
Spain
Tel.: (34) 911146586
Web Site: http://www.intermec.es
Automated Identification & Data Capture
Equipment Mfr & Whslr
N.A.I.C.S.: 334118

Intermec by Honeywell (6)
Gydevang 31-33, 3450, Allerod, Denmark
Tel.: (45) 48166166
Web Site: http://www.intermec.dk
Sales Range: $10-24.9 Million
Emp.: 7
Automated Identification & Data Capture
Equipment Mfr
N.A.I.C.S.: 334118

Subsidiary (Domestic):

Vocollect, Inc. (5)
703 Rodi Rd, Pittsburgh, PA 15235
Tel.: (412) 829-8145
Web Site: http://www.vocollectvoice.com
Sales Range: $75-99.9 Million
Emp.: 300
Residential Mfr
N.A.I.C.S.: 334512

Subsidiary (Non-US):

Vocollect International Limited (6)

Wycombe Lane Gemini House Mercury
Park, Wooburn Green, HP10 0HH, Bucking-
hamshire, United Kingdom
Tel.: (44) 1628 55 2900
Web Site: http://www.vocollect.co.uk
Sales Range: $25-49.9 Million
Emp.: 19
Voice Activated Computer
N.A.I.C.S.: 541512

Subsidiary (Domestic):

Metrologic Instruments, Inc. (4)
90 Coles Rd Route 42, Blackwood, NJ
08012-4683
Tel.: (856) 228-8100
Barcode Scanning Hardware, Software &
Accessories Developer & Mfr
N.A.I.C.S.: 334118

Subsidiary (Non-US):

Metrologic Asia (Pte) Ltd. (5)
17 Changi Business Park Central 1, Singa-
pore, 486073, Singapore
Tel.: (65) 63552828
Sales Range: $25-49.9 Million
Emp.: 10
Barcode Scanner Hardware, Software &
Accessory Mfr
N.A.I.C.S.: 334118

Subsidiary (Non-US):

Metrologic Japan Co., Ltd. (6)
Matsunoya Building 6F 3-14-8 Higashiueno,
Taitou-ku, Tokyo, 110-0015, Japan
Tel.: (81) 3 3839 8511
Web Site: http://www.metrologic.co.jp
Emp.: 8
Barcode Scanner Hardware, Software &
Accessory Whslr
N.A.I.C.S.: 423430

Subsidiary (Non-US):

Metrologic Instruments GmbH (5)
Dornierstrasse 2, 82178, Puchheim, Ger-
many
Tel.: (49) 89890190
Web Site: http://www.honeywellaidc.com
Sales Range: $25-49.9 Million
Emp.: 35
Barcode Scanner Hardware, Software &
Accessory Mfr
N.A.I.C.S.: 423430

Metrologic do Brasil Ltda. (5)
Rue da Paz 2059, Chacara Santo Antonio,
CEP 04513 002, Sao Paulo, Brazil
Tel.: (55) 1151858222
Sales Range: $10-24.9 Million
Emp.: 21
Laser & Holographic Bar Code Scanners,
Data Collectors, PC Keyboard Wedges, La-
sers & Accessories Mfr
N.A.I.C.S.: 334118

Branch (Non-US):

**Honeywell Security & Communica-
tions - Canada** (3)
10 Whitmore Road, Woodbridge, L4L 7Z4,
ON, Canada
Tel.: (905) 856-2384
Sales Range: $25-49.9 Million
Emp.: 1
Security & Communications Equipment
Distr
N.A.I.C.S.: 423610

Subsidiary (Non-US):

Honeywell Security UK Limited (3)
140 Waterside Road Hamilton Industrial
Park, Leicester, LE5 1TN, Leics, United
Kingdom
Tel.: (44) 1928378005
Web Site:
    http://www.security.honeywell.com
Security Services & Systems
N.A.I.C.S.: 561621

Unit (Domestic):

Honeywell Video Systems (3)
2700 Blankenbaker Pkwy Ste 150, Louisville, KY 40299
Tel.: (502) 297-5700

Web Site:
    http://www.honeywellsystems.com
Rev.: $14,000,000
Emp.: 5
TV Cameras, Electronic Security, Access
Control Systems, Data Acquisition & Pro-
cess Monitoring Systems Mfr
N.A.I.C.S.: 561621

Subsidiary (Non-US):

Notifier (Benelux) S.A. (3)
Liege Airport Business Park B50, 4460,
Grace-Hollogne, Belgium   (100%)
Tel.: (32) 42470300
Web Site: https://www.notifier.be
Sales Range: $25-49.9 Million
Emp.: 14
Distr of Fire Alarm Systems
N.A.I.C.S.: 444180

Subsidiary (Domestic):

Notifier Co. (3)
12 Clintonville Rd, Northford, CT
06472   (100%)
Tel.: (203) 484-7161
Web Site: http://www.notifier.com
Emp.: 500
Fire Alarm & Emergency Lighting Products;
Fire Alarm Control Panels & Compatible
Indicating & Initiating Devices Mfr
N.A.I.C.S.: 334290
Todd Reif (Pres)

Subsidiary (Non-US):

Notifier Deutschland GmbH (3)
Berliner Strasse 91, 40880, Ratingen,
Germany   (100%)
Tel.: (49) 2102700690
Web Site: http://www.notifier.de
Sales Range: $10-24.9 Million
Emp.: 109
Distr of Fire Alarm Systems
N.A.I.C.S.: 444180

Notifier Espana S.L. (3)
C/Pau Vila 15-19, Badalona, 08911, Barce-
lona, 08911, Spain   (100%)
Tel.: (34) 931334760
Web Site: http://www.notifier.es
Sales Range: $25-49.9 Million
Emp.: 56
Distribution of Fire Alarm Systems
N.A.I.C.S.: 444110

Notifier Inertia Fire System (3)
9 Columbia Way Norwest Business Park,
PO Box 6832, Baulkham Hills, 2153, NSW,
Australia   (100%)
Tel.: (61) 298941444
Web Site: http://www.notifier.com.au
Sales Range: $10-24.9 Million
Emp.: 40
Distr of Fire Alarm Systems
N.A.I.C.S.: 561621
Steven Heiggins (Mng Dir)

Notifier Italia S.r.l. (3)
Via Grandi 22, San Donato Milanese,
20097, Milan, Italy   (100%)
Tel.: (39) 02518971
Web Site: https://www.notifier.it
Sales Range: $50-74.9 Million
Emp.: 100
Distr of Fire Alarm Systems
N.A.I.C.S.: 444180

Division (Domestic):

Honeywell Sensing & Control (2)
1985 Douglas Dr N, Golden Valley, MN
55422-3992   (100%)
Tel.: (763) 954-5204
Web Site: http://www.honeywell.com
Emp.: 1,500
Sensor, Control & Switch Mfr
N.A.I.C.S.: 334513

Unit (Domestic):

Honeywell Sensing & Control (3)
2520 S Walnut Rd, Freeport, IL 61032
Tel.: (815) 235-5500
Sales Range: $600-649.9 Million
Emp.: 2,300
Sensors, Switches & Control Products Mfr
N.A.I.C.S.: 335313

Subsidiary (Domestic):

Intelligrated, Inc. (3)
7901 Innovation Way, Mason, OH 45040
Web Site: http://www.intelligrated.com
Emp.: 3,100
Integrated Material Handling Systems, Services & Products
N.A.I.C.S.: 333922
Christopher C. Cole (Founder)

Honeywell Automation India Ltd. (1)
56 & 57 Hadapsar Industrial Estate, Hadapsar, Pune, 411013, Maharashtra, India (81%)
Tel.: (91) 2066039400
Web Site: https://www.honeywell.com
Sales Range: $300-349.9 Million
Emp.: 3,000
Integrated Automation & Software Solutions
N.A.I.C.S.: 541512
Suresh Senapaty (Chm)
Amit Kumar Tantia (CFO)
Ashish Gaikwad (Mng Dir)
Farah Irani (Sec)
Abhishek Kumar (Head-HR)
Rahul Sharma (Head-Global Svcs)
Gajanan Lahane (Head-Global Mfg)
Aseem Joshi (Head-Building Solutions)
Nikhil Thakkar (Head-Audit & Internal Controls)

Honeywell Avionics Systems Limited (1)
Edison Rd, Basingstoke, RG21 6QD, Hampshire, United Kingdom
Tel.: (44) 1256 722200
Web Site: http://www.honeywell.com
Emp.: 100
Electric Equipment Mfr
N.A.I.C.S.: 335999

Honeywell Burdick & Jackson (1)
1953 Harvey St, Muskegon, MI 49442
Tel.: (231) 726-3171
Web Site: http://www.honeywell-burdickandjackson.com
Rev.: $21,500,000
Emp.: 90
High Purity Solvents Mfr
N.A.I.C.S.: 325199

Honeywell Canada, Inc. (1)
200 Marcel Laurin Blvd, Montreal, H4M 2L5, QC, Canada (100%)
Tel.: (514) 744-2811
Web Site: http://www51.honeywell.com
Sales Range: $50-74.9 Million
Emp.: 200
Aerospace & Defense-Related Products Mfr
N.A.I.C.S.: 334511

Subsidiary (Domestic):

Honeywell ASCa Inc. (2)
3333 Unity Dr, Mississauga, L5L 3S6, ON, Canada
Tel.: (905) 608-6325
Web Site: http://www.honeywell.ca
Emp.: 3,000
Measuring & Controlling Products Mfr
N.A.I.C.S.: 334519

Honeywell Video Systems (2)
6554 176th St, Surrey, V3S 4G5, BC, Canada
Tel.: (604) 574-1526
Web Site: http://www.honeywellvideo.com
Sales Range: $25-49.9 Million
Emp.: 165
Video Surveillance Systems Mfr
N.A.I.C.S.: 334310

Matrikon Inc. (2)
Suite 1800 10405 Jasper Avenue, Edmonton, T5J 3N4, AB, Canada
Tel.: (780) 448-1010
Web Site: https://www.matrikonopc.com
Sales Range: $50-74.9 Million
Emp.: 588
Computer System Integration Services
N.A.I.C.S.: 541511

Subsidiary (Non-US):

Matrikon Deutschland AG (3)
Venloer Str 25, 50672, Cologne, Germany
Tel.: (49) 221969770
Web Site: https://www.matrikonopc.de

Sales Range: $25-49.9 Million
Emp.: 20
Computer System Integration Services
N.A.I.C.S.: 541512

Subsidiary (US):

Matrikon International Inc. (3)
1800 W Loop S Ste 1250, Houston, TX 77027-3520
Tel.: (713) 490-3737
Web Site: http://www.matrikonopc.com
Sales Range: $25-49.9 Million
Emp.: 30
System Integration Services
N.A.I.C.S.: 541512

Subsidiary (Non-US):

Matrikon Middle East Co WLL (3)
Suite 14 Business Centre BIIP Bldg 731 Road 1510 Block 324, Al-Hidd, Bahrain
Tel.: (973) 17465363
Sales Range: $25-49.9 Million
Emp.: 4
Computer System Integration Services
N.A.I.C.S.: 541512

Honeywell Co., Ltd. (1)
4 5 7th Floor Sangam IT Tower Sangamdong Cupbuk-ro 434 World, Mapo-gu, Seoul, 03922, Korea (South)
Tel.: (82) 27 996 1145
Web Site: https://www.honeywell.com
Automation Control Products Mfr
N.A.I.C.S.: 336413

Honeywell Control Systems Ltd. (1)
Honeywell House Skimped Hill Lane, Bracknell, RG12 1EB, Berks, United Kingdom (100%)
Tel.: (44) 1344656000
Aircraft Engine & Engine Part Whslr
N.A.I.C.S.: 423860

Subsidiary (US):

Novar Controls Corporation (2)
6060 Rockside Woods Blvd Ste 400, Cleveland, OH 44131
Tel.: (216) 682-1600
Web Site: http://www.novar.com
Sales Range: $150-199.9 Million
Emp.: 500
Control Components Mfr
N.A.I.C.S.: 334413

Subsidiary (Non-US):

Novar GmbH (2)
Forumstr 30, 41468, Neuss, Germany (100%)
Tel.: (49) 698 088 5333
Web Site: https://www.esser-systems.com
Sales Range: $100-124.9 Million
Emp.: 270
Residential Mfr
N.A.I.C.S.: 334512

Honeywell Electronic Materials (Thailand) Co., Ltd. (1)
32 Moo 8 Chonburi Industrial Estate Bo-Win Highway 331, Si Racha, 20230, Chonburi, Thailand
Tel.: (66) 38344020
Electrical & Electronic Product Distr
N.A.I.C.S.: 423610
Sasitron Boonyaratsuntron (Mgr-HR)

Honeywell Europe NV (1)
Haasrode Research Park Grauwmeer 1, Heverlee, 3001, Belgium
Tel.: (32) 16391278
Aircraft Engine & Engine Parts Whslr
N.A.I.C.S.: 423860

Honeywell Holdings Pty. Ltd. (1)
Level 3 2 Richardson Place, North Ryde, 2113, NSW, Australia
Tel.: (61) 293537000
Web Site: http://www.honeywell.com
Emp.: 300
Aircraft Engine & Engine Part Whslr
N.A.I.C.S.: 423860

Honeywell International Sdn. Bhd. (1)
Suite 25-1 Level 25 The Vertical Avenue 10 Bangsar South City UOA, Corporate Tower Lobby B No 8 Jalan Kerinchi, 59200, Kuala Lumpur, Malaysia

Tel.: (60) 327773100
Emp.: 1,500
Aircraft Mfr
N.A.I.C.S.: 336411
Brian Davis (Pres)

Honeywell International, Inc. - Puerto Rico Office (1)
Rezxo Industrial Park 400 St C Ste 100, Guaynabo, PR 00968
Tel.: (787) 792-7075
Web Site: http://www.honeywell.com
Sales Range: $1-4.9 Billion
Emp.: 50
Industrial Organic Chemicals
N.A.I.C.S.: 425120

Honeywell Japan Inc. (1)
New Pier Takeshiba South Tower 20F 1-16-1 Kaigan, Minato-Ku, Tokyo, 105-0022, Japan
Tel.: (81) 367307275
Web Site: http://www.honeywell-japan.com
Emp.: 150
Aerospace Component Mfr
N.A.I.C.S.: 334511

Honeywell Korea, Ltd. (1)
2095-3 Jeongwang-dong 26 Mayu-ro 70 beon-gil Smart-hub 3 Ma 819-1, Siheung, Gyeonggi, Korea (South)
Tel.: (82) 8191209510
Automotive Engine Mfr
N.A.I.C.S.: 336110

Honeywell Life Safety Romania SRL (1)
Str George Constantinescu no 3 Upground - BOC office Building, Entrance A Floor 4, 020339, Bucharest, Romania
Tel.: (40) 317107919
Web Site: https://www.hls-romania.com
Gas Detector Equipment Mfr
N.A.I.C.S.: 333248

Honeywell Limited (1)
Level 3 2 Richardson Place, North Ryde, 2113, NSW, Australia
Tel.: (61) 293537000
Web Site: https://www.honeywell.com
Aircraft Engine Mfr
N.A.I.C.S.: 336412

Honeywell Nylon LLC (1)
101 Columbia Rd, Morristown, NJ 07960-4640
Tel.: (877) 841-2840
Web Site: http://www.honeywell.com
Sales Range: $25-49.9 Million
Emp.: 14
Nylon, Nylon Yarn, Fiber Tinitermediate, Caprolactam & Polycaprolactam Mfr
N.A.I.C.S.: 313110

Honeywell Pte. Ltd. (1)
17 Changi Business Park Central 1 Honeywell Building, Singapore, 486073, Singapore
Tel.: (65) 67146999
Aerospace Component Mfr
N.A.I.C.S.: 334511

Honeywell Safety Products Europe SAS (1)
Immeuble Edison Paris Nord 2 33 rue des Vanesses, CS 55288 Villepinte Roissy, 95958, Paris, France
Tel.: (33) 149907979
Web Site: http://www.honeywellsafety.com
Emp.: 150
Aerospace Component Mfr
N.A.I.C.S.: 334511

Honeywell Sensors, Inc. (1)
245 Railroad St, Woonsocket, RI 02895-3039
Tel.: (401) 727-1300
Web Site: http://sensing.honeywell.com
Sales Range: $25-49.9 Million
Emp.: 120
Commercial Thermostats Mfr
N.A.I.C.S.: 334512

Honeywell Specialty Chemicals Seelze GmbH (1)
Wunstorfer Strasse 40, 30926, Seelze, Germany
Tel.: (49) 51379990
Web Site: https://advancedmaterials.honeywell.com

Emp.: 600
Specialty Chemical Whslr
N.A.I.C.S.: 325998

Honeywell Technologies Sarl (1)
Z A La Piece 16, 1180, Rolle, Vaud, Switzerland
Tel.: (41) 216442700
Sales Range: $50-74.9 Million
Emp.: 300
Aircraft Engine & Engine Part Whslr
N.A.I.C.S.: 423860

Honeywell Technology Solutions Lab Pvt. Ltd. (1)
Survey 96 & 97 Boganahalli Village Survey 72/2 & 72/5, Doddakananahalli Village Varthur Hobli, Bengaluru, 560103, Karnataka, India
Tel.: (91) 124403136165
Web Site: http://www.honeywell.com
Automobile Parts Distr
N.A.I.C.S.: 423140

Honeywell Technology Solutions Qatar Ltd. (1)
5th Floor Amwal Tower Al Wahdah Street 820, PO Box 63757, Al Dafna, Doha, Qatar
Tel.: (974) 44066200
Industrial Automation Equipment Mfr & Distr
N.A.I.C.S.: 334513

Honeywell Teknoloji Anonim Sirketi (1)
Kucukbakkalkoy Mah Kayisdagi Cad No 1 Allianz Tower Kat 27, Atasehir, 34750, Istanbul, Turkiye
Tel.: (90) 2165787100
Industrial Automation Equipment Mfr & Distr
N.A.I.C.S.: 334513

Honeywell UK Limited (1)
5 The Old Granary, Chichester, PO18 OES, West Sussex, United Kingdom
Tel.: (44) 1243783763
Aerospace Component Mfr
N.A.I.C.S.: 334511

Honeywell spol. sr.o. (1)
Havrankova 33, 61900, Brno, Czech Republic
Tel.: (420) 543558121
Web Site: http://www.honeywell.com
Emp.: 70
Electronic Appliances Whslr
N.A.I.C.S.: 423690

KAC Alarm Company Limited (1)
Honeywell House Skimped Hill Lane, Bracknell, RG12 1EB, Berks, United Kingdom
Tel.: (44) 2034091779
Web Site: https://www.kac.co.uk
Emp.: 170
Manual Call Point & Visual Alarm Device Mfr
N.A.I.C.S.: 334290

Life Safety Distribution AG (1)
Javastrasse 2, 8604, Hegnau, Switzerland
Tel.: (41) 449434380
Aircraft Engine & Engine Part Whslr
N.A.I.C.S.: 423860

Novar ED & S Limited (1)
The Arnold Centre Paycocke Road, Basildon, SS14 3EA, Essex, United Kingdom
Tel.: (44) 1268563000
Web Site: http://www.mkelectric.co.uk
Emp.: 200
Aircraft Engine & Engine Part Whslr
N.A.I.C.S.: 423860

Rebellion Photonics, Inc. (1)
2327 Commerce St Ste 200, Houston, TX 77002
Tel.: (713) 218-0101
Optical Instrument & Lens Mfr
N.A.I.C.S.: 333310

Rocky Research (1)
1598 Foothill Dr, Boulder City, NV 89005
Tel.: (702) 293-0851
Web Site: http://rockyresearch.com
Commercial Nonphysical Research
N.A.I.C.S.: 541910

Saia-Burgess Electronics Holding AG (1)
Freiburgstrasse 33, 3280, Murten, Switzerland
Tel.: (41) 266727111

Honeywell International Inc.—(Continued)

Sales Range: $75-99.9 Million
Emp.: 340
Holding Company; Development, Production & Sale of Electronic Components & Systems for Control/Automation Engineering
N.A.I.C.S.: 551112

Subsidiary (Non-US):

SBC Deutschland GmbH (2)
Strahlenbergerstrasse 110-112, 63067, Offenbach, Germany
Tel.: (49) 698064040
Web Site: http://www.saia-pcd.de
Sales Range: $25-49.9 Million
Emp.: 30
Development, Production & Sale of Electronic Components & Systems for Control/Automation Engineering
N.A.I.C.S.: 334419
Stefan Pfutzer (Mng Dir)

Subsidiary (Domestic):

Saia Burgess Controls AG (2)
Route Jo-Siffert 4, 1762, Givisiez, Switzerland
Tel.: (41) 265803000
Web Site: https://www.saia-pcd.com
Electronic Control System Mfr & Distr
N.A.I.C.S.: 334419

Subsidiary (Non-US):

Saia Burgess Controls Italia S.r.l. (2)
Via Alesssandro Volta 16 Scala C - Piano 7, Cologno Monzese, 20093, Milan, Italy
Tel.: (39) 0392165228
Web Site: http://www.saia-pcd.it
Electronic Control System Distr
N.A.I.C.S.: 423690

Subsidiary (US):

Saia Burgess Controls USA Inc. (2)
500 Lake Cook Rd, Deerfield, IL 60015
Tel.: (847) 597-7007
Web Site: http://www.saia-pcd.com
Sales Range: $25-49.9 Million
Emp.: 12
Sales & Distribution of Electronic Components
N.A.I.C.S.: 423690

Subsidiary (Non-US):

Saia-Burgess Benelux B.V. (2)
Hanzeweg 12c, 2803 MC, Gouda, Netherlands
Tel.: (31) 182 54 31 54
Web Site: http://www.saia-pcd.com
Sales Range: $25-49.9 Million
Emp.: 13
Electronic Components Mfr & Distr
N.A.I.C.S.: 334419

Salisbury Electrical Safety L.L.C. (1)
101 E Crossroads Pkwy Ste A, Bolingbrook, IL 60440
Tel.: (630) 343-3800
Web Site: http://www.salisburybyhoneywell.com
Electrical Safety Equipment Mfr
N.A.I.C.S.: 335932

TRANSNORM SYSTEM GmbH (1)
Forster Str 2, 31177, Harsum, Germany
Tel.: (49) 51274020
Industrial Automation Equipment Mfr & Distr
N.A.I.C.S.: 334513

Tridium, Inc. (1)
3951 Westerre Pkwy Ste 350, Richmond, VA 23233
Tel.: (804) 747-4771
Web Site: https://www.tridium.com
Software Development Services
N.A.I.C.S.: 541511
Ed Merwin (Dir-Strategic Bus)

UOP LLC (1)
25 E Algonquin Rd, Des Plaines, IL 60017-5017
Tel.: (847) 391-2000
Web Site: http://uop.honeywell.com
Sales Range: $1-4.9 Billion
Emp.: 2,500

Supplier of Process Technology, Catalysts, Process Plants & Consulting Services
N.A.I.C.S.: 325180

Subsidiary (Non-US):

UOP CH Sarl (2)
La Piece 16, 1180, Rolle, 1180, Switzerland
Tel.: (41) 216953039
Oil & Gas Industry Machinery & Equipment Distr
N.A.I.C.S.: 484220
Steven Eshelman (Gen Mgr)

Unit (Domestic):

UOP Callidus (2)
7130 S Lewis Ave Ste 335, Tulsa, OK 74136
Tel.: (918) 496-7599
Sales Range: $100-124.9 Million
Emp.: 200
Combustion Products & Systems Mfr
N.A.I.C.S.: 333994
Jeff Lewallen (Mgr-Sls Application)

Branch (Domestic):

UOP LLC - Houston (2)
1250 W Sam Houston Pkwy S Ste 450, Houston, TX 77042
Tel.: (713) 744-2800
Web Site: http://www.uop.com
Sales Range: $1-9.9 Million
Emp.: 50
Supplier of Process Technology, Catalysts, Process Plants & Consulting Services
N.A.I.C.S.: 325180

Subsidiary (Non-US):

UOP Limited (2)
Liongate Ladymead, Guildford, GU1 1AT, Surrey, United Kingdom
Tel.: (44) 1483304848
Oil & Gas Industry Machinery & Equipment Distr
N.A.I.C.S.: 484220
Gyan Pandey (Sr Mgr-Tech Svcs)

Subsidiary (Domestic):

UOP Russell LLC (2)
7130 S Lewis Ave Ste 500, Tulsa, OK 74136 (100%)
Tel.: (539) 664-4800
Engineeering Services
N.A.I.C.S.: 541330

HONG KONG WINALITE GROUP, INC.
3445 Lawrence Ave, Oceanside, NY 11572
Tel.: (646) 768-8417 NV
HKWO—(OTCIQ)
Health Product Distr
N.A.I.C.S.: 456199
David Lazar (CEO)

HOOKER FURNISHINGS CORPORATION
440 E Commonwealth Blvd E, Martinsville, VA 24112
Tel.: (276) 632-2133 VA
Web Site:
https://www.hookerfurnishings.com
Year Founded: 1924
HOFT—(NASDAQ)
Rev.: $540,081,000
Assets: $352,273,000
Liabilities: $94,770,000
Net Worth: $257,503,000
Earnings: ($10,426,000)
Emp.: 1,148
Fiscal Year-end: 01/31/21
Mfr & Importer of Household & Office Furniture
N.A.I.C.S.: 337122
Paul A. Huckfeldt (CFO & Sr VP-Fin & Acctg)
Jeremy R. Hoff (CEO)
W. Christopher Beeler Jr. (Chm)

Subsidiaries:

Bradington-Young LLC (1)
4040 10th Ave Dr SW, Hickory, NC 28602
Tel.: (276) 656-3335
Web Site: https://www.bradington-young.com
Sales Range: $10-24.9 Million
Emp.: 220
Upholstered Household Furniture Mfr
N.A.I.C.S.: 337121
Cheryl Sigmon (Dir-Mdsg)

Home Meridian International, Inc. (1)
2485 Penny Rd, High Point, NC 27265
Tel.: (336) 819-7200
Web Site: http://www.homemeridian.com
Holding Company; Furniture Mfr & Whslr
N.A.I.C.S.: 551112
Lee Boone (Pres)
Page Wilson (Pres-Pulaski Furniture)
Mary-Price Furr (VP-Mktg)
David Gusler (Sr VP-Far East Ops)
Kevin Walker (Pres-Accentrics Home)
Rebecca Colyn (Sr VP-Ops)

Subsidiary (Domestic):

Samuel Lawrence Furniture (2)
440 E Commonwealth Blvd, Martinsville, VA 24112
Tel.: (276) 656-3335
Web Site: https://www.slf-co.com
Wood Bedroom, Dining Room, Home Office & Youth Furniture Mfr
N.A.I.C.S.: 337122

Sam Moore Furniture LLC (1)
1556 Dawn Dr, Bedford, VA 24523
Tel.: (540) 586-8253
Web Site: http://www.sammoore.com
Sales Range: $100-124.9 Million
Emp.: 350
Furniture Mfr
N.A.I.C.S.: 337121

HOOKIPA PHARMA INC.
350 Fifth Ave Room Ste 7240, New York, NY 10118
Tel.: (431) 890-6360 DE
Web Site:
https://www.hookipapharma.com
Year Founded: 2011
HOOK—(NASDAQ)
Rev.: $14,249,000
Assets: $170,454,000
Liabilities: $67,937,000
Net Worth: $102,517,000
Earnings: ($64,915,000)
Emp.: 156
Fiscal Year-end: 12/31/22
Biotechnology Research & Development Services
N.A.I.C.S.: 541714
Daniel Pinschewer (Co-Founder)
Klaus Orlinger (Exec VP-Res)
Rolf Zinkernagel (Co-Founder)
Andreas Bergthaler (Co-Founder)
Lukas Flatz (Co-Founder)
Matt Beck (Exec Dir-IR)
Roman Necina (COO)
Gwenaelle Kerforn (Exec Dir-HR)
Michael Szumera (Exec Dir-Comm)
Malte Peters (Pres & CEO)
Terry Coelho (CFO & Exec VP)

HOOPS SCOUTING USA
63 Rocio Ct, Palm Desert, CA 92260
Tel.: (760) 636-4353 WY
Web Site:
http://www.hoopsscoutingusa.com
Year Founded: 2016
HSCT—(OTCIQ)
Assets: $10,586
Liabilities: $43,235
Net Worth: ($32,649)
Earnings: ($36,592)
Emp.: 1
Fiscal Year-end: 06/30/21
Online Sports Services
N.A.I.C.S.: 513199

Jamie Oei (Pres, CEO, CFO, Principal Acctg Officer, Treas & Sec)

HOP-ON, INC.
31938 Temecula Pkwy Ste A323, Temecula, CA 92592
Tel.: (949) 756-9008
Web Site: https://www.hop-on.com
Year Founded: 1993
HPNN—(OTCIQ)
Sales Range: Less than $1 Million
Telecommunications Resellers
N.A.I.C.S.: 517121
Peter D. Michaels (Chm & CEO)

HOPE BANCORP, INC.
3200 Wilshire Blvd Ste 1400, Los Angeles, CA 90010
Tel.: (213) 639-1700 DE
Web Site:
https://www.bankofhope.com
Year Founded: 1988
HOPE—(NASDAQ)
Rev.: $767,512,000
Assets: $19,164,491,000
Liabilities: $17,145,163,000
Net Worth: $2,019,328,000
Earnings: $218,277,000
Emp.: 1,549
Fiscal Year-end: 12/31/22
Bank Holding Company
N.A.I.C.S.: 551111
Kevin Sung Kim (Chm, Pres & CEO)
Peter Koh (Chief Credit Officer)
Julianna Balicka (CFO & Exec VP)
Peter Koh (Chief Credit Officer & Exec VP-Bank of Hope)
Angie Yang (Sr VP & Dir-IR & Comm)
Thomas P. Stenger (Chief Risk Officer)

Subsidiaries:

Bank of Hope (1)
3200 Wilshire Blvd Ste 1400, Los Angeles, CA 90010 (100%)
Tel.: (213) 639-1700
Web Site: https://www.bankofhope.com
Sales Range: $350-399.9 Million
Commericial Banking
N.A.I.C.S.: 522110
Kevin Sung Kim (Chm, Pres & CEO)
Peter Koh (COO & Exec VP)
Julianna Balicka (CFO & Exec VP)
Peter Koh (Chief Credit Officer & Exec VP)
Thomas P. Stenger (Sr Exec VP)

HOPTO INC.
189 N Main St Ste 102, Concord, NH 03301
Tel.: (408) 688-2674 DE
Web Site: https://www.hopto.com
Year Founded: 1996
HPTO—(OTCIQ)
Rev.: $3,908,600
Assets: $6,049,600
Liabilities: $1,968,100
Net Worth: $4,081,500
Earnings: $123,000
Emp.: 14
Fiscal Year-end: 12/31/22
Prepackaged Software; Application Software Developer
N.A.I.C.S.: 513210
Jonathon R. Skeels (CEO, Interim CFO & Sec)

Subsidiaries:

GraphOn Corporation (1)
6 Loudon Rd Ste 200, Concord, NH 03301
Tel.: (603) 225-3525
Web Site: https://www.graphon.com
Software Publishing Services
N.A.I.C.S.: 513210

HORACE MANN EDUCATORS CORPORATION
Tel.: (217) 789-2500 DE

Web Site:
https://www.horacemann.com
Year Founded: 1945
HMN—(NYSE)
Rev.: $1,491,900,000
Assets: $14,049,900,000
Liabilities: $12,874,600,000
Net Worth: $1,175,300,000
Earnings: $45,000,000
Emp.: 1,700
Fiscal Year-end: 12/31/23
Insurance Holding Company
N.A.I.C.S.: 524126
Bret A. Conklin *(CFO & Exec VP)*
Marita Zuraitis *(Pres & CEO)*
Kimberly A. Johnson *(Sr VP & Controller)*
Heather J. Wietzel *(VP-IR & Enterprise Comm)*
Stephen J. McAnena *(COO & Exec VP)*
Donald M. Carley *(Chief Compliance Officer)*
Jennifer E. Thayer *(Chief HR Officer)*
Micael B. Weckenbrock *(Sr VP)*

Subsidiaries:

Benefit Consultants Group, Inc.   **(1)**
51 Haddonfield Rd Ste 200, Cherry Hill, NJ 08002
Tel.: (856) 368-2000
Web Site: https://www.bcgbenefits.com
Retirement Plan Services
N.A.I.C.S.: 524298

Horace Mann Insurance
Company   **(1)**
1 Horace Mann Plz, Springfield, IL 62715-0001   **(100%)**
Tel.: (217) 789-2500
Web Site: http://www.horacemann.com
Sales Range: $700-749.9 Million
Provider of Property & Casualty Insurance
N.A.I.C.S.: 524126

Horace Mann Life Insurance
Company   **(1)**
1 Horace Mann Plz, Springfield, IL 62715-0001   **(100%)**
Tel.: (217) 789-2500
Web Site: http://www.horacemann.com
Sales Range: $150-199.9 Million
Emp.: 800
Life Insurance & Retirement Annuities
N.A.I.C.S.: 524113

NTA Life Business Services Group,
Inc.   **(1)**
PO Box 1392, Addison, TX 75001-1392
Business Management Consulting Services
N.A.I.C.S.: 541611

NTA Life Insurance Company of New
York   **(1)**
30 BRd St 14th Fl Ste 1426, New York, NY 10004
Business Management Consulting Services
N.A.I.C.S.: 541611

National Teachers Associates Life
Insurance Company   **(1)**
4949 Keller Springs Rd, Addison, TX 75001
Tel.: (972) 532-2100
Web Site: https://www.ntalife.com
Health & Life Insurance
N.A.I.C.S.: 524113

Teachers Insurance Company   **(1)**
2101 Sardis Rd N Ste 209, Charlotte, NC 28227
Tel.: (704) 532-1111
Insurance Services
N.A.I.C.S.: 524113
Marita Zuraitis *(Pres)*

HORIZON ACQUISITION COR-
PORATION
600 Steamboat Rd Ste 200, Greenwich, CT 06830
Tel.: (203) 298-5300   Ky
Year Founded: 2020
HZAC—(NYSE)
Investment Services

N.A.I.C.S.: 523999
Todd L. Boehly *(CEO & CFO)*
Robert Ott *(VP)*

HORIZON ACQUISITION COR-
PORATION II
600 Steamboat Rd Ste 200, Greenwich, CT 06830
Tel.: (203) 298-5300
Web Site: https://www.sec.gov
HZON—(NYSE)
Investment Services
N.A.I.C.S.: 523999
Todd L. Boehly *(CEO & CFO)*

HORIZON BANCORP, INC.
515 Franklin St, Michigan City, IN 46360
Tel.: (219) 879-0211   IN
Web Site:
https://www.horizonbank.com
Year Founded: 1873
HBNC—(NASDAQ)
Rev.: $283,484,000
Assets: $7,872,518,000
Liabilities: $7,195,143,000
Net Worth: $677,375,000
Earnings: $93,408,000
Emp.: 852
Fiscal Year-end: 12/31/22
Bank Holding Company
N.A.I.C.S.: 551111
Mark E. Secor *(Chief Administration Officer & Exec VP)*
Mark E. Secor *(CFO & Exec VP)*
Thomas M. Prame *(Pres)*
Lynn M. Kerber *(Chief Comml Banking Officer)*
Dennis J. Kuhn *(Reg Pres-Southwest Michigan)*
Thomas M. Prame *(Pres & CEO)*
Lynn Kerber *(Officer-Credit Admin & Exec VP)*

Subsidiaries:

Horizon Bank   **(1)**
515 Franklin St, Michigan City, IN 46360   **(100%)**
Tel.: (219) 874-9245
Web Site: https://www.horizonbank.com
Sales Range: $100-124.9 Million
Emp.: 550
Commercial Banking Services
N.A.I.C.S.: 522110
Mark E. Secor *(Chief Administration Officer & Exec VP)*
Thomas M. Prame *(Pres)*
Lynn M. Kerber *(Chief Comml Banking Officer)*
Dennis J. Kuhn *(Reg Pres-Southwest Michigan)*
Thomas M. Prame *(Pres & CEO)*
Grayson Fenwick *(VP-Central Indiana)*
Dennis J. Kuhn *(Chief Comml Banking Officer & Exec VP)*

Subsidiary (Domestic):

Horizon Insurance Services, Inc.   **(2)**
515 Franklin St, Michigan City, IN 46360
Tel.: (219) 874-0211
Web Site: http://www.horizonbank.com
Insurance Brokerage Services
N.A.I.C.S.: 524210

HORIZON GROUP PROPER-
TIES, INC.
10275 W Higgins Rd Ste 260, Rosemont, IL 60018
Tel.: (847) 292-1870   MD
Web Site:
https://www.horizongroup.com
Year Founded: 1998
HGPI—(OTCIQ)
Rev.: $8,146,000
Assets: $141,274,000
Liabilities: $75,221,000
Net Worth: $66,053,000
Earnings: ($19,145,000)
Emp.: 129

Fiscal Year-end: 12/31/20
Factory Outlet Shopping Centers Owner; Planned Communities Developer
N.A.I.C.S.: 531390
Gary J. Skoien *(Chm & CEO)*
David R. Tinkham *(CFO)*
Andrew F. Pelmoter *(Exec VP-Leasing)*
Thomas A. Rumptz *(Exec VP-Real Estate & Asset Mgmt)*
James S. Harris *(Mng Dir-Bus Dev)*

HORIZON MINERALS CORP.
9101 W Sahara Ave Ste 105-197, Las Vegas, NV 89117
Tel.: (587) 984-2321   DE
Web Site:
http://www.horizonmineralscorp.com
Year Founded: 2011
HZNM—(OTCIQ)
Gold & Mineral Mining
N.A.I.C.S.: 212220
Robert D. Fedun *(CEO & CFO)*
Francisco Flores *(Dir-Advisory)*

HORIZON TECHNOLOGY FI-
NANCE CORPORATION
312 Farmington Ave, Farmington, CT 06032
Tel.: (860) 676-8654
Web Site:
https://www.horizontechfinance.com
Year Founded: 2010
HRZN—(NASDAQ)
Rev.: $60,015,000
Assets: $513,960,000
Liabilities: $268,625,000
Net Worth: $245,335,000
Earnings: $28,220,000
Fiscal Year-end: 12/31/21
Venture Lending
N.A.I.C.S.: 523999
Diane C. Earle *(Chief Credit Officer & Sr VP)*
John C. Bombara *(Co-Founder, Chief Compliance Officer, Gen Counsel, Sec & Sr VP)*
Daniel S. Devorsetz *(Co-Founder, COO & Chief Investment Officer)*
Daniel R. Trolio *(CFO, Treas & Sr VP)*
Kevin J. May *(Sr Mng Dir-West Coast)*
Kevin T. Walsh *(Mng Dir-Tech-West Coast)*
Gary P. Moro *(Officer-Credit & VP)*
Megan N. Bacon *(Dir-IR & Mktg)*
Mishone B. Donelson *(Mng Dir-Life Science-East Coast)*
Lynn D. Dombrowski *(Controller)*
Haitham Shehadah *(Portfolio Mgr)*
Todd A. McDonald *(Mng Dir-Tech-Mid-Atlantic & Southeast)*
Lindsay A. Fouty *(Officer-Credit & VP)*
Bryce C. Bewley *(VP-Bus Dev)*
Sara M. Johnson *(Mng Dir-Tech-South West & Mid West)*
Robert D. Pomeroy Jr. *(Chm & CEO)*
Gerald A. Michaud *(Pres)*

HORIZONS HOLDINGS INTER-
NATIONAL, INC.
3651 Lindell Rd Ste D459, Las Vegas, NV 89103
Tel.: (702) 425-8627   DE
Web Site:
https://www.horizonsholdings.com
HZHI—(OTCIQ)
Rev.: $26,523
Assets: $168,202
Liabilities: $227,010
Net Worth: ($58,808)
Earnings: ($52,015)
Fiscal Year-end: 06/30/19

Investment Management Service
N.A.I.C.S.: 523999
Brian Conrad *(Chm, Pres & CEO)*

HORMEL FOODS CORPORA-
TION
1 Hormel Pl, Austin, MN 55912-3680
Tel.: (507) 437-5611   DE
Web Site:
https://www.hormelfoods.com
Year Founded: 1891
HRL—(NYSE)
Rev.: $11,386,189,000
Assets: $12,696,329,000
Liabilities: $5,717,969,000
Net Worth: $6,978,360,000
Earnings: $908,839,000
Emp.: 20,000
Fiscal Year-end: 10/31/21
Food Products Mfr
N.A.I.C.S.: 311611
Mark A. Coffey *(Grp VP-Supply Chain)*
James P. Snee *(Chm, Pres & CEO)*
Mark J. Ourada *(Grp VP-Foodservice)*
Paul Kuehneman *(VP & Controller)*
Brian D. Johnson *(Sec & VP)*
Jeffrey A. Grev *(VP-Legislative Affairs)*
Swen Neufeldt *(Grp VP)*
Kevin L. Myers *(Sr VP-R&D & Quality Control)*
Wendy A. Watkins *(Chief Comm Officer & Sr VP)*
Mark D. Vaupel *(VP-IT Svcs)*
Jacinth C. Smiley *(CFO & Exec VP)*
Steven L. Lykken *(Grp VP)*
Tyler Hulsebus *(VP-Engrg)*
Mark Morey *(VP-Affiliated)*
Nathan P. Annis *(Dir-IR)*
Natosha Walsh *(Sr VP-Sls-Consumer Products Sls & VP)*
Pierre M. Lilly *(Chief Compliance Officer & Sr VP)*
Leslie Lee *(VP-Digital Experience)*
Paul Kuehneman *(Asst Controller)*
Eldon Quam *(Asst Controller)*
Tony Hoffman *(Sr VP-Sls-Consumer Products Sls & VP)*
Lisa Selk *(VP-Mktg-Meat Products)*
Annemarie Vaupel *(VP-Mktg-Foodservice)*
Jacinth C. Smiley *(CFO & Exec VP)*
Jen Ehresmann *(VP-Supply Chain)*
John Forsythe *(VP-Ops Grocery Products)*
Clint Walters *(VP-Refrigerated Foods Ops)*
Florence Makope *(Treas & VP)*
Katie Larson *(Sr VP-HR)*
Henry Hsia *(VP-Retail Mktg-Snacking & Entertaining)*
Richard Carlson *(VP)*
David Weber *(VP)*

Subsidiaries:

Alma Foods, LLC   **(1)**
110 1st St, Alma, KS 66401
Tel.: (785) 765-3396
Emp.: 100
Food Products Mfr
N.A.I.C.S.: 311999
Shane Weers *(Gen Mgr)*

Beijing Hormel Foods Co. Ltd.   **(1)**
Room 902 Guangming Hotel Liangmaqiao Road, Chaoyang District, Beijing, China
Tel.: (86) 10 8491 4595
Food Products Mfr
N.A.I.C.S.: 311999

Burke Corporation   **(1)**
1516 S D Ave, Nevada, IA 50201   **(100%)**
Tel.: (515) 382-3575
Web Site: http://www.burkecorp.com
Sales Range: $150-199.9 Million
Emp.: 300

Hormel Foods Corporation—(Continued)

Fully Cooked Ethnic & Specialty Meats for
Foodservice, Industrial & Retail Markets
N.A.I.C.S.: 424470
Scott Miller *(Dir-Foodsvc Sls-East)*
Chad Randick *(Pres)*
Tracy Brown *(VP-Ops)*
Thomas R. Burke *(VP-Pur)*
Mike Dougherty *(VP-Sls & Mktg)*
Casey B. Frye *(VP-R&D)*
Valarie Rossman *(Dir-Foodsvc Sls-West)*
Paul Sheehan *(Dir-Industrial Sls)*
Bob Darling *(Reg Sls Mgr-Northwest)*
George Hennion *(Reg Sls Mgr-Southwest)*
Chris Reyes *(Reg Sls Mgr-Mid-Central)*
Jay Clough *(Reg Sls Mgr-South Central)*
Connie McGowin *(Reg Sls Mgr-Midwest)*
Julie Fernandez *(Reg Sls Mgr-Mid-South)*
Dan Canale *(Reg Sls Mgr-East)*
Joseph Suero *(Reg Sls Mgr-Mid-Northeast)*
Shelli Seibert *(Mgr-HR)*
Doug Jones *(Controller)*
Sue Trzebiatowski *(Dir-Quality Assurance &
Technical Svcs)*
John Ogdon *(Sls Mgr-Northwest Reg)*
William J. Burke Sr. *(Founder)*

Century Foods International, LLC (1)
400 Century Ct, Sparta, WI 54656
Tel.: (608) 269-1900
Web Site: https://www.centuryfoods.com
Sales Range: $125-149.9 Million
Emp.: 400
Specialty Food Supplements & Consumer
Products Developer & Mfr
N.A.I.C.S.: 311999
Tom Miskowski *(Pres)*
Joe Leinfelder *(Dir-Bus Dev)*
Pawel Noland *(VP-Ops)*
Kevin Mead *(VP-R&D)*
Michael White *(VP-Sls & Mktg)*
Bob Jones *(Dir-HR)*

Champ, LLC (1)
515 Albin St, Albin, WY 82050
Tel.: (307) 246-3581
Food Products Mfr
N.A.I.C.S.: 311999

Columbus Manufacturing, Inc. (1)
30977 San Antonio St, Hayward, CA 94544
Web Site: http://www.columbussalame.com
Premium Processed Meat Products Mfr &
Distr
N.A.I.C.S.: 311612
Marisa Vladislavich *(Dir-HR)*

**Creative Contract Packaging
Corp.** (1)
3777 Exchange Ave, Aurora, IL
60504 **(100%)**
Tel.: (630) 851-6226
Sales Range: $1-9.9 Million
Emp.: 80
Dry Powder Desserts Mfr
N.A.I.C.S.: 311423

Dan's Prize, Inc. (1)
930 Interstate Ridge Dr Ste A, Gainesville,
GA 30501 **(100%)**
Tel.: (770) 503-1881
Web Site: http://www.dansprize.com
Sales Range: $100-124.9 Million
Emp.: 275
Meats & Meat Products Whslr
N.A.I.C.S.: 424470

Dold Foods (1)
2929 N Ohio St, Wichita, KS
67219 **(100%)**
Tel.: (316) 838-9101
Web Site: http://www.hormelfoods.com
Sales Range: $50-74.9 Million
Emp.: 250
Meat Products Mfr & Distr
N.A.I.C.S.: 445240

FJ Foodservice, LLC (1)
3049 E Vernon Ave, Los Angeles, CA 90058-
1718
Tel.: (323) 583-4621
Web Site: http://www.farmerjohn.com
Emp.: 1,500
Food Products Distr
N.A.I.C.S.: 445298

Fort Dodge Foods, Inc. (1)
1 Hormel Pl, Austin, MN
55912-3673 **(100%)**

Tel.: (515) 955-3377
Sales Range: Less than $1 Million
Emp.: 12
Food Preparations Mfr
N.A.I.C.S.: 311999

Hormel Canada Ltd. (1)
200 Bay Street Suite 3800, Toronto, M5J
2Z4, ON, Canada
Tel.: (905) 336-8821
Web Site: http://www.hormel.ca
Emp.: 3
Food Products Distr
N.A.I.C.S.: 445298

Hormel Foods Australia Pty Ltd. (1)
PO Box 589, Moorabbin BC, Moorabbin,
3189, VIC, Australia **(100%)**
Tel.: (61) 800770015
Web Site: https://www.hormelfoods.com.au
Food & Meat Products Marketer & Mfr
N.A.I.C.S.: 424410

**Hormel Foods Corp. - Deli
Division** (1)
1 Hormel Pl, Austin, MN 55912-3673
Tel.: (507) 437-5000
Web Site: http://www.hormel.com
Sales Range: $75-99.9 Million
Emp.: 80
Luncheon Meat Products
N.A.I.C.S.: 424470

**Hormel Foods Corp. - Foodservice
Division** (1)
1 Hormel Pl, Austin, MN 55912-3673
Tel.: (507) 437-5611
Web Site: http://www.hormelfoods.com
Sales Range: $150-199.9 Million
Emp.: 400
Food for Restaurants & Other Foodservice
Operations
N.A.I.C.S.: 722310
Mark J. Ourada *(Grp VP)*
David Weber *(VP-Sls)*

Subsidiary (Domestic):

Mark-Lynn Foods, Inc. (2)
1090 Pacific Ave, Bremen, GA 30110-2238
Tel.: (770) 537-5813
Sales Range: $1-9.9 Million
Emp.: 150
Food Packaging & Labeling Services
N.A.I.C.S.: 561910

**Hormel Foods Corp. - Grocery Prod-
ucts Division** (1)
1 Hormel Pl, Austin, MN 55912-3673
Tel.: (507) 437-5611
Web Site: http://www.hormel.com
Sales Range: $400-449.9 Million
Emp.: 282
Canned Food Products Mfr
N.A.I.C.S.: 112320

Subsidiary (Domestic):

Justin's LLC (2)
736 Pearl St, Boulder, CO 80302
Tel.: (844) 448-0302
Web Site: http://www.justins.com
Nut Butters & Candy Mfr
N.A.I.C.S.: 311911

**Hormel Foods Corp. - Refrigerated
Foods Division** (1)
1 Hormel Pl, Austin, MN 55912
Tel.: (507) 437-5363
Web Site: http://www.hormel.com
Sales Range: $450-499.9 Million
Emp.: 1,000
Packaged Foods
N.A.I.C.S.: 311412
Thomas R. Day *(Exec VP)*

Subsidiary (Domestic):

Provena Foods Inc. (2)
1560 Eucalyptus Ave, Chino, CA 91710
Tel.: (909) 627-1082
Specialty Food Processors
N.A.I.C.S.: 311412

**Hormel Foods Corp. - Specialty Prod-
ucts Division** (1)
1 Hormel Pl, Austin, MN 55912-3673
Tel.: (507) 437-5611
Web Site: http://www.hormeleterna.com

Sales Range: $75-99.9 Million
Emp.: 160
Gelatin Products, Specialized Proteins used
in Cosmetics; Concentrated Meat Stocks,
Private Label Desserts
N.A.I.C.S.: 311999

Subsidiary (Domestic):

Hormel Healthlabs, Inc. (2)
10783 Tea Olive Ln, Boca Raton, FL
33498 **(100%)**
Tel.: (561) 451-1100
Web Site: http://www.hormelhealthlabs.com
Sales Range: $1-9.9 Million
Food Testing Laboratory
N.A.I.C.S.: 541380

**Hormel Foods Corporate Services,
LLC** (1)
901 N Lake Destiny Rd 345 Ste 101, Mait-
land, FL 32751-4844
Tel.: (407) 660-1433
Web Site: http://www.hormelfoods.com
Emp.: 4
Meat Product Whslr
N.A.I.C.S.: 424470

**Hormel Foods International
Corporation** (1)
1 Hormel Pl, Austin, MN 55912 **(100%)**
Tel.: (507) 437-5478
Web Site: http://www.hormel.com
Sales Range: $10-24.9 Million
Emp.: 50
License & Royalty Agreements for Over-
seas Mfg of Food Products & Food Packag-
ing
N.A.I.C.S.: 561499
Richard A. Bross *(Pres & Grp VP)*

Hormel Foods Japan K.K. (1)
1-12-1 Dogenzaka Shibuya Mark City Bldg
22f, Shibuya-Ku, Tokyo, 150-0043, Japan
Tel.: (81) 343605341
Food Products Mfr & Distr
N.A.I.C.S.: 311999

**Jennie-O Turkey Store International
Inc.** (1)
2505 Willmar Ave SW, Willmar, MN 56201
Tel.: (320) 214-2870
Food Products Distr
N.A.I.C.S.: 445298

**Jennie-O Turkey Store Sales,
LLC** (1)
16847 Sheldon Lane Sw, Rochester, WA
98579-9453
Tel.: (360) 273-6896
Web Site:
http://www.jennieofoodservice.com
Food Products Distr
N.A.I.C.S.: 424420

Jennie-O Turkey Store, Inc. (1)
2505 SW Willmar Ave, Willmar, MN
56201 **(100%)**
Tel.: (320) 214-5888
Web Site: https://www.jennieo.com
Sales Range: $900-999.9 Million
Emp.: 7,000
Turkey Processor
N.A.I.C.S.: 311615

Lloyds Barbeque Company, LLC (1)
1455 Mendota Hts Rd, Mendota Heights,
MN 55120 **(100%)**
Tel.: (651) 688-6000
Web Site: http://www.hormel.com
Cooked Meats From Purchased Meat
N.A.I.C.S.: 311612

Logistic Services, Inc. (1)
2951 S 1st St, Eldridge, IA 52748 **(100%)**
Tel.: (563) 285-7846
Sales Range: $1-9.9 Million
Emp.: 73
Warehouse & Storage Services
N.A.I.C.S.: 493110

MegaMex Foods, LLC (1)
333 S Anita Dr Ste 1000, Orange, CA
92868 **(50%)**
Web Site: http://www.megamexfoods.com
Mexican Food Products & Ingredients Mfr
N.A.I.C.S.: 311941

Subsidiary (Domestic):

Don Miguel Mexican Foods, Inc. (2)

1501 W Orangewood Ave, Orange, CA
92868
Tel.: (714) 634-8441
Web Site: http://www.donmiguel.com
Mexican Food Product Mfr
N.A.I.C.S.: 311422

Mexican Accent, LLC (1)
16675 W Glendale Dr, New Berlin, WI
53151
Tel.: (262) 784-4422
Food Products Mfr & Distr
N.A.I.C.S.: 311999

Mountain Prairie, LLC (1)
540 Carson Ave, Las Animas, CO 81054-
1732
Tel.: (719) 456-0834
Hog & Pig Farming Services
N.A.I.C.S.: 112210

Osceola Foods, Inc. (1)
1027 Warren Ave, Osceola, IA
50213 **(100%)**
Tel.: (641) 342-8000
Sales Range: $10-24.9 Million
Emp.: 700
Prepared Meat Mfr
N.A.I.C.S.: 311611

Progressive Processing, LLC (1)
1205 Chavenelle Ct, Dubuque, IA 52002-
9778
Tel.: (563) 557-4500
Food Products Mfr
N.A.I.C.S.: 311999

Rochelle Foods, Inc. (1)
1001 S Main St, Rochelle, IL
61068 **(100%)**
Tel.: (815) 562-4141
Sales Range: $250-299.9 Million
Emp.: 1,000
Prepared Meat Mfr
N.A.I.C.S.: 311611

Shanghai Hormel Foods Co. Ltd. (1)
No 30 Nanda Road, Baoshan District,
Shanghai, 200436, China
Tel.: (86) 2156500878
Food Products Mfr
N.A.I.C.S.: 311999

Stagg Foods, Inc. (1)
PO Box 800, Austin, MN 55912 **(100%)**
Tel.: (507) 437-5611
Web Site: http://www.staggchili.com
Sales Range: $25-49.9 Million
Emp.: 25
Canned Meat Product Mfr
N.A.I.C.S.: 311422

HOST HOTELS & RESORTS,
INC.
4747 Bethesda Ave Ste 1300,
Bethesda, MD 20814
Tel.: (240) 744-1000 MD
Web Site:
https://www.hosthotels.com
Year Founded: 1993
HST—(NASDAQ)
Rev.: $5,311,000,000
Assets: $12,243,000,000
Liabilities: $5,606,000,000
Net Worth: $6,637,000,000
Earnings: $740,000,000
Emp.: 163
Fiscal Year-end: 12/31/23
Hospitality Real Estate Investment
Trust
N.A.I.C.S.: 525990
James F. Risoleo *(Pres & CEO)*
Nathan S. Tyrrell *(Chief Investment
Officer & Exec VP)*
Michael E. Lentz *(Exec VP-Dev, De-
sign & Construction)*
Julie P. Aslaksen *(Gen Counsel, Sec
& Exec VP)*
Joseph C. Ottinger *(Principal Acctg
Officer, Sr VP & Controller)*
Mari Sifo *(Chief HR Officer & Exec
VP)*

Subsidiaries:

CCHP Waikiki LLC (1)

175 Paoakalani Ave, Honolulu, HI 96815-3743
Tel.: (808) 931-4395
Real Estate Services
N.A.I.C.S.: 531390

HHR Holdings Pty Ltd. (1)
L 18 126-130 Phillip St, Sydney, 2000, NSW, Australia
Tel.: (61) 290095500
Hotel Services
N.A.I.C.S.: 721110

HMC Gateway, Inc. (1)
10400 Fernwood Rd Rm 507, Bethesda, MD 20817-1109
Tel.: (301) 380-5045
Hotel & Resort Rental Services
N.A.I.C.S.: 721110

HMC NGL LP (1)
10400 Fernwood Rd, Bethesda, MD 20817-1102
Tel.: (202) 380-9000
Hotel Services
N.A.I.C.S.: 721110

Host Hotels & Resorts L.P. (1)
4747 Bethesda Ave Ste 1300, Bethesda, MD 20814
Tel.: (240) 744-1000
Web Site: https://www.hosthotels.com
Rev.: $5,310,999,999
Assets: $12,242,999,999
Liabilities: $5,605,999,999
Net Worth: $6,636,999,999
Earnings: $751,000,000
Emp.: 162
Fiscal Year-end: 12/31/2023
Real Estate Investment Services
N.A.I.C.S.: 531110
Richard E. Marriott (Chm)

Manchester Grand Resorts, Inc. (1)
5300 Grand Del Mar Ct, San Diego, CA 92130
Tel.: (858) 509-2140
Emp.: 7
Hotel Services
N.A.I.C.S.: 721110

Phoenician Operating LLC (1)
6000 E Camelback Rd, Scottsdale, AZ 85251
Tel.: (480) 941-8200
Home Management Services
N.A.I.C.S.: 721110

Polserv S.A. de C.V. (1)
Andres Bello No 29, Palmas Polanco, Mexico, 11560, DF, Mexico
Tel.: (52) 5539990096
Emp.: 450
Hotel Services
N.A.I.C.S.: 721110

Tiburon Golf Ventures Limited Partnership (1)
2620 Tiburon Dr, Naples, FL 34109
Tel.: (239) 593-2200
Web Site: https://www.tiburonnaples.com
Hotel Services
N.A.I.C.S.: 721110
Kevin DeDonato (Gen Mgr)
Allison Sweat (Controller-Property)
Scott Finer (Dir-Engrg)
Brandon Jordan (Dir-F&B)
Kathy Zalewski (Mgr-Catering & Event)
Chad Nigro (Dir-Golf)
Jim Simpson (Sls Dir)

HOTH THERAPEUTICS, INC.
590 Madison Ave 21st Fl, New York, NY 10022
Tel.: (646) 756-2997   NV
Web Site:
  https://www.hoththerapeutics.com
Year Founded: 2017
HOTH—(NASDAQ)
Rev.: $6,370
Assets: $6,759,381
Liabilities: $1,637,731
Net Worth: $5,121,650
Earnings: ($11,371,953)
Emp.: 2
Fiscal Year-end: 12/31/22
Biotechnology Research & Development Services

N.A.I.C.S.: 541714
Robb Knie (Pres & CEO)
David Briones (CFO)
Hayley Springer (VP-Ops)
Mary Beth Jones (Dir-Project Mgmt)

HOULIHAN LOKEY, INC.
10250 Constellation Blvd 5th Fl, Los Angeles, CA 90067
Tel.: (310) 788-5200   DE
Web Site: https://www.hl.com
Year Founded: 1972
HLI—(NYSE)
Rev.: $1,914,404,000
Assets: $3,170,759,000
Liabilities: $1,334,009,000
Net Worth: $1,836,750,000
Earnings: $280,301,000
Emp.: 2,601
Fiscal Year-end: 03/31/24
Financial Restructuring, Acquisition Management & Capital Raising Services
N.A.I.C.S.: 523940
David A. Preiser (Vice Chm)
Charles A. Yamarone (Chief Corp Governance Officer)
Christopher M. Crain (Gen Counsel)
P. Eric Siegert (Co-Head-Fin Restructuring-Global)
Scott Jospeh Adelson (CEO)
Irwin N. Gold (Co-Founder)
J. Lindsey Alley (CFO)
Shea Goggin (Co-Head-Private Funds Grp-Global)
Andy Lund (Co-Head-Private Funds Grp-Global)
Maria Ruderman Singer (Executives)
David Villa (Mng Dir-Fin Svcs Grp)
Andy Cairns (Mng Dir & Head-Capital Markets-Middle East & Africa)
Jay Novak (Head-Consumer, Food, and Retail Grp-Global)

Subsidiaries:

Freeman & Co., LLC. (1)
645 Fifth Ave 9th Fl, New York, NY 10022
Tel.: (212) 830-6161
Web Site: http://www.freeman-co.com
Financial Services, Management Consulting & Competitor Benchmarking Data
N.A.I.C.S.: 541611
James L. Freeman (Founder & CEO)
Gagan Sawhney (Mng Dir)
Eric C. Weber (CEO)
Christopher Pedone (Exec Dir)
Greg Stevenson (Exec Dir)
Matthew Capozzi (Exec Dir)

GCA Corporation (1)
Pacific Century Place Marunouchi Floor 30, 11-1 Marunouchi 1-chome Chiyoda-ku, Tokyo, 100-6230, Japan   (81.2%)
Tel.: (81) 362127100
Web Site: http://www.gcaglobal.com
Rev.: $217,503,230
Assets: $336,328,090
Liabilities: $134,230,460
Net Worth: $202,097,630
Earnings: $21,760,410
Emp.: 435
Fiscal Year-end: 12/31/2019
Holding Company; Investment & Business Support Services
N.A.I.C.S.: 551112
Todd J. Carter (Co-CEO & Mng Dir)
Akihiro Watanabe (Founder)
Geoffrey D. Baldwin (Co-CEO, Mng Dir & Head-M&A)
Akikazu Ida (Mng Dir)
Ritsuko Nonomiya (Mng Dir)
Phil Adams (Mng Dir)
Sascha Pfeiffer (Mng Dir)
Alexander M. Grunwald (Mng Dir)
Rich Jasen (Mng Dir & Head-Private Capital)
Susan Moran (VP-Mktg & Client Engagement)
Kate Staunton (Dir-Talent Mgmt & People Ops)
Marcus Anthony (VP)
Rushi Bhanderi (VP)

Kirk Bloede (VP)
Charlie Wheatley (VP)
John F. Lambros (Pres-Global Investment Bank-US)

Subsidiary (Domestic):

Due Diligence Corporation (2)
30th Fl 1 11 1 Marunouchi, Tokyo, 100 6230, Chiyoda-ku, Japan
Tel.: (81) 362121850
Financial Advisory Services
N.A.I.C.S.: 523999
Yasuyuki Tanaka (Partner)

Subsidiary (Non-US):

GCA China Company, Limited (2)
B02 22F Tower 3 Jing An Kerry Centre 1228 Yanan Road Middle, Shanghai, 200040, China
Tel.: (86) 2131076056
Financial Investment Services
N.A.I.C.S.: 523999

GCA India Investment Advisers Private Limited (2)
146 Maker Chambers 6 Nariman Point, Mumbai, 400 021, India
Tel.: (91) 2261069000
Financial Investment Services
N.A.I.C.S.: 523999

Subsidiary (Domestic):

GCA Savian Holdings Corporation (2)
30th Fl Pac Century Pl Marunouchi, Tokyo, 100 6230, Japan
Tel.: (81) 362127100
Sales Range: $100-124.9 Million
Emp.: 150
Investment Banking Advisory Services
N.A.I.C.S.: 523940

Subsidiary (US):

GCA Savvian Advisors LLC (2)
One Maritime Plaza, San Francisco, CA 94111
Tel.: (415) 318-3600
Sales Range: $100-124.9 Million
Emp.: 60
Financial Advisory Services
N.A.I.C.S.: 523999
James B. Avery (Mng Dir)

GCA Savvian Capital LLC (2)
150 California St, San Francisco, CA 94111
Tel.: (415) 318-3600
Investment Management Service
N.A.I.C.S.: 541618
Todd J. Carter (Mng Dir)

GCA Savvian LLC (2)
1 Maritime Plz 25th Fl, San Francisco, CA 94111
Tel.: (415) 318-3600
Web Site: http://gcaglobal.com
Emp.: 50
Financial Advisory Services
N.A.I.C.S.: 523999

Subsidiary (Non-US):

GCA Singapore Private Limited (2)
9 Temasek Boulevard 41-04 Suntec Tower 2, Singapore, 038989, Singapore
Tel.: (65) 64553051
Financial Investment Services
N.A.I.C.S.: 523999

Subsidiary (Domestic):

Mezzanine Corporation (2)
Tokyo Tatemono Nihonbashi Building 11th Floor 3-13 Nihonbashi 1-chome, Chuo-ku, Tokyo, 103-0027, Japan
Tel.: (81) 363677970
Web Site: https://www.mcokk.com
Sales Range: $50-74.9 Million
Emp.: 30
Investment Banking Advisory Services
N.A.I.C.S.: 523940
Osamu Matsuno (Mng Dir)

Houlihan Lokey (China) Limited (1)
Suites 506-508 One International Finance Centre 1 Harbour View Street, Central, China (Hong Kong)
Tel.: (852) 35512300

Investment Advice Management Services
N.A.I.C.S.: 523900
Jeffrey Wilson (Mng Dir)

Houlihan Lokey (Corporate Finance) Limited (1)
One Curzon Street, London, W1J 5HD, United Kingdom   (100%)
Tel.: (44) 20 7839 3355
Web Site: http://hl.com
Mergers & Acquisitions Advisory Services
N.A.I.C.S.: 561499
Andrew D. Adams (Mng Dir & Co-Head-Corp Fin-UK)
Shaun Browne (Mng Dir & Co-Head-Fin-UK)
Joseph Swanson (Sr Mng Dir-Fin Restructuring)

Houlihan Lokey (Espana) S.A. (1)
Edificio Torre Serrano Marques de Villamagna 3, 28001, Madrid, Spain
Tel.: (34) 918335470
Web Site: http://www.hl.com
Investment Advisory Services
N.A.I.C.S.: 523940
Manuel Martinez-Fidalgo (Mng Dir)
Carlos Parames (Mng Dir)
Juan Luis Munoz (Mng Dir)

Houlihan Lokey (Europe) Limited (1)
83 Pall mall, London, SW1Y 5ES, United Kingdom
Tel.: (44) 2078393355
Web Site: http://www.hl.com
Financial Restructuring, Acquisition Management & Capital Raising Services
N.A.I.C.S.: 523940
Anthony Forshaw (Mng Dir & Head-Capital Markets)
Joseph Swanson (Sr Mng Dir & Head-Fin Restructuring)
Matteo Manfredi (Mng Dir & Head-Corp Fin-Milan)
Andrew Adams (Mng Dir & Co-Head-Corp Fin)
Shaun Browne (Mng Dir & Co-Head-Corp Fin)

Houlihan Lokey (Netherlands) B.V. (1)
Roemer Visscherstraat 43-45, 1054 EW, Amsterdam, Netherlands
Tel.: (31) 20 58 91 831
Web Site: http://www.hl.com
Emp.: 15
Investment Advisory Services
N.A.I.C.S.: 523940
Rob Oudman (Mng Dir)

Houlihan Lokey Capital, Inc. (1)
10250 Constellation Blvd 5th Fl, Los Angeles, CA 90067
Tel.: (310) 553-8871
Web Site: http://www.hl.com
Emp.: 300
Corporate Capital Raising Services
N.A.I.C.S.: 541611

Houlihan Lokey EMEA, LLP (1)
One Curzon Street, London, W1J 5HD, United Kingdom
Tel.: (44) 2078393355
Financial Advisory Services
N.A.I.C.S.: 523940
David A. Preiser (Chm)
Jonathan Harrison (Mng Dir-Bus Svcs Grp)

Houlihan Lokey Financial Advisors, Inc. (1)
10250 Constellation Blvd 5th Fl, Los Angeles, CA 90067
Tel.: (310) 553-8871
Web Site: http://www.hl.com
Emp.: 300
Corporate Financial Advisory Services
N.A.I.C.S.: 541611

Houlihan Lokey GmbH (1)
OpernTurm Bockenheimer Landstrasse 2-4, 60306, Frankfurt am Main, Germany
Tel.: (49) 69 170099 0
Web Site: http://www.hl.com
Investment Advisory Services
N.A.I.C.S.: 523940
Steffen Leckert (Mng Dir-Industrials Grp)

Leonardo & Co. S.p.A. (1)
Via dell'orso 8, 20121, Milan, Italy
Tel.: (39) 02873311

Houlihan Lokey, Inc.—(Continued)

Web Site: http://www.leonardo-co.com
Emp.: 25
Investment Advisory Services
N.A.I.C.S.: 523940
Andrea Mainetti *(Mng Dir)*
Andre Pichler *(Mng Dir & Co-Head-Corp Fin)*
Pietro Braicovich *(Mng Dir & Co-Head-Corp Fin)*

HOUR LOOP, INC.

8201 164th Ave NE Ste 200, Redmond, WA 98052-7615
Tel.: (206) 385-0488   **DE**
Web Site: https://www.hourloop.com
Year Founded: 2015
HOUR—(NASDAQ)
Rev.: $95,930,091
Assets: $25,731,976
Liabilities: $18,899,120
Net Worth: $6,832,856
Earnings: ($1,477,623)
Emp.: 186
Fiscal Year-end: 12/31/22
Gift Product Distr
N.A.I.C.S.: 424990
Sau Kuen Yu *(Sr VP)*
Randy Wu *(Fin Mgr)*
Peri Wu *(Mgr-Human Resources)*
Sam Lai *(Chm, CEO & Interim CFO)*

HOUSTON AMERICAN ENERGY CORPORATION

801 Travis St Ste 1425, Houston, TX 77002
Tel.: (713) 222-6966   **DE**
Web Site:
   https://www.houstonamerican.com
Year Founded: 2001
HUSA—(NYSEAMEX)
Rev.: $1,638,841
Assets: $11,731,183
Liabilities: $414,309
Net Worth: $11,316,874
Earnings: ($744,279)
Emp.: 2
Fiscal Year-end: 12/31/22
Crude Oil & Natural Gas Exploration & Production
N.A.I.C.S.: 211120
John F. Terwilliger *(Founder, Pres & CEO)*

HOUSTON NATURAL RESOURCES CORP.

12 Greenway Plz Ste 1100, Houston, TX 77046
Tel.: (713) 425-4901   **NV**
Web Site: https://hnrcholdings.gcs-web.com
HNRC—(OTCIQ)
Sewage Treatment Services
N.A.I.C.S.: 221320
Frank Kristan *(Pres)*

HOVNANIAN ENTERPRISES, INC.

90 Matawan Rd 5th Fl, Matawan, NJ 07747
Tel.: (732) 747-7800   **DE**
Web Site: https://www.khov.com
Year Founded: 1959
HOV—(NYSE)
Rev.: $3,004,918,000
Assets: $2,605,574,000
Liabilities: $1,805,225,000
Net Worth: $800,349,000
Earnings: $242,008,000
Emp.: 1,878
Fiscal Year-end: 10/31/24
Holding Company; New Housing Operative Builder & Marketer
N.A.I.C.S.: 551112
Ara K. Hovnanian *(Founder, Chm, Pres & CEO)*

Brad G. O'Connor *(CFO, Chief Acctg Officer, Treas & Sr VP)*
Kevork S. Hovnanian *(Founder)*

Subsidiaries:

2700 Empire, LLC   (1)
Empire Ave and Claudia Ln, Brentwood, CA 94513
Tel.: (916) 945-5380
Commercial Building Construction Services
N.A.I.C.S.: 236220

Amber Ridge, LLC   (1)
741 Amber Ridge Ave, Glen Ellyn, IL 60137
Tel.: (630) 547-2942
Real Estate Development Services
N.A.I.C.S.: 531390

Arbor Trails, LLC   (1)
5871 Oak Ridge Way, Lisle, IL 60532
Tel.: (331) 281-0171
Real Estate Development Services
N.A.I.C.S.: 531390

EASTERN TITLE AGENCY, INC.   (1)
2 Indus Way W, Eatontown, NJ 07724
Tel.: (732) 389-0009
Web Site: http://www.khov.com
Title Abstract & Settlement Services
N.A.I.C.S.: 541191

FOUNDERS TITLE AGENCY,
INC.   (1)
4090-A Lafayette Center Dr, Chantilly, VA 20151
Tel.: (703) 885-7330
Web Site:
   http://www.founderstitleagency.com
Real Estate Development Services
N.A.I.C.S.: 531390

Fair Land Title Company, Inc.   (1)
5160 Village Creek Dr Ste 200, Plano, TX 75093
Tel.: (972) 380-9200
Real Estate Development Services
N.A.I.C.S.: 531390

Glenrise Grove, LLC   (1)
741 Amber Ridge Ave, Glen Ellyn, IL 60137
Tel.: (630) 547-2942
Real Estate Development Services
N.A.I.C.S.: 531390

HovSite Firenze LLC   (1)
3601 Quantum Blvd, Boynton Beach, FL 33426-8638
Tel.: (561) 420-9075
Real Estate Development Services
N.A.I.C.S.: 531390

K. HOVNANIAN AT TAMARACK
SOUTH LLC   (1)
3807 Formby Rd, Naperville, IL 60564
Tel.: (331) 702-2645
Real Estate Development Services
N.A.I.C.S.: 531390

K. HOVNANIAN GREAT WESTERN
BUILDING COMPANY, LLC   (1)
20830 N Tatum Blvd Ste 250, Phoenix, AZ 85050
Tel.: (480) 824-4171
Construction Engineering Services
N.A.I.C.S.: 237990

K. HOVNANIAN GREAT WESTERN
HOMES, LLC   (1)
715 E Center Ave, Buckeye, AZ 85326
Tel.: (623) 393-8909
Multifamily Housing Construction Services
N.A.I.C.S.: 236116

K. HOVNANIAN'S FOUR SEASONS
AT BAKERSFIELD, L.L.C.   (1)
6311 Barcelona Dr, Bakersfield, CA 93306
Tel.: (661) 872-8140
Real Estate Development Services
N.A.I.C.S.: 531390

K. Hovnanian American Mortgage
LLC   (1)
3601 Quantum Blvd, Boynton Beach, FL 33426   (100%)
Tel.: (561) 752-1762
Web Site: http://www.khovmortgage.com
Sales Range: $25-49.9 Million
Real Estate Development of Planned Communities

Jessica Blair *(Acct Mgr)*
Jennifer Borunda *(Acct Mgr)*
John Dilbert *(Acct Mgr)*
Lorena Fatica *(Acct Mgr)*
Andrew Gentille *(Acct Mgr)*
Christi Hill *(Acct Mgr)*
Jodie Kutner *(Acct Mgr)*
Adeleine Maloney *(Acct Mgr)*
Christopher Montague *(Acct Mgr)*

K. Hovnanian Aspire at Apricot
Grove, LLC   (1)
814 Holdenhurst Ln, Patterson, CA 95363
Tel.: (209) 231-7774
Home Rental Services
N.A.I.C.S.: 531110

K. Hovnanian Aspire at Auld Farms,
LLC   (1)
624 Diagonal Rd, Akron, OH 44320
Tel.: (330) 302-9970
Residential Building Construction Services
N.A.I.C.S.: 236115

K. Hovnanian Aspire at Caliterra
Ranch, LLC   (1)
Wheatland Rd & Oakley Ln, Wheatland, CA 95692
Residential Building Construction Services
N.A.I.C.S.: 236115

K. Hovnanian Aspire at Hawks Ridge,
LLC   (1)
678 NE Waters Edge Ln, Port Saint Lucie, FL 34983
Tel.: (772) 837-6006
Housing Construction Services
N.A.I.C.S.: 236117

K. Hovnanian Aspire at Port St. Lucie, LLC   (1)
2961 SW Savona Blvd, Port Saint Lucie, FL 34953
Tel.: (561) 532-1280
Home Rental Services
N.A.I.C.S.: 531110

K. Hovnanian Aspire at River Terrace,
LLC   (1)
1402 Delta River Ave, Stockton, CA 95206
Tel.: (209) 249-0954
Commercial Building Construction Services
N.A.I.C.S.: 236220

K. Hovnanian Aspire at Solaire,
LLC   (1)
2182 Daylight Dr, Roseville, CA 95747
Tel.: (916) 269-5620
Residential Building Construction Services
N.A.I.C.S.: 236115

K. Hovnanian Aspire at Stones
Throw, LLC   (1)
West Main St and Niemann St, Winters, CA 95694
Tel.: (916) 945-5505
Home Rental Services
N.A.I.C.S.: 531110

K. Hovnanian Aspire at Waterstone,
LLC   (1)
5226 Armina Pl, Fort Pierce, FL 34951
Tel.: (561) 532-1221
Commercial Building Construction Services
N.A.I.C.S.: 236220

K. Hovnanian Belden Pointe,
LLC   (1)
3790 Case Rd, Avon, OH 44011
Tel.: (440) 934-3760
Real Estate Development Services
N.A.I.C.S.: 531390

K. Hovnanian Brittany Manor Borrower, LLC   (1)
2001 Damon Dr, Mount Airy, MD 21771
Commercial Building Construction Services
N.A.I.C.S.: 236220

K. Hovnanian Building Company,
LLC   (1)
20830 N Tatum Blvd Ste 250, Phoenix, AZ 85050
Tel.: (480) 824-4200
Construction Engineering Services
N.A.I.C.S.: 237990

K. Hovnanian Cambridge Homes,
LLC   (1)

151 Southhall Lane Suite 120 Maitland, Orlando, FL 32751
Tel.: (407) 865-9600
Web Site: http://www.khov.com
Sales Range: $150-199.9 Million
Emp.: 40
Single-Family Housing Construction
N.A.I.C.S.: 236115
Kyla Upper *(Pres)*

K. Hovnanian Companies Northeast,
Inc.   (1)
110 Fieldcrest Ave, Edison, NJ 08837-3626   (100%)
Tel.: (732) 225-4001
Web Site: http://www.khov.com
Sales Range: $50-74.9 Million
Emp.: 200
Real Estate Development of Planned Communities
N.A.I.C.S.: 236115

K. Hovnanian Cornerstone Farms,
LLC   (1)
4351 Weathervane Dr, Lorain, OH 44053
Tel.: (440) 271-8503
Commercial Building Construction Services
N.A.I.C.S.: 236220

K. Hovnanian DFW Ascend at Justin
Crossing, LLC   (1)
FM 156 at John Wiley Rd, Justin, TX 76247
Tel.: (469) 737-1485
Home Rental Services
N.A.I.C.S.: 531110

K. Hovnanian DFW Auburn Farms,
LLC   (1)
3637 Fletcher Ct, Flower Mound, TX 75022
Tel.: (972) 588-6138
Real Estate Development Services
N.A.I.C.S.: 531390

K. Hovnanian DFW Bayside,
LLC   (1)
2122 Hermosa Dr, Rowlett, TX 75088
Tel.: (469) 737-6582
Commercial Building Construction Services
N.A.I.C.S.: 236220

K. Hovnanian DFW Canyon Falls,
LLC   (1)
4105 Silver Lace Ln Northlake, Roanoke, TX 76262
Tel.: (469) 737-6532
Commercial Building Construction Services
N.A.I.C.S.: 236220

K. Hovnanian DFW Commodore at
Preston, LLC   (1)
8084 Ingram Dr, Plano, TX 75024
Tel.: (469) 737-6583
Commercial Building Construction Services
N.A.I.C.S.: 236220

K. Hovnanian DFW Diamond Creek
Estates, LLC   (1)
NW of FM 548 and Diamond Creek Dr, Forney, TX 75126
Tel.: (469) 737-6544
Commercial Building Construction Services
N.A.I.C.S.: 236220

K. Hovnanian DFW Harmon Farms,
LLC   (1)
8721 Everglade Dr, North Richland Hills, TX 76182
Tel.: (972) 588-6133
Real Estate Development Services
N.A.I.C.S.: 531390

K. Hovnanian DFW Heron Pond,
LLC   (1)
5729 Heron Dr W, Colleyville, TX 76034
Tel.: (972) 588-6146
Real Estate Development Services
N.A.I.C.S.: 531390

K. Hovnanian DFW High Pointe,
LLC   (1)
5301 Waterview Ct, Haltom City, TX 76137
Tel.: (972) 588-6145
Commercial Building Construction Services
N.A.I.C.S.: 236220

K. Hovnanian DFW Homestead,
LLC   (1)
395 Mitchell Dr, Sunnyvale, TX 75182
Tel.: (972) 588-6137

Real Estate Development Services
N.A.I.C.S.: 531390

K. Hovnanian DFW Liberty Crossing, LLC (1)
8159 Declaration Dr, Frisco, TX 75035
Tel.: (972) 588-6130
Real Estate Development Services
N.A.I.C.S.: 531390

K. Hovnanian DFW Liberty, LLC (1)
3703 Republic Trl, Melissa, TX 75454
Tel.: (972) 474-1227
Commercial Building Construction Services
N.A.I.C.S.: 236220

K. Hovnanian DFW Midtown Park, LLC (1)
9915 Wiltshire Dr, Houston, TX 77089
Tel.: (713) 817-7201
Housing Construction Services
N.A.I.C.S.: 236117

K. Hovnanian DFW Oakmont Park, LLC (1)
602 Pinehurst Rd, Red Oak, TX 75154
Tel.: (214) 466-8443
Commercial Building Construction Services
N.A.I.C.S.: 236220

K. Hovnanian DFW Sanford Park, LLC (1)
416 Vawter Dr, Van Alstyne, TX 75495
Tel.: (469) 737-6510
Commercial Building Construction Services
N.A.I.C.S.: 236220

K. Hovnanian DFW Sapphire Bay, LLC (1)
806 Resort Dr, Rowlett, TX 75088
Tel.: (469) 283-5596
Residential Building Construction Services
N.A.I.C.S.: 236115

K. Hovnanian DFW Seventeen Lakes, LLC (1)
4508 Duck Creek Ln, Roanoke, TX 76247
Tel.: (972) 588-6134
Real Estate Development Services
N.A.I.C.S.: 531390

K. Hovnanian DFW Trailwood, LLC (1)
5232 Ravine Ridge Ct, Flower Mound, TX 76262
Tel.: (469) 737-6531
Commercial Building Construction Services
N.A.I.C.S.: 236220

K. Hovnanian DFW Villas at Mustang Park, LLC (1)
4677 Maverick Way, Carrollton, TX 75010
Tel.: (469) 737-6578
Housing Construction Services
N.A.I.C.S.: 236117

K. Hovnanian DFW Watson Creek, LLC (1)
Alta Vista Rd at Golden Triangle Blvd, Fort Worth, TX 76244
Tel.: (972) 588-6133
Commercial Building Construction Services
N.A.I.C.S.: 236220

K. Hovnanian DFW Wellington Villas, LLC (1)
12116 Howell Ct, Haslet, TX 76052
Tel.: (469) 737-6540
Commercial Building Construction Services
N.A.I.C.S.: 236220

K. Hovnanian DFW Wildridge, LLC (1)
9716 Grouse Ridge Ln, Little Elm, TX 75068
Tel.: (469) 737-6532
Housing Construction Services
N.A.I.C.S.: 236117

K. Hovnanian Estates at Wekiva, LLC (1)
2205 Argo Wood Way, Apopka, FL 32712
Tel.: (407) 326-2072
Real Estate Development Services
N.A.I.C.S.: 531390

K. Hovnanian Four Seasons at Chestnut Ridge, LLC (1)
288 Kensington Way, Elyria, OH 44035
Tel.: (440) 271-8488

Commercial Building Construction Services
N.A.I.C.S.: 236220

K. Hovnanian Four Seasons at Homestead, LLC (1)
400 Farmhouse Way, Dixon, CA 95620
Tel.: (707) 348-0505
Residential Building Construction Services
N.A.I.C.S.: 236115

K. Hovnanian Grand Cypress, LLC (1)
4489 Grand Preserve Pl, Palm Harbor, FL 34684
Tel.: (813) 375-0640
Real Estate Development Services
N.A.I.C.S.: 531390

K. Hovnanian Homes - DFW, L.L.C. (1)
5808 W Plano Pkwy, Plano, TX 75093-4636
Tel.: (469) 737-1400
Real Estate Development Services
N.A.I.C.S.: 531390
Jimmy Brownlee *(Pres)*

K. Hovnanian Homes at Brook Manor, LLC (1)
409 Birkby Way, Holly Springs, NC 27540
Tel.: (919) 238-5132
Real Estate Development Services
N.A.I.C.S.: 531390

K. Hovnanian Homes at Creekside, LLC (1)
110 Smoke Rise Rd, Richmond Hill, GA 31324
Tel.: (843) 706-7646
Real Estate Development Services
N.A.I.C.S.: 531390

K. Hovnanian Homes at Shell Hall, LLC (1)
53 Shell Hall Way, Bluffton, SC 29910
Tel.: (843) 706-7644
Real Estate Development Services
N.A.I.C.S.: 531390

K. Hovnanian Homes at Shenandoah Springs, LLC (1)
263 Mountain Laurel Blvd, Ranson, WV 25438
Tel.: (703) 885-7114
Commercial Building Construction Services
N.A.I.C.S.: 236220

K. Hovnanian Homes at Summit Pointe, LLC (1)
360 Dillon Cir, Middletown, DE 19709
Tel.: (302) 202-2415
Home Rental Services
N.A.I.C.S.: 531110

K. Hovnanian Homes at The Abby, LLC (1)
81 Western Trace, Beaufort, SC 29907
Tel.: (843) 706-7670
Real Estate Development Services
N.A.I.C.S.: 531390

K. Hovnanian Homes of Maryland I, LLC (1)
1802 Brightseat Rd 5th Fl, Landover, MD 20785
Tel.: (301) 772-8900
Real Estate Development Services
N.A.I.C.S.: 531390

K. Hovnanian Homes of Maryland, LLC (1)
1802 Brightseat Rd, Hyattsville, MD 20785-4232 **(100%)**
Tel.: (301) 772-8900
Web Site: http://www.khov.com
Sales Range: $50-74.9 Million
Emp.: 140
General Contractors
N.A.I.C.S.: 236115

K. Hovnanian Homes of Minnesota at Arbor Creek, LLC (1)
12078 78th St NE, Otsego, MN 55301
Tel.: (763) 777-9010
Real Estate Development Services
N.A.I.C.S.: 531390

K. Hovnanian Homes of Minnesota at Autumn Meadows, LLC (1)
17874 Fielding Way, Lakeville, MN 55044
Tel.: (952) 683-1627

Real Estate Development Services
N.A.I.C.S.: 531390

K. Hovnanian Homes of Minnesota at Cedar Hollow, LLC (1)
4420 Walnut Grove Ln N, Plymouth, MN 55446
Tel.: (763) 270-5476
Real Estate Development Services
N.A.I.C.S.: 531390

K. Hovnanian Homes of Minnesota at Founder's Ridge, LLC (1)
3836 Founders Way, Chaska, MN 55318
Tel.: (952) 500-9183
Real Estate Development Services
N.A.I.C.S.: 531390

K. Hovnanian Homes of Minnesota at Harpers Street Woods, LLC (1)
3105 129th Ave NE, Blaine, MN 55449
Tel.: (763) 208-2982
Real Estate Development Services
N.A.I.C.S.: 531390

K. Hovnanian Homes of Minnesota, L.L.C. (1)
12701 Whitewater Dr Ste 120, Minnetonka, MN 55343-4109
Tel.: (952) 944-3455
Real Estate Development Services
N.A.I.C.S.: 531390

K. Hovnanian Houston Balmoral, LLC (1)
11919 Lewisvale Green Dr, Humble, TX 77346
Tel.: (281) 559-7680
Home Rental Services
N.A.I.C.S.: 531110

K. Hovnanian Houston Bayou Oaks at West Orem, LLC (1)
14003 Inland Hill St, Houston, TX 77045
Tel.: (832) 409-5600
Commercial Building Construction Services
N.A.I.C.S.: 236220

K. Hovnanian Houston Creek Bend, LLC (1)
508 Moore St, Richwood, TX 77531
Tel.: (979) 265-2582
Commercial Building Construction Services
N.A.I.C.S.: 236220

K. Hovnanian Houston Dry Creek Village, LLC (1)
3106 Trishelle Ct, Missouri City, TX 77459
Tel.: (713) 955-6853
Commercial Building Construction Services
N.A.I.C.S.: 236220

K. Hovnanian Houston Eldridge Park, LLC (1)
13802 Andover Park Dr, Houston, TX 77083
Tel.: (713) 590-4511
Home Rental Services
N.A.I.C.S.: 531110

K. Hovnanian Houston Greatwood Lake, LLC (1)
326 Arbor Ranch Cir, Richmond, TX 77469
Tel.: (713) 538-1626
Commercial Building Construction Services
N.A.I.C.S.: 236220

K. Hovnanian Houston Katy Pointe, LLC (1)
24130 Prairie Glen Ln, Katy, TX 77493
Tel.: (281) 574-1324
Commercial Building Construction Services
N.A.I.C.S.: 236220

K. Hovnanian Houston Lakes of Bella Terra West, LLC (1)
6038 Jenna Way, Rosenberg, TX 77406
Tel.: (713) 590-4500
Home Rental Services
N.A.I.C.S.: 531110

K. Hovnanian Houston Laurel Glen, LLC (1)
7710 Autumn Run Dr, Spring, TX 77379
Tel.: (832) 717-6842
Commercial Building Construction Services
N.A.I.C.S.: 236220

K. Hovnanian Houston Midtown Park I, LLC (1)

1841 Alyssa Way, Alvin, TX 77511
Tel.: (281) 800-8865
Commercial Building Construction Services
N.A.I.C.S.: 236220

K. Hovnanian Houston Park Lakes East, LLC (1)
15235 Yellowstone Lk Dr, Humble, TX 77396
Tel.: (713) 590-4514
Commercial Building Construction Services
N.A.I.C.S.: 236220

K. Hovnanian Houston Parkway Trails, LLC (1)
Commercial Building Construction Services
N.A.I.C.S.: 236220

K. Hovnanian Houston River Farms, LLC (1)
14231 Angelina Dr, Baytown, TX 77523
Tel.: (281) 609-6038
Commercial Building Construction Services
N.A.I.C.S.: 236220

K. Hovnanian Houston Sunset Ranch, LLC (1)
1841 Alyssa Way, Alvin, TX 77511
Tel.: (713) 590-4500
Home Rental Services
N.A.I.C.S.: 531110

K. Hovnanian Houston Terra Del Sol, LLC (1)
7606 Granite Terrace Ln, Houston, TX 77083
Tel.: (281) 988-5518
Home Rental Services
N.A.I.C.S.: 531110

K. Hovnanian Houston Thunder Bay Subdivision, LLC (1)
11703 St Augustine Dr, Mont Belvieu, TX 77535
Tel.: (281) 573-4249
Commercial Building Construction Services
N.A.I.C.S.: 236220

K. Hovnanian Houston Tranquility Lake Estates, LLC (1)
3034 Tranquility Lake Estates Blvd, Pearland, TX 77581
Tel.: (713) 590-4512
Commercial Building Construction Services
N.A.I.C.S.: 236220

K. Hovnanian Houston Westwood, LLC (1)
609 Westwood Dr, League City, TX 77573
Tel.: (832) 234-9769
Home Rental Services
N.A.I.C.S.: 531110

K. Hovnanian Lake Parker, LLC (1)
1378 Heritage Landings Dr, Lakeland, FL 33805
Tel.: (813) 518-6779
Real Estate Development Services
N.A.I.C.S.: 531390

K. Hovnanian Landings 40s, LLC (1)
3997 Abigail Dr, Lorain, OH 44053
Tel.: (440) 960-5400
Commercial Building Construction Services
N.A.I.C.S.: 236220

K. Hovnanian Legacy at Via Bella, LLC (1)
3265 E Indigo Bay Ct, Gilbert, AZ 85234
Tel.: (602) 824-7820
Housing Construction Services
N.A.I.C.S.: 236117

K. Hovnanian Liberty on Bluff Creek, LLC (1)
1988 Commonwealth Blvd Ste 1, Chanhassen, MN 55317
Tel.: (952) 239-9662
Real Estate Development Services
N.A.I.C.S.: 531390

K. Hovnanian Magnolia at Westside, LLC (1)
2407 Biscotto Cir, Davenport, FL 33897
Tel.: (407) 279-3634
Commercial Building Construction Services
N.A.I.C.S.: 236220

K. Hovnanian Meadow Lakes, LLC (1)

Hovnanian Enterprises, Inc.—(Continued)

36833 Sandy Ridge Dr, North Ridgeville, OH 44039
Tel.: (440) 271-8425
Commercial Building Construction Services
N.A.I.C.S.: 236220

K. Hovnanian Meadow View at Mountain House, LLC (1)
1040 S Prosperity St Mountain House, San Joaquin, CA 95391
Commercial Building Construction Services
N.A.I.C.S.: 236220

K. Hovnanian Norton Place, LLC (1)
2209 Norton Pl, Avon, OH 44011
Commercial Building Construction Services
N.A.I.C.S.: 236220

K. Hovnanian Ocoee Landings, LLC (1)
1896 Ibis Bay Ct, Ocoee, FL 34761
Tel.: (407) 326-0293
Commercial Building Construction Services
N.A.I.C.S.: 236220

K. Hovnanian Preserve at Avonlea, LLC (1)
215 Preserve Trl S, Stuart, FL 34994
Tel.: (772) 758-1022
Home Rental Services
N.A.I.C.S.: 531110

K. Hovnanian Redfern Trails, LLC (1)
Redfern Rd, Columbia Station, OH 44028
Commercial Building Construction Services
N.A.I.C.S.: 236220

K. Hovnanian San Sebastian, LLC (1)
2100 Emerald Springs Dr, Apopka, FL 32712
Tel.: (407) 214-4522
Commercial Building Construction Services
N.A.I.C.S.: 236220

K. Hovnanian Sereno, LLC (1)
5010 Bella Armonia Cir, Wimauma, FL 33598
Tel.: (813) 513-9613
Housing Construction Services
N.A.I.C.S.: 236117

K. Hovnanian Sherwood at Regency, LLC (1)
Royal Glen Dr & Killingsworth Dr, Cary, NC 27518
Tel.: (919) 274-1710
Real Estate Development Services
N.A.I.C.S.: 531390

K. Hovnanian Sterling Ranch, LLC (1)
5125 E Sterling Ranch Cir, Davie, FL 33314
Web Site: http://www.khov.com
Real Estate Development Services
N.A.I.C.S.: 531390

K. Hovnanian Summit Homes, L.L.C. (1)
13025 Jerry City Rd, Cygnet, OH 43413
Tel.: (419) 655-2077
Construction Engineering Services
N.A.I.C.S.: 237990

K. Hovnanian T&C Homes at Illinois, L.L.C. (1)
1806 S Highland Ave, Lombard, IL 60148
Tel.: (630) 953-2222
Rev.: $11,900,000
Emp.: 50
Single-Family Housing Construction
N.A.I.C.S.: 236115
William J. Ryan (Pres)

K. Hovnanian Union Park, LLC (1)
32230 Watoga Loop, Wesley Chapel, FL 33543
Tel.: (813) 375-0373
Real Estate Development Services
N.A.I.C.S.: 531390

K. Hovnanian Village Glen, LLC (1)
851 Asbury Pointe Ln, Painesville, OH 44077
Commercial Building Construction Services
N.A.I.C.S.: 236220

K. Hovnanian Villas at The Commons, LLC (1)
6 Commons Cir, Hawthorn Woods, IL 60047
Tel.: (331) 701-7875
Commercial Building Construction Services
N.A.I.C.S.: 236220

K. Hovnanian Winding Bay Preserve, LLC (1)
11030 Hanlon Terrace Aly, Winter Garden, FL 34787
Tel.: (407) 641-1359
Commercial Building Construction Services
N.A.I.C.S.: 236220

K. Hovnanian Windward Homes, LLC (1) (100%)
5439 Beaumont Ctr Blvd Ste 1050, Tampa, FL 33634
Tel.: (813) 885-7744
Web Site: http://www.windwardhomes.com
Sales Range: $50-74.9 Million
Emp.: 50
Provider of Single-Family Housing Construction
N.A.I.C.S.: 236115

K. Hovnanian Woodridge Place, LLC (1)
10556 Herrington Dr, Reminderville, OH 44202
Tel.: (330) 348-0200
Real Estate Development Services
N.A.I.C.S.: 531390

K. Hovnanian at 240 Missouri, LLC (1)
240 W Missouri Ave, Phoenix, AZ 85013
Tel.: (602) 824-7835
Housing Construction Services
N.A.I.C.S.: 236117

K. Hovnanian at Alameda Point, LLC (1)
45th Ave Alameda Rd, Phoenix, AZ 85310
Tel.: (602) 737-1750
Residential Building Construction Services
N.A.I.C.S.: 236115

K. Hovnanian at Alexander Lakes, LLC (1)
14342 Trotters Ridge Pl, Nokesville, VA 20181
Tel.: (703) 885-7274
Commercial Building Construction Services
N.A.I.C.S.: 236220

K. Hovnanian at Amberley Woods, LLC (1)
1835 Amberley Ct, Lake Forest, IL 60045
Tel.: (224) 706-6132
Real Estate Development Services
N.A.I.C.S.: 531390

K. Hovnanian at Ashby Place, LLC (1)
802 Ashby Dr, Middletown, DE 19709
Tel.: (302) 319-5530
Emp.: 3
Real Estate Development Services
N.A.I.C.S.: 531390
Jason Farissier (Mgr-Sls)

K. Hovnanian at Ashley Pointe LLC (1)
2061 Wren Rd, Yorkville, IL 60560
Tel.: (331) 701-7849
Commercial Building Construction Services
N.A.I.C.S.: 236220

K. Hovnanian at Aspire at Apricot Grove PH2, LLC (1)
814 Holdenhurst Ln, Patterson, CA 95363
Tel.: (209) 231-7774
Residential Building Construction Services
N.A.I.C.S.: 236116

K. Hovnanian at Autumn Ridge, LLC (1)
Pioneer Rd, Milford, DE 19963
Commercial Building Construction Services
N.A.I.C.S.: 236220

K. Hovnanian at Beacon Park Area 129, LLC (1)
121 Derailer, Irvine, CA 92618
Tel.: (949) 336-7351
Housing Construction Services

K. Hovnanian at Bellewood, LLC (1)
15835 Beau Ridge Dr, Woodbridge, VA 22193
Tel.: (703) 783-3422
Home Rental Services
N.A.I.C.S.: 531110

K. Hovnanian at Bensen's Mill Estates, LLC (1)
104 Pender Ct, Fredericksburg, VA 22406
Tel.: (703) 864-0579
Commercial Building Construction Services
N.A.I.C.S.: 236220

K. Hovnanian at Blackstone, LLC (1)
5051 Brentford Way, El Dorado Hills, CA 95762
Tel.: (916) 349-4060
Real Estate Development Services
N.A.I.C.S.: 531390

K. Hovnanian at Boca Dunes, LLC (1)
10226 Akenside Dr, Boca Raton, FL 33428
Tel.: (561) 623-3306
Commercial Building Construction Services
N.A.I.C.S.: 236220

K. Hovnanian at Booth Farm, LLC (1)
4425 Main St, Perry, OH 44081
Tel.: (440) 271-8816
Residential Building Construction Services
N.A.I.C.S.: 236115

K. Hovnanian at Bradwell Estates, LLC (1)
5191 Carriana Ct, Hoffman Estates, IL 60010
Tel.: (331) 201-9554
Real Estate Development Services
N.A.I.C.S.: 531390

K. Hovnanian at Brittany Manor, LLC (1)
2001 Damon Dr, Mount Airy, MD 21771
Tel.: (301) 205-5060
Commercial Building Construction Services
N.A.I.C.S.: 236220

K. Hovnanian at Burch Kove, LLC (1)
359 Lena Cir, Chapel Hill, NC 27514
Tel.: (919) 238-5134
Real Estate Development Services
N.A.I.C.S.: 531390

K. Hovnanian at Cadence Park, LLC (1)
520 Cultivate, Irvine, CA 92618
Tel.: (714) 368-4599
Commercial Building Construction Services
N.A.I.C.S.: 236220

K. Hovnanian at Casa Del Mar, LLC (1)
N Federal Hwy Near Dimick Rd, Boynton Beach, FL 33435
Tel.: (561) 536-4487
Real Estate Development Services
N.A.I.C.S.: 531390

K. Hovnanian at Cedar Lane, LLC (1)
39850 Cedar Blvd, Newark, CA 94560
Tel.: (916) 349-4073
Real Estate Development Services
N.A.I.C.S.: 531390

K. Hovnanian at Christina Court, LLC (1)
22W101 Busch Rd, Glen Ellyn, IL 60137
Tel.: (630) 793-9478
Housing Construction Services
N.A.I.C.S.: 236117

K. Hovnanian at Churchill Farms LLC (1)
312 Palomino Dr, Plano, IL 60545
Tel.: (331) 701-7854
Commercial Building Construction Services
N.A.I.C.S.: 236220

K. Hovnanian at Cooper's Landing, LLC (1)
4351 Weathervane Dr, Lorain, OH 44053
Home Rental Services
N.A.I.C.S.: 531110

K. Hovnanian at Coral Lago, LLC (1)
University Dr & NW 40th St, Coral Springs, FL 33075
Tel.: (954) 900-6855
Real Estate Development Services
N.A.I.C.S.: 531390

K. Hovnanian at Country View Estates, LLC (1)
1160 23rd St SW, Massillon, OH 44647
Tel.: (440) 271-8775
Residential Building Construction Services
N.A.I.C.S.: 236115

K. Hovnanian at Deer Ridge, LLC (1)
1914 Eagle Dr, Morris, IL 60450
Tel.: (331) 701-7865
Commercial Building Construction Services
N.A.I.C.S.: 236220

K. Hovnanian at Dorado at Twelve Bridges, LLC (1)
1281 Stark Bridge Rd, Lincoln, CA 95648
Tel.: (916) 945-5505
Home Rental Services
N.A.I.C.S.: 531110

K. Hovnanian at Doylestown, LLC (1)
6 Green St, Doylestown, PA 18901
Tel.: (267) 454-7895
Real Estate Development Services
N.A.I.C.S.: 531390

K. Hovnanian at Eden Terrace, LLC (1)
6 Eden Terrace Ln, Catonsville, MD 21228
Tel.: (301) 683-6363
Commercial Building Construction Services
N.A.I.C.S.: 236220

K. Hovnanian at Embrey Mill Village, LLC (1)
506 Sourwood Ct, Stafford, VA 22554
Tel.: (703) 885-7305
Commercial Building Construction Services
N.A.I.C.S.: 236220

K. Hovnanian at Estates of Chancellorsville, LLC (1)
8705 Formation Dr, Fredericksburg, VA 22407
Tel.: (703) 844-3768
Commercial Building Construction Services
N.A.I.C.S.: 236220

K. Hovnanian at Estates of Fox Chase, LLC (1)
200 Gates Creek Dr, Oswego, IL 60543
Tel.: (331) 701-7844
Commercial Building Construction Services
N.A.I.C.S.: 236220

K. Hovnanian at Fairfield Ridge, LLC (1)
14924 Case St, Plainfield, IL 60544
Tel.: (815) 782-7165
Real Estate Development Services
N.A.I.C.S.: 531390

K. Hovnanian at Firefly at Winding Creek, LLC (1)
4016 Backwater Cove Cir, Roseville, CA 95747
Tel.: (916) 269-5642
Home Rental Services
N.A.I.C.S.: 531110

K. Hovnanian at Fork Landing, LLC (1)
37 Pontoon Dr, Felton, DE 19943
Tel.: (302) 204-6227
Home Rental Services
N.A.I.C.S.: 531110

K. Hovnanian at Glen Oaks, LLC (1)
Home Rental Services
N.A.I.C.S.: 531110

K. Hovnanian at Grande Park, LLC (1)
26910 Summergrove Dr, Plainfield, IL 60585
Tel.: (331) 701-7840
Commercial Building Construction Services
N.A.I.C.S.: 236220

K. Hovnanian at Hammock Breeze, LLC (1)
178 Mitchelville Rd, Hilton Head Island, SC 29926
Tel.: (843) 706-7650
Commercial Building Construction Services
N.A.I.C.S.: 236220

K. Hovnanian at Hampshire Farms, LLC (1)
6117 Oberlin Rd, Amherst, OH 44001
Tel.: (440) 271-5888
Residential Building Construction Services
N.A.I.C.S.: 236115

K. Hovnanian at Hampton Cove, LLC (1)
Ellison Wilson Rd & Valerie Ln, North Palm Beach, FL 33408
Tel.: (561) 571-8752
Housing Construction Services
N.A.I.C.S.: 236117

K. Hovnanian at Harbor's Edge at Bayside, LLC (1)
21408 Sweetwater Sq, Selbyville, DE 19975
Tel.: (302) 202-2700
Home Rental Services
N.A.I.C.S.: 531110

K. Hovnanian at Harvest Meadows, LLC (1)
105 Harvest Way, Elyria, OH 44035
Tel.: (440) 271-8720
Residential Building Construction Services
N.A.I.C.S.: 236115

K. Hovnanian at Hidden Brook, LLC (1)
437 Moorton Rd, Dover, DE 19904
Commercial Building Construction Services
N.A.I.C.S.: 236220

K. Hovnanian at Hilltop Reserve, LLC (1)
1913 Marden Rd, Apopka, FL 32703
Tel.: (407) 705-2429
Web Site: http://www.khov.com
Real Estate Development Services
N.A.I.C.S.: 531390

K. Hovnanian at Hunter's Pond, LLC (1)
16105 Hunters Pond Trail, Centreville, VA 20120
Tel.: (571) 528-4574
Real Estate Development Services
N.A.I.C.S.: 531390

K. Hovnanian at Indian Wells, LLC (1)
7008 Indian Wells Rd, Cary, NC 27519
Tel.: (919) 238-5200
Real Estate Development Services
N.A.I.C.S.: 531390

K. Hovnanian at Jacks Run, LLC (1)
17835 Silcott Springs Rd, Purcellville, VA 20132
Commercial Building Construction Services
N.A.I.C.S.: 236220

K. Hovnanian at Lake Burden, LLC (1)
11201 Grander Dr, Windermere, FL 34786
Tel.: (407) 326-2041
Real Estate Development Services
N.A.I.C.S.: 531390

K. Hovnanian at Lake LeClare, LLC (1)
5155 Lakecastle Dr, Tampa, FL 33624
Tel.: (813) 517-8964
Housing Construction Services
N.A.I.C.S.: 236117

K. Hovnanian at Lake Rancho Viejo, LLC (1)
8799 Balboa Ave, San Diego, CA 92123
Tel.: (858) 751-0511
Real Estate Development Services
N.A.I.C.S.: 531390

K. Hovnanian at Laurel Hills Crossing, LLC (1)
8950 Hubbard Way, Lorton, VA 22079
Tel.: (703) 885-7118
Home Rental Services
N.A.I.C.S.: 531110

K. Hovnanian at Lily Orchard, LLC (1)
3333 Regency Pkwy Ste 100, Cary, NC 27518-7700
Tel.: (919) 238-5128
Real Estate Development Services
N.A.I.C.S.: 531390

K. Hovnanian at Link Crossing, LLC (1)
258 Saddle Ct, Buffalo Grove, IL 60089
Tel.: (331) 701-7870
Commercial Building Construction Services
N.A.I.C.S.: 236220

K. Hovnanian at Luke Landing, LLC (1)
127th Ave and Glendale Ave, Glendale, AZ 85307
Tel.: (602) 671-0410
Commercial Building Construction Services
N.A.I.C.S.: 236220

K. Hovnanian at Luna Vista, LLC (1)
13342 Sunchief Ct, Victorville, CA 92392
Tel.: (714) 368-4595
Commercial Building Construction Services
N.A.I.C.S.: 236220

K. Hovnanian at Main Street Square, LLC (1)
6019 Kentworth Dr, Holly Springs, NC 27540
Tel.: (919) 238-5126
Real Estate Development Services
N.A.I.C.S.: 531390

K. Hovnanian at Maple Hill LLC (1)
1880 Savannah Cir, Mundelein, IL 60060
Tel.: (331) 701-7863
Commercial Building Construction Services
N.A.I.C.S.: 236220

K. Hovnanian at Marlboro Grove, LLC (1)
8 Buckley Rd, Marlboro, NJ 07746
Tel.: (732) 845-6507
Residential Building Construction Services
N.A.I.C.S.: 236115

K. Hovnanian at McCartney Ranch, LLC (1)
2515 N Kenna Pl, Casa Grande, AZ 85122
Tel.: (602) 671-0027
Real Estate Rental Services
N.A.I.C.S.: 531110

K. Hovnanian at Meadowridge Villas, LLC (1)
1175 Woodridge Dr Ste B, Sugar Grove, IL 60554
Tel.: (630) 466-4733
Real Estate Development Services
N.A.I.C.S.: 531390

K. Hovnanian at Neuse River, LLC (1)
3333 Regency Pkwy Ste 100, Cary, NC 27518-7700
Tel.: (919) 462-0070
Construction Engineering Services
N.A.I.C.S.: 237990

K. Hovnanian at New Post, LLC (1)
10053 Premier St, Fredericksburg, VA 22408
Tel.: (703) 844-3768
Residential Building Construction Services
N.A.I.C.S.: 236115

K. Hovnanian at North Grove Crossing, LLC (1)
200 Gates Creek Dr, Oswego, IL 60543
Tel.: (331) 701-7844
Commercial Building Construction Services
N.A.I.C.S.: 236220

K. Hovnanian at North Pointe Estates LLC (1)
1201 N Pointe Dr, Libertyville, IL 60048
Tel.: (331) 401-2251
Commercial Building Construction Services
N.A.I.C.S.: 236220

K. Hovnanian at North Ridge, LLC (1)
122 Brafferton Blvd, Stafford, VA 22701
Tel.: (703) 782-4108
Residential Building Construction Services
N.A.I.C.S.: 236115

K. Hovnanian at Oyster Cove, LLC (1)
33126 Oyster Cove Dr, Lewes, DE 19958
Residential Building Construction Services
N.A.I.C.S.: 236115

K. Hovnanian at Palm Valley, L.L.C. (1)
15631 W Coronado Rd, Goodyear, AZ 85395
Tel.: (623) 215-2656
Construction Engineering Services
N.A.I.C.S.: 237990

K. Hovnanian at Park Paseo, LLC (1)
Phelps Rd and 73rd Ave, Peoria, AZ 85308
Commercial Building Construction Services
N.A.I.C.S.: 236220

K. Hovnanian at Pinckney Farm, LLC (1)
1123 Cultivator St, Mount Pleasant, SC 29466
Tel.: (843) 706-7670
Commercial Building Construction Services
N.A.I.C.S.: 236220

K. Hovnanian at Prairie Pointe, LLC (1)
1385 Prairie Pointe, South Elgin, IL 60177
Tel.: (847) 717-4270
Real Estate Development Services
N.A.I.C.S.: 531390

K. Hovnanian at Quail Creek, L.L.C. (1)
19235 E Peartree Ln, Queen Creek, AZ 85142
Tel.: (602) 824-7816
Construction Engineering Services
N.A.I.C.S.: 237990

K. Hovnanian at Rancho Cabrillo, LLC (1)
26316 N 131st Dr, Peoria, AZ 85383
Tel.: (480) 824-4222
Construction Engineering Services
N.A.I.C.S.: 237990

K. Hovnanian at Rancho El Dorado, LLC (1)
40290 W Chambers Dr, Maricopa, AZ 85138
Tel.: (520) 277-3760
Residential Building Construction Services
N.A.I.C.S.: 236115

K. Hovnanian at Randall Highlands, LLC (1)
1201 Kilbery Ln, North Aurora, IL 60542
Tel.: (630) 340-5795
Real Estate Development Services
N.A.I.C.S.: 531390

K. Hovnanian at Redtail, LLC (1)
32049 Red Tail Blvd, Sorrento, FL 32776
Tel.: (407) 641-3823
Housing Construction Services
N.A.I.C.S.: 236117

K. Hovnanian at Retreat at Millstone, LLC (1)
19068 Jackstone Way, Millsboro, DE 19966
Tel.: (302) 223-0120
Commercial Building Construction Services
N.A.I.C.S.: 236220

K. Hovnanian at River Hills, LLC (1)
1145 Winding Way, Bolingbrook, IL 60490
Tel.: (815) 782-7078
Real Estate Development Services
N.A.I.C.S.: 531390

K. Hovnanian at Rockland Village Green, LLC (1)
13921 Vernon St, Chantilly, VA 20151
Tel.: (703) 885-7118
Commercial Building Construction Services
N.A.I.C.S.: 236220

K. Hovnanian at Sage II Harvest at Limoneira, LLC (1)
Tangelo Way & Limoneira Ln, Santa Paula, CA 93060
Tel.: (805) 261-2402
Residential Building Construction Services
N.A.I.C.S.: 236115

K. Hovnanian at Sagebrook, LLC (1)

1991 Sagebrook Dr, South Elgin, IL 60177
Tel.: (331) 701-7840
Housing Construction Services
N.A.I.C.S.: 236117

K. Hovnanian at Sandpiper Place, LLC (1)
930 Railroad Ave, Ocean, NJ 08087
Tel.: (609) 739-7010
Residential Building Construction Services
N.A.I.C.S.: 236115

K. Hovnanian at Sauganash Glen, LLC (1)
5404 W Devon Ave, Chicago, IL 60646
Tel.: (773) 853-0062
Real Estate Development Services
N.A.I.C.S.: 531390

K. Hovnanian at Scottsdale Heights, LLC (1)
7289 E Camino Rayo De Luz, Scottsdale, AZ 85266
Tel.: (602) 671-0611
Commercial Building Construction Services
N.A.I.C.S.: 236220

K. Hovnanian at Seabrook, LLC (1)
32072 Apple Ridge Run, Millsboro, DE 19966
Tel.: (302) 223-0133
Commercial Building Construction Services
N.A.I.C.S.: 236220

K. Hovnanian at Seasons Landing, LLC (1)
4090 Lafayette Center Dr Ste A, Chantilly, VA 20151-1244
Tel.: (703) 631-7432
Real Estate Development Services
N.A.I.C.S.: 531390

K. Hovnanian at Sierra Vista, LLC (1)
310 Mono Lk Ave, Merced, CA 95341
Tel.: (916) 945-5412
Commercial Building Construction Services
N.A.I.C.S.: 236220

K. Hovnanian at Silver Leaf, LLC (1)
610 Silver Leaf Dr, Joliet, IL 60431
Tel.: (331) 701-7842
Commercial Building Construction Services
N.A.I.C.S.: 236220

K. Hovnanian at Somerset, LLC (1)
12824 Timberwood Cir, Plainfield, IL 60585
Tel.: (815) 267-6899
Housing Construction Services
N.A.I.C.S.: 236117

K. Hovnanian at Summerlake, LLC (1)
7741 Green Mountain Way, Winter Garden, FL 34787
Tel.: (321) 263-2662
Housing Construction Services
N.A.I.C.S.: 236117

K. Hovnanian at Summit Crossing Estates, LLC (1)
9001 Walnut Hill Rd, Fredericksburg, VA 22408
Tel.: (703) 468-1167
Residential Building Construction Services
N.A.I.C.S.: 236115

K. Hovnanian at Sun City West, LLC (1)
Sandridge Dr and RH Johnson Blvd, Sun City West, AZ 85375
Home Rental Services
N.A.I.C.S.: 531110

K. Hovnanian at Tanglewood Oaks, LLC (1)
3034 Trillium Ct E, Aurora, IL 60506
Tel.: (331) 302-5948
Real Estate Development Services
N.A.I.C.S.: 531390

K. Hovnanian at The Highlands at Summerlake Grove, LLC (1)
11030 Hanlon Terrace Aly, Winter Garden, FL 34787
Tel.: (321) 263-2663
Real Estate Development Services
N.A.I.C.S.: 531390

K. Hovnanian at The Preserve, LLC (1)

Hovnanian Enterprises, Inc.—(Continued)

16204 Solitude Ave, Chino, CA 91708
Tel.: (909) 606-7451
Real Estate Development Services
N.A.I.C.S.: 531390

K. Hovnanian at Tortosa South,
LLC (1)
18658 N Los Gabrieles Way, Maricopa, AZ
85138
Tel.: (520) 263-1152
Residential Building Construction Services
N.A.I.C.S.: 236115

K. Hovnanian at Townes at County
Center, LLC (1)
5060 Dimples Ct, Woodbridge, VA 22192
Tel.: (703) 885-7125
Commercial Building Construction Services
N.A.I.C.S.: 236220

K. Hovnanian at Townsend Fields,
LLC (1)
35 Peach Peddler Path, Dover, DE 19934
Tel.: (302) 202-2777
Home Rental Services
N.A.I.C.S.: 531110

K. Hovnanian at Union Park,
LLC (1)
19th Ln and Union Pk Dr, Phoenix, AZ
85085
Tel.: (602) 824-7839
Commercial Building Construction Services
N.A.I.C.S.: 236220

K. Hovnanian at Upper Providence,
LLC (1)
290 Fairfield Cir W, Royersford, PA 19468
Tel.: (610) 792-3094
Real Estate Development Services
N.A.I.C.S.: 531390

K. Hovnanian at Valletta, LLC (1)
100 NW 70th St, Boca Raton, FL 33487
Tel.: (561) 257-5886
Real Estate Development Services
N.A.I.C.S.: 531390

K. Hovnanian at Verrado Marketside,
LLC (1)
21007 W Almeria Rd, Buckeye, AZ 85396
Tel.: (602) 824-7837
Commercial Building Construction Services
N.A.I.C.S.: 236220

K. Hovnanian at Victory at Verrado,
LLC (1)
20818 W Pasadena Ave, Buckeye, AZ
85396
Tel.: (602) 671-3511
Home Rental Services
N.A.I.C.S.: 531110

K. Hovnanian at Village Center,
LLC (1)
4032 Parkmoor Ln, Roseville, CA 95747
Commercial Building Construction Services
N.A.I.C.S.: 236220

K. Hovnanian at Vineyard Heights,
LLC (1)
35829 Sea Smoke St, Winchester, CA
92596
Tel.: (951) 599-4352
Real Estate Development Services
N.A.I.C.S.: 531390

K. Hovnanian at Wade's Grant,
LLC (1)
8406 Amber Beacon Cir, Millersville, MD
21108
Tel.: (301) 205-5120
Commercial Building Construction Services
N.A.I.C.S.: 236220

K. Hovnanian at Walkers Grove,
LLC (1)
709 Walkers Grove Ln, Winter Garden, FL
34787
Tel.: (407) 705-3103
Real Estate Development Services
N.A.I.C.S.: 531390

K. Hovnanian at West Windsor,
L.L.C. (1)
110 W Front St, Red Bank, NJ 07701
Tel.: (732) 747-7800
Web Site: http://www.khov.com

Emp.: 200
Real Estate Development Services
N.A.I.C.S.: 531390

K. Hovnanian at Willowsford Greens
III, LLC (1)
25955 Cullen Run Pl, Aldie, VA 20105
Tel.: (703) 885-7175
Commercial Building Construction Services
N.A.I.C.S.: 236220

K. Hovnanian of Houston II,
L.L.C. (1)
13111 NW Freeway Ste 200, Houston, TX
77040
Tel.: (713) 460-0264
Real Estate Development Services
N.A.I.C.S.: 531390

K. Hovnanian's Aspire at Union Village, LLC (1)
303 Woolrich Bay Dr, Bakersfield, CA
93307
Tel.: (661) 543-0714
Commercial Building Construction Services
N.A.I.C.S.: 236220

K. Hovnanian's Cove at Asbury Park
Urban Renewal, LLC (1)
320 Asbury Ave, Asbury Park, NJ 07712
Tel.: (732) 517-7495
Residential Building Construction Services
N.A.I.C.S.: 236116

K. Hovnanian's Four Seasons at Bay-
mont Farms LLC (1)
206 Northern Oak St, Middletown, DE
19709
Tel.: (302) 202-2460
Commercial Building Construction Services
N.A.I.C.S.: 236220

K. Hovnanian's Four Seasons at
Belle Terre, LLC (1)
19173 Chartres St, Lewes, DE 19958
Tel.: (302) 223-0130
Commercial Building Construction Services
N.A.I.C.S.: 236220

K. Hovnanian's Four Seasons at
Carolina Oaks, LLC (1)
SC-170 and SC-46, Bluffton, SC 29909
Commercial Building Construction Services
N.A.I.C.S.: 236220

K. Hovnanian's Four Seasons at
Lakes of Cane Bay LLC (1)
109 Magnolia House Dr, Summerville, SC
29486
Tel.: (843) 891-6675
Residential Building Construction Services
N.A.I.C.S.: 236116

K. Hovnanian's Four Seasons at New
Kent Vineyards, L.L.C. (1)
7723 Rockbridge Run Pl, New Kent, VA
23124
Tel.: (703) 885-7265
Emp.: 5
Real Estate Development Services
N.A.I.C.S.: 531390
Ceilie Holmes (VP-Sls)

K. Hovnanian's Four Seasons at
Rush Creek, L.L.C. (1)
7550 Ranier Ln N, Maple Grove, MN 55311
Tel.: (763) 424-9991
Real Estate Development Services
N.A.I.C.S.: 531390

K. Hovnanian's Four Seasons at The
Lakes at Cane Bay, LLC (1)
Cane Bay Blvd, Summerville, SC 29483
Tel.: (843) 706-7666
Real Estate Development Services
N.A.I.C.S.: 531390

K. Hovnanian's Four Seasons at The
Manor, LLC (1)
10915 W Edgewood Dr, Sun City, AZ
85351
Tel.: (602) 824-7833
Housing Construction Services
N.A.I.C.S.: 236117

K. Hovnanian's Four Seasons,
LLC (1)
339 Enchanted Park N, Beaumont, CA
92223
Tel.: (951) 769-4115

Construction Engineering Services
N.A.I.C.S.: 237990

LAUREL HIGHLANDS, LLC (1)
9101 Purvis Dr, Lorton, VA 22079
Tel.: (703) 646-5611
Real Estate Development Services
N.A.I.C.S.: 531390

MILLENNIUM TITLE AGENCY,
LTD. (1)
5061 N Abbe Rd Ste 3, Sheffield Village,
OH 44035
Tel.: (440) 934-9910
Real Estate Development Services
N.A.I.C.S.: 531390

New Land Title Agency, L.L.C. (1)
20830 N Tatum Blvd Ste 250, Phoenix, AZ
85050
Tel.: (480) 824-4243
Web Site: http://www.newlandtitle.com
Title Agency & Real Estate Services
N.A.I.C.S.: 541191

WH PROPERTIES, INC. (1)
62 Bohemia Ln, Earleville, MD 21919
Tel.: (410) 275-8216
Emp.: 3
Real Estate Development Services
N.A.I.C.S.: 531390

HOWARD HUGHES HOLDINGS INC.
9950 Woodloch Forest Dr Ste 1100,
The Woodlands, TX 77380
Tel.: (281) 719-6100 DE
Web Site:
https://www.howardhughes.com
HHH—(NYSE)
Rev.: $1,024,102,000
Assets: $9,577,003,000
Liabilities: $6,518,079,000
Net Worth: $3,058,924,000
Earnings: ($551,773,000)
Emp.: 608
Fiscal Year-end: 12/31/23
Real Estate Investment Services
N.A.I.C.S.: 525990
Elena Verbinskaya (Chief Acctg Offi-
cer)
David R. O'Reilly (CEO)
Peter Helfer (VP-Strategic
Partnerships-Global)
Randy Kostroske (Exec VP-Risk
Mgmt)
Greg Fitchitt (Pres-Columbia)
Carlos Olea (CFO)
Valerie Qualls (Sr VP-Capital Mar-
kets)
Cristina Carlson (Sr VP & Head-Corp
Comm)
Jim Carman (Pres-Houston)
L. Jay Cross (Pres)
Andrew D. Davis (Sr VP & Head-
Investments)
Jesse Carrillo (Chief Innovation Offi-
cer)
Alex Hancock (Sr VP)
Eric Holcomb (Sr VP)
Doug Johnstone (Pres)
Heath Melton (Pres)
Gautami Palanki (Sr VP)
Frank Stephan (Pres)
Elena Verbinskaya (Exec VP)
Bonnie Wedemeyer (Exec VP)
Zach Winick (Co-Pres)

Subsidiaries:

70 CC, LLC (1)
11000 Broken Land Pkwy, Columbia, MD
21044
Tel.: (410) 997-5175
Business Support Services
N.A.I.C.S.: 561499

HL Multi-Family Holdings, LLC (1)
1950 Hughes Landing Blvd, Spring, TX
77380
Tel.: (281) 298-8361
Holding Company
N.A.I.C.S.: 551112

Howard Hughes Management Ser-
vices Company, LLC (1)
1440 Lk Frnt Cir Ste 150, Spring, TX 77380
Tel.: (281) 475-2081
Emp.: 43
Real Estate Development Services
N.A.I.C.S.: 237210

Kai Investments, LLC (1)
318 Richards Way Dr, Cordova, TN 38018-
7428
Tel.: (901) 859-3816
Real Estate Development Services
N.A.I.C.S.: 237210

Kewalo Harbor, LLC (1)
1125 Ala Moana Blvd B1, Honolulu, HI
96814
Tel.: (808) 594-0849
Web Site: https://www.kewaloharbor.com
Real Estate Development Services
N.A.I.C.S.: 237210

Landmark Mall L.L.C. (1)
5801 Duke St, Alexandria, VA 22304
Tel.: (703) 354-8405
Web Site: http://www.landmarkmall.com
Nonresidential Building Services
N.A.I.C.S.: 531120

One Hughes Landing, LLC (1)
1800 Hughes Landing Blvd, Woodlands, TX
77380
Tel.: (281) 292-2211
Real Estate Development Services
N.A.I.C.S.: 237210

Riverwalk Marketplace (New Or-
leans), LLC (1)
500 Port of New Orleans Pl Ste 101, New
Orleans, LA 70130-1694
Tel.: (504) 522-1555
Web Site:
https://www.riverwalkneworleans.com
Shopping Center Leasing Services
N.A.I.C.S.: 531120
Yvette Gremillion-Watkins (Gen Mgr)
Troy Thibodeaux (Asst Mgr)

South Street Seaport Limited
Partnership (1)
10275 Little Patuxent Pkwy, Columbia, MD
21044
Tel.: (214) 741-7744
Residential Buildings & Dwellings Services
N.A.I.C.S.: 531110

Stewart Title of Montgomery County
Inc. (1)
6875 FM 1488 Ste 800, Magnolia, TX
77354
Tel.: (832) 482-1880
Property Management Services
N.A.I.C.S.: 531390

Summerlin Development, LLC (1)
4994 Lower Roswell Rd Ste 8, Marietta, GA
30068
Tel.: (770) 973-9761
Emp.: 5
Real Estate Development Services
N.A.I.C.S.: 237210

Summerlin Las Vegas Baseball Club,
LLC (1)
850 Las Vegas Blvd N, Las Vegas, NV
89101-2062
Tel.: (702) 386-7200
Real Estate Development Services
N.A.I.C.S.: 237210
Chuck Johnson (Gen Mgr)

The Woodlands Beverage, Inc. (1)
2301 N Millbend Dr, Spring, TX 77380-1399
Tel.: (281) 367-1100
Property Management Services
N.A.I.C.S.: 237210

WECCR General Partnership (1)
2301 N Millbend Dr, The Woodlands, TX
77380-1360
Tel.: (281) 367-1100
Web Site: http://www.woodlandsresort.com
Property Management Services
N.A.I.C.S.: 237210

WRCC Holdings, LLC (1)
2301 N Millbend Dr, The Woodlands, TX
77380
Tel.: (281) 364-6311

Emp.: 500
Holding Company
N.A.I.C.S.: 551112

Ward Village Properties, LLC (1)
1240 Ala Moana Blvd, Honolulu, HI 96814
Tel.: (808) 369-9600
Web Site: https://www.wardvillage.com
Real Estate Development Services
N.A.I.C.S.: 237210
Chelsea McKay (Sr Dir-Development)
Doug Johnstone (Pres)
Bonnie Wedemeyer (Exec VP-Natl Sls & Strategy)
Jon Moore (Sr VP-Design & Construction Mgmt)
Ka'iulani Sodaro (Sr VP-Planning & Development)
Lee Cranmer (VP-Planning & Development)
David Major (Deputy Gen Counsel-Hawai, ', i, and Arizona)
Deborah Cho (Gen Counsel)
Brian Smith (Sr VP-Finance)
Stacy Starmer (VP-Accounting)
Taylor Herring Starmer (Gen Mgr)
Nelson Burton (Project Mgr-Tenant Coordination)
Cord Anderson (Sr Dir-Development)
Paul Hayes (Sr Dir-Development)
Gayna Buranelli (Dir-Planning & Development)
Lynn Toma (VP-Sls Ops & Broker in Charge)
Sharon Hanamoto (Sr Dir-Design & Construction Mgmt)
Kawai Yamashiro (VP-Owner Svcs)
Eric Sls (Sr Dir-Design & Construction Mgmt)
Bill Wright (Sr Dir-Design & Construction Mgmt)
Larry Schenk (Sr Dir-Construction Mgmt)
Rebecca Wright (Dir-Design & Construction Mgmt)
Chuck O'Neill (Dir-Construction Mgmt)
Lakaysha Lee-Hill (Mgr-Design & Construction Mgmt)
Mandy Davis (VP-Marketing)
Yan Hasegawa (Dir-Marketing)
Heidi Kuia (Mgr-Marketing)
Tiffany Tokuuke (Dir-Accounting)
Kevin Chan (Sr Mgr-Dev Acctg)

Waterway Hotel Holdings, LLC (1)
2 Waterway Square Pl, Spring, TX 77380-2660
Tel.: (281) 419-4300
Holding Company
N.A.I.C.S.: 551112
Micheal Speicher (Gen Mgr)

HOWMET AEROSPACE INC.
201 Isabella St Ste 200, Pittsburgh, PA 15212-5872
Tel.: (412) 553-2500   PA
Web Site: https://www.howmet.com
Year Founded: 1888
HWM—(NYSE)
Rev.: $6,640,000,000
Assets: $10,428,000,000
Liabilities: $6,391,000,000
Net Worth: $4,037,000,000
Earnings: $765,000,000
Emp.: 23,200
Fiscal Year-end: 12/31/23
Holding Company; Primary & Fabricated Aluminum & Alumina Products Mfr
N.A.I.C.S.: 551112
Ken Giacobbe (CFO & Exec VP)
Margaret Lam (Asst Sec & Assoc Gen Counsel)
Michael Chanatry (Chief Comml Officer & VP)
Christopher Favo (Chief Ethics & Compliance Officer)
Barbara L. Shultz (Principal Acctg Officer, VP & Controller)
Vagner Finelli (Pres-Howmet Fastening Sys)
Ramiro Gutierrez (Pres)
John C. Plant (Exec Chm & CEO)

Subsidiaries:

Arconic Domestic LLC (1)

201 Isabella St, Pittsburgh, PA 15212-5858
Tel.: (412) 992-2500
Web Site: https://www.arconic.com
Rev.: $8,961,000,000
Assets: $6,015,000,000
Liabilities: $4,658,000,000
Net Worth: $1,357,000,000
Earnings: ($181,000,000)
Emp.: 11,550
Fiscal Year-end: 12/31/2022
Other Aluminum Rolling, Drawing & Extruding
N.A.I.C.S.: 331318
Christopher L. Ayers (CEO)

Subsidiary (Domestic):

Howmet International, Inc. (2)
3960 S Marginal Rd, Cleveland, OH 44114   (100%)
Tel.: (216) 641-3600
Holding Company
N.A.I.C.S.: 551112

Subsidiary (Domestic):

Howmet Corporation (3)
6450 Rockside Woods Blvd S Ste 350, Independence, OH 44131-2238
Tel.: (216) 641-4400
Emp.: 250
Nonferrous Metals Rolling, Drawing & Extruding
N.A.I.C.S.: 331491
Michael A. Pepper (Pres-Alcoa Power & Propulsion)

Subsidiary (Non-US):

Howmet Aluminum Casting Ltd. (4)
93 Mountainview Road, Georgetown, L7G 4J6, ON, Canada   (100%)
Tel.: (905) 877-6936
Web Site: https://www.howmet.com
Sales Range: $25-49.9 Million
Emp.: 100
Aluminum & Copper-Based Castings
N.A.I.C.S.: 331524

Howmet CIRAL s.n.c (4)
Zone de la Presaie, 53602, Evron, France   (100%)
Tel.: (33) 243666161
Web Site: http://www.howmet.com
Sales Range: $25-49.9 Million
Emp.: 296
Aluminum Investment Castings Mfr
N.A.I.C.S.: 331524
Xavier Dunant (Mng Dir)

Subsidiary (Domestic):

Howmet Castings & Services, Inc. (4)
3850 White Lake Dr, Whitehall, MI 49461
Tel.: (231) 894-5686
Sales Range: $750-799.9 Million
Mfr of Metal Molds Castings
N.A.I.C.S.: 331512

Plant (Domestic):

Howmet Castings & Services, Inc. - Dover (5)
9 Roy St, Dover, NJ 07801-4308
Tel.: (973) 361-0300
Sales Range: $750-799.9 Million
Emp.: 1,000
Complex Investment Cast Turbine Airfoils Supplier & Engineered Solutions
N.A.I.C.S.: 331512

Unit (Domestic):

Howmet Castings & Services, Inc. - Dover Alloy (5)
10 Roy St, Dover, NJ 07801-4325
Tel.: (973) 361-2310
Vacuum & Air-Melted Nickel & Cobalt-Based Superalloys Supplier
N.A.I.C.S.: 331512

Plant (Domestic):

Howmet Castings & Services, Inc. - Hampton (5)
1 Howmet Dr, Hampton, VA 23661
Tel.: (757) 838-4680
Web Site: http://www.arconic.com
Investment Cast Tubine Airfoils
N.A.I.C.S.: 331512

Howmet Castings & Services, Inc. - La Porte (5)
1110 E Lincoln Way, La Porte, IN 46350-3954
Tel.: (219) 326-7400
Web Site: http://www.alcoa.com
Sales Range: $300-349.9 Million
Emp.: 600
Castings For Aerospace & Investment Gas Turbine Applications
N.A.I.C.S.: 331512

Howmet Castings & Services, Inc. - Morristown (5)
5650 Commerce Blvd, Morristown, TN 37814-1048
Tel.: (423) 587-4910
Web Site: http://www.alcoa.com
Sales Range: $300-349.9 Million
Emp.: 600
Complex Ceramic Cores Producer
N.A.I.C.S.: 331512

Howmet Castings & Services, Inc. - Structural Casting (5)
1 Howmet Dr, Hampton, VA 23661
Tel.: (757) 838-4680
Web Site: http://www.howmet.com
Superalloy & Titanium Aerospace Structural Components Producer
N.A.I.C.S.: 331512

Division (Domestic):

Howmet Castings & Services, Inc. - Titanium Castings (5)
3850 White Lake Dr, Whitehall, MI 49461
Tel.: (231) 894-5686
Web Site: http://www.alcoa.com
Sales Range: $75-99.9 Million
Emp.: 260
Titanium-Investment Casting Services
N.A.I.C.S.: 331523

Plant (Domestic):

Howmet Castings & Services, Inc. - Whitehall Casting (5)
1 Misco Dr, Whitehall, MI 49461
Tel.: (231) 894-5686
Web Site: http://www.howmet.com
Sales Range: $400-449.9 Million
Emp.: 1,500
Complex Investment-Cast Turbine Components Mfr
N.A.I.C.S.: 333611

Howmet Castings & Services, Inc. - Wichita Falls (5)
6200 Central Fwy N, Wichita Falls, TX 76305-6605
Tel.: (940) 855-8100
Web Site: http://www.alcoa.com
Sales Range: $350-399.9 Million
Emp.: 800
Equiax Superalloy Blades & Vanes Producer
N.A.I.C.S.: 331110

Subsidiary (Domestic):

Howmet Holdings Corporation (4)
1 Misco Dr, Whitehall, MI 49461-1799
Tel.: (231) 894-5686
Sales Range: $300-349.9 Million
Holding Company; Castings Mfr
N.A.I.C.S.: 551112

Subsidiary (Non-US):

Howmet Laval Casting Ltd. (4)
4001 Autoroute Des Laurentides, Laval, H7L 3H7, QC, Canada   (100%)
Tel.: (450) 680-2500
Sales Range: $125-149.9 Million
Emp.: 250
Structural Helicopter & Aircraft Parts, Electronic Boxes, Structural Missile Parts, Gear Boxes, Front Frames & Other Engine Parts Mfr
N.A.I.C.S.: 336412
John Pellegrino (Gen Mgr)

Howmet Limited (4)
Kestrel Way, Exeter, EX2 7LG, United Kingdom   (100%)
Tel.: (44) 1392429700
Web Site: http://www.arconic.com
Sales Range: $125-149.9 Million
Emp.: 600

Complex Investment-Cast Turbine Airfoils; Vacuum & Air-Melted Master Alloy Supplier
N.A.I.C.S.: 336412

Subsidiary (Domestic):

Howmet Research Corporation (4)
1500 S Warner St, Whitehall, MI 49461-1895
Tel.: (231) 894-7200
Web Site: http://www.howmet.com
Sales Range: $50-74.9 Million
Emp.: 200
Commercial Laboratory Testing Services
N.A.I.C.S.: 541380

Subsidiary (Non-US):

Howmet S.A.S. (4)
68 A 78 Rue du Moulin de Cage, 92230, Gennevilliers, France
Tel.: (33) 140853600
Web Site: http://www.howmet.com
Sales Range: $100-124.9 Million
Emp.: 250
Aircraft & Industrial Gas Turbine Castings
N.A.I.C.S.: 336411

Subsidiary (Domestic):

Alcoa Holding France SAS (5)
68 Rue Du Moulin De Cage, 92230, Gennevilliers, France
Tel.: (33) 140853600
Holding Company
N.A.I.C.S.: 551112

Arconic Global Fasteners & Rings, Inc. (1)
3000 W Lomita Blvd, Torrance, CA 90505
Tel.: (310) 530-2220
Web Site: http://www.arconic.com
Designer & Mfr of Specialty Fastening Systems, Components & Installation Tools for Aerospace & Industrial Applications
N.A.I.C.S.: 332722

Plant (Non-US):

Arconic Fasteners SAS - Us Operations (2)
US Par Vigny, PO Box 4, 95450, Clos d'Asseville, France
Tel.: (33) 130279500
Fasteners
N.A.I.C.S.: 212290
Roland Monet (Mgr-Ops)

Plant (Domestic):

Arconic Fastening Systems & Rings - Carson (2)
900 Watson Center Rd, Carson, CA 90745-4201
Tel.: (310) 830-8200
Emp.: 280
Collars, Lockbolts, Bolts & Pins Fastening Systems Mfr
N.A.I.C.S.: 332722
Vitaliy V. Rusakov (COO-Forgings & Extrusions)

Arconic Fastening Systems & Rings - Kingston (2)
1 Corporate Dr, Kingston, NY 12401-5536
Tel.: (845) 331-7300
Fastening Systems Mfr
N.A.I.C.S.: 332722

Arconic Fastening Systems & Rings - Tucson (2)
3724 E Columbia St, Tucson, AZ 85714
Tel.: (520) 519-7400
Fastening Systems Mfr
N.A.I.C.S.: 423840

Arconic Fastening Systems & Rings - Waco (2)
8001 Imperial Dr, Waco, TX 76712
Tel.: (254) 751-5543
Web Site: http://www.afshuck.net
Fastening Systems Mfr
N.A.I.C.S.: 332722
Don C. Busby (Pres)

Subsidiary (Non-US):

Arconic Fastening Systems & Rings-Australia Pty. Ltd. (2)

Howmet Aerospace, Inc.—(Continued)

1508 Centre Road, Clayton, 3168, VIC, Australia
Tel.: (61) 1300363049
Fastener Mfr
N.A.I.C.S.: 339993

Plant (Non-US):

Arconic Global Fasteners Limited - Leicester (2)
Viking Road, Wigston, LE18 2BL, Leics, United Kingdom
Tel.: (44) 1162881192
Web Site: http://www.arconic.com
Forged Engine Bolts Mfr
N.A.I.C.S.: 332722

Arconic Global Fasteners Limited - Redditch (2)
Crossgate Road, Park Farm, Redditch, B98 7TD, Worcs, United Kingdom
Tel.: (44) 1527525719
Sales Range: $25-49.9 Million
Emp.: 200
Mfr of Fasteners for Aircraft Industry
N.A.I.C.S.: 332722

Arconic Global Fasteners Limited - Telford (2)
Unit C Stafford Park 7, Telford, TF3 3BQ, Shropshire, United Kingdom
Tel.: (44) 1952290011
Fastening Systems Mfr
N.A.I.C.S.: 339993

Arconic International Holding Company LLC (1)
201 Isabella St, Pittsburgh, PA 15212
Tel.: (412) 992-2500
Holding Company
N.A.I.C.S.: 551112

Subsidiary (Non-US):

Arconic (China) Investment Company Ltd. (2)
Room 3118 Beijing Yintai Center 2 Jianguomenwai Avenue, Chaoyang District, Beijing, 100022, China
Tel.: (86) 1065876131
Aluminum Products Mfr & Distr
N.A.I.C.S.: 331315

Arconic Architectural Products SAS (2)
2 rue Marie Curie, 68500, Merxheim, 68500, France (100%)
Tel.: (33) 389744600
Sales Range: $75-99.9 Million
Emp.: 268
Aluminum Producer
N.A.I.C.S.: 331318

Arconic GmbH (2)
Heinrichstrasse 24, 40239, Dusseldorf, Germany
Tel.: (49) 211471110
Aluminium Product Distr
N.A.I.C.S.: 423510
Bernd Schaefer (Mgr-Sls)

Arconic International (Asia) Limited (2)
Room 1301 Admiralty Centre Tower 1 13th Fl, Hong Kong, China (Hong Kong)
Tel.: (852) 25292333
Aluminum Products Whslr
N.A.I.C.S.: 423510

Arconic Inversiones Espana S.L. (2)
Calle Pedro Teixeira 8 Edificio Iberia Mart Planta 3, Madrid, 28020, Spain
Tel.: (34) 914068200
Sales Range: $250-299.9 Million
Emp.: 50
Holding Company
N.A.I.C.S.: 551112
Rosa Maria Garcia Pineiro (Pres)

Kawneer Company, Inc. (1)
555 Guthridge Ct Technology Park, Norcross, GA 30092 (100%)
Tel.: (770) 449-5555
Web Site: http://www.kawneer.com
Sales Range: $450-499.9 Million
Emp.: 1,400
Architectural Aluminum Building Products & Systems Mfr

N.A.I.C.S.: 332321

Subsidiary (Non-US):

Kawneer Company Canada Ltd. (2)
4000 18th Ave North, Lethbridge, T1H 5S8, AB, Canada (100%)
Tel.: (403) 320-7755
Web Site: https://www.kawneer.us
Sales Range: $125-149.9 Million
Emp.: 300
Store Fronts & Windows Mfr
N.A.I.C.S.: 332321

Plant (Domestic):

Kawneer Company, Inc. (2)
7200 Doe Ave, Visalia, CA 93291-9296
Tel.: (559) 651-4000
Web Site: http://www.kawneer.com
Sales Range: $50-74.9 Million
Emp.: 120
Aluminum Building Products
N.A.I.C.S.: 423390

Kawneer Company, Inc. (2)
500 E 12th St, Bloomsburg, PA 17815
Tel.: (570) 784-8000
Web Site: http://www.kawneer.com
Sales Range: $75-99.9 Million
Emp.: 400
Store Fronts & Windows Mfr
N.A.I.C.S.: 332321

Kawneer Company, Inc. (2)
2031 Deyerle Ave, Harrisonburg, VA 22801
Tel.: (540) 433-2711
Web Site: http://www.kawneer.com
Sales Range: $50-74.9 Million
Emp.: 80
Store Fronts & Windows Mfr
N.A.I.C.S.: 332321

Kawneer Company, Inc.- Springdale (2)
600 Kawneer Dr, Springdale, AR 72764
Tel.: (479) 756-2740
Web Site: http://www.kawneer.com
Architectural Aluminum Products & Systems Mfr & Marketer
N.A.I.C.S.: 332312

Subsidiary (Non-US):

Kawneer France SA (2)
Zone Industrielle, Rue de la Garenne, 34748, Vendargues, Cedex, France (100%)
Tel.: (33) 240247576
Web Site: http://www.kawneer.com
Sales Range: $25-49.9 Million
Emp.: 90
Aluminum Architectural Systems Including Doors & Windows Mfr
N.A.I.C.S.: 332321

Subsidiary (Non-US):

Kawneer Maroc SA (3)
Parc Industriel de Bouskoura, Casablanca, 27182, Morocco
Tel.: (212) 522593060
Web Site: http://www.alcoa.com
Sales Range: $1-9.9 Million
Emp.: 35
Aluminum Architectural Systems Including Doors & Windows Mfr
N.A.I.C.S.: 332321

Subsidiary (Non-US):

Kawneer UK Limited (2)
Astmoor Road Astmoor Industrial Estate, Runcorn, WA7 1QQ, Cheshire, United Kingdom
Tel.: (44) 1928502500
Web Site: https://www.kawneer.co.uk
Curtain Wallings, Frames, Window & Door Systems Mfr
N.A.I.C.S.: 337920

Subsidiary (Domestic):

TRACO Inc. (2)
71 Progress Ave, Cranberry Township, PA 16066
Tel.: (724) 776-7000
Web Site: http://www.traco.com
Sales Range: $150-199.9 Million
Emp.: 600

Commercial & Residential Windows, Doors, Skylights, Solariums, Folding Glass Walls & Sunrooms Mfr
N.A.I.C.S.: 332321

HP INC.

1501 Page Mill Rd, Palo Alto, CA 94304
Tel.: (650) 857-1501 DE
Web Site: https://www.hp.com
Year Founded: 1939
HPQ—(NYSE)
Rev.: $53,718,000,000
Assets: $37,004,000,000
Liabilities: $38,073,000,000
Net Worth: ($1,069,000,000)
Earnings: $3,263,000,000
Emp.: 58,000
Fiscal Year-end: 10/31/23
Computer Equipment & Software Mfr
N.A.I.C.S.: 334118
Tuan Tran (Pres-Imaging, Printing & Solutions)
Enrique J. Lores (Pres & CEO)
Alex Cho (Pres-Personal Sys Bus)
Kristen M. Ludgate (Chief People Officer)
Dave McQuarrie (Chief Comml Officer)
Karen L. Parkhill (CFO & Exec VP)
Julie Jacobs (Chief Legal Officer & Gen Counsel)
Anneliese Olson (Pres-Imaging, Printing, and Solutions)
Ernest Nicolas (Chief Enterprise Ops Officer)

Subsidiaries:

Alpha Holding Two B.V. (1)
Startbaan 16, 1187XR, Amstelveen, Netherlands
Tel.: (31) 205476911
Holding Company
N.A.I.C.S.: 551112

Apogee Corporation (Jersey) Limited (1)
94 Halkett Place, Saint Helier, JE2 4WH, Jersey
Tel.: (44) 1534872345
Printing Services
N.A.I.C.S.: 323111

Aruba Networks, Inc. (1)
1344 Crossman Ave, Sunnyvale, CA 94089-1113
Tel.: (408) 227-4500
Web Site: http://www.arubanetworks.com
Sales Range: $700-749.9 Million
Wireless & Wireline Enterprise Network Mobility Services
N.A.I.C.S.: 517112
Vishal Lall (COO)
Jim Bergkamp (CFO)
Alain Carpentier (Sr VP-Sls-Worldwide)
Partha Narasimhan (CTO)
Tom Black (Sr VP & Gen Mgr-Switching)
Ash Chowdappa (Sr VP & Gen Mgr-Cloud & Security Software)
Pradeep Iyer (Chief Architect)
J. D. Singh (VP-Global Customer Ops)
Jeff Lipton (VP-Strategy & Corp Dev)
Kathy Winters (VP-HR)
Willie Hernandez (VP & Deputy Gen Counsel)

Subsidiary (Non-US):

Aruba Networks India Pvt. Ltd. (2)
Salarpuria Hallmark Outer Ring Road Sy No 15/3 & 16 Kadubeesanahalli, Varthur Hobli, Bengaluru, 560 103, South Talluk, India
Tel.: (91) 8033176000
Web Site: http://www.arubanetworks.com
Emp.: 400
Wireless & Wireline Enterprise Network Mobility Services
N.A.I.C.S.: 517112

BAS Burosysteme GmbH (1)
Magdeburger Strasse 5, 530880, Laatzen, Germany
Tel.: (49) 51 029 1970

Web Site: https://www.apogeecorp.de
Business Management Consulting Services
N.A.I.C.S.: 541611

Bromium UK Limited (1)
Lockton House 2nd Floor Clarendon Road, Cambridge, CB2 8FH, United Kingdom
Tel.: (44) 1223314914
Software Development Services
N.A.I.C.S.: 541511
Ian Pratt (Founder & Pres)

China HP Co., Ltd. (1)
No 8 Guang Shun Avenue South Bldg 1 5th Floor Lei Shing Hong Center, ChaoYang District, Beijing, 100102, China
Tel.: (86) 1058704833
Printer Mfr
N.A.I.C.S.: 333248

Computing and Printing Global Services Mexico, S. de R.L. de C.V. (1)
Montemorelos 299, 45060, Guadalajara, Jalisco, Mexico
Tel.: (52) 3331347400
Web Site: https://www.hp.com
Electronic Computer Mfr
N.A.I.C.S.: 334111

Computing and Printing Mexico, S. de R.L. de C.V. (1)
Av Basco of Surgery No 2999, Distrito Federal, 01210, Mexico, Mexico
Tel.: (52) 5550912455
Electronic Computer Mfr
N.A.I.C.S.: 334111

Datatron Document Image Archiving Limited (1)
Unit 6 Mercury Orion Business Park, Tyne & Wear, North Shields, NE29 7SN, United Kingdom
Tel.: (44) 1912728466
Web Site: https://www.datatron.co.uk
Information Technology Services
N.A.I.C.S.: 541519

Electronic Data SystemsBelgium BVBA (1)
Blarenberglaan 2, Mechelen, 2800, Belgium
Tel.: (32) 15783711
Software Publishing Services
N.A.I.C.S.: 513210

HP Austria GmbH (1)
Technologiestrasse 5, 1120, Vienna, Austria
Tel.: (43) 13400210100
Web Site: https://www.hp.com
Electronic Computer Mfr
N.A.I.C.S.: 334111

HP Belgium BVBA (1)
Hermeslaan 1B Floor B1, 1831, Diegem, Belgium
Tel.: (32) 26201600
Web Site: https://www.hp.com
Electronic Computer Mfr
N.A.I.C.S.: 334111

HP Brasil Industria e Comercio de Equipamentos Eletronicos Ltda (1)
ITower Alameda Xingu 350, Barueri, 06455-030, Sao Paulo, Brazil
Tel.: (55) 1129337986
Web Site: https://www.hp.com
Electronic Computer Mfr
N.A.I.C.S.: 334111

HP Computing and Printing Systems India Private Limited (1)
5F Salarpuria GR Tech Park Khatha No 69/3 Mahadevapura CMC 5 &9 FL, Whitefield Road, Bengaluru, 560 066, Karnataka, India
Tel.: (91) 8033837405
Electronic Computer Mfr
N.A.I.C.S.: 334111

HP Computing and Printing d.o.o. (1)
Radnicka cesta 41 5th Floor North Wing, 10000, Zagreb, Croatia
Tel.: (385) 15790475
Web Site: https://www.hp.com
Electronic Computer Mfr
N.A.I.C.S.: 334111

HP Deutschland GmbH (1)
Schickardstrasse 32, 71034, Boblingen, Germany

Tel.: (49) 7031 450 7000
Web Site: https://www.hp.com
Electronic Computer Mfr
N.A.I.C.S.: 334111
Peter Kleiner *(Mng Dir)*

HP Finland Oy (1)
Piispankalliontie 17 Pt Ground Floor, 02200,
Espoo, Finland
Tel.: (358) 10 277 4000
Web Site: https://www.hp.com
Electronic Computer Mfr
N.A.I.C.S.: 334111

HP Imaging & Printing Group (1)
3000 Hanover St, Palo Alto, CA 94304
Tel.: (650) 857-1501
Web Site: http://welcome.hp.com
Sales Range: $125-149.9 Million
Office Machines
N.A.I.C.S.: 333310

Unit (Domestic):

HP ColorSpan (2)
11311 K-Tel Dr, Minnetonka, MN 55343
Tel.: (952) 944-9330
Sales Range: $100-124.9 Million
Emp.: 90
Laser Printer & Display Systems, Subsystems for Electronic Printing & High-
Resolution Plain-paper Typesetters Mfr,
Sales & Marketer
N.A.I.C.S.: 333248

HP Exstream Software (2)
810 Bull Lea Run, Lexington, KY 40511
Tel.: (859) 296-0600
Web Site: http://www.exstream.com
Sales Range: $25-49.9 Million
Emp.: 300
Document Creation Business Software
N.A.I.C.S.: 541511

Logoworks (2)
825 E 1180 S Ste 300, American Fork, UT
84003
Tel.: (801) 805-3700
Web Site: http://www.logoworks.com
Rev.: $5,700,000
Emp.: 200
Graphic Design Services
N.A.I.C.S.: 541430
Aaron Bernabi *(Pres & Project Mgr)*
Laurie Coreas *(Mgr-Project)*
Linsey Dudley *(Office Mgr)*
Amber Nacrelli *(Mgr-Project)*
Meek Banks *(Mgr-Project)*
Joyce Gomez *(Mgr-Print Design & Production)*

HP Inc Argentina S.R.L. (1)
Vedia 3616 - Piso 7 Ciudad Autonoma de,
C1430DAL, Buenos Aires, Argentina
Tel.: (54) 1152833537
Web Site: https://www.hp.com
Electronic Computer Mfr
N.A.I.C.S.: 334111

HP Inc Chile Comercial Limitada (1)
Mariano Sanchez Fontecilla 310 Piso 13,
7550296, Santiago, Chile
Tel.: (56) 227227051
Web Site: https://www.hp.com
Electronic Computer Mfr
N.A.I.C.S.: 334111

HP Inc Costa Rica Limitada (1)
Centro Corporativo Plaza Roble Edificio 5,
San Jose, Costa Rica
Tel.: (506) 525552584000
Electronic Computer Mfr
N.A.I.C.S.: 334111

HP Inc Czech Republic s.r.o. (1)
Computer Terminal & Computer Peripheral
Equipment Mfr
N.A.I.C.S.: 333248
Patrik Toifl *(Mgr-Bus Dev)*

HP Inc Danmark ApS (1)
Engholm Parkvej 8, 3450, Allerod, Denmark
Tel.: (45) 3 515 0600
Web Site: https://www.hp.com
Electronic Computer Mfr
N.A.I.C.S.: 334111

HP Inc Magyarorszag Kft. (1)
Ujbuda Allee Corner October twenty-third u
8-10, 1117, Budapest, Hungary
Tel.: (36) 1 777 7545

Web Site: https://www.hp.com
Electronic Computer Mfr
N.A.I.C.S.: 334111
Zoltan Szalai *(CFO)*

HP Inc Polska sp. z o.o. (1)
Dominikanski Office Complex ul Piotra
Skargi 1A, 50-082, Wroclaw, Poland
Tel.: (48) 227261400
Web Site: https://www.hp.com
Electronic Computer Mfr
N.A.I.C.S.: 334111

HP Inc Romania SRL (1)
Glucose Factory No 5 Building F floors P
and 8, 2nd District, 020337, Bucharest,
Romania
Tel.: (40) 316304796
Web Site: https://www.hp.com
Electronic Computer Mfr
N.A.I.C.S.: 334111

HP Inc Slovakia, s.r.o. (1)
Galvaniho 7 4th Floor, 820 02, Bratislava,
Slovakia
Tel.: (421) 23 918 3100
Web Site: https://www.hp.com
Electronic Computer Mfr
N.A.I.C.S.: 334111

HP Inc Tunisie SARL (1)
Immeuble NIDA ZI Chotrana Technopole El
Ghazala Lot n45, 2088, Ariana, Tunisia
Tel.: (216) 70164430
Electronic Computer Mfr
N.A.I.C.S.: 334111

HP Italy S.r.l. (1)
Via Carlo Donat Cattin 5, 20063, Cernusco
sul Naviglio, Milan, Italy
Tel.: (39) 0292121
Web Site: https://www.hp.com
Electronic Computer Mfr
N.A.I.C.S.: 334111
Stefano Venturi *(CEO)*

HP KSA Ltd. (1)
Floor 14 King Fahad Highway, Olaya District, Riyadh, Saudi Arabia
Tel.: (966) 112803990
Web Site: https://www.hp.com
Computer Peripheral Equipment Distr
N.A.I.C.S.: 423430

HP Nederland B.V. (1)
Krijgsman 75, 1186 DR, Amstelveen, Netherlands
Tel.: (31) 207213400
Web Site: https://www.hp.com
Electronic Computer Mfr
N.A.I.C.S.: 334111
Ken Wilson *(Acct Mgr)*

HP Norge AS (1)
Rolfsbuktveien 4, 1364, Fornebu, Oslo,
Norway
Tel.: (47) 23502019
Web Site: https://www.hp.com
Electronic Computer Mfr
N.A.I.C.S.: 334111

HP PPS Australia Pty Ltd (1)
Office Number 203 Level 2 East The Wentworth Buildin 300 Murray Street, Off Raine
Lane, Perth, 6000, WA, Australia
Tel.: (61) 288232485
Web Site: https://www.hp.com
Electronic Computer Mfr
N.A.I.C.S.: 334111
Manpal Jagpal *(Bus Mgr)*

HP PPS Malaysia Sdn. Bhd. (1)
Plaza Zurich No 12 Block A Level 5, Jalan
Gelenggang Bukit Damansara Wilayah
Persekutuan, 50490, Kuala Lumpur, Malaysia
Tel.: (60) 379533333
Web Site: https://www.hp.com
Electronic Computer Mfr
N.A.I.C.S.: 334111
Matthew Choon Howe Sia *(Mgr-Fin-Asia
Pacific & Japan)*

HP PPS Maroc SARL (1)
Boulevard Des Almohades Office N5 Immeuble Crystal 1 4eme Etage, Annexe A,
20030, Casablanca, Morocco
Tel.: (212) 522642464
Electronic Computer Mfr
N.A.I.C.S.: 334111

HP PPS Multimedia Sdn. Bhd. (1)
Hp Global Centre, Persiaran Rimba Permai,
Cyberjaya, 63000, Malaysia
Tel.: (60) 383108686
Electronic Computer Mfr
N.A.I.C.S.: 334111

**HP PPS Singapore (Sales) Pte.
Ltd.** (1)
1 Depot Close, Singapore, 109841, Singapore
Tel.: (65) 67407838
Electronic Computer Mfr
N.A.I.C.S.: 334111
Albert Seah *(Mgr-Printing Supplies)*

HP PPS Sverige AB (1)
Gustav III s boulevard 34, 169 73, Solna,
Sweden
Tel.: (46) 105200700
Web Site: https://www.hp.com
Electronic Computer Mfr
N.A.I.C.S.: 334111

**HP Printing & Computing Solutions,
S.L.U.** (1)
Cami de Can Graells 1-21 Bldg BCN01,
08174, Sant Cugat del Valles, Spain
Tel.: (34) 902027020
Electronic Computer Mfr
N.A.I.C.S.: 334111

**HP Printing and Personal Systems
Hellas EPE** (1)
Tzavella 1-3 2nd floor, Chalandri, 15231,
Athens, Greece
Tel.: (30) 2109696416
Electronic Computer Mfr
N.A.I.C.S.: 334111
Vassilis Avzotis *(Mng Dir)*

HP Schweiz GmbH (1)
Smooth Tower Neue Winterthurerstrasse
99, Wallisellen, 8304, Zurich, Switzerland
Tel.: (41) 43 547 0500
Web Site: https://www.hp.com
Electronic Computer Mfr
N.A.I.C.S.: 334111

HP Solutions Creation and Development Services S.L.U. (1)
Julia Morros 1 Pt Ground Floor, 24009,
Leon, Spain
Tel.: (34) 902027020
Electronic Computer Mfr
N.A.I.C.S.: 334111

**HP South Africa Proprietary
Limited** (1)
12 Autumn Street Pt 1st Floor, Wendywood,
Sandton, 2128, South Africa
Tel.: (27) 110695400
Web Site: https://www.hp.com
Electronic Computer Mfr
N.A.I.C.S.: 334111

**HP Taiwan Information Technology
Ltd.** (1)
10F-2 No 66 Jing Mao 2 Road, Hsin-Yi
Road, Taipei, 11568, Taiwan
Tel.: (886) 237899900
Electronic Computer Mfr
N.A.I.C.S.: 334111
Steven Lai *(Mgr-WKS Mktg Bus Dev)*

HP Technology Ireland Limited (1)
Liffey Valley Office Campus 1st floor Block
B, Quarryvale, Dublin, D22 X0Y3, Ireland
Tel.: (353) 16161140
Computer Peripheral Equipment Distr.
N.A.I.C.S.: 423430

HP-PPS Ecuador Cia. Ltda (1)
Avenue Republica del Salvador Number
1082 y Naciones Unidas, Torre Paris Edificio Mansion Blanca, Quito, Ecuador
Tel.: (593) 22990500
Electronic Computer Mfr
N.A.I.C.S.: 334111

HPCP-Computing and Printing Portugal, Unipessoal, Lda. (1)
Quinta da Fonte Pt Ground Floor, Paco de
Arcos, 2774-528, Lisbon, Portugal
Tel.: (351) 210608062
Electronic Computer Mfr
N.A.I.C.S.: 334111

HPQ Holdings, LLC (1)

11445 Compaq Center Dr W, Houston, TX
77070
Tel.: (650) 857-5144
Holding Company
N.A.I.C.S.: 551112

**Hewlett-Packard - Business
Intelligence** (1)
2001 Butterfield Rd Ste 700, Downers
Grove, IL 60515-5471
Tel.: (312) 577-0210
Sales Range: $10-24.9 Million
Emp.: 70
Data Warehousing & Systems Integration
Consulting & Services
N.A.I.C.S.: 541611

Hewlett-Packard Arabia LLC (1)
Al Fasaliah Tower, Riyadh, 11598, Saudi
Arabia
Tel.: (966) 12731200
Electronic Computer Mfr
N.A.I.C.S.: 334111

Hewlett-Packard Development Company, L.P. (1)
10300 Energy Dr, Spring, TX 77389
Tel.: (650) 857-1501
Web Site: https://www.hp.com
Computer Mfr
N.A.I.C.S.: 334111

**Hewlett-Packard Enterprises,
LLC** (1)
6080 Tennyson Pkwy Ste 400, Plano, TX
75024
Tel.: (972) 604-6000
Web Site: https://www.hpe.com
Electronic Computer Mfr
N.A.I.C.S.: 334111

Hewlett-Packard Espanola S.L. (1)
Calle Vicente Aleixandre 1, Parque Empresarial, Madrid, 28230, Spain
Tel.: (34) 916348800
Electronic Computer Mfr
N.A.I.C.S.: 334111
Timo Kinzelmann *(Engr-HP Store Bus Process)*

Hewlett-Packard Espanola, S.A. (1)
C/ Vicente Alexandre 1 Parque Empresarial
Las Rozas, Las Rozas de Madrid, E-28230,
Madrid, Las Rozas, Spain
Tel.: (34) 916311600
Sales Range: $100-124.9 Million
Sales & Marketing of Computer Products
N.A.I.C.S.: 449210

Branch (Domestic):

Hewlett-Packard Espanola, S.A. (2)
Camgrablls 1, 08174, Barcelona,
Spain (100%)
Tel.: (34) 934019100
Web Site: http://www.hp.es
Sales & Marketing of Computer Products
N.A.I.C.S.: 449210

Hewlett-Packard Espanola, S.A. (2)
Calle General Aviles 35-37, 46015, Valencia, Spain
Tel.: (34) 902027020
Web Site: http://welcome.hp.com
Sales Range: $100-124.9 Million
Sales & Marketing of Computer Products
N.A.I.C.S.: 449210

**Hewlett-Packard Europa Holding
B.V.** (1)
Startbaan 16, Amstelveen, 1187 XR, Netherlands
Tel.: (31) 205476911
Web Site: http://www.hp.nl
Holding Company
N.A.I.C.S.: 551112

**Hewlett-Packard India Sales Pvt.
Ltd.** (1)
G 3 4 Fl Salapuria Arena, Hosur Main
Road, Bengaluru, 560030, India
Tel.: (91) 8025041862
Computer Related Services
N.A.I.C.S.: 541512
Balu Doraisamy *(Mng Dir & Sr VP)*

Hewlett-Packard Indigo B.V. (1)
Startbaan 16, 1187 XR, Amstelveen,
Netherlands (100%)
Tel.: (31) 205476911

HP Inc.—(Continued)

Sales Range: $50-74.9 Million
Emp.: 150
Develops, Licenses, Manufactures, Distributes & Services Liquid, Ink-Based Electrophotographic Products
N.A.I.C.S.: 325910

Hewlett-Packard Indigo Ltd.   **(1)**
Kiryat Weizmann, Rehovot, 7610101, Israel
Tel.: (972) 89381818
Electronic Computer Mfr
N.A.I.C.S.: 334111
Alon Bar-Shany *(Gen Mgr)*

Hewlett-Packard Industrial Printing Ltd.   **(1)**
8B Hatzoran, Netanya, 42506, Israel
Tel.: (972) 98924644
Electronic Computer Mfr
N.A.I.C.S.: 334111
Asaf Dobrin *(Controller)*

Hewlett-Packard International Pte. Ltd.   **(1)**
450 Alexandra Road, Singapore, 119960, Singapore
Tel.: (65) 62753888
Holding Company
N.A.I.C.S.: 551112

Hewlett-Packard Ireland Ltd.   **(1)**
Barnhall Rd Bldg DUB01, Leixlip, Ireland   **(100%)**
Tel.: (353) 19079337
Web Site: http://www.welcome.hp.com
Sales & Marketing of Computer Products
N.A.I.C.S.: 449210

Hewlett-Packard Luxembourg S.C.A.   **(1)**
Vegacenter 75 parc d'Activities, Capellen, Luxembourg
Tel.: (352) 499261
Computer Peripherals Mfr
N.A.I.C.S.: 334210
Lahaye Stephane *(Gen Mgr)*

Hewlett-Packard Polska Sp. z.o.o.   **(1)**
University Business Center II Ul Szturmowa 2A, Warsaw, 02-678, Poland
Tel.: (48) 225657700
Web Site: http://www.hp.com
Computer Peripherals Mfr
N.A.I.C.S.: 334111

Hewlett-Packard Services Saudi Arabia Company   **(1)**
King Fahad Rd 5th Floor, Riyadh, Saudi Arabia
Tel.: (966) 12827429
Electronic Computer Mfr
N.A.I.C.S.: 334111

Hewlett-Packard Singapore (Private) Limited   **(1)**
450 Alexandra Rd, Singapore, 119960, Singapore
Tel.: (65) 62753888
Web Site: http://www.hp.com.sg
Sales Range: $25-49.9 Million
Emp.: 100
Sales & Marketing of Computer Products
N.A.I.C.S.: 449210

Hewlett-Packard Technology (Shanghai) Co. Ltd.   **(1)**
No 20 Jiafeng Rd Waigaoqiao Free Trade Zone Pudong New Area, Shanghai, 200131, Shanghai, China
Tel.: (86) 2128938888
Electronic Computer Mfr
N.A.I.C.S.: 334111

Hewlett-Packard Trading (Shanghai) Co. Ltd.   **(1)**
2nd Floor No 20 Jia Feng Road Waigaoqiao Free Trade Zone, Pudong, Shanghai, 200131, Shanghai, China
Tel.: (86) 2128938888
Electronic Computer Mfr
N.A.I.C.S.: 334111

Hewlett-Packard Vietnam Ltd.   **(1)**
Saigon Tower Building 10th Floor 29 Le Duan Street, District 1, Ho Chi Minh City, Vietnam
Tel.: (84) 838234151

Computer Sales, Marketing, Customer Service & Information Technology Consulting
N.A.I.C.S.: 423430

OOO Hewlett-Packard RUS   **(1)**
Leningradskoye Highway 16A Block 3 9th Floor, 125171, Moscow, Russia
Tel.: (7) 8499 921 3250
Web Site: https://www.hp.com
Electronic Computer Mfr
N.A.I.C.S.: 334111

PT Hewlett-Packard Indonesia   **(1)**
9th Floor Jl Casablanca Kav 88 Prudential Center, E4/6 Mega Kuningan, Jakarta, 12870, Indonesia
Tel.: (62) 2157991088
Electronic Computer Mfr
N.A.I.C.S.: 334111

Palm Comercio de Aparelhos Eletronicos Ltda.   **(1)**
Avenida Maria Coelho Aguiar, 215 Bl F Cenesp, Sao Paulo, 05805-000, Brazil
Tel.: (55) 1135237280
Electronic Computer Mfr
N.A.I.C.S.: 334111

Palm Europe Limited   **(1)**
59-60 Thames Street, Windsor, SL4 1TX, United Kingdom
Tel.: (44) 2071122333
Electronic Computer Mfr
N.A.I.C.S.: 334111

Plantronics, Inc.   **(1)**
345 Encinal St, Santa Cruz, CA 95060
Tel.: (831) 420-3002
Web Site: http://www.poly.com
Rev.: $1,681,144,000
Assets: $2,225,354,000
Liabilities: $2,205,192,000
Net Worth: $20,162,000
Earnings: $17,917,000
Emp.: 6,500
Fiscal Year-end: 04/02/2022
Lightweight Communications Headsets, Telephone Headset Systems, Accessories & Related Services Designer, Mfr & Marketer
N.A.I.C.S.: 334210
Marvin Tseu *(Vice Chm)*
Paul Johnson *(CIO & VP)*
Anja Hamilton *(Chief HR Officer & Exec VP)*
Darrius Jones *(Chief Strategy Officer, Chief Mktg Officer-Acting & Exec VP)*
Mike Iburg *(VP-IR)*
Carl James Wiese *(Chief Revenue Officer & Exec VP)*
Shannon Shamoon *(Mgr-PR)*
Navin Mehta *(Exec VP-Svcs)*
Edie Kissko *(VP-Corp Comm)*
David M. Shull *(Pres & CEO)*
Lisa Bodensteiner *(Chief Legal & Compliance Officer & Exec VP)*
John Goodwin *(Sr VP-Pub Affairs)*
Grant Hoffman *(Chief Supply Chain Officer & Exec VP)*

Subsidiary (Non-US):

Brazil Plantronics Telecommunicacoes Ltda.   **(2)**
R Iguatemi 192-18, Sao Paulo, 01451-010, SP, Brazil
Tel.: (55) 1130782934
Telecommunication Servicesb
N.A.I.C.S.: 517810

Unit (Non-US):

Clarity   **(2)**   **(100%)**
Tel.: (423) 622-7793
Web Site: http://www.clarityproducts.com
Sales Range: $10-24.9 Million
Emp.: 30
Telecommunications Equipment
N.A.I.C.S.: 334210

Subsidiary (Domestic):

Plamex, S.A. de C.V.   **(2)**
345 Encinal St, Santa Cruz, CA 95060
Tel.: (831) 426-5858
Web Site: http://www.plantronics.com
Communications Headsets, Telephone Headset Systems & Accessories Mfr
N.A.I.C.S.: 334210

Subsidiary (Non-US):

Plantronics Acoustics Italia, S.r.l.   **(2)**
Via Torri Bianche 9, Vimercate, 20059, Milan, Italy
Tel.: (39) 039685971
Web Site: http://www.plantronics.com
Sales Range: $10-24.9 Million
Emp.: 7
Telephone Headsets & Telecommunications Products
N.A.I.C.S.: 517810

Plantronics B.V.   **(2)**
Tel.: (31) 235648010
Web Site: http://www.plantronics.com
Sales Range: $25-49.9 Million
Emp.: 100
Telephone Headsets & Telecommunications Products
N.A.I.C.S.: 517810

Plantronics Canada Limited   **(2)**
151 Hymus Blvd ste 10, Pointe-Claire, H9R 1E9, QC, Canada   **(100%)**
Tel.: (514) 694-3185
Web Site: http://www.plantronics.com
Sales Range: $1-9.9 Million
Emp.: 4
Mfr of Telephone Headsets & Telecommunications Products
N.A.I.C.S.: 517810

Plantronics GmbH   **(2)**
Gildenweg 7, 50354, Hurth, Germany   **(100%)**
Tel.: (49) 22333990
Web Site: http://www.plantronics.de
Sales Range: $10-24.9 Million
Emp.: 15
Telephone Headsets & Telecommunications Products
N.A.I.C.S.: 517810

Plantronics International   **(2)**
Interface Business Pk Bincknoll Ln, Wootton Bassett, SN4 8QQ, United Kingdom   **(100%)**
Tel.: (44) 1793848999
Web Site: http://www.plantronics.com
Sales Range: $25-49.9 Million
Emp.: 100
Marketing & Sales of Telecommunications Equipment
N.A.I.C.S.: 238210

Plantronics International do Brasil, Ltda.   **(2)**
Av Joao Carlos Silva Borges 693, 01451-010, Sao Paulo, SP, Brazil   **(100%)**
Tel.: (55) 1156416310
Web Site: http://www.plantronics.com
Sales Range: $1-9.9 Million
Emp.: 5
Telephone Headsets & Telecommunications Products
N.A.I.C.S.: 517810

Plantronics Japan Ltd.   **(2)**
Daido Seimei Kasumigaseki Building 8F 1-4-2 Kasumigaseki, Chiyoda-ku, Tokyo, 100-0013, Japan
Tel.: (81) 335096400
Web Site: http://www.plantronics.com
Telephone Headsets & Telecommunications Products
N.A.I.C.S.: 517810

Plantronics Limited   **(2)**
Interface Business Park Bincknoll Lane, Wootton Bassett, SN4 8QQ, Wiltshire, United Kingdom
Tel.: (44) 1793812200
Web Site: http://www.plantronics.com
Sales Range: $25-49.9 Million
Emp.: 100
Audio Communication Equipment Mfr
N.A.I.C.S.: 334290

Plantronics Pty. Limited   **(2)**
12 Hall Street, Moonee Ponds, Melbourne, 3039, VIC, Australia
Tel.: (61) 393261653
Web Site: http://www.plantronics.com
Audio Communication Equipment Mfr
N.A.I.C.S.: 334290

Plantronics Rus LLC   **(2)**
Presnenskaya Embankment 6 Bld 2 Floor 19 Location I-Room 14, 123317, Moscow, Russia

Tel.: (7) 4959677993
Audio Communication Equipment Mfr
N.A.I.C.S.: 334290

Plantronics Singapore Pte. Ltd.   **(2)**
6 Eu Tong Sen Street 08-17, soho 1 Central, Singapore, 059817, Singapore
Tel.: (65) 63245858
Web Site: http://www.plantronics.com
Telephone Headsets & Telecommunications Products
N.A.I.C.S.: 517810

Subsidiary (Domestic):

Polycom, Inc.   **(2)**
6001 America Ctr Dr, San Jose, CA 95002
Tel.: (408) 586-6000
Web Site: http://www.polycom.com
Teleconferencing Equipment Developer, Mfr & Marketer
N.A.I.C.S.: 334210
Gary Nelson *(VP-Ops)*

Subsidiary (Domestic):

Obihai Technology Inc.   **(3)**
2105 S Bascom Ave Ste 285, Campbell, CA 95008-3277
Tel.: (408) 890-6000
Web Site: http://www.obihai.com
Electronic Shopping
N.A.I.C.S.: 425120

Subsidiary (Non-US):

Polycom (France), S.A.R.L.   **(3)**
Tour Prisma 4-6 avenue d Alsace, 92400, Courbevoie, France
Tel.: (33) 141321999
Web Site: http://www.polycom.fr
Teleconferencing Equipment Mfr & Distr
N.A.I.C.S.: 334210
Frederic Batut *(Mng Dir)*

Polycom (Japan) K.K.   **(3)**
Shinjuku Eastside Square 6-27-30 3 F, Shinjuku-ku, Tokyo, 160-0022, Japan
Tel.: (81) 345603645
Web Site: http://www.polycom.co.jp
Teleconferencing Equipment Mfr & Distr
N.A.I.C.S.: 334210

Polycom AG   **(3)**
Thurgauerstrasse 40, PO Box 6463, Zurich, 8050, Switzerland
Tel.: (41) 443073585
Sales of Videoteleconferencing Equipment
N.A.I.C.S.: 449210

Polycom Asia Pacific Pte Ltd.   **(3)**
9 Changi Business Park Vista 07-01, Singapore, 486041, Singapore
Tel.: (65) 63899200
Web Site: http://www.poly.com
Teleconferencing Equipment Mfr & Distr
N.A.I.C.S.: 334210

Polycom Danmark ApS   **(3)**
c / o Regus Larsbjornstrade 3, 1454, Naestved, Denmark
Tel.: (45) 8088 4610
Web Site: http://www.poly.com
Wireless Communication Services
N.A.I.C.S.: 517112

Polycom Global Limited   **(3)**
The Offices at Central World 29th Floor Suite 2969, 999/9 Rama I Road, Bangkok, 10330, Thailand
Tel.: (66) 22072558
Web Site: http://www.poly.com
Teleconferencing Equipment Mfr & Distr
N.A.I.C.S.: 334210

Polycom GmbH   **(3)**
Walter-Gropius-Strasse 7, Munich, 80807, Germany   **(100%)**
Tel.: (49) 8119994100
Web Site: http://www.polycom.com
Sales of Teleconferencing Equipment
N.A.I.C.S.: 449210

Polycom Israel Ltd.   **(3)**
2 Jabotinsky Street Atrium Tower Floor 18 Offices 1839-1844 & 1846-1, Ramat Gan, 5250501, Israel
Tel.: (972) 39251444
Web Site: http://www.poly.com
Teleconferencing Equipment Mfr & Distr
N.A.I.C.S.: 334210

Polycom Norway AS (3)
c/o Regus, Aker Brygge, Filipstad Brygge 1,
0252, Oslo, Norway
Tel.: (47) 31237440600
Web Site: http://www.poly.com
Teleconferencing Equipment Mfr & Distr
N.A.I.C.S.: 334210

Polycom Russia (3)
st Enthusiastov 1st 15 building 1, Business
Center Paveletskaya Plaza, Moscow,
115054, Russia
Tel.: (7) 4951270575
Web Site: https://www.polycom.moscow
Teleconferencing Equipment Mfr & Distr
N.A.I.C.S.: 334210

**Polycom Technology (R&D) Center
Private Limited** (3)
Level 7 Unit 3B Octave Block Plot No 2 In-
orbit Mall Road Hi-tech City, One India Bulls
Centre 841, Hyderabad, 500 081, India
Tel.: (91) 4069041400
Web Site: http://www.polycom.co.in
Teleconferencing Equipment Distr
N.A.I.C.S.: 423690

**Polycom Telecomunicacoes do Brasil
Ltda.** (3)
9th Floor Suite N-1002 Storage Spaces 36
and 37, 04578-000, Sao Paulo, SP, Brazil
Tel.: (55) 1136384463
Web Site: http://www.poly.com
Teleconferencing Equipment Mfr & Distr
N.A.I.C.S.: 334210

Polycom UK Ltd. (3)
Building 4 First Floor Foundation Park Rox-
borough Way, Maidenhead, SL6 3UD, Berk-
shire, United Kingdom
Tel.: (44) 01753723000
Web Site: http://www.polycom.com
Teleconferencing Equipment Developer, Mfr
& Marketer
N.A.I.C.S.: 333310

**Polycom Unified Communications
Solutions Pvt. Ltd.** (3)
The Executive Center Prestige Khoday
Tower, 5 Raj Bhavan Road, Bengaluru,
560001, India
Tel.: (91) 8049339001
Web Site: http://www.polycom.com.in
Software Development Services
N.A.I.C.S.: 541511

**Polycom Unified Iletisim Sanayi ve
Ticaret Limited Sirketi** (3)
Maslak Veko Giz Plaza 43/45 Meydan
Sokak, Maslak 13-14, Istanbul, Turkiye
Tel.: (90) 2127084220
Web Site: http://www.polycom.com
Teleconferencing Equipment Distr
N.A.I.C.S.: 423690

Branch (Domestic):

Polycom, Inc. - Austin (3)
7700 W Parmer Ln Bldg C 1st Fl, Austin,
TX 78729-8101
Tel.: (512) 372-7000
Web Site: http://www.polycom.com
Teleconferencing Equipment Developer, Mfr
& Marketer
N.A.I.C.S.: 334210

Polycom, Inc. - Boston (3)
100 Minuteman Rd, Andover, MA 01810-
1031
Tel.: (978) 292-5000
Web Site: http://www.polycom.com
Sales & Distribution of Videoteleconferenc-
ing Equipment
N.A.I.C.S.: 518210

Polycom, Inc. - Westminster (3)
Primectr At Northridge Bldg B First Fl 1765
W 121st Ave, Westminster, CO 80234-2301
Tel.: (303) 223-5003
Web Site: http://www.polycom.com
Teleconferencing Equipment Developer, Mfr
& Marketer
N.A.I.C.S.: 334210

Subsidiary (Domestic):

SpectraLink Corporation (3)
2560 55th St, Boulder, CO 80301
Tel.: (303) 441-7500
Web Site: https://www.spectralink.com

Electronic Computer Mfr
N.A.I.C.S.: 334111

PrinterOn Corporation (1)
221 McIntyre Drive, Kitchener, N2R 1G1,
ON, Canada
Tel.: (519) 748-2848
Web Site: http://www.printeron.com
Printing Services
N.A.I.C.S.: 323111

Teradici Corporation (1)
4601 Canada Way Suite 301, Burnaby,
V5G 4X7, BC, Canada
Tel.: (604) 451-5800
Web Site: http://www.teradici.com
Software Development Services
N.A.I.C.S.: 541511

UAB Hewlett-Packard (1)
V Gerulaicio g 1, Vilnius, 08222, Lithuania
Tel.: (370) 52103300
Web Site: http://www.hp.lt
Emp.: 26
Computer Peripherals Mfr
N.A.I.C.S.: 334111

ZAO Hewlett-Packard AO (1)
52/1 Kosmodamianskaja Naberezhnaya,
115054, Moscow, Russia
Tel.: (7) 4957973500
Web Site: http://www.hp.com
Sales Range: $100-124.9 Million
Computers & Computer Peripherals Distr
N.A.I.C.S.: 423430

HPIL HOLDING

134 Landing St, Southampton, NJ
08088
Tel.: (231) 676-2232   NV
Web Site: http://www.hpilholding.com
HPIL—(OTCIQ)
Health Care & Environmental Prod-
ucts
N.A.I.C.S.: 339112

HPN HOLDINGS, INC.

14749 Crystal Tree Dr, Orland Park,
IL 60462
Tel.: (815) 370-8318   OK
Year Founded: 2008
KICK—(OTCIQ)
Software Development Services
N.A.I.C.S.: 541511
Douglas Stukel (CEO)
Michael Profita (Co-Pres & Co-Sec)
John Heskett (Co-Pres, Treas & Co-
Sec)

HQDA ELDERLY LIFE NET-
WORK CORP.

8780 Vly Blvd Ste J, Rosemead, CA
91770
Tel.: (626) 877-8187   NV
Year Founded: 2004
HQDA—(OTCIQ)
Rev.: $838,578
Assets: $26,491,216
Liabilities: $6,574,432
Net Worth: $19,916,784
Earnings: ($1,242,355)
Emp.: 18
Fiscal Year-end: 06/30/21
Senior Retirement Services Compa-
ny;Senior Housing & Retirement Ser-
vices
N.A.I.C.S.: 525110

HST GLOBAL, INC.

509 Old Great Neck Rd Ste 105, Vir-
ginia Beach, VA 23454
Tel.: (757) 766-6100   NV
Web Site: https://www.hstglobal.com
HSTC—(OTCIQ)
Assets: $1,526
Liabilities: $593,593
Net Worth: ($592,067)
Earnings: ($146,210)
Emp.: 1
Fiscal Year-end: 12/31/23
Pharmaceuticals Mfr

N.A.I.C.S.: 325412
Ronald R. Howell (Chm)
Jason Andrew Murphy (CEO & VP)
Michael Lee Field Jr. (Pres & CFO)

HTG MOLECULAR DIAGNOS-
TICS, INC.

3430 E Global Loop, Tucson, AZ
85706   DE
Web Site:
  https://www.htgmolecular.com
HTGM—(NASDAQ)
Rev.: $6,366,220
Assets: $17,777,655
Liabilities: $12,385,958
Net Worth: $5,391,697
Earnings: ($21,594,476)
Emp.: 53
Fiscal Year-end: 12/31/22
Molecular Profiling Applications, In-
cluding Tumor Profiling, Molecular
Diagnostic Testing & Biomarker De-
velopment
N.A.I.C.S.: 621512
John L. Lubniewski (Pres & CEO)
Shaun D. McMeans (CFO, Treas,
Sec & Sr VP-Fin & Admin)
Laura L. Godlewski (Principal Acctg
Officer & VP-Fin)
Byron T. Lawson (Chief Comml Offi-
cer & Sr VP)
Stephen Barat (Sr VP-Therapeutics)
Carl Kaub (VP-Chemistry Ops)

HUB DEALS CORP.

200 Rector Pl Ste 17F, New York, NY
10280
Tel.: (646) 928-2902   NV
Year Founded: 2001
HDLS—(OTCIQ)
Assets: $600,341
Liabilities: $345,220
Net Worth: $255,121
Earnings: ($79,582)
Fiscal Year-end: 12/31/19
Online Shopping Services
N.A.I.C.S.: 519290
William Drury (Pres, CEO, Treas &
Sec)

HUB GROUP, INC.

2001 Hub Group Way, Oak Brook, IL
60523
Tel.: (630) 271-3600   DE
Web Site: https://www.hubgroup.com
Year Founded: 1971
HUBG—(NASDAQ)
Rev.: $5,340,490,000
Assets: $2,810,081,000
Liabilities: $1,210,479,000
Net Worth: $1,599,602,000
Earnings: $356,948,000
Emp.: 5,900
Fiscal Year-end: 12/31/22
Freight Transportation Management
Services
N.A.I.C.S.: 488510
David P. Yeager (Chm)
Phillip D. Yeager (Vice Chm, Pres &
CEO)
Matthew Yeager (Exec VP-
Procurement)
Kevin W. Beth (CFO, Chief Acctg Of-
ficer, Treas & Exec VP)
Dhruv Bansal (CIO & Exec VP)
Jessica Pokrajac (Exec VP-Customer
Solutions)
Geoff Turner (Exec VP-Truck Broker-
age)
Matthew Fletchall (Exec VP-Final
Mile)
Tom LaFrance (Chief Legal Officer,
Chief HR Officer, Sec & Exec VP)
Brent Rhodes (Chief Acctg Officer)
Brandon Folck (Exec VP-Human Re-
sources)

Michael Daly (Sr VP-Corporate De-
velopment & Strategy)
Lorna Williams (VP-Investor Rela-
tions)
Scott Robider (Exec VP-Final Mile)
Joby Homesley (Exec VP-
Consolidation & Fulfillment)
Shannon McCullough (Sr VP-
Dedicated Ops)
Steve Wilson (Sr VP-Logistics)
Jakub Cerny (Exec VP-Fleet Svcs)

Subsidiaries:

CaseStack, Inc. (1)
3000 Ocean Park Blvd Ste 1000, Santa
Monica, CA 90405
Tel.: (866) 828-7120
Web Site: http://www.cloud.casestack.com
Logistics Outsourcing Services; Warehous-
ing, Fulfillment & Transportation Infrastruc-
ture Services
N.A.I.C.S.: 541614
Daniel A. Sanker (Pres & CEO)
Steve Sezna (COO)
David Isaksen (CFO)
Guillermo Pardon (CTO)
Craig Long (VP-Transport Svcs)
Ryan Casady (VP-Logistics Partners)
Nathan Schmies (VP-Ops)
Colby Beland (VP-Sls & Mktg)
Spencer Smith (Sr Dir-Client Dev)
Jordan Korss (Sr Dir-Bus Analytics & Pric-
ing)
Daisy McKenna (Sr Dir-Ops)
Perry Johnson (Sr Dir-Transportation)
Joe Grover (Dir-Consolidation Programs)
Cullen Brown (Sr Dir-Warehouse Providers)
Pei-Ching Ling (VP-Fin & Bus Process)

Choptank Transport Inc (1)
3601 Choptank Rd, Preston, MD 21655
Tel.: (410) 673-2240
Web Site: http://www.choptanktransport.com
Rev.: $7,743,000
Emp.: 400
Freight Transportation Arrangement
N.A.I.C.S.: 488510
Geoff A. Turner (Pres & CEO)
Marcia Wood (CFO)

Hub Group Canada, L.P (1)
2660 Sherwood Heights Dr Ste 101, Oak-
ville, CT 06037
Tel.: (905) 829-2070
Web Site: http://www.hubgroup.com
Sales Range: $25-49.9 Million
Emp.: 43
Freight Transportation Services
N.A.I.C.S.: 488510

Hub Group Trucking, Inc. (1)
5660 Universal Dr, Memphis, TN 38118-
7923
Tel.: (901) 541-8000
Web Site: https://www.hubgroup.com
Sales Range: $75-99.9 Million
Emp.: 400
Freight Transportation Services
N.A.I.C.S.: 488510

Subsidiary (Domestic):

Estenson Logistics LLC (2)
560 W Brown Rd Ste 3001, Mesa, AZ
85201
Tel.: (480) 940-8800
Web Site: http://www.estensonlogistics.com
Freight Transportation Arrangement Ser-
vices
N.A.I.C.S.: 488510

Hub Group Trucking (2)
263 Roy Rd SW, Pacific, WA 98047-2148
Tel.: (253) 826-7686
Web Site: http://www.hubgroup.com
Sales Range: $25-49.9 Million
Emp.: 25
General Freight Trucking Services
N.A.I.C.S.: 484110

Mode Freight Services, LLC (1)
17330 Preston Rd Ste 200c, Dallas, TX
75252
Tel.: (972) 447-0075
Freight Transportation Services

Hub Group, Inc.—(Continued)
N.A.I.C.S.: 488510

NonstopDelivery, LLC (1)
4500 Southgate Pl Ste 300, Chantilly, VA 20151
Web Site: http://www.shipnsd.com
Freight Transportation Arrangement
N.A.I.C.S.: 488510
Stephen Senkus (Founder & CEO)

TAGG Logistics, LLC (1)
372 Hazelwood Logistics Center Dr, Saint Louis, MO 63042
Tel.: (314) 991-1900
Web Site: http://www.tagglogistics.com
Emp.: 150
Logistics Consulting Servies
N.A.I.C.S.: 541614
Tod Yazdi (Principal)
Gary Patterson (Principal)

Subsidiary (Domestic):

ABC Fulfillment LLC (2)
300 Brookside Ave, Ambler, PA 19002-3436
Tel.: (215) 628-3154
Web Site: http://www.abcfulfillment.com
Packaging & Labeling Services
N.A.I.C.S.: 561910
Eileen Maginnis (Pres)

HUBBELL INCORPORATED

40 Waterview Dr, Shelton, CT 06484-1000
Tel.: (475) 882-4000   **CT**
Web Site: https://www.hubbell.com
Year Founded: 1888
HUBB—(NYSE)
Rev.: $5,372,900,000
Assets: $6,914,000,000
Liabilities: $4,024,700,000
Net Worth: $2,889,300,000
Earnings: $759,800,000
Emp.: 18,317
Fiscal Year-end: 12/31/23
Lighting, Wiring & Power System & Electrical Component Mfr
N.A.I.C.S.: 335999
William R. Sperry (CFO & Exec VP)
Rodd R. Ruland (Exec VP)
Susan Huppertz (Chief Mfg & Supply Chain Officer)
Katherine A. Lane (Gen Counsel, Sec & VP)
Jonathan M. Del Nero (Principal Acctg Officer, VP & Controller)
Gerben W. Bakker (Chm, Pres & CEO)

Subsidiaries:

Acme Electric LLC (1)
N65 W13385 Silver Spring Dr, Menomonee Falls, WI 53051
Web Site: http://www.hubbell.com
Power Conditioning Equipment Mfr
N.A.I.C.S.: 335311

Anderson Electrical Products (1)
1615 Moore St NW, Leeds, AL 35094
Tel.: (205) 699-2411
Web Site:
http://www.hubbellpowersystems.com
Rev.: $41,000,000
Emp.: 200
Manufacture Electronic Connectors, Clamps & Fittings
N.A.I.C.S.: 449210

Architectural Area Lighting/Moldcast Co. (1)
16555 Gale Ave, City of Industry, CA 91745-1713 (100%)
Tel.: (714) 994-2700
Web Site: http://www.aal.net
Sales Range: $10-24.9 Million
Emp.: 140
Outdoor Lighting Equipment
N.A.I.C.S.: 335139

Artesanias Baja, S. A. de C.V. (1)
Blvd Universidad No 12965 Parque Industrial Int, Tijuana, 22575, Baja California, Mexico
Tel.: (52) 6566249341

Electrical Product Whslr
N.A.I.C.S.: 423610

Austdac Pty. Limited (1)
Unit 1 42 Carrington Road, Castle Hill, 2154, NSW, Australia
Tel.: (61) 288515000
Web Site: https://www.austdac.com.au
Mining,Industrial & Communication Equipment Design & Mfr
N.A.I.C.S.: 334290

Bel Manufacturera, S.A. de C.V. (1)
Ave Santiago Blancas 551 Terrazas Del Valle, Ciudad Juarez, 32599, Chihuahua, Mexico
Tel.: (52) 6566290951
Electrical Product Whslr
N.A.I.C.S.: 423610

Bryant Electric Company (1)
40 Waterview Dr, Shelton, CT 06460-2473
Tel.: (475) 882-4804
Web Site: http://www.bryant-electric.com
Sales Range: $25-49.9 Million
Emp.: 100
Industrial, Commercial & Residential Wiring Devices Mfr
N.A.I.C.S.: 335931
Christian Thompson (Dir-Mktg)
Mike Sullivan (VP-Sls)

Burndy Canada Inc. (1)
870 Brock Rd S, Pickering, L1W 1Z8, ON, Canada
Tel.: (905) 752-5400
Current-Carrying Wiring Device Mfr
N.A.I.C.S.: 335931

Burndy LLC (1)
47 E Industrial Park Dr, Manchester, NH 03109-5311
Tel.: (603) 647-5000
Web Site: https://www.hubbell.com
Emp.: 150
Electronic Connector Design & Mfr
N.A.I.C.S.: 334417

Burndy Products Mexico, S.A. de C.V. (1)
Calle 5 Sur No 104 Parque Industrial Toluca 2000, 50200, Toluca, Mexico
Tel.: (52) 7222654400
Web Site: http://www.burndy.com
Electric Equipment Mfr
N.A.I.C.S.: 335999

Burndy do Brasil Industria, Comercio, Importacao e Exportacao de Conectores Ltda. (1)
Av Guarapiranga 2400, Sao Paulo, 049110-905, Brazil
Tel.: (55) 1155157201
Electrical Equipment & Component Mfr
N.A.I.C.S.: 335999

CDR de Mexico S. de R.L. de C.V. (1)
Avenida Zaragoza S/N Poniente 2 Esquina, Matamoros, 87550, Tamaulipas, Mexico
Tel.: (52) 8688430535
Electrical Product Whslr
N.A.I.C.S.: 423610

Cantega Technologies Inc. (1)
11603 - 165 Street, Edmonton, T5M 3Z1, AB, Canada
Tel.: (780) 448-9700
Web Site: https://www.cantega.com
Electrical & Electronic Equipment Mfr
N.A.I.C.S.: 336320
Brent Stankowski (Chm & CEO)
Mike Dunham (COO)
Marshall Rosichuk (CFO)
Keith Yeats (VP-Field Svcs)
Gayle Howard (Exec VP-Corp Dev)

Chalmit Lighting Limited (1)
388 Hillington Road Hillington Park, PO Box 5575, Glasgow, G52 9AP, United Kingdom
Tel.: (44) 1418109644
Web Site: http://www.chalmit.com
Sales Range: $25-49.9 Million
Fluorescent & Lighting Product Mfr
N.A.I.C.S.: 335139

Dual Lite Manufacturing Inc. (1)
Intl Rd 192 Rr 31, Naguabo, PR 00718 (100%)
Tel.: (787) 874-2060

Web Site: http://www.duallite.com
Sales Range: $10-24.9 Million
Emp.: 55
Lighting Equipment Mfr
N.A.I.C.S.: 335139

English Road Holdings, LLC (1)
546 English Rd, Rocky Mount, NC 27804
Tel.: (252) 467-2210
Electrical Equipment & Component Mfr
N.A.I.C.S.: 335999

Fargo Mfg. Company, Inc. (1)
210 N Allen St, Centralia, MO 65240
Tel.: (573) 682-5521
Electrical Fitting & Accessories Mfr
N.A.I.C.S.: 335999

GAI-Tronics Limited (1)
Brunel Drive, Stretton Park, Burton-on-Trent, DE13 0BZ, Staffordshire, United Kingdom
Tel.: (44) 1283500500
Web Site: http://www.gai-tronics.org.uk
Communication Equipment Mfr
N.A.I.C.S.: 334290

GAI-Tronics S.r.l. (1)
Via Cristoforo Colombo n 12, 20094, Corsico, MI, Italy
Tel.: (39) 0248601460
Sales Range: $25-49.9 Million
Emp.: 50
Electrical Products Mfr
N.A.I.C.S.: 335999

Gai-Tronics Corporation (1)
3030 Kutztown Rd, Reading, PA 19605
Tel.: (610) 777-1374
Web Site: http://www.gai-tronics.com
Sales Range: $50-74.9 Million
Electric Equipment Mfr
N.A.I.C.S.: 335999

Gleason Reel Corporation (1)
600 S Clark St, Mayville, WI 53050 (100%)
Tel.: (920) 387-4120
Web Site: http://www.gleasonreel.com
Sales Range: $50-74.9 Million
Electric Equipment Mfr
N.A.I.C.S.: 335999

Greenjacket Inc. (1)
27151 Burbank St, Foothill Ranch, CA 92610
Web Site: https://greenjacketinc.com
Dielectric Polymer Mfr
N.A.I.C.S.: 336320

Hawke Asia Pacific Pte. Ltd. (1)
130 Joo Seng Road 03-02 Olivine Building, Olivine Building, Singapore, 368357, Singapore
Tel.: (65) 6 282 2242
Web Site: http://www.ehawke.com
Sales Range: $10-24.9 Million
Emp.: 20
Electric Equipment Mfr
N.A.I.C.S.: 335999
Geoffrey Low (Sls Mgr-Area)

Hawke International (1)
Oxford Street West, Ashton under Lyne, OL7 0NA, Lancashire, United Kingdom (100%)
Tel.: (44) 1418109644
Web Site: https://www.ehawke.com
Sales Range: $25-49.9 Million
Emp.: 200
Provider of Cable Glands & Pneumatic Components
N.A.I.C.S.: 334513

Hipotronics, Inc. (1)
1650 Route 22 N, Brewster, NY 10509-0414
Tel.: (845) 279-3644
Web Site: http://www.hipotronics.com
Sales Range: $25-49.9 Million
Mfr of High Voltage Power Supplies & Test Equipment
N.A.I.C.S.: 334515

Hubbell Building Automation (1)
9601 Dessau Rd Bldg 1, Austin, TX 78754
Tel.: (512) 450-1100
Web Site: http://www.hubbell-automation.com
Sales Range: $10-24.9 Million
Emp.: 40

Designer, Manufacturer & Marketer of Microprocessor Based Digital Self Adjusting Occupancy Sensors, HID Dimming Controls, Photo Cells & Other Lighting Related Electrical Control Products
N.A.I.C.S.: 541512

Hubbell Canada, Inc. (1)
870 Brock Road South, PO Box 100, Pickering, L1W 1Z8, ON, Canada (100%)
Tel.: (905) 839-1138
Web Site: http://www.hubbellonline.com
Sales Range: $50-74.9 Million
Sales of Electrical Wiring Devices
N.A.I.C.S.: 423610

Subsidiary (Domestic):

Hubbell Canada (2)
870 Brock Road South, Pickering, L1W 1Z8, ON, Canada (100%)
Tel.: (905) 839-1138
Web Site: https://www.hubbell.com
Sales Range: $25-49.9 Million
Emp.: 80
Mfr Noncurrent-Carrying Wiring Devices
N.A.I.C.S.: 335932

Hubbell Caribe Ltd (1)
Km 17 Hm 3 Rr 686, Vega Baja, PR 00693 (100%)
Tel.: (787) 855-1075
Web Site: http://www.hubbell.com
Sales Range: $250-299.9 Million
Emp.: 900
Manufacture Connector & Electrical Device Mfr
N.A.I.C.S.: 335931

Hubbell Distribution, Inc. (1)
20 Glenn Bridge Rd, Arden, NC 28704-9450
Tel.: (828) 687-8505
Sales Range: $50-74.9 Million
Emp.: 200
Electrical Product Whslr
N.A.I.C.S.: 423610
Kal West (Gen Mgr)

Hubbell Industrial Controls, Inc. (1)
4301 Cheynne Dr, Archdale, NC 27263
Tel.: (336) 434-2800
Web Site: http://www.hubbell-icd.com
Sales Range: $50-74.9 Million
Industrial Control Product Mfr
N.A.I.C.S.: 335314

Hubbell Korea, Ltd. (1)
426 512 Gangseo-ro, Gangseo-gu, Seoul, 157-030, Korea (South)
Tel.: (82) 226071363
Web Site: http://www.hubbell.kr
Sales Range: $10-24.9 Million
Electrical Product Whslr
N.A.I.C.S.: 423610
Megan Klinghoffer (Mng Dir)

Hubbell Lighting - Progress Lighting Division (1)
701 Millennium Blvd, Greenville, SC 29607
Tel.: (864) 678-1000
Web Site: http://www.hubbelllighting.com
Sales Range: $250-299.9 Million
Emp.: 500
Residential & Commercial Lighting Fixtures
N.A.I.C.S.: 335210

Subsidiary (Non-US):

Progress Lighting (2)
1616 Autoroute Laval 440, Ville de Laval, H7S 2E7, QC, Canada
Tel.: (450) 687-0433
Web Site: http://www.progresslighting.com
Sales Range: $10-24.9 Million
Emp.: 8
Lighting Mfr
N.A.I.C.S.: 335139

Hubbell Limited (1)
Brunel Drive Stretton Park, Stretton Business Park, Burton-on-Trent, DE13 0BZ, Staffordshire, United Kingdom (100%)
Tel.: (44) 1283500500
Web Site: http://www.hubbell.co.uk
Sales Range: $25-49.9 Million
Emp.: 100
Electric Equipment Mfr
N.A.I.C.S.: 335999

Hubbell Pickering LP (1)

870 Brock Road South, Pickering, L1W
1Z8, ON, Canada
Tel.: (905) 839-1138
Electrical Equipment Distr
N.A.I.C.S.: 423610

Hubbell Power Systems, Inc. (1)
210 N Allen, Centralia, MO 65240
Tel.: (573) 682-5521
Web Site: https://www.hubbell.com
Power Transmission & Distribution Compo-
nent Mfr
N.A.I.C.S.: 335999

Subsidiary (Domestic):

Aclara Technologies LLC (2)
77 W Port Plz Ste 500, Saint Louis, MO
63146-3126
Tel.: (314) 895-6400
Web Site: http://www.aclara.com
Utilities Metering & Data Management Com-
munication Products Mfr
N.A.I.C.S.: 334290
Allan Connolly *(Pres)*
Michael Garcia *(Sr VP-HR & Org Effective-
ness)*
Rick Riccardi *(Sr VP-Major Projects)*
Kumi Premathilake *(Sr VP-Advanced Meter-
ing Infrastructure)*
Greg Bodenhamer *(Sr VP-Global Sls)*
Erik Christian *(Sr VP-Fin, Strategy & IT)*
Jason Subirana *(VP-Intl)*

Subsidiary (Domestic):

Aclara Power-Line Systems Inc. (3)
945 Hornet Dr, Hazelwood, MO 63042
Tel.: (314) 895-6400
Web Site: http://www.aclara.com
Sales Range: $75-99.9 Million
Emp.: 230
Power Line Data Communications Equip-
ment Mfr
N.A.I.C.S.: 334290

Division (Domestic):

Aclara Software (3)
16 Laurel Ave, Wellesley, MA 02481
Tel.: (781) 694-3300
Web Site: http://www.aclara.com
Utilities Information Management Software
Developer & Publisher
N.A.I.C.S.: 513210

Subsidiary (Domestic):

CDR Systems Corporation (2)
146 S Atlantic Ave, Ormond Beach, FL
32176
Tel.: (386) 615-9510
Web Site: http://www.cdrsystems.com
Sales Range: $75-99.9 Million
Polymer, Concrete & Fiberglass Storage
Products Mfr
N.A.I.C.S.: 326199

Subsidiary (Non-US):

Electro Composites (2008) ULC (2)
325 Scott Street, Saint-Jerome, J7Z 1H3,
QC, Canada
Tel.: (450) 431-2777
Electric Equipment Mfr
N.A.I.C.S.: 335999

Branch (Domestic):

**Hubbell Power Systems, Inc. -
Centralia** (2)
210 N Allen St, Centralia, MO 65240
Tel.: (573) 682-5521
Web Site:
   http://www.hubbellpowersystems.com
Emp.: 1,000
Mfr & Distributors of Electrical Transformers
& Products
N.A.I.C.S.: 335931

Plant (Domestic):

**Hubbell Power Systems, Inc. -
Wadsworth** (2)
8711 Wadsworth Rd State, Wadsworth, OH
44281
Tel.: (330) 335-2361
Web Site:
   http://www.hubbellpowersystems.com
Sales Range: $25-49.9 Million
Emp.: 70

Electric Utility Transmission & Distribution
Products
N.A.I.C.S.: 334416

Subsidiary (Domestic):

RFL Electronics, Inc. (2)
353 Powerville Rd, Boonton, NJ 07005
Tel.: (973) 334-3100
Web Site: http://www.rflelect.com
Protection Signaling, Relaying, Meter Cali-
bration & Applications Requiring Rugged
Data Communications Design & Mfr
N.A.I.C.S.: 334515

Hubbell Premise Wiring (1)
23 Clara Dr Ste 103, Mystic, CT 06355-
1959
Tel.: (860) 535-5310
Web Site: http://www.hubbell-premise.com
Sales Range: $10-24.9 Million
Emp.: 25
Mfr of Telecommunications Products
N.A.I.C.S.: 334210

**Hubbell Products Mexico S. de R.L.
de C.V.** (1)
Calle Cinco Sur 104 Col Parque Industrial
Toluca 2000, 50200, Toluca, Mexico
Tel.: (52) 7222654400
Electrical Equipment Distr
N.A.I.C.S.: 423610

Hubbell Wiring Device-Kellems (1)
40 Waterview Dr, Shelton, CT
06484   **(100%)**
Tel.: (475) 882-4800
Web Site: http://www.hubbell-wiring.com
Sales Range: $50-74.9 Million
Emp.: 150
Custom Plastic Molding Services
N.A.I.C.S.: 335132

Hubbell Wiring Systems (1)
40 Waterview Dr, Shelton, CT 06484
Tel.: (203) 882-4800
Web Site: http://www.hubbell-wiring.com
Sales Range: $25-49.9 Million
Emp.: 300
Mfr of Wire Mesh Mechanical Holding De-
vices
N.A.I.C.S.: 335931

Hubbell de Mexico, S.A. de C.V. (1)
Av Insurgentes Sur 1228 Piso 8, Col Tlaco-
quemecatl del Valle, Mexico, 03200, Mexico
Tel.: (52) 5591519999
Web Site: http://www.hubbell.com.mx
Sales Range: $25-49.9 Million
Emp.: 75
Electric Equipment Mfr
N.A.I.C.S.: 335999

Hubbell-Taian Co., Ltd. (1)
7F No 19-8 San-Chong Road Nangang
Dist, Taipei, 11501, Taiwan
Tel.: (886) 226551028
Web Site: http://www.hubbell-taian.com.tw
Electrical Equipment & Component Mfr
N.A.I.C.S.: 335999

**Industria Eletromecanica Balestro
Ltda.** (1)
Av Geraldo Potyguara Silveira Franco 298
Parque da Empresa, Mogi Mirim, Sao
Paulo, 13803-280, Brazil
Tel.: (55) 1938149000
Web Site: https://balestro.com.br
Electronic Component Mfr & Distr
N.A.I.C.S.: 334416

**Jiangsu Xiangyuan Electric Equip-
ment Co., Ltd.** (1)
Chaiwan Industrial Park Rugao Economic
Development Zone, Jiangsu, China
Tel.: (86) 51387195828
Web Site: http://www.xydqgroup.com
Electrical Product Mfr & Distr
N.A.I.C.S.: 335999

KV Holding Co., Inc. (1)
1001 Alaskan Way, Seattle, WA 98104-
1028
Tel.: (206) 587-2500
Web Site: http://www.kiddvalley.com
Emp.: 500
Holding Company
N.A.I.C.S.: 551112
Bob Donegan *(CEO)*

Killark Electric (1)

2112 Fenton Logistics Park Blvd, Fenton,
MO 63026   **(100%)**
Tel.: (314) 531-0460
Web Site: http://www.hubbell-killark.com
Sales Range: $25-49.9 Million
Emp.: 150
Weatherproof & Hazardous Location Prod-
ucts Mfr
N.A.I.C.S.: 335932
John Hastings *(Dir-Intl Bus)*
Brent Birchler *(VP-Sls)*
Dan Dahm *(Dir-Customer Svc)*

Kim Lighting (1)
17760 Rowland St, Rowland Heights, CA
91748
Tel.: (626) 968-5666
Web Site: http://www.kimlighting.com
Sales Range: $75-99.9 Million
Emp.: 250
Mfr of Outdoor Lighting Equipment
N.A.I.C.S.: 335139

Kurt Versen, Inc. (1)
10 Charles St, Westwood, NJ 07675
Tel.: (201) 664-8200
Web Site: http://www.kurtversen.com
High Performance Lighting Product Mfr
N.A.I.C.S.: 335139

**Meramec Instrument Transformer
Company** (1)
1 Andrews Way, Cuba, MO 65453
Tel.: (573) 885-2521
Web Site: https://meramecusa.com
Electrical Products Mfr
N.A.I.C.S.: 335311
Nick Sanazaro *(Pres & CEO)*
Vinod George *(Mgr-Mfg)*
Brad Armstrong *(Mgr-Sls & Mktg)*
Les Norman *(Mgr-Bus Unit)*
Dennis Dreyer *(Mgr-Engrg)*
Brenda Smith *(Mgr-Pur)*
Joe Moreland *(Mgr-Safety)*
Antonio Ceballos *(Engr-Product Dev)*
Serhat Tekin *(Engr-Product Dev)*
John Isaac *(Supvr-Quality)*

Multiwave Sensors Inc. (1)
110 Parr Boulevard Unit 1, Bolton, L7E 4J4,
ON, Canada
Tel.: (905) 857-4481
Web Site:
   https://www.multiwavesensors.com
Antenna Alignment Services
N.A.I.C.S.: 238290

PCORE Electric Company, Inc. (1)
135 Gilbert St, Le Roy, NY 14482
Tel.: (585) 768-1200
Web Site: http://www.hubbell.com
Sales Range: $25-49.9 Million
Emp.: 70
Capacitance Product Mfr
N.A.I.C.S.: 334515

PCX Corp. (1)
33 Pony Farm Rd, Clayton, NC 27520-4811
Tel.: (919) 550-2800
Web Site: http://www.pcxcorp.com
Prefabricated Metal Building & Component
Mfr
N.A.I.C.S.: 332311
Gary Pollock *(VP)*

Prescolite Inc. (1)
701 Millennium Blvd, Greenville, SC 29607
Tel.: (864) 599-6000
Web Site: http://www.prescolite.com
Sales Range: $10-24.9 Million
Emp.: 100
Residential Electric Lighting Fixture Mfr
N.A.I.C.S.: 335131

Progress Lighting Inc. (1)
701 Millennium Blvd, Greenville, SC 29607
Tel.: (864) 678-1000
Web Site: https://www.hubbell.com
Residential & Commercial Lighting Product
Mfr & Distr
N.A.I.C.S.: 335131
Timothy H. Powers *(Pres & CEO)*

**Progressive Lighting, Inc. (North
Carolina)** (1)
215 Huntersville Gateway Blvd, Hunters-
ville, NC 28078
Tel.: (704) 948-1899
Lighting Fixture Mfr
N.A.I.C.S.: 335132

R.W. Lyall & Company Inc. (1)
2665 Research Dr, Corona, CA 92882
Web Site: http://www.rwlyall.com
Plastics Plumbing Fixtures Mfr
N.A.I.C.S.: 326191
Tony Mauer *(CFO)*

Racoo, Inc. (1)
3902 W Sample St, South Bend, IN
46634   **(100%)**
Tel.: (574) 234-7151
Sales Range: $100-124.9 Million
Emp.: 330
Mfr of Fittings, Switches, Outlet Boxes
N.A.I.C.S.: 335932

Reuel, Inc. (1)
200 W Dewey St, Goldsboro, NC 27530
Tel.: (919) 734-0460
Web Site: http://www.reuel.com
Electrical Equipment & Component Mfr
N.A.I.C.S.: 335999

Ripley Europe Limited (1)
Building 47 Second Avenue, The Pensnett
Estate, Kingswinford, DY6 7UZ, West Mid-
lands, United Kingdom
Tel.: (44) 1384400070
Fiber Optic Cable Mfr & Distr
N.A.I.C.S.: 335921

The Wiegmann Company (1)
501 W Apple St, Freeburg, IL 62243
Tel.: (618) 539-3193
Web Site:
   http://www.hubbell-wiegmann.com
Rev.: $12,000,000
Emp.: 250
Mfr Of Electric Junction Boxes
N.A.I.C.S.: 335932

Wiring Device-Kellems (1)
1613 State St PO Box 3999, Bridgeport, CT
06602
Tel.: (203) 337-3333
Web Site: http://www.hubbell-premise.com
Sales Range: $25-49.9 Million
Emp.: 85
Mfr of High Quality Wiring Devices & Acces-
sories
N.A.I.C.S.: 335931

iDevices, LLC (1)
50 Tower Ln, Avon, CT 06001
Tel.: (860) 352-5252
Web Site: http://www.idevicesinc.com
App-Enabled Products Developer
N.A.I.C.S.: 334419
Christopher Allen *(Pres)*
Mike Daigle *(COO)*
Shawn Monteith *(CTO)*
Warren Katz *(CMO)*
Kelley McIntyre *(CFO)*

HUBILU VENTURE CORPORA-
TION
205 S Beverly Dr Ste 205, Beverly
Hills, CA 90212
Tel.: (310) 308-7887   **DE**
Web Site: https://www.hubilu.com
Year Founded: 2015
HBUV—(OTCIQ)
Rev.: $1,579,682
Assets: $17,089,666
Liabilities: $17,982,243
Net Worth: ($892,577)
Earnings: ($114,286)
Fiscal Year-end: 12/31/22
Real Estate Professionals & Investors
Consulting & Advisory Services
N.A.I.C.S.: 531390
David Behrend *(Founder, Chm, Pres,
CEO, CFO, Principal Acctg Officer &
Co-Sec)*
Tracy Black-Van Wier *(Co-Sec & VP-
IR)*

HUBSPOT, INC.
2 Canal Pk, Cambridge, MA 02141
Tel.: (857) 829-5060   **DE**
Web Site: https://www.hubspot.com
Year Founded: 2005
HUBS—(NYSE)
Rev.: $2,170,230,000
Assets: $3,071,392,000

HUBSPOT, INC.

HubSpot, Inc.—(Continued)

Liabilities: $1,751,283,000
Net Worth: $1,320,109,000
Earnings: ($176,295,000)
Emp.: 7,663
Fiscal Year-end: 12/31/23
Marketing Software
N.A.I.C.S.: 513210
Eric Richard (Chief Info Security Officer & Sr VP-Engrg)
Katie Burke (Chief People Officer)
Andrew Lindsay (Sr VP-Dev & Bus Dev)
Kathleen Burke (Chief People Officer)
Rob Giglio (Chief Customer Officer)
Whitney Sorenson (Co-CTO)
Andy Pitre (Exec VP)
Alyssa Harvey Dawson (Chief Legal Officer)
Brian Halligan (Co-Founder)
Dharmesh Shah (Co-Founder & CTO)
Kathryn A. Bueker (CFO)
Yamini Rangan (Pres & CEO)

Subsidiaries:

HubSpot Asia Pte. Ltd.   (1)
60 Anson Road Mapletree Anson 10-03, Singapore, 079914, Singapore
Tel.: (65) 8008523301
Marketing Software Distr
N.A.I.C.S.: 423430
Jeetu Mahtani (Mng Dir-Intl)

HubSpot Australia Pty. Ltd.   (1)
20 Hunter St Level 7, Sydney, 2000, NSW, Australia
Tel.: (61) 13004827768
Software Services
N.A.I.C.S.: 513210
Jonathan Williams (Head-Mktg-Australia & New Zealand)

HubSpot Ireland Limited   (1)
1 Sir John Rogerson's Quay, Dublin, 2, Ireland
Tel.: (353) 15187500
Web Site: http://www.hubspot.com
Sales Range: $10-24.9 Million
Marketing Software Services
N.A.I.C.S.: 513210

HubSpot Japan K.K.   (1)
ShinOtemachi Building 3F 2-2-1 Otemachi, Chiyoda-ku, Tokyo, 100-0004, Japan
Tel.: (81) 368635293
Software Distr
N.A.I.C.S.: 423430

HubSpot Latin America S.A.S.   (1)
Carrera 11 79 35 5th Floor, Bogota, Colombia
Tel.: (57) 6016284810
Broadcast Graphic Hardware & Software Services
N.A.I.C.S.: 513210

PieSync NV   (1)
Notarisstraat 1, 9000, Gent, Belgium
Tel.: (32) 479954190
Information & Technology Services
N.A.I.C.S.: 541519

HUDSON EXECUTIVE CAPITATL LP

570 Lexington Ave 35th Fl, New York, NY 10022
Tel.: (212) 521-8495   DE
Year Founded: 2020
HECCU—(NASDAQ)
Emp.: 2
Investment Services
N.A.I.C.S.: 523999
Jonathan Dobres (CFO)
Douglas L. Braunstein (Chm & Pres)
Douglas G. Bergeron (CEO)

HUDSON GLOBAL, INC

53 Forest Ave 1st Fl, Old Greenwich, CT 06870
Tel.: (475) 988-2068   DE

Web Site:
https://www.hudsonrpo.com
Year Founded: 2003
HSON—(NASDAQ)
Rev.: $200,917,000
Assets: $67,942,000
Liabilities: $22,150,000
Net Worth: $45,792,000
Earnings: $7,129,000
Emp.: 1,440
Fiscal Year-end: 12/31/22
Holding Company; Specialty Staffing & Talent Management Services
N.A.I.C.S.: 551112
Jeffrey E. Eberwein (CEO)
Kimberley Hubble (CEO-APAC)
Darren Lancaster (CEO-EMEA)

Subsidiaries:

Hudson Europe BV   (1)
Emmaplein 8-10, 1075 AW, Amsterdam, Netherlands
Tel.: (31) 204711111
Web Site: http://www.nl.hudson.com
Holding Company; Regional Managing Office
N.A.I.C.S.: 551112

Hudson Global Resources Management, Inc.   (1)
1325 Ave of Americas 12th Fl, New York, NY 10019   (100%)
Tel.: (212) 351-7400
Web Site: http://www.us.hudson.com
Sales Range: $50-74.9 Million
Specialty Staffing & Talent Management Services
N.A.I.C.S.: 561311

HUDSON PACIFIC PROPERTIES, INC.

11601 Wilshire Blvd 9th Fl, Los Angeles, CA 90025
Tel.: (310) 445-5700   MD
Web Site:
https://www.hudsonpacificproperties.com
Year Founded: 2009
HPP—(NYSE)
Rev.: $812,375,000
Assets: $8,282,050,000
Liabilities: $4,787,878,000
Net Worth: $3,494,172,000
Earnings: ($192,181,000)
Emp.: 758
Fiscal Year-end: 12/31/23
Real Estate Investment Services
N.A.I.C.S.: 525990
Mark T. Lammas (Pres)
Dale Shimoda (Exec VP-Fin)
Kay Lee Tidwell (Chief Risk Officer, Gen Counsel & Exec VP)
Drew B. Gordon (Chief Investment Officer)
Harout Diramerian (CFO)
Victor J. Coleman (Chm & CEO)
Arthur X. Suazo (Exec VP-Leasing)
Steven M. Jaffe (Exec VP-Bus Affairs)
Laura Campbell (Exec VP-IR & Mktg)
Andy Wattula (COO)
Laura Murray (Sr Dir-Comm)
Lisa Burelli (Chief HR Officer)
Shawn McGarry (Exec VP)
Jeff Stotland (Exec VP)
Ryan Karchner (Sr VP)
Anne Mehrtens (Sr VP)
Chris Pearson (Sr VP)
Nader Shah (Sr VP)
Jim Soutter (Sr VP)
Erik Thoreen (Sr VP)
Daniel Walbrun (Sr VP)
Wolf Wirth (Sr VP)
Ken Young (Sr VP)
Christopher J. Barton (Exec VP-Dev & Capital Investments)

Subsidiaries:

Hudson 1099 Stewart REIT, LLC   (1)

11601 Wilshire Blvd 9th Fl, Los Angeles, CA 90025
Tel.: (310) 445-5700
Real Estate Property Management Services
N.A.I.C.S.: 531190

Hudson 1455 Market Street, LLC   (1)
1455 Market St, San Francisco, CA 94103-1331
Tel.: (415) 777-4100
Web Site:
http://www.hudsonpacificproperties.com
Property Management Services
N.A.I.C.S.: 531210

Hudson 6922 Hollywood, LLC   (1)
6922 Hollywood Blvd, Los Angeles, CA 90028
Tel.: (323) 443-7950
Web Site:
http://www.hudsonpacificproperties.com
Real Estate Investment Services
N.A.I.C.S.: 525990

Hudson 901 Market, LLC   (1)
11601 Wilshire Blvd, Los Angeles, CA 90025
Tel.: (310) 445-5700
Web Site:
https://www.hudsonpacificproperties.com
Emp.: 180
Nonresidential Building Operators
N.A.I.C.S.: 531120

Hudson Met Park North, LLC   (1)
1220 Howell St, Seattle, WA 98101
Tel.: (206) 467-5002
Web Site:
http://www.hudsonpacificproperties.com
Nonresidential Building Operators
N.A.I.C.S.: 531120

Hudson Pacific Properties, L.P.   (1)
11601 Wilshire Blvd 9th Fl, Los Angeles, CA 90025
Tel.: (310) 445-5700
Web Site:
https://www.hudsonpacificproperties.com
Rev.: $812,374,999
Assets: $8,282,049,999
Liabilities: $4,787,877,999
Net Worth: $3,494,171,999
Earnings: ($173,889,000)
Emp.: 757
Fiscal Year-end: 12/31/2023
Real Estate Asset Management Services
N.A.I.C.S.: 531390
Mark Lammas (Pres)
Lisa Burelli (Chief People Officer)
Harout Diramerian (CFO)
Drew B. Gordon (Chief Investment Officer)
Kay L. Tidwell (Chief Risk Officer)
Andy Wattula (COO)
Christopher Barton (Exec VP)
Laura Campbell (Exec VP)
Gary Hansel (Exec VP)
Steven Jaffe (Exec VP)
Shawn McGar (Exec VP)
Dale Shimoda (Exec VP)
Jeff Stotland (Exec VP)
Arthur X. Suazo (Exec VP)
Chuck We (Exec VP)
Brad Cleveringa (Sr VP)
Derric Dubourdieu (Sr VP)
Ryan Karchner (Sr VP)
Anne Mehrtens (Sr VP)
Chris Pearson (Sr VP)
Nader Shah (Sr VP)
Jim Soutter (Sr VP)
Natalie Teear (Sr VP)
Erik Thoreen (Sr VP)
Daniel Walbrun (Sr VP)
Wolf Wirth (Sr VP)
Ken Young (Sr VP)

Quixote Studios, LLC   (1)
1011 N Fuller Ave, Los Angeles, CA 90046
Tel.: (323) 851-5030
Web Site: http://www.quixote.com
Sales Range: $1-9.9 Million
Emp.: 50
Consumer Goods Rental
N.A.I.C.S.: 532289

Rincon Center Commercial, LLC   (1)
121 Spear St Ste 220, San Francisco, CA 94101
Tel.: (310) 445-5700
Web Site:
http://www.hudsonpacificproperties.com

Emp.: 9
Real Estate Investment Services
N.A.I.C.S.: 525990

HUDSON TECHNOLOGIES, INC.

300 Tice Blvd Ste 290 2nd Fl, Woodcliff Lake, NJ 07677
Tel.: (845) 735-6000   NY
Web Site:
https://www.hudsontech.com
Year Founded: 1991
HDSN—(NASDAQ)
Rev.: $325,225,000
Assets: $272,493,000
Liabilities: $97,618,000
Net Worth: $174,875,000
Earnings: $103,801,000
Emp.: 232
Fiscal Year-end: 12/31/22
Commercial & Industrial Machinery & Equipment (except Automotive & Electronic) Repair & Maintenance
N.A.I.C.S.: 811310
Kenneth Gaglione (VP-Ops)
Stephen P. Mandracchia (Founder)
Kathleen L. Houghton (Sr VP-Mktg & Sls)
Brian F. Coleman (Chm, Pres & CEO)

Subsidiaries:

ASPEN Refrigerants, Inc.   (1)
38-18 33rd St, Long Island City, NY 11101
Tel.: (718) 392-8002
Web Site: http://www.aspenrefrigerants.com
Refrigerants Gases Distr & Reclaimer
N.A.I.C.S.: 423730
Mary John Coats (Acct Mgr)

ASPEN Refrigerants, Inc.   (1)
38 18 33rd St, Long Island City, NY 11101
Tel.: (718) 392-8002
Web Site: http://www.aspenrefrigerants.com
Refrigeration Equipment & Supplies Merchant Whslr
N.A.I.C.S.: 423740

HUGOTON ROYALTY TRUST

3838 Oak Lawn Ave Ste 1720, Dallas, TX 75219   TX
Web Site: https://hgt-hugoton.com
Year Founded: 1998
HGTXU—(OTCQB)
Rev.: $19,561,208
Assets: $2,034,300
Liabilities: $2,834,360
Earnings: $16,585,039
Fiscal Year-end: 12/31/22
Trust, Fiduciary & Custody Activities
N.A.I.C.S.: 523991

HUMACYTE, INC.

2525 NC-54, Durham, NC 27713
Tel.: (919) 313-9633   DE
Web Site: https://www.humacyte.com
Year Founded: 2020
HUMA—(NASDAQ)
Rev.: $1,565,000
Assets: $204,302,000
Liabilities: $87,374,000
Net Worth: $116,928,000
Earnings: ($11,965,000)
Emp.: 164
Fiscal Year-end: 12/31/22
Investment Services
N.A.I.C.S.: 523999
Kathleen Sebelius (Chm)
Laura E. Niklason (Co-Founder, Pres & CEO)
Dale A. Sander (CFO, Chief Corp Dev Officer & Treas)
Heather Prichard (COO)
Shamik Parikh (Chief Medical Officer)
William Scheessele (Chief Comml Officer)
Cindy Cao (Chief Regulatory Officer)

Sabrina Osborne *(Chief People Officer)*
Harold Alterson *(Chief Quality Officer)*
Juliana L. Blum *(Co-Founder)*

Subsidiaries:

Humacyte Global, Inc. (1)
2525 NC Hwy 54, Durham, NC 27713
Tel.: (919) 313-9633
Web Site: http://www.humacyte.com
Chemicals Mfr
N.A.I.C.S.: 325412
Chris Fang *(Chief Medical Officer)*

HUMAN UNITEC INTERNATIONAL INC.
551 Warren St Ste 304, Hudson, NY 12534
Tel.: (438) 364-2277   NV
Year Founded: 2002
HMNU—(OTCIQ)
Business Services
N.A.I.C.S.: 541611
Kurt M. Gaensel *(Pres & Sec)*
Fabio De Stefano *(CFO & VP)*

HUMANA, INC.
500 W Main St, Louisville, KY 40202
Tel.: (502) 580-1000   DE
Web Site: https://www.humana.com
Year Founded: 1961
HUM—(NYSE)
Rev.: $106,374,000,000
Assets: $47,065,000,000
Liabilities: $30,747,000,000
Net Worth: $16,318,000,000
Earnings: $2,489,000,000
Emp.: 67,600
Fiscal Year-end: 12/31/23
Health Insurance Coverage & Related Services
N.A.I.C.S.: 525190
Elizabeth D. Bierbower *(Executives)*
Timothy S. Huval *(Chief Admin Officer & Chief HR Officer)*
Sam M. Deshpande *(Chief Tech & Risk Officer)*
Vishal Agrawal *(Chief Strategy & Corp Dev Officer)*
Joseph C. Ventura *(Chief Legal Officer)*
Susan M. Diamond *(CFO)*
William H. Shrank *(Chief Medical & Corp Affairs Officer)*
Carolyn Tandy *(Chief Inclusion & Diversity Officer & Sr VP)*
John-Paul W. Felter *(Chief Acctg Officer, Sr VP & Controller)*
Sanjay Shetty *(Pres-CenterWell)*
George Renaudin *(Pres-Medicare & Medicaid)*
Samir M. Deshpande *(CIO)*
Andrew C. Agwunobi *(Pres-Home Solutions)*
Susan D. Schick *(Pres-Grp Military & Specialty Bus)*
James A. Rechtin *(Pres & CEO)*

Subsidiaries:

154th Street Medical Plaza, Inc. (1)
5801 Miami Lakes Dr E, Miami Lakes, FL 33014
Tel.: (305) 821-9115
Emp.: 6
Ambulatory Health Care Services
N.A.I.C.S.: 621999

54th Street Medical Plaza, Inc. (1)
5385 Ne 2Nd Ave, Miami, FL 33137
Tel.: (305) 756-9977
Emp.: 25
Ambulatory Health Care Services
N.A.I.C.S.: 621999

Agile Technology Solutions, Inc. (1)
46090 Lk Ctr Plz Ste 100, Potomac Falls, VA 20165
Tel.: (703) 856-2415
Web Site: http://www.agile-inc.com

Health Insurance Services
N.A.I.C.S.: 524114

Ambulatory Care Solutions of Ohio LLC (1)
103 Plz Dr, Saint Clairsville, OH 43950
Tel.: (740) 695-9321
Ambulatory Health Care Services
N.A.I.C.S.: 621999

American Eldercare, Inc. (1)
14565 Sims Rd, Delray Beach, FL 33484
Tel.: (561) 499-9656
Web Site:
   http://providerportal.americanelder
   care.com
Sales Range: $75-99.9 Million
Health Maintenance Organization Services
N.A.I.C.S.: 621491

Asian American Home Care, Inc. (1)
1301 Marina Vlg Pkwy Ste 103, Alameda, CA 94501
Tel.: (510) 835-3268
Women Healthcare Services
N.A.I.C.S.: 621610
Nancy Liu *(Dir-Sls)*

Availity, L.L.C. (1)
5555 Gate Pkwy Ste 110, Jacksonville, FL 32256
Web Site: https://www.availity.com
Health Insurance Services
N.A.I.C.S.: 524114

Availity, LLC (1)
5555 Gate Pkwy Ste 110, Jacksonville, FL 32256
Tel.: (904) 470-4900
Web Site: https://www.availity.com
Sales Range: $10-24.9 Million
Emp.: 32
Health Information Services
N.A.I.C.S.: 519290
Russ Thomas *(CEO)*
Julie D. Klapstein *(Founder)*
Nathan von Colditz *(Chief Strategy Officer)*
Frank Petito *(CFO)*
Frank Manzella *(Sr VP)*
Bobbi Coluni *(Chief Product Officer)*
Leslie Antunes *(Chief Growth Officer)*
Jim McNary *(COO)*

Avalon Hospice Iowa, LLC (1)
4601 Westown Pkwy Ste 105, West Des Moines, IA 50266
Tel.: (515) 218-9600
Personal Home Care Services
N.A.I.C.S.: 621610

Avalon Hospice Minnesota, LLC (1)
1821 University Ave W Ste 252, Saint Paul, MN 55101
Tel.: (612) 361-0022
Personal Home Care Services
N.A.I.C.S.: 621610

Avalon Hospice Missouri, LLC (1)
2024 S Maiden Ln Ste 202, Joplin, MO 64804
Tel.: (417) 782-6811
Personal Home Care Services
N.A.I.C.S.: 621610

Avalon Hospice Ohio, LLC (1)
4010 Executive Park Dr Ste 225, Cincinnati, OH 45241
Tel.: (513) 904-6189
Personal Home Care Services
N.A.I.C.S.: 621610

B-Cycle, LLC (1)
1140 NE 7th Ave Unit 4, Fort Lauderdale, FL 33304
Tel.: (754) 200-5672
Web Site: http://www.broward.bcycle.com
Bicycle Rental Services
N.A.I.C.S.: 532284

CAC Medical Center Holdings, Inc. (1)
641 NW 183rd St, Miami, FL 33169
Tel.: (305) 654-9009
Web Site: http://www.caccares.com
Emp.: 30
Health Maintenance Organization Services
N.A.I.C.S.: 621491
Bruce Broussard *(Pres)*

CAC-Florida Medical Centers, LLC (1)

8350 NW 52nd Ter Ste 301, Miami, FL 33166
Tel.: (305) 463-6600
Web Site:
   http://www.cacmedicalcenters.com
Emp.: 100
Health Maintenance Organization Medical Services
N.A.I.C.S.: 621491

CarePlus Health Plans, Inc. (1)
PO Box 277810, Miramar, FL 33027
Web Site:
   https://www.careplushealthplans.com
Emp.: 1,100
Health Insurance Services
N.A.I.C.S.: 524114

CenterWell Senior Primary Care (FL), Inc. (1)
360 Douglas Ave, Altamonte Springs, FL 32714
Tel.: (407) 848-3952
Web Site:
   https://www.centerwellprimarycare.com
Health Insurance Services
N.A.I.C.S.: 524114

Certify Data Systems, Inc. (1)
910 E Hamilton Ave Ste 500, Campbell, CA 95008
Tel.: (408) 426-3150
Web Site:
   http://www.certifydatasystems.com
Custom Computer Programming Services
N.A.I.C.S.: 541511

Community Home Care of Vance County, LLC (1)
946 W Andrews Ave Ste S, Henderson, NC 27536
Tel.: (252) 430-7760
Personal Home Care Services
N.A.I.C.S.: 621610

CompBenefits Corp. (1)
100 Mansell Ct E Ste 400, Roswell, GA 30076
Tel.: (770) 552-7101
Web Site: http://www.mycompbenefits.com
Sales Range: $50-74.9 Million
Emp.: 685
Health Care Insurance Services
N.A.I.C.S.: 524114

Continucare MDHC, LLC (1)
7200 Corporate Ctr Dr Ste 600, Miami, FL 33126
Tel.: (305) 500-2000
Health Maintenance Organization Services
N.A.I.C.S.: 621491

Conviva Care Solutions, LLC (1)
6101 Blue Lagoon Dr Ste 400, Miami, FL 33126
Tel.: (305) 662-5200
Web Site:
   https://www.convivacaresolutions.com
Health Insurance Services
N.A.I.C.S.: 524114

Conviva Physician Group, LLC (1)
6101 Blue Lagoon Dr Ste 400, Miami, FL 33126
Tel.: (305) 662-5200
Web Site:
   https://www.convivaphysicians.com
Health Insurance Services
N.A.I.C.S.: 524114

DefenseWeb Technologies, Inc. (1)
10188 Telesis Ct Ste 300, San Diego, CA 92121
Tel.: (858) 272-8505
Web Site: http://www.defenseweb.com
Sales Range: $25-49.9 Million
Emp.: 90
Software Designing Services
N.A.I.C.S.: 513210

Enclara Pharmacia, Inc. (1)
1601 Cherry St Ste 1800, Philadelphia, PA 19102
Web Site:
   https://www.enclarapharmacia.com
Healtcare Services
N.A.I.C.S.: 524114
Mark Morse *(CEO)*
Deanna R. Douglass *(Sr VP-Bus Dev)*
Megha Kadiyala *(Sr VP)*

Kerry Lord *(Sr VP)*
Ellen Schneider *(Sr VP)*
Anthony Dameika *(VP)*
Ryan Krout *(VP)*
Patrick Leary *(VP)*

Enhanz DCE, LLC (1)
1700 79th St Cswy Ste 120, North Bay Village, FL 33141
Web Site: https://www.enhanzdce.com
Medicare & Medicaid Services
N.A.I.C.S.: 524114
Steven Schnur *(CEO)*
Perry Krichmar *(COO & Chief Compliance Officer)*
Jose Rios *(Chief Medical Officer)*
Fernando Valverde *(Chief Strategy Officer)*
Andres Valverde *(Dir-Operations)*

Family Physicians Group, Inc. (1)
6350 W Colonial Dr, Orlando, FL 32818
Tel.: (407) 447-4264
Web Site: http://www.fpg-florida.com
Health Care Srvices
N.A.I.C.S.: 621111
Nayana Vyas *(Founder & Dir-Medical)*

Family Physicians of Winter Park, Inc. (1)
5745 Canton Cove Ste 121, Winter Park, FL 32708
Tel.: (407) 647-2550
Web Site: https://www.winterparkfamilyphysi
   cians.com
Health Care Srvices
N.A.I.C.S.: 621498

Healthfield Home Health, LLC (1)
410 Peachtree Pkwy Ste 4245, Cumming, GA 30041
Tel.: (833) 453-1107
Health Care Services
N.A.I.C.S.: 621610

HomeCare Health Solutions, Inc. (1)
630 N Wymore Rd Ste 370, Maitland, FL 32751
Tel.: (407) 339-6500
Emp.: 25
Women Healthcare Services
N.A.I.C.S.: 621610

Hospice of Mesilla Valley, LLC (1)
299 Montana Ave, Las Cruces, NM 88005
Tel.: (575) 523-4700
Web Site: https://www.mvhospice.org
Personal Home Care Services
N.A.I.C.S.: 621610

Humana At Home (Dallas), Inc. (1)
100 N Central Expy Ste 600/600 B, Richardson, TX 75080-5332
Tel.: (972) 422-1375
Women Healthcare Services
N.A.I.C.S.: 621610

Humana At Home (Houston), Inc. (1)
8303 Southwest Fwy Ste 280, Houston, TX 77074-1600
Tel.: (713) 523-2329
Women Healthcare Services
N.A.I.C.S.: 621610

Humana Behavioral Health, Inc. (1)
2101 W John Carpenter Freeway, Irving, TX 75063
Tel.: (800) 207-5101
Web Site:
   http://www.humanabehavioralhealth.com
Health Maintenance Organization Services
N.A.I.C.S.: 621491
Brian P. LeClaire *(CIO)*
Alan J. Bailey *(Treas & VP)*
William Mark Preston *(VP-Investments)*
Donald Hank Robinson *(Sr VP-Tax)*
Ralph M. Wilson *(VP)*
Vanessa M. Olson *(Chief Actuary & Sr VP)*
Douglas A. Edwards *(VP)*
Sean J. O'Reilly *(Chief Compliance Officer & VP)*
Susan L. Mateja *(Actuary)*

Humana Employers Health Plan of Georgia, Inc. (1)
1200 Ashwood Pkwy ste 350, Atlanta, GA 30338   **(100%)**
Tel.: (770) 508-2388
Web Site: http://www.humana.com
Health Maintenance Organization

Humana, Inc.—(Continued)

N.A.I.C.S.: 524114

Humana Government Business, Inc. (1)
500 W Main St Fl 19, Louisville, KY 40202
Tel.: (502) 580-6474
Health & Well Being Program Services
N.A.I.C.S.: 923120
Tim McClain *(Pres)*
Brent Densford *(VP-Bus Dev)*
Dave Lewis *(CFO & VP)*
Sandra Delgado *(Chief Medical Officer)*

Humana Health Benefit Plan of Louisiana, Inc. (1)
1 Galleria Blvd Ste 850, Metairie, LA 70001   (100%)
Tel.: (504) 219-6600
Web Site: http://www.humana.com
Sales Range: $150-199.9 Million
Health Care Insurance Services
N.A.I.C.S.: 524114

Humana Health Insurance Company of Florida, Inc. (1)
76 S Laura St, Jacksonville, FL 32202
Tel.: (904) 376-1000
Web Site: http://www.humana.com
Sales Range: $150-199.9 Million
Health Care Insurance Services
N.A.I.C.S.: 524114

Humana Health Plan of Ohio, Inc. (1)
640 Eden Park Dr, Cincinnati, OH 45202   (100%)
Tel.: (513) 784-5200
Web Site: http://www.humanahealth.com
Sales Range: $500-549.9 Million
Emp.: 800
Health Care Insurance Services
N.A.I.C.S.: 524114

Humana Health Plan of Texas, Inc. (1)
8431 Fredericksburg Rd Ste 570, San Antonio, TX 78229
Tel.: (210) 617-1000
Web Site: http://www.humana.com
Sales Range: $200-249.9 Million
Emp.: 175
Health Care Insurance Services
N.A.I.C.S.: 524114

Humana Health Plan, Inc. (1)
500 W Main St, Louisville, KY 40202   (100%)
Tel.: (800) 486-2620
Web Site: http://www.humana.com
Sales Range: $5-14.9 Billion
Emp.: 20,000
Health Care Insurance Services
N.A.I.C.S.: 524114

Humana Health Plans of Puerto Rico, Inc. (1)
383 Ave FD Roosevelt, San Juan, PR 00918-2131
Tel.: (787) 282-7900
Web Site: https://www.humana.pr
Hospital & Medical Health Plans
N.A.I.C.S.: 524114

Humana Insurance of Puerto Rico, Inc. (1)
383 Ave FD Roosevelt, San Juan, PR 00918
Tel.: (787) 282-7900
Web Site: https://www.humana.pr
Women Healthcare Services
N.A.I.C.S.: 621610

Humana Medical Plan, Inc. (1)
3501 SW 160th Ave, Miramar, FL 33027-4695   (100%)
Tel.: (305) 621-4222
Web Site: http://www.humana.com
Sales Range: $50-74.9 Million
Emp.: 100
Health Care Insurance Services
N.A.I.C.S.: 524114

Humana Ventures (1)
500 W Main St, Louisville, KY 40202
Tel.: (502) 580-3906
Web Site: http://www.humana.com
Sales Range: $150-199.9 Million
Emp.: 100
Investment Services

N.A.I.C.S.: 523999
Busy Burr *(Founder-Health)*

Humana Wisconsin Health Organization Insurance Corporation (1)
N19 W24133 Riverwood Dr Ste 300, Waukesha, WI 53188   (100%)
Tel.: (262) 951-2300
Sales Range: $100-124.9 Million
Emp.: 200
Health Maintenance Organization
N.A.I.C.S.: 524114

Humana at Home, Inc. (1)
845 3rd Ave, New York, NY 10022
Tel.: (212) 994-6100
Web Site: http://www.seniorbridge.com
Health Care Insurance Services
N.A.I.C.S.: 524114

Humco, Inc. (1)
201 W 5th St Fl 12, Austin, TX 78701
Tel.: (410) 485-4000
Web Site: https://www.humco.com
Vehicle Insurance Services
N.A.I.C.S.: 524126

Hummingbird Coaching Systems LLC (1)
640 Eden Park Dr, Cincinnati, OH 45202
Tel.: (513) 287-6529
Web Site:
    http://www.hummingbirdcoaching.com
Emp.: 36
Ambulatory Health Care Services
N.A.I.C.S.: 621999

Independent Care Health Plan, Inc. (1)
1555 River Ctr Dr Ste 206, Milwaukee, WI 53212
Tel.: (414) 223-4847
Web Site: https://www.icarehealthplan.org
Sales Range: $75-99.9 Million
Emp.: 150
Health Care Insurance Services
N.A.I.C.S.: 524114
Bill Jensen *(VP-Sls & Mktg)*
Tom Lutzow *(Pres & CEO)*
Lisa Holden *(VP-Accountable Care)*
Mary Ellen Benzik *(Chief Medical Officer)*
Margaret Kristan *(VP-Long Term Care & Community Inclusion)*

Iowa Hospice, L.L.C. (1)
1526 Sycamore St, Iowa City, IA 52240
Tel.: (319) 351-5665
Web Site: https://www.iowacityhospice.org
Personal Home Care Services
N.A.I.C.S.: 621610
Karla Kamal *(CEO & Chm)*
Sara Krieger *(COO)*
Kara Thoma *(Mgr-Social Svcs)*
Martha Lubaroff *(Founder)*

Kindred Hospice Missouri, LLC (1)
12125 Woodcrest Executive Dr Ste 220, Saint Louis, MO 63141
Tel.: (314) 275-6100
Personal Home Care Services
N.A.I.C.S.: 621610

Metcare of Florida, Inc. (1)
2900 N Military Trail Ste 200, Boca Raton, FL 33431
Tel.: (561) 823-2932
Web Site: http://www.metcare.com
Health Maintenance Organization Medical Services
N.A.I.C.S.: 621491
Bruce Devereau Perkins *(Pres)*

Metropolitan Health Networks, Inc. (1)
777 Yamato Rd Ste 510, Boca Raton, FL 33431
Tel.: (561) 805-8500
Web Site: http://www.metcare.com
Sales Range: $450-499.9 Million
Emp.: 1,140
Health Care Insurance Services
N.A.I.C.S.: 524114

Subsidiary (Domestic):

Continucare Corporation (2)
7200 Corporate Ctr Dr Ste 600, Miami, FL 33126
Tel.: (305) 500-2000
Web Site: http://www.continucare.com

Sales Range: $300-349.9 Million
Emp.: 870
Health Care Insurance Services
N.A.I.C.S.: 524114
Gemma Rosello *(Pres)*

Subsidiary (Domestic):

Continucare MSO, Inc. (3)
2627 NE 203rd St, Miami, FL 33180
Tel.: (305) 937-4833
Sales Range: $50-74.9 Million
Provider of Mental & Physical Rehabilitation Management Services
N.A.I.C.S.: 621610

One Homecare Solutions, LLC (1)
3351 Executive Way, Miramar, FL 33025
Tel.: (954) 628-5360
Web Site: https://www.onehome.health
Personal Home Care Services
N.A.I.C.S.: 621610
Kirk Allen *(CEO)*
J. Matthew Stimac *(Sr VP-)*
Norman McGee *(Sr VP-)*

Partners in Integrated Care, Inc. (1)
301 NW 84th Ave Ste 301, Plantation, FL 33324-1807
Tel.: (305) 500-2000
Web Site:
    http://www.partnersinintegratedcare.com
Health Care Insurance Services
N.A.I.C.S.: 524114

SeniorBridge (NC), Inc. (1)
200 Queens Rd Ste 101, Charlotte, NC 28204
Tel.: (704) 377-2273
Web Site: http://www.seniorbridge.com
Emp.: 10
Health Maintenance Organization Services
N.A.I.C.S.: 621491

SeniorBridge Care Management, Inc. (1)
845 3rd Ave, New York, NY 10022
Tel.: (212) 994-6100
Women Healthcare Services
N.A.I.C.S.: 621610

SeniorBridge Family Companies (FL), Inc. (1)
2570 W International Speedway Blvd, Daytona Beach, FL 32114
Tel.: (386) 310-4360
Health Maintenance Organization Services
N.A.I.C.S.: 621491

SeniorBridge Family Companies (IL), Inc. (1)
550 W Adams St 6th Fl, Chicago, IL 60661
Tel.: (312) 329-9060
Ambulatory Health Care Services
N.A.I.C.S.: 621999
Sherry Kostman *(Gen Mgr)*

SeniorBridge Family Companies (MD), Inc. (1)
1829 Reisterstown Rd 435, Baltimore, MD 21208
Tel.: (410) 580-0400
Health Maintenance Organization Services
N.A.I.C.S.: 621491

SeniorBridge Family Companies (NY), Inc. (1)
845 3rd Ave Fl 7, New York, NY 10022
Tel.: (212) 994-6100
Web Site: http://www.seniorbridge.com
Emp.: 200
Women Healthcare Services
N.A.I.C.S.: 621610

SeniorBridge Family Companies (PA), Inc. (1)
400 Penn Center Blvd Ste 630, Pittsburgh, PA 15235
Tel.: (412) 317-6985
Web Site: http://www.seniorbridge.com
Emp.: 50
Ambulatory Health Care Services
N.A.I.C.S.: 621999

SeniorBridge Family Companies, Inc. (1)
845 3rd Ave, New York, NY 10022
Tel.: (212) 994-6100
Web Site: http://www.seniorbridge.com

Sales Range: $50-74.9 Million
Emp.: 30
Home Geriatric Care
N.A.I.C.S.: 621610

SeniorBridge-Florida, LLC (1)
8751 W Broward Blvd Ste 200, Fort Lauderdale, FL 33324-2630
Tel.: (954) 423-2217
Web Site: http://locations.seniorbridge.com
Women Healthcare Services
N.A.I.C.S.: 621610

Sensei, Inc. (1)
2300 Glades Rd Ste 220 W, Boca Raton, FL 33431
Tel.: (561) 208-4480
Web Site: http://www.sensei.com
Mobile Telephone Services
N.A.I.C.S.: 517112
Sean McDevitt *(Chm & CEO)*

TLC Plus of Texas, Inc. (1)
2201 Main St Ste 300, Dallas, TX 75201
Tel.: (214) 350-1213
Emp.: 150
Women Healthcare Services
N.A.I.C.S.: 621610

Transcend Insights, Inc. (1)
910 E Hamilton Ave Ste 500, Campbell, CA 95008
Tel.: (408) 426-3150
Web Site: http://www.transcendinsights.com
Healthcare Software Development Services
N.A.I.C.S.: 541511
Marc Willard *(Pres)*

Trueshore S.R.I. (1)
Av Los Proceres 50 Unicorp Bldg, Arroyo Hondo Los Pinos, Santo Domingo, Dominican Republic
Tel.: (809) 3059022338
Web Site: https://www.trueshore.com
Health Insurance Services
N.A.I.C.S.: 524114

Valor Healthcare, Inc. (1)
14643 Dallas Pkwy Ste 100, Dallas, TX 75254
Web Site: https://valorhealthcare.com
Health Insurance Services
N.A.I.C.S.: 524114

HUMANCO ACQUISITION CORP.
PO Box 90608, Austin, TX 78709
Tel.: (512) 535-0440   DE
Year Founded 2020
HMCOU—(NASDAQ)
Rev.: $13,884,218
Assets: $313,137,998
Liabilities: $316,335,315
Net Worth: ($3,197,317)
Earnings: $11,717,478
Emp.: 99
Fiscal Year-end: 12/31/21
Investment Services
N.A.I.C.S.: 523999
Jason H. Karp *(Co-Chm)*
Ross Berman *(CEO)*
Brett Thomas *(Pres)*
Amy Zipper *(COO)*
Rohan Oza *(Co-Chm)*

HUMANIGEN, INC.
830 Morris Tpke 4th Fl, Short Hills, NJ 07078
Tel.: (973) 200-3100   DE
Web Site:
    https://www.humanigen.com
HGEN—(NASDAQ)
Rev.: $2,514,000
Assets: $11,195,000
Liabilities: $57,960,000
Net Worth: ($46,765,000)
Earnings: ($70,730,000)
Emp.: 6
Fiscal Year-end: 12/31/22
Biopharmaceutical Product Research & Development
N.A.I.C.S.: 325412

Cameron Durrant *(Chm & CEO)*
Omar Ahmed *(Sr VP-Clinical, Medical & Scientific Affairs)*
Ken Trbovich *(Sr VP-IR)*

HUMBL, INC.
600 B St Ste 300, San Diego, CA 92101
Tel.: (786) 738-9012   DE
Web Site: https://www.humbl.com
Year Founded: 2009
HMBL—(OTCIQ)
Rev.: $2,768,534
Assets: $3,825,997
Liabilities: $39,115,565
Net Worth: ($35,289,568)
Earnings: ($48,567,938)
Emp.: 16
Fiscal Year-end: 12/31/22
Floor & Wall Covering Materials Distr & Installer
N.A.I.C.S.: 238330

HUMBLE ENERGY, INC.
447 Broadway 2nd Fl Unit 103, New York, NY 10013
Tel.: (501) 821-5509   NV
Web Site: https://humlinc.com
Year Founded: 2008
HUML—(OTCIQ)
Oil & Gas Exploration Services
N.A.I.C.S.: 213112

HUNTER CREEK MINING CO.
PO Box 487, Portland, OR 97207-0487
Tel.: (503) 281-8699   ID
Year Founded: 1945
HTRC—(OTCIQ)
Metal Mining & Exploration Services
N.A.I.C.S.: 213114
Burton A. Onstine *(Pres)*
Jack Rititus *(Co-Sec)*
John Henley *(Co-Sec)*

HUNTINGTON BANCSHARES INCORPORATED
Huntington Ctr 41 S High St, Columbus, OH 43287
Tel.: (614) 480-2265   MD
Web Site: https://ir.huntington.com
Year Founded: 1966
HBAN—(NASDAQ)
Rev.: $10,837,000,000
Assets: $189,368,000,000
Liabilities: $169,970,000,000
Net Worth: $19,398,000,000
Earnings: $1,971,000,000
Emp.: 19,955
Fiscal Year-end: 12/31/23
Commercial Banking Services
N.A.I.C.S.: 551111
Stephen D. Steinour *(Chm, Pres & CEO)*
Helga S. Houston *(Chief Risk Officer & Sr Exec VP)*
Zachary J. Wasserman *(CFO & Sr Exec VP)*
Michael Van Treese *(Exec VP)*
Amit Dhingra *(Chief Enterprise Payments Officer)*
Marcy Hingst *(Gen Counsel & Sr Exec VP)*
Kendall Kowalski *(CIO & Exec VP)*
Brendan A. Lawlor *(Chief Credit Officer & Exec VP)*
Tim Miller *(Chief Comm Officer & Exec VP)*
Prashant Nateri *(Chief Corp Ops Officer & Exec VP)*
Sarah Pohmer *(Chief HR Officer & Sr Exec VP)*
Donnell White *(Inclusion Officer, Sr VP & Chief Diversity, Equity)*
Brant J. Standridge *(Pres, Pres-Consumer & Reg Banking & Sr Exec VP)*

Subsidiaries:

Capstone Partners LLC   (1)
176 Federal St, Boston, MA 02110
Tel.: (617) 619-3300
Investment Banking Services
N.A.I.C.S.: 523940
Leonard A. Potter *(Founder)*
John Ferrara *(Founder & CEO)*
Shannon Cullen *(Head-Admin & HR)*
Steve Standbridge *(Mng Dir)*
Jim Calandra *(Mng Dir)*
Mark Casper *(CFO)*
Doug Usifer *(Mng Dir)*

Subsidiary (Domestic):

Capstone Headwaters LLC   (2)
176 Federal St 3rd Fl, Boston, MA 02110
Tel.: (617) 619-3300
Web Site:
    https://www.capstonepartners.com
Investment Services
N.A.I.C.S.: 523999

Subsidiary (Domestic):

Headwaters MB LLC   (3)
1225 17th St Ste 1725, Denver, CO 80202
Tel.: (303) 572-6000
Investment Banking & Securities Dealing
N.A.I.C.S.: 523150

Creditron Canada, Inc.   (1)
2265 Upper Middle Road East Suite 601, Oakville, L6H0G5, ON, Canada
Tel.: (888) 721-9510
Web Site: http://www.creditron.com
Sales Range: $25-49.9 Million
Emp.: 20
Payment Processing Software Provider
N.A.I.C.S.: 522320

HBI Title Services, Inc.   (1)
37 S High St, Canal Winchester, OH 43110-1212
Tel.: (614) 480-0073
Sales Range: $25-49.9 Million
Emp.: 20
Insurance Agency & Brokerage Services
N.A.I.C.S.: 524210
Pam Moore *(Mgr)*

HPCKAL, LLC   (1)
3993 Howard Hughes Pkwy, Las Vegas, NV 89169-0961
Tel.: (702) 734-2233
Commercial Banking Services
N.A.I.C.S.: 522110

Haberer Registered Investment Advisor, Inc.   (1)
201 E 5th St Ste 1100, Cincinnati, OH 45202
Tel.: (513) 381-8200
Web Site: http://www.haberer.com
Emp.: 13
Bank Holding Company
N.A.I.C.S.: 551111
Adonis Saneris *(Dir-Compliance)*

Huntington Distribution Finance, Inc.   (1)
1475 E Woodfield Rd Ste 1000, Schaumburg, IL 60173
Web Site: https://www.huntingtondf.com
Financial Services
N.A.I.C.S.: 523999

Huntington Municipal Securities, Inc.   (1)
3993 Howard Hughes Pkwy, Las Vegas, NV 89169
Tel.: (702) 734-6633
Emp.: 2
Trust Management Services
N.A.I.C.S.: 523991

Huntington Public Capital Corporation   (1)
3993 Howard Hughes Pkwy Ste 250, Las Vegas, NV 89169
Tel.: (702) 836-3436
Commercial Banking Services
N.A.I.C.S.: 522110
Jeffry D. Elliott *(Mng Dir)*

Huntington Technology Finance, Inc.   (1)

2285 Franklin Rd, Bloomfield Hills, MI 48302
Tel.: (248) 253-9000
Web Site: https://www.huntington.com
Emp.: 180
Commercial Banking Services
N.A.I.C.S.: 522110

TCF Commercial Finance Canada, Inc.   (1)
700 Dorval Dr Ste 705, Oakville, L6K 3V3, ON, Canada
Tel.: (905) 844-4430
Sales Range: $25-49.9 Million
Emp.: 25
Mortgage & Nonmortgage Loan Broker
N.A.I.C.S.: 522310

TCF Foundation   (1)
Mail Code EX0-01-C 200 Lake St E, Wayzata, MN 55391
Tel.: (952) 745-2757
Web Site: http://www.tcfbank.com
Charitable Grantmaking Organization
N.A.I.C.S.: 813211

The Huntington National Bank   (1)
41 S High St, Columbus, OH 43215   **(100%)**
Tel.: (614) 480-3278
Web Site: http://www.huntington.com
Sales Range: $1-4.9 Billion
Commercial Banking Services
N.A.I.C.S.: 522110
Gary H. Torgow. *(Chm)*

Subsidiary (Domestic):

Cumberland Trail Golf Course, LLC   (2)
8244 Columbia Rd SW, Pataskala, OH 43062
Tel.: (740) 964-9336
Web Site: http://www.cumberlandtgc.com
Golf Course & Club Management Services
N.A.I.C.S.: 713910

FMRC, Inc.   (2)
300 Delaware Ave, Wilmington, DE 19801
Tel.: (302) 421-7361
Financial Investment Services
N.A.I.C.S.: 523999

FirstMerit Equipment Finance, Inc.   (2)
106 S Main St, Akron, OH 44308
Tel.: (330) 996-8013
Emp.: 8
Mortgage & Nonmortgage Loan Brokers
N.A.I.C.S.: 522310
Tim Evans *(Gen Mgr)*

FirstMerit Mortgage Corporation   (2)
4455 Hills & Dales Rd NW, Canton, OH 44708   **(100%)**
Tel.: (330) 478-3400
Rev.: $6,294,000
Emp.: 85
Banking & Mortgage
N.A.I.C.S.: 522110

Huntington Insurance, Inc.   (2)
519 Madison Ave, Toledo, OH 43604   **(100%)**
Tel.: (419) 720-7900
Web Site: http://www.huntington.com
Commercial Banking Services
N.A.I.C.S.: 522110

Huntington Preferred Capital, Inc.   (2)
41 S High St, Columbus, OH 43287
Tel.: (614) 480-5676
Web Site: http://www.huntington-ir.com
Rev.: $137,706,000
Assets: $3,983,385,000
Liabilities: $564,869,000
Net Worth: $3,418,516,000
Earnings: $153,783,000
Fiscal Year-end: 12/31/2012
Real Estate Investment Trust
N.A.I.C.S.: 523999

The Huntington Investment Company   (2)
41 S High St, Columbus, OH 43215-0001   **(100%)**
Tel.: (614) 480-3600
Web Site: http://www.huntington.com

Sales Range: $1-4.9 Billion
Emp.: 1,000
Investment Banking
N.A.I.C.S.: 523150

The Huntington Mortgage Group   (2)
7 Easton Oval, Columbus, OH 43219   **(100%)**
Tel.: (614) 480-6505
Web Site: http://www.huntington.com
Sales Range: $150-199.9 Million
Emp.: 400
Mortgage Banking
N.A.I.C.S.: 522292

Unizan Capital, LLC   (1)
3993 Howard Hughes Pkwy Ste 250, Las Vegas, NV 89169-6754
Tel.: (702) 693-6351
Commercial Banking Services
N.A.I.C.S.: 522110

Winthrop Resources Corporation   (1)
11100 Wayzata Blvd Ste 800, Minnetonka, MN 55305
Tel.: (952) 936-0226
Web Site:
    http://www.winthropresources.com
Investment Advisory Services
N.A.I.C.S.: 523940
Richard Chenitz *(Pres & COO)*
Tom Vasilakos *(Sr VP & Sr Dir-Tech Fin)*
Shea Huston *(VP-Sls-Central)*
Paul Stenberg *(VP-Sls-Eastern)*
Dan Mandy *(VP-Bus Dev-Western)*
Tim Haugen *(Natl Dir-Healthcare)*
Ken Heimbach *(VP-Sls-Southern)*

HUNTINGTON INGALLS INDUSTRIES, INC.
4101 Washington Ave, Newport News, VA 23607
Tel.: (757) 380-2000   DE
Web Site: https://www.hii.com
Year Founded: 2011
HII—(NYSE)
Rev.: $11,454,000,000
Assets: $11,215,000,000
Liabilities: $7,122,000,000
Net Worth: $4,093,000,000
Earnings: $681,000,000
Emp.: 44,000
Fiscal Year-end: 12/31/23
Ship Building & Repairing Services
N.A.I.C.S.: 336611
William R. Ermatinger *(Chief HR Officer & Exec VP)*
Chad N. Boudreaux *(Chief Legal Officer & Exec VP)*
Christopher D. Kastner *(Pres & CEO)*
Nicolas G. Schuck *(Chief Acctg Officer, VP, Controller & Other)*
D. R. Wyatt *(Treas & VP)*
Julia Jones *(VP-Manufacturing-Newport News Shipbuilding)*
Gary Fuller *(VP-Newport News Shipbuilding)*
Paul Harris *(Chief Compliance & Privacy Officer & Chief Compliance & Privacy Officer)*
Jeffrey Bauer *(VP)*
Todd West *(VP-Svc Aircraft Carrier Programs, Newport News Shipbuilding)*
Matt Needy *(VP)*
Thomas E. Stiehle *(CFO & Exec VP)*
Keith Munn *(CFO-Ingalls Shipbuilding & VP-Business Development-Ingalls Shipbuilding)*
Thomas Moore *(VP-Nuclear, Environmental Svcs)*
DeWolfe Miller *(VP)*
Kari R. Wilkinson *(Pres-Ingalls Shipbuilding & Exec VP)*
Ashutosh Gokhale *(CFO & VP-Technical Solutions)*
Jason Sutton *(CIO)*
Danny Hernandez *(Dir-Pub Affairs)*
Todd Borkey *(CTO & Exec VP)*

Huntington Ingalls Industries, Inc.—(Continued)

Jeff Showalter *(VP-Ops-Mission Technologies)*
Eric Chewning *(Exec VP-Strategy & Dev)*

Subsidiaries:

Camber Corporation (1)
670 Discovery Dr NW, Huntsville, AL 35806
Tel.: (256) 922-0200
Web Site: http://tsd.huntingtoningalls.com
Emp.: 597
Professional Training Services
N.A.I.C.S.: 611430

Camber Technical Services LLC (1)
635 Discovery Dr NW, Huntsville, AL 35806
Tel.: (256) 922-0200
Emp.: 5
Ship Building & Repairing Services
N.A.I.C.S.: 336611
Joe Reale *(Pres)*

Enlighten IT Consulting LLC (1)
10960 Grantchester Way Ste 300, Columbia, MD 21044
Tel.: (410) 449-1201
Web Site: https://www.eitccorp.com
Information Technology Services
N.A.I.C.S.: 541519

Fulcrum IT Services, LLC (1)
5870 Trinity Pkwy Ste 400, Centreville, VA 20120
Tel.: (703) 543-2900
Computer System Design Services
N.A.I.C.S.: 541512
Jeff Handy *(Pres)*
Carroll Johnson *(CFO & Chief Admin Officer)*

Subsidiary (Domestic):

The PTR Group, LLC (2)
5870 Trinity Pkwy Ste 320, Centerville, VA 20120
Tel.: (703) 543-2880
Web Site: http://theptrgroup.com
Custom Computer Programming Services
N.A.I.C.S.: 541511
Dean Thompson *(Founder, COO & Dir-Engrg)*
Michael E. Anderson *(Co-Founder & CTO)*
Phil Moroco *(Mng Dir)*
Cody Wall *(Mgr-Energy Indus)*

Huntington Ingalls Incorporated (1)
4101 Washington Ave, Newport News, VA 23607
Tel.: (757) 380-2000
Web Site: http://www.huntingtoningalls.com
Naval Architecture & Marine Engineering Services
N.A.I.C.S.: 541330

Hydroid, Inc. (1)
1 Henry Dr, Pocasset, MA 02559-4900
Tel.: (508) 563-6565
Web Site: http://www.hydroid.com
Sales Range: $10-24.9 Million
Autonomous Underwater Vehicle Mfr
N.A.I.C.S.: 334511
Tom Reynolds *(Sr Dir-Bus Dev)*
Ian Moss *(Sr Dir-Legal)*
Derek Daly *(Sr Dir-Production & Mfg)*
Sandor Becz *(Sr Dir-Engrg)*
Janice Norton *(Sr Mgr-Fin)*
Carolyn Martin *(Sr Dir-HR)*

Subsidiary (Non-US):

Hydroid Europe (2)
Unit 17 Murrills Estate, Portchester, Fareham, PO16 9RD, United Kingdom
Tel.: (44) 2392417222
Web Site: http://www.km.kongsberg.com
Autonomous Underwater Vehicle Mfr
N.A.I.C.S.: 336612

Ingalls Shipbuilding, Inc. (1)
1000 Jerry St Pe Hwy, Pascagoula, MS 39568-0149
Tel.: (228) 935-1122
Emp.: 11,000
Shipbuilding & Repair
N.A.I.C.S.: 336611
Thomas E. Stiehle *(CFO, CIO & VP)*
Frank D. Martin *(VP-Fin & Controller)*

Mike Lipski *(VP-Strategy)*
George S. Jones *(VP-Ops)*
Jim McIngvale *(Dir-Comm & Pub Affairs)*
Mike Duthu *(VP-Bus Dev)*
Edmond E. Hughes *(VP-HR & Admin)*
Scott G. Weldon *(VP-Supply Chain Mgmt)*
Brian Blanchette *(VP-Quality & Engrg)*

Subsidiary (Domestic):

AMSEC LLC (2)
5701 Cleveland St, Virginia Beach, VA 23462 **(100%)**
Tel.: (757) 463-6666
Web Site: http://www.amsec.com
Sales Range: $200-249.9 Million
Emp.: 2,000
Naval Architecture & Marine Engineering Services
N.A.I.C.S.: 541330
Mark Harris Leonard *(VP-Ops)*
Kelly J. Carlan *(Dir-HR)*
Harris Leonard *(Pres)*
Cathy Cope *(Dir-Contracts, Pricing, Procurement & Matl Mgmt)*
Ryan Norris *(Dir-Strategic Plng & Bus Dev)*

Continental Maritime of San Diego, Inc. (2)
1995 Bay Front St, San Diego, CA 92113 **(100%)**
Tel.: (619) 234-8851
Web Site: https://cmsd-msr.com
Sales Range: $150-199.9 Million
Emp.: 325
Ship Repair & Maintenance Services
N.A.I.C.S.: 336611

Newport News Shipbuilding and Dry Dock Company (1)
4101 Washington Ave, Newport News, VA 23607-2700
Tel.: (757) 380-2000
Web Site: http://www.huntingtoningalls.com
Ship Building & Repairing
N.A.I.C.S.: 336611
Jennifer R. Boykin *(Pres)*
Brandi Smith *(VP-Columbia-Class Program)*
David Horne *(VP-Trades)*
Xavier Beale *(VP-HR & Admin)*

Subsidiary (Domestic):

Newport News Industrial Corporation (2)
182 Enterprise Dr, Newport News, VA 23603 **(100%)**
Tel.: (757) 380-7053
Web Site: http://tsd.huntingtoningalls.com
Power Plant Equipment Construction Services
N.A.I.C.S.: 237120

Newport News Nuclear, Inc. (2)
4101 Washington Ave, Newport News, VA 23607
Tel.: (757) 380-2000
Web Site: http://nnn.huntingtoningalls.com
Nuclear Program Management & Technical Services
N.A.I.C.S.: 541618
Dave Carlson *(Mgr)*
Neal Quesnel *(Mgr)*
Gerald Boyd *(VP-Bus Dev)*

Subsidiary (Non-US):

Newport News Nuclear BWXT-Los Alamos, LLC (3)
Web Site: http://www.n3b-la.com
Electric Power Generation & Nuclear Services
N.A.I.C.S.: 221113

Joint Venture (Domestic):

Savannah River Nuclear Solutions, LLC (3)
Park Ave & Laurens St, Aiken, SC 29808
Tel.: (803) 725-6211
Web Site:
http://www.savannahrivernuclearsolutions.com
Emp.: 6,000
Nuclear Weapons & Materials Storage & Processing Facility Operation Management Services
N.A.I.C.S.: 493190
Jennifer T. Curtis *(Gen Counsel & Sr VP)*
Vahid Majidi *(Dir & Exec VP)*

Dave Olson *(Exec VP)*
Dennis Carr *(Pres & CEO)*
Sean Alford *(Chief Admin Officer & Exec VP)*
Wyatt Clark *(Sr VP)*
Mark Davis *(Sr VP-NNSA Ops & Programs)*
Chris Harkins *(Officer-Nuclear Safety & Sr VP)*
Sharon Marra *(Deputy Dir & Sr VP)*
Ted Myers *(Sr VP)*
Norman Powell *(Sr VP-Bus Svcs)*
Rick Sprague *(Sr VP-Environment, Safety, Health & Quality)*
Michael Swain *(Sr VP-Technical Svcs)*
James Toler *(Exec VP)*
James G. Angelos *(Sr VP-Operations)*
Francine Burroughs *(Sr VP)*
Janice Lawson *(Sr VP)*
James Toler *(Exec VP)*
James G. Angelos *(Sr VP-Operations)*
Francine Burroughs *(Sr VP)*
Janice Lawson *(Sr VP)*
James Toler *(Exec VP)*
James G. Angelos *(Sr VP-Operations)*
Francine Burroughs *(Sr VP)*
Janice Lawson *(Sr VP)*

Stoller Newport News Nuclear, Inc. (1)
105 Technology Dr Ste 190, Broomfield, CO 80021 **(100%)**
Tel.: (303) 546-4300
Web Site: http://sn3.huntingtoningalls.com
Emp.: 35
Environmental Consulting Services
N.A.I.C.S.: 541620
Nick Lombardo *(Pres)*

Undersea Solutions Corporation (1)
4101 Washington Ave, Newport News, VA 23607
Tel.: (757) 688-5672
Emp.: 30
Ship Building & Repair Services
N.A.I.C.S.: 336611
Ross Lindman *(Sr VP-Ops)*

UniversalPegasus International Canada, Inc. (1)
Suite 900 707-7th Avenue SW, Calgary, T2P 3H6, AB, Canada
Tel.: (403) 767-9990
Engineeering Services
N.A.I.C.S.: 541330
Aaron Kraus *(Engr-Pipeline)*

UniversalPegasus International Trinidad and Tobago Limited (1)
Central Warehousing Complex, Chaguanas, Trinidad & Tobago
Tel.: (868) 671 5670
Engineeering Services
N.A.I.C.S.: 541330
Stephen de Gannes *(Reg Mgr)*

HUNTSMAN CORPORATION
10003 Woodloch Forest Dr, The Woodlands, TX 77380
Tel.: (281) 719-6000 DE
Web Site: https://www.huntsman.com
Year Founded: 1982
HUN—(NYSE)
Rev.: $6,111,000,000
Assets: $7,248,000,000
Liabilities: $3,770,000,000
Net Worth: $3,478,000,000
Earnings: $101,000,000
Emp.: 6,000
Fiscal Year end: 12/31/20
Holding Company; Chemical Products Mfr & Whslr
N.A.I.C.S.: 551112
Peter R. Huntsman *(Chm, Pres & CEO)*
Twila M. Day *(CIO & VP)*
Kevin C. Hardman *(VP-Tax)*
R. Wade Rogers *(Chief Compliance Officer & Sr VP-HR-Global)*
Anthony P. Hankins *(Pres-Polyurethanes Div & CEO-Asia Pacific)*
David Stryker *(Gen Counsel, Sec & Exec VP)*
Cynthia L. Egan *(Vice Chm)*

Scott J. Wright *(Pres-Advanced Materials)*
Pierre Poukens *(VP-Internal Audit)*
Claire Mei *(Treas & VP)*
Philip M. Lister *(CFO & Exec VP)*
Jan Buberl *(Pres-Performance Products Div)*
Rachel Muir *(VP, Asst Sec & Deputy Gen Counsel)*

Subsidiaries:

CVC Thermoset Specialties (1)
844 N Lenola Rd, Maple Shade, NJ 08057
Tel.: (856) 533-3000
Web Site: http://www.emeraldmaterials.com
Sales Range: $10-24.9 Million
Epoxy Resins Mfr
N.A.I.C.S.: 325998

Demilec (USA) Inc. (1)
3315 E Division St, Arlington, TX 76011
Web Site: http://www.demilec.com
Emp.: 150
Spray Foam Insulation Mfr
N.A.I.C.S.: 326150

Demilec Inc. (1)
870 Boulevard du Cure-Boivin, Boisbriand, J7G 2A7, QC, Canada
Web Site: http://www.demilec.ca
Polyurethane Spray Foam Insulation Product Mfr
N.A.I.C.S.: 326150

Huntsman (UAE) FZE (1)
Plot No MO0474 JAFZA, PO Box 16942, Dubai, United Arab Emirates
Tel.: (971) 48813800
Chemical Products Mfr
N.A.I.C.S.: 325998
Gulum Selen Kabil *(Mng Dir)*
Mustafa Orcan *(Mgr-Site)*
Zehra Butun *(Mgr-EHS)*

Huntsman Advanced Materials (Deutschland) GmbH (1)
Ernst-Schering-Str 14, 59192, Bergkamen, Germany
Tel.: (49) 230720882550
Specialty Component Mfr
N.A.I.C.S.: 335999

Huntsman Building Solutions (Central Europe) A.S. (1)
Druzstevni 2, 27351, Pleteny Ujezd, Czech Republic
Tel.: (420) 725419713
Spray Foam Insulation Mfr
N.A.I.C.S.: 326140

Huntsman Building Solutions (Europe) BV (1)
Cloo Chapelle aux Champs 30 boite, 0000, Brussels, Belgium
Tel.: (32) 28806233
Spray Foam Insulation Mfr
N.A.I.C.S.: 326140

Huntsman Building Solutions (France) SAS (1)
103 Ronsard, Villefranche-sur-Saone, France
Tel.: (33) 474669410
Coatings & Spray Polyurethane Mfr
N.A.I.C.S.: 325510

Huntsman Building Solutions (USA) LLC (1)
10003 Woodloch Forest Dr, The Woodlands, TX 77380
Tel.: (281) 719-6000
Web Site:
http://www.huntsmanbuildingsolutions.com
Spray Polyurethane Foam Product Mfr
N.A.I.C.S.: 326150

Huntsman Gomet S.r.l. (1)
Strada Tomboleto 12, Azeglio, 10010, Turin, Italy
Tel.: (39) 0125728800
Web Site: https://www.gomet.it
Automobile Spare Parts Mfr
N.A.I.C.S.: 336390

Huntsman IFS Polyurethanes Limited (1)
Station Road Kings Lynn, Norfolk, PE32 1AW, United Kingdom
Tel.: (44) 1485601155
Web Site: http://www.ifs-group.com

Polyurethane Chemical Mfr
N.A.I.C.S.: 326150
Iain Stanton *(Mng Dir)*

Huntsman International LLC   **(1)**
10003 Woodloch Forest Dr, The Wood-
lands, TX 77380   **(100%)**
Tel.: (281) 719-6000
Web Site: http://www.huntsman.com
Rev.: $8,022,000,000
Assets: $8,226,000,000
Liabilities: $4,374,000,000
Net Worth: $3,852,000,000
Earnings: $461,000,000
Emp.: 7,000
Fiscal Year-end: 12/31/2022
Chemical Products Mfr & Whslr
N.A.I.C.S.: 325998
Nolan D. Archibald *(Vice Chm)*
Peter R. Huntsman *(Chm, Pres & CEO)*
Twila M. Day *(CIO & VP)*
Philip M. Lister *(CFO)*
Cynthia L. Egan *(Vice Chm)*
Chuck Hirsch *(Pres)*
Brittany Benko *(Sr VP)*

Subsidiary (Non-US):

Arabian Amines Company   **(2)**
PO Box 11140, Jubail Industrial City, Al
Jubayl, 31961, Eastern Province, Saudi
Arabia
Tel.: (966) 3 358 5100
Web Site: https://www.aminat.com.sa
Differentiated Chemical Mfr
N.A.I.C.S.: 325199

Subsidiary (Domestic):

Chemical Specialties, LLC   **(2)**
5910 Pharr Mill Rd, Harrisburg, NC 28075-
8625
Tel.: (704) 454-4811
Web Site: http://www.mrdc.com
Wood Preservative Mfr
N.A.I.C.S.: 321212

Division (Domestic):

**Mineral Research &
Development**   **(3)**
5910 Pharr Mill Rd, Harrisburg, NC 28075
Tel.: (704) 454-4811
Web Site: http://www.mrdc.com
Emp.: 3,700
Mineral Chemical Mfr
N.A.I.C.S.: 424690
Thorn Baccich *(Pres)*
Trey Asberry *(Mgr-Sls-SW, E & West Coast)*

Subsidiary (Non-US):

**EMA Kimya Sistemleri Sanayi ve Ti-
caret A.S.**   **(2)**
Organize Deri Sanayi Yan Sanayi Gelis-
tirme YA-1, Tuzla, 34953, Istanbul, Turkiye
Tel.: (90) 2165910808
Web Site: https://www.ema.gen.tr
Chemicals Mfr
N.A.I.C.S.: 325199

Holliday Chemical Espana S.A.   **(2)**
Marie Curie Passage Pol Industrial Santa
Margarita Ii 17, Terrassa, Barcelona, 08223,
Spain
Tel.: (34) 937842234
Web Site: http://www.holliday-espana.com
Specialty Chemicals Mfr
N.A.I.C.S.: 325998
Alberto Zubiaur *(Sls Dir)*
Cinta Gacen *(Mgr-Sls)*

Holliday France S.A.S.   **(2)**
ZAC de la moinerie 2 rue du Languedoc,
Paris, 91220, Bretigny-sur-Orge, France
Tel.: (33) 160847700
Web Site: http://www.holliday-france.fr
Chemicals Mfr
N.A.I.C.S.: 325199

Huntsman (Argentina) S.r.l.   **(2)**
Reconquista 2780 El Talar, 1617, Buenos
Aires, Argentina
Tel.: (54) 114 736 6000
Web Site: http://www.huntsman.com
Emp.: 22
Polyurethane Chemical Blending, Wahous-
ing & Distr
N.A.I.C.S.: 325998
Javier Wetzler Malbran *(Gen Mgr)*

Huntsman (Colombia) Limitada   **(2)**
Calle 20A No 43A-50 Int 5, Bogota, Colom-
bia
Tel.: (57) 1 335 5000
Web Site: http://www.huntsman.com
Specialty Chemicals Mfr
N.A.I.C.S.: 325998

**Huntsman (Czech Republic)
Spol.sr.o**   **(2)**
Vladislova St 17-47/16, 11 000, Prague,
Czech Republic
Tel.: (420) 222523560
Web Site: http://www.huntsman.com
Sales Range: $50-74.9 Million
Polyurethane Mfr
N.A.I.C.S.: 325998

Huntsman (Europe) BVBA   **(2)**
Everslaan 45, 3078, Everberg, Belgium
Tel.: (32) 27589211
Web Site: http://www.huntsman.com
Emp.: 600
Differentiated Chemical Mfr
N.A.I.C.S.: 325199

Subsidiary (Domestic):

Huntsman (Belgium) BVBA   **(3)**
Everslaan 45, 3078, Everberg, Belgium
Tel.: (32) 27589211
Sales Range: $150-199.9 Million
Organic Chemical Mfr
N.A.I.C.S.: 325199
Steen Weien Hansen *(VP)*

Subsidiary (Domestic):

**Huntsman Textile Effects (Belgium)
BVBA**   **(4)**
Everslaan 45, 3078, Kortenberg, Belgium
Tel.: (32) 27589244
Web Site: http://www.huntsman.com
Sales Range: $25-49.9 Million
Emp.: 4
Organic Chemical Mfr
N.A.I.C.S.: 325199

Subsidiary (Domestic):

**Huntsman Advanced Materials (Eu-
rope) BVBA**   **(3)**
Everslaan 45, 3078, Everberg, Belgium
Tel.: (32) 27589211
Web Site: http://www.huntsman.be
Sales Range: $50-74.9 Million
Emp.: 400
Synthetic & Formulated Polymer Systems
N.A.I.C.S.: 326119
Steen Weien Hansen *(VP)*

Subsidiary (Non-US):

**Huntsman Advanced Materials (Aus-
tria) GmbH**   **(4)**
Breitnerfurterstrasse 251, 1231, Vienna,
Wien, Austria
Tel.: (43) 1801320
Sales Range: $25-49.9 Million
Emp.: 5
Organic Chemical Mfr
N.A.I.C.S.: 325199

**Huntsman Advanced Materials (Italy)
Srl**   **(4)**
Via Mazzini 58, Ternate, 21020, Varese,
Italy
Tel.: (39) 0332941111
Emp.: 70
Polyurethane Mfr
N.A.I.C.S.: 325199

**Huntsman Advanced Materials (UK)
Limited**   **(4)**
Ickleton Road, Duxford, Cambridge, CB22
4XQ, Cambs, United Kingdom
Tel.: (44) 1223832121
Organic Chemical Mfr
N.A.I.C.S.: 325199

Subsidiary (Non-US):

Huntsman (Germany) GmbH   **(2)**
Baumwall 5, 20459, Hamburg, Germany
Tel.: (49) 40376700
Web Site: http://www.huntsman.com
Sales Range: $10-24.9 Million
Emp.: 10
Distr of Performance Chemicals

N.A.I.C.S.: 325998

Subsidiary (Domestic):

Huntsman P&A Germany GmbH   **(3)**
Dr Rudolf Sachtleben Strasse 4, 47198,
Duisburg, Germany
Tel.: (49) 2066220
Web Site: http://www.huntsman.com
Emp.: 2,250
Chemicals Mfr
N.A.I.C.S.: 325180

Subsidiary (Non-US):

Huntsman P&A Finland Oy   **(4)**
Titaanitie, Pori, 28840, Finland
Tel.: (358) 104301000
Web Site: http://www.sachtleben.de
Pigment Mfr
N.A.I.C.S.: 325130

Subsidiary (Domestic):

**Huntsman P&A Uerdingen
GmbH**   **(4)**
Rheinuferstrasse 7-9, Krefeld, 47829, Ger-
many
Tel.: (49) 215147973000
Chemical Mfr & Distr
N.A.I.C.S.: 424690

**Huntsman P&A Wasserchemie
GmbH**   **(4)**
Zeppelinstrasse 23, 49479, Ibbenburen,
Germany
Tel.: (49) 2066222685
Web Site: http://www.sachtleben-
wasserchemie.de
Emp.: 50
Water Treatment Chemical Distr
N.A.I.C.S.: 424690

Subsidiary (Domestic):

**Huntsman Pigments Holding
GmbH**   **(3)**
Muhlstr 118, 65396, Walluf, Germany
Tel.: (49) 61237970
Web Site: http://www.hpigments.com
Holding Company
N.A.I.C.S.: 551112

Huntsman Verwaltungs GmbH   **(3)**
Baumwall 5, 20459, Hamburg, Germany
Tel.: (49) 40376700
Emp.: 7
Office Administrative Services
N.A.I.C.S.: 561110
Jan Kruetzfldt *(Mgr)*

PUR-Systems GmbH   **(3)**
Werner-von-Sie-mens-Strasse 22, 49124,
Georgsmarienhutte, Germany
Tel.: (49) 54 018 3550
Web Site: https://pursystems.com
Chemical Mfr & Distr
N.A.I.C.S.: 325199

Subsidiary (Domestic):

**PUR-SYSTEMS Verwantungsgesell-
schaft mbH**   **(4)**
Werner-Von-Siemens-Str 22, Georgs-
marienhutte, Germany
Tel.: (49) 5401 8355 0
Web Site: http://www.puresystems.de
Emp.: 20
Organic & Inorganic Chemical Mfr
N.A.I.C.S.: 325180

Subsidiary (Non-US):

**Huntsman (Holdings) Netherlands
B.V.**   **(2)**
Merseyweg 10, Botlek, Rotterdam, 3197
KG, Netherlands
Tel.: (31) 2817196000
Holding Company
N.A.I.C.S.: 551112
Peter R. Huntsman *(CEO)*

Huntsman (Korea) Limited   **(2)**
9Fl Dukmyung Bldg 170-9 Samsung-dong,
Gangnam-gu, Seoul, 135-741, Korea
(South)
Tel.: (82) 23 404 6800
Web Site: http://www.huntsman.com
Emp.: 25
Polyurethane Whlsr
N.A.I.C.S.: 424690

Huntsman (Netherlands) BV   **(2)**
Merseyweg 10, Rozenburg, 3197 KG, Rot-
terdam, Netherlands
Tel.: (31) 181299111
Web Site: http://www.huntsman.com
Sales Range: $50-74.9 Million
Organic Chemical Distr
N.A.I.C.S.: 423490

Subsidiary (Domestic):

**Huntsman (Russia Investments)
B.V.**   **(3)**
Merseyweg 10, Botlek, 3197 KG, Rotter-
dam, Netherlands
Tel.: (31) 181299111
Web Site: http://www.huntsman.com
Emp.: 50
Organic Chemical Mfr
N.A.I.C.S.: 325199

Subsidiary (Non-US):

Huntsman (Poland) Sp. z o.o.   **(2)**
7 Szyszkowa Street, 02-285, Warsaw, Po-
land
Tel.: (48) 22 825 8826
Web Site: http://www.huntsman.com
Sales Range: $50-74.9 Million
Emp.: 40
Polyurethane Products
N.A.I.C.S.: 325998
Michael Gabryszewski *(Mng Dir)*

**Huntsman Advanced Materials (Hong
Kong) Ltd**   **(2)**
Room 3108-11 31/F Tower 1 Millennium
City 1 No 388 Kwun Tong Road, Kowloon,
China (Hong Kong)
Tel.: (852) 21488800
Basic Inorganic Chemical Mfr
N.A.I.C.S.: 325180

**Huntsman Advanced Materials (India)
Private Limited**   **(2)**
782/882 Solitaire Corporate Park 5TH Floor
Building No 10 Road No 167, Guru Hargov-
indji Marg Andheri East, Mumbai, 400093,
Maharashtra, India
Tel.: (91) 22 4095 1556
Organic Chemical Mfr
N.A.I.C.S.: 325199

**Huntsman Advanced Materials (Nan-
jing) Company Limited.**   **(2)**
No 168 Guanqu South Road Chemical In-
dustry Park, Luhe District, Nanjing, 210047,
China
Tel.: (86) 2558390810
Chemicals Mfr
N.A.I.C.S.: 325199

**Huntsman Advanced Materials (Tai-
wan) Corporation**   **(2)**
No 19 Industrial Third Road, Kuan Yin,
Taoyuan, 80143, Taiwan
Tel.: (886) 34838616
Sales Range: $25-49.9 Million
Emp.: 6
Organic Chemical Mfr
N.A.I.C.S.: 325199
Steen Weien Hansen *(Dir)*

**Huntsman Advanced Materials (UAE)
FZE**   **(2)**
Street No 732A Jebel Ali Free Zone, PO
Box 16942, Dubai, 16942, United Arab
Emirates
Tel.: (971) 48813800
Web Site: http://www.huntsman.com
Sales Range: $25-49.9 Million
Emp.: 15
Advanced Material Mfr
N.A.I.C.S.: 325199

Subsidiary (Domestic):

**Huntsman Advanced Materials
LLC**   **(2)**
5121 San Fernando Rd W, Los Angeles,
CA 90039-1011
Tel.: (818) 265-7298
Web Site: http://www.huntsman.com
Sales Range: $50-74.9 Million
Synthetic & Formulated Polymer System
Distr
N.A.I.C.S.: 325199

Subsidiary (Non-US):

**Huntsman Chemical Trading (Shang-
hai) Ltd.**   **(2)**

Huntsman Corporation—(Continued)

45/F Wandu Mansion No 8 Xingyi Road,
Changning District, Shanghai, 200336,
China
Tel.: (86) 2122087587
Sales Range: $50-74.9 Million
Emp.: 200
Organic Chemical Mfr
N.A.I.C.S.: 325199
Frank Xing (Mgr-Office)

Huntsman Corporation Canada Inc. (2)
2795 Slough Street, Mississauga, L4T 1G2,
ON, Canada
Tel.: (905) 678-9150
Web Site: http://www.huntsman.com
Sales Range: $25-49.9 Million
Holding Company; Polyurethane Products
Mfr
N.A.I.C.S.: 551112

Subsidiary (Domestic):

Huntsman International (Canada) Corporation (3)
2795 Slough Street, Mississauga, L4T 1G2,
ON, Canada
Tel.: (905) 678-9150
Web Site: https://www.huntsman.com
Sales Range: $1-9.9 Million
Emp.: 13
Polyurethane Products Mfr
N.A.I.C.S.: 326150

Subsidiary (Non-US):

Huntsman Corporation Hungary Rt. (2)
Sport u 40/b, Solymar, 2083, Hungary
Tel.: (36) 309408891
Web Site: http://www.huntsman.com
Sales Range: Less than $1 Million
Emp.: 108
Polyurethanes
N.A.I.C.S.: 325998
Csaba Mikulai (Mgr)

Huntsman Corporation UK Limited (2)
Bynea, Carms, Llanelli, SA14 9TE, Car-
marthenshire, United Kingdom
Tel.: (44) 155 474 5225
Web Site: http://www.huntsman.com
Chemicals Manufacturing
N.A.I.C.S.: 325199

Subsidiary (Domestic):

Huntsman Pigments (UK) Limited (3)
Liverpool Road East, Kidsgrove, Stoke-on-
Trent, ST7 3AA, Staffordshire, United King-
dom
Tel.: (44) 1782794400
Web Site: http://www.hpigments.com
Pigment Mfr
N.A.I.C.S.: 325130

Subsidiary (Non-US):

Huntsman Holland B.V. (2)
Merseyweg 10, Rozenburg, 3197 KG, Rot-
terdam, Netherlands
Tel.: (31) 18 129 9111
Web Site: http://www.huntsman.com
Sales Range: $150-199.9 Million
Emp.: 400
Polyurethanes
N.A.I.C.S.: 325998

Huntsman International (India) Private Limited (2)
Hiranandani Business Park Lighthall B-wing
Saki Vihar Road, Chandivali Andheri, Mum-
bai, 400072, India
Tel.: (91) 2242875100
Organic Chemical Mfr
N.A.I.C.S.: 325199
Rohit Aggarwal (Pres-Textile Effects)
Harshad Naik (Mng Dir-India Subcontinent)

Huntsman MA Investments (Nether-lands) CV (2)
Merseyweg 10 3197 KG Botlek, Rotterdam,
3197 KG, Zuid-Holland, Netherlands
Tel.: (31) 181292261
Financial Services
N.A.I.C.S.: 523999

Huntsman Norden AB (2)
Reningsverksg 5, Goteborg, Vastra Frol-
unda, 421 26, Sweden
Tel.: (46) 31892375
Differentiated Chemical Mfr
N.A.I.C.S.: 325199

Subsidiary (Domestic):

Huntsman Petrochemical LLC (2)
500 Huntsman Way, Salt Lake City, UT
84108
Tel.: (801) 584-5700
Web Site: http://www.huntsman.com
Molecular Chemical Distr
N.A.I.C.S.: 424690

Plant (Domestic):

Huntsman Pigments & Additives (2)
7 Swisher Dr, Cartersville, GA 30120
Tel.: (770) 386-4766
Web Site: http://www.huntsman.com
Chemical Product Packaging Services
N.A.I.C.S.: 561910

Subsidiary (Non-US):

Huntsman Pigments & Trading Pty. Ltd. (100%)
21 David Street, Dandenong, 3175, VIC,
Australia
Tel.: (61) 392123300
Emp.: 12
Inorganic Pigment Developer Whslr
N.A.I.C.S.: 424690
Scott Colquhoun (Dir-Comml)

Subsidiary (Domestic):

Huntsman Pigments Americas LLC (2)
7101 Muirkirk Rd, Beltsville, MD 20705
Tel.: (301) 210-3400
Web Site: http://www.hpigments.com
Chemicals Mfr
N.A.I.C.S.: 325199

Subsidiary (Non-US):

Huntsman Pigments Hong Kong Limited (2)
Room No 6A 20/F Tower 1 China Hong
Kong City, 33 Canton Road Tsim Sha Tsui,
Kowloon, China (Hong Kong)
Tel.: (852) 23683031
Web Site: http://www.huntsman.com
Chemical Product Whslr
N.A.I.C.S.: 424690

Huntsman Pigments S.p.A. (2)
44/12 Via Reiss Romoli Guglielmo, 10148,
Turin, TO, Italy
Tel.: (39) 0112280501
Chemicals Mfr
N.A.I.C.S.: 325199

Division (Non-US):

Huntsman Polyurethanes (2)
Everslaan 45, 3078, Everberg, Belgium
Tel.: (32) 27589211
Web Site: http://www.huntsman.com
Sales Range: $25-49.9 Million
Emp.: 522
Mfr of Household & Industrial Surfactants
N.A.I.C.S.: 325613

Subsidiary (Non-US):

Huntsman Polyurethanes (3)
Suite 16-01 Level 16 The Pinnacle Persi-
aran Lagoon, bandar sunway, 46150, Petal-
ing Jaya, Selangor Darul Ehsan, Malaysia
Tel.: (60) 376699700
Web Site: http://www.huntsman.com
Sales Range: $1-9.9 Million
Emp.: 4
Polyurethanes Sales & Marketing
N.A.I.C.S.: 325211

Subsidiary (US):

Huntsman Polyurethanes (3)
52 Kendall Pond Rd, Derry, NH 03038
Tel.: (603) 421-3507
Web Site: http://www.huntsman.com
Sales Range: $25-49.9 Million
Emp.: 10
Polyurethane Mfr
N.A.I.C.S.: 326150

Plant (Domestic):

Huntsman - Polyurethanes Division (4)
101 Concrete St, Houston, TX 77012
Tel.: (713) 924-6419
Web Site: http://www.oxid.net
Sales Range: $75-99.9 Million
Mfr & Supplier of Chemicals for Urethane
Industry
N.A.I.C.S.: 325998

Subsidiary (Non-US):

Huntsman Polyurethanes (Australia) Pty Ltd. (3)
Gate 3 765 Ballarat Rd, Deer Park, 3023,
VIC, Australia
Tel.: (61) 393616000
Web Site: http://www.huntsman.com
Sales Range: $10-24.9 Million
Mfr & Distributor of Polyurethanes
N.A.I.C.S.: 325211

Huntsman Polyurethanes (China) Limited (3)
No 452 Wen Jing Road Minhang Develop-
ment Zone, Dev Zone, Shanghai, 200245,
China
Tel.: (86) 2124037288
Web Site: http://www.huntsman.com
Sales Range: $50-74.9 Million
Polyruethane & Chemical Sales
N.A.I.C.S.: 325998

Subsidiary (Domestic):

Huntsman Polyurethanes Shanghai Ltd. (4)
No 452 Wen Jing Road, Minhang Develop-
ment Zone, Shanghai, 200245, China
Tel.: (86) 2124037288
Organic Chemical Mfr
N.A.I.C.S.: 325199

Shanghai Huntsman Polyurethanes Specialties Co., Ltd. (4)
Weiliu Lu Jinshanwei No 1209 Weiliu Road
Number 2 Industrial Park, Jinshan District,
Shanghai, China
Tel.: (86) 2123257965
Emp.: 55
Polyurethane Coating Mfr
N.A.I.C.S.: 325510

Subsidiary (Non-US):

Huntsman Polyurethanes (UK) Ltd. (3)
Wilton International, PO Box 99, Redcar,
TS10 4YA, United Kingdom
Tel.: (44) 1642834700
Web Site: http://www.huntsman.com
Sales Range: $25-49.9 Million
Mfr of Polyurethane Polyester, Polyols &
Formulated Blends
N.A.I.C.S.: 325211

Subsidiary (Non-US):

Huntsman Quimica Brasil Ltda. (2)
Avenida Professor Vicente Rao 90 Predio
1222 andar 90 Santo Amaro, Sao Paulo,
04706-900, SP, Brazil
Tel.: (55) 1123922486
Web Site: http://www.huntsman.com
Sales Range: $25-49.9 Million
Sample Preparations for Industrial Trials
N.A.I.C.S.: 325998

Huntsman Saint-Mihiel SAS (2)
Z I de Han sur Meuse, 55300, Saint-Mihiel,
France
Tel.: (33) 329917300
Web Site: http://www.huntsman.com
Sales Range: $50-74.9 Million
Emp.: 200
Mfr of Surface Active Agent Products
N.A.I.C.S.: 325998

Huntsman Surface Sciences France SAS (2)
PO Box 19, Han-sur-Meuse, 55300, Saint-
Mihiel, France
Tel.: (33) 3.299 17300
Surfactants Mfr
N.A.I.C.S.: 325199

Huntsman Surface Sciences Italia S.r.l. (2)

Via Camillo Benso Conte Di Cavour 50
Castiglione Delle Stiviere, Mantua, 46043,
Italy
Tel.: (39) 03766371
Organic Chemical Mfr
N.A.I.C.S.: 325199

Huntsman Textile Effects (Mexico) S. de R.L. de C.V. (2)
Km 43 5 Carretera Guadalajara-Ocotlan,
Chapala, 45930, Jalisco, Mexico
Tel.: (52) 37 6737 4200
Chemical Product & Preparation Mfr
N.A.I.C.S.: 325998

Huntsman Textile Effects (Qingdao) Co., Ltd (2)
Room 1804 China Overseas Building No 76
Yanji Road, Shibei District, Qingdao,
266034, Shandong, China
Tel.: (86) 2133572550
Web Site: http://www.huntsman.com
Organic Chemical Mfr
N.A.I.C.S.: 325199

Division (Non-US):

Huntsman Textile Effects Division (2)
152 Beach Road 29-00 Gateway East, Sin-
gapore, 189721, Singapore
Tel.: (65) 62973363
Web Site: http://www.huntsman.com
Textile Chemicals & Dyes Mfr
N.A.I.C.S.: 325130
Rajiv Banavali (VP-Technology)
Rohit Aggarwal (Pres)

Subsidiary (Non-US):

Huntsman Textile Effects (Germany) GmbH (3)
Rehlinger Strasse 1, 86462, Langweid, Ger-
many
Tel.: (49) 823041212
Emp.: 220
Textile Chemicals & Dyes Mfr
N.A.I.C.S.: 325130
Martin Brokatzky (Mng Dir & Plant Mgr)
Bernd Trunk (Mgr-Sls & Technical Support)

Plant (US):

Huntsman Textile Effects - Charlotte Plant (3)
3400 Westinghouse Blvd, Charlotte, NC
28273
Tel.: (704) 587-5000
Web Site: http://www.huntsman.com
Rev.: $2,300,000
Emp.: 30
Textile Chemicals & Dyes Mfr
N.A.I.C.S.: 325130

Huntsman Textile Effects - High Point Plant (3)
4050 Premier Dr, High Point, NC 27265
Tel.: (336) 801-2002
Web Site: http://www.huntsman.com
Textile Chemicals & Dyes Mfr
N.A.I.C.S.: 325130

Subsidiary (Non-US):

Huntsman de Mexico, S.A. de C.V. (2)
Rio Lerma 32 Fracc Industrial Tlaxcolpan
Tlalnepantla Edo de, Col Naples, 54030,
Mexico, DF, Mexico
Tel.: (52) 5553902780
Web Site: http://www.huntsman.com
Petrochemical Distr
N.A.I.C.S.: 325110

International Polyurethane Invest-ments B.V. (2)
Merseyweg 10, Rozenburg, 3197 KG, Rot-
terdam, Netherlands
Tel.: (31) 181299111
Web Site: https://www.huntsman.com
Emp.: 400
Organic Chemical Mfr
N.A.I.C.S.: 325199

Laffans Petrochemicals Limited (2)
ONE BKC 13th Floor 1302 BWing Plot C66
GBlock Bandra Kurla Complex, Bandra E,
Mumbai, 400051, India
Tel.: (91) 2266930813

Web Site:
https://www.laffanspetrochemical.com
Rev.: $3,303,593
Assets: $9,296,106
Liabilities: $1,109,466
Net Worth: $8,186,641
Earnings: $455,156
Fiscal Year-end: 03/31/2021
Chemical Product Whslr
N.A.I.C.S.: 424690
Sandeep Seth (Mng Dir)
Anisha Sandeep Seth (Exec Dir)
S. R. Narayanan (Compliance Officer & Sec)
Rajesh Udharam Thadani (Exec Dir)
Mahalinga Booba Kotian (CFO)

Limited Liability Company Huntsman (Ukraine)   (2)
Peremogy Avenue 67 4nd Floor, Kiev, 03062, Ukraine
Tel.: (380) 442773208
Chemical Distr
N.A.I.C.S.: 424690
Marchuk Nikolai (Mgr-Sls)

Mineral Feed, S.L.   (2)
Avenida Francisco Montenegro s/n Transversal 5, 21001, Huelva, Spain
Tel.: (34) 959255799
Web Site: https://www.mineralfeed.es
Agricultural Chemical Mfr
N.A.I.C.S.: 325320

Subsidiary (Domestic):

Nanocomp Technologies, Inc.   (2)
57 Daniel Webster Hwy, Merrimack, NH 03054
Tel.: (603) 442-8992
Web Site: http://www.miralon.com
Electrical Equipment & Component Mfr
N.A.I.C.S.: 335999
Dave Gailus (VP-Engineering)
John Gargasz (Mng Dir)
Paul Hallee (Dir-Finance)
Eitan Zeira (VP-Product Development)
Matt Bangert (VP-Manufacturing)

Subsidiary (Non-US):

Oligo SA   (2)
Pol Ind Nuevo Puerto A, 21810, Palos de la Frontera, Spain
Tel.: (34) 959369125
Fertilizer & Soil Conditioner Mfr
N.A.I.C.S.: 325199

PT Huntsman Indonesia   (2)
Jl Raya Bogor Km 27 3, Jakarta, 13710, Indonesia
Tel.: (62) 21 871 1500
Web Site: https://www.huntsman.com
Technical & Sales Expertise to Local Industries, Particularly in Footwear, Appliance, Furniture & Leisure, Construction & CWP (composite wood products) & Adhesives
N.A.I.C.S.: 561110
Chze Kian Kek (Mgr-Sales)

Affiliate (Domestic):

Rubicon LLC   (2)
9156 LA Hwy 75, Geismar, LA 70734
Tel.: (225) 744-5000
Web Site: https://www.rubiconllc.us
Sales Range: $350-399.9 Million
Polyurethane Mfr
N.A.I.C.S.: 326150
Shannon M. Arceneaux (Mgr-HR & Pub Affairs)
Mark Dearman (Gen Mgr)

Affiliate (Non-US):

SASOL-HUNTSMAN Verwaltungs-GmbH   (2)
Romerstr 733, Moers, 47443, Germany
Tel.: (49) 2841492512
Web Site: http://www.sasol-huntsman-germany.de
Emp.: 8
Organic Chemical Mfr
N.A.I.C.S.: 325199
Herbert Peters (Mgr)

Subsidiary (Non-US):

UP Huntsman-NMG   (2)
Office 32 Behtereva lane 8, Minsk, 20026, Belarus

Tel.: (375) 172965926
Chemicals Mfr
N.A.I.C.S.: 325199

Division (Non-US):

Venator Materials PLC   (2)
Titanium House Hanzard Drive Wynyard Park, Stockton-On-Tees, Durham, TS22 5FD, United Kingdom
Tel.: (44) 1740608001
Web Site: http://www.venatorcorp.com
Rev.: $2,173,000,000
Assets: $2,069,000,000
Liabilities: $1,759,000,000
Net Worth: $310,000,000
Earnings: ($188,000,000)
Emp.: 3,413
Fiscal Year-end: 12/31/2022
Chemical Products Mfr & Distr
N.A.I.C.S.: 325998
Simon Turner (Pres & CEO)
Kurt D. Ogden (CFO & Exec VP)
Russ R. Stolle (Chief Compliance Officer, Gen Counsel & Exec VP)
Mahomed Maiter (Exec VP-Bus Ops)
Barry B. Siadat (Chm)
Kevin Wilson (Sr VP)
Stefano Soccol (Sr VP)

Subsidiary (Domestic):

Venator Group   (3)
Titanium House Hanzard Drive Wynyard Park, Stockton-on-Tees, TS22 5FD, United Kingdom
Tel.: (44) 1740608001
Web Site: https://www.venatorcorp.com
Holding Company; Titanium Dioxide, Iron Sulphate & Other Pigments Mfr & Whslr
N.A.I.C.S.: 551112

Subsidiary (Non-US):

Tioxide (Malaysia) Sdn. Bhd.   (4)
Kawasan Industri Teluk Kalong, PO Box 29, Kuala Terengganu, Kemaman, 24007, Terengganu DI, Malaysia
Tel.: (60) 98631688
Web Site: http://www.huntsman.com
Titanium Dioxide & Other Pigments Mfr
N.A.I.C.S.: 325130

Subsidiary (US):

Tioxide Americas LLC   (4)
10003 Woodloch Forest Dr, The Woodlands, TX 77380
Tel.: (281) 719-4269
Web Site: http://www.huntsman.com
Rev.: $4,500,000
Emp.: 35
Titanium Dioxide & Other Pigments Whslr
N.A.I.C.S.: 424690

Subsidiary (Non-US):

Tioxide Europe S.r.l.   (4)
Stablimento DI Scarlino 113, Contrada Casone, Scarlino, GR, Italy
Tel.: (39) 056671111
Sales Range: $100-124.9 Million
Emp.: 250
Titanium Dioxide & Other Pigments Mfr & Whslr
N.A.I.C.S.: 325130

Tioxide Europe SAS   (4)
1 Rue Des Garennes, BP 89, F-62102, Calais, Cedex, France
Tel.: (33) 321464500
Web Site: http://www.huntsman.com
Sales Range: $75-99.9 Million
Emp.: 100
Titanium Dioxide & Other Pigments Mfr & Whslr
N.A.I.C.S.: 325130

Tioxide Southern Africa (Pty) Ltd.   (4)
Private Bag X504, Umbogintwini Kwazulu, 4120, Natal, South Africa
Tel.: (27) 319103611
Sales Range: $75-99.9 Million
Emp.: 250
Titanium Dioxide & Other Pigments Mfr & Whslr
N.A.I.C.S.: 325130

Joint Venture (Domestic):

Viance, LLC   (2)

8001 IBM Dr Bldg 403, Charlotte, NC 28262
Tel.: (704) 522-0825
Web Site: http://www.treatwood.com
Timber Treatment Products Mfr
N.A.I.C.S.: 325180
Steve Furr (Dir-Engrg & Tech Svcs)
John Hussa (Pres)
Edie Kello (Dir-Mktg)
Jonathan Moyes (CFO)
Kevin Archer (Dir-R&D)

Subsidiary (Non-US):

ZAO Huntsman-NMG   (2)
110 Km Kievskoe Shosse, Kaluga region, 249032, Obninsk, Russia
Tel.: (7) 4843993444
Web Site: http://www.huntsman-nmg.com
Sales Range: $50-74.9 Million
Emp.: 15
Organic Chemical Mfr
N.A.I.C.S.: 325199
Andij Borysov (Mng Dir)

Huntsman Mexico S. de R.L. de C.V.   (1)
Rio Lerma 32 Fracc Industrial Tlaxcolpan, 54030, Tlalnepantla, Mexico, Mexico
Tel.: (52) 5553902780
Plastics Product Mfr
N.A.I.C.S.: 325211

Huntsman P&A Americas LLC   (1)
10003 Woodloch Forest Dr, The Woodlands, TX 77380
Tel.: (281) 719-6000
Chemicals Mfr
N.A.I.C.S.: 325211

Huntsman Products GmbH   (1)
Roemerstrasse 733, D-47443, Moers, Germany
Tel.: (49) 2841492515
Web Site: https://www.its-all-maleic.com
Plastics Product Mfr
N.A.I.C.S.: 325211

Huntsman Pursan Chemicals Kimya Sanayi Ve Ticaret Limited Sirketi   (1)
N 218 211 Yesilkoy Havaalani Kavsag 5, 34149, Istanbul, Türkiye
Tel.: (90) 2124657677
Chemicals Mfr
N.A.I.C.S.: 325211

Huntsman Solutions India Private Limited   (1)
Lighthall B Wing Saki Vihar Road, Andheri East, Mumbai, 400072, India
Tel.: (91) 2242875307
Chemical Product Mfr & Distr
N.A.I.C.S.: 325998

Huntsman Specialty Chemicals Kimya Sanayi ve Ticaret Anonim Sirketi   (1)
Palladium Tower Barbaros Mah Kardelen Sok No 2 Kat 18 D 63-64, Atasehir, 34746, Istanbul, Turkiye
Tel.: (90) 2162756800
Chemical Products Mfr
N.A.I.C.S.: 325998
Burcak Ozer (Country Mgr)

Huntsman Textile Effects (Switzerland) GmbH   (1)
Klybeckstrasse 200, 4057, Basel, Switzerland
Tel.: (41) 612991111
Chemicals Mfr
N.A.I.C.S.: 325211

Icynene Asia Pacific Inc.   (1)
2-4-2 Shinjuku, Shinjuku-ku, Tokyo, 106-0022, Japan
Tel.: (81) 442011800
Web Site: https://www.icynene.co.jp
Spray Foam Insulation Product Mfr
N.A.I.C.S.: 326150

Icynene Lapolla France SAS   (1)
103 rue Ronsard, 69400, Villefranche-sur-Saone, France
Tel.: (33) 474669410
Web Site: https://www.icynene.fr
Construction Renovation Services
N.A.I.C.S.: 236118

Icynene, Inc.   (1)

15402 Vantage Pkwy E 322, Houston, TX 77032
Tel.: (905) 363-4040
Web Site: http://www.icynene.com
Foam Products Mfr
N.A.I.C.S.: 326140
Eric De Groot (Pres)
Mark Sarvary (Chm)
Larry Genyn (VP-R&D)
Monica Longtin (VP-Customer Service)
Randal W. Scott (VP & Gen Mgr-North America)

Subsidiary (Domestic):

LaPolla Industries, Inc.   (2)
Intercontinental Business Park 15402 Vantage Pkwy E Ste 322, Houston, TX 77032
Tel.: (281) 219-4100
Web Site: http://www.lapolla.com
Coatings, Foam, Paints, Sealants, Adhesives & Related Equipment Mfr & Distr
N.A.I.C.S.: 325510
Douglas J. Kramer (Pres & CEO)
David Feitl (VP-Sls)
Mark Sarvary (Chm)
Scott Campbell (VP-Mfg & Supply Chain)
Shiela Cipriani (VP-HR)

Joint Stock Company Huntsman-NMG B.V.   (1)
110 km Kievskoe Shosse, Obninsk, Russia
Tel.: (7) 4843993444
Plastics Product Mfr
N.A.I.C.S.: 325211

Tecnoelastomeri S.r.l.   (1)
Via Magelano 7/9/11, Castelfranco Emilia, 41013, Modena, Italy
Tel.: (39) 059920707
Web Site: https://www.tecnoelastomeri.com
Chemicals Mfr
N.A.I.C.S.: 325211

HUNTWICKE CAPITAL GROUP INC.
7 Grove St Ste 201, Topsfield, MA 01983
Tel.: (978) 887-5981   DE
Web Site: https://www.huntwicke.com
Year Founded: 2009
HCGI—(OTCIQ)
Sales Range: Less than $1 Million
Emp.: 70
Real Estate Investment Services
N.A.I.C.S.: 531390
Brian Woodland (Pres, CEO & CFO)
Fernando Garcia (VP-Operations)

HURCO COMPANIES, INC.
1 Technology Way, Indianapolis, IN 46268
Tel.: (317) 293-5309   IN
Web Site: http://www.hurco.com
Year Founded: 1968
HURC—(NASDAQ)
Rev.: $227,807,000
Assets: $290,589,000
Liabilities: $68,358,000
Net Worth: $222,231,000
Earnings: $4,389,000
Emp.: 716
Fiscal Year-end: 10/31/23
Computerized Metal Component Production Services
N.A.I.C.S.: 541511
Sonja K. McClelland (CFO, Treas & Exec VP)
Michael Doar (Exec Chm)
Gregory S. Volovic (Pres & CEO)
HaiQuynh Jamison (Principal Acctg Officer & Controller)
Jonathon Wright (Gen Counsel & Sec)

Subsidiaries:

Hurco (S.E. Asia) Pte Ltd.   (1)
21 Toh Guan Road East 01-06 Toh Guan Centre, Singapore, 608609, Singapore
Tel.: (65) 67426177
Web Site: http://www.hurco.com

Hurco Companies, Inc.—(Continued)

Computerized Metal Component Production Services
N.A.I.C.S.: 541512

Hurco Europe Limited (1)
12 Merlin Centre Lancaster Road, Cressex Business Park, High Wycombe, HP12 3TB, Buckinghamshire, United Kingdom
Tel.: (44) 1494442222
Computerized Metal Component Production Services
N.A.I.C.S.: 541512

Hurco GmbH (1)
Gewerbestrasse 5a, 85652, Pliening, Germany
Tel.: (49) 899050940
Web Site: https://www.hurco.eu
Machine Tools Mfr
N.A.I.C.S.: 333517
Michael Auer (Mng Dir)

Hurco India Pte. Ltd. (1)
No 69 2nd Main Road, Ambattur Industrial Estate, Chennai, 600 058, India
Tel.: (91) 4443108726
Web Site: http://www.hurco.com
Sales Range: $25-49.9 Million
Computerized Metal Component Production Services
N.A.I.C.S.: 541512
Sanjib Chakraborty (Head-Country)

Hurco Machine Tool Production Company (1)
1 Technology Way, Indianapolis, IN 46268-5106 (100%)
Tel.: (317) 614-1549
Web Site: http://www.hurco.com
Sales Range: $25-49.9 Million
Emp.: 100
Mfr, Designer & Marketer of Advanced CNC Systems & Associated Software
N.A.I.C.S.: 334513

Hurco Manufacturing Ltd. (1)
No 899 Sec 2 Chung-Shan Rd Ta-Chia, Ta-Chia Town, Taichung, 437, Hsien, Taiwan
Tel.: (886) 4 2682 1993
Web Site: http://www.hurco.com
Machine Tool Whslr
N.A.I.C.S.: 423830

Hurco S.a.r.l. (1)
Alpha Park Activity Park 14 rue Gustave Eiffel, PO Box 40702, 95190, Goussainville, Cedex, France
Tel.: (33) 139886400
Web Site: http://www.hurco.com
Computerized Metal Component Production Services
N.A.I.C.S.: 541512

Hurco S.r.l. (1)
Via E Torricelli 5, 20089, Rozzano, MI, Italy
Tel.: (39) 0290006047
Web Site: http://www.hurco.it
Sales Range: $100-124.9 Million
Computerized Metal Component Production Services
N.A.I.C.S.: 541512

LCM Precision Technology S.r.l. (1)
Via Statale 25/k, 14033, Castellalfero, AT, Italy
Tel.: (39) 0141296035
Web Site: https://www.lcmitalia.it
Machine Tool Mfr & Distr
N.A.I.C.S.: 333517

Milltronics Europe B.V. (1)
Basisweg 10, 1043 AP, Amsterdam, Netherlands
Tel.: (31) 3471756261
Vertical Machine Product Mfr & Distr
N.A.I.C.S.: 332721

Milltronics USA, Inc. (1)
1400 Mill Ln, Waconia, MN 55387
Tel.: (952) 442-1410
Web Site: https://milltronics.com
Emp.: 80
Industrial Machinery Whslr
N.A.I.C.S.: 423830
Bill Bender (Dir-Bus Dev-Intl)
Jill Weinand (Mgr-Customer Svc)
Bill Miracco (Mgr-Sls-Central)
Juan Vizoso (Mgr-Sls & Svc-Latin America)

Brian Starnes (Mgr-Sls-Eastern)
Gary Voltolina (Mgr-Sls-Natl)
Ed Korb (Mgr-Sls-Western)

Takumi Precision Co., Ltd. (1)
No 10 Gong 10th Rd, Dajia Dist, Taichung, 437, Taiwan
Tel.: (886) 426811215
Web Site: https://www.takumi.com.tw
Emp.: 110
Graphite Machine Product Mfr & Distr
N.A.I.C.S.: 335991

HURON CONSULTING GROUP INC.
550 W Van Buren St, Chicago, IL 60607
Tel.: (312) 583-8700   DE
Web Site: https://www.huronconsultinggroup.com
Year Founded: 2002
HURN—(NASDAQ)
Rev.: $1,158,961,000
Assets: $1,199,040,000
Liabilities: $647,000,000
Net Worth: $552,040,000
Earnings: $75,552,000
Emp.: 5,660
Fiscal Year-end: 12/31/22
Holding Company; Operational & Financial Consulting Services
N.A.I.C.S.: 551112
James H. Roth (Founder & Vice Chm-Client Svcs)
John D. Kelly (CFO, Treas & Exec VP)
C. Mark Hussey (Pres & CEO)
Rick Rohrbach (Mng Dir-Higher Education-Healthcare & Non Profit)
J. Ronald Dail (COO)
David Devine (Mng Dir-Healthcare)
Larry Hagenbuch (Mng Dir)
Andrew Laws (Mng Dir-Strategy & Ops)
BG Weiss (Mng Dir-Industrials & Mfg, Financial Svcs & Public Sector)
Kyle D. Featherstone (Chief Acctg Officer & VP)
Ronnie Dail (COO)
Kristen Bruner (Chief HR Officer)

Subsidiaries:

Huron Consulting Services LLC (1)
550 W Van Buren St, Chicago, IL 60607
Tel.: (312) 583-8700
Operational & Financial Consulting Services
N.A.I.C.S.: 541611
James H. Roth (CEO)
C. Mark Hussey (Pres & CEO)

Subsidiary (Domestic):

The Studer Group, LLC (2)
350 W Cedar St Ste 300, Pensacola, FL 32502
Tel.: (850) 439-5839
Web Site: http://www.studergroup.com
Emp.: 166
Healthcare Related Management Consulting Services
N.A.I.C.S.: 541618
Quint Studer (Founder)

Huron Transaction Advisory LLC (1)
550 W Van Buren St Ste 1700, Chicago, IL 60607
Tel.: (312) 583-8700
Financial Advisory Services
N.A.I.C.S.: 523940
Casey Webb (Mgr)
Steven A. Mermelstein (Mng Dir)
Geoffrey Frankel (Mng Dir)

Innosight Consulting Asia Pacific PTE. LTD. (1)
8 Eu Tong Sen Street 15-89 The Central, Singapore, 059818, Singapore
Tel.: (65) 6 884 9375
Web Site: http://www.innosight.com
Business Management Consulting Services
N.A.I.C.S.: 541611

Innosight Consulting, LLC (1)
225 Franklin St Ste 2010, Boston, MA 02110
Tel.: (781) 652-7200
Web Site: https://www.innosight.com
Emp.: 84
Business Management Consulting Services
N.A.I.C.S.: 541611

Pope Woodhead and Associates (1)
The Old Grammar School 1 Ramsey Road, Saint Ives, PE27 5BZ, Cambridgeshire, United Kingdom
Tel.: (44) 1480300300
Web Site: http://www.popewoodhead.com
Business Management Consulting Services
N.A.I.C.S.: 541611

Rittman Mead Consulting Private Limited (1)
Unit No 105-106 Regent Prime Whitefield Main Road, Bengaluru, Whitefield, 560066, Karnataka, India
Tel.: (91) 8040935800
Marketing Consulting Services
N.A.I.C.S.: 541613

Studer Holdings, Inc. (1)
350 W Cedar St Ste 300, Pensacola, FL 32502
Tel.: (850) 439-5839
Holding Company
N.A.I.C.S.: 551112

HURON VALLEY BANCORP, INC.
130 S Milford Rd, Milford, MI 48381
Tel.: (248) 684-9626   Ca
Web Site: https://www.hvsb.com
HVLM—(OTCIQ)
Rev.: $12,673,000
Assets: $232,295,000
Liabilities: $211,496,000
Net Worth: $20,799,000
Earnings: $2,522,000
Emp.: 40
Fiscal Year-end: 12/31/23
Banking Holding Company
N.A.I.C.S.: 551111
Jack J. Shubitowski (Pres & CFO)

HUT 8 CORP.
1101 Brickell Ave Ste 1500, Miami, FL 33131
Tel.: (305) 224-6427   DE
Web Site: https://hut8.com
Year Founded: 2023
HUT—(NASDAQ)
Holding Company
N.A.I.C.S.: 551112

Subsidiaries:

Hut 8 Mining Corp. (1)
130 King Street West Suite 1800, Toronto, M5X 2A2, ON, Canada
Tel.: (647) 256-1992
Web Site: http://www.hut8mining.com
Rev.: $117,875,515
Assets: $323,032,356
Liabilities: $48,146,987
Net Worth: $274,885,369
Earnings: $(189,947,754)
Emp.: 98
Fiscal Year-end: 12/31/2022
Holding Company
N.A.I.C.S.: 551112
Shenif Visram (CFO)
Bill Tai (Chm)
Jaime Leverton (CEO)
Aniss Amdiss (Chief Legal Officer)
Erin Dermer (Sr VP)
James Beer (Sr VP)
Sue Ennis (VP)
Josh Rayner (VP)

U.S. Data Mining Group, Inc. (1)
1101 Brickell Ave Ste 1500, Miami, FL 33131
Tel.: (305) 224-6427
Bitcoin Asset Mining
N.A.I.C.S.: 518210

HYATT HOTELS CORPORATION

150 N Riverside Plz 8th Fl, Chicago, IL 60606
Tel.: (312) 750-1234   DE
Web Site: https://www.hyatt.com
Year Founded: 1957
H—(NYSE)
Rev.: $6,667,000,000
Assets: $12,833,000,000
Liabilities: $9,266,000,000
Net Worth: $3,567,000,000
Earnings: $220,000,000
Emp.: 206,000
Fiscal Year-end: 12/31/23
Hotel Owner, Operator & Franchiser
N.A.I.C.S.: 721110
Thomas J. Pritzker (Exec Chm)
Mark S. Hoplamazian (Pres & CEO)
David Udell (Grp Pres-Asia Pacific)
Peter Sears (Grp Pres-Americas)
Peter Fulton (Grp Pres-Europe, Africa, Middle East & Southwest Asia)
Mark R. Vondrasek (Chief Comml Officer)
Margaret C. Egan (Gen Counsel & Sec)
Malaika Myers (Chief HR Officer)
Joan Bottarini (CFO & Exec VP)
Javier Aguila (Pres)
Jerry Lewin (Sr VP-Ops)

Subsidiaries:

3385434 CANADA INC. (1)
1255 Jeanne-Mance, Montreal, H5B 1E5, QC, Canada
Tel.: (514) 982-1234
Web Site: http://www.montreal.regency.hyatt.com
Hotels & Motels Operator
N.A.I.C.S.: 721110

ATRIUM HOTEL, L.L.C. (1)
18700 MacArthur Blvd, Irvine, CA 92612
Tel.: (949) 833-2770
Web Site: http://www.atriumhotel.com
Emp.: 90
Hotels & Motels Operator
N.A.I.C.S.: 721110

Alila Hotels & Resorts Pte. Ltd. (1)
15 Scotts Road 04-10 Thong Teck building, Singapore, 228218, Singapore
Tel.: (65) 67358300
Web Site: http://www.alilahotels.com
Convention & Laundry Services
N.A.I.C.S.: 721110

Andaz Amsterdam Prinsengracht (1)
Prinsengracht 587, 1016 HT, Amsterdam, Netherlands
Tel.: (31) 205231234
Web Site: http://www.amsterdamprinsengracht.andaz.hyatt.com
Home Management Services
N.A.I.C.S.: 721110

Andaz Liverpool Street (1)
40 Liverpool Street, London, EC2M 7QN, United Kingdom
Tel.: (44) 207 961 1234
Web Site: http://www.londonliverpoolstreet.andaz.hyatt.com
Sales Range: $10-24.9 Million
Emp.: 400
Hotel Operator
N.A.I.C.S.: 721110

BOSTON HOTEL COMPANY, L.L.C. (1)
1 Ave De Lafayette, Boston, MA 02111-1739
Tel.: (617) 912-1234
Hotels & Motels Operator
N.A.I.C.S.: 721110

Classic Residence by Hyatt (1)
71 S Wacker Dr 900, Chicago, IL 60606
Tel.: (312) 750-1234
Web Site: http://www.hyatt.com
Sales Range: $25-49.9 Million
Emp.: 91
Senior Housing Industry
N.A.I.C.S.: 541611

DH Carolina Management LLC (1)
211 Pittsboro St, Chapel Hill, NC 27516

Tel.: (919) 933-2001
Web Site: http://www.carolinainn.com
Hotel Room & Resort Services
N.A.I.C.S.: 721110

DH DBHL Management LLC (1)
150 DuBose Home Ln, Chapel Hill, NC
27517
Tel.: (919) 913-2098
Hotel Room & Resort Services
N.A.I.C.S.: 721110

DH Del Mar Management LLC (1)
1540 Camino Del Mar, Del Mar, CA 92014
Tel.: (858) 259-1515
Boutique Luxury Hotel Services
N.A.I.C.S.: 721110

DH Kirkland Management LLC (1)
1200 Carillon Pt, Kirkland, WA 98033
Tel.: (425) 822-3700
Luxurious Boutique Hotel Services
N.A.I.C.S.: 721110

**DH Mission Bay Management
LLC** (1)
1404 Vacation Rd, San Diego, CA 92109
Tel.: (858) 240-4913
Room Amenitie & Guest Services
N.A.I.C.S.: 721110

**DH Mission Palms Management
LLC** (1)
60 E 5th St, Tempe, AZ 85281
Tel.: (480) 894-1400
Hotel Room & Resort Services
N.A.I.C.S.: 721110

DH RSC Management LLC (1)
135 Saint Charles Ave, New Orleans, LA
70130
Tel.: (504) 587-3700
Hotel Room & Resort Services
N.A.I.C.S.: 721110

DH Richmond Management LLC (1)
201 W Broad St, Richmond, VA 23220
Tel.: (804) 340-6040
Hotel Room & Resort Services
N.A.I.C.S.: 721110

DH Roslyn Management LLC (1)
3600 Suncadia Trl, Cle Elum, WA 98922
Tel.: (509) 649-6400
Luxury Hotel & Conference Center Services
N.A.I.C.S.: 721110

DH SJ Management LLC (1)
233 W Santa Clara St, San Jose, CA 95113
Tel.: (408) 286-1000
Finest Boutique Hotel Services
N.A.I.C.S.: 721110

**DH San Antonio Management
LLC** (1)
16641 La Cantera Pkwy, San Antonio, TX
78256
Tel.: (210) 558-6500
Web Site: https://www.lacanteraresort.com
Hotel Room & Resort Services
N.A.I.C.S.: 721110

DH Scottsdale Management LLC (1)
7700 E McCormick Pkwy, Scottsdale, AZ
85258
Tel.: (480) 991-9000
Hotel Room & Resort Services
N.A.I.C.S.: 721110

DH Seattle Management LLC (1)
1415 5th Ave, Seattle, WA 98101
Luxury & Boutique Hotel Services
N.A.I.C.S.: 721110

DH Stowe Management LLC (1)
7412 Mountain Rd, Stowe, VT 05672
Tel.: (802) 282-4625
Web Site: https://www.sprucepeak.com
Lodge & Restaurant Services
N.A.I.C.S.: 721110

DH Sunriver Management LLC (1)
17600 Center Dr, Sunriver, OR 97707
Hotel Room & Resort Services
N.A.I.C.S.: 721110

DH Tahoe Management LLC (1)
400 Squaw Creek Rd, Olympic Valley, CA
96146
Tel.: (530) 412-7034
Hotel Room & Resort Services
N.A.I.C.S.: 721110

**DH Washington Management
LLC** (1)
1131 SW Skamania Lodge Way, Stevenson, WA 98648
Tel.: (509) 314-4177
Web Site: https://www.skamania.com
Hotel & Fitness Center Services
N.A.I.C.S.: 721110

DH West Loop Management (1)
2525 West Loop S, Houston, TX 77027
Tel.: (713) 961-3000
Hotel Room & Resort Services
N.A.I.C.S.: 721110

**DH Wild Dunes Management
LLC** (1)
5757 Palm Blvd, Isle of Palms, SC 29451
Hotel Room & Resort Services
N.A.I.C.S.: 721110

DH York Management LLC (1)
591 Shore Rd, Cape Neddick, ME 03902
Tel.: (207) 361-1000
Web Site: https://www.cliffhousemaine.com
Guest Room & Cottage Services
N.A.I.C.S.: 721199

**Destination Residences Hawaii
LLC** (1)
68-1050 Mauna Lani Point Dr, Wailea, HI
96743
Tel.: (808) 495-4546
Web Site: https://www.destinationhotels.com
Hotel Room & Resort Services
N.A.I.C.S.: 721110
Michael Cuthbertson *(VP)*

Destination Residences LLC (1)
PO Box 5629, Snowmass Village, CO
81615
Hotel Room & Resort Services
N.A.I.C.S.: 721110

Exhale Enterprises XXXI, LLC (1)
Hamilton Princess And Beach Club 76 Pitts
Bay Road, Pembroke, Hamilton, Bermuda
Tel.: (441) 2986046
Yoga Class & Spa Therapy Services
N.A.I.C.S.: 812199

Exhale Enterprises, LLC (1)
150 Central Park S, New York, NY 10019
Tel.: (212) 561-7400
Web Site: https://www.exhalespa.com
Spa Operator
N.A.I.C.S.: 713940
Annbeth Eschbach *(Founder & CEO)*

Subsidiary (Domestic):

Exhale Enterprises II, LLC (2)
2415 Main St, Bridgehampton, NY 11932
Tel.: (631) 537-2401
Yoga Class & Spa Therapy Services
N.A.I.C.S.: 812199

Exhale Enterprises III, Inc. (2)
150 Central Park S, New York, NY 10019
Tel.: (212) 561-7400
Yoga Class & Spa Therapy Services
N.A.I.C.S.: 812199

Exhale Enterprises IV, LLC (2)
28 Arlington St, Boston, MA 02116
Tel.: (617) 532-7000
Yoga Class & Spa Therapy Services
N.A.I.C.S.: 812199

Exhale Enterprises V, LLC (2)
945 N State St, Chicago, IL 60610
Tel.: (312) 753-6500
Yoga Class & Spa Therapy Services
N.A.I.C.S.: 812199

Exhale Enterprises VIII, Inc. (2)
5300 E Mockingbird Ln, Dallas, TX 75206
Tel.: (214) 370-5800
Yoga Class & Spa Therapy Services
N.A.I.C.S.: 812199

Exhale Enterprises XIV, LLC (2)
420 Park Ave S, New York, NY 10016
Tel.: (646) 380-5330
Yoga Class & Spa Therapy Services
N.A.I.C.S.: 812199

Exhale Enterprises XIX, LLC (2)
2 Battery Wharf, Boston, MA 02109
Tel.: (617) 603-3100
Yoga Class & Spa Therapy Services

N.A.I.C.S.: 812199

Exhale Enterprises XVI, LLC (2)
101 Wilshire Blvd, Santa Monica, CA 90401
Tel.: (310) 319-3193
Yoga Class & Spa Therapy Services
N.A.I.C.S.: 812199

Exhale Enterprises XVIII, LLC (2)
1065 Peachtree St NE, Atlanta, GA 30309
Tel.: (404) 720-5000
Yoga Class & Spa Therapy Services
N.A.I.C.S.: 812199

Exhale Enterprises XX, LLC (2)
150 Washington Blvd, Stamford, CT 06902
Tel.: (203) 391-5350
Yoga Class & Spa Therapy Services
N.A.I.C.S.: 812199

Exhale Enterprises XXI, LLC (2)
500 Boardwalk, Atlantic City, NJ 08401
Tel.: (609) 783-8700
Web Site: https://exhalespa.com
Yoga Class & Spa Therapy Services
N.A.I.C.S.: 812199

Exhale Enterprises XXIV, LLC (2)
2400 Aviation Dr DFW Airport, Dallas, TX
75261
Tel.: (214) 370-5800
Yoga Class & Spa Therapy Services
N.A.I.C.S.: 812199

Exhale Enterprises XXVI, LLC (2)
1601 Collins Ave, Miami Beach, FL 33139
Tel.: (305) 200-1301
Yoga Class & Spa Therapy Services
N.A.I.C.S.: 812199

Exhale Enterprises XXVIII, LLC (2)
10295 Collins Ave, Bal Harbour, FL 33154
Tel.: (305) 455-5411
Yoga Class & Spa Therapy Services
N.A.I.C.S.: 812199

Exhale Enterprises XXXII, LLC (2)
2100 NW 42nd Ave, Miami, FL 33126
Tel.: (305) 423-3900
Yoga Class & Spa Therapy Services
N.A.I.C.S.: 812199

GRAND HYATT BERLIN GMBH (1)
Marlene-Dietrich-Platz 2, Berlin, Germany
Tel.: (49) 3025531234
Web Site: http://berlin.grand.hyatt.com
Emp.: 250
Hotels & Motels Operator
N.A.I.C.S.: 721110

**GRAND HYATT SAN ANTONIO,
L.L.C.** (1)
600 E Market St, San Antonio, TX 78205
Tel.: (210) 224-1234
Web Site: http://sanantonio.grand.hyatt.com
Hotels & Motels Operator
N.A.I.C.S.: 721110

GRAND HYATT SF, L.L.C. (1)
345 Stockton St, San Francisco, CA 94108
Tel.: (415) 398-1234
Web Site: http://www.hyatt.com
Hotels & Motels Operator
N.A.I.C.S.: 721110

**GRAND HYATT SINGAPORE (PTE.)
LIMITED** (1)
10 Scotts Road, Singapore, 228211, Singapore
Tel.: (65) 67381234
Web Site: http://singapore.grand.hyatt.com
Sales Range: $75-99.9 Million
Emp.: 800
Hotel & Spa Operations
N.A.I.C.S.: 721110

**GRAND TORONTO VENTURE,
L.P.** (1)
4 Ave Road, Toronto, M5R 2E8, ON,
Canada
Tel.: (416) 925-1234
Sales Range: $25-49.9 Million
Emp.: 400
Hotel & Motel Operator
N.A.I.C.S.: 721110

Grand Hyatt Seoul (1)
322 Sowol-ro Hannam-dong, Yongsan-gu,
Seoul, 04347, Korea (South)
Tel.: (82) 27971234
Web Site: http://www.seoul.grand.hyatt.com

Sales Range: $75-99.9 Million
Emp.: 1,000
Hotel Operator
N.A.I.C.S.: 721110

H.E. PROPERTIES, INC. (1)
3077 NW Saint Helens Rd, Portland, OR
97210
Tel.: (503) 552-5800
Emp.: 10
Commercial Building Rental & Leasing Services
N.A.I.C.S.: 531120

HDG ASSOCIATES (1)
1111 E Cabrillo Blvd, Santa Barbara, CA
93103
Tel.: (805) 963-0744
Web Site: http://www.hyatt.com
Emp.: 120
Hotels & Motels Operator
N.A.I.C.S.: 721110

**HIHCL HP Amsterdam Airport
B.V.** (1)
Rijnlanderweg 800, Amsterdam, Netherlands
Tel.: (31) 205421234
Hotel Room & Resort Services
N.A.I.C.S.: 721110

**HR MC HOTEL COMPANY, S. DE
R.L. DE C.V.** (1)
Avenida Campos Eliseos 204, 11560, Polanco, Distrito Federal, Mexico
Tel.: (52) 5550831234
Web Site:
http://www.mexicocity.regency.hyatt.com
Emp.: 700
Hotel Owner & Franchiser Operator
N.A.I.C.S.: 721110

HTS-LOAN SERVICING, INC. (1)
450 Carillon Pkwy Ste 210, Saint Petersburg, FL 33716-1209
Tel.: (727) 803-9400
Credit Intermediation Provider
N.A.I.C.S.: 522390

HYATT ARCADE, L.L.C. (1)
420 E Superior Ave, Cleveland, OH 44114
Tel.: (216) 575-1234
Web Site: http://www.cleveland.hyatt.com
Hotels & Motels Operator
N.A.I.C.S.: 721110

**HYATT CHAIN SERVICES
LIMITED** (1)
Rm 1301 13/F The Gateway Twr 1, Tsim
Tsa Tsui, China (Hong Kong)
Tel.: (852) 27681234
Home Management Services
N.A.I.C.S.: 561110

HYATT CRYSTAL CITY, L.L.C. (1)
2799 Jefferson Davis Hwy, Arlington, VA
22202
Tel.: (703) 418-1234
Web Site: http://www.crystalcity.hyatt.com
Emp.: 600
Hotels & Motels Operator
N.A.I.C.S.: 721110

HYATT GTLD, L.L.C. (1)
71 S Wacker Dr, Chicago, IL 60606
Tel.: (312) 750-1234
Emp.: 3
Restaurant Operating Services
N.A.I.C.S.: 722511

**HYATT HOTELS CORPORATION OF
MARYLAND** (1)
1 Bethesda Metro Ctr 7400 Wisconsin Ave,
Bethesda, MD 20814
Tel.: (301) 657-1234
Web Site: http://www.hyatt.com
Hotels & Motels Operator
N.A.I.C.S.: 721110

**HYATT HOTELS OF CANADA,
INC.** (1)
700 Centre St SE, Calgary, T2G 5P6, AB,
Canada
Tel.: (403) 717-1234
Web Site: http://www.hyatthotels.com
Hotels & Motels Operator
N.A.I.C.S.: 721110

**HYATT HOTELS OF FLORIDA,
INC.** (1)

Hyatt Hotels Corporation—(Continued)

335 Beard St, Tallahassee, FL 32303
Tel.: (850) 561-1234
Web Site: http://www.hyatt.com
Restaurant Operating Services
N.A.I.C.S.: 722511

HYATT INTERNATIONAL (EUROPE AFRICA MIDDLE EAST) LLC (1)
Balz-Zimmermannstrasse 7 Kloten, 8302, Zurich, Switzerland
Tel.: (41) 442791234
Web Site: http://www.hyatt.com
Emp.: 55
Hotel & Motel Operator Services
N.A.I.C.S.: 721110
Peter Fulton (Pres)

HYATT INTERNATIONAL (OSAKA) CORPORATION (1)
1-13-11 Nanko-Kita, Suminoe-Ku, Osaka, 559-0034, Japan
Tel.: (81) 666121234
Web Site:
  http://www.osaka.regency.hyatt.com
Hotels & Motels Operator
N.A.I.C.S.: 721110

HYATT INTERNATIONAL - SOUTH-WEST ASIA, LIMITED (1)
Unit Precinct 3-3rd Floor-Units 301 & 310 Level 3, PO Box 506727, Gate Precinct Building 3 Dubai International Financial Centre, Dubai, 506727, United Arab Emirates
Tel.: (971) 47031234
Web Site: http://www.hyatt.com
Hotel & Motel Operator Services
N.A.I.C.S.: 721110

HYATT MINNEAPOLIS, LLC (1)
1300 Nicollet Mall, Minneapolis, MN 55403
Tel.: (612) 370-1234
Web Site: http://www.minneapolis.hyatt.com
Hotels & Motels Operator
N.A.I.C.S.: 721110
Mark Peker (Mng Dir)

HYATT REGENCY COLOGNE GMBH (1)
Kennedy-Ufer 2A, 50679, Cologne, Germany
Tel.: (49) 221 828 1234
Web Site: https://www.hyatt.com
Emp.: 230
Hotels & Motels Operator
N.A.I.C.S.: 721110

HYATT SERVICES GMBH (1)
Roemerpassage 1, 55116, Mainz, Germany
Tel.: (49) 6131731234
Web Site: http://www.hyatt.com
Sales Range: $10 24.0 Million
Emp.: 80
Hotels & Motels Operator
N.A.I.C.S.: 721110

Hyatt Regency Cambridge (1)
575 Memorial Dr, Cambridge, MA 02139-4896
Tel.: (617) 492-1234
Web Site: http://www.cambridge.hyatt.com
Hotel Operator
N.A.I.C.S.: 721110

Hyatt Regency Lake Tahoe Resort & Casino (1)
111 Country Club Dr, Incline Village, NV 89451
Tel.: (775) 832-1234
Web Site: http://www.laketahoe.hyatt.com
Sales Range: $75-99.9 Million
Emp.: 850
Resort Hotel & Casino
N.A.I.C.S.: 721120

INTERNATIONAL RESERVATIONS LIMITED (1)
Birkbeck House Colliers Way Phoenix Business Park Nottinghamshire, Nottingham, NG6 6AT, United Kingdom
Tel.: (44) 1823444644
Hotel Reservation Services
N.A.I.C.S.: 561599

Joint Venture Italkyr Closed Joint Stock Company (1)
191 Abdrahmanov Street, Bishkek, Kyrgyzstan

Tel.: (996) 312661234
Hotel Room & Resort Services
N.A.I.C.S.: 721110

LOST PINES BEVERAGE, LLC (1)
575 Hyatt Lost Pines Rd, Cedar Creek, TX 78612
Tel.: (512) 308-1234
Web Site: http://www.hyattlostpines.com
Spa & Resort Hotel Operator
N.A.I.C.S.: 721110

MUNICH OPCO GMBH (1)
Sedanstrasse 8, 81667, Munich, Bayern, Germany
Tel.: (49) 8967971560
Web Site: http://www.opco-gmbh.de
Restaurant Operating Services
N.A.I.C.S.: 722511

Miraval Group, LLC (1)
5000 E Via Estancia, Tucson, AZ 85739
Web Site: http://www.miravalresorts.com
Hotel Room & Resort Services
N.A.I.C.S.: 721110
Philippe Brenot (Dir-Retail Procurement)
Cecil Hopper (Dir-Revenue Optimization)
Susan Santiago (Head-Lifestyle & Ops)
Fenili Niekamp (Dir-Brand & Mktg)
Simon Marxer (Dir-Spa & Wellbeing)

Miraval Resort Arizona, LLC (1)
5000 E Via Estancia, Tucson, AZ 85739
Web Site: http://www.miravalarizona.com
Hotel & Resort Operator
N.A.I.C.S.: 721110

Mrg ATX Holdings, LLC (1)
13500 FM2769, Austin, TX 78726
Tel.: (512) 531-5700
Hotel Spa & Golf Resort Services
N.A.I.C.S.: 721110

Mrg CRW Holdings, LLC (1)
55 Lee Rd, Lenox, MA 01240
Tel.: (413) 637-1364
Web Site: http://www.cranwell.lpages.co
Hotel Spa & Golf Resort Services
N.A.I.C.S.: 721110

PARK HYATT HOTEL GMBH (1)
Beethovenstrasse 21, 8002, Zurich, 8002, Switzerland
Tel.: (41) 438831234
Hotels & Motels Operator
N.A.I.C.S.: 721110

PARK HYATT WATER TOWER ASSOCIATES, L.L.C. (1)
800 N Michigan Ave, Chicago, IL 60611
Tel.: (312) 335-1234
Web Site: http://www.parkhyattchicago.com
Hotels & Motels Operator
N.A.I.C.S.: 721110

Park HYATT Hamburg GmbH (1)
Bugenhagenstrasse 8, Hamburg, Germany
Tel.: (49) 4033321234
Hotel Room & Resort Services
N.A.I.C.S.: 721110

Rosemont Project Management, LLC (1)
71 S Wacker Dr Ste 4700, Chicago, IL 60606
Tel.: (312) 780-6234
Emp.: 25
Hotel & Motel Operator Services
N.A.I.C.S.: 721110

SELECT HOTELS GROUP, L.L.C. (1)
8741 International Dr, Orlando, FL 32819
Tel.: (407) 370-4720
Web Site: http://www.hyatte.com
Emp.: 40
Hotels & Motels Operator
N.A.I.C.S.: 721110

Sao Paulo Investment Company Inc. (1)
52 Bella Vista, Panama, Panama
Tel.: (507) 3071234
Hotel Spa & Golf Resort Services
N.A.I.C.S.: 721110

Standard International Management LLC (1)
23 East 4th Street 5th Floor, New York, NY 10003
Tel.: (212) 226-5656

Web Site: http://www.standardhotels.com
Hotels Owner & Management Services
N.A.I.C.S.: 721110
Laura Nolte (Dir-Mktg)
Edward Farwick (VP-Sls)
Lauren Casamassima (VP-Team Dev)
Kevin Osterhaus (Exec VP-Ops)
Amber Asher (Gen Counsel & Exec VP)

Holding (Domestic):

Bunkhouse Group LLC (2)
1402 E Cesar Chavez, Austin, TX 78702   (51%)
Tel.: (512) 852-2300
Web Site: http://www.bunkhousegroup.com
Hotel
N.A.I.C.S.: 721110
Elizabeth Ann Lambert (Principal & Mgr)

Unit (Domestic):

Standard Hotel Hollywood (2)
8300 Sunset Blvd, Hollywood, CA 90069
Tel.: (323) 650-9090
Web Site: http://www.standardhotels.com
Sales Range: $1-9.9 Million
Emp.: 189
Hotel
N.A.I.C.S.: 721110
David Vialli (Gen Mgr)

TR BIG SUR Management LLC (1)
48123 Highway 1, Big Sur, CA 93920
Tel.: (831) 667-2331
Web Site: https://www.ventanabigsur.com
Hotel Spa & Golf Resort Services
N.A.I.C.S.: 721110

TR Camino Management LLC (1)
860 E EL Camino Real, Mountain View, CA 94040
Tel.: (650) 940-1000
Hotel & Resort Services
N.A.I.C.S.: 721110

TR Excelsior Manaement LLC (1)
401 Regent St, Excelsior Springs, MO 64024
Tel.: (816) 630-5500
Web Site: https://www.elmshotelandspa.com
Hotel Room & Resort Services
N.A.I.C.S.: 721110

TR Lakeshore Management LLC (1)
4104 Lakeshore Blvd, South Lake Tahoe, CA 96150
Tel.: (530) 541-5263
Web Site: http://www.thelandingtahoe.com
Resort & Spa Services
N.A.I.C.S.: 721110

TR New York Management LLC (1)
123 Nassau St, New York, NY 10038
Tel.: (212) 233-2300
Web Site: http://www.thompsonhotels.com
Hotel Room & Resort Services
N.A.I.C.S.: 721110

TR Park South Management LLC (1)
124 E 28th St, New York, NY 10016
Tel.: (212) 448-0888
Boutique Hotel Services
N.A.I.C.S.: 721110

TR Post Management LLC (1)
1625 Post St, San Francisco, CA 94115
Tel.: (415) 922-3200
Boutique Hotel Services
N.A.I.C.S.: 721110

TR Presidio Management LLC (1)
444 Presidio Ave, San Francisco, CA 94115
Tel.: (415) 567-8467
Boutique Hotel Services
N.A.I.C.S.: 721110

TR Santa Clara Management LLC (1)
4200 Great America Pkwy, Santa Clara, CA 95054
Tel.: (408) 235-8900
Boutique Hotel Services
N.A.I.C.S.: 721110

TR Seattle Management LLC (1)
110 Stewart St, Seattle, WA 98101-1019
Tel.: (206) 623-4600
Web Site: http://www.thompsonhotels.com
Restaurant & Bar Services

N.A.I.C.S.: 721110

TR Sedona Management LLC (1)
301 Lauberge Ln, Sedona, AZ 86336
Tel.: (928) 399-7002
Web Site: https://www.lauberge.com
Resort & Spa Services
N.A.I.C.S.: 721110
Joe Mottershead (COO)

TR Sunnyvale Management LLC (1)
910 E Fremont Ave, Sunnyvale, CA 94087
Tel.: (408) 738-0500
Boutique Hotel Services
N.A.I.C.S.: 721110

Tijuana Partners, S. De R.L. DE C.V. (1)
Blvd Agua Caliente 10488 Col Aviacion, Tijuana, Mexico
Tel.: (52) 6649001234
Hotel Room & Resort Services
N.A.I.C.S.: 721110

Wall Street Manager, LLC (1)
15 Gold St, New York, NY 10038-4803
Tel.: (212) 232-7700
Hotel Room & Resort Services
N.A.I.C.S.: 721110

HYBRID COATING TECHNOLOGIES INC.
950 John Daly Blvd Ste 260, Daly City, CA 94015
Tel.: (650) 491-3449   NV
Web Site:
  http://www.hybridcoatingtech.com
Year Founded: 2010
HCTI—(OTCIQ)
Sales Range: Less than $1 Million
Emp.: 3
Coatings & Other Chemicals Mfr
N.A.I.C.S.: 325510
Darin Nellis (Sec, Dir-Sls & Mktg)
Joseph Kristul (Pres, CEO & Treas)

HYBRID ENERGY HOLDINGS, INC.
9267 Yankee Rd, Springboro, OH 45066
Tel.: (443) 334-8840   DE
Year Founded: 1966
HYBE—(OTCIQ)
Alternative Fuel Energy Generation Services
N.A.I.C.S.: 221112
Roxanne McDade (Chm)

HYCROFT MINING HOLDING CORPORATION
PO Box 3030, Winnemucca, NV 89446
Tel.: (775) 304-0260   DE
Web Site:
  https://www.hycroftmining.com
Year Founded: 2017
HYMC—(NASDAQ)
Rev.: $33,229,000
Assets: $248,954,000
Liabilities: $185,648,000
Net Worth: $63,306,000
Earnings: ($60,828,000)
Emp.: 74
Fiscal Year-end: 12/31/22
Gold & Silver Mining
N.A.I.C.S.: 212220
Jeffrey Stieber (Treas & Sr VP-Fin)
David B. Thomas (Sr VP-Ops & Gen Mgr)
Diane Renee Garrett (Pres & CEO)
Mike Eiselein (VP & Gen Mgr-Hycroft Mine)
John William Henris (COO & Exec VP)
Stanton K. Rideout (CFO & Exec VP)
Lily He (VP-Finance & Treasury)
Alex Davidson (VP-Exploration)
Rebecca Jennings (Gen Counsel, Sec & Sr VP)

Subsidiaries:

Hycroft Mining Corporation (1)
9790 Gateway Dr Ste 200, Reno, NV 89521
Tel.: (775) 358-4455
Web Site: http://www.hycroftmining.com
Sales Range: $300-349.9 Million
Emp.: 70
Gold Mining & Exploration Services
N.A.I.C.S.: 212220
Jeffrey Stieber (Interim CFO)
David Kirsch (Chm)
Tracey M. Thom (VP-IR)

Subsidiary (Domestic):

Vista Gold Holdings Inc. (2)
9604 Prototype Ct, Reno, NV 89600
Tel.: (775) 358-4455
Web Site: http://www.alliednevada.com
Sales Range: $1-9.9 Million
Holding Company; Gold Mining
N.A.I.C.S.: 551112

Subsidiary (Domestic):

Hycroft Resources & Development, Inc. (3)
PO Box 3030, Winnemucca, NV 89446-3030
Tel.: (775) 623-5260
Sales Range: $1-9.9 Million
Mining Operation
N.A.I.C.S.: 212220
Randy Buffington (Gen Mgr)

HYDROFARM HOLDINGS GROUP, INC.
1510 Main St, Shoemakersville, PA 19555
Tel.: (707) 765-9990 DE
Web Site: https://www.hydrofarm.com
Year Founded: 2017
HYFM—(NASDAQ)
Rev.: $344,501,000
Assets: $573,559,000
Liabilities: $223,678,000
Net Worth: $349,881,000
Earnings: ($285,415,000)
Emp.: 498
Fiscal Year-end: 12/31/22
Offices of Other Holding Companies
N.A.I.C.S.: 551112
William Douglas Toler (Chm & CEO)
B. John Lindeman (CFO & Exec VP)

Subsidiaries:

Aurora Innovations, LLC (1)
901 D St Sw Ste 901, Washington, DC 20024
Tel.: (202) 479-4009
Software Development Services
N.A.I.C.S.: 541511

Aurora Peat Products ULC (1)
13704 170 Street NW, Edmonton, T5V 1T2, AB, Canada
Tel.: (780) 447-1802
Web Site: https://www.aurorapeat.com
Peat Moss Harvesting Services
N.A.I.C.S.: 113210

Eltac XXI S.L. (1)
Parque Empresarial Sector P 9 EDIFICIO C puerta 1 10, Figueruelas, 50639, Zaragoza, Spain
Tel.: (34) 976655461
Web Site: https://www.eltacnet.com
Farming Services
N.A.I.C.S.: 115116

GreenStar Plant Products Inc. (1)
9430 198st, Langley, V1M 3C8, BC, Canada
Tel.: (604) 882-7699
Web Site: https://www.getgreenstar.com
Grain & Oilseed Shipping Services
N.A.I.C.S.: 111120

Innovative Growers Equipment Canada, Inc. (1)
1166 Gorham Street Unit 8, Newmarket, L3Y 8W4, ON, Canada
Farm Equipment Mfr
N.A.I.C.S.: 333111

Innovative Growers Equipment, Inc. (1)
421 N California St Bldg 6, Sycamore, IL 60178
Tel.: (815) 991-5010
Farm Equipment Mfr
N.A.I.C.S.: 333111

Sunblaster Holdings ULC (1)
5744 268th Street, Langley, V4W 3X9, BC, Canada
Tel.: (604) 381-1166
Web Site: https://www.sunblasterlighting.com
Farming Services
N.A.I.C.S.: 115116

HYDROMER, INC.
4715 Corporate Dr, Concord, NC 28027
Tel.: (908) 722-5000 NJ
Web Site: https://www.hydromer.com
Year Founded: 1980
HYDI—(OTCIQ)
Sales Range: $1-9.9 Million
Emp.: 39
Bio-Polymer Researcher & Developer
N.A.I.C.S.: 541715
Manfred F. Dyck (Chm & Exec VP-R&D)
Robert Y. Lee (CFO, Treas & VP-Fin)
Martin C. Dyck (Exec VP-Ops)
John Konar (VP-Quality Assurance & Dir-HR)
Richard A. Merkt (Gen Counsel & Sec)
Peter M. Von Dyck (Pres & CEO)
Cortney Wells (Dir-Fin)
Michael Torti (VP-Sls, Mktg & Bus Dev)

HYLIION HOLDINGS CORP.
1202 BMC Dr Ste 100, Cedar Park, TX 78613 DE
Web Site: https://www.hyliion.com
Year Founded: 2018
HYLN—(NYSE)
Rev.: $672,000
Assets: $328,383,000
Liabilities: $22,117,000
Net Worth: $306,266,000
Earnings: ($123,510,000)
Emp.: 85
Fiscal Year-end: 12/31/23
Electrified Powertrain Services
N.A.I.C.S.: 488210
Thomas Healy (Founder & CEO)
Jon T. Panzer (CFO)
Josh Mook (CTO)
Cheri Lantz (Chief Strategy Officer)
Jose Oxholm (Chief Compliance Officer, Gen Counsel & VP)
Govi Ramasamy (Chief Comml Officer)

HYPERFINE, INC.
351 New Whitfield St, Guilford, CT 06437
Tel.: (203) 458-7100 DE
Web Site: https://hyperfine.io
Year Founded: 2020
HCAQ—(NASDAQ)
Rev.: $6,814,000
Assets: $134,051,000
Liabilities: $10,329,000
Net Worth: $123,722,000
Earnings: ($73,164,000)
Emp.: 136
Fiscal Year-end: 12/31/22
Surgical Appliance & Supplies Manufacturing
N.A.I.C.S.: 551112
Jonathan M. Rothberg (Founder & Chm)
Arthur B. Cohen (CEO)

HYPERTENSION DIAGNOSTICS, INC.

730 2nd Ave S 730 Building Ste 295, Minnetonka, MN 55402
Tel.: (952) 545-2457 MN
Web Site: http://www.hypertensiondiagnostics.com
Year Founded: 1988
HDII—(OTCIQ)
Sales Range: $1-9.9 Million
Non-Invasive Devices to Measure Large & Small Artery Elasticity
N.A.I.C.S.: 339112
Maury Taylor (Exec Dir)

HYPHA LABS, INC.
5940 S Rainbow Blvd, Las Vegas, NV 89118
Tel.: (702) 744-0640 NV
Web Site: https://hyphalabs.com
Year Founded: 2010
FUNI—(OTCQB)
Assets: $1,409,464
Liabilities: $3,614,570
Net Worth: ($2,205,106)
Earnings: $246,774
Emp.: 17
Fiscal Year-end: 09/30/23
Digital Pathology Solutions & Advisory Services
N.A.I.C.S.: 513210
Todd Denkin (Founder)
Angus Stone Douglass (CFO)
Dennis Hartmann (Interim Pres)

Subsidiaries:

DigiPath Labs, Inc. (1)
6450 Cameron St Ste 113, Las Vegas, NV 89118
Tel.: (702) 209-2429
Web Site: https://www.digipathlabs.com
Laboratory Testing Services
N.A.I.C.S.: 621511

HYRECAR, INC.
355 S Grand Ave Ste 1650, Los Angeles, CA 90071
Tel.: (888) 688-6769 DE
Web Site: http://www.hyrecar.com
Year Founded: 2014
HYRE—(OTCBB)
Rev.: $35,716,031
Assets: $16,444,370
Liabilities: $10,827,053
Net Worth: $5,617,317
Earnings: ($25,953,717)
Emp.: 76
Fiscal Year-end: 12/31/21
Car Rental Services
N.A.I.C.S.: 532111
Anshu Bansal (Co-Founder)
Greg Tatem (CTO)
Abhishek Arora (Co-Founder)
Grace Mellis (Chm)
Megan Behrens (Sr VP-Ops & Product)
Nate Ryan (VP-Mktg)
A. J. Lee (COO)
Eduardo Vazquez Iniguez (CEO & CFO)

HYSTER-YALE MATERIALS HANDLING, INC.
5875 Landerbrook Dr Ste 300, Cleveland, OH 44124
Tel.: (440) 449-9600 DE
Web Site: https://www.hyster-yale.com
HY—(NYSE)
Rev.: $4,118,300,000
Assets: $2,079,100,000
Liabilities: $1,687,100,000
Net Worth: $392,000,000
Earnings: $125,900,000
Emp.: 8,600
Fiscal Year-end: 12/31/23
Holding Company; Materials Handling Equipment Mfr & Distr

N.A.I.C.S.: 551112
Alfred Marshall Rankin Jr. (Exec Chm)
Jennifer M. Langer (VP-European Div)
Suzanne S. Taylor (Gen Counsel, Sec & Sr VP)
Scott A. Minder (CFO, Treas & Sr VP)
Gregory J. Breier (VP-Tax)
Stephen J. Karas (Pres-Asia Pacific & Sr VP)
Rajiv K. Prasad (Pres & CEO)
Anthony J. Salgado (COO)
Brian A. Jennings (VP)
Stewart D. Murdoch (Mng Dir)
Charles F. Pascarelli (Pres)
David M. LeBlanc (Pres)
Michele Corini (VP)
Tracy S. Hixson (VP)
Gopi Somayajula (Sr VP)
Jon C. Taylor (Co-CFO)

Subsidiaries:

Bolzoni (Hebei) Forks (1)
Industrial Base of Long Hua Town, Jing, Hebei, 053511, China
Tel.: (86) 318 583 5388
Web Site: http://www.bolzoni-auramo.de
Emp.: 900
Trucks Mfr
N.A.I.C.S.: 333924

Bolzoni Auramo (Wuxi) Forklift Truck Attachment Co. Ltd. (1)
No 2566 Antai 2nd Road, Xishan Economic and Technological Development Zone, Wuxi, 214106, Jiangsu, China
Tel.: (86) 51088789395
Web Site: https://www.bolzoni-auramo.com.cn
Emp.: 900
Trucks Mfr
N.A.I.C.S.: 333924

Bolzoni Auramo Inc. (1)
17635 Hoffman Way, Homewood, IL 60430
Tel.: (708) 957-8809
Web Site: https://us.bolzonigroup.com
Emp.: 1,500
Trucks Mfr
N.A.I.C.S.: 333924

Bolzoni Capital Holding B.V. (1)
Nijverheidsweg 29, 6541 CL, Nijmegen, Netherlands
Tel.: (31) 243742444
Trucks Mfr
N.A.I.C.S.: 333924

Bolzoni Italia Srl (1)
Via del Mandorlo 28, 59100, Prato, Italy
Tel.: (39) 057 457 1353
Web Site: https://it.bolzonigroup.com
Emp.: 900
Trucks Mfr
N.A.I.C.S.: 333924
Paolo Chiesi (Dir)

Bolzoni S.p.A. (1)
Via I Maggio 103 Casoni di Podenzano, 29027, Piacenza, Italy (62.5%)
Tel.: (39) 0523555511
Web Site: https://www.bolzonigroup.com
Sales Range: $150-199.9 Million
Emp.: 737
Lift Truck Attachments & Industrial Material Handling Equipment Mfr
N.A.I.C.S.: 333248

Subsidiary (Non-US):

AURAMO OY (2)
Yrittajankatu 4, PL 1001, 04401, Jarvenpaa, Finland
Tel.: (358) 982931
Web Site: https://fi.bolzonigroup.com
Fork Lift Trucks Mfr
N.A.I.C.S.: 333924

Bolzoni Auramo (Pty) Ltd (2)
Unit 2 12 Avalli Road, Prestons, Liverpool, 2170, NSW, Australia
Tel.: (61) 28 783 8377

Hyster-Yale Materials Handling,
Inc.—(Continued)

Web Site: https://au.bolzonigroup.com
Fork Lift Trucks Mfr
N.A.I.C.S.: 333924

Bolzoni Auramo AB   (2)
Beckasinvagen 9A, SE-803 09, Gavle,
Sweden
Tel.: (46) 26647230
Web Site: https://www.se.bolzonigroup.com
Lift Truck Attachments Distr
N.A.I.C.S.: 423120

Bolzoni Auramo BV   (2)
Waterbeemd 6a Industrieterrein nr 8955,
5705 DN, Helmond, Netherlands
Tel.: (31) 49 250 9777
Web Site: https://www.nl.bolzonigroup.com
Emp.: 3
Fork Lift Trucks Mfr
N.A.I.C.S.: 333924

Bolzoni Auramo Canada Ltd   (2)
211 ave Labrosse, Pointe-Claire, H9R 1A3,
QC, Canada
Tel.: (514) 685-7871
Industrial Truck Machinery Distr
N.A.I.C.S.: 423830

Bolzoni Auramo GmbH   (2)
Muhlenstr 74, 41352, Korschenbroich, Germany
Tel.: (49) 2161999360
Web Site: http://www.bolzoni-auramo.de
Fork Lift Trucks Mfr
N.A.I.C.S.: 333924

Bolzoni Auramo Polska Sp Zoo   (2)
Tokarska 9C, 20-210, Lublin, Poland
Tel.: (48) 814465491
Web Site: https://pl.bolzonigroup.com
Lift Truck Attachments Distr
N.A.I.C.S.: 423120
Krzysztof Pomykaa *(Dir-Sls)*

Bolzoni Auramo S.A.R.L.   (2)
Rue Avogadro Technopole De Forbach-Sud,
Forbach, 57600, France
Tel.: (33) 387846540
Web Site: http://fr.bolzonigroup.com
Lift Truck Attachments Distr
N.A.I.C.S.: 423120

Bolzoni Auramo S.L.   (2)
c/ Segre 8-10 P I Pla d en Coll, 08110,
Montcada i Reixac, Barcelona, Spain
Tel.: (34) 938648633
Web Site: http://www.es.bolzonigroup.com
Sales Range: $50-74.9 Million
Emp.: 9
Lift Truck Attachments Distr
N.A.I.C.S.: 423120

Bolzoni Limited   (2)
Unit 10 Taurus Park Europa Boulevard,
Warrington, WA5 7ZT, Cheshire, United
Kingdom
Tel.: (44) 192 562 4570
Web Site: https://uk.bolzonigroup.com
Sales Range: $25-49.9 Million
Emp.: 10
Industrial Truck Machinery Distr
N.A.I.C.S.: 423830

Bolzoni SARL   (2)
3 Rue Gutenberg Za De la Butte, 91620,
Nozay, France
Tel.: (33) 178854574
Web Site: https://fr.bolzonigroup.com
Emp.: 4
Fork Lift Trucks Mfr & Distr
N.A.I.C.S.: 333924
Benoit Delaporte *(Acct Mgr)*
Yohann Cario *(Engr-Sls)*
Pierre Romero *(Engr-Sls)*

Hans H. MEYER GmbH   (2)
Gittertor 14, D-38259, Salzgitter, Germany
Tel.: (49) 53418030
Web Site: http://www.meyer-world.com
Sales Range: $50-74.9 Million
Emp.: 145
Fork Lift Trucks Mfr
N.A.I.C.S.: 333924

Bolzoni South America Ltda.   (1)
Rua Porto de Praia Mole 124-CIVIT I,
29168-005, Serra, Espirito Santo, Brazil
Tel.: (55) 27996467907

Industrial Material Handling Equipment Mfr
N.A.I.C.S.: 333924

Hyster France S.A.R.L.   (1)
10 Rue de la Fontaine Rouge Immeuble le
Galilee, 77700, Chessy, France
Tel.: (33) 160435870
Web Site: http://www.hyster.com
Sales Range: $10-24.9 Million
Emp.: 12
Lift Truck & Related Part Whslr
N.A.I.C.S.: 333924

**Hyster-Yale Australia Holding Pty
Ltd.**   (1)
1 Bullecourt Avenue, Milperra, 2214, NSW,
Australia
Tel.: (61) 297953800
Industrial Truck Machinery Distr
N.A.I.C.S.: 423830

Hyster-Yale Deutschland GmbH   (1)
Siemensstr 9, 63263, Neu-Isenburg, Germany
Tel.: (49) 6102368680
Industrial Truck Machinery Distr
N.A.I.C.S.: 423830

Hyster-Yale Group, Inc.   (1)
1400 Sullivan Dr, Greenville, NC 27834
Tel.: (252) 931-5100
Emp.: 1,217
Industrial Truck Machinery Mfr
N.A.I.C.S.: 333924
Rajiv K. Prasad *(Pres)*
Anthony J. Salgado *(COO)*
Suzanne S. Taylor *(Sr VP)*

Hyster-Yale Group, Inc.   (1)
5875 Landerbrook Dr, Cleveland, OH
44124-4069
Tel.: (440) 449-9600
Web Site: http://www.hyster-yale.com
Holding Company; Forklift Truck & Auto-
mated Handling Equipment Mfr & Distr
N.A.I.C.S.: 551112
Rajiv K. Prasad *(Pres & CEO)*

Subsidiary (Non-US):

**NACCO Materials Handling Group
Brasil Ltda.**   (2)
Av das Nacoes Unidas 22777, Sao Paulo,
04795-100, Brazil   **(100%)**
Tel.: (55) 1156838500
Web Site: http://www.hyster.com.br
Sales Range: $100-124.9 Million
Emp.: 200
Forklift Mfr & Distr
N.A.I.C.S.: 333924

**NACCO Materials Handling Group
Pty. Ltd.**   (2)
1 Dullecourt Avenue, Milperra, 2214, NSW,
Australia   **(100%)**
Tel.: (61) 2 9795 3800
Web Site: http://www.hyster.com
Fork Lift Truck Mfr & Whslr
N.A.I.C.S.: 333924

**NACCO Materials Handling Group,
Ltd.**   (2)
Centennial House 4 5 Frimley Business
Park Frimley, Camberley, GU16 7SG, Sur-
rey, United Kingdom   **(100%)**
Tel.: (44) 1252810261
Web Site: http://www.hyster.com
Sales Range: $25-49.9 Million
Emp.: 80
Fork Lift Truck Mfr & Whslr
N.A.I.C.S.: 333924

Plant (Domestic):

**NACCO Materials Handling Ltd. -
Craigavon Plant**   (3)
Armagh Carn Industrial Area, PO Box 11,
Craigavon, BT63 5RY, United Kingdom
Tel.: (44) 2838354499
Web Site: http://www.nmhg.com
Forklift Truck Mfr
N.A.I.C.S.: 333924

Subsidiary (Non-US):

NMHG Australia Holding Pty Ltd.   (2)
1 Bullecourt Ave, Milperra, 2214, NSW,
Australia
Tel.: (61) 297953800
Investment Management Service

N.A.I.C.S.: 551112

NMHG Distribution Pty. Limited   (2)
Somerville Rd, Yarraville, 3013, VIC, Aus-
tralia
Tel.: (61) 1300367577
Industrial Truck Machinery Distr
N.A.I.C.S.: 423830

NMHG Mexico S.A. de C.V.   (2)
Industria Automotriz No 3090 Parque, Coa-
huila, Ramos Arizpe, 25900, Mexico
Tel.: (52) 8444110500
Lift Truck & Related Part Mfr
N.A.I.C.S.: 336120
Daniela Chapa *(Supvr-Fin)*
Mike Gorham *(Mgr-Matls)*

Subsidiary (Domestic):

NMHG Oregon, LLC   (2)
4000 NE Blue Lake Rd, Fairview, OR
97024-8710
Tel.: (503) 721-6000
Web Site: http://www.hyster-yale.com
Industrial Machinery & Equipment Whslr
N.A.I.C.S.: 423830

Joint Venture (Non-US):

**Sumitomo NAACO Materials Han-
dling Co., Ltd.**   (2)
2-75 Daito-cho Obu-shi, Nagoya, 474-8555,
Japan   **(50%)**
Tel.: (81) 562485251
Web Site: http://www.sumitomonacco.co.jp
Sales Range: $125-149.9 Million
Emp.: 1,200
Fork-Lift Trucks & Logistic Handling Equip-
ment Mfr & Distr
N.A.I.C.S.: 333924

Subsidiary (Domestic):

**Sumitomo NACCO Materials Han-
dling Sales Co., Ltd.**   (3)
2-75 Daito-cho Obu-shi, Nagoya, 474-8555,
Japan
Tel.: (81) 562485251
Web Site: http://www.sumitomonacco.co.jp
Emp.: 1,200
Sales, Lease, Repair & Service of Forklift
Trucks & Logistics Machinery & Equipment
N.A.I.C.S.: 423830

Hyster-Yale Italia SpA   (1)
Tel.: (39) 02953991
Industrial Machinery & Equipment Whslr
N.A.I.C.S.: 423830

**Hyster-Yale Materials Handling
GmbH**   (1)
Siemensstr 9, 63263, Neu-Isenburg, Ger-
many
Tel.: (49) 6102882710
Industrial Truck & Vehicle Whslr
N.A.I.C.S.: 333924

**Hyster-Yale Maximal Forklift (Zheji-
ang) Co., Ltd.**   (1)
No 1 Jinxin Road Lushan Industrial Area,
Fuyang, Hangzhou, Zhejiang,
China   **(75%)**
Tel.: (86) 57128037691
Web Site: https://www.maxforklift.com
Emp.: 500
Forklift Truck Mfr & Distr
N.A.I.C.S.: 333120

**Hyster-Yale UK Pension Co.
Limited**   (1)
Centennial House Centennial House Build-
ing 4 5, Frimley Business Park, Frimley,
GU16 7SG, Surrey, United Kingdom
Tel.: (44) 1276538500
Industrial Truck Machinery Services
N.A.I.C.S.: 532490

LLC Hans H. Meyer OOO   (1)
Krasnogo Mayka Str 26, 117570, Moscow,
Russia
Tel.: (7) 4953745434
Trucks Mfr
N.A.I.C.S.: 333924

Meyer GmbH   (1)
Dr Doernemann-Str 1, 38259, Salzgitter,
Germany
Tel.: (49) 53418030
Trucks Mfr
N.A.I.C.S.: 333924

**NACCO Materials Handling France
S.A.R.L.**   (1)
10 Rue De La Fontaine Rouge, Chessy,
77700, France
Tel.: (33) 160435870
Web Site: http://www.hyster.com
Emp.: 23
Industrial Machinery & Equipment Distr
N.A.I.C.S.: 423830

Nuvera Fuel Cells Europe Srl   (1)
Via XXV Aprile 2, 20097, San Donato Mila-
nese, Italy
Tel.: (39) 0251616701
Web Site: https://www.nuvera.com
Chemical Research & Development Ser-
vices
N.A.I.C.S.: 541715

Nuvera Fuel Cells, Inc.   (1)
129 Concord Rd Bldg 1, Billerica, MA
01821
Tel.: (617) 245-7500
Web Site: https://www.nuvera.com
Chemical Research & Development Ser-
vices
N.A.I.C.S.: 541715

Shanghai Hyster Forklift, Ltd.   (1)
No 588 Rongqiao Road Jinqiao Expo, Pu
Dong New Area, Shanghai, 201206,
China   **(75%)**
Tel.: (86) 21583496
Industrial Truck Machinery Distr
N.A.I.C.S.: 423830
Richard Lin *(Mng Dir)*

**Yale Fordertechnik Handelsgesell-
schaft mbH**   (1)
Keniastr 32, 47269, Duisburg, Germany
Tel.: (49) 203710180
Forklift Truck Mfr
N.A.I.C.S.: 336120

HYZON MOTORS INC.
475 Quaker Meeting House Rd, Ho-
neoye Falls, NY 14472
Tel.: (585) 484-9337   **DE**
Web Site:
    https://www.hyzonfuelcell.com
Year Founded: 2017
HYZN—(NASDAQ)
Assets: $338,600
Liabilities: $314,000
Net Worth: $24,600
Earnings: ($216,960)
Emp.: 2
Fiscal Year-end: 12/31/19
Investment Services
N.A.I.C.S.: 520999
John P. Waldron *(Chief Acctg Officer
& Sr VP-Fin & Acctg)*
Erik J. Anderson *(Chm)*
Parker Meeks *(Pres & CEO)*
John Edgley *(Pres-Intl Ops)*
John Zavoli *(Chief Legal Officer &
Gen Counsel)*
Sue Sun-LaSovage *(Chief HR Offi-
cer)*
Bappaditya Banerjee *(COO)*
Stephen Weiland *(CFO)*
Christian Mohrdieck *(CTO-Europe)*
Stephanie J. Mudgett *(Head-Global
Comm & Branding)*

I-80 GOLD CORP.
5190 Neil Rd Ste 460, Reno, NV
89502
Tel.: (202) 572-3133   **BC**
Web Site: https://www.i80gold.com
Year Founded: 2020
IAUX—(NYSE)
Rev.: $36,958,000
Assets: $641,959,000
Liabilities: $308,547,000
Net Worth: $333,412,000
Earnings: $79,197,000
Fiscal Year-end: 12/31/22
Gold Exploration Services
N.A.I.C.S.: 212220
Ryan Snow *(CFO)*

I-WELLNESS MARKETING GROUP, INC.
3651 Lindell Rd Ste D612, Las Vegas, NV 89103
Tel.: (702) 318-7545   NV
IWMG—(OTCIQ)
Healtcare Services
N.A.I.C.S.: 541219

I3 VERTICALS, INC.
40 Burton Hills Blvd Ste 415, Nashville, TN 37215
Tel.: (615) 465-4487   DE
Web Site: https://www.i3verticals.com
Year Founded: 2018
IIIV—(NASDAQ)
Rev.: $370,239,000
Assets: $881,493,000
Liabilities: $553,197,000
Net Worth: $328,296,000
Earnings: ($811,000)
Emp.: 1,663
Fiscal Year-end: 09/30/23
Offices of Other Holding Companies
N.A.I.C.S.: 551112
Gregory S. Daily *(Chm & CEO)*
Clay M. Whitson *(Chief Strategy Officer)*
Geoff Smith *(CFO & Principal Acctg Officer)*
Paul J. Christians *(Chief Revenue Officer)*
Rick Stanford *(Pres)*
Paul Maple *(Gen Counsel & Sec)*
Pete Panagakis *(CTO)*
Diana Day-Cartee *(VP-Customer Experience)*
Amber Murphy *(VP-HR)*
Chris Laisure *(Pres-Public Sector)*

Subsidiaries:

Accufund Inc   (1)
400 Hillside Ave, Needham, MA 02494
Tel.: (781) 433-0233
Web Site: http://www.accufund.com
Rev.: $1,200,000
Emp.: 5
Software Publisher
N.A.I.C.S.: 513210
Gordon Holfelder *(Pres)*
Ian Scotland *(VP & Gen Mgr)*

Ad Valorem Records, Inc.   (1)
12332 Cutten Rd, Houston, TX 77066
Web Site: http://www.avrub.com
Software Development Services
N.A.I.C.S.: 513210
Ron Emberg *(Founder)*
Sonny Perlacia *(VP-Ops & Fin)*
Steve Popchock *(VP-Tech)*

Business Information Systems, Inc.   (1)
333 Industrial Park Road, Piney Flats, TN 37686
Tel.: (423) 538-1900
Web Site: http://www.bisonline.com
Rev.: $7,000,000
Emp.: 60
Other Computer Related Services
N.A.I.C.S.: 541519

Celtic Systems Private Limited   (1)
405-410 4th Floor Ocean Sarabhai Compound Nr Centre Square Mall, Dr Vikram Sarabhai Marg, Vadodara, 390 003, Gujarat, India
Tel.: (91) 2652311304
Software Development Services
N.A.I.C.S.: 541511

DuxWare, LLC   (1)
64026 Hwy 434 Ste 230, Lacombe, LA 70445
Tel.: (985) 646-1665
Web Site: https://duxware.com
Software Development Services
N.A.I.C.S.: 541511
Mike Perkins *(Pres)*

ImageSoft, Inc.   (1)
25900 W 11 Mile Rd Ste 100, Southfield, MI 48034
Tel.: (248) 948-8100
Web Site: http://www.imagesoftinc.com
Sales Range: $1-9.9 Million
Emp.: 55
Content Management
N.A.I.C.S.: 541512
Scott Bade *(Pres)*

Kiriworks, LLC   (1)
Software Development Services
N.A.I.C.S.: 541511
Geoff Barber *(Project Mgr)*
Nate Anderson *(Mgr-Customer Support)*
Lorri Howski *(VP)*
Jon Swisher *(VP)*
Greg Wheeler *(CTO)*
Earl Williams *(VP)*
Eric Willis *(CEO)*

Monetra Technologies, LLC   (1)
123 Main St Ste 54, Gainesville, FL 32606
Tel.: (904) 312-9575
Web Site: https://www.monetra.com
Software Development Services
N.A.I.C.S.: 513210

San Diego Cash Register Company, Inc.   (1)
7940 Arjons Dr, San Diego, CA 92126
Web Site: http://www.sdcr.com
Software Development Services
N.A.I.C.S.: 513210

The Northeast Texas Data Corp.   (1)
1110 Enterprise Dr, Sulphur Springs, TX 75482
Tel.: (903) 885-0818
Web Site: http://www.netdatacorp.net
Custom Computer Programming Services
N.A.I.C.S.: 541511

i3 Verticals, LLC   (1)
40 Burton Hills Blvd Ste 415, Nashville, TN 37215
Tel.: (615) 465-4487
Web Site: https://www.i3verticals.com
Electronic Payment Processing Software & Services
N.A.I.C.S.: 561499
Gregory S. Daily *(Founder & CEO)*
Scott Meriwether *(Sr VP-Fin)*
Clay M. Whitson *(CFO)*
Rick Stanford *(Pres)*
Paul Maple *(Gen Counsel)*
Pete Panagakis *(CTO)*
Amber Murphy *(Sr VP)*
Michael O'Keefe *(Sr VP)*

Subsidiary (Domestic):

CP-DBS, LLC   (2)
4100 Holiday St NW Ste 101, Canton, OH 44718
Tel.: (303) 779-6573
Web Site: https://www.payschools.com
School Electronic Payment Technologies Developer
N.A.I.C.S.: 541511
Hume Miller *(CEO)*
Logan Knight *(VP-Sls)*
Rick Killian *(VP-Ops)*
Chelsea Brown *(Mgr-Implementation)*
Adrian Drlik *(Mgr-Support)*
Chris O'Neil *(Mgr-Key Acct)*
Alex Pollema *(VP)*
Lisa Good *(VP)*

Fairway Payments, LLC   (2)
300 N Lee St Ste 500, Alexandria, VA 22314
Web Site: http://www.fairwaypayments.com
Transaction Processing Software & Services
N.A.I.C.S.: 541511

i3-Infin, LLC   (2)
4455 Carver Woods Dr Ste 110, Blue Ash, OH 45242
Web Site: https://i3commercetech.com
Payment Processing Software & Services
N.A.I.C.S.: 541511
Chad Stephens *(VP-Sls)*
Rob Kroeger *(VP-Ops)*

i3-PBS, LLC   (2)
40 Burton Hills Blvd Ste 415, Nashville, TN 37215
Tel.: (615) 465-4499
Web Site: http://www.rupractical.com
Payment Processing Solutions & Services

N.A.I.C.S.: 541511
i3-Randall, LLC   (2)
40000 Grand River Ave Ste 504, Novi, MI 48375
Tel.: (734) 453-9200
Web Site: http://www.randalldata.com
Computer & Computer Peripheral Equipment & Software Merchant Whslr
N.A.I.C.S.: 423430

i3-Software & Services, LLC   (2)
1120 S Pointe Pkwy Ste A, Shreveport, LA 71105
Web Site: https://www.softwareservices.net
Emp.: 35
Local Government Technical Software & Services
N.A.I.C.S.: 541511
Gregory R. Teeters *(Pres)*

i3-Axia, LLC   (1)
1933 Cliff Dr Ste 12, Santa Barbara, CA 93109
Web Site: http://www.axiapayments.com
Payment Processing Services
N.A.I.C.S.: 541214
Joff Moine *(CEO)*

i3-EZPay, LLC   (1)
4055 Executive Park Dr Ste 400, Cincinnati, OH 45241
Web Site: http://www.spsezpay.com
Payment Processing Services
N.A.I.C.S.: 541214

i3-LL, LLC   (1)
40 Burton Hills Blvd Ste 415, Nashville, TN 37215
Web Site: http://www.locallevelevents.com
Software Development Services
N.A.I.C.S.: 513210

i3-One, LLC   (1)
8280 Willow Oaks Corporate Dr Ste 600, Fairfax, VA 22031
Tel.: (571) 408-1010
Web Site: https://i3llc.us
Software Development Services
N.A.I.C.S.: 541511

i3-RS, LLC   (1)
115 Broadway, New York, NY 10006
Web Site: http://www.placepay.com
Payment Processing Services
N.A.I.C.S.: 541214

mobileAxept North America, Inc.   (1)
400 S 4th St Ste 401, Minneapolis, MN 55415
Web Site: https://www.mobileaxept.com
Software Services
N.A.I.C.S.: 541511

IAC INC.
555 W 18th St, New York, NY 10011
Tel.: (212) 314-7300   DE
Web Site: https://www.iac.com
Year Founded: 1986
IAC—(NASDAQ)
Rev.: $4,365,235,000
Assets: $10,371,177,000
Liabilities: $3,616,174,000
Net Worth: $6,755,003,000
Earnings: $265,942,000
Emp.: 9,500
Fiscal Year-end: 12/31/23
Holding Company; Media & Internet Services
N.A.I.C.S.: 516120
Barry Diller *(Chm)*
Joseph Levin *(CEO)*
Victor A. Kaufman *(Vice Chm)*
Christopher Halpin *(CFO & Exec VP)*
Valerie Combs *(Sr VP & Head-Comm)*
Jonathan Miller *(Pres & CEO)*
Joshua Koplik *(Chief Information Sec Officer & Sr VP)*
Nick Stoumpas *(Treas & Sr VP)*
Mark Schneider *(Sr VP-Fin & IR)*
Kendall Fox Handler *(Chief Legal Officer, Exec VP & Sr VP)*
Russell Farscht *(Sr VP-Strategy, M, and A)*

Layren Geer *(Chief HR Officer & Sr VP)*
Shruti Choudhari *(Sr VP-Internal Audit)*

Subsidiaries:

About, Inc.   (1)
225 Liberty St 4th Fl, New York, NY 10281
Tel.: (212) 204-4000
Web Site: https://www.dotdashmeredith.com
Sales Range: $75-99.9 Million
Emp.: 500
Internet Publishing & Broadcasting Services
N.A.I.C.S.: 516210
Scott P. Kurnit *(Founder)*
Alex Ellerson *(COO-Dotdash)*
Neil Vogel *(CEO)*
Tim Quinn *(CFO & Head-Strategy)*
Nabil Ahmad *(CTO)*
Andrew Gorenstein *(Pres-Adv & Partnerships)*
Adam McClean *(Chief Product Officer)*
Vincent Holleran *(Chief Design Officer)*
Ellen Shultz *(Chief HR Officer)*
Patrice Sosoo *(Sr VP)*

Subsidiary (Domestic):

ConsumerSearch, Inc.   (2)
555 12th St Ste 400, Oakland, CA 94607
Tel.: (510) 985-7400
Web Site: https://www.consumersearch.com
Internet Publishing & Broadcasting Services
N.A.I.C.S.: 516210

Modern Bride Group   (2)
1 World Trade Ctr, New York, NY 10007
Tel.: (212) 286-3953
Web Site: http://www.brides.com
Sales Range: $10-24.9 Million
Emp.: 130
Bridal Magazine Publisher
N.A.I.C.S.: 513120

Angi Inc.   (1)
130 E Washington St, Indianapolis, IN 46204   **(98.1%)**
Tel.: (303) 963-7200
Web Site: https://www.angi.com
Rev.: $1,891,524,000
Assets: $1,907,778,000
Liabilities: $856,400,000
Net Worth: $1,051,378,000
Earnings: ($128,450,000)
Emp.: 4,599
Fiscal Year-end: 12/31/2022
Holding Company; Digital Marketing Services
N.A.I.C.S.: 551112
Joseph Levin *(Chm & CEO)*
Dhanusha Sivajee *(CMO)*
Jeffrey W. Kip *(CEO)*
Andrew Russakoff *(CFO)*
Angela R. Hicks Bowman *(Chief Customer Officer)*
Michael Wanderer *(Chief People Officer)*
Shannon Shaw *(Chief Legal Officer)*
Kulesh Shanmugasundaram *(CTO)*
Dave Fleischman *(Chief Product Officer)*
Sandra Buchanan Hurse *(Mng Dir & Chief HR Officer)*

Subsidiary (Domestic):

Angie's List, Inc.   (2)
130 E Washington St, Indianapolis, IN 46204
Tel.: (303) 963-7200
Web Site: https://www.angi.com
Emp.: 5,000
Information Services
N.A.I.C.S.: 519290
Joseph Levin *(CEO)*
William S. Oesterle *(Co-Founder)*
Joey Levin *(CEO)*
Andrew Russakoff *(CFO)*
Kulesh Shanmugasundaram *(CTO)*
Dhanusha Sivajee *(CMO)*
Angie Hicks *(Chief Customer Officer)*
Michael Wanderer *(Chief People Officer)*
Ercan Kamber *(Chief Data Officer)*

HomeAdvisor, Inc.   (2)
3601 Walnut St Ste 81, Denver, CO 80205
Tel.: (303) 963-7200
Web Site: https://www.homeadvisor.com
Internet Publishing & Broadcasting Services
N.A.I.C.S.: 516210

IAC Inc.—(Continued)

Mile High Insights, LLC (2)
117 Lost Oak Ct, Roseville, CA 95661-4052
Tel.: (916) 412-5824
Software Publishing Services
N.A.I.C.S.: 513210

Subsidiary (Non-US):

Werkspot BV (2)
Herengracht 469, 1017 BS, Amsterdam,
Netherlands
Tel.: (31) 889375793
Web Site: https://www.werkspot.nl
Internet Publishing & Broadcasting Services
N.A.I.C.S.: 516210
Joost Gielen (Co-Founder)
Sjoerd Eikenaar (Co-Founder)
Ronald Egas (CEO)

Ask Applications, Inc. (1)
1 N Lexington 9th Fl, White Plains, NY
10601
Tel.: (914) 826-2000
Web Site: http://www.askapplications.com
Internet Publishing & Broadcasting Services
N.A.I.C.S.: 517810

Ask Jeeves UK Partnership (1)
53 Parker St, London, WC2B 5PT, United
Kingdom
Tel.: (44) 207211677
Application Service Provider
N.A.I.C.S.: 518210

Care.com, Inc. (1)
816 Congress Ste 800, Austin, TX 78701
Tel.: (512) 842-7520
Web Site: https://www.care.com
Online Caregiver Services
N.A.I.C.S.: 513199
Nancy Bushkin (Sr VP-Global Comm)
Michelle Arbov (CFO)
Roman Degtyur (CIO)
John W. Buchanan (CMO)
Wes Burke (Chief HR Officer)
Bill Chase (Gen Mgr-Consumer)
Amit Goyal (CTO)
Cindi Moreland (Gen Counsel)
Naaz Nichols (Chief Customer Svc Experi-
ence Officer)
Glenn Petersen (Gen Mgr-Enterprise)
Elizabeth Sartin (Chief Product Officer)
Brad E. Wilson (CEO)
Natasha Fellion (Mgr-Communications)
Margarita Junowitsch (Mgr-Public Relations)

Subsidiary (Non-US):

Care.com Europe GmbH (2)
Rotherstr 17, 10245, Berlin, Germany
Tel.: (49) 3029363890
Web Site: https://www.betreut.de
Family Welfare Services
N.A.I.C.S.: 624190
Dirk Kasten (Mng Dir)

Care.com Switzerland AG (2)
Limmatquai 94, 8001, Zurich, Switzerland
Tel.: (41) 435881418
Web Site: https://www.care.com
Family Welfare Services
N.A.I.C.S.: 624190

Subsidiary (Domestic):

Trusted Labs, Inc. (2)
217 2nd St Fl 5, San Francisco, CA 94105
Child Care Services
N.A.I.C.S.: 624410

Citysearch (1)
8833 Sunset Blvd, West Hollywood, CA
90069
Tel.: (310) 360-4500
Web Site: http://www.citysearch.com
Sales Range: $100-124.9 Million
Emp.: 450
Database Information Retrieval Services
N.A.I.C.S.: 517810

Conversant France (1)
30-34 rue du Chemin Vert, 75011, Paris,
France
Tel.: (33) 186651360
Web Site: https://www.conversantmedia.eu
Advetising Agency
N.A.I.C.S.: 541810

Delightful.com, LLC (1)

8300 Douglas Ave Ste 800, Dallas, TX
75225-5826
Tel.: (415) 799-2000
Emp.: 15
Executive Placement Services
N.A.I.C.S.: 561312

Dotdash Meredith, Inc. (1)
225 Liberty St 4th Fl, New York, NY 10281
Tel.: (212) 204-4000
Web Site: https://www.dotdashmeredith.com
Magazine Publishing Services
N.A.I.C.S.: 513120
Alysia Borsa (Pres, Pres, Chief Bus Officer
& Chief Bus Officer)
Jon Roberts (Pres-Finance)
Neil Vogel (CEO)
Alex Ellerson (COO)
Tim Quinn (CFO & Head-Strategy)
Adam McClean (Chief Product Officer)
Melanie Berliet (Sr VP)
Rachel Berman (Sr VP)
Eric Handelsman (Sr VP)
Sara Michael (Sr VP)
Elspeth Velten (Sr VP)
Leah Wyar (Pres-Entertainment, Beauty,
and Style Grp)
Dylan Zurawell (Sr VP)
Nabil Ahmad (CTO)
Tory Brangham (Chief Commerce Officer)
Andrew Gorenstein (Pres-Advertising &
Partnerships)
Jack Griffin (Chm-Operating)
Jeff Hartwig (Gen Counsel & Sr VP)
Vincent Holleran (Chief Design Officer)
Melissa Inman (Sr VP-Brand Partnerships &
Licensing)
Matt Petersen (Pres-Specialty Mktg Solu-
tions)
DeLonzo Rhodes (Head-Diversity, Equity, ,
&, and Inclusion)
Ellen Shultz (Chief HR Officer)
Nicole Silver (CMO-Advertising & Partner-
ships)
Lindsay Van Kirk (Sr VP)
Meredith Worsham (Head-Communications)

Filios, Inc. (1)
9640 W Tropicana Ste 200, Las Vegas, NV
89147
Tel.: (702) 869-8023
Web Site: https://www.filios.com
Real Estate Services
N.A.I.C.S.: 531390

HSE24 (1)
Munchener Strasse 101 h, Ismaning,
85737, Germany
Tel.: (49) 89 960 60 6100
Web Site: http://www.hse24.de
Sales Range: $75-99.9 Million
Emp.: 700
Internet & Online Shopping Services
N.A.I.C.S.: 425120
Richard Reitzner (Chm-Supervisory Bd)

HSN, LLC (1)
1 HSN Dr, Saint Petersburg, FL 33729
Tel.: (727) 872-7443
Web Site: https://www.hsn.com
Sales Range: $750-799.9 Million
Internet Publishing & Broadcasting Services
N.A.I.C.S.: 516210
Eric Yonkin (Assoc Gen Counsel)

IAC Search & Media, Inc. (1)
555 12th St Ste 500, Oakland, CA 94607
Tel.: (510) 985-7400
Web Site: http://www.ask.com
Sales Range: $250-299.9 Million
Emp.: 505
Online Search Engine Services
N.A.I.C.S.: 519290
Andrew Moers (Pres-Askcom Partner Net-
work)

INKD LLC (1)
3131 Western Ave Ste 327, Seattle, WA
98121
Tel.: (206) 343-0405
Web Site: https://inkd.com
Graphic Design Services
N.A.I.C.S.: 513199

Investopedia LLC (1)
28 Liberty St 7th Fl, New York, NY 10005
Tel.: (510) 985-7400
Web Site: https://www.investopedia.com
Internet Publishing & Broadcasting Services
N.A.I.C.S.: 516210

Megan LaCava (Sr VP-Client Services)
Caleb Silver (Editor-in-Chief)
Anna Attkisson (Sr Dir-Editorial)
Hilarey Gould (Sr Dir-Editorial-Fin Prod-
ucts,Svcs)
Yasmin Ghahremani (Assoc Dir-Editorial-Fin
Products,Svcs)
Ben Woolsey (Assoc Dir-Editorial-Fin Kith-
ucts,Svcs)
Stella Osoba (Sr Editor-Trading & Investing)
Michael Sacchitello (Sr Editor-Investing &
Trading Product Reviews)
Sienna Wrenn (Sr Editor-Special Projects)
Lars Peterson (Sr Editor-Fin Product Re-
views)
Brendan Harkness (Sr Editor-Fin Product
Reviews)
Clay Halton (Editor-Bus)
Ward Williams (Editor-Fin Products & Svcs)
Mia Davis (Assoc Editor-Special Projects)
Katie Reilly (Assoc Editor-Trading & Invest-
ing)
Will Baker (Assoc Editor-Investing & Trad-
ing Product Reviews)
Caroline Dilone (Editor-Social Media)
Stephen Wisnefski (Exec Editor-News)
Kara Greenberg (Sr Editor)
Mrinalini Krishna (Sr Editor-Investing News)
Taylor Tompkins (Editor-Economics-News)
Colin Laidley (Assoc Editor-News)
Hiranmayi Srinivasan (Assoc Editor)
Isaac Braun (Mgr-Res)
Marisa Figat (Assoc Dir-Content Compli-
ance)
Dylan Zurawell (Gen Mgr)
Katherine Divney (Chief Revenue Officer)
Michael Capecci (VP-Marketing & Sales)
Alexandra Kerr (Dir-Brand Mktg & Commu-
nications)

Investopedia, LLC (1)
4208-97 Street Suite 200, Edmonton, T6E
5Z9, AB, Canada
Tel.: (780) 421-0555
Web Site: http://www.investopedia.com
Investor Education Website
N.A.I.C.S.: 513199
Caleb Silver (Editor-in-Chief)
Megan LaCava (VP-Client Svcs)
Dylan Zurawell (Gen Mgr)
Katherine Divney (Chief Revenue Officer)
Michael Capecci (VP)

LifeCare, Inc. (1)
2 Armstrong Rd, Shelton, CT 06405
Tel.: (203) 291-3453
Web Site: https://www.lifecare.com
Business Management Services
N.A.I.C.S.: 541618
Peter Burki (Co-Founder & Chm)
Jeffrey Burki (Co-Founder, Vice Chm &
Chief Strategy Officer)

Massive Media Match NV (1)
Emile Braunplein 18, 9000, Gent, Belgium
Tel.: (32) 24004321
Internet Publishing & Broadcasting Services
N.A.I.C.S.: 516210

Match Group, Inc. (1)
8750 N Central Expy Ste 1400, Dallas, TX
75231
Tel.: (214) 576-9352
Web Site: https://www.mtch.com
Rev.: $3,364,504,000
Assets: $4,507,886,000
Liabilities: $4,526,959,000
Net Worth: ($19,073,000)
Earnings: $651,539,000
Emp.: 2,600
Fiscal Year-end: 12/31/2023
Online Dating Services
N.A.I.C.S.: 812990
Gary Swidler (Pres & CFO)
Philip D. Eigenmann (Chief Acctg Officer)
Peter Foster (Gen Mgr-Adv & Brand
Solutions-Global)
Justine Sacco (Chief Comm Officer)
Jennifer Zephirin (Head-Diversity, Equity,
and Inclusion)
Justin McLeod (Founder/CEO-Hinge)
D. V. Williams (Chief People Officer)
Malgosia Green (CEO)
Will Wu (CTO)
Sam Ahn (Co-Founder)
Amanda Bradford (Co-Founder)

Subsidiary (Domestic):

Chemistry.com (2)

8300 Douglas Ave, Dallas, TX 75225
Tel.: (214) 576-9352
Web Site: http://www.chemistry.com
Online Dating Services
N.A.I.C.S.: 812990

Humor Rainbow, Inc. (2)
809 Washington St 3rd Fl, New York, NY
10014
Tel.: (646) 216-8762
Web Site: https://www.okcupid.com
Emp.: 36
Internet Publishing & Broadcasting Services
N.A.I.C.S.: 516210
Ariel Charytan (CEO)

Subsidiary (Non-US):

Match.com Canada Ltd. (2)
100 de La Gauchetiere Street West Suite
2100, Montreal, H3B 4W5, QC, Canada
Tel.: (214) 576-9352
Internet & Online Service Provider
N.A.I.C.S.: 517810

Match.com Nordic AB (2)
Grev Turegatan 30, Stockholm, 114 38,
Sweden
Tel.: (46) 852500850
Internet Publishing & Broadcasting Services
N.A.I.C.S.: 516210

Meetic SA (2)
66 Route De La Reine, Boulogne-
Billancourt, 92100, France **(87.5%)**
Tel.: (33) 800944949
Web Site: http://www.meetic-corp.com
Sales Range: $200-249.9 Million
Emp.: 367
Online Dating Services
N.A.I.C.S.: 812990
Christophe Simmer (Chief Analytics Officer)
Christophe Ozimek (CIO)

Subsidiary (Domestic):

Tinder, Inc. (2)
8750 N Central Expy Ste 1400, Dallas, TX
75231
Tel.: (214) 853-4309
Web Site: https://tinder.com
Emp.: 86
Location Based Social Search Mobile Appli-
cation Services
N.A.I.C.S.: 513210
Sean Rad (Founder & Chm)
Whitney Wolfe Herd (Co-Founder)

Pronto, LLC (1)
555 W 18th St 4th Fl, New York, NY 10011
Tel.: (212) 915-3846
Web Site: http://www.pronto.com
Sales Range: $50-74.9 Million
Emp.: 58
Internet Publishing & Broadcasting Services
N.A.I.C.S.: 516210
John Foley (Co-Founder)

ReserveAmerica Inc. (1)
40 South St, Ballston Spa, NY
12020-9904 **(100%)**
Tel.: (518) 583-6200
Web Site: http://www.reserveamerica.com
Rev.: $220,000
Emp.: 300
Reservation Services for Camping
N.A.I.C.S.: 561599

ServiceMagic Limited (1)
Union House 182 194 Union Street Greater,
London, SE1 0LH, United Kingdom
Tel.: (44) 8006125305
Emp.: 30
Internet & Online Service Provider
N.A.I.C.S.: 517810

Shoptouch, Inc. (1)
156 2nd St, San Francisco, CA 94105
Tel.: (415) 994-2954
Emp.: 3
Internet Publishing & Broadcasting Services
N.A.I.C.S.: 516210

Slimware Utilities Holdings, Inc. (1)
555 W 18th St, New York, NY 10011
Tel.: (228) 447-3175
Web Site: https://www.slimware.com
Holding Company
N.A.I.C.S.: 551112
Bob Bryant (CTO & Gen Mgr)

Synapse Services, LLC (1)
360 Erie Blvd E, Syracuse, NY 13202
Tel.: (315) 475-3700
Web Site: https://www.synapsellc.com
Insurance Brokerage Services
N.A.I.C.S.: 524210

TelTech Systems, Inc. (1)
102 Main St, Garnerville, NY 10923
Tel.: (845) 362-6700
Web Site: https://www.teltechsystems.com
Telecommunication Servicesb
N.A.I.C.S.: 517810

The Daily Beast Company LLC (1)
555 W 18th St, New York, NY 10011
Tel.: (212) 445-4600
Web Site: https://www.thedailybeast.com
Online News Magazine Publisher
N.A.I.C.S.: 513120
Barry Diller *(Chm)*
Tracy Connor *(Exec Editor)*
Katie Baker *(Mng Editor)*
Andrew Kirell *(Editor-Cheat Sheet & Express)*
Tim Teeman *(Editor-Arts & Culture)*
Ben Sherwood *(CEO)*
Joanna Coles *(Chief Creative Officer)*
Noor Ibrahim *(Mng Editor)*
Elizabeth Hunt Brockway *(Dir-Editorial Visual)*
Kevin Hechtkopf *(Dir-Audience)*
Anthony Fisher *(Sr Editor-Opinion)*
Kevin Fallon *(Sr Editor-Obsessed)*
Nico Hines *(Editor-World News)*
Mathew Murphy *(Sr Editor-News)*
Rachel Olding *(Sr Editor-Breaking News)*
Matt Wilstein *(Sr Editor-Entertainment)*

Division (Domestic):

The Daily Beast (2)
555 W 18th St, New York, NY 10011
Tel.: (347) 537-5494
Web Site: https://www.thedailybeast.com
Emp.: 80
Online News Website
N.A.I.C.S.: 513110
Barry Diller *(Chm)*
Noah Shachtman *(Editor-in-Chief)*

Tutor.com, Inc. (1)
110 E 42nd St Fl 7, New York, NY 10017
Tel.: (212) 528-3101
Web Site: https://www.tutor.com
Consumer Support Services
N.A.I.C.S.: 812990
Sandi White *(VP-Institutional Sls)*

Subsidiary (Domestic):

Education Holdings 1 (2)
111 Speen St, Framingham, MA 01701
Tel.: (508) 663-5050
Web Site: http://www.princetonreview.com
Emp.: 854
Online & Offline Test Preparation Software,
Books & Magazines Publisher; College Admissions Help & Financial Advice; Classroom Base & Online Test Preparation
Courses
N.A.I.C.S.: 611710

Subsidiary (Domestic):

Penn Foster, Inc. (3)
925 Oak St, Scranton, PA 18515-0999
Tel.: (570) 961-4033
Web Site: https://www.pennfoster.edu
Sales Range: $75-99.9 Million
Emp.: 750
Home Study Educational Services
N.A.I.C.S.: 611699
Frank F. Britt *(CEO)*
Lisa Prince Rutsky *(VP-Education)*
Pat Gaffey *(VP-Admissions)*
Mark Slayton *(Sr VP-Student Success)*
Michelle Rothenbecker *(Sr Dir-Instructional Design & Content)*

Subsidiary (Domestic):

Ashworth College (4)
6625 The Corners Pkwy Ste 500, Norcross, GA 30092
Tel.: (770) 729-8400
Web Site: https://www.ashworthcollege.edu
Online Education; Online College Degrees,
Online Career Training, Online High School
Diplomas

N.A.I.C.S.: 611699
Kimberley Winfield *(Dir-Faculty & Academic Affairs)*
Frank F. Britt *(Pres)*
Tracey Jerauld *(Sr Dir-Learning Strategy & Ops)*
Megan Andrews *(Dir-Veterinary Academy)*
Megan Bowen *(Dir-High School Programs)*
Kelsha Abraham *(Mgr-Faculty & Academic Affairs)*

IAHL CORP.
1037 Pathfinder Way Ste 136, Rockledge, FL 32955
Tel.: (239) 277-3883
Web Site: https://www.altenesol.com
IAHL—(OTCIQ)
Electric Power Distribution
N.A.I.C.S.: 221122
Peter Van Dyke *(CEO)*

IANTHUS CAPITAL HOLDINGS, INC.
420 Lexington Ave Ste 414, New York, NY 10170
Tel.: (646) 518-9411　　ON
Web Site: https://www.ianthus.com
ITHUF—(OTCIQ)
Rev.: $163,213,000
Assets: $303,467,000
Liabilities: $292,478,000
Net Worth: $10,989,000
Earnings: ($449,391,000)
Emp.: 748
Fiscal Year-end: 12/31/22
Holding Company
N.A.I.C.S.: 551112
Hadley Ford *(Co-Founder)*
Randy Maslow *(Co-Founder)*
Richard Boxer *(Chief Medical Officer)*
John Henderson *(Sr VP-Ops-Eastern)*
Robert Galvin *(Interim COO)*
Andrew Ryan *(Gen Counsel)*
Ethan Anderson *(Sr VP-Mktg)*
Richard Proud *(CEO)*

Subsidiaries:

MPX Bioceutical Corporation (1)
Yonge Norton Centre 5255 Yonge Street
Suite 701, Toronto, M2N 6P4, ON, Canada
Tel.: (416) 840-3725
Web Site: http://www.mpxbioceutical.com
Pharmaceuticals Product Mfr
N.A.I.C.S.: 325412
Jonathan Chu *(Interim CFO)*

IBC ADVANCED ALLOYS CORP.
401 Arvin Rd, Franklin, IN 46131
Tel.: (317) 738-2558　　BC
Web Site:
https://www.ibcadvancedalloys.com
IAALF—(OTCQB)
Rev.: $28,547,000
Assets: $28,319,000
Liabilities: $25,358,000
Net Worth: $2,961,000
Earnings: ($5,932,000)
Emp.: 74
Fiscal Year-end: 06/30/23
Nonferrous Metal Die-Casting Foundries
N.A.I.C.S.: 331523
Rajeev Jain *(VP-Sls)*
Mark Alan Smith *(Chm, Pres, Pres & CEO)*
Jim Sims *(Dir-Investor & PR)*
Toni Wendel *(CFO & Sec)*

Subsidiaries:

Freedom Alloys, Inc. (1)
155 Railrd Plz, Royersford, PA 19468
Tel.: (610) 792-3202
Copper Mining Services
N.A.I.C.S.: 212230

IBERE PHARMACEUTICALS

2005 Market St Ste 2030, Philadelphia, PA 19103
Tel.: (267) 765-3222　　Ky
Web Site:
http://www.iberepharma.com
Year Founded: 2020
IBER—(NYSE)
Rev.: $2,565,895
Assets: $138,710,328
Liabilities: $149,556,284
Net Worth: ($10,845,956)
Earnings: $1,561,747
Emp.: 3
Fiscal Year-end: 12/31/21
Investment Services
N.A.I.C.S.: 523999
Osagie Imasogie *(Chm & CEO)*
Lisa Gray *(CFO & Exec VP)*
Zoltan Kerekes *(COO & Exec VP)*

IBIO, INC.
8800 HSC Pkwy, Bryan, TX 77807-1107
Tel.: (302) 355-0650　　DE
Web Site: https://www.ibioinc.com
IBIO—(NYSEAMEX)
Rev.: $225,000
Assets: $28,734,000
Liabilities: $7,410,000
Net Worth: $21,324,000
Earnings: ($24,907,000)
Emp.: 16
Fiscal Year-end: 06/30/24
Biopharmaceutical Mfr
N.A.I.C.S.: 325412
William D. Clark *(Chm)*
Martin B. Brenner *(CEO & Chief Scientific Officer)*
Lisa Middlebrook *(Chief HR Officer)*
Brian F. Berquist *(VP-Process Dev & Tech Transfer)*
Melissa Berquist *(Head-Animal Health Programs)*
Peter Kipp *(VP-Translational Sciences & Alliance Mgmt)*
Matthew Parker *(VP-Ops)*
Dillon Phan *(VP & Head-Early Res & Dev)*
Jack Owens *(Dir-Quality Assurance)*
Felipe Duran *(CFO)*
Marc Banjak *(Corp Counsel)*
Nick DeLong *(VP)*
Matthew P. Greving *(VP)*
Mike Jenkins *(VP)*
Matthew Luter *(VP)*

IBW FINANCIAL CORPORATION
4812 Georgia Ave NW, Washington, DC 20011-4113
Tel.: (202) 722-2000　　MD
Web Site: http://www.industrial-bank.com
Year Founded: 1997
IBWC—(OTCIQ)
Sales Range: $10-24.9 Million
Emp.: 146
Bank Holding Company
N.A.I.C.S.: 551111
B. Doyle Mitchell Jr. *(Pres & CEO)*
Clinton W. Chapman *(Chm)*
Patricia Mitchell *(Exec VP-Retail Programs)*
Rodney Epps *(COO & Sr VP)*
Thomas A. Wilson Jr. *(CFO & Sr VP)*

Subsidiaries:

Industrial Bank (1)
4812 Georgia Ave NW, Washington, DC 20011
Tel.: (202) 722-2000
Web Site: http://www.industrial-bank.com
Sales Range: $50-74.9 Million
Emp.: 136
Commericial Banking
N.A.I.C.S.: 522110

ICAD, INC.
98 Spit Brook Rd Ste 100, Nashua, NH 03062
Tel.: (603) 882-5200　　DE
Web Site: https://www.icadmed.com
Year Founded: 1984
ICAD—(NASDAQ)
Rev.: $27,944,000
Assets: $51,705,000
Liabilities: $16,803,000
Net Worth: $34,902,000
Earnings: ($13,656,000)
Emp.: 108
Fiscal Year-end: 12/31/22
Digital Image Scanners, Film Digitizers & Related Software for Applications in the Medical Imaging, Graphic Arts & Photographic Markets
N.A.I.C.S.: 334118
Michelle Strong *(COO)*
Stacey M. Stevens *(Pres & CEO)*
Dana Brown *(Exec Chm)*
Vasu Avadhanula *(Chief Product Officer)*
William Keyes *(Sr VP-US Comml Sls & AI)*
Eric Lonnqvist *(CFO)*
Jonathan Go *(CTO)*

Subsidiaries:

Xoft, Inc. (1)
101 Nicholson Ln, San Jose, CA 95134
Tel.: (408) 493-1500
Web Site: https://www.xoftinc.com
Sales Range: $1-9.9 Million
Emp.: 25
Medical Equipment Mfr
N.A.I.C.S.: 334510

iCad, Inc. (1)
98 Spit Brook Rd Ste 100, Nashua, NH 03062
Tel.: (603) 882-5200
Web Site: https://www.icadmed.com
Sales Range: $200-249.9 Million
Emp.: 50
Provider of Office Equipment & Computer Hardware, Internet
N.A.I.C.S.: 221118

ICAHN ENTERPRISES L.P.
16690 Collins Ave Ph Ste, Sunny Isles Beach, FL 33160
Tel.: (305) 422-4100　　DE
Web Site: https://www.ielp.com
Year Founded: 1987
IEP—(NASDAQ)
Rev.: $13,378,000,000
Assets: $27,914,000,000
Liabilities: $18,356,000,000
Net Worth: $9,558,000,000
Earnings: $183,000,000
Emp.: 20,000
Fiscal Year-end: 12/31/22
Investment Holding Company
N.A.I.C.S.: 551112
Carl Celian Icahn *(Chm)*
Hunter C. Gary *(Sr Mng Dir)*
Andrew J. Teno *(Pres & CEO)*
Jesse A. Lynn *(Gen Counsel)*
Michael Nevin *(Mng Dir)*
Ted Papapostolou *(CFO & Sec)*

Subsidiaries:

ACC-U-TUNE (1)
2023 S Percy St, Philadelphia, PA 19148
Tel.: (215) 551-7559
Automotive Parts Holding Company Services
N.A.I.C.S.: 551112

Ace Nevada Corp. (1)
9017 S Pecos Rd, Henderson, NV 89074
Tel.: (702) 586-8246

Icahn Enterprises L.P.—(Continued)

Financial Investment Services
N.A.I.C.S.: 523999

Bayswater Brokerage Mass. LLC (1)
PO Box 1730, Rutherford, NJ 07070
Tel.: (508) 539-8200
Real Estate Development Services
N.A.I.C.S.: 531390

Bayswater Falling Waters LLC (1)
2055 Cascades Dr, Naples, FL 34112
Tel.: (239) 774-5457
Financial Investment Services
N.A.I.C.S.: 523999

Beck Arnley Holdings LLC (1)
2375 Midway Ln, Smyrna, TN 37167
Tel.: (615) 220-3200
Emp.: 74
Automotive Parts Holding Company Services
N.A.I.C.S.: 551112

CAPPCO Tubular Products USA, LLC (1)
26777 Lorain Rd Ste 216, North Olmsted, OH 44070
Tel.: (216) 641-2218
Web Site: http://www.cappco.com
Environmental Consulting Services
N.A.I.C.S.: 541620

CVR Energy, Inc. (1)
2277 Plz Dr Ste 500, Sugar Land, TX 77479 (82%)
Tel.: (281) 207-3200
Web Site: https://www.cvrenergy.com
Rev.: $9,247,000,000
Assets: $4,707,000,000
Liabilities: $3,669,000,000
Net Worth: $1,038,000,000
Earnings: $769,000,000
Emp.: 1,566
Fiscal Year-end: 12/31/2023
Holding Company; Petroleum Refiner & Transportation Fuels & Nitrogen Fertilizer Mfr
N.A.I.C.S.: 551112
Michael H. Wright Jr. (COO & Exec VP)
David L. Lamp (Pres & CEO)
Mark A. Pytosh (Exec VP-Corp Svcs)
Jeffrey D. Conaway (Chief Acctg Officer, VP & Controller)
Melissa M. Buhrig (Gen Counsel, Sec & Exec VP)
C. Douglas Johnson (Chief Comml Officer)

Subsidiary (Domestic):

CVR Partners, LP (2)
2277 Plz Dr Ste 500, Sugar Land, TX 77479
Tel.: (281) 207-3200
Web Site: https://www.cvrpartners.com
Rev.: $681,477,000
Assets: $975,332,000
Liabilities: $672,452,000
Net Worth: $302,880,000
Earnings: $172,433,000
Emp.: 310
Fiscal Year-end: 12/31/2023
Holding Company; Nitrogen Fertilizer Products Mfr & Marketer
N.A.I.C.S.: 551112
David L. Lamp (Chm)
Mark A. Pytosh (Pres & CEO)
Dane J. Neumann (CFO & Exec VP)
Jeffrey D. Conaway (Chief Acctg Officer, VP & Controller)
Matthew W. Bley (Chief Acctg officer & Controller)
Melissa M. Buhrig (Gen Counsel, Sec & Exec VP)

Subsidiary (Domestic):

Coffeyville Resources Nitrogen Fertilizers, LLC (3)
400 N Linden St, Coffeyville, KS 67337
Tel.: (620) 251-4360
Sales Range: $25-49.9 Million
Emp.: 100
Financial Investment Services
N.A.I.C.S.: 523999

East Dubuque Nitrogen Fertilizers, LLC (3)
16675 Us Hwy 20 W, East Dubuque, IL 61025

Tel.: (815) 747-3101
Emp.: 145
Financial Investment Services
N.A.I.C.S.: 523999
Dan Poster (Controller)

Subsidiary (Domestic):

CVR Refining, LP (2)
2277 Plz Dr Ste 500, Sugar Land, TX 77479 (100%)
Tel.: (281) 207-3200
Web Site: https://www.cvrrefining.com
Oil Refining
N.A.I.C.S.: 324110

Subsidiary (Domestic):

Coffeyville Resources Crude Transportation, LLC (3)
411 NE Washington Blvd, Bartlesville, OK 74006
Tel.: (918) 333-4111
Web Site: http://www.cvrrefining.com
Sales Range: $25-49.9 Million
Financial Investment Services
N.A.I.C.S.: 523999
Don Sloan (VP-Pipeline Ops)
Mike Rowe (Mgr-Pipeline Integrity)

Coffeyville Resources Refining & Marketing, LLC (3)
3982 Cr 1675, Coffeyville, KS 67337-9437
Tel.: (620) 251-1166
Web Site: http://www.coffeyvillecrude.com
Sales Range: $250-299.9 Million
Emp.: 300
Financial Investment Services
N.A.I.C.S.: 523999
Bill Copeland (VP-Crude Oil Supply)
Allen Rempe (Mgr-Crude Supply)
Chad Arnold (Mgr-Crude Supply)
Scott Wayman (Mgr-Crude Supply)
Brian Blood (Mgr-Crude Supply)
Ty Peck (Mgr-Crude Supply)
Eric Schlecht (Mgr-Crude Supply)

Subsidiary (Domestic):

Coffeyville Finance Inc. (2)
102 W 7th St, Coffeyville, KS 67337
Tel.: (620) 252-6103
Financial Investment Services
N.A.I.C.S.: 523999

Coffeyville Nitrogen Fertilizers, Inc. (2)
10 E Cambridge Cir Dr, Kansas City, KS 66103
Tel.: (620) 252-1900
Web Site: http://www.cvrpartners.com
Emp.: 3
Financial Investment Services
N.A.I.C.S.: 523999

Coffeyville Resources Terminal, LLC (2)
1589 Hwy 183, Phillipsburg, KS 67661
Tel.: (785) 543-5246
Financial Investment Services
N.A.I.C.S.: 523999

Carbon Plate Steel Products, LLC (1)
26777 Lorain Rd Ste 216, North Olmsted, OH 44070
Tel.: (216) 641-2218
Web Site: http://www.carbonplate.com
Plate Work Mfr
N.A.I.C.S.: 332313

Darmex Casings SP.ZO.O (1)
Sulnowo 53 D, 86-100, Swiecie, Poland
Tel.: (48) 523310600
Sausage Casing Whslr
N.A.I.C.S.: 424490
Adam Szymanski (Gen Mgr)

Felt Products Mfg. Co. (1)
7450 N McCormick Blvd, Skokie, IL 60076
Tel.: (847) 674-7700
Financial Investment Services
N.A.I.C.S.: 523999

Grand Harbor Management, LLC (1)
4985 Club Ter, Vero Beach, FL 32967
Tel.: (772) 778-9000
Web Site: http://www.grandharbor.com
Hotel & Resort Management Services
N.A.I.C.S.: 721110

Subsidiary (Domestic):

GHG Asset Management LLC (2)
1590 NE 162 St Ste 500, North Miami Beach, FL 33162
Tel.: (305) 374-3529
Web Site: https://www.ghg-am.com
Property Management Services
N.A.I.C.S.: 531311

IEH Auto Parts LLC (1)
1155 Roberts Blvd Ste 175, Kennesaw, GA 30144
Tel.: (770) 701-5000
Web Site: http://www.autoplusap.com
Financial Investment Services
N.A.I.C.S.: 523999

Subsidiary (Domestic):

IEH ARI Holdings LLC (2)
445 Hamilton Ave, White Plains, NY 10601
Tel.: (646) 861-7060
Financial Investment Services
N.A.I.C.S.: 523999

IEH GH Management LLC (2)
1155 Roberts Blvd Ste 175, Kennesaw, GA 30144
Tel.: (770) 701-5000
Web Site: http://www.grandharbor.com
Financial Investment Services
N.A.I.C.S.: 523999

ISA Installations-,Steurerungs und Automatisierungs GmbH (1)
Bismarckstrasse 66, 01257, Dresden, Germany
Tel.: (49) 351272900
Web Site: http://www.isa-elektrik.de
Control Equipment Merchant Whslr
N.A.I.C.S.: 423730

Icahn Automotive Group LLC (1)
1155 Roberts Blvd. Ste. 175, Kennesaw, GA 30144
Tel.: (215) 430-9720
Web Site: https://www.icahnautomotive.com
Emp.: 22,000
Automotive Parts Distr & Related Services
N.A.I.C.S.: 441330
Matt Flannery (Chief Legal & Admin Officer)

Subsidiary (Domestic):

Tecnicentros Mundial Inc. (2)
PO Box 29423, San Juan, PR 00929-0423
Tel.: (787) 276-5630
Web Site: http://www.tecnicentrospr.com
Sales Range: $10-24.9 Million
Emp.: 78
Automotive Tires
N.A.I.C.S.: 441340
Efrain Tirado (Pres)
Victor Caraballo (Controller)
Roberto Tirado (VP-Ops)

Icahn Capital Management LP (1)
767 5th Ave Ste 4700, New York, NY 10153
Tel.: (212) 702-4300
Web Site: http://www.ielp.com
Investment Management Service
N.A.I.C.S.: 523940
Nicholas Francis Graziano (Portfolio Mgr)
Carl Icahn (CEO)

Icahn Enterprises Holdings L.P. (1)
16690 Collins Ave PH-1, Sunny Isles Beach, FL 33160
Tel.: (305) 422-4100
Rev.: $6,814,999,999
Assets: $24,986,999,999
Liabilities: $15,732,000,000
Net Worth: $9,255,000,000
Earnings: ($1,652,000,000)
Emp.: 23,832
Fiscal Year-end: 12/31/2020
Holding Company
N.A.I.C.S.: 551112
Keith Cozza (Pres & CEO)

Icahn Nevada Management Corp. (1)
445 Hamilton Ave Ste 1210, White Plains, NY 10601
Tel.: (914) 614-7062
Hotel & Resort Management Services
N.A.I.C.S.: 721110

Icahn Partners Master Fund LP (1)
767 5th Ave 47th Fl, New York, NY 10153

Tel.: (212) 702-4300
Investment Advisory Services
N.A.I.C.S.: 523940

M W Recycling, LLC (1)
3144 N Broadway, Saint Louis, MO 63147-3513
Tel.: (314) 381-1938
Financial Investment Services
N.A.I.C.S.: 523999

MB Development, LLC (1)
3540 Crain Hwy Ste 150, Bowie, MD 20716
Tel.: (301) 744-8218
Web Site: https://www.mbdevel.com
Real Estate Development Services
N.A.I.C.S.: 531390

Miracle Industries, Inc (1)
259 Great Hill Rd, Naugatuck, CT 06770
Tel.: (203) 723-0928
Web Site: http://www.weboffsetparts.com
Automotive Parts Holding Company Services
N.A.I.C.S.: 551112

New Seabury Properties, LLC (1)
20 Red Brook Rd, Mashpee, MA 02649
Tel.: (508) 539-8200
Web Site: http://www.newseabury.com
Sales Range: $10-24.9 Million
Emp.: 40
Financial Investment Services
N.A.I.C.S.: 523999

Subsidiary (Domestic):

New Seabury Beach Club LLC (2)
95 Shore Dr W, New Seabury, MA 02649
Tel.: (508) 477-9400
Beach Club Operating Services
N.A.I.C.S.: 713990

New Seabury Golf Club LLC (2)
95 Shore Dr W, Mashpee, MA 02649
Tel.: (508) 539-8322
Web Site: https://www.newseabury.com
Golf Club Operating Services
N.A.I.C.S.: 713910

PSC Metals Inc. (1)
5875 Landerbrook Rd Ste 200, Mayfield, OH 44124-5350
Tel.: (440) 753-5400
Web Site: http://www.pscmetals.com
Sales Range: $750-799.9 Million
Emp.: 80
Industrial Cleaning & Maintenance; Metal, Scrap Recycling, Brokerage & Mill Services
N.A.I.C.S.: 423930

Division (Domestic):

PSC Metals (2)
3101 Varloy Avo SW, Canton, OH 44706
Tel.: (330) 484-7610
Web Site: http://www.pscmetals.com
Sales Range: $50-74.9 Million
Emp.: 75
Scrap Metal Whslr
N.A.I.C.S.: 423930

PSC Metals (2)
710 S 1st St, Nashville, TN 37213
Tel.: (615) 271-3300
Web Site: http://www.pscmetals.com
Sales Range: $50-74.9 Million
Non-Woven Felt, Cushioning, Padding & Soundproofing for the Bedding, Furniture & Automotive Industries
N.A.I.C.S.: 423930

Subsidiary (Domestic):

PSC Metals - Akron, LLC (2)
701 W Hopocan Ave, Barberton, OH 44203
Tel.: (330) 745-4437
Web Site: http://www.pscmetals.com
Scrap Metal Collection & Processing Services
N.A.I.C.S.: 331491

PSC Metals - Aliquippa, LLC (2)
12 Woodland Rd, Aliquippa, PA 15001
Tel.: (724) 378-3734
Scrap Metal Collection & Processing Services
N.A.I.C.S.: 331491

PSC Metals - Alliance, LLC (2)
826 N Webb Ave, Alliance, OH 44601
Tel.: (330) 823-3643

Financial Investment Services
N.A.I.C.S.: 523999

PSC Metals - CAW, LLC (2)
2700 Youngstown Hubbard Rd, Youngstown, OH 44505
Tel.: (330) 759-2820
Web Site: http://www.pscmetals.com
Scrap Metal Collection & Processing Services
N.A.I.C.S.: 331491

PSC Metals - Elyria, LLC (2)
800 Infirmary Rd, Elyria, OH 44035
Tel.: (440) 322-1333
Web Site: http://www.pscmetals.com
Scrap Metal Collection & Processing Services
N.A.I.C.S.: 331491

PSC Metals - Garn, LLC (2)
972 Old Columbus Rd, Wooster, OH 44691
Tel.: (330) 263-0984
Recyclable Material Whslr
N.A.I.C.S.: 423930

PSC Metals - Joyce, LLC (2)
1283 Joyce Ave, Columbus, OH 43219
Tel.: (614) 299-4175
Web Site: http://www.pscmetals.com
Scrap Metal Collection & Processing Services
N.A.I.C.S.: 331491

PSC Metals - Knoxville, LLC (2)
2826 Central St N, Knoxville, TN 37917
Tel.: (865) 637-4353
Web Site: http://www.pscmetals.com
Scrap Metal Collection & Processing Services
N.A.I.C.S.: 331491

PSC Metals - Metallics, LLC (2)
1375 Old Mansfield Rd, Wooster, OH 44691
Tel.: (330) 264-5455
Financial Investment Services
N.A.I.C.S.: 523999

PSC Metals - Mitco, LLC (2)
3312 Barber Rd, Norton, OH 44203
Tel.: (330) 753-1700
Financial Investment Services
N.A.I.C.S.: 523999

PSC Metals - Wooster, LLC (2)
972 Old Columbus Rd, Wooster, OH 44691
Tel.: (330) 264-8956
Web Site: http://www.pscmetals.com
Scrap Metal Collection & Processing Services
N.A.I.C.S.: 331491

PSC Metals Inc. (2)
9th Delmar St, Festus, MO 63028
Tel.: (636) 937-9185
Sales Range: $25-49.9 Million
Emp.: 65
Scrap Metal Processing Services
N.A.I.C.S.: 423930

PSC Metals Massillon, LLC (1)
359 State Ave NW, Massillon, OH 44647
Tel.: (330) 236-2250
Web Site: http://www.pscmetals.com
Motor Vehicle Parts Mfr
N.A.I.C.S.: 336390

Precision Auto Care, Inc. (1)
748 Miller Dr SE, Leesburg, VA 20175
Tel.: (703) 777-9095
Web Site: http://www.precisiontune.com
General Automotive Repair Services
N.A.I.C.S.: 811111
Joel Burrows (VP-Trng & R&D)
Robert R. Falconi (Pres & CEO)
John T. Wiegand (Sr VP-Operational Programs & Dev)
Frederick F. Simmons (Gen Counsel & Sec)
Lee Oppenheim (VP-Bus Dev)

Subsidiary (Domestic):

Miracle Partners, Inc. (2)
22449 Conservancy Dr, Ashburn, VA 20148
Automotive Services
N.A.I.C.S.: 811111

Precision Franchising LLC (2)
748 Miller Dr SE, Leesburg, VA 20175
Tel.: (703) 777-9095
Financial Investment Services

N.A.I.C.S.: 523999

Precision Tune Auto Care, Inc. (2)
748 Miller Dr SE, Leesburg, VA 20175
Tel.: (703) 777-9095
Web Site: https://www.precisiontune.com
Automobile Maintenance Services
N.A.I.C.S.: 811111

Precision Printing, Inc. (1)
1613 Industrial Dr, Wilkesboro, NC 28697
Tel.: (828) 265-0004
Web Site:
https://www.precisionprintinggroup.com
Commercial Printing Services
N.A.I.C.S.: 323111

TLH LLC (1)
3917 Wrights Wharf Rd, Hurlock, MD 21643
Tel.: (410) 330-4357
Financial Investment Services
N.A.I.C.S.: 523999

The Pep Boys - Manny, Moe & Jack (1)
3111 W Allegheny Ave, Philadelphia, PA 19132
Web Site: http://www.pepboys.com
Automotive Parts, Accessories & Services
N.A.I.C.S.: 441330
Keith Cozza (Pres)

Subsidiary (Domestic):

The Pep Boys Manny Moe & Jack of California (2)
3111 W Allegheny Ave, Philadelphia, PA 19132-1116 **(100%)**
Tel.: (215) 430-9000
Web Site: http://www.pepboys.com
Auto Parts, Accessories & Service
N.A.I.C.S.: 441330

VTD Vakuumtecknik Dresden GmbH (1)
Niedersedlitzer Strasse 75, 01257, Dresden, Germany
Tel.: (49) 35128050
Web Site: http://www.vtd.de
Customer Consulting Services
N.A.I.C.S.: 541613

Vision Linens Limited (1)
Darwen House Walker Park Walker Road, Blackburn, BB1 2QE, Lancashire, United Kingdom
Tel.: (44) 1254589550
Web Site: https://www.visionlinens.com
Textile Performance & Luxury Textile Mfr
N.A.I.C.S.: 313310

Vision Support Services Limited (1)
Darwen House Walker Park Walker Road, Blackburn, BB1 2QE, Lancashire, United Kingdom
Tel.: (44) 1254589550
Web Site:
http://www.visionsupportservices.com
Textile Product Mfr & Distr
N.A.I.C.S.: 314999
Laurie Thomas (Grp Mng Dir)

Vision Support Services Pakistan Ltd. (1)
48- Abubakr Block New Garden Town, Lahore, 54700, Pakistan
Tel.: (92) 4235868788
Textile Product Mfr & Distr
N.A.I.C.S.: 314999
Nayyar Riaz (Mgr-Mdsg)

Vision Support Services Pvt. Ltd. (1)
89 Mangal Puri Ismail Ganj Lucknow, Maradu, Lucknow, 227 105, UP, India
Tel.: (91) 4842986171
Textile Product Mfr & Distr
N.A.I.C.S.: 314999
K. Joshy Michael (Reg Dir)

Viskase Companies, Inc. (1)
333 E Butterfield Rd Ste 400, Lombard, IL 60148-5679
Tel.: (630) 874-0700
Web Site: https://www.viskase.com
Sales Range: $125-149.9 Million
Cellulose, Fibrous & Plastic Packaging & Casings Mfr & Supplier
N.A.I.C.S.: 326199
Thomas D. Davis (Pres & CEO)

Subsidiary (Non-US):

Viskase Brasil Embalagens Ltda. (2)
Rod Dom Pedro I Km 87, Atibaia, 12954-260, Sao Paulo, Brazil
Tel.: (55) 114 417 7820
Web Site: http://www.viskase.com
Financial Investment Services
N.A.I.C.S.: 523999

Subsidiary (Domestic):

Viskase Films, Inc. (2)
8205 S Cass Ave Ste 115, Darien, IL 60561-5319
Tel.: (630) 874-0700
Plastic Utensils Mfr
N.A.I.C.S.: 326199

Subsidiary (Non-US):

Viskase GmbH (2)
Hamburger Strasse 28, Dormagen, 41540, Germany
Tel.: (49) 2133976130
Web Site: http://www.viskase.com
Sales Range: $25-49.9 Million
Emp.: 16
Financial Investment Services
N.A.I.C.S.: 523999

Viskase Polska Sp z o.o. (2)
Ul Pilsudskiego 101, 50-016, Wroclaw, Poland
Tel.: (48) 71 756 7960
Web Site: http://www.viskase.com
Sales Range: $25-49.9 Million
Emp.: 11
Sales of Cellulosic Casings
N.A.I.C.S.: 326199

Viskase S.A.S. (2)
134 Rue Danton, Levallois-Perret, 92300, France
Tel.: (33) 1 819 39000
Web Site: http://www.viskase.com
Meat Casings & Packaging Mfr
N.A.I.C.S.: 326199

Viskase S.p.A. (2)
Via Enrico Fermi 606, Caronno Pertusella, Varese, 21042, Italy
Tel.: (39) 029639901
Web Site: http://www.viskase.com
Sales Range: $25-49.9 Million
Emp.: 23
Sales of Cellulosic Casings
N.A.I.C.S.: 326199

Walsroder Casings GmbH (2)
Bahnhofstrasse 13, Bomlitz, 29699, Walsrode, Germany
Tel.: (49) 516150300
Web Site: http://www.walsroder.com
Cellulose & Plastic Sausage Casing Mfr
N.A.I.C.S.: 325220

Walsroder Casings Polska Sp.zo.o (1)
Legnicka 107, Legnickie Pole, Nowa Wies, 59-241, Poland
Tel.: (48) 767233950
Web Site: http://www.walsroder.com
Home Fashion Holding Company Services
N.A.I.C.S.: 531390

WestPoint International, Inc. (1)
28 E 28th St, New York, NY 10016
Tel.: (212) 930-2000
Web Site: http://www.westpointhome.com
Sales Range: $350-399.9 Million
Emp.: 2,148
Holding Company; Bedding & Household Products
N.A.I.C.S.: 551112

Subsidiary (Domestic):

WestPoint Home LLC (2)
777 3rd Ave 7th Fl, New York, NY 10017
Tel.: (212) 930-2000
Web Site: https://www.westpointhome.com
Bed Linens & Towels Mfr
N.A.I.C.S.: 314120

Subsidiary (Non-US):

WestPoint Home (Bahrain) W.L.L. (3)
Alba Industrial Area Road 5146 Building

1912 Block 951, Riffa, Askar, 39308, Bahrain
Tel.: (973) 17838018
Web Site: http://www.westpointhome.com
Financial Investment Services
N.A.I.C.S.: 523999

ICC HOLDINGS, INC.
225 20th St, Rock Island, IL 61201
Tel.: (309) 793-1700   PA
Web Site:
https://ir.iccholdingsinc.com
Year Founded: 2016
ICCH—(NASDAQ)
Rev.: $69,679,838
Assets: $192,162,211
Liabilities: $131,721,280
Net Worth: $60,440,931
Earnings: ($581,662)
Emp.: 102
Fiscal Year-end: 12/31/22
Holding Company
N.A.I.C.S.: 551112
Gerald J. Pepping (Chm)
Arron K. Sutherland (Pres & CEO)
Michael R. Smith (CFO & VP)
Julia B. Suiter (Chief Legal Officer)

Subsidiaries:

ICC Realty, LLC (1)
225 20th St, Rock Island, IL 61201
Tel.: (309) 324-7368
Web Site: https://www.icc-realty.com
Real Estate Services
N.A.I.C.S.: 531390

ICF INTERNATIONAL, INC.
1902 Reston Metro Plz, Reston, VA 20190
Tel.: (703) 934-3000   DE
Web Site: https://www.icf.com
Year Founded: 1969
ICFI—(NASDAQ)
Rev.: $1,779,964,000
Assets: $2,092,258,000
Liabilities: $1,239,047,000
Net Worth: $853,211,000
Earnings: $64,243,000
Emp.: 9,000
Fiscal Year-end: 12/31/22
Consulting & Technology Services
N.A.I.C.S.: 541690
John George (CIO)
Robert F. Toth (Sr VP-Contracts & Admin)
David M. Speiser (Exec VP-Corp Strategy)
Kristen Klovsky (Sr VP-Corp Growth)
Tobias Schaefer (Sr VP)
Jennifer Welham (Sr VP-Health, People, and Human Svcs)
James Morgan (COO)
Barry Broadus (CFO & Sr VP)
Matt Maurer (CMO)
Caryn McGarry (Chief HR Officer)
Ranjit S. Chadha (Principal Acctg Officer, VP & Controller)
Philip Mihlmester (Exec VP-Global Energy)
Sergio Ostria (EVP-Growth & Innovation)
James E. Daniel III (Gen Counsel & Exec VP)
John M. Wasson (Chm, Pres & CEO)

Subsidiaries:

Blanton & Associates, Inc. (1)
5 Lakeway Centre Ct, Austin, TX 78734
Tel.: (512) 264-1095
Web Site: http://www.blantonassociates.com
Scientific & Technical Consulting Services
N.A.I.C.S.: 541690
Donald R. Blanton (Pres)
Mark Kainer (Project Mgr)
Clifton Ladd (Project Mgr)

CITYTECH, Inc. (1)
211 W Wacker Dr Suite 1300, Chicago, IL 60606

ICF International, Inc.—(Continued)

Tel.: (312) 673-6433
Web Site: http://www.citytechinc.com
Sales Range: $10-24.9 Million
Emp.: 100
Web Experience Management, Managed
Services, Application Development & Cloud
Enablement Services
N.A.I.C.S.: 513210

GHK Holdings Ltd. (1)
Clerkenwell House 67 Clerkenwell Road,
London, EC1R 5BL, United Kingdom
Tel.: (44) 2076111100
Management Consulting Services
N.A.I.C.S.: 541611

ICF Consulting Group, Inc. (1)
9300 Lee Hwy, Fairfax, VA 22031-1207
Tel.: (703) 934-3000
Business Management Consulting Services
N.A.I.C.S.: 518210

Branch (Domestic):

ICF Consulting (2)
5300 International Blvd Ste 207, North
Charleston, SC 29418
Tel.: (843) 760-2908
Web Site: http://www.icfi.com
Sales Range: $10-24.9 Million
Emp.: 20
Technology Consulting Services
N.A.I.C.S.: 541690

ICF Consulting (2)
601 W 5th St, Los Angeles, CA 90071
Tel.: (213) 312-1700
Web Site: http://www.icfi.com
Sales Range: $10-24.9 Million
Emp.: 8
Management Consulting Services; Technology & Product Development
N.A.I.C.S.: 541611

Subsidiary (Non-US):

ICF Consulting Canada, Inc. (1)
400 University Avenue 17th Floor, Toronto,
M5G 1S5, ON, Canada
Tel.: (416) 341-0990
Emp.: 15
Management Consulting Services
N.A.I.C.S.: 541611

ICF Consulting India Private, Ltd. (2)
2nd Floor Caddie Commercial Tower,
Aerocity, New Delhi, 110 037, India
Tel.: (91) 1143533040
Business Management Consulting Services
N.A.I.C.S.: 541611

ICF Consulting Limited (2)
Riverscape 3rd Floor 10 Queens Street
Place, Clerkenwell House, London, EC4R
1BE, United Kingdom
Tel.: (44) 2030964800
Web Site: http://www.ghkint.com
Emp.: 150
Management Consulting Services
N.A.I.C.S.: 541611

**ICF International Consulting (Beijing)
Company, Ltd.** (2)
2 Jianwai Avenue Unit 3125 Level 31/F
Tower C Yintai Office Building, Chaoyang
District, Beijing, 100022, China
Tel.: (86) 1065628300
Sales Range: $25-49.9 Million
Emp.: 10
Business Management Consulting Services
N.A.I.C.S.: 541611

ICF Consulting Services, India Private, Ltd. (1)
Ashoka Estate 24 Barakhamba Road 301-
307 314 Third Floor, New Delhi, 110001,
India
Tel.: (91) 1143543000
Emp.: 70
Business Management & Consulting Services
N.A.I.C.S.: 541614
Nitin Zamre (Mng Dir)

ICF Consulting Services, Ltd. (1)
Heckfield Pl 526 Fulham Rd, London, SW6
5NR, United Kingdom
Tel.: (44) 20 7471 8000
Management Consulting Services

N.A.I.C.S.: 541611
Jonathan Lonsdale (Dir-Consulting)

ICF Jones & Stokes, Inc. (1)
980 9th St Ste 1200, Sacramento, CA
95814
Tel.: (916) 737-3000
Web Site: http://www.icfi.com
Sales Range: $50-74.9 Million
Emp.: 743
Management Consulting Services
N.A.I.C.S.: 541611

ICF Macro, Inc. (1)
530 Gaither Rd Ste 500, Rockville, MD
20850-1478
Tel.: (301) 315-2800
Web Site: http://www.icfi.com
Management Consulting Services
N.A.I.C.S.: 541611

ICF Olson (1)
420 N 5th St Ste 1000, Minneapolis, MN
55401
Tel.: (612) 215-9800
Web Site: http://www.olson.com
Sales Range: $75-99.9 Million
Emp.: 800
Advetising Agency
N.A.I.C.S.: 541810

Subsidiary (Domestic):

Olson Engage (2)
564 W Randolph Ste 500, Chicago, IL
60661
Tel.: (312) 577-1750
Web Site: http://www.olsonengage.com
Sales Range: $25-49.9 Million
Emp.: 75
Public Relations Agency
N.A.I.C.S.: 541820

ICF SH&E, Inc. (1)
630 3rd Ave Fl 11, New York, NY 10017
Tel.: (212) 656-9200
Emp.: 65
Management Consulting Services
N.A.I.C.S.: 541611

Subsidiary (Non-US):

ICF SH&E Limited (2)
3rd Floor Kean House 6 Kean Street, London, WC2B 4AS, United Kingdom
Tel.: (44) 2072429333
General Management Consulting Services
N.A.I.C.S.: 541611

**Incentive Technology Group,
LLC** (1)
2550 S Clark St 12th Fl, Arlington, VA
22202
Tel.: (571) 842-4500
Web Site: http://www.itgfirm.com
Sales Range: $10-24.9 Million
Emp.: 57
IT Consulting, Engineering & System Integration Services to Government Agencies
N.A.I.C.S.: 519290
JC Chidiac (COO)

Macro International Inc. (1)
530 Gater Rd Rockfield, Calverton, MD
20850
Tel.: (301) 572-0200
Web Site:
http://www.macrointernational.com
Sales Range: $125-149.9 Million
Emp.: 1,200
Research Services
N.A.I.C.S.: 541910

Mostra, SA (1)
Globe Village 1001 Chaussee d'Alsemberg,
1180, Brussels, Belgium
Tel.: (32) 25374400
Web Site: http://www.mostra.com
Business Management & Consulting Services
N.A.I.C.S.: 541614

Olson Canada, Inc. (1)
400 University Avenue 17th Floor, Toronto,
M7A 1T7, ON, Canada
Tel.: (416) 848-4115
Web Site: http://www.icfolson.ca
Advertising Service
N.A.I.C.S.: 541810

PulsePoint Group, LLC (1)

2700 Via Fortuna Dr Ste 200, Austin, TX
78746
Tel.: (512) 582-7450
Web Site: http://www.pulsepointgroup.com
Emp.: 23
Management Consulting Services
N.A.I.C.S.: 541611

SemanticBits, LLC (1)
13921 Park Ctr Rd Ste 420, Herndon, VA
20171-3241
Tel.: (703) 787-9656
Web Site: http://www.semanticbits.com
Computer Related Services
N.A.I.C.S.: 541519
Ram Chilukuri (Co-Founder & CEO)

ICG HYPERSONIC ACQUISITION CORP.
717 Fifth Ave 18th Fl, New York, NY
10022
Tel.: (212) 705-5000 DE
Year Founded: 2020
ICGAU—(NASDAQ)
Investment Services
N.A.I.C.S.: 523999
Andrew L. Farkas (Chm)
Jeffrey P. Cohen (CEO)
Matthew J. Stern (Pres & CFO)
Marc W. Levy (Co-Chief Investment
Officer)
Geoffrey H. Woodward (Co-Chief Investment Officer)

ICOA, INC.
3651 Lindell Rd Ste D, Las Vegas,
NV 89103
Tel.: (917) 539-4271 NV
Web Site: http://www.icoacorp.com
Year Founded: 1983
ICOA—(OTCIQ)
Sales Range: Less than $1 Million
Emp.: 9
Broadband Wireless Services
N.A.I.C.S.: 334220
George Strouthopoulos (Chm & CEO)
Hadria Yanneck Wong Yen Cheong
(CEO)
James Paul Soyangco Botonez
(COO)
Ashwin Lutchmeenaraidoo (CTO)
Erwin Vahlsing Jr. (CFO)

ICON MEDIA HOLDINGS, INC.
5520 McNeely Dr Ste 101, Raleigh,
NC 27612
Tel.: (919) 237-5700
Web Site:
https://www.iconmediaholdings.com
ICNM—(OTCIQ)
Sales Range: $1-9.9 Million
Other Scientific & Technical Consulting Services
N.A.I.C.S.: 541690
Chris Horne (CTO)
Rob Deakin (Chm & CEO)
Jerry Brown (Pres & COO)
Mike Scheiber (Dir-Ops)

ICONIC BRANDS, INC.
44 Seabro Ave, Amityville, NY 11701
Tel.: (631) 464-4050 NV
Web Site:
https://www.iconicbrandsusa.com
Year Founded: 2005
ICNB—(OTCQB)
Rev.: $14,745,261
Assets: $18,358,748
Liabilities: $17,998,506
Net Worth: $360,242
Earnings: ($30,771,062)
Emp.: 42
Fiscal Year-end: 12/31/22
Alcoholic Beverage Importer, Marketer & Sales
N.A.I.C.S.: 424820
Richard J. DeCicco (Founder, Chm,
Pres, CEO & CFO)

Roseann Faltings (Bd of Dirs & VP-Sls)
John Cosenza (COO)

ICONSUMER CORP.
73 Greentree Dr 558, Dover, DE
19904
Web Site:
https://www.iconsumer.com
RWRDP—(OTCIQ)
Online Investment Services
N.A.I.C.S.: 541519
Rob Grosshandler (Founder & CEO)

ICORECONNECT INC.
105 S Maple St, Itasca, IL 60143
Tel.: (847) 773-1665 DE
Web Site: https://www.fgmerger.com
ICCT—(NASDAQ)
Emp.: 100
Investment Holding Company
N.A.I.C.S.: 551112
M. Wesley Schrader (CEO)
Mark Penway (CFO)

Subsidiaries:

iCoreConnect Inc. (1)
529 E Crown Point Rd Ste 250, Ocoee, FL
34761-3618
Web Site: https://www.icoreconnect.com
Rev.: $7,987,902
Assets: $6,556,184
Liabilities: $9,057,688
Net Worth: ($2,501,504)
Earnings: ($6,079,824)
Emp.: 41
Fiscal Year-end: 12/31/2022
Online Information Services
N.A.I.C.S.: 519290
Muralidar Chakravarthi (CTO)
Robert P. McDermott (Pres & CEO)
David Fidanza (COO & CIO)

ICTV BRANDS INC.
489 Devon Park Dr Ste 306, Wayne,
PA 19087
Tel.: (484) 598-2300 NV
Web Site: http://www.ictvonline.com
Year Founded: 1998
ICTV—(OTCIQ)
Sales Range: $25-49.9 Million
Emp.: 29
Health & Beauty Product Telemarketing
N.A.I.C.S.: 561422
Kelvin Claney (Chm & CEO)
Douglas M. Crouthers (Interim Pres &
VP-Sls)
Vince Dargush (VP-Ops)
Craig J. Millman (Interim CFO & VP-Fin Reporting)

ICU MEDICAL, INC.
951 Calle Amanecer, San Clemente,
CA 92673
Tel.: (949) 366-2183 DE
Web Site: https://www.icumed.com
Year Founded: 1984
ICUI—(NASDAQ)
Rev.: $2,259,126,000
Assets: $4,378,439,000
Liabilities: $2,255,029,000
Net Worth: $2,123,410,000
Earnings: ($29,655,000)
Emp.: 14,000
Fiscal Year-end: 12/31/23
Disposable Medical Connection Systems Mfr
N.A.I.C.S.: 339112
George A. Lopez (Founder)
Vivek Jain (Chm & CEO)
Christian Voigtlander (COO)
Dan Woolson (VP & Gen Mgr-Infusion Sys)
Virginia Sanzone (Gen Counsel &
VP)
Brian M. Bonnell (CFO)

Subsidiaries:

BMDi Tuta Healthcare Pty Ltd **(1)**
Unit U 10 - 16 South St, Rydalmere, 2116,
NSW, Australia
Tel.: (61) 294665300
Emp.: 23
Medical Product Whslr
N.A.I.C.S.: 423450

Excelsior Medical Corporation **(1)**
1933 Heck Ave, Neptune, NJ 07753
Tel.: (732) 776-7525
Web Site:
https://www.swabflush.excelsiormedi
cal.com
Flush Syringe & Syringe Pump Mfr
N.A.I.C.S.: 339112

Fannin (UK) Limited **(1)**
Westminister Industrial Estate Repton Road
Measham, Swadlincote, DE12 7DT, Derbs,
United Kingdom
Tel.: (44) 1530514566
Web Site: http://www.fannin.eu
Medical Device Mfr & Distr
N.A.I.C.S.: 334510

ICU Medical (Utah), Inc. **(1)**
4455 S Atherton Dr, Salt Lake City, UT
84123
Tel.: (801) 262-2688
Sales Range: $500-549.9 Million
Emp.: 1,425
Surgical & Medical Instruments
N.A.I.C.S.: 339112
George A. Lopez *(Executives)*

**ICU Medical Australia Pty
Limited** **(1)**
207/33 Lexington Dr, Bella Vista, Sydney,
2153, NSW, Australia
Tel.: (61) 296296977
Web Site: http://www.icumedical.com.au
Medical Instrument Mfr
N.A.I.C.S.: 339112

ICU Medical Fleet Services, LLC **(1)**
3900 Howard Ln, Austin, TX 78728
Tel.: (512) 255-2000
Emp.: 100
Medical Product Whslr
N.A.I.C.S.: 423450

ICU Medical Germany GmbH **(1)**
Altenaer Strasse 136, 58513, Ludenscheid,
Germany
Tel.: (49) 235195480
Medical Product Whslr
N.A.I.C.S.: 423450

Medical Australia Limited **(1)**
Unit 4B 128-130 Frances Street, Lidcombe,
2141, NSW, Australia
Tel.: (61) 294665300
Web Site: https://www.medaust.com
Medical Device Mfr
N.A.I.C.S.: 339112

Pursuit Vascular, Inc. **(1)**
6901 E Fish Lake Rd Ste 166, Maple
Grove, MN 55369
Tel.: (612) 424-9006
Web Site: http://www.pursuitvascular.com
Medical Instrument Mfr
N.A.I.C.S.: 339112
Doug Killion *(Pres & CEO)*
Bob Ziebol *(Founder & Sr VP-R&D)*
Keith Modert *(VP-Mfg)*
Renee Koziol *(Dir-Mktg)*

Smiths Medical Group Limited **(1)**
1500 Eureka Park, Lower Pemberton, Ash-
ford, TN25 4BF, Kent, United Kingdom
Tel.: (44) 123 372 2153
Web Site: https://www.smiths-medical.com
Medical Device Distr
N.A.I.C.S.: 423450
Brett Landrum *(CTO & Sr VP-R&D)*
John Kowalczyk *(Sr VP-Sls-Global)*
Brenda McCormick *(CFO & Sr VP-Fin)*
Chris Percival *(Sr VP-Ops-Global)*
Gretchen Randall *(Gen Counsel)*

Subsidiary (US):

Access Scientific, LLC **(2)**
12526 High Bluff Dr Ste 360, San Diego,
CA 92130
Tel.: (858) 259-8333
Web Site: http://www.accessscientific.com

Professional Equipment & Supplies Mer-
chant Whslr
N.A.I.C.S.: 423490
Richard Pluth *(VP-R&D)*

Subsidiary (Non-US):

Graseby Medical Ireland Ltd. **(2)**
Unit 3 Leopard stown Business Centre,
Bally Ogan Rd, Dublin, 18, Ireland **(100%)**
Tel.: (353) 012941133
Web Site: http://www.smiths-medical.com
Sales Range: $25-49.9 Million
Emp.: 4
Medical Equipment Mfr
N.A.I.C.S.: 339112

Subsidiary (US):

Level 1, Inc. **(2)**
160 Weymouth St, Rockland, MA
02370-1136 **(100%)**
Tel.: (781) 878-8011
Web Site: http://www.smiths-medical.com
Sales Range: $25-49.9 Million
Laboratory & Medical Equipment Mfr
N.A.I.C.S.: 334519

Subsidiary (Non-US):

Medex Medical GmbH **(2)**
Hauptstreet 25 47, 40880, Ratingen, Ger-
many
Tel.: (49) 80915510
N.A.I.C.S.: 327211

Subsidiary (US):

**Respiratory Support Products
Inc.** **(2)**
9255 Custom House Plz Ste N, San Diego,
CA 92154 **(100%)**
Tel.: (619) 710-1000
Sales Range: $450-499.9 Million
Emp.: 1,400
Mfr of Healthcare Equipment
N.A.I.C.S.: 339112

Smiths Medical **(2)**
10 Bowman Dr, Keene, NH
03431-5911 **(100%)**
Tel.: (603) 352-3812
Web Site: http://www.smiths-medical.com
Sales Range: $25-49.9 Million
Medical Equipment Mfr
N.A.I.C.S.: 326199

Smiths Medical **(2)**
5700 W 23rd Ave, Gary, IN 46406-2617
Tel.: (219) 989-9150
Web Site: http://www.smithmedical.com
Sales Range: $25-49.9 Million
Orthopedic & Surgical Appliances
N.A.I.C.S.: 339112
Dennis Sullivan *(Gen Mgr)*

Smiths Medical **(2)**
160 Weymouth St, Rockland, MA
02370-1136 **(100%)**
Tel.: (781) 878-8011
Web Site: http://www.smiths-medical.com
Medical Equipment Mfr
N.A.I.C.S.: 334519

Smiths Medical **(2)**
201 W Queen St, Southington, CT 06489-
1138
Tel.: (860) 621-9111
Web Site: http://www.smiths-medical.com
Sales Range: $75-99.9 Million
Mfr of IV Catheters
N.A.I.C.S.: 339112

Subsidiary (Non-US):

**Smiths Medical (Beijing) Co.,
Ltd.** **(2)**
Landgent Center Tower A Level 29 No 20
East 3rd Ring Middle Road, Chao Yang
District, Beijing, 100022, China
Tel.: (86) 1056320888
Web Site: http://www.smiths-medical.com
Medical Device Distr
N.A.I.C.S.: 423450

**Smiths Medical (Portugal) Unipessoal
Lda.** **(2)**
Av Eng Duarte Pacheco Amoreiras Torre 2
15 A, 1070-102, Lisbon, Portugal
Tel.: (351) 22 532 3010
Web Site: http://www.smiths-medical.com

Sales Range: $25-49.9 Million
Emp.: 15
Medical Device Distr
N.A.I.C.S.: 423450

**Smiths Medical (South Africa) Pty.
Ltd.** **(2)**
San Croy Office Park Die Agora Road Croy-
don, Isando, 1619, South Africa **(100%)**
Tel.: (27) 0119747134
Web Site: http://www.smiths-medical.com
Sales Range: $25-49.9 Million
Emp.: 30
Medical Equipment Mfr
N.A.I.C.S.: 334510

Subsidiary (US):

Smiths Medical ASD Inc. **(2)**
5200 Upper Metro Pl Ste 200, Dublin, OH
43017
Tel.: (614) 210-7300
Web Site: http://www.smiths-medical.com
Medical Device Mfr & Distr
N.A.I.C.S.: 339113

Subsidiary (Non-US):

**Smiths Medical Australasia Pty.
Ltd.** **(2)**
Unit U 10 - 16 South Street, Rydalmere,
2116, NSW, Australia **(100%)**
Tel.: (61) 294665300
Web Site: http://www.smiths-medical.com
Sales Range: $25-49.9 Million
Emp.: 13
Provider of Medical Equipment
N.A.I.C.S.: 334510

Smiths Medical Belgium N.V. **(2)**
Pegasuslaan 5, 1831, Diegem, Belgium
Tel.: (32) 27044900
Web Site: http://www.smiths-medical.com
Emp.: 40
Medical Equipment Distr
N.A.I.C.S.: 423450

Smiths Medical Canada Ltd. **(2)**
301 Gough Road, Markham, L3R 4Y8, ON,
Canada
Tel.: (905) 477-2000
Medical Device Distr
N.A.I.C.S.: 423450

Smiths Medical Denmark ApS **(2)**
Winghouse Orestads Boulevard 73, 2300,
Copenhagen, Denmark
Tel.: (45) 7 027 2090
Web Site: http://www.smiths-medical.com
Sales Range: $50-74.9 Million
Emp.: 7
Medical Equipment Distr
N.A.I.C.S.: 423450

**Smiths Medical Deutschland
GmbH** **(2)**
Bretonischer Ring 3, 85630, Grasbrunn,
Germany **(100%)**
Tel.: (49) 89242959370
Web Site: http://www.smiths-medical.com
Sales Range: $75-99.9 Million
Medical Equipment Mfr
N.A.I.C.S.: 334510

Smiths Medical Espana, S.R.L. **(2)**
Avenida Diagonal no 635, 08028, Barce-
lona, Spain
Tel.: (34) 93 363 8400
Web Site: http://www.smiths-medical.com
Medical Equipment Distr
N.A.I.C.S.: 423450

Smiths Medical France S.A. **(2)**
3-5 rue du Pont des Halles Batiment A,
94150, Rungis, France **(100%)**
Tel.: (33) 800944148
Web Site: http://www.smiths-medical.com
Sales Range: $25-49.9 Million
Medical Equipment Mfr
N.A.I.C.S.: 339112

**Smiths Medical Instrument (Zhejiang)
Co., Ltd.** **(2)**
No 26 The 3rd Avenue, Hangzhou Eco-
nomic & Technological Development Zone,
Hangzhou, 310018, China
Tel.: (86) 57186717228
Web Site: http://www.smiths-medical.com
Sales Range: $50-74.9 Million
Health Care Equipment Mfr
N.A.I.C.S.: 339112

Subsidiary (Domestic):

Smiths Medical International Ltd. **(2)**
1500 Eureka Park, Lower Pemberton, Ash-
ford, TN25 4BF, Kent, United
Kingdom **(100%)**
Tel.: (44) 8458500445
Web Site: https://www.smiths-medical.com
Medical Equipment Mfr
N.A.I.C.S.: 334510

Subsidiary (Non-US):

Smiths Medical Italia S.r.l. **(2)**
Via della stazione 2, 04100, Latina Scalo,
Italy
Tel.: (39) 0773 408 4350
Web Site: http://www.smiths-medical.com
Medical Device Distr
N.A.I.C.S.: 423450

Smiths Medical Japan Ltd. **(2)**
2-38-3 Hongo Bunkyo Ku, Tokyo, 113 0033,
Japan **(100%)**
Tel.: (81) 356840612
Web Site: http://www.smithsmedical.jp
Sales Range: $25-49.9 Million
Emp.: 40
Medical Equipment Mfr
N.A.I.C.S.: 334510

Smiths Medical Limited **(2)**
80 Vitoria St Circinal Place 2nd Fl, SW1E
5JL, London, United Kingdom -
England **(100%)**
Tel.: (44) 2078085500
Web Site: http://www.smiths-medical.com
Sales Range: $25-49.9 Million
Emp.: 45
Laboratory & Medical Equipment Mfr
N.A.I.C.S.: 339112

Subsidiary (US):

Smiths Medical MD, Inc. **(2)**
1265 Grey Fox Rd, Saint Paul, MN
55112-6929 **(100%)**
Tel.: (651) 633-2556
Web Site: http://www.smiths-medical.com
Sales Range: $25-49.9 Million
Laboratory & Medical Equipment Mfr
N.A.I.C.S.: 339112

Subsidiary (Non-US):

Smiths Medical Nederland B.V. **(2)**
Hofspoor 3, 3994 VZ, Houten,
Netherlands **(100%)**
Tel.: (31) 735285050
Web Site: http://www.smiths-medical.com
Sales Range: $25-49.9 Million
Medical Equipment Mfr
N.A.I.C.S.: 335999

Subsidiary (US):

Smiths Medical PM Inc. **(2)**
5200 Upper Metro Pl Ste 200, Dublin, OH
43017-5379 **(100%)**
Tel.: (614) 210-7300
Web Site: http://www.smiths-medical.com
Sales Range: $25-49.9 Million
Laboratory & Medical Equipment Mfr
N.A.I.C.S.: 339112

Subsidiary (Non-US):

Smiths Medical Sverige AB **(2)**
Orrvaegen 26-28, 192 55, Sollentuna, Swe-
den
Tel.: (46) 859477250
Web Site: http://www.smiths-medical.com
Medical Equipment Distr
N.A.I.C.S.: 423450

IDACORP, INC.

1221 W Idaho St, Boise, ID 83702-
5627
Tel.: (208) 388-2200   **ID**
Web Site:
https://www.idacorpinc.com
Year Founded: 1998
IDA—(NYSE)
Rev.: $264,013,000
Assets: $2,967,647,000
Liabilities: $60,078,000
Net Worth: $2,907,569,000
Earnings: $261,195,000

IDACORP, Inc.—(Continued)

Emp.: 2,100
Fiscal Year-end: 12/31/23
Energy Holding Company
N.A.I.C.S.: 551112
Richard J. Dahl (Chm)
Lisa A. Grow (Pres & CEO)
Jeffrey L. Malmen (Sr VP/Sr VP-Pub Affairs)
Kenneth W. Petersen (Chief Acctg Officer, Treas & VP)
Brian R. Buckham (CFO & Sr VP)
Amy I. Shaw (Chief Acctg Officer & VP-Compliance, Fin, and Risk)
Justin S. Forsberg (Dir-IR & Treasury)
Jeff Malmen (Sr VP-Pub Affairs)

Subsidiaries:

IDACORP Financial Services, Inc.　　　　　　　　　　(1)
205 N 10th St Ste 510, Boise, ID 83702
Tel.: (208) 388-2820
Investment Office
N.A.I.C.S.: 525990
Steve R. Keen (Pres)

Ida-West Energy Company　　　(1)
PO Box 7867, Boise, ID
83707-1867　　　　　　　　　(100%)
Tel.: (208) 388-2820
Web Site: https://www.ida-west.com
Sales Range: $10-24.9 Million
Emp.: 5
Maintains & Operates Power Generation Facilities
N.A.I.C.S.: 221122

Idaho Power Company　　　　　(1)
1221 W Idaho St, Boise, ID
83702-5627　　　　　　　　　(100%)
Tel.: (208) 388-2200
Web Site: https://www.idahopower.com
Rev.: $1,641,040,000
Assets: $7,411,104,000
Liabilities: $4,779,441,000
Net Worth: $2,631,663,000
Earnings: $254,867,000
Emp.: 2,062
Fiscal Year-end: 12/31/2022
Electric Generation Purchase Transmission Distr
N.A.I.C.S.: 221122
Lisa A. Grow (Pres & CEO)
Jeffrey L. Malmen (Sr VP-Pub Affairs)
Kenneth W. Petersen (Chief Acctg Officer, Treas & VP)
Brian R. Buckham (CFO & Sr VP)
Amy I. Shaw (Chief Acctg Officer & VP-Fin, Compliance, and Risk)
Adam J. Richins (COO & Sr VP)
Tim E. Tatum (VP-Regulatory Affairs)
Ryan N. Adelman (VP-Power Supply)
James Bo D. Hanchey (Chief Safety Officer & VP-Customer Ops)
Sarah E. Griffin (VP-HR)
Debra Leithauser (VP-Corp Svcs & Comm)
Mitch Colburn (VP-Plng, Engrg & Construction)
Jason Huszar (CIO & VP-IT)
Julia Hilton (Corp Counsel)
Andres Valdepena-Delgado (Engr)
Lindsay Barretto (Sr Mgr)
Bryan Brandel (Mgr)
Angelique Rood (Reg Mgr)
Allison Murray (Mgr)
Fred Noland (Mgr)

Subsidiary (Domestic):

Idaho Energy Resources Company　　　　　　　　　　(2)
1221 W Idaho St, Boise, ID 83702-5626
Tel.: (208) 388-2200
Web Site: http://www.idahopower.com
Electric Power Distr
N.A.I.C.S.: 221122
Darrel T. Anderson (Pres & CEO)

IDAHO COPPER CORPORATION

800 W Main St Ste 1460, Boise, ID 83702
Tel.: (208) 274-9220　　　　　NV

Web Site: https://www.idaho-copper.com
Year Founded: 2003
COPR—(OTCIQ)
Assets: $151,770
Liabilities: $6,212,379
Net Worth: ($6,060,609)
Earnings: ($3,712,047)
Fiscal Year-end: 01/31/24
Holding Company; Copper Ore Mining
N.A.I.C.S.: 551112
Yuan Huang (CFO & Treas)
Jinghe Zhang (Chm)
Andrew A. Brodkey (Pres, CEO, COO & Sec)

Subsidiaries:

International CuMo Mining Corporation　　　　　　　　(1)
800 W Main St Ste 1460, Boise, ID 83702
Tel.: (208) 274-9220
Web Site: https://cumoproject.com
Copper Exploration & Mining Services
N.A.I.C.S.: 212230
Trevor Burns (Chm)
Shaun M. Dykes (Pres)

IDAHO STRATEGIC RESOURCES, INC.

201 N 3rd St, Coeur D'Alene, ID 83814
Tel.: (208) 625-9001　　　　　ID
Web Site: https://idahostrategic.com
IDR—(NYSE)
Rev.: $13,656,733
Assets: $23,889,789
Liabilities: $3,354,191
Net Worth: $20,535,598
Earnings: $1,073,449
Emp.: 42
Fiscal Year-end: 12/31/23
Gold, Silver & Base Metal Mining
N.A.I.C.S.: 212220
Monique Hayes (Sec)
Grant A. Brackebusch (CFO & VP)
John A. Swallow (Chm, Pres & CEO)
Robert Morgan (VP-Exploration)

IDDRIVEN, INC.

13355 Moss Rock Dr, Auburn, CA 95602
Tel.: (415) 226-7773　　　　　NV
Web Site: http://www.iddriven.com
Year Founded: 2014
IDDR—(OTCIQ)
Sales Range: Less than $1 Million
Emp.: 7
Identity & Access Management Services
N.A.I.C.S.: 513210
Arend Dirk Verweij (CEO)
Geurt van Wijk (COO)
Remy De Vries (CTO)
Neil Kleinman (Mgr-Sls-North America)

IDEAL POWER INC.

5508 Hwy 290 W Ste 120, Austin, TX 78735
Tel.: (512) 264-1542　　　　　DE
Web Site: https://www.idealpower.com
Year Founded: 2007
IPWR—(NASDAQ)
Rev.: $198,871
Assets: $12,248,070
Liabilities: $2,188,370
Net Worth: $10,059,700
Earnings: ($9,954,020)
Emp.: 11
Fiscal Year-end: 12/31/23
Electronic Power Converters & Inverters Mfr
N.A.I.C.S.: 335311
Michael C. Turmelle (Chm)
R. Daniel Brdar (Pres & CEO)

IDEANOMICS, INC.

1441 Broadway Ste 5116, New York, NY 10018
Tel.: (212) 206-1216　　　　　NV
Web Site: https://www.ideanomics.com
Year Founded: 2004
IDEX—(NASDAQ)
Rev.: $100,936,000
Assets: $242,801,000
Liabilities: $106,350,000
Net Worth: $136,451,000
Earnings: ($260,692,000)
Emp.: 565
Fiscal Year-end: 12/31/22
Holding Company; Video On Demand Services
N.A.I.C.S.: 551112
Macy Neshati (Chief Comml Officer)
Bruno Wu (Founder)
Shane McMahon (Chm)
James S. Cassano (Vice Chm)
Robin J. Mackie (COO)
Alfred Poor (CEO & Chm)
Tony Sklar (Sr VP-IR)
Steve Heckeroth (Founder)

Subsidiaries:

Energica Motor Company S.p.A.　(1)
Via Cesare della Chiesa 150, 41126, Modena, Italy
Tel.: (39) 0597231722
Web Site: https://www.energicamotor.com
Rev.: $7,422,575
Assets: $12,788,123
Liabilities: $13,372,461
Net Worth: ($584,338)
Earnings: ($7,780,764)
Emp.: 58
Fiscal Year-end: 12/31/2020
Motorcycle Manufacturing
N.A.I.C.S.: 336991
Franco Cevolini (Chm)
Livia Cevolini (CEO)
Giampiero Testoni (CTO)
Andrea Vezzani (CFO)

Solectrac, Inc.　　　　　　　　(1)
5600 Earhart Ct, Windsor, CA 95492
Web Site: https://solectrac.com
Agriculture Machinery Mfr & Distr
N.A.I.C.S.: 333111

Timios Holdings Corp.　　　　　(1)
5716 Corsa Ave Ste 102, Westlake Village, CA 91362
Tel.: (818) 706-6404
Web Site: http://www.timios.com
Sales Range: $10-24.9 Million
Emp.: 285
Holding Company; Real Estate Title Insurance, Escrow, Settlement, Appraisal & Default Services
N.A.I.C.S.: 551112
Trevor G. Stoffer (Chm)
Raymond B. Davison (CEO)

Subsidiary (Domestic):

Timios Appraisal Management, Inc.　　　　　　　　　　(2)
4955 Steubenville Pike Ste 305, Pittsburgh, PA 15205
Tel.: (412) 593-2021
Real Estate Appraisal Services
N.A.I.C.S.: 531320

Timios Default Services, Inc.　　(2)
4 Penn Ctr Blvd Ste 404, Pittsburgh, PA 15276
Tel.: (502) 968-1400
Web Site: http://www.timios.com
Emp.: 20
Default Asset Management Services
N.A.I.C.S.: 523940

Timios, Inc.　　　　　　　　　(2)
5716 Corsa Ave Ste 102, Westlake Village, CA 91362
Tel.: (818) 706-6400
Web Site: http://www.timios.com
Title, Escrow & Settlement Services
N.A.I.C.S.: 541191
Trevor G. Stoffer (Chm)
Raymond B. Davison (CEO)
Dominic Janero (Sr VP-Appraisal Ops)

Subsidiary (Domestic):

Timios Title, a California Corporation　　　　　　　　(3)
250 W Sycamore St, Willows, CA 95988
Tel.: (530) 934-3338
Web Site: http://www.timios.com
Title & Escrow Services
N.A.I.C.S.: 531390
Richard M. Thomas (Pres)

US Hybrid Corporation　　　　　(1)
445 Maple Ave, Torrance, CA 90503
Tel.: (310) 212-1200
Web Site: http://www.ushybrid.com
Hazardous Waste Treatment & Disposal
N.A.I.C.S.: 562211
Gordon Abas Goodarzi (CEO)

VIA Motors Inc.　　　　　　　　(1)
3900 Automation Ave, Auburn Hills, MI 48326
Tel.: (801) 764-9111
Web Site: https://www.viamotors.com
Automobile Mfr
N.A.I.C.S.: 336110
Pablo Acedo (Pres-Latin America)

IDEAYA BIOSCIENCES, INC.

5000 Shoreline Ct Ste 300, South San Francisco, CA 94080
Tel.: (650) 443-6209　　　　　DE
Web Site: https://www.ideayabio.com
Year Founded: 2015
IDYA—(NASDAQ)
Rev.: $23,385,000
Assets: $649,316,000
Liabilities: $28,226,000
Net Worth: $621,090,000
Earnings: ($112,961,000)
Emp.: 124
Fiscal Year-end: 12/31/23
Biotechnology Research & Development Services
N.A.I.C.S.: 541714
Timothy M. Shannon (Chm)
Andres Ruiz Briseno (Principal Acctg Officer, Sr VP & Head-Fin & IR)
Michael White (Chief Scientific Officer)
Darrin M. Beaupre (Chief Medical Officer)
Jasgit Sachdev (VP)
Claire L. Neilan (VP)
Yujiro S. Hata (Founder, Pres & CEO)

IDENTILLECT TECHNOLOGIES CORP.

14781 Pomerado Rd Ste 578, Poway, CA 92064
Tel.: (949) 215-1244
Web Site: https://www.identillect.com
8ID—(STU)
Software Development Services
N.A.I.C.S.: 541511
Todd Sexton (CEO)
Einar Mykletun (CTO)
Robert Chrisholm (CFO)

IDENTIV, INC.

2201 Walnut Ave Ste 100, Fremont, CA 94538
Tel.: (949) 250-8888　　　　　DE
Web Site: https://www.identiv.com
Year Founded: 1990
INVE—(NASDAQ)
Rev.: $112,915,000
Assets: $102,765,000
Liabilities: $27,371,000
Net Worth: $75,394,000
Earnings: ($392,000)
Emp.: 343
Fiscal Year-end: 12/31/22
Physical & Logical Access Control, Identity Management & Radio Frequency Identification Systems Mfr, Designer & Retailer
N.A.I.C.S.: 334220

Manfred W. Mueller (COO & Gen Mgr-Identity)
Justin Scarpulla (CFO)
James E. Ousley (Chm)
Mark Allen (Gen Mgr-Premises)
Mike Taylor (VP-Global Sls)
Leigh Dow (VP-Global Mktg)
Tanya Freedland (VP)

Subsidiaries:

3VR Security, Inc. (1)
1 Kaiser Pl, Ste 1030, Oakland, CA 94612
Tel.: (415) 513-4611
Web Site: http://www.identiv.com
Software Publisher
N.A.I.C.S.: 513210

ACIG TECHNOLOGY Corp. (1)
6135 NW 167 St Ste E18, Hialeah, FL 33015
Tel.: (305) 513-4090
Web Site: https://www.acigintl.com
Identity Management Solutions & Services
N.A.I.C.S.: 326199

Identiv Australia Pty Ltd (1)
Unit 13 16 Metroplex Avenue, Murarrie, 4172, QLD, Australia
Tel.: (61) 731984400
Software Development Services
N.A.I.C.S.: 541511

Identiv GmbH (1)
Oskar-Messter-Str 12, 85737, Ismaning, Germany
Tel.: (49) 8995955441
Web Site: http://www.identiv.com
Identity Management Solutions & Services
N.A.I.C.S.: 423690

Identiv GmbH (1)
Oskar-Messter-Str 12, 85737, Ismaning, Germany
Tel.: (49) 8995955441
Security Identification Provider
N.A.I.C.S.: 518210

Identiv KK (1)
GoogolPlex Millennium Building 6F 4-4-20 Shiba, Minato-ku, Tokyo, 108-0014, Japan
Tel.: (81) 364146611
Security Identification Provider
N.A.I.C.S.: 518210

Identiv Pte. Ltd. (1)
6 Serangoon North Ave 5 04-06/07/08, Singapore, 554910, Singapore
Tel.: (65) 66351600
Software Development Services
N.A.I.C.S.: 541511
Hazel Viroya (Asst Mgr-QA)

Identiv Pvt. Ltd. (1)
5th Floor Block A Tecci Park No 173 Rajiv Gandhi Salai, Sholinganallur, Chennai, 600 119, Tamil Nadu, India
Tel.: (91) 4442931300
Software Development Services
N.A.I.C.S.: 541511

Identive (Japan) KK (1)
GoogolPlex Millennium Building 6F 4-4-20 Shiba, Minato-ku, Tokyo, 108-0014, Japan
Tel.: (81) 364146611
Identity Management Solutions & Services
N.A.I.C.S.: 423690

Multicard Australia Pty Ltd (1)
Unit 13 16 Metroplex Avenue, Murarrie, 4172, QLD, Australia
Tel.: (61) 1300666910
Web Site: http://www.multicard.com.au
Emp.: 5
Secure Identity Management Services
N.A.I.C.S.: 326199

RockWest Technology Group LLC (1)
6820 N Broadway Unit J, Denver, CO 80221
Tel.: (303) 477-3338
Web Site: http://www.multicard.com
Sales Range: $25-49.9 Million
Emp.: 8
Identity Card Management Services
N.A.I.C.S.: 423690

SCM Microsystems India Pvt. Ltd. (1)
Module No 0506 0507 & 0508 D Block South 5th Floor, Tidel Park 4 Canal Bank Road Taramani, Chennai, 600 113, Sholinganallur, India
Tel.: (91) 2254 0020
Web Site: http://www.identiv.com
Sales Range: $25-49.9 Million
Emp.: 60
Computer Programming Services
N.A.I.C.S.: 541511

SCM Microsystems Japan, Inc. (1)
8F Hirakawacho Ronstate 2-11-1 Hirakawacho, Chiyoda-ku 4-4-20 Minato-Ku, Tokyo, 102-0093, Shiba, Japan
Tel.: (81) 335118511
Web Site: http://www.identive-group.com
Sales Range: $10-24.9 Million
Emp.: 6
Computer Hardware Mfr
N.A.I.C.S.: 334118

SCM Microsystems Ltd. (1)
11 Tunbridge Close Bottisham, Cambridge, CB25 9EA, United Kingdom
Tel.: (44) 1223811015
Secure Identity Card Management Services
N.A.I.C.S.: 326199

Thursby Software Systems, Inc. (1)
8777 N Stemmons Freeway Suite #150, Dallas, TX 75247
Tel.: (817) 478-5070
Web Site: http://www.thursby.com
Custom Computer Programing
N.A.I.C.S.: 513210
Paul Nelson (CTO)

VISCOUNT SYSTEMS, INC. (1)
Unit 650 3711 N Fraser Way, Burnaby, V5J 5J2, BC, Canada
Tel.: (604) 327-9446
Web Site: https://www.identiv.com
Sales Range: $1-9.9 Million
Emp.: 36
Security System Mfr & Distr
N.A.I.C.S.: 561621
Scott Sieracki (Interim CEO)
Zhi Yuan Zheng (CFO)
Boris Margovskiy (VP-Ops)
Mitch Storey (Dir-Res & Dev)
Sarah James (Sr Dir-Sls)
Zhi Yuan Zheng (CFO & Controller)

IDEX CORP
3100 Sanders Rd Ste 301, Northbrook, IL 60062
Tel.: (847) 498-7070   DE
Web Site: https://www.idexcorp.com
Year Founded: 1987
IEX—(NYSE)
Rev.: $3,273,900,000
Assets: $5,865,200,000
Liabilities: $2,324,000,000
Net Worth: $3,541,200,000
Earnings: $596,100,000
Emp.: 8,800
Fiscal Year-end: 12/31/23
Fluid Handling & Industrial Products Mfr, Designer & Marketer
N.A.I.C.S.: 333995
Eric D. Ashleman (Pres & CEO)
Allison S. Lausas (Chief Acctg Officer & VP)
Abhishek Khandelwal (CFO & Sr VP)
Abigail Roche (Chief Compliance Officer, VP & Asst Gen Counsel)
Melissa S. Flores (Chief HR Officer & Sr VP)
Allison S. Lausas (Chief Acctg Officer)

Subsidiaries:

40Seven Ltd (1)
Cross Green Industrial Estate Cross Green Way, Leeds, LS9 0SE, United Kingdom
Tel.: (44) 1132019700
Web Site: http://www.40seven.com
Emp.: 50
Gas Hazard Surveying Services
N.A.I.C.S.: 541370
Ian Edwards (Mng Dir)
Richard Bond (Fin Dir)
Isabell Holling (Head-Ops)
Martyn Utley (Mgr-Bus Dev)

Jon Steers (Mgr-Delivery)
Graeme Jamieson (Project Mgr)
Lee Peters (Project Mgr)
Ed Elbrow (Project Mgr)
Andy Grigg (Project Mgr)
Byron Checketts (Project Mgr)
Maddy Lees (Mgr-Trng & Quality)
Susanne Hudson (Mgr-HR)
Steve Wood (Mgr-Compliance)

ADS LLC (1)
340 The Bridge St Ste 204, Huntsville, AL 35806
Tel.: (256) 430-6242
Web Site: https://www.adsenv.com
Sales Range: $50-74.9 Million
Emp.: 60
Water & Wastewater Metering Technologies Developer & Mfr; Flow Monitoring Services
N.A.I.C.S.: 334513

Division (Domestic):

ADS Environmental Services (2)
340 The Bridge St Ste 204, Huntsville, AL 35806
Tel.: (256) 430-3366
Web Site: http://www.adsenv.com
Sales Range: $10-24.9 Million
Emp.: 50
Flow Monitoring Services
N.A.I.C.S.: 561990

Subsidiary (Domestic):

Accusonic Technologies (2)
28 Patterson Brook Rd Ste 1, West Wareham, MA 02576
Tel.: (508) 273-9600
Web Site: http://www.accusonic.com
Sales Range: $25-49.9 Million
Emp.: 50
Water & Wastewater Flow Metering Systems Developer & Mfr
N.A.I.C.S.: 334513

Hydra-Stop, Inc. (2)
144 Tower Dr Ste A, Burr Ridge, IL 60527
Tel.: (708) 389-5111
Web Site: http://www.hydra-stop.com
Sales Range: $75-99.9 Million
Emp.: 30
Water & Wastewater Utility Pipe Maintenance Equipment Mfr & Support Services
N.A.I.C.S.: 332919
Steve Roehrig (VP-Sls & Mktg)
Amy Van Meter (CFO)
Gary Brewer (CEO)
A. J. Nelson (COO)
Herman Ruiz (VP-Ops)

AWG Fittings GmbH (1)
Bergstrasse 25, 89177, Ballendorf, Germany
Tel.: (49) 73409188980
Web Site: https://www.awg-fittings.com
Fire Protection System Mfr
N.A.I.C.S.: 333998

Abel Pumps, L.P. (1)
Foster Plz 9 750 Dr Ste 400, Pittsburgh, PA 15220
Tel.: (412) 741-3222
Web Site: http://www.abelpumps.com
Emp.: 50
Displacement Pumps Design & Mfr
N.A.I.C.S.: 333914

Advanced Thin Films LLC (1)
5733 Central Ave, Boulder, CO 80301-2848
Tel.: (303) 815-1545
Web Site:
    https://www.advancedthinfilms.com
Sales Range: $10-24.9 Million
Emp.: 60
Optical Instrument Mfr
N.A.I.C.S.: 333310

Aegis Flow Technologies (1)
6041 Industrial Dr, Geismar, LA 70734
Tel.: (225) 673-9990
Web Site: https://www.aegisvalves.com
Emp.: 40
Industrial Valve Mfr
N.A.I.C.S.: 332911

Airtech Group, Inc. (1)
301 Veterans Blvd, Rutherford, NJ 07070
Tel.: (201) 569-1173
Web Site: https://www.airtechusa.com

Sales Range: $1-9.9 Million
Emp.: 13
Industrial Machinery & Equipment Merchant Whslr
N.A.I.C.S.: 423830
Chris Latsos (Treas & Sec)

Akron Brass Company (1)
343 Venture Blvd, Wooster, OH 44691   (100%)
Tel.: (330) 264-5678
Web Site: https://www.akronbrass.com
Fire Fighting Equipment Mfr
N.A.I.C.S.: 333914

Division (Domestic):

Weldon Technologies Inc. (2)
3656 Paragon Dr, Columbus, OH 43228
Tel.: (614) 529-7230
Web Site: https://www.akronbrass.com
Automotive Lighting Equipment Mfr
N.A.I.C.S.: 336320

Atul Sugar Screens Private Limited (1)
Plot No B-23 Village Shinde Vasuli MIDC Chakan Phase II, Tal Khed Dist, Pune, 410501, Maharashtra, India
Tel.: (91) 2135686646
Web Site: https://www.atulscreens.com
Sugar Screen Mfr & Distr
N.A.I.C.S.: 311314

Band-It Clamps (Asia) Pte., Ltd. (1)
11 Second Chin Bee Road, Singapore, 618777, Singapore
Tel.: (65) 62658853
Hose Clamps Mfr
N.A.I.C.S.: 332722

Band-It-Idex, Inc. (1)
4799 Dahlia St, Denver, CO 80216-3222   (100%)
Tel.: (303) 320-4555
Web Site: https://www.band-it-idex.com
Sales Range: $75-99.9 Million
Emp.: 150
Mfr of Stainless Steel Bands, Buckles, Preformed Clamps & Installation Tools
N.A.I.C.S.: 332510

Subsidiary (Non-US):

Band-It Company Ltd. (2)
Speedwell Industrial Estate Staveley N, Chesterfield, S43 3PF, Derbyshire, United Kingdom
Tel.: (44) 1246479479
Web Site: https://www.band-it-idex.com
Sales Range: $75-99.9 Million
Emp.: 150
Mfr of Stainless Steel Bands, Buckles, Preformed Clamps & Installation Tools
N.A.I.C.S.: 332510

Band-It R.S.A. (Pty) Ltd. (2)
Unit No 3 22 Buwbes Road Sebenza Ext 1 Edenvale, PO Box 10240, Edenglen, 1613, South Africa   (51%)
Tel.: (27) 114521288
Sales Range: $100-124.9 Million
Mfr of Stainless Steel Bands, Buckles, Preformed Clamps & Installation Tools
N.A.I.C.S.: 332510

Banjo Corporation (1)
150 Banjo Dr, Crawfordsville, IN 47933
Tel.: (765) 362-7367
Web Site: https://www.banjocorp.com
Emp.: 250
Fluid Handling & Industrial Products Mfr & Distr
N.A.I.C.S.: 333914

Blagdon Pump Holdings Ltd. (1)
2 Lambert Road Armstrong Industrial Estate, Sunderland, NE37 1QP, United Kingdom
Tel.: (44) 1914177475
Industrial Machinery & Equipment Whslr
N.A.I.C.S.: 423830

CVI Laser International LLC (1)
200 Dorado Pl SE, Albuquerque, NM 87123
Tel.: (505) 296-9541
Web Site: http://www.cvilaseroptics.com
Optical Instrument & Lens Mfr
N.A.I.C.S.: 333310

CVI Laser Limited (1)

IDEX Corp—(Continued)

28 Ashville Way, Leicester, Whetstone, LE8 6NU, Leicestershire, United Kingdom
Tel.: (44) 1162846200
Web Site: https://www.idexot.com
Sales Range: $25-49.9 Million
Emp.: 25
Optical Component & Spectral Products Design Mfr
N.A.I.C.S.: 333310

CVI Laser Optics   **(1)**
200 Dorado Pl SE, Albuquerque, NM 87123
Tel.: (505) 296-9541
Web Site: https://www.cvilaseroptics.com
Optical Components Designer & Mfr
N.A.I.C.S.: 333310

CVI Laser SAS   **(1)**
12 Avenue Jean Bart, Voisins-le-Bretonneux, 78960, France
Tel.: (33) 130120680
Web Site: http://marketplace.idexop.com
Emp.: 5
Fluid Handling & Industrial Products Mfr & Distr
N.A.I.C.S.: 333995

CVI Technical Optics Company Ltd.   **(1)**
Second Avenue, Onchan, IM3 4PA, United Kingdom
Tel.: (44) 1624647000
Sales Range: $25-49.9 Million
Emp.: 50
Laser Optics & Spectrum Analyzer Mfr
N.A.I.C.S.: 333310

CiDRA Precision Services, LLC   **(1)**
50 Barnes Park N, Wallingford, CT 06492-5920
Tel.: (203) 265-0035
Web Site: https://www.cidra.com
Mfr of Microfluidic Components for Life Science, Health & Industrial Markets
N.A.I.C.S.: 334419

Class 1   **(1)**
607 NW 27th Ave, Ocala, FL 34475
Tel.: (352) 629-5020
Web Site: http://www.haleproducts.com
Sales Range: $100-124.9 Million
Emp.: 100
Provider of Pumping Equipment
N.A.I.C.S.: 335314

Envirosight, LLC   **(1)**
111 Canfield Ave Unit A14, Randolph, NJ 07869
Tel.: (973) 252-6700
Web Site: http://www.envirosight.com
Sales Range: $1-9.9 Million
Emp.: 10
Industrial Machinery & Equipment Merchant Whslr
N.A.I.C.S.: 423830
Richard Lindner *(Pres)*
Christopher Helliwell *(Mgr-Sls-Western Reg)*
Venay Sehgal Bhatia *(Mgr-Digital Mktg)*
Christopher Begbie *(Mgr-Svc)*
Marie Weinberg *(Dir-Ops)*
Doug Ehrlich *(Asst Controller)*
Ron Falcone *(CFO)*
Mike Putney *(Mgr-Sls-Northeast)*
Jamie Winters *(Mgr-Sls-Midwest)*
Mike Vislay *(Dir-Sls)*

FAST & Fluid Management Australia Pty. Ltd.   **(1)**
Unit 4 10 Doyle Ave Dr, Unanderra, 2526, NSW, Australia
Tel.: (61) 242717111
Web Site: https://asia.fast-fluid.com
Emp.: 16
Paint Dispensers, Mixers & Shakers Mfr
N.A.I.C.S.: 325510

FAST & Fluid Management East Europe Sp. z.o.o.   **(1)**
Ul Bolesawa Chrobrego 135 /137, 87-100, Torun, Kujawsko-Pomorskie, Poland
Tel.: (48) 566644500
Industrial Machinery & Equipment Whslr
N.A.I.C.S.: 423830

FAST & Fluid Management S.r.l.   **(1)**
Via Pelizza da Volpedo 40, Cinisello Balsamo, 20092, Milan, Italy
Tel.: (39) 02660911

Sales Range: $10-24.9 Million
Emp.: 5
Precision Designed Tinting & Measuring Equipment Mfr
N.A.I.C.S.: 334519

FTL Ltd.   **(1)**
Howley Park Rd, Leeds, LS27 0QS, United Kingdom
Tel.: (44) 1132530331
Web Site: http://www.ftlsolutions.co.uk
Metal Hose Mfr
N.A.I.C.S.: 332999
Steve Reed *(Mng Dir)*
Marcus Armitage *(Dir-Fin)*
Mark Walker *(Dir-Ops)*
Steve Quarmby *(Engr-Dev)*

FTL Seals Technology Ltd   **(1)**
Bruntcliffe Avenue Leeds 27 Business Park, Morley, Leeds, LS27 0TG, United Kingdom
Tel.: (44) 1132521061
Web Site: https://ftl.technology
Sales Range: $10-24.9 Million
Emp.: 32
Sealing & Bearing Products Distr
N.A.I.C.S.: 423840
Mark McCormack *(Dir-Engrg)*
Hannah Bradbury *(Acct Mgr-Internal)*
Trina Haynes *(Acct Mgr-Internal)*

Fast & Fluid Management B.V.   **(1)**
Hub van Doorneweg 31, 2171 KZ, Sassenheim, Netherlands
Tel.: (31) 252240800
Web Site: https://emea.fast-fluid.com
Emp.: 120
Paint & Allied Product Mfr
N.A.I.C.S.: 325510

Flow Management Devices, LLC   **(1)**
5225 S 37th St Ste 5, Phoenix, AZ 85040
Tel.: (602) 233-9885
Web Site: https://www.flowmd.com
Emp.: 160
Sampler Petroleum Fluid Mfr
N.A.I.C.S.: 324191
Jennifer Harthun *(Dir-HR)*

Fluid Management   **(1)**
1023 Wheeling Rd, Wheeling, IL 60090
Tel.: (847) 537-0880
Web Site: http://fluidman.com
Sales Range: $100-124.9 Million
Emp.: 150
Paint Mixing & Dispensing Equipment
N.A.I.C.S.: 333248

Subsidiary (Non-US):

Fast & Fluid Management Australia   **(2)**
10 Resolution Drive, Unanderra, 2526, NSW, Australia   **(100%)**
Tel.: (61) 242717111
Web Site: http://www.fast-fluid.com
Sales Range: $1-9.9 Million
Emp.: 16
Industrial Machinery
N.A.I.C.S.: 423830

Fast & Fluid Management Iberica   **(2)**
Calle Agricultura Pg Industrial Sector Centro 37 - A, Villadecans, Barcelona, Spain   **(100%)**
Tel.: (34) 936375655
Web Site: http://www.fast-fluid.com
Sales Range: $75-99.9 Million
Emp.: 9
Sales of Paint Colorant Dispensers & Mixers
N.A.I.C.S.: 332999

Fast & Fluid Management Netherlands   **(2)**
Hub Van Doorneweg 31, 2171 KZ, Sassenheim, Netherlands   **(100%)**
Tel.: (31) 252240800
Web Site: http://emea.fast-fluid.com
Sales Range: $50-74.9 Million
Emp.: 150
Metering & Mixing Equipment
N.A.I.C.S.: 325510

Fast & Fluid Management SRL   **(2)**
Via Pelizza da Volpedo 40, 20092, Cinisello Balsamo, Milan, Italy   **(100%)**
Tel.: (39) 02660911

Web Site: http://www.fast-fluid.com
Sales Range: $50-74.9 Million
Paint & Colorant Dispensers & Mixes Mfr
N.A.I.C.S.: 325510

Fluid Management France SARL   **(2)**
7 Rue Fosse Blanc, Gennevilliers, F 92230, Paris, France   **(100%)**
Tel.: (33) 0140863636
Web Site: http://www.fast-fluid.com
Sales Range: $1-9.9 Million
Emp.: 7
Sales of Paint Colorant Dispensers & Mixers
N.A.I.C.S.: 332999

Fluid Management Canada, Inc.   **(1)**
140 Milner Avenue Unit 42 Scarborough, Toronto, M1S 3R3, ON, Canada
Tel.: (416) 293-2460
Emp.: 4
Wood Finishing Supplies Whslr
N.A.I.C.S.: 424950
Michael Hurley *(Mng Dir)*

Fluid Management Europe B.V.   **(1)**
Hub van Doorneweg 31, Sassenheim, 2171, Netherlands
Tel.: (31) 252240800
Web Site: http://www.fast-fluid.com
Emp.: 150
Paint & Allied Products Mfr
N.A.I.C.S.: 325510

Fluid Management, Inc.   **(1)**
1023 Wheeling Rd, Wheeling, IL 60090
Tel.: (847) 537-0880
Web Site: https://www.fluidman.com
Automatic Dispenser Mfr & Distr
N.A.I.C.S.: 333914

Gast Group Ltd.   **(1)**
Unit 11 The I 0 Centre Nash Road, Redditch, B98 7AS, Worcestershire, United Kingdom
Tel.: (44) 1527504040
Web Site: https://www.gastmfg.com
Compressor & Gear Motor Accessories Mfr
N.A.I.C.S.: 333998

Gast Manufacturing, Inc.   **(1)**
2300 M-139 Hwy, Benton Harbor, MI 49022   **(100%)**
Tel.: (269) 926-6171
Web Site: https://www.gastmfg.com
Sales Range: $100-124.9 Million
Emp.: 250
Air Pumps & Pneumatic Motors Mfr & Distr
N.A.I.C.S.: 333912

Subsidiary (Domestic):

Gast Asia, Inc.   **(2)**
2300 M-109 Hwy, Denton Harbor, MI 49023
Tel.: (269) 926-6171
Web Site: http://www.idex.com
Holding Company
N.A.I.C.S.: 333912

Hale Products Inc.   **(1)**
607 NW 27th Ave, Ocala, FL 34475
Tel.: (610) 825-6300
Web Site: https://www.haleproducts.com
Sales Range: $75-99.9 Million
Emp.: 150
Fire Pumps, Pumping Units, Rescue Tools, Pump Accessories; Fire Irrigation, Contractors, Industry, G
N.A.I.C.S.: 333914

Subsidiary (Non-US):

Godiva Ltd.   **(2)**
Charles Street, Warwick, CV34 5LR, Warwickshire, United Kingdom   **(100%)**
Tel.: (44) 1926623600
Web Site: https://www.godiva.co.uk
Sales Range: $25-49.9 Million
Emp.: 75
Fire & Safety Relief Services
N.A.I.C.S.: 339999

Halox Technologies, Inc.   **(1)**
304 Bishop Ave, Bridgeport, CT 06610
Tel.: (203) 334-6278
Web Site: http://www.haloxtech.com
Sales Range: $10-24.9 Million
Emp.: 18
Provider of Pumping Products
N.A.I.C.S.: 333310

Hemina SpA   **(1)**
Via Piemonte 2, Montagnana, 35044, Padua, Padova, Italy   **(30%)**
Tel.: (39) 0049615541
Web Site: https://www.hemina.eu
Sales Range: $125-149.9 Million
Mfr of Industrial Equipment
N.A.I.C.S.: 333248

Hurst Jaws of Life, Inc   **(1)**
711 N Post Rd, Shelby, NC 28150
Tel.: (704) 487-6961
Web Site: https://www.jawsoflife.com
Industrial Machinery & Equipment Whslr
N.A.I.C.S.: 423830

IDEX Asia Pacific Pte. Ltd.   **(1)**
63 Hillview Avenue No 07-08 Lam Soon Industrial Building, Singapore, 669569, Singapore
Tel.: (65) 67636633
Web Site: https://www.idexfmt-asia.com
Sales Range: $10-24.9 Million
Emp.: 8
Industrial Equipment Mfr
N.A.I.C.S.: 333914

IDEX Fluid & Metering Pvt. Ltd.   **(1)**
Survey No 256 GIDC Manjusar Savli, Near Bombardier Cir, Vadodara, 391 770, Gujarat, India
Tel.: (91) 2667662001
Web Site: http://www.indexcorp.com
Sales Range: $25-49.9 Million
Emp.: 150
Fluid Handling & Industrial Products Mfr & Distr
N.A.I.C.S.: 333914
Rajesh Prasad *(Mng Dir & VP)*

IDEX Health & Science GmbH   **(1)**
Futtererstrasse 16a, 97877, Wertheim, Baden-Wurttemberg, Germany
Tel.: (49) 937792030
Web Site: http://www.ismatec.de
Emp.: 15
Liquid Subassemblies & Precision Components Design & Mfr
N.A.I.C.S.: 334513

IDEX Health & Science KK   **(1)**
5-8-6 Nishiaoki, Kawaguchi, 332-0035, Saitama, Japan
Tel.: (81) 482405750
Research & Development Biotechnology Services
N.A.I.C.S.: 541714

IDEX Health & Science LLC   **(1)**
600 Park Ct, Rohnert Park, CA 94928
Tel.: (360) 679-2528
Web Site: https://www.idex-hs.com
Sales Range: $10-24.9 Million
Emp.: 109
Precision-Engineered Fluidics Solutions
N.A.I.C.S.: 541380

IDEX Health & Science LLC   **(1)**
619 Oak St, Oak Harbor, WA 98277
Tel.: (360) 679-2528
Web Site: http://www.idex-hs.com
Liquid Subassemblies & Precision Components Design & Mfr
N.A.I.C.S.: 334513

Subsidiary (Domestic):

Finger Lakes Instrumentation, LLC   **(2)**
7287 W Main St, Lima, NY 14485-4485
Tel.: (585) 624-3760
Web Site: http://www.flicamera.com
Photographic & Photocopying Equipment Mfr
N.A.I.C.S.: 333310

IDEX Heath & Science GmbH   **(1)**
Futtererstrasse 16, 97877, Wertheim, Germany
Tel.: (49) 937792030
Web Site: http://www.ismatec.com
Emp.: 20
Health Care Equipment Mfr
N.A.I.C.S.: 339112

IDEX Holdings GmbH   **(1)**
Durenbodenstrasse 7, 6992, Hirschegg, Austria
Tel.: (43) 551731250
Financial Holding Services

N.A.I.C.S.: 551112

IDEX Holdings, Inc. (1)
630 Dundee Rd Ste 400, Northbrook, IL
60062
Tel.: (847) 498-7070
Holding Company
N.A.I.C.S.: 551114

IDEX India Private Ltd. (1)
4th Floor S 14 Solitaire Corporate Park
Guru Hargovindji Rd, Chakala Andheri East,
Mumbai, 400 093, Maharashtra, India
Tel.: (91) 2266435555
Web Site: https://www.idexindia.in
Fluid Handling & Industrial Products Mfr &
Distr
N.A.I.C.S.: 333914

IDEX Optical Technologies B.V. (1)
Aalsbergen 2, 6942 SE, Didam, Nether-
lands
Tel.: (31) 316333041
Optical Product Mfr & Distr
N.A.I.C.S.: 339115

IDEX Pump Technologies (Ireland)
Limited (1)
79 Shannon Industrial Estate, Shannon,
Clare, Ireland
Tel.: (353) 61471933
Web Site: https://www.blagdonpump.com
Sales Range: $25-49.9 Million
Emp.: 50
Pumping Equipment Distr
N.A.I.C.S.: 423830

IDEX SAS (1)
12 Quai du Commerce, 69009, Lyon,
France
Tel.: (33) 147124212
Industrial Metal Products Mfr
N.A.I.C.S.: 332323

IDEX Technology (Suzhou) Co.,
Ltd. (1)
428 Xing Long Steet Su Chun Industrial
Square, Changning, Shanghai, 215021, Su-
zhou, China
Tel.: (86) 2152415599
Web Site: https://www.idexcorp.cn
Fluid Handling & Industrial Products Mfr &
Distr
N.A.I.C.S.: 333995

Idex do Brasil Servicos e Vendas
Ltda. (1)
Highway 1662 - Building 8, Valinhos, Sao
Paulo, 13277 650, Brazil
Tel.: (55) 5519387551
Sales Range: $10-24.9 Million
Emp.: 9
Fluid Systems Mfr
N.A.I.C.S.: 333995
Guillaume Dupont *(Dir-Bus Dev-Latin
America)*

Iridian Spectral Technologies,
Ltd. (1)
2700 Swansea Crescent, Ottawa, K1G
6R8, ON, Canada
Tel.: (613) 741-4513
Web Site: https://www.iridian.ca
Emp.: 130
Optical Product Mfr & Distr
N.A.I.C.S.: 339115

KZ CO. (1)
23860 Kz Pkwy, Greenwood, NE 68366
Tel.: (402) 944-2767
Web Site: http://www.kzvalve.com
Sales Range: $1-9.9 Million
Emp.: 30
Mfg Farm Machinery/Equipment Mfg
Valves/Pipe Fittings Mfg Industrial Valves
N.A.I.C.S.: 333111
Ardith Ziegenbein *(Treas)*
Nathaniel Rasmussen *(Engr-Mechanical
Design)*

Knight, LLC (1)
15340 Barranca Pkwy, Irvine, CA 92618
Tel.: (949) 595-4800
Web Site: https://www.knightequip.com
Sales Range: $50-74.9 Million
Emp.: 40
Mfr of Chemical Delivery Systems
N.A.I.C.S.: 333998

Subsidiary (Non-US):

Knight Canada Limited (2)

2880 Argentia Rd Unit 6, Mississauga, L5N
7X8, ON, Canada **(100%)**
Tel.: (905) 542-2333
Web Site: http://www.knightequip.com
Sales Range: $50-74.9 Million
Emp.: 6
Chemical Delivery Systems Mfr & Distr
N.A.I.C.S.: 333914

Knight Equipment Pty., Ltd. (2)
Unit 3 1B Kleins Rd, Northmead, 2152,
Australia **(100%)**
Tel.: (61) 2 9352 1801
Web Site: http://www.knightequip.com
Sales Range: $50-74.9 Million
Emp.: 2
Mfr of Chemical Delivery Systems
N.A.I.C.S.: 424690

Knight U.K. Ltd. (2)
Unit 12 13 Edison Road Highfield Industrial
Estate, Eastbourne, BN23 6PT, E Sussex,
United Kingdom
Tel.: (44) 1323514855
Web Site: http://www.knighteurope.eu
Chemical Delivery System Distr
N.A.I.C.S.: 424690

Liquid Controls, Inc. (1)
105 Albrecht Dr, Lake Bluff, IL 60044
Tel.: (847) 295-1050
Web Site: http://www.lcmeter.com
Sales Range: $25-49.9 Million
Emp.: 150
Mfr of Positive Displacement Flow Meters &
Accessories
N.A.I.C.S.: 334514

Subsidiary (Domestic):

Circuit Works Corporation (2)
3135 N Oak Grove Ave, Waukegan, IL
60087
Tel.: (847) 283-8600
Web Site: https://www.cwcems.com
Sales Range: $100-124.9 Million
Circuit Board Mfr
N.A.I.C.S.: 334412
Tom Thompson *(Founder)*

Corken, Inc. (2)
3805 NW 36th St, Oklahoma City, OK
73112 **(100%)**
Tel.: (405) 946-5576
Web Site: http://www.corken.com
Sales Range: $75-99.9 Million
Emp.: 150
Mfr of Small Horsepower Compressors,
Pumps & Valves
N.A.I.C.S.: 333912

LouwersHanique B.V. (1)
Energieweg 3A, 5527 AH, Hapert, Nether-
lands
Tel.: (31) 497339696
Web Site: https://www.louwershanique.com
Technical Glass Mfr & Distr
N.A.I.C.S.: 327215

Lukas Hydraulik GmbH (1)
Weinstrasse 39, 91058, Erlangen,
Germany **(100%)**
Tel.: (49) 91316980
Web Site: https://lukas.com
Sales Range: $50-74.9 Million
Emp.: 180
Mfr of Industrial Machinery
N.A.I.C.S.: 333248
Fabio Ferrari *(Mng Dir)*
Keith Miller *(Mng Dir)*
Jenna Myszak *(Mng Dir)*

Matcon Limited (1)
Bramley Drive Vale Park West, Evesham,
WR11 1JH, Worcestershire, United King-
dom
Tel.: (44) 1386769000
Web Site: https://www.matconibc.com
Industrial Machinery & Equipment Whslr
N.A.I.C.S.: 423830

Melles Griot AB (1)
Bangardsgatan 13, 753 21, Uppsala, Swe-
den
Tel.: (46) 18120400
Web Site: http://www.mellesgriot.com
Optical Component & Optomechanical
Hardware Mfr & Distr
N.A.I.C.S.: 333310

Melles Griot B.V. (1)

Aalsbergen 2, 6942 SE, Didam, Nether-
lands
Tel.: (31) 316333041
Web Site: http://www.mellesgriot.com
Optical Component & Machinery Parts Mfr
& Distr
N.A.I.C.S.: 333310

Microfluidics International
Corporation (1)
90 Glacier Dr Ste 1000, Westwood, MA
02090
Tel.: (617) 969-5452
Web Site: https://www.microfluidics-mpt.com
Sales Range: $10-24.9 Million
Emp.: 50
Mfr of High Performance Fluid Processing
Equipment for the Pharmaceutical, Chemi-
cal, Biotechnology, Cosmetic/Personal Care
& Food Industries
N.A.I.C.S.: 333248

Division (Domestic):

Morehouse-COWLES (2)
13930 Magnolia Ave, Chino, CA 91710
Tel.: (909) 627-7222
Web Site: http://www.morehousecowles.com
Emp.: 30
Technology & Equipment Mfr for Material
Production, Purification & Processing
N.A.I.C.S.: 333248

Micropump, Inc. (1)
1402 NE 136th Ave, Vancouver, WA
98684-0818 **(100%)**
Tel.: (360) 253-2008
Web Site: http://www.micropump.com
Sales Range: $50-74.9 Million
Emp.: 110
Mfr of Pumps & Pumping Equipment
N.A.I.C.S.: 333914

Millux B.V. (1)
Bijsterhuizen 24-29, 6604 LK, Wijchen,
Netherlands
Tel.: (31) 243787564
Web Site: https://www.millux.nl
Electronic Equipment Mfr & Distr
N.A.I.C.S.: 335311

Mott Corp. (1)
84 Spring Ln, Farmington, CT 06032
Tel.: (860) 747-6333
Web Site: http://www.mottcorp.com
Sales Range: $10-24.9 Million
Emp.: 157
Distributions Of Filters
N.A.I.C.S.: 333998
Kevin McGuffin *(Dir-High Purity Sls)*
Boris F. Levin *(Pres & CEO)*

Novotema SpA (1)
Via S Giovanni delle Formiche 2, 24060,
Villongo, BG, Italy
Tel.: (39) 03 592 6530
Web Site: https://www.novotema.com
Emp.: 170
Valve Gasket Mfr
N.A.I.C.S.: 339991

OBL Srl (1)
Via Kennedy 12, 20090, Segrate, MI, Italy
Tel.: (39) 02269191
Web Site: https://oblpumps.it
Metering Pumps Mfr & Supplier
N.A.I.C.S.: 333914

Pipeline Renewal Technologies Lim-
ited Liability Company (1)
111 Canfield Ave, Randolph, NJ 07869
Web Site: https://www.pipelinert.com
Electronic Equipment Mfr & Distr
N.A.I.C.S.: 335311

Precision Photonics Corporation (1)
2901 55th St, Boulder, CO 80301
Tel.: (303) 444-9948
Web Site:
    http://www.precisionphotonics.com
Wired Telecommunications Carriers
N.A.I.C.S.: 517111

Precision Polymer Engineering Inter-
national Limited (1)
1st Floor Al Ajmi Business Center 2682 9,
Al Olaya District, Al Khobar, 34448 - 7353,
Saudi Arabia
Tel.: (966) 596400650
Web Site: https://sa.prepol.com

Rubber Material Mfr & Distr
N.A.I.C.S.: 326299

Precision Polymer Engineering
Limited (1)
Greenbank Road, Blackburn, BB1 3EA,
Lancashire, United Kingdom
Tel.: (44) 1254295400
Web Site: https://www.prepol.com
Emp.: 300
Rubber Seal & Compound Mfr
N.A.I.C.S.: 326291
Ben Green *(Gen Mgr)*
Neil Thompson *(Pres)*
Stefano Arrigoni *(Head-R&D)*
Ashley McCarrick *(Mgr-HR)*
Chris Allan *(Mgr-Mfg Engrg)*
Carlos Uribe *(Pres-)*
Shauna Smith *(VP-Operations)*

Subsidiary (US):

PPE, LLC (2)
3201 S Blue Bell Rd, Brenham, TX 77833
Tel.: (979) 353-7350
Rubber Seals Mfr
N.A.I.C.S.: 339991

Pulsafeeder Inc. (1)
2883 Brighton-Henrietta Townline Rd, Roch-
ester, NY 14623 **(100%)**
Tel.: (585) 292-8000
Web Site: https://www.pulsa.com
Sales Range: $50-74.9 Million
Emp.: 100
Gasoline Measuring & Pump Mfr
N.A.I.C.S.: 333914

Subsidiary (Non-US):

Pulsafeeder Europe B.V. (2)
Marssteden 68, Enschede,
Netherlands **(100%)**
Tel.: (31) 534282230
Web Site: http://www.pulsafeeder.com
Sales Range: $10-24.9 Million
Emp.: 4
Mfr of Pumping Equipment
N.A.I.C.S.: 333914

Quadro Engineering Corp (1)
613 Colby Drive, Waterloo, N2V 1A1, ON,
Canada
Tel.: (519) 884-9660
Web Site: https://www.quadro-mpt.com
Pharmaceutical & Food Industry Processing
Equipment Mfr
N.A.I.C.S.: 333310

Richter Pumps and Valves Inc. (1)
406 State St, Cedar Falls, IA 50613
Tel.: (319) 268-8038
Web Site: http://www.richter-ct.com
Pumps Valves & Control Equipment Mfr &
Distr
N.A.I.C.S.: 333914

Richter-Chemie-Technik GmbH (1)
Otto-Schott-Str 2, 47906, Kempen, Ger-
many
Tel.: (49) 21521460
Web Site: https://www.richter-ct.com
Pumps Valves & Control Equipment Mfr &
Distr
N.A.I.C.S.: 333914
Peter Olschewski *(Mng Dir)*
Jenna Michelle Myszak *(Mng Dir)*
Steven Hamelin *(Mng Dir)*

Roplan AB (1)
Skyttbrinksvagen 20, 147 39, Tumba, Swe-
den
Tel.: (46) 84499900
Web Site: http://www.roplan.com
Emp.: 160
Mechanical Shaft Seal Mfr
N.A.I.C.S.: 339991

Roplan Inc. (1)
5020 World Dairy Dr, Madison, WI 53718
Tel.: (608) 229-5225
Mechanical Shaft Seal Mfr
N.A.I.C.S.: 339991
Daniel Buss *(Mgr-Production Control)*

Roplan Ltd. (1)
Prince Henry House Kingsclere Park, King-
sclere, Newbury, RG20 4SW, Berkshire,
United Kingdom
Tel.: (44) 1635299091
Mechanical Shaft Seal Mfr

IDEX Corp—(Continued)
N.A.I.C.S.: 339991

Roplan Machinery (Ningbo) Co., Ltd. (1)
1F No 15 Jinxi Road, Nordic Industrial Park
Zhenhai, Ningbo, 315221, Zhejiang, China
Tel.: (86) 57486308516
Mechanical Shaft Seal Mfr
N.A.I.C.S.: 339991
Jerry Wang (Ops Mgr)

SFC KOENIG AG (1)
Lagerstrasse 8, 8953, Dietikon, Switzerland
Tel.: (41) 447434600
Web Site: https://www.sfckoenig.com
Metalworking Machines Mfr
N.A.I.C.S.: 333514

SFC KOENIG GmbH (1)
Max-Eyth-Strasse 14 Illerrieden, 89186,
Baden-Baden, Germany
Tel.: (49) 73062062300
Industrial Metal Product Distr
N.A.I.C.S.: 423510

SFC KOENIG LLC (1)
73 Defco Park Rd, North Haven, CT 06473
Tel.: (203) 245-1100
Industrial Metal Products Mfr
N.A.I.C.S.: 332323

Semrock, Inc. (1)
3625 Buffalo Rd Ste 6, Rochester, NY
14624
Tel.: (585) 594-7000
Web Site: http://www.semrock.com
Sales Range: $10-24.9 Million
Emp.: 50
Optical Filter Mfr
N.A.I.C.S.: 333310
Moez Adatia (VP-Sls)
Mike Ransford (VP-Ops)
Alan Heaney (Dir-Quality & Continuous Improvement)
Craig Hodgson (Dir-R&D)
Jamie Dargan (Dir-Supply Chain)

Steridose Sales AB (1)
Himmelsbodavagen 7, 147 39, Tumba,
Sweden
Tel.: (46) 84499900
Web Site: http://www.steridose.com
Mixer & Diaphragm Valve Mfr
N.A.I.C.S.: 332919

Steridose Sales Inc. (1)
5020 World Dairy Dr, Madison, WI 53718
Tel.: (608) 229-5225
Mixer & Diaphragm Valve Mfr
N.A.I.C.S.: 332919

The Fitzpatrick Company (1)
832 Industrial Dr, Elmhurst, IL 60126
Tel.: (630) 530-3333
Web Site: http://www.fitzmill.com
Sales Range: $25-49.9 Million
Emp.: 100
Pharmaceutical & Food Industry Processing
Equipment Mfr
N.A.I.C.S.: 332999

The Fitzpatrick Company Europe N.V. (1)
Entrepotstraat 8, B-9100, Saint-Niklaas,
Belgium
Tel.: (32) 37777208
Mechanical Engineering Services
N.A.I.C.S.: 541330

Toptech Systems N.V. (1)
Nieuwe Weg 1 - Haven 1053, 2070, Zwijn-
drecht, Belgium
Tel.: (32) 32506060
Web Site: https://www.toptech.com
Sales Range: $25-49.9 Million
Emp.: 20
Terminal Automation Software & Hardware
Solutions
N.A.I.C.S.: 541512

Toptech Systems, Inc. (1)
1124 Florida Central Pkwy, Longwood, FL
32750
Tel.: (407) 332-1774
Web Site: https://www.toptech.com
Sales Range: $10-24.9 Million
Emp.: 90
Terminal Automation Software & Hardware
Solution Provider

N.A.I.C.S.: 541512

Trebor International, Inc. (1)
8100 S 1300 W, West Jordan, UT 84088
Tel.: (801) 561-0303
Web Site: https://www.treborintl.com
Sales Range: $10-24.9 Million
Emp.: 26
Mfr of Chemical Pump & Heating Equip-
ment
N.A.I.C.S.: 334413

Viking Pump, Inc. (1)
406 State St, Cedar Falls, IA 50613-3343
Tel.: (319) 266-1741
Web Site: https://www.vikingpump.com
Emp.: 500
Positive Displacement Rotary, Internal Gear,
Spur Gear & Metering Pumps Mfr
N.A.I.C.S.: 333914

Subsidiary (Non-US):

Viking Pump (Europe) Ltd. (2)
Shannon Ind Est Unit 79 Shannon Clare,
Shannon, Monster, Ireland (100%)
Tel.: (353) 61471933
Web Site: http://www.vikingpump.com
Sales Range: $25-49.9 Million
Emp.: 28
Mfr of Pumps
N.A.I.C.S.: 333914

Viking Pump of Canada, Inc. (2)
661 Grove Avenue, PO Box 398, Windsor,
N9A 6M3, ON, Canada (100%)
Tel.: (519) 256-5438
Web Site:
https://www.vikingpumpcanada.com
Sales Range: $25-49.9 Million
Emp.: 35
Mfr of Pumps
N.A.I.C.S.: 333914

Subsidiary (Domestic):

Wright Flow Technologies (2)
S84 W18693 Enterprise Dr, Muskego, WI
53150
Tel.: (262) 679-8000
Web Site: http://www.wrightpump.com
Emp.: 2
Circumferential Piston & Ultra-Pure Cen-
trifugal Pumps Mfr
N.A.I.C.S.: 333914

Warren Rupp, Inc. (1)
800 N Main St, Mansfield, OH
44902 (100%)
Tel.: (419) 524-8388
Web Site: https://warrenruppinc.com
Sales Range: $50-74.9 Million
Emp.: 127
Mfr of Air-Operated, Motor-Driven & Double-
Diaphragm Pumps & Accessories
N.A.I.C.S.: 333914

Subsidiary (Domestic):

Pumper Parts LLC (2)
800 N Main St, Mansfield, OH 44902
Tel.: (419) 526-7296
Web Site: http://www.pumperparts.com
Sales Range: $125-149.9 Million
Provider of Pumping Equipment
N.A.I.C.S.: 333914

Versa-Matic Tool, Inc. (2)
800 North Main St, Mansfield, OH 44902
Tel.: (419) 526-7296
Web Site: http://www.versamatic.com
Sales Range: $50-74.9 Million
Emp.: 120
Mfr of Pumping Products
N.A.I.C.S.: 333914

WinCan Deutschland GmbH (1)
Krumme Jauchert 15, 88085, Langenargen,
Germany
Tel.: (49) 75439344770
Software Development Services
N.A.I.C.S.: 541511

Wright Flow Technologies, Inc. (1)
406 State St, Cedar Falls, IA 50613
Tel.: (319) 268-8013
Web Site:
http://www.wrightflowtechnologies.com
Emp.: 400

Pharmaceutical & Food Industries Pumping
Solution Provider
N.A.I.C.S.: 333914

Wright Flow Technologies Limited (1)
Highfield Industrial Estate Edison Road,
Eastbourne, BN23 6PT, East Sussex,
United Kingdom
Tel.: (44) 1323509211
Web Site:
http://www.wrightflowtechnologies.com
Emp.: 31
Pharmaceutical & Food Industries Pumping
Solution Provider
N.A.I.C.S.: 333914

Wright Flow Technologies Ltd. (1)
Highfield Industrial Estate, Edison Road,
Eastbourne, BN23 6PT, East Sussex,
United Kingdom
Tel.: (44) 1323509211
Web Site: http://www.johnsonpump.com
Mfr of Pumps
N.A.I.C.S.: 333914

iPEK Spezial-TV GmbH (1)
Durenbodenstrasse 7, 6992, Hirschegg,
Austria
Tel.: (43) 55173125
Web Site: https://www.ipek.at
Sales Range: $25-49.9 Million
Emp.: 150
Infrastructure Inspection Cameras & Re-
mote Control Systems Design & Mfr
N.A.I.C.S.: 333310

Subsidiary (Non-US):

IDEX Health & Science GmbH (2)
Futtererstrasse 16, esmatec, 97877,
Wertheim, Germany (100%)
Tel.: (49) 937792030
Web Site: http://www.ismatec.de
Sales Range: $10-24.9 Million
Pumps Mfr
N.A.I.C.S.: 333914

thinXXS Microtechnology AG (1)
Amerikastrasse 21, 66482, Zweibrucken,
Germany
Tel.: (49) 633280020
Web Site: https://www.thinxxs.com
Industrial Metal Products Mfr
N.A.I.C.S.: 332323

IDEXX LABORATORIES, INC.
1 IDEXX Dr, Westbrook, ME 04092
Tel.: (207) 556-0300 DE
Web Site: https://www.idexx.com
Year Founded: 1984
IDXX—(NASDAQ)
Rev.: $3,660,953,000
Assets: $3,259,925,000
Liabilities: $1,775,395,000
Net Worth: $1,484,530,000
Earnings: $845,042,000
Emp.: 11,000
Fiscal Year-end: 12/31/23
Diagnostic Testing Materials & Drugs
Mfr for Pets & Livestock
N.A.I.C.S.: 325413
Brian P. McKeon (CFO, Treas & Exec
VP)
Jonathan J. Mazelsky (Pres & CEO)
Ken Grady (CIO & Sr VP)
Michael Lane (Exec VP & Gen Mgr-
Reference Laboratories & IT)
Murthy Yerramilli (Sr VP-R&D)

Subsidiaries:

Animana B.V. (1)
Galvanistraat 1, 6716 AE, Ede, Netherlands
Tel.: (31) 881111222
Web Site: http://www.animana.nl
Software Development Services
N.A.I.C.S.: 541511

Beijing IDEXX Laboratories Co. Limited (1)
1F No 10 Building No 28 Yuhua Road, Beijing Airport Economic Core Zone, Beijing,
101318, China
Tel.: (86) 1080451300
Diagnostic Substance Mfr
N.A.I.C.S.: 325413

IDEXX B.V. (1)
Scorpius 60 Building F, 2132 LR, Hoofd-
dorp, Netherlands
Tel.: (31) 235587000
Veterinary Product Mfr & Distr
N.A.I.C.S.: 325412

IDEXX Computer Systems (1)
2536 Alpine Rd, Eau Claire, WI
54703-9560 (100%)
Tel.: (715) 834-0355
Sales Range: $50-74.9 Million
Emp.: 200
Veterinarian Practice Management Solu-
tions
N.A.I.C.S.: 513210

IDEXX Diavet AG (1)
Schlyffistrasse 10, Bach, 8806, Schwyz,
Switzerland
Tel.: (41) 447869020
Web Site: https://www.idexx.ch
Veterinary Laboratory Testing Services
N.A.I.C.S.: 541940

IDEXX Europe B.V. (1)
Scorpius 60 Building F, 2132 LR, Hoofd-
dorp, Netherlands (100%)
Tel.: (31) 235587000
Web Site: https://www.idexx.nl
Sales Range: $50-74.9 Million
Diagnostic Health & Well-Being Products for
People, Pets & Livestock
N.A.I.C.S.: 325412

IDEXX GmbH (1)
Humboldtstrasse 2, 70806, Kornwestheim,
Germany (100%)
Tel.: (49) 69153253290
Web Site: https://www.idexx.de
Diagnostic Products Mfr
N.A.I.C.S.: 325412

IDEXX Holding B.V. (1)
Scorpius 60 BuildingF, Hoofddorp, 2132 LR,
Netherlands
Tel.: (31) 235587000
Holding Company
N.A.I.C.S.: 551112

IDEXX Laboratories Inc. (1)
6F-1 No 88 Ruihu Street, Neihu District,
Taipei, 11494, Taiwan
Tel.: (886) 266039728
Provider of Diagnostic Products & Services
N.A.I.C.S.: 325412

IDEXX Laboratories Italia S.r.l. (1)
Via Gugliemo Silva 36, 20149, Milan, MI,
Italy (100%)
Tel.: (39) 023192031
Web Site: https://www.idexx.it
Sales Range: $1-9.9 Million
Emp.: 10
Provider of Diagnostic Products
N.A.I.C.S.: 325412

IDEXX Laboratories Limited (1)
Unit 4 Oakhurst Business Pk Wilberforce
Way Southwater, Horsham, RH139RT,
United Kingdom (100%)
Tel.: (44) 2037887508
Web Site: https://www.idexx.co.uk
Pets & Livestock Diagnostic Testing Mate-
rial Mfr
N.A.I.C.S.: 325412

IDEXX Laboratories Limited (1)
Grange House Sandbeck Way, Wetherby,
LS22 7DN, West Yorkshire, United Kingdom
Tel.: (44) 193 754 4000
Web Site: https://www.idexx.co.uk
Provider of Diagnostic Products
N.A.I.C.S.: 325412

IDEXX Laboratories Norge AS (1)
Bryggetorget 1, 0250, Oslo, Norway
Tel.: (47) 90073259
Web Site: https://www.idexx.no
Scientific Research & Development Ser-
vices
N.A.I.C.S.: 541715

IDEXX Laboratories Private Limited (1)
Unit No 2239/2241 22nd floor WTC Banga-
lore Brigade Gateway, Rajajinager Exten-
sion Malleswaram, Bengaluru, 560 055,
Karnataka, India
Tel.: (91) 8067935424
Diagnostic Equipment Distr

N.A.I.C.S.: 423450

IDEXX Laboratories Pty. Ltd. (1)
Metro Centre Unit 6 38-46 South Street,
Rydalmere, 2116, NSW, Australia (100%)
Tel.: (61) 298987300
Web Site: https://www.idexx.com.au
Sales Range: $25-49.9 Million
Emp.: 60
Provider of Diagnostic Products
N.A.I.C.S.: 325412

IDEXX Laboratories Pty. Ltd. (1)
Metro Centre Unit 6 38-46 South Street,
Rydalmere, 2116, NSW, Australia (100%)
Tel.: (61) 300443399
Web Site: https://www.idexx.com.au
Sales Range: $10-24.9 Million
Emp.: 60
Provider of Diagnostic Products & Services
N.A.I.C.S.: 325412

IDEXX Laboratories Singapore Pte.
Ltd. (1)
21 Biopolis Road Nucleos Unit 03-06, Sin-
gapore, 138567, Singapore
Tel.: (65) 68076288
Scientific Research & Development Ser-
vices
N.A.I.C.S.: 541715

IDEXX Laboratories Sp. z o.o. (1)
Ul Dominikanska 5, 02-736, Warsaw, Po-
land
Tel.: (48) 228534001
Web Site: https://www.idexx.pl
Veterinary Services
N.A.I.C.S.: 541940

IDEXX Laboratories, KK (1)
2F Asahi Seimei Daitabashi Building
1-22-19 Izumi, Suginami-ku, Tokyo, 168-
0063, Japan (100%)
Tel.: (81) 353016700
Web Site: https://www.idexx.co.jp
Sales Range: $10-24.9 Million
Emp.: 40
Provider of Diagnostic Products & Services
N.A.I.C.S.: 325412

IDEXX Laboratorios, S.L. (1)
c/ Plom n 2-8 3, 08038, Barcelona,
Spain (100%)
Tel.: (34) 932672660
Web Site: https://www.idexx.es
Sales Range: $1-9.9 Million
Provider of Diagnostic Products
N.A.I.C.S.: 325412

IDEXX Operations, Inc. (1)
6100 E Shelby Dr, Memphis, TN
38141-7602 (100%)
Tel.: (901) 565-2100
Sales Range: $1-9.9 Million
Distr of Laboratory Instruments
N.A.I.C.S.: 424990

IDEXX Pharmaceuticals, Inc. (1)
7009 Albert Pick Rd, Greensboro, NC
27409
Tel.: (336) 834-6500
Web Site: http://www.idexx.com
Emp.: 18
Pharmaceutical Products Distr
N.A.I.C.S.: 424210

IDEXX Reference Laboratories
Ltd. (1)
1345 Denison Street, Markham, L3R 5V2,
ON, Canada
Tel.: (416) 798-4988
Web Site: https://ca.idexx.com
Veterinary Services
N.A.I.C.S.: 541940

IDEXX Reference Laboratories,
Inc. (1)
1 Idexx Dr, Westbrook, ME 04092
Tel.: (207) 556-0300
Web Site: http://www.idexx.com
Holding Company; Veterinary Research &
Testing Laboratories
N.A.I.C.S.: 551112

Unit (Domestic):

IDEXX Reference Laboratories -
Dallas (2)
4444 Trinity Mills Rd Ste 300, Dallas, TX
75287

Tel.: (972) 447-2769
Web Site: http://www.idexx.com
Sales Range: $10-24.9 Million
Emp.: 32
Veterinary Research & Testing Laboratories
N.A.I.C.S.: 541380

IDEXX Reference Laboratories -
Denver (2)
1020 W 124th Ave Ste 800, Westminster,
CO 80234
Tel.: (720) 977-6100
Web Site: http://www.idexx.com
Sales Range: $100-124.9 Million
Veterinary Research & Testing Laboratories
N.A.I.C.S.: 541380

IDEXX Reference Laboratories -
Elmhurst (2)
655 W Grand Ave Ste 390, Elmhurst, IL
60126
Tel.: (708) 834-3012
Web Site: http://www.idexx.com
Sales Range: $25-49.9 Million
Emp.: 100
Veterinary Research & Testing Laboratories
N.A.I.C.S.: 541380

IDEXX Reference Laboratories -
Irvine (2)
1370 Reynolds Ave Ste 109, Irvine, CA
92614
Tel.: (949) 477-2840
Web Site: http://www.idexx.com
Sales Range: $10-24.9 Million
Emp.: 55
Veterinary Research & Testing Laboratories
N.A.I.C.S.: 541380

IDEXX Reference Laboratories -
Phoenix (2)
2320 W Peoria Ave B148, Phoenix, AZ
85029
Tel.: (602) 906-2900
Web Site: http://www.idexx.com
Sales Range: $10-24.9 Million
Emp.: 55
Veterinary Research & Testing Laboratories
N.A.I.C.S.: 541380

IDEXX Reference Laboratories -
Sacramento (2)
2825 Kovr Dr, West Sacramento, CA 95605
Tel.: (916) 372-4200
Web Site: http://www.idexx.com
Sales Range: $50-74.9 Million
Veterinary Research & Testing Laboratories
N.A.I.C.S.: 541380

IDEXX Reference Laboratories -
Totowa (2)
80H Commerce Way Ste H, Totowa, NJ
07512
Tel.: (973) 237-0331
Web Site: http://www.idexx.com
Sales Range: $10-24.9 Million
Emp.: 70
Veterinary Research & Testing Laboratories
N.A.I.C.S.: 541380

IDEXX S.A.R.L. (1)
84 rue Charles Michels Batiment A, 93200,
Saint Denis, France
Tel.: (33) 149218321
Web Site: http://www.idexx.com
Provider of Diagnostic Products
N.A.I.C.S.: 325412

IDEXX Technologies Limited (1)
Units 1B and 1C Newmarket Business Park
Studlands Park Avenue, Newmarket, CB8
7ER, Suffolk, United Kingdom
Tel.: (44) 1638676800
Web Site: https://www.idexx.com
Laboratory Testing Services
N.A.I.C.S.: 541380

IDEXX Telemedicine Consultants (1)
9200 SE Sunnybrook Blvd Ste 460, Clacka-
mas, OR 97015 (100%)
Tel.: (973) 339-2290
Web Site: http://www.idexx.com
Sales Range: Less than $1 Million
Emp.: 30
Veterinary Hospital, Consultant & Lab Ser-
vices
N.A.I.C.S.: 541940

In Vitro-Labor fur veterinarmedizinis-
che Diagnostik und Hygiene

GmbH (1)
Rennweg 95/Ecke Dr Bohrgasse, 1030, Vi-
enna, Austria
Tel.: (43) 179962290
Web Site: http://www.invitro.at
Laboratory Services
N.A.I.C.S.: 541380
Ernst Leidinger (Mgr)

Movet Oy (1)
Bioteknia 1 Neulaniementie 2, 70210, Kuo-
pio, Finland
Tel.: (358) 50 502 0770
Web Site: https://www.movet.fi
Veterinary Services
N.A.I.C.S.: 541940

OPTI Medical Systems, Inc. (1)
235 Hembree Park Dr, Roswell, GA 30076
Tel.: (770) 510-4444
Web Site: https://www.optimedical.com
Sales Range: $25-49.9 Million
Analytical Laboratory Instrument Mfr
N.A.I.C.S.: 334516

OPTI Medical, Inc. (1)
235 Hembree Park Dr, Roswell, GA 30076
Tel.: (770) 510-4444
Web Site: http://www.optimedical.com
Sales Range: $25-49.9 Million
Emp.: 170
Diagnostic Technology Services
N.A.I.C.S.: 339112

Vetlab Oy (1)
Peltokatu 16 C, 33100, Tampere, Finland
Tel.: (358) 103874455
Web Site: http://www.vetlab.fi
Veterinary Laboratory Testing Services
N.A.I.C.S.: 541940

labor-zentral.ch AG (1)
Stationsweg 3, Geuensee, 6232, Sursee,
Switzerland
Tel.: (41) 419222444
Web Site: https://www.labor-zentral.ch
Veterinary Medical Equipment Mfr
N.A.I.C.S.: 339112

IDLE MEDIA, INC.
216 S Centre Avenue, Leesport, PA
19533
Tel.: (484) 671-2241 NV
Web Site: http://www.idlemedia.net
Year Founded: 2008
IDLM—(OTCIQ)
Sales Range: $1-9.9 Million
Emp.: 14
Music Downloading Services
N.A.I.C.S.: 513210

IDT CORPORATION
520 Broad St, Newark, NJ 07102
Tel.: (973) 438-1000 DE
Web Site: https://www.idt.net
Year Founded: 1990
IDT—(NYSE)
Rev.: $1,238,854,000
Assets: $510,810,000
Liabilities: $310,814,000
Net Worth: $199,996,000
Earnings: $40,492,000
Emp.: 1,880
Fiscal Year-end: 07/31/23
VoIP Telecommunications Services
N.A.I.C.S.: 517121
Joyce J. Mason (Gen Counsel, Sec &
Exec VP)
Howard S. Jonas (Founder & Chm)
Mitch Silberman (Chief Acctg Officer
& Controller)
Bill S. Pereira (Pres & COO)
Shmuel Jonas (CEO)
Menachem Ash (Exec VP-Strategy &
Legal Affairs)
David Wartell (CTO)
Nadine Shea (Exec VP & Head-HR-
Global)
Nick Ford (Pres-Carrier Svcs)

Subsidiaries:

D.P.S.I. Digital Production Solutions
Israel Ltd. (1)

PO Box 81044, Bet Shemesh 9900, Jerusa-
lem, 99052, Israel
Tel.: (972) 29937000
Sales Range: $100-124.9 Million
Computer-Generated Animation Services
N.A.I.C.S.: 512110

IDT Card Services Ireland
Limited (1)
3rd Floor 64 Lower Mount Street, Dublin,
Ireland
Tel.: (353) 14323400
Web Site: http://www.idteurope.com
Sales Range: $10-24.9 Million
Emp.: 13
Telecommunication Calling Card Distr
N.A.I.C.S.: 517121

IDT Corporation de Argentina
S.A. (1)
Av Cabildo 642 piso 3, CP 1426, Buenos
Aires, Argentina
Tel.: (54) 1153659000
Web Site: http://www.idtlatinamerica.com
Sales Range: $10-24.9 Million
Emp.: 50
Telecommunication Servicesb
N.A.I.C.S.: 517111

IDT Global Limited (1)
Tel.: (44) 2075496000
Sales Range: $75-99.9 Million
Emp.: 150
Telecommunication Servicesb
N.A.I.C.S.: 517111

Division (Non-US):

IDT Europe BVBA (2)
Uitbreidingstraat 60 62, 2600 Berchem, Ant-
werp, Belgium
Tel.: (32) 11551065
Web Site: https://idteurope.eu
Sales Range: $1-9.9 Million
Emp.: 4
Telecommunication Servicesb
N.A.I.C.S.: 517111
Angelo Marinelli (Mgr-Sls)

IDT France SARL (2)
Tel.: (33) 155350308
Telecommunication Servicesb
N.A.I.C.S.: 517111

IDT Inter Direct Tel Sweden AB (2)
Naas Fabriker Fack 5031, 44851, Tollered,
Sweden
Tel.: (46) 317851970
Sales Range: $1-9.9 Million
Emp.: 3
Pre-Paid Telephone Calling Cards
N.A.I.C.S.: 517111

IDT Italia S.R.L. (2)
Varese 18, Milan, 20121, Italy
Tel.: (39) 0297069062
Telecommunication Servicesb
N.A.I.C.S.: 517111
Filippo Percario (VP)

IDT Netherlands BV (2)
Olympia 1A, 1213 NS, Hilversum, Nether-
lands
Tel.: (31) 1 04 400 902
Telecommunication Servicesb
N.A.I.C.S.: 517111

IDT Spain S.L. (2)
Sales Range: $1-9.9 Million
Emp.: 6
Telecommunication Servicesb
N.A.I.C.S.: 517111

Interdirect Tel Ltd. (2)
3rd Floor 64 Lower Mount Street, Dublin, 2,
Ireland
Tel.: (353) 014323400
Sales Range: $25-49.9 Million
Emp.: 20
Pre-Paid Telephone Calling Cards
N.A.I.C.S.: 517121

IDT Retail Europe Limited (1)
44 Featherstone Street, London, EC1Y
8RN, United Kingdom
Tel.: (44) 2075496000
Sales Range: $25-49.9 Million
Emp.: 100
Consumer Prepaid Cards Development &
Distr
N.A.I.C.S.: 517121

IDT Corporation—(Continued)

Katrona Tyrrell (Dir-HR)
Nicholas Ford (COO)
Filippo Percario (VP-Carrier Svcs)

IDT Telecom Asia Pacific (Australia) PTY. LTD. (1)
Suite 1601 Level 16 122 Arthur Street,
North Sydney, 2060, Australia
Tel.: (61) 299222208
Web Site: http://www.idtasia.net
Emp.: 5
Telecommunication Calling Card Distr
N.A.I.C.S.: 517121

Net2Phone, Inc. (1)
520 Broad St, Newark, NJ 07102
Tel.: (973) 438-3111
Web Site: https://www.net2phone.com
Sales Range: $75-99.9 Million
Emp.: 273
Internet-Based Telecommunications Services
N.A.I.C.S.: 517111

Subsidiary (Domestic):

Net2Phone Cable Telephony, LLC (2)
550 Broad St, Newark, NJ 07102
Tel.: (973) 438-3111
Web Site: http://www.net2phone.com
Sales Range: $100-124.9 Million
Communication Service
N.A.I.C.S.: 517121

Subsidiary (Non-US):

Versature Corp. (2)
5424 Canotek Road, Ottawa, K1J 1E9, ON,
Canada
Tel.: (613) 237-9329
Telecommunication Servicesb
N.A.I.C.S.: 517810

Telecard Network, L.L.C. (1)
5156 Eisenhower Ave, Alexandria, VA
22304
Tel.: (703) 823-7515
Web Site: http://www.telecardnetwork.com
Emp.: 25
Consumer Prepaid Cards Distr
N.A.I.C.S.: 517810
Armin Torres (Owner & Pres)

Touch-N-Buy, LLC (1)
11600 NW 34th St, Miami, FL 33178
Tel.: (305) 639-9590
Web Site: http://www.touch-n-buy.com
Telecommunication Calling Card Distr
N.A.I.C.S.: 517121

Union Telecard Alliance, LLC (1)
120 Vfw Pkwy, Revere, MA 02151-2540
Tel.: (781) 289-2220
Web Site: http://www.uniontelecard.com
Consumer Prepaid Cards Distr
N.A.I.C.S.: 517810

Union Telecard Arizona, LLC (1)
2150 E Highland Ave Ste 107, Phoenix, AZ
85016
Tel.: (602) 667-3333
Sales Range: $10-24.9 Million
Emp.: 3
Telecom Platform & Consumer Phone Services
N.A.I.C.S.: 517121
Rosa Atencia (Mgr)

Union Telecom Texas LLC (1)
7447 Harwin Dr Ste 135, Houston, TX
77036
Tel.: (713) 266-6661
Telephone Communication Services
N.A.I.C.S.: 517121

WMET 1160 (1)
8121 Georgia Ave Ste 806, Silver Spring,
MD 20910
Tel.: (202) 969-9884
Web Site: http://www.wmet1160.com
Sales Range: $10-24.9 Million
Emp.: 22
Radio Stations
N.A.I.C.S.: 516110

IDW MEDIA HOLDINGS, INC.
520 Broad St, Newark, NJ 07102

Tel.: (203) 323-5161
Web Site:
https://www.idwmediaholdings.com
IDWM—(OTCQB)
Rev.: $32,425,000
Assets: $31,398,000
Liabilities: $8,761,000
Net Worth: $22,637,000
Earnings: ($5,392,000)
Emp.: 78
Fiscal Year-end: 10/31/21
Books Publishing Services
N.A.I.C.S.: 513130
Howard S. Jonas (Chm)
Davidi Jonas (CEO & Chm)
Allan I. Grafman (CEO)
Sanford R. Climan (Vice Chm)
Amber Huerta (COO)
Nachie Marsham (Publr)
Paul Davidson (Exec VP)

IEH CORPORATION
140 58th St 8E, Brooklyn, NY 11220
Tel.: (718) 492-4440   NY
Web Site: https://www.iehcorp.com
Year Founded: 1943
IEHC—(OTCIQ)
Rev.: $21,524,544
Assets: $26,913,454
Liabilities: $5,113,936
Net Worth: $21,799,518
Earnings: ($2,916,902)
Emp.: 154
Fiscal Year-end: 03/31/24
Printed Circuit Board Connector Mfr
N.A.I.C.S.: 334417
David Offerman (Chm, Pres & CEO)
Subrata Purkayastha (CFO)

IES HOLDINGS, INC.
2 Riverway Ste 1730, Houston, TX
77056
Tel.: (713) 860-1500   DE
Web Site: https://www.ies-co.com
Year Founded: 1997
IESC—(NASDAQ)
Rev.: $2,884,358,000
Assets: $1,244,026,000
Liabilities: $591,917,000
Net Worth: $652,109,000
Earnings: $232,501,000
Emp.: 9,423
Fiscal Year-end: 09/30/24
Holding Company; Electrical & Communications Contracting Solutions
N.A.I.C.S.: 551112
Dwayne Collier (Pres-Comml & Industrial)
Tracy A. McLauchlin (CFO, Principal Acctg Officer, Treas & Sr VP)
Michael T. Rice (Pres-Infrastructure Solutions)
Matthew J. Simmes (Pres & COO)
Jeffrey L. Gendell (Chm & CEO)

Subsidiaries:

Bayonet Plumbing, Heating & Air Conditioning, LLC (1)
8950 New York Ave, Hudson, FL 34667
Heating & Air Conditioning Services
N.A.I.C.S.: 238220

Calumet Armature & Electric, LLC (1)
1050 W 134th St, Riverdale, IL 60827
Tel.: (708) 841-6880
Web Site: http://www.calumetarmature.com
Electric Motor & Component Mfr
N.A.I.C.S.: 335312

Freeman Enclosure Systems, LLC (1)
4160 Half Acre Rd, Batavia, OH 45103
Web Site:
http://www.freemanenclosures.com
Turbine Generator Set Mfr
N.A.I.C.S.: 333611
Rick Elcessor (VP-Admin)
Jim Dovel (Mgr-Project Design & Sls)

Steve Tatum (Engr-Sls)
Cassie Freeman (Mgr-Engrg)
Eric Davis (VP-Ops)
Lee Hofmann (Engr-Sls)
Jim Newcomb (Mgr-Field Svc)

Greiner Industries, Inc. (1)
1650 Steel Way, Mount Joy, PA 17552
Tel.: (717) 738-1010
Web Site: http://www.greinerindustries.com
Rev.: $4,000,000
Emp.: 50
Fabricated Structural Metal Mfr
N.A.I.C.S.: 332312
Franklin Greiner (Founder)

IES Commercial & Industrial, LLC (1)
14425 Torrey Chase Blvd Ste 250, Houston,
TX 77014
Tel.: (713) 588-4792
Commercial & Industrial Electrical Contractor
N.A.I.C.S.: 238210
John Werner (Pres)

Branch (Domestic):

IES Commercial & Industrial, LLC - Greenville (2)
920 Frontage Rd, Greenville, SC 29611
Tel.: (864) 250-2500
Web Site: http://www.iesci.net
Sales Range: $10-24.9 Million
Emp.: 12
Electrical & Instrumentation Contractor
N.A.I.C.S.: 238210
Jack Roberts (VP & Gen Mgr)

Subsidiary (Domestic):

Shanahan Mechanical & Electrical, Inc. (2)
202 W 2nd St, Valparaiso, NE 68065
Tel.: (402) 784-2381
Web Site: http://www.iesci.net
Mechanical & Electrical Contracting Services
N.A.I.C.S.: 238210

IES Communications, LLC (1)
2801 S Fair Ln, Tempe, AZ 85282
Tel.: (480) 379-6200
Web Site: http://www.iescomm.com
Communication Product Mfr
N.A.I.C.S.: 335929

IES Infrastructure Solutions, LLC (1)
800 Nave Rd SE, Massillon, OH 44646
Tel.: (330) 830-3500
Industrial Machinery & Equipment Repair
Services
N.A.I.C.S.: 811310

Subsidiary (Domestic):

Plant Power & Control Systems, LLC (2)
179 Airpark Industrial Rd, Alabaster, AL
35007-9583
Tel.: (205) 663-4433
Web Site: http://www.plantpower.com
Sales Range: $10-24.9 Million
Miscellaneous Electrical Equipment & Component Mfr
N.A.I.C.S.: 335999
Ken Miller (Mgr-Bus Dev)
Anthony Robinson (Ops Mgr)
Corey Foster (Project Mgr)
Beth Luketic (Dir-Admin)
Patrick Whatley (Gen Mgr)

IES Renewable Energy, LLC (1)
1240 Railroad St, Corona, CA 92882
Tel.: (951) 737-8870
Web Site: http://www.iesre.com
Solar Electric Generation Services
N.A.I.C.S.: 221114

IES Residential, Inc. (1)
10203 Mula Cir, Stafford, TX 77477
Tel.: (281) 498-2212
Web Site: https://www.iesresidential.com
Emp.: 60
Residential Electrical Installation Services
N.A.I.C.S.: 238210
Dwayne Collier (Pres)
Alison M. Petersen (Interim Sr VP-Fin)
William Wilks (Sr VP-Fin & Ops)
Christine Kirklin (Gen Counsel & VP)

William Crist (VP)
Randall Allen (VP-Safety)
Jim Johnson (VP-Multi-Family Ops)

Subsidiary (Domestic):

Aerial Lighting & Electric Inc. (2)
26 Hotchkiss St, Naugatuck, CT 06770
Tel.: (203) 720-0900
Web Site: http://www.aerialelectric.com
Electrical Contractor
N.A.I.C.S.: 238210
Jeff Johnson (Mgr-Fin)
Paul Simko (CEO)
Bob Carlson (VP & Gen Mgr)
Gary R. Hennessy (CIO)
Roland St. Germain (VP & Sr Mgr-Field Ops)
Joseph Luzzi (VP & Sr Mgr-Talent Acquisition)

Edmonson Electric, LLC (2)
5611 Land O Lakes Blvd, Land O Lakes, FL
34639   (80%)
Tel.: (813) 910-3403
Web Site: http://www.edmonsonelectric.com
Sales Range: $1-9.9 Million
Emp.: 115
Residential Electric, Heating, Ventilation &
Air Conditioning Installation Services
N.A.I.C.S.: 238220
Kevin Edmonson (Pres)
Michele Eleyet (VP)

Wedlake Fabricating, Inc. (2)
3989 N Osage Dr, Tulsa, OK 74127
Tel.: (918) 428-1641
Web Site: https://www.wedlake.net
Sales Range: $1-9.9 Million
Emp.: 30
Miscellaneous Fabricated Metal Product Mfr
N.A.I.C.S.: 332999
Brian Wedlake (Gen Mgr)

IES Subsidiary Holdings, Inc. (1)
800 Nave Rd SE, Massillon, OH 44646
Tel.: (330) 830-3500
Web Site: http://www.miscor.com
Emp.: 100
Holding Company
N.A.I.C.S.: 551112
Mike Rice (Pres)
Steve Lolli (Dir-Safety)

Subsidiary (Domestic):

Magnetech Industrial Services, Inc. (2)
800 Nave Rd SE, Massillon, OH 44646-
9476
Tel.: (330) 830-3500
Web Site: https://www.magnetech.com
Repair Services
N.A.I.C.S.: 811114

K.E.P. Electric, Inc. (1)
1114 Ferris Rd, Amelia, OH 45102
Tel.: (513) 752-3043
Web Site: https://www.kepelectric.com
Sales Range: $1-9.9 Million
Emp.: 17
Electrical Contracting Services

NEXT Electric, LLC (1)
1121 Marlin Ct, Waukesha, WI 53186
Tel.: (262) 506-3200
Web Site: http://www.nextelectricllc.com
Electrical Contractor Services
N.A.I.C.S.: 238210
Chris Surges (Pres)

Southern Industrial Sales and Services, Inc. (1)
5277 Chumar Dr, Columbus, GA 31904
Tel.: (706) 317-5545
Web Site:
http://www.southernrewinding.com
Electric Motor Repair, Sales & Services
N.A.I.C.S.: 811310

Technibus, Inc. (1)
1501 Raff Rd SW, Canton, OH 44710
Tel.: (330) 479-4202
Metal Enclosed Bus Duct Mfr
N.A.I.C.S.: 423610

IEXALT, INC.
12000 Aerospace Ave Ste 375, Houston, TX 77034

Tel.: (281) 464-8400
IEXA—(NASDAQ)
Books Publishing Services
N.A.I.C.S.: 513130
Donald W. Sapaugh *(CEO)*

IF BANCORP, INC.
201 E Cherry St, Watseka, IL 60970-0190
Tel.: (815) 432-2476   MD
Web Site:
    https://www.iroquoisfed.com
IROQ—(NASDAQ)
Rev.: $45,370,000
Assets: $887,745,000
Liabilities: $813,829,000
Net Worth: $73,916,000
Earnings: $1,790,000
Emp.: 109
Fiscal Year-end: 06/30/24
Bank Holding Company
N.A.I.C.S.: 551111
Pamela J. Verkler *(CFO, Treas & Sr Exec VP)*
Gary Martin *(Chm)*
Walter H. Hasselbring III *(Pres & CEO)*
Linda L. Hamilton *(COO & Exec VP)*
Thomas J. Chamberlain *(Chief Lending Officer, Sr Exec VP & Exec VP)*

Subsidiaries:

Iroquois Federal Savings & Loan
Association   **(1)**
201 E Cherry St, Watseka, IL 60970
Tel.: (815) 432-2476
Web Site: http://www.iroquoisfed.com
Sales Range: $10-24.9 Million
Emp.: 82
Federal Savings & Loan Associations
N.A.I.C.S.: 522180
Pamela J. Verkler *(CFO, Treas & Sr Exec VP)*
Gary Martin *(Chm)*
Walter H. Hasselbring III *(Pres & CEO)*

IFAN FINANCIAL, INC.
3517 Camino Del Rio S Ste 407, San Diego, CA 92108
Tel.: (619) 537-9998   NV
Web Site:
    https://www.ifanfinancial.com
IFAN—(OTCIQ)
Sales Range: Less than $1 Million
Miscellaneous Financial Investment Activities
N.A.I.C.S.: 523999
J. Christopher Mizer *(Pres & CEO)*
Steven Scholl *(CFO, Tres & Sec)*

IFB HOLDINGS, INC.
522 Washington St, Chillicothe, MO 64601
Tel.: (660) 646-3733   DE
IFBH—(OTCIQ)
Banking Holding Company
N.A.I.C.S.: 551111
Charles Bigler *(Pres & CEO)*

IFRESH INC.
137-80 Northern Blvd 2nd Fl, Flushing, NY 11354
Tel.: (718) 359-2518
Web Site:
    http://www.ifreshmarket.com
IFMK—(OTCEM)
Rev.: $89,453,031
Assets: $99,259,161
Liabilities: $101,809,308
Net Worth: ($2,550,147)
Earnings: ($8,286,854)
Emp.: 276
Fiscal Year-end: 03/31/20
Specialty Grocery Store Operator
N.A.I.C.S.: 424490

IG ACQUISITION CORP.

251 Park Ave S 8th Fl, New York, NY 10010
Tel.: (917) 765-5588   DE
Web Site:
    http://www.igacquisition.com
Year Founded: 2020
IGACU—(NASDAQ)
Investment Services
N.A.I.C.S.: 523999
Bradley Tusk *(Chm)*
Christian Goode *(CEO)*
Edward Farrell *(CFO)*

IGC PHARMA, INC.
10224 Falls Rd, Potomac, MD 20854
Tel.: (301) 983-0998   MD
Web Site: https://igcpharma.com
Year Founded: 2005
IGC—(NYSEAMEX)
Rev.: $1,345,000
Assets: $9,902,000
Liabilities: $2,581,000
Net Worth: $7,321,000
Earnings: ($13,000,000)
Emp.: 67
Fiscal Year-end: 03/31/24
Cannabis-Based Biopharmaceutical Research & Development; Construction Equipment Rental Services; Real Estate Management Services
N.A.I.C.S.: 541714
Ram Mukunda *(Pres & CEO)*
Richard K. Prins *(Chm)*
Claudia Grimaldi *(CFO, Chief Compliance Officer & VP)*
Benysh Qureshi *(Dir-Operations)*

Subsidiaries:

IGC Pharma LLC   **(1)**
PO Box 60642, Potomac, MD 20859-0642
Tel.: (301) 983-0998
Web Site: http://www.igcpharma.com
Pharmaceuticals Product Mfr
N.A.I.C.S.: 325412
Ram Mukunda *(CEO)*
Richard K. Prins *(Chm)*
Claudia Grimaldi *(VP)*

Techni Bharathi Private Limited   **(1)**
34 136A Florance Ist Floor NH Bypass Road Edappally, Kochi, 682024, India   **(100%)**
Tel.: (91) 4842344906
Web Site: http://www.technibharathi.in
Sales Range: $250-299.9 Million
Emp.: 15
Construction Equipment Leasing Services
N.A.I.C.S.: 532412
Deepak M. P. *(Deputy Gen Mgr-Technical)*
Sankaran Nair P. *(Deputy Gen Mgr-Accounts)*
Shaji M. S. *(Asst Gen Mgr-Accounts)*
M. S. Shaji *(Deputy Gen Mgr)*

IGEN NETWORKS CORP.
Tel.: (951) 226-7142   NV
Web Site:
    https://www.igennetworks.net
Year Founded: 2006
IGN—(CNSX)
Rev.: $318,016
Assets: $616,290
Liabilities: $1,593,944
Net Worth: ($977,654)
Earnings: ($1,159,190)
Emp.: 10
Fiscal Year-end: 12/31/22
Entertainment Industry Investment Services
N.A.I.C.S.: 523999
Robert Nealon *(Chm)*
Neil Gene Chan *(CEO)*
Abel I. Sierra *(COO)*

IGENE BIOTECHNOLOGY, INC.
9110 Red Branch Rd, Columbia, MD 21045-2024
Tel.: (410) 997-2599   MD
Web Site: http://www.igene.com

IGNE—(OTCIQ)
Animal Products Mfr
N.A.I.C.S.: 311119
Stephen A. Hiu *(Pres)*

IGM BIOSCIENCES, INC.
325 E Middlefield Rd, Mountain View, CA 94043
Tel.: (650) 965-7873   DE
Web Site: https://www.igmbio.com
Year Founded: 1993
IGMS—(NASDAQ)
Rev.: $1,069,000
Assets: $513,499,000
Liabilities: $226,236,000
Net Worth: $287,263,000
Earnings: ($221,102,000)
Emp.: 258
Fiscal Year-end: 12/31/22
Biotechnology Research & Development Services
N.A.I.C.S.: 541714
Fred M. Schwarzer *(Pres & CEO)*
Misbah Tahir *(CFO)*
Suzette Tauber *(Chief HR Officer)*
Lisa L. Decker *(Chief Bus Officer)*
Steven Weber *(Principal Acctg Officer, Sr VP & Controller)*
Chris H. Takimoto *(Chief Medical Officer)*
George A. Gauthier *(Chief Comml Officer)*
Lisa L. Decker *(Chief Bus Officer)*

IHEARTMEDIA, INC.
20880 Stone Oak Pkwy, San Antonio, TX 78258
Tel.: (210) 822-2828   DE
Web Site:
    https://www.iheartmedia.com
Year Founded: 2007
IHRT—(NASDAQ)
Rev.: $3,751,025,000
Assets: $6,952,611,000
Liabilities: $7,337,369,000
Net Worth: ($384,758,000)
Earnings: ($1,102,660,000)
Emp.: 10,800
Fiscal Year-end: 12/31/23
Media Holding Company
N.A.I.C.S.: 551112
Robert W. Pittman *(Chm & CEO)*
Richard J. Bressler *(Pres, CFO & COO)*
John L. Sykes *(Pres-Entertainment Enterprises)*
Steve Mills *(CIO-Global)*
Greg Ashlock *(CEO-Multiplatform Grp)*
Wendy Goldberg *(Chief Comm Officer)*
Joe Robinson *(Pres-Corp Dev & Ventures)*
Mark Gray *(CEO-Katz Media Group)*
Michele Laven *(Chief HR Officer & Chief Diversity Officer)*
Michael B. McGuinness *(Deputy CFO, Exec VP & Head-IR)*
Jordan Fasbender *(Gen Counsel & Exec VP)*
Juliana F. Hill *(Executives)*
Jeff Howard *(Pres-Sls-Natl)*
Tony Coles *(Pres-Black Information Network)*
Conal Byrne *(CEO-Digital Audio Grp)*
Jon Kurland *(Exec VP-Bus Affairs)*
Jay C. Lowe *(Pres-Oklahoma)*
Hartley Adkins *(Pres-Markets Grp)*
Paul McNicol *(Exec VP)*

Subsidiaries:

Aircheck India Pvt. Ltd.   **(1)**
07/104 Nesco IT Park C Wing 7th Floor NH 8, Nesco Goregaon E, Mumbai, 400 063, Maharashtra, India
Tel.: (91) 2240030113
Web Site: https://www.aircheckindia.com

Emp.: 250
Radio Monitoring Services
N.A.I.C.S.: 516210
Krittika Banerjee *(Dir-Global Processing)*
Diana Stokey *(VP-Mktg Ops & Comm)*
Barry Hill *(VP-Customer Experience)*
Chris Bean *(VP-IT)*
Biju Thomas *(VP-Product Mgmt)*
Heather Dwyer *(VP-Global Fin & Admin)*
Mike Powell *(Chief Compliance Officer & Sr VP-Intl Ops)*
Philippe Generali *(Pres & CEO)*
Chip Jellison *(Exec VP-Tech & Dev)*
Shankar Balakrishnan *(Gen Mgr)*

All Access Music Group, Inc.   **(1)**
28955 Pacific Coast Hwy, Malibu, CA 90265
Tel.: (310) 457-6616
Web Site: http://www.allaccess.com
Sales Range: $1-9.9 Million
Emp.: 20
Business Services, Nec, Nsk
N.A.I.C.S.: 512290
Joel Denver *(Co-Founder, Pres & Publr)*
Mark Capuano *(VP-Bus Dev)*
Matt Parvis *(VP & Mgr-Sls)*
Matt Shapo *(VP-Digital Content)*
Paul Colbert *(Acct Exec)*
Perry Michael Simon *(VP & Editor-News, Talk & Sports)*
Shawn Alexander *(VP-Editorial & Editor-Alternative Format)*
John Kilgo *(Exec VP-Music & Entertainment)*

Clear Channel Belgium Sprl   **(1)**
Laurent-Benoit Dewezplein 5, 1800, Vilvoorde, Belgium
Tel.: (32) 26417300
Web Site: https://www.clearchannel.be
Emp.: 200
Advertising Services
N.A.I.C.S.: 541810

Clear Channel Chile Publicidad Ltda   **(1)**
Magdalena 140 Floor -1, Las Condes, Santiago, Chile
Tel.: (56) 24305800
Web Site: https://www.clearchannel.cl
Outdoor Advertising Services
N.A.I.C.S.: 541850

IN-TER-SPACE Services, Inc.   **(1)**
4635 Crackersport Rd, Allentown, PA 18104
Tel.: (610) 395-8002
Outdoor Advertising Services
N.A.I.C.S.: 541850

KMS Advertising Ltd.   **(1)**
33 Golden Square, London, W1F 9JT, United Kingdom
Tel.: (44) 2082024141
Advertising Agency Services
N.A.I.C.S.: 541810

Los Angeles Broadcasting Partners, LLC   **(1)**
7136 S Yale Ave Ste 501, Tulsa, OK 74136
Tel.: (918) 664-4581
Media Broadcasting Services
N.A.I.C.S.: 541830

Radio Computing Services (Africa) Pty Ltd.   **(1)**
Regus Business Centre 292 Surrey Avenue, Randburg, Ferndale, 2194, South Africa
Tel.: (27) 11 477 1229
Web Site: https://www.rcsafrica.com
Emp.: 6
Radio Broadcasting Services
N.A.I.C.S.: 516210

Radio Computing Services (India) Pvt. Ltd.   **(1)**
314 Raheja Plaza Off New Link Road, Andheri West, Mumbai, 400 053, India
Tel.: (91) 2261413131
Web Site: http://www.rcs.in
Sales Range: $10-24.9 Million
Emp.: 20
Broadcast Software Services
N.A.I.C.S.: 513210

Radio Computing Services (SEA) Pte Ltd.   **(1)**
16 Raffles Quay 41-07 Hong Leong Building, Singapore, 048581, Singapore

iHeartMedia, Inc.—(Continued)

Tel.: (65) 63246658
Web Site: http://www.rcsworks.com
Emp.: 1
Radio Broadcasting Services
N.A.I.C.S.: 516210

**Radio Computing Services (UK)
Ltd.** (1)
Abbey Mill Business Park Lower Eashing,
Godalming, GU7 2QJ, Surrey, United King-
dom
Tel.: (44) 148 342 2411
Web Site: https://www.rcsuk.com
Emp.: 10
Radio Broadcasting Services
N.A.I.C.S.: 516210
Jon Earley (Mng Dir)

**Radio Computing Services Canada
Ltd.** (1)
189 Stonebriar Drive, Maple, L6A 4A3, ON,
Canada
Tel.: (604) 986-4468
Radio Broadcasting Services
N.A.I.C.S.: 516210

Rockbox Ltd. (1)
34 Obelisk Way The Square Shopping Cen-
tre, Camberley, GU15 3SG, Surrey, United
Kingdom
Tel.: (44) 127626628
Web Site: https://www.rockbox.co.uk
Disco Equipment Whslr
N.A.I.C.S.: 334610

SIA Clear Channel Latvia (1)
Valnu iela 3-1 6th floor, Riga, 1050, Latvia
Tel.: (371) 67221777
Web Site: http://www.clearchannel.lv
Outdoor Advertising Services
N.A.I.C.S.: 541850
Inese Sukste (Project Mgr-Dev)
Janis Puravs (Exec Dir)

Street Furniture (NSW) Pty Ltd. (1)
Bldg N 6 Regents Park Estate Segal ST
Commercial Drive, Regents Park, 2143,
Australia
Tel.: (61) 280960100
Web Site: http://www.streetfurniture.com
Furniture Mfr
N.A.I.C.S.: 337127

Supersigns Polska SP ZO.o. (1)
ul Saska 62/5, 03-914, Warsaw, Poland
Tel.: (48) 226229426
Web Site: https://www.supersigns.com.pl
Advertising Services
N.A.I.C.S.: 541810

UAB Clear Channel Lietuva (1)
Vokieciu st 20, 01130, Vilnius, Lithuania
Tel.: (370) 52312060
Web Site: http://www.clearchannel.lt
Outdoor Advertising Services
N.A.I.C.S.: 541850
Arturas Staude (Mng Dir)
Karolina Strazdiene (Project Mgr)

iHeartCommunications, Inc. (1)
8044 Montgomery Rd Ste 650, Cincinnati,
OH 45236
Tel.: (513) 241-1550
Web Site: http://www.iheartmedia.com
Rev.: $6,170,993,000
Assets: $12,260,430,000
Liabilities: $23,587,885,000
Net Worth: ($11,327,454,000)
Earnings ($393,890,000)
Emp.: 17,899
Fiscal Year-end: 12/31/2017
Radio Broadcasting Services
N.A.I.C.S.: 516210
Robert W. Pittman (CEO)

Subsidiary (Non-US):

Clear Channel Hillenaar BV (2)
Geversstraat 30, Oegstgeest, 2342 AA,
Netherlands
Tel.: (31) 715157343
Web Site: http://www.hillenaar.com
Advertising Services
N.A.I.C.S.: 541890

Clear Channel International Ltd. (2)
33 Golden Square, London, W1F 9JT,
United Kingdom
Tel.: (44) 2074782200

Web Site: https://www.clearchannel.co.uk
Emp.: 200
Outdoor Advertising Services
N.A.I.C.S.: 541850
Justin Cochrane (CEO)
Martin Corke (CMO)

Clear Channel Latvia (2)
Valnu iela 3-1 6th floor, Riga, 1050, Latvia
Tel.: (371) 67221777
Web Site: http://www.clearchannel.lv
Advertising Services
N.A.I.C.S.: 541890

Clear Channel Norway AS (2)
Schweigaardsgate 16, 0191, Oslo, Norway
Tel.: (47) 22023400
Web Site: http://www.clearchannel.no
Outdoor Advertising Services
N.A.I.C.S.: 541890

**Clear Channel Outdoor Mexico, Op-
eraciones SA de CV** (2)
Blvrd BManuel Avila Camacho 138 Lomas
de Chapultepec, Lomas De Chapultepec
Miguel Hidalgo, 11560, Mexico, Mexico
Tel.: (52) 52810392
Web Site: http://www.clearchannel.com.mx
Emp.: 75
Advertising Services
N.A.I.C.S.: 541890

Clear Channel Poland Sp ZO.o. (2)
st Polna 11, 00-633, Warsaw, Poland
Tel.: (48) 228253606
Web Site: http://www.clearchannel.com.pl
Sales Range: $25-49.9 Million
Emp.: 80
Advertising Services
N.A.I.C.S.: 541850

Clear Channel Sverige AB (2)
Birger Jarlsgatan 43, 111 45, Stockholm,
Sweden
Tel.: (46) 852240000
Web Site: http://www.clearchannel.se
Advertising Services
N.A.I.C.S.: 541890

Subsidiary (Domestic):

Critical Mass Media, Inc. (2)
8044 Montgomery Rd Ste 650, Cincinnati,
OH 45236-2959
Tel.: (513) 631-4266
Web Site: http://www.criticalmassmedia.com
Sales Range: $75-99.9 Million
Emp.: 15
Radio Market Research & Analysis Services
N.A.I.C.S.: 541910
Lainie Fertick (Gen Mgr)

Katz Media Group, Inc. (2)
3525 Piedmont Rd NE, Atlanta, GA 30305
Tel.: (404) 365-3100
Web Site: http://www.katz-media.com
Sales Range: $250-299.9 Million
Emp.: 600
Radio Broadcasting Services
N.A.I.C.S.: 516210
Mark Gray (CEO)
Joe Brewer (Pres-Bus Ops & Innovation)
Jennifer Savage (Dir-Comm & Mktg)

Subsidiary (Domestic):

Katz Communications, Inc. (3)
1 Dag Hammarskjold Plz, New York, NY
10017
Tel.: (212) 572-5000
Web Site: http://www.katz-media.com
Sales Range: $100-124.9 Million
Emp.: 500
Radio Broadcasting Services
N.A.I.C.S.: 516210

Division (Domestic):

Clear Channel Radio Sales (4)
125 W 55th St 4th Fl, New York, NY 10019-
5366
Tel.: (212) 424-6000
Sales Range: $100-124.9 Million
Radio Advertising Representatives
N.A.I.C.S.: 541840

Katz 360 Digital Sales (4)
125 W 55th St, New York, NY 10019
Tel.: (212) 424-6000
Web Site: http://www.katz-media.com

Sales Range: $100-124.9 Million
Online Digital Audio, Mobile, Database &
Display Advertising Representatives
N.A.I.C.S.: 541840

Katz Advantage (4)
125 W 55th St, New York, NY 10019-5369
Tel.: (212) 424-6000
Web Site: http://www.katz-media.com
Sales Range: $100-124.9 Million
Radio Advertising Representatives
N.A.I.C.S.: 541840

Katz Marketing Solutions (4)
125 W 55th St 7th Fl, New York, NY 10019
Tel.: (212) 424-6000
Web Site: https://www.raisingthevolume.com
Sales Range: $75-99.9 Million
Multiplatform Marketing Services
N.A.I.C.S.: 541613

Group (Domestic):

Katz Radio Group (4)
125 W 55th St, New York, NY 10019
Tel.: (212) 424-6500
Web Site: http://www.katz-media.com
Sales Range: $100-124.9 Million
Radio Advertising Representatives
N.A.I.C.S.: 541840
Christine Travaglini (Pres)
Kimberly Browne (Bus Mgr)

Subsidiary (Domestic):

Christal Radio Sales, Inc. (5)
125 W 55th St Fl 7, New York, NY 10019-
5369
Tel.: (212) 424-6000
Web Site: http://www.katz-media.com
Sales Range: $10-24.9 Million
Emp.: 80
Radio Broadcasting Services
N.A.I.C.S.: 516210

Unit (Domestic):

Eastman Radio Sales (5)
125 W 55th St, New York, NY 10019
Tel.: (212) 424-6000
Web Site: http://www.katz-media.com
Sales Range: $100-124.9 Million
Radio Advertising Representatives
N.A.I.C.S.: 541840

Subsidiary (Domestic):

Katz Net Radio Sales, Inc. (5)
125 W 55th St 7th Fl, New York, NY 10019-
5366
Tel.: (212) 424-6000
Sales Range: $100-124.9 Million
Emp.: 500
Radio Advertising Representatives
N.A.I.C.S.: 541840

Unit (Domestic):

Univision Radio National Sales (5)
125 W 55th St, New York, NY 10019-5366
Tel.: (212) 424-6000
Web Site: http://www.katz-media.com
Sales Range: $10-24.9 Million
Emp.: 50
Spanish-Language Radio Advertising Rep-
resentatives
N.A.I.C.S.: 541840

Group (Domestic):

Katz Television Group (4)
125 W 55th St, New York, NY 10019
Tel.: (212) 424-6000
Web Site: http://www.katz-media.com
Sales Range: $100-124.9 Million
Television Advertising Representatives
N.A.I.C.S.: 541840
Leo MacCourtney (Pres)
Craig Broitman (COO & Exec VP)
Doug Pfaff (Exec VP-Dev & Partnerships)
Artie Altman (Exec VP)
Michael Lawless (VP & Dir-Ad Sls Ops)
Ben Buchwald (VP & Gen Sls Mgr-Direct
Mktg)

Unit (Domestic):

Continental Television Sales (5)
125 W 55th St, New York, NY 10019-5366
Tel.: (212) 424-6000
Web Site: http://www.katz-media.com

Sales Range: $25-49.9 Million
Emp.: 100
Television Advertising Representatives
N.A.I.C.S.: 541840

Eagle Television Sales (5)
125 W 55th St Fl 11, New York, NY 10019
Tel.: (212) 408-3614
Web Site: http://www.katz-media.com
Sales Range: $25-49.9 Million
Emp.: 150
Television Advertising Representatives
N.A.I.C.S.: 541840

Katz Direct (5)
125 W 55th St, New York, NY 10019
Tel.: (212) 424-6950
Web Site: http://www.katzdirect.com
Sales Range: $75-99.9 Million
Emp.: 20
Television Direct Marketing Services
N.A.I.C.S.: 541613

Subsidiary (Domestic):

**Katz Millennium Sales & Marketing
Inc.** (5)
211 E Ontario St Ste 700, Chicago, IL
60611-3281
Tel.: (312) 642-2450
Web Site: http://www.katz-media.com
Sales Range: $100-124.9 Million
Radio Broadcasting Services
N.A.I.C.S.: 516210

Subsidiary (Domestic):

Premiere Networks, Inc. (2)
15260 Ventura Blvd, Sherman Oaks, CA
91403
Tel.: (818) 377-5300
Web Site:
　　https://www.premierenetworks.com
Radio Program Syndication Services
N.A.I.C.S.: 516210
Michael Kindhart (VP)
Peter Tripi (Exec VP-Affiliate Sls)

Radio Computing Services, Inc. (2)
1 N Broadway 14th Fl, White Plains, NY
10601
Tel.: (914) 428-4600
Web Site: https://www.rcsworks.com
Sales Range: $10-24.9 Million
Emp.: 200
Radio & Television Broadcast Programming
Software Developer & Publisher
N.A.I.C.S.: 513210
Mike Powell (Chief Compliance Officer & Sr
VP-Ops-Intl)
Philippe Generali (Pres & CEO)
Chip Jellison (CTO)
Neal Perchuk (Sr VP-Sls & Mktg)
Keith Williams (VP-Asia Pacific)
Barry Hill (VP-Customer Experience)
Chris Bean (VP-IT)
Heather Dwyer (VP-Global Fin & Admin)

Terrestrial RF Licensing, Inc. (2)
7136 S Yale Ave Ste 501, Tulsa, OK 74136
Web Site: http://www.rflicensing.com
Advertising Services
N.A.I.C.S.: 541890

Group (Domestic):

**iHeartMedia + Entertainment,
Inc.** (2)
1501 13th Ave, Columbus, GA 31901-1908
Tel.: (706) 576-3000
Web Site: http://www.iheartmedia.com
Emp.: 70
Radio Broadcasting Services
N.A.I.C.S.: 516210

Unit (Domestic):

94 Country WKKJ (3)
45 W Main St, Chillicothe, OH 45601
Tel.: (740) 773-3000
Web Site: http://wkkj.iheart.com
Radio Stations
N.A.I.C.S.: 516110

Cat Country 107 Fm (3)
13320 Metro Pkwy Ste 1, Fort Myers, FL
33966
Tel.: (239) 225-4300
Web Site: https://catcountry1071.iheart.com
Radio Broadcasting Stations
N.A.I.C.S.: 516110

Fox Sports Radio 1350 AM (3)
2030 Iowa Ave Ste 100, Riverside, CA
92507
Tel.: (951) 369-1350
Web Site:
    https://foxsportsradio1350.iheart.com
Radio Stations
N.A.I.C.S.: 516110

Kdon 102 5 Fm (3)
1550 Moffett St Unit C, Salinas, CA 93905
Tel.: (831) 755-8181
Web Site: https://kdon.iheart.com
Radio Broadcasting Stations
N.A.I.C.S.: 516110

Subsidiary (Domestic):

Triton Digital Inc. (3)
15303 Ventura Blvd Ste 1500, Sherman
Oaks, CA 91403
Tel.: (866) 448-4037
Web Site: http://www.tritondigital.com
Radio Station Web Content & Interactive
Media Services
N.A.I.C.S.: 513210
John Rosso (Pres-Market Dev)
Neal Schore (Pres & CEO)
Mark Rosenbaum (CFO)
Micheline Sebbag (Exec VP-HR)
Alex Fournier (Sr VP-Product & Tech)
Kristin Charron (VP-Mktg)
Nicole Kuntz (Chief Compliance Officer &
Sr VP-Compliance & Industry Rels)
Stephanie Donovan (Sr VP-Publr Dev-North
America)
Daryl Battaglia (Sr VP-Market Dev, Strategy
& Audience Res)
Sharon Taylor (Mng Dir)
Brendan Collins (Sr VP-Bus & Legal Affairs)

Unit (Domestic):

WDLA-FM (3)
Townsquare Media 34 Chestnut St, Oneo-
nta, NY 13820
Tel.: (607) 432-1030
Web Site: http://bigcat921.com
Radio Stations
N.A.I.C.S.: 516110
Michele Clapperton (Dir-Sls)

WGCHAM 1490 (3)
71 Lewis St, Greenwich, CT 06830
Tel.: (203) 869-1490
Web Site: https://www.wgch.com
Radio Stations
N.A.I.C.S.: 516110
Bob Small (Mgr-Ops)
Tony Savino (Dir-News)

WSRW 101.5 (3)
5675 State Route 247, Hillsboro, OH 45133
Tel.: (937) 393-1590
Web Site: http://wsrw.iheart.com
Radio Stations
N.A.I.C.S.: 516110

WWNC AM (3)
13 Summerlin Rd, Asheville, NC 28806
Tel.: (828) 257-2700
Web Site: http://wwnc.iheart.com
Radio Stations
N.A.I.C.S.: 516110

Wlde Oldies 101 7 Fm (3)
347 W Berry St 600, Fort Wayne, IN 46802
Tel.: (260) 423-3676
Web Site: https://www.classichits1017.com
Radio Stations
N.A.I.C.S.: 516110

Wmmb Am 1240 (3)
1388 S Babcock St, Melbourne, FL 32901
Tel.: (321) 821-7100
Web Site: https://wmmbam.iheart.com
Radio Broadcasting Stations
N.A.I.C.S.: 516110

Wrwd Country 1073 (3)
20 Tucker Dr, Poughkeepsie, NY 12603
Tel.: (845) 471-2300
Web Site: https://wrwdcountry.iheart.com
Radio Stations
N.A.I.C.S.: 516110

Wtks Real Radio 104 1 Fm (3)
2500 Maitland Ctr Pkwy Ste 401, Maitland,
FL 32751
Tel.: (407) 916-1041
Web Site: https://realradio.iheart.com

Radio Broadcasting Stations
N.A.I.C.S.: 516110

**iHeartMedia + Entertainment, Inc. -
Albany, GA** (3)
1501 13th Ave, Albany, GA 31901
Tel.: (706) 576-3000
Sales Range: $25-49.9 Million
Emp.: 60
Radio Broadcasting Stations
N.A.I.C.S.: 516110

**iHeartMedia + Entertainment, Inc. -
Albany, NY** (3)
1203 Troy Schenectady Rd, Latham, NY
12110
Tel.: (518) 452-4800
Web Site:
    https://albany.iheartadvertising.com
Sales Range: $25-49.9 Million
Emp.: 85
Radio Broadcasting Stations
N.A.I.C.S.: 516110

**iHeartMedia + Entertainment, Inc. -
Albuquerque, NM** (3)
5411 Jefferson St NE Ste 100, Albuquer-
que, NM 87109
Tel.: (505) 830-6400
Web Site:
    https://albuquerque.iheartadvertising.com
Sales Range: $25-49.9 Million
Emp.: 70
Radio Broadcasting Stations
N.A.I.C.S.: 516110
Chuck Hammond (VP & Gen Mgr)

**iHeartMedia + Entertainment, Inc. -
Anchorage, AK** (3)
800 E Dimond Blvd Ste 3-370, Anchorage,
AK 99515
Tel.: (907) 522-1515
Web Site:
    https://anchorage.iheartadvertising.com
Sales Range: $10-24.9 Million
Emp.: 35
Radio Broadcasting Stations
N.A.I.C.S.: 516110

**iHeartMedia + Entertainment, Inc. -
Ashland, OH** (3)
1400 Radio Ln, Mansfield, OH 44906
Tel.: (419) 529-2211
Web Site:
    https://midohio.iheartadvertising.com
Sales Range: $10-24.9 Million
Emp.: 17
Radio Broadcasting Stations
N.A.I.C.S.: 516110

Unit (Domestic):

**iHeartMedia + Entertainment, Inc. -
Mansfield, OH** (4)
1400 Radio Ln, Mansfield, OH 44906
Tel.: (419) 529-2211
Web Site: http://www.iheartmedia.com
Sales Range: $10-24.9 Million
Emp.: 17
Radio Broadcasting Stations
N.A.I.C.S.: 516110

Unit (Domestic):

**iHeartMedia + Entertainment, Inc. -
Atlanta, GA** (3)
1819 Peachtree Rd NE Ste 700, Atlanta,
GA 30309-1848
Tel.: (404) 875-8080
Web Site:
    https://atlanta.iheartadvertising.com
Sales Range: $200-249.9 Million
Emp.: 130
Radio Broadcasting Stations
N.A.I.C.S.: 516110

**iHeartMedia + Entertainment, Inc. -
Augusta, GA** (3)
2743 Perimeter Pkwy 100 Ste 300, Au-
gusta, GA 30909
Tel.: (706) 396-6000
Web Site:
    https://augusta.iheartadvertising.com
Sales Range: $10-24.9 Million
Emp.: 20
Radio Broadcasting Stations
N.A.I.C.S.: 516110
Tim Snell (Sr VP-Programming)

**iHeartMedia + Entertainment, Inc. -
Baton Rouge, LA** (3)
5555 Hilton Ave Ste 500, Baton Rouge, LA
70808
Tel.: (225) 231-1860
Web Site:
    https://batonrouge.iheartadvertising.com
Sales Range: $10-24.9 Million
Emp.: 23
Radio Broadcasting Stations
N.A.I.C.S.: 516110
Michael Hudson (Pres)

**iHeartMedia + Entertainment, Inc. -
Beaumont, TX** (3)
2885 I-10 E, Beaumont, TX 77702
Tel.: (409) 896-5555
Web Site:
    https://beaumont.iheartadvertising.com
Sales Range: $10-24.9 Million
Emp.: 23
Radio Broadcasting Stations
N.A.I.C.S.: 516110
Tim Thomas (VP & Mgr-Market)

**iHeartMedia + Entertainment, Inc. -
Biloxi, MS** (3)
286 Debuys Rd, Biloxi, MS 39531
Tel.: (228) 388-2323
Web Site: https://biloxi.iheartadvertising.com
Sales Range: $200-249.9 Million
Radio Broadcasting Stations
N.A.I.C.S.: 516110

**iHeartMedia + Entertainment, Inc. -
Binghamton, NY** (3)
320 N Jensen Rd, Vestal, NY 13850
Tel.: (607) 584-5800
Web Site:
    https://binghamton.iheartadvertising.com
Radio Broadcasting Stations
N.A.I.C.S.: 516110

**iHeartMedia + Entertainment, Inc. -
Birmingham, AL** (3)
600 Beacon Pkwy W Ste 400, Birmingham,
AL 35209-3152
Tel.: (205) 439-9600
Web Site:
    https://birmingham.iheartadvertising.com
Sales Range: $10-24.9 Million
Emp.: 45
Radio Broadcasting Stations
N.A.I.C.S.: 516110

**iHeartMedia + Entertainment, Inc. -
Bismarck, ND** (3)
3500 E Rosser Ave, Bismarck, ND 58501-
4004
Tel.: (701) 255-1234
Web Site:
    https://bismarck.iheartadvertising.com
Sales Range: $10-24.9 Million
Emp.: 30
Radio Broadcasting Stations
N.A.I.C.S.: 516110

**iHeartMedia + Entertainment, Inc. -
Boston, MA** (3)
1170 Soldiers Field Rd, Boston, MA 02134
Tel.: (781) 663-2500
Sales Range: $10-24.9 Million
Emp.: 85
Radio Broadcasting Stations
N.A.I.C.S.: 516110

**iHeartMedia + Entertainment, Inc. -
Cedar Rapids, IA** (3)
600 Old Marion Rd, Cedar Rapids, IA
52402-2152
Tel.: (319) 395-0530
Web Site:
    https://cedarrapids.iheartadvertising.com
Sales Range: $10-24.9 Million
Emp.: 20
Radio Broadcasting Stations
N.A.I.C.S.: 516110

**iHeartMedia + Entertainment, Inc. -
Charleston, SC** (3)
950 Houston Northcutt Blvd, Mount Pleas-
ant, SC 29464-3482
Tel.: (843) 856-6148
Web Site:
    https://charleston.iheartadvertising.com
Sales Range: $10-24.9 Million
Emp.: 40
Radio Broadcasting Stations
N.A.I.C.S.: 516110

**iHeartMedia + Entertainment, Inc. -
Chicago, IL** (3)
233 N Michigan Ave Ste 2800, Chicago, IL
60601-4504
Tel.: (312) 540-2000
Web Site:
    https://chicago.iheartadvertising.com
Sales Range: $75-99.9 Million
Emp.: 250
Radio Broadcasting Stations
N.A.I.C.S.: 516110

**iHeartMedia + Entertainment, Inc. -
Chillicothe, OH** (3)
45 W Main St, Chillicothe, OH 45601-3103
Tel.: (740) 773-3000
Web Site:
    https://chillicothe.iheartadvertising.com
Sales Range: $10-24.9 Million
Emp.: 9
Radio Broadcasting Stations
N.A.I.C.S.: 516110
Josh Koch (Sr VP-Sls)

Unit (Domestic):

WCHO Radio (4)
1535 N North St, Washington Court House,
OH 43160
Tel.: (740) 335-0941
Web Site: http://www.wchoam.com
Radio Broadcasting Stations
N.A.I.C.S.: 516110

Unit (Domestic):

**iHeartMedia + Entertainment, Inc. -
Cincinnati, OH** (3)
8044 Montgomery Rd Ste 650, Cincinnati,
OH 45236
Tel.: (513) 686-8300
Web Site:
    https://cincinnati.iheartadvertising.com
Sales Range: $25-49.9 Million
Emp.: 100
Radio Broadcasting Stations
N.A.I.C.S.: 516110

**iHeartMedia + Entertainment, Inc. -
Cleveland, OH** (3)
6200 Oak Tree Blvd 4th Fl, Independence,
OH 44131-2510
Tel.: (216) 520-2600
Web Site:
    https://cleveland.iheartadvertising.com
Sales Range: $25-49.9 Million
Emp.: 120
Radio Broadcasting Stations
N.A.I.C.S.: 516110

**iHeartMedia + Entertainment, Inc. -
Columbia, SC** (3)
316 Greystone Blvd, Columbia, SC 29210
Tel.: (803) 343-1100
Web Site:
    https://columbia.iheartadvertising.com
Sales Range: $25-49.9 Million
Emp.: 60
Radio Broadcasting Stations
N.A.I.C.S.: 516110
L. J. Smith (Sr VP-Programming)

**iHeartMedia + Entertainment, Inc. -
Columbus, GA** (3)
1501 13th Ave, Columbus, GA 31901
Tel.: (706) 576-3000
Web Site: https://columbus-
ga.iheartadvertising.com
Sales Range: $25-49.9 Million
Emp.: 150
Radio Broadcasting Stations
N.A.I.C.S.: 516110

Unit (Domestic):

**iHeartMedia + Entertainment, Inc. -
LaGrange-Newnan, GA** (4)
154 Boone Dr, Newnan, GA 30263
Tel.: (770) 683-7234
Web Site: http://www.iheartmedia.com
Sales Range: $10-24.9 Million
Emp.: 50
Radio Broadcasting Stations
N.A.I.C.S.: 516110

Unit (Domestic):

**iHeartMedia + Entertainment, Inc. -
Columbus, OH** (3)

iHeartMedia, Inc.—(Continued)

2323 W 5th Ave Ste 200, Columbus, OH 43204-7000
Tel.: (614) 486-6101
Web Site:
https://columbus.iheartadvertising.com
Sales Range: $25-49.9 Million
Emp.: 125
Radio Broadcasting Stations
N.A.I.C.S.: 516110

iHeartMedia + Entertainment, Inc. - Corpus Christi, TX (3)
501 Tupper Ln, Corpus Christi, TX 78417
Tel.: (361) 289-0111
Web Site:
https://corpuschristi.iheartadvertising.com
Sales Range: $25-49.9 Million
Emp.: 40
Radio Broadcasting Stations
N.A.I.C.S.: 516110

iHeartMedia + Entertainment, Inc. - Dallas, TX (3)
14001 Dallas Pkwy Ste 300, Dallas, TX 75240
Tel.: (214) 866-8000
Web Site:
https://dallas.iheartadvertising.com
Sales Range: $25-49.9 Million
Emp.: 100
Radio Broadcasting Stations
N.A.I.C.S.: 516110

iHeartMedia + Entertainment, Inc. - Dayton, OH (3)
101 Pine St, Dayton, OH 45402
Tel.: (937) 224-1137
Web Site:
https://dayton.iheartadvertising.com
Sales Range: $25-49.9 Million
Emp.: 40
Radio Broadcasting Stations
N.A.I.C.S.: 516110

iHeartMedia + Entertainment, Inc. - Denver, CO (3)
4695 S Monaco St, Denver, CO 80237-3403
Tel.: (303) 713-8000
Web Site:
https://denver.iheartadvertising.com
Sales Range: $100-124.9 Million
Emp.: 250
Radio Broadcasting Stations
N.A.I.C.S.: 516110
Tim Hager (Pres)

iHeartMedia + Entertainment, Inc. - Des Moines, IA (3)
2141 Grand Ave, Des Moines, IA 50312
Tel.: (515) 245-8900
Web Site:
https://desmoines.iheartadvertising.com
Sales Range: $25-49.9 Million
Emp.: 80
Radio Broadcasting Stations
N.A.I.C.S.: 516110

Unit (Domestic):

iHeartMedia + Entertainment, Inc. - Ames, IA (4)
415 Main St, Ames, IA 50010-6149
Tel.: (515) 232-1430
Web Site: http://www.1430kasi.iheart.com
Radio Broadcasting Stations
N.A.I.C.S.: 516110

Unit (Domestic):

iHeartMedia + Entertainment, Inc. - Detroit, MI (3)
27675 Halsted Rd, Farmington Hills, MI 48331
Tel.: (248) 324-5800
Web Site:
https://detroit.iheartadvertising.com
Sales Range: $10-24.9 Million
Emp.: 50
Radio Broadcasting Stations
N.A.I.C.S.: 516110

iHeartMedia + Entertainment, Inc. - Dickinson, ND (3)
11291 39th St SW, Dickinson, ND 58601
Tel.: (701) 483-1876
Web Site:
https://dickinson.iheartadvertising.com

Sales Range: $10-24.9 Million
Emp.: 5
Radio Broadcasting Stations
N.A.I.C.S.: 516110

iHeartMedia + Entertainment, Inc. - El Paso, TX (3)
4045 N Mesa St, El Paso, TX 79902
Tel.: (915) 351-5400
Web Site: http://www.clearchannel.com
Sales Range: $200-249.9 Million
Emp.: 30
Radio Broadcasting Stations
N.A.I.C.S.: 516110

iHeartMedia + Entertainment, Inc. - Fairbanks, AK (3)
546 9th Ave, Fairbanks, AK 99701-4902
Tel.: (907) 450-1000
Web Site:
https://fairbanks.iheartadvertising.com
Sales Range: $10-24.9 Million
Emp.: 25
Radio Broadcasting Stations
N.A.I.C.S.: 516110

iHeartMedia + Entertainment, Inc. - Farmington, NM (3)
200 E BRdway Avre, Farmington, NM 87401-6418
Tel.: (505) 325-1716
Web Site:
https://farmington.iheartadvertising.com
Sales Range: $10-24.9 Million
Emp.: 10
Radio Broadcasting Stations
N.A.I.C.S.: 516110

iHeartMedia + Entertainment, Inc. - Fayetteville, AR (3)
2049 E Joyce Blvd, Fayetteville, AR 72703-5002
Tel.: (479) 582-1079
Web Site:
https://fayetteville.iheartadvertising.com
Sales Range: $10-24.9 Million
Emp.: 37
Radio Broadcasting Stations
N.A.I.C.S.: 516110

iHeartMedia + Entertainment, Inc. - Florida Keys (Tavernier), FL (3)
93351 Overseas Hwy, Tavernier, FL 33070
Tel.: (305) 852-9085
Web Site: http://www.iheart.com
Radio Broadcasting Stations
N.A.I.C.S.: 516110

Unit (Domestic):

iHeartMedia + Entertainment, Inc. - Florida Keys (Key West), FL (4)
5450 MacDonald Ave, Key West, FL 33040-5000
Tel.: (305) 296-7511
Sales Range: $10-24.9 Million
Emp.: 7
Radio Broadcasting Stations
N.A.I.C.S.: 516110
Robert H. Holladay (Owner)

Unit (Domestic):

iHeartMedia + Entertainment, Inc. - Fort Myers, FL (3)
13320 Metro Pkwy, Fort Myers, FL 33966
Tel.: (239) 225-4300
Web Site: https://fortmyers-naples.iheartadvertising.com
Sales Range: $200-249.9 Million
Emp.: 50
Radio Broadcasting Stations
N.A.I.O.O.: 510110

Unit (Domestic):

iHeartMedia + Entertainment, Inc. - Punta Gorda, FL (4)
24100 Tiseo Blvd Unit 10, Port Charlotte, FL 33980
Tel.: (941) 206-1188
Web Site: http://www.iheartmedia.com
Sales Range: $10-24.9 Million
Emp.: 25
Radio Broadcasting Stations
N.A.I.C.S.: 516110

Unit (Domestic):

iHeartMedia + Entertainment, Inc. - Fort Smith, AR (3)

311 Lexington Ave, Fort Smith, AR 72901
Tel.: (479) 782-8888
Web Site:
https://fortsmith.iheartadvertising.com
Sales Range: $10-24.9 Million
Emp.: 18
Radio Broadcasting Stations
N.A.I.C.S.: 516110

iHeartMedia + Entertainment, Inc. - Gadsden, AL (3)
6510 Whorton Bend Rd, Gadsden, AL 35901-5213
Tel.: (256) 543-9229
Web Site: http://www.iheartmedia.com
Sales Range: $10-24.9 Million
Emp.: 3
Radio Broadcasting Stations
N.A.I.C.S.: 516110

iHeartMedia + Entertainment, Inc. - Grand Forks, ND (3)
505 University Ave, Grand Forks, ND 58203
Tel.: (701) 746-1417
Web Site:
https://grandforks.iheartadvertising.com
Sales Range: $10-24.9 Million
Emp.: 40
Radio Broadcasting Stations
N.A.I.C.S.: 516110

iHeartMedia + Entertainment, Inc. - Grand Rapids, MI (3)
77 Monroe Ctr St NW Ste 1000 10th Fl, Grand Rapids, MI 49503
Tel.: (616) 459-1919
Web Site: http://www.clearchannel.com
Sales Range: $10-24.9 Million
Emp.: 50
Radio Broadcasting Stations
N.A.I.C.S.: 516110
Tim Feagan (Gen Mgr & Office Mgr)

iHeartMedia + Entertainment, Inc. - Greenville, SC (3)
101 N Main St Ste 1000, Greenville, SC 29607
Tel.: (864) 242-1005
Web Site:
https://greenville.iheartadvertising.com
Radio Broadcasting Stations
N.A.I.C.S.: 516110

iHeartMedia + Entertainment, Inc. - Harrisburg, PA (3)
600 Corporate Cir, Harrisburg, PA 17110
Tel.: (717) 540-8800
Web Site:
https://harrisburg.iheartadvertising.com
Sales Range: $25-49.9 Million
Emp.: 30
Radio Broadcasting Stations
N.A.I.C.S.: 516110

iHeartMedia + Entertainment, Inc. - Hartford, CT (3)
10 Columbus Blvd Ste 10 1 Fl, Hartford, CT 06106-1976
Tel.: (860) 723-6000
Web Site:
https://hartford.iheartadvertising.com
Radio Broadcasting Stations
N.A.I.C.S.: 516110
Steve Honeycomb (Reg Pres-Market)
Vanessa Wojtusiak (VP-Mktg-Hartford & New Haven)

iHeartMedia + Entertainment, Inc. - Honolulu, HI (3)
650 Iwilei Rd Ste 400, Honolulu, HI 96817-5319
Tel.: (808) 550-9253
Web Site:
https://honolulu.iheartadvertising.com
Sales Range: $10-24.9 Million
Emp.: 50
Radio Broadcasting Stations
N.A.I.C.S.: 516110

iHeartMedia + Entertainment, Inc. - Houston, TX (3)
2000 W Loop S Ste 300, Houston, TX 77027
Tel.: (713) 212-8000
Web Site:
https://houston.iheartadvertising.com
Radio Broadcasting Stations
N.A.I.C.S.: 516110
Mark West (Gen Mgr-Sls)

iHeartMedia + Entertainment, Inc. - Huntsville, AL (3)
26869 Peoples Rd, Madison, AL 35756
Tel.: (256) 309-2400
Web Site:
https://huntsville.iheartadvertising.com
Sales Range: $10-24.9 Million
Emp.: 20
Radio Broadcasting Stations
N.A.I.C.S.: 516110
Carmelita Palmer (Pres-Market)

iHeartMedia + Entertainment, Inc. - Indianapolis, IN (3)
6161 Fall Creek Rd, Indianapolis, IN 46220
Tel.: (317) 257-7565
Web Site:
https://indianapolis.iheartadvertising.com
Sales Range: $10-24.9 Million
Emp.: 50
Radio Broadcasting Stations
N.A.I.C.S.: 516110

iHeartMedia + Entertainment, Inc. - Iowa City, IA (3)
1 Stephans Atkins Dr, Iowa City, IA 52240
Tel.: (319) 354-9500
Web Site: http://www.clearchannel.com
Sales Range: $10-24.9 Million
Emp.: 25
Radio Broadcasting Stations
N.A.I.C.S.: 516110

iHeartMedia + Entertainment, Inc. - Jackson, MS (3)
1375 Beasley Rd, Jackson, MS 39206
Tel.: (601) 982-1062
Web Site:
https://jackson.iheartadvertising.com
Sales Range: $10-24.9 Million
Emp.: 30
Radio Broadcasting Stations
N.A.I.C.S.: 516110

iHeartMedia + Entertainment, Inc. - Jacksonville, FL (3)
11700 Central Pkwy, Jacksonville, FL 32224-2600
Tel.: (904) 636-0507
Web Site:
https://jacksonville.iheartadvertising.com
Radio Broadcasting Stations
N.A.I.C.S.: 516110

iHeartMedia + Entertainment, Inc. - Lancaster, PA (3)
600 Corporate Cir Ste 100, Harrisburg, PA 17110
Tel.: (717) 540-8800
Web Site:
https://lancaster.iheartadvertising.com
Sales Range: $10-24.9 Million
Emp.: 20
Radio Broadcasting Stations
N.A.I.C.S.: 516110

iHeartMedia + Entertainment, Inc. - Lancaster/Antelope, CA (3)
352 E Ave K4, Lancaster, CA 93535-4505
Tel.: (661) 942-1121
Web Site: http://www.ktpifm.com
Radio Broadcasting Stations
N.A.I.C.S.: 516110

iHeartMedia + Entertainment, Inc. - Las Vegas, NV (3)
2880 Meade Ave Ste 250, Las Vegas, NV 89102
Tel.: (702) 238-7389
Web Site:
https://lasvegas.iheartadvertising.com
Sales Range: $10-24.9 Million
Emp.: 40
Radio Broadcasting Stations
N.A.I.C.S.: 516110

iHeartMedia + Entertainment, Inc. - Lexington, KY (3)
2601 Nicholasville Rd, Lexington, KY 40503
Tel.: (859) 422-1000
Web Site:
https://lexington.iheartadvertising.com
Sales Range: $25-49.9 Million
Emp.: 100
Radio Broadcasting Stations
N.A.I.C.S.: 516110

iHeartMedia + Entertainment, Inc. - Lima, OH (3)

667 Market St, Lima, OH 45801-4603
Tel.: (419) 223-2060
Web Site: https://lima.iheartadvertising.com
Sales Range: $10-24.9 Million
Emp.: 50
Radio Broadcasting Stations
N.A.I.C.S.: 516110

**iHeartMedia + Entertainment, Inc. -
Little Rock, AR** (3)
10800 Colonel Glenn Rd, Little Rock, AR
72204
Tel.: (501) 217-5000
Web Site:
https://littlerock.iheartadvertising.com
Sales Range: $25-49.9 Million
Emp.: 125
Radio Broadcasting Stations
N.A.I.C.S.: 516110

**iHeartMedia + Entertainment, Inc. -
Los Angeles, CA** (3)
3400 W Olive Ave Ste 550, Burbank, CA
91505
Tel.: (818) 559-2252
Web Site:
https://losangeles.iheartadvertising.com
Sales Range: $75-99.9 Million
Emp.: 300
Radio Broadcasting Stations
N.A.I.C.S.: 516110

**iHeartMedia + Entertainment, Inc. -
Louisville, KY** (3)
4000 Radio Dr Ste 1, Louisville, KY 40218
Tel.: (502) 479-2222
Web Site:
https://louisville.iheartadvertising.com
Radio Broadcasting Stations
N.A.I.C.S.: 516110
Karen Manley (Bus Mgr)

**iHeartMedia + Entertainment, Inc. -
Macon, GA** (3)
7080 Industrial Hwy, Macon, GA 31216
Tel.: (478) 781-1063
Web Site: http://www.clearchannel.com
Sales Range: $25-49.9 Million
Emp.: 90
Radio Broadcasting Stations
N.A.I.C.S.: 516110

**iHeartMedia + Entertainment, Inc. -
Madison, WI** (3)
2651 S Fish Hatchery Rd, Madison, WI
53711
Tel.: (608) 274-5450
Web Site:
https://madison.iheartadvertising.com
Radio Broadcasting Stations
N.A.I.C.S.: 516110
Drew Lauter (Pres)

**iHeartMedia + Entertainment, Inc. -
Marion, OH** (3)
1330 N Main St, Marion, OH 43302-1525
Tel.: (740) 383-1131
Web Site:
https://marion.iheartadvertising.com
Sales Range: $10-24.9 Million
Emp.: 12
Radio Broadcasting Stations
N.A.I.C.S.: 516110

**iHeartMedia + Entertainment, Inc. -
Memphis, TN** (3)
2650 Thousand Oaks Blvd Ste 4100, Memphis, TN 38118
Tel.: (901) 259-1300
Web Site: http://www.clearchannel.com
Sales Range: $200-249.9 Million
Radio Broadcasting Stations
N.A.I.C.S.: 516110

**iHeartMedia + Entertainment, Inc. -
Miami/Fort Lauderdale, FL** (3)
7601 Riviera Blvd, Miramar, FL 33023
Tel.: (954) 862-2000
Web Site:
https://miami.iheartadvertising.com
Sales Range: $75-99.9 Million
Emp.: 250
Radio Broadcasting Stations
N.A.I.C.S.: 516110

**iHeartMedia + Entertainment, Inc. -
Milwaukee, WI** (3)
12100 W Howard Ave, Milwaukee, WI
53228

Tel.: (414) 545-8900
Web Site:
https://milwaukee.iheartadvertising.com
Sales Range: $50-74.9 Million
Emp.: 165
Radio Broadcasting Stations
N.A.I.C.S.: 516110

**iHeartMedia + Entertainment, Inc. -
Minneapolis, MN** (3)
1600 Utica Ave S Ste 500, Minneapolis, MN
55416
Tel.: (952) 417-3000
Web Site:
https://minneapolis.iheartadvertising.com
Sales Range: $25-49.9 Million
Emp.: 200
Radio Broadcasting Stations
N.A.I.C.S.: 516110

**iHeartMedia + Entertainment, Inc. -
Minot, ND** (3)
1000 20th Ave SW, Minot, ND 58701
Tel.: (701) 582-4646
Web Site:
https://minot.iheartadvertising.com
Sales Range: $10-24.9 Million
Emp.: 20
Radio Broadcasting Stations
N.A.I.C.S.: 516110

**iHeartMedia + Entertainment, Inc. -
Mobile, AL** (3)
555 Broadcast Dr 3rd Fl, Mobile, AL 36606
Tel.: (251) 450-0100
Web Site:
https://mobile.iheartadvertising.com
Sales Range: $25-49.9 Million
Emp.: 100
Radio Broadcasting Stations
N.A.I.C.S.: 516110

Unit (Domestic):

**iHeartMedia + Entertainment, Inc. -
Pensacola, FL** (4)
6485 Pensacola Blvd, Pensacola, FL
32505-1701
Tel.: (850) 473-0400
Web Site: http://www.clearchannel.com
Sales Range: $10-24.9 Million
Emp.: 40
Radio Broadcasting Stations
N.A.I.C.S.: 516110

Unit (Domestic):

**iHeartMedia + Entertainment, Inc. -
Modesto/Stockton, CA** (3)
2121 Lancey Dr, Modesto, CA 95355
Tel.: (209) 551-1306
Web Site:
https://modesto.iheartadvertising.com
Sales Range: $10-24.9 Million
Emp.: 40
Radio Broadcasting Stations
N.A.I.C.S.: 516110

**iHeartMedia + Entertainment, Inc. -
Monterey, CA** (3)
903 N Main St, Salinas, CA 93906
Tel.: (831) 755-8181
Web Site:
https://monterey.iheartadvertising.com
Sales Range: $10-24.9 Million
Emp.: 65
Radio Broadcasting Stations
N.A.I.C.S.: 516110

**iHeartMedia + Entertainment, Inc. -
Montgomery, AL** (3)
203 Gunn Rd, Montgomery, AL 36117
Tel.: (334) 274-6423
Web Site:
https://montgomery.iheartadvertising.com
Sales Range: $10-24.9 Million
Emp.: 30
Radio Broadcasting Stations
N.A.I.C.S.: 516110

**iHeartMedia + Entertainment, Inc. -
Nashville, TN** (3)
55 Music Sq W, Nashville, TN 37203
Tel.: (615) 664-2400
Web Site:
https://nashville.iheartadvertising.com
Sales Range: $50-74.9 Million
Emp.: 60
Radio Broadcasting Stations

N.A.I.C.S.: 516110

**iHeartMedia + Entertainment, Inc. -
Nassau/Suffolk, NY** (3)
66 Colonial Dr, Patchogue, NY 11772-5849
Tel.: (631) 475-5200
Web Site: http://www.walkradio.com
Radio Broadcasting Stations
N.A.I.C.S.: 516110

**iHeartMedia + Entertainment, Inc. -
New Orleans, LA** (3)
929 Howard Ave, New Orleans, LA 70113
Tel.: (504) 679-7300
Web Site: http://www.clearchannel.com
Sales Range: $10-24.9 Million
Emp.: 60
Radio Broadcasting Stations
N.A.I.C.S.: 516110
Steve Mcnair (Pres)

**iHeartMedia + Entertainment, Inc. -
New York City, NY** (3)
125 W 55th St, New York, NY 10019
Tel.: (212) 377-7900
Web Site: https://nyc.iheartadvertising.com
Sales Range: $25-49.9 Million
Emp.: 250
Radio Broadcasting Stations
N.A.I.C.S.: 516110
Tom Poleman (Philadelphia & Miami & Mgr-Ops)
Angel Aristone (Exec VP-Comm)

**iHeartMedia + Entertainment, Inc. -
Norfolk, VA** (3)
1003 Norfolk Sq, Norfolk, VA 23502
Tel.: (757) 466-0009
Web Site: http://www.iheartmedia.com
Sales Range: $10-24.9 Million
Emp.: 25
Radio Broadcasting Stations
N.A.I.C.S.: 516110

**iHeartMedia + Entertainment, Inc. -
Omaha, NE** (3)
5010 Underwood Ave, Omaha, NE 68132
Tel.: (402) 561-2000
Web Site:
https://omaha.iheartadvertising.com
Sales Range: $10-24.9 Million
Emp.: 50
Radio Broadcasting Stations
N.A.I.C.S.: 516110
Taylor Walet (Pres-Mktg)

**iHeartMedia + Entertainment, Inc. -
Orlando, FL** (3)
2500 Maitland Center Pkwy Ste 401, Orlando, FL 32751
Tel.: (407) 916-7800
Web Site:
https://orlando.iheartadvertising.com
Radio Broadcasting Stations
N.A.I.C.S.: 516110
Pam Volkman (Natl Specialist)

**iHeartMedia + Entertainment, Inc. -
Panama City, FL** (3)
1834 Lisenby Ave, Panama City, FL 32405
Tel.: (850) 769-1408
Web Site:
https://panamacity.iheartadvertising.com
Sales Range: $10-24.9 Million
Emp.: 20
Radio Broadcasting Stations
N.A.I.C.S.: 516110

**iHeartMedia + Entertainment, Inc. -
Parkersburg, WV** (3)
6006 Grand Central Ave, Vienna, WV
26105
Tel.: (304) 295-6070
Web Site: http://www.iheartmedia.com
Sales Range: $10-24.9 Million
Emp.: 15
Radio Broadcasting Stations
N.A.I.C.S.: 516110

**iHeartMedia + Entertainment, Inc. -
Philadelphia, PA** (3)
111 Presidential Blvd Ste 100, Philadelphia,
PA 19004
Tel.: (610) 784-3333
Web Site:
https://philadelphia.iheartadvertising.com
Sales Range: $50-74.9 Million
Emp.: 200
Radio Broadcasting Stations

N.A.I.C.S.: 516110
Jeff Moore (Sr VP-Sls)

**iHeartMedia + Entertainment, Inc. -
Phoenix, AZ** (3)
4686 E Van Buren St Ste 400, Phoenix, AZ
85008
Tel.: (602) 374-6000
Web Site:
https://phoenix.iheartadvertising.com
Sales Range: $50-74.9 Million
Emp.: 180
Radio Broadcasting Stations
N.A.I.C.S.: 516110
Linda Little (Pres)

**iHeartMedia + Entertainment, Inc. -
Pittsburgh, PA** (3)
44 Abele Rd Ste 102, Bridgeville, PA 15017
Tel.: (412) 937-1441
Web Site:
https://pittsburgh.iheartadvertising.com
Sales Range: $25-49.9 Million
Emp.: 100
Radio Broadcasting Stations
N.A.I.C.S.: 516110
Tracey Baumgard (Pres-Huntington)

**iHeartMedia + Entertainment, Inc. -
Portland, OR** (3)
13333 SW 68th Pkwy Ste 310, Tigard, OR
97223
Tel.: (503) 323-6400
Web Site:
https://portland.iheartadvertising.com
Sales Range: $25-49.9 Million
Emp.: 75
Radio Broadcasting Stations
N.A.I.C.S.: 516110

**iHeartMedia + Entertainment, Inc. -
Portsmouth, NH** (3)
815 Lafayette Rd, Portsmouth, NH 03801
Tel.: (603) 436-7300
Web Site:
https://portsmouth.iheartadvertising.com
Sales Range: $10-24.9 Million
Emp.: 60
Radio Broadcasting Stations
N.A.I.C.S.: 516110

**iHeartMedia + Entertainment, Inc. -
Raleigh, NC** (3)
3100 Smoketree Ct Ste 700, Raleigh, NC
27604
Tel.: (919) 878-1500
Web Site:
https://raleigh.iheartadvertising.com
Sales Range: $10-24.9 Million
Emp.: 50
Radio Broadcasting Stations
N.A.I.C.S.: 516110

**iHeartMedia + Entertainment, Inc. -
Richmond, VA** (3)
3245 Basie Rd, Richmond, VA 23228
Tel.: (804) 474-0000
Web Site:
http://www.clearchannelrichmond.com
Sales Range: $25-49.9 Million
Emp.: 130
Radio Broadcasting Stations
N.A.I.C.S.: 516110
Amy Kusmin (Dir-HR)
Stacey Trexler (Gen Mgr-Sls-WBTJ-FM &
WRVQ-FM)
Dave Carwile (Pres)

**iHeartMedia + Entertainment, Inc. -
Riverside/San Bernardino, CA** (3)
2030 Iowa Ave Ste 100, Riverside, CA
92507
Tel.: (909) 684-1991
Web Site:
https://riverside.iheartadvertising.com
Sales Range: $25-49.9 Million
Emp.: 80
Radio Broadcasting Stations
N.A.I.C.S.: 516110

**iHeartMedia + Entertainment, Inc. -
Rochester, MN** (3)
1530 Greenview Dr SW Ste 200, Rochester, MN 55902
Tel.: (507) 288-3888
Web Site: https://rochester-
mn.iheartadvertising.com
Sales Range: $10-24.9 Million
Emp.: 17
Radio Broadcasting Stations

iHeartMedia, Inc.—(Continued)
N.A.I.C.S.: 516110

**iHeartMedia + Entertainment, Inc. -
Rochester, NY** **(3)**
100 Chestnut St, Rochester, NY 14604
Tel.: (585) 454-4884
Web Site:
https://rochester.iheartadvertising.com
Sales Range: $25-49.9 Million
Emp.: 100
Radio Broadcasting Stations
N.A.I.C.S.: 516110

**iHeartMedia + Entertainment, Inc. -
Sacramento, CA**
1545 River Park Dr, Sacramento, CA 95815
Tel.: (916) 929-5325
Web Site:
https://sacramento.iheartadvertising.com
Sales Range: $10-24.9 Million
Emp.: 60
Radio Broadcasting Stations
N.A.I.C.S.: 516110
Bill White *(Program Dir)*

**iHeartMedia + Entertainment, Inc. -
Saint Louis, MO** **(3)**
1001 Highlands Plz Dr W Ste 200, Saint
Louis, MO 63110
Tel.: (314) 333-8000
Web Site:
https://stlouis.iheartadvertising.com
Sales Range: $25-49.9 Million
Emp.: 100
Radio Broadcasting Stations
N.A.I.C.S.: 516110
Derrick Michael *(Pres)*

**iHeartMedia + Entertainment, Inc. -
Salisbury/Ocean City, MD**
351 Tilghman Rd, Salisbury, MD 21804-
1920
Tel.: (410) 742-1923
Web Site:
https://salisbury.iheartadvertising.com
Sales Range: $25-49.9 Million
Emp.: 25
Radio Broadcasting Stations
N.A.I.C.S.: 516110

**iHeartMedia + Entertainment, Inc. -
Salt Lake City, UT** **(3)**
2801 S Decker Lake Dr, Salt Lake City, UT
84119
Tel.: (801) 908-1300
Web Site:
https://saltlakecity.iheartadvertising.com
Sales Range: $25-49.9 Million
Emp.: 80
Radio Broadcasting Stations
N.A.I.C.S.: 516110

**iHeartMedia + Entertainment, Inc. -
San Antonio, TX** **(3)**
6222 NW Interstate 10, San Antonio, TX
78201
Tel.: (210) 736-9700
Web Site:
https://sanantonio.iheartadvertising.com
Sales Range: $25-49.9 Million
Emp.: 110
Radio Broadcasting Stations
N.A.I.C.S.: 516110

**iHeartMedia + Entertainment, Inc. -
San Diego, CA** **(3)**
9660 Granite Ridge Dr, San Diego, CA
92123-2688
Tel.: (858) 292-2000
Web Site:
https://sandiego.iheartadvertising.com
Sales Range: $25-49.9 Million
Emp.: 125
Radio Broadcasting Stations
N.A.I.C.S.: 516110
Debbie Wagner *(Pres & Gen Mgr)*

**iHeartMedia + Entertainment, Inc. -
San Francisco, CA** **(3)**
340 Townsend St, San Francisco, CA
94107
Tel.: (415) 975-5555
Web Site:
https://sanfrancisco.iheartadvertising.com
Radio Broadcasting Stations
N.A.I.C.S.: 516110

Unit (Domestic):

**iHeartMedia + Entertainment, Inc. -
San Jose, CA** **(4)**
1420 Koll Cir, San Jose, CA 95112
Tel.: (408) 453-5400
Web Site: http://bolly923fm.com
Radio Broadcasting Stations
N.A.I.C.S.: 516110

Unit (Domestic):

**iHeartMedia + Entertainment, Inc. -
Sarasota, FL** **(3)**
1779 Independence Blvd, Sarasota, FL
34234
Tel.: (941) 552-4800
Web Site:
https://sarasota.iheartadvertising.com
Sales Range: $10-24.9 Million
Emp.: 30
Radio Broadcasting Stations
N.A.I.C.S.: 516110

**iHeartMedia + Entertainment, Inc. -
Savannah, GA** **(3)**
245 Alfred St, Savannah, GA 31408-3205
Tel.: (912) 964-7794
Web Site:
https://savannah.iheartadvertising.com
Radio Broadcasting Stations
N.A.I.C.S.: 516110

**iHeartMedia + Entertainment, Inc. -
Seattle, WA** **(3)**
645 Elliot Ave W Ste 400, Seattle, WA
98119
Tel.: (206) 494-2000
Web Site:
https://seattle.iheartadvertising.com
Sales Range: $25-49.9 Million
Emp.: 100
Radio Broadcasting Stations
N.A.I.C.S.: 516110

**iHeartMedia + Entertainment, Inc. -
Spokane, WA** **(3)**
808 E Sprague, Spokane, WA 99202
Tel.: (509) 242-2400
Web Site:
https://spokane.iheartadvertising.com
Emp.: 40
Radio Broadcasting Stations
N.A.I.C.S.: 516110

**iHeartMedia + Entertainment, Inc. -
Springfield, MA** **(3)**
1331 Main St, Springfield, MA 01103
Tel.: (413) 781-1011
Web Site:
https://springfield.iheartadvertising.com
Sales Range: $200-240.0 Million
Emp.: 16
Radio Broadcasting Stations
N.A.I.C.S.: 516110

**iHeartMedia + Entertainment, Inc. -
Sussex, NJ** **(3)**
45 Mitchell Ave, Franklin, NJ 07416
Tel.: (973) 827-2525
Web Site:
https://sussex.iheartadvertising.com
Radio Broadcasting Stations
N.A.I.C.S.: 516110

**iHeartMedia + Entertainment, Inc. -
Syracuse, NY** **(3)**
500 Plum St Ste 400, Syracuse, NY 13204-
0000
Tel.: (315) 472-9797
Web Site:
https://syracuse.iheartadvertising.com
Sales Range: $25-49.9 Million
Emp.: 60
Radio Broadcasting Stations
N.A.I.C.S.: 516110

**iHeartMedia + Entertainment, Inc. -
Tallahassee, FL** **(3)**
325 John Knox Rd Bldg G, Tallahassee, FL
32303
Tel.: (850) 422-3107
Sales Range: $10-24.9 Million
Emp.: 25
Radio Broadcasting Stations
N.A.I.C.S.: 516110
Christina Lynch *(Bus Mgr)*
John Lund *(Mgr-Ops)*

**iHeartMedia + Entertainment, Inc. -
Tampa, FL** **(3)**
4002 Gandy Blvd, Tampa, FL 33611
Tel.: (813) 832-1000
Web Site:
https://tampa.iheartadvertising.com
Sales Range: $50-74.9 Million
Emp.: 175
Radio Broadcasting Stations
N.A.I.C.S.: 516110

**iHeartMedia + Entertainment, Inc. -
Toledo, OH** **(3)**
125 S Superior St, Toledo, OH 43602
Tel.: (419) 244-8321
Web Site:
https://toledo.iheartadvertising.com
Sales Range: $25-49.9 Million
Emp.: 70
Radio Broadcasting Stations
N.A.I.C.S.: 516110

**iHeartMedia + Entertainment, Inc. -
Tucson, AZ** **(3)**
3202 N Oracle Rd, Tucson, AZ 85705
Tel.: (520) 618-2100
Web Site:
https://tucson.iheartadvertising.com
Sales Range: $25-49.9 Million
Emp.: 40
Radio Broadcasting Stations
N.A.I.C.S.: 516110
Mike Saffer *(Pres-Market)*

Branch (Domestic):

**iHeartMedia + Entertainment, Inc. -
Tulsa Corporate Office** **(3)**
7136 S Yale Ave Ste 500, Tulsa, OK 74136
Tel.: (918) 388-5100
Web Site: https://tulsa.iheartadvertising.com
Sales Range: $250-299.9 Million
Emp.: 10
Radio Broadcasting Regional Corporate
Office
N.A.I.C.S.: 551114
Steve Davis *(Sr VP-Engrg)*

Unit (Domestic):

**iHeartMedia + Entertainment, Inc. -
Tulsa, OK** **(3)**
2625 S Memorial Dr, Tulsa, OK 74129
Tel.: (918) 388-5100
Web Site: http://www.iheartmedia.com
Sales Range: $200-249.9 Million
Emp.: 50
Radio Broadcasting Stations
N.A.I.C.S.: 516110

**iHeartMedia + Entertainment, Inc. -
Tupelo, MS** **(3)**
5028 Cliff Gookin Blvd, Tupelo, MS 39531
Tel.: (662) 842-1067
Web Site:
https://tupelo.iheartadvertising.com
Emp.: 29
Radio Broadcasting Stations
N.A.I.C.S.: 516110

**iHeartMedia + Entertainment, Inc. -
Waco, TX** **(3)**
314 W State Hwy 6, Waco, TX 76712
Tel.: (254) 776-3900
Web Site: https://waco.iheartadvertising.com
Sales Range: $10-24.9 Million
Emp.: 35
Radio Broadcasting Stations
N.A.I.C.S.: 516110

**iHeartMedia + Entertainment, Inc. -
Washington, DC** **(3)**
1801 Rockville Pike, Rockville, MD 20852
Tel.: (240) 747-2700
Web Site: https://dc.iheartadvertising.com
Sales Range: $25-49.9 Million
Emp.: 110
Radio Broadcasting Stations
N.A.I.C.S.: 516110

Unit (Domestic):

**iHeartMedia + Entertainment, Inc. -
Baltimore, MD** **(4)**
711 W 40th St, Baltimore, MD 21211
Tel.: (240) 747-2700
Web Site:
https://baltimore.iheartadvertising.com

Sales Range: $10-24.9 Million
Emp.: 30
Radio Broadcasting Stations
N.A.I.C.S.: 516110

Unit (Domestic):

**iHeartMedia + Entertainment, Inc. -
West Palm Beach, FL** **(3)**
3071 Continental Dr, West Palm Beach, FL
33407
Tel.: (561) 616-6600
Web Site:
https://westpalmbeach.iheartadverti
sing.com
Sales Range: $25-49.9 Million
Emp.: 180
Radio Broadcasting Stations
N.A.I.C.S.: 516110

**iHeartMedia + Entertainment, Inc. -
Wichita, KS** **(3)**
9323 E 37th St N, Wichita, KS 67226
Tel.: (316) 494-6600
Web Site:
https://wichita.iheartadvertising.com
Sales Range: $10-24.9 Million
Emp.: 35
Radio Broadcasting Stations
N.A.I.C.S.: 516110

**iHeartMedia + Entertainment, Inc. -
Williamsport, PA** **(3)**
1559 W 4th St, Williamsport, PA 17701
Tel.: (570) 327-1400
Web Site:
https://williamsport.iheartadvertising.com
Sales Range: $10-24.9 Million
Emp.: 20
Radio Broadcasting Stations
N.A.I.C.S.: 516110

**iHeartMedia + Entertainment, Inc. -
Wilmington, DE** **(3)**
920 W Basin Rd Ste 400, New Castle, DE
19720
Tel.: (302) 395-9800
Web Site:
https://wilmington.iheartadvertising.com
Sales Range: $10-24.9 Million
Emp.: 40
Radio Broadcasting Stations
N.A.I.C.S.: 516110

**iHeartMedia + Entertainment, Inc. -
Youngstown, OH** **(3)**
7461 S Ave, Youngstown, OH 44512
Tel.: (330) 729-2500
Web Site:
https://youngstown.iheartadvertising.com
Sales Range: $10-24.9 Million
Emp.: 60
Radio Broadcasting Stations
N.A.I.C.S.: 516110

IIOT-OXYS, INC.
705 Cambridge St, Cambridge, MA
02141
Tel.: (401) 307-3092 **NV**
Web Site: https://www.oxyscorp.com
Year Founded: 2003
ITOX—(OTCIQ)
Rev.: $114,666
Assets: $207,495
Liabilities: $2,830,759
Net Worth: ($2,623,264)
Earnings: ($1,067,929)
Emp.: 2
Fiscal Year-end: 12/31/23
Edge Computing Systems Services
N.A.I.C.S.: 513199
Clifford L. Emmons *(Pres, CEO &
Interim CFO)*
Karen McNemar *(COO)*

IJJ CORP.
1325 Cavendish Dr Ste 201, Silver
Spring, MD 20905-7033
Tel.: (301) 202-7762 **WY**
Web Site: https://www.ijjc.com
Year Founded: 2003
IJJP—(OTCIQ)
Sales Range: Less than $1 Million
Emp.: 4

Business & Management Consulting
Services
N.A.I.C.S.: 541611
Clifford Pope (Founder, Chm, Pres,
CEO, Treas & Sec)
Oscar O. Lawson II (COO & Exec
VP)

IKENA ONCOLOGY, INC.

645 Summer St Ste 101, Boston, MA
02210
Tel.: (857) 273-8343   DE
Web Site:
https://www.ikenaoncology.com
Year Founded: 2006
IKNA—(NASDAQ)
Rev.: $15,618,000
Assets: $172,259,000
Liabilities: $25,290,000
Net Worth: $146,969,000
Earnings: ($68,765,000)
Emp.: 80
Fiscal Year-end: 12/31/22
Biotechnology Research & Develop-
ment Services
N.A.I.C.S.: 541714
Owen Patrick Hughes Jr. (Chm)
Mark Manfredi (Pres & CEO)
Jeffrey Ecsedy (Chief Dev Officer)
Maude Tessier (Chief Bus Officer)
Alexander Constan (Sr VP-Non Clini-
cal Safety & DMPK)
Michelle Zhang (Chief Scientific Offi-
cer)
Karen McGovern (VP-Early Discov-
ery)
James Nolan (VP-Therapeutics Dev
& Mfr)
Francisco Oliveira (Interim Principal
Acctg Officer & VP-Fin)
Caroline Germa (Chief Medical Offi-
cer)
Jotin Marango (CFO, COO & Head-
Corp Dev)

ILEARNINGENGINES, INC.

6701 Democracy Blvd Ste 300,
Bethesda, MD 20817
Tel.: (310) 566-5966   DE
Web Site:
https://ilearningengines.com
Year Founded: 2020
AILE—(NASDAQ)
Assets: $47,004,462
Liabilities: $71,489,142
Net Worth: ($24,484,680)
Earnings: ($5,848,628)
Emp.: 2
Fiscal Year-end: 12/31/23
Investment Services
N.A.I.C.S.: 523999
Matthew Safaii (Chm & CEO)
Thomas Olivier (Pres, Mng Dir, Head-
Entertainment Transformation Divi-
sion & Dir-Rep)
Priya Pinto (Asst VP-Marketing)
Ratish Nair (Asst VP-Sales & Busi-
ness Development)
A. P. Balakrishnan (Pres & Chief Bus
Officer)
Farhan Naqvi (CFO & Head)
David Samuels (Chief Legal Officer,
Sec & Exec VP)
Harish Chidambaran (CEO)
Sanjeev Menon (Chief Architect-AI)
Ram Parameswaran (Sr VP-
Technology & Products)
Shan Wang (VP-Customer Success
& Architectures)
Roger Duffield (Gen Mgr-Risk Man-
agement)
Vivek Chary (VP-Consulting & Bus
Ops)

Subsidiaries:

iLearningEngines Holdings, Inc. (1)

6701 Democracy Blvd, Bethesda, MD
20817
Tel.: (240) 812-1734
Web Site: https://ilearningengines.com
Emp.: 100
Software Publisher
N.A.I.C.S.: 518210
Bala Krishnan (Pres & Chief Bus Officer)
Harish Chidambaran (CEO)

Subsidiary (Domestic):

in2vate, llc. (2)
321 S Boston Aveste 900, Tulsa, OK 74103
Tel.: (918) 582-5262
Sales Range: $1-9.9 Million
Emp.: 14
Labor Unions & Similar Labor Organizations
N.A.I.C.S.: 813930
Patricia Neal (CFO)
Roger Duffield (Pres)

ILLINOIS COMMUNITY BAN-CORP, INC.

301 N Main St, Chatham, IL 62629
Tel.: (217) 374-7127   IL
ILCM—(OTCIQ)
Bank Holding Company
N.A.I.C.S.: 551111
Robert Narmont (CEO)

ILLINOIS TOOL WORKS INC.

155 Harlem Ave, Glenview, IL 60025
Tel.: (224) 661-8870   DE
Web Site: https://www.itw.com
Year Founded: 1912
ITW—(NYSE)
Rev.: $16,107,000,000
Assets: $15,518,000,000
Liabilities: $12,505,000,000
Net Worth: $3,013,000,000
Earnings: $2,957,000,000
Emp.: 45,000
Fiscal Year-end: 12/31/23
Fasteners, Components, Equipment,
Consumable Systems, Specialty
Products & Equipment Mfr
N.A.I.C.S.: 333998
Mary K. Lawler (Chief HR Officer &
Sr VP)
Axel R. J. Beck (Exec VP)
T. Kenneth Escoe (Exec VP)
Sharon A. Szafranski (Exec VP)
Xavier Gracia (Exec VP)
Patricia A. Hartzell (Exec VP)
Jennifer Schott (Sec, Sr VP & Gen
Counsel)
Michael M. Larsen (CFO & Sr VP)
Christopher A. O'Herlihy (Pres &
CEO)

Subsidiaries:

ACCU-LUBE Manufacturing
GmbH (1)
Glaitstr 29, 75433, Maulbronn, Germany
Tel.: (49) 70435612
Web Site: https://www.accu-lube.com
Industrial Equipment Whsr
N.A.I.C.S.: 423830

Accessories Marketing, Inc. (1)
125 Venture Dr Ste 210, San Luis Obispo,
CA 93401
Tel.: (805) 489-0490
Web Site: https://www.slime.com
Sales Range: $25-49.9 Million
Emp.: 60
Tire Product & Inner Tube Mfr
N.A.I.C.S.: 325199

Allen Coding GmbH (1)
Friedrich-Bergius-Ring 30, 97076,
Wurzburg, Germany
Tel.: (49) 931250760
Web Site: https://www.diagraph.de
Emp.: 50
Industrial Machinery Whsr
N.A.I.C.S.: 423830
Juan Lopez (Gen Mgr)

Allen France SAS (1)
11 Rue Marie de Lorraine, 37700, La Ville-
aux-Dames, France

Tel.: (33) 247304121
Web Site: https://www.allenfrance.com
Machine Tools Mfr
N.A.I.C.S.: 333517

Alpine Automation Limited (1)
Threemilestone Industrial Estate, Truro,
TR4 9LD, Cornwall, United Kingdom
Tel.: (44) 1872245450
Compressor Product Distr
N.A.I.C.S.: 423830

Alpine Systems Corporation (1)
1701 Creditstone Rd, Concord, L4K 5V6,
ON, Canada
Tel.: (905) 417-2766
Web Site: http://www.alpineitw.com
Industrial Machinery Whslr
N.A.I.C.S.: 423830

American Safety Technologies (1)
565 Eagle Rock Ave, Roseland, NJ 07068
Tel.: (973) 403-2600
Sales Range: $10-24.9 Million
Emp.: 50
Non-Slip Stair Treads & Non-Slip Floor
Coatings
N.A.I.C.S.: 326199

Anaerobicos Srl (1)
Calle 117 No 6274, Loma Hermosa,
B1655CTB, San Martin, Buenos Aires, Ar-
gentina
Web Site: https://www.anaerobicos.com
Emp.: 20
Basic Organic Chemical Mfr
N.A.I.C.S.: 325199

Anahol S.A. (1)
Calle 108 0, San Luis, 5700, Argentina
Tel.: (54) 2664426707
Emp.: 9
Industrial Equipment Mfr
N.A.I.C.S.: 332510

AppliChem GmbH (1)
Ottoweg 4, 64291, Darmstadt, Germany
Tel.: (49) 615193570
Web Site: http://www.applichem.com
Sales Range: $10-24.9 Million
Chemical Products Mfr
N.A.I.C.S.: 325998

AppliChem, Inc. (1)
3211 Nebraska Ave Ste 300, Council Bluffs,
IA 51501
Tel.: (402) 731-9300
Web Site: https://forzabuilt.com
Adhesive Product Mfr
N.A.I.C.S.: 325520

Archem Quimica Ltda (1)
Av Julio Victorello 765 Distrito Industrial V,
PO Box 365, 13609-586, Araras, Sao
Paulo, Brazil
Tel.: (55) 1935435000
Web Site: http://www.archem.com.br
Chemical Products Mfr
N.A.I.C.S.: 325199

Arylux Hungary Elektromechanikus
Alkatreszgyarto Kft (1)
Zichy Jeno utca 4, Budapest, 1066, Hun-
gary
Tel.: (36) 37570034
Emp.: 45
Industrial Equipment Mfr
N.A.I.C.S.: 333310

Avery Berkel France SAS (1)
Campus Saint Christophe 10 Avenue de l
Entreprise, 95800, Cergy, France
Tel.: (33) 825870800
Web Site: https://www.averyberkel.com
Weighing Equipment Maintenance Services
N.A.I.C.S.: 811310

Avery India Limited (1)
Plot Nos 50-59 Sector 25, Ballabgarh,
121004, Haryana, India
Tel.: (91) 1294094400
Web Site: https://www.averyweigh-
tronix.com
Machine Tool & Industrial Machinery Mfr
N.A.I.C.S.: 333517

Avery Malaysia Sdn Bhd (1)
No 12-i Jalan Tandang, 46050, Petaling
Jaya, Selangor, Malaysia
Tel.: (60) 37 781 4344

Web Site: https://www.averyweigh-
tronix.com
Machine Tool & Industrial Machinery Mfr
N.A.I.C.S.: 333517

Avery Weigh-Tronix (Suzhou) Weigh-
ing Technology Co. Ltd. (1)
G2 Export processing Zone B No 288
Shengpu Road, Suzhou, China
Tel.: (86) 5128 885 9930
Web Site: http://www.averyweigh-tronix.com
Machine Tool & Industrial Machinery Mfr
N.A.I.C.S.: 333517

Avery Weigh-Tronix Holdings
Limited (1)
Foundry Lane, Smethwick, B66 2LP, West
Midlands, United Kingdom
Tel.: (44) 8453070314
Web Site: http://www.averyweigh-tronix.com
Holding Company
N.A.I.C.S.: 551112

Avery Weigh-Tronix International
Limited (1)
Foundry Lane, Thamebridge, Smethwick,
B66 2LP, West Midlands, United Kingdom
Tel.: (44) 845 307 0314
Web Site: https://www.averyweigh-
tronix.com
General Purpose Machinery Mfr
N.A.I.C.S.: 333998

Avery Weigh-Tronix UK Limited (1)
Foundry Lane, Smethwick, B66 2LP, West
Midlands, United Kingdom
Tel.: (44) 8453070314
Web Site: http://www.averyweigh-tronix.com
Emp.: 100
Weighing Equipment Mfr
N.A.I.C.S.: 333310

Avery Weigh-Tronix, Inc. (1)
1000 Armstrong Dr, Fairmont, MN 56031-
1439
Tel.: (507) 238-4461
Web Site: http://www.averyweigh-tronix.com
Sales Range: $200-249.9 Million
Emp.: 400
Industrial & Retail Weighing Systems Mfr
N.A.I.C.S.: 333998
Ross Hunwardsen (CEO)

Avery Weigh-Tronix, LLC (1)
1000 Armstrong Dr, Fairmont, MN 56031-
1439
Tel.: (507) 238-4461
Web Site: https://www.averyweigh-
tronix.com
Industrial Product & Weighing System Mfr
N.A.I.C.S.: 333993

Bangalore Integrated System Solu-
tions Private Ltd (1)
No 497E 14th Cross 4th Phase Peenya In-
dustrial Area, Bengaluru, 560058, Karna-
taka, India
Tel.: (91) 8028360184
Web Site: https://www.biss.in
Machine Tools Mfr
N.A.I.C.S.: 333517

Bates Cargo-Pak ApS (1)
Stigsborgvej 36, 9400, Norresundby, Den-
mark
Tel.: (45) 96328800
Web Site: https://www.bates-cargopak.com
Emp.: 50
Air & Paper Bag Mfr
N.A.I.C.S.: 322220

Bayshore Truck Equipment
Company (1)
1379 San Mateo Ave, South San Francisco,
CA 94080
Tel.: (650) 871-9193
Web Site: http://www.bayshoretruck.com
General Purpose Machinery Mfr
N.A.I.C.S.: 333998

Berkel (Ireland) Limited (1)
Unit L11 Greenogue Business Park,
Rathcoole, Dublin, Ireland
Tel.: (353) 14580036
Web Site: https://www.averyberkel.com
Weighing & Food Equipment Distr
N.A.I.C.S.: 423610

Bernard Welding (1)

Illinois Tool Works Inc.—(Continued)

449 W Corning Rd, Beecher, IL
60401-3127   **(100%)**
Tel.: (708) 946-2281
Web Site: http://www.bernardwelds.com
Sales Range: $50-74.9 Million
Emp.: 115
MIG Welding Guns, Consumables & Electrode Holders Mfr
N.A.I.C.S.: 333992

Binks   (1)
Anchor Brook Industrial Estate, Lockside
Aldridge, Walsall, WS9 8EG, West Midlands, United Kingdom
Tel.: (44) 1922423700
General Purpose Machinery Mfr
N.A.I.C.S.: 333998

Brapenta Eletronica Ltda.   (1)
Rua Padre Leonardo 504 Jardim Aeroporto,
Sao Paulo, 04753 001, Brazil
Tel.: (55) 1131232850
Web Site: http://www.brapenta.com
Industrial Machinery Whslr
N.A.I.C.S.: 423830

Brooks Instrument B.V.   (1)
Einsteinstraat 57, 3902 HN, Veenendaal,
Netherlands
Tel.: (31) 318549300
Web Site: http://www.brooksinstrument.com
Industrial Equipment Mfr
N.A.I.C.S.: 332510
Remco Wever (Mng Dir & Mgr-Global Bus Unit)

Brooks Instrument GmbH   (1)
Zur Wetterwarte 50 Gebaude 337/B, 01109,
Dresden, Germany
Tel.: (49) 3512152040
Web Site: http://www.brooksinstrument.com
Industrial Machinery Whslr
N.A.I.C.S.: 423830

Brooks Instrument India Private Limited   (1)
320 Prabhadevi Industrial Estate 408 Veer
Savarkar Marg, Near Siddhivinayak Temple
Pradhadevi, Mumbai, 400025, Maharashtra,
India
Tel.: (91) 9833511600
Machine Tools Mfr
N.A.I.C.S.: 333517

Brooks Instrument KFT   (1)
Berenyi Ut 72-100, 8000, Szekesfehervar,
Hungary
Tel.: (36) 22539600
Web Site: http://www.brooksinstrument.com
Emp.: 130
Industrial Machinery Whslr
N.A.I.C.S.: 423830

Brooks Instrument Korea, Ltd.   (1)
D-806 Bundang Techno Park 700 Pangyoro, Bundang-gu, Seongnam, 13516,
Gyeonggi-do, Korea (South)
Tel.: (82) 317082521
Web Site: http://www.brooksinstrument.com
Industrial Equipment Mfr
N.A.I.C.S.: 332510

Brooks Instrument Singapore Pte, Ltd.   (1)
61 Ubi Ave 1 UB Point 06-01, Singapore,
408941, Singapore
Tel.: (65) 98245228
Machine Tools Mfr
N.A.I.C.S.: 333517

Brooks Instrument, LLC   (1)
407 W Vine St, Hatfield, PA 19440-0903
Tel.: (215) 362-3500
Web Site: http://www.brooksinstrument.com
Sales Range: $200-249.9 Million
Flow & Level Measurement Control Equipment Mfr
N.A.I.C.S.: 334519

Subsidiary (Non-US):

Brooks Instrument K.K.   (2)
1-4-4 Kitasuna, Koto-ku, Tokyo, 136-0073,
Japan
Tel.: (81) 356337100
Web Site:
   https://www.brooksinstrument.com
Sales Range: $10-24.9 Million
Emp.: 40
Industrial Flow Meter Mfr

N.A.I.C.S.: 334519

Buehler, Ltd.   (1)
41 Waukegan Rd, Lake Bluff, IL 60044
Tel.: (847) 295-6500
Web Site: https://www.buehler.com
Rev.: $70,000,000
Emp.: 150
Scientific Instruments & Supplies Mfr
N.A.I.C.S.: 334516

Subsidiary (Non-US):

Buehler   (2)
Warwick Manufacturing Group IMC Building, University of Warwick Coventry, Coventry, CV4 7AL, United Kingdom   **(100%)**
Tel.: (44) 8007076273
Web Site: http://www.buehler.co.uk
Sales Range: $10-24.9 Million
Emp.: 15
Metallographic Preparation Equipment
N.A.I.C.S.: 334516
Julien Noel (Gen Mgr)

Buehler GmbH   (2)
In der Steele 2, 40599, Dusseldorf, Germany
Tel.: (49) 211974100
Web Site: http://www.buehler-met.de
Sales Range: $25-49.9 Million
Emp.: 40
Scientific Instruments & Supplies Sales
N.A.I.C.S.: 334516

Division (Domestic):

Buehler Ltd., Irvine   (1)
41 Waukegan Rd, Lake Bluff, IL
60044-1699   **(100%)**
Tel.: (847) 295-6500
Web Site: https://www.buehler.com
Sales Range: $10-24.9 Million
Emp.: 2
Metallographic Laboratory Equipment Mfr
N.A.I.C.S.: 423490

Burseryds Bruk AB   (1)
Storgatan 15-17, Burseryd, 333 77,
Gislaved, Sweden
Tel.: (46) 37137500
Web Site: https://www.burserydsbruk.se
Steel Products Mfr
N.A.I.C.S.: 332999
Per Myhrberg (Dir-Sls-Europe)

CFC International, Inc.   (1)
500 State St, Chicago Heights, IL 60411-1206
Tel.: (708) 891-3456
Web Site: http://www.cfcintl.com
Sales Range: $75-99.9 Million
Emp.: 150
Specialty Coated Film Designer, Mfr & Marketer
N.A.I.C.S.: 325510

Subsidiary (Non-US):

CFC Europe GmbH   (2)
Rigistrasse 20, 73037, Goppingen, Germany
Tel.: (49) 716180090
Web Site: https://www.cfceurope.com
Sales Range: $25-49.9 Million
Specialty Coated Films Mfr
N.A.I.C.S.: 325510

CS (Australia) Pty Limited   (1)
L3 74 Doncaster Rd, Balwyn, 3104, VIC,
Australia
Tel.: (61) 388622400
Electric Equipment Mfr
N.A.I.C.S.: 423090

Celcor Ltd.   (1)
25 Sheffield St Suite 3, Cambridge, N3C
1C4, ON, Canada
Tel.: (519) 220-0743
General Purpose Machinery Mfr
N.A.I.C.S.: 333998

Celeste Industries Corporation   (1)
8007 Industrial Park Rd, Easton, MD 21601
Tel.: (410) 822-5775
Web Site: https://www.celestecorp.com
Emp.: 54
Chemical Products Mfr
N.A.I.C.S.: 325199

Coeur Medical Products Services, S. De R.L. De C.V.   (1)

Calle 17 No 3820, Saltillo, Mexico
Tel.: (52) 8444300695
Medical Product Distr
N.A.I.C.S.: 423450

Coeur Medical Products, S. De R.L. De C.V.   (1)
Calle 17 No 3820, Saltillo, 25013, Coahuila,
Mexico
Tel.: (52) 8444300695
Emp.: 10
Medical & Surgical Instrument Mfr
N.A.I.C.S.: 339112

Coeur, Inc.   (1)
209 Creekside Dr, Washington, NC 27889
Tel.: (615) 547-7923
Web Site: https://www.coeurinc.com
Emp.: 10
Medical Device Mfr
N.A.I.C.S.: 339112

Compagnie Hobart S.A.S.   (1)
Allee du 1er Mai, BP 68, 77183, Croissy-Beaubourg, France   **(100%)**
Tel.: (33) 164116000
Web Site: http://www.hobart.fr
Sales Range: $125-149.9 Million
Emp.: 400
Industrial Machinery Whslr
N.A.I.C.S.: 423830
Fabrice Mezzomo (Pres)

Corporacion Coral S. de R.L. de C.V.   (1)
Calle E No 20, Naucalpan, 53020, Mexico
Tel.: (52) 5555600100
Plastics Product Mfr
N.A.I.C.S.: 326199

Dacro B.V.   (1)
Sydneystraat 11, 3047 BP, Rotterdam,
Netherlands
Tel.: (31) 102383880
Web Site: http://www.dacro.nl
Chemical Products Mfr
N.A.I.C.S.: 325199

Danley Construction Products Pty Ltd   (1)
21 Steel Place, Morningside, Brisbane,
4170, QLD, Australia
Tel.: (61) 738993466
Web Site: http://www.danley.com.au
Building Materials Mfr
N.A.I.C.S.: 333120

Densit ApS   (1)
Gasvaerksvej 46, 9000, Aalborg, Denmark
Tel.: (45) 98167011
Web Site: http://www.densit.com
Emp.: 30
Building Materials Mfr
N.A.I.C.S.: 333120

Densit Asia Pacific Sdn Bhd   (1)
Suite 7 Sea View 12th Floor Wisma Perindustrian, Jalan Istiadat Likas, Kota Kinabalu, 88400, Malaysia
Tel.: (60) 88272671
Building Materials Mfr
N.A.I.C.S.: 333120

Despatch Industries Inc.   (1)
8860 207th St, Minneapolis, MN 55044
Tel.: (952) 469-5424
Web Site: http://www.despatch.com
Sales Range: $200-249.9 Million
Emp.: 250
Industrial Furnace & Oven Mfr
N.A.I.C.S.: 333994

Subsidiary (Non-US):

Despatch Industries (Shanghai) Trading Co., Ltd.   (2)
Bldg 2 No 858 Zhujiang Road, Suzhou New
District, Suzhou, 215129, Jiangsu, China
Tel.: (86) 2162365868
Thermal Processing Services
N.A.I.C.S.: 541715

Despatch Industries GmbH EMEA Operation   (2)
Behrenstr 29, 10117, Berlin, Germany
Tel.: (49) 30 629 073 410
Web Site: http://www.despatch.com
Thermal Processing Services
N.A.I.C.S.: 541990

Despatch Industries Taiwan Ltd,   (2)

13F-2 No 229 Fuxing 2nd Rd, GuangMing
6th Road, Zhubei, 30271, Hsinchu, Taiwan
Tel.: (886) 36588484
Thermal Processing Services
N.A.I.C.S.: 541715

Subsidiary (Domestic):

Despatch Industries, Inc.   (2)
1801 Solar Dr Ste 190, Oxnard, CA 93030
Tel.: (805) 981-1518
Sales Range: $10-24.9 Million
Emp.: 18
Providers of Engineering Services, Temperature & Humidity Chambers, Thermal
Shock Chambers, Environmental Test Facilities, Durability Test Systems, Supervisory
Software
N.A.I.C.S.: 333994

Despatch Industries Limited Partnership   (1)
8860 207th St, Minneapolis, MN 55044
Tel.: (952) 469-5424
Web Site: http://www.despatch.com
Machine Tool & Industrial Machinery Mfr
N.A.I.C.S.: 333517

Diagraph   (1)
1 Research Park Dr, Saint Charles, MO
63304-5685
Tel.: (636) 300-2000
Web Site: https://www.diagraph.com
Product Identification & Bar Coding Systems Mfr
N.A.I.C.S.: 339940
Meesha Robinson (Coord-HR)

Diagraph Corporation Sdn. Bhd   (1)
No41 Jalan Serendah 26/41, Hicom Industrial Estate, 40400, Shah Alam, Selangor,
Malaysia
Tel.: (60) 356144688
Web Site: https://www.diagraph.com.my
Automated Label Distr
N.A.I.C.S.: 424310

Diagraph Marking & Stenciling Products Group   (1)
5307 Meadowland Pkwy, Marion, IL 62959
Tel.: (618) 997-3321
Web Site: https://www.diagraphmsp.com
Sales Range: $10-24.9 Million
Emp.: 55
Marking & Stenciling Products
N.A.I.C.S.: 339940

Diagraph Mexico, S.A. DE C.V.   (1)
Tezcatlipoca 22 San Miguel Xochimanga,
Atizapan de Zaragoza, 52927, Ciudad Lopez Mateos, Estado de Mexico, Mexico
Tel.: (52) 5553213190
Web Site: https://www.diagraph.com.mx
Automated Label Distr
N.A.I.C.S.: 424310

Duo-Fast Corporation   (1)
13825 W Business Center Dr, Lake Forest,
IL 60045-1100   **(100%)**
Tel.: (847) 783-5500
Web Site: https://www.paslode.com
Sales Range: $50-74.9 Million
Emp.: 100
Nailers, Staplers, Tackers, Nails & Staples
Mfr
N.A.I.C.S.: 332216

Duo-Fast Korea Co. Ltd.   (1)
333-1 Yusan Youngsan City Kyungnam,
Seoul, 626 230, Korea (South)
Tel.: (82) 553877800
Industrial Machinery Whslr
N.A.I.C.S.: 423830

Duo-Fast LLC   (1)
155 Harlem Ave, Glenview, IL 60025
Web Site: http://www.duo-fastconstruction.com
Construction Services
N.A.I.C.S.: 236220

Duo-Fast de Espana S.A.   (1)
Pol Industrial Villalonquejar Calle Lopez
Bravo 77, Burgos, 09001, Spain
Tel.: (34) 947298546
Industrial Machinery Whslr
N.A.I.C.S.: 423830

E.C.S. d.o.o.   (1)
Maksimirska 120, 10000, Zagreb, Croatia
Tel.: (385) 12336344

Web Site: https://www.ecs.hr
Emp.: 20
Information Technology Consulting Services
N.A.I.C.S.: 541512

ECS Cable Protection Sp. z o.o. (1)
Ul Poznanska 375, Inowroclaw, 88-100, Poland
Tel.: (48) 523527524
Web Site:
    http://www.ecscableprotection.com
Cable Insulation Material Mfr & Distr
N.A.I.C.S.: 326150

ELRO (U.K.) LIMITED (1)
3 Furzton Lake Shirwell Crescent, Milton Keynes, MK4 1GA, Bucks, United Kingdom
Tel.: (44) 1908526444
General Purpose Machinery Mfr
N.A.I.C.S.: 333998

ELRO Grosskuchen Gmbh (1)
Industriering Ost 31, 47906, Kempen, Germany
Tel.: (49) 21522055992
Web Site: https://elro.ch
Kitchen Appliance Mfr & Distr
N.A.I.C.S.: 332215

ELRO-WERKE AG (1)
Wohlerstrasse 47, 5620, Bremgarten, Switzerland
Tel.: (41) 566489111
Web Site: https://www.elro.ch
Kitchen Appliance Mfr & Distr
N.A.I.C.S.: 332215

EMIC Equipamentos E Sistemas De Ensaio Ltda. (1)
Rua Quirino Zagonel 257, 83020-250, Sao Jose dos Pinhais, Brazil
Tel.: (55) 4130359400
Web Site: http://www.emic.com.br
Machine Tool & Industrial Machinery Mfr
N.A.I.C.S.: 333517

Electro Static Technology (1)
31 Winterbrook Rd, Mechanic Falls, ME 04256
Tel.: (207) 998-5140
Web Site: https://www.est-aegis.com
Sales Range: $10-24.9 Million
Emp.: 50
Static Control Devices Mfr & Designer
N.A.I.C.S.: 334519

Elga AB (1)
Jarntradsvagen 2, 433 30, Partille, 433 30, Sweden
Tel.: (46) 317264600
Web Site: https://elgawelding.com
Emp.: 25
General Purpose Machinery Mfr
N.A.I.C.S.: 333998

Elga Aktiebolag (1)
Jarntradsvagen 2, 433 30, Partille, Sweden
Tel.: (46) 317264600
Web Site: http://www.elga.se
Welding Consumables Mfr
N.A.I.C.S.: 333514

Eltex-Elektrostatik-Gesellschaft mit beschrankter Haftung (1)
Blauenstrasse 67-69, 79576, Weil am Rhein, Germany
Tel.: (49) 76217905422
Web Site: https://www.eltex.de
Industrial Machinery Whslr
N.A.I.C.S.: 423830

Envases Multipac S.A. De C.V. (1)
Emilio Cardenas 166, Tlalnepantla, 54030, Edo De Mexico, Mexico (49%)
Tel.: (52) 5553215250
Web Site: http://www.hi-cone.com
Sales Range: $10-24.9 Million
Emp.: 40
Packaging Products Sales
N.A.I.C.S.: 326199

Eurotec Srl (1)
Via Lirone 60/i, 40013, Castel Maggiore, BO, Italy
Tel.: (39) 0516321595
Web Site: www.eurotecsrl.com
Industrial Machinery Distr
N.A.I.C.S.: 423610

Exactrak Limited (1)
Foundry Lane, Smethwick, B66 2LP, West

Midlands, United Kingdom
Tel.: (44) 8452462778
Web Site: https://www.exactrak.co.uk
Emp.: 6
Software Development Services
N.A.I.C.S.: 541511

Fasver SAS (1)
286 Rue Charles Gide ZAE La Biste II, 34670, Baillargues, France
Tel.: (33) 467876699
Web Site: http://www.fasver.com
Emp.: 44
Industrial Machinery Whslr
N.A.I.C.S.: 423830

Fasver Technology, Inc. (1)
3505 Silverside Rd Ste 208f, Wilmington, DE 19810
Tel.: (302) 478-4878
Computer Peripheral Distr
N.A.I.C.S.: 423430

Filtertek Do Brasil Industria E Comercio Ltda. (1)
Avenida Otavio Braga De Mesquita 324 Vila Florida, Guarulhos, 07191-000, Brazil
Tel.: (55) 1124429204
Web Site: http://www.filtertek.com.br
Medical Device Mfr
N.A.I.C.S.: 339112

Filtertek Inc. (1)
11411 Price Rd, Hebron, IL 60034-8936
Tel.: (815) 648-2416
Web Site: https://www.filtertek.com
Sales Range: $250-299.9 Million
Emp.: 900
Custom Filters & Filtration Equipment Designer & Mfr
N.A.I.C.S.: 333998

Subsidiary (Non-US):

Filtertek B.V. (2)
Industrial Estate Newcastle West County, Limerick, Ireland
Tel.: (353) 6962666
Web Site: http://www.filtertek.com
Sales Range: $25-49.9 Million
Emp.: 56
Custom Filters & Filtration Equipment Designer & Mfr
N.A.I.C.S.: 333998

Filtertek de Mexico, S.A. de C.V. (2)
Faraday 8231 Parque Industrial Antonio J Bermudez, Ciudad Juarez, 32470, Chihuahua, Mexico
Tel.: (52) 6566250535
Web Site: http://www.filtertek.com
Filtration Equipment Mfr
N.A.I.C.S.: 333998

Filtertek do Brazil Industria E Commercio Ltda. (2)
Av Otavio Braga De Mesquita 258 Macedo, Guarulhos, 07140-230, SP, Brazil
Tel.: (55) 1124619300
Web Site: http://www.filtertek.com
Sales Range: $100-124.9 Million
Emp.: 300
Custom Filters & Filtration Equipment Designer & Mfr
N.A.I.C.S.: 333998

Filtertek, S.A. (2)
ZA Du pre de la Dame Jeanne, B P 11, 60128, Plailly, France
Tel.: (33) 344541990
Web Site: http://www.filtertek.com
Sales Range: $25-49.9 Million
Custom Filters & Filtration Equipment Designer & Mfr
N.A.I.C.S.: 333998

Forte Lubricants Limited (1)
Unit 7 Westwood House Westwood Way, Westwood Business Park, Coventry, CV4 8HS, West Midlands, United Kingdom
Tel.: (44) 2476474069
Web Site: https://www.forteuk.co.uk
Emp.: 25
General Purpose Machinery Mfr
N.A.I.C.S.: 333998

Forte Noord-West-Europa B.V. (1)
Geijsterseweg 11A, Wanssum, 5861 BK, Venray, Netherlands
Tel.: (31) 478537555

Web Site: http://www.forte-nwe.com
Automobile Parts Mfr
N.A.I.C.S.: 336390

Foster Refrigerator (U.K.) (1)
Oldmedow Road, King's Lynn, PE30 4JU, United Kingdom
Tel.: (44) 1553691122
Web Site: https://www.fosterrefrigerator.com
General Purpose Machinery Mfr
N.A.I.C.S.: 333998

Foster Refrigerator France S.A.S. (1)
Park Bellevues Rue Gros Murger, PO Box 246, Eragny-sur-Oise, 95615, Cergy-Pontoise, France
Tel.: (33) 134302222
Web Site: http://www.fosterfrance.com
Industrial Machinery Mfr
N.A.I.C.S.: 333517

GRK Canada Limited (1)
1499 Rosslyn Road, Thunder Bay, P7E 6W1, ON, Canada
Tel.: (807) 474-4300
Web Site: http://www.grkfasteners.com
Machine Tool Mfr & Distr
N.A.I.C.S.: 333517

Gamko B.V. (1)
Mon Plaisir 75, 4879 AL, Etten-Leur, Netherlands
Tel.: (31) 155 378 0515
Web Site: https://www.gamko.com
Sales Range: $25-49.9 Million
Emp.: 120
Commercial Refrigeration Equipment Mfr
N.A.I.C.S.: 333415
Peter Naaikans (Mng Dir)

Subsidiary (Non-US):

Gamko Refrigeration U.K. Limited (2)
Old Meadow Road Kings Lynn, Trafford Park Village, Norfolk, PE30 4JU, United Kingdom
Tel.: (44) 1553691122
Web Site: https://www.gamko.com
General Purpose Machinery Mfr
N.A.I.C.S.: 333998

Gamko Refrigeration Eurl (1)
26-28 Rue de Piscop, 95350, Saint-Brice-sous-Foret, France
Tel.: (33) 134294141
Web Site: http://www.gamko.com
Emp.: 15
Industrial Machinery Mfr
N.A.I.C.S.: 333517

GloboPlastt s.r.o. (1)
Vysielac 486, 082 53, Presòv, Slovakia
Tel.: (421) 512850285
Web Site: https://www.globoplastt.com
Packaging Material Mfr & Distr
N.A.I.C.S.: 326112

HOBART Gesellschaft mit beschrankter Haftung (1)
Robert-Bosch-Strasse 17, 77656, Offenburg, Germany
Tel.: (49) 7816000
Web Site: https://www.hobart.de
Emp.: 1,100
Industrial Machinery Mfr
N.A.I.C.S.: 333517

Hartness International Europe, Gmbh (1)
Siemensstr 32, 47533, Kleve, Germany
Tel.: (49) 28217776505
Industrial Machinery Mfr
N.A.I.C.S.: 333517
Anne Dams (Mgr-Bus Unit)

Hartness International Inc. (1)
50 Beechtree Blvd, Greenville, SC 29605 (100%)
Tel.: (864) 297-1200
Web Site: https://www.hartness.com
Rev.: $44,188,000
Emp.: 400
Packaging Machinery Mfr
N.A.I.C.S.: 333993

Hobart (Japan) K.K. (1)
1F Suzunaka Building 6-16-16 Minamioi, Shinagawa-ku, Tokyo, 140-0013, Japan
Tel.: (81) 357678672

Web Site: https://www.hobart.co.jp
Industrial Machinery Distr
N.A.I.C.S.: 423610

Hobart Andina S.A.S. (1)
Tel.: (57) 13794600
Web Site: http://hobartandina.com
Emp.: 32
Machine Tools Mfr
N.A.I.C.S.: 333517

Hobart Canada Corp. (1)
105 Gordon Baker Rd Ste 801, Toronto, M2H 3P8, ON, Canada
Tel.: (866) 334-2371
Web Site: http://www.hobart.ca
Sales Range: $25-49.9 Million
Emp.: 35
General Purpose Machinery Mfr
N.A.I.C.S.: 333998

Hobart Corporation (1)
701 S Ridge Ave, Troy, OH 45373 (100%)
Tel.: (937) 332-3000
Web Site: https://www.hobartcorp.com
Sales Range: $300-349.9 Million
Emp.: 900
Commercial Food Equipment Mfr
N.A.I.C.S.: 333310
Bob Bilokonsky (VP & Gen Mgr)

Division (Domestic):

Hobart Brothers Company (2)
101 Trade Sq E, Troy, OH 45373 (100%)
Tel.: (937) 332-4000
Web Site: https://www.hobartbrothers.com
Sales Range: $200-249.9 Million
Emp.: 700
Welding Systems & Equipment, Industrial Battery Chargers, Aircraft Ground Power & Support Equipment Mfr
N.A.I.C.S.: 333992

Subsidiary (Domestic):

ITW GSE Inc. (3)
11001 US Highway 41 N, Palmetto, FL 34221
Tel.: (941) 721-1000
Web Site: https://itwgse.com
Aircraft Ground Support Equipment Solutions
N.A.I.C.S.: 221118

Division (Non-US):

AXA Power ApS (4)
Smedebakken 31-33, 5270, Odense, Denmark
Tel.: (45) 63186000
Web Site: http://www.itwgse.com
Sales Range: $25-49.9 Million
Aircraft Ground Power Solutions
N.A.I.C.S.: 221118

Division (Domestic):

Hobart Ground Power (4)
1177 Trade Rd E, Troy, OH 45373
Tel.: (937) 332-5080
Web Site: http://www.itwgsegroup.com
Sales Range: $25-49.9 Million
Emp.: 50
Aircraft Ground Power Solutions
N.A.I.C.S.: 221118

J&B Aviation Services Inc. (4)
Ste A 907 Cotting Ln, Vacaville, CA 95688
Tel.: (707) 469-2600
Web Site: http://www.jandbaviation.com
Rev.: $11,000,000
Emp.: 20
Aircraft Parts & Equipment, Nec
N.A.I.C.S.: 336413

Unit (Non-US):

Hobart Food Equipment Group Canada (2)
105 Gordon Baker Road Suite 801, Toronto, M2H 3P8, ON, Canada (100%)
Tel.: (866) 334-2371
Web Site: http://www.hobart.ca
Sales Range: $125-149.9 Million
Emp.: 25
Commercial Food Equipment & Home Appliances Mfr, Sales & Service
N.A.I.C.S.: 335220

Illinois Tool Works Inc.—(Continued)

Subsidiary (Non-US):

Hobart GmbH (2)
Robert-Bosch-Strasse 17, 77656, Offenburg, Germany **(100%)**
Tel.: (49) 7816000
Web Site: https://www.hobart.de
Sales Range: $300-349.9 Million
Emp.: 700
Appliances Sales & Marketer
N.A.I.C.S.: 423620

Hobart Nederland B.V. (2)
Pompmolenlaan 12, 3447 GK, Woerden, Netherlands **(100%)**
Tel.: (31) 348462626
Web Site: http://www.hobart.nl
Appliances Mfr & Distr
N.A.I.C.S.: 449210

Hobart UK Limited (2)
Southgate Way Orton Southgate, Peterborough, PE2 6GN, United Kingdom **(100%)**
Tel.: (44) 8448887777
Web Site: https://www.hobartuk.com
Sales Range: $25-49.9 Million
Emp.: 80
Commercial Food Equipment & Home Appliances Mfr
N.A.I.C.S.: 335210

Unit (Domestic):

Traulsen (2)
4401 Blue Mound Rd, Fort Worth, TX 76106-1928
Tel.: (817) 625-9671
Web Site: https://www.traulsen.com
Sales Range: $100-124.9 Million
Emp.: 350
Refrigeration & Heating Equipment
N.A.I.C.S.: 333415

Hobart Dayton Mexicana, S. de R.L. de C.V. (1)
Viveros de la colina No 238 Col Viveros de la Loma, 54080, Tlalnepantla, Mexico
Tel.: (52) 5550628200
Emp.: 200
Kitchen Appliance Mfr & Distr
N.A.I.C.S.: 332215

Hobart Food Equipment Co., Ltd. (1)
Tel.: (86) 2134182288
Kitchen Appliance Mfr & Distr
N.A.I.C.S.: 332215

Hobart Foster Belgium B.V.B.A. (1)
Industriestraat 6, 1910, Kampenhout, Belgium
Tel.: (32) 16606040
Web Site: https://nl.hobart.be
Industrial Machinery Distr
N.A.I.C.S.: 423610

Hobart International (Singapore) Pte. Ltd. (1)
158 Kallang Way 06-03/05, Singapore, 349245, Singapore
Tel.: (65) 6 846 7117
Web Site: https://www.hobart.com.sg
Kitchen Appliance Mfr & Distr
N.A.I.C.S.: 332215

Hobart Korea Co. Ltd. (1)
7th floor Woongsan Bldg 463 Baekjegobun-ro, Songpa-gu, 05550, Seoul, Korea (South)
Tel.: (82) 2344369014
Web Site: https://www.hobart.co.kr
Industrial Machinery Distr
N.A.I.C.S.: 423610

Hobart Nederland B.V. (1)
Pompmolenlaan 12, 3447 GK, Woerden, Netherlands
Tel.: (31) 348462626
Web Site: http://www.hobart.nl
Industrial Machinery Mfr
N.A.I.C.S.: 333517

Hobart Sales & Service, Inc. (1)
701 S Ridge Ave, Troy, OH 45373
Tel.: (937) 332-3000
Sales Range: $125-149.9 Million
Emp.: 600
General Purpose Machinery Mfr
N.A.I.C.S.: 333998

Hobart Scandinavia ApS (1)
Handvaerkerbyen 27, 2670, Greve, Denmark
Tel.: (45) 4 390 5012
Web Site: https://www.hobart.dk
Industrial Machinery Mfr
N.A.I.C.S.: 333517

Hobart do Brasil Ltd. (1)
Avenida Forte do Leme 195, 08340-010, Sao Paulo, SP, Brazil
Tel.: (55) 1120148080
Web Site: https://www.hobart.com.br
Food Industry Machinery & Equipment Mfr & Distr
N.A.I.C.S.: 423830

Hopital Services Systemes S.A.S. (1)
13/15 Rue Paul Langevin, Ris Orangis, Paris, 91130, France
Tel.: (33) 169021860
Web Site: http://www.hmsante.com
Medical Product Distr
N.A.I.C.S.: 423450

Horis SAS (1)
17 rue des Freres Lumiere - Z I Compans, 77292, Mitry-Mory, Cedex, France
Tel.: (33) 164676100
Web Site: https://www.horis-services.fr
Household Appliance Repair & Maintenance Services
N.A.I.C.S.: 811412

I.KELA Company (1)
4405 Independence Ct, Sarasota, FL 34234
Tel.: (941) 355-6498
Web Site: http://www.ikela.com
Sales Range: $25-49.9 Million
Emp.: 6
UV Curing & Rotary Hot Foil Stamping Products Mfr & Distr
N.A.I.C.S.: 332119

I.T.W. Inc. (1)
155 Harlem Ave, Glenview, IL 60025
Tel.: (224) 661-8870
Web Site: https://www.itw.com
General Purpose Machinery Mfr
N.A.I.C.S.: 333998
Moe Berger (Owner & Pres)

INN SP Z.o.o. (1)
Lubuska Street 21a, 41-811, Zabrze, Poland
Tel.: (48) 322484505
Web Site: https://www.inn.com.pl
Emp.: 50
Industrial Machinery Mfr
N.A.I.C.S.: 333517

ITECMA S.A.S. (1)
Parc De l a Fontaine De Jouvenc, 4 Rue Angiboust, Marcoussis, 91460, France
Tel.: (33) 164497238
Sales Range: $25-49.9 Million
Emp.: 28
Maintenance & Cleaning Services
N.A.I.C.S.: 333998

ITW (Deutschland) GmbH (1)
Muhlacker Strasse 149, 75417, Muhlacker, Germany
Tel.: (49) 704196340
Web Site: http://www.itwcp.de
Machine Tools Mfr
N.A.I.C.S.: 333517

ITW (Ningbo) Components & Fastenings Systems Co., Ltd. (1)
Ningbo Science Technology Zone, Jiangdong District, Ningbo, 315040, Zhejiang, China
Tel.: (86) 57487901966
Industrial Equipment Distr
N.A.I.C.S.: 423830

ITW - Evercoat (1)
6600 Cornell Rd, Cincinnati, OH 45242 **(100%)**
Tel.: (513) 489-7600
Web Site: https://www.evercoat.com
Sales Range: $50-74.9 Million
Emp.: 130
Marine & Automotive Repair Products Mfr
N.A.I.C.S.: 325510

Subsidiary (Domestic):

ITW Auto Wax Company, Inc. (2)

1275 Round Table Dr, Dallas, TX 75247-3503
Tel.: (214) 631-1689
Web Site: http://www.autowaxcompany.com
Polishing Preparations & Related Products Mfr
N.A.I.C.S.: 325612

ITW Air Management (1)
10125 Carver Rd, Cincinnati, OH 45242 **(100%)**
Tel.: (513) 891-7485
Web Site: https://www.itw-air.com
Sales Range: $50-74.9 Million
Emp.: 27
Centrifugal Blowers & Drying Systems Mfr
N.A.I.C.S.: 333413

ITW Angleboard AB (1)
Sandared, Boras, 518 22, Sweden
Tel.: (46) 33205290
Web Site: http://www.itwangleboard.net
Industrial Machinery Mfr
N.A.I.C.S.: 333517

ITW Appliance Components d.o.o. (1)
Poljubinj 89E, 5220, Tolmin, Slovenia
Tel.: (386) 53820200
Web Site: http://www.itwmetalflex.com
Appliance Component Mfr
N.A.I.C.S.: 335999

ITW Ark-Les Corporation (1)
1490 Central St, Stoughton, MA 02072
Tel.: (781) 297-6000
Industrial Equipment Whsr
N.A.I.C.S.: 423830
Juan Barrena (Engr-Design)

ITW Australia Property Holdings Pty Ltd. (1)
Doncaster Road 74, Melbourne, 3104, VIC, Australia
Tel.: (61) 398598020
Holding Company
N.A.I.C.S.: 551114

ITW Australia Pty. Ltd. (1)
74-94 Newton Road, Wetherill Park, 2164, NSW, Australia **(100%)**
Tel.: (61) 29 757 0777
Web Site: https://www.itwproline.com.au
Emp.: 60
Hardware Distr
N.A.I.C.S.: 423710

Subsidiary (Domestic):

Cyclone Industries Pty Ltd (2)
317 Abbotts Road Dandenong South, Dandenong, 3175, VIC, Australia
Tel.: (61) 387919300
Web Site: http://www.cyclone.com.au
Sales Range: $400-449.9 Million
Emp.: 100
Hand & Edge Tools Mfr
N.A.I.C.S.: 332216

ITW Automotive Components (Langfang) Co., Ltd. (1)
Yaohua Road LandFang Economic and Techn Development Zone, Lang Sen Automotive Industry Park, Langfang, 065001, China
Tel.: (86) 3166070868
Industrial Equipment Distr
N.A.I.C.S.: 423830

ITW Automotive Finishing (1)
320 Phillips Ave, Toledo, OH 43612
Tel.: (419) 470-2000
Sales Range: $25-49.9 Million
Emp.: 60
Liquid Electrostatic Paint Application Equipment Mfr & Distr
N.A.I.C.S.: 333248

ITW Automotive Korea, LLC (1)
12 16 Gueo ri Oedong eup, 780-823, Gyeoji, Gyeongsangbuk, Korea (South)
Tel.: (82) 547464991
Emp.: 133
Industrial Equipment Mfr
N.A.I.C.S.: 332510

ITW Automotive Products GmbH (1)
Im Wasen 1, Rottingen, 97285, Wurzburg, Germany
Tel.: (49) 9338800
Web Site: https://www.itw-deltar.de

Emp.: 350
Automobile Assembly Parts Mfr
N.A.I.C.S.: 336330
Martin Raida (Mng Dir)
Jose Luis Serrada (Mng Dir)
Alberto Andena (Mng Dir)

ITW Automotive Products Mexico, S. de R.L. de C.V. (1)
Ave Fomento Industrial s/n Parque Industrial del Norte Reynosa, Tamaulipas, 88736, Mexico
Tel.: (52) 9566328100
Automobile Assembly Parts Mfr
N.A.I.C.S.: 336330
Karim Montante (Head-Sys)

ITW Bailly Comte S.A.S. (1)
Parc D Activite Lyon Nord 239 Rue Jacquard, Genay, France
Tel.: (33) 478986969
Industrial Machinery Mfr
N.A.I.C.S.: 423830

ITW Befestigungssysteme Alpen GmbH (1)
Gewerbestrasse 6, Biel-Benken, 4105, Biel, Switzerland
Tel.: (41) 617221212
Web Site: http://www.haubold-deutschland.com
Emp.: 9
Industrial Machinery Mfr
N.A.I.C.S.: 423830
Thorsten Eckstein (Gen Mgr)

ITW Befestigungssysteme GmbH (1)
Carl-Zeiss-Str 19, 30966, Hemmingen, Germany **(100%)**
Tel.: (49) 51142040
Web Site: https://www.itw-befestigungssysteme.de
Sales Range: $25-49.9 Million
Fasteners & Other Hardware Products Sales & Distr
N.A.I.C.S.: 423710

ITW Belgium S.p.r.l. (1)
t Hofveld 3, 1702, Groot-Bijgaarden, Belgium **(100%)**
Tel.: (32) 3323900
Web Site: https://www.spitpaslode.be
Sales Range: $10-24.9 Million
Specialty Product & Equipment Mfr
N.A.I.C.S.: 333514

ITW Brands (1)
955 National Pkwy Ste 95500, Schaumburg, IL 60173
Tel.: (847) 944-2260
Web Site: http://www.itwbrands.com
Home Improvement & Do-It-Yourself Construction Products Mfr
N.A.I.C.S.: 332510

ITW Buildex (1)
1349 W Bryn Mawr Ave, Itasca, IL 60143-1313
Tel.: (630) 595-3500
Web Site: https://www.itwbuildex.com
Sales Range: $50-74.9 Million
Emp.: 100
Fasteners & Building Products Mfr
N.A.I.C.S.: 339993

ITW Buildex (1)
600 South Rd, PO Box 1154, Moorabbin, 3189, VIC, Australia
Tel.: (61) 395556433
Web Site: http://www.buildex.com.au
Sales Range: $50-74.9 Million
Emp.: 100
Self Drilling Screws Mfr & Supplier
N.A.I.C.S.: 332722

ITW Building Components Group Inc. (1)
155 Harlem Ave N Bldg 4 Fl, Glenview, IL 60025 **(100%)**
Tel.: (224) 681-8870
Web Site: https://alpineitw.com
Sales Range: $250-299.9 Million
Emp.: 450
Commercial Construction Product Support Services
N.A.I.C.S.: 551112

ITW CER (1)
85 Rue Castellion, 01100, Oyonnax, 01117, France

Tel.: (33) 474732600
Web Site: https://www.itwcer.com
Industrial Machinery Distr
N.A.I.C.S.: 423830

ITW CP Distribution Center Holland BV (1)
van Heemskerckweg 5, 5928 LL, Venlo, Netherlands
Tel.: (31) 857821821
Emp.: 35
Industrial Machinery Distr
N.A.I.C.S.: 423610
B. Jaukan *(Gen Mgr)*

Subsidiary (Non-US):

Davall Gears Ltd. (2)
Travellers Ln, Welham Green, Hatfield, AL9 7JB, Hertfordshire, United Kingdom
Tel.: (44) 1707283100
Web Site: https://mtimotion.com
Gear Mfr
N.A.I.C.S.: 333612

ITW CPM S.A.S. (1)
45 Avenue Du General De Gaulle, Thiers, 63300, France
Tel.: (33) 473804855
Industrial Machinery Mfr
N.A.I.C.S.: 333517

ITW Canada Investments Limited Partnership (1)
10 Carlow Crt Unit 2, Whitby, L1N 9T7, ON, Canada
Tel.: (905) 430-4643
Industrial Machinery Mfr
N.A.I.C.S.: 333517

Division (Domestic):

ITW Construction Products (2)
120 Travail Road, Markham, L3S 3J1, ON, Canada (100%)
Tel.: (905) 471-7403
Web Site: https://www.itwconstruction.ca
Emp.: 30
Fasteners & Construction Products Mfr
N.A.I.C.S.: 339993

ITW Canada Management Company (1)
10 Carlow Crt Unit 2, Whitby, L1N9T7, ON, Canada (100%)
Tel.: (905) 403-4643
Web Site: http://www.itw.com
Sales Range: $10-24.9 Million
Emp.: 45
Management Services
N.A.I.C.S.: 541611

ITW Chemical Products Ltda (1)
Av Jorge Alfredo Camasmie 670, Parque Industrial Ramos de Freitas Embu das Artes, Sao Paulo, 06816-050, Sau Paulo, Brazil
Web Site: https://itwpf.com.br
Chemical Products Mfr
N.A.I.C.S.: 325199

ITW Chemical Products Scandinavia ApS (1)
Priorsvej 36, Silkeborg, 8600, Denmark
Tel.: (45) 86826444
Chemical Product Mfr & Distr
N.A.I.C.S.: 325199

ITW Coding Products (1)
111 W Park Dr, Kalkaska, MI 49646 (100%)
Tel.: (231) 258-5521
Web Site: http://www.codingproducts.com
Sales Range: $50-74.9 Million
Emp.: 100
Heat Transfer Ink Systems & Products Mfr
N.A.I.C.S.: 332999

ITW Colombia S.A.S. (1)
Industrial Park Robles V Bodega 7 Vereda Canavita, Tocancipa, Colombia
Tel.: (57) 6018698710
Web Site: http://www.itwcolombia.com
Industrial Machinery Whslr
N.A.I.C.S.: 423830

ITW Construction Products (Singapore) Pte. Ltd. (1)
4 Changi South Lane 06-01 Nan Wah

Building, Singapore, 486127, Singapore (100%)
Tel.: (65) 6 746 1177
Web Site: https://www.itwcpsea.com
Sales Range: $10-24.9 Million
Construction Materials & Fasteners Mfr
N.A.I.C.S.: 339993

ITW Construction Products AB (1)
Betongv 5, PO Box 406, 691 42, Karlskoga, Sweden
Tel.: (46) 857893020
Web Site: http://www.spitpaslode.se
General Purpose Machinery Mfr
N.A.I.C.S.: 333998

ITW Construction Products AS (1)
Kobbervikdalen 65, PO Box 111, 3036, Drammen, Norway
Tel.: (47) 6 717 3600
Web Site: https://www.itw.no
Construction Machinery Mfr
N.A.I.C.S.: 333120

ITW Construction Products ApS (1)
Gl Banegardsvej 25, 5500, Middelfart, Denmark
Tel.: (45) 6 341 1010
Web Site: https://www.itwbyg.dk
Industrial Machinery Mfr
N.A.I.C.S.: 333517

ITW Construction Products CZ s.r.o. (1)
Zdebradska 8, Ricany, Czech Republic
Tel.: (420) 32 320 2202
Web Site: https://www.itw.cz
Industrial Equipment Mfr
N.A.I.C.S.: 333248
Ales Dohanic *(Mng Dir)*

ITW Construction Products Espana S.A. (1)
Calle Lopez Bravo 77, 09001, Burgos, Spain
Tel.: (34) 936307689
Construction Machinery Mfr
N.A.I.C.S.: 333120

ITW Construction Products Italy Srl (1)
Via Lombardia 10 Cazzago di, 30030, Pianiga, VE, Italy
Tel.: (39) 0415135511
Web Site: https://www.itw-elematic.com
Construction Machinery Mfr
N.A.I.C.S.: 333120

ITW Construction Products OU (1)
Turi 10D, 11313, Tallinn, Harju, Estonia
Tel.: (372) 6512462
Web Site: https://www.itwconstruction.ee
Industrial Machinery Whslr
N.A.I.C.S.: 423830

Division (Non-US):

ITW Construction Products UK (2)
Fleming Way, Crawley, RH10 9DP, West Sussex, United Kingdom (100%)
Tel.: (44) 1293523372
Web Site: http://www.itwcp.co.uk
Sales Range: $25-49.9 Million
Emp.: 60
Construction Product Distr
N.A.I.C.S.: 423390
Andrew Mines *(Pres-Grp)*

ITW Construction Products OY (1)
Timmermalmintie 19A, 01680, Vantaa, Finland
Tel.: (358) 207859200
Web Site: https://www.itwconstruction.fi
Construction Machinery Mfr
N.A.I.C.S.: 333120

ITW Construction Products UK (1)
Diamond Point Fleming Way, Crawley, RH10 9DP, United Kingdom (100%)
Tel.: (44) 1413421660
Web Site: http://www.itwcp.co.uk
Sales Range: $25-49.9 Million
Emp.: 20
Fasteners & Components
N.A.I.C.S.: 339993

ITW Contamination Control B.V. (1)
Saffierlaan 5, 2132 VZ, Hoofddorp, Netherlands
Tel.: (31) 88 130 7400
Web Site: https://www.itw-cc.com

Emp.: 25
Industrial Machinery Mfr
N.A.I.C.S.: 333517

ITW Covid Security Group Inc. (1)
32 Commerce Dr N Ste 1, Cranbury, NJ 08512
Tel.: (609) 395-5600
Web Site: http://www.itwsecuritydivision.com
Emp.: 70
Miscellaneous General Purpose Machinery Mfr
N.A.I.C.S.: 333998

ITW DelFast do Brasil Ltda. (1)
Av Guarapiranga 1 389 Capela Do Socorro, Sao Paulo, 04901-010, Brazil
Tel.: (55) 1155155800
Web Site: http://www.itw.com.br
Automobile Parts Mfr
N.A.I.C.S.: 336390

ITW Denmark ApS (1)
Priorsvej 36, Silkeborg, 8600, Denmark
Tel.: (45) 87205157
Machine Tools Mfr
N.A.I.C.S.: 333517

ITW Devcon (1)
30 Endicott St, Danvers, MA 01923-3712 (100%)
Tel.: (978) 777-1100
Web Site: https://itwperformancepolymers.com
Sales Range: $50-74.9 Million
Emp.: 130
Adhesives, Epoxies, Flexanes Mfr
N.A.I.C.S.: 325520

Subsidiary (Domestic):

ITW Devcon Futura Coatings (2)
1685 Galt Industrial Blvd, Saint Louis, MO 63132-1021
Tel.: (314) 733-1110
Web Site: http://www.futuracoatings.com
Sales Range: $10-24.9 Million
Emp.: 15
Polyurethane Coatings, Elastomers & Structural Resins Mfr
N.A.I.C.S.: 325510

Division (Non-US):

ITW Devcon Japan (2)
30-32 Enokicho, Osaka, 564-0053, Japan
Tel.: (81) 663307118
Web Site: http://www.itwppfjapan.com
Sales Range: $10-24.9 Million
Emp.: 17
Metal & Rubber Repair Services
N.A.I.C.S.: 339993

ITW Dymon (1)
805 E Old 56 Hwy, Olathe, KS 66061-4914
Tel.: (913) 829-6296
Web Site: http://www.dymon.com
Sales Range: $25-49.9 Million
Emp.: 100
Specialty Chemicals & Marking Systems Mfr
N.A.I.C.S.: 325998

ITW Dynatec (1)
ZI Croix de Raville, 28500, Cherisy, France
Tel.: (33) 237625647
Web Site: http://fr.itwdynatec.com
Adhesive Product Mfr & Distr
N.A.I.C.S.: 325520

ITW Dynatec (1)
31 Volunteer Dr, Hendersonville, TN 37075
Tel.: (615) 824-3634
Web Site: https://www.itwdynatec.com
Industrial Adhesive Application Equipment Mfr
N.A.I.C.S.: 333248

Subsidiary (Non-US):

ITW Dynatec G.m.b.H. (2)
Industriestrasse 28, 40822, Mettmann, Germany (100%)
Tel.: (49) 2 104 9150
Web Site: https://www.itwdynatec.com
Sales Range: $25-49.9 Million
Dispensing Sealants & Adhesives Equipment & Hot Melting Systems Mfr
N.A.I.C.S.: 333914

ITW Dynatec Kabushiki Kaisha (2)

Flos Kamata 1st 2nd Floor 26-11 Nishikamata 7-chome, Ota-ku, Tokyo, 144-0051, Japan (100%)
Tel.: (81) 35 703 5501
Web Site: https://www.itwdynatec.com
Sales Range: $10-24.9 Million
Sealants, Adhesives & Hot Melting Systems Mfr
N.A.I.C.S.: 333992
Susumu Hasegawa *(Pres)*

ITW Dynatec Adhesive Equipment (Suzhou) Co. Ltd. (1)
No 2 Anzhi Street SIP, Suzhou, 215122, China
Tel.: (86) 51262890620
Web Site: http://www.itwdynatec.com
Adhesive Mfr
N.A.I.C.S.: 325520

ITW EAE Mexico, S de RL de CV (1)
Jose Maria Pino Suarez 1039-31 Colonia el Vigia, 45140, Zapopan, Jalisco, Mexico
Tel.: (52) 8007181614
Electronic Assembly Products Mfr
N.A.I.C.S.: 334418

ITW EF&C France SAS (1)
4 Rue due Wittholz, 67340, Ingwiller, France
Tel.: (33) 388894754
Industrial Equipment Distr
N.A.I.C.S.: 423830

ITW EF&C Selb GmbH (1)
Am Schreinersteich 4, 95100, Selb, Germany
Tel.: (49) 928799650
Web Site: http://www.itw-efc.com
Automobile Parts Mfr
N.A.I.C.S.: 336390

ITW Electronic Business Asia Co., Limited (1)
Tel.: (886) 78119206
Emp.: 200
Electronic Equipment Mfr & Distr
N.A.I.C.S.: 334419

ITW Electronics (Suzhou) Co., Ltd. (1)
No 5 Xiang st Tai Shan Road, Suzhou, 215129, Jiangsu, China
Tel.: (86) 51262588850
Industrial Equipment Mfr
N.A.I.C.S.: 332510

ITW Espana, S.A. (1)
De Ribes km 31 7, 08520, Les Franqueses del Valles, Spain (100%)
Tel.: (34) 938443125
Web Site: http://eu.itwnexus.com
Sales Range: $150-199.9 Million
Plastic Buckles, Engineered Closures & Components Mfr
N.A.I.C.S.: 339993

ITW FEG Hong Kong Limited (1)
2516 Technology Park 18 On Lai Street, Shekmun, Sha Tin, New Territories, China (Hong Kong)
Tel.: (852) 2 341 9315
Web Site: https://www.hobart.com.hk
Kitchen Appliance Mfr & Distr
N.A.I.C.S.: 332215

ITW Fastex (1)
195 Algonquin Rd, Des Plaines, IL 60016 (100%)
Tel.: (847) 299-2222
Web Site: http://www.itw-fastex.com
Sales Range: $75-99.9 Million
Emp.: 150
Plastic Fasteners Mfr
N.A.I.C.S.: 339993

ITW Foilmark (1)
5 Malcolm Hoyt Dr, Newburyport, MA 01950
Tel.: (978) 225-8200
Web Site: http://www.foilmark.com
Sales Range: $75-99.9 Million
Emp.: 435
Hot Stamping Foil, Holographic Media & Laminated Paper Mfr
N.A.I.C.S.: 332999

Division (Non-US):

ITW Foils (2)

Illinois Tool Works Inc.—(Continued)

2285 Ambassador Dr, Windsor, N9C 3R5, ON, Canada
Tel.: (519) 966-4721
Sales Range: $50-74.9 Million
Emp.: 100
Hot-Stamping Foil for the Graphics & Plastic Industry Mfr
N.A.I.C.S.: 322220

ITW Foils B.V. (1)
Havenweg 1, Waalwijk, 5145 NJ, Netherlands
Tel.: (31) 416569400
Web Site: http://www.itwfolls.com
Emp.: 30
Films & Foil Laminate Mfr
N.A.I.C.S.: 322220

ITW Food Equipment Group LLC (1)
701 S Ridge Ave, Troy, OH 45374-0001
Tel.: (937) 332-3000
Web Site:
  https://www.itwfoodequipment.com
Commercial Equipments Mfr
N.A.I.C.S.: 333998

ITW GSE ApS (1)
Smedebakken 31-33, 5270, Odense, Denmark
Tel.: (45) 63186000
Industrial Equipment Distr
N.A.I.C.S.: 423830

ITW German Real Estate Management GmbH & Co. KG (1)
Magnusstrasse 18, 46535, Dinslaken, Germany
Tel.: (49) 2064690
Real Estate Development Services
N.A.I.C.S.: 531390

ITW Global Investments Inc. (1)
3600 West Lake Avenue, Glenview, IL 60026
Tel.: (847) 724-7500
Web Site: http://www.itw.com
Sales Range: $75-99.9 Million
Emp.: 400
Miscellaneous General Purpose Machinery Mfr
N.A.I.C.S.: 333998

ITW Global Tire Repair Europe GmbH (1)
Carl-Benz-Strasse 10, D-88696, Owingen, Germany
Tel.: (49) 755192000
Web Site: https://www.itwgtr.com
Tire Repair Product Mfr
N.A.I.C.S.: 326211
William Keller (Mng Dir)

ITW Global Tire Repair Inc. (1)
125 Venture Dr Ste 210, San Luis Obispo, CA 93401
Tel.: (805) 489-0490
Web Site: https://www.itwgtr.com
Tire Repairing Services
N.A.I.C.S.: 811198

ITW Graphics (1)
375 New State Rd, Manchester, CT 06042 (100%)
Tel.: (860) 646-8153
Web Site: http://www.itwgraphics.com
Sales Range: $50-74.9 Million
Emp.: 200
Heat Transfer Decals Mfr
N.A.I.C.S.: 323113

ITW Graphics (Thailand) Ltd. (1)
30/132 Moo 1 Chetsadawithi Road Khok Kham, Muang Samutsakhon, Samut Sakhon, 74000, Thailand
Tel.: (66) 24022180
Web Site: http://www.itwgraphics.com
Industrial Machinery Whslr
N.A.I.C.S.: 423830

ITW Graphics Asia Limited (1)
3/F 47 Hung To Road, Kwun Tong, Kowloon, China (Hong Kong)
Tel.: (852) 3 589 2000
Web Site: http://www.itwgraphics.com
Printing Machinery Mfr
N.A.I.C.S.: 333248

ITW Graphics Korea Co. Ltd. (1)
1619 East Hanshin Inter-valley B/D 707-34

Yeoksam-dong, Kangnam-gu, Seoul, 135-080, Korea (South)
Tel.: (82) 221830066
Printing Machinery Mfr
N.A.I.C.S.: 333248

ITW Gunther S.A.S. (1)
Zone Industrielle des Joncs, Tournus, 71700, France
Tel.: (33) 385322380
Web Site: http://www.itwgunther.com
Industrial Machinery Mfr
N.A.I.C.S.: 333517
Abderrahim Rachidia (Mgr)

ITW Heartland - Standard Machines (1)
1205 36th Ave, Alexandria, MN 56308
Tel.: (320) 762-0138
Web Site: https://www.itwheartland.com
Sales Range: $25-49.9 Million
Emp.: 80
Custom Automated Machine Mfr & Builder
N.A.I.C.S.: 333248

ITW Heartland Gears (1)
1205 36th Ave W, Alexandria, MN 56308-3304
Tel.: (320) 762-0138
Web Site: https://www.itwheartland.com
Sales Range: $25-49.9 Million
Emp.: 80
Precision Instruments & Systems
N.A.I.C.S.: 332710

ITW Hi-Cone (1)
1140 W Bryn Mawr Ave, Itasca, IL 60143-1509 (100%)
Tel.: (630) 438-5300
Web Site: https://www.hi-cone.com
Sales Range: $50-74.9 Million
Emp.: 100
Packaging Systems Mfr
N.A.I.C.S.: 333993

ITW Highland (1)
1240 Wolcott St, Waterbury, CT 06705
Tel.: (203) 574-3200
Web Site: https://www.itwhighland.com
Sales Range: $50-74.9 Million
Emp.: 150
Industrial Machinery & Equipment Mfr
N.A.I.C.S.: 333310

Division (Domestic):

ITW Drawform (2)
500 N Fairview Rd, Zeeland, MI 49464
Tel.: (616) 772-1910
Web Site: https://www.itwdrawform.com
Sales Range: $75-99.9 Million
Metal Stamping Mfr
N.A.I.C.S.: 332119

ITW Imagedata (1)
Factory Lane, Brantham, Manningtree, CO11 1NL, Essex, United Kingdom
Tel.: (44) 1206 716200
Web Site: http://www.itw-imagedata.com
Sales Range: $25-49.9 Million
Emp.: 50
Mfr of Coatings for Polyethylene Films Used in Card Printing
N.A.I.C.S.: 326113

ITW Imtran (1)
475 N Gary Ave, Carol Stream, IL 60188-1820
Tel.: (978) 372-3443
Sales Range: $10-24.9 Million
Pad Printing Supplies & Machine Accessories
N.A.I.C.S.: 322230

ITW India Limited (1)
No 995/2/1 Dingrajwadi Near Kalyani Sharp Pune Nagar Road, Near Kalyani Sharp Dingrajwadi, Pune, 412207, Maharashtra, India (96.67%)
Tel.: (91) 9921993395
Web Site: http://www.itwindia.com
Sales Range: $10-24.9 Million
Emp.: 30
Steel & Plastic Strapping, Stretch Film, Pressure Sensitive Carton Sealing Tape Equipment & Accessories
N.A.I.C.S.: 325520

ITW Industrial Finishing (1)
195 Internationale Blvd, Glendale Heights, IL 60139-2092

Tel.: (630) 237-5000
Web Site: http://www.itwif.com
Sales Range: $25-49.9 Million
Emp.: 55
Industrial Spray Finishing Equipment Mfr
N.A.I.C.S.: 333914

ITW Industry B.V. (1)
Van Heemskerckweg 1a, Postbus 3069, 5902 RB, Venlo, Netherlands
Tel.: (31) 773999600
Web Site: http://www.itwindustry.nl
Electronic Equipment Mfr & Distr
N.A.I.C.S.: 334419

ITW Insulation Systems Malaysia Sdn Bhd (1)
Lot PT33 Jalan 2 Kawasan Perindustrian Salak Tinggi, 43900, Sepang, Selangor Darul Ehsan, Malaysia
Tel.: (60) 387062486
Web Site: https://www.temperlite.com.my
Insulator Mfr
N.A.I.C.S.: 335932

ITW International Holdings LLC (1)
3600 W Lake Ave, Glenview, IL 60026
Tel.: (847) 724-7500
Holding Company
N.A.I.C.S.: 551112

ITW Ireland (1)
Farm Lane, Kinsale, P17 K223, Cork, Ireland
Tel.: (353) 214772050
Web Site: http://www.itwspi.com
Emp.: 50
Industrial Machinery Whslr
N.A.I.C.S.: 423830
Joanne Hayes (Mng Dir)

ITW Japan Ltd. (1)
1-4-4 Kitasuna, Koto-Ku, Tokyo, 136-0073, Japan
Tel.: (81) 356337100
Web Site: http://www.buehler.com
Industrial Machinery Mfr
N.A.I.C.S.: 333517

ITW LLC & Co. KG (1)
Muhlacker Strasse 149, 75417, Muhlacker, Germany
Tel.: (49) 704196340
Web Site: https://www.itwcp.de
Chemical Products Mfr
N.A.I.C.S.: 325199

ITW Limited (1)
(100%)
Tel.: (44) 1753836800
Web Site: http://www.itwcp.co.uk
Sales Range: $10-24.9 Million
Emp.: 25
Fastener Mfr
N.A.I.C.S.: 339993

ITW Lys Fusion S.r.l. (1)
Via Le Bois-Vuillermoz 30, Pralormo, 11020, Hone, Italy
Tel.: (39) 0125800500
Web Site: http://www.itw-efc.com
Industrial Equipment Mfr
N.A.I.C.S.: 332510

ITW Magnaflux (1)
155 Harlem Ave, Glenview, IL 60025
Tel.: (847) 657-5300
Web Site: https://www.magnaflux.com
Sales Range: $10-24.9 Million
Emp.: 25
Magnetic Particle & Dye Penetrant Inspection Equipment Mfr & Supplier
N.A.I.C.S.: 334513

ITW Marking & Coding (Shanghai) Co., Ltd. (1)
Bldg 9 Unit 1 Section E 353 Ri Ying North Rd China Shanghai, Pilot Free Trade Zone, Shanghai, 200131, China
Tel.: (86) 2151379159
Web Site: http://www.diagraph.com
Industrial Equipment Mfr
N.A.I.C.S.: 332510

ITW Medical Products Inc (1)
11411 Price Rd, Hebron, IL 60034-8936
Tel.: (815) 648-2416
Web Site: https://www.itwmedical.com
Medical & Surgical Instrument Mfr
N.A.I.C.S.: 339112

ITW Meritex Sdn. Bhd. (1)
Bayan Lepas FIZ Phase 3, 11900, Penang, Malaysia
Tel.: (60) 48207100
Web Site: http://www.itwecps.com
Packaging Machinery Mfr
N.A.I.C.S.: 333993

ITW Metal Fasteners, S.L. (1)
Passeig Can Feu 60-66, 08205, Sabadell, Spain
Tel.: (34) 93 700 7700
Web Site: https://itwmikalor.es
Metal Stamping Mfr
N.A.I.C.S.: 332119

ITW Mima Systems S.A.S. (1)
26 Rue Paul Girod, 73000, Chambery, France
Tel.: (33) 479685353
Packaging Machinery Mfr
N.A.I.C.S.: 333993

ITW Morlock GmbH (1)
Lise Meitner Street 9, Dornstetten, 72280, Freudenstadt, Germany
Tel.: (49) 7 443 2850
Web Site: https://itwmorlock.com
Printing Machinery Mfr
N.A.I.C.S.: 333248

ITW Mortgage Investments II, Inc. (1)
16479 Dallas Pkwy Ste 500, Addison, TX 75001
Tel.: (972) 447-2529
Emp.: 3
Real Estate Manangement Services
N.A.I.C.S.: 531390

ITW Motion (1)
21601 S Harlem Ave, Frankfort, IL 60423
Tel.: (708) 720-0300
Web Site: http://www.itwmotion.com
Emp.: 80
Plastic Automotive Products Mfr
N.A.I.C.S.: 326199

ITW Muller (1)
16715 Hymus Blvd, Kirkland, H9H 5M8, QC, Canada (100%)
Tel.: (514) 426-9248
Web Site: http://www.itwmuller.com
Sales Range: $10-24.9 Million
Emp.: 70
Packaging Machinery Mfr
N.A.I.C.S.: 333993

ITW New Zealand Limited (1)
Level 7 The Bayleys Building 28 Brandon st, Wellington, 632, New Zealand (100%)
Tel.: (64) 94773000
Web Site: https://www.paslode.co.nz
Sales Range: $10-24.9 Million
Emp.: 35
Packaging Products Mfr
N.A.I.C.S.: 322220

ITW Nexus (1)
21601 S Harlem Ave, Frankfort, IL 60423
Tel.: (708) 720-3025
Web Site: https://na.itwnexus.com
Sales Range: $75-99.9 Million
Emp.: 200
Plastic Buckles & Hardware Products Mfr
N.A.I.C.S.: 326199

ITW Nexus UK (1)
Unit 12 Bilton Rd Kingsland Industrial Estate, Basingstoke, RG24 8NJ, Hampshire, United Kingdom (100%)
Tel.: (44) 1256317663
Web Site: https://www.itwnexus.com
Sales Range: $150-199.9 Million
Emp.: 50
Plastic Buckles, Engineered Closures & Components Sales
N.A.I.C.S.: 423710

ITW PPF Brasil Adesivos Ltda. (1)
Rua Antonio Felamingo 430, Macuco, Valinhos, 13279-452, Sao Paulo, Brazil
Tel.: (55) 1921387600
Web Site: http://www.itwpolymers.com.br
Chemical Products Mfr
N.A.I.C.S.: 325520

ITW Performance Plastic (Shanghai) Co., Ltd. (1)
JiangSu Rd, Shanghai, 200050, China

Tel.: (86) 2152300521
Specialty Products & Equipment Mfr
N.A.I.C.S.: 333998
Tracy Wang *(Bus Mgr)*

ITW Performance Polymers & Fluids Japan Co. Ltd.   **(1)**
30-32 Enoki-cho, Suita, 564-0053, Osaka, Japan
Tel.: (81) 663307118
Web Site: https://www.itwppfjapan.com
Emp.: 18
Adhesive Distr
N.A.I.C.S.: 424690

ITW Performance Polymers & Fluids OOO   **(1)**
Novoryazanskaya Str 18 Bld 16, 107891, Moscow, Russia
Tel.: (7) 4959333424
Web Site: http://www.itwppf.ru
Chemical Products Distr
N.A.I.C.S.: 424690

ITW Performance Polymers & Fluids Pte. Ltd.   **(1)**
73 Upper Paya Lebar Rd 02-04 Centro Bianco, Singapore, 534818, Singapore
Tel.: (65) 62812996
Web Site: http://www.itwpolymersasia.com
Chemical Products Distr
N.A.I.C.S.: 424690

ITW Performance Polymers ApS   **(1)**
Rordalsvej 44, 9220, Aalborg, Denmark
Tel.: (45) 98167011
Industrial Equipment Distr
N.A.I.C.S.: 423830

ITW Performance Polymers Trading (Shanghai) Co. Ltd.   **(1)**
10 27F Xingyuan Building No 418 Guiping Rd Cao He Jing Hi-Tech Park, Shanghai, China
Tel.: (86) 2154261212
Web Site: http://www.itwppfchina.com
Chemical Products Mfr
N.A.I.C.S.: 325520
Bruce Kang *(Mng Dir)*

ITW Permatex, Inc.   **(1)**
10 Columbus Blvd, Hartford, CT 06106
Tel.: (860) 543-7500
Web Site: https://www.permatex.com
Rev.: $12,300,000
Emp.: 40
Adhesive, Sealant & Cleaning Product Mfr
N.A.I.C.S.: 325520

Subsidiary (Domestic):

Spray Nine Corporation   **(2)**
309 W Montgomery St, Johnstown, NY 12095-2435
Tel.: (518) 762-4591
Web Site: http://www.spraynine.com
Specialty Cleaning Product Mfr
N.A.I.C.S.: 325612

Subsidiary (Non-US):

ITW Permatex Canada   **(3)**
35 Brownridge Road Unit 1, Halton Hills, L7G 0C6, ON, Canada
Tel.: (905) 693-8900
Web Site: http://www.permatex.com
Sales Range: $150-199.9 Million
Emp.: 25
Cleaning Product Mfr
N.A.I.C.S.: 325612

ITW Philadelphia Resins   **(1)**
130 Commerce Dr, Montgomeryville, PA 18936-9624   **(100%)**
Tel.: (215) 855-8450
Web Site: http://www.philadelphiaresins.com
Sales Range: $25-49.9 Million
Emp.: 60
Polymer-Based Grouting, Chocking, Coatings, Castables & Other Specialized Products Mfr
N.A.I.C.S.: 325211
Rick Budweg *(Gen Mgr)*

ITW Plastiglide   **(1)**
952 South Main St PO Box 1188, Waterbury, CT 06721   **(100%)**
Tel.: (203) 753-1161
Sales Range: $25-49.9 Million
Emp.: 50
Casters & Wheels Mfr

N.A.I.C.S.: 332510

ITW Poly Mex, S. de R.L. de C.V.   **(1)**
Avenida del Marques 40 Parque Industrial Bernardo Quintana, Queretaro, 76246, El Marques, Queretaro, Mexico   **(100%)**
Tel.: (52) 5550892870
Web Site: https://www.itwpolymex.com
Adhesive Mfr
N.A.I.C.S.: 325520

ITW Polymers & Fluids Pty. Ltd.   **(1)**
100 Hassall Street, Wetherill Park, 2164, NSW, Australia   **(100%)**
Tel.: (61) 800000945
Web Site: https://www.itwpf.com.au
Sales Range: $50-74.9 Million
Emp.: 30
Chemicals & Plastics Mfr
N.A.I.C.S.: 325998

Subsidiary (Domestic):

Epirez Construction Products Pty Limited   **(2)**
100 Hassall St, PO Box 35, Wetherill Park, Sydney, 2164, New South Wales, Australia
Tel.: (61) 297578800
Web Site: http://www.itwpf.com.au
Chemical Construction Products Mfr
N.A.I.C.S.: 424690

ITW Polymers Adhesives North America   **(1)**
30 Endicott St, Danvers, MA 01923
Tel.: (978) 777-1100
Web Site: http://www.itwadhesives.com
Adhesive & Sealant Mfr
N.A.I.C.S.: 325520

ITW Polymers Sealants North America Inc.   **(1)**
12055 Cutten Rd, Houston, TX 77066
Tel.: (972) 438-9111
Web Site: https://itwsealants.com
Sales Range: $10-24.9 Million
Emp.: 100
Sealants
N.A.I.C.S.: 325520

Branch (Domestic):

ITW Polymers Sealants North America Inc. - Eastern Division Office   **(2)**
6385 Atlantic Blvd A, Norcross, GA 30071
Tel.: (770) 448-6801
Web Site: http://www.schnee-morehead.com
Emp.: 25
Adhesive Mfr
N.A.I.C.S.: 325520

ITW Polymex, S. DE R.L. DE C.V.   **(1)**
Avenida de la Industria s/n Manzana 1 L-5 y 6 Parque, Industrial del Convento Colonia El Trebol Tepotzotlan, Tepotzotlan, 54614, Mexico
Tel.: (52) 5550892870
Web Site: https://www.itwpolymex.com
Emp.: 150
Chemical Products Distr
N.A.I.C.S.: 424690

ITW Powertrain Fastening   **(1)**
2001 Buck Ln, Lexington, KY 40511
Tel.: (859) 255-6400
Web Site: http://www.crestproducts.com
Sales Range: $10-24.9 Million
Emp.: 155
Metal Fasteners Mfr
N.A.I.C.S.: 332722
Lee Wallace *(Mgr-Sls)*
Jeremy Tuttle *(Mgr-Bus Dev)*

ITW Produx   **(1)**
3700 West Lake Ave, Glenview, IL 60026   **(100%)**
Tel.: (847) 657-5100
Sales Range: $75-99.9 Million
Emp.: 24
Highly Engineered Products for Vehicle Chassis & Suspensions Designer & Mfr
N.A.I.C.S.: 332999

ITW Ramset/Red Head   **(1)**
155 Harlem Ave, Glenview, IL 60025
Tel.: (630) 350-0370
Web Site: https://www.ramset.com

Sales Range: $75-99.9 Million
Emp.: 30
Fastening Products Designer & Mfr
N.A.I.C.S.: 332510

ITW Real Estate Management GmbH   **(1)**
Magnusstrasse 18, 46535, Dinslaken, Germany
Tel.: (49) 704196340
Real Estate Manangement Services
N.A.I.C.S.: 531390

ITW Reyflex France S.A.S.   **(1)**
Zone Industrielle les Pochons 488 Avenue des Bouleaux, Thyez, 74300, France
Tel.: (33) 450981388
Electric Equipment Mfr
N.A.I.C.S.: 334419

ITW Richmond Technology   **(1)**
95 Commerce Dr, Somerset, NJ 88733-3469   **(100%)**
Tel.: (732) 873-5500
Web Site: http://www.richmond-technology.com
Sales Range: $100-124.9 Million
Emp.: 40
Grounding Products, Mats, Monitors & Test Equipment Mfr, Sales & Distr
N.A.I.C.S.: 423830

ITW Rippey Corporation   **(1)**
5000 Hillsdale Cir, El Dorado Hills, CA 95762
Tel.: (916) 939-4332
Web Site: https://www.rippey.com
Sales Range: $10-24.9 Million
Emp.: 74
Computers, Peripherals & Software
N.A.I.C.S.: 423430

ITW Rivex S.A.S.   **(1)**
Route De Lonege, 25290, Ornans, 25290, France
Tel.: (33) 381624100
Industrial Machinery Whslr
N.A.I.C.S.: 423830

ITW Rocol   **(1)**
ROCOL House Wakefield Road, Swillington, Leeds, LS26 8BS, United Kingdom
Tel.: (44) 1132322600
Web Site: https://www.rocol.com
Sales Range: $25-49.9 Million
Emp.: 10
Oil & Grease Mfr
N.A.I.C.S.: 324191

ITW SMPI S.A.S.   **(1)**
525 avenue d'italie, 74300, Cluses, France
Tel.: (33) 450980749
Plastics Product Mfr
N.A.I.C.S.: 325211
Batot Bertrand *(Gen Mgr)*

ITW Shakeproof   **(1)**
2002 Stephenson Hwy, Troy, MI 48083   **(100%)**
Tel.: (248) 589-2500
Web Site:
   https://shakeproof.itwautomotive.com
Sales Range: $150-199.9 Million
Emp.: 700
Fasteners Mfr & Distr
N.A.I.C.S.: 339993

ITW Shakeproof Automotive Products   **(1)**
100 Kirts Blvd, Troy, MI 48084
Tel.: (248) 589-2500
Web Site: https://www.itwshakeproof.com
Sales Range: $75-99.9 Million
Emp.: 85
Plastic & Metal Fasteners Mfr
N.A.I.C.S.: 326199

ITW Shakeproof Group   **(1)**
W 6331 Bee Rd, Watertown, WI 53098   **(100%)**
Tel.: (920) 261-2652
Web Site: https://www.shakeproof.com
Sales Range: $10-24.9 Million
Emp.: 50
Threaded Fastener Assemblies & Products Mfr
N.A.I.C.S.: 339993

ITW Shippers S.p.r.l.   **(1)**
Rue Louis De Brouckere 66, La Louviere, 7100, Belgium

Tel.: (32) 64430511
Web Site: http://www.itw-shippers.com
Emp.: 7
Miscellaneous General Purpose Machinery Mfr
N.A.I.C.S.: 333998

ITW Spain Holdings, S.L.   **(1)**
Carretera Ribes Corro D Avall Km 31 7 Les Franqueses Del Valles, 8520, Barcelona, Spain
Tel.: (34) 938443125
Financial Management Services
N.A.I.C.S.: 551112

ITW Specialty Film LLC   **(1)**
5F Rocket Bldg 747-29 Yeoksam Dong Kangnam-ku, Teheran-ro Gangnam-gu, Seoul, 135 080, Korea (South)
Tel.: (82) 221049200
Web Site: http://www.itwsfk.co.kr
Emp.: 100
Coating Mfr
N.A.I.C.S.: 325510

ITW Specialty Films Italy S.r.l.   **(1)**
Strada per Solero Zona Industriale D 4, Valenza, 15048, Italy
Tel.: (39) 0131973211
Web Site: http://www.itwspecialtyfilms.it
Emp.: 20
Plastics Product Mfr
N.A.I.C.S.: 325211

ITW Specialty Materials (Suzhou) Co., Ltd.   **(1)**
Hengqiao Road, Wujiang Economic Development Z, Suzhou, 215200, Jiangsu, China
Tel.: (86) 51263033700
Web Site: http://www.itw.com
Coating Mfr
N.A.I.C.S.: 325510

ITW Speedline Equipment (Suzhou) Co. Ltd.   **(1)**
Blk F Export Processing Zone 200 Su Hong Middle Road, Suzhou Industrial Park, Suzhou, 215021, Jiangsu, China
Tel.: (86) 51262588850
Electric Equipment Mfr
N.A.I.C.S.: 334419

ITW Spraytec S.A.S.   **(1)**
42 rue Gallieni, 92601, Asnieres-sur-Seine, Cedex, France
Tel.: (33) 140803232
Web Site: https://www.itwpc.com
Industrial Machinery Mfr
N.A.I.C.S.: 333248

ITW Stretch Packaging Parts & Technical Assistance   **(1)**
5271 NW 108th Ave, Tamarac, FL 33321   **(100%)**
Tel.: (954) 724-7788
Sales Range: $100-124.9 Million
Stretch Wrapping Machinery, Packaging Systems & Consumables Mfr
N.A.I.C.S.: 333998

ITW Sverige AB   **(1)**
As Bredaryd, 333 73, Varnamo, Sweden   **(100%)**
Tel.: (46) 37170500
Web Site: http://www.itw.se
Sales Range: $125-149.9 Million
Plastics Product Mfr
N.A.I.C.S.: 326199
Per-Arne Axelsson *(Gen Mgr)*

Division (Non-US):

ITW Switches   **(2)**
Edgington Way, Sidcup, DA14 5EF, Kent, United Kingdom   **(100%)**
Tel.: (44) 2083088000
Web Site: http://www.itwswitches.co.uk
Sales Range: $10-24.9 Million
Switch Mfr
N.A.I.C.S.: 335313

ITW Switches   **(1)**
195 E Algonquin Rd, Des Plaines, IL 60016
Tel.: (847) 376-6701
Web Site: https://www.itwswitches.com
Sales Range: $75-99.9 Million
Emp.: 250
Electrical Switches Mfr
N.A.I.C.S.: 334419

ITW TekFast   **(1)**

Illinois Tool Works Inc.—(Continued)

21555 S Harlem Ave, Frankfort, IL 60423
Tel.: (708) 720-2600
Web Site: https://www.itwtekfast.com
Sales Range: $150-199.9 Million
Emp.: 100
Injection Molded Routing & Fastening Products Mfr
N.A.I.C.S.: 326199

ITW Temb (QUFU) Automotive Cooling Systems Co. Ltd. (1)
Building 2 No 66 Tianying Rd, Qingpu District, Shanghai, 201700, China
Tel.: (86) 2169225880
Chemical Products Distr
N.A.I.C.S.: 424690

ITW Test & Measurement (China) Co., Ltd. (1)
No 15 Lane 1985 ChunShen Road Suzhou Industrial Park, Shanghai, 200237, China
Tel.: (86) 2154293761
Specialty Product & Equipment Mfr
N.A.I.C.S.: 333998
Daisy Wang (Controller-Fin)

ITW Test & Measurement GmbH (1)
Meisenweg 35, 70771, Leinfelden-Echterdingen, Germany
Tel.: (49) 7114 904 6900
Web Site: https://www.buehler-met.de
Industrial Machinery Mfr
N.A.I.C.S.: 333248

ITW Test & Measurement Italia Srl (1)
Via Airauda 12, 10044, Pianezza, Torino, Italy
Tel.: (39) 0119685511
Web Site: https://www.instron.com
Laboratory Equipment Mfr
N.A.I.C.S.: 334516

ITW Texwipe (1)
1210 S Park Dr, Kernersville, NC 27284
Tel.: (336) 996-7046
Web Site: https://www.texwipe.com
Sales Range: $10-24.9 Million
Emp.: 14
Contamination Control Supplies & Cleaning Products Mfr
N.A.I.C.S.: 325612

ITW Thermal Films (Shanghai) Co., Ltd. (1)
201 2nd Bldg No 1507 Hong Mei Road South, Shanghai, 200237, China
Tel.: (86) 215 430 5701
Web Site: https://www.itwthermalfilms.com
Coating Mfr
N.A.I.C.S.: 325510

ITW V.A.C. B.V. (1)
H A Lorentzstraat 1, 3331 EE, Zwijndrecht, Netherlands
Tel.: (31) 786126744
Web Site: http://www.vac-bv.nl
Cardboard Mfr
N.A.I.C.S.: 322130

ITW Welding Products B.V. (1)
Edisonstraat 10, 3261 LD, Oud-Beijerland, Netherlands
Tel.: (31) 18 664 1444
Web Site: https://www.itwwelding.com
Emp.: 20
Industrial Machinery Whslr
N.A.I.C.S.: 423830

ITW Welding Products Group FZE (1)
S3 A2SR10 Jebel Ali Free Zone, PO Box 16774, Dubai, United Arab Emirates
Tel.: (971) 4 255 9194
Web Site: https://www.itwwelding.com
Welding Equipment Mfr
N.A.I.C.S.: 333992

ITW Welding Products Italy Srl (1)
Via Primo Maggio 19/21, San Zenone al Lambro, 20070, Milan, Italy
Tel.: (39) 0298 2901
Web Site: https://www.itwwelding.com
Welding Equipment Mfr
N.A.I.C.S.: 333992

ITW Welding Products Limited Liability Company (1)

9 Neverovskogo Str Office 107, 121170, Moscow, Russia
Tel.: (7) 4952325329
Welding Product Distr
N.A.I.C.S.: 423840

ITW Zip-Pak Packaging (Shanghai) Ltd. (1)
Room A 20F Zhao-Feng World Trade Building No 369 Jiangsu Road, Shanghai, 200050, China
Tel.: (86) 2152300521
Packaging Material Distr
N.A.I.C.S.: 423840

ITW de France S.A.S. (1)
305 Chaussee Jules Cesar, 95250, Beauchamp, 95250, France (100%)
Tel.: (33) 130404040
Web Site: http://www.itw-fasteners.com
Plastics Product Mfr
N.A.I.C.S.: 326199

ITW do Brasil Industrial e Comercial Ltda. (1)
Rua Forte do Ribeira 271, Sao Paulo, 08340-145, Brazil
Tel.: (55) 1120147455
Web Site: http://www.itwpack.com.br
Industrial Machinery Whslr
N.A.I.C.S.: 423830

Impar Comercio E Representacoes Ltda. (1)
Av 15 De Novembro 191A Campos dos Goytacazes, Rio de Janeiro, 28035, Brazil
Tel.: (55) 247232729
Emp.: 2
Automotive Part Whslr
N.A.I.C.S.: 423120

Industria e Comercio de Maquinas Perfecta Curitiba Ltda. (1)
Rod Do Cafe, Curitiba, 82305, Parana, Brazil
Tel.: (55) 4133701000
Emp.: 250
Food Product Machinery Mfr
N.A.I.C.S.: 332510

Industrie Plastic Elsasser GmbH (1)
Saarburger Ring 11, 68229, Mannheim, Germany
Tel.: (49) 6214802530
Web Site: http://www.ipe-mannheim.de
Industrial Machinery Whslr
N.A.I.C.S.: 423830
Jens Sturies (CEO)
Daniela Engelen (Mgr-Quality)

Inmobiliaria Cit., S.A. de C.V. (1)
Calle Emilio Cardenas Suite 166 Colonia Industrial Center Tlalnepantla, Tlalnepantla, 50040, Tlalnepantla De Baz, Mexico
Tel.: (52) 15553215250
Industrial Machinery Mfr
N.A.I.C.S.: 423830

Instron (Shanghai) Ltd. (1)
Room 1708 Shanghai CVIC Plaza No 819 Nanjing Road W, Shanghai, 200041, China
Tel.: (86) 2162158568
Industrial Equipment Mfr & Distr
N.A.I.C.S.: 333248

Instron Brasil Equipamentos Cientificos Ltda. (1)
Rua Quirino Zagonel 257, Pinhais, Sao Jose dos Pinhais, 83020-250, Parana, Brazil
Tel.: (55) 4130359400
Web Site: https://www.emic.com.br
Tooting Instrument Mfr
N.A.I.C.S.: 334519
Scott Santi (CEO)

Instron Corporation (1)
825 University Ave, Norwood, MA 02062
Tel.: (781) 575-5246
Web Site: https://www.instron.com
Sales Range: $200-249.9 Million
Emp.: 350
Markets & Services Materials; Structural Testing Systems, Software & Accessories Mfr
N.A.I.C.S.: 334519

Holding (Non-US):

Equipamentos Cientificos Instron Ltda. (2)

Alameda Tocantins 280, Alphaville Ind Barueri, Sao Paulo, 06455-020, Brazil (100%)
Tel.: (55) 1146895496
Sales Range: $25-49.9 Million
Emp.: 3
Testing Equipment Sales & Services
N.A.I.C.S.: 423830

Instron Deutschland GmbH (2)
Landwehrstrasse 65, 64293, Darmstadt, Germany (100%)
Tel.: (49) 615139170
Web Site: https://www.instron.com
Sales Range: $25-49.9 Million
Emp.: 55
Testing Equipment Sales & Services
N.A.I.C.S.: 423830

Subsidiary (Domestic):

Instron Industrial Products Group (2)
900 Liberty St, Grove City, PA 16127-9045
Tel.: (724) 458-9610
Web Site: http://www.instron.com
Sales Range: $25-49.9 Million
Emp.: 85
Physical Properties Testing Equipment Mfr
N.A.I.C.S.: 334519

Holding (Non-US):

Instron Japan Co. Ltd. (2)
1-8-9 Miyamaedaira, Miyamae Ward, Kawasaki, 216-0006, Kanagawa-ken, Japan (100%)
Tel.: (81) 448538520
Web Site: https://www.instron.jp
Sales Range: $25-49.9 Million
Emp.: 40
Testing Equipment Sales & Services
N.A.I.C.S.: 423830

Instron Limited (2)
Coronation Road, High Wycombe, HP12 3SY, Buckinghamshire, United Kingdom (100%)
Tel.: (44) 1494456815
Web Site: https://www.instron.com
Sales Range: $50-74.9 Million
Emp.: 350
Instruments & Systems for Advanced Materials Testing Mfr & Distr
N.A.I.C.S.: 334511

Instron Pty. Ltd. (2)
15 Stud Rd Factory 15, PO Box 352, Bayswater, Melbourne, 3153, VIC, Australia (100%)
Tel.: (61) 397203477
Web Site: http://www.instron.com.au
Sales Range: $25-49.9 Million
Emp.: 6
Testing Equipment Sales & Services
N.A.I.C.S.: 459410

Instron S.A.S. (2)
3 boulevard Jean Moulin Omega Parc Batiment 2, Batiment C, 78990, Elancourt, France (100%)
Tel.: (33) 139306630
Web Site: http://www.instron.tm.fr
Sales Range: $25-49.9 Million
Emp.: 30
Test Equipment Sales & Mfr
N.A.I.C.S.: 459410

Instron France S.A.S. (1)
3 boulevard Jean Moulin Omega Parc Batiment 2, 78990, Elancourt, Cedex, France
Tel.: (33) 139306630
Web Site: http://www.instron.fr
Industrial Machinery Whslr
N.A.I.C.S.: 423830

Instron GmbH (1)
Landwehrstrasse 65, 64293, Darmstadt, Germany
Tel.: (49) 61513917457
Industrial Equipment Mfr & Distr
N.A.I.C.S.: 333248

Instron Korea LLC (1)
16FI Hae-Am Building Daechi-dong 325 Yonungdongdae-ro, Gangnam-gu, Seoul, 06188, Korea (South)
Tel.: (82) 2 552 2311
Web Site: https://www.instron.com
Emp.: 26
Industrial Machinery Whslr
N.A.I.C.S.: 423830

Instron Singapore Pte Limited (1)
3A International Business Park ICON IBP 06-16, Singapore, 609935, Singapore
Tel.: (65) 65860838
Web Site: http://www.instron.com.sg
Emp.: 26
General Purpose Machinery Mfr
N.A.I.C.S.: 333998

Instron Structural Testing Systems GmbH (1)
Landwehrstrasse 65, Darmstadt, 64293, Germany
Tel.: (49) 615139170
Web Site: http://www.instron.com
Emp.: 150
Industrial Machinery Mfr
N.A.I.C.S.: 333517
Graham Rogers (Mng Dir)

International Leasing Company LLC (1)
3337 Calder Ave, Beaumont, TX 77706
Tel.: (409) 833-8021
Web Site: http://www.itw.com
Industrial Machinery Leasing Services
N.A.I.C.S.: 532490

International Truss Systems Proprietary Limited (1)
28 Bisset Rd Jet Park, Boksburg, 1469, Gauteng, South Africa
Tel.: (27) 113974441
Web Site: https://www.rooftruss.co.za
Emp.: 50
Software Development Services
N.A.I.C.S.: 513210
Emmanuel Piyackis (Mng Dir)

Isolenge Termo Construcoes Ltda. (1)
Silvabuino St No 1808 Apartment 72, Sao Paulo, 04208-001, Brazil
Tel.: (55) 1129690311
Web Site: http://www.isolenge.com.br
Emp.: 3
Industrial Machinery Distr
N.A.I.C.S.: 423610

Japan Polymark Co. Ltd. (1)
45-300 Shimizusugitanicho, Fukui, 910-3607, Japan
Tel.: (81) 776982233
Web Site: https://www.polymark.co.jp
Emp.: 145
Industrial Machinery Mfr
N.A.I.C.S.: 333248

Jetline Engineering (1)
15 Goodyear St, Irvine, CA 92618
Tel.: (949) 951-1515
Web Site: http://www.millerwelds.com
Sales Range: $25-49.9 Million
Emp.: 35
Welding Product Mfr
N.A.I.C.S.: 333992

Josef Kihlberg AB (1)
Industrigatan 37B, 544 50, Hjo, Sweden
Tel.: (46) 50332800
Web Site: https://kihlberg.com
Emp.: 35
Packaging Material Distr
N.A.I.C.S.: 423840

KaiRak Inc. (1)
1158 N Gilbert St, Anaheim, CA 92801
Tel.: (714) 870-8661
Web Site: http://www.kairak.com
Sales Range: $50-74.9 Million
Emp.: 130
Commercial Refrigeration Equipment Mfr
N.A.I.C.S.: 333415

Kester Components (M) Sdn. Bhd. (1)
Plo 113 Phase 3 Kawasan Perindustrian Senai, 81400, Senai, Johor, Malaysia
Tel.: (60) 75984113
Web Site: http://www.kester.com
Emp.: 1
Industrial Supplies Merchant Whslr
N.A.I.C.S.: 423840

Kiwiplan GmbH (1)
Mina-Rees-Str 5, 64295, Darmstadt, Germany
Tel.: (49) 6151860990
Web Site: http://www.kiwiplan.com
Software Development Services

N.A.I.C.S.: 541511

Kiwiplan Inc. (1)
7870 E Kemper Rd Ste 200, Cincinnati, OH 45249
Tel.: (656) 444-9855
Web Site: http://www.kiwiplan.com
Sales Range: $25-49.9 Million
Emp.: 43
Software Development Sales & Technical Support Services
N.A.I.C.S.: 541511
Rodney McGee (Pres)

Kleinmann GmbH (1)
Am Trieb 13, Sonnenbuhl, 72820, Reutlingen, Germany
Tel.: (49) 71 289 2920
Web Site: https://www.kleinmann.net
Emp.: 40
Industrial Machinery Mfr
N.A.I.C.S.: 333248
Thomas Brown (Head-Logistics)

Lachenmeier ApS (1)
Fynsgade 6-10, 6400, Sonderborg, Denmark
Tel.: (45) 73422200
Web Site: http://www.lachenmeier.com
Emp.: 75
Industrial Machinery Mfr
N.A.I.C.S.: 333248
Gynter Lorenzen (Mng Dir)

Liljendals Bruk AB (1)
Krogarintie 9 Liljendal, 07880, Lovisa, Southern Finland, Finland
Tel.: (358) 207969818
Fabricated Metal Products Mfr
N.A.I.C.S.: 332312

Lock Inspection Systemes France Sarl (1)
12 Avenue du Quebec Silic Bat H 8, 91140, Villebon-sur-Yvette, France
Tel.: (33) 169591620
Industrial Machinery & Equipment Mfr
N.A.I.C.S.: 333998

Lock Inspection Systems BV (1)
Daalderweg 17, 4879 AX, Etten-Leur, Netherlands
Tel.: (31) 765030212
Industrial Machinery Mfr
N.A.I.C.S.: 333248

Lock Inspection Systems Limited (1)
Lock House Neville Street, Oldham, OL9 6LF, Lancashire, United Kingdom
Tel.: (44) 1616240333
Web Site: http://www.lockinspection.com
Industrial Machinery Mfr
N.A.I.C.S.: 333248

Loma Systems BV (1)
Steenovenweg 44, 5708 HN, Helmond, Netherlands
Tel.: (31) 765030212
Web Site: https://www.loma.com
Metal Detector Mfr
N.A.I.C.S.: 334519

Loma Systems Ltd (1)
Summit Avenue, Farnborough, GU14 0NY, Hampshire, United Kingdom (100%)
Tel.: (44) 1252893300
Web Site: https://www.loma.com
Sales Range: $25-49.9 Million
Emp.: 60
Food, Pharmaceutical & Textile Inspection Systems
N.A.I.C.S.: 333248

Subsidiary (Non-US):

Loma Systems (Canada) Inc. (2)
333 Wyecroft Road, Oakville, L6K 2H2, ON, Canada
Tel.: (905) 842-4581
Web Site: http://www.loma.com
Industrial Machinery Whslr
N.A.I.C.S.: 423830

Subsidiary (US):

Loma Systems-Illinois (2)
550 Kehoe Blvd, Carol Stream, IL 60188-1838
Tel.: (630) 588-0900
Web Site: https://www.loma.com

Sales Range: $25-49.9 Million
Emp.: 25
End-of-Line Inspection System Designer & Mfr
N.A.I.C.S.: 333248

Subsidiary (Domestic):

Magnaflux Limited (2)
Faraway Rd S Dorcan Industrial Estate, Swindon, SN3 5HE, Wiltshire, United Kingdom (100%)
Tel.: (44) 1793524566
Web Site: http://www.eu.magnaflux.com
Sales Range: $10-24.9 Million
Emp.: 25
Penetrant & Magnetic Particle Processing Materials, Equipment & Accessories Mfr
N.A.I.C.S.: 325613

Loma Systems sro (1)
U Lomy 1069, 334 41, Dobrany, Czech Republic
Tel.: (420) 377183810
Web Site: http://www.loma.com
Industrial Machinery Mfr
N.A.I.C.S.: 333248

Loveshaw (1)
2206 Easton Tpke, South Canaan, PA 18459
Tel.: (570) 937-4921
Web Site: https://www.loveshaw.com
Sales Range: $25-49.9 Million
Emp.: 70
Corrugated Box Sealing Machinery Mfr
N.A.I.C.S.: 333993

Lumex, Inc. (1)
425 N Gary Ave, Carol Stream, IL 60188
Web Site: https://www.lumex.com
Emp.: 30
Electric Equipment Mfr
N.A.I.C.S.: 334419

M&C Specialties Company (1)
90 James Way, Southampton, PA 18966
Tel.: (215) 322-1600
Web Site: https://www.mcspecialties.com
Sales Range: $100-124.9 Million
Emp.: 2,000
Distr & Converter of Pressure Sensitive Tapes
N.A.I.C.S.: 322220

Subsidiary (Non-US):

M&C Specialties (Ireland) Limited (2)
Athlone Business & Technology Park, Dublin Road, Athlone, Co Westmeath, Ireland (100%)
Tel.: (353) 906476900
Web Site: http://www.mcspecialties.com
Sales Range: $10-24.9 Million
Emp.: 16
Diecutter & Distributor of Pressure Sensitive Tape Products
N.A.I.C.S.: 322216

MAGNAFLUX GmbH (1)
Tel.: (49) 7365810
Web Site: https://maconaflux.eu
Industrial Machinery Mfr
N.A.I.C.S.: 333248

MTS Europe Holdings LLC (1)
14000 Technology Dr, Eden Prairie, MN 55344
Tel.: (952) 937-4000
Web Site: https://www.mts.com
Emp.: 1,700
Technical Consulting Services
N.A.I.C.S.: 541690

Magna Industrial Company Limited (1)
1801 Guardian House 32 Oi Kwan Road, Wanchai, China (Hong Kong)
Tel.: (852) 25775187
Web Site: http://www.magnagroup.com
Industrial Machinery Mfr
N.A.I.C.S.: 333248

Maxal International, Inc. (1)
1631 International Dr, Traverse City, MI 49686
Tel.: (231) 933-1234
Web Site: http://www.maxal.com
Electric Equipment Mfr
N.A.I.C.S.: 335999

Meritex Technology (Suzhou) Co. Ltd. (1)
Land No 1 Factory Building Kuatang Sub-District Suzhou Industrial Park, Suzhou, 215122, China
Tel.: (86) 51262746798
Electric Equipment Mfr
N.A.I.C.S.: 335999

Meurer Verpackungssysteme Gmbh (1)
Von-Tambach-Strasse 3-5, Fürstenau, 49584, Osnabruck, Germany
Tel.: (49) 59019550
Web Site: http://www.meurer-group.com
Emp.: 600
Industrial Machinery Mfr
N.A.I.C.S.: 333248

Mezger Heftsysteme Gmbh (1)
Saganer Str 24, 90475, Nuremberg, Germany
Tel.: (49) 911984940
Web Site: https://www.mezger.eu
Industrial Machinery Mfr
N.A.I.C.S.: 333248

Midwest Industrial Packaging, Inc. (1)
1940 Usg Dr, Libertyville, IL 60048
Tel.: (847) 918-0220
Web Site: http://www.miptools.com
Sales Range: $25-49.9 Million
Emp.: 25
Hand Packaging Tools Mfr
N.A.I.C.S.: 332216

Miller Electric Manufacturing Co. (1)
1635 W Spencer St, Appleton, WI 54912-1079 (100%)
Tel.: (920) 734-9821
Web Site: https://www.millerwelds.com
Sales Range: $400-449.9 Million
Welding & Cutting Equipment Mfr
N.A.I.C.S.: 333992

Mima Films Sprl (1)
Zoning Industriel De Latour, Virton, 6761, Luxembourg, Belgium
Tel.: (32) 63588700
Chemical Products Mfr
N.A.I.C.S.: 325520

Minigrip/Zip-Pak (1)
1650 N Heideke St, Seguin, TX 78155
Tel.: (830) 433-6033
Web Site: http://www.minigrip.com
Sales Range: $50-74.9 Million
Emp.: 160
Plastic Reclosable Bags Mfr
N.A.I.C.S.: 322220

Division (Domestic):

Minigrip, LLC (2)
209 Medegen Dr, Gallaway, TN 38036
Tel.: (770) 422-4187
Web Site: https://medegenmed.com
Sales Range: $10-24.9 Million
Emp.: 15
Reclosable Plastic Bag Mfr & Packaging Products Supplier
N.A.I.C.S.: 326111

Zip-Pak (2)
1800 Sycamore Rd, Manteno, IL 60950
Tel.: (815) 468-6500
Web Site: https://www.zippak.com
Sales Range: $10-24.9 Million
Emp.: 50
Reclosable Polyethylene Zipper Bags, Plastic Zippers, Reclosable Bagging Equipment Mfr
N.A.I.C.S.: 322220

Division (Domestic):

Zip-Pak (3)
4250 NE Expy, Atlanta, GA 30340-3304 (100%)
Tel.: (770) 458-8189
Web Site: https://www.zippak.com
Mfr of Plastics Working Machinery
N.A.I.C.S.: 333248

Multi-Wall Packaging (1)
50 Taylor Dr, East Providence, RI 02916
Web Site: https://www.signode.com
Protective Packaging Products Mfr
N.A.I.C.S.: 424130

Subsidiary (Domestic):

Multi-Wall Packaging Corp. (2)
130 S 20th St, Irvington, NJ 07111
Tel.: (973) 374-0704
Web Site: http://www.multiwall.com
Rev.: $2,600,000
Emp.: 30
Paperboard Mills
N.A.I.C.S.: 322130

MultiBind Biotech GmbH (1)
Gottfried-Hagen-Str 62, 51105, Cologne, Germany
Tel.: (49) 2212780211
Web Site: https://www.multibind.com
Chemical Products Mfr
N.A.I.C.S.: 325520

National Truck Parts of the Midwest, Inc. (1)
4845 Provident Dr, Cincinnati, OH 45246-1018
Tel.: (513) 874-3680
Sales Range: $10-24.9 Million
Emp.: 6
Industrial Machinery Mfr
N.A.I.C.S.: 333248

National Truck Parts, Inc. (1)
6550 E 42nd St, Tulsa, OK 74145
Tel.: (918) 660-0310
Web Site: http://www.ntpsurplus.com
Sales Range: $25-49.9 Million
Emp.: 4
Truck Parts Whslr
N.A.I.C.S.: 423120
Cecil Keeling (Mgr)

North Star Imaging Europe SAS (1)
Les Fregates 6 Hall F Paris Nord II 13 Rue De La Perdrix, BP66151, 93290, Tremblay-en-France, France
Tel.: (33) 148170200
Web Site: http://4nsi.com
Industrial Machinery & Equipment Distr
N.A.I.C.S.: 423830

North Star Imaging, Inc. (1)
19875 S Diamond Lake Rd, Rogers, MN 55374
Tel.: (763) 312-8836
Web Site: https://4nsi.com
Sales Range: $25-49.9 Million
Industrial Non Destructive Testing Equipment Mfr
N.A.I.C.S.: 334519

Norwood Marking Systems (1)
1 Research Park Dr, Saint Charles, MO 63304
Tel.: (636) 300-2000
Web Site: http://www.itwnorwood.com
Sales Range: $10-24.9 Million
Emp.: 96
Food Industry Marking Systems Mfr
N.A.I.C.S.: 339940

Nova Chimica, S.r.l. (1)
Via G Galilei 47, 20092, Cinisello Balsamo, MI, Italy
Tel.: (39) 0266045392
Web Site: http://www.novachimica.com
Chemical Products Distr
N.A.I.C.S.: 424690

Novadan ApS (1)
Platinvej 21, 6000, Kolding, Denmark
Tel.: (45) 76348400
Web Site: https://www.novadan.dk
Chemical Research & Development Services
N.A.I.C.S.: 541715

Orbitalum Tools GmbH (1)
Josef-Schuettler-Str 17, 78224, Singen, Germany
Tel.: (49) 77317920
Web Site: https://www.orbitalum.com
Industrial Machinery Mfr
N.A.I.C.S.: 333248
Markus Tamm (Gen Mgr)

Orgapack GmbH (1)
Silbernstrasse 14, 8953, Dietikon, Switzerland
Tel.: (41) 447455050
Packaging Machinery Mfr
N.A.I.C.S.: 333993

PENTA-91 OOO (1)

Illinois Tool Works Inc.—(Continued)

Kosmodamianskaya embankment 26/55 building 6, Moscow, 109316, Russia
Tel.: (7) 4957300530
Web Site: https://www.itwpenta.ru
Silicone Product Mfr
N.A.I.C.S.: 325199

PR. A. I. Srl (1)
Via Nobel 15/17, Gravina in Puglia, 70024, Bari, Italy
Tel.: (39) 080 325 5817
Web Site: https://www.praigroup.it
Welding Equipment Mfr
N.A.I.C.S.: 333992

Pacific Concept Industries (USA) LLC (1)
39 W 37th St Fl 12, New York, NY 10018
Tel.: (212) 736-6533
Emp.: 3
Decorative Product Whslr
N.A.I.C.S.: 459420

Packaging Leasing Systems Inc. (1)
3600 W Lake Ave, Glenview, IL 60026-1215
Tel.: (847) 724-7500
Web Site: http://www.itwinc.com
Sales Range: $100-124.9 Million
Emp.: 4
Industrial Machinery Equipment Rental & Leasing Services
N.A.I.C.S.: 532490

Paslode (1)
888 Forest Edge Dr, Vernon Hills, IL 60061 (100%)
Tel.: (847) 634-1900
Web Site: https://www.paslode.com
Rev.: $100,000,000
Emp.: 100
Pneumatic & Cordless Fastening Systems Mfr & Marketer
N.A.I.C.S.: 339993

Paslode Fasteners (Shanghai) Co., Ltd. (1)
No 900 Songzheng Highway Zone B, Shanghai, 201614, China
Tel.: (86) 21578565
Emp.: 200
Metal Household Furniture Mfr
N.A.I.C.S.: 337126
Sunmay Shi (Gen Mgr)

Penta Don OOO (1)
ul Pavlenko 15, 344039, Rostov Oblast, Russia
Tel.: (7) 8632903741
Industrial Machinery Whslr
N.A.I.C.S.: 423830

Pillar Technologies (1)
475 Industrial Dr, Hartland, WI 53029-0110
Tel.: (262) 912-7200
Web Site: https://www.pillartech.com
Sales Range: $10-24.9 Million
Emp.: 25
Cap Sealing Systems Mfr
N.A.I.C.S.: 339991
Alex Schwarzkopf (Founder & CEO)

Pistora Oy (1)
Latomaentie 5, Rauma, 26510, Finland
Tel.: (358) 28383800
Industrial Machinery Mfr
N.A.I.C.S.: 333248

Propaper Industria e Comercio de Papeis Ltda. (1)
Avenida Pedro I N 6201 Jardim Baronesa Distrito Industrial, Sao Goncalo, 12091-000, Taubate, Sao Paulo, Brazil
Tel.: (55) 1236095300
Web Site: http://www.propaper.com.br
Tissue paper Mfr & Whslr
N.A.I.C.S.: 322291

Pryda Australia (1)
153 -187 Discovery Rd, Dandenong South, 3175, VIC, Australia
Tel.: (61) 300657052
Web Site: https://www.pryda.com.au
Sales Range: $150-199.9 Million
Emp.: 300
Building Truss, Frame Systems & Timber Connectors Mfr
N.A.I.C.S.: 321215

QSA Global Inc. (1)

40 North Ave, Burlington, MA 01803
Tel.: (781) 272-2000
Web Site: https://www.qsa-global.com
Sales Range: $25-49.9 Million
Radioactive Material Disposal Services & Radiation Detection Equipment, Medical Product & Radioactive Reference Device Mfr
N.A.I.C.S.: 334517
Lawrence K. Swift (Pres)

Quandel Verpackungs- und Foerdertechnik GmbH (1)
Dieselstrasse 4, 57290, Neunkirchen, Germany
Tel.: (49) 273561184
Web Site: http://www.e-quandel.de
Packaging Machinery Equipment Mfr
N.A.I.C.S.: 333993

Quimica Industrial Mediterraneo, S.L. (1)
Rosa De Los Vientos 75, 29006, Malaga, Spain
Tel.: (34) 952041199
Web Site: https://www.quimsaitw.com
Industrial Machinery Whslr
N.A.I.C.S.: 423830

Regent Hose & Hydraulics Limited (1)
Unit 15-18 Rabans Close Rabans Lane Ind Estate, Aylesbury, HP19 8RS, Buckinghamshire, United Kingdom
Tel.: (44) 1296420171
Web Site: http://www.regenttrist.co.uk
Emp.: 6
Hydraulic Hoses equipment Mfr
N.A.I.C.S.: 326220

RxSafe LLC (1)
237 Via Vera Cruz, San Marcos, CA 92078-2617
Tel.: (760) 736-0122
Web Site: http://www.rxsafe.com
Pharmacy Automation Technology Services
N.A.I.C.S.: 423450
William Holmes (CEO)

S.E.E. Sistemas Industria E Comercio Ltda. (1)
Av Forte do Leme 195, Parque Sao Lourenco, Sao Paulo, Brazil
Tel.: (55) 1136236500
Web Site: https://www.seesistemas.com.br
Machine Tools Mfr
N.A.I.C.S.: 333517

SPG Netherlands B.V. (1)
Sterrebaan 10, 3542 DK, Utrecht, Netherlands
Tel.: (31) 302480311
Web Site: http://www.ctrapox.nl
Industrial Machinery Mfr
N.A.I.C.S.: 333517

SPG Packaging UK Ltd (1)
Unit 51 Empire Industrial Park Brickyard Road, Aldridge, Walsall, WS9 8UQ, United Kingdom
Tel.: (44) 1922742500
Web Site: https://www.signodegroup.co.uk
Machine Tools Mfr
N.A.I.C.S.: 333517

SWT Holdings B.V. (1)
Leliegracht 10, 1015 DE, Amsterdam, Netherlands
Tel.: (31) 205216344
Investment Management Service
N.A.I.C.S.: 541611

Sealant Systems International, Inc. (1)
125 Venture Dr Ste 210, San Luis Obispo, CA 93401
Tel.: (805) 489-0490
Machine Tools Mfr
N.A.I.C.S.: 333517

Shanghai ITW Plastics & Metal Co., Ltd. (1)
Building 1 66 Tian Ying Road QingPu industrial Development Zone, West Foundation Park, Shanghai, 201712, China
Tel.: (86) 69225880300
Web Site: http://www.itw-deltar.com
Injection Molding Plastic Component Mfr
N.A.I.C.S.: 333511

Signode India Limited (1)
914 915 9th Floor Rupa Solitaire Building No A-1, Millennium Business Park Mahape, Navi Mumbai, 400710, Maharashtra, India
Tel.: (91) 2227780271
Web Site: http://www.itwsignodeindia.co.in
Plastic Product Mfr & Distr
N.A.I.C.S.: 326150

Signode Packaging Espana, S.L. (1)
Carretera del Mig 83-87, Cornella del Llobregat, 08940, Barcelona, Spain
Tel.: (34) 934800720
Web Site: http://www.signode-europe.com
Machines & Hand Tools Parts Services
N.A.I.C.S.: 811411

Signode Packaging Systems Limited (1)
Mombasa Road next to Mabati Rolling Mills, PO Box 78160-00507, Nairobi, Kenya
Tel.: (254) 202135002
Web Site: http://www.signodekenya.co.ke
Steel & Plastic Strapping Product Mfr
N.A.I.C.S.: 332999

Signode Systems (Thailand) Ltd. (1)
44/120 2nd Fl Moo 4 Soi Watpromrangsi Rama 2 Road, Samaedam Bangkhunthien, Bangkok, 10150, Thailand
Tel.: (66) 28495501
Web Site: http://www.signode.com
Steel & Plastic Strapping Product Mfr
N.A.I.C.S.: 332999

Simco (Nederland) B.V. (1)
Aalsvoort 74, 7241 MB, Lochem, Netherlands (100%)
Tel.: (31) 573288333
Web Site: https://www.simco-ion.nl
Sales Range: $10-24.9 Million
Emp.: 60
Electrostatic Equipment Sales & Services
N.A.I.C.S.: 335999

Simco Japan Inc. (1)
1-2-4 Minatojima-Nakamachi, Chuo-ku, Kobe, 650-0046, Hyogo, Japan (100%)
Tel.: (81) 78 303 4651
Web Site: http://www.simcoion.jp
Sales Range: $10-24.9 Million
Electrostatic Equipment Sales & Services
N.A.I.C.S.: 335999
Katsumi Shiji (Pres)

Simco-Ion, Industrial Group (1)
2257 N Penn Rd, Hatfield, PA 19440
Tel.: (215) 822-6401
Web Site: https://www.simco-ion.com
Static Control Products Mfr
N.A.I.C.S.: 335999

Smith Equipment (1)
2601 Lockheed Ave, Watertown, SD 57201
Tel.: (605) 882-3200
Web Site: http://www.smithequipment.com
Sales Range: $125-149.9 Million
Welding & Cutting Equipment Mfr
N.A.I.C.S.: 333992

Societe de Prospection et d'Inventions Techniques S.A.S. (1)
150 Route de Lyon, BP 104, 26501, Bourgles-Valence, Cedex, France
Tel.: (33) 475822020
Web Site: http://www.spitpaslode.fr
Construction Equipment Mfr
N.A.I.C.S.: 333120

Somat Company (1)
165 Independence Ct, Lancaster, PA 17601
Tel.: (717) 397-5100
Web Site: https://www.somatcompany.com
Sales Range: $25-49.9 Million
Emp.: 34
Waste Reduction Systems Mfr
N.A.I.C.S.: 333310

Speedline Technologies GmbH (1)
Im Gefierth 14, 63303, Dreieich, Germany
Tel.: (49) 61038320
Web Site: http://www.itweae.com
Electronic Assembly Equipment & Printing Machinery Mfr
N.A.I.C.S.: 333242

Stokvis Celix Portugal Unipessoal LDA (1)
Transformadora de Espumas Tecnicas, Pq Industrial de Sequeira Pav 16 A/B, 4705-

629, Braga, Portugal
Tel.: (351) 253305610
Web Site: https://www.stokvistapes.pt
Industrial Equipment Mfr
N.A.I.C.S.: 333248

Stokvis Danmark AS (1)
Gydevang 40, 3450, Allerod, Denmark
Tel.: (45) 48171211
Web Site: https://www.stokvistapes.dk
Adhesive Product Mfr
N.A.I.C.S.: 325520

Stokvis Tape Group B.V. (1)
Van Hennaertweg 10, 2952 CA, Alblasserdam, Netherlands
Tel.: (31) 786992100
Web Site: https://www.stokvistapes.nl
Adhesive Product Mfr
N.A.I.C.S.: 325520

Stokvis Tapes (Beijing) Co. Ltd. (1)
Ground fl Bldg 7 GuoSheng Science & Technology Zone No 1 Kangding St, Beijing, 100176, China
Tel.: (86) 1067856115
Web Site: http://www.stokvistapes.cn
Adhesive Product Mfr
N.A.I.C.S.: 325520

Stokvis Tapes (Shanghai) Co. Ltd. (1)
Building 9 Section B No 353 Ri Ying North Road, Waigaoqiao Free Trade Zone, Shanghai, 200131, China
Tel.: (86) 2150461945
Web Site: http://www.stokvistapes.cn
Adhesive Product Mfr
N.A.I.C.S.: 325520

Stokvis Tapes (Shenzhen) Co. Ltd. (1)
West Part North Side 1st Floor Building 1 Huaya Industrial Park, Yousong Village East Industry Road Longhua Street, Shenzhen, 518109, China
Tel.: (86) 75528158300
Web Site: http://www.stokvistapes.cn
Adhesive Product Mfr
N.A.I.C.S.: 325520

Stokvis Tapes (Taiwan) Co. Ltd. (1)
2 Floor 58 Lane 316 Rd Rui-Guang, Nei-hu district, Taipei, 114, Taiwan
Tel.: (886) 27987198
Web Site: http://www.stokvistapes.tw
Adhesive Product Mfr
N.A.I.C.S.: 325520

Stokvis Tapes (Tianjin) Co. Ltd. (1)
Xinghua Rd, 4 Xiging Economic Development Area, Tianjin, 300385, China
Tel.: (86) 2283969927
Web Site: http://www.stokvistapes.cn
Adhesive Product Mfr
N.A.I.C.S.: 325520

Stokvis Tapes BVBA (1)
Mechelsesteenweg 586C 18 1 2, Cargovil, 1800, Vilvoorde, Belgium
Tel.: (32) 22550611
Web Site: http://www.stokvistapes.be
Emp.: 8
Adhesive Product Mfr
N.A.I.C.S.: 325520

Stokvis Tapes Benelux B.V. (1)
Van Hennaertweg 10, 2952 CA, Alblasserdam, Netherlands
Tel.: (31) 786992100
Web Site: https://stokvistapes.nl
Adhesive Tape Mfr
N.A.I.C.S.: 339113

Stokvis Tapes Deutschland GmbH (1)
Jagerwald 11, 42897, Remscheid, Germany
Tel.: (49) 21 913 7600
Web Site: https://stokvistapes.de
Emp.: 16
Adhesive Product Mfr
N.A.I.C.S.: 325520

Stokvis Tapes Estonia OU (1)
Piirimae 8 Tanassilma kula, Saku vald, Harjumaa, 76401, Estonia
Tel.: (372) 6799680
Web Site: http://www.stokvistapes.ee
Electronic Parts Equipment Merchant Whslr
N.A.I.C.S.: 423690

Stokvis Tapes France SAS (1)
Z I De Mont de Magny Rue De La Haute
Borne, 27140, Gisors, France
Tel.: (33) 232559302
Web Site: http://www.stokvistapes.com
Adhesive Product Mfr
N.A.I.C.S.: 325520

Stokvis Tapes Italia s.r.l. (1)
Via Monza 116, 20060, Gessate, MI, Italy
Tel.: (39) 0295746051
Web Site: https://www.stokvistapes.it
Adhesive Product Mfr
N.A.I.C.S.: 325520

**Stokvis Tapes Limited Liability
Company** (1)
Build 21 75 Fridrikha Engelsa Street,
105082, Moscow, Russia
Tel.: (7) 4997695087
Web Site: http://www.stokvis.ru
Emp.: 5
Adhesive Product Mfr
N.A.I.C.S.: 325520

Stokvis Tapes Magyarorszag Kft (1)
Kossuth Lajos Utca 7-9, 1053, Budapest,
Hungary
Tel.: (36) 14392020
Web Site: http://www.stokvistapes.hu
Adhesive Product Mfr
N.A.I.C.S.: 325520

Stokvis Tapes Norge AS (1)
Gamle Drammensvei 120, 1363, Hovik,
Norway
Tel.: (47) 67177900
Web Site: https://www.stokvistapes.no
Adhesive Product Mfr
N.A.I.C.S.: 325520

Stokvis Tapes Oy (1)
Tehtaantie 1 Suomi, 03100, Nummela, Vihti,
Finland
Tel.: (358) 207199940
Web Site: https://www.stokvistapes.fi
Adhesive Product Mfr
N.A.I.C.S.: 325520

Stokvis Tapes Sverige AB (1)
Zinkgatan 6, 602 23, Norrkoping, Sweden
Tel.: (46) 11280400
Web Site: https://www.stokvistapes.se
Adhesive Product Mfr
N.A.I.C.S.: 325520

Strapex Austria Ges. mbH (1)
Gewerbeparkstrasse 45, 3500, Krems, Austria
Tel.: (43) 273273501
Web Site: https://www.strapex.co.at
Packaging Machinery Equipment Mfr
N.A.I.C.S.: 333993

Strapex Embalagem L.d.a. (1)
Estrada da Outurela 121, 2794-051, Carnaxide, Portugal
Tel.: (351) 214164785
Web Site: https://www.strapex.pt
Packaging Machinery Equipment Mfr
N.A.I.C.S.: 333993

Strapex GmbH (1)
Maybachstrasse 1, 71088, Holzgerlingen,
Germany
Tel.: (49) 703168040
Web Site: https://www.strapex.de
Packaging Machinery Equipment Mfr
N.A.I.C.S.: 333993

Strapex GmbH (1)
Silbernstrasse 14, 8953, Dietikon, Switzerland
Tel.: (41) 447455050
Web Site: http://www.strapex.ch
Packaging Machinery Equipment Mfr
N.A.I.C.S.: 333993

Strapex S.A.S. (1)
31 Rue Jean Jacques Rousseau, 94204,
Ivry-sur-Seine, Cedex, France
Tel.: (33) 149870160
Web Site: http://www.strapex.fr
Packaging Machinery Equipment Mfr
N.A.I.C.S.: 333993

Strapex S.p.r.l. (1)
Rue de la Science 1, 1400, Nivelles, Belgium
Tel.: (32) 67346910
Web Site: http://www.strapex.be

Emp.: 5
Packaging Machinery Equipment Mfr
N.A.I.C.S.: 333993

Strapex Srl (1)
Via Murri 24/26, 20013, Magenta, Milan,
Italy
Tel.: (39) 029700751
Web Site: https://www.strapex.it
Packaging Machinery Equipment Mfr
N.A.I.C.S.: 333993

Superior Spring Company (1)
1260 S Talt Ave, Anaheim, CA 92806
Tel.: (714) 490-0881
Web Site: https://www.superiorspring.com
Automotive Repair
N.A.I.C.S.: 811198

Sweldx AB (1)
Sisjo Kullegata 11 Vastra Frolunda, PO Box
9246, 40095, Gothenburg, Sweden
Tel.: (46) 317875000
Web Site: http://www.sweldx.com
Machine Tools Mfr
N.A.I.C.S.: 333517

Systemcare Products Limited (1)
6-7 Maybrook Industrial Estate, Walsall
Wood, Walsall, WS8 7DG, United Kingdom
Tel.: (44) 1543454872
Web Site: http://www.systemcare.co.uk
Organic Chemical Mfr
N.A.I.C.S.: 325199

Tag Fasteners Sdn. Bhd. (1)
No 1081 Jalan Aman 2 Kawasan Industrial
Taman Makmur, Lunas, 09600, Kedah, Kedah Darul Aman, Malaysia
Tel.: (60) 44842660
Web Site: https://www.tagfasteners.com.my
Fastener Product Mfr
N.A.I.C.S.: 339993

Tarutin Kester Co., Ltd. (1)
2-20-11 Yokokawa, Tokyo, 130-0003,
Sumida-ku, Japan
Tel.: (81) 336245351
Web Site: http://www.kester.com
Emp.: 4
Semiconductor Product Mfr
N.A.I.C.S.: 334419

Tech Spray, L.P. (1)
1001 NW 1st St, Amarillo, TX 79107
Tel.: (806) 372-8523
Web Site: http://www.techspray.com
Sales Range: $100-124.9 Million
Emp.: 44
Chemical Cleaners & Anti-Static Solutions
N.A.I.C.S.: 424690
Brett Robinson *(Mgr-Sls-West US & West
Canada)*
Samantha Luedke *(Mgr-Life Sciences)*
Bill Martin *(Mgr-Aerospace)*

Teknek (China) Limited (1)
Flat E 4/F Winfield Industrial Building 3 Kin
Kwan Street, Tuen Mun, New Territories,
China (Hong Kong)
Tel.: (852) 24683160
Web Site: http://www.teknek.com
Cleaning Solution Product Mfr
N.A.I.C.S.: 325998

Teknek (Japan) Limited (1)
1-2-4 Minatojima-Nakamachi, Chuo-ku,
Kobe, 650-0046, Japan
Tel.: (81) 783045780
Web Site: https://teknek.co.jp
Cleaning Solution Product Mfr
N.A.I.C.S.: 325998

Teknek Limited (1)
River Drive Inchinnan Business Park, Renfrew, PA4 9RT, Renfrewshire, United Kingdom
Tel.: (44) 1415688100
Web Site: https://www.teknek.com
Cleaning Solution Product Mfr
N.A.I.C.S.: 325998
Richard Feenan *(Mgr-Bus Dev)*

Tempil, Inc. (1)
2901 Hamilton Blvd, South Plainfield, NJ
07080
Tel.: (908) 757-8300
Web Site: http://www.tempil.com
Sales Range: $25-49.9 Million
Emp.: 100
Temperature Indication Products Mfr

N.A.I.C.S.: 325120

The Peerless Group (1)
500 S Vandemark Rd, Sidney, OH 45365
Tel.: (937) 492-4158
Sales Range: $50-74.9 Million
Emp.: 120
Bakery & Food Equipment Mfr
N.A.I.C.S.: 333241
David Alexander *(CFO)*

**Thirode Grandes Cuisines Poligny
SAS** (1)
Zone Industrielle, Poligny, 39800, Jura,
France
Tel.: (33) 384737577
Machine Tools Mfr
N.A.I.C.S.: 333517

Twinaplate Limited (1)
Threemilestone Industrial Estate, Truro,
TR4 9LD, Cornwall, United Kingdom
Tel.: (44) 1872245450
Machine Tools Mfr
N.A.I.C.S.: 333517

**Unichemicals Industria e Comercio
Ltda.** (1)
Avenida Jonia 520, Sao Paulo, 04634-011,
Brazil
Tel.: (55) 11950319859
Machine Tools Mfr
N.A.I.C.S.: 333517

United Silicone (1)
4471 Walden Ave, Lancaster, NY
14086 **(100%)**
Tel.: (716) 681-8222
Web Site: https://www.unitedsilicone.com
Sales Range: $10-24.9 Million
Emp.: 4,471
Mfr & Supply Of Hot Coal Machines
N.A.I.C.S.: 333248

Valeron Strength Films (1)
9505 Bamboo Rd, Houston, TX 77041-7705
Tel.: (713) 996-4200
Web Site: https://www.valeron.com
Sales Range: $25-49.9 Million
Emp.: 100
Polyethylene Film Mfr
N.A.I.C.S.: 326113

Valeron Strength Films B.V.B.A. (1)
Nieuwmoersesteenweg 145, 2910, Essen,
Belgium
Tel.: (32) 36700753
Web Site: http://www.valeron.eu
Plastic Foam Product Mfr
N.A.I.C.S.: 326111

Versachem Chile S.A. (1)
Calle Los Industriales 639, Huechuraba,
Santiago, Chile
Tel.: (56) 22 625 3487
Web Site: https://www.itwversachem.cl
General Purpose Machinery Mfr
N.A.I.C.S.: 333998

Vesta (Guangzhou) Catering Equipment Co. Ltd (1)
Kitchen Appliance Mfr & Distr
N.A.I.C.S.: 332215

Vesta Global Limited (1)
Unit 902 9F 113 Aotyle Street, Mongkok,
Kowloon, China (Hong Kong)
Tel.: (852) 27697908
Web Site: http://www.vesta-china.com
Kitchen Appliance Mfr & Distr
N.A.I.C.S.: 332215

Vitronics Soltec B.V. (1)
Innovatiepark 12, 4906 AA, Oosterhout,
Netherlands
Tel.: (31) 162483280
Web Site: http://www.vitronics-soltec.com
Machine Tools Mfr
N.A.I.C.S.: 333517

Vitronics Soltec Corporation (1)
2 Marin Way, Stratham, NH 03885
Tel.: (603) 772-7778
General Purpose Machinery Mfr
N.A.I.C.S.: 333998

Vitronics Soltec Technologies (Suzhou) Co., Ltd. (1)
No 5 Xiang St 858 Zhujiang Lu New District, Suzhou, 215129, Jiangsu, China
Tel.: (86) 51268413378

Web Site: http://www.vitronics-soltec.com
Emp.: 220
General Purpose Machinery Mfr
N.A.I.C.S.: 333998

Vulcan-Hart (1)
3600 N Point Blvd, Baltimore, MD
21222 **(100%)**
Tel.: (410) 284-0660
Web Site: http://www.vulcanequipment.com
Sales Range: $50-74.9 Million
Emp.: 130
Commercial Cooking Equipment Mfr & Distr
N.A.I.C.S.: 335220

Wachs Canada Ltd. (1)
1250 Journeys End Circle Unit 5, Newmarket, L3Y 0B9, ON, Canada
Tel.: (905) 830-8888
Web Site: http://www.ehwachs.com
Sales Range: $10-24.9 Million
Specific Machinery Mfr
N.A.I.C.S.: 333998

**Warehouse Automation Iberia,
S.L.** (1)
Cl Regordonbo 37 Poligono Prado Regordono, 28936, Mostoles, Spain
Tel.: (34) 917364196
Industrial Machinery Mfr
N.A.I.C.S.: 333248
Alejandro Cox *(Dir-Sls)*

Weigh-Tronix Canada, ULC (1)
6429 Abrams, St-Laurent, Montreal, H4S
1X9, QC, Canada
Tel.: (902) 468-7551
Web Site: http://www.averyweigh-tronix.com
Sales Range: $10-24.9 Million
Scale Sales
N.A.I.C.S.: 333998

Welding Industries Pty Limited (1)
5 Allan St, Melrose Park, 5039, SA, Australia
Tel.: (61) 882766494
Web Site: http://www.welding.com.au
Sales Range: $50-74.9 Million
Emp.: 30
General Purpose Machinery Mfr
N.A.I.C.S.: 333998
Mahi Rao *(Mgr-Customer Support & Distr-
Oceania)*

**Wynn Oil (South Africa) (Pty)
Ltd.** (1)
Mopedi Road 22, PO Box 680, Sebenza
Edenvale, Johannesburg, 1610, South Africa
Tel.: (27) 116093708
Web Site: https://www.wynns.co.za
Chemical Products Mfr
N.A.I.C.S.: 325998

Wynn Oil Company (1)
1050 W 5th St, Azusa, CA 91702
Tel.: (626) 334-0231
Web Site: http://www.wynnsusa.com
Sales Range: $75-99.9 Million
Emp.: 135
Specialty Chemical Products Marketer
N.A.I.C.S.: 324191

Wynn's Automotive France SAS (1)
Avenue leonard de vinci 2, 33608, Pessac,
Cedex, France
Tel.: (33) 557262900
Web Site: http://www.wynns.fr
Chemical Products Mfr
N.A.I.C.S.: 325998

Zip-Pak International B.V. (1)
AJ Romijnweg 27 NL, 9672 AH, Winschoten, Netherlands
Tel.: (31) 597670170
Web Site: http://zippak.com
Fiber Can Tube & Drum Mfr
N.A.I.C.S.: 325220

ILLUMINA, INC.

5200 Illumina Way, San Diego, CA
92122
Tel.: (858) 202-4500 DE
Web Site: https://www.illumina.com
Year Founded: 1998
ILMN—(NASDAQ)
Rev.: $4,504,000,000
Assets: $10,111,000,000
Liabilities: $4,366,000,000

ILLUMINA, INC.

Illumina, Inc.—(Continued)

Net Worth: $5,745,000,000
Earnings: ($1,161,000,000)
Emp.: 9,250
Fiscal Year-end: 12/31/23
Large-scale Genetic Variation & Biological Function Analytical Technologies & Systems Developer, Mfr & Marketer
N.A.I.C.S.: 334516
David R. Walt (Founder)
Charles E. Dadswell (Gen Counsel & Sr VP)
Aimee Hoyt (Chief People Officer & Sr VP)
Gretchen Weightman (VP/Gen Mgr-Asia Pacific & Japan)
Li Qing (VP/Gen Mgr-Greater China)
Nicole Berry (Sr VP/Gen Mgr-Comml Ops-Americas)
Ankur Dhingra (CFO)
Jose Torres (Chief Acctg Officer & VP)
John Frank (Chief Pub Affairs Officer)
Carissa L. Rollins (Executives)
Scott Ericksen (Chief Acctg Officer & VP)
Salli Schwartz (VP)
Bas Verhoef (Interim Chief Comml Officer & Head-Europe)
Steven Barnard (CTO)
Stephen P. MacMillan (Chm)
Jacob Thaysen (CEO)

Subsidiaries:

Emedgene Technologies Ltd.   (1)
Emedgene 126 Yigal Alon St Building A, Tel Aviv, Israel
Tel.: (972) 3 554 4490
Web Site: https://www.emedgene.com
Information Technology Services
N.A.I.C.S.: 541511
Einat Metzer (Co-Founder)
Niv Mizrahi (Co-Founder & CTO)
Ori Sarfaty (VP-Research & Development)
Josh Forsythe (VP)
Orit Livnat Levi (Mktg Dir)

Epicentre Technologies
Corporation   (1)
5602 Research Park Blvd Ste 200, Madison, WI 53719
Tel.: (608) 258-3080
Web Site: http://www.epibio.com
Sales Range: $25-49.9 Million
Emp.: 50
Biological Product Mfr
N.A.I.C.S.: 325411

IDbyDNA Inc.   (1)
675 Arapeen Dr, Salt Lake City, UT 84108
Pharmaceutical Product Mfr & Distr
N.A.I.C.S.: 325411

Illumina Australia Pty. Ltd.   (1)
Level 3 535 Elizabeth Street, Melbourne, 3000, VIC, Australia
Tel.: (61) 392129900
Sales Range: $25-49.9 Million
Emp.: 15
Biotechnology Research & Development
N.A.I.C.S.: 541714
Robert Blaylock (Gen Mgr)

Illumina Brasil Produtos de Biotecnologia Ltda.   (1)
Avenida Paulista 1063 - suite 301, Sao Paulo, 01311-200, Brazil
Tel.: (55) 113 500 3900
Web Site: https://www.illumina.com
Biotechnology Research & Development
N.A.I.C.S.: 541714

Illumina Cambridge, Ltd.   (1)
Chesterford Research Park Little Chesterford, Saffron Walden, CB10 1XL, Essex, United Kingdom
Tel.: (44) 1799532300
Web Site: http://www.illumina.com
Biotechnology Research & Development
N.A.I.C.S.: 541714

Illumina K.K.   (1)

Tokyo Office 22nd floor Mita Berge Building 5-36-7 Shiba, Minato-ku, Tokyo, 108-0014, Japan
Tel.: (81) 345782800
Web Site: https://jp.illumina.com
Medical Device Mfr & Distr
N.A.I.C.S.: 339112

Illumina Korea Ltd.   (1)
Hi Investment Securities building 66 Yeoidaero, Yeoungdeungpo-gu, Seoul, Korea (South)
Tel.: (82) 27405300
Analytical Laboratory Instrument Mfr
N.A.I.C.S.: 334516

Illumina Middle East FZE   (1)
Office Nos T02 FLR01-01 03 & 01 04 Offices 2 One Central, Dubai World Trade Centre, Dubai, United Arab Emirates
Tel.: (971) 4264986
Medical Device Mfr & Distr
N.A.I.C.S.: 339112

Illumina Shanghai (Trading) Co.,
Ltd.   (1)
12F Building 23 1999 Yishan Road, Shanghai Business Park Phase III, Shanghai, 200233, China
Tel.: (86) 2160321066
Laboratory Instrument Mfr
N.A.I.C.S.: 334519

Illumina Singapore Pte. Ltd.   (1)
11 Biopolis Way 09-05 Helios, Singapore, 138667, Singapore
Tel.: (65) 6 773 0188
Web Site: http://www.illumina.com
Sales Range: $10-24.9 Million
Developer of Tools for Analysis of Genetic Variation
N.A.I.C.S.: 339112

Illumina Trading (Shanghai) Co.,
Ltd.   (1)
12F Building 23 1999 Yishan Road, Shanghai Business Park Phase III, Shanghai, 200233, China
Tel.: (86) 2160321066
Biotechnology Research & Development
N.A.I.C.S.: 541714

Illumina, Inc.-Hayward   (1)
25861 Industrial Blvd, Hayward, CA 94545
Tel.: (510) 670-9300
Web Site: http://www.illumina.com
Sales Range: $1-9.9 Million
Emp.: 118
Genetic Analysis System & Technology Developer & Marketer
N.A.I.C.S.: 334516
Jay T. Flatley (CEO)

NextBio   (1)
451 El Camino Real Ste 210, Santa Clara, CA 95050
Tel.: (408) 861-3610
Web Site: http://www.nextbio.com
Software Development Services
N.A.I.C.S.: 541511
Mostafa Ronaghi (Co-Founder)
Yeongmi Jeon (Sr Engr-Software)

thromboDx BV   (1)
Linnaeusparkweg 10-2, 1098 EA, Amsterdam, Netherlands
Tel.: (31) 646767255
Web Site: http://www.thrombodx.nl
Healtcare Services
N.A.I.C.S.: 622310
Rolf Jan Rutten (CEO)
Jonas Nilsson (COO)
Robert Al (CFO)
Bastiaan van der Baan (Co-Founder)

IMAC HOLDINGS, INC.
1605 Westgate Cir, Brentwood, TN 37027   DE
Web Site:
https://imacregeneration.gcs-web.com
Year Founded: 2000
BACK—(NASDAQ)
Rev.: $16,185,682
Assets: $11,081,606
Liabilities: $6,430,350
Net Worth: $4,651,256
Earnings: ($18,312,806)

Emp.: 85
Fiscal Year-end: 12/31/22
Holding Company
N.A.I.C.S.: 551112
Daniel M. Bradbury (Co-Founder)
Jeffrey S. Ervin (Co-Founder, Chm & CEO)
Sheri F. Gardzina (CFO)
Matthew C. Wallis (Founder-Regeneration Center-Kentucky & Co-Founder)
Faith Zaslavsky (CEO)

IMAGE INTERNATIONAL GROUP, INC.
8105 Birch Bay Sq St Ste 205, Blaine, WA 98230
Tel.: (518) 638-8192   NV
Web Site:
http://www.imageinternationalgroupinc.com
Year Founded: 2005
IMGL—(OTCIQ)
Emp.: 2
Mineral Mining & Distr
N.A.I.C.S.: 212390
Hoi Ming Chan (Pres, COO & Sec)

IMAGE METRICS, INC.
5th Fl 110 W 11th St, Los Angeles, CA 90031
Tel.: (310) 656-6555   NV
Web Site: https://www.image-metrics.com
IMGX—(OTCIQ)
Sales Range: Less than $1 Million
Emp.: 30
Facial Animation Solutions
N.A.I.C.S.: 541519
David Rolston (Chm)
Ron Ryder (CEO)
Kevin Walker (Founder & CTO)
Armando Pena (VP-Mobile Tech)
Mike Rogers (VP-Res)
Nick Ramsay (VP-Product)

IMAGE PROTECT, INC.
3001 N Rocky Point Dr E Ste 200, Tampa, FL 33607
Tel.: (845) 338-3366   DE
Year Founded: 2002
IMTL—(OTCIQ)
Sales Range: Less than $1 Million
Medical Imaging & Information Management
N.A.I.C.S.: 339112
James Andrew Ballas (CEO)
Francis Casella (Pres-Subsidiary)

IMMEDIATEK INC.
3301 Airport Fwy Ste 200, Bedford, TX 76021-6034   NV
Web Site:
http://www.immediatek.com
IMKI—(OTCIQ)
Sales Range: $1-9.9 Million
Emp.: 20
Online Back-Up, File Storage & Other Web-Based Services
N.A.I.C.S.: 513210
Timothy M. Rice (Pres & CEO)
Timothy McCrory (CFO & VP)
Paul Marin (COO & VP)

IMMERSION CORPORATION
2999 N E 191st St Ste 610, Aventura, FL 33180
Tel.: (408) 467-1900   DE
Web Site:
https://www.immersion.com
Year Founded: 1993
IMMR—(NASDAQ)
Rev.: $38,461,000
Assets: $190,110,000
Liabilities: $32,410,000
Net Worth: $157,700,000

Earnings: $30,664,000
Emp.: 19
Fiscal Year-end: 12/31/22
Haptic Feedback Technology Developer & Licensor
N.A.I.C.S.: 334610
J. Michael Dodson (CFO)
Eric B. Singer (Chm, Pres & CEO)
William C. Martin (Chief Strategy Officer)
Yeshwant Muthusamy (CTO)

Subsidiaries:

511220 N.B. Inc.   (1)
6705 Millcreek Drive Unit #4, Mississauga, L5N 5M4, ON, Canada
Tel.: (905) 363-3634
Web Site: http://www.blutipower.com
Engine Equipment Mfr
N.A.I.C.S.: 333618

Immersion (Shanghai) Science & Technology Co., Ltd.   (1)
43F Maxdo Centre No 8 Xing Yi Road, Changning District, Shanghai, 200336, China
Tel.: (86) 2160273166
Web Site: http://www.immersion.com
Electronic Components Mfr
N.A.I.C.S.: 334419

Immersion Canada, Inc.   (1)
4200 Boulevard Saint-Laurent Suite 1105, Montreal, H2W 2R2, QC, Canada (100%)
Tel.: (514) 987-9800
Web Site: http://www.immersion.com
Sales Range: Less than $1 Million
Emp.: 25
Mfr of Peripheral Device Technology
N.A.I.C.S.: 334118

Immersion Japan K.K.   (1)
Otemachi Financial City Grand Cube 18F
1-9-2 Otemachi, Chiyoda-ku, Tokyo, 100-0004, Japan
Tel.: (81) 36 262 3400
Web Site: http://www.immersion.com
Electronic Components Mfr
N.A.I.C.S.: 334419

Immersion Limited   (1)
905 Silvercord Tower 2 30 Canton Road, Tsimshatsui Kowloon, Hong Kong, China (Hong Kong)
Tel.: (852) 6598150765
Web Site: http://www.immersion.com
Electronic Components Mfr
N.A.I.C.S.: 334419

IMMIX BIOPHARMA, INC.
11400 W Olympic Blvd Ste 200, Los Angeles, CA 90064
Tel.: (310) 651-8041   DE
Web Site: https://www.immixbio.com
Year Founded: 2012
IMMX—(NASDAQ)
Assets: $14,908,101
Liabilities: $1,748,296
Net Worth: $13,159,805
Earnings: ($8,229,713)
Emp.: 9
Fiscal Year-end: 12/31/22
Research & Development in Biotechnology (except Nanobiotechnology)
N.A.I.C.S.: 541714
Ilya Rachman (Co-Founder, Chm & CEO)
Gabriel Morris (CFO)
Graham Ross (Chief Medical Officer & Head-Clinical Dev)
Vladimir Torchilin (Co-Founder)
Nandan Oza (Head-Chemistry, Mfg & Control)
Sean Senn (Co-Founder)

IMMUCELL CORPORATION
56 Evergreen Dr, Portland, ME 04103
Tel.: (207) 878-2770   DE
Web Site: https://www.immucell.com
Year Founded: 1982
ICCC—(NASDAQ)
Rev.: $18,567,962
Assets: $44,860,649

Liabilities: $14,480,600
Net Worth: $30,380,049
Earnings: ($2,493,805)
Emp.: 67
Fiscal Year-end: 12/31/22
Mfr of Diagnostic Biotechnology Products for Dairy & Beef Industries
N.A.I.C.S.: 325413
Elizabeth L. Williams (VP-Mfg Ops)
Michael F. Brigham (Pres, CEO, Treas & Sec)
Bobbi Jo Brockmann (VP-Mktg & Sls)

IMMUNE PHARMACEUTICALS INC.

550 Sylvan Ave, Englewood Cliffs, NJ 07632
Tel.: (201) 464-2677   DE
Web Site:
  http://www.immunepharma.com
Year Founded: 1993
IMNPQ—(OTCIQ)
Emp.: 7
Pharmaceuticals Mfr
N.A.I.C.S.: 325412
John Clark (Controller)
John Zhang (VP-R&D)
Adeel Ahmed-Daudpota (Pres & Interim CEO)

Subsidiaries:

EpiCept Corporation   (1)
777 Old Saw Mill River Rd, Tarrytown, NY 10591
Tel.: (914) 606-3500
Web Site: http://www.epicept.com
Sales Range: $150-199.9 Million
Emp.: 4
Pharmaceuticals Product Mfr
N.A.I.C.S.: 325412

EpiCept GmbH   (1)
Goethestrasse 4, 80336, Munich, Germany
Tel.: (49) 896808720
Web Site: http://www.epicept.de
Sales Range: $10-24.9 Million
Emp.: 5
Pharmaceuticals Product Mfr
N.A.I.C.S.: 325412

Immune Pharmaceuticals Ltd.   (1)
11C Galgale Haplada 1st Floor, Herzliya Pituach, 46722, Israel
Tel.: (972) 98866612
Web Site: http://www.immunepharma.com
Biotechnology Research & Development Services
N.A.I.C.S.: 541714

IMMUNE THERAPEUTICS, INC.

2431 Aloma Ave Ste 124, Winter Park, FL 32792   FL
Web Site:
  http://www.immunetherapeutics.com
IMUN—(OTCIQ)
Assets: $963,719
Liabilities: $3,477,173
Net Worth: ($2,513,454)
Earnings: ($3,536,076)
Emp.: 18,975
Fiscal Year-end: 12/31/22
Pharmaceuticals Mfr
N.A.I.C.S.: 325412
Glen A. Farmer (CFO)
Kelly O'Brien Wilson (Interim Pres & Interim CEO)
Roscoe M. Moore Jr. (Chm)

IMMUNEERING CORP.

245 Main St 2nd Fl, Cambridge, MA 02142
Tel.: (617) 500-8080   DE
Web Site:
  https://www.immuneering.com
Year Founded: 2008
IMRX—(NASDAQ)
Rev.: $316,952
Assets: $122,367,283
Liabilities: $12,517,028

Net Worth: $109,850,255
Earnings: ($50,513,568)
Emp.: 73
Fiscal Year-end: 12/31/22
Research & Development in Biotechnology (except Nanobiotechnology)
N.A.I.C.S.: 541714
Scott Barrett (Chief Medical Officer)
Brett Hall (Chief Scientific Officer)
Michael D. Bookman (Gen Counsel & Sec)
Jenny Zhang (Dir-Genomic Data Science)
Chris Walker (VP-Clinical Dev Scientist)
Rajeev Shrimali (VP-Discovery Oncology Therapeutics)
Stephen Sebastian (Sr Dir & Controller-Corp)
J.L. Ross (VP & Head-Neuroscience)
Mallory Morales (Chief Acctg Officer, Principal Fin Officer & Treas)
Andrew Lysaght (VP & Head-Bioinformatics)
Rebecca Kusko (VP-Bus Dev & Corp Affairs)
Rajaraman Krishnan (Sr Dir-Neurosciences)
Sarah Kolitz (VP-Translational Medicine)
Peter King (VP & Head-Discovery)
Jason Kim (Assoc Dir-Biomedical Informatics)
Mo Kagalwala (Sr Dir-Neurosciences)
Anastasia Gutierrez (VP-Clinical Ops)
Paula George (Sr Mgr-Acctg & Ops)
Jason Funt (VP-Translational Genomics)
Kevin D. Fowler (VP-Translational Res)
Elisabeth Madec Foley (Dir-Clinical Ops)
Renan Escalante-Chong (Dir-Disease Cancelling Tech)
Yoonjeong Cha (Sr Dir-Computational Biology)
Amy Axel (Assoc Dir-Ops)
Christian Alaia (Dir-Fin Plng & Analysis)
Rimma Steinhertz (VP-Project & Alliance Mgmt)
Benjamin J. Zeskind (Co-Founder, Pres & CEO)
John Brothers II (Sr Dir-Bioinformatics)

IMMUNIC, INC.

1200 Ave of the Americas Ste 200, New York, NY 10036
Tel.: (332) 255-9811   DE
Web Site: https://www.imux.com
Year Founded: 2003
IMUX—(NASDAQ)
Rev.: $3,075,000
Assets: $54,299,000
Liabilities: $25,368,000
Net Worth: $28,931,000
Earnings: ($93,612,000)
Emp.: 77
Fiscal Year-end: 12/31/23
Pharmaceuticals Mfr
N.A.I.C.S.: 325412
Hella Kohlhof (Chief Scientific Officer)
Andreas Muehler (Chief Medical Officer)
Tamara A. Favorito (Interim CFO)
Jessica Breu (Head-IR & Comm)
Inderpal Singh (Gen Counsel)
Patrick Walsh (Chief Bus Officer)
Duane D. Nash (Chm)
Jason Tardio (Pres & COO)
Daniel Vitt (CEO)

Subsidiaries:

Immunic AG   (1)
Lochhamer Schlag 21, Martinsried, 82166,

Grafelfing, Germany
Tel.: (49) 89208047700
Pharmaceuticals Product Mfr
N.A.I.C.S.: 325412
Erika Von Der Decken (Office Mgr)

IMMUNOME, INC.

18702 N Creek Pkwy Ste 100, Bothell, WA 98011
Tel.: (610) 321-3700   DE
Web Site:
  https://www.immunome.com
Year Founded: 2006
IMNM—(NASDAQ)
Rev.: $5,000
Assets: $24,046,000
Liabilities: $7,393,000
Net Worth: $16,653,000
Earnings: ($37,518,000)
Emp.: 37
Fiscal Year-end: 12/31/22
Biotechnology Research & Development Services
N.A.I.C.S.: 541714
Philip Roberts (Chief Technical Officer)
Matthew K. Robinson (Sr VP-R&D)
Jillian DiMuzio (Sr Dir-High Throughput Screening & Automation)
Benjamin Harman (Dir-Target ID & Validation)
Pavel Nikitin (Dir-Antibody Engrg)
Michael Rapp (Chm)
Dennis Giesing (Chief Dev Officer)
Sandra G. Stoneman (Chief Legal Officer & Sec)
Dennis Dong (VP-Product Dev)
Fang Shen (VP-Res & Translational Biology)
Clay Siegall (Pres & CEO)
Max Rosett (CFO, Principal Acctg Officer & Exec VP-Ops)

IMPAC MORTGAGE HOLDINGS, INC.

4000 MacArthur Blvd Ste 6000, Newport Beach, CA 92660
Tel.: (949) 475-3600   MD
Web Site:
  https://www.impaccompanies.com
Year Founded: 1995
IMH—(NYSEAMEX)
Rev.: $8,595,000
Assets: $60,331,000
Liabilities: $71,934,000
Net Worth: ($11,603,000)
Earnings: ($39,432,000)
Emp.: 98
Fiscal Year-end: 12/31/22
Other Financial Vehicles
N.A.I.C.S.: 525990
George A. Mangiaracina (Chm & CEO)
Tiffany Entsminger (COO)
Joe Joffrion (Gen Counsel)

Subsidiaries:

Impac Funding Corporation   (1)
19500 Jamboree Rd, Irvine, CA 92651
Tel.: (949) 475-3600
Sales Range: $150-199.9 Million
Provider of Short-Term Credit to Mortgage Banks
N.A.I.C.S.: 522310
Joseph R. Tomkinson (Chm & CEO)

IMPACT FUSION INTERNATIONAL, INC.

204 Hwy 1011, Napoleonville, LA 70390   NV
Web Site:
  https://impactfusionbrands.com
Year Founded: 2006
IFUS—(OTCIQ)
Medicinal & Botanical Product Mfr
N.A.I.C.S.: 325411
Marc Walther (Chm, Pres & CEO)

IMPEL PHARMACEUTICALS INC.

201 Elliott Ave W Ste 260, Seattle, WA 98119
Tel.: (206) 568-1466   DE
Web Site:
  https://www.impelpharma.com
Year Founded: 2008
IMPL—(NASDAQ)
Rev.: $12,652,000
Assets: $88,550,000
Liabilities: $132,707,000
Net Worth: ($44,157,000)
Earnings: ($106,312,000)
Emp.: 160
Fiscal Year-end: 12/31/22
Biotechnology Research & Development Services
N.A.I.C.S.: 541714
John Hoekman (Chief Scientific Officer)
Stephen Shrewsberry (Chief Medical Officer)
Leonard S. Paolillo (Interim Pres & Interim CEO)
Lynn Gold (Sr VP-Regulatory)
Scott Youmans (Sr VP-Technical Ops)
Michael Malafronte (VP-Quality Assurance)
Jen Berman (VP-Mktg)
Sheena K. Aurora (VP-Medical Affairs-Migraine)
Rigo Canal (VP-Comml Ops & Analytics)
Gerald F. Penn (VP-Market Access & Trade)
Patty Billingsley (VP-Sls)
Rajiv Amin (VP & Controller)

IMPINJ, INC.

400 Fairview Ave N Ste 1200, Seattle, WA 98109
Tel.: (206) 517-5300   DE
Web Site: https://www.impinj.com
Year Founded: 2000
PI—(NASDAQ)
Rev.: $307,539,000
Assets: $359,409,000
Liabilities: $325,278,000
Net Worth: $34,131,000
Earnings: ($43,366,000)
Emp.: 475
Fiscal Year-end: 12/31/23
Radio Frequency Identification Systems Mfr
N.A.I.C.S.: 334220
Yukio Morikubo (Gen Counsel)
Hussein K. Mecklai (COO)
Cary L. Baker (CFO)
Andy Cobb (VP-Strategic Fin)
Jeff Dossett (Chief Revenue Officer)
Jill West (VP-Strategic Comm)
Christina Balam (Sr VP-Human Resources & VP)
Alberto Pesavento (CTO)
Gahan Richardson (Exec VP & Gen Mgr-Bus Unit)
Jukka Voutilainen (Sr VP & Voyantic Gen Mgr-Bus Unit)
Cathal Phelan (Chief Innovation Officer)

Subsidiaries:

Impinj RFID Technology (Shanghai) Co., Ltd.   (1)
Room 1003-1004 Shanghai Times Square Office Building, No 93 Huihai Zhong Road Huangpu District, Shanghai, 200021, China
Tel.: (86) 2163901886
Information Technology & Consulting Services
N.A.I.C.S.: 541690

Impreso, Inc.—(Continued)

IMPRESO, INC.

652 SWern Blvd, Coppell, TX 75019
Tel.: (972) 462-0100   DE
Web Site:
    https://www.tstimpreso.com
Year Founded: 1976
ZCOM—(OTCIQ)
Sales Range: $75-99.9 Million
Emp.: 200
Offices of Other Holding Companies
N.A.I.C.S.: 551112
Marshall D. Sorokwasz *(Founder, Chm, Pres & CEO)*
Susan M. Atkins *(CFO & VP-Fin)*
Richard D. Bloom *(Founder)*
Jeffrey W. Boren *(VP-Sls & Mktg)*
John L. Graves *(VP-Mfg)*

Subsidiaries:

TST/Impreso, Inc.   **(1)**
865 W Irving Pk Rd, Itasca, IL
60143-2021   **(100%)**
Tel.: (630) 775-9555
Web Site: http://www.tstimpreso.com
Sales Range: $10-24.9 Million
Emp.: 40
Mfr of Paper Mills
N.A.I.C.S.: 322120

TST/Impreso, Inc.   **(1)**
652 SW Blvd, Coppell, TX
75019-0506   **(100%)**
Tel.: (972) 462-0100
Web Site: http://www.tstimpreso.com
Sales Range: $25-49.9 Million
Emp.: 75
Specialty Paper Mfr
N.A.I.C.S.: 322220

IMRIS INC.

5101 Shady Oak Rd, Minnetonka,
MN 55343
Tel.: (763) 203-6300   Ca
Web Site: http://www.imris.com
Year Founded: 2005
IMRSQ—(OTCIQ)
Surgical Imaging Products Mfr
N.A.I.C.S.: 339112
Andrew M. Flanagan *(Pres & CEO)*
Robert Korn *(Sr VP-Global Sls & Mktg)*
Sarah Fyfe *(VP-Talent & Culture)*
Christopher Monnot *(VP-Fin)*
A. Gregory Sorensen *(Exec Chm)*

Subsidiaries:

IMRIS (Europe) SPRL   **(1)**
Rue De Spontin 3, 5530, Yvoir, Namur,
Belgium
Tel.: (32) 495586871
Sales Range: $10-24.9 Million
Emp.: 1
Medical Imaging Services
N.A.I.C.S.: 621512
Gregory Vanesse *(Mgr-Sls)*
Hartmut Warnken *(VP & Gen Mgr-Europe & Middle East)*

IMRIS Singapore Pte. Ltd.   **(1)**
18 Holland Hill 08-17, 278746, Singapore,
Singapore
Tel.: (65) 9180 9879
Web Site: http://www.imris.com
Medical Imaging
N.A.I.C.S.: 621512

IMUNON, INC.

997 Lenox Dr Ste 100, Lawrenceville,
NJ 08648
Tel.: (609) 896-9100   DE
Web Site: https://www.imunon.com
Year Founded: 1982
IMNN—(NASDAQ)
Rev.: $500,000
Assets: $43,975,894
Liabilities: $14,648,028
Net Worth: $29,327,866
Earnings: ($35,898,234)
Emp.: 31

Fiscal Year-end: 12/31/22
Medical Treatment Systems Developer & Mfr
N.A.I.C.S.: 334510
Jeffrey W. Church *(Sec & Exec VP)*
Corinne Le Goff *(Pres & CEO)*
Sebastien Hazard *(Chief Medical Officer & Exec VP)*
Stacy R. Lindborg *(Pres & CEO)*
Michael H. Tardugno *(Chm)*
David Gaiero *(CFO & Principal Acctg Officer)*

IN-SYSTCOM, INC.

1360 Union Hill Rd Ste 11A, Alpharetta, GA 30004
Tel.: (770) 751-0003
ISYX—(OTCIQ)
Media Advertising Services
N.A.I.C.S.: 541850
Peter Demilio *(Pres)*

IN8BIO, INC.

350 5th Ave Ste 5330, New York, NY
10118
Tel.: (646) 600-6438   DE
Web Site: https://www.in8bio.com
Year Founded: 2016
INAB—(NASDAQ)
Assets: $33,039,000
Liabilities: $10,307,000
Net Worth: $22,732,000
Earnings: ($28,521,000)
Emp.: 26
Fiscal Year-end: 12/31/22
Research & Development in Biotechnology (except Nanobiotechnology)
N.A.I.C.S.: 541714
Alan S. Roemer *(Chm)*
William Ho *(Co-Founder & CEO)*
Lawrence Lamb *(Co-Founder, Chief Scientific Officer & Exec VP)*
Melissa Beelen *(VP-Clinical Ops)*
Kate Rochlin *(COO)*
Lou Vaickus *(Chief Medical Officer-Interim)*
Alan S. Roemer *(Chm)*

INARI MEDICAL, INC.

6001 Oak Canyon Ste 100, Irvine,
CA 92618
Tel.: (299) 999-9999   DE
Web Site:
    https://www.inarimedical.com
Year Founded: 2011
NARI—(NASDAQ)
Rev.: $383,471,000
Assets: $504,152,000
Liabilities: $87,150,000
Net Worth: $417,002,000
Earnings: ($28,016,000)
Emp.: 1,100
Fiscal Year-end: 12/31/22
Medical Device Mfr
N.A.I.C.S.: 334510
Andrew J. Hykes *(Pres & CEO)*
Thomas Tu *(Chief Medical Officer)*
Paul Koehn *(VP-Ops)*
John Borrell *(VP-Sls)*
Brian Strauss *(VP-Engrg)*
Ebon Gordon *(VP Quality Assurance & Regulatory Affairs)*
Eric Khairy *(VP-Mktg)*
Robert Rosenbluth *(Co-Founder)*
Paul Lubock *(Co-Founder)*
Brian Cox *(Co-Founder)*
Tara Dunn *(VP-Clinical Affairs & Market Dev)*
Mitchell Hill *(CFO)*
Eric Louw *(VP-Mfg)*
Janet Byk *(VP-Fin & Acctg)*
Angela Ahmad *(Gen Counsel)*
Vitas Sipelis *(VP-Intl)*
Kevin Strange *(CFO, Principal Acctg Officer & Sr VP-Fin, Acctg, Strategy, and Bus Dev)*

INBANKSHARES CORP.

6380 S Fiddlers Green Cir Ste 108A,
Greenwood Village, CO 80111
Tel.: (720) 552-8325   DE
Web Site: https://inbank.com
Year Founded: 2017
INBC—(OTCQX)
Rev.: $67,822,000
Assets: $1,340,349,000
Liabilities: $1,220,885,000
Net Worth: $119,464,000
Earnings: $8,811,000
Emp.: 182
Fiscal Year-end: 12/31/23
Banking Holding Company
N.A.I.C.S.: 551111
Edward Guy Francis *(Founder, Chm, Pres & CEO)*
J. Daniel Patten *(CFO & Exec VP)*
Mike Katz *(Chief Credit Officer)*
Brian Kreps *(Exec VP)*
Bo Scott *(Pres & Chief Comml Banking Officer)*
Amy Lovell *(Chief Acctg Officer, Exec VP & Controller-Corp)*
Steve Shear *(Officer-Operations, Chief Deposit Officer & Exec VP)*
Adrianne Tracy *(Pres-Boulder Market & Sr VP)*
Lisa Gregory *(Sr VP & Ops Mgr-Loan)*
Molly E. Kufeldt *(Pres-Denver Tech Center Market & Sr VP)*
Shawn Gullixson *(Pres-Community Bank & Sr VP)*
Steve Sahli *(Sr VP & Dir-Treasury Mgmt & Payments)*
Tim Romano *(Sr VP & Mng Dir-INTQ Fin)*
Vince Abrue *(Pres-Denver Market & Sr VP)*

Subsidiaries:

Legacy Bank   **(1)**
220 Main St, Wiley, CO 81092
Tel.: (719) 546-0800
Web Site: http://www.legacyib.com
Sales Range: $1-9.9 Million
Emp.: 20
Commercial Banking Services
N.A.I.C.S.: 522110
Andrew Trainor *(Pres-Pueblo)*
Angie Peterie *(Sr VP-Colorado Springs)*
Curt Wyeno *(Pres-Colorado Springs)*
Josh Stensrud *(VP-Colorado Springs)*
Dave Esgar *(Chm, Pres & CEO)*

INCAPTA, INC.

1876 Horse Creek Rd, Cheyenne,
WY 82009
Tel.: (682) 229-7476   WY
Web Site: https://www.incapta.com
Year Founded: 1997
INCT—(OTCIQ)
Sales Range: Less than $1 Million
Emp.: 1
Miscellaneous Financial Investment Activities
N.A.I.C.S.: 523999
Gregory Martin *(Chm, Pres, Treas & Sec)*

INCEPTION GROWTH ACQUISITION LIMITED

875 Washington St, New York, NY
10014
Tel.: (315) 636-6638   DE
Web Site:
    https://www.inceptiongrowth1.com
Year Founded: 2021
IGTA—(NASDAQ)
Rev.: $2,737,549
Assets: $32,115,642
Liabilities: $4,295,884
Net Worth: $27,819,758
Earnings: $640,087
Emp.: 2

Fiscal Year-end: 12/31/23
Investment Services
N.A.I.C.S.: 523999
Felix Yun Pun Wong *(CFO)*
Eddie Chow *(CEO)*

INCEPTION MINING, INC.

5530 S 900 E Ste 280, Murray, UT
84117
Tel.: (801) 312-8113   NV
Web Site:
    https://www.inceptionmining.com
Year Founded: 2007
IMII—(OTCIQ)
Assets: $1,153,403
Liabilities: $35,284,446
Net Worth: ($34,131,043)
Earnings: ($4,148,849)
Emp.: 1
Fiscal Year-end: 12/31/22
Gold Mining Services
N.A.I.C.S.: 212220
Trent D'Ambrosio *(CEO & CFO)*

Subsidiaries:

Compania Minera Cerros del Sur,
S.A. de C.V.   **(1)**
Colonia Linda Vista Este, Morazan, Tegucigalpa, Honduras
Tel.: (504) 2214307
Emp.: 250
Gold Ore Mining Services
N.A.I.C.S.: 212220
Alina Larissa Nunez Bulnes *(Supvr-Health, Safety & Environment)*

INCOME OPPORTUNITY REALTY INVESTORS, INC.

1603 LBJ Fwy Ste 800, Dallas, TX
75234
Tel.: (469) 522-4200   NV
Web Site: https://www.incomeopp-realty.com
Year Founded: 1985
IOR—(NYSEAMEX)
Rev.: $6,602,000
Assets: $111,989,000
Liabilities: $4,000
Net Worth: $111,985,000
Earnings: $3,931,000
Fiscal Year-end: 12/31/22
Real Estate Investment Trust
N.A.I.C.S.: 525990
Louis J. Corna *(Gen Counsel, Sec & Exec VP)*
Erik L. Johnson *(Pres & CEO)*
Erik L. Johnson *(CFO)*
Henry A. Butler *(Chm)*

INCYTE CORPORATION

1801 Augustine Cut-Off, Wilmington,
DE 19803
Tel.: (302) 498-6700   DE
Web Site: https://www.incyte.com
Year Founded: 2002
INCY—(NASDAQ)
Rev.: $3,695,649,000
Assets: $6,782,107,000
Liabilities: $1,592,270,000
Net Worth: $5,189,837,000
Earnings: $597,599,000
Emp.: 2,524
Fiscal Year-end: 12/31/23
Enzyme-Inhibiting Drug Mfr
N.A.I.C.S.: 541715
Christiana Stamoulis *(CFO & Exec VP)*
Paula J. Swain *(Exec VP-HR)*
Herve Hoppenot *(Chm, Pres & CEO)*
Barry P. Flannelly *(Exec VP & Gen Mgr-North America)*
Steven H. Stein *(Chief Medical Officer & Exec VP)*
Pablo J. Cagnoni *(Pres & Head-R&D)*
Jonathan E. Dickinson *(Exec VP & Gen Mgr-Europe)*

Michael Morrissey *(Exec VP & Head-Tech Ops-Global)*
Wenqing Yao *(Exec VP)*
Lauren Ayala *(Sr Dir-Investor Relations)*
Christine Chiou *(Sr Dir-Investor Relations)*
Xiaozhao Wang *(Exec VP, VP, Head & Assoc VP)*

Subsidiaries:

BIOBASE Corporation   (1)
100 Cummings Ctr 107a, Beverly, MA 01915
Tel.: (978) 922-1643
Web Site: http://www.biobase-international.com
Sales Range: $75-99.9 Million
Proteome Research
N.A.I.C.S.: 541715

Incyte Biosciences Austria GmbH   (1)
DC Tower 1 Donau-City-Strasse 7, 1220, Vienna, Austria
Tel.: (43) 13580803
Web Site: http://www.incyte.com
Biopharmaceutical Product Distr
N.A.I.C.S.: 424210

Incyte Biosciences Benelux B.V. (1)
Paasheuvelweg 25, 1105 BP, Amsterdam, Netherlands
Tel.: (31) 202619300
Web Site: https://www.incyte.nl
Pharmaceuticals Product Mfr
N.A.I.C.S.: 325412

Incyte Biosciences France   (1)
35 ter avenue Andre Morizet, 92100, Boulogne-Billancourt, France
Tel.: (33) 171109300
Web Site: https://www.incyte.fr
Biopharmaceutical Product Distr
N.A.I.C.S.: 424210

Incyte Biosciences Germany GmbH   (1)
Fraunhoferstr 9, Martinsried, 82152, Planegg, Germany
Tel.: (49) 8986399230
Web Site: http://www.incyte.com
Biopharmaceutical Product Distr
N.A.I.C.S.: 424210

Incyte Biosciences Iberia S.L.   (1)
Plaza de la Encina 10-11 Nucleo 5 Planta 2 Modulo A, 28760, Tres Cantos, Spain
Tel.: (34) 911141446
Web Site: https://www.incyte.es
Biopharmaceutical Product Distr
N.A.I.C.S.: 424210

Incyte Biosciences International S.a r.l.   (1)
Rue Docteur-Yersin 12, 1110, Morges, Switzerland
Tel.: (41) 215815000
Biopharmaceutical Product Distr
N.A.I.C.S.: 424210

Incyte Biosciences Italy S.R.L. (1)
Via Melchiorre Gioia nr 26, 20124, Milan, Italy
Tel.: (39) 0266668200
Web Site: https://www.incyte.it
Biopharmaceutical Product Distr
N.A.I.C.S.: 424210

Incyte Biosciences Japan G.K.   (1)
Imperial Hotel Tower 15Fl 1-1-1 Uchisaiwai-cho Chiyoda, Tokyo, 100-0011, Japan
Tel.: (81) 335075774
Biopharmaceutical Product Distr
N.A.I.C.S.: 424210
Eiji Ueda *(Exec Dir-R&D)*

Incyte Biosciences Nordic AB   (1)
Barnhusgatan 3, 111 23, Stockholm, Sweden
Pharmaceuticals Product Mfr
N.A.I.C.S.: 325412

Incyte Biosciences Technical Operations S.a r.l.   (1)
Rue Du Pre-de-la-Bichette 1, Geneva, 1202, Switzerland
Tel.: (41) 225812000

Biopharmaceutical Product Distr
N.A.I.C.S.: 424210

Incyte Biosciences UK Ltd   (1)
First Floor Q1 The Square Randalls Way, Leatherhead, KT22 7TW, United Kingdom
Tel.: (44) 8007833711
Web Site: https://www.incytebiosciences.uk
Biopharmaceutical Product Distr
N.A.I.C.S.: 424210

INDAPTUS THERAPEUTICS, INC.

3 Columbus Cir 15th Fl, New York, NY 10019
Tel.: (646) 427-2727   DE
Web Site:
  https://www.indaptusrx.com
Year Founded: 2021
INDP—(NASDAQ)
Rev.: $588,108
Assets: $28,063,806
Liabilities: $3,433,341
Net Worth: $24,630,465
Earnings: ($14,322,798)
Emp.: 6
Fiscal Year-end: 12/31/22
Research & Development in Biotechnology (except Nanobiotechnology)
N.A.I.C.S.: 541714
Jeffrey A. Meckler *(CEO)*
Michael J. Newman *(Founder)*
Nir Sassi *(CFO)*
Walt A. Linscott *(Chief Bus Officer)*

INDEPENDENCE CONTRACT DRILLING, INC.

20475 SH 249 Ste 300, Houston, TX 77070
Tel.: (281) 598-1230   DE
Web Site: https://www.icdrilling.com
ICD—(NYSE)
Rev.: $210,106,000
Assets: $394,677,000
Liabilities: $213,098,000
Net Worth: $181,579,000
Earnings: ($37,697,000)
Emp.: 450
Fiscal Year-end: 12/31/23
Drilling Services
N.A.I.C.S.: 213111
Philip A. Choyce *(CFO, Treas, Sec & Exec VP)*
James G. Minmier *(Chm)*
Philip A. Dalrymple *(Sr VP-Ops)*
Scott A. Keller *(Sr VP-Bus Dev)*
Katherine Kokenes *(Chief Acctg Officer & VP)*
Marc S. Noel *(VP-Sls & Mktg)*
J. Anthony Gallegos Jr. *(Pres & CEO)*

INDEPENDENCE HOLDINGS CORP.

277 Park Ave 29th Fl Ste B, New York, NY 10172
Tel.: (212) 704-3000   Ky
Web Site:
  http://www.indholdings.com
Year Founded: 2020
ACQRU—(NASDAQ)
Investment Services
N.A.I.C.S.: 523999
Steven J. McLaughlin *(Co-Chm)*
Eugene Yoon *(Co-Chm)*
John Lawrence Furlong *(CEO)*
Jaskaran Heir *(CFO)*

INDEPENDENCE REALTY TRUST, INC.

1835 Market St Ste 2601, Philadelphia, PA 19103
Tel.: (312) 924-1600   MD
Web Site: https://www.irtliving.com
Year Founded: 2009
IRT—(NYSE)
Rev.: $628,525,000
Assets: $6,532,095,000

Liabilities: $2,794,228,000
Net Worth: $3,737,867,000
Earnings: $120,659,000
Emp.: 923
Fiscal Year-end: 12/31/22
Real Estate Investment Trust
N.A.I.C.S.: 525990
Scott F. Schaeffer *(Chm & CEO)*
Jason R. Delozier *(Chief Acctg Officer)*
Ella S. Neylan *(COO)*
James J. Sebra *(Pres & CFO)*

Subsidiaries:

BSF-Arbors River Oaks   (1)
225 Arbor Commons Cir, Memphis, TN 38120
Tel.: (901) 747-2011
Web Site: http://www.arborsriveroaks.com
Apartment Rental & Leasing Services
N.A.I.C.S.: 531110

Bayview Club Apartments Indiana, LLC   (1)
7545 Bayview Club Dr, Indianapolis, IN 46250
Tel.: (317) 841-7858
Web Site:
  http://www.bayviewclubapartments.com
Apartment Rental & Leasing Services
N.A.I.C.S.: 531110

Bennington Pond LLC   (1)
4261 Hamilton Sq Blvd, Columbus, OH 43230
Tel.: (614) 833-3308
Web Site:
  http://www.benningtonpondapts.com
Apartment Rental & Leasing Services
N.A.I.C.S.: 531110

Brunswick Point North Carolina, LLC   (1)
1001 Hunterstone Dr, Leland, NC 28451
Tel.: (910) 383-2345
Web Site: http://www.brunswickpoint.com
Apartment Rental & Leasing Services
N.A.I.C.S.: 531110

Cherry Grove South Carolina, LLC   (1)
1100 David St, North Myrtle Beach, SC 29582
Tel.: (843) 272-2070
Web Site:
  https://www.cherrygrovecommons.com
Apartment Rental & Leasing Services
N.A.I.C.S.: 531110

Creekside Corners Georgia, LLC   (1)
5301 W Fairington Pkwy, Lithonia, GA 30038
Tel.: (770) 580-1147
Web Site:
  https://www.liveatcreeksidecorners.com
Apartment Rental & Leasing Services
N.A.I.C.S.: 531110

HPI Collier Park LLC   (1)
2201 Collier Crest, Grove City, OH 43123
Tel.: (614) 539-3600
Web Site: http://www.liveatcollierpark.com
Apartment Rental & Leasing Services
N.A.I.C.S.: 531110

HPI Hartshire LLC   (1)
3170 Hartshire S Dr, Bargersville, IN 46106
Tel.: (317) 535-3345
Web Site: https://www.hartshirelakes.com
Apartment Rental & Leasing Services
N.A.I.C.S.: 531110

HPI Kensington Commons LLC   (1)
6300 Refugee Rd, Canal Winchester, OH 43110
Tel.: (614) 322-9120
Web Site:
  https://www.livethecommonscw.com
Apartment Rental & Leasing Services
N.A.I.C.S.: 531110

HPI Riverchase LLC   (1)
2730 Riverchase Dr, Indianapolis, IN 46214
Tel.: (317) 387-1900
Web Site: http://www.riverchaseapts.net
Apartment Rental & Leasing Services
N.A.I.C.S.: 531110

HPI Schirm Farms LLC   (1)
6340 Saddler Way, Canal Winchester, OH 43110
Tel.: (614) 920-6611
Web Site: http://www.schirmfarmsapts.com
Apartment Rental & Leasing Services
N.A.I.C.S.: 531110

Haverford Place Apartments Owner, LLC   (1)
101 Haverford Path, Georgetown, KY 40324
Tel.: (502) 570-0227
Web Site:
  http://www.haverfordplaceapts.com
Apartment Rental & Leasing Services
N.A.I.C.S.: 531110

Hilliard Grand Apartments, LLC   (1)
5399 Grand Dr, Dublin, OH 43016
Tel.: (614) 494-4212
Property Management & Investment Services
N.A.I.C.S.: 531110

IRT Live Oak Trace Louisiana, LLC   (1)
7615 Magnolia Beach Rd, Denham Springs, LA 70726
Tel.: (225) 791-5998
Web Site:
  http://www.liveoaktraceapartments.com
Apartment Rental & Leasing Services
N.A.I.C.S.: 531110

IRT Stonebridge Crossing Apartments Owner, LLC   (1)
9135 Morning Ridge Rd, Cordova, TN 38016
Tel.: (901) 386-7473
Web Site:
  http://www.stonebridgecrossing.net
Apartment Rental & Leasing Services
N.A.I.C.S.: 531110

IRT Waterford Landing Apartments, LLC   (1)
1900 Waterford Landing, McDonough, GA 30253
Tel.: (770) 898-9595
Web Site:
  http://www.livewaterfordlanding.com
Apartment Rental & Leasing Services
N.A.I.C.S.: 531110

Jamestown CRA-B1, LLC   (1)
902 Markham Ln, Louisville, KY 40207
Tel.: (502) 893-2541
Web Site:
  http://www.jamestownatstmatthews.com
Apartment Rental & Leasing Services
N.A.I.C.S.: 531110

King's Landing LLC   (1)
618 N New Ballas Rd, Creve Coeur, MO 63141
Tel.: (314) 579-0200
Web Site:
  http://www.kingslandingapartments.com
Apartment Leasing & Rental Services
N.A.I.C.S.: 531110

Lakes of Northdale Apartments LLC   (1)
16297 Northdale Oaks Dr, Tampa, FL 33624
Tel.: (813) 969-3333
Web Site: http://www.lakesofnorthdale.com
Apartment Rental & Leasing Services
N.A.I.C.S.: 531110

Lucerne Apartments Tampa, LLC   (1)
1419 Lake Lucerne Way, Brandon, FL 33511
Tel.: (813) 661-0061
Web Site: http://www.liveatlucerne.com
Apartment Rental & Leasing Services
N.A.I.C.S.: 531110

Meadows CRA-B1, LLC   (1)
2204 Deercross Dr, Louisville, KY 40220
Tel.: (502) 499-1626
Web Site: http://www.meadows-apthomes.com
Apartment Rental & Leasing Services
N.A.I.C.S.: 531110

Millenia 700, LLC   (1)
4150 Eastgate Dr, Orlando, FL 32839
Tel.: (407) 345-7944

Independence Realty Trust, Inc.—(Continued)

Web Site: http://www.millenia700.com
Apartment Rental & Leasing Services
N.A.I.C.S.: 531110

Oxmoor CRA-B1, LLC (1)
7400 Steeplecrest Cir, Louisville, KY 40222
Tel.: (502) 412-5533
Web Site: http://www.oxmoor-apthomes.com
Apartment Rental & Leasing Services
N.A.I.C.S.: 531110

Pointe at Canyon Ridge, LLC (1)
8350 Roswell Rd, Sandy Springs, GA
30350
Tel.: (770) 587-3796
Web Site:
http://www.thepointeatcanyonridge.com
Apartment Rental & Leasing Services
N.A.I.C.S.: 531110

Prospect Park CRA-B1, LLC (1)
2300 Glen Eagle Dr, Louisville, KY 40222
Tel.: (502) 426-8300
Web Site: http://www.prospectpark-
apthomes.com
Apartment Rental & Leasing Services
N.A.I.C.S.: 531110

Steadfast Apartment REIT, Inc. (1)
18100 Von Karman Ave Ste 500, Irvine, CA
92612
Tel.: (949) 569-9700
Web Site: http://www.steadfastliving.com
Rev.: $300,101,159
Assets: $3,301,739,045
Liabilities: $2,220,113,590
Net Worth: $1,081,625,455
Earnings: ($114,089,541)
Fiscal Year-end: 12/31/2020
Real Estate Investment Trust
N.A.I.C.S.: 525990
Rodney F. Emery (Chm & CEO)
Tim Middleton (Chief Investment Officer)
Jason Stern (Chief Strategy & Admin Offi-
cer)
Gustav Bahn (Chief Legal Officer & Sec)
Tiffany Stanley (Exec VP-Property Mgmt)
David Miller (Chief Acctg Officer)

TS Big Creek, LLC (1)
50 Estuary Trl, Alpharetta, GA 30005
Tel.: (678) 393-7368
Web Site:
http://www.waterstoneatbigcreek.com
Residential Services
N.A.I.C.S.: 531110

TS Brier Creek, LLC (1)
10022 Meadow Chase Dr, Raleigh, NC
27617
Tel.: (919) 293-1100
Web Site:
http://www.waterstoneatbriercreek.com
Residential Services
N.A.I.C.S.: 531110

TS Craig Ranch, LLC (1)
8700 Stacy Rd, McKinney, TX 75070
Tel.: (972) 529-2700
Web Site:
http://www.avenuesatcraigranch.com
Residential Services
N.A.I.C.S.: 531110

TS Creekstone, LLC (1)
5472 S Miami Blvd, Durham, NC 27703
Tel.: (919) 472-0420
Web Site: http://www.creekstoneatrtp.com
Residential Services
N.A.I.C.S.: 531110

TS GooseCreek, LLC (1)
900 Channing Way, Goose Creek, SC
29445
Tel.: (843) 771-0870
Web Site:
http://www.stjamesgoosecreek.com
Resident Services
N.A.I.C.S.: 531110

TS Miller Creek, LLC (1)
3769 Skipping Stone Trace, Memphis, TN
38125
Tel.: (901) 624-9404
Web Site: http://www.millercreekapts.com
Resident Services
N.A.I.C.S.: 531110

TS Talison Row, LLC (1)

480 7 Farms Dr Daniel Island, Charleston,
SC 29492
Tel.: (843) 471-2220
Web Site: http://www.talisonrow.com
Resident Services
N.A.I.C.S.: 531110

TS Westmont, LLC (1)
120 Chamberlain Dr, Asheville, NC 28806
Tel.: (828) 225-4044
Web Site:
http://www.westmontcommons.com
Resident Services
N.A.I.C.S.: 531110

**Tides at Calabash North Carolina,
LLC** (1)
7112 Town Center Rd, Sunset Beach, NC
28468
Tel.: (910) 579-8433
Web Site: http://www.tidesatcalabash.com
Apartment Rental & Leasing Services
N.A.I.C.S.: 531110

INDEPENDENT BANK CORP.

2036 Washington St, Hanover, MA
02339
Tel.: (781) 878-6100 MA
Web Site:
https://www.rocklandtrust.com
Year Founded: 1992
INDB—(NASDAQ)
Rev.: $757,507,000
Assets: $19,294,174,000
Liabilities: $16,407,473,000
Net Worth: $2,886,701,000
Earnings: $263,813,000
Emp.: 1,739
Fiscal Year-end: 12/31/22
Bank Holding Company
N.A.I.C.S.: 551111
Jeffrey J. Tengel (Pres & CEO)
Donna Lopolito Abelli (Chm)
Mark J. Ruggiero (CFO)
Maureen A. Gaffney (Principal Acctg
Officer, Sr VP & Controller)
Stefanie M. Kimball (Chief Risk Offi-
cer)
Larry R. Daniel Jr. (Exec VP)
Patrick J. Ervin (Exec VP)
Gavin A. Mohr (CFO)
Joel Rahn (Exec VP)

Subsidiaries:

Rockland Trust Company (1)
288 Union St, Rockland, MA
02370 (100%)
Tel.: (701) 002-0110
Web Site: https://www.rocklandtrust.com
Sales Range: $550-599.9 Million
Commercial Banking
N.A.I.C.S.: 522110
Donna Lopolito Abelli (Chm)
Gerard F. Nadeau (Pres & Chief Comml
Banking Officer)
Jeffrey J. Tengel (Pres & CEO)
Donna Lopolito Abelli (Chm)
Mark J. Ruggiero (CFO & Exec VP-
Consumer Lending)
Maureen A. Gaffney (Principal Acctg Officer,
Sr VP & Controller)
Emily McDonald (Project Mgr-Mktg Strategy
& Analysis)

Subsidiary (Domestic):

**Compass Exchange Advisors
LLC** (2)
288 Union St Rockland, Plymouth, MA
02370
Tel.: (508) 830-1188
Investment Services
N.A.I.C.S.: 523999

INDEPENDENT BANK CORPO-RATION

4200 E Beltline, Grand Rapids, MI
49525
Tel.: (616) 527-5820 MI
Web Site:
https://www.independentbank.com
Year Founded: 1973

IBCP—(NASDAQ)
Rev.: $230,917,000
Assets: $4,999,787,000
Liabilities: $4,652,191,000
Net Worth: $347,596,000
Earnings: $63,351,000
Emp.: 803
Fiscal Year-end: 12/31/22
Offices of Bank Holding Companies
N.A.I.C.S.: 551111
William Bradford Kessel (Pres &
CEO)
Michael M. Magee Jr. (Chm)
Gavin A. Mohr (CFO & Exec VP)
Larry Russ Daniel Jr. (Exec VP-Ops
& Digital Banking)
Stefanie M. Kimball (Chief Risk Offi-
cer & Exec VP)
Patrick J. Ervin (Exec VP-Mortgage
Banking)

Subsidiaries:

Independent Bank (1)
4200 E Beltline, Grand Rapids, MI 49525
Tel.: (616) 363-1207
Web Site: http://www.independentbank.com
Sales Range: $10-24.9 Million
Emp.: 55
Commercial Banking
N.A.I.C.S.: 522110
William Bradford Kessel (Pres & CEO)
Michael M. Magee Jr. (Chm)
Kaye Weaver (Officer-Mortgage Loan)
Lisa Brown (Asst VP-South)

Subsidiary (Domestic):

IB Wealth Management, Inc. (2)
230 W Main St, Ionia, MI 48846
Tel.: (616) 527-5818
Web Site:
https://www.ibwealthmanagement.com
Commercial Banking Services
N.A.I.C.S.: 522110

Independent Title Services, Inc. (2)
4200 E Beltline NE, Grand Rapids, MI
49525-9325
Tel.: (616) 363-1436
Web Site:
https://www.independenttitle.services
Sales Range: $150-199.9 Million
Emp.: 5
Title Insurance Services
N.A.I.C.S.: 524127
Melissa Hewlett (Sr VP)

INDEPENDENT BANK GROUP, INC.

7777 Henneman Way, McKinney, TX
75070-1711
Tel.: (972) 562-9004 TX
Web Site: https://www.ifinancial.com
Year Founded: 2002
IBTX—(NASDAQ)
Rev.: $922,845,000
Assets: $19,035,102,000
Liabilities: $16,632,509,000
Net Worth: $2,402,593,000
Earnings: $43,201,000
Emp.: 1,517
Fiscal Year-end: 12/31/23
Bank Holding Company
N.A.I.C.S.: 551111
Paul B. Langdale (CFO & Exec VP)
David R. Brooks (Chm & CEO)
Michael B. Hobbs (Pres & COO)
James P. Tippit (Exec VP-Corp Re-
sponsibility)
Mark S. Haynie (Gen Counsel &
Exec VP)
Wendi Costlow (CMO & Exec VP)
Brenda K. Montgomery (Chief Acctg
Officer)
John G. Turpen (Chief Risk Officer)

Subsidiaries:

Guaranty Bancorp (1)
1331 17th St Ste 200, Denver, CO 80202
Tel.: (303) 675-1194

Web Site: http://www.gbnk.com
Rev.: $159,746,000
Assets: $3,698,890,000
Liabilities: $3,293,991,000
Net Worth: $404,899,000
Earnings: $38,624,000
Emp.: 487
Fiscal Year-end: 12/31/2017
Bank Holding Company
N.A.I.C.S.: 551111
John M. Eggemeyer III (Founder)

Subsidiary (Domestic):

Guaranty Bank & Trust Company (2)
1331 17th St Ste 300, Denver, CO 80202-
1566
Tel.: (303) 293-5500
Web Site: http://www.guarantybankco.com
Sales Range: $75-99.9 Million
Emp.: 300
Commercial Banking
N.A.I.C.S.: 522110
Hue Townsend (CEO)

**Private Capital Management,
Inc.** (2)
210 University Blvd Ste 400, Denver, CO
80206
Tel.: (303) 370-0055
Web Site: http://www.pcm-inc.com
Rev.: $150,000,000
Investment Management Service
N.A.I.C.S.: 523940
Justin R. Apt (Mng Principal)
Gary Wagner (Mng Principal)
Giles R. A. Fox (Dir-Res)
Peter Keilman (Portfolio Mgr)

IBG Adriatica Holdings, Inc. (1)
6625 Mediterranean Dr, McKinney, TX
75070
Tel.: (972) 540-5955
Web Site: http://www.adriaticavillage.com
Holding Company
N.A.I.C.S.: 551112

IBG Real Estate Holdings, Inc. (1)
1600 Redbud Blvd, McKinney, TX 75069
Tel.: (972) 547-6416
Web Site: http://www.johnchristieres.com
Holding Company
N.A.I.C.S.: 551112

Independent Bank (1)
1650 N Central Expy, McKinney, TX 75070
Tel.: (972) 548-5910
Web Site: http://www.ibtx.com
Sales Range: $75-99.9 Million
Emp.: 200
Commercial Banking
N.A.I.C.S.: 522110
Paul B. Langdale (CFO & Exec VP)
David R. Brooks (Chm & CEO)
Michael B. Hobbs (Pres & COO)
Wendi Costlow (CMO & Exec VP)

INDIE SEMICONDUCTOR, INC.

32 Journey Ste 100, Aliso Viejo, CA
92656
Tel.: (949) 608-0854
Web Site: https://www.indiesemi.com
INDI—(NASDAQ)
Rev.: $110,797,000
Assets: $603,351,000
Liabilities: $289,019,000
Net Worth: $314,332,000
Earnings: ($43,400,000)
Emp.: 600
Fiscal Year-end: 12/31/22
Software Development Services
N.A.I.C.S.: 541511
K. Raja S. Bal (Chief Acctg Officer)

Subsidiaries:

GEO Semiconductor Inc. (1)
101 Metro Dr Ste 620, San Jose, CA 95110
Tel.: (408) 638-0400
Web Site: http://www.geosemi.com
Semiconductor & Related Device Mfr
N.A.I.C.S.: 334413
Paul Russo (CEO)

INDOOR HARVEST, CORP.

7401 W Slaughter Ln No 5078, Austin, TX 78739

Tel.: (512) 309-1776   **TX**
Web Site:
    https://www.indoorharvest.com
Year Founded: 2011
INQD—(OTCIQ)
Rev.: $3,373
Assets: $573,258
Liabilities: $1,355,607
Net Worth: ($782,349)
Earnings: ($2,407,688)
Emp.: 2
Fiscal Year-end: 12/31/23
Aeroponic Fixtures & Systems Mfr &
Distr
N.A.I.C.S.: 333112
Leslie Bocskor *(Chm, CEO & CFO)*

INDUSTRIAL NANOTECH, INC.
999 Vanderbilt Beach Rd Ste 200,
Naples, FL 34108
Tel.: (239) 417-4803
Web Site: https://www.industrial-
    nanotech.com
INTK—(OTCIQ)
Sales Range: Less than $1 Million
Emp.: 12
All Other Miscellaneous Chemical
Product & Preparation Manufacturing
N.A.I.C.S.: 325998
Stuart Burchill *(CEO & CTO)*

INDUSTRIAL TECH ACQUISI-
TIONS, INC.
5090 Richmond Ave Ste 319, Hous-
ton, TX 77056
Tel.: (713) 599-1300   **DE**
Year Founded: 2020
ITAQ—(NASDAQ)
Rev.: $6,932,740
Assets: $179,153,691
Liabilities: $186,317,308
Net Worth: ($7,163,617)
Earnings: $4,892,914
Emp.: 2
Fiscal Year-end: 12/31/22
Investment Services
N.A.I.C.S.: 523999
E. Scott Crist *(Chm & CEO)*
R. Greg Smith *(CFO)*

INDVR BRANDS, INC.
821 22nd St, Denver, CO 80205
Tel.: (720) 399-0599
Web Site:
    http://www.cannabisone.life
CAAOF—(OTCEM)
Rev.: $903,927
Assets: $7,444,927
Liabilities: $5,990,648
Net Worth: $1,454,279
Earnings: ($5,659,697)
Emp.: 10
Fiscal Year-end: 01/31/21
Holding Company
N.A.I.C.S.: 551112
Joshua Mann *(Pres)*
P. J. Rinker *(VP-Product Dev)*
Ryan Atkins *(Gen Counsel)*

INFINERA CORPORATION
6373 San Ignacio Ave, San Jose, CA
95119
Tel.: (408) 572-5200   **DE**
Web Site: https://www.infinera.com
Year Founded: 2000
INFN—(NASDAQ)
Rev.: $1,614,128,000
Assets: $1,679,238,000
Liabilities: $1,462,647,000
Net Worth: $216,591,000
Earnings: ($25,213,000)
Emp.: 3,389
Fiscal Year-end: 12/30/23
Digital Optical Networking Systems
Mfr
N.A.I.C.S.: 334220

Alexander Derecho *(Sr VP-Svcs-
Global)*
Nancy Erba *(CFO & Principal Acctg
Officer)*
Jagdeep Singh *(Co-Founder)*
David F. Welch *(Co-Founder & Chief
Innovation Officer)*
David W. Heard *(CEO)*
Brett Hooper *(Chief HR Officer)*
Robert Shore *(Sr VP-Mktg)*
Regan J. MacPherson *(Chief Legal
Officer & Sec)*
Craig Cocchi *(Sr VP-Ops-Global)*
Nick Walden *(Sr VP-Worldwide Sls)*
Amitabh Passi *(Head-IR)*
Ryan Perera *(Sr VP-Sls-Asia Pacific)*
Scotty Benda *(Sr VP-Worldwide Sys
Engrg)*
Tom Burns *(Gen Mgr)*
Ron Johnson *(Gen Mgr)*
Russ Esmacher *(Sr VP)*

Subsidiaries:

Infinera Asia Limited   **(1)**
Ngee Ann City Tower B 391B Orchard Road
23-01, 3 Church Street, Singapore, 238874,
Singapore
Tel.: (65) 68328099
Web Site: http://www.infinera.com
Digital Optical Networking Systems Sales
N.A.I.C.S.: 423690

Infinera India Pvt. Ltd   **(1)**
Prestige Solitarire 401 Level 4 6 Brunton
Road, Bengaluru, 560 001, KA, India
Tel.: (91) 8066731300
Web Site: http://www.infinera.com
Electronic Parts & Equipment Distr
N.A.I.C.S.: 423690

Infinera Japan K.K.   **(1)**
Oak Kanda Ogawamachi Building 4th floor
2-5 Kanda Ogawamachi, Chiyoda-ku, To-
kyo, 101-0052, Japan
Tel.: (81) 355773607
Web Site: http://www.infinera.com
Digital Optical Network Provider
N.A.I.C.S.: 541512

Infinera Limited   **(1)**
New Penderel House 4th Floor 283-288
High Holborn, 1 Ropemaker Street, London,
WC1V 7HP, United Kingdom
Tel.: (44) 2070651340
Web Site: http://www.infinera.com
Sales Range: $150-199.9 Million
Digital Optical Networking Systems Sales
N.A.I.C.S.: 423690

Transmode Ltd.   **(1)**
Unit 3 Suite 11a Orwell House Ferry Lane,
Felixstowe, IP11 3QU, Suffolk, United King-
dom
Tel.: (44) 1394675635
Web Site: https://www.transmode.co.uk
Inland Water Freight Transportation Ser-
vices
N.A.I.C.S.: 483211
Angela O'Reilly *(Mgr-Accounts)*

Transmode Systems, Inc.   **(1)**
1302 E Collins Blvd, Richardson, TX 75081
Tel.: (214) 576-9881
Telecommunication Servicesb
N.A.I.C.S.: 517810

INFINITE ACQUISITION CORP.
745 5th Ave 15th Fl, New York, NY
10151
Tel.: (212) 644-4200   **Ky**
Year Founded: 2021
NFNT—(NYSE)
Rev.: $4,061,486
Assets: $286,150,923
Liabilities: $296,044,084
Net Worth: ($9,893,161)
Earnings: $2,426,964
Emp.: 4
Fiscal Year-end: 12/31/22
Investment Services
N.A.I.C.S.: 523999
Kevin Durant *(Co-CEO)*
Rich Kleiman *(Co-CEO)*

Alexander Michael *(Chief Dev Officer)*
Aryeh B. Bourkoff *(Chm)*
David Farber *(CFO)*

INFINITE GRAPHICS INCOR-
PORATED
4611 E Lake St, Minneapolis, MN
55406
Tel.: (612) 728-1300   **MN**
Web Site: http://www.igi.com
Year Founded: 1969
INFG—(OTCIQ)
Software Products Distr
N.A.I.C.S.: 423430
Cliff Stritch *(Founder & Pres)*

Subsidiaries:

MicroCraft K.K.   **(1)**
617-17 Tanaka, Kita-ku, Okayama, 700-
0951, Japan
Tel.: (81) 862416681
Web Site: http://www.usamicrocraft.com
Inkjet Printer & Electronic Product Mfr
N.A.I.C.S.: 334419
Yorio Hidehira *(CEO)*

INFINITE GROUP, INC.
175 Sullys Trl Ste 202, Pittsford, NY
14534
Tel.: (585) 385-0610   **DE**
Web Site:
    https://www.igicybersecurity.com
Year Founded: 1994
IMCI—(OTCQB)
Rev.: $7,224,242
Assets: $1,552,765
Liabilities: $5,650,654
Net Worth: ($4,097,889)
Earnings: ($1,568,813)
Emp.: 65
Fiscal Year-end: 12/31/21
Information Technology Services
N.A.I.C.S.: 335910
James A. Villa *(CEO)*
Donald J. Reeve *(Chm)*
Andrew Hoyen *(Pres & COO)*
Richard Glickman *(Chief Acctg Officer
& VP-Fin)*

INFINITY BANK
6 Hutton Centre Dr Ste 100, Santa
Ana, CA 92707
Tel.: (657) 223-1000
Web Site: https://www.infinity.bank
Year Founded: 2018
INFT—(OTCIQ)
Rev.: $2,843,000
Assets: $116,632,000
Liabilities: $90,853,000
Net Worth: $25,779,000
Earnings: ($1,932,000)
Emp.: 23
Fiscal Year-end: 12/31/19
Commericial Banking
N.A.I.C.S.: 522110
Ray Gagnon *(Chm)*

INFINITY PHARMACEUTICALS,
INC.
1100 Massachusetts Ave Fl 4, Cam-
bridge, MA 02138
Tel.: (617) 453-1000   **DE**
Web Site: http://www.infi.com
Year Founded: 1995
INFI—(NASDAQ)
Rev.: $2,593,000
Assets: $42,151,000
Liabilities: $61,202,000
Net Worth: ($19,051,000)
Earnings: ($44,369,000)
Emp.: 30
Fiscal Year-end: 12/31/22
Cancer Drug Discovery & Develop-
ment
N.A.I.C.S.: 325412
Adelene Q. Perkins *(Chm)*
Lawrence E. Bloch *(Pres & Treas)*

Seth A. Tasker *(CEO)*
Robert Ilaria Jr. *(Chief Medical Offi-
cer)*
Stephane Peluso *(Chief Scientific
Officer)*

Subsidiaries:

Infinity Discovery, Inc.   **(1)**
780 Memorial Dr, Cambridge, MA 02139
Tel.: (617) 453-1000
Web Site: http://www.infi.com
Sales Range: $150-199.9 Million
Pharmaceutical Preparation Mfr
N.A.I.C.S.: 325412

INFORMATICA INC.
2100 Seaport Blvd, Redwood City,
CA 94063
Tel.: (650) 385-5000   **DE**
Year Founded: 2021
INFA—(NYSE)
Rev.: $1,595,160,000
Assets: $5,202,082,000
Liabilities: $2,989,484,000
Net Worth: $2,212,598,000
Earnings: ($125,283,000)
Emp.: 5,000
Fiscal Year-end: 12/31/23
Software Development Services
N.A.I.C.S.: 541511
Michael I. McLaughlin *(CFO & Exec
VP-Global Fin)*
Amit Walia *(CEO)*
John Schweitzer *(Chief Revenue Offi-
cer & Exec VP)*
Bruce Chizen *(Chm)*
Amit Walia *(CEO)*

INFORMATION SERVICES
GROUP, INC.
2187 Atlantic St, Stamford, CT 06902
Tel.: (203) 517-3100   **DE**
Web Site: https://www.isg-one.com
Year Founded: 2006
III—(NASDAQ)
Rev.: $286,267,000
Assets: $243,028,000
Liabilities: $142,597,000
Net Worth: $100,431,000
Earnings: $19,726,000
Emp.: 1,599
Fiscal Year-end: 12/31/22
Information Technology & Business
Process Outsourcing
N.A.I.C.S.: 541618
Lyonel Rouast *(Pres & Partner-ISG-
South Europe, Middle East & Africa)*
Todd D. Lavieri *(Vice Chm & Pres-
ISG-Americas & Asia Pacific)*
Thomas S. Kucinski *(Chief HR Officer
& Exec VP)*
Lois Coatney *(Pres & Partner-Sls-
Americas)*
Todd Dreger *(Pres & Partner-
Governx)*
Chip Wagner *(CEO-Automation)*
Kathy Rudy *(Chief Data & Analytics
Officer)*
Paul Gottsegen *(Pres & Partner-ISG
Res & Client Experience)*
Michael A. Sherrick *(CFO & Exec VP)*
Prashant Kelker *(Partner)*
Dieter Thompson *(Member-Exec Bd)*
Michael P. Connors *(Founder, Chm &
CEO)*

Subsidiaries:

CTP Italia S.p.A.   **(1)**
Via Tribolina 30, Grumello Del Monte,
24064, Bergamo, Italy
Tel.: (39) 035832555
Web Site: https://www.ctp-srl.it
Clothing Plastic Product Mfr
N.A.I.C.S.: 326199

Compass America Inc.   **(1)**
700 Commerce Dr Ste 400, Oak Brook, IL
60523

Information Services Group, Inc.—(Continued)

Tel.: (630) 955-0999
Emp.: 36
Office Administrative Services
N.A.I.C.S.: 561110

Compass Consulting AB (1)
Engelbrektsgatan 9-11, SE 114 32, Stockholm, Sweden
Tel.: (46) 705734773
Web Site: http://www.isg-one.com
Information Technology & Business Process Outsourcing
N.A.I.C.S.: 541618
Jerker Runnquist (Partner)

Compass Management Consulting Iberica SA (1)
w Paseo de la Castellana 102 Segunda, 28046, Madrid, Spain
Tel.: (34) 911851716
Business Consulting Services
N.A.I.C.S.: 541618

Compass Management Consulting S.A. (1)
250 Bureaux de la Colline, Saint Cloud, 92213, Paris, France
Tel.: (33) 1 41 12 81 81
Web Site: http://www.isg-one.com
Emp.: 40
Business Management Consulting Services
N.A.I.C.S.: 541618

ISG Information Services Group Americas, Inc. (1)
2002 Timberloch Pl Ste 200, The Woodlands, TX 77380
Tel.: (281) 465-5700
Investment Advisory Services
N.A.I.C.S.: 523940

Information Services Group Denmark ApS (1)
Tuborg Boulevard no 12 3rd Floor, 2900, Hellerup, Denmark
Tel.: (45) 705734773
Management Consulting Services
N.A.I.C.S.: 541618

Information Services Group Europe Limited (1)
Hays House Millmead, Guildford, GU2 4HJ, Surrey, United Kingdom
Tel.: (44) 1483514500
Investment Advisory Services
N.A.I.C.S.: 523940

Information Services Group Germany GmbH (1)
The Squaire 12 Am Flughafen, 60549, Frankfurt am Main, Germany
Tel.: (49) 6969/6900
Management Consulting Services
N.A.I.C.S.: 541618

Information Services Group Netherlands B.V. (1)
Burgemeester de Manlaan 2, 4837 BN, Breda, Netherlands
Tel.: (31) 655705371
Management Consulting Services
N.A.I.C.S.: 541618

Information Services Group Oy (1)
Pohjoisesplanadi 39, 00100, Helsinki, Finland
Tel.: (358) 201550510
Management Consulting Services
N.A.I.C.S.: 541618

Information Services Group SA (1)
27 Quai Alphonse Le Gallo, Boulogne-Billancourt, 92210, Paris, Cedex, France
Tel.: (33) 141128181
Management Consulting Services
N.A.I.C.S.: 541618

Information Services Group Sweden AB (1)
Kungsgatan 56, 111 22, Stockholm, Sweden
Tel.: (46) 1483514500
Management Consulting Services
N.A.I.C.S.: 541618

Information Services Group Switzerland GmbH (1)
The Circle 6, 8058, Zurich, Switzerland

Tel.: (41) 445676107
Management Consulting Services
N.A.I.C.S.: 541618

Saugatuck Technology Inc. (1)
8 Wright St 1st Fl, Westport, CT 06880
Tel.: (203) 454-3900
Web Site:
　　http://www.saugatucktechnology.com
Sales Range: $1-9.9 Million
Emp.: 20
Consulting Services
N.A.I.C.S.: 541611
William S. McNee (Founder, Pres & CEO)

TPI Advisory Services India Pvt. Ltd. (1)
4th Floor Shankaranarayana Building 25 Mahatma Gandhi Road, Bengaluru, 560001, India
Tel.: (91) 8067680549
Web Site: http://www.tpi.net
Sales Range: $10-24.9 Million
Emp.: 40
Management Consulting Services
N.A.I.C.S.: 541618
Siddharth A. Pai (Mng Dir)

TPI Europe Ltd. (1)
Longley House International Drive Southgate, Crawley, RH10 6AQ, West Sussex, United Kingdom
Tel.: (44) 1293530196
Web Site: http://www.tpieurope.com
Professional, Scientific & Technical Services
N.A.I.C.S.: 541990

INFRASTRUCTURE DEVELOPMENTS CORP.
299 S Main St 13th Fl, Salt Lake City, UT 84111
Tel.: (801) 488-2006　　　　NV
Web Site: http://www.idvc.us
Year Founded: 2006
IDVC—(OTCIQ)
Construction Services
N.A.I.C.S.: 236220
Stanley Loo (CFO)
Cyril Means III (Sec)

INFRASTRUCTURE MATERIALS CORP.
1135 Terminal Way Ste 106, Reno, NV 89502
Tel.: (775) 322-4448　　　　DE
Year Founded: 1999
IFAM—(OTCIQ)
Silver Mining Services
N.A.I.C.S.: 212220
Todd Montgomery (CEO)

INFUSYSTEM HOLDINGS, INC.
3851 W Hamlin Rd, Rochester Hills, MI 48309
Tel.: (248) 291-1210
Web Site:
　　https://www.infusystem.com
INFU—(NYSEAMEX)
Rev.: $109,914,000
Assets: $99,388,000
Liabilities: $51,385,000
Net Worth: $48,003,000
Earnings: $18,000
Emp.: 420
Fiscal Year-end: 12/31/22
Ambulatory Infusion Pumps & Clinical Support Services
N.A.I.C.S.: 339112
Richard A. Dilorio (CEO)
Carrie A. Lachance (Pres & COO)
Barry Steele (CFO & Exec VP)
Addam Chupa (CIO)

Subsidiaries:

OB Healthcare Corporation (1)
11130 Strang Line Rd, Lenexa, KS 66215
Web Site: http://www.obhealthcare.com
Other Ambulatory Health Care Services
N.A.I.C.S.: 621999

INGEN TECHNOLOGIES, INC.

3410 La Sierra Ave Ste F507, Riverside, CA 92503
Tel.: (951) 688-7840
Web Site: https://www.ingentech.com
IGNT—(OTCIQ)
Sales Range: Less than $1 Million
Surgical & Medical Instrument Manufacturing
N.A.I.C.S.: 339112

INGERSOLL RAND INC.
525 Harbour Place Dr 600, Davidson, NC 28036-7444
Tel.: (704) 655-4000　　　　DE
Web Site: https://www.irco.com
Year Founded: 2013
IR—(NYSE)
Rev.: $6,876,100,000
Assets: $15,563,500,000
Liabilities: $5,716,800,000
Net Worth: $9,846,700,000
Earnings: $778,700,000
Emp.: 18,000
Fiscal Year-end: 12/31/23
Industruial Equipmnt Mfr
N.A.I.C.S.: 551112
Matthew J. Emmerich (CIO & Sr VP)
Vicente Reynal (Chm, Pres & CEO)

Subsidiaries:

Air Dimensions, Inc. (1)
1371 W Newport Center Dr Ste 101, Deerfield Beach, FL 33442
Tel.: (954) 428-7333
Web Site: https://www.airdimensions.com
Mfg Pumps/Pumping Equipment
N.A.I.C.S.: 333914
David English (VP)

Albin Pump SAS (1)
6 Avenue du Meyrol, 26200, Montelimar, France
Tel.: (33) 475909292
Web Site: http://www.albinpump.fr
Industrial Peristaltic Pump Mfr
N.A.I.C.S.: 333996

Comercial Ingersoll-Rand (Chile) Limitada (1)
Av Americo Vespucio 2512 El Cortijo Business Center, Conchali, Santiago, Chile
Tel.: (56) 232103159
Air Compressor Repair Services
N.A.I.C.S.: 811310

Comingersoll-Comercio E Industria De Equipamentos S A (1)
Rua Fraternidade Operaria n 8, 2790-076, Carnaxide, Portugal
Tel.: (351) 214244481
Web Site: http://www.comingersoll.pt
Industrial Equipment Distr
N.A.I.C.S.: 423830

Dosatron International SAS (1)
Rue Pascal, Tresses, 33370, Gironde, France
Tel.: (33) 557971111
Web Site: https://www.dosatron.com
Pumps Mfr
N.A.I.C.S.: 333996

Enza Air Proprietary Limited (1)
255 Berrange Road Wadeville, Germiston, South Africa
Tel.: (27) 118240808
Web Site: https://www.enza-air.co.za
Compressor & Related Equipment Distr
N.A.I.C.S.: 423830

Gardner Denver (Thailand) Co., Ltd. (1)
36 Soi Bangna-Trad 23, Kwang Bangna Khet, Bangkok, Thailand
Tel.: (66) 23961134
Air Compressor & Vacuum Product Mfr
N.A.I.C.S.: 333912

Gardner Denver Canada Corp. (1)
105 6303 39th Street, Leduc, T9E 0Z3, AB, Canada
Tel.: (780) 612-2600
Air Compressor & Vacuum Product Mfr
N.A.I.C.S.: 333912

Gardner Denver Petroleum Pumps, LLC (1)
4747 S 83rd E Ave, Tulsa, OK 74145
Tel.: (918) 664-1151
Air Compressor & Vacuum Product Mfr
N.A.I.C.S.: 333912

Gardner Denver Pte. Ltd. (1)
No 1 Gul Link, Singapore, 629371, Singapore
Tel.: (65) 64170786
Air Compressor & Vacuum Product Mfr
N.A.I.C.S.: 333912

Gardner Denver, Inc. (1)
1500 Liberty Rdg Dr Ste 3000, Wayne, PA 19087
Tel.: (610) 249-2000
Web Site: http://www.gardnerdenver.com
Sales Range: $1-4.9 Billion
Emp.: 7,000
Blowers, Stationary Air Compressors, Petroleum Drilling & Production Pumps & Water Jetting Equipment Mfr
N.A.I.C.S.: 333132
Larry Kerr (VP & Gen Mgr)

Subsidiary (Domestic):

Emco Wheaton USA, Inc. (2)
9111 Jackrabbit Rd, Houston, TX 77095
Tel.: (281) 856-1300
Web Site: http://www.emcowheaton.com
Engineered Industrial Products Marketer & Mfr
N.A.I.C.S.: 423830

Subsidiary (Non-US):

Emco Wheaton Corp. (3)
2390 South Service Road, Oakville, L6L 5M9, ON, Canada
Tel.: (905) 829-8619
Web Site: http://www.emcowheaton.com
Sales Range: $25-49.9 Million
Emp.: 25
Fluid Handling Equipment & Accessories Mfr & Supplier
N.A.I.C.S.: 423830

Emco Wheaton GmbH (3)
Emcostrasse 2-4, 35274, Kirchhain, Germany
Tel.: (49) 6422 840
Web Site: http://www.emcowheaton.com
Air Compressor & Vacuum Pump Mfr
N.A.I.C.S.: 333912
Gerd Heikamp (Mng Dir)

Division (Non-US):

Emco Wheaton UK (3)
Channel Road Westwood Industrial Estate, Margate, CT9 4JR, Kent, United Kingdom
Tel.: (44) 1843221521
Web Site: http://www.emcowheaton.com
Emp.: 80
Fluid Handling Equipment & Accessories Mfr & Supplier
N.A.I.C.S.: 423830

Subsidiary (Non-US):

GD Industrial Products Malaysia Sdn (2)
No 21-5F Bandar Puchong Jaya IOI Business Park, 47170, Puchong, Selangor Darul Ehsan, Malaysia
Tel.: (60) 380757500
Web Site: http://www.emcowheaton.com
Emp.: 3
Fiscal Year-end: 12/31/2014
Air Compressor & Vacuum Pump Mfr
N.A.I.C.S.: 333912

Gardner Denver Austria GmbH (2)
Donau-City-Strsse 7, 1220, Vienna, Austria
Tel.: (43) 7323208800
Industrial Compressor, Blower & Pump Mfr
N.A.I.C.S.: 333912

Gardner Denver Belgium NV (2)
Luithagen 7a-haven 200, 2030, Antwerp, Belgium
Tel.: (32) 35415040
Emp.: 9
Industrial Compressor, Blower & Pump Mfr
N.A.I.C.S.: 333912
Paul Keegel (Gen Mgr)

Gardner Denver CZ + SK, s.r.o. (2)

Veveri 111, 616 00, Brno, Czech Republic
Tel.: (420) 539093101
Emp.: 85
Air Compressor & Vacuum Pump Mfr
N.A.I.C.S.: 333912
Milan Klatorvsku *(Mgr)*

Gardner Denver Denmark A/S (2)
Ejby Industrivej 26, 2600, Glostrup, Denmark
Tel.: (45) 43202600
Web Site: https://www.gardnerdenver.com
Industrial Air Compressor Mfr
N.A.I.C.S.: 333912

Gardner Denver Deutschland GmbH (2)
Industriestrasse 26, 97616, Bad Neustadt an der Saale, Germany
Tel.: (49) 977168880
Air Compressors, Blowers & Pumps Mfr & Distr
N.A.I.C.S.: 333912

Division (Domestic):

CompAir Drucklufttechnik (3)
Argenthaler Strasse 11, D-55469, Simmern, Germany
Tel.: (49) 6761 832 0
Web Site: http://www.compair.com
Air & Gas Compressors Mfr
N.A.I.C.S.: 333912

Subsidiary (Non-US):

Gardner Denver Drum Ltd. (2)
Springmill Street, PO Box 178, Bradford, BD5 7YH, West Yorkshire, United Kingdom
Tel.: (44) 1274718160
Web Site:
    http://www.gardnerdenverproducts.com
Sales Range: $25-49.9 Million
Emp.: 100
Compressor Mfr
N.A.I.C.S.: 333912

Gardner Denver Engineered Products India Pte Ltd. (2)
Block No 878, Sarkhej Bavla Road Rajoda Bavla, Ahmedabad, 382220, Gujarat, India
Tel.: (91) 2714619300
Sales Range: $10-24.9 Million
Emp.: 60
Air & Gas Compressor Mfr
N.A.I.C.S.: 333912
Krutesh Shat *(Product Mgr)*

Gardner Denver France SAS (2)
15-17 Boulevard du General de Gaulle, 92542, Montrouge, Cedex, France
Tel.: (33) 146124141
Industrial Compressor Blower & Pump Mfr
N.A.I.C.S.: 333912

Gardner Denver Hong Kong Ltd. (2)
Units 1-5 25F Metropole Square 1 On Yiu Street Siu Lek Yuen, Sha Tin, New Territories, China (Hong Kong)
Tel.: (852) 26903502
Compressor & Blower Mfr
N.A.I.C.S.: 333912
Warren Beese *(Gen Mgr)*

Gardner Denver Iberica, SL (2)
Avenida La Recomba, Madrid-de-France, 41500, Leganes, Spain
Tel.: (34) 916499200
Web Site: http://www.gardnerdenver.com
Air Compressors, Pumps & Blowers Distr
N.A.I.C.S.: 423830

Gardner Denver Industries Australia Pty Ltd. (2)
13-17 Progress Street, Dandenong South, 3164, VIC, Australia
Tel.: (61) 3 9212 5800
Web Site: http://www.gardnerdenver.com.au
Emp.: 45
Air Compressor & Pump Mfr
N.A.I.C.S.: 333912

Division (Domestic):

Gardner Denver Nash Australia (3)
13 Arnott Place, Wetherill Park, 2164, NSW, Australia
Tel.: (61) 2 9725 5199
Web Site:
    http://www.gardnerdenvernash.com
Air Compressor & Pump Mfr

N.A.I.C.S.: 333912

Subsidiary (Non-US):

Gardner Denver Industries SA (2)
Immeuble Le Miroir 15-17 boulevard du General de Gaulle, 92542, Montrouge, Cedex, France
Tel.: (33) 1 46 1241 41
Sales Range: $25-49.9 Million
Emp.: 70
Holding Company
N.A.I.C.S.: 551112

Gardner Denver Japan Ltd. (2)
239 Shimohirama, Saiwai-Ku, Kawasaki, 211-8560, Japan
Tel.: (81) 445556961
Industrial Air Compressor Mfr
N.A.I.C.S.: 333912

Gardner Denver Ltd. (2)
Claybrook Drive, Washford Industrial Estate, Redditch, B98 0DS, Worcs, United Kingdom
Tel.: (44) 1527838200
Web Site: http://www.gardnerdenver.com
Blowers, Stationary Air Compressors, Petroleum Drilling & Production Pumps & Water Jetting Equipment Mfr
N.A.I.C.S.: 333912

Subsidiary (Non-US):

CompAir (Australasia) Ltd. (3)
13-17 Progress Street, Dandenong South, Melbourne, 3175, VIC, Australia
Tel.: (61) 392125800
Web Site: http://www.compair.com.au
Emp.: 120
Air Compressors & Pumps Mfr
N.A.I.C.S.: 333912
Gary Woodhead *(Mng Dir)*

CompAir GmbH (3)
Im Sudpark 207, 4030, Linz, Austria
Tel.: (43) 7323208800
Web Site: https://www.compair.com
Emp.: 17
Air Compressor & Vacuum Pump Whslr
N.A.I.C.S.: 423830

CompAir Korea Co., Ltd. (3)
Room 1006 10th Ace Techno Tower 470-5 Gasan-dong Geumcheon-gu, Seoul, 153-789, Korea (South)
Tel.: (82) 28535000
Web Site: http://www.gardnerdenver.com
Sales Range: $125-149.9 Million
Emp.: 40
Air & Gas Compressor
N.A.I.C.S.: 333912

CompAir South Africa (Pty) Ltd. (3)
255 Berrange Road, Wadeville, 1422, South Africa
Tel.: (27) 113452200
Web Site: http://www.compair.com
Emp.: 50
Air Compressor & Vacuum Pump Mfr
N.A.I.C.S.: 333912

Subsidiary (US):

Gardner Denver Nash LLC (3)
200 Simko Blvd, Charleroi, PA 15022
Tel.: (724) 239-1500
Web Site: https://www.nashpumps.com
Vacuum Pumps & Compressors
N.A.I.C.S.: 333912

Holding (Non-US):

Gardner Denver Nash Brasil Industria e Comercio de Bombas Ltda. (4)
Avenida Mercedes Benz, Sao Paulo, 13054-750, SP, Brazil
Tel.: (55) 19 3765 8000
Web Site: http://www.gdnash.com
Air Compressor Mfr
N.A.I.C.S.: 333912

Subsidiary (Non-US):

Gardner Denver Machinery (Shanghai) Co. Ltd. (2)
Room 1006 10/F Building B, Shanghai, 200000, China
Tel.: (86) 4000121268
Pump & Compressor Equipment Mfr
N.A.I.C.S.: 333912

Gardner Denver Nash Singapore Pte Ltd. (2)
5 Toh Guan Rd E,, Singapore, 608831, Singapore
Tel.: (65) 64170777
Air Compressor & Vacuum Pump Mfr
N.A.I.C.S.: 333912

Gardner Denver Nederland BV (2)
Kabelweg 2, 1014 BA, Amsterdam, Netherlands
Tel.: (31) 205829111
Industrial Air Compressor Mfr
N.A.I.C.S.: 333912

Gardner Denver New Zealand Ltd. (2)
40 Anvil Road, PO Box 45, Auckland, 0932, New Zealand
Tel.: (64) 94260370
Web Site: http://www.gd-elmorietschle.com
Emp.: 6
Air Compressor & Vacuum Pump Mfr
N.A.I.C.S.: 333912

Subsidiary (Domestic):

Gardner Denver Oberdorfer Pumps, Inc. (2)
5900 Firestone Dr, Syracuse, NY 13206
Tel.: (315) 437-0361
Web Site: http://www.oberdorferpumps.com
Sales Range: $25-49.9 Million
Emp.: 2
Pumps Mfr
N.A.I.C.S.: 333914

Subsidiary (Non-US):

Gardner Denver Slovakia s.r.o. (2)
Hranicna 4533/2A, 058 01, Poprad, Slovakia
Tel.: (421) 527723108
Industrial Air Compressor Mfr
N.A.I.C.S.: 333912

Gardner Denver Srl (2)
Via Tevere 6, Lonate Pozzolo, 21015, Varese, Italy
Tel.: (39) 0331349411
Web Site: http://www.bottarini.it
Compressors Mfr & Sales
N.A.I.C.S.: 333912

Division (Domestic):

Gardner Denver - Robuschi Division (3)
Via San Leonardo 71/a, Parma, 43122, Italy
Tel.: (39) 0521274911
Compressor & Blower Mfr
N.A.I.C.S.: 333912
Cristina Cavazzini *(Mgr-Mktg)*
Massimo Moracchioli *(Mgr-EHS)*
Anca Dumitru *(Mgr-Sls)*

Subsidiary (Non-US):

Robuschi Benelux BV (4)
Kanaaldijk 100, 6956 AX, Spankeren, Netherlands
Tel.: (31) 313 415570
Web Site: http://www.robuschi.nl
Pumps, Blowers & Compressors Sales
N.A.I.C.S.: 423830

Robuschi Fluid Technology (Shanghai) Co. Ltd. (4)
218 Tianmu Road West Suite 1208 Building No 2, Kerry Everbright City, Shanghai, 200070, China
Tel.: (86) 21 6317 5461
Web Site: http://www.gardnerdenver.com
Compressors, Blowers & Pumps Mfr
N.A.I.C.S.: 333912

Robuschi France SARL (4)
6 rue de la Grande Borne, 77990, Le Mesnil-Amelot, France
Tel.: (33) 1 60 03 7569
Web Site: http://www.robuschi.fr
Emp.: 7
Air Compressor & Blower Mfr
N.A.I.C.S.: 333912

Robuschi do Brasil Ltd. (4)
Al Rio Negro 585 Alphaville Industrial, 06454-000, Barueri, SP, Brazil
Tel.: (55) 1141912378
Web Site: http://www.robuschi.com.br

Air Compressors, Pumps & Blowers Mfr & Whslr
N.A.I.C.S.: 333912

Subsidiary (Non-US):

Gardner Denver Taiwan Ltd. (2)
2f No 101 Wugong 3rd Rd, Wugu Shiang, Taipei, 00248, Taiwan
Tel.: (886) 222995533
Web Site: http://www.gardnerdenver.com
Air Compressor & Vacuum Pump Mfr
N.A.I.C.S.: 333912

Gardner Denver Thomas GmbH (2)
Livry-Gargan-Str 10, 82256, Fuerstenfeldbruck, Germany
Tel.: (49) 814122800
Web Site: https://www.thomaspumps.com
Emp.: 850
Pump & Compressor Equipment Mfr
N.A.I.C.S.: 333912

Subsidiary (Non-US):

Gardner Denver Thomas Pneumatic Systems (Wuxi) Co., Ltd. (3)
No 1 Dong An Road Shuo Fang Town, Wuxi, 214142, China
Tel.: (86) 51068782235
Web Site:
    http://www.gardnerdenvermedical.com
Emp.: 150
Air Compressors & Pumps Mfr
N.A.I.C.S.: 333912

Subsidiary (US):

Gardner Denver Thomas, Inc. (3)
1419 Illinois Ave, Sheboygan, WI 53081
Tel.: (920) 457-4891
Web Site: http://www.gd-thomas.com
Compressors & Pumps Designer, Mfr & Retailer
N.A.I.C.S.: 333912

Plant (Domestic):

Gardner Denver Thomas - Monroe (4)
4601 Central Ave, Monroe, LA 71203-6003
Tel.: (318) 387-4280
Web Site: http://www.gd-thomas.com
Sales Range: $50-74.9 Million
Emp.: 300
Compressors & Vacuum Pumps Mfr
N.A.I.C.S.: 333912

Division (Domestic):

Welch-Ilmvac (4)
5621 W Howard St, Niles, IL 60714 (100%)
Tel.: (847) 676-8800
Web Site: http://www.welchvacuum.com
Sales Range: $25-49.9 Million
Emp.: 15
Mfr of Industrial Vacuum Pumps
N.A.I.C.S.: 333996

Subsidiary (Non-US):

Gardner Denver Trading (Shanghai) Co. Ltd. (2)
Room E & F 5/F Hai Yi Commercial Building 310 Tian Shan Road, Shanghai, 200336, China
Tel.: (86) 862162919525
Web Site: http://www.gardnerdenver.com
Emp.: 100
Air Compressor & Vacuum Pump Mfr
N.A.I.C.S.: 333912

Subsidiary (Domestic):

Gardner Denver Water Jetting Systems, Inc. (2)
12300 N Houston Rosslyn Rd, Houston, TX 77086
Tel.: (281) 448-5800
Web Site:
    http://www.gardnerdenverproducts.com
Sales Range: $25-49.9 Million
Emp.: 100
Pumping Equipment Mfr
N.A.I.C.S.: 333914

Subsidiary (Non-US):

ILMVAC Trading (Shanghai) Co. Ltd. (2)

Ingersoll Rand Inc.—(Continued)

Room 2206 22th Floor Quiangshen Mansion No 145 Pu Jian Road, Pudong New District, Shanghai, 200127, China
Tel.: (86) 215039622318
Web Site: http://www.wechvaccum.com
Emp.: 6
Air Compressor & Vacuum Pump Mfr
N.A.I.C.S.: 333912

Tamrotor Kompressorit OY (2)
Martinkylantie 39, Vantaa, 01720, Finland
Tel.: (358) 9751761
Web Site: http://www.tamrotor.fi
Sales Range: $10-24.9 Million
Emp.: 20
Compressor Mfr
N.A.I.C.S.: 333912
Jukka Pirhonen (Mgr-Field Svc)
Jussi Nurminen (Mng Dir)

Affiliate (Non-US):

Tamrotor Marine Compressors AS (2)
Prof Birkelands Vei 24D, 1081, Oslo, Norway
Tel.: (47) 22918500
Web Site: http://www.tmc.no
Sales Range: $25-49.9 Million
Emp.: 25
Marine Compressors
N.A.I.C.S.: 333912
Tom Erik Ranheim (Area Mgr-Sls)

Subsidiary (Domestic):

Thomas Industries Inc. (2)
211 Industrial Ct, Wabasha, MN 55981
Tel.: (651) 565-3395
Web Site:
https://www.thomasindustriesinc.com
Industrial Air Compressor Mfr
N.A.I.C.S.: 333912

TriContinent Scientific, Inc. (2)
12740 Earhart Ave, Auburn, CA 95602
Tel.: (530) 273-8888
Web Site: http://www.tricontinent.com
Emp.: 750
Syringe Pumps Mfr
N.A.I.C.S.: 332710

Subsidiary (Non-US):

Zinsser Analytic GmbH (2)
Schwalbacher Strasse 62, 65760, Eschborn, Germany
Tel.: (49) 6196586930
Web Site: https://www.zinsser-analytic.com
Liquid Handling Solutions & Equipment Mfr
N.A.I.C.S.: 621511
Patrick Bennett (CEO)

Division (Non-US):

Zinsser Analytic GmbH (3)
5 Avenue Gallieni, 92160, Antony, France
Tel.: (33) 670858330
Web Site: http://www.zinsser-analytic.com
Medical Equipment Distr
N.A.I.C.S.: 423450

Subsidiary (US):

Zinsser NA, Inc. (3)
19145 Parthenia St Ste C, Northridge, CA 91324
Tel.: (818) 341-2906
Web Site: https://www.zinsserna.com
Emp.: 10
Medical Equipment Distr
N.A.I.C.S.: 423450

ILS Inovative Laborsysteme GmbH (1)
Franz-Ferdinand-Greiner Str 37, 98694, Ilmenau, Germany
Tel.: (49) 3678452524
Web Site: https://www.microsyringes.com
Air Compressor & Vacuum Product Mfr
N.A.I.C.S.: 333912

Ingersoll-Rand Colombia S.A.S. (1)
Terminal Terrestre de Carga-Autopista Medellin Km 3 0 Bodega 4, Modulo 5 Bogota, Cota, Cundinamarca, Colombia
Tel.: (57) 14898231
Air Compressor Mfr
N.A.I.C.S.: 333912

Ingersoll-Rand Company Limited (1)
Canon's Court 22 Victoria Street, Hamilton, HM 12, Bermuda
(100%)
Tel.: (441) 2952838
Web Site: http://www.ingersollrand.com
Sales Range: $5-14.9 Billion
Holding Company
N.A.I.C.S.: 551112

Subsidiary (US):

GPSI Holdings, LLC (2)
1074 N Orange Ave, Sarasota, FL 34236
Tel.: (941) 306-3890
Web Site: http://www.gpsindustries.com
Holding Company; Golf Global Positioning System Equipment Developer, Mfr & Distr
N.A.I.C.S.: 551112

Subsidiary (Domestic):

GPS Industries, LLC (2)
1074 N Orange Ave, Sarasota, FL 34236
Tel.: (941) 306-3890
Web Site: http://www.gpsindustries.com
Golf Global Positioning System Equipment Developer, Mfr & Distr
N.A.I.C.S.: 334419
Ben Porter (CEO)

Subsidiary (US):

Ingersoll-Rand Company (2)
155 Chestnut Ridge Rd, Montvale, NJ 07645
Tel.: (201) 573-0123
Web Site: http://www.irco.com
Pneumatic, Hydraulic & General Machinery & Tools, Pumps, Compressors, Drilling Equipment, Locks, Bearings, Hoists, Winches, Off-Road Forklifts Mfr
N.A.I.C.S.: 333248

Subsidiary (Non-US):

A/S PARTS LIMITED (3)
4 Hayes Road, Southall, UB2 5LZ, United Kingdom
Tel.: (44) 20 8571 5262
Industrial Machinery Distr
N.A.I.C.S.: 423830

AB Best Matic (3)
V Industrigatan 3c, PO Box 525, 372 25, Ronneby, Sweden
Tel.: (46) 45734500
Web Site: http://www.kmtrobotic.eu
Rev.: $9,678,000
Emp.: 50
Mfr of Pneumatic, Hydraulic & General Machinery & Tools, Pumps, Compressors, Drilling Equipment, Locks, Bearings, Hoists, Winches, Off-Road Forklifts
N.A.I.C.S.: 333998

ABG-France E.U.R.L (3)
5 Rue Ampere, 69680, Chassieu, France
Tel.: (33) 472476131
Web Site: http://www.ir-abg.com
Sales Range: $25-49.9 Million
Emp.: 21
Mfr of Pneumatic, Hydraulic & General Machinery & Tools, Pumps, Compressors, Drilling Equipment, Locks, Bearings, Hoists, Winches, Off-Road Forklifts
N.A.I.C.S.: 333998

ABG-Iberica (3)
Tierra De Barros 2, Coslada, 28820, Madrid, Spain
Tel.: (34) 916277489
Sales Range: $25-49.9 Million
Emp.: 40
Mfr of Pneumatic, Hydraulic & General Machinery & Tools, Pumps, Compressors, Drilling Equipment, Locks, Bearings, Hoists, Winches, Off-Road Forklifts
N.A.I.C.S.: 333998

AIRCO (3)
1126/2 Vanit Building II 30th-31st Floor New Petchburi Road, Makkasan Rachthevee, Bangkok, 10400, Thailand
Tel.: (66) 27049999
Web Site: http://www.tranethailand.com
Air Conditioner Mfr
N.A.I.C.S.: 333413

AIRTEC LIMITED (3)
Sefton House Northgate Close Middlebrook

Business Park, Bolton, BL6 6PQ, United Kingdom
Tel.: (44) 844 474 1000
Web Site: http://www.airtec-oilfree.com
Sales Range: $25-49.9 Million
Emp.: 6
Compressor Repair & Maintenance Services
N.A.I.C.S.: 811310

Subsidiary (Domestic):

ALLIANCE COMPRESSORS INC. (3)
100 Industrial Dr, Natchitoches, LA 71457
Tel.: (318) 356-4600
Emp.: 700
Industrial Machinery & Equipment Mfr
N.A.I.C.S.: 423830
Ken Gardner (Office Mgr)

Subsidiary (Non-US):

Aro GmbH (3)
Englerstrasser 9A, Durchhausen, 78591, Ratingen, Germany
Tel.: (49) 7816392880
Sales of Diaphragm Pumps, Piston Pumps, Valves, Controls & Tools
N.A.I.C.S.: 423830

Subsidiary (Domestic):

BMM, INC. (3)
1724 Douglas Dr N Ste 100, Golden Valley, MN 55422
Tel.: (763) 541-4886
Web Site:
https://www.buildingmaintenancemanagement.com
Sales Range: $10-24.9 Million
Emp.: 30
Building Maintenance Services
N.A.I.C.S.: 541350
Jim Rognlie (Owner)

Subsidiary (Non-US):

BRICARD S.A. (3)
1 rue Paul Henri Spaak, 77400, Saint-Thibault-des-Vignes, France
Tel.: (33) 164121111
Web Site: https://bricard.com
Electronic Lock Mfr & Distr
N.A.I.C.S.: 334419

CISA CERRADURAS S.A. (3)
Pl La Charluca C/F, Calatayud, 50300, Zaragoza, Spain
Tel.: (34) 976889230
Sales Range: $25-49.9 Million
Emp.: 60
Lock Mfr
N.A.I.C.S.: 332510
Jesus Castellon (Reg Mgr)

CISA S.P.A. (3)
Via Oberdan 42, 48018, Faenza, Ravenna, Italy
Tel.: (39) 0546677111
Web Site: https://www.cisa.com
Sales Range: $100-124.9 Million
Emp.: 500
Hardware & Security systems Mfr
N.A.I.C.S.: 332510

Subsidiary (Domestic):

CLEAN AIR, INC. (3)
250 S Whiting St, Alexandria, VA 22304
Tel.: (703) 987-3944
Web Site: http://www.cleanaireinc.com
Air Duct Cleaning Services
N.A.I.C.S.: 561720

Dixie Pacific Manufacturing Co. (3)
1015 Brundidge Blvd, Troy, AL 36081
Tel.: (256) 442-4513
Web Site: http://www.dixiepacific.com
Sales Range: $125-149.9 Million
Emp.: 30
Wood Porch Columns
N.A.I.C.S.: 321918

Energy Equipment & Supply, Inc. (3)
7421 W 6 Wn Rd, Casper, WY 82604
Web Site: http://www.energyeq.com
Emp.: 15
Equipment Sales
N.A.I.C.S.: 423830

Subsidiary (Non-US):

FRIGOBLOCK Grosskopf GmbH (3)
Weidkamp 274, 45356, Essen, Germany
(100%)
Tel.: (49) 201613010
Web Site: https://www.frigoblock.com
Emp.: 150
Transport Refrigeration Machines Mfr
N.A.I.C.S.: 333415
Frank den Brok (Mng Dir)

HIBON INC. (3)
100 Voyageur Pointe Claire, Quebec, H9R 6A8, QC, Canada
Tel.: (514) 631-3501
Air Blower & Compression Equipment Distr
N.A.I.C.S.: 423830

HUSSMANN (THAILAND) COMPANY LIMITED (3)
Room 2903 29th Floor Vanit Building II 1126/2 New Petchburi Road, Makkasan Rachthevee, Bangkok, 10400, Thailand
Tel.: (66) 2 704 9999
Web Site: http://www.hussmann.com
Sales Range: $125-149.9 Million
Emp.: 300
Industrial Machinery Whslr
N.A.I.C.S.: 423830

HUSSMANN SERVICE DO BRASIL LTDA. (3)
Alam Caiapos 311 Parte 275 Tambore, Barueri, 06460-110, Brazil
Tel.: (55) 11 2109.8729
Air Conditioning System Installation Services
N.A.I.C.S.: 238220

Subsidiary (Domestic):

IMPROVED MACHINERY INC. (3)
111 Ingersoll Rand Dr, Atlanta, GA 30341
Tel.: (770) 936-6200
Industrial Machinery Distr
N.A.I.C.S.: 423830

Subsidiary (Non-US):

INGERSOLL-RAND (CHINA) INDUSTRIAL EQUIPMENT MANUFACTURING CO., LTD. (3)
2333 Pangjin Road Wujiang Economics Development Zone, Wujiang, China
Tel.: (86) 512 6363 6888
Industrial Equipment Mfr
N.A.I.C.S.: 333248

INGERSOLL-RAND (CHINA) INVESTMENT COMPANY LIMITED (3)
10/F Tower B City Center of Shanghai 100 Zun Yi Road, Shanghai, 200051, China
Tel.: (86) 21 2208 1288
Web Site: http://www.ingersollrand.com
Air Conditioning Equipment Mfr
N.A.I.C.S.: 333415

INGERSOLL-RAND (GUILIN) TOOLS COMPANY LIMITED (3)
No 55 Chaoyang Road Qixing District, Guilin, 541004, Guangxi, China
Tel.: (86) 7735876019
Pneumatic Tool & Diaphragm Pump Mfr
N.A.I.C.S.: 333991

INGERSOLL-RAND (HONG KONG) LIMITED (3)
139 Hennessy Road Units A-E 15/F China Overseas Building, Wanchai, China (Hong Kong)
Tel.: (852) 22350600
Industrial Machinery Whslr
N.A.I.C.S.: 423830

INGERSOLL-RAND AIR SOLUTIONS HIBON SARL (3)
2 Avenue Jean-paul Sartre, 59290, Wasquehal, France
Tel.: (33) 32 045 3939
Web Site: https://www.hibon.com
Air Compressor Mfr & Distr
N.A.I.C.S.: 333912

INGERSOLL-RAND ARCHITECTURAL HARDWARE (AUSTRALIA) PTY LIMITED (3)
31-33 Alfred Street, Sunshine, Blackburn,

3130, VIC, Australia
Tel.: (61) 393009300
Web Site: http://www.ingersollrand.com.au
Sales Range: $25-49.9 Million
Emp.: 20
Door Hardware Mfr
N.A.I.C.S.: 423830

INGERSOLL-RAND ARCHITEC-TURAL HARDWARE LIMITED (3)
437 Rosebank Road, Avondale, Auckland, 1026, New Zealand
Tel.: (64) 98290550
Web Site: https://www.allegion.co.nz
Sales Range: $25-49.9 Million
Emp.: 50
Door Locks Mfr
N.A.I.C.S.: 332510

INGERSOLL-RAND BEST-MATIC AB (3)
Krossverksgatan 5 L, Limhamn, 216 16, Sweden
Tel.: (46) 40 16 20 60
Industrial Engineering Services
N.A.I.C.S.: 541330

Subsidiary (Domestic):

INGERSOLL-RAND CHARITABLE FOUNDATION (3)
1 Centennial Ave Ste 101, Piscataway, NJ 08854-3921
Tel.: (732) 652-7000
Industrial Machinery & Equipment Mfr
N.A.I.C.S.: 423830

Subsidiary (Non-US):

INGERSOLL-RAND COMPANY LIMITED (UK) (3)
Sefton House Northgate Close Middlebrook Business Park, Bolton, BL6 6PQ, United Kingdom
Tel.: (44) 1204479500
Air & Gas Compressor Mfr
N.A.I.C.S.: 333912

INGERSOLL-RAND EQUIPEMENTS DE PRODUCTION S.A.S. (3)
529 Avenue R Salengro, 59450, Sin-le-Noble, 59450, France
Tel.: (33) 327930808
Sales Range: $25-49.9 Million
Emp.: 80
Industrial Lifting Equipment Mfr
N.A.I.C.S.: 333998

INGERSOLL-RAND EUROPEAN HOLDING COMPANY B.V. (3)
Driemansseeweg 60, 3084 CB, Rotterdam, Netherlands
Tel.: (31) 715823456
Sales Range: $50-74.9 Million
Emp.: 65
Investment Management Service
N.A.I.C.S.: 523940
Louis van Kampen (Gen Mgr)

INGERSOLL-RAND EUROPEAN SALES LIMITED (3)
Swan Lane Hindley Green, Lancashire, Wigan, WN2 4EZ, United Kingdom
Tel.: (44) 1942257171
Industrial Machinery & Tool Mfr & Whslr
N.A.I.C.S.: 333248

INGERSOLL-RAND FINLAND OY (3)
Rajamaankaari 16, 02970, Espoo, Finland
Tel.: (358) 20544141
Web Site: https://ingersollrand.fi
Sales Range: $50-74.9 Million
Emp.: 270
Industrial Machinery Leasing Services
N.A.I.C.S.: 532490
Juha Saari (Office Mgr)

INGERSOLL-RAND INTERNATIONAL LIMITED (3)
170/175 Lakeview Drive Airside Business Park, Swords, K67 EW96, Co Dublin, Ireland
Tel.: (353) 1 870 7000
Sales Range: $50-74.9 Million
Emp.: 200
Industrial Machinery Mfr
N.A.I.C.S.: 333248

INGERSOLL-RAND IRISH HOLDINGS (3)
170/175 Lakeview Drive, Swords, K67EW96, Co Dublin, Ireland
Tel.: (353) 18707000
Investment Management Service
N.A.I.C.S.: 523999

INGERSOLL-RAND ITALIA S.R.L. (3)
Strada Provinciale Cassanese 108, Vignate, Italy
Tel.: (39) 02 950561
Industrial Machinery Mfr
N.A.I.C.S.: 333248

INGERSOLL-RAND ITALIANA S.P.A. (3)
Strada Provinciale Cassanese 108-110, Vignate, 20060, Italy
Tel.: (39) 02950561
Web Site:
  http://www.ingersollrandproducts.com
Air Compressor Mfr
N.A.I.C.S.: 333912

INGERSOLL-RAND ITS JAPAN LTD. (3)
4-5-37 Kami-Osaki, Shinagawa-ku, Tokyo, 141-0021, Japan
Tel.: (81) 369106600
Web Site:
  http://www.ingersollrandproducts.com
Sales Range: $50-74.9 Million
Emp.: 10
Air Compressor Distr
N.A.I.C.S.: 423730

INGERSOLL-RAND KOREA LIMITED (3)
World Cupbuk-ro 56-gil Trutech Building 10th floor, Mapo-gu Sangam-dong, Seoul, Korea (South)
Tel.: (82) 260160800
Sales Range: $25-49.9 Million
Emp.: 40
Turbine Distr
N.A.I.C.S.: 423830

INGERSOLL-RAND MACHINERY (SHANGHAI) COMPANY LIMITED (3)
11F Tower B City Center of Shanghai No 100 Zun Yi Road, Shanghai, China
Tel.: (86) 21 2208 1288
Industrial Machinery Whslr
N.A.I.C.S.: 423830

INGERSOLL-RAND MALAYSIA CO. SDN. BHD. (3)
Lot 4881 Jalan SS13/2, 47500, Petaling Jaya, Selangor, Malaysia
Tel.: (60) 39 078 4011
Web Site: https://www.irco.com
Emp.: 50
Industrial Machinery Whslr
N.A.I.C.S.: 423830

INGERSOLL-RAND NETHERLANDS B.V. (3)
Produktieweg 10, 2382 PB, Zoeterwoude, Netherlands
Tel.: (31) 858887908
Web Site: http://www.ingersollrand.com
Sales Range: $25-49.9 Million
Emp.: 65
Industry Machinery & Equipment Distr
N.A.I.C.S.: 423830

INGERSOLL-RAND POLSKA SP.ZO.O. (3)
ul Kolejowa 5/7, 01-217, Warsaw, 01-217, Poland
Tel.: (48) 224347770
Web Site:
  http://www.ingersollrandproducts.com
Air Compressor Mfr
N.A.I.C.S.: 333912

INGERSOLL-RAND S.A. DE C.V. (3)
Boulevard Centro Industrial No 11 Industrial Puente de Vigas, Tlalnepantla, 54070, Mexico
Tel.: (52) 55 50056600
Web Site: http://www.ingersollrand.com
Air Conditioning Equipment Distr
N.A.I.C.S.: 423730

INGERSOLL-RAND SERVICES AND TRADING LIMITED LIABILITY COMPANY (3)
Sergeya Makeeva St 13, 123022, Moscow, Russia
Tel.: (7) 4959 33 03 21
Web Site: http://www.ingersollrand.com
Sales Range: $25-49.9 Million
Emp.: 70
Refrigeration Equipment Distr
N.A.I.C.S.: 423740

INGERSOLL-RAND SERVICIOS, S.A. (3)
Pol Ind Casas De Miravete 22 Edificio 1B 3 Planta, Madrid, 28031, Spain
Tel.: (34) 913623934
Sales Range: $25-49.9 Million
Emp.: 25
Road Construction Machinery Mfr
N.A.I.C.S.: 333120
Francisco Gomez (Pres)

INGERSOLL-RAND SOUTH EAST ASIA (PTE.) LTD. (3)
42 Benoi Rd, Singapore, 629903, Singapore
Tel.: (65) 68611555
Industrial Machinery Mfr
N.A.I.C.S.: 333248

Subsidiary (Domestic):

INGERSOLL-RAND US TRANE HOLDINGS CORPORATION (3)
1 Centennial Ave, Piscataway, NJ 08854
Tel.: (732) 652-7100
Investment Management Service
N.A.I.C.S.: 551112

Subsidiary (Non-US):

INGERSOLL-RAND WORLDWIDE CAPITAL S.A.R.L. (3)
16 Ave Pasteur, Luxembourg, 2310, Luxembourg
Tel.: (352) 26649263
Air & Gas Compressor Mfr
N.A.I.C.S.: 333912

INTERFLEX Datensysteme GmbH & Co. KG (3)
Epplestrasse 225, 70567, Stuttgart, Germany
Tel.: (49) 71113220
Web Site: https://interflex.com
Sales Range: $125-149.9 Million
Emp.: 550
Security & Employee Management System Mfr & Distr
N.A.I.C.S.: 336320

Subsidiary (Non-US):

INTERFLEX Datensysteme GesmbH (4)
Leonard-Bernstein-Strasse 10/8, 1220, Vienna, Austria
Tel.: (43) 18774646
Web Site: http://www.interflex.de
Office Equipment Mfr & Distr
N.A.I.C.S.: 333310

Subsidiary (Non-US):

INVERSORA LOCKEY DE VENEZUELA CA (3)
Calle Los Pinos Sector Los Mangos El Tambor, Los Taques, 1021, Venezuela
Tel.: (58) 212 321 0744
Web Site: http://www.cisaven.com
Sales Range: $100-124.9 Million
Emp.: 425
Lock Mfr
N.A.I.C.S.: 332510

INVERSORA LOCKEY LTDA. (3)
Calle 80 N 69-70 Bodega 12 Parque Comercial Av 80, Bogota, Colombia
Tel.: (57) 15331258
Web Site: https://lockeycolombia.com
Construction Materials Distr
N.A.I.C.S.: 423390

IR DEUTSCHE HOLDING GMBH (3)
Schwarzwaldstr 15, 77871, Renchen, Germany
Tel.: (49) 7843 7040

Emp.: 250
Investment Management Service
N.A.I.C.S.: 523940
Peter Deglow (Gen Mgr)

IR Security Technologies (3)
1076 Lakeshore Rd E, Mississauga, L5E 1E4, ON, Canada
Tel.: (905) 403-1800
Web Site:
  http://www.irsecurityandsafety.com
Sales Range: $75-99.9 Million
Emp.: 150
Mfr of Fabricated Metal Products
N.A.I.C.S.: 332919

Ingersoll Rand S.E. Asia (Private) Limited (3)
42 Benoi Road, Jurong, 629903, Singapore
Tel.: (65) 68611555
Web Site: http://www.ap.irco.com
Sales Range: $75-99.9 Million
Emp.: 160
Industrial Mfr
N.A.I.C.S.: 333912

Ingersoll-Rand (Australia) Ltd. (3)
13-17 Progress Street, Dandenong, 3175, VIC, Australia (100%)
Tel.: (61) 41588282
Sales Range: $25-49.9 Million
Emp.: 5
Pump & Compressor Mfr
N.A.I.C.S.: 333914
Amanda Yao (Mgr-Fin)

Ingersoll-Rand (India) Private Ltd. (3)
8th FloorTower D IBC Knowledge Park, No 4/1 Bannerghatta Main Road, Bengaluru, 560029, Bidadi, India
Tel.: (91) 8022166000
Web Site: http://www.ingersollrand.co.in
Rev.: $60,267,000
Emp.: 1,366
Mfr of Mobile Drills
N.A.I.C.S.: 333131

Ingersoll-Rand AB (3)
Lindberghs GaTa 9, 195 61, Arlandastad, Sweden
Tel.: (46) 40162060
Air Compressor Distr
N.A.I.C.S.: 423730
Martijn Nanning (Mgr-Europe)

Ingersoll-Rand Company (Chile) y Cia Ltda. (3)
Avenida Americo Vespucio 2512 El Cortijo, Conchali, Santiago, Chile
Tel.: (56) 224858300
Sales Range: $25-49.9 Million
Emp.: 35
Mfr of Machines
N.A.I.C.S.: 333998

Ingersoll-Rand Company SA (Pty) Ltd. (3)
Innes Road, Jet Park, Boksburg, 1459, South Africa
Tel.: (27) 115658600
Web Site: http://www.ingersollrand.com
Sales Range: $50-74.9 Million
Emp.: 120
Mfr of Compressors & Mobile Drill Rigs
N.A.I.C.S.: 333912

Ingersoll-Rand GmbH (3)
Max Planck Ring 27, 46049, Oberhausen, Germany
Tel.: (49) 20899940
Web Site: http://www.ingersollrand.de
Sales Range: $50-74.9 Million
Emp.: 126
Air Conditioning Equipment Whslr
N.A.I.C.S.: 423730

Ingersoll-Rand Holdings Ltd. (3)
Swam Ln Hindley Green, Wigan, WN2 4EZ, United Kingdom
Tel.: (44) 942257171
Rev.: $110,000,000
Emp.: 200
Mfr of Pneumatic, Hydraulic & General Machinery & Tools, Pumps, Compressors, Drilling Equipment, Locks, Bearings, Hoists, Winches, Off-Road Forklifts
N.A.I.C.S.: 333998

Unit (Domestic):

Ingersoll-Rand Industrial Technologies - Compressed Air Solutions (3)

Ingersoll Rand Inc.—(Continued)

800-D Beaty St, Davidson, NC 28036-1840
Tel.: (704) 655-4000
Web Site: http://www.cagi.org
Sales Range: $350-399.9 Million
Emp.: 2,000
Reciprocating & Rotary Air Compressors
Mfr
N.A.I.C.S.: 333912

Ingersoll-Rand Industrial Technologies - Tools & Lifting/Material Handling Solutions **(3)**
1467 State Rte 31 S, Annandale, NJ 08801-3118
Tel.: (908) 238-5800
Web Site:
http://www.ingersollrandproducts.com
Industrial Tools & Material Handling Equipment Mfr, Distr & Support Services
N.A.I.C.S.: 333991

Subsidiary (Non-US):

Ingersoll-Rand do Brasil Ltda. **(3)**
Alameda dos Caiapo 311 - Barueri, Vila Olimpia, Sao Paulo, 05331-040, Brazil
Tel.: (55) 1121098933
Web Site: https://www.irco.com
Sales Range: $25-49.9 Million
Emp.: 50
Mfr of Mechanical Refrigeration Systems for Trucks, Trailers & Rail Cars; Bus Air Conditioning
N.A.I.C.S.: 333415

Subsidiary (Domestic):

LOCKEY CORP. **(3)**
10851 NW 29th St, Doral, FL 33172
Tel.: (954) 716-8393
Web Site: https://lockeycorp.net
Emp.: 3
Door Lock Distr
N.A.I.C.S.: 423710

Subsidiary (Non-US):

Marquinarias Ingersoll-Rand de Colombia S.A. **(3)**
Cra 86 No 18A 14, Bogota, Colombia
Tel.: (57) 16386169
Web Site:
http://www.ingersollrandproducts.com
Sales
N.A.I.C.S.: 561499

NORMBAU BESCHLAGE UND AUSSTATTUNGS GMBH **(3)**
Schwarzwaldstrasse 15, 77871, Renchen, Germany
Tel.: (49) 78427040
Web Site: https://www.normbau.de
Emp.: 250
Hardware Distr
N.A.I.C.S.: 423710

NORMBAU FRANCE S.A.S. **(3)**
1 rue de l'Artisanat, CS 50056, 67242, Bischwiller, Cedex, France
Tel.: (33) 388062323
Web Site: https://www.normbau.fr
Hardware Mfr & Distr
N.A.I.C.S.: 332510

Joint Venture (Domestic):

Niject Services Company **(3)**
222 Pennbright Dr Ste 300, Houston, TX 77090
Tel.: (512) 217-4833
Sales Range: $25-49.9 Million
Emp.: 2
Enhanced Oil Recovery Services
N.A.I.C.S.: 541990

Subsidiary (Non-US):

PLURIFILTER D.O.O. **(3)**
Obrtna Cona 14, 1370, Logatec, 1370, Slovenia
Tel.: (386) 17508282
Web Site: https://www.plurifilter.com
Sales Range: $25-49.9 Million
Emp.: 26
Hydraulic Equipment Distr
N.A.I.C.S.: 423830
Lovro Cuden (Gen Mgr)

PT INGERSOLL-RAND INDONESIA **(3)**
Pondok Indah Office Tower 2 16th Floor Suite 1601, Jl Sultan Iskandar Muda Kav V TA Pondok Pinang Kebayoran Lama, Jakarta, 12310, Indonesia
Tel.: (62) 2150996906
Industrial Machinery Mfr & Distr
N.A.I.C.S.: 333248

SCHLAGE DE MEXICO S.A. DE C.V. **(3)**
Olives Street No 698 Col Chavez, Tecale, 21440, Baja California, Mexico
Tel.: (52) 6656540622
Hardware Mfr
N.A.I.C.S.: 332510

Subsidiary (Domestic):

SILVER HOLDING CORP. **(3)**
5350 Joliet St Unit 3, Denver, CO 80239-2148
Tel.: (303) 373-2311
Industrial Machinery & Equipment Mfr
N.A.I.C.S.: 423830

Steelcraft Manufacturing Company **(3)**
9017 Blue Ash Rd, Cincinnati, OH 45242-6816
Tel.: (513) 745-6400
Web Site: http://www.steelcraft.com
Sales Range: $150-199.9 Million
Emp.: 800
Mfr of Commercial Steel Doors & Door Frames
N.A.I.C.S.: 332321

Subsidiary (Non-US):

TRANE DEUTSCHLAND GMBH **(3)**
Max-Planck-Ring 27, 46049, Oberhausen, Germany
Tel.: (49) 8009994240
Air Conditioning Equipment Mfr
N.A.I.C.S.: 333415

TRATAMAQ CA **(3)**
Zona Industrial Los Tres Puentes Final Avda, Oswaldo Brandani, Los Teques, Miranda, Venezuela
Tel.: (58) 2123214595
Web Site: http://www.tratamaq.com
Industrial Machinery & Equipment Mfr
N.A.I.C.S.: 423830

Subsidiary (Domestic):

ZEKS COMPRESSED AIR SOLUTIONS LLC **(3)**
1302 Goshen Pkwy, West Chester, PA 19380
Tel.: (610) 692-9100
Web Site: http://www.zeks.com
Emp.: 130
Air Treatment Equipment Mfr
N.A.I.C.S.: 333415
Michelle Trumpower (Officer-Data Protection & Privacy-Global)

MB Air Systems Limited **(1)**
149 Glasgow Road, Wishaw, ML2 7QJ, United Kingdom
Tel.: (44) 1698355711
Web Site: https://www.mbairsystems.co.uk
Industrial & Offshore Lifting Equipment Mfr
N.A.I.C.S.: 333132

Milton Roy Industrial (Shanghai) Co., Ltd. **(1)**
Building 1 No 879 Shen Fu Road, Xin-Zhuang Industrial Zone Min Hang District, Shanghai, 201108, China
Tel.: (86) 4000121268
Metering Pump & Equipment Mfr
N.A.I.C.S.: 333996

Oina VV Aktiebolag **(1)**
Fraktflyggatargatan 3, 128 30, Skarpnack, Sweden
Tel.: (46) 841016370
Air Compressor Mfr
N.A.I.C.S.: 333912

Runtech Systems OY **(1)**
Lemminkaisenkatu 50, 20520, Turku, Finland
Tel.: (358) 34711000
Air Compressor Mfr

N.A.I.C.S.: 333912

Runtech Systems, Inc. **(1)**
258 Beartooth Pkwy Ste 100-204, Dawsonville, GA 30534
Tel.: (770) 205-7494
Air Compressor Mfr
N.A.I.C.S.: 333912

Tecno Matic Europe s.r.o. **(1)**
Malhotice 128, Vsechovice, 753 53, Prerov, Czech Republic
Tel.: (420) 608939629
Web Site: http://www.tecnomaticpump.com
Mold Product Mfr
N.A.I.C.S.: 333511

Tuthill Vacuum & Blower Systems, Inc. **(1)**
4840 W Kearney St, Springfield, MO 65803-8702 **(100%)**
Tel.: (417) 865-8715
Sales Range: $25-49.9 Million
Emp.: 160
Displacement Blowers & Vacuum Pumps Mfr
N.A.I.C.S.: 333914
Tamara Coday (Acct Mgr-Admin)
Craig Keeling (Accountant)
Keith Bucher (Dir-Fin-Tuthill Vacuum & Blower Sys)
Andy Tuthill (Pres)

INGEVITY CORPORATION
4920 O'Hear Ave Ste 400, North Charleston, SC 29405
Tel.: (843) 740-2300   DE
Web Site: https://www.ingevity.com
NGVT—(NYSE)
Rev.: $1,668,300,000
Assets: $2,736,500,000
Liabilities: $2,038,200,000
Net Worth: $698,300,000
Earnings: $211,600,000
Emp.: 2,050
Fiscal Year-end: 12/31/22
Holding Company; Specialty Chemicals Mfr & Whslr
N.A.I.C.S.: 551112
Stuart Edward Woodcock (Pres-Performance Materials & Exec VP)
Mary Dean Hall (CFO & Exec VP)
Ed Woodcock (Pres, Pres-Performance Materials & Exec VP)
John C. Fortson (Pres, CEO & Dir)
Rich White (Pres-Performance Chemicals & Sr VP)
Steve Hulme (Pres-Advanced Polymer Technologies & Sr VP)
Terry Dyer (Chief HR Officer & Sr VP)
Ryan C. Fisher (Gen Counsel, Sec & Sr VP)

Subsidiaries:

Ingevity Georgia, LLC **(1)**
1000 Gary Way, Waynesboro, GA 30830
Tel.: (706) 526-0000
Chemical Products Distr
N.A.I.C.S.: 424690

Ingevity Holdings Sprl **(1)**
Avenue des Olympiades 2, Brussels, 1140, Belgium
Tel.: (32) 27712017
Holding Company; Specialty Chemicals Whslr
N.A.I.C.S.: 551112

Ingevity South Carolina, LLC **(1)**
5598 Virginia Ave, North Charleston, SC 29406
Tel.: (843) 740-4500
Web Site: https://www.ingevity.com
Emp.: 230
Specialty Chemicals Mfr & Whslr
N.A.I.C.S.: 325998

Perstorp UK Ltd. **(1)**
Baronet Road, Warrington, WA4 6HA, Cheshire, United Kingdom
Tel.: (44) 1925 591111
Web Site: http://www.perstorp.com
Polyethylene, PVC, Polystyrene Distr
N.A.I.C.S.: 424690

Purification Cellutions, LLC **(1)**
1000 Gary Way, Waynesboro, GA 30830
Tel.: (706) 526-0000
Sales Range: $25-49.9 Million
Emp.: 52
Air Purification Parts Mfr
N.A.I.C.S.: 333413
Chuck Sabo (Mgr-Quality & Safety)

INGLES MARKETS, INCORPORATED
2913 US Hwy 70 W, Black Mountain, NC 28711
Tel.: (828) 669-2941   NC
Web Site: https://shop.ingles-markets.com
Year Founded: 1963
IMKTA—(NASDAQ)
Rev.: $5,639,609,434
Assets: $2,527,882,715
Liabilities: $982,133,625
Net Worth: $1,545,749,090
Earnings: $105,541,301
Emp.: 26,360
Fiscal Year-end: 09/28/24
Grocery Store Owner & Operator
N.A.I.C.S.: 445110
James W. Lanning (Pres & CEO)
Patricia E. Jackson (CFO & VP)
Catherine L. Phillips (Sec & Controller)
Robert P. Ingle II (Founder & Chm)

Subsidiaries:

Milkco, Inc. **(1)**
220 Deaverview Rd, Asheville, NC 28806-1710 **(100%)**
Tel.: (828) 254-9560
Sales Range: $150-199.9 Million
Emp.: 300
Mfr of Dairy Products
N.A.I.C.S.: 311511
David Hogan (Pres)

INGREDION INCORPORATED
5 Westbrook Corporate Ctr, Westchester, IL 60154
Tel.: (708) 551-2600   DE
Web Site: https://www.ingredion.com
Year Founded: 1906
INGR—(NYSE)
Rev.: $8,160,000,000
Assets: $7,642,000,000
Liabilities: $4,090,000,000
Net Worth: $3,552,000,000
Earnings: $643,000,000
Emp.: 11,600
Fiscal Year-end: 12/31/23
Corn Refiner; Starches, Liquid Sweeteners & Other Corn-Derived Food Ingredients Supplier
N.A.I.C.S.: 311221
Javier A. Echevarria (Chief Procurement Officer & VP)
Pierre Perez Y. Landazuri (Pres-EMEA & Sr VP-Texture, Protein & Performance Specialties)
James D. Gray (CFO & Exec VP)
Valdirene Bastos-Licht (Pres-Asia Pacific, Sr VP & Head-Pharma, Home & Beauty-Global)
Larry Fernandes (Chief Comml & Sustainability Officer & Sr VP)
Bob Border (CIO-Global)
Eric Seip (Chief Supply Chain Officer & Sr VP-Ops-Global)
Tanya Jaeger de Foras (Chief Compliance Officer, Chief Legal Oficer, Sec & Sr VP)
Rob Ritchie (Sr VP-Food & Industrial Ingredients-Americas)
Nancy Wolfe (Chief HR Officer)
Lori Arnold (VP)

James P. Zallie *(Pres & CEO)*
C. Kevin Wilson *(Treas & VP)*

Subsidiaries:

Avnet (Shanghai) Limited (1)
12th Floor Innov Tower No 1801 Hongmei
Road, Shanghai, 200233, China
Tel.: (86) 2134167000
Electronic Component & Semiconductor
Distr
N.A.I.C.S.: 423690

Avnet Asia Pte Ltd (1)
151 Lorong Chuan 05-02A&03 New Tech
Park, Singapore, 556741, Singapore
Tel.: (65) 65806000
Web Site: http://www.em.avnetasia.com
Sales Range: $75-99.9 Million
Emp.: 300
Electronic Component & Semiconductor
Distr
N.A.I.C.S.: 423690

Avnet Electronics Marketing (Austra-lia) Pty Ltd (1)
Unit 9B/9-11 South St, Rydalmere, 2116,
NSW, Australia
Tel.: (61) 295855511
Emp.: 20
Electronic Component & Semiconductor
Distr
N.A.I.C.S.: 423690

Avnet Korea, Inc. (1)
6th Floor KT&G Bundang Tower 26
Hwangsaeul-ro 312beon-gil, Bundang-gu,
Seongnam, 13591, Gyeonggi-do, Korea
(South)
Tel.: (82) 262776300
Web Site: http://www.avnetkorea.com
Sales Range: $25-49.9 Million
Emp.: 80
Electronic Components Distr
N.A.I.C.S.: 423690

**CP Ingredients India Private
Limited** (1)
1701 17th Floor Kesar Solitaire Plot No 5
Sector 19 Sanpada, Navi Mumbai, 400706,
Maharashtra, India
Tel.: (91) 2266097672
Web Site: http://www.ingredion.com
Starch & Sweetener Ingredient Distr
N.A.I.C.S.: 325199

CP Ingredients India Pvt. ltd. (1)
1701 17th Floor Kesar Solitaire, Plot No 5
Sector 19, Mumbai, 400706, India
Tel.: (91) 22 6609 7672
Corn Refiner; Starches, Liquid Sweeteners
& Other Corn-Derived Food Ingredients
Supplier
N.A.I.C.S.: 311211

CPIngredientes, S.A. de C.V. (1)
Av Mariano Otero No 1249 Floor 9 Torre
Atlantico, Rinconada del Bosque, Guadala-
jara, 44530, Jalisco, Mexico
Tel.: (52) 3338849000
Web Site: http://www.ingredion.mx
Pharmaceutical Preparation Mfr
N.A.I.C.S.: 325412

**Corn Products (Thailand) Co.
Ltd.** (1)
40/14 Moo 12 Bangna Tower C 12th fl, Unit
A Bangna-Trad rd Tambol, Bangkok, 10540,
Thailand
Tel.: (66) 2 725 0200
Corn Refiner; Starches, Liquid Sweeteners
& Other Corn-Derived Food Ingredients
Supplier
N.A.I.C.S.: 311211

**Corn Products Brasil Ingredientes
Industriais Ltda.** (1)
Av Do Cafe 277 Torre B 2, Sao Paulo,
106551, SP, Brazil **(100%)**
Tel.: (55) 1150707700
Web Site: http://www.cornproducts.com.br
Sales Range: $50-74.9 Million
Emp.: 100
Wet Corn Milling
N.A.I.C.S.: 311221

**Corn Products Chile-Inducorn
S.A.** (1)
Canaveral 240 Quilicura, Santiago,
Chile **(100%)**

Tel.: (56) 2 685 6000
Web Site: http://www.inducorn.cl
Sales Range: $50-74.9 Million
Emp.: 55
Wet Corn Milling
N.A.I.C.S.: 311221

Corn Products Kenya Ltd. (1)
Tulip House 5th Floor Mombasa Road, PO
Box 1952, 00606, Nairobi, Kenya
Tel.: (254) 0203628215
Web Site:
https://www.ingredionincorporated.com
Wet Corn Milling
N.A.I.C.S.: 311221

**Corn Products Southern Cone
S.A.** (1)
Cazadores De Coquimbo 2860, Munro,
Buenos Aires, 1605, Argentina
Tel.: (54) 1155448500
Corn Product Development Services
N.A.I.C.S.: 311221

Corn Products Thailand Co., Ltd. (1)
40/14 Moo 12 Bangna Trad Road Km 6 5
11th & 12th Floors, Bangna Towers C
Bangkaew Bangplee, Samut Prakan,
10540, Thailand
Tel.: (66) 27250200
Web Site: http://www.ingredion.com
Sales Range: $75-99.9 Million
Emp.: 400
Corn Product Development Services
N.A.I.C.S.: 311221

GTC Oats, Inc. (1)
5840 Expressway, Missoula, MT 59808
Tel.: (406) 541-6382
Corn Product Development Services
N.A.I.C.S.: 311221

**Golden Technologies Company,
Inc.** (1)
401 Bridge St, Old Forge, PA 18518
Tel.: (303) 216-2489
Web Site: https://www.goldentech.com
Sales Range: $25-49.9 Million
Emp.: 22
Corn Refiner Mfr to the Food Processing,
Dietary Supplement & Animal Feed Indus-
tries
N.A.I.C.S.: 311221

Industrias del Maiz C.A. (1)
Carretera Nacional La Encrucijada, Turmero
Km 1 Turmero, 2115, Maracay, 2115, Ara-
gua, Venezuela
Tel.: (58) 2446632320
Web Site: https://www.indelma.com.ve
Corn Refiner; Starches, Liquid Sweeteners
& Other Corn-Derived Food Ingredients
Supplier
N.A.I.C.S.: 311211

**Industrias del Maiz S.A.-Corn Prod-
ucts Andina** (1)
Cr 5 No 52-56, Cali, 076001,
Colombia **(100%)**
Tel.: (57) 24135000
Web Site:
http://www.cornproductsaldina.com
Sales Range: $250-299.9 Million
Emp.: 500
Wet Corn Milling
N.A.I.C.S.: 311221
Fabio Cadavid *(Pres)*

Ingredion (Thailand) Ltd. (1)
40/14 Moo 12 Bangna Trad Road Km 6 5
11th & 12th Floors, Bangna Towers C
Bangkaew, Bang Phli, 10540, Samut Pra-
kan, Thailand
Tel.: (66) 27250200
Web Site: https://www.ingredion.com
Emp.: 80
Food Ingredient Mfr
N.A.I.C.S.: 325998

Ingredion ANZ Pty Ltd (1)
Unit 5 706 Great South Road, Penrose,
Auckland, 1061, New Zealand
Tel.: (64) 95820284
Corn Refiner; Starches, Liquid Sweeteners
& Other Corn-Derived Food Ingredients
Supplier
N.A.I.C.S.: 311211

Ingredion ANZ Pty Ltd. (1)
Suite 3 02 Level 3 Building 1 3 Richardson

Place, Riverview Business Park, North
Ryde, 2113, NSW, Australia
Tel.: (61) 299111200
Web Site: http://www.ingredion.com.au
Corn Product Development Services
N.A.I.C.S.: 311221
Ilene S. Gordon *(Chm, Pres & CEO)*

**Ingredion APAC EMEA Shared Ser-
vices Sdn. Bhd.** (1)
1 Jalan Kontraktor U1/14 Level 5, Wisma
Samudra Hicom-Glenmarie Industrial Park,
40150, Shah Alam, Selangor, Malaysia
Tel.: (60) 355692633
Food & Beverage Mfr
N.A.I.C.S.: 311999

Ingredion Argentina S.A. (1)
Complejo Empresarial Urbana I Avalos,
Planta baja, 2829, Munro, Buenos Aires,
Argentina
Tel.: (54) 1155448500
Web Site: https://www.ingredion.com
Corn Product Development Services
N.A.I.C.S.: 311221
James P. Zallie *(CEO)*
James D. Gray *(Exec VP)*
Valdirene Bastos-Licht *(Sr VP-
Pacific,Global)*
Larry Fernandes *(Sr VP-Commercial)*
Eric Seip *(Chief Supply Chain Officer)*
Jeremy Xu *(Chief Innovation Officer)*
Nancy Wolfe *(Sr VP)*

**Ingredion Brasil Ingredientes Industri-
ais Ltda.** (1)
Rochavera - Av Nacoes Unidas 14171 4
andar - Torre B Ebony, Av Dr Chucri Zaidan
1170 - Vila Cordeiro, Sao Paulo, 04794-
000, Brazil
Tel.: (55) 1150707700
Corn Product Development Services
N.A.I.C.S.: 311221

Ingredion Canada Corporation (1)
405 The West Mall Ste 600, Etobicoke,
M9C 0A1, ON, Canada **(100%)**
Tel.: (416) 620-2300
Web Site: https://www.ingredion.ca
Wet Corn Milling
N.A.I.C.S.: 311221

Ingredion Chile S.A. (1)
Canaveral N 240, Quilicura, Santiago, Chile
Tel.: (56) 26856000
Web Site: http://cl.ingredion.com
Corn Product Development Services
N.A.I.C.S.: 311221

Ingredion China Limited (1)
450 Hua Tie Road, Song Jiang Industrial
Estate, Shanghai, 201600, China
Tel.: (86) 2137740066
Emp.: 185
Food Ingredient Mfr
N.A.I.C.S.: 325998
Christina Jhang *(Mgr-HR)*

Ingredion Colombia S.A. (1)
Carrera 5 No 52-56, PO Box 6560, Cali,
Colombia
Tel.: (57) 6024315111
Web Site: https://www.ingredion.com
Corn Product Development Services
N.A.I.C.S.: 311221

Ingredion India Private Limited (1)
1605 16th Floor Rupa Solitaire Millennium
Business Park, Thane Belapur Road Ma-
hape Navi, Mumbai, 400710, Maharashtra,
India
Tel.: (91) 2239530600
Web Site: http://www.ingredion.com
Food Ingredient Mfr
N.A.I.C.S.: 325998

Ingredion Japan K.K. (1)
3-5-10 Shimbashi Shinsan Building 2F,
Minato-ku, Tokyo, 105-0004, Japan
Tel.: (81) 335049690
Emp.: 35
Corn Refiner; Starches, Liquid Sweeteners
& Other Corn-Derived Food Ingredients
Supplier
N.A.I.C.S.: 311211

Ingredion Malaysia Sdn. Bhd. (1)
No 1 Jalan Kontraktor U1/14 Level 5 Wisma
Samudra, Hicom-Glenmarie Industrial Park,
40150, Shah Alam, Selangor Darul Ehsan,
Malaysia

Tel.: (60) 355692633
Emp.: 12
Food Ingredient Mfr
N.A.I.C.S.: 325998
Shue Peng Law *(Bus Mgr)*

Ingredion Mexico, S.A. de C.V. (1)
Av Mariano Otero 1249 Floor 9 Torre Atlan-
tico, Rinconada del Bosque, 44530, Guada-
lajara, 44530, Jalisco, Mexico
Tel.: (52) 3338849000
Corn Refiner; Starches, Liquid Sweeteners
& Other Corn-Derived Food Ingredients
Supplier
N.A.I.C.S.: 311211

Ingredion Philippines, Inc. (1)
Unit 5B Suntree Tower, No 13 Meralco Av-
enue Ortigas Center, Pasig, 1605, Philip-
pines
Tel.: (63) 26503081
Corn Refiner; Starches, Liquid Sweeteners
& Other Corn-Derived Food Ingredients
Supplier
N.A.I.C.S.: 311211

Ingredion Singapore Pte. Ltd. (1)
21 Biopolis Road 05-21/27 Nucleos, Singa-
pore, 138567, Singapore
Tel.: (65) 68726006
Corn Refiner; Starches, Liquid Sweeteners
& Other Corn-Derived Food Ingredients
Supplier
N.A.I.C.S.: 311211

**Ingredion South Africa (Pty)
Limited** (1)
Suite 6 Block C Infinte Office Park 2 Robin
Close, PO Box 14528, Meyersdal, Alberton,
1448, Gauteng, South Africa
Tel.: (27) 118207222
Web Site: https://www.ingredion.com
Sales Range: $25-49.9 Million
Emp.: 9
Food Ingredient Mfr
N.A.I.C.S.: 311999

Ingredion South Africa (Pty) Ltd. (1)
Infinity Office Park Suite 6 Block C 2 Robin
Close, Meyersdal, Alberton, 1448, Gauteng,
South Africa
Tel.: (27) 118679260
Web Site: http://www.ingredion.com
Emp.: 8
Corn Product Development Services
N.A.I.C.S.: 311221

**Ingredion Sweetener & Starch (Thai-
land) Co., Ltd.** (1)
40/14 Moo 12 Bangna Trad Road Km 6 5
11th 12th floors, Bangna Towers C Bangkaew Bangplee, Samut Prakan, 10540,
Thailand
Tel.: (66) 27250200
Food Products Mfr
N.A.I.C.S.: 311999

Ingredion UK Limited (1)
Ingredion House Manchester Green Busi-
ness Park 339 Styal Road, Manchester,
M22 5LW, Greater Manchester, United
Kingdom
Tel.: (44) 1614353200
Corn Product Development Services
N.A.I.C.S.: 311221

Ingredion Uruguay S.A. (1)
Complejo World Trade Center Montevideo,
Luis Alberto de Herrera 1248 O, 11300,
Montevideo, Uruguay
Tel.: (598) 2 628 9009
Emp.: 4
Corn Refiner; Starches, Liquid Sweeteners
& Other Corn-Derived Food Ingredients
Supplier
N.A.I.C.S.: 311211
Gabriel Paz *(Gen Mgr & Mgr-Comml)*

**Ingredion Vietnam Company
Limited** (1)
Room 817 8th Floor Pakson Paragon No 3
Nguyen Luong Bang, District 7, Ho Chi
Minh City, Vietnam
Tel.: (84) 854133368
Food & Beverage Mfr
N.A.I.C.S.: 333241

**Inter-National Starch & Chemical Co.,
Inc.** (1)
2 Perfecto Dr Santa Maria Ind Est Bagum-

Ingredion Incorporated—(Continued)

bayan Taguig, Manila, 1600, Philippines
Tel.: (63) 2 838 5201
Sales Range: $25-49.9 Million
Emp.: 30
Adhesives & Starches Mfr
N.A.I.C.S.: 325520

Inter-National Starch Inc. (1)
No 8 Perfecto Drive Sta Maria Industrial
Estate, Bagumbayan, Taguig, 1631, Philip-
pines
Tel.: (63) 28370631
Web Site: http://www.ingredion.com
Corn Product Development Services
N.A.I.C.S.: 311221

**KaTech Ingredient Solutions
GmbH** (1)
Aegidienstrasse 22, 23552, Lubeck, Ger-
many
Tel.: (49) 451407020
Web Site: https://katech-solutions.com
Food & Beverage Services
N.A.I.C.S.: 722511
Cyril Carrat (Mng Dir)
Michael O'Riordan (Mng Dir)
Marcel Hergett (Mng Dir)

KaTech Ingredient Solutions Ltd. (1)
Unit 19 Venture Point Stanney Mill Road,
Ellesmere Port, CH2 4NE, Cheshire, United
Kingdom
Tel.: (44) 1513573700
Food & Beverage Services
N.A.I.C.S.: 722511

**KaTech Ingredient Solutions Sp. z
o.o.** (1)
Ul Powstancow Wlkp 49, 62-060, Steszew,
Poland
Tel.: (48) 616707001
Food & Beverage Services
N.A.I.C.S.: 722511

Kerr Concentrates, Inc. (1)
2340 Hyacinth St NE, Salem, OR 97301-
3108
Tel.: (503) 378-0493
Web Site: http://www.kerrconcentrates.com
Sales Range: $1-9.9 Million
Emp.: 75
Syrup & Concentrate Mfr
N.A.I.C.S.: 311930

N-Starch Sdn. Bhd. (1)
Level 5 Wisma Samudra No 1 Jalan Kon-
traktor U1/14, Hicom-Glenmarie Industrial
Par, 40150, Shah Alam, Selangor, Malaysia
Tel.: (60) 355692633
Web Site: http://www.ingredion.com
Sales Range: $25-49.9 Million
Emp.: 17
Corn Product Development Services
N.A.I.C.S.: 311221

National Starch & Chemical (1)
14351 Hwy 221, Enoree, SC 29335-2017
Tel.: (864) 969-2811
Sales Range: $25-49.9 Million
Emp.: 50
Adhesives & Specialty Synthetic Polymers
Mfr
N.A.I.C.S.: 325520

**National Starch & Chemical (Hold-
ings) Ltd.** (1)
Prestbury Court, Greencourts Business
Park, 333 Styal Road, Manchester, M22
5lw, United Kingdom
Tel.: (44) 161 435 3200
Sales Range: $25-49.9 Million
Emp.: 60
Holding Company
N.A.I.C.S.: 551112

**National Starch & Chemical (Thai-
land) Ltd.** (1)
40/14 Moo 12 Bangna Trad Road Km 6 5
11th & 12th floors, Bangna Towers C Bang-
kaew Bangplee, Samut Prakan, 10540,
Thailand
Tel.: (66) 27250200
Web Site: http://www.ici.com
Starch Mfr
N.A.I.C.S.: 339999

**National Starch & Chemical (Thai-
land) Ltd.** (1)

40/14 Moo 12 Bangna Tower Building,
Bangna-Trad Rd (6th K.M) Tambol, Bang-
kok, 10540, Thailand
Tel.: (66) 2 725 0200
Corn Refiner; Starches, Liquid Sweeteners
& Other Corn-Derived Food Ingredients
Supplier
N.A.I.C.S.: 311211

**National Starch & Chemical Ltd.-Nam
Dinh** (1)
23 VSIP St 2 Vietnam Singapore Industrial
Park, Nam Dinh, Binh Duong, Vietnam
Tel.: (84) 650757060
Web Site: http://www.nstarch.com
Sales Range: $25-49.9 Million
Emp.: 31
Adhesive Mfr
N.A.I.C.S.: 325520

**National Starch & Chemical Pty
Ltd.** (1)
Suite 3 02 Level 3 Building 1 Riverview
Business Park, 3 Richardson Place, North
Ryde, 2113, NSW, Australia
Tel.: (61) 299111200
Web Site: http://www.foodinnovation.com
Sales Range: $50-74.9 Million
Emp.: 150
Mfr of Adhesives, Specialty Synthetic Poly-
mers & Starches
N.A.I.C.S.: 325520

**National Starch &
Chemical-Lincolnshire** (1)
25 Tri State International, Lincolnshire, IL
60069
Tel.: (847) 945-7500
Web Site: http://www.foodinnovation.com
Sales Range: $25-49.9 Million
Emp.: 7
Starch Mfr
N.A.I.C.S.: 325998

National Starch Company (1)
10 Finderne Ave, Bridgewater, NJ 08807-
0500
Tel.: (908) 685-5000
Industrial Adhesive & Specialty Polymer
Product Mfr
N.A.I.C.S.: 325998

**National Starch Servicios, S.A. de
C.V.** (1)
Paraiso No 1936-A Del Fresno, 44900, Za-
popan, Jalisco, Mexico
Tel.: (52) 3339421060
Chemical Product & Preparation Mfr
N.A.I.C.S.: 325998

**National Starch Specialties (Shang-
hai) Ltd.** (1)
No 450 HuaTie Road SongJiang Industrial
Estate, Shanghai, 201600, China
Tel.: (86) 21 37740066
Corn Products Mfr
N.A.I.C.S.: 325520

**PT National Starch & Chemical
Indonesia** (1)
Jl Agung Perkasa 8 Blok K1 No 42, Sumer
Agung Podomoro, Jakarta, 14350, Indone-
sia
Tel.: (62) 21 6507542
Sales Range: $50-74.9 Million
Emp.: 125
Adhesive Mfr
N.A.I.C.S.: 325520

PT. Ingredion Indonesia (1)
Mezzanine Floor Talavera Suite - Talavera
Office Park, Jl Letjen TB Simatupang Kav
22-26 Cilandak, Jakarta Selatan, 12430,
Indonesia
Tel.: (62) 2175924377
Emp.: 25
Corn Refiner; Starches, Liquid Sweeteners
& Other Corn-Derived Food Ingredients
Supplier
N.A.I.C.S.: 311211

Productos de Maiz S.A. (1)
Complejo Empresarial Urbana 1 Cazadores
de Coquimbo 2860 - 1er Piso, Buenos Ai-
res, B1605DXP, Argentina (100%)
Tel.: (54) 1143418500
Web Site: http://www.pdm.com.ar
Sales Range: $25-49.9 Million
Emp.: 40
Wet Corn Milling

N.A.I.C.S.: 311221

Productos de Maiz Uruguay S.A. (1)
Luis B Cavia 2724 Office 501 Departa-
mento de, 11300, Montevideo,
Uruguay (100%)
Tel.: (598) 27079009
Web Site: http://www.pdm.com.ua
Sales Range: $1-9.9 Million
Emp.: 200
Wet Corn Milling
N.A.I.C.S.: 311221

PureCircle Africa Limited (1)
Ereto Plaza 6th Floor Mburu Gichua Road,
PO Box 4550, Nakuru, Nairobi, Kenya
Tel.: (254) 518002540
Food & Beverage Mfr
N.A.I.C.S.: 311999

PureCircle Limited (1)
Level 12 West Wing Rohas PureCircle No 9
Jalan P Ramlee, 50250, Kuala Lumpur,
Malaysia
Tel.: (60) 321662206
Web Site: http://www.purecircle.com
Natural High Intensity Sweetener Producer
N.A.I.C.S.: 311930
DeLio Tony (CEO)
SukGu Kim (CFO)

Subsidiary (Non-US):

PureCircle (Jiangxi) Co. Ltd (2)
Yangtang Industrial Zone Maodian ganxian,
341108, Ganzhou, China
Tel.: (86) 7974601666
Sales Range: $100-124.9 Million
Emp.: 300
Natural Sweetners Mfr
N.A.I.C.S.: 311999

Subsidiary (Domestic):

PureCircle Sdn, Bhd (2)
Unit 19-03-02 3rd Floor Pnb Damansara No
19 Lorong Dungun, Damansara Heights,
Kuala Lumpur, Malaysia
Tel.: (60) 320939333
Natural Sweeteners Mfr
N.A.I.C.S.: 325199

Subsidiary (US):

PureCircle USA Holdings Inc (2)
915 Harger Rd Ste 250, Oak Brook, IL
60523
Tel.: (630) 361-0374
Web Site: https://www.purecircle.com
Food & Beverage Products Mfr
N.A.I.C.S.: 311999

**PureCircle Natural Ingredient India
Private Limited** (1)
DLF Building 9 14th Floor Tower A DLF Cy-
ber City Phase III, Gurgaon, 122 002, Hary-
ana, India
Tel.: (91) 1244775603
Food & Beverage Mfr
N.A.I.C.S.: 311999

**PureCircle South America Sociedad
Anonima** (1)
Paraguay Campos Cervera 5639 c Nudel-
mann, Asuncion, Paraguay
Tel.: (595) 21612691
Food & Beverage Mfr
N.A.I.C.S.: 311999

Rafhan Maize Products Co. Ltd (1)
Rakh Canal East Road, PO Box 62, Fais-
alabad, 38060, Pakistan
Tel.: (92) 418540121
Web Site: https://www.rafhanmaize.com
Corn Refiner; Starches, Liquid Sweeteners
& Other Corn-Derived Food Ingredients
Supplier
N.A.I.C.S.: 311211

Rafhan Maize Products Co. Ltd. (1)
Rakh Canal East Road, PO Box 62, Fais-
alabad, 38060, Punjab, Pakistan (70.3%)
Tel.: (92) 4185401212233
Web Site: https://www.rafhanmaize.com
Wet Corn Milling
N.A.I.C.S.: 311221
Michael Fergus O'Riordan (Chm)
Humair Ijaz Ahmed (Mng Dir)
Adil Saeed Khan (CFO)
Mustafa Kamal Zuberi (Sec)

**Stamford Food Industries Sdn.
Bhd.** (1)
11th Fl Menara Manulife 1B, Lenggang Da-
mansara Heights, Kuala Lumpur, 50490,
Malaysia (100%)
Tel.: (60) 320842888
Sales Range: $10-24.9 Million
Emp.: 20
Wet Corn Milling
N.A.I.C.S.: 311221
Jane Lim (Mgr-HR)

TIC Gums China. (1)
Building A8 Clifford Huashan Industrial Park
No 288 Juhuashi Street, Guangzhou,
510800, China
Tel.: (86) 2036871386
Web Site: http://www.ticgums.com.cn
Food Mfr
N.A.I.C.S.: 311999

TIC Gums, Inc. (1)
4609 Richlynn Dr, Belcamp, MD 21017
Tel.: (410) 273-7300
Web Site: http://www.ticgums.com
Emp.: 200
Prepared Sauces Mfr
N.A.I.C.S.: 311941

Western Polymer Corporation (1)
32 Rd R SE, Moses Lake, WA 98837
Tel.: (509) 765-1803
Web Site: http://www.westernpolymer.com
Rev.: $13,100,000
Emp.: 50
Wet-End & Specialty Potato Starches Mfr &
Distr
N.A.I.C.S.: 325199
Lynn Townsend-White (Pres & CEO)

INHIBIKASE THERAPEUTICS,
INC.
3350 Riverwood Pkwy Ste 1900, At-
lanta, GA 30339
Tel.: (678) 392-3419 DE
Web Site: https://www.inhibikase.com
Year Founded: 2008
IKT—(NASDAQ)
Rev.: $123,440
Assets: $24,936,297
Liabilities: $3,900,896
Net Worth: $21,035,401
Earnings: ($18,054,155)
Emp.: 6
Fiscal Year-end: 12/31/22
Research & Development in Biotech-
nology (except Nanobiotechnology)
N.A.I.C.S.: 541714
Milton H. Werner (Co-Founder, Pres
& CEO)
Dan Williams (Controller)
Dennis Berman (Co-Founder)
C. Warren Olanow (Chief Medical
Interim Officer)

INHIBITOR THERAPEUTICS,
INC.
900 W Platt St Ste 200, Tampa, FL
33606
Tel.: (888) 841-6811 VA
Web Site: https://inhibitortx.com
Year Founded: 1992
INTI—(OTCQB)
Assets: $11,975,124
Liabilities: $3,678,782
Net Worth: $8,296,342
Earnings: $12,106,230
Emp.: 3
Fiscal Year-end: 12/31/22
Basic Research Services in
Protein/Peptide & DNA/RNA Chemis-
tries
N.A.I.C.S.: 541715
Nicholas J. Virca (Pres & CEO)
Garrison J. Hasara (CFO, Chief Com-
pliance Officer, Treas & Sec)
William Mark Watson (Chm)
Amy McCord (VP-Regulatory Affairs)

INLAND REAL ESTATE IN-
COME TRUST, INC.

2901 Butterfield Rd, Oak Brook, IL 60523
Tel.: (630) 218-8000   MD
Web Site: https://www.inland-investments.com
Year Founded: 2011
INRE—(OTCIQ)
Rev.: $149,972,000
Assets: $1,344,040,000
Liabilities: $935,685,000
Net Worth: $408,355,000
Earnings: ($15,123,000)
Emp.: 1
Fiscal Year-end: 12/31/23
Real Estate Investment Services
N.A.I.C.S.: 531210
Mark E. Zalatoris *(Pres & CEO)*
Daniel L. Goodwin *(Chm)*
Catherine L. Lynch *(CFO & Treas)*
Cathleen M. Hrtanek *(Sec)*
Daniel W. Zatloukal *(Sr VP)*
Judy Fu *(VP)*

INMUNE BIO, INC.
225 NE Mizner Blvd Ste 640, Boca Raton, FL 33432
Tel.: (858) 964-3720   NV
Web Site: https://www.inmunebio.com
Year Founded: 2015
INMB—(NASDAQ)
Rev.: $374,000
Assets: $81,795,000
Liabilities: $21,691,000
Net Worth: $60,104,000
Earnings: ($27,299,000)
Emp.: 10
Fiscal Year-end: 12/31/22
Research & Development in Biotechnology (except Nanobiotechnology)
N.A.I.C.S.: 541714
Raymond Joseph Tesi *(Chm, Pres, CEO & Chief Medical Officer)*
David J. Moss *(CFO, Treas & Sec)*
Mark Lowdell *(Chief Scientific Officer & Chief Mfg Officer)*
Christopher J. Barnum *(Dir-Neuroscience)*
Joshua S. Schoonover *(Assoc Gen Counsel)*

INNERSCOPE HEARING TECHNOLOGIES, INC.
2151 Professional Dr 2nd Fl, Roseville, CA 95661   NV
Web Site: http://www.innd.com
Year Founded: 2012
INND—(OTCIQ)
Rev.: $165,860
Assets: $4,039,825
Liabilities: $10,107,164
Net Worth: ($6,067,339)
Earnings: ($1,174,442)
Emp.: 10
Fiscal Year-end: 12/31/20
Advertising Services
N.A.I.C.S.: 541810
Kimberly Moore *(CFO)*
Mark Moore *(Co-Founder & Chm)*
Matthew Moore *(Co-Founder, Pres & CEO)*

INNO HOLDINGS, INC.
2465 Farm Market 359 S, Brookshire, TX 77423   TX
Web Site: https://www.innoholdings.com
INHD—(NASDAQ)
Rev.: $799,747
Assets: $2,545,762
Liabilities: $4,489,348
Net Worth: ($1,943,586)
Earnings: ($4,023,204)
Emp.: 11
Fiscal Year-end: 09/30/23
Holding Company

N.A.I.C.S.: 551112
Tianwei Li *(CEO & CFO)*

INNODATA, INC.
55 Challenger Rd, Ridgefield Park, NJ 07660
Tel.: (201) 371-8000   DE
Web Site: https://www.innodata.com
Year Founded: 1988
INOD—(NASDAQ)
Rev.: $79,001,000
Assets: $48,042,000
Liabilities: $29,269,000
Net Worth: $18,773,000
Earnings: ($11,935,000)
Emp.: 4,205
Fiscal Year-end: 12/31/22
On-Line Data Conversion & Content Management Services
N.A.I.C.S.: 518210
Amy R. Agress *(Gen Counsel & Sr VP)*
Marissa B. Espineli *(Interim CFO)*
Nauman Toor *(Chm)*
Jack S. Abuhoff *(Pres & CEO)*

Subsidiaries:

Innodata Knowledge Services, Inc.   **(1)**
HVG IT Park Subangdaku, Mandaue, 6014, Cebu, Philippines
Tel.: (63) 322307000
Data Management Services
N.A.I.C.S.: 541513
Jemima Villa *(Head-Country)*

MediaMiser Ltd.   **(1)**
319 McRae Avenue Suite 500, Ottawa, K1Z 0B9, ON, Canada
Tel.: (613) 232-7797
Web Site: http://www.mediamiser.com
Emp.: 35
Software Development Services
N.A.I.C.S.: 541511
Allison Murphy *(Mng Dir-UK)*

INNOSPEC INC.
8310 S Vly Hwy Ste 350, Englewood, CO 80112
Tel.: (303) 792-5554   DE
Web Site: https://innospec.com
Year Founded: 1940
IOSP—(NASDAQ)
Rev.: $1,963,700,000
Assets: $1,603,700,000
Liabilities: $563,300,000
Net Worth: $1,040,400,000
Earnings: $133,000,000
Emp.: 2,100
Fiscal Year-end: 12/31/22
Fuel Additives & Specialty Chemicals Mfr
N.A.I.C.S.: 325180
Milton C. Blackmore *(Chm)*
Patrick S. Williams *(Pres & CEO)*
Ian McRobbie *(CTO & Sr VP)*
Philip J. Boon *(COO & Exec VP)*
Trey Griffin *(Sr VP-Human Resources)*
Corbin Barnes *(Sr VP-Corporate Development & Investor Relations)*
Ian P. Cleminson *(CFO & Exec VP)*

Subsidiaries:

Bachman Services Inc.   **(1)**
2220 S Prospect Ave, Oklahoma City, OK 73129
Tel.: (405) 677-8296
Web Site: http://www.bachmanservices.com
Sales Range: $1-9.9 Million
Emp.: 12
Specialty Chemical Product & Preparation Mfr
N.A.I.C.S.: 325998

Chemsil Silicones, Inc.   **(1)**
21900 Marilla St, Chatsworth, CA 91311
Tel.: (818) 700-0302
Web Site: https://www.chemsil.com

Sales Range: $1-9.9 Million
Silicones Mfr & Whslr
N.A.I.C.S.: 325199
Robert Griffiths *(VP-Sls & Mktg)*
Andrew Shearer *(Dir-Quality Assurance & Regulatory)*

Independence Oilfield Chemicals LLC   **(1)**
1450 Lake Robbins Dr Ste 400, The Woodlands, TX 77380
Tel.: (713) 936-4340
Web Site: http://www.innospecoilfield.com
Emp.: 250
Petroleum Refining Services
N.A.I.C.S.: 324110

Innospec Active Chemicals LLC   **(1)**
510 W Grimes Ave, High Point, NC 27260
Tel.: (336) 882-3308
Chemical Products Mfr
N.A.I.C.S.: 325998

Innospec Deutschland GmbH   **(1)**
Thiesstrasse 61, 44649, Herne, Germany   **(100%)**
Tel.: (49) 23259800
Web Site: http://www.innospecinc.com
Sales Range: $25-49.9 Million
Lubricants, Auto Care Products, Boat Care Products & Ferrocene
N.A.I.C.S.: 324191
Uwe Plattes *(Mng Dir)*

Innospec Developments Limited   **(1)**
Innospec Manufacturing Park Oil Sites Road Merseyside, Ellesmere Port, CH65 4EY, Cheshire, United Kingdom
Tel.: (44) 1513553611
Emp.: 300
Chemical Products Mfr
N.A.I.C.S.: 325998

Innospec France S.A.   **(1)**
17 Route de Rouen, 27950, Saint Marcel, France   **(100%)**
Tel.: (33) 232643535
Petroleum Refining
N.A.I.C.S.: 324110

Innospec Fuel Specialties LLC   **(1)**
8310 S Valley Hwy Ste 350, Englewood, CO 80112
Tel.: (303) 792-5554
Web Site: https://innospec.com
Sales Range: $25-49.9 Million
Petroleum Refining
N.A.I.C.S.: 324110

Innospec Hellas Ltd.   **(1)**
Il Merachias Street 11, 18535, Piraeus, Greece   **(100%)**
Tel.: (30) 2104110727
Web Site: http://www.innospecinc.com
Sales Range: $25-49.9 Million
Emp.: 5
Petroleum Refining
N.A.I.C.S.: 324110

Innospec Performance Chemicals Italia s.r.l   **(1)**
Via Cavour 50, 46043, Castiglione della Stiviere, Italy
Tel.: (39) 03766371
Chemicals Mfr
N.A.I.C.S.: 325998

Innospec Performance Chemicals Spain S.L.   **(1)**
Poligono Zona Franca Sector F Calle 43 No 10, 08040, Barcelona, Spain
Tel.: (34) 933369700
Chemicals Mfr
N.A.I.C.S.: 325998

Innospec Russ OOO   **(1)**
ul Tverskaja Dom 9/7 Room 508, 125009, Moscow, Russia
Tel.: (7) 4956601022
Chemical Mfr & Distr
N.A.I.C.S.: 335311

Innospec Specialty Chemicals   **(1)**
Innospec Manufacturing Park Oil Sites Road, PO Box 17, Ellesmere Port, CH65 4EY, Cheshire, United Kingdom
Tel.: (44) 1513553611
Sales Range: $125-149.9 Million
Emp.: 400
Fine & Specialty Chemicals Mfr

N.A.I.C.S.: 325998

Innospec Sweden AB   **(1)**
Kopmannagatan 2, 652 26, Karlstad, Varmland, Sweden
Tel.: (46) 54190012
Chemical Additive Mfr
N.A.I.C.S.: 325998

Vijall, Inc.   **(1)**
21900 Marilla St, Chatsworth, CA 91311
Tel.: (818) 700-0071
Web Site: https://www.chemteccc.com
Chemical Components Distr
N.A.I.C.S.: 424690

INNOVACOM, INC.
525 Inner Cir, The Villages, FL 32162
Tel.: (352) 750-0751
MPEG—(NASDAQ)
Computer Chip Mfr
N.A.I.C.S.: 334310
Michael Manion *(Pres)*

INNOVATE CORP.
295 Madison Ave 12th Fl, New York, NY 10017
Tel.: (954) 663-1147   DE
Web Site: https://www.innovatecorp.com
Year Founded: 1994
VATE—(NYSE)
Rev.: $1,637,300,000
Assets: $1,151,300,000
Liabilities: $1,242,300,000
Net Worth: ($90,600,000)
Earnings: ($35,900,000)
Emp.: 3,565
Fiscal Year-end: 12/31/22
Holding Company; Integrated Telecommunications Services
N.A.I.C.S.: 551112
Michael J. Sena *(CFO)*
Paul K. Voigt *(Interim CEO)*
Avram A. Glazer *(Chm)*

Subsidiaries:

Aitken Manufacturing Inc.   **(1)**
4920 Airline Dr, Houston, TX 77022
Tel.: (281) 441-5438
Web Site: https://www.aitkenmfg.com
Gas & Pipeline Industry Equipment Mfr
N.A.I.C.S.: 333132
Rick Kuhn *(Exec VP)*

American Natural Gas, LLC   **(1)**
19 Railroad PL Ste 201, Saratoga Springs, NY 12866
Tel.: (866) 264-6220
Web Site: http://www.americannaturalgas.com
Emp.: 20
Natural Gas Distr
N.A.I.C.S.: 221210
Drew West *(Founder & CEO)*
Bryan Berry *(Chief Revenue & Sustainability Officer)*
Bridget Buckley *(Controller)*
Brent Tesla *(VP-Ops)*
Greg Mountain *(Corp Counsel)*

DBM Global Inc.   **(1)**
3020 E Camelback Rd Ste 100, Phoenix, AZ 85016   **(89%)**
Tel.: (602) 257-7838
Web Site: https://www.dbmglobal.com
Sales Range: $400-449.9 Million
Emp.: 1,800
Holding Company; Structural Steel Construction & Fabrication
N.A.I.C.S.: 551112
James Rustin Roach *(Chm & CEO)*
Michael R. Hill *(CFO & VP)*

Subsidiary (Domestic):

Mountain States Steel, Inc.   **(2)**
1971 W 700 N Ste 101, Lindon, UT 84042-1621
Tel.: (385) 256-9200
Web Site: http://www.schuff.com
Fabricated Structural Metal Mfr
N.A.I.C.S.: 332312

Schuff Steel Company   **(2)**

INNOVATE Corp.—(Continued)

3003 N Central Ave Ste 1500, Phoenix, AZ 85012
Tel.: (602) 252-7787
Web Site: https://www.schuff.com
Structural Steel Construction & Fabrication
N.A.I.C.S.: 238120
Rustin Roach *(Pres & CEO)*
Robb Waldrep *(Exec VP)*
Kevin McKenna *(Exec VP-West)*
Scott Esmeier *(Exec VP-Fabrication)*
Jay Allen *(Exec VP-Engrg)*
Tony Hannan *(VP-Safety)*
Roland Oxborrow *(VP-Field Ops)*

Subsidiary (Domestic):

Schuff Steel Management Company
SE, LLC   **(3)**
1920 Ledo Rd, Albany, GA 31707
Tel.: (229) 883-4506
Rolled Steel Mfr
N.A.I.C.S.: 331221

Schuff Steel Management Company
SW, Inc.   **(3)**
4320 E Presidio St Ste 111, Mesa, AZ 85215
Tel.: (480) 892-7509
Rolled Steel Mfr
N.A.I.C.S.: 331221

Schuff Steel-Atlantic, LLC   **(3)**
7351 Overland Rd, Orlando, FL 32810-3409
Tel.: (407) 295-6434
Web Site: http://www.schuff.com
Sales Range: $75-99.9 Million
Emp.: 200
Design, Fabricate & Erect Structural Steel;
Joist Manufacturing
N.A.I.C.S.: 332312

Schuff Steel-Gulf Coast, Inc.   **(3)**
14500 Smith Rd, Humble, TX 77396
Tel.: (281) 441-5400
Web Site: http://www.schuff.com
Sales Range: $10-24.9 Million.
Emp.: 150
Provider of Structural Steel Services
N.A.I.C.S.: 334513

Schuff Steel-Pacific, Inc.   **(3)**
2324 Navy Dr, Stockton, CA 95206
Tel.: (209) 938-0869
Web Site: http://www.schuff.com
Sales Range: $25-49.9 Million
Emp.: 75
Structural Steel Fabrication Services
N.A.I.C.S.: 238120

DBM Vircon Services (Canada)
Ltd.   **(1)**
889 Carnarvon Street, New Westminster,
V3M 1G2, BC, Canada
Tel.: (604) 525-0055
Construction Services
N.A.I.C.S.: 236220

DBM Vircon Services (NZ) Ltd.   **(1)**
Level 1 16 St Marks Road, Epsom, Auck-
land, 1051, New Zealand
Tel.: (64) 99417460
Job Training Services
N.A.I.C.S.: 624310

DBM Vircon Services (Philippines)
Inc.   **(1)**
6th Floor The 30th Corporate Center Mer-
alco Avenue, Pasig, 1604, Metro Manila,
Philippines
Tel.: (63) 277309727
Job Training Services
N.A.I.C.S.: 624310

DBM Vircon Services (Thailand) Co.,
Ltd.   **(1)**
24 Prime Building 14th Floor Sukhumvit 21
Asoke Road, Kweang Klongtoey Nue Khet
Wattana, Bangkok, 10110, Thailand
Tel.: (66) 20178200
Job Training Services
N.A.I.C.S.: 624310

Genovel Orthopedics, Inc.   **(1)**
460 Herndon Pkwy, Herndon, VA 20170
Tel.: (703) 902-2800
Health Care Equipment Mfr
N.A.I.C.S.: 339112

Global Marine Cable Systems Pte,
Ltd   **(1)**
331 North Bridge Road 07-03/04 Odeon
Towers, Singapore, 188720, Singapore
Tel.: (65) 65131300
Web Site: http://www.globalmarine.co.uk
Emp.: 17
Marine Construction Engineering Services
N.A.I.C.S.: 541330

Global Marine Search, Ltd   **(1)**
New Saxon House 1 Winsford Way,
Chelmsford, CM2 5PD, United Kingdom
Tel.: (44) 1245702181
Trading Stamp Promotion Services
N.A.I.C.S.: 561990

Global Marine Systems Oil and Gas,
LTD   **(1)**
New Saxon House 1Winsford Way Bore-
ham Interchange, Chelmsford, CM2.5PD,
Essex, United Kingdom
Tel.: (44) 1245702180
Web Site: http://www.newglobalconnect.com
Emp.: 60
Underwater Construction Services
N.A.I.C.S.: 237990

Global Marine Systems Pension
Trustee, Ltd   **(1)**
Ocean House 1 Winsford Way, Boreham
Interchange, Chelmsford, CM2 5PD, Essex,
United Kingdom
Tel.: (44) 1245702000
Web Site: http://globalmarine.co.uk
Pension Fund Management Services
N.A.I.C.S.: 525110
Ian Douglas *(CEO)*
Bruce Neilson-Watts *(Mng Dir)*
Graham Boyle *(Dir-RQHSE)*
David Green *(Head-Sls)*
Paul Deslandes *(Head-Project Delivery)*
Rob Twell *(Head-Fleet)*
John /Walters *(Dir-Asia)*

Go2Tel.com, Inc.   **(1)**
1100 NW 163rd Dr, Miami, FL 33169
Tel.: (305) 614-2030
Web Site: http://www.go2tel.com
Telecommunication Servicesb
N.A.I.C.S.: 517112

GrayWolf Industrial, Inc.   **(1)**
2205 Ragu Dr, Owensboro, KY 42303
Tel.: (270) 854-2299
Web Site:
      https://www.graywolfindustrial.com
Construction Maintenance & Fabrication
Services
N.A.I.C.S.: 236220
Kelly Duncan *(CFO & Chief Admin Officer)*
Weldon Mann *(Dir-Safety)*
Tracy Peoples *(Dir-I/T)*

Subsidiary (Domestic):

Milco National Constructors, Inc.   **(2)**
1115 Industrial Dr, Owensboro, KY 42301
Tel.: (270) 926-2534
Web Site: https://www.milconational.com
Plant Construction & Industrial Construction
Services
N.A.I.C.S.: 236210
Patrick Phister *(VP)*

ICS Group Holdings Inc.   **(1)**
300 1st Ave S Ste 401, Saint Petersburg,
FL 33701
Tel.: (727) 440-3559
Web Site: http://www.vault.insurance
Global Insurance Services
N.A.I.C.S.: 524210
Charles Williamson *(CEO)*
Stephen Bitterman *(Chief Risk Svcs Officer)*
Peter Piotrowski *(Chief Claims Officer)*
Nick Muqtadir *(CFO)*
Mary Qualls *(Chief Underwriting Officer)*
Brandy Roth *(Chief Actuary)*
Stacy Warren *(Chief Sls & Customer Svc
Experience Officer)*

Inco Services, Inc.   **(1)**
3550 Francis Cir, Alpharetta, GA 30004
Tel.: (770) 740-0029
Construction Services
N.A.I.C.S.: 237990

On-Time Steel Management Holding,
Inc.   **(1)**

1841 W Buchanan St, Phoenix, AZ 85007-
3335
Tel.: (602) 417-8865
Holding Company
N.A.I.C.S.: 551112

PTGi International Carrier Services
Ltd.   **(1)**
3rd Floor 130 City Road, London, EC1V
2NW, United Kingdom   **(100%)**
Tel.: (44) 2076696000
Web Site: http://www.ptgi-ics.com
Sales Range: $10-24.9 Million
Emp.: 55
Global Telecommunications Services
N.A.I.C.S.: 517112

Subsidiary (Non-US):

PTGi Europe, B.V.   **(2)**
Zuidplein 116 Tower H Lev, Amsterdam,
1077 XV, Noord-Holland, Netherlands
Tel.: (31) 203338320
Communication Equipment Distr
N.A.I.C.S.: 423690

Pansend, LLC   **(1)**
460 Herndon Pkwy Ste 150, Herndon, VA
20170
Tel.: (703) 456-4100
Health Care Equipment Mfr
N.A.I.C.S.: 339112

R2 Dermatology Incorporated   **(1)**
2633 Camino Ramon Ste 130 Bishop
Ranch 3, San Ramon, CA 94583
Tel.: (925) 378-4400
Web Site: http://www.r2derm.com
Dermatology Services
N.A.I.C.S.: 621111
Kevin Springer *(Dir-Clinical Engrg)*

Titan Fabricators, Inc.   **(1)**
280 Ellis Smeathers Rd, Owensboro, KY
42303
Tel.: (270) 686-7436
Sales Range: $1-9.9 Million
Emp.: 54
Construction Services
N.A.I.C.S.: 237990

United Teacher Associates Insurance
Company   **(1)**
PO Box 26580, Austin, TX 78717-0580
Tel.: (512) 451-2224
Web Site: http://www.utaic.com
Medical Insurance Products & Services
N.A.I.C.S.: 524114

INNOVATION PHARMACEUTI-
CALS INC.

301 Edgewater Pl Ste 100, Wake-
field, MA 01880
Tel.: (978) 921-4125   NV
Web Site: https://www.ipharminc.com
Year Founded: 2007
IPIX—(OTCIQ)
Assets: $7,517,000
Liabilities: $5,478,000
Net Worth: $2,039,000
Earnings: ($3,168,000)
Emp.: 4
Fiscal Year-end: 06/30/23
Biopharmaceutical Company; Medical
Therapies With Dermatology, Oncol-
ogy, Anti-inflammatory & Antibiotic
Applications
N.A.I.C.S.: 325412
Leo Ehrlich *(Founder, Chm, CFO,
CFO, Principal Acctg Officer & Sec)*
Jane Harness *(Sr VP-Clinical Sci-
ences & Portfolio Mgmt)*

INNOVATION1 BIOTECH INC.

7 Grand View Ave, Somerville, MA
02143
Tel.: (617) 447-8299   NV
Web Site:
      http://www.gridironbionutrients.com
IVBT—(OTCQB)
Assets: $75,993
Liabilities: $3,505,956
Net Worth: ($3,429,963)
Earnings: ($5,988,266)

Emp.: 5
Fiscal Year-end: 08/31/23
Supplement Product Distr
N.A.I.C.S.: 456191
Charles W. Allen *(Treas & Sec)*

INNOVATIVE CLIMATIC TECH-
NOLOGIES CORP.

13835 N Tatum Blvd Ste 9-419,
Phoenix, AZ 85032
Tel.: (818) 349-2870
Year Founded: 2015
INVL—(OTCIQ)
Thermostat Product Mfr
N.A.I.C.S.: 334512
George H. Roundy *(CEO & CFO)*

INNOVATIVE DESIGNS, INC.

124 Cherry St, Pittsburgh, PA 15223
Tel.: (412) 799-0350   DE
Web Site: https://www.idigear.com
IVDN—(OTCQB)
Rev.: $347,763
Assets: $1,503,627
Liabilities: $394,993
Net Worth: $1,108,634
Earnings: ($301,378)
Emp.: 2
Fiscal Year-end: 10/31/23
Insulated Sporting Apparel Mfr
N.A.I.C.S.: 339920
Joseph Riccelli *(Chm, CEO, CFO &
Principal Acctg Officer)*

INNOVATIVE EYEWEAR, INC.

11900 Biscayne Blvd Ste 630, North
Miami Beach, FL 33138
Tel.: (786) 785-5178   FL
Year Founded: 2019
LUCY—(NASDAQ)
Rev.: $659,788
Assets: $4,689,884
Liabilities: $665,455
Net Worth: $4,024,429
Earnings: ($5,681,833)
Emp.: 9
Fiscal Year-end: 12/31/22
Optical Product Mfr & Distr
N.A.I.C.S.: 333310
Harrison R. Gross *(CEO & Co-
Founder)*
Konrad Dabrowski *(CFO)*

INNOVATIVE FOOD HOLD-
INGS, INC.

9696 Bonita Beach Rd Ste 208, Bo-
nita Springs, FL 34135
Tel.: (239) 596-0204   FL
Web Site: https://www.ivfh.com
Year Founded: 2004
IVFH—(OTCQB)
Rev.: $80,102,964
Assets: $23,420,202
Liabilities: $6,587,063
Net Worth: $16,833,139
Earnings: ($1,350,002)
Emp.: 128
Fiscal Year-end: 12/31/22
Perishable & Specialty Food Products
Distr
N.A.I.C.S.: 424410
Gary Schubert *(CFO)*
Robert William Bennett *(CEO)*
Brady Smallwood *(COO)*

Subsidiaries:

Artisan Specialty Foods, Inc.   **(1)**
2528 S 27th Ave, Broadview, IL 60155
Tel.: (708) 447-5500
Web Site: https://www.artisanspecialty.com
Sales Range: $1-9.9 Million
Emp.: 30
Specialty Foods Distr
N.A.I.C.S.: 424490

Food Innovations, Inc.   **(1)**
28411 Race Track Rd, Bonita Springs, FL
34135

Tel.: (239) 596-0204
Web Site: https://www.foodinno.com
Food Products Distr
N.A.I.C.S.: 424420

Golden Organics　　　　　　　　(1)
5350 Pecos St, Denver, CO 80221
Tel.: (303) 456-5616
Web Site: https://www.goldenorganics.org
Rev.: $5,908,000
Emp.: 7
Other Grocery & Related Products Merchant Whslr
N.A.I.C.S.: 424490
David Rickard *(Owner)*

Innovative Gourmet, LLC　　　　(1)
11 E Gwynns Mill Ct, Owings Mills, MD 21117
Tel.: (410) 363-1317
Web Site:
　　https://www.innovativegourmet.com
Catering Services
N.A.I.C.S.: 722320

Organic Food Brokers, LLC　　　(1)
28411 Race Track Rd, Bonita Springs, FL 34135
Tel.: (303) 440-7378
Web Site:
　　http://www.organicfoodbrokers.com
Brand Management Services
N.A.I.C.S.: 541430
Ross Schold *(Exec VP)*
George Wright *(Dir-Sls & Strategy)*
Colleen Noonan *(Coord-Category Review & Promo)*
Brittany Robertson *(Assoc Mgr-Brand)*
Salleigh Knox *(Sls Dir-Ops)*

INNOVATIVE HOLDINGS ALLIANCE, INC.

12460 Crabapple Rd Ste 202-224, Alpharetta, GA 30004
Tel.: (770) 777-6641　　　　　DE
Web Site:
　　https://www.innovativeholdingsalliance.com
IHAI—(OTCIQ)
Medicinal & Botanical Product Mfr
N.A.I.C.S.: 325411

INNOVATIVE INDUSTRIAL PROPERTIES, INC.

11440 W Bernardo Ct Ste 100, San Diego, CA 92127
Tel.: (858) 997-3332　　　　　DE
Web Site:
　　https://www.innovativeindustrialproperties.com
Year Founded: 2016
IIPR—(NYSE)
Rev.: $276,359,000
Assets: $2,414,836,000
Liabilities: $452,943,000
Net Worth: $1,961,893,000
Earnings: $153,034,000
Emp.: 19
Fiscal Year-end: 12/31/22
Real Estate Asset Management Services
N.A.I.C.S.: 531390
Alan D. Gold *(Co-Founder & Exec Chm)*
Paul E. Smithers *(Co-Founder, Pres & CEO)*
Brian J. Wolfe *(Gen Counsel, Sec & VP)*
Gary A. Kreitzer *(Co-Founder & Vice Chm)*
Catherine Hastings *(COO)*
Ben Regin *(Chief Investment Officer)*
Andy Bui *(Chief Acctg Officer & VP)*
Tracie Hager *(VP-Asset Mgmt)*
Kelly C. Spicher *(VP-Real Estate Counsel)*
David Smith *(CFO & Treas)*

INNOVATIVE PAYMENT SOLUTIONS, INC.

56B 5th St Lot 1, Carmel, CA 93921　　　　　　　　　　　　NV
Web Site: https://www.ipsipay.com
Year Founded: 2013
IPSI—(OTCQB)
Rev.: $847
Assets: $2,752,572
Liabilities: $6,707,222
Net Worth: ($3,954,650)
Earnings: ($10,288,157)
Emp.: 3
Fiscal Year-end: 12/31/22
Digital Payment Services
N.A.I.C.S.: 522320
Richard Rosenblum *(Pres)*
William Corbett *(Chm)*

INNOVATIVE SOLUTIONS & SUPPORT, INC.

720 Pennsylvania Dr, Exton, PA 19341-1129
Tel.: (610) 646-9800　　　　　PA
Web Site: https://www.innovative-ss.com
Year Founded: 1988
ISSC—(NASDAQ)
Rev.: $34,808,513
Assets: $62,957,451
Liabilities: $24,320,467
Net Worth: $38,636,984
Earnings: $6,027,755
Emp.: 95
Fiscal Year-end: 09/30/23
Flight Avionics Products Designer, Mfr & Sales
N.A.I.C.S.: 325991
Brian Urbanski *(VP-Quality)*
Shahram Askarpour *(Pres & CEO)*
Markus Knopf *(VP-Product Dev)*
Kevin Cravens *(VP-Program Mgmt)*
Jeffrey DiGiovanni *(CFO)*

Subsidiaries:

IS&S Aviation, Inc.　　　　　　(1)
720 Pennsylvania Dr, Exton, PA 19341
Tel.: (610) 646-9800
Web Site: http://www.innovative-ss.com
Sales Range: $50-74.9 Million
Emp.: 100
Holding Company
N.A.I.C.S.: 336413

IS&S Aviation, LLC　　　　　　(1)
720 Pennsylvania Ave, Exton, PA 19341
Tel.: (610) 646-9800
Web Site: http://www.innovative-ss.com
Sales Range: $250-299.9 Million
Holding Company
N.A.I.C.S.: 336413

IS&S Delaware, Inc.　　　　　　(1)
720 Pennsylvania Dr, Exton, PA 19341
Tel.: (610) 646-9800
Web Site: http://www.innovative-ss.com
Sales Range: $75-99.9 Million
Emp.: 100
Holding Company
N.A.I.C.S.: 336413

IS&S Holdings, Inc.　　　　　　(1)
720 Pennsylvania Dr, Exton, PA 19341
Tel.: (610) 646-9800
Web Site: http://www.innovative-ss.com
Sales Range: $250-299.9 Million
Holding Company
N.A.I.C.S.: 336413

Innovative Solutions and Support, LLC　　　　　　　　　　　(1)
720 Pennsylvania Dr, Exton, PA 19341
Tel.: (610) 646-9800
Rev.: $47,198,020
Assets: $82,382,261
Liabilities: $35,743,606
Net Worth: $46,638,655
Earnings: $6,998,380
Emp.: 133
Fiscal Year-end: 09/30/2024
Holding Company
N.A.I.C.S.: 336413

INNOVEREN SCIENTIFIC, INC.

2202 N W Shore Blvd Ste 200, Tampa, FL 33607
Tel.: (312) 445-2870　　　　　NV
Web Site:
　　https://www.innoverenscientific.com
Year Founded: 2013
IVRN—(OTCQB)
Rev.: $453,460
Assets: $137,357
Liabilities: $9,494,743
Net Worth: ($9,357,386)
Earnings: ($10,299,580)
Emp.: 2
Fiscal Year-end: 12/31/22
Medical Device Developer
N.A.I.C.S.: 339112
Jeremy Daniel *(CFO)*
Michael Yurkowsky *(CEO)*

INNOVEST GLOBAL, INC.

8834 Mayfield Rd, Chesterland, OH 44026
Tel.: (440) 644-1027
Web Site:
　　http://www.innovestglobal.net
Year Founded: 1999
IVST—(OTCIQ)
Holding Company
N.A.I.C.S.: 551112
Daniel G. Martin *(Founder, Chm, Pres & CEO)*

Subsidiaries:

Chagrin Safety Supply, Inc.　　(1)
8227 E Washington St, Chagrin Falls, OH 44023
Tel.: (440) 543-2777
Web Site:
　　http://www.chagrinsafetysupply.com
Sales Range: $1-9.9 Million
Emp.: 1
Safety Supplies & Equipment Whslr
N.A.I.C.S.: 423990
Bill Oler *(Pres)*
Victor Lombardi *(Dir-Bus Dev)*

INNOVIVA, INC.

1350 Old Bayshore Hwy Ste 400, Burlingame, CA 94010
Tel.: (650) 238-9600　　　　　DE
Web Site: https://www.inva.com
Year Founded: 1996
INVA—(NASDAQ)
Rev.: $331,339,000
Assets: $1,231,497,000
Liabilities: $665,709,000
Net Worth: $565,788,000
Earnings: $213,921,000
Emp.: 101
Fiscal Year-end: 12/31/22
Pharmaceutical Developer & Mfr
N.A.I.C.S.: 325412
Pavel Raifeld *(CEO)*
Marianne Zhen *(Chief Acctg Officer)*
Stephen Basso *(CFO)*
David Altarac *(Chief Medical Officer)*
Marcie Cain *(Chief People Officer)*
Patricia Drake *(Chief Comml Officer)*
Mark DiPaolo *(Chm)*

Subsidiaries:

Entasis Therapeutics Holdings Inc.　　　　　　　　　　　　(1)
35 Gatehouse Dr, Waltham, MA 02451　　　　　　　　　(99.99%)
Tel.: (781) 810-0120
Web Site: http://www.entasistx.com
Rev.: $5,176,000
Assets: $40,920,000
Liabilities: $9,708,000
Net Worth: $31,212,000
Earnings: ($47,141,000)
Emp.: 51
Fiscal Year-end: 12/31/2021
Biopharmaceutical Product Mfr & Distr
N.A.I.C.S.: 325412
John Mueller *(Chief Dev Officer)*
Ruben Tommasi *(Chief Scientific Officer)*
David Altarac *(Chief Medical Officer)*
Elizabeth Kelley *(Gen Counsel)*

Colleen Tucker *(Head-HR)*
Matthew Ronsheim *(Chief Pharmaceutical Sciences & Mfg Officer)*
Kristie Wagner *(VP & Interim Principal Fin & Acctg Officer)*

LABA Royalty Sub LLC　　　　(1)
901 Gateway Blvd, San Francisco, CA 94080
Tel.: (650) 808-6000
Restaurant Operating Services
N.A.I.C.S.: 722511

La Jolla Pharmaceutical Company　　　　　　　　　　　(1)
201 Jones Rd Ste 400, Waltham, MA 02451
Tel.: (617) 715-3600
Web Site:
　　http://www.lajollapharmaceutical.com
Rev.: $75,720,000
Assets: $101,230,000
Liabilities: $167,968,000
Net Worth: ($66,738,000)
Earnings: $19,660,000
Emp.: 61
Fiscal Year-end: 12/31/2021
Biopharmaceutical Products Developer
N.A.I.C.S.: 325414
Michael S. Hearne *(CFO)*
Stew Kroll *(Chief Dev Officer)*
Larry Edwards *(Pres & CEO)*
Steven Ferris *(VP-Quality Assurance)*
Tom Ouellette *(VP-Sls & Mktg)*
Paula Rusu *(VP-Ops)*
Tony Hodges *(Chief Medical Officer)*

Subsidiary (Non-US):

La Jolla Pharmaceutical II B.V.　(2)
Strawinskylaan 569, 1077 XX, Amsterdam, Netherlands
Tel.: (31) 207372218
Biotechnology Research & Development Services
N.A.I.C.S.: 541714

Pulmoquine Therapeutics, Inc.　(1)
1155 Camino Del Mar Ste 481, Del Mar, CA 92014
Tel.: (858) 777-9750
Web Site: http://www.pulmoquine.com
Pharmaceuticals Mfr
N.A.I.C.S.: 325412
Robert S Hillman *(Pres & CEO)*

INNSUITES HOSPITALITY TRUST

1730 E Nern Ave Ste 122, Phoenix, AZ 85020
Tel.: (602) 944-1500　　　　　OH
Web Site:
　　https://www.innsuitestrust.com
Year Founded: 1971
IHT—(NYSEAMEX)
Rev.: $7,145,687
Assets: $17,019,972
Liabilities: $13,337,827
Net Worth: $3,682,145
Earnings: $737,051
Emp.: 52
Fiscal Year-end: 01/31/23
Real Estate Investment Trust
N.A.I.C.S.: 525990
Marc E. Berg *(Treas, Sec & Exec VP)*
James F. Wirth *(Chm & CEO)*
Sylvin Lange *(CFO)*

Subsidiaries:

IBC Hotels, LLC　　　　　　　(1)
1625 E Northern Ave Ste 105, Phoenix, AZ 85020
Tel.: (602) 944-1500
Web Site: http://www.ibchotels.com
Restaurant Operators
N.A.I.C.S.: 722511

InnSuites Hotels, Inc.　　　　　(1)
1730 E Northern Ave Ste 122, Phoenix, AZ 85020
Tel.: (602) 944-1500
Web Site: https://www.innsuites.com
Sales Range: $650-699.9 Million
Hotel Operator
N.A.I.C.S.: 721110

InnSuites Hospitality Trust—(Continued)

Affiliate (Domestic):

Albuquerque Suite Hospitality LLC (2)
2400 Yale Blvd SE, Albuquerque, NM 87106
Tel.: (505) 242-7022
Web Site:
    http://www.albuquerque.innsuites.com
Sales Range: $250-299.9 Million
Emp.: 25
Hotel Operator
N.A.I.C.S.: 721110
Victoria Lombardelli (Gen Mgr)

Buena Park Suite Hospitality LLC (2)
7555 Beach Blvd, Buena Park, CA 90620
Tel.: (714) 522-7360
Web Site: http://www.buenapark.com
Sales Range: $250-299.9 Million
Emp.: 40
Operator of Hotels
N.A.I.C.S.: 721110

Holding (Domestic):

Ontario Hospitality Properties Limited Partnership (2)
3400 Shelby St, Ontario, CA 91764-4873
Tel.: (909) 466-9600
Web Site: http://ontario.innsuites.com
Sales Range: Less than $1 Million
Emp.: 66
Operator of Hotels
N.A.I.C.S.: 721110

Tucson Hospitality Properties, Ltd (2)
6201 N Oracle Rd, Tucson, AZ 85704
Tel.: (520) 297-8111
Web Site: http://www.innsuites.com
Emp.: 40
Operator of Hotels
N.A.I.C.S.: 721110

Tucson St. Mary's Suite Hospitality LLC (2)
475 N Granada Ave, Tucson, AZ 85701
Tel.: (520) 622-3000
Hotel Operations
N.A.I.C.S.: 721110
Charles Wetegrove (Gen Mgr)

Yuma Hospitality Properties, Ltd. (2)
1450 S Castle Dome Ave, Yuma, AZ 85365
Tel.: (928) 783-8341
Web Site: http://www.yuma.innsuites.com
Sales Range: $125-149.9 Million
Operator of Hotels
N.A.I.C.S.: 721110

Ontario Hospitality Properties L.L.L.P. (1)
1625 E Northern Ave Ste 105, Phoenix, AZ 85020
Tel.: (602) 944-1500
Restaurant Operators
N.A.I.C.S.: 722511

RRF Limited Partnership (1)
1615 E Northern Ave Ste 102, Phoenix, AZ 85020-3998
Tel.: (602) 944-1500
Web Site: http://www.innsuites.com
Sales Range: $25-49.9 Million
Emp.: 10
Operator of Hotels
N.A.I.C.S.: 721110
Pamela Barnhill (Pres)

INOGEN, INC.
859 Ward Dr Ste 200, Goleta, CA 93111
Tel.: (805) 562-0500   DE
Web Site: https://www.inogen.com
Year Founded: 2001
INGN—(NASDAQ)
Rev.: $377,241,000
Assets: $405,041,000
Liabilities: $107,635,000
Net Worth: $297,406,000
Earnings: ($83,772,000)
Emp.: 1,026
Fiscal Year-end: 12/31/22

Portable Oxygen Concentrators & Other Medical Devices Mfr
N.A.I.C.S.: 339112
Alison Bauerlein (Co-Founder)
Gregoire Ramade (Chief Comml Officer)
Michael J. Bourque (CFO, Treas & Exec VP)
Kevin R. M. Smith (Pres & CEO)

INOTIV, INC.   IN
Web Site: https://www.inotiv.com
Year Founded: 1974
NOTV—(NASDAQ)
Rev.: $572,425,000
Assets: $856,530,000
Liabilities: $588,040,000
Net Worth: $268,490,000
Earnings: ($105,140,000)
Emp.: 1,955
Fiscal Year-end: 09/30/23
Life Science Research & Development Services; Analytical Instruments Mfr
N.A.I.C.S.: 541715
John E. Sagartz (Chief Strategy Officer)
Beth A. Taylor (CFO & VP-Fin)
Greg Beattie (COO)
Jeff Krupp (Chief HR Officer)
Beth A. Taylor (CFO & VP-Fin)
Lizanne Muller (Pres & Pres-RMS)
Adrian Hardy (Chief Comml Officer & Exec VP)
Andrea Castetter (Chief Compliance Officer, Gen Counsel, Sec & Sr VP)
Robert W. Leasure Jr. (Pres & CEO)

Subsidiaries:

BAS Evansville, Inc. (1)
10424 Middle Mount Vernon Rd, Mount Vernon, IN 47620
Tel.: (812) 985-5900
Web Site: http://www.basinc.com
Preclinical Toxicology Testing Laboratory
N.A.I.C.S.: 541380

Bolder BioPATH, Inc. (1)
5541 Central Ave Ste 160, Boulder, CO 80301-2944
Tel.: (303) 633-5400
Web Site: http://www.bolderbiopath.com
Research & Development in the Physical, Engineering & Life Sciences
N.A.I.C.S.: 541715
Phil Bendele (CFO & COO)
Alison Bendele (Pres)

Histion LLC (1)
2615 W Casino Rd Ste 6G, Everett, WA 98204-2113
Tel.: (425) 347-0439
Web Site: http://www.histion.com
Emp.: 100
Research & Development in Biotechnology
N.A.I.C.S.: 541714
Peggy Lalor (Founder & Pres)

HistoTox Labs, Inc. (1)
2108 55th St Ste 12, Boulder, CO 80301
Tel.: (303) 633-5401
Web Site: http://www.histotoxlabs.com
Research & Development in the Physical, Engineering & Life Sciences
N.A.I.C.S.: 541715
Jon Bishop (Pres)

Plato Bio Pharma Inc. (1)
7581 W 103rd Ave, Westminster, CO 80021
Tel.: (720) 987-8384
Web Site: http://www.platobiopharma.com
Testing Laboratories
N.A.I.C.S.: 541380
Craig F. Plato (Founder & CEO)

Seventh Wave Laboratories, LLC (1)
19 Worthington Access Dr, Maryland Heights, MO 63043
Tel.: (636) 519-4885
Consultative Contract Research
N.A.I.C.S.: 541715
John E. Sagartz (Founder)

INOVALON HOLDINGS, INC.

4321 Collington Rd, Bowie, MD 20716
Tel.: (301) 809-4000   DE
Web Site: http://www.inovalon.com
Year Founded: 2014
INOV—(NASDAQ)
Rev.: $667,524,000
Assets: $1,971,398,000
Liabilities: $1,262,684,000
Net Worth: $708,714,000
Earnings: $22,579,000
Emp.: 1,836
Fiscal Year-end: 12/31/20
Holding Company; Data Analytics & Data-Driven Intervention Platforms
N.A.I.C.S.: 551112
Keith R. Dunleavy (Chm & CEO)
Ingrid E. Olsen (Chief People Officer)
Matt Brow (Pres/Gen Mgr-Pharmacy, Life Sciences & Advisory)
Bud Meadows (Pres/Gen Mgr-Provider Bus)
Beverly Allen (Chief Compliance & Privacy Officer, Gen Counsel, Sec & Sr VP)
Geoff Charron (CTO)
Monica Keeneth (Chief Information Security Officer)
Paige Kilian (Chief Medical Officer)
Eron S. Kelly (Pres)
Lanie Schenkelberg (VP-Product Mktg)

Subsidiaries:

ABILITY Network Inc. (1)
Butler Sq 100 N 6th St Ste 900A, Minneapolis, MN 55403
Tel.: (612) 460-4301
Web Site: http://www.abilitynetwork.com
Secure Healthcare Information Services
N.A.I.C.S.: 541519
Bud Meadows (Pres & Gen Mgr)
John Agostino (Sr VP-Fin)
John Carter (Sr VP-Platform Ops)
Julie Lambert (Sr VP-Custom Ops)

Creehan & Company Corporation (1)
8 Grandview Cir, Canonsburg, PA 15317   (100%)
Tel.: (724) 743-9154
Web Site: http://www.creehan.com
Sales Range: $25-49.9 Million
Emp.: 30
Software Application Platforms & Implementation of Services for Pharmacy, Drug Mfr & Distr
N.A.I.C.S.: 541511
R. Sean Creehan (Founder & Gen Mgr)

Inovalon, Inc. (1)
4321 Collington Rd, Bowie, MD 20716
Tel.: (301) 809-4000
Web Site: http://www.inovalon.com
Sales Range: $250-299.9 Million
Healthcare Technology & Software Developer
N.A.I.C.S.: 513210
Keith R. Dunleavy (Chm & CEO)

Vigilanz Corporation (1)
5775 Wayzata Blvd Ste 970, Minneapolis, MN 55416-2669
Web Site: http://www.vigilanzcorp.com
Computer Related Services
N.A.I.C.S.: 541519
Ohar Oohodes (Dir-I IR & Admin)

INOVIO PHARMACEUTICALS, INC.
660 W Germantown Pike Ste 110, Plymouth Meeting, PA 19462
Tel.: (267) 440-4200   DE
Web Site: https://www.inovio.com
Year Founded: 1983
INO—(NASDAQ)
Rev.: $10,262,268
Assets: $348,533,302
Liabilities: $126,170,546
Net Worth: $222,362,756
Earnings: ($279,818,065)
Emp.: 184

Fiscal Year-end: 12/31/22
Surgical & Medical Instrument Manufacturing
N.A.I.C.S.: 339112
Peter Kies (CFO)
Laurent Humeau (Chief Scientific Officer)
E. J. Brandreth (Sr VP-Quality Assurance)
Stephen Kemmerrer (Sr VP-Engrg Dev)
Daniel Jordan (Sr VP-Device Mfg Ops)
Jeffrey Skolnik (Sr VP-Clinical Dev)
Shawn D. Bridy (Sr VP-Bus Dev)
Jacqueline E. Shea (Pres & CEO)
Mark Twyman (Chief Comml Officer)
Rob Crotty (Gen Counsel)
Asli Gevgilili (Chief HR Officer)
Michael Sumner (Chief Medical Officer)
Cheryl Elder (Sr VP)
Robert J. Juba Jr. (Sr VP-Biological Mfg & Clinical Supply Mgmt)

Subsidiaries:

VGX Animal Health, Inc. (1)
2700 Research Forest Dr Ste 180, The Woodlands, TX 77381
Tel.: (281) 296-7300
Web Site: http://www.vgxah.com
Biotechnology Research
N.A.I.C.S.: 541714

INOZYME PHARMA, INC.
321 Summer St Ste 400, Boston, MA 02210
Tel.: (857) 330-4340   DE
Web Site: https://www.inozyme.com
Year Founded: 2015
INZY—(NASDAQ)
Rev.: $1,933,000
Assets: $139,195,000
Liabilities: $20,801,000
Net Worth: $118,394,000
Earnings: ($67,061,000)
Emp.: 56
Fiscal Year-end: 12/31/22
Biotechnology Research & Development Services
N.A.I.C.S.: 541714
Axel Bolte (Pres & CEO)
Douglas A. Treco (Chm)
Sanjay S. Subramanian (CFO & Principal Acctg Officer)
Douglas Treco (Chm)
Yves Sabbagh (Chief Scientific Officer & Sr VP)
Gayle Gironda (Chief People Officer)
Kurt Gunter (Chief Medical Officer)
Soojin Kim (Chief Technical Ops Officer)
Matt Winton (COO)

INSCORP, INC.
2106 Crestmoor Rd, Nashville, TN 37215
Tel.: (615) 515-2265
Web Site: https://www.insbank.com
IBTN—(OTCIQ)
Rev.: $23,861,392
Assets: $617,229,587
Liabilities: $566,136,022
Net Worth: $51,093,565
Earnings: $2,432,636
Emp.: 47
Fiscal Year-end: 12/31/20
Offices of Bank Holding Companies
N.A.I.C.S.: 551111
Mark Edward Bruchas (CFO & Exec VP-INS Bank)
James H. Rieniets Jr. (Pres & CEO-INS Bank)
J. Scott Gupton (COO & Exec VP-INS Bank)
Philip C. Fons (Chief Credit Officer & Exec VP-INS Bank)

Chad Hankins *(Officer-Lending & Exec VP-INS Bank)*

Subsidiaries:

INSBANK **(1)**
2106 Crestmoor Rd, Nashville, TN 37215
Tel.: (615) 515-2265
Web Site: http://www.insbanktn.com
Sales Range: $1-9.9 Million
Emp.: 30
Commericial Banking
N.A.I.C.S.: 522110
Mark Edward Bruchas *(CFO & Exec VP)*
James H. Rieniets Jr. *(Pres & CEO)*
Michael A. Qualls *(Chm)*
Andy Hawkins *(First VP & Mgr-Relationship)*
Tina Melton *(Officer-Loan Admin & First VP)*
Maya Demonbreum *(Asst Controller)*
Ellis Simmons *(Sr VP & Mgr-Relationship)*
Aaron Lawyer *(VP)*
Blake Adams *(VP & Mgr-Relationship)*
Blake Wilson *(VP & Head-Tma Medical Banking)*
Heather Carr *(Asst VP-Ops)*
Jana Spicer *(Mgr-Deposit Portfolio)*
Jason Stout *(VP & Mgr-Is)*
Leslie Smith *(Officer-Mgmt, Treas & Asst VP)*
Patrick Wright *(First VP & Mgr-Relationship)*
Lauren Cannon *(VP & Dir-Treasury Mgmt & Deposit Svcs)*

INSEEGO CORP.
9710 Scranton Rd Ste 200, San Diego, CA 92121
Tel.: (858) 812-3400   DE
Web Site: https://www.inseego.com
Year Founded: 1996
INSG—(NASDAQ)
Rev.: $195,688,000
Assets: $121,797,000
Liabilities: $223,902,000
Net Worth: ($102,105,000)
Earnings: ($49,176,000)
Emp.: 331
Fiscal Year-end: 12/31/23
Wireless Communications Access Solutions
N.A.I.C.S.: 541511
Robert G. Barbieri *(CFO)*
Steven A. Sherman *(Founder)*
Simon Rayne *(Sr VP & Mng Dir-UK, EMEA & APAC)*
Steven H. Gatoff *(CFO)*
Douglas Kahn *(Exec VP-Ops & Customer Success)*
Dan Picker *(CTO)*
Mark Frisch *(Exec VP-Americas-Sls)*
Stephen Brown *(Sr VP-Enterprise Sls)*
Ritesh Mukherjee *(Sr VP)*
Vishal Donthireddy *(Sr VP)*
Steve Harmon *(Chief Revenue Officer)*
Keri Bolding *(Sr VP-Global Channel Sls & Distr)*
Philip G. Brace *(Exec Chm)*

Subsidiaries:

Ctrack (Pty) Ltd **(1)**
Suite 4 Level 4 6 Eden Park Drive, Macquarie Park, 2113, NSW, Australia
Tel.: (61) 1300304033
Web Site: https://inseego.com
Vehicle Tracking Mfr & Distr
N.A.I.C.S.: 325199

Ctrack (SA) (Pty) Limited **(1)**
Regency Office Park 9 Regency Drive, Route 21 Corporate Park Irene, Centurion, 0157, South Africa
Tel.: (27) 124502222
Web Site: https://www.ctrack.com
Vehicle Tracking & Fleet Management Solutions
N.A.I.C.S.: 517810
Hein Jordt *(Mng Dir)*

Ctrack Benelux BV **(1)**
Ketelweg 44, 3356 LE, Papendrecht, Netherlands
Tel.: (31) 786449334

Web Site: https://inseego.com
Software Development Services
N.A.I.C.S.: 541511

Ctrack Deutschland GmbH **(1)**
Business Park 18, 49143, Bissendorf, Germany
Tel.: (49) 5402702800
Web Site: https://inseego.com
Sales Range: $25-49.9 Million
Emp.: 30
Software Development Services
N.A.I.C.S.: 541511
Maria Johanning *(Mng Dir)*

Ctrack Finance Limited **(1)**
Park House Ground Floor Headingley Office Park, Victoria Road, Leeds, LS6 1LG, United Kingdom
Tel.: (44) 8452001215
Sales Range: $25-49.9 Million
Emp.: 20
Vehicle Tracking & Fleet Management Services
N.A.I.C.S.: 517810

Ctrack UK Ltd **(1)**
Stockdale House 8 Victoria Road, Leeds, LS6 1PF, United Kingdom
Tel.: (44) 3450558555
Web Site: https://inseego.com
Vehicle Tracking Mfr & Distr
N.A.I.C.S.: 325199
Ian Holt *(Mng Dir-Fin & Ops)*
Steve Thomas *(Mng Dir-Sls & Mktg)*

Enfora, Inc. **(1)**
251 Renner Pkwy, Richardson, TX 75080
Tel.: (972) 633-4400
Wireless Network Hardware & Software Developer & Mfr
N.A.I.C.S.: 334118

Inseego Australia Pty Ltd. **(1)**
Suite 4 Level 4 6 Eden Park Drive, Macquarie Park, 2113, NSW, Australia
Tel.: (61) 294293999
Telecommunication Servicesb
N.A.I.C.S.: 517111

Inseego Belgium B.V. **(1)**
Mechelsesteenweg 277, 1800, Vilvoorde, Belgium
Tel.: (32) 22548557
Information Technology Services
N.A.I.C.S.: 541511

Inseego Benelux B.V. **(1)**
Ketelweg 44, 3356 LE, Papendrecht, Netherlands
Tel.: (31) 786449334
Information Technology Services
N.A.I.C.S.: 541511

Inseego Deutschland GmbH **(1)**
Gewerbepark 18, 49143, Bissendorf, Germany
Tel.: (49) 5402702800
Information Technology Services
N.A.I.C.S.: 541511

Inseego International Holdings Ltd. **(1)**
Suite G3 South Central Millshaw Court Global Avenue, Leeds, LS11 8PG
Tel.: (44) 0345055855
Web Site: https://inseego.com
Wireless Communications Access Solutions
N.A.I.C.S.: 334111

Inseego Ireland Limited **(1)**
Unit 24 Kilcarberry Business Park Nangor Road, Clondalkin, Dublin, 22, Ireland
Tel.: (353) 14611025
Information Technology Services
N.A.I.C.S.: 541511

Inseego New Zealand Ltd. **(1)**
Level 2 6 Clayton Street, Newmarket, Auckland, 1023, New Zealand
Tel.: (64) 93361591
Telecommunication Servicesb
N.A.I.C.S.: 517111

Inseego North America, LLC **(1)**
180 W 8th Ave, Eugene, OR 97401
Tel.: (877) 685-9040
Web Site: https://www.inseego.com
Mobile Broadband Services
N.A.I.C.S.: 517112

Novatel Wireless Solutions, Inc. **(1)**
9645 Scranton Rd Ste 205, San Diego, CA 92121-1764
Tel.: (858) 812-3400
Web Site: http://www.novatelinc.com
Sales Range: $25-49.9 Million
Emp.: 100
Wireless Communication Services
N.A.I.C.S.: 517112

Novatel Wireless Technologies, Ltd. **(1)**
6715 8 St NE Ste 200, Calgary, T2E 7H7, AB, Canada
Tel.: (403) 295-4800
Sales Range: $25-49.9 Million
Emp.: 70
Software Development Services
N.A.I.C.S.: 513210

INSIGHT ACQUISITION CORP.
333 E 91st St, New York, NY 10128
Tel.: (917) 374-2922   DE
Web Site:
  https://www.insightacqcorp.com
Year Founded: 2021
INAQ—(NASDAQ)
Rev.: $2,826,777
Assets: $12,353,755
Liabilities: $23,340,899
Net Worth: ($10,987,144)
Earnings: ($651,138)
Emp.: 2
Fiscal Year-end: 12/31/23
Investment Services
N.A.I.C.S.: 523999
Michael E. Singer *(Exec Chm & CEO)*
Glenn C. Worman *(CFO)*
Michael E. Singer *(Chm)*
Jeffrey Gary *(Asst Mgr-Fin)*

INSIGHT ENTERPRISES, INC.
2701 E Insight Way, Chandler, AZ 85286
Tel.: (480) 333-3000   DE
Web Site: https://www.insight.com
Year Founded: 1988
NSIT—(NASDAQ)
Rev.: $10,431,191,000
Assets: $5,112,581,000
Liabilities: $3,474,513,000
Net Worth: $1,638,068,000
Earnings: $280,608,000
Emp.: 13,448
Fiscal Year-end: 12/31/22
Information Technology Products, Services & Solutions
N.A.I.C.S.: 541512
Rachael A. Bertrandt Crump *(Principal Acctg Officer & Controller-Global)*
Timothy A. Crown *(Co-Founder & Chm)*
Helen K. Johnson *(CFO-North America & Sr VP-Fin)*
Jen Vasin *(Sr VP-HR)*
Mike Tatum *(Dir-Product Mgmt, Infrastructure & Security)*
Joyce A. Mullen *(Pres & CEO)*
Jeffery Shumway *(CIO-Global)*
Dee Burger *(Pres-North America)*
Megan Amdahl *(COO & Sr VP-Client Experience-North America)*
Rob Green *(Chief Digital Officer-North America)*
Bob Kane *(Chief Revenue Officer & Sr VP-Enterprise Sls & North America)*
Hilary Kerner *(CMO)*
Jason Rader *(Chief Information Security Officer & VP)*
Adrian Gregory *(Pres-Europe, Middle East & Africa)*
Samuel C. Cowley *(Gen Counsel, Sec & Sr VP)*

Subsidiaries:

Amdaris Bulgaria EOOD **(1)**

Georgi Benkovski 11 3rd Floor, 1000, Sofia, Bulgaria
Tel.: (359) 883433832
Software Development Services
N.A.I.C.S.: 541511

Amdaris Group Ltd. **(1)**
Countership, Bristol, BS1 6BX, United Kingdom
Tel.: (44) 1179353444
Web Site: https://amdaris.com
Software Development Services
N.A.I.C.S.: 541511

Amdaris Romania S.R.L. **(1)**
11 Dinu Vintila Street 8th Floor, 021101, Bucharest, Romania
Tel.: (40) 356171535
Software Development Services
N.A.I.C.S.: 541511

Amdaris S.R.L. **(1)**
Mt Varlaam 63/23 Str, Chisinau, Moldova
Tel.: (373) 60755228
Software Development Services
N.A.I.C.S.: 541511

Caase Group BV **(1)**
Rigtersbleek-Zandvoort 10 1, 7521 BE, Enschede, Netherlands
Tel.: (31) 884320000
Computer Support Services
N.A.I.C.S.: 541519

Datalink Corporation **(1)**
10050 Crosstown Cir Ste 500, Eden Prairie, MN 55344
Tel.: (952) 944-3462
Web Site: http://www.datalink.com
Sales Range: $750-799.9 Million
Data Storage Systems Mfr
N.A.I.C.S.: 541512

Hanu Software Solutions (India) Private Ltd. **(1)**
Unit F2 1st Floor Plot No 6 Signature Tower Ansal IT City Park, Noida, 201308, UP, India
Tel.: (91) 18001202726
Information Technology Services
N.A.I.C.S.: 541519

Hanu Software Solutions, Inc. **(1)**
5 Independence Way Ste 300, Princeton, NJ 08540
Tel.: (609) 945-2242
Web Site: http://www.HanuSoftware.com
Sales Range: $1-9.9 Million
Emp.: 120
Custom Computer Programming Services
N.A.I.C.S.: 541511
Anil Singh *(Founder & CEO)*
Manoj Srivastava *(COO)*

Insight Direct UK Limited **(1)**
1st Floor St Paul's Place 121 Norfolk Street, Sheffield, S1 2JF, South Yorkshire, United Kingdom
Tel.: (44) 3448463333
Web Site: https://www.uk.insight.com
Sales Range: $150-199.9 Million
Computer & Software Retail
N.A.I.C.S.: 423430
Joyce Mullen *(CEO)*
Glynis Bryan *(CFO)*
Dee Burger *(Pres-)*
Megan Amdahl *(Sr VP- &)*
Rachael A. Crump *(Chief Acctg Officer)*
Rob Green *(Chief Digital Officer-)*
Adrian Gregory *(Pres-)*
Hilary Kerner *(CMO)*
Bob Kane *(Chief Revenue Officer)*
Stan Lequin *(Pres-)*
Mike Morgan *(Sr VP-)*
Jason Rader *(Chief Information Security Officer)*
Jen Vasin *(Chief HR Officer)*
Karim Adatia *(Sr VP)*
John Carnahan *(Sr VP-Business Development &)*
Scott Friedlander *(Sr VP-)*
Suzanne Gallagher *(Sr VP-)*
Mike Gaumond *(Sr VP-Strategy)*
Reem Gedeon *(Sr VP)*
Jet Golia *(Sr VP- &)*
Lynn Wilden *(Sr VP-Treasury & Tax)*
Brenda Hudson *(Sr VP-)*
Russell Leighton *(Sr VP- & Operations)*
Karen McLaughlin *(Sr VP- &)*
James Morgado *(Sr VP-Finance)*

Insight Enterprises, Inc.—(Continued)

Stephen Moss (Sr VP-)
Aneema Rawat (Sr VP-)
Gary Richards (Sr VP-)
Kate Savage (Sr VP-)

Insight Direct USA, Inc. (1)
6820 S Harl Ave, Tempe, AZ 85283-4318
Tel.: (480) 902-1000
Web Site: http://www.insight.com
Emp.: 3,000
Computer Peripheral & Software Whslr
N.A.I.C.S.: 423430

Insight Direct Worldwide, Inc. (1)
6820 S Harl Ave, Tempe, AZ 85283
Tel.: (480) 889-9500
Web Site: https://www.insight.com
Data Center Management & Information
Technology Services
N.A.I.C.S.: 541519

Insight Enterprises BV (1)
Wapenrustlaan 11, 7321 DL, Apeldoorn,
Netherlands
Tel.: (31) 555382382
Emp.: 150
Computer Related Services
N.A.I.C.S.: 423430

Insight Enterprises Hong Kong (1)
Suites 1203-4 12th Floor 625 King's Road,
North Point Island East, Hong Kong, China
(Hong Kong)
Tel.: (852) 2 972 8200
Web Site: http://www.insight.com
Information Technology Consulting Services
N.A.I.C.S.: 541512

**Insight Enterprises Netherlands
BV** (1)
Faustraat 3, 7323 BA, Apeldoorn, Nether-
lands
Tel.: (31) 55 538 2382
Web Site: https://www.nl.insight.com
Computer Related Services
N.A.I.C.S.: 423430

Insight Enterprises UK, Ltd. (1)
Technoloy Building Insight Campus Terry
Street, Sheffield, S9 2BU, United Kingdom
Tel.: (44) 344 846 3333
Web Site: https://www.uk.insight.com
Computer Related Services
N.A.I.C.S.: 541519
Jet Golia (VP-Comml & Legal)

Insight Enterprises, Inc. (1)
444 Scott Dr, Bloomingdale, IL 60108
Tel.: (630) 924-6700
Web Site: http://www.insight.com
Sales Range: $700-749.9 Million
Emp.: 1,364
Distr of Computer Media & Peripheral
Equipment
N.A.I.C.S.: 423430

Insight Enterprises, Inc. (1)
3480 Lotus Dr, Plano, TX 75075
Tel.: (469) 443-3900
Web Site: http://www.insight.com
Sales Range: $1-4.9 Billion
Business Software Reseller
N.A.I.C.S.: 423430

Insight North America (1)
6820 S Harl Ave, Tempe, AZ 85283
Web Site: http://www.insight.com
Computer Related Services
N.A.I.C.S.: 423430

Insight Technology Solutions AB (1)
Kistagangen 12 Plan 2, 164-40, Kista, Swe-
den
Tel.: (46) 85 221 0010
Web Site: https://se.insight.com
Computer Network Systems Design & Man-
agement Products & Services
N.A.I.C.S.: 541512

Insight Technology Solutions AG (1)
Richtistrasse 7, 8304, Wallisellen, Switzer-
land
Tel.: (41) 44 878 7606
Web Site: https://ch.insight.com
Computer Network Management Services
N.A.I.C.S.: 541512

**Insight Technology Solutions
N.U.F.** (1)

Nydalsveien 33, PO Box 4814, Oslo, 422,
Norway
Tel.: (47) 8522 100 10
Web Site: http://no.insight.com
Computer Network System Design & Man-
agement Products & Services
N.A.I.C.S.: 541512
Glynis A. Bryan (CFO)
Marten Blixt (Country Mgr-Nordics)
Alexander Kaatz (VP-Sls & Mktg-EMEA)
Kenneth Lamneck (Pres & CEO)
Wolfgang Ebermann (Pres-EMEA)
Jet Golia (VP-Comml & Legal-EMEA)
Peter Ricahrdson (SR VP-EMEA)
Rolf Adam (VP-Svcs-EMEA)
Russell Leighton (Sr VP-Fin & Ops)

**Insight Technology Solutions Pte
Ltd** (1)
16 Collyer Quay 32-01 Hitachi Tower, Sin-
gapore, 049318, Singapore
Tel.: (65) 6 438 2995
Web Site: https://sg.insight.com
Computer Products Whslr
N.A.I.C.S.: 423430

**Insight Technology Solutions
S.R.L.** (1)
Viale Piero e Alberto Pirelli 6, 20126, Milan,
Italy
Tel.: (39) 022 108 0210
Web Site: https://it.insight.com
Computer Network Systems Design & Man-
agement Products & Services
N.A.I.C.S.: 541513
Russell Leighton (Sr VP-Ops & Fin-EMEA)

**Insight Technology Solutions
SAS** (1)
6th Avenue Morane Saulnier, 78140, Velizy-
Villacoublay, France
Tel.: (33) 130672500
Web Site: https://fr.insight.com
Computer Network Systems Design & Man-
agement Products & Services
N.A.I.C.S.: 541512

**Insight Technology Solutions,
Inc.** (1)
Romeinsesteenweg 468, 1853, Grimbergen,
Belgium
Tel.: (32) 22636020
Web Site: http://www.be.insight.com
Software Development Services
N.A.I.C.S.: 513210
Glynis A. Bryan (CFO)
Kenneth T. Lamneck (Pres & CEO)

**Insight Technology Solutions,
S.L.** (1)
Calle Francisca Delgado 11-4, 28108, Al-
cobendas, Madrid, Spain
Tel.: (34) 91 384 0790
Web Site: https://es.insight.com
Computer Network System Design & Man-
agement Products & Services
N.A.I.C.S.: 541512

MicroWarehouse BV (1)
Aletta Jacobslaan 7, Amsterdam, 1066 BG,
Netherlands
Tel.: (31) 203551425
Electronic Equipment & Component Whslr
N.A.I.C.S.: 423430
Ferdi Van Der Zwaag (Mgr-Bus Partner-
ships)

PCM, Inc. (1)
1940 E Mariposa Ave, El Segundo, CA
90245
Tel.: (310) 354-5600
Web Site: http://www.pcm.com
IT Products & Services
N.A.I.C.S.: 423430
Simon M. Abuyounes (Exec VP-IT, Ops &
Comml Sls)

Subsidiary (Domestic):

AF Services, LLC (2)
2555 W 190th St, Torrance, CA 90504
Tel.: (310) 354-5600
Computer Equipment Store
N.A.I.C.S.: 449210

Subsidiary (Non-US):

Acrodex Inc. (2)
11420 170 Street NW, Edmonton, T5S 1L7,
AB, Canada

Tel.: (780) 426-4444
Web Site: http://www.acrodex.com
IT Services
N.A.I.C.S.: 541513

Subsidiary (Domestic):

**En Pointe Technologies Sales,
Inc.** (2)
1940 E Mariposa Ave, El Segundo, CA
90245
Tel.: (310) 337-5200
Information Technology Consulting, Software Licensing & Cloud Services & Computer & Parts Distr
N.A.I.C.S.: 541512

Subsidiary (Non-US):

OSRP, LLC (2)
2nd Floor Edsa Central Pavilion Building
Edsa corner United Street, Greenfield Dis-
trict Metro Manila, Mandaluyong, 1550, Phil-
ippines
Tel.: (63) 2 238 6400
Back Office Services & Support for IT, Call
Center, Graphics & Accounting
N.A.I.C.S.: 561499

PC Mall Canada, Inc. (2)
1100 Rue University, Montreal, H3B 3A5,
QC, Canada
Tel.: (514) 373-8700
Computer & Software Store
N.A.I.C.S.: 423430

Subsidiary (Domestic):

PC Mall Gov, Inc. (2)
14120 Newbrook Dr Ste 100, Chantilly, VA
20151
Tel.: (703) 594-8100
Web Site: http://www.pcmg.com
Sales Range: $25-49.9 Million
Emp.: 70
Direct Marketing Reseller of IT Products &
Services to Public Sector
N.A.I.C.S.: 541512

PC Mall Services, Inc. (2)
8337 Green Meadows Dr N, Lewis Center,
OH 43035-9451
Tel.: (614) 854-1399
Web Site: http://www.pcm.com
Consumer Electronics Product Marketer
N.A.I.C.S.: 423690

Subsidiary (Non-US):

**PCM Technology Solutions UK,
Ltd.** (2)
Suite 1 3rd Floor 11-12 St Jamess Square,
London, SW1Y 4LB, United Kingdom
Tel.: (44) 8000698512
Computer Parts Distr
N.A.I.C.S.: 423430

Subsidiary (Domestic):

PCM-Logistics, LLC (2)
1940 E Mariposa Ave, El Segundo, CA
90245
Tel.: (855) 444-1438
Web Site: https://pcmlogisticsllc.com
Transportation Services
N.A.I.C.S.: 488999
Daniel Reid (Mgr-Credit Card Ops)

PCMG Inc. (2)
13755 Sunrise Valley Dr Ste 750, Herndon,
VA 20171
Tel.: (703) 594-8100
Web Site: https://www.pcmg.com
Electronic Product Marketing Services
N.A.I.C.S.: 561422

TigerDirect, Inc. (2)
7795 W Flagner St Ste 35, Miami, FL
33144
Tel.: (305) 415-2200
Web Site: http://www.tigerdirect.com
Rev.: $37,300,000
Emp.: 500
Catalog & Mail-Order Houses
N.A.I.C.S.: 449210

Subsidiary (Domestic):

CompUSA Inc. (3)
7795 W Flagler St Ste 35, Miami, FL
33144-2367

Tel.: (305) 415-2199
Web Site: http://www.compusa.com
Sales Range: $125-149.9 Million
Computers, Computer Software & Com-
puter Accessories Retailer
N.A.I.C.S.: 449210

Tiger Corp. Direct, Inc. (3)
7795 W Flagler St Ste 35, Miami, FL 33144
Tel.: (919) 319-0600
Web Site: http://www.tigerdirect.com
Rev.: $7,800,000
Emp.: 40
Catalog & Mail-Order Houses
N.A.I.C.S.: 423620

Subsidiary (Domestic):

eCOST.com, Inc. (2)
200 N Sepulveda Blvd Ste 360, El Se-
gundo, CA 90245 (100%)
Tel.: (310) 658-5000
Web Site: http://www.ecost.com
Sales Range: $75-99.9 Million
Emp.: 93
Retailer of Discounted New, Close-Out &
Refurbished Brand-Name Merchandise
N.A.I.C.S.: 423620
Robert Rich (Pres)

Sada Systems, Inc. (1)
5250 Lankersham Blvd, North Hollywood,
CA 91601
Tel.: (818) 766-2400
Web Site: http://www.sadasystems.com
Sales Range: $1-9.9 Million
Emp.: 100
IT Consulting Services
N.A.I.C.S.: 541512
Tony Safoian (Pres & CEO)
Michael Higby (Sr Mgr-Bus Dev)
Narine Galstian (VP-Mktg)
Patrick Watson (VP-Mktg)
Brandon Woods (Sr Mgr-Bus Dev)
Annie Safoian (Co-Founder)
Matthew Lawrence (CFO)
Lisa Freeman (Dir-HR, Comm & Virgin Mo-
bile)
Orkideh Shahidi (Dir-People Ops)
Hovig Safoian (Co-Founder & CTO)
Joe Kosco (VP-Sls)
Tom Marek (Dir-Enterprise Solutions)
Mitesh Patel (Head-Svc Delivery-Microsoft
Practice)
Mark Haddad (VP-Microsoft Sls)
Dana Berg (COO)
Patrick Monaghan (Chief Legal Officer)

INSIGHT SELECT INCOME
FUND
200 Park Ave 7th Fl, New York, NY
10166 DE
INSI—(NYSE)
Rev.: $10,232,874
Assets: $214,259,498
Liabilities: $3,627,900
Net Worth: $210,631,598
Earnings: $8,518,770
Fiscal Year-end: 03/31/20
Investment Management Service
N.A.I.C.S.: 525990
Daniel Haff (Chief Compliance Offi-
cer)

INSMED INCORPORATED
700 US Hwy 202-206, Bridgewater,
NJ 08807
Tel.: (908) 977-9900 VA
Web Site: https://www.insmed.com
Year Founded: 1988
INSM—(NASDAQ)
Rev.: $305,208,000
Assets: $1,329,837,000
Liabilities: $1,661,760,000
Net Worth: ($331,923,000)
Earnings: ($749,567,000)
Emp.: 912
Fiscal Year-end: 12/31/23
Metabolic, Endocrine & Degenerative
Diseases Treatment Developer
N.A.I.C.S.: 325412
William H. Lewis (Chm, Pres & CEO)

S. Nicole Schaeffer (Chief People Strategy Officer)
Martina Flammer (Chief Medical Officer)
Michael Smith (Gen Counsel & Sr VP)
Eugene Sullivan (Chief Product Strategy Officer)
Roger Adsett (COO)
Drayton Wise (Chief Comml Officer)
Sara M. Bonstein (CFO & Principal Acctg Officer)

Subsidiaries:

Insmed Germany GmbH   (1)
The Squaire 12 Am Flughafen, 60549, Frankfurt am Main, Germany
Tel.: (49) 6105 708 3870
Web Site: http://insmed.com
Pharmaceutical Preparation Distr
N.A.I.C.S.: 424210

Insmed Netherlands B.V.   (1)
Stadsplateau 7, 3521 AZ, Utrecht, Netherlands
Tel.: (31) 203080754
Pharmaceutical Preparation Distr
N.A.I.C.S.: 424210

INSPERITY, INC.

19001 Crescent Springs Dr, Kingwood, TX 77339
Tel.: (832) 432-1773   DE
Web Site: https://www.insperity.com
Year Founded: 1986
NSP—(NYSE)
Rev.: $6,485,871,000
Assets: $2,119,659,000
Liabilities: $2,026,035,000
Net Worth: $93,624,000
Earnings: $171,382,000
Emp.: 4,400
Fiscal Year-end: 12/31/23
Personnel Management Services
N.A.I.C.S.: 541611
Paul J. Sarvadi (Co-Founder, Chm & CEO)
A. Steve Arizpe (Pres & COO)
Gregory R. Clouse (Sr VP)
Ross L. Astramecki (Sr VP-Sls)
Larry Shaffer (Sr VP-Mktg & Bus Dev)
JaNette Connell (Sr VP-Corp HR)
James D. Allison (CFO, Treas & Exec VP-Fin)

Subsidiaries:

Insperity Business Services, L.P.   (1)
19001 Crescent Springs Dr, Kingwood, TX 77339-3802   (99%)
Web Site: http://www.insperity.com
Human Resources & Business Consulting Services
N.A.I.C.S.: 541611

Subsidiary (Domestic):

Insperity Payroll Services, L.L.C.   (2)
19001 Crescent Springs Dr, Kingwood, TX 77339
Tel.: (281) 312-3397
Database Management Software Development Services
N.A.I.C.S.: 541511

Insperity Employment Screening, L.L.C   (1)
1300 Rollingbrook St, Baytown, TX 77521
Tel.: (281) 425-2300
Web Site: http://www.insperityscreening.com
Sales Range: $25-49.9 Million
Emp.: 50
Employment Placement Agencies Services
N.A.I.C.S.: 561311

Insperity Expense Management, Inc.   (1)
2211 Michelson Dr Ste 540, Irvine, CA 92612
Tel.: (949) 510-0776
Web Site: http://www.insperity.com

Administrative Management Consulting Services
N.A.I.C.S.: 541611

Insperity Time and Attendance   (1)
2990 Triverton Pike Dr, Madison, WI 53711
Tel.: (608) 836-9096
Web Site: http://www.galaxy-inc.com
Sales Range: $10-24.9 Million
Emp.: 3
Time & Attendance Software Mfr
N.A.I.C.S.: 513210

INSPIRATION LEAD CO., INC.

PO Box 487, Portland, OR 97207-0487
Tel.: (503) 281-8699   ID
ILDIA—(OTCIQ)
Metal Mining & Exploration Services
N.A.I.C.S.: 213114
Jack Rititus (Sec)

INSPIRATO INCORPORATED

1544 Wazee St, Denver, CO 80202
Tel.: (303) 586-7771   DE
Web Site: https://www.inspirato.com
Year Founded: 2020
ISPO—(NASDAQ)
Rev.: $345,530,000
Assets: $430,367,000
Liabilities: $505,357,000
Net Worth: ($74,990,000)
Earnings: ($24,057,000)
Emp.: 900
Fiscal Year-end: 12/31/22
Investment Services
N.A.I.C.S.: 523999
Brad Handler (Co-Founder)
Eric Grosse (CEO)

Subsidiaries:

Bayside Villas, LLC   (1)
1406 S Berthe Ave, Panama City, FL 32404
Tel.: (850) 374-5226
Web Site: https://www.baysidevillasfl.com
Interior Design Services
N.A.I.C.S.: 541410

Best of 52 LLC   (1)
1544 Wazee St, Denver, CO 80202
Tel.: (303) 586-7771
Travel Arrangement Services
N.A.I.C.S.: 561599

Faraway Land, LLC   (1)
5680 Hwy 6 Ste 214, Missouri City, TX 77459
Tel.: (832) 856-2430
Web Site: https://farawayinc.com
Real Estate Services
N.A.I.C.S.: 531390

Point Break Holdings LLC   (1)
304 S Jones Blvd Ste 5051, Las Vegas, NV 89701
Web Site: https://pointbreakholdings.com
Investment Management Service
N.A.I.C.S.: 523940

INSPIRE MEDICAL SYSTEMS, INC.

5500 Wayzata Blvd Ste 1600, Golden Valley, MN 55416   DE
Web Site:
   https://www.inspiresleep.com
Year Founded: 2007
INSP—(NYSE)
Rev.: $624,799,000
Assets: $676,811,000
Liabilities: $104,297,000
Net Worth: $572,514,000
Earnings: ($21,153,000)
Emp.: 1,011
Fiscal Year-end: 12/31/23
Biotechnology Research & Development Services
N.A.I.C.S.: 541714
Timothy P. Herbert (Founder, Chm, Pres & CEO)
Richard Buchholz (CFO)
Randy Ban (Chief Comml Officer)

Steve Jandrich (VP-HR)
Kathy Sherwood (Sr VP-Market Access-Global)
Martin Abrams (VP-Mktg & Customer Experience)
Ivan Lubogo (Sr VP-Sls)
Bryan Phillips (Chief Compliance Officer, Gen Counsel, Sec & Sr VP)
Charisse Y. Sparks (Chief Medical Officer)
Carlton Weatherby (Chief Strategy Officer)

INSPIRE VETERINARY PARTNERS, INC.

780 Lynnhaven Pkwy Ste 400, Virginia Beach, VA 23452
Tel.: (757) 734-5464   NV
Web Site: https://www.inspirevet.com
Year Founded: 2020
IVP—(NASDAQ)
Rev.: $9,834,778
Assets: $20,185,695
Liabilities: $25,321,176
Net Worth: ($5,135,481)
Earnings: ($4,911,926)
Fiscal Year-end: 12/31/22
Veterinary Care Services
N.A.I.C.S.: 541940
Alexandra Quatri (VP-Medical Ops)
Richard Paul Frank (CFO)
Kimball Carr (Chm, Pres & CEO)
Charles Stith Keiser (Vice Chm, COO & Dir)
Zander Carraway (Dir-Acquisitions)
Lynley Kees (VP-Human Resources)
Lauren Silva (Sr Mgr-Hospital Partnerships)
Morgan Wood (CEO & Office Mgr)
Debbe Bastian (Controller-Finance)

INSPIRED ENTERTAINMENT INC

250 W 57th St Ste 415, New York, NY 10107
Tel.: (646) 565-3861   DE
Web Site: https://www.inseinc.com
Year Founded: 2014
INSE—(NASDAQ)
Rev.: $323,000,000
Assets: $340,900,000
Liabilities: $418,900,000
Net Worth: ($78,000,000)
Earnings: $7,600,000
Emp.: 1,700
Fiscal Year-end: 12/31/23
Investment Services
N.A.I.C.S.: 523999
A. Lorne Weil (Exec Chm)
Brooks H. Pierce (Pres & CEO)
Steven Collett (Chief Product Officer)
Lorna Evans (VP-People & Organisational Dev)
Claire Osborne (VP-Interactive)
Colleen Stanton Kakavetsis (VP-Mktg)
Ian Freeman (Chief Comml Officer-Virtuals)
Lee Gregory (Chief Comml Officer-Gaming)
Simona Camilleri (Gen Counsel)

Subsidiaries:

Fun House Leisure Limited   (1)
Unit S40 Wood Lane, Hastingwood Industrial Park Erdington, Birmingham, B24 9QR, West Midlands, United Kingdom
Tel.: (44) 1212701221
Web Site: http://www.funhouse-leisure.com
Vending Machine Operating Services
N.A.I.C.S.: 445132
Nassir Ghanchi (CEO)

Inspired Gaming (Gibraltar) Limited   (1)
4 Pitmans Alley, Gibraltar, Gibraltar
Tel.: (350) 20077616

Gaming Software Services
N.A.I.C.S.: 513210

Inspired Gaming (Italy) Limited   (1)
Via Fabio Massimo 72, 00192, Rome, Italy
Tel.: (39) 0695550550
Software Development Services
N.A.I.C.S.: 513210

Inspired Gaming Group Limited   (1)
First Floor 107 Station Street, Burton-on-Trent, DE14 1SZ, Staffordshire, United Kingdom
Tel.: (44) 1283512777
Electronic Gaming Terminal Mfr & Software Publisher
N.A.I.C.S.: 334111
Daniel B. Silvers (Chief Strategy Officer & Exec VP)

Subsidiary (Domestic):

Inspired Gaming (UK) Limited   (2)
First Floor 107 Station Street, Burton-on-Trent, DE14 1SZ, Staffordshire, United Kingdom
Tel.: (44) 1283512777
Web Site: http://www.inseinc.com
Amusement Arcades Services
N.A.I.C.S.: 713120

Inspired Technology UK Limited   (1)
Technology House 2 Lissadel Street Salford, Manchester, M6 6AP, United Kingdom
Tel.: (44) 1612782454
Web Site: http://www.inspire-tech.net
Software Development Services
N.A.I.C.S.: 513210

INSTALLED BUILDING PRODUCTS, INC.

495 S High St Ste 50, Columbus, OH 43215
Tel.: (614) 221-3399   DE
Web Site:
   https://www.installedbuildingproducts.com
Year Founded: 1977
IBP—(NYSE)
Rev.: $2,669,844,000
Assets: $1,778,932,000
Liabilities: $1,285,433,000
Net Worth: $493,499,000
Earnings: $223,428,000
Emp.: 10,300
Fiscal Year-end: 12/31/22
Residential Insulation Installer
N.A.I.C.S.: 238310
Todd R. Fry (Chief Acctg Officer & Treas)
Michael T. Miller (CFO & Exec VP-Fin)
Shelley A. McBride (Gen Counsel & Sec)
Jeffrey W. Edwards (Chm & CEO)
W. Jeffrey Hire (Pres-External Affairs)
R. Scott Jenkins (Reg Pres)
William W. Jenkins (Sr VP-Pur & Supply Chain)
Matthew J. Momper (Reg Pres)
Warren W. Pearce (Reg Pres)
Randall S. Williamson (Reg Pres)
Jason R. Niswonger (Chief Admin & Sustainability Officer)
Brad A. Wheeler (COO)

Subsidiaries:

5 Star Building Products LLC   (1)
944 N 1200 W, Orem, UT 84057
Tel.: (801) 231-5562
Web Site:
   https://www.fivestarbuildingproducts.com
Garage Door Repair & Insulation Services
N.A.I.C.S.: 238350

A+ Insulation of Kansas City, LLC   (1)
14324 W 96th Ter, Lenexa, KS 66215
Tel.: (913) 281-2250
Web Site:
   https://www.insulatekansascity.com
Building Insulation Services
N.A.I.C.S.: 238290

Installed Building Products, Inc.—(Continued)

ABS Coastal Insulating Company, LLC (1)
600 11th Ave S, Myrtle Beach, SC 29577
Tel.: (843) 353-1502
Web Site: https://www.abscoastal.com
Commercial & Building Insulation Services
N.A.I.C.S.: 238310

ABS Insulating Company, Inc. (1)
1077 Van Buren Ave, Indian Trail, NC 28079
Tel.: (704) 821-4343
Web Site: https://absinsulating.com
Commercial & Building Insulation Services
N.A.I.C.S.: 238310

Accurate Insulation LLC (1)
15121 Marlboro Pike, Upper Marlboro, MD 20772
Tel.: (240) 303-2401
Web Site:
https://www.accurateinsulation.com
Emp.: 300
Building Insulation Services
N.A.I.C.S.: 238310

Advanced Fiber, LLC (1)
100 Crossroads Blvd, Bucyrus, OH 44820
Tel.: (419) 562-1337
Web Site: https://www.advanced-fiber.com
Cellulose Industrial Fiber Products Mfr
N.A.I.C.S.: 325220

All Construction Services, LLC (1)
945 Industrial Pkwy N, Brunswick, OH 44212
Tel.: (330) 220-6666
Web Site:
https://www.allconstructionohio.com
Building Insulation Services
N.A.I.C.S.: 238290

All in One & Moore Building Systems, LLC (1)
350 Worcester St, West Boylston, MA 01583
Tel.: (508) 719-8781
Web Site:
https://www.allinonemooreinsulation.com
Building Insulation Services
N.A.I.C.S.: 238290

Alpha Insulation & Water Proofing Company (1)
670 Village Trce Bldg 19-A, Marietta, GA 30067
Tel.: (678) 325-2960
Web Site: https://www.alphaiwp.com
Commercial Insulation Services
N.A.I.C.S.: 238390

Alpha Insulation & Water Proofing Inc (1)
1649 Universal City Blvd, Universal City, TX 78148
Tel.: (210) 907-8630
Building Insulation Services
N.A.I.C.S.: 238290

Alpine Insulation Co, Inc. (1)
1941 Ashland Ave, Sheboygan, WI 53081
Tel.: (920) 458-8188
Web Site: https://www.alpineinsulation.com
Sales Range: $1-9.9 Million
Emp.: 100
Drywall & Insulation Contractors
N.A.I.C.S.: 238310

Anchor Insulation Co., Inc. (1)
435 Narragansett Park Dr, Pawtucket, RI 02861
Tel.: (401) 438-6720
Web Site: http://www.anchorinsulation.com
Rev.: $10,000,000
Emp.: 70
Drywall & Insulation Contractors
N.A.I.C.S.: 238310
Gregory A. Fiske (Pres)
David Oberg (CFO & Controller)

Apple Valley Insulation, a BDI Company, Inc. (1)
17525 Catalpa St Ste 109, Hesperia, CA 92345
Tel.: (760) 813-5583
Web Site:
https://www.applevalleyinsulation.com
Sales Range: $1-9.9 Million
Drywall & Insulation Contractors
N.A.I.C.S.: 238310

Arctic Express Insulation LLC (1)
3802 Apollo Rd, Corpus Christi, TX 78413
Tel.: (361) 887-2099
Residential/Commercial insulation Installation
N.A.I.C.S.: 238310

B-Organized Insulation, LLC (1)
6051-E Lakeview Rd, Charlotte, NC 28269
Web Site:
https://www.borganizedinsulation.net
Building Insulation Services
N.A.I.C.S.: 238290

BDI Insulation of Idaho Falls, Inc. (1)
1460 Commerce Way Bldg A, Idaho Falls, ID 83401
Tel.: (986) 497-5586
Web Site: https://www.bdiidahofalls.com
Insulation Installation Services
N.A.I.C.S.: 238310

BDI Insulation of Salt Lake, LLC (1)
2507 S 300 W Unit B, Salt Lake City, UT 84115
Tel.: (801) 485-0391
Web Site: https://www.bdiidahofalls.com
Insulation Installation Services
N.A.I.C.S.: 238310

Baytherm Insulation, LLC (1)
3370 Bay Rdg Ct, Oneida, WI 54155
Tel.: (920) 347-8540
Web Site:
https://www.baytherminsulation.com
Building Insulation Services
N.A.I.C.S.: 238310

Big City Insulation of Idaho, Inc. (1)
1314 Shilo Dr, Nampa, ID 83687
Tel.: (986) 249-5812
Web Site:
https://www.bigcityinsulationidaho.com
Insulation Installation Services
N.A.I.C.S.: 238310

Big City Insulation, Inc. (1)
1140 S 1900 E Unit 2, Washington, UT 84780
Tel.: (435) 275-2430
Web Site:
https://www.bigcityinsulationutah.com
Insulation Installation Services
N.A.I.C.S.: 238310

Broken Drum Insulation Visalia, Inc. (1)
751 N Miller Park St, Visalia, CA 93291
Tel.: (559) 372-0028
Web Site: https://www.bdivisalia.com
Drywall & Insulation Contractors
N.A.I.C.S.: 238310

Broken Drum of Bakersfield, Inc. (1)
34779 Lencioni Ave, Bakersfield, CA 93308
Tel.: (661) 744-1289
Web Site: https://www.bdiinsulation.com
Insulation Installation Services
N.A.I.C.S.: 238310

Builders Installed Products of Vermont, LLC (1)
51 Industrial Park Dr, Westmoreland, NH 03467-4430
Tel.: (603) 607-6691
Web Site:
https://www.buildersinstalledproducts
vt.com
Emp.: 70
Building Insulation Services
N.A.I.C.S.: 238290

Building Materials Finance, Inc. (1)
136 Tivoli St, Albany, NY 12207
Tel.: (518) 434-9657
Building Materials Distr
N.A.I.C.S.: 423990

C.Q. Insulation, Inc. (1)
1408 N Westshore Blvd Ste 500, Tampa, FL 33607
Tel.: (813) 635-9103
Web Site: https://www.cqinsulation.com
Insulation Installation Services
N.A.I.C.S.: 238310
Matt Winn (Mng Dir)
Thomas Fluharty (Mng Dir)
Jamie Keyes (Dir-Support)

CFI Insulation, Inc. (1)

908 Ault Rd, Knoxville, TN 37914
Tel.: (865) 588-4464
Web Site: http://www.cfiinsulation.com
Rev.: $2,800,000
Emp.: 34
Drywall & Insulation Contractors
N.A.I.C.S.: 238310
Chris Davenport (Project Mgr)
Greg Greene (Mgr-Ops)

CLS Insulation, LLC (1)
2915 E Randol Mill Rd, Arlington, TX 76011
Tel.: (945) 910-9907
Web Site: https://www.clsinsulation.com
Commercial Insulation Services
N.A.I.C.S.: 238390

Carolina Management, Inc. (1)
3501 Integrity Dr, Garner, NC 27529-6203
Tel.: (919) 662-9050
Web Site: http://www.carolinaglass.com
Glass & Glazing Installation Contractors
N.A.I.C.S.: 238150
Mike Wilkins (Founder & Branch Mgr)
Mike House (Mgr-Warehouse & Pur)

Central Aluminum Supply Corp. (1)
115 Muirhead Ave, Trenton, NJ 08638
Tel.: (609) 393-2222
Web Site:
http://www.centralaluminumsupply.com
Sales Range: $1-9.9 Million
Emp.: 15
Building Finishing Contractors
N.A.I.C.S.: 238390
Karen Sanger (Mgr)

Columbia Shelving & Mirror Co, Inc. (1)
1211 Oakcrest Dr, Columbia, SC 29223
Tel.: (803) 227-4669
Web Site:
https://www.columbiashelvingandmir
ror.com
Trade Contractor; Home Improvement Distr
N.A.I.C.S.: 238990

Combee Insulation Company, Inc. (1)
3802 N Combee Rd, Lakeland, FL 33805
Tel.: (863) 682-5783
Web Site: http://www.combeeinsulation.com
Sales Range: $1-9.9 Million
Emp.: 50
Drywall/Insulating Contractor
N.A.I.C.S.: 238310
Iva Combee (Controller)

Cornhusker Insulation, Inc. (1)
2201 River Road Dr, Waterloo, NE 68069
Tel.: (531) 319-2533
Web Site:
https://www.cornhuskerinsulation.com
Building Insulation Services
N.A.I.C.S.: 238310

Custom Glass & Doors, Inc. (1)
430 Fairmont Dr, Norcross, GA 30071-2401
Tel.: (770) 849-9520
Sales Range: $1-9.9 Million
Emp.: 49
Glass Products Mfr
N.A.I.C.S.: 327215
Fran Lash (Acct Mgr)

Custom Glass Atlanta, Inc. (1)
7040 Jonesboro Rd, Morrow, GA 30260
Tel.: (770) 960-9622
Web Site:
https://www.customglassatlanta.com
Sales Range: $10-24.9 Million
Emp.: 50
Bathroom & Custom Glass Installation Services
N.A.I.C.S.: 238150

Affiliate (Domestic):

Atlanta Commercial Glazing Inc. (2)
116 Rock Quarry Rd, Stockbridge, GA 30281
Tel.: (678) 565-5040
Web Site: https://www.atlantacommercialgla
zing.com
Commercial Glass & Glazing Services
N.A.I.C.S.: 238150
Mike Mitchell (Pres)

Eastern Contractor Services, Limited Liability Company (1)

121 Bartley Flanders Rd, Flanders, NJ 07836
Tel.: (862) 866-5723
Web Site: https://www.easterninsulation.com
Emp.: 135
Insulation Installation Services
N.A.I.C.S.: 238310
Todd Sawyer (Owner & CEO)

Ecologic Energy Solutions, LLC (1)
48 Union St Ste 1A, Stamford, CT 06906
Tel.: (203) 889-9559
Web Site: https://www.ecologices.com
Building Insulation Services
N.A.I.C.S.: 238290

Edwards/Mooney & Moses, LLC (1)
1320 McKinley Ave Ste B, Columbus, OH 43222
Tel.: (614) 321-5984
Web Site: https://www.edwardsmooneyand
moses.com
Building Insulation Services
N.A.I.C.S.: 238290

Expert Insulation of Minnesota, LLC (1)
6894 10th Ave SW, Rochester, MN 55902
Tel.: (507) 923-2097
Web Site: https://www.expertinsulation.com
Residential, Commercial & Agriculture Insulation Services
N.A.I.C.S.: 423330
Clay Hazelman (Production Mgr)
Lucas Hines (Branch Mgr)
Chris Fryxell (Production Mgr)

FiberClass Insulation, LLC (1)
50370 Dennis Ct, Wixom, MI 48393
Tel.: (248) 669-0660
Web Site: https://www.fiberclass.net
Insulation Products & Installation Services
N.A.I.C.S.: 238390

General Ceiling & Partitions, Inc. (1)
1435 Paonia St, Colorado Springs, CO 80915
Tel.: (719) 574-6450
Sales Range: $1-9.9 Million
Emp.: 50
Drywall & Insulation Contractors
N.A.I.C.S.: 238310
Brian Pring (Pres)

Gold Star Insulation LP (1)
210 N 10th St, Sacramento, CA 95811
Tel.: (916) 526-1321
Web Site:
https://www.goldstarinsulation.com
Emp.: 45
Building Insulation Services
N.A.I.C.S.: 238310

Gulf Coast Insulation LLC (1)
107 Bulldog Rd, Freeport, FL 32439
Tel.: (850) 307-5660
Web Site:
https://www.gulfcoastinsulation.com
Residential Building Construction Services
N.A.I.C.S.: 236118

Hinkle Insulation & Drywall Company, Incorporated (1)
2013 Centimeter Cir Ste B, Austin, TX 78758
Tel.: (737) 345-0326
Web Site: https://www.hinkleinsulation.com
Building Insulation Services
N.A.I.C.S.: 238310

IBP Asset, LLC (1)
495 S High St Ste 50, Columbus, OH 43215
Tel.: (614) 221-3399
Building Material Transportation Services
N.A.I.C.S.: 484110

IBP Holdings, LLC (1)
3010 Lyndon B Johnson Fwy Ste 715, Dallas, TX 75234
Tel.: (614) 221-3241
Web Site: https://www.ibpholdings.com
Holding Company
N.A.I.C.S.: 551114

Installed Building Products - Panhandle, LLC (1)
209 Massachusetts Ave, Pensacola, FL 32505
Tel.: (850) 400-6291
Web Site: https://www.ibppanhandle.com
Construction Equipment Mfr

N.A.I.C.S.: 333120

Installed Building Products - Portland, LLC (1)
2738 N Hayden Is Dr, Portland, OR 97217
Tel.: (503) 608-7878
Web Site: https://www.ibpportland.com
Building Insulation Services
N.A.I.C.S.: 238310

Installed Building Products of Fort Myers, LLC (1)
5641 Zip Dr, Fort Myers, FL 33905
Tel.: (239) 944-9958
Web Site: https://www.ibpftmyers.com
Construction Equipment Mfr
N.A.I.C.S.: 333120

Installed Building Products of Jacksonville, LLC (1)
9009 Regency Square Blvd, Jacksonville, FL 32211
Tel.: (904) 870-8376
Web Site: https://www.ibpjacksonville.com
Construction Equipment Mfr
N.A.I.C.S.: 333120

Installed Building Products of Maine, LLC (1)
84C Warren Ave, Westbrook, ME 04092
Tel.: (207) 797-8887
Web Site: https://ne-spray.com
Insulation Services
N.A.I.C.S.: 238310

Installed Building Products of Miami, LLC (1)
12605 NW 115th Ave Units B-107/108, Medley, FL 33178
Tel.: (305) 982-7952
Web Site: https://www.ibpmiami.com
Construction Equipment Mfr
N.A.I.C.S.: 333120

Installed Building Products of Tampa, LLC (1)
1909 US Hwy 301 Ste 160, Tampa, FL 33637
Tel.: (813) 291-4064
Web Site: https://www.ibptampa.com
Construction Equipment Mfr
N.A.I.C.S.: 333120

Installed Building Products of West Palm, LLC (1)
377 N Cleary Rd Ste 1, West Palm Beach, FL 33414
Tel.: (561) 292-0015
Web Site: https://www.ibpwestpalm.com
Construction Equipment Mfr
N.A.I.C.S.: 333120

Installed Building Products, LLC (1)
2431 W Main St, Fort Wayne, IN 46808
Tel.: (260) 432-7543
Web Site: https://www.installedbuildingproducts.com
Building Insulation Services
N.A.I.C.S.: 238310

Installed Building Solutions II, LLC (1)
21025 Edmonton Ave, Farmington, MN 55024
Tel.: (651) 968-1017
Web Site: https://www.installbuild.com
Building Insulation Services
N.A.I.C.S.: 238310

InsulVail, LLC (1)
147 Airpark Dr Unit 1A, Gypsum, CO 81637
Tel.: (970) 609-3321
Web Site: https://www.insulvail.com
Building Insulation Services
N.A.I.C.S.: 238310

Insulation Contractors Inc. (1)
22706 58th Pl S, Kent, WA 98032
Tel.: (253) 395-1895
Web Site: http://www.magellaninsulation.com
Insulation, Buildings
N.A.I.C.S.: 238310
Gary Trauter (Co-Founder & Pres)
Fletcher Vinson (Co-Founder)
Chantha Uch (Controller)

Insulation Wholesale Supply, LLC (1)
34779 Lencioni Ave, Bakersfield, CA 93308

Angela Genal ...
Tel.: (661) 744-3129
Web Site: https://www.insulationwholesalesupply.com
Insulation Material Distr
N.A.I.C.S.: 423330

Kern Door Company (1)
34779 Lencioni Ave, Bakersfield, CA 93380
Tel.: (661) 401-7730
Web Site: https://www.kerndoor.com
Sales Range: $1-9.9 Million
Emp.: 15
Door Mfr
N.A.I.C.S.: 321911

LKS Transportation, LLC (1)
495 S High St Ste 50, Columbus, OH 43215
Tel.: (614) 221-3320
Building Material Transportation Services
N.A.I.C.S.: 484110

Lakeside Insulation, LLC (1)
770 Industrial Dr Unit A, Cary, IL 60013
Web Site: https://www.thermaseallakeside.com
Building Insulation Services
N.A.I.C.S.: 238310

Layman Brothers Insulation, LLC (1)
2409 New Dorset Ter, Powhatan, VA 23139
Tel.: (804) 598-8640
Web Site: https://laymanbros.com
Building Insulation Services
N.A.I.C.S.: 238290

Lynch Insulation of Montana, LLC (1)
7145 US Hwy 10 W, Missoula, MT 59808
Tel.: (406) 728-6785
Web Site: https://lynchinsulation.com
Fiberglass Insulation & Mineral Wool Mfr
N.A.I.C.S.: 327993

M & D Insulation, LLC (1)
330 Weaver Rd Ste 300, Florence, KY 41042
Tel.: (859) 488-2964
Web Site: https://www.mdinsulation.com
Building Insulation Services
N.A.I.C.S.: 238290

MIG Building Systems, LLC (1)
100 Ontario St, East Rochester, NY 14445
Tel.: (585) 651-0300
Web Site: https://www.mighome.com
Insulation Services
N.A.I.C.S.: 238390

Marv's Insulation, Inc. (1)
2790 E Lanark St, Meridian, ID 83642
Tel.: (208) 629-5936
Web Site: https://www.marvsinsulation.com
Building Insulation Services
N.A.I.C.S.: 238310

Metro Home Insulation, LLC (1)
5861 Queens Ave NE, Elk River, MN 55330
Tel.: (763) 726-8942
Web Site: https://www.metrohomeinsulate.com
Emp.: 57
Building Insulation & Waterproof Services
N.A.I.C.S.: 238310

Mid South Construction and Building Products, Inc. (1)
5355 Palmero Ct, Buford, GA 30518
Tel.: (770) 932-1247
Web Site: http://www.tcimidsouth.com
Emp.: 26
Building Insulation Services
N.A.I.C.S.: 238310

Nationwide Gutter, LLC (1)
4312 Reeder Dr Carrollton, Dallas, TX 75010
Tel.: (972) 241-2900
Web Site: http://www.nationwidegutter.com
Other Building Finishing Contractors
N.A.I.C.S.: 238390

Norkote of Washington, LLC (1)
2330 106th St SW, Everett, WA 98204
Tel.: (425) 212-3813
Web Site: https://www.norkote.com
Industrial Construction Services
N.A.I.C.S.: 236220

Northwest Insulation, LLC (1)

1615 Dundee Ave Unit I, Elgin, IL 60120
Tel.: (847) 695-9999
Web Site: https://www.northwestinsulation.net
Building Insulation Services
N.A.I.C.S.: 238310

OJ Insulation, L.P. (1)
2061 Aldergrove Ave, Escondido, CA 92029
Tel.: (323) 347-7665
Web Site: https://www.ojinc.com
Emp.: 34
Building Insulation Services
N.A.I.C.S.: 238310

Orr Industries of Pennsylvania, LLC (1)
835 Enterprise St, Dickson City, PA 18519
Tel.: (570) 382-3046
Web Site: https://www.orrindustries.com
Fiberglass Insulation & Mineral Wool Mfr
N.A.I.C.S.: 327993

PEG, LLC (1)
3975 Fair Ridge Dr Ste 400S, Fairfax, VA 22033
Tel.: (703) 934-2777
Web Site: https://www.pegenv.com
Engineering Consulting Services
N.A.I.C.S.: 541330
Joann Spence (Pres & CEO)
Josh Spence (VP)

Pacific Partners Insulation North, a BDI Company, LLC (1)
6405 172nd St NE Ste C, Arlington, WA 98223
Tel.: (564) 333-1188
Web Site: https://www.pacificpartnersinsulationnorth.com
Insulation Installation Services
N.A.I.C.S.: 238310

Pacific Partners Insulation South, a BDI Company, LLC (1)
5207 187th St E Bldg A, Tacoma, WA 98446
Tel.: (253) 256-1097
Web Site: https://www.pacificpartnersinsulationsouth.com
Insulation Installation Services
N.A.I.C.S.: 238310

Parker Insulation and Building Products, LLC (1)
2920 N Twin City Hwy, Nederland, TX 77627
Tel.: (409) 527-3190
Web Site: https://www.absolute-insulation.com
Door Installation Services
N.A.I.C.S.: 238350

Pisgah Insulation and Fireplaces of NC, LLC (1)
5120 Old Haywood Rd, Mills River, NC 28759
Tel.: (828) 786-3575
Web Site: https://pisgahinsulation.com
Fiberglass Insulation & Building Contracting Services
N.A.I.C.S.: 236220

Red Rock Insulation LLC (1)
6630 S Arroyo Springs St Ste 700, Las Vegas, NV 89113
Tel.: (702) 262-6933
Web Site: https://www.redrockinsulation.com
Sales Range: $1-9.9 Million
Emp.: 28
Drywall & Insulation Contractors
N.A.I.C.S.: 238310
Rebecca Merrihew (Pres)

Royals Commercial Services, Inc. (1)
212 Najoles Rd Ste A, Millersville, MD 21108-2650
Tel.: (410) 729-0405
Web Site: http://www.royalscommercialservices.com
Sales Range: $1-9.9 Million
Emp.: 25
Construction Services
N.A.I.C.S.: 236220

Sierra Insulation Contractors, Inc. (1)

120 S Wineville Ave, Ontario, CA 91761
Tel.: (909) 390-9944
Web Site: https://www.sierrainsulation.com
Sales Range: $1-9.9 Million
Emp.: 45
Plastering, Drywall, And Insulation, Nsk
N.A.I.C.S.: 238310

Southern Insulators, LLC (1)
78389 Hwy 1081, Covington, LA 70435
Tel.: (985) 867-3430
Web Site: https://www.southerninsulators.com
Building Insulation Services
N.A.I.C.S.: 238290

Spec 7 Insulation Co., LLC (1)
5945 Broadway St Unit C, Denver, CO 80216
Tel.: (303) 558-6786
Web Site: https://www.spec7insulation.com
Building Insulation Services
N.A.I.C.S.: 238310

Statewide Insulation, Inc. (1)
910 George St, 95054, Santa Clara, CA
Tel.: (831) 475-2205
Web Site: https://tricountyinsulation.com
Drywall & Insulation Contractors
N.A.I.C.S.: 238310
Marie Geiseke (Chm)

Storm Master Co., Inc. (1)
1860 Old Cuthbert Rd, Cherry Hill, NJ 08034
Tel.: (732) 521-4989
Sales Range: $1-9.9 Million
Emp.: 17
Building Finishing Contractors
N.A.I.C.S.: 238390
Joel Lunney (Pres)

Suburban Insulation, Inc. (1)
250 W Kensinger Dr Ste 600, Cranberry Township, PA 16066
Tel.: (724) 625-2257
Web Site: https://www.suburban-insulation.com
Emp.: 40
Building Insulation Services
N.A.I.C.S.: 238310

Superior Insulation Services, LLC (1)
264 Vauxhall St, New London, CT 06320
Tel.: (860) 238-3113
Web Site: https://superiorinsulationservices.com
Building Insulation Services
N.A.I.C.S.: 238290

Superior Insulation, LLC (1)
14410 Creosote Rd, Gulfport, MS 39503
Tel.: (228) 214-2303
Web Site: https://www.superiorinsulationms.com
Emp.: 20
Insulation Services
N.A.I.C.S.: 238390

TCI Contracting of Hilton Head, LLC (1)
1118 Honey Hill Rd, Hardeeville, SC 29927
Tel.: (843) 784-6536
Emp.: 23
Building Insulation Services
N.A.I.C.S.: 238290

Tci Contracting, LLC (1)
4080 Mcginnis Ferry Rd, Alpharetta, GA 30005
Tel.: (678) 990-5491
Web Site: http://www.tcicon.com
Rev.: $5,000,000
Emp.: 61
Drywall & Insulation Contractors
N.A.I.C.S.: 238310

Therm-Con, LLC (1)
730 Airport Rd, Chattanooga, TN 37421
Tel.: (423) 704-9029
Web Site: http://www.therm-con.com
Insulation & Complementary Building Products Mfr
N.A.I.C.S.: 423330

Thermal Control Insulation, LLC (1)
PO Box 1151, Frederick, MD 21702
Tel.: (301) 748-3741
Web Site: https://www.thermalcontrolinsulation.com
Building Insulation Services
N.A.I.C.S.: 238310
Leslie Bronstein (Owner)

Installed Building Products, Inc.—(Continued)

Tidewater Insulators, LLC (1)
5610B E Virginia Beach Blvd, Norfolk, VA 23502
Tel.: (757) 828-0023
Web Site:
https://www.tidewaterinsulators.com
Building Insulation Services
N.A.I.C.S.: 238290

Town Building Systems, LLC (1)
4083 Saunders Settlement Rd, Sanborn, NY 14132
Tel.: (716) 790-6986
Web Site:
https://www.townbuildingsystems.net
Building Insulation Services
N.A.I.C.S.: 238290

Trademark Roofing Company, Inc. (1)
PO Box 2759, Vacaville, CA 95687
Tel.: (707) 455-7663
Web Site:
https://www.trademarkroofingco.com
Roofing & Building Construction Services
N.A.I.C.S.: 238310

U.S. Insulation Corp. (1)
24 Andover Dr, West Hartford, CT 06110
Tel.: (860) 829-8881
Web Site: https://www.usinsulation.net
Building Insulation Services
N.A.I.C.S.: 238310

Water-Tite Company, LLC (1)
850 York St, Plymouth, MI 48170
Tel.: (734) 663-0600
Web Site: https://www.miwatertite.com
Waterproofing Contractor Services
N.A.I.C.S.: 313320

WeatherSeal Company, LLC (1)
1600 Quail Run, Charlottesville, VA 22911
Tel.: (434) 974-1818
Web Site:
https://www.weathersealinsulation.com
Fiberglass Insulation & Building Contracting Services
N.A.I.C.S.: 236220

WeatherSeal Insulation Co., LLC (1)
1600 Quail Run, Charlottesville, VA 22911-9053
Tel.: (434) 974-1818
Web Site:
http://www.weathersealinsulation.com
Drywall & Insulation Contractors
N.A.I.C.S.: 238310

Wilson Insulation Company, LLC (1)
1584 McCurdy Dr, Stone Mountain, GA 30083
Tel.: (770) 441-4798
Web Site: http://www.wilsoninsulation.com
Emp.: 30
Building Insulation Services
N.A.I.C.S.: 238310

INSTEEL INDUSTRIES, INC.
1373 Boggs Dr, Mount Airy, NC 27030
Tel.: (336) 786-2141   NC
Web Site: https://www.insteel.com
Year Founded: 1953
IIIN—(NYSE)
Rev.: $529,198,000
Assets: $422,552,000
Liabilities: $71,697,000
Net Worth: $350,855,000
Earnings: $19,305,000
Emp.: 929
Fiscal Year-end: 09/28/24
Steel Wire Reinforcing Products Mfr
N.A.I.C.S.: 331110
Howard Osler Woltz III (Chm, Pres & CEO)
Richard T. Wagner (COO & Sr VP)
James R. York (Sr VP-Sourcing & Logistics)
Elizabeth C. Southern (Chief Legal Officer, Sec & VP-Administration)
James F. Petelle (Chief Legal Officer, Sec & VP-Admin)
James F. Petelle (Chief Legal Officer, Sec & VP-Admin)

Subsidiaries:

Insteel Wire Products Company (1)
1373 Boggs Dr, Mount Airy, NC 27030-2145
Tel.: (336) 719-9000
Wire Product Mfr
N.A.I.C.S.: 332618
Howard Osler Woltz III (Pres)
Richard T. Wagner (VP & Gen Mgr)

Subsidiary (Domestic):

Ortiz Engineered Products, Inc. (2)
314 Main St Ste B, Sugarloaf, PA 18249-3832
Tel.: (570) 501-3780
Web Site: http://www.ortizengineered.com
Welded Steel Reinforcement Mats Design & Application
N.A.I.C.S.: 423510
Blaine Rampulla (VP-Engrg)

Strand-Tech Martin Incorporated (1)
258 Deming Way, Summerville, SC 29483
Web Site: http://www.strandtech.com
Strand & Wire Manufacturing
N.A.I.C.S.: 332618

INSTIL BIO, INC.
3963 Maple Ave Ste 350, Dallas, TX 75219
Tel.: (972) 499-3350   DE
Web Site: https://www.instilbio.com
Year Founded: 2018
TIL—(NASDAQ)
Rev.: $3,655,000
Assets: $482,128,000
Liabilities: $118,523,000
Net Worth: $363,605,000
Earnings: ($223,177,000)
Emp.: 80
Fiscal Year-end: 12/31/22
Biotechnology Research & Development Services
N.A.I.C.S.: 541714
Bronson Crouch (CEO & Chm)
Zachary Roberts (Chief Medical Officer)
Sandeep Laumas (CFO & Chief Bus Officer)

INSTRUCTIVISION, INC.
93 Edward Dr, Ringwood, NJ 07456
Tel.: (973) 575-9992
Year Founded: 1981
ISTC—(OTCIQ)
Educational Support Services
N.A.I.C.S.: 611710
Rosemary Middelmann (Pres)

INSULET CORPORATION
100 Nagog Park, Acton, MA 01720
Tel.: (978) 600-7000   DE
Web Site: https://www.insulet.com
Year Founded: 2000
PODD—(NASDAQ)
Rev.: $1,697,100,000
Assets: $2,588,200,000
Liabilities: $1,855,500,000
Net Worth: $732,700,000
Earnings: $206,300,000
Emp.: 3,000
Fiscal Year-end: 12/31/23
Insulin Infusion System Developer, Mfr & Marketer
N.A.I.C.S.: 339112
Deborah R. Gordon (VP-IR)
Curtis Kopf (Grp VP-Customer Experience)
Trang Ly (Sr VP & Dir-Medical)
Lauren Budden (Chief Acctg Officer, Grp VP & Controller)
James R. Hollingshead (Pres & CEO)
Dan Manea (Chief HR Officer & Sr VP)
Ana Maria Chadwick (CFO, Treas & Exec VP)

Angela Geryak Wiczek (Sr Dir-Comm)
Prem Singh (Sr VP-Global Ops)
Laetitia Cousin (Sr VP)

Subsidiaries:

Shelbourn Chemists, Inc. (1)
958 E 2nd St, Brooklyn, NY 11230
Tel.: (718) 438-9302
Sales Range: $25-49.9 Million
Emp.: 30
Pharmaceutical Product Whslr
N.A.I.C.S.: 456110

INSURAGUEST TECHNOLO-GIES, INC.
2725 E Parleys Way Ste 170, Salt Lake City, UT 84109
Tel.: (801) 560-4605
Web Site:
https://www.insuraguest.com
Year Founded: 2017
ISGI—(TSXV)
Assets: $77,396
Liabilities: $248,802
Net Worth: ($171,406)
Earnings: ($358,867)
Software Development Services
N.A.I.C.S.: 541511
Douglas Anderson (Chm & CEO)
Logan Anderson (CFO)
Charles James Cayias (Pres)
Tony Sansone (COO & VP-Fin)
Alexander Walker (Gen Counsel)

INTAPP, INC.
3101 Park Blvd, Palo Alto, CA 94306
Tel.: (650) 852-0400
Web Site: https://www.intapp.com
INTA—(NASDAQ)
Rev.: $430,523,000
Assets: $732,999,000
Liabilities: $329,761,000
Net Worth: $403,238,000
Earnings: ($32,021,000)
Emp.: 1,235
Fiscal Year-end: 06/30/24
Law Software & Services
N.A.I.C.S.: 513210
David H. Morton Jr. (CFO)
John Hall (CEO & Chm)
Dan Tacone (Pres & Chief Client Officer)
Don Coleman (COO)
Thad Jampol (Chief Product Officer)
Dan Harsell (Sr VP-Tech)
David H. Morton Jr. (CFO)
Costa Harbilas (Sr VP-Sls)
Kalyani Tandon (Chief Acctg Officer)
Michele Murgel (Chief People & Places Officer)
Scott Fitzgerald (CMO)
Ben Harrison (Co-Pres-Financial Svcs)
Mark Holman (Chief Strategy Officer & Pres-Accounting-Consulting)
Steve Todd (Gen Counsel & Sr VP)
Lokesh Seth (Co-Pres-Financial Svcs)
Karthik Srinivasan (Sr VP-Cloud)
Duane Rusten (Sr VP-Client Services)
Lavinia Calvert (Gen Mgr-Marketing-Bus Dev Solutions)
Nigel Riley (Gen Mgr-Risk-Compliance Solutions)
Christopher Kraft (Gen Mgr-Operations-Fin Solutions)
Alan McMillen (Gen Mgr-Collaboration-Content Solutions)
Eldean Ward (VP-Client Success-Support)
David Trone (Sr VP-IR)
Ali Robinson (Dir-Global Media Rels)

Subsidiaries:

The Frayman Group, Inc. (1)

128 Brighton Beach Ave 5th Fl Ste 400, Brooklyn, NY 11235
Tel.: (718) 648-7700
Web Site: http://www.fraymangroup.com
Sales Range: $1-9.9 Million
Emp.: 75
Risk Management Software & Services
N.A.I.C.S.: 541618
Yelena Chervinsky (VP-Risk Mgmt Consulting)

INTEGER HOLDINGS CORPORATION
5830 Granite Pkwy Ste 1150, Plano, TX 75024
Tel.: (214) 618-5243   DE
Web Site: https://www.integer.net
Year Founded: 1940
ITGR—(NYSE)
Rev.: $1,596,673,000
Assets: $2,942,653,000
Liabilities: $1,423,611,000
Net Worth: $1,519,042,000
Earnings: $90,650,000
Emp.: 10,500
Fiscal Year-end: 12/31/23
Holding Company; Implantable Medical Device Power Sources, Wet Tantalum Capacitors & Precision Engineered Components Mfr
N.A.I.C.S.: 551112
Joseph W. Dziedzic (Pres & CEO)
Kirk Thor (Chief HR Officer & Exec VP)
Tom P. Thomas (Chief Acctg Officer, VP & Controller)
Andrew Senn (Sr VP-Strategy, Business Development, and Investor Relations)
Diron Smith (CFO & Exec VP)
McAlister Marshall (Chief Compliance Officer, Chief Ethics Officer, Sec & Sr VP)
Payman Khales (Pres-Cardio & Vascular)
Margaret Carthy (Exec VP-Global Quality & Regulatory Affairs & Sr VP)
Jim Stephens (Pres-Cardiac Rhythm Mgmt & Neuromodulation)

Subsidiaries:

Aran Biomedical Teoranta Ltd. (1)
Coilleach Spiddal Co, Galway, H91 C2NF, Ireland
Tel.: (353) 91896900
Web Site: https://www.aranbiomedical.com
Medical Device Component Mfr & Distr
N.A.I.C.S.: 339113

Brivant Limited (1)
Parkmore West Business Park, Galway, Ireland
Tel.: (353) 91385037
Medical Instrument Mfr
N.A.I.C.S.: 339113

Greatbatch Ltd. (1)
10000 Wehrle Dr, Clarence, NY 14031
Tel.: (716) 759-5600
Web Site: https://greatbatchmedical.com
Design & Manufacture of Technologies used in Medical Devices & Procedures
N.A.I.C.S.: 339112

Subsidiary (Domestic):

Electochem Solutions, Inc. (2)
670 Paramount Dr, Raynham, MA 02767   (100%)
Tel.: (781) 830-5800
Web Site:
https://www.electrochemsolutions.com
Designer & Mfr of Customized Battery & Wireless Sensing Technology Solutions
N.A.I.C.S.: 335910
Jennifer M. Bolt (Pres)

Plant (Domestic):

Electrochem Solutions, Inc. - Beaverton Design & Development Center (3)

9305 SW Nimbus Ave, Beaverton, OR 97008
Tel.: (503) 693-7600
Storage Battery Mfr
N.A.I.C.S.: 335910

Plant (Domestic):

Greatbatch Ltd. - Plymouth Plant (2)
2300 Berkshire Ln N, Plymouth, MN 55441
Tel.: (763) 951-8200
Web Site:
https://www.greatbatchmedical.com
Sales Range: $25-49.9 Million
Emp.: 260
Venous Vessel Introducers Developer, Mfr & Supplier
N.A.I.C.S.: 339112

Subsidiary (Non-US):

Greatbatch Medical SA (2)
Bahnhofstrasse 15, Bienne, 2501, Biel, Switzerland
Tel.: (41) 32 358 0111
Web Site: https://www.integer.net
Sales Range: $50-74.9 Million
Orthopedic Instruments Developer & Mfr
N.A.I.C.S.: 339112

Subsidiary (Non-US):

Centro de Construccion de Cardioe-
stimuladores del Uruguay SA (3)
General Paz 1371, Montevideo, 11400, Uruguay
Tel.: (598) 26007629
Surgical & Medical Instrument Mfr
N.A.I.C.S.: 339112
Oscar DeOliveira (Gen Mgr)

Greatbatch Medical SAS (3)
4 Rue Louis et Renee Landanger ZI La Vendue, 52000, Chaumont, France
Tel.: (33) 325307777
Medical Devices & Components Mfr
N.A.I.C.S.: 339112

Subsidiary (Domestic):

Greatbatch-Globe Tool, Inc. (2)
730 24th Ave SE, Minneapolis, MN 55414 (88%)
Tel.: (612) 676-7200
Web Site:
http://www.greatbatchmedical.com
Sales Range: $125-149.9 Million
Emp.: 215
Mfr of Precision Metal Casings
N.A.I.C.S.: 332119

Greatbatch MCSO, S. de R.L. de C.V (1)
Blvd Hector Teran Teran No 20120 Parque Industrial Prologi, Ciudad Industrial, Tijuana, 22444, Baja California, Mexico
Tel.: (52) 6649734222
Surgical Instrument Mfr
N.A.I.C.S.: 339112

Lake Region Medical Holdings, Inc (1)
169 Callender Rd, Watertown, CT 06795-1627
Tel.: (860) 945-0601
Holding Company
N.A.I.C.S.: 551112
Clayton Parr (Mgr-Technical Program)

Lake Region Medical Limited (1)
Butlersland, New Ross, Ireland
Tel.: (353) 51440500
Medical Instrument Mfr
N.A.I.C.S.: 339113

Lake Region Medical Sdn. Bhd. (1)
No 91-B Lebuhraya Kampung Jawa 23 Y Electro-Mechanical, 11900, Bayan Lepas, Malaysia
Tel.: (60) 6048101800
Pharmaceutical Product Whslr
N.A.I.C.S.: 424210

Lake Region Medical, Inc. (1)
100 Fordham Rd Bldg C, Wilmington, MA 01887
Tel.: (978) 570-6900
Medical Device Mfr
N.A.I.C.S.: 339112

Subsidiary (Domestic):

American Technical Molding, Inc. (2)
2052 W 11th St, Upland, CA 91786-3509
Tel.: (909) 982-1025
Plastic Injection Molding
N.A.I.C.S.: 326199

Lake Region Manufacturing, Inc. (2)
1234 Lakeview Dr, Chaska, MN 55318
Tel.: (952) 361-6045
Medical Devices for Diagnostic Use Mfr
N.A.I.C.S.: 339112

Plant (Domestic):

Lake Region Medical - Salem (3)
200 S Yorkshire St, Salem, VA 24153
Tel.: (540) 389-7860
Tubes & Pipes Mfr
N.A.I.C.S.: 334419

Lake Region Medical - Trenton (3)
395 S Industrial Blvd, Trenton, GA 30752
Tel.: (706) 657-7700
Medical Instrument Mfr
N.A.I.C.S.: 339112

Subsidiary (Domestic):

Viant Collegeville, LLC (3)
200 W 7th Ave, Collegeville, PA 19426
Tel.: (610) 409-2322
Web Site: http://www.viantmedical.com
Medical Instrument Mfr
N.A.I.C.S.: 339112

Subsidiary (Non-US):

Lake Region Medical GmbH (2)
Staatsstrasse 5, 97773, Aura im Sinngrund, Germany
Tel.: (49) 93569810
Web Site: https://en.viant-aura.de
Tubes & Precision Wire Products Mfr
N.A.I.C.S.: 334419

Lake Region Medical Ltd (2)
Butlersland, New Ross, Y34 K825, Co Wexford, Ireland
Tel.: (353) 51440500
Web Site: http://www.integer.net
Medical Device Mfr
N.A.I.C.S.: 339112

Subsidiary (Domestic):

Spectrum Manufacturing, Inc. (2)
140 E Hintz Rd, Wheeling, IL 60090
Tel.: (847) 520-1553
Medical Instrument Mfr
N.A.I.C.S.: 339112

Subsidiary (Non-US):

Star Guide Limited (2)
Parkmore West Business Park, Oranmore, Galway, Ireland
Tel.: (353) 51 440500
Web Site: http://www.integer.net
Wire Product Mfr
N.A.I.C.S.: 332618

Venusa de Mexico, S.A. de C.V. (2)
1525-6 Hertz Street, Ciudad Juarez, 32470, Chihuahua, Mexico
Tel.: (52) 6561461900
Web Site: https://www.integer.net
Medical Instrument Mfr
N.A.I.C.S.: 339112

Subsidiary (Domestic):

Venusa, Ltd. (2)
6456 New Taylor Rd, Orchard Park, NY 14127
Tel.: (480) 272-4066
Web Site: https://beautybyvictoriaj.com
Medical Instrument Mfr
N.A.I.C.S.: 339112

MedSource Technologies, LLC (1)
200 W 7th Ave, Trappe, PA 19426
Tel.: (610) 409-2420
Surgical Instrument Mfr
N.A.I.C.S.: 339112

Portlyn, LLC (1)
200 W 7th Ave, Collegeville, PA 19426
Tel.: (610) 409-2225
Surgical Instrument Mfr
N.A.I.C.S.: 339112

INTEGRA LIFESCIENCES HOLDINGS CORPORATION

1100 Campus Rd, Princeton, NJ 08540
Tel.: (609) 275-0500 DE
Web Site: https://www.integralife.com
Year Founded: 1989
IART—(NASDAQ)
Rev.: $1,541,573,000
Assets: $3,781,988,000
Liabilities: $2,194,104,000
Net Worth: $1,587,884,000
Earnings: $67,741,000
Emp.: 3,946
Fiscal Year-end: 12/31/23
Holding Company; Medical Devices, Implants & Biomaterials Developer & Mfr
N.A.I.C.S.: 551112
Stuart M. Essig (Exec Chm)
Robert T. Davis Jr. (Pres-Orthopedics & Tissue Technologies-Global & Exec VP)
Judith E. O'Grady (VP-Regulatory Affairs-Global)
Andrea Caruso (VP-Bus Dev)
Kenneth E. Burhop (Chief Scientific Officer & VP)
Lisa Evoli (Chief HR Officer & Exec VP)
Jeffrey A. Mosebrook (Chief Acctg Officer & Sr VP-Fin)
Eric Schwartz (Chief Legal Officer, Sec & Exec VP)
Michael McBreen (Pres-Codman Specialty Surgical & Exec VP)
Steve Leonard (VP-Ops & Supply Chain-Global)
Lea Daniels Knight (CFO & Exec VP)
Stuart Hart (Chief Medical Officer)
Mark Jesser (Chief Digital Officer)
Gurpreet Kaur (CIO)
Susan Krause (Chief Quality Officer)
Harvinder Singh (Pres-Intl)
Jessica Smith (Chief Regulatory Officer)

Subsidiaries:

ACell, Inc. (1)
6640 Eli Whitney Dr Ste 200, Columbia, MD 21046
Web Site: http://www.acell.com
Rev.: $100,794,336
Assets: $43,397,322
Liabilities: $24,426,341
Net Worth: $18,970,981
Earnings: $1,448,710
Emp.: 400
Fiscal Year-end: 12/31/2019
Medical Product Mfr & Distr
N.A.I.C.S.: 339112

Acclarent, Inc. (1)
33 Technology Dr, Irvine, CA 92618
Tel.: (650) 687-5888
Web Site: http://www.acclarent.com
Sales Range: $10-24.9 Million
Emp.: 210
Ear, Nose & Throat Medical Device Mfr
N.A.I.C.S.: 339112

Ascension Orthopedics, Inc. (1)
8700 Cameron Rd Ste 100, Austin, TX 78754
Tel.: (512) 836-5001
Web Site: http://www.integralife.com
Sales Range: $25-49.9 Million
Emp.: 50
Orthopedic Product Mfr & Distr
N.A.I.C.S.: 423450

Ascension Orthopedics, Ltd. (1)
BioPark Broadwater Road, Welwyn Garden City, AL7 3AX, Herts, United Kingdom
Tel.: (44) 1763222505
Medical Devices & Biomaterials Mfr
N.A.I.C.S.: 339112

BioD,LLC (1)
7740A Trinity Rd Ste 107, Cordova, TN 38018
Tel.: (901) 417-7868

Web Site: http://www.biodlogics.com
Biological Product Mfr
N.A.I.C.S.: 325414
Tim Brahm (Chief Dev Officer)

CardioDyne, Inc. (1)
25901 Commercentre Dr, Lake Forest, CA 92630
Tel.: (949) 951-3800
Web Site: http://www.trimedyne.com
Lasers & Disposable Fiber Optic Mfr
N.A.I.C.S.: 334510

Derma Sciences, Inc. (1)
311 Enterprise Dr, Plainsboro, NJ 08536
Tel.: (609) 514-4744
Web Site: http://www.dermasciences.com
Wound Closure & Catheter Securement Skin Products Supplier & Mfr
N.A.I.C.S.: 339112

EndoSolutions, Inc. (1)
581 Davies Dr, York, PA 17402
Tel.: (800) 215-4245
Web Site: http://www.endosolutions.net
Surgical & Medical Instrument Mfr
N.A.I.C.S.: 339112

ILS Services Switzerland Ltd. (1)
Chemin des Aulx 18, 1228, Plan-les-Ouates, Switzerland
Tel.: (41) 227212311
Web Site: http://www.integralife.eu
Sales Range: $10-24.9 Million
Emp.: 6
Medical Devices Implants & Biomaterials Developer & Mfr
N.A.I.C.S.: 339112

Integra Burlington MA, Inc. (1)
22 Terry Ave, Burlington, MA 01803
Tel.: (781) 565-1401
Healthcare Equipment Distr
N.A.I.C.S.: 456199

Integra GmbH (1)
Borsigstrasse 11-15, 40880, Ratingen, Germany
Tel.: (49) 210255356200
Web Site: http://www.integralife.eu
Sales Range: $25-49.9 Million
Emp.: 150
Medical Instrument Mfr
N.A.I.C.S.: 339112

Integra LS (Benelux) NV (1)
Leuvensesteenweg 542, 1930, Zaventem, Belgium
Tel.: (32) 22574130
Sales Range: $25-49.9 Million
Emp.: 30
Medical Devices Implants & Biomaterials Developer & Mfr
N.A.I.C.S.: 339112

Integra LifeSciences (Shanghai) Co., Ltd. (1)
Tel.: (86) 2153860808
Web Site: https://www.integralife.com
Surgical Equipment Distr
N.A.I.C.S.: 423450
Eva Xu (Gen Mgr)

Integra LifeSciences Corporation (1)
1100 Campus Rd, Princeton, NJ 08540
Tel.: (609) 275-0500
Medical Devices Implants & Biomaterials Developer & Mfr
N.A.I.C.S.: 339112
Robert T. Davis Jr. (Pres-Orthopedics & Tissue Tech & Exec VP)

Integra LifeSciences Italy S.r.l. (1)
Centro Direzionale Milanofiori - Strada 6 - Pal N3 Rozzano, 20089, Milan, Italy
Tel.: (39) 025778921
Medical Device Mfr
N.A.I.C.S.: 339113
Roberto Galofaro (Mktg Mgr)

Integra LifeSciences Services (France) SAS (1)
Immeuble Sequoia II 97 allee Alexandre Borodine, Parc Technologique de la Porte des Alpes, 69800, Saint Priest, France
Tel.: (33) 437475900
Web Site: http://www.integralife.eu
Sales Range: $25-49.9 Million
Emp.: 130
Medical Devices Implants & Biomaterials Developer & Mfr

Integra LifeSciences Holdings
Corporation—(Continued)

N.A.I.C.S.: 339112
John B. Henneman III *(CFO & Exec VP-Fin & Admin)*

Integra Luxtec, Inc. **(1)**
99 Hardwell St, West Boylston, MA 01583
Tel.: (508) 835-9700
Web Site: http://www.integralife.com
Emp.: 143
Medical Lighting & Visualization Systems
N.A.I.C.S.: 339112

Integra MicroFrance SAS **(1)**
Le Pavillon, Bourbon l'Archambault, 03160,
Saint-Aubin-le-Monial, France
Tel.: (33) 470679800
Web Site: https://www.microfrance.fr
Healthcare Equipment Distr
N.A.I.C.S.: 456199

Integra NeuroSciences Limited **(1)**
Kingsgate House Newbury Road, Andover,
SP10 4DU, Hampshire, United Kingdom
Tel.: (44) 1264345780
Web Site: http://www.integrals.com
Sales Range: $25-49.9 Million
Emp.: 100
Medical Instrument Mfr
N.A.I.C.S.: 339112

Integra OrthoBiologics, Inc. **(1)**
2 Goodyear, Irvine, CA 92618-2054
Tel.: (949) 595-8710
Web Site: http://www.integralife.com
Sales Range: $25-49.9 Million
Emp.: 143
Orthobiologics Developer, Mfr & Marketer
N.A.I.C.S.: 325414

Integra York PA, Inc. **(1)**
589 Davies Dr, York, PA 17402-8630
Tel.: (717) 840-9335
Web Site: http://www.miltex.com
Sales Range: $50-74.9 Million
Emp.: 250
Hand-Held Surgical Instruments Mfr & Supplier
N.A.I.C.S.: 423450

Jarit GmbH **(1)**
Langes Gewand 9, 78604, Rietheim-
Weilheim, Germany
Tel.: (49) 746196600
Medical Devices Implants & Biomaterials
Developer & Mfr
N.A.I.C.S.: 339112

Medtronic Xomed, Inc. **(1)**
4102 Southpoint Blvd, Jacksonville, FL
32216
Tel.: (004) 206 0600
Web Site: https://www.medtronic.com
Emp.: 724
Surgical Instrument Mfr
N.A.I.C.S.: 339112

Newdeal SAS **(1)**
Immeuble 2 97 Alexander Borodin, ave Alexander Borodine, 69800, Saint Priest,
France
Tel.: (33) 437475151
Web Site: http://www.newdeal.info
Sales Range: $10-24.9 Million
Emp.: 35
Orthopaedic Solutions for Feet & Ankles
N.A.I.C.S.: 339112

Precise Dental Internacional, S.A. de **(1)**
C.V.
Calle Eugenio Cuzin 925, Belenes Norte
Guadalajara, 45150, Zapopan, Jalisco,
Mexico
Tel.: (52) 3336563536
Web Site: http://www.integralifescience.com
Surgical & Medical Instrument Distr
N.A.I.C.S.: 423450

Rebound Therapeutics
Corporation **(1)**
13900 Alton Pkwy Ste 120, Irvine, CA
92618
Tel.: (949) 305-8111
Web Site: http://www.reboundtx.com
Medical Device Mfr
N.A.I.C.S.: 339112

TGX Medical Systems, LLC **(1)**

12220 N Meridian St Ste 175, Carmel, IN
46032
Tel.: (317) 575-0300
Web Site: http://www.tgxmedical.com
Surgical & Medical Instrument Mfr
N.A.I.C.S.: 339112
Chris Sogard *(Pres)*
Michael Mancebo *(Sr VP-Sls)*
Melissa Achtien *(Controller)*
Jeff Haskett *(Dir-Product Dev)*

Tarsus Medical Inc. **(1)**
465 Fairchild Dr Ste 230, Menlo Park, CA
94043
Tel.: (650) 237-0070
Healthcare Equipment Distr
N.A.I.C.S.: 456199

Tei Biosciences Inc **(1)**
7 Elkins St, Boston, MA 02127
Tel.: (617) 268-1616
Web Site: http://www.teibio.com
Rev.: $7,800,000
Emp.: 65
Surgical & Medical Instrument Mfr
N.A.I.C.S.: 339112

INTEGRAL AD SCIENCE HOLDING CORP.
12 E 49th St Fl 20, New York, NY
10017
Tel.: (646) 278-4871   DE
Web Site:
     https://www.integralads.com
Year Founded: 2009
IAS—(NASDAQ)
Rev.: $408,348,000
Assets: $1,168,683,000
Liabilities: $360,467,000
Net Worth: $808,216,000
Earnings: $15,373,000
Emp.: 835
Fiscal Year-end: 12/31/22
Offices of Other Holding Companies
N.A.I.C.S.: 551112
Tania Secor *(CFO)*
Lisa Utzschneider *(CEO)*
Tom Sharma *(Chief Product Officer)*

INTEGRATED BIOPHARMA, INC.
225 Long Ave, Hillside, NJ 07205
Tel.: (973) 926-0816   DE
Web Site: https://ir.ibiopharma.com
INBP—(OTCQX)
Rev.: $50,317,000
Assets: $26,207,000
Liabilities: $6,969,000
Net Worth: $19,238,000
Earnings: $112,000
Emp.: 147
Fiscal Year-end: 06/30/24
Pharmaceutical Preparation Manufacturing
N.A.I.C.S.: 325412
Christina Kay *(Co-CEO)*
Dina L. Masi *(CFO & Sr VP)*
Riva Kay Sheppard *(Co-CEO)*

Subsidiaries:

AgroLabs, Inc. **(1)**
101 Clukey Dr, Harrington, DE
19952   **(100%)**
Tel.: (302) 566-6094
Web Site: https://www.agrolab.us
Sales Range: $10-24.9 Million
Emp.: 25
Mfr & Sales of Nutritional Products
N.A.I.C.S.: 456191

IHT Health Products, Inc. **(1)**
225 Long Ave Bldg 15, Hillside, NJ 07205
Tel.: (973) 926-0816
Web Site: http://www.ihthealthproducts.com
Sales Range: $150-199.9 Million
Emp.: 100
Sales & Distribution of Fine Chemicals &
Formulations for the Nutritional, Pharmaceutical, Food & Cosmetic Industries
N.A.I.C.S.: 424690

Manhattan Drug Company, Inc. **(1)**
225 Long Ave Bldg 15, Hillside, NJ 07205

Tel.: (973) 926-0816
Web Site: https://www.manhattandrug.com
Sales Range: $10-24.9 Million
Emp.: 45
Mfr of Vitamins, Nutritional Supplements &
Herbal Products
N.A.I.C.S.: 325412
Christina Kay *(VP)*

Vitamin Factory, Inc. **(1)**
225 Long Ave Bldg 15, Hillside, NJ
07205   **(100%)**
Tel.: (973) 926-0816
Web Site: http://www.vitafac.com
Sales Range: $50-74.9 Million
Emp.: 45
Sales of Nutritional Supplements
N.A.I.C.S.: 424210

INTEGRATED BUSINESS SYSTEMS & SERVICES, INC.
1601 Shop Rd Ste E, Columbia, SC
29201
Tel.: (803) 736-5595   SC
Web Site: https://www.ibss.net
Year Founded: 1990
IBSS—(OTCIQ)
Sales Range: $1-9.9 Million
Emp.: 28
Online Transaction Processing Tools
& Vertical Application Software Developer, Mfr & Marketer
N.A.I.C.S.: 513210

INTEGRATED CANNABIS SOLUTIONS, INC.
1300 N Florida Mango Rd Ste 30,
West Palm Beach, FL 33409
Tel.: (561) 235-2295   NV
Web Site: http://www.igpk.org
Year Founded: 1995
IGPK—(OTCIQ)
Assets: $10,000
Liabilities: $1,069,951
Net Worth: ($1,059,951)
Earnings: ($373,858)
Fiscal Year-end: 12/31/21
Farm Management Services
N.A.I.C.S.: 115116
Gene Caiazzo *(Chm, Pres, CEO,
CFO & Pres-Consolidated Apparel,
Inc)*

INTEGRATED ENERGY TRANSITION ACQUISITION CORP.
24 E Market St, West Chester, PA
19381   DE
Web Site:
     http://www.intenergyco.com
Year Founded: 2020
ETA'U—(NYSE)
Investment Services
N.A.I.C.S.: 523999
Christopher J. Close *(CFO)*
Narinder Singh *(Chief Strategy Officer)*
Richard W. Westerdale II *(Chm &
CEO)*

INTEGRATED ENVIRONMENTAL TECHNOLOGIES, LTD.
4235 Commerce St, Little River, SC
29566
Tel.: (843) 390-2500
Web Site: http://www.ietltd.net
Year Founded: 1999
IEVM—(OTCIQ)
Sales Range: Less than $1 Million
Emp.: 12
Innovative Technology Equipment Mfr
N.A.I.C.S.: 339999
David R. LaVance Jr. *(Chm, Pres &
CEO)*
Thomas S. Gifford *(CFO)*
Chad L. Crady *(VP-Sls & Ops-Oil &
Gas)*

INTEGRATED RAIL & RE-

SOURCES ACQUISITION CORP.
6100 SW Blvd Ste 320, Fort Worth,
TX 76109
Tel.: (817) 737-5885   DE
Year Founded: 2021
IRRX—(NYSE)
Rev.: $12,222,522
Assets: $238,025,021
Liabilities: $249,455,206
Net Worth: ($11,430,185)
Earnings: $9,584,028
Emp.: 3
Fiscal Year-end: 12/31/22
Investment Services
N.A.I.C.S.: 523999
Mark A. Michel *(Chm & CEO)*
Timothy J. Fisher *(Vice Chm, Pres &
CFO)*

INTEGRATED VENTURES, INC.
18385 Route 287, Tioga, PA 16946
Tel.: (215) 613-9898   NV
Web Site:
     https://www.integratedventures
     inc.com
Year Founded: 2011
INTV—(OTCQB)
Rev.: $5,863,935
Assets: $3,942,691
Liabilities: $3,683,142
Net Worth: $259,549
Earnings: ($11,524,357)
Emp.: 1
Fiscal Year-end: 06/30/24
Software Company; Acquiring,
Launching & Operating Companies In
The Cryptocurrency Sector
N.A.I.C.S.: 513210
Steve Rubakh *(Pres, CEO, CFO,
Principal Acctg Officer, Treas & Sec)*

INTEGRATED WELLNESS ACQUISITION CORP.
59 N Main St Ste 1, Florida, NY
10921
Tel.: (914) 618-4521   Ky
Web Site:
     https://integratedwellnesshold
     ings.com
Year Founded: 2021
WEL—(NYSE)
Rev.: $1,691,913
Assets: $119,794,791
Liabilitio: $123,312,212
Net Worth: ($3,517,421)
Earnings: $567,541
Emp.: 3
Fiscal Year-end: 12/31/22
Investment Services
N.A.I.C.S.: 523999
Suren Ajjarapu *(CEO)*
Matthew Malriat *(CFO)*
Binson Lau *(Chm)*

INTEL CORPORATION
2200 Mission College Blvd, Santa
Clara, CA 95054
Tel.: (408) 765-8080   DE
Web Site: https://www.intel.com
Year Founded: 1968
INTC—(NASDAQ)
Rev.: $54,228,000,000
Assets: $191,572,000,000
Liabilities: $81,607,000,000
Net Worth: $109,965,000,000
Earnings: $1,689,000,000
Emp.: 124,800
Fiscal Year-end: 12/30/23
Electronics & Semiconductors Mfr
N.A.I.C.S.: 334413
Karen Kahn *(Chief Comm Officer &
VP-Corp)*
Christopher Schell *(Chief Comml Officer, Exec VP & Gen Mgr-Comm,
Mktg, and Sls)*
David P. Flanagan *(Mng Dir & VP)*

Ramamurthy Sivakumar (Mng Dir)
Leslie S. Culbertson (Exec VP & Gen Mgr-Security)
Jacklyn A. Sturm (VP & Gen Mgr)
Matthew J. Adiletta (Dir)
Babak Sabi (VP & Gen Mgr)
Laura G. Crone (VP-Sales & Gen Mgr-Volatile Memory Solutions Grp)
Joshua M. Walden (Sr VP & Gen Mgr)
Xu Yang (Pres & VP)
Lorie Wigle (VP & Gen Mgr)
Steven T. Holmes (VP & Gen Mgr)
Peter C. Baker (Dir & VP)
Zane A. Ball (VP & Gen Mgr)
Koushik Banerjee (Dir & VP)
Jerry Rodolfo Bautista (VP & Gen Mgr-Communications)
Genevieve Bell (VP-Security)
Darren B. Bernhard (Dir & VP-Legal Department)
Morris Beton (VP & Gen Mgr)
Cheng Gang Bian (VP-Manufacturing-Operations)
Melton C. Bost (Dir & VP)
Wendell M. Brooks (Pres & Sr VP)
Peter K. Charvat (VP & Gen Mgr-Sort Mfg)
Li-Sheng Chen (VP-Sales)
Gaurang N. Choksi (Dir & VP)
Changhong Dai (Dir-Global & VP-Supply Chain-Global)
Albert D. Diaz (VP-Sales & Gen Mgr)
David M. Dixon (Dir-Product Development-Non,Volatile Memory Solutions Grp & VP)
Ellen Z. Doller (Dir-Operations-Non,Volatile Memory Solutions Grp & VP)
Ryszard Dyrga (VP & Gen Mgr)
Christin Eisenschmid (VP & Gen Mgr)
Ali Reza Farhang (Dir & VP)
Maxine Fassberg (VP & Gen Mgr)
Mohsen Fazlian (VP & Gen Mgr-Operations-Security)
Mark Friedman (Assoc Gen Counsel & VP-Legal Department)
Alison M. Gardyne (Dir-Labor Relations & VP-Human Resources)
Thomas M. Garrison (VP & Gen Mgr)
Raghupathy V. Giridhar (Dir-Volatile Memory Tech Dev & VP)
Rahul Goyal (Dir-Research & Development & VP-Technology)
Marc D. Graff (Dir-Corporate Planning-Strategy & VP-Finance)
Michael A. Greene (VP & Gen Mgr)
Matthew B. Haycock (Dir & VP)
Robert C. Hays (VP & Gen Mgr)
Rajeeb Hazra (VP & Gen Mgr)
Bradley G. Heaney (Dir & VP)
Mark H. Henninger (VP-Finance)
Richard A. Howarth (VP-Volatile Memory Solutions Grp & Gen Mgr-Volatile Memory Solutions Grp)
Michael A. Hurley (VP & Gen Mgr)
Vida Ilderem (Dir & VP)
Sridhar R. Iyengar (Dir-Security & VP)
James A. Johnson (Interim Sr VP & Interim Gen Mgr)
Asha R. Keddy (VP & Gen Mgr-Next Generation Sys & Standards)
Christopher N. Kenyon (Dir & VP)
Gary Kershaw (Asst Treas-Investments & VP-Finance)
Shervin Kheradpir (Dir & VP)
Shahaf Kieselstein (VP & Gen Mgr)
Upendra M. Kulkarni (Dir-Volatile Memory Solutions Grp & VP-Volatile Memory Solutions Grp)
Ravishankar Kuppuswamy (VP & Gen Mgr-Engineering)
Clare Lawson (VP & Gen Mgr)
Gloria Leong (VP & Gen Mgr)

Jo S. Levy (VP & Gen Counsel)
Chee Chyuan Liong (VP-Volatile Memory Solutions Grp & Gen Mgr-Volatile Memory Solutions Grp)
Steven A. Long (VP-Sales & Gen Mgr)
Zhiyong Ma (Dir & VP-Manufacturing-Operations)
Patricia A. McDonald (VP-Volatile Memory Solutions Grp & Gen Mgr-Volatile Memory Solutions Grp)
Joseph J. McDonnell (Mgr-Strategic Planning & VP-Manufacturing-Operations)
Myra J. McDonnell (Dir & VP)
Julie Coppernoll McGee (VP & Gen Mgr)
Daniel J. McKeon (VP-Information Technology & Gen Mgr)
Christina S. Min (CFO-Volatile Memory Solutions Grp & VP-Volatile Memory Solutions Grp)
Kaizad R. Mistry (Dir & VP)
James A. Murray (VP-Legal Department)
Kim Huat Ooi (VP-Manufacturing-Operations & Gen Mgr)
Alexander D. Peleg (Dir-Technology & VP)
Jeffrey S. Pettinato (Dir & VP)
Shannon J. Poulin (COO-Programmable Solutions Grp)
Anita K. Rao (VP & Gen Mgr)
Robert A. Reid (VP-Finance)
Anthony L. Romero (VP-Supply Chain-Global & Gen Mgr-Planning-Global)
Steven P. Rowe (VP-Finance)
Patrick T. Ruark (VP-Finance & Controller)
Thomas G. Rucker (Dir & VP)
Aziz M. Safa (Chief Data Officer & Chief Data Officer-Information Technology)
Eric H. Samuels (VP-Finance & Controller-Security)
Armin Sarstedt (Dir-Global & VP-Global)
Ralph A. Schweinfurth (Dir-Manufacturing-Operations & VP)
Steven P. Sciarappo (VP-Information Technology & Gen Mgr)
Ran Itzhak Senderovitz (VP & Gen Mgr)
Carolin T. Seward (Dir-Global & VP)
Raheel A. Shah (Dir & VP)
Sanjiv M. Shah (VP & Gen Mgr)
Isic Silas (Dir & VP)
Eamonn A. Sinnott (VP-Manufacturing-Operations & Gen Mgr)
Mostafa A. Aghazadeh (Dir & VP)
Mohsen Alavi (VP-Manufacturing-Operations & Gen Mgr)
Niraj Anand (Dir & VP)
Christopher P. Auth (Dir & VP)
Hamid R. Azimi (Dir & VP)
Peng Bai (Dir & VP)
Greg S. Slater (Gen Counsel & Gen Counsel)
Samuel G. Spangler (VP & Gen Mgr)
Kumud M. Srinivasan (Pres-Volatile Memory Solutions Grp)
Allon Stabinsky (Sr VP)
Mark A. Stettler (Dir & VP)
Weng Kuan Tan (VP & Gen Mgr)
Maurits Tichelman (VP-Sales & Gen Mgr-Global,Partners EMEA)
Bruce J. Tufts (VP)
Sanjay V. Vora (VP)
Rui Wang (Mgr-Sales-China & VP-Sales)
Jason P. Waxman (VP & Gen Mgr)
David Weigand (VP & Gen Mgr)

Jeffrey L. Woolard (VP-Finance & Controller-Finance)
Jeanne Yuen-Hum (Dir & VP-Manufacturing-Operations)
Ahmad A. Zaidi (VP & Gen Mgr)
Thomas P. Lantzsch (Sr VP & Gen Mgr)
Noel T. Murphy (VP & Gen Mgr)
Paul S. Scully (Dir & VP-Human Resources)
Abhay A. Joshi (VP-Communications & Gen Mgr)
Adam J. King (VP & Gen Mgr)
Alan J. Schijf (VP-Manufacturing-Operations & Gen Mgr)
Alexander D. Quach (VP & Gen Mgr)
Alper Ilkbahar (VP & Gen Mgr)
Alyson L. Crafton (VP & Gen Mgr)
Amir Khosrowshahi (VP)
Anil V. Nanduri (VP & Gen Mgr)
Anil R. Rao (VP & Gen Mgr)
Anish Ramachandran (VP-Human Resources)
Ann-Marie M. Holmes (Mgr-Fab 24 & VP-Manufacturing-Operations)
Anurag Handa (VP & Gen Mgr)
Anwar Awad (VP & Gen Mgr)
Ari Rauch (VP & Gen Mgr)
Boyd S. Phelps (VP & Gen Mgr)
Bradley M. Dendinger (VP & Gen Mgr)
Brent Conran (VP-Information Technology)
Brian J. McIntyre (Dir & VP)
C. Matt Swafford (Assoc Gen Counsel & VP-Legal Department)
Christian Erben (VP-Communications & Gen Mgr)
Christopher M. Walker (VP & Gen Mgr)
Cristina Rodriguez (VP & Gen Mgr)
Curren Krishnan (VP-Finance & Controller-Manufacturing)
Daniel C. Rodriguez (VP & Gen Mgr)
Daniel Benatar (Asst Gen Mgr-Worldwide)
Daniel T. Wood (Dir-Strategic Planning & VP)
Darcy L. Ortiz (VP-Manufacturing-Operations & Gen Mgr)
David R. Aubin (VP & Gen Mgr)
David A. Bloss (Dir-Global & VP-Supply Chain-Global)
David M. McCloskey (VP-Sales & Gen Mgr)
David J. Moore (VP & Gen Mgr)
Donald D. Parker (VP-Security & Gen Mgr)
Doug B. Klucevek (VP-Finance & Controller)
Elkana Ben-Sinai (VP-Communications & Gen Mgr)
Eugene Scuteri (VP & Gen Mgr)
Frank E. Abboud (VP & Gen Mgr)
Frank A. Sanders (Dir-Global & VP-Supply Chain-Global)
Gilberto A. Vargas (Dir & VP-Sales)
Gregory G. Baur (Dir & VP-Sales)
Hans P. H. Chuang (Dir & VP-Sales)
Hillarie Prestopine (Dir & VP)
Isaura Gaeta (VP-Security & Gen Mgr)
Jagannath Keshava (Dir-Silicon Strategies,Capabilities & VP)
James D. Jackson (VP & Gen Mgr)
Jeffery J. Rittener (Chief Govt Affairs Officer & Chief Govt Affairs Officer)
Jeffrey S. Draeger (Dir & VP-Legal Department)
Jeffrey S. McVeigh (VP & Gen Mgr)
Joe D. Jensen (VP & Gen Mgr)
John F. Bonini (VP & Gen Mgr)
John D. Vossoughi (VP & Gen Mgr-Sales)
Jonathan Ballon (VP & Gen Mgr)

Jose Alvaro Avalos (Dir-IOT Solutions Grp)
Jose A. Vargas (VP & Gen Mgr)
Kapil Wadhera (VP-Communications & Gen Mgr-China)
Karen M. Perry (Dir-Bus Ops & VP-Sales)
Karin Eibschitz Segal (Dir & VP)
Katherine S. Winter (VP & Gen Mgr)
Kenneth P. Caviasca (VP & Gen Mgr)
Kevin J. Fischer (Dir & VP)
Kit Ho Chee (VP-Sales & Gen Mgr)
Li-Chung Lin (Mng Dir-Intl & VP-Intl)
Lisa M. Pearce (Dir & VP)
Lori L. Weber (Dir & VP-Human Resources)
Marina B. Alekseeva (Dir & VP)
Mark P. Hocking (Dir-Global & VP-Sales)
Mark L. Skarpness (Dir & VP)
Messay Amerga (VP-Communications & Gen Mgr)
Michael L. Forrest (Dir & VP-Human Resources)
Michael C. Uhl (VP & Gen Mgr)
Myung-sook Kwon (Pres & VP-Sales)
Naveen G. Rao (VP & Gen Mgr)
Pushkar Jain (Dir-Yield Dev & VP)
Rebecca A. Brown (VP-Sales & Gen Mgr)
Remi S. El-Ouazzane (VP)
Robert C. DeLine (VP-Sales & Gen Mgr-Global)
Ryan T. McCurdy (VP-Sales)
Sagi Ben Moshe (VP & Gen Mgr)
Sambit Sahu (VP & Gen Mgr-India)
Sandeep G. Bharathi (Dir & VP)
Shaheen Dayal (Dir-Global & VP-Global)
Sherry S. Boger (VP & Gen Mgr)
Song Gao (VP & Gen Mgr)
Tahir Ghani (Dir)
Upendra Puntambekar (VP & Gen Mgr)
Valentin D. Kaplan (VP & Gen Mgr)
Viktor A. Tymchenko (Dir & VP)
Vincent Y. Hu (VP & Gen Mgr-Strategy)
Ying Zhang (Dir & VP)
Yosef Takserman (VP & Gen Mgr)
Yu Teong Chow (VP-Manufacturing-Operations & Gen Mgr)
Yung H. Hahn (Dir-Strategy-Planning & VP)
Jon Carvill (VP)
Jim Keller (Sr VP-Technology & Gen Mgr)
Randhir Thakur (Chief Supply Chain Officer, Chief Supply Chain Officer & Chief Supply Chain Officer)
Kalyan Thumaty (VP & Gen Mgr)
Sumeet Agrawal (VP & Gen Mgr)
Evangelina Almirantearena (Assoc Gen Counsel & VP-Legal Department)
Itay Bar-Chen (Dir-Engineering & VP)
Brad M. Benson (VP & Gen Mgr-Strategic Planning)
Wai Phang Chan (VP & Gen Mgr)
Wei Chen (VP & Gen Mgr-China)
Lynn Comp (VP & Gen Mgr)
Adrian Criddle (Mgr-Sales-UK & VP-Sales)
Phillip A. Harris (VP & Gen Mgr)
Reynette Au (VP-Programmable Solutions Grp & Gen Mgr-Mktg)
Sharon L. Heck (Chief Tax Officer, Chief Tax Officer & Chief Tax Officer)
Sandra L. Rivera (CEO-Programmable Solutions Grp, Exec VP & Gen Mgr-Datacenter & AI)
Sarah E. Kemp (VP-Intl Gov Affairs)
Gordon Moore (Co-Founder)
Richard A. Uhlig (Dir & VP-Technology)

Intel Corporation—(Continued)

William Archer *(CFO & VP-Finance)*
Robert Bedichek *(VP & Gen Mgr)*
Jill Bennett *(Dir & VP)*
Ameet S. Bhansali *(Mng Dir & VP)*
Selim Bilgin *(VP & Gen Mgr)*
Susan Blocher *(Dir & VP-Sales)*
Christine Boles *(VP & Gen Mgr)*
Premal Buch *(VP & Gen Mgr)*
James M. Carwana *(VP & Gen Mgr)*
Avinash P. Chakravarthy *(VP & Gen Mgr)*
Chad R. Chambers *(Assoc Gen Counsel & VP-Legal Department)*
Sze-Ming A. Chan *(VP & Gen Mgr)*
Roger Chandler *(VP & Gen Mgr)*
Guangli Che *(Mgr-Fab 68 & VP-Volatile Memory Solutions Grp)*
Srinivas Chennupaty *(VP & Gen Mgr)*
Julie Choi *(VP & Gen Mgr)*
Chad Constant *(Dir & VP-Sales)*
John Coyne *(VP-Sales & Gen Mgr)*
Donald R. Cunningham *(Dir & VP)*
Kathleen D. Deibert *(Sr Dir & VP)*
Charles H. Dennison *(Dir-Volatile Memory Solutions Grp & VP-Volatile Memory Solutions Grp)*
Mariya Zorotovich *(Dir)*
Aleksandr Shargorodskiy *(Mgr)*
Christy Pambianchi *(Chief People Officer & Exec VP)*
Bruce H. Andrews *(Chief Govt Affairs Officer & Chief Govt Affairs Officer)*
Patricia L. Kummrow *(VP-Network & Edge Grp & Gen Mgr-Ethernet Div)*
Greg Lavender *(CTO, Sr VP & Gen Mgr-Software & Advanced Tech Grp)*
David Zinsner *(CFO & Exec VP)*
Santhosh Viswanathan *(Mng Dir-Sls, Mktg & Comm Grp-India)*
Herbert D. Kelleher *(Co-Founder)*
Scott Gawel *(Chief Acctg Officer & VP)*
Christoph Schell *(Chief Comml Officer, Sr VP & Gen Mgr-Comm, Mktg, and Sls)*
Kari Aakre *(Sr Dir-Tech & Exec Comms)*
April Miller Boise *(Chief Legal Officer & Exec VP)*
Michelle C. Johnston Holthaus *(Interim Co-CEO)*
David A. Zinsner *(Interim Co-CEO, CFO & Exec VP)*
James B. Kirkland Jr. *(Dir & VP)*
Albert Blaha Jr. *(VP-Volatile Memory Solutions Grp)*
Christine M. Pambianchi *(Chief People Officer & Exec VP)*
Safroadu Yeboah-Amankwah *(Chief Strategy Officer & Sr VP)*

Subsidiaries:

Componentes Intel de Costa Rica **(1)**
Calle 129 La Ribera De, Belen, Heredia, Costa Rica **(100%)**
Tel.: (506) 22986000
Web Site: http://www.intel.com
Sales Range: $100-124.9 Million
Electronics & Semiconductors Mfr
N.A.I.C.S.: 334413

Fulcrum Microsystems, Inc. **(1)**
26630 Agoura Rd, Calabasas, CA 91302
Tel.: (818) 871-8100
Web Site: http://www.fulcrummicro.com
Sales Range: $25-49.9 Million
Emp.: 50
Semiconductor & Related Device Mfr
N.A.I.C.S.: 334413

Ineda Systems Pvt. Ltd. **(1)**
Plot No 89&90 H No 8-2-120/115/c, Road No 2 Banjara Hills, Hyderabad, 500 034, India
Tel.: (91) 40 3061 5555
Web Site: http://www.inedasystems.com

Emp.: 180
Computer Chip Mfr
N.A.I.C.S.: 334412
Balaji Kanigicherla *(Founder & CEO)*

Subsidiary (US):

Ineda Systems Inc. **(2)**
2901 Tasman Dr Ste 113, Santa Clara, CA 95054
Tel.: (408) 400-7374
Computer Chip Mfr
N.A.I.C.S.: 334412

Intel Australia Pty. Ltd. **(1)**
111 Pacific Highway, North Sydney, 2060, NSW, Australia **(100%)**
Tel.: (61) 415519635
Web Site: http://www.intel.com
Sales Range: $10-24.9 Million
Emp.: 30
Sales & Marketing
N.A.I.C.S.: 449210

Intel Capital Corporation **(1)**
2200 Mission College Blvd, Santa Clara, CA 95054
Tel.: (408) 765-8080
Web Site: http://www.intelcapital.com
Venture Capital & Private Equity Investment Services
N.A.I.C.S.: 523999
Nick Washburn *(Sr Mng Dir)*
Avram Miller *(Co-Founder)*

Subsidiary (Non-US):

Brainlab AG **(2)**
Olof-Palme-Strasse 9, 81829, Munich, Germany
Tel.: (49) 899915680
Medical Technology Services
N.A.I.C.S.: 621511
Jan Meker *(COO)*

Subsidiary (US):

VisionTree Software, Inc. **(3)**
8885 Rio San Diego Dr Ste 220, San Diego, CA 92108
Tel.: (619) 295-2800
Web Site: http://www.visiontree.com
Other Personal Services
N.A.I.C.S.: 812990
Martin Pellinat *(Founder & Pres)*

Intel China Ltd. **(1)**
6th Floor North Office Tower 06-01 Beijing Kerry Centre, 1 Guang Hua Road Chao Yang District, Beijing, 100020, China
Tel.: (86) 1085298800
Web Site: http://www.intel.com.cn
Sales Range: $100-124.9 Million
Emp.: 600
Electronics & Semiconductors Mfr
N.A.I.C.S.: 334413

Intel China Ltd. **(1)**
2F 751 Ziri Road Zizhu Science Park Minhang District, 2299 Yan an Road West, Shanghai, 200241, China
Tel.: (86) 2161165778
Web Site: http://www.intel.com.cn
Sales Range: $100-124.9 Million
Electronics & Semiconductors Mfr
N.A.I.C.S.: 334413

Intel Corp. Iberia, S.A. **(1)**
Torre Picasso Plaza Pablo Ruiz Picasso 1, Madrid, 28020, Spain **(100%)**
Tel.: (34) 914329090
Web Site: http://www.intel.com
Sales Range: $25-49.9 Million
Emp.: 30
Computer Equipment Mfr
N.A.I.C.S.: 334118

Intel Corp. S.A.R.L. **(1)**
Les Montalets 2 Rue De Paris, 92196, Meudon, France **(100%)**
Tel.: (33) 158877115
Web Site: http://www.intel.fr
Sales Range: $100-124.9 Million
Computer Sales
N.A.I.C.S.: 449210

Intel Corporation - Chandler Office **(1)**
5000 W Chandler Blvd, Chandler, AZ 85226
Tel.: (480) 715-8080
Web Site: http://www.intel.cn

Semiconductor & Related Device Mfr
N.A.I.C.S.: 334413

Intel Corporation - Parsippany Office **(1)**
6 Campus Dr, Parsippany, NJ 07054-4538
Tel.: (973) 993-3000
Web Site: http://www.intel.com
Sales Range: $400-449.9 Million
Emp.: 1,200
Telephony Equipment Mfr
N.A.I.C.S.: 334210

Intel Corporation U.K. Ltd. **(1)**
Pipers Way, Swindon, SN3 1RJ, Wiltshire, United Kingdom **(100%)**
Tel.: (44) 1793403000
Web Site: http://www.intel.com
Computer Mfr
N.A.I.C.S.: 334111

Intel Czech Tradings, Inc. **(1)**
IBC Business Ctr, Pobrezni 3 7th Fl, 186 00, Prague, Czech Republic **(100%)**
Tel.: (420) 222090301
Web Site: http://www.intel.com
Sales Range: $10-24.9 Million
Emp.: 6
Electronics & Semiconductors Distr & Whslr
N.A.I.C.S.: 334413

Intel Deutschland GmbH **(1)**
Am Campeon 10, 85579, Neubiberg, Germany
Tel.: (49) 899988530
Web Site: https://www.intel.de
Software Development Services
N.A.I.C.S.: 541511
Gustl Maurer *(Sr Dir-R&D)*

Intel Electronics (Malaysia) Sdn. Bhd. **(1)**
Level 14 Seuite 14-8 Wisma UOA Damansara II No 6 Changkat Semantan, Damansara Heights, 50490, Kuala Lumpur, Malaysia
Tel.: (60) 3 21 466400
Web Site: http://www.intel.com
Sales Range: $1-4.9 Billion
Emp.: 5,200
Electronics & Semiconductors Mfr
N.A.I.C.S.: 334413

Intel Finland OY **(1)**
Itamerenkatu 1, PO Box 281, 00180, Helsinki, Finland
Tel.: (358) 108504759
Sales Range: $10-24.9 Million
Emp.: 10
Sales & Marketing
N.A.I.C.S.: 449210

Intel GmbH **(1)**
Dornacher Strasse 1, Feldkirchon, 80106, Germany **(100%)**
Tel.: (49) 89991430
Web Site: http://www.intel.com
Sales Range: $150-199.9 Million
Emp.: 325
Computer & Peripheral Equipment Whslr
N.A.I.C.S.: 423430

Intel Holdings B.V. **(1)**
Capronilaan 37, 1119 NG, Schiphol-Rijk, Netherlands
Tel.: (31) 206591800
Holding Company
N.A.I.C.S.: 551112

Intel Indonesia Corporation **(1)**
14th Floor World Trade Centre 1 Jalan Jend Sudirman Kav 31, Jakarta, 12920, JK, Indonesia
Tel.: (62) 2125578500
Web Site: http://www.intel.co.id
Sales Range: $100-124.9 Million
Electronics & Semiconductors Mfr
N.A.I.C.S.: 334413

Intel Ireland Ltd. **(1)**
Collinstown, Leixlip, W23 CX68, Ireland
Tel.: (353) 016067000
Web Site: http://www.intel.ie
Electronics & Semiconductors Mfr
N.A.I.C.S.: 334413

Intel Israel (74) Limited **(1)**
Merkaz Marahot Mada Hofhacarnel, PO Box 1659, Haifa, Hefa, Israel **(100%)**
Tel.: (972) 48655711
Web Site: http://www.intel.co.il

Sales Range: $550-599.9 Million
Emp.: 2,040
Electronics & Semiconductors Mfr
N.A.I.C.S.: 334413

Intel Italia, S.p.A. **(1)**
Viale Milanofiori Palazzo E/4, Assago, 20090, Milan, MI, Italy **(100%)**
Tel.: (39) 02575441
Web Site: http://www.intel.it
Sales Range: $100-124.9 Million
Emp.: 60
Microprocessor & Multimedia Equipment Mfr
N.A.I.C.S.: 541512

Intel Kabushiki Kaisha **(1)**
5 6 Tokodai, PO Box 115 Tsukubact, Tsukuba, 300- 2635, Ibaraki, Japan **(100%)**
Tel.: (81) 298478511
Web Site: http://www.intel.co.jp
Sales Range: $50-74.9 Million
Emp.: 200
Semiconductor Distr
N.A.I.C.S.: 449210

Intel Kabushiki Kaisha **(1)**
Kokusai Bldg 5F 3-1-1 Marunouchi, Chiyoda-ku, Tokyo, 100-0005, Japan **(100%)**
Tel.: (81) 352239100
Web Site: http://www.intel.co.jp
Sales Range: $100-124.9 Million
Electronics & Semiconductors Mfr
N.A.I.C.S.: 334413

Intel Korea Ltd. **(1)**
5/F Dae Han Investment Trust Co Building 27-3 Yoido-doing, Youngdeungpo-ku, Seoul, 150-705, Korea (South) **(100%)**
Tel.: (82) 27672500
Web Site: http://www.intel.com
Sales Range: $25-49.9 Million
Emp.: 117
Sales & Marketing
N.A.I.C.S.: 449210

Intel Malaysia Sdn. Berhad **(1)**
Plot 6 Bayan Lepas Technoplex Medan Bayaln Lepas, 11900, Penang, Malaysia
Tel.: (60) 42530000
Computer Peripheral Equipment Mfr
N.A.I.C.S.: 334118

Intel Massachusetts, Inc. **(1)**
75 77 Reed Rd, Hudson, MA 01749 **(100%)**
Tel.: (978) 553-4000
Web Site: http://www.intel.com
Sales Range: $100-124.9 Million
Electronics & Semiconductors Mfr
N.A.I.C.S.: 334413

Intel Mediterranean Trading Company **(1)**
Maya Meridyen Is Merkezi Ebulula Cd Kat 6 Akatlar, 34335, Istanbul, Akatlar, Turkiye
Tel.: (90) 2123491500
Sales Range: $100-124.9 Million
Electronics & Semiconductors Distr
N.A.I.C.S.: 334413

Intel Microelectronics Asia **(1)**
8/F Bank Tower Building 205 Tun Hwa North Road, Taipei, 796, Taiwan
Tel.: (886) 227169660
Web Site: http://www.intel.com
Sales Range: $100-124.9 Million
Sales & Marketing
N.A.I.C.S.: 449210

Intel Mobile Communications GmbH **(1)**
Am Campeon 10, Neubiberg, Germany
Tel.: (49) 899988530
Semiconductor Devices Mfr
N.A.I.C.S.: 334413

Intel SA Corp **(1)**
Western Service Rd, PO Box 1085, 2052, Gallo Manor, Woodmead, South Africa
Tel.: (27) 118064530
Web Site: http://www.intel.co.za
Sales Range: $10-24.9 Million
Emp.: 30
Electronics & Semiconductors Mfr
N.A.I.C.S.: 334413

Intel Semiconductor (Dalian) Ltd. **(1)**
No 109 Huaihe Rd E DETD, 116600, Dalian, China

bai, 400 051, India **(100%)**
Tel.: (91) 2226415579
Web Site: http://www.intel.com
Sales Range: $10-24.9 Million
Emp.: 30
Electronics & Semiconductors Mfr
N.A.I.C.S.: 334413

Intel Technology Philippines, Inc. **(1)**
Gateway Business Park Javalera Gen Trias,
Cavite, Philippines **(100%)**
Tel.: (63) 28928610
Web Site: http://www.intel.com
Sales Range: $550-599.9 Million
Emp.: 3,000
Electronics & Semiconductors Mfr
N.A.I.C.S.: 334413

Intel Technology Poland **(1)**
Jerozolimskie Business Park, Al Jerozolim-
skie 146 C, 02 305, Warsaw, Poland
Tel.: (48) 225708100
Web Site: http://www.intel.com
Sales Range: $100-124.9 Million
Electronics & Semiconductors Mfr
N.A.I.C.S.: 334413

Intel Tecnologia de Argentina
S.A. **(1)**
Olga Cossettini 240 Dock IV Edificio 3 Piso
3, C1107BBA, Buenos Aires, Argentina
Tel.: (54) 1145154200
Sales Range: $10-24.9 Million
Emp.: 25
Electronics & Semiconductors Mfr
N.A.I.C.S.: 334413

Intel Tecnologia de Colombia
S.A. **(1)**
Calle 100 13-21 Piso 11 Bogota FSO
Megatower Distrito Capital, Bogota, Colom-
bia
Tel.: (57) 1 651 5300
Sales Range: $100-124.9 Million
Emp.: 25
Electronics & Semiconductors Mfr
N.A.I.C.S.: 334413

Intel Tecnologia de Mexico, S.A. de
C.V. **(1)**
Blvd Manuel Avila Camacho No 36 Torre 2
Piso 7 Lomas De Chapultepec, 11000,
Mexico, DF, Mexico
Tel.: (52) 5552847000
Sales Range: $10-24.9 Million
Emp.: 40
Electronics & Semiconductors Mfr
N.A.I.C.S.: 334413
Gaby Gallarzo *(Gen Mgr)*

Inteltech S.A. de C.V. **(1)**
Poniente 150 No 978 Industrial Vallejo
Azcapotzalco, Mexico, 02300, DF,
Mexico **(100%)**
Tel.: (52) 55 5333 9800
Web Site: http://www.inteltech.com.mx
Sales Range: $100-124.9 Million
Emp.: 120
Electronics & Semiconductors Mfr
N.A.I.C.S.: 334413
Victor Rodiguez *(Gen Mgr)*

Mobileye Global Inc. **(1)**
Har Hotzvim 13 Hartom Street, PO Box
45157, Jerusalem, 9777513, Israel
Tel.: (972) 25417333
Web Site: http://www.mobileye.com
Rev.: $2,079,000,000
Assets: $15,577,000,000
Liabilities: $653,000,000
Net Worth: $14,924,000,000
Earnings: ($27,000,000)
Emp.: 3,700
Fiscal Year-end: 12/30/2023
Software Development Services
N.A.I.C.S.: 541511
Amnon Shashua *(Co-Founder, Pres &*
CEO)

Mobileye N.V. **(1)**
Har Hotzvim 13 Hartom Street, PO Box
45157, Jerusalem, 9777513, Israel
Tel.: (972) 2 541 7333
Web Site: http://www.mobileye.com
Sales Range: $350-399.9 Million
Camera-Based Advanced Driver Assistance
Systems Software Developer
N.A.I.C.S.: 513210
Amnon Shashua *(Pres & CEO)*
Gaby Hayon *(Exec VP-Res & Dev)*

Elchanan Rushinek *(Exec VP-Engrg)*
Pini Segal *(VP-Fin & HR)*
Erez Dagan *(Exec VP-Products & Strategy)*
Liz Cohen-Yerushalmi *(Chief Legal Officer &*
Gen Counsel)
Elad Serfaty *(Sr VP & Gen Mgr-Intelligent*
Mobility Solutions Div)
Shai Shalev-Shwartz *(CTO)*
Kobi Ohayon *(Sr VP-Ops)*
Tal Babaioff *(VP-Mapping & Localization &*
Gen Mgr-REM)
Johann Jungwirth *(VP-Mobility as a Svc)*
Nir Erez *(Exec VP)*
Anat Heller *(CFO)*
Shay Assoolin *(VP-Dev Infrastructure)*
Tomer Baba *(VP-Sensing Algorithms)*
Diane Be'ery *(VP-Mktg)*
Efim Belman *(VP-Sys Architecture)*
Orna Etzion *(VP-Compute Software)*
Yossi Hadad *(VP-Dev Integration & Prod-*
ucts)
Yosef Kreinin *(VP & Gen Mgr-Platform &*
Application Software)
Danielle Mann *(VP-Corp Comm)*
Tsachi Namir *(VP-Functionality & Product*
Validation)
Lior Sethon *(VP & Deputy Gen Mgr-*
Intelligent Mobility Solutions Div)
Leonid Smolansky *(VP-Soc Architecture)*
Jack Weast *(VP-Autonomous Vehicle Stan-*
dards)

Subsidiary (US):

Mobileye Inc. **(2)**
1350 Broadway, New York, NY 10018
Tel.: (877) 867-4900
Web Site: http://www.mobileye.com
Motor Vehicle Driver Assistance & Collision
Avoidance Systems Developer
N.A.I.C.S.: 513210

Subsidiary (Non-US):

Mobileye Japan Ltd. **(2)**
La Piazzola 6F 2-9-3 Higashi-Shinbashi,
Minato-ku, Tokyo, 105-0021, Japan
Tel.: (81) 3 6721 5530
Motor Vehicle Driver Assistance & Collision
Avoidance Systems Developer
N.A.I.C.S.: 513210
Shotaro Kawahara *(CEO)*

Subsidiary (Domestic):

Mobileye Vision Technologies
Ltd. **(2)**
Har Hotzvim 13 Hartom Street, PO Box
45157, Jerusalem, 9777513, Israel
Tel.: (972) 2 541 7333
Web Site: http://www.mobileye.com
Motor Vehicle Driver Assistance & Collision
Avoidance Systems Developer
N.A.I.C.S.: 513210

Saffron Technology, Inc. **(1)**
1000 CentreGreen Way, Cary, NC 27513-
2282
Tel.: (919) 468-8201
Web Site: http://www.saffrontech.com
Cognitive Computing Technologies Devel-
oper
N.A.I.C.S.: 541511

INTELLIA THERAPEUTICS, INC.
40 Erie St Ste 130, Cambridge, MA
02139
Tel.: (857) 285-6200 DE
Web Site: https://www.intelliatx.com
Year Founded: 2014
NTLA—(NASDAQ)
Rev.: $36,275,000
Assets: $1,300,977,000
Liabilities: $250,808,000
Net Worth: $1,050,169,000
Earnings: ($481,192,000)
Emp.: 526
Fiscal Year-end: 12/31/23
Biological Research & Development
Services
N.A.I.C.S.: 541715
John M. Leonard *(Pres & CEO)*
Laura Sepp-Lorenzino *(Chief Scien-*
tific Officer & Exec VP)

David Lebwohl *(Chief Medical Officer*
& Exec VP)
James Basta *(Gen Counsel, Sec &*
Exec VP)
Ian Karp *(Sr VP-Corp Comm & IR)*
Aron Stein *(Sr VP-Regulatory Affairs)*
Yuanxin Xu *(Sr VP-Early Dev &*
Translational Medicine)
Frank A. G. M. Verwiel *(Chm)*
Glenn Goddard *(CFO & Exec VP)*
Marika Amand *(Chief HR Officer & Sr*
VP)
Derk Hicks *(Chief Bus Officer & Exec*
VP)
Edward Dulac *(CFO & Exec VP)*
Maria Natale *(Sr VP-Commercial)*
Mary Ferguson *(Sr VP & Head-*
Intellectual Property)
Birgit Schultes *(Sr VP & Head-Cell*
Therapies)
Kristy Wood *(Sr VP-Technical Ops)*

INTELLICENTRICS GLOBAL HOLDINGS LTD.
777 International Pkwy Ste 400,
Flower Mound, TX 75028
Tel.: (817) 732-3873 Ky
Web Site: https://www.intellicentrics-
global.com
Year Founded: 2016
6819—(HKG)
Rev.: $43,980,000
Assets: $58,563,000
Liabilities: $62,647,000
Net Worth: ($4,084,000)
Earnings: ($8,839,000)
Emp.: 172
Fiscal Year-end: 06/30/23
Holding Company
N.A.I.C.S.: 551112
Michael McDonald *(COO)*
Simone Pringle *(Chief Product Offi-*
cer)
Tzung-Liang Lin *(Founder)*

INTELLICHECK, INC.
200 BRdhollow Rd, Melville, NY
11747
Tel.: (516) 992-1900 DE
Web Site:
https://www.intellicheck.com
Year Founded: 1994
IDN—(NASDAQ)
Rev.: $15,966,000
Assets: $22,453,000
Liabilities: $3,949,000
Net Worth: $18,504,000
Earnings: ($3,851,000)
Emp.: 53
Fiscal Year-end: 12/31/22
Identity Authentication & Access Man-
agement Services
N.A.I.C.S.: 513210
Bryan Lewis *(CEO)*
Frank Lubin *(VP-Engrg)*
Bruce Ackerman *(Sr VP-Sls)*
David Andrews *(VP-Mktg)*
Adam Sragovicz *(CFO)*

INTELLIGENT BIO SOLUTIONS INC.
135 W 41st St Fl 5, New York, NY
10036
Tel.: (646) 828-8258 DE
Web Site: https://www.ibs.inc
Year Founded: 2016
INBS—(NASDAQ)
Rev.: $3,111,781
Assets: $13,778,863
Liabilities: $5,595,672
Net Worth: $8,183,191
Earnings: ($10,190,932)
Emp.: 50
Fiscal Year-end: 06/30/24
Offices of Other Holding Companies
N.A.I.C.S.: 551112

Tel.: (86) 41139231001
Computer Peripheral Equipment Mfr & Distr
N.A.I.C.S.: 334118

Intel Semiconductor Limited **(1)**
2200 Mission College Blvd, Santa Clara,
CA 95054-1537 **(100%)**
Tel.: (408) 765-8080
Sales Range: $150-199.9 Million
Electronics & Semiconductors Mfr & Whslr
N.A.I.C.S.: 423690

Subsidiary (Domestic):

Fujitsu Semiconductor Wireless Prod-
ucts, Inc. **(2)**
2100 E Elliot Rd, Tempe, AZ 85284
Tel.: (800) 866-8608
Wireless Communication Equipment Mfr
N.A.I.C.S.: 334220

Intel Semiconductor Ltd. **(1)**
69/F Central Plz 18 Harbour Rd, Wanchai,
China (Hong Kong) **(100%)**
Tel.: (852) 28444555
Web Site: http://www.intel.com
Sales Range: $75-99.9 Million
Emp.: 180
Semiconductor Mfr
N.A.I.C.S.: 334413

Intel Semiconductor Ltd. **(1)**
Tung Shing Sq Ste 1106 2 Ngo Quyen St,
Hanoi, Vietnam
Tel.: (84) 438262929
Web Site: http://www.intel.com
Sales Range: $10-24.9 Million
Emp.: 10
Electronics & Semiconductors Mfr
N.A.I.C.S.: 334413

Intel Semiconductor Ltd. **(1)**
Lot I2 D1 Road Saigon Hi-Tech Park District
9, Ho Chi Minh City, Vietnam
Tel.: (84) 4 826 2929
Web Site: http://www.intel.vn
Sales Range: $100-124.9 Million
Electronics & Semiconductors Mfr
N.A.I.C.S.: 334413

Intel Semiconductor Ltd. **(1)**
Matam Bldg 6 Matam Industrial Park, PO
Box 1659, Matam Industrial Park, Haifa,
31015, Israel **(100%)**
Tel.: (972) 4 865 5711
Web Site: http://www.intel.com
Semiconductor Mfr & Sales
N.A.I.C.S.: 334413

Intel Semicondutores do Brasil
Ltda. **(1)**
Av Dr Chucri Zaidan 940 Brooklin 10 Andar,
04583-110, Sao Paulo, Brazil
Tel.: (55) 33655500
Web Site: http://www.intel.com.br
Sales Range: $25-49.9 Million
Emp.: 90
Semiconductor Mfr
N.A.I.C.S.: 334413

Intel Sweden AB **(1)**
Isafjordsgatan 30 b, 164 40, Kista,
Sweden **(100%)**
Tel.: (46) 859461700
Sales Range: $25-49.9 Million
Emp.: 30
Computer Software & Equipment Sales
N.A.I.C.S.: 423430

Intel Technologies, Inc. **(1)**
Krylatsky Hills 17 Krylatskaya Str Bldg 4,
121614, Moscow, Russia
Tel.: (7) 4956414500
Web Site: http://www.intel.ru
Sales Range: $75-99.9 Million
Electronics & Semiconductors Mfr
N.A.I.C.S.: 334413

Intel Technology Asia Pte. Ltd. **(1)**
180 Clemenceau Ave Haw Par Centre 0401
04 Haw Par Centre, Singapore, 239922,
Singapore
Tel.: (65) 62131000
Sales Range: $50-74.9 Million
Emp.: 100
Microprocessor Whslr
N.A.I.C.S.: 423690

Intel Technology India Pvt. Ltd. **(1)**
3F B Wing Pt 2 Exchange Plaza Block G,
Bandra Kurla Complex Bandra East, Mum-

Intelligent Bio Solutions Inc.—(Continued)

Harry Simeonidis (Pres & CEO)
Spiro Sakiris (CFO)
Steven Boyages (Chm)
Alex Arzeno (VP-IR & Comm)

Subsidiaries:

Intelligent Fingerprinting Limited **(1)**
14-17 Evolution Business Park Milton Road,
Impington, Cambridge, CB24 9NG, United
Kingdom
Tel.: (44) 1223941941
Web Site:
    https://www.intelligentfingerprinting.com
Fingerprint Drug Testing Product Distr
N.A.I.C.S.: 424210

**INTELLIGENT MEDICINE AC-
QUISITION CORP.**
9001 Burdette Rd, Bethesda, MD
20817
Tel.: (202) 905-5834   DE
Year Founded: 2021
IQMD—(NASDAQ)
Rev.: $13,255,472
Assets: $214,034,334
Liabilities: $224,890,993
Net Worth: ($10,856,659)
Earnings: $11,408,859
Emp.: 1
Fiscal Year-end: 12/31/22
Investment Services
N.A.I.C.S.: 523999
Gregory C. Simon (CEO & CFO)
Jack D. Hidary (Chm)

INTELLINETICS, INC.
2190 Dividend Dr, Columbus, OH
43228
Tel.: (614) 921-8170   NV
Web Site:
    https://www.intellinetics.com
INLX—(NYSEAMEX)
Rev.: $14,016,928
Assets: $19,943,142
Liabilities: $11,374,340
Net Worth: $8,568,802
Earnings: $24,027
Emp.: 139
Fiscal Year-end: 12/31/22
Software Developer
N.A.I.C.S.: 513210
Matthew L. Chretien (Founder, CTO,
Chief Strategy Officer & Sec)
Joseph D. Spain (CFO & Treas)
James F. DeSocio (Pres & CEO)
Danielle Patterson (Sls Mgr)

Subsidiaries:

CEO Imaging Systems, Inc.   **(1)**
340 North Main St, Plymouth, MI 48170
Tel.: (734) 354-8874
Web Site: http://www.ceoimage.com
Rev.: $2,586,886
Emp.: 12
Software Reproducing
N.A.I.C.S.: 334610
Brad Lahr (Pres)

**INTENSITY THERAPEUTICS,
INC.**
1 Enterprise Dr Ste 430, Shelton, CT
06484-4779
Tel.: (203) 221-7381   DE
Web Site:
    https://www.intensitytherapeu
tics.com
Year Founded: 2012
INTS—(NASDAQ)
Pharmacies & Drug Retailers
N.A.I.C.S.: 456110
Joseph Talamo (CFO)
Robert Cooke (Sr VP)
John Wesolowski (Principal Acctg
Officer & Controller)
Lewis H. Bender (Pres & CEO)

INTER PARFUMS, INC.
551 5th Ave, New York, NY 10176
Tel.: (212) 983-2640   DE
Web Site:
    https://www.interparfumsinc.com
Year Founded: 1983
IPAR—(NASDAQ)
Rev.: $1,317,675,000
Assets: $1,369,329,000
Liabilities: $477,159,000
Net Worth: $892,170,000
Earnings: $187,776,000
Emp.: 607
Fiscal Year-end: 12/31/23
Alternative Designer Fragrances &
Cosmetics Distr
N.A.I.C.S.: 456120
Jean Madar (Chm & CEO)
Philippe Benacin (Vice Chm)
Michel Atwood (CFO & Exec VP)

Subsidiaries:

Divabox SAS   **(1)**
CS 14001, 20700, Ajaccio, Cedex, France
Tel.: (33) 969321310
Web Site: https://www.my-origines.com
Beauty Care Product Distr
N.A.I.C.S.: 456120

IP Beauty, Inc.   **(1)**
551 5th Ave, New York, NY 10176
Tel.: (212) 983-2640
Perfume Mfr
N.A.I.C.S.: 325199

Inter Parfums Holdings, S.A.   **(1)**
4 Rond Pt des Champs Elysees, 75008,
Paris, 75008, France   **(100%)**
Tel.: (33) 153770000
Web Site: http://www.interparfums.fr
Sales Range: $75-99.9 Million
Emp.: 240
Holding Company
N.A.I.C.S.: 551112

Affiliate (Domestic):

Interparfums SA   **(2)**
4 rond-point des Champs Elysees, 75008,
Paris, France   **(27%)**
Tel.: (33) 153770000
Web Site: http://www.interparfums.fr
Rev.: $762,598,748
Assets: $1,066,238,938
Liabilities: $424,492,769
Net Worth: $641,746,169
Earnings: $107,406,648
Emp.: 317
Fiscal Year-end: 12/31/2022
Fragrance Mfr
N.A.I.C.S.: 325620
Philippe Santi (Chief Financial & Legal Offi-
cer & Exec VP)
Philippe Benacin (Chm)
Frederic Garcia-Pelayo (Chief Intl Officer &
Exec VP)
Axel Marot (VP-Supply Chain & Ops)
Jerome Thermoz (VP-French Distr)
Pierre Desaulles (Mng Dir-Luxury Brands)
Renaud Boisson (Mng Dir-Interparfums Asia
Pacific)
Stanislas Archambault (Exec Dir-
Operational & Digital Mktg)
Veronique Duretz (VP-HR)
Natacha Cennac-Finateu (Corp Counsel)

Subsidiary (Domestic):

Inter Parfums Grand Public, S.A.   **(3)**
4 Rond PointChamps Elysees Marcel Das-
sault, 75008, Paris, France   **(100%)**
Tel.: (33) 153770000
Web Site: http://www.inter-parfums.fr
Sales Range: $25-49.9 Million
Emp.: 160
Mfr of Frangrances
N.A.I.C.S.: 325620

Interparfums Singapore Pte.   **(1)**
163 Penang Rd 06-03 Winsland Hse 2 S,
Singapore, 238463, Singapore
Tel.: (65) 66439130
Web Site: http://www.interparfums.fr
Designer Perfumes & Fragrances Distr
N.A.I.C.S.: 456120

Jean Philippe Fragrances, LLC   **(1)**

551 5th Ave, New York, NY 10176
Tel.: (212) 983-2640
Budget Line of Fragrances
N.A.I.C.S.: 325620

**INTERACT HOLDINGS GROUP,
INC.**
9625 Mission Gorge Rd Ste B2366,
Santee, CA 92071
Tel.: (619) 342-7443   FL
Web Site:
    https://www.interactholdings.com
IHGP—(OTCIQ)
Led Product Distr
N.A.I.C.S.: 423610
William Yates (CFO & Treas)
Michel Johnson (CEO)
Jim Nelson (Pres & COO)
Zonghan Wu (Sec)

**INTERACT-TV, INCORPO-
RATED**
4023 Kennett Pike Ste 590, Wilming-
ton, DE 19807
Tel.: (302) 777-1642   DE
Web Site: https://www.interact-tv-
    inc.com
Year Founded: 2000
ITVI—(OTCIQ)
Television Broadcasting Services
N.A.I.C.S.: 516120
Robert Bryan (Pres, Treas & Sec)

**INTERACTIVE BROKERS
GROUP, INC.**
1 Pickwick Plz, Greenwich, CT 06830
Tel.: (203) 618-5800
Web Site:
    https://www.interactivebrokers.com
Year Founded: 1977
IBKR—(NASDAQ)
Rev.: $4,340,000,000
Assets: $128,423,000,000
Liabilities: $114,356,000,000
Net Worth: $14,067,000,000
Earnings: $600,000,000
Emp.: 2,932
Fiscal Year-end: 12/31/23
Investment Management Service
N.A.I.C.S.: 523910
Thomas Peterffy (Founder & Chm)
Earl H. Nemser (Vice Chm)
Paul J. Brody (CFO, Treas & Sec)
Milan Galik (Pres & CEO)
Thomas A. Frank (CIO & Exec VP)
Michael J. Domka (Mng Dir-Sls-
Chicago)

Subsidiaries:

Covestor Limited   **(1)**
Floor 12 20 Fenchurch Street, London,
EC3M 3BY, United Kingdom
Tel.: (44) 8668253005
Financial Company Services
N.A.I.C.S.: 523910

IBG LLC   **(1)**
1 Pickwick Plz, Greenwich, CT 06830-5551
Tel.: (203) 618-5800
Sales Range: $125-149.9 Million
Emp.: 400
Stocks & Bonds Brokerage Services
N.A.I.C.S.: 523150
Earl H. Nemser (Vice Chm & Officer)
Paul J. Brody (CFO)
Milan Galik (Pres)

Subsidiary (Non-US):

Interactive Brokers (India) Private
Limited   **(2)**
502/A Times Square Andheri Kurla Road,
Andheri East, Mumbai, 400 059, Maharash-
tra, India
Tel.: (91) 226 128 9888
Web Site:
    https://www.interactivebrokers.co.in
Sales Range: $25-49.9 Million
Emp.: 20
Stocks & Bonds Brokerage Services

N.A.I.C.S.: 523150

Interactive Brokers (UK) Limited   **(1)**
Level 20 Heron Tower 110 Bishopsgate,
London, EC2N 4AY, United Kingdom
Tel.: (44) 2077105632
Web Site:
    http://www.interactivebrokers.co.uk
Sales Range: $650-699.9 Million
Securities Brokerage Services
N.A.I.C.S.: 523150

Interactive Brokers Australia Nomi-
nees Pty Limited   **(1)**
Grosvenor Place Level 40 225 George
Street, Sydney, 2000, NSW, Australia
Tel.: (61) 280937301
Miscellaneous Business Intermediation Ser-
vices
N.A.I.C.S.: 523910

Interactive Brokers Canada, Inc.   **(1)**
1800 McGill College Avenue Suite 2106,
Montreal, H3A 3J6, QC, Canada
Web Site: https://www.interactivebrokers.ca
Sales Range: $75-99.9 Million
Emp.: 15
Securities Brokerage Services
N.A.I.C.S.: 523150

Interactive Brokers Central Europe
Zrt.   **(1)**
Madach Imre ut 13-14, 1075, Budapest,
Hungary
Tel.: (36) 17010350
Web Site: https://www.interactivebrokers.hu
Banking Services
N.A.I.C.S.: 522110

Interactive Brokers Hong Kong
Limited   **(1)**
Suite 1512 Two Pacific Place 88 Queen-
sway Admiralty, Hong Kong, China (Hong
Kong)
Tel.: (852) 2 156 7990
Web Site:
    https://www.interactivebrokers.com.hk
Financial Services
N.A.I.C.S.: 523150
Thomas Peterffy (Chm & CEO)

Interactive Brokers, LLC   **(1)**
1 Pickwick Plz, Greenwich, CT 06830
Tel.: (203) 618-4030
Web Site:
    https://www.interactivebrokers.com
Sales Range: $650-699.9 Million
Emp.: 2,400
Securities Brokerage Services
N.A.I.C.S.: 523150

Timber Hill Europe AG   **(1)**
Gubelstrasse 28, 6300, Zug, Switzerland
Tel.: (41) 7205088
Sales Range: $650-699.9 Million
Securities Brokerage Services
N.A.I.C.S.: 523150

**INTERACTIVE LEISURE SYS-
TEMS, INC.**
8310 S Vly Hwy Ste 300, Englewood,
CO 80112
Tel.: (303) 524-1110   NV
IALS—(OTCIQ)
Industrial Organic Chemicals Mfr
N.A.I.C.S.: 325199
Joseph Wade (CEO)

INTERACTIVE STRENGTH INC.
1005 Congress Ave Ste 925 C14,
Austin, TX 78701-3051
Tel.: (310) 697-8655   DE
Web Site: https://www.formelife.com
Year Founded: 2017
TRNR—(NASDAQ)
Rev.: $323,000
Assets: $22,066,000
Liabilities: $41,729,000
Net Worth: ($19,663,000)
Earnings: ($32,840,000)
Emp.: 108
Fiscal Year-end: 12/31/21
Software Development Services
N.A.I.C.S.: 541511
Trent A. Ward (Founder)

INTERCARE DX, INC.
20280 S Vermont Ave Ste 215, Torrance, CA 90502　　　　CA
Web Site: https://www.intercare.com
Year Founded: 1991
ICCO—(OTCIQ)
Information Technology Services
N.A.I.C.S.: 541512
Anthony C. Dike (Founder)

INTERCLOUD SYSTEMS, INC.
980 N Federal Hwy Ste 304, Boca Raton, FL 33432
Tel.: (561) 988-1988　　　　DE
Web Site:
　　http://www.intercloudsys.com
Year Founded: 1999
ICLD—(OTCIQ)
Sales Range: $25-49.9 Million
Emp.: 241
Cloud, Managed, Professional Consulting, Voice, Data & Optical Services & Solutions
N.A.I.C.S.: 513210
Daniel Sullivan (CFO & Chief Acctg Officer)
Timothy A. Larkin (CFO)
Mark Munro (Chm & CEO)

Subsidiaries:

Integration Partners - NY
Corporation　　　　(1)
1719 Route 10 E Ste 114, Parsippany, NJ 07054
Tel.: (973) 871-2100
Information Services
N.A.I.C.S.: 519290

Integration Partners Corp.　　　　(1)
12 Hartwell Ave, Lexington, MA 02421
Tel.: (781) 357-8100
Web Site:
　　http://www.integrationpartners.com
Sales Range: $25-49.9 Million
Emp.: 50
Computer System Design Services
N.A.I.C.S.: 541512

Localloop, Inc.　　　　(1)
1820B N Columbia St, Milledgeville, GA 31061
Tel.: (478) 453-8324
Web Site: http://www.www.dpsonline.co
Information Services
N.A.I.C.S.: 519290

Rives-Monteiro Engineering, LLC　(1)
2736 Southside Dr, Tuscaloosa, AL 35401　　　　(49%)
Tel.: (205) 248-0111
Web Site: http://www.monteiro-eng.com
Engineering Services for Telecommunications Industry
N.A.I.C.S.: 541330
Diana Patricia Gomez Molina (Gen Mgr)

INTERCONTINENTAL EXCHANGE, INC.
5660 New Northside Dr 3rd Fl, Atlanta, GA 30328
Tel.: (770) 857-4700　　　　DE
Web Site: https://www.ice.com
Year Founded: 2001
ICE—(NYSE)
Rev.: $9,903,000,000
Assets: $136,084,000,000
Liabilities: $110,298,000,000
Net Worth: $25,786,000,000
Earnings: $2,368,000,000
Emp.: 13,222
Fiscal Year-end: 12/31/23
Holding Company; Securities & Commodities Exchange Operator
N.A.I.C.S.: 551112
Christopher S. Edmonds (Pres-Fixed Income & Data Svcs)
Jeffrey C. Sprecher (Founder, Chm & CEO)
Christopher Edmonds (Chief Dev Officer-Global)
Mark P. Wassersug (COO)

Benjamin R. Jackson (Pres)
Mayur Kapani (CTO)
Lynn C. Martin (Pres-Fixed Income & Data Svcs)
Warren Gardiner (CFO)
Timothy J. Bowler (Pres-ICE Benchmark Admin)
Douglas Foley (Sr VP-HR & Admin)
James W. Namkung (Chief Acctg Officer & Controller)
Andrew J. Surdykowski (Gen Counsel)
Elizabeth King (Chief Regulatory Officer)
Brookly McLaughlin (VP-Corp Affairs & Sustainability)
Joanne Rowe (Officer-Corp Risk)
John Tuttle (Chief Comml Officer & Vice Chm)
Joe Tyrrell (Pres)
Trabue Bland (Pres)
Stuart Williams (Pres)
Kevin McClear (Pres)
Stanislav Ivanov (Pres)
Hester Serafini (Pres)
John Tuttle (Chief Comml Officer & Vice Chm)
Joe Tyrrell (Pres)
Trabue Bland (Pres)
Stuart Williams (Pres)
Kevin McClear (Pres)
Stanislav Ivanov (Pres)
Amanda Hindlian (Pres)
Hester Serafini (Pres)
John Tuttle (Chief Comml Officer & Vice Chm)
Joe Tyrrell (Pres)
Trabue Bland (Pres)
Stuart Williams (Pres)
Kevin McClear (Pres)
Stanislav Ivanov (Pres)
Amanda Hindlian (Pres)
Hester Serafini (Pres)
Warren A. Gardiner (Founder, CFO, Sec, VP-Sales & VP)
Christopher Rhodes (Pres, Founder, CFO, Sec, VP-Sales & VP)

Subsidiaries:

Bakkt Holdings, LLC　　　　(1)
5660 New Northside Dr, Atlanta, GA 30328
Tel.: (770) 916-7863
Web Site: http://www.bakkt.com
Holding Company
N.A.I.C.S.: 551112
Adam White (Pres)
Marc D'Annunzio (Gen Counsel)
Gavin Michael (CEO)
Drew LaBenne (CFO & Exec VP)
Dan O'Prey (Exec VP-Digital Assets)
Lauren Post (VP-Comm)

Subsidiary (Domestic):

Bakkt Marketplace, LLC　　　　(2)
5660 New Northside Dr, Atlanta, GA 30328
Tel.: (770) 916-7863
Web Site: http://www.bakkt.com
Commodity Exchange Services
N.A.I.C.S.: 523160

Bakkt, LLC　　　　(2)
5660 New Northside Dr, Atlanta, GA 30328
Tel.: (770) 916-7863
Web Site: http://www.bakkt.com
Software Publisher
N.A.I.C.S.: 513210
Adam White (Pres)

Black Knight, Inc.　　　　(1)
601 Riverside Ave, Jacksonville, FL 32204
Tel.: (904) 854-5100
Web Site: https://www.blackknightinc.com
Rev.: $1,551,900,000
Assets: $5,831,600,000
Liabilities: $3,258,300,000
Net Worth: $2,573,300,000
Earnings: $452,500,000
Emp.: 6,100
Fiscal Year-end: 12/31/2022
Holding Company; Integrated Technology, Workflow Automation, Data & Analytics

N.A.I.C.S.: 551112
Joseph M. Nackashi (CEO)
Michael L. Gravelle (Gen Counsel & Exec VP)
Richard Gagliano (Pres-Origination Technologies)
Ben Graboske (Pres-Data & Analytics)
Colleen Haley (Sec)
Bob Pinder (Chief Compliance Officer)
Anthony Reyes (Chief Audit Officer)
Kirk T. Larsen (Pres, CFO & Principal Acctg Officer)
Peter Carrara (CIO)
Ryan Hallett (Chief Risk Officer)
Sandra Madigan (Chief Digital Officer & Exec VP)
George FitzGerald (Exec VP)
Kevin McMahon (Pres)
Victor Soler-Sala (Exec VP)
Ravi Varma (Pres)

Subsidiary (Domestic):

Black Knight InfoServ, LLC　　　　(2)
601 Riverside Ave, Jacksonville, FL 32204
Tel.: (904) 854-5100
Web Site: http://www.blackknightinc.com
Sales Range: $1-4.9 Billion
Emp.: 7,800
Holding Company; Mortgage Processing, Settlement, Performance Analytics & Default Solutions Services
N.A.I.C.S.: 551112

Collateral Analytics, LLC　　　　(2)
Hawaii Kai Towne Ctr 6700 Kalanianaole Hwy Ste 210, Honolulu, HI 96825
Tel.: (808) 527-2428
Web Site: http://www.collateralanalytics.com
Custom Computer Programming Services
N.A.I.C.S.: 541511
Michael Sklarz (Mng Dir & Exec VP)
Jonah Ungacta (VP-IT)
Stefan Pampulov (VP-Product Dev)
Keith Agena (VP-Bus Ops)
Darlene Swain (VP-Bus Dev)
John Holbrook (VP-Bus Strategy)

Compass Analytics, LLC　　　　(2)
650 California St Ste 2025, San Francisco, CA 94108
Tel.: (415) 462-7500
Web Site: https://compass-analytics.blackknightinc.com
Mortgage Capital & Risk Management Services
N.A.I.C.S.: 541618
Rob Kessel (CEO)

HeavyWater, Inc.　　　　(2)
1650 Market St Ste 3600, Philadelphia, PA 19103
Tel.: (610) 564-1000
Web Site: http://www.heavywater.com
Software Development Services
N.A.I.C.S.: 513210

Motivity Solutions LLC　　　　(2)
3033 S Parker Rd 11th Fl, Aurora, CO 80014　　　　(100%)
Tel.: (303) 721-9000
Web Site: http://www.motivitysolutions.com
Emp.: 50
Mortgage Software & Financial Services
N.A.I.C.S.: 513210

Joint Venture (Domestic):

The Dun & Bradstreet
Corporation　　　　(2)
103 JFK Pkwy, Short Hills, NJ 07078
Tel.: (973) 921-5500
Web Site: http://www.dnb.com
Business Information, Publishing & Marketing Services
N.A.I.C.S.: 519290
Anthony M. Jabbour (CEO)
Tim Solms (Gen Mgr-Govt Segment)
Gary Kotovets (Chief Data Officer)
Brian Hipsher (CFO & Treas)
Colleen Haley (Sec)
Virginia Green Gomez (Chief Product Officer)
Michael Manos (CTO)
Anthony Pietrontone Jr. (Principal Acctg Officer & Controller)

Subsidiary (Domestic):

AllBusiness.com, Inc.　　　　(3)

N.A.I.C.S.: 551112
Joseph M. Nackashi (CEO)
650 Townsend St Ste 450, San Francisco, CA 94103
Tel.: (415) 694-5000
Web Site: http://www.allbusiness.com
Sales Range: $25-49.9 Million
Emp.: 40
Business Resource Website Operator
N.A.I.C.S.: 513199

Corinthian Leasing Corporation　　(3)
103 John F Kennedy Pkwy, Short Hills, NJ 07078-2708
Tel.: (973) 921-5500
Office Machinery Rental & Leasing Services
N.A.I.C.S.: 532420

D&B Acquisition Corp.　　　　(3)
12194 Monaco Dr, Brighton, CO 80602
Tel.: (303) 909-4502
Financial Investment Services
N.A.I.C.S.: 523999

Subsidiary (Non-US):

D&B Europe Limited　　　　(3)
The Point 37 North Wharf Road, London, W2 1AF, Buckinghamshire, United Kingdom
Tel.: (44) 1628492109
Web Site: http://www.db.com
Emp.: 400
Management Consulting Services
N.A.I.C.S.: 541618
Janets Storle (Mgr-IT & HR)

D&B Group Holdings (UK)　　　　(3)
The Point 37 North Wharf Road, London, W2 1AF, Buckinghamshire, United Kingdom
Tel.: (44) 1628492342
Investment Management Service
N.A.I.C.S.: 551112

D&B Holdings Australia Limited　　(3)
The Point 37 North Wharf Road, London, W2 1AF, United Kingdom
Tel.: (44) 1628492000
Web Site: http://www.dnb.co.uk
Emp.: 400
Investment Management Service
N.A.I.C.S.: 551112

Subsidiary (Domestic):

D&B Management Services Co.　　(3)
103 JFK Pkwy, Short Hills, NJ 07078-2708
Tel.: (973) 921-5500
Web Site: http://www.schooldata.com
Holding Company
N.A.I.C.S.: 551112

D&B Sales & Marketing
Solutions　　　　(3)
460 Totten Pond Rd, Waltham, MA 02451
Tel.: (781) 672-9200
Sales Range: $10-24.9 Million
Emp.: 30
Computer Software Development
N.A.I.C.S.: 541511

Subsidiary (Non-US):

DBXB Netherlands B.V.　　　　(3)
Stationsplein 45 4th floor C, 3013 AK, Rotterdam, Netherlands
Tel.: (31) 107109400
Web Site: http://www.dnb-nederland.nl
Emp.: 25
Management Consulting Services
N.A.I.C.S.: 541618

DBXB S.r.l.　　　　(3)
48 Via Valtorta, 20127, Milan, Italy
Tel.: (39) 022814941
Management Consulting Services
N.A.I.C.S.: 541618

Dun & Bradstreet (HK) Ltd.　　　(3)
13/F BEA Tower Millennium City 5, 418 Kwun Tong Rd, Kwun Tong, Kowloon, China (Hong Kong)
Tel.: (852) 25161111
Web Site: https://www.dnb.com.hk
Sales Range: $25-49.9 Million
Emp.: 100
Credit Services
N.A.I.C.S.: 561450
Thomas Tam (Controller)

Dun & Bradstreet (Israel) Ltd.　　(3)
53 Derech Hashalom St, Givatayim, 5345433, Israel
Tel.: (972) 37330330

Intercontinental Exchange, Inc.—(Continued)

Web Site: https://www.dbisrael.co.il
Sales Range: $25-49.9 Million
Emp.: 150
Credit Services
N.A.I.C.S.: 561450

Dun & Bradstreet (Singapore) Pte. Ltd. (3)
6 Shenton Way OUE Downtown 2 17-10,
Singapore, 068809, Singapore
Tel.: (65) 65656161
Web Site: https://www.dnb.com.sg
Sales Range: $100-124.9 Million
Business Information Services
N.A.I.C.S.: 519290

Dun & Bradstreet (Vietnam) LLC (3)
Unit 2104 Floor 21 Saigon Trade Center, 37
Ton Duc Thang District 1, Ho Chi Minh City,
Vietnam
Tel.: (84) 839117288
Web Site: http://www.dnb.com
Management Consulting Services
N.A.I.C.S.: 541611
Nhi Le Thi Phuong (Dir-Bus Dev)

Dun & Bradstreet B.V. (3)
Otto Reuchlinweg 1032, 3072 MD, Rotter-
dam, Netherlands
Tel.: (31) 107109400
Web Site: http://www.dnb-nederland.nl
Sales Range: $25-49.9 Million
Emp.: 100
Business Information Services
N.A.I.C.S.: 519290
D. Tebbitt (Mgr-Site)

Dun & Bradstreet Belgium N.V. (3)
Inter Access Park Pontbeekstraat 4, Dil-
beek, 1702, Brussels, Belgium
Tel.: (32) 24818300
Web Site: http://www.dnb.com
Sales Range: $10-24.9 Million
Emp.: 40
Business Information Services
N.A.I.C.S.: 519290
Coraline van Hoeymissen (Dir-HR)

Dun & Bradstreet CIS (3)
3rd Khoroshevsky Proyezd 1 corpus 1,
123007, Moscow, Russia
Tel.: (7) 959401816
Web Site: http://www.dnb.ru
Sales Range: $10-24.9 Million
Emp.: 15
N.A.I.C.S.: 561450

Dun & Bradstreet Canada BV (3)
Otto Reuchlinweg 1032, Rotterdam, 3072
MD, Netherlands
Tel.: (31) 107109400
Web Site: http://www.dnb-netherlands.com
Emp.: 120
Management Consulting Services
N.A.I.C.S.: 541611
Darren Tebbitt (Gen Mgr)

Dun & Bradstreet Canada Ltd. (3)
B1-5770 Hurontario St, Mississauga, L5R
3G5, ON, Canada
Tel.: (800) 668-3033
Web Site: http://www.dnb.ca
Information Services
N.A.I.C.S.: 519290
Jenal Embry (VP-Supply Chain Solutions)
Brian Alster (Global Head-of Supply & Com-
pliance Product)
Nipa Basu (Chief Analytics Officer)
Ilio Krumins-Beens (Global Head-PMO)
Daniel Sherman (Dir-Vulnerability Mgmt)

Subsidiary (Domestic):

**Dun & Bradstreet Credibility
Corp.** (3)
22761 Pacific Coast Hwy Ste 226, Malibu,
CA 90265
Tel.: (424) 644-0601
Web Site: http://www.dandb.com
Emp.: 575
Credit Monitoring Services
N.A.I.C.S.: 522390

Dun & Bradstreet Europe, Ltd. (3)
103 JFK Pkwy, Short Hills, NJ 07078
Tel.: (973) 921-5500
Web Site: http://www.dunandbradstreet.com
Management Consulting Services

N.A.I.C.S.: 541611

Subsidiary (Non-US):

**Dun & Bradstreet Information Ser-
vices India Pvt Ltd.** (3)
iSprout Business Center 5th Floor Kochar
Jade PLOT NO SP 22, T-S No 25 SIDCO
Industrial Estate Guindy, Chennai, 600032,
India
Tel.: (91) 2228574190
Web Site: http://www.dnb.com
Sales Range: $75-99.9 Million
Emp.: 350
Information Services
N.A.I.C.S.: 519290

**Dun & Bradstreet International Con-
sultant (Shanghai) Ltd.** (3)
9th Floor Building 6 Hongqiao Vanke Center
No 988 Shenchang Road, 318 Fu Zhou
Road, Shanghai, 200001, China
Tel.: (86) 2123213636
Web Site: https://www.dnbchina.com
Sales Range: $50-74.9 Million
Emp.: 200
Credit Bureau Services
N.A.I.C.S.: 561450

**Dun & Bradstreet Investments
Limited** (3)
The Point 37 North Wharf Road, London,
W2 1AF, Buckinghamshire, United Kingdom
Tel.: (44) 1628492319
Web Site: http://www.dnb.co.uk
Investment Management Service
N.A.I.C.S.: 523999

Dun & Bradstreet Ltd. (3)
The Point 37 North Wharf Road, London,
W2 1AF, Buckinghamshire, United Kingdom
Tel.: (44) 1628492000
Web Site: https://www.dnb.co.uk
Sales Range: $75-99.9 Million
Emp.: 400
Business Information Services
N.A.I.C.S.: 519290

Subsidiary (Domestic):

Dun & Bradstreet NetProspex (3)
300 3rd Ave, Waltham, MA 02451
Tel.: (888) 826-4877
Web Site: http://www.netprospex.com
B2B Business & Marketing Services
N.A.I.C.S.: 561499

Subsidiary (Non-US):

Dun & Bradstreet SpA (3)
Via Dei Valtorta 48, 20127, Milan, Italy
Tel.: (39) 02284551
Web Site: http://www.dnb.it
Sales Range: $75-99.9 Million
Emp.: 300
Credit Services
N.A.I.C.S.: 561450

**Dun & Bradstreet Technologies &
Data Services Private Limited** (3)
Level 9 Prince Info City Phase 1 286/1,
Kandanchavadi Rajiv Gandhi Salai OMR,
Chennai, 600 096, India
Tel.: (91) 4466779999
Internet Service Provider
N.A.I.C.S.: 517121

Subsidiary (Domestic):

**Dun & Bradstreet, Inc. - Credit
Services** (3)
400 Penn Ctr Blvd, Pittsburgh, PA 15235
Tel.: (412) 829-3731
Sales Range: $125-149.9 Million
Business Credit Management
N.A.I.C.S.: 522390

Duns Investing Corporation (3)
801 N West St Fl 2, Wilmington, DE 19801-
1525
Tel.: (302) 656-8981
Investment Management Service
N.A.I.C.S.: 523940

Dunsnet, LLC (3)
189 S Orange Ave Ste 1500 S, Orlando, FL
32801
Tel.: (407) 476-9854
Web Site: https://www.dunsnet.com
Financial Transaction Services

N.A.I.C.S.: 541611

Subsidiary (Non-US):

First Research, Inc. (3)
7700 W Parmer Ln Bldg A, Austin, TX
78729
Tel.: (512) 380-4808
Web Site: https://www.firstresearch.com
Sales Range: $1-9.9 Million
Emp.: 14
Industry Analysis & Marketing Products &
Services
N.A.I.C.S.: 513199

Hoover's, Inc. (3)
5800 Airport Blvd, Austin, TX 78752-4204
Tel.: (512) 374-4500
Web Site: http://www.hoovers.com
Sales Range: $50-74.9 Million
Emp.: 231
Publisher of Business Information
N.A.I.C.S.: 541990

Subsidiary (Domestic):

Visible Path Corp. (4)
181 Metro Dr Ste 290, San Jose, CA
95110-1344
Tel.: (650) 356-2254
Sales Range: $10-24.9 Million
Emp.: 30
Online Business Networking Solutions
N.A.I.C.S.: 513210
Stephen Charles Pusey (CMO)

Subsidiary (Domestic):

Lattice Engines, Inc. (3)
1825 S Grant Ave Ste 510, San Mateo, CA
94402
Tel.: (877) 460-0010
Web Site: http://www.lattice-engines.com
Sales Range: $1-9.9 Million
Emp.: 40
Predictive Analytics to Sales & Marketing
Consumers
N.A.I.C.S.: 513210
Shashi Upadhyay (CEO)
Kent McCormick (CTO)
Ian J. Scott (VP-Pro Svcs)
Scott Harralson (VP-Pro Svcs)
Jean-Paul Gomes (VP-Bus Dev)

Market Data Retrieval (3)
5335 Gate Pkwy, Jacksonville, FL 32256
Tel.: (973) 921-5500
Web Site: https://mdreducation.com
Sales Range: $25-49.9 Million
Emp.: 166
School Marketing Information & Services
N.A.I.C.S.: 541910

Purisma, Inc. (3)
2211 Bridgepointe Pkwy Ste 300, San Ma-
teo, CA 94404
Tel.: (650) 350-3500
Web Site: http://www.purisma.com
Sales Range: $25-49.9 Million
Emp.: 15
Data Management Services
N.A.I.C.S.: 541511

Subsidiary (Non-US):

**Shanghai Huaxia Dun & Bradstreet
Business Information Consulting Co.,
Limited** (3)
Unit 907-910 Cross Tower 318 Fu Zhou
Road, Shanghai, 200001, China
Tel.: (86) 2123213636
Web Site: http://www.huaxiadnb.com
Commercial Information Consulting Ser-
vices
N.A.I.C.S.: 541611

**The D&B Companies of Canada
Ltd.** (3)
6750 Century Ave Suite 305, Mississauga,
L5N 0B7, ON, Canada
Tel.: (800) 668-3033
Web Site: http://www.dnb.com
Management Consulting Services
N.A.I.C.S.: 541611

Subsidiary (Domestic):

coAction.com LLC (3)
300 Carnegie Dr, Princeton, NJ 08540
Web Site: http://www.coaction.com
Sales Range: $1-9.9 Million
Business Collaboration Software
N.A.I.C.S.: 513210

Jagdish Talreja (CEO)

Subsidiary (Domestic):

Top of Mind Networks, LLC (2)
3621 Vinings Slope SE Unit #4250, Atlanta,
GA 30339
Tel.: (415) 823-4766
Web Site: http://www.topofmind.com
Advertising Agencies
N.A.I.C.S.: 541810
Mark Green (Founder & Chief Strategy Offi-
cer)
Bill Hayes (CEO)
Nick Belenky (Chief Revenue Officer)

eMBS, Inc. (2)
5023 Wesley Dr, Tampa, FL 33647
Tel.: (813) 971-8982
Web Site: http://www.embs.com
Other Accounting Services
N.A.I.C.S.: 541219
Andrea Schmidt (Owner)

Ellie Mae, Inc. (1)
4420 Rosewood Dr Ste 500, Pleasanton,
CA 94588
Tel.: (925) 227-7000
Web Site: http://www.elliemae.com
Electronic Mortgage Origination Network;
Software Publisher
N.A.I.C.S.: 513210
Selim Aissi (Chief Security Officer & Sr VP)
Parvesh Sahi (Sr VP-Bus & Client Dev)
Jonas Moe (Sr VP-Mktg)
Joe Tyrrell (Pres)
Georgeann Beville (Sr VP-Customer Svcs)
Shea Haley (Sr VP-Professional Svcs)
Satheesh Ravala (Sr VP-Engrg)
Eric Connors (Sr VP-Product Strategy &
Mgmt)
Linh Lam (CIO & Sr VP)
Robert Baca (Sr VP-Technical Ops)

Subsidiary (Domestic):

Mortgage Returns, LLC (2)
1335 Strassner Dr, Saint Louis, MO 63144
Tel.: (314) 989-9100
Web Site:
    http://www.web.mortgagereturns.com
Sales Range: $1-9.9 Million
Emp.: 29
Software for Mortgages
N.A.I.C.S.: 513210
Jim Blatt (Founder & VP-CRM Strategy)

Velocify, Inc. (2)
222 N Pacific Coast Hwy Ste 1800, El Se-
gundo, CA 90245
Tel.: (844) 327-3296
Web Site: http://www.velocify.com
Sales Acceleration Platform
N.A.I.C.S.: 541511

ICE Clear Netherlands B.V. (1)
Atlas Arena Amsterdam Australia Building
3rd Floor, Hoogoorddreef 7, Amsterdam,
1101 BA, Netherlands
Tel.: (31) 20 305 5155
Web Site: http://www.theice.com
Clearing Services for Derivative Products
N.A.I.C.S.: 523999

ICE Data Indices, LLC (1)
100 Church St, New York, NY 10007
Tel.: (212) 497-3008
Web Site: http://www.theice.com
Investment Banking & Securities Dealing
N.A.I.C.S.: 523150

ICE Endex Markets B.V. (1)
Hoogoorddreef 7 Australia Building 3rd
Floor, 1101 BA, Amsterdam, Netherlands
Tel.: (31) 20 305 5100
Web Site: http://www.theice.com
Securities & Commodity Exchanges
N.A.I.C.S.: 523210

ICE Futures Singapore Pte. Ltd. (1)
6 Battery Road #36-01, Singapore, 049909,
Singapore
Tel.: (65) 65940160
Web Site: http://www.theice.com
Commodity Exchange Services
N.A.I.C.S.: 523160

Subsidiary (Domestic):

ICE Clear Singapore Pte. Ltd (2)

6 Battery Road #36-01, Singapore, 049909, Singapore
Tel.: (65) 65 940160
Commodity Exchange Services
N.A.I.C.S.: 523160

ICE Trade Vault Europe Limited (1)
Milton Gate 60 Chiswell Street, London, EC1Y 4SA, United Kingdom
Tel.: (44) 2074885100
Web Site: http://www.theice.com
Securities & Commodity Exchanges
N.A.I.C.S.: 523210

ICE UK LP, LLC (1)
2100 Riveredge Pkwy, Atlanta, GA 30328
Tel.: (770) 857-4700
Security & Commodity Exchange Operator
N.A.I.C.S.: 523210

Intercontinental Exchange Holdings, Inc. (1)
2100 RiverEdge Pkwy Ste 500, Atlanta, GA 30328
Tel.: (770) 857-4700
Web Site: http://www.theice.com
Rev.: $1,716,000,000
Assets: $64,422,000,000
Liabilities: $52,041,000,000
Net Worth: $12,381,000,000
Earnings: $270,000,000
Emp.: 4,232
Fiscal Year-end: 12/31/2013
Holding Company; Commodity Futures, Financial Contracts & Derivatives Exchange Operator, Trade Processing & Clearinghouse Services
N.A.I.C.S.: 551112
Sharon Y. Bowen (Chm)

Subsidiary (Non-US):

Climate Exchange plc (2)
IOMA House Hope Street, Douglas, IM1 1AP, Isle of Man
Tel.: (44) 1624681250
Web Site: http://www.climateexchangeplc.com
Sales Range: $50-74.9 Million
Emp.: 67
Environmental Financial Exchange Services
N.A.I.C.S.: 523210
Philip Scales (Sec)

Subsidiary (US):

Chicago Climate Exchange, Inc. (3)
353 North Clark St Ste 3100, Chicago, IL 60654
Tel.: (312) 229-5134
Web Site: http://www.theice.com
Rev.: $6,000,000
Emp.: 52
Security/Commodity Exchange
N.A.I.C.S.: 523210

Subsidiary (Domestic):

Creditex Group, Inc. (2)
875 3rd Ave 29th Fl, New York, NY 10022 (100%)
Tel.: (212) 323-8520
Credit Derivative Execution & Processing Services
N.A.I.C.S.: 522320
John Grifonetti (Pres & COO)

ICE Data Services, Inc. (2)
100 Church St Fl 11th, New York, NY 10007
Tel.: (212) 497-3000
Stock Exchange Services
N.A.I.C.S.: 523210
Patrick Smith (Dir-Municipal Evaluations)

Subsidiary (Non-US):

ICE Futures Canada, Inc. (2)
85A Pembina Hwy, Winnipeg, R3M 2M7, MB, Canada (100%)
Tel.: (204) 925-5000
Sales Range: $75-99.9 Million
Commodity Futures Exchange
N.A.I.C.S.: 523210
Brad Vannan (Pres & COO)
Trabue Bland (Pres-US)

ICE Futures Europe (2)
Milton Gate 60 Chiswell Street 1 St Katherines Way, London, EC1Y4SA, United Kingdom (100%)

Tel.: (44) 2074810643
Web Site: http://www.theice.com
Sales Range: $125-149.9 Million
Commodity Futures Exchange
N.A.I.C.S.: 523210
William Jefferson Hague (Chm)

Subsidiary (Domestic):

LIFFE (Holdings) Ltd. (3)
Cannon Bridge House, 1 Cousin Lane, London, EC4R 3XX, United Kingdom
Tel.: (44) 2076230444
Holding Company; Financial Futures & Options Market Exchange
N.A.I.C.S.: 551112

Subsidiary (Domestic):

ICE Futures U.S., Inc. (2)
55 E 52nd St 40th Fl, New York, NY 10055
Tel.: (212) 748-4000
Web Site: https://www.theice.com
Sales Range: $300-349.9 Million
Emp.: 160
Commodity Futures Exchange
N.A.I.C.S.: 523210
Frederick W. Hatfield (Chm)

Subsidiary (Non-US):

ICE Markets Limited (2)
Milton Gate 60 Chiswell Street, London, EC1Y 4SA, United Kingdom
Tel.: (44) 2070657700
Web Site: http://www.intercontinentalexchange.com
Investment Banking & Securities Dealing
N.A.I.C.S.: 523150

ICE NGX Canada, Inc. (2)
10th Floor 300-5th Avenue SW, Calgary, T2P 3C4, AB, Canada
Tel.: (403) 974-1700
Web Site: http://www.theice.com
Electronic Natural Gas Trading Services
N.A.I.C.S.: 523210

Subsidiary (Domestic):

Super Derivatives Inc. (2)
100 Church St 11th Fl, New York, NY 10003
Tel.: (770) 999-4501
Web Site: http://www.superderivatives.com
Option Pricing, Risk Management & Independent Revaluation Services
N.A.I.C.S.: 519290

The Clearing Corporation (2)
353 N Clark St Fl 31, Chicago, IL 60654
Tel.: (312) 786-5700
Rev.: $42,897,186
Emp.: 35
Holding Company; Exchange Clearinghouse Operator
N.A.I.C.S.: 551112

Subsidiary (Non-US):

ICE Clear Canada, Inc. (3)
850A Pembina Highway, Winnipeg, R3M 2M7, MB, Canada
Tel.: (204) 925-5009
Web Site: http://www.theice.com
Clearinghouse Services
N.A.I.C.S.: 522320

Subsidiary (Domestic):

ICE Clear Credit LLC (3)
353 N Clark St, Chicago, IL 60654
Tel.: (312) 836-6890
Web Site: http://www.theice.com
Credit Clearing Services
N.A.I.C.S.: 522320
Stanislav Ivanov (Pres)

Subsidiary (Non-US):

ICE Clear Europe, Ltd. (3)
5th Floor Milton Gate 60 Chiswell Street, London, EC1Y 4SA, United Kingdom
Tel.: (44) 2070657600
Clearinghouse Services
Robert Reid (Chm)
Caroline L. Silver (Chm)
Hester Serafini (Pres)

Subsidiary (Domestic):

ICE Clear U.S., Inc. (3)

140 Broadway 23rd Fl, New York, NY 10005
Tel.: (212) 785-2939
Web Site: http://www.theice.com
Sales Range: $650-699.9 Million
Clearinghouse Services
N.A.I.C.S.: 522320
Kevin McClear (Pres)

MERSCORP Holdings, Inc. (1)
11819 Miami St Ste 100, Omaha, NE 68164 (100%)
Tel.: (703) 761-1270
Web Site: http://www.mersinc.org
Sales Range: $1-9.9 Million
Emp.: 5,000
Holding Company; Nondepository Credit Intermediation
N.A.I.C.S.: 551112

NYSE Group, Inc. (1)
86 Trinity Pl, New York, NY 10005 (100%)
Tel.: (212) 656-5264
Web Site: http://www.nyse.com
Holding Company; Securities & Commodities Exchanges
N.A.I.C.S.: 551112
Stacey Cunningham (Pres)
John Tuttle (Vice Chm & Chief Comml Officer)
Jaime L. Klima (Chief Regulatory Officer)

Subsidiary (Domestic):

NYSE American LLC (2)
11 Wall St, New York, NY 10005
Tel.: (212) 306-1000
Web Site: http://www.nyse.com
Sales Range: $75-99.9 Million
Emp.: 200
Securities & Commodities Exchange
N.A.I.C.S.: 523210

NYSE Arca, Inc. (2)
100 S Wacker Dr Ste 1800, Chicago, IL 60606
Tel.: (312) 960-1696
Web Site: http://www.nyse.com
Sales Range: $250-299.9 Million
Emp.: 234
Securities & Commodities Exchange
N.A.I.C.S.: 523210

NYSE Chicago Holdings, Inc. (2)
1 Financial Pl 440 S LaSalle St, Chicago, IL 60605
Tel.: (312) 663-2222
Web Site: http://www.nyse.com
Holding Company; Securities Exchange
N.A.I.C.S.: 551112
John K. Kerin (Pres & CEO)

Subsidiary (Domestic):

NYSE Chicago, Inc. (3)
440 S LaSalle St Ste 800, Chicago, IL 60605
Tel.: (312) 663-2222
Web Site: https://www.nyse.com
Security & Commodity Exchange
N.A.I.C.S.: 523210

Subsidiary (Domestic):

NYSE Liffe US LLC (2)
20 Broad St Fl 5, New York, NY 10005-2625 (100%)
Tel.: (212) 482-3000
Web Site: http://www.nyseliffeus.com
Securities & Commodity Exchange
N.A.I.C.S.: 523210
Marco Bianchi (Sr VP & Head-Bus Dev)
Lynn Martin (CEO)
Andy Booth (CTO)

NYSE Technologies, Inc. (2)
11 Wall St, New York, NY 10005 (100%)
Tel.: (212) 656-3000
Web Site: http://www.nyse.com
Sales Range: $125-149.9 Million
Emp.: 400
Electronic Trading Services
N.A.I.C.S.: 523999

New York Stock Exchange LLC (2)
11 Wall St, New York, NY 10005
Tel.: (212) 656-5264
Web Site: http://www.nyse.com
Sales Range: $650-699.9 Million
Securities & Commodities Exchange
N.A.I.C.S.: 523210

Jeffrey B. Osher (Trustee)
Sharon Y. Bowen (Chm)
Michael Blaugrund (COO)
Meaghan Dugan (Head-Options)

Subsidiary (Domestic):

NYSE Market (DE), Inc. (3)
55 E 52nd St, New York, NY 10055
Tel.: (770) 857-2395
Security & Commodity Exchange Operator
N.A.I.C.S.: 523210

NYSE National, Inc. (3)
One Financial Pl 440 Lasalle St Ste 2600, Chicago, IL 60605
Tel.: (212) 896-2830
Web Site: http://www.nyse.com
Securities Exchange
N.A.I.C.S.: 523210

NYSE Regulation, Inc. (3)
20 Broad St 18th Fl, New York, NY 10005
Tel.: (212) 656-4542
Web Site: http://www.nyse.com
Securities Exchange Regulatory Services
N.A.I.C.S.: 926150

Securities Industry Automation Corporation (3)
20 Broad St Fl 9, New York, NY 10005-2601
Tel.: (212) 656-2880
Web Site: http://www.siac.com
Technical Services
N.A.I.C.S.: 541519

OTC Commodity Markets, LLC (1)
5660 New Northside Dr 3rd Fl, Atlanta, GA 30328
Tel.: (770) 857-4700
Securities & Commodity Exchanges
N.A.I.C.S.: 523210

Simplifile LC (1)
5072 N 300 W, Provo, UT 84604
Web Site: http://www.simplifile.com
Software Publisher; E-recording Network
N.A.I.C.S.: 513210

TMC Bonds, LLC (1)
850 3rd Ave, New York, NY 10022
Tel.: (646) 375-1145
Web Site: http://www.tmcbonds.com
Trading & Clearing Services
N.A.I.C.S.: 523150
Stuart R. Henderson (CFO)

INTERDIGITAL, INC.
200 Bellevue Pkwy Ste 300, Wilmington, DE 19809-3727
Tel.: (302) 281-3600 PA
Web Site: https://www.interdigital.com
Year Founded: 1972
IDCC—(NASDAQ)
Rev.: $457,794,000
Assets: $1,900,105,000
Liabilities: $1,169,592,000
Net Worth: $730,513,000
Earnings: $93,693,000
Emp.: 425
Fiscal Year-end: 12/31/22
Digital Wireless Telephone Systems Mfr
N.A.I.C.S.: 334413
Michael G. Cortino (CIO & Exec VP)
Rajesh Pankaj (CTO & Exec VP)
Joshua D. Schmidt (Chief Legal Officer, Sec & Exec VP)
Eeva K. Hakoranta (Chief Licensing Officer & Exec VP)
Ken Kaskoun (Chief Growth Officer & Exec VP)
Skip Maloney (Chief People Officer & Exec VP)
Lawrence Chen (Pres & CEO)

Subsidiaries:

6GWorld, Inc. (1)
200 Bellevue Pkwy Ste 300, Wilmington, DE 19809
Web Site: https://www.6gworld.com
News Wire Services
N.A.I.C.S.: 516210

InterDigital, Inc.—(Continued)

IPR Licensing, Inc. (1)
200 Bellevue Pkwy Ste 300, Wilmington,
DE 19809-3727 **(100%)**
Tel.: (302) 477-2500
Patent Buying & Licensing Services
N.A.I.C.S.: 533110

InterDigital - Melville (1)
2 Huntington Quadrangle 4th Fl S Wing,
Melville, NY 11747-4508 **(100%)**
Tel.: (631) 622-4000
Web Site: http://www.interdigital.com
Sales Range: $25-49.9 Million
Emp.: 125
Digital Wireless Telephone Systems Mfr
N.A.I.C.S.: 334210
William C. Miller (Exec VP)

InterDigital Canada Ltee. (1)
1000 Sherbrooke Street West 10th Floor,
Montreal, H3A 3G4, QC, Canada
Tel.: (514) 904-6300
Web Site: http://www.interdigital.com
Wireless Telecommunication Services
N.A.I.C.S.: 517112

InterDigital Facility Company (1)
200 Bellevue Pkwy Ste 300, Wilmington,
DE 19809
Tel.: (302) 281-3600
Sales Range: $25-49.9 Million
Emp.: 80
Wireless Telecommunication Services
N.A.I.C.S.: 517112

InterDigital International, Inc. (1)
200 Bellevue Pkwy Ste 300, Wilmington,
DE 19809
Tel.: (302) 281-3600
Wireless Communication Equipment Mfr
N.A.I.C.S.: 334220

NexStar Capital, LLC (1)
780 3rd Ave, New York, NY 10017
Tel.: (212) 994-7001
Asset Management Services
N.A.I.C.S.: 531390

WoT.io, Inc. (1)
30 W 24th St Fl 6, New York, NY 10010
Tel.: (212) 675-3904
Web Site: http://www.wot.io
Emp.: 10
Information Technology Services
N.A.I.C.S.: 541512

INTERDYNE COMPANY, INC.
26 Briarwood, Irvine, CA 92604
Tel.: (805) 322-3883 CA
Year Founded: 1946
ITDN—(OTCIQ)
Assets: $52,273
Liabilities: $40,071
Net Worth: $12,202
Earnings: ($30,625)
Fiscal Year-end: 06/30/21
Investment Services
N.A.I.C.S.: 523999
Sun Tze Whang (Chm & CEO)
Kit Heng Tan (CFO, Principal Acctg
Officer & Sec)

INTERFACE, INC.
1280 W Peachtree St NW, Atlanta,
GA 30309
Tel.: (770) 437-6800 GA
Web Site: https://www.interface.com
Year Founded: 1973
TILE—(NASDAQ)
Rev.: $1,297,919,000
Assets: $1,266,503,000
Liabilities: $904,966,000
Net Worth: $361,537,000
Earnings: $19,560,000
Emp.: 3,671
Fiscal Year-end: 01/01/23
Offices of Other Holding Companies
N.A.I.C.S.: 551112
Robert Pridgen (Chief Acctg Officer &
VP)
Bruce A. Hausmann (CFO & VP)

David B. Foshee (Gen Counsel, Sec
& VP)
Laurel M. Hurd (Pres & CEO)
Greg Minano (Chief HR Officer & VP)
Jake Elson (CIO & VP)
John Bradford (Chief Science & Tech
Officer & VP)
Anna Webb (VP)

Subsidiaries:

Interface Americas Holdings,
LLC (1)
1280 W Peachtree St NE, Atlanta, GA
30309
Tel.: (404) 887-5002
Investment Management Service
N.A.I.C.S.: 523940

Subsidiary (Domestic):

Interface Americas, Inc. (2)
1503 Orchard Hill Rd, LaGrange, GA
30240-5709
Tel.: (706) 882-1891
Emp.: 4,100
Commercial Carpet Mfr
N.A.I.C.S.: 314110

Interface Aust. Holdings Pty
Limited (1)
14 Henry St, Picton, 2571, NSW, Australia
Tel.: (61) 246778800
Emp.: 215
Holding Company
N.A.I.C.S.: 551112

Interface Aust. Pty Limited (1)
101 Chalmers St, Surry Hills, 2010, NSW,
Australia
Tel.: (61) 1800804361
Web Site: https://www.interface.com
Carpet Tile Mfr
N.A.I.C.S.: 327120

Interface Europe B.V. (1)
Industrielaan 15, 3925 BD, Scherpenzeel,
Netherlands **(100%)**
Tel.: (31) 332775555
Web Site: https://www.interface.com
Holding Company; Regional Managing Of-
fice
N.A.I.C.S.: 551112

Interface Europe, Ltd. (1)
3rd Floor West F Mill Dean Clough, Halifax,
HX3 5AX, West Yorkshire, United Kingdom
Tel.: (44) 8003134465
Sales Range: $25-49.9 Million
Emp.: 90
Commercial Carpet Mfr
N.A.I.C.S.: 314110

Interface International B.V. (1)
Industrielaan 15, 3925 BD, Scherpenzeel,
3925 BD, Netherlands
Tel.: (31) 332775555
Commercial Carpet Mfr
N.A.I.C.S.: 314110

Interface Overseas Holdings,
Inc. (1)
2859 Paces Ferry Rd SE, Atlanta, GA
30339
Tel.: (770) 437-6800
Holding Company
N.A.I.C.S.: 551112

Interface Singapore Pte. Ltd. (1)
80 Marine Parade Road 18-02 Parkway Pa-
rade, Singapore, 449269, Singapore
Tel.: (65) 64781510
Web Site: https://www.interface.com
Carpet Tile Mfr
N.A.I.C.S.: 327120

nora systems GmbH (1)
Hohnerweg 2-4, 69469, Weinheim, Ger-
many
Tel.: (49) 6201806633
Web Site: https://www.nora.com
Rubber Floorcovering & Footwear Compo-
nents Mfr & Marketer
N.A.I.C.S.: 326299
Anton van Keken (Mng Dir)
Robert Heeres (Mng Dir)

Subsidiary (US):

nora systems, Inc. (2)

9 Northeastern Blvd, Salem, NH 03079
Tel.: (603) 894-1021
Web Site: https://www.nora.com
Rubber Floor Covering Mfr & Distr
N.A.I.C.S.: 326299
Benjamin P. Cowart (Pres)

INTERFOUNDRY, INC.
4505 Allstate Dr Ste 108, Riverside,
CA 92501
Tel.: (909) 367-2463
ITFY—(OTCIQ)
Diesel Fuel Distr
N.A.I.C.S.: 457210
William O. Sheaffer (Exec VP-Sls &
Mktg)

INTERGROUP CORPORATION
1516 S Bundy Dr Ste 200, Los Ange-
les, CA 90025
Tel.: (310) 889-2500 DE
Web Site:
https://www.intergroupcorpora
tion.com
Year Founded: 1965
INTG—(NASDAQ)
Rev.: $58,140,000
Assets: $107,811,000
Liabilities: $214,278,000
Net Worth: ($106,467,000)
Earnings: ($12,556,000)
Emp.: 214
Fiscal Year-end: 06/30/24
Real Estate Buyer, Developer & Man-
ager
N.A.I.C.S.: 531110
David C. Gonzalez (VP-Real Estate)
John V. Winfield (Chm, Pres & CEO)
Jolie Kahn (Sec)
Ann Marie Blair (Treas & Controller)

Subsidiaries:

Intergroup Meadowbrook Gardens,
Inc. (1)
3579 Us Hwy 46, Parsippany, NJ 07054
Tel.: (973) 335-3111
Web Site:
http://www.meadowbrookgardensapart
ments.com
Residential Building Leasing Services
N.A.I.C.S.: 531110

Intergroup Pine Lake, Inc. (1)
1100 Glendon Ave Ste PH 1, Los Angeles,
CA 90024
Tel.: (310) 889-2500
Web Site: http://www.intgla.com
Apartment Building Rental & Leasing Ser-
vices
N.A.I.C.S.: 531110

Santa Fe Financial Corporation (1)
12121 Wilshire Blvd Ste 610, Los Angeles,
CA 90025
Tel.: (310) 889-2500
Web Site:
http://www.santafemortgagerates.com
Rev.: $43,156,000
Assets: $68,256,000
Liabilities: $142,390,000
Net Worth: ($74,134,000)
Earnings: ($2,966,000)
Emp.: 2
Fiscal Year-end: 06/30/2020
Commercial & Residential Real Estate In-
vestment
N.A.I.C.S.: 523999
John V. Winfield (Chm, Pres & CEO)
Danfeng Xu (Treas, Sec & Controller)

Subsidiary (Domestic):

Portsmouth Square, Inc. (2)
1516 S Bundy Dr Ste 200, Los Angeles, CA
90025 **(68.8%)**
Tel.: (310) 889-2500
Rev.: $41,886,000
Assets: $41,402,000
Liabilities: $156,412,000
Net Worth: ($115,010,000)
Earnings: ($11,375,000)
Emp.: 4
Fiscal Year-end: 06/30/2024

Commercial Real Estate Brokerage & Man-
agement
N.A.I.C.S.: 531210
David C. Gonzalez (Pres)
John V. Winfield (Chm & CEO)

INTERLINK ELECTRONICS,
INC.
15707 Rockfield Blvd Ste 105, Irvine,
CA 92618
Tel.: (805) 484-8855 DE
Web Site:
https://www.interlinkelectronics.com
Year Founded: 1985
LINK—(NASDAQ)
Rev.: $7,493,000
Assets: $14,983,000
Liabilities: $1,135,000
Net Worth: $13,848,000
Earnings: $1,672,000
Emp.: 98
Fiscal Year-end: 12/31/22
Intuitive Interface Components & So-
lution Services
N.A.I.C.S.: 334610
Ryan J. Hoffman (CFO & Sec)
Eugene Vlad Robin (Executives)
Peter Roussak (Gen Counsel & VP)
Sreeni Rao (Gen Mgr-Gas, Environ-
mental & Air Quality Sensing)
Steven N. Bronson (Chm & CEO)

Subsidiaries:

Interlink Electronics, K.K. (1)
Kannai-Keihin Bldg 10F/1004 2-4-2 Ougi-
cyo, Naka-ku, Yokohama, 101 0031, Kana-
gawa, Japan
Tel.: (81) 45 263 6500
Web Site:
http://www.interlinkelectronics.com
Sales Range: $100-124.9 Million
Mfr of Human Interface Products
N.A.I.C.S.: 334419

KWJ Engineering, Inc. (1)
8430 Central Ave Ste C, Newark, CA
94560-3453
Tel.: (510) 794-4296
Web Site: https://www.kwjengineering.com
Engineering Services
N.A.I.C.S.: 541330

INTERLINK PRODUCTS IN-
TERNATIONAL, INC.
1315 E Elizabeth Ave, Linden, NJ
07036
Tel.: (908) 862-0023 NJ
ITLK—(OTCIQ)
Health Care Products Mfr
N.A.I.C.S.: 339112
Eli Zhadanov (Pres & CEO)

INTERMAP TECHNOLOGIES
CORPORATION
385 Inverness Pkwy Ste 105, Engle-
wood, CO 80112
Tel.: (303) 708-0955 AB
Web Site: https://www.intermap.com
Year Founded: 1997
IMP—(TSX)
Rev.: $4,720,000
Assets: $7,644,000
Liabilities: $6,158,000
Net Worth: $1,406,000
Earnings: $26,532,000
Emp.: 124
Fiscal Year-end: 12/31/20
Geospatial Surveying &
3-Dimensional Terrain Mapping Ser-
vices
N.A.I.C.S.: 541360
Greg Hoffman (VP-HR)
Patrick A. Blott (Chm & CEO)
Jennifer Bakken (CFO & Exec VP-
Fin)
Ivan Maddox (Exec VP-Comml Solu-
tions)
Stephen Griffiths (CTO & Exec VP-
Value Added Data Solutions)

Jack Schneider *(COO)*
Andrew P. Hines *(Sec)*

Subsidiaries:

Intermap Technologies Inc. **(1)**
8310 S Valley Hwy Ste 400, Englewood,
CO 80112-5809
Tel.: (303) 708-0955
Web Site: http://www.intermap.com
Geospatial Surveying & 3-Dimensional Terrain Mapping Services
N.A.I.C.S.: 541360

INTERNATIONAL BALER CORP.

5400 Rio Grande Ave, Jacksonville,
FL 32254
Tel.: (904) 358-3812   DE
Web Site: http://www.intl-baler.com
Year Founded: 1975
IBAL—(OTCIQ)
Rev.: $10,002,443
Assets: $10,366,010
Liabilities: $2,045,435
Net Worth: $8,320,575
Earnings: ($130,814)
Emp.: 45
Fiscal Year-end: 12/31/21
Waste Material Compression Machines & Balers Mfr
N.A.I.C.S.: 562213
William E. Nielsen *(CFO)*
D. Roger Griffin *(Pres & CEO)*
Ronald L. McDaniel *(Chm)*

INTERNATIONAL BANCSHARES CORPORATION

1200 San Bernardo Ave, Laredo, TX
78042-1359
Tel.: (956) 722-7611   TX
Web Site: https://www.ibc.com
Year Founded: 1979
IBOC—(NASDAQ)
Rev.: $712,915,000
Assets: $15,501,476,000
Liabilities: $13,456,717,000
Net Worth: $2,044,759,000
Earnings: $300,232,000
Emp.: 1,974
Fiscal Year-end: 12/31/22
Bank Holding Company
N.A.I.C.S.: 551111
Imelda Navarro *(Pres-Retail Banking-International Bank of Commerce)*
Judith I. Wawroski *(CFO, Chief Acctg Officer & Treas)*
Dennis E. Nixon *(Chm, Pres & CEO)*
Hilda V. Torres *(Asst Sec)*
Dalia F. Martinez *(VP)*

Subsidiaries:

IBC Life Insurance Company **(1)**
1200 San Bernardo Ave, Laredo, TX 78042
Tel.: (956) 722-7611
Fire Insurance Services
N.A.I.C.S.: 524113

International Bank of Commerce **(1)**
1200 San Bernardo Ave, Laredo, TX 78042-1359
Tel.: (956) 722-7611
Sales Range: $800-899.9 Million
Emp.: 3,000
Federal Savings Institutions
N.A.I.C.S.: 518210
Imelda Navarro *(Pres-Retail Banking)*
Dennis E. Nixon *(Pres & CEO)*
Eliza V. Gonzalez *(Exec VP-Corp Div)*
Nativido Lozano *(Exec VP)*
Rosalinda Ramirez *(Exec VP)*
Mike K. Sohn *(Pres, Pres/CEO-San Antonio & Texas & CEO-San Antonio)*
Adrian Villarreal *(Pres, Pres/CEO-McAllen & Texas & CEO-McAllen)*
Guillermo Garcia *(Exec VP)*
Eliza Gonzalez *(Officer)*
Derek Schmidt *(Pres & Pres/CEO-Port Lavaca)*
Gustavo A. Barrera *(Pres & Pres/CEO-Corpus Christi & Texas)*

Hector J. Cerna *(Pres & Pres/CEO-Eagle Pass & Texas)*
Jay Rogers *(Pres & Pres/CEO-Houston-Texas)*
Jeff Samples *(Pres)*
Kyle McElvaney *(Pres)*
Ricardo Ramirez *(Pres)*
Robert B. Barnes *(Pres & Pres/CEO-Austin-Texas)*

Subsidiary (Domestic):

International Bank of Commerce,
Brownsville **(2)**
1600 Ruben Torres Blvd, Brownsville, TX
78526
Tel.: (956) 547-1000
Web Site: http://www.ibc.com
Sales Range: $75-99.9 Million
Emp.: 218
Commercial Banking Services
N.A.I.C.S.: 522110

International Bank of Commerce,
Zapata **(2)**
US Hwy 83 at 10th Ave, Zapata, TX 78076-1030
Tel.: (956) 765-8361
Web Site: https://www.ibc.com
Sales Range: $50-74.9 Million
Emp.: 123
Commericial Banking
N.A.I.C.S.: 522110
Ricardo Ramirez *(Pres)*

International Bank of Commerce,
Oklahoma **(1)**
3817 NW Expy Ste 100, Oklahoma City,
OK 73112
Tel.: (405) 841-2100
Company Holding Services
N.A.I.C.S.: 551111
Kyle McElvaney *(Pres)*

INTERNATIONAL BUSINESS MACHINES CORPORATION

1 New Orchard Rd, Armonk, NY
10504-1722
Tel.: (914) 499-1900   NY
Web Site: https://www.ibm.com
Year Founded: 1911
IBM—(NYSE)
Rev.: $61,860,000,000
Assets: $135,241,000,000
Liabilities: $112,628,000,000
Net Worth: $22,613,000,000
Earnings: $7,502,000,000
Emp.: 305,300
Fiscal Year-end: 12/31/23
Software Development Services
N.A.I.C.S.: 541511
Jonathan H. Adashek *(Chief Comm Officer)*
Gary Cohn *(Vice Chm)*
Dario Gil *(Sr VP & Dir-Res)*
Nickle LaMoreaux *(Chief HR Officer & Sr VP)*
Roger Premo *(Gen Mgr-Corp Strategy)*
Ric Lewis *(Sr VP-Infrastructure)*
Dinesh Nirmal *(Sr VP-Products & IBM Software)*
Alexander Stern *(Sr VP)*
Joanne Wright *(Sr VP-Transformation & Operations)*
Kareem Yusuf *(Sr VP-Product Mgmt & Growth)*
Chandar Pattabhiram *(Executives)*
Arvind Krishna *(Chm & CEO)*
James J. Kavanaugh *(CFO, CFO & Sr VP)*

Subsidiaries:

7Summits, LLC **(1)**
1110 N Old World 3rd St Ste 500, Milwaukee, WI 53203-1121
Web Site: http://www.7summitsagency.com
Advertising Agencies
N.A.I.C.S.: 541810
R. J. Reimers *(Chief Customer Officer)*
Paul Stillmank *(Founder & CEO)*
Matt Henwood *(Exec VP-Svc Delivery)*

Nick Ulfers *(Sr VP-Sls & Alliances)*
Bethany K. Perkins *(VP-Mktg)*
John Price *(Sr VP-Tech Svcs & Solutions)*
Michelle Hicks-Tobias *(Controller)*

Apptio, Inc. **(1)**
11100 NE 8th St Ste 600, Bellevue, WA
98004
Web Site: http://www.apptio.com
Rev.: $188,519,000
Assets: $234,251,000
Liabilities: $146,001,000
Net Worth: $88,250,000
Earnings: ($25,621,000)
Fiscal Year-end: 12/31/2017
Technology Business Management Solutions
N.A.I.C.S.: 513210
Susanna Morgan *(Sr VP-Fin & IR)*
Paul McLachlan *(Co-Founder & CTO)*
Lawrence Blasko *(Chief Revenue Officer)*
Dione Hedgpeth *(Sr VP-Customer Success)*
Britt Provost *(Sr VP-People & Culture)*
John Morrow *(Gen Counsel & Exec VP-Corp Dev)*
Susanna Morgan *(Sr VP-Fin & IR)*
Theo Beack *(Exec VP-Products & Engrg)*
Mark Jancola *(VP & Gen Mgr-Digital Fuel Bus)*
Mahesh Gidwani *(Sr VP-Professional Svcs)*
Colin Rowland *(Sr VP-EMEA)*
Sunny Gupta *(CEO)*
Subramanian Krishnan *(VP/Gen Mgr-India)*
Anton Van Deth *(CMO)*
Abuna Demoz *(VP-Engrg)*

Subsidiary (Non-US):

Apptio Europe Limited **(2)**
10 Fenchurch Street 5th Floor, London,
EC3M 3BE, United Kingdom
Tel.: (44) 2030148300
Business Management Software Development Services
N.A.I.C.S.: 541511
Catherine Picknell *(Sr Mgr-Mktg)*

Apptio France SAS **(2)**
15 Rue Beaujon, 75008, Paris, France
Tel.: (33) 142999533
Business Management Software Development Services
N.A.I.C.S.: 541511

Apptio Italy S.r.l. **(2)**
Via Paleocapa 7, 20121, Milan, Italy
Tel.: (39) 0230315841
Business Management Software Development Services
N.A.I.C.S.: 541511

Apptio Pty Ltd. **(2)**
44 Market Street, Sydney, 2000, NSW,
Australia
Tel.: (61) 290918092
Business Management Software Development Services
N.A.I.C.S.: 541511
Jing Wang *(Sr Engr-Technical Support)*

Banco IBM S.A. **(1)**
Rua Tutoia 1157, 04007-900, Sao Paulo,
Brazil
Tel.: (55) 1121325114
Web Site: http://www.ibm.com
Computer Peripheral Equipment & Software Whslr
N.A.I.C.S.: 423430

Bermuda Computer Services
Ltd. **(1)**
20 Dundonald Street, PO Box HM 1196,
Hamilton, HM 12, Bermuda
Tel.: (441) 2952969
Web Site: http://www.ibm.com
Sales Range: $150-199.9 Million
Computers & Computer Products Sales & Services
N.A.I.C.S.: 423430

Compagnie IBM France, S.A. **(1)**
Center de Relations Clients, BP 51,
F-45802, Saint Jean de Braye,
France **(100%)**
Tel.: (33) 238557777
Web Site: http://www.ibm.com
Sales Range: $150-199.9 Million
Office Machines & Computers Sales & Services
N.A.I.C.S.: 423430

Subsidiary (Non-US):

IBM Tunisie **(2)**
Rue du Lac d'Annecy, Les Berges du Lac,
1053, Tunis, Tunisia **(100%)**
Tel.: (216) 7 116 1800
Web Site: https://www.ibm.com
Office Machines & Computers Sales & Services
N.A.I.C.S.: 811210

Companhia IBM Portuguesa,
S.A. **(1)**
Rua do Mar da China n3, 1990-138, Lisbon, Portugal **(100%)**
Tel.: (351) 218927000
Web Site: http://www.ibm.com
Sales Range: $150-199.9 Million
Emp.: 100
Software Development Services
N.A.I.C.S.: 513210

Emptoris, Inc. **(1)**
200 Wheeler Road, Burlington, MA 01803
Tel.: (781) 993-9212
Web Site: http://www.emptoris.com
Sales Range: $50-74.9 Million
Emp.: 725
Strategic Supply & Contract Management Software Publisher
N.A.I.C.S.: 513210

Gravitant, Inc. **(1)**
11501 Burnet Rd Bldg 905 Fl 2, Austin, TX
78758-3400
Tel.: (512) 535-7399
Web Site: http://www.gravitant.com
Sales Range: $1-9.9 Million
Emp.: 200
Software & IT Service Solutions
N.A.I.C.S.: 513210
Robert Erickson *(VP-Products & Mktg)*
Mohammed Farooq *(Chm & CEO)*
Raghunath Sapuram *(CTO)*
Jay Link *(Sr VP-Sls)*
Manish Modh *(CTO)*
Bob Pujman *(VP-Customer Svcs)*
Prasad Bandreddi *(VP-Engrg)*

Guardium, Inc. **(1)**
550 King St # 1, Littleton, MA 01460-6245
Tel.: (781) 487-9400
Web Site: http://www.guardium.com
Sales Range: $1-9.9 Million
Emp.: 160
Data Security Solutions
N.A.I.C.S.: 518210

IBM (China) Investment Company
Limited **(1)**
25/F Pangu Plaza No 27 Central North
Fourth Ring Road, Chaoyang District, Beijing, 100101, China
Tel.: (86) 1063618888
Web Site: http://www.ibm.com
Personal Computer Mfr
N.A.I.C.S.: 334111

IBM (International Business Machines) Turk Ltd Sirketi **(1)**
Buyukdere Caddesi Yapi Kredi Plaza B Blok
Levent, Istanbul, 34330, Turkiye **(100%)**
Tel.: (90) 2123171000
Web Site: http://www.ibm.com
Sales Range: $75-99.9 Million
Office Machines & Computers Sales & Services
N.A.I.C.S.: 811210

Joint Venture (Domestic):

I-Bimsa Uluslararasi Is Bilgi
Veyonetim Sistemleri A.S. **(2)**
Acarlar yp Merkezi D Blok Kat 3-4 Kavacyk,
Istanbul, 34805, Turkiye
Tel.: (90) 2164251050
Web Site: http://www.bimsa.com.tr
Sales Range: $50-74.9 Million
Emp.: 100
Business Information & Management Systems; Owned 50% by Haci Omer Sabanci Holding A.S. & 50% by International Business Machines Corporation
N.A.I.C.S.: 551112

IBM Argentina Sociedad de Responsabilidad Limitada **(1)**
Ingeniero Butty 275, C1001AFA, Buenos

International Business Machines
Corporation—(Continued)

Aires, Argentina
Tel.: (54) 115 286 4898
Web Site: https://www.ibm.com
Information Technology Services
N.A.I.C.S.: 519290

IBM Argentina, S.A.   **(1)**
Ingeniero Butty 275, C1001AFA, Buenos
Aires, Argentina   **(100%)**
Tel.: (54) 1152864898
Web Site: https://www.ibm.com
Sales Range: $1-4.9 Billion
Emp.: 5,000
Computers & Computer Products Sales &
Services
N.A.I.C.S.: 423430

IBM Australia Limited   **(1)**
Level 13 IBM Centre 601 Pacific Highway,
Saint Leonards, 2065, NSW, Australia
Tel.: (61) 293544000
Web Site: http://www.ibm.com.au
Sales Range: $650-699.9 Million
Emp.: 1,000
Personal Computer & Other Computer
Products Whslr
N.A.I.C.S.: 423430
David La Rose *(Gen Mgr)*

IBM Bahamas Limited   **(1)**
2nd Terrace & Collins Ave, PO Box SS
6400, Nassau, SS6400, Bahamas **(100%)**
Tel.: (242) 3237350
Web Site: http://www.ibm.com
Sales Range: $25-49.9 Million
Emp.: 12
Computers & Computer Products Sales &
Services
N.A.I.C.S.: 423430

**IBM Brasil - Industria, Maquinas e
Servicos Limitada**   **(1)**
Rua Tutoia 1157, Sao Paulo, 04007-900,
SP, Brazil   **(100%)**
Tel.: (55) 1130032717
Web Site: https://www.ibm.com
Computers & Computer Products Sales &
Services
N.A.I.C.S.: 423430

**IBM Brasil-Industria, Maquinas e Ser-
vicos Limitada**   **(1)**
Rua Tutoia 1157, 04007-900, Sao Paulo,
Brazil
Tel.: (55) 8007014262
Web Site: http://www.ibm.com
Computer Peripheral Equipment & Software
Whslr
N.A.I.C.S.: 423430

IBM Bulgaria Ltd.   **(1)**
36 Dragan Tzankov Str, Sofia, 1040,
Bulgaria   **(100%)**
Tel.: (359) 29733171
Web Site: http://www.ibm.com
Sales Range: $75-99.9 Million
Emp.: 150
Office Machines & Computers Sales & Ser-
vices
N.A.I.C.S.: 423430

IBM Burkina Faso SARL   **(1)**
01 - Cite Sonar villa N3, BP 1778, Ouaga-
dougou, Burkina Faso
Tel.: (226) 5 031 5916
Web Site: http://www.ibm.com
Information Technology Services
N.A.I.C.S.: 519290

IBM Canada Limited   **(1)**
3600 Steeles Avenue East, Markham, L3R
9Z7, ON, Canada   **(100%)**
Tel.: (905) 316-5000
Web Site: https://www.ibm.com
Sales Range: $150-199.9 Million
Computers & Computer Products Sales &
Services
N.A.I.C.S.: 423430

Subsidiary (Domestic):

Groupe LGS Inc.   **(2)**
1360 Rene-Levesque West Ste 400, Mon-
treal, H3G 2W6, QC, Canada   **(100%)**
Tel.: (514) 964-0939
Web Site: http://www.lgs.com
Sales Range: $100-124.9 Million
Emp.: 300
Information Technology Consulting Services

N.A.I.C.S.: 541611 &

Subsidiary (Non-US):

IBM Application Services   **(3)**
6 avenue Usines, 90000, Belfort, France
Tel.: (33) 384586400
Sales Range: $75-99.9 Million
Information Technology Management Ser-
vices
N.A.I.C.S.: 541611

Subsidiary (Domestic):

LGS Group Inc   **(3)**
2700 Laurier Blvd Tour Champlain Suite
4000 Sainte-Foy, Quebec, G1V 4K5, QC,
Canada   **(100%)**
Tel.: (418) 653-6574
Web Site: http://www.lgs.com
Sales Range: $10-24.9 Million
Emp.: 300
Computer Services
N.A.I.C.S.: 541519
Gratien Cote *(VP)*
Bernard Roy *(Pres)*
Jean Louis Proulx *(Dir-Human Resources)*
Sylvain Roy *(Sr Dir)*
Michel Dumas *(Co-Pres)*
Francois Dufresne *(Co-Pres)*
Eliane Martel *(Dir)*
Paula Morris *(Dir)*
Joelle Gaudet *(Dir)*
Diane Bouchard *(Dir)*
Lyne Savaria *(Dir-Human Resources)*
Claude Fortin *(Dir)*
Marie B. Deschamps *(Dir-Communications)*
Marco Siconolfi *(CFO)*

Branch (Domestic):

IBM Canada Limited   **(2)**
23 boulevard de lAeroport, Bromont, J2L
1A3, QC, Canada   **(100%)**
Tel.: (450) 534-6967
Web Site: http://www.ibm.com
Emp.: 300
Computers & Computer Products Sales &
Services
N.A.I.C.S.: 423430

IBM Canada Limited   **(2)**
227 11th Ave SW, Calgary, T2R 1R9, AB,
Canada   **(100%)**
Tel.: (403) 539-3100
Web Site: http://www.can.ibm.com
Sales Range: $125-149.9 Million
Emp.: 600
Computers & Computer Products Sales &
Services
N.A.I.C.S.: 423430

IBM Canada Limited   **(2)**
10044 108th St Nw, Edmonton, T5J 3S7,
AB, Canada
Tel.: (780) 642-4100
Web Site: http://www.ca.ibm.com
Sales Range: $25-49.9 Million
Emp.: 200
Computers & Computer Products Sales &
Services
N.A.I.C.S.: 423430

Subsidiary (Domestic):

**ISM Information Systems Manage-
ment Corporation**   **(2)**
200-1 Research Drive, Regina, S4S 7H1,
SK, Canada
Tel.: (306) 781-8488
Web Site: https://www.ismcanada.com
Custom Computer Programming Services
N.A.I.C.S.: 541511
Kerry Cibart *(Chief Privacy Officer)*
Kevin Neish *(VP-Sales-Marketing)*
Hasnain Versi *(Pres & CEO)*

IBM Ceska Republika spol. sr.o.   **(1)**
V Parku 2294/4 The Park, Chodov, 148 00,
Prague, 4, Czech Republic   **(100%)**
Tel.: (420) 272131111
Web Site: http://www.ibm.com
Sales Range: $150-199.9 Million
Computers & Computer Products Sales &
Services
N.A.I.C.S.: 423430

IBM China Company Limited   **(1)**
25/F Pangu Plaza No 27 Central North
Fourth Ring Road, Chaoyang District, Bei-

jing, 100101, Chaoyang, China   **(100%)**
Tel.: (86) 1063618888
Web Site: https://www.ibm.com
Sales Range: $500-549.9 Million
Emp.: 2,000
Computers & Computer Products Sales &
Services
N.A.I.C.S.: 811210
Chen Liming *(Chm-Greater China)*

IBM China/Hong Kong Limited   **(1)**
10/Fl PCCW Tower Taikoo Place 979 King's
Road, 979 Kings Road, Quarry Bay, China
(Hong Kong)   **(100%)**
Tel.: (852) 2 825 6222
Web Site: https://www.ibm.com
Sales Range: $25-49.9 Million
Emp.: 30
Computers & Computer Products Sales &
Services
N.A.I.C.S.: 423430

IBM Congo SARL   **(1)**
4 Avenue Foch Centre-Ville, Brazzaville,
Congo, Republic of
Tel.: (242) 44535353
Web Site: http://www.ibm.com
Personal Computer Mfr
N.A.I.C.S.: 334111

IBM Credit LLC   **(1)**
1 N Castle Dr, Armonk, NY 10504
Tel.: (914) 765-1900
Rev.: $1,128,000,000
Assets: $23,953,000,000
Liabilities: $21,731,000,000
Net Worth: $2,222,000,000
Earnings: $413,000,000
Emp.: 2,100
Fiscal Year-end: 12/31/2020
Financial Support Services
N.A.I.C.S.: 541611
Adam Wilson *(CFO & VP-Fin)*
Henry Voldman *(Controller & Dir-Fin)*
Simon J. Beaumont *(Chm, Pres & CEO)*
Robert F. Del Bene *(Mgr)*
Andrew P. Urbansky *(Mgr)*

IBM Croatia Ltd.   **(1)**
Miramarska 23, 10000, Zagreb,
Croatia   **(100%)**
Tel.: (385) 16308100
Web Site: https://www.ibm.com
Sales Range: $50-74.9 Million
Emp.: 175
Computers & Computer Products Sales &
Services
N.A.I.C.S.: 811210

IBM Danmark A/S   **(1)**
Provensvej 1, 2605, Brondby,
Denmark   **(100%)**
Tel.: (45) 45240000
Web Site: http://www.ibm.com
Sales Range: $1-4.9 Billion
Emp.: 4,000
Office Equipment & Computers Sales &
Services
N.A.I.C.S.: 423430

IBM Deutschland GmbH   **(1)**
IBM Allee 1, 71139, Ehningen,
Germany   **(100%)**
Tel.: (49) 1803313233
Web Site: http://www.ibm.de
Sales Range: $600-649.9 Million
Emp.: 2,500
Computers & Computer Products Mfr, Sales
& Services
N.A.I.C.S.: 334111

Subsidiary (Non-US):

**IBM Oesterreich Internationale Buero-
maschinen Gesellschaft m.b.H.**   **(2)**
Obere Donaustrasse 95, 1020, Vienna,
Austria   **(100%)**
Tel.: (43) 121 1450
Web Site: https://www.ibm.com
Sales Range: $50-74.9 Million
Emp.: 75
Computers & Computer Products Sales &
Services
N.A.I.C.S.: 423430

IBM Schweiz AG   **(2)**
Vulkanstrasse 106, 8010, Zurich,
Switzerland   **(100%)**
Tel.: (41) 583334455
Web Site: https://www.ibm.com

Sales Range: $75-99.9 Million
Computers & Computer Products Sales &
Services
N.A.I.C.S.: 811210

**IBM Deutschland Kreditbank
GmbH**   **(1)**
IBM-Allee 1, 71139, Ehningen, Germany
Tel.: (49) 7034150
Web Site: http://www.ibm.com
Computer Peripheral Equipment & Software
Whslr
N.A.I.C.S.: 423430
Marco Kempf *(Co-CEO)*
Robert Staudinger *(Co-CEO)*

IBM East Africa Limited   **(1)**
04th Floor Atrium Building Cnr Chaka and
Lenana Road, PO Box 35475, Kilimani,
00200, Nairobi, Kenya   **(100%)**
Tel.: (254) 20 515 3000
Web Site: https://www.ibm.com
Sales Range: $100-124.9 Million
Computers & Computer Products Sales &
Services
N.A.I.C.S.: 811210

IBM East Europe/Asia Ltd.   **(1)**
10 Presnenskaya Emb, Moscow, 123112,
Russia   **(100%)**
Tel.: (7) 4957758800
Web Site: https://www.ibm.com
Sales Range: $75-99.9 Million
Emp.: 200
Office Machines & Computers Sales & Ser-
vices
N.A.I.C.S.: 811210

IBM Eesti Osauhing   **(1)**
Toompuiestee 33 A, 10149, Tallinn, Estonia
Tel.: (372) 660 0800
Web Site: https://www.ibm.com
Personal Computer Mfr
N.A.I.C.S.: 334111

IBM Estonia Ou   **(1)**
Toompuiestee 33a, 10149, Tallinn,
Estonia   **(100%)**
Tel.: (372) 6600800
Web Site: https://www.ibm.com
Sales Range: $10-24.9 Million
Emp.: 30
Office Machines & Computers Sales & Ser-
vices
N.A.I.C.S.: 811210

IBM Finans Norge AS   **(1)**
Lakkegata 53, 0187, Oslo, Norway
Tel.: (47) 66998000
Software & Networking Development Ser-
vices
N.A.I.C.S.: 513210

IBM Foreign Sales Corporation   **(1)**
Radley Court Collymore Rock Street, PO
Box 184, Saint Michael, Barbados
Tel.: (246) 4260670
Web Site: http://www.ibm.com
Sales Range: $150-199.9 Million
Emp.: 30
Computers & Computer Products Sales &
Services
N.A.I.C.S.: 423430

IBM France Financement, S.A.   **(1)**
17 avenue de l'Europe, 92275, Bois-
Colombes, Cedex, France
Tel.: (33) 158750000
Web Site: http://www.ibm.com
Computer Peripheral Equipment & Software
Whslr
N.A.I.C.S.: 423430

IBM Global Financing   **(1)**
1 New Orchard Rd, Armonk, NY 10504-
1785
Tel.: (914) 499-1900
Web Site: https://www.ibm.com
Information Technology Sales Financing &
Leasing Services
N.A.I.C.S.: 522220

**IBM Global Financing Australia
Limited**   **(1)**
Level 13 IBM Centre 601 Pacific Highway,
Saint Leonards, 2065, NSW, Australia
Tel.: (61) 293 544 0002
Web Site: http://www.ibm.com.au
Computer Peripheral Equipment & Software
Whslr

N.A.I.C.S.: 423430

IBM Global Financing Canada Corporation (1)
3600 Steeles Ave E, Markham, L3R 9Z7, ON, Canada
Tel.: (800) 426-3889
Computer Mfr
N.A.I.C.S.: 334111

IBM Global Financing Deutschland GmbH (1)
IBM-Allee 1, 71139, Ehningen, Germany
Tel.: (49) 8002255426
Computer Mfr
N.A.I.C.S.: 334111

IBM Global Financing Espana, S.L.U. (1)
Santa Hortensia 26-28, 28002, Madrid, Spain
Tel.: (34) 902022005
Computer Mfr
N.A.I.C.S.: 334111

IBM Global Financing Finland Oy (1)
Laajalahdentie 23, 00330, Helsinki, Finland
Tel.: (358) 94591
Computer Mfr
N.A.I.C.S.: 334111

IBM Global Financing Schweiz GmbH (1)
Vulkanstrasse 106, 8010, Zurich, Switzerland
Tel.: (41) 583335100
Computer Mfr
N.A.I.C.S.: 334111

IBM Global Financing Sweden AB (1)
Kista Allecag 60, Kista, 164 55, Stockholm, Sweden
Tel.: (46) 87931000
Software & Networking Development Services
N.A.I.C.S.: 513210

IBM Global Services (1)
1 New Orchard Rd, Armonk, NY 10504
Tel.: (914) 499-1900
Web Site: http://www.ibm.com
Information Technology Infrastructure, Application Management, System Integration & Consulting Services
N.A.I.C.S.: 541519

Division (Domestic):

IBM Global Business Services (2)
294 Route 100, Somers, NY 10589
Tel.: (914) 766-4900
Web Site: http://www.ibm.com
Application Management, System Integration & Consulting Services
N.A.I.C.S.: 541519
Jesus B. Mantas (*Mng Partner-Strategy, Innovation, and Corp Dev-Global*)

IBM Global Technology Services (2)
Rte 100, Somers, NY 10589
Tel.: (914) 766-4900
Web Site: https://www.ibm.com
Sales Range: $100-124.9 Million
Emp.: 200
Information Technology Infrastructure Services
N.A.I.C.S.: 541513
Bridget E. Karlin (*CTO & VP*)
Violeta Fabe (*Head-Retail*)

Unit (Domestic):

IBM Business Continuity & Resiliency Services (3)
294 Rte 100, Somers, NY 10589
Tel.: (914) 766-4900
Web Site: http://www.ibm.com
Sales Range: $100-124.9 Million
Data Recovery Technology & Services
N.A.I.C.S.: 541511

IBM Global Services Espana, S.A. (1)
Calle Del Mar Adriatico 2, San Fernando de Henares, 28830, Spain
Tel.: (34) 913976611
Software & Networking Development Services
N.A.I.C.S.: 513210

IBM Hellas Information Handling Systems S.A. (1)
284 Kifissias Ave, 15232, Halandri, Greece (100%)
Tel.: (30) 2106881220
Web Site: http://www.ibm.com
Sales Range: $75-99.9 Million
Emp.: 200
Office Machines & Computers Sales & Services
N.A.I.C.S.: 423430
Spyros Poulidas (*Gen Mgr*)

IBM India Private Limited (1)
No 12 Subramanya Arcade Bannerghatta Main Road, Bengaluru, 560 029, India
Tel.: (91) 8026788015
Web Site: https://www.ibm.com
Computers & Computer Products Sales & Services
N.A.I.C.S.: 811210

IBM International Group Capital LLC (1)
1 New Orchard Rd, Armonk, NY 10504-1722
Tel.: (914) 499-5454
Web Site: http://www.ibm.com
Emp.: 500
Computer System Design Services
N.A.I.C.S.: 541512

IBM Ireland Limited (1)
IBM House Shelbourne Road, Dublin, 4, Ireland (100%)
Tel.: (353) 1 815 4000
Web Site: https://www.ibm.com
Sales Range: $1-4.9 Billion
Computers & Computer Products Sales & Services
N.A.I.C.S.: 423430

IBM Ireland Product Distribution Limited (1)
IBM House Shelbourne Road, Ballsbridge, Dublin, Ireland
Tel.: (353) 18810085
Web Site: http://www.ibm.com
Personal Computer Mfr
N.A.I.C.S.: 334111

IBM Israel Limited (1)
94 shlomo shmeltzer, 49527, Petah Tikva, Israel
Tel.: (972) 80 060 0888
Web Site: https://www.ibm.com
Computers & Computer Products Sales & Services
N.A.I.C.S.: 423430

IBM Italia S.p.A. (1)
Circonvallazione Idroscalo, 20090, Segrate, Milan, Italy (100%)
Tel.: (39) 0270312168
Web Site: http://www.ibm.com
Sales Range: $75-99.9 Million
Computers & Computer Products Sales, Distr & Services
N.A.I.C.S.: 811210

Branch (Non-US):

IBM Italia S.p.A. - Cyprus (2)
42-44 Grivas Dighenis Avenue, PO Box 22019, 1080, Nicosia, Cyprus
Tel.: (357) 22841100
Web Site: http://www.ibm.com.cy
Sales Range: $75-99.9 Million
Emp.: 40
Computers & Computer Products Sales & Services
N.A.I.C.S.: 811210

IBM Jamaica (1)
52 Knutsford Boulevard Kingston 5, PO Box 391, New Kingston, Kingston, Jamaica (100%)
Tel.: (876) 9263170
Web Site: http://www.ibm.com
Sales Range: $50-74.9 Million
Emp.: 50
Computers & Computer Products Sales & Services
N.A.I.C.S.: 423430

IBM Japan Ltd (1)
19-21 Nihonbashi Hakozakicho, Chuo-ku, Tokyo, 103-8510, Japan (100%)
Tel.: (81) 36 667 1111
Web Site: https://www.ibm.com

Sales Range: $1-4.9 Billion
Emp.: 20,000
Computers & Computer Products Sales & Services
N.A.I.C.S.: 423430
Toshiyuki Fukuchi (*Exec VP*)
Akio Yamaguchi (*Pres & Exec Officer*)
Anthony Luna (*Mng Exec Officer-Intellectual Property*)
Toshimitsu Misawa (*VP-Business Development*)

Affiliate (Domestic):

NI Information System Co., Ltd. (2)
3-4-1 Marunouchi Shinkokusai, Chiyoda-ku, Tokyo, 100-8360, Japan (51%)
Tel.: (81) 3 3216 5800
Web Site: http://www.ibm.com
Sales Range: $25-49.9 Million
Emp.: 188
Information Technology Support & System Integration Services
N.A.I.C.S.: 541513
Kazumi Wakamatsu (*Pres*)

Joint Venture (Domestic):

Nippon Information & Communication Corporation (2)
St Luke's Garden Tower 15F 8-1 Akashi-cho, Chuo-ku, Tokyo, 104-0044, Japan (50%)
Tel.: (81) 362781111
Web Site: http://www.niandc.co.jp
Sales Range: $450-499.9 Million
Emp.: 1,193
Software Development Services
N.A.I.C.S.: 541511
Yujiro Hirose (*Pres & CEO*)
Goichi Suzaki (*COO & Sr Exec VP*)
Kiyoshi Nohara (*Sr VP*)
Susumu Uchida (*Sr VP*)
Fumio Harukawa (*Sr Exec Officer*)
Takashi Date (*Sr Exec Officer*)
Nobuki Yasuyama (*Sr Exec Officer*)
Shin Takahashi (*Sr Exec Officer*)
Shiro Yuuki (*Exec Officer*)
Kimio Tamura (*Auditor*)
Katsumi Kuroda (*Auditor*)

Subsidiary (Domestic):

NIandC NETSYSTEM Inc. (3)
580 Solid Square West Building 15F 580 Horikawacho, Saiwai-ku, Kawasaki, 212-0013, Japan
Tel.: (81) 44 556 8540
Web Site: http://www.niandcnetsystem.co.jp
Emp.: 171
Information Technology Consulting Services
N.A.I.C.S.: 541512
Hideki Yamauchi (*Pres*)

NIandC SOFT Inc. (3)
Akashi-cho 6-4 Nichirei Akashi-cho Building 2F, Chuo-ku, Tokyo, 104-0044, Japan
Tel.: (81) 362781212
Web Site: http://www.nicsoft.co.jp
Emp.: 155
Software Development Services
N.A.I.C.S.: 513210
Shiro Yuki (*Pres*)

IBM Korea, Inc. (1)
3 IFC 10 Gukjegeumyung-ro, Yeongdeungpo-gu, Seoul, Korea (South) (100%)
Tel.: (82) 237817114
Web Site: http://www.ibm.com
Sales Range: $1-4.9 Billion
Emp.: 3,000
Computers & Computer Products Sales & Services
N.A.I.C.S.: 423430

IBM Kuwait SPC (1)
Al Hamra Tower Shuhada Street, PO Box 5819, Safat, 13059, Kuwait, Kuwait
Tel.: (965) 22203550
Software Development Services
N.A.I.C.S.: 541511
Takreem El-Tohamy (*Gen Mgr*)

IBM Lietuva (1)
Seimyniskiu 3, 09312, Vilnius, Lithuania (100%)
Tel.: (370) 52786600
Web Site: https://www.ibm.com

Sales Range: $50-74.9 Million
Emp.: 200
Computers & Computer Products Sales & Services
N.A.I.C.S.: 811210

IBM Luxembourg Sarl (1)
23 - 25 Rue du puits Romain, 8070, Bertrange, Luxembourg
Tel.: (352) 23603851
Web Site: https://www.ibm.com
Information Technology Development Services
N.A.I.C.S.: 541511

IBM Magyarorszagi Kft (1)
Neumann Janos u 1, 1117, Budapest, Hungary
Tel.: (36) 1 382 5720
Web Site: https://www.ibm.com
Computer Design Services
N.A.I.C.S.: 541512

IBM Malaysia Sdn. Bhd. (1)
19th Floor Plaza IBM No 8 First Avenue, Persiaran Bandar Utama, 47800, Petaling Jaya, Selangor, Malaysia (100%)
Tel.: (60) 32 301 8888
Web Site: https://www.ibm.com
Sales Range: $100-124.9 Million
Emp.: 4,000
Computers & Computer Products Sales & Services
N.A.I.C.S.: 811210

IBM Malta Limited (1)
85 St John St, Valletta, VLT 1165, Malta
Tel.: (356) 8664037638
Web Site: https://www.ibm.com
Computer System Design Services
N.A.I.C.S.: 541512

IBM Maroc (1)
Casablanca Nearshore Park Shore 19, 1100 Bd Al Qods - Quartier Sidi Maarouf, 20270, Casablanca, Morocco
Tel.: (212) 522509035
Web Site: https://www.ibm.com
Information Technology Services
N.A.I.C.S.: 513210

IBM Mauritius (1)
Unit 2EF 2nd Floor Standard Chartered Tower Cybercity, Ebene, Mauritius
Tel.: (230) 4679801
Web Site: http://www.ibm.com
Emp.: 15
Personal Computer Mfr
N.A.I.C.S.: 334111

IBM Middle East FZ-LLC (1)
Dubai Internet City IBM Building 3rd Level, PO Box 27242, Dubai, United Arab Emirates (100%)
Tel.: (971) 43907000
Web Site: http://www.ibm.com
Sales Range: $75-99.9 Million
Emp.: 1,000
Office Machines & Computers Sales & Services
N.A.I.C.S.: 423430

IBM Nederland B.V. (1)
Johan Huizingalaan 765, PO Box 9999, 1066 VH, Amsterdam, Netherlands (100%)
Tel.: (31) 205135151
Web Site: http://www.ibm.com
Sales Range: $150-199.9 Million
Emp.: 200
Computers & Computer Products Sales & Services
N.A.I.C.S.: 423430

IBM Nederland Financieringen B.V. (1)
Johan Huizingalaan 765, 1066 VH, Amsterdam, Netherlands
Tel.: (31) 205145461
Computer Mfr
N.A.I.C.S.: 334111

IBM Netherlands Antilles (1)
Schottegatweg Oost 18, PO Box 3612, Willemstad, Curacao (100%)
Tel.: (599) 97341400
Web Site: http://www.ibm.com
Sales Range: $25-49.9 Million
Emp.: 23
Computers & Computer Products Sales & Services

International Business Machines
Corporation—(Continued)

N.A.I.C.S.: 423430

IBM New Zealand Limited (1)
Level 4 30 Gaunt Street Wellesley Street,
PO Box 6840, Auckland, 1010, New
Zealand **(100%)**
Tel.: (64) 45765999
Web Site: http://www.ibm.com
Sales Range: $700-749.9 Million
Emp.: 1,000
Computer & Computer Products Sales &
Services
N.A.I.C.S.: 423430
David La Rose (Gen Mgr)

IBM Pakistan (1)
1st & 2nd Floors Nice Trade Orbit Building
Plot No 44, A & B PECHS Block 6 Shahrah-
e-Faisal, Karachi, 75400, Pakistan
Tel.: (92) 21111426426
Web Site: http://www.ibm.com
Sales Range: $75-99.9 Million
Emp.: 150
Computers & Computer Products Sales &
Services
N.A.I.C.S.: 423430

IBM Philippines, Incorporated (1)
28/F One World Place Bldg 32nd Street
corner 9th Avenue, Bonifacio Global City,
Taguig, 1634, Philippines **(100%)**
Tel.: (63) 289952426
Web Site: https://www.ibm.com
Computers & Computer Products Sales &
Services
N.A.I.C.S.: 423430
Aileen Judan-Jiao (Mng Dir)

IBM Polska Sp.z.o.o. (1)
Ul Krakowiakow 32, 02-255, Warsaw,
Poland **(100%)**
Tel.: (48) 22 878 6777
Web Site: https://www.ibm.com
Sales Range: $700-749.9 Million
Emp.: 1,000
Office Machines & Computers Sales, Distr
& Services
N.A.I.C.S.: 423430

IBM Qatar SSC (1)
Level 14 Commercial Bank Plaza West Bay,
PO Box 27111, Doha, Qatar
Tel.: (974) 4527970
Web Site: http://www.ibm.com
Personal Computer Mfr
N.A.I.C.S.: 334111

IBM Romania Srl (1)
Sos Orhideelor 15D Building A - The Bridge
5th Floor Sector 6, 060071, Bucharest,
Romania **(100%)**
Tel.: (40) 214058100
Web Site: http://www.ibm.com
Sales Range: $100-124.9 Million
Office Machines & Computers Sales & Ser-
vices
N.A.I.C.S.: 811210

IBM Singapore Pte. Ltd. (1)
7 Changi Business Park Central 1 IBM
Place, Singapore, 486072, Singapore
Tel.: (65) 64181000
Web Site: https://www.ibm.com
Computers & Computer Products Sales &
Services
N.A.I.C.S.: 423430
Martin Chee (Mng Dir)

IBM Slovenija d.o.o. (1)
Ameriska Ulica 8, 1000, Ljubljana,
Slovenia **(100%)**
Tel.: (386) 1 320 8600
Web Site: https://www.ibm.com
Office Machines & Computers Sales &
Cloud-based Services
N.A.I.C.S.: 811210

IBM Slovensko spol. s.r.o. (1)
Krasovskeho 14, Mestska Cast Petrzalka,
851 01, Bratislava, Slovakia **(100%)**
Tel.: (421) 249541111
Web Site: http://www.ibm.com
Sales Range: $400-449.9 Million
Emp.: 1,453
Office Machines & Computers Sales & Ser-
vices
N.A.I.C.S.: 811210

IBM Software Group (1)
IBM Corporation Bldg 1 294 Route 100,
Somers, NY 10589-0100
Tel.: (914) 766-1640
Web Site: http://www.ibm.com
Sales Range: $100-124.9 Million
Software Producer
N.A.I.C.S.: 513210
Lauren C. States (CTO)

Subsidiary (Domestic):

Acoustic, L.P. (2)
100 Summit Dr Ste 911 912, Burlington, MA
01803
Web Site: https://acoustic.com
Internet Marketing Services
N.A.I.C.S.: 541613

Aspera, Inc. (2)
5900 Hollis St Ste E, Emeryville, CA 94608
Tel.: (510) 849-2386
Web Site: http://www.asperasoft.com
Cloud-Based Software Application Devel-
oper
N.A.I.C.S.: 513210

Cleversafe, Inc. (2)
222 S Riverside Plz Ste 1700, Chicago, IL
60606
Tel.: (312) 423-6640
Web Site: http://www.cleversafe.com
Sales Range: $1-9.9 Million
Emp.: 60
Data Storage Software Publisher
N.A.I.C.S.: 513210

Subsidiary (Non-US):

DataMirror Corporation (2)
3100 Steeles Avenue East Suite 1100,
Markham, L3R 8T3, ON, Canada
Tel.: (905) 415-0310
Web Site: http://www.datamirror.com
Sales Range: $25-49.9 Million
Emp.: 229
Real-Time Data Integration & Data Protec-
tion Solutions
N.A.I.C.S.: 541512

Unit (Domestic):

**IBM Software - Enterprise Content
Management** (2)
3565 Harbor Blvd, Costa Mesa, CA 92626-
1405
Tel.: (714) 327-3400
Web Site: http://www.ibm.com
Enterprise E-Content & E-Process Software
Solutions Developer, Publisher & Marketer
N.A.I.C.S.: 513210

Subsidiary (Domestic):

Kenexa Corporation (2)
650 E Swedesford Rd 2nd Fl, Wayne, PA
19087
Tel.: (610) 971-9171
Web Site: http://www.kenexa.com
Sales Range: $250-299.9 Million
Emp.: 2,800
Corporate Communications, Recruitment,
Strategic Planning/Research
N.A.I.C.S.: 541612

Subsidiary (Domestic):

Devon Royce, Inc. (3)
650 E Swedesford Rd, Wayne, PA 19087-
1610
Tel.: (610) 971-6133
Executive Search & Consulting Services
N.A.I.C.S.: 561312

Branch (Domestic):

Kenexa (3)
343 Winter St, Waltham, MA 02451
Tel.: (781) 530-5000
Web Site: http://www.kenexa.com
Sales Range: $75-99.9 Million
Emp.: 300
Online & Offline Recruitment Tools & Ser-
vices
N.A.I.C.S.: 513210

Subsidiary (Non-US):

Kenexa Limited (3)
47 Mark Lane, London, EC3R 7QQ, United
Kingdom

Tel.: (44) 2035458000
Sales Range: $50-74.9 Million
Emp.: 200
Employment Placement Services
N.A.I.C.S.: 561311

**Kenexa Technologies Private
Limited** (3)
No 12 Subramanya Arcade Bannerghatta
Main Road, Bengaluru, 560 029, KA, India
Tel.: (91) 4023351270
Sales Range: $125-149.9 Million
Emp.: 300
Corporate Communications, Recruitment,
Strategic Planning/Research
N.A.I.C.S.: 513210

Subsidiary (Domestic):

Phytel, Inc. (2)
11511 Luna Rd Ste 600, Dallas, TX 75234
Tel.: (214) 750-9922
Web Site: http://www3.phytel.com
Health Care Management Software & Data
Services
N.A.I.C.S.: 518210

Subsidiary (Non-US):

Platform Computing (2)
3760 14th Ave, Markham, L3R 3T7, ON,
Canada
Tel.: (905) 948-8448
Web Site: http://www.ibm.com
Sales Range: $50-74.9 Million
Emp.: 500
Computing Services & Solutions
N.A.I.C.S.: 541513

Subsidiary (Domestic):

SPSS Inc. (2)
233 S Wacker Dr 11th Fl, Chicago, IL
60606-6307 **(100%)**
Tel.: (312) 651-3000
Web Site: http://www.spss.com
Emp.: 1,203
Predictive Analytics Software & Data Mining
Solutions
N.A.I.C.S.: 513210

Branch (Domestic):

SPSS Inc. - Rochester (3)
4115 W Frontage Hwy 52 Rd NW Ste 300,
Rochester, MN 55901
Tel.: (507) 288-5922
Web Site: http://www.spss.com
Sales Range: $25-49.9 Million
Emp.: 300
Computer Software & Services Including
Predictive Analytics & Data Mining
N.A.I.C.S.: 513210

Subsidiary (Non-US):

SPSS South Asia (Pvt.) Ltd. (3)
5DC-701 2nd Floor 5Th D cross 2nd Block
HRBR Layout Kalyan Nagar, kacharaka-
nahalli, Bengaluru, 560043, India
Tel.: (91) 8040117300
Web Site: https://www.spss.co.in
Sales Range: $25-49.9 Million
Emp.: 45
Predictive Analytics & Data Mining Software
Distr & Technical Consulting Services
N.A.I.C.S.: 423430

IBM South Africa (Pty) Ltd. (1)
90 Grayston, Sandton, 2196, South
Africa **(100%)**
Tel.: (27) 11 302 9111
Web Site: https://www.ibm.com
Sales Range: $450-499.9 Million
Emp.: 3,000
Office Machines & Computers Sales & Ser-
vices
N.A.I.C.S.: 811210

IBM Suriname (1)
Hogarhu St 9211, PO Box 735, Paramaribo,
Suriname
Tel.: (597) 403060
Web Site: http://www.ibm.com
Sales Range: $25-49.9 Million
Emp.: 4
Computers & Computer Products Sales &
Services
N.A.I.C.S.: 423430

IBM Systems & Technology (1)

1 New Orchard Rd, Armonk, NY 10504
Tel.: (914) 499-1900
Web Site: http://www.ibm.com
Computers & Other Information Technology
Equipment & Components Mfr
N.A.I.C.S.: 334111

Subsidiary (Domestic):

**Blade Network Technologies,
Inc.** (2)
2051 Mission College Blvd, Santa Clara,
CA 95054
Tel.: (408) 850-8999
Web Site: http://www.bladenetwork.net
Sales Range: $25-49.9 Million
Emp.: 102
Computer Network Design Services
N.A.I.C.S.: 541512

Initiate Systems, Inc. (2)
200 W Madison Ste 2300, Chicago, IL
60606
Tel.: (312) 759-5030
Web Site: http://www.initiate.com
Sales Range: $25-49.9 Million
Emp.: 241
Real-Time Data Management Systems
N.A.I.C.S.: 518210

IBM Taiwan Corporation (1)
3F No 7 Shong-Ren Rd, Taipei, Taiwan
Tel.: (886) 287238888
Web Site: http://www.ibm.com
Personal Computer Mfr
N.A.I.C.S.: 334111
Lisa Kao (Gen Mgr)

IBM Tanzania Limited (1)
Amani Place 7th Floor Ohio Street, Dar es
Salaam, Tanzania
Tel.: (255) 222196800
Information Technology Services
N.A.I.C.S.: 513210

IBM Thailand Company Ltd. (1)
IBM Building 388 Phaholyothin Road, Bang-
kok, 10400, Thailand **(100%)**
Tel.: (66) 2 273 0041
Web Site: https://www.ibm.com
Sales Range: $150-199.9 Million
Emp.: 400
Computers & Computer Products Sales &
Services
N.A.I.C.S.: 423430
Patama Chantaruck (Mng Dir & VP-
Indochina Expansion)

IBM Trinidad & Tobago (1)
Level 2 Invaders Bay Tower Invaders Bay,
PO Box 658, Port of Spain, Trinidad & To-
bago
Tel.: (868) 6245111
Web Site: https://www.ibm.com
Sales Range: $25-49.9 Million
Emp.: 25
Computers & Office Machines Services
N.A.I.C.S.: 811210

IBM Ukraine (1)
Horizon Park BC 12 Amosova Str, Kiev,
03680, Ukraine
Tel.: (380) 44 501 1888
Web Site: https://www.ibm.com
Computer System Design Services
N.A.I.C.S.: 541512

**IBM United Kingdom Financial Ser-
vices Limited** (1)
PO Box 41, North Harbour, Portsmouth,
PO6 3AU, Hampshire, United Kingdom
Tel.: (44) 2392561000
Web Site: http://www.ibm.com
Computer Peripheral Equipment & Software
Whslr
N.A.I.C.S.: 423430

**IBM United Kingdom Holdings
Limited** (1)
PO Box 41, North Harbour, Portsmouth,
PO6 3AU, Hants, United Kingdom **(100%)**
Tel.: (44) 2392561000
Web Site: http://www.ibm.com
Sales Range: $1-4.9 Billion
Emp.: 18,000
Holding Company; Computer Mfr, Sales &
Services
N.A.I.C.S.: 551112

Subsidiary (Domestic):

IBM United Kingdom Limited (2)

PO Box 41, North Harbour, Portsmouth, P06 3AU, Hampshire, United Kingdom **(100%)**
Tel.: (44) 2392561000
Web Site: https://www.ibm.com
Sales Range: $900-999.9 Million
Computers & Computer Products Mfr, Sales & Services
N.A.I.C.S.: 334111

Branch (Domestic):

IBM United Kingdom Ltd. - Greenford **(3)**
Greenford Green Business Park Green Parkway, Greenford, UB6 0AD, Middlesex, United Kingdom **(100%)**
Tel.: (44) 2088325095
Web Site: http://www.ibm.com
Sales Range: $50-74.9 Million
Emp.: 100
Computers & Computer Products Sales, Distr & Services
N.A.I.C.S.: 423430

IBM Vietnam Company **(1)**
2nd Floor Pacific Place 83B Ly Thuong Kiet, Hanoi, Vietnam
Tel.: (84) 243 946 2021
Web Site: https://www.ibm.com
Computer Whslr
N.A.I.C.S.: 811210

IBM de Chile, S.A.C **(1)**
Av Providencia 655, Providencia, 7500261, Santiago, Chile **(100%)**
Tel.: (56) 2 200 6000
Web Site: https://www.ibm.com
Computer Products Mfr & Computer Maintenance Services
N.A.I.C.S.: 423430

IBM de Colombia, S.A. **(1)**
Carrera 53 100-25, Bogota, Colombia **(100%)**
Tel.: (57) 13901000
Web Site: https://www.ibm.com
Sales Range: $150-199.9 Million
Computers & Computer Products Sales & Services
N.A.I.C.S.: 423430

IBM de Mexico, Comercializacion y Servicios S. de R.L. de C.V. **(1)**
Alfonso Napoles Gandara 3111, Col Parque corporativo de Pena Blanca, 01210, Mexico, Mexico
Tel.: (52) 5552703000
Web Site: http://www.ibm.com
Computer Peripheral Equipment & Software Whslr
N.A.I.C.S.: 423430

IBM de Mexico, S. de R.L. **(1)**
Alfonso Napoles Gandara No 3111 Col Parque Corporativo de Pena Blanca, Delegacion Alvaro Obregon, CP 01210, Mexico, DF, Mexico **(99.99%)**
Tel.: (52) 55 5270 3000
Web Site: http://www.ibm.com.mx
Sales Range: $500-549.9 Million
Emp.: 700
Computers & Computer Products Sales & Services
N.A.I.C.S.: 423430

IBM de Venezuela, S.A **(1)**
Edificio IBM Avda Ernesto Blohm, Chuao, Caracas, 1064, Venezuela **(100%)**
Tel.: (58) 2129088111
Web Site: http://www.ibm.com
Sales Range: $150-199.9 Million
Computers & Computer Products Sales & Services
N.A.I.C.S.: 423430

IBM del Ecuador, C.A. **(1)**
Diego de Almagro N 32-48 Y Whimper, Quito, Ecuador **(100%)**
Tel.: (593) 2 500 0100
Web Site: https://www.ibm.com
Computers & Computer Products Sales & Services
N.A.I.C.S.: 423430

IBM del Peru, S.A. **(1)**
Av Javier Prado 6230 La Molina, Lima, 15026, Peru **(100%)**
Tel.: (51) 1 625 6000
Web Site: https://www.ibm.com

Sales Range: $125-149.9 Million
Emp.: 300
Computers & Computer Products Sales & Services
N.A.I.C.S.: 423430

IBM del Uruguay, S.A. **(1)**
La Cumparsita 1475, Edificio Plaza Alemania, 11000, Montevideo, Uruguay **(100%)**
Tel.: (598) 2 902 3617
Web Site: https://www.ibm.com
Computers & Computer Products Sales & Services
N.A.I.C.S.: 811210

IBM-International Business Machines d.o.o., Belgrade **(1)**
Bulevar Mihajla Pupina 6, 11070, Belgrade, Serbia
Tel.: (381) 112013500
Information Technology Services
N.A.I.C.S.: 513210

International Business Machines A/S **(1)**
Rosenholmveinen 25, Kolbotn, 1411, Norway **(100%)**
Tel.: (47) 66998000
Web Site: http://www.ibm.com
Sales Range: $1-4.9 Billion
Emp.: 1,400
Office Machines & Computers Sales & Services
N.A.I.C.S.: 423430

Joint Venture (Domestic):

PetroData AS **(2)**
Eldfiskvegen 1, 4056, Tananger, Norway
Tel.: (47) 51838250
Sales Range: $25-49.9 Million
Emp.: 100
Data Management & Storage Services;
Owned 66% by Landmark Graphics Corporation & 33% by International Business Machines Corporation
N.A.I.C.S.: 513140

International Business Machines AS **(1)**
Sundtkvartalet Lakkegata 53, 0134, Oslo, Norway
Tel.: (47) 66998000
Web Site: https://www.ibm.com
Emp.: 1,200
Computer Peripheral Equipment & Software Whslr
N.A.I.C.S.: 423430

International Business Machines Corporation Magysrorssyagi Kft. **(1)**
Neumann Janos u 1, 1117, Budapest, Hungary **(100%)**
Tel.: (36) 13825500
Web Site: http://www.ibm.com
Sales Range: $75-99.9 Million
Emp.: 150
Office Machines & Computers Sales & Services
N.A.I.C.S.: 423430

International Business Machines Senegal **(1)**
KM 8 Route de OUAKAM Immeuble Atryium 1er etage, PO Box 24596, Dakar, 50555, Senegal
Tel.: (221) 33 869 5885
Web Site: https://www.ibm.com
Personal Computer Mfr
N.A.I.C.S.: 334111

International Business Machines Svenska AB **(1)**
Kistagangen 6, Kista, 164 92, Stockholm, Sweden **(100%)**
Tel.: (46) 87931000
Web Site: https://www.ibm.com
Sales Range: $1-4.9 Billion
Emp.: 2,800
Computers & Computer Products Sales, Distr & Services
N.A.I.C.S.: 423430

International Business Machines West Africa Limited **(1)**
7th Floor Africa Re Building Plot 1679 Karimu Kotun Street, Victoria Island, Lagos, Nigeria **(100%)**
Tel.: (234) 113027036

Web Site: http://www.ibm.com
Office Machines & Computers Sales & Services
N.A.I.C.S.: 423430

International Business Machines, S.A. **(1)**
Santa Hortensia 26-28, 28002, Madrid, Spain **(100%)**
Tel.: (34) 91 397 6611
Web Site: https://www.ibm.com
Sales Range: $75-99.9 Million
Emp.: 250
Office Machines & Computers Sales & Services
N.A.I.C.S.: 423430

MDTVISION **(1)**
31 Ave de la Baltique Parc d'Activites, de Courtaboeuf 1, 91954, Les Ulis, Cedex, France **(100%)**
Tel.: (33) 169822400
Web Site: http://www.mdtvision.com
Sales Range: $125-149.9 Million
Emp.: 460
Computer Consulting & Engineering Services
N.A.I.C.S.: 541519

Subsidiary (Non-US):

Matra Products **(2)**
21 11e Rue Ouest, Saint Martine, G0M 1B0, QC, Canada
Tel.: (418) 382-5151
Web Site: http://www.produitsmatra.com
Sales Range: $10-24.9 Million
Emp.: 150
Computer Aided Design Software Mfr
N.A.I.C.S.: 334610

Merge Healthcare Incorporated **(1)**
71 S Wacker Dr 20th Fl, Chicago, IL 60606
Tel.: (262) 367-0700
Web Site: http://www.merge.com
Sales Range: $200-249.9 Million
Networking & Data Management Systems for Radiology & Diagnostic Imaging Applications
N.A.I.C.S.: 541512
Jen Naylor (CFO)

Netezza Corporation **(1)**
26 Forest St, Marlborough, MA 01752
Tel.: (508) 382-8200
Web Site: http://www.netezza.com
Sales Range: $150-199.9 Million
Emp.: 469
Data Warehouse Appliances
N.A.I.C.S.: 334112

Subsidiary (Non-US):

Netezza Corporation Ltd. **(2)**
The Quadrant 55-57 High Street, Windsor, SL4 1LP, United Kingdom
Tel.: (44) 1753835980
Web Site: http://www.netezza.com
Sales Range: $100-124.9 Million
Data Warehouse Appliances
N.A.I.C.S.: 519290

Neudesic, LLC **(1)**
200 Spectrum Center Dr Ste 2000, Irvine, CA 92618
Tel.: (949) 754-4500
Web Site: http://www.neudesic.com
Sales Range: $25-49.9 Million
Emp.: 400
Information Technology Services
N.A.I.C.S.: 541990

Subsidiary (Domestic):

Web4, Inc. **(2)**
8175 E Kaiser Blvd, Anaheim, CA 92808
Tel.: (714) 974-2670
Web Site: http://www.web4inc.com
Computer Softwares Mfr
N.A.I.C.S.: 513210
Michelle Stamm (Office Mgr)

Oy IBM Finland AB **(1)**
Laajalahdentie 23, PL 265, 00330, 00101, Helsinki, Finland
Tel.: (358) 94591
Web Site: https://www.ibm.com
Personal Computer Mfr
N.A.I.C.S.: 334111

Oy IBM Finland Ab **(1)**

Laajalahdentie 23, 00330, Helsinki, Finland
Tel.: (358) 94595900
Web Site: http://www.ibm.com
Cognitive Computing & Cloud Platform Services
N.A.I.C.S.: 518210
Tuomo Haukkovaara (Chm)

PT IBM Indonesia **(1)**
The Plaza Office Tower 16-18th Floor JI MH Thamrin Kav 28-30, JI MH Thamrin Kav 28-30, Jakarta, 10350, Indonesia **(100%)**
Tel.: (62) 212512 992 5000
Web Site: https://www.ibm.com
Office Machines & Computers Sales & Services
N.A.I.C.S.: 811210

Promontory Financial Group LLC **(1)**
801 17th St Ste 1100, Washington, DC 20006 **(100%)**
Tel.: (202) 384-1200
Web Site: https://www.promontory.com
Risk Management & Regulatory Compliance Consulting Firm
N.A.I.C.S.: 541618
Arthur G. Angulo (Mng Dir)
S. Trezevant Moore Jr. (Mng Dir)
William Lang (Mng Dir-New York)
Eric Schwartz (Mng Dir-Washington)
Barak J. Sanford (Mng Dir)

Subsidiary (Non-US):

Promontory Financial Group (UK) Limited **(2)**
2nd Floor 30 Old Broad Street, London, EC2N 1HT, United Kingdom
Tel.: (44) 2039009800
Web Site: http://www.promontory.com
Financial Consulting Firm
N.A.I.C.S.: 541618
Henry Raine (Mng Dir & Head-London)
Munib Ali (Mng Dir)
Tony Boorman (Mng Dir)
Jon W. Harvey (Mng Dir)
Huseyin Sahin (Dir)
Sam Tymms (Mng Dir)
Priya Giuliani (Mng Dir)
Prashant Jobanputra (Mng Dir)

Promontory Financial Group Australasia, LLP **(2)**
10 Marina Boulevard 42-01 Marina Bay Financial Centre Tower 2, Singapore, 018983, Singapore
Tel.: (65) 64189000
Web Site: http://www.promontory.com
Financial Consulting Firm
N.A.I.C.S.: 541618
Jeffrey Carmichael (Mng Dir & Head-Australasia)
Alexander Carmichael (COO-Promontory Australasia)

Promontory Financial Group Global Services - Japan, LLC **(2)**
Teikoku Hotel Tower 9F 1-1-1 Uchisaiwaicho, Chiyoda-ku, Tokyo, 100-0011, Japan
Tel.: (81) 338084940
Web Site: http://www.promontory.com
Financial Consulting Firm
N.A.I.C.S.: 541618

Subsidiary (Non-US):

Q1 Labs Inc. **(1)**
890 Winter St Ste 300, Waltham, MA 02451
Tel.: (781) 250-5800
Web Site: http://q1labs.com
Sales Range: $25-49.9 Million
Emp.: 4
Computer System Design Services
N.A.I.C.S.: 541512

Red Hat, Inc. **(1)**
100 E Davie St, Raleigh, NC 27601
Tel.: (919) 754-3700
Web Site: http://www.redhat.com
Rev.: $3,362,069,000
Assets: $5,588,289,000
Liabilities: $3,974,357,000
Net Worth: $1,613,932,000
Earnings: $433,988,000
Emp.: 13,360
Fiscal Year-end: 02/28/2019
Open Source Internet Infrastructure Solutions Developer
N.A.I.C.S.: 513210
Marco Bill-Peter (Sr VP)
Mark Enzweiler (Sr VP)

International Business Machines
Corporation—(Continued)

Michael R. Cunningham *(Gen Counsel & Exec VP)*
Timothy B. Yeaton *(Chief Mktg Officer & Chief Mktg Officer)*
Narendra K. Gupta *(Executives)*
DeLisa Alexander *(Chief HR Officer & Exec VP)*
Craig Muzilla *(Sr VP)*
Werner Knoblich *(Sr VP & Gen Mgr)*
Dirk-Peter Van Leeuwen *(Sr VP/Gen Mgr-Comml Sls-North America)*
Michael A. Kelly *(CIO)*
Chris Wright *(CTO & Sr VP)*
Paul J. Cormier *(Chm)*
Marjet Andriesse *(VP/Gen Mgr-Asia Pacific)*
Nathan Jones *(VP-Federal Bus)*
Ben McNeal *(Dir-Navy & Marine Corps Strategy & Sls)*
Clara Conti *(Sr VP/Gen Mgr-Pub Sector)*
Carolyn Nash *(COO & Sr VP)*
Robert Leibrock *(CFO & Sr VP)*
Jim Palermo *(CIO & Sr VP)*
Matt Hicks *(Pres & CEO)*
Andrew Brown *(Chief Revenue Officer)*
Andrew Brown *(Chief Revenue Officer & Sr VP)*

Subsidiary (Non-US):

FeedHenry Ltd. (2)
6700 Cork Airport Business Park Kinsale Road, Cork, Ireland
Tel.: (353) 51275106
Web Site: http://www.feedhenry.com
Emp.: 65
Software Development Services
N.A.I.C.S.: 513210

Subsidiary (Domestic):

FeedHenry (Ireland) Limited (3)
6700 Cork Airport Business Park Kinsale Road, Cork, Ireland
Tel.: (353) 19197544499
Software Development Services
N.A.I.C.S.: 513210

Subsidiary (US):

FeedHenry LLC (3)
15 New England Executive Park, Burlington, MA 01803
Tel.: (339) 221-0809
Emp.: 8
Software Publisher
N.A.I.C.S.: 513210
Cathal McGloin *(VP-Mobile Platforms)*
Stephen Drake *(Dir-Partners & Strategic Alliances-Mobile-Global)*

Group (Non-US):

Red Hat Asia Pacific Pty. Ltd. (2)
Levels 1 to 4 193 North Quay, Brisbane, 4000, QLD, Australia
Tel.: (61) 735148100
Web Site: http://www.redhat.com.au
Sales Range: $25-49.9 Million
Emp.: 100
Information Technology Services
N.A.I.C.S.: 517810

Subsidiary (Non-US):

PT. Red Hat Indonesia (3)
Revenue Tower 21st Floor No 119 Jl Jenderal Sudirman No 52-53, Sudirman Central Business District Kebayoran Baru Senayan, Jakarta, 12190, Indonesia
Tel.: (62) 8067935000
Web Site: http://www.redhat.com
Emp.: 16
Software Development Services
N.A.I.C.S.: 513210

Red Hat (Thailand) Limited (3)
No 127 Room 25 11 25 12 25 13 25 39 Floor 25 Gaysorn Tower, Ratchadamri Road, Lumpini Sub-district Pathumwan District, Bangkok, 10330, Thailand
Tel.: (66) 26240601
Information Technology Services
N.A.I.C.S.: 541511

Red Hat Asia Pacific Pte Ltd. (3)
8 Shenton Way 11-01 AXA Tower, Singapore, 068811, Singapore
Tel.: (65) 64904200

Web Site: http://www.redhat.com
Sales Range: $25-49.9 Million
Emp.: 200
Software Development Services
N.A.I.C.S.: 513210
Dirk-peter van Leeuwen *(Sr VP & Gen Mgr)*

Branch (Domestic):

Red Hat Asia Pacific Pty Ltd (3)
Level 1 193 North Quay, PO Box 13547, Brisbane, 4000, QLD, Australia
Tel.: (61) 735148100
Web Site: http://www.au.redhat.com
Emp.: 200
Software Development Services
N.A.I.C.S.: 513210

Subsidiary (Non-US):

Red Hat India Pvt. Ltd. (3)
Supreme Business Park Supreme City A-201 2nd Floor, Hiranandani Gardens Powai, Mumbai, 400 076, India
Tel.: (91) 2261147559
Web Site: http://redhat.com
Sales Range: $10-24.9 Million
Emp.: 50
Software Development Services
N.A.I.C.S.: 513210

Subsidiary (Domestic):

Red Hat Software Services (India) Pvt. Ltd. (4)
Tower X Level-1 Cybercity, Magarpatta City Hadapsar, Pune, 411 013, India
Tel.: (91) 2030467000
Sales Range: $50-74.9 Million
Emp.: 250
Software Development Services
N.A.I.C.S.: 541511
N. Murty *(Mgr-HR & Facilities)*

Subsidiary (Non-US):

Red Hat KK (3)
Ebisu Neonart 3F 4-1-18 Ebisu, Shibuya-ku, Tokyo, 150-0013, Japan
Tel.: (81) 345907472
Web Site: https://www.redhat.com
Software Development Services
N.A.I.C.S.: 513210

Red Hat Malaysia SDN. BHD. (3)
Level 17 01 The Gardens South Tower Mid Valley City, Lingkaran Syed Putra, 59200, Kuala Lumpur, Malaysia
Tel.: (60) 327330500
Software Development Services
N.A.I.C.S.: 513210

Subsidiary (Non-US):

Red Hat Brasil Limitada (2)
Av Brig Faria Lima 3900 Cj 81, Faria Lima n 3 900, Sao Paulo, 04538-132, Brazil
Tel.: (55) 1135296000
Software Development Services
N.A.I.C.S.: 513210

Red Hat Chile Limitada (2)
Avda Apoquindo N 2827 Oficina 701 Piso 7, Las Condes, Santiago, Chile
Tel.: (56) 232783691
Information Technology Services
N.A.I.C.S.: 513210

Red Hat Colombia S.A.S (2)
Cra 9 N0 115-06 Piso 19 Of 1906 Edificio Tierra Firme, Bogota, Colombia
Tel.: (57) 15802703
Software Development Services
N.A.I.C.S.: 513210
Monica Paredes Narvaez *(Mgr-Sls Accts)*

Group (Non-US):

Red Hat GmbH (2)
Werner-von-Siemens Ring 14 Technopark II Haus C, Grasbrunn, 85630, Germany
Tel.: (49) 892050710
Web Site: http://www.redhat.com
Information Technology Services
N.A.I.C.S.: 541519

Subsidiary (Non-US):

Red Hat AB (3)
Kista Science Tower, Farogatan 33, 164 51, Kista, Stockholm, Sweden

Tel.: (46) 850575600
Web Site: http://www.redhat.se
Sales Range: $100-124.9 Million
Emp.: 25
Software Development Services
N.A.I.C.S.: 513210

Red Hat BV (3)
7th Floor Entree II Entree 238, Amsterdam Zuidoost Weesperkarspel, 3821 AD, Amsterdam, Netherlands
Tel.: (31) 205651200
Web Site: http://www.redhat.nl
Sales Range: $10-24.9 Million
Emp.: 20
Software Development Services
N.A.I.C.S.: 513210

Red Hat Czech, s.r.o. (3)
Purkynova 71/99 3080/97b & 647/111, 612 00, Brno, Czech Republic
Tel.: (420) 532294111
Web Site: http://www.europe.redhat.com
Sales Range: $100-124.9 Million
Software Development Services
N.A.I.C.S.: 513210

Red Hat FZ LLC (3)
Office Park Building Dubai Knowledge Village Office 406A, PO Box 502579, Dubai, United Arab Emirates
Tel.: (971) 44494100
Web Site: http://www.europe.redhat.com
Software Development Services
N.A.I.C.S.: 513210

Red Hat France SARL (3)
Immeuble Defense Plaza 23-25 Rue Delariviere Lefoullon, Puteaux, 92800, Paris, France
Tel.: (33) 141912323
Web Site: http://www.redhat.com
Sales Range: $25-49.9 Million
Emp.: 30
Software Development Services
N.A.I.C.S.: 513210

Branch (Domestic):

Red Hat GmbH (3)
Wankelstrasse 1-5, Stuttgart, Germany
Tel.: (49) 711964370
Web Site: http://www.redhat.com
Sales Range: $10-24.9 Million
Emp.: 24
Software Development Services
N.A.I.C.S.: 513210

Subsidiary (Non-US):

Red Hat Israel Ltd. (3)
34 Sderot Yerushalayim, Ra'anana, 43501, Israel
Tel.: (972) 97692222
Sales Range: $25-49.9 Million
Emp.: 110
Software Development Services
N.A.I.C.S.: 513210
Michal Keneph *(Gen Mgr)*

Red Hat Limited (3)
6700 Cork Airport Business Park Phase II 1st Floor, Kinsale Road, Cork, T12 XR60, Ireland
Tel.: (353) 21 230 3400
Web Site: https://www.redhat.com
Sales Range: $25-49.9 Million
Emp.: 86
Software Development Services
N.A.I.C.S.: 513210

Red Hat Poland sp.zo.o (3)
ul Krucza 50, 00-022, Warsaw, Poland
Tel.: (48) 226570000
Web Site: https://www.redhat.com
Software Development Services
N.A.I.C.S.: 513210

Red Hat S.R.L. (3)
Via Gustavo Fara 26 4 piano, 20124, Milan, Italy
Tel.: (39) 0236047601
Web Site: http://www.redhat.it
Software Development Services
N.A.I.C.S.: 513210

Red Hat UK Ltd. (3)
200 Fowler Avenue, Farnborough Business Park, Farnborough, GU14 7JP, Hampshire, United Kingdom
Tel.: (44) 1252362700

Web Site: http://www.europe.redhat.com
Sales Range: $100-124.9 Million
Software Development Services
N.A.I.C.S.: 513210

Red Hat, S.L. (3)
Travessera de Gracia 11 3, Planta 3D, 08021, Barcelona, Spain
Tel.: (34) 932204205
Web Site: http://www.redhat.es
Sales Range: $25-49.9 Million
Emp.: 40
Software Development Services
N.A.I.C.S.: 513210

Red Hat, bvba (3)
Leonardo Da Vincilaan 19, Diegem, 1831, Brussels, 1831, Belgium
Tel.: (32) 27190340
Web Site: http://www.redhat.be
Software Development Services
N.A.I.C.S.: 513210

Subsidiary (Non-US):

Red Hat Philippines Software Solutions Corp. (2)
Regus Ascott 7/F Ascott Makati Ayala Center, Makati, 1224, Philippines
Tel.: (63) 26516530
Software Development Services
N.A.I.C.S.: 513210

Red Hat South Africa (Pty) Ltd (2)
The Link Building 173 Oxford Road We-Work Rosebank, Johannesburg, 2196, South Africa
Tel.: (27) 115134109
Information Technology Services
N.A.I.C.S.: 513210

Red Hat Yazilim Servisleri A.S. (2)
Barbaros Mahallesi Kardelen Sokak Palladium Tower No 2 Kat 13, Atasehir, 34746, Istanbul, Turkiye
Tel.: (90) 2166870313
Information Technology Services
N.A.I.C.S.: 513210

Resource/Ammirati (1)
250 S High St Ste 400, Columbus, OH 43215
Tel.: (614) 621-2888
Web Site: http://www.resourceammirati.com
Digital Marketing Services
N.A.I.C.S.: 541810
Nancy J. Kramer *(Chm)*

Sabiedriba ar irobezotu atbildibu IBM Latvija (1)
Bauskas iela 58a, Riga, LV-1004, Latvia (100%)
Tel.: (371) 6 707 0300
Web Site: https://www.ibm.com
Office Machines & Computers Sales & Services
N.A.I.C.S.: 811210

SoftLayer Technologies, Inc. (1)
4849 Alpha Rd, Dallas, TX 75244
Tel.: (214) 442-0600
Web Site: http://www.softlayer.com
Sales Range: $50-74.9 Million
Emp.: 250
Web Hosting Services; Software Developer
N.A.I.C.S.: 518210

Subsidiary (Non-US):

SoftLayer Technologies Asia (2)
29A International Business Park, Jurong, Singapore
Tel.: (65) 6622 2131
Web Hosting Services; Software Publisher
N.A.I.C.S.: 518210

SoftLayer Technologies Europe (2)
Paul van Vlissingenstraat 16, 1096, Amsterdam, Netherlands
Tel.: (31) 203080540
Web Site: http://www.softlayer.com
Web Hosting Services; Software Publisher
N.A.I.C.S.: 518210

TRIRIGA Inc. (1)
6700 Via Austi Pkwy Ste 500, Las Vegas, NV 89119
Tel.: (702) 932-4444
Web Site: http://www.tririga.com
Sales Range: $100-124.9 Million
Emp.: 500

Real Estate & Facilities Management Software
N.A.I.C.S.: 513210

TWC Product and Technology, LLC (1)
1001 Summit Blvd 20th Fl, Atlanta, GA 30319
Web Site: https://www.weather.com
Weather Forecasting & Digital Publishing Platform Services
N.A.I.C.S.: 541990
Sheri Bachstein *(CEO)*

Subsidiary (Domestic):

WSI Corporation (2)
400 Minuteman Rd, Andover, MA 01810
Tel.: (978) 983-6300
Web Site: http://www.wsicorp.com
Emp.: 220
Business-to-Business Weather Data Services
N.A.I.C.S.: 541990
Peter P. Neilley *(VP-Global)*
Bill Dow *(VP & Gen Mgr)*
Jim Menard *(VP)*
Linda Maynard *(VP-Corporate Marketing)*

Subsidiary (Domestic):

Enterprise Electronics Corporation (3)
128 S Industrial Blvd, Enterprise, AL 36330
Tel.: (334) 347-3478
Web Site: https://www.eecradar.com
Sales Range: $10-24.9 Million
Emp.: 100
Meteorological Radar Systems Mfr
N.A.I.C.S.: 334511
Michael Knight *(VP-Engrg)*

Taos Mountain LLC (1)
121 Daggett Dr, San Jose, CA 95134-1204
Tel.: (408) 588-1200
Web Site: http://www.taos.com
Sales Range: $10-24.9 Million
Emp.: 200
IT Consulting & Services
N.A.I.C.S.: 561320
Mary Hale *(CFO)*
Ric Urrutia *(Co-Founder)*
Aditya Joglekar *(VP-Sls)*
Hamilton Yu *(CEO)*
Gopal Bhat *(Sr VP-Intl)*
Ken Grohe *(Chief Revenue Officer)*
Rachel Beckler *(Mktg Dir)*
Alexis Tatatsky *(Co-Founder)*
Kevin O'Hare *(CFO)*
Patty Shrum *(Sr VP)*
Peter Newton *(Sr VP)*
Trish Palumbo *(Sr VP)*
Melissa Munnerlyn *(Sr Dir-Human Resources-Administration)*

Truven Health Analytics Inc. (1)
100 Phoenix Dr, Ann Arbor, MI 48108
Tel.: (734) 913-3000
Web Site: https://www.truvenhealth.com
Healthcare Database, Analysis & Research Products & Services
N.A.I.C.S.: 513140

Ustream, Inc. (1)
274 Castro St Ste 204, Mountain View, CA 94041
Tel.: (650) 864-9588
Web Site: http://www.ustream.tv
Sales Range: $10-24.9 Million
Emp.: 254
Television Broadcasting Services
N.A.I.C.S.: 516120
Brad Hunstable *(Co-CEO & Co-Founder)*
Gyula Feher *(Co-Founder & Co-CTO)*

WTC Insurance Corp, Ltd. (1)
2 Church Street, Hamilton, HM11, Bermuda (100%)
Tel.: (441) 2951422
Web Site: http://www.conyersdill.com
Sales Range: $100-124.9 Million
Insurance Services
N.A.I.C.S.: 524298

WTC Insurance Corporation, Ltd. (1)
2 Church Street, Hamilton, Bermuda
Tel.: (441) 4412994912
Insurance Services
N.A.I.C.S.: 524210

INTERNATIONAL CARD ESTABLISHMENT, INC.
555 Airport Way Ste A, Camarillo, CA 93010   DE
Web Site: https://www.icepmt.com
ICRD—(OTCIQ)
Sales Range: $1-9.9 Million
Emp.: 15
Credit Card Authorization & Payment Systems Software
N.A.I.C.S.: 513210
Jonathan A. Severn *(Chm, Pres & CFO)*
William A. Lopshire *(CEO)*

INTERNATIONAL DALECO CORPORATION
711 W 17th St Ste E-6, Costa Mesa, CA 92627
Tel.: (949) 515-1301   CA
Web Site: http://www.interdaleco.com
ILDO—(OTCIQ)
Healtcare Services
N.A.I.C.S.: 621310

INTERNATIONAL DISPENSING CORPORATION
89 Little Neck Rd, Southampton, NY 11968
Tel.: (212) 464-7203   DE
IDND—(OTCIQ)
Rev.: $18,344,000
Assets: $456,644,000
Liabilities: $406,921,000
Net Worth: $49,723,000
Earnings: $5,065,000
Fiscal Year-end: 12/31/19
Packaging Services
N.A.I.C.S.: 561910
Jay Weil *(Sec)*
Pepe Martinez *(CEO)*

INTERNATIONAL DISPLAY ADVERTISING, INC.
745 5th Ave, New York, NY 10151
Tel.: (646) 768-4285   NV
IDAD—(OTCIQ)
Advertising Agency Services
N.A.I.C.S.: 541810
Yoram Drucker *(CEO)*

INTERNATIONAL ENDEAVORS CORPORATION
5451 Avenida Encinas Ste B126, Carlsbad, CA 92008
Tel.: (619) 343-3199   NV
Web Site:
    http://internationalendeavors corp.com
Year Founded: 2014
IDVV—(OTCIQ)
Real Estate Manangement Services
N.A.I.C.S.: 531190
Bill Martin *(VP)*
Ray Valdez *(CEO)*

INTERNATIONAL FLAVORS & FRAGRANCES INC.
521 W 57th St, New York, NY 10019-2960
Tel.: (212) 765-5500   NY
Web Site: https://www.iff.com
Year Founded: 1958
IFF—(NYSE)
Rev.: $11,479,000,000
Assets: $30,978,000,000
Liabilities: $16,336,000,000
Net Worth: $14,642,000,000
Earnings: ($2,567,000,000)
Emp.: 21,500
Fiscal Year-end: 12/31/23
Chemical Products Mfr
N.A.I.C.S.: 325998

J. Erik Fyrwald *(CEO)*
Michael DeVeau *(Chief IR & Comm Officer & Sr VP)*
Gregory Yep *(Chief R&D, Integrated Solutions & Sustainability Officer& Exec VP)*
Deborah Borg *(Chief HR & Diversity, Equity & Inclusion Officer & Exec VP)*
Vic Verma *(CIO & Exec VP)*
Simon Herriott *(Pres-Health & Biosciences)*
Angela Strzelecki *(Pres-Pharma Solutions)*
Frank Clyburn *(CEO)*
Relf Finzel *(Exec VP)*
Ana Paula Mendonca *(Sr VP)*
Christophe Fauchon de Villeplee *(Pres)*

Subsidiaries:

Agtech Products, Inc. (1)
8801 Anderson Ave, Manhattan, KS 66503
Tel.: (785) 776-3863
Web Site: https://www.agtechinc.com
Veterinary Medicine Mfr
N.A.I.C.S.: 325412
John L. Curtis *(Pres & CEO)*
Matthew Curtis *(Mgr-Distr-Intl)*
Orlando Quiroga *(Sls Mgr-Intl)*
Matt Coffey *(Mgr-Warehouse)*

Amco Sp. z o. o. (1)
UI Kasztanowa 88, Dybow-Kolonia, 05-250, Radzymin, Poland
Tel.: (48) 227635280
Web Site: https://www.amco.pl
Seafood Product Mfr
N.A.I.C.S.: 311710

Aroma S.A. (1)
17 Avenida 51-40 Zona 12, Guatemala, Guatemala
Tel.: (502) 23270400
Chemical Products Distr
N.A.I.C.S.: 424690

Aromco Ltd. (1)
Bell Farm Industrial Park, Nuthampstead, Royston, SG8 8ND, Herts, United Kingdom
Tel.: (44) 1763848889
Web Site: http://www.aromco.com
Chemical Products Mfr
N.A.I.C.S.: 325199

Aromor Flavors & Fragrances Inc. (1)
560 Sylvan Ave, Englewood Cliffs, NJ 07632
Tel.: (201) 503-1662
Web Site: http://www.aromor.com
Flavours & Fragrances Mfr
N.A.I.C.S.: 311999

BSA India Food Ingr. Pvt. Ltd. (1)
F-29 Agro Food Park Mia Extn Alwar, Alwar, 301 030, RJ, India
Tel.: (91) 9982627280
Web Site: http://www.bsaindia.in
Processed Meat Mfr
N.A.I.C.S.: 311612

Bush Boake Allen do Brasil Industria e Comercio Ltda. (1)
Av Mal Castelo Branco 761 Taboao da Serra, Sao Paulo, 06790, Brazil
Tel.: (55) 1147873099
Emp.: 15
Organic Chemical Mfr
N.A.I.C.S.: 325180

CitraSource Holdings, LLC (1)
1000 American Superior Blvd, Winter Haven, FL 33880
Tel.: (863) 293-0326
Web Site: http://www.citrasource.com
Chemical Product & Preparation Mfr
N.A.I.C.S.: 325998

Dandy Lions Limited (1)
5 Whittle Close Drayton Fields Industrial Estate, Daventry, NN11 8RQ, Northants, United Kingdom
Tel.: (44) 1327312912
Web Site: https://www.dandylions.co.uk
Honey & Syrup Distr
N.A.I.C.S.: 424490

Danisco Austria GmbH (1)
Arnbruckerstrasse 1 A, 4860, Lenzing, Austria
Tel.: (43) 7672935500
Medical Device Mfr
N.A.I.C.S.: 339112

Danisco Italia S.p.A. (1)
Corso di Porta Nuova 46, 20121, Milan, Italy
Tel.: (39) 02926291
Food Products Distr
N.A.I.C.S.: 424490

Danisco Poland Sp. z.o.o (1)
Paddock 6, 61-315, Poznan, Poland
Tel.: (48) 618719700
Chemical Product Whslr
N.A.I.C.S.: 424690

DuPont de Nemours Kenya Limited (1)
Afriq Center Unit 5 Masai Road Behind Libra House Off Mombasa Road, Nairobi, Kenya
Tel.: (254) 726436124
Web Site: http://www.dupontkenya.com
Building Materials Mfr
N.A.I.C.S.: 327120

Enzymotec USA, Inc. (1)
55 Railroad Ave, Ridgefield, NJ 07657
Tel.: (201) 941-8777
Pharmaceutical Products Distr
N.A.I.C.S.: 424210

Etol Aroma Ve Baharat Gida Urunleri San. Ve Tic.A.S. (1)
GOSP Ihsan Dede Caddesi No 129, Gebze, 41400, Kocaeli, Turkiye
Tel.: (90) 5322577463
Web Site: http://www.etol.com
Chemical Product & Preparation Mfr
N.A.I.C.S.: 325998

Flavors and Essences UK Limited (1)
Flavours House Mercer Way Shadsworth Business Park, Blackburn, BB1 2QD, United Kingdom
Tel.: (44) 1254667447
Web Site: http://www.irishcountrygold.com
Chemical Products Mfr
N.A.I.C.S.: 325199

Frutarom (UK) Ltd. (1)
Turnells Mill Lane Denington Industrial Estate, Wellingborough, NN8 2RN, United Kingdom
Tel.: (44) 1933440343
Chemical Products Distr
N.A.I.C.S.: 424690
Gary Waterston *(Mgr-Comml)*

Frutarom Belgium N.V. (1)
Ambachtsstraat 6, 1840, Londerzeel, Belgium
Tel.: (32) 523195424
Chemical Products Distr
N.A.I.C.S.: 424690
Sven Friday *(Mgr- Warehouse & Coord-Logistics)*

Frutarom Chile S.A. (1)
Hermanos Carrera Pinto 97 A Parque Industrial Los Libertadores, Colina, Santiago, Chile
Tel.: (56) 227538527
Food Products Distr
N.A.I.C.S.: 424490

Frutarom France S.A.R.L. (1)
5 Rue Louis Neel, 21000, Dijon, France
Tel.: (33) 380739391
Chemical Products Distr
N.A.I.C.S.: 424690
Jean-Michel Papin *(Comml Dir)*

Frutarom Germany GmbH (1)
Reeser Strasse 60, 46446, Emmerich am Rhein, Germany
Tel.: (49) 2822920114
Chemical Products Distr
N.A.I.C.S.: 424690
Petra Fisch *(Mgr-Comml)*

Frutarom Industries Ltd. (1)
Manofim St Herzeliya, PO Box 3088, Herzliya Pituach, 46104, Israel
Tel.: (972) 49877600
Web Site: http://www.frutarom.com

International Flavors & Fragrances Inc.—(Continued)

Sales Range: $1-4.9 Billion
Emp.: 5,600
Flavors & Ingredients Mfr
N.A.I.C.S.: 311930
Adi Melamed *(VP-Strategic Bus Dev)*

Subsidiary (Non-US):

Frutarom (Switzerland) AG **(2)**
Florhofstrasse 13, 8820, Wadenswil, Aargan, Switzerland **(100%)**
Tel.: (41) 66263821201
Web Site: http://www.frutarom.com
Sales Range: $25-49.9 Million
Emp.: 100
Marketing & Creative Laboratory
N.A.I.C.S.: 541380

Subsidiary (Non-US):

Etol d.d. **(3)**
Skofja Vas 39, 3211, Celje, Slovenia **(56%)**
Tel.: (386) 34277100
Web Site: http://www.etol.si
Sales Range: $50-74.9 Million
Emp.: 200
Flavors & Fragrances Mfr
N.A.I.C.S.: 311930

Subsidiary (Non-US):

ETOL RUS, Ltd. **(4)**
Leninskiy District Aparinki 5/2, 117335, Moscow, Russia
Tel.: (7) 4959815313
Sales Range: $50-74.9 Million
Emp.: 4
Flavor Mfr
N.A.I.C.S.: 311930

ETOL Ukrajina TzOV **(4)**
Vul Kovaliva 46B, 82300, Borislav, Lviv Oblast, Ukraine
Tel.: (380) 324765577
Web Site: http://www.etol.com.ua
Sales Range: $50-74.9 Million
Emp.: 32
Confectionery Flavors Mfr
N.A.I.C.S.: 311930

Etol JVE d.o.o. **(4)**
Bulevar Vojvode Stepe 40, 21000, Novi Sad, Serbia
Tel.: (381) 216302011
Sales Range: $50-74.9 Million
Emp.: 8
Beverage Flavors Mfr
N.A.I.C.S.: 311930

Etol SK s.r.o. **(4)**
Nevadzova 5, 821 01, Bratislava, Slovakia
Tel.: (421) 248287412
Web Site: http://www.etol.com
Sales Range: $50-74.9 Million
Emp.: 6
Flavor Mfr
N.A.I.C.S.: 311930

Frutarom Etol d.o.o. **(4)**
Moldawska 9, 02 127, Warsaw, Poland
Tel.: (48) 226685109
Web Site: http://www.etol.pl
Sales Range: $50-74.9 Million
Emp.: 9
Beverage Flavors Mfr
N.A.I.C.S.: 311930

Subsidiary (US):

Frutarom USA Inc. **(2)**
9500 Railroad Ave, North Bergen, NJ 07047-1422
Tel.: (201) 861-9500
Web Site: http://www.frutarom.com
Sales Range: $25-49.9 Million
Emp.: 120
Botanicals, Water Soluble Gums, Flavors, Oleoresins Enhancers, Extracts, Oils
N.A.I.C.S.: 325411

Subsidiary (Domestic):

Frutarom USA Inc. **(3)**
10139 Commerce Park Dr, Cincinnati, OH 45246
Tel.: (513) 870-4900

Sales Range: $10-24.9 Million
Emp.: 55
Flavoring Syrup & Concentrate Mfr
N.A.I.C.S.: 311930
Reed Lynn *(Gen Mgr)*

Subsidiary (US):

Grow Company Inc **(2)**
55 Railroad Ave, Ridgefield, NJ 07657
Tel.: (201) 941-8777
Web Site: http://www.growco.us
Rev.: $2,700,000
Emp.: 20
Manufactures & Markets Food Flavors, Natural Food Coloring Agents, Dietary Supplements for Human & Animal Consumption & Cosmetic Ingredients
N.A.I.C.S.: 311930

Subsidiary (Non-US):

Ingredientes Naturales Seleccionados S.L. **(2)**
Finca La Almazara Santa Ana, 30319, Cartagena, Murcia, Spain
Tel.: (34) 968161500
Web Site: http://www.ingrenat.com
Natural Colors, Flavors, Cultures, Biotechnological Services
N.A.I.C.S.: 325414

Frutarom Peru S.A. **(1)**
Av Los Rosales 280, Santa Anita, Lima, Peru
Tel.: (51) 2306000
Web Site: https://iff.pe
Food Products Mfr
N.A.I.C.S.: 311999
Aharon Ran Cohen *(CFO)*

Frutarom Production GmbH **(1)**
Eichendorffstr 25, 83395, Freilassing, Germany
Tel.: (49) 86544700
Sausage & Meat Product Distr
N.A.I.C.S.: 424470
Alexander Klein *(Head-Logistics)*

Frutarom Russia Ltd. **(1)**
Kaspiyskaya Ulitsa 22, Moscow, 115304, Russia
Tel.: (7) 66263821201
Chemical Products Distr
N.A.I.C.S.: 424690
Svetlana Lobova *(Gen Mgr)*

Frutarom Savory Solutions Austria GmbH **(1)**
A-Schemel-Str 9, 5020, Salzburg, Austria
Tel.: (43) 66263820
Web Site: https://www.frutaromsavory.com
Sausage & Meat Product Mfr
N.A.I.C.S.: 311615

Frutarom Savory Solutions Germany GmbH **(1)**
Eichendorffstr 25, 83395, Freilassing, Germany
Tel.: (49) 86544700
Sausage & Meat Product Distr
N.A.I.C.S.: 424470

Frutarom South Africa (Proprietary) Limited **(1)**
70 Lechwe Road Corporate Park South, Midrand, 1682, Gauteng, South Africa
Tel.: (27) 829559518
Chemical Products Distr
N.A.I.C.S.: 424690

Health Wright Products, Inc. **(1)**
12482 SE Capps Rd, Clackamas, OH 97015
Tel.: (503) 722-4344
Web Site: http://www.healthwrightproducts.com
Sales Range: $1-9.9 Million
Emp.: 225
Health Capsule Mfr
N.A.I.C.S.: 325412
Mark Wright *(Co-Founder & Pres)*
Megan Westbrook *(Dir-HR)*

Henry H. Ottens Manufacturing Co., Inc. **(1)**
7800 Holstein Ave, Philadelphia, PA 19153
Tel.: (215) 365-7800
Organic Chemical Mfr
N.A.I.C.S.: 325180

IFF (Korea) Inc. **(1)**
Floor 2 336 Gamasan-ro Daesong Building, Yeongdeungpo-gu, Seoul, 7412, Korea (South)
Tel.: (82) 28350181
Flavor & Fragrance Product Mfr & Supplier
N.A.I.C.S.: 325199

IFF Aroma Esans Sanayi Ve Ticaret A.S. **(1)**
Ihsan Dede Caddesi 1100 Sokak, Gebze, 41480, Kocaeli, Turkiye **(100%)**
Tel.: (90) 2626770777
Sales Range: $10-24.9 Million
Emp.: 5
Creates & Produces Flavors, Fragrances & Aroma Chemicals
N.A.I.C.S.: 311930

IFF Fragrance GmbH **(1)**
Borstelmannsweg 169, 20537, Hamburg, Germany
Tel.: (49) 402111900
Flavor & Aroma Chemical Product Whslr
N.A.I.C.S.: 424490

IFF International Flavors & Fragrances Inc. **(1)**
600 Hwy 36, Hazlet, NJ 07730 **(100%)**
Tel.: (732) 264-4500
Web Site: http://www.iss.com
Sales Range: $300-349.9 Million
Emp.: 600
International Sales of Flavorings, Fragrances & Related Chemicals
N.A.I.C.S.: 325199

IFF Latin American Holdings (Espana), S.L. **(1)**
Paseo de la Castellana 149, 28046, Madrid, Spain
Tel.: (34) 915708935
Flavor & Aroma Chemical Product Whslr
N.A.I.C.S.: 424490

IFF Turkey Aroma Ve Esans Urunleri Satis Ticaret Anonim Sirketi **(1)**
Gebze Organize Sanayi Bolgesi Ihsan Dede Caddesi 1100 Sokak, 41480, Gebze, Kocaeli, Turkiye
Tel.: (90) 2626770777
Organic Chemical Mfr
N.A.I.C.S.: 325180

International Flavors & Fragrances (Asia Pacific) Pte. Ltd. **(1)**
41 Science Park Road Unit 02-22 The Gemini Lobby D, Singapore Science Park 2, Singapore, 117610, Singapore **(100%)**
Tel.: (65) 591500
Web Site: http://www.iff.com
Sales Range: $100-124.9 Million
Emp.: 150
Flavors & Ingredients Sales
N.A.I.C.S.: 424490

International Flavors & Fragrances (China) Ltd. **(1)**
9 Jinhua 2nd Street, Guangzhou Economic and Technological Development District, Guangzhou, 510730, China **(100%)**
Tel.: (86) 2082219838
Web Site: http://www.iff.com
Sales Range: $100-124.9 Million
Emp.: 200
Marketing & Sales
N.A.I.C.S.: 424490

Branch (Domestic):

International Flavors & Fragrances (China) Ltd. - Beijing Office **(2)**
Room 0409-0410 4th Floor No 60 North Street Xizhimen, haidian District, Beijing, 100088, China
Tel.: (86) 10 5881 0288
Web Site: http://www.iff.com
Creates & Produces Flavors, Fragrances & Aroma Chemicals
N.A.I.C.S.: 311930

International Flavors & Fragrances (China) Ltd. - Shanghai Office **(2)**
Floor 2-4 No 6 Bldg F Tatuhe road, Da Du He Road, Shanghai, 200062, China
Tel.: (86) 2160865500
Emp.: 100
Creates & Produces Flavors, Fragrances & Aroma Chemicals

N.A.I.C.S.: 311930

Subsidiary (Domestic):

International Flavors & Fragrances (Hangzhou) Co., Ltd. **(2)**
No 321 20 Ave, Hangzhou Economic & Technological Development Area, Hangzhou, 310018, Zhejiang, China
Tel.: (86) 57128928321
Grocery & Related Product Whslr
N.A.I.C.S.: 424490

International Flavors & Fragrances (Zhejiang) Co., Ltd. **(2)**
No 88 GuoXiang Road, Yangxi Community, Jiande, 311600, Zhejiang, China **(100%)**
Tel.: (86) 57164743488
Web Site: http://www.iff.com
Sales Range: $75-99.9 Million
Emp.: 190
Creates & Produces Flavors, Fragrances & Aroma Chemicals
N.A.I.C.S.: 311930

International Flavors & Fragrances (Hangzhou) Co. Ltd **(1)**
321 20 Ave Hangzhou Economic & Technological Development Area, Zhenjiang, 310018, China
Tel.: (86) 57128928321
Flavors & Fragrances Mfr
N.A.I.C.S.: 311999

International Flavors & Fragrances (Japan) Ltd. **(1)**
Gotemba 35 Aza Hotta Itazumi, Shinagawaku, Gotemba, 412-0048, Shizuoka, Japan **(100%)**
Tel.: (81) 18854963
Sales Range: $1-9.9 Million
Emp.: 50
Mfr & Sales of Flavors & Fragrances
N.A.I.C.S.: 325620
Masaharu Waki *(Pres)*

Plant (Domestic):

International Flavors & Fragrances (Japan) Ltd. - Gotemba Plant **(2)**
35 Itazuma, Gotemba, 412-0048, Shizuoka, Japan
Tel.: (81) 550896377
Creates & Produces Flavors, Fragrances & Aroma Chemicals
N.A.I.C.S.: 311930

International Flavors & Fragrances (Korea), Inc. **(1)**
2nd Floor Daesung Building 775 3 Daerim Dong Youngdeungpo Ku, Seoul, 150 070, Korea (South) **(100%)**
Tel.: (82) 28350181
Web Site: http://www.iff.com
Sales Range: $50-74.9 Million
Emp.: 9
Marketing
N.A.I.C.S.: 424490

International Flavors & Fragrances (Luxembourg) S.a.r.l. **(1)**
Tour A E-BRC 5 rue Eugene R, 2453, Luxembourg, Luxembourg
Tel.: (352) 8854961
Flavor & Fragrance Product Mfr & Supplier
N.A.I.C.S.: 325180

International Flavors & Fragrances (Mexico) S.A. de C.V. **(1)**
San Nicholas No 5 Fracc Indl, San Nicolas, Tlalnepantla, 54030, Mexico **(100%)**
Tel.: (52) 5553331900
Web Site: http://www.iff.com
Sales Range: $75-99.9 Million
Emp.: 190
Flavorings Mfr, Marketer & Retailer
N.A.I.C.S.: 311930

International Flavors & Fragrances (Mexico), S. de R.L. de C.V. **(1)**
San Nicolas No 5 Fracc Indl San Nicolas, 54030, Tlalnepantla, Estado de Mexico, Mexico
Tel.: (52) 5553331900
Flavor & Aroma Chemical Product Whslr
N.A.I.C.S.: 424490

International Flavors & Fragrances (Middle East) FZ-LLC **(1)**

Dubiotech Nucleoti Complex Ground Floor
Wing 4, PO Box 485030, Dubai, United
Arab Emirates
Tel.: (971) 44544500
Web Site: http://www.iff.com
Sales Range: $25-49.9 Million
Emp.: 30
Flavor & Fragrance Product Mfr & Supplier
N.A.I.C.S.: 325180

**International Flavors & Fragrances
(Nederland) Holding B.V.** (1)
Liebergerweg 72, 1221 JT, Hilversum,
Netherlands
Tel.: (31) 356883911
Sales Range: $75-99.9 Million
Emp.: 350
Investment Management Service
N.A.I.C.S.: 551112
Jeroen Van Noorden (Gen Mgr)

Subsidiary (Domestic):

**International Flavors & Fragrances
I.F.F. (Nederland) B.V.** (2)
Liebergerweg 72, 1221 JT, Hilversum,
1221JT, Netherlands (100%)
Tel.: (31) 356883911
Web Site: http://www.isf.com
Sales Range: $75-99.9 Million
Emp.: 350
Marketing & Creative Laboratory
N.A.I.C.S.: 541380
Cyndy Loomis (CEO)

Plant (Domestic):

**International Flavors & Fragrances
I.F.F. (Nederland) B.V. - Tilburg
Plant** (3)
Zevenheuvelenweg 60, 5048 AN, Tilburg,
Netherlands
Tel.: (31) 134642211
Web Site: http://www.iff.com
Creates & Produces Flavors, Fragrances &
Aroma Chemicals
N.A.I.C.S.: 311930

**International Flavors & Fragrances
(Philippines), Inc.** (1)
PH Distribution Center - 143 Mercedes Av-
enue San Miguel, Pasig, 1600,
Philippines (100%)
Tel.: (63) 8854963
Web Site: http://www.iff.com.ph
Sales Range: Less than $1 Million
Emp.: 25
Manufacturing, Sales & Creative Laboratory
N.A.I.C.S.: 311930

**International Flavors & Fragrances
(Poland) Sp.z.o.o.** (1)
Wiertnicza 109, 02-952, Warsaw, Poland
Tel.: (48) 228582560
Web Site: http://www.iff.com
Sales Range: $50-74.9 Million
Emp.: 20
Flavors & Ingredients Sales
N.A.I.C.S.: 424490

**International Flavors & Fragrances
(Thailand) Ltd.** (1)
989 Siam Piwat Tower 29th Floor Rama 1
Rd Pathumwan, Bangkok, 10330,
Thailand (100%)
Tel.: (66) 26645555
Web Site:
   http://www.internationalflavors.com
Sales Range: $75-99.9 Million
Emp.: 60
Marketing & Sales of Flavors & Fragrances
N.A.I.C.S.: 424490

**International Flavors & Fragrances
I.F.F. (Deutschland) GmbH** (1)
Units 3 16 17 18 Centroallee 275 277,
46047, Oberhausen, Germany (100%)
Tel.: (49) 20878240
Web Site: http://www.iff.com
Sales Range: $50-74.9 Million
Emp.: 30
Flavors & Fragrances Mfr & Sales
N.A.I.C.S.: 311930
Nicola Mueller (Mng Dir)

**International Flavors & Fragrances
I.F.F. (Espana) S.A.** (1)
Paseo de la Castellana 149-9 Planta, Ma-
drid, 28046, Spain (100%)

Tel.: (34) 915708935
Web Site: http://www.iff.com
Sales Range: $25-49.9 Million
Emp.: 15
Also Located at Barcelona & Benicarlo MC;
Sales & Marketing of Flavorings, Fra-
grances & Aroma
N.A.I.C.S.: 311930

Subsidiary (Domestic):

IFF Benicarlo, S.A. (2)
Avda Felipe Klein 2, 12580, Benicarlo, Cas-
tellon, Spain (100%)
Tel.: (34) 8854961
Web Site: http://www.iff.com
Sales Range: $75-99.9 Million
Emp.: 210
Mfr of Flavors, Fragrances & Aroma Chemi-
cals
N.A.I.C.S.: 325620

Branch (Domestic):

**International Flavors & Fragrances
I.F.F. (Espana) S.A. - Barcelona** (2)
Edificio Astrolabio Avenida Cerdanyola 92-
94, 08172, Barcelona, Spain
Tel.: (34) 932684122
Web Site: http://www.iffs.com
Sales Range: $10-24.9 Million
Emp.: 8
Sales Office & Creative Laboratory for IFF
N.A.I.C.S.: 311930

**International Flavors & Fragrances
I.F.F. (France) S.a.r.l.** (1)
61 Rue Des Villiers CS 30063, 92523,
Neuilly-sur-Seine, France (100%)
Tel.: (33) 146494347
Web Site: http://www.iff.com
Sales Range: $100-124.9 Million
Emp.: 300
Sales of Flavors & Fragrances
N.A.I.C.S.: 424490

Subsidiary (Domestic):

**International Flavors & Fragrances
I.F.F. (France) S.A.S.** (1)
9b rue Rene Char, PO Box 36514, 21065,
Dijon, Cedex, France (100%)
Tel.: (33) 380737878
Web Site: http://www.iff.com
Sales Range: $25-49.9 Million
Emp.: 30
Creates & Produces Flavors, Fragrances &
Aroma Chemicals
N.A.I.C.S.: 311930

Laboratoire Monique Remy (2)
Parc Industriel Les Bois De, 06130, Grasse,
France (100%)
Tel.: (33) 492424344
Web Site: http://www.iff.com
Sales Range: $10-24.9 Million
Emp.: 40
Mfr of Flavors, Fragrances & Aroma Chemi-
cals
N.A.I.C.S.: 325199

**International Flavors & Fragrances
I.F.F. (Israel) Ltd.** (1)
Hayezira St 3, Ramat Gan, 52521,
Israel (100%)
Tel.: (972) 37511545
Web Site: http://www.iff.com
Sales Range: $150-199.9 Million
Flavors & Ingredients Sales
N.A.I.C.S.: 424490

**International Flavors & Fragrances
I.F.F. (Italia) S.r.l.** (1)
Via F LLI Cervi 13, Trezzano sul Naviglio,
20090, Milan, Italy
Tel.: (39) 02484721
Web Site: http://www.iff.com
Sales Range: $10-24.9 Million
Emp.: 30
Manufacturing, Sales & Creative Laboratory
N.A.I.C.S.: 334516

**International Flavors & Fragrances
I.F.F. (Middle East) FZE** (1)
Ground floor Wing 4 Unit RO11 G01 G02
G06C G06B G06A G05, PO Box 485030,
DSP Laboratory Complex Dubai Science
Park, Dubai, United Arab Emirates
Tel.: (971) 97144544500
Flavor & Fragrance Product Mfr & Supplier

N.A.I.C.S.: 325180

**International Flavors & Fragrances
I.F.F. (Norden) AB** (1)
Fargerigatan 3, PO Box 107, 289 21, Knisl-
inge, Sweden (100%)
Tel.: (46) 8854961
Web Site: http://www.iff.com
Sales Range: $25-49.9 Million
Emp.: 35
Creates & Produces Flavors, Fragrances &
Aroma Chemicals
N.A.I.C.S.: 311930

**International Flavors & Fragrances
I.F.F. (S.A.) (Pty) Ltd.** (1)
34 Diesel Road, Isando, 1600, Gauteng,
South Africa (100%)
Tel.: (27) 119228815
Web Site: http://www.iff.com
Sales Range: $50-74.9 Million
Emp.: 120
Creates & Produces Flavors, Fragrances &
Aroma Chemicals
N.A.I.C.S.: 311930

**International Flavors & Fragrances
S.R.L.** (1)
Einstein 824, B1619CQA, Garin, Buenos
Aires, Argentina
Tel.: (54) 3327445000
Web Site: http://www.iff.com
Flavoring Material Mfr
N.A.I.C.S.: 325199

**International Flavors & Fragrances
S.R.L.** (1)
Einstein 824 Garin, B1619CQA, Buenos
Aires, Argentina (100%)
Tel.: (54) 3327445000
Web Site: http://www.iff.com
Sales Range: $50-74.9 Million
Emp.: 160
Mfr of Fragrances & Flavors
N.A.I.C.S.: 311930

**International Flavors e Fragrances
IFF (Italia) S.r.l.** (1)
Via Fratelli Cervi 13, 20090, Trezzano sul
Naviglio, MI, Italy
Tel.: (39) 02484721
Flavoring Material Mfr
N.A.I.C.S.: 325199

**International Flavours & Fragrances
(Australia) Pty. Ltd.** (1)
310 Frankston Dandenong Road, PO Box
1455, Dandenong, 3175, VIC,
Australia (100%)
Tel.: (61) 397889200
Web Site: http://www.iff.com
Sales Range: $50-74.9 Million
Emp.: 160
Grocery & Related Products Whslr
N.A.I.C.S.: 424490

**International Flavours & Fragrances
(India) Ltd.** (1)
1-5 Seven Wells Street, St thomas Mount,
Chennai, 600 016, TN, India (100%)
Tel.: (91) 4422341131
Web Site: http://www.iff.com
Sales Range: $25-49.9 Million
Emp.: 140
Mfr of Flavors, Fragrances & Aroma Chemi-
cals
N.A.I.C.S.: 325199
Sridhar Balakrishnan (CEO)

**International Flavours & Fragrances
(NZ) Limited** (1)
Central Park Building 2 Level 4 666 Great
South Road Ellerslie, Auckland, 1051, New
Zealand
Tel.: (64) 96212000
Flavoring Material Mfr
N.A.I.C.S.: 325199

**International Flavours & Fragrances
(NZ) Ltd** (1)
128 Stoddard Road Mt Roskill, PO Box
27162, Auckland, 1041, New Zealand
Tel.: (64) 96212000
Web Site: http://www.iff.com
Emp.: 10
Flavours & Fragrances Mfr
N.A.I.C.S.: 311999

**International Flavours & Fragrances
(New Zealand) Ltd.** (1)

128 Stoddard Road Mt Roskill, Auckland,
1041, New Zealand (100%)
Tel.: (64) 96212000
Web Site: http://www.iff.com
Sales Range: $10-24.9 Million
Emp.: 10
Mfr of Flavors, Fragrances & Aroma Chemi-
cals
N.A.I.C.S.: 325199

**International Flavours & Fragrances
(Thailand) Limited** (1)
29th Floor Siam Piwat Tower Rama 1 Road,
Patumwan, Bangkok, 10330, Thailand
Tel.: (66) 26645555
Organic Chemical Mfr
N.A.I.C.S.: 325180

**International Flavours & Fragrances
(Vietnam) Limited Liability
Company** (1)
TMS Building 11th Floor 172 Hai Ba Trung
Street, Da Kao Ward District 1, Ho Chi
Minh City, Vietnam
Tel.: (84) 822202700
Organic Chemical Mfr
N.A.I.C.S.: 325180

**International Flavours & Fragrances
I.F.F. (Great Britain) Ltd.** (1)
The Grange Bank Lane, London, SW15
5JT, United Kingdom (100%)
Tel.: (44) 2083924000
Web Site: http://www.iff.com
Sales Range: $50-74.9 Million
Emp.: 25
Sales of Cosmetics & Perfumes
N.A.I.C.S.: 456120

Subsidiary (Domestic):

**International Flavours & Fragrances
(CIL) Limited** (2)
Duddery Hill, Haverhill, CB9 8LG, Suffolk,
United Kingdom (100%)
Tel.: (44) 1440715000
Web Site: http://www.iff.com
Emp.: 275
Creates & Produces Flavors, Fragrances &
Aroma Chemicals
N.A.I.C.S.: 311930

**International Flavours & Fragrances
India Private Limited** (1)
1-5 Seven Wells Street St Thomas Mount,
Chennai, 600016, India
Tel.: (91) 4422341131
Pharmaceutical Chemicals Mfr
N.A.I.C.S.: 325998

**Inventive Food Technology (ZQ)
Ltd.** (1)
San Rong Industrial Zone Jidong Road,
Duanzhou District, Zhaoqing, Guangdong,
China
Tel.: (86) 7582915668
Food Products Distr
N.A.I.C.S.: 424490

Kelp Industries Pty. Ltd. (1)
89 Netherby Road, PO Box 314, King Is-
land, Currie, 7256, TAS, Australia
Tel.: (61) 364621340
Web Site: https://www.kelpind.com.au
Alginate Mfr
N.A.I.C.S.: 325199

Leagel S.r.l. (1)
Strada delle Seriole 55, Chiesanuova,
47894, San Marino, San Marino
Tel.: (378) 549999435
Web Site: https://www.leagel.com
Ice Cream & Cake Product Mfr
N.A.I.C.S.: 311813
Cesare Di Paolo (Mgr-Export)

**Les Ingredients Alimentaires BSA
Inc.** (1)
6005 Boulevard Couture, Montreal, H1P
3E1, QC, Canada
Tel.: (514) 852-2719
Web Site: http://www.bsa.ca
Chemical Products Distr
N.A.I.C.S.: 424690
Marcel Baril (Pres & CEO)

**Lucas Meyer Cosmetics Australia Pty
Ltd** (1)
Hinterland Way 226, Knockrow, 2479,

International Flavors & Fragrances Inc.—(Continued)

NSW, Australia
Tel.: (61) 266878828
Organic Chemical Mfr
N.A.I.C.S.: 325180

Misr Co. for Aromatic Products (MARP) S.A.E. **(1)**
6 October City 1st Industrial Area No 26, PO Box 114, Haram, Cairo, 12556, Egypt **(100%)**
Tel.: (20) 238200540
Web Site: http://www.iff.com
Sales Range: $10-24.9 Million
Emp.: 35
Mfr of Flavors, Fragrances & Aroma Chemicals
N.A.I.C.S.: 325199

Muhlehof Gewurze AG **(1)**
Marktstrasse 34, Niederuzwil, 9244, Uzwil, Switzerland
Tel.: (41) 719518711
Web Site: http://www.muehlehof-gewuerze.ch
Food Products Mfr
N.A.I.C.S.: 311999

Nardi Armoas Ltda. **(1)**
Av Alberto Jafet 407, Diadema, 09951-110, Sao Paulo, Brazil
Tel.: (55) 11998977475
Organic Chemical Product Mfr
N.A.I.C.S.: 325199

Nardi Aromas Ltda. **(1)**
Av Alberto Jafet 407 Vila Nogueira, Diadema, SP, Brazil
Tel.: (55) 1140714073
Web Site: http://www.fatima.dominiotemporario.com
Chemical Products Distr
N.A.I.C.S.: 424690

Nutrafur S.A. **(1)**
Camino Viejo de Pliego Km 2, PO Box 182, Alcantarilla, 30820, Murcia, Spain
Tel.: (34) 968892855
Web Site: http://www.nutrafur.com
Organic Chemical Product Mfr
N.A.I.C.S.: 325199
Adolfo Aliaga Ruiz (Mgr-Pur)

Proveedores de Ingenieria Alimentaria, S.A. de C.V. **(1)**
Ave Industrias Num 140 Esq Privada Las Mitras, Postal 65, Fracc Pimsa Ote KRONOS Parque Industrial, 66603, Apodaca, NL, Mexico
Tel.: (52) 8112539990
Web Site: https://www.piasa.com
Prepared Sauces Mfr
N.A.I.C.S.: 311941

Pucheng Yongfang Fragrance Technology Co., Ltd. **(1)**
No 5 Industrial park, Nanping, 353400, Fujian, China
Tel.: (86) 5992838333
Web Site: http://www.pcffcn.com
Food Products Mfr
N.A.I.C.S.: 311999

Redbrook Blentech Limited **(1)**
Warehouse Unit Blyry Industrial Estate, Athlone, Co Westmeath, Ireland
Tel.: (353) 906470984
Chemical Products Distr
N.A.I.C.S.: 424690

Redbrook Ingredient Services Limited **(1)**
Unit 1 Plato Business Park Damastown, Mulhuddart, Dublin, 15, Ireland
Tel.: (353) 18604900
Web Site: http://www.redbrookingredients.com
Food Products Mfr
N.A.I.C.S.: 311999

Rene Laurent, a Societe par Actions Simplifiee **(1)**
107 Avenue Franklin Roosevelt, PO Box 40016, 06117, Le Cannet-Rocheville, Cedex, France
Tel.: (33) 493692727
Web Site: http://www.rene-laurent.fr
Distillery Mfr
N.A.I.C.S.: 312140

Sabores y Fragancias S.A. **(1)**
Cra 98 No 25G 10 Interior 14, Bogota, Colombia
Tel.: (57) 14222240
Sales Range: $25-49.9 Million
Emp.: 60
Creates & Produces Flavors, Fragrances & Aroma Chemicals
N.A.I.C.S.: 311930

Savoury Flavours Ltd. **(1)**
Unit 1A Riverside Avenue West Lawford, Manningtree, CO11 1UN, Essex, United Kingdom
Tel.: (44) 1206393540
Web Site: http://www.savouryflavours.co.uk
Food Products Mfr
N.A.I.C.S.: 311999

Speximo AB **(1)**
Scheelevagen 2, Medicon Village, 223 63, Lund, Skane lan, Sweden
Tel.: (46) 721669144
Web Site: http://www.speximo.com
Cosmetics Products Mfr
N.A.I.C.S.: 325620
Malin Sjoo (Founder & CEO)

Tastepoint Inc. **(1)**
7800 Holstein Ave, Philadelphia, PA 19153
Tel.: (215) 365-7800
Web Site: http://www.tastepoint.com
Flavoring Material Mfr
N.A.I.C.S.: 325199

Subsidiary (Non-US):

Sonarome Private Limited **(1)**
One Sonarome Way Kiadb Industrial Area, Doddaballapur, Bengaluru, India **(70%)**
Tel.: (91) 8068902200
Web Site: https://www.sonarome.com
Chemical Products Distr
N.A.I.C.S.: 424690

Subsidiary (Domestic):

Tastepoint, Inc. **(2)**
10801 Decatur Rd, Philadelphia, PA 19154-3209
Tel.: (215) 632-3100
Web Site: http://www.tastepoint.com
Flavorings for Processed Food Industry Mfr
N.A.I.C.S.: 311930

Subsidiary (Non-US):

David Michael Europe S.A.S. **(3)**
ZI de Marcerolles Rue E Rutherford, 26500, Bourg-les-Valence, France
Tel.: (33) 475834025
Sales Range: $10-24.9 Million
Emp.: 23
Food Additives Mfr
N.A.I.C.S.: 311930
Claude Simon (Mng Dir)

Taura Natural Ingredients (North America) Inc. **(1)**
9950 Commerce Park Dr Ste1, West Chester, OH 45246-1332
Tel.: (540) 723-8691
Food Products Distr
N.A.I.C.S.: 424490

Taura Natural Ingredients Ltd. **(1)**
16 Owens Place, PO Box 4149, Mount Maunganui, 3149, New Zealand
Tel.: (64) 75726700
Web Site: https://www.tauraurc.com
Food Products Mfr
N.A.I.C.S.: 311999

Taura Natural Ingredients NV **(1)**
I Z 3-De Heze Lammerdries-oost 30, 2250, Olen, 2250, Belgium
Tel.: (32) 14257300
Food Products Distr
N.A.I.C.S.: 424490
Wim De Mol (VP-Global Ops)

The Mighty Company Limited **(1)**
9 Soi Sangkomsongkraw 6, Ladprao, Bangkok, 10230, Thailand
Tel.: (66) 29331155
Web Site: https://www.mighty.co.th
Organic Chemical Product Mfr
N.A.I.C.S.: 325199
Watchareekul Rattananupap (VP)

Unique Ingredients Limited **(1)**

5 Whittle Close Drayton Fields Industrial Estate, Daventry, NN11 8RQ, Northants, United Kingdom
Tel.: (44) 1327876200
Web Site: https://www.uniqueingredients.co.uk
Food Products Mfr
N.A.I.C.S.: 311999

VAYA Pharma, Inc. **(1)**
10480 Little Patuxent Pkwy Ste 900, Columbia, MD 21044
Tel.: (410) 297-0020
Web Site: http://www.vayapharma.com
Pharmaceutical Products Distr
N.A.I.C.S.: 424210
Michelle Cuccia (CEO)

VITIVA proizvodnja in storitve d.d. **(1)**
Nova Vas Pri Markovcih 98, Markovci, 2281, Ptuj, Slovenia
Tel.: (386) 27888730
Web Site: http://www.vitiva.eu
Chemical Product & Preparation Mfr
N.A.I.C.S.: 325998

WIBERG Canada Inc. **(1)**
931 Equestrian Court, Oakville, L6L 6L7, ON, Canada
Tel.: (905) 825-9900
Web Site: https://www.wiberg.ca
Food Products Mfr
N.A.I.C.S.: 311412

WIBERG Corporation of California **(1)**
11258 Regentview Ave, Downey, CA 90241
Tel.: (562) 869-5240
Food Products Distr
N.A.I.C.S.: 424490

INTERNATIONAL ISOTOPES INC.
4137 Commerce Cir, Idaho Falls, ID 83401
Tel.: (208) 524-5300　　TX
Web Site: https://www.intisoid.com
Year Founded: 1995
INIS—(OTCQB)
Rev.: $11,181,988
Assets: $16,244,596
Liabilities: $11,902,054
Net Worth: $4,342,542
Earnings: $303,238
Emp.: 32
Fiscal Year-end: 12/31/22
Radioisotopes & Radiochemicals Mfr
N.A.I.C.S.: 325998
Christopher G. Grosso (Chm)
W. Matthew Cox (CFO & Sec)
Shahe Bagderjian (Pres & CEO)

INTERNATIONAL LAND ALLIANCE, INC.
350 10th Ave Ste 1000, San Diego, CA 92101　　WY
Web Site: https://www.ila.company
Year Founded: 2013
ILAL—(OTCQB)
Rev.: $7,058,479
Assets: $30,353,831
Liabilities: $28,656,801
Net Worth: $1,697,030
Earnings: ($2,073,281)
Emp.: 4
Fiscal Year-end: 12/31/23
Real Estate Manangement Services
N.A.I.C.S.: 531390
Roberto Jesus Valdes (Founder & CEO)
Jason Sunstein (CFO, Chief Acctg Officer & VP-Fin)
Frank A. Ingrande (Pres)

INTERNATIONAL LUXURY PRODUCTS, INC.
8 The Green Ste R, Dover, DE 19901
Tel.: (302) 601-2133　　NV
Year Founded: 1998
ILXP—(OTCIQ)

Watchcases & Clock Distr
N.A.I.C.S.: 458310
Andrew Gaudet (COO)
Tejas Bansilal Parikh (Chm, CEO, CFO & Sec)

INTERNATIONAL MEDIA ACQUISITION CORP.
1604 US Highway 130, North Brunswick, NJ 08902
Tel.: (993) 080-9579　　DE
Web Site: https://www.imac.org.in
Year Founded: 2021
IMAQ—(OTCIQ)
Assets: $11,393,873
Liabilities: $25,386,351
Net Worth: ($13,992,478)
Earnings: ($814,487)
Emp.: 1
Fiscal Year-end: 03/31/24
Investment Services
N.A.I.C.S.: 523999
Shibasish Sarkar (Chm & CEO)

INTERNATIONAL MONETARY SYSTEMS, LTD.
16901 W Glendale Dr, New Berlin, WI 53151-0305
Tel.: (262) 780-3640　　WI
Web Site: http://www.imsbarter.com
Year Founded: 1985
ITNM—(OTCIQ)
Rev.: $11,726,000
Assets: $7,490,000
Liabilities: $3,646,000
Net Worth: $3,844,000
Earnings: $370,000
Emp.: 110
Fiscal Year-end: 12/31/19
Holding Company; Trade Exchanges & Barter Networks Owner, Manager & Operator
N.A.I.C.S.: 551112
Donald F. Mardak (Founder)
John E. Strabley (CEO)
Dale L. Mardak (Pres & CFO)
Kimberly A. Strabley (VP)

INTERNATIONAL MONEY EXPRESS INC.
9100 S Dadeland Blvd Ste 1100, Miami, FL 33156
Tel.: (305) 671-8000　　DE
Web Site: https://www.intermexonline.com
Year Founded: 2015
IMXI—(NASDAQ)
Rev.: $546,805,000
Assets: $512,072,000
Liabilities: $362,166,000
Net Worth: $149,906,000
Earnings: $57,331,000
Emp.: 893
Fiscal Year-end: 12/31/22
Holding Company
N.A.I.C.S.: 551112
Robert W. Lisy (Chm, Pres & CEO)
Randall Nilsen (Exec VP-Intermex Retail Sls-US & Canada)
Mike Gallentine (VP-IR)
Andras Bende (CFO)

Subsidiaries:

Envios de Valores La Nacional Corp. **(1)**
566 W 207th St, New York, NY 10034
Tel.: (917) 529-0700
Sales Range: $1-9.9 Million
Emp.: 50
Financial Transactions Processing, Reserve & Clearinghouse Activities
N.A.I.C.S.: 522320
Jon Ness (Pres & CEO)

Intermex Wire Transfer, LLC **(1)**
9480 S Dixie Hwy, Miami, FL 33156
Tel.: (305) 671-8000
Web Site: http://www.intermexonline.com

Wired Telecommunications Carriers
N.A.I.C.S.: 517111
Andreas Bende *(CFO)*

Intermex Wire Transfers de Guatemala S.A. (1)
12 Calle 1-25 Zona 10 Edificio Geminis 10 Torre Sur Oficina 301, Guatemala, Guatemala
Tel.: (502) 24233200
Web Site: https://www.intermexonline.com
Financial Management Services
N.A.I.C.S.: 551112

INTERNATIONAL PAPER COMPANY
6400 Poplar Ave, Memphis, TN 38197
Tel.: (901) 419-9000   TN
Web Site:
https://www.internationalpaper.com
Year Founded: 1898
IP—(NYSE)
Rev.: $18,916,000,000
Assets: $23,261,000,000
Liabilities: $14,906,000,000
Net Worth: $8,355,000,000
Earnings: $288,000,000
Emp.: 39,000
Fiscal Year-end: 12/31/23
Pulp & Paper, Converted Paper Products, Paperboard, Wood & Specialty Products Mfr
N.A.I.C.S.: 322120
Andrew K. Silvernail *(Chm & CEO)*
Jean-Michel Ribieras *(Sr VP)*
John V. Sims *(Sr VP-Corp Dev)*
Holly G. Goughnour *(VP-Fin & Controller)*
Joseph R. Saab *(Gen Counsel, Sec & Sr VP)*
James P. Royalty Jr. *(Sr VP)*
Aimee Gregg *(Sr VP)*
Allison Magness *(Sr VP)*
Tim S. Nicholls *(Chief Fin Officer)*
W. Thomas Hamic *(Pres-North American Packaging Solutions & Exec VP)*

Subsidiaries:

Baoding International Paper Packaging Co., Ltd. (1)
Gaoxin Industrial Park Tianwei Road, Baoding New District West, Baoding, 71051, Hebei, China
Tel.: (86) 312 3210213
Web Site: http://www.internationalpaper.com
Paper Packaging Mfr
N.A.I.C.S.: 322211

CMCP - INTERNATIONAL PAPER S.A.S. (1)
Quartier Industriel Ain Sebaa Bd El Hanch Ben Bouazza, PO Box 2595, 20250, Casablanca, Morocco
Tel.: (212) 522667878
Web Site: http://www.internationalpaper.com
Paper Packaging Mfr
N.A.I.C.S.: 322211

Carton y Papel Reciclado, S.A. (1)
Calle del Papel 1, 28947, Fuenlabrada, Madrid, Spain
Tel.: (34) 913716570
Web Site: https://www.carpasa.es
Packaging Paperboard Product Mfr
N.A.I.C.S.: 322211

Cartonajes International S.L. (1)
General Yague 20 2 B, Madrid, 28020, Spain   (100%)
Tel.: (34) 915557141
Sales Range: $1-9.9 Million
Paper Mills
N.A.I.C.S.: 322120

Cartonajes Union S.L. (1)
Camino Viejo del Grao s/n, 46700, Gandia, Spain
Tel.: (34) 962840350
Corrugated & Solid Fibre Boxes Mfr
N.A.I.C.S.: 322211

Cartonajes Union S.L. (1)
Laderita del Pilar, 38107, Santa Cruz de

Tenerife, Spain
Tel.: (34) 922629121
Paper Packaging Mfr
N.A.I.C.S.: 322211

Chocolate Bayou Water Company (1)
1920 FM 2917 Rd, Alvin, TX 77512
Tel.: (281) 393-1596
Water Supply Services
N.A.I.C.S.: 221310

Branch (Domestic):

International Paper Realty Corp. - Savannah Office (2)
1200 W Lathrop Ave 201, Savannah, GA 31415-1061
Tel.: (912) 238-6000
Residential Land Development & Management
N.A.I.C.S.: 113210

Comptoir des Bois de Brive SAS (1)
17 Avenue Maillard, CS 40160, 19104, Brive-la-Gaillarde, France
Tel.: (33) 555927392
Emp.: 30
Wood Sourcing Services; Extraction of Timber
N.A.I.C.S.: 113110

Emballages Laurent SAS (1)
Z I Nord rue Colbert, 71109, Chalon-sur-Saone, Cedex, France
Tel.: (33) 385476800
Packaging Products Mfr
N.A.I.C.S.: 322211

Envases Grau, S.L. (1)
Ctra Tavernes - Lliria PK3, Tavernes de la Valldigna, 46760, Valencia, Spain
Tel.: (34) 962824004
Web Site: http://www.envasesgrau.es
Packaging Paperboard Product Mfr & Distr
N.A.I.C.S.: 322211

Hammermill Paper (1)
6400 Poplar Ave, Memphis, TN 38197-0100
Tel.: (901) 419-9000
Web Site: http://www.hammermill.com
Sales Range: $900-999.9 Million
Emp.: 3,000
Printing & Office Paper Mfr
N.A.I.C.S.: 322120

I.P. CONTAINER HOLDINGS (SPAIN) S.L. (1)
Oquendo 23-2, 28006, Madrid, Spain
Tel.: (34) 915557141
Paper Products Mfr
N.A.I.C.S.: 322299

IP Belgian Services Company SPRL (1)
Chaussee de la Hulpe 166, 1170, Brussels, Belgium
Tel.: (32) 26761311
Web Site: http://www.ipaper.com
Administrative Management Services
N.A.I.C.S.: 336360

IP Canadian Packaging Operations Inc. (1)
203-26596 Gloucester Way, Langley, V4W 4A8, BC, Canada
Tel.: (604) 856-8868
Packaging Paper Product Whslr
N.A.I.C.S.: 424120

IP Commercial Properties Inc. (1)
8665 Argent St Ste C, Santee, CA 92071
Tel.: (619) 596-1880
Web Site: http://ipcommercialproperties.com
Commercial Real Estate Consulting Services
N.A.I.C.S.: 531210

IP EMPAQUES DE MEXICO, S. DE R.L. DE C.V. (1)
Blvd Independencia 2550 Parque Industrial Independencia 1, Chihuahua, 32575, Ciudad Juarez, Mexico
Tel.: (52) 6562520800
Emp.: 23
Industrial Equipment Mfr
N.A.I.C.S.: 333248
Alsredo Ancaondo *(Mgr)*

IP India Foundation (1)

Krishe Sapphire 8th Floor Madhapur Road Hitech City, Hyderabad, 500 081, India
Tel.: (91) 4033121000
Web Site: http://www.ipindiafoundation.org
All Other Personal Services
N.A.I.C.S.: 812990

IP Singapore Holding Pte. Ltd. (1)
101 Thomas Road 06-01 United Square, Singapore Land Tower, Singapore, 307591, Singapore
Tel.: (65) 6 829 5344
Web Site:
https://www.internationalpaper.com
Pulp & Paper Mfr
N.A.I.C.S.: 322120

Subsidiary (Domestic):

International Paper Singapore (2)
101 Thomas Road 06-01 United Square, Singapore, 307591, Singapore
Tel.: (65) 68295343
Sales Range: $25-49.9 Million
Emp.: 10
Corrugated Sheetboards, Packaging Cartons, Paper Pallets & Laminated Cartons Mfr
N.A.I.C.S.: 322211

Instituto International Paper (1)
Avenida Paulista 37 14th floor, 01311-902, Bela Vista, Brazil
Tel.: (55) 1938618637
Public Interest Civil Services
N.A.I.C.S.: 813312

International Paper (1)
Fedorova Str 12, 03150, Kiev, Ukraine   (100%)
Tel.: (380) 442897677
Sales Range: $10-24.9 Million
Emp.: 3
Printing & Communications Papers
N.A.I.C.S.: 322120

International Paper & Sun Cartonboard Co., Ltd. (1)
1 Youyi Road Yanzhou, 272100, Shangdong, China
Tel.: (86) 5373898902
Paperboard Mill Operating Services
N.A.I.C.S.: 322130
Li Bernard *(Gen Mgr)*

International Paper (Chongqing) Packaging Co., Ltd (1)
No. 27 Xiangyu Road Air Industrial Zone, Yubei District, 401120, Chongqing, China
Tel.: (86) 2367282666
Paper Packaging Mfr
N.A.I.C.S.: 322211

International Paper (Deutschland)GmbH (1)
Volmerswerther Strasse 20, 40221, Dusseldorf, Germany
Tel.: (49) 211901780
Paper Packaging Mfr
N.A.I.C.S.: 322211

International Paper (Espana), S. L. (1)
C/Paris 162 3- 2, 08036, Barcelona, Spain
Tel.: (34) 934110034
Paper Packaging Mfr
N.A.I.C.S.: 322211

International Paper (Europe) S.A. (1)
Chaussee de la Hulpe 166, Brussels, 1170, Belgium   (100%)
Tel.: (32) 27741211
Sales Range: $10-24.9 Million
Emp.: 70
Paper Mills
N.A.I.C.S.: 322120

International Paper (India) Private Limited (1)
Krishe Sapphire Building 8th Floor 1-89/3/B/40 to 42/KS/801, Hitech City Main Road Madhapur, Hyderabad, 500 081, Telangana, India
Tel.: (91) 4033121000
Paper Packaging Mfr
N.A.I.C.S.: 322211

International Paper (Malaysia) Sdn Bhd (1)

Suite 4 03 Level 4 Amoda Building 22 Jalan Imbi, 55100, Kuala Lumpur, Malaysia
Tel.: (60) 321444306
Paper Packaging Mfr
N.A.I.C.S.: 322211

International Paper (UK) Limited (1)
Crichiebank Business Centre Office 2 Mill Road Port Elphinstone, Aberdeenshire, Inverurie, AB51 5NQ, United Kingdom
Tel.: (44) 8706001693
Printing Paper Mfr
N.A.I.C.S.: 322120

International Paper - Kwidzyn Sp. Z O.O. (1)
ul Lotnicza 1, 82-500, Kwidzyn, Poland
Tel.: (48) 556108000
Paper Mill Operator
N.A.I.C.S.: 322120
Aneta Muskala *(Dir-Finance-Mgmt Bd & Vice Chm-Mgmt Bd)*
Piotr Klimek *(Dir & Member-Exec Bd)*
Krzysztof Grosser *(Dir-Operations & Member-Exec Bd)*
Tomasz Brodecki *(Mgr-Mill & Chm-Exec Bd)*

International Paper APPM Limited (1)
Door No 1-89/3/B/40 to 42/KS/107/A 1 st Floor, MSR Block Krishe Sapphire Building Hitech City Main Road Madhapur, Hyderabad, 500 081, Telangana, India
Tel.: (91) 4049839999
Web Site: https://andhrapaper.com
Emp.: 2,500
Printing Paper Mfr
N.A.I.C.S.: 322120
Prabhakar Cherukumudi *(Sec & Sr VP)*
Sreenivas Pamidimukkala *(CIO & VP-Information Technology)*
Anish Mathew *(CFO)*
Sura Mallidi *(Sr VP)*
Shyam Srivastava *(VP-Purchase-Forestry)*
Atanu Chakrabarti *(Sr VP-Sales-Supply Chain)*
Joseph Kammara *(Gen Mgr)*
Lakshmi Prasad *(Gen Mgr-Government Relations)*
S. K. Bangur *(Co-Mng Dir & Chm)*
Saurabh Bangur *(Co-Mng Dir)*
Virendraa Bangur *(Vice Chm)*
Mukesh Jain *(Comml Dir)*
Aravind Matta *(Sec & VP)*

International Paper Agroflorestal Ltda. (1)
Telemaco Carneiro 669 SL 3 Centro, 84990-000, Arapoti, Parana, Brazil
Tel.: (55) 4391196644
Paper Packaging Mfr
N.A.I.C.S.: 322211

International Paper Asia Limited (1)
28F Ascendas Plaza 333 Tian Yao Qiao Road, Xuhui District, Shanghai, 200030, China   (100%)
Tel.: (86) 2161133200
Web Site:
https://www.internationalpaper.com
Sales Range: $100-124.9 Million
General Trading, Bleached Board, Paperboard Mfr
N.A.I.C.S.: 322130

International Paper CTA (Mexico), S. de R.L. de C.V. (1)
Av 5 de Febrero No 1351 Empresalia Tower 1 Sequoia PB01 Col Fracc, 76120, Queretaro, Mexico
Tel.: (52) 4424276150
Corrugated Packaging Product Mfr
N.A.I.C.S.: 322211

International Paper Cabourg SAS (1)
ZAC de Cabourg Village Cabourg, 14390, Normandie, France
Tel.: (33) 231281880
Paper Products Mfr
N.A.I.C.S.: 322299

International Paper Canada, Inc. (1)
1550 Enterprise Road Suite 108, Mississauga, L4W 4P4, ON, Canada   (100%)
Tel.: (905) 696-7550
Sales Range: $300-349.9 Million
Mfr of White Papers & Coated Publication Papers

International Paper Company—(Continued)

N.A.I.C.S.: 322220

International Paper Cartones Ltda. (1)
Longitudinal Sur Km 75, Comuna de Graneros, Rancagua, Chile
Tel.: (56) 72208200
Paper Packaging Mfr
N.A.I.C.S.: 322211

International Paper Cartovar, S.A. (1)
R de Ovar 16, 3880-102, Ovar, Portugal
Tel.: (351) 256579360
Pulp & Paper Product Mfr
N.A.I.C.S.: 322120

International Paper Cellulose Fibers (Poland) sp. z o.o. (1)
ul Maszynowa 20, 80-298, Gdansk, Poland
Tel.: (48) 587600300
Paper Products Mfr
N.A.I.C.S.: 322299

International Paper Cellulose Fibers Sales Sarl (1)
Route de Florissant 13 5th Floor, 1206, Geneva, Switzerland
Tel.: (41) 228495811
Paper Products Mfr
N.A.I.C.S.: 322299

International Paper Chalon SAS (1)
Z I Nord rue Colbert, 71103, Chalon-sur-Saone, Cedex, France
Tel.: (33) 385476800
Corrugated Packaging Product Mfr
N.A.I.C.S.: 322211

International Paper Co. - Georgetown Container (1)
1480 International Dr, Georgetown, SC 29442
Tel.: (843) 546-0528
Sales Range: $50-74.9 Million
Emp.: 200
Boxes Corrugated: Made From Purchased Materials
N.A.I.C.S.: 322299

International Paper Co. - Mansfield Mill (1)
1202 Hwy 509, Mansfield, LA 71052-6789
Tel.: (318) 872-5100
Web Site: http://www.ipaper.com
Sales Range: $400-449.9 Million
Emp.: 560
Paper Mills
N.A.I.C.S.: 322120

International Paper Co. - Phoenix (1)
301 S 30th St, Phoenix, AZ 85034-2714
Tel.: (602) 225-0560
Web Site: http://www.map.ipaper.com
Sales Range: $50-74.9 Million
Emp.: 70
Waste Material Recycling Services
N.A.I.C.S.: 562920
Nicholas Stull (Mgr)

International Paper Co. - Snow Hill Chip Mill (1)
335 Jesse Hill Rd, Snow Hill, NC 28580-8834
Tel.: (252) 747-8381
Web Site: http://www.rpaper.com
Sales Range: $10-24.9 Million
Emp.: 10
Chip Mill
N.A.I.C.S.: 322120

International Paper Co. - Statesville Container Mill (1)
930 Meacham Rd, Statesville, NC 28677-2990
Tel.: (704) 872-6541
Web Site: http://www.myip.com
Sales Range: $50-74.9 Million
Emp.: 140
Boxes Corrugated: Made From Purchased Materials
N.A.I.C.S.: 322211

International Paper Co. - Ticonderoga Mill (1)
568 Shore Airport Rd, Ticonderoga, NY 12883

Tel.: (518) 585-5300
Sales Range: $400-449.9 Million
Emp.: 600
Paper Mills
N.A.I.C.S.: 322120

International Paper Co. - Wood Products (1)
1201 W Lathrop Ave, Savannah, GA 31415
Tel.: (912) 238-6750
Sales Range: $300-349.9 Million
Emp.: 300
Containerboard Mill
N.A.I.C.S.: 113210

International Paper Company (1)
6850 W 62nd St, Chicago, IL 60638 **(100%)**
Tel.: (773) 586-3200
Sales Range: $25-49.9 Million
Emp.: 135
Corrugated & Solid Fiber Boxes
N.A.I.C.S.: 322211

International Paper Company (1)
5200 Fairfield Rd, Pine Bluff, AR 71611 **(100%)**
Tel.: (870) 541-5600
Web Site: http://www.ipaper.com
Sales Range: $500-549.9 Million
Emp.: 1,150
Mfr of Printing Paper
N.A.I.C.S.: 322120

International Paper Company (1)
1655 S Interstate 35 E, Carrollton, TX 75006-7415
Tel.: (972) 446-9890
Web Site: http://www.ipaper.com
Sales Range: $25-49.9 Million
Emp.: 100
Corrugated Boxes Partitions Display Items
N.A.I.C.S.: 322211

International Paper Company (1)
1501 N Closner Blvd, Edinburg, TX 78541-2563
Tel.: (956) 383-3811
Web Site: http://www.ipaper.com
Sales Range: $25-49.9 Million
Emp.: 130
Corrugated Boxes
N.A.I.C.S.: 541990

International Paper Company (1)
300 Williams Lk Rd, Pineville, LA 71360-9301
Tel.: (318) 441-4100
Web Site: http://www.ippaper.com
Sales Range: $75-99.9 Million
Emp.: 2
Paperboard Mills
N.A.I.C.S.: 322130

International Paper Company (1)
100 Jensen Rd, Prattville, AL 36067 **(100%)**
Tel.: (334) 361-5000
Web Site: http://www.ipaper.com
Sales Range: $450-499.9 Million
Emp.: 600
Paper Mills
N.A.I.C.S.: 322120

International Paper Company (1)
175 Allied Rd, Auburn, ME 04210 **(100%)**
Tel.: (207) 784-4051
Web Site: http://www.ipaper.com
Sales Range: $50-74.9 Million
Emp.: 138
Mft Corrugated & Solid Fiber Boxes
N.A.I.C.S.: 322211

International Paper Company (1)
204 S Park Rd, Lafayette, LA 70508-3609 **(100%)**
Tel.: (337) 839-9091
Sales Range: $50-74.9 Million
Emp.: 120
Corrugated & Solid Fibre Boxes
N.A.I.C.S.: 322211

International Paper Company (1)
Hwy 3 N, Redwood, MS 39156 **(100%)**
Tel.: (601) 638-3665
Sales Range: $250-299.9 Million
Emp.: 350
Paper Mills
N.A.I.C.S.: 322120

International Paper Company (1)

---

100 Dickman Rd, Bay Minette, AL 36507
Tel.: (251) 937-1900
Sales Range: $50-74.9 Million
Emp.: 150
Mfr of Corrugated Boxes
N.A.I.C.S.: 322211

International Paper Company (1)
4015 Emerald Dr, Kalamazoo, MI 49001 **(100%)**
Tel.: (269) 382-7900
Web Site: http://www.ipc.com
Sales Range: $25-49.9 Million
Emp.: 120
Corrugated & Solid Fiber Boxes
N.A.I.C.S.: 322211

International Paper Company (1)
4400 Progress Blvd, Louisville, KY 40218
Tel.: (502) 451-5610
Web Site: http://www.ipaper.com
Rev.: $50,229,863
Emp.: 101
Corrugated Boxes Made From Purchased Materials
N.A.I.C.S.: 322211

International Paper Company (1)
151 Ipsco St, Decatur, AL 35601 **(100%)**
Tel.: (256) 355-7610
Web Site: http://www.ip.com
Sales Range: $25-49.9 Million
Emp.: 100
Boxes Corrugated: Made From Purchased Materials
N.A.I.C.S.: 322211

International Paper Company (1)
660 S Mariposa Rd, Modesto, CA 95354
Tel.: (209) 526-4700
Web Site: http://maps.ipaper.com
Sales Range: $50-74.9 Million
Emp.: 130
Mft Corrugated & Solid Fiber Boxes
N.A.I.C.S.: 322130

International Paper Company (1)
1300 Red Fox Rd, Saint Paul, MN 55112 **(100%)**
Tel.: (651) 636-3300
Sales Range: $25-49.9 Million
Emp.: 120
Mfr of Corrugated Boxes Made from Purchased Materials
N.A.I.C.S.: 322211

International Paper Company (1)
700 S Kaminski St, Georgetown, SC 29440
Tel.: (843) 546-0427
Paper Mills
N.A.I.C.S.: 322120

International Paper Company (1)
5115 Pine Tree St, Forest Park, GA 30297 **(100%)**
Tel.: (404) 366-9118
Web Site: http://maps.ipaper.com
Sales Range: $50-74.9 Million
Emp.: 130
Mfr of Corrugated & Solid Fiber Boxes
N.A.I.C.S.: 322211

International Paper Company (1)
175 Park Rd, Putnam, CT 06260
Tel.: (860) 928-7901
Web Site: http://www.ip.com
Sales Range: $50-74.9 Million
Emp.: 130
Container Board
N.A.I.C.S.: 322130

International Paper Company (1)
4343 Clary Blvd, Kansas City, MO 64130-2330 **(100%)**
Tel.: (816) 861-4343
Sales Range: $50-74.9 Million
Emp.: 130
Mfr of Corrugated Boxes
N.A.I.C.S.: 423310

International Paper Company (1)
3900 International Dr, Russellville, AR 72802 **(100%)**
Tel.: (479) 964-2248
Sales Range: $50-74.9 Million
Emp.: 134
Mfr of Corrugated Boxes
N.A.I.C.S.: 322211

International Paper Company (1)

2575 Palumbo Dr, Lexington, KY 40509-1202
Tel.: (859) 269-8877
Sales Range: $25-49.9 Million
Emp.: 130
Boxes Corrugated
N.A.I.C.S.: 322211
Don Noort (Product Mgr)

International Paper Company (1)
511 3rd St, Houston, MS 38851 **(100%)**
Tel.: (662) 456-4251
Web Site: http://www.ipaper.com
Sales Range: $50-74.9 Million
Emp.: 150
Corrugated And Solid Fiber Boxes
N.A.I.C.S.: 322211

International Paper Company (1)
801 Fountain Ave, Lancaster, PA 17601-4532 **(100%)**
Tel.: (717) 391-3400
Web Site: http://www.ipaper.com
Sales Range: $25-49.9 Million
Emp.: 70
Fiber Cans Drums & Similar Products
N.A.I.C.S.: 322219

International Paper Company (1)
9301 Billy The Kid St, El Paso, TX 79907-4807 **(100%)**
Tel.: (915) 858-8877
Sales Range: $25-49.9 Million
Emp.: 125
Mfr of Corrugated & Solid Fiber Boxes
N.A.I.C.S.: 322211

International Paper Company (1)
6600 Lyndon B Johnson Fwy, Dallas, TX 75240-6514
Tel.: (972) 934-6000
Web Site: http://www.ipaper.com
Sales Range: $100-124.9 Million
Emp.: 145
Paper & Paper Products Distribution Center
N.A.I.C.S.: 424110

International Paper Company (1)
730 Enterprise Dr, Conway, AR 72032 **(100%)**
Tel.: (501) 329-9456
Web Site: http://map.ipaper.com
Sales Range: $75-99.9 Million
Emp.: 242
Mfr of Corrugated & Solid Fiber Boxes
N.A.I.C.S.: 322211

International Paper Company (1)
1145 Union Camp Blvd, Sumter, SC 29154 **(100%)**
Tel.: (803) 481-6700
Web Site: http://www.ipc.com
Sales Range: $25-49.9 Million
Emp.: 100
Paper Cutting
N.A.I.C.S.: 323120

International Paper Company (1)
4049 Willow Lk Blvd, Memphis, TN 38118 **(100%)**
Tel.: (901) 363-2231
Sales Range: $300-349.9 Million
Emp.: 450
Financial Services
N.A.I.C.S.: 322120

International Paper Company (1)
2811 Cofer Rd, Richmond, VA 23224
Tel.: (804) 230-3100
Web Site: http://www.ipaper.com
Sales Range: $50-74.9 Million
Emp.: 130
Pallets Corrugated: Made From Purchased Materials
N.A.I.C.S.: 322211

International Paper Company (1)
730 Enterprise Ave, Conway, AR 72032 **(100%)**
Tel.: (501) 329-9456
Sales Range: $25-49.9 Million
Emp.: 100
Sales of Corrugated & Solid Fiber Boxes
N.A.I.C.S.: 322211

International Paper Company (1)
981 S Hickory St, Fond Du Lac, WI 54936 **(100%)**
Tel.: (920) 921-9600
Sales Range: $50-74.9 Million
Emp.: 140
Mfr of Container Packaging & Boxboard

N.A.I.C.S.: 322130

International Paper Company **(1)**
3000 Brittmoore Rd, Houston, TX
77043   **(100%)**
Tel.: (713) 996-9877
Mineral Resources
N.A.I.C.S.: 211120

International Paper Company (Europe) Limited **(1)**
Balz-Zimmermannstrasse 7, 8302, Kloten,
Switzerland   **(100%)**
Tel.: (41) 442253131
Sales Range: $1-9.9 Million
Emp.: 4
Pulp & Paper Products
N.A.I.C.S.: 322120

International Paper Company (Japan) Ltd. **(1)**
3rd Floor Toranomon Takagi Building 7-2
Nishishinbashi 1-Chome, Minato-Ku, Tokyo,
105-0003, Japan   **(100%)**
Tel.: (81) 8006758316
Pulp, Paper Products, Beverage Packaging
& Bleached Board Dist & Mfr
N.A.I.C.S.: 322299

International Paper Company - Augusta Lumber Mill **(1)**
4206 Mike Padgett Hwy, Augusta, GA
30906-9784
Tel.: (706) 793-8753
Rev.: $2,000,000
Emp.: 1,000
Lumber Mill
N.A.I.C.S.: 322120

International Paper Company - Courtland **(1)**
16504 County Rd 150, Courtland, AL 35618
Tel.: (256) 637-7300
Paper Mills
N.A.I.C.S.: 459410

International Paper Company - Fort Wayne **(1)**
3904 Ferguson Rd, Fort Wayne, IN 46809-3150
Tel.: (260) 747-9111
Industrial Packaging & Paper Mfr
N.A.I.C.S.: 322211

International Paper Company - Fort Worth Container **(1)**
2400 Shamrock Ave, Fort Worth, TX
76107-1429   **(100%)**
Tel.: (817) 338-4000
Sales Range: $10-24.9 Million
Emp.: 50
Corrugated Box Mfr
N.A.I.C.S.: 322211

International Paper Company - Loveland **(1)**
6283 Tri Rdg Blvd, Loveland, OH 45140-8325
Tel.: (513) 248-6000
Paper Research & Testing Center
N.A.I.C.S.: 541380

International Paper Company - Memphis Southwind Information Technology Center **(1)**
3232 Players Club Pkwy, Memphis, TN
38125-8844
Tel.: (901) 419-9000
Information Technology Facilities Management & Data Processing Services
N.A.I.C.S.: 541513

International Paper Company - Mount Carmel Container **(1)**
2164 Locust Gap Hwy, Mount Carmel, PA
17851
Tel.: (570) 339-1611
Web Site:
    http://www.internationalpapers.com
Sales Range: $50-74.9 Million
Emp.: 160
Corrugated Box Mfr
N.A.I.C.S.: 322211

International Paper Company - Murfreesboro **(1)**
2220 NW Broad St, Murfreesboro, TN
37129
Tel.: (615) 896-2240

Web Site: http://www.ipaper.com
Industrial Packaging & Corrugated Box Mfr
N.A.I.C.S.: 322211
Mark Snipe *(Pres)*

International Paper Company - Riegelwood Mill **(1)**
865 John L Riegel Rd, Riegelwood, NC
28456-9500
Tel.: (910) 362-4900
Coated Paperboard & Cellulose Fibers Mill
N.A.I.C.S.: 322130
Floyd Whitmier *(Mgr)*

International Paper Company - San Antonio **(1)**
610 Pop Gunn Dr, San Antonio, TX 78219
Tel.: (210) 661-8543
Corrugated & Solid Fiber Boxes Mfr
N.A.I.C.S.: 322211

International Paper Company - Springhill Container **(1)**
3000 S Arkansas St, Springhill, LA 71075
Tel.: (318) 994-6262
Sales Range: $75-99.9 Million
Emp.: 150
Corrugated Board
N.A.I.C.S.: 322130

International Paper Company - Stamford **(1)**
400 Atlantic St, Stamford, CT 06901
Tel.: (203) 541-8000
Web Site: http://www.ipaper.com
Sales Range: $25-49.9 Million
Emp.: 100
Personal Service Agents Brokers &Bureaus
N.A.I.C.S.: 322120

International Paper Company - Wooster Container Plant **(1)**
689 Palmer St, Wooster, OH 44691
Tel.: (330) 264-1322
Emp.: 200
Industrial & Corrugated Packaging Plant &
Converting Facility
N.A.I.C.S.: 322211

International Paper Czech Republic, s.r.o. **(1)**
Na Zertvach 2247/29, 180 00, Prague,
Czech Republic
Tel.: (420) 227133181
Web Site: http://www.ipaper.com
Paper Packaging Mfr
N.A.I.C.S.: 322211

International Paper Distribution (Shanghai) Limited **(1)**
17/F West Buidling Greenland Center 600,
Middle Longhua Road, Shanghai, 200032,
China
Tel.: (86) 2161133200
Paper Packaging Mfr
N.A.I.C.S.: 322211

International Paper Distribution Group (Taiwan) Limited **(1)**
5/F No 261 Sec 3 Nanjing E Rd, Songshan
District, Taipei, 10550, Taiwan
Tel.: (886) 227134321
Paper Packaging Mfr
N.A.I.C.S.: 322211

International Paper Empaques Industriales de Mexico S. de R.L. de C.V. **(1)**
Av Comerciantes S/N Esquina Blvd Industriales Parque Industrial Fipasi, 36100, Silao,
Guanajuato, Mexico
Tel.: (52) 4727226800
Paper Packaging Mfr
N.A.I.C.S.: 322211

International Paper Espaly SAS **(1)**
34 avenue de la Bernarde CS90038,
43009, Le Puy, France
Tel.: (33) 471072000
Corrugated Packaging Product Mfr
N.A.I.C.S.: 322211

International Paper Foodservice Europe Limited **(1)**
Units 10 & 11 Navigation Park Road One,
Winsford Industrial Estate, Winsford, CW7
3RL, Cheshire, United Kingdom
Tel.: (44) 1606552537
Food Packaging & Paper Cup Mfr

N.A.I.C.S.: 322299

International Paper Grinon, S.L. **(1)**
Ctra Fuenlabrada a Grinon Km 6700, Grinon, 28971, Madrid, Spain
Tel.: (34) 91 814 9200
Pulp & Paper Product Mfr
N.A.I.C.S.: 322299

International Paper Group, S. de R.L. de C.V. **(1)**
Carretera No 57-Entronque A San, 37980,
San Jose Iturbide, Guanajuato, Mexico
Tel.: (52) 4191988800
Food Packaging & Paper Cup Mfr
N.A.I.C.S.: 322299

International Paper Investments France S.A. **(1)**
4 Parc Ariane - Immeuble Pluton Boulevard
Des Chenes, 78280, Guyancourt,
France   **(100%)**
Tel.: (33) 0139303400
Sales Range: $300-349.9 Million
Provider of Real Estate Services
N.A.I.C.S.: 531210

International Paper Italia S.p.A. **(1)**
Via Ornago 55, 20882, Bellusco, MB,
Italy   **(100%)**
Tel.: (39) 0396 0621
Web Site:
    https://www.internationalpaper.com
Sales Range: $50-74.9 Million
Paper & Pulp Mills
N.A.I.C.S.: 322120

International Paper Madrid Mill, S.L. **(1)**
Parque Industrial La Cantuena c/del Papel
1, 28947, Fuenlabrada, Madrid, Spain
Tel.: (34) 916420603
Packaging Paperboard Product Distr
N.A.I.C.S.: 424130

International Paper Manufacturing and Distribution Ltd. **(1)**
11/F Tower 5 China Hong Kong City 33
Canton Road, Tsimshatsui, Kowloon, China
(Hong Kong)
Tel.: (852) 8006758315
Paper Mfr & Whslr
N.A.I.C.S.: 322120

International Paper Montblanc, S.L. **(1)**
Carretera Tarragona - Lleida Km 35 5 Tarragona, 43400, Montblanc, Spain
Tel.: (34) 977860900
Pulp & Paper Product Mfr
N.A.I.C.S.: 322120
Francesc Benet *(Mgr-Quality)*

International Paper Monterrey, S. de R.L. de C.V. **(1)**
Carretera Villa De Garcia Km 2 5 Santa
Catarina, 66350, Monterrey, Nuevo Leon,
Mexico
Tel.: (52) 8181247000
Paper Mfr & Whslr
N.A.I.C.S.: 322120

International Paper Mortagne S.A.S. **(1)**
2 Rue Paul Sabatier-BP 30275, 71 107,
Chalon-sur-Saone, France
Tel.: (33) 385476890
Packaging Product Mfr & Distr
N.A.I.C.S.: 332439

International Paper Packaging Malaysia (Kuala Lumpur) Sdn. Bhd. **(1)**
PLO 59 Jalan Perindustrian 4 Kawasan
Perindustrian Senai, 81400, Senai, Malaysia
Tel.: (60) 7599553
Paper Packaging Product Mfr
N.A.I.C.S.: 322220

International Paper Polska Sp. z o.o. **(1)**
ul Lubicz 23, 31-503, Krakow, Poland
Tel.: (48) 122526000
Paper Products Mfr
N.A.I.C.S.: 322299

International Paper Retail Display & Packaging **(1)**
33 Phoenix Dr, Thorofare, NJ 08086
Tel.: (856) 853-7000

Web Site: http://www.ipaper.com
Sales Range: $100-124.9 Million
Emp.: 250
Corrugated Papers & Boxes
N.A.I.C.S.: 322219

International Paper S.A. **(1)**
Kraport Kina 1st Senator, Saint Petersburg,
190000, Russia   **(100%)**
Tel.: (7) 8123345730
Sales Range: $25-49.9 Million
Emp.: 40
Printing & Communications Papers
N.A.I.C.S.: 322110
Franz Josef Marx *(Pres)*

International Paper Saint-Amand **(1)**
4 Parc Ariane - Immeuble Pluton Boulevard
des Chenes, 78280, Guyancourt, France
Tel.: (33) 233775050
Pulp & Paper Product Mfr
N.A.I.C.S.: 322120

International Paper Switzerland GmbH **(1)**
Balz-Zimmermannstrasse 7, Kloten, 8302,
Switzerland
Tel.: (41) 442253131
Paper Packaging Product Mfr
N.A.I.C.S.: 322220

International Paper Taiwan Ltd. **(1)**
6th Floor 1 49 Lane 35 Jihu Road, Nei Hu
Taipei, Neihu, 114, Taiwan   **(100%)**
Tel.: (886) 287977771
Sales Range: $10-24.9 Million
Emp.: 20
Beverage Packaging
N.A.I.C.S.: 488991

International Paper Valls, S.A. **(1)**
Carretera del Pla 229 Poligono Industrial,
43800, Valls, Tarragona, Spain
Tel.: (34) 97 760 1115
Pulp & Paper Product Mfr
N.A.I.C.S.: 322299

International Paper do Brasil Ltda. **(1)**
Rodovia Sp 340 Km 171, Sao Paulo, Mogi-Guacu, 13840-970, SP, Brazil   **(100%)**
Tel.: (55) 1938618121
Sales Range: $1-4.9 Billion
Emp.: 3,682
Provider of Paper Products
N.A.I.C.S.: 322120

International Paper-Hungary Kerekedelmi Kft. **(1)**
Liget U 1 Pest, 2040, Budaors,
Hungary   **(100%)**
Tel.: (36) 23501144
Web Site: http://www.ipnet.ipaper.com
Sales Range: $10-24.9 Million
Emp.: 4
Printing & Communications Papers
N.A.I.C.S.: 424110
Konrad Sipos *(Mng Dir)*

International Pulp Sales Company **(1)**
6400 Poplar Ave, Memphis, TN
38197   **(100%)**
Tel.: (901) 419-9000
Sales Range: $300-349.9 Million
Emp.: 5,000
Mfr of Paper & Paper Products
N.A.I.C.S.: 322120

Med Packaging SARL **(1)**
Tanger Automotive City Lot A, Commune
Jouamaa, 90024, Tangiers, Fahs Anjra,
Morocco
Tel.: (212) 531060820
Packaging Paperboard Product Distr
N.A.I.C.S.: 424130

PT International Paper Packaging Indonesia Batam **(1)**
Jalan Hang Kesturi No 1 Lot B039 Kuang
Hwa Industrial Zone Kabil Centr, 29467,
Pulau Batam, Indonesia
Tel.: (62) 778711011
Emp.: 100
Packaging Products Mfr
N.A.I.C.S.: 322211
John Loh *(Gen Mgr)*

Polyrey Benelux **(1)**

International Paper Company—(Continued)

Haachtsesteenweg 162, Melsbroek, 1820, Belgium **(100%)**
Tel.: (32) 27530909
Web Site: http://www.polyrey.com
Sales Range: $10-24.9 Million
Emp.: 6
Decorative Wood Products
N.A.I.C.S.: 337211

Przedsiebiorstwo Produkcyjno-Handlowe "Tor-Pal" Spolka z Ograniczona Odpowiedzialnoscia **(1)**
ul Lotnicza 1, 82-500, Kwidzyn, Poland
Tel.: (48) 552798194
Web Site: https://www.tor-pal.com.pl
Emp.: 500
Wood Container & Pallet Mfr
N.A.I.C.S.: 321920

Sabine River & Northern Railroad Company **(1)**
5830 Old Highway 87 N, Orange, TX 77632
Tel.: (409) 746-2453
Freight Transportation Services
N.A.I.C.S.: 482112

Societe Guadeloupeenne de Carton Ondule SAS **(1)**
Peres Blancs, Guadeloupe, 97123, Baillif, France
Tel.: (33) 590813875
Packaging Products Mfr
N.A.I.C.S.: 322211

Societe Martiniquaise de Carton Ondule **(1)**
Zone Industrielle du Lamentin, BP 244, 97232, Lamentin, Cedex 2, Martinique, France **(100%)**
Sales Range: $250-299.9 Million
Paper Mills
N.A.I.C.S.: 322120

Societe Mediterraneenne d Emballages SAS **(1)**
15 rue Gaspard Monge, 13200, Arles, France
Tel.: (33) 490934155
Packaging Products Mfr
N.A.I.C.S.: 322211

Societe Normande de Carton Ondule SAS **(1)**
Zone Industrielle de Nogent sur Oise 5 rue du Clos Barrois, 60107, Creil, Cedex, France
Tel.: (33) 344558282
Packaging Products Mfr
N.A.I.C.S.: 322211

TIN Inc. **(1)**
1300 S Mopac Expy Fl 3, Austin, TX 78746-6933
Tel.: (512) 434-5800
Web Site: http://www.templeinland.com
Packaging Products Mfr
N.A.I.C.S.: 322211

Templar Essex Inc. **(1)**
103 Foulk Rd, Wilmington, DE 19803-3742
Tel.: (302) 656-1950
Investment Advisory Services
N.A.I.C.S.: 523940

Temple-Inland Inc. **(1)**
1300 S MoPac Expy 3rd Fl, Austin, TX 78746-6933
Tel.: (512) 434-5800
Web Site: http://www.templeinland.com
Sales Range: $1-4.9 Billion
Emp.: 10,500
Paper & Packaging Manufacturing, Building Products, Saw, Pulp & Paperboard Mills
N.A.I.C.S.: 322130

Subsidiary (Domestic):

Temple-Inland Resource Company **(2)**
101 Convention Ctr Ste 850, Las Vegas, NV 89109
Tel.: (702) 949-0022
Investment Banking Services
N.A.I.C.S.: 523150

Texas South-Eastern Railroad Company **(2)**

515 Pine Vly Rd, Diboll, TX 75941-1422 **(100%)**
Tel.: (936) 829-5613
Sales Range: $25-49.9 Million
Emp.: 6
Railroad
N.A.I.C.S.: 482111
Mike Smith (Gen Mgr)

Tianjin Bohai International Paper Packaging Co., Ltd. **(1)**
No 11 Qijing Road Dongli Economic and Technical Development Area, Tianjin, China
Tel.: (86) 2224981933
Packaging Products Mfr
N.A.I.C.S.: 322211

Western Papers **(1)**
2700 S 600th W, Salt Lake City, UT 84115 **(100%)**
Tel.: (801) 972-1261
Sales Range: $25-49.9 Million
Emp.: 30
Printing & Writing Paper
N.A.I.C.S.: 423830

ZAO International Paper **(1)**
14 Malaya Pirogovskaya St Bld 1, Moscow, 119435, Russia **(100%)**
Tel.: (7) 4999226939
Sales Range: $10-24.9 Million
Printing & Communications Papers
N.A.I.C.S.: 424110

INTERNATIONAL POWER GROUP LTD.
1420 Celebration Blvd Ste 313, Celebration, FL 34747
Tel.: (407) 566-0318   DE
Web Site: https://www.international-power.com
Year Founded: 1998
IPWG—(OTCIQ)
Hazardous Waste Treatment & Disposal Services
N.A.I.C.S.: 562211
Daniel Conte (Chm, Treas & Sec)
John Benvengo (Pres & Co-CEO)
Subramanyeswara S. Vempati (Co-CEO)
Jose Garcia (VP)

INTERNATIONAL SEAWAYS, INC.
600 3rd Ave 39th Fl, New York, NY 10016
Tel.: (212) 578-1600   MH
Web Site: https://www.intlseas.com
Year Founded: 2016
INSW—(NYSE)
Rev.: $864,665,000
Assets: $2,615,334,000
Liabilities: $1,127,582,000
Net Worth: $2,615,334,000
Earnings: $387,891,000
Emp.: 1,800
Fiscal Year-end: 12/31/22
Oil & Gas Transportation Services
N.A.I.C.S.: 486210
Jeffrey D. Pribor (CFO, Treas & Sr VP)
Adewale O. Oshodi (VP & Controller)
Derek Solon (Chief Comml Officer & Sr VP)
William Nugent (Chief Technical & Sustainability Officer & Sr VP)
James D. Small III (Chief Admin Officer, Gen Counsel, Sec & Sr VP)
Lois K. Zabrocky (Pres & CEO)

Subsidiaries:

Lightering LLC **(1)**
10001 Woodloch Forest Dr 325, Woodlands, TX 77380
Tel.: (281) 445-5098
Web Site: http://www.lightering.com
Marine Cargo Handling Services
N.A.I.C.S.: 488320

INTERNATIONAL SILVER, INC.

16 Park Ave Ste 301, Rutherford, NJ 07070
Tel.: (212) 683-4240   AZ
Web Site: https://www.international-silver.com
Year Founded: 1992
ISLV—(OTCIQ)
Silver Mining Services
N.A.I.C.S.: 212220
Harold Roy Shipes (Chm, Pres & CEO)
John A. McKinney (CFO & Exec VP)
Matthew J. Lang (Sec & VP-Admin & Admin)

INTERNATIONAL STEM CELL CORPORATION
9745 Businesspark Ave, San Diego, CA 92131
Tel.: (760) 940-6383   DE
Web Site: https://www.internationalstemcell.com
Year Founded: 2005
ISCO—(OTCQB)
Rev.: $8,180,000
Assets: $5,135,000
Liabilities: $9,655,000
Net Worth: ($4,520,000)
Earnings: ($331,000)
Emp.: 29
Fiscal Year-end: 12/31/22
Therapeutic, Biomedical & Cosmeceutical Research & Development
N.A.I.C.S.: 541714
Russell Kern (Chief Scientific Officer, Principal Fin Officer & Exec VP)
Andrey Semechkin (Chm & CEO)

Subsidiaries:

Lifeline Skincare, Inc **(1)**
2595 Jason Ct, Oceanside, CA 92056
Tel.: (760) 940-6383
Web Site: http://www.lifelineskincare.com
Cosmetics Products Mfr
N.A.I.C.S.: 325620
Russell Kern (CEO)

INTERNETARRAY, INC.
7954 Transit Rd Ste 232, Williamsville, NY 14221-4117
Tel.: (917) 387-4410
Year Founded: 2008
INAR—(OTCEM)
Broadcasting Services
N.A.I.C.S.: 516210
Michael J. Black (Pres)

INTERPACE BIOSCIENCES, INC.
2001 Rte 46 Waterview Plz Ste 310, Parsippany, NJ 07054   DE
Web Site: https://www.interpace.com
Year Founded: 1988
IDXG—(OTCQX)
Rev.: $31,838,000
Assets: $15,979,000
Liabilities: $79,051,000
Net Worth: ($63,072,000)
Earnings: ($21,958,000)
Emp.: 94
Fiscal Year-end: 12/31/22
Holding Company; Molecular Diagnostics Products Developer & Mfr
N.A.I.C.S.: 551112
Thomas W. Burnell (Pres & CEO)
Christopher McCarthy (CFO)

Subsidiaries:

Interpace Diagnostics, LLC **(1)**
Morris Corporate Ctr 1 Bldg C 300 Interpace Pkwy, Parsippany, NJ 07054
Web Site: http://www.interpacediagnostics.com
Molecular Diagnostic Products Developer & Mfr
N.A.I.C.S.: 325413

Greg Richard (Chief Comml Officer)
Sara A. Jackson (VP-Clinical Dev)
Glenn Gershon (Sr VP-Ops)
Syd Finkelstein (Chief Scientific Officer)
Christina M. Narick (VP-Pathology)

Subsidiary (Domestic):

Interpace Diagnostics Corporation **(2)**
Morris Corporate Ctr 1 Bldg A 300 Interpace Pkwy, Parsippany, NJ 07054
Web Site: http://www.interpacediagnostics.com
Molecular Diagnostic Products Developer & Mfr
N.A.I.C.S.: 325413

JS Genetics, Inc. **(2)**
2 Church St S Ste B-05B, New Haven, CT 06519-1760
Tel.: (203) 624-5742
Web Site: https://www.jsgenetics.com
Molecular Diagnostic Products Developer & Mfr
N.A.I.C.S.: 325413

INTERPLAY ENTERTAINMENT CORP.
12301 Wilshire Blvd Ste 407, Los Angeles, CA 90025-1007
Tel.: (310) 432-1958   DE
Web Site: https://www.interplay.com
Year Founded: 1982
IPLY—(OTCIQ)
Entertainment Software Developer & Publisher
N.A.I.C.S.: 513210
Herve Caen (Chm, CEO & Interim CFO)

Subsidiaries:

Interplay OEM, Inc. **(1)**
16815 Von Karman Ave Ste 100, Irvine, CA 92606-4920
Tel.: (310) 432-1958
Sales Range: $1-9.9 Million
Emp.: 4
Software Bundles to the Computer Hardware Industry
N.A.I.C.S.: 513210

INTERUPS INC.
645 5th Ave Ste 400, New York, NY 10022
Tel.: (646) 575-9161   NV
Web Site: https://www.itupglobal.com
Year Founded: 2012
ITUP—(OTCIQ)
Sales Range: Less than $1 Million
Emp.: 1
Daily Deal Website
N.A.I.C.S.: 541890
Satyendra Thakur (Mng Dir-High Value Transactions & Govt Liaisons-India)
Murali Kuppa (CEO-Asean)
Mahesh Vellaboyina (Vice Chm & CTO)
Suryanarayanan Venkataraman (Sec & Head)
Vinay Kapoor (Vice Chm)

INTEST CORPORATION
Tel.: (856) 505-8800   DE
Web Site: https://www.intest.com
Year Founded: 1981
INTT—(NYSEAMEX)
Rev.: $116,828,000
Assets: $110,066,000
Liabilities: $45,110,000
Net Worth: $64,956,000
Earnings: $8,461,000
Emp.: 327
Fiscal Year-end: 12/31/22
Docking Hardware, Test Head Manipulators & Tester Interfaces Mfr
N.A.I.C.S.: 334514
Duncan Gilmour (CFO, Treas & Sec)
Richard Rogoff (VP-Dev)
Michael Tanniru (Pres-Environmental Technologies)

Joe McManus *(Pres)*
Richard Nolen *(VP)*
Meghan Moseley *(VP)*
Richard N. Grant, Jr. *(Pres & CEO)*

Subsidiaries:

Ambrell B.V. (1)
Holtersweg 1, 7556 BS, Hengelo, Netherlands
Tel.: (31) 880150100
Heating Equipment Mfr
N.A.I.C.S.: 333414

Ambrell Corporation (1)
1655 Lyell Ave, Rochester, NY 14606
Tel.: (585) 889-9000
Web Site: https://www.ambrell.com
Precision Induction Heating Equipment Designer, Mfr & Whslr
N.A.I.C.S.: 333994
Girish Dahake *(Sr VP-Global Applications)*

Ambrell Limited (1)
Unit 6 Space Business Centre Tewkesbury Road, Cheltenham, GL51 9FL, Gloucestershire, United Kingdom
Tel.: (44) 1242514042
Heating Equipment Mfr
N.A.I.C.S.: 333414

SigmaSYS Corp. (1)
41 Hampden Rd, Mansfield, MA 02048
Tel.: (781) 688-2354
Web Site: http://www.sigmasys.com
Emp.: 40
Temperature testing & Conditioning Chamber Product Mfr
N.A.I.C.S.: 334513

Temptronic Corporation (1)
41 Hampden Rd, Mansfield, MA 02048-1807
Tel.: (781) 688-2300
Web Site: https://www.intestthermal.com
Sales Range: $10-24.9 Million
Emp.: 60
Environmental Testing Services
N.A.I.C.S.: 541620

Subsidiary (Non-US):

Temptronic GmbH (2)
Gewerbeparkring 18, Brandenburg, 15299, Germany
Tel.: (49) 3360677700
Web Site: http://www.temptronic.com
Sales Range: $1-9.9 Million
Emp.: 4
Developer of Environmental Testing Systems
N.A.I.C.S.: 334516

Subsidiary (Domestic):

Thermonics, Inc. (2)
41 Hampden Rd, Mansfield, MA 02048
Tel.: (781) 688-2345
Web Site: http://www.thermonics-chillers.com
Sales Range: $25-49.9 Million
Emp.: 60
Semiconductor Thermal Test Systems Developer & Mfr
N.A.I.C.S.: 333242

inTEST PTE, Ltd. (1)
Blk 4010 Ang Mo Kio Ave 10 05-02 Techplace 1, Singapore, 569626, Singapore
Tel.: (65) 65522404
Web Site: https://www.intest.com
Semiconductor Equipment Mfr
N.A.I.C.S.: 333242

inTEST Silicon Valley Corporation (1)
48860 Milmont Dr Ste 105C, Fremont, CA 94538
Tel.: (408) 678-9167
Web Site: https://www.intest.com
Sales Range: $100-124.9 Million
Developer of Circuit Board Testing Instruments
N.A.I.C.S.: 334413

inTEST Thermal Solutions GmbH (1)
Gewerbeparkring 18, 15299, Mullrose, Germany
Tel.: (49) 3360677700

Web Site: http://www.intestthermal.com
Emp.: 5
Semiconductor Equipment Mfr
N.A.I.C.S.: 333242

INTEVAC, INC.
3560 Bassett St, Santa Clara, CA 95054
Tel.: (408) 986-9888   CA
Web Site: https://www.intevac.com
Year Founded: 1991
IVAC—(NASDAQ)
Rev.: $52,665,000
Assets: $156,506,000
Liabilities: $40,989,000
Net Worth: $115,517,000
Earnings: ($12,610,000)
Emp.: 128
Fiscal Year-end: 12/30/23
Photonics & Equipment to Apply Magnetic Films Onto Computer Disks Design, Mfr & Sales
N.A.I.C.S.: 332410
Nigel D. Hunton *(Pres & CEO)*
Mark P. Popovich *(VP-Bus Dev)*
Nigel Hunton *(Pres & CEO)*
John Dickinson *(VP-Ops)*
Sam Harkness *(VP)*
Eva Valencia *(VP)*
Cameron McAulay *(CFO)*
Kevin H. Soulsby *(Controller)*

Subsidiaries:

Intevac (Shenzhen) Co. Ltd. (1)
Room 1807A Shenzhen International Exchange Square No 1 Fuhua 1st Road, PO Box 37, Futian District, Shenzhen, 518000, Guangdong, China
Tel.: (86) 75583484020
Web Site: http://www.intevac.com
Sales Range: $10-24.9 Million
Magnetic Media Processing Device Distr
N.A.I.C.S.: 334112

Intevac Asia Private Limited (1)
6 Marsiling Lane Block C 01-00, Singapore, 739145, Singapore (100%)
Tel.: (65) 63686863
Web Site: http://www.intevac.com
Sales Range: $1-9.9 Million
Design, Manufacture & Sale of Photonics & Equipment to Apply Magnetic Films onto Computer Disks
N.A.I.C.S.: 333310

INTRA-CELLULAR THERAPIES, INC.
135 Rte 202 206 Ste 6, Bedminster, NJ 07921
Tel.: (646) 440-9333   DE
Year Founded: 2012
ITCI—(NASDAQ)
Sales Range: $25-49.9 Million
Emp.: 1
Investment Services
N.A.I.C.S.: 325412
Samir N. Masri *(Pres, CEO, CFO & Sec)*

Subsidiaries:

ITI, Inc. (1)
Tel.: (646) 440-9333
Web Site: https://www.intracellulartherapies.com
Rev.: $464,370,000
Assets: $728,295,000
Liabilities: $136,871,000
Net Worth: $591,424,000
Earnings: ($139,674,000)
Emp.: 610
Fiscal Year-end: 12/31/2023
Drug Mfr
N.A.I.C.S.: 325412
Michael I. Halstead *(Gen Counsel & Exec VP)*
Michael Olchaskey *(Sr VP & Head-Regulatory Affairs)*
Mark Neumann *(Chief Comml Officer & Exec VP)*
John A. Bardi *(Sr VP-Market Access, Policy & Govt Affairs)*

Karen Sheehy *(Chief Compliance Officer & Sr VP)*
Willie R. Earley *(Sr VP)*
Sanjeev Narula *(CFO, Treas & Exec VP)*
Sharon Mates *(Founder, Chm & CEO)*
Michael I. Halstead *(Pres)*
Juan Sanchez *(VP-Corp Comm & IR)*
Robert E. Davis *(Chief Scientific Officer & Sr VP)*

INTREPID CAPITAL CORP.
1400 Marsh Landing Pkwy Ste 106, Jacksonville Beach, FL 32250
Tel.: (904) 246-3433   FL
Web Site:
https://www.intrepidcapitalfunds.com
Year Founded: 1994
ITPC—(OTCIQ)
Miscellaneous Financial Investment Activities
N.A.I.C.S.: 523999
Mark A. Travis *(Pres, CEO & CIO)*
Don White *(CFO)*
Matt Berquist *(COO)*
Clay Kirkland *(VP & Portfolio Mgr)*
Matt Parker *(VP & Portfolio Mgr)*

INTREPID POTASH, INC.
707 17th St Ste 4200, Denver, CO 80202
Tel.: (303) 296-3006   DE
Web Site:
https://www.intrepidpotash.com
Year Founded: 2000
IPI—(NYSE)
Rev.: $279,083,000
Assets: $768,474,000
Liabilities: $84,046,000
Net Worth: $684,428,000
Earnings: ($35,673,000)
Emp.: 485
Fiscal Year-end: 12/31/23
Potash, Solar Salt, Magnesium Chloride Brine & Sulfate Producer
N.A.I.C.S.: 325314
Robert P. Jornayvaz III *(Co-Founder & CEO)*
Hugh E. Harvey Jr. *(Co-Founder)*

Subsidiaries:

Intrepid Potash-Moab, LLC (1)
Hwy 279 Mine Site Rd, Moab, UT 84532
Tel.: (435) 259-7171
Sales Range: $25-49.9 Million
Emp.: 55
Chemical Product Whslr
N.A.I.C.S.: 424690

Intrepid Potash-New Mexico, LLC (1)
1996 Potash Mines Rd, Carlsbad, NM 88202
Tel.: (575) 887-5591
Nonmetallic Mineral Mining Services
N.A.I.C.S.: 212390
Robert Baldridge *(Sr VP)*

INTRICON CORPORATION
1260 Red Fox Rd, Arden Hills, MN 55112
Tel.: (651) 636-9770
Web Site: http://www.intricon.com
Year Founded: 1977
IIN—(NASDAQ)
Rev.: $125,206,000
Assets: $122,459,000
Liabilities: $28,709,000
Net Worth: $93,750,000
Earnings: ($106,000)
Emp.: 873
Fiscal Year-end: 12/31/21
Microminiature Electronic Components Mfr
N.A.I.C.S.: 334419
J. Scott Longval *(Pres & CEO)*
Mark S. Gorder *(Executives)*
Michael P. Geraci *(Sr VP-Sls & Mktg)*
Philip I. Smith *(Exec Chm)*
Doug Pletcher *(VP-Medical Bus Dev)*

Craig Sandbulte *(VP-Corp Quality Assurance & Regulatory Affairs)*
Sara Hill *(Chief HR Officer)*
David Liebl *(VP-R&D)*
Annalee Lutgen *(Interim CFO)*
Tim Deraney *(VP-Global Ops)*

Subsidiaries:

Emerald Medical Services Pte. Ltd. (1)
08 Admiralty Street 06-16 Admirax Building, Singapore, 757438, Singapore
Tel.: (65) 66849410
Web Site: http://www.emmedservices.com
Complex Catheter Mfr
N.A.I.C.S.: 339112

Hearing Help Express, Inc. (1)
1714 Sycamore Rd, Dekalb, IL 60115
Web Site:
https://www.hearinghelpexpress.com
Sales Range: $1-9.9 Million
Emp.: 60
Hearing Aid Product Distr
N.A.I.C.S.: 423450

IntriCon Datrix Corporation (1)
340 State Pl, Escondido, CA 92029
Tel.: (760) 480-8874
Sales Range: $10-24.9 Million
Emp.: 7
Patient Monitoring Equipment Mfr
N.A.I.C.S.: 334510
Jon Barron *(Gen Mgr)*

IntriCon GmbH (1)
Kesselschmiedstrasse 10, 85354, Freising, Germany
Tel.: (49) 816148040
Web Site: http://www.intricon.com
Sales Range: $250-299.9 Million
Emp.: 3
Sales of Hearing Instruments, Medical & Communication Products
N.A.I.C.S.: 456199

IntriCon Pte. Ltd. (1)
8 Admiralty Street 02-01 to 06 Admirax, Singapore, 757438, Singapore
Tel.: (65) 6 776 1021
Web Site: https://www.intricon.com.sg
Sales Range: $75-99.9 Million
Emp.: 200
Resistance Technology, Microminiature Components & Molded Plastic Parts for Hearing Instruments
N.A.I.C.S.: 326199
Juan Yeow Goh *(Sr Mgr-Fin)*
Woei Sing Yap *(Mgr-Product Dev)*
Vivien Chua *(Mgr-HR)*
William Lee *(Mgr-Supply Chain)*
Winson Chan *(Mng Dir & Gen Mgr)*
Vincent Teo *(Sr Mgr-Ops)*
Timothy Teo *(Sls Mgr-PADA)*
Nancy Gan *(Mgr-Customer Support)*
Yong Khian Chew *(Sr Mgr-Quality & Regulatory)*

INTRUSION INC.
101 E Park Blvd Ste 1200, Plano, TX 75074
Tel.: (312) 445-2869   DE
Web Site: https://www.intrusion.com
Year Founded: 1983
INTZ—(NASDAQ)
Rev.: $7,529,000
Assets: $9,275,000
Liabilities: $13,490,000
Net Worth: ($4,215,000)
Earnings: ($16,229,000)
Emp.: 63
Fiscal Year-end: 12/31/22
Security Networking Products
N.A.I.C.S.: 334290
Anthony J. LeVecchio *(Chm)*
Brandy Schade *(VP-People Dev & Culture)*
Mike McClure *(VP-Consulting)*
Blake Dumas *(VP-Engrg)*
Anthony Scott *(Pres & CEO)*
Kimberly Pinson *(CFO & Principal Acctg Officer)*

INTUIT INC.

Intuit Inc.—(Continued)

2700 Coast Ave, Mountain View, CA 94043
Tel.: (650) 944-6000   DE
Web Site: https://www.intuit.com
Year Founded: 1984
INTU—(NASDAQ)
Rev.: $16,285,000,000
Assets: $32,132,000,000
Liabilities: $13,696,000,000
Net Worth: $18,436,000,000
Earnings: $2,963,000,000
Emp.: 18,800
Fiscal Year-end: 07/31/24
Accounting & Tax Preparation Software Publisher & Online Banking Services
N.A.I.C.S.: 513210
Scott D. Cook (Bd of Dirs, Executives)
Laura A. Fennell (Chief People & Places Officer & Exec VP)
Kerry J. McLean (Sec, Exec VP & Gen Counsel)
Lara H. Balazs (Exec VP & Gen Mgr-Strategic Partner Grp)
Mark Notarainni (Gen Mgr-Consumer Grp)
Shveta Mujumdar (Sr VP/VP-Corp Dev)
Marianna Tessel (Exec VP & Gen Mgr-Small Bus & Self-Employed Grp)
CeCelia G. Morken (Executives)
Lauren D. Hotz (Chief Acctg Officer & VP)
Atticus N. Tysen (Chief Information Security & Fraud Prevention Officer & Sr VP-Product Dev)
Sandeep Singh Aujla (CFO & Exec VP)
Alex Balazs (CTO & Exec VP)
Anton Hanebrink (Chief Corp Strategy & Dev Officer & Exec VP)
Sasan K. Goodarzi (Pres & CEO)

Subsidiaries:

Courier Holdings Ltd. (1)
88 Hanbury Street Level 1, London, E1 5JL, United Kingdom
Tel.: (44) 7418335248
Web Site:
   https://www.courierholdingsltd.com
Transportation Services
N.A.I.C.S.: 488510

Credit Karma, Inc. (1)
760 Market St 2nd Fl, San Francisco, CA 94102
Tel.: (415) 692-5722
Web Site: http://www.creditkarma.com
Emp.: 120
Free Access & Ongoing Tracking of Consumers' Credit Scores & Reports
N.A.I.C.S.: 561450
Joseph Kauffman (Pres)
Greg Lull (CMO)
Nichole Mustard (Co-Founder & Chief Revenue Officer)
Ryan Graciano (Co-Founder & CTO)
Susannah Wright (Chief Legal Officer)
Gannesh Bharadhwaj (Gen Mgr-Karma Scale)
Colleen McCreary (Chief People, Places & Publicity Officer)

Electronic Clearing House, Inc. (1)
730 Paseo Camarillo, Camarillo, CA 93010
Tel.: (818) 706-8999
Sales Range: $75-99.9 Million
Emp.: 222
Credit Card Approval & Processing Services
N.A.I.C.S.: 522320

Intuit Canada Limited (1)
10423-101 Street Suite 2200, Edmonton, T5H 0E7, AB, Canada   **(100%)**
Tel.: (780) 466-9996
Web Site: http://www.intuit.ca
Sales Range: $125-149.9 Million
Emp.: 350
Accounting & Tax Preparation Software
N.A.I.C.S.: 513210

Division (Domestic):

Intuit Greenpoint (2)
400 138th Ave SE, Calgary, T2G 4Z6, AB, Canada
Tel.: (780) 466-9996
Web Site: http://www.accountant.intuit.ca
Sales Range: $75-99.9 Million
Accounting & Tax Preparation Software
N.A.I.C.S.: 513210

Intuit Inc.-Consumer Tax Group (1)
7535 Torrey Santa Fe Rd, San Diego, CA 92129   **(100%)**
Tel.: (858) 525-8000
Web Site: http://about.intuit.com
Sales Range: $200-249.9 Million
Emp.: 800
Accounting & Tax Preparation Software
N.A.I.C.S.: 513210

Intuit Inc.-Customer Contact Center (1)
110 Juliad Ct, Fredericksburg, VA 22406-1171   **(100%)**
Tel.: (540) 752-6100
Web Site: http://www.intuit.com
Sales Range: $125-149.9 Million
Emp.: 500
Accounting & Tax Preparation Software
N.A.I.C.S.: 513210

Intuit Limited (1)
5th Floor Cardinal Place 80 Victoria Street, London, SW1E 5JL, United Kingdom   **(100%)**
Tel.: (44) 8083046376
Web Site: https://quickbooks.intuit.com
Sales Range: $10-24.9 Million
Emp.: 40
Accounting & Tax Preparation Software & Products
N.A.I.C.S.: 513210

Intuit Technology Services Private Limited (1)
Campus 4A PriTech Park-Ecospace 7th & 8th Floor Belandur Villg, Varthur Hobli East Taluk, Bengaluru, 560 103, India
Tel.: (91) 8041769200
Web Site: http://www.about.intuit.com
Sales Range: $10-24.9 Million
Emp.: 50
Accounting & Tax Preparation Software Developer
N.A.I.C.S.: 513210

Lacerte Software Corporation (1)
5601 Headquarters Dr, Plano, TX 75024
Tel.: (214) 387-2000
Web Site: http://www.intuit.com
Accounting & Tax Preparation Software Publisher
N.A.I.C.S.: 513210

Lettuce Inc. (1)
11 Brooks Ave Unit A, Venice, CA 90291
Tel.: (310) 961-3580
Web Site: http://www.lettuceapps.com
Software Publisher
N.A.I.C.S.: 513210

Origami Logic Ltd. (1)
3 Aluf Kalman Magen St 3rd Floor, Tel Aviv, Israel
Tel.: (972) 526632320
Tax Preparation Software & Related Services
N.A.I.C.S.: 541213

The Rocket Science Group LLC (1)
675 Ponce de Leon Ave NE Ste 5000, Atlanta, GA 30308
Tel.: (678) 999-0141
Web Site: http://www.mailchimp.com
Sales Range: $10-24.9 Million
Emp.: 110
Email Marketing Software
N.A.I.C.S.: 513210
Amy Ellis (Head-Integrations & Partnerships)
Ben Chestnut (Founder & CEO)
Tom Klein (VP-Mktg)
Scott Culpepper (Gen Counsel)

TradeGecko Pte Ltd (1)
02 121 Telok Ayer, Singapore, 068590, Singapore
Tel.: (65) 31639910
Web Site: https://www.tradegecko.com

Software Development Services
N.A.I.C.S.: 541511
Cameron Priest (CEO & Co-Founder)
Bradley Priest (Co-Founder & CTO)
Alberto Rodriguez (Mgr)
Alex Smee (Dir)
Cat Williams-Treloar (Chief Revenue Officer)

INTUITIVE MACHINES, INC.
3700 Bay Area Blvd, Houston, TX 77058
Tel.: (281) 520-3703   DE
Web Site:
   https://www.intuitivemachines.com
Year Founded: 2021
LUNR—(NASDAQ)
Rev.: $4,833,790
Assets: $334,940,408
Liabilities: $325,152,995
Net Worth: $9,787,413
Earnings: ($190,408)
Emp.: 163
Fiscal Year-end: 12/31/22
Aerospace Component Mfr
N.A.I.C.S.: 334511
Stephen Altemus (Co-Founder, Pres & CEO)
Bob Pavelko (Exec Dir-Defense Programs)
Jack Fischer (VP-Production, Operations, and Infrastructure)
Jade Marcantel (Chief Human Capital Officer)
Stephen Zhang (Sr Dir-Investor Relations)
Steve Labbe (VP-Engineering)
Steve Vontur (Controller)
Tom Niemeyer (VP-Federal Svcs)
Trent Martin (Sr VP-Space Systems)
Annachiara Jones (Gen Counsel & Sec)
Peter McGrath (COO & Sr VP)
Kamal Ghaffarian (Co-Founder)

Subsidiaries:

Intuitive Machines, LLC (1)
3700 Bay Area Blvd Ste 100, Houston, TX 77058-1159
Tel.: (281) 520-3703
Web Site: http://www.intuitivemachines.com
Scientific & Technical Consulting Services
N.A.I.C.S.: 541690

INTUITIVE SURGICAL, INC.
1020 Kifer Rd, Sunnyvale, CA 94086-5304
Tel.: (408) 523-2100   DE
Web Site: https://www.intuitive.com
Year Founded: 1995
ISRG—(NASDAQ)
Rev.: $7,124,100,000
Assets: $15,441,500,000
Liabilities: $2,044,200,000
Net Worth: $13,397,300,000
Earnings: $1,798,000,000
Emp.: 13,676
Fiscal Year-end: 12/31/23
Robotic Surgical Systems Mfr
N.A.I.C.S.: 339112
Marshall L. Mohr (Exec VP-Global Bus Svcs)
Gary S. Guthart (CEO)
Myriam J. Curet (Chief Medical Officer & Exec VP)
Colin Morales (Sr VP & Gen Mgr)
Bob DeSantis (Chief Product Officer & Exec VP)
Brian Miller (Chief Digital Officer)
Craig Child (Sr VP-Human Resources)
Kara Andersen Reiter (Chief Compliance Officer, Gen Counsel & Sr VP)
Glenn Vavoso (Sr VP & Gen Mgr-Asia & Worldwide Indirect)
Julian Nikolchev (Sr VP-Corp Dev & Strategy)

Chris Carlson (Sr VP & Gen Mgr-Endoluminal)
Gillian Duncan (Sr VP-Professional Education & Program SvcsWorldwide)
Fredrik Widman (Principal Acctg Officer, VP & Controller)
Fredrik C. Widman (VP & Controller)
Lesly Marban (Sr VP-Corporate Marketing)
Dirk Barten (Sr VP & Gen Mgr-Marketing)
Marc Bland (Sr VP & Gen Mgr-Commercial-Marketing-US)
Michele DiMartino (Chief HR Officer)
Gary Loeb (Chief Compliance Officer)
Iman Jeddi (Sr VP)
Charlie Dean (Sr VP)
Ian Purdy (Sr VP)
David J. Rosa (Pres)

Subsidiaries:

Intuitive Surgical Deutschland GmbH (1)
Am Flughafen 6, 79108, Freiburg, Germany
Tel.: (49) 76188787700
Medical Instrument Mfr
N.A.I.C.S.: 339112

Intuitive Surgical GK (1)
Ark Mori Building 1-12-32 Akasaka, Minato-ku, Tokyo, 107-6032, Japan
Tel.: (81) 355751341
Medical Instrument Mfr
N.A.I.C.S.: 339112
Toshiyuki Tachibana (Dir-Fin)

Intuitive Surgical Holdings, Inc. (1)
1020 Kifer Rd, Sunnyvale, CA 94086
Tel.: (408) 523-2100
Web Site: http://www.Intuitivesurgical.com
Emp.: 43
Investment Management Service
N.A.I.C.S.: 523940

Intuitive Surgical Korea Limited (1)
3F Bldg A DMC Hi-Tech Industry Center 330 Seongam-ro, Mapo-gu, Seoul, Korea (South)
Tel.: (82) 232713200
Medical Instrument Mfr
N.A.I.C.S.: 339112
Kyewon Choi (Area Mgr-Sls)

Intuitive Surgical Medical Device Science & Technology (Shanghai) Co., Ltd. (1)
Room 2022 20th Floor The Center No 989 Chang Le Road, Shanghai, 200031, China
Tel.: (86) 2151166834
Surgical Medical Device Mfr
N.A.I.C.S.: 339112
Tong Wang (Mgr-Regulatory Affairs)

Intuitive Surgical, Sarl (1)
1 Chemin des Muriers, 1170, Aubonne, Switzerland
Tel.: (41) 218212000
Web Site: http://www.intuitivesurgical.com
Robotic Surgical Systems Mfr
N.A.I.C.S.: 339112

KindHeart, LLC (1)
8295 Tournament Dr Ste 150, Memphis, TN 38125
Tel.: (901) 969-4448
Web Site: https://kindheartsllc.com
Healtcare Services
N.A.I.C.S.: 621111
Brenda Westbrook (Owner)

Orpheus Medical GmbH (1)
Westendstrasse 21, 60325, Frankfurt am Main, Germany
Tel.: (49) 6979588870
Medical Device Mfr
N.A.I.C.S.: 339112

Orpheus Medical Ltd. (1)
Matam Park Building 25 8th Floor, Haifa, 3190501, Israel
Tel.: (972) 46968800
Web Site: http://www.orpheus-medical.com
Medical Device Mfr
N.A.I.C.S.: 339112

Gaddi Menahem *(CEO)*
Daniel Fink *(CFO)*
Tomer Ben-Sira *(VP-Product & Mktg)*

Orpheus Medical USA Inc.   **(1)**
430 Indiana St Ste 100, Golden, CO 80401
Tel.: (720) 798-2378
Medical Device Mfr
N.A.I.C.S.: 339112

Schoelly, Inc.   **(1)**
360 Church St Ste 130, Northborough, MA 01532
Tel.: (508) 926-8855
Web Site: http://www.schoelly-usa.com
Emp.: 750
Medical Equipment & Device Mfr
N.A.I.C.S.: 339112
Jim Bonneville *(Pres & CEO)*

INUVO, INC.
500 President Clinton Ave Ste 300, Little Rock, AR 72201
Tel.: (501) 205-8508   **NV**
Web Site: https://www.inuvo.com
Year Founded: 1987
INUV—(NYSEAMEX)
Rev.: $75,603,745
Assets: $35,557,310
Liabilities: $13,807,994
Net Worth: $21,749,316
Earnings: ($13,106,539)
Emp.: 87
Fiscal Year-end: 12/31/22
Marketing & Technological Business Software & Solutions
N.A.I.C.S.: 513210
John B. Pisaris *(Gen Counsel & Sec)*
Wallace D. Ruiz *(Principal Acctg Officer)*
Dana Robbins *(Sr VP-ValidClick)*
Barry Lowenthal *(Pres)*
Amir Bakhshaie *(Sr VP-IntentKey)*
Richard K. Howe *(Chm & CEO)*

Subsidiaries:

Vertro, Inc.   **(1)**
143 Varick St, New York, NY 10013
Tel.: (212) 231-2000
Sales Range: $25-49.9 Million
Online Advertising Network; Software Publisher
N.A.I.C.S.: 513210

INVECH HOLDINGS, INC.
2901 W Coast Hwy Ste 140, Costa Mesa, CA 92663
Tel.: (646) 322-9440
Year Founded: 1998
IVHI—(OTCIQ)
Financial Investment Services
N.A.I.C.S.: 523999
Limei Zhang *(Pres)*

INVENTERGY GLOBAL, INC.
19925 Stevens Creek Blvd Ste 100, Cupertino, CA 95014
Tel.: (408) 973-7896   **DE**
Web Site: http://www.inventergy.com
Year Founded: 2012
INVT—(OTCIQ)
Telephone Communication Services
N.A.I.C.S.: 561421
Joe Beyers *(Founder, Chm & CEO)*
Clifford Loeb *(Dir-Bus Dev)*
Ken Cannizzaro *(Pres)*

Subsidiaries:

Inventergy, Inc.   **(1)**
900 E Hamilton Ave Ste 180, Campbell, CA 95008
Tel.: (408) 389-3510
Intellectual Property Asset Investment & Licensing Services
N.A.I.C.S.: 533110
Jon Rortveit *(Sr VP-Intellectual Property Acq & Licensing)*
Paul Roberts *(VP)*
Anna Johns *(VP-Licensing)*
Charlie Bedard *(Dir-Tech)*

Clifford Loeb *(Dir-Bus Intelligence)*
Molly McAuliffe *(Dir-Ops)*
Christopher M. Camarra *(Dir-IR)*

INVENTRUST PROPERTIES CORP.
3025 Highland Pkwy Ste 350, Downers Grove, IL 60515
Tel.: (630) 570-0700   **MD**
Web Site:
https://www.inventrustproperties.com
Year Founded: 2004
IVT—(NYSE)
Rev.: $258,676,000
Assets: $2,487,331,000
Liabilities: $933,287,000
Net Worth: $1,554,044,000
Earnings: $5,269,000
Emp.: 104
Fiscal Year-end: 12/31/23
Real Estate Investment Trust
N.A.I.C.S.: 525990
Christy L. David *(COO, Gen Counsel, Sec & Exec VP)*
Daniel J. Busch *(Pres & CEO)*
Michael Phillips *(CFO, Treas & Exec VP)*
Dan Lombardo *(VP-IR)*
David Bryson *(Chief Acctg Officer & Sr VP)*
Matt Hagan *(Sr VP)*
James Puzon *(Sr VP)*

INVESCO ADVANTAGE MUNICIPAL INCOME TRUST II
1555 Peachtree St NE Ste 1800, Atlanta, GA 30309
Tel.: (404) 439-3217   **MA**
VKI—(NYSEAMEX)
Rev.: $36,292,594
Assets: $922,391,937
Liabilities: $369,520,348
Net Worth: $552,871,589
Earnings: $22,634,911
Fiscal Year-end: 02/29/20
Investment Management Service
N.A.I.C.S.: 525990

INVESCO BOND FUND
1331 Spring St NW Ste 2500, Atlanta, GA 30309
Tel.: (404) 439-3217   **DE**
VBF—(NYSE)
Rev.: $10,033,482
Assets: $241,320,234
Liabilities: $1,554,366
Net Worth: $239,765,868
Earnings: $8,815,083
Fiscal Year-end: 02/29/20
Investment Management Service
N.A.I.C.S.: 525990
Christopher L. Wilson *(Vice Chm)*

INVESCO CALIFORNIA VALUE MUNICIPAL INCOME TRUST
1331 Spring St NW Ste 2500, Atlanta, GA 30309
Tel.: (404) 439-3217   **MA**
VCV—(NYSE)
Rev.: $40,454,471
Assets: $1,022,104,970
Liabilities: $357,007,009
Net Worth: $665,097,961
Earnings: $26,009,428
Fiscal Year-end: 02/29/20
Investment Management Service
N.A.I.C.S.: 525990

INVESCO DYNAMIC CREDIT OPPORTUNITIES FUND
7800 E Union Ave Ste 1100, Denver, CO 80237
VTA—(NYSE)
Rev.: $84,091,273
Assets: $1,362,768,185

Liabilities: $585,123,704
Net Worth: $777,644,481
Earnings: $51,798,265
Fiscal Year-end: 02/29/20
Investment Management Service
N.A.I.C.S.: 525990
Philip Yarrow *(Mgr-Fund)*

INVESCO HIGH INCOME 2023 TARGET TERM FUND
7800 E Union Ave Ste 1100, Denver, CO 80237
IHIT—(NYSE)
Rev.: $19,686,948
Assets: $335,531,656
Liabilities: $80,648,871
Net Worth: $254,882,785
Earnings: $14,043,507
Fiscal Year-end: 02/29/20
Investment Management Service
N.A.I.C.S.: 525990
Kevin Collins *(Mgr-Fund)*

INVESCO HIGH INCOME 2024 TARGET TERM FUND
1555 Peachtree St NE, Atlanta, GA 30309   **DE**
IHTA—(NYSE)
Investment Services
N.A.I.C.S.: 525910

INVESCO HIGH INCOME TRUST II
1331 Spring St NW Ste 2500, Atlanta, GA 30309
Tel.: (212) 296-6963   **MA**
VLT—(NYSE)
Rev.: $10,056,954
Assets: $140,320,113
Liabilities: $43,313,427
Net Worth: $97,006,686
Earnings: $7,149,426
Fiscal Year-end: 02/29/20
Investment Management Service
N.A.I.C.S.: 525990

INVESCO LTD.
Midtown Union 1331 Spring St NW, Atlanta, GA 30309
Tel.: (404) 892-0896   **BM**
Web Site: https://www.invesco.com
Year Founded: 1935
IVZ—(NYSE)
Rev.: $5,716,400,000
Assets: $28,933,800,000
Liabilities: $13,763,500,000
Net Worth: $15,170,300,000
Earnings: ($333,700,000)
Emp.: 8,489
Fiscal Year-end: 12/31/23
Holding Company; Investment Management Services
N.A.I.C.S.: 551112
Laura Allison Dukes *(Sr Mng Dir & CFO)*
Douglas J. Sharp *(Sr Mng Dir & Head-Americas & EMEA)*
Stephanie Butcher *(Sr Mng Dir & Co-Head-Investments)*
Tony Wong *(Sr Mng Dir & Co-Head-Investments)*
Andrew Schlossberg *(Sr Mng Dir)*
Andrew Ryan Schlossberg *(Pres & CEO)*
Shannon Johnston *(Sr Mng Dir, CIO & Chief Ops Officer)*
Jeff Kupor *(Sr Mng Dir & Gen Counsel)*
Alan Smith *(Sr Mng Dir & Chief HR Officer)*

Subsidiaries:

Aim Trimark Investments   **(1)**
5140 Yonge St Ste 900, Toronto, M2N 6X7, ON, Canada   **(100%)**
Tel.: (416) 228-5500

Web Site: http://www.invesco.ca
Sales Range: $1-4.9 Billion
Emp.: 108
Investment Services
N.A.I.C.S.: 523940

Finemost Limited   **(1)**
Rm 311 3/F Hunghom Commercial Ctr Blk A, Ma Tau Wai Road Hung Hom, Hong Kong, China (Hong Kong)
Tel.: (852) 27744778
Electronic Part & Equipment Mfr
N.A.I.C.S.: 423690

INVESCO Global Asset Management Limited   **(1)**
Central Quay Riverside IV Sir John Rogerson's Quay, Dublin, Ireland
Tel.: (353) 14398000
Web Site: http://invescointernational.co.uk
Real Estate Asset Management Services
N.A.I.C.S.: 531390

INVESCO Real Estate s.r.o.   **(1)**
Praha City Center Klimenstska 46, 110 02, Prague, Czech Republic
Tel.: (420) 227202420
Web Site: http://www.invesco.com
Emp.: 6
Real Estate Asset Management Services
N.A.I.C.S.: 531390

IVZ Bahamas Private Limited   **(1)**
Lyford Manor East Satellite Bldg, PO Box N-7776, Lyford Cay West Bay Street, Nassau, Bahamas
Tel.: (242) 2426772880
Investment Management Service
N.A.I.C.S.: 523940

Invesco (Hyderabad) Private Limited   **(1)**
DivyaSree Orion 14th & 15th Floor Block 6-North Tower Survey 66/1 Ra, RangaReddy District, Hyderabad, 500 032, Andhra Pradesh, India
Tel.: (91) 4067480000
Investment Management Service
N.A.I.C.S.: 551112

Invesco (NY) Inc.   **(1)**
1166 Ave of the Americas 27th Fl, New York, NY 10036-2708   **(100%)**
Tel.: (212) 278-9128
Web Site: http://www.invesco.com
Sales Range: $150-199.9 Million
Emp.: 250
Investment Products
N.A.I.C.S.: 523940

Invesco Administration Services Limited   **(1)**
6th Floor 125 London Wall, London, EC2Y 5AS, United Kingdom
Tel.: (44) 2037531000
Web Site:
https://www.invescoperpetual.co.uk
Investment Management Service
N.A.I.C.S.: 551112

Invesco Advisers, Inc.   **(1)**
2 Peachtree Pointe 1555 Peachtree St NE Ste 1800, Atlanta, GA 30309
Tel.: (404) 892-0896
Web Site:
http://www.institutional.invesco.com
Investment Advisory & Management Services
N.A.I.C.S.: 523940

Invesco Asset Management (Japan) Ltd.   **(1)**
6-10-1 Roppongi Roppongi Hills Mori Tower 14th floor, PO Box 115, Minato-ku, Tokyo, 106-6114, Japan   **(100%)**
Tel.: (81) 36 447 3000
Web Site: https://www.invesco.com
Emp.: 126
Investment Management, Marketing & Client Services
N.A.I.C.S.: 523999

Invesco Asset Management (Schweiz) AG   **(1)**
Talacker 34, 8001, Zurich, Switzerland
Tel.: (41) 44 287 9000
Web Site: https://www.invesco.com
Investment Management Service
N.A.I.C.S.: 523940

Invesco Ltd.—(Continued)

Invesco Asset Management (Switzerland) Ltd. **(1)**
Talacker 34, 8001, Zurich, Switzerland
Tel.: (41) 442879000
Web Site: http://www.invesco.com
Investment Advisory Services
N.A.I.C.S.: 525910

Invesco Asset Management Limited **(1)**
C/Goya 6-3, 28001, Madrid, Spain
Tel.: (34) 917813020
Web Site: http://www.invesco.es
Financial Investment Services
N.A.I.C.S.: 523999

Invesco Asset Management Osterreich GmbH **(1)**
Rotenturmstrasse 16-18, 1010, Vienna, 1010, Austria
Tel.: (43) 1316200
Web Site: http://www.invesco.at
Investment Products & Services
N.A.I.C.S.: 525910
Michael Wurzl *(Head-Client Svcs)*

Invesco Asset Management S.A. **(1)**
5th Floor 16-18 rue de Londres, 75009, Paris, France **(100%)**
Tel.: (33) 156624302
Web Site: http://www.invesco.fr
Sales Range: $25-49.9 Million
Emp.: 45
Investment Products
N.A.I.C.S.: 525910

Branch (Non-US):

Invesco Asset Management S.A. **(2)**
Vinoly Building Claude Debussylaan 26, 1082 MD, Amsterdam, Netherlands **(100%)**
Tel.: (31) 208880221
Web Site: http://www.invesco.nl
Investment Products
N.A.I.C.S.: 525910

Invesco Asset Management S.A. **(1)**
Avenue Louise 235, 1050, Brussels, Belgium
Tel.: (32) 26410170
Web Site: http://www.invesco.be
Emp.: 20
Investment Products
N.A.I.C.S.: 525910

Invesco Asset Management Singapore Ltd. **(1)**
9 Raffles Place 18-01 Republic Plaza, Singapore, 048619, Singapore **(100%)**
Tel.: (65) 66039180
Sales Range: $1-9.9 Million
Emp.: 18
Investment Management Service
N.A.I.C.S.: 523999

Invesco Australia Ltd **(1)**
Level 26 333 Collins St, Melbourne, 3000, VIC, Australia **(100%)**
Tel.: (61) 396113600
Web Site: https://www.invesco.com
Sales Range: $250-299.9 Million
Emp.: 550
Investment Products
N.A.I.C.S.: 525910
Martin Franc *(CEO)*
Nick Burrell *(Sec & Head-Legal)*
Neil Lahy *(Sr Portfolio Mgr-IQS Australian Equities)*
Ritchard Longmire *(Sr Portfolio Mgr-IQS Australian Equities)*
Andre Roberts *(Sr Portfolio Mgr-IQS Australian Equities)*
Nicole Schnuderl *(Sr Portfolio Mgr-IQS Australian Equities)*
Richard C. J. Tsai *(Portfolio Mgr-Invesco Quantitative Strategies)*

Invesco Canada Ltd. **(1)**
120 Bloor Street East Suite 700, Toronto, M4W 1B7, ON, Canada
Web Site: https://www.invesco.com
Investment Management Service
N.A.I.C.S.: 523940

Invesco Capital Markets, Inc. **(1)**
3500 Lacey Rd Ste700, Downers Grove, IL 60515

Tel.: (630) 684-6000
Web Site: https://www.invesco.com
Investment Advisory Services
N.A.I.C.S.: 523940

Invesco Continental Europe Services S.A. **(1)**
The Blue Twr Ave Louise 326, Brussels, B, 1050, Belgium **(100%)**
Tel.: (32) 26410111
Web Site: http://www.invescoeurope.com
Sales Range: $25-49.9 Million
Emp.: 12
Investment Products
N.A.I.C.S.: 525910

Invesco CurrencyShares Australian Dollar Trust **(1)**
3500 Lacey Rd Ste 700, Downers Grove, IL 60515
Web Site: https://www.invesco.com
Rev.: $187,406
Assets: $87,320,105
Liabilities: $6,738,824
Net Worth: $80,581,281
Earnings: ($180,023)
Fiscal Year-end: 12/31/2022
Currency-Focused Closed-End Investment Fund
N.A.I.C.S.: 525990
Brian Hartigan *(CEO)*

Invesco CurrencyShares British Pound Sterling Trust **(1)**
3500 Lacey Rd Ste 700, Downers Grove, IL 60515
Web Site: https://www.invesco.com
Rev.: $719,312
Assets: $109,962,007
Liabilities: $36,432
Net Worth: $109,925,575
Earnings: $299,826
Fiscal Year-end: 12/31/2022
Currency-Focused Closed-End Investment Fund
N.A.I.C.S.: 525990
Brian Hartigan *(CEO)*

Invesco CurrencyShares Canadian Dollar Trust **(1)**
3500 Lacey Rd Ste 700, Downers Grove, IL 60515
Web Site: https://www.invesco.com
Rev.: $613,343
Assets: $97,531,777
Liabilities: $38,328
Net Worth: $97,493,449
Earnings: $146,701
Fiscal Year-end: 12/31/2022
Currency-Focused Closed-End Investment Fund
N.A.I.C.S.: 525990
Brian Hartigan *(CEO)*

Invesco CurrencyShares Euro Trust **(1)**
3500 Lacey Rd Ste 700, Downers Grove, IL 60515
Web Site: https://www.invesco.com
Rev.: $330,793
Assets: $285,725,144
Liabilities: $118,683
Net Worth: $285,606,461
Earnings: ($1,785,713)
Fiscal Year-end: 12/31/2022
Currency-Focused Closed-End Investment Fund
N.A.I.C.S.: 525990
Brian Hartigan *(CEO)*
Kelli Gallegos *(Principal Fin & Acctg Officer-Investments Pools)*
John M. Zerr *(Mgr)*
Jordan Krugman *(Mgr)*

Invesco CurrencyShares Japanese Yen Trust **(1)**
3500 Lacey Rd Ste 700, Downers Grove, IL 60515
Web Site: https://www.invesco.com
Assets: $187,461,552
Liabilities: $96,658
Net Worth: $187,364,894
Earnings: $1,053,063
Fiscal Year-end: 12/31/2022
Currency-Focused Closed-End Investment Fund
N.A.I.C.S.: 525990
Brian Hartigan *(CEO)*

Invesco CurrencyShares Swiss Franc Trust **(1)**

3500 Lacey Rd Ste 700, Downers Grove, IL 60515
Web Site: https://www.invesco.com
Assets: $217,032,018
Liabilities: $73,878
Net Worth: $216,958,140
Earnings: ($2,258,055)
Fiscal Year-end: 12/31/2022
Currency-Focused Closed-End Investment Fund
N.A.I.C.S.: 525990
Brian Hartigan *(CEO)*

Invesco Dublin **(1)**
2 Sandyford Business Centre Burtonhall Road Sandyford, Dublin, 18, Ireland **(100%)**
Tel.: (353) 12947600
Web Site: http://www.invescooffshore.com
Sales Range: $250-299.9 Million
Investment Products
N.A.I.C.S.: 525910

Invesco Far East Limited **(1)**
Perpetual Park Dr, Henley-on-Thames, RG9 1HH, Oxfordshire, United Kingdom
Tel.: (44) 2070654000
Investment Advisory Services
N.A.I.C.S.: 523940

Invesco Gestion S.A. **(1)**
Calle Recoletos 15 Piso 1, 28001, Madrid, Spain **(100%)**
Tel.: (34) 917813020
Web Site: http://www.es.invesco.com
Sales Range: $10-24.9 Million
Emp.: 5
Investment Products
N.A.I.C.S.: 525910

Invesco Global Real Estate Asia Pacific Inc.M **(1)**
Roppongi Hills Mori Tower 14F, PO Box 116, 6-10-1 Minato-ku, Tokyo, 106-6114, Japan
Tel.: (81) 364473300
Web Site: http://www.invesco-gre.co.jp
Investment Advisory Services
N.A.I.C.S.: 523940

Invesco Great Wall Fund Management Company Limited **(1)**
21/F Tower 1 Kerry Plaza No 1 Zhong Xin Si Road, Futian District, Shenzhen, 518048, China
Tel.: (86) 75582370388
Web Site: https://www.igwfmc.com
Fund Management Services
N.A.I.C.S.: 523150

Invesco Hong Kong Limited **(1)**
45/F Jardine House 1 Connaught Place, Central, China (Hong Kong) **(100%)**
Tel.: (852) 31918282
Web Site: https://www.invesco.com
Sales Range: $50-74.9 Million
Emp.: 240
Holding Company; Investment Management Services
N.A.I.C.S.: 551112

Subsidiary (Non-US):

Invesco Asset Management (India) Pvt. Ltd. **(2)**
Unit No 2101 A 21st Floor A - Wing Marathon Futurex N M Joshi Marg, Lower Parel, Mumbai, 400 013, Maharashtra, India **(100%)**
Tel.: (91) 226 731 0000
Web Site: https://www.invescomutualfund.com
Sales Range: $10-24.9 Million
Investment Asset Management Services
N.A.I.C.S.: 523940
Saurabh Nanavati *(CEO)*
Ketan Ugrankar *(CFO & COO)*
Rohit Goyal *(Head-Institutional Sls)*
Haresh Sadani *(Head-Products & Mktg)*
Taher Badshah *(Chief Investment Officer)*
Dhimant Kothari *(Mgr-Fund)*
Vikas Garg *(Head-Fixed Income)*
Sandhir Sharma *(Head-Retail Sls)*
Hiten Jain *(Mgr-Fund)*
Kuber Mannadi *(Mgr-Fund)*

Subsidiary (Domestic):

Invesco Trustee Pvt. Ltd. **(3)**

2101-A A Wing 21st Floor Marathon Futurex N M Joshi Marg Lower Parel, Vile Parle East, Mumbai, 400 013, India
Tel.: (91) 2267310105
Mutual Fund Holding Company
N.A.I.C.S.: 551112

Subsidiary (Domestic):

Invesco Asset Management Asia Limited **(2)**
41/F Champion Tower Three Garden Road, Central, China (Hong Kong) **(100%)**
Tel.: (852) 31918282
Web Site: http://www.invesco.com.hk
Sales Range: $250-299.9 Million
Investment Management Service
N.A.I.C.S.: 523940

Invesco IP Holdings (Canada) Ltd. **(1)**
5140 Yonge Street Suite 800, Toronto, M2N 6X7, ON, Canada
Web Site: https://www.invesco.com
Other Financial Advisory Services
N.A.I.C.S.: 523940

Invesco Institutional (N.A.) Inc. **(1)**
1555 Peachtree St NE Ste 1800, Atlanta, GA 30309 **(100%)**
Tel.: (404) 479-1095
Web Site: http://www.institutional.invesco.com
Sales Range: $650-699.9 Million
Emp.: 588
Investment Management
N.A.I.C.S.: 523940

Branch (Domestic):

Invesco Institutional **(2)**
The Aegon Bldg 400 W Market St Ste 3300, Louisville, KY 40202 **(100%)**
Tel.: (502) 589-2011
Web Site: http://www.institutional.invesco.com
Sales Range: $150-199.9 Million
Emp.: 120
Investment Management
N.A.I.C.S.: 523940
Martin L. Flanagan *(Pres)*

Invesco Institutional **(2)**
1000 SW Broadway Ste 1720, Portland, OR 97205 **(100%)**
Tel.: (503) 241-6515
Web Site: http://www.invesco.com
Sales Range: $25-49.9 Million
Emp.: 4
Investment Management
N.A.I.C.S.: 525910

Invesco International Ltd. **(1)**
Orviss House 17A Queen Street, PO Box 1588, Saint Helier, JE4 2PH, Jersey **(100%)**
Tel.: (44) 153 460 7600
Web Site: https://www.invesco.com
Investment Products Services
N.A.I.C.S.: 525910

Invesco Investment Advisers LLC **(1)**
11 Greenway Plz Ste 1000, Houston, TX 77046-1173
Tel.: (713) 214-1919
Investment Advisory Services
N.A.I.C.S.: 523940

Invesco Investment Management (Shanghai) Limited **(1)**
Hang Seng Bank Tower 5F Unit 032 1000 Lujiazui Ring Rd, Pudong New Area, Shanghai, 200120, China
Tel.: (86) 2138937206
Financial Advisory Services
N.A.I.C.S.: 523940

Invesco Investment Services, Inc. **(1)**
11 Greenway Plz Ste 1000, Houston, TX 77046-1173 **(100%)**
Tel.: (713) 626-1919
Web Site: http://www.invescoaim.com
Sales Range: $125-149.9 Million
Emp.: 1,400
Investment Services
N.A.I.C.S.: 523999

Branch (Domestic):

Invesco Investment Services, Inc. **(2)**

3500 Lacey Rd Ste 700, Downers Grove, IL
60515
Tel.: (630) 684-6000
Sales Range: $150-199.9 Million
Emp.: 400
Mutual Fund & Investment Advisory Firm
N.A.I.C.S.: 525910

Invesco Managed Accounts, LLC (1)
2001 6th Ave Ste 2310, Seattle, WA 98121
Web Site: https://www.snwam.com
Investment Management Service
N.A.I.C.S.: 523940
Tim Benzel (Portfolio Mgr)
Lisa Cook (COO)
Brittany Russo (Mgr-Client Service)
David Richardson (Portfolio Mgr)
Jennifer Tandler (Mgr-Client Service)

Invesco Mortgage Capital, Inc. (1)
1331 Spring St NW Ste 2500, Atlanta, GA
30309
Tel.: (404) 439-4843
Web Site:
   https://www.invescomortgagecapital.com
Rev.: $277,929,000
Assets: $5,284,209,000
Liabilities: $4,501,544,000
Net Worth: $782,665,000
Earnings: ($37,541,000)
Fiscal Year-end: 12/31/2023
Mortgage-Backed Securities Investment
Services
N.A.I.C.S.: 523999
Kevin M. Collins (Pres)
John M. Anzalone (CEO)
David Lyle (COO)
Richard Lee Phegley Jr. (CFO)

Invesco North America (1)
1555 Peachtree St NE, Atlanta, GA
30309-3262   (100%)
Tel.: (404) 892-0896
Web Site: http://www.invesco.com
Sales Range: $1-4.9 Billion
Emp.: 500
Investment Management
N.A.I.C.S.: 523940

**Invesco North American Holdings,
Inc.**   (1)
2001 Ross Avenue Ste 3400, Dallas, TX
75201
Tel.: (972) 715-7400
Web Site: http://www.invescorealestate.com
Sales Range: $25-49.9 Million
Emp.: 150
Investment Management Service
N.A.I.C.S.: 551112

Invesco Pensions Limited (1)
Post Handling Centre Maclaren House Tal-
bot Road, Stretford, M32 0FP, Manchester,
United Kingdom
Tel.: (44) 1344464400
Web Site:
   https://www.pensions.invesco.co.uk
Pension Services
N.A.I.C.S.: 525110

**Invesco Perpetual (Nominees)
Limited**   (1)
Perpetual Park Perpetual Park Dr, Henley-
on-Thames, RG9 1HH, Oxfordshire, United
Kingdom
Tel.: (44) 1491417000
Other Financial Advisory Services
N.A.I.C.S.: 523940

**Invesco PowerShares Capital Man-
agement LLC**   (1)
3500 Lacey Rd Ste 700, Downers Grove, IL
60515
Tel.: (630) 933-9600
Web Site: http://www.invesco.com
Investment Management Service
N.A.I.C.S.: 523940
Dan Draper (Mng Dir)

Invesco Puerto Rico (1)
250 Munoz Rivera Ave Ste 406 American
International Plz, Hato Rey, PR
00918   (100%)
Tel.: (787) 771-2960
Web Site: http://www.invesco.com
Sales Range: $50-74.9 Million
Emp.: 2
Investment Products
N.A.I.C.S.: 523999

Invesco Real Estate (1)
2001 Ross Ave Ste 3400, Dallas, TX
75201   (100%)
Tel.: (972) 715-7400
Web Site: http://www.invescorealestate.com
Sales Range: $25-49.9 Million
Emp.: 170
Real Estate Investment Advice & Products
N.A.I.C.S.: 525990

**Invesco Real Estate Advisors (Shang-
hai) Limited**   (1)
Hang Seng Bank Tower 5F Unit 031 1000
Lujiazui Ring Rd, Pudong New Area,
Shanghai, 200120, China
Tel.: (86) 2138937268
Financial Advisory Services
N.A.I.C.S.: 523940

Invesco Real Estate GmbH (1)
Sendlinger Strasse 12, 80331, Munich,
80331, Germany
Tel.: (49) 8920606000
Web Site: http://www.invescorealestate.de
N.A.I.C.S.: 531390
Simon Redman (Mng Dir & Head-Product
Mgmt)

Invesco Real Estate Korea (1)
18/F Seoul Finance Center 136 Sejong-
daero, Youngdeungpo-gu, Seoul, 04520,
Korea (South)
Tel.: (82) 263307310
Investment Management Service
N.A.I.C.S.: 523940

**Invesco Real Estate Management
S.a.r.l.**   (1)
37A Avenue JF Kennedy, 1855, Luxem-
bourg, Luxembourg
Tel.: (352) 27118000
Web Site: http://www.invesco.com
Emp.: 21
Real Estate Asset Management Services
N.A.I.C.S.: 531390

**Invesco Ruihe (Shanghai) Private
Equity Investment Management Com-
pany Limited**   (1)
Hang Seng Bank Tower 5F Unit 031 1000
Lujiazui Ring Road, Pudong New Area,
Shanghai, 200120, China
Tel.: (86) 2138937268
Investment Management Service
N.A.I.C.S.: 523999

Invesco Select Trust plc (1)
6th Floor 125 London Wall, London, EC2Y
5AS, United Kingdom
Tel.: (44) 2037531000
Rev.: $5,716,400,000
Assets: $28,933,800,000
Liabilities: $13,763,500,000
Net Worth: $15,170,300,000
Earnings: ($168,200,000)
Emp.: 8,489
Fiscal Year-end: 12/31/2023
Financial Investment Services
N.A.I.C.S.: 523940
Victoria Muir (Chm)

Invesco Taiwan Ltd. (1)
22F No1 Songzhi Road, Taipei, 11047,
Taiwan   (100%)
Tel.: (886) 287299999
Web Site: http://www.invesco.com.tw
Sales Range: $25-49.9 Million
Emp.: 75
Investment Products
N.A.I.C.S.: 525910

Invesco Trimark Ltd. (1)
5140 Yonge Street Suite 800, Toronto, M2N
6X7, ON, Canada
Tel.: (800) 874-6275
Web Site: http://www.invesco.ca
Investment Management Service
N.A.I.C.S.: 523940

Invesco UK Ltd. (1)
Perpetual Park Perpetual Park Drive,
Henley-on-Thames, RG9 1HH, Oxfordshire,
United Kingdom   (100%)
Tel.: (44) 1491417000
Web Site: https://www.invesco.com
Sales Range: $300-349.9 Million
Emp.: 300
Holding Company; Investment Management
Services
N.A.I.C.S.: 551112

Allison Dukes (Sr Mng Dir)
Jeff Kupor (Gen Counsel)
Tony Wong (Sr Mng Dir)
Stephanie Butcher (Sr Mng Dir)
Andrew Lo (Sr Mng Dir)

Subsidiary (Domestic):

Invesco Asset Management Ltd. (2)
125 London Wall Sixth Floor, London,
EC2Y 5AS, United Kingdom   (100%)
Tel.: (44) 2037531000
Web Site: http://www.invescoperpetual.co.uk
Sales Range: $125-149.9 Million
Emp.: 500
Holding Company Involved in Investment
Management & Insurance in the US & UK
N.A.I.C.S.: 551112

Subsidiary (Domestic):

Invesco Global Advisors, Inc. (3)
30 Finsbury Sq, London, EC2A 1AG, United
Kingdom   (100%)
Tel.: (44) 2070653003
Web Site:
   http://www.invescoglobalcash.com
Investment Advice & Fund Management
N.A.I.C.S.: 523940

Subsidiary (Domestic):

Invesco Fund Managers Limited (2)
Perpetual Park Perpetual Park Drive,
Henley-on-Thames, RG9 1HH, Oxon,
United Kingdom
Tel.: (44) 1491417000
Investment & Fund Management Services
N.A.I.C.S.: 523940

Affiliate (Domestic):

**Invesco Bond Income Plus
Limited**   (3)
c/o Invesco Fund Managers - Perpetual
Park Perpetual Park Drive, Henley-on-
Thames, RG9 1HH, Oxon, United Kingdom
Tel.: (44) 1534607600
Web Site: https://www.invesco.com
Investment Trust
N.A.I.C.S.: 525990
Timothy Scholefield (Mgr-Fund)

Subsidiary (Domestic):

Invesco Real Estate Ltd. (2)
43-45 Portman Sq, London, W1H 6LY,
United Kingdom   (100%)
Tel.: (44) 2075433500
Web Site: http://www.invescoperpetual.co.uk
Sales Range: $25-49.9 Million
Emp.: 25
Provider of Investment Products
N.A.I.C.S.: 525910
Anna Duchnowska (Head-Europe)
Andy Rofe (Mng Dir)
Andrew Gordon (Head-Real Estate Debt-
Europe)

**Invesco Verwaltungsgesellschaft
mbH**   (1)
Bleichstr 60-63, 60313, Frankfurt,
Germany   (100%)
Tel.: (49) 69298070
Web Site: http://www.de.invesco.com
Sales Range: $50-74.9 Million
Emp.: 130
Holding Company
N.A.I.C.S.: 551111

Subsidiary (Domestic):

**Invesco Asset Management
GmbH**   (2)
An der Welle 5, 60322, Frankfurt,
Germany   (100%)
Tel.: (49) 69298070
Web Site: http://www.de.invesco.com
Sales Range: $50-74.9 Million
Emp.: 130
Commercial Bank & Provider of Investment
Products
N.A.I.C.S.: 525910

Subsidiary (Domestic):

**Invesco Asset Management
Deutschland GmbH**   (3)
An der Welle 5, D-60322, Frankfurt am
Main, Germany   (100%)

Tel.: (49) 69298070
Web Site: https://www.invesco.com
Sales Range: $50-74.9 Million
Emp.: 120
Investment Products
N.A.I.C.S.: 525910

Jemstep, Inc. (1)
5150 W El Camino Real Ste B-16, Los Al-
tos, CA 94022
Web Site: http://www.jemstep.com
Other Financial Advisory Services
N.A.I.C.S.: 523940

OppenheimerFunds, Inc. (1)
225 Liberty St 14th Fl, New York, NY
10281-1008
Tel.: (212) 323-0200
Web Site:
   http://www.oppenheimerfunds.com
Rev.: $256,005,234
Emp.: 1,380
Holding Company; Asset Management Ser-
vices
N.A.I.C.S.: 551112

Subsidiary (Domestic):

**OppenheimerFunds Distributor,
Inc.**   (2)
2 World Financial Ctr 225 Liberty St 11th Fl,
New York, NY 10281-1008
Tel.: (212) 323-0200
Web Site:
   http://www.oppenheimerfunds.com
Sales Range: $150-199.9 Million
Emp.: 600
Provider of Asset Management Services
N.A.I.C.S.: 523940

Branch (Domestic):

**OppenheimerFunds, Inc. - Rochester
Office**   (2)
350 Linden Oaks, Rochester, NY 14625-
2807
Tel.: (585) 383-1300
Web Site:
   http://www.oppenheimerfunds.com
Sales Range: $75-99.9 Million
Emp.: 35
Independent Mutual Fund Group
N.A.I.C.S.: 525910

PCM Properties LLC (1)
7575 E Redfield Rd Ste 219, Scottsdale, AZ
85260
Tel.: (480) 361-1130
Web Site:
   https://www.pcmpropertiesmanage
   ment.com
Property Management Services
N.A.I.C.S.: 523940

**RedBlack Software Private
Limited**   (1)
Noel Focus 7th Floor AB1 Division Seaport-
Airport Road, Kakkanad Chittethukara,
Kochi, 682037, India
Tel.: (91) 9605623900
Software Development Services
N.A.I.C.S.: 541511

RedBlack Software, LLC (1)
1 Bedford Farms Dr Ste 104, Bedford, NH
03110
Tel.: (603) 232-9404
Web Site: https://www.redblacksoftware.com
Investment Management Service
N.A.I.C.S.: 523940

**The Edinburgh Investment Trust
plc**   (1)
First Floor 9 Haymarket Square, Edinburgh,
EH3 8RY, United Kingdom
Tel.: (44) 2074121700
Web Site:
   https://www.edinburgh-investment.co.uk
Rev.: $125,088,362
Assets: $1,593,985,107
Liabilities: $161,206,766
Net Worth: $1,432,778,341
Earnings: $166,252,209
Fiscal Year-end: 03/31/2024
Investment Management Service
N.A.I.C.S.: 523940

W.L. Ross & Co., LLC (1)
1166 Avenue of the Americas, New York,
NY 10036
Tel.: (212) 826-1100

Invesco Ltd.—(Continued)

Web Site: http://www.wlross.com
Sales Range: $75-99.9 Million
Emp.: 30
Privater Equity Firm
N.A.I.C.S.: 523999
Harold L. Malone (Head-Transportation)

Holding (Non-US):

International Automotive Components
Group, S.A.   (2)
53 Boulevard Royal, Findel, 2449, Luxem-
bourg, Luxembourg
Tel.: (352) 2484557000
Web Site: https://www.iacgroup.com
Sales Range: $5-14.9 Billion
Automotive Components Mfr & Distr
N.A.I.C.S.: 336390
Iwona Niec Villaire (Chief Admin Officer)
David Pascoe (Chief Technical Officer)
Kevin Graham (CFO)
David Prystash (CEO)
Prashant Arya (CIO)
Michael Andrews (COO)
Thomas Boney (COO)

Subsidiary (US):

International Automotive Components
Group, LLC   (3)
5300 Auto Club Dr, Dearborn, MI
48126-2628   (75%)
Tel.: (313) 240-3000
Web Site: http://www.iacgroup.com
Sales Range: $1-4.9 Billion
Emp.: 23,000
Automotive Carpet, Interior & Exterior Prod-
uct Mfr
N.A.I.C.S.: 336360
Manfred Gingl (Chm)
David Prystash (CEO)
Iwona Niec Villaire (Chief Admin Officer)
David Pascoe (Chief Technical Officer)
Kelly Bysouth (Chief Supply Chain Officer)
Kevin Graham (CFO)
Sebastian de Coster (Exec VP-Global
Comml)

Division (Non-US):

International Automotive Components
Group Europe   (4)
Theodorstrasse 178, 40472, Dusseldorf,
Germany
Tel.: (49) 211447780
Web Site: http://www.iacgroup.eu
Sales Range: $1-4.9 Billion
Emp.: 80
Automotive Carpet, Interior & Exterior Prod-
uct Mfr
N.A.I.C.S.: 336360

Subsidiary (Non-US):

IAC Group AB   (5)
Assarebyn, 458 81, Fargelanda, Sweden
Tel.: (46) 528 68 32 00
Web Site: http://www.iacgroup.eu
Automotive Components & Systems (includ-
ing Interior & Exterior Trim) Supplier & Mfr
N.A.I.C.S.: 423110

IAC Group B.V.B.A.   (5)
Mondeolaan 5, Genk, 3600, Belgium
Tel.: (32) 89328141
Web Site: http://www.iacgroup.eu
Sales Range: $75-99.9 Million
Automotive Carpet, Interior & Exterior Prod-
uct Mfr
N.A.I.C.S.: 336360

IAC Group S.L.   (5)
c Mendigorritxu Industriale Area 57 PI Jun-
diz, Vitoria, 1015, Spain
Tel.: (34) 945290852
Web Site: http://www.iacgroup.eu
Sales Range: $150-199.9 Million
Automotive Carpet, Interior & Exterior Prod-
uct Mfr
N.A.I.C.S.: 336360

Subsidiary (Domestic):

International Automotive Components
Group North America Inc.   (4)
28333 Telegraph Rd, Southfield, MI 48034
Tel.: (248) 455-7000
Web Site: http://www.iacna.com

Sales Range: $1-4.9 Billion
Emp.: 500
Supplier of Automotive Components & Sys-
tems, Including Interior & Exterior Trim &
Structural & Functional Applications
N.A.I.C.S.: 336390
Manfred Gingl (Chm)
David Prystash (CEO)
Iwona Niec Villaire (Chief Admin Officer)
David Pascoe (CTO)
Kelly Bysouth (Chief Supply Chain Officer)
Nick Skwiat (Pres)
Kevin Graham (CFO)
Sebastian de Coster (Exec VP-Global
Comml)

Subsidiary (Domestic):

IAC Canton LLC   (5)
1212 7th St Southwest, Canton, OH 44707-
4434
Tel.: (330) 456-4543
Sales Range: $75-99.9 Million
Emp.: 1,100
Mfr of Car Mats
N.A.I.C.S.: 326299

IAC Mendon, LLC   (5)
236 W Clark St, Mendon, MI 49072
Tel.: (269) 496-2215
Web Site: http://www.iacgroup.com
Sales Range: $300-349.9 Million
Emp.: 700
Mfr of Automotive Molded Plastic Products
& Assemblies
N.A.I.C.S.: 336390

Holding (Non-US):

Invesco Asia Trust plc   (2)
Perpetual Park Perpetual Park Drive,
Henley-on-Thames, RG9 1HH, Oxfordshire,
United Kingdom
Tel.: (44) 2037531000
Rev.: $8,540,059
Assets: $352,893,152
Liabilities: $10,508,753
Net Worth: $342,384,399
Earnings: ($25,588,949)
Fiscal Year-end: 04/30/2022
Financial Investment Services
N.A.I.C.S.: 523940

INVESCO MUNI INCOME OPPS TRUST
1331 Spring St NW Ste 2500, At-
lanta, GA 30309
Tel.: (404) 439-3217   MA
OIA—(NYSE)
Rev.: $23,505,769
Assets: $502,961,326
Liabilitio: $121,673,116
Net Worth: $381,288,210
Earnings: $17,853,613
Fiscal Year-end: 02/29/20
Investment Management Service
N.A.I.C.S.: 525990

INVESCO MUNICIPAL OPPOR-TUNITY TRUST
1331 Spring St NW Ste 2500, At-
lanta, GA 30309
Tel.: (404) 439-3217   MA
VMO—(NYSE)
Rev.: $61,595,146
Assets: $1,570,576,470
Liabilities: $631,013,134
Net Worth: $939,563,336
Earnings: $38,300,140
Fiscal Year-end: 02/29/20
Investment Management Service
N.A.I.C.S.: 525990

INVESCO MUNICIPAL TRUST
1331 Spring St NW Ste 2500, At-
lanta, GA 30309
Tel.: (404) 439-3217   MA
VKQ—(NYSE)
Rev.: $49,455,383
Assets: $1,268,379,455
Liabilities: $495,450,254
Net Worth: $772,929,201
Earnings: $31,309,179

Fiscal Year-end: 02/29/20
Investment Management Service
N.A.I.C.S.: 525990

INVESCO PENNSYLVANIA VALUE MUNICIPAL INCOME TRUST
1331 Spring St NW Ste 2500, At-
lanta, GA 30309
Tel.: (404) 439-3217   PA
VPV—(NYSE)
Rev.: $22,973,087
Assets: $551,838,475
Liabilities: $205,510,675
Net Worth: $346,327,800
Earnings: $13,884,897
Fiscal Year-end: 02/29/20
Investment Management Service
N.A.I.C.S.: 525990

INVESCO QUALITY MUNICI-PAL INCOME TRUST
1331 Spring St NW Ste 2500, At-
lanta, GA 30309
Tel.: (404) 439-3217   MA
IQI—(NYSE)
Rev.: $46,961,320
Assets: $1,194,483,978
Liabilities: $448,218,147
Net Worth: $746,265,831
Earnings: $30,300,132
Fiscal Year-end: 02/29/20
Investment Management Service
N.A.I.C.S.: 525990

INVESCO SENIOR INCOME TRUST
1331 Spring St NW Ste 2500, At-
lanta, GA 30309
Tel.: (404) 439-3217   MA
VVR—(NYSE)
Rev.: $71,887,012
Assets: $1,187,866,671
Liabilities: $481,735,314
Net Worth: $706,131,357
Earnings: $45,749,599
Fiscal Year-end: 02/29/20
Investment Management Service
N.A.I.C.S.: 525990

INVESCO TRUST FOR INVEST-MENT GRADE MUNICIPALS
1331 Spring St NW Ste 2500, At-
lanta, GA 30309
Tel.: (404) 439-3217   MA
VGM—(NYSE)
Rev.: $50,344,550
Assets: $1,301,761,872
Liabilities: $521,658,724
Net Worth: $780,103,148
Earnings: $31,405,712
Fiscal Year-end: 02/29/20
Investment Management Service
N.A.I.C.S.: 525990

INVESCO TRUST FOR INVEST-MENT GRADE NEW YORK MU-NICIPALS
1331 Spring St NW Ste 2500, At-
lanta, GA 30309
Tel.: (404) 439-3217   MA
VTN—(NYSE)
Rev.: $17,907,956
Assets: $474,313,669
Liabilities: $181,496,864
Net Worth: $292,816,805
Earnings: $11,033,248
Fiscal Year-end: 02/29/20
Investment Management Service
N.A.I.C.S.: 525990

INVESCO VALUE MUNICIPAL INCOME TRUST
1331 Spring St NW Ste 2500, Atlanta, GA 30309

Tel.: (404) 439-3217   MA
IIM—(NYSE)
Rev.: $50,075,366
Assets: $1,299,814,439
Liabilities: $492,960,900
Net Worth: $806,853,539
Earnings: $31,583,441
Fiscal Year-end: 02/29/20
Investment Management Service
N.A.I.C.S.: 525990

INVESQUE INC.
8701 E 116th St Ste 260, Fishers, IN
46038
Tel.: (317) 643-4017   BC
Web Site: https://www.invesque.com
Year Founded: 2007
IVQ—(TSX)
Rev.: $217,387,000
Assets: $1,498,424,000
Liabilities: $1,205,095,000
Net Worth: $293,329,000
Earnings: ($184,004,000)
Fiscal Year-end: 12/31/20
Other Financial Vehicles
N.A.I.C.S.: 525990
Scott White (Chm & CEO)
Scott Higgs (CFO)
Dennis Dechow (Sr VP-Asset Svcs)
Adlai Chester (Chief Investment Offi-
cer)
Vineet Bedi (Chief Strategy Officer)
Bryan Hickman (Sr VP-Investments)
Quinn Haselhorst (Sr VP-Fin)
Julie Michael (Coord-HR)
Emily Molitor (Mgr-Internal Ops)
Kari Onweller (VP-Partner Rels &
Portfolio Mgmt)
Jim Rees (Dir-Acctg)

INVESTAR HOLDING CORPO-RATION
10500 Coursey Blvd 3rd Fl, Baton
Rouge, LA 70816
Tel.: (225) 227-2222   LA
Web Site:
https://www.investarbank.com
Year Founded: 2009
ISTR—(NASDAQ)
Rev.: $139,739,000
Assets: $2,815,155,000
Liabilities: $2,588,387,000
Net Worth: $226,768,000
Earnings: $16,678,000
Emp.: 320
Fiscal Year-end: 12/31/23
Bank Holding Company
N.A.I.C.S.: 551111
John J. D'Angelo (Pres & CEO)
Travis M. Lavergne (Chief Credit &
Risk Mgmt Officer & Exec VP)
Corey E. Moore (Chief Acctg Officer)
John R. Campbell (CFO & Exec VP)

Subsidiaries:

Cheaha Financial Group, Inc.   (1)
1320 Highway Dr, Oxford, AL 36203
Tel.: (256) 835-8855
Bank Holding Companies
N.A.I.C.S.: 551111
Barbara Montgomery (VP)
Shad Williams (Proc & CEO)

Subsidiary (Domestic):

Cheaha Bank   (2)
1320 Hwy Dr, Oxford, AL 36203-1998
Tel.: (256) 835-8855
Web Site: http://www.cheahabank.com
Credit Card Issuing
N.A.I.C.S.: 522210
Shad Williams (Mgr)

Investar Bank, N.A.   (1)
7244 Perkins Rd, Baton Rouge, LA 70808
Tel.: (225) 448-5451
Web Site: https://www.investarbank.com
Sales Range: $25-49.9 Million
Savings Bank
N.A.I.C.S.: 522180

John J. D'Angelo (Co-Founder, Pres &
CEO)
Suzanne O. Middleton (Chm)
Corey E. Moore (Chief Acctg Officer)
John R. Campbell (CFO & Exec VP)

INVESTCORP CREDIT MAN-
AGEMENT BDC, INC.
280 Park Ave 39th Fl, New York, NY
10017
Tel.: (646) 690-5034   MD
Web Site: https://www.icmbdc.com
Year Founded: 2012
ICMB—(NASDAQ)
Rev.: $23,878,302
Assets: $192,237,745
Liabilities: $117,227,536
Net Worth: $75,010,209
Earnings: ($4,092,470)
Emp.: 500
Fiscal Year-end: 06/30/24
Closed-End Debt Investment Fund
N.A.I.C.S.: 525990
Suhail A. Shaikh (Pres & CEO)

INVESTORS TITLE COMPANY
121 N Columbia St, Chapel Hill, NC
27514
Tel.: (919) 968-2200   NC
Web Site: https://www.invtitle.com
Year Founded: 1972
ITIC—(NASDAQ)
Rev.: $283,392,000
Assets: $339,757,000
Liabilities: $98,746,000
Net Worth: $241,011,000
Earnings: $23,903,000
Emp.: 626
Fiscal Year-end: 12/31/22
Holding Company; Title Insurance
N.A.I.C.S.: 551112
W. Morris Fine (Sec & Exec VP)
James Allan Fine Jr. (Co-Pres, CFO
& Treas)
James Allen Fine (Founder, Chm &
CEO)
Beth Adams (Mktg Mgr)
Rhonda Debruhl (Mktg Mgr)
W. Andrew Foley (VP & Atty)
Judy Medford (Mktg Mgr)
Kathy Baum (Mktg Mgr)
Michael W. Aiken (Compliance Officer
& Sr VP)
Carol Hayden (Exec VP-Investors
Title Exchange Corp & VP)
Jackie Thomas (Mktg Mgr)
Ryan E. Wainio (Sr VP-Underwriting
Ops-North Carolina & Atty)
C. Todd Murphy (Sr VP-Fin)
L. Dawn Martin (VP-Corp Admin)
Kirsten Pollock (VP & Dir-Audit)
Elizabeth B. Lewter (VP & Controller)
Brandee Garren (VP-Underwriting &
Ops Support)
Jonathan W. Biggs (VP & Dir-Risk
Mgmt & Education)
Kim Wells (VP-Mktg-Southeast Reg &
Mgr-Ops)
Mary Sajfar (VP-Ops, Trng & Dev)
Elizabeth A. Wainio (VP)
Gates Grainger (VP-Comml Svcs Div)
Jane Barkley (VP, Mgr-Comml Svcs
Div & Atty)
Tabatha Cruden (VP-Comml Svcs
Div)
Marcus G. Garren (VP & Atty)
Jodi Harelson (Mktg Mgr)
Missy Lawhorne (Dir-Mktg)
Dana Lyons (VP-Multi-State Mktg)
Dawn Royle (Mktg Mgr)
Sky Weaver (VP-Natl Markets Mktg)
Kim Long (VP-Natl Markets Ops &
Market Dev)
Daniel W. Minto (Sr VP-Engrg & IT)
Ned Manning (VP & Atty)
Shanna Bryant (VP-NC Agency Mktg)

Susan Harris (Sr VP-Agency & Mar-
ket Dev)
Tom Berry (Exec VP-Market Dev)
Kevin Joyce (VP & Atty)
Johanne Hindman (Mktg Mgr)
Jeffrey A. Benson (Exec VP)
John Herath (VP)
Brooke Mathosian (VP)
Andrew Wert (Sr VP)
Kristi Moretz-Icard (VP)
Kinsley Johnson (Mktg Mgr)
Matt Linville (VP)
Victoria Templeton (VP)
Stephen B. Brown Sr. (VP-Comm &
Market Dev & Atty)
James L. Bryan Jr. (VP-NC Legal
Support Svcs & Atty)

Subsidiaries:

Investors Capital Management
Company   **(1)**
121 N Columbia St, Chapel Hill, NC 27514
Tel.: (919) 968-2200
Web Site: http://www.invtitle.com
Emp.: 100
Portfolio Management Services
N.A.I.C.S.: 523940

Investors Title Exchange
Corporation   **(1)**
121 N Columbia St, Chapel Hill, NC 27514
Tel.: (984) 364-2752
Insurance Related Services
N.A.I.C.S.: 524298

Investors Title Insurance
Company   **(1)**
121 N Columbia St, Chapel Hill, NC
27514   **(100%)**
Tel.: (919) 968-2200
Sales Range: $50-74.9 Million
Emp.: 100
Land Title Insurance Primary Insurer & Un-
derwriter
N.A.I.C.S.: 524127
W. Morris Fine (Pres & COO)
James Allen Fine (Chm)
J. Allen Fine (Chm)
James A. Fine Jr. (Exec VP)
A. James Fine Jr. (CFO, Treas & Exec VP)

Investors Trust Company   **(1)**
121 N Columbia St, Chapel Hill, NC 27514
Tel.: (919) 945-2457
Web Site: https://www.invtrust.com
Financial Management Consulting Services
N.A.I.C.S.: 541611
Jim Fine (CEO)
Robert G. Fontana (Chief Investment Offi-
cer)
Charles Wright (Asst VP & Office Mgr-
Middle)
Craig Lewis (Pres)
Ty Powers (Dir-Asset Allocation)
Robby Scholes (VP-Wealth Advisor)

National Investors Title Insurance
Company   **(1)**
3445 Executive Ctr Dr Ste 110, Austin, TX
78731   **(100%)**
Tel.: (919) 968-2200
Web Site: https://www.nititle.com
Sales Range: $25-49.9 Million
Emp.: 100
Title Insurance
N.A.I.C.S.: 524127
W. Morris Fine (Pres & COO)
James Allan Fine Jr. (CFO, Treas & Exec
VP)

National Investors Title Insurance
Company   **(1)**
3445 Executive Center Dr Ste 110, Austin,
TX 78731
Web Site: https://www.nititle.com
Insurance Services
N.A.I.C.S.: 524210
W. Morris Fine (Co-Pres & COO)
James Allen Fine Jr. (Founder, Chm, Co-
Pres, CEO & Treas)
C. Todd Murphy (Sr VP-Fin)
Brandi Abercrombie (VP)
J. Allen Fine (Founder)
Jason Boss (VP)
L. Dawn Martin (VP)

Lauren Blair (VP)
Lisa Monti (VP)
Stephanie Stigant (VP)
Tom Berry (Exec VP)
James A. Fine Jr. (Co-Pres)
Summer Swope (Dir-Marketing & Real Es-
tate Education)
Tava Patterson (VP-Texas Agency Licens-
ing & Support)
Elizabeth A. Wainio (Sr VP-Risk Manage-
ment & Claims Counsel)
Jyoti Mehta (VP-Fin Ops)

University Title Company   **(1)**
1021 University Dr E, College Station, TX
77840
Tel.: (979) 260-9818
Web Site: https://www.utitle.com
Insurance Carrier Services
N.A.I.C.S.: 524127
Alexis Thornton (Officer-Escrow)
Kim Tomme (Officer-Escrow)
Michelle Merritt (VP-HR & Ops)
Eric McNeese (Gen Counsel-Legal)
Heath Poole (VP-Market Exec)
Stephanie Lozano (COO)
Crystal Gallo (Chief Revenue Officer)
Amber Patteson (Dir-Texas Fin)
Cully Lipsey (VP-Associate Counsel)
Darlene Fairchild (VP-Compliance)
Marianne Havey (Dir-Operations)
Kelsey Buell (Mgr-Escrow)
Trent C. Bailey (Pres-Houston)
Angie Shults (Pres-Brownwood)
Melissa Torres (Pres-San Antonio)
Romey Jackson (VP-Comml Svcs Group)
Amber Libert (VP-Sales & Marketing)

INVESTVIEW, INC.
234 Industrial Way W Ste A202,
Eatontown, NJ 07724
Tel.: (732) 889-4300   NV
Web Site:
https://www.investview.com
Year Founded: 2005
INVU—(OTCQB)
Rev.: $67,920,871
Assets: $33,688,971
Liabilities: $14,898,673
Net Worth: $18,790,298
Earnings: $2,831,920
Emp.: 24
Fiscal Year-end: 12/31/23
Investor & Financial Educational
Products
N.A.I.C.S.: 519290
Annette Raynor (Co-Founder & COO)
Mario Romano (Co-Founder, Treas &
Dir-Fin & IR)
Jayme Lin McWidener (Chief Acctg
Officer)
James R. Bell (Pres & Acting COO)
David B. Rothrock (Chm)
Ralph R. Valvano (CFO)
Victor M. Oviedo (CEO)
Myles Gill (Dir-Ops)

INVITAE CORPORATION
1400 16th St, San Francisco, CA
94103
Tel.: (415) 374-7782   DE
Web Site: https://www.invitae.com
Year Founded: 2010
NVTA—(NYSE)
Rev.: $516,303,000
Assets: $1,954,116,000
Liabilities: $1,852,280,000
Net Worth: $101,836,000
Earnings: ($3,106,293,000)
Emp.: 1,700
Fiscal Year-end: 12/31/22
Genetic Testing Services
N.A.I.C.S.: 621511
Randal W. Scott (Co-Founder &
Chm)
Thomas R. Brida (Chief Compliance
Officer, Gen Counsel & Sec)
Kenneth D. Knight (Pres & CEO)

Subsidiaries:

Clear Genetics, Inc.   **(1)**

2 Harrison St, San Francisco, CA 94105
Tel.: (415) 598-9489
Web Site: http://www.cleargenetics.com
Genetic Testing Services
N.A.I.C.S.: 621511
Motti Shohat (Co-Founder)
Guy Snir (Co-Founder & COO)
Moran Snir (Co-Founder & CEO)
Brian Cerceo (Sr Engr-Software)
Jeff Froom (Sr Engr-Software)

CombiMatrix Corporation   **(1)**
300 Goddard Ste 100, Irvine, CA 92618
Tel.: (949) 753-0624
Customizable Biological Arrays
N.A.I.C.S.: 334516

Subsidiary (Domestic):

CombiMatrix Molecular Diagnostics,
Inc.   **(2)**
300 Goddard Ste 100, Irvine, CA 92618
Tel.: (949) 753-0624
Web Site: http://combimatrix.com
Molecular Diagnostic Laboratory Operator
N.A.I.C.S.: 621512

Good Start Genetics, Inc.   **(1)**
237 Putnam Ave Ste 2, Cambridge, MA
02139
Tel.: (617) 714-0800
Genetic Testing Laboratory Services
N.A.I.C.S.: 621511

Invitae Australia Pty. Ltd.   **(1)**
73 Kenneth Road, Balgowlah, 2093, NSW,
Australia
Tel.: (61) 299495857
Web Site: http://www.invitaaust.com.au
Food Mfr & Distr
N.A.I.C.S.: 311999
Megan Mouat (Mng Dir)

INVITATION HOMES INC.
1717 Main St Ste 2000, Dallas, TX
75201
Tel.: (972) 421-3600   MD
Web Site: https://www.invh.com
Year Founded: 2012
INVH—(NYSE)
Rev.: $2,432,278,000
Assets: $19,220,967,000
Liabilities: $9,030,532,000
Net Worth: $10,190,435,000
Earnings: $518,774,000
Emp.: 1,555
Fiscal Year-end: 12/31/23
Real Estate Investment Services
N.A.I.C.S.: 531210
Dallas B. Tanner (Co-Founder)
Kimberly K. Norrell (Chief Acctg Offi-
cer & Exec VP)
Scott A. McLaughlin (Sr VP-IR & Tax)
Charles D. Young (Pres & COO)
Peter DiLello (Sr VP-Investment
Mgmt Grp)
Jonathan S. Olsen (CFO, Treas &
Exec VP)
David Ayers (Sr VP-Engrg)
Marnie Vaughn (Sr VP-
Transformation & Innovation)
Brad Greiwe (Co-Founder)

Subsidiaries:

Invitation Homes L.P.   **(1)**
901 Main St Ste 4700, Dallas, TX 75202
Tel.: (800) 339-7368
Web Site: https://www.invitationhomes.com
Real Estate Investment Services
N.A.I.C.S.: 531210

INVITRO INTERNATIONAL
330 E Orangethorpe Ave Ste D, Pla-
centia, CA 92870
Tel.: (949) 851-8356   CA
Web Site: https://www.invtrointl.com
Year Founded: 1985
IVRO—(OTCQB)
Rev.: $792,628
Assets: $1,534,007
Liabilities: $78,990
Net Worth: $1,455,017
Earnings: $1,553

InVitro International—(Continued)

Emp.: 6
Fiscal Year-end: 09/30/23
Medical Laboratories
N.A.I.C.S.: 621511
W. Richard Ulmer (CEO)

INVIVO THERAPEUTICS HOLDINGS CORP.

1 Kendall Sq Bldg 1400 W 4th Fl Ste B14402, Cambridge, MA 02139
Tel.: (617) 863-5524   NV
Web Site:
https://www.invivotherapeutics.com
Year Founded: 2003
NVIV—(NASDAQ)
Rev.: $160,000
Assets: $18,822,000
Liabilities: $3,076,000
Net Worth: $15,746,000
Earnings: ($10,490,000)
Emp.: 6
Fiscal Year-end: 12/31/22
Medical Device Mfr
N.A.I.C.S.: 339112
Richard C. Christopher (CFO & Treas)
Richard M. Toselli (Pres, CEO & Chief Medical Officer)
C. Ann Merrifield (Chm)

INVIVYD, INC.

1601 Trapelo Rd Ste 178, Waltham, MA 02451
Tel.: (781) 819-0080   DE
Web Site: https://invivyd.com
Year Founded: 2020
IVVD—(NASDAQ)
Rev.: $6,714,000
Assets: $383,167,000
Liabilities: $27,197,000
Net Worth: $355,970,000
Earnings: ($241,317,000)
Emp.: 84
Fiscal Year-end: 12/31/22
Biotechnology Research & Development Services
N.A.I.C.S.: 541714
William E. Duke Jr. (CFO, Principal Acctg Officer & Principal Executive Officer)
Timothy Lee (Chief Comml Officer)
Tillman U. Gerngross (Co-Founder)
Laura Walker (Co-Founder & Chief Scientific Officer)
Becky Dabora (Chief Tech & Mfg Officer)
Eric Kimble (Chief Comml Officer)
Pete Schmidt (Chief Medical Officer)

INVO BIOSCIENCE, INC.

5582 Broadcast Ct, Sarasota, FL 34240
Tel.: (978) 878-9505   NV
Web Site:
https://www.invobioscience.com
INVO—(NASDAQ)
Rev.: $822,196
Assets: $4,103,715
Liabilities: $5,081,327
Net Worth: ($977,612)
Earnings: ($10,892,511)
Emp.: 15
Fiscal Year-end: 12/31/22
Fertility Medical Device Mfr
N.A.I.C.S.: 339112
Steven M. Shum (CEO)
Andrea Goren (CFO)
Michael J. Campbell (COO & VP-Bus Dev)
J. Chris Jensen (VP-Quality, Quality, and Quality)
Bojan Mitrovic (Dir-Sales)
April McGhee (VP-Clinical Ops)
Terah Krigsvold (Controller)

ION GEOPHYSICAL CORPORATION

2105 City W Blvd Ste 100, Houston, TX 77042-2839
Tel.: (281) 933-3339   DE
Web Site: http://www.iongeo.com
Year Founded: 1968
IO—(NYSE)
Rev.: $122,674,000
Assets: $193,593,000
Liabilities: $264,683,000
Net Worth: ($71,090,000)
Earnings: ($37,225,000)
Emp.: 428
Fiscal Year-end: 12/31/20
Seismic Imaging Technology & Equipment
N.A.I.C.S.: 334519
Christopher T. Usher (Pres & CEO)
Ken Williamson (COO-E&P Tech & Svcs & Exec VP)
Scott Schwausch (VP-Fin & Controller)
Matt Powers (Gen Counsel, Sec & Exec VP)
Dale Lambert (Exec VP-Ops Optimization)
Lisa Ruiz (Sr VP-HR-Global)
Steven Bate (Chief Admin Officer)

Subsidiaries:

Concept Systems Ltd.   (1)
1 Logie Mill, Edinburgh, EH7 4HG, Scotland, United Kingdom
Tel.: (44) 1315575595
Web Site: http://www.iongeo.com
Sales Range: $100-124.9 Million
Navigation & Global Positioning Products
N.A.I.C.S.: 488330

GMG/AXIS, Inc.   (1)
225 E 16th Ave Ste 1200, Denver, CO 80203
Tel.: (303) 318-7780
Web Site: http://www.iongeo.com
Emp.: 50
Software Development Services
N.A.I.C.S.: 541511

GX Technology Australia Pty Ltd.   (1)
Suite 1 Ground Floor 578-586 Murray Street, West Perth, 6005, WA, Australia
Tel.: (61) 863369740
Web Site: http://www.iongeo.com
Oil & Gas Field Exploration Services
N.A.I.C.S.: 213112

GX Technology Corporation   (1)
2105 CityWest Blvd Ste 900, Houston, TX 77042-2837
Tel.: (713) 789-7250
Web Site: http://www.gxt.com
Sales Range: $75-99.9 Million
Seismographic Technology Services
N.A.I.C.S.: 541360

Subsidiary (Non-US):

GX Technology Canada, Ltd.   (2)
800 350 - 7th Avenue SW, Calgary, T2P 3N9, AB, Canada
Tel.: (403) 263-9139
Web Site: http://www.iongeo.com
Sales Range: $1-9.9 Million
Seismographic Technology Services
N.A.I.C.S.: 541360

GX Technology EAME Limited   (2)
31 Windsor Street, Chertsey, KT16 8AT, Surrey, United Kingdom
Tel.: (44) 1932792200
Web Site: http://www.iongeo.com
Seismographic Technology Services
N.A.I.C.S.: 541360

GX Technology Processamento de Dados Ltda.   (1)
Av Nilo Pecanha 50 Grp 2817/2818-centro, Rio de Janeiro, Brazil
Tel.: (55) 2135095420
Geophysical Surveying Services
N.A.I.C.S.: 541360

GX Technology Trinidad, Ltd.   (1)
Albion Plaza Energy Centre 22 - 24 Victoria

Avenue 7th Floor West, Port of Spain, Trinidad & Tobago
Tel.: (868) 6249756
Geophysical Technology Services
N.A.I.C.S.: 541330

I/O Marine Systems Limited   (1)
Unit 1 Little Mead Industrial Estate, Little Mead, Cranleigh, GU6 8ND, United Kingdom
Tel.: (44) 1483277644
Electronic Equipment & Instrument Mfr
N.A.I.C.S.: 335999

I/O Marine Systems, Inc.   (1)
5000 River Rd, Harahan, LA 70123
Tel.: (504) 733-6061
Sales Range: $75-99.9 Million
Seismographic Technology Services
N.A.I.C.S.: 541360

ION Exploration Products (U.S.A.), Inc.   (1)
2105 Citywest Blvd Ste 400, Houston, TX 77042-2839
Tel.: (281) 933-3339
Oil & Gas Field Exploration Services
N.A.I.C.S.: 213112

ION Geophysical CIS LLC   (1)
1 10 Letnikovskaya street Building 1, 115114, Moscow, Russia
Tel.: (7) 4959899902
Web Site: http://www.iongeo.ru
Electric Equipment Mfr
N.A.I.C.S.: 335999

Inco Industrial Components 's-Gravenhage B.V.   (1)
Kanaalpark 140, 2321 JV, Leiden, Netherlands
Tel.: (31) 715601234
Electronic Equipment & Instrument Mfr
N.A.I.C.S.: 335999

OceanGeo B.V.   (1)
Prins Bernhardplein 200, 1097 JB, Amsterdam, Netherlands
Tel.: (31) 205214777
Electric Equipment Mfr
N.A.I.C.S.: 335999

Sensor Nederland B.V.   (1)
Kanaalpark 140, 2321 JV, Leiden, Netherlands
Tel.: (31) 715601234
Web Site: http://www.ingo.com
Sales Range: $25-49.9 Million
Emp.: 100
Seismographic Technology Services
N.A.I.C.S.: 541360

IONIS PHARMACEUTICALS, INC.

2855 Gazelle Ct, Carlsbad, CA 92010
Tel.: (760) 931-9200   DE
Web Site:
https://www.ionispharma.com
Year Founded: 1989
IONS—(NASDAQ)
Rev.: $787,647,000
Assets: $2,990,072,000
Liabilities: $2,603,386,000
Net Worth: $386,686,000
Earnings: ($366,286,000)
Emp.: 927
Fiscal Year-end: 12/31/23
Biopharmaceutical Drug Developer
N.A.I.C.S.: 325412
Stanley T. Crooke (Founder)
Kyle Jenne (Chief Global Product Strategy Officer & Exec VP-Comml)
Brett P. Monia (CEO)
David J. Ecker (VP-Strategic Innovation)
C. Frank Bennett (Chief Scientific Officer & Exec VP)
Shannon Devers (Sr VP-HR)
Richard S. Geary (Chief Dev Officer & Exec VP)
Sanjay Bhanot (Chief Medical Officer & Sr VP)
Eugene Schneider (Chief Clinical Dev Officer & Exec VP)
Adam Mullick (VP-Drug Discovery)

Anthony Scozzari (Sr VP-DevChem & Mfg)
Brian Lemay (VP-Tax)
Charles Asare (VP & Head-Drug Safety)
Cliff Ford (VP-Patents)
Daniel Capaldi (VP-Analytical & Process Chemistry)
Darren Gonzales (Chief Acctg Officer & Sr VP)
Ken Newman (VP-Clincial Dev)
Leo Sahelijo (VP-Translational Medicine)
Matt Buck (VP-Regulatory Affairs)
Eric E. Swayze (Exec VP-Res)
Ewa Karwatowska-Prokopczuk (VP-Cardiovascular Medicine)
Roger Lane (VP-Clinical Dev)
Scott Henry (Sr VP-Preclinical Dev)
Shuling Guo (VP-Drug Discovery)
Alexey S. Revenko (VP)
Anne V. Smith (VP)
Bret A. Coldren (VP)
Bryan J. Tayefeh (VP)
Christopher Kramer (VP)
Dawn Henson-Hannough (VP)
Eric P. Bastings (VP)
Hala B. Mirza (Sr VP)
James J. Haney (VP)
Jason P. Zwerner (VP)
Kara Malewicz (VP)
Kim P. Doan (VP)
Melissa M. Yoon (VP)
Michael Pollock (Sr VP)
Rachel M. Carnes (Sr VP)
Shay Bujanover (VP)
Sheetal K. Patel (VP)
Sujit K. Basu (VP)
Tae-Won Kim (VP)
Tiffany L. Baumann (VP)
Tracy Berns (Sr VP)
Xiang Gao (VP)
Joseph T. Baroldi (Chief Bus Officer)
Lisa R. Johnson-Pratt (Sr VP-New Product Comml Strategy)

Subsidiaries:

Akcea Therapeutics, Inc.   (1)
22 Boston Wharf Rd Fl 9, Boston, MA 02210   (100%)
Tel.: (617) 207-0202
Web Site: http://www.akceatx.com
Rev.: $488,543,000
Assets: $599,250,000
Liabilities: $56,246,000
Net Worth: $543,004,000
Earnings: $40,772,000
Emp.: 294
Fiscal Year-end: 12/31/2019
Biotechnology Research & Development Services
N.A.I.C.S.: 541713
Kyle Jenne (Chief Comml Officer)
Brett P. Monia (Pres)
Elizabeth L. Hougen (Treas)
Jared Rhines (Sr VP & Head-Americas)
Kathleen Gallagher (VP-Corp Comm & IR)
Maura Bullock (VP-HR)
Richard Jones (Sr VP & Head-Europe)
Joshua Patterson (Gen Counsel)
Carla Poulson (Chief HR Officer)
Tracy Palmer Berns (Chief Compliance Officer)
William T. Andrews (Chief Medical Officer)
Melissa Yoon (Sec)

IONQ, INC.

4505 Campus Dr, College Park, MD 20740
Tel.: (301) 298-7997   DE
Web Site: https://ionq.com
Year Founded: 2015
IONQ—(NYSE)
Rev.: $11,131,000

Assets: $597,992,000
Liabilities: $29,781,000
Net Worth: $568,211,000
Earnings: ($48,511,000)
Emp.: 202
Fiscal Year-end: 12/31/22
Software Publr
N.A.I.C.S.: 513210
Thomas Kramer *(CFO)*
Jungsang Kim *(Bd of Dirs, Founder & CTO)*
Stacey Giamalis *(Chief Legal Officer & Sec)*
Rima Alameddine *(Chief Revenue Officer)*
Tom Jones *(Chief People Officer)*
Ariel Braunstein *(Sr VP-Product)*
Dean Kassmann *(Sr VP-Engineering & Technology)*
Dave Mehuys *(VP-Production Engrg)*
Jordan Shapiro *(Sr VP-Fin Planning & Analysis)*
Peter Chapman *(Pres & CEO)*
Jungsang Kim *(Co-Founder)*

IOTA COMMUNICATIONS, INC.

540 Union Square, New Hope, PA 18938   DE
Web Site:
   http://www.iotacommunications.com
Year Founded: 1998
IOTC—(OTCIQ)
Rev.: $2,305,144
Assets: $12,977,628
Liabilities: $107,735,606
Net Worth: ($94,757,978)
Earnings: ($56,777,401)
Emp.: 30
Fiscal Year-end: 05/31/19
Semiconductor Devices Mfr
N.A.I.C.S.: 334413
Terrence M. DeFranco *(Pres & CEO)*
Barclay Knapp *(Chm)*
Brian Ray *(CTO)*
M.Rob Somers *(Mgr & Gen Counsel)*

Subsidiaries:

Solbright Renewable Energy, LLC   (1)
701 E Bay St Ste 302, Charleston, SC 29403
Tel.: (843) 535-8500
Web Site: http://www.solbrightre.com
Solar Energy Power Generation Services
N.A.I.C.S.: 221114
Andrew Streit *(Dir-Bus Dev)*
Corey Mitchell *(Sr Project Mgr)*

IOVANCE BIOTHERAPEUTICS, INC.

825 Industrial Rd Ste 400, San Carlos, CA 94070
Tel.: (650) 260-7120   NV
Web Site: https://www.iovance.com
Year Founded: 2007
IOVA—(NASDAQ)
Rev.: $1,189,000
Assets: $780,351,000
Liabilities: $195,738,000
Net Worth: $584,613,000
Earnings: ($444,037,000)
Emp.: 557
Fiscal Year-end: 12/31/23
Biopharmaceutical Mfr
N.A.I.C.S.: 325412
Jean-Marc Bellemin *(CFO, Principal Acctg Officer & Treas)*
Igor P. Bilinsky *(COO)*
Frederick G. Vogt *(Interim Pres, Interim CEO & Gen Counsel)*
Friedrich Graf Finckenstein *(Chief Medical Officer)*
Raj K. Puri *(Exec VP)*
Brian Shew *(Sr VP)*
Kevin Smyth *(Sr VP)*
Tracy Winton *(Sr VP)*

Hequn Yin *(Sr VP)*
Jim Ziegler *(Exec VP)*
Iain Dukes *(Chm)*

IPG PHOTONICS CORPORATION

377 Simarano Dr, Marlborough, MA 01752
Tel.: (508) 373-1100   DE
Web Site:
   https://www.ipgphotonics.com
Year Founded: 1990
IPGP—(NASDAQ)
Rev.: $1,287,439,000
Assets: $2,698,898,000
Liabilities: $283,513,000
Net Worth: $2,415,385,000
Earnings: $218,878,000
Emp.: 6,180
Fiscal Year-end: 12/31/23
Fiber Optics Communications Equipment Developer & Mfr
N.A.I.C.S.: 334413
Angelo P. Lopresti *(Gen Counsel, Sec & Sr VP)*
Timothy P. V. Mammen *(CFO & Sr VP)*
Felix Stukalin *(COO & Sr VP)*
Mark M. Gitin *(CEO)*
Thomas J. Burgomaster *(VP & Controller)*

Subsidiaries:

Genesis Systems Group, LLC   (1)
8900 N Harrison St, Davenport, IA 52806
Tel.: (563) 445-5600
Web Site: http://www.genesis-systems.com
Industrial & Commercial Robotic Systems Designer & Mfr
N.A.I.C.S.: 333998
Harlon Neumann *(Dir-Engineering)*
Keith Bernier *(Mgr-Business Development)*
Patrick Pollock *(COO)*
Carol Woten *(Mgr-Business Development)*

IPG (Beijing) Fiber Laser Technology Co., Ltd.   (1)
F28 2 Jingyuan North St Bda, Beijing, 100176, China
Tel.: (86) 1067873377
Web Site: http://www.ipgphotonics.com
Emp.: 200
Photonics Research & Developement Services
N.A.I.C.S.: 541715

IPG Fibertech S.r.l.   (1)
Via Kennedy 21, 20025, Legnano, MI, Italy   **(100%)**
Tel.: (39) 03311706900
Web Site: http://www.ipgphotonics.com
Sales Range: $10-24.9 Million
Emp.: 12
Provider of Fiber Optics Communications Equipment
N.A.I.C.S.: 335921

IPG IRE-Polus   (1)
Vvedenskogo Sq 1, Fryazino, 141190, Moscow, Russia
Tel.: (7) 8007752829
Web Site: http://www.ipgphotonics.com
Provider of Fiber Optics Communications Equipment
N.A.I.C.S.: 335921

IPG Laser GmbH   (1)
Carl-Benz-Strasse 28, 57299, Burbach, Germany   **(100%)**
Tel.: (49) 273644208100
Web Site: https://www.ipgphotonics.com
Sales Range: $200-249.9 Million
Emp.: 800
Provider of Fiber Optics Communications Equipment
N.A.I.C.S.: 335921
Valentin Fomin *(Mng Dir)*
Andrey Mashkin *(Mng Dir)*

IPG Photonics (India) Pvt. Ltd.   (1)
Indiqube-ETA No 38/4 Ground Floor, Adjacent to Dell EMC2 Doddanekundi Outer Ring Road, Bengaluru, 560037, Karnataka, India

Tel.: (91) 8071172555
Web Site: http://www.ipgphotonics.com
Provider of Fiber Optics Communications Equipment
N.A.I.C.S.: 335921

IPG Photonics (Japan) Ltd.   (1)
920 Nippa-cho, Kohoku-ku, Yokohama, 223-0057, Kanagawa, Japan
Tel.: (81) 457169831
Web Site: http://japanese.ipgphotonics.com
Emp.: 50
Fiber Optic Communications Equipment Mfr
N.A.I.C.S.: 334413
Valentin P. Gapontsev *(Pres)*

IPG Photonics (Korea) Ltd.   (1)
Techno 2ro 80-12, Yuseong-gu, Daejeon, 34014, Korea (South)
Tel.: (82) 429302000
Web Site: http://www.ipgphotonics.com
Emp.: 24
Fiber Optic Communications Equipment Mfr
N.A.I.C.S.: 334413

IPG Photonics (UK) Ltd.   (1)
2 Viggen Way Ansty Park, Coventry, CV7 9RE, Warwickshire, United Kingdom
Tel.: (44) 2031782111
Web Site: http://www.ipgphotonics.com
Sales Range: $10-24.9 Million
Emp.: 4
Fiber Optics Communications Equipment
N.A.I.C.S.: 335921

Innovative Laser Technologies, Inc.   (1)
5110 Main St NE Ste 1400, Minneapolis, MN 55421
Tel.: (763) 574-7374
Web Site: http://www.iltinc.com
Laser System Mfr
N.A.I.C.S.: 335999
David Billings *(Engr-Mechanical)*
Derek Kranig *(Sr Engr-Electrical)*
Felix Lin *(Engr-Mechanical)*

Menara Networks, Inc.   (1)
3400 Carlisle St Ste 210, Dallas, TX 75204
Tel.: (214) 303-1600
Web Site: http://www.menaranet.com
Electronic Parts & Equipment Merchant Whslr
N.A.I.C.S.: 423690
Siraj Nour El-Ahmadi *(Co-Founder, Pres & CEO)*
Salam El-Ahmadi *(Co-Founder)*

Optigrate Corporation   (1)
562 S Econ Cir, Oviedo, FL 32765-4311
Tel.: (407) 542-7704
Web Site: https://www.optigrate.com
Holographic Optical Elements Design, Development & Production
N.A.I.C.S.: 333310
Alexei Glebov *(Pres & Gen Mgr)*
Vadim Smirnov *(CTO & Dir-Holography)*
Leon Glebov *(Dir-R&D)*
Oleg Smolski *(Dir-Glass Mfg)*
Igor Ciapurin *(Dir-Ops)*

IPIC ENTERTAINMENT INC.

301 Plaza Real, Boca Raton, FL 33432
Tel.: (561) 299-3000   DE
Web Site: https://www.ipic.com
Year Founded: 2017
IPIC—(OTCQB)
Rev.: $148,345,000
Assets: $158,724,000
Liabilities: $277,945,000
Net Worth: ($119,221,000)
Earnings: ($23,199,000)
Emp.: 250
Fiscal Year-end: 12/31/18
Entertainment Services
N.A.I.C.S.: 512131

Subsidiaries:

Bay Colony Realty, LLC   (1)
205B Willow St S, Hamilton, MA 01982
Tel.: (978) 626-0126
Web Site: http://www.baycolonyrealty.com
Real Estate Services
N.A.I.C.S.: 531390

IPOWER INC.

Tel.: (626) 863-7344   NV
Web Site:
   https://www.meetipower.com
Year Founded: 2018
IPW—(NASDAQ)
Rev.: $86,071,485
Assets: $51,295,857
Liabilities: $28,279,824
Net Worth: $23,016,033
Earnings: ($1,541,448)
Emp.: 60
Fiscal Year-end: 06/30/24
Lawn & Garden Tractor & Home Lawn & Garden Equipment Manufacturing
N.A.I.C.S.: 333112
Kevin Vassily *(CFO)*
Allan Huang *(Co-Founder)*
Chenlong Tan *(Co-Founder, Chm, Pres & CEO)*
Chenlong Tan *(Co-Founder, Chm, Pres & CEO)*
Kevin Dean Vassily *(CFO)*

IPURE LABS, INC.

871 Coronado Center Dr Ste 200, Henderson, NV 89052
Tel.: (702) 996-7106
Web Site: http://www.ipurelabs.com
Year Founded: 2014
IPLB—(OTCIQ)
Digital Marketing Services
N.A.I.C.S.: 541613
Gary L. Killoran *(CFO)*

IQSTEL INC.

300 Aragon Ave Ste 375, Coral Gables, FL 33134
Tel.: (954) 951-8191   NV
Web Site: https://www.iqstel.com
Year Founded: 2011
IQST—(OTCQX)
Rev.: $144,502,351
Assets: $22,155,653
Liabilities: $14,109,781
Net Worth: $8,045,872
Earnings: ($219,436)
Emp.: 70
Fiscal Year-end: 12/31/23
Internet Distr
N.A.I.C.S.: 517121
Juan Carlos Lopez Silva *(Co-Founder)*
Leandro Jose Iglesias *(Chm, Pres & CEO)*
Alvaro Quintana Cardona *(CFO, COO, Principal Acctg Officer, Treas & Sec)*

Subsidiaries:

ItsBchain, LLC   (1)
300 Aragon Ave Ste 375, Coral Gables, FL 33134
Tel.: (954) 951-8191
Web Site: https://www.itsbchain.com
Telecommunication Servicesb
N.A.I.C.S.: 517121

QGlobal SMS, LLC   (1)
300 Aragon Ave Ste 375, Coral Gables, FL 33134
Tel.: (786) 654-4450
Web Site: https://www.qglobalsms.com
Telecommunication Servicesb
N.A.I.C.S.: 517121

Smartbiz Telecom LLC   (1)
6303 Blue Lagoon Dr Ste 400, Miami, FL 33126
Tel.: (973) 341-5761
Web Site: https://www.smartbiztel.com
Telecommunication Servicesb
N.A.I.C.S.: 517121

SwissLink Carrier AG   (1)
Neuhausweg 5, 8810, Horgen, Switzerland
Tel.: (41) 435771000
Web Site: https://www.swisslink-carrier.com
Telecommunication Servicesb

IQSTEL Inc.—(Continued)

N.A.I.C.S.: 517121
Juan Carlos Lopez Silva (CEO)

IQVIA HOLDINGS INC.

2400 Ellis Rd, Durham, NC 27703
Tel.: (919) 998-2000　　　　　　　**DE**
Web Site: https://www.iqvia.com
Year Founded: 2009
IQV—(NYSE)
Rev.: $14,984,000,000
Assets: $26,681,000,000
Liabilities: $20,569,000,000
Net Worth: $6,112,000,000
Earnings: $1,358,000,000
Emp.: 87,000
Fiscal Year-end: 12/31/23
Holding Company; Biological & Pharmaceutical Development Services
N.A.I.C.S.: 551112
Ronald E. Bruehlman (CFO & Exec VP)
Jeffrey A. Spaeder (Chief Medical & Scientific Officer)
Trudy Stein (Chief HR Officer & Exec VP)
Karl Guenault (CIO & Sr VP)
W. Richard Staub III (Pres-R&D Solutions)
Eric Sherbet (Gen Counsel & Exec VP)
Jim Berkshire (Sr VP-Bus Ops)
Rob Kotchie (Pres-Real-World Solutions)
Brian Mi (Pres-Asia Pacific)
Sanjay Chikarmane (Chief Product Officer)
Keriann Cherofsky (Principal Acctg Officer, Sr VP & Controller)
Bhavik Patel (Pres)
Bhavani Sivalingam (Sr VP)
Fumihiko Ugajin (Pres)
Nick Childs (Sr VP)
Ari Bousbib (Chm & CEO)

Subsidiaries:

159 Solutions, Inc.　　　　　　**(1)**
1850 Gateway Dr Ste 250, San Mateo, CA 94404
Web Site: http://www.159solutions.com
Technical Consulting Services
N.A.I.C.S.: 541690
Prasanna Sridharan (Partner)
Deepak Gopinath (Principal)
Yogooh Maddan (Principal)
Mukesh Masand (Principal)
Sepp Saljoughi (Principal)
Sriram Rangarajan (Principal)

Allcare Plus Pharmacy LLC　　**(1)**
50 Bearfoot Rd, Northborough, MA 01532
Web Site:
　　https://www.allcarepluspharmacy.com
Patient Support Services
N.A.I.C.S.: 621999
H. Tim (Program Mgr)
V. Harry (Mgr-Logistics)

Aposphare GmbH　　　　　　　**(1)**
Clouth 104, Niehler Strasse 104, 50733, Cologne, Germany
Tel.: (49) 22165072950
Web Site: https://www.aposphaere.de
Healthcare Training Services
N.A.I.C.S.: 611430

Ascott Sales Integration Pty. Ltd. **(1)**
Level 8 201 Pacific Highway, St Leonards, North Shore, 2065, NSW, Australia
Tel.: (61) 294399770
Web Site: https://www.ascottsales.com.au
Nurse Advisory Services
N.A.I.C.S.: 621610

BITAC MAP S.L.U.　　　　　　　**(1)**
Recinte Modernista de Sant Pau Pabellon de Sant Manuel, Carrer de Sant Antoni Maria Claret 167, 08025, Barcelona, Spain
Tel.: (34) 672398195
Web Site: https://www.bitac.com
Clinical Terminology Training Services
N.A.I.C.S.: 621399

Benefit Holding, Inc.　　　　　**(1)**
4709 Creekstone Dr Ste 200, Durham, NC 27703
Tel.: (919) 998-2000
Pharmaceutical Products Distr
N.A.I.C.S.: 424210

BioFortis, Inc.　　　　　　　　**(1)**
10320 Little Patuxent Pkwy Ste 410, Columbia, MD 21044
Tel.: (443) 276-2464
Web Site: http://www.biofortis.com
Commercial Biotechnical Research Services
N.A.I.C.S.: 541714

CTcue B.V.　　　　　　　　　　**(1)**
Science Park 406, 1098 XH, Amsterdam, Netherlands
Tel.: (31) 85 600 1037
Web Site: https://ctcue.com
Hospital & Health Care Services
N.A.I.C.S.: 622110
Roel Lakmaker (CEO & Co-Founder)
Jochem de Boer (Co-Founder & CTO)

Cenduit (India) Services Private Company Limited　　　　　　　**(1)**
Safina Towers No 3 Ground And First Floor Ali Askar Road, Bengaluru, 560 052, India
Tel.: (91) 8040196600
Software Development Services
N.A.I.C.S.: 513210

Cenduit GmbH　　　　　　　　**(1)**
3rd Floor Kirschgartenstrasse 12/14, 4051, Basel, Switzerland
Tel.: (41) 614874040
Pharmaceutical Products Distr
N.A.I.C.S.: 424210

Cenduit Japan GK　　　　　　**(1)**
IQVIA Japan Tokyo 7th Floor Keikyu Daiichi Bldg Takanawa 4-10-18, Minato-Ku, Tokyo, 108-0074, Japan
Tel.: (81) 345309638
Pharmaceutical Products Distr
N.A.I.C.S.: 424210

Centrix Innovations (Pty) Ltd.　**(1)**
BCX Building 3rd Floor 1021 Lenchen Ave North, Centurion, South Africa
Tel.: (27) 120035200
Web Site: http://www.centrix.co.za
Software Development Services
N.A.I.C.S.: 541512

ClinTec International Ltd.　　　**(1)**
133 Finnieston Street, Glasgow, G3 8HB, United Kingdom
Tel.: (44) 1412261120
Web Site: http://www.clintec.com
Health Care Srvices
N.A.I.C.S.: 621999
Karen Garland (Mgr-Global)

Clintec International, Inc.　　　**(1)**
590 Madison Ave, New York, NY 10022
Tel.: (212) 521-4472
Health Care Services
N.A.I.C.S.: 621999

Comline GmbH　　　　　　　　**(1)**
Lise-Meitner-Strasse 16, 24941, Flensburg, Germany
Tel.: (49) 4617 730 8300
Web Site: https://www.comline-shop.de
Technical Consulting Services
N.A.I.C.S.: 541511
Andreas Christensen (Mgr-Business Development)
Richard Gabel (Mng Dir)
Anja Sobottka (Mng Dir)
Oliver Bartsch (Mng Dir)

DAVASO GmbH　　　　　　　　**(1)**
Sommerfelder Strasse 120, 04316, Leipzig, Germany
Tel.: (49) 34 125 9200
Web Site: https://www.davaso.de
Medical Insurance Services
N.A.I.C.S.: 524114

DAVASO Holding GmbH　　　　**(1)**
Sommerfelder Strasse 120, 04316, Leipzig, Germany
Tel.: (49) 3416 586 3398
Web Site: https://www.davaso-holding.de
Human Resource Management Services
N.A.I.C.S.: 541612

Dimensiions Healthcare LLC　　**(1)**

20th Floor Al Wahda City Tower Hazaa Bin Zayed the First Street, PO Box 114521, Abu Dhabi, United Arab Emirates
Tel.: (971) 28157929
Web Site: http://www.dimensions-healthcare.com
Health Care Consulting Services
N.A.I.C.S.: 541611
Omar Ghosheh (CEO)

Drug Dev Inc.　　　　　　　　**(1)**
1170 Devon Park Dr Ste 300, Wayne, PA 19087
Web Site: https://www.drugdev.com
Health Care Consulting Services
N.A.I.C.S.: 541611
Brian Fisher (Pres-Trial Mgmt)
Brett Kleger (Chief Comml Officer)
Elisa Cascade (Chief Product Officer)
Stuart Thiede (Pres-Payments)
Eric Delente (Pres-Patient Solutions)

EPG Communication Holdings Limited　　　　　　　　　　**(1)**
Wellington Gate 7 & 9 Church Road, Tunbridge Wells, TN1 1HT, United Kingdom
Tel.: (44) 1892577706
Web Site: https://epghealth.com
Medical Education & Communication Services
N.A.I.C.S.: 624190

EPID Research Oy　　　　　　　**(1)**
Metsanneidonkuja 6, 02130, Espoo, Finland
Tel.: (358) 942413800
Web Site: http://www.epidresearch.com
Data Management Services
N.A.I.C.S.: 518210

Educom S.r.l.　　　　　　　　　**(1)**
Via Fabio Filzi 29, 20124, Milan, Italy
Tel.: (39) 02697861
Web Site: https://www.educom.it
Advertising Services
N.A.I.C.S.: 541810

Foundry Health, LLC　　　　　**(1)**
1350 14th Ave St 13, Grafton, WI 53024
Web Site: https://www.foundryhealth.com
Health Research & Development Services
N.A.I.C.S.: 541715

GCE Solutions, GmbH　　　　　**(1)**
Greifengasse 38, 4058, Basel, Switzerland
Tel.: (41) 1618706667
Health Care Srvices
N.A.I.C.S.: 621999

Highpoint Solutions, LLC　　　**(1)**
Cours de Rive 13, 1204, Geneva, Switzerland
Tel.: (41) 227359581
Biological & Pharmaceutical Development Services
N.A.I.C.S.: 541714

IM Associates BV　　　　　　　**(1)**
Persilstraat 52 Building E, PO Box 5, 3020, Herent, Belgium
Tel.: (32) 16224743
Web Site: https://www.im-associates.eu
Information Technology Services
N.A.I.C.S.: 541519

IMS Health Analytics Services Private Limited　　　　　　　　　　**(1)**
Omega Embassy TechSquare Marathahalli-Sarjapur Outer Ring Road, Kadubeesana-halli, Bengaluru, 560 103, India
Tel.: (91) 8037690100
Biological & Pharmaceutical Development Services
N.A.I.C.S.: 541714

IMS Health Holdings, Inc.　　　**(1)**
83 Wooster Heights Rd, Danbury, CT 06810
Tel.: (203) 448-4600
Web Site: http://www.iqvia.com
Healthcare Information & Technology Services
N.A.I.C.S.: 551112

Subsidiary (Domestic):

IQVIA Inc.　　　　　　　　　　**(2)**
83 Wooster Heights Rd, Danbury, CT 06810
Tel.: (203) 448-4600
Web Site: http://www.iqvia.com

Information Solutions for the Pharmaceutical & Health Care Industries
N.A.I.C.S.: 513210
Ari Bousbib (Bd of Dirs, Executives)
Suzanne Kain (Dir-Bus Svcs)

Subsidiary (Non-US):

IMS Health Korea Ltd　　　　　**(3)**
23rd Fl Namsan Square, 173 Toegye-ro Junggu, Seoul, 04554, Korea (South)
Tel.: (82) 234597307
Web Site: https://www.iqvia.com
Healthcare Software Development Services
N.A.I.C.S.: 541511

IMS Health Market Research Consulting (Shanghai) Co. Ltd.　**(3)**
12&15F, No.968 West Beijing Road,, Shanghai, China
Tel.: (86) 2133252288
Market Research Consulting Services
N.A.I.C.S.: 541910

IQVIA AG　　　　　　　　　　**(3)**
Kirschgartenstrasse 14, 4051, Basel, Switzerland
Tel.: (41) 612045000
Web Site: http://www.iqvia.com
Health Care Srvices
N.A.I.C.S.: 621999

IQVIA Consulting and Information Services India Pvt. Ltd.　　**(3)**
902 9th floor B-Wing Supreme Business Park, Hiranandani Gardens Powai, Mumbai, 400076, India
Tel.: (91) 2271097200
Web Site: http://www.iqvia.com
Healthcare Software Development Services
N.A.I.C.S.: 541511

Subsidiary (Domestic):

IQVIA Government Solutions, Inc.　　　　　　　　　　　　**(3)**
8280 Willow Oaks Corporate Dr Ste 775, Fairfax, VA 22031
Tel.: (703) 204-3800
Web Site: http://www.iqvia.com
Professional Advisory Services
N.A.I.C.S.: 561499

Subsidiary (Non-US):

IQVIA Solutions (NZ) Limited　　**(3)**
2A Rothwell Ave, Rosedale, Auckland, 632, New Zealand
Tel.: (64) 94149000
Health Care Srvices
N.A.I.C.S.: 621999

IQVIA Solutions Argentina S.A.　**(3)**
Leandro N Alem 1050 7th Floor, C1001AAS, Buenos Aires, Argentina
Tel.: (54) 1141236700
Web Site: https://www.iqvia.com
Healthcare Software Development Services
N.A.I.C.S.: 541511

IQVIA Solutions Asia Pte. Ltd.　**(3)**
79 Anson Road 19-01, Singapore, 079906, Singapore
Tel.: (65) 69629100
Web Site: https://www.iqvia.com
Health Care Srvices
N.A.I.C.S.: 621999

IQVIA Solutions Bangladesh Limited　　　　　　　　　　　**(3)**
Unique Trade Centre Level 09 M2/SW 8 Panthapath Karwan Bazar, Dhaka, 1215, Bangladesh
Tel.: (880) 1570011
Healthcare Software Development Services
N.A.I.C.S.: 541511

IQVIA Solutions Philippines Inc.　**(3)**
Unit 6A 6th Floor Hidalgo Drive 8 Rockwell Building Rockwell Center, Makati, 1210, Philippines
Tel.: (63) 26836111
Web Site: http://www.iqvia.com
Health Care Srvices
N.A.I.C.S.: 621999

IQVIA Solutions Taiwan Ltd.　　**(3)**
8F no 134 sec 3 Min-sheng East Rd, Taipei, 105, Taiwan
Tel.: (886) 221756500
Web Site: https://www.iqvia.com

Data Processing & Hosting Services
N.A.I.C.S.: 518210

IQVIA Solutions UK Limited (3)
210 Pentonville Road, London, N19JY,
United Kingdom
Tel.: (44) 20 3075 5000
Web Site: http://www.iqvia.com
Media Marketing Services
N.A.I.C.S.: 541890

IQVIA Solutions do Brasil Ltda. (3)
Verbo Divino Street 2001 Tower A 9th Floor,
Chacara Santo Antonio, Sao Paulo, Brazil
Tel.: (55) 1151851500
Web Site: http://www.iqvia.com
Health Care Srvices
N.A.I.C.S.: 621999

**IQVIA Technology and Services
AG** (3)
Kirschgartenstrasse 14, 4051, Basel, Switzerland
Tel.: (41) 612045000
Web Site: http://www.iqvia.com
Health Care Srvices
N.A.I.C.S.: 621999

Subsidiary (Domestic):

ImpactRx, Inc. (3)
550 Blair Mill Rd Ste100, Horsham, PA
19044
Tel.: (215) 444-8700
Web Site: http://www.impactrx.com
Pharmaceutical Promotional Activity Evaluation Services
N.A.I.C.S.: 541910
John Ouren (CEO)

Subsidiary (Domestic):

AlphaDetail, Inc. (4)
777 Mariners Island Blvd, San Mateo, CA
94404
Tel.: (650) 581-3100
Web Site: http://www.alphadetail.com
Management Consulting Services
N.A.I.C.S.: 541613
Rishi Varma (CEO)

Subsidiary (Non-US):

Medical Data Management, Inc. (3)
7 Krasilovskaya St, Kiev, 03040, Ukraine
Tel.: (380) 444960430
Web Site: https://www.mdmworld.com
Web & Mobile Telecommunications & Telemarketing Services
N.A.I.C.S.: 561422

Branch (Domestic):

Quintiles IMS Inc. - Parsippany (3)
Waterview Corporate Ctr 10 Waterview
Blvd, Parsippany, NJ 07054
Tel.: (866) 267-4479
Web Site: http://www.iqvia.com
Pharmaceutical & Health Care Industries
Information Solutions
N.A.I.C.S.: 541690

Subsidiary (Non-US):

Schwarzeck-Verlag GmbH (3)
Einsteinring 24, 85609, Aschheim, Germany
Tel.: (49) 89608040
Web Site: https://www.schwarzeck.de
Healthcare Operational Marketing Services
N.A.I.C.S.: 541613
Arnim Jost (Mng Dir)
Frank Wartenberg (Mng Dir)
Karsten Immel (Mng Dir)

IMS Health Information Solutions India Private Ltd. (1)
902 9th floor B-wing supreme Business
Park Hiranandani Gardens Powai, Mumbai,
400 076, India
Tel.: (91) 2271097200
Biological & Pharmaceutical Development
Services
N.A.I.C.S.: 541714

**IMS Health Pakistan (Private)
Limited** (1)
502-503 5th Floor Business Avenue P E C
H S Block 6, Main Shahrah e-Faisal, Karachi, 75350, Pakistan
Tel.: (92) 2134314650

Biological & Pharmaceutical Development
Services
N.A.I.C.S.: 541714

IMS Health Technology Solutions India Private Ltd. (1)
Omega Embassy TechSquare Marathahalli-
Sarjapur Outer Ring Road, Kadubeesana-
halli, Bengaluru, 560 103, India
Tel.: (91) 8037690000
Biological & Pharmaceutical Development
Services
N.A.I.C.S.: 541714

IQVIA (Thailand) Co. Ltd. (1)
23rd Floor Room No 1-5 Silom Complex
Building 191 Silom Road, Kwaeng Silom
Khet Bangrak, Bangkok, 10500, Thailand
Tel.: (66) 26862300
Health Care Srvices
N.A.I.C.S.: 621999

IQVIA (Thialand) Co. Ltd. (1)
23rd Floor Room No 1-5 Silom Complex
Building, 191 Silom Road Kwaeng Silom
Khet Bangrak, Bangkok, 10500, Thailand
Tel.: (66) 26862300
Biological & Pharmaceutical Development
Services
N.A.I.C.S.: 541714

IQVIA AG (1)
Dorfplatz 4, Cham, 6330, Zug, Switzerland
Tel.: (41) 7856868
Biological & Pharmaceutical Development
Services
N.A.I.C.S.: 541714

IQVIA Biotech LLC (1)
1700 Perimeter Park Dr, Morrisville, NC
27560
Tel.: (919) 484-1921
Web Site: http://www.iqviabiotech.com
Medical Device Distr
N.A.I.C.S.: 423450

Subsidiary (Non-US):

IQVIA Biotech Ltd. (2)
3 Forbury Place 23 Forbury Road,
RG1 3JH, Berkshire, United Kingdom
Tel.: (44) 1438221122
Medical Device Distr
N.A.I.C.S.: 423450
Joanne Hackett (Executives)

**IQVIA Commercial GmbH & Co.
OHG** (1)
Unterschweinstiege 2-14, 60549, Frankfurt
am Main, Germany
Tel.: (49) 6966040
Biological & Pharmaceutical Development
Services
N.A.I.C.S.: 541714

Subsidiary (Domestic):

**IQVIA Commercial Software
GmbH** (2)
Schwertberger Str 14, 53177, Bonn, Germany
Tel.: (49) 2283365100
Web Site: http://www.iqvia.com
Healthcare Software Development Services
N.A.I.C.S.: 541511

IQVIA Commercial Sp. z o.o. (1)
Ul Domaniewska 48, 02-672, Warsaw, Poland
Tel.: (48) 223891000
Biological & Pharmaceutical Development
Services
N.A.I.C.S.: 541714

**IQVIA Commerical Consulting Sp. z
o.o.** (1)
Ul Domaniewska 48, 02-672, Warsaw, Poland
Tel.: (48) 223891000
Biological & Pharmaceutical Development
Services
N.A.I.C.S.: 541714

IQVIA Consulting & Information Services India Private Limited (1)
902 9th Floor B-Wing Supreme Business
Park Hiranandani Gardens Powai, Mumbai,
400 076, India
Tel.: (91) 2271097200

Biological & Pharmaceutical Development
Services
N.A.I.C.S.: 541714

IQVIA Ltd. (1)
3 Forbury Palce 23 Forbury Road, Reading,
RG1 3JH, Berks, United Kingdom
Tel.: (44) 1184508000
Medical Product Sales & Marketing Services
N.A.I.C.S.: 541613

IQVIA Quality Metric Inc. (1)
1301 Atwood Ave Ste 216E, Johnston, RI
02919
Web Site: https://www.qualitymetric.com
Health Care Srvices
N.A.I.C.S.: 621610

**IQVIA RDS (India) Private
Limited** (1)
Omega Embassy TechSquare Marathahalli,
Sarjapur Outer Ring Road Kadubeesana-
halli, Bengaluru, 560 103, India
Tel.: (91) 8037690100
Biological & Pharmaceutical Development
Services
N.A.I.C.S.: 541714

IQVIA RDS AG (1)
Kirschgartenstrasse 14, 4051, Basel, Switzerland
Tel.: (41) 1612708150
Biological & Pharmaceutical Development
Services
N.A.I.C.S.: 541714

IQVIA RDS Estonia OU (1)
Turu Street 2, Tartu, 51014, Estonia
Tel.: (372) 7371150
Biological & Pharmaceutical Development
Services
N.A.I.C.S.: 541714

IQVIA RDS Latvia SIA (1)
G Astras Street 8B, Riga, 1082, Latvia
Tel.: (371) 67146660
Biological & Pharmaceutical Development
Services
N.A.I.C.S.: 541714

IQVIA RDS Slovakia s.r.o. (1)
Polus Tower II Vajnorska 100/B, 831 04,
Bratislava, Slovakia
Tel.: (421) 220515111
Emp.: 500
Biological & Pharmaceutical Development
Services
N.A.I.C.S.: 541714

IQVIA RDS Switzerland sarl (1)
Route de Pallatex 29, 1162, Saint Prex,
Switzerland
Tel.: (41) 213213560
Biological & Pharmaceutical Development
Services
N.A.I.C.S.: 541714

IQVIA RDS d.o.o. Beograd (1)
Business Center Usce 16th floor Bulevar
Mihajla Pupina 6, 11070, Novi Beograd,
Serbia
Tel.: (381) 62275107
Biological & Pharmaceutical Development
Services
N.A.I.C.S.: 541714

IQVIA Romania S.R.L. (1)
1B Menuetului Street, Bucharest, 013713,
Romania
Tel.: (40) 212007072
Emp.: 160
Clinical Research Services
N.A.I.C.S.: 541715

IQVIA Solutions GmbH (1)
Erlenstrasse 4, 6343, Rotkreuz, Switzerland
Tel.: (41) 2086111
Biological & Pharmaceutical Development
Services
N.A.I.C.S.: 541714

**IQVIA Solutions Pakistan (Private)
Limited** (1)
502-503 5th Floor Business Avenue P E C
H S Block-6, Main Shahrah-e-Faisal, Karachi, 75350, Pakistan
Tel.: (92) 2134314650
Health Care Srvices
N.A.I.C.S.: 621999

IQVIA Solutions Philipines, Inc. (1)
Unit 6A 6th Floor Hidalgo Drive 8 Rockwell
Building Rockwell Center, Makati, Philippines
Tel.: (63) 26836111
Biological & Pharmaceutical Development
Services
N.A.I.C.S.: 541714

IQVIA Solutions Philippines, Inc. (1)
Unit 6A 6th Floor Hidalgo Drive 8 Rockwell
Building Rockwell Center, Makati, Philippines
Tel.: (63) 26836111
Biological & Pharmaceutical Development
Services
N.A.I.C.S.: 541714

IQVIA Technology & Services AG (1)
Theaterstrasse 4, 4051, Basel, Switzerland
Tel.: (41) 612045000
Biological & Pharmaceutical Development
Services
N.A.I.C.S.: 541714

ImmunXperts BV (1)
Street Clement Ader 16, 6041, Charleroi,
Belgium
Tel.: (32) 71960133
Pharmaceutical Product Research & Development Services
N.A.I.C.S.: 541714

Incarnus Malaysia Sdn. Bhd. (1)
Unit 301 Level 3 Uptown 1 No 1 Jalan
SS21/58, Damansara Uptown, 47400, Petaling Jaya, Selangor, Malaysia
Tel.: (60) 377350300
Health Care Srvices
N.A.I.C.S.: 621999

Interface Clinical Services Ltd. (1)
Schofield House Gate Way Drive, Yeadon,
Leeds, LS19 7XY, United Kingdom
Tel.: (44) 1132029799
Web Site: https://www.interface-cs.co.uk
Emp.: 100
Clinical Support Services
N.A.I.C.S.: 621498
Michael Drakard (Mng Dir)
Omar Patel (Dir-Clinical)
Jim Mcardle (Comml Dir)
Steve Davis (Dir-Client Svcs)

Jager Health Koln GmbH (1)
Clouth 104 Niehler Str 104, 50733, Cologne, Germany
Tel.: (49) 22165072900
Web Site: https://www.jaeger.health
Health Care Srvices
N.A.I.C.S.: 621999
Andreas Gerads (Sr Dir-Art)

Lasso Marketing, Inc. (1)
7701 N Lamar Blvd Ste 300, Austin, TX
78752
Tel.: (512) 761-7639
Web Site: https://www.lassoplatform.io
Pharmaceutical Products Distr
N.A.I.C.S.: 424210

Linguamatics Limited (1)
324 Cambridge Science Park Milton Road,
Cambridge, CB4 0WG, United Kingdom
Tel.: (44) 122 365 1910
Web Site: https://www.linguamatics.com
Software Development Services
N.A.I.C.S.: 541511
John M. Brimacombe (Sr Dir)
David Milward (Sr Dir-NLP Tech)
Roger Hale (Sr Dir-Operations)
Phil Hastings (Sr Dir-Business Development)
Heather Stewart (Office Mgr-Human Resources)

MTouch SRL (1)
Da Vincilaan 7, 1930, Zaventem, Belgium
Tel.: (32) 26273211
Web Site: https://www.mtouch.be
Event Management Services
N.A.I.C.S.: 711310

MedData Group, LLC (1)
3210 El Camino Real Ste 150, Irvine, CA
92602
Tel.: (978) 887-0039
Web Site: https://www.meddatagroup.com
Marketing Management Services
N.A.I.C.S.: 541810

IQVIA Holdings Inc.—(Continued)

Clare O'Brien *(Dir-Solutions Sls)*
Bob Whiting *(Dir-Bus Dev)*
Danielle Thorne *(Dir-Production Ops)*

Medineos S.r.l. **(1)**
Viale Virgilio 54/U, 41123, Modena, Italy
Tel.: (39) 059 886 0134
Web Site: www.medineos.com
Medical Research Services
N.A.I.C.S.: 541713

Medpages International Proprietary Limited **(1)**
2nd Floor 50 Riebeek Street, Cape Town, 8001, Western Cape, South Africa
Tel.: (27) 214419700
Web Site: https://www.medpages.info
Software Development Services
N.A.I.C.S.: 541511

Metrika Business Intelligence Consulting, Inc. **(1)**
8-1457 Laurier East, Montreal, H2J 1H8, QC, Canada
Tel.: (514) 807-2150
Web Site: https://www.metrikagroup.com
Business Consulting Services
N.A.I.C.S.: 541611

Novasyte, LLC **(1)**
5999 Avenida Encinas Ste 100, Carlsbad, CA 92008
Web Site: https://novasyte.com
Medical Device Mfr
N.A.I.C.S.: 339112

Onkodatamed GmBH **(1)**
Friedenstrasse 58, Neuenhagen, 15366, Berlin, Germany
Tel.: (49) 33424268910
Web Site: http://www.onkodatamed.de
Physical & Biological Research Services
N.A.I.C.S.: 541713

Open Applications Consulting Limited **(1)**
Avoca House 189-193 Parnell Street, Dublin, D01 H578, Ireland
Tel.: (353) 18729331
Web Site: https://www.openapp.ie
Software Development Services
N.A.I.C.S.: 541511

Optimum Contact Limited **(1)**
166 Northwood Way Northwood, Northwood, HA6 1RB, Middlesex, United Kingdom
Tel.: (44) 1249554232
Web Site: http://www.optimumcontact.com
Health Care Srvices
N.A.I.C.S.: 621999
Chris Williams *(CFO)*
Gary Smith *(Dir-IT)*
Alistair Rowley *(Dir-Sls)*

Outcome Sciences, LLC **(1)**
201 Broadway 5th Fl, Cambridge, MA 02139
Tel.: (617) 621-1600
Healthcare Research Services
N.A.I.C.S.: 541714

PharmaReview Limited **(1)**
U6 / Building 7 Chiswick Park, London, W4 5YG, United Kingdom
Tel.: (44) 2081238474
Web Site: https://pharmareview.com
Emp.: 60
Pharmaceutical Product Research & Development Services
N.A.I.C.S.: 541714

Privacy Analytics Inc. **(1)**
251 Laurier Avenue W Suite 1000, Ottawa, K1P 5J6, ON, Canada
Tel.: (613) 369-4313
Web Site: https://www.privacy-analytics.com
Health Care Srvices
N.A.I.C.S.: 621999
Andrew Baker *(Sr Engr-Res)*

Q Squared Solutions (Beijing) Co. Ltd. **(1)**
Unit 302 Building 15 No 8 Liangshuihe 2nd Street, Hans Enterprise Bay BDA, Beijing, 100176, China
Tel.: (86) 1087835000
Laboratory Services
N.A.I.C.S.: 621511

Q Squared Solutions (Shanghai) Co. Ltd. **(1)**
5F Building A Fenglin International Tower 388 Fenglin Road, Xuhui District, Shanghai, 200032, China
Tel.: (86) 2124228886
Laboratory Services
N.A.I.C.S.: 621511

Q Squared Solutions Expression Analysis LLC **(1)**
2400 Ellis dir, Durham, NC 27703
Tel.: (919) 998-7000
Web Site: http://www.q2labsolutions.com
Biotechnology Research & Development Services
N.A.I.C.S.: 541714
Annette Balog *(Chief Comml Officer)*
Tony Brown *(VP & Gen Mgr-Global Central Labs)*
Patrice Hugo *(Chief Scientific Officer)*
Caroline Keane *(Sr VP-Project Svcs)*
Brian O'Dwyer *(CEO)*
Simon Thornley *(VP-Quality & Compliance)*
Jenny Zhang *(VP & Gen Mgr-Asia Pacific Ops)*
Kevin Dooley *(Chief HR Officer)*
Kevin Jones *(VP & Gen Mgr-Bioanalytical, ADME & Vaccines Svcs)*
Darlene Godsey *(Dir-Bus Ops)*
Mike Hamill *(VP-IT)*
Jian Wang *(VP & Head-Digital Innovation)*
Todd Regelsberger *(CFO)*
Ralph L. McDade *(VP)*
Chuck Drucker *(VP)*
David Kaye *(VP)*

Q Squared Solutions K.K. **(1)**
Telecom Center Building 2-5-10 Aomi, Koto-ku, Tokyo, 135-0064, Japan
Tel.: (81) 368599620
Laboratory Services
N.A.I.C.S.: 621511

Q Squared Solutions Limited **(1)**
The Alba Campus Rosebank, West Lothian, Livingston, EH54 7EG, United Kingdom
Tel.: (44) 1506814000
Web Site: https://www.q2labsolutions.com
Laboratory Services
N.A.I.C.S.: 621511

Q Squared Solutions Pte. Ltd. **(1)**
438B Alexandra Road 07-01/04, Alexandra Technopark, Singapore, 119968, Singapore
Tel.: (65) 66021002
Laboratory Services
N.A.I.C.S.: 621511

Quality Health Limited **(1)**
Unit 1 Holmewood Business Park Chesterfield Road, Holmewood, Chesterfield, S42 5US, Derbyshire, United Kingdom
Tel.: (44) 1246856263
Web Site: http://www.quality-health.co.uk
Health Care Consulting Services
N.A.I.C.S.: 541611

Quintiles Transnational Corp. **(1)**
4820 Emperor Blvd, Durham, NC 27703
Tel.: (919) 998-2000
Web Site: http://www.iqvia.com
Research, Sales, Marketing, Healthcare Policy Consulting & Information Management Services to Pharmaceutical, Biotechnology, Medical Device & Healthcare Industries
N.A.I.C.S.: 541714

Subsidiary (Non-US):

IQVIA Nederland **(2)**
Herikerbergweg 314, 1101 CT, Amsterdam, Netherlands
Tel.: (31) 235670910
Web Site: https://www.iqvia.com
Health Care Srvices
N.A.I.C.S.: 621498

IQVIA RDS AG **(2)**
Kirschgartenstr 14, 4051, Basel, Switzerland
Tel.: (41) 612708150
Web Site: http://www.iqvia.com
Clinical Research Services
N.A.I.C.S.: 541715

IQVIA RDS East Asia Pte Ltd. **(2)**
79 Science Park Dr, Singapore, 118264, Singapore

Tel.: (65) 66021000
Web Site: http://www.iqvia.com
Medical Laboratory Operator
N.A.I.C.S.: 621511

IQVIA RDS Eastern Holdings GmBH **(2)**
Stella-klein-low-weg 15 Haus B 5 Stock, Vienna, 1020, Austria
Tel.: (43) 17263010
Web Site: http://www.iqvia.com
Pharmaceutical Products Distr
N.A.I.C.S.: 424210

IQVIA RDS Estonia OU **(2)**
Turu 2, 51014, Tartu, Estonia
Tel.: (372) 7371150
Clinical Research Services
N.A.I.C.S.: 541715

IQVIA RDS France SAS **(2)**
151-161 Blvd Victor Hugo, 93400, Saint-Ouen, France
Tel.: (33) 0141277272
Clinical Research Services
N.A.I.C.S.: 541715

IQVIA RDS Ges.m.b.H **(2)**
Stella klein loew weg, 1030, Vienna, Austria
Tel.: (43) 172630100
Clinical Research Services
N.A.I.C.S.: 541715

IQVIA RDS Ireland Limited **(2)**
Estuary House East Point Business Park, Dublin, 3, Ireland
Tel.: (353) 18195100
Clinical Research Services
N.A.I.C.S.: 541715

IQVIA RDS Magyarorszag Gyogyszerfejlesztesi es Tanacsado Kft. **(2)**
Dombovari ut 9, Alphagon Office Building 5 floor, 1117, Budapest, Hungary
Tel.: (36) 18839700
Web Site: http://www.iqvia.com
Clinical Research Services
N.A.I.C.S.: 541715

IQVIA RDS Pty. Limited **(2)**
Unit A 2 Rothwell Avenue Rosedale, Auckland, 0632, New Zealand
Tel.: (64) 94406200
Web Site: http://www.iqvia.com
Clinical Research Services
N.A.I.C.S.: 541715

IQVIA RDS UK Holdings Limited **(2)**
3 Forbury Place 23 Forbury Road, Reading, RG1 3JH, Berkshire, United Kingdom
Tel.: (44) 1184508000
Web Site: http://www.iqvia.com
Pharmaceutical Products Distr
N.A.I.C.S.: 424210

IQVIA RDS and Integrated Services Belgium NV **(2)**
Corporate Village Davos Building Da Vinci-laan 7, 1930, Zaventem, Belgium
Tel.: (32) 26273211
Web Site: https://www.iqvia.com
Clinical Research Services
N.A.I.C.S.: 541715

IQVIA Technology Solutions Ukraine LLC **(2)**
12 Amosova str, 03038, Kiev, Ukraine
Tel.: (380) 444903738
Web Site: http://www.iqvia.com
Clinical Research Services
N.A.I.C.S.: 541715

Quintiles B.V. **(2)**
Herikerbergweg 314, 1101 CT, Amsterdam, Netherlands
Tel.: (31) 235670910
Web Site: http://www.iqvia.com
Clinical Research Services
N.A.I.C.S.: 541715

Quintiles Enterprise Management (Shanghai) Co. Ltd. **(2)**
3F 5F Building A Fenglin International Tower 388 Fenglin Road, Xuhui District, Shanghai, 200032, China
Tel.: (86) 2124228888
Web Site: http://www.iqvia.com
Pharmaceutical Products Distr
N.A.I.C.S.: 424210

Quintiles Hong Kong Limited **(2)**

Unit 2212-2219 Level 22 Metroplaza Tower 1 223 Hing Fong Road, Kwai Fong, New Territories, China (Hong Kong)
Tel.: (852) 28309200
Web Site: https://www.iqvia.com
Pharmaceutical Products Distr
N.A.I.C.S.: 424210

Quintiles Israel Ltd. **(2)**
3 HaMachshev St Poleg Industrial Park, PO Box 8567, Netanya, 4250713, Israel
Tel.: (972) 98645645
Web Site: http://www.iqvia.com
Contract Pharmaceutical Services
N.A.I.C.S.: 541715

Quintiles Lithuania **(2)**
Savanoriu pr 349, LT-49425, Kaunas, Lithuania
Tel.: (370) 37306500
Web Site: http://www.iqvia.com
Sales Range: $25-49.9 Million
Emp.: 40
Clinical Research Services
N.A.I.C.S.: 541715

Quintiles Russia LLC **(2)**
Leningradskiy Prospekt 37A Bldg.14, Floor 4, Moscow, 125167, Russia
Tel.: (7) 4957211964
Web Site: http://www.iqvia.com
Sales Range: $75-99.9 Million
Emp.: 300
Clinical Research Services
N.A.I.C.S.: 541715

STI Technologies Limited **(1)**
38 Solutions Drive Suite 200, Halifax, B3S 0H1, NS, Canada
Web Site: https://www.smartsti.com
Health Care Insurance Services
N.A.I.C.S.: 524130

Silverbullet A/S **(1)**
Soren Frichs Vej 42F 1 tv, Abyhoj, 8230, Aarhus, Denmark
Tel.: (45) 20606701
Web Site: https://silverbullet.io
Information Technology Consulting Services
N.A.I.C.S.: 541512

Smart I.T. Systems BV **(1)**
Turnhoutsebaan 570, 2110, Wijnegem, Belgium
Tel.: (32) 33552979
Web Site: https://www.smartit.be
Medical Software Development Services
N.A.I.C.S.: 541511

Strategique Sante **(1)**
Carre Haussmann Evry 52 Boulevard de Yerres, 91000, Evry, France
Tel.: (33) 160871483
Web Site: http://www.strategique-sante.fr
Consulting & Training Services
N.A.I.C.S.: 541613
Sandrine Bourguignon *(Founder)*

VCG&A, Inc. **(1)**
137 Hill St, Holliston, MA 01746
Tel.: (781) 964-4864
Web Site: http://www.iqvia.com
Pharmaceuticals Product Mfr
N.A.I.C.S.: 325412

Vivacity Health Pty. Ltd. **(1)**
8/201 Pacific Highway, Saint Leonards, 2065, NSW, Australia
Tel.: (61) 28 404 4951
Web Site: https://www.vivacityhealth.com.au
Digital Marketing Services
N.A.I.C.S.: 541613

genae Americas, Inc. **(1)**
10000 Cedar Ave, Cleveland, OH 44106
Tel.: (216) 255-5005
Web Site: http://www.genae.com
Health Care Srvices
N.A.I.C.S.: 621999
Jorn O. Balzer *(CMO)*
Peter Bossier *(CTO)*
Wouter Tack *(COO)*
Aly Talen *(Co-Founder)*

genae Associates NV **(1)**
Justitiestraat 6B, 2018, Antwerp, Belgium
Tel.: (32) 32900306
Health Care Srvices
N.A.I.C.S.: 621999
Julie Bosiers *(Dir-Bus Dev)*

gradient.SystemIntegration
GmbH **(1)**
Weiherstrasse 10, 78224, Singen, Germany
Tel.: (49) 773 179 7720
Web Site: https://www.gradient.de
Emp.: 50
Software Development Services
N.A.I.C.S.: 541511

IR BIOSCIENCES HOLDINGS, INC.

8777 E Via de Ventura, Scottsdale,
AZ 85258
Tel.: (480) 922-3926 **DE**
IRBS—(OTCIQ)
Holding Company
N.A.I.C.S.: 551112
Micheal K. Wilhelm *(Pres & CEO)*
John A. Fermanis *(CFO)*

IRADIMED CORPORATION

1025 Willa Springs Dr, Winter
Springs, FL 32708
Tel.: (407) 677-8022 **DE**
Web Site: https://www.iradimed.com
Year Founded: 1992
IRMD—(NASDAQ)
Rev.: $53,303,145
Assets: $85,513,747
Liabilities: $11,840,760
Net Worth: $73,672,987
Earnings: $12,828,487
Emp.: 123
Fiscal Year-end: 12/31/22
Electromedical & Electrotherapeutic
Apparatus Manufacturing
N.A.I.C.S.: 334510
Roger Susi *(Founder, Chm, Chm, Pres & CEO)*
Steven Kachelmeyer *(VP-Regulatory Affairs & Quality Assurance)*
Lynn Neuhardt *(VP-R&D)*
Randy Waddell *(VP)*

IRELAND INC.

2360 W Horizon Ridge Pkwy Ste
100, Henderson, NV 89052
Tel.: (702) 932-0353 **NV**
Web Site: http://irelandminerals.com
Year Founded: 2001
IRLD—(OTCIQ)
Sales Range: Less than $1 Million
Emp.: 7
Gold, Silver & Tungsten Exploration &
Mining
N.A.I.C.S.: 212220
Douglas D.G. Birnie *(Pres, CEO & Sec)*
David Z. Strickler Jr. *(CFO & COO)*

IRHYTHM TECHNOLOGIES, INC.

699 8th St Ste 600, San Francisco,
CA 94103
Tel.: (415) 632-5700
Web Site:
https://www.irhythmtech.com
Year Founded: 2006
IRTC—(NASDAQ)
Rev.: $492,681,000
Assets: $433,144,000
Liabilities: $223,047,000
Net Worth: $210,097,000
Earnings: ($123,406,000)
Emp.: 2,000
Fiscal Year-end: 12/31/23
Health Care Information Services
N.A.I.C.S.: 518210
Marc Rosenbaum *(Chief Acctg Officer)*
Quentin S. Blackford *(Pres & CEO)*
Reyna Fernandez *(Chief HR Officer & Exec VP)*
Chad Patterson *(Chief Comml Officer)*
Sumi Shrishrimal *(Chief Risk Officer)*
Daniel G. Wilson *(CFO)*

Subsidiaries:

iRhythm Technologies Limited **(1)**
Seal House 56 London Road, Bagshot,
GU19 5HL, Surrey, United Kingdom
Tel.: (44) 8081893411
Web Site: https://irhythmtech.co.uk
Medical Healthcare Services
N.A.I.C.S.: 621910

IRIDEX CORPORATION

1212 Terra Bella Ave, Mountain View,
CA 94043
Tel.: (650) 940-4700 **DE**
Web Site: https://www.iridex.com
Year Founded: 1989
IRIX—(NASDAQ)
Rev.: $53,903,000
Assets: $48,687,000
Liabilities: $25,388,000
Net Worth: $23,299,000
Earnings: ($5,225,000)
Emp.: 119
Fiscal Year-end: 01/01/22
Semiconductor-Based Laser Systems
for Ophthalmology, Dermatology &
Research
N.A.I.C.S.: 334510
Scott A. Shuda *(Co-Chm)*
David I. Bruce *(Pres & CEO)*
Robert A. Gunst *(Co-Chm)*
Patrick Mercer *(COO)*

Subsidiaries:

IRIDEX S.A. **(1)**
17 Rue du Bel Air, Lisses, 91090, France
Tel.: (33) 160862049
Web Site: http://www.cutera.com
Sales Range: $1-9.9 Million
Emp.: 6
Laser Systems for Ophthalmology, Dermatology & Research
N.A.I.C.S.: 339112

IRIDIUM COMMUNICATIONS INC.

1750 Tysons Blvd Ste 1400, McLean,
VA 22102
Tel.: (703) 287-7400 **DE**
Web Site: https://www.iridium.com
Year Founded: 2007
IRDM—(NASDAQ)
Rev.: $790,723,000
Assets: $2,661,775,000
Liabilities: $1,773,676,000
Net Worth: $888,099,000
Earnings: $15,415,000
Emp.: 760
Fiscal Year-end: 12/31/23
Satellite Communication Services
N.A.I.C.S.: 517410
Thomas D. Hickey *(Chief Legal Officer & Sec)*
Matthew J. Desch *(CEO)*
Scott T. Scheimreif *(Exec VP-Govt Programs)*
Timothy Kapalka *(VP & Controller-Iridium Satellite LLC)*
Suzanne E. McBride *(COO)*
Kathleen A. Morgan *(Chief Legal Officer)*
Vincent O'Neill *(CFO)*

Subsidiaries:

Aireon LLC **(1)**
8484 Westpark Dr Ste 300, McLean, VA
22102
Tel.: (571) 401-1500
Web Site: https://www.aireon.com
Surveillance System & Equipment Mfr
N.A.I.C.S.: 334511
Don Thoma *(CEO)*
Marc Courtois *(Chm)*
Vincent Capezzuto *(CTO & VP-Engrg)*
Cyriel Kronenburg *(VP)*
Rich Nyren *(CFO)*
Peter Cabooter *(VP-Customer Affairs)*

Iridium Government Services
LLC **(1)**

8440 S River Pkwy, Tempe, AZ 85284
Tel.: (480) 752-1100
Web Site: http://www.iridium.com
Sales Range: $25-49.9 Million
Emp.: 100
Satellite Operations
N.A.I.C.S.: 517410
Matthew J. Desch *(CEO)*

Iridium Satellite LLC **(1)**
1750 Tysons Blvd Ste 1400, McLean, VA
22102
Tel.: (703) 287-7400
Web Site: https://www.iridium.com
Sales Range: $25-49.9 Million
Communication Service
N.A.I.C.S.: 517810
Vincent O'Neill *(Sr VP-Fin)*

OOO Iridium Communications **(1)**
St Skladochnaya House 1 Building 18 Entrance 3 2nd Floor Office 208, 127018,
Moscow, Russia
Tel.: (7) 4952219379
Web Site: https://www.iridium-russia.com
Iridium Refining Services
N.A.I.C.S.: 331410

IRIDIUM WORLD COMMUNICATIONS LTD.

1750 Tysons Blvd Ste 1400, McLean,
VA 22102
Tel.: (703) 287-7400
Web Site: https://www.iridium.com
IRIDQ—(NASDAQ)
Rev.: $560,444,000
Assets: $3,623,557,000
Liabilities: $2,164,275,000
Net Worth: $1,459,282,000
Earnings: ($166,193,000)
Emp.: 497
Fiscal Year-end: 12/31/19
Wireless Telecommunications Carriers (except Satellite)
N.A.I.C.S.: 517112
Matthew J. Desch *(CEO)*

IROBOT CORP.

8 Crosby Dr, Bedford, MA 01730
Tel.: (781) 430-3000 **DE**
Web Site: https://www.irobot.com
Year Founded: 1990
IRBT—(NASDAQ)
Rev.: $1,564,987,000
Assets: $1,184,429,000
Liabilities: $467,706,000
Net Worth: $716,723,000
Earnings: $30,390,000
Emp.: 1,372
Fiscal Year-end: 01/01/22
Household & Military Robot Mfr
N.A.I.C.S.: 333310
Jeffrey Engel *(COO)*
Julie Zeiler *(CFO & Exec VP)*
Tonya Drake *(Gen Counsel & Exec VP)*
Barry Schliesmann *(Chief Product Officer)*
Gary S. Cohen *(Pres & CEO)*

Subsidiaries:

iRobot (HK) Limited **(1)**
06 11/F Exchange Tower 33 Wang Chiu
Road, Kowloon Bay, Kowloon, China (Hong
Kong) **(100%)**
Tel.: (852) 35863671
Web Site: http://www.irobot.com
Sales Range: $125-149.9 Million
Emp.: 500
Mfr of Industrial & Household Robots
N.A.I.C.S.: 333248

iRobot (India) Private Limited **(1)**
#2940 I D8 3rd Floor Temple Road V V
Puram, Mysore, 570 002, India **(100%)**
Tel.: (91) 8214004100
Web Site: http://www.irobot.com
Sales Range: $25-49.9 Million
Emp.: 40
Mfr & Distr of Industrial & Household Robots
N.A.I.C.S.: 333248

iRobot (Shanghai) Ltd. **(1)**
No 288 South Shaanxi Road Suite 2814-16
Two ICC, Xuhui District, Shanghai, 200031,
China
Tel.: (86) 2160918258
Computer & Electronic Mfr
N.A.I.C.S.: 334111

iRobot - UK **(1)**
111 Buckingham Palace Road, London,
SW1W 0SR, United Kingdom **(100%)**
Tel.: (44) 1414030566
Web Site: https://support.irobot.co.uk
Sales Range: $125-149.9 Million
Mfr & Distr of Industrial & Household Robots
N.A.I.C.S.: 333248

iRobot Austria GmbH **(1)**
EURO PLAZA AM Euro Platz Geb G, 1120,
Vienna, Austria
Tel.: (43) 720116671
Web Site: https://www.irobot.at
Household Robot Distr
N.A.I.C.S.: 423620

iRobot italia S.r.l. **(1)**
Via Victims of Piazza Fontana n 54, 10024,
Moncalieri, TO, Italy
Tel.: (39) 0110888345
Web Site: https://www.irobot.it
Mobile Accessory Distr
N.A.I.C.S.: 449210

IRON MOUNTAIN INCORPORATED

85 New Hampshire Ave Ste 150,
Portsmouth, NH 03801
Tel.: (617) 535-4766 **DE**
Web Site:
https://www.ironmountain.com
Year Founded: 1951
IRM—(NYSE)
Rev.: $5,480,289,000
Assets: $17,473,802,000
Liabilities: $17,262,029,000
Net Worth: $211,773,000
Earnings: $184,234,000
Emp.: 27,000
Fiscal Year-end: 12/31/23
Real Estate Investment Trust; Records Management, Data Protection
& Information Destruction Solutions &
Services
N.A.I.C.S.: 525990
Barry A. Hytinen *(CFO & Exec VP)*
Raymond C. Fox *(Chief Risk Officer & Exec VP)*
Mark Kidd *(Exec VP & Gen Mgr-Asset Lifecycle Mgmt)*
William L. Meaney *(Pres & CEO)*
Greg Mcintosh *(Chief Comml Officer & Exec VP)*
Edward E. Greene *(Chief HR Officer & Exec VP)*
Mithu Bhargava *(Exec VP & Gen Mgr-Digital Solutions)*

Subsidiaries:

AB Archyvu Sistemos **(1)**
Vaike-Sojamae Tn 3G, Harju Maakond,
11415, Tallinn, Estonia
Tel.: (372) 6034050
Document Storage Services
N.A.I.C.S.: 493190

AB Archyvu Sistemos **(1)**
Zirgu str 3, Gineitiskes, Vilnius, 14159,
Lithuania
Tel.: (370) 52319484
Web Site: http://www.archyvusistemos.lt
Document Storage Services
N.A.I.C.S.: 493190

AB Archyvu Sistemos **(1)**
Zirgu g 3, Gineitiskes, LT-14159, Vilnius,
Lithuania
Tel.: (370) 52319484
Web Site: http://www.archyvusistemos.lt
Document Storage Services

Iron Mountain Incorporated—(Continued)
N.A.I.C.S.: 493190

AS Archivu Serviss (1)
Ganibu Dambis 7a, Riga, 1045, Latvia
Tel.: (371) 67245640
Web Site: http://www.arhivuserviss.lv
Data Storage & Information Management
Services
N.A.I.C.S.: 518210

AS Iron Mountain Latvia AS (1)
Ganibu Dam 7a, Riga, 1045, Latvia
Tel.: (371) 28369359
Information Technology Services
N.A.I.C.S.: 541519

Archivex S.A. (1)
Rue Madadan Ex Rue L Quartier Industriel
Est, Hay Sidi Bernossi, 20590, Casablanca,
Morocco
Tel.: (212) 52266458990
Information Management Services
N.A.I.C.S.: 541511

Bonded Services (International)
B.V. (1)
Tokyostraat 13 - 15, Lijnden, 1175 RB, Am-
sterdam, Netherlands
Tel.: (31) 206015031
Web Site: http://www.bonded.nl
Document Storage Services
N.A.I.C.S.: 493190

Bonded Services International
Limited (1)
Rm 7-8 11/F Block B Tung Chun Industrial
Bldg, 11-13 Tai Yuen Street, Kwai Chung,
New Territories, China (Hong Kong)
Tel.: (852) 24256036
Data Storage & Information Management
Services
N.A.I.C.S.: 518210

Bonded Services Limited (1)
5 Space Waye, Feltham, TW14 0TH,
Middlesex, United Kingdom
Tel.: (44) 2034055560
Data Storage & Information Management
Services
N.A.I.C.S.: 518210

Capital Vision SAS (1)
3 rue de Messine, 75008, Paris, France
Tel.: (33) 143796800
Web Site: http://www.capitalvision.fr
Audiovisual Services
N.A.I.C.S.: 512191

Crozier Fine Arts Limited (1)
5 Glasshouse Walk, London, SE11 5ES,
United Kingdom
Tel.: (44) 2077350566
Web Site: https://www.crozierfinearts.com
Storage Facility & Warehouse Services
N.A.I.C.S.: 493110

Crozier Fine Arts, Inc. (1)
525 W 20th St, New York, NY 10011-2831
Tel.: (212) 741-2024
Web Site: http://www.crozierarts.com
Logistic Consulting Services for Art
N.A.I.C.S.: 541614
Simon Hornby (Pres)
Tom Hale (Sr VP & Gen Mgr-North
America)
Jamez Basora (Dir-Artist Projects & Exhibi-
tions)
Nicole Bouchard (Dir-Tech)
Joseph Carlucci (Chief Comml Officer &
VP)
Rachel Stein Dickinson (COO & VP)
Lauren Gentile (Dir-Client Accounts)
James Pantoleon (Dir-Engrg & Design)
Chuck Agro (Dir-Special Projects)
Jeff Colburn (Dir-Crating & Packing)
Andrew Deock (Dir-Storage & Inventory)
Joseph Hale (Dir-Transportation & Logistics)
Johan Kritzinger (Dir-Project Mgmt)
Ilana Skolnick (Dir-Bus Dev)

Crozier Schweiz AG (1)
Steinackerstrasse 47, 8302, Kloten, Swit-
zerland
Tel.: (41) 434889999
Logistic Services
N.A.I.C.S.: 488510

DBJ Limited (1)
Haut Bois La Grande Route de St Laurent,

Saint Lawrence, JE3 1NN, Jersey
Tel.: (44) 1534483311
Web Site: https://www.dbj.co.je
Outsourced Record Management Services
N.A.I.C.S.: 541611

DOCUGROUP PAPIR Szolgaltato
Korlatolt Felelossegu Tarsasag (1)
Jozsef Attila u 57-59, 9151, Gyor, Hungary
Tel.: (36) 96410688
Web Site: http://www.docugroup.hu
Data Management Services
N.A.I.C.S.: 541513

Data Outsourcing Centre doo (1)
Prva Industrijska 11, 22330, Nova Pazova,
Serbia
Tel.: (381) 22326327
Web Site: https://www.data-outsourcing-
centre.com
Data Storage & Information Management
Services
N.A.I.C.S.: 518210

Disaster Recovery Services
Limited (1)
PO Box 256, Manchester, M24 0BL, United
Kingdom
Tel.: (44) 1706362000
Web Site:
http://www.securemediastorage.co.uk
Data Storage & Information Management
Services
N.A.I.C.S.: 518210

Fontis International, Inc. (1)
200 Quebec St Bldg 300 Ste 111, Denver,
CO 80230
Tel.: (719) 694-2480
Web Site: https://notifications.igpolicy.net
Information Management Services
N.A.I.C.S.: 519290
Steven Formica (Pres & CEO)

Hamilton Data Services EOOD (1)
4 Adama Mitckevich Str, 1360, Sofia, Bul-
garia
Tel.: (359) 28321100
Data Storage & Information Management
Services
N.A.I.C.S.: 518210

IM Mortgage Solutions, LLC (1)
4020 Fee Fee Rd, Bridgeton, MO 63044
Tel.: (314) 264-5325
Financial Loan Services
N.A.I.C.S.: 522390
Stacey Whyte (Ops Mgr-Mortgage)
Stacey Ash (Officer-Comp)
Chris Smith (Mgr-Mortgage Sls & Bus Dev)
Gregg Merkel (Officer-Mortgage Loan)

IM Tape Storage Oy (1)
Kuuoillantie 27, 01200, Vantaa, Finland
Tel.: (358) 98256020
Web Site: http://www.ironmountain.fi
Data Storage & Information Management
Services
N.A.I.C.S.: 518210

ITRenew, Inc. (1)
7575 Gateway Blvd, Newark, CA
94560 (80%)
Tel.: (408) 744-9600
Web Site: http://www.itrenew.com
IT Lifecycle Management Solutions
N.A.I.C.S.: 513210
Aidin Aghamiri (CEO)
Charlie Leeming (Pres-Sesame)
Erik Riedel (Sr VP-Compute & Storage So-
lutions)
Bill Vasquez (Sr VP-Strategy & Bus Dev)
Andrew Perlmutter (Chief Strategy Officer)
Rhonda Walker (CMO)
Brandon Manley (COO)
Ali Fenn (Pres)
Colin Fisher (CFO)
Kate Lechner (VP-Strategic Partnerships)
Shivani Puri (VP-HR)
Kien Duong (Controller)
Chris Henderson (Sr VP-Engrg & Tech)

InfoFort Bahrain CO.WLL (1)
Avenue 19 Bahrain International Investment
Park, Block 115 Road 13 Building 11 Hidd,
Manama, Bahrain
Tel.: (973) 17467536
Data Processing Services
N.A.I.C.S.: 518210

InfoFort Egypt S.A.E. (1)

Giza Governorate Egypt Infofort g2 b Engi-
neering Square, E Square IDG Developers
Area, Cairo, Egypt
Tel.: (20) 216915
Data Processing Services
N.A.I.C.S.: 518210

InfoFort Muscat SPC (1)
Ghala Industrial Area Infofort, Al Hooqani
Warehouse, Muscat, Oman
Tel.: (968) 24503392
Data Processing Services
N.A.I.C.S.: 518210

Iron Mountain (India) Pvt Ltd. (1)
Plot-36 Gandhinagar C I E Extn Balanagar
IDPL Cross Road, Hyderabad, 500 037,
India
Tel.: (91) 4064578009
Web Site: http://www.ironmountain.com
Sales Range: $900-999.9 Million
Emp.: 75
Records Management, Data Protection &
Information Destruction Solutions & Ser-
vices
N.A.I.C.S.: 541519

Iron Mountain (Ireland) Services
Limited (1)
Damastown Rise Damastown Industrial Es-
tate Damastown, Dublin, Ireland
Tel.: (353) 1800732673
Data Storage & Management Services
N.A.I.C.S.: 518210

Iron Mountain (Thailand) Limited (1)
69 Village No 2 Soi Wat Nam Daeng Srina-
karin Road, Bang Kaeo Subdistrict, Bang
Phli, 10540, Samut Prakan, Thailand
Tel.: (66) 24073333
Information Management Services
N.A.I.C.S.: 541511

Iron Mountain Assurance
Corporation (1)
565 Sinclair Frontage Rd, Milpitas, CA
95035
Tel.: (408) 945-1600
Emp.: 100
Direct Mail Advertising Services
N.A.I.C.S.: 541860

Iron Mountain Australia Group Pty.
Ltd. (1)
Level 2 170-180 Bourke Rd, Alexandria,
2015, NSW, Australia
Tel.: (61) 296779315
Web Site: http://www.ironmtn.com.au
Information & Document Management Ser-
vices
N.A.I.C.S.: 519290

Subsidiary (Domestic):

Iron Mountain Australia Pty. Ltd. (2)
Level 4 973 Nepean Highway, Melbourne,
3204, VIC, Australia
Tel.: (61) 397971400
Web Site: https://www.zircodata.com.au
Sales Range: $900-999.9 Million
Emp.: 260
Records Management, Data Protection &
Information Destruction Solutions & Ser-
vices
N.A.I.C.S.: 541519

Subsidiary (Domestic):

Iron Mountain Australia Services Pty
Ltd (3)
L 1 785 Toorak Rd, Hawthorn East, 3123,
VIC, Australia
Tel.: (61) 397971400
Emp.: 20
Information Management Services
N.A.I.C.S.: 519290

Iron Mountain Bahrain Co., Ltd. (1)
Avenue 19 Bahrain International Investment
Park Block 115 Road, 13 Building 11 Hidd,
Manama, Bahrain
Tel.: (973) 17467536
Web Site: https://www.ironmountain.com
Information Technology Services
N.A.I.C.S.: 541511

Iron Mountain Bulgaria (1)
4 Adam Mitskevich Str, 1360, Sofia, Bulgaria
Tel.: (359) 28321100

Web Site: https://www.ironmountain.com
Data Management Services
N.A.I.C.S.: 518210
William Meaney (Pres)
Mithu Bhargava (Exec VP)
Edward E. Greene (Chief HR Officer)
Barry A. Hytinen (CFO)
Mark Kidd (Exec VP)
Deborah Marson (Gen Counsel)
Greg McIntosh (Exec VP)
John Tomovcsik (COO)

Iron Mountain Canada
Corporation (1)
195 Summerlea Rd, Brampton, L6T 4T6,
ON, Canada
Tel.: (905) 792-7099
Web Site: http://www.ironmountain.ca
Sales Range: $900-999.9 Million
Emp.: 1,300
Records Management, Data Protection &
Information Destruction Solutions & Ser-
vices
N.A.I.C.S.: 541519

Subsidiary (Domestic):

Iron Mountain Canada Operations
ULC (2)
195 Summerlea Road, Brampton, L6T 4P6,
ON, Canada
Web Site: https://www.ironmountain.ca
Document Storage & Information Manage-
ment Services
N.A.I.C.S.: 493190

Iron Mountain Colombia, S.A.S. (1)
Calle 11 No 32-47 Conjunto de Bodegas
Arroyohondo Bod 5, Cali, Colombia
Tel.: (57) 24899544
Web Site: http://www.ironmountain.com.co
Information Management Services
N.A.I.C.S.: 519290

Iron Mountain Cyprus Limited (1)
PO Box 16237, 2087, Nicosia, Cyprus
Tel.: (357) 77778666
Web Site: https://www.ironmountain.com
Data Storage & Information Management
Services
N.A.I.C.S.: 518210

Iron Mountain Data Management
(Beijing) Co., Ltd. (1)
Rm 912 Block 2 Kylin Zone No 2 Wangjing
Street, Chaoyang District, Beijing, China
Tel.: (86) 1057389051
Data Management Solution Services
N.A.I.C.S.: 518210

Iron Mountain Data Management
Consulting (Beijing) Co., Ltd. (1)
Rm 912 Block 2 Kylin Zone No 2 Wangjing
Street, Chaoyang District, Beijing, China
Tel.: (86) 61057389051
Information Management Services
N.A.I.C.S.: 541511

Iron Mountain Europe Limited (1)
Ground Floor 4 More London Riverside,
London, SE1 2AU, United Kingdom
Tel.: (44) 2079391500
Holding Company; Regional Managing Of-
fice; Records Management, Data Protection
& Information Destruction Solutions & Ser-
vices
N.A.I.C.S.: 551112

Subsidiary (Non-US):

A.L.C.Z a s (2)
Mezi Uvozy 2000/0 Praha 9, Horni Poceri-
nice, Prague, 193 00, Czech Republic
Tel.: (420) 777252903
Web Site: http://www.alcz.cz
Document Storage & Information Manage-
ment Services
N.A.I.C.S.: 493190

Archivages et Services (2)
4/6 Rue Dauphine, 76600, Le Havre,
France
Tel.: (33) 232749825
Web Site: http://www.archivages-services.fr
Information Management Services
N.A.I.C.S.: 519290

Subsidiary (Domestic):

Iron Mountain (UK) Ltd. (2)

Third Floor Cottons Centre Tooley Street, London, SE1 2TT, United Kingdom
Tel.: (44) 2079391500
Web Site: http://www.ironmountain.co.uk
Sales Range: $10-24.9 Million
Records Management, Data Protection & Information Destruction Solutions & Services
N.A.I.C.S.: 541519
Mark Duale *(Mng Dir)*

Subsidiary (Domestic):

Iron Mountain (UK) Services Limited (3)
Ground Floor 4 More London Riverside, Waterloo, London, SE1 2AU, United Kingdom
Tel.: (44) 12558281738
Web Site: http://www.ironmountain.co.uk
Emp.: 550
Document Storage & Information Management Services
N.A.I.C.S.: 493190

Iron Mountain DIMS Ltd. (3)
Ground Floor 4 More London Riverside, London, SE1 2AU, United Kingdom
Tel.: (44) 8445607080
Web Site: http://www.ironmountain.co.uk
Record Storage & Information Management Services
N.A.I.C.S.: 493190

Subsidiary (Non-US):

Iron Mountain A/S. (2)
Greve Main 20, 2670, Greve, Denmark
Tel.: (45) 70217700
Web Site: https://www.ironmountain.com
Emp.: 50
Information Management Services
N.A.I.C.S.: 519290

Iron Mountain Anamnis GDM SAS (2)
CS 36859 ZA Cap Malo La Meziere, Rennes, 35520, France
Tel.: (33) 299131330
Electronic Document Management & Protection Services
N.A.I.C.S.: 541519

Iron Mountain Arsivleme Hizmetleri AS (2)
Etiler Nisbetiye Cad Akmerkez B3 Blok K 11, 34340, Besiktas, Turkiye
Tel.: (90) 2122889503
Web Site: http://www.ironmountain.com.tr
Information Management Services
N.A.I.C.S.: 519290

Iron Mountain Ceska Republika S.R.O. (2)
Zahradni 105, 252 61, Jenec, Czech Republic
Tel.: (420) 233900638
Web Site: https://www.ironmountain.com
Management Data Protection Service Provider
N.A.I.C.S.: 541519

Iron Mountain Deutschland GmbH (2)
Randstrasse 11, 22525, Hamburg, Germany
Tel.: (49) 8004080000
Web Site: https://www.ironmountain.com
Records Management, Data Protection & Information Destruction Solutions & Services
N.A.I.C.S.: 541519
Ralf Reich *(Mng Dir)*

Iron Mountain Espana, S.A. (2)
Avda Reyes Catolicos 6 Poligono Industrial Valgrande, Alcobendas, 28108, Spain
Tel.: (34) 900222324
Web Site: http://www.ironmountain.es
Records Management & Storage System Provider
N.A.I.C.S.: 493190

Iron Mountain France S.A.S. (2)
6/12 Avenue Descartes ZI Les Sables, 91420, Morangis, France
Tel.: (33) 800215218
Web Site: https://www.ironmountain.com
Records Management, Data Protection & Information Destruction Solutions & Services

N.A.I.C.S.: 541519

Iron Mountain Hellas SA (2)
Thessi Dio Pefka Lofos Kirillou, 19300, Aspropyrgos, Greece
Tel.: (30) 2105584084
Web Site: http://www.ironmountain.gr
Document Management Services
N.A.I.C.S.: 541611

Iron Mountain Ireland Ltd. (2)
Damastown Rise Damastown, Damastown Industrial Estate, Dublin, 15, Ireland
Tel.: (353) 800732673
Web Site: https://www.ironmountain.com
Record Storage & Retrieval Services
N.A.I.C.S.: 493190

Iron Mountain Italia S.p.A. (2)
Via Zaccarini 1, San Nicolo, Piacenza, 29010, Italy
Tel.: (39) 0523766111
Web Site: http://www.ironmountain.it
Records Management, Data Protection & Information Destruction Solutions & Services
N.A.I.C.S.: 541519

Iron Mountain Magyarorszag Kereskedelmi es Szolgaltato Kft. (2)
Czuczor utca 10, 1093, Budapest, Hungary
Tel.: (36) 18153683
Web Site: http://www.ironmountain.hu
Document Storage & Information Management Services
N.A.I.C.S.: 493190

Subsidiary (Domestic):

DocuTar Iratrendezo es Tarolo Szolgaltato Kft. (3)
Czuczor u 10, 1093, Budapest, Hungary
Tel.: (36) 18153600
Web Site: https://www.docutar.hu
Document Storage & Information Management Services
N.A.I.C.S.: 493190

Subsidiary (Non-US):

Iron Mountain Magyarorszaq kft (2)
Czuczor 10, 1093, Budapest, Hungary
Tel.: (36) 18153600
Web Site: https://www.ironmountain.com
Sales Range: $25-49.9 Million
Record Storage & Information Management Service Provider
N.A.I.C.S.: 493190

Iron Mountain Nederland B.V. (2)
Cairostraat 1, Postbus 6303, 3002 AH, Rotterdam, Netherlands
Tel.: (31) 104254444
Web Site: http://www.ironmountain.nl
Sales Range: $75-99.9 Million
Emp.: 50
Records Management, Data Protection & Information Destruction Solutions & Services
N.A.I.C.S.: 541519

Subsidiary (Domestic):

Iron Mountain (Nederland) Services BV (3)
Cairostraat 1, 3047 BB, Rotterdam, Netherlands
Tel.: (31) 104254444
Web Site: http://www.ironmountain.com
Emp.: 40
Information Management Services
N.A.I.C.S.: 519290

Subsidiary (Non-US):

Iron Mountain Norge AS (2)
Hamrasletta 6, Postboks 235, 4098, Tananger, Norway
Tel.: (47) 51719800
Web Site: http://www.ironmountain.no
Records Management, Data Protection & Information Destruction Solutions & Services
N.A.I.C.S.: 541519
Bengt Nordang *(Ops Mgr)*
Josefin Gramel *(Dir-HR-Nordics & Baltics)*

Iron Mountain Polska Sp. z o.o. (2)
ul Regulska 2, Reguly k/ Warszawy, 05-820, Piastow, Poland
Tel.: (48) 227536141

Web Site: http://www.ironmountain.pl
Emp.: 500
Records Management, Data Protection & Information Destruction Solutions & Services
N.A.I.C.S.: 541519

Iron Mountain SRL (2)
North Business Center Str Siriului no 6 - 8 3rd floor Sector 1, 014354, Bucharest, 014354, Romania
Tel.: (40) 212325212
Web Site: http://www.ironmountain.ro
Record Storage & Information Management Service Provider
N.A.I.C.S.: 493190

Iron Mountain Slovakia s.r.o. (2)
Near Sajba 1, 831 06, Bratislava, 831 06, Slovakia
Tel.: (421) 249106900
Web Site: http://www.ironmountain.sk
Emp.: 120
Records Management, Data Protection & Information Destruction Solutions & Services
N.A.I.C.S.: 541519

Iron Mountain Ukraine LLC (2)
Lunacharskogo Str 13th Floor Kiev 4, Kiev, 02002, Ukraine
Tel.: (380) 444981314
Web Site: http://www.ironmountain.com.ua
Emp.: 25
Record Storage & Information Management Services
N.A.I.C.S.: 493190

Iron Mountain FZ-LLC (1)
City Tower 2 Office 2004A Sheikh Zayed Road, Al Karama, Dubai, United Arab Emirates
Tel.: (971) 43589881
Web Site: http://www.ironmountain.ae
Data Storage & Information Management Services
N.A.I.C.S.: 518210

Iron Mountain Finland Oy (1)
Kuussillantie 27, 01230, Vantaa, Finland
Tel.: (358) 982560214
Web Site: https://www.ironmountain.com
Data Management Services
N.A.I.C.S.: 541513
Juha-Pekka Lehto *(Country Mgr)*

Iron Mountain Holdings Group, Inc. (1)
745 Atlantic Ave, Boston, MA 02111
Tel.: (617) 535-4964
Holding Company
N.A.I.C.S.: 551112

Iron Mountain Hong Kong Limited (1)
Room 605-606 6/F Greenfield Tower Concordia Plaza, No 1 Science Museum Road, Tsim Tsa Tsui, China (Hong Kong)
Tel.: (852) 23318000
Web Site: https://www.ironmountain.com
Sales Range: $25-49.9 Million
Emp.: 40
Record Storage & Information Management Service Provider
N.A.I.C.S.: 541519

Iron Mountain Information Management, LLC (1)
745 Atlantic Ave, Boston, MA 02111-2735
Tel.: (719) 896-0394
Information Management Services
N.A.I.C.S.: 519290

Iron Mountain International Holdings B.V. (1)
Cairostraat 1, 3047 BB, Rotterdam, Netherlands
Tel.: (31) 104254444
Web Site: http://www.ironmountain.com
Holding Company
N.A.I.C.S.: 551112
Jerome Strike *(CEO)*

Iron Mountain Kuwait for Documents Preservation and Destruction Services (1)
Fahad Al Salem Street Saadon Jassem AL Yaqoub Building Floor M1, Office 14 Qibla Block 11, Kuwait, Kuwait
Tel.: (965) 50936868

Information Management Services
N.A.I.C.S.: 541511

Iron Mountain Muscat SPC (1)
Ghala Industrial Area Infofort Al Hooqani Warehouse, Muscat, Oman
Tel.: (968) 24503392
Information Technology Services
N.A.I.C.S.: 541519

Iron Mountain Peru S.A. (1)
Av Elmer Faucett, 3462, Callao, Peru
Tel.: (51) 15751000
Web Site: http://www.ironmountain.com.pe
Record Storage & Information Management Service Provider
N.A.I.C.S.: 493190

Iron Mountain Philippines Inc. (1)
Warehouse 2 Brgy, Batino, 4027, Calamba, Laguna, Philippines
Tel.: (63) 28381761
Web Site: http://www.ironmountain.ph
Data Management Solution Services
N.A.I.C.S.: 518210

Iron Mountain Records Management (Shanghai) Co Limited (1)
Suite 7C Jian Gong Building, 33 Fushan Road Pudong New District, Shanghai, China
Tel.: (86) 2168913738
Web Site: http://www.ironmountain.com.cn
Information Management Services
N.A.I.C.S.: 519290

Iron Mountain Shanghai Co. Ltd (1)
Suite 702 Jianfa International Buidling 288 Yangshupu Road, Pudong New District, Shanghai, China
Tel.: (86) 4001664766
Web Site: https://www.ironmountain.com
Record Storage & Information Management Service Provider
N.A.I.C.S.: 493190

Iron Mountain South Africa (Pty) Ltd (1)
85 Morkels Close Capital Hill Commercial Estate, Midrand, 1682, Johannesburg, Gauteng, South Africa
Tel.: (27) 861476668
Web Site: http://www.ironmountain.co.za
Document Storage Services
N.A.I.C.S.: 493190

Iron Mountain Taiwan Ltd. (1)
No 110 Ln 228 Sec 2 Nankan Rd, Luzhu District, Taoyuan, 338, Taiwan
Tel.: (886) 33119228
Web Site: http://www.ironmountain.com.tw
Data Management Solution Services
N.A.I.C.S.: 518210

Iron Mountain d.o.o. (1)
Third Logistics 1, Novi Banovci, 22304, Stara Pazova, Serbia
Tel.: (381) 113239336
Web Site: http://www.ironmountain.rs
Record Storage Facility Services
N.A.I.C.S.: 493190
Benil Misini *(Mng Dir)*

Iron Mountain do Brasil Ltda. (1)
avenida Goncalo Madeira 401 Jaguare, Sao Paulo, 05438-000, Brazil
Tel.: (55) 1137670888
Web Site: https://www.ironmountain.com
Records Management & Storage System Services
N.A.I.C.S.: 493190

Iron Mountain for Information Documents Storing PSC (1)
Shipping Road, Al-Qastal Industrial Area, Amman, Jordan
Tel.: (962) 62002425
Information Management Services
N.A.I.C.S.: 541511

Iron Trust doo Beograd (1)
46th Kneza Danila Street, 11000, Belgrade, Serbia
Tel.: (381) 113239466
Web Site: https://www.iron-trust.com
Document Storage Services
N.A.I.C.S.: 493190

Keepers Brasil Ltda (1)
Av Prefeito Joao Villalobo Quero 2253 Jd Belval, Barueri, 06400-001, Brazil

Iron Mountain Incorporated—(Continued)

Tel.: (55) 1147893000
Web Site: https://www.keepersbrasil.com.br
Document Storage & Information Management Services
N.A.I.C.S.: 493190

Navbharat Archive Xpress Private Limited (1)
501 A Wing 5TH Floor Navbharat Estates
Zakaria Bunder Road, Sewri, Mumbai, 400 A
015, India
Tel.: (91) 2224150000
Web Site: http://www.naxworld.com
Data Processing & Management Services
N.A.I.C.S.: 518210
Ganesh Narkar (Branch Mgr)

OEC Records Management Company Private Limited (1)
302 B-Wing Third Floor Times Square Andheri Kurla Road, Opp Mittal Est Andheri-East, Mumbai, 400 059, India
Tel.: (91) 2227812244
Web Site: http://oecrecords.com
Document Storage Services
N.A.I.C.S.: 493190

OSG Records Management Crypto LLC (1)
3rd Floor BC Alkon Leningradsky Prospect 72/3, 125315, Moscow, Russia
Tel.: (7) 4953636050
Web Site: http://www.osgrm.ru
Data Management Services
N.A.I.C.S.: 518210

OSG Records Management LLC (1)
Raffu 111, Yerevan, 0034, Armenia
Tel.: (374) 10743460
Web Site: https://www.osgrm.am
Data Management Solution Services
N.A.I.C.S.: 518210
Lilya Abrahamyan (Dir-OSG Records Mgmt)

OSG Records Management LLC (1)
St Surganova 43, 220013, Minsk, 220013, Belarus
Tel.: (375) 293486050
Web Site: https://www.osgrm.by
Data Management Solution Services
N.A.I.C.S.: 518210

OSG Records Management LLC (1)
St Shovkovichna 42-44, Kiev, 01004, Ukraine
Tel.: (380) 444901277
Data Management Services
N.A.I.C.S.: 518210

OSG Records Management LLP (1)
28B Timiryazev Street office 305/2, 050051, Almaty, Kazakhstan
Tel.: (7) 7750074855
Web Site: https://www.osgrm.kz
Data Management Solution Services
N.A.I.C.S.: 518210
Mikhail Betin (Gen Mgr-Kazakhstan)

PT Santa Fe Properties (1)
Jl Karanggan Muda Raya 59, 16961, Bogor, West Java, Indonesia
Tel.: (62) 2129612990
Document Storage Services
N.A.I.C.S.: 493190

Prism Integrated Sdn. Bhd. (1)
2A Jalan Tiang U9/91 Bukit Jeloutong, 40150, Shah Alam, Selangor, Malaysia
Tel.: (60) 377341111
Web Site: https://www.prism.com.my
Data Storage & Information Management Services
N.A.I.C.S.: 518210

Prism Intergrated Sdn Bhd (1)
2A Jalan Tiang U8/91, Bukit Jeloutong, Shah Alam, Selangor, Malaysia
Tel.: (60) 377341111
Web Site: https://www.prism.com.my
Computer Peripheral Equipment Mfr
N.A.I.C.S.: 334112

SIA RIA Tech (1)
Bauskas Street 22, Riga, LV-1004, Latvia
Tel.: (371) 28369359
Web Site: http://www.riatech.lv
Electronic Document Archive Services
N.A.I.C.S.: 519210

Safe House Information Management Solutions Private Limited (1)
3rd Floor Currimjee Building 111 M G Road Fort, Mumbai, 400001, Maharashtra, India
Tel.: (91) 2265277623
Web Site: http://www.safehouse.in
Data Management Services
N.A.I.C.S.: 541513
Carl Cooper (CEO)
Kunal Gandhi (CTO)
V. S. Iyer (Sr VP-SIs)
P. V. Ramana (Mgr-Facilities)

Superior Storage Limited (1)
Unit 12 Dunshaughlin Business Park, Dunshaughlin, Meath, A85 T924, Ireland
Tel.: (353) 18240600
Web Site: http://www.documentstorage.ie
Data Storage & Information Management Services
N.A.I.C.S.: 518210

Ulshofer IT GmbH & Co. KG. (1)
Raiffeisenstrasse 17, 61191, Rosbach vor der Hohe, Germany
Tel.: (49) 600391230
Web Site: http://www.ulshoefer.de
Record Storage Facility Services
N.A.I.C.S.: 493190

IRONNET, INC.
7900 Tysons 1 Pl Ste 400, McLean, VA 22102
Tel.: (443) 300-6761   DE
Year Founded: 2019
IRNT—(NYSE)
Rev.: $808,527
Assets: $174,077,031
Liabilities: $169,077,030
Net Worth: $5,000,001
Earnings: $141,312
Emp.: 8
Fiscal Year-end: 12/31/20
Cyber Security Services
N.A.I.C.S.: 518210
Linda K. Zecher-Higgins (CEO)
Marc J. Gabelli (Chm)
Keith B. Alexander (Founder)
Cameron D. Pforr (Pres & CFO)
John P. O'Hara (Sr VP-Corp Dev & Partnerships)

IRONWOOD PHARMACEUTICALS, INC.
100 Summer St Ste 2300, Boston, MA 02110
Tel.: (617) 621-7722   DE
Web Site:
https://www.ironwoodpharma.com
Year Founded: 1998
IRWD—(NASDAQ)
Rev.: $442,735,000
Assets: $471,073,000
Liabilities: $817,368,000
Net Worth: ($346,295,000)
Earnings: ($1,002,239,000)
Emp.: 267
Fiscal Year-end: 12/31/23
Pharmaceuticals Mfr
N.A.I.C.S.: 325412
Sravan K. Emany (CFO & Sr VP)
Peter M. Hecht (Co-Founder)
Brian M. Cali (Co-Founder)
G. Todd Milne (Co-Founder)
Matt Roache (Dir-IR)
John Minardo (Chief Legal Officer & Sr VP)
Thomas McCourt (CEO)
Susanna Y. Huh (VP)
Diane Stroehmann (VP)
Tammi Gaskins (VP)
Andrew Davis (Chief Bus Officer)
Beth Calitri (Head)
Mike Nanfito (Exec VP)
Marcel Moulaison (VP)
Thomas A. McCourt (CEO)

Subsidiaries:

VectivBio Holding AG (1)

Aeschenvorstadt 36, 4051, Basel, Switzerland (100%)
Tel.: (41) 615513030
Rev.: $27,341,000
Assets: $252,599,000
Liabilities: $39,231,000
Net Worth: $213,368,000
Earnings: ($93,735,000)
Emp.: 42
Fiscal Year-end: 12/31/2022
Holding Company
N.A.I.C.S.: 551112
Claudia D'Augusta (CFO)
Christian Meyer (Chief Dev Officer)
Kevin Harris (Chief Comml Officer)
Alain Bernard (CTO)
Sarah Holland (Chief Bus Officer)
Andrew Davis (Chm)

ISABELLA BANK CORPORATION
401 N Main St, Mount Pleasant, MI 48804-0100
Tel.: (989) 772-9471   MI
Web Site:
https://www.isabellabank.com
Year Founded: 1988
ISBA—(OTCQX)
Rev.: $79,464,000
Assets: $2,030,267,000
Liabilities: $1,844,057,000
Net Worth: $186,210,000
Earnings: $22,238,000
Emp.: 347
Fiscal Year-end: 12/31/22
Financial Services Holding Company; Banking, Employee Leasing & Financial Information Services
N.A.I.C.S.: 551111
Jerome E. Schwind (Pres & CEO)
Jennifer L. Gill (Controller)

Subsidiaries:

Isabella Bank (1)
1416 E Pickard, Mount Pleasant, MI 48858
Tel.: (989) 773-2129
Web Site: https://www.isabellabank.com
Commercial Banking Services
N.A.I.C.S.: 522110
Jerome E. Schwind (CEO)
Neil M. McDonnell (Pres)

ISHARES GOLD BULLION FUND
400 Howard St, San Francisco, CA 94105
Tel.: (415) 670-2000   Ca
Web Site: https://www.ishares.com
Year Founded: 2009
CGL—(TSX)
Sales Range: Less than $1 Million
Miscellaneous Financial Investment Activities
N.A.I.C.S.: 523999

ISHARES GOLD TRUST
c/o iShares Delaware Trust Sponsor LLC 400 Howard St, San Francisco, CA 94105
Tel.: (415) 670-2000
Web Site: https://www.ishares.com
Year Founded: 2005
IAU—(NYSA)
Assets: $26,160,403,760
Liabilities: $5,511,616
Net Worth: $26,154,892,134
Earnings: ($71,451,301)
Fiscal Year-end: 12/31/22
Bond Investment Services
N.A.I.C.S.: 523999
Paul Lohrey (CEO)
Mary Cronin (CFO)
Shannon Ghia (Pres)
Bryan Bowers (COO)

ISIGN SOLUTIONS INC.
2033 Gateway Pl Ste 659, San Jose, CA 95110
Tel.: (650) 802-7888   DE

Web Site: https://www.isignnow.com
Year Founded: 1986
ISGN—(OTCIQ)
Rev.: $987,000
Assets: $203,000
Liabilities: $6,724,000
Net Worth: ($6,521,000)
Earnings: ($711,000)
Emp.: 5
Fiscal Year-end: 12/31/22
Digital Transaction Management Software Publisher
N.A.I.C.S.: 513210
Philip S. Sassower (Co-Chm & CEO)
Michael W. Engmann (Co-Chm, Pres, CFO & COO)

ISLEWORTH HEALTHCARE ACQUISITION CORP.
970 Lake Carillon Dr Feather Sound Ste 300, Saint Petersburg, FL 33716
Tel.: (727) 245-0146   DE
Year Founded: 2020
ISLE—(NASDAQ)
Rev.: $5,677,372
Assets: $207,967,067
Liabilities: $215,590,355
Net Worth: ($7,623,288)
Earnings: $4,840,854
Emp.: 2
Fiscal Year-end: 12/31/21
Investment Services
N.A.I.C.S.: 523999
Robert Whitehead (CEO)
Dan Halvorson (CFO & Exec VP)

ISOS ACQUISITION CORP.
55 Post Rd W Ste 200, Westport, CT 06880
Tel.: (203) 554-5641   Ky
Year Founded: 2020
ISOS—(NYSE)
Investment Services
N.A.I.C.S.: 523999
George Barrios (Co-Chm & Co-CEO)
Winston Meade (CFO)
Michelle D. Wilson (Co-Chm & Co-CEO)

ISPECIMEN INC.
450 Bedford St, Lexington, MA 02420
Tel.: (781) 301-6700   DE
Web Site: https://www.ispecimen.com
Year Founded: 2009
ISPC—(NASDAQ)
Rev.: $10,402,303
Assets: $24,617,653
Liabilities: $4,308,483
Net Worth: $20,309,170
Earnings: ($10,245,922)
Emp.: 75
Fiscal Year-end: 12/31/22
Research & Development in Biotechnology (except Nanobiotechnology)
N.A.I.C.S.: 541714
Jill Mullan (Treas & Sec)
Tracy Wilson Curley (CEO, CFO & Treas)
David Wages (Chief Medical Officer)
Erik Uribe (Dir-Implementations-Global)
Annette Arnold (VP)
Evan Cox (VP)
Jeff Ladino (VP)

ISPIRE TECHNOLOGY INC.
19700 Magellan Dr, Los Angeles, CA 90502
Tel.: (310) 742-9975   DE
Web Site:
https://www.ispiretechnology.com
Year Founded: 2022
ISPR—(NASDAQ)
Rev.: $151,908,691
Assets: $122,640,966

Liabilities: $88,184,626
Net Worth: $34,456,340
Earnings: ($14,767,822)
Emp.: 98
Fiscal Year-end: 06/30/24
Small Electrical Appliance Manufac-
turing
N.A.I.C.S.: 335210

ISRAEL ACQUISITIONS CORP.
12600 Hill Country Blvd Bldg R Ste
275, Bee Cave, TX 78738   Ky
Web Site:
    https://israelacquisitionscorp.com
ISRL—(NASDAQ)
Investment Services
N.A.I.C.S.: 523999
Ziv Elul (CEO)

ISRAEL AMPLIFY PROGRAM
CORP.
10 E 53rd St Ste 1301 13th Fl, New
York, NY 10022
Tel.: (646) 699-8282   Ky
Year Founded: 2021
ISAP—(NYSE)
Investment Services
N.A.I.C.S.: 523999
Chemi Peres (Chm)
Asher Levy (CEO)
Amichai Steimberg (Pres & COO)
Tim Surzyn (CFO)
Abraham Gross (CTO)

ISSUER DIRECT CORPORA-
TION
1 Glenwood Ave Ste 1001, Raleigh,
NC 27603
Tel.: (919) 769-3576   DE
Web Site:
    https://www.issuerdirect.com
ISDR—(NYSEAMEX)
Rev.: $23,514,000
Assets: $66,325,000
Liabilities: $33,102,000
Net Worth: $33,223,000
Earnings: $1,934,000
Emp.: 137
Fiscal Year-end: 12/31/21
All Other Business Support Services
N.A.I.C.S.: 561499
Brian R. Balbirnie (Pres & CEO)
William H. Everett (Chm)
Steven Knerr (Interim CFO, Interim
Principal Acctg Officer, VP-Fin & Con-
troller)
Mark Lloyd (CTO)
Jennifer Hammers (Exec VP)

Subsidiaries:

Filing Services Canada Inc.   (1)
440 10816 Macleod Trail SE, Calgary, T2J
5N8, AB, Canada
Tel.: (403) 717-3898
Web Site: http://www.fscwire.com
Business Support Services
N.A.I.C.S.: 561499
Nancy Gautreau (Mgr-Client Care)

ISUN, INC.
400 Ave D, Williston, VT 05495
Tel.: (802) 658-3378   DE
Web Site:
    https://www.isunenergy.com
Year Founded: 2014
ISUN—(NASDAQ)
Rev.: $76,453,000
Assets: $67,481,000
Liabilities: $48,194,000
Net Worth: $19,287,000
Earnings: ($53,779,000)
Emp.: 290
Fiscal Year-end: 12/31/22
Investment Targeting
N.A.I.C.S.: 523999
Jeffrey Peck (CEO)
Frederick Myrick (Exec VP-Solar)

ITAFOS
5151SanFelipeStSte2015, Houston,
TX 77056
Tel.: (713) 242-8446   Ca
Web Site: https://itafos.com
Year Founded: 2009
IFOS—(TSXV)
Rev.: $260,185,000
Assets: $477,304,000
Liabilities: $394,881,000
Net Worth: $82,423,000
Earnings: ($63,060,000)
Fiscal Year-end: 12/31/20
Phosphate & Potash Fertilizer Mfr
N.A.I.C.S.: 325312
Anthony Cina (Chm & Chm)
G. David Delaney (CEO)
David Brush (Chief Strategy Officer)
Tim Vedder (VP-Ops & Gen Mgr-
Itafos Canada)
Wynand van Dyk (VP-Engrg, R&D,
and Dev)
Geoff Williams (Gen Counsel, Sec &
VP)
Lee Reeves (Gen Counsel & Corp
Sec)

Subsidiaries:

MBAC Brazil Holdings B.V.   (1)
Prins Bernhardplein 200, Amsterdam, 1097
JB, Noord-Holland, Netherlands
Tel.: (31) 205270100
Investment Holding Services
N.A.I.C.S.: 551112

ITEKNIK HOLDING CORPORA-
TION
7750 Okeechobee Blvd Ste 4-561,
West Palm Beach, FL 33411
Tel.: (561) 459-3809   WY
Web Site: http://www.iteknik.com
Year Founded: 2007
ITKH—(OTCIQ)
Telecommunication Products Distr &
Retailer
N.A.I.C.S.: 423620

ITEM 9 LABS CORP.
2727 N 3rd St Ste 201, Phoenix, AZ
85004   DE
Web Site:
    https://www.item9labscorp.com
Year Founded: 2010
INLB—(OTCIQ)
Rev.: $21,937,227
Assets: $116,809,133
Liabilities: $30,707,690
Net Worth: $86,101,443
Earnings: ($10,905,772)
Emp.: 103
Fiscal Year-end: 09/30/21
Nasal Breathing Devices Developer,
Mfr & Distr
N.A.I.C.S.: 423450
Robert E. Mikkelsen (CFO, Treas &
Sec)
Christopher Wolven (COO)
Bobby Mikkelsen (CFO)

ITEOS THERAPEUTICS, INC
321 Arsenal St Bldg 312 Ste 301,
Watertown, MA 02472
Tel.: (339) 217-0161   DE
Web Site:
    https://www.iteostherapeutics.com
Year Founded: 2019
ITOS—(NASDAQ)
Rev.: $267,630,000
Assets: $754,991,000
Liabilities: $91,659,000
Net Worth: $663,332,000
Earnings: $96,652,000
Emp.: 125
Fiscal Year-end: 12/31/22
Research & Development in Biotech-
nology (except Nanobiotechnology)
N.A.I.C.S.: 541714

Matthew Call (COO)
Matthew Gall (CFO)
Yvonne McGrath (VP-R&D)
Philippe Brantegem (VP-HR)
Michel Detheux (Pres & CEO)

ITEX CORPORATION
13555 SE 36th St Ste 210, Bellevue,
WA 98006
Tel.: (425) 463-4000   NV
Web Site: https://www.itex.com
Year Founded: 1982
ITEX—(OTCIQ)
Rev.: $6,877,000
Assets: $8,212,000
Liabilities: $986,000
Net Worth: $7,226,000
Earnings: $802,000
Emp.: 7
Fiscal Year-end: 07/31/21
All Other Business Support Services
N.A.I.C.S.: 561499
Steven White (Chm & CEO)
John A. Wade (CFO, Treas & Sec)

ITIQUIRA ACQUISITION CORP.
430 Park Ave Ste 202, New York, NY
10022
Tel.: (646) 350-0341   Ky
Web Site: http://www.itiquiracorp.com
Year Founded: 2020
ITQR—(NASDAQ)
Investment Services
N.A.I.C.S.: 523999
Paulo Carvalho De Gouvea (CEO &
Chm)
Marcus Leonardo Silberman (CFO)
Pedro Chomnalez (Co-Chief Invest-
ment Officer)
Maria Alejandra Herrera (Co-Chief
Investment Officer)
Gabriela Yu (Officer-IR, Treas & Con-
troller)
Tainah Salles Mendes (VP-Corp Fin)

ITOKK, INC.
1712 Pioneer Ave Ste 500, Chey-
enne, WY 82001
Tel.: (408) 419-1719   NV
Web Site: https://www.itokk.com
Year Founded: 2003
IRBS—(OTCIQ)
Telecommunication Servicesb
N.A.I.C.S.: 517112
Paul Lucien Strickland (Sec)

ITONIS, INC.
22630 C Lambert St Ste 902, Lake
Forest, CA 92630
Tel.: (949) 200-8887
Web Site:
    https://www.itonisholdings.com
ITNS—(OTCIQ)
Sales Range: $10-24.9 Million
Pharmaceuticals Product Mfr
N.A.I.C.S.: 325412
Stephen R. Pidliskey Jr. (Sec & VP)
Mark Cheung (Pres & CEO)
Donald L. Jolly (CFO & Treas)

ITRON, INC.
2111 N Molter Rd, Liberty Lake, WA
99019
Tel.: (509) 924-9900   WA
Web Site: https://na.itron.com
Year Founded: 1977
ITRI—(NASDAQ)
Rev.: $1,795,564,000
Assets: $2,378,078,000
Liabilities: $1,186,522,000
Net Worth: $1,191,556,000
Earnings: ($9,732,000)
Emp.: 5,477
Fiscal Year-end: 12/31/22

Energy Information & Communica-
tions Solutions to Utility Industries
Worldwide
N.A.I.C.S.: 334220
Michel Charles Cadieux (Sr VP-HR)
Thomas L. Deitrich (Pres & CEO)
Joan S. Hooper (CFO & Sr VP)
Donald L. Reeves (Sr VP-Outcomes)
Justin K. Patrick (Sr VP-Device Solu-
tions)
John F. Marcolini (Sr VP-Networked
Solutions)
Kenneth P. Gianella (VP-IR)
Paul Vincent (VP)
David Means (Dir)
Christopher E. Ware (Gen Counsel)
Laurie Hahn (Sr VP)

Subsidiaries:

Actaris Pty Ltd   (1)
8 Rosberg Road, Wingfield, Adelaide, 5013,
SA, Australia
Tel.: (61) 881692500
Web Site: http://www.itron.com
Sales Range: $10-24.9 Million
Emp.: 27
Testing, Measuring & Scientific Equipment
Mfr
N.A.I.C.S.: 334515
Philip Mazay (Pres)

Allmess GmbH   (1)
Am Vossberg 11, D-23758, Oldenburg, Ger-
many
Tel.: (49) 43616250
Web Site: https://www.allmess.de
Emp.: 200
Water Meters, Heat & Cooling Meters &
Remote Reading Systems Mfr & Distr
N.A.I.C.S.: 334513
Harald Jollenbeck (Mng Dir)
Johannes Huizing (Mng Dir)
Chantel Landers (Mng Dir)
Joel Vach (Mng Dir)

Arabian Metering Company   (1)
PO Box 4793, Baglaf Industrial Area, Al
Khobar, 31952, Saudi Arabia
Tel.: (966) 3 890 1614
Electricity Meters Mfr & Marketer
N.A.I.C.S.: 334513

Asais S.A.S.   (1)
39 41 Rue De l Universite, 93160, Noisy-le-
Grand, France
Tel.: (33) 1 43 05 58 00
Web Site: http://www.asais.fr
Develops & Implements Sales Solutions for
Energy Producers & Suppliers; Consulting
Services
N.A.I.C.S.: 334519

Compania Chilena de Medicion
S.A.   (1)
Avenida General Freire 725, La Cisterna,
Santiago, Chile
Tel.: (56) 2 328 5000
Web Site: http://www.medidores.cl
Water Meters Mfr & Distr
N.A.I.C.S.: 334519

Comverge, Inc.   (1)
5390 Triangle Pkwy Ste 300, Norcross, GA
30092
Tel.: (678) 392-4954
Electric Utility Measuring & Control Device
Mfr
N.A.I.C.S.: 334512
Jason Cigarran (VP-Mktg & IR)
David Neal (COO)
Chris Ash (VP-Product Mgmt)
Tracy Caswell (Chief Admin Officer & Gen
Counsel)

Contigea SA   (1)
142 rue de Stalle, Brussels, 1180, Belgium
Tel.: (32) 2 333 18 11
Sales of Measuring Meters
N.A.I.C.S.: 423830

GANZ Meter Company Ltd.   (1)
Tancsics M u 11, PO Box 396, 2101,
Godollo, Hungary
Tel.: (36) 28520600
Sales Range: $100-124.9 Million
Emp.: 300

Itron, Inc.—(Continued)

Electrical Measuring Instruments Mfr &
Sales
N.A.I.C.S.: 334515

Itron Argentina S.A. (1)
Av Monsenor Bufano 5010 La Tablada,
B1766DIT, Buenos Aires, Argentina
Tel.: (54) 1144804901
Web Site: http://www.itron.com
Sales Range: $10-24.9 Million
Emp.: 75
Gas Meter Mfr
N.A.I.C.S.: 334519
Luis Manuel Rossi *(Mng Dir)*

Itron Austria GmbH (1)
Am Concorde Park 1/B2, Schwechat, 2320,
Austria
Tel.: (43) 170640000
Web Site: http://www.itron.com
Emp.: 6
Measuring Meters Distr
N.A.I.C.S.: 423830

Itron BV (1)
Kamerlingh Onnesweg 55, Postbus 42,
3316 GK, Dordrecht, Netherlands
Tel.: (31) 786545454
Web Site: http://www.itron.com
Sales Range: $25-49.9 Million
Emp.: 17
Gas & Water Meters Mfr & Sales
N.A.I.C.S.: 334519

Itron Canada, Inc. (1)
2624 Dunwin Drive Unit 4, Mississauga,
L5L 3T6, ON, Canada
Tel.: (905) 593-1707
Web Site: http://www.itron.com
Industrial Machinery & Equipment Distr
N.A.I.C.S.: 423830

Itron Czech Republic s.r.o. (1)
Bucharova 2657/12 budova C 4te patro,
158 00, Prague, 13, Czech Republic
Tel.: (420) 226522221
Web Site: http://www.itron.cz
Emp.: 20
Sales of Measuring Meters
N.A.I.C.S.: 811310

Itron Distribucion S.A. de C.V. (1)
Periferico Sur No 5739 - Nave 5 6 y 7, Za-
popan, 45134, Jalisco, Mexico
Tel.: (52) 13316054652
Web Site: http://www.itron.com
Sales of Measuring Meters
N.A.I.C.S.: 423830

Itron France S.A.S. (1)
Immeuble Les Montale 2 Rue De Paris,
92190, Meudon, 92190, France
Tel.: (33) 146622300
Read Meter Mfr
N.A.I.C.S.: 334516

Itron Holding Company GmbH (1)
Hardeckstrasse 2, 76185, Karlsruhe, Ger-
many
Tel.: (49) 72159810
Web Site: http://www.itron.com
Emp.: 200
Holding Company
N.A.I.C.S.: 551112
Guillaume de Contenson *(Mng Dir)*

Subsidiary (Domestic):

Itron GmbH (2)
Hardeckstr 2, 76185, Karlsruhe, Germany
Tel.: (49) 721 598 1100
Web Site: http://www.itron.com
Gas Meters Mfr & Distr
N.A.I.C.S.: 334519

Itron India Private Limited (1)
5th Floor Campus 6B RMZ Eco world Devarabeesanahalli Outer Ring Road, Lal Tap-
par, Bengaluru, 560103, Karnataka, India
Tel.: (91) 8061459000
Water Meters Mfr
N.A.I.C.S.: 334513

Itron Italia SpA (1)
Strada Valcossera 16, 14100, Asti, Italy
Tel.: (39) 0141477077
Web Site: https://www.itron.com
Water Meters Mfr
N.A.I.C.S.: 334519

Itron Japan Co., Ltd. (1)
Level 1 Yusen Building 2-3-2, Marunouchi
Chiyoda-ku, Tokyo, 100-0005, Japan
Tel.: (81) 355338870
Measuring Equipment Mfr
N.A.I.C.S.: 334515

Itron LLC (1)
17 Vorontsovskaya st BC Mosenka Capital
Plaza 4th Floor, 109147, Moscow, Russia
Tel.: (7) 4959357626
Emp.: 2
Measuring Meters Distr
N.A.I.C.S.: 423830

Itron Liquid Measurement (1)
1310 Emerald Rd, Greenwood, SC 29646
Tel.: (864) 223-1212
Web Site:
   http://www.redsealmeasurement.com
Fluid Meter/Counting Devices Mfr
N.A.I.C.S.: 334514

**Itron Management Services Ireland,
Limited** (1)
Block 1000 Unit 1105 City Gate, Cork, Ire-
land
Tel.: (353) 214410000
Web Site: http://www.itron.com
Energy Company
N.A.I.C.S.: 541618

Subsidiary (Domestic):

SELC Ireland Ltd. (2)
Office 3 Unit 11 Faber Castell Business
Campus, Fermoy, Co Cork, Ireland
Tel.: (353) 2548020
Web Site: http://www.selc.ie
Lighting Equipment Mfr
N.A.I.C.S.: 335139
Pat Gayer *(CEO)*
Amanda Dixon *(VP-Sls & Bus Dev-
Americas)*
Linda Mellerick *(Dir-Ops)*
Frank Magee *(Dir-Value Engrg)*
Liam Kerrigan *(Mgr-R&D)*

**Itron Measurements & Systems (Pro-
prietary) Limited** (1)
Itron House Tygerberg Office Park 136
Hendrik Verwoerd Drive, Plattekloof, Cape
Town, 7500, South Africa
Tel.: (27) 21 928 1700
Web Site: http://www.itron.com
Electrical Measuring Instruments Marketer
N.A.I.C.S.: 423830

Itron Metering Solutions UK Ltd (1)
Unit 10 Haven Exchange, Felixstowe, IP11
2QX, Suffolk, United Kingdom
Tel.: (44) 1394694000
Web Site: http://www.itron.com
Sales Range: $250-299.9 Million
Emp.: 200
Electrical Measuring Instrument Mfr
N.A.I.C.S.: 334513

Branch (Domestic):

Itron Metering Solutions UK Ltd (2)
Langer Road, Felixstowe, IP11 2ER, Suf-
folk, United Kingdom
Tel.: (44) 1394276030
Web Site: http://www.itron.com
Sales Range: $100-124.9 Million
Emp.: 415
Electrical Measuring Instrument Mfr
N.A.I.C.S.: 334515

**Itron Metering Systems (Chongqing)
Co., Ltd.** (1)
No 4 Dian Ce Cun Guan Yinqiao, Jiang Bei
District, Chongqing, 400020, China
Tel.: (86) 23 6751 5829
Gas Meters Mfr
N.A.I.C.S.: 334519

**Itron Metering Systems (Suzhou) Co.,
Ltd.** (1)
No 50 Weihe Road, Suzhou Industrial Park,
Suzhou, 215121, Jiangsu, China
Tel.: (86) 51269368066
Mfr of Measuring Meters for Water Utilities
N.A.I.C.S.: 334519
Chang Silio *(Sr Mgr-Ops)*

**Itron Metering Systems Singapore
Pte Ltd.** (1)
Novena Square Tower A, 238A Thomson

Road Unit 10-08, Singapore, 307 684, Sin-
gapore
Tel.: (65) 65574410
Measuring Meters Sales
N.A.I.C.S.: 423830

Itron Nederland B.V. (1)
Kamerlingh Onnesweg 55, 3316 GK, Dor-
drecht, Netherlands
Tel.: (31) 786545454
Measuring Equipment Mfr
N.A.I.C.S.: 334515

Itron Polska sp. z o.o. (1)
ul T Romanowicza 6, 30-702, Krakow, Po-
land
Tel.: (48) 12 257 10 27
Web Site: http://www.itron.com
Sales of Measuring Meters
N.A.I.C.S.: 423830

Itron Portugal, Unipessoal, LDA. (1)
R Jose Carvalho N 671, Vila Nova de Fa-
malicao, 4760-353, Portugal
Tel.: (351) 252320300
Measuring Equipment Mfr
N.A.I.C.S.: 334515

Itron Sistemas de Medicao Lda. (1)
Rua Jose Carvalho 671, 4760-353, Vila
Nova de Famalicao, Portugal
Tel.: (351) 252320300
Web Site: https://www.itron.com
Electricity & Water Meters Mfr & Distr
N.A.I.C.S.: 334519

**Itron Soluciones de Medida Espana
SL** (1)
Montornes del Valles, Montornes del Valles,
8170, Barcelona, Spain
Tel.: (34) 93 565 36 00
Web Site: http://www.itron.com
Sales Range: $25-49.9 Million
Emp.: 90
Measuring & Controlling Devices Mfr & Distr
N.A.I.C.S.: 334519
Antoine Pimenta De Miranda *(CEO)*

**Itron Solucoes para Energia e Agua
Ltda.** (1)
Av Joaquim Boer 792 - Jd Helena, Ameri-
cana, 13477-360, Sao Paulo, Brazil
Tel.: (55) 1934718400
Web Site: http://www.itron.com
Mfr & Distr of Measuring Meters for Electric
& Water Utilities; Software Developer
N.A.I.C.S.: 334519

Itron Spain SLU (1)
Pol Ind El Congost - Parcela 8 Sector J,
Montornes del Valles, 08170, Barcelona,
Spain
Tel.: (34) 935653600
Measuring Equipment Mfr
N.A.I.C.S.: 334515
Frederic Tarruell Rodriguez *(Dir-Mktg)*

Itron Sweden AB (1)
Adolfsbergsvagen 29, 168 67, Bromma,
Sweden
Tel.: (46) 856200500
Web Site: https://www.itron.com
Sales Range: $25-49.9 Million
Emp.: 20
Measuring Meters Whslr
N.A.I.C.S.: 423830

Itron US Gas, LLC (1)
970 Hwy 127 N, Owenton, KY 40359
Tel.: (502) 484-5747
Sales Range: $50-74.9 Million
Emp.: 200
Gas Meters & Regulators Mfr
N.A.I.C.S.: 334519

Itron Ukraine (1)
103 Oleksy Tykhoho Street, 03067, Kiev,
Ukraine
Tel.: (380) 444907710
Emp.: 7
Mfr of Gas Meters
N.A.I.C.S.: 334519

Itron Unterstutzungskasse GmbH (1)
Hardeckstr 2, 76185, Karlsruhe, Germany
Tel.: (49) 72159810
Web Site: http://www.actaris.com
Measuring Equipment Mfr
N.A.I.C.S.: 334515

**Itron Zahler & Systemtechnik
GmbH** (1)

Brekelbaumstrasse 5, 31789, Hameln, Ger-
many
Tel.: (49) 5 151 7820
Web Site: http://www.itron.com
Emp.: 16
Electricity Meters Mfr & Distr
N.A.I.C.S.: 334519

Itron, Inc. - Oakland (1)
1111 Bdwy Ste 1800, Oakland, CA 94607
Tel.: (510) 844-2800
Web Site: http://www.itron.com
Sales Range: $25-49.9 Million
Emp.: 85
Provider of Application Computer Software
N.A.I.C.S.: 513210

Itron-Australasia Pty Limited (1)
Level 2 Suite 2 0210 Barrack Street, Syd-
ney, 2000, NSW, Australia
Tel.: (61) 28 235 5700
Web Site: http://www.itron.com
Emp.: 30
Information Technology Solutions for Utility
Industry, Including Communications, Hard-
ware, Software, Service & Consulting
N.A.I.C.S.: 541519

Metertek Sdn Bhd (1)
c/o Level 8 MCT Tower Sky Park One City
Jalan USJ25/1, 47650, Subang Jaya, Se-
langor, Malaysia
Tel.: (60) 380228201
Mfr of Measuring Meters for Electric & Wa-
ter Utilities
N.A.I.C.S.: 334519

PT Mecoindo (1)
EJIP Plot 6B-2, Cikarang Selatan, Jakarta
Barat, 17550, Indonesia
Tel.: (62) 218970270
Web Site: http://www.itron.com
Sales Range: $200-249.9 Million
Emp.: 600
Electricity, Gas & Water Meters Mfr & Distr
N.A.I.C.S.: 334513

SEWA GmbH (1)
Hardeckstr 2, 76185, Karlsruhe, Germany
Tel.: (49) 7215981282
Measuring Meters for Gas Utilities; Software
Developer
N.A.I.C.S.: 334519

Temetra Limited (1)
Gortnafleur, Clonmel, Co Tipperary, Ireland
Tel.: (353) 52 615 0035
Web Site: https://en.temetra.com
Software Development Services
N.A.I.C.S.: 541511

Thielmann Energietechnik GmbH (1)
Dormannweg 48, 34123, Kassel, Germany
Tel.: (49) 561507850
Web Site: https://www.gts-thielmann.de
Emp.: 13
Mfr of Pressure Vessels for Gas Industry
N.A.I.C.S.: 334519
Remy Brill *(Mng Dir)*

ITRONICS INC.

6490 S McCarran Blvd Bldg C Ste
23, Reno, NV 89509
Tel.: (775) 689-7696   TX
Web Site: https://www.itronics.com
Year Founded: 1988
ITRO—(OTCIQ)
Research & Development in the
Physical, Engineering & Life Sciences
(except Nanotechnology & Biotech-
nology)
N.A.I.C.S.: 541715
John W. Whitney *(Pres)*
John Key *(Sr VP)*

Subsidiaries:

Itronics Metallurgical, Inc. (1)
6490 S McCarran Blvd Bldg C Ste 23,
Reno, NV 89509
Tel.: (775) 677-6044
Web Site: http://www.itromet.com
Manufactures, Sells & Services Advanced
Silver Recovery Units; Recycles Used
Photo-Chemicals into Fertilizer Products
N.A.I.C.S.: 325312

Whitney & Whitney, Inc. (1)

6490 S McCarran Blvd Bldg C Ste 23, Reno, NV 89509
Tel.: (775) 677-6049
Web Site: http://www.whitneywhitney.com
Technical & Management Consulting Services for Mineral Resource Industry
N.A.I.C.S.: 541611

Division (Domestic):

InsideMetals.com **(2)**
6490 S McCarran Blvd Bldg C Ste 23, Reno, NV 89510
Tel.: (775) 677-6049
Web Site: http://www.insidemetals.com
Website Subscription Service for Precious Metals Investors
N.A.I.C.S.: 513199

ITT INC.

100 Washington Blvd 6th FL, Stamford, CT 06902
Tel.: (914) 641-2000 **IN**
Web Site: https://www.itt.com
Year Founded: 1995
ITT—(NYSE)
Rev.: $3,283,000,000
Assets: $3,932,600,000
Liabilities: $1,393,500,000
Net Worth: $2,539,100,000
Earnings: $410,500,000
Emp.: 10,600
Fiscal Year-end: 12/31/23
Advanced Engineering Services, Design & Mfr
N.A.I.C.S.: 423830
Luca Savi (Pres & CEO)
Mary Beth Gustafsson (Chief Compliance Officer, Gen Counsel & Sr VP)
Bartek Makowiecki (Chief Strategy Officer, Pres-Industrial Process & Sr VP)
Carlo Ghirardo (Pres-Motion Technologies & Sr VP)
Ryan Flynn (Pres-Connect & Control Technologies & Sr VP)
Maurine C. Lembesis (Chief HR Officer & Sr VP)
Davide Barbon (Pres-Asia Pacific & Sr VP)
Cheryl de Mesa Graziano (Chief Acctg Officer & VP)

Subsidiaries:

1026128 Alberta Ltd **(1)**
1924 11 Ave Nw, Medicine Hat, T1C 1T6, AB, Canada
Tel.: (403) 504-4214
Web Site:
http://www.precisionpumpservice.com
Emp.: 11
Precision Equipment Repair & Maintenance Services
N.A.I.C.S.: 811210

AcousticFab, LLC **(1)**
25395 Rye Canyon Rd, Valencia, CA 91355
Tel.: (661) 257-2242
Noise Attenuation Component Mfr
N.A.I.C.S.: 336413
Mark Hughes (Controller)

Axtone GmbH **(1)**
Rheinstrasse 15, 57638, Neitersen, Germany
Tel.: (49) 26818080
Rail Gear Mfr & Distr
N.A.I.C.S.: 336510

Axtone HSW sp. z.o.o. **(1)**
Ul Kwiatkowskiego 1, 37-450, Stalowa Wola, Poland
Tel.: (48) 158135482
Rail Spring Mfr & Distr
N.A.I.C.S.: 332613
Grzegorz Jedynak (Plant Dir)

Axtone S.A. **(1)**
Ul Zielona 2, 37-220, Kanczuga, Poland
Tel.: (48) 166492400
Rail Spring Mfr & Distr
N.A.I.C.S.: 332613

Axtone s.r.o. **(1)**

Dolni 100, 796 01, Prostejov, Czech Republic
Tel.: (420) 58231268498
Rail Spring Mfr & Distr
N.A.I.C.S.: 332613

Bombas Bornemann S.R.L. **(1)**
Mariano Moreno 4380, B1605BOD, Munro, Buenos Aires, Argentina
Tel.: (54) 1147568008
Web Site: http://www.bornemann-ar.com
Pumps Mfr
N.A.I.C.S.: 333914

Bombas Goulds S.A. **(1)**
Mariano Moreno 4380, Buenos Aires, B1605BOF, Argentina
Tel.: (54) 1147568008
Industrial Machinery & Equipment Distr
N.A.I.C.S.: 423830

Bombas Goulds de Mexico S. de R.L. de C.V. **(1)**
Avenue Eje Oriente Poniente L4 M9 Ciudad Industrial, Tizayuca, 43800, HG, Mexico
Tel.: (52) 7797962193
Industrial Pump Mfr & Distr
N.A.I.C.S.: 333914

Bornemann Exzenterschneckenpumpen GmbH **(1)**
Industriestrasse 2, 31683, Obernkirchen, Germany
Tel.: (49) 57243900
Web Site: http://www.borex-pumps.com
Pumps Mfr
N.A.I.C.S.: 333914

Bornemann Inc. **(1)**
200 625 4th Avenue SW, Calgary, T2P 0K2, AB, Canada
Tel.: (587) 233-1278
Pumps Mfr
N.A.I.C.S.: 333914

Bornemann Middle East FZE **(1)**
PO Box 293582, Dubai, United Arab Emirates
Tel.: (971) 42146531
Pumps Mfr
N.A.I.C.S.: 333914

Bornemann Pumps & Systems Co. Ltd **(1)**
Jinbin Bldg No 6 No 45 Muning Rd, Tianjin, 300457, China
Tel.: (86) 2266297800
Pumps Mfr
N.A.I.C.S.: 333914

Bornemann Pumps Asia Pte. Ltd. **(1)**
10 Jalan Kilang 06-01 Sime Darby Enterprise Centre, Singapore, 159410, Singapore
Tel.: (65) 65616782
Pumps Mfr
N.A.I.C.S.: 333914
Elson Tan (Dir-Sls)

Bornemann S.A. DE C.V. **(1)**
Calle Horacio 1840 1er Piso Col Chapultepec los Morales Polanco, 11510, Mexico, Mexico
Tel.: (52) 791780
Web Site: http://www.bornemann-ch.com
Pumps Mfr
N.A.I.C.S.: 333914

Electrofilm Manufacturing Company LLC **(1)**
25395 Rye Canyon Rd, Valencia, CA 91355
Tel.: (661) 257-2242
Electric Air Heater Mfr
N.A.I.C.S.: 334512
Joe Maddison (Dir-Fin)

EnviroTech LLC **(1)**
2931 Whittington Ave, Baltimore, MD 21230
Tel.: (410) 525-0045
Web Site: http://www.envirotechllc.com
Water Remediation Services
N.A.I.C.S.: 562910

European Pump Services B.V. **(1)**
Neon 13, 4751 XA, Oud Gastel, Netherlands
Tel.: (31) 18 044 2266
Web Site: https://epsbv.com
Pump Installation System Services
N.A.I.C.S.: 238290

Menno De Visser (Acct Mgr-Strategic Sls)
Joost van Linden (Mgr-Technical)
Max De Vries (Mgr-Svc)

Goulds Pumps (NY), Inc. **(1)**
Av Defensores Del Morro 1788, Chorrillos, Lima, 09, Huaylas, Peru
Tel.: (51) 13990466
Web Site: http://www.gouldspumps.com
Industrial Pump Distr
N.A.I.C.S.: 423830

Goulds Pumps, Inc. **(1)**
240 Fall St, Seneca Falls, NY 13148
Tel.: (315) 568-2811
Web Site: http://www.gouldspumps.com
Sales Range: $800-899.9 Million
Emp.: 5,250
Mfr of Centrifugal Pumps For Industrial Markets
N.A.I.C.S.: 333914

Subsidiary (Domestic):

Goulds Pumps (NY), Inc. **(2)**
240 Fall St, Seneca Falls, NY 13148 **(100%)**
Tel.: (315) 568-2811
Web Site: https://www.gouldspumps.com
Sales Range: $300-349.9 Million
Emp.: 1,000
Pumps And Pumping Equipment
N.A.I.C.S.: 333914

Subsidiary (Non-US):

Goulds Pumps Co. Ltd. **(2)**
Rm 501 Ducksoo Bldg 608, Seoul, 135-010, Korea (South)
Tel.: (82) 234444202
Web Site: https://www.gouldspumps.com
Emp.: 10
Industrial Products Mfr
N.A.I.C.S.: 333914

Goulds Pumps U.K. Ltd. **(2)**
Millwey Rise Industrial Estate, Axminster, EX13 5HU, Devon, United Kingdom **(100%)**
Tel.: (44) 1297639100
Web Site: http://www.gouldspumps.com
Sales Range: $1-9.9 Million
Emp.: 50
Industrial Pumps
N.A.I.C.S.: 333914

Branch (Domestic):

Goulds Pumps, Inc. - Huntington **(2)**
20 24th St, Huntington, WV 25703
Tel.: (304) 529-4161
Web Site: http://www.gouldspumps.com
Sales Range: $25-49.9 Million
Emp.: 17
Automotive, Defense, Electronics & Fluid Technologies
N.A.I.C.S.: 423830

Goulds Pumps, Inc. - Los Angeles **(2)**
3951 Capitol Ave, City of Industry, CA 90601
Tel.: (562) 908-4125
Web Site: http://www.proservices.com
Sales Range: $25-49.9 Million
Emp.: 20
Pumps And Pumping Equipment
N.A.I.C.S.: 333914

Goulds Pumps, Inc. - Memphis **(2)**
5815 E Shelby Dr, Southaven, TN 38671-6804
Tel.: (901) 366-4010
Web Site: http://www.goulds.com
Sales Range: $25-49.9 Million
Emp.: 17
Pumps & Pumping Equipments
N.A.I.C.S.: 333914

ITT Aerospace Controls LLC **(1)**
28150 Industry Dr, Valencia, CA 91355
Tel.: (661) 295-4000
Web Site: https://www.ittaerospace.com
Sales Range: $125-149.9 Million
Emp.: 401
Aerospace Relays, Switches, Actuators & Other Control Components Mfr
N.A.I.C.S.: 334419

ITT Blakers PTY Ltd **(1)**

29 Paramount Drive, Wangara, 6065, WA, Australia
Tel.: (61) 130 033 3488
Web Site: https://www.ittblakers.com
Pump Distr
N.A.I.C.S.: 423830

ITT Bombas Goulds do Brasil Ltda. **(1)**
Rodovia Itu-Salto Km 40 4 - Guarau, Salto, Sao Paulo, Brazil
Tel.: (55) 1146029200
Pump Mfr & Distr
N.A.I.C.S.: 333914

ITT Bornemann GmbH **(1)**
Industriestrasse 2, 31683, Obernkirchen, Germany **(100%)**
Tel.: (49) 5 724 3900
Web Site: https://www.bornemann.com
Sales Range: $150-199.9 Million
Emp.: 550
Oil & Gas Industry Pump & Pumping System Mfr
N.A.I.C.S.: 333132
Markus Schwarte (Mng Dir)
Arne Stuckenberg (Mng Dir)
Jorg Narewski (Mng Dir)

ITT Brasil Equipamentospara Bombeamento e Tratamento de Agua e Efluentes Ltda **(1)**
Rue Telmo Coelho Filho 40, Sao Paulo, 05543-020, Brazil
Tel.: (55) 1137320150
Electronic Products Mfr
N.A.I.C.S.: 334419

ITT C'treat LLC **(1)**
309 Briar Rock Rd, The Woodlands, TX 77380
Tel.: (281) 367-2800
Emp.: 2,400
Industrial Machinery Mfr
N.A.I.C.S.: 333248

ITT Cannon International, Inc. **(1)**
56 Technology Dr, Irvine, CA 92618
Tel.: (714) 557-4700
Web Site: https://www.ittcannon.com
Sales Range: $550-599.9 Million
Emp.: 700
International Supplier of Connectors, Interconnectors, Cable Assemblies, Switches, Multi-Function Grips, I/O Card Kits, Smart Card Systems & LAN Components; Network Systems & Services
N.A.I.C.S.: 334417

Subsidiary (Domestic):

ITT BIW Connector Systems, LLC **(2)**
500 Tesconi Cir, Santa Rosa, CA 95401-4692
Tel.: (707) 523-2300
Web Site: https://www.ittbiw.com
Sales Range: $25-49.9 Million
Emp.: 120
High-Durability Electronic Connector Mfr
N.A.I.C.S.: 334417

Subsidiary (Non-US):

ITT Cannon De Mexico S.A. De C.V. **(2)**
Parque Industrial Nuevo, 84000, Nogales, Sonora, Mexico
Tel.: (52) 6313110050
Electronic Connector Mfr
N.A.I.C.S.: 334417

ITT Cannon GmbH **(2)**
Cannonstr 1, 71384, Weinstadt, Germany
Tel.: (49) 71516990
Web Site: https://www.jobs-cannon.de
Electronics Instrument Mfr
N.A.I.C.S.: 334511

ITT Cannon Korea Ltd. **(2)**
Rm 1712 Kbiz Tower 1622 Sang-Am Dong, Mapo-gu, Seoul, 03929, Korea (South)
Tel.: (82) 27027111
Electronics Instrument Mfr
N.A.I.C.S.: 334511

ITT Cannon Veam Italia S.r.l. **(2)**
Corso Europa 41/43, 20020, Lainate, MI, Italy
Tel.: (39) 02938721

ITT Inc.—(Continued)

Web Site: http://www.ittcannon.com
Industrial Equipment Mfr
N.A.I.C.S.: 333248

Subsidiary (Domestic):

ITT Veam LLC (2)
100 New Wood Rd, Watertown, CT 06795
Tel.: (860) 274-9681
Web Site: http://www.ittcannon.com
Sales Range: $25-49.9 Million
Emp.: 7
Multipin, Cylindrical, Electrical, Optical &
Pneumatic Connector Mfr & Distr
N.A.I.C.S.: 334417

**ITT Community Development
Corp.** (1)
1133 Westchester Ave, White Plains, NY
10604
Tel.: (914) 641-2000
Community Support Services
N.A.I.C.S.: 561499

**ITT Control Technologies EMEA
GmbH** (1)
Werkstrasse 5, 64732, Bad Konig, Germany
Tel.: (49) 606393140
Web Site: https://www.enidine.com
Transportation Equipment Distr
N.A.I.C.S.: 423860

ITT Control Technologies GmbH (1)
Werkstrasse 5, Bad Konig, 64732, Hessen,
Germany
Tel.: (49) 606393140
Web Site: http://www.ittcontrols.com
Emp.: 17
Information Technology Services
N.A.I.C.S.: 519290

ITT Corp. - Newton (1)
15 Riverdale Ave, Newton, MA 02458
Tel.: (617) 969-3700
Web Site: http://www.ittcannon.com
Sales Range: $75-99.9 Million
Emp.: 105
Mfr Switches
N.A.I.C.S.: 541715

ITT Corp. - Santa Ana (1)
56 Technology Dr, Irvine, CA 92618
Tel.: (714) 557-4700
Web Site: https://www.ittcannon.com
Sales Range: $75-99.9 Million
Emp.: 200
Motor Pumps Mfr
N.A.I.C.S.: 333914

ITT Corp. - Sumter (1)
2635b Hardee Cv, Sumter, SC 29150
Tel.: (803) 469-4880
Sales Range: $10-24.9 Million
Emp.: 6
Telecommunications
N.A.I.C.S.: 517810

ITT Corporation India Pvt. Ltd. (1)
Plot No 731 A GIDC Savli Savli-Manjusar
Road, Vadodara, 391775, Gujarat, India
Tel.: (91) 2667665700
Sales Range: $25-49.9 Million
Emp.: 150
Engineering Component Mfr
N.A.I.C.S.: 334511

ITT Delaware Investments Inc. (1)
1133 Weschester Ave, White Plains, NY
10604
Tel.: (914) 641-2000
Sales Range: $1-9.9 Million
Emp.: 3
Investment Services
N.A.I.C.S.: 561499

ITT Engineered Valves, LLC (1)
33 Centerville Rd, Lancaster, PA
17603 (100%)
Tel.: (717) 509-2200
Web Site: https://www.engvalves.com
Sales Range: $50-74.9 Million
Emp.: 200
Valves & Pipe Fittings
N.A.I.C.S.: 332919

**ITT Fluid Technology Asia Pte
Ltd.** (1)
1 Jalan Kilang Timor 04-06, Singapore,
159303, Singapore

Tel.: (65) 66974205
Sales Range: $300-349.9 Million
Emp.: 35
Automotive, Defense, Electronics & Fluid
Technologies
N.A.I.C.S.: 336340

**ITT Fluid Technology International,
Inc.** (1)
Unit 1403 Level 14 U Bora Tower Business
Bay, PO Box 35249, Dubai, United Arab
Emirates
Tel.: (971) 42525345
Industrial Pump Distr
N.A.I.C.S.: 423830

**ITT Goulds Pumps Columbia
S.A.S.** (1)
Carrera 85D No 46A 65 Bodega 9, Bogota,
Colombia
Tel.: (57) 14109024
Pumps Mfr
N.A.I.C.S.: 333914

**ITT High Precision Manufactured
Products (Wuxi) Co., Ltd** (1)
No 570 Xida Road, Meicun Xinwu District,
Wuxi, 214112, Jiangsu, China
Tel.: (86) 51088556188
Web Site: https://www.itt.com.cn
Sales Range: $75-99.9 Million
Emp.: 400
Instrument Mfr
N.A.I.C.S.: 339999

**ITT Industries Engineered Products
Division** (1)
240 Fall St, Seneca Falls, NY 13148-1590
Tel.: (315) 568-2811
Web Site: http://www.ittindustries.com
Sales Range: $350-399.9 Million
Emp.: 1,200
Mfr of Centrifugal End Suction, Double Suc-
tion & Multi-Stage Pumps
N.A.I.C.S.: 326199

ITT Industries Inc. (1)
1110 Bankhead Ave, Amory, MS
38821 (100%)
Tel.: (662) 256-7185
Web Site: https://www.engvalves.com
Sales Range: $75-99.9 Million
Emp.: 100
Mfr of Specialty Valves
N.A.I.C.S.: 332919

ITT Industries Inc. (1)
450 W 100 N, North Salt Lake, UT
84054 (100%)
Tel.: (801) 936-7924
Web Site: http://www.ittind.com
Sales Range: $10-24.9 Million
Emp.: 14
Repair of Gear Boxes & Industrial Refinery
Equipments
N.A.I.C.S.: 335314

ITT Industries Inc. (1)
Off Air Force Base Bldg, Bellevue, NE
68123 (100%)
Tel.: (402) 291-5332
Sales Range: $10-24.9 Million
Emp.: 13
Provider of Training & Development Consul-
tant Services
N.A.I.C.S.: 541612

ITT Industries Inc. (1)
268 Appin Rd, PO Box 4, Glencoe, N0L
1M0, ON, Canada (100%)
Tel.: (519) 287-2450
Web Site: http://www.ittindustries.com
Sales Range: $150-199.9 Million
Emp.: 425
Mfr of Motor Vehicle Parts & Accessories
N.A.I.C.S.: 336390

ITT Industries Inc. (1)
59 Technology Dr, Lowell, MA 01851
Tel.: (978) 441-0200
Sales Range: $10-24.9 Million
Emp.: 35
Research Services Except Laboratory
N.A.I.C.S.: 541910

ITT Industries Inc. (1)
16700 NE 79th St, Redmond, WA 98052
Tel.: (425) 895-1975
Web Site: http://www.ittcannon.com

Sales Range: $10-24.9 Million
Emp.: 2
Electric Connectors
N.A.I.C.S.: 423610

ITT Industries Spain SL (1)
Francisco Cantu C/Miguel Faraday No 20 B
Office 202 Getafe, 28906, Madrid, Spain
Tel.: (34) 916845947
Web Site: http://www.bornemann-ve.com
Pumps Mfr
N.A.I.C.S.: 333914

ITT Italia S.r.l. (1)
Via San Martino 87, Cuneo, 12032, Cuneo,
Italy
Tel.: (39) 0175347111
Inspection Equipment Mfr
N.A.I.C.S.: 334511

ITT Korea Holding B.V. (1)
Keplerstraat 34Â , 1171 CD, Badhoevedorp,
Netherlands
Tel.: (31) 203055700
Holding Company
N.A.I.C.S.: 551112

ITT Pure-Flo (UK) Ltd. (1)
Selby Industrial Estate Richards Street,
Kirkham, PR4 2HU, United Kingdom
Tel.: (44) 1772682696
Industrial Equipment Distr
N.A.I.C.S.: 423830

ITT Rheinhutte Benelux B.V. (1)
Steenpad 5, 4797 SG, Willemstad, Nether-
lands
Tel.: (31) 168473651
Pumping Equipment Mfr
N.A.I.C.S.: 333914

ITT Rheinhutte Pumpen Co., Ltd. (1)
1st Floor No 51 Mingdong Road, Pudong
New Area, Shanghai, 201209, China
Tel.: (86) 18616311323
Industrial Pump Mfr
N.A.I.C.S.: 333914

ITT Rheinhutte Pumpen GmbH (1)
Rheingaustrasse 96-98, 65203, Wiesbaden,
Germany
Tel.: (49) 6116040
Web Site: https://www.rheinhuette.de
Emp.: 201
Pumping Equipment Mfr
N.A.I.C.S.: 333914
Duncan Morgan *(Mng Dir)*
Bernhard Wuermeling *(Mng Dir)*
Jorg Narewski *(Mng Dir)*
Bernhard Wuermeling *(Mng Dir)*
Jorg Narewski *(Mng Dir)*

**ITT Water & Wastewater U.S.A.,
Inc.** (1)
35 Nutmeg Dr, Trumbull, CT 06611
Tel.: (203) 380-4700
Water Treatment Equipment Mfr
N.A.I.C.S.: 333310

Impeller Repair Service (1)
1725 Childhaven NE, Cullman, AL 35056-
1247
Tel.: (256) 737-5061
Web Site: http://www.gouldspumps.com
Sales Range: $1-9.9 Million
Emp.: 30
Pumps & Pumping Equipment Repair
N.A.I.C.S.: 811210

Industrial Tube Company LLC (1)
3091 Indian Ave, Perris, CA 92571
Tel.: (951) 657-2611
Aircraft Hose & Composite Mfr
N.A.I.C.S.: 336413

International Motion Control, Inc. (1)
45 Bryant Woods N, Buffalo, NY 14228-
3600
Tel.: (716) 855-2500
Sales Range: $200-249.9 Million
Emp.: 1,120
Motion Control Devices
N.A.I.C.S.: 336412

Subsidiary (Domestic):

ITT Enidine Inc. (2)
7 Centre Dr, Orchard Park, NY 14127-2281
Tel.: (716) 662-1900
Web Site: https://www.enidine.com

Sales Range: $150-199.9 Million
Emp.: 300
Energy Absorption & Vibration Isolation
Products
N.A.I.C.S.: 336412

Koni BV (1)
Korteweg 2, 3261 NH, Oud-Beijerland,
Netherlands
Tel.: (31) 186635500
Web Site: https://www.koni.com
Instrument Mfr
N.A.I.C.S.: 334511

Koni NA LLC (1)
1961 International Way, Hebron, KY 41048
Tel.: (859) 586-4100
Web Site: https://www.koni-na.com
Shock Absorber Mfr
N.A.I.C.S.: 336330

Koni North America, Inc. (1)
1961 International Way, Hebron, KY 41048-
9526
Tel.: (859) 586-4100
Web Site: https://www.koni-na.com
Sales Range: $25-49.9 Million
Emp.: 25
Wholesale Distributors of Shock Absorbers
And Struts
N.A.I.C.S.: 333415

Leland Properties (1)
4401 Morella Dr, Studio City, CA 91607
Tel.: (818) 769-5680
Web Site: https://www.lelandproperties.com
Real Estate Manangement Services
N.A.I.C.S.: 531390

Matrix Composites, Inc. (1)
275 Barnes Blvd, Rockledge, FL 32955
Tel.: (321) 633-4480
Web Site: http://www.matrixcomp.com
Precision Moulding Mfr
N.A.I.C.S.: 333511
Ken Swarner *(Co-Founder)*
David A. Nesbitt Jr. *(Co-Founder)*

Micro-Mode Products, Inc. (1)
1870 John Towers Ave, El Cajon, CA 92020
Tel.: (619) 449-3844
Web Site: http://www.micromode.com
Sales Range: $1-9.9 Million
Emp.: 110
Microwave Connectors & Cable Assemblies
Mfr
N.A.I.C.S.: 334220
Andy Dukes *(Mgr)*

PCU, Inc. (1)
3017 James L Redman Pkwy, Plant City,
FL 33566
Tel.: (813) 717-7717
Web Site: https://www.pcucomputers.com
Computer Peripheral Equipment Distr
N.A.I.C.S.: 423430
Jim Brown *(Founder)*

**PT ITT Fluid Technology
Indonesia** (1)
L23 06 Menara Palma Jl Hr Rasuna Said
Kav 6 Kuningan Timur, Setiabudi, 12950,
Jakarta, Indonesia
Tel.: (62) 213867801
Pumps Mfr
N.A.I.C.S.: 333514

**Qingdao Kamax Buffer Equipment
Company Ltd.** (1)
No 1-11 Shibei High & New Technic Indus-
try Zone, ShangMa area AoDong Road
Chengyang district, Qingdao, 266000,
China
Tel.: (86) 53266965008
Rail Gear Mfr & Distr
N.A.I.C.S.: 336510

**Shanghai Goulds Pumps Co.
Ltd.** (1)
No 135 Futexiyi Rd Waigaoqiao Ftz, Shang-
hai, 200131, China
Tel.: (86) 2158669730
Industrial Equipment Mfr
N.A.I.C.S.: 333248

Svanehoj Danmark A/S (1)
Fabriksparken 6, DK-9230, Svenstrup, Denmark

Tel.: (45) 96372200
Web Site: http://www.wartsila.com
Marine Cargo Pumping Systems Mfr
N.A.I.C.S.: 333914

Subsidiary (US):

Complete Cryogenic Services, Inc. (2)
1155 Warner Ave, Tustin, CA 92780-6458
Tel.: (714) 258-8531
Web Site: http://www.completecryogenicser
vices.com
Flat Glass Mfr
N.A.I.C.S.: 327211

TDS Corporate Services LLC (1)
2 Corporate Dr, Palm Coast, FL 32137-0020
Tel.: (386) 446-6166
Web Site: http://www.itt-tds.com
Freight Transportation Services
N.A.I.C.S.: 481212

Wolverine Advance Materials GmbH (1)
Verrenberger Weg 20, 74613, Ohringen, 74613, Germany
Tel.: (49) 79416030
Rubber Products Mfr
N.A.I.C.S.: 326220
Peter Ernst (Mng Dir)

Wolverine Advanced Materials GmbH (1)
Verrenberger Weg 20, Ohringen, 74613, Germany
Tel.: (49) 79416030
Automotive Parts Mfr & Distr.
N.A.I.C.S.: 336340

Wolverine Advanced Materials, LLC (1)
5850 Mercury Dr Ste 250, Dearborn, MI 48126
Tel.: (313) 749-6100
Web Site: https://www.wamglobal.com
Emp.: 70
Gasket Product Mfr
N.A.I.C.S.: 339991
Abdul-hafiz Afaneh (VP-Global Engrg)
Jerome Pedretti (CFO)
Marcelo Teixeira (Exec Dir-Ops-USA)
Kristine Frost (Exec Dir-HR-Global)
Marco Walter (Exec Dir-Pur-Global)
Ivan Martinez-Rivera (Dir-Quality-Global)
Laurent Crosnier (VP & Gen Mgr)

Wolverine Press (Changshu) Co. Ltd. (1)
4 Jingshun Industrial Shop Riverside Indus-trial Park, Changshu, 215536, Jiangsu, China
Tel.: (86) 51252267355
Motor Vehicle Parts Mfr
N.A.I.C.S.: 336211
Patrick Xu (Gen Mgr)

kSARIA Corporation (1)
300 Griffin Brook Dr, Methuen, MA 01844
Tel.: (978) 933-0003
Web Site: https://ksaria.com
Aerospace Services
N.A.I.C.S.: 334511
Anthony Christopher (Pres & CEO)

Division (Domestic):

Charles E. Gillman Company (2)
907 E Frontage Rd, Rio Rico, AZ 85648
Tel.: (520) 281-1141
Web Site: http://www.gillman.com
Electronic Components Mfr
N.A.I.C.S.: 334419
Alan Gillman (Pres)

Subsidiary (Domestic):

Co-Operative Industries Defense, LLC (2)
1401 S Cherry Ln, Fort Worth, TX 76108
Tel.: (817) 740-4700
Web Site: http://www.coopind.com
Electronic Components Mfr
N.A.I.C.S.: 334419
Amber Chavez (CFO & Controller)

CompuLink Cable Assemblies of Florida Inc. (2)

1205 Gandy Blvd N, Saint Petersburg, FL 33702-2428
Tel.: (727) 579-1500
Web Site: http://www.compulink-usa.com
Provider of Wiring Device Services
N.A.I.C.S.: 335931
Steven Shevlin (Pres)

IVEDA SOLUTIONS, INC.
1744 S Val Vista Dr Ste 213, Mesa, AZ 85204
Tel.: (480) 307-8700 NV
Web Site: https://www.iveda.com
Year Founded: 2006
IVDA—(NASDAQ)
Rev.: $4,468,279
Assets: $9,863,070
Liabilities: $2,293,320
Net Worth: $7,569,750
Earnings: ($3,345,270)
Emp.: 32
Fiscal Year-end: 12/31/22
Security Systems Services (except Locksmiths)
N.A.I.C.S.: 561621
Robert J. Brilon (CFO, Treas & Sec)
David Ly (Founder, Chm, Pres & CEO)
Gregory Omi (CTO)

IVY HIGH INCOME OPPORTU-NITIES FUND
6300 Lamar Ave, Shawnee Mission, KS 66202-4200
IVH—(NYSE)
Rev.: $28,740,000
Assets: $363,191,000
Liabilities: $113,759,000
Net Worth: $249,432,000
Earnings: $20,795,000
Fiscal Year-end: 09/30/19
Investment Management Service
N.A.I.C.S.: 525990
Joseph W. Kauten (VP & Treas)
Philip J. Sanders (Pres)
Joseph Harroz Jr. (Chm)

IZEA WORLDWIDE, INC.
1317 Edgewater Dr Ste 1880, Or-lando, FL 32804
Tel.: (407) 674-6911 NV
Web Site: https://www.izea.com
Year Founded: 2006
IZEA—(NASDAQ)
Rev.: $41,095,937
Assets: $85,674,890
Liabilities: $15,408,943
Net Worth: $70,265,947
Earnings: ($4,469,498)
Emp.: 123
Fiscal Year-end: 12/31/22
Advertising Services
N.A.I.C.S.: 541810
Sandra Carbone (Gen Counsel, Sec & Sr VP)
Peter Biere (CFO & Treas)
Edward H. Murphy (Founder)
Patrick J. Venetucci (CEO)

Subsidiaries:

Ebyline, Inc. (1)
15260 Ventura Blvd Ste 800, Sherman Oaks, CA 91403
Tel.: (661) 731-3239
Web Site: http://www.ebyline.com
Document Preparation Services
N.A.I.C.S.: 561410

Zuberance, Inc. (1)
628 El Camino Real, San Carlos, CA 94070
Tel.: (647) 494-4932
Web Site: http://www.zuberance.com
Professional, Scientific & Technical Services
N.A.I.C.S.: 541990
Devin Chojnacki (Sr Dir-Sls & Bus Dev)

IZON NETWORK, INC.
20751 N Pima Rd Ste 100, Scotts-dale, AZ 85255

Tel.: (623) 252-2551 OK
Year Founded: 2011
IZNN—(OTCIQ)
Telecommunication Servicesb
N.A.I.C.S.: 517112
Giles Sommerville (Chm)
Jeff Hosek (Pres, Treas & Sec)

J&J SNACK FOODS CORPO-RATION
350 Fellowship Rd, Mount Laurel, NJ 08054
Tel.: (856) 665-9533 NJ
Web Site: https://www.jjsnack.com
Year Founded: 1971
JJSF—(NASDAQ)
Rev.: $1,574,755,000
Assets: $1,365,101,000
Liabilities: $408,131,000
Net Worth: $956,970,000
Earnings: $86,551,000
Emp.: 5,000
Fiscal Year-end: 09/28/24
Ice Cream & Frozen Dessert Manu-facturing
N.A.I.C.S.: 311520
Ken A. Plunk (CFO, Treas & Sr VP)
Lynwood Mallard (CMO & Sr VP)
Robert Cranmer (VP-Ops)
Jay Montgomery (VP-Ops)
Bjoern Leyser (Sr VP-Sls)
Matt Inderlied (Sr VP-Sls)
James Hamill (VP & Controller)
Mary Lou Kehoe (VP-HR)
Deborah Kane (VP-Food Safety, Quality, EHS & Regulatory)
Dan Crossan (VP-Retail Sls)
Bo Powell (VP-Foodservice Sls)
John Stefanik (VP-Bakery Sls)
Norma Abbattista (Sr Dir-Mktg)
Joanne Mizner (Sr Dir-Mktg)
Michael Pollner (Corp Counsel)
Gerald B. Shreiber (Founder)
Daniel J. Fachner (Chm, Pres & CEO)

Subsidiaries:

Bakers Best Snack Food Corp. (1)
1880 N Penn Rd, Hatfield, PA 19440-1950
Tel.: (215) 822-3511
Snacks & Baked Food Mfr
N.A.I.C.S.: 311919

Bakers Best Trotter (1)
1880 N Penn Rd, Hatfield, PA 19440-1950 (100%)
Tel.: (215) 822-3511
Sales Range: $25-49.9 Million
Emp.: 54
Mfr & Distributor of Soft Pretzels
N.A.I.C.S.: 311919
Joel Shreiver (Pres)

California Churros Corp. (1)
751 Via Lata, Colton, CA 92324
Tel.: (909) 370-4777
Web Site: http://www.churros.com
Sales Range: $10-24.9 Million
Emp.: 130
Pastries Mfr
N.A.I.C.S.: 311812

Country Home Bakers, Inc. (1)
361 Benigno Blvd, Bellmawr, NJ 08031
Tel.: (856) 931-7052
Web Site:
 http://www.countryhomebakers.com
Sales Range: $10-24.9 Million
Emp.: 500
Mfr of Frozen Bread & Other Bakery Prod-ucts
N.A.I.C.S.: 424490

DADDY RAY (1)
1070 Industrial Ct, Moscow Mills, MO 63362-1045
Tel.: (636) 366-9900
Web Site: http://www.daddyrays.com
Emp.: 300
Fig & Fruit Bar Mfr
N.A.I.C.S.: 311340

DADDY RAY'S, Inc. (1)
PO Box 186, Moscow Mills, MO 63362
Tel.: (636) 366-9900
Web Site: http://www.daddyrays.com
Cookie Mfr
N.A.I.C.S.: 311821
Ray Henry (Pres & CEO)

Dippin' Dots Australia Pty. Ltd. (1)
Unit 7 / 810 Princes Highway, Springvale, 03171, VIC, Australia
Tel.: (61) 395408466
Web Site: https://dippindots.com.au
Ice Cream Mfr & Distr
N.A.I.C.S.: 311520

Dippin' Dots, LLC (1)
5101 Charter Oak Dr, Paducah, KY 42001
Tel.: (270) 443-8994
Web Site: https://www.dippindots.com
Sales Range: $200-249.9 Million
Emp.: 165
Ice Cream & Frozen Dessert Mfr & Shops Franchisor
N.A.I.C.S.: 311520
Scott Fischer (CEO)

Subsidiary (Domestic):

Dippin' Dots Franchising, LLC (2)
2775 W Park Dr, Paducah, KY 42001
Tel.: (270) 575-6990
Web Site: http://www.dippindots.com
Sales Range: $10-24.9 Million
Emp.: 5
Ice Cream & Frozen Dessert Shops Fran-chisor
N.A.I.C.S.: 533110
Dana Knudsen (Sr Dir-Mktg)
Steve Rothenstein (Sr Dir-Franchising)

Federal Pretzel Baking Company, LLC (1)
300 Eagle Ct, Bridgeport, NJ 08014
Tel.: (215) 467-0505
Web Site: http://www.federalpretzel.biz
Sales Range: $125-149.9 Million
Pretzel Mfr
N.A.I.C.S.: 311919

Hill & Valley, Inc. (1)
320 44th St, Rock Island, IL 61201
Tel.: (309) 793-0161
Web Site: http://www.hillandvalley.net
Emp.: 150
Snack Food Mfr
N.A.I.C.S.: 311813
Scott Bell (CFO)

Hom/Ade Foods, Inc. (1)
90 E Garden St, Pensacola, FL 32502
Tel.: (850) 444-4740
Web Site: http://www.homadefoods.com
Sales Range: $25-49.9 Million
Emp.: 9
Frozen Biscuit Dough Mfr
N.A.I.C.S.: 311813

ICEE de Mexico, S.A. De C.V. (1)
Presidentes No 52 Portales, Benito Juarez, 03300, Mexico, DF, Mexico
Tel.: (52) 5556120770
Web Site: http://www.icee.mx
Frozen Foods & Beverages Mfr & Distr
N.A.I.C.S.: 311412

ICEE of Hawaii, Inc. (1)
94-497 Ukee St Ste A, Waipahu, HI 96797
Tel.: (808) 671-5402
Web Site: http://www.icee.com
Sales Range: $25-49.9 Million
Emp.: 9
Snack Foods & Beverages Mfr
N.A.I.C.S.: 311812

ICEE-USA Corp. (1)
265 Mason Rd, La Vergne, TN 37086 (100%)
Tel.: (248) 374-2000
Web Site: https://www.icee.com
Sales Range: $1-9.9 Million
Emp.: 20
Distr of Refrigerated Soft Drink Dispensing Equipment
N.A.I.C.S.: 811490

J & J Snack Foods Investment Corp. (1)
919 N Market St Ste 200, Wilmington, DE 19801

J&J Snack Foods Corporation—(Continued)

Tel.: (302) 571-0884
Snack Food Mfr
N.A.I.C.S.: 311919

J&J Snack Foods Corp. (1)
PO Box 3777, Scranton, PA
18505-0777 (100%)
Tel.: (570) 457-7431
Web Site: http://www.jjsnack.com
Sales Range: $25-49.9 Million
Emp.: 50
Mfr of Pretzels, Baked Goods & Whipped &
Frozen Juice Products
N.A.I.C.S.: 311919
Dennis G. Moore (CFO)

J&J Snack Foods Corp. of
California (1)
5353 S Downey Rd, Vernon, CA
90058 (100%)
Tel.: (323) 581-0171
Sales Range: $50-74.9 Million
Emp.: 250
Mfr of Snack Foods, Baked Goods, Frozen
& Whipped Juice Products
N.A.I.C.S.: 311919
Gerald Law (Gen Mgr)

J&J Snack Foods Corp. of New
Jersey (1)
6000 Central Hwy, Pennsauken, NJ
08109-4607 (100%)
Tel.: (856) 665-9533
Web Site:
   http://www.jjsnackfoodservice.com
Sales Range: $125-149.9 Million
Emp.: 250
Mfr of Snack Foods, Baked Goods & Fro-
zen Juice Bars
N.A.I.C.S.: 311813

J&J Snack Foods Corp./Mia (1)
Rocky Glenn Industrial Pa, Moosic, PA
18507
Tel.: (570) 457-7431
Emp.: 300
Frozen Food Products & Beverages Mfr
N.A.I.C.S.: 424420
Melissa Learn (Office Mgr)

J&J Snack Foods Handhelds
Corp. (1)
103 Depot St, Weston, OR 97886
Tel.: (541) 566-3511
Sales Range: $25-49.9 Million
Emp.: 110
Baked Snacks & Cookies Mfr
N.A.I.C.S.: 311991

J&J Snack Foods Transport
Corp. (1)
6000 Central Hwy, Pennsauken, NJ 08109
Tel.: (856) 665-9533
Sales Range: $100-124.9 Million
Emp.: 200
Mfr of Frozen Foods
N.A.I.C.S.: 311813

New York Pretzel, LLC (1)
200 Moore St, Brooklyn, NY 11206
Tel.: (718) 366-9800
Web Site: http://www.nypretzel.com
Snack Food Mfr
N.A.I.C.S.: 311919

Philly's Famous Water Ice, Inc. (1)
1102 N 28th St, Tampa, FL 33605
Tel.: (813) 353-8645
Web Site: http://www.phillyswirl.com
Sales Range: $25-49.9 Million
Emp.: 75
Ice Cream Mfr
N.A.I.C.S.: 311520

Pretzels, Inc. (1)
2305 E Belt Line Rd, Carrollton, TX 75006-
5463
Tel.: (972) 416-3660
Sales Range: $75-99.9 Million
Emp.: 250
Soft Pretzels Mfr
N.A.I.C.S.: 311812
Gary Powell (Pres)

The ICEE Company (1)
265 Mason Rd, La Vergne, TN
37086 (100%)
Tel.: (909) 390-4233

Web Site: http://www.icee.com
Sales Range: $100-124.9 Million
Emp.: 1,000
Frozen Beverage Distr
N.A.I.C.S.: 311919
Daniel J. Fachner (Pres & CEO)

J.B. HUNT TRANSPORT SER-
VICES, INC.
615 JB Hunt Corporate Dr, Lowell,
AR 72745-0130
Tel.: (479) 820-0000   AR
Web Site: https://www.jbhunt.com
Year Founded: 1961
JBHT—(NASDAQ)
Rev.: $12,829,665,000
Assets: $8,538,260,000
Liabilities: $4,434,502,000
Net Worth: $4,103,758,000
Earnings: $728,287,000
Emp.: 34,718
Fiscal Year-end: 12/31/23
Logistic Services
N.A.I.C.S.: 484121
John N. Roberts III (Exec Chm)
Shelley Simpson (Pres & CEO)
John Kenneth Kuhlow (CFO & Exec
VP)
Nicholas Hobbs (COO, Pres-Contract
Svcs & Exec VP)
Stuart Scott (CIO & Exec VP)
Kevin Bracy (Treas & Sr VP-Fin)
Jennifer Boattini (Gen Cousel, Sec &
Sr VP-Legal & Litigation)
Darren Field (Pres-Intermodel & Exec
VP)
Bradley Hicks (Pres-Highway Svcs &
Exec VP-People)
Brittnee Davie (VP-Mktg)
Spencer Frazier (Exec VP-Sls &
Mktg)
Eric McGee (Exec VP)
Brian Webb (Exec VP)
David Keefauver (Exec VP)
Greer Woodruff (Exec VP-Safety,
Sustainability, and Maintenance)

Subsidiaries:

J.B. Hunt Logistics, Inc. (1)
615 JB Hunt Corporate Dr, Lowell, AR
72745
Tel.: (479) 820-0000
Sales Range: $25-49.9 Million
Provider of Transportation Services
N.A.I.C.S.: 485999

J.B. Hunt Transport, Inc. (1)
615 JB Hunt Corporate Dr, Lowell, AR
72745 (100%)
Tel.: (479) 820-0000
Web Site: http://www.jbhunt.com
Trucking Service
N.A.I.C.S.: 484121
Kirk Thompson (Chm)

Subsidiary (Domestic):

Joseph Cory Holdings LLC (2)
150 Meadowlands Pkwy, Secaucus, NJ
07094
Tel.: (201) 795-1000
Web Site: http://www.corycompanies.com
Rev.: $40,798,225
Emp.: 30
Trucking Except Local
N.A.I.C.S.: 493110

L.A. Inc. (1)
615 JB Hunt Corporate Dr, Lowell, AR
72745-9143
Tel.: (479) 820-0000
Web Site: http://www.jbhunt.com
Sales Range: $50-74.9 Million
Provider of Transportation Services
N.A.I.C.S.: 484121

Special Dispatch of San Antonio,
Inc. (1)
4430 Director Dr, San Antonio, TX 78219
Tel.: (210) 359-6997
Emp.: 50
Courier Service
N.A.I.C.S.: 492210

Al Diaz (VP-Sls & Mktg)

J.JILL, INC.
4 Batterymarch Park, Quincy, MA
02169
Tel.: (617) 376-4300   DE
Web Site: https://www.jjill.com
Year Founded: 2011
JILL—(NYSE)
Rev.: $615,268,000
Assets: $466,417,000
Liabilities: $466,636,000
Net Worth: ($219,000)
Earnings: $42,175,000
Emp.: 1,115
Fiscal Year-end: 01/28/23
Women's Apparel Mfr & Retailer
N.A.I.C.S.: 315250
Claire Spofford (Pres & CEO)
Mark Webb (CFO, COO & Exec VP)
Maria Martinez (Chief HR Officer &
Sr VP)

J.W. MAYS, INC.
9 Bond St, Brooklyn, NY 11201
Tel.: (718) 624-7400   NY
Web Site: https://www.jwmays.com
Year Founded: 1924
MAYS—(NASDAQ)
Rev.: $21,593,264
Assets: $89,525,035
Liabilities: $36,626,898
Net Worth: $52,898,137
Earnings: ($406,568)
Emp.: 30
Fiscal Year-end: 07/31/24
Commercial Real Estate Property
Operator
N.A.I.C.S.: 531120
Ward N. Lyke Jr. (CFO)
Lloyd J. Shulman (Chm, Pres, CEO &
COO)
Ward N. Lyke Jr. (VP & Asst Treas)

JABIL INC.
10800 Roosevelt Blvd N, Saint Pe-
tersburg, FL 33716
Tel.: (727) 577-9749   DE
Web Site: https://www.jabil.com
Year Founded: 1966
JBL—(NYSE)
Rev.: $28,883,000,000
Assets: $17,351,000,000
Liabilities: $15,614,000,000
Net Worth: $1,737,000,000
Earnings: $1,388,000,000
Emp.: 140,000
Fiscal Year-end: 08/31/24
Electronic Components Mfr
N.A.I.C.S.: 334418
Thomas A. Sansone (Vice Chm)
Mark T. Mondello (Exec Chm)
Steven D. Borges (Exec VP-Global
Bus Units)
Michelle Smith (VP-Comm & Brand
Strategy)
Robert L. Katz (Chief Ethics & Com-
pliance Officer, Gen Counsel, Sec &
Exec VP)
Bruce A. Johnson (Chief HR Officer &
Exec VP)
Daryn Smith (Sr VP-Enterprise &
Controller-Comml)
Aileen Han (Dir-Comm & Brand Strat-
egy)
May Yap (CIO & Sr VP)
Frederic McCoy (CEO-Electronics
Mfg Svcs)
Frank McKay (Sr VP)
Roberto Ferri (Sr VP)
LaShawne Meriwether (Chief HR Offi-
cer)
Kim Newman (Acct Mgr-Global)
Michael Dastoor (CEO)

Subsidiaries:

Celetronix USA, Inc. (1)

2125 B Madera Rd, Simi Valley, CA 93065
Tel.: (805) 955-3600
Sales Range: $25-49.9 Million
Emp.: 45
High-Density Power Supplies & Power
Adapters Designer, Mfr & Distr
N.A.I.C.S.: 334419

Clothing Plus Zhejiang Ltd. (1)
No 3 Tiao Xi Dong Street, Qianyuan Town
Deqing County, Huzhou, 313216, Zhejiang,
China
Tel.: (86) 5728233027
Web Site: http://www.clothingplus.com
Apparels Mfr
N.A.I.C.S.: 313310

Digitek Electronics Ltd. (1)
Suites 1108-1111 11/F Tower 6, The Gate-
way Harbour City, Tsim Sha Tsui, Kowloon,
China (Hong Kong)
Tel.: (852) 2668 7668
Sales Range: $50-74.9 Million
Provider of Electronic Manufacturing Ser-
vices
N.A.I.C.S.: 811210

Ecologic Brands, Inc. (1)
550 Carnegie St, Manteca, CA 95337
Tel.: (510) 451-1197
Web Site: http://www.ecologicbrands.com
Chemicals Mfr
N.A.I.C.S.: 325998
Julie Corbett (CEO)

Green Point (Suzhou) Technology
Co., Ltd. (1)
No 128 Tongyuan Road Suzhou Industrial
Park, Suzhou, 215021, Jiangsu, China
Tel.: (86) 51262556917
Emp.: 3,000
Plastics Product Mfr
N.A.I.C.S.: 326199

Green Point Precision (M) Sdn,
Bhd. (1)
Lot 200 Jalan Pknk 2, Kawasan Perindus-
trian SG Petani, 08000, Sungai Petani, Ke-
dah, Malaysia
Tel.: (60) 44428688
Plastics Product Mfr
N.A.I.C.S.: 326199

Green Point Technology (ShenZhen)
Co., Ltd. (1)
No 2073 Building A2 Floors 1 to 2 Building
A3 A5 A6 & 2071Building A1, Jincheng
Road Democratic Community Shajing Street
Bao'an District, Shenzhen, 518104, Guang-
dong, China
Tel.: (86) 75581768888
Printed Circuit Assembly Mfr
N.A.I.C.S.: 334418

Jabil (Mauritius) Holdings Ltd. (1)
Les Cascades Building C/O Sim Global
Business, Edith Cavell Street, Port Louis,
Mauritius
Tel.: (230) 2129800
Web Site: http://www.jabilinc.com
Printed Circuit Assembly Mfr
N.A.I.C.S.: 334418

Jabil Advanced Mechanical Solutions
de Mexico, S de RL de C.V. (1)
Paseo Del Valle 5200-A, Guadalajara Tech-
nology Park, 45010, Zapopan, Jalisco,
Mexico
Tel.: (52) 3338191357
Business Support Services
N.A.I.C.S.: 541611

Jabil Advanced Mechanical Solutions,
Inc. (1)
10560 Dr Martin Luther King Jr Str N, Saint
Petersburg, FL 33716 (51%)
Tel.: (727) 577-9749
Web Site: http://www.jabil.com
Printed Circuit Assembly Mfr
N.A.I.C.S.: 334418

Jabil Chad Automation (1)
1565 S Sinclair St, Anaheim, CA 92806
Tel.: (714) 938-0080
Web Site: http://www.chadautomation.com
Robotics Automation Equipment, Motion
Controllers & Machine Vision Mfr
N.A.I.C.S.: 333998

Jabil Circuit (Beijing) Limited (1)

Yeqing No 9 Wangjing North RD, Chaoyang District, Beijing, 100102, China
Tel.: (86) 1067881372
Electronic Product Mfr & Distr
N.A.I.C.S.: 334413

Jabil Circuit (Shanghai) Co. Ltd. (1)
600 Tian Lin Road, Shanghai, 200233, China
Tel.: (86) 2164858585
Web Site: http://www.jabil.com
Sales Range: $75-99.9 Million
Provider of Manufacturing Services
N.A.I.C.S.: 541614

Jabil Circuit (Shenzhen) Co. Ltd. (1)
Electronics Factory Sha Jing San Yi SBI 2nd Industrial Estate, San Yi Cun Sha Jing Zhen, Shenzhen, China
Tel.: (86) 755 2725 4691
Sales Range: $75-99.9 Million
Provider of Manufacturing Services
N.A.I.C.S.: 541614

Jabil Circuit (Singapore) Pte. Ltd. (1)
16 Tampines Industrial Crescent, Singapore, 528604, Singapore (100%)
Tel.: (65) 68718200
Provider of Electronic Manufacturing Services
N.A.I.C.S.: 811210

Jabil Circuit (Suzhou) Ltd. (1)
No 7 Yang Qing Road Lou Feng Demonstrative Zone, Suzhou Industrial Park, Suzhou, 215021, China
Tel.: (86) 51267451710
Electronic Product Mfr & Distr
N.A.I.C.S.: 334413

Jabil Circuit Austria GmbH (1)
Gutheil Schoder Gasse 17, 1230, Vienna, Austria (100%)
Tel.: (43) 1661053423
Sales Range: $75-99.9 Million
Emp.: 200
Provider of Manufacturing Services
N.A.I.C.S.: 333310

Jabil Circuit Automotive, SAS (1)
8 Rue De Kervezennec, 29228, Brest, France (100%)
Tel.: (33) 298142000
Web Site: http://www.jabilcircuit.com
Sales Range: $25-49.9 Million
Emp.: 500
Provider of Electronic Manufacturing Services
N.A.I.C.S.: 811210

Jabil Circuit Financial, Inc. (1)
103 Foulk Rd, Wilmington, DE 19803
Tel.: (302) 576-2710
Electronics Design Mfr
N.A.I.C.S.: 334418

Jabil Circuit Gyarto K.F.T. (1)
Huszar Andor Ut 1, Tiszaujvaros, 3580, Hungary (100%)
Tel.: (36) 49548500
Sales Range: $800-899.9 Million
Emp.: 4,000
Provider of Manufacturing Services
N.A.I.C.S.: 333310

Jabil Circuit India Pvt. Ltd. (1)
B-26 MIDC Industrial Area, Ranjangaon Taluka Shirur, Pune, 412220, Maharashtra State, India
Tel.: (91) 2138662109
Web Site: http://www.jabil.com
Mfr Services
N.A.I.C.S.: 333310

Jabil Circuit Italia, S.r.l (1)
(100%)
Tel.: (39) 0823582499
Web Site: http://www.jabilitaly.com
Electrical & Electronic Components Manufacturing Services
N.A.I.C.S.: 333310

Jabil Circuit Italia, S.r.l. (1)
Strada provinciale per Casapuzzano, Zona Industriale ASI, 81025, Marcianise, Caserta, Italy
Tel.: (39) 0823582600
Sales Range: $125-149.9 Million
Provider of Manufacturing Services
N.A.I.C.S.: 333310

Jabil Circuit Japan, Inc. (1)
7/F Tamachi Nikko Bldg 5-29-14 Shiba, Minato-ku, Tokyo, Japan
Tel.: (81) 3 3452 8611
Sales Range: $100-124.9 Million
Printed Circuit Board Mfr
N.A.I.C.S.: 334412

Jabil Circuit Poland sp. z o.o. (1)
Ul Lotnicza 2, Kwidzyn, 82-500, Poland
Tel.: (48) 552622793
Web Site: http://www.jabil.com
Sales Range: $125-149.9 Million
Emp.: 5,000
Provider of Manufacturing Services
N.A.I.C.S.: 333310

Jabil Circuit Technology India Pvt. Ltd. (1)
B-26 Midc Rd Midc Industrial Area Ranjangaon Shirur Taluka, Pune, 412209, Maharashtra, India
Tel.: (91) 2138662109
Information Technology Services
N.A.I.C.S.: 423430

Jabil Circuit U.K., Limited (1)
Progress Cl, Coventry, West Midlands, United Kingdom
Tel.: (44) 2476561250
Emp.: 55
Electrical Component Repair & Maintenance Services
N.A.I.C.S.: 811210

Jabil Circuit de Chihuahua S. de R.L. de C.V. (1)
Tel.: (52) 6144426000
Web Site: http://www.jabil.com
Mfr Services
N.A.I.C.S.: 333310

Jabil Circuit de Mexico, S de RL de C.V. (1)
No 1993-1 floor Colonia Lomas de Zapopan, 45130, Guadalajara, Mexico
Tel.: (52) 3338191300
Industrial Equipment & Machinery Mfr
N.A.I.C.S.: 333998

Jabil Circuit of Michigan, Inc. (1)
3800 Giddings Rd, Auburn Hills, MI 48326-1519
Tel.: (248) 292-6000
Web Site: http://www.jabil.com
Sales Range: $1-4.9 Billion
Emp.: 100
N.A.I.C.S.: 334220

Jabil Circuit, Inc. - San Jose Plant (1)
30 Great Oaks Blvd, San Jose, CA 95119
Tel.: (408) 361-3200
Web Site: http://www.jabil.com
Sales Range: $125-149.9 Million
Emp.: 400
N.A.I.C.S.: 334220

Jabil Circuit, Inc. - Tempe Plant (1)
615 S River Dr, Tempe, AZ 85281-3099
Tel.: (480) 968-6790
Web Site: http://www.jabil.com
Sales Range: $250-299.9 Million
Emp.: 800
Mfr of Circuit Boards
N.A.I.C.S.: 334412

Jabil Circuit, LLC (1)
10500 Dr Martin Luther King Jr St N, Saint Petersburg, FL 33716-2307
Tel.: (408) 361-3200
Information Technology Consulting Services
N.A.I.C.S.: 541512

Jabil Circuit, LLC (1)
8 Deer Park, Fairways Business Park, Livingston, EH54 8GA, United Kingdom (100%)
Tel.: (44) 1506432266
Sales Range: $125-149.9 Million
Emp.: 250
N.A.I.C.S.: 334220

Jabil Circuit, SAS (1)
8 Rue De Kervezennec, Brest, 29228, Finistere, France
Tel.: (33) 298142000
Emp.: 70
Electronic Parts & Equipment Distr
N.A.I.C.S.: 423690

Forbes Ian James Alexander (Pres)

Jabil Global Services India Private Limited (1)
107-A First Floor S107-A First Flooralcon Aurum Jasola District Centre, Jasola Vihar, Delhi, 110025, India
Tel.: (91) 1141060073
Electronic Parts & Equipment Distr
N.A.I.C.S.: 423690

Jabil Global Services Netherlands B.V. (1)
(100%)
Tel.: (31) 203167459
Web Site: http://www.iqor.com
Sales Range: $25-49.9 Million
Emp.: 80
Provider of Manufacturing Services
N.A.I.C.S.: 333310

Jabil Global Services Poland sp z.o.o. (1)
Fordonska 248/G, Bydgoszcz, 85-766, Poland
Tel.: (48) 525259000
Software Development Services
N.A.I.C.S.: 541511

Jabil Global Services de Mexico, S.A. de C.V. (1)
Blvd Montebello No 737, Parque Industrial Colonial, Reynosa, 88787, Mexico
Tel.: (52) 8999211200
Electrical & Electronic Component Repair & Maintenance Services
N.A.I.C.S.: 811210

Jabil Japan, Inc. (1)
Tel.: (81) 353247111
Web Site: http://www.jabil.com
Electronic Assembly Products Mfr
N.A.I.C.S.: 334418

Jabil Sdn Bhd Ltd. (1)
Level 3 4 GBS Mayang Jalan Mayang Pasir 1, Bayan Baru, 11950, Bayan Lepas, Pulau Pinang, Malaysia
Tel.: (60) 48105000
Information Technology Consulting Services
N.A.I.C.S.: 541512

Jabil do Brasil Industria Eletro-eletronica Ltda. (1)
Avenida Matrinxa 687, Distrito Industrial, Manaus, 69075-150, Amazonas, Brazil
Tel.: (55) 9221219400
Emp.: 1,700
Electronic Components Mfr
N.A.I.C.S.: 334413

Kasalis Inc. (1)
11 N Ave, Burlington, MA 01803
Tel.: (781) 273-6200
Web Site: http://www.kasalis.com
Printed Circuit Assembly Mfr
N.A.I.C.S.: 334418

Lewis Engineering Company (1)
1608 E Houston St, Marshall, TX 75670
Tel.: (903) 938-6754
Web Site: http://lewisengineingco.com
Miscellaneous Fabricated Metal Product Mfr
N.A.I.C.S.: 332999
Doug Lewis (VP)
Steve Lewis (Pres)
Donna Bell (Office Mgr)
Jeff Thomas (Mgr-Fabrication)
Todd Aucoin (Mgr-Quality Control)
Josh Hopkins (Supvr-CNC)
Dereck Bible (Supvr-Engrg)

NPA de Mexico S de RL de CV (1)
Sor Juana Ines de la Cruz 20150-5 Cd Industrial Otay, 20150, Tijuana, Baja California, Mexico
Tel.: (52) 6642313700
Transportation Services
N.A.I.C.S.: 488490

New Ventures Group LLC (1)
3246 Sharp Rd, Glenwood, MD 21738
Tel.: (301) 509-1899
Business Management Consulting Services
N.A.I.C.S.: 541618

Nypro Alabama LLC (1)
208 Nypro Ln, Dothan, AL 36305
Tel.: (334) 702-2583
Injection Molded Product Distr

N.A.I.C.S.: 423310

Nypro Denmark ApS (1)
Arne Jacobsens Alle 7, 2300, Copenhagen, Denmark
Tel.: (45) 70204221
Technical Professional & Scientific Services
N.A.I.C.S.: 541990

Nypro Deutschland GmbH (1)
Pflegmuhleweg 61, 75438, Stuttgart, Germany
Tel.: (49) 704393450
Emp.: 300
Electronic Parts & Equipment Distr
N.A.I.C.S.: 423690

Nypro France SAS (1)
ZA Jean Monnet, Fontenay-sur-Eure, 28630, France
Tel.: (33) 237258151
Emp.: 150
Rubber & Plastic Product Mfr
N.A.I.C.S.: 326199
Tiequrart Thierry (Gen Mgr)

Nypro Global Holdings CV (1)
Keplerstraat 34, Badhoevedorp, 1171 CD, Netherlands
Tel.: (31) 203055700
Holding Company
N.A.I.C.S.: 551112

Nypro Healthcare Baja Inc. (1)
2195 Britannia Blvd Ste 107, San Diego, CA 92154
Tel.: (619) 498-9250
Surgical & Medical Instrument Distr
N.A.I.C.S.: 423450

Nypro Hungary Muanyagtechnika Kft (1)
Bacso Bela Utca 41, 2890, Tata, Hungary
Tel.: (36) 34556420
Chemical Products Distr
N.A.I.C.S.: 424690

Nypro Inc. (1)
101 Union St, Clinton, MA 01510
Tel.: (978) 365-9721
Medical Diagnostics Equipment & Analytic Instruments Designer & Mfr
N.A.I.C.S.: 339112
Chuck Henry (VP-Ops & Engrg)

Subsidiary (Domestic):

NP Medical Inc. (2)
101 Union St, Clinton, MA 01510-2908
Tel.: (978) 365-9721
Web Site: https://www.npmedical.com
Sales Range: $50-74.9 Million
Emp.: 103
Plastics Product Mfr
N.A.I.C.S.: 326199

Nypro Asheville Inc. (2)
100 Vista Blvd, Arden, NC 28704-9457
Tel.: (828) 684-3141
Sales Range: $50-74.9 Million
Emp.: 350
Plastics Product Mfr
N.A.I.C.S.: 326199

Unit (Domestic):

Nypro Chicago (2)
955 Tri-State Pkwy, Gurnee, IL 60031-5113
Tel.: (847) 855-9555
Web Site: http://www.nypro.com
Sales Range: $50-74.9 Million
Emp.: 200
Plastics Product Mfr
N.A.I.C.S.: 326199

Subsidiary (Non-US):

Nypro Guadalajara (2)
Avenida Ignacio Jacobo 20, Parque Industrial Los Belenes, Zapopan, 45184, Jalisco, Mexico
Tel.: (52) 33 3819 5000
Web Site: http://www.jabil.com
Sales Range: $50-74.9 Million
Emp.: 300
Packaging & Molding/Assembly Operations
N.A.I.C.S.: 326199

Subsidiary (Domestic):

Nypro Kanaak Iowa Inc. (2)

Jabil Inc.—(Continued)

400 N Harvey Rd, Mount Pleasant, IA 52641-3100 **(100%)**
Tel.: (319) 385-4426
Web Site: http://www.nypro.com
Sales Range: $25-49.9 Million
Emp.: 80
Plastics Product Mfr
N.A.I.C.S.: 326199

Nypro Kanaak-Alabama LLC **(2)**
208 Nypro Ln, Dothan, AL 36305-1081
Tel.: (334) 702-2583
Web Site: http://www.nypro.com
Rev.: $29,800,000
Emp.: 105
Plastics Product Mfr
N.A.I.C.S.: 326199

Subsidiary (Non-US):

Nypro Puerto Rico Inc. **(2)**
(100%)
Tel.: (787) 738-4211
Web Site: http://www.nypro.com
Sales Range: $125-149.9 Million
Emp.: 400
Plastics Product Mfr
N.A.I.C.S.: 326199

Subsidiary (Domestic):

Nypro San Diego Inc. **(2)**
505 Main St, Chula Vista, CA 91911-6065
Tel.: (619) 482-7033
Web Site: http://www.nypro.com
Sales Range: $50-74.9 Million
Emp.: 135
Plastics Product Mfr
N.A.I.C.S.: 326199

Nypro Iowa Inc. **(1)**
400 N Harvey Rd, Mount Pleasant, IA 52641
Tel.: (319) 385-4426
Web Site: http://www.jabil.com
Emp.: 85
Injection Mold Product Mfr
N.A.I.C.S.: 333248

Nypro Limited **(1)**
Corke Abbey Ave, Cork Great, Bray, Dublin, Ireland
Tel.: (353) 12043300
Emp.: 350
Medical Equipment Mfr
N.A.I.C.S.: 339992

Nypro Nagyigmand Vagyonkezelo Kft **(1)**
Acsi ut 26, 2942, Budapest, Hungary
Tel.: (36) 34556423
Rubber & Plastic Product Mfr
N.A.I.C.S.: 326199
Andres Bondor *(Plant Mgr)*

Nypro Realty Corp **(1)**
101 Union St, Clinton, MA 01510
Tel.: (978) 368-8966
Emp.: 5
Real Estate Development Services
N.A.I.C.S.: 531390

Nypro de la Frontera, S de RL de CV **(1)**
Manuel Sandoval Vallarta No 420, Ciudad Juarez, 32557, Chihuahua, Mexico
Tel.: (52) 6568925100
Plastics Product Mfr
N.A.I.C.S.: 326199
Antonio Rangel *(Gen Mgr)*

Plasticast Hungary Korlatolt Felel-ossegu Tarsasag **(1)**
Acsi ut 26, 2942, Budapest, Hungary
Tel.: (36) 34556420
Web Site: http://www.plasticoscastella.com
Injection Mold Product Mfr
N.A.I.C.S.: 333248

Precision Communication Services Corp. **(1)**
99 Signet Dr, North York, ON, Canada
Tel.: (416) 749-0110
Communication Equipment Mfr
N.A.I.C.S.: 334220

Procureability, Inc. **(1)**
221 N Hogan St 389, Jacksonville, FL 32202

Tel.: (904) 432-7001
Web Site: http://www.procureability.com
Sales Range: $10-24.9 Million
Emp.: 56
Staffing & Recruitment Services
N.A.I.C.S.: 541612

Radius Hong Kong Ltd **(1)**
513 5/F Building 12 W No 12 Science Park West Ave, Hong Kong Science Park Shatin, Hong Kong, NT, China (Hong Kong)
Tel.: (852) 26555790
Emp.: 12
Engineering & Design Services
N.A.I.C.S.: 541330

Retronix Global Inc. **(1)**
1007 S Heatherwilde Blvd Ste 300, Pfluger-ville, TX 78660
Tel.: (737) 787-8555
Laser Reballing Services
N.A.I.C.S.: 518210

Retronix Ltd. **(1)**
North Caldeen Road, Scotland, Coatbridge, ML5 4EF, United Kingdom
Tel.: (44) 1236433345
Web Site: https://retronix.com
Laser Reballing Services
N.A.I.C.S.: 518210

Somera Communications Pte. Ltd. **(1)**
Level 25 Bank Of China Tower 1 Garden Road, Central, China (Hong Kong)
Tel.: (852) 22511868
Communication Equipment Mfr
N.A.I.C.S.: 334220

Taiwan Green Point Enterprises Co., Ltd **(1)**
No 256 Sec 1 Shenlin Rd, Daya Dist Ta-Ya Dist, Taichung, 428, Taiwan
Tel.: (886) 425666123
Plastics Product Mfr
N.A.I.C.S.: 326199

Tel-NT Brazil Comercio de Equipa-mentos de Telecomunicaoes Ltda. **(1)**
Rua Antonio Felamingo 162, Valinhos, 13279-452, Sao Paulo, Brazil
Tel.: (55) 1921017300
Web Site: http://www.tel-nt.com.br
Telecommunication Maintenance Services
N.A.I.C.S.: 811210
Cristian Nusimovich *(Dir-Ops-South America)*

Telmar Network Technology B.V. **(1)**
Maasheseweg 87B, 5804 AB, Venray, Neth-erlands
Tel.: (31) 478470100
Telecommunication Repair Services
N.A.I.C.S.: 811210

Telmar Network Technology Co., Ltd. **(1)**
No 43 Wenxing Rd, Taipei, 333, Taoyuan, Taiwan
Tel.: (886) 33187688
Telecommunication Repair Services
N.A.I.C.S.: 811210

Telmar Network Technology Inc. **(1)**
Tel.: (972) 836-0400
Web Site: http://www.iqor.com
Sales Range: $125-149.9 Million
Emp.: 200
Telecommunication Equipment Distr
N.A.I.C.S.: 423690

Division (Non-US):

Telmar Network Technology-Council Bluffs **(2)**
Tel.: (712) 322-2725
Web Site: http://www.telmarnt.com
Sales Range: $50-74.9 Million
Emp.: 100
Provider of Reused Telecommunication Equipment
N.A.I.C.S.: 423690

Telmar Network Technology S.r.l. **(1)**
Callao Avenue 852 8th Fl, Buenos Aires, 1023, Argentina
Tel.: (54) 1135355050
Telecommunication Repair Services
N.A.I.C.S.: 811210

Telmar Network Technology Sdn Bhd **(1)**
Plot 50 Hilir Sungai Keluang 2 Bayan Lepas Industrial Park, 11900, Penang, Malaysia
Tel.: (60) 46439977
Telecommunication Repair Services
N.A.I.C.S.: 811210

Westing Green (Tianjin) Plastic Co., Ltd **(1)**
Tel.: (86) 2223802046
Printed Circuit Assembly Manufacturing
N.A.I.C.S.: 334418

YouTransactor SAS **(1)**
32 Rue Brancion, 75015, Paris, France
Tel.: (33) 178054906
Web Site: https://www.youtransactor.com
Payment Transaction Services
N.A.I.C.S.: 522320

JACK HENRY & ASSOCIATES, INC.

663 Highway 60, Monett, MO 65708
Tel.: (417) 235-6652 DE
Web Site: https://www.jackhenry.com
Year Founded: 1976
JKHY—(NASDAQ)
Rev.: $2,215,543,000
Assets: $2,924,481,000
Liabilities: $1,082,117,000
Net Worth: $1,842,364,000
Earnings: $381,816,000
Emp.: 7,170
Fiscal Year-end: 06/30/24
Integrated Computer Systems for In-House & Service Bureau Data Pro-cessing to Banks & Other Financial Institutions
N.A.I.C.S.: 541512
David B. Foss *(Chm)*
Matthew C. Flanigan *(Vice Chm)*
Stacey E. Zengel *(Sr VP)*
Gregory R. Adelson *(Pres & CEO)*
Craig K. Morgan *(Gen Counsel & Sec)*
Mimi L. Carsley *(CFO & Treas)*

Subsidiaries:

Audiotel Corporation **(1)**
15510 Wright Brothers Dr, Addison, TX 75001
Tel.: (972) 239-4486
Software Publishing Services
N.A.I.C.S.: 513210

Banno, LLC **(1)**
6525 Chancellor Dr Ste 101, Cedar Falls, IA 50613
Tel.: (319) 266-7574
Web Site: http://www.banno.com
Software Development Services
N.A.I.C.S.: 541511

Ensenta Corporation **(1)**
303 Twin Dolphin Dr Ste 201, Redwood City, CA 94065-1417
Web Site: http://www.ensenta.com
Custom Computer Programming Services
N.A.I.C.S.: 541511

Gladiator Technology Services, Inc. **(1)**
11395 Old Roswell Rd, Alpharetta, GA 30009
Tel.: (678) 461-4620
Web Site: http://www.gladiatortechnology.com
Sales Range: $900-999.9 Million
Emp.: 50
Information Technology Security Services for Financial Institutions
N.A.I.C.S.: 541519

Goldleaf Technologies, LLC **(1)**
9020 Overlook Blvd 3rd Fl, Brentwood, TN 37027
Tel.: (615) 250-2100
Software Development Services
N.A.I.C.S.: 541511

JHA Payment Processing Solutions, Inc. **(1)**
1100 Olive Way Ste 320, Seattle, WA 98101-1861

Tel.: (206) 352-3500
Web Site: http://www.weknowpayments.com
Software Development Services
N.A.I.C.S.: 541511

Jack Henry Banking **(1)**
663 W Hwy 60, Monett, MO 65708
Tel.: (417) 235-6652
Web Site: http://www.jackhenry.com
Sales Range: $700-749.9 Million
Emp.: 3,700
Integrated Computer Systems for Banks
N.A.I.C.S.: 541512
Stacey E. Zengel *(Pres)*

Jack Henry Services, LP **(1)**
663 W Hwy 60, Monett, MO 65708
Tel.: (417) 235-6652
Web Site: http://www.jackhenry.com
Sales Range: $400-449.9 Million
Emp.: 1,300
Provider of Integrated Computer Systems for In-House & Service Bureau Data Pro-cessing to Banks & other Financial Institu-tions
N.A.I.C.S.: 541512

Jack Henry Systems, LP **(1)**
663 W Hwy 60, Monett, MO 65708
Tel.: (417) 235-6652
Web Site: http://www.jackhenry.com
Sales Range: $400-449.9 Million
Emp.: 1,300
Integrated Computer Systems for In-House & Service Bureau Data Processing to Banks & other Financial Institutions
N.A.I.C.S.: 541512

Jack Henry, LLC **(1)**
663 Hwy 60, Monett, MO 65708
Tel.: (417) 235-6652
Web Site: http://www.jackhenry.com
Sales Range: $350-399.9 Million
Emp.: 1,100
Provider of Integrated Computer Systems for In-House & Service Bureau Data Pro-cessing to Banks & other Financial Institu-tions
N.A.I.C.S.: 541512

ProfitStars/Alogent **(1)**
350 Technology Blvd Ste 200, Norcross, GA 30092 **(100%)**
Tel.: (770) 752-6400
Web Site: http://www.profitstars.com
Sales Range: $75-99.9 Million
Emp.: 493
Financial & Retail Institution Deposit Auto-mation & Payment Processing Software & Services
N.A.I.C.S.: 513210

Unit (Domestic):

ProfitStars **(2)**
1025 Central Expy S, Allen, TX 75013-2790 **(100%)**
Tel.: (972) 359-5500
Web Site: http://www.profitstars.com
Sales Range: $50-74.9 Million
Emp.: 200
Products & Services Designed to Improve Financial Institutions Operating Perfor-mance
N.A.I.C.S.: 513210

Subsidiary (Domestic):

ProfitStars **(2)**
8 Cadillac Dr Ste 300, Brentwood, TN 37027
Tel.: (615) 221-8400
Web Site: http://www.profitstars.com
Sales Range: $75-99.9 Million
Emp.: 100
Financial Institution Automated Clearing House & Remote Deposit Software & Ser-vices
N.A.I.C.S.: 513210
Russ Bernthal *(Pres)*

Unit (Domestic):

ProfitStars - DataTrade Division **(2)**
3653 S Ave, Springfield, MO 65807
Tel.: (417) 882-1576
Sales Range: $100-124.9 Million
Financial Institution Banking & Transaction Processing Software & Services

N.A.I.C.S.: 513210
Colin McAllister (Sr VP)

Subsidiary (Domestic):

Vanguard Software Group LLC (2)
195 Wekiva Springs Rd Ste 340, Longwood, FL 32779
Tel.: (407) 475-0005
Web Site: http://www.vsgsolutions.com
Information Technology Solutions
N.A.I.C.S.: 513210
Mark Hill (Pres)

Symitar Systems, Inc. (1)
8985 Balboa Ave, San Diego, CA 92123-1507
Tel.: (619) 542-6700
Web Site: http://www.symitar.com
Sales Range: $100-124.9 Million
Emp.: 500
Integrated Computer Systems for In-House & Service Bureau Data Processing to Banks & Other Financial Institutions
N.A.I.C.S.: 541511

Sys-Tech, Inc. (1)
23001 W 81st St, Shawnee Mission, KS 66227-2619
Tel.: (913) 422-3232
Web Site: http://www.jackhenry.com
Sales Range: $25-49.9 Million
Emp.: 20
Provider of Electronic Parts & Equipment
N.A.I.C.S.: 423690

iPay Technologies, LLC (1)
2323 Ring Road, Elizabethtown, KY 42701
Tel.: (270) 737-0590
Web Site: http://www.jackhenry.com
Electronic Financial Payment Services
N.A.I.C.S.: 522320
Robert Forman (Sr VP-Payment Strategy)

JACK IN THE BOX INC.
9357 Spectrum Center Blvd, San Diego, CA 92123
Tel.: (858) 571-2121   DE
Web Site:
https://www.jackinthebox.com
Year Founded: 1951
JACK—(NASDAQ)
Rev.: $1,143,670,000
Assets: $1,750,137,000
Liabilities: $2,568,019,000
Net Worth: ($817,882,000)
Earnings: $165,755,000
Emp.: 5,300
Fiscal Year-end: 10/03/21
Fast Food Restaurant Owner, Operator & Franchisor
N.A.I.C.S.: 722513
Darin S. Harris (CEO)
Sarah Super (Chief Legal & Risk Officer, Sec & Sr VP)
Dawn E. Hooper (Interim Principal Financial Officer)
Tim Linderman (Chief Franchise & Corp Dev Officer & Sr VP)
Tony Darden (COO & Sr VP)
Ryan Ostrom (CMO & Exec VP)
Doug Cook (CTO & Sr VP)
Steven Piano (Chief People Officer & Sr VP)
Dean Gordon (Chief Supply Chain Officer & Sr VP)

Subsidiaries:

Del Taco Restaurants, Inc. (1)
25521 Commercentre Dr, Lake Forest, CA 92630
Tel.: (949) 462-9300
Web Site: http://www.deltaco.com
Holding Company; Restaurant Operator & Franchisor
N.A.I.C.S.: 551112
Steven L. Brake (CFO & Exec VP)
Chad Gretzema (Pres)
Tim Hackbardt (CMO)

Subsidiary (Domestic):

Del Taco LLC (2)

25521 Commercentre Dr, Lake Forest, CA 92360
Tel.: (949) 462-9300
Web Site: https://www.deltaco.com
Quick Service Mexican Restaurant Franchisor
N.A.I.C.S.: 722513

Qdoba Mexican Grill Inc. (1)
4865 Ward Rd Ste 500, Wheat Ridge, CO 80033   (100%)
Tel.: (720) 898-2300
Web Site: http://www.qdoba.com
Sales Range: $50-74.9 Million
Emp.: 175
Mexican Restaurant Operator
N.A.I.C.S.: 722513
Keith Guilbault (CEO)
Eric Williams (VP-Franchise & License Ops)
Jim Sullivan (Chief Dev Officer)

JACKSAM CORPORATION
3100 Airway Ave Ste 138, Costa Mesa, CA 92626   NV
Web Site:
https://www.convectium.com
Year Founded: 1989
JKSM—(OTCIQ)
Rev.: $1,455,880
Assets: $276,754
Liabilities: $5,259,790
Net Worth: ($4,983,036)
Earnings: ($1,259,191)
Emp.: 7
Fiscal Year-end: 12/31/23
Vaporizer Cartridge Filling & Capping Mfr
N.A.I.C.S.: 325998
Mark Adams (Pres & CEO)

JACKSON ACQUISITION COMPANY
2655 Northwinds Pkwy, Alpharetta, GA 30009
Tel.: (678) 690-1079   DE
Web Site:
https://www.jacksonacquisitions.com
Year Founded: 2021
RJAC—(NYSE)
Rev.: $13,537,755
Assets: $229,635,335
Liabilities: $237,547,518
Net Worth: ($7,912,183)
Earnings: $11,484,257
Emp.: 2
Fiscal Year-end: 12/31/22
Investment Services
N.A.I.C.S.: 523999
John Ellis Bush (Chm)
Richard L. Jackson (Pres & CEO)
Douglas B. Kline (CFO & Treas)

JACKSON FINANCIAL INC.
1 Corporate Way, Lansing, MI 48951
Tel.: (517) 381-5500   DE
Web Site: https://www.jackson.com
Year Founded: 1961
JXN—(NYSE)
Rev.: $3,159,000,000
Assets: $330,255,000,000
Liabilities: $319,921,000,000
Net Worth: $10,334,000,000
Earnings: $899,000,000
Emp.: 3,015
Fiscal Year-end: 12/31/23
Financial Holding Company; Insurance Products & Services
N.A.I.C.S.: 551111
Don W. Cummings (CFO, Chief Acctg Officer & Exec VP)

Subsidiaries:

Jackson National Life Insurance Company (1)
1 Corporate Way, Lansing, MI 48951
Tel.: (517) 381-5500
Web Site: https://www.jackson.com

Sales Range: $1-4.9 Billion
Emp.: 3,500
Insurance & Annuities
N.A.I.C.S.: 524113
Marcia L. Wadsten (Chief Actuary & Sr VP)
Laura L. Prieskorn (COO & Exec VP)
Dana Rapier (Chief HR Officer & Sr VP)
Scott E. Romine (Pres/CEO-NPH)
Dev D. Ganguly (COO & Exec VP)
Michael Falcon (CEO-Jackson Holdings, LLC)
Scott Golde (VP & Deputy Gen Counsel-Insurance)
Liz Werner (Sr VP-IR)
Carrie Chelko (Gen Counsel)

Subsidiary (Domestic):

Jackson National Asset Management LLC (2)
225 W Wacker Dr Ste 900 Ste 1200, Chicago, IL 60606
Tel.: (312) 634-2500
Asset Management Services
N.A.I.C.S.: 523940
Erin Balcaitis (Mgr-Sub-Adviser Oversight)
Mike Piszczek (VP)
Nora Platt (Supvr-Fund Acctg)

Jackson National Life Distributors LLC (2)
7601 Technology Way, Denver, CO 80237
Tel.: (720) 489-6400
Life Insurance Agency
N.A.I.C.S.: 524210

PPM America, Inc. (1)
225 W Wacker Dr Ste 1200, Chicago, IL 60606-1276
Tel.: (312) 634-2500
Web Site: https://www.ppmamerica.com
Sales Range: $100-124.9 Million
Emp.: 225
Investment Management
N.A.I.C.S.: 523940
Julie Bruzek (Mng Dir-Mktg & Comm)
Eric Maskalunas (Exec VP, Head-Distr & Reg Dir-Midwest)
Michael Markowitz (Exec VP & Head-Bus Dev)
Robert Boles (Sr VP & Head-HR)
Melissa Binder (Mng Dir-Distr)

JACO ELECTRONICS, INC.
145 Oser Ave, Hauppauge, NY 11788
Tel.: (631) 273-5500   NY
Web Site:
http://www.jacodisplays.com
Year Founded: 1961
JACO—(OTCIQ)
Electronic Components & Display Products Mfr & Distr
N.A.I.C.S.: 334419
Herbert Entenberg (Sec)
Joel A. Girsky (Pres)
Jeffrey A. Gash (CFO)

JACOBS ENGINEERING GROUP, INC.
1999 Bryan St Ste 3500, Dallas, TX 75201   DE
Web Site: https://www.jacobs.com
Year Founded: 1947
J—(NYSE)
Rev.: $16,352,414,000
Assets: $14,617,109,000
Liabilities: $8,017,027,000
Net Worth: $6,600,082,000
Earnings: $665,777,000
Emp.: 60,000
Fiscal Year-end: 09/29/23
Architectural Engineering & Construction Services
N.A.I.C.S.: 541330
Robert V. Pragada (Chm & CEO)
Marietta Hannigan (Chief Strategy, Corp Dev & Comm Officer & Exec VP)
Joanne E. Caruso (Chief Legal & Admin Officer & Exec VP)
Bruce T. Crawford (Sr VP-Strategic Dev & Critical Mission Solutions)

Shelie Gustafson (Chief People & Inclusion Officer & Exec VP)
Caesar Nieves (Sr VP-Cyber & Intelligence)
Jennifer Richmond (Sr VP-Sls-Federal & Environmental Solutions)
Patrick X. Hill (Pres-People & Places Solutions & Exec VP)
Steve Arnette (Pres-Critical Mission Solutions & Exec VP)
Madhuri A. Andrews (Chief Digital & Info Officer & Exec VP)
William B. Allen Jr. (Chief Acctg Officer & Sr VP)
William B. Allen Jr. (Chief Acctg Officer & Sr VP)

Subsidiaries:

Aquenta Consulting Pty Ltd (1)
Level 6 30 Flinders, PO Box 152, Rundle Mall, Adelaide, 5000, SA, Australia
Tel.: (61) 871005352
Web Site: http://www.aquenta.com.au
Business Management Consulting Services
N.A.I.C.S.: 541611
Mike McClosky (Mng Dir)

Blue Canopy Group, LLC (1)
11091 Sunset Hills Rd Ste 777, Reston, VA 20190   (100%)
Tel.: (703) 896-4000
Web Site: http://www.bluecanopy.com
Computer System Design Services
N.A.I.C.S.: 541512
Brendan Harris (VP-Div & Deputy Gen Mgr)

CH2M HILL Argentina S.A (1)
Azara 841 Piso 1 Ciudad Autonama de Buenos Aires, Buenos Aires, 1267, Argentina
Tel.: (54) 1143090200
Engineering & Construction Services
N.A.I.C.S.: 236220
Manuel Aguirre (Sr VP & Reg Mng Dir)

CH2M HILL Companies, Ltd. (1)
9191 S Jamaica St, Englewood, CO 80112   (100%)
Tel.: (303) 771-0900
Sales Range: $5-14.9 Billion
Engineering, Planning, Economics, Construction Operations & Management Services
N.A.I.C.S.: 541330
Rick Abelson (Dir-Master Plng-Urban Programs)
Manuel Aguirre (Mgr-Area-Construction)

Subsidiary (Domestic):

CH2M HILL Engineers, Inc. (2)
9191 S Jamaica St, Englewood, CO 80112   (100%)
Tel.: (303) 771-0900
Engineeering Services
N.A.I.C.S.: 541330

CH2M HILL, Inc. (2)
9191 S Jamaica St, Englewood, CO 80112   (100%)
Tel.: (303) 771-0900
Environmental & Transportation Engineering Services
N.A.I.C.S.: 541330
Chien Hsu (Engr-Mechanical)
Rick Abelson (Dir-Master Plng-Urban Programs)
Omur Akay (Sr VP)

Subsidiary (Domestic):

CH2M HILL Alaska, Inc. (3)
949 E 36th Ave Ste 500, Anchorage, AK 99508
Tel.: (907) 762-1500
Engineering, Planning, Construction Operations & Management Services
N.A.I.C.S.: 541330
Bryan Clemenz (Dir-Bus Dev-Alaska)

Subsidiary (Non-US):

CH2M HILL United Kingdom (3)
2nd Floor Cottons Centre Cottons Lane, London, SE1 2QG, United Kingdom

Jacobs Engineering Group, Inc.—(Continued)

Tel.: (44) 203 980 2000
Engineering, Construction Operations &
Management Services
N.A.I.C.S.: 541330

Subsidiary (Domestic):

Operations Management International, Inc. (3)
9191 S Jamaica St, Englewood, CO
80112 **(100%)**
Tel.: (303) 740-0019
Utility Operation & Environmental Facility
Management Services
N.A.I.C.S.: 221320

Subsidiary (Non-US):

Halcrow Holdings Limited (2)
2nd Floor Cottons Centre Cottons Lane,
London, SE1 2QG, United
Kingdom **(100%)**
Tel.: (44) 2039802000
Web Site: http://www.halcrow.com
Holding Company; Engineering & Management Consulting Services
N.A.I.C.S.: 551112

Subsidiary (Non-US):

Halcrow China Limited (3)
6th Floor 633 Kings Road North Point,
Hong Kong, China (Hong Kong)
Tel.: (852) 2880 9788
Engineeering Services
N.A.I.C.S.: 541330

Halcrow Group Ireland Limited (3)
Saint Johns House High Street, Tallaght,
Dublin, 24, Ireland
Tel.: (353) 1 404 3900
Engineering & Management Consulting
Services
N.A.I.C.S.: 541330

Subsidiary (US):

Halcrow, Inc. (3)
2591 Knapp St, Brooklyn, NY 11235
Tel.: (347) 713-1290
Engineering Design, Construction & Program Management Services
N.A.I.C.S.: 541330

CH2M HILL Singapore Pte. Ltd. (1)
150 Beach Road Level 32 33 34, Singapore, 189720, Singapore
Tel.: (65) 63910350
Architectural & Engineering Consultant Services
N.A.I.C.S.: 541330

CH2M HILL do Brasil Engenharia Ltda. (1)
Rua do Rocio 351 CJ 11 12 61 e 62 Vila
Olimpia, Sao Paulo, 04552-000, Brazil
Tel.: (55) 1130400800
Engineering & Construction Services
N.A.I.C.S.: 236220
Vanessa Sousa *(Mgr-HR)*

Compass Technology Services, Inc. (1)
5449 Bells Ferry Rd, Acworth, GA 30102
Tel.: (770) 701-2500
Web Site: http://www.compassts.com
Sales Range: $10-24.9 Million
Emp.: 71
Engineeering Services
N.A.I.C.S.: 541330

Consulting Engineering Services LLC. (1)
B/H Al Najah School Way No 2102 Bldg No
24 Rex Road, PO Box 2302, Ruwi, Oman
Tel.: (968) 24705152
Engineering & Consulting Services
N.A.I.C.S.: 541330

EK Design Services, Inc. (1)
7300 N Kendall Dr Ste 400, Miami, FL
33156
Tel.: (305) 670-1233
Construction Engineering Services
N.A.I.C.S.: 541330

FMHC Corp. (1)
1700 Sherwin Ave, Des Plaines, IL 60018
Tel.: (773) 380-3800

Web Site: http://www.fmhc.com
Emp.: 10
Wired Telecommunications Carriers
N.A.I.C.S.: 517111

Guimar Engenharia Ltda. (1)
Av Marechal Camara 160 Ed Le Bourget 5
andar, Rio de Janeiro, 20020-080, Brazil
Tel.: (55) 2125179000
Web Site: http://www.m.jacobsguimar.com
Engineering Consulting Services
N.A.I.C.S.: 541330

Iffland Kavanagh Waterbury, P.L.L.C. (1)
1501 Broadway Ste 606, New York, NY
10036
Tel.: (212) 944-2000
Emp.: 70
Construction Engineering Services
N.A.I.C.S.: 541330

JE Architects/Engineers, P.C. (1)
2 Penn Plz Rm 2495, New York, NY 10121
Tel.: (212) 946-2255
Construction Engineering Services
N.A.I.C.S.: 541330

JEG Architecture Nevada, Inc. (1)
7160 Bermuda Rd Ste 200, Las Vegas, NV
89119
Tel.: (702) 938-5400
Emp.: 4
Construction Engineering Services
N.A.I.C.S.: 541330

JPL Project Sp. z o. o. (1)
Al Niepodleglosci 58, Warsaw, 02-626, Poland
Tel.: (48) 225640600
Web Site: http://www.jplproject.com
Engineering & Consulting Services
N.A.I.C.S.: 541330
Wojciech Mieszkowski *(CEO)*
Jakub Loch *(Pres & CEO)*

Jacobs Advisers Inc. (1)
155 N Lake Ave, Pasadena, CA
91101 **(100%)**
Tel.: (626) 578-3500
Web Site: http://www.jacobs.com
Engineeering Services
N.A.I.C.S.: 541330

Jacobs Belgie NV (1)
Haven 190 Noorderlaan 127, 2030, Antwerp, Belgium **(100%)**
Tel.: (32) 35409411
Sales Range: $75-99.9 Million
Emp.: 500
Engineeering Services
N.A.I.C.S.: 541330

Jacobs Brasil Holdings S.A. (1)
Av Rio Branco 100-Sala 1001-Parte, Rio de
Janeiro, 20040-070, Brazil
Tel.: (55) 2122522500
Holding Company
N.A.I.C.S.: 551112

Jacobs China Limited (1)
6th Fl 633 King's Road, Hong Kong, China
(Hong Kong)
Tel.: (852) 28809788
Web Site: http://www.jacobschina.com
Emp.: 200
Chemicals Mfr
N.A.I.C.S.: 325180

Jacobs Clean Energy s.r.o. (1)
Krenova 58, Brno, 602 00, Czech Republic
Tel.: (420) 543 428 311
Web Site: http://www.jacobscz.cz
Environmental Consulting Services
N.A.I.C.S.: 541620
Petr Vymazal *(Mng Dir & Project Mgr)*
Zuzana Flegrova *(Mgr-Comml)*
Stanislav Postbiegl *(Project Mgr)*
Tomas Bartos *(Project Mgr)*
Pavel Mitev *(Project Mgr)*
Jitka Heikenwaelderova *(Project Mgr)*
Jana Svabova Nezvalova *(Project Mgr)*
Eliska Smrzova *(Sec & Mgr-Admin)*

Jacobs Colombia S.A.S. (1)
Calle 99 10 08 Of 304, Bogota, Colombia
Tel.: (57) 14764444
Construction Engineering Services
N.A.I.C.S.: 541330

Jacobs Consultancy Spol s.r.o (1)

Zlatnicka 10, 110 00, Prague, Czech Republic
Tel.: (420) 251 019 231
Web Site: http://www.jacobsconsultancy.cz
Industrial Maintenance & Construction
N.A.I.C.S.: 236210

Jacobs Consultants, Inc. (1)
777 Main St Ste 3800, Fort Worth, TX
76102
Tel.: (817) 735-6000
Web Site:
http://www.jacobsconsultancy.com
Engineering Consulting Services
N.A.I.C.S.: 541330

Jacobs Eagleton LLC (1)
12140 Wickchester Ln Ste 100, Houston,
TX 77079
Tel.: (281) 589-5002
Engineeering Services
N.A.I.C.S.: 541330
Jeff Durand *(Mgr-Engrg)*

Jacobs Engineering Deutschland GmbH (1)
Josef Lammerting Allee 25, Cologne,
50933, Germany **(100%)**
Tel.: (49) 221337330
Sales Range: $50-74.9 Million
Emp.: 175
Engineeering Services
N.A.I.C.S.: 541330
Rene Gonkers *(VP-Ops-Germany)*

Jacobs Engineering Group Malaysia Sdn Bhd (1)
Suite E-17-P2 Level 17 Penthouse Block E
Plaza, Mont Kiara No 2 Jalan Kiara, Kuala
Lumpur, 50480, Malaysia
Tel.: (60) 362046688
Construction Engineering Services
N.A.I.C.S.: 541330

Jacobs Engineering Group, Inc. - Arlington (North Glebe Road), VA (1)
1100 N Glebe Rd Ste 500, Arlington, VA
22201
Tel.: (571) 218-1000
Web Site: http://www.jacobs.com
Sales Range: $75-99.9 Million
Emp.: 350
Engineering , Architectural & Constructional
Services
N.A.I.C.S.: 541330

Jacobs Engineering Group, Inc. - Baton Rouge, LA (1)
4949 Essen Ln, Baton Rouge, LA 70809-3406
Tel.: (225) 769-7700
Web Site: http://www.jacobs.com
Sales Range: $150-199.9 Million
Emp.: 700
Engineering
N.A.I.C.S.: 541330
R. Terry Jones *(VP-Opers)*

Jacobs Engineering Group, Inc. - Boston, MA (1)
343 Congress St, Boston, MA 02210
Tel.: (617) 242-9222
Web Site: http://www.jacobs.com
Sales Range: $25-49.9 Million
Emp.: 135
Construction Services
N.A.I.C.S.: 541330

Jacobs Engineering Group, Inc. - Cincinnati, OH (1)
1880 Waycross Rd, Cincinnati, OH 45240-5600
Tel.: (513) 595-7500
Web Site: http://www.jacobs.com
Sales Range: $100-124.9 Million
Emp.: 315
Engineering Works
N.A.I.C.S.: 541330

Jacobs Engineering Group, Inc. - Conshohocken, PA (1)
3 Tower Bridge 2 Ash St Ste 3000, Conshohocken, PA 19428
Tel.: (610) 238-1000
Web Site: http://www.jacobs.com
Sales Range: $25-49.9 Million
Emp.: 250
Building Construction
N.A.I.C.S.: 237990

Jacobs Engineering Group, Inc. - Denver, CO (1)
707 17th St Ste 2400, Denver, CO 80202-5131
Tel.: (303) 820-5240
Web Site: http://www.jacobs.com
Sales Range: $50-74.9 Million
Emp.: 200
Engineeering Services
N.A.I.C.S.: 541330

Jacobs Engineering Group, Inc. - Greenville, SC (1)
1041 E Butler Rd, Greenville, SC 29607-5725
Tel.: (864) 676-6000
Web Site: http://www.jacobs.com
Sales Range: $75-99.9 Million
Emp.: 500
Pulp Paper Engineering
N.A.I.C.S.: 541330

Jacobs Engineering Group, Inc. - Morristown, NJ (1)
299 Madison Ave, Morristown, NJ 07960-6107
Tel.: (973) 267-0555
Web Site: http://www.jacobs.com
Sales Range: $200-249.9 Million
Emp.: 3,000
Consulting Engineering & Planning Organization; Construction Management
N.A.I.C.S.: 541330

Jacobs Engineering Group, Inc. - New York, NY (1)
2 Penn Plz 6th Fl, New York, NY 10121
Tel.: (212) 944-2000
Sales Range: $25-49.9 Million
Emp.: 100
Structural & Architectural Engineering Services
N.A.I.C.S.: 541330

Jacobs Engineering India Private Limited (1)
Jacobs House, Mumbai, 400059, Maharashtra, India
Tel.: (91) 2226812000
Engineeering Services
N.A.I.C.S.: 327910
Vijay Paranjape *(Mng Dir)*

Jacobs Engineering Ireland Limited (1)
Merrion House Merrion Road, Merrion
Road, Dublin, 4, Ireland **(100%)**
Tel.: (353) 12695666
Web Site: http://www.jacobs.com
Sales Range: $25-49.9 Million
Emp.: 300
Engineeering Services
N.A.I.C.S.: 541330

Branch (Domestic):

Jacobs Engineering Ireland Limited - Blackrock (2)
Mahon Indsutrial Est, Blackrock, Cork, Ireland
Tel.: (353) 214515777
Web Site: http://www.jacobs.com
Sales Range: $50-74.9 Million
Engineering & Construction Services
N.A.I.C.S.: 541330

Jacobs Engineering New York Inc. (1)
2 Penn Plz Ste 603, New York, NY 10121
Tel.: (212) 944-2000
Emp.: 200
Engineeering Services
N.A.I.C.S.: 541330
Vincent A. Mangiere *(CEO)*

Jacobs Engineering SA International (1)
Imm No 5 Zenith Millenium, Casablanca,
20270, Morocco
Tel.: (212) 522877000
Web Site: http://www.jesa.africa
Building Construction Services
N.A.I.C.S.: 236210
Anne Duval *(Dir-Academy)*

Jacobs Engineering and Construction (Thailand) Limited (1)
9 Pakin Building Room No 1203 12th Floor

Ratchadaphisek Road, Din Daeng, Bangkok, 10400, Thailand
Tel.: (66) 22065000
Engineeering Services
N.A.I.C.S.: 541330

Jacobs Field Services Americas Inc. (1)
333 E Wetmore Rd Ste 600, Tucson, AZ 85705
Tel.: (520) 620-1530
Engineering & Construction Services
N.A.I.C.S.: 541330

Jacobs Field Services North America, Inc. (1)
5995 Rogerdale Rd, Houston, TX 77072 **(100%)**
Tel.: (832) 351-6000
Web Site: http://www.jocobsconnect.com
Sales Range: $1-9.9 Million
Emp.: 70
Engineeering Services
N.A.I.C.S.: 237990

Subsidiary (Non-US):

JFSL Projects Ltd. (2)
2301 Premier Way Ste 168 Broadmoor Place III, Sherwood Park, T8H 2K8, AB, Canada
Tel.: (780) 400-2800
Web Site: http://www.jfslprojects.com
Industrial Fabrication & Construction Services
N.A.I.C.S.: 332999
David Haddock (Mgr-Project Svcs)
Lorisa Watt (Mgr-Quality Assurance & Quality Control)
Stuart Boyd (Mgr-Supply Chain Mgmt)
Ray Scriven (Mgr-Fabrications Ops)

Triton Projects (2)
10010 106 Street Suite 600, Edmonton, T5J 3L8, AB, Canada **(89%)**
Tel.: (780) 485-6700
Web Site: http://www.tritonprojects.com
Commercial & Industrial Construction Services
N.A.I.C.S.: 236220

Jacobs Group (Australia) Pty Ltd (1)
177 Pacific Hwy, North Sydney, 2060, Australia
Tel.: (61) 2 9928 2100
Sales Range: $1-4.9 Billion
Emp.: 7,000
Engineering & Scientific Consulting Services
N.A.I.C.S.: 541690
Lesley Morris (Grp Mgr-Industry)
Michael Shirley (VP-ANZ Infrastructure & Environment)
Philip Lory (VP-ANZ Resources & Power)
Paul Casamento (Sr VP-Integration)
Tim Dilnot (Mgr-Corp Comm)

Subsidiary (Non-US):

Enviros Consulting Ltd. (2)
Regus House 1010 Cambourne Business Park, Cambourne, Cambridge, CB23 6DP, United Kingdom
Tel.: (44) 8701652400
Environmental Compliance Consulting Services
N.A.I.C.S.: 541620
Peter Young (Dir-Strategy & Dev)

Subsidiary (Non-US):

Enviros, s. r. o. (3)
Na Rovnosti 1/2246 Level 1-3, 130 00, Prague, Czech Republic
Tel.: (420) 207 939 6337
Sales Range: $25-49.9 Million
Emp.: 35
Environmental Compliance Consulting Services
N.A.I.C.S.: 541620
Rajaroslav Vich (Mng Dir)

Jacobs International Limited (1)
Merrion House Merrion Road, Dublin, D4 R2C5, Ireland
Tel.: (353) 12695666
Construction Engineering Services
N.A.I.C.S.: 541330

Jacobs Italia SpA (1)

Via Alessandro Volta N° 16, Cologno Monzese, 20093, Milan, Italy **(100%)**
Tel.: (39) 02250981
Web Site: http://www.jacobs.com
Sales Range: $50-74.9 Million
Emp.: 200
Engineeering Services
N.A.I.C.S.: 541330

Jacobs Matasis (Pty) Ltd. (1)
15 Forest Road Waverley Office Park Building 2, Bramley, 2090, Johannesburg, South Africa
Tel.: (27) 114828198
Web Site: http://www.matasis.co.za
Investment Management Service
N.A.I.C.S.: 523940

Jacobs Minerals, Inc. (1)
8 Penn Ctr W, Pittsburgh, PA 15276
Tel.: (412) 249-3432
Emp.: 40
Engineeering Services
N.A.I.C.S.: 541330
Joseph Perri (Gen Mgr)

Jacobs Nederland BV (1)
Plesmanlaan 100, Leiden, 2332 CB, Netherlands **(100%)**
Tel.: (31) 715827111
Web Site: http://www.jacobs.com
Sales Range: $150-199.9 Million
Emp.: 1,100
Engineeering Services
N.A.I.C.S.: 541330

Subsidiary (Non-US):

Chemetics, Inc. (2)
Ste 200 2930 Virtual Way, Vancouver, V5M 0A5, BC, Canada
Tel.: (604) 734-1200
Web Site: http://www.jacobs.com
Sales Range: $50-74.9 Million
Emp.: 200
Process Technology Services Offering Engineered Systems, Proprietary Equipment & Turnkey Plants to the Chemical, Pulp & Paper, Water Treatment, Fertilizer & Non-Ferrous Metals Industries
N.A.I.C.S.: 325998

Subsidiary (Domestic):

Jacobs Minerals Canada Inc. (3)
1920 Yonge St Ste 301 S, Toronto, M4S 3E2, ON, Canada
Tel.: (416) 340-1145
Emp.: 50
Mineral Mining Services
N.A.I.C.S.: 213113
Andrew Berryman (Principal)

Subsidiary (Domestic):

Jacobs Advanced Manufacturing BV (2)
Plesmanlaan 100, Leiden, 2332 CB, Zuid-Holland, Netherlands
Tel.: (31) 715827900
Web Site: http://www.jacobs.com
Emp.: 1,100
Oil & Gas Mining Services
N.A.I.C.S.: 325180

Subsidiary (Non-US):

Jacobs Norway AS (2)
Simonsen Advokatfirma DA Filipstad Brygge 1, Oslo, 0252, Norway
Tel.: (47) 67513000
Engineeering Services
N.A.I.C.S.: 541330

Subsidiary (Non-US):

Jacobs Chile S.A. (3)
Monsenor Sotero Sanz 161, Providencia, Santiago, Chile
Tel.: (56) 229246000
Industrial Fabrication & Construction Services
N.A.I.C.S.: 332999

Jacobs Peru S.A. (3)
Avenida 28 de Julio No 1044 Piso 10, Miraflores, Lima, 18, Peru
Tel.: (51) 12079200
Coal Mining Services
N.A.I.C.S.: 213113
Sam Izaguirre (Gen Mgr)

Subsidiary (Domestic):

Jacobs Process B.V. (2)
Plesmanlaan 100, Leiden, 2332CB, Netherlands
Tel.: (31) 715827111
Web Site: http://www.jacobs.com
Engineeering Services
N.A.I.C.S.: 541330

Subsidiary (Non-US):

Jacobs Russia LLC. (2)
3 Of 667 Pl Smolenskaya, Moscow, Russia
Tel.: (7) 4959806755
Engineeering Services
N.A.I.C.S.: 541330

Jacobs Professional Services Inc. (1)
PO Box 7, Monon, IN 47959
Tel.: (219) 253-5150
Web Site: http://www.jacobsservices.com
Human Resource Consulting Services
N.A.I.C.S.: 541612
Stacy Jacobs (Pres & CEO)
Edward D. Jacobs (Project Mgr)

Jacobs Projects (Philippines) Inc. (1)
5th Floor Makati Stock Exchange Building 6767 Ayala Avenue, Barangay Bel Air, Makati, 1226, Manila, Philippines
Tel.: (63) 29678600
Construction Engineering Services
N.A.I.C.S.: 541330
Gemma Estember (Project Mgr)

Jacobs Projects (Shanghai) Co., Ltd. (2)
Unit 02-10 6/F South Tower No 1701 Century Avenue, Pudong Ne, Shanghai, 200122, China
Tel.: (86) 2150818811
Web Site: http://www.jacobs.com
Engineeering Services
N.A.I.C.S.: 541330

Subsidiary (Domestic):

Jacobs Engineering (Suzhou) Co., Ltd (2)
Room 2409 Sovereign Building No 8 Avenue West, Suzhou Industrial Park, Suzhou, China
Tel.: (86) 51287656540845
Web Site: http://www.szhsce.com
Construction Engineering Services
N.A.I.C.S.: 541330

Jacobs Sverige AB (1)
Industrivagen, Stenungsund, 444 32, Sweden **(100%)**
Tel.: (46) 30386900
Web Site: http://www.jacobs.com
Sales Range: $25-49.9 Million
Emp.: 125
Engineeering Services
N.A.I.C.S.: 541330

Jacobs Technology, Inc. (1)
600 William Northern Blvd, Tullahoma, TN 37388 **(100%)**
Tel.: (931) 455-6400
Web Site: http://www.jacobstechnology.com
Sales Range: $400-449.9 Million
Emp.: 4,000
Advanced Technology Engineering Services Design Build of Test Facilities Scientific Engineering & Op
N.A.I.C.S.: 541330

Subsidiary (Domestic):

DM Petroleum Operations Company (2)
850 S Clearview Pkwy EF-29, New Orleans, LA 70123-3401 **(80%)**
Tel.: (504) 734-4200
Web Site: http://www.dmpetroleumoperations.com
Crude Oil Pipeline Management & Operating Services
N.A.I.C.S.: 213112

Subsidiary (Non-US):

Jacobs Australia Pty. Limited (2)
L 7 8-10 Hobart Pl, Canberra, 2601, ACT, Australia
Tel.: (61) 0262306972

Web Site: http://www.jacobs.com.au
Emp.: 25
Engineeering Services
N.A.I.C.S.: 541330
Dieter Rogiers (Mng Dir)

Subsidiary (Domestic):

Jacobs E&C Australia Pty. Ltd. (3)
Level 11 452 Flinders St, Melbourne, 3000, VIC, Australia
Tel.: (61) 386683000
Web Site: http://www.jacobs.com
Engineeering Services
N.A.I.C.S.: 541330

Subsidiary (Domestic):

Jacobs Strategic Solutions Group, Inc. (2)
3863 Centerview Dr No 150, Chantilly, VA 20151
Tel.: (703) 956-8200
Sales Range: $50-74.9 Million
Emp.: 150
Computer Services for Government
N.A.I.C.S.: 541512

TYBRIN Corporation (2)
1030 Titan Ct, Fort Walton Beach, FL 32547
Tel.: (850) 337-2500
Systems & Software Engineering
N.A.I.C.S.: 541511

Jacobs Telecommunications Inc. (1)
450 Raritan Ctr Pkwy, Edison, NJ 08837
Tel.: (732) 225-3330
Web Site: http://www.jacobs.com
Emp.: 30
Telecommunication Engineering Services
N.A.I.C.S.: 238210

Jacobs U.K. Limited (1)
1180 Eskdale Road, Winnersh, Wokingham, RG41 5TU, Berks, United Kingdom
Tel.: (44) 118 946 7000
Web Site: http://www.jacobs.com
Emp.: 1,000
Engineering & Consulting Services
N.A.I.C.S.: 541330

Subsidiary (Domestic):

Jacobs Engineering UK Limited (2)
Park Square Birdhall Lane, Cheadle Heath, Stockport, SK3 0XF, Cheshire, United Kingdom
Tel.: (44) 1617417800
Construction Engineering Services
N.A.I.C.S.: 541330

Jacobs One Limited (2)
95 Bothall Street, Glasgow, G2 7HX, Scotland, United Kingdom **(100%)**
Tel.: (44) 1412042511
Engineeering Services
N.A.I.C.S.: 541330

Subsidiary (Domestic):

BEAR Scotland Limited (3)
BEAR House Inveralmond Road Inveralmond Industrial Estate, Perth, PH1 3TW, United Kingdom
Tel.: (44) 1738448600
Web Site: http://www.bearscot.com
Engineering Consulting Services
N.A.I.C.S.: 541330

Subsidiary (Non-US):

Jacobs China Limited (2)
6th Fl 633 King's Road, North Point, Quarry Bay, China (Hong Kong) **(100%)**
Tel.: (852) 28809788
Web Site: http://www.jacobschina.com
Sales Range: $50-74.9 Million
Emp.: 200
Engineering & Consulting Services
N.A.I.C.S.: 541330
Mark Trey (Mng Dir)

Subsidiary (Domestic):

Jacobs European Holdings Limited (3)
1180 Eskdale Road, Winnersh Wokingham, Reading, RG41 5TU, United Kingdom
Tel.: (44) 1189467000
Holding Company

Jacobs Engineering Group, Inc.—(Continued)
N.A.I.C.S.: 551112

Subsidiary (Domestic):

Inspire Defence Ltd (4)
Eskdale Road, Winnersh, Wokingham,
RG41 5TU, Berkshire, United Kingdom
Tel.: (44) 7873449952
Construction Engineering Services
N.A.I.C.S.: 541330

Subsidiary (Domestic):

Jacobs SKM Ltd (3)
Eskdale Road, Winnersh, Wokingham,
RG41 5TU, Berkshire, United Kingdom
Tel.: (44) 2076301137
Construction Engineering Services
N.A.I.C.S.: 541330

Ringway Babtie Limited (3)
Albion House 38 Springfield Road, Hor-
sham, RH12 2RW, West Sussex, United
Kingdom
Tel.: (44) 1403215800
Construction Engineering Services
N.A.I.C.S.: 541330

Ringway Jacobs Limited (3)
Victoria House 101-105 Victoria Rd,
Chelmsford, CM1 1JR, Essex, United King-
dom
Tel.: (44) 1245204954
Web Site: http://www.ringway-jacobs.co.uk
Highway Construction Services
N.A.I.C.S.: 237310
Emma Bedford (Project Mgr)

Subsidiary (Domestic):

Jacobs Process Limited (2)
1 Port Way, Port Solent, Portsmouth, P06
4TZ, Hampshire, United Kingdom
Tel.: (44) 2392394000
Emp.: 200
Engineering Services
N.A.I.C.S.: 541330
Steve Randle (Dir-Ops)

Subsidiary (Domestic):

Jacobs E&C Limited (3)
Phoenix House, Stockton, TS18 3HR,
Cleveland, United Kingdom
Tel.: (44) 1642334000
Web Site: http://www.jacobs.com
Emp.: 250
Engineering Services
N.A.I.C.S.: 541330

Subsidiary (Domestic):

Jacobs Stobbarts Ltd (2)
Tarn Howe Lakes Road, Workington, CA14
3YP, Cumbria, United Kingdom
Tel.: (44) 190087078
Construction Engineering Services
N.A.I.C.S.: 541330

Jordan, Jones and Goulding, Inc. (1)
6801 Governors Lk Pkwy, Norcross, GA
30071-1119
Tel.: (770) 455-8555
Web Site: http://www.jjg.com
Engineering Planning & Consulting Services
N.A.I.C.S.: 541330

LeighFisher Inc. (1)
4 Embarcadero Ctr Ste 3800, San Fran-
cisco, CA 94111
Tel.: (650) 579-7722
Web Site: http://www.leighfisher.com
Management Consultants
N.A.I.C.S.: 541611

LeighFisher Ltd. (1)
2nd Floor Cottons Centre Cottons Lane,
London, SE1 2QG, United Kingdom
Tel.: (44) 2039802195
Web Site: http://www.leighfisher.com
Emp.: 40
Civil Construction Engineering Services
N.A.I.C.S.: 541330

SKM (Singapore) Pte Ltd (1)
29 International Business Pk 03-01, Singa-
pore, 609923, Singapore
Tel.: (65) 63453055
Engineering Consulting Services
N.A.I.C.S.: 541330

Jevgeni Andronenko (Engr-Civil & Structural)

**SKM Investments Australia Pty
Ltd** (1)
100 Christie St, Saint Leonards, 2065,
NSW, Australia
Tel.: (61) 299282100
Financial Management Services
N.A.I.C.S.: 551112

**Sinclair Knight Merz (NZ) Holdings
Ltd** (1)
12-16 Nicholls Lane, Parnell, Auckland,
New Zealand
Tel.: (64) 99138900
Holding Company
N.A.I.C.S.: 551112

Subsidiary (Domestic):

Jacobs New Zealand Limited (2)
Carlaw Park 12-16 Nicholls Lane Level 2,
Parnell, Auckland, 1010, New Zealand
Tel.: (64) 99285500
Construction Engineering Services
N.A.I.C.S.: 541330
John Heap (CEO)

Subsidiary (Non-US):

PT Jacobs Group Indonesia (3)
Talavera Office Park 15th Floor Jalan
LetJen TB, Simatupang Kav 22-26, Jakarta,
12340, Indonesia
Tel.: (62) 2127588200
Construction Engineering Services
N.A.I.C.S.: 541330
Wedha Aditiawan Mardi (Project Mgr)

Sula Systems Ltd. (1)
Old Crown House, Market Street, Wotton-
under-Edge, GL12 7AE, Gloucestershire,
United Kingdom
Tel.: (44) 1453 844660
Web Site: http://www.jacobssula.co.uk
Engineering Consultancy Company
N.A.I.C.S.: 541330

The Buffalo Group, LLC (1)
1851 Alexander Bell Dr Ste 300, Reston,
VA 20191-1553
Tel.: (571) 346-3300
Web Site: http://www.thebuffalogroup.com
Professional, Scientific & Technical Services
N.A.I.C.S.: 541990
Paul Courtney (Pres)

The KEYW Holding Corporation (1)
7740 Milestone Pkwy Ste 400, Hanover,
MD 21076
Tel.: (443) 733-1600
Web Site: http://www.keywcorp.com
Rev.: $506,840,000
Assets: $675,981,000
Liabilities: $385,751,000
Net Worth: $290,230,000
Earnings: ($22,280,000)
Emp.: 1,790
Fiscal Year-end: 12/31/2018
Computer Security Solutions to National
Security, Defense & Intelligence Agencies
N.A.I.C.S.: 541512
Kirk Herdman (Exec VP-Corp Strategy &
Bus Dev)
Caroline S. Pisano (Chm)
Phil Luci (Gen Counsel & Exec VP)
William J. Weber (Pres & CEO)
Michael J. Alber (CFO & Exec VP)
John Sutton (COO & Exec VP)
Marion Ruzecki (Chief People Officer &
Exec VP)

Subsidiary (Domestic):

Geovantage, Inc. (2)
250 Clark St, North Andover, MA 01845
Tel.: (978) 242-7344
Web Site: http://www.geovantage.com
Computer System Design Services
N.A.I.C.S.: 541512
William Pevear (Co-Founder & Pres)
Matthew Herring (Co-Founder & Sr VP)

The KEYW Corporation (2)
1334 Ashton Rd Ste A, Hanover, MD 21076
Tel.: (443) 270-5300
Web Site: http://www.keywcorp.com
Imaging Equipment Mfr
N.A.I.C.S.: 811210

Dave Wallen (Sr VP-Advanced Cyber)
Michael Alber (CFO & Exec VP)
Phil Luci (Gen Counsel & Exec VP)
Kevin Gunde (Sr VP-Survey & Exploration
Sys)
Jack Hess (Sr VP-Natl Intelligence Div)
Janet Schoenfeld (VP-Sector-Defense Mis-
sion)

Subsidiary (Domestic):

Flight Landata, Inc. (3)
250 Clark St, North Andover, MA 01845
Tel.: (978) 682-7767
Web Site: http://www.flightlandata.com
Sales Range: $25-49.9 Million
Emp.: 6
Airborne Surveillance & Reconnaissance
Solutions
N.A.I.C.S.: 541990

Poole & Associates, Inc. (3)
10820 Guilford Rd Ste 201, Annapolis Junc-
tion, MD 20701
Tel.: (301) 617-2796
Web Site: http://www.pooleinc.com
Engineering Services for Both Systems &
Software Capabilities & Technologies
N.A.I.C.S.: 541519

Sotera Defense Solutions, Inc. (3)
2121 Cooperative Way Ste 2300, Herndon,
VA 20171
Tel.: (703) 230-8200
Web Site: http://www.soteradefense.com
Emp.: 1,133
Mission-Critical Technology-Based Systems,
Solutions & Services
N.A.I.C.S.: 928110

**The Van Dyke Technology Group,
Inc.** (3)
6716 Alexander Bell Dr Ste 205, Columbia,
MD 21046
Tel.: (443) 832-4700
Web Site: http://www.vdtg.com
Computer System Design Services
N.A.I.C.S.: 541512

Traffic Services, Inc. (1)
2260 Southwind Blvd, Bartlett, IL 60103
Tel.: (630) 497-3478
Management Consulting Services
N.A.I.C.S.: 541611

VEI Inc. (1)
2011 Stefani Ct, Carrollton, TX 75007-3529
Tel.: (972) 492-3017
Management Consulting Services
N.A.I.C.S.: 541611

**JADE GLOBAL HOLDINGS,
INC**
8950 SW 74th Ct Ste 2201-A44, Mi-
ami, FL 33156
Tel.: (786) 363-0136   FL
Web Site:
  http://jadeglobalholdings.com
Year Founded: 2011
JADG—(OTCIQ)
Assets: $9,805
Liabilities: $480,163
Net Worth: ($470,358)
Earnings: ($214,963)
Fiscal Year-end: 12/31/19
Investment Services
N.A.I.C.S.: 523999
Guoqiang Qian (Chm, Pres & CEO)
Min Shi (Sec)

JAGUAR HEALTH, INC.
200 Pine St Ste 400, San Francisco,
CA 94104
Tel.: (415) 371-8300   DE
Web Site: https://www.jaguar.health
Year Founded: 2013
JAGX—(NASDAQ)
Rev.: $9,761,000
Assets: $50,763,000
Liabilities: $45,866,000
Net Worth: $4,897,000
Earnings: ($41,300,000)
Emp.: 49
Fiscal Year-end: 12/31/23
Pharmaceuticals Mfr

N.A.I.C.S.: 325412
Lisa A. Conte (Founder, Pres & CEO)
Steven R. King (Chief Sustainable
Supply, Ethnobotanical Res & IP Offi-
cer)
James J. Bochnowski (Chm)
Pravin R. Chaturvedi (Chief Scientific
Officer-Acting)
Michael K. Guy (VP-Preclinical &
Nonclinical Studies)
Jonathan Wolin (Chief Compliance
Officer & Gen Counsel)
Carol R. Lizak (CFO, Chief Acctg Of-
ficer & Sr VP)
Ian H. Wendt (Chief Comml Officer)
Brian Sutton (Natl Dir-Bus)
Karen J. Brunke (Exec VP-Corp &
Bus Dev)

Subsidiaries:

Napo Pharmaceuticals, Inc. (1)
200 Pine St Ste 400, San Francisco, CA
94104   (100%)
Tel.: (415) 963-9938
Web Site: https://www.napopharma.com
Proprietary Pharmaceuticals Development &
Commercialization
N.A.I.C.S.: 325412

JAKKS PACIFIC, INC.
2951 28th St, Santa Monica, CA
90405
Tel.: (424) 268-9444   DE
Web Site: https://www.jakks.com
Year Founded: 1995
JAKK—(NASDAQ)
Rev.: $796,187,000
Assets: $405,342,000
Liabilities: $258,644,000
Net Worth: $146,698,000
Earnings: $91,413,000
Emp.: 622
Fiscal Year-end: 12/31/22
Toys & Related Products Mfr, Devel-
oper & Marketer
N.A.I.C.S.: 339930
John Joseph McGrath (COO)
Stephen G. Berman (Founder, Chm,
Pres, CEO & Sec)
John L. Kimble (CFO & Exec VP)

Subsidiaries:

A.S. Design Limited (1)
75 Mody Road Rm 210 Tower 2 South
Seas Centre, Tsim Sha Tsui, Kowloon,
China (Hong Kong)
Tel.: (852) 23121668
Web Site: http://www.mauitoys.com
Toy Mfr
N.A.I.C.S.: 339930

Disguise Inc. (1)
12120 Kear Pl, Poway, CA 92064
Tel.: (858) 391-3600
Web Site: https://www.disguise.com
Game Toy & Childrens Vehicle Mfr
N.A.I.C.S.: 339930

Go Fly A Kite (1)
21749 Baker Pkwy, Walnut, CA 91789
Tel.: (909) 594-7771
Web Site: http://www.jakks.com
Designing Developing & Marketing of Kites
N.A.I.C.S.: 339930

JAKKS Pacific (UK) Ltd. (1)
1st Floor One Arlington Square Downshire
Way, Bracknell, RG12 1WA, Berkshire,
United Kingdom
Tel.: (44) 8000318226
Sales Range: $10-24.9 Million
Emp.: 8
Game Toy & Childrens Vehicle Mfr
N.A.I.C.S.: 339930

JAKKS Pacific Germany GmbH (1)
Lindenstr 26a, 91126, Schwabach, Ger-
many
Tel.: (49) 91228758092
Toys & Related Product Mfr
N.A.I.C.S.: 339930

JAKKS Sales Corporation (1)

22619 Pacific Coast Hwy Ste 250, Malibu,
CA 90265-5054
Tel.: (310) 456-7799
Sales Range: $50-74.9 Million
Emp.: 100
Toy & Hobby Goods Whslr
N.A.I.C.S.: 423920
John Joseph McGrath *(COO)*
Joel Bennett *(Exec VP & CFO)*

Kids Only, Inc. (1)
7701 E 21st St, Indianapolis, IN 46219
Tel.: (317) 329-1000
Web Site: https://www.kidsonlyinc.com
Game Toy & Childrens Vehicle Mfr
N.A.I.C.S.: 339930

Maui Toys, Inc. (1)
1275 Crescent St, Youngstown, OH 44502
Tel.: (330) 747-4333
Web Site: http://www.mauitoys.com
Toy Mfr & Distr
N.A.I.C.S.: 339930
Brian D. Kessler *(Founder & CEO)*

JAMES MARITIME HOLDINGS, INC.

9360 S 300 W Ste 101, Sandy, UT
84070
Tel.: (801) 706-9429   NV
Year Founded: 1992
JMTM—(OTCIQ)
Rev.: $4,063,122
Assets: $5,774,808
Liabilities: $3,592,115
Net Worth: $2,182,693
Earnings: $204,894
Emp.: 152
Fiscal Year-end: 12/31/22
Agriculture Product Distr
N.A.I.C.S.: 424910
Kip Eardley *(Pres)*
Ray Sheets *(CFO, Treas & Sec)*

JAMES MONROE CAPITAL CORPORATION

175 S Main 17th Fl Walker Ctr, Salt
Lake City, UT 84111
Tel.: (801) 303-6730   DE
Year Founded: 2005
JMON—(OTCIQ)
Mortgage Finance Services
N.A.I.C.S.: 522292
Joseph Herran *(CEO)*
William Sklar *(CFO)*

JAMF HOLDING CORP.

100 Washington Ave S Ste 1100,
Minneapolis, MN 55401
Tel.: (612) 605-6625   DE
Web Site: https://www.jamf.com
Year Founded: 2002
JAMF—(NASDAQ)
Rev.: $478,776,000
Assets: $1,529,542,000
Liabilities: $828,204,000
Net Worth: $701,338,000
Earnings: ($141,301,000)
Emp.: 2,796
Fiscal Year-end: 12/31/22
Holding Company
N.A.I.C.S.: 551112
Dave Alampi *(CMO)*
Sam Johnson *(Chief Customer Offi-
cer)*
Jeff Lendino *(Gen Counsel)*
Jason Wudi *(CTO)*
Linh Lam *(CIO)*
John Strosahl *(CEO)*
David Rudow *(CFO)*

Subsidiaries:

JAMF Software Pacific Limited (1)
48-102B 48/F Lee Garden One 33 Hysan
Avenue, Causeway Bay, China (Hong
Kong)
Tel.: (852) 30085865
Software Development Services
N.A.I.C.S.: 541511

JAMF Software UK Limited (1)
C/O Freeths Llp Routeco Office Park Davy
Avenue, Knowlhill, Milton Keynes, MK5
8HJ, United Kingdom
Tel.: (44) 2038161409
Software Development Services
N.A.I.C.S.: 541511

Jamf Japan KK (1)
25/F Kamiyacho Trust Tower 4-1-1, Tora-
nomon Minato-ku, Tokyo, 105-0001, Japan
Tel.: (81) 5017902200
Software Development Services
N.A.I.C.S.: 541511

Jamf Sweden AB (1)
Kungsgatan 60, 111 22, Stockholm, Swe-
den
Tel.: (46) 844685304
Software Development Services
N.A.I.C.S.: 541511

JAMMIN JAVA CORP.

447 Broadway Fl 2 Unit 103, New
York, NY 10013
Tel.: (424) 224-5358   NV
Web Site:
http://www.marleycoffee.com
JAMN—(OTCIQ)
Sales Range: $10-24.9 Million
Emp.: 12
Roasted Coffee Distr
N.A.I.C.S.: 311920
Rohan Marley *(Founder)*
Paul Strickland *(Treas & Sec)*

JANEL CORPORATION

80 8th Ave, New York, NY 10011
Tel.: (212) 373-5895   NV
Web Site: https://www.janelcorp.com
Year Founded: 1980
JANL—(OTCIQ)
Rev.: $183,184,000
Assets: $110,610,000
Liabilities: $91,109,000
Net Worth: $19,501,000
Earnings: $551,000
Emp.: 334
Fiscal Year-end: 09/30/24
Freight Transportation Arrangement
N.A.I.C.S.: 492110
Brendan James Killackey *(CIO)*
Vincent A. Verde *(Chief Acctg Officer)*

Subsidiaries:

Antibodies Incorporated (1)
25242 County Rd 95, Davis, CA 95616
Tel.: (530) 758-4400
Web Site: http://www.antibodiesinc.com
Reagent Developer
N.A.I.C.S.: 325414
Will Fry *(Pres)*

ELFS Brokerage LLC (1)
3031 Eastveld Dr, Houston, TX 77073-2020
Tel.: (281) 442-3323
Logistics Transportation Services
N.A.I.C.S.: 488510

**Expedited Logistics & Freight Ser-
vices, Ltd.** (1)
Tel.: (281) 442-3323
Web Site: http://www.elfsfreight.com
Sales Range: $50-74.9 Million
Emp.: 152
Freight Transportation & Logistics
N.A.I.C.S.: 488510
Randy Cockrell *(Co-Owner & Partner)*
Mike Womack *(Dir-Intl)*

Global Trading Resources, Inc. (1)
5933 NE 80th Ave, Portland, OR 97218
Tel.: (503) 262-5506
Freight Transportation Arrangement
N.A.I.C.S.: 488510

**ImmunoChemistry Technologies,
LLC** (1)
PO Box 1560, Davis, CA 95617-1560
Tel.: (530) 758-4400
Web Site:
https://www.immunochemistry.com
Biotechnologies Research & Development
Services

N.A.I.C.S.: 541715

Indco, Inc. (1)
4040 Earnings Way, New Albany, IN 47150
Tel.: (812) 945-4383
Web Site: http://www.indco.com
Industrial Mixing Equipment Mfr & Distr
N.A.I.C.S.: 333248
Mark C. Hennis *(Pres)*
Kris Wilberding *(VP & Controller)*
Tricia Thien *(Mgr-Sls & Customer Svc)*
Mike Grady *(Engr-Applications)*
Trent Pickerill *(Production Mgr)*

Janel Group, Inc. (1)
233 7th St Ste 100, Garden City, NY 11530
Tel.: (516) 593-1390
Web Site: http://www.janelgroup.com
Freight Transportation Arrangement
N.A.I.C.S.: 488510

Subsidiary (Domestic):

The Janel Group of Georgia, Inc. (2)
795SPkwy ste 900, Atlanta, GA 30349
Tel.: (404) 361-6610
Web Site: http://www.janelgroup.net
Rev.: $2,030,293
Emp.: 5
Freight Transportation Arrangement
N.A.I.C.S.: 488510

PhosphoSolutions, LLC (1)
12635 E Montview Blvd Ste 213, Aurora,
CO 80045-7337
Tel.: (720) 859-4050
Web Site:
https://www.phosphosolutions.com
Antibody Biomedical Product Mfr
N.A.I.C.S.: 325414
Kristin Nixon *(Pres)*
Kameron Simpson *(Sr Mgr-Product)*
Patti Pickell *(VP-Admin)*
Amy Archuleta *(Dir-Scientific Mktg)*

W.J. Byrnes & Co. (1)
1111 Bayhill Dr Ste 205, San Bruno, CA
94066
Tel.: (650) 583-8300
Provider of Transportation Services
N.A.I.C.S.: 488510
John A. Leitner *(Pres & CEO)*

Branch (Domestic):

**W.J. Byrnes & Co. -
Arizona-Phoenix** (2)
509 S 48th St Ste 102, Tempe, AZ 85281
Tel.: (480) 284-4747
Provider of Transportation Services
N.A.I.C.S.: 488510
Jim Steel *(Gen Mgr)*

W.J. Byrnes & Co. - Oregon (2)
8383 NE Sandy Blvd, Portland, OR 97220
Tel.: (503) 252-6400
Provider of Transportation Services
N.A.I.C.S.: 488510

W.J. Byrnes & Co. - Wisconsin (2)
13890 Bishops Dr Ste 310, Brookfield, WI
53005
Tel.: (262) 860-7777
Provider of Transportation Services
N.A.I.C.S.: 488510

JANOVER INC.

6401 Congress Ave Ste 250, Boca
Raton, FL 33487
Tel.: (561) 559-4111   DE
Web Site: https://www.janover.co
Year Founded: 2018
JNVR—(NASDAQ)
Emp.: 13
Real Estate Management Services
N.A.I.C.S.: 531210
Bruce S. Rosenbloom *(CFO)*
Blake E. Janover *(Founder)*
Patrick Stinus *(Sr VP)*

JANUX THERAPEUTICS, INC.

10955 Vista Sorrento Pkwy Ste 200,
San Diego, CA 92130
Tel.: (858) 751-4493   DE
Web Site: https://www.januxrx.com
Year Founded: 2017

JANX—(NASDAQ)
Rev.: $8,612,000
Assets: $364,010,000
Liabilities: $43,270,000
Net Worth: $320,740,000
Earnings: ($63,059,000)
Emp.: 60
Fiscal Year-end: 12/31/22
Research & Development in Biotech-
nology (except Nanobiotechnology)
N.A.I.C.S.: 541714
David David *(Founder)*
Tighe Reardon *(CFO)*
Andy Meyer *(Chief Bus Officer)*
Charles Winter *(Sr VP-Chemistry,
Mfg & Controls)*
Tommy Diraimondo *(Chief Scientific
Officer)*
David Campbell *(Pres & CEO)*

JAPAN SMALLER CAPITAL-IZATION FUND, INC.

World Wide Plz 309 W 49th St, New
York, NY 10019   MD
JOF—(NYSE)
Rev.: $6,089,225
Assets: $231,034,860
Liabilities: $1,084,156
Net Worth: $229,950,704
Earnings: $2,847,201
Fiscal Year-end: 02/28/23
Investment Management Service
N.A.I.C.S.: 525990
Makoto Ito-Aim *(Mgr-Fund)*
Hiroaki Tanaka *(Portfolio Mgr)*
Atsushi Katayama *(Portfolio Mgr-
Lead)*

JASPER THERAPEUTICS, INC.

2200 Bridge Pkwy Ste 102, Redwood
City, CA 94065
Tel.: (650) 549-1400   DE
Web Site: https://www.jaspertx.com
JSPR—(NASDAQ)
Rev.: $13,511,000
Assets: $48,361,000
Liabilities: $12,372,000
Net Worth: $35,989,000
Earnings: ($37,685,000)
Emp.: 35
Fiscal Year-end: 12/31/22
Research & Development in Biotech-
nology
N.A.I.C.S.: 541714
Jeet Mahal *(COO)*
Herbert Cross *(CFO)*
Edwin Tucker *(Chief Medical Officer)*
Wendy Pang *(Sr VP-Research &
Translational Medicine)*
Patricia Carlos *(Sr VP-Regulatory
Affairs & Quality)*
Luca Di Noto *(Sr VP-Technical Ops)*
David Ku *(VP-Corporate Develop-
ment, Portfolio Strategy, and Mgmt)*
Annette Marcantonio *(VP-Clinical
Ops)*
Matt Ford *(VP-Human Resources)*
Ronald A. Martell *(Pres & CEO)*

JAWS HURRICANE ACQUISI-TION CORPORATION

1601 Washington Ave Ste 800, Miami
Beach, FL 33139
Tel.: (305) 695-5500   DE
Year Founded: 2021
HCNE—(NASDAQ)
Rev.: $14,396,675
Assets: $321,268,748
Liabilities: $334,645,428
Net Worth: ($13,376,680)
Earnings: $12,180,586
Emp.: 2
Fiscal Year-end: 12/31/22
Investment Services

Jaws Hurricane Acquisition
Corporation—(Continued)

N.A.I.C.S.: 523999
Barry Stuart Sternlicht *(Founder & Chm)*
Matthew Walters *(CEO)*
Michael Racich *(CFO)*

JAWS JUGGERNAUT ACQUISITION CORPORATION

1601 Washington Ave Ste 800, Miami Beach, FL 33139
Tel.: (203) 422-7718   Ky
Year Founded: 2020
JUGG—(NASDAQ)
Rev.: $13,841,605
Assets: $280,397,520
Liabilities: $291,026,697
Net Worth: ($10,629,177)
Earnings: $12,722,346
Emp.: 3
Fiscal Year-end: 12/31/22
Investment Services
N.A.I.C.S.: 523999
Barry Stuart Sternlicht *(Founder & Chm)*
Paul E. Jacobs *(CEO)*
Wilcoln Lee *(CIO)*
Michael Racich *(CFO)*

JAWS MUSTANG ACQUISITION CORPORATION

2340 Collins Ave, Miami Beach, FL 33139
Tel.: (305) 695-5500   Ky
Year Founded: 2020
JWSM—(NYSE)
Rev.: $50,898,041
Assets: $1,050,467,874
Liabilities: $1,092,955,123
Net Worth: ($42,487,249)
Earnings: $46,703,589
Emp.: 3
Fiscal Year-end: 12/31/22
Investment Services
N.A.I.C.S.: 523999
Barry Stuart Sternlicht *(Founder & Chm)*
Andrew Klaber *(CEO)*
Michael Reidler *(CFO)*
Matthew Walters *(COO)*

JBG SMITH PROPERTIES

4747 Bethesda Ave Ste 200,
Bethesda, MD 20814
Tel.: (240) 333-3600   MD
Web Site: https://www.jbgsmith.com
Year Founded: 2017
JBGS—(NYSE)
Rev.: $605,824,000
Assets: $5,903,438,000
Liabilities: $3,189,326,000
Net Worth: $2,714,112,000
Earnings: $85,371,000
Emp.: 912
Fiscal Year-end: 12/30/22
Real Estate Investment Services
N.A.I.C.S.: 531210
W. Matthew Kelly *(CEO)*
Madhumita Moina Banerjee *(CFO)*
Kai Reynolds *(Chief Dev Officer)*
Steven A. Museles *(Chief Legal Officer & Sec)*
Angela Valdes *(Chief Acctg Officer)*
Patrick Tyrrell *(Chief Admin Officer)*
Carey Goldberg *(Chief HR Officer)*
George Xanders *(Chief Investment Officer)*
Barbat Rodgers *(Sr VP-IR)*

JEFFERIES FINANCIAL GROUP INC.

520 Madison Ave 10th Fl, New York, NY 10022
Tel.: (212) 284-2300   NY

Web Site: https://www.jefferies.com
Year Founded: 1968
JEF—(NYSE)
Rev.: $7,441,399,000
Assets: $57,905,161,000
Liabilities: $48,102,620,000
Net Worth: $9,802,541,000
Earnings: $263,072,000
Emp.: 7,564
Fiscal Year-end: 11/30/23
Holding Company
N.A.I.C.S.: 551112
Richard B. Handler *(CEO)*
Brian P. Friedman *(Pres)*
Matthew S. Larson *(CFO & Exec VP)*
Mark L. Cagno *(Controller & Principal Acctg Officer)*

Subsidiaries:

Chrome Capital Group LLC   **(1)**
720 Goodlette Rd N Ste 400, Naples, FL 34102
Tel.: (239) 213-9922
Web Site: http://www.chromecapital.com
Motor Vehicle Distr
N.A.I.C.S.: 441227

HomeFed Corporation   **(1)**
1903 Wright Pl Ste 220, Carlsbad, CA 92008   **(100%)**
Tel.: (760) 918-8200
Web Site:
http://www.homefed.com
Sales Range: $125-149.9 Million
Emp.: 39
Real Estate Development Services
N.A.I.C.S.: 531110
Christian E. Foulger *(Pres)*
Erin N. Ruhe *(COO)*
Trevor Anderson *(Dir-EB-5 Financing)*
Thomas W. Blessent *(VP-Plng & Entitlement)*
Leon Hayden *(VP-Construction)*
Karima Knee *(Controller)*
Steven H. Levenson *(VP-Dev)*
Jeff O'Connor *(VP-Community Dev)*
Bob Penner *(VP-Asset Mgmt)*
Hale Richardson *(VP)*
Curt Smith *(VP-Community Dev)*
Jacob Fish *(VP-Community Dev)*
John Kent Aden Jr. *(Sr VP)*

Subsidiary (Domestic):

BRP Leasing, LLC   **(2)**
315 Park Ave S Fl 20, New York, NY 10010
Tel.: (212) 358-6552
Real Estate Services
N.A.I.C.S.: 531390

HOFD Ashville Park LLC   **(2)**
1868 Ashville Park Blvd, Virginia Beach, VA 23456
Tel.: (757) 689-8541
Web Site: http://www.ashvilleparkva.com
Real Estate Management Service Provider
N.A.I.C.S.: 531210

HomeFed Resources
Corporation   **(2)**
1903 Wright Pl Ste 220, Carlsbad, CA 92008-6584
Tel.: (760) 918-8200
Land Development Services
N.A.I.C.S.: 237210

Maine Seaboard Realty LLC   **(2)**
22 Central St, Rockport, ME 04856
Tel.: (207) 236-0036
Real Estate Services
N.A.I.C.S.: 531390

Otay Land Company, LLC   **(2)**
1903 Wright Pl Ste 220, Carlsbad, CA 92008-6584
Tel.: (760) 918-8200
Web Site: http://www.otaylandcompany.com
Real Estate Rorperty Leasing Services
N.A.I.C.S.: 531190

San Elijo Hills Town Center, LLC   **(2)**
1277 San Elijo Rd S, San Marcos, CA 92078-1073
Tel.: (760) 798-1765
Web Site: https://www.sanelijohills.com
Real Estate Services
N.A.I.C.S.: 531390

St. Andrew Bay Land Company,
LLC   **(2)**
416 Jenks Ave, Panama City, FL 32401-2626
Tel.: (850) 215-0097
Web Site: http://www.sweetbayfl.com
Real Estate Services
N.A.I.C.S.: 531390

Idaho Timber Corporation   **(1)**
4800 Production St, Boise, ID 83705
Tel.: (208) 345-1202
Web Site: http://www.idahotimber.com
Sales Range: $75-99.9 Million
Emp.: 23
Lumber Products Mfr & Distr
N.A.I.C.S.: 321113
Ted Ellis *(Pres & CEO)*
Brock Lenon *(VP-Transportation & Logistics)*
Tom Griffith *(Mgr-Traffic)*
Darrell Gottschalk *(Gen Mgr-Plants & Equipment)*
Mike Jacobs *(Gen Mgr-Mktg)*
Bill Grzanic *(Gen Mgr-IT)*
Byron Cannon *(Gen Mgr-Cedar Sls)*
Dave Taugher *(VP-HR & Gen Counsel)*
Ash Cockcroft *(Controller)*
Scott Beechie *(CFO & VP)*

Subsidiary (Domestic):

Sagebrush Sales Company   **(2)**
6300 State Rd 303, Albuquerque, NM 87105
Tel.: (505) 877-7331
Web Site: http://www.idahotimber.com
Sales Range: $75-99.9 Million
Timber Product Mfr
N.A.I.C.S.: 321113

Jefferies (Australia) Pty. Ltd.   **(1)**
Level 22 60 Martin Place, Sydney, 2000, NSW, Australia
Tel.: (61) 293642800
Investment Banking Services
N.A.I.C.S.: 523999
Shyamal Chand *(VP)*

Jefferies Group LLC   **(1)**
520 Madison Ave, New York, NY 10022   **(100%)**
Tel.: (212) 284-2550
Web Site: http://www.jefferies.com
Rev.: $7,907,287,000
Assets: $54,768,900,000
Liabilities: $47,690,292,000
Net Worth: $7,078,608,000
Earnings: $1,618,731,000
Emp.: 4,508
Fiscal Year-end: 11/30/2021
Holding Company; Securities & Investment Banking Services
N.A.I.C.S.: 551112
Richard B. Handler *(Chm & CEO)*
Michael J. Sharp *(Gen Counsel, Sec & Exec VP)*
Matthew S. Larson *(CFO & Exec VP)*
Mark L. Cagno *(Mng Dir & Controller)*
Peter Forlenza *(Head-Equities-Global)*
Andrew R. Whittaker *(Vice Chm)*
John F. Stacconi *(Treas-Global)*
Fred Orlan *(Head-Fixed Income-Global)*
John M. Dalton *(VP)*
Rocco J. Nittoli *(Chief Compliance Officer)*
Laura E. Ulbrandt DiPierro *(Sec)*
James P. Walsh *(Vice Chm)*

Affiliate (Domestic):

Jefferies Capital Partners LLC   **(2)**
520 Madison Ave 10th Fl, New York, NY 10022
Tel.: (212) 284-2300
Web Site: http://www.jefcap.com
Sales Range: $75-99.9 Million
Emp.: 20
Privater Equity Firm
N.A.I.C.S.: 523999
Brian P. Friedman *(Founder)*
James L. Luikart *(Exec VP)*
James J. Dowling *(Mng Dir)*
Nicholas Daraviras *(Mng Dir)*

Division (Domestic):

Jefferies Energy Group   **(2)**
3 Allen Ctr 333 Clay St Ste 1000, Houston, TX 77002
Tel.: (281) 774-2000

Web Site: http://www.jefferies.com
Sales Range: $650-699.9 Million
Emp.: 80
Oil & Natural Gas Industry Financial Advisory Services
N.A.I.C.S.: 523940
Ralph Eads III *(Chm)*

Subsidiary (Domestic):

Jefferies Execution Services, Inc.   **(2)**
520 Madison Ave 11th Fl, New York, NY 10022   **(100%)**
Tel.: (646) 805-5400
Web Site: http://www.jefferies.com
Financial Transaction Processing Services
N.A.I.C.S.: 522320

Jefferies Finance, LLC   **(2)**
520 Madison Ave, New York, NY 10022
Tel.: (212) 284-2550
Web Site: http://www.jefferies.com
Management Consulting Services
N.A.I.C.S.: 541611
J. R. Young *(Head-Active Mgmt & Portfolio Mgr)*

Jefferies Financial Services, Inc.   **(2)**
520 Madison Ave 10th Fl, New York, NY 10022
Tel.: (212) 284-2300
Web Site: http://www.jefferies.com
Commodities Futures Dealing & Brokerage Services
N.A.I.C.S.: 523160

Jefferies Funding LLC   **(2)**
520 Madison Ave Fl 12, New York, NY 10022
Tel.: (212) 284-2550
Open End Investment Fund Services
N.A.I.C.S.: 525910

Jefferies High Yield Holdings,
LLC   **(2)**
The Metro Ctr 1 Station Pl, Stamford, CT 06902
Tel.: (203) 708-5800
Investment Management Service
N.A.I.C.S.: 523940

Subsidiary (Non-US):

Jefferies International (Holdings)
Limited   **(2)**
Vintners Place, London, EC4V 3BJ, United Kingdom
Tel.: (44) 2070298000
Emp.: 468
Investment Management Service
N.A.I.C.S.: 551112
Sara-Louise Boyes *(Head-Comm-EMEA)*

Subsidiary (Domestic):

Jefferies Bache Limited   **(3)**
Vintners Place 68 Upper Thames Street, London, EC4V 3BJ, United Kingdom
Tel.: (44) 2070298000
Web Site: http://www.jefferiesbache.com
Sales Range: $50-74.9 Million
Emp.: 120
Securities & Investment Banking Services
N.A.I.C.S.: 523150

Jefferies International Limited   **(3)**
100 Bishopsgate, London, EC2N 4JL, United Kingdom
Tel.: (44) 2070298000   **(100%)**
Web Site: http://www.jefferies.com
Sales Range: $1-4.9 Billion
Securities & Investment Banking Services
N.A.I.C.S.: 523150
Huw Tucker *(CEO & CFO)*

Subsidiary (Non-US):

Jefferies (Japan) Limited   **(4)**
1-1-2 Yurakucho, Chiyoda-ku, Tokyo, 100-0006, Japan   **(100%)**
Tel.: (81) 352516100
Web Site: http://www.jefferies.com
Sales Range: $75-99.9 Million
Securities Trading
N.A.I.C.S.: 523150

Jefferies (Switzerland) Ltd.   **(4)**
Uraniastrasse 12, Zurich, Switzerland   **(100%)**
Tel.: (41) 442271600

Sales Range: $50-74.9 Million
Emp.: 12
Securities Trading
N.A.I.C.S.: 523150

Jefferies Hong Kong Limited (4)
Cheung Kong Center 22nd Floor 2 Queen's
Road, Central, China (Hong Kong)
Tel.: (852) 37438000
Web Site: http://www.jefferies.com
Security Brokerage Services
N.A.I.C.S.: 523150

Jefferies India Private Ltd. (4)
42/43 2 North Avenue Maker Maxity
Bandra-Kurla Complex BKC Bandra East,
Mumbai, 400 051, Maharashtra, India
Tel.: (91) 2243566000
Web Site: http://www.jefferies.com
Sales Range: $25-49.9 Million
Emp.: 50
Securities & Investment Banking Services
N.A.I.C.S.: 523150

Subsidiary (Domestic):

Jefferies Investment Advisers,
LLC (2)
520 Madison Ave, New York, NY 10022
Tel.: (212) 284-2300
Capital Market Investment Services
N.A.I.C.S.: 523940

Jefferies LLC (2)
520 Madison Ave Fl 10, New York, NY
10022
Tel.: (212) 284-2300
Web Site: http://www.jefferies.com
Emp.: 3,438
Investment Banking Services
N.A.I.C.S.: 523150

Division (Domestic):

Jefferies Broadview (3)
520 Madison Ave, New York, NY 10022
Tel.: (212) 284-8100
Emp.: 65
Investment Banking
N.A.I.C.S.: 523150

Branch (Domestic):

Jefferies LLC - Los Angeles (3)
11100 Santa Monica Blvd, Los Angeles, CA
90025
Tel.: (310) 914-6611
Sales Range: $50-74.9 Million
Emp.: 70
Investment Banking, Securities Brokerage &
Dealing Services
N.A.I.C.S.: 523150
Karen Armstrong (Mng Dir-Private Client
Svcs)
David Luse (Mng Dir-Fin Sponsors Invest-
ment Grp)

Subsidiary (Domestic):

Jefferies Mortgage Finance, LLC (2)
1 Station Pl Ste 21, Stamford, CT 06902
Tel.: (203) 708-5800
Emp.: 9
Real Estate Credit Lending Services
N.A.I.C.S.: 522292

Leucadia Asset Management
LLC (1)
520 Madison Ave, New York, NY 10022
Tel.: (212) 284-2300
Web Site: http://www.leucadia-am.com
Investment Management Service
N.A.I.C.S.: 523940
Nicholas Daraviras (Co-Pres)
Solomon Jamshid Kumin (Co-Pres)
David Cranston (Head-Bus Dev-Global)
Sonia Han Levovitz (Gen Counsel)
Matt Smith (COO)

Leucadia Financial Corporation (1)
529 E S Temple, Salt Lake City, UT
84102 (100%)
Tel.: (801) 521-5400
Real Estate Lending Services
N.A.I.C.S.: 531190

Leucadia LLC (1)
315 Park Ave S Fl 20, New York, NY 10010
Tel.: (212) 460-1900
Investment Management Service
N.A.I.C.S.: 551112

M Science LLC (1)
45 W 25th St 9th Fl, New York, NY 10010
Tel.: (646) 751-1433
Web Site: http://www.mscience.com
Investment Banking Services
N.A.I.C.S.: 523999
Michael V. Marrale (CEO)
Joseph Napoli (COO)
Alessandro De Giorgis (Chief Compliance
Officer & Gen Counsel)
Elizabeth Coleman (Head-Product)
Dana Donnelly (Head-HR)

OpNet S.p.A. (1)
Viale Citta d Europa 681, 00144, Rome,
Italy
Tel.: (39) 0652097001
Web Site: https://opnet.it
Emp.: 250
Telecommunication Servicesb
N.A.I.C.S.: 517111

ResortQuest International, Inc. (1)
546 Mary Esther Cut-Off NW Ste 3, Fort
Walton Beach, FL 32548
Tel.: (850) 275-5000
Web Site: http://www.resortquest.com
Sales Range: $150-199.9 Million
Emp.: 4,000
Vacation Condominium & Home Sales &
Rentals; Property Management Services
N.A.I.C.S.: 531390
Elan J. Blutinger (Founder)

Sangart, Inc. (1)
6175 Lusk Blvd, San Diego, CA 92121
Tel.: (858) 450-2400
Web Site: http://www.sangart.com
Biopharmaceutical Product Mfr
N.A.I.C.S.: 325412

Tessellis S.p.A. (1)
Loc Sa Illetta SS 195 Km 2300, 09123, Ca-
gliari, Italy
Tel.: (39) 07046011
Web Site: https://www.tessellis.it
Emp.: 1,145
Telecommunication Servicesb
N.A.I.C.S.: 517111

JEFFERSONVILLE BANCORP

4864 State Rte 52, Jeffersonville, NY
12748
Tel.: (845) 482-4000 NY
Web Site: https://www.jeff.bank
Year Founded: 1982
JFBC—(OTCIQ)
Rev.: $20,529,000
Assets: $616,596,000
Liabilities: $542,166,000
Net Worth: $74,430,000
Earnings: $4,810,000
Emp.: 130
Fiscal Year-end: 12/31/20
Bank Holding Company
N.A.I.C.S.: 551111
Tatiana C. Hahn (Chief Lending Offi-
cer & Exec VP)
Virginia Sanborn (VP & Controller)
Claire C. Taggart (VP-HR)
John A. Russell (CFO & Exec VP)
LeighAnne Pfriender (Asst VP)
George W. Kinne Jr. (Pres & CEO)
Kenneth C. Klein (Chm & Chm)
Florence Horecky (Officer-Ops & VP)
Tanja McKerrell (Officer-Loan & VP)
Valerie A. Panich (VP & Mgr-Loan
Origination)
Jill Atkins (Asst Controller)
Amber Benson (Compliance Officer,
VP & Coord-Audit)
Marisa Heisler (VP & Dir-IT)
Anna Milucky (VP)
Deborah Muzuruk (Asst VP)
Leanne Stuhlmiller (Officer-BSA &
Information Security & VP)
Rhonda L. Decker (Officer-Security &
Sr VP)
Jillian Bertot (Branch Mgr-Eldred)
Margaret Blaut (VP & Branch Mgr-
Anawana Lake)
Michelle Brockner (Officer-Trng)

Krista Brink (Asst VP & Branch Mgr-
Loch Sheldrake)
Linda Browne (Branch Mgr-White
Lake)
Joseph Coleman (Officer-Comml
Loan & VP)
Bertha Donohue (Asst VP & Branch
Mgr-Liberty)
Bryan Flynn (Officer-Comml Loan, VP
& Portfolio Mgr)
Melanie Karkos (Asst VP & Mgr-
Deposit Ops)
Patricia Korth (Branch Mgr-Port Jer-
vis)
Kristin Lockwood (Branch Mgr-
Narrowsburg)
Diane McGrath (Asst VP & Mgr-Loan
Servicing)
Amber Novikov (Branch Mgr)
Patricia Olsen (Asst VP)
Abigail Opper (Controller & Asst VP)
Kimberly White (Branch Mgr-
Wurtsboro)
Heinrich Strauch (Officer-Comml
Loan & VP)
Melinda Stratton (Asst VP & Branch
Mgr-Monticello)
Brandy Smith (Officer-Loan-II)
Sandra Ross (Branch Mgr-Callicoon)
Jaclene Poley (Coord-Mktg)
Kelsey Conklin (Asst Mgr-Loan Ser-
vicing)
Ursula Curry (Asst Mgr-Deposit Ops)

Subsidiaries:

Jeff Bank (1)
4866 State Rte 52 PO Box 398, Jefferson-
ville, NY 12748 (100%)
Tel.: (845) 482-4000
Web Site: http://www.jeffbank.com
Rev.: $22,923,000
Assets: $427,187,000
Liabilities: $378,253,000
Net Worth: $48,934,000
Earnings: $4,539,000
Emp.: 117
Fiscal Year-end: 12/31/2012
Savings, Loans, Commercial & Investment
Banking Services
N.A.I.C.S.: 522110
Tatiana C. Hahn (Exec VP)
Virginia Sanborn (Controller)
Claire C. Taggart (VP-HR)
Rhonda Decker (VP, Branch Mgr-Liberty &
Security Officer)
Anna Milucky (VP)
Debbie Muzuruk (Asst VP)
Tanjay McKerrell (VP & Mgr-Loan Servicing)
John A. Russell (Exec VP)
Jackie Austin (Asst VP)
Linda Fisk (VP)
Joseph Coleman (VP)

Subsidiary (Domestic):

FNBJ Holding Corp. (2)
4864 State Rte 52, Jeffersonville, NY 12748
Tel.: (845) 482-4000
Web Site: http://www.jeffbank.com
Emp.: 35
Investment Management Service
N.A.I.C.S.: 523940
Stacy Kuhn (Branch Mgr)

JERASH HOLDINGS (US), INC.

277 Fairfield Rd Ste 338, Fairfield, NJ
07004
Tel.: (201) 285-7973 DE
Web Site:
https://www.jerashholdings.com
Year Founded: 2016
JRSH—(NASDAQ)
Rev.: $117,187,340
Assets: $80,245,566
Liabilities: $15,814,903
Net Worth: $64,430,663
Earnings: $2,041,926)
Emp.: 4,700
Fiscal Year-end: 03/31/24
Holding Company
N.A.I.C.S.: 551112

Lin Hung Choi (Chm, Pres, CEO &
Treas)
Wei Yang (Sec & VP)
Tsze Lun Ng (Head-Mktg)
Baiju Chellamma (Gen Mgr)
Gilbert K. Lee (CFO)

JET.AI INC.

10845 Griffith Peak Dr Ste 200, Las
Vegas, NV 89135
Tel.: (702) 747-4000 DE
Web Site: https://jet.ai
JTAI—(NASDAQ)
Rev.: $4,065
Assets: $13,049,940
Liabilities: $17,906,373
Net Worth: ($4,856,433)
Earnings: $7,175,980
Emp.: 2
Fiscal Year-end: 12/31/22
Software Publr
N.A.I.C.S.: 513210
Wrendon Timothy (CFO, Treas &
Sec)
Mark Winston (Exec Chm & Interim
CEO)
George Murnane (CEO)
Patrick McNulty (COO)
Kienan Franklin (VP-Sales)
Jake Vale (CMO)

JETBLACK CORP.

304SJonesBlvdSte5058, Las Vegas,
NV 89107
Tel.: (870) 888-8880 NV
Web Site:
https://www.jetblackcorp.com
Year Founded: 2002
JTBK—(OTCIQ)
Sales Range: Less than $1 Million
Emp.: 4
Jewelry, Furniture & Crafts Designer
& Retailer
N.A.I.C.S.: 339910
Daniel A. Goldin (Chm & CEO)
Emilia S. Olvera (Mgr-Corporate Mar-
keting & Investor Relations)

JETBLUE AIRWAYS CORPO-
RATION

Tel.: (718) 286-7900 DE
Web Site: https://www.jetblue.com
Year Founded: 1999
JBLU—(NASDAQ)
Rev.: $9,615,000,000
Assets: $13,853,000,000
Liabilities: $10,516,000,000
Net Worth: $3,337,000,000
Earnings: ($310,000,000)
Emp.: 19,232
Fiscal Year-end: 12/31/23
Airline Operations
N.A.I.C.S.: 481111
Robert Land (Head-Govt Affairs &
Assoc Gen Counsel)
Martin St. George (Pres)
Warren Christie (COO)
Warren Christie (Head-Safety, Secu-
rity, and Fleet Ops)
Tracy Lawlor (Chief Strategy & Bus
Dev Officer)
Jayne O'Brien (Head-Mktg & Loyalty)
Ursula Hurley (CFO)
Doug McGraw (Chief Comm Officer)
Carol Clements (Chief Digital Officer
& Chief Tech Officer)
Dave Clark (Head-Finance & Strat-
egy)
Daniel Shurz (Head-Revenue, Net-
work, and Enterprise Planning)
Eileen McCarthy (Gen Counsel &
Sec)
Joanna L. Geraghty (CEO)

JEWETT-CAMERON TRADING
COMPANY LTD.

Jewett-Cameron Trading Company
Ltd.—(Continued)

32275 NW Hillcrest, North Plains, OR
97133
Tel.: (503) 647-0110   BC
Web Site:
  https://www.jewettcameron.com
JCTCF—(NASDAQ)
Rev.: $47,145,176
Assets: $27,490,514
Liabilities: $2,639,370
Net Worth: $24,851,144
Earnings: $721,753
Emp.: 62
Fiscal Year-end: 08/31/24
Holding Company; Lumber & Building
Products Whslr.
N.A.I.C.S.: 444180
Chad Summers (Pres & CEO)
Mitch Van Domelen (CFO & Sec)
Charles E. Hopewell (Chm)

Subsidiaries:

Greenwood Products, Inc.   (1)
PO Box 249, North Plains, OR 97133
Tel.: (503) 670-9663
Web Site:
  https://www.greenwoodproducts.com
Sales Range: $10-24.9 Million
Emp.: 8
Plywood & Related Products
N.A.I.C.S.: 423310
Don Boone (CEO)

Jewett-Cameron Lumber
Corporation   (1)
32275 NW Hillcrest St, North Plains, OR
97133
Tel.: (503) 647-0110
Web Site: http://www.jewettcameron.com
Sales Range: $50-74.9 Million
Lumber & Building Materials
N.A.I.C.S.: 423310

Jewett-Cameron Seed Company   (1)
32275 NW Hillcrest, North Plains, OR
97133
Tel.: (503) 647-0110
Web Site: http://www.jewett-cameron.com
Sales Range: $150-199.9 Million
Emp.: 40
Feed
N.A.I.C.S.: 423310

MSI-PRO Company   (1)
32275 NW Hillcrest St, North Plains, OR
97133
Tel.: (503) 647-7351
Web Site: http://www.msipro.com
Sales Range: $150-199.9 Million
Emp.: 5
Tools & Clamps
N.A.I.C.S.: 423830

JFROG LTD.
270 E Caribbean Dr, Sunnyvale, CA
94089
Tel.: (408) 329-1540   II
Web Site: https://www.jfrog.com
Year Founded: 2008
FROG—(NASDAQ)
Rev.: $280,040,000
Assets: $871,221,000
Liabilities: $246,448,000
Net Worth: $624,773,000
Earnings: ($90,184,000)
Emp.: 1,300
Fiscal Year-end: 12/31/22
Software Development Services
N.A.I.C.S.: 541511
Frederic Ben Simon (Co-Founder)
Shlomi Ben Haim (Co-Founder, Chm
& CEO)
Yoav Landman (Co-Founder & CTO)
Tali Notman (Chief Revenue Officer)
Keren Massad (Chief HR Officer)
Orit Goren (COO)
Micheline Nijmeh (CMO)
Sagi Dudai (Exec VP-Product & En-
grg)
Siobhan Lyons (Sr Mgr-MarComm)

Jeff Schreiner (VP-IR)
Aran Azarzar (CIO)
Gal Marder (Exec VP-Strategy)

JIYA ACQUISITION CORP.
628 Middlefield Rd, Palo Alto, CA
94301
Tel.: (650) 285-4270   DE
Web Site: http://www.jiyacorp.com
Year Founded: 2020
JYAC—(NASDAQ)
Assets: $104,427,748
Liabilities: $107,485,618
Net Worth: ($3,057,870)
Earnings: ($1,923,038)
Emp.: 4
Fiscal Year-end: 12/31/21
Investment Services
N.A.I.C.S.: 551112
Srinivas Akkaraju (Chm)
Richard Van Doren (CFO & Sec)
Cory Freedland (Chief Investment
Officer)
Mayank Gandhi (VP-Corp Dev)

JLM COUTURE, INC.
525 7th Ave Ste 1703, New York, NY
10018
Tel.: (212) 764-6960   DE
Web Site:
  https://www.jlmcouture.com
Year Founded: 1986
JLMCQ—(OTCIQ)
Sales Range: $25-49.9 Million
Emp.: 70
Cut & Sew Apparel Manufacturing
(except Contractors)
N.A.I.C.S.: 315250
Joseph L. Murphy (Pres & CEO)

JMD PROPERTIES INC.
139 Fulton St Ste 412, New York, NY
10038
Tel.: (516) 946-1288   WY
TDEY—(OTCIQ)
Holding Company; Residential Real
Estate Investment, Renovation & As-
set Management
N.A.I.C.S.: 551112
Marissa Julia Welner (CEO)

Subsidiaries:

JMD MHC LLC   (1)
139 Fulton St Ste 412, New York, NY
10038
Tel.: (516) 946-1288
Residential Real Estate Investment, Reno-
vation & Asset Management
N.A.I.C.S.: 531390
Marissa Julia Welner (CEO)

JNS HOLDINGS CORPORA-
TION
830 Seton Ct, Wheeling, IL 60090
Tel.: (773) 467-8180   DE
Web Site:
  https://www.jnsholdings.com
JNSH—(OTCIQ)
Other Gasoline Stations
N.A.I.C.S.: 457120
Brian Howe (Pres & CEO)

Subsidiaries:

Evolve USA Charging
Corporation   (1)
830 Seton Ct, Wheeling, IL 60090
Tel.: (847) 520-2899
Electric Vehicle Charging Station Operator
N.A.I.C.S.: 457120

JNS Power & Control Systems,
Inc.   (1)
830 Seton Ct, Wheeling, IL 60090
Tel.: (773) 467-8180
Web Site: http://www.jnspower.com
Electrical & Wiring Installation Contracting
Services
N.A.I.C.S.: 238210

JOANN INC.
5555 Darrow Rd, Hudson, OH 44236
Tel.: (330) 656-2600   DE
Web Site: https://www.joann.com
Year Founded: 2012
JOAN—(NASDAQ)
Rev.: $2,216,900,000
Assets: $2,180,800,000
Liabilities: $2,229,900,000
Net Worth: ($49,100,000)
Earnings: ($200,600,000)
Emp.: 20,000
Fiscal Year-end: 01/28/23
Holding Company
N.A.I.C.S.: 551112
Varadheesh Chennakrishnan (CIO &
Sr VP)
Christopher DiTullio (Chief Customer
Officer & Sr VP)
Janet Duliga (Chief Admin Officer &
Sr VP)
Sharyn Hejcl (Chief Innovation &
Sourcing Officer & Sr VP)
Michael Joyce (Sr VP-Plng, Replen-
ishment & Supply Chain Optimiza-
tion)
Robert Will (Chief Mdsg Officer & Sr
VP)
Ann Aber (Gen Counsel, Sec & VP)
Joe Thibault (Sr VP-Store Ops)
Lisa Wittman-Smith (Sr VP-Inventory
Mgmt & Bus Insights)
Scott N. Sekella (CFO & Sr VP)

JOBY AVIATION, INC.
Tel.: (831) 201-6700   DE
Web Site:
  https://www.jobyaviation.com
Year Founded: 2020
JOBY—(NYSE)
Rev.: $134,252,000
Assets: $1,292,984,000
Liabilities: $128,243,000
Net Worth: $1,164,741,000
Earnings: ($258,043,000)
Emp.: 1,422
Fiscal Year-end: 12/31/22
Aviation & Aerospace Component Mfr.
N.A.I.C.S.: 334511
Bonny W. Simi (Head-People & Air
Ops)
Matt Field (CFO)
Greg Bowles (Head-Govt)
Eric Allison (Head-Product)
Kate DeHoff (Gen Counsel & Sec)
Didier Papadopoulos (Head-Aircraft
OEM)
JoeBen Bevirt (Founder, CEO &
Chief Architect)
Paul Sciarra (Exec Chm)

Subsidiaries:

Avionyx, S.A.   (1)
America Free Trade Zone, San Jose, Costa
Rica
Tel.: (506) 3218212365
Web Site: https://www.avionyx.com
Software Development Services
N.A.I.C.S.: 541511
Jose Arias (Mgr-Project)

Joby Aero, Inc.   (1)
2155 Delaware Ave Ste 225, Santa Cruz,
CA 95060
Tel.: (831) 426-3733
Web Site: http://www.jobyaviation.com
All-Electric Aircraft Developer & Mfr.
N.A.I.C.S.: 336411
JoeBen Bevirt (Founder & CEO)

JOEY NEW YORK, INC.
Trump Tower I 16001 Collins Ave,
Sunny Isles Beach, FL 33160
Tel.: (305) 948-9998   NV
Web Site:
  http://www.joeynewyork.com
Year Founded: 2011
JOEY—(NASDAQ)

Sales Range: Less than $1 Million
Emp.: 5
Natural Skincare & Beauty Products
Distr
N.A.I.C.S.: 424210
Joey Chancis (CEO)

JOFF FINTECH ACQUISITION
CORP.
1345 Ave of the Americas, New York,
NY 10105
Tel.: (212) 370-1300   DE
Web Site: http://www.joffspac.com
Year Founded: 2020
JOFF—(NASDAQ)
Rev.: $18,050,100
Assets: $415,473,211
Liabilities: $443,983,241
Net Worth: ($28,510,030)
Earnings: $15,152,975
Emp.: 4
Fiscal Year-end: 12/31/21
Investment Services
N.A.I.C.S.: 523999
Joel Leonoff (CEO)
Hillel Frankel (Pres & Sec)
Peter J.S. Smith (CFO)
Fraz Ahmed (Sr VP-Corp & Bus Dev)

JOHN ADAMS LIFE CORPO-
RATION
5776 Lindero Cyn Rd Ste D 417,
Westlake Village, CA 91362
Tel.: (310) 431-9769   CA
Web Site: https://www.jalifecorp.com
JALC—(OTCIQ)
Financial Investment Services
N.A.I.C.S.: 524210
Alvin S. Milder (Gen Counsel, Sec &
VP)

JOHN B. SANFILIPPO & SON,
INC.
1703 N Randall Rd, Elgin, IL 60123-
7820
Tel.: (847) 289-1800   DE
Web Site: https://www.jbssinc.com
Year Founded: 1922
JBSS—(NASDAQ)
Rev.: $1,066,783,000
Assets: $515,575,000
Liabilities: $192,962,000
Net Worth: $322,613,000
Earnings: $60,249,000
Emp.: 1,800
Fiscal Year-end: 06/27/24
Nuts, Snacks & Confections Mfr. &
Distr
N.A.I.C.S.: 311911
Michael J. Valentine (Grp Pres)
Jeffrey T. Sanfilippo (Chm & CEO)
Jasper Brian Sanfilippo Jr. (Pres,
COO & Asst Sec)
Frank S. Pellegrino (CFO, Treas &
Exec VP-Fin & Admin)
John E. Sanfilippo (Plant Engr & Mgr-
Engrg Projects)

Subsidiaries:

John B. Sanfilippo & Son, Inc.   (1)
1703 N Randall Rd, Elgin, IL
60123-7820   (100%)
Tel.: (847) 289-1800
Web Site: https://jbssinc.com
Sales Range: $300-349.9 Million
Emp.: 384
Supplier of Farm Product Raw Materials
N.A.I.C.S.: 424450

Squirrel Brand, L.P.   (1)
113 Industrial Blvd, McKinney, TX 75069-
7233
Tel.: (214) 585-0100
Web Site: http://www.squirrelbrand.com
Roasted Nut Mfr
N.A.I.C.S.: 445292

Brent Meyer *(Owner)*

JOHN BEAN TECHNOLOGIES CORPORATION
70 W Madison St Ste 4400, Chicago, IL 60602
Tel.: (312) 861-5900   DE
Web Site: https://www.jbtc.com
JBT—(NYSE)
Rev.: $2,166,000,000
Assets: $2,584,100,000
Liabilities: $1,721,400,000
Net Worth: $862,700,000
Earnings: $130,700,000
Emp.: 7,200
Fiscal Year-end: 12/31/22
Food Processing, Packaging & Air Transportation Machinery & Equipment Mfr
N.A.I.C.S.: 333241
David C. Burdakin *(Pres-AeroTech & Exec VP)*
Luiz Rizzolo *(Pres-Diversified Food & Health & Exec VP)*
Brian A. Deck *(Pres & CEO)*
James L. Marvin *(Gen Counsel, Exec VP & Asst Sec)*
Jessi L. Corcoran *(Chief Acctg Officer, VP & Controller)*
Matthew J. Meister *(CFO & Exec VP)*
Kristina Paschall *(Chief Information & Digital Officer & Exec VP)*
Robert Petrie *(Pres-Protein & Exec VP)*
Shelley Bridarolli *(Chief HR Officer)*
Jack Martin *(Exec VP)*

Subsidiaries:

A & B Process Systems Corp.   (1)
212700 Stainless Ave, Stratford, WI 54484
Tel.: (715) 687-4332
Food Processing & Pharmaceutical Distr
N.A.I.C.S.: 424210

Aircraft Maintenance Support Services Limited   (1)
Eagle House Village Farm Industrial Estate, Bridgend, CF33 6NU, United Kingdom
Tel.: (44) 1656743700
Food Processing & Pharmaceutical Distr
N.A.I.C.S.: 424210

Avure Technologies Inc.   (1)
2601 S Verity Pkwy Bldg 13, Middletown, OH 45044
Tel.: (513) 433-2500
Web Site: http://www.avure-hpp-foods.com
High-Pressure Isostatic, Sheet Metal Forming & Food Processing Press Designer, Mfr & Distr
N.A.I.C.S.: 333248
Errol Raghubeer *(Sr VP-HPP Science & Tech)*
Austin Lowder *(Mgr-Food Science)*

Subsidiary (Non-US):

Quintus Technologies AB   (2)
Quintusvagen 2, 721 66, Vasteras, Sweden
Tel.: (46) 21327000
Web Site: http://www.quintustechnologies.com
High-Pressure Isostatic & Sheet Metal Forming Press Mfr & Distr
N.A.I.C.S.: 333248

Bevcorp, LLC   (1)
37200 Research Dr, Eastlake, OH 44095
Tel.: (440) 954-3500
Web Site: https://www.bevcorp.com
Packaging Equipment Mfr & Distr
N.A.I.C.S.: 333993

FTNON Almelo B.V.   (1)
Bedrijvenpark Twente 20, 7602 KA, Almelo, Netherlands
Tel.: (31) 546574222
Web Site: http://www.ftnon.com
Food Processing Equipment Mfr & Distr
N.A.I.C.S.: 333310

FTNON Delft B.V.   (1)
Rotterdamseweg 402E, 2629 HH, Delft, Netherlands

Tel.: (31) 157440150
Food Processing Equipment Distr
N.A.I.C.S.: 423830
Mathijs Vermeulen *(CTO)*

FTNON USA Inc.   (1)
30 E San Joaquin Ste 203, Salinas, CA 93901
Tel.: (831) 274-6007
Food Processing Equipment Distr
N.A.I.C.S.: 423830
Angela Green *(Mgr-Admin)*

JBT AeroTech Singapore Pte. Ltd.   (1)
6 Loyang Lane 03-00, Young Heng Industrial Building, Singapore, 508920, Singapore
Tel.: (65) 65429255
Aircraft Related Equipment Mfr
N.A.I.C.S.: 336413
Karthick Soundararajan *(Mgr-Customer Care)*

JBT AeroTech UK Limited   (1)
Arnold Hawker House Central Way, Feltham, TW14 0XQ, Middlesex, United Kingdom
Tel.: (44) 2085870666
Aircraft Related Equipment Mfr
N.A.I.C.S.: 336413
Richard Hale *(Mgr-Customer Care-EMEA)*

JBT Alco-food-machines GmbH   (1)
Kreienbrink 3 5, 49186, Bad Iburg, Germany
Tel.: (49) 540379330
Web Site: https://www.alco-food.com
Food Product Equipment Mfr & Distr
N.A.I.C.S.: 333241

JBT Food & Dairy Systems Inc.   (1)
6430 Shiloh Rd E C, Alpharetta, GA 30005
Tel.: (800) 653-0304
Food Processing & Pharmaceutical Distr
N.A.I.C.S.: 424210

JBT Food and Dairy Systems B.V.   (1)
Deccaweg 32, 1042 AD, Amsterdam, Netherlands
Tel.: (31) 206348911
Food Processing & Pharmaceutical Distr
N.A.I.C.S.: 424210

JBT FoodTech Citrus Systems   (1)
400 Fairway Ave, Lakeland, FL 33801
Tel.: (863) 683-5411
Web Site: http://www.jbtcorporation.com
Sales Range: $75-99.9 Million
Emp.: 200
Mfr of Citrus Processing Machinery & Coatings; Fresh Produce Preservation; Produce Labeling
N.A.I.C.S.: 333993

JBT FoodTech Fort Pierce   (1)
3206 Industrial 33rd St, Fort Pierce, FL 34946
Tel.: (772) 461-5471
Web Site: http://www.jbtcorporation.com
Sales Range: $25-49.9 Million
Emp.: 6
Fresh Produce Preservation; Produce Labeling
N.A.I.C.S.: 325998

JBT FoodTech Lindsay   (1)
70 W Madison St Ste 4400, Chicago, IL 60602
Tel.: (312) 861-5900
Web Site: http://www.jbtcorporation.com
Sales Range: $25-49.9 Million
Emp.: 55
Fresh Produce Preservation, Produce Labeling & Citrus Processing
N.A.I.C.S.: 325998
Charles H. Cannon Jr. *(Chm)*

JBT FoodTech Madera   (1)
2300 Industrial Ave, Madera, CA 93639
Tel.: (559) 661-3200
Web Site: http://www.jbtc.com
Rev.: $20,000,000
Emp.: 180
In-Container & In-Flow Processing Systems Mfr
N.A.I.C.S.: 333241

JBT FoodTech Redmond   (1)
15304 NE 95th St, Redmond, WA 98052
Tel.: (425) 883-1101

Web Site: http://www.jbtcorporation.com
Sales Range: $25-49.9 Million
Emp.: 32
Freezing, Frying, Coating & Cooking Equipment Mfr
N.A.I.C.S.: 333241

JBT FoodTech Sandusky   (1)
1622 1st St, Sandusky, OH 44870
Tel.: (419) 626-0304
Web Site: http://www.jbtcorporation.com
Sales Range: $125-149.9 Million
Freezing, Frying, Coating & Cooking Equipment Mfr
N.A.I.C.S.: 333241

JBT Netherlands B.V.   (1)
Deccaweg 32, 1042 AD, Amsterdam, Netherlands
Tel.: (31) 206348911
Web Site: http://www.jbtc.com
Conveying Equipment Mfr
N.A.I.C.S.: 335311

JBT Wolf-tec   (1)
134 Flatbush Ave, Kingston, NY 12401
Tel.: (845) 340-9727
Web Site: http://www.wolf-tec.com
Food Products Machinery Mfr & Whslr
N.A.I.C.S.: 333241

John Bean Technologies (Proprietary) Ltd.   (1)
Koper Street, Brackenfell, Cape Town, 7560, South Africa
Tel.: (27) 219821130
Web Site: http://www.jbtcorporation.com
Sales Range: $25-49.9 Million
Emp.: 79
General Industrial Machinery Mfr
N.A.I.C.S.: 333248

John Bean Technologies (Shanghai) Co., Ltd.   (1)
Units 711 & 712 No 763 of Mengzi Road, Huangpu District, Shanghai, 200023, China
Tel.: (86) 2163411616
Food Product Machinery Mfr
N.A.I.C.S.: 333241

John Bean Technologies (Thailand) Ltd.   (1)
No 2525 FYI Center Building 2 9th Floor Unit No 2/901-2/903, Rama IV Road Klongtoei, Bangkok, 10110, Thailand
Tel.: (66) 22574000
Web Site: http://www.jbtfoodtech.com
Emp.: 30
Food Processing Equipment Whslr
N.A.I.C.S.: 423830

John Bean Technologies AB   (1)
Rusthallsgatan 21, SE-251 09, Helsingborg, Sweden
Tel.: (46) 424904000
Sales Range: $75-99.9 Million
Emp.: 500
Mfr of Freezers for Food Production
N.A.I.C.S.: 335220

Subsidiary (Domestic):

John Bean Technologies International AB   (2)
Rusthallsgatan 21, 251 09, Helsingborg, Sweden
Tel.: (46) 424904000
Web Site: http://www.jbtfoodtech.com
Emp.: 180
Holding Company; Food Processing Equipment Whslr
N.A.I.C.S.: 551112

John Bean Technologies Australia Ltd.   (1)
Level 1 385 Macarthur Ave, Hamilton, 4007, QLD, Australia
Tel.: (61) 738966100
Sales Range: $50-74.9 Million
Emp.: 12
Food Processing Equipment Mfr
N.A.I.C.S.: 333241

John Bean Technologies GmbH   (1)
Esch 11, 33824, Werther, Germany
Tel.: (49) 52039700970
Sales Range: $10-24.9 Million
Emp.: 20
Food Processing Equipment Mfr & Whslr
N.A.I.C.S.: 333241

John Bean Technologies Hong Kong Limited   (1)
31/F Tower Two Times Square 1 Matheson Street, Causeway Bay, China (Hong Kong)   (100%)
Tel.: (852) 61318828
Web Site: http://www.jbtcorporation.com
Sales Range: $10-24.9 Million
Emp.: 10
Food Processing Equipment Whslr
N.A.I.C.S.: 423830
Patrick Tan *(Dir Gen)*

Representative Office (Non-US):

John Bean Technologies Hong Kong Ltd. - Philippines Office   (1)
4th Fl Pilipinas Bank Bldg 111 Paseo De Roxas, Makati, 1229, Metro Manila, Philippines
Tel.: (63) 28175546
Web Site: http://www.jbtfoodtech.com
Emp.: 20
Food Processing Equipment Whslr
N.A.I.C.S.: 423830

John Bean Technologies Iberica S.L.   (1)
Sucursal Espana C Julian Camarillo 26 4 Local 2, Alcala de Henares, 28805, Madrid, Spain
Tel.: (34) 913046698
Web Site: http://www.jbtfoodtech.com
Sales Range: $25-49.9 Million
Emp.: 14
Food Processing Equipment Mfr
N.A.I.C.S.: 333241

John Bean Technologies India Private Limited   (1)
Gat no 255 Chikhali Moshi Road Borhadewadi Moshi, Pune, 412 105, Maharashtra, India   (100%)
Tel.: (91) 772 202 9071
Web Site: http://www.jbtc.com
Sales Range: $10-24.9 Million
Emp.: 20
Food Processing Equipment Mfr
N.A.I.C.S.: 333241

John Bean Technologies K.K.   (1)
Forecast Ningyocho Place 5F 3-4-14, Nihonbashi-Ningyocho Chuo-ku, Tokyo, 103-0013, Japan
Tel.: (81) 336605550
Web Site: http://www.jbtfoodtech.com
Food Processing Equipment Mfr & Whslr
N.A.I.C.S.: 333241

Division (Domestic):

John Bean Technologies K.K. - Citrus Division   (2)
845-3 Yamanishi-cho, Matsuyama, 791-8026, Ehime, Japan
Tel.: (81) 89 907 1446
Web Site: http://www.jbtfoodtech.com
Fruit & Vegetable Processing Equipment Mfr
N.A.I.C.S.: 333241

John Bean Technologies Ltd.   (1)
Heather Park Kirkton South Road, West Lothian, Livingston, EH54 7BT, United Kingdom
Tel.: (44) 1506857112
Food Processing Equipment Distr
N.A.I.C.S.: 423830

John Bean Technologies Middle East FZE   (1)
Office No LB190502 Building No LB19 Jebel Ali Free Zone, PO Box 263001, Dubai, United Arab Emirates
Tel.: (971) 488112009
Web Site: http://www.jbtcorporation.com
Food Processing Machinery Whslr
N.A.I.C.S.: 423830

John Bean Technologies N.V.   (1)
Breedstraat 3, 9100, Saint-Niklaas, Belgium
Tel.: (32) 37801211
Web Site: http://www.jbtfoodtech.com

John Bean Technologies
Corporation—(Continued)
(1)
Sales Range: $25-49.9 Million
Emp.: 200
Mfr of Industrial Food Processing Equipment
N.A.I.C.S.: 333241

John Bean Technologies S.p.A. (1)
Via Mantova 63/A, 43100, Parma, Italy
Tel.: (39) 0521908411
Web Site: http://www.jbtfoodtech.com
Sales Range: $125-149.9 Million
Emp.: 120
Food Processing Equipment Mfr & Whslr
N.A.I.C.S.: 333241

John Bean Technologies SA (1)
Taverparc - Batiment 2 1 62 Boulevard
Henri Navier, PO Box 55, 95150, Taverny,
France
Tel.: (33) 18 428 0200
Web Site: http://www.jbtc.com
Sales Range: $150-199.9 Million
Food Processing Equipment
N.A.I.C.S.: 423830

John Bean Technologies Sp. z (1)
o.o.
Ul Stryjenskich 19 lok usl 21/21A, 02-791,
Warsaw, Poland
Tel.: (48) 22 894 9025
Web Site: http://www.jbtfoodtech.com
Food Processing Machinery Whslr
N.A.I.C.S.: 423830

John Bean Technologies Spain (1)
S.L.
Carretera A2 Km 34 400 Alcala de Henares,
28805, Madrid, Spain
Tel.: (34) 918775880
Web Site: http://www.jbtc.com
Food Processing Equipment Mfr
N.A.I.C.S.: 333241

John Bean Technologies Spain (1)
S.L.U.
Carretera A2 Km 34 400, 28805, Alcala de
Henares, Madrid, Spain
Tel.: (34) 918775880
Conveying Equipment Mfr
N.A.I.C.S.: 335311
Urban Drotz (Mgr-European Shared Svc
Center)

Lektro Inc. (1)
1190 SE Flightline Dr, Warrenton, OR
97146-7146
Tel.: (503) 861-2288
Web Site: http://www.lektro.com
Industrial Truck, Tractor, Trailer & Stacker
Machinery Mfr
N.A.I.C.S.: 333924
Steven Hill (Mgr-Parts)
Travis Boggs (Mgr-Pur)
Jeremiah Scott (Mgr-Engrg)
Patrick Reed (Mgr-Svc)
Jesse A. Long (Dir-Sls & Customer Care)
Paul Davis (Dir-Ops)
Tyler Bellmore (Dir-Trng)
Grant North (Comptroller)
Matt Talley (Mgr-Quality Control)
Henry A. Balensifer III (Mgr-Govt Rels &
Mktg)

PLF International Limited (1)
Ardleigh House Dedham Road Ardleigh,
Harwich, CO12 4EN, Essex, United Kingdom
Tel.: (44) 1255552994
Food Processing & Pharmaceutical Distr
N.A.I.C.S.: 424210

Prime Equipment Group, Inc. (1)
2000 E Fulton St, Columbus, OH 43205
Tel.: (614) 253-8590
Web Site:
   http://www.primeequipmentgroup.com
Sales Range: $1-9.9 Million
Emp.: 19
Food Product Machinery Mfr
N.A.I.C.S.: 333241
Michael Gasbarro (Pres)

Proseal America, Inc. (1)
7611 Whitepine Rd, Richmond, VA 23237
Tel.: (804) 447-9038
Food Related Machinery Mfr
N.A.I.C.S.: 333241

Gari Wyatt (CEO)

Proseal Australia Pty. Ltd. (1)
24-26 Lindon Court, Tullamarine, Melbourne, 3043, VIC, Australia
Tel.: (61) 393970955
Web Site:
   http://www.prosealaustralia.com.au
Sealing & Packaging Machinery Mfr
N.A.I.C.S.: 333993
Scott Templeton (Gen Mgr)

Proseal UK Limited (1)
Adlington Industrial Estate, Adlington, SK10
4NL, Cheshire, United Kingdom
Tel.: (44) 1625856600
Web Site: https://www.proseal.com
Food Related Machinery Mfr
N.A.I.C.S.: 333241
Eddie Holmes (Project Mgr)

Schroder Maschinenbau GmbH & Co
KG (1)
Esch 11, 33824, Werther, Germany
Tel.: (49) 520397000
Web Site: https://schroeder-maschinen.de
Food Processing Equipment Mfr & Distr
N.A.I.C.S.: 333310

Shanghai FTNON Food Processing
Equipment Co., Ltd. (1)
No 2888 of Jiuxin Road Area C Floor 3
Block 4, Songjiang District, Shanghai, China
Tel.: (86) 18651708915
Food Processing Equipment Distr
N.A.I.C.S.: 423830

Stork Food & Dairy Systems
B.V. (1)
Deccaweg 32, Amsterdam, 1042 AD, Netherlands
Tel.: (31) 206348911
Web Site: http://www.sfds.eu
Dairy, Juice, Food Processing & Pharmaceutical Industries Integrated Processing &
Filling Lines Mfr
N.A.I.C.S.: 333241

Subsidiary (Non-US):

JBT Food & Dairy Systems
SARL (2)
62 Boulevard Henri Navier, 95150, Taverny,
France
Tel.: (33) 184280200
Web Site: http://www.jbtfoodtech.com
Packaging Machinery Distr
N.A.I.C.S.: 423830

Tipper Tie, Inc. (1)
2000 Lufkin Rd, Apex, NC 27539
Tel.: (919) 362-8811
Web Site: http://www.tippertie.com
Food Product Machinery Mfr
N.A.I.C.S.: 333241

JOHN HANCOCK HEDGED
EQUITY & INCOME FUND
200 Berkeley St, Boston, MA 02116
Tel.: (617) 663-4497
Web Site:
   https://www.jhinvestments.com
Year Founded: 2010
HEQ—(NYSE)
Rev.: $9,281,326
Assets: $182,715,134
Liabilities: $1,194,244
Net Worth: $181,520,890
Earnings: $7,213,124
Fiscal Year-end: 12/31/19
Investment Services
N.A.I.C.S.: 523999
Charles A. Rizzo (CFO)
Salvatore Schiavone (Treas)
Hassell H. McClellan (Chm)
Francis Vincent Knox Jr. (Chief Compliance Officer)

JOHN MARSHALL BANCORP,
INC.
1943 Isaac Newton Sq E Ste 100,
Reston, VA 20190
Tel.: (703) 584-0840 VA
Web Site:
   https://www.johnmarshallbank.com

JMSB—(NASDAQ)
Rev.: $85,757,000
Assets: $2,348,235,000
Liabilities: $2,135,435,000
Net Worth: $212,800,000
Earnings: $31,803,000
Emp.: 139
Fiscal Year-end: 12/31/22
Offices of Bank Holding Companies
N.A.I.C.S.: 551111
Jason R. McDonough (Chief Lending
Officer & Exec VP)
Kelly J. Bell (COO)
Christopher W. Bergstrom (Pres &
CEO)
Kent D. Carstater (CFO & Exec VP)
Andrew J. Peden (Chief Banking Officer & Exec VP)
Mike Bell (Chief Acctg Officer)
Sheila Yosufy (Exec VP-John Marshall Bank, Exec VP, Dir-Sls-John
Marshall Bank & Dir-Sls)
Devika Wimalkantha (VP-Sls-John
Marshall Bank)
Melanie Williams (Sr VP & Dir-IR)

JOHN WILEY & SONS, INC.
111 River St, Hoboken, NJ 07030-
5774
Tel.: (201) 748-6000 NY
Web Site: https://www.wiley.com
Year Founded: 1807
WLY—(NYSE)
Rev.: $1,872,987,000
Assets: $2,725,495,000
Liabilities: $1,985,779,000
Net Worth: $739,716,000
Earnings: ($200,319,000)
Emp.: 6,400
Fiscal Year-end: 04/30/24
Educational, Scientific, Technical,
Medical, Professional, Reference &
Trade Books, Journals & Multimedia
Products Publisher
N.A.I.C.S.: 513130
Kevin Monaco (Treas & Sr VP)
Danielle McMahan (Chief People &
Ops Officer & Exec VP)
Jesse Caleb Wiley (Chm)
Aref Matin (CTO & Exec VP)
Deirdre Silver (Gen Counsel & Exec
VP)
Jay Flynn (Exec VP & Gen Mgr-Res
& Learning-Res)
Josh Jarrett (Sr VP-Strategy)
Andrew Weber (Sr VP-Operations)
Christopher Caridi (Sr VP &
Controller-Corp)
Marjorie Pierre-Merrit (Sec & VP-
Corp)
Matthew S. Kissner (Pres & CEO)
Christopher F. Caridi (Interim CFO)

Subsidiaries:

Atypon Systems, LLC (1)
111 River St, Hoboken, NJ 07030
Tel.: (212) 364-2330
Web Site: https://www.atypon.com
Emp.: 500
Software Publisher
N.A.I.C.S.: 513210
Gordon Tibbitts (Gen Mgr)
Hisham Shahtout (Sr VP-Engrg)
Christos Nikolakakos (Product Mgr-Ebooks)
Dino Paravandis (VP-User Experience)
Himanshu Jhamb (VP-Strategic Accounts)
Megan Prosser (Sr Dir-Mktg)
Michael Markey (VP-Security & Governance)
Nash Pal (Dir-Client Mgmt)
Nikos Markantonatos (Head-Ops-Greece &
Dir-Engrg)
Rob Posadas (VP-Solution Architecture)
Doreen Hall (Dir-Program Mgmt)
Bruce Rosenblum (VP-Content & Workflow
Solutions)
Mike Markey (VP)
Josh Pyle (VP)

Subsidiary (Non-US):

Atypon Systems Jordan (2)
141 Makkah Al Mukaramah Street Hamadani 1 Complex 3rd Floor, Amman, 11181,
Jordan
Tel.: (962) 65519262
Web Site: http://www.atypon.com
Software Publisher
N.A.I.C.S.: 513210

Atypon Systems UK (2)
9600 Garsington Road, Oxford, OX4 2DQ,
United Kingdom
Tel.: (44) 1865476602
Emp.: 464
Software Publisher
N.A.I.C.S.: 513210

Blackwell Verlag GmbH (1)
Rotherstrasse 21, 10245, Berlin, Germany
Tel.: (49) 3047031467
Web Site: http://www.blackwell.de
Emp.: 100
Book Publishers
N.A.I.C.S.: 513130

CrossKnowledge Group Limited (1)
40 Gracechurch St, London, EC3V 0BT,
United Kingdom
Tel.: (44) 2037145620
Learning Services
N.A.I.C.S.: 513199

Subsidiary (Non-US):

E-Learning SAS (2)
4 Rue Du Port Aux Vins, 92150, Suresnes,
France
Tel.: (33) 141381499
Learning Services
N.A.I.C.S.: 513199

John Wiley & Sons (Asia) Pte.
Ltd. (1)
1 Fusion Tolis Walk 0701 Solaris S Tower,
Singapore, 138628, Singapore (100%)
Tel.: (65) 64632400
Web Site: http://www.wiley.com
Sales Range: $25-49.9 Million
Emp.: 200
N.A.I.C.S.: 513130

John Wiley & Sons (HK) Limited (1)
Room 2203 Apec Plaza 49 Hoi Yuen Road,
Kwun Tong, Kowloon, China (Hong Kong)
Tel.: (852) 27934652
Books Publishing Services
N.A.I.C.S.: 513130

John Wiley & Sons Australia,
Ltd. (1)
42 McDougall Street, PO Box 1226, Milton,
4064, QLD, Australia (100%)
Tel.: (61) 738599755
Web Site: http://www.johnwiley.com
Sales Range: $75-99.9 Million
Emp.: 100
Professional, Educational & Scientific
Books, Journals & Software Publisher
N.A.I.C.S.: 513130

John Wiley & Sons Canada, Ltd. (1)
(100%)
Tel.: (416) 236-4433
Web Site: https://www.wiley.ca
Sales Range: $25-49.9 Million
Emp.: 34
Marketing & Distribution of Educational,
Professional & Reference Books, Journals
& Encyclopedics
N.A.I.C.S.: 513130

John Wiley & Sons Commercial Ser-
vice (Beijing) Co., Ltd. (1)
Room 805-808 Floor 8 Sun Palace No 12A
Taiyanggong Middle Road, Chaoyang District, Beijing, 100028, China
Tel.: (86) 1084187800
Educational Software Development Services
N.A.I.C.S.: 541511

John Wiley & Sons GmbH (1)
Boschstrasse 12, 69469, Weinheim, Germany
Tel.: (49) 62016060
Web Site: http://www.whiley.com
Sales Range: $100-124.9 Million
Emp.: 450
Books Publishing Services

N.A.I.C.S.: 513130
Peter Gregory (CFO & COO)

John Wiley & Sons International Rights, Inc. (1)
3773 Howard Hughes Pkwy, Las Vegas, NV 89169-0949
Tel.: (702) 866-2225
Book Publishers
N.A.I.C.S.: 513130

John Wiley & Sons LTD A/S (1)
Tel.: (45) 77333333
Journal & Book Publisher
N.A.I.C.S.: 513130

John Wiley & Sons, Inc. - Somerset (1)
1 Wiley Dr, Somerset, NJ 08875-1222
Tel.: (732) 469-4400
Web Site: http://www.wiley.com
Sales Range: $50-74.9 Million
Provider of Print Services
N.A.I.C.S.: 493110

Jossey-Bass, Inc. (1)
1 Montgomery St, San Francisco, CA 94104-1741
Tel.: (415) 433-1740
Web Site: http://www.josseybass.com
Sales Range: $50-74.9 Million
Emp.: 75
Professional Books & Resource Materials Publisher
N.A.I.C.S.: 513130
Debrah Hunter (Mng Dir)

Wiley Blackwell Publishing Ltd. (1)
9600 Garsington Rd, Oxford, OX4 2DQ, United Kingdom
Tel.: (44) 1865776868
Web Site: http://eu.wiley.com
Sales Range: $350-399.9 Million
Emp.: 500
Academic Books & Journals Publisher
N.A.I.C.S.: 513130

Subsidiary (Non-US):

Blackwell Munksgaard (2)
Rosenorns Alle 1, DK-1970, Frederiksberg, Copenhagen, Denmark   **(100%)**
Tel.: (45) 77333333
Web Site:
    http://www.blackwellpublishing.com
Sales Range: $750-799.9 Million
Academic Books & Journals Publisher
N.A.I.C.S.: 513130

John Wiley & Sons Australia, Ltd. (2)
155 Cremorne St, Richmond, 3121, VIC, Australia
Tel.: (61) 383591011
Web Site:
    http://www.blackwellpublishing.com
Sales Range: $75-99.9 Million
Emp.: 110
Academic Books & Journals Publisher
N.A.I.C.S.: 513130

Branch (US):

Wiley Blackwell Publishing (2)
350 Main St Commerce Place, Malden, MA 02148   **(100%)**
Tel.: (781) 388-8200
Web Site: http://www.wiley.com
Sales Range: $75-99.9 Million
Emp.: 100
Academic Books & Journals Publisher
N.A.I.C.S.: 513130

Wiley Europe Limited (1)
                 (100%)
Tel.: (44) 1243779777
Web Site: http://www.wiley.co.uk
Sales Range: $250-299.9 Million
Emp.: 1,000
Academic, Professional & Reference Books Publisher
N.A.I.C.S.: 513130

Subsidiary (Non-US):

Wiley-VCH Verlag GmbH & Co. KGaA (2)
Boschstrasse 12, 69469, Weinheim, Germany   **(100%)**
Tel.: (49) 62016060

Web Site: http://www.wiley-vch.de
Sales Range: $150-199.9 Million
Emp.: 400
Scientific, Technical & Professional Books Publisher
N.A.I.C.S.: 513130
Hartmut Gante (Dir-Publ Professional & Trade)
Jose Oliveira (Sr Dir-Editorial-Materials Science & Physics)
Heiko Baumgartner (Dir-Publ-Chemistry & Laboratory)

Subsidiary (Non-US):

Wiley-VHCA AG (3)
Seefeldstrasse 69, 8024, Zurich, Switzerland
Tel.: (41) 443602434
Web Site: https://wiley-vhca.ch
Book Publishers
N.A.I.C.S.: 513130

Subsidiary (Domestic):

Wilhelm Ernst & Sohn GmbH & Co. KG (3)
Lopherstrasse 21, 10245, Berlin, Germany   **(100%)**
Tel.: (49) 3047031200
Web Site: http://www.ernst-und-sohn.de
Sales Range: $50-74.9 Million
Emp.: 25
Architectural & Technical Science Books Publisher
N.A.I.C.S.: 513130

Wiley Global Technology (Private) Limited (1)
Level 37 West Tower World Trade Center, Colombo, Sri Lanka
Tel.: (94) 117494241
Software Development Services
N.A.I.C.S.: 513210

Wiley Higher Education Publishing (1)
111 River St, Hoboken, NJ 07030   **(100%)**
Tel.: (201) 748-6000
Web Site: http://he-cda.wiley.com
Sales Range: $150-199.9 Million
Educational Books, Journals & Software Publisher
N.A.I.C.S.: 513130

Wiley Japan KK (1)
Frontier Koishikawa Building 4F 1-28-1 Koishikawa, Bunkyo-ku, Tokyo, 112-0002, Japan
Tel.: (81) 338301221
Web Site: http://www.wiley.co.jp
Books Publishing Services
N.A.I.C.S.: 513130

Wiley Professional/Trade Publishing (1)
111 River St, Hoboken, NJ 07030-5774   **(100%)**
Tel.: (201) 748-6000
Web Site: http://www.wiley.com
Sales Range: $350-399.9 Million
Professional & Trade Books, Journals & Software Publisher
N.A.I.C.S.: 513130

Unit (Domestic):

CliffsNotes, Inc. (2)
111 River St, Hoboken, NJ 07030-5774
Tel.: (201) 748-6000
Web Site: http://www.wiley.com
Sales Range: $10-24.9 Million
Emp.: 40
Literature Guidebooks Publisher
N.A.I.C.S.: 513130

Wiley Publishing Australia Pty Ltd. (1)
Tel.: (61) 738599755
Sales Range: $50-74.9 Million
Emp.: 160
Book Publishers
N.A.I.C.S.: 513130

Wiley Publishing Japan KK (1)
Tel.: (81) 345209011
Web Site: https://www.wiley.co.jp
Book Publishers
N.A.I.C.S.: 513130

Wiley Publishing Services, Inc. (1)
10475 Crosspoint Blvd, Indianapolis, IN 46256-3386
Tel.: (317) 572-3000
Sales Range: $75-99.9 Million
Emp.: 350
Books Publishing Services
N.A.I.C.S.: 513130

Wiley Publishing, Inc. (1)
9200 Keystone Crossing Ste 800, Indianapolis, IN 46240
Tel.: (317) 572-3000
Web Site: http://www.wiley.com
Sales Range: $100-124.9 Million
Emp.: 300
Professional & Trade Publishing
N.A.I.C.S.: 513130

Subsidiary (Non-US):

Wiley India Private Ltd. (2)
1402 14th Floor World Trade Tower Plot No C-1 Sector - 16, Noida, 201 301, India
Tel.: (91) 1206291100
Web Site: https://www.wileyindia.com
Book Publishers
N.A.I.C.S.: 513130
Vikas Gupta (Mng Dir)

Wiley Scientific, Technical & Medical Publishing (1)
111 River St, Hoboken, NJ 07030-5774   **(100%)**
Tel.: (201) 748-6000
Web Site: http://www.wiley.com
Sales Range: $200-249.9 Million
Scientific, Technical & Medical Books, Journals & Software Publisher
N.A.I.C.S.: 513130

Wiley-VCH GmbH (1)
Boschstrasse 12, 69469, Weinheim, Germany
Tel.: (49) 62016060
Web Site: https://www.wiley-vch.de
Magazine & Ebook Retailer
N.A.I.C.S.: 424920

JOHNSON & JOHNSON

One Johnson & Johnson Plaza, New Brunswick, NJ 08933
Tel.: (732) 524-0400   NJ
Web Site: https://www.jnj.com
Year Founded: 1887
JNJ—(NYSE)
Rev.: $85,159,000,000
Assets: $167,558,000,000
Liabilities: $98,784,000,000
Net Worth: $68,774,000,000
Earnings: $35,153,000,000
Emp.: 131,900
Fiscal Year-end: 12/31/23
Surgical Dressings, Baby Products, Pharmaceuticals & Healthcare Products Mfr
N.A.I.C.S.: 424210
Joaquin Duato (Chm & CEO)
Kathleen M. Widmer (Chm-Consumer-North America & Latin America)
Kathryn E. Wengel (Chief Technical Operations & Risk Officer & Exec VP)
Jennifer L. Taubert (Exec VP)
Joseph J. Wolk (CFO & Exec VP)
Thibaut Mongon (Chm-Consumer Health-Worldwide & Exec VP)
Liz Forminard (Gen Counsel)
William N. Hait (Exec VP)
James Swanson (CIO)
R. J. Decker Jr. (Chief Acctg Officer & Controller)

Subsidiaries:

ABIOMED, Inc. (1)
22 Cherry Hill Dr, Danvers, MA 01923
Tel.: (978) 646-1400
Web Site: http://www.abiomed.com
Rev.: $1,031,753,000
Assets: $1,673,393,000
Liabilities: $170,067,000
Net Worth: $1,503,326,000
Earnings: $136,505,000
Emp.: 2,003

Fiscal Year-end: 03/31/2022
Developer of Cardiac & Heart Replacement Technology
N.A.I.C.S.: 339112
Jeffrey Blizard (Head-Surgical Sls-Global & Sr Dir-Sls)

Subsidiary (Non-US):

ABIOMED Europe (2)
Neuenhofer Weg 3, 52074, Aachen, Germany
Tel.: (49) 24188600
Web Site: http://www.abiomed.com
Blood Pump Mfr
N.A.I.C.S.: 339112

Subsidiary (Domestic):

Abiomed R&D, Inc. (2)
22 Cherry Hill Dr, Danvers, MA 01923
Tel.: (978) 646-1400
Web Site: https://www.abiomed.com
Surgical & Medical Instrument Mfr
N.A.I.C.S.: 339112

AMO (Shanghai) Medical Devices Trading Co., Ltd. (1)
Unit 3104-3109 Westgate Mall 1038 West Nanjing Road, 1038 Nanjing Road West, Shanghai, China
Tel.: (86) 2123077666
Vision Care Product Distr
N.A.I.C.S.: 423460

Actelion Ltd. (1)
Gewerbestrasse 16, CH-4123, Allschwil, Switzerland
Tel.: (41) 615656565
Web Site: http://www.actelion.com
Holding Company; Biopharmaceutical Research, Development & Manufacturing Services
N.A.I.C.S.: 541715

Subsidiary (Non-US):

Actelion Pharmaceuticals Australia Pty. Limited (2)
Suite 6 13B Narabang Way, Belrose, 2085, NSW, Australia
Tel.: (61) 294864600
Web Site: http://www.actelion.com.au
Biopharmaceutical Research, Development & Manufacturing Services
N.A.I.C.S.: 541714

Actelion Pharmaceuticals Canada, Inc. (2)
3111 Saint-Martin Blvd West, Suite 300, Laval, H7T 0K2, QC, Canada
Tel.: (450) 681-1664
Web Site: http://www.actelion.com
Sales Range: $25-49.9 Million
Emp.: 20
Biopharmaceutical Research, Development & Manufacturing Services
N.A.I.C.S.: 541715

Actelion Pharmaceuticals Espana, SL (2)
Via Augusta 281-3-B, 08017, Barcelona, Spain
Tel.: (34) 933664399
Web Site: http://www.actelion.com
Biopharmaceutical Research, Development & Manufacturing Services
N.A.I.C.S.: 541715

Actelion Pharmaceuticals France SAS (2)
21 Bd de la Madeleine, 75001, Paris, France
Tel.: (33) 158623232
Web Site: http://www.actelion.com
Biopharmaceutical Research, Development & Manufacturing Services
N.A.I.C.S.: 541715

Actelion Pharmaceuticals Hellas SA (2)
68 Agisilaou Str Blue Land Center GR Agios Thomas, Marousi, 151 23, Athens, Greece
Tel.: (30) 210 675 25 00
Web Site: http://www.actelion.com
Pharmaceutical Products Distr
N.A.I.C.S.: 424210

Actelion Pharmaceuticals Italia Srl (2)

Johnson & Johnson—(Continued)

Via delle Valli 25, 18100, Imperia, Italy
Tel.: (39) 0183576200
Web Site: http://www.actelion.com
Biopharmaceutical Research, Development & Manufacturing Services
N.A.I.C.S.: 541715

Actelion Pharmaceuticals Japan Ltd. (2)
Tokyo Midtown Tower 9-7-1 Akasaka, Minato-ku, Tokyo, 107-6235, Japan
Tel.: (81) 357853262
Web Site: http://www.actelion.com
Biopharmaceutical Research, Development & Manufacturing Services
N.A.I.C.S.: 541714

Actelion Pharmaceuticals Korea Ltd. (2)
6F Gangnam Finance Center, 152 Teheran-ro Gangnam-gu, Seoul, 006-236, Korea (South)
Tel.: (82) 2 2112 2833
Web Site: http://www.actelion.com
Pharmaceutical Products Distr
N.A.I.C.S.: 424210

Subsidiary (Domestic):

Actelion Pharmaceuticals Ltd. (2)
Gewerbestrasse 16, 4123, Allschwil, Switzerland
Tel.: (41) 615656565
Web Site: http://www.actelion.com
Biopharmaceutical Research, Development & Manufacturing Services
N.A.I.C.S.: 541715
Robert Etherington (Executives)

Subsidiary (Non-US):

Actelion Pharmaceuticals Mexico S.A. De C.V. (2)
Diego Rivera N40 Col Altavista Deleg Alvaro Obregon, Mexico, 01060, Mexico
Tel.: (52) 55 5484 2300
Web Site: http://www.actelion.mx
Pharmaceutical Products Distr
N.A.I.C.S.: 424210

Actelion Pharmaceuticals UK Ltd. (2)
50-100 Holmers Farm Way, High Wycombe, HP12 4DP, United Kingdom
Tel.: (44) 2089873333
Web Site: http://www.actelion.co.uk
Biopharmaceutical Research, Development & Manufacturing Services
N.A.I.C.S.: 541715

Actelion Pharmaceuticals do Brasil Ltda. (2)
Rua Dalcidio Jurandir n 255 - salas 306 a 308, Condominio Island Personal Offices Barra da Tijuca, Rio de Janeiro, 22631-250, Brazil
Tel.: (55) 8009420808
Web Site: http://www.actelion.com.br
Biopharmaceutical Research, Development & Manufacturing Services
N.A.I.C.S.: 541715

Subsidiary (US):

Actelion US Holding Co. (2)
5000 Shoreline Ct Ste 200, South San Francisco, CA 94080-1956
Tel.: (650) 624-6900
Web Site: http://www.actelion.com
Investment Management Service
N.A.I.C.S.: 523999

Subsidiary (Domestic):

Actelion Clinical Research, Inc. (3)
1820 Chapel Ave W Ste 300, Cherry Hill, NJ 08002
Tel.: (856) 773-4300
Web Site: http://www.actelion.com
Biopharmaceutical Research & Development Services
N.A.I.C.S.: 541714

Actelion Pharmaceuticals US, Inc. (3)
5000 Shoreline Ct Ste 200, South San Francisco, CA 94080
Tel.: (650) 624-6900

Web Site: http://www.actelionus.com
Biopharmaceutical Research, Development & Manufacturing Services
N.A.I.C.S.: 541715
Gary Palmer (Sr VP-Medical-US)
Robert P. Smith (Sr VP-Sales)
Rahsaan Thompson (VP)
Volker Mehlo (Sr Dir)
Bill Kaminski (Sr Dir)
Serge Messerlian (Pres)
Kaylynn Callister (Head-Human Resources)
Bryan Huff (Head-Finance)
Assaf Guterman (Dir)

Ceptaris Therapeutics, Inc. (3)
101 Lindenwood Dr Ste 400, Malvern, PA 19355
Tel.: (610) 975-9290
Pharmaceutical Research & Development
N.A.I.C.S.: 541715

Ambrx Biopharma Inc. (1)
10975 N Torrey Pines Rd, La Jolla, CA 92037
Tel.: (858) 875-2400
Web Site: https://www.ambrx.com
Rev.: $7,402,000
Assets: $146,977,000
Liabilities: $29,127,000
Net Worth: $117,850,000
Earnings: ($77,996,000)
Emp.: 66
Fiscal Year-end: 12/31/2022
Biotechnology Research & Development Services
N.A.I.C.S.: 541714
Simon Allen (Chief Bus Officer)
Simon Allen (Chief Bus Officer)
Shawn Zhang (Sr VP-R&D Ops)
Ying Buechler (VP-Dev)
Dana Zhang (VP-Fin)
Sukumar Sakamuri (VP & Head-Chemistry)
Janice Lu (Chief Medical Officer)
Sandra Aung (Exec VP & Head-Clinical Dev)
Sonja Nelson (CFO)

Animas LLC (1)
200 Lawrence Dr, West Chester, PA 19380
Tel.: (610) 644-8990
Insulin Delivery Products Mfr
N.A.I.C.S.: 339112
Katherine D. Crothall (Founder)

Aragon Pharmaceuticals, Inc. (1)
12780 El Camino Real Ste 301, San Diego, CA 92130
Tel.: (858) 369-7600
Medicinal & Botanical Product Mfr
N.A.I.C.S.: 325411

Auris Health, Inc. (1)
150 Shoreline Dr, Redwood City, CA 94065
Tel.: (650) 610-0750
Web Site: http://www.aurishealth.com
Medical Device Mfr
N.A.I.C.S.: 339112

Auris Health, Inc. (1)
125 Shoreway Rd ste D, San Carlos, CA 94070
Tel.: (650) 610-0750
Web Site: http://www.aurisrobotics.com
Technology Services
N.A.I.C.S.: 541715

Subsidiary (Domestic):

Hansen Medical, Inc. (2)
800 East Middlefield Road, Mountain View, CA 94043 **(100%)**
Tel.: (650) 404-5800
Web Site: https://www.hansenmedical.com
Sales Range: $10-24.9 Million
Robotic Control Catheter Systems Mfr
N.A.I.C.S.: 339112

Subsidiary (Non-US):

Hansen Medical Deutschland GmbH (3)
Universitatsstrasse 71, 50931, Koln, Germany
Tel.: (49) 71178892179
Surgical Appliance & Supplies Mfr
N.A.I.C.S.: 339113

Hansen Medical UK Ltd. (3)
53 Chandos Place, London, WC2N 4HS, United Kingdom
Tel.: (44) 2073931900

Web Site: https://www.hansenmedical.com
Surgical & Medical Instrument Mfr
N.A.I.C.S.: 339112

Beijing Dabao Cosmetics Co., Ltd. (1)
No 12 Ronghua M Rd Economic Technology Development Zone, Beijing, 100176, China
Tel.: (86) 4008188778
Web Site: https://www.dabao.com
Emp.: 1,200
Cosmetics Products Mfr
N.A.I.C.S.: 325620

Biosense Webster (Israel) Ltd. (1)
4 Hatnufa St Levinstein Bldg, Yokneam, 2066717, Israel
Tel.: (972) 48131111
Health Care Products Mfr
N.A.I.C.S.: 325412

Biosense Webster Inc. (1)
31 Technology Dr Ste 200, Irvine, CA 92618 **(100%)**
Tel.: (909) 839-8500
Web Site: http://www.biosensewebster.com
Sales Range: $100-124.9 Million
Emp.: 5,000
Diagnostic & Therapeutic Cardiac Catheters Mfr
N.A.I.C.S.: 334510

Subsidiary (Domestic):

Coherex Medical, Inc. (2)
3598 W 1820 S, Salt Lake City, UT 84104
Tel.: (801) 433-9900
Web Site: http://www.coherex.com
Rev.: $3,500,000
Emp.: 30
Surgical & Medical Instrument Mfr
N.A.I.C.S.: 339112

NuVera Medical, Inc. (2)
140 Knowles Dr, Los Gatos, CA 95032
Tel.: (408) 560-2500
Web Site: http://www.nuveramedical.com
Medical Device Mfr
N.A.I.C.S.: 339112

Calibra Medical, Inc. (1)
220 Saginaw Dr Ste 1440, Redwood City, CA 94063
Tel.: (650) 216-7722
Medical Support Services
N.A.I.C.S.: 456199
Clif Alferness (Mgr)

Campus-Foyer Apotheke GmbH (1)
Gubelstrasse 30, 6300, Zug, Switzerland
Tel.: (41) 417109151
Web Site: http://www.campus-foyer.ch
Pharmaceutical Products Distr
N.A.I.C.S.: 456110
Norbert Penteker (Mng Officer)

Ci:z Holdings Co. Ltd. (1)
14 F Ebisu Prime Square 1-1-39 Hiroo, Shibuya-ku, Tokyo, 150-0012, Japan **(69.1%)**
Tel.: (81) 3 6419 2500
Web Site: http://www.ci-z-holdings.com
Rev.: $452,329,440
Assets: $470,648,880
Liabilities: $156,225,840
Net Worth: $314,423,040
Earnings: $50,695,920
Emp.: 905
Fiscal Year-end: 07/31/2018
Cosmetic Product Mfr & Whslr
N.A.I.C.S.: 325620
Tomomi Ishihara (Pres & COO)
Yoshinori Shirono (Chm & CEO)
Humio Yoshioka (Auditor)
Yoshiki Kuroiwa (Auditor)
Hirofumi Suzuki (Auditor)
Kiyoshi Suda (Auditor)

Cilag Pharmaceuticals GmbH (1)
High Street 201, Schaffhausen, 8205, Switzerland
Tel.: (41) 526309111
Web Site: http://www.cilag.ch
Emp.: 1,000
Pharmaceuticals Product Mfr
N.A.I.C.S.: 424210

Cilag Products GmbH (1)
Gubelstrasse 34, 6003, Zug, Switzerland
Tel.: (41) 526309111

Web Site: http://www.jnj.ch
Emp.: 700
Pharmaceuticals Product Mfr
N.A.I.C.S.: 424210
David Bruce Bancroft (Chm)

Codman Neurovascular Inc. (1)
821 Fox Ln, San Jose, CA 95131-1601
Tel.: (408) 433-1400
Sales Range: $75-99.9 Million
Emp.: 307
Implantable & Disposable Medical Devices Mfr & Marketer
N.A.I.C.S.: 339112

Cordis Europa NV (1)
Oosteinde 8, Roden, 9301 LJ, Netherlands
Tel.: (31) 505022222
Web Site: http://www.cordis.europa.eu
Surgical & Medical Instrument Mfr
N.A.I.C.S.: 339112

Cordis LLC (1)
5452 Betsy Ross Dr, Santa Clara, CA 95054
Tel.: (408) 273-3700
Web Site: http://www.cordis.com
Surgical Product Mfr
N.A.I.C.S.: 339112

Covagen AG (1)
Wagistrasse 25, Zurich, 8952, Switzerland
Tel.: (41) 447324660
Web Site: http://www.covagen.com
Healtcare Services
N.A.I.C.S.: 456199

CrossRoads Extremity Systems, LLC (1)
6423 Shelby View Dr Ste 101, Memphis, TN 38134
Tel.: (901) 221-8406
Web Site: https://www.crextremity.com
Medical Equipment Mfr & Distr
N.A.I.C.S.: 334510

Crucell N.V. (1)
Main Building Archimedesweg 4-6, 2333 CN, Leiden, Netherlands
Tel.: (31) 7151248701
Research, Production & Marketing of Biopharmaceuticals
N.A.I.C.S.: 541714

Subsidiary (Non-US):

Berna Biotech Korea Corp. (2)
23 Harmony-ro 303 Beon-gil 13-42 Songdodong Yeonsu-gu, Incheon, 406-840, Korea (South) **(100%)**
Tel.: (82) 322908400
Web Sito: http://www.oruooll.kr
Sales Range: $75-99.9 Million
Emp.: 300
Pharmaceutical Research, Development, Manufacturing, Sales & Marketing
N.A.I.C.S.: 325412
Sang Jeom Ahn (Gen Mgr)

Subsidiary (Domestic):

Crucell Holland B.V. (2)
Archimedesweg 4, Leiden, 2333 CN, Netherlands **(100%)**
Tel.: (31) 715199100
Web Site: http://www.crucell.com
Emp.: 700
Pharmaceuticals Mfr
N.A.I.C.S.: 325412

Subsidiary (Non-US):

Crucell Spain, S.A. (2)
Paseo de la Castellana 163, 28046, Madrid, Spain **(100%)**
Tel.: (34) 915716888
Web Site: http://www.crucell.es
Sales Range: $25-49.9 Million
Emp.: 70
Pharmaceuticals Mfr, Sales & Marketing
N.A.I.C.S.: 325412

Crucell UK Ltd. (2)
50-100 Holmers Farm Way, High Wycombe, HP12 4EG, Buckinghamshire, United Kingdom
Tel.: (44) 1494567447
Web Site: http://www.crucell.co.uk

Sales & Marketing of Pharmaceuticals
N.A.I.C.S.: 424210

Subsidiary (US):

Crucell Vaccines Inc. (2)
14201 NW 60th Ave, Miami Lakes, FL
33014 **(100%)**
Tel.: (305) 443-2900
Web Site: http://www.crucell.com
Sales Range: $25-49.9 Million
Emp.: 12
Pharmaceuticals Sales & Marketing
N.A.I.C.S.: 424210

Subsidiary (Non-US):

Janssen Vaccines AG (2)
Rehhagstrasse 79, CH-3018, Bern,
Switzerland **(100%)**
Tel.: (41) 319806111
Web Site: http://www.crucell.ch
Sales Range: $125-149.9 Million
Emp.: 200
Biopharmaceutical Developer, Mfr & Mar-
keter
N.A.I.C.S.: 325412
Jan Fejen (CEO)

Affiliate (US):

Percivia LLC (2)
1 Hampshire St 5th Fl, Cambridge, MA
02139
Tel.: (617) 301-8800
Web Site: https://www.percivia.com
Sales Range: $25-49.9 Million
Emp.: 35
Pharmaceutical Research & Development;
Joint Venture of Crucell N.V. (50%) & DSM
Biologics B.V. (50%)
N.A.I.C.S.: 541714

DePuy International Limited (1)
Number One White Rose Office Park
Millshaw Park Lane, Leeds, LS11 0BG,
United Kingdom
Tel.: (44) 1133877800
Surgical Product Mfr
N.A.I.C.S.: 339112

DePuy Synthes, Inc. (1)
700 Orthopaedic Dr, Warsaw, IN 46582
Tel.: (574) 267-8143
Web Site: http://www.depuysynthes.com
Emp.: 1,000
Holding Company; Orthopedic Devices &
Equipment Mfr
N.A.I.C.S.: 551112

Division (Domestic):

DePuy Orthopaedics, Inc. (2)
700 Orthopaedic Dr, Warsaw, IN
46581 **(100%)**
Tel.: (574) 267-8143
Web Site: http://www.depuy.com
Sales Range: $650-699.9 Million
Emp.: 1,500
Orthopedic Products Mfr & Whslr
N.A.I.C.S.: 339113
Andrew Ekdahl (Pres)

Subsidiary (Domestic):

BioMedical Enterprises, Inc. (3)
14785 Omicron Dr Ste 205, San Antonio,
TX 78245
Tel.: (210) 677-0354
Web Site: http://www.bme-tx.com
Sales Range: $1-9.9 Million
Medical Implant Mfr & Whslr
N.A.I.C.S.: 339113

Codman & Shurtleff, Inc. (3)
325 Paramount Dr, Raynham, MA 02767
Tel.: (508) 880-8100
Web Site: http://www.codman.com
Sales Range: $550-599.9 Million
Emp.: 1,140
Developer & Mfr of Diagnostic & Therapeu-
tic Products for Treatment of Central Ner-
vous System Disorders
N.A.I.C.S.: 334510

Subsidiary (Domestic):

DePuy Synthes Products, Inc. (4)
325 Paramount Dr, Raynham, MA 02767
Medical Device Mfr
N.A.I.C.S.: 339112

Shane Maher (Dir-Prod Planning & Logistics)

Subsidiary (Domestic):

Pulsar Vascular, Inc. (5)
130 Knowles Dr Ste E, Los Gatos, CA
95032
Tel.: (408) 260-9264
Web Site: http://www.pulsarvascular.com
Invasive Medical Devices Designer & De-
veloper
N.A.I.C.S.: 339112

Subsidiary (Non-US):

DePuy (Ireland) Limited (3)
Loughbeg Ringaskiddy, Cork, Ireland
Tel.: (353) 214914000
Web Site: http://www.depuy.com
Sales Range: $150-199.9 Million
Emp.: 750
Orthopedic Products Mfr & Whslr
N.A.I.C.S.: 339112

DePuy France S.A. (3)
7 Allee Irene Joliot Curie, Saint Priest,
69800, France
Tel.: (33) 472792727
Web Site: http://www.jnj.com
Sales Range: $150-199.9 Million
Emp.: 350
Orthopaedic Product Mfr
N.A.I.C.S.: 423450

Subsidiary (Domestic):

DePuy Mitek, Inc. (3)
325 Paramount Dr, Raynham, MA
02767 **(100%)**
Web Site: http://www.jandj.com
Sales Range: $50-74.9 Million
Emp.: 1,600
Suture Anchoring Implants & Sports Medi-
cine Reconstructive Surgical Devices Mfr
N.A.I.C.S.: 339112

Subsidiary (Non-US):

DePuy Orthopedie S.A. (3)
7 Allee Irene Joliot Curie, 69801, Saint
Priest, France
Tel.: (33) 472792727
Web Site: http://www.depuy.com
Sales Range: $25-49.9 Million
Emp.: 150
Orthopedic Products Mfr & Whslr
N.A.I.C.S.: 339112

Subsidiary (Domestic):

DePuy Products, Inc. (3)
700 Orthopaedic Dr, Warsaw, IN 46581
Tel.: (574) 267-8143
Web Site: http://www.depuysynthes.com
Sales Range: $450-499.9 Million
Emp.: 1,200
Prosthetic Implants, Surgical Instruments,
Surgical & Hospital Specialty Products Mfr
N.A.I.C.S.: 339999

DePuy Spine, Inc. (3)
325 Paramount Dr, Raynham, MA 02767
Tel.: (508) 880-8100
Sales Range: $450-499.9 Million
Emp.: 1,300
Medical Equipment Mfr for Spine Treatment
N.A.I.C.S.: 339112

Subsidiary (Non-US):

**DePuy International (Holdings)
Ltd.** (4)
St Anthonys Road, Leeds, LS11 8DT,
United Kingdom
Tel.: (44) 1132700461
Web Site: http://www.depuy.com
Sales Range: $25-49.9 Million
Emp.: 300
Holding Company
N.A.I.C.S.: 551112

DePuy Spine Sarl (4)
Chemin Blanc 36, Le Locle, 2400, NE, Swit-
zerland
Tel.: (41) 329338300
Web Site: http://www.jnj.com
Sales Range: $400-449.9 Million
Emp.: 1,200
Orthopedic Products Mfr & Whslr
N.A.I.C.S.: 339112

Division (Domestic):

Synthes, Inc. (2)
1302 Wrights Ln E, West Chester, PA
19380
Tel.: (610) 719-5000
Web Site: http://www.synthes.com
Sales Range: $1-4.9 Billion
Emp.: 12,000
Implants & Biomaterial Medical Devices De-
veloper & Mfr
N.A.I.C.S.: 339113

Subsidiary (Non-US):

Synthes Argentina S.A. (3)
Lavalle 4066 Almagro Ciudad de 1190,
Buenos Aires, Argentina
Tel.: (54) 11 4867 4949
Web Site: http://www.synthes.com
Sales Range: $25-49.9 Million
Emp.: 35
Medical Products, Instruments & Implants
Mfr
N.A.I.C.S.: 423450

Synthes Colombia Ltda (3)
Calle 97A N 9A-50 Second floor, 100228,
Bogota, Colombia **(100%)**
Tel.: (57) 16460200
Web Site: http://www.sythes.com
Sales Range: $50-74.9 Million
Emp.: 150
Medical Equipment Mfr
N.A.I.C.S.: 423450

Synthes Ind. Com. Ltda. (3)
Avenida Pennwalt 501, CEP 13505 650,
Rio Claro, Brazil **(100%)**
Tel.: (55) 935356600
Web Site: http://www.synthes.com
Sales Range: $50-74.9 Million
Emp.: 150
Medical Equipment Mfr
N.A.I.C.S.: 423450

Branch (Non-US):

**Synthes, GmBH - European
Headquarters** (3)
Eimattstrasse 3, CH 4436, Basel, Oberdorf,
Switzerland
Tel.: (41) 327204060
Medical Equipment Mfr
N.A.I.C.S.: 423450

Subsidiary (Non-US):

DePuy Synthes A/S (4)
Horkaer 28 3rd Floor, 2730, Herlev,
Denmark **(100%)**
Tel.: (45) 44534544
Web Site: http://emea.depuysynthes.com
Sales Range: $25-49.9 Million
Emp.: 31
Sales, Marketing, Customer Support & Ad-
ministration in Medical Implants & Instru-
ments
N.A.I.C.S.: 423450

N.V. STRATEC Medical S.A. (4)
Havenlaan 86C B406, 1000, Brussels, Bel-
gium
Tel.: (32) 25138015
Sales Range: $150-199.9 Million
Medical Equipment Mfr
N.A.I.C.S.: 423450

STRATEC Medical Lda. (4)
Rua Latino Coelho Bl A-3-1 19-D, 1050-
132, Lisbon, Portugal **(100%)**
Tel.: (351) 213531287
Sales Range: $25-49.9 Million
Emp.: 15
Medical Equipment Mfr
N.A.I.C.S.: 423450

**STRATEC Medical Medizintechnik
GmbH** (4)
Durlacher Strasse 35, 75172, Pforzheim,
Germany **(100%)**
Tel.: (49) 723114540
Web Site: http://www.galileo-training.com
Sales Range: $1-9.9 Million
Emp.: 10
Medical Equipment Mfr
N.A.I.C.S.: 423450

STRATEC Medical S.p.A. (4)
Via San Francesco D'Assisi, I-40128, Bolo-

gna, Italy
Tel.: (39) 025300011
Sales Range: $25-49.9 Million
Emp.: 60
Medical Equipment Mfr
N.A.I.C.S.: 423450

Synthes AB (4)
Korta Gatan 9, 171 54, Solna,
Sweden **(100%)**
Tel.: (46) 87437110
Sales Range: $1-9.9 Million
Emp.: 20
Medical Equipment Mfr
N.A.I.C.S.: 423450

Synthes GmbH (4)
Laitermatten 5A, Umkirch, 79224, Germany
Tel.: (49) 76655030
Medical Equipment Mfr
N.A.I.C.S.: 423450

Synthes Ltd. (4)
Tewin Rd, Welwyn Garden City, AL7 1LG,
Hertfordshire, United Kingdom **(100%)**
Tel.: (44) 1707332212
Web Site: http://www.synthes.com
Sales Range: $25-49.9 Million
Emp.: 80
Medical Equipment Mfr
N.A.I.C.S.: 423450

Synthes Medical Kft. (4)
Otvos Janos U 1-3, 1021, Budapest,
Hungary **(100%)**
Tel.: (36) 13914560
Web Site:
   http://www.synthesmedicalkft.kozuleti.com
Sales Range: $200-249.9 Million
Emp.: 15
Medical Equipment Mfr
N.A.I.C.S.: 423450

Synthes S.R.O. (4)
Radlicka 740 113 D, 15800, Prague, Czech
Republic **(100%)**
Tel.: (420) 220515006
Web Site: http://www.synthes.com
Sales Range: $25-49.9 Million
Emp.: 30
Medical Equipment Mfr
N.A.I.C.S.: 423450

Synthes Stratec (4)
Calle Rozabella 2 Europa Empresarial-
Edificio Las Rozas, Edificio Berlin, Madrid,
28290, Spain **(100%)**
Tel.: (34) 902190128
Sales Range: $25-49.9 Million
Emp.: 43
Medical Equipment Mfr
N.A.I.C.S.: 423450
Fernando Oliveros (Mng Dir)

EES, S.A. de C.V. (1)
Calle Durango 2751 Lote Bravo, Ciudad
Juarez, 32575, Mexico
Tel.: (52) 6566373000
Surgical Equipment Mfr
N.A.I.C.S.: 339113

Ethicon, Inc. (1)
Route 22 W, Somerville, NJ 08876
Tel.: (908) 218-3500
Web Site: http://www.ethicon.com
Sales Range: $1-4.9 Billion
Emp.: 9,000
Surgical Sutures, Wound Management,
Women's Health & Cardiovascular Surgery
Products Mfr & Whslr
N.A.I.C.S.: 339113

Subsidiary (Domestic):

**Advanced Sterilization Products,
Inc.** (2)
33 Technology Dr, Irvine, CA 92618-2346
Tel.: (949) 581-5799
Sterilization Systems Mfr
N.A.I.C.S.: 339113
Amy Higgins (Dir-Comm)
Chad Rohrer (Pres)
Matt Dicker (Dir-Communications)

Ethicon Endo-Surgery Inc (2)
4545 Creek Rd, Cincinnati, OH 45242-2839
Tel.: (513) 337-7000
Web Site:
   http://www.ethiconendosurgery.com
Sales Range: $100-124.9 Million
Emp.: 2,000

Johnson & Johnson—(Continued)

Endoscopic & Small Incision Surgical Products Mfr
N.A.I.C.S.: 339112

Subsidiary (Non-US):

Ethicon Endo-Surgery (Europe) GmbH **(3)**
Hummelsbutteler Steindamm 71, 22851, Norderstedt, Germany
Tel.: (49) 4052973200
Web Site: http://www.ethicon.com
Surgical Equipment Researcher & Developer
N.A.I.C.S.: 339112

Subsidiary (Domestic):

Megadyne Medical Products Inc. **(3)**
11506 State St, Draper, UT 84020-9453
Tel.: (801) 576-9669
Web Site: http://www.megadyne.com
Surgical & Medical Instrument Mfr
N.A.I.C.S.: 339112

Subsidiary (Domestic):

Ethicon Endo-Surgery, LLC **(2)**
3801 University Blvd SE, Albuquerque, NM 87106-5605
Tel.: (505) 768-5200
Web Site: http://www.ethiconendo.com
Sales Range: $200-249.9 Million
Emp.: 800
Surgical Appliances & Supplies Mfr
N.A.I.C.S.: 339113

Subsidiary (Non-US):

Ethicon GmbH
Robert-Koch-Strasse 1, 22851, Norderstedt, Germany
Tel.: (49) 4052973200
Web Site: https://www.jnjmedtech.com
Sales Range: $450-499.9 Million
Emp.: 1,500
Precise Wound Closure Instruments, Sutures & Related Products Mfr & Marketer
N.A.I.C.S.: 339112
Kristof Boogaerts (Mng Dir)
Andrew Morris (Mng Dir)
Hans Christian Wirtz (Mng Dir)

Ethicon Ireland Limited **(2)**
Airton Road, Tallaght, Dublin, 24, Ireland
Tel.: (353) 14510544
Web Site: http://www.ethicon.com
Sales Range: $100-124.9 Million
Emp.: 30
Surgical Sutures Mfr
N.A.I.C.S.: 339113

Ethicon SAS **(2)**
1 rue Camille Desmoulins, 92787, Issy-les-Moulineaux, France
Tel.: (33) 0155002200
Web Site: http://www.ethicon.com
Sales Range: $450-499.9 Million
Emp.: 1,500
Surgical Sutures Mfr
N.A.I.C.S.: 339113

Branch (Domestic):

Ethicon, Inc. **(2)**
655 Ethicon Cir, Cornelia, GA 30531-2112
Tel.: (706) 778-2281
Web Site: http://www.ethicon.com
Sales Range: $75-99.9 Million
Emp.: 500
Medical Device Mfr
N.A.I.C.S.: 339112

Ethicon, Inc. **(2)**
3348 Pulliam St, San Angelo, TX 76905
Tel.: (325) 482-5200
Web Site: http://www.ethicon.com
Sales Range: $550-599.9 Million
Emp.: 1,900
Surgical Appliances & Supplies Mfr
N.A.I.C.S.: 339113

Subsidiary (Domestic):

Ethicon, LLC **(2)**
183 Km 8 3, San Lorenzo, PR 00754
Tel.: (787) 783-7070
Web Site: http://www.ethicon.com

Sales Range: $450-499.9 Million
Emp.: 1,000
Surgical Sutures Mfr
N.A.I.C.S.: 339999
Michelle M. Brennan (Pres-Worldwide)

Mentor Corporation **(2)**
201 Mentor Dr, Santa Barbara, CA 93111
Tel.: (805) 879-6000
Web Site: http://www.mentorcorp.com
Sales Range: $350-399.9 Million
Emp.: 1,190
Cosmetic Surgery Products Mfr
N.A.I.C.S.: 339113

Subsidiary (Non-US):

Mentor Deutschland GmbH **(3)**
Lilienthalstrasse 27-29, 85399, Hallbergmoos, Germany
Tel.: (49) 811600500
Web Site: http://www.mentorcorp.com
Sales Range: $150-199.9 Million
Emp.: 25
Cosmetic Surgery Products Distr
N.A.I.C.S.: 423450

Mentor Medical Systems B.V. **(3)**
Zernikedreef 2, 2333 CL, Leiden, Netherlands
Tel.: (31) 715249600
Web Site: http://www.mentormedical.nl
Sales Range: $50-74.9 Million
Emp.: 200
Cosmetic Surgery Products Mfr
N.A.I.C.S.: 339113

Mentor Medical Systems Ltd. **(3)**
Elizabeth House 13-19 London Road, Newbury, RG14 1JL, Berkshire, United Kingdom
Tel.: (44) 1635511800
Web Site: http://www.mentorwllc.eu
Sales Range: $150-199.9 Million
Emp.: 14
Cosmetic Surgery Products Distr
N.A.I.C.S.: 423450

Mentor Medical Systems Pty. Ltd. **(3)**
1-5 Khartoum Road, North Ryde, 2113, Australia
Tel.: (61) 292518111
Web Site: http://www.mentordirect.com.au
Sales Range: $150-199.9 Million
Emp.: 100
Cosmetic Surgery Products Distr
N.A.I.C.S.: 423450

Plant (Domestic):

Mentor Texas **(3)**
3041 Skwy Cir N, Irving, TX 75038
Tel.: (972) 252-6060
Web Site: http://www.tx-mentor.com
Sales Range: $75-99.9 Million
Emp.: 300
Reconstructive Surgery Products Mfr
N.A.I.C.S.: 339113

Subsidiary (Domestic):

NeuWave Medical, Inc. **(2)**
3529 Anderson St, Madison, WI 53704-2500
Tel.: (608) 512-1500
Web Site: http://www.neuwave.com
Electromedical & Electrotherapeutic Apparatus Mfr
N.A.I.C.S.: 334510

Subsidiary (Non-US):

Omrix Biopharmaceuticals LTD **(2)**
MDA Blood Bank Tel Hashomer Hospital, PO Box 888, Tel Aviv, 52621, Israel
Tel.: (972) 35316531
Web Site: http://www.omrix.com
Sales Range: $150-199.9 Million
Pharmaceuticals Mfr
N.A.I.C.S.: 325412

Subsidiary (Domestic):

Torax Medical, Inc. **(2)**
4188 Lexington Ave N, Shoreview, MN 55126
Tel.: (651) 361-8900
Web Site: http://www.toraxmedical.com
Surgical & Medical Instrument Mfr
N.A.I.C.S.: 339112

GATT Technologies B.V. **(1)**
Novio Tech Campus-Transistorweg 5, 6534 AT, Nijmegen, Netherlands
Tel.: (31) 850644369
Web Site: https://www.jnjmedtech.com
Medical Device Mfr & Distr
N.A.I.C.S.: 339112

GMED Healthcare BVBA **(1)**
Leonardo Da Vincilaan 15, 1831, Diegem, Belgium
Tel.: (32) 2 746 30 00
Pharmaceuticals Product Mfr
N.A.I.C.S.: 325412

Independence Technology, LLC **(1)**
45 Technology Dr, Warren, NJ 07059
Tel.: (908) 412-2200
Sales Range: $25-49.9 Million
Emp.: 25
Technological Products Mfr for People with Disabilities
N.A.I.C.S.: 423430

JOM Pharmaceutical Services, Inc. **(1)**
1 Cottontail Ln, Somerset, NJ 08873
Web Site: https://www.jom.com
Emp.: 125
Pharmaceutical Product Whslr
N.A.I.C.S.: 424210

Janssen Pharmaceuticals, Inc. **(1)**
1125 Trenton Harbourton Rd, Titusville, NJ 08560 **(100%)**
Tel.: (609) 730-2000
Sales Range: $500-549.9 Million
Emp.: 2,000
Pharmaceutical Preparation Mfr
N.A.I.C.S.: 325412
David York Norton (Pres)

Subsidiary (Domestic):

Alios BioPharma, Inc. **(2)**
260 E Grand Ave 2nd Fl, South San Francisco, CA 94080
Tel.: (650) 635-5500
Biopharmaceutical Research & Development Services
N.A.I.C.S.: 541715
Leonid Beigelman (Co-Founder)
Bruce Bryan (Sr Dir-Ops & Project Mgmt)

Subsidiary (Non-US):

Cilag AG **(2)**
Hochstrasse 201, 8200, Schaffhausen, Switzerland **(100%)**
Tel.: (41) 52 630 9111
Web Site: https://www.cilag.ch
Emp.: 1,200
Industrial Chemicals & Pharmaceuticals Mfr
N.A.I.C.S.: 325412
Thomas Moser (Head-External Comm)

Subsidiary (Domestic):

Cilag Advanced Technologies GmbH **(3)**
Hochstrasse 201, 8200, Schaffhausen, Switzerland
Tel.: (41) 526309111
Web Site: http://www.cilag.ch
Pharmaceutical & Consumer Goods Mfr
N.A.I.C.S.: 325412

Cilag Holding AG **(3)**
Landis Gyr-Strasse 1, Zug, 6300, Switzerland
Tel.: (41) 7255050
Web Site: http://www.jnc.ch
Holding Company
N.A.I.C.S.: 551112

Subsidiary (Domestic):

Janssen Alzheimer Immunotherapy Research & Development, LLC **(2)**
700 Gateway Blvd, South San Francisco, CA 94080
Tel.: (650) 794-2500
Web Site: http://www.janimm.com
Sales Range: $50-74.9 Million
Emp.: 200
Pharmaceuticals Product Mfr
N.A.I.C.S.: 325412

Subsidiary (Non-US):

Janssen Biologics (Ireland) **(2)**

Ringaskiddy Co, Cork, Ireland
Tel.: (353) 214973000
Pharmaceutical & Consumer Goods Mfr
N.A.I.C.S.: 325412

Janssen Biologics B.V. **(2)**
Einsteinweg 101, Leiden, 2333 CB, Netherlands
Tel.: (31) 71 524 2444
Web Site: http://www.janssen-biologics.nl
Pharmaceutical & Consumer Goods Mfr
N.A.I.C.S.: 325412

Subsidiary (Domestic):

Janssen Biotech, Inc. **(2)**
800 Ridgeview Rd, Horsham, PA 19044 **(100%)**
Tel.: (610) 651-6000
Web Site: http://www.janssenbiotech.com
Pharmaceuticals Mfr
N.A.I.C.S.: 541720

Subsidiary (Domestic):

BeneVir Biopharm, Inc. **(3)**
2736 E Baltimore St, Baltimore, MD 21224 **(100%)**
Tel.: (240) 498-6824
Research & Development in Biotechnology
N.A.I.C.S.: 541714
Matthew Mulvey (CEO)

Subsidiary (Non-US):

Janssen Cilag Farmaceutica S.A. **(2)**
Mendoza 1259, 1428, Buenos Aires, Argentina
Tel.: (54) 114 789 7200
Web Site: https://www.janssen.com
Pharmaceuticals Product Mfr
N.A.I.C.S.: 325412

Janssen Inc. **(2)**
19 Green Belt Dr, Toronto, M3C 1L9, ON, Canada
Tel.: (416) 449-9444
Web Site: https://www.janssen.com
Emp.: 400
Pharmaceutical Products Distr
N.A.I.C.S.: 424210

Subsidiary (Domestic):

Janssen Ortho LLC **(2)**
State Rd 933 Km 0 1 Mamey, Gurabo, PR 00778
Tel.: (787) 789-5000
Pharmaceuticals Product Mfr
N.A.I.C.S.: 325412

Subsidiary (Non-US):

Janssen Ortho, LLC **(2)**
19 Green Belt Dr, Toronto, M3C 1L9, ON, Canada
Tel.: (416) 449-9444
Web Site: http://www.janssen-ortho.com
Sales Range: $400-449.9 Million
Emp.: 420
Pharmaceutical Research Services
N.A.I.C.S.: 325412
Chris Halyk (Pres)
Sandy Heymann (VP-HR)

Subsidiary (Domestic):

Janssen Pharmaceutica **(2)**
1000 Route 202, Raritan, NJ 08869-1425
Tel.: (800) 526-7736
Pharmaceuticals Product Mfr
N.A.I.C.S.: 325412

Subsidiary (Non-US):

Janssen Pharmaceutica (Pty) Limited **(2)**
Johnson & Johnson Campus 2 Medical road, Midrand, 1685, Gauteng, South Africa **(100%)**
Tel.: (27) 112651000
Web Site:
http://www.janssenpharmaceutica.co.za
Sales Range: $50-74.9 Million
Emp.: 150
Pharmaceuticals Mfr
N.A.I.C.S.: 325412

Janssen Pharmaceutica N.V. **(2)**

Turnhoutseweg 30, 2340, Beerse,
Belgium **(100%)**
Tel.: (32) 1 460 2111
Web Site: https://www.janssen.com
Pharmaceuticals Mfr
N.A.I.C.S.: 325412

Subsidiary (Domestic):

Janssen Internationaal CVBA **(3)**
Turnhoutseweg 30, 2340, Beerse, Belgium
Tel.: (32) 14602111
Web Site:
    http://www.janssenpharmaceutica.be
Sales Range: $1-4.9 Billion
Emp.: 4,700
Pharmaceuticals Mfr
N.A.I.C.S.: 551112

Subsidiary (Non-US):

Janssen Pharmaceutical K.K. **(2)**
3-5-2 Nishikanda, Chiyoda-ku, Tokyo, 101-
0065, Japan **(100%)**
Tel.: (81) 34 411 7700
Web Site: https://www.janssen.com
Emp.: 2,500
Pharmaceuticals Whslr
N.A.I.C.S.: 456191
Shuhei Sekiguchi *(Pres)*

Janssen Pharmaceutical Ltd. **(2)**
Cork, Little Island, Ireland **(100%)**
Tel.: (353) 214353321
Web Site: http://www.janssen.ie
Sales Range: $100-124.9 Million
Emp.: 300
Pharmaceuticals Mfr
N.A.I.C.S.: 325412

Janssen-Cilag A/S **(2)**
Bregnerodvej 133, 3460, Birkerod,
Denmark **(100%)**
Tel.: (45) 4 594 8282
Web Site: https://www.janssen.com
Sales Range: $10-24.9 Million
Emp.: 40
Pharmaceutical Preparation Mfr
N.A.I.C.S.: 325412
Bert Patrik Ringblom *(Mng Dir)*

Janssen-Cilag A/S **(2)**
Drammensveien 288, 0283, Oslo,
Norway **(100%)**
Tel.: (47) 2 412 6500
Web Site: https://www.janssen.com
Sales Range: $10-24.9 Million
Emp.: 65
Pharmaceutical Product Whslr
N.A.I.C.S.: 424210

Janssen-Cilag AB **(2)**
Kolonnvagen 45, 170 67, Solna,
Sweden **(100%)**
Tel.: (46) 86265000
Web Site: http://www.janssen.com
Sales Range: $25-49.9 Million
Emp.: 100
Surgical Dressings, Baby Products, Phar-
maceuticals & Health Products Mfr
N.A.I.C.S.: 339113

Janssen-Cilag AG **(2)**
Hochstrasse 201, 8200, Schaffhausen,
Switzerland
Tel.: (43) 52 630 9111
Web Site: https://www.cilag.ch
Pharmaceuticals Whslr
N.A.I.C.S.: 424210

Janssen-Cilag B.V. **(2)**
Graaf Engelbertlaan 75, 4837 DS, Breda,
Netherlands **(100%)**
Tel.: (31) 800 242 4242
Web Site: https://www.janssen.com
Sales Range: $150-199.9 Million
Emp.: 250
Pharmaceuticals Whslr
N.A.I.C.S.: 456191

**Janssen-Cilag Farmaceutica
Ltda.** **(2)**
Av Presidente Juscelino Kubitschek 2 041
Complexo JK-Bloco B-7o andar, Sao Paulo,
04543-011, SP, Brazil
Tel.: (55) 800 701 1851
Web Site: https://www.janssen.com
Human Drug & Medicine Mfr
N.A.I.C.S.: 325412

**Janssen-Cilag Farmaceutica,
Lda.** **(2)**
Estrada Consiglieri Pedroso No 69 A, que-
luz de baixo, 2734-503, Barcarena, Portu-
gal
Tel.: (351) 21 436 8835
Web Site: http://www.janssencilag.com
Sales Range: $50-74.9 Million
Emp.: 150
Pharmaceuticals Mfr
N.A.I.C.S.: 325412

Janssen-Cilag GmbH **(2)**
Johnson & Johnson-Platz 1, 41470, Neuss,
Germany **(100%)**
Tel.: (49) 2 137 9550
Web Site: https://www.janssen.com
Sales Range: $550-599.9 Million
Emp.: 910
Pharmaceuticals Whslr
N.A.I.C.S.: 424210

Janssen-Cilag Ltd. **(2)**
106 Moo 4 Lard Krabang Industrial Estate
Chalongkrung Rd, Lamplatew Lard Kra-
bang, Bangkok, 10520, Thailand
Tel.: (66) 27397200
Pharmaceutical & Consumer Goods Mfr
N.A.I.C.S.: 325412

Janssen-Cilag Ltd. **(2)**
50-100 Holmers Farm Way, High Wy-
combe, HP12 4EG, United
Kingdom **(100%)**
Tel.: (44) 1494567567
Web Site: https://www.janssen.com
Sales Range: $400-449.9 Million
Emp.: 900
Pharmaceuticals Mfr
N.A.I.C.S.: 325412

Janssen-Cilag NV **(2)**
Antwerpseweg 15-17, 2340, Beerse,
Belgium **(100%)**
Tel.: (32) 8 009 3377
Web Site: https://www.janssen.com
Surgical Dressings, Baby Products, Phar-
maceuticals & Health Products Mfr
N.A.I.C.S.: 339999

Janssen-Cilag OY **(2)**
Tel.: (358) 20 753 1300
Web Site: https://www.janssen.com
Emp.: 280
Pharmaceuticals Mfr
N.A.I.C.S.: 325412

Janssen-Cilag Pharma GmbH **(2)**
Vorgartenstrasse 206B, 1020, Vienna,
Austria **(100%)**
Tel.: (43) 161 0300
Web Site: https://www.janssen.com
Emp.: 155
Pharmaceuticals Mfr
N.A.I.C.S.: 424210

**Janssen-Cilag Pharmaceutica
Limited** **(2)**
1550 Grand Amarin Tower 11th Floor New
Petchburi Road, Makasan Rachtevee,
Bangkok, 10310, Thailand
Tel.: (66) 22070252
Pharmaceuticals Mfr
N.A.I.C.S.: 325412

**Janssen-Cilag Pharmaceutical
S.A.C.I.** **(2)**
56 Irini Ave, Pefki, 15121, Athens,
Greece **(100%)**
Tel.: (30) 2108090000
Web Site: https://www.janssen.com
Emp.: 200
Pharmaceuticals Mfr & Whslr
N.A.I.C.S.: 424210

Janssen-Cilag Pty. Limited **(2)**
1-5 Khartoum Rd, Macquarie Park, 2113,
NSW, Australia **(100%)**
Tel.: (61) 298153333
Web Site: https://www.janssen.com
Sales Range: $50-74.9 Million
Emp.: 250
Baby, Personal & Health Care Products Mfr
N.A.I.C.S.: 621999
Chris Hourigan *(Chm-Grp-Asia Pacific)*

Janssen-Cilag S.A. **(2)**
1 Rue Camille Desmoulins, TSA 91003,
TSA 91003, 92787, Issy-les-Moulineaux,

Cedex, France **(100%)**
Tel.: (33) 155004500
Web Site: https://www.jnj.fr
Pharmaceuticals Mfr
N.A.I.C.S.: 325412
Titeux Cyiril *(Mng Dir)*
Delphine Aguilera-Caron *(Pres)*

Janssen-Cilag S.A. **(2)**
Paseo De Las Doce Estrellas 5 7, Madrid,
28042, Spain **(100%)**
Tel.: (34) 917228100
Web Site: http://www.janssen-cilag.es
Sales Range: $300-349.9 Million
Emp.: 500
Pharmaceutical Preparation Whslr
N.A.I.C.S.: 424210
Martin Selles *(Mng Dir)*

Janssen-Cilag S.p.A. **(2)**
Via Michelangelo Buonarroti 23, 20093, Co-
logno Monzese, MI, Italy **(100%)**
Tel.: (39) 0270 707 0963
Web Site: https://www.janssen.com
Sales Range: $300-349.9 Million
Emp.: 1,500
Pharmaceuticals Mfr & Whslr
N.A.I.C.S.: 325412

Janssen-Cilag s.r.o **(2)**
Karla Englise 3201/6, Prague, 15000,
Czech Republic
Tel.: (420) 227012227
Pharmaceuticals Product Mfr
N.A.I.C.S.: 325412

Janssen-Cilag, C.A. **(2)**
Av Romulo Gallego Edificio Johnson &
Johnson piso 12, Los Dos Caminos, Cara-
cas, Edo Miranda, Venezuela
Tel.: (58) 2122375335
Web Site: http://www.janssen.com.ve
Sales Range: $25-49.9 Million
Emp.: 200
Surgical Dressings, Baby Products, Phar-
maceuticals & Health Products Mfr
N.A.I.C.S.: 339113

Janssen-Cilag, S.A. de C.V. **(2)**
3720 Adolfo Ruiz Cortines Boulevard Tower
1 Floor 3, jardines del pedregal, 01900,
Mexico, DF, Mexico
Tel.: (52) 555 142 1000
Web Site: https://www.janssen.com
Sales Range: $750-799.9 Million
Emp.: 1,000
Pharmaceuticals Mfr
N.A.I.C.S.: 325412

Janssen-Ortho, Inc. **(2)**
Green Belt Dr, North York, M3C 1L9, ON,
Canada **(100%)**
Tel.: (416) 382-5000
Web Site: http://www.janssen-ortho.com
Sales Range: $400-449.9 Million
Emp.: 840
Pharmaceuticals Mfr
N.A.I.C.S.: 325412

Subsidiary (Domestic):

**Johnson & Johnson Holdco (NA)
Inc.** **(2)**
7050 Camp Hill Rd, Fort Washington, PA
19034
Tel.: (215) 273-7000
Holding Company
N.A.I.C.S.: 551112

Momenta Pharmaceuticals, Inc. **(2)**
301 Binney St, Cambridge, MA 02142
Tel.: (617) 491-9700
Pharmaceutical Services; Complex Sugar
Engineering
N.A.I.C.S.: 541715
Jo-Ann Beltramello *(Chief HR & Infrastruc-
ture Officer)*
Young T. Kwon *(CFO & Chief Bus Officer)*
Ganesh Venkataraman Kaundinya *(Co-
Founder)*
Anthony M. Manning *(Chief Scientific Offi-
cer)*

OMJ Pharmaceuticals, Inc. **(2)**
PO Box 367, San German, PR 00683
Tel.: (787) 892-2245
Web Site: http://www.jnj.com
Sales Range: $150-199.9 Million
Emp.: 4
Medical Devices, Anglographic & Neurosci-
ence Products Mfr & Services

N.A.I.C.S.: 325414

Ortho Biologics, LLC **(2)**
Rr 2, Manati, PR 00674
Tel.: (787) 854-1800
Web Site: http://www.jnj.com
Sales Range: $150-199.9 Million
Pharmaceuticals Mfr
N.A.I.C.S.: 325412

**Ortho-McNeil Pharmaceutical,
Inc.** **(2)**
1000 US Hwy 202, Raritan, NJ
08869 **(100%)**
Tel.: (908) 231-0712
Web Site: http://www.jnj.com
Pharmaceuticals Mfr
N.A.I.C.S.: 325411

Subsidiary (Non-US):

**Xian-Janssen Pharmaceutical
Ltd.** **(2)**
14F Tower 3 China Central Place No 77
Jian Guo Road, Chaoyang District, Beijing,
100025, China
Tel.: (86) 105 821 8888
Web Site: https://www.xian-janssen.com.cn
Emp.: 3,000
Pharmaceuticals Product Mfr
N.A.I.C.S.: 325412

Janssen Products, LP **(1)**
1125 Trenton Harbourton Rd, Titusville, NJ
08560
Tel.: (908) 218-6095
Medicinal & Botanical Product Mfr
N.A.I.C.S.: 325411

Janssen Sciences Ireland UC **(1)**
Airton Road, Dublin, D24WR89, Ireland
Tel.: (353) 14665200
Web Site: https://www.janssen.com
Pharmaceuticals Product Mfr
N.A.I.C.S.: 424210

Janssen Sciences Ireland UC **(1)**
Airton Road, Eastgate, Dublin, D24WR89,
County Cork, Ireland
Tel.: (353) 14665200
Web Site: http://www.janssen.com
Emp.: 70
Health Care Srvices
N.A.I.C.S.: 456199

Janssen Vaccine Corp. **(1)**
23 Harmony-Ro 303beon-Gil Yeonsu-Gu,
Incheon, 022-014, Korea (South)
Tel.: (82) 220943695
Pharmaceutical Preparation Mfr
N.A.I.C.S.: 325412
HeungSeub Ahn *(Mgr-Site Procurement)*

**Janssen Vaccines & Prevention
B.V.** **(1)**
Main Building Archimedesweg 4-6, 2333
CN, Leiden, Netherlands
Tel.: (31) 715199100
Pharmaceuticals Product Mfr
N.A.I.C.S.: 325412
Edison Wiesken *(Head-Ops Clinical Immu-
nology & GLAD Support Team)*

**Janssen-Cilag (New Zealand)
Limited** **(1)**
507 Mount Wellington Hwy, Mount Welling-
ton, Auckland, 1060, New Zealand
Tel.: (64) 95881343
Web Site: http://www.janssen.com
Pharmaceutical Research & Development
Services
N.A.I.C.S.: 541714

Janssen-Cilag Kft. **(1)**
Nagyenyed u 8-14, 1123, Budapest, Hun-
gary
Tel.: (36) 1 884 2858
Web Site: https://www.janssenmed.hu
Health Care Srvices
N.A.I.C.S.: 456199

Janssen-Cilag Polska, Sp. z o.o. **(1)**
Ul Ilzecka 24 Building F, 02-135, Warsaw,
Poland
Tel.: (48) 222376000
Human Drug & Medicine Mfr
N.A.I.C.S.: 325412

Janssen-Cilag S.A. **(1)**
Carrera 11 A Suite 94-45 Piso 10, Bogota,
Colombia

Johnson & Johnson—(Continued)

Tel.: (57) 12192500
Human Drug & Medicine Mfr
N.A.I.C.S.: 325412

Johnson & Johnson (China) Ltd. (1)
3/F Wanbao Center 660 Xinhua Road,
Shanghai, 200052, China
Tel.: (86) 2122058888
Web Site: http://www.jnj.com
Sales Range: $75-99.9 Million
Emp.: 500
Surgical & Medical Instruments Mfr
N.A.I.C.S.: 339112

Johnson & Johnson (Hong Kong)
Limited (1)
Room 1001 Grand Century Place 193
Prince Edward Road West, Kowloon, China
(Hong Kong) (100%)
Tel.: (852) 27382888
Web Site: http://www.jnjgateway.com
Sales Range: $25-49.9 Million
Emp.: 150
Hospital Products Mfr
N.A.I.C.S.: 339112
Jesse Wu (Chm)

Johnson & Johnson (Ireland)
Ltd. (1)
Airton Road, Tallaght, Dublin, Ireland
Tel.: (353) 14665200
Web Site: https://www.janssen.com
Sales Range: $25-49.9 Million
Emp.: 100
Hospital Products, Sanitary Towels, Tooth-
brushes & Toiletries Mfr
N.A.I.C.S.: 322291

Johnson & Johnson (Middle East)
Inc. (1)
1 Johnson & Johnson Plz, New Brunswick,
NJ 08933
Tel.: (732) 524-0400
Web Site: http://www.jnj.com
Sales Range: $150-199.9 Million
Emp.: 300
Surgical Dressings, Baby Products, Phar-
maceuticals & Health Products Mfr
N.A.I.C.S.: 325412

Johnson & Johnson (New Zealand)
Limited (1)
Tel.: (64) 28 260 8000
Web Site: https://www.jnjnz.co.nz
Sales Range: $50-74.9 Million
Emp.: 62
Surgical Dressings, Baby Products, Phar-
maceuticals & Health Products Whslr
N.A.I.C.S.: 424210

Johnson & Johnson (Philippines),
Inc. (1)
Edison Road, Bo Ibayo, Paranaque, 1700,
Metro Manila, Philippines (100%)
Tel.: (63) 368 8230
Web Site: https://www.jnj.com.ph
Sales Range: $50-74.9 Million
Emp.: 182
Hospital Products Mfr
N.A.I.C.S.: 339112

Johnson & Johnson (Proprietary)
Limited (1)
241 Main Road, Retreat, Cape Town, 7945,
South Africa
Tel.: (27) 86 041 0032
Web Site: https://www.jnjconsumer.co.za
Pharmaceuticals Product Mfr
N.A.I.C.S.: 325412

Johnson & Johnson AB (1)
Kolonnvagen Vag44, Solna, 17067,
Sweden (100%)
Tel.: (46) 86262200
Web Site: http://www.jjsweden.com
Sales Range: $25-49.9 Million
Emp.: 100
Hospital Products Mfr
N.A.I.C.S.: 339112

Johnson & Johnson AG (1)
Gubelstrasse 34, 6300, Zug,
Switzerland (100%)
Tel.: (41) 582315050
Web Site: http://www.jnj.ch
Sales Range: $100-124.9 Million
Emp.: 200

Cosmetics, Textiles, Clothing, Hospital &
Medical Equipment & Supplies Whslr
N.A.I.C.S.: 456199

Johnson & Johnson Comercio E Dis-
tribuicao Ltda. (1)
Rua Gerivatiba 207, 05501-900, Sao Paulo,
SP, Brazil
Tel.: (55) 1130308564
Web Site: http://www.jnjbrasil.com.br
Sales Range: $1-4.9 Billion
Emp.: 2,300
Toiletry, Hospital & Health Care Products
Mfr
N.A.I.C.S.: 325620

Johnson & Johnson Finance
Corporation (1)
501 George St, New Brunswick, NJ 08901-
1161
Tel.: (732) 524-2604
Web Site: http://www.jnj.com
Sales Range: $75-99.9 Million
Financial Services
N.A.I.C.S.: 541611

Johnson & Johnson Finance
Limited (1)
Pine Wood Campus Nine Mile Ride, Wok-
ingham, RG40 3EW, Berkshire, United
Kingdom
Tel.: (44) 1344871000
Web Site: http://www.jnj.com
Sales Range: $150-199.9 Million
Emp.: 300
Financial Services
N.A.I.C.S.: 525990

Johnson & Johnson Financial Ser-
vices GmbH (1)
Oststrasse 1, Norderstedt, 22844, Germany
Tel.: (49) 4052207700
Web Site: http://www.jandj.com
Sales Range: $650-699.9 Million
Financial Services
N.A.I.C.S.: 523940

Johnson & Johnson Group Holdings
GmbH (1)
Hekinghauser Str Bldg SSE 263, Wupper-
tal, 42289, Germany
Tel.: (49) 20262980
Sales Range: $125-149.9 Million
Emp.: 300
Holding Company; Pharmaceutical Mfr
N.A.I.C.S.: 551112

Johnson & Johnson Health Care Sys-
tems Inc. (1)
425 Hoes Ln, Piscataway, NJ
08854 (100%)
Tel.: (732) 562-3000
Web Site: http://www.jnjgateway.com
Sales Range: $50-74.9 Million
Emp.: 100
Account Management & Business Support
Services for Large Managed Care Organi-
zations, Hospitals & Government Custom-
ers
N.A.I.C.S.: 423450

Johnson & Johnson Health and Well-
ness Solutions, Inc. (1)
130 S First St, Ann Arbor, MI 48104
Tel.: (734) 623-0000
Web Site: http://jnjhws.com
Health Care Srvices
N.A.I.C.S.: 621491
Len Greer (Pres)
Jennifer Turgiss (VP-Behavior Science &
Advanced Analytics)

Johnson & Johnson Hellas S.A. (1)
4 Epidavrou & Aegialias St, Maroussi, 151
25, Greece
Tel.: (30) 16875555
Web Site: http://www.jnj.com
Sales Range: $50-74.9 Million
Emp.: 390
Hospital Products Mfr
N.A.I.C.S.: 339112

Johnson & Johnson Hemisferica
S.A. (1)
475 Calle C, Guaynabo, PR 00969
Tel.: (787) 272-1848
Health Care Products Mfr
N.A.I.C.S.: 325412

Johnson & Johnson Holding AB (1)

Staffans Vag 2, Sollentuna, 191 84, Swe-
den
Tel.: (46) 86262200
Web Site: http://www.jjsweden.com
Sales Range: $50-74.9 Million
Emp.: 100
Holding Company
N.A.I.C.S.: 551112

Johnson & Johnson Holding
GmbH (1)
Robert-Koch-Strasse 1, 22851, Norderstedt,
Germany
Tel.: (49) 40529701
Web Site: http://www.jnj.com
Sales Range: $750-799.9 Million
Emp.: 2,000
Holding Company
N.A.I.C.S.: 551112

Johnson & Johnson India Ltd. (1)
501 Arena Space Behind Majas Bus Depot
Off, Jogeshwari Vikhroli Link Road Jogesh-
wari E, Mumbai, 400 060, India (100%)
Tel.: (91) 2266464464
Web Site: http://www.jnjindia.in
Sales Range: $50-74.9 Million
Emp.: 500
Health Care Products Mfr
N.A.I.C.S.: 339113

Johnson & Johnson Innovation -
JJDC, Inc. (1)
410 George St, New Brunswick, NJ 08901
Tel.: (732) 524-3218
Web Site: https://jnjinnovation.com
Sales Range: $250-299.9 Million
Venture Capital Services
N.A.I.C.S.: 523999
Jeanne Bolger (VP-Venture Investments)
Stacy Feld (Head-West North America, Aus-
tralia & New Zealand)
V. Kadir Kadhiresan (VP-Venture Invest-
ments)
Tamir Meiri (Sr Mgr-Venture Investments)
Marian Nakada (VP-Venture Investments)
Asish K. Xavier (VP-Venture Investments)
Zeev Zehavi (VP-Venture Investments)
Naom Krantz (VP-Venture Investments)
Claire Leurent (Principal-Venture Invest-
ments)
Fiona MacLaughlin (Principal-Venture In-
vestments)
Anurag Mehta (Principal-Venture Invest-
ments)
Asha Nayak (VP-Venture Investments)
Wei Wu (Principal-Venture Investments)
Maike Stenull (Head-Strategy & Bus Ops-
Global)
Sarah Brennan (VP-Bus Dev, Cardiovascu-
lar & Metabolism)
Herwig Janssen (VP-Bus Dev & Emerging
Markets)
Elizabeth Wu (Mgr-Venture Investments,
Consumer & Pharm Sectors)
Chris Picariello (Pres)

Johnson & Johnson Innovation
LLC (1)
255 Main St, Cambridge, MA 02142
Tel.: (617) 225-4700
Web Site: https://jnjinnovation.com
Health Care Products Mfr
N.A.I.C.S.: 325412

Johnson & Johnson Innovation
Limited (1)
One Chapel Place, London, W1G 0BG,
United Kingdom
Tel.: (44) 2075734500
Web Site: https://www.jnjinnovation.com
Health Care Srvices
N.A.I.C.S.: 456199
Maike Stenull (Head-Strategy & Bus Ops-
Global)
Sue Hohenleitner (VP-Fin)
Chris Picariello (Pres)

Johnson & Johnson International (1)
1 Johnson & Johnson Plz, New Brunswick,
NJ 08933
Tel.: (732) 524-0400
Web Site: http://www.jnj.com
Holding Company
N.A.I.C.S.: 551112

Johnson & Johnson International
S.A. (1)
1 Rue Camille Desmoulins, Issy-les-

Moulineaux, 92130, France
Tel.: (33) 155004800
Web Site: http://www.jnj.com
Sales Range: $75-99.9 Million
Emp.: 1,300
Sanitary Protection Products, Toiletries &
Health Care Products Whslr
N.A.I.C.S.: 424210

Johnson & Johnson K.K. (1)
3-5-2 Nishikanda, Chiyoda-ku, Tokyo, 101-
0065, Japan
Tel.: (81) 34 411 7100
Web Site: https://www.jnj.co.jp
Sales Range: $150-199.9 Million
Emp.: 2,490
Sanitary Protection Products, Toiletries &
Health Care Products Whslr
N.A.I.C.S.: 424210

Johnson & Johnson Lda. (1)
Estrada Consiglieri Pedroso 69 A Queluz de
Baixo, Barcarena, 2730-055,
Portugal (100%)
Tel.: (351) 214351414
Web Site: http://www.janssen-cilag.pt
Sales Range: $75-99.9 Million
Emp.: 250
Toiletries & Sanitary Products Mfr
N.A.I.C.S.: 325620

Johnson & Johnson Ltd. (1)
Pinewood Camtus Nine miles ride, Woking-
ham, RG40 3EW, Berkshire, United King-
dom
Tel.: (44) 344864000
Web Site: http://www.jnjvisioncare.co.uk
Sales Range: $150-199.9 Million
Emp.: 310
Surgical Dressings, Baby Products, Phar-
maceuticals & Health Products Whslr
N.A.I.C.S.: 424210

Johnson & Johnson Medical (Pty)
Limited (1)
Halfway House 2 Medical Street, PO Box
273, Isando, 1685, Gauteng, South
Africa (100%)
Tel.: (27) 112651000
Web Site: http://www.jnjgateway.com
Sales Range: $150-199.9 Million
Emp.: 350
Pharmaceuticals Mfr
N.A.I.C.S.: 325412

Johnson & Johnson Medical (Shang-
hai) Ltd. (1)
4F Chengkai Guoji Building 355 Hongqiao
Road, Shanghai, 200030, China
Tel.: (86) 2122058888
Web Site: http://www.jnj.com
Pharmaceutical Product Whslr
N.A.I.C.S.: 424210

Johnson & Johnson Medical B.V. (1)
Computerweg 14, PO Box 188, Amersfoort,
3821 AD, Netherlands (100%)
Tel.: (31) 334500500
Web Site: http://www.jnjmedical.nl
Sales Range: $50-74.9 Million
Emp.: 153
Surgical Products Whslr
N.A.I.C.S.: 423450

Johnson & Johnson Medical Korea
Limited (1)
92 Hangang-daero LS Yongsan Tower 24
layer, Yongsan-gu, Seoul, 04386, Korea
(South)
Tel.: (82) 220943500
Web Site: http://www.jnjmedicaldevices.com
Sales Range: $25-49.9 Million
Emp.: 300
Surgical Dressings, Baby Products, Phar-
maceuticals & Health Products Mfr
N.A.I.C.S.: 325412
Sae Yul Park (Mng Dir)

Johnson & Johnson Medical Ltd. (1)
Pinewood Campus Nine Mile Ride, Woking-
ham, RG403EW, Berkshire, United King-
dom
Tel.: (44) 1344864000
Web Site: http://www.jnj.com
Sales Range: $900-999.9 Million
Emp.: 300
Medical & Hospital Equipment Mfr
N.A.I.C.S.: 325412

Johnson & Johnson Medical Ltd. (1)

Pinewood Campus Nine Mile Ride, Woking-ham, RG40 3EW, Berkshire, United Kingdom **(100%)**
Tel.: (44) 1344864000
Web Site: http://www.ethiconedo.com
Sales Range: $150-199.9 Million
Emp.: 300
Pharmaceuticals Mfr
N.A.I.C.S.: 325412
Stephen O'Callaghan *(Mng Dir)*

Johnson & Johnson Medical N.V. **(1)**
Leonardo Da Vincilaan 15, Diegem, 1831, Belgium
Tel.: (32) 27463000
Web Site: http://www.jnjmedical.be
Surgical Dressings, Baby Products, Pharmaceuticals & Health Products Whslr
N.A.I.C.S.: 325412

Johnson & Johnson Medical Products GmbH **(1)**
Vorgartenstrasse 206 B, 1020, Vienna, Austria
Tel.: (43) 136 0250
Web Site: http://www.jnjmedical.at
Pharmaceutical & Consumer Goods Mfr
N.A.I.C.S.: 325412

Johnson & Johnson Medical Pty. Limited **(1)**
1-5 Khartoum Rd, North Ryde, 2113, NSW, Australia **(100%)**
Tel.: (61) 298154000
Web Site: http://www.jnj.com
Sales Range: $125-149.9 Million
Emp.: 300
Medicinal Product Mfr
N.A.I.C.S.: 551112

Johnson & Johnson Medical S.A. **(1)**
Monsenor Magliano 3061, B1642GLA, San Isidro, Argentina
Tel.: (54) 1147086600
Web Site: http://www.jnjgateway.com
Sales Range: $75-99.9 Million
Emp.: 400
Surgical Dressings, Baby Products, Pharmaceuticals & Health Products Whslr
N.A.I.C.S.: 424210

Johnson & Johnson Medical S.p.A. **(1)**
Via del Mare 56 Pratica di Mare, Pomezia, 00071, Rome, Italy
Tel.: (39) 0691 1941
Web Site: https://www.jnjmedicaldevices.com
Pharmaceuticals Product Mfr
N.A.I.C.S.: 424210

Johnson & Johnson Medikal Sanayi ve Ticaret Limited Sirketi **(1)**
Erturk Sok Keceli Plaza No 13, Kavacik, 34810, Istanbul, Turkiye
Tel.: (90) 2165382000
Pharmaceutical Research & Development Services
N.A.I.C.S.: 541714

Johnson & Johnson Middle East FZ-LLC **(1)**
Building 14 Level 7, PO Box 505080, Dubai Healthcare City, Dubai, 505080, United Arab Emirates
Tel.: (971) 4 429 7377
Web Site: https://www.johnsonsbabyarabia.com
Health Care Srvices
N.A.I.C.S.: 621491

Johnson & Johnson Nordic AB **(1)**
Kolonnvagen 45, Solna, 170 67, Sweden
Tel.: (46) 8 626 22 00
Web Site: http://www.jjsweden.com
Pharmaceutical & Consumer Goods Mfr
N.A.I.C.S.: 325412
David Follovs *(Mng Dir)*

Johnson & Johnson Pharmaceutical Research & Development, LLC **(1)**
920 Us Hwy 202, Raritan, NJ 08869-1420 **(100%)**
Tel.: (908) 704-4000
Web Site: http://www.jnjpharmarnd.com
Sales Range: $400-449.9 Million
Emp.: 2,513
Pharmaceutical Research & Development Services

N.A.I.C.S.: 541715

Johnson & Johnson Private Limited **(1)**
501 Arena Space Behind Majas Bus Depot Off, Jogeshwari Vikhroli Link Road Jogeshwari E, Mumbai, 400 060, India
Tel.: (91) 2266646464
Web Site: https://www.jnj.in
Emp.: 3,500
Human Drug & Medicine Mfr
N.A.I.C.S.: 325412

Johnson & Johnson Products Inc. **(1)**
200 Whitehall Dr, Markham, L3R 0T5, ON, Canada
Tel.: (905) 946-1611
Web Site: http://www.jjmp.ca
Sales Range: $300-349.9 Million
Emp.: 350
Surgical Dressings, Baby Products, Pharmaceuticals & Health Products Whslr
N.A.I.C.S.: 424210

Johnson & Johnson Professional Co. (P.R.) Inc. **(1)**
Carr 183 Km83, San Lorenzo, PR 00754 **(100%)**
Tel.: (787) 736-7070
Sales Range: $400-449.9 Million
Emp.: 1,000
Surgical & Medical Instruments Mfr
N.A.I.C.S.: 339112

Johnson & Johnson Romania S.R.L. **(1)**
Str Tipografilor Nr 11-15 S-Park Building Corpul B3 3rd Floor, Room 1 Corps B4 3rd Floor and LB Corp 3rd Floor Sector 1, Bucharest, 013714, Romania
Tel.: (40) 212071800
Pharmaceuticals Product Mfr
N.A.I.C.S.: 325412

Johnson & Johnson S.A. **(1)**
Paseo Doce Estrellas 3, 28042, Madrid, Spain
Tel.: (34) 917228000
Web Site: http://www.jnjgateway.com
Sales Range: $400-449.9 Million
Emp.: 600
Surgical Dressings, Baby Products, Pharmaceuticals & Health Products Whslr
N.A.I.C.S.: 424210

Johnson & Johnson S.E. d.o.o. **(1)**
Radnicka 210, Zagreb, 10000, Croatia
Tel.: (385) 16610750
Pharmaceuticals Product Mfr
N.A.I.C.S.: 325412

Johnson & Johnson S.p.A. **(1)**
Via Degli Agrostemmi, Pomezia, 00134, Rome, Italy **(100%)**
Tel.: (39) 0671304058
Web Site: http://www.jnjgateway.com
Sales Range: $50-74.9 Million
Emp.: 400
Hospital Products Mfr
N.A.I.C.S.: 339112

Johnson & Johnson Sdn. Bhd. **(1)**
Level 8 The Pinnacle Persiaran Lagoon Bandar Sunway, Selangor Darul Ehsan, 46150, Petaling Jaya, Selangor Darul Ehsan, Malaysia **(100%)**
Tel.: (60) 800222565
Web Site: https://www.johnsonsbaby.com.my
Sales Range: $50-74.9 Million
Emp.: 300
Hospital Products Mfr
N.A.I.C.S.: 339112
Vaibhav Saran *(Mng Dir)*

Johnson & Johnson Services Inc. **(1)**
1 Johnson & Johnson Plz, New Brunswick, NJ 08933
Tel.: (732) 524-0400
Web Site: https://www.jnj.com
Sales Range: $1-4.9 Billion
Emp.: 50
Surgical Dressings, Baby Products, Pharmaceuticals & Health Products Mfr
N.A.I.C.S.: 325412

Johnson & Johnson Sihhi Malzeme Sanayi Ve Ticaret Limited Sirketi **(1)**

Erturk Sok Keceli Plaza No 13 Kavacik Beykoz, 34810, Istanbul, Turkiye
Tel.: (90) 2165382200
Web Site: http://www.jnjconsumer.com.tr
Contact Lens & Blood Glucose Monitoring System Whslr
N.A.I.C.S.: 423460

Johnson & Johnson Surgical Vision, Inc. **(1)**
1700 E Saint Andrew Pl, Santa Ana, CA 92705
Web Site: http://www.surgical.jnjvision.com
Eye Surgical Services
N.A.I.C.S.: 621111

Johnson & Johnson Surgical Vision, Inc. **(1)**
1700 E St Andrew Pl, Santa Ana, CA 92705
Tel.: (714) 247-8200
Web Site: http://www.jjvision.com
Ophthalmic Surgical & Medical Products Mfr & Distr
N.A.I.C.S.: 339112

Johnson & Johnson Taiwan Ltd. **(1)**
4F 319 DunHua S Rd Sec 2 Da an District, Taipei, 10669, Taiwan **(100%)**
Tel.: (886) 27327999
Web Site: http://www.jnjgateway.com
Sales Range: $50-74.9 Million
Emp.: 170
Health Care Products Mfr
N.A.I.C.S.: 325620

Johnson & Johnson Vision Care, Inc. **(1)**
7500 Centurion Pkwy Ste 100 D-CREL, Jacksonville, FL 32256-0517
Tel.: (904) 443-1000
Web Site: http://www.jjvision.com
Sales Range: $650-699.9 Million
Emp.: 3,475
Ophthalmic Product Mfr
N.A.I.C.S.: 339115
Xiao-Yu Song *(Head-R&D-Global)*
Rajesh Rajpal *(Chief Medical Officer & Head-Medical Affairs & Clinical Affairs)*
Peter Menziuso *(Pres-Vision Care-Worldwide)*
Christoph Vonwiller *(Pres-)*
Jacqueline Henderson *(Pres-)*
Lori Tierney *(Pres-)*
Jun Morimura *(Pres-)*
Matt Ryno *(VP-)*
Philip Kowalczyk *(VP-Business Development)*
Abdiel Alvarez *(VP-Quality & Compliance)*
Jeanne Bennett *(VP-)*
Sahar Shepperd *(VP-)*
A. Krishnan *(VP-Finance)*
Ryan Reinhardt *(VP-Supply Chain)*

Subsidiary (Non-US):

Johnson & Johnson Vision Care (Ireland) Limited **(2)**
Innovation Centre, National Technological Park, Limerick, Ireland
Tel.: (353) 61203203
Web Site: http://www.acuvue.com
Sales Range: $150-199.9 Million
Emp.: 750
Ophthalmic Product Mfr
N.A.I.C.S.: 339113

Johnson & Johnson d.o.o. **(1)**
Smartinska 53, 1000, Ljubljana, Slovenia
Tel.: (386) 14011830
Pharmaceutical Research & Development Services
N.A.I.C.S.: 541714
Asja Ljubanovic *(Controller-Fin)*

Johnson & Johnson de Uruguay S.A. **(1)**
Avenida Italia 7519 of 301, 11500, Montevideo, Uruguay
Tel.: (598) 8005553333
Web Site: https://www.jnjuruguay.com
Health Care Products Mfr
N.A.I.C.S.: 325412

Johnson & Johnson de Venezuela, S.A. **(1)**
Romulo Gallegos Av Johnson Johnson Building Los Dos Caminos, Chiyoda-ku, Caracas, 1060, Venezuela
Tel.: (58) 2122383122

Web Site: https://www.jnjvenezuela.com
Sales Range: $50-74.9 Million
Emp.: 360
Sanitation Products Mfr
N.A.I.C.S.: 339112

Johnson & Johnson, Prodaja medicinskih in farmacevtskih izdelkov, d.o.o **(1)**
Smartinska cesta 53, 1000, Ljubljana, Slovenia
Tel.: (386) 14011800
Web Site: http://www.jnj.com
Sales Range: $50-74.9 Million
Emp.: 100
Pharmaceutical & Consumer Goods Mfr
N.A.I.C.S.: 325412

Johnson & Johnson, Spol. s.r.o. **(1)**
Karla Englise 3201/6 Smichov Praha 5, 150 00, Prague, 15000, Czech Republic **(100%)**
Tel.: (420) 227012111
Web Site: https://www.jnj.cz
Sales Range: $50-74.9 Million
Emp.: 200
Pharmaceuticals Mfr
N.A.I.C.S.: 325412

Johnson & Johnson, s.r.o. **(1)**
Walterovo namesti 329/1, Jinonice, 158 00, Prague, Smichov, Czech Republic
Tel.: (420) 22 700 7001
Web Site: https://www.jnj.cz
Pharmaceuticals Product Mfr
N.A.I.C.S.: 325412

Johnson & Johnson, s.r.o. **(1)**
Karadzicova 12, 821 08, Bratislava, 821 08, Slovakia
Tel.: (421) 232408400
Pharmaceutical Healthcare Product Mfr
N.A.I.C.S.: 325412

LifeScan Products, LLC **(1)**
Rd 110 Km 5/9 St Ro, Aguadilla, PR 00603
Tel.: (787) 819-5200
Emp.: 300
Medical Equipment Mfr
N.A.I.C.S.: 339113
Ana Myriam Irizarry *(Gen Mgr)*

LifeScan Scotland Limited **(1)**
Beechwood Park North, Inverness, IV2 3ED, United Kingdom
Tel.: (44) 1463721000
Web Site: http://www.lifescan-scotland.co.uk
Emp.: 1,200
Medical Equipment Mfr
N.A.I.C.S.: 339113

Lifescan **(1)**
1 Rue Camille Desmoulins, Issy-les-Moulineaux, 92787, Paris, Cedex 09, France
Tel.: (33) 800459459
Web Site: http://www.lifescan.fr
Health Care Srvices
N.A.I.C.S.: 456199

Medical Devices International LLC **(1)**
1200 Bunn Ave, Springfield, IL 62703
Tel.: (217) 793-9469
Web Site: http://www.medicaldevicesinternational.net
Medical Equipment & Device Mfr
N.A.I.C.S.: 339112

Medos International Sarl **(1)**
Chemin-Blanc 38, Le Locle, 2400, Switzerland
Tel.: (41) 329348000
Web Site: http://www.jnj.ch
Holding Company
N.A.I.C.S.: 551112

Mentor B.V. **(1)**
Zernikedreef 2, Leiden, 2333 CL, Netherlands
Tel.: (31) 715249600
Medical Instrument Mfr
N.A.I.C.S.: 339112

Mentor Texas L.P. **(1)**
3041 Skyway Cir N, Irving, TX 75038-3540
Tel.: (972) 252-6060
Surgical & Medical Instrument Mfr
N.A.I.C.S.: 339112

Mentor Worldwide LLC **(1)**

Johnson & Johnson—(Continued)

31 Technology Dr, Irvine, CA 92618
Tel.: (805) 879-6000
Web Site: https://www.mentordirect.com
Medical Equipment Mfr
N.A.I.C.S.: 339113

Micro Typing Systems, Inc. (1)
1295 SW 29th Ave, Pompano Beach, FL
33069
Tel.: (954) 970-9500
Analytical Laboratory Instrument Mfr
N.A.I.C.S.: 334516

Neuravi Limited (1)
Block 3 Ballybrit Business Park, Galway,
H91 K5YD, Ireland
Tel.: (353) 91394123
Web Site: http://www.neuravi.com
Medical & Dental Instrument Mfr
N.A.I.C.S.: 339112

Neutrogena Corporation (1)
5760 W 96th St, Los Angeles, CA
90045 **(100%)**
Tel.: (310) 642-1150
Web Site: http://www.neutrogena.com
Sales Range: $500-549.9 Million
Emp.: 700
Skin & Hair Care Products Mfr
N.A.I.C.S.: 325620

Novira Therapeutics, Inc. (1)
3805 Old Easton Rd, Doylestown, PA
18902
Tel.: (267) 337-6913
Web Site:
http://www.noviratherapeutics.com
Pharmaceutical Preparation Mfr
N.A.I.C.S.: 325412
Osvaldo Flores (Pres & Chief Scientific Officer)

Obtech Medical AG (1)
Dammstrasse 19, 6300, Zug, Switzerland
Tel.: (41) 417255070
Web Site: http://www.obtech.com
Sales Range: $100-124.9 Million
Medical Equipment Mfr
N.A.I.C.S.: 339112

Rutan Realty, LLC (1)
1 Johnson & Johnson Plz, New Brunswick,
NJ 08933
Tel.: (732) 524-0400
Web Site: http://www.jnj.com
Holding Company
N.A.I.C.S.: 551112

**S.C. Johnson and Son Kenya
Limited**
SC Johnson A Family Company Premises
Off Baba Dogo Rd Baba Dogo, PO Box
30467-00100, Nairobi, Kenya
Tel.: (254) 203635000
Sales Range: $75-99.9 Million
Emp.: 70
Sanitary Protection Products, Toiletries &
Health Care Products Whslr
N.A.I.C.S.: 424210

**SYNTHES Medical Immobilien
GmbH** (1)
In Kirchenhurstle 6-8, 79224, Umkirch, Germany
Tel.: (49) 76655030
Real Estate Services
N.A.I.C.S.: 531190

**Shanghai Johnson & Johnson
Ltd.** (1)
120 Nanya Road, Minhang District, Shanghai, 200245, China
Tel.: (86) 2164302410
Sales Range: $150-199.9 Million
Emp.: 1,000
Band-Aid Adhesive Bandages Mfr
N.A.I.C.S.: 325520

Subsidiary (Domestic):

Shanghai Johnson & Johnson Pharmaceuticals, Ltd. (2)
No 139 Lvchun Road, Minhang Economic
and Technological Development Zone,
Shanghai, 200245, China
Tel.: (86) 800 820 1188
Web Site: https://sjjp.jnj.com.cn
Sales Range: $100-124.9 Million
Emp.: 300
Pharmaceuticals Mfr

N.A.I.C.S.: 325412

ShockWave Medical, Inc. (1)
5403 Betsy Ross Dr, Santa Clara, CA
95054
Tel.: (510) 279-4262
Web Site:
https://www.shockwavemedical.com
Rev.: $489,733,000
Assets: $646,089,000
Liabilities: $134,773,000
Net Worth: $511,316,000
Earnings: $215,996,000
Emp.: 1,001
Fiscal Year-end: 12/31/2022
Medical Device Mfr & Distr
N.A.I.C.S.: 339113
Douglas E. Godshall (Pres & CEO)
Isaac Zacharias (Chief Comml Officer)
Beaux Alexander (VP-Clinical Affairs)
Robert Fletcher (VP-Mktg)
Cathy Harnett (Dir-HR)
Mike Maszy (VP-Ops)
Trinh Phung (VP-Fin)
Patrick Stephens (VP-R&D)
Rob Williamson (VP-Sls)
Renee M. Gaeta (CFO)
Hajime Tada (Gen Counsel)
Keith D. Dawkins (Chief Medical Officer)
Meg Carr (VP-Regulatory Affairs)
Peter Nowakowski (VP-Quality)
Debbie Kaster (Head-IR)
C. Raymond Larkin Jr. (Chm)
C. Raymond Larkin Jr. (Chm)

Subsidiary (Non-US):

Neovasc Inc. (2)
13700 Mayfield Place, Suite 2135, Richmond, V6V2E4, BC, Canada
Tel.: (604) 270-4344
Rev.: $2,547,406
Assets: $66,224,839
Liabilities: $13,996,728
Net Worth: $52,228,111
Earnings: ($24,889,069)
Emp.: 54
Fiscal Year-end: 12/31/2021
Holding Company; Medical Products Developer & Mfr
N.A.I.C.S.: 551112

Subsidiary (Domestic):

Neovasc Medical Inc. (3)
13562 Maycrest Way Suite 5138, Richmond, V6V 2J7, BC, Canada
Tel.: (604) 270-4344
Web Site: http://www.neovasc.com
Cardiovascular Medical Device Mfr
N.A.I.C.S.: 339112

Spine Solutions GmbH (1)
Neuhauser Strasse 47, 78532, Tuttlingen,
Germany
Tel.: (49) 7461966275
Web Site: http://www.spinesolutions.de
Pharmaceuticals Product Mfr
N.A.I.C.S.: 325412

SterilMed, Inc. (1)
5010 Cheshire Pkwy Ste 2, Plymouth, MN
55446
Tel.: (763) 488-3400
Web Site: http://www.sterilmed.com
Emp.: 500
Medical Equipment Mfr
N.A.I.C.S.: 339113
Tom Schlick (Office Mgr)

**Surgical Process Institute
Deutschland GmbH** (1)
Kreuzstrasse 5, 04103, Leipzig, Germany
Tel.: (49) 3413086740
Web Site: http://www.sp-institute.com
Surgical Center Operator
N.A.I.C.S.: 621493

Synthes (Canada) Ltd. (1)
2566 Meadowpine Boulevard, Mississauga,
L5N 6P9, ON, Canada
Tel.: (905) 567-0440
Web Site: http://www.synthes.com
Medical Equipment Mfr
N.A.I.C.S.: 339113

**Synthes (Shanghai) Medical Trading
Co., Ltd.** (1)
Floor 3 85 Taoyuan Road Silver Court,
Shanghai, 200021, China

Tel.: (86) 2123275200
Medical Equipment Mfr
N.A.I.C.S.: 339113

**Synthes (Suzhou) Medical Co.,
Ltd.** (1)
428 Zhong Nan Street Suzhou Industrial
Park, Suzhou, 215021, China
Tel.: (86) 51262897607
Medical Equipment Mfr
N.A.I.C.S.: 339113

Synthes Australia Pty Ltd (1)
1 Lucknow Rd Riverside Corporate Park,
North Ryde, 2113, NSW, Australia
Tel.: (61) 298554600
Web Site: http://www.synthes.com
Emp.: 140
Medical Equipment Mfr
N.A.I.C.S.: 339113

**Synthes Industria e Comercio
Ltda.** (1)
Av Pennwalt 501, 13505-650, Rio Claro,
Sao Paulo, Brazil
Tel.: (55) 1921126600
Computer System Design Services
N.A.I.C.S.: 541512

Synthes Produktions GmbH (1)
Luzernstrasse 21, Solothurn, 4528, Zuchwil,
Switzerland
Tel.: (41) 32 720 4060
Web Site: http://www.synthes.com
Medical Equipment Mfr
N.A.I.C.S.: 339113

Synthes Tuttlingen GmbH (1)
Unter Hasslen 5, 78532, Tuttlingen, Germany
Tel.: (49) 746220010
Medical Equipment Mfr
N.A.I.C.S.: 339113

Synthes USA, LLC (1)
1101 Synthes Ave, Monument, CO 80132-7117
Tel.: (719) 481-5300
Surgical Product Mfr
N.A.I.C.S.: 339112

TearScience, Inc. (1)
5151 Mccrimmon Pkwy Ste 250, Morrisville,
NC 27560
Tel.: (919) 459-4891
Web Site: http://www.tearscience.com
Pharmaceuticals Product Mfr
N.A.I.C.S.: 325412

The Anspach Effort, LLC (1)
4500 Riverside Dr, Palm Beach Gardens,
FL 33410
Tel.: (561) 627-1080
Emp.: 300
Surgical Instrument Mfr
N.A.I.C.S.: 339112
Tony Meserve (Gen Mgr)

The Tylenol Company (1)
1 Johnson & Johnson Plz, New Brunswick,
NJ 08901-1241
Tel.: (732) 524-0400
Web Site: http://www.jnj.com
Sales Range: $25-49.9 Million
Emp.: 100
Pharmaceuticals Mfr
N.A.I.C.S.: 325412

Tibotec BVBA (1)
Gen De Wittelaan L 11B 3, Mechelen,
2800, Belgium
Tel.: (32) 15293100
Sales Range: $200-249.9 Million
Emp.: 500
Pharmaceutical Researcher & Developer of
New Drugs for HIV/AIDS & Other Infectious
Diseases
N.A.I.C.S.: 325412

Subsidiary (Non-US):

Tibotec Pharmaceuticals Ltd. (2)
Unit 4 Block 4B Blanchardstown Corporate
Park, Blanchardstown, Dublin, Ireland
Tel.: (353) 1 820 8114
Sales Range: $10-24.9 Million
Emp.: 15
Pharmaceutical Researcher & Developer of
New Drugs for HIV/AIDS & Other Infectious
Diseases
N.A.I.C.S.: 325412

Paulus A. Stoffels (Founder)

Subsidiary (Domestic):

Tibotec-Virco Virology BVBA (2)
Turnhoutseweg 30, Beerse, 2340, Belgium
Tel.: (32) 1 460 21 11
Web Site:
http://www.janssenpharmaceutica.be
Pharmaceuticals Product Mfr
N.A.I.C.S.: 325412

UAB Johnson & Johnson (1)
Konstitucijos pr 21C Verslo centras
QUADRUM North 5 aukstas, 08130, Vilnius,
Lithuania
Tel.: (370) 52786888
Web Site: https://www.janssen.com
Pharmaceutical Research & Development
Services
N.A.I.C.S.: 541714

Veridex, LLC (1)
1001 US Hwy Route 202, Raritan, NJ
08869
Tel.: (585) 453-3240
Web Site: http://www.veridex.com
Sales Range: $1-9.9 Million
Emp.: 110
Medical Instrument Mfr
N.A.I.C.S.: 339112

Virco BVBA (1)
Turnhoutseweg 30, Beerse, 2340, Belgium
Tel.: (32) 14641332
Web Site: http://www.vircolab.com
Sales Range: $25-49.9 Million
Emp.: 105
Pharmaceutical Researcher & Developer of
New Drugs for HIV/AIDS & Other Infectious
Diseases
N.A.I.C.S.: 325412
Werner Verbiest (Gen Mgr)

JOHNSON OUTDOORS INC.
555 Main St, Racine, WI 53403
Tel.: (262) 631-6600
Web Site:
https://www.johnsonoutdoors.com
Year Founded: 1985
JOUT—(NASDAQ)
Rev.: $592,846,000
Assets: $635,212,000
Liabilities: $171,788,000
Net Worth: $463,424,000
Earnings: ($26,533,000)
Emp.: 1,200
Fiscal Year-end: 09/27/24
Sporting Goods Mfr
N.A.I.C.S.: 339920
Helen P. Johnson-Leipold (Chm &
CEO)
David W. Johnson (CFO & VP)
Patricia Penman (VP-Mktg Svcs &
Global Comm)

Subsidiaries:

Humminbird (1)
678 Humminbird Ln, Eufaula, AL 36027
Tel.: (770) 888-6292
Web Site: http://www.humminbird.com
Rev.: $60,000,000
Emp.: 30
Mfr of Marine Electronics & Fishing Gear
N.A.I.C.S.: 334511

Jetboil, Inc. (1)
540 North Commercial St, Manchester, NH
03101
Tel.: (603) 518-1600
Web Site: https://www.jetboil.com
Sales Range: $10-24.9 Million
Emp.: 30
Cooking & Heating Equipment Mfr
N.A.I.C.S.: 423440

Johnson Outdoors Canada, Inc. (1)
4180 Harvester Road, Burlington, L7L 6B6,
ON, Canada **(100%)**
Tel.: (905) 634-0023
Web Site: https://www.johnsonoutdoors.com
Sales Range: $25-49.9 Million
Emp.: 16
Distr of Motors & Outdoor Equipment
N.A.I.C.S.: 459110

Johnson Outdoors Diving (1)
1166 Fesler St Ste A, El Cajon, CA 92020-1812
Tel.: (619) 402-1023
Web Site: http://www.scubapro.com
Sales Range: $10-24.9 Million
Emp.: 41
Scuba Diving Buoyancy Vest Mfr
N.A.I.C.S.: 339920

Johnson Outdoors France (1)
Nova Antipolis Les Terriers Nord 175 Allee Belle Vue, Chemin de St Claude, 06600, Antibes, France
Tel.: (33) 493339096
Web Site: http://www.johnsonoutdoors.fr
Sales Range: $25-49.9 Million
Emp.: 40
Sporting Goods Mfr
N.A.I.C.S.: 339920

Johnson Outdoors Gear LLC (1)
625 Conklin Rd, Binghamton, NY 13903-2700
Tel.: (607) 779-2222
Sporting Goods Mfr
N.A.I.C.S.: 339920
Christopher Martens (Dir-Bus-Camping)

Johnson Outdoors Inc.-Marine Electronics Group (1)
121 Power Dr, Mankato, MN 56002
Tel.: (507) 345-4623
Web Site: http://www.johnsonoutdoors.com
Sales Range: $25-49.9 Million
Emp.: 200
Motor & Generator Mfr
N.A.I.C.S.: 335312

Johnson Outdoors Marine Electronics. Inc. (1)
678 Humminbird Ln, Eufaula, AL 36027
Tel.: (334) 687-6613
Sales Range: $50-74.9 Million
Emp.: 300
Sonar & Electronic Product Mfr
N.A.I.C.S.: 334511
Helen P. Johnson-Leipold (Chm & CEO)

Johnson Outdoors Vertriebsgesellschaft GmbH (1)
Bremer Str 4, 90451, Nuremberg, Germany
Tel.: (49) 91 196 2620
Web Site: https://www.scubapro.eu
Outdoor Recreational Product Mfr
N.A.I.C.S.: 336214

Johnson Outdoors Watercraft Inc. (1)
125 Gilman Falls Ave Bldg B, Old Town, ME 04468
Tel.: (207) 827-5514
Web Site: http://www.oldtowncanoe.com
Sales Range: $25-49.9 Million
Emp.: 200
Sporting Boat Mfr
N.A.I.C.S.: 336612
Helen P. Johnson-Leipold (Chm & CEO)

Johnson Outdoors Watercraft Ltd. (1)
2 Furnace Pl, Silverdale, 0932, Auckland, New Zealand
Tel.: (64) 94275234
Outdoor Recreational Product Mfr
N.A.I.C.S.: 336214

Old Town Canoe Co. (1)
125 Gilman Salls Ave Bldg B, Old Town, ME 04468
Tel.: (207) 827-5513
Web Site: http://www.oldtowncanoe.com
Sales Range: $25-49.9 Million
Emp.: 150
Mfr of Kayaks & Accessories
N.A.I.C.S.: 336612

Scubapro AG (1)
Bodenackerstrasse 3, 8957, Spreitenbach, Switzerland
Tel.: (41) 62 767 9400
Web Site: http://www.johnsonoutdoors.com
Emp.: 15
Outdoor Recreational Product Mfr & Distr
N.A.I.C.S.: 336214

Scubapro Asia Pacific Ltd. (1)
608 Block B M P Industrial Centre 18 Ka Yip Street, Chai Wan, China (Hong Kong)
Tel.: (852) 2 556 7338

Web Site: https://ww2.scubapro.com
Water Sport Equipment Mfr
N.A.I.C.S.: 339920

Scubapro Asia, Ltd. (1)
Mitsubishi Juko Yokohama Bldg 3-3-1 Minato Mirai, Nishi-ku, Yokohama, 220-0012, Japan
Tel.: (81) 454894800
Outdoor Recreational Product Mfr & Distr
N.A.I.C.S.: 336214

Scubapro Espana, S.A. (1)
c/Pere IV no 359 2nd Floor, 08020, Barcelona, Spain
Tel.: (34) 933035550
Outdoor Recreational Product Mfr & Distr
N.A.I.C.S.: 336214

Scubapro Europe Benelux, S.A. (1)
De Vunt 13 Bus 4, 3220, Holsbeek, Belgium
Tel.: (32) 22503710
Outdoor Recreational Product Mfr & Distr
N.A.I.C.S.: 336214

Scubapro Europe S.r.l (1)
16 Via Tangoni, Casarza Ligure, 16030, Genoa, Italy
Tel.: (39) 0185467100
Web Site: http://www.scubapro.com
Outdoor Recreational Product Mfr & Distr
N.A.I.C.S.: 336214

Scubapro Italy S.r.l. (1)
Via Tangoni 16, Casarza Ligure, 16030, Genoa, Italy
Tel.: (39) 0185467100
Outdoor Recreational Product Mfr & Distr
N.A.I.C.S.: 336214

Scubapro-Uwatec Australia Pty. Ltd. (1)
Unit 21 / Building 38 Eastern Valley Way, Chatswood, 2067, NSW, Australia
Tel.: (61) 29 417 1011
Web Site: http://ww2.scubapro.com
Emp.: 6
Outdoor Recreational Product Mfr & Distr
N.A.I.C.S.: 336214
Rick Payne (Mng Dir)

Scubapro-Uwatec France S.A. (1)
Nova Antipolis Les Terriers Nord, 175 Allee Belle Vue, 06600, Antibes, France (100%)
Tel.: (33) 492913030
Web Site: http://www.scubapro.com
Sales Range: $10-24.9 Million
Emp.: 30
Mfr & Retailer of Diving Equipment
N.A.I.C.S.: 339920
Jose Stelle (Pres)

Scubapro/Uwatec France S.A. (1)
Nova Antipolis Les Terriers Nord 175 Allee Belle Vue, 06600, Antibes, France
Tel.: (33) 492913030
Outdoor Product Mfr
N.A.I.C.S.: 337126
Valerie Chovelon (Mgr-Export)

Seemann Sub GmbH & Co KG (1)
Johann-Hollfritsch-Strasse 47, Wendelstein, 90530, Germany
Tel.: (49) 9129909950
Sales Range: $25-49.9 Million
Emp.: 40
Scuba Diving Equipment Supplier
N.A.I.C.S.: 423910
Tina Kopseel (Mgr-Mktg)

Uwatec AG (1)
Bodenackerstrasse 3, 8957, Spreitenbach, Switzerland
Tel.: (41) 627679400
Web Site: http://www.johnsonoutdoors.com
Emp.: 50
Water Sport Equipment Mfr
N.A.I.C.S.: 339920

JONES LANG LASALLE INCORPORATED
200 E Randolph Dr Fl 43-48, Chicago, IL 60601
Tel.: (312) 782-5800   MD
Web Site: https://www.us.jll.com
Year Founded: 1997
JLL—(NYSE)
Rev.: $20,760,800,000

Assets: $16,064,800,000
Liabilities: $9,654,900,000
Net Worth: $6,409,900,000
Earnings: $225,400,000
Emp.: 106,100
Fiscal Year-end: 12/31/23
Real Estate Management Services
N.A.I.C.S.: 551112
Herman E. Bulls (Founder-JLL's Public Institutions bus unit, Vice Chm-Americas & Dir-Intl)
Mark D. Gibson (CEO-Capital Markets-Americas)
John Gates (CEO-Markets-Americas)
Christian Ulbrich (Pres & CEO)
John Gates (CEO-Markets-Americas)
Laura Adams (Chief HR Officer)
Amit Koren (Chief Product Officer)
Tanya Earley (Head-Marketing)
Nashunda Williams (Head-Diversity, Equity, and Inclusion)
Tara Gibney (Head-Human Resources & work Dynamics)
Karen Brennan (CFO)
James Gregory (CFO-Work Dynamics)
Siddharth Taparia (CMO-Global)
Alan K. Tse (Chief Legal Officer-Global & Sec)
Richard Bloxam (CEO-Capital Markets)
Neil Murray (CEO-Work Dynamics-Global)
Peter Downie (Exec Mng Dir-Comml-Work Dynamics)
Andy Poppink (CEO-Market Advisory)
Mihir Shah (CEO-JLL Technologies)
Ben Hawke (Chief Acctg Officer)
Cynthia Kantor (Chief Client Value & Growth Officer & CEO-Project, Dev Svcs, and Work Dynamics)

Subsidiaries:

Advanced Technologies Group, Inc. (1)
377 E Butterfield Rd Ste 900, Lombard, IL 60148
Tel.: (630) 964-9700
Web Site: http://www.site.atginc.com
Facility Management Software Development Services
N.A.I.C.S.: 541511
Mike Hakbaz (Pres & Mng Dir-Healthcare Solutions)
Ted Pappas (Principal & VP-Facility Svcs Div)
Jay Balapa (Principal & VP-Enterprise Solutions Div)
Ken Mustafa (Reg Dir-Healthcare)
Mike Mostardi (Reg Dir-Healthcare)

Alkas Consulting (1)
5 Gazeteciler Sit 2 Soltas Evleri Hare Sokak No 9 G 10, Levent, Istanbul, 34335, Turkiye
Tel.: (90) 2122848650
Web Site: http://www.alkas.com.tr
Emp.: 15
Real Estate Brokerage Services
N.A.I.C.S.: 531210

Appraisal Property Management Sdn Bhd (1)
Lot 7 2 Level 7 Menara 1Sentrum No 201, Jalan Tun Sambanthan, 50470, Kuala Lumpur, Malaysia
Tel.: (60) 22600777
Web Site: http://www.appraisal.my
Property Management Services
N.A.I.C.S.: 531312
Jamie Tan Mun Onn (Exec Dir)

Area Zero Consulting de Arquitectura e Interiorismo, S.L. (1)
Calle Raimundo Fernandez Villaverde Ent 53, Madrid, 28003, Spain
Tel.: (34) 917589820
Interior Design Services
N.A.I.C.S.: 541410

BRG International, LLC (1)
605 Lincoln Rd Ste 302, Miami Beach, FL 33139

Tel.: (305) 397-8788
Web Site: https://www.brgintl.com
Real Estate Management Services
N.A.I.C.S.: 531210

Big Red Rooster, Inc. (1)
121 Thurman Ave, Columbus, OH 43206
Tel.: (614) 607-7900
Web Site: http://www.bigredrooster.com
Emp.: 200
Industrial Design Services
N.A.I.C.S.: 541420
Stephen Jay (Sr VP)
Aaron Spiess (Founder & Exec VP)
Diane Rambo (Sr VP-Creative-Columbus Studio)
Josh Broehl (Sr VP & Acct Dir)
Staci Mandrell (Sr VP & Mng Dir-Atlanta)
Jaymie Gelino (Sr VP-Ops)
Russell Baumann (Sr VP)
Maureen Millard (VP-Client Svcs)
Beth Dorsey (VP & Dir-Acct Grp)
Jennifer Harbeson (VP & Dir-Acct Grp)
Tammy Kavicky (VP-Strategy)
Maggie Honious (Sr VP-Strategy)
David Denniston (Creative Dir)
Todd Haislip (VP & Creative Dir-Atlanta Studio)
Leah Miller (VP-Brand Activation)
Katherine Kline (Creative Dir)
Ashley Rowland Taylor (Dir-Strategy)
Bobby Donathan (Dir-Interactive)
Stefanie Mowery (Sr Mgr-Mktg)
Michael Brindley (VP-Creative)
Greg Feist (Creative Dir)
Kelly Truitt (Dir-Accounts)
Mary Margaret Connell (VP-Dev)
Emily Albright Miller (VP-Strategy)
Julia Toth (VP & Creative Dir)
Joe Nevin (Sr VP-Dev)
Keith Heinemann (VP-Phoenix Studio)

Corporate Concierge Services, Inc. (1)
135 S LaSalle St, Chicago, IL 60603
Tel.: (312) 329-1234
Web Site: https://www.corporateconcierge.com
Concierge Services
N.A.I.C.S.: 812990
Thomas S. Larance (CEO)
Meghan Rooney (VP-Ops)
Sue Morrison (Controller)
Teresa Bomkamp (Mgr-Acct)
Nicole Targa (Mgr-Acct)

Corrigo Incorporated (1)
8245 SW Tualatin Sherwood Rd, Tualatin, OR 97062-8441
Tel.: (503) 218-4200
Web Site: http://www.corrigo.com
Software & Services for Facilities Maintenance
N.A.I.C.S.: 513210
David Rainton (Exec VP-Tech)
Lyle Newkirk (Exec VP-Fin & Admin)
Tim Bernardez (Pres)
Jack Watkinson (Exec VP-Strategy)

Coverpoint Catering Consultancy Limited (1)
8 The Square Stockley Park, Uxbridge, UB11 1FW, United Kingdom
Tel.: (44) 2082832544
Web Site: http://www.coverpoint.co.uk
Retail Food Services Consulting Services
N.A.I.C.S.: 541611

Facility Associates Recruitment Limited (1)
2nd Floor 47-49 Borough High Street, London, SE1 1NB, United Kingdom
Tel.: (44) 2032072068
Web Site: http://www.farecruit.co.uk
Engineering, Maintenance, Automotive, Infrastructure & Real Estate Placement Services
N.A.I.C.S.: 561311

Fitoutetris SA (1)
Edificio Heron Castilho Rua Braamcamp, 1250-050, Lisbon, Portugal
Tel.: (351) 504952234
Real Estate Management Services
N.A.I.C.S.: 531210

H Park Germany LP GmbH (1)
Viktualienmarkt 8 / 5th floor, 80331, Munich, Germany

Jones Lang LaSalle Incorporated—(Continued)

Tel.: (49) 892111130
Real Estate Related Services
N.A.I.C.S.: 531390

HFF, Inc. (1)
1 Victory Park 2323 Victory Ave Ste 1200,
Dallas, TX 75219
Tel.: (214) 265-0880
Web Site: http://www.hfflp.com
Rev.: $662,042,000
Assets: $858,053,000
Liabilities: $507,507,000
Net Worth: $350,546,000
Earnings: $135,988,000
Emp.: 1,074
Fiscal Year-end: 12/31/2018
Commercial Real Estate & Capital Markets
Services
N.A.I.C.S.: 531390

**Homebay Residential Private
Limited** (1)
129 Berger House 4th Floor Near Mallick
Bazar Crossing, Park Street Circus Avenue,
Kolkata, 700017, West Bengal, India
Tel.: (91) 3322273293
Real Estate Brokerage Services
N.A.I.C.S.: 531210

ID Conseil (1)
57 rue de Lancry, 75010, Paris, France
Tel.: (33) 140400297
Web Site: http://www.idconseil.com
Investment Management Service
N.A.I.C.S.: 523940

Integral Facility Services Limited (1)
Styne House Upper Hatch Street, Dublin,
Ireland
Tel.: (353) 16775220
Real Estate Investment Management Ser-
vices
N.A.I.C.S.: 531120

Integral UK Ltd (1)
730 Waterside Drive Aztec West, Almonds-
bury, BS32 4UE, United Kingdom
Tel.: (44) 145 427 8900
Web Site: http://www.integral.co.uk
Building Services, Maintenance & Contract
Facilities Management
N.A.I.C.S.: 561210
Yash Kapila (Mng Dir)

JLL Capital Markets AB (1)
PO Box 1147, 111 81, Stockholm, Sweden
Tel.: (46) 86113107
Real Estate Related Services
N.A.I.C.S.: 531390
Susan B. Carras (Sr Mng Dir-
Washington,DC)

**JLL Corretagem e Trasacoes Imobil-
iarias Ltda.** (1)
Av Presidente Juscelino Kubitschek 1909 4
Andar Conj 41 Sala 01, Torre Norte Vila
Nova Conceicao, Sao Paulo, 04543-907,
Brazil
Tel.: (55) 1130436900
Emp.: 72
Real Estate Related Services
N.A.I.C.S.: 531390
Jairo Meneghelli Lima (Mgr-Real Estate
Transactions)

JLL Knightsbridge (1)
174 Brompton Road, London, SW3 1HP,
United Kingdom
Tel.: (44) 203 757 6499
Web Site: http://www.waellis.com
Property Management Services
N.A.I.C.S.: 531312

JLL Ltd (1)
Styne House Upper Hatch Street, Dublin,
D02 DY27, Ireland
Tel.: (353) 1 673 1600
Web Site: http://www.jll.ie
Emp.: 98
Real Estate Brokerage Services
N.A.I.C.S.: 531210
Deirdre Costello (Sr Dir-Office Agency)
Nigel Healy (Sr Dir-Industrial Agency)
John Moran (CEO & Member-Exec Bd)
Daniel O'Connor (Sr VP-Hotels)
Camilla Taaffe (COO & Member-Exec Bd)
Fionnuala O'Buachalla (Sr Dir-Tenant Rep-
resentation)

Woody O'Neill (Dir-Industrial Agency)
Stephen Murray (Sr Dir-Retail Agency)
Conor O'Gallagher (Sr Dir-Residential)
Andrew McCracken (Sr Dir-Project & Dev
Svcs)
Max Reilly (Sr Dir-Investments)

JLL Macau Limited (1)
Unit H 16/F Finance and IT Center of Ma-
cau, Avenida Doutor Mario Soares N 320,
Macau, China (Macau)
Tel.: (853) 28718822
Investment Management Service
N.A.I.C.S.: 523940

JLL Mortgage Services Pty Ltd (1)
Level 25 420 George Street, Sydney, 2000,
NSW, Australia
Tel.: (61) 292208500
Real Estate Investment Management Ser-
vices
N.A.I.C.S.: 531120

**JLL Property Services (Malaysia) Sdn
Bhd** (1)
Unit 7 2 Level 7 Menara 1 Sentrum No 201,
Jalan Tun Sambanthan KL Sentral, 50470,
Kuala Lumpur, Malaysia
Tel.: (60) 22600700
Web Site: http://www.jll.com.my
Real Estate Related Services
N.A.I.C.S.: 531390
Y. Y. Lau (Mng Dir)

JLL Technology Solutions (1)
10440 N Central Expy Ste 1150, Dallas, TX
75231
Tel.: (214) 777-5100
Web Site: http://www.brg.com
Management Consulting Services
N.A.I.C.S.: 541618
Traci Doane (Pres)
Reeves Davis (Exec VP)

JLL Valoraciones SA (1)
Paseo de la Castellana 79 - 3 Planta,
28046, Madrid, Spain
Tel.: (34) 7891100
Web Site: http://www.jllvaloraciones.es
Real Estate Consulting Service
N.A.I.C.S.: 531390

Japan H. L. Limited (1)
101-111 Kensington High Street, London,
W8 5SA, United Kingdom
Tel.: (44) 2039727100
Web Site: https://www.japanhouselondon.uk
Real Estate Manangement Services
N.A.I.C.S.: 531210

**Jones Lang LaSalle (Beijing) Co.,
Ltd.** (1)
11/F China World Tower A 1 Jianguomenwai
Avenue, Beijing, 100004, China (100%)
Tel.: (86) 1059221300
Web Site:
http://www.joneslanglasalle.com.cn
Sales Range: $100-124.9 Million
Emp.: 200
N.A.I.C.S.: 531210
Julien Zhang (Mng Dir)

**Jones Lang LaSalle (China)
Limited** (1)
7/F One Taikoo Place 979 King's Road,
Hong Kong, China (Hong Kong)
Tel.: (852) 28465000
Web Site: http://www.jll.com.hk
Real Estate Related Services
N.A.I.C.S.: 531390

**Jones Lang LaSalle (Geneva)
SA** (1)
Rue Vallin 2, 1201, Geneva, Switzerland
Tel.: (41) 228397373
Web Site: https://www.jll.ch
Real Estate Manangement Services
N.A.I.C.S.: 531210

**Jones Lang LaSalle (India) Private
Limited** (1)
1110 Ashoka Estate Barakhamba Rd, Con-
naught Place, New Delhi, 110 001,
India (100%)
Tel.: (91) 1143317070
Web Site: http://www.joneslanglasalle.com
Sales Range: $25-49.9 Million
Emp.: 35
Rel Estate Services
N.A.I.C.S.: 531210

Juggy Marwaha (Exec Mng Dir)
Manish Aggarwal (Mng Dir-North & East)
Abhay Kumar (Head-Mktg)
Dinesh Wadehra (Mng Dir-Property & Asset
Mgmt)
M. V. Harish (Mng Dir-Project & Dev Svcs)
Tanvi Choksi (Head-HR)
Aveek Sinha (CFO & Head-Ops)
Surekha Bihani (Mng Dir-East)
Sandeep Sethi (Chm-Corp Solutions)
Ashok Jayakumar (CIO)
Shubhranshu Pani (Mng Dir-Retail Svcs &
Stressed Asset-Mgmt Grp)
Nitish Bhasin (Mng Dir-Corp Dev)

**Jones Lang LaSalle (Philippines),
Inc.** (1)
19th floor NEX Tower 6786 Ayala Avenue,
Makati, Philippines
Tel.: (63) 2 902 0888
Web Site: https://www.jll.ph
Emp.: 150
Real Estate Brokerage Services
N.A.I.C.S.: 531210

**Jones Lang LaSalle (Puerto Rico),
Inc.** (1)
27 Gonzalez Giusti St Tres Rios Bldg,
Guaynabo, PR 00968
Tel.: (787) 777-5800
Real Estate Manangement Services
N.A.I.C.S.: 531210

**Jones Lang LaSalle (Thailand)
Limited** (1)
19/F Sathorn City Tower 175 South Sathorn
Road, Sathorn District, Bangkok, 10120,
Thailand
Tel.: (66) 26246400
Web Site: http://www.joneslanglasalle.co.th
Emp.: 1,200
Real Estate Brokerage Services
N.A.I.C.S.: 531210
Suphin Mechuchep (Mng Dir)

Jones Lang LaSalle - Atlanta (1)
3344 Peachtree Rd NE Ste 1100, Atlanta,
GA 30326
Tel.: (404) 995-2100
Web Site: http://www.jll.com
Emp.: 260
Real Estate Brokerage Services
N.A.I.C.S.: 531210
Michael J. Sivewright (Dir-Market)
Adam Viente (Exec Mng Dir)
Wit Truitt (Sr Mng Dir)
Brian Terrell (Mng Dir)
Randy Fink (Mng Dir-Property & Asset
Mgmt)
Eric Weatherholtz (Sr Mng Dir-Retail)
Rob Metcalf (Exec Mng Dir-Tenant Repre-
sentation)
Tami Rubison (Acct Dir-Rey)
Ed Coco (Sr Mng Dir-Capital Markets & Co-
Head-Office)
Richard Reid (Sr Mng Dir-Capital Markets &
Co-Head-Office)
Ryan Hoyt (Sr Mng Dir)
Tim McCarthy (Exec Mng Dir)
Bill Teberg (Pres-Div-MidWest & South
Reg)

Jones Lang LaSalle - Houston (1)
1400 Post Oak Blvd Ste 1100, Houston, TX
77056
Tel.: (713) 888-4000
Web Site: http://www.joneslanglasalle.com
Sales Range: $50-74.9 Million
Emp.: 150
Real Estate Brokerage Services
N.A.I.C.S.: 531210
Dan Bellow (Pres & Dir-Market)
Russell Hodges (Mng Dir-Agency Leasing)
Colby Mueck (Sr Mng Dir-Capital Markets &
Co-Head-Office)
Matt Kafka (Sr Mng Dir-Capital Markets &
Co-Head-Office)
Jeff Venghaus (Exec VP-Industrial)
Simmi Jaggi (Mng Dir-Land Svcs Grp)
John Roberts (Mng Dir-Project & Dev Svcs)
Connie O'Murray (Mng Dir-Property Mgmt)
Mark Raines (Mng Dir-Retail)
Ronnie Deyo (Exec VP-Tenant Representa-
tion)
David Dominy (Mng Dir-Valuation Advisory)

Jones Lang LaSalle - San Diego (1)
8910 University Ctr Ln Ste 100, San Diego,
CA 92122

Tel.: (858) 410-1200
Web Site: http://www.jll.com
Sales Range: $50-74.9 Million
Emp.: 60
Real Estate Brokerage Services
N.A.I.C.S.: 531210
Jay Alexander (Mng Dir)
Peter Belisle (Dir-Market-Southwest Reg)
Shawn Lorentzen (Mng Dir)
Darcy Miramontes (Mng Dir-Capital Mar-
kets)
Bob Prendergast (Mng Dir-Capital Markets)
Lynn LaChapelle (Mng Dir-Capital Markets)
Joe Anderson (Sr VP)
Andy Irwin (VP)
Bob Nowak (Mng Dir-Bus Dev)
Wyn H. Channer (Mng Dir-Integrated Port-
folio Svcs)
Aldon Cole (Sr Mng Dir & Head-Capital
Markets)
Scott Hall (Sr Mng Dir-Capital Markets &
Head-Office)
Jan Pope (Pres-Corp Solutions-West Reg)
Jay Pich (Mng Dir-Project & Dev Svcs)

Jones Lang LaSalle - Seattle (1)
601 Union St Ste 2800, Seattle, WA 98101
Tel.: (206) 607-1700
Web Site: http://www.joneslanglasalle.com
Emp.: 50
Real Estate Brokerage Services
N.A.I.C.S.: 531210

**Jones Lang LaSalle - Silicon
Valley** (1)
4085 Campbell Ave Ste 150, Menlo Park,
CA 94025
Tel.: (650) 480-2200
Web Site: http://www.jll.com
Sales Range: $50-74.9 Million
Emp.: 60
Real Estate Brokerage Services
N.A.I.C.S.: 531210
Bart Lammersen (Exec Mng Dir)

Jones Lang LaSalle - Texas, Inc. (1)
1703 W 5th St Ste 850, Austin, TX 78703
Tel.: (512) 225-2700
Real Estate Manangement Services
N.A.I.C.S.: 531210

Jones Lang LaSalle AB (1)
Lastmakargatan 20, PO Box 1147, Stock-
holm, 111 44, Sweden
Tel.: (46) 84535000
Web Site: http://www.joneslanglasalle.se
Sales Range: $50-74.9 Million
Emp.: 80
Real Estate Brokerage Services
N.A.I.C.S.: 531210

Jones Lang LaSalle AG (1)
Prime Tower Hardstrasse 201, 8005, Zurich,
Switzerland
Tel.: (41) 44 215 7500
Web Site: https://www.jll.ch
Sales Range: $25-49.9 Million
Real Estate Brokerage Services
N.A.I.C.S.: 531210
Jan P. Eckert (CEO)

**Jones Lang LaSalle Arizona,
LLC** (1)
51 W 3rd St Ste 201, Tempe, AZ 85281
Tel.: (480) 626-6304
Real Estate Manangement Services
N.A.I.C.S.: 531210

**Jones Lang LaSalle Australia Pty.
Limited** (1)
Level 25 420 George Street, Sydney, 2000,
NSW, Australia
Tel.: (61) 29 220 8500
Web Site:
http://www.joneslanglasalle.com.au
Sales Range: $100-124.9 Million
Offices of Real Estate Agents & Brokers
N.A.I.C.S.: 531210
Stephen William Conry (CEO-Australia &
New Zealand)
Jamie Guerra (Head-Industrial & Logistics)
John Talbot (Mng Dir-Advisory & Consulting
Svcs)
John Williams (Mng Dir-Western)
Kathleen Stubbs (CIO-Australia & New Zea-
land)
Tracey Annear (Dir-External Comm)

Subsidiary (Domestic):

**Jones Lang LaSalle (ACT Integrated)
Pty Limited** (2)

Level 7 121 Marcus Clarke Street, Canberra, 2600, ACT, Australia
Tel.: (61) 262749888
Web Site: http://www.jll.com.au
Emp.: 160
Real Estate Brokerage Services
N.A.I.C.S.: 531210
Andrew Balzanelli *(Mng Dir)*

Jones Lang LaSalle (ACT) Pty Limited (2)
Ngunnawal Country Level 7 121 Marcus Clarke Street, Canberra, 2600, ACT, Australia
Tel.; (61) 262749888
Real Estate Manangement Services
N.A.I.C.S.: 531210

Jones Lang LaSalle (NSW) Pty Limited (2)
Level 25 420 George Street, Sydney, 2000, NSW, Australia
Tel.: (61) 29 220 8500
Web Site: http://www.jll.com.au
Emp.: 450
Real Estate Brokerage Services
N.A.I.C.S.: 531210

Jones Lang LaSalle (QLD) Pty Limited (2)
Level 39 Central Plaza 345 Queen Street, Brisbane, 4000, QLD, Australia
Tel.: (61) 73 231 1311
Web Site: http://www.jll.com.au
Real Estate Brokerage Services
N.A.I.C.S.: 531210

Jones Lang LaSalle (SA) Pty Limited (2)
Level 18 Grenfell Centre 25 Grenfell Street, Adelaide, 5000, SA, Australia
Tel.: (61) 88 233 8888
Web Site: http://www.jll.com.au
Sales Range: $50-74.9 Million
Real Estate Brokerage Services
N.A.I.C.S.: 531210
Jamie Guerra *(Head-Industrial & Logistics-SA)*
Stephen Conry *(CEO)*

Jones Lang LaSalle (VIC) Pty Limited (2)
Wurundjeri Country Level 40 101 Collins Street, Melbourne, 3000, VIC, Australia
Tel.: (61) 396726666
Real Estate Manangement Services
N.A.I.C.S.: 531210

Jones Lang LaSalle (WA) Pty Limited (2)
Level 31 Central Park 152-158 St Georges Terrace, Perth, 6000, WA, Australia
Tel.: (61) 89 322 5111
Web Site: http://www.jll.com.au
Real Estate Brokerage Services
N.A.I.C.S.: 531210

Jones Lang LaSalle Hotels (NSW) Pty Limited (2)
Level 21 200 George Street, Sydney, 2000, NSW, Australia
Tel.: (61) 292847925
Web Site: http://www.jll.com.au
Sales Range: $25-49.9 Million
Investment Management Service
N.A.I.C.S.: 523940

Jones Lang LaSalle Hotels (QLD) Pty Limited (2)
Level 33 Central Plaza One, 345 Queen Street, Brisbane, 4000, QLD, Australia
Tel.: (61) 732311400
Sales Range: $25-49.9 Million
Emp.: 10
Real Estate Brokerage Services
N.A.I.C.S.: 531210

LaSalle Funds Management Limited (2)
200 George Street Level 21, Sydney, 2000, NSW, Australia
Tel.: (61) 29 284 7925
Web Site: http://www.lasalle.com
Sales Range: $50-74.9 Million
Emp.: 26
Real Estate Investment Services
N.A.I.C.S.: 531110
Matthew Bailey *(Head-Dev)*
Benjamin Daley *(VP-Acquisitions)*

Simon Howard *(Head-Asset Mgmt)*
Simon Juniper *(Sr VP-Dev)*
Joshua Mudge *(Mng Dir-Acquisitions)*
Michael Stratton *(Head-Acquisitions)*
Gareth Sneade *(Sr VP-Asset Mgmt)*
Emily Wills *(VP-Asset Mgmt)*
David Swann *(Sr VP-Asset Mgmt)*

Jones Lang LaSalle Co., Ltd. (1)
32F One IFC 10 Gukjegeumyung-ro, Yeongdeungpo-gu, Seoul, 07326, Korea (South)
Tel.: (82) 237048888
Web Site: https://www.jll.co.kr
Real Estate Manangement Services
N.A.I.C.S.: 531210.

Jones Lang LaSalle Construction Company, Inc. (1)
1 Post Ofc Sq Ste 2600, Boston, MA 02109
Tel.: (617) 523-8000
Real Estate Brokerage Services
N.A.I.C.S.: 531210
Joshua Jacoby *(Sr Mgr-Proposal)*

Jones Lang LaSalle Espana, S.A. (1)
Paseo de la Castellana 79 4 planta, 28046, Madrid, Spain
Tel.: (34) 91 789 1100
Web Site: http://www.jll.es
Real Estate Brokerage Services
N.A.I.C.S.: 531210

Jones Lang LaSalle Europe Limited (1)
30 Warwick Street, London, W1B 5NH, United Kingdom
Tel.: (44) 207 493 4933
Web Site: http://www.jll.co.uk
Real Estate Brokerage Services
N.A.I.C.S.: 531210
Alex Ash *(Dir-Corp Consulting)*

Subsidiary (Domestic):

AMAS Limited (2)
22 Hanover Square, London, W1S 1JA, United Kingdom
Tel.: (44) 2073995656
Real Estate Brokerage Services
N.A.I.C.S.: 531210

Churston Heard Ltd (2)
7 Hanover Square, London, W1S 1HQ, United Kingdom
Tel.: (44) 2074092199
Real Estate Brokerage Services
N.A.I.C.S.: 531210

Environmental Governance Ltd (2)
70 Cowcross St, London, EC1M 6EJ, United Kingdom
Tel.: (44) 2070616430
Management Consulting Services
N.A.I.C.S.: 541618

Jones Lang LaSalle (Scotland) Limited (2)
150 St Vincent Street, Glasgow, G2 5ND, United Kingdom
Tel.: (44) 1412486040
Sales Range: $50-74.9 Million
Emp.: 60
Real Estate Brokerage Services
N.A.I.C.S.: 531210
Ann Agnew *(Sec)*
Laura Cassells *(Sec-Industrial and Logistics)*
Keith McBain *(Dir)*
Andrew McCracken *(Assoc Dir)*
Sarka Novakova *(Mgr-Facilities)*
Diane Wilson *(Sec-Planning)*
Kerrie Currie *(Mgr-Property)*

Jones Lang LaSalle AP Limited (2)
40 Berkeley Square, Bristol, BS8 1HU, Avon, United Kingdom
Tel.: (44) 1179276691
Sales Range: $75-99.9 Million
Emp.: 180
Real Estate Brokerage Services
N.A.I.C.S.: 531210

Jones Lang LaSalle Corporate Finance Limited (2)
22 Hanover Square, London, W1S 1JA, United Kingdom
Tel.: (44) 2074936040
Web Site: http://www.jll.com

Sales Range: $25-49.9 Million
Emp.: 500
Investment Management Service
N.A.I.C.S.: 523940

Jones Lang LaSalle Machinery & Business Assets Limited (2)
1 Piccadilly Gardens, Manchester, M1 1RG, United Kingdom
Tel.: (44) 1612368793
Web Site: http://www.joneslanglasalle.com
Emp.: 120
Real Estate Asset Management Services
N.A.I.C.S.: 531390

Jones Lang LaSalle Facilities Kabushiki Kaisha (1)
2-5-5 Keihan-Hondori, Moriguchi-shi, Osaka, 570-8677, Japan
Tel.: (81) 669949365
Real Estate Brokerage Services
N.A.I.C.S.: 531210

Jones Lang LaSalle Finland OY (1)
Keskuskatu 7 4th floor, 00100, Helsinki, Finland
Tel.: (358) 207619960
Web Site: https://www.jll.fi
Real Estate Manangement Services
N.A.I.C.S.: 531210

Jones Lang LaSalle Gayrimenkul Hizmetleri Ticaret Anonim Sirketi (1)
Maslak Link Plaza Ayazaga Mah Eski Buyukdere Cad No 3/5, Maslak, 34398, Istanbul, Türkiye
Tel.: (90) 212 350 0800
Web Site: https://www.jll.com.tr
Real Estate Related Services
N.A.I.C.S.: 531390

Jones Lang LaSalle Global Finance Luxembourg Sarl (1)
Atrium Business Park 37 rue du Puits Romain, Bertrange, Luxembourg
Tel.: (352) 464540
Web Site: http://www.jll.lu
Investment Management Service
N.A.I.C.S.: 523940

Jones Lang LaSalle Global Services - RR, Inc. (1)
8343 Dougls Ave, Dallas, TX 75225
Tel.: (972) 361-5000
Management Consulting Services
N.A.I.C.S.: 541618

Jones Lang LaSalle Holdings BV (1)
Strawinskylaan 3103, PO Box 75208, Amsterdam, 1077 ZX, Netherlands
Tel.: (31) 205405405
Holding Company
N.A.I.C.S.: 551112

Jones Lang LaSalle Hotels & Hospitality (1)
200 E Randolph Dr, Chicago, IL 60601
Tel.: (312) 782-5800
Web Site:
 http://www.joneslanglasallehotels.com
Sales Range: $800-899.9 Million
Emp.: 7,000
Provider of Hotel Investment Services
N.A.I.C.S.: 531120
Mark Wynne-Smith *(CEO-Global)*

Jones Lang LaSalle Investment Management (1)
200 E Randolph Dr, Chicago, IL 60601
Tel.: (312) 782-5800
Web Site: http://www.jll.com
Sales Range: $1-4.9 Billion
Emp.: 600
Real Estate Investment Management Services
N.A.I.C.S.: 531120

Subsidiary (Non-US):

LaSalle Investment Management (Canada) (2)
22 Adelaide Street West Suite 2600, PO Box 407, Toronto, M5H 4E3, ON, Canada
Tel.: (416) 304-6000
Web Site: http://www.lasalle.com
Real Estate Investment Management Services
N.A.I.C.S.: 531190
John McKinlay *(CEO)*
Michael Cornelissen *(VP-Acquisitions)*

Stephen Robertson *(Head-Acquisitions)*
Sam Barbieri *(Mgr-Asset & Portfolio)*
Chris Lawrence *(Dir-Asset & Portfolio Mgmt)*
Edmund Lee *(Mgr-Asset & Portfolio)*

LaSalle Investment Management Asia Pte Ltd (2)
9 Raffles Place 37-01 Republic Plaza, Singapore, 048619, Singapore
Tel.: (65) 64943500
Web Site: http://www.lasalle.com
Commercial Real Estate Property Management Services
N.A.I.C.S.: 523940
Philip Ling *(CEO)*

LaSalle Investment Management BV (2)
De Lairessestraat 127 C en D, 1075 HJ, Amsterdam, Netherlands
Tel.: (31) 20 530 8888
Web Site: http://www.lasalle.com
Real Estate Investment Management Services
N.A.I.C.S.: 531210

Subsidiary (Non-US):

LaSalle Investment Management (3)
One Curzon Street, PO Box 2326, London, W1J 5HD, United Kingdom **(100%)**
Tel.: (44) 207 852 4200
Web Site: http://www.lasalle.com
Sales Range: $100-124.9 Million
Real Estate Management
N.A.I.C.S.: 531210
Tiziana Galassini *(COO-Client Capital Grp)*
Jon Zehner *(Head-Client Capital Grp-Global)*
Gary Moore *(Head-Accounts-Intl)*
Alok Gaur *(Head-Global-Client Capital Grp-Chicago)*
Jeff Jacobson *(Chm)*
Julian Agnew *(Chief Investment Officer)*
Amy Klein Aznar *(Head-Debt Investment & Special Situations)*
Alistair Dryer *(Head-Client Capital-Global Partner Solutions)*
Rebecca Gates *(Head-Asset Mgmt)*
Chris Lewis *(Head-Transactions)*
Simon Marx *(Reg Dir-Res & Strategy)*
Philip Nell *(Head-Real Return Assets)*
Tom Rose *(Head-Relative Return Strategies)*
Steve Spray *(Head-Absolute Return Funds & Mgr-Fund)*
Nayda Arslanian *(Head-Mktg & Comm)*
Petra Blazkova *(Mng Dir-Res & Strategy)*
James Boyd-Phillips *(Head-Retail Asset Mgmt)*
Ben Collis *(VP-HR)*
Andrew Jeanes *(Mgr-Fund)*
Tal Lev-Ari *(Mng Dir & Head-Ops-DEBT & Special Situations)*
Anne Lucking *(Sr Mng Dir-IR)*
Stuart Richmond-Watson *(Mgr-Fund)*
Alistair Seaton *(Dir-Bus Support)*

Subsidiary (Domestic):

LaSalle Investment Management BV (3)
De Lairessestraat 127 C en D, 1075 HJ, Amsterdam, Netherlands
Tel.: (31) 205308888
Commercial Real Estate Property Management Services
N.A.I.C.S.: 523940

Subsidiary (Non-US):

LaSalle Investment Management Espana, S.L.U. (3)
Paseo de la Castellana 79 3a planta, 28046, Madrid, Spain
Tel.: (34) 917453312
Sales Range: $25-49.9 Million
Emp.: 2
Commercial Real Estate Property Management Services
N.A.I.C.S.: 523940

LaSalle Investment Management S.A.S. (3)
112 Avenue Kleber, 75784, Paris, Cedex 16, France **(100%)**
Tel.: (33) 15 643 4646
Web Site: http://www.lasalle.com

Jones Lang LaSalle Incorporated—(Continued)

Sales Range: $25-49.9 Million
N.A.I.C.S.: 531210
Loic Sanieres (Head-Asset Mgmt)
Alexandre Arhuis-Grumbach (Mgr-Fund Transactions)
Marianne Hemon-Laurens (Mgr-Deputy Fund)
Samer Honein (Sr Mng Dir-IR)
Beverley Kilbride (Country Mgr)
Nora Yazane (VP-IR)

Lasalle Investment (Luxembourg)
SARL   **(3)**
41 Ave De La Liberte, Luxembourg, 1931, Luxembourg
Tel.: (352) 2686891
Sales Range: $25-49.9 Million
Emp.: 15
Commercial Real Estate Property Management Services
N.A.I.C.S.: 523940
Stephanie Duval (Gen Mgr)

Subsidiary (Non-US):

LaSalle Investment Management Luxembourg SARL   **(2)**
34-38 Avenue de la Liberte, 1930, Luxembourg, Luxembourg
Tel.: (352) 2686891
Real Estate Management Services
N.A.I.C.S.: 531210

Subsidiary (Domestic):

LaSalle Investment Management, Inc.   **(2)**
100 E Pratt St 20th Fl, Baltimore, MD 21202-1009   **(100%)**
Tel.: (410) 878-4800
Web Site: http://www.lasalle.com
Sales Range: $25-49.9 Million
Emp.: 900
Real Estate Asset Management
N.A.I.C.S.: 531210
Steve Bolen (Head-Healthcare Real Estate)
Hank Feibusch (Mng Dir-Due Diligence)
Richard Reese (Officer-Acquisitions)
Steven Schnur (Mgr-Asset)

Subsidiary (Domestic):

LaSalle Investment Management Securities, LLC   **(3)**
100 E Pratt St 20th Fl, Baltimore, MD 21202
Tel.: (410) 878-4800
Web Site: http://www.lasalle.com
Real Estate Investment Management Services
N.A.I.C.S.: 531190

Latitude Management Real Estate Investors, Inc.   **(3)**
350 S Beverly Dr Ste 300, Beverly Hills, CA 90212   **(80%)**
Tel.: (310) 234-2100
Web Site: http://www.lmrei.com
Emp.: 20
Commercial Real Estate Investment Services
N.A.I.C.S.: 531390
Glen Sonnenberg (Pres & CEO)
Chip Sellers (Exec VP)
Craig Oram (Mng Dir)

Subsidiary (Domestic):

Dakota Hospitality Company   **(4)**
3803 13th Ave S, Fargo, ND 58103
Tel.: (701) 277-7349
Web Site: http://www.fchhotels.com
Hotel Property Management Services
N.A.I.C.S.: 531312

Unit (Domestic):

Holiday Inn Austin Midtown   **(5)**
6000 Middle Fiskville Rd, Austin, TX 78752-4315
Tel.: (512) 451-5757
Web Site: http://www.hiausmid.com
Sales Range: $10-24.9 Million
Hotel Operator
N.A.I.C.S.: 721110

Jones Lang LaSalle Israel
Limited   **(1)**

HaSheizaf 4 Ra'anana Wopa Building, Ra'anana, Israel
Tel.: (972) 733822796
Web Site: https://www.jll.co.il
Real Estate Management Services
N.A.I.C.S.: 531210

Jones Lang LaSalle KFT   **(1)**
Szabadsag ter 14 Budapest Office, 1054, Budapest, Hungary
Tel.: (36) 1 489 0202
Web Site: https://www.jll.hu
Sales Range: $50-74.9 Million
Real Estate Brokerage Services
N.A.I.C.S.: 531210
Gabor Onczay (Head-Project & Dev Svcs & Dir-Natl)
Ferenc Furulyas (Mng Dir)
Peter Wursching (Head-Leasing & Office-Grp)
Jaroslav Kopac (Head-Valuation)
Eva Sreter (Head-Retail)
Roland Kis (Head-Industrial & Assoc Dir)
Kornelia Kiraly (Head-Fin)

Jones Lang LaSalle Kabushki
Kaisha   **(1)**
Prudential Tower 2-13-10 Nagata-cho, Chiyoda-ku, Tokyo, 100-0014, Japan
Tel.: (81) 355019200
Web Site: http://www.joneslanglasalle.co.jp
Emp.: 1,000
Real Estate Brokerage Services
N.A.I.C.S.: 531210

Jones Lang LaSalle Kenya Ltd   **(1)**
Sanlam Tower 4thFloor 1 Waiyaki Way, Westlands, Nairobi, 00800, Kenya
Tel.: (254) 709324324
Real Estate Investment Management Services
N.A.I.C.S.: 531120

Jones Lang LaSalle LLC   **(1)**
St Letnikovskaya 2 Bld 1 Vivaldi Plaza Business Center, Moscow, Russia
Tel.: (7) 4957378000
Web Site: http://www.jll.ru
Real Estate Brokerage Services
N.A.I.C.S.: 531210
Tim Millard (Head-Advisory Grp)

Jones Lang LaSalle LLP   **(1)**
BC Sunkar MD 2 Bldg 47B Suite 728, 130000, Aktau, Kazakhstan
Tel.: (7) 7292545258
Web Site: http://www.joneslanglasalle.kz
Sales Range: $25-49.9 Million
Emp.: 48
Real Estate Brokerage Services
N.A.I.C.S.: 531210

Jones Lang LaSalle Lanka (Private)
Limited   **(1)**
Unit 3 Level 4 West Tower, World Trade Centre Echelon Square, 01, Colombo, Sri Lanka
Tel.: (94) 112324124
Web Site: https://www.jll.com.lk
Real Estate Management Services
N.A.I.C.S.: 531210

Jones Lang LaSalle Limited   **(1)**
Level 16 188 Quay Street, PO Box 165, Auckland, 1140, New Zealand
Tel.: (64) 9 366 1666
Web Site: http://www.jll.nz
Real Estate Brokerage Services
N.A.I.C.S.: 531210
Graham Barton (Dir-Valuation & Advisory)
Todd Lauchlan (Mng Dir)
Jolyon Thomson (Head-Indus)

Jones Lang LaSalle Limited   **(1)**
32F One IFC 10 Gukjegeumyung-ro, Yeongdeungpo-gu, Seoul, 07326, Korea (South)
Tel.: (82) 237048888
Investment Management Service
N.A.I.C.S.: 523940

Jones Lang LaSalle Limited Liability
Company   **(1)**
Moskovskaya St 32/2 Senator business centre, Kiev, Ukraine
Tel.: (380) 444904444
Investment Management Service
N.A.I.C.S.: 523940

Jones Lang LaSalle Ltd   **(1)**

7/F One Taikoo Place 979 King's Road, Hong Kong, China (Hong Kong)
Tel.: (852) 2 846 5000
Web Site: http://www.jll.com.hk
Real Estate Management Services
N.A.I.C.S.: 531210
Joseph Tsang (Chm & Head-Capital Markets)

Jones Lang LaSalle Ltd.   **(1)**
Styne House Upper Hatch Street, Dublin, D02 DY27, Ireland
Tel.: (353) 16731600
Investment Management Service
N.A.I.C.S.: 523940

Jones Lang LaSalle Michigan,
LLC   **(1)**
24 Frank Lloyd Wright Dr Ste J4200, Ann Arbor, MI 48105
Tel.: (734) 769-3200
Real Estate Management Services
N.A.I.C.S.: 531210

Jones Lang LaSalle Property Consultants Pte Ltd   **(1)**
9 Raffles Place 39-00 Republic Plaza, Singapore, 048619, Singapore
Tel.: (65) 62203888
Web Site: http://www.jll.com.sg
Sales Range: $200-249.9 Million
Real Estate Brokerage Services
N.A.I.C.S.: 531210
Chris Archibold (Head-Leasing)
Nihat Ercan (Mng Dir & Head-Investment Sls-Asia)
Mok Sze Sze (Sr Dir-Auctions)

Jones Lang LaSalle Real Estate Services Incorporated   **(1)**
150 King Street West Suite 2103, Toronto, M5L 1J9, ON, Canada   **(100%)**
Tel.: (416) 304-6000
Web Site: http://www.jll.ca
Sales Range: $25-49.9 Million
Emp.: 100
N.A.I.C.S.: 531210

Jones Lang LaSalle Real Estate Services, Inc.   **(1)**
Bay Adelaide Centre East Tower 22 Adelaide Street West 26th Floor, Toronto, M5H 4E3, ON, Canada
Tel.: (416) 304-6000
Web Site: http://www.jll.ca
Real Estate Related Services
N.A.I.C.S.: 531390

Jones Lang LaSalle Residential Development GmbH   **(1)**
Unter den Linden 14, 10117, Berlin, Germany
Tol.: (40) 308866000
Web Site: http://www.residential.jll.de
Residential Property Development Services
N.A.I.C.S.: 531311

Jones Lang LaSalle Residential Private Limited   **(1)**
H No 8-2-418 Level 4 Krishnama House Road No 7 Banjara Hills, Hyderabad, 500034, India
Tel.: (91) 8688909501
Web Site: http://www.jllresidential.co.in
Sales Range: $25-49.9 Million
Emp.: 11
Real Estate Brokerage Services
N.A.I.C.S.: 531210

Jones Lang LaSalle S.A.   **(1)**
Av Presidente Juscelino Kubitschek 1,909 Torre Norte - 4 andar, Sao Paulo, 04543-907, Brazil
Tel.: (55) 113 043 6900
Web Site: http://www.jll.com
Sales Range: $150-199.9 Million
Emp.: 600
Real Estate Brokerage Services
N.A.I.C.S.: 531210
Fabio Maceira (CEO)

Jones Lang LaSalle S.R.L.   **(1)**
Carlos Pellegrini 719 7th floor, C1009ABO, Buenos Aires, Argentina
Tel.: (54) 1139848600
Web Site: https://www.jll.com.ar
Sales Range: $50-74.9 Million
Emp.: 85
Real Estate Brokerage Services

N.A.I.C.S.: 531210

Jones Lang LaSalle S.p.A.   **(1)**
Via Agnello 8, 20121, Milan, Italy
Tel.: (39) 02 858 6861
Web Site: http://www.jll.it
Emp.: 80
Real Estate Brokerage Services
N.A.I.C.S.: 531210
Claudia Bisignani (Head-Hotels & Hospitality)
Davide Dalmiglio (Head-Capital Markets & Retail Grp)
Pierre Marin (CEO)

Jones Lang LaSalle SAS   **(1)**
40-42 rue La Boetie, 75008, Paris, France
Tel.: (33) 140551515
Web Site: http://www.jll.fr
Emp.: 100
Real Estate Brokerage Services
N.A.I.C.S.: 531210
Emmanuel Joachim (COO)
Charles Boudet (CEO)
Benoit Du Passage (Mng Dir-EMEA)

Jones Lang LaSalle SE   **(1)**
Rahel-Hirsch-Strasse 10, 10557, Berlin, Germany
Tel.: (49) 302039800
Investment Management Service
N.A.I.C.S.: 523940

Jones Lang LaSalle SSC (Philippines), Inc.   **(1)**
19th floor NEX Tower 6786 Ayala Avenue, Makati, Philippines
Tel.: (63) 2 902 0888
Web Site: http://www.jll.com.ph
Real Estate Related Services
N.A.I.C.S.: 531390
Lindsay Orr (Chm)

Jones Lang LaSalle Sarl   **(1)**
13 rue Ibnou Toufail - Quartier Palmiers Espace les Palmiers 2nd floor, Casablanca, Morocco
Tel.: (212) 520447700
Investment Management Service
N.A.I.C.S.: 523940

Jones Lang LaSalle Saudi Arabia
Limited   **(1)**
Level 21 Al Khobar Gate Tower King Fahed Road, PO Box 32348, Al Khobar, Saudi Arabia
Tel.: (966) 133308401
Real Estate Related Services
N.A.I.C.S.: 531390
Frank Gleeson (Project Mgr)

Jones Lang LaSalle Secs   **(1)**
Atrium Business Park 41 Rue du Puits Romain, Bertrange, 8070, Luxembourg
Tel.: (352) 464540
Web Site: http://www.joneslanglasalle.lu
Sales Range: $25-49.9 Million
Emp.: 34
Real Estate Brokerage Services
N.A.I.C.S.: 531210

Jones Lang LaSalle Services AB   **(1)**
Birger Jarlsgatan 25 4th floor, Box 1147, 111 81, Stockholm, Sweden
Tel.: (46) 8 453 5000
Web Site: http://www.jllsweden.se
Real Estate Brokerage Services
N.A.I.C.S.: 531210

Jones Lang LaSalle South Africa (Proprietary) Ltd   **(1)**
Office 303 Cnr Craddock & Biermann Road, Rosebank, Johannesburg, 2196, South Africa
Tel.: (27) 115072200
Web Site: http://www.jll.co.za
Sales Range: $50-74.9 Million
Real Estate Brokerage Services
N.A.I.C.S.: 531210
Peter Harris (CFO & COO)

Jones Lang LaSalle Sp. z o.o.   **(1)**
Plac Europejski 1, 00-844, Warsaw, Poland
Tel.: (48) 22 167 0000
Web Site: http://www.jll.pl
Sales Range: $75-99.9 Million
Real Estate Brokerage Services
N.A.I.C.S.: 531210
Tomasz Trzoslo (Mng Dir)
Malgorzata Zoltowska (COO & Head-Valuations)

Jones Lang LaSalle Srl (1)
Victoria Center 145 Calea Victoriei 10th Floor Sector 1, Bucharest, 10072, Romania
Tel.: (40) 213023400
Web Site: http://www.jll.ro
Sales Range: $25-49.9 Million
Emp.: 35
Real Estate Brokerage Services
N.A.I.C.S.: 531210
Mariana Stamate (Head-Property Mgmt)
Silviana Petre Badea (Mng Dir)
Marius Scuta (Head-Office Dept & Tenant Representation)
Maria Florea (Dir-Client)
Andrei Vacaru (Head-Capital Markets)
Costin Banica (Head-Industrial Agency)
Alina Cojocaru (Head-Valuation Advisory)
Cezar Florea (Head-Project & Dev Svcs)
Attila Peli (Head-Dev & Land)
Viorel Opait (Dir-Bus Dev)

Jones Lang LaSalle Taiwan Limited (1)
20/F-1 Taipei 101 Tower No 7 Xinyi Road Section 5, Taipei, 11049, Taiwan
Tel.: (886) 287589898
Web Site: https://www.jll.com.tw
Real Estate Manangement Services
N.A.I.C.S.: 531210

Jones Lang LaSalle UAE Limited (1)
30 Warwick Street, London, W1B 5NH, United Kingdom
Tel.: (44) 2074934933
Web Site: http://www.jll.com
Real Estate Related Services
N.A.I.C.S.: 531390

Jones Lang LaSalle Vietnam Company Limited (1)
26/F Saigon Trade Center 37 Ton Duc Thang Str, District 1, Ho Chi Minh City, 7000, Vietnam
Tel.: (84) 83 911 9399
Web Site:
http://www.joneslanglasalle.com.vn
Sales Range: $50-74.9 Million
Real Estate Agents & Broker Services
N.A.I.C.S.: 531210

Jones Lang LaSalle d.o.o. (1)
Danube Business Center 10L Mihajla Pupina Blvd, Belgrade, 11070, Serbia
Tel.: (381) 11 785 0600
Web Site: http://www.jll.rs
Real Estate Related Services
N.A.I.C.S.: 531390

Jones Lang LaSalle of New York, LLC (1)
330 Madison Ave 4th Fl, New York, NY 10017
Tel.: (212) 812-5700
Real Estate Manangement Services
N.A.I.C.S.: 531210

Jones Lang LaSalle s.r.o (1)
Blumental Offices II Namestie Mateja Korvina 1, 811 07, Bratislava, Slovakia
Tel.: (421) 25 920 9911
Web Site: https://www.jll.sk
Real Estate Related Services
N.A.I.C.S.: 531390
Miroslav Barnas (CEO, Member-Exec Bd & Head-Capital Markets)
Peter Nitschneider (Member-Exec Bd, Head-Advisory & Country Mgr)

Jones Lang LaSalle spoka z ograniczon odpowiedzialnoceci (1)
Plac Europejski 1, 00-844, Warsaw, Poland
Tel.: (48) 223180000
Real Estate Investment Management Services
N.A.I.C.S.: 531120
Dagmara Filipiak (Head-Retail Tenant Representation)
Anna Wysocka (Head-Retail)

Jones Lang LaSalle sprl (1)
Avenue Marnixlaan 23 B1, 1000, Brussels, Belgium
Tel.: (32) 2 550 2525
Web Site: http://www.jll.be
Sales Range: $50-74.9 Million
Real Estate Brokerage Services
N.A.I.C.S.: 531210
Walter Goossens (Head-Industrial & Logistics Agency)

Rod Scrivener (Head-Valuation & Consulting)
Valina Sempot (Head-Mktg, Comm, Res & Data Knowledge)
Bernard Sergeant (Head-Corp Solutions & Bus Dev)
Erik Verbruggen (Head-Office Agency)
Jean-philip Vroninks (CEO)
Evelien Van Hoecke (Head-Retail Agency)
Adrian Glatt (Head-Capital Markets-Belux)
Ignace de Haut de Sigy (Head-Tetris)
Pierre-paul Verelst (Head-Res)

Jones Lang LaSalle, Sociedad Anonima de Capital Variable (1)
Monte Pelvoux 111 Floor 5 Col Lomas de Chapultepec Del Miguel Hidalgo, Mexico, 11000, Mexico
Tel.: (52) 55 5980 8003
Web Site:
http://www.joneslanglasalle.com.mx
Real Estate Broker
N.A.I.C.S.: 531210
Pedro Azcue (CEO)

Jones Lang LaSalle, Sociedade de Mediacao Imobiliaria, S.A. (1)
Edificio Heron Castilho Rua Braamcamp 40-8, 1250-050, Lisbon, Portugal
Tel.: (351) 21 358 3222
Web Site: http://www.jll.com
Sales Range: $50-74.9 Million
Emp.: 40
Real Estate Brokerage Services
N.A.I.C.S.: 531210
Patricia Araujo (Member-Exec Bd & Head-Retail)

Jones Lang Lasalle (Luxembourg) Secs (1)
Atrium Business Park 37 rue du Puits Romain, 8070, Bertrange, Luxembourg
Tel.: (352) 464540
Web Site: http://www.jll.lu
Real Estate Brokerage Services
N.A.I.C.S.: 531210
Angelique Sabron (Mng Dir-Head-Markets)

Jones Lang Lasalle BV (1)
Parnassusweg 727 Entrance parking at the Strawinskylaan, 1077 DG, Amsterdam, Netherlands
Tel.: (31) 20 540 5405
Web Site: http://www.jll.nl
Sales Range: $50-74.9 Million
Real Estate Brokerage Services
N.A.I.C.S.: 531210
Reynout Vroegop (CFO, COO & Member-Exec Bd)

Kensington CA, LLC (1)
4064 Colony Rd Ste 400, Charlotte, NC 28211
Tel.: (704) 644-3681
Web Site: https://www.kensington-advisors.com
Real Estate Manangement Services
N.A.I.C.S.: 531210

Kensington Capital Advisors, LLC (1)
4064 Colony Rd Ste 400, Charlotte, NC 28211
Tel.: (704) 644-3681
Web Site: http://www.kensington-advisors.com
Management Consulting Services
N.A.I.C.S.: 541618
Karen Jahnke (Owner)

King Sturge Management SPRL (1)
Avenue Marnix 23, 1000, Brussels, Belgium
Tel.: (32) 22307900
Property Management Services
N.A.I.C.S.: 531312

LaSalle GmbH (1)
Viktualienmarkt 8, 80331, Munich, Germany
Tel.: (49) 892111130
Commercial Real Estate Property Management Services
N.A.I.C.S.: 523940

LaSalle Investment Management (Shanghai) Co., Ltd. (1)
Unit 1 & 2 49F One Museum Place No 669 Xinzha Road, Jing'An District, Shanghai, China
Tel.: (86) 2122506000
Real Estate Manangement Services

N.A.I.C.S.: 531210

LaSalle Investment Management Australia Pty Ltd (1)
200 George Street Level 21, Sydney, 2000, NSW, Australia
Tel.: (61) 292847925
Emp.: 18
Real Estate Investment Management Services
N.A.I.C.S.: 531120

LaSalle Investment Management Co., Ltd. (1)
16F Two IFC 10 Gukjegeumyung-ro, Yeongdeungpo-gu, Seoul, 07326, Korea (South)
Tel.: (82) 261376137
Web Site: http://www.lasalle.com
Real Estate Related Services
N.A.I.C.S.: 531390

LaSalle Investment Management Hong Kong Limited (1)
Suite 3008 30/F AIA Central 1 Connaught Road, Central, China (Hong Kong)
Tel.: (852) 31825333
Real Estate Manangement Services
N.A.I.C.S.: 531210

LaSalle Partners, S. de R.L. de C.V. (1)
Monte Pelvoux 111 Floor 5 Col Lomas de Chapultepec, Del Miguel Hidalgo, 11000, Mexico, Mexico
Tel.: (52) 555 980 8003
Web Site: https://www.jll.com.mx
Real Estate Manangement Services
N.A.I.C.S.: 531390

LaSalle REIT Advisors K.K. (1)
14th Floor Pacific Century Place Marunouchi 1-11-1, Marunouchi Chiyoda-ku, Tokyo, Japan
Tel.: (81) 36 367 5600
Web Site: https://www.lasalle-reit-advisors.com
Emp.: 18
Real Estate Investment Management Services
N.A.I.C.S.: 531120
Toshimitsu Fujiwara (Pres & CEO)

Merritt & Harris, Inc. (1)
148 W 37th St 4th Fl, New York, NY 10018
Tel.: (212) 915-2954
Web Site: http://www.merrittandharris.com
Sales Range: $1-9.9 Million
Construction Consulting Services
N.A.I.C.S.: 541690
Craig Van Steenbergen (VP)
James L. Mako (VP-Florida)
Edward J. Bellavigna (Sr VP)
James G. Cockinos (Sr VP)
Joseph Marciano (Sr VP)
Margaret Asimakis (VP)
Rita O'Grady (Project Mgr)
David Humphrey (Sr Project Mgr)

Metropolitan Valuation Services, Inc. (1)
44 E 32nd St Rm 602, New York, NY 10016-5508
Tel.: (212) 213-8650
Web Site: http://www.mvsappraisal.com
Offices of Real Estate Appraisers
N.A.I.C.S.: 531320

Morii Appraisal & Investment Consulting Inc. (1)
1-8-3 Nihonbashi Kayabacho, Chuo-ku, Tokyo, 103-0025, Japan
Tel.: (81) 356455733
Web Site: http://www.maic.jp
Real Estate Investment Management Services
N.A.I.C.S.: 531120

PDM International (Beijing) Limited (1)
Level 25 Tower A Chaowai SOHO Chaiwai Street 6B Chaoyang District, Beijing, 100020, China
Tel.: (86) 1059001380
Web Site: http://www.pdmdesign.com
Interior Design Services
N.A.I.C.S.: 541410

PDM International (Chengdu) Limited (1)

29/F Tower 1 Chengdu International Finance Square 1 Hongxing Road, Chengdu, 610021, Sichuan, China
Tel.: (86) 2866805000
Web Site: http://www.pdmdesign.com
Interior Design Services
N.A.I.C.S.: 541410

PDM International China Limited (1)
Level 5 Bldg B 98 Yanping Road, Shanghai, 200042, China
Tel.: (86) 2162728833
Web Site: http://www.pdmdesign.com
Interior Design Services
N.A.I.C.S.: 541410

PDM International Limited (1)
23 Finkle Street, Thirsk, YO7 1DA, North Yorkshire, United Kingdom
Tel.: (44) 1765602600
Web Site: https://www.pd-m.com
Real Estate Manangement Services
N.A.I.C.S.: 531210

Prime Property Consultants Limited (1)
Unit 1803-4 Chinachem Tower 34-37 Connaught Road, Central, China (Hong Kong)
Tel.: (852) 28542856
Web Site: http://www.primeoffice.com.hk
Real Estate Agency Services
N.A.I.C.S.: 531210

SRS Real Estate Partners, LLC (1)
8343 Douglas Ave Ste 200, Dallas, TX 75225
Tel.: (214) 560-3200
Web Site: http://www.srsre.com
Sales Range: $200-249.9 Million
Emp.: 40
Commercial Real Estate
N.A.I.C.S.: 531390
Janie French (Principal & VP-Bus Dev)
Enid Husby (Principal & VP-HR)
Jimmy Dockal (CFO)
John Artope (Exec VP)
Woody McMinn (Pres-Brokerage-North America)
Tara Tolomeo (Coord-Mktg-Chicago)
Kyle Stonis (Mng Principal-Investment Properties Grp)
Pierce Mayson (Mng Principal-Investment Properties Grp-Atlanta)
Kevin Yaryan (Sr VP-Investment Properties Grp)
Ed Beeh (Mng Principal & Exec VP)
Garrett Colburn (Mng Principal & Exec VP)
Matias Campins (VP-Res & Analytics)
Ashley Loyd (Principal & Sr VP-Mktg)

Subsidiary (Domestic):

Cypress Equities (2)
8343 Douglas Ave Ste 200, Dallas, TX 75225
Tel.: (214) 561-8800
Web Site: http://cypressequities.com
Sales Range: $10-24.9 Million
Real Estate Development
N.A.I.C.S.: 531390
Chris Maguire (CEO)
Brian Parro (CFO)
Scott Harrington (COO & Mng Principal)
Cameron Aderhold (VP)
Hugh Kelly (Mng Principal-NE Reg)
Jeff Coker (Mng Dir-Dev)
Kirk Williams (Mng Dir)
Michael Wheat (Mng Dir-Leasing)
Mike Holsomback (Mng Dir-Capital Markets)
Julie Schreiber (Dir-Events)
Jennifer Doughty (Mgr-Property Acctg)
Darrell Gage (Sr Dir-Property Mgmt)
Stephanie Hooper (Project Mgr-Tenant Improvement)
Emma Nicodemus (VP-Capital Markets)
Kourtney Karvas (Project Mgr)
Jeff Maguire (Dir-Design)
Stephen Schmidt (Mng Dir)
David Shute (Sr Project Mgr)
Chad Huffman (Mgr-Fin Reporting)
Carolyn Hutchison (Dir-HR)
Demetria Miles (Coord-Acctg)
Kim Phillips (Coord-Acctg)
Sandy Holbrook (Sr Mgr-Property)
Callie Sallee (Controller)

Branch (Domestic):

SRS Real Estate Partners, LLC - San Jose Office (2)

Jones Lang LaSalle Incorporated—(Continued)

901 Campisi Way Ste 245, Campbell, CA 95126
Tel.: (408) 553-6135
Web Site: http://srsre.com
Real Estate Investment
N.A.I.C.S.: 525990
Sarah D. Edwards (First VP)
Bruce H. Frazer (Sr VP)
Robert G. Quigley (Sr VP)

Shelter Bay Retail Group, Inc.   **(1)**
655 Redwood Hwy Ste 177, Mill Valley, CA 94941
Tel.: (415) 388-4460
Web Site: http://www.shelterbay.com
Sales Range: $1-9.9 Million
Emp.: 45
Commercial Property Management
N.A.I.C.S.: 531210

Strategic Advisory Group Inc.   **(1)**
3848 St Annes Court Ste 300, Duluth, GA 30096
Tel.: (631) 725-7746
Web Site:
    http://www.strategicadvisorygroup.com
Emp.: 100
Corporate Finance & Investment Services
N.A.I.C.S.: 523940

Tetris Design & Build BV   **(1)**
Parnassusweg 727, 1077 DG, Amsterdam, Netherlands
Tel.: (31) 205405405
Real Estate Manangement Services
N.A.I.C.S.: 531210

Tetris Design & Build Sarl   **(1)**
Rue Docteur-Alfred-Vincent 5, 1201, Geneva, Switzerland
Tel.: (41) 227500680
Real Estate Manangement Services
N.A.I.C.S.: 531210

Tetris Design & Build sprl   **(1)**
Avenue Marnix 23, 1000, Brussels, Belgium
Tel.: (32) 25502617
Real Estate Manangement Services
N.A.I.C.S.: 531210

Tetris Design and Build (Pty) Ltd.   **(1)**
1 Biermann Ave, Rosebank, Johannesburg, 2196, South Africa
Tel.: (27) 105009206
Real Estate Manangement Services
N.A.I.C.S.: 531210

Tetris Design and Build S.R.L   **(1)**
Via San Paolo 7, 20121, Milan, Italy
Tel.: (39) 06696771
Web Site: http://www.it.tetris-db.com
Property Management Services
N.A.I.C.S.: 531312
Philippe Sourdois (Mng Dir)

Tetris Design and Build Sarl   **(1)**
37 Rue du puits Romain, 8070, Bertrange, Luxembourg
Tel.: (352) 46454034
Real Estate Manangement Services
N.A.I.C.S.: 531210

Tetris Projects GmbH   **(1)**
Bockenheimer Landstrasse 55, 60325, Frankfurt am Main, Germany
Tel.: (49) 6920032000
Web Site: http://de.tetris-db.com
Property Management Services
N.A.I.C.S.: 531312

Tetris SAS   **(1)**
110 Esplanade Du General De Gaulle, 92931, Paris, France
Tel.: (33) 149003250
Web Site: http://www.tetris.com
Site Preparation & Related Services
N.A.I.C.S.: 238910

Travis Commercial Real Estate Services, Ltd.   **(1)**
9601 McAllister Fwy Ste 1100, San Antonio, TX 78216
Tel.: (210) 308-9888
Offices of Real Estate Agents & Brokers
N.A.I.C.S.: 531210
Lee Cantu (Engr-Building)

JONES SODA COMPANY

4786 1st Ave S Ste 103, Seattle, WA 98134
Tel.: (206) 624-3357   **WA**
Web Site:
    https://www.jonessoda.com
JSDA—(CNSX)
Rev.: $19,085,000
Assets: $15,102,000
Liabilities: $3,335,000
Net Worth: $11,767,000
Earnings: ($6,404,000)
Emp.: 29
Fiscal Year-end: 12/31/22
Soda & Beverage Mfr
N.A.I.C.S.: 312111
David A. Knight (Pres & CEO)
Maisie Antoniello (VP-Mktg)
Joe Culp (Interim CFO, Principal Acctg Officer & Controller)
Jerry Goldner (Chief Growth Officer)

Subsidiaries:

Jones Soda (Canada) Inc.   **(1)**
1501 Haro St Suite 1007, Vancouver, V6G 1G4, BC, Canada   **(100%)**
Tel.: (604) 682-3013
Soda Drinks Distr
N.A.I.C.S.: 312111

JOURNEY MEDICAL CORPORATION

9237 E Via De Ventura Ste 105, Scottsdale, AZ 85258
Tel.: (480) 434-6670   **DE**
Web Site:
    https://www.journeymedical corp.com
Year Founded: 2014
DERM—(NASDAQ)
Rev.: $73,669,000
Assets: $105,160,000
Liabilities: $88,178,000
Net Worth: $16,982,000
Earnings: ($29,628,000)
Emp.: 20
Fiscal Year-end: 12/31/22
Pharmaceutical Preparation Manufacturing
N.A.I.C.S.: 325412
Claude Maraoui (Pres, CEO & Founder)
Robert Nevin (Chief Comml Officer)
Ramsey Alloush (Gen Counsel)
Lindsay A. Rosenwald (Chm)
Joseph M. Benesch (CFO)

JPMORGAN CHASE & CO.

270 Pk Ave, New York, NY 10179
Web Site:
    https://www.jpmorganchase.com
Year Founded: 1799
JPM—(NYSE)
Rev.: $158,104,000,000
Assets: $3,875,393,000,000
Liabilities: $3,547,515,000,000
Net Worth: $327,878,000,000
Earnings: $49,552,000,000
Emp.: 7,600
Fiscal Year-end: 12/31/23
Investment Management Service
N.A.I.C.S.: 523999
Jamie Dimon (Chm & CEO)

JPMORGAN CHASE & CO.

277 Park Ave, New York, NY 10172-0003
Tel.: (212) 270-2479   **DE**
Web Site:
    https://www.jpmorganchase.com
Year Founded: 1968
JPM—(NYSE)
Rev.: $158,104,000,000
Assets: $3,875,393,000,000
Liabilities: $3,547,515,000,000
Net Worth: $327,878,000,000
Earnings: $47,760,000,000
Emp.: 309,926

Fiscal Year-end: 12/31/23
Bank Holding Company; Commercial & Investment Banking & Other Financial Services
N.A.I.C.S.: 551111
Jerry L. Levens (Mng Dir-Treasury & Securities Solutions Bus)
Carol J. Burt (Founder)
Leslie Wims Morris (Pres-Private Label Captive Fin & Chase Auto)
Michelle M. MacKay (VP-Fixed Income)
Mary Callahan Erdoes (CEO-Asset & Wealth Mgmt)
Douglas B. Petno (CEO-Comml Banking)
Ashley Bacon (Chief Risk Officer)
Lori A. Beer (CIO-Global)
Sanjay Saraf (Executives)
Richard W. Smith (Partner)
Michelle M. MacKay (VP-Fixed Income)
James Dimon (Chm & CEO)
Teresa Heitsenrether (Head-Securities Svcs-Global)
Troy Rohrbaugh (Head-Markets-Global)
Kenneth J. Kencel (Founder-High Yield Fin Bus)
Elena Korablina (Principal Acctg Officer & Controller)
Marc Badrichani (Head)
Jeremy Barnum (CFO)
Peter L. Scher (Vice Chm)

Subsidiaries:

Banc One Capital Holdings LLC   **(1)**
270 Park Ave Fl 35, New York, NY 10017-2014
Tel.: (614) 217-1043
Holding Company
N.A.I.C.S.: 551112

Carr Properties   **(1)**
1615 L St NW Ste 650, Washington, DC 20036
Tel.: (202) 303-3080
Web Site: https://www.carrprop.com
Sales Range: $10-24.9 Million
Emp.: 60
Acquires, Renovates, Owns & Manages Small to Midsized Office Buildings
N.A.I.C.S.: 531110
John A Schissel (Pres)
Michael Comer (Chief Acctg Officer)
James Berkon (Sr VP-Design & Construction)
Alison Wertzler (VP-Design & Construction)
Jason Bockenek (VP-Dev)
Glen Holsinger (VP-Asset Mgmt)
Oliver T. Carr III (CEO)

Chase Card Services, Inc.   **(1)**
360 Bay St, San Francisco, CA 94133
Tel.: (415) 477-9028
Web Site: http://www.chase.com
Credit Card Services
N.A.I.C.S.: 522210

Chase Education Finance   **(1)**
3900 Westerre Pkwy Ste 301, Henrico, VA 23233-1339
Tel.: (540) 374-1600
Web Site: http://www.cfsloans.com
Sales Range: $150-199.9 Million
Emp.: 806
Student Loans
N.A.I.C.S.: 522291
J. Barry Morrow (Pres & CEO)

Chase Home Finance LLC   **(1)**
343 Thornall St Ste 7, Edison, NJ 08837
Tel.: (732) 205-0600
Financial Services
N.A.I.C.S.: 523999

Chase Manhattan Mortgage Corp.   **(1)**
194 Wood Ave S 2nd Fl, Iselin, NJ 08830-2710
Tel.: (732) 452-8627
Web Site: http://www.chase.com
Sales Range: $5-14.9 Billion
Emp.: 9,000
Mortgage Banker

N.A.I.C.S.: 522292

Chase Mortgage Holdings, Inc.   **(1)**
76 S 1250 E, Logan, UT 84321-6770
Tel.: (435) 755-6622
Real Estate Services
N.A.I.C.S.: 525990

Chase Paymentech Solutions, LLC   **(1)**
14221 Dallas Pkwy Bldg 2, Dallas, TX 75254
Tel.: (214) 849-3000
Credit Card Processing Services
N.A.I.C.S.: 522320

Subsidiary (Non-US):

Chase Paymentech Solutions   **(2)**
100 Consilium Place Suite 1700, Toronto, M1H 3E3, ON, Canada
Tel.: (416) 940-6395
Web Site: http://www.chasepaymentech.ca
Sales Range: $75-99.9 Million
Emp.: 200
Credit Card Processing Services
N.A.I.C.S.: 522320

Subsidiary (Domestic):

WePay, Inc.   **(2)**
3223 Hanover St, Palo Alto, CA 94304
Tel.: (855) 469-3729
Web Site: https://go.wepay.com
Online Payment Services
N.A.I.C.S.: 522320
Bill Clerico (Co-Founder & CEO)
Rich Aberman (Co-Founder & Chief Strategy Officer)

Chase Student Loans, Inc.   **(1)**
6510 Old Canton Rd, Ridgeland, MS 39157
Tel.: (866) 306-0868
Web Site:
    http://www.chasestudentloans.com
Banking & Financial Services
N.A.I.C.S.: 523150

Custodial Trust Company   **(1)**
14201 Dallas Pkwy # 2, Dallas, TX 75254-2916
Tel.: (609) 951-2300
Sales Range: $25-49.9 Million
Emp.: 41
Custody & Securities Portfolio Servicing
N.A.I.C.S.: 523991

Dauphine Mauritius Investment Limited   **(1)**
4th Flr Ebene Heights 34 Cybercity, Rose Hill, Ebene, Mauritius
Tel.: (230) 4034409
Investment Management Service
N.A.I.C.S.: 523940

EMC Mortgage Corp.   **(1)**
2780 Lake Vista Dr, Lewisville, TX 75067
Tel.: (972) 956-1000
Sales Range: $400-449.9 Million
Emp.: 1,600
Residential Mortgage Loan Servicing
N.A.I.C.S.: 522310

El Paso Electric Company   **(1)**
Stanton Tower 100 N Stanton, El Paso, TX 79901
Tel.: (915) 543-5711
Web Site: http://www.epelectric.com
Sales Range: $800-899.9 Million
Electric Power Generation & Distribution
N.A.I.C.S.: 221122
Robert Clay Doyle (VP-Transmission & Distr)
H. Wayne Soza (Chief Risk Officer & VP-Compliance)
Steven T. Buraczyk (Sr VP-Ops)
David C. Hawkins (VP-Strategy & Sustainability)
James A. Schichtl (VP-Regulatory Affairs)
Victor F. Rueda (VP-HR & Safety)
Kelly Tomblin (Pres & CEO)
Frank Cassidy (Chm)
Richard Ostberg (CFO)
Cynthia Henry (Gen Counsel & VP)
Cheryl Mele (VP-Customer Care & Corp Comm)
Cynthia S. Prieto (Controller & VP)
Robert Heimer (Dir-Customer Care)

First Republic Bank   **(1)**
Tel.: (415) 392-1400

Web Site: https://www.firstrepublic.com
Rev.: $4,156,699,000
Assets: $116,263,634,000
Liabilities: $106,412,527,000
Net Worth: $9,851,107,000
Earnings: $930,329,000
Emp.: 4,812
Fiscal Year-end: 12/31/2019
Commercial Banking & Investment Management Services
N.A.I.C.S.: 522110
Arthur A. Pensato (Mgr-Wealth-First Republic Investment Mgmt)
Robert Lee Thornton (Pres-First Republic Private Wealth Mgmt & Exec VP)
Cary Biren (Mgr-Wealth-First Republic Investment Mgmt)
Edward Joseph Dobranski (Gen Counsel, Sec & Exec VP)
David C. Tateosian (Pres-First Republic Securities Company)
David B. Lichtman (Chief Credit Officer & Sr Exec VP)
Jason C. Bender (COO & Exec VP)
Michael D. Selfridge (Chief Banking Officer & Sr Exec VP)
Shelley M. Gill (Sr Mng Dir-Foreign Exchange)
Sean F. Bricmont (Mgr-Wealth-First Republic Investment Mgmt)
Barbara Bruser (Mgr-Wealth-First Republic Investment Mgmt)
Rebecca DeCesaro (Mgr-Wealth-First Republic Investment Mgmt)
Tom Egan (Mgr-Wealth-First Republic Investment Mgmt)
Maureen A. Flanagan (Mgr-Wealth-First Republic Investment Mgmt)
Vito Gioiello (Mgr-Wealth-First Republic Investment Mgmt)
Mary W. Hayes (Mgr-Wealth-First Republic Investment Mgmt)
Robin Kopeikin (Mgr-Wealth-First Republic Investment Mgmt)
Gene Martino (Mgr-Wealth-First Republic Investment Mgmt)
Brian P. Nagle (Mgr-Wealth-First Republic Investment Mgmt)
Lucas Newman (Mgr-Wealth-First Republic Investment Mgmt)
Libby Palomeque (Mgr-Wealth-First Republic Investment Mgmt)
Devon Porpora (Mgr-Wealth-First Republic Investment Mgmt)
Nicolas Gentin (Exec VP-First Republic Investment Mgmt-Los Angeles)
Sheri Ann T. Chang Yamaguchi (Mgr-Wealth-First Republic Investment Mgmt)
Fred Przekop (Mgr-Wealth-First Republic Investment Mgmt)
Justin Sean Raymond Tipp (Mgr-Wealth-First Republic Investment Mgmt)
Jeffrey K. Yandle (Mgr-Wealth-First Republic Investment Mgmt)
Bart F. Zitnitsky (Mgr-Wealth-First Republic Investment Mgmt)
Brett W. Berry (Mgr-Wealth-First Republic Investment Mgmt)
Jon S. Bull (Mgr-Wealth-First Republic Investment Mgmt)
Glenn S. Degenaars (Mgr-Wealth-First Republic Investment Mgmt)
Kristin Nicholson (Mgr-Wealth-First Republic Investment Mgmt)
Gary Pollock (Mgr-Wealth-First Republic Investment Mgmt)
Bill Ward (Chief BSA, AML & Security Officer & Exec VP)
Mollie M. Richardson (Chief Admin Officer, Chief People Officer & Exec VP)
Theresa Allen (Mgr-Wealth-First Republic Investment Mgmt)
Dan Bessey (Mgr-Wealth-First Republic Investment Mgmt)
Hugh Beecher (Mgr-Wealth-First Republic Investment Mgmt)
Rick Gordon (Mgr-Wealth-First Republic Investment Mgmt)
Tim Woodall (Mgr-Wealth-First Republic Investment Mgmt)
Dustin Raring (Mgr-Wealth-First Republic Investment Mgmt)
Dagny Maidman (Mgr-Wealth-First Republic Investment Mgmt)
Chris Chase (Mgr-Wealth-First Republic Investment Mgmt)
Erik Ralston (Mgr-Wealth-First Republic Investment Mgmt)

Jeffrey Titus (Mgr-Wealth-First Republic Investment Mgmt)
Mark A. Friedman (Mgr-Wealth-First Republic Investment Mgmt)
Mitchell Peters (Mgr-Wealth-First Republic Investment Mgmt)
Mary Kasaris (Sr Exec Mng Dir)
Ronald Weckbacher (Mgr-Wealth-First Republic Investment Mgmt)
Gregory Webster (Mgr-Wealth-First Republic Investment Mgmt)
Stephanie Bontemps (Chief Risk Officer & Exec VP)
Scott D. Finder (Chief Digital Officer & Sr VP)
Justin Gibson (Exec VP)
Shannon Houston (Chief Mktg & Comm Officer & Sr VP)
Jim Hughes (CIO & Exec VP)
Neal Holland (CFO & Exec VP)
James H. Herbert II (Founder & Co-CEO)
James Buckley (Mgr-Wealth-First Republic Investment Mgmt)

Subsidiary (Domestic):

First Republic Investment Management, Inc. (2)
1230 Avenue of the Americas, New York, NY 10020-6601
Tel.: (212) 759-7755
Web Site:
http://www.firstrepublicinvestmentmanagement.com
Sales Range: $10-24.9 Million
Emp.: 40
Investment Services
N.A.I.C.S.: 523940
Michael Martini (VP)
Michael Hickey (Mng Dir)
Paul E. Tramontano (Sr Mng Dir, Portfolio Mgr & Mgr-Wealth)
Vincent Lovoy (Mng Dir & Mgr-Wealth)
Adam MacDonald (Mng Dir & Mgr-Wealth)
Todd Halbrook (Mng Dir & Mgr-Wealth)
Kieran Lynch (Mng Dir/Mgr-Wealth-Paramus)
Jack Inserra (Mng Dir/Mgr-Wealth-Paramus)
Craig Kaufman (Mng Dir/Mgr-Wealth-Paramus)
Joel Kaufman (VP/Mgr-Wealth-Paramus)
Maureen Raihle (Mng Dir & Mgr-Wealth)
John Ver Bockel (Mng Dir & Mgr-Wealth)
Joseph P. Lally (Mng Dir/Mgr-Wealth-Century)
J. Joseph Lally (Mng Dir/Mgr-Wealth-Century)
Sanah Chung (Mng Dir/Mgr-Wealth-Century)
John Barnes (Mng Dir/Mgr-Wealth-Century)
Bob Thornton (Pres)
William W. Marden III (Mng Dir)

First Republic Preferred Capital Corporation (2)
111 Pine St 2nd Fl, San Francisco, CA 94111
Tel.: (415) 392-1400
Web Site: http://www.firstrepublic.com
Real Estate Investment Services
N.A.I.C.S.: 525990

First Republic Securities Company, LLC (2)
111 Pine St, San Francisco, CA 94111
Tel.: (415) 392-1400
Web Site: http://www.firstrepublic.com
Sales Range: $650-699.9 Million
Private Banking Services
N.A.I.C.S.: 523150
Lisa Garey (Mng Dir)

First Republic Trust Company (2)
111 Pine St at Front, San Francisco, CA 94111
Tel.: (415) 392-1400
Web Site: http://www.firstrepublic.com
Sales Range: $1-4.9 Billion
Emp.: 400
Investment Services
N.A.I.C.S.: 523940
Michael J. Harrington (Chm)
Dale A. Smith (CIO & Exec VP)
David C. Tateosian (Pres-First Republic Securities Company)
Jason C. Bender (Sr VP-Fin)

David B. Lichtman (Exec VP & Chief Credit Officer)
Joseph M. Petitti (Exec VP-Sls)
Dianne Snedaker (Exec VP & CMO)
Kelly Johnston (Pres)

First Republic Wealth Advisors, LLC (2)
111 Pine Street, San Francisco, CA 94111
Tel.: (415) 296-5709
Web Site: http://www.firstrepublic.com
Sales Range: $100-124.9 Million
Emp.: 50
Wealth Management Services
N.A.I.C.S.: 523940

HCP Properties, Inc. (1)
3760 Kilroy Airport Way Ste 300, Long Beach, CA 90806
Tel.: (562) 733-5100
Web Site: http://www.hcpi.com
Real Estate Services
N.A.I.C.S.: 531190

HMP Properties, Inc. (1)
5388 Discovery Park Blvd Ste 300, Williamsburg, VA 23188
Tel.: (757) 229-9650
Web Site: https://www.hmphotels.com
Emp.: 20
Management Services
N.A.I.C.S.: 541618
Hitesh M. Patel (CEO & Dir-Dev)
Divya H. Patel (Dir-Interior Design)
Kimberly Armstead (VP-Ops & Revenue)
Lewis Tedesco (Sr Dir-Sls & Mktg-Reg)
Ginger Jenkins (Reg Dir-Sls-Market)
Kathy McKinney (Acct Mgr)
John Yannitello (Mgr-Construction)

Joint Venture (Domestic):

SouthWest Water Company (2)
1 Wilshire Bldg 624 S Grand Ave Ste 2900, Los Angeles, CA 90017
Tel.: (213) 929-1800
Web Site: http://www.southwestwater.com
Sales Range: $200-249.9 Million
Holding Company; Owner of Water & Wastewater Management Operations
N.A.I.C.S.: 221310
Anton C. Garnier (Pres & CEO)
Michael O. Quinn (Mng Dir-West Utilities)

Subsidiary (Domestic):

SWWC Utilities, Inc., (3)
9511 Ranch Rd 620 N, Austin, TX 78726-2908
Tel.: (512) 335-7580
Web Site: http://www.swwc.com
Water & Wastewater Utility Services
N.A.I.C.S.: 221310

Suburban Water Systems (3)
1325 N Grand Ave Ste 100, Covina, CA 91724-3603
Tel.: (626) 543-2640
Web Site: https://www.swwc.com
Sales Range: $50-74.9 Million
Water Utility Services
N.A.I.C.S.: 221310

Windermere Utility Company (3)
2700 Pecan St W Ste 430, Pflugerville, TX 78660
Tel.: (713) 405-1717
Web Site: http://www.swwc.com
Water Management Operations
N.A.I.C.S.: 221310

Highbridge Capital Management, LLC (1)
277 Park Ave 23rd Fl, New York, NY 10172
Tel.: (212) 287-2500
Web Site: https://www.highbridge.com
Sales Range: $1-4.9 Billion
Assets: $21,000,000,000
Emp.: 150
Investment Fund Management Services
N.A.I.C.S.: 523940

Subsidiary (Domestic):

Currax Holdings LLC (2)
10 N Park Pl Ste 201, Morristown, NJ 07960
Tel.: (800) 793-2145
Web Site: http://www.curraxpharma.com
Holding Company

N.A.I.C.S.: 551112

Subsidiary (Domestic):

Currax Holdings USA LLC (3)
10 N Park Pl Ste 201, Morristown, NJ 07960
Tel.: (800) 793-2145
Holding Company
N.A.I.C.S.: 551112

Subsidiary (Domestic):

Currax Pharmaceuticals LLC (4)
155 Franklin Rd Ste 450, Brentwood, TN 37027
Web Site: https://www.curraxpharma.com
Pharmaceuticals Product Mfr
N.A.I.C.S.: 325412
George Hampton (Pres)
Michael Kyle (Chief Medical Officer)
Hope Mueller (Sr VP)
Laura Lustig (VP)
Aaron Chesnut (VP)

Subsidiary (Non-US):

Gavea Investimentos Ltda. (2)
R Jeronimo da Veiga 384 - 12th floor, Itaim Bibi, Sao Paulo, 04536-001, Brazil (55%)
Tel.: (55) 1135269100
Web Site: https://www.gaveainvest.com.br
Sales Range: $5-14.9 Billion
Emp.: 68
Asset Management
N.A.I.C.S.: 523999
Luiz H. Fraga (Co-Founder & Co-CIO-Private Equity)
Gabriel Srour (Co-CIO-Hedge Funds)
Bernardo Carvalho (Mng Dir)

Highbridge Capital Management (Hong Kong), Limited (2)
14/F Rm 1401 14th floor York House the Landmark 15 Queens Rd Central, Hong Kong, China (Hong Kong)
Tel.: (852) 21627100
Web Site: http://www.highbridge.com
Sales Range: $25-49.9 Million
Emp.: 15
Financial Investment Services
N.A.I.C.S.: 523999
Arjun Menon (Mng Dir)

Highbridge Capital Management (UK), Ltd. (2)
5 Tudor Street 2nd Floor, 1 May Fair, London, EC4Y 0JP, United Kingdom
Tel.: (44) 2074846000
Web Site: http://www.highbridge.com
Investment Management Service
N.A.I.C.S.: 523940

Joint Venture (Domestic):

Nalpropion Pharmaceuticals, Inc. (2)
3344 N Torrey Pines Ct Ste 200, La Jolla, CA 92037
Tel.: (858) 875-8600
Web Site: http://www.nalpropion.com
Pharmaceuticals Mfr
N.A.I.C.S.: 325412
John Sedor (Chm & CEO)
Kenneth R. Pina (Exec VP)
Angus Smith (Exec VP)
Salma Jutt (Chief Comml Officer & Sr VP)
Amy Fox (VP-HR)
Amy Halseth (VP-Clinical Dev)
Kris Hanson (VP-Legal & Compliance)

InstaMed Holdings, Inc. (1)
1528 Walnut St Ste 1902, Philadelphia, PA 19102
Tel.: (215) 789-3680
Web Site: http://www.instamed.com
Healthcare Payment Platform
N.A.I.C.S.: 522320
Bill Marvin (Co-Founder, Pres & CEO)
Deirdre Ruttle (CMO)
Jeff Lin (Chief Product Officer)
Richard M. Croswell (COO)
Jon Neal (Head-Bus Dev)
Mark Krapels (Chief Information Security & Controls Officer)
Chris Seib (Co-Founder & CTO)

Subsidiary (Domestic):

InstaMed Communications, LLC (2)

JPMorgan Chase & Co.—(Continued)

1880 John F Kennedy Blvd 12th Fl, Philadelphia, PA 19103
Tel.: (215) 789-3680
Web Site: https://www.instamed.com
Telecommunication Servicesb
N.A.I.C.S.: 517810
Mark Krapels *(Chief Information Security & Compliance Officer)*
Richard M. Croswell *(COO)*
Bill Marvin *(Co-Founder, Pres & CEO)*

J.P. Morgan (China) Venture Capital Investment Company Limited (1)
20th Floor North Beijing Winland International Finance Center No 7, Jinrong Street Xicheng, Beijing, 100033, China
Tel.: (86) 1059318500
Investment Management Service
N.A.I.C.S.: 523940

J.P. Morgan (S.E.A.) Limited (1)
88 Market Street 30-00, 168 Robinson Road, Singapore, 048948, Singapore
Tel.: (65) 68822888
Financial Investment Services
N.A.I.C.S.: 523999
Matthew McGrath *(Head-Mktg)*

J.P. Morgan AG (1)
TaunusTurm Taunustor 1, 60310, Frankfurt, Germany
Tel.: (49) 6971240
Web Site: http://www.jpmorgan.com
Financial Investment Services
N.A.I.C.S.: 523999

J.P. Morgan Administrative Services Australia Limited (1)
Level 18 85 Castlereagh Street, Sydney, 2000, NSW, Australia
Tel.: (61) 290038888
Web Site: http://www.jpmorgan.com
Financial Investment Services
N.A.I.C.S.: 523999

J.P. Morgan Australia Group Pty Limited (1)
L 32 Grosvenor Pl 225 George St, Sydney, 2000, NSW, Australia
Tel.: (61) 292504111
Financial Services
N.A.I.C.S.: 523999
Paul Uren *(CEO-Australia & New Zealand)*

J.P. Morgan Bank (Ireland) plc (1)
JP Morgan House Intl Financial Services Ctr, Dublin, Ireland
Tel.: (353) 16123203
Emp.: 20
Financial Services
N.A.I.C.S.: 523999

J.P. Morgan Bank Canada (1)
200 Bay Street Royal Bank Plaza Suite 1800 South Tower, 200 Bay Street, Toronto, M5J 2J2, ON, Canada
Tel.: (416) 981-9200
Web Site: http://www.jpmorgan.com
Investment Banking Services
N.A.I.C.S.: 523150

J.P. Morgan Bank Luxembourg S.A. (1)
European Bank and Business Centre 6 route de Treves, Senningerberg, 2633, Luxembourg, 2633, Luxembourg
Tel.: (352) 4626851
Web Site: http://www.jpmorgan.com
Financial Consulting Services
N.A.I.C.S.: 541611

J.P. Morgan Broking (Hong Kong) Limited (1)
27/F Chater House 8 Connaught Road, Central, Hong Kong, China (Hong Kong)
Tel.: (852) 28001000
Financial Security Brokerage Services
N.A.I.C.S.: 523150

J.P. Morgan Chase Community Development Group (1)
1 Chase Manhattan Plz Fl 6, New York, NY 10005-1401 **(100%)**
Tel.: (212) 552-1798
Web Site: http://www.jpmorganchase.com
Sales Range: $25-49.9 Million
Emp.: 150
Community Development Company

N.A.I.C.S.: 813410

J.P. Morgan Chile Limitada (1)
Apoqimdo, Santiago, 2827, Chile
Tel.: (56) 24255100
Financial Investment Services
N.A.I.C.S.: 523999

J.P. Morgan Clearing Corp. (1)
1 Metrotech Ctr N Lobby 4, Brooklyn, NY 11201
Tel.: (212) 272-1000
Sales Range: $125-149.9 Million
Emp.: 2,000
Securities Investment Clearing Services
N.A.I.C.S.: 522320
Michael Minikes *(CEO)*
Joe Triarsi *(Mng Dir)*

J.P. Morgan Corretora de Cambio e Valores Mobiliarios S.A. (1)
Avenida Brigadeiro Faria Lima n 3729 13 andar parte Itaim Bibi, Sao Paulo, 04538-905, Brazil
Tel.: (55) 1131057942
Financial Investment Services
N.A.I.C.S.: 523999

J.P. Morgan Equities Limited (1)
1 Fricker Road, Illovo, 2197, Gauteng, South Africa
Tel.: (27) 115070300
Financial Services
N.A.I.C.S.: 523999

J.P. Morgan Europe Limited (1)
25 Bank Street, Canary Wharf, London, E14 5JP, United Kingdom
Tel.: (44) 2077772000
Web Site: http://www.jpmorgan.com
Emp.: 14,000
Financial Investment Services
N.A.I.C.S.: 523999

J.P. Morgan Fonds Services GmbH (1)
Junghofstrasse 14, 60311, Frankfurt am Main, Germany **(100%)**
Tel.: (49) 6971241150
Web Site: http://www.jpmorgan.com
Sales Range: $1-4.9 Billion
Emp.: 450
Financial Services
N.A.I.C.S.: 523999

J.P. Morgan Futures Inc. (1)
4 New York Plz, New York, NY 10004-2413 **(100%)**
Tel.: (212) 623-3336
Web Site: http://www.jpmorganchase.com
Sales Range: $100-124.9 Million
Emp.: 70
Futures Brokers & Dealers
N.A.I.C.S.: 523160

J.P. Morgan Grupo Financiero S.A. de C.V. (1)
Paseo de las Palmas No 405 Piso 16 Col Lomas de Chapultepec, PO Box 1415Y16, Delegacion Miguel Hidalgo, 11000, Mexico, 11000, DF, Mexico
Tel.: (52) 55409333
Web Site: http://www.jpmorganchase.com
Bank Holding Company
N.A.I.C.S.: 551111

Subsidiary (Domestic):

Banco J.P. Morgan S.A., Institucion de Banca Multiple, J.P. Morgan Grupo Financiero (2)
Paseo De Las Palmas No 405 Piso 16, Ciudad De Mexico, Mexico, 11000, Distrito Federal, Mexico
Tel.: (52) 5555409333
Financial Consulting Services
N.A.I.C.S.: 541611

J.P. Morgan Investment Management (1)
270 Park Ave, New York, NY 10154-0004
Tel.: (212) 464-1900
Web Site: http://www.jpmorganchase.com
Sales Range: $150-199.9 Million
Emp.: 400
Investment Fund Management Services
N.A.I.C.S.: 525910

Subsidiary (Domestic):

J.P. Morgan Research Total Return Fund LLC (2)

270 Park Ave, New York, NY 10017
Tel.: (212) 648-0757
Investment Management Service
N.A.I.C.S.: 523940

J.P. Morgan Nominees Australia Limited (1)
L 32 225 George St, Sydney, 2000, NSW, Australia
Tel.: (61) 292504111
Emp.: 20
Financial Services
N.A.I.C.S.: 523999

J.P. Morgan Partners, LLC (1)
1221 Avenue Of The Americas, New York, NY 10020
Tel.: (212) 899-3400
Web Site: http://www.jpmorganpartners.com
Consumer Lending
N.A.I.C.S.: 522291
Jeffrey C. Walker *(CEO)*

J.P. Morgan Securities (Asia Pacific) Limited (1)
Chater House 25/F 8 Connaught Road, Central, Hong Kong, China (Hong Kong)
Tel.: (852) 28007878
Web Site: http://www.jpmorgan.com
Financial Security Brokerage Services
N.A.I.C.S.: 523150

J.P. Morgan Securities Asia Pte. Ltd. (1)
168 Robinson Road 17th Floor Capital Tower, Singapore, 068912, Bangrak, Singapore **(87%)**
Tel.: (65) 68822888
Web Site: http://www.jpmorgan.com
Sales Range: $1-4.9 Billion
Emp.: 700
Security Brokerage Services
N.A.I.C.S.: 523150

J.P. Morgan Securities LLC (1)
925 Westchester Ave Ste 405, White Plains, NY 10604
Tel.: (914) 899-5999
Web Site:
    http://www.jpmorgansecurities.com
Financial Investment Services
N.A.I.C.S.: 523999

J.P. Morgan Securities Singapore Private Limited (1)
88 Market Street 30-00, Singapore, 048948, Singapore
Tel.: (65) 68822888
Financial Services
N.A.I.C.S.: 523999

J.P. Morgan Securities plc (1)
25 Bank Street, Canary Wharf, London, E14 5JP, United Kingdom
Tel.: (44) 2077772000
Financial Security Brokerage Services
N.A.I.C.S.: 523150

J.P. Morgan Services (Malaysia) Sdn. Bhd. (1)
Level 18 Integra Tower The Intermark 348 Jalan Tun Razak, 50400, Kuala Lumpur, Malaysia
Tel.: (60) 327180500
Financial Consulting Services
N.A.I.C.S.: 541611

J.P. Morgan Services Inc. (1)
500 Stanton Christiana Rd, Newark, DE 19713
Tel.: (302) 634-1000
Emp.: 1,000
Financial Investment Services
N.A.I.C.S.: 523999

J.P. Morgan Services India Private Limited (1)
Prestige Tech Park Next To Innovative Multiplex Outer Ring Road, Sarjapur Main Road Marathahalli, Bengaluru, India
Tel.: (91) 8044160000
Financial Consulting Services
N.A.I.C.S.: 541611

J.P. Morgan Ventures Energy Corporation (1)
383 Madison Ave 10th Fl, New York, NY 10017
Tel.: (713) 236-3000
Financial Investment Services

N.A.I.C.S.: 523999

J.P.Morgan Services India Private Limited (1)
JP Morgan Tower Off CST Road Kalina Santacruz East, Mumbai, 400 098, India
Tel.: (91) 2261573000
Commercial Banking Services
N.A.I.C.S.: 522110

JPMP Capital Corp. (1)
60 Wall St 14th Fl, New York, NY, 10017
Tel.: (212) 483-2323
Financial Consulting Services
N.A.I.C.S.: 541611

JPMorgan Asset Management Holdings Inc. (1)
522 5th Ave, New York, NY 10036-7601 **(100%)**
Tel.: (212) 483-2323
Web Site: http://www.jpmorgan.com
Sales Range: $550-599.9 Million
Emp.: 1,000
International Brokers, Money Management, Investment Bankers
N.A.I.C.S.: 525910
Lauren M. Tyler *(Exec VP & Head-HR-Global)*
George Gatch *(CEO)*
Jared B. Gross *(Head-Institutional Portfolio Strategy)*
Keith Cahill *(Head-North America)*

Subsidiary (Domestic):

Campbell Global, LLC (2)
1 SW Columbia Ste 1700, Portland, OR 97258
Tel.: (503) 275-9675
Web Site: http://www.campbellglobal.com
Investment Services
N.A.I.C.S.: 113110
Duncan Campbell *(Founder)*
John S. Gilleland *(Chm & CEO)*
Stan Renecker *(Mng Dir-Acquisitions)*
Dave Rumker *(Mng Dir & Chief Investment Officer)*
Angie Davis *(Pres)*
Mark Oergel *(Reg Mgr-Northwest)*
Mark Simmons *(Mng Dir & CFO)*
Gary L. Combs *(Vice Chm & Mng Dir)*
Stephen Levesque *(Mng Dir-Ops)*
Matthew Thuman *(Reg Mgr-Southern)*
Ian Aguilar *(CTO & Dir)*
Matt Armstrong *(Dir-Resource Plng)*
Guadalupe Folegatti *(Mgr-Strategic Solutions)*
Andy Hoyt *(Dir-Fin & Strategy)*
Steven King *(Dir-Global Bus Strategy)*
John Miller *(Chief Compliance Officer & Assoc Gen Counsel)*
Matt Muller *(Mgr-Budget & Forecast)*
Nell Radzins *(Dir-Acctg)*
Rhonda Stephens *(Dir-HR)*
Kyle Stinchfield *(Gen Counsel)*
Jenny West *(Dir-Strategic Solutions)*
Carrie Wheeler *(Mgr-Log Acctg)*

Subsidiary (Non-US):

J.P. Morgan (Suisse) SA (2)
Dreikonigstrasse 37, 8002, Zurich, 8002, Switzerland
Tel.: (41) 445674500
Web Site: http://www.jpmam.ch
International Brokers, Money Management, Investment Bankers
N.A.I.C.S.: 523910

J.P. Morgan Asset Management (2)
14 Place Vendome, 75001, Paris, France **(100%)**
Tel.: (33) 140154500
Web Site: https://www.jpmorgan.com
Sales Range: $150-199.9 Million
Emp.: 120
International Brokers, Money Management, Investment Bankers
N.A.I.C.S.: 523160
James Peagam *(Head-Global Insurance Solutions-Europe)*
Mike O'Brien *(Global Head-Institutional Bus)*
Maria Ryan *(Head--Global Fixed Income Bus,EMEA)*
Ashbel C. Williams *(Vice Chm)*

Subsidiary (Domestic):

JPMorgan Asset Management (Asia) Inc. (2)

270 Park Ave Ste 12, New York, NY 10017
Tel.: (212) 483-2323
Asset Management Services
N.A.I.C.S.: 531390

Subsidiary (Non-US):

JPMorgan Asset Management (Korea) Company Limited (3)
Jeong-dong 34-35, Jung-gu, Seoul, 100-120, Korea (South)
Tel.: (82) 27585200
Web Site: http://www.jpmorgan.co.kr
Emp.: 30
Financial Investment Services
N.A.I.C.S.: 523999

JPMorgan Asset Management (Singapore) Limited (3)
88 Market Street 30th Floor, CapitaSpring, Singapore, 048948, Singapore
Tel.: (65) 68821328
Web Site: https://am.jpmorgan.com
Asset Management Services
N.A.I.C.S.: 531390

JPMorgan Asset Management (Taiwan) Limited (3)
3F & 17F 65 Tun Hua S Rd Sec 2, 17th Floor cum 65 67 69 71 Section 65, Taipei, 10682, Taiwan
Tel.: (886) 227558686
Financial Investment Services
N.A.I.C.S.: 523999

JPMorgan Asset Management India Private Limited (3)
JP Morgan Tower Off CST Road Kalina, Santacruz East, Mumbai, 400098, India
Tel.: (91) 2261573000
Web Site: http://www.jpmorganmf.com
Emp.: 5,700
Asset Management Services
N.A.I.C.S.: 531390
Kalpana Morparia *(Chm)*

Subsidiary (Non-US):

JPMorgan Asset Management (Australia) Limited (2)
Level 31 101 Collins Street, Melbourne, 3000, VIC, Australia
Tel.: (61) 396334000
Web Site: https://am.jpmorgan.com
Emp.: 80
Asset Management Services
N.A.I.C.S.: 531390
Jacqui Crothers *(Mgr-Key Acct-Northern Reg)*

JPMorgan Asset Management (Canada) Inc. (2)
Royal Bank Plaza South Tower Suite 1800 200 Bay Street, Toronto, M5J 2J2, ON, Canada (100%)
Tel.: (416) 981-9200
Sales Range: $25-49.9 Million
Emp.: 5
Investment Advisory & Asset Management Services
N.A.I.C.S.: 523940
Katie Babatsikos *(Mgr-Bus)*
Robert Stark *(Head-Strategic Relationships)*

JPMorgan Asset Management (Japan) Limited (2)
Tokyo Building 7-3 Marunouchi 2-chome, Chiyoda-ku, Tokyo, 100-6432, Japan (100%)
Tel.: (81) 367362000
Asset Management Services
N.A.I.C.S.: 523150

JPMorgan Asset Management (UK) Limited (2)
25 Bank Street Canary Wharf, London, E14 5JP, United Kingdom (100%)
Tel.: (44) 2077424000
Web Site: http://www.jpmorganchase.com
International Brokers, Money Management, Investment Bankers
N.A.I.C.S.: 523910

JPMorgan Asset Management Holdings (Luxembourg) S.a r.l. (2)
Route De Treves 6, Niederanven, 2633, Luxembourg
Tel.: (352) 34103060

Web Site:
http://www.jpmorganassetmanagement.lu
Financial Investment Services
N.A.I.C.S.: 523999

Subsidiary (Domestic):

JPMorgan Asset Management (Europe) S.a.r.l (3)
6 route de Treves, Senningerberg, 2633, Luxembourg, Luxembourg (100%)
Tel.: (352) 4640107280
Web Site: https://am.jpmorgan.com
Sales Range: $150-199.9 Million
Emp.: 350
Asset Management
N.A.I.C.S.: 523940

Subsidiary (Domestic):

JPMorgan Asset Management Luxembourg S.A. (4)
Route De Treves 6, Senningerberg, 2633, Luxembourg
Tel.: (352) 34103060
Web Site:
http://www.jpmorganassetmanagement.lu
Financial Services
N.A.I.C.S.: 523999

Holding (Non-US):

Koole Tanktransport B.V. (4)
Sluispolderweg 67, 1505 HJ, Zaandam, Netherlands
Tel.: (31) 756812812
Web Site: http://www.koole.com
Bulk Chemical Storage & Shipping Services
N.A.I.C.S.: 483111

Joint Venture (Non-US):

Nortegas Energia Distribucion, S.A.U. (4)
Plaza Euskadi 5- Planta 23, 48009, Bilbao, Spain
Tel.: (34) 944035700
Web Site: http://www.nortegas.es
Rev.: $109,384,982
Assets: $3,479,107,707
Liabilities: $2,243,707,972
Net Worth: $1,235,399,735
Earnings: $14,359,946
Emp.: 250
Fiscal Year-end: 12/31/2017
Natural Gas Distribution Services
N.A.I.C.S.: 221210
Alejandro Legarda Zaragueta *(Chm)*

Subsidiary (Domestic):

NED Espana Distribucion Gas, S.A.U. (5)
Calle General Concha 20, 48010, Bilbao, Spain
Tel.: (34) 946 140 020
Web Site: http://www.nortegas.es
Gas Distr
N.A.I.C.S.: 221210

JPMorgan Cazenove Ltd. (1)
25 Bank Street Canary Wharf, London, E14 5JP, United Kingdom
Tel.: (44) 2077772000
Web Site:
http://www.jpmorgancazenove.com
Sales Range: $1-4.9 Billion
Emp.: 600
Investment Banking & Asset Management Services
N.A.I.C.S.: 523150

JPMorgan Chase Bank, Dearborn (1)
18800 Hubbard Dr Ste 101, Dearborn, MI 48126-4296
Tel.: (313) 271-7720
Web Site: http://www.chase.com
Sales Range: $25-49.9 Million
Emp.: 6
Financial Investment Services
N.A.I.C.S.: 523999

JPMorgan Chase Bank, N.A. (1)
270 Park Ave, New York, NY 10172
Tel.: (212) 270-0589
Web Site: http://www.jpmorganchase.com
Sales Range: $250-299.9 Million
Bank Holding Company
N.A.I.C.S.: 551111

J. Albert Smith Jr. *(Chm)*

Subsidiary (Domestic):

Chase Paymentech Solutions, LLC (2)
14221 Dallas Pkwy, Dallas, TX 75254
Tel.: (302) 282-1100
Web Site:
http://www.chasepaymentech.com
Emp.: 499
Credit Card Processing Solutions
N.A.I.C.S.: 522320
Rob Cameron *(Pres)*

Chase Ventures Holdings Inc. (2)
194 Wood Ave S, Iselin, NJ 08830
Tel.: (732) 452-8349
Web Site: http://www.chase.com
Sales Range: $25-49.9 Million
Emp.: 25
Bank Holding Company
N.A.I.C.S.: 551111

J.P. Morgan International Inc. (2)
270 Park Ave, New York, NY 10017-2070 (100%)
Tel.: (212) 270-6000
Web Site: http://www.jpmorganchase.com
Sales Range: $250-299.9 Million
Bank Holding Company
N.A.I.C.S.: 551111

Subsidiary (Non-US):

J.P. Morgan (Suisse) S.A. (3)
Rue du Rhone 35, 1204, Geneva, Switzerland (100%)
Tel.: (41) 227441111
Web Site: http://www.jpmorgan.com
Sales Range: $250-299.9 Million
Emp.: 500
Banking Services
N.A.I.C.S.: 522299

J.P. Morgan Bank (3)
TaunusTurm Taunustor 1, Frankfurt, 60310, Germany (100%)
Tel.: (49) 6971241601
Web Site: http://www.jpmorgan.com
Sales Range: $125-149.9 Million
Emp.: 300
Bank Holding Company
N.A.I.C.S.: 551111
Stephen A. Berenson *(Co-Founder)*

Subsidiary (Domestic):

J.P. Morgan Bank (4)
Taunustar 1, Frankfurt am Main, 60310, Germany (100%)
Tel.: (49) 6971241601
Web Site: http://www.jpmorgan.com
Sales Range: $500-549.9 Million
Emp.: 269
Financial & Banking Services
N.A.I.C.S.: 523999

Subsidiary (Non-US):

J.P. Morgan Bank International (LLC) (3)
10 Butyrsky Val, 125047, Moscow, Russia
Tel.: (7) 4959671000
Web Site: http://www.jpmorgan.ru
Financial Services
N.A.I.C.S.: 523910

J.P. Morgan Chase (UK) Holdings Ltd. (3)
(100%)
Tel.: (44) 2077772000
Web Site: http://www.jpmorgan.com
Sales Range: $250-299.9 Million
Emp.: 4,000
Bank Holding Company
N.A.I.C.S.: 551111

Subsidiary (Non-US):

J.P. Morgan Limited (4)
Tel.: (44) 2077773190
Financial Consulting Services
N.A.I.C.S.: 541611

Subsidiary (Non-US):

J.P. Morgan Securities India Private Limited (3)
J P Morgan Tower Off C S T Road Kalina, Santacruz - East, Mumbai, 400098, Maharashtra, India
Tel.: (91) 2261573000
Web Site: http://www.jpmipl.com
Financial Services
N.A.I.C.S.: 523999

Subsidiary (Domestic):

Paymentech Salem Services, LLC (3)
4 Northeastern Blvd, Salem, NH 03079-5916
Tel.: (603) 896-6000
Financial Investment Services
N.A.I.C.S.: 523999

Subsidiary (Non-US):

Chase Paymentech Europe Limited (4)
EastPoint Plaza 2nd Floor EastPoint Business Park, Dublin, 3, Ireland
Tel.: (353) 17262909
Web Site:
http://www.merchantservices.chase.com
Credit Card Processing Services
N.A.I.C.S.: 522320

Branch (Domestic):

JPMorgan Chase - Midwest Regional Office (2)
10 S Dearborn, Chicago, IL 60603
Tel.: (312) 732-5177
Web Site: http://www.jpmorganchase.com
Retail Financial & Commercial Banking Services
N.A.I.C.S.: 523910

JPMorgan Chase - Southern Regional Office (2)
6303 N Portland Ave Fl 1, Oklahoma City, OK 73112
Tel.: (405) 231-3555
Web Site: http://www.chase.com
Sales Range: $150-199.9 Million
Emp.: 300
Commercial Banking Services
N.A.I.C.S.: 522110

JPMorgan Chase - Western Regional Office (2)
560 Mission St Ste 2400, San Francisco, CA 94105
Tel.: (415) 772-2900
Web Site: http://www.jpmorganchase.com
Rev.: $9,500,000
Emp.: 450
Full-Service Banking
N.A.I.C.S.: 523150

Subsidiary (Non-US):

JPMorgan Chase Bank (China) Company Limited (2)
19th Floor Beijing Winland International Finance Center No 7, Jinrong Street Xicheng District, Beijing, 100033, China
Tel.: (86) 1059318000
Sales Range: $75-99.9 Million
Emp.: 200
Financial Investment Services
N.A.I.C.S.: 523999
Frank Gong *(Chm-Investment Banking)*

Subsidiary (Domestic):

JPMorgan Chase Bank, N.A. - Louisville (2)
416 W Jefferson St, Louisville, KY 40202
Tel.: (502) 566-2002
Web Site: http://www.jpmorganchase.com
Sales Range: $150-199.9 Million
Emp.: 1,140
Commercial Banking Services
N.A.I.C.S.: 522110

JPMorgan Funds (Asia) Limited (1)
19th Floor Chater House 8 Connaught Road Central, Hong Kong, China (Hong Kong)
Tel.: (852) 22651188
Web Site: http://www.jpmorganam.com.hk
Financial Services
N.A.I.C.S.: 523999

JPMorgan Securities Japan Co., Ltd. (1)
Tokyo Building 2-7-3 Marunouchi, Chiyoda-ku, Tokyo, 100-6432, Japan

JPMorgan Chase & Co.—(Continued)

Tel.: (81) 367361111
Web Site: https://www.jpmorgan.co.jp
Financial Investment Services
N.A.I.C.S.: 523999

JPMorgan Servicios Auxiliares,
S.A. **(1)**
Calle Jose Ortega Y Gasset 29 - 2, Madrid,
28006, Spain
Tel.: (34) 914356041
Sales Range: $550-599.9 Million
Emp.: 200
Financial Services
N.A.I.C.S.: 523999

JPMorgan Trust Company (Bahamas)
Limited **(1)**
Bahamas Financial Centre 3rd Floor Shirley
& Charlotte Streets, PO Box N4899, Nas-
sau, New Providence, Bahamas **(100%)**
Tel.: (242) 3978712
Web Site: http://www.jpmorgan.com
Sales Range: $25-49.9 Million
Emp.: 100
Commercial Banking & Trust Services
N.A.I.C.S.: 522110

Madison Tax Capital, LLC **(1)**
5619 DTC Pkwy Ste 800, Greenwood Vil-
lage, CO 80111
Tel.: (303) 597-2000
Web Site: http://www.madisoncap.com
Emp.: 30
Financial Investment Services
N.A.I.C.S.: 523999

Max Recovery Limited **(1)**
25 Bank Street Canary Wharf, London, E14
5JP, Dorsetshire, United Kingdom
Tel.: (44) 8454983939
Financial Consulting Services
N.A.I.C.S.: 541611

MorServ, Inc. **(1)**
343 Thornall St, Edison, NJ 07675
Tel.: (212) 552-1358
Mortgage Loan Brokerage Services
N.A.I.C.S.: 522310

Neovest, Inc. **(1)**
1145 S 800 E Ste 310, Orem, UT 84097
Tel.: (212) 622-2724
Web Site: https://www.neovest.com
Financial Services
N.A.I.C.S.: 523999
Jarrett Sydell (Dir-Product Mgmt)

Plymouth Park Tax Services LLC **(1)**
300 Convergence Way Fl 1, Whippany, NJ
07981
Tel.: (973) 793-4811
Web Site: http://www.xspand.com
Real Estate Taxation Services
N.A.I.C.S.: 541213

Robert Fleming Holdings Limited **(1)**
25 Copthall Avenue, London, EC2B 7PQ,
United Kingdom
Tel.: (44) 2076385858
Web Site: http://www.jpmorgan.com
Sales Range: $1-4.9 Billion
Emp.: 500
Financial Investment Services
N.A.I.C.S.: 523999

Security Capital Research & Manage-
ment Incorporated **(1)**
10 S Dearborn St Ste 1400, Chicago, IL
60603 **(100%)**
Tel.: (312) 385-8300
Web Site: http://www.securitycapital.com
Sales Range: $75-99.9 Million
Emp.: 40
Investment Services
N.A.I.C.S.: 523999

South Jersey Industries, Inc. **(1)**
1 S Jersey Plz, Folsom, NJ 08037
Tel.: (609) 561-9000
Web Site: http://www.sjindustries.com
Rev.: $1,991,996,000
Assets: $7,308,672,000
Liabilities: $2,120,222,000
Net Worth: $5,188,450,000
Earnings: $88,091,000
Emp.: 1,173
Fiscal Year-end: 12/31/2021
Holding Company; Natural Gas Distr
N.A.I.C.S.: 551112

Steven R. Cocchi (CFO & Sr VP)
Melissa J. Orsen (Pres-SJI Utilities & Sr
VP)
Eric Stein (Gen Counsel & Sr VP)
Leonard Brinson Jr. (CIO & Sr VP)

Subsidiary (Domestic):

Elizabethtown Gas Company **(2)**
520 Green Ln, Union, NJ 07083 **(100%)**
Web Site:
https://www.elizabethtowngas.com
Natural Gas Distr
N.A.I.C.S.: 221210

South Jersey Energy Solutions,
LLC **(2)**
1 S Jersey Plz Rte 54, Folsom, NJ 08037
Tel.: (609) 561-9000
Holding Company
N.A.I.C.S.: 551112

Subsidiary (Domestic):

Marina Energy LLC **(3)**
1 S Jersey Plz, Folsom, NJ 08037
Tel.: (609) 561-9000
Web Site: http://www.sjindustries.com
Sales Range: $100-124.9 Million
On-Site Energy-Related Projects Operator
N.A.I.C.S.: 561499

South Jersey Energy Company **(3)**
1 S Jersey Plz, Folsom, NJ 08037 **(100%)**
Tel.: (609) 561-9000
Web Site: http://www.sjindustries.com
Sales Range: $10-24.9 Million
Emp.: 6
Natural Gas Distr & Energy Consulting Ser-
vices
N.A.I.C.S.: 221210
Michael J. Renna (Executives)

Subsidiary (Domestic):

SJ EnerTrade, Inc. **(4)**
1 S Jersey Plz, Hammonton, NJ 08037
Tel.: (609) 561-9000
Natural Gas Distr
N.A.I.C.S.: 221210

Subsidiary (Domestic):

South Jersey Energy Services Plus,
LLC **(3)**
420 N 2nd Rd Unit 1, Hammonton, NJ
08037
Tel.: (888) 246-2610
Heating, Air Conditioning & Water Heating
Systems Installation, Maintenance & Ser-
vices
N.A.I.C.S.: 238210

South Jersey Resources Group,
LLC **(3)**
2350 Airport Fwy, Bedford, TX 76022
Tel.: (817) 283-0450
Marketing & Risk Management Services
N.A.I.C.S.: 561499

Subsidiary (Domestic):

South Jersey Gas Company **(2)**
1 S Jersey Plz, Folsom, NJ 08037 **(100%)**
Tel.: (609) 561-9000
Web Site: https://southjerseygas.com
Natural Gas Distr
N.A.I.C.S.: 221210
Brent W. Schomber (Pres & COO)

Division (Domestic):

South Jersey Gas Co. - Glassboro
Division **(3)**
142 S Main St, Glassboro, NJ
08028 **(100%)**
Tel.: (856) 881-7000
Sales Range: $25-49.9 Million
Emp.: 80
Utility Company
N.A.I.C.S.: 221210
Thomas Harrell (Reg Dir)

clearXchange, LLC **(1)**
333 Market St 26th Fl, San Francisco, CA
94105
Tel.: (415) 371-4111
Financial Management Services
N.A.I.C.S.: 541611
Michael J. Kennedy (Co-Founder)
Michael Kennedy (CEO)

cxLoyalty Group, Inc. **(1)**
6 High Ridge Park, Stamford, CT 06905
Tel.: (203) 956-1000
Rev.: $969,400,000
Assets: $766,300,000
Liabilities: $2,305,100,000
Net Worth: ($1,538,800,000)
Earnings: $16,500,000
Emp.: 3,150
Fiscal Year-end: 12/31/2016
Holding Company; Consumer Membership,
Insurance & Package Enhancement Pro-
grams & Services Direct Marketer
N.A.I.C.S.: 551112
Todd H. Siegel (CEO)
Scott Lazear (Pres-Connexions Loyalty)
Brian Fisher (Gen Counsel & Exec VP)
Robert A. Lyons (COO)
Michele Conforti (Pres & Mng Dir)
Robert Dudacek (Pres-Insurance Svcs)
Michael Bush (Dir-PR)
Lori A. Tansley (Chief Acctg Officer & Sr
VP)
Gregory Miller (CFO & Exec VP)
James C. Daly Jr. (Chief HR Officer & Exec
VP)

Subsidiary (Domestic):

Trilegiant Corporation **(2)**
6 High Ridge Park, Stamford, CT 06905
Tel.: (203) 956-1000
Web Site: https://www.trilegiant.com
Rev.: $180,000,000
Emp.: 520
Marketing Consumer Services
N.A.I.C.S.: 561499

cxLoyalty, Inc. **(2)**
6 High Ridge Park, Stamford, CT 06905
Tel.: (804) 217-8090
Web Site: https://www.cxloyalty.com
Rewards & Incentive Programs; Loyalty
Management & Marketing Services
N.A.I.C.S.: 541618

JPX GLOBAL INC.
370 Amapola Ave Ste 200-A, Tor-
rance, CA 90501
Tel.: (424) 358-1046 NV
Year Founded: 2008
JPEX—(OTCIQ)
Emp.: 10
Copper, Molybdenum & Other Mineral
Mining Services
N.A.I.C.S.: 212230
Frank Lkechukwu Igwealor (CFO)
Ambrose Okechukwu Egbuonu (Pres
& CEO)
Chene C. Gardner (Sec)

JTNB BANCORP, INC.
12 Broadway, Jim Thorpe, PA 18229
Tel.: (570) 325-3631
Web Site: https://www.jtnb.com
Year Founded: 1988
JTNB—(OTCIQ)
Bank Holding Company
N.A.I.C.S.: 551111
Craig A. Zurn (Pres & CEO)
Gregory C. Hartman (CFO & Exec
VP)

Subsidiaries:

Jim Thorpe Neighborhood Bank **(1)**
12 Broadway, Jim Thorpe, PA 18229
Tel.: (570) 325-3631
Web Site: http://www.jtnb.com
Commercial Banking
N.A.I.C.S.: 522110
Craig A. Zurn (Pres & CEO)
Gregory C. Hartman (CFO & Exec VP)
Richard T. Kuhn (COO & Exec VP)

JUMA TECHNOLOGY CORP.
154 Toledo St, Farmingdale, NY
11735
Tel.: (631) 300-1000 DE
Year Founded: 2004
JUMT—(OTCIQ)
Telecommunication Services
N.A.I.C.S.: 517111

JUNIATA VALLEY FINANCIAL
CORP.
Bridge and Main St, Mifflintown, PA
17059-0066
Tel.: (717) 436-8211 PA
Web Site:
https://juniatavalley.q4ir.com
Year Founded: 1983
JUVF—(OTCQX)
Rev.: $32,780,000
Assets: $830,875,000
Liabilities: $793,926,000
Net Worth: $36,949,000
Earnings: $8,320,000
Emp.: 124
Fiscal Year-end: 12/31/22
Bank Holding Company
N.A.I.C.S.: 551111
Marcie A. Barber (Pres & CEO)
Gary E. Kelsey (Vice Chm)
Tina J. Smith (Sr VP & Dir-HR-
Juniata Valley Bank)
Jeremiah J. Trout (Sr VP & Mgr-
Lending Div-Juniata Valley Bank)
Lisa M. Synder (Sr VP & Mgr-Credit
Admin-Juniata Valley Bank)
Curtis M. Crouse (Officer-Security, Sr
VP & Mgr-IT-Juniata Valley Bank)
Thomas Weldon (Sr VP)
Brenda A. Brubaker (Sr VP)

Subsidiaries:

The Juniata Valley Bank **(1)**
1 S Main St, Mifflintown, PA 17059
Tel.: (717) 436-8211
Web Site: https://www.jvbonline.com
Sales Range: $10-24.9 Million
Emp.: 50
Commercial Banking
N.A.I.C.S.: 522110
Marcie A. Barber (Pres & CEO)

JUNIPER NETWORKS, INC.
1133 Innovation Way, Sunnyvale, CA
94089
Tel.: (408) 745-2000 DE
Web Site: https://www.juniper.net
Year Founded: 1996
JNPR—(NYSE)
Rev.: $5,564,500,000
Assets: $9,518,500,000
Liabilities: $5,025,800,000
Net Worth: $4,492,700,000
Earnings: $310,200,000
Emp.: 11,144
Fiscal Year-end: 12/31/23
Holding Company; Information Tech-
nology Network Equipment Designer,
Mfr & Whslr
N.A.I.C.S.: 551112
Kevin Hutchins (Sr VP-Strategy &
Corp Dev)
Jean English (CMO & Sr VP)
Rami Rahim (CEO)
Penny Still (Sr Dir-Corp Comm-
Europe, Middle East & Africa)
Michael Marcellin (CMO & Sr VP)
Kenneth B. Miller (CFO & Exec VP)
Brian M. Martin (Gen Counsel, Gen
Counsel & Gen Counsel)
Manoj Leelanivas (COO & Exec VP)
Eva Andres (Chief HR Officer & Sr
VP)
Derrell James (Interim Chief Revenue
Officer & Exec VP-Customer Experi-
ence)
Jonathan Coleman (Dir-NA)
Robin Drago (Mgr-SD-WAN & Con-
nected Security-North America)
Thomas A. Austin (Chief Acctg Offi-
cer, VP & Controller)
Raj Yavatkar (CTO & Sr VP)
Athena Murphy (VP-Transformation)
Sharon Mandell (CIO & Sr VP)
Sujai Hajela (Sr VP-AI-Driven Enter-
prise)

Brad Tallman *(Sr VP-Supply Chain Ops)*
Bill Burtis *(Chief Compliance Officer)*
Kevin Cumming *(Executives)*
Timothy W. Gray *(Chief Compliance Officer & Gen Counsel)*
Joshua Schmidt *(Executives)*
Robert Mobassaly *(Sr VP & Gen Counsel)*
Leslie Moore *(Chief Comm Officer)*
Chris Kaddaras *(Chief Revenue Officer)*
A. E. Natarajan *(Chief Dev Officer)*

Subsidiaries:

Juniper Networks (US), Inc. **(1)**
1133 Innovation Way, Sunnyvale, CA 94089
Tel.: (408) 745-2000
Web Site: https://www.juniper.net
Sales Range: $450-499.9 Million
Emp.: 9,400
Information Technology Network Equipment Designer, Mfr & Whslr
N.A.I.C.S.: 334118

Juniper Networks Holdings International, Inc. **(1)**
1133 Innovation Way, Sunnyvale, CA 94089
Tel.: (408) 745-2000
Web Site: http://www.juniper.net
Holding Company
N.A.I.C.S.: 551112

Subsidiary (Non-US):

JNPR Sweden AB **(2)**
Arstaangfvagen 1 A, Stockholm, 117 43, Sweden **(100%)**
Tel.: (46) 86726800
Sales Range: $1-4.9 Billion
Emp.: 27
Provider of Internet Infrastructure Solutions
N.A.I.C.S.: 334290

Juniper Networks (Hong Kong) Ltd. **(2)**
26/F City Plaza 1 1111 King's Road, 3 Garden Road, Taikoo Shing, China (Hong Kong) **(100%)**
Tel.: (852) 23323636
Web Site: http://www.juniper.net
Sales Range: $25-49.9 Million
Emp.: 80
Provider of Internet Infrastructure Solutions
N.A.I.C.S.: 334290

Juniper Networks (Singapore) Pte. Ltd. **(2)**
3 Anson Road 11-02 Springleaf Tower, Singapore, 079909, Singapore
Tel.: (65) 65113500
Web Site: http://www.juniper.net
Sales Range: $100-124.9 Million
Provider of Internet Infrastructure Solutions
N.A.I.C.S.: 334290

Juniper Networks Australia Ltd. **(2)**
Level 1 181 Miller Street, Sydney, 2060, NSW, Australia **(100%)**
Tel.: (61) 289139800
Web Site: http://www.junipernetworks.com
Sales Range: $25-49.9 Million
Emp.: 100
Provider of Internet Infrastructure Solutions
N.A.I.C.S.: 334290

Juniper Networks B.V. **(2)**
Boeing Ave 240, 1119 PZ, Schiphol-Rijk, 1119 PZ, Netherlands **(100%)**
Tel.: (31) 207125700
Provider of Internet Infrastructure Solutions
N.A.I.C.S.: 334290

Juniper Networks Brazil Ltd. **(2)**
Av Das Nacoes Unidas 12551, World Trade Centre, Sao Paulo, 04578-903, SP, Brazil **(100%)**
Tel.: (55) 1134431468
Web Site: http://www.juniper.net
Sales Range: $100-124.9 Million
Internet Infrastructure Solutions
N.A.I.C.S.: 334290

Juniper Networks China Ltd. **(2)**
Suite 1508 15/F Tower W3 Oriental Plaza Number 1 East Chang An Avenue, Dong Cheng District, Beijing, 100738, China

Tel.: (86) 1065288800
Web Site: http://www.juniper.net
Sales Range: $10-24.9 Million
Emp.: 10
Provider of Internet Infrastructure Solutions
N.A.I.C.S.: 334290

Juniper Networks Finland Oy **(2)**
Kone Bldg Keilasatama 3, 02150, Espoo, Finland **(100%)**
Tel.: (358) 925107320
Web Site: http://www.junipernetworks.com
Sales Range: $1-9.9 Million
Emp.: 4
Provider of Internet Infrastructure Solutions
N.A.I.C.S.: 334290

Juniper Networks France SARL **(2)**
4143 Rue De Villiers, 92200, Neuilly-sur-Seine, France **(100%)**
Tel.: (33) 147756180
Sales Range: $10-24.9 Million
Emp.: 60
Provider of Internet Infrastructure Solutions
N.A.I.C.S.: 334290

Juniper Networks India Private Ltd. **(2)**
Unit 306&307 Trade Centre Building 3rd Floor Off CST Road Bandra West, Bandra Kurla Complex, Mumbai, 400 098, Maharashtra, India
Tel.: (91) 2240843700
Web Site: http://www.juniper.net
Sales Range: $100-124.9 Million
Internet Infrastructure Solutions
N.A.I.C.S.: 334290

Juniper Networks Ireland Ltd. **(2)**
Airside Business Park, Swords, Dublin, Ireland **(100%)**
Tel.: (353) 18903600
Web Site: http://www.juniper.net
Internet Infrastructure Solutions Provider
N.A.I.C.S.: 334290

Juniper Networks Italy S.r.l. **(2)**
Via Robert Koch 1/2 Torre A-14mo Piano, 20152, Milan, Italy
Tel.: (39) 02 3601 4300
Web Site: http://www.juniper.net
Internet Infrastructure Solutions Provider
N.A.I.C.S.: 334290

Juniper Networks Korea, Inc. **(2)**
19th Fl Capital Tower 736-1 Yeoksam 1 Dong, Kangnam-gu, Seoul, 135-983, Korea (South) **(100%)**
Tel.: (82) 234833400
Web Site: http://www.juniper.net
Provider of Internet Infrastructure Solutions
N.A.I.C.S.: 334290

Juniper Networks Malaysia Sdn. Bhd. **(2)**
Level 36 Menara Citibank, 50450, Kuala Lumpur, Malaysia **(100%)**
Tel.: (60) 321697710
Sales Range: $10-24.9 Million
Emp.: 10
Provider of Internet Infrastructure Solutions
N.A.I.C.S.: 334290

Juniper Networks Mexico S.A. de C.V. **(2)**
10th Floor Lagrange Corporate 103 Jose Luis Lagrange Street, Col Los Morales Polanco, Mexico, 11510, CP, Mexico **(100%)**
Tel.: (52) 5547395026
Web Site: http://www.juniper.net
Sales Range: $1-9.9 Million
Emp.: 8
Internet Infrastructure Solutions
N.A.I.C.S.: 334290

Juniper Networks Spain Srl **(2)**
Complejo Mb 1 Planta Baja Mod A Avda Europa 19, Alcobendas, 28108, Madrid, Spain **(100%)**
Tel.: (34) 914 143 400
Web Site: http://www.juniper.net
Sales Range: $10-24.9 Million
Emp.: 13
Internet Infrastructure Solutions
N.A.I.C.S.: 334290

Juniper Networks Switzerland GmbH **(2)**
Leutschenbachstrasse 95, 8050, Zurich, Switzerland

Tel.: (41) 443083811
Web Site: http://www.juniper.net
Internet Infrastructure Services
N.A.I.C.S.: 334290

Juniper Networks Taiwan Limited Co. **(2)**
Section 2 Nanking E Rd Unit B 5th Floor No 167, Taipei, 105, Taiwan **(100%)**
Tel.: (886) 221756300
Sales Range: $10-24.9 Million
Emp.: 25
Provider of Internet Infrastructure Solutions
N.A.I.C.S.: 334290
Eric Lee *(Gen Mgr)*

Juniper Networks U.K. Ltd. **(2)**
1 Aviator Park Station Road, Addlestone, KT15 2PJ, Surrey, United Kingdom **(100%)**
Tel.: (44) 372385500
Web Site: http://www.juniper.net
Provider of Internet Infrastructure Solutions
N.A.I.C.S.: 334290

JUPITER ACQUISITION CORPORATION
11450 SE Dixie Hwy Ste 105, Hobe Sound, FL 33455
Tel.: (212) 207-8884 DE
Year Founded: 2020
JAQC—(NASDAQ)
Rev.: $5,612,563
Assets: $160,162,502
Liabilities: $166,063,415
Net Worth: ($5,900,913)
Earnings: $3,429,080
Emp.: 4
Fiscal Year-end: 12/31/22
Investment Services
N.A.I.C.S.: 523999
James N. Hauslein *(Co-Founder, Chm, CEO & CFO)*
C. Blake Saunders *(VP-Strategy & Dev)*
Gaurav Burman *(Pres)*
Louis G. Zachary Jr. *(Co-Founder)*

JUPITER MARINE INTERNATIONAL HOLDINGS, INC.
1103 12th Ave E, Palmetto, FL 34221
Tel.: (941) 729-5000 FL
Web Site:
https://www.jupitermarine.com
Year Founded: 1989
JMIH—(OTCIQ)
Boat Mfr
N.A.I.C.S.: 336612
Bryan Harris *(Pres)*

JUPITER NEUROSCIENCES, INC.
1001 N US Hwy 1 Ste 504, Jupiter, FL 33477
Tel.: (561) 406-6154 DE
Year Founded: 2016
JUNS—(NASDAQ)
Rev.: $1,126,233
Assets: $549,983
Liabilities: $4,260,961
Net Worth: ($3,710,978)
Earnings: ($1,654,699)
Emp.: 5
Fiscal Year-end: 12/31/20
Biotechnology Research & Development Services
N.A.I.C.S.: 541714
Christer Rosen *(CEO, Co-Founder & Chm)*
Marshall Hayward *(Chief Scientific Officer)*
Alexander Rosen *(Co-Founder & Chief Admin Officer)*
Alison D. Silva *(Pres & Chief Bus Officer)*
Dana Eschenburg Perez *(CFO, Treas & Sec)*

JUPITER WELLNESS ACQUISITION CORP.
1061 E Indiantown Rd Ste 110, Jupiter, FL 33477
Tel.: (561) 244-0710 DE
Year Founded: 2021
JWAC—(NASDAQ)
Investment Services
N.A.I.C.S.: 523999
Brian S. John *(CEO & Chm)*
Ryan Allison *(COO)*
Ke Li *(CFO)*

JUSHI HOLDINGS INC.
301 Yamato Rd Ste 3250, Boca Raton, FL 33431
Tel.: (561) 617-9100 BC
Web Site: https://jushico.com
Year Founded: 2018
JUSHF—(OTC)
Holding Company
N.A.I.C.S.: 551112
Trent Woloveck *(Chief Strategy Officer)*
Todd West *(COO)*
Michelle Mosier *(CFO)*
Matt Leeth *(Exec VP)*
Jon Barack *(Co-Founder & Pres)*
Tobi Lebowitz *(Chief Legal Officer & Sec)*
Andreas Neumann *(Chief Creative Officer)*
Shaunna Patrick *(Chief Comml Officer)*
James Cacioppo *(Co-Founder, Chm & CEO)*

JUSTWORKS, INC.
55 Water St 29th Fl, New York, NY 10041 DE
Web Site: https://www.justworks.com
Year Founded: 2012
JW—(NASDAQ)
Rev.: $982,700,000
Assets: $454,300,000
Liabilities: $499,400,000
Net Worth: ($45,100,000)
Earnings: $10,900,000
Emp.: 768
Fiscal Year-end: 05/31/21
Software Development Services
N.A.I.C.S.: 541511
Isaac Oates *(CEO & Founder)*
Michael Seckle *(Pres & COO)*
Aida Sukys *(CFO & Sr VP)*
Mario Springer *(Sr VP & Gen Counsel)*
Robert Lopez *(Sr VP-Sales-Customer Success)*

KAANAPALI LAND, LLC
900 N Michigan Ave, Chicago, IL 60611
Tel.: (312) 915-1987 DE
Web Site:
http://www.kaanapalidevelopment.com
KANP—(OTCIQ)
Rev.: $9,224,000
Assets: $98,514,000
Liabilities: $18,510,000
Net Worth: $80,004,000
Earnings: $2,850,000
Emp.: 24
Fiscal Year-end: 12/31/22
Land Development & Leasing Services
N.A.I.C.S.: 237210
Stephen Lovelette *(Exec Officer & Principal)*
Gailen A. Hull *(CFO)*

Subsidiaries:

Kaanapali Land Management Corporation **(1)**
275 Lahainaluna Rd, Lahaina, HI 96761

Kaanapali Land, LLC—(Continued)

Tel.: (808) 661-9652
Web Site:
  https://www.kaanapalidevelopment.com
Farm Management Services
N.A.I.C.S.: 115116
Puanani Lindsey (Coord-Project)

**MauiGrown Coffee Distributors,
LLC** (1)
277 Lahainaluna Rd Maui, Lahaina, HI
96761
Tel.: (808) 661-2728
Web Site:
  https://www.mauigrowngreencoffee.com
Coffee Mfr
N.A.I.C.S.: 311920
James Falconer (Pres)

KADANT INC.
1 Technology Park Dr, Westford, MA
01886
Tel.: (978) 776-2000   DE
Web Site: https://www.kadant.com
Year Founded: 1991
KAI—(NYSE)
Rev.: $786,579,000
Assets: $1,132,212,000
Liabilities: $566,596,000
Net Worth: $565,616,000
Earnings: $84,043,000
Emp.: 2,900
Fiscal Year-end: 01/01/22
Papermaking & Paper Recycling
Equipment Mfr
N.A.I.C.S.: 333243
Michael J. McKenney (CFO & Exec
VP)
Jeffrey L. Powell (Pres & CEO)
Deborah S. Selwood (Chief Acctg
Officer & Sr VP)
Peter J. Flynn (VP)
Michael C. Colwell (VP)
Fredrik Han Westerhout (VP)
Thomas Andrew Blanchard (VP)

Subsidiaries:

Amadeo Farell S.A.U. (1)
AV Can Jofresa 73, 08223, Terrassa, Spain
Tel.: (34) 937470900
Millwork Machinery Mfr
N.A.I.C.S.: 314999

**Cogent Industrial Technologies
Ltd.** (1)
Suite 2208-13353 Commerce Parkway,
Richmond, V6V 3A1, BC, Canada
Tel.: (604) 207-8880
Web Site: https://www.cogentind.com
Software Services
N.A.I.C.S.: 541511
Bijan Shams (Pres)
Jonathan Long (Dir-Technical)
Cristian Zaharia (Head-Electrical & Power
Sys)

**Dynamic Sealing Technologies,
Inc.** (1)
13829 Jay St NW, Andover, MN 55304
Tel.: (763) 786-3758
Web Site: http://www.dsti.com
Sales Range: $1-9.9 Million
Emp.: 14
Mechanical Power Transmission Equipment
Mfr
N.A.I.C.S.: 333613
Jeffrey S. Meister (Pres)
Christopher Larson (Mgr-Mktg)
Eric Powell (Project Mgr)

**East Chicago Machine Tool
Corporation** (1)
980 Crown Ct, Crown Point, IN 46307-2732
Tel.: (219) 663-4525
Web Site: https://www.balemaster.com
Rev.: $5,000,000
Emp.: 60
Scrap Paper Handling & Baling Equipment
Mfr
N.A.I.C.S.: 333998

Subsidiary (Non-US):

Balemaster Europe BV (2)

Industriestrat 11, 6361 HD, Nuth, Nether-
lands
Tel.: (31) 45 524 43 43
Web Site: http://www.balemaster.nl
Emp.: 8
Baler & Shredder Mfr
N.A.I.C.S.: 333248
Hans Habets (Gen Mgr)

Johnson-Fluiten S.r.l. (1)
Via Newton 21, 20016, Pero, MI, Italy
Tel.: (39) 023394091
Web Site: https://johnson-fluiten.com
Millwork Machinery Mfr
N.A.I.C.S.: 314999

**KWS Manufacturing Company,
Ltd.** (1)
3041 Conveyor Dr, Burleson, TX 76028-
1857
Tel.: (817) 293-3018
Web Site: http://www.kwsmfg.com
Emp.: 165
Broom, Brush & Mop Mfr
N.A.I.C.S.: 339994
Jim Collins (VP-Sls & Mktg)

Kadant Black Clawson LLC (1)
1425 Kingsview Dr, Lebanon, OH 45036
Tel.: (513) 229-8100
Fiberline Process Equipment Mfr & Supplier
N.A.I.C.S.: 333243

Kadant Canada Corp. (1)
Unit 8 - 15050 - 54A Avenue, Surrey, V3S
5X7, BC, Canada   (100%)
Tel.: (604) 299-3431
Web Site: https://kadantcarmanah.com
Sales Range: $25-49.9 Million
Emp.: 60
Mfr of Process Control Equipment for Paper
Making Machinery
N.A.I.C.S.: 333243

Kadant Fiberline (China) Co. (1)
No 99 Jidianyi Lu, Hi-New Technical Indus-
try Development District, Jining, 272023,
Shandong, China
Tel.: (86) 105372073000
Paper Making Equipment Mfr
N.A.I.C.S.: 333243

**Kadant Johnson Corporation (Wuxi)
Ltd.** (1)
No 11 Hanjiang Road, Wuxi National Hi-
Tech Industrial Development Zone Hanji-
ang, Nanjing, 214028, China
Tel.: (86) 51085212218
Paper Making Equipment Mfr
N.A.I.C.S.: 333243

**Kadant Johnson Deutschland
GmbH** (1)
Elisabeth-Selbert-Str 5b, D - 40764, Lan-
genfeld, Germany
Tel.: (49) 217397490
Emp.: 40
Industrial Machinery & Equipment Mfr
N.A.I.C.S.: 333998

Kadant Johnson Europe BV (1)
Nijverheidslaan 23-25, Postbus 68, 1380
AB, Weesp, Netherlands
Tel.: (31) 29 449 4200
Web Site: http://www.kadant.com
Emp.: 60
Industrial Machinery & Equipment Mfr
N.A.I.C.S.: 333248

Kadant Johnson France B.V. (1)
13 rue Calmette et Guerin, 78500, Sartrou-
ville, France
Tel.: (33) 161043010
Sales Range: $10-24.9 Million
Emp.: 6
Paper Idustry Machinery Mfr
N.A.I.C.S.: 333248
Jose Oliveira (Gen Mgr)

Kadant Johnson Inc. (1)
805 Wood St, Three Rivers, MI 49093
Tel.: (269) 278-1715
Web Site: http://www.kadant.com
Sales Range: $75-99.9 Million
Emp.: 120
Mfr of Rotary Joints, Syphons, Condensate
Systems, Cylinder & Solenoid Valves,
Vacuum Breakers, Separators & Sight Flow
Indicators
N.A.I.C.S.: 332919

Subsidiary (Non-US):

Kadant Australia Pty. Ltd. (2)
8/820 Princes Highway, Springvale, 3171,
VIC, Australia
Tel.: (61) 395460355
Paper Processing Machinery Mfr
N.A.I.C.S.: 333243

Kadant Johnson Argentina S.r.l. (2)
Bartolome Mitre 315, Lomas de Zamora,
1832, Buenos Aires, Argentina   (100%)
Tel.: (54) 1142440519
Paper Idustry Machinery Mfr
N.A.I.C.S.: 333248

Kadant Lamort AB (1)
Kallebasbag 3, PO Box 79, 430 63, Hindas,
Sweden   (100%)
Tel.: (46) 30110550
Web Site: http://www.kadant.com
Sales Range: $10-24.9 Million
Emp.: 8
Provider of Papermaking Services
N.A.I.C.S.: 333243

Kadant Lamort S.A.S. (1)
39 rue de la Fontaine Ludot, CS 30046,
51302, Vitry-le-Francois, Cedex,
France   (100%)
Tel.: (33) 32 674 8080
Web Site: http://www.kadanteurope.com
Sales Range: $25-49.9 Million
Emp.: 140
Industrial Machinery & Equipment Mfr
N.A.I.C.S.: 333248
Alain Serres (Pres)

Subsidiary (Non-US):

Kadant BC- Lamort UK Limited (2)
12 Waterside Court Albany Street, Newport,
NP20 5NT, South Wales, United Kingdom
Tel.: (44) 1633820030
Fiber Processing Services
N.A.I.C.S.: 314999

Kadant M-Clean AB (1)
Birkagatan 36, Huskvarna, 561 33, Sweden
Tel.: (46) 3613 6080
Web Site: http://www.kadant.com
Emp.: 22
Paper Making Equipment Mfr
N.A.I.C.S.: 333243

Kadant Mexico S.A. de C.V. (1)
Apartado Postal 44940 Calle 6 no 2559
Zona Industrial, 44940, Guadalajara,
Jalisco, Mexico   (100%)
Tel.: (52) 333 812 2215
Web Site: http://www.kadant.com
Industrial Machinery & Equipment Mfr
N.A.I.C.S.: 333248

Kadant Nordic AB (1)
Birkagatan 36, 561 33, Huskvarna, Sweden
Tel.: (46) 36136080
Fiber Processing Production Equipment
Distr
N.A.I.C.S.: 424310

Kadant PAAL S.A.U. (1)
Av Can Jofresa 73, 08223, Terrassa, Spain
Tel.: (34) 937470900
Web Site: https://www.kadantpaal.com
Industrial Equipment Mfr
N.A.I.C.S.: 334513

Kadant Paal GmbH (1)
Raiffeisenstrasse 15-17, 49124, Georgs-
marienhutte, Germany
Tel.: (49) 54014880
Web Site: https://kadantpaal.com
Fiber Processing Production Equipment
Distr
N.A.I.C.S.: 424310

Kadant Solutions (1)
35 Sword St, Auburn, MA 01501
Tel.: (508) 791-8171
Web Site: http://www.kadant.com
Distr of Auxiliary Equipment for Paper Ma-
chines
N.A.I.C.S.: 333243

Kadant South America Ltda. (1)
Via Anhanguera km 83 5, Valinhos, Sao
Paulo, Brazil
Tel.: (55) 1938498700
Emp.: 100
Industrial Machinery & Equipment Mfr

N.A.I.C.S.: 333248

Kadant UK Ltd. (1)
Riverside Works Woodhill Road, Bury, BL8
1BD, Lancashire, United Kingdom
Tel.: (44) 161 764 9111
Web Site: http://www.kadant.com
Provider of Papermaking Services
N.A.I.C.S.: 333243

Subsidiary (Non-US):

Radiance SAS (2)
Rue du Moulin de la Rousseliere, 44 800,
Saint-Herblain, France
Tel.: (33) 228000228
Web Site: http://www.radiance-com.fr
Communication Solution Provider
N.A.I.C.S.: 541618

Kadant Unaflex LLC (1)
1715 Hwy 29 S, Anderson, SC 29626
Tel.: (864) 222-1710
Expansion Joint & Hose Mfr
N.A.I.C.S.: 332912

Key Knife Inc. (1)
19100 SW 125th Ct, Tualatin, OR 97062
Tel.: (503) 403-2000
Web Site: http://www.keyknife.com
Sales Range: $10-24.9 Million
Emp.: 80
Mfr of Knives, Agricultural or Industrial
N.A.I.C.S.: 332216
Rick Ornduff (Engr-Mechanical Design)
Christopher McDonald (Pres)
Dan Szydlowski (Mgr-Western United
States)
Pamela Anderson (Sr VP)
Tom Hinchliff (Mgr-Engrg)
Eric Larsen (Mgr-IT)
Les Boatsman (VP-Fin)

Nicholson Manufacturing Ltd. (1)
9896 Galaran Road, PO Box 2128, Sidney,
V8L 3S6, BC, Canada
Tel.: (250) 656-3131
Web Site: https://www.debarking.com
Fiber Production Equipment Parts Mfr &
Distr
N.A.I.C.S.: 314999

**Syntron Material Handling Group,
LLC** (1)
2730 Hwy 145 S, Saltillo, MS 38866
Tel.: (662) 869-5711
Web Site: https://www.syntronmh.com
Emp.: 300
Material Handling Product Mfr
N.A.I.C.S.: 333922

Thermo Fibergen Inc. (1)
81 Wyoming St, Waltham, MA 02451
Tel.: (781) 622-1000
Web Site: http://www.thermofibertek.com
Sales Range: $10-24.9 Million
Emp.: 47
Develops & Commercializes Technologies
to Recover Valuable Components
N.A.I.C.S.: 334513

Subsidiary (Domestic):

Kadant GranTek Inc. (2)
607 Liberty St, Green Bay, WI 54304
Tel.: (920) 435-5200
Web Site: https://kadantgrantek.com
Industrial Machinery & Equipment Mfr
N.A.I.C.S.: 333248

VK North America LLC (1)
3808 N Sullivan Rd Bldg 15 Ste C, Spo-
kane, WA 99216
Tel.: (509) 434-6436
Emp.: 6
Fiber Processing Production Equipment
Distr
N.A.I.C.S.: 424310

Valon Kone OY (1)
Honkatie 5, 08500, Lohja, Finland
Tel.: (358) 1936061
Web Site: https://www.valonkone.com
Millwork Machinery Mfr
N.A.I.C.S.: 314999
Henrik Wikstrom (Mng Dir)
Tomi Hassinen (VP)

Valon Kone OY (1)
Honkatie 5, 08500, Lohja, Finland
Tel.: (358) 1936061

Web Site: https://www.valonkone.com
Millwork Machinery Mfr
N.A.I.C.S.: 314999
Henrik Wikstrom *(Mng Dir)*
Tomi Hassinen *(VP)*

Subsidiary (Non-US):

Valon Kone AB   (2)
Kvarnvagen 7, 821 43, Bollnas, Sweden
Tel.: (46) 27820480
Rotary Barking Machine Mfr
N.A.I.C.S.: 333517

Valon Kone OOO   (2)
Mitrofanjevskoe shosse 10, Saint Peters-
burg, 198095, Russia
Tel.: (7) 8126779850
Web Site: https://www.valonkone.ru
Rotary Barking Machine Mfr
N.A.I.C.S.: 333111

Valon Kone OY   (1)
Honkatie 5, 08500, Lohja, Finland
Tel.: (358) 1936061
Web Site: https://www.valonkone.com
Millwork Machinery Mfr
N.A.I.C.S.: 314999
Henrik Wikstrom *(Mng Dir)*
Tomi Hassinen *(VP)*

Valon Kone OY   (1)
Honkatie 5, 08500, Lohja, Finland
Tel.: (358) 1936061
Web Site: https://www.valonkone.com
Millwork Machinery Mfr
N.A.I.C.S.: 314999
Henrik Wikstrom *(Mng Dir)*
Tomi Hassinen *(VP)*

Subsidiary (Non-US):

Valon Kone AB   (2)
Kvarnvagen 7, 821 43, Bollnas, Sweden
Tel.: (46) 27820480
Rotary Barking Machine Mfr
N.A.I.C.S.: 333517

Valon Kone OOO   (2)
Mitrofanjevskoe shosse 10, Saint Peters-
burg, 198095, Russia
Tel.: (7) 8126779850
Web Site: https://www.valonkone.ru
Rotary Barking Machine Mfr
N.A.I.C.S.: 333111

KADEM SUSTAINABLE IM-
PACT CORPORATION
152 W 57th St 52nd Fl, New York,
NY 10019
Tel.: (212) 218-4092   DE
Web Site: http://www.kademcorp.com
Year Founded: 2020
KSI—(NASDAQ)
Rev.: $5,394,396
Assets: $175,909,703
Liabilities: $189,950,187
Net Worth: ($14,040,484)
Earnings: $3,820,335
Emp.: 3
Fiscal Year-end: 12/31/21
Investment Services
N.A.I.C.S.: 523999
Charles Gassenheimer *(CEO & Sec)*
Golchehreh Abtahian *(CFO)*
Raj Chudgar *(Pres)*
Raymond E. Mabus Jr. *(Chm)*

KAIROS ACQUISITION CORP.
1345 Avenue of the Americas, New
York, NY 10105
Tel.: (917) 783-4057   Ky
Year Founded: 2020
KAIR—(NASDAQ)
Rev.: $10,376,354
Assets: $276,631,029
Liabilities: $296,756,824
Net Worth: ($20,125,795)
Earnings: $8,245,382
Emp.: 2
Fiscal Year-end: 12/31/21
Investment Services
N.A.I.C.S.: 523999

Peter Bang *(Chm & CEO)*
Jerry De St. Paer *(CFO)*

KAISER ALUMINUM CORPO-
RATION
1550 W McEwen Dr Ste 500, Frank-
lin, TN 37067
Tel.: (629) 252-7040   DE
Web Site:
    https://www.kaiseraluminum.com
Year Founded: 1946
KALU—(NASDAQ)
Rev.: $3,427,900,000
Assets: $2,288,800,000
Liabilities: $1,657,600,000
Net Worth: $631,200,000
Earnings: ($29,600,000)
Emp.: 4,000
Fiscal Year-end: 12/31/22
Aluminum Products Producer & Mar-
keter
N.A.I.C.S.: 331313
Melinda C. Ellsworth *(VP-IR & Corp
Comm)*
Jack A. Hockema *(Chm)*
Blain A. Tiffany *(Exec VP-Sls & Mktg)*
Keith A. Harvey *(Pres & CEO)*
Neal E. West *(CFO & Exec VP)*
Ray Parkinson *(Sr VP-Advanced En-
grg)*
Mark R. Krouse *(VP-HR)*
Jason D. Walsh *(Exec VP-Mfg)*
Brant Weaver *(VP-Strategy Dev)*
Vijai Narayan *(Chief Acctg Officer &
VP)*

Subsidiaries:

Imperial Machine & Tool Co.   (1)
8 W Crisman Rd, Columbia, NJ 07832
Tel.: (908) 496-8100
Web Site: http://www.imperialmachine.com
Instrument Mfr for Measuring & Testing
Electricity & Electrical Signals
N.A.I.C.S.: 334515
Michael Clifford *(Dir-Sls)*
Tom Golembeski *(CFO)*
John Shelp *(CTO)*
Robert Preg *(Dir-Quality)*
Joseph Sinclair *(Dir-Additive & Hybrid Pro-
cesses)*
Michael Pereira *(Accountant)*

Kaiser Aluminum Canada
Limited   (1)
3021 Gore Rd, London, N5V 5A9, ON,
Canada
Tel.: (519) 457-3610
Sales Range: $75-99.9 Million
Emp.: 250
Aluminum Extrusions
N.A.I.C.S.: 331314

Kaiser Aluminum Fabricated Prod-
ucts, LLC   (1)
27422 Portola Pkwy Ste 200, Foothill
Ranch, CA 92610-2831
Tel.: (949) 614-1740
Web Site: http://www.kaiseraluminum.com
Aluminium Products Mfr
N.A.I.C.S.: 331318

Subsidiary (Domestic):

Kaiser Aluminum Alexco LLC   (2)
6520 W Allison Rd, Chandler, AZ 85226
Tel.: (520) 796-1206
Sales Range: $10-24.9 Million
Emp.: 130
Aerospace Aluminum Extrusions
N.A.I.C.S.: 331318

Kaiser Aluminum Fabricated
Products   (2)
1547 Helton Dr, Florence, AL 35630
Tel.: (256) 764-4271
Sales Range: $10-24.9 Million
Emp.: 130
Aluminum Alloy Wire, Rod & Bar Mfr
N.A.I.C.S.: 331318

Kaiser Aluminum Fabricated
Products   (2)
4300 Hwy 75 S, Sherman, TX 75091

Tel.: (903) 893-5566
Web Site: http://www.kaiseraluminum.com
Sales Range: $50-74.9 Million
Emp.: 200
Semi-Finished Aluminum Extrusions & Fab-
ricated Products Mfr
N.A.I.C.S.: 331314

Kaiser Aluminum Washington,
LLC   (2)
E 15000 Euclid Ave, Spokane Valley, WA
99216-1813
Tel.: (509) 924-1500
Fabricated Aluminum Mfr
N.A.I.C.S.: 331315

Kaiser Aluminum Warrick, LLC   (1)
4000 W State Rd 66, Newburgh, IN 47629
Tel.: (812) 853-6111
Metal Products Mfr
N.A.I.C.S.: 332313

KAIVAL BRANDS INNOVA-
TIONS GROUP, INC.
401 N Wickham Rd Ste 130, Mel-
bourne, FL 32935   DE
Web Site:
    https://www.kaivalbrands.com
KAVL—(NASDAQ)
Rev.: $13,087,018
Assets: $19,385,006
Liabilities: $5,827,995
Net Worth: $13,557,011
Earnings: ($11,245,272)
Emp.: 18
Fiscal Year-end: 10/31/23
Miscellaneous Financial Investment
Activities
N.A.I.C.S.: 523999
Nirajkumar Patel *(Founder, CEO,
Chief Science Officer & Chief Regula-
tory Officer)*

KALA BIO, INC.
1167 Massachusetts Ave, Arlington,
MA 02476
Tel.: (781) 996-5252   DE
Web Site: https://www.kalarx.com
Year Founded: 2009
KALA—(NASDAQ)
Rev.: $3,892,000
Assets: $86,820,000
Liabilities: $67,846,000
Net Worth: $18,974,000
Earnings: ($44,822,000)
Emp.: 34
Fiscal Year-end: 12/31/22
Research & Development in Nano-
technology
N.A.I.C.S.: 541713
Mary Reumuth *(CFO)*
Robert Paull *(Treas)*
Todd Bazemore *(COO)*
Eric L. Trachtenberg *(Chief Compli-
ance Officer, Gen Counsel & Sec)*
Darius Kharabi *(Chief Bus Officer)*
Mark T. Iwicki *(Pres & CEO)*

KALEIDO BIOSCIENCES, INC.
65 Hayden Ave, Lexington, MA 02421
Tel.: (617) 674-9000   DE
Year Founded: 2015
KLDO—(NASDAQ)
Rev.: $1,104,000
Assets: $50,137,000
Liabilities: $39,530,000
Net Worth: $10,607,000
Earnings: ($90,288,000)
Emp.: 76
Fiscal Year-end: 12/31/21
Biotechnology Research & Develop-
ment Services
N.A.I.C.S.: 541714
Noubar B. Afeyan *(Co-Founder)*
Geoffrey von Maltzahn *(Co-Founder)*
Theodose Melas-Kyriazi *(Chm)*
Clare Fisher *(Chief Bus Officer)*

Kimberly Hocknell *(VP-Technical
Ops)*
Mark Wingertzahn *(Sr VP-R&D &
Head-Dev)*

KALERA PUBLIC LIMITED
COMPANY
7455 Emerald Dunes Dr Ste 2100,
Orlando, FL 32822
Tel.: (407) 559-5536
Web Site: https://kalera.com
KALRQ—(OTCQB)
All Other Miscellaneous Crop Farm-
ing
N.A.I.C.S.: 111998

Subsidiaries:

Agrico Acquisition Corp.   (1)
Boundary Hall Cricket Square, Georgetown,
KY1-1102, Grand Cayman, Cayman Islands
Tel.: (345) 3468005508
Rev.: $19,675
Assets: $147,315,186
Liabilities: $151,859,113
Net Worth: ($4,543,927)
Earnings: ($372,974)
Emp.: 2
Fiscal Year-end: 12/31/2021
Investment Services
N.A.I.C.S.: 523999
Brent De Jong *(Chm & CEO)*
Roberto Perez Silva *(CFO)*

KALEYRA, INC.
85 Broad St, New York, NY 10004
Tel.: (39) 022885841   DE
Web Site:
    http://investors.kaleyra.com
Year Founded: 2017
KLR—(NYSE)
Rev.: $339,168,000
Assets: $370,173,000
Liabilities: $327,960,000
Net Worth: $42,213,000
Earnings: ($98,528,000)
Emp.: 675
Fiscal Year-end: 12/31/22
Investment Services
N.A.I.C.S.: 523999
Mauro Carobene *(Chief Bus Officer &
Exec VP)*
Avishay S. Katz *(Chm)*
Dario Calogero *(Founder & CEO)*
Giacomo Dall'Aglio *(CFO)*
Mauro Carobene *(Chief Bus Officer)*

KALTURA, INC.
860 Broadway 3rd Fl, New York, NY
10003
Tel.: (646) 290-5445   DE
Web Site: https://corp.kaltura.com
Year Founded: 2006
KLTR—(NASDAQ)
Rev.: $175,172,000
Assets: $183,736,000
Liabilities: $153,416,000
Net Worth: $30,320,000
Earnings: ($46,366,000)
Emp.: 580
Fiscal Year-end: 12/31/23
Software Development Services
N.A.I.C.S.: 541511
John N. Doherty *(CFO & Principal
Acctg Officer)*
Ron Yekutiel *(Co-Founder, Chm, Pres
& CEO)*
Shay David *(Co-Founder)*
Michal Tsur *(Co-Founder)*
Eran Etam *(Co-Founder)*
Sigal Srur *(Chief HR Officer)*
Zohar Babin *(Exec VP)*
Renan Gutman *(Exec VP)*
Claire Rotshten *(Exec VP)*
Liad Eshkar *(Exec VP)*
Zvi Maayan *(Gen Counsel)*

Subsidiaries:

Kaltura Ltd.   (1)

Kaltura, Inc.—(Continued)

Ha-Yarkon Street 2 10th Floor, Bnei Brak,
5126012, Israel
Tel.: (972) 37512995
Software Development Services
N.A.I.C.S.: 541511

KALVISTA PHARMACEUTI-CALS, INC.
55 Cambridge Pkwy Ste 901 E, Cambridge, MA 02142
Tel.: (857) 999-0075   **DE**
Web Site: https://www.kalvista.com
Year Founded: 2004
KALV—(NASDAQ)
Rev.: $13,801,000
Assets: $235,404,000
Liabilities: $28,822,000
Net Worth: $206,582,000
Earnings: ($126,644,000)
Emp.: 150
Fiscal Year-end: 04/30/24
Pharmaceuticals Mfr
N.A.I.C.S.: 325412
Brian J. G. Pereira *(Chm)*
Thomas Andrew Crockett *(Co-Founder)*
Benjamin L. Palleiko *(CEO & Principal Fin Officer)*
Edward P. Feener *(Co-Founder & Chief Scientific Officer)*
Christopher M. Yea *(Chief Dev Officer)*
Michael D. Smith *(Sr VP-Development)*
Nicole Sweeny *(Chief Comml Officer)*
Paul K. Audhya *(Chief Medical Officer)*
Jarrod Aldom *(VP-Corp Comm)*
Ryan Baker *(Head-IR)*
Brian Piekos *(CFO)*

KANSAS CITY LIFE INSURANCE COMPANY
3520 Broadway, Kansas City, MO
64121 9139
Tel.: (816) 753-7000   **MO**
Web Site: https://www.kclife.com
Year Founded: 1895
KCLI—(OTCIQ)
Rev.: $523,910,000
Assets: $5,463,012,000
Liabilities: $4,554,273,000
Net Worth: $908,739,000
Earnings: $15,170,000
Emp.: 473
Fiscal Year-end: 12/31/20
Individual & Group Life Insurance Services
N.A.I.C.S.: 524130
Walter E. Bixby III *(Vice Chm & Exec VP)*
R. Philip Bixby *(Chm, Pres & CEO)*
Mark Alan Milton *(Sr VP & Actuary)*
Donald E. Krebs *(Sr VP-Sls & Mktg)*
Stephen E. Ropp *(Sr VP-Ops)*
Philip A. Williams *(Sr VP-Fin)*
Alan Craig Mason Jr. *(Gen Counsel, Sec & Sr VP)*

Subsidiaries:

Grange Life Insurance Company   **(1)**
671 S High St, Columbus, OH 43206-1014
Tel.: (614) 445-2900
Web Site: http://www.grangeinsurance.com
Life Insurance Products & Services
N.A.I.C.S.: 524113
Theresa Mason *(Pres)*

Old American Insurance
Company   **(1)**
3520 Broadway, Kansas City, MO 64111-2565
Tel.: (816) 753-4900
Web Site: http://www.oaic.com
Insurance Services
N.A.I.C.S.: 524113
Walter E. Bixby III *(Pres)*

Sunset Life Insurance Company   **(1)**
3520 Broadway, Kansas City, MO
64111-2502   **(100%)**
Tel.: (816) 753-7000
Web Site: http://www.sunsetlife.com
Fire Insurance Services
N.A.I.C.S.: 524113
R. Philip Bixby *(Chm & Pres)*

KARAT PACKAGING INC.
6185 Kimball Ave, Chino, CA 91708
Tel.: (626) 965-8882   **DE**
Web Site:
   https://www.karatpackaging.com
Year Founded: 2018
KRT—(NASDAQ)
Rev.: $422,957,000
Assets: $252,175,000
Liabilities: $100,242,000
Net Worth: $151,933,000
Earnings: $23,648,000
Emp.: 781
Fiscal Year-end: 12/31/22
Disposable Food Packaging Product Mfr & Distr
N.A.I.C.S.: 327213
Marvin Cheng *(Co-Founder, Sec & VP-Mfg)*
Alan Yu *(Co-Founder, Chm & CEO)*
Jian Guo *(CFO)*

KARTOON STUDIOS, INC.
190 N Canon Dr Fl 4, Beverly Hills,
CA 90210
Tel.: (310) 273-4222   **NV**
Web Site:
   https://www.kartoonstudios.com
Year Founded: 2006
TOON—(NYSEAMEX)
Rev.: $62,299,000
Assets: $237,918,000
Liabilities: $125,049,000
Net Worth: $112,869,000
Earnings: ($45,595,000)
Emp.: 743
Fiscal Year-end: 12/31/22
Motion Picture & Video Production
N.A.I.C.S.: 512110
Margaret Loesch *(Exec Chm-Kartoon Channel)*
Lloyd Mintz *(Sr VP & Head-Consumer Products-Worldwide)*
Anthony D. Thomopoulos *(Vice Chm)*
Andrew A. Heyward *(Chm & CEO)*
David Neuman *(Chief Creative Officer-Kartoon Channel)*

Subsidiaries:

A Squared Entertainment LLC   **(1)**
9401 Wilshire Blvd Ste 608, Beverly Hills,
CA 90212
Tel.: (310) 273-4222
Brand Entertainment Services
N.A.I.C.S.: 533110
Gregory Payne *(COO & Gen Counsel)*

ChizComm Ltd.   **(1)**
245 Fairview Mall Dr Suite 301, North York,
M2J 4T1, ON, Canada
Tel.: (416) 551-0822
Web Site: http://www.chizcomm.com
Marketing & Advertising Services
N.A.I.C.S.: 541613
Harold Chiziok *(CEO)*
Jennifer Chizick *(COO)*
Donna MacNeil *(Pres)*
Kathleen Campisano *(CMO)*

Subsidiary (US):

Beacon Media Group   **(2)**
1050 Wall Wtreet W Ste 665, 07071,
Lyndhurst, NJ
Tel.: (201) 335-0032
Web Site: https://www.beaconmediagrp.com
Full-service Marketing, Communications & Media Agency Group
N.A.I.C.S.: 541810

Wow Unlimited Media Inc.   **(1)**
200-2025 West Broadway, Vancouver, V6J
1Z6, BC, Canada

Tel.: (604) 714-2600
Web Site: http://www.wowunlimited.co
Rev.: $47,815,279
Assets: $56,060,277
Liabilities: $53,422,939
Net Worth: $2,637,337
Earnings: ($3,885,082)
Emp.: 105
Fiscal Year-end: 12/31/2020
Computer Animated Film Production Services
N.A.I.C.S.: 512110

Subsidiary (US):

Frederator Networks Inc.   **(2)**
22 W 21st St, New York, NY 10010
Tel.: (212) 779-4133
Web Site: http://www.frederatorstudios.com
Data Processing Services
N.A.I.C.S.: 518210
Kenny Ash *(VP-Talent & Brand)*

KARYOPHARM THERAPEU-TICS INC.
85 Wells Ave Ste 210, Newton, MA
02459-3298
Tel.: (617) 658-0600   **DE**
Web Site:
   https://www.karyopharm.com
Year Founded: 2008
KPTI—(NASDAQ)
Rev.: $146,033,000
Assets: $240,438,000
Liabilities: $376,644,000
Net Worth: ($136,206,000)
Earnings: ($143,099,000)
Emp.: 325
Fiscal Year-end: 12/31/23
Pharmaceuticals Mfr
N.A.I.C.S.: 325412
Michael K. Kauffman *(Founder)*
Brian Austad *(Sr VP-Pharmaceutical Sciences)*
Steven Rotman *(Chief People & Corp Engagement Officer)*
Michael Mano *(Gen Counsel, Sec & Sr VP)*
Stephen Mitchener *(Chief Bus Officer & Sr VP)*
Stuart Poulton *(Chief Dev Officer & Exec VP)*
James Accumanno *(Chief Compliance Officer)*
Lisa DiPaulo *(Chief HR Officer)*
Reshma Rangwala *(Chief Medical Officer)*
Amana Sadiq *(Sr VP)*
Elhan Webb *(Sr VP)*
Richard A. Paulson *(Pres & CEO)*

Subsidiaries:

Karyopharm Europe GmbH   **(1)**
Franziska-Bilek-Weg 9, 80339, Munich,
Germany
Tel.: (49) 895484860
Emp.: 10
Pharmaceuticals Mfr
N.A.I.C.S.: 325412

KASHIN, INC.
112 N Curry St, Carson City, NV
89703-4934
Tel.: (626) 429-2780   **NV**
KUSA—(OTCIQ)
Rev.: $7,000
Assets: $126
Liabilities: $97,988
Net Worth: ($97,862)
Earnings: ($64,748)
Fiscal Year-end: 04/30/24
Education Services
N.A.I.C.S.: 611710
Carl Maybin *(Pres, CEO, CFO & Principal Acctg Officer)*

KASPIEN HOLDINGS INC.
2818 N Sullivan Rd, Spokane, WA
99216

Tel.: (509) 900-6287   **NY**
Web Site: https://www.kaspien.com
Year Founded: 1972
KSPN—(NASDAQ)
Rev.: $128,228,000
Assets: $40,739,000
Liabilities: $41,840,000
Net Worth: ($1,101,000)
Earnings: ($19,044,000)
Emp.: 80
Fiscal Year-end: 01/28/23
Retailer of Music, Pre-Recorded Videocassettes, DVD's & Related Products Mfr
N.A.I.C.S.: 449210
Edwin Sapienza *(CFO, Chief Acctg Officer & Exec VP)*

Subsidiaries:

Kaspien Holdings Inc.   **(1)**
8000 Freedom Ave, North Canton, OH
44720-6912   **(100%)**
Tel.: (330) 494-2282
Sales Range: $150-199.9 Million
Retailer of Music, Pre-Recorded Videocassettes, DVD & Related Products
N.A.I.C.S.: 423990

Kaspien, Inc.   **(1)**
2128 N Sullivan Rd Ste 130, Spokane Valley, WA 99216
Web Site: http://www.kaspien.com
Emp.: 150
Online Retailer of Eco-Friendly Products from Various Suppliers
N.A.I.C.S.: 459999
Brock Kowalchuk *(CFO)*
Tom Simpson *(Co-Founder)*
Lisa Wideman *(Chief HR Officer)*

KATAHDIN BANKSHARES CORP.
11 Main St, Patten, ME 04765
Tel.: (207) 528-2211   **ME**
Web Site:
   http://www.katahdintrust.com
Year Founded: 1986
KTHN—(OTCQX)
Rev.: $42,208,000
Assets: $937,007,000
Liabilities: $860,805,000
Net Worth: $76,202,000
Earnings: $9,519,000
Emp.: 161
Fiscal Year-end: 12/31/20
Bank Holding Company
N.A.I.C.S.: 551111
Jon J. Prescott *(Pres & CEO)*
Steven L. Richardson *(Chm)*
Matthew M. Nightingale *(CFO, Treas & Exec VP)*
William P. Lucy *(Exec VP-Comml Svcs)*
Krista K. Putnam *(Sr VP-Mktg)*
Angela T. Butler *(Sr VP-Retail & Bus Banking)*
James P. Amabile *(VP)*
Tori A. Barber *(Asst VP & Mgr-Trng)*
Annette J. Beaton *(VP)*
Bradley A. Berthiaume *(Sr VP)*
Vicki L. Bessette *(Officer-Comml Svcs & VP)*
Cindy L. Boot *(Officer-Comml Svcs & Asst VP)*
David H. Cambridge *(Officer-Comml Svcs & Sr VP)*
Samuel S. Clockedile *(Officer-Mktg & Asst VP)*
Melissa A. Dahlgren *(Asst VP)*
Janet M. Doak *(Asst VP)*
Sunny G. Flannery *(Asst VP)*
Sue A. Fox *(Mgr-Appraisal Dept)*
Angela M. Franck *(Asst VP)*
John S. Frohock *(Officer-Managed Assets & VP)*
Sarah J. Gardiner *(Asst VP)*
Leslie M. Gardne *(VP-Retail Loans)*
Allissa M. Given *(Officer-Retail Svcs & Branch Mgr)*

Jonathan P. Glazier *(Officer-Bus Dev)*
Alison N. Gould *(Officer-Comml Svcs & Asst VP)*
Billi B. Griffeth *(Reg VP-Retail Banking)*
Katherine H. Hil *(VP & Mgr-Bank Ops)*
Richard J. York Jr. *(Vice Chm)*

Subsidiaries:

Katahdin Trust Company **(1)**
11 Main St, Patten, ME 04765
Tel.: (207) 528-2211
Web Site: http://www.katahdintrust.com
Rev.: $10,634,000
Emp.: 20
Banking Services
N.A.I.C.S.: 522110
Jon J. Prescott *(Pres & CEO)*
Leslie M. Gardner *(Asst VP)*
Patty A. Hersey *(Asst VP)*
Natasha McCarthy *(Dir-HR-Houlton)*

KAVTEK SOFTWARE CORP.
17011 Beach Blvd Ste 900, Huntington Beach, CA 92647
Tel.: (714) 841-2670   DE
IMSU—(OTCIQ)
Surgical & Medical Instrument Mfr
N.A.I.C.S.: 339112
Wayne Cockburn *(CEO)*

KAYA HOLDINGS, INC.
915 Middle River Dr Ste 316, Fort Lauderdale, FL 33304
Tel.: (954) 892-6911   DE
Web Site:
   https://www.kayaholdings.com
Year Founded: 1993
KAYS—(OTCQB)
Rev.: $685,379
Assets: $843,241
Liabilities: $18,446,982
Net Worth: ($17,603,741)
Earnings: ($3,576,614)
Emp.: 4
Fiscal Year-end: 12/31/22
Legal Medical & Recreational Marijuana Support Services
N.A.I.C.S.: 561499
Craig R. Frank *(Chm, Pres & CEO)*
David A. Levine *(Chief Compliance Officer)*

KB HOME
10990 Wilshire Blvd, Los Angeles, CA 90024
Tel.: (310) 231-4000   DE
Web Site: https://www.kbhome.com
Year Founded: 1957
KBH—(NYSE)
Rev.: $5,724,930,000
Assets: $5,835,918,000
Liabilities: $2,816,443,000
Net Worth: $3,019,475,000
Earnings: $564,746,000
Emp.: 2,244
Fiscal Year-end: 11/30/21
Homes & Commercial Project Builder
N.A.I.C.S.: 236117
Brian J. Woram *(Gen Counsel & Exec VP)*
Brian J. Woram *(Gen Counsel & Exec VP)*
Jeffrey T. Mezger *(Chm & CEO)*
William R. Hollinger *(Chief Acctg Officer & Sr VP)*
Albert Z. Praw *(Exec VP-Real Estate & Bus Dev)*
Thomas F. Norton *(Sr VP-HR)*
Jeff J. Kaminski *(CFO & Exec VP)*
Thad Johnson *(Treas & Sr VP)*
Dan Bridleman *(Sr VP-Sustainability, Tech & Strategic Sourcing)*
Robert V. McGibney *(Pres & COO)*
Ken Gancarczyk *(Sr VP-Builder Svcs)*

Jill Peters *(Sr VP-IR)*
Amit Desai *(CMO & Sr VP)*
Bill Kiselick *(Pres-Charlotte)*

Subsidiaries:

KB HOME California LLC **(1)**
5000 Executive Pkwy Ste 175, San Ramon, CA 94583
Tel.: (925) 983-4600
Building Construction Services
N.A.I.C.S.: 236117

KB HOME Greater Los Angeles Inc. **(1)**
10990 Wilshire Blvd Fl 7, Los Angeles, CA 90024
Tel.: (310) 231-4000
Web Site: http://www.kbhome.com
Building Reconstruction Services
N.A.I.C.S.: 236118

KB HOME Nevada Inc. **(1)**
5655 Badura Ave, Las Vegas, NV 89118-4713
Tel.: (702) 266-8400
Emp.: 350
Building Construction Services
N.A.I.C.S.: 236116

KB HOME Phoenix Inc. **(1)**
4127 E Van Buren St 150, Phoenix, AZ 85008
Tel.: (602) 282-3090
Building Construction Services
N.A.I.C.S.: 236117
Sam Griffin *(Dir-Land Acq)*

Subsidiary (Domestic):

KB Home **(2)**
10800 Pecan Park Blvd Ste 110, Austin, TX 78750
Tel.: (512) 721-3550
Web Site: http://www.kbhome.com
Sales Range: $50-74.9 Million
Emp.: 80
Single Family Home Builder
N.A.I.C.S.: 236117

KB HOME Raleigh-Durham Inc. **(1)**
4506 S Miami Blvd Ste 100, Durham, NC 27703-8001
Tel.: (919) 768-7974
Emp.: 75
Residential Buildings Contractor
N.A.I.C.S.: 236117

KB HOME Sacramento Inc. **(1)**
3005 Douglas Blvd Ste 250, Roseville, CA 95661
Tel.: (916) 945-5400
Web Site: http://www.kbhome.com
Home Building Contractor
N.A.I.C.S.: 236117

KB HOME Sacramento Inc. **(1)**
9141 Sea Ridge Ct, Sacramento, CA 95829
Tel.: (916) 688-3567
Building Construction Services
N.A.I.C.S.: 236117

KB HOME South Bay Inc. **(1)**
5000 Executive Pkwy Ste 175, San Ramon, CA 94583
Tel.: (925) 983-4600
Web Site: http://www.kbhome.com
Building Construction Services
N.A.I.C.S.: 236117

KB Home **(1)**
4800 Fredericksburg Rd, San Antonio, TX 78229-3628 **(100%)**
Tel.: (210) 349-1111
Web Site: http://search.kbhome.com
Sales Range: $50-74.9 Million
Emp.: 100
Residential Builders
N.A.I.C.S.: 236117

KB Home Colorado, Inc. **(1)**
7807 E Pkview Ave Ste 300, Centennial, CO 80111 **(100%)**
Tel.: (303) 323-1100
Web Site: http://www.kbhome.com
Residential Construction
N.A.I.C.S.: 236115

KB Home Greater Los Angeles, Inc. **(1)**

10990 Wilshire Blvd, Los Angeles, CA 90024 **(100%)**
Tel.: (310) 231-4000
Web Site: http://www.kbhome.com
Sales Range: $150-199.9 Million
Emp.: 75
Home Construction Services
N.A.I.C.S.: 236115

KB Home Jacksonville LLC **(1)**
10475 Fortune Pkwy Ste 100, Jacksonville, FL 32256 **(100%)**
Tel.: (904) 596-6800
Web Site: http://www.kbhome.com
Home Construction Services
N.A.I.C.S.: 236115

KB Home Mortgage Company **(1)**
10990 Wilshire Blvd Fl 7, Los Angeles, CA 90024 **(100%)**
Tel.: (310) 231-4000
Sales Range: $50-74.9 Million
Emp.: 75
Mortgage Banking
N.A.I.C.S.: 236115

KB Home Nevada Inc. **(1)**
5655 Badura Ave, Las Vegas, NV 89118-4713 **(100%)**
Tel.: (702) 266-8400
Web Site: http://www.kbhome.com
Sales Range: $50-74.9 Million
Emp.: 100
Single-Family Home Contractor
N.A.I.C.S.: 236115

KB Home Northern California **(1)**
5000 Executive Pkwy Ste 175, San Ramon, CA 94583 **(100%)**
Tel.: (925) 983-4600
Web Site: http://www.kbhome.com
Sales Range: $50-74.9 Million
Emp.: 70
Home Construction Services
N.A.I.C.S.: 236115
Chris Apostolopoulos *(Pres)*

KB Home Orlando LLC **(1)**
9102 S Park Ctr Loop Ste 100, Orlando, FL 32819 **(100%)**
Tel.: (407) 587-3800
Web Site: http://www.kbhome.com
Real Estate Services
N.A.I.C.S.: 531390

KB Home Tampa LLC **(1)**
3450 Buschwood Park Dr Ste 240, Tampa, FL 33618-4467 **(100%)**
Tel.: (813) 775-7800
Web Site: http://www.kbhome.com
Home Construction Services
N.A.I.C.S.: 236115

KB Home/Shaw Louisiana LLC **(1)**
10990 Wilshire Blvd Fl 7, Los Angeles, CA 90024-3907
Tel.: (310) 231-4000
Web Site: http://www.kbhome.com
Testing Laboratories
N.A.I.C.S.: 541380

KBR, INC.
601 Jefferson St Ste 3400, Houston, TX 77002
Tel.: (713) 753-2000   DE
Web Site: https://www.kbr.com
Year Founded: 1901
KBR—(NYSE)
Rev.: $6,956,000,000
Assets: $5,565,000,000
Liabilities: $4,171,000,000
Net Worth: $1,394,000,000
Earnings: ($265,000,000)
Emp.: 34,000
Fiscal Year-end: 12/29/23
Holding Company; Engineering, Construction & Government Contracting Services
N.A.I.C.S.: 551112
Mark W. Sopp *(CFO & Exec VP)*
Stuart J. B. Bradie *(Pres & CEO)*
Gregory Sean Conlon *(Chief Digital & Dev Officer)*
Alison Vasquez *(Chief Acctg Officer & Sr VP)*
Byron Bright *(Pres-Govt Solutions)*

Doug Kelly *(Pres-Tech)*
Shad E. Evans *(CFO-Sustainable Tech Solutions)*
Pete Green *(Sr VP-Govt Solutions US-Defense & Intel Solutions)*
Ella Studer *(Sr VP-Govt Solutions US-Readiness & Sustainment Solutions)*
Sonia Galindo *(Gen Counsel & Exec VP)*
Jay Ibrahim *(Pres)*
Paul Kahn *(Pres)*

Subsidiaries:

Aspire Defence Capital Works JV **(1)**
Aspire Business Centre Ordnance Road, Tidworth, SP9 7QD, United Kingdom
Tel.: (44) 1980886739
Construction Management Services
N.A.I.C.S.: 236116

Bristol Management Centre Limited **(1)**
Armada House Telephone Avenue, Bristol, BS1 4BQ, United Kingdom
Tel.: (44) 1179491500
Web Site: https://www.lyly.co.uk
Management Training Services
N.A.I.C.S.: 611430

CCC Cayman, Ltd. **(1)**
Artemis House 67 Fort Street, PO Box 2775, Georgetown, KY1-1111, Cayman Islands
Tel.: (345) 769 1890
Web Site: https://www.cccapital.ky
Investment Banking Services
N.A.I.C.S.: 523999

FTX Logistics Limited **(1)**
Wing House Marlborough Road, Bulford Barracks, Salisbury, SP4 9LZ, Wiltshire, United Kingdom
Tel.: (44) 1980667100
Web Site: https://www.ftxlog.com
Heavy Equipment Transportation Services
N.A.I.C.S.: 561910

Frazer-Nash Australia Pty. Ltd. **(1)**
Level 8 99 Gawler Place, PO Box 3471, Rundle Mall, Adelaide, 5000, SA, Australia
Tel.: (61) 873254200
Web Site: https://www.fnaustralia.com.au
Engineering Service Provider
N.A.I.C.S.: 541330

Frazer-Nash Consultancy Ltd. **(1)**
Styonebridge House Dorking Business Park, Dorking, RH4 1HJ, Surrey, United Kingdom
Tel.: (44) 130 688 5050
Web Site: https://www.fnc.co.uk
Engineering & Technical Services for Defense, Aerospace, Power & Transportation Industries
N.A.I.C.S.: 541330

Subsidiary (Non-US):

Frazer-Nash Consultancy (Australia) Pty Ltd **(2)**
Level 8 99 Gawler Place, PO Box 3471, Rundle Mall, Adelaide, 5000, SA, Australia
Tel.: (61) 873254200
Web Site: http://www.fnaustralia.com.au
Engineering Consulting Services
N.A.I.C.S.: 541330
Neil McDougall *(Mng Dir)*

Granherne Pty Ltd **(1)**
L 17 100 St Georges Tce, Perth, 6000, Australia
Tel.: (61) 864443000
Engineeering Services
N.A.I.C.S.: 541330

Harmonic Limited **(1)**
The Hatchery Eaglewood Park, Ilminster, TA19 9DQ, Somerset, United Kingdom
Tel.: (44) 1460256500
Web Site: https://harmonic.co.uk
Business Management Consulting Services
N.A.I.C.S.: 541618

KBR Al-Yusr Limited Company **(1)**
Patchi Building 3rd Floor Prince Sultan Bin Abdulaziz Road, PO Box 2959, Rakah, Al

KBR, Inc.—(Continued)

Khobar, 31952, Saudi Arabia
Tel.: (966) 138477260
Software Development Services
N.A.I.C.S.: 541511

KBR Holdings Pty Ltd. (1)
186 Greenhill Rd Parkside, Adelaide, 5063, SA, Australia
Tel.: (61) 883011234
Emp.: 1,723
Holding Company
N.A.I.C.S.: 551112

KBR Industrial Canada Co. (1)
1302 10 St, Nisku, T9E 8K2, AB, Canada
Tel.: (780) 468-1341
Construction & Engineering Services
N.A.I.C.S.: 237990

KBR Netherlands Investments B.V. (1)
Laan van Vredenoord 33, 2289 DA, Rijswijk, Netherlands
Tel.: (31) 703071300
Construction & Engineering Services
N.A.I.C.S.: 237990

KBR Overseas, Inc. (1)
601 Jefferson St Ste 7911, Houston, TX 77002
Tel.: (713) 597-7527
Engineeering Services
N.A.I.C.S.: 541330

KBR Wyle Services LLC (1)
601 Jefferson St Ste 7911, Houston, TX 77002-4003
Tel.: (713) 753-2000
Web Site: https://www.kbr.com
Commercial Solutions Services
N.A.I.C.S.: 541613

Kellogg Brown & Root Asia Pacific Pte Ltd (1)
80 Bendemeer Road 06-01, Singapore, 339949, Singapore
Tel.: (65) 6 210 7000
Web Site: https://www.kbr.com
Emp.: 200
Construction & Engineering Services
N.A.I.C.S.: 237990

Kellogg Brown & Root LLC (1)
601 Jefferson St, Houston, TX 77002
Tel.: (713) 753-3011
Engineering, Construction & Government Contracting Services
N.A.I.C.S.: 541330

Joint Venture (Domestic):

Brown & Root Industrial Services, LLC (2)
2600 Citiplace Dr Ste 500, Baton Rouge, LA 70808 (50%)
Tel.: (225) 778-7655
Web Site: https://www.brownandroot.com
Emp.: 1,600
Industrial Services, Including Engineering, Construction & Maintenance
N.A.I.C.S.: 541330
Charlie Heath (CFO)
Brandon Politz (Gen Counsel)
Crista Stokes Wynne (VP-Finance)
Mary Bihlmeyer (VP-, , and)
Jerry Redden (VP-, Safety, and)
Mike Firmin (Pres)
Jack Penley (Pres-Engineering &)
Grant Landry (Pres)
Ross Campesi (Pres-)
Donnie Hopkins (Pres-)
Katie Richardson (VP-Human Resources)
Shannon Wild (VP-, Technology, and)

Subsidiary (Domestic):

Maintenance Enterprises LLC (3)
52410 Clark Rd, White Castle, LA 70788
Tel.: (225) 545-3970
Web Site: http://maintenanceenterprise.com
Renovation, Remodeling & Repairs; Industrial Buildings
N.A.I.C.S.: 236220

Petrin Corp. (3)
1405 Commercial Dr, Port Allen, LA 70767-0330
Tel.: (225) 343-0471
Web Site: https://www.petrinllc.com

Sales Range: $50-74.9 Million
Emp.: 670
Industrial Insulation Services
N.A.I.C.S.: 238310
Bob Hall (Mgr-Northern Div)
Kenny Freeman (Pres)
Michael Shipp (Exec VP)

Affiliate (Domestic):

Scaffolding Rental & Erection Services, LLC (4)
1423 Commercial Dr, Port Allen, LA 70767
Tel.: (225) 339-0871
Web Site: http://www.scaffold-rental.com
Emp.: 350
Scaffolding Rental & Erection Services
N.A.I.C.S.: 532490
Mike Shipp (Exec VP)
Sonny Jordan (Gen Mgr)
Richard Trisler (Dir-Safety & Health)

Subsidiary (Domestic):

KBR Construction Company, LLC (2)
3000 Riverchase Galleria Ste 1400, Birmingham, AL 35244
Tel.: (205) 972-6000
Web Site: https://www.kbr.com
Commercial & Industrial Building Construction Services
N.A.I.C.S.: 236210
Stuart J. B. Bradie (Pres & CEO)

KBR Engineering Company, LLC (2)
2000 International Park Dr, Birmingham, AL 35243 (100%)
Tel.: (205) 972-6000
Web Site: https://www.kbr.com
Sales Range: $125-149.9 Million
Emp.: 600
Engineeering Services
N.A.I.C.S.: 541330

KBRwyle Technology Solutions, LLC (2)
7000 Columbia Gateway Dr, Columbia, MD 21046-2119
Tel.: (410) 964-7557
Integrated Management & Field Engineering Services
N.A.I.C.S.: 517410

Subsidiary (Domestic):

Stinger Ghaffarian Technologies Inc. (3)
7701 Greenbelt Rd Ste 400, Greenbelt, MD 20770
Tel.: (301) 614-8600
Web Site: http://www.sgt-inc.com
Engineering Services, Mission Operations, Scientific & IT Solutions
N.A.I.C.S.: 541330

Subsidiary (Domestic):

Kellogg Brown & Root International, Inc. (2)
4100 Clinton Dr, Houston, TX 77020
Tel.: (713) 753-2000
Holding Company
N.A.I.C.S.: 551112

Subsidiary (Non-US):

GVA Consultants AB (3)
Ostra Hamngatan 7, PO Box 11450, 404 29, Gothenburg, Sweden
Tel.: (46) 31106700
Web Site: http://www.gvac.se
Sales Range: $25-49.9 Million
Emp.: 100
Marine & Offshore Engineering & Design Consultancy Services
N.A.I.C.S.: 541330

Kellogg Brown & Root (Canada) Company (3)
3300 76th Ave, Edmonton, T6P 1J4, AB, Canada
Tel.: (780) 468-1341
Web Site: http://www.kbr.com
Sales Range: $650-699.9 Million
Emp.: 2,400
Engineering, Construction & Government Contracting Services
N.A.I.C.S.: 237990

Kellogg Brown & Root Holdings (U.K.) Limited (3)
park Court Springfield Dr, Leatherhead, KT22 7NL, United Kingdom
Tel.: (44) 01372865000
Web Site: https://www.kbr.com
Engineering, Construction & Government Contracting Services
N.A.I.C.S.: 237990

Subsidiary (Domestic):

Kellogg Brown & Root (Greenford) Limited (4)
Kellogg Tower Greenford Road, Greenford, UB6 0JA, Middlesex, United Kingdom (100%)
Tel.: (44) 2088727000
Sales Range: $150-199.9 Million
Emp.: 1,000
Engineering & Construction Services
N.A.I.C.S.: 541330

Subsidiary (Non-US):

Servicios Halliburton de Venezuela S.A. (3)
Ave 3E Calles 78 y 79 Torre Empresarial Claret, Piso 10 Ofic 10 01, Maracaibo, 4001, Edo Zulia, Venezuela
Tel.: (58) 261 2005211
Sales Range: $700-749.9 Million
Emp.: 1,095
Oil & Gas Drilling Services
N.A.I.C.S.: 213111

Joint Venture (Non-US):

United Water International (3)
Level 1 180 Greenhill Road, Parkside, 5063, Australia
Tel.: (61) 883012700
Web Site: http://www.uwi.com.au
Sales Range: $50-74.9 Million
Emp.: 500
Water Utility Company
N.A.I.C.S.: 221310
Alan Hesketh (Mng Dir)

Subsidiary (Domestic):

Kellogg Brown & Root Services, Inc. (2)
4100 Clinton Dr, Houston, TX 77020
Tel.: (713) 676-3011
Web Site: http://www.kbr.com
Oil Field Services & Products Whslr
N.A.I.C.S.: 237120

Subsidiary (Non-US):

Roberts & Schaefer Company (2)
Tel.: (312) 236-7292
Engineering & Construction Services
N.A.I.C.S.: 541330

Subsidiary (Non-US):

Clinch River Corporation (3)
Tel.: (276) 963-5271
Industrial Metal Fabrications & Vacuum Pump Repair
N.A.I.C.S.: 332312

Roberts & Schaefer Company (3)
Tel.: (801) 984-0900
Engineering & Construction Services
N.A.I.C.S.: 541330

Subsidiary (Domestic):

Wyle Laboratories, Inc. (2)
1960 E Grand Ave Ste 900, El Segundo, CA 90245-5023
Tel.: (310) 563-6800
Web Site: http://ww2.wyle.com
Governmental Engineering, Professional, Scientific & Technical Support Services
N.A.I.C.S.: 541990

Subsidiary (Domestic):

CAS, Inc. (3)
100 Quality Cir, Huntsville, AL 35806
Tel.: (256) 922-4200
Web Site: http://ww2.wyle.com
Technical Engineering, Logistics Support & Weapons Systems Analysis Services
N.A.I.C.S.: 541990

Group (Domestic):

KBRwyle Aerospace Group (3)
22309 Exploration Dr, Lexington Park, MD 20653
Tel.: (301) 863-4200
Web Site: http://ww2.wyle.com
Aerospace Research & Technical Consulting Services
N.A.I.C.S.: 927110

KBRwyle Science, Technology & Engineering Group (3)
2400 NASA Pkwy, Houston, TX 77058
Tel.: (281) 212-1200
Web Site: http://www.kbr.com
Space Medical Operations Research, Engineering & Technical Support Services
N.A.I.C.S.: 927110

Kord Technologies, Inc. (1)
635 Discovery Dr NW, Huntsville, AL 35806
Tel.: (256) 489-2346
Web Site: https://www.kordtechnologies.com
Information Technology Consulting Services
N.A.I.C.S.: 541511
Scott Schnorrenberg (Pres)
Scott Schnorrenberg (Pres)

LinQuest Corporation (1)
5140 W Goldleaf Cir Ste 400, Los Angeles, CA 90056
Tel.: (323) 924-1600
Web Site: http://www.linquest.com
Networks, Communications & Information Systems
N.A.I.C.S.: 541519
Stephen Chambal (Chief Growth Officer & Exec VP)
Greg Young (Pres & CEO)
Doug Manya (Gen Counsel & Sec)
Matt Klein (CFO)
Rich Martin (CIO)
Silvia Van Dussen (Chief HR Officer)
Ronald Gembarosky (Chief Security Officer & Exec VP)

Subsidiary (Domestic):

TMC Design Corporation (2)
4325 Del Rey Blvd, Las Cruces, NM 88012
Tel.: (575) 382-4600
Web Site: http://www.tmcdesign.com
Engineeering Services
N.A.I.C.S.: 541330
Troy Scoughton (Chm)
Kimball Edwards (Chief Technical Officer & Exec VP)
Christopher V. Ham (Pres & CEO)

Unit (Domestic):

The Perduco Group, Inc. (2)
2647 Commons Blvd, Beavercreek, OH 45431
Tel.: (937) 401-0268
Web Site: http://www.theperducogroup.com
Business Support & General Management Consulting Services
N.A.I.C.S.: 541611
Stephen Chambal (Founder)

Sigma Bravo Pty Ltd (1)
3/15 Dundas Court, Phillip, 2606, ACT, Australia
Tel.: (61) 261730700
Web Site: https://www.sigmabravo.com
Software Development Services
N.A.I.C.S.: 541511
Tim Wedding (Mng Dir)
Karen Schilling (Gen Mgr)
Mike Wagstaff (Dir)
Ben Finney (Dir)

Technical Staffing Resources, LLC (1)
3000 Riverchase Galleria Ste 1400, Birmingham, AL 35244
Tel.: (205) 972-6658
Web Site: https://www.technicalstaffingresources.com
Professional Employment Services
N.A.I.C.S.: 561330

KBS GROWTH & INCOME REIT, INC.
800 Newport Ctr Dr Ste 700, Newport Beach, CA 92660
Tel.: (949) 417-6500   MD.

Web Site: https://kbs-cmg.com
Year Founded: 2015
KBSG—(OTCIQ)
Rev.: $14,602,000
Assets: $114,910,000
Liabilities: $113,824,000
Net Worth: $1,086,000
Earnings: ($19,896,000)
Fiscal Year-end: 12/31/22
Real Estate Investment Trust
N.A.I.C.S.: 525990
Charles Jay Schreiber Jr. (Chm, Pres & CEO)
Jeffrey K. Waldvogel (CFO, Treas & Sec)
Stacie K. Yamane (Chief Acctg Officer & Asst Sec)

KBS REAL ESTATE INVESTMENT TRUST III, INC.

800 Newport Ctr Dr Ste 700, Newport Beach, CA 92660
Tel.: (949) 417-6500   MD
Year Founded: 2009
KBSR—(OTCIQ)
Rev.: $300,677,000
Assets: $2,139,385,000
Liabilities: $1,871,973,000
Net Worth: $267,412,000
Earnings: ($157,533,000)
Fiscal Year-end: 12/31/23
Real Estate Investment Trust
N.A.I.C.S.: 523999
Jeffrey K. Waldvogel (CFO, Treas & Sec)
Charles Jay Schreiber Jr. (Pres & CEO)
Stacie K. Yamane (Chief Acctg Officer & Asst Sec)

Subsidiaries:

KBSIII Almaden Financial Plaza, LLC   (1)
99 Almaden Blvd, San Jose, CA 95113
Tel.: (408) 289-8310
Web Site: http://www.kbs.com
Real Estate Investment Services
N.A.I.C.S.: 531390

KBSIII Anchor Centre, LLC   (1)
2201 E Camelback Rd Ste 122, Phoenix, AZ 85016
Tel.: (602) 955-7030
Web Site: http://www.anchorcentre.com
Real Estate Services
N.A.I.C.S.: 531390

KBSIII One Washingtonian, LLC   (1)
6700 Rockledge Dr Ste 500-A, Bethesda, MD 20817
Tel.: (301) 571-0900
Web Site: https://transwestern.com
Real Estate Agency Services
N.A.I.C.S.: 531390

KBSIII Ten Almaden, LLC   (1)
10 Almaden Blvd Ste 440, San Jose, CA 95113
Tel.: (408) 572-8450
Web Site: https://www.tenalmaden.com
Real Estate Services
N.A.I.C.S.: 531390

KEARNY FINANCIAL CORP.

120 Passaic Ave, Fairfield, NJ 07004
Tel.: (973) 244-4500
Web Site:
     https://www.kearnybank.com
Year Founded: 2001
KRNY—(NASDAQ)
Rev.: $328,868,000
Assets: $7,683,461,000
Liabilities: $6,929,890,000
Net Worth: $753,571,000
Earnings: ($86,667,000)
Emp.: 552
Fiscal Year-end: 06/30/24
Bank Holding Company
N.A.I.C.S.: 551111

Craig L. Montanaro (Pres & CEO)
Patrick M. Joyce (Chief Lending Officer & Exec VP)
Erika K. Parisi (Chief Admin Officer & Exec VP)
Keith Suchodolski (CFO & Sr Exec VP)
John J. Mazur Jr. (Chm)
Thomas D. DeMedici (Chief Credit Officer & Exec VP)
John V. Dunne (Chief Risk Officer & Exec VP)
Timothy A. Swansson (CTO, Chief Innovation Officer & Exec VP)
Anthony V. Bilotta Jr. (Chief Banking Officer & Exec VP)

Subsidiaries:

Kearny Bank   (1)
120 Passaic Ave, Fairfield, NJ 07004
Tel.: (973) 244-4500
Web Site: https://www.kearnybank.com
Federal Savings Bank
N.A.I.C.S.: 522180
Craig L. Montanaro (Pres & CEO)
Keith Suchodolski (CFO & Sr Exec VP)
John J. Mazur Jr. (Chm)
Patrick M. Joyce (Chief Lending Officer & Exec VP)
Erika K. Parisi (Chief Admin Officer & Exec VP)
Keith Suchodolski (CFO & Exec VP)

MSB Financial Corp.   (1)
1902 Long Hill Rd, Millington, NJ 07946-0417
Tel.: (908) 647-4000
Web Site: http://www.millingtonbank.com
Rev.: $25,529,000
Assets: $593,086,000
Liabilities: $527,711,000
Net Worth: $65,375,000
Earnings: $4,103,000
Emp.: 53
Fiscal Year-end: 12/31/2019
Bank Holding Company
N.A.I.C.S.: 551111
John S. Kaufman (CFO & First VP)

Subsidiary (Domestic):

Millington Bank   (2)
1902 Long Hill Rd, Millington, NJ 07946-0417
Tel.: (908) 647-4000
Web Site: http://www.millingtonbank.com
Commercial Banking Services
N.A.I.C.S.: 522110

KEEN VISION ACQUISITION CORPORATION

37 Greenbriar Dr, Summit, NJ 07901
Tel.: (203) 609-1394   VG
Web Site: https://www.kv-ac.com
Year Founded: 2021
KVAC—(NASDAQ)
Rev.: $1,933,434
Assets: $155,688,933
Liabilities: $157,827,318
Net Worth: ($2,138,385)
Earnings: $1,454,758
Fiscal Year-end: 12/31/23
Investment Management Service
N.A.I.C.S.: 523999

KELLANOVA

1 Kellogg Sq, Battle Creek, MI 49016-3599
Tel.: (269) 961-2000   DE
Web Site: https://www.kellanova.com
Year Founded: 1906
K—(NYSE)
Rev.: $13,122,000,000
Assets: $15,621,000,000
Liabilities: $12,252,000,000
Net Worth: $3,369,000,000
Earnings: $951,000,000
Emp.: 23,000
Fiscal Year-end: 12/30/23
Alcoholic Beverages Mfr
N.A.I.C.S.: 312140

Amit Banati (Vice Chm)
Steven A. Cahillane (Chm, Pres & CEO)
David Lawlor (Pres-Europe & Sr VP)
Kurt D. Forche (Chief Acctg Officer, VP & Controller)
Juliann M. Bowerman (CMO)
Lesley Salmon (CIO & Sr VP)
Nicolas Amaya (Pres-North America & Sr VP)
Shumit Kapoor (Pres-Asia Pacific, Middle East, and Africa & Sr VP)
Rodrigo Lance (Sr VP-Supply Chain-Global)

Subsidiaries:

Austin Quality Foods, Inc.   (1)
1 Quality Ln, Cary, NC 27513
Tel.: (919) 677-3400
Snacks & Related Products Mfr
N.A.I.C.S.: 311919

BiscoMisr   (1)
32 El Sawah St, Al-Ameria, Cairo, Egypt
Tel.: (20) 22 286 6600
Web Site: https://www.biscomisr.com
Biscuits, Chocolates, Chewing Gum, Wafers, Cakes, Cereal & Candy Mfr
N.A.I.C.S.: 311352
Mahmoud Abdel Sattar Hammam (Mng Dir-Finance)
Sahar Youssef (Dir-Human Resources)
Adel Mahmoud (Plant Dir)
Ahmed Elsayad (CEO & Vice Chm)
Shahir Nathan (Dir-Sales)
Ahmed Mostafa (Plant Dir)
May Hashad (Mgr-Marketing)
Walid Farouk (Mgr-Accounting)
Hossam Zikry (Mgr)
Samir Moawad Lotfallah (Mgr)
Hany A. Rahim (Mgr-Information Technology)
Ahmed Abd el Aziz (Mktg Dir)

Keebler Company   (1)
Snack Food Mfr & Merchant Whslr

Kellanova Canada Inc.   (1)
5350 Creekbank Rd, Mississauga, L4W 5S1, ON, Canada
Web Site: https://www.kellanova.ca
Snacks & Frozen Food Product Mfr
N.A.I.C.S.: 311813

Kellogg (Deutschland) GmbH   (1)
Mary-Somerville- 9, 28359, Bremen, Germany   (100%)
Tel.: (49) 42139990
Web Site: https://www.kellogg.de
Sales Range: $200-249.9 Million
Emp.: 500
Mfr, Distr & Retailer of Ready-to-eat Breakfast Cereals, Snacks & Beverage Products
N.A.I.C.S.: 311230

Subsidiary (Non-US):

Kellogg (Osterreich) GmbH   (2)
Am Handelskai 388, Vienna, A-1020, Austria
Tel.: (43) 172823150
Web Site: https://www.kellogg.at
Emp.: 5
Breakfast Foods Mfr
N.A.I.C.S.: 311230
Volker Tratz (Mng Dir)

Subsidiary (Domestic):

Kellogg Manufacturing GmbH & Co. KG   (2)
Auf Der Muggenburg 30, Bremen, 28217, Germany
Tel.: (49) 421399910
Web Site: http://www.kelloggs.de
Food Merchant Whslr
N.A.I.C.S.: 424420

Kellogg (Qingdao) Food Co., Ltd.   (1)
13/14 F Block 1 Shenghe Building Shandongtou Rd 58, LaoShan District, Qingdao, China
Tel.: (86) 53289098000
Food Product Whslr
N.A.I.C.S.: 424420

Kellogg (Thailand) Limited   (1)
60 Moo 4, Pluak Daeng Sub-district Pluak

Daeng District, Rayong, 21150, Thailand
Tel.: (66) 38927129
Breakfast Cereal Mfr
N.A.I.C.S.: 311230

Kellogg Asia Pacific Pte. Ltd   (1)
238B Thomson Road Suite 10-01/08 Novena Square Tower B, Singapore, 307685, Singapore
Tel.: (65) 66616200
Web Site: https://www.kelloggs.com
Grocery Product Distr
N.A.I.C.S.: 424410

Kellogg Asia Products Sdn. Bhd.   (1)
Lot G 01c Ground Floor 1 First Avenue Bandar Utama, 47800, Petaling Jaya, Selangor, Malaysia
Tel.: (60) 377180800
Breakfast Cereal Mfr
N.A.I.C.S.: 311230

Kellogg Asia Sdn. Bhd.   (1)
Unit 9 05 Level 9 Menara Uac 12 Jalan Pju 7/5, Petaling Jaya, 47800, Malaysia
Tel.: (60) 377180800
Grocery Product Distr
N.A.I.C.S.: 424410

Kellogg Australia Holdings Pty Ltd   (1)
41-51 Wentworth Ave, Pagewood, 2035, NSW, Australia
Tel.: (61) 293845555
Web Site: https://www.kellog.com
Emp.: 10
Holding Companies
N.A.I.C.S.: 551112

Subsidiary (Domestic):

Kellogg (Aust.) Pty. Ltd.   (2)
41-51 Wentworth Ave, Pagewood, 2035, NSW, Australia
Tel.: (61) 800000474
Web Site: https://www.kelloggs.com.au
Breakfast Cereal Mfr
N.A.I.C.S.: 311230
Andrew Towle (Mng Dir)

Kellogg (Australia) Proprietary Ltd.   (2)
41 51 Wentworth Ave, Pagewood, 2035, NSW, Australia   (100%)
Tel.: (61) 1800000474
Web Site: http://www.kellogg.com.au
Sales Range: $200-249.9 Million
Ready-to-Eat Cereals & Other Food Products
N.A.I.C.S.: 311230
Andrew Towell (Mng Dir)

Specialty Cereals Pty Limited   (2)
41-51 Wentworth Ave, Pagewood, 2035, NSW, Australia
Tel.: (61) 299321000
Web Site:
     https://www.specialtycereals.com.au
Food Products Mfr
N.A.I.C.S.: 311999

Kellogg Canada, Inc.   (1)
5350 Creekbank Rd, Mississauga, L4W 5S1, ON, Canada   (100%)
Tel.: (905) 290-5200
Web Site: http://www.kelloggs.ca
Sales Range: $75-99.9 Million
Emp.: 200
Ready to Eat Cereal & Other Food Products
N.A.I.C.S.: 311230

Division (Domestic):

Kellogg Canada Inc.   (2)
100 Kellogg Ln Stn B, London, N6A 4P9, ON, Canada   (100%)
Tel.: (519) 455-9600
Web Site: http://www.kellog.com
Emp.: 650
Breakfast Cereal Mfr
N.A.I.C.S.: 311230

Kellogg Caribbean Services Company, Inc.   (1)
305 Carr 5, Bayamon, PR 00961
Tel.: (787) 273-8888
Emp.: 88
Grocery Product Distr

Kellanova—(Continued)

N.A.I.C.S.: 424410

Kellogg Company Mexico, S. de R.L. de C.V. (1)
Km 1 Carr al Campo Militar s/n Col San Antonio de la Punta CP, 76135, Queretaro, Mexico
Tel.: (52) 5556242105
Web Site: https://www.kelloggs.com.mx
Breakfast Cereal Mfr
N.A.I.C.S.: 311230

Kellogg Company of Great Britain Limited (1)
The Kellogg Bldg Talbot Road, Manchester, M16 OPU, United Kingdom (100%)
Tel.: (44) 01618692000
Web Site: https://www.kellogg.com
Emp.: 250
Ready-to-Eat Cereals & Other Food Products
N.A.I.C.S.: 311230

Subsidiary (Non-US):

Kellogg Company of Ireland Limited (2)
7 St Johns Court Swords Road Santry, Kellogg Bldg Lakeshore Rd Drive A, Dublin, Ireland
Tel.: (353) 18429100
Web Site: https://www.kelloggs.ie
Food Merchant Whslr
N.A.I.C.S.: 424420

Kellogg Europe Trading Limited (2)
The Kellog Building Lakeshore Dr Airside Retail park, Swords, K67 XF79, Ireland
Tel.: (353) 18830600
Web Site: http://www.kellogg.com
Emp.: 250
Food Merchant Whslr
N.A.I.C.S.: 424420

Subsidiary (Domestic):

Kellogg Marketing and Sales Company (UK) Limited (2)
The Kellogg Building Talbot Road, Manchester, M16 0PU, United Kingdom
Tel.: (44) 1618692000
Web Site: https://www.kelloggs.co.uk
Packaging Products Mfr
N.A.I.C.S.: 424420

Portable Foods Manufacturing Company Limited (2)
Orange Tower Media City Uk, Salford, M50 2HF, Greater Manchester, United Kingdom
Tel.: (44) 1506413311
Food Mfr
N.A.I.C.S.: 311999

Kellogg Company of South Africa (Pty.) Ltd. (1)
7 Woodmead Estate Woodmead Drive, Woodmead, Johannesburg, 2146, South Africa
Tel.: (27) 11 233 6685
Web Site: https://www.kelloggs
Ready-to-Eat Cereals & Drink Mixes Mfr
N.A.I.C.S.: 311230

Kellogg Espana, S.L. (1)
Poligono Industrial de Valls, Tarragona, 43800, Spain
Tel.: (34) 902237323
Web Site: https://www.kelloggs.es
Ready-to-Eat Cereals & Drink Mixes Mfr
N.A.I.C.S.: 311230

Subsidiary (Domestic):

Kellogg Manufacturing Espana, S.L. (2)
Calle Dels Licoristes Corders 2, Valls, 43800, Spain
Tel.: (34) 977603114
Breakfast & Snacks Products Mfr
N.A.I.C.S.: 311230

Kellogg Foods (Shanghai) Co. Ltd (1)
Shanghai Waigaoqiao Bonded Area Jiatai Rd 39 four part-31, Shanghai, 200131, China
Tel.: (86) 58391533
Food Merchant Whslr

N.A.I.C.S.: 424420

Kellogg Group Limited (1)
The Kellogg Building Talbot Road, Manchester, M16 0PU, United Kingdom
Tel.: (44) 1618692000
Web Site: https://www.kellogg.com
Emp.: 250
Breakfast Cereal Mfr
N.A.I.C.S.: 311230

Kellogg India Private Limited (1)
1001-1002 10th Floor Hiranandani Knowledge Park Hiranandani Business P, Powai, Mumbai, 400076, India
Tel.: (91) 1800223500
Web Site: https://www.kelloggs.com
Breakfast Cereal Mfr
N.A.I.C.S.: 311230
Prashant Peres *(Mng Dir)*

Kellogg Sales Company (1)
1 Kellogg Sq, Battle Creek, MI 49016
Tel.: (269) 961-2000
Ready to Eat Cereal & Other Food Products Mfr & Distr
N.A.I.C.S.: 424490

Subsidiary (Domestic):

545 LLC (2)
1590 US Hwy 259 S, Daingerfield, TX 75638
Tel.: (903) 520-6746
Breakfast Cereal Mfr
N.A.I.C.S.: 311230

Gardenburger, LLC (2)
15615 Alton Pkwy Ste 350, Irvine, CA 92618
Tel.: (949) 255-2000
Emp.: 156
Restaurant Services
N.A.I.C.S.: 722513

Kellogg de Mexico, S. de R.L. de C.V. (1)
Km 1 Carr Al Campo Militar s / n, Col San Antonio de la Punta, CP 76135, Queretaro, Mexico
Tel.: (52) 5556242105
Web Site: https://www.kelloggs.com.mx
Food Products Distr
N.A.I.C.S.: 311999

Subsidiary (Domestic):

Kellman, S. de R.L. de C.V. (2)
Calle Ninguno 0 Int 0 Colonia San Antonio De La Punta, Queretaro, 76135, Mexico
Tel.: (52) 4422111300
Food Merchant Whslr
N.A.I.C.S.: 424420

Kellogg Servicios, S.C. (2)
Campo Militar Km 1 Entroque Km 3 S L P S/N San Antonio De La Punta, Queretaro, 76135, Mexico
Tel.: (52) 4422111300
Food Merchant Whslr
N.A.I.C.S.: 424420

Servicios Argkel, S.C. (2)
Lazaro Cardenas No 2785, Tlaquepaque, 45550, Jalisco, Mexico
Tel.: (52) 3336669519
Grain & Field Bean Distr
N.A.I.C.S.: 424510

Kellogg's Produits Alimentaires, S.A. (1)
245 Rue du Vieux Pont de Sevres, 92100, Boulogne-Billancourt, France (100%)
Tel.: (33) 149352121
Sales Range: $25-49.9 Million
Emp.: 100
Ready-to-Eat Cereals
N.A.I.C.S.: 311230

Klux A S.a.r.l. (1)
91 Montee St Crepin, 1365, Luxembourg, Luxembourg
Tel.: (352) 26683785
Breakfast Cereal Mfr
N.A.I.C.S.: 311230

Mass Food SAE (1)
Plot 43 44 3rd Industrial Zone, Giza, 6th of October City, 12451, Egypt
Tel.: (20) 238204001
Web Site: https://www.massfood.com

Breakfast Cereal Mfr
N.A.I.C.S.: 311230

Nhong Shim Kellogg Co. Ltd. (1)
142 Sinsohyeon-dong 29 Gongdan 2-ro, Anseong, 17567, Gyeonggi-Do, Korea (South)
Tel.: (82) 800236411
Web Site: https://www.kellogg.co.kr
Food Merchant Whslr
N.A.I.C.S.: 424420

Nordisk Kelloggs ApS (1)
Stationsparken 24, Glostrup, 2600, Denmark (100%)
Tel.: (45) 43281000
Web Site: http://www.kelloggs.dk
Sales Range: $25-49.9 Million
Emp.: 51
Ready-to-Eat Cereals
N.A.I.C.S.: 311230

North America Cereal Co. (1)
1 Kellogg Sq, Battle Creek, MI 49016
Web Site: https://www.wkkellogg.ca
Snacks & Frozen Food Product Mfr
N.A.I.C.S.: 311813

Parati Industria e Comercio De Alimentos Ltda (1)
Rua Tirandentes 475 Sao Lourenco D Oeste, Sao Francisco do Sul, 89990-000, Brazil
Tel.: (55) 4933447000
Web Site: https://www.parati.com.br
Cookie Mfr
N.A.I.C.S.: 311821

Pringles Manufacturing Company (1)
1306 Highway 70 Byp, Jackson, TN 38301-5072
Tel.: (731) 423-5940
Breakfast Cereal Mfr
N.A.I.C.S.: 311230

The Eggo Company (1)
1 Kellogg Sq, Battle Creek, MI 49017
Tel.: (269) 660-7553
Web Site: https://www.leggowitheggo.com
Frozen Breakfast Foods Mfr
N.A.I.C.S.: 311230

Wimble Manufacturing Belgium BVBA (1)
Eggestraat 1, 2800, Mechelen, Belgium
Tel.: (32) 15263940
Snack Food Mfr
N.A.I.C.S.: 311919

KELLER MANUFACTURING COMPANY, INC.
2603 Grassland Dr, Louisville, KY 40299
Tel.: (828) 261-5123
Web Site: https://kmfi.net
Year Founded: 1866
KMFI—(OTCIQ)
Fabricated Metal Mfr
N.A.I.C.S.: 332312
Douglas W. Rink *(CEO)*
S. Oden Howell Jr. *(Chm)*

KELLY SERVICES, INC.
999 W Big Beaver Rd, Troy, MI 48084-4782
Tel.: (248) 362-4444
Web Site:
  https://www.kellyservices.com
Year Founded: 1946
KELYA—(NASDAQ)
Rev.: $4,909,700,000
Assets: $2,894,200,000
Liabilities: $1,558,000,000
Net Worth: $1,336,200,000
Earnings: $156,100,000
Emp.: 7,400
Fiscal Year-end: 01/01/22
Temporary Staffing Services
N.A.I.C.S.: 561320
Vanessa P. Williams *(Gen Counsel & Sr VP)*
Peter W. Quigley *(Pres & CEO)*
Laura S. Lockhart *(Chief Acctg Officer, VP & Controller)*

Pete M. Boland *(CMO & Sr VP)*
Jocelyn Lincoln *(Chief Talent Officer)*
Vanessa P. Williams *(Gen Counsel)*
Troy R. Anderson *(CFO & Exec VP)*

Subsidiaries:

Global Technology Associates, LLC (1)
1890 Preston White Dr Ste 150, Reston, VA 20191
Tel.: (703) 476-8999
Web Site: https://www.gtatelecom.com
Engineering Consulting Services
N.A.I.C.S.: 541330

Greenwood/Asher & Associates, LLC (1)
42 Business Center Dr Ste 206, Miramar Beach, FL 32550
Tel.: (850) 650-2277
Web Site:
  https://www.greenwoodsearch.com
Recruiting Consulting & Training Services
N.A.I.C.S.: 541612
Susanne Griffin *(Mng Dir & VP)*
Betty Asher *(Co-Founder)*
Tracey Weldon *(VP-)*
Jim Johnsen *(VP-)*
Jeremy Duff *(VP-)*
Robert Caret *(VP-)*

Kelly Properties, Inc. (1)
999 W Big Beaver Rd, Troy, MI 48084-4716 (100%)
Tel.: (248) 244-4300
Web Site: http://www.kellyservices.com
Sales Range: $550-599.9 Million
Emp.: 2,000
Property Management Services
N.A.I.C.S.: 531312

Kelly Services (Australia), Ltd. (1)
Level G 15 Castlereagh Street, Sydney, 2000, NSW, Australia
Tel.: (61) 292466000
Web Site: http://www.kellyservices.com.au
Human Resource Consulting Services
N.A.I.C.S.: 541612

Kelly Services GmbH (1)
Domstrasse 19, 20095, Hamburg, Germany
Tel.: (49) 403680700
Web Site: https://www.kellyservices.de
Employment Services
N.A.I.C.S.: 561311
Sladjan Petkovic *(Mng Dir)*
Jacqueline S. Luttjohann *(Dir-Human Resources)*
Berendina Bekhuis *(Mng Dir)*
Stefano Tomasi *(Mng Dir)*

Kelly Services Hungary Staffing, Kft. (1)
Vaci Ut 35 34, 1134, Budapest, Hungary
Tel.: (36) 13017800
Web Site: https://www.kellyservices.hu
Staffing & Recruitment Services
N.A.I.C.S.: 541612

Kelly Services, Inc. - International Division (1)
999 W Big Beaver Rd, Troy, MI 48084-4716
Tel.: (248) 362-4444
Web Site: http://www.kellyservices.com
Sales Range: $550-599.9 Million
Emp.: 2,000
International Office, Marketing & Staffing Services
N.A.I.C.S.: 561320

Subsidiary (Non-US):

Kelly Services (S) Pte Ltd (2)
36 Robinson Road 20-01 City House, Singapore, 68877, Singapore
Tel.: (65) 67093388
Web Site: https://www.persolkelly.com.sg
Temporary & Permanent Staffing Services
N.A.I.C.S.: 561311

Subsidiary (Domestic):

BTI Consultants Pte. Ltd. (3)
36 Robinson Road 20-01 City House, Singapore, 68877, Singapore
Tel.: (65) 66033368
Employment Placement Agencies
N.A.I.C.S.: 561311
Wanna Assavakarint *(Dir-Consulting)*

Subsidiary (Non-US):

BTI Consultants (India) Private Limited (4)
707 Prestige Meridian-II 30 M G Road Bangalore Bazaar, Indiranagar, Bengaluru, 560001, India (100%)
Tel.: (91) 8025591263
Sales Range: $50-74.9 Million
Consulting Services
N.A.I.C.S.: 611710

BTI Consultants Hong Kong Limited (4)
Unit 1001 10th Floor 100 Queen's Road, Central, China (Hong Kong)
Tel.: (852) 25221186
Temporary Help Service
N.A.I.C.S.: 561320

BTI Executive Placement (Thailand) Co. (4)
27th floorTower 2 Unit 2706 195 South Sathorn Road, Bangkok, 10120, Thailand
Tel.: (66) 26703388
Web Site: http://www.bticonsultants.com
Sales Range: $25-49.9 Million
Emp.: 7
Executive Placement Services
N.A.I.C.S.: 561311
James Agrawal (Mng Dir)

Subsidiary (Non-US):

Kelly Services (India) Pvt. Ltd. (3)
Unitech Cyber Park Tower C 12th Floor Unit No 1202 - 1204 Sector 39, Gurgaon, 122 002, Haryana, India
Tel.: (91) 8882404613
Web Site: https://www.persolkelly.co.in
Emp.: 83
Employment Placement Agencies
N.A.I.C.S.: 561311
Bn Thammaiah (Mng Dir)

Kelly Services (Malaysia) Sdn. Bhd. (3)
Level 19 Menara AIA Sentral No 30 Jalan Sultan Ismail, 6 Changkat Raja Chulan, 50250, Kuala Lumpur, Malaysia (100%)
Tel.: (60) 322030808
Web Site: https://www.persolkelly.com.my
Sales Range: $100-124.9 Million
Temporary & Permanent Staffing Services
N.A.I.C.S.: 561311

Subsidiary (Domestic):

Agensi Pekerjaan Kerjaya Sukses Sdn. Bhd (4)
17th Floor MCB Plaza 13 Changkat Raja Chulan, 50200, Kuala Lumpur, Malaysia
Tel.: (60) 320318923
Web Site: http://www.kerjayasukses.com.my
Sales Range: $25-49.9 Million
Emp.: 10
Recruitment Services
N.A.I.C.S.: 561320

Subsidiary (Non-US):

Kelly Services (New Zealand), Ltd. (3)
35b Leslie Hills Dr Riccarton, Christchurch, 8011, New Zealand
Tel.: (64) 33792963
Web Site: http://www.kellyservices.co.nz
Sales Range: $10-24.9 Million
Emp.: 40
Temporary & Permanent Staffing Services
N.A.I.C.S.: 561311

Kelly Services Australia (3)
Level G 15 Castlereagh Street, Sydney, 2000, NSW, Australia (100%)
Tel.: (61) 292466000
Web Site: http://www.kellyservices.com.au
Sales Range: $25-49.9 Million
Emp.: 40
Temporary & Permanent Staffing Services
N.A.I.C.S.: 561320

Kelly Services Staffing & Recruitment (Thailand) Co., Ltd. (3)
27th Floor Empire Tower 3 Unit 2707 1 South Sathorn Road, Yannawa, Bangkok, 10120, Thailand
Tel.: (66) 26700505
Web Site: https://www.persolkelly.co.th

Sales Range: $25-49.9 Million
Emp.: 16
Recruitment Services
N.A.I.C.S.: 561320
Wanna Assavakarint (Mng Dir)

Subsidiary (Domestic):

P-Serv Pte. Ltd. (3)
36 Robinson Road 20-01 City House, Singapore, 068877, Singapore
Tel.: (65) 67093388
Web Site: https://www.p-serv.com.sg
Sales Range: $25-49.9 Million
Emp.: 2
Employment Placement Agencies
N.A.I.C.S.: 561311

Joint Venture (Non-US):

Tempstaff (Hong Kong) Limited (3)
Unit 2001 20F Hing Wai Building 36 Queen's Road, Central, China (Hong Kong) (49%)
Tel.: (852) 25258121
Web Site: http://www.tempstaff.com.hk
Recruitment & Employment Consulting Services
N.A.I.C.S.: 561311

Subsidiary (Non-US):

Kelly Services Canada, Ltd. (2)
77 City Centre Drive Suite 401, Mississauga, L5B 1M5, ON, Canada (100%)
Tel.: (905) 949-0428
Web Site: https://www.kellyservices.ca
Sales Range: $10-24.9 Million
Temporary Services for Office, Marketing, Technical & Light Industrial & Home Care
N.A.I.C.S.: 335132

Kelly Services Healthcare Unipessoal, Lda. (2)
Gare do Oriente Espaco F1, 1990 - 233, Lisbon, Portugal
Tel.: (351) 218933050
Human Resource Consulting Services
N.A.I.C.S.: 541612

Kelly Services Management S.a.r.l. (2)
Av Edouard-Dubois 20, CH-2002, Neuchatel, Switzerland
Tel.: (41) 327321100
Sales Range: $25-49.9 Million
Emp.: 25
Temporary Help Service
N.A.I.C.S.: 561320

Subsidiary (Non-US):

Kelly Services (3)
Pr Mira d 33 / 1 business center Olympic Plaza, 129110, Moscow, Russia
Tel.: (7) 4957777756
Web Site: http://www.kellyservices.ru
Sales Range: $100-124.9 Million
Temporary & Permanent Staffing Services
N.A.I.C.S.: 561311

Kelly Services (Ireland), Ltd. (3)
21-22 Grafton Street, Dublin, Ireland (100%)
Tel.: (353) 0016793111
Web Site: https://www.kellyservices.ie
Sales Range: $1-9.9 Million
Temporary Staffing Services
N.A.I.C.S.: 561320
Richard Bradley (Mng Dir & VP)
Donal Cahill (Mgr-Human Resources-Operations)
Gwen Leyden (Head-Operations)
Chris Morris (Fin Dir)
Maggie Old (Dir-HR & Support Svcs)
Ben Forde (Branch Mgr)
Ben Forde (Branch Mgr)

Kelly Services (Nederland) B.V. (3)
Neptunusstraat 37, 2132 JA, Hoofddorp, Netherlands (100%)
Tel.: (31) 237111182
Web Site: https://www.kellyservices.nl
Sales Range: $25-49.9 Million
Temporary & Permanent Staffing Services
N.A.I.C.S.: 561330

Subsidiary (Domestic):

Kelly Services (Suisse) S.A. (3)

Rue Saint-Honore 2, 2000, Neuchatel, Switzerland (100%)
Tel.: (41) 327298080
Sales Range: $10-24.9 Million
Emp.: 200
Temporary & Permanent Staffing Services
N.A.I.C.S.: 561320

Subsidiary (Non-US):

Kelly Services (UK) Ltd. (3)
Apple Market House 17 Union Street, Kingston upon Thames, KT1 1RR, Surrey, United Kingdom (100%)
Tel.: (44) 2084811200
Web Site: http://www.kellyservices.co.uk
Temporary & Permanent Staffing Services
N.A.I.C.S.: 561330

Division (Domestic):

Kelly Educational Staffing (4)
Premier House 150 Southampton Row, London, WC1B 5AL, United Kingdom
Tel.: (44) 2078330865
Web Site: http://www.kellyservices.co.uk
Sales Range: $1-9.9 Million
Emp.: 10
Educational Staffing Services & Marketing
N.A.I.C.S.: 541613

Subsidiary (Domestic):

Kelly Payroll Services Limited (4)
Apple Market House 17 Union Street, Kingston upon Thames, KT1 1RR, Surrey, United Kingdom
Tel.: (44) 2084811200
Web Site: http://www.kellyservices.co.uk
Recruitment Services
N.A.I.C.S.: 541214

Toner Graham Limited (4)
The Limes Bayshill Road, Cheltenham, GL50 3AW, Gloucestershire, United Kingdom
Tel.: (44) 1242227711
Web Site: http://www.tonergraham.com
Sales Range: $75-99.9 Million
Financial & Accounting Professional Recruitment Services
N.A.I.C.S.: 541612
Helen Palmer (Mng Dir)

Subsidiary (Non-US):

Kelly Services - Empressa De Trabalho Temporario, Unipessoal, Lda. (3)
Rua Joshua Benoliel 6, Edificio Alto das Amoreiras 10B, 1250-133, Lisbon, Portugal
Tel.: (351) 213715250
Web Site: https://www.kellyservices.pt
Sales Range: $25-49.9 Million
Emp.: 100
Temporary Help Service
N.A.I.C.S.: 561320

Kelly Services AB (3)
Regeringsgatan 77, Stockholm, 111 39, Sweden
Tel.: (46) 854651100
Web Site: http://www.kellyservices.se
Sales Range: $25-49.9 Million
Emp.: 7
Recruitment Services
N.A.I.C.S.: 561320

Kelly Services France S.A. (3)
9 cours du Triangle - BAT D, La Defense, 92937, Paris, France (100%)
Tel.: (33) 158746767
Web Site: https://www.kellyservices.fr
Sales Range: $10-24.9 Million
Temporary Services for Office, Marketing, Technical & Light Industrial & Home Care
N.A.I.C.S.: 561320

Kelly Services GMBH NCO Ohg (3)
Lubecker Strasse 128, 22087, Hamburg, Germany (100%)
Tel.: (49) 403680700
Web Site: http://www.kellyservices.de
Sales Range: $100-124.9 Million
Temporary & Permanent Staffing Services
N.A.I.C.S.: 561311

Kelly Services Interim (Belgium) (3)
Jan Emiel Mommaertslaan 18/A, 1831, Machelen, Belgium (100%)
Tel.: (32) 2 211 0890

Web Site: https://www.kellyservices.be
Sales Range: $100-124.9 Million
Temporary & Permanent Staffing Services
N.A.I.C.S.: 561311

Kelly Services Luxembourg, S.a.r.l. (3)
7/11 Route d'Esch, 1470, Luxembourg, Luxembourg
Tel.: (352) 4662661
Web Site: https://www.kellyservices.lu
Recruitment Services
N.A.I.C.S.: 561320

Kelly Services Norge A/S (3)
Ovre Slottsgate 2B, PO Box 1573, Oslo, 0157, Norway (100%)
Tel.: (47) 81500044
Web Site: https://www.kellyservices.no
Sales Range: $10-24.9 Million
Temporary Services for Offices, Marketing, Technical & Light Industrial & Home Care
N.A.I.C.S.: 561320
Thomas Schenk (Mng Dir)
Gunn Marie Henningsen (Country Mgr-)
Thomas Lund (Branch Mgr)
Philip Lindholm (Partner-)
Frances Toney (Branch Mgr)
Tina Eriksen (Partner)

Kelly Services S.A.R.L. (3)
7-11 Route d'Esch, 1470, Luxembourg, Luxembourg
Tel.: (352) 4662661
Sales Range: $1-9.9 Million
Emp.: 5
Permanent & Temporary Staffing Services
N.A.I.C.S.: 561311

Kelly Services Societa di Fornitura di Lavoro Temporaneo S.p.A. (3)
Viale Sarca 235, 20126, Milan, Italy
Tel.: (39) 02880731
Web Site: https://www.kellyservices.it
Sales Range: $100-124.9 Million
Temporary & Permanent Staffing Services
N.A.I.C.S.: 561311
Stefano Giorgetti (CEO)

Kelly Services of Denmark, Inc. (3)
Kultorvet 11 1 tv, Copenhagen, 1175, Denmark (100%)
Tel.: (45) 33117070
Web Site: https://www.kellyservices.dk
Sales Range: $10-24.9 Million
Temporary & Permanent Staffing Services
N.A.I.C.S.: 561320
Thommas Schenk (CEO)
Winnie Andersen (Ops Mgr)
Janni Thornborg Sorensen (Sls Mgr)

access KellyOCG GmbH (3)
Schanzenstr 23, 51063, Cologne, 51063, Germany
Tel.: (49) 2219564900
Web Site: http://www.access.de
Emp.: 8
Human Resources & Executive Search Consulting Services
N.A.I.C.S.: 541612

Subsidiary (Non-US):

Kelly Services Mexico S.A. de C.V. (2)
Ejercito Nacional 579 Piso 5th Fl, Colonia, 44190, Granada, Mexico (100%)
Tel.: (52) 5511011200
Web Site: http://www.kellyservices.com.mx
Sales Range: $75-99.9 Million
Emp.: 300
Temporary Services for Office, Marketing, Technical & Light Industrial & Home Care
N.A.I.C.S.: 561320

LLC Kelly Services IT solutions (2)
Karl Marx 7, Tomsk, Russia
Tel.: (7) 8123320406
Information Technology Consulting Services
N.A.I.C.S.: 541512
Dmitry Lizinsky (Coord-Projects)

Kelly Services, Inc. - Professional Technical & Staffing Alternatives Division (1)
999 W Big Beaver Rd, Troy, MI 48084-4716
Tel.: (248) 362-4444
Web Site: http://www.kellyservices.com
Sales Range: $550-599.9 Million
Emp.: 2,000
Professional, Technical & Staffing Services

Kelly Services, Inc.—(Continued)

N.A.I.C.S.: 561320

Unit (Domestic):

Kelly Automotive Services Group (2)
999 W Big Beaver Rd, Troy, MI
48084-4716   **(100%)**
Tel.: (248) 362-4444
Sales Range: $100-124.9 Million
Temporary & Contract Automotive Employee Services
N.A.I.C.S.: 561320

Kelly Engineering Resources (2)
999 W Big Beaver Rd, Troy, MI
48084-4716   **(100%)**
Tel.: (248) 362-4444
Web Site: http://www.kellyengineering.com
Sales Range: $75-99.9 Million
Emp.: 30
Aeronautical, Automotive, Chemical, Electrical, Mechanical & Process Engineering Staffing Services
N.A.I.C.S.: 561320

Kelly Financial Resources (2)
999 W Big Beaver Rd, Troy, MI
48084-4716   **(100%)**
Tel.: (248) 362-4444
Web Site: http://www.kellyfinance.com
Sales Range: $400-449.9 Million
Multi-Disciplined Financial & Accounting Staffing Services
N.A.I.C.S.: 561330

Kelly Information Technology Resources (2)
999 W Big Beaver Rd, Troy, MI
48084-4716   **(100%)**
Tel.: (248) 362-4444
Web Site: http://www.kellyit.com
Sales Range: $100-124.9 Million
Information Technology Staffing Services
N.A.I.C.S.: 561320

Kelly Managed Services (2)
999 W Big Beaver Rd, Troy, MI
48084-4716   **(100%)**
Tel.: (248) 362-4444
Web Site:
   http://www.kellycareernetwork.com
Office, Light Industrial & Home Care Services
N.A.I.C.S.: 561330

Kelly Scientific Resources (2)
999 W Big Beaver Rd, Troy, MI
48084-4716   **(100%)**
Tel.: (248) 362-4444
Web Site: http://www.kellyscientific.com
Sales Range: $10-24.9 Million
Emp.: 10
Scientific Professional Staffing for Disciplines Including Biology, Chemistry, Geology, Biochemistry & Physics
N.A.I.C.S.: 561320

NextGen Global Resources, LLC (1)
300 S Wacker Dr Ste 1313, Chicago, IL 60606
Tel.: (858) 999-8668
Web Site: https://www.kellytelecom.com
Telecommunications Consulting Services
N.A.I.C.S.: 541618
Jonathan Langley (Chief Talent Officer)
Julie Pieters (VP-Ops)
Michelle Cadena (VP-Sales)
Alice Mahoney (VP-Sales)
Mark Walker (Pres)
Rashid Iqbal (Chief Growth Officer)
Liz Fiallo (Sr VP-Sales & Business Development)
Dexter Lee (VP-)
Mike Cutler (VP-)
Christian Atienza (VP-Finance)
Michael Kefauver (VP-)
Irene Stone (VP-Client Services)
Nikhil Dogra (VP-)
Henrik Centerham (VP-Sales)
Darren Horton (VP-Sales)
Mike Dawkins (VP- &)

Pediatric Therapeutic Services, Inc. (1)
525 Fayette St, Conshohocken, PA 19428
Tel.: (610) 941-7020
Web Site: https://mypts.com
Healthcare Services

N.A.I.C.S.: 621111
Philip Puleo (Exec Dir)
Pamela Hackett (Mng Partner)
Diana Fongheiser (Mng Partner)
Candice Donnelly-Knox (Dir-Clinical Svcs)

Softworld, Inc. (1)
281 Winter St Ste 301, Waltham, MA 02451
Tel.: (781) 466-8882
Web Site: https://www.softworldinc.com
Employment Placement Agencies
N.A.I.C.S.: 561311
Tim Southwick (Chief Revenue Officer)
David S Teitelman (Pres)
Steve Cooper (Sr VP)
Alan Sarasohn (Sr VP-Financial Services)
Peter Niejadlik (VP)
Michael Tolk (Pres)
Mark Finocchario (COO)
Maura Mohan (VP-Human Resources)
Steven Edwards (VP-Finance)
Jonathan Anderson (VP)
Megan Altmayer (VP-Information Technology-Engineering)
Hasan Hammad (Controller)

Teachers On Call, Inc. (1)
3001 Metro Dr Ste 200, Bloomington, MN 55425
Web Site: https://www.teachersoncall.com
Educational Staff Recruitment Services
N.A.I.C.S.: 611710

KELVIN MEDICAL, INC.
10930 Skyranch Pl, Nevada City, CA 95959
Tel.: (530) 388-8706
Year Founded: 2016
KVMD—(OTCEM)
Medical Device Mfr & Distr
N.A.I.C.S.: 339113
William Mandel (Pres, CEO, CFO & Treas)

KELYNIAM GLOBAL, INC.
97 River Rd, Collinsville, CT 06019   **NV**
Web Site: https://www.kelyniam.com
Year Founded: 2005
KLYG—(OTCIQ)
Engineeering Services
N.A.I.C.S.: 541330
Ross Bjella (Chm & CEO)
Christopher Breault (COO)
Mark V. Smith (VP-Sls & Bus Dev)

KEMIAO GARMENT HOLDING GROUP
6910 S Cimarron Rd Ste 240, Las Vegas, NV 89114
Tel.: (213) 893-2525   **NV**
Web Site:
   http://www.aivtechgroup.com
Year Founded: 2007
KMGH—(OTCIQ)
Liabilities: $41,695
Net Worth: ($41,695)
Earnings: ($41,695)
Emp.: 1
Fiscal Year-end: 12/31/19
Consumer Electronics Product Mfr
N.A.I.C.S.: 334419
Yanping Sheng (CEO & CFO)

KEMPER CORPORATION
200 E Randolph St Ste 3300, Chicago, IL 60601
Tel.: (312) 661-4600   **DE**
Web Site: https://www.kemper.com
KMPR—(NYSE)
Rev.: $4,944,200,000
Assets: $12,742,700,000
Liabilities: $10,237,700,000
Net Worth: $2,505,000,000
Earnings: ($272,100,000)
Emp.: 8,100
Fiscal Year-end: 12/31/23
Property & Casualty Insurance, Life & Health Insurance & Consumer Finance Services

N.A.I.C.S.: 524126
Christopher Wade Flint (Pres-Kemper Life)
Joseph P. Lacher Jr. (Pres & CEO)
Charles T. Brooks (Exec VP-Ops & Sys)
Mark A. Green (Exec VP-Business Development)
Barbara Ciesemier (Asst VP-Corp Comm)
Duane Sanders (Pres-Property & Casualty Div & Exec VP)
Kimberly A. Holmes (Chief Actuary, Strategic Analytics Officer & Exec VP)
Ismat Aziz (Chief Admin Officer, Chief HR Officer & Exec VP)
Erich Sternberg (Pres-Life & Health Div & Exec VP)
James A. Alexander (Chief Acctg Officer & Sr VP)
C. Thomas Evans Jr. (Gen Counsel, Sec & Exec VP)

Subsidiaries:

Alliance United Insurance Services, Inc. (1)
5300 Adolfo Rd Suite 200, Camarillo, CA 93012
Tel.: (805) 650-2100
Web Site: http://www.allianceunited.com
Sales Range: $1-9.9 Million
Emp.: 500
Automobile Insurance Services
N.A.I.C.S.: 524298
Brian Duffy (Pres)

Alpha Property & Casualty Insurance Company (100%)
400 S Executive Dr Ste 200, Brookfield, WI 53005
Tel.: (972) 690-5500
Web Site: http://www.kemper.com
Property & Casualty Insurance Operating Company
N.A.I.C.S.: 524126

American Access Casualty Company (1)
2211 Butterfield Rd Ste 200, Downers Grove, IL 60515
Tel.: (630) 645-7750
Web Site: https://www.aains.com
Automobile Insurance Services
N.A.I.C.S.: 524126
Raquel Alfaro (Coord-Marketing)
Michelle Thibault (Mktg Dir)

Fireside Bank (1)
5050 Hopyard Rd Ste 200, Pleasanton, CA 94588
Tel.: (925) 460-9020
Sales Range: $200-249.9 Million
Emp.: 300
Banking Services
N.A.I.C.S.: 522110

Infinity Property & Casualty Corporation (1)
2201 4th Ave N, Birmingham, AL 35203
Tel.: (205) 870-4000
Web Site: http://www.infinityauto.com
Property & Casualty Insurance
N.A.I.C.S.: 524126
James R. Gober (Chm)

Subsidiary (Domestic):

Infinity Casualty Insurance Company (2)
11700 Great Oaks Way Ste 300, Alpharetta, GA 30022
Tel.: (678) 627-7000
Web Site: http://www.infinityauto.com
Property & Casualty Insurance Services
N.A.I.C.S.: 524126

Subsidiary (Domestic):

Infinity Insurance Agency Inc. (3)
11700 Great Oaks Way, Alpharetta, GA 30022-2448
Tel.: (678) 627-7000
Web Site: http://www.infinityauto.com
Insurance Agents

N.A.I.C.S.: 524210

Subsidiary (Non-US):

Infinity Specialty Insurance Company (4)
3760 River Run Dr, Birmingham, AL 35243
Tel.: (678) 627-7000
Web Site: http://www.infinityauto.com
Property Damage Insurance Services
N.A.I.C.S.: 524126

Subsidiary (Domestic):

Infinity Group, L.L.C. (2)
3700 Colnnade Pkwy, Birmingham, AL 35243
Tel.: (205) 870-4000
Web Site: http://www.infinityauto.com
Insurance Holding Company
N.A.I.C.S.: 551112
James R. Gober (Chm, Pres & CEO)

Subsidiary (Domestic):

Infinity Auto Insurance Company (3)
3700 Colonnade Pkwy Ste 600, Birmingham, AL 35243
Tel.: (205) 870-4000
Web Site: http://www.infinityauto.com
Property & Casualty Insurance Services
N.A.I.C.S.: 524210
James R. Gober (Pres & CEO)

Subsidiary (Domestic):

Infinity Insurance Agency, Inc. (2)
15357 Crenshaw Blvd Ste A, Gardena, CA 90249
Tel.: (424) 757-4893
Web Site: http://www.infinityauto.com
Insurance Management Services
N.A.I.C.S.: 524298

Infinity Property & Casualty Services (2)
11700 Great Oaks Way, Alpharetta, GA 30022
Tel.: (678) 627-6000
Web Site: http://www.infinityproperty.com
Property & Casualty Insurance Services
N.A.I.C.S.: 524298
Thomas Smith (Dir-IT)

Kemper Home Service Companies (1)
12115 Lackland Rd, Saint Louis, MO 63146
Tel.: (314) 819-4300
Web Site: http://www.kemper.com
Sales Range: $125-149.9 Million
Life & Property Insurance Services
N.A.I.C.S.: 524113

Subsidiary (Domestic):

Mutual Savings Life Insurance Company (2)
1420 5th Ave, Decatur, AL 35601
Tel.: (256) 353-1031
Web Site: http://www.kemperhsc.com
Holding Company: Life Insurance Services
N.A.I.C.S.: 524113

Subsidiary (Domestic):

Mutual Savings Fire Insurance Co. Inc. (3)
401 Lee St NE, Decatur, AL 35601
Web Site:
   http://www.unitrincareeragencycompanies.com
Sales Range: $50-74.9 Million
Emp.: 100
Home Owner Fire Insurance Services
N.A.I.C.S.: 524126

Mutual Savings Life Insurance Co. Inc. (3)
12115 Lackland Rd, Saint Louis, MO 63146-4003
Tel.: (314) 819-4300
Sales Range: $50-74.9 Million
Emp.: 100
Fire Insurance Services
N.A.I.C.S.: 524113
Thom Myers (Pres, COO & Gen Mgr)

Subsidiary (Domestic):

The Reliable Life Insurance
Company **(2)**
12115 Lackland Rd, Saint Louis, MO 63146
Tel.: (314) 963-1480
Web Site: http://www.kemperhsc.com
Sales Range: $100-124.9 Million
Fire Insurance Services
N.A.I.C.S.: 524113

Affiliate (Domestic):

Capitol County Mutual Fire Insurance
Co. **(3)**
12115 Lackland Rd, Saint Louis, MO 63146
Tel.: (314) 819-4300
Web Site: http://www.unitrin.com
Sales Range: $10-24.9 Million
Emp.: 2
Fire Insurance & Other Coverage
N.A.I.C.S.: 524126

Subsidiary (Domestic):

Old Reliable Casualty Co. **(4)**
12115 Lackland Rd, Saint Louis, MO
63146 **(100%)**
Tel.: (314) 819-4300
Fire Insurance & Related Coverage
N.A.I.C.S.: 524113

Kemper Independence Insurance
Company **(1)**
5555 Gate Pkwy Ste 500, Jacksonville, FL
32256
Tel.: (904) 245-5600
Sales Range: $300-349.9 Million
Life, Property & Casualty Insurance Services
N.A.I.C.S.: 524113

Kemper Specialty **(1)**
21650 Oxnard St Ste 1800, Woodland Hills,
CA 91367-4944
Tel.: (818) 313-8500
Web Site: http://www.kemper.com
Sales Range: $125-149.9 Million
Emp.: 250
Insurance Services
N.A.I.C.S.: 524126

Newins Insurance Agency Holdings,
LLC **(1)**
2211 Butterfield Rd Ste 155, Downers
Grove, IL 60515
Tel.: (630) 570-7172
Art Insurance Services
N.A.I.C.S.: 524210

Security One Insurance Agency **(1)**
117 E Pershing St, New Iberia, LA 70560
Tel.: (337) 560-1601
Sales Range: $25-49.9 Million
Emp.: 2
Property & Casualty Insurance Services
N.A.I.C.S.: 524126

Trinity Universal Insurance Co. **(1)**
12790 Merrit Dr Ste 400, Dallas, TX
75251 **(100%)**
Tel.: (312) 661-4930
Web Site: http://www.unitrin.com
Sales Range: $100-124.9 Million
Emp.: 200
Property & Casualty Insurance Services
N.A.I.C.S.: 524126

Subsidiary (Domestic):

Direct Response Corporation **(2)**
500 S Broad St, Meriden, CT 06450-6643
Tel.: (203) 634-7200
Web Site: http://www.response.com
Sales Range: $125-149.9 Million
Emp.: 150
Investment Holding Company Services
N.A.I.C.S.: 524126

Subsidiary (Domestic):

Response Insurance Company **(3)**
500 S Broad St PO Box 1014, Meriden, CT
06450
Tel.: (203) 634-7200
Web Site: http://www.response.com
Sales Range: $75-99.9 Million
Emp.: 150
Online Auto Insurance Services
N.A.I.C.S.: 524126

Subsidiary (Domestic):

National Merit Insurance Co. **(4)**
500 S Broad St Ste 1, Meriden, CT 06450-
6643
Web Site: http://www.nationalmerit.com
Rev.: $13,081,863
Emp.: 50
Auto Insurance
N.A.I.C.S.: 524126

Subsidiary (Domestic):

Merastar Insurance Co. **(2)**
5600 Brainerd Rd Ste 1A, Chattanooga, TN
37411-5394
Tel.: (423) 296-7700
Web Site: http://www.merastar.com
Fire, Marine & Casualty Insurance
N.A.I.C.S.: 524126

United Casualty Insurance Company
of America **(1)**
One E Wacker Dr, Chicago, IL
60601-1802 **(100%)**
Tel.: (312) 661-4500
Sales Range: $50-74.9 Million
Emp.: 200
Accidental Insurances
N.A.I.C.S.: 524210

Unitrin Advantage Insurance
Company **(1)**
12926 Gran Bay Pkwy W, Jacksonville, FL
32258
Tel.: (904) 245-5600
Sales Range: $150-199.9 Million
Emp.: 500
Property & Casualty Insurance Services
N.A.I.C.S.: 524126

Unitrin County Mutual Insurance
Company **(1)**
Executive Ctr II 8360 LBJ Fwy Ste 400,
Dallas, TX 75243
Tel.: (972) 690-5500
Web Site: http://www.kemper.com
Personal & Commercial Automobile Insurance
N.A.I.C.S.: 524128

Unitrin Direct Property & Casualty
Company **(1)**
5927 Priesly Dr Ste 200, Carlsbad, CA
92008
Tel.: (760) 599-4700
Web Site: http://www.unitrindirect.com
Sales Range: $150-199.9 Million
Automobile Insurance Services
N.A.I.C.S.: 524126

KENILWORTH SYSTEMS
CORP.
721 Beach St, Daytona Beach, FL
32114
Tel.: (516) 741-1352   **WY**
Year Founded: 1968
KENS—(OTCIQ)
Assets: $300,499,198
Liabilities: $300,059,835
Net Worth: $439,363
Earnings: ($13,358)
Fiscal Year-end: 12/31/22
Information Technology Consulting
Services
N.A.I.C.S.: 541512
Dan Snyder (Pres)
Steven W. Swank (sec)

KENNAMETAL INC.
525 William Penn Pl Ste 3300, Pittsburgh, PA 15219-2706
Tel.: (412) 790-0792   **PA**
Web Site:
  https://www.kennametal.com
Year Founded: 1938
KMT—(NYSE)
Rev.: $2,046,899,000
Assets: $2,503,758,000
Liabilities: $1,215,159,000
Net Worth: $1,288,599,000
Earnings: $113,641,000
Emp.: 8,400
Fiscal Year-end: 06/30/24

Machine Tool Manufacturing
N.A.I.C.S.: 333517
William M. Lambert (Chm)
Judith L. Bacchus (Chief Admin Officer & VP)
Kelly Boyer (VP-IR)
Michelle R. Keating (Gen Counsel,
Sec & VP)
Patrick S. Watson (CFO & VP)
Carlonda R. Reilly (CTO & VP)
Sanjay K. Chowbey (Pres & CEO)
Franklin G. Cardenas (Pres-
Infrastructure Bus Segment & VP)
Naeem Rahman (VP-Ops-Metal Cutting)
Nicholas Pflugh (VP-Inserts & Steel
Mfg-America & Interim Chief Comml
Officer)
John W. Witt (VP-Fin & Controller)

Subsidiaries:

Comericializadora Kennametal Bolivia
S.R.L. **(1)**
Calle Villanueva 18, El Alto, La Paz, Bolivia
Tel.: (591) 22852690
Steel Products Mfr
N.A.I.C.S.: 327910
Robert Martin (Gen Mgr)

Deloro Stellite, L.P. **(1)**
1201 Eisenhower Dr N, Goshen, IN 46526
Tel.: (574) 534-2585
Web Site: https://www.stellite.com
Fabricated Metal Products Mfr
N.A.I.C.S.: 332999

Subsidiary (Non-US):

Deloro Stellite UK Limited **(2)**
Unit 3 Kembrey Business Park, Swindon,
SN2 8UU, Wiltshire, United Kingdom
Tel.: (44) 1793498500
Web Site: http://www.stellite.co.uk
Fabricated Metal Products Mfr
N.A.I.C.S.: 332999

Hanita Metal Works, Ltd. **(1)**
PO Box 1121, Shlomi, 22832, Israel
Tel.: (972) 49850034
Emp.: 250
Machine Tools Mfr
N.A.I.C.S.: 333517
David Amir (Gen Mgr)

Kennametal (Shanghai) Co., Ltd. **(1)**
No 750 Jin Yu Rd Jin Qiao Export Processing Zone, Pudong, Shanghai,
China **(100%)**
Tel.: (86) 2138608288
Web Site: http://www.kennametal.com
Sales Range: $125-149.9 Million
Emp.: 200
Metals & Metalworking
N.A.I.C.S.: 333519

Kennametal (Singapore) Pte.
Ltd. **(1)**
3A International Business Park Unit 01-
02/03/05 ICON IBP, Singapore, 609935,
Singapore **(100%)**
Tel.: (65) 62659222
Web Site: http://www.kennametal.com
Sales Range: $25-49.9 Million
Emp.: 14
Sales & Warehousing of Metalworking Tools
N.A.I.C.S.: 444140

Kennametal (Thailand) Co., Ltd. **(1)**
121/35 RS Tower 8th Floor Ratchadapisek
Road, Bangkok, 10400, Dindaeng,
Thailand **(100%)**
Tel.: (66) 24607039
Sales Range: $10-24.9 Million
Emp.: 17
Metals & Metalworking
N.A.I.C.S.: 333519

Kennametal Advanced Materials Solutions Group **(1)**
1600 Technology Way, Latrobe, PA
15650 **(100%)**
Tel.: (724) 539-5000
Web Site: http://www.kennametal.com
Sales Range: $150-199.9 Million
Emp.: 700

Specialty Metal Products, Industrial Advanced Metal Components & Custom Surface & Wear Technologies Mfr
N.A.I.C.S.: 332919

Subsidiary (Domestic):

Conforma Clad, Inc. **(2)**
501 Park E Blvd, New Albany, IN 47150
Tel.: (812) 948-2118
Web Site: http://www.conformaclad.com
Sales Range: $50-74.9 Million
Emp.: 100
Wear-Resistant Industrial Metal Components Mfr
N.A.I.C.S.: 332117

Unit (Domestic):

Extrude Hone LLC **(2)**
235 Industry Blvd, Irwin, PA 15642-2794
Tel.: (724) 863-5900
Web Site: http://www.extrudehone.com
Metal Cutting Tool Mfr
N.A.I.C.S.: 333517
Christian Bernert (CEO)

Subsidiary (Non-US):

Kennametal Extrude Hone
Limited **(3)**
East Park, Shannon, County Clare, Ireland
Tel.: (353) 61705060
Web Site: http://www.extrudehone.com
Sales Range: $10-24.9 Million
Emp.: 11
Machine Tools Mfr
N.A.I.C.S.: 333517

Subsidiary (Non-US):

Extrude Hone KK **(4)**
3-139-1 Shinwa, Misato, 341-0034, Saitama, Japan
Tel.: (81) 489540811
Emp.: 30
Machine Tools Mfr
N.A.I.C.S.: 333517
Okano Yasuki (Gen Mgr)

Subsidiary (Non-US):

Kennametal Extrude Hone Ltd. **(3)**
1 Sovereign Business Park Joplin Court,
Crownhill, Milton Keynes, MK8 0JP, Buckinghamshire, United Kingdom
Tel.: (44) 1908263636
Web Site: http://www.extrudehone.co.uk
Emp.: 10
Machine Tools Mfr
N.A.I.C.S.: 333517

Kennametal Argentina S.A. **(1)**
Edificio Uruguay III Virasoro 2656 Piso 2,
Beccar, B1643HDB, Buenos Aires, Argentina
Tel.: (54) 1151732250
Web Site: http://www.kennametal.com
Emp.: 25
Engineered Component & Advanced Material Distr
N.A.I.C.S.: 423830

Kennametal Australia Pty. Ltd. **(1)**
Unit 10 899 Willington Rd, Roseville, 3178,
NSW, Australia **(100%)**
Tel.: (61) 1800666667
Web Site: https://www.kennametal.com
Sales & Warehousing of Metalworking Tools
N.A.I.C.S.: 444140

Kennametal Chile Ltda. **(1)**
Alferez Real No 1150, Santiago, Chile
Tel.: (56) 22641177
Engineered Component & Advanced Material Distr
N.A.I.C.S.: 423830

Kennametal Energy, Mining & Construction Solutions **(1)**
1600 Technology Way, Latrobe, PA
15650-4647 **(100%)**
Tel.: (724) 539-5000
Web Site: http://www.kennametal.com
Sales Range: $300-349.9 Million
Emp.: 700
Mining & Construction; Machine Bits Mfr
N.A.I.C.S.: 423830

Kennametal Europe Holding
GmbH **(1)**

Kennametal Inc.—(Continued)

Rheingoldstrasse 50, 8212, Neuhausen,
Switzerland
Tel.: (41) 526750100
Web Site: https://www.kennametal.com
Emp.: 30
Machine Tools Mfr
N.A.I.C.S.: 333517
Joost Berting (Mng Dir)

Kennametal GmbH (1)
Wehlauer Strasse 73, 90766, Furth, 90766,
Germany (94%)
Tel.: (49) 91197350
Sales Range: $100-124.9 Million
Emp.: 280
Holding Company
N.A.I.C.S.: 551112
Joachim Fabry (Mng Dir)

Subsidiary (Non-US):

Kenci S.L. (2)
Poligono Industrial Rubi Sur Avda Antonio
Gaudi 192, Rubi, 08191, Barcelona, Spain
Tel.: (34) 935860350
Web Site: http://www.kenci.com
Sales Range: $25-49.9 Million
Emp.: 50
Metal Cutting Tool Mfr
N.A.I.C.S.: 333517

Subsidiary (Domestic):

Kennametal AMSG GmbH (2)
Postfach 1347, Friedrichsdorf, 61364, Germany
Tel.: (49) 6172285220
Web Site: http://www.kennametal.com
Emp.: 120
Engineered Component & Advanced Material Distr
N.A.I.C.S.: 423830

Subsidiary (Non-US):

Kennametal Belgium S.p.r.l. (2)
PO Box 0016, Brussels, 1000,
Belgium (100%)
Tel.: (32) 42484848
Web Site: http://www.kennametal.be
Sales Range: $10-24.9 Million
Emp.: 20
Mfr of Metric Toolholding Products; Rotating
Tooling
N.A.I.C.S.: 333517
Annette Flagothier (Sec)

Subsidiary (Domestic):

Kennametal Deutschland Gmbh (2)
Raiffeisenstrasse 10, PO Box 1347, 61191,
Rosbach vor der Hohe, Germany (100%)
Tel.: (49) 600382770
Web Site: http://www.kennametal.de
Sales Range: $75-99.9 Million
Emp.: 200
Tool Mfr
N.A.I.C.S.: 332216

Kennametal Infrastructure GmbH (2)
Wehlauer Str 73, 90766, Furth, Germany
Tel.: (49) 91197350
Industrial Machinery Mfr
N.A.I.C.S.: 334519

Subsidiary (Non-US):

Kennametal Italia S.p.A. (2)
Via Lombardia 32, San Giuliano Milanese,
20098, Milan, Italy (40%)
Tel.: (39) 02895961
Web Site: https://www.kennametal.com
Hand & Edge Tool Mfr
N.A.I.C.S.: 332216

Subsidiary (Domestic):

**Kennametal Italia Produzione
S.R.L.** (3)
San Giuliano Milanese, Milan, 20098, Lombardy, Italy
Tel.: (39) 0289596307
Engineered Component & Advanced Material Distr
N.A.I.C.S.: 423830
Davide Russo (Mgr-Pur & Logistics)

Subsidiary (Non-US):

**Kennametal Kesici Takimlar Sanayi
Ve Ticaret Anonim Sirketi** (2)

DES Sanayi Sitesi 110 S D29 Blok No 45,
Yukari Dudullu Umraniye, 34776, Istanbul,
Turkiye
Tel.: (90) 2165744780
Sales Range: $25-49.9 Million
Emp.: 25
Machine Tools Mfr
N.A.I.C.S.: 333517
Ilhan Eryener (Country Mgr)

Kennametal Nederland B.V. (2)
Nieuwe Havenweg 29, Postbus 159, NL
6800 AD, Arnhem, Gelderland, (100%)
Netherlands
Tel.: (31) 767995220
Sales Range: $25-49.9 Million
Emp.: 10
Sales & Warehousing of Metalworking Tools
N.A.I.C.S.: 444140

Subsidiary (Domestic):

**Nederlandse Hardmetaal Fabrieken
B.V.** (3)
Nieuwe Havenweg 29, Postbus 159, 6800,
Arnhem, Netherlands
Tel.: (31) 263699611
Web Site: http://www.nhf.nl
Sales Range: $50-74.9 Million
N.A.I.C.S.: 332216

Subsidiary (Non-US):

Kennametal Polska Sp. Z.o.o. (2)
Krzywoustego No 7, Poznan, 61-144, Poland
Tel.: (48) 616656501
Emp.: 50
Machine Tools Mfr
N.A.I.C.S.: 333517
Thomas Kroneisl (Mng Dir)

Subsidiary (Domestic):

**Kennametal Produktions GmbH &
Co. KG.** (2)
Altweiherstrasse 27 -31, 91320, Ebermannstadt, Germany
Tel.: (49) 9194720159
Hand Tool Mfr & Distr
N.A.I.C.S.: 332216

Subsidiary (Non-US):

Kennametal UK Limited (2)
Pensnett Trading Estate Building 14, Kingswinford, DY6 7NP, West Midlands, United
Kingdom (100%)
Tel.: (44) 1384408060
Web Site: http://www.kennametal.com
Sales Range: $100-124.9 Million
Emp.: 180
Hand & Edge Tool Mfr
N.A.I.C.S.: 332216

Subsidiary (Domestic):

Kennametal Logistics UK Ltd. (3)
Building 14 Pensnett Trading Estate, PO
Box 29, Kingswinford, DY6 7NP, West Midlands, United Kingdom
Tel.: (44) 1384401000
Web Site: http://www.kennametal.com
Sales Range: $25-49.9 Million
Emp.: 60
Machine Tools Mfr
N.A.I.C.S.: 333517
Keith Dodd (Mng Dir)

Subsidiary (Domestic):

**Kennametal Widia Produktions GmbH
& Co. KG** (2)
Munchener Str 125 - 127, PO Box 10 21
61, 45145, Essen, Germany
Tel.: (49) 2017250
Industrial Machinery Mfr
N.A.I.C.S.: 334519

**Kennametal Widia Real Estate GmbH
& Co. KG** (2)
Wehlauer Strasse 73, 90766, Furth, Germany
Tel.: (49) 91197350
Web Site: http://www.kennametal.com
Real Estate Development Services
N.A.I.C.S.: 531390

Subsidiary (Domestic):

**Kennametal Hardpoint (Taiwan)
Inc.** (1)

8F No 192 Junggung 2nd Road, Hsi Tun
District, Taichung, 407, Taiwan
Tel.: (886) 423501920
Emp.: 6
Machine Tools Mfr
N.A.I.C.S.: 333517

**Kennametal Holdings Europe
Inc.** (1)
1600 Technology Way, Latrobe, PA 15650-
4647
Tel.: (724) 539-5000
Web Site: http://www.kennametal.com
Investment Management Service
N.A.I.C.S.: 551112

Subsidiary (Non-US):

Kennametal Holdings, LLC Luxembourg S.C.S. (2)
Rue des Bruyeres 23, 1274, Hesperange,
Luxembourg
Tel.: (352) 404448
Web Site: http://www.kennametal.com
Holding Company
N.A.I.C.S.: 551112

Kennametal Hungaria Kft. (1)
Tihanyi Arpad ut 10/B, 9024, Gyor, Gyor-
Moson-Sopron, Hungary
Tel.: (36) 96618150
Sales Range: $25-49.9 Million
Emp.: 7
Engineered Component & Advanced Material Distr
N.A.I.C.S.: 423830

Kennametal India Ltd. (1)
8/9th Mile Tumkur Road, Bengaluru, 560
073, India
Tel.: (91) 8028394321
Web Site: https://www.kennametal.com
Rev.: $136,513,650
Assets: $113,267,700
Liabilities: $25,047,750
Net Worth: $88,219,950
Earnings: $15,574,650
Emp.: 749
Fiscal Year-end: 06/30/2022
Industrial Machinery Mfr
N.A.I.C.S.: 333248
Sanjay K. Chowbey (VP)
Bhagya Chandra Rao (Mng Dir)
K. V. Suresh Reddy (CFO)
Alexander Broetz (VP)
Naveen Chandra Prakash (Compliance Officer & Co-Compliance Officer)
Sanjay Chowbey (VP)

Kennametal Japan Ltd. (1)
MA Building 4 Floor 2 15 12 Kiba Koto Ku,
Tokyo, 1350042, Japan
Tel.: (81) 338202855
Hand & Edge Tool Mfr
N.A.I.C.S.: 332216

Kennametal Korea Ltd. (1)
801 11 Digital-ro 33-gil, Guro-gu, Seoul,
152780, Korea (South)
Tel.: (82) 7047315051
Sales Range: $25-49.9 Million
Emp.: 39
Machine Tools Mfr
N.A.I.C.S.: 333517
J. Song (Mng Dir)

Kennametal Logistics GmbH (1)
Zweibrucker Str 105, 66538, Neunkirchen,
Saarland, Germany
Tel.: (49) 682198090
Web Site: http://www.kennametal.com
Sales Range: $25-49.9 Million
Emp.: 70
Fabricated Metal Products Mfr
N.A.I.C.S.: 332999

**Kennametal Metalworking Solutions &
Services Group** (1)
1600 Technology Way, Latrobe, PA
15650-4647 (100%)
Tel.: (724) 539-5000
Web Site: http://www.kennametal.com
Sales Range: $250-299.9 Million
Emp.: 800
Metal Cutting Tools & Tooling Systems Mfr
N.A.I.C.S.: 333515

Subsidiary (Domestic):

Adaptive Technologies Corp. (2)

6865 Cochran Rd, Solon, OH
44139-4335 (100%)
Tel.: (248) 585-5340
Sales Range: $50-74.9 Million
Emp.: 30
Steel Cutting Tool Mfr & Refurbishing Services
N.A.I.C.S.: 333514

Circle Machine Co. (2)
8782 Lanyard Ct, Rancho Cucamonga, CA
91730-0804 (100%)
Tel.: (626) 357-7046
Web Site: http://www.circlemachine.com
Sales Range: $50-74.9 Million
Emp.: 45
Hand & Edge Tool Mfr
N.A.I.C.S.: 332216
Carlos M. Cardoso (Chm, Pres & CEO)

Kennametal IPG (2)
1662 MacMillan Park Dr, Fort Mill, SC
29707
Tel.: (800) 892-9919
Web Site: http://www.kennametal.com
Sales Range: $150-199.9 Million
Emp.: 100
Expendable Cutting Tools & Accessories
Mfr
N.A.I.C.S.: 332216
Steven R. Hanna (CIO & VP)

**Kennametal Shared Services Private
Limited** (1)
Unit 3 4 5 & 6 Navigator Bldg 5th Flr,
Whitefield, Bengaluru, 560066, Karnataka,
India
Tel.: (91) 8040238400
Machine Tools Mfr
N.A.I.C.S.: 333517
Krishnaveni Iyengar (Asst Mgr-Product Engrg)

**Kennametal Sintec Keramik
GmbH** (1)
Ingenrieder Strasse 2a, 86956, Schongau,
86956, Bavaria, Germany
Tel.: (49) 886123080
Web Site: https://www.kennametal.com
Non-Oxide Ceramics & Powder Metallurgical Steel Mfr
N.A.I.C.S.: 327110

Subsidiary (US):

Sintec Keramik USA Inc. (2)
580 Barnum Ave, Bridgeport, CT 06608
Tel.: (203) 331-0778
Web Site: http://www.sintec-keramik.com
Emp.: 9
Non Oxide Ceramics & Powder Metallurgical Steel Mfr
N.A.I.C.S.: 327110

**Kennametal South Africa (Pty.)
Ltd.** (1)
15 Reservoir Road, Boksburg East, Boksburg, 1478, Gauteng, South Africa (100%)
Tel.: (27) 117489300
Web Site: https://www.kennametal.com
Sales Range: $25-49.9 Million
Emp.: 50
Metals & Metalworking
N.A.I.C.S.: 333519
Mike Hankin (Mng Dir)

Kennametal Sp. z o.o. (1)
Ul Boczna 8, 44-240, Zory, Poland (100%)
Tel.: (48) 324789100
Web Site: http://www.kennametal.com
Sales Range: $125-149.9 Million
Emp.: 30
Energy, Mining & Construction
N.A.I.C.S.: 333131

Subsidiary (Non-US):

**Kennametal Stellite Coatings
S.r.l.** (2)
Tel.: (39) 02907871
Steel Products Mfr
N.A.I.C.S.: 327910

Kennametal Stellite S.r.l. (1)
Via Per Ornago 26, 20882, Bellusco, MI,
Italy

Tel.: (39) 0396204411
Web Site: http://www.stellite.com
Emp.: 19
Fabricated Metal Products Mfr
N.A.I.C.S.: 332999
Sinatra Claudio *(CEO)*

Kennametal Stellite, L.P. (1)
1201 Eisenhower Dr N, Goshen, IN 46526
Tel.: (574) 534-2585
Steel Products Mfr
N.A.I.C.S.: 327910

Kennametal Stellram Limited (1)
Hercules Way, SN126, Trowbridge, Wiltshire, United Kingdom
Tel.: (44) 1225897100
Hand Tool Mfr & Distr
N.A.I.C.S.: 332216

Kennametal Xuzhou Co., Ltd. (1)
Room 1203 Kai Wei Building No 10 Ya Bao Road, Chaoyang District, Beijing, 100020, China **(100%)**
Tel.: (86) 1085634883
Sales Range: $1-9.9 Million
Emp.: 30
Tool Mfr
N.A.I.C.S.: 332216

Kennametal de Mexico, S.A. de C.V. (1)
Bosques de Ciruelos No 186-piso 10, Miguel Hidalgo, Mexico, 11700, Mexico
Tel.: (52) 5559505055
Web Site: http://www.kennametal.com
Machine Tools Mfr
N.A.I.C.S.: 333517

Kennametal do Brasil Ltda. (1)
Rua Eduardo Borsari 1715, Distrito Industrial, Indaiatuba, 13347-320, Sao Paulo, Brazil
Tel.: (55) 1939369200
Engineered Component & Advanced Material Distr
N.A.I.C.S.: 423830

OOO Kennametal (1)
Vavilova str 5 bld 3 office 214, 119334, Moscow, Russia
Tel.: (7) 4954115386
Web Site: http://www.kennametal.com
Sales Range: $10-24.9 Million
Emp.: 20
Machine Tools Mfr
N.A.I.C.S.: 333517

KENNEDY-WILSON HOLDINGS, INC.
151 S El Camino Dr, Beverly Hills, CA 90212
Tel.: (310) 887-6400   DE
Web Site:
    https://www.kennedywilson.com
Year Founded: 2007
KW—(NYSE)
Rev.: $540,000,000
Assets: $8,271,800,000
Liabilities: $6,261,400,000
Net Worth: $2,010,400,000
Earnings: $64,800,000
Emp.: 230
Fiscal Year-end: 12/31/22
Holding Company; Real Estate Investment & Property Management Services
N.A.I.C.S.: 551112
William J. McMorrow *(Chm & CEO)*
Justin Enbody *(CFO)*
Matthew Windisch *(Pres)*
In Ku Lee *(Gen Counsel & Exec VP)*
Daven Bhavsar *(VP-IR)*
Michael Eadie *(Mng Dir)*
Alex Spilger *(Head)*
Gautam Doshi *(Sr Mng Dir)*

Subsidiaries:

Guardian/KW Hayward LLC (1)
25800 Industrial Blvd, Hayward, CA 94545
Tel.: (510) 887-8185
Residential Building & Dwelling Leasing Services
N.A.I.C.S.: 531110

Hotel Majestic LLC (1)
1500 Sutter St, San Francisco, CA 94109
Tel.: (415) 441-1100
Web Site: https://www.thehotelmajestic.com
Hotel Services
N.A.I.C.S.: 721199

KW Cantata Trail, LLC (1)
6700 Cantata St NW, Albuquerque, NM 87114
Tel.: (505) 221-6010
Web Site:
    https://www.cantataatthetrails.com
Apartment Rental Services
N.A.I.C.S.: 531110

KW Four Points, LLC (1)
9701 Wilshire Blvd Ste 700, Beverly Hills, CA 90212
Tel.: (310) 887-6495
Real Estate Related Services
N.A.I.C.S.: 531210

KW Marina View, LLC (1)
13274 Fiji Way, Marina Del Rey, CA 90292-7119
Tel.: (310) 823-2400
Real Estate Related Services
N.A.I.C.S.: 531210

KW Sacramento, LLC (1)
4080 Truxel Rd Ste 100, Sacramento, CA 95834
Tel.: (916) 283-7500
Web Site: https://www.kwsacmetro.com
Real Estate Services
N.A.I.C.S.: 531120

KW Transportation Services, LLC (1)
871 N Hanover St, Pottstown, PA 19464
Tel.: (610) 323-1691
Web Site:
    https://www.kwtransportationservices.com
Freight Forwarding & Transportation Services
N.A.I.C.S.: 541614

KW Tricenter, LLC (1)
5990 Sepulveda Blvd Ste 220, Van Nuys, CA 91411
Tel.: (818) 988-0007
Real Estate Related Services
N.A.I.C.S.: 531210

KW/LF Malibu Sands, LLC (1)
22333 Pacific Coast Hwy, Malibu, CA 90265
Tel.: (424) 644-0261
Real Estate Related Services
N.A.I.C.S.: 531210

Kennedy Wilson Ireland Limited (1)
94 St Stephen's Green, Dublin, 2, Ireland
Tel.: (353) 15884000
Real Estate Related Services
N.A.I.C.S.: 531210

Kennedy-Wilson, Inc. (1)
9701 Wilshire Blvd Ste 700, Beverly Hills, CA 90212
Tel.: (310) 887-6400
Web Site: https://www.kennedywilson.com
Sales Range: $100-124.9 Million
Real Estate Investment & Property Management Services
N.A.I.C.S.: 531390

Subsidiary (Domestic):

Kennedy Wilson Auction Group Inc. (2)
151 S El Camino Dr, Beverly Hills, CA 90212
Tel.: (310) 887-6446
Web Site: https://www.bidkw.com
Sales Range: $50-74.9 Million
Emp.: 50
Real Estate Auctioneer
N.A.I.C.S.: 531210
Richard Rhett Winchell *(Pres)*
Marty Clouser *(Sr VP)*
Dean Cullum *(VP)*
Shannon Hayon *(Mgr-Operations)*

Subsidiary (Non-US):

Kennedy Wilson Europe Limited (2)
94 St Stephen's Green, Dublin, 2, Leinster, Ireland
Tel.: (353) 15884000

Web Site: https://www.kennedywilson.com
Emp.: 50
Holding Company; Real Estate Investment & Property Management Services
N.A.I.C.S.: 551112
Michael Pegler *(Pres)*
Padmini Singla *(Gen Counsel)*

Branch (Non-US):

Kennedy Wilson UK Limited (3)
50 Grosvenor Hill, London, W1K 3QT, United Kingdom
Tel.: (44) 2071235700
Web Site: http://www.kennedywilson.com
Emp.: 50
Real Estate Investment & Property Management Services; Executive Office
N.A.I.C.S.: 531210
Mary L. Ricks *(Pres)*
Fiona D'Silva *(Head-Origination-Europe)*
Peter Richard Hewetson *(Head-Direct Real Estate)*

Subsidiary (Non-US):

KW Investment Management Ltd. (4)
47 Esplanade, Saint Helier, JE1 0BD, Jersey
Tel.: (44) 1534859440
Real Estate Investment Management Services
N.A.I.C.S.: 523940

Subsidiary (Domestic):

Kennedy Wilson Pennsylvania Management, Inc. (2)
1101 Market St Ste 105, Philadelphia, PA 19107
Tel.: (215) 592-1400
Web Site: http://www.kennedywilson.com
Real Estate Investment & Property Management Services
N.A.I.C.S.: 531390

Kennedy-Wilson International (2)
9701 Wilshire Blvd Ste 700, Beverly Hills, CA 90210-5213
Tel.: (310) 887-6400
Web Site: https://www.kennedywilson.com
Sales Range: $10-24.9 Million
Emp.: 50
Real Estate Agents & Managers
N.A.I.C.S.: 531210

Palms At Peccole Ranch (1)
9599 W Charleston Blvd, Las Vegas, NV 89117-6654
Tel.: (702) 233-0677
Web Site:
    http://www.palmsatpeccoleranch.com
Lessors of Residential Buildings & Dwellings
N.A.I.C.S.: 531110
Liz Ritchey *(Mgr-Property)*

Southern Oaks Apartment Homes (1)
5900 Park Hamilton Blvd, Orlando, FL 32808
Tel.: (407) 307-2729
Web Site: https://www.southernoaksfl.com
Real Estate Services
N.A.I.C.S.: 531390

Village Square Apartment Homes (1)
4014 Fairmount St, Dallas, TX 75219
Tel.: (214) 646-3907
Web Site: http://www.villagesquareinfo.com
Real Estate Services
N.A.I.C.S.: 531390

Vintage Housing Holdings, LLC (1)
369 San Miguel Dr Ste 135, Newport Beach, CA 92660 **(61.5%)**
Tel.: (949) 721-6775
Web Site: http://www.vintagehousing.com
Sales Range: $1-9.9 Million
Emp.: 10
Property Development & Residential Housing Management
N.A.I.C.S.: 236117

KENVUE INC.
199 Grandview Rd, Skillman, NJ 08558

Tel.: (908) 874-1200   DE
Web Site: https://www.kenvue.com
Year Founded: 2022
KVUE—(NYSE)
Rev.: $15,444,000,000
Assets: $27,851,000,000
Liabilities: $16,640,000,000
Net Worth: $11,211,000,000
Earnings: $1,664,000,000
Emp.: 22,000
Fiscal Year-end: 12/31/23
Holding Company; Personal Care Products Mfr & Whslr
N.A.I.C.S.: 551112
Thibaut Mongon *(CEO)*

Subsidiaries:

Ci:z.Labo Co., Ltd. (1)
1-1-40 Hiroo Shibuya-ku, Tokyo, Japan
Tel.: (81) 337974000
Web Site: http://www.ci-z.com
Beauty Care Services
N.A.I.C.S.: 713940
Tomomi Ishihara *(Pres & COO)*

Johnson & Johnson Consumer Inc. (1)
199 Grandview Rd, Skillman, NJ 08558
Tel.: (908) 874-1200
Personal Care Products Mfr & Whslr
N.A.I.C.S.: 325620

Subsidiary (Non-US):

Johnson & Johnson Consumer B.V. (2)
Computerweg 14, 3821 AB, Amersfoort, Netherlands
Tel.: (31) 334500500
Web Site: http://www.jnjconsumer.nl
Emp.: 25
Pharmaceutical & Consumer Goods Mfr
N.A.I.C.S.: 325412

Johnson & Johnson Consumer France SAS (2)
1 Rue Camille Desmoulins, 92130, Issy-les-Moulineaux, France
Tel.: (33) 0155004800
Web Site: http://www.jnj.com
Sales Range: $400-449.9 Million
Emp.: 545
Pharmaceuticals Product Mfr
N.A.I.C.S.: 424210

Johnson & Johnson Consumer NV/SA (2)
Antzerpseweg 15-17, 2340, Beerse, 2340, Belgium
Tel.: (32) 14649440
Web Site: https://www.sinutab.be
Sales Range: $50-74.9 Million
Emp.: 100
Sanitary Protection Products, Toiletries & Health Care Products Whslr
N.A.I.C.S.: 424210

Unit (Domestic):

Johnson & Johnson Consumer Products (2)
199 Grandview Rd, Skillman, NJ 08558
Tel.: (908) 874-1000
Consumer Personal Care & Health Products Mfr
N.A.I.C.S.: 325412

Unit (Non-US):

Johnson & Johnson Consumer Products (2)
88 McNabb Street, Markham, L3R5L2, ON, Canada
Tel.: (905) 968-2000
Emp.: 350
Consumer Personal Care & Health Products Mfr
N.A.I.C.S.: 325412

Johnson & Johnson Gesellschaft m.b.H (1)
Vorgartenstrasse 206B, 1020, Vienna, Austria
Tel.: (43) 1725150
Web Site: https://www.jnjaustria.at

Kenvue Inc.—(Continued)

Sales Range: $50-74.9 Million
Emp.: 30
Pharmaceuticals Mfr
N.A.I.C.S.: 325412

Johnson & Johnson GmbH (1)
Johnson and Johnson Platz 2 Raiffeisen-
strasse 9, Raiffeisenstrasse 9, 41470,
Neuss, Germany
Tel.: (49) 21379360
Web Site: https://www.jnjgermany.de
Emp.: 750
Professional Medical Equipment & External
Sanitary Products Mfr
N.A.I.C.S.: 322291

**Johnson & Johnson Hellas Commer-
cial & Industrial S.A.** (1)
Aegialias & Epidavrou 4, Maroussi, Athens,
15125, Greece
Tel.: (30) 2106875555
Medical Equipment Mfr
N.A.I.C.S.: 339113

Johnson & Johnson Inc. (1)
890 Woodlawn Road West, Guelph, N1K
1A5, ON, Canada
Tel.: (519) 826-6226
Web Site: https://www.jnjcanada.com
Emp.: 350
Orthopedic Prosthetic Surgical Appliances,
Perfumes, Cosmetics & Toilet Preparations
Mfr
N.A.I.C.S.: 339112

**Johnson & Johnson Industrial
Ltda.** (1)
Rodovia Presidente Dutra S/N Km 154
Jardim Das Industrias, Sao Jose dos Cam-
pos, 12240-420, SP, Brazil
Tel.: (55) 1127881000
Pharmaceuticals Product Mfr
N.A.I.C.S.: 424210

Johnson & Johnson Korea, Ltd. (1)
F22 LS Yongsan Tower 92 Hangang-daero,
Yongsan-gu, Seoul, 140-012, Korea (South)
Tel.: (82) 220944162
Web Site: http://www.jnj.com
Pharmaceuticals Mfr
N.A.I.C.S.: 325412
Stephanie Choi (Mng Dir)

**Johnson & Johnson Pacific Pty.
Ltd.** (1)
45 Jones Street, PO Box 5, Ultimo, 2007,
NSW, Australia
Tel.: (61) 82608000
Web Site: https://www.jnj.com.au
Sales Range: $400-449.9 Million
Emp.: 1,050
Hospital Products Mfr
N.A.I.C.S.: 339112

Johnson & Johnson Pte. Ltd. (1)
2 International Business Park the Strategy
Tower One Number 07-01, Singapore,
609930, Singapore
Tel.: (65) 68276000
Web Site: http://www.jnj.com
Sales Range: $200-249.9 Million
Emp.: 400
Pharmaceuticals Mfr
Products
N.A.I.C.S.: 325412

Johnson & Johnson Pty. Limited (1)
Locked Bag 5 Ultimo, Broadway, 2007,
NSW, Australia
Tel.: (61) 282608000
Emp.: 1,180
Pharmaceuticals Product Mfr
N.A.I.C.S.: 325412

**Johnson & Johnson Sante Beaute
France** (1)
41-43 rue Camille Desmoulins, 92787, Issy-
les-Moulineaux, France
Tel.: (33) 155004800
Web Site: https://www.jjsbf.fr
Pharmaceutical & Consumer Goods Mfr
N.A.I.C.S.: 325412

**Johnson & Johnson de Argentina,
S.A.C.e I.** (1)
Ruta 8 Km 63 500, Fatima Pilar,
B1630CFA, Buenos Aires, Argentina
Tel.: (54) 2322490101
Web Site: http://www.jnjarg.com

Sales Range: $100-124.9 Million
Emp.: 300
Sanitary Protection Products, Toiletries &
Health Care Products Mfr
N.A.I.C.S.: 322291

**Johnson & Johnson de Colombia
S.A.** (1)
Av Calle 26 No 69 - 76, Bogota, Colombia
Tel.: (57) 13441315
Web Site: http://www.jnjcolombia.com.co
Sales Range: $10-24.9 Million
Emp.: 25
Polish & Sanitation Goods Mfr
N.A.I.C.S.: 339112

**Johnson & Johnson del Ecuador
S.A.** (1)
Avenida Rodriguez Chavez Gonzalez
parque empresarial Colon, Edificio Corpora-
tivo II piso 5, Guayaquil, Ecuador
Tel.: (593) 800222555
Web Site: https://www.jnjecuador.com
Health Care Products Mfr
N.A.I.C.S.: 325412

**Johnson & Johnson del Peru
S.A.** (1)
Avenida Canaval y Moreyra 4 80 Piso 9
Edificio Citibank, San Isidro, Peru
Tel.: (51) 80053233
Web Site: https://www.jnjperu.com
Health Care Srvices
N.A.I.C.S.: 621491

**Johnson & Johnson, S.A. de
C.V.** (1)
Miguel Angel De Quevedo 247 Col Romero
De Terreros, 04310, Mexico, DF, Mexico
Tel.: (52) 5554842300
Web Site: http://www.jnjgateway.com
Sales Range: $25-49.9 Million
Emp.: 150
Baby Products, Surgical, Medical & Dental
Products Mfr
N.A.I.C.S.: 339112

**McNeil Consumer Pharmaceuticals
Co.** (1)
7050 Camp Hill Rd, Fort Washington, PA
19034
Web Site: https://www.pepcid.com
Heartburn Relief Product Mfr
N.A.I.C.S.: 325412

McNeil GmbH & Co. OHG (1)
Johnson & Johnson Platz 2 Raiffeisen-
strasse 9, 41470, Neuss, Germany
Tel.: (49) 21379360
Web Site: http://www.jnjgermany.de
Sales Range: $75-99.9 Million
Emp.: 250
Marketer of Over the Counter Products
N.A.I.C.S.: 325412

Subsidiary (Non-US):

McNeil AB (2)
Norrbroplatsen 2, Box 941, 251 09, Helsing-
borg, Sweden
Tel.: (46) 42288000
Web Site: https://www.mcneilab.se
Pharmaceutical & Consumer Goods Mfr
N.A.I.C.S.: 325412

Subsidiary (Domestic):

**McNeil Consumer Healthcare
GmbH** (2)
Johnson & Johnson Platz 2, Neuss, 41470,
Germany
Tel.: (49) 213729360
Web Site: http://www.jnjgermany.de
Pharmaceutical & Consumer Goods Mfr
N.A.I.C.S.: 325412

Subsidiary (Non-US):

**McNeil Consumer Nutritionals
Ltd.** (2)
Millennium Way Derbyshire, Chesterfield,
S41 8ND, United Kingdom
Tel.: (44) 2076658372
Web Site: http://www.benecol.co.uk
Sales Range: $1-9.9 Million
Emp.: 10
Nutritional Products Marketer
N.A.I.C.S.: 541613

McNeil Denmark ApS (2)

Bregnerodvej 133, 3460, Birkerod, Denmark
Tel.: (45) 70205212
Web Site:
https://www.consumerhealthcare.dk
Pharmaceutical Healthcare Product Mfr
N.A.I.C.S.: 325412

McNeil Healthcare (UK) Limited (2)
Foundation Park Roxborough Way, Maiden-
head, SL6 3UG, Berkshire, United Kingdom
Tel.: (44) 1344864042
Pharmaceuticals Product Mfr
N.A.I.C.S.: 424210

Subsidiary (US):

McNeil Nutritionals, LLC (2)
601 Office Center Dr, Fort Washington, PA
19034
Tel.: (215) 273-7000
Sugar Substitute & Other Nutritional Products Mfr
N.A.I.C.S.: 311999

Subsidiary (Non-US):

McNeil Sweden AB (2)
Frosundaviks Alle 1, Solna, Solna, 169 70,
Sweden
Tel.: (46) 850338500
Pharmaceutical & Consumer Goods Mfr
N.A.I.C.S.: 325412

McNeil Healthcare LLC (1)
Km 19 8 Bo Mo Hc 183, Las Piedras, PR
00771
Tel.: (787) 733-1000
Emp.: 99
Commercial Construction Services
N.A.I.C.S.: 236220
Debbie Vacquez (Gen Mgr)

Neostrata Company Inc (1)
199 Grandview Rd, Skillman, NJ 08558
Tel.: (609) 520-0715
Web Site: https://www.neostrata.com
Cosmetics Mfr & Distr
N.A.I.C.S.: 456120
Eugene J. Van Scott (Co-Founder)
Ruey J. Yu (Co-Founder)

**P.T. Johnson & Johnson
Indonesia** (1)
Mampang Park Office 3rd Floor Jl Mam-
pang Prapatan Raya No 1, Jakarta, 12790,
Selatan, Indonesia
Tel.: (62) 217988905
Web Site: http://www.jnj.com
Sales Range: $75-99.9 Million
Emp.: 300
Pharmaceutial Mfr
N.A.I.C.S.: 334516

Vogue International LLC (1)
2600 Mccormick Dr Ste 320, Clearwater, FL
33759
Tel.: (727) 216-1600
Pharmaceuticals Product Mfr
N.A.I.C.S.: 325412
Holly Shackleton (Editor-in-Chief)

Zarbee's, Inc. (1)
11650 State St Ste 101, Draper, UT 84020
Web Site: https://www.zarbees.com
Human Drug & Medicine Mfr
N.A.I.C.S.: 325412
Zak Zarbock (Founder)

**KERNEL GROUP HOLDINGS,
INC.**
515 Madison Ave 8th Fl Ste 8078,
New York, NY 10022
Tel.: (415) 404-6356   Ky
Web Site: https://www.kernelcap.com
Year Founded: 2020
KRNL—(NASDAQ)
Rev.: $4,469,702
Assets: $309,369,883
Liabilities: $322,943,505
Net Worth: ($13,573,622)
Earnings: $15,656,029
Fiscal Year-end: 12/31/22
Investment Services
N.A.I.C.S.: 523999
Howard A. Doss (CFO)
Surendra Ajjarapu (Chm & CEO)

KEROS THERAPEUTICS, INC.
1050 Waltham St Ste 302, Lexington,
MA 02421
Tel.: (617) 314-6297   DE
Web Site: https://www.kerostx.com
Year Founded: 2015
KROS—(NASDAQ)
Rev.: $10,111,000
Assets: $306,781,000
Liabilities: $29,358,000
Net Worth: $277,423,000
Earnings: ($104,679,000)
Emp.: 105
Fiscal Year-end: 12/31/22
Biotechnology Research & Develop-
ment Services
N.A.I.C.S.: 541714
Jasbir Seehra (CEO)
Keith Regnante (CFO)
Christopher Rovaldi (Pres & COO)
Esther Cho (Gen Counsel, Sec, Sr
VP & Head-Legal)
John Oram (Sr VP-Program & Portfo-
lio Mgmt)
Robin Wagner (Sr VP-Human Re-
sources & VP-HR)
Jasbir S. Seehra (CEO)

KETER1 ACQUISITION CORP.
2093 Philadelphia Pike Ste 1866,
Claymont, DE 19703
Tel.: (408) 263-1040   Ky
Year Founded: 2021
KETAU—(NASDAQ)
Investment Services
N.A.I.C.S.: 523999
Oren Dobronsky (CEO)
Omer Cygler (Pres & CFO)

**KEWAUNEE SCIENTIFIC COR-
PORATION**
2700 W Front St, Statesville, NC
28677
Tel.: (704) 873-7202   DE
Web Site:
https://www.kewaunee.com
Year Founded: 1906
KEQU—(NASDAQ)
Rev.: $203,755,000
Assets: $134,766,000
Liabilities: $78,557,000
Net Worth: $56,209,000
Earnings: $19,057,000
Emp.: 1,006
Fiscal Year-end: 04/30/24
Laboratory & Technical Furniture
Products Designer, Mfr & Installer
N.A.I.C.S.: 337127
David S. Rhind (Chm)
William F. Peters (VP)
Kurt P. Rindoks (VP-Strategic Alli-
ances & Product Dev-Global)
Elizabeth D. Phillips (VP-HR)
Boopathy Sathyamurthy (Mng Dir-
Ops-Intl)
Ryan S. Noble (VP-Sls & Mktg-
Americas)
Mandar M. Ranade (VP-IT & Engrg)
Douglas J. Batdorff (VP-Mfg Ops)
Thomas D. Hull III (Pres & CEO)
Donald T. Gardner III (CFO, Treas,
Sec & VP-Fin)

Subsidiaries:

Kewaunee Labway Asia Pte. Ltd. (1)
194 Pandan Loop 06-22 Pantech Business
Hub, Singapore, 128383,
Singapore   **(100%)**
Tel.: (65) 67730288
Sales Range: $10-24.9 Million
Emp.: 7
Mfr & Installer of Scientific & Technical Fur-
niture
N.A.I.C.S.: 337127

Subsidiary (Non-US):

**Kewaunee Scientific Corporation In-
dia Pvt. Ltd.** (2)

Plot No 186 Jigani Link Road, Jigani Anekal
Taluk, Bengaluru, 562106, India
Tel.: (91) 8027812040
Emp.: 250
Laboratory Furniture Mfr
N.A.I.C.S.: 337127
Hari Krishan (Gen Mgr)

Kewaunee Labway India Pvt.
Ltd.　　　　　　　　　　　　　　　　(1)
Tel.: (91) 8003091906
Web Site: https://www.kewaunee.in
Emp.: 57
Laboratory Furniture Mfr
N.A.I.C.S.: 337127
Srinivas P. N. (Dir-Sls & Mktg)
P. N. Srinivas (Dir)

Koncepo Scientech International Pvt.
Ltd.　　　　　　　　　　　　　　　　(1)
1st Floor Venkatadri IT City 236 HP Avenue
Electronic City Phase 01, Bengaluru,
560100, India
Tel.: (91) 8142066007
Web Site: https://koncepo.com
Emp.: 40
Engineeering Services
N.A.I.C.S.: 541330
Satish Hiremath (Mng Dir)
Jaykumar Gowda (Chief Dev Officer)
C. Ranjan (Gen Mgr)
Kundan Thakur (Mgr-Bus Dev & Strategic
Advisory)

NuAire Inc.　　　　　　　　　　　　(1)
2100 Fernbrook Ln N, Minneapolis, MN
55447
Tel.: (763) 553-1270
Web Site: http://www.nuaire.com
Rev.: $16,000,000
Emp.: 300
Incubators, Laboratory
N.A.I.C.S.: 334516
William F. Peters (Pres)
Fred McElveen (Mgr-Production Control)
Jim Sande (VP-Fin)
Matt Squire (Engr-Mechanical)
Michael Lenz (Dir-IT)
Walter Johnson (Mgr-Tech Svc)
Jeanne Lippert (Dir-Quality Sys)
Earl Cornell (Supvr-Plant)
Steve Winget (Mgr-Tech Svc)
Mark Huxtable (CEO)

KEWEENAW LAND ASSOCIA-TION, LTD.

Tel.: (906) 932-3410　　　　　　　　MI
Web Site:
　　https://www.keweenaw.com
KEWL—(OTCIQ)
Rev.: $292,415
Assets: $15,675,747
Liabilities: $321,127
Net Worth: $15,354,620
Earnings: $168,602
Emp.: 2
Fiscal Year-end: 12/31/23
Forestry & Logging Services
N.A.I.C.S.: 115310
Timothy G. Lynott (Pres)
Paula J. Aijala (Sec)
Jamie Mai (Chm)

KEY ENERGY SERVICES, INC.

1500 CityWest Blvd Ste 800, Hous-
ton, TX 77042
Tel.: (713) 651-4300　　　　　　　　MD
Web Site: http://www.keyenergy.com
Year Founded: 1978
KEGXD—(OTCIQ)
Rev.: $413,854,000
Assets: $347,870,000
Liabilities: $399,123,000
Net Worth: ($51,253,000)
Earnings: ($97,418,000)
Emp.: 2,000
Fiscal Year-end: 12/31/19
Natural Gas Transportation & Market-
ing; Drilling Oil & Gas Wells; Oil &
Gas Exploration Services
N.A.I.C.S.: 213111
John Marshall Dodson (Pres & CEO)
Katherine I. Hargis (Chief Admin Offi-
cer, Gen Counsel, Sec & Sr VP)

Harry F. Quarls (Chm)
Louis Coale (VP & Controller)

Subsidiaries:

Key Energy QTS　　　　　　　　　　(1)
1301 McKinney Ste 1800, Houston, TX
77101　　　　　　　　　　　　　　(100%)
Tel.: (713) 869-6020
Sales Range: $25-49.9 Million
Emp.: 12
Oil & Gas Field Services
N.A.I.C.S.: 213112

Key Energy Services, Inc.-
Appalachian Division　　　　　　　(1)
2 Players Club Rd, Charleston, WV 25311
Tel.: (303) 342-9700
Sales Range: $250-299.9 Million
Oil Well Drilling & Maintenance Services
N.A.I.C.S.: 213111

Key Energy Services, Inc.-California
Division　　　　　　　　　　　　　(1)
5080 California Ave Ste 150, Bakersfield,
CA 93309
Tel.: (661) 334-8100
Sales Range: $250-299.9 Million
Oil Well Drilling & Maintenance Services
N.A.I.C.S.: 213111

Key Energy Services, Inc.-Permian
Basin North Division　　　　　　　(1)
2626 W Marland Ave, Hobbs, NM 88240
Tel.: (505) 393-9171
Sales Range: $250-299.9 Million
Oil Well Drilling & Maintenance Services
N.A.I.C.S.: 213111
Ray Ramsey (Div Mgr)

Key Energy Services, Inc.-Rocky
Mountain Division　　　　　　　　(1)
2377 Clover Rd, Casper, WY 82604
Tel.: (307) 265-0054
Sales Range: $250-299.9 Million
Oil Well Drilling & Maintenance
N.A.I.C.S.: 213111

Leader Energy Services Ltd.　　　(1)
Sierra Place Ste 700 706 - 7th Avenue SW,
Calgary, T2P 0Z1, AB, Canada
Tel.: (403) 716-3175
Tubing, Cementing & Nitrogen Plumbing
Products & Services
N.A.I.C.S.: 322219

KEY TRONIC CORPORATION

4424 Sullivan Rd, Spokane Valley,
WA 99216
Tel.: (509) 928-8000　　　　　　　　WA
Web Site: https://www.keytronic.com
Year Founded: 1969
KTCC—(NASDAQ)
Rev.: $566,942,000
Assets: $355,343,000
Liabilities: $231,353,000
Net Worth: $123,990,000
Earnings: ($2,787,000)
Emp.: 4,122
Fiscal Year-end: 06/29/24
Printed Circuit Assembly (Electronic
Assembly) Manufacturing
N.A.I.C.S.: 334418
Ronald F. Klawitter (Chm)
Philip S. Hochberg (Exec VP-Bus
Dev)
Brett R. Larsen (Pres, CEO & COO)
Duane D. Mackleit (Exec VP-Ops)
Chad T. Orebaugh (VP-Engrg)
David H. Knaggs (Exec VP-Quality &
Information Sys)
Thomas Despres (VP-Ops-
Southwest)
Mark Courtney (VP-Supply Chain)
Craig Green (Sr VP-Bus Dev)
Nicholas S. Fasciana (Sr VP-Ops)

Subsidiaries:

Key Tronic Computer Peripherals
(Shanghai) Co. LTD　　　　　　　(1)
Part A 2F 6th Workshop No 350 Xiya Road,
Waigaoqiao Ftz, Shanghai, China
Tel.: (86) 2150460756
Computer Peripherals Mfr

N.A.I.C.S.: 334118

Key Tronic Juarez S.A. de CV　　(1)
Tel.: (52) 6566292100
Sales Range: $50-74.9 Million
Emp.: 1,500
Electronics Mfr
N.A.I.C.S.: 811210
Doug Burkhardt (VP-Ops)

Key Tronic Reynosa, S.A. de CV　(1)
Ave Pedregal S/N, Pargue Industrial Colo-
nial, Reynosa, Tam, Mexico
Tel.: (52) 6566292100
Web Site: http://www.keytronic.com
Sales Range: $25-49.9 Million
Emp.: 100
Electronics Mfr
N.A.I.C.S.: 811210

KeyTronicEMS Computer Peripheral
Co.　　　　　　　　　　　　　　　(1)
No 350 Xi Ya Road Plot FM7 Area F Part A,
2nd Fl of No 6 Factory Bldg, Shanghai,
200137, China
Tel.: (86) 2150460756
Web Site: http://www.keytronic.com
Sales Range: $75-99.9 Million
Emp.: 200
Electronics Mfr
N.A.I.C.S.: 811210

KEYARCH ACQUISITION COR-PORATION

275 Madison Ave 39th Fl, New York,
NY 10016
Tel.: (914) 434-2030　　　　　　　　Ky
Year Founded: 2021
KYCH—(NASDAQ)
Rev.: $2,222
Assets: $118,133,929
Liabilities: $118,017,272
Net Worth: $116,657
Earnings: $843,672
Fiscal Year-end: 12/31/22
Investment Services
N.A.I.C.S.: 523999
Fang Zhang (Chm)
Kai Xiong (CEO)
Jing Lu (CFO)

KEYCORP

127 Public Sq, Cleveland, OH 44114-
1306
Tel.: (216) 689-3000　　　　　　　　OH
Web Site: https://www.key.com
Year Founded: 1958
KEY—(NYSE)
Rev.: $10,397,000,000
Assets: $188,281,000,000
Liabilities: $173,644,000,000
Net Worth: $14,637,000,000
Earnings: $967,000,000
Emp.: 17,333
Fiscal Year-end: 12/31/23
Bank Holding Company
N.A.I.C.S.: 551111
Christopher Marrott Gorman (Chm &
CEO)
Clark H. I. Khayat (CFO, Chief Strat-
egy Officer & Exec VP)
Brian L. Fishel (Chief HR Officer &
Exec VP)
Jamie Warder (Exec VP & Head-
Digital Banking)
Victor B. Alexander (Exec VP &
Head-Consumer Banking)
Andrew J. Paine III (Head)
Ally Kidik (Chief Risk Review Officer)

Subsidiaries:

KeyBank National Association　　(1)
127 Public Sq, Cleveland, OH
44114-1306　　　　　　　　　　　(100%)
Tel.: (216) 689-8481
Web Site: https://www.key.com
Emp.: 18,000
Federal Savings Bank
N.A.I.C.S.: 522110
Christopher Marrott Gorman (Chm, Pres &
CEO)
Tim Burke (Pres-Market-Northeast Ohio)

Subsidiary (Domestic):

HelloWallet, LLC　　　　　　　　　(2)
2121 Ward Ct NW 3rd Fl, Washington, DC
20037
Tel.: (866) 554-3556
Web Site: http://www.key.com
Emp.: 64
Investment Advisory Services
N.A.I.C.S.: 523940

Key Community Development
Corporation　　　　　　　　　　　(2)
127 Public Sq, Cleveland, OH
44114-1221　　　　　　　　　　　(100%)
Tel.: (216) 689-5580
Web Site: http://www.key.com
Sales Range: $125-149.9 Million
Affordable Housing Equity Investment Ser-
vices
N.A.I.C.S.: 523999

Division (Domestic):

KeyBank N.A. - Key Community Bank
Division　　　　　　　　　　　　　(2)
127 Public Sq, Cleveland, OH 44114
Tel.: (216) 689-3000
Web Site: http://www.key.com
Retail & Commercial Banking
N.A.I.C.S.: 522110
Edward J. Burke (Pres-Comml Banking,
Residential Mortgage & Private Banking)

KeyBank N.A. - Key Corporate Bank
Division　　　　　　　　　　　　　(2)
127 Public Sq, Cleveland, OH 44114
Tel.: (216) 689-3000
Web Site: http://www.key.com
Investment Banking, Private Equity, Real
Estate & Equipment Finance Services
N.A.I.C.S.: 523999

Subsidiary (Domestic):

Key Equipment Finance Inc.　　　(3)
1000 S McCaslin Blvd, Superior, CO
80027　　　　　　　　　　　　　(100%)
Tel.: (720) 304-1000
Web Site:
　　https://www.keyequipmentfinance.com
Sales Range: $100-124.9 Million
Emp.: 250
Holding Company; Equipment Financing &
Leasing Services
N.A.I.C.S.: 551112
Shawn Arnone (Sr VP & Head-Mfr & Govt
Alliances Bus)
Philip Turner (Exec VP & Mng Dir)
Deborah Brady (Sr VP & Dir-Fin)
Rain W. Emmett (Mng Dir-Specialty Fin
Lending)
Amy Gross (Exec VP-Govt & Comml Ven-
dor)
Sarah Palmer (Sr VP-Underwriting)
Jennifer L. Martin (VP-Leasing & Vendor
Program Support)
Joe Messineo (Reg Dir-Sls)
Shawn Arnone (Sr VP & Head-Mfr & Govt
Alliances Bus)
Derek Chauvette (Grp Head-Pub Sector &
Native American Fin Svcs)

Subsidiary (Domestic):

Key Equipment Finance International
Inc.　　　　　　　　　　　　　　　(4)
1000 S McCaslin Blvd, Superior, CO 80027
Tel.: (720) 304-1000
Web Site: http://www.kefonline.com
Consumer & Equipment Financing & Leas-
ing Services
N.A.I.C.S.: 522220

Unit (Domestic):

Key Education Resources　　　　　(5)
127 Public Sq, Cleveland, OH 44114
Tel.: (216) 689-8481
Web Site: http://www.key.com
Educational Finances & Loans
N.A.I.C.S.: 611710

Subsidiary (Domestic):

KeyBanc Capital Markets Inc.　　(3)
1861 S Trenton Dr, Trenton, MI 48183
Tel.: (734) 556-4054
Web Site: https://mcfingroup.com

KeyCorp—(Continued)

Sales Range: Less than $1 Million
Investment Banking & Brokerage
N.A.I.C.S.: 523150
Mark Kovachick *(CFO)*

Subsidiary (Domestic):

Cain Brothers & Company, LLC (4)
277 Pk Ave 40th Fl, New York, NY 10172
Tel.: (212) 869-5600
Web Site: http://www.cainbrothers.com
Pre-eminent Healthcare Investment Bank
N.A.I.C.S.: 523150
James E. Cain *(Founder)*
Bartlett A. Plank *(Mng Dir & Co-Head-Healthcare Pub Fin)*
Scott A. James *(Mng Dir)*
Edward S. Fishman *(Mng Dir)*
Andrew Labovitz *(Dir-)*
Todd Rudsenske *(Mng Dir)*
Matthew H. Goldreich *(Mng Dir)*
James M. Moloney *(Mng Dir & Co-Head-Health Sys M&A)*
Court H. Houseworth *(Mng Dir)*
Bill Pomeranz *(Mng Dir)*
Mike Elizondo *(Dir)*
Wyatt Ritchie *(Mng Dir)*
David Morlock *(Mng Dir & Co-Head)*
James R. King *(Mng Dir)*
Jill Frew *(Mng Dir)*
John V. Soden *(Mng Dir & Head)*
Joseph P. Mulligan *(Mng Dir)*
Katherine A. Kirchhoff *(Mng Dir)*
Matthew Margulies *(Mng Dir)*
Rafe B. Hanahan *(Mng Dir)*
Bryan Clones *(Mng Dir)*
Christian Pesci *(Mng Dir)*
Joanna Stephenson *(Dir-)*
John Kerins *(Mng Dir)*
Taaha Shaikh *(Dir-)*
James Conahan *(VP)*
Michael Jackson *(Mng Dir)*
Zach Kau *(Mng Dir & Co-Head-Healthcare Pub Fin)*
Stacy Guffanti *(Dir-)*
Elizabeth Kim *(VP)*
Ila Afsharipour *(Mng Dir)*
Steven Alcauskas *(Mng Dir)*
Donald Persinski *(Mng Dir)*
Kris Beth *(VP)*
Thomas Culhane *(VP)*
Sean Gomez *(VP)*
Erika Haanpaa *(Dir-)*
Ted Kaehler *(VP)*
Colby Kittrell *(Dir--Physician Grp)*
Danielle LeBenger *(Chief Admin Officer)*
David Levine *(Dir--Hospitals)*
Ricky Ng *(Dir)*
Daren Oddenino *(VP)*
Jonah Schutzman *(VP)*
Lee Sophocleous *(VP)*
Alice Tan *(VP)*
Sean Trail *(VP)*
Jenny Watson *(Dir)*
Carsten Beith *(Vice Chm)*
Matthew O'Grady *(Mng Dir)*
Joe Pollock *(Mng Dir)*
Maura Davalos *(Dir)*
Kyle Hemminger *(Dir)*
Benton Au *(VP)*
Eugene Bord *(VP)*
Garrett Colgan *(VP)*
Brian Gierman *(VP)*
Dan Gold *(VP)*
David Iklodi *(VP)*
Joseph Quinn *(VP)*
Casey Wade *(VP)*
Carsten Beith *(Vice Chm)*
Matthew O'Grady *(Mng Dir)*
Joe Pollock *(Mng Dir)*
Maura Davalos *(Dir)*
Kyle Hemminger *(Dir)*
Benton Au *(VP)*
Eugene Bord *(VP)*
Garrett Colgan *(VP)*
Brian Gierman *(VP)*
Dan Gold *(VP)*
David Iklodi *(VP)*
Joseph Quinn *(VP)*
Casey Wade *(VP)*
Robert J. Fraiman Jr. *(Pres)*

Subsidiary (Domestic):

KeyCorp Real Estate Capital Markets, Inc. (3)
127 Public Sq, Cleveland, OH
44114-1221 (100%)

Tel.: (216) 689-3574
Web Site: http://www.key.com
Sales Range: $50-74.9 Million
Real Estate Banking Services
N.A.I.C.S.: 522292
Angela G. Mago *(Head)*
Dan Baker *(Head-Comml Mortgage)*
Norm Nichols *(Head-Income Property Grp)*
Bryan Nitcher *(Head-Loan Servicing & Asset Mgmt)*
Brandon Nowac *(Head-Real Estate Payments)*
Dan Haberle *(Head-Institutional Real Estate Grp)*
James McLaughlin *(Head-Healthcare Real Estate Lending)*

Subsidiary (Domestic):

Pacific Crest Securities LLC (2)
111 SW 5th Ave Fl 42, Portland, OR 97204
Tel.: (503) 248-0721
Web Site: http://www.pacific-crest.com
Sales Range: $10-24.9 Million
Emp.: 170
Securities Brokerage
N.A.I.C.S.: 523150

KEYSIGHT TECHNOLOGIES, INC.

1400 Fountaingrove Pkwy, Santa Rosa, CA 95403-1738
Tel.: (707) 577-5030
Web Site: https://www.keysight.com
Year Founded: 2013
KEYS—(NYSE)
Rev.: $4,979,000,000
Assets: $9,269,000,000
Liabilities: $4,164,000,000
Net Worth: $5,105,000,000
Earnings: $614,000,000
Emp.: 15,500
Fiscal Year-end: 10/31/24
Communications & Electronics Industry Measurement Instruments, Software & Services
N.A.I.C.S.: 334513
Ingrid A. Estrada *(Chief People & Admin Officer & Sr VP)*
Soon Chai Gooi *(Pres-Order Fulfillment & Digital Ops & Sr VP)*
Satish C. Dhanasekaran *(Pres & CEO)*
Lisa Poole *(Chief Acctg Officer, VP & Controller-Corp)*
Marie Hattar *(CMO & Sr VP)*
Huei Sin Ee *(Board of Directors, Pres-Electronic Industrial Solutions Grp & Sr VP)*
Jeffrey Li *(Gen Counsel, Sec & Sr VP)*
Mark Wallace *(Sr VP-Global)*

Subsidiaries:

Cliosoft, Inc. (1)
39500 Stevenson Pl Ste 110, Fremont, CA 94539-3102
Tel.: (510) 790-4732
Web Site: http://www.cliosoft.com
Software Publisher
N.A.I.C.S.: 513210
Johan Gardelius *(Mgr-Sls)*

ESI Group S.A. (1)
Batiment Le Seville 3 bis Rue Saarinen, 94528, Hungis, France
Tel.: (33) 141735800
Web Site: http://www.esi-group.com
Rev.: $142,783,372
Assets: $213,015,032
Liabilities: $117,052,767
Net Worth: $95,962,265
Earnings: $16,441,870
Emp.: 985
Fiscal Year-end: 12/31/2022
Digital Simulation Software for Product Prototyping & Manufacturing Processes
N.A.I.C.S.: 334610
Alain de Rouvray *(Chm)*
Vincent Chaillou *(Reg Dir-EMEA)*
Cristel de Rouvray *(CEO)*
Corinne Romefort-Regnier *(Dir-Corp Governance)*

Mike Salari *(COO-Revenue Generation)*
Marco Gremaud *(Exec Mng Dir)*
Yannick Charron *(VP-HR)*
Olfa Zorgati *(CFO)*
Dominique Lefebvre *(Exec VP-Product Ops)*
Alex Davern *(Chm)*
Francis Griffiths *(Exec VP-Sls)*
Olfa Zorgati *(Deputy CEO)*

Subsidiary (US):

Amoeba Technologies Inc. (2)
11809 La Barzola Bend, Austin, TX 78738-6023
Tel.: (512) 879-3065
Web Site: http://www.amoebatech.com
Software Publisher
N.A.I.C.S.: 513210
Prabhu Sathyamurt *(Co-Founder)*
Sanjay Mathur *(Co-Founder)*

Subsidiary (Non-US):

Calcom ESI SA (2)
Parc Scientifique EPFL, Lausanne, CH-1015, Switzerland
Tel.: (41) 216932918
Web Site: http://www.esigroup.ch
Sales Range: $25-49.9 Million
Emp.: 18
Simulation Software Distr & Sales
N.A.I.C.S.: 423430
Alaen Derougray *(Pres)*

ESI CFD Services (2)
K502 MegaCenter Pune Solapur Road, Hadapsar, Pune, 411013, Maharashtra, India
Tel.: (91) 20 26890656
Web Site: http://www.esi-group.com
Sales Range: $25-49.9 Million
Emp.: 35
Industrial Software Development Services
N.A.I.C.S.: 541511

ESI China (2)
Unit 1006-1008 Metropolis Tower No 2, Haidiandongsanjie, Haidian District, Beijing, 100080, China
Tel.: (86) 1065544907
Web Site: http://www.esi-group.com
Software Development Services
N.A.I.C.S.: 541511

Subsidiary (Domestic):

ESI France SARL (2)
Le Recamier 70 rue Robert, 69458, Lyon, France
Tel.: (33) 478141200
Web Site: http://www.esi-group.com
Sales Range: $25-49.9 Million
Emp.: 85
Digital Simulation Software Development Services
N.A.I.C.S.: 541511
Eric Daubourg *(Mng Dir)*

Subsidiary (Non-US):

ESI Germany GmbH (2)
Liebknechtstr 33, 70565, Stuttgart, Germany
Tel.: (49) 711273030
Software Development Services
N.A.I.C.S.: 541511

Subsidiary (Domestic):

Engineering System International GmbH (3)
Siemensstr 12 B, 63263, Neu-Isenburg, Germany
Tel.: (49) 610220670
Computer Programming Services
N.A.I.C.S.: 541511

Subsidiary (Non-US):

ESI GmbH (2)
Mergenthalerallee 15-21, 65760, Eschborn, Germany
Tel.: (49) 619695830
Web Site: http://www.esigmbh.de
Sales Range: $25-49.9 Million
Emp.: 40
Simulation Software Sales & Technical Services
N.A.I.C.S.: 423430

ESI Group Hispania, S.L. (2)

Parque Empresarial Arroyo De La Vega C Francisca Delgado 11 Planta 2, 28108, Alcobendas, Madrid, Spain
Tel.: (34) 914840256
Web Site: http://www.esi-group.com
Software Development Services
N.A.I.C.S.: 541511

ESI Group Netherlands (2)
Radex Innovation Centre Room 4.57, Rotterdamseweg 183 C, 2629 HD, Delft, Netherlands
Tel.: (31) 152682501
Web Site: http://www.esi-group.com
Simulation Software Distr & Sales
N.A.I.C.S.: 423430

ESI ITI GmbH (2)
Schweriner Strasse 1, 01067, Dresden, Germany
Tel.: (49) 351260500
Web Site: http://www.simulationx.com
Computer Programming Services
N.A.I.C.S.: 541511
Egon Wiedekind *(Head-Mktg)*

ESI Italia srl (2)
Via San Donato 191, 40127, Bologna, Italy
Tel.: (39) 0516335577
Web Site: http://www.esi-italia.it
Sales Range: $25-49.9 Million
Emp.: 5
Digital Simulation Software Development Services
N.A.I.C.S.: 541511
Denis Luci *(Mng Dir)*

ESI Japan Ltd (2)
16F Shinjuku Green Tower Bldg 6-14-1 Nishi-Shinjuku, Shinjuku-ku, Tokyo, 160-0023, Japan
Tel.: (81) 363818490
Web Site: http://www.esi.co.jp
Sales Range: $25-49.9 Million
Emp.: 50
Digital Simulation Software Development Services
N.A.I.C.S.: 541511

ESI Nordics AB (2)
Lagerhyddsvagen 2 Hus 7, 752 37, Uppsala, Sweden
Tel.: (46) 841003511
Computer Programming Services
N.A.I.C.S.: 541511

Subsidiary (US):

ESI North America, Inc. (2)
32605 W 12 Mile Rd Ste 350, Farmington Hills, MI 48334
Tel.: (248) 381-8040
Web Site: http://www.esi-group.com
Sales Range: $25-49.9 Million
Emp.: 55
Simulation Software Distr & Sales
N.A.I.C.S.: 423430
Adi Sholapurwalla *(Gen Mgr)*

Subsidiary (Non-US):

ESI Services Tunisia SARL (2)
Annexe Immeuble La Carte 3eme et 4eme Etage, Centre Urbain Nord, 1082, Tunis, Tunisia
Tel.: (216) 71946906
Computer Programming Services
N.A.I.C.S.: 541511
Yacine Gargouri *(Gen Mgr)*

ESI Services Vietnam Co., Ltd. (2)
5F Thanh Long Tower 456 Xo Viet Nghe Tinh, Ward 25 Binh Thanh District, Ho Chi Minh City, Vietnam
Tel.: (84) 854454556
Computer Programming Services
N.A.I.C.S.: 541511
Nguyen Van Trong *(Engr-Vibration & Acoustic CAE)*

ESI Software Pvt. Ltd (2)
No 42 Block B 2nd floor 27th Cross Industrial Layout Banashankari, Brigade Software Park-1, Bengaluru, 560070, India
Tel.: (91) 8068285555
Web Site: http://www.esi-group.com
Sales Range: $25-49.9 Million
Emp.: 100
Simulation Software
N.A.I.C.S.: 334610

ESI South America Comercio E Servicos De Informatica Ltda (2)
Av Pedroso de Morais 1619 cj 312, Pinheiros, Sao Paulo, 05419-001, SP, Brazil
Tel.: (55) 1130316221
Computer Programming Services
N.A.I.C.S.: 541511

ESI UK Limited (2)
16 Morston Court, Kingswood Lakeside, Cannock, WS11 8JB, United Kingdom
Tel.: (44) 1543 397 900
Simulation Software Distr & Sales
N.A.I.C.S.: 423430

Subsidiary (US):

ESI US R&D, Inc. (2)
12555 High Bluff Dr Ste 160, San Diego, CA 92130
Tel.: (248) 381-8040
Computer Programming Services
N.A.I.C.S.: 541511

Subsidiary (Domestic):

Engineering System International SAS (2)
3 bis Rue Saarinen, 94528, Rungis, France
Tel.: (33) 149782800
Computer Programming Services
N.A.I.C.S.: 541511

Subsidiary (Non-US):

Hankook ESI (2)
157-033 5F Misung Building 660-6 Deungchon-3Dong, Gangseo-ku, Seoul, Korea (South)
Tel.: (82) 53300743
Web Site: http://www.esi.co.kr
Digital Simulation Software Development Services
N.A.I.C.S.: 541511

MECAS ESI s.r.o. (2)
Uslavska 10, Plzen, 32600, Czech Republic
Tel.: (420) 377432931
Web Site: http://www.mecasesi.cz
Sales Range: $25-49.9 Million
Emp.: 50
Simulation Software Distr & Sales
N.A.I.C.S.: 423430
Karel Lunacek *(Mng Dir, Dir-Sls & Mktg)*

OpenCFD Ltd. (2)
Unit 6 the Courtyard Eastern Road, Bracknell, RG12 2XB, Berkshire, United Kingdom
Tel.: (44) 7903169878
Web Site: http://www.openfoam.com
Computer Programming Services
N.A.I.C.S.: 541511
Fred Mendonca *(Mng Dir)*

The Virtual Try-Out Space S.L. (2)
Edificio IKEA Oficina 311, C/ Estartetxe 5, 48940, Leioa, Bizkaia, Spain
Tel.: (34) 944804760
Simulation Software Distr & Sales
N.A.I.C.S.: 423430

Eggplant Group Limited (1)
6 Snow Hill, London, EC1A 2AY, United Kingdom
Tel.: (44) 20 7002 7888
Web Site: http://www.eggplantsoftware.com
Holding Company; Testing Software Developer, Publisher & Whslr
N.A.I.C.S.: 551112
Chris Verdin *(CFO)*
Antony Edwards *(COO)*
Richard Ward *(Exec VP-Worldwide Sls)*
Teddy George *(VP-People)*
Gareth Smith *(CTO)*
Candice Arnold *(CMO)*

Subsidiary (US):

Eggplant (2)
2995 Wilderness Place, Boulder, CO 80301
Tel.: (800) 640-3842
Web Site: http://www.eggplantsoftware.com
Testing Software Developer, Publisher & Whslr
N.A.I.C.S.: 513210
Richard Ward *(Exec VP-Worldwide Sls)*
Candice Arnold *(CMO)*
Antony Edwards *(COO)*
Gareth Smith *(CTO)*
Teddy George *(VP-People)*
Chris Verdin *(CFO)*

Subsidiary (Domestic):

TestPlant UK Limited (2)
Unit 3 Barn 2 Somerford Business Court Holmes Chapel Road, Congleton, CW12 4SN, Cheshire, United Kingdom
Tel.: (44) 20 7002 7888
Web Site: http://www.testplant.com
Testing Software Developer, Publisher & Whslr
N.A.I.C.S.: 513210

IXIA (1)
26601 W Agoura Rd, Calabasas, CA 91302
Tel.: (818) 871-1800
Web Site: http://www.ixiacom.com
Emp.: 1,810
High Speed, Multi-Port Network Performance Analysis Systems Mfr
N.A.I.C.S.: 334515
Mark Pierpoint *(Pres-Ixia Solutions Grp)*

Subsidiary (Domestic):

IXIA - Austin (2)
8310 N Capital of Tx Hwy Bld 2 Ste 300, Austin, TX 78731
Tel.: (512) 600-5400
Web Site: http://www.ixiacom.com
Computer Network Diagnostic Equipment Mfr
N.A.I.C.S.: 541519

Subsidiary (Non-US):

Ixia Pte. Ltd. (2)
101 Thomson Road #29-04/05 United Square, Singapore, 307591, Singapore
Tel.: (65) 63320125
Web Site: http://www.ixiacom.com
Computer Network Testing Services
N.A.I.C.S.: 541519
Naveen Bhat *(Mng Dir-Asia Pacific)*

Ixia Technologies Europe Limited (2)
Main Building Hartham Park, Corsham, SN13 0RP, Wilts, United Kingdom
Tel.: (44) 1628 408 750
Computer Network Testing Services
N.A.I.C.S.: 541519

Subsidiary (Domestic):

Net Optics, Inc. (2)
5303 Betsy Ross Dr, Santa Clara, CA 95054
Tel.: (408) 737-7777
Web Site: http://www.ixiacom.com
Computer Network Security Services
N.A.I.C.S.: 541519

Keysight Technologies Japan G.K. (1)
9-1 Takakura-cho, Hachioji, 192-8550, Tokyo, Japan
Tel.: (81) 42 660 3000
Communications & Electronics Industry Measurement Instruments, Software & Services
N.A.I.C.S.: 334513

Keysight Technologies UK Limited (1)
5 Lochside Avenue, Edinburgh, Edinburgh, EH12 9DJ, United Kingdom
Tel.: (44) 1314520600
Electronic Measurement Instrument Mfr
N.A.I.C.S.: 334513
Roy MacNaughton *(Mgr-R&D-Signal Networks)*

Sanjole Inc. (1)
711 Kapiolani Blvd Ste 1050, Honolulu, HI 96813-5285
Tel.: (808) 457-1452
Web Site: http://www.sanjole.com
Wireless Network Test & Measurement Equipment Mfr
N.A.I.C.S.: 517112
Joe Fala *(Pres)*

Scalable Network Technologies, Inc. (1)
6167 Bristol Pkwy Ste 400, Culver City, CA 90230
Tel.: (310) 338-3318
Web Site: http://www.scalable-networks.com
Sales Range: $1-9.9 Million
Emp.: 43
Custom Computer Programming Services

N.A.I.C.S.: 541511
Rajive Bagrodia *(Founder)*
Christine Van Slyke *(VP-Sls & Bus Dev)*
Jim Zierick *(CEO)*
Paul Dumais *(VP-Product Dev)*

KEYSTAR CORP.
9620 Las Vegas Blvd S Ste E4-98, Las Vegas, NV 89123
Tel.: (702) 800-2511   NV
Web Site:
http://www.keystarshop.com
Year Founded: 2020
KEYR—(OTCIQ)
Rev.: $47,172
Assets: $108,573
Liabilities: $111,327
Net Worth: ($2,754)
Earnings: ($51,638)
Emp.: 2
Fiscal Year-end: 06/30/21
Ecommerce Services
N.A.I.C.S.: 541511
James G. Mackey *(CFO, Principal Acctg Officer & Treas)*
Bruce A. Cassidy Sr. *(Chm, Interim CEO & Sec)*
Steven Lane *(Pres)*

KEZAR LIFE SCIENCES, INC.
4000 Shoreline Ct Ste 300, South San Francisco, CA 94080
Tel.: (650) 822-5600   DE
Web Site:
https://www.kezarlifesciences.com
Year Founded: 2015
KZR—(NASDAQ)
Rev.: $4,108,000
Assets: $299,568,000
Liabilities: $29,696,000
Net Worth: $269,872,000
Earnings: ($68,239,000)
Emp.: 84
Fiscal Year-end: 12/31/22
Biotechnology Research & Development Services
N.A.I.C.S.: 541714
John Fowler *(Co-Founder)*
Christopher Kirk *(Co-Founder & CEO)*
Marc L. Belsky *(CFO & Sec)*
Jack Taunton *(Co-Founder)*
Gitanjali Jain *(VP-IR & External Affairs)*
Neel K. Anand *(Sr VP-Res & Drug Discovery)*
Kieron Wesson *(Sr VP-CMC & Supply Chain)*
Nick Mordwinkin *(Chief Bus Officer)*
Rafael Sarabia *(VP)*

KFG RESOURCES LTD.
150-A Providence Rd, Natchez, MS 39120
Tel.: (214) 526-2030   BC
Year Founded: 1994
KFG—(TSXV)
Rev.: $1,091,392
Assets: $635,390
Liabilities: $534,908
Net Worth: $100,482
Earnings: ($462,162)
Fiscal Year-end: 04/30/20
Natural Gas Exploration Service
N.A.I.C.S.: 213112
James F. Gilbert *(CFO)*
G. Stephen Guido *(COO & VP-Ops)*
Robert A. Kadane *(CEO)*

KFORCE INC.
1150 Assembly Dr Ste 500, Tampa, FL 33607
Tel.: (813) 552-5000   FL
Web Site: https://www.kforce.com
Year Founded: 1994
KFRC—(NASDAQ)
Rev.: $1,710,765,000

Assets: $392,004,000
Liabilities: $209,806,000
Net Worth: $182,198,000
Earnings: $75,431,000
Emp.: 2,000
Fiscal Year-end: 12/31/22
Temporary Staffing & Permanent Placement of Professional & Technical Personnel in the Information Technology, Accounting, Finance, Human Resources, Manufacturing, Health Care & Life Insurance Areas
N.A.I.C.S.: 561320
Joseph J. Liberatore *(Pres & CEO)*
Michael R. Blackman *(Chief Corp Dev Officer)*
David M. Kelly *(COO & Sec)*
Jeffrey B. Hackman *(CFO & Principal Acctg Officer)*
Denis Edwards *(CIO)*
Virgil Palumbo *(Reg Pres-Central)*
Steve Soares *(Pres-Vertical)*
Jennifer Smayda *(Gen Counsel)*
Jeffrey Hackman *(Principal Acctg Officer)*

Subsidiaries:

Kforce (1)
10790 Parkridge Blvd Ste 410, Reston, VA 20191
Tel.: (703) 342-3100
Web Site: https://www.kforce.com
Sales Range: $75-99.9 Million
Emp.: 650
Professional Staffing & Solutions Services
N.A.I.C.S.: 561311

Kforce Government Holdings, Inc. (1)
1001 E Palm Ave, Tampa, FL 33605
Tel.: (813) 552-5000
Web Site: http://www.kforce.com
Emp.: 800
Professional Staffing Services
N.A.I.C.S.: 561311
David L. Dunkel *(Chm & CEO)*

KHOSLA VENTURES ACQUISITION CO.
2128 Sand Hill Rd, Menlo Park, CA 94025
Tel.: (650) 376-8500   DE
Year Founded: 2021
KVSA—(NASDAQ)
Assets: $350,187,282
Liabilities: $357,954,324
Net Worth: ($7,767,042)
Earnings: $1,873,625
Fiscal Year-end: 12/31/22
Investment Services
N.A.I.C.S.: 523999
Vinod Khosla *(Founder)*
Samir Kaul *(CEO)*
Peter Buckland *(CFO, COO, Sec & Treas)*

KIDPIK CORP.
200 Park Ave S, New York, NY 10003
Tel.: (212) 399-2323   DE
Web Site: https://www.kidpik.com
Year Founded: 2015
PIK—(NASDAQ)
Rev.: $16,477,984
Assets: $16,148,346
Liabilities: $7,398,592
Net Worth: $8,749,754
Earnings: ($7,615,261)
Emp.: 25
Fiscal Year-end: 12/31/22
Ecommerce Services
N.A.I.C.S.: 458110
Ezra Dabah *(Chm, Pres & CEO)*
Moshe Dabah *(COO, CTO, Sec & VP)*
Jill Pasechnick *(Chief Acctg Officer & Principal Acctg Officer)*

Kidpik Corp.—(Continued)

KIDVILLE, INC.
205 W 88th St, New York, NY 10024
Tel.: (212) 362-7792 DE
Web Site: https://www.kidville.com
Year Founded: 2004
KVIL—(OTCIQ)
Sales Range: Less than $1 Million
Emp.: 30
Children's Playground & Other Related Facilities
N.A.I.C.S.: 713990
Rammy Harwood (Pres)

KILEY GROUP, INC.
2910 Belmeade Dr Ste 106, Carrollton, TX 75006
Tel.: (972) 850-8628 DE
Year Founded: 1997
KGRI—(OTCIQ)
Business Consulting Services
N.A.I.C.S.: 541611
William Smart (Pres)

KILLBUCK BANCSHARES, INC.
Tel.: (330) 276-4881 OH
Web Site:
http://www.killbuckbank.com
Year Founded: 1991
KLIB—(OTCIQ)
Bank Holding Company
N.A.I.C.S.: 551111
Craig A. Lawhead (Bd of Dirs, Pres & CEO)
Rachel Miller (Pres & CEO)
Justin J. Pike (CFO)
Lisa Kauffman (Sec)
Matthew Miller (Sr VP & CLO)
James Mirich (COO & Sr VP)
Theodore G. Thorpe (VP)
Dean Mullet (Chm)
Max Miller (Vice Chm)

Subsidiaries:

The Killbuck Savings Bank Company (1)
165 N Main St, Killbuck, OH 44637 (100%)
Tel.: (330) 276-4881
Web Site: http://www.killbuckbank.com
Rev.: $19,192,000
Emp.: 30
Commericial Banking
N.A.I.C.S.: 522110
Craig A. Lawhead (Pres & CEO)

KILROY REALTY CORPORATION
12200 W Olympic Blvd Ste 200, Los Angeles, CA 90064
Tel.: (310) 481-8400 MD
Web Site:
https://www.kilroyrealty.com
Year Founded: 1997
KRC—(NYSE)
Rev.: $1,129,694,000
Assets: $11,401,045,000
Liabilities: $5,741,352,000
Net Worth: $5,659,693,000
Earnings: $212,241,000
Emp.: 248
Fiscal Year-end: 12/31/23
Real Estate Investment Trust
N.A.I.C.S.: 525990
Tyler H. Rose (Pres & Sec)
Justin W. Smart (Exec VP-Dev & Construction Svcs)
Heidi Rena Roth (Chief Admin Officer & Exec VP)
Michelle Ngo (CFO, Treas & Sr VP)
Merryl E. Werber (Chief Acctg Officer, Sr VP & Controller)
Angela M. Aman (CEO)
John A. Osmond (Sr VP & Head-Asset Mgmt)

William E. Hutcheson (Sr VP-IR & Capital Markets)
Eliott L. Trencher (Chief Investment Officer & Exec VP)

Subsidiaries:

Kilroy Realty, L.P. (1)
12200 W Olympic Blvd Ste 200, Los Angeles, CA 90064
Tel.: (310) 481-8400
Web Site: https://www.kilroyrealty.com
Rev.: $1,129,693,999
Assets: $11,401,044,999
Liabilities: $5,741,351,999
Net Worth: $5,659,692,999
Earnings: $214,324,000
Emp.: 247
Fiscal Year-end: 12/31/2023
Real Estate Investment Trust
N.A.I.C.S.: 525990
Michelle Ngo (CFO, Treas & Sr VP)
John B. Kilroy Sr. (Chm & CEO)
Merryl E. Werber (Chief Acctg Officer, Sr VP & Controller)
Justin W. Smart (Pres)
A. Robert Paratte (Chief Leasing Officer)

Subsidiary (Domestic):

Kilroy Realty Finance Partnership, L.P. (2)
12200 W Olympic Blvd Ste 200, Los Angeles, CA 90064
Tel.: (310) 481-8400
Web Site: http://www.kilroyrealty.com
Sales Range: $10-24.9 Million
Emp.: 100
Finance, Insurance & Real Estate
N.A.I.C.S.: 524298

Kilroy Services, LLC (2)
12200 W Olympic Blvd Ste 200, Los Angeles, CA 90064
Tel.: (310) 481-8400
Real Estate Manangement Services
N.A.I.C.S.: 531210

KIMBALL ELECTRONICS, INC.
1205 Kimball Blvd, Jasper, IN 47546
Tel.: (812) 634-4000 IN
Web Site:
https://www.kimballelectronics.com
Year Founded: 1961
KE—(NASDAQ)
Rev.: $1,714,510,000
Assets: $1,207,919,000
Liabilities: $667,458,000
Net Worth: $540,461,000
Earnings: $20,511,000
Emp.: 7,000
Fiscal Year-end: 06/30/24
Electronic Products Mfr
N.A.I.C.S.: 334111
Steven T. Korn (COO)
Kathy R. Thomson (Chief Comml Officer)
Christopher J. Thyen (VP-New Platforms)
Jessica L. DeLorenzo (VP-Human Resources)
Douglas A. Hass (Chief Legal Officer, Chief Compliance Officer & Sec)
Kathy R. Thomson (VP-Design Svcs & Bus Dev-Global)
LeRoy W. Kemper (VP-Diversified Contract Mfg Svcs)
Richard D. Phillips (CEO)
Jana T. Croom (CFO)
Adam M. Baumann (Chief Acctg Officer)
Steven T. Korn (COO)

Subsidiaries:

Aircom Manufacturing, Inc. (1)
6205 E 30th St, Indianapolis, IN 46219 (100%)
Tel.: (317) 545-5383
Web Site: http://www.aircommfg.com
Emp.: 100
Metal Fabricating Services
N.A.I.C.S.: 332999
Ron Lyon (Pres)

Global Equipment Services & Manufacturing Vietnam Company Limited (1)
Lot I3 - 1 D1 Street, Saigon Hi-Tech Park Tan Phu Ward District 9, Ho Chi Minh City, Vietnam
Tel.: (84) 2837362388
Electric Equipment Mfr
N.A.I.C.S.: 334419

Kimball Electronics (Nanjing) Co., Ltd. (1)
Jiyindadao 3098, Jiangning District, Nanjing, 211100, Jiangsu, China
Tel.: (86) 2552728701
Web Site: https://www.kegroup.com
Sales Range: $100-124.9 Million
Emp.: 600
Electronics Mfr
N.A.I.C.S.: 334419

Kimball Electronics (Thailand), Ltd. (1)
49 45 Moo 5 Laem Chabang Industrial Estate, Sukhumvit Road Thungsukhla Sriracha, Chon Buri, 20230, Thailand.
Tel.: (66) 38401566
Sales Range: $100-124.9 Million
Emp.: 800
Complete Electronic Manufacturing Services
N.A.I.C.S.: 334220

Kimball Electronics Indianapolis, Inc. (1)
2950 N Catherwood Ave, Indianapolis, IN 46219
Tel.: (317) 547-3640
Medical Equipment Mfr & Distr
N.A.I.C.S.: 334418

Kimball Electronics Mexico, Inc. (1)
1501 W Produce Dr, Pharr, TX 78577 (100%)
Tel.: (956) 205-4600
Sales Range: $100-124.9 Million
Electronics Mfr
N.A.I.C.S.: 334419

Subsidiary (Non-US):

Kimball Electronics - Mexico, S.A. de C.V. (2)
Mike Allen 1145, Parque Industrial Reynosa Cd, 88780, Reynosa, Tamaulipas, Mexico (100%)
Tel.: (52) 8999094600
Emp.: 100
Provider of Electronic Manufacturing Services
N.A.I.C.S.: 423610

Kimball Electronics Poland Sp. z o.o (1)
ul Poznanska 1C, Tarnowo Podgorne, 62-080, Poznan, Poland (100%)
Tel.: (48) 618609600
Web Site: http://kimball.pl
Sales Range: $25-49.9 Million
Emp.: 100
Complete Electronic Manufacturing Services
N.A.I.C.S.: 811210
Janusz Kasprzyk (VP-Ops-Europe)

Kimball Electronics Tampa, Inc. (1)
13750 Reptron Blvd, Tampa, FL 33626-3040 (100%)
Tel.: (813) 814-5039
Sales Range: $125-149.9 Million
Emp.: 315
Electronic Parts Mfr
N.A.I.C.S.: 334419

KIMBELL ROYALTY PARTNERS, LP
777 Taylor St Ste 810, Fort Worth, TX 76102
Tel.: (817) 945-9700 DE
Web Site: https://www.kimbellrp.com
Year Founded: 2015
KRP—(NYSE)
Rev.: $294,068,612
Assets: $1,337,789,216
Liabilities: $309,322,464
Net Worth: $1,028,466,752
Earnings: $60,141,679
Emp.: 29

Fiscal Year-end: 12/31/23
Crude Petroleum Extraction Services
N.A.I.C.S.: 211120
Robert D. Ravnaas (Chm & CEO)
R. Blayne Rhynsburger (Controller)
Rand Ravnaas (VP-Bus Dev)
Andrew Cardwell (VP-Fin & IR)
Daniel C. Przyojski Jr. (VP)

KIMBELL TIGER ACQUISITION CORP.
777 Taylor St ste 810, Fort Worth, TX 76102
Tel.: (817) 945-9700 DE
Web Site:
https://www.kimbelltiger.com
Year Founded: 2021
TGR—(NYSE)
Rev.: $3,721,145
Assets: $241,047,197
Liabilities: $246,125,467
Net Worth: ($5,078,270)
Earnings: $1,156,000
Emp.: 2
Fiscal Year-end: 12/31/22
Investment Services
N.A.I.C.S.: 523999
Zachary M. Lunn (Pres & CEO)
Robert D. Ravnaas (Chm)
R. Blayne Rhynsburger (Controller)

KIMBERLY PARRY ORGANICS, CORP.
276 E Main St Ste 10-77, Denville, NJ 07834
Tel.: (727) 274-0077 NV
Year Founded: 2006
KPOC—(OTCIQ)
Personal Care Product Mfr
N.A.I.C.S.: 325620
Guy Papineau (CEO)
Theodore Collas (Pres)
Richard Edelson (Accountant)

KIMBERLY-CLARK CORPORATION
PO Box 619100, Dallas, TX 75261-9100
Tel.: (972) 281-1200 WI
Web Site: https://www.kimberly-clark.com
Year Founded: 1872
KMB—(NYSE)
Rev.: $20,431,000,000
Assets: $17,344,000,000
Liabilities: $16,276,000,000
Net Worth: $1,068,000,000
Earnings: $1,764,000,000
Emp.: 41,000
Fiscal Year-end: 12/31/23
Consumer Products, Health Care Products, Newsprint & Specialty Paper Products Mfr
N.A.I.C.S.: 322120
Tristram Wilkinson (Pres-Consumer Bus-EMEA)
Zackery A. Hicks (Chief Digital & Tech Officer)
Nelson Urdaneta (CFO & Sr VP)
Andrew S. Drexler (VP & Controller)
Alison Lewis (Chief Growth Officer)
Gustavo Ghory (Chief Supply Chain Officer & Chief Supply Chain Officer)
Sandi Karrmann (Chief HR Officer & Sr VP)
Preeti Binoy (Head-Communications)
Gonzalo Uribe (Pres-Consumer Bus-Latin)
Robert Long (Chief R&D Officer)
Bryan Haynes (Dir-Technical-R&E)
Ehab Abou-Oaf (Pres)
Tamera Fenske (Chief Supply Chain Officer)
Michael D. Hsu (Chm & CEO)

Subsidiaries:

Balder d.o.o. (1)
Teslova ulica 30, 1000, Ljubljana, Slovenia
Tel.: (386) 14264579
Web Site: http://www.balder.si
Optoelectronic Device Mfr
N.A.I.C.S.: 334413

Chapel Valley Housing II LLC (1)
5781 Chapel Valley Rd, Fitchburg, WI
53711
Tel.: (608) 277-8887
Health Care Products Mfr
N.A.I.C.S.: 621610

**Colombiana Kimberly Colpapel
S.A.** (1)
c/o Kimberly-Clark Argentina S.A., Libertador 498 piso 24, CP 1001, Buenos Aires,
Argentina (69%)
Tel.: (54) 11 4321 5838
Web Site: http://www.kimberly-clark.com
Sales Range: $400-449.9 Million
Emp.: 6,400
Mfr & Distr of Personal Care & Household
Products
N.A.I.C.S.: 812199

Hogla-Kimberly Ltd. (1)
Ramie Way Machsanai Ha'Sochnoot, PO
Box 231, Tel-Aviv Ramie, Ramla, 72101,
Tzrifin, Israel (50.1%)
Tel.: (972) 8 9771277
Web Site: http://www.hadera-paper.co.il
Emp.: 250
Marketing of Paper Products, Toilet Tissue
& Paper Towels
N.A.I.C.S.: 424130

Unit (Domestic):

Shikma (2)
20 Hata as St, PO Box 231, Kfar Saba,
44425, Israel
Tel.: (972) 97687684
Web Site: http://www.shikma.biz
Mfr of Absorbent Disposable Products for
Incontinence & Geriatric Use
N.A.I.C.S.: 322291

I-Flow, LLC (1)
20202 Windrow Dr, Lake Forest, CA 92630
Tel.: (949) 206-2700
Web Site: http://www.iflo.com
Sales Range: $125-149.9 Million
Emp.: 430
Drug Delivery Systems Developer & Marketer
N.A.I.C.S.: 339112
Mark A. Buthman (CFO)

**K-C AFC Manufacturing, S. de R.L.
de C. V.** (1)
Calzada Industrial de las Maquiladoras 14,
Nogales, Mexico
Tel.: (52) 6313115830
Personal Care Product Mfr
N.A.I.C.S.: 322291
Martha Soto (Supvr-Acctg)

K-C Advertising, Inc. (1)
N Lake St, Neenah, WI 54956
Tel.: (920) 721-2000
Sales Range: $100-124.9 Million
Advetising Agency
N.A.I.C.S.: 541810

K-C Equipment Finance L.P. (1)
75 Stafford St, Gillingham, ME7 5EN,
United Kingdom
Tel.: (44) 1634856956
Used Car Dealers
N.A.I.C.S.: 441120

K.C.S.A. Holdings (Pty.) Ltd. (1)
8 Leicester Road Bedford Gardens, Bedfordview, 2007, Gauteng, South Africa
Tel.: (27) 114565700
Web Site: http://www.kimberly-clark.co.za
Holding Company
N.A.I.C.S.: 551112

KCA Super Pty Limited (1)
52 Alfred Street, Milsons Point, 2061, NSW,
Australia
Tel.: (61) 135228
Financial Trust Services
N.A.I.C.S.: 523991

KCSSA East Africa Limited (1)
Cove Court Watermark Business Park
Ndege Road, Karen, Nairobi, Kenya
Tel.: (254) 27114565700
Sanitary Paper Product Mfr
N.A.I.C.S.: 322291

Kalayaan Land Corporation (1)
Maharlika, 4023, Laguna, Philippines
Tel.: (63) 28848595
Personal Care Product Distr
N.A.I.C.S.: 424130

Kimberly Bolivia S.A. (1)
Los Cedros Street No 100ITC Tower Building 4th Floor, North Equipetrol, Santa Cruz,
Bolivia
Tel.: (591) 33122900
Web Site: http://www.kimberly-clark.com.bo
Emp.: 206
Sanitation Goods Mfr
N.A.I.C.S.: 322291

Kimberly Clark Uruguay S.A. (1)
Camino Carrasco 5975, Montevideo, Uruguay
Tel.: (598) 225250105
Sanitary Paper Product Mfr
N.A.I.C.S.: 322291

**Kimberly-Clark (China) Company
Ltd.** (1)
12F Bldg A SOHO Fuxing Plz No 299 Danshui Rd, Huangpu District, Shanghai,
200025, China
Tel.: (86) 85223343361
Household Products Mfr
N.A.I.C.S.: 811490

**Kimberly-Clark (Hong Kong)
Limited** (1)
12F Building A SOHO Fuxing Plaza No 299
Danshui Road, Huangpu District, Shanghai,
200025, China
Tel.: (86) 23343361
Sanitary Paper Product Mfr
N.A.I.C.S.: 322291

**Kimberly-Clark (Singapore) Finance
Pte. Ltd.** (1)
81 Tuas South Ave 8, Singapore, 637558,
Singapore
Tel.: (65) 64905600
Web Site: http://www.kimberlyclark.com
Paper Products Mfr
N.A.I.C.S.: 322291

**Kimberly-Clark Amsterdam Holdings
B.V.** (1)
Copernicuslaan 35, 6716 BM, Ede, Netherlands
Tel.: (31) 318697697
Web Site: http://www.kimberly-clark.com
Sales Range: $25-49.9 Million
Paper Products Mfr
N.A.I.C.S.: 322291

Kimberly-Clark Argentina S.A. (1)
Olga Cossettini 1031, CP 1103, Buenos
Aires, 1001, Argentina
Tel.: (54) 1143215700
Sanitary Paper Product Mfr
N.A.I.C.S.: 322291

**Kimberly-Clark Asia Holdings Pte.
Ltd.** (1)
81 Tuas S Ave 8, Singapore, 637558, Singapore
Tel.: (65) 62262882
Paper Products Mfr
N.A.I.C.S.: 322291

**Kimberly-Clark Asia Pacific Pte.
Ltd.** (1)
81 Tuas S Ave 8, Singapore, 637558, Singapore
Tel.: (65) 64905600
Web Site: http://www.kimberly-clark.com
Emp.: 100
Sanitary Paper Product Mfr
N.A.I.C.S.: 322291

**Kimberly-Clark Australia Holdings Pty.
Limited** (1)
100 Arthur Street, Sydney, 2060, NSW,
Australia
Tel.: (61) 135228
Web Site:
https://www.kcprofessional.com.au
Holding Company
N.A.I.C.S.: 551112

Kimberly-Clark Australia Pty. Ltd. (1)
52 Alfred Street, PO Box 343, Milsons
Point, 1565, NSW, Australia
Tel.: (61) 299638888
Web Site: http://www.kimberly-clark.com.au
Sales Range: $100-124.9 Million
Paper & Paper Products Mfr & Distr
N.A.I.C.S.: 322120
Rahul Asthana (Sr Dir-Mktg)
Doug Cunningham (Mng Dir)
Annelise Tregoning (Head-Comm & Govt
Affairs)
Ignacio Suit (Gen Mgr)
Cam Scott (Gen Mgr)
George Papanikitas (Gen Counsel)
Nathan McLachlan (Fin Dir)
Geoff Walker (Dir-Supply Chain)
Ian Flemington (Dir-HR)
Matthew Kelly (Dir-Consumer Sls)

Kimberly-Clark Bolivia S.A. (1)
Parque Industrial Manzana 5, Santa Cruz,
Bolivia
Tel.: (591) 33126300
Web Site: http://www.kimberly-clark.com.bo
Sales Range: $150-199.9 Million
Emp.: 500
Paper Products Mfr
N.A.I.C.S.: 322291

**Kimberly-Clark Brasil Industria e Comercio de Produtos de Higiene
Ltda.** (1)
Tel.: (55) 1145034500
Paper Products Mfr
N.A.I.C.S.: 322291

Kimberly-Clark Canada Inc. (1)
50 Burnhamthorpe Rd W, Mississauga, L5B
3C2, ON, Canada
Tel.: (905) 277-6500
Paper Mill Operator
N.A.I.C.S.: 322120

**Kimberly-Clark Central American
Holdings, S.A.** (1)
PO Box 6-6611, El Dorado, Panama,
Panama
Tel.: (507) 3600400
Paper Products Mfr
N.A.I.C.S.: 322120

Kimberly-Clark Chile S.A. (1)
Av Del Valle 732 Piso 4 Ciudad Empresarial, Huechuraba, Chile
Tel.: (56) 225498001
Sanitary Paper Product Mfr
N.A.I.C.S.: 322291

Kimberly-Clark Chile S.A. (1)
Av Del Valle 732 Piso 4 Ciudad Empresarial, Huechuraba, 8580659, Chile
Tel.: (56) 80 020 1717
Web Site: http://www.kimberlyclark.com
Sanitary Paper Product Mfr
N.A.I.C.S.: 322291

**Kimberly-Clark Colombia Holding
Limitada** (1)
Carrera 11 94-45 Piso 5, Bogota, Colombia
Tel.: (57) 16003300
Holding Company
N.A.I.C.S.: 551112

Kimberly-Clark Corporation (1)
520 W Summit Hill Dr, Knoxville, TN 37902-
2007
Tel.: (865) 541-7000
Web Site: http://www.kimberly-clark.com
Sales Range: $300-349.9 Million
Emp.: 400
Administrative Management Services
N.A.I.C.S.: 322120

Kimberly-Clark Corporation - Consumer Tissue Sector (1)
1400 Holcomb Bridge Rd, Roswell, GA
30076
Tel.: (770) 587-8000
Web Site: http://www.kimberly-clark.com
Sales Range: $650-699.9 Million
Emp.: 1,600
Paper Mills
N.A.I.C.S.: 322299

Branch (Domestic):

Kimberly-Clark Corporation (2)
13219 Kimberly Clark Pl, Jenks, OK 74037-
3000

Tel.: (918) 366-5000
Web Site: http://www.kcc.com
Sales Range: $350-399.9 Million
Emp.: 500
Paper Mills
N.A.I.C.S.: 322120

Kimberly-Clark Corporation (2)
3120 Riverside Ave, Marinette, WI 54143-
1123
Tel.: (715) 735-6644
Sales Range: $100-124.9 Million
Emp.: 270
Paper Mills
N.A.I.C.S.: 322120

Kimberly-Clark Corporation (2)
1 Ave of the States, Chester, PA 19013
Tel.: (610) 874-4331
Web Site: http://www.kimberly-clark.com
Sales Range: $550-599.9 Million
Emp.: 840
Paper Mills
N.A.I.C.S.: 322120

Kimberly-Clark Corporation (2)
5600 Kimberly Way, Loudon, TN
37774 (100%)
Tel.: (865) 988-5536
Web Site: http://www.kcprofessional.com
Sales Range: $250-299.9 Million
Emp.: 350
Towels Tissues & Napkins; Paper & Stock
N.A.I.C.S.: 322120

Kimberly-Clark Corporation (2)
58 Pickett District Rd, New Milford, CT
06776
Tel.: (860) 354-4481
Towels Tissues & Napkins; Paper & Stock
N.A.I.C.S.: 322120

Kimberly-Clark Corporation (2)
2001 E Orangethorpe Ave, Fullerton, CA
92831-5326 (100%)
Tel.: (714) 773-7500
Web Site: http://www.kimberlyclark.com
Sales Range: $350-399.9 Million
Emp.: 500
Paper
N.A.I.C.S.: 322120

Kimberly-Clark Corporation - Household Products Sector (2)
2300 County Rd Ii, Neenah, WI 54956-9321
Tel.: (920) 721-5215
Web Site: http://www.kimberly-clark.com
Sales Range: $10-24.9 Million
Emp.: 15
Mfr of Facial & Bathroom Tissue, Disposable Household Towels & Table Napkins
N.A.I.C.S.: 513110

**Kimberly-Clark Corporation -
Mobile** (2)
200 Bay Bridge Rd, Mobile, AL
36610 (100%)
Tel.: (251) 330-3000
Web Site: http://www.kimberlyclark.com
Sales Range: $10-24.9 Million
Emp.: 400
Sanitary Paper Product Mfr
N.A.I.C.S.: 322291

Subsidiary (Domestic):

**Kimberly-Clark International Services
Corp.** (2)
401 N Lake St, Neenah, WI 54956-2018
Tel.: (920) 721-2000
Web Site: http://www.kimberly-clark.com
Sales Range: $10-24.9 Million
Paper Mills
N.A.I.C.S.: 322120

**Kimberly-Clark Corporation - Neenah
Paper** (1)
1376 Kimberly Dr, Neenah, WI 54956-1641
Tel.: (715) 735-6644
Web Site: http://www.neenahpaper.com
Sales Range: $10-24.9 Million
Emp.: 56
Consortium of Subsidiaries & Equity Companies in 18 Countries
N.A.I.C.S.: 322120

Branch (Domestic):

Kimberly-Clark Corporation (2)

Kimberly-Clark Corporation—(Continued)

2100 Winchester Rd, Neenah, WI
54956-9317 **(100%)**
Tel.: (920) 721-5499
Web Site: http://www.kimberly-clark.com
Paper Mills
N.A.I.C.S.: 322120

Services Plus, Inc. **(2)**
1001 Discovery Rd, Green Bay, WI 54311-8001
Tel.: (920) 469-5222
Web Site: http://www.servicesplus.com
Emp.: 100
Paper Mills
N.A.I.C.S.: 322120
Tad Campana *(Pres)*
Jennifer Brown *(Mgr-Contact Pkg Value Stream)*

Kimberly-Clark Corporation - Personal Care Sector **(1)**
401 N Lake St, Neenah, WI 54956-2018
Tel.: (920) 721-3617
Web Site: http://www.kimberly-clark.com
Sales Range: $10-24.9 Million
Emp.: 12
Diapers, Feminine Pads, Tampons & Incontinence Products
N.A.I.C.S.: 513110

Subsidiary (Domestic):

Kimberly-Clark Conway Mills
480 Exchange Ave, Conway, AR 72032-7808
Tel.: (501) 329-2973
Web Site: http://www.kimberly-clark.com
Mfr of Sanitary Paper Products
N.A.I.C.S.: 322291

Branch (Domestic):

Kimberly-Clark Corporation **(2)**
2466 Farm Rd 137, Paris, TX 75460
Tel.: (903) 737-5100
Web Site: http://www.kimberly-clark.com
Mfr of Diapers
N.A.I.C.S.: 322291

Kimberly-Clark Corporation **(2)**
2010 Rulon White Blvd, Ogden, UT 84404 **(100%)**
Tel.: (801) 782-2500
Web Site: http://www.kimberly-clark.com
Diapers Paper (Disposable); Made From Purchased Paper
N.A.I.C.S.: 322291

Kimberly-Clark Corporation **(2)**
500 Murphy Dr, Maumelle, AR 72113
Tel.: (501) 212-2200
Web Site: http://www.kcc.com
Cleansing Tissues Made From Purchased Paper
N.A.I.C.S.: 322291

Subsidiary (Non-US):

Kimberly-Clark Inc. **(2)**
1402 50 Burnhamthorpe Rd W, Mississauga, L5B 3Y5, ON, Canada
Tel.: (905) 277-6500
Personal Care Consumer Tissue & Travel Products Retailer & Marketer
N.A.I.C.S.: 322291

Subsidiary (Domestic):

Kimberly-Clark, Inc.-Huntsville **(3)**
570 Ravenscliffe Rd, Huntsville, P1H 2A1, ON, Canada **(100%)**
Tel.: (705) 788-5200
Web Site: http://www.kimberly-clark.com
Sales Range: $50-74.9 Million
Emp.: 200
Paper Mills
N.A.I.C.S.: 322120

Kimberly-Clark Corporation - Professional & Other and Health Care Sector **(1)**
1400 Holcomb Bridge Rd, Roswell, GA 30076
Tel.: (770) 587-8000
Web Site: http://www.kcprofessional.com
Sales Range: $450-499.9 Million
Emp.: 600
Durable & Single Use Nonwoven Materials; Disposable Medical Accessories

N.A.I.C.S.: 322299
Jan B. Spencer *(Pres)*

Subsidiary (Domestic):

Jackson Products, Inc. **(2)**
801 Corporate Ctr Dr No 300, Saint Charles, MO 63304-8685
Tel.: (636) 717-6600
Web Site: http://www.jacksonsafety.com
Holding Company; Protective & Safety Equipment Mfr
N.A.I.C.S.: 339113

Kimberly-Clark Ballard Medical **(2)**
12050 Lone Peak Pkwy, Draper, UT 84020 **(100%)**
Tel.: (801) 572-6800
Web Site: http://www.kchealthcare.com
Sales Range: $450-499.9 Million
Earnings: $32,000,000
Surgical & Medical Instruments
N.A.I.C.S.: 339112

Plant (Domestic):

Kimberly-Clark Corporation **(2)**
3461 CR 100, Corinth, MS 38834
Tel.: (662) 287-8011
Sales Range: $10-24.9 Million
Nonwoven Fabrics
N.A.I.C.S.: 322120

Branch (Domestic):

Kimberly-Clark Corporation **(2)**
32 Smyth Ave, Hendersonville, NC 28792 **(100%)**
Tel.: (828) 692-9611
Web Site: http://www.surftran.com
Sales Range: $350-399.9 Million
Emp.: 300
Nonwoven Fabrics
N.A.I.C.S.: 322120

Kimberly-Clark Corporation **(2)**
Frnt Ave of the State, Chester, PA 19013
Tel.: (610) 874-4331
Web Site: http://www.kimberly-clark.com
Sales Range: $300-349.9 Million
Emp.: 400
Mfr of Nonwoven Fabrics
N.A.I.C.S.: 322120

Plant (Domestic):

Kimberly-Clark Corporation **(2)**
1400 Holcomb Bridge Rd, Roswell, GA 30076 **(100%)**
Tel.: (770) 587-8000
Web Site: http://www.kimberlyclark.com
Corrugated & Solid Fiber Boxes
N.A.I.C.S.: 322211

Kimberly-Clark Ecuador S.A. **(1)**
Mapasingue Este Calle 5ta y Av Las Aguas, Guayaquil, Guayas, Ecuador
Tel.: (593) 1800200500
Sanitary Paper Product Mfr
N.A.I.C.S.: 322291

Kimberly-Clark Europe Limited **(1)**
Calle Juan Esplandiu 11 13, Madrid, 28007, Spain
Tel.: (34) 915579700
Sanitary Paper Product Mfr
N.A.I.C.S.: 322291

Kimberly-Clark Finance Limited **(1)**
1 Tower View Kings Hill, West Malling, ME19 4HA, Kent, United Kingdom
Tel.: (44) 1732594000
Emp.: 250
Sanitary Paper Product Mfr
N.A.I.C.S.: 322291

Kimberly-Clark Global Sales, LLC **(1)**
2001 Marathon Ave, Neenah, WI 54957
Tel.: (920) 721-2000
Paper Mill Operator
N.A.I.C.S.: 322120

Kimberly-Clark GmbH **(1)**
Wienerbergstrasse 11, Vienna, 1100, Austria
Tel.: (43) 16051700
Web Site: http://www.kchealthcare.com
Emp.: 1
Sanitary Paper Product Mfr
N.A.I.C.S.: 322291

Kimberly-Clark GmbH **(1)**
Carl-Spaeter-Strasse 17, 56070, Koblenz, Germany
Tel.: (49) 26192270
Web Site: http://www.kcprofessional.de
Sanitary Products Mfr
N.A.I.C.S.: 322291
Frank Fleck *(Mng Dir)*
Joachim Gutschmidt *(Mng Dir)*

Kimberly-Clark GmbH **(1)**
Rotboden 1, Niederbipp, 4704, Bern, Switzerland
Tel.: (41) 326335111
Sanitary Paper Product Mfr
N.A.I.C.S.: 322291

Kimberly-Clark Guatemala, Limitada **(1)**
Calzada Astanasio Tzul 47-70 zona 12, Guatemala, Guatemala
Tel.: (502) 18010002473
Sanitary Paper Product Mfr
N.A.I.C.S.: 322291

Kimberly-Clark Health Care Inc. **(1)**
1400 Holcomb Bridge Rd, Roswell, GA 30076
Tel.: (770) 587-8000
Web Site: https://www.kcprofessional.com
Surgical & Medical Instrument Mfr
N.A.I.C.S.: 339112

Subsidiary (Non-US):

Kimberly-Clark Holding Ltd **(2)**
1 Tower View Kings Hill, West Malling, ME19 4HA, United Kingdom
Tel.: (44) 01732594000
Web Site: http://www.kimberly-clark.com
Sales Range: $250-299.9 Million
Holding Company
N.A.I.C.S.: 551112

Subsidiary (Non-US):

Hainz-Kimberly Deutschland GmbH **(3)**
PO Box 22 60, Mainz, 55012, Germany **(100%)**
Tel.: (49) 6131607000
Web Site: http://www.hakle.de
Sales Range: $25-49.9 Million
Emp.: 60
Manufacture & Conversion of Creped Wadding
N.A.I.C.S.: 313210
Andy Kistler *(Pres & CEO)*

Subsidiary (Domestic):

Kimberly-Clark Limited **(3)**
1 Tower View Kings Hill, West Malling, ME19 4HA, Kent, United Kingdom **(100%)**
Tel.: (44) 1732594000
Web Site: http://www.kimberly-clark.com
Sales Range: $125-149.9 Million
Manufacture & Conversion of Creped Wadding & Nonwoven Fabrics
N.A.I.C.S.: 313210

Subsidiary (Non-US):

Kimberly-Clark S.L.U. **(3)**
C/ Quintanavides 17 planta 1, 28050, Madrid, Spain
Tel.: (34) 915579700
Web Site: http://www.kimberlyclark.es
Sales Range: $300-349.9 Million
Sanitary Paper Product Mfr
N.A.I.C.S.: 322291

Kimberly-Clark s.r.l. **(3)**
C So Francesco Ferrucci 112, 10138, Turin, TO, Italy **(100%)**
Tel.: (39) 01188141
Sales Range: $300-349.9 Million
Emp.: 100
Sanitary Tissue Products Mfr
N.A.I.C.S.: 322291

Subsidiary (Non-US):

YuHan-Kimberly, Limited **(2)**
29th floor Lotte World Tower 300 Olympic-ro, Songpa-gu, Seoul, 05551, Korea (South) **(100%)**
Tel.: (82) 26 411 0100
Web Site: https://www.yuhan-kimberly.co.kr

Sales Range: $600-649.9 Million
Mfr & Conversion of Creped Wadding; Consumer Disposable Products for Feminine Care Personal Tissue
N.A.I.C.S.: 313210

Subsidiary (Non-US):

Kimberly Clark Trading (Malaysia) Sdn. Bhd. **(3)**
2nd Floor Tower 2 Wisma AmFirst Jalan SS7/15 Kelana Jaya, 47301, Petaling Jaya, Selanger, Malaysia
Tel.: (60) 378068288
Web Site: http://www.kcprofessional.com.my
Mfr of Sanitary Tissue Products
N.A.I.C.S.: 322291

Kimberly-Clark Singapore Pte. Ltd. **(3)**
83 Clemenceau Avenue 14-05 UE Square, Singapore, 239920, Singapore **(100%)**
Tel.: (65) 18005625275
Sales Range: $10-24.9 Million
Emp.: 30
Mfr of Sanitary Paper Products
N.A.I.C.S.: 322291

Kimberly-Clark Thailand Ltd. **(3)**
323 United Ctr 32nd 33rd Fl Silom Road, 323 Silom Rd Bangrak, Bangkok, 10500, Thailand **(100%)**
Tel.: (66) 22303000
Web Site: http://www.kcc.com
Sales Range: $250-299.9 Million
Mfr & Conversion Mill
N.A.I.C.S.: 322120

Kimberly-Clark Holding srl **(1)**
Via Della Rocca 49, Turin, 10123, Italy
Tel.: (39) 01188141
Emp.: 578
Holding Company
N.A.I.C.S.: 551112

Kimberly-Clark Hygiene Products Private Limited **(1)**
Art Guild House B-16-17 3rd Floor Phoenix Market City, LBS Marg Kurla, Mumbai, 400 070, India
Tel.: (91) 2233220111
Sanitary Paper Product Mfr
N.A.I.C.S.: 322291

Kimberly-Clark India Private Limited **(1)**
Art Guild House A 09 3rd Floor Phoenix Market City LBS Marg, Kurla West, Mumbai, 400 070, India
Tel.: (91) 2233220000
Sanitary Paper Product Mfr
N.A.I.C.S.: 322291

Kimberly-Clark Integrated Services Corporation **(1)**
351 Phelps Dr, Irving, TX 75038
Tel.: (972) 281-1200
Medical Equipment Distr
N.A.I.C.S.: 423450

Kimberly-Clark Kazakhstan Limited Liability Partnership **(1)**
Furmanova st 240 V BC CDC-2 2nd Floor, Almaty, 050059, Kazakhstan
Tel.: (7) 87272502046
Baby Care Product Mfr
N.A.I.C.S.: 325620

Kimberly-Clark LDA **(1)**
Estrada De Alfragide Km 1 5 Edificio F-Piso 3-Norte, Alfrapark, Amadora, 2610-008, Portugal
Tel.: (351) 214705800
Sales Range: $25-49.9 Million
Emp.: 7
Sanitary Paper Product Mfr
N.A.I.C.S.: 322291

Kimberly-Clark Manufacturing (Thailand) Limited **(1)**
323 Silom Rd 32-33 United Center Silom, Bangrak, Bangkok, 10500, Thailand
Tel.: (66) 275590114
Web Site: http://www.th.careersatkc.com
Paper Mill Operator
N.A.I.C.S.: 322120

Kimberly-Clark Paper (Shanghai) Co. Ltd. **(1)**
Number 139 Jinshatan Songjiang District,

Shanghai, 201600, Shanghai, China
Tel.: (86) 2157822671
Paper Products Mfr
N.A.I.C.S.: 322291

Kimberly-Clark Paraguay, S.A. (1)
Herib Campos Cervera 886 c/Aviadores del
Chaco Edificio, Australia-Of 2 Entrepiso,
Asuncion, Paraguay
Tel.: (595) 21610990
Web Site: http://www.kimberly-clark.com.py
Sanitary Paper Product Mfr
N.A.I.C.S.: 322291

**Kimberly-Clark Pension Trusts
Ltd.** (1)
Tower View, West Malling, ME19 4HA,
United Kingdom
Tel.: (44) 1732594000
Emp.: 250
Intermediation Services
N.A.I.C.S.: 523910
Kate Goodman (Gen Mgr)

Kimberly-Clark Peru S.R.L. (1)
Av Del Pinar 180 oficina 505 Urb Chacarilla
del Estanque, Surco, Lima, 33, Peru
Tel.: (51) 6181800
Web Site: http://www.kimberly-
clarkperutemp.com
Sales Range: $125-149.9 Million
Sanitary Paper Product Mfr
N.A.I.C.S.: 322291

Kimberly-Clark Philippines Inc. (1)
Skincare, Air Fresheners, Paper Hand &
Towel Dipensers;Bathroom & Facial Tissue
Mfr
N.A.I.C.S.: 322299

Kimberly-Clark Puerto Rico, Inc. (1)
Santander Tower St Tabonuco B-7 Ste
1100, Guaynabo, PR 00918
Tel.: (787) 785-3625
Web Site: http://www.kimberlyclark.com
Paper Mill Operator
N.A.I.C.S.: 322120

Kimberly-Clark S.A.S. (1)
55 Avenue des Champs Pierreux, 92000,
Nanterre, France
Tel.: (33) 141919700
Sanitary Paper Product Mfr
N.A.I.C.S.: 322291

Kimberly-Clark S.L.U. (1)
P E Via Norte C/ Quintanavides 17 edf 3
1st floor, 28050, Madrid, Spain
Tel.: (34) 915579700
Sanitary Paper Product Mfr
N.A.I.C.S.: 322291

Kimberly-Clark SAS (1)
55 Avenue des Champs Pierreux, 92000,
Nanterre, France
Tel.: (33) 141919700
Web Site: http://www.kimberly-clark.fr
Sanitary Paper Product Mfr
N.A.I.C.S.: 322291

Kimberly-Clark Taiwan (1)
8F Number 8 Sec 5 Hsin-I Rd, Taipei,
11049, Taiwan
Tel.: (886) 277372888
Web Site: https://www.kimberly-clark.com.tw
Paper Products Mfr
N.A.I.C.S.: 322291

**Kimberly-Clark Trading (M) Sdn.
Bhd.** (1)
2nd Floor Tower 2 Wisma AmFirst Jalan
SS7/15 Jalan Stadium Kelana Jaya, 47301,
Petaling Jaya, Selangor, Malaysia (100%)
Tel.: (60) 1800889466
Web Site:
https://www.kcprofessional.com.my
Converting Facility Producing Feminine
Pads & Facial Tissue
N.A.I.C.S.: 322291

**Kimberly-Clark Tuketim Mallari
Sanayi ve Ticaret A.s.** (1)
Yayalar Mah Tandogan Cad No 3
Dolayoba-Pendik, Istanbul, Turkiye
Tel.: (90) 2164108182
Sanitary Paper Product Mfr
N.A.I.C.S.: 322291

**Kimberly-Clark UK Operations
Limited** (1)
Beech House 35 London Rd, Reigate,

RH29PZ, United Kingdom
Tel.: (44) 1737736127
Sanitary Paper Product Mfr
N.A.I.C.S.: 322291

Kimberly-Clark Ukraine LLC (1)
2/1 M Hrinchenka Str, 03038, Kiev, Ukraine
Tel.: (380) 444905810
Sanitary Paper Product Mfr
N.A.I.C.S.: 322291

Kimberly-Clark Vietnam Ltd. (1)
Level 18 etown Central Building 11 Doan
Van Bo Street, Ward 12 District 4, Ho Chi
Minh City, Vietnam
Tel.: (84) 839979639
Web Site: http://www.kimberly-clark.com.vn
Sanitary Paper Product Mfr
N.A.I.C.S.: 322291

Kimberly-Clark Worldwide, Inc. (1)
351 Phelps Dr, Irving, TX 75261
Tel.: (972) 281-1200
Sales Range: $50-74.9 Million
Personal Care Product Mfr
N.A.I.C.S.: 812990
Thomas J. Falk (Chm & CEO)

**Kimberly-Clark de Centro America
S.A.** (1)
KM 32 5 Carretera a San Juan Opico Sitio
del Nino Departamento de, La Libertad, El
Salvador
Tel.: (503) 80025062473
Sanitary Paper Product Mfr
N.A.I.C.S.: 322291

**Kimberly-Clark de Mexico, S.A.B. de
C.V.** (1)
Av Jaime Balmes No 8 piso 9 Los Morales
Polanco, 11510, Mexico, DF, Mexico
Tel.: (52) 5552827300
Web Site: http://www.kimberly-clark.com.mx
Rev.: $2,357,359,520
Assets: $2,452,371,278
Liabilities: $2,164,644,448
Net Worth: $287,726,830
Earnings: $224,191,029
Emp.: 8,000
Fiscal Year-end: 12/31/2021
Disposable Paper Products Mfr & Sales
N.A.I.C.S.: 322291
Pablo Roberto Gonzalez Guajardo (CEO)
Xavier Cortes Lascurain (CFO)
Jesus A. Gonzalez Laporte (Dir-Strategic
Ops Plng)
Jesus Gonzalez Urevig (Dir-Tissue Mfg)
Alejandro Lascurain Curbelo (Dir-HR)
Fernando Vergara Rosales (Controller)
Carlos Conss Curiel (Deputy Dir-Info Svcs)
Roberto Garcia Palacios (Dir-Product Inno-
vation, Tech Dev & Quality)
Alejandro Arguelles de la Torre (Gen Coun-
sel)
Luiz Roberto Neves Rodrigues (Dir-Supply
Chain)
Ernesto Reyes Diaz (Dir-Personal Care
Mfg)
Ommar H. Parra de la Rocha (Dir-
Consumer Product Sls)
Claudio X. Gonzalez Laporte (Chm)
Valentin Diez Morodo (Vice Chm)

**Kimberly-Clark of South Africa (Pty)
Ltd.** (1)
Kimberly-Clark House 8 Leicester Road,
Bedford Gardens, Bedfordview, Gauteng,
South Africa
Tel.: (27) 114565700
Web Site: http://www.kimberly-clark.co.za
Sales Range: $250-299.9 Million
Emp.: 800
Personal Care Product Mfr
N.A.I.C.S.: 456199

Kimberly-Clark s.r.l. (1)
Turin Office Via E Lugaro 15, 10126, Turin,
Italy
Tel.: (39) 01188141
Sanitary Paper Product Mfr
N.A.I.C.S.: 322291

Kimnica Sociedad Anonima (1)
Edificio Eco 2 do piso de la rotonda Univer-
sitaria 200mts al norte, 50 mts al oeste,
Managua, Nicaragua
Tel.: (505) 2666403
Sanitary Paper Product Mfr
N.A.I.C.S.: 322291

**La Ada de Acuna, S. de R.L. de
C.V.** (1)
Carretera Presa La Amistad Km 4 5 Indus-
trial Coahuila, 26220, Acuna, Mexico
Tel.: (52) 87730088
Surgical Instrument Mfr
N.A.I.C.S.: 339112

OOO Kimberly-Clark (1)
Obrucheva 30/1 bld 2, 117485, Moscow,
Russia
Tel.: (7) 4999562577
Web Site: http://www.kimberly-clark.com
Personal Care Product Mfr
N.A.I.C.S.: 322291

PT Softex Indonesia (1)
The Prominence Tower Lantai 5 Jl Jalur
Sutera Barat No 15, Alam Sutera,
Tangerang, 15325, Indonesia
Tel.: (62) 2130055108
Web Site: http://www.softexindonesia.com
Baby Care Product Mfr
N.A.I.C.S.: 325620
Djali Halim (Chief Sls Officer)
Chrisdianto Tedjawidjaja (CFO)
Danny Tan Chong Hian (Chief Comml Offi-
cer)
Hendra Setiawan (CEO)

Providence Leasing LLC (1)
5 Ave Of The Arts, Providence, RI 02903-
1103
Tel.: (401) 276-0010
Web Site: http://www.renaissance-
hotels.marriott.com
Emp.: 200
Home Management Services
N.A.I.C.S.: 721110
Michael Canini (Gen Mgr)

**Safeskin Medical & Scientific (Thai-
land) Limited** (1)
200 Moo 8 Karnchanavanich Rd, Tambol
Prik Amphur Sadad, Songkhla, 90120, Thai-
land
Tel.: (66) 7446090611
Medical Equipment & Supplies
N.A.I.C.S.: 423450

Tecnosur S.A. (1)
Calle 23 Ste 7 39, San Nicolas, Cali, Valle,
Colombia
Tel.: (57) 28825555
Paper Products Mfr
N.A.I.C.S.: 322291

KIMCO REALTY CORPORA-
TION
500 N Broadway Ste 201, Jericho,
NY 11753
Tel.: (516) 869-9000   **MD**
Web Site:
https://www.kimcorealty.com
Year Founded: 2022
KIM—(NYSE)
Rev.: $1,783,400,000
Assets: $18,274,022,000
Liabilities: $8,620,564,000
Net Worth: $9,653,458,000
Earnings: $654,273,000
Emp.: 660
Fiscal Year-end: 12/31/23
Real Estate Investment Trust
N.A.I.C.S.: 525990
Glenn Gary Cohen (CFO & Exec VP)
Paul Westbrook (Chief Acctg Officer
& VP)
Chris Freeman (Sr VP-Property
Mgmt)
Bruce M. Rubenstein (Gen Counsel,
Sec & Exec VP)
Leah Landro (Chief HR Officer &
Exec VP)
Thomas R. Taddeo (CIO & Exec VP)
David F. Bujnicki (Sr VP-IR & Strat-
egy)
Joshua Weinkranz (Pres-Eastern
Reg)
Harvey G. Weinreb (VP-Tax)
Ross Cooper (Pres & Chief Invest-
ment Officer)
Geoffrey Glazer (Sr VP-Dev-Natl)

David Jamieson (COO & Exec VP)
Barbara E. Briamonte (VP-Legal)
Scott Gerber (VP-Risk)
Carmen Decker (Pres-Western Reg)
David Domb (VP-Res & Data Analyt-
ics)
Paul C. Dooley (VP-Insurance & Real
Estate Tax)
Brett N. Klein (VP-Analysis & Fin
Plng)
Kathleen Thayer (Treas & Sr VP-
Corp Acctg)
Ken Fisher (CTO & VP)
Will Teichman (Sr VP-Strategic Ops)
Tamara Chernomordik (VP-Corp Re-
sponsibility)
Jennifer Maisch (VP-Corp Comm &
Mktg)
Jonathon Siswick (VP-Lease Admin)
Kraig Elliott (Chief Info Security Offi-
cer & VP)
Milton Cooper (Exec Chm & Chm)
Wilbur Tom Simmons (Pres-Southern)
Conor C. Flynn (CEO)
Raymond Edwards (Exec VP-Retailer
Svcs)
Marissa Garcia (VP-Investments)
Heather Medica (VP-HR)

Subsidiaries:

Kimco Realty OP, LLC (1)
500 N Broadway Ste 201, Jericho, NY
11753
Tel.: (516) 869-9000
Web Site: http://www.kimcorealty.com
Rev.: $1,783,400,000
Assets: $18,274,022,000
Liabilities: $8,620,564,000
Net Worth: $9,653,458,000
Earnings: $654,273,000
Emp.: 660
Fiscal Year-end: 12/31/2023
Real Estate Investment Trust
N.A.I.C.S.: 525990
Glenn Gary Cohen (CFO & Exec VP)
Paul Westbrook (Chief Acctg Officer & VP)
Chris Freeman (Sr VP-Property Mgmt)
Bruce M. Rubenstein (Gen Counsel, Sec &
Exec VP)
Leah Landro (Chief HR Officer & Exec VP)
Thomas R. Taddeo (CIO & Exec VP)
David F. Bujnicki (Sr VP-IR & Strategy)
Joshua Weinkranz (Pres-Eastern Reg)
Harvey G. Weinreb (VP-Tax)
Ross Cooper (Pres & Chief Investment Offi-
cer)
Geoffrey Glazer (Sr VP-Dev-Natl)
David Jamieson (COO & Exec VP)
Barbara E. Briamonte (VP-Legal)
Scott Gerber (VP-Risk)
Carmen Decker (Pres-Western Reg)
David Domb (VP-Res & Data Analytics)
Paul C. Dooley (VP-Insurance & Real Es-
tate Tax)
Brett N. Klein (VP-Analysis & Fin Plng)
Kathleen Thayer (Treas & Sr VP-Corp
Acctg)
Ken Fisher (CTO & VP)
Will Teichman (Sr VP-Strategic Ops)
Tamara Chernomordik (VP-Corp Responsi-
bility)
Jennifer Maisch (VP-Corp Comm & Mktg)
Jonathon Siswick (VP-Lease Admin)
Kraig Elliott (Chief Info Security Officer &
VP)
Milton Cooper (Co-Founder & Exec Chm)
Wilbur Tom Simmons (Pres-Southern)
Conor C. Flynn (CEO)

Subsidiary (Domestic):

KIMCO OCALA 665, INC. (2)
3333 New Hyde Park Rd Ste 100, New
Hyde Park, NY 11042
Tel.: (516) 869-9000
Web Site: https://www.kimcorealty.com
Emp.: 4
Commercial Property Managing Services
N.A.I.C.S.: 531312

Joint Venture (Domestic):

Kimco Realty Inc (2)
3333 New Hyde Park Rd Ste 100, New
Hyde Park, NY 11042-0020

Kimco Realty Corporation—(Continued)

Tel.: (516) 869-9000
Web Site: http://www.kimcorealty.com
Sales Range: $125-149.9 Million
Emp.: 250
Owner & Operator of Retail Shopping Centers
N.A.I.C.S.: 525990
Ross Cooper *(Chief Investment Officer & Exec VP)*
Raymond Edwards *(VP-Retailer Svcs)*
Robert Nadler *(Pres-Central)*
Wilbur Simmons *(Pres-Mid-Atlantic)*
Kelly Smith *(Mng Dir-Canadian Ops)*
Thomas R. Taddeo *(CIO & Sr VP)*
Armand Vasquez *(Pres-Western)*
Joshua Weinkranz *(Pres-Northeast)*

Subsidiary (Domestic):

Kimco, Inc.　　　　　　　　　　　　**(2)**
15608 Whittwood Ln, Los Angeles, CA 90603
Tel.: (310) 284-6000
Web Site: https://www.kimcorealty.com
Sales Range: $125-149.9 Million
Emp.: 4
Real Estate Investment Services
N.A.I.C.S.: 525990

RPT Realty　　　　　　　　　　　　**(2)**
19 W 44th St Ste 1002, New York, NY 10036
Tel.: (212) 221-1261
Web Site: https://www.rptrealty.com
Rev.: $217,656,000
Assets: $1,946,439,000
Liabilities: $967,786,000
Net Worth: $978,653,000
Earnings: $84,050,000
Emp.: 138
Fiscal Year-end: 12/31/2022
Real Estate Investment
N.A.I.C.S.: 525990

Subsidiary (Domestic):

Ramco/Lion Venture LP　　　　　　**(3)**
31500 NW Hwy 3 Ste 300, Farmington Hills, MI 48334-2501
Tel.: (248) 350-9900
Web Site: https://www.rgpt.com
Emp.: 80
Real Estate Investment Services
N.A.I.C.S.: 531210

Subsidiary (Domestic):

Weingarten Realty Investors　　　　**(2)**
2600 Citadel Plaza Dr Ste 125, Houston, TX 77008
Tel.: (713) 866-6000
Web Site: https://www.weingarten.com
Rev.: $433,917,000
Assets: $3,961,400,000
Liabilities: $2,160,898,000
Net Worth: $1,800,502,000
Earnings: $112,149,000
Emp.: 243
Fiscal Year-end: 12/31/2020
Real Estate Investment Trust
N.A.I.C.S.: 531390
C. Park Shaper *(Mgr-Trust)*
Bill Goeke *(Sr VP-Property Mgmt)*
Mark D. Stout *(Gen Counsel & Sr VP)*
Timothy M. Frakes *(Sr VP-Dev & Acquisitions)*
Michael Townsell *(Sr VP-HR)*
William M. Crook *(VP-Div & Assoc Gen Counsel)*
Gerald Crump *(Sr VP & Dir-Central Reg)*
Marc A. Kasner *(VP-Div & Assoc Gen Counsel)*
Alan R. Kofoed *(Sr VP-Construction)*
Richard H. Carson *(Sr VP-Dev & Acquisitions)*
Jenny Hyun *(VP-Div & Assoc Gen Counsel)*
Kristen L. Seaboch *(VP-Div & Controller)*
Christopher B. Byrd *(VP-Leasing)*
Lee Brody *(Sr VP & Dir-Mid-Atlantic)*
Frank Rollow *(Reg VP-Property Mgmt)*
Gary Wankum *(VP-Construction Div)*
Patrick Manchi *(VP-Leasing)*
Michelle Wiggs *(VP-IR)*
Terri Klages *(VP & Asst Controller)*
Darren Amato *(Sr VP-Investments)*
Taylor Vaughan *(VP-Leasing)*
Karl Brinkman *(Reg VP & Dir-Southeast Reg)*

Ken Wygle *(VP-Leasing)*
Alexander C. Evans *(VP-Leasing)*
Cynthia A. Krist *(VP-Tax)*
Scott A. Henson *(VP-Construction)*
Kent Maxey *(VP-Property Mgmt)*
Andrew Bell *(VP-Leasing)*

Subsidiary (Domestic):

Miller Real Estate Investments, LLC　　　　　　　　　　　　**(3)**
6900 E Belleview Ave Ste 300, Greenwood Village, CO 80111
Tel.: (303) 799-6300
Web Site: https://www.millerre.com
Sales Range: $125-149.9 Million
Real Estate Agencies & Brokerage Services
N.A.I.C.S.: 531210
Stewart A. Miller *(Chm)*
Steven A. Shoflick *(Founder & Principal)*
John S. Loss *(Co-CFO & Exec VP)*
Scott Goldammer *(Dir-Property Mgmt)*
Dean Insalaco *(VP-Leasing & New Bus)*
David Goldberg *(Principal)*
Bobby Kline *(VP)*
Brandi Lundberg *(Dir)*
Anette Trujillo *(Mgr-Property)*
Mike Smith *(Co-CFO & Controller)*

WRI Flamingo Pines, LLC　　　　　**(3)**
100 South Flamingo Rd, Pembroke Pines, FL 33027
Tel.: (954) 351-7002
Real Estate Investment Trust
N.A.I.C.S.: 531190

WRI Golden State, LLC　　　　　　**(3)**
2600 Citadel Plz Dr Ste 300, Houston, TX 77008
Tel.: (713) 868-6515
Real Estate Agencies & Brokerage Services
N.A.I.C.S.: 531210

Weingarten Realty Management Company　　　　　　　　　　**(3)**
2600 Citadel Plaza Dr Ste 125, Houston, TX 77008
Tel.: (713) 866-6000
Web Site: https://www.weingarten.com
Sales Range: $75-99.9 Million
Real Estate Management Services
N.A.I.C.S.: 531312
Andrew M. Alexander *(Pres)*

Waterford Lakes Town Center, LLC　　　　　　　　　　　　**(1)**
413 N Alafaya Trl, Orlando, FL 32828
Tel.: (407) 737-2866
Nonresidential Building Leasing Services
N.A.I.C.S.: 531120

KINDER MORGAN, INC.

1001 Louisiana St Ste 1000, Houston, TX 77002
Tel.: (713) 369-9000　　　　　**KS**
Web Site:
　https://www.kindermorgan.com
Year Founded: 1997
KMI—(NYSE)
Rev.: $15,334,000,000
Assets: $71,020,000,000
Liabilities: $39,291,000,000
Net Worth: $31,729,000,000
Earnings: $2,391,000,000
Emp.: 10,891
Fiscal Year-end: 12/31/23
Oil & Gas Storage, Transportation & Distribution Services
N.A.I.C.S.: 221210
Kimberly Allen Dang *(CEO)*
Patrick Bourgoyne *(VP-Internal Audit)*
Dax A. Sanders *(Pres-Products Pipelines)*
Mark Huse *(CIO & VP)*
David P. Michels *(CFO & VP)*
John W. Schlosser *(Pres-Terminals)*
David W. Conover *(VP-Govt Rels & Comm)*
Matthew J. Wojtalewicz *(VP & Controller)*
James E. Holland *(COO)*
Catherine Callaway James *(Gen Counsel & VP)*
Kevin Grahmann *(VP-Corp Dev)*

Chris Graeter *(Treas & VP)*
Tom Martin *(Pres)*
Richard D. Kinder *(Co-Founder, Chm & Exec Chm)*
Eric McCord *(Sec, VP & Deputy Gen Counsel)*
Michael J. Pitta *(Chief Admin Officer & VP)*
Jordan H. Mintz *(VP)*

Subsidiaries:

American Petroleum Tankers II LLC　　　　　　　　　　　　**(1)**
1001 Louisiana Ste 1000, Houston, TX 77002
Tel.: (713) 369-9000
Crude Oil Transportation Services
N.A.I.C.S.: 486110

American Petroleum Tankers LLC　　　　　　　　　　　　**(1)**
600 W Germantown Pike Ste 400, Plymouth Meeting, PA 19462
Tel.: (610) 940-1677
Petroleum Transportation Services
N.A.I.C.S.: 483111

Battleground Oil Specialty Terminal Company LLC　　　　　　**(1)**
1836 Miller Cut Off Rd, La Porte, TX 77571
Tel.: (281) 241-3838
Web Site: https://www.bostco.net
Emp.: 20
Oil Terminal Operating Services
N.A.I.C.S.: 424710

CDE Pipeline LLC　　　　　　　　**(1)**
1001 Louisiana St Ste 1000, Houston, TX 77002
Tel.: (713) 369-9000
Crude Oil Transportation Services
N.A.I.C.S.: 486110

Citrus LLC　　　　　　　　　　　**(1)**
448 S Hill St, Los Angeles, CA 90013
Tel.: (213) 542-5121
Web Site: http://www.perchla.com
Emp.: 100
Restaurant Operating Services
N.A.I.C.S.: 722511

Dakota Bulk Terminal LLC　　　　**(1)**
925 Hardman Ave, North Saint Paul, MN 55075
Tel.: (651) 451-1414
Oil Terminal Operator
N.A.I.C.S.: 424710

El Paso CNG Company, L.L.C.　　**(1)**
1001 Louisana St Ste 1000, Houston, TX 77002
Tel.: (713) 369-9000
Pipeline Transportation of Natural Gas
N.A.I.C.S.: 486210

El Paso LLC　　　　　　　　　　**(1)**
El Paso Bldg 1001 Louisiana St, Houston, TX 77002
Tel.: (713) 420-2600
Web Site: https://www.elpaso.com
Sales Range: $1-4.9 Billion
Emp.: 4,858
Holding Company; Natural Gas Extraction, Transportation & Distribution
N.A.I.C.S.: 551112

Subsidiary (Domestic):

El Paso CGP Company, L.L.C.　　**(2)**
1001 Louisiana St Ste 1000, Houston, TX 77002　　　　　　　　　**(100%)**
Tel.: (713) 420-2600
Web Site: https://www.elpaso.com
Sales Range: $1-4.9 Billion
Emp.: 900
Holding Company
N.A.I.C.S.: 486210

El Paso Pipeline Partners, L.P.　　**(2)**
1001 Louisiana St Ste 1000, Houston, TX 77002
Tel.: (713) 369-9000
Web Site:
　http://www.eppipelinepartners.com
Wire Line Services
N.A.I.C.S.: 486210

Subsidiary (Domestic):

Cheyenne Plains Gas Pipeline Company, L.L.C.　　　　　　　**(3)**

1001 Louisiana St, Houston, TX 77002-5089
Tel.: (713) 420-2600
Gas Pipeline Transportation Services
N.A.I.C.S.: 486210

Colorado Interstate Gas Company, L.L.C.　　　　　　　　　　**(3)**
1001 Louisiana St Ste 1000, Houston, TX 77002　　　　　　　　　**(100%)**
Tel.: (713) 369-9305
Web Site: https://www.cigco.com
Sales Range: $400-449.9 Million
Natural Gas Transport Services
N.A.I.C.S.: 486210

Southern Natural Gas Company, L.L.C.　　　　　　　　　　**(3)**
1001 Louisiana St, Houston, TX 77002
Tel.: (713) 420-2600
Web Site:
　http://www.eppipelinepartners.com
Pipeline Transportation of Natural Gas
N.A.I.C.S.: 486210

Wyoming Interstate Company, L.L.C.　　　　　　　　　　**(3)**
2 N Nevada Ave, Colorado Springs, CO 80903-1700　　　　　　　**(100%)**
Tel.: (719) 473-2300
Emp.: 12,000
Pipeline Transportation of Natural Gas
N.A.I.C.S.: 486210

Joint Venture (Domestic):

Young Gas Storage Company　　　**(3)**
2 N Nevada Ave, Colorado Springs, CO 80903-1715
Tel.: (719) 473-2300
Web Site: http://www.kindermorgan.com
Sales Range: $10-24.9 Million
Emp.: 20
Natural Gas Storage & Pipeline Transporation
N.A.I.C.S.: 486210
Kimberly Allen Dang *(Pres)*
Richard D. Kinder *(Chm)*
Steven L. Kean *(CEO)*
Adam Forman *(Sec & VP)*
Anthony B. Ashley *(Treas & VP-IR)*
David P. Michels *(CFO & VP)*
Dax A. Sanders *(Chief Strategy Officer & Exec VP)*
James Holland *(Pres-Products Pipelines)*
Jesse Arenivas *(Officer-Ops)*
John W. Schlosser *(Pres-Terminals)*
Jordan H. Mintz *(Chief Tax Officer & VP)*
Mark Huse *(CIO & VP)*
Tom Martin *(Pres-Natural Gas Pipelines)*

Subsidiary (Domestic):

Southern Gulf LNG Company, L.L.C.　　　　　　　　　　**(2)**
569 Brookwood Village Ste 501, Birmingham, AL 35209　　　　　**(100%)**
Tel.: (205) 325-7410
Pipeline Transportation of Natural Gas
N.A.I.C.S.: 486210

El Paso Natural Gas Company, LLC　　　　　　　　　　　**(1)**
Western Pipelines, Colorado Springs, CO 80944　　　　　　　　　**(50%)**
Tel.: (719) 520-4514
Web Site:
　https://pipeportal.kindermorgan.com
Natural Gas Distr & Marketer
N.A.I.C.S.: 221210
Paul Haas *(Dir-Scheduling & Nominations)*
Freddie Salas *(Mgr-Scheduling & Nominations)*

Subsidiary (Domestic):

Mojave Pipeline Company, L.L.C.　　　　　　　　　　　**(2)**
5401 E Brundage Ln, Bakersfield, CA 93307-2960　　　　　　　　**(100%)**
Tel.: (661) 363-4000
Web Site: https://www.kindermorgan.com
Sales Range: $25-49.9 Million
Emp.: 14
Pipeline Transportation of Natural Gas

N.A.I.C.S.: 486210

Subsidiary (Domestic):

**Mojave Pipeline Operating
Company** (3)
2 N Nevada Ave, Colorado Springs, CO
80903-1700
Tel.: (719) 667-7517
Web Site:
    https://www.pipeline2.kindermorgan.com
Pipeline Transportation of Natural Gas
N.A.I.C.S.: 486210

Fort Union Gas Gathering, LLC (1)
2 N Nevada Ave, Colorado Springs, CO
80903
Tel.: (719) 667-7774
Web Site: http://www.fortuniongg.com
Gas Transportation Services
N.A.I.C.S.: 221210
Dessie Sharpton *(Mgr-IC-Comml)*

Greens Port CBR, LLC (1)
315 W 3rd St, Pittsburg, KS 66762-4706
Tel.: (620) 235-7316
Oil & Gas Exploration Services
N.A.I.C.S.: 213112

K N Gas Gathering, Inc. (1)
4200 W Hwy 96, Scott City, KS 67871
Tel.: (620) 872-2149
Natural Gas Distr
N.A.I.C.S.: 221210

Kinder Morgan (Delaware), Inc. (1)
1301 McKinney Ste 3400, Houston, TX
77010
Tel.: (713) 844-9500
Oil & Gas Field Operating Services
N.A.I.C.S.: 213112

Kinder Morgan Altamont LLC (1)
17790 W 3750 N, Altamont, UT 84001
Tel.: (435) 454-3927
Emp.: 49
Natural Gas Distr
N.A.I.C.S.: 221210

Kinder Morgan G.P., Inc. (1)
1301 McKinney St Ste 3450, Houston, TX
77010
Tel.: (713) 844-9500
Web Site: http://www.kindermorgan.com
Holding Company
N.A.I.C.S.: 551112

Subsidiary (Domestic):

**Kinder Morgan Energy Partners,
L.P.** (2)
1001 Louisiana St Ste 1000, Houston, TX
77002
Tel.: (713) 369-9000
Web Site: https://www.kindermorgan.com
Rev.: $12,530,000,000
Assets: $42,764,000,000
Liabilities: $25,543,000,000
Net Worth: $17,221,000,000
Earnings: $3,317,000,000
Fiscal Year-end: 12/31/2013
Natural Gas & Petroleum Terminals & Pipe-
line Systems
N.A.I.C.S.: 486110
Kimberly Allen Dang *(CFO)*

Subsidiary (Domestic):

Dakota Bulk Terminal, Inc. (3)
925 Hardman Ave, Saint Paul, MN 55075
Tel.: (651) 451-1414
Web Site: http://www.kindermorgan.com
Salt & Grain Product Transportation
N.A.I.C.S.: 488999

Elizabeth River Terminals LLC (3)
4100 Buell St, Chesapeake, VA 23324
Tel.: (757) 543-0335
Marine Cargo Handling Services
N.A.I.C.S.: 488320
Gary Pullen *(Gen Mgr)*

**Kinder Morgan CO2 Company,
L.P.** (3)
1001 Louisiana St Ste 1000, Houston, TX
77002
Web Site: https://www.kindermorgan.com
Oil & Gas Pipeline Services
N.A.I.C.S.: 237120

Unit (Domestic):

**Kinder Morgan Energy Partners, L.P.
- Pacific Operations** (3)
1100 W Twn Cntry Rd 621, Orange, CA
92868
Tel.: (714) 560-4400
Emp.: 125
Refined Petroleum Products Pipeline Op-
erator
N.A.I.C.S.: 486910

Subsidiary (Domestic):

**Kinder Morgan Pipelines (USA)
Inc.** (3)
800 Werner Ct Ste 352, Casper, WY
82601-1364
Tel.: (307) 237-5590
Oil & Gas Pipeline Services
N.A.I.C.S.: 237120

Subsidiary (Domestic):

**Kinder Morgan Texas Pipeline,
LP** (4)
500 Dallas St, Houston, TX 77002-4718
Tel.: (713) 369-9000
Web Site: http://www.kindermorgan.com
Natural Gas Pipeline Operator
N.A.I.C.S.: 486210

Unit (Domestic):

**Kinder Morgan Southeast Terminals
LLC - Knoxville** (3)
5009 Middlebrook Pike, Knoxville, TN
37921-5939
Tel.: (865) 584-4611
Web Site: https://www.kindermorgan.com
Sales Range: $25-49.9 Million
Emp.: 4
Petroleum Fuels Bulk Terminal
N.A.I.C.S.: 424710

**Kinder Morgan Southeast Terminals
LLC - Roanoke** (3)
835 Hollins Rd NE, Roanoke, VA 24012-
8034
Tel.: (540) 982-3515
Web Site: http://www.kindermorgan.com
Sales Range: $25-49.9 Million
Emp.: 5
Petroleum Fuels Bulk Terminal
N.A.I.C.S.: 424710

Subsidiary (Domestic):

**Kinder Morgan Texas Terminals,
L.P.** (3)
1001 Louisiana St Ste 1000, Houston, TX
77002
Tel.: (713) 369-9000
Web Site: https://www.kindermorgan.com
Natural Gas Pipeline Transmission Services
N.A.I.C.S.: 486210

Kinder Morgan Treating LP (3)
1001 Louisiana St Ste 1000, Houston, TX
77002
Tel.: (713) 369-8515
Web Site:
    https://www.kindermorgantreating.com
Natural Gas Distribution Services
N.A.I.C.S.: 486210

Milwaukee Bulk Terminals LLC (3)
1900 S Harbor Dr, Milwaukee, WI 53207-
1027
Tel.: (414) 769-1901
Natural Gas Pipeline Transmission Services
N.A.I.C.S.: 493190

Plantation Pipe Line Company (3)
1000 Windward Concourse Ste 450, Al-
pharetta, GA 30005
Tel.: (770) 751-4000
Web Site: http://www.kindermorgan.com
Refined Petroleum Products Pipeline Trans-
portation Services
N.A.I.C.S.: 486910

Queen City Terminals, Inc. (3)
3806 Kellogg Ave, Cincinnati, OH 45226
Tel.: (513) 871-9018
Web Site: http://www.kindermorgan.com
Warehousing & Packaging Plant Services
N.A.I.C.S.: 493110

SouthTex Treaters, Inc. (3)
13405 E Hwy 191, Odessa, TX 79765
Tel.: (432) 563-2733
Web Site: http://www.southtex.com
Sales Range: $50-74.9 Million
Natural Gas Processing Plant Construction
& Equipment Mfr
N.A.I.C.S.: 333132

**Tennessee Gas Pipeline Company,
L.L.C.** (3)
Po Box 2511, Houston, TX
77252-2511 (100%)
Tel.: (713) 420-2600
Web Site:
    https://pipeline2.kindermorgan.com
Natural Gas Pipeline Operator
N.A.I.C.S.: 486210

Transload Services, LLC (3)
3115 W 167th St, Hazel Crest, IL 60429
Tel.: (708) 755-4100
Transportation & Material Handling Services
N.A.I.C.S.: 486990

Watco Companies, LLC (3)
315 W 3rd St, Pittsburg, KS 66762
Tel.: (620) 231-2230
Web Site: https://www.watco.com
Holding Company; Short Line Railroad Op-
erator, Locomotive Repair & Other Trans-
portation Services & Supply Chain Services
N.A.I.C.S.: 551112
Rick Baden *(Pres & CFO)*
Richard D. Webb *(Founder)*
Craig Richey *(Gen Counsel & Exec VP)*
Dan Smith *(CEO)*
Rachael Peterson *(Chief People Officer &
Exec VP)*
Ed McGuire *(Chief Investment Officer &
Exec VP)*
Nick Coomes *(COO & Exec VP)*

Joint Venture (Domestic):

GBW Railcar Services, LLC (4)
10895 Grandview Dr Ste 350, Overland
Park, KS 66210
Tel.: (888) 968-4364
Web Site: http://www.gbwservices.com
Emp.: 2,100
Locomotive & Railcar Repair Services
N.A.I.C.S.: 811310
Ray Pericola *(Pres)*

Plant (Domestic):

**Watco Mechanical Services, LLC -
Cudahy** (5)
5000 S Whitnall Ave, Cudahy, WI 53110
Tel.: (414) 744-1612
Web Site: http://www.gbwservices.com
Sales Range: $10-24.9 Million
Emp.: 35
Railcar Repair & Maintenance Services
N.A.I.C.S.: 811310

**Watco Mechanical Services, LLC -
Jacksonville** (5)
7305 Old Kings Rd N, Jacksonville, FL
32219
Tel.: (904) 786-1700
Web Site: http://www.watcocompanies.com
Sales Range: $25-49.9 Million
Emp.: 80
Railcar Repair Services
N.A.I.C.S.: 811310

Subsidiary (Domestic):

**Watco Railroad Company Holdings,
Inc.** (4)
315 W 3rd St, Pittsburg, KS 66762 (100%)
Tel.: (620) 231-2230
Web Site: http://www.watcocompanies.com
Emp.: 31
Holding Company; Short Line Railroads
N.A.I.C.S.: 551112

Holding (Domestic):

Birmingham Terminal Railway (5)
1390 Watco Way, Fairfield, AL 35064
Tel.: (205) 781-5715
Web Site: http://www.watcocompanies.com
Railway Transportation Services for Raw
Materials
N.A.I.C.S.: 488210

Eastern Idaho Railroad (5)

618 Shoshone St W, Twin Falls, ID 83301
Tel.: (208) 735-1049
Web Site: http://www.watcocompanies.com
Sales Range: $1-9.9 Million
Emp.: 30
Short Line Railroad
N.A.I.C.S.: 482112
Darin Price *(Gen Mgr)*

Mission Mountain Railroad (5)
100 Railroad St, Eureka, MT 59933
Tel.: (406) 270-4159
Web Site: http://www.watcocompanies.com
Line-Haul Railroads
N.A.I.C.S.: 482111

Stillwater Central Railroad, LLC (5)
900 S Byers Ave, Oklahoma City, OK
73129
Tel.: (405) 616-3000
Web Site: http://www.watcocompanies.com
Short Line Railroad Operator
N.A.I.C.S.: 482112

**Wisconsin & Southern Railroad
Company** (5)
5300 N 33rd St, Milwaukee, WI 53209-4825
Tel.: (414) 438-8820
Web Site: http://www.wsorrailroad.com
Railroads & Line Haul Operations
N.A.I.C.S.: 482111

Affiliate (Domestic):

**Wisconsin & Southern Railroad
Company** (6)
203 S Pearl St, Janesville, WI 53545-4521
Tel.: (414) 438-8820
Web Site: http://www.wsorrailroad.com
Sales Range: $25-49.9 Million
Emp.: 100
Railroad
N.A.I.C.S.: 482111

**Wisconsin & Southern Railroad
Company** (6)
1890 E Johnson St, Madison, WI 53704-
4745
Tel.: (608) 620-2074
Web Site: http://www.watcocompanies.com
Sales Range: $25-49.9 Million
Emp.: 5
Railroad
N.A.I.C.S.: 482111

**Wisconsin & Southern Railroad
Company** (6)
PO Box 116, Horicon, WI 53032-0116
Tel.: (920) 485-4783
Web Site: http://www.wsorrailroad.com
Sales Range: $25-49.9 Million
Emp.: 40
Railroad
N.A.I.C.S.: 488210

Subsidiary (Domestic):

**Watco Supply Chain Services,
LLC** (4)
3905 Elliott Ave, Springdale, AR 72762
Web Site: http://www.watcosupplychain.com
Supply Chain Services
N.A.I.C.S.: 541614
Eric Wolfe *(Pres)*
Lynda Patterson *(VP-Growth Strategies)*
Judd Gilgen *(VP-Risk Mgmt)*

Kinder Morgan Services LLC (1)
500 Dallas St Ste 1000, Houston, TX
77002-4718
Tel.: (713) 369-9000
Web Site: http://www.kindermorgan.com
Emp.: 1,000
Eletric Power Generation Services
N.A.I.C.S.: 221118

Mid-Ship Group LLC (1)
145 Main St, Port Washington, NY 11050
Tel.: (516) 944-3500
Web Site: http://www.midship.com
Marine Shipping & Cargo Transportation
Services
N.A.I.C.S.: 488320
Craig Ahrens *(COO & CIO)*
Matthew I. DeLuca Jr. *(Founder, Chm &
CEO)*

Midco LLC (1)
3901 N Louise Ave, Sioux Falls, SD 57107
Web Site: https://www.midco.com

Kinder Morgan, Inc.—(Continued)

Natural Gas Distribution Services
N.A.I.C.S.: 486210

**Natural Gas Pipeline Company of
America LLC**
1001 Louisiana St Ste 1000, Houston, TX
77002
Tel.: (713) 369-9000
Interstate Gas Transmission Services
N.A.I.C.S.: 486210

**North American Natural Resources,
LLC**   **(1)**
4121 Okemos Rd Ste 17, Okemos, MI
48864
Tel.: (517) 351-5400
Web Site: https://nanr.net
Renewable Energy Services
N.A.I.C.S.: 221112

North Denton Pipeline, L.L.C.   **(1)**
3314 E Highway 82, Gainesville, TX 76240-
7311
Tel.: (940) 668-8344
Natural Gas Transmission Services
N.A.I.C.S.: 237120

PI 2 Pelican State LLC   **(1)**
345 Park Ave 29th Fl, New York, NY 10154-
2900
Tel.: (215) 776-0173
Oil & Gas Exploration Services
N.A.I.C.S.: 213112

Queen City Terminals LLC   **(1)**
3806 Kellogg Ave, Cincinnati, OH 45226
Tel.: (513) 871-9018
Oil Terminal Operator
N.A.I.C.S.: 424710

Red Cedar Gathering Company   **(1)**
125 Mercado St Ste 201, Durango, CO
81301
Tel.: (970) 764-6900
Web Site:
http://www.redcedargathering.com
Emp.: 120
Natural Gas Treating Services
N.A.I.C.S.: 213112
Jake Mallett (Dir-Bus Dev & Comml Ops)
Coy Bryant (Pres & COO)
Dan Jefferson (Dir-Environmental, Health &
Safety)
Tom Weinheimer (Dir-Engrg)
Leila McSween (Controller)
Eddie Malcom (Mgr-Sys Maintenance)

Sage Refined Products, Ltd.   **(1)**
1800 Post Oak Blvd Ste 6360, Houston, TX
77056
Tel.: (713) 655-1010
Natural Gas Pipeline Transportation Services
N.A.I.C.S.: 486210

Sierrita Gas Pipeline LLC   **(1)**
2 N Nevada Ave, Colorado Springs, CO
80903
Tel.: (800) 334-8047
Natural Gas Pipeline Transportation Ser-
vices
N.A.I.C.S.: 486210
Greg Ruben (VP-Bus Dev)

**KINDERCARE LEARNING
COMPANIES, INC.**
650 NE Holladay Ste 1400, Portland,
OR 97232
Tel.: (503) 872-1300   DE
Web Site: https://www.kc-
learning.com
Year Founded: 2017
KLC—(NYSE)
Rev.: $1,366,556,000
Assets: $3,266,542,000
Liabilities: $3,130,257,000
Net Worth: $136,285,000
Earnings: ($129,496,000)
Emp.: 34,000
Fiscal Year-end: 01/02/21
Holding Company
N.A.I.C.S.: 551112
John T. Wyatt (CEO & Chm)
Paul Thompson (Pres)

Anthony Amandi (CFO)
Elanna Yalow (Chief Academic Officer)

KINDLY MD, INC.
5097 S 900 E Ste 100, Salt Lake
City, UT 84117
Tel.: (385) 388-8220   UT
Web Site: https://kindlymd.com
Year Founded: 2019
KDLY—(NASDAQ)
Rev.: $3,787,077
Assets: $1,001,269
Liabilities: $620,255
Net Worth: $381,014
Earnings: ($2,540,593)
Emp.: 21
Fiscal Year-end: 12/31/22
Health Care Srvices
N.A.I.C.S.: 621610

KINETA, INC.
219 Terry Ave N Ste 300, Seattle, WA
98109
Tel.: (206) 378-0400   DE
Web Site: https://kinetabio.com
KA—(NASDAQ)
Rev.: $5,442,000
Assets: $10,281,000
Liabilities: $72,220,000
Net Worth: $30,590,000
Earnings: ($14,099,000)
Emp.: 64
Fiscal Year-end: 12/31/23
Pharmaceutical Preparation Manufac-
turing
N.A.I.C.S.: 325412
Shawn Iadonato (Co-Founder)
Keith A. Baker (CFO)

KINETIC GROUP INC.
2801 NW 74th Ave, Miami, FL 33122
Tel.: (786) 712-6827   NV
Web Site: https://www.knitgrp.com
Year Founded: 2014
KNIT—(OTCIQ)
Assets: $550,113
Liabilities: $152,026
Net Worth: $398,087
Earnings: ($121,776)
Emp.: 2
Fiscal Year-end: 09/30/23
Website & Content Development Ser-
vices
N.A.I.C.S.: 511613
Jason R. Vanderbrink (CEO)
Nathan Rosenberg (Pres, CEO, CFO,
Chief Acctg Officer, Treas & Sec)
Jeffrey Ehrich (Gen Counsel & Sec)

**KINETIC SEAS INCORPO-
RATED**
1501 E Woodfield Rd Ste 114E,
Schaumburg, IL 60173
Tel.: (404) 816-8240   CO
Web Site:
https://www.kineticseas.com
ECGR—(OTCIQ)
Assets: $1,376
Liabilities: $157,525
Net Worth: ($156,149)
Earnings: ($94,131)
Fiscal Year-end: 12/31/22
Vaporizer Product Mfr & Distr
N.A.I.C.S.: 335210
Atom Miller (CEO)
Jeffrey William Lozinski (COO)
Joseph Lehman (CTO)
Erik Nelson (Sec)
Edward Scott Honour (Chm & CEO)

**KING OF PINE CREEK MINING
LTD.**
PO Box 487, Portland, OR 97207
Tel.: (503) 281-8699   ID
KPCM—(OTCIQ)

Mineral Mining Services
N.A.I.C.S.: 213115
Burton A. Onstine (Pres)
Jack A. Titus (Sec)
John Henley (Treas)

KING RESOURCES, INC.
215 N Jefferson St, Ossian, IN 46777
Tel.: (260) 490-9990   DE
KRFG—(OTCIQ)
Rev.: $198,816
Assets: $1,089,496
Liabilities: $2,722,831
Net Worth: ($1,633,335)
Earnings: ($1,315,508)
Emp.: 7
Fiscal Year-end: 03/31/23
Electric Equipment Mfr
N.A.I.C.S.: 335999
Brian K. Kistler (CEO)

KINGSTONE COMPANIES, INC.
15 Joys Ln, Kingston, NY 12401
Tel.: (845) 802-7900   DE
Web Site:
https://www.kingstonecompa
nies.com
Year Founded: 1886
KINS—(NASDAQ)
Rev.: $130,159,290
Assets: $320,332,531
Liabilities: $284,163,099
Net Worth: $36,169,432
Earnings: ($22,524,794)
Emp.: 95
Fiscal Year-end: 12/31/22
Insurance Services
N.A.I.C.S.: 524210
Victor J. Brodsky (Chief Acctg Officer)
Meryl S. Golden (Pres & CEO)
Jennifer Gravelle (CFO & VP)
Floyd R. Tupper (Sec)

**KINGSWAY FINANCIAL SER-
VICES INC.**
10 S Riverside Plz Ste 1520, Chi-
cago, IL 60606
Tel.: (312) 766-2138   ON
Web Site: https://www.kingsway-
financial.com
Year Founded: 1989
KFS—(NYSE)
Rev.: $93,280,000
Assets: $285,650,000
Liabilities: $269,542,000
Net Worth: $16,108,000
Earnings: $24,416,000
Emp.: 471
Fiscal Year-end: 12/31/22
Holding Company; Property, Casu-
alty, Automobile & Non-Standard Au-
tomobile Insurance
N.A.I.C.S.: 551112
John Taylor Maloney Fitzgerald (Pres
& CEO)
Kent A. Hansen (CFO & Exec VP)

Subsidiaries:

Argo Management Group, LLC   **(1)**
2108 E 2nd St, Coal Valley, IL 61240
Tel.: (309) 738-2872
Web Site: https://www.amgrecovery.com
Travel Trailer & Camper Mfr
N.A.I.C.S.: 336214

IWS Acquisition Corporation   **(1)**
5901 Broken Sound Pkwy NW Ste 400,
Boca Raton, FL 33487
Tel.: (561) 981-7000
Web Site: https://iwsgroup.com
Insurance Management Services
N.A.I.C.S.: 524298
Kathy Semanate (VP-Finance)

Kingsway America Inc.   **(100%)**
150 NW Point Blvd, Elk Grove Village, IL
60007-1015
Tel.: (847) 871-6400
Web Site: http://www.kingswayamerica.com

Sales Range: $75-99.9 Million
Emp.: 15
N.A.I.C.S.: 524128

Subsidiary (Domestic):

Fundamental Global Inc.   **(2)**
108 Gateway Blvd Ste 204, Mooresville, NC
28117
Tel.: (704) 994-8279
Web Site: https://www.fgfinancial.com
Rev.: $20,095,000
Assets: $49,475,000
Liabilities: $12,180,000
Net Worth: $37,295,000
Earnings: ($701,000)
Emp.: 7
Fiscal Year-end: 12/31/2022
Insurance Holding Company
N.A.I.C.S.: 551112
Daniel Kyle Cerminara (Chm)

Subsidiary (Domestic):

FG Group Holdings Inc.   **(3)**
5960 Fairview Rd Ste 275, Charlotte, NC
28210
Tel.: (704) 994-8279
Web Site: https://fg.group
Rev.: $41,237,000
Assets: $71,753,000
Liabilities: $25,055,000
Net Worth: $46,698,000
Earnings: ($7,154,000)
Emp.: 174
Fiscal Year-end: 12/31/2022
Commercial Motion Picture Equipment &
Lighting Systems Mfr, Designer & Distr
N.A.I.C.S.: 333310
Daniel Kyle Cerminara (Co-Chm)
Ray F. Boegner (Pres-Strong Entertain-
ment)
Mark D. Roberson (CEO)
Todd R. Major (CFO)

Subsidiary (Domestic):

Strong Technical Services, Inc.   **(4)**
14565 Portal Cir Ste 106, La Vista, NE
68138
Tel.: (402) 453-4444
Web Site: https://strong-tech.com
Emp.: 70
Electric Lighting Fixture Mfr
N.A.I.C.S.: 335132
Ray F. Boegner (Pres)

Subsidiary (Domestic):

**Strong Global Entertainment,
Inc.**   **(3)**
5960 Fairview Rd Ste 275, Charlotte, NC
28210
Tel.: (704) 471-6784
Web Site:
https://www.strong-entertainment.com
Rev.: $25,972,000
Assets: $22,199,000
Liabilities: $13,389,000
Net Worth: $8,810,000
Earnings: $821,000
Emp.: 167
Fiscal Year-end: 12/31/2021
Holding Company
N.A.I.C.S.: 551112
Ray F. Boegner (Pres)
Mark D. Roberson (CEO)
Todd R. Major (CFO, Treas & Sec)
D. Kyle Cerminara (Chm)

Subsidiary (Non-US):

Hamilton Risk Management Co.   **(2)**
Tel.: (305) 716-6000
Sales Range: $75-99.9 Million
Insurance Services
N.A.I.C.S.: 524210

Subsidiary (Non-US):

Hamilton Investments, Inc.   **(3)**
Tel.: (646) 285-0345
Web Site:
http://www.hamiltoninvestment.com
Investment Brokers
N.A.I.C.S.: 561450

**Kingsway Amigo Insurance
Company**   **(3)**
Tel.: (305) 716-6000
Web Site: http://www.kingswayamigo.com

Property & Casualty Insurance Services
N.A.I.C.S.: 524126

U.S. Security Insurance Co.   (3)
Tel.: (305) 716-6100
Web Site: http://www.hamiltonrisk.com
Insurance Services
N.A.I.C.S.: 524126

Joint Venture (Domestic):

Lincoln General Insurance
Company   (2)
3501 Concord Rd, York, PA
17402-8607   (49%)
Tel.: (717) 757-0000
Web Site: http://www.lincolngeneral.com
Property & Casualty Insurance Products &
Services
N.A.I.C.S.: 524126
Frank Amodeo (COO)

Subsidiary (Domestic):

Southern United Fire Insurance
Company   (2)
3155 North West 77th Ave, Miami, FL
33122
Tel.: (251) 661-8008
Sales Range: $75-99.9 Million
Fire Insurance
N.A.I.C.S.: 524126

Kingsway Reinsurance
Corporation   (1)
Whitepark House, PO Box 1174, Bridge-
town, BB11000, Barbados
Tel.: (246) 4369929
Sales Range: $50-74.9 Million
Emp.: 2
Reinsurance
N.A.I.C.S.: 524130

Prime Auto Care Inc.   (1)
1081 Hanover St, Wilkes Barre, PA 18706-
2028
Web Site: http://www.primeautocare.com
Automobile Repair & Maintenance Services
N.A.I.C.S.: 811198

Ravix Financial, Inc.   (1)
2109 Landings Dr, Mountain View, CA
94043
Tel.: (650) 691-1500
Web Site: http://www.ravixgroup.com
Sales Range: $1-9.9 Million
Emp.: 40
Management Consulting Services
N.A.I.C.S.: 541611
Daniel Saccani (Pres)
Ingrid Glazebrook (VP)

Secure Nursing Service, Inc.   (1)
3333 Wilshire Blvd, Los Angeles, CA 90010
Tel.: (213) 736-6771
Web Site: http://www.securenursing.com
Employment Agencies, Nsk
N.A.I.C.S.: 561311
Haesook Kim (Pres)
Charles Mokuolu (Pres & CEO)

Systems Products International,
Inc.   (1)
2600 SW 3rd Ave Fl 5, Miami, FL 33129
Tel.: (305) 858-9505
Web Site: https://spisoftware.com
Sales Range: $1-9.9 Million
Emp.: 30
Computer & Computer Peripheral Equip-
ment & Software Merchant Whslr
N.A.I.C.S.: 423430
Matt Brosious (VP-Sls & Mktg)
Karl Lange (Founder)
George Stemper (CEO)
Gordon McClendon (CEO)
Jeff Wilder (VP-Software Dev)
Steve Schmidt (CFO)

KINGSWOOD ACQUISITION CORP.
17 Battery Pl Rm 625, New York, NY
10004
Tel.: (212) 404-7002   DE
Year Founded: 2020
KWAC—(OTCIQ)
Rev.: $6,173,524
Assets: $5,850,146
Liabilities: $15,141,749

Net Worth: ($9,291,603)
Earnings: $1,352,234
Emp.: 2
Fiscal Year-end: 12/31/22
Investment Services
N.A.I.C.S.: 523999
Gary Wilder (Chm)
Michael NessimC (CEO)
David Hudd (Gen Counsel)

KINSALE CAPITAL GROUP, INC.
2035 Maywill St Ste 100, Richmond,
VA 23230
Tel.: (804) 289-1300   DE
Web Site:
   https://www.kinsalecapitalgroup.com
Year Founded: 2009
KNSL—(NYSE)
Rev.: $1,224,449,000
Assets: $3,772,974,000
Liabilities: $2,686,142,000
Net Worth: $1,086,832,000
Earnings: $308,093,000
Emp.: 561
Fiscal Year-end: 12/31/23
General Insurance Services
N.A.I.C.S.: 524210
Michael P. Kehoe (Founder, Chm &
CEO)
Brian D. Haney (Pres, COO & Exec
VP)
Bryan P. Petrucelli (CFO, Treas &
Exec VP)
Diane D. Schnupp (CIO & Exec VP)
Mark J. Beachy (Chief Claims Officer
& Exec VP)
Amber Sheridan (Chief HR Officer &
Sr VP)
Brendan McMorrow (Sr VP-
Underwriting)
Eric Gentry (VP-Underwriting)
Chris Tangard (VP-Fin)

Subsidiaries:

Aspera Insurance Services, Inc.   (1)
2035 Maywill St Ste 100, Richmond, VA
23230
Tel.: (804) 774-2101
Web Site: https://www.asperains.com
Casualty Insurance Services
N.A.I.C.S.: 524128
Heather Mawn (Product Mgr)

KINTARA THERAPEUTICS, INC.
9920 Pacific Heights Blvd Ste 150,
San Diego, CA 92121
Tel.: (858) 350-4364   NV
Web Site: https://www.kintara.com
Year Founded: 2009
KTRA—(NASDAQ)
Rev.: $147,000
Assets: $3,979,000
Liabilities: $3,248,000
Net Worth: $731,000
Earnings: ($15,019,000)
Emp.: 2
Fiscal Year-end: 06/30/23
Pharmaceuticals Mfr
N.A.I.C.S.: 325412
Robert E. Hoffman (Chm, Pres, CEO
& Interim CFO)
Dennis M. Brown (Founder)
Steven Rychnovsky (VP-R&D)
Greg A. Johnson (Acting Head-Ops)

Subsidiaries:

Adgero Biopharmaceuticals Holdings,
Inc.   (1)
4365 US 1 S Ste 211, Princeton, NJ 08540
Tel.: (609) 917-9796
Web Site: http://www.adgerobiopharm.com
Biotechnology Research & Development
Services
N.A.I.C.S.: 541713
Laura Edgerly-Pflug (VP-Technical Ops)

KIORA PHARMACEUTICALS, INC.
332 Encinitas Blvd Ste 102, Encini-
tas, CA 92024
Tel.: (781) 788-8869   DE
Web Site:
   https://www.kiorapharma.com
Year Founded: 2004
KPRX—(NASDAQ)
Rev.: $173,989
Assets: $13,711,870
Liabilities: $7,602,216
Net Worth: $6,109,654
Earnings: ($12,513,896)
Emp.: 12
Fiscal Year-end: 12/31/23
Pharmaceuticals Mfr
N.A.I.C.S.: 325412
Brian M. Strem (Pres & CEO)
Melissa Tosca (Principal Acctg Offi-
cer, Principal Fin Officer & Exec VP-
Fin)
Eric Daniels (Chief Dev Officer)
Stefan Sperl (Exec VP)

Subsidiaries:

EyeGate Pharma S.A.S.   (1)
52 rue du Theatre, Paris, 75015, France
Tel.: (33) 146410498
Pharmaceutical Products Distr
N.A.I.C.S.: 424210

Panoptes Pharma Ges.m.b.H.   (1)
Reisnerstrasse 34/1, 1030, Vienna, Austria
Tel.: (43) 6648557369
Web Site: http://www.panoptes-pharma.com
Bio Technology Services
N.A.I.C.S.: 541714
Franz Obermayr (CEO)
Stefan Sperl (COO)

KIRBY CORPORATION
55 Waugh Dr Ste 1000, Houston, TX
77007
Tel.: (713) 435-1000   NV
Web Site: https://www.kirbycorp.com
Year Founded: 1921
KEX—(NYSE)
Rev.: $3,091,640,000
Assets: $5,722,197,000
Liabilities: $2,535,520,000
Net Worth: $3,186,677,000
Earnings: $222,935,000
Emp.: 5,450
Fiscal Year-end: 12/31/23
Holding Company; Marine Freight
Transportation & Diesel Engine Ser-
vices
N.A.I.C.S.: 551112
Kim B. Clarke (Chief HR Officer &
VP)
Christian G. O'Neil (Pres & COO)
Ronald A. Dragg (VP, Controller &
Asst Sec)
Amy D. Husted (Gen Counsel, Sec &
VP)
David W. Grzebinski (CEO)
Scott P. Miller (CIO & VP)
Raj Kumar (CFO & Exec VP)
Julie M. Kruger (VP)

Subsidiaries:

Kirby Engine Systems, Inc.   (1)
175 Freight Rd, Rocky Mount, NC 27804
Tel.: (252) 977-2720
Web Site: https://www.kirbycorp.com
Sales Range: $25-49.9 Million
Emp.: 80
Diesel Engine Repair & Maintenance Ser-
vices
N.A.I.C.S.: 333618
Dorman Lynn Strahan (Pres)

Subsidiary (Domestic):

Engine Systems, Inc.   (2)
175 Freight Rd, Rocky Mount, NC 27804
Tel.: (252) 977-2720
Web Site: http://www.enginesys.com

Sales Range: $25-49.9 Million
Emp.: 5,800
Diesel Engine Services
N.A.I.C.S.: 333618
P. Scott Mangan (VP-East Coast)

Marine Systems, Inc.   (2)
1763 Wooddale Ct, Baton Rouge, LA 70806
Tel.: (225) 300-9325
Web Site:
   https://www.marinesystemsinc.com
Marine Vessel Support Operations
N.A.I.C.S.: 336611
Thomas W. Bottoms (VP-Midwest)
Troy A. Bourgeois (VP-Sales)
D. Lynn Strahan (Pres)
P. Scott Mangan (VP-East Coast)

Branch (Domestic):

Marine Systems, Inc.   (3)
840 Dumaine Rd, Mobile, AL 36610
Tel.: (251) 410-6900
Web Site: http://www.kirbycorp.com
Sales Range: $10-24.9 Million
Emp.: 15
Diesel Engine Repair Services
N.A.I.C.S.: 336611

Subsidiary (Domestic):

United Holdings LLC   (2)
5555 W Reno Ave, Oklahoma City, OK
73127
Web Site: https://unitedholdingscorp.com
General Freight Trucking Services
N.A.I.C.S.: 484110

Subsidiary (Domestic):

Thermo King of Houston, LP   (3)
772 McCarty St, Houston, TX 77029
Tel.: (713) 671-2700
Web Site: https://www.tkofhouston.com
Sales Range: $25-49.9 Million
Emp.: 40
Refrigerated Transportation Services
N.A.I.C.S.: 488999

Subsidiary (Domestic):

San Antonio Thermo King, Inc.   (4)
5807 Dietrich Rd, San Antonio, TX 78220
Tel.: (210) 661-4611
Web Site: http://www.tkofhouston.net
Sales Range: $25-49.9 Million
Emp.: 25
Refrigeration Equipment Whslr
N.A.I.C.S.: 423740

Subsidiary (Domestic):

UE Manufacturing LLC   (3)
10000 NW 2nd St, Oklahoma City, OK
73127-6621
Tel.: (405) 494-2400
Web Site: https://www.uemanufacturing.com
Emp.: 280
Oilfield Pumping Equipment Mfr & Whslr
N.A.I.C.S.: 333914

United Engines, LLC   (3)
5555 W Reno Ave, Oklahoma City, OK
73127-6340
Tel.: (405) 947-3321
Web Site: https://www.unitedengines.com
Industrial Machinery Whslr & Distr
N.A.I.C.S.: 423830

Kirby Inland Marine, LP   (1)
55 Waugh Dr Ste 1000, Houston, TX 77007
Tel.: (713) 435-1000
Web Site: https://www.kirbycorp.com
Sales Range: $450-499.9 Million
Emp.: 1,000
Marine Transportation Services
N.A.I.C.S.: 483211

Subsidiary (Domestic):

Kirby Inland Marine   (2)
18350 Market St, Channelview, TX 77530
Tel.: (713) 435-1600
Web Site: http://kirbycorp.com
Barge Fleeting Operations; Marine Trans-
portation
N.A.I.C.S.: 483211

Kirby Marine Transport
Corporation   (1)

Kirby Corporation—(Continued)

55 Waugh Dr Ste 1000, Houston, TX
77007-1537
Tel.: (713) 435-1000
Web Site: http://www.kirby.com
Sales Range: $75-99.9 Million
Emp.: 260
Marine Transport Service Provider
N.A.I.C.S.: 488999

Kirby Ocean Transport Company (1)
55 Waugh Dr Ste 1000, Houston, TX 77007
Tel.: (713) 435-1000
Web Site: https://kirbycorp.com
Emp.: 35
Marine Transportation Services
N.A.I.C.S.: 488999

Subsidiary (Domestic):

**Kirby Ocean Transport Co. - Houston
Office** (2)
55 Waugh Dr Ste 1000, Houston, TX 77007
Tel.: (713) 435-1000
Web Site: http://www.kirbycorp.com
Sales Range: $10-24.9 Million
Emp.: 2
N.A.I.C.S.: 524128

**Kirby Offshore Marine Hawaii,
LLC** (1)
Pier 21, Honolulu, HI 96817
Tel.: (808) 522-1000
Ship Building & Repair Services
N.A.I.C.S.: 336611

Osprey Line, LLC (1)
55 Waugh Dr Ste 1000, Houston, TX
77007 (66.67%)
Tel.: (713) 435-1000
Sales Range: $25-49.9 Million
Emp.: 7
Container Terminal Operator
N.A.I.C.S.: 483211
Charles J. Duet (VP-Project Cargo)

Penn Maritime Inc. (1)
1 Stamford Plz 263 Tresser Blvd, Stamford,
CT 06901
Tel.: (203) 356-0009
Marine Transportation Services
N.A.I.C.S.: 488390

Smith Maritime LLC (1)
967 Bulkhead Rd, Green Cove Springs, FL
32043
Tel.: (904) 284-0503
Web Site: http://www.smithmaritime.us
Emp.: 45
Marine Transportation Services
N.A.I.C.S.: 488390
Robert Remmer (Dir-Marketing)
Latham Smith (Founder & Owner)
David Rattray (Mgr-Compliance)
Mike Murphy (Mgr-Shipyard)

**Stewart & Stevenson de las Americas
Colombia Ltda.** (1)
Avenida Calle 23 No 32 A 51, Bogota, Co-
lombia
Tel.: (57) 15190449
Web Site: https://ssss.com.co
Mining Equipment Mfr & Distr
N.A.I.C.S.: 333131

Stewart & Stevenson, LLC (1)
8631 E Fwy, Houston, TX 77029
Tel.: (713) 671-6220
Web Site:
https://www.stewartandstevenson.com
Oil & Gas Equipment Mfr, Sales & Rental
Services
N.A.I.C.S.: 333132
John Merrifield (Pres)
Julie Kruger (VP)

Subsidiary (Domestic):

Stewart & Stevenson FDDA LLC (2)
4141 Sw 30th Ave, Fort Lauderdale, FL
33312-6805
Tel.: (954) 327-4440
Web Site: https://www.fdda.com
Industrial Equipment Distr
N.A.I.C.S.: 423830

**Stewart & Stevenson Power Prod-
ucts, LLC** (2)
5840 Dahlia St, Commerce City, CO 80022
Tel.: (303) 287-7441

Web Site:
http://www.stewartandstevenson.com
Integrated Oilfield Services
N.A.I.C.S.: 213112

KIRKLAND'S INC.
5310 Maryland Way, Brentwood, TN
37027
Tel.: (615) 872-4800 TN
Web Site: https://www.kirklands.com
Year Founded: 1966
KIRK—(NASDAQ)
Rev.: $498,825,000
Assets: $274,246,000
Liabilities: $244,473,000
Net Worth: $29,773,000
Earnings: ($44,694,000)
Emp.: 1,000
Fiscal Year-end: 01/28/23
Gifts & Home Decor Store Owner &
Operator
N.A.I.C.S.: 459420
Tracy R. Parker (VP-Store Ops &
Mdse Presentation)
Amy A. Sullivan (Pres & CEO)
Jeffrey R. McGowan (VP-
eCommerce)
Michael A. Holland (CTO & Sr VP)
Lisa Foley (VP-Mktg)
Gregg W. Sayers (VP-Supply Chain)
R. Wilson Orr III (Chm)
Carter R. Todd (Gen Counsel, Sec &
VP)
Carter R. Todd (Gen Counsel, Sec &
VP)

Subsidiaries:

Kirkland of Chattanooga Inc. (1)
431 Smith Ln, Jackson, TN 38301-9670
Tel.: (731) 668-2444
Sales Range: $50-74.9 Million
Emp.: 10
Operator of Gift Stores
N.A.I.C.S.: 459420

KIROMIC BIOPHARMA, INC.
7707 Fannin Ste 140, Houston, TX
77054
Tel.: (832) 968-4888 DE
Web Site: https://www.kiromic.com
KRBP—(NASDAQ)
Assets: $11,967,500
Liabilities: $17,742,200
Net Worth: ($5,774,700)
Earnings: ($34,731,000)
Emp.: 31
Fiscal Year-end: 12/31/22
Research & Development in Biotech-
nology (except Nanobiotechnology)
N.A.I.C.S.: 541714
Brian Hungerford (Interim CFO)
Michael Nagel (Chm)
Pietro Bersani (CEO)
Scott Dahlbeck (Chief Medical Offi-
cer, Head-Clinical, Head-Staff & Pres)
Leonardo Mirandola (Chief Scientific
Officer)
Linda Phelan Dyson (Head-Corp
Comm-Global)

Subsidiaries:

In Silico Solutions LLC (1)
8280 Willow Oaks Corporate Dr Ste 600,
Fairfax, VA 22031
Tel.: (703) 626-5653
Web Site: https://www.insilico.us.com
Research & Development in Biotechnology
N.A.I.C.S.: 541714

KISH BANCORP, INC.
4255 E Main St Rt 655, Belleville, PA
17004
Tel.: (814) 861-4747 PA
Year Founded: 1986
KISB—(OTCQX)
Emp.: 253
Bank Holding Company
N.A.I.C.S.: 551111

William P. Hayes (Chm & CEO)
Debra Weikel (Sr VP & Dir-Loan Ad-
min)
Mark J. Cvrkel (CFO, Treas & Exec
VP)
Robert S. McMinn (Gen Counsel &
Exec VP)
James L. Lakso (Vice Chm)
William L. Dancy (Sec)

Subsidiaries:

Kish Bank (1)
4255 E Main St, Belleville, PA 17004
Tel.: (717) 935-2191
Web Site: https://www.mykish.com
National Commercial Banks
N.A.I.C.S.: 522110
William P. Hayes (Chm & CEO)
Arthur Dangel (Sr VP & Dir-Trust Svcs)
Robert McMinn (Gen Counsel & Exec VP)
Kayelene Sunderland (VP-Wealth Mgmt)
Mark Cvrkel (CFO & Exec VP)
Peter Collins (Chief Credit Officer & Exec
VP)
Jim Shilling (Chief Business Banking Officer
& Exec VP)
Richard Sarfert (Sr Lending Officer & Exec
VP)
Robert Crane (Sr VP & Dir-Profitability)
Carol Herrmann (CEO-Kish Travel, Sr VP &
Dir-Admin & Comm)
Amy Muchler (Sr VP & Dir-Ops & Support)
Debra Weikel (Sr VP & Dir-Loan Administra-
tion)
Suzanne White (Sr VP & Dir-HR & Organi-
zational Dev)
Stanley Ayers (VP & Mgr-Special Assets)
Douglas Baxter (VP & Mgr-Acctg & Con-
trols)
Kathleen Boop (VP & Mgr-Personal Lines
Insurance)
Kimberly Bubb (VP & Dir-Sys & Client Solu-
tions)
Larry Burger (VP & Mgr-Comml Relation-
ship)
John Cunningham (VP & Mgr-Mifflin County
Market)
Wade Curry (VP-Kish Financial Solutions)
Terra Decker (Officer-BSA, VP, & Dir-
Compliance & BSA Trng)
Ann Guss (VP-Residential Lender)
Allana Hartung (VP & Mgr-Comml Mgr)
Marsha Kuhns (VP-Residential Lender)
Terry Horner (Officer-Bus Dev & VP)
John Massie (VP-Comml)
Virginia McAdoo (VP & Mgr-Lending Svcs)
Kristie McKnight (VP & Mgr-Comml Rela-
tionship)
Thomas Minichiello (VP & Mgr-Centre
County Market)
Denise Quinn (VP & Mgr-Comml Relation-
ship)
Melissa Rover (VP)
Cheryl Shope (VP)
Norman Robert (Compliance Officer & VP)
Jeffrey Wilson (CEO-Kish Insurance & Mgr-
Comml Lines)
Bill Yaudes (VP & Mgr-Huntingdon County)
Gregory T. Hayes (Pres & COO)

KISSES FROM ITALY, INC.
80 SW 8th St Ste 2000, Miami, FL
33304
Tel.: (305) 423-7129 FL
Web Site:
https://www.kissesfromitaly.com
Year Founded: 2013
KITL—(OTCIQ)
Rev.: $225,953
Assets: $85,473
Liabilities: $934,002
Net Worth: ($848,529)
Earnings: ($4,871,545)
Emp.: 3
Fiscal Year-end: 12/31/23
Restaurant Management Services
N.A.I.C.S.: 722511
Michele Di Turi (Co-Founder, Chm,
Pres & Co-CEO)
Claudio Ferri (Co-Founder, Co-CEO,
CFO & Chief Investment Officer)
Leonardo Fraccalvieri (COO)

KITE REALTY GROUP TRUST
30 S Meridian St Ste 1100, India-
napolis, IN 46204
Tel.: (317) 577-5600 MD
Web Site: https://www.kiterealty.com
Year Founded: 2004
KRG—(NYSE)
Rev.: $801,996,000
Assets: $7,341,982,000
Liabilities: $3,570,097,000
Net Worth: $3,771,885,000
Earnings: ($12,636,000)
Emp.: 236
Fiscal Year-end: 12/30/22
Real Estate Investment Trust
N.A.I.C.S.: 525990
John A. Kite (Chm & CEO)
Heath R. Fear (CFO & Exec VP)
Thomas K. McGowan (Pres & COO)
Mellissa Boggs (Exec VP-Employee
Experience)
David E. Buell (Chief Acctg Officer &
Sr VP)
Matthew Gabet (Sr VP-Operational
Strategy)
Mark Jenkins (Sr VP-Dev)
Gregg Poetz (Sr VP-Leasing)
Mitch Rippe (Sr VP-Acquisition & Dis-
position)
Randy Burke (Sr VP-Construction)
Neil Burka (Sr VP)
Pat Casey (CTO)
Kimberly Fuhrman (Sr VP)
Tyler Henshaw (Sr VP)
Dean Papadakis (Chief Legal Officer)

Subsidiaries:

KRG Rivers Edge, LLC (1)
30 S Meridian St Ste 1100, Indianapolis, IN
46204-3565
Tel.: (317) 577-5600
Web Site: http://www.kiterealty.com
Property Management Services
N.A.I.C.S.: 531110

Kite Realty Group, L.P. (1)
30 S Meridian St Ste 1100, Indianapolis, IN
46204
Tel.: (317) 577-5600
Web Site: https://www.kiterealty.com
Rev.: $801,995,999
Assets: $7,341,981,999
Liabilities: $3,570,096,999
Net Worth: $3,771,884,999
Earnings: ($12,777,000)
Emp.: 236
Fiscal Year-end: 12/31/2022
Real Estate Investment Services
N.A.I.C.S.: 531210
John A. Kite (Chm & CEO)

Retail Properties of America, Inc. (1)
2021 Spring Rd Ste 200, Oak Brook, IL
60523
Tel.: (630) 634-4200
Web Site: http://www.rpai.com
Rev.: $430,043,000
Assets: $3,637,203,000
Liabilities: $2,055,073,000
Net Worth: $1,582,130,000
Earnings: $14,571,000
Emp.: 214
Fiscal Year-end: 12/31/2020
Real Estate Investment Trust
N.A.I.C.S.: 525990
Shane C. Garrison (Pres & COO)
Julie M. Swinehart (CFO, Treas & Exec VP)
Matthew Beverly (Pres-Eastern Div)
Michael Hazinski (Sr VP & Dir-Investments)
Gregory Goldberg (VP & Dir-Leasing-
Eastern Div)
Jason N. Kasal (VP & Sr Dir-Leasing-
Western Div)
Ann Smith (VP & Sr Dir-Leasing-Eastern
Div)
Lauren Whaley (Officer-Compliance, VP &
Dir-HR)
Gerald Wright (Pres-Western Div)
Stacy Short (VP & Dir-Leasing-Western Div)
Fran Davanzo (VP-Property Mgmt-Eastern
Div)
Daniel Upton (VP-Property Mgmt-Western
Div)

David Bennett (VP-Asset Mgmt-Eastern Div)
Michael Tchang (VP-Asset Mgmt-Eastern Div)
Nick Over (VP & Dir-Dev-Eastern Div)
Kevin Woods (Sr VP & Dir-Ops & Construction)
Scott Miller (VP & Dir-Dev-Western Div)
Mike Gaiden (VP-Capital Markets & IR)
Mike Lubinski (Asst VP-Asset Mgmt-Western Div)
Ann M. Sharp Hult (Sec & VP)
Colin Joynt (Sr VP-IT)

Subsidiary (Domestic):

Centre at Laurel, LLC (2)
13600 Baltimore Ave, Laurel, MD 20707
Tel.: (704) 541-1042
Real Estate Investment Services
N.A.I.C.S.: 531190

RPAI Chicago Brickyard, L.L.C. (2)
2021 Spring Rd Ste 200, Oak Brook, IL 60523
Tel.: (630) 634-4200
Emp.: 11
Property Managing Services
N.A.I.C.S.: 531312

RPAI Pacific Property Services LLC (2)
1851 E 1st St, Santa Ana, CA 92705
Tel.: (714) 569-0033
Real Estate Manangement Services
N.A.I.C.S.: 531210

RPAI Southwest Management LLC (2)
6363 De Zavala Rd Ste 302, San Antonio, TX 78249
Tel.: (210) 265-5255
Real Estate Manangement Services
N.A.I.C.S.: 531210

RPAI US Management LLC (2)
8 Griffin Rd N Fl 103, Windsor, CT 06095-1574
Tel.: (860) 787-1880
Real Estate Manangement Services
N.A.I.C.S.: 531210
Pam Delfino (Mgr-Propery)

RPAI Williston Maple Tree, L.L.C. (2)
2021 Spring Rd Ste 200, Oak Brook, IL 60523-1845
Tel.: (410) 246-5588
Real Estate Manangement Services
N.A.I.C.S.: 531210

Reisterstown Plaza Associates, LLC (2)
6564 Reisterstown Rd, Baltimore, MD 21215-2346
Tel.: (410) 764-3224
Web Site:
    http://www.shopreisterstownroadplaza.com
Real Estate Investment Services
N.A.I.C.S.: 531190

University Square Parking LLC (2)
101 N 14th St, Lincoln, NE 68508-3800
Tel.: (402) 441-6477
Real Estate Investment Services
N.A.I.C.S.: 531190

KIWA BIO-TECH PRODUCTS GROUP CORP.

3200 Guasti Rd Ste 100, Ontario, CA 91761
Tel.: (909) 456-8828
Web Site:
    http://www.kiwabiotech.com
Year Founded: 2004
KWBT—(OTCIQ)
Rev.: $40,089,457
Assets: $24,069,329
Liabilities: $14,384,041
Net Worth: $9,685,288
Earnings: ($6,635,296)
Emp.: 16
Fiscal Year-end: 12/31/19
Bio-Fertilizer Mfr
N.A.I.C.S.: 325314

Hon Man Yun (CFO)
Qi Wang (VP-Tech)
Xiao Qiang Yu (COO)
Weijun Xu (Chief Strategy Officer)
Wade Li (Chm, Pres & CEO)
Qiansheng Wang (VP)
Yanan Tong (CTO)

KKR & CO. INC.

30 Hudson Yards, New York, NY 10001
Tel.: (212) 750-8300   DE
Web Site: https://www.kkr.com
Year Founded: 1976
KKR—(NYSE)
Rev.: $14,499,312,000
Assets: $317,294,194,000
Liabilities: $259,530,709,000
Net Worth: $57,763,485,000
Earnings: $5,357,086,000
Emp.: 4,490
Fiscal Year-end: 12/31/23
Holding Company; Investment Services
N.A.I.C.S.: 523999
Joshua T. Weisenbeck (Partner)
Emmanuel Lagarrigue (Partner & Co-Head)
Todd C. Builione (Partner & Head-Private Wealth-Global)
George R. Roberts (Co-Founder & Co-Chm)
Kendra L. Decious (Mng Dir-Finance)
David J. Sorkin (Partner & Chief Legal Officer)
Henry R. Kravis (Co-Founder & Co-Chm)
Dinesh C. Paliwal (Partner-Private Equity Bus)
Ryan Stork (COO)
Kendra Decious (Mng Dir-Fin)
Craig Larson (Partner & Head-IR)
Kristi Huller (Mng Dir & Head-Corp Mktg & Comm-Global)
Paul E. Raether (Sr Partner-Advisory)
Ali Allahbachani (Mng Dir-KKR Credit)
Webster B. Chua (Partner-Private Equity-New York)
Christopher Kim (Head-Benefits-Human Capital-Global)
George Aitken (Mng Dir & Head-Global Impact-APAC)
Johannes P. Huth (Partner)
Dane E. Holmes (Chief Admin Officer)
Felix Gernburd (Partner-Private Equity-Menlo Park)
Domenico AcriGarofalo (Mng Dir-Real Estate)
Paula Campbell Roberts (Chief Investment Strategist-Private Wealth)
Stephen Shanley (Executives)
Kathryn King Sudol (Partner, Gen Counsel & Sec)
Paula Campbell Roberts (Chief Investment Strategist-Private Wealth)
Henry McVey (CIO-Balance Sheet & Head-Global Macro & Asset Allocation)
Lester Lim (Dir-Family Capital-Asia-Pacific)
Sahar Abdulahad (Dir-Human Capital)
Rajesh Addy (Principal-Legal-Compliance)
Ankit Aggarwal (Principal-Private Equity)
Barkha Agrawal (Principal-Infrastructure)
Ruchika Agrawal (Principal-KKR Asset Finance-India)
Amy Alcock (Principal-Compliance)
Pamela Alexander (Mng Dir & Head-Corp Citizenship-Public Affairs)
Omar Alfukaha (Principal-Finance)
Amit Alleck (Principal-Global Impact)

Jessica Allen (Principal-Tech Growth)
Nishi Anand (Principal-KKR Capstone)
Ian Anderson (Mng Dir-Credit)
Nina Anderson (Principal-Client & Partner Group)
Kei Ando (Dir-KKR Capital Markets)
Mike Angelon (Dir-Technology-Engrg & Data)
Neil Arora (Partner-Infrastructure)
Hans Arstad (Mng Dir-Private Equity)
Ahmad Ashraf (Dir-Enterprise Risk Mgmt)
Paul Atefi (Mng Dir-Credit)
Mohamed Attar (Dir-Client & Partner Group)
Aidan Bailey (Dir-Legal & Compliance)
Ludo Bammens (Mng Dir & Head--EMEA)
Soumya Banerjee (Dir-Tech,Engrg & Data)
Projesh Banerjea (Dir-Infrastructure)
Jennifer McGroarty (Dir)
Ashish Shastry (Partner)
Craig Lee (Partner)
Wonda Quinn (Dir)
John Ihn Park (Partner-Private Equity-Menlo Park)
Joseph Y. Bae (Co-CEO)
Scott C. Nuttall (Co-CEO)

Subsidiaries:

A-Gas International Ltd. (1)
Units 7 8 Gordano Court Serbert Close, Portishead, Bristol, BS20 7FS, United Kingdom
Tel.: (44) 1275376600
Web Site: https://www.agas.com
Refrigerant Whslr
N.A.I.C.S.: 423740
Richard Stewart (CFO-Grp)
Jack Govers (CEO)
Louise McCann (Mng Dir)
John Ormerod (Mng Dir)
Mike Armstrong (Pres)

Accel-KKR Company LLC (1)
2500 Sand Hill Rd Ste 300, Menlo Park, CA 94025
Tel.: (650) 289-2460
Web Site: https://www.accel-kkr.com
Privater Equity Firm
N.A.I.C.S.: 523999
Patrick J. Fallon (Mng Dir & COO)
Gregory Williams (Mng Dir-Growth Capital Investments)
David Cusimano (Principal)
Kristy Curtis (Office Mgr)
Park Durrett (Mng Dir)
Maurice Hernandez (VP-London office)
Dean Jacobson (Mng Dir)
Matt Marinaro (VP)
Joe Porten (VP)
Joe Savig (Principal)
Clara Yee (Sr VP-Fin)
Phil Cunningham (Mng Dir)
Roy Kelvin (CFO)
Samantha Shows (Mng Dir)
Weston Ahlswede (VP)
Eric Armagost (VP)
Scotty Lu (VP)
Dave Moore (VP)
Adam Malinowski (VP)
Gordon MacNeill (VP)
Alissa Palatiello (VP)
Nishant Patel (Principal)
Andy Rich (Principal)
Christian Stewart (VP)
Johnny Van Siclen (VP)
Andrew Zbella (Principal)
Jason Klein (Mng Dir)
Adam Malinowski (VP)
Paul Hazen (Chm)

Holding (Domestic):

Accertify, Inc. (2)
2 Pierce Pl Ste 900, Itasca, IL 60143
Tel.: (630) 735-4400
Web Site: https://www.accertify.com
Software Development Services
N.A.I.C.S.: 541511

Joint Venture (Non-US):

Basware Oyj (2)
Linnoitustie 2 Cello-rakennus, PL 97, 02601, Espoo, Finland
Tel.: (358) 9879171
Web Site: https://www.basware.com
Rev.: $188,111,097
Assets: $271,097,133
Liabilities: $181,481,058
Net Worth: $89,616,075
Earnings: ($17,481,540)
Emp.: 1,347
Fiscal Year-end: 12/31/2021
Software Publisher
N.A.I.C.S.: 513210
Jane Broberg (Chief HR Officer)
Lars Madsen (CMO)
Klaus Andersen (CEO)
Martti Nurminen (CFO)
Alwin Schauer (Chief Revenue Officer)
Jason Kurtz (CEO-Basware)
Barrett Schiwitz (CIO)
Sam Pathmasiri (Gen Counsel)

Subsidiary (Non-US):

Basware A/S (3)
Kirkebjerg Alle 84 1 Sal, 2605, Brondby, Denmark
Tel.: (45) 7 022 9955
Web Site: https://www.basware.com
Emp.: 25
Software Development Services
N.A.I.C.S.: 541511

Basware AB (3)
Gustavslundsv 151 C, 167 51, Bromma, Stockholm, Sweden
Tel.: (46) 85 057 4400
Web Site: https://www.basware.com
Sales Range: $25-49.9 Million
Emp.: 35
Software Development Services
N.A.I.C.S.: 541511
Jukka Virkkunen (Sr VP)

Basware AS (3)
Vollsveien 6, PO Box 241, Lilleaker, 1366, Lysaker, Norway
Tel.: (47) 2 337 0300
Web Site: http://www.basware.com
Financial Software Development Services
N.A.I.C.S.: 541511

Basware B.V. (3)
Krijn Taconiskade 436, Duivendrecht, 1087 HW, Amsterdam, Netherlands
Tel.: (31) 20 850 8020
Web Site: https://www.basware.com
Software Development Services
N.A.I.C.S.: 541511

Basware Belgium NV (3)
Clinton Park Ninovesteenweg 196, Erembodegem, 9320, Belgium
Tel.: (32) 53 60 11 11
Web Site: http://www.basware.be
Emp.: 50
Software Development Services
N.A.I.C.S.: 541511
Pieter Geeraerts (Gen Mgr)

Basware Corporation (3)
Ocean Financial Centre Level 40 10 Collyer, Quay, Singapore, 49315, Singapore
Tel.: (65) 6808 6494
Software Development Services
N.A.I.C.S.: 541511
Ben Selby (Head-IR)
Jukka Janonen (Dir-Comm)

Basware GmbH (3)
Rossstr 96, 40476, Dusseldorf, Germany
Tel.: (49) 211 41 55 95 50
Sales Range: $25-49.9 Million
Emp.: 70
Software Development Services
N.A.I.C.S.: 541511
Frank Wuschech (Mng Dir)

Basware Holdings Ltd. (3)
4th Floor 120 Old Broad Street, London, EC2N 1AR, United Kingdom
Tel.: (44) 845 603 2885
Software Services
N.A.I.C.S.: 541511

Basware India Private Limited (3)
Rajiv Gandhi IT Park DLF Building Tower A Ground Floor, Chandigarh, 160 001, India

KKR & Co. Inc.—(Continued)

Tel.: (91) 172 301 2020
Web Site: http://www.basware.com
Software Development Services
N.A.I.C.S.: 541511

Basware Pty Ltd (3)
Level 15 67 Albert Ave, PO Box 148, Chatswood, 2067, NSW, Australia
Tel.: (61) 2 8622 5850
Software Development Services
N.A.I.C.S.: 541511
Niclas Hill *(Dir-Consulting)*

Basware Russia (3)
Helsinki House 4 Rostovsky per 1/2, Moscow, 119121, Russia
Tel.: (7) 499 248 16 73
Web Site: http://www.basware.ru
Software Development Services
N.A.I.C.S.: 541511

Basware SAS (3)
20 Rue Caumartin, 75009, Paris, France
Tel.: (33) 14 008 1820
Web Site: https://www.basware.com
Software Development Services
N.A.I.C.S.: 541511

Basware UK Ltd. (3)
1-3 Berkeley Court Borough Road, Newcastle, ST5 1TT, Staffordshire, United Kingdom
Tel.: (44) 845 6711953
Software Development Services
N.A.I.C.S.: 541511

Subsidiary (US):

Basware, Inc. (3)
1245 Rosemont Dr Ste 200, Fort Mill, SC 29707
Tel.: (203) 487-7900
Web Site: https://www.basware.com
Sales Range: $25-49.9 Million
Emp.: 50
Software Development Services
N.A.I.C.S.: 541511
Tehseen Dahya *(Gen Mgr-North America)*

Subsidiary (Domestic):

Verian Technologies, Inc. (4)
8701 Mallard Creek Rd, Charlotte, NC 28262
Tel.: (704) 547-7301
Web Site: http://www.verian.com
Sales Range: $10-24.9 Million
Emp.: 75
Procurement Technology Solutions
N.A.I.C.S.: 513210
Tehseen Ali Dahya *(Pres & CEO)*
Lindsay Munn *(Mgr-Mktg Comm)*
Bilal Soylu *(CTO)*
Tommy Benston *(VP-Customer Svc)*
Dana Saylors *(VP-Mktg & Product Strategy)*
Jerry Ellis *(VP-Sls)*
Steve Ayala *(VP-Tech)*
Bhavin Shah *(Dir-Product Strategy)*

Subsidiary (Non-US):

Glantus Holdings Plc (3)
Marina House Block V Eastpoint Business Park, Dublin, D03 AX24, Ireland
Tel.: (353) 18895300
Rev.: $12,925,013
Assets: $32,981,867
Liabilities: $20,630,120
Net Worth: $12,351,748
Earnings: ($2,806,273)
Emp.: 124
Fiscal Year-end: 12/31/2021
Holding Company
N.A.I.C.S.: 551112

Holding (Domestic):

GPS Insight LLC (2)
7201 E Henkel Way Ste 400, Scottsdale, AZ 85255
Tel.: (480) 663-9454
Web Site: http://www.gpsinsight.com
Sales Range: $1-9.9 Million
Emp.: 65
GPS Tracking, Navigation & Messaging Technologies
N.A.I.C.S.: 334511
Rob Donat *(Founder)*
Tyler Mortensen *(Sr Acct Mgr)*

Elliot Batcheller *(Dir-Ops)*
Gary Fitzgerald *(CEO)*
Wayne Holder *(CFO)*
Jason Walker *(Chief Revenue Officer)*
Geoffrey Garrett *(Chief Revenue Officer)*

National Electronic Attachment, Inc. (2)
3577 Pkwy Ln Ste 250, Norcross, GA 30092
Tel.: (770) 441-3203
Web Site: http://www.nea-fast.com
Sales Range: $1-9.9 Million
Internet Based Solutions for Health Information Exchange
N.A.I.C.S.: 541519
Kent McAllister *(Chief Dev Officer & Chief Ops Officer)*
Melinda H. Benton *(CEO)*
Claudia Stein-Martin *(CFO)*
Nicole Smith *(VP-Govt Svcs)*
Scott Hefner *(VP-Sls)*

Subsidiary (Domestic):

The White Stone Group Inc. (3)
6422 E Main St Ste 100, Reynoldsburg, OH 43068
Tel.: (614) 501-7007
Web Site: https://www.whitestonegroup.us
Sales Range: $1-9.9 Million
Emp.: 65
Healthcare Management Consulting
N.A.I.C.S.: 541618
Randy Smith *(CFO)*
Jeff Peters *(Pres & CEO)*
Dave Stridde *(COO)*
Phillip McClure *(VP-Bus Dev)*
Jo Norris *(VP-Strategic Acct Dev)*
Blair Wright *(Exec VP-Bus Dev)*
Jerry Thomas *(Exec VP-Accts Dev)*
Scott Overholt *(CMO & Exec VP-Market Dev)*
Matt Jernigan *(Dir-Product Mgmt)*

Joint Venture (Non-US):

Reapit Ltd (2)
67 - 74 Saffron Hill 3rd Floor London, Greater, London , EC1N 8QX, United Kingdom
Tel.: (44) 8453302965
Web Site: https://www.reapit.com
Software Publisher
N.A.I.C.S.: 513210
Mark Armstrong *(CEO)*

Subsidiary (Non-US):

Console Australia Pty Ltd (3)
Level 8 Elizabeth Plaza North Sydney, Sydney, 2060, NSW, Australia
Tel.: (61) 1300131311
Web Site: http://www.console.com.au
Real Estate Software Development Services
N.A.I.C.S.: 541511

Subsidiary (Non-US):

Console New Zealand Limited (4)
Level 7 203 Queen Street, Auckland, 1010, New Zealand
Tel.: (64) 508 641 199
Web Site: http://www.console.co.nz
Emp.: 10
Real Estate Software Development Services
N.A.I.C.S.: 541511
Jose Antonio Cadarso *(Office Mgr)*

Holding (Domestic):

Salary.com, LLC (2)
610 Lincoln St North Ste 200, Waltham, MA 02451
Tel.: (617) 631-8000
Web Site: http://www.salary.com
On-Demand Compensation & Performance Management Services
N.A.I.C.S.: 518210
G. Kent Plunkett *(Founder, Pres & CEO)*
Yong Zhang *(COO, CTO & Pres-Global Ops)*
Robert Merklinger *(Sr VP-Sls)*
Anne Huemme *(CFO)*
ALys Reynders Scott *(CMO)*
Brian Davis *(Head-People)*

SciQuest, Inc. (2)

3020 Carrington Mill Blvd Ste 100, Morrisville, NC 27560
Tel.: (919) 659-2100
Web Site: https://www.jaggaer.com
Technology & Services to Optimize Procurement & Materials Management
N.A.I.C.S.: 513210
Zia Zahiri *(CTO)*

Subsidiary (Non-US):

BravoSolution S.p.A. (3)
Via Rombon 11, 20134, Milan, Italy
Tel.: (39) 022105121
Web Site: http://www.jaggaer.com
Electronic Sourcing Software & Services Developer
N.A.I.C.S.: 513210

Subsidiary (Domestic):

BravoBus S.r.l. (4)
Via Rombon 11, Milan, 20134, Italy
Tel.: (39) 022105121
Web Site: http://www.jaggaer.com
Software Development Services
N.A.I.C.S.: 541511

Subsidiary (Non-US):

BravoSolution Benelux B.V. (4)
Nieuwezijds Voorburgwal 162, Amsterdam, 1012 SJ, Netherlands
Tel.: (31) 0208203825
Web Site: http://www.jaggaer.com
Supply Management Software Development Services
N.A.I.C.S.: 541511

BravoSolution China Co. Ltd (4)
Room C06 No 13 Lane 345 Danshui Road, Huangpu District, Shanghai, 200003, China
Tel.: (86) 21 6145 8500
Web Site: http://www.jaggaer.com
Software Development & Management Services
N.A.I.C.S.: 541511

BravoSolution Espana S.A. (4)
Avenida Manoteras 42 Calle 3 Edificio Esindus 1 Planta, 28050, Madrid, Spain
Tel.: (34) 917870200
Web Site: http://www.jaggaer.com
Supply Management Software Development Services
N.A.I.C.S.: 541511

BravoSolution France S.a.s. (4)
81 83 Le Quintet Batiment E 81 Avenue Edouard Vaillant, 92100, Boulogne-Billancourt, France
Tel.: (33) 146095678
Web Site: http://www.jaggaer.com
Software Development Services
N.A.I.C.S.: 541511

BravoSolution GmbH (4)
Ottobrunner Str 41, 82008, Munich, Germany
Tel.: (49) 89 121 93 35 0
Software Development & Management Services
N.A.I.C.S.: 541511

BravoSolution Mexico S.r.l. de C.V. (4)
Av Homero 1933-301 Col Los Morales, 11510, Mexico, Mexico
Tel.: (52) 55 5395 8936
Supply Chain Software Development Services
N.A.I.C.S.: 541511

Subsidiary (US):

BravoSolution Software, Inc. (4)
120 Plaza Dr Ste F, Vestal, NY 13850
Tel.: (607) 231-6000
Web Site: http://www.jaggaer.com
Software Development & Management Services
N.A.I.C.S.: 541511

Subsidiary (Non-US):

BravoSolution Technologies Ltd (4)
103 St John Street, London, EC1M 4AS, United Kingdom
Tel.: (44) 20 7796 4170
Web Site: http://www.jaggaer.com
Software Development Services

N.A.I.C.S.: 541511

BravoSolution UK Ltd (4)
103 St John Street, London, EC1M 4AS, United Kingdom
Tel.: (44) 2077964170
Web Site: http://www.jaggaer.com
Software Development Services
N.A.I.C.S.: 541511

Holding (Domestic):

SugarCRM, Inc. (2)
10050 N Wolfe Rd Ste SW2-130, Cupertino, CA 95014
Tel.: (408) 454-6900
Web Site: http://www.sugarcrm.com
Sales Range: $10-24.9 Million
Emp.: 150
Open Source Customer Relationship Management (CRM) Software
N.A.I.C.S.: 513210
Chuck Coulson *(VP-Bus Dev)*
Clint Oram *(Co-Founder & VP-Product Mgmt)*
Larry Augustin *(Chm)*
Majed Itani *(VP-Dev)*
Jennifer Stagnaro *(CMO)*
Sherry Pulvers *(VP-People & Places)*
Remy Malan *(Chief Customer Officer)*
Fred Gewant *(Exec VP-Worldwide Sls)*
Rich Green *(Chief Product Officer)*
Juan Herrera *(Exec VP-Sls-Worldwide)*
Mark Liu *(Gen Counsel, Sec & VP)*
Craig Charlton *(CEO)*
John Donaldson *(CFO)*
Shana Sweeney *(Chief HR Officer)*
Jason Rushforth *(Gen Mgr-Americas)*
Clare Dorrian *(CMO)*

Subsidiary (Domestic):

Salesfusion Inc. (3)
3565 Piedmont Rd NE Building 2, Atlanta, GA 30305
Tel.: (770) 217-1228
Web Site: http://www.salesfusion.com
Holding Company
N.A.I.C.S.: 551112
Malinda Wilkinson *(CMO)*
Matt Barman *(Exec VP-Client Svcs)*
Gavin Harris *(VP-Sls)*
Logan Henderson *(CEO)*

Subsidiary (Non-US):

SugarCRM Deutschland GmbH (3)
Luise-Ullrich-Strasse 20, 80636, Munich, Germany
Tel.: (49) 89189172000
Web Site: http://www.sugarcrm.com
Emp.: 55
Open Source Customer Relationship Management (CRM) Software
N.A.I.C.S.: 513210
Kevan Baker *(Gen Mgr)*

Division (Non-US):

SugarCRM Sweden (4)
Master Samuelsgatan 60 8th Floor, 111 21, Stockholm, Sweden
Tel.: (46) 8 44 68 02 56
Open Source Customer Relationship Management (CRM) Software
N.A.I.C.S.: 513210

SugarCRM UK (4)
Work Life 20 Red Lion St, Holborn, London, WC1R 4PS, Cambridge, United Kingdom
Tel.: (44) 2038088507
Web Site: http://www.sugarcrm.com
Open Source Customer Relationship Management (CRM) Software
N.A.I.C.S.: 513210

Holding (Domestic):

Team Software, Inc. (2)
407 S 27th Ave, Omaha, NE 68131
Tel.: (402) 345-5660
Web Site: https://www.teamsoftware.com
Sales Range: $1-9.9 Million
Emp.: 25
Computer Related Services
N.A.I.C.S.: 541519
Colleen Slepicka *(Accountant)*

Subsidiary (Non-US):

Innovise Ltd. (3)

Keypoint 17-23 High Street, Slough, SL1
1DY, Berks, United Kingdom
Tel.: (44) 370 626 0400
Web Site: http://www.innovise.com
Sales Range: $25-49.9 Million
Information Technology Management Services
N.A.I.C.S.: 541513
Mike Taylor (CEO)
Graeme Hughes (Mng Dir)

Holding (Non-US):

TimeTarget Pty Ltd (2)
Level 14 90 Arthur St, North Sydney, 2060,
NSW, Australia
Tel.: (61) 300886698
Web Site: https://humanforce.com
Payroll Solutions Provider
N.A.I.C.S.: 513210
Clayton Pyne (CEO)
Alex Panich (CFO)
Sylvia Vasas (CMO)

Subsidiary (Domestic):

IntelliHR Limited (3)
Level 28 345 Queen Street, Brisbane,
4000, QLD, Australia
Tel.: (61) 300993803
Web Site: http://www.intellihr.com.au
Rev.: $2,151,780
Assets: $7,523,029
Liabilities: $3,702,803
Net Worth: $3,820,226
Earnings: ($5,847,812)
Emp.: 45
Fiscal Year-end: 06/30/2021
Software Management Services
N.A.I.C.S.: 541512
Robert Bromage (Founder & CEO)
Suzanne M. Yeates (CFO & Sec)
Paul Trappett (COO)
Kelly Harvey (Head-Mktg)
Andrew Smith (CTO)
Laura Butler (Head)
Gemma Murdoch (Head)
Kate Charge (Head)
Tony Lehner (Head)

Subsidiary (Domestic):

VisiQuate, Inc. (2)
500 Bicentennial Way Ste 300, Santa Rosa,
CA 95403
Tel.: (707) 546-4377
Web Site: http://www.visiquate.com
Web Based Content Management Services
N.A.I.C.S.: 541511
Rich Waller (CTO)
Keith Eggert (Exec VP & Gen Mgr-
Healthcare)
Leonid Nekhymchuk (Sr VP-Engrg)
Brian Robertson (Co-Founder & CEO)
Jim Kolmansberger (Co-Founder & Pres)
Andrii Svydlo (Sr Engr-Data)
Greg Karraker (CMO & Sr VP)
Lurii Mekesha (Sr Engr-Data)
Mykola Kryvenchuk (Engr-R&D)
Nataliya Vasyutyn (Project Mgr)
Sven P. Zabka (Chief Legal Officer & Exec
VP)
Svitlana Sharypina (Project Mgr)
Valerie R. Gallo-Pompa (Sr Project Mgr)
Vitaliy Gontovoi (Sr Engr-Data)
Melissa Ross (COO)
Chuck Rackley (Exec VP-Velocity Consult-
ing & HealthMobile.D Ecosystem)
Terry Blessing III (Sr VP-Client Dev)

**Acco Material Handling Solutions,
Inc.** (1)
76 Acco Dr, York, PA 17402-0792
Tel.: (717) 741-4863
Web Site: https://www.accomhs.com
Sales Range: $50-74.9 Million
Emp.: 150
Chain & Lifting Equipment Mfr
N.A.I.C.S.: 333923
David Eshelman (CFO & VP-HR)

Division (Domestic):

**Acco Material Handling Solutions,
Inc. - Nutting Division** (2)
450 Pheasant Ridge Dr, Watertown, SD
57201-5610
Tel.: (605) 882-3000
Web Site: http://www.acconutting.com

Sales Range: $1-9.9 Million
Emp.: 26
Floor Trucks, Wheels & Casters: Cargo
Carts, Pallet Trucks, Two Wheel Hand
Trucks, Custom Engineered Material Han-
dling Equipment & Contract Mfr
N.A.I.C.S.: 333924
Darla Becking (Mgr-Product)
Kevin Lemieux (Mgr-Product)

Al Futtaim Carillion (1)
Near Dubai Municipality Used Car Show-
room Complex Aweer, Dubai, 1811, United
Arab Emirates (50%)
Tel.: (971) 43331200
Web Site: http://www.afcarillion.ae
Sales Range: $1-4.9 Billion
Emp.: 24,000
Civil Engineering Contractors
N.A.I.C.S.: 237990
Richard Howson (CEO)
Simon Web (Mng Dir)

Albioma SA (1)
Tour Opus 12 77 esplanade du General de
Gaulle, La Defense, 92914, Paris, Cedex,
France (92.19%)
Tel.: (33) 147766700
Web Site: http://www.albioma.com
Rev.: $622,349,208
Assets: $2,150,648,240
Liabilities: $1,497,224,560
Net Worth: $653,423,680
Earnings: $67,921,672
Emp.: 606
Fiscal Year-end: 12/31/2020
Power Generation Services
N.A.I.C.S.: 221117
Julien Gauthier (CFO & Deputy CEO-Fin)
Pascal Langeron (COO-Reunion Island &
Mayotte)
Frederic Moyne (Chm & CEO)
Louis Decrop (COO & Head-Dev)
Xavier Becquey (Dir-Industrial)
Paul Mayer (Dir-HR)
Charlotte Neuvy (Head-Comm & Comm
Mgr)

Alchemer LLC (1)
168 Centennial Pkwy Ste 250, Louisville,
CO 80027
Tel.: (800) 609-6480
Web Site: https://www.alchemer.com
Integrated Feedback Management Platform
N.A.I.C.S.: 513210
Brandon Hodges (Chief Revenue Officer)
David Roberts (CEO)

Subsidiary (Domestic):

Apptentive, Inc. (2)
1205 Queen Anne Ave N Ste 201, Seattle,
WA 98109
Tel.: (415) 939-7143
Web Site: http://www.apptentive.com
Software Publisher
N.A.I.C.S.: 513210
Mike Saffitz (Co-Founder & CTO)
Emily Carrion (Dir-Mktg)
Charlie Morss (VP-Engrg)
Vageesh Kumar (Dir-Product Mgmt)
Marisa Nolan (VP-Sls)
Robi Ganguly (Co-founder & CEO)
Melody Jones (Dir-Engrg)
Ken Clements (VP-Mktg)
Pat Goodwin (VP-Fin & Ops)

**American Indian Health & Services
Corp.** (1)
4141 State St, Santa Barbara, CA 93110-
1814
Tel.: (805) 681-7144
Web Site: https://www.aihscorp.org
Miscellaneous Ambulatory Health Care Ser-
vices
N.A.I.C.S.: 621999

Angelica Corporation (1)
1901 S Meyers Rd Ste 630, Oakbrook Ter-
race, IL 60181
Tel.: (678) 823-4100
Web Site: https://www.angelica.com
Hospital Linen & Medical Laundry Services
N.A.I.C.S.: 812320
Carol Landry (Sr VP-Sls & Svc)

Subsidiary (Domestic):

Angelica Textile Services, Inc. (2)

1901 S Meyers Rd Ste 630, Oakbrook Ter-
race, IL 60181
Tel.: (678) 823-4100
Web Site: http://www.angelica.com
Textile Rental & Laundry Services
N.A.I.C.S.: 812331

Apex Analytix, LLC (1)
1501 Highwoods Blvd Ste 200-A, Greens-
boro, NC 27410
Tel.: (336) 272-4669
Web Site: http://www.apexanalytix.com
Rev.: $37,200,000
Emp.: 220
Software Publisher
N.A.I.C.S.: 513210
Steve Yurko (CEO)
Albert Peynsaert (Mng Dir-European Ops)
Phil Beane (Sr VP-Global Field Ops)
Derek Binnicker (Sr VP-Global Sls)
Sarah Stevens (VP-Enterprise Trng & Sup-
port)
Akhilesh Agarwal (VP-R&D)
Jason Street (VP-Retail Ops)
Danny Thompson (Sr VP-Market & Product
Strategy)

Asure Software UK Ltd. (1)
Sutherland House 3 Lloyd s Avenue
Fenchurch Street, London, EC3N 3DS,
United Kingdom
Tel.: (44) 2083289460
Web Site: http://www.asuresoftware.com
Software Development Services
N.A.I.C.S.: 541511

Subsidiary (US):

MP Pumps, Inc. (2)
34800 Bennett Dr, Fraser, MI 48026-1694
Tel.: (586) 293-8240
Web Site: http://www.mppumps.com
Pumps & Pumping Equipment Mfr
N.A.I.C.S.: 333914

Axius Water (1)
53 Portside Dr, Pocasset, MA 02559
Tel.: (866) 642-7621
Web Site: https://www.axiuswater.com
Environmental Services
N.A.I.C.S.: 541620
Chris McIntire (CEO)
Patrick Hill (Gen Mgr-Triplepoint)
Brady Galbreath-O'Leary (Gen Mgr-
Triplepoint)

Subsidiary (Domestic):

Triplepoint Environmental, LLC (2)
6586 S Kenton St, Centennial, CO 80111
Web Site: http://www.triplepointwater.com
Sales Range: $1-9.9 Million
Emp.: 8
Environmental Services
N.A.I.C.S.: 541620
Erica Velasco (Ops Mgr)

BIS Industries Limited (1)
Level 5 146 Arthur Street, North Sydney,
2060, NSW, Australia
Tel.: (61) 292456333
Web Site: http://www.bisindustries.com
Sales Range: $400-449.9 Million
Emp.: 30
Resource & Steel Industry Freight Transpor-
tation & Logistic Support Services
N.A.I.C.S.: 488510
Brad Rogers (CEO)
Graeme Hunt (Chm)

BMC Software, Inc. (1)
2103 CityWest Blvd, Houston, TX 77042-
2828
Tel.: (713) 918-2950
Web Site: https://www.bmc.com
Sales Range: Less than $1 Million
Emp.: 6,000
Software Publisher
N.A.I.C.S.: 513210
Hannah Cho (VP-Comm)
T. Cory Bleuer (Chief Acctg Officer, Sr VP &
Controller)
Patrick K. Tagtow (Chief Compliance Offi-
cer, Gen Counsel, Sec & Sr VP)
Imran Khan (Sr VP-Customer Success)
Gur Steif (Pres-Digital Bus Automation)
Jason Andrew (Sr VP-ESO America Sls)
Scott Crowder (CIO & Sr VP)
John McKenny (Sr VP-ZSolutions Strategy
& Innovation)

Michael Beaver (Sr VP-ZSolutions Sls &
Customer Success)
Eric Olmo (Sr VP-People & Spaces)
Ayman Sayed (Pres & CEO)
Ram Chakravarti (CTO)
Saar Shwartz (CMO)
Ali Siddiqui (Chief Product Officer)
Marc E. Rothman (CFO & Sr VP)
Paul Cant (Chief Revenue Officer)

Subsidiary (Non-US):

**BMC Software (Australia) Pty.
Ltd.** (2)
Level 13 383 Kent Street, Macquarie Park,
Sydney, 2000, NSW, Australia
Tel.: (61) 288992900
Sales Range: $10-24.9 Million
Emp.: 40
Systems Software Products Mfr
N.A.I.C.S.: 334610
Chris Gibbs (Mng Dir)

Branch (Domestic):

**BMC Software (Australia) Pty.
Ltd.** (3)
Level 10 Twenty 8 Freshwater Place, Mel-
bourne, 3006, VIC, Australia
Tel.: (61) 396574400
Web Site: https://www.bmc.com
Sales Range: $10-24.9 Million
Emp.: 30
Computer Software
N.A.I.C.S.: 334610

Subsidiary (Non-US):

BMC Software (China) Limited (2)
Room 502 Level 5 W1 Oriental Plaza No 1
East Chang An Ave, Dong Cheng District,
Beijing, 100738, China
Tel.: (86) 1085170600
Web Site: https://www.bmcsoftware.cn
Sales Range: $10-24.9 Million
Emp.: 25
Computer Software
N.A.I.C.S.: 334610

Branch (Domestic):

BMC Software China (3)
Unit 2101 The Platinum No 233 Taicang
Road, Huangpu District, Shanghai, 200120,
China
Tel.: (86) 2180114000
Web Site: http://www.bmc.com
Sales Range: $10-24.9 Million
Emp.: 15
Computer Software
N.A.I.C.S.: 423430

Subsidiary (Non-US):

**BMC Software (Hong Kong)
Limited** (2)
Suite 2706 27/F Devon House Taikoo Place
979 Kings Road, 979 Kings Road, Quarry
Bay, China (Hong Kong)
Tel.: (852) 25881182
Web Site: http://www.bmc.com
Sales Range: $10-24.9 Million
Emp.: 20
Systems Software Products Mfr
N.A.I.C.S.: 334610

**BMC Software (New Zealand)
Ltd.** (2)
Level 27 PWC Tower 188 Quay Street,
Auckland, 1010, New Zealand
Tel.: (64) 93632700
Web Site: http://www.bmc.com
Emp.: 5
Systems Software Product & Enterprise
Management Solution Provider
N.A.I.C.S.: 513210
Chris Gibbs (Mng Dir)

BMC Software (Thailand) Limited (2)
63 Wireless Road Level 23 Athenee Tower
Pathumwan, Lumpini, Bangkok, 10330,
Thailand
Tel.: (66) 21268065
Web Site: http://www.bmc.com
Software Development Services
N.A.I.C.S.: 541511

BMC Software A/S (2)
Lottenborgvej 24, 2800, Kongens Lyngby,
Denmark

KKR & Co. Inc.—(Continued)

Tel.: (45) 44731000
Web Site: https://www.bmc.com
Sales Range: $10-24.9 Million
Emp.: 15
Computer Softwares Mfr
N.A.I.C.S.: 334610

BMC Software AB (2)
Farogatan 33, Box 1036, 164 21, Kista,
Sweden
Tel.: (46) 854496300
Sales Range: $10-24.9 Million
Emp.: 25
Computer Software
N.A.I.C.S.: 423430

BMC Software AS (2)
Karenslyst alle 8b 3rd Floor, 0278, Oslo,
Norway
Tel.: (47) 23120500
Sales Range: $25-49.9 Million
Emp.: 10
Computer Software
N.A.I.C.S.: 423430

Branch (Domestic):

BMC Software Asia Pacific Pte. (2)
Ltd.
210 Middle Road #12-01/08, Singapore,
188994, Singapore
Tel.: (65) 63389400
Web Site: http://www.bmc.com.sg
Sales Range: $25-49.9 Million
Emp.: 85
Systems Software Products Mfr
N.A.I.C.S.: 334610

BMC Software Asia Sdn Bhd (2)
No 18 Jalan Persiaran Barat Unit E-10-27,
Petaling Jaya, Kuala Lumpur, 46050, Ma-
laysia
Tel.: (60) 35632184
Sales Range: $25-49.9 Million
Systems Software Products Mfr
N.A.I.C.S.: 334610

BMC Software Belgium NV (2)
Park Lane C Culliganlaan 2C, 1831, Di-
egem, Belgium
Tel.: (32) 27115860
Web Site: http://www.bmc.com
Sales Range: $10-24.9 Million
Emp.: 20
Prepackaged Software
N.A.I.C.S.: 334610

BMC Software Canada, Inc. (2)
50 Minthorn Blvd Suite 200, Markham, L3T
7X8, ON, Canada
Tel.: (905) 747-2800
Web Site: http://www.bmc.com
Sales Range: $100-124.9 Million
Computer Software
N.A.I.C.S.: 334610

Branch (Domestic):

BMC Software Canada (3)
1010 Sherbrooke St W Ste 1514, Montreal,
H3A 2R7, QC, Canada
Tel.: (514) 982-1000
Web Site: http://www.bmc.com
Sales Range: $25-49.9 Million
Emp.: 10
Systems Software Products Mfr
N.A.I.C.S.: 334610

Subsidiary (Non-US):

BMC Software Distribution B.V. (2)
Vision Plaza West Boeingavenue 220, 1119
PN, Schiphol-Rijk, Netherlands
Tel.: (31) 203648600
Web Site: https://www.bmc.com
Sales Range: $25-49.9 Million
Prepackaged Software Distr
N.A.I.C.S.: 423430

BMC Software Europe (2)
Building 3 The Campus Cherrywood,
Foxrock, Dublin, D18 TF72, Ireland
Tel.: (353) 14406800
Web Site: http://www.bmc.com
Sales Range: $25-49.9 Million
Design & Distribution of Software
N.A.I.C.S.: 541512

BMC Software France SAS (2)
Paris La Defense 4 - Coeur Defense 100
Esplanade du General de Gaulle, La De-
fense, 10th Floor Tower A Courbevoie,

92400, Paris, France
Tel.: (33) 157006100
Web Site: https://www.bmc.com
Sales Range: $50-74.9 Million
Emp.: 200
Computer Software
N.A.I.C.S.: 334610

BMC Software GmbH (2)
Herriotstrasse 1, Astro Park, 60528, Frank-
furt am Main, Germany
Tel.: (49) 69664060
Web Site: http://www.bmc.com
Sales Range: $25-49.9 Million
Software Developer
N.A.I.C.S.: 334610

Branch (Domestic):

BMC Software GmbH (3)
Einsteinring 31-39, Aschheim-Dornach,
85609, Munich, Germany
Tel.: (49) 899455290
Sales Range: $50-74.9 Million
Systems Software Products Mfr
N.A.I.C.S.: 334610

BMC Software GmbH (3)
Sarrazinstr 17, 12159, Berlin, Germany
Tel.: (49) 308598970
Web Site: http://www.bmc.com
Sales Range: $25-49.9 Million
Emp.: 4
Computer Software
N.A.I.C.S.: 334610

Subsidiary (Non-US):

BMC Software GmbH (2)
Handelskai 94-96 Millennium Tower 24th
Floor, 1200, Vienna, Austria
Tel.: (43) 1240800
Web Site: http://www.bmc.com
Sales Range: $10-24.9 Million
Emp.: 25
Prepackaged Software Developer
N.A.I.C.S.: 334610

BMC Software GmbH (2)
Obstgartenstrasse 29, Kloten, Kloten, 8302,
Switzerland
Tel.: (41) 432114343
Web Site: http://www.bmc.com
Sales Range: $10-24.9 Million
Emp.: 30
Systems Software Products Mfr
N.A.I.C.S.: 334610

BMC Software India Private (2)
Limited
Wing 1 Tower B Poonawala Business Bay
Survey No 103 Hissa No 2, Airport Road
Yerwada, Pune, 411006, Maharashtra, India
Tel · (91) 2040175000
Web Site: http://www.bmc.com
Sales Range: $125-149.9 Million
Software Development Services
N.A.I.C.S.: 541511

Subsidiary (Domestic):

BMC Software Investment, (2)
L.L.C.
2101 Citywest Blvd Bldg 1, Houston, TX
77042-2828
Tel.: (713) 918-8800
Software Development Services
N.A.I.C.S.: 541511

Subsidiary (Non-US):

BMC Software Ireland Limited (2)
Building 3 The Campus Cherrywood. Dub-
lin, D18 TF72, Ireland
Tel.: (353) 14406800
Web Site: http://www.bmc.com
Sales Range: $25-49.9 Million
Software Development Services
N.A.I.C.S.: 541511

BMC Software Israel Ltd. (2)
10 Habarzel St, PO Box 61581, Tel Aviv,
6158101, Israel
Tel.: (972) 36451111
Web Site: http://www.bmc.com
Sales Range: $150-199.9 Million
Emp.: 160
Computer Software
N.A.I.C.S.: 541511

BMC Software K.K. (2)

Harmony Tower 24F 1-32-2 Honcho,
Nakano-ku, Tokyo, 164-8721, Japan
Tel.: (81) 353028400
Web Site: https://www.bmcsoftware.jp
Computer Softwares Mfr
N.A.I.C.S.: 334610

BMC Software Korea, Ltd. (2)
9 FL Two IFC 10 Gukjekeumyung-ro,
Yeongdeungpo-gu, Seoul, 07326, Korea
(South)
Tel.: (82) 260010100
Web Site: http://www.bmc.com
Sales Range: $10-24.9 Million
Emp.: 30
Prepackaged Software
N.A.I.C.S.: 334610

BMC Software Limited (2)
1020 Eskdale Road 2nd Floor, Vicarage
Road, Winnersh, RG41 5TS, Berkshire,
United Kingdom
Tel.: (44) 1189218000
Sales Range: $50-74.9 Million
Computer Software
N.A.I.C.S.: 334610

BMC Software Oy (2)
Ayritie 12 C 5 krs, 1510, Vantaa, Finland
Tel.: (358) 9540670
Web Site: http://www.bmc.com
Sales Range: $25-49.9 Million
Emp.: 6
Systems Software Products Distr
N.A.I.C.S.: 423430

BMC Software S.A. (2)
Camino Cerro de los Gamos 1 Edificio 3,
Pozuelo de Alarcon, E 28224, Madrid,
Spain
Tel.: (34) 917099000
Sales Range: $25-49.9 Million
Emp.: 100
Computer Software
N.A.I.C.S.: 334610
Mirella Jimenez (Mgr-HR)

Branch (Domestic):

BMC Software S.A. (3)
Gran Via Business & Meeting Center, Gran
Via 630 4th Floor, Barcelona, 08007, Spain
Tel.: (34) 934 458 309
Sales Range: $25-49.9 Million
Systems Software Products Mfr
N.A.I.C.S.: 334610

Subsidiary (Non-US):

BMC Software S.r.l. (2)
Via Angelo Scarsellini No 14 Light Building
10th Floor, 20161, Milan, Italy
Tel.: (39) 02607351
Web Site: https://www.bmc.com
Sales Range: $10-24.9 Million
Emp.: 45
Computer Software
N.A.I.C.S.: 334610

Branch (Domestic):

BMC Software S.r.l. (3)
Via del Serafico 200, 144, Rome, Italy
Tel.: (39) 06515701
Web Site: http://www.bmc.com
Sales Range: $10-24.9 Million
Emp.: 15
Systems Software Products Mfr
N.A.I.C.S.: 334610

Subsidiary (Non-US):

BMC Software Sales (Poland) Sp. (2)
o.o.
Zlota 59 lok 625-626, Mazowieckie, 00-120,
Warsaw, Poland
Tel.: (48) 69664060
Web Site: http://www.bmc.com
Software Development Services
N.A.I.C.S.: 541511

BMC Software de Argentina S.A. (2)
Ing Butty 220 Fl 18, Capital Federal, Bue-
nos Aires, C1001AFB, Argentina
Tel.: (54) 11 5776 7500
Sales Range: $10-24.9 Million
Emp.: 30
Systems Software Products Mfr
N.A.I.C.S.: 334610
Jader Carrique (VP)

BMC Software de Mexico, S.A. de (2)
C.V.
Volcan 150 Col II Seccion Del Miguel Hi-
dalgo Ciudad De, Lomas de Chapultepec,
11000, Mexico, Mexico
Tel.: (52) 5552845700
Web Site: http://www.bmc.com
Software Development Services
N.A.I.C.S.: 541511

BMC Software do Brasil Ltda. (2)
Avenida das Nacoes Unidas 8501 Fl 22,
Sao Paulo, 05425-070, SP, Brazil
Tel.: (55) 11 2183 6000
Web Site: http://www.bmc.com
Sales Range: $10-24.9 Million
Emp.: 60
Systems Software Products Mfr
N.A.I.C.S.: 334610

Subsidiary (Domestic):

Compuware Corporation (2)
1 Campus Martius, Detroit, MI 48226-5099
Tel.: (313) 227-7300
Web Site: http://www.compuware.com
Data Processing, Professional Services &
System Software Products Mfr
N.A.I.C.S.: 513210
Christopher O'Malley (CEO)

Subsidiary (Non-US):

Compuware S.A. (3)
Paseo de la Castellana 95-15 Torre Europa,
28046, Madrid, Spain
Tel.: (34) 910851820
Applications Software Programming Ser-
vices
N.A.I.C.S.: 541511

Compuware Software Group Pty. (3)
Ltd.
Level 19 1 OConnell Street, Sydney, 2000,
NSW, Australia (100%)
Tel.: (61) 2 8249 8857
Web Site: http://www.compuware.com
Mainframe Computer Management Services
N.A.I.C.S.: 541511
Chris O'Malley (CEO)

Dynatrace A/S (3)
Frederiksborggade 15, 1360, Copenhagen,
Denmark
Tel.: (45) 44209000
Applications Software Programming Ser-
vices
N.A.I.C.S.: 541511

Dynatrace BV (3)
Ikaroslaan 21, 1930, Zaventem, Belgium
Tel.: (32) 27159900
Web Site: https://www.dynatrace.com
Sales Range: $25-49.9 Million
Emp.: 25
Applications Software Programming Ser-
vices
N.A.I.C.S.: 541511
Geert Speltincx (Mng Dir)

Dynatrace Finland Oy (3)
Aleksanterinkatu 15-B 6th Floor, 00100,
Helsinki, Finland
Tel.: (358) 400384399
Web Site: https://www.dynatrace.com
Applications Software Programming Ser-
vices
N.A.I.C.S.: 541511

Dynatrace Limited (3)
Quantum 60 Norden Road, Maidenhead,
SL6 4AY, Berkshire, United Kingdom
Tel.: (44) 1020010000
Web Site: https://www.dynatrace.com
Applications Software Programming Ser-
vices
N.A.I.C.S.: 541511

Dynatrace SARL (3)
27/33 Quai Alphonse Le Gallo, 92100,
Boulogne-Billancourt, France
Tel.: (33) 42610955
Web Site: https://www.dynatrace.com
Applications Software Programming Ser-
vices
N.A.I.C.S.: 541511

Subsidiary (Domestic):

Standardware Inc. (3)
424 Pelham Manor Rd, Pelham, NY 10803

Tel.: (914) 738-6382
Web Site: http://www.standardware.com
Custom Online Programming Services
N.A.I.C.S.: 513210
David Evans (Owner)

Subsidiary (Non-US):

Coradiant (Canada) Inc. (2)
1100 Rue De La Gauchetiere O Bureau
C-25, Montreal, H3B 2S2, QC, Canada
Tel.: (514) 908-6300
Software Development Services
N.A.I.C.S.: 541511

MQSoftware GmbH Middleware
Solutions (2)
Sarrazinstr 17, Berlin, 12159, Germany
Tel.: (49) 308598970
Software Development Services
N.A.I.C.S.: 541511

Numara Software (France) SAS (2)
16 Rue de Solferino, 92100, Boulogne-sur-
Mer, France
Tel.: (33) 146109380
Web Site: http://www.numarasoftware.fr
Software Development Services
N.A.I.C.S.: 541511

Numara Software Limited (2)
The Innovation CentreÂ 1 Devon Way,
Longbridge Technology Park, Birmingham,
B31 2TS, United Kingdom
Tel.: (44) 1189000900
Web Site: http://www.numarasoftware.co.uk
Software Development Services
N.A.I.C.S.: 541511

Simulus Limited (2)
Corinthian Court 80 Milton Park, Abingdon,
OX14 4RY, United Kingdom
Tel.: (44) 1235827400
Software Development Services
N.A.I.C.S.: 541511

Subsidiary (Domestic):

Software Credit LP (2)
2101 Citywest Blvd, Houston, TX 77042-
2829
Tel.: (713) 918-1928
Systems Software Product & Enterprise
Management Solution Provider
N.A.I.C.S.: 513210

Streamweaver, Inc. (2)
4322 Harding Pike Ste 417, Nashville, TN
37205
Tel.: (615) 541-5273
Web Site: http://www.streamweaver.com
Software Publisher
N.A.I.C.S.: 513210
Jamin Guy (Dir-Product Dev)

BOASSO Global, Inc. (1)
615 Channelside Dr. Ste 206, Tampa, FL
33602
Tel.: (813) 797-3271
Web Site: https://www.boassoglobal.com
Transportation, Logistics, Supply Chain &
Storage
N.A.I.C.S.: 336999

Subsidiary (Domestic):

Linden Bulk Transportation Co.,
LLC (2)
4200 Tremley Point Rd, Linden, NJ 07036
Tel.: (908) 862-3883
Web Site: http://www.lindenbulk.com
Sales Range: $75-99.9 Million
Emp.: 142
Commoditie Chemical & Intermodal Tank
Warehousing & Transportation Distr
N.A.I.C.S.: 484121
Michael Salz (Pres)
John Malgieri (VP-Sls)

Subsidiary (Domestic):

Linden Warehouse & Distribution Co.,
Inc. (3)
1300 Lower Rd, Linden, NJ 07036 (100%)
Tel.: (908) 862-1400
Web Site: http://www.lindenwarehouse.com
Sales Range: $25-49.9 Million
General & Hazardous Commodities &
Chemicals Warehousing & Distribution Ser-
vices
N.A.I.C.S.: 493110

Jared Stadlin (VP-Client Svcs)

Subsidiary (Domestic):

QualaWash Holdings, LLC (2)
500 N Westshore Blvd Ste 435, Tampa, FL
33609
Tel.: (813) 321-6485
Web Site: http://www.quala.us.com
Bulk Container Cleaning & Maintenance
Services
N.A.I.C.S.: 811310
Terry O'Brien (Pres)
Erik Leto (COO)
Paul Woodbury (VP-HR)
Eric Speiser (Exec VP-Sls & Mktg)
Jason Carney (VP-IT)
John Jolly (Exec VP-Industrial Svcs)
Scott Harrison (CEO)
Scott Harris (CFO)
Amit Mohanty (Chief Transformation Officer)

Subsidiary (Domestic):

Alpha Technical Services
Corporation (3)
5100 Underwood Rd, Pasadena, TX 77507
Tel.: (281) 291-7453
Web Site: http://www.alphatechserv.com
Industrial Cleaning & Hazardous Waste Dis-
posal Services
N.A.I.C.S.: 562211
Andy Lyons (VP-Admin)
Jim Robbins (Mgr-HSE)
Mike Howerton (Pres)
Steve Dodds (VP-Ops)
Steve Martin (VP-Sls & Mktg)
Moe Barbarawi (CIO & Officer-Process)
Lynda Goldstein (Mgr-HR)

Barracuda Networks, Inc. (1)
3175 S Winchester Blvd, Campbell, CA
95008
Tel.: (408) 342-5400
Web Site: http://www.barracuda.com
Security Appliances Email, Internet & IM
Protection
N.A.I.C.S.: 561621
William D. Jenkins Jr. (Pres)
Diane C. Honda (Chief Admin Officer & Gen
Counsel)
Zachary S. Levow (Founder, CTO & Exec
VP)
Brian Babineau (Sr VP & Gen Mgr-
Barracuda MSP)
Hossein Ghazizadeh (Sr VP-Worldwide
Customer Support & Success)
Ken Martin (Sr VP-Worldwide Mfg Ops)
Rod Mathews (Sr VP-Corp Dev & Aliances)
Chris Ross (Chief Revenue Officer)
Dustin Driggs (CFO)
Erin Hintz (CMO & Sr VP)
Fleming Shi (CTO)
Simon Yeo (Sr VP-Global Ops & Infrastruc-
ture)
Jason Beal (VP-Worldwide Partner Ecosys-
tems)
Hatem H. Naguib (Pres & CEO)

Subsidiary (Domestic):

Barracuda MSP (2)
100 Apollo Dr, Chelmsford, MA 01824
Tel.: (978) 328-1680
Web Site: https://www.barracudamsp.com
Online Backup Software Service
N.A.I.C.S.: 513210

Subsidiary (Non-US):

Barracuda Networks (Hong Kong)
Limited (2)
Level 19 Two International Finance Centre
8 Finance Street, Central, China (Hong
Kong)
Tel.: (852) 30023718
Software Development Services
N.A.I.C.S.: 513210

Barracuda Networks (India) Private
Limited (2)
Dairy Colony Adugodi, Bengaluru, 560029,
Karnataka, India
Tel.: (91) 8049048600
Software Development Services
N.A.I.C.S.: 513210

Barracuda Networks AG (2)
Eduard-Bodem-Gasse 1, 6020, Innsbruck,
Austria

Tel.: (43) 508 100
Web Site:
   http://www.barracudanetworksag.com
Communications IT Security Technologies
N.A.I.C.S.: 541511
Klaus Gheri (VP-Product Mgmt)

Barracuda Networks Japan, K.K. (2)
8 Chome Building 5th Fl 8-3-16 Nishigo-
tanda, Shinagawa-ku, Tokyo, 141-0031,
Japan
Tel.: (81) 17910524
Web Site: http://www.barracuda.co.jp
Email, Internet & IM Product Security Appli-
ances
N.A.I.C.S.: 561621
Daizo Ohkoshi (Exec Dir)

Barracuda Networks Singapore PTE
LTD. (2)
8 Temasek Boulevard Level 42 Suntec
Tower Three, 038988, Singapore, Singa-
pore
Tel.: (65) 69290970
Software Development Services
N.A.I.C.S.: 513210

Barracuda Networks Technology Co.
Ltd. (2)
4F Building 2 Shanghai New Withub, S&T
Creation Center No 799 Hutai Road,
Shanghai, 200072, China
Tel.: (86) 2151810518
Email, Internet & IM Product Security Appli-
ances
N.A.I.C.S.: 561621

Barracuda Networks, Limited (2)
Brunel House Stephenson Road, Basings-
toke, RG21 6XR, United Kingdom
Tel.: (44) 1256300100
Software Development Services
N.A.I.C.S.: 513210

Bettcher Industries Inc. (1)
6801 State Rte 60, Birmingham, OH 44889
Tel.: (440) 965-4422
Web Site: https://www.bettcher.com
Sales Range: $25-49.9 Million
Emp.: 150
Food Products Machinery
N.A.I.C.S.: 333241
Paul Pirozzola (VP-Mktg)
Peter Taft (Chm)

Subsidiary (Non-US):

Frontmatec Group ApS (2)
Albuen 37, 6000, Kolding, Denmark
Tel.: (45) 76342700
Web Site: https://www.frontmatec.com
Sales Range: $150-199.9 Million
Emp.: 840
Holding Company; Food Industry Equip-
ment & Solutions Designer, Mfr & Whslr
N.A.I.C.S.: 551112
Henrik Andersen (CEO)

Subsidiary (Domestic):

Carometec A/S (3)
Hasselunden 9, 2765, Smorum, Denmark
Tel.: (45) 44503700
Web Site: http://www.carometec.com
Commercial Meat Carcass Grading & Qual-
ity Control Equipment Mfr & Distr
N.A.I.C.S.: 334513

Subsidiary (Non-US):

Carometec S.L. (4)
Calle Carretera 67, 08650, Sallent, Spain
Tel.: (34) 938380835
Web Site: http://www.carometec.net
Commercial Meat Carcass Grading & Qual-
ity Control Equipment Distr
N.A.I.C.S.: 423440

Subsidiary (Non-US):

Frontmatec Hygiene GmbH (3)
Auf dem Tigge 60 b c, 59269, Beckum,
Germany
Tel.: (49) 252185070
Web Site: https://www.itec-hygiene.com
Emp.: 85
Hygiene Systems & Other Food Industry
Equipment Developer, Mfr & Whslr
N.A.I.C.S.: 333241
Petra Pawlewski-Voge (Sec)

Subsidiary (Domestic):

Frontmatec Kolding A/S (3)
Platinvej 8, PO Box 69, 6000, Kolding, Den-
mark
Tel.: (45) 76342700
Web Site: http://www.sfkleblanc.com
Sales Range: $75-99.9 Million
Emp.: 487
Animal Slaughtering & Meat Processing
Equipment Mfr & Whslr
N.A.I.C.S.: 333248

Subsidiary (Non-US):

Frontmatec B.V. (4)
Butaanstraat 22a, 7463 PG, Rijssen, Neth-
erlands
Tel.: (31) 886294000
Web Site: http://www.frontmatec.com
Animal Slaughtering & Meat Processing
Equipment Mfr & Whslr
N.A.I.C.S.: 333248

Subsidiary (Domestic):

Frontmatec Skive A/S (3)
Osterbro 5, 7800, Skive, Denmark
Tel.: (45) 97525022
Web Site: http://www.frontmatec.com
Industrial Food Processing Automation
Equipment Mfr
N.A.I.C.S.: 333241
Stuart McBride (Sls Mgr)

Frontmatec Tandslet A/S (3)
Mommarkvej 293-301, Tandslet Sydals,
6470, Sonderborg, Denmark
Tel.: (45) 74407644
Web Site: http://www.attec.dk
Emp.: 150
Slaughterhouse Automated Cutting, Debon-
ing & Storage Systems Mfr
N.A.I.C.S.: 333241

Subsidiary (Non-US):

MHM Automation Limited (2)
53 Lunns Road, Middleton, Christchurch,
New Zealand
Tel.: (64) 33487039
Web Site: http://www.mercers.co.nz
Rev.: $25,543,184
Assets: $16,162,544
Liabilities: $13,874,665
Net Worth: $2,287,879
Earnings: ($692,728)
Emp.: 145
Fiscal Year-end: 06/30/2019
Stainless Steel Products Mfr
N.A.I.C.S.: 331221
Ian McGregor (CFO)
Mike Lee (Gen Mgr-H&C)

Subsidiary (Domestic):

Mercer Stainless Limited (3)
53 Lunns Road, PO Box 6020,
Christchurch, 8442, New Zealand
Tel.: (64) 33487039
Web Site: http://www.mercerstainless.com
Stainless Steel Products Mfr
N.A.I.C.S.: 331210

Borden Dairy Company (1)
8750 N Central Expy Ste 400, Dallas, TX
75231
Tel.: (214) 526-2653
Web Site: http://www.bordendairy.com
Holding Company; Dairy & Milk Production
N.A.I.C.S.: 551112
Lazzy Oroza (Gen Mgr)

Subsidiary (Domestic):

Borden Dairy Company of
Florida (2)
308 Avenue G SW, Winter Haven, FL
33880-3433
Tel.: (863) 297-7300
Web Site: http://www.bordenonline.com
Sales Range: $150-199.9 Million
Processing, Distribution & Sale of Milk &
Dairy Products
N.A.I.C.S.: 311511
Tim Long (Controller)
Michael Lasky (Gen Mgr)

Coburg Dairy (2)
5001 LaCross Rd, North Charleston, SC
29406

KKR & Co. Inc.—(Continued)

Tel.: (843) 554-4870
Web Site: http://www.bordendairy.com
Sales Range: $75-99.9 Million
Milk & Milk By-Products Processor
N.A.I.C.S.: 311511

H. Meyer Dairy (2)
415 John St, Cincinnati, OH 45215-5481
Tel.: (513) 948-8811
Sales Range: $25-49.9 Million
N.A.I.C.S.: 311511
Tim Alger (Mgr-HR)

Milk Products, L.P. (2)
5327 S Lamar St, Dallas, TX 75215-4972
Tel.: (214) 565-0332
Sales Range: $350-399.9 Million
Mfr of Milk & Dairy Products
N.A.I.C.S.: 311520
William Charters (CFO)

Plant (Domestic):

Borden Milk Products (3)
71 Strandtman Cove, Austin, TX 78702-5100
Tel.: (512) 385-2100
Web Site: http://www.milkproductslp.com
Sales Range: $100-124.9 Million
Emp.: 270
Dairy Products
N.A.I.C.S.: 311511
Ruben Morales (Chief Engr)
Craig Nguyen (Mgr-Production)

BrightView Landscapes, LLC (1)
24151 Ventura Blvd, Calabasas, CA 91302
Tel.: (818) 223-8500
Web Site: http://www.brightview.com
Landscape Development & Maintenance Services
N.A.I.C.S.: 541320
Thomas C. Donnelly (Pres-Dev Svcs)

CIRCOR International, Inc. (1)
30 Corporate Dr Ste 200, Burlington, MA 01803-4238
Tel.: (781) 270-1200
Web Site: https://www.circor.com
Rev.: $786,919,000
Assets: $1,012,687,000
Liabilities: $853,641,000
Net Worth: $159,046,000
Earnings: $19,388,000
Emp.: 3,060
Fiscal Year-end: 12/31/2022
Designs, Manufactures & Supplies Valves & Related Products & Services
N.A.I.C.S.: 332919
Joseph Losak (Principal Acctg Officer, VP-Fin & Controller)
Dan Daniel (Chm)

Subsidiary (Domestic):

CIRCOR Aerospace, Inc. (2)
2301 Wardlow Cir, Corona, CA 92878
Tel.: (951) 270-6200
Web Site: http://www.circoraerospace.com
Sales Range: $25-49.9 Million
Emp.: 235
Valves & Controls for Aerospace, Military & Industrial Applications Mfr
N.A.I.C.S.: 332911

Subsidiary (Domestic):

CIRCOR Aerospace (3)
2301 Wardlow Cir, Corona, CA 92880-2881
Tel.: (951) 270-6200
Web Site: http://www.circoraerospace.com
Sales Range: $50-74.9 Million
Precision Machining Mfr
N.A.I.C.S.: 333517

CIRCOR Instrumentation Technologies, Inc. (3)
405 Centura Ct, Spartanburg, SC 29303-6603
Tel.: (864) 574-7966
Web Site: https://hoke.com
Fluid Power Valve & Hose Fitting Mfr
N.A.I.C.S.: 332912

Subsidiary (Domestic):

Dopak Inc. (4)
4540 S Pinemont Ste 118, Houston, TX 77041

Tel.: (713) 460-8311
Web Site: https://www.dopak.com
Emp.: 4
Industrial Supplies Whslr
N.A.I.C.S.: 423840

Subsidiary (Non-US):

CIRCOR Dovianus Holdings B.V. (2)
Leeuwenhoekweg 24, 2661 CZ, Bergschenhoek, Netherlands
Tel.: (31) 105242000
Industrial Equipment Distr
N.A.I.C.S.: 423830

CIRCOR Energy Products (Canada) ULC (2)
9430-39th Avenue, Edmonton, T6E 5T3, AB, Canada
Tel.: (780) 463-8633
Sales Range: $25-49.9 Million
Emp.: 2
Industrial Supplies Whslr
N.A.I.C.S.: 423840

Subsidiary (Domestic):

CIRCOR Energy Products, Inc (2)
1500 SE 89th St, Oklahoma City, OK 73149
Tel.: (405) 631-1533
Web Site: http://www.circor.com
Emp.: 100
Industrial Pattern Mfr
N.A.I.C.S.: 332999

Subsidiary (Non-US):

CIRCOR Maroc SARL A.U. (2)
ILot n 23 Lots n 4, Tangiers, 90000, Morocco
Tel.: (212) 538800054
Aerospace Component Mfr
N.A.I.C.S.: 336413

Subsidiary (Domestic):

CIRCOR Naval Solutions, LLC (2)
82 Bridges Ave, Warren, MA 01083-0969
Tel.: (413) 436-7711
Web Site: http://www.warrenpumps.com
Industrial Products Mfr
N.A.I.C.S.: 333996

CIRCOR Pumping Technologies (2)
1710 Airport Rd, Monroe, NC 28110
Tel.: (704) 289-6511
Web Site: http://www.circor.com
Fuel, Lube Oil, Elevator & Hydraulic Pumps Mfr
N.A.I.C.S.: 336412

Subsidiary (Non-US):

Allwoilor GmbH (3)
Allweiler Strasse 1, 78315, Radolfzell, Germany
Tel.: (49) 7732860
Web Site: https://www.allweiler.de
Pump & Pumping Equipment Mfr
N.A.I.C.S.: 333914

Subsidiary (Non-US):

Allweiler A/S (4)
Nye Vakaasvei 4 N-1, 1395, Hvalstad, Norway
Tel.: (47) 66775050
Web Site: https://www.allweiler.no
Pump & Pumping Equipment Mfr
N.A.I.C.S.: 333914
Matthias Probian (CEO)

Allweiler Finland Oy AR (4)
Karkikuja 3, 01740, Vantaa, Finland
Tel.: (358) 95655880
Web Site: http://www.allweiler.fi
Industrial Valve Distr
N.A.I.C.S.: 423830

Subsidiary (Domestic):

CIRCOR Naval Solutions, LLC (3)
82 Bridge Ave, Warren, MA 01083-0969
Tel.: (413) 436-7711
Web Site: http://www.warrenpumps.com
Pumps Mfr
N.A.I.C.S.: 333914

Subsidiary (Non-US):

Houttuin B.V. (3)

Sluisstraat 12, 7491 GA, Delden, Netherlands
Tel.: (31) 881030400
Web Site: http://www.houttuin.nl
Pump & Pumping Equipment Mfr
N.A.I.C.S.: 333914

Subsidiary (Domestic):

Imo Industries Inc. (3)
1710 Airport Rd, Monroe, NC 28110
Tel.: (704) 289-6511
Web Site: http://www.imo-pump.com
Fuel, Lube Oil, Elevator & Hydraulic Pumps Mfr
N.A.I.C.S.: 333914

Subsidiary (Non-US):

Sicelub Colombia Ltda. (3)
Carrera 68 5 93, Bogota, Colombia
Tel.: (57) 56676439
Web Site: http://www.sicelub.com
Fan & Compressor Mfr
N.A.I.C.S.: 333413

Sicelub Iberico S.L. (3)
Calle Bratislava 65, 30353, Murcia, Cartagena, Spain
Tel.: (34) 968541042
Fan & Compressor Mfr
N.A.I.C.S.: 333413

Unit (Domestic):

Zenith Corporation (3)
1710 Airport Rd, Monroe, NC 28110
Tel.: (704) 289-6511
Web Site: https://www.zenithpumps.com
Precision Gear Metering Pumps & Systems Mfr
N.A.I.C.S.: 336413

Subsidiary (Domestic):

CIRCOR, Inc. (2)
30 Corporate Dr Ste 200, Burlington, MA 01803-4232
Tel.: (781) 270-1200
Web Site: http://www.circor.com
Sales Range: $25-49.9 Million
Emp.: 40
Fluid Power Valve & Hose Fitting Mfr
N.A.I.C.S.: 332912

Hoke, Inc. (2)
405 Centura CT, Spartanburg, SC 29303-6603
Tel.: (864) 574-7966
Web Site: https://www.hoke.com
Sales Range: $50-74.9 Million
Emp.: 500
Fluid Controls Mfr
N.A.I.C.S.: 332912

KF Industries, Inc. (2)
1500 SE 89th St, Oklahoma City, OK 73149-4607 **(100%)**
Tel.: (405) 631-1533
Web Site: http://www.circorenergy.com
Sales Range: $125-149.9 Million
Emp.: 300
Mfr of Valves
N.A.I.C.S.: 332919

Leslie Controls, Inc. (2)
12501 Telecom Dr, Tampa, FL 33637
Tel.: (813) 978-1000
Web Site: http://www.lesliecontrols.com
Sales Range: $150-199.9 Million
Mfr of Regulators, Control Valves, Control Instrumentation, Steam Water Heaters & Air Whistles
N.A.I.C.S.: 332911

Subsidiary (Non-US):

Pipeline Engineering LTD (2)
Gatherley Road Catterick Bridge, Richmond, DL10 7JQ, North Yorkshire, United Kingdom
Tel.: (44) 1748813000
Web Site: http://www.pipelineengineering.com
Emp.: 60
Metalworking Machines Mfr
N.A.I.C.S.: 333519
Allan Mather (Mng Dir)

SCHROEDAHL-ARAPP Spezialarmaturen GmbH & Co. KG (2)

Alte Schonenbacher Str 4, Mittelagger, 51580, Reichshof, Germany
Tel.: (49) 226599270
Web Site: http://www.schroedahl.de
Industrial Equipment Mfr
N.A.I.C.S.: 332911
Roger Ingemey (Mng Dir & Member-Mgmt Bd)

TapcoEnpro UK Limited (2)
Shawfield Road, Carlton Industrial Estate, Barnsley, S71 3HS, United Kingdom
Tel.: (44) 1226323160
Web Site: https://www.tapcoenpro.com
Industrial Equipment Mfr
N.A.I.C.S.: 332911

Cardenas Market, LLC (1)
2501 E Guasti Rd, Ontario, CA 91761
Tel.: (909) 923-7426
Web Site: https://www.cardenasmarkets.com
Fresh Product Store
N.A.I.C.S.: 445298
John Gomez (CEO)

Chase Corporation (1)
375 University Ave, Westwood, MA 02090
Tel.: (781) 332-0700
Web Site: https://www.chasecorp.com
Rev.: $293,336,000
Assets: $404,159,000
Liabilities: $59,835,000
Net Worth: $344,324,000
Earnings: $44,920,000
Emp.: 661
Fiscal Year-end: 08/31/2021
Protective Materials for Electrical Cables, Steel Highway Bridges, Underground Pipelines & Printed Circuitry & Conformal Coatings for Electronics Systems
N.A.I.C.S.: 335999
Adam P. Chase (Pres & CEO)
Jeffery D. Haigh (Gen Counsel, Sec & VP)
Lance Reisman (Chm)

Subsidiary (Non-US):

ABchimie (2)
1230 Route de la Porte ZA La Rivoire, Corbelin, 38630, Isere, France
Tel.: (33) 474831219
Electronic Circuit Mfr & Distr
N.A.I.C.S.: 334419

Subsidiary (Domestic):

C.I.M. Industries, Inc. (2)
23 Elm St, Peterborough, NH 03458
Tel.: (603) 924-9481
Web Site: http://www.chasecorp.com
Sales Range: $25-49.9 Million
Emp.: 12
Industrial Lining & Coating Systems Mfr
N.A.I.C.S.: 324122

Division (Domestic):

Chase & Sons Division (2)
295 University Ave, Westwood, MA 02090 **(100%)**
Tel.: (781) 963-2600
Web Site: http://www.chasecorp.com
Sales Range: $75-99.9 Million
Emp.: 45
Mfr Of Insulating & Semi-Conductive Tapes For Power & Telecommunications Cables
N.A.I.C.S.: 314910
Adam P. Chase (Pres & COO)

Chase Corporation - Pittsburgh (2)
128 1st St, Pittsburgh, PA 15238
Tel.: (412) 828-1500
Web Site: http://www.chasecorp.com
Industrial Coatings & Tapes Mfr
N.A.I.C.S.: 325211
Adam P. Chase (Pres & CEO)

Subsidiary (Non-US):

Chase Protective Coatings Limited (2)
Harbour Road, Rye, TN31 7TE, East Sussex, United Kingdom
Tel.: (44) 1797223561
Sales Range: $25-49.9 Million
Emp.: 30
Waterproofing & Corrosion Protection Systems Mfr
N.A.I.C.S.: 237120
Paul Barkley (Dir-Sls & Ops)

Division (Domestic):

Fluid Polymers (2)
201 Zeta Dr, Pittsburgh, PA 15238-3223
Tel.: (412) 828-0232
Web Site: http://www.fluidpolymers.com
Sales Range: $25-49.9 Million
Emp.: 100
Mfr of Solventless Sealants, Adhesives,
Coatings & Dialectric Materials for Fluid Pu-
rification, Construction & Wire & Cable In-
dustries
N.A.I.C.S.: 325211

Subsidiary (Non-US):

HumiSeal India Private Limited (2)
J-154 M I D C Bhosari Industrial Estate,
Pune, 411026, Maharashtra, India
Tel.: (91) 2066308098
Protective Coatings Mfr
N.A.I.C.S.: 325510
Bhavesh Joshi *(Mgr-Production)*

Subsidiary (Domestic):

NEPTCO Incorporated (2)
30 Hamlet St, Pawtucket, RI 02861
Tel.: (401) 722-5500
Web Site: http://www.neptco.com
Sales Range: $50-74.9 Million
Emp.: 150
Woven Wire Products Mfr
N.A.I.C.S.: 332618
Guy Marini *(Pres)*

Resin Designs, LLC (2)
11 State St, Woburn, MA
01801-2050 (100%)
Tel.: (781) 935-3133
Web Site: http://www.resindesigns.com
Sales Range: $10-24.9 Million
Emp.: 30
Develops & Manufactures Custom Adhe-
sives & Fabricated Silicones
N.A.I.C.S.: 325520

Stewart Superabsorbents, LLC (2)
1954 Main Ave SE, Hickory, NC 28602
Tel.: (828) 632-5664
Web Site: http://chasecorp.com
Other Chemical & Allied Products Merchant
Whslr
N.A.I.C.S.: 424690

Division (Domestic):

TapeCoat Company (2)
1527 Lyons St, Evanston, IL 60201-3551
Tel.: (847) 866-8500
Web Site: http://www.tapecoat.com
Sales Range: $25-49.9 Million
Emp.: 50
Mfr of Miscellaneous Plastic Products, Flex-
ible Film Packaging, Laminating & Adhesive
Coatings; Corrosion Prevention Products;
Packaging Products
N.A.I.C.S.: 322220

Cloudera, Inc. (1)
5470 Great America Pkwy, Santa Clara, CA
95054
Tel.: (650) 362-0488
Web Site: http://www.cloudera.com
Rev.: $869,258,000
Assets: $2,508,601,000
Liabilities: $1,380,671,000
Net Worth: $1,127,930,000
Earnings: ($162,734,000)
Emp.: 2,728
Fiscal Year-end: 01/31/2021
Business & Financial Data Management
Software Development Services
N.A.I.C.S.: 541511
Kevin Cook *(VP-Corp Dev & IR)*
Amr Awadallah *(Founder)*
Mick Hollison *(Pres)*
Scott Aronson *(COO)*
Scott Reasoner *(Chief Acctg Officer)*
Arun C. Murthy *(Chief Product Officer)*
Bob Mahan *(Chief HR Officer)*

Subsidiary (Non-US):

**Cloudera (Shanghai) Software Co.
Ltd.** (2)
Shanghai Mart Office Tower Floor 26 Suite
2612 No 2299, Yan'an Road, Shanghai,
200336, China
Tel.: (86) 2162369001

Software Development Services
N.A.I.C.S.: 541511

Cloudera (UK) Limited (2)
30 Old Broad Street 5th Floor, London,
EC2N 1HT, United Kingdom
Tel.: (44) 2038261405
Software Development Services
N.A.I.C.S.: 541511

Cloudera GmbH (2)
Birketweg 31, 80639, Munich, Germany
Tel.: (49) 22165078699
Software Development Services
N.A.I.C.S.: 541511

Cloudera Hungary Kft. (2)
Roosevelt Building Szechenyi Istvan ter 7-8
level 7, 1051, Budapest, Hungary
Tel.: (36) 17011201
Software Development Services
N.A.I.C.S.: 541511

Cloudera Inc. (2)
81 Rivington Street, London, EC2A 3AY,
United Kingdom
Tel.: (44) 203 178 4857
Software Publisher
N.A.I.C.S.: 513210

Cloudera K.K. (2)
26th Floor Kyobashi Edogrand Kyobashi
2-2-1, Chuo-ku, Tokyo, 104-0031, Japan
Tel.: (81) 367481506
Web Site: http://www.cloudera.com
Software Publisher
N.A.I.C.S.: 513210

Cloudera Korea, Inc. (2)
41/F Gangnam Finance Center 152
Teheran-ro, Gangnam-gu, Seoul, 06236,
Korea (South)
Tel.: (82) 220084595
Software Development Services
N.A.I.C.S.: 541511

Subsidiary (Domestic):

Hortonworks Inc. (2)
5470 Great America Pkwy, Santa Clara, CA
95054
Tel.: (408) 916-4121
Web Site: http://www.hortonworks.com
Rev.: $261,810,000
Assets: $250,733,000
Liabilities: $315,769,000
Net Worth: ($65,036,000)
Earnings: ($204,507,000)
Emp.: 1,175
Fiscal Year-end: 12/31/2017
Software Developer
N.A.I.C.S.: 513210
Paul A. Krieger *(Mgr-Revenue)*

Subsidiary (Domestic):

Agniv, Inc. (3)
7100 Stevenson Blvd, Fremont, CA 94538-
2485
Tel.: (510) 585-3289
Business Support Services
N.A.I.C.S.: 561499

**Colonial First State Investments
Limited** (1)
11 Harbour Street, Sydney, 2000, NSW,
Australia (55%)
Tel.: (61) 293033000
Web Site:
http://www.colonialfirststate.com.au
Sales Range: $350-399.9 Million
Emp.: 1,000
Investment Services
N.A.I.C.S.: 523150
Nicolette Rubinsztein *(Gen Mgr-Retirement)*
Steve McGregor *(Gen Mgr-IT)*
Linda Elkins *(Exec Gen Mgr-Mktg)*

Subsidiary (Non-US):

**First Sentier Investors (Hong Kong)
Limited** (2)
Level 25 One Exchange Square, Central,
China (Hong Kong)
Tel.: (852) 28467555
Web Site:
https://www.firstsentierinvestors.com
Financial Management Services
N.A.I.C.S.: 523999

**First Sentier Investors
(Singapore)** (2)
79 Robinson Road 17-01, CapitaSky, Sin-
gapore, 068897, Singapore
Tel.: (65) 65380008
Web Site:
https://www.firstsentierinvestors.com
Emp.: 50
Investment Management Service
N.A.I.C.S.: 523999

**First Sentier Investors (UK) Funds
Limited** (2)
Finsbury Circus House 15 Finsbury Circus,
London, EC2M 7EB, United Kingdom
Tel.: (44) 2073326500
Web Site:
https://www.firstsentierinvestors.com
Sales Range: $50-74.9 Million
Emp.: 80
Investment Management Service
N.A.I.C.S.: 523940

Corel Corporation (1)
1600 Carling Ave, Ottawa, K1Z 8R7, ON,
Canada (100%)
Tel.: (877) 582-6735
Web Site: http://www.corel.com
Software Products Mfr, Development, Li-
censing & Sales
N.A.I.C.S.: 334610
Christa S. Quarles *(CEO)*
John Ihn Park *(Chm)*
Jason Wesbecher *(Exec VP-Mktg & Sls)*
Brad Jewett *(CFO)*
Gerard Metrailler *(Exec VP-Global Prod-
ucts)*
Rob Charlebois *(Exec VP-Global eCom-
merce & Digital Mktg)*
Prasannaa Ganesan *(COO)*
Michelle Chiantera *(CMO)*
Scott Day *(Chief People Officer)*

Subsidiary (Non-US):

Corel Company (2)
7F 399 Rueiguang Road, Taipei, 114, ROC,
Taiwan
Tel.: (886) 226597588
Web Site: http://www.ulead.com
Sales Range: $25-49.9 Million
Digital Media Software Developer
N.A.I.C.S.: 334610

Subsidiary (Non-US):

Ulead Systems GmbH (3)
Hrmmer Land St strasse 89 41460 Neuss,
D-41564, Kaarst, Germany
Tel.: (49) 21315125850
Web Site: http://www.ulead.de
Digital Media Software.
N.A.I.C.S.: 334610

Ulead Systems K.K. (3)
Queens Tower C 12F 2-3-5 Minatomirai,
Nishi-ku, Yokohama, 220-6212, Kanagawa,
Japan
Tel.: (81) 3 5491 5661
Web Site: http://www.corel.com
Digital Media Software
N.A.I.C.S.: 334610

Subsidiary (US):

Ulead Systems, Inc. (3)
3460 Torrance Blvd Ste 300, Torrance, CA
90503-5811
Tel.: (510) 979-7118
Web Site: http://www.ulead.com
Software for Video, Imaging & Multimedia
Creation
N.A.I.C.S.: 541511

Subsidiary (Non-US):

Corel UK Limited (2)
Sapphire Court, Bell Street, Maidenhead,
SL6 1BU, Berks, United Kingdom
Tel.: (44) 1628589800
Web Site: http://www.apps.corel.com
Sales Range: $25-49.9 Million
Emp.: 20
Software Distr
N.A.I.C.S.: 513210

Subsidiary (US):

Corel USA (2)

385 Ravendale Dr, Mountain View, CA
94043-5240
Tel.: (510) 200-0438
Sales Range: $100-124.9 Million
Software Products Mfr, Development, Li-
censing & Sales
N.A.I.C.S.: 334610

Parallels, Inc. (2)
110 110th Ave NE Ste 410, Renton, WA
98004-5861
Tel.: (425) 282-6400
Web Site: http://www.parallels.com
Virtualization & Automation Software
N.A.I.C.S.: 513210
Yuriy Tsybrovskyy *(Founder & Dir-Tech)*

WinZip Computing LLC (2)
PO Box 540, Mansfield, CT 06268
Tel.: (860) 429-3539
Web Site: https://www.winzip.com
Sales Range: $25-49.9 Million
File Compression Software Developer
N.A.I.C.S.: 513210

**Covenant Physician Partners,
Inc.** (1)
401 Commerce St Ste 600, Nashville, TN
37219
Tel.: (615) 345-6900
Web Site:
https://www.covenantphysicianpart
ners.com
Ambulatory Health Care Services
N.A.I.C.S.: 621999
Goran Dragolovic *(CEO)*
Ijeoma Odu *(Sr VP)*
Trey Melancon *(Sr VP)*
Donna Keehner-Nowak *(Sr VP)*
Mike Field *(Sr VP)*
Viva Elia *(Sr VP)*
Wes Chick *(Sr VP)*
Bill Balaun *(COO)*
Henry Artime *(Sr VP)*
Yousif A-Rahim *(Chief Medical Officer)*
Andrew Ard *(Reg VP)*
Mike Burney *(VP)*
Carol Crump *(Reg VP)*
Jeanne Desautels *(Reg VP)*
Felisha Faulkner *(VP)*
Kristi F. Lewis *(VP)*
AnnaLyn Ogata *(Reg VP)*
Lance Perkins *(VP)*
Kyle Phillips *(VP)*
Connie StClair *(Reg VP)*
Jim Turner *(Reg VP)*

Crescent Energy Company (1)
600 Travis St Ste 7200, Houston, TX 77002
Tel.: (713) 332-7001
Web Site:
https://www.crescentenergyco.com
Rev.: $2,382,602,000
Assets: $6,803,335,000
Liabilities: $5,068,825,000
Net Worth: $1,734,510,000
Earnings: $67,610,000
Emp.: 904
Fiscal Year-end: 12/31/2023
Oil & Gas Operations Services
N.A.I.C.S.: 213112
John Goff *(Chm)*
David Rockecharlie *(CEO)*
Brandi Kendall *(CFO)*
Todd Falk *(Chief Acctg Officer)*
Clay Rynd *(Exec VP)*

Subsidiary (Domestic):

Contango Oil & Gas Company (2)
111 E 5th St Ste 300, Fort Worth, TX 76102
Tel.: (817) 529-0059
Web Site: http://www.contango.com
Rev.: $112,920,000
Assets: $170,267,000
Liabilities: $154,700,000
Net Worth: $15,567,000
Earnings: ($165,342,000)
Emp.: 205
Fiscal Year-end: 12/31/2020
Oil & Gas Exploration Services
N.A.I.C.S.: 213112
Michael J. Autin *(CEO)*
Chad Roller *(COO & Sr VP)*
Chad McLawhorn *(Gen Counsel & Sr VP)*
E. Joseph Grady *(CFO & Sr VP)*
Farley Dakan *(Pres)*

Subsidiary (Domestic):

Contango Operators, Inc. (3)

KKR & Co. Inc.—(Continued)

3700 Buffalo Speedway Ste 960, Houston,
TX 77098　　　　　　　　　**(100%)**
Tel.: (713) 960-1901
Web Site: http://www.contango.com
Oil & Natural Gas Exploration & Production
Services
N.A.I.C.S.: 213112

Mid-Con Energy Partners, LP　　**(3)**
2431 E 61st St Ste 850, Tulsa, OK 74136
Tel.: (918) 743-7575
Web Site:
　http://www.midconenergypartners.com
Rev.: $63,163,000
Assets: $202,769,000
Liabilities: $146,906,000
Net Worth: $55,863,000
Earnings: ($599,000)
Emp.: 100
Fiscal Year-end: 12/31/2019
Oil & Natural Gas Exploration Services
N.A.I.C.S.: 211112
Charles R. Olmstead (Chm)

Subsidiary (Domestic):

SilverBow Resources, Inc.　　　**(2)**
920 Memorial City Way Ste 850, Houston,
TX 77024
Tel.: (281) 874-2700
Web Site: https://www.sbow.com
Rev.: $652,358,000
Assets: $2,734,462,000
Liabilities: $1,545,134,000
Net Worth: $1,189,328,000
Earnings: $297,716,000
Emp.: 20
Fiscal Year-end: 12/31/2023
Oil & Gas Exploration, Acquisition, Production & Management Services
N.A.I.C.S.: 211120

Subsidiary (Domestic):

Sundance Energy Inc.　　　　　**(3)**
1050 17th St Ste 700, Denver, CO 80265
Tel.: (303) 543-5700
Web Site: http://sundanceenergy.net
Rev.: $91,812,000
Assets: $415,939,000
Liabilities: $432,685,000
Net Worth: ($16,746,000)
Earnings: ($370,462,000)
Emp.: 59
Fiscal Year-end: 12/31/2020
Oil & Gas Exploration Services
N.A.I.C.S.: 213112
James R. Redfearn (COO & Exec VP)
Christopher L. Humber (Gen Counsel, Sec
& Exec VP)

Swift Energy Operating, LLC　　**(3)**
920 Memorial City Way Ste 850, Houston,
TX 77024
Tel.: (281) 874-2700
Web Site: https://www.sbow.com
Sales Range: $150-199.9 Million
Oil & Gas Exploration Services
N.A.I.C.S.: 213112
Mary Kenner (Mgr-HR)

CyrusOne Inc.　　　　　　　　**(1)**
2850 N Harwood St Ste 2200, Dallas, TX
75201
Tel.: (972) 350-0060
Web Site: http://www.cyrusone.com
Rev.: $1,205,700,000
Assets: $7,452,000,000
Liabilities: $4,528,300,000
Net Worth: $2,923,700,000
Earnings: $25,300,000
Emp.: 456
Fiscal Year-end: 12/31/2021
Real Estate Investment Trust; Information
Technology Networks Designer & Operator
N.A.I.C.S.: 525990
Lynn A. Wentworth (Chm)
John Hatem (COO & Exec VP)
David H. Ferdman (Founder)
Mark E. Skomal (Chief Acctg Officer & Sr
VP)
Matt Pullen (Mng Dir-Europe & Exec VP)
Michael Nudelman (Sr VP-Project Dev)
Eric Schwartz (Pres & CEO)
Michael Schafer (Interim CFO & Sr VP-Fin)

Subsidiary (Domestic):

CyrusOne LLC　　　　　　　　**(2)**

1649 W Frankford Rd, Carrollton, TX 75007
Tel.: (972) 350-0060
Web Site: http://www.cyrusone.com
Information Technology Networks Designer
& Operator
N.A.I.C.S.: 541513

Ensono, LP　　　　　　　　　**(1)**
3333 Finley Rd, Downers Grove, IL 60515
Tel.: (866) 880-8611
Web Site: http://www.ensono.com
Emp.: 500
Information Technology Outsourcing Services
N.A.I.C.S.: 541519
Peter Brazil (Chief Legal Officer)
Lisa Agona (CMO & Sr VP)
Marc Capri (Pres)
Jeff VonDeylen (CEO)
Brian Klingbeil (COO)
Tim Beerman (CTO)
Brett Moss (Sr VP-Hyperscale Cloud)
Meredith Graham (Sr VP-HR)
William Flannery (Sr VP-Bus Innovation &
Consulting)
Paul Morris (Sr VP-Global Svc Assurance)
Richard Dresden (Sr VP-Sls & Field Ops)
Jason Deck (VP-Hyperscale Cloud Products
& Mktg)
Norman Smagley (CFO)
Duan Van Der Westhuizen (Sr VP-Public
Cloud)

Subsidiary (Non-US):

Ensono GmbH　　　　　　　　**(2)**
Dusseldorfer Strasse 71b, 40667, Meerbusch, Germany
Tel.: (49) 6950507750
Web Site: http://www.ensono.com
Information Technology Managed Services
N.A.I.C.S.: 518210
Maik Bunge (Dir-Delivery Svc)

Ensono Limited　　　　　　　**(2)**
Regus Centurion House London Road,
Staines-upon-Thames, TW18 4AX, Mddx,
United Kingdom
Tel.: (44) 1784211100
Web Site: http://www.ensono.com
Infomation Technology Managed Services
N.A.I.C.S.: 518210

Envision Healthcare Corporation　**(1)**
1A Burton Hills Blvd, Nashville, TN 37215
Tel.: (615) 665-1283
Web Site: https://www.envisionhealth.com
Medical Devices
N.A.I.C.S.: 621111
James A. Rechtin (Pres & CEO)
Jim Rechtin (Pres & CEO)
Chan Chuang (Chief Medical Officer)
Henry Howe (CFO & Exec VP-Enterprise
Strategy)
Ash Goulatia (Pres)
Megan Barney (CIO)
April Zepeda (Chief Comm Officer)
Meg Lafave (Chief People Officer)
Karey L. Witty (COO & Exec VP)

Subsidiary (Domestic):

Affiliated Endoscopy Services of Clifton, LLC　　　　　　　　　**(3)**
925 Clifton Ave Ste 100, Clifton, NJ 07013
Tel.: (973) 425-5015
Web Site: https://www.affiliatedendo.com
Gastroenterology Specialist Services
N.A.I.C.S.: 621111

AmSurg Corp.　　　　　　　　**(2)**
1A Burton Hills Blvd, Nashville, TN 37215
Tel.: (615) 665-1283
Web Site: https://www.amsurg.com
Hospital & Health Care Services
N.A.I.C.S.: 622110
Nina Goins (VP-Quality & Clinical Svcs)
Jeff Snodgrass (Pres)
Sarah Belmont (CFO)
Mauricio Camargo (Sr VP)
Robert Cook (CIO)
John Lamberth (Sr VP)
Tesha Simpson (COO)

Subsidiary (Domestic):

32nd Street Surgery Center, LLC (3)
1531 E 32nd St Ste 6, Joplin, MO 64804-
2970
Tel.: (417) 553-0210

Web Site:
　https://www.32ndstreetsurgery.com
Health Care Srvices
N.A.I.C.S.: 621111

**All Women's Healthcare Services,
Inc.**　　　　　　　　　　　　**(3)**
8890 W Oakland Park Blvd Ste 102, Sunrise, FL 33351
Tel.: (954) 742-3536
Web Site: http://www.floridaabortion.com
Women Healthcare Services
N.A.I.C.S.: 621111

Subsidiary (Domestic):

**All Women's Healthcare of Sawgrass,
Inc.**　　　　　　　　　　　　**(4)**
603 N Flamingo Rd, Pembroke Pines, FL
33026
Tel.: (954) 845-1190
Women Healthcare Services
N.A.I.C.S.: 622110

All Women's Healthcare of West Broward, Inc.　　　　　　　　　　**(4)**
140 SW 84th Ave Ste D, Plantation, FL
33324
Tel.: (954) 251-0431
Web Site:
　http://www.obgynwestbroward.com
Women Healthcare Services
N.A.I.C.S.: 621111

Subsidiary (Domestic):

AmSurg Burbank, Inc.　　　　**(3)**
2829 W Burbank Blvd, Burbank, CA 91505-
2300
Tel.: (818) 567-0348
Web Site: http://www.amsurg.com
Ambulatory Surgery Center Operator
N.A.I.C.S.: 621493

**AmSurg Cincinnati Anesthesia,
LLC**　　　　　　　　　　　　**(3)**
9275 Montgomery Rd, Cincinnati, OH
45242-7779
Tel.: (513) 936-4518
Health Care Srvices
N.A.I.C.S.: 622110

AmSurg Citrus Anesthesia, LLC (3)
2861 S Delaney Ave Ste A, Orlando, FL
32806-5409
Tel.: (407) 472-5095
Web Site: http://www.amsurg.com
Ambulatory Surgery Services
N.A.I.C.S.: 621910

Unit (Domestic):

**AmSurg Corp - Central Regional
Office**　　　　　　　　　　　**(3)**
5500 Greenville Ave Ste 1100, Dallas, TX
75231
Tel.: (214) 739-9544
Web Site: http://www.amsurg.com
Ambulatory Surgery Center Operator
N.A.I.C.S.: 621493

Subsidiary (Domestic):

AmSurg El Paso, Inc.　　　　**(3)**
1300 Murchison Dr Ste 180, El Paso, TX
79902
Tel.: (915) 544-5000
Web Site: http://www.epgastro.com
Ambulatory Surgical & Emergency Services
N.A.I.C.S.: 621493

AmSurg Fresno CA, Inc.　　　**(3)**
1843 E Fir Ave Ste 104, Fresno, CA 93720
Tel.: (559) 323-6611
Web Site: http://www.amsurg.com
Ambulance Surgery Services
N.A.I.C.S.: 621910

**AmSurg Greensboro Anesthesia,
LLC**　　　　　　　　　　　　**(3)**
1593 Yanceyville St Ste 100, Greensboro,
NC 27405-6948
Tel.: (336) 553-3190
Web Site: http://www.amsurg.com
Health Care Srvices
N.A.I.C.S.: 621610

**AmSurg Hermitage Anesthesia,
LLC**　　　　　　　　　　　　**(3)**

5653 Frist Blvd Ste 532, Hermitage, TN
37076-2062
Tel.: (615) 316-3066
Web Site: http://www.amsurg.com
Ambulance Health Care Services
N.A.I.C.S.: 622110

**AmSurg Kentucky Ophthalmology,
LLC**　　　　　　　　　　　　**(3)**
9202 Leesgate Rd, Louisville, KY 40222
Tel.: (502) 637-4800
Web Site: http://www.amsurg.com
Health Care Srvices
N.A.I.C.S.: 622110

AmSurg Louisville GI, LLC　　**(3)**
1400 Poplar Level Rd Ste 2, Louisville, KY
40217
Tel.: (502) 442-7303
Web Site:
　http://louisvilleendoscopycenter.com
Ambulance Surgery Services
N.A.I.C.S.: 622110

**AmSurg Northern Kentucky GI,
LLC**　　　　　　　　　　　　**(3)**
340 Thomas More Pkwy Ste 160B, Crestview Hills, KY 41017-5101
Tel.: (859) 331-6466
Web Site:
　https://www.stelizabethphysicians.com
Ambulance Surgery Services
N.A.I.C.S.: 622110

**AmSurg Rockledge FL Anesthesia,
LLC**　　　　　　　　　　　　**(3)**
1974 Rockledge Blvd Ste 102, Rockledge,
FL 32955-3756
Tel.: (321) 504-4440
Web Site: http://www.amsurg.com
Ambulance Surgery Services
N.A.I.C.S.: 622110

**AmSurg Tampa Bay Anesthesia,
LLC**　　　　　　　　　　　　**(3)**
4809 N Aremnia Ave Ste 100, Tampa, FL
33603-1447
Tel.: (813) 658-5037
Web Site:
　https://www.tampaendocenter.com
Ambulance Surgery Services
N.A.I.C.S.: 622110

AmSurg Toledo Anesthesia, LLC (3)
4841 Monroe St Ste 111, Toledo, OH
43623-4385
Tel.: (419) 474-3949
Web Site: http://www.amsurg.com
Health Care Srvices
N.A.I.C.S.: 621610

**Ambulatory Anesthesia Associates
Inc.**　　　　　　　　　　　　**(3)**
2 Pkwy Ctr G-1, Pittsburgh, PA 15220
Tel.: (412) 937-1900
Web Site: https://www.ambanes.com
Anesthesiology Services
N.A.I.C.S.: 622110

**Anesthesia Associates of Pinellas
County Division, LLC**　　　　**(3)**
300 Pinellas St, Clearwater, FL 33756-3804
Tel.: (727) 462-7000
Health Care Srvices
N.A.I.C.S.: 621111

**Anesthesiologists of Greater Orlando,
Inc.**　　　　　　　　　　　　**(3)**
851 Trafalgar Ct Se 300W, Maitland, FL
32751-7425
Tel.: (407) 896-9500
Web Site: https://www.aqomd.com
Health Care Srvices
N.A.I.C.S.: 622110
Phoebe Bradshaw (Gen Mgr)

Anesthesiology Associates of Tallahassee, Inc.　　　　　　　　**(3)**
2173 Cinville Pl, Tallahassee, FL 32308
Tel.: (850) 385-0144
Health Care Srvices
N.A.I.C.S.: 622110

Austin Endoscopy Center I, LP　**(3)**
8015 Shoal Creek Blvd Ste 300, Austin, TX
78757-8066
Tel.: (512) 371-1519
Web Site: http://www.austingastro.com
Health Care Srvices
N.A.I.C.S.: 621610

Bay Area Anesthesia, LLC (3)
5433 Clayton Rd Ste K 304, Clayton, CA 94517
Tel.: (925) 787-5652
Web Site: https://www.bayareaanesthesia.com
Health Care Srvices
N.A.I.C.S.: 622110

Bethesda Anesthesia Associates, Inc. (3)
55 Douglas Dr, Boynton Beach, FL 33435-7307
Tel.: (561) 274-8375
Health Care Srvices
N.A.I.C.S.: 622110

Bethesda Outpatient Surgery Center, LLC (3)
10301 Hagen Ranch Rd Ste 520, Boynton Beach, FL 33437
Tel.: (561) 374-5550
Web Site: http://www.physicianpartnersofamerica.com
Outpatient Care Center Operator
N.A.I.C.S.: 621498

Blaine MN Multi-Specialty ASC, LLC (3)
11855 Ulysses St Ste 270, Blaine, MN 55434
Tel.: (763) 447-4310
Web Site: https://www.northmetrosurgerycenter.com
Health Care Srvices
N.A.I.C.S.: 622110

Boca Anesthesia Service, Inc. (3)
800 Meadows Rd, Boca Raton, FL 33486-2304
Tel.: (561) 395-7100
Health Care Srvices
N.A.I.C.S.: 622110

Boston Endoscopy Center, LLC (3)
175 Worcester St, Wellesley Hills, MA 02481
Tel.: (617) 936-7693
Web Site: https://www.bostonendoscopycenter.com
Health Care Srvices
N.A.I.C.S.: 622110

Boston Out-Patient Surgical Suites, L.L.C. (3)
840 Winter St, Waltham, MA 02451
Tel.: (781) 209-5645
Web Site: https://www.bostonoutpatient.com
Out Patient Health Care Services
N.A.I.C.S.: 622110

COA ASC of Franklin County, LLC (3)
5965 E Broad St, Columbus, OH 43213
Tel.: (614) 751-4080
Web Site: https://www.columbuseyesurgerycenter.com
Health Care Srvices
N.A.I.C.S.: 622110

Campus Surgery Center, LLC (3)
901 Campus Dr Ste 102, Daly City, CA 94015
Tel.: (650) 351-7616
Web Site: https://www.campussurgery.com
Surgical & Other Health Care Services
N.A.I.C.S.: 622110

Cascade Endoscopy Center, LLC (3)
1007 Harlow Rd Ste 110, Springfield, OR 97477
Tel.: (541) 228-9127
Web Site: https://www.cascadeendocenter.com
Health Care Srvices
N.A.I.C.S.: 621111

Central Park Endoscopy Center, LLC (3)

1600 Central Dr Ste 300, Bedford, TX 76022
Tel.: (817) 789-4575
Web Site: http://www.dhcoftx.com
Colorectal Cancer Screening Center
N.A.I.C.S.: 622310

Central Texas Endoscopy Center, LLC (3)
2206 E Villa Maria Rd, Bryan, TX 77802
Tel.: (979) 774-4211
Web Site: https://www.centraltexasendoscopy.com
Colon Cancer Screening Center
N.A.I.C.S.: 622310

Clearwater Pain Management Associates Division, LLC (3)
430 Morton Plant St Ste 210, Clearwater, FL 33756
Tel.: (727) 446-4506
Web Site: https://www.clearwaterpain.com
Health Care Srvices
N.A.I.C.S.: 621111
Edward Chen (Dir-Medical)

Colton CA Multi ASC, L.P. (3)
900 E Washington St Ste 155, Colton, CA 92324
Tel.: (909) 370-2190
Web Site: http://www.premierosc.com
Health Care Srvices
N.A.I.C.S.: 622110

Coral Springs Ambulatory Surgery Center, LLC (3)
967 University Dr, Coral Springs, FL 33071
Tel.: (954) 341-5553
Web Site: http://www.surgerycentercoralsprings.com
Health Care Srvices
N.A.I.C.S.: 622110

Diagnostic Endoscopy Center, LLC (3)
778 Long Rdg Rd, Stamford, CT 06902
Tel.: (203) 428-4643
Web Site: https://www.diagnosticendoscopy.com
Health Care Srvices
N.A.I.C.S.: 622110

Digestive Endoscopy Center, LLC (3)
1530 Needmore Rd Ste 100 101, Dayton, OH 45414
Tel.: (937) 534-7330
Web Site: https://www.digestivespecialists.com
Endoscopic Facility Center Operator
N.A.I.C.S.: 621493

Digestive Health Center, LLC (3)
570 White Pond Dr Ste 150, Akron, OH 44320
Tel.: (330) 899-4194
Web Site: https://www.dhcakron.com
Endoscopic Facility Center Operator
N.A.I.C.S.: 621493

Discovery Clinical Research, Inc. (3)
1613 N Harrison Pkwy Ste 200, Sunrise, FL 33323-2896
Tel.: (954) 838-2729
Health Care Srvices
N.A.I.C.S.: 622110

Doctors Park Surgery Center, LLC (3)
2090 NE Wyatt Ct Ste 102, Bend, OR 97701-7687
Tel.: (541) 389-5931
Ambulatory Surgery Center Operator
N.A.I.C.S.: 621493

Drs. Ellis, Rojas, Ross & Debs, Inc. (3)
8900 N Kendall Dr, Miami, FL 33176
Tel.: (305) 595-4510
Health Care Srvices
N.A.I.C.S.: 622110

Eagle Eye Surgery and Laser Center, LLC (3)
3090 E Gentry Way Ste 100, Meridian, ID 83642-3548
Tel.: (208) 288-1600
Web Site: https://www.eagleeyesurgery.com
Ambulatory Surgery Center Operator
N.A.I.C.S.: 621493

East Valley Endoscopy, LLC (3)
6020 E Arbor Ave Ste 105, Mesa, AZ 85206
Tel.: (480) 210-6853
Ambulatory Surgery Center Operator
N.A.I.C.S.: 621493

Elms Endoscopy Center, LLC (3)
2671 Elms Plantation Blvd, Charleston, SC 29406-9165
Tel.: (843) 797-6800
Web Site: https://www.elmsdigestive.com
Health Care Srvices
N.A.I.C.S.: 621610

Emergency Physician Solutions of South Florida, LLC (3)
11750 SW 40th St, Miami, FL 33175
Tel.: (305) 227-5544
Health Care Srvices
N.A.I.C.S.: 622110

Emergency Professional Services, PC (3)
645 E Missouri Ave Ste 300, Phoenix, AZ 85012
Tel.: (480) 500-2540
Web Site: https://www.envisionphysicianservices.com
Freestanding Ambulatory Surgical & Emergency Centers
N.A.I.C.S.: 621493
Richard Bruno (Reg Dir-Medical)
Mandy Limberg (Dir-Recruiting)
Nichole Logan (Coord-Credentialing)
Katie McDonald (Coord-Ops & Website Admin)
Elizabeth Mehrer (Dir-Ops)
David Streitwieser (Dir-Billing)
Robert Baron (Dir-QA & QI)
Dayanne Bernaola (Coord-Lead Scribe & Scribe)

Envision Healthcare Clinical Research, Inc. (3)
7700 W Sunrise Blvd, Plantation, FL 33322
Tel.: (954) 838-2729
Web Site: http://www.envisionphysicianservices.com
Health Care Srvices
N.A.I.C.S.: 621111
Jay S. Cohen (Dir-Medical)

Eye Surgery Center of Western Ohio, LLC (3)
855 W Market St, Lima, OH 45805
Tel.: (419) 228-9991
Web Site: https://www.amsurg.com
Eye Care Service
N.A.I.C.S.: 621111

Eye Surgery Center, LLC (3)
445 Ashley Rdg Blvd, Shreveport, LA 71106
Tel.: (318) 869-1130
Health Care Srvices
N.A.I.C.S.: 622110

EyeCare Consultants Surgery Center, LLC (3)
101 NW 1st St Ste 112, Evansville, IN 47708-1220
Tel.: (812) 618-4330
Web Site: https://www.eyecare-consultants.net
Ophthalmology Surgical Services
N.A.I.C.S.: 621493

Flamingo Anesthesia Associates, Inc. (3)
501 N Flamingo Rd, Pembroke Pines, FL 33028
Tel.: (954) 889-6223
Web Site: http://www.memorialsameday.com
Health Care Srvices
N.A.I.C.S.: 622110

Fresno CA Endoscopy ASC, L.P. (3)
7055 N Fresno St Ste 100, Fresno, CA 93720
Tel.: (559) 385-2838
Web Site: http://www.ccendoscopy.com
Health Care Srvices
N.A.I.C.S.: 622110

Fresno CA Multi ASC, L.P. (3)
1843 E Fir Ave Ste 104, Fresno, CA 93720
Tel.: (559) 323-6611
Web Site: http://www.herndonsurgerycenter.com

Health Care Srvices
N.A.I.C.S.: 621111

General Surgery of Jupiter Medical Specialists, LLC (3)
1002 S Old Dixie Hwy Ste 206, Jupiter, FL 33458-7202
Tel.: (561) 972-5721
Web Site: http://www.jupitermedicalspecialists.com
Health Care Srvices
N.A.I.C.S.: 622110

Glen Endoscopy Center, LLC (3)
2551 Compass Rd Ste 115, Glenview, IL 60026
Tel.: (847) 656-2400
Web Site: https://www.glenendo.com
Health Care Srvices
N.A.I.C.S.: 621111

Glendale Ophthalmology ASC, L.P. (3)
500 N Central Ave Ste 400, Glendale, CA 91203-1804
Tel.: (818) 956-1010
Web Site: http://www.glendaleeye.com
Ophthalmology Surgical Services
N.A.I.C.S.: 621493

Global Surgical Partners, Inc. (3)
3059 Grand Ave Ste 300, Miami, FL 33133
Tel.: (305) 577-0551
Health Care Srvices
N.A.I.C.S.: 622110

Greater Florida Anesthesiologists, LLC (3)
5380 Tech Data Dr Ste 101, Clearwater, FL 33760
Tel.: (727) 573-7777
Web Site: https://www.gfamed.com
Health Care Srvices
N.A.I.C.S.: 621111

Greenspring Station Endoscopy, LLC (3)
10751 Falls Rd Ste 401, Lutherville, MD 21093
Tel.: (410) 457-7240
Web Site: http://www.gssendo.com
Endoscopic Facility Center Operator
N.A.I.C.S.: 621493

Gynecologic Oncology Associates, Inc. (3)
3700 Washington St, Hollywood, FL 33021
Tel.: (305) 324-7300
Health Care Srvices
N.A.I.C.S.: 622110

Hudson Crossing Surgery Center, LLC (3)
2 Executive Dr, Fort Lee, NJ 07024
Tel.: (201) 470-6977
Web Site: https://www.hudsoncrossingsc.com
Health Care Srvices
N.A.I.C.S.: 622110

Jacksonville Beaches Anesthesia Associates, Inc. (3)
3316 3rd Rd St S Ste 200, Jacksonville Beach, FL 32250-6073
Tel.: (904) 247-8181
Health Care Srvices
N.A.I.C.S.: 622110

Jupiter Anesthesia Associates, LLC (3)
1210 S Old Dixie Hwy, Jupiter, FL 33458-7205
Tel.: (516) 515-5910
Web Site: http://www.jupitermed.com
Health Care Srvices
N.A.I.C.S.: 622110

Jupiter Imaging Associates, Inc. (3)
1210 S Old Dixie Hwy, Jupiter, FL 33458
Tel.: (561) 744-4411
Web Site: http://www.jupitermed.com
Health Care Srvices
N.A.I.C.S.: 621111

Kenwood ASC, LLC (3)
8250 Kenwood Crossing Way, Cincinnati, OH 45236
Tel.: (513) 793-6011
Health Care Srvices
N.A.I.C.S.: 622110

KKR & Co. Inc.—(Continued)

Long Beach Surgery Center, L.P. (3)
2880 Atlantic Ave Ste 160, Long Beach, CA 90806
Tel.: (562) 453-3814
Web Site:
https://surgerycenteroflongbeach.com
Ambulatory Surgery Services
N.A.I.C.S.: 621910

MDSINE, LLC (3)
55 Saint George Rd, Springfield, MA 01104-3333
Tel.: (413) 306-4005
Web Site:
http://www.surgerycenterofneweng
land.com
Health Care Srvices
N.A.I.C.S.: 622110

MSC Anesthesia, Inc. (3)
601 Manatee Ave W, Bradenton, FL 34205
Tel.: (941) 745-2727
Web Site:
https://manateesurgicalcenter.com
Ambulatory Surgery Services
N.A.I.C.S.: 621910

Manatee Surgical Center, LLC (3)
601 Manatee Ave W, Bradenton, FL 34205
Tel.: (941) 745-2727
Web Site:
http://www.manateesurgicalcenter.com
Health Care Srvices
N.A.I.C.S.: 621111
Linda Nash (Mgr-Risk)
Kurt Slotabec (Dir-Medical)
Michael Gurucharri (Pres)
Mark Kocab (Treas & Sec)
Erin Paris (Mgr-Nurse)

Marin Endoscopy Center, LLC (3)
1100 S Eliseo Dr Ste 3, Greenbrae, CA 94904
Tel.: (415) 798-9711
Web Site:
https://endoscopycentermarin.com
Endoscopic Facility Center Operator
N.A.I.C.S.: 621493

Maryland Endoscopy Center Limited Liability Company (3)
100 W Rd Ste 115, Towson, MD 21204
Tel.: (410) 698-6432
Web Site:
https://www.marylandendoscopycen
ter.com
Endoscopic Facility Center Operator
N.A.I.C.S.: 621493

May Street Surgi Center, LLC (3)
205 May St Ste 103, Edison, NJ 08837
Tel.: (732) 820-4566
Web Site:
https://www.maystreetsurgicenter.com
Endoscopic Facility Center Operator
N.A.I.C.S.: 621493

Meadows Surgery Center, LLC (3)
75 Orient Way, Rutherford, NJ 07070
Tel.: (201) 574-0566
Web Site: https://www.meadowssurgery.com
Health Care Srvices
N.A.I.C.S.: 622110
Rebecca Anne Vitillo (Gen Mgr)

Medical Anesthesia Consultants Medical Group, Inc. (3)
2175 N California Blvd Ste 425, Walnut Creek, CA 94596
Tel.: (925) 543-0140
Web Site: http://www.macmgi.com
Health Care Srvices
N.A.I.C.S.: 622111
David Fitzgerald (Pres)
Jeffrey Poage (Dir-Medical)
Kurt Dittman (Reg Dir-Medical)
Allison Duffy (Dir-Medical)
Mir Ali (Dir-Medical)
Raymond Cheung (Dir-Medical)
Oscar Fernandez (Dir-Medical)
Michele Collier (Dir-Medical)
Haywon Lieh (Dir-Medical)
Andrew Knight (Dir-Medical)

Mercer County Surgery Center, LLC (3)
2A Princess Rd, Lawrenceville, NJ 08648
Tel.: (609) 895-0290

Web Site:
https://www.mercercountysurgerycen
ter.com
Outpatient Surgical Center
N.A.I.C.S.: 621498

Mid Atlantic Endoscopy Center, LLC (3)
4923 Ogletown-Stanton Rd Ste 100, Newark, DE 19713
Tel.: (302) 613-0436
Web Site: https://midatlanticendoscopy.com
Health Care Srvices
N.A.I.C.S.: 621111

Montgomery Eye Surgery Center, LLC (3)
2752 Zelda Rd, Montgomery, AL 36106
Tel.: (334) 513-1675
Web Site:
https://www.montgomeryeyesurgery.com
Outpatient Surgical Center
N.A.I.C.S.: 621498

Mount Dora Ophthalmology ASC, LLC (3)
17560 US Hwy 441, Mount Dora, FL 32757-6711
Tel.: (352) 735-2020
Web Site: https://www.midfloridaeye.com
Health Care Srvices
N.A.I.C.S.: 622110

North Florida Perinatal Associates, Inc. (3)
6440 W Newberry Rd Ste 410, Gainesville, FL 32605
Tel.: (352) 224-1840
Web Site: https://www.gainesvillemfm.com
Health Care Srvices
N.A.I.C.S.: 621111

North Richland Hills Endoscopy Center, LLC (3)
7640 NE Loop 820 Ste 96, North Richland Hills, TX 76180
Tel.: (469) 713-3740
Web Site: http://www.dhcoftx.com
Health Care Srvices
N.A.I.C.S.: 622110

North Valley Endoscopy Center, LLC (3)
15255 N 40th St Bldg 8-157, Phoenix, AZ 85032
Tel.: (602) 633-9396
Web Site: https://www.northvalleyendo.com
Endoscopic Facility Center Operator
N.A.I.C.S.: 621493

Northside Gastroenterology Endoscopy Center, LLC (3)
8424 Naab Rd Ste 3G, Indianapolis, IN 46260
Tel.: (317) 872-7396
Web Site: https://www.northsidegastro.com
Ambulatory Surgical Center Operator
N.A.I.C.S.: 621493

Oak Lawn IL Endoscopy ASC, LLC (3)
9921 Southwest Hwy, Oak Lawn, IL 60453-3767
Tel.: (708) 459-9553
Health Care Srvices
N.A.I.C.S.: 621111

Ocean Endosurgery Center (3)
129 New Jersey 37, Toms River, NJ 08755
Tel.: (732) 606-4440
Web Site:
https://www.oceanendosurgery.com
Health Care Srvices
N.A.I.C.S.: 622110

Old Town Endoscopy Center, LLC (3)
9500 N Central Expy Ste 200B, Dallas, TX 75231
Tel.: (214) 739-9544
Web Site: http://www.dhcoftx.com
Health Care Srvices
N.A.I.C.S.: 622110

Parity Healthcare, Inc. (3)
1613 NW 136th Ave Ste 200 Bldg C, Sunrise, FL 33323
Tel.: (954) 838-2717
Health Care Srvices
N.A.I.C.S.: 622110

Park Ventura Endoscopy Center, LLC (3)
981 State Hwy 121 Ste 2100, Allen, TX 75013
Tel.: (214) 383-8210
Web Site: http://www.amsurg.com
Health Care Srvices
N.A.I.C.S.: 622110

Phoenix Endoscopy, L.L.C. (3)
349 E Coronado Rd, Phoenix, AZ 85004-1525
Tel.: (602) 635-4948
Web Site:
https://www.phoenixendoscopy.com
Endoscopic Facility Center Operator
N.A.I.C.S.: 621493

Phoenix Orthopaedic Ambulatory Center, L.L.C. (3)
690 N Cofco Ctr Ct Ste 150, Phoenix, AZ 85008-6469
Tel.: (602) 910-6839
Web Site:
http://www.gatewaysurgerycenter.com
Health Care Srvices
N.A.I.C.S.: 622110
Peggy Jahn-Pacu (Mgr-Nurse)
Cynthia Bensoni (Mgr-Operating Room)
Michael Vital (Mgr-Bus)
Marty Quihuis (Mgr-Materials)

Physician Office Partners, Inc. (3)
6050 Sprint Pkwy Ste 300, Overland Park, KS 66211
Tel.: (913) 754-0467
Web Site:
https://www.physicianofficepartners.com
Health Care Srvices
N.A.I.C.S.: 621111
Rob Davey (Pres & CEO)

Physicians' Eye Surgery Center, LLC (3)
2060 Charlie Hall Blvd Ste 301, Charleston, SC 29414
Tel.: (843) 571-4800
Web Site:
https://www.charlestoneyesurgery.com
Health Care Srvices
N.A.I.C.S.: 621111

Pioneer Valley Surgicenter, LLC (3)
3550 Main St Ste 103, Springfield, MA 01107
Tel.: (413) 241-6471
Web Site: https://www.pvsurgery.com
Health Care Srvices
N.A.I.C.S.: 622110

Radiology Services of Jupiter Medical Specialists, LLC (3)
1240 S Old Dixie Hwy, Jupiter, FL 33450-7205
Tel.: (561) 263-4400
Health Care Srvices
N.A.I.C.S.: 622110

Redbird Square Endoscopy Center, LLC (3)
3107 W Camp Wisdom Rd Ste 189, Dallas, TX 75237
Tel.: (214) 331-2922
Web Site: http://www.dhcoftx.com
Health Care Srvices
N.A.I.C.S.: 622110

San Antonio ASC, LP (3)
5225 Prue Rd Ste 100, San Antonio, TX 78240-1331
Tel.: (210) 384-2129
Web Site: https://www.specialtyasc.com
Health Care Srvices
N.A.I.C.S.: 622110

Sarasota Physicians Surgical Center, LLC (3)
3201 S Tamiami Trl, Sarasota, FL 34239-5112
Tel.: (941) 757-3205
Web Site: https://www.spsc.info
Health Care Srvices
N.A.I.C.S.: 622110

Sheridan Anesthesia Services of Louisiana, Inc. (3)
1613 N Harrison Pkwy Ste 200, Sunrise, FL 33323
Tel.: (954) 514-4844

Health Care Srvices
N.A.I.C.S.: 621111

Sheridan Radiology Services of Central Florida, Inc. (3)
1401 W Sunrise Blvd, Plantation, FL 33322
Tel.: (954) 838-2371
Health Care Srvices
N.A.I.C.S.: 622110

Sheridan Radiology Services of Kentucky, Inc. (3)
3200 N Ocean Blvd, Fort Lauderdale, FL 33308-7152
Tel.: (954) 565-5249
Health Care Srvices
N.A.I.C.S.: 622110

Sheridan Radiology Services of Pinellas, Inc. (3)
6500 38th Ave N, Saint Petersburg, FL 33710
Tel.: (727) 338-1414
Health Care Srvices
N.A.I.C.S.: 622110

Sheridan Radiology Services of Virginia, Inc. (3)
7700 W Sunrise Blvd, Plantation, FL 33322
Tel.: (954) 838-2371
Health Care Srvices
N.A.I.C.S.: 622110

Short Hills Surgery Center, LLC (3)
187 Millburn Ave Ste 102, Millburn, NJ 07041
Tel.: (973) 671-0555
Web Site: https://www.shorthillssc.com
Health Care Srvices
N.A.I.C.S.: 622110

Southeast Perinatal Associates, Inc. (3)
1951 SW 172nd Ave Ste 411, Miramar, FL 33029
Tel.: (954) 431-7372
Web Site:
https://www.southeastperinatal.com
Health Care Srvices
N.A.I.C.S.: 621111

Southern Idaho Ambulatory Surgery Center, LLC (3)
115 Falls Ave W, Twin Falls, ID 83301
Tel.: (208) 733-1662
Web Site: https://www.sawtoothsurgery.com
Outpatient Care Center Operator
N.A.I.C.S.: 621498

St. Clair Shores MI Ophthalmology ASC, LLC (3)
21711 Greater Mack Ave, Saint Clair Shores, MI 48080-2418
Tel.: (586) 782-4915
Web Site:
http://www.lakeshoreeyesurgery.com
Health Care Srvices
N.A.I.C.S.: 622110

St. George Endoscopy Center, LLC (3)
368 E Riverside Dr Ste B, Saint George, UT 84790
Tel.: (435) 767-0404
Web Site: https://www.utahendocenter.com
Eye Care Surgery Center Operator
N.A.I.C.S.: 621493

Subsidiary (Domestic):

AmSurg St. George Anesthesia, LLC (4)
368 E Riverside Dr Ste B, Saint George, UT 84790
Tel.: (435) 674-3109
Web Site: http://www.amsurg.com
Ambulatory Surgery Center Operator
N.A.I.C.S.: 621493

Subsidiary (Domestic):

Sunrise Ambulatory Surgical Center, LLC (3)
5448 S White Mountain Blvd Ste 100, Lakeside, AZ 85929
Tel.: (928) 358-1862
Web Site: https://www.sunriseasc.com
Health Care Srvices
N.A.I.C.S.: 621111

Surgery Center of Allentown,
LLC   (3)
250 Centronia Rd Ste 300, Allentown, PA
18104
Tel.: (484) 477-0622
Web Site: http://www.scoallentown.com
Health Care Srvices
N.A.I.C.S.: 621111

Surgery Center of Northeast Texas,
LLC   (3)
1902 Moores Ln Ste B, Texarkana, TX
75503-4668
Tel.: (903) 729-2108
Web Site: https://www.scnetx.com
Health Care Srvices
N.A.I.C.S.: 621111

Surgery Center of South Central
Kansas   (3)
1708 E 23rd Ave, Hutchinson, KS 67502
Tel.: (620) 236-6492
Web Site:
   https://www.hutchinsonsurgery.com
Health Care Srvices
N.A.I.C.S.: 622110

Surgery Center of Volusia, LLC   (3)
3635 Clyde Morris Blvd Ste 500, Port Or-
ange, FL 32129
Tel.: (386) 868-5034
Web Site:
   https://www.surgerycenterofvolusia.com
Ambulatory Surgery Center Operator
N.A.I.C.S.: 621493

Surgery Specialists of Broward,
Inc.   (3)
350 NW 84th Ave Ste 311, Plantation, FL
33324
Tel.: (954) 476-9899
Health Care Srvices
N.A.I.C.S.: 621111

Temecula CA United Surgery,
L.P.   (3)
31469 Rancho Pueblo Rd Ste 100, Te-
mecula, CA 92592-0000
Tel.: (951) 303-6890
Web Site: http://www.unitedgi.com
Health Care Srvices
N.A.I.C.S.: 621111

The Abilene Eye ASC, L.P.   (3)
2120 Antilley Rd, Abilene, TX 79606-5211
Tel.: (325) 695-2020
Web Site:
   http://www.abileneeyeinstitute.com
Lasik, Cataract & Refractive Surgery
N.A.I.C.S.: 622310

The Alexandria Ophthalmology ASC,
LLC   (3)
4100 Parliament Dr, Alexandria, LA 71303-
2717
Tel.: (318) 487-8342
Web Site:
   http://www.wallaceeyeassociates.com
Laser And Surgery Center
N.A.I.C.S.: 622110

The Altamonte Springs FL Endoscopy
ASC, LLC   (3)
623 Maitland Ave Ste 1100, Altamonte
Springs, FL 32701
Tel.: (407) 219-9510
Web Site: https://www.palmendoscopy.com
Endoscopic Facility Center Operator
N.A.I.C.S.: 621493

The Arcadia CA Endoscopy ASC,
L.P.   (3)
488 E Santa Clara St Ste 102, Arcadia, CA
91006
Tel.: (626) 264-8065
Web Site:
   https://www.valleydigestivehealthcen
   ter.com
Outpatient Surgical Center
N.A.I.C.S.: 621498

The Baltimore Endoscopy ASC,
LLC   (3)
700 Geipe Rd Ste 220, Catonsville, MD
21228
Tel.: (410) 753-2255
Web Site: https://www.gibaltimore.com
Outpatient Surgical Center
N.A.I.C.S.: 621498

The Blue Ridge/Clemson Orthopaedic
ASC, LLC   (3)
10630 Clemson Blvd Ste 200, Seneca, SC
29678
Tel.: (864) 324-0466
Web Site:
   https://www.blueridgesurgerycentersc.com
Health Care Srvices
N.A.I.C.S.: 622110

The Boca Raton Ophthalmology ASC,
LLC   (3)
950 NW 13th St, Boca Raton, FL 33486-
2310
Tel.: (561) 910-0782
Web Site: http://www.bocaeyecenter.com
Ophthalmology Ambulatory Surgical Ser-
vices
N.A.I.C.S.: 621493

The Burbank Ophthalmology ASC,
L.P.   (3)
2829 W Burbank Blvd, Burbank, CA 91505-
2300
Tel.: (818) 237-3553
Web Site:
   http://www.pacificeyesurgerycenter.com
Eye Health Care Services
N.A.I.C.S.: 622110

The Cape Coral/Ft. Myers Endoscopy
ASC, LLC   (3)
665 Del Prado Blvd, Cape Coral, FL 33990
Tel.: (239) 772-3800
Ambulatory Surgery Center Operator
N.A.I.C.S.: 621493

The Chattanooga Endoscopy ASC,
LLC   (3)
1501 Riverside Dr ste 117, Chattanooga,
TN 37406
Tel.: (423) 822-2393
Web Site:
   https://www.chattanoogaendo.com
Outpatient Surgical Center
N.A.I.C.S.: 621498

The Chevy Chase ASC, LLC   (3)
5530 Wisconsin Ave Ste 500, Chevy
Chase, MD 20815
Tel.: (301) 654-8020
Web Site: https://www.ccendo.com
Outpatient Surgical Center
N.A.I.C.S.: 621498

The Columbia ASC Northwest,
LLC   (3)
100 Palmetto Health Pkwy Ste 100, Colum-
bia, SC 29212-1747
Tel.: (803) 753-7282
Web Site: http://www.columbiagastro.com
Health Care Srvices
N.A.I.C.S.: 622110

The Columbia ASC, LLC   (3)
2739 Laurel St Ste 1-B, Columbia, SC
29204
Tel.: (803) 254-9588
Web Site: https://columbiagicenter.com
Health Care Srvices
N.A.I.C.S.: 622110

The Columbia MD Orthopaedic ASC,
LLC   (3)
10700 Charter Dr Ste 301, Columbia, MD
21044-4000
Tel.: (410) 910-2301
Ambulatory Surgery Center Operator
N.A.I.C.S.: 621493

The Crystal River Endoscopy ASC,
L.P.   (3)
6412 W Gulf to Lk Hwy, Crystal River, FL
34429-7622
Tel.: (352) 400-4459
Web Site:
   https://www.citrusendoscopycenter.com
Health Care Srvices
N.A.I.C.S.: 622110

The Dover Ophthalmology ASC,
LLC   (3)
655 Bay Rd Ste 5-B, Dover, DE 19901
Tel.: (302) 724-4720
Web Site:
   http://www.bluehensurgerycenter.com
Health Care Srvices
N.A.I.C.S.: 622110

The El Paso ASC, L.P.   (3)

1300 Murchison Dr Ste 180, El Paso, TX
79902
Tel.: (915) 613-0811
Web Site: http://www.epgastro.com
Health Care Srvices
N.A.I.C.S.: 622110

The Endoscopy Center of El Paso,
L.P.   (3)
1300 Murchison Dr Ste 180, El Paso, TX
79902
Tel.: (915) 613-0811
Web Site: http://www.epgastro.com
Outpatient Surgical Center
N.A.I.C.S.: 621498

The Endoscopy Center of Knoxville,
L.P.   (3)
1311 Dowell Springs Blvd, Knoxville, TN
37909-2706
Tel.: (865) 684-4686
Web Site:
   https://www.knoxvilleendocenter.com
Health Care Srvices
N.A.I.C.S.: 622110
Jeff Dew (CEO)

The Endoscopy Center of Santa Fe,
L.P.   (3)
1630 Hospital Dr Ste A, Santa Fe, NM
87505
Tel.: (505) 819-0662
Web Site:
   https://www.endocentersantafe.com
Outpatient Surgical Center
N.A.I.C.S.: 621498

The Endoscopy Center of Southeast
Texas, L.P.   (3)
950 N 14th St Ste 200, Beaumont, TX
77702
Tel.: (409) 299-3550
Web Site:
   https://www.southeasttexasendo.com
Outpatient Surgical Center
N.A.I.C.S.: 621498

The Endoscopy Center of St.
Thomas, L.P.   (3)
4230 Harding Rd Ste 400, Nashville, TN
37205
Tel.: (615) 338-7530
Web Site: https://stmgendo.com
Endoscopy Surgical Services
N.A.I.C.S.: 621493

The Endoscopy Center of Topeka,
L.P.   (3)
2200 SW 6th St Ste 103, Topeka, KS
66606
Tel.: (785) 354-1254
Outpatient Surgical Center
N.A.I.C.S.: 621498

The Endoscopy Center of Washing-
ton D.C., L.P.   (3)
2021 K St NW Ste T-115, Washington, DC
20006
Tel.: (202) 640-1426
Web Site: https://www.endodc.com
Outpatient Surgical Center
N.A.I.C.S.: 621498

The Endoscopy Center of the South
Bay, L.P.   (3)
23560 Madison St Ste 109, Torrance, CA
90505
Tel.: (310) 325-6331
Web Site: http://www.southbaygastro.com
Outpatient Surgery Center
N.A.I.C.S.: 621498

The Englewood ASC, LLC   (3)
499 E Hampden Ave Ste 420, Englewood,
CO 80113
Tel.: (303) 788-8888
Web Site:
   http://www.southdenverendoscopy.com
Outpatient Surgical Center
N.A.I.C.S.: 621498

The Florham Park Endoscopy ASC,
LLC   (3)
195 Columbia Tpke Ste 110, Florham Park,
NJ 07932
Tel.: (973) 947-7511
Web Site: https://www.florhamparkendo.com
Outpatient Surgical Center
N.A.I.C.S.: 621498

The Glendora CA Endoscopy ASC,
L.P.   (3)
1794 S Barranca Ave, Glendora, CA 91740
Tel.: (626) 723-3844
Web Site:
   https://www.glendoradigestive.com
Health Care Srvices
N.A.I.C.S.: 622110
Cecilia Giancanelli (Dir-Center)

The Greensboro NC Endoscopy ASC,
LLC   (3)
1593 Yancyville St Ste 100, Greensboro,
NC 27405-6948
Tel.: (336) 740-9916
Web Site:
   https://www.guilfordendoscopy.com
Health Care Srvices
N.A.I.C.S.: 622110

The Greensboro Opthalmology ASC,
LLC   (3)
3312 Battleground Ave, Greensboro, NC
27410
Tel.: (336) 282-8331
Outpatient Surgical Center
N.A.I.C.S.: 621498

The Greenville ASC, LLC   (3)
14 Hawthorne Park Ct, Greenville, SC
29615-3194
Tel.: (864) 610-3750
Web Site:
   http://www.endocenterupstate.com
Health Care Srvices
N.A.I.C.S.: 622110

The Hanover NJ Endoscopy ASC,
LLC   (3)
91 Jefferson Rd Ste 300, Whippany, NJ
07981
Tel.: (973) 658-5022
Web Site: https://www.hanoverendo.com
Cancer Screening & Gastroenterology Cen-
ter
N.A.I.C.S.: 621493

The Hillmont ASC, L.P.   (3)
1528 Bethlehem Pike, Flourtown, PA 19031
Tel.: (215) 395-8007
Web Site: https://www.springfieldasc.com
Health Care Srvices
N.A.I.C.S.: 622110

The Kissimmee FL Endoscopy ASC,
LLC   (3)
715 Oak Commons Blvd, Kissimmee, FL
34741
Tel.: (407) 910-3071
Web Site:
   https://www.kissimmeeendocenter.com
Endoscopic Facility Center Operator
N.A.I.C.S.: 621493

The La Jolla Endoscopy Center,
L.P.   (3)
9850 Genesee Ave Ste 980, La Jolla, CA
92037
Tel.: (858) 412-7190
Web Site: http://www.lajollaendoscopy.com
Outpatient Surgical Center
N.A.I.C.S.: 621498

The Lakeland FL Endoscopy ASC,
LLC   (3)
3340 Lakeland Hills Blvd, Lakeland, FL
33805
Tel.: (863) 682-3239
Web Site: https://www.lakelandgi.com
Colon Cancer Screening Center Operator
N.A.I.C.S.: 622310

The Lancaster PA Endoscopy ASC,
L.P.   (3)
2112 Harrisburg Pike Ste 323, Lancaster,
PA 17601
Tel.: (717) 925-8888
Web Site:
   http://www.midatlanticendoscopycen
   ter.com
Outpatient Surgical Center
N.A.I.C.S.: 621498

The Las Vegas East Ophthalmology
ASC, LLC   (3)
3575 Pecos-McLeod, Las Vegas, NV
89121-3803
Tel.: (702) 819-8417
Web Site: https://www.shepherdeye.com

KKR & Co, Inc.—(Continued)

Health Care Srvices
N.A.I.C.S.: 622110

The Laurel MD Endoscopy ASC, LLC
7350 Van Dusen Rd Ste 230, Laurel, MD 20707
Tel.: (301) 867-0492
Web Site:
https://www.endocentermaryland.com
Eye Care Surgery Center Operator
N.A.I.C.S.: 622310

The Main Line PA Endoscopy ASC, L.P. (3)
325 W Central Ave Lowr Level, Malvern, PA 19355
Tel.: (610) 482-4529
Web Site:
https://www.mainlineendoscopy.com
Cancer Screening & Gastroenterology Center
N.A.I.C.S.: 622310

The Maryville ASC, L.P. (3)
1706 E Lamar Alexander Pkwy, Maryville, TN 37804-6204
Tel.: (865) 238-5621
Web Site: https://www.tenneseeendo.com
Health Care Srvices
N.A.I.C.S.: 622110

The Melbourne ASC, L.P. (3)
1401 S Apollo Blvd Ste B, Melbourne, FL 32901
Tel.: (321) 369-9610
Web Site:
https://www.surgerymelbourne.com
Health Care Srvices
N.A.I.C.S.: 622110

The Middletown Endoscopy ASC, LLC (3)
257 N Breiel Blvd, Middletown, OH 45042
Tel.: (513) 422-5990
Web Site: https://www.thegiendocenter.com
Health Care Srvices
N.A.I.C.S.: 622110

The Minneapolis Ophthalmology ASC, LLC
8401 Golden Vly Rd Ste 340, Golden Valley, MN 55427
Tel.: (763) 447-3321
Web Site: https://www.mplseye.com
Outpatient Surgical Center
N.A.I.C.S.: 621498

The Nashville TN Ophthalmology ASC, LLC (3)
907 Rivergate Pkwy, Goodlettsville, TN 37072-2324
Tel.: (615) 859-3121
Health Care Srvices
N.A.I.C.S.: 622110

The Newark Endoscopy ASC, LLC (3)
1090 Old Churchmans Rd, Newark, DE 19713-2102
Tel.: (302) 246-5140
Web Site:
https://www.endoscopycenterofdelaware.com
Health Care Srvices
N.A.I.C.S.: 622110

The Northern NV Endoscopy ASC, LLC (3)
5250 Kietzke Ln, Reno, NV 89511-2073
Tel.: (775) 473-6949
Web Site:
https://www.digestivehealthreno.com
Health Care Srvices
N.A.I.C.S.: 622110

The Oakland CA Endoscopy ASC, L.P. (3)
300 Frank Ogawa Plz Ste 135, Oakland, CA 94612
Tel.: (510) 984-2740
Web Site: https://www.eastbayendo.com
Health Care Srvices
N.A.I.C.S.: 622110

The Ocala Endoscopy ASC, L.P. (3)
1160 SE 18th Pl, Ocala, FL 34471
Tel.: (352) 261-0499

Web Site:
https://www.endoscopycenterofocala.com
Health Care Srvices
N.A.I.C.S.: 622110

The Orlando FL Endoscopy ASC, LLC (3)
11140 W Colonial Dr Ste 3, Ocoee, FL 34761
Tel.: (407) 656-2700
Web Site:
https://www.centralfloridagicenters.com
Health Care Srvices
N.A.I.C.S.: 622110

The Orlando/Mills FL Endoscopy ASC, LLC (3)
1817 N Mills Ave, Orlando, FL 32803
Tel.: (407) 896-1726
Web Site:
https://www.centerfordigestivehealth.net
Health Care Srvices
N.A.I.C.S.: 622110

The Overland Park KS Endoscopy ASC, LLC (3)
10200 W 105th St Ste 100, Overland Park, KS 66212-5750
Tel.: (913) 492-0800
Web Site: http://www.kc-gi.com
Health Care Srvices
N.A.I.C.S.: 622110

The Paducah Ophthalmology ASC, LLC (3)
100 Medical Ctr Dr, Paducah, KY 42003-7909
Tel.: (270) 908-0564
Web Site:
https://www.eyesurgerypaducah.com
Health Care Srvices
N.A.I.C.S.: 622110

The Phoenix Ophthalmology ASC, LLC (3)
300 E Osborn Rd Ste 102, Phoenix, AZ 85012-2383
Tel.: (602) 910-6870
Web Site:
https://www.arizonaeyesurgerycenter.com
Ambulatory Surgery Center Operator
N.A.I.C.S.: 621493

The Pikesville MD Endoscopy ASC, LLC (3)
1838 Greene Tree Rd Ste 180, Baltimore, MD 21208
Tel.: (410) 505-4461
Web Site:
https://www.endocentreofbaltimore.com
Health Care Srvices
N.A.I.C.S.: 622110

The Pottsville PA Endoscopy ASC, L.P. (3)
48 Tunnel Rd 103, Pottsville, PA 17901
Tel.: (507) 225-4077
Web Site:
https://www.schuylkillendoscopy.com
Health Care Srvices
N.A.I.C.S.: 622110

The Raleigh NC Endoscopy ASC, LLC (3)
8300 Health Park Ste 210, Raleigh, NC 27615
Tel.: (919) 249-5902
Web Site:
https://www.raleighendoscopy.com
Health Care Srvices
N.A.I.C.S.: 622110

The Rockledge FL Endoscopy ASC, LLC (3)
1974 Rockledge Blvd Ste 102, Rockledge, FL 32955
Tel.: (321) 252-4411
Web Site:
https://www.spacecoastendocenter.com
Outpatient Surgery Center Operator
N.A.I.C.S.: 621498

The Rockville/ESC-North MD Endoscopy ASC, LLC (3)
15005 Shady Grove Rd Ste 300, Rockville, MD 20850
Tel.: (301) 825-9701
Web Site: https://www.escm-north.com
Health Care Srvices

N.A.I.C.S.: 622110
Jamie Spencer *(CFO)*

The Rogers AR Ophthalmology ASC, LLC (3)
3737 W Walnut St, Rogers, AR 72756-1839
Tel.: (479) 246-1700
Web Site: https://www.boozmanhof.com
Health Care Srvices
N.A.I.C.S.: 622110

The Salem OR Ophthalmology ASC, LLC (3)
1330 Commercial St SE, Salem, OR 97302
Web Site: https://salemeyesurgery.com
Eye Care Surgery Center
N.A.I.C.S.: 622310

The San Antonio TX Endoscopy ASC, L.P. (3)
150 E Sonterra Blvd Ste 110, San Antonio, TX 78258
Tel.: (210) 775-2265
Web Site: http://www.saendocenter.com
Health Care Srvices
N.A.I.C.S.: 622110

The San Diego CA Multi-Specialty ASC, LLC (3)
7485 Mission Vly Rd Ste 106, San Diego, CA 92108-4422
Tel.: (619) 274-8522
Web Site: https://www.mvhsc.com
Health Care Srvices
N.A.I.C.S.: 622110
Alexander Gavin *(Office Mgr)*

The San Luis Obispo CA Endoscopy ASC, L.P. (3)
77 Casa St Ste 106, San Luis Obispo, CA 93405
Tel.: (805) 771-4041
Web Site:
http://www.centralcoastendoscopy.com
Outpatient Surgical Center
N.A.I.C.S.: 621498

The Sarasota Endoscopy ASC, LLC (3)
2800 Bahia Vista St Ste 300, Sarasota, FL 34239
Tel.: (941) 373-9808
Web Site: https://www.bayviewsurgeryfl.com
Outpatient Surgical Center
N.A.I.C.S.: 621498

The Sarasota Ophthalmology ASC, LLC (3)
2121 S Tamiami Trl, Sarasota, FL 34233-1207
Tel.: (941) 955-6363
Web Site: https://www.srqeye.com
Eye Care Surgery Center Operator
N.A.I.C.S.: 622310

The Seneca PA ASC, LLC (3)
3744 State Route 257, Seneca, PA 16346-3318
Tel.: (814) 677-6700
Outpatient Surgical Center
N.A.I.C.S.: 621498

The Sidney ASC, LLC (3)
283 Looney Rd, Piqua, OH 45356
Tel.: (937) 778-3848
Web Site:
https://www.valleyregionalsurgery.com
Ambulatory Surgery Center Operator
N.A.I.C.S.: 621493

The Silver Spring MD Endoscopy ASC, LLC (3)
10801 Lockwood Dr Ste 110, Silver Spring, MD 20901
Tel.: (301) 825-9680
Web Site: https://www.escm-silverspring.com
Outpatient Surgical Center
N.A.I.C.S.: 621498

The South Bend IN Endoscopy ASC, LLC (3)
53830 Generations Dr, South Bend, IN 46635
Tel.: (574) 271-0174
Web Site: https://www.michianaendo.com
Health Care Srvices
N.A.I.C.S.: 622110

The St. Cloud MN Ophthalmology ASC, LLC (3)

2055 N 15th St Ste B, Saint Cloud, MN 56303
Tel.: (320) 310-0951
Web Site:
https://www.stcloudeyesurgery.com
Health Care Srvices
N.A.I.C.S.: 622110

The St. Louis MO Orthopaedic ASC, LLC (3)
1050 Old Des Peres Rd Ste 150, Saint Louis, MO 63131-1874
Tel.: (314) 775-2264
Web Site: https://www.desperessquare-sc.com
Health Care Srvices
N.A.I.C.S.: 622110

The Suncoast Endoscopy ASC, L.P. (3)
3621 E Forest Dr, Inverness, FL 34453-0787
Tel.: (352) 637-4368
Web Site:
http://www.suncoastendoscopycenter.com
Health Care Srvices
N.A.I.C.S.: 622110

The Surgery Center of Middle Tennessee, LLC (3)
1050 N James Campbell Blvd Ste 120, Columbia, TN 38401
Tel.: (931) 548-4768
Web Site:
https://www.surgerycenterofmidtn.com
Outpatient Surgical Center
N.A.I.C.S.: 621498

The Temecula CA Endoscopy Center ASC, L.P. (3)
25150 Hancock Ave Ste 208, Murrieta, CA 92562-5989
Tel.: (951) 698-8805
Web Site: http://www.unitedgi.com
Outpatient Surgical Center
N.A.I.C.S.: 621498

The Toledo Endoscopy ASC, LLC (3)
4841 Monroe St, Toledo, OH 43623
Tel.: (419) 471-1350
Web Site: https://www.nwogastro.com
Health Care Srvices
N.A.I.C.S.: 622110

The Torrance CA Multi-Specialty ASC, LLC (3)
23500 Madison St, Torrance, CA 90505-4702
Tel.: (310) 803-9401
Web Site:
https://www.surgerycentersouthbay.com
Health Care Srvices
N.A.I.C.S.: 622110
Joe Devine *(Dir-Medical)*

The Tulsa OK Ophthalmology ASC, LLC (3)
7191 S Yale Ave, Tulsa, OK 74136
Tel.: (918) 894-5757
Web Site:
https://www.eyesurgerycenteroftulsa.com
Health Care Srvices
N.A.I.C.S.: 622110

The Voorhees NJ Endoscopy ASC, LLC (3)
93 Cooper Rd Ste 100, Voorhees, NJ 08043-4910
Tel.: (856) 432-4116
Web Site: https://www.theendocenter.com
Endoscopic Facility Specializing Services
N.A.I.C.S.: 621493

The Waldorf Endoscopy ASC, LLC (3)
3510 Old Washington Rd Ste 200, Waldorf, MD 20602-3233
Tel.: (301) 861-3660
Web Site: https://www.waldorfendo.com
Health Care Srvices
N.A.I.C.S.: 622110

The West Orange NJ Endoscopy ASC, LLC (3)
741 Northfield Ave Ste 102, West Orange, NJ 07052
Tel.: (973) 542-2470
Web Site: https://www.northfieldsurgical.com

Colon Cancer Screening Center Operator
N.A.I.C.S.: 622310

The Westglen Endoscopy Center, LLC (3)
16663 Midland Dr Ste 200, Shawnee, KS 66217-3042
Tel.: (913) 227-4618
Web Site: https://www.westglenendo.com
Health Care Srvices
N.A.I.C.S.: 622110

The Wichita Orthopaedic ASC, LLC (3)
7550 W Vlg Cir Ste 2, Wichita, KS 67205-9364
Tel.: (316) 838-8388
Web Site: https://surgerycenterkansas.com
Health Care Srvices
N.A.I.C.S.: 622110

The Willoughby ASC, LLC (3)
6025 Commerce Cir, Willoughby, OH 44094
Tel.: (440) 585-2750
Web Site:
http://www.willoughbysurgerycenter.com
Health Care Srvices
N.A.I.C.S.: 622110

The Winter Haven/Sebring FL Ophthalmology ASC, LLC (3)
409 Ave K SE, Winter Haven, FL 33880-4126
Tel.: (863) 594-1368
Web Site:
https://eyesurgeryandlasercenter.com
Health Care Srvices
N.A.I.C.S.: 622110

The Yuma AZ Endoscopy ASC, LLC (3)
1030 W 24th St Ste I, Yuma, AZ 85364-8384
Tel.: (928) 343-1717
Health Care Srvices
N.A.I.C.S.: 327910

Tiva Healthcare, Inc. (3)
1613 N Harrison Pkwy Ste 200, Sunrise, FL 33323
Tel.: (954) 858-1443
Web Site: http://staging.tivahealthcare.com
Human Resource Consulting Services
N.A.I.C.S.: 541612
Steven Samalekis (VP)
Gillian Arbas (VP)
Jackie Foster (VP-Ops)

Torrance Surgery Center, L.P. (3)
23560 Crenshaw Blvd Ste 104, Torrance, CA 90505
Tel.: (310) 986-2005
Web Site: https://www.torranceasc.com
Orthopedic Surgery Center Operator
N.A.I.C.S.: 622310

Towson Surgical Center, LLC (3)
1122 Kenilworth Dr Ste 17, Towson, MD 21204
Tel.: (410) 561-6743
Web Site: https://www.towsonasc.com
Outpatient Care Center Operator
N.A.I.C.S.: 621498

Triangle Endoscopy Center, LLC (3)
249 E NC 54 Ste 210, Durham, NC 27713
Tel.: (919) 544-4887
Web Site: https://www.dukehealth.org
Endoscopic Facility Center
N.A.I.C.S.: 621493
John Lytle (Dir-Center & Mgr)

Waco Gastroenterology Endoscopy Center, LLC (3)
364 Richland W Cir, Waco, TX 76712
Tel.: (254) 230-1109
Web Site: https://www.wacoendocenter.com
Endoscopic Facility Center Operator
N.A.I.C.S.: 621493

West Bank Surgery Center, LLC (3)
3704 Lapalco Blvd, Harvey, LA 70058-2332
Tel.: (504) 208-1846
Web Site: https://www.westbanksurgery.com
Health Care Srvices
N.A.I.C.S.: 622110

West Bridgewater MA Endoscopy ASC, LLC (3)

120 W Ctr St, West Bridgewater, MA 02379-1600
Tel.: (508) 659-4260
Web Site:
http://www.gastrointestinalspecialists.com
Health Care Srvices
N.A.I.C.S.: 622110

West Palm Outpatient Surgery & Laser Center, LTD (3)
200 Northpoint Pkwy, West Palm Beach, FL 33407
Tel.: (561) 615-0110
Health Care Srvices
N.A.I.C.S.: 622110

Weston Outpatient Surgical Center, Ltd. (3)
2229 N Commerce Pkwy, Weston, FL 33326-3239
Tel.: (954) 703-6559
Web Site: https://westonoutpatient.com
Outpatient Surgical Services
N.A.I.C.S.: 621999

Wilton Surgery Center, LLC (3)
195 Danbury Rd, Wilton, CT 06897
Tel.: (203) 423-8151
Web Site:
https://www.wiltonsurgerycenter.com
Ambulatory Surgery Center Operator
N.A.I.C.S.: 621493

Women's Health and Wellness of Jupiter Medical Specialists, LLC (3)
1210 S Old Dixie Hwy, Jupiter, FL 33458
Tel.: (561) 462-8540
Web Site: http://www.jupitermed.com
Health Care Srvices
N.A.I.C.S.: 622110

Subsidiary (Domestic):

Associated Eye Surgical Center, LLC (2)
1100 N Topeka St, Wichita, KS 67214
Tel.: (316) 844-7184
Web Site: https://associatedeyewichita.com
Health Care Srvices
N.A.I.C.S.: 621610

Brit Systems, LLC (2)
13737 Noel Rd Ste 120, Dallas, TX 75240
Tel.: (214) 630-0636
Web Site: https://www.brit.com
Medical Imaging & Ris Product Services
N.A.I.C.S.: 621512

Care Connection of Cincinnati, LLC (2)
4420 Cooper Rd Ste 120, Blue Ash, OH 45242
Tel.: (513) 842-1101
Web Site: http://www.gemcityhc.com
Health Care Srvices
N.A.I.C.S.: 621610

Community EMS, Inc. (2)
25400 W 8 Mile, Southfield, MI 48033
Tel.: (210) 260-8444
Web Site: https://www.communityems.net
Fiscal Year-end: 03/31/2014
Mobile Intensive Ambulance Services
N.A.I.C.S.: 621910
Nicholle Mehr (VP-Ops)

Connecticut Eye Surgery Center South, LLC (2)
60 Wellington Rd, Milford, CT 06461
Web Site:
https://www.connecticuteyesurgerycenter.com
Eye Surgery Center Services
N.A.I.C.S.: 621493

Direct Medical Supply, LLC (2)
1A Burton Hills Blvd, Nashville, TN 37215
Tel.: (615) 846-3835
Web Site:
https://www.directmedicalsupply.net
Medical Equipment Mfr
N.A.I.C.S.: 339112

Doctors Billing Service, Inc. (2)
335 14th Ave, San Francisco, CA 94118
Tel.: (415) 831-9000
Web Site:
https://www.doctorsbillingservices.org
Medical Billing Services
N.A.I.C.S.: 561110

Emergency Medical Transport, Inc. (2)
7100 Whipple Ave NW, North Canton, OH 44720
Tel.: (330) 478-4111
Web Site: https://www.emtambulance.com
Emergency Medical Transportation Services
N.A.I.C.S.: 621910

Envision Healthcare Holdings, Inc. (2)
1A Burton Hills Blvd, Nashville, TN 37215
Tel.: (615) 665-1283
Web Site: http://www.evhc.net
Holding Company; Emergency Medical Transportation & Other Medical Services
N.A.I.C.S.: 551112
James A. Rechtin (Pres & CEO)
Teresa Sparks (Exec VP & CFO)
Dave Esler (Chief Admin Officer)
Kristin Darby (Chief Information Officer)
Doug Smith (Pres-Envision Physician Svcs)

Subsidiary (Domestic):

BestPractices, Inc. (3)
10306 Eaton Pl Ste 180, Fairfax, VA 22030
Tel.: (703) 667-3499
Web Site: http://www.best-practices.com
Health Care Srvices
N.A.I.C.S.: 621610
Thom Mayer (Founder & CEO)

Guardian Health Care, Inc. (3)
1320 S Universirty Dr Ste 220, Fort Worth, TX 76107-5743
Tel.: (817) 882-8200
Web Site: http://www.guardmyhealth.com
Health Care Srvices
N.A.I.C.S.: 622110

Medics Ambulance Service, Inc. (3)
2500 NW 29th Manor, Pompano Beach, FL 33442-3106
Tel.: (305) 687-4040
Web Site: http://www.medicsambulance.com
Medical Devices
N.A.I.C.S.: 622110
Adam Ross (Mgr-Fin)
Stephanie Shaffer (Acct Exec)
Daniel Southwick (Mgr-Palm Beach County Ops)
Ernie Ferrara (Mgr-Fleet)
Stephen Webb (Mgr-Comm)

Reimbursement Technologies, Inc. (3)
1000 River Rd Ste 100, Conshohocken, PA 19428-2437
Tel.: (610) 834-9100
Health Care Srvices
N.A.I.C.S.: 622110

River Medical Incorporated (3)
415 El Camino Way, Lake Havasu City, AZ 86403
Tel.: (928) 855-4104
Web Site: http://www.amr.net
Health Care Srvices
N.A.I.C.S.: 622110
Frank Foti (CEO)

Rural/Metro Corporation (3)
8465 N Pima Rd, Scottsdale, AZ 85258
Tel.: (480) 627-6200
Ambulance & Fire Protection Services
N.A.I.C.S.: 561612

S. Fisher and S. Thomas, Inc. (3)
117 SE 1st St, Paris, TX 75460
Tel.: (903) 737-9865
Health Care Srvices
N.A.I.C.S.: 622110

Vista Staffing Solutions, Inc. (3)
2800 E Cottonwood Pkwy Ste 400, Cottonwood Heights, UT 84121
Tel.: (801) 487-8190
Web Site: https://www.vistastaff.com
Physician Staffing Services
N.A.I.C.S.: 561311
Andrea Nelson (Pres)

Subsidiary (Domestic):

Envision Physician Services, LLC (2)
1A Burton Hills Blvd, Nashville, TN 37215
Tel.: (615) 665-1283

Web Site:
https://www.envisionphysicianservices.com
Physician Services
N.A.I.C.S.: 622110

Gem City Home Care, LLC (2)
565 Metro Pl S Ste 160, Dublin, OH 43017
Tel.: (614) 588-0228
Web Site: http://www.gemcityhc.com
Women Healthcare Services
N.A.I.C.S.: 621610

Gold Cross Ambulance Services, Inc. (2)
1055 Wittmann Dr, Menasha, WI 54952-3606
Tel.: (920) 727-3020
Web Site: https://www.goldcross.org
Healthcare Ambulance Services
N.A.I.C.S.: 621910
Mark Fredrickson (Exec Dir)

Grace Behavioral Health, LLC (2)
1A Brookfield Glen Dr, Belvidere, NJ 07823
Tel.: (908) 652-5311
Web Site:
https://www.gracebehavioralhealth.org
Healtcare Services
N.A.I.C.S.: 623220

Herren Enterprises, Inc. (2)
46714 - 254th St, Crooks, SD 57020
Tel.: (605) 543-6010
Web Site: https://www.herreninc.com
Freight Brokerage Truck Services
N.A.I.C.S.: 327910

KMAC, Inc. (2)
19437 Vale Ave, Hutchinson, MN 55350
Tel.: (320) 587-9697
Web Site: https://www.kmacmn.com
Commercial Contract Services
N.A.I.C.S.: 236220
Rodney Krasen (Mgr-Comml Sls)
Jim McClure (Mgr-Comml Sls)

Knoxville Eye Anesthesia, LLC (2)
1A Burton Hills Blvd, Nashville, TN 37215-6187
Tel.: (865) 588-1037
Health Care Srvices
N.A.I.C.S.: 621610

LaSalle Ambulance, Inc. (2)
481 William L Gaiter Pkwy, Buffalo, NY 14215
Tel.: (716) 882-8400
Health Care Srvices
N.A.I.C.S.: 621610

Lifeline Ambulance Service, Inc. (2)
1439 Ferris Pl, Bronx, NY 10461
Tel.: (718) 824-4500
Web Site:
http://www.lifelineambulanceservice.com
Ambulance Service
N.A.I.C.S.: 621910
Cheryl Hampton-Smith (Pres)

Los Angeles/Inglewood Endoscopy ASC, LP (2)
8110 Airport Blvd 1st Fl, Los Angeles, CA 90045
Tel.: (213) 387-9000
Health Care Srvices
N.A.I.C.S.: 621610

Marlboro Hudson Ambulance & Wheelchair Service, Inc. (2)
401 Cedar Hill St, Marlborough, MA 01752-3036
Tel.: (508) 485-4544
Health Care Srvices
N.A.I.C.S.: 621610

Maryland Endoscopy Anesthesia, LLC (2)
1A Burton hills Blvd, Nashville, TN 37215
Tel.: (410) 494-0144
Health Care Srvices
N.A.I.C.S.: 621610

Maryland Surgery Center for Women, LLC (2)
11400 Rockville Pike Ste C25, Rockville, MD 20852-3063
Tel.: (301) 761-4760
Web Site:
http://www.marylandsurgerycenter.com
Elective Surgical Care Services

KKR & Co. Inc.—(Continued)
N.A.I.C.S.: 621493

Medics Emergency Services of Palm Beach County, Inc. (2)
6363 S Fifflers Green Cir Ste 1400, Greenwood Village, CO 80111
Tel.: (954) 763-1776
Health Care Srvices
N.A.I.C.S.: 621610

Mid-Atlantic Endoscopy, LLC (2)
2112 Harrisburg Pike 1st Fl Ste 100, Lancaster, PA 17601-2644
Tel.: (717) 925-8888
Web Site:
https://www.midatlanticendoscopycenter.com
Colorectal Cancer Screening Services
N.A.I.C.S.: 622310

Mississippi Coast Endoscopy and Ambulatory Surgery Center, Inc. (2)
2406 Catalpa Ave, Pascagoula, MS 39567-1813
Tel.: (228) 696-0818
Web Site: https://www.mscoastsurgery.com
Ambulatory Surgery Center Services
N.A.I.C.S.: 621493
Jennifer Cochran (Mgr-Nurse)

Nashville Gastrointestinal Specialists, LLC (2)
3443 Dickerson Pike Skyline Medical Plz Ste 750, Nashville, TN 37207
Tel.: (615) 868-1064
Web Site: http://www.nashvillegi.com
Health Care Services
N.A.I.C.S.: 621610

North Florida Anesthesia Consultants, P.A. (2)
1301 RiverPl Blvd Ste 2540, Jacksonville, FL 32207
Tel.: (904) 387-4030
Web Site:
https://www.northfloridaanesthesia.com
Anesthesia Care & Surgeons Services
N.A.I.C.S.: 621111

North Jersey Gastroenterology & Endoscopy Center, PA (2)
1825 Rte 23 S, Wayne, NJ 07470-7526
Tel.: (973) 996-4009
Web Site: https://www.njgastro.com
Health Care Srvices
N.A.I.C.S.: 621610

Northeast Endoscopy Center, LLC (2)
59 Lowes Way, Lowell, MA 01851-5018
Tel.: (978) 513-8755
Web Site:
https://www.northeastendoscopy.com
Health Care Srvices
N.A.I.C.S.: 621610

Ocean Springs Surgical and Endoscopy Center, LLC (2)
3301 Bienville Blvd, Ocean Springs, MS 39564-4318
Tel.: (228) 872-8854
Web Site: https://www.ossurgical.com
Endoscopy Surgical Services
N.A.I.C.S.: 621493

Phoenix Emergency Services of Inverness, LLC (2)
502 W Highland Blvd, Inverness, FL 34452
Tel.: (919) 425-1565
Health Care Srvices
N.A.I.C.S.: 621610

ProvidaCare, LLC (2)
21 Cypress Blvd Ste 1150, Round Rock, TX 78664
Tel.: (512) 733-6500
Web Site: http://www.providacare.com
Chronic Respiratory Care Services
N.A.I.C.S.: 621399

QRx Medical Management, LLC (2)
12221 Merit Dr Ste 1500, Dallas, TX 75251
Tel.: (214) 705-1155
Web Site: http://www.qrxmed.com
Medical Management & Practice Services
N.A.I.C.S.: 622110

Radiology Associates of Hollywood, Inc. (2)

500 N Hiatus Rd Ste 200, Pembroke Pines, FL 33026
Tel.: (954) 437-4800
Web Site: https://www.rahrad.com
Health Care Services
N.A.I.C.S.: 621610

River Drive Surgery Center, LLC (2)
619 River Dr 1st Fl, Elmwood Park, NJ 07407
Tel.: (201) 693-4330
Web Site: https://www.riverdrivesurgery.com
Health Care Srvices
N.A.I.C.S.: 621610

SXR Medical, LLC (2)
645 E Missouri Ave Ste 300, Phoenix, AZ 85012
Tel.: (479) 667-4000
Web Site:
http://www.envisionphysicianservices.com
Digital Radiology Services
N.A.I.C.S.: 621512

Sentinel Healthcare Services, LLC (2)
3155 N Point Pkwy F100, Alpharetta, GA 30005
Tel.: (770) 645-9181
Health Care Srvices
N.A.I.C.S.: 621610

South Portland Surgical Center, LLC (2)
6370 SW Borland Rd Ste 100, Tualatin, OR 97062-9768
Tel.: (503) 218-1105
Web Site:
https://www.southportlandsurgicalcenter.com
Ambulatory Surgery Care Services
N.A.I.C.S.: 621493

Surgical Center at Millburn, LLC (2)
37 E Willow St, Millburn, NJ 07041-1416
Tel.: (973) 821-3387
Web Site:
https://www.millburnsurgicalcenter.com
Outpatient Surgical Center Services
N.A.I.C.S.: 621493

Surgical Specialty Center of Northeastern Pennsylvania, LLC (2)
190 Welles St Ste 150, Forty Fort, PA 18704-4968
Tel.: (570) 263-4091
Web Site:
https://www.surgicalspecialtycenterofnepa.com
Surgical Specialty Center Services
N.A.I.C.S.: 621493

Waverly Surgery Center, LLC (2)
400 Forest Ave, Palo Alto, CA 94301
Tel.: (650) 285-6919
Web Site: https://www.waverleysurgery.com
Surgery Center Services
N.A.I.C.S.: 621493

Westmed Ambulance Service, Inc. (2)
14275 Wicks Blvd, San Leandro, CA 94577
Tel.: (510) 614-1420
Web Site:
https://www.westmedambulance.com
Healthcare Ambulance Services
N.A.I.C.S.: 621910

Exact Holding N.V. (1)
Molengraaffsingel 33, 2629 JD, Delft, Netherlands
Tel.: (31) 15 711 50 00
Web Site: http://www.exact.com
Sales Range: $250-299.9 Million
Emp.: 1,400
Holding Company; Business Software Publisher & Distr
N.A.I.C.S.: 551112
Paul Ramakers (Member-Mgmt Bd & Mng Dir-Bus Solutions)
Onno Krap (CFO & Member-Mgmt Bd)
Hartmut Wagner (Member-Mgmt Bd & Mng Dir-Cloud Solutions)
Ken Leong Lee (Mgr-Dev)
Shamin Khurana (Principal-Infrastructure & Ops)
Olivier Constant (Sls Mgr)
Sanjeev Bharadwaj (Engr-Software)
Marco Kastrop (Mgr-UX Dev)
Phill Robinson (CEO)

Subsidiary (Domestic):

Exact EMEA B.V. (2)
Molengraaffsingel 33, 2629 JD, Delft, Netherlands (100%)
Tel.: (31) 157115100
Web Site: http://www.exact.com
Sales Range: $50-74.9 Million
Emp.: 60
Holding Company; Regional Managing Office
N.A.I.C.S.: 551112
Neeta Solanki-Unger (Mktg Mgr)

Subsidiary (Non-US):

Exact Espana SL (3)
Paseo de la Castellana 200 Planta 9, 28046, Madrid, Spain (100%)
Tel.: (34) 912309632
Web Site: https://www.exact.com
Sales Range: $25-49.9 Million
Emp.: 40
Cloud Software Applications & Integration
N.A.I.C.S.: 513210

Exact Software (UK) Ltd. (3)
1 Bartholomew Lane, London, EC2N 2AX, United Kingdom
Tel.: (44) 2083964058
Web Site: https://www.exact.com
Sales Range: $50-74.9 Million
Emp.: 10
Software Publisher
N.A.I.C.S.: 513210
Jaime Stewart (Mng Dir)

Subsidiary (Domestic):

Exact Manufacturing Systems (UK) Ltd (4)
The Mille 5th Floor 1000 Great West Road, Brentford, TW8 9HH, United Kingdom (100%)
Tel.: (44) 208 396 4058
Web Site: http://www.exact.com.uk
Sales Range: $25-49.9 Million
Emp.: 5
Business & Manufacturing Software
N.A.I.C.S.: 541511
Jason Palmer (Sr Mgr-Sls)
Malcom Coton (Mgr-Channel Dev)

Subsidiary (Non-US):

Exact Software Belgium N.V. (3)
Koningin Astridlaan 166, 1780, Wemmel, Belgium (100%)
Tel.: (32) 27111511
Web Site: https://www.exact.com
Sales Range: $25-49.9 Million
Emp.: 60
Software Publisher
N.A.I.C.S.: 513210

Exact Software Czech Republic, s.r.o. (3)
Antala Staska 510/38, 14000, Prague, 4, Czech Republic
Tel.: (420) 241 049 011
Web Site: http://www.exact.co.cz
Emp.: 14
Information Technology Software Solutions
N.A.I.C.S.: 541511

Exact Software France SARL (3)
6 rue Marius Aufan, 92300, Levallois-Perret, France (100%)
Tel.: (33) 173098749
Web Site: http://www.exact.com
Sales Range: $25-49.9 Million
Emp.: 15
Accounting Software & Services
N.A.I.C.S.: 513210

Exact Software Poland Sp. z o.o. (3)
ul Krzemowa 1, Zlotniki, 62-002, Suchy Las, Poland
Tel.: (48) 618580600
Web Site: https://www.exact.com
Sales Range: $25-49.9 Million
Emp.: 50
Financial & Cloud Software Publishers
N.A.I.C.S.: 513210

Subsidiary (Domestic):

Exact Group B.V (2)
Molengraaffsingel 33, 2629 JD, Delft, Netherlands

Tel.: (31) 157115000
Web Site: http://www.exact.nl
Software Development Services
N.A.I.C.S.: 541511

Subsidiary (Domestic):

Exact International Development B.V. (3)
Dr Klinkertweg 25a, Zwolle, 8025 BR, Netherlands
Tel.: (31) 15 711 51 00
Web Site: http://www.exact.nl
Sales Range: $75-99.9 Million
Cloud Software Development Services
N.A.I.C.S.: 541512
Erik van der Meijden (CEO)
Sanjeev Bharadwaj Venu Gopala (Engr & Android Developer)

Exact Online B.V. (3)
Molengraaffsingel 33, 2629 JD, Delft, Netherlands
Tel.: (31) 15 711 51 00
Web Site: http://www.exact.com
Emp.: 500
Online Accounting Software Development Services
N.A.I.C.S.: 541511
Serge Leloux (Dir-Acctg)

Subsidiary (Domestic):

Exact Nederland B.V. (2)
Molengraaffsingel 33, 2629 JD, Delft, Netherlands (100%)
Tel.: (31) 157115100
Web Site: https://www.exact.com
Sales Range: $350-399.9 Million
Holding Company; Business Software Publisher & Distr
N.A.I.C.S.: 551112
Hartmut Wagner (Mng Dir-Cloud Solutions)

Subsidiary (Domestic):

Exact Software Nederland B.V. - Eindhoven (3)
Sciencepark 5008, 5692 EA, Son, Netherlands (100%)
Tel.: (31) 157115100
Web Site: http://www.exact.nl
Sales Range: $150-199.9 Million
Business Accounting Software Publisher
N.A.I.C.S.: 513210
Paul Ramakers (Mng Dir-Bus Solutions)

Subsidiary (Non-US):

Exact Software (Antilles) N.V. (2)
Schottegatweg Oost 82-84 B1, Willemstad, Curacao
Tel.: (599) 9 4650077
Web Site: http://www.exactcaribbean.com
Sales Range: $25-49.9 Million
Emp.: 1
Software Development Services
N.A.I.C.S.: 541511
Densie Marie Testing (Gen Mgr-Willemstad & Curacao)

Exact Software (Shanghai) Co., Ltd. (2)
Park Place 38F No1601 Nanjing West Rd, Jing'an District, Shanghai, 200040, China
Tel.: (86) 2152925666
Web Site: https://www.exact.com
Sales Range: $25-49.9 Million
Emp.: 25
Software Development Services
N.A.I.C.S.: 541511

Exact Software Asia Sdn. Bhd. (2)
Suite A6-1,2&3 Northpoint Mid Valley City No 1 Medan Syed Putra Utara, 59200, Kuala Lumpur, Malaysia (100%)
Tel.: (60) 3 2081 6888
Web Site: http://www.exact.asia
Holding Company; Regional Managing Office
N.A.I.C.S.: 551112

Subsidiary (Domestic):

Exact Software (Malaysia) Sdn. Bhd. (3)
Suite A6-1,2&3 Northpoint Mid Valley City No 1 Medan Syed Putra Utara, 59200, Kuala Lumpur, Malaysia
Tel.: (60) 3 2081 6888

Web Site: http://www.exact.asia
Business Software Developer, Publisher,
Distr & Support Services
N.A.I.C.S.: 513210
Onno Krap (CFO)

Subsidiary (Non-US):

Exact Software Australia Pty Ltd (2)
Suite 401 Level 4 15 Help Street, Chatswood, 2067, NSW, Australia
Tel.: (61) 284481900
Web Site: http://www.exactsoftware.com.au
Sales Range: $25-49.9 Million
Emp.: 6
Software Development Services
N.A.I.C.S.: 541511
Elisabeth Schindler (Mgr-Territory)

Subsidiary (US):

**Exact Software North America
LLC** (2)
3600 American Blvd W, Bloomington, MN
55431
Web Site: http://www.exact.com
Sales Range: $50-74.9 Million
Emp.: 200
Business Software Publisher, Distr & Support Services
N.A.I.C.S.: 513210
Robin W. Foster (Gen Counsel)
Dan Griffin (Dir-Product Mktg & Product
Mgmt)
Mike Stadelman (Dir-Mktg)

Subsidiary (Non-US):

**Exact Software Singapore Pte
Ltd.** (2)
30 Cecil Street 19-08 Prudential Tower, Singapore, 049712, Singapore
Tel.: (65) 65365719
Web Site: http://www.exact.com
Sales Range: $25-49.9 Million
Emp.: 7
Software Development Services
N.A.I.C.S.: 541511

**Exact Software de Mexico S.A. de
C.V.** (2)
Av Mariano Otero No 1249 B-243 Col
Rinconada del Bosque, CP 44530, Guadalajara, Jalisco, Mexico
Tel.: (52) 33 31 34 4333
Web Site: http://la.exact.com
Software Development Services
N.A.I.C.S.: 541511

Exact Southeast Asia Sdn. Bhd. (2)
199 Jalan Tun Razak Suite 8-01 8-02 Level
8 G Tower, 50400, Kuala Lumpur, Malaysia
Tel.: (60) 321794241
Web Site: https://www.exact.com
Software Development & Cloud Solutions
Services
N.A.I.C.S.: 541511

Subsidiary (Non-US):

**Exact Software (International)
N.V.** (3)
Schottegatweg Oost 82-84 B1, Willemstad,
Curacao
Tel.: (599) 9 4650077
Web Site: http://www.exactcaribbean.com
Sales Range: $25-49.9 Million
Emp.: 1
Software Development Services
N.A.I.C.S.: 541511
Denise Marie Testing (Gen Mgr-Willemstad
& Curacao)

**Global Atlantic Financial Group
Limited** (1)
4 World Trade Ctr 51st Fl 150 Greenwich
St, New York, NY 10282 (63.3%)
Tel.: (866) 645-2449
Web Site: http://www.globalatlantic.com
Holding Company; Life, Annuity, Property &
Casualty Reinsurance Products & Services
N.A.I.C.S.: 551112
Jamie Kosharek (Head-Independent Channel Distr)
Allan Levine (Founder, Chm & CEO)
Kim Lee (CFO)
Dan O'Shea (Chief HR Officer)
Dave Wilken (Pres-Traditional Life-Global
Atlantic)
Sam Barnett (Head-Sls-Life Insurance Bus)

Rob Arena (Pres & Head-Individual Markets)
Samuel Ramos (Chief Legal Officer, Gen
Counsel & Sec)
Padma Elmgart (CTO & Mng Dir)
Peggy Poon (Treas)
Philip Sherrill (Chief Strategy Officer)
Dave Schalleur (Head-Partnerships)
Emily LeMay (COO)

Subsidiary (Domestic):

**Accordia Life and Annuity
Company** (2)
215 10th St Ste 100, Des Moines, IA 50309
Tel.: (515) 283-2371
Web Site: http://www.athene.com
Sales Range: $200-249.9 Million
Emp.: 300
Life Insurance
N.A.I.C.S.: 524113
Steven L. Hinrichs (Sr VP-Sls)
Maureen H. Henderson (Sr VP, Chief Compliance Officer, Sec & Assoc Gen Counsel)
Nicholas Von Moltke (CEO)
Chris K. Guttin (VP-Analytics & Data Mgmt)
Virginia L. Craig (VP-New Bus, Underwriting
& Ops)
Kathy J. Bauer (Sr VP-HR)
Tom Doruska (VP-Pricing & Product Dev)
David E. Neve (VP & Chief Actuary)
Mark Elming (Sr VP-Tech)
Brock Scheck (VP-Bus Ops)
Dave Wilken (Pres)

Commonwealth Annuity & Life Insurance Company (2)
132 Turnpike Rd Ste 210, Southborough,
MA 01772 (100%)
Tel.: (508) 460-2400
Web Site:
http://www.commonwealthannuity.com
Rev.: $517,631,116
Assets: $9,112,717,357
Liabilities: $8,762,382,778
Net Worth: $350,334,579
Earnings: ($7,389,090)
Fiscal Year-end: 12/31/2012
Life & Pension Reinsurance Products &
Services
N.A.I.C.S.: 524130
Margot Kibbe Wallin (Chief Compliance Officer & VP)
Allan Steven Levine (Chm)
Kevin Francis Leavey (VP & Actuary-Product)
Robert Evan Winawer (VP-Risk)
Mark Andelin (VP)

**Forethought Financial Group,
Inc.** (1)
300 N Meridian St Ste 1800, Indianapolis,
IN 46204
Tel.: (713) 212-4610
Web Site: http://www.forethought.com
Sales Range: $800-899.9 Million
Emp.: 275
Fire Insurance Services
N.A.I.C.S.: 524113
Craig Anderson (Chief Acctg Officer, Sr VP
& Controller)
Paula Nelson (Pres-Forethought Distributors)
David de Gorter (Pres)

Global Medical Response, Inc. (1)
6363 S Fiddlers Green Cir, Greenwood Village, CO 80111
Tel.: (303) 495-1264
Web Site:
http://www.globalmedicalresponse.com
Medical Transportation; Emergency Airlifts &
Ambulance Medical Services
N.A.I.C.S.: 621910

Subsidiary (Domestic):

Air Evac EMS, Inc. (2)
1001 Boardwalk Springs Pl Ste 250,
O'Fallon, MO 63368
Tel.: (636) 695-5400
Web Site: https://www.lifeteam.net
Sales Range: $75-99.9 Million
Emp.: 4,000
Air Medical Transport Service
N.A.I.C.S.: 481219
Daniel Sweeza (COO)

Air Medical Ltd. (2)

402 E Ramsey Rd, San Antonio, TX 78216
Tel.: (210) 945-8959
Web Site: http://www.air-medical.com
Sales Range: $1-9.9 Million
Emp.: 24
Air Ambulance Services
N.A.I.C.S.: 621910
Joe V. McCart (Chm)
Marty Dyer (Dir-Ops)
Dan Thompson (Controller)
Tim Morgan (CEO)
Steve Soliz (Dir-Bus Dev)

**American Medical Response,
Inc.** (2)
6363 S Fiddlers Green Cir 14th Fl, Greenwood Village, CO 80111
Tel.: (303) 495-1200
Web Site: http://www.amr.net
Emergency & Non-Emergency Transportation
N.A.I.C.S.: 621910
Edward M. Racht (Chief Medical Officer)
Tom Maxian (Pres-Northeast)
Jeffery McCollom (Sr VP-Bus Dev)
Randy Strozyk (Exec VP-Ops)
Richard Barr (VP-HR)
Sven Johnson (COO)
Timothy J. Dorn (CFO)
Tom Wagner (Pres-West Reg)
Amanda Doran (Chief Compliance Officer)
Donna Itzoe (VP-Mktg & Comm)
Steve Dralle (Pres-South)
Erik Rohde (Pres-Southeast)

Subsidiary (Domestic):

Abbott Ambulance, Inc. (3)
2500 Abbott Pl, Saint Louis, MO 63143
Tel.: (314) 768-1212
Health Care Srvices
N.A.I.C.S.: 622110

**American Medical Response Mid-
Atlantic, Inc.** (3)
426 N 8th St # 440, Philadelphia, PA 19123
Tel.: (215) 629-2600
Web Site: http://www.amr.net
Health Care Srvices
N.A.I.C.S.: 621610

American Medical Response Northwest, Inc. (3)
1 Se 2nd Ave, Portland, OR 97214
Tel.: (503) 239-0389
Web Site: http://www.amr.net
Ambulance Service
N.A.I.C.S.: 621910

American Medical Response of Colorado, Inc. (3)
6363 S Fiddlers Green Cir 14th Fl, Greenwood Village, CO 80111
Tel.: (303) 495-1200
Web Site: http://www.amr.net
Ambulance Service
N.A.I.C.S.: 621910

American Medical Response of Connecticut, Inc. (3)
55 Church St Fl 6, New Haven, CT 06510-3014
Tel.: (203) 562-4107
Web Site: http://www.amrwny.net
Health Care Srvices
N.A.I.C.S.: 621610

American Medical Response of Inland Empire (3)
7925 Ctr Ave, Rancho Cucamonga, CA
91730
Tel.: (909) 477-5000
Web Site: http://www.amr.net
Ambulance Service
N.A.I.C.S.: 621910

**American Medical Response of New
York, LLC** (3)
35 Bartels Pl, New Rochelle, NY 10801
Tel.: (844) 375-8747
Ambulance Service
N.A.I.C.S.: 621910
Michael Addario (VP-Ops-Northeast US)

Blythe Ambulance Service (3)
129 S 1st St, Blythe, CA 92225-2518
Tel.: (760) 922-8460
Health Care Srvices
N.A.I.C.S.: 621610

ComTrans, Inc. (3)
2336 E Magnolia St, Phoenix, AZ 85034
Tel.: (602) 231-0102
Web Site: https://www.gocomtrans.com
Ambulance Service
N.A.I.C.S.: 621910
L. Neal Thomas (Pres)
Mona Lee (Mgr-HR)
Anthony Jackson (Program Mgr)
Chris Soplop (Program Mgr)
Jay Meyer (Dir-Ops)
Bob Morrone (Mgr-Safety Program)
Tawana Scott (Supvr-Program)
Cyndi Cross (Exec VP)
Ricardo Bedoy (Mgr-Dispatch)
Lynne Carrel (Mgr-Program)
Jamerson Savant (Mgr-Fleet)
Chris Vanbrunt (Supvr-Driver)
Stephanie Cervantes (Supvr-Program)
Linda Des Lauriers (Supvr-Program)
Kimberly Foster (Supvr-Program)
Faray Gibson (Supvr-Program)
Larry Hintz (Supvr-Program)
Dayana Parra (Supvr-Program)
Donald Williams (Supvr-Program)
Diana Colin (Supvr-DCS New Hire)
Blanca Villalobos (Mgr-Billing)
Bruce Wilson (Coord-Trng)

International Life Support, Inc. (3)
6363 S Fiddlers Green Cir 14th fl, Greenwood Village, CO 80111
Tel.: (303) 495-1200
Web Site: https://www.amr.net
Emp.: 250
Ambulance Service
N.A.I.C.S.: 621910
Kurt Lorimoto (Dir)

Kurtz Ambulance Service, Inc. (3)
1900 Garnet Ct, New Lenox, IL 60451
Tel.: (815) 722-1900
Web Site: https://www.amr.net
Health Care Srvices
N.A.I.C.S.: 621610

LifeFleet Southeast, Inc. (3)
4914 W Knox St Ste 400, Tampa, FL
33634-8026
Tel.: (813) 885-3955
Web Site: http://www.amrwny.net
Health Care Srvices
N.A.I.C.S.: 621610

Medic West Ambulance, Inc. (3)
9 W Delhi Ave, North Las Vegas, NV 89032
Tel.: (702) 650-9900
Ambulance Service
N.A.I.C.S.: 621910

Puckett Ambulance Service, Inc. (3)
3760 Tramore Pointe Pkwy, Austell, GA
30106
Tel.: (770) 222-5045
Web Site: http://www.priorityambulance.com
Ambulance Service
N.A.I.C.S.: 621910

Rural/Metro Fire Dept., Inc. (3)
807 NE 6th St, Grants Pass, OR 97526
Tel.: (541) 474-1218
Web Site: http://www.ruralmetrofire.com
Fire Protection, Rescue & First Responder
Medical Services
N.A.I.C.S.: 922160

**Sunrise Handicap Transport
Corp.** (3)
1160 Lincoln Ave, Holbrook, NY 11741
Tel.: (631) 218-4070
Sales Range: $1-9.9 Million
Emp.: 60
Non-Emergency Ambulance Services
N.A.I.C.S.: 621910
Richard Barr (VP-HR)
Timothy J. Dorn (CFO & COO)
Jeffery McCollom (Sr VP-Innovative Practices & Bus Dev)
Tom McEntee (CEO-East Reg)
Leslie Mueller (CEO-South Div)
Edward M. Racht (Chief Medical Officer)
Randy Strozyk (Sr VP-Ops)
Ron Thackery (Sr VP-Pro Svcs & Integration)
Edward Van Horne (Pres & CEO)
Tom Wagner (CEO-West Reg)

Subsidiary (Domestic):

EMS Management, LLC (2)

KKR & Co. Inc.—(Continued)

321 Broadway St, Houston, TX 77012
Tel.: (832) 834-6459
Web Site:
  https://www.emsmanagement.com
Emp.: 50
Industrial Cleaning Services
N.A.I.C.S.: 562998

EagleMed LLC (2)
6601 W Pueblo Dr, Wichita, KS 67209
Tel.: (316) 613-4855
Web Site: https://www.flyeaglemed.com
Air Medical Transport Service
N.A.I.C.S.: 481219
Jon Wilson *(Dir-Maintenance)*

Guardian Flight, LLC (2)
10888 S 300 W, South Jordan, UT 84095
Tel.: (801) 619-4900
Web Site: https://guardianflight.com
Air Medical Transportation Services
N.A.I.C.S.: 481219

Med-Trans Corporation (2)
209 State Hwy 121 Bypass Ste 21, Lewis-
ville, TX 75067
Tel.: (972) 459-4919
Web Site: http://www.med-trans.net
Air Medical Transport Services
N.A.I.C.S.: 481219
Dennis Rohlfs *(Founder)*

Subsidiary (Domestic):

MidAtlantic MedEvac, L.L.C. (3)
230 N Broad St Ste 487, Philadelphia, PA
19102-1121
Tel.: (215) 762-4713
Sales Range: $10-24.9 Million
Emp.: 38
Air Medical Care Transport Services
N.A.I.C.S.: 624230
Brett Greenfield *(Dir-Medical)*

SevenBar Aviation, LLC (3)
8111 Lemmon Ave Hangar 4, Dallas, TX
75209
Tel.: (214) 904-9911
Web Site: http://www.7bar.com
Air Medical Operator & Fixed & Rotor Wing
Services
N.A.I.C.S.: 621999
Kim Montgomery *(Pres)*
Rolfe Black *(Chm)*
B. J. Raysor *(Sr VP-Ops)*
Darrell Rickert *(Dir-Maintenance)*
Calvin Folds *(Mgr-Fin)*
Steve Moody *(Dir-Ops)*
Sean Mulholland *(Dir-Safety)*
Analia Vaca *(Mgr-HR)*
Betsy Casanave *(Sr VP-Bus Dev & Strate-
gic Svcs)*

Subsidiary (Domestic):

**Professional Medical Transport,
Inc.** (2)
222 E Main St, Mesa, AZ 85201
Tel.: (480) 804-7400
Health Care Srvices
N.A.I.C.S.: 621610

**REACH Air Medical Services,
LLC** (2)
880 Cal Ctr Dr Ste 125, Sacramento, CA
95826
Tel.: (916) 921-4000
Web Site: https://www.reachair.com
Air Ambulance Services
N.A.I.C.S.: 621910
Rosemary Pitts *(Mng Dir)*
Eric Lampe *(Mng Dir)*

Rural Metro Corporation (2)
8465 N Pima Rd, Scottsdale, AZ 85258
Tel.: (800) 352-2309
Web Site: http://www.ruralmetro.com
Emergency Ambulance & Fire Protection
Services
N.A.I.C.S.: 922160

Subsidiary (Domestic):

**Rural/Metro of Northern Ohio,
Inc.** (3)
1380 Rio Rancho Dr SE Ste 349, Rio Ran-
cho, NM 87124
Tel.: (505) 433-2755
Web Site: https://www.physicianslifeline.com

Healthcare Ambulance Services
N.A.I.C.S.: 621910

GoDaddy, Inc. (1)
100 S Mill Ave Ste 1600, Tempe, AZ 85281
Tel.: (406) 760-7600
Web Site: https://www.godaddy.com
Rev.: $4,254,100,000
Assets: $7,564,900,000
Liabilities: $7,502,700,000
Net Worth: $62,200,000
Earnings: $1,374,800,000
Emp.: 6,159
Fiscal Year-end: 12/31/2023
Holding Company; Domain Name Registra-
tion Services
N.A.I.C.S.: 551112
Jared Sine *(Chief Strategy Officer & Chief
Legal Officer)*
Amanpal S. Bhutani *(CEO)*
Auguste Goldman *(Pres-Care & Svcs)*
Charles Beadnall *(CTO)*
Monica Bailey *(Chief People Officer)*
Fara Howard *(CMO)*
Roger Chen *(COO)*
Nick Daddario *(Chief Acctg Officer)*
Osama Bedier *(Pres-Commerce)*
Mark D. McCaffrey *(CFO)*
Paul Nicks *(Pres-Domain Registrars & In-
vestors)*
Laura Messerschmitt *(Pres-Intl Independ-
ents)*
Gourav Pani *(Pres-US Independents)*
Paul Bindel *(Pres-Partners)*

Subsidiary (Domestic):

GoDaddy.com, LLC (2)
14455 N Hayden Rd, Scottsdale, AZ 85260
Tel.: (480) 505-8800
Web Site: http://www.godaddy.com
Domain Name Registration Services
N.A.I.C.S.: 518210
Amanpal S. Bhutani *(CEO)*

Subsidiary (Non-US):

Host Europe Group Limited (2)
The Shipping Building Old Vinyl Factory
252-254 Blyth Road, Hayes, London, UB3
1HA, Mddx, United Kingdom
Tel.: (44) 345 450 2310
Web Site: http://www.heg.com
Domain Registrar Services
N.A.I.C.S.: 517810
Richard Winslow *(Brand Dir-123 Reg)*

Subsidiary (Domestic):

123-Reg Limited (3)
The Shipping Building Old Vinyl Factory
252-254 Blyth Road, Hayes, London, UB3
1HA, Mddx, United Kingdom
Tel.: (44) 3454502310
Web Site: https://www.123-reg.co.uk
Custom Web Hosting Services
N.A.I.C.S.: 517810
Richard Winslow *(Brand Dir)*

Subsidiary (Non-US):

Host Europe GmbH (3)
c/o WeWork Friesenplatz 4, 50672, Co-
logne, Germany
Tel.: (49) 22199999301
Web Site: https://www.hosteurope.de
Internet Hosting Services
N.A.I.C.S.: 518210
Claus Boyens *(Mng Dir)*
Tobias Mohr *(Mng Dir)*

Subsidiary (Domestic):

Main Street Hub Inc. (2)
600 Congress Ave Ste 1200, Austin, TX
78701
Tel.: (888) 900-0920
Online Reputation Management Services
N.A.I.C.S.: 561499

Media Temple, Inc. (2)
12655 W Jefferson Blvd Ste 400, Los Ange-
les, CA 90066
Tel.: (310) 841-5500
Web Site: https://www.mediatemple.net
Sales Range: $1-9.9 Million
Emp.: 225
Hosts Websites for Motion Graphic Artists,
Art Directors & Broadcast & Web Design
Firms
N.A.I.C.S.: 518210

Lou Kikos *(VP-Mktg)*

Outright, Inc. (2)
100 Mathilda Pl, Sunnyvale, CA 94086
Tel.: (650) 440-6352
Web Site: http://www.outright.com
Sales Range: $1-9.9 Million
Billing & Accounting Software Mfr
N.A.I.C.S.: 513210

Subsidiary (Non-US):

Special Domains Services, Inc. (2)
Tel.: (480) 505-8800
Domain Name Registration Services
N.A.I.C.S.: 541519

Subsidiary (Non-US):

Domains by Proxy, LLC (3)
Tel.: (480) 505-8800
Web Site: http://www.domainsbyproxy.com
Domain Name Registration Services
N.A.I.C.S.: 541519

Subsidiary (Domestic):

Starfield Technologies, Inc. (2)
14455 N Hayden Rd, Scottsdale, AZ 85260
Tel.: (480) 505-8825
Web Site: http://www.starfieldtech.com
Technology-Based Business Solutions De-
veloper
N.A.I.C.S.: 541512

Wild West Domains, Inc. (2)
2150 E Warner Rd, Tempe, AZ 85284
Tel.: (480) 624-2500
Web Site: https://www.wildwestdomains.com
Domain-Related Products & Services Re-
seller
N.A.I.C.S.: 541519
Blake J. Irving *(CEO)*

**Greenvolt - Energias Renovaveis,
S.A.** (1)
Rua Manuel Pinto de Azevedo 818, 4100-
320, Porto, Portugal (100%)
Tel.: (351) 213307722
Web Site: http://greenvolt.com
Rev.: $260,765,916
Assets: $1,879,523,202
Liabilities: $1,307,438,868
Net Worth: $572,084,333
Earnings: $31,310,168
Emp.: 486
Fiscal Year-end: 12/31/2022
Renewable Energy Services
N.A.I.C.S.: 221210
Joao Manso Neto *(CEO)*
Clementina Barroso *(Pres)*

Subsidiary (Domestic):

Greenvolt Next Portugal, Lda. (2)
Nucleo Empresarial da Venda do Pinheiro
Rua C Arm 56, 2665-602, Venda do Pin-
heiro, Portugal
Tel.: (351) 215801233
Solar Energy Distr
N.A.I.C.S.: 423330

Subsidiary (Non-US):

Tilbury Green Power Limited (2)
Port of Tilbury, Essex, Tilbury, RM18 7NU,
United Kingdom
Tel.: (44) 8000209634
Web Site: https://tilburygreenpower.com
Renewable Biomass Power Plant Services
N.A.I.C.S.: 221117

Headlands Research, Inc. (1)
145 Corte Madera Town Ctr, Corte Madera,
CA 94925
Tel.: (727) 543-4604
Web Site:
  https://www.headlandsresearch.com
Clinical Research Organization
N.A.I.C.S.: 541714
Mark Blumling *(Founder & CEO)*

Subsidiary (Domestic):

Clinical Research Atlanta (2)
175 Country Club Dr Ste 100A, Stockbridge, GA 30281-7380
Tel.: (404) 252-0699
Web Site:
  http://www.clinicalresearchatlanta.com

**Offices of Physicians (except Mental Health
Specialists)**
N.A.I.C.S.: 621111
Michelle Sowell *(Dir-Site)*
Nathan Segall *(Dir-Bus Dev)*
Karen Hickson *(Dir-Bus Dev)*

Pharmasite Research Inc. (2)
1314 Bedford Ave Ste 205, Pikesville, MD
21208-6605
Tel.: (410) 602-1440
Web Site:
  http://www.pharmasiteresearch.com
All Other Ambulatory Health Care Services
N.A.I.C.S.: 621999

Summit Research Network, Inc. (2)
2701 NW Vaughn St Ste 350, Portland, OR
97210-5354
Tel.: (206) 292-2273
Web Site:
  http://www.summitresearchnetwork.com
Diagnostic Imaging Centers
N.A.I.C.S.: 621512
Tawnya Andersen *(Mgr-Adv & Recruitment
Dept)*
James Hockley *(Pres)*

Heartland Dental, LLC (1)
1200 Network Centre Dr, Effingham, IL
62401
Tel.: (217) 540-5100
Web Site: https://heartland.com
Dental Practice Management Services
N.A.I.C.S.: 621210
Richard Workman *(Founder & Chm)*
Patrick Bauer *(Pres & CEO)*
DeAnn McClain *(COO)*
Travis J. Franklin *(CFO & Exec VP)*
Mark Greenstein *(Chief Growth Officer)*
Stacy DeWalt *(CMO)*
Jason Mattes *(Exec VP)*
Mohamed Attar *(Exec VP)*
Kirsty Leyland *(Chief HR Officer)*

**Hyperion Materials & Technologies,
Inc.** (1)
6325 Huntley Rd, Worthington, OH 43085
Tel.: (614) 438-2000
Web Site: https://www.hyperionmt.com
Emp.: 2,000
Hard Materials, Abrasives, Cutting-Tools &
Other Related Products Mfr
N.A.I.C.S.: 331492
Ron Voigt *(CEO)*
Brian Coate *(Sr VP)*
Rosemary Pitts *(Sr VP)*
Matthew Seymour *(VP)*
Marcy Ungar *(Chief HR Officer)*
Biju Varghese *(Sr VP)*

Subsidiary (Domestic):

Dura-Metal Products Corp. (2)
1552 Arona Road, Irwin, PA 15642
Tel.: (724) 864-9770
Web Site: http://www.dura-metal.com
Rev.: $6,666,666
Emp.: 100
Special Die & Tool, Die Set, Jig & Fixture
Mfr
N.A.I.C.S.: 333514
Joseph B. Freiland *(Pres)*
Joseph Freiland *(CEO)*

Subsidiary (Non-US):

**Hyperion Materials & Technologies
(Sweden) AB** (2)
Vastbergavagen 32, 126 30, Hagersten,
Sweden (100%)
Tel.: (46) 87266300
Web Site: http://www.hyperionmt.com
Cemented Carbide Powder & Wear Parts
Mfr
N.A.I.C.S.: 331492

Subsidiary (US):

Craftstech, Inc. (3)
91 Joey Dr, Elk Grove Village, IL 60007-
1301
Tel.: (847) 758-3100
Web Site: http://www.craftstech.net
Ultra-Hard Wear Parts & Specialized Cut-
ting Tools from Cemented Carbides Mfr
N.A.I.C.S.: 333515
Jeffrey Taylor *(Pres & CEO)*

Diamond Innovations, Inc. (3)

6325 Huntley Rd, Worthington, OH 43085
Tel.: (614) 438-2000
Industrial Diamond, Cubic Boron Nitride &
Polycrystalline Abrasive Products Mfr &
Distr
N.A.I.C.S.: 327910

Unit (Non-US):

Diamond Innovations International
Sales (4)
Clonshaugh Industrial Estate Clonshaugh,
Dublin, Ireland
Tel.: (353) 1 8037723
Metal Cutting Tool & Equipment Mfr
N.A.I.C.S.: 333515

Diamond Innovations International,
Inc. - European Headquarters (4)
Eibenstrasse 1D, D-63303, Dreieich, Germany
Tel.: (49) 61038920
Web Site: http://www.hyperionmt.com
Industrial Diamond, Cubic Boron Nitride &
Polycrystalline Abrasive Products Distr; Regional Managing Office
N.A.I.C.S.: 423840

Diamond Innovations, Inc. - Pacific
Headquarters (4)
Nisso 18 Building 7F 3-7-18 Shinyokohama,
Kohoku-ku, Yokohama, 222-0033, Kanagawa, Japan
Tel.: (81) 364201070
Web Site: http://www.hyperionmt.com
Industrial Diamond, Cubic Boron Nitride &
Polycrystalline Abrasive Products Distr; Regional Managing Office
N.A.I.C.S.: 423840

Subsidiary (Non-US):

Hyperion Materials & Technologies
(France) S.A.S. (3)
Quartier de la Gare, F-26210, Epinouze,
France (100%)
Tel.: (33) 475313800
Web Site: http://www.hyperionmt.com
Tungsten Carbide Wear Parts Mfr
N.A.I.C.S.: 332999

Hyperion Materials & Technologies
Germany GmbH (3)
Heerdter Landstrasse 243, Postfach
104451, 40035, Dusseldorf, Germany
Tel.: (49) 2115027557
Web Site: http://www.hyperionmt.com
Cemented Carbide Products Distr
N.A.I.C.S.: 423710

Subsidiary (Domestic):

Arno Friedrichs Hartmetall GmbH &
Co. KG (4)
Burgkunstadter Strasse 7, 95336, Mainleus,
Germany
Tel.: (49) 922996470
Web Site: https://www.afcarbide.com
Solid Carbide Mfr
N.A.I.C.S.: 331492
Patrick Andre *(Mng Dir)*
Brian Coate *(Mng Dir)*

Subsidiary (Non-US):

Hyperion Materials & Technologies de
Mexico S.A. de C.V. (3)
Avenida Gustavo Baz No 352 Col La Loma,
Tlalnepantla, 54060, Mexico
Tel.: (52) 555 729 3900
Web Site: http://www.hyperionmt.com
Metal Cutting Tool & Equipment Mfr
N.A.I.C.S.: 333515

Sandvik Hyperion (Wuxi) Co.,
Ltd. (3)
No 5 South Xinchang Road, New District,
Wuxi, 214028, Jiangsu, China (100%)
Tel.: (86) 51081130160
Web Site: http://www.hyperionmt.com
Cemented Carbide Products Mfr & Distr
N.A.I.C.S.: 332999

Sandvik Hyperion Taiwan Limited (3)
1 Tzu Chiang 1st Rd, 320, Chung-li,
Taiwan (100%)
Tel.: (886) 34523172
Web Site:
http://www.hardmaterials.sandvik.com
Cemented Carbide Products Mfr & Distr

N.A.I.C.S.: 332999
Menderes Kayhan *(Mng Dir)*

IQGeo Group plc (1)
Nine Hills Road, Cambridge, CB2 1GE,
United Kingdom
Tel.: (44) 1223606655
Web Site: https://www.iqgeo.com
Rev.: $18,803,064
Assets: $37,215,105
Liabilities: $13,928,849
Net Worth: $23,286,256
Earnings: ($2,619,042)
Emp.: 102
Fiscal Year-end: 12/31/2021
Real-Time Location System Mfr
N.A.I.C.S.: 334511
Riccardo Ettore Petti *(CEO)*

Subsidiary (US):

IQGeo America Inc. (2)
1670 Broadway Ste 2215, Denver, CO
80202
Tel.: (720) 577-4732
Design & Construction Services
N.A.I.C.S.: 237110

Subsidiary (Non-US):

IQGeo Germany GmbH (2)
Friedrich-Ebert-Anlage 49, 60308, Frankfurt
am Main, Germany
Tel.: (49) 69506067511
Design & Construction Services
N.A.I.C.S.: 237110

IQGeo Japan KK (2)
Level 45 Sunshine 60 3-1-1, Higashi-
Ikebukuro Toshima-ku, Tokyo, Japan
Tel.: (81) 359575350
Design & Construction Services
N.A.I.C.S.: 237110

Subsidiary (Domestic):

IQGeo UK Limited (2)
Nine Hills Road, Cambridge, United Kingdom
Tel.: (44) 1223606655
Design & Construction Services
N.A.I.C.S.: 237110

Subsidiary (US):

Ubisense America LLC (2)
1630 Welton St Ste 1000E, Denver, CO
80202
Tel.: (720) 549-7553
Software Development Services
N.A.I.C.S.: 541511

Subsidiary (Non-US):

Ubisense GmbH (2)
Franz-Rennefeld-Weg 6, 40472, Dusseldorf,
Germany
Tel.: (49) 2112297330
Software Development Services
N.A.I.C.S.: 541511

Ubisense Japan K.K. (2)
Otemachi Building 6F Otemachi 1-6-1,
Chiyoda-ku, Tokyo, 100-0004, Japan
Tel.: (81) 345778372
Software Development Services
N.A.I.C.S.: 541511

Ubisense SAS (2)
52 Boulevard de Sebastopol, 75003, Paris,
France
Tel.: (33) 183790682
Software Development Services
N.A.I.C.S.: 541511

Instructure Holdings, Inc. (1)
6330 S 3000 E Ste 700, Salt Lake City, UT
84121
Web Site: https://www.instructure.com
Rev.: $475,194,000
Assets: $2,153,489,000
Liabilities: $877,362,000
Net Worth: $1,276,127,000
Earnings: ($34,242,000)
Emp.: 1,466
Fiscal Year-end: 12/31/2022
Offices of Other Holding Companies
N.A.I.C.S.: 551112
Mitch Benson *(Chief Product Officer)*
Matt Kaminer *(Chief Legal Officer)*
Melissa Loble *(Chief Customer Experience
Officer)*

Jeff Weber *(Exec VP-People & Places)*
Steve Townsend *(Sr VP-Engrg)*
Peter Walker *(CFO & Exec VP)*
Chris Ball *(Pres & COO)*
Steve Daly *(CEO)*

Subsidiary (Domestic):

Parchment LLC (2)
6263 N Scottsdale Rd Ste 330, Scottsdale,
AZ 85250
Tel.: (480) 719-1646
Web Site: http://www.parchment.com
Software Development Services
N.A.I.C.S.: 513210
Matthew Pittinsky *(CEO)*

Internet Brands, Inc. (1)
909 N Pacific Coast Hwy 11th Fl, El Segundo, CA 90245
Tel.: (310) 280-4000
Web Site: http://www.internetbrands.com
Holding Company; Media & E-Commerce
Sites Investment, Development & Operator
N.A.I.C.S.: 551112
Robert N. Brisco *(Pres & CEO)*
Charles E. Hoover *(CMO)*
B. Lynn Walsh *(Gen Counsel & Exec VP-
Corp Dev)*
Lisa Morita *(COO)*
Joe Rosenblum *(CTO)*
Kevin Hayes *(Chief Product Officer)*
Scott A. Friedman *(CFO)*

Subsidiary (Domestic):

Auto Credit Express, Inc. (2)
3252 University Dr Ste 250, Auburn Hills,
MI 48326
Tel.: (248) 370-6600
Web Site:
https://www.autocreditexpress.com
Emp.: 125
Consumer Lending Solutions
N.A.I.C.S.: 522291
Jack Lintol *(COO)*

Avvo, Inc. (2)
720 Olive Wy Ste 1400, Seattle, WA 98101
Tel.: (206) 734-4111
Web Site: http://www.avvo.com
Online Legal Directory, Information & Forum
Hosting Services
N.A.I.C.S.: 513140
Diana Schulz *(Pres)*
Suke Jawanda *(Sr VP-Sls & Mktg & Head-
Avvo)*
Andrew Crow *(Dir-Sls & Acq)*
Jenny Leaverenz *(Dir-Client Relations)*
Tony Jones *(Dir-Engrg)*
Randy Laub *(Dir-Mktg)*
Ria Emsley *(Mgr-HR)*

CarsDirect.com, Inc. (2)
909 N Sepulveda Blvd, El Segundo, CA
90245
Tel.: (310) 280-4000
Web Site: http://www.internetbrands.com
Sales Range: $50-74.9 Million
Emp.: 150
Online Provider of Automobile Research,
Price, Design, Order & Delivery Services
N.A.I.C.S.: 441110

Demandforce, Inc. (2)
222 Kearny St Ste 600, San Francisco, CA
94108
Web Site: https://www.demandforce.com
Small Business Management Software Developer
N.A.I.C.S.: 513210
Stu MacFarlane *(CMO)*

DentalPlans.com, Inc. (2)
8100 S W 10th St Ste 2000, Plantation, FL
33324
Web Site: https://www.dentalplans.com
Dental Plans
N.A.I.C.S.: 524114

Nolo Inc. (2)
950 Parker St, Berkeley, CA 94710-2524
Tel.: (510) 549-1976
Web Site: http://www.nolo.com
Sales Range: $10-24.9 Million
Emp.: 110
Do-It-Yourself Legal Solutions For Consumers & Small Businesses
N.A.I.C.S.: 541199

Chris Braun *(Pres & Gen Mgr)*
Chelsey Langan *(VP-Sls & Ops)*
Micah Schwartzbach *(Mng Editor)*
E. A. Gjelten *(Editor)*

Subsidiary (Domestic):

Martindale, LLC (3)
121 Chanlon Rd Ste 110, New Providence,
NJ 07974-1541
Tel.: (908) 464-6800
Web Site: https://www.martindale.com
Legal Directories Publisher; Online Marketing & Advertising Services
N.A.I.C.S.: 513140

Subsidiary (Domestic):

Sesame Communications, Inc. (2)
720 Olive Way Ste 1100, Seattle, WA
98101
Tel.: (206) 458-7700
Web Site:
https://www.sesamecommunications.com
Computer System Design Services
N.A.I.C.S.: 541512
Travis Heimbigner *(VP-Bus Ops)*
Todd Martini *(Sr Dir-Mktg)*
Teo Hunter *(Sr Dir-Engrg)*
Christine Williams *(Controller)*

WebMD Health Corp. (2)
395 Hudson St, New York, NY 10014
Tel.: (212) 624-3700
Web Site: http://www.webmd.com
Holding Company; Health Information Online Services
N.A.I.C.S.: 551112
John Whyte *(Co-Chief Medical Officer)*
Michael Smith *(Co-Chief Medical Officer)*
Neha Pathak *(Chief Physician Editor)*

Subsidiary (Domestic):

Aptus Health, Inc. (3)
55 Walkers Brook Dr Ste 500, Reading, MA
01867
Tel.: (888) 225-4852
Health Care Srvices
N.A.I.C.S.: 813212

Subsidiary (Domestic):

Physicians Interactive Inc. (4)
950 Technology Way Ste 202, Libertyville,
IL 60048
Tel.: (847) 984-1700
Web Site:
http://www.physiciansinteractive.com
Sales Range: $25-49.9 Million
Healthcare Marketing Solutions
N.A.I.C.S.: 541890
Donato J. Tramuto *(Chm & CEO)*
Bonnie Schirato *(VP-HR)*
Ted Dometita *(VP-Fin)*

Subsidiary (Domestic):

Skyscape.com Inc. (5)
293 Boston Post Rd W, Marlborough, MA
01752 (100%)
Tel.: (508) 460-6500
Web Site: http://www.skyscape.com
Mobile & Desktop References for the Medical Community
N.A.I.C.S.: 541511
Sandeep Shah *(Founder, Pres & CEO)*
Kartik Shah *(VP-Engrg)*

Tomorrow Networks, LLC (5)
1270 6th Ave Ste 2920, New York, NY
10020
Tel.: (212) 554-4657
Custom Computer Programming Services
N.A.I.C.S.: 541511

Subsidiary (Domestic):

Frontline Medical Communications
Inc. (3)
7 Century Dr Ste 302, Parsippany, NJ
07054-4609
Tel.: (973) 290-8200
Web Site: http://www.frontlinemedcom.com
Sales Range: $50-74.9 Million
Medical Trade Periodical & Media Publisher
N.A.I.C.S.: 513120
Carolyn Caccavelli *(VP-HR & Facility Ops)*
JoAnn Wahl *(Pres-Custom Solutions)*
Mark Branca *(VP, Publr-Grp & Dir-Society
Partners)*

KKR & Co. Inc.—(Continued)

Mike Guire *(VP-Sls)*
Amy Pfeiffer *(VP-Digital Content & Strategy)*
Wendy Raupers *(VP-Custom Solutions)*
Tim LaPella *(Sr Dir-Sls & Classified)*
Toni Haggerty *(Sr Dir-Bus Dev & Neurology Reviews)*
Devin Gregorie *(Sls Mgr)*
Melissa Whitty *(Mgr-Digital Adv)*
Julian Knight *(Dir-Engagement)*
Alison Paton *(Dir-eBus Dev)*
Patrick Finnegan *(Dir-Custom Solutions)*
Jared Sonners *(Dir-Circulation)*
Monique Michowski *(Dir-Bus Dev)*
Josh Norton *(Acct Mgr-Natl)*

Healthwise, Incorporated (3)
2601 N Bogus Basin Rd, Boise, ID 83702-0909
Tel.: (208) 345-1161
Web Site: http://www.healthwise.org
Emp.: 220
Fiscal Year-end: 06/30/2008
Medical Information
N.A.I.C.S.: 813410
Donald W. Kemper *(Founder)*
Molly Mettler *(Sr VP)*
Jim Giuffre *(Pres & COO)*
Margaret O'Kane *(Chm)*
Adam C. Husney *(CEO)*
Benjamin W. Moulton *(Sr VP-Informed Medical Decisions Foundation)*
Darra Wray *(Sr VP)*
Eileen Casal *(Gen Counsel)*
Kevin Harbauer *(CTO)*
Michael J. Barry *(Chief Science Officer)*
Neal Benz *(CIO)*
Paul Sonnenschein *(Sr VP)*
Tammy A. Zokan *(Gen Counsel & Corp Sec)*
Dave Mink *(Chief Client Officer)*
Christy Calhoun *(Chief Content Solutions Officer)*

Medscape, LLC (3)
395 Hudson St 3rd Fl, New York, NY 10014
Tel.: (212) 301-6700
Web Site: https://www.medscape.com
Health Information Online Services
N.A.I.C.S.: 519290

Subsidiary (Domestic):

SNTC Holding, Inc. (3)
4005 Kennett Pike, Wilmington, DE 19807-2018
Tel.: (302) 777-5261
Holding Company
N.A.I.C.S.: 551112

The StayWell Company, LLC (3)
800 Township Line Rd, Yardley, PA 19067
Tel.: (267) 685-2800
Web Site: http://www.staywell.com
Publiohor & Providor of Hoalth Management Products, Services & Programs
N.A.I.C.S.: 513130
David Anderson *(Founder)*
David Gregg *(Chief Medical Officer)*

WebMD Global LLC (3)
111 8th Ave Fl 7, New York, NY 10011
Tel.: (212) 624-3700
Web Site: http://www.wbmd.com
Emp.: 10
Health Information Online Services
N.A.I.C.S.: 519290

WebMD, LLC (3)
395 Hudson St 3rd Fl, New York, NY 10014
Tel.: (212) 624-3700
Web Site: https://www.webmd.com
Online Health Information Publisher
N.A.I.C.S.: 519290
Arefa Cassoobhoy *(Sr Dir-Medical)*
Robert N. Brisco *(CEO)*
Joshua Conrad *(VP)*
Leah Gentry *(VP)*
Jeffrey T. Arnold *(Founder & Pres)*

Subsidiary (Domestic):

MedicineNet, Inc. (4)
395 Hudson St 3rd Fl, New York, NY 10014
Tel.: (212) 624-3700
Web Site: http://www.medicinenet.com
Online Health Information Publisher
N.A.I.C.S.: 519290

Group (Domestic):

WebMD Health Services Group, Inc. (4)

2701 NW Vaughn St Ste 700, Portland, OR 97210
Tel.: (503) 205-5066
Web Site: https://www.webmdhealthservices.com
Communications Platforms Services for the Healthcare Industry
N.A.I.C.S.: 923120
John Harrison *(Gen Mgr)*
Phil Oester *(VP-Tech Ops)*
Alex Nguyen *(VP-Product & Solutions)*
Shelley Blouin *(VP)*
Bruce Foyt *(VP)*
Melissa Voigt *(VP)*
Kellie Hand *(Sr VP)*

Subsidiary (Domestic):

Limeade, Inc. (5)
10885 NE 4th St Ste 400, Bellevue, WA 98004
Tel.: (425) 908-0216
Web Site: https://www.limeade.com
Rev.: $56,017,000
Assets: $49,351,000
Liabilities: $39,100,000
Net Worth: $10,251,000
Earnings: ($13,225,000)
Emp.: 320
Fiscal Year-end: 12/31/2022
Health Care & Employee Engagement Software Publisher
N.A.I.C.S.: 513210
Mia F. Mends *(Corp Dir)*
Henry Albrecht *(CEO)*
Dave Smith *(Pres & COO)*
Paul Crick *(VP)*
Liz Carver *(Chief People Officer)*
Lauren Chucko *(Chief Customer Officer)*
Patti Fletcher *(CMO)*
Alan Saporta *(CTO)*
Kathy Xanthos *(Chief Information Security Officer)*
Colette Foreman *(VP)*
Sarah Visbeek *(Gen Counsel)*

Subsidiary (Domestic):

9Slides, Inc. (6)
6710 108th Ave NE, Kirkland, WA 98052
Tel.: (888) 716-2560
Web Site: http://www.9slides.com
Custom Computer Programming Services
N.A.I.C.S.: 541511
Aaron Khoo *(Dir-Engrg)*
Ruchit Garg *(Co-Founder & CEO)*
Volodymyr Otryshko *(Co-Founder)*

Jitterbit, Inc. (1)
1101 Marina Village Pkwy Ste 201, Alameda, CA 94501
Tel.: (510) 250-3330
Web Site: https://www.jitterbit.com
Application Integration Platform Developer & Data Services
N.A.I.C.S.: 541511
George Gallegos *(CEO)*
Dan Moore *(Sr VP-Client Svcs)*
Joost De Bot *(VP-EMEA)*
Philippe Turpault *(VP-Customer Success)*
Vito Salvaggio *(Sr VP-Product Mgmt)*
Ron Wastal *(Sr VP-Partner Dev, Channels & Alliances)*
Manoj Chaudhary *(CTO & Sr VP-Engrg)*
Jill Ransome *(CMO)*
Jeremy Parker *(COO)*
Avner Alkhas *(CFO)*
Diogo Lupinari *(VP)*
Singu Srinivas *(Sr VP)*

KEDI Holdings S.a.r.l. (1)
Rue de Rollingergrund 59, 2440, Luxembourg, Luxembourg
Tel.: (352) 2702431
Holding Company
N.A.I.C.S.: 551112

KFN Sentinel REIT LLC (1)
9 W 57th St Ste 4200, New York, NY 10019
Tel.: (212) 230-9486
Real Estate Investment Trust
N.A.I.C.S.: 525990

KION Group AG (1)
Thea-Rasche-Strasse 8, 60549, Frankfurt am Main, Germany
Tel.: (49) 69201100
Web Site: https://www.kiongroup.com
Rev.: $12,339,412,907
Assets: $18,765,810,490

Liabilities: $12,535,829,916
Net Worth: $6,229,980,574
Earnings: $330,023,743
Emp.: 41,552
Fiscal Year-end: 12/31/2023
Industrial Equipment Mfr
N.A.I.C.S.: 551112
Pong Quek Ching *(Chief Asia Pacific & Americas Officer & Member-Exec Bd)*
Ozcan Pancarci *(Deputy Chm-Supervisory Bd)*
Michael Macht *(Chm-Supervisory Bd)*
Hasan Dandashly *(Pres)*
Andreas Krinninger *(Pres)*
Henry Puhl *(CTO)*
Marcus A. Wassenberg *(CFO)*

Subsidiary (US):

Dematic Corp. (2)
507 Plymouth Ave NE, Grand Rapids, MI 49505
Tel.: (877) 725-7500
Web Site: http://www.dematic.com
Materials Handling Equipment & Logistics Systems Mfr & Distr
N.A.I.C.S.: 333922
Hasan Dandashly *(Pres & CEO)*
Michele Longo *(Sr VP-HR)*
Michael Larsson *(Exec VP)*
Michael Jerogin *(Sr VP)*
Meraj Anas *(Sr VP)*
Shibu Sasidharan *(Sr VP)*
Deidre Cusack *(Exec VP)*
David Dechavassine *(Sr VP)*
Howard Yntema *(CFO)*
Erin Dillard *(Sr VP)*
Eric Sharon *(Sr VP)*
Chris Petitt *(Sr VP)*
Chris Steiner *(Sr VP)*

Subsidiary (Non-US):

Dematic GmbH (3)
Martinseestrasse 1, D-63150, Heusenstamm, Germany
Tel.: (49) 69 58 30 25 0
Web Site: http://www.dematic.com
Holding Company; Regional Managing Office
N.A.I.C.S.: 551112
Jens Hardenacke *(Mng Dir)*

Subsidiary (Domestic):

Dematic GmbH (4)
Carl-Legien-Strasse 15, Offenbach, D-63073, Germany
Tel.: (49) 6989030
Web Site: http://www.dematic.com
Materials Handling Equipment & Electronics Assembly Systems Mfr
N.A.I.C.S.: 333922

Subsidiary (Non-US):

Dematic GmbH (4)
Industriestrasse 50, 8112, Otelfingen, Switzerland
Tel.: (41) 434556065
Web Site: https://www.dematic.com
Materials Handling Equipment & Electronics Assembly Systems Mfr
N.A.I.C.S.: 333922

Subsidiary (Domestic):

Dematic Logistics GmbH (4)
Marie-Curie-Strasse 3a, 48599, Gronau, Germany
Tel.: (49) 2562 70108 0
Web Site: http://www.dematic.com
Automated Material Handling Systems & Solutions
N.A.I.C.S.: 541614

Dematic Logistics GmbH (4)
Schelpmilser Weg 20, 33609, Bielefeld, Germany
Tel.: (49) 521 92277 100
Web Site: http://www.dematic.com
Material Handling Equipment Solutions & Electronics Assembly Systems Mfr
N.A.I.C.S.: 541614

Subsidiary (Non-US):

Dematic Ltd. (4)
Banbury Business Park Trinity Way, Adderbury, Banbury, OX17 3SN, Oxon, United Kingdom

Tel.: (44) 1295 274 600
Web Site: http://www.dematic.com
Automated Logistics Solutions
N.A.I.C.S.: 541614

Subsidiary (Non-US):

Dematic Holdings Pty. Ltd. (3)
24 Narabang Way, Belrose, 2085, NSW, Australia
Tel.: (61) 294865555
Web Site: http://www.dematic.com
Emp.: 4,000
Holding Company
N.A.I.C.S.: 551112
Hasan Dandashly *(Pres & CEO)*
Michael Jerogin *(Sr VP-APAC Reg)*
Deidre Cusack *(Sr VP-Global Products & Solutions)*
Michele Longo *(Sr VP-HR)*
Michael Larsson *(Exec VP)*
Bernard Biolchini *(Exec VP)*
Meraj Anas *(Sr VP)*
Shibu Sasidharan *(Sr VP)*
David Dechavassine *(Pres)*
Howard Yntema *(CFO)*
Erin Dillard *(VP)*
Eric Sharon *(Sr VP)*
Chris Petitt *(Sr VP)*
Chris Steiner *(Sr VP)*

Subsidiary (Domestic):

Dematic Pty. Ltd. (4)
24 Narabang Way, Belrose, 2085, NSW, Australia
Tel.: (61) 294865555
Web Site: http://www.dematic.com.au
Emp.: 500
Materials Handling Equipment & Logistics Systems Mfr & Distr
N.A.I.C.S.: 333922

Subsidiary (Domestic):

Dematic Reddwerks (3)
1122 S Capital of Texas Hwy Ste 150, Austin, TX 78746
Tel.: (512) 597-6810
Web Site: http://www.dematicreddwerks.com
Emp.: 200
Warehouse Management System Software
N.A.I.C.S.: 513210
Francisco Arzu *(CTO)*

Subsidiary (Domestic):

Linde Material Handling GmbH (2)
Schweinheimer Strasse 34, PO Box 62, 63743, Aschaffenburg, Germany
Tel.: (49) 6021990
Web Site: http://www.linde mh.de
Sales Range: $1-4.9 Billion
Emp.: 12,531
Forklifts, Industrial Trucks & Hydraulic Engineering Equipment Mfr
N.A.I.C.S.: 333924

Subsidiary (Non-US):

A.G. Pruden & Cia. S.A. (3)
Av Hipolito Yrigoyen 2441/2465 Martinez, B1640HFW, Buenos Aires, Argentina
Tel.: (54) 1147332500
Web Site: https://www.agpruden.com
Sales Range: $25-49.9 Million
Emp.: 120
Forklifts, Industrial Trucks & Hydraulics Equipment Distr
N.A.I.C.S.: 333924

EDNIL d.o.o. Sarajevo (3)
Izeta Delica Br 1A, 71320, Sarajevo, Bosnia & Herzegovina
Tel.: (387) 33 425 200
Web Site: http://www.toyota-viljuskari.ba
Sales Range: $25-49.9 Million
Emp.: 30
Forklifts & Industrial Trucks Sales & Maintenance
N.A.I.C.S.: 333924
Mesud Rizvo *(Mng Dir)*

Fenwick-Linde S.A.R.L. (3)
1 RUE Du Marechal De Lattre De Tassigny, Saint-Quentin-en-Yvelines, 78854, France
Tel.: (33) 130684412
Web Site: http://www.fenwick-linde.com

Sales Range: $300-349.9 Million
Emp.: 350
Forklifts & Industrial Trucks Mfr
N.A.I.C.S.: 333924

Division (Domestic):

Fenwick-Linde Hydraulics   (4)
1 rue du Marechal de Lattre de Tassigny,
78854, Saint-Quentin-en-Yvelines, Cedex,
France
Tel.: (33) 130684647
Web Site: http://www.fl-hydraulics.fr
Sales Range: $100-124.9 Million
Emp.: 300
Hydraulic Pumps & Motors Mfr
N.A.I.C.S.: 333996

Subsidiary (US):

KION North America Corporation   (3)
2450 W 5th N St, Summerville, SC 29483
Tel.: (843) 875-8000
Web Site: http://www.kion-na.com
Forklifts & Industrial Trucks Mfr
N.A.I.C.S.: 333924
Max Heller *(Pres, CEO & CFO)*
Michael Gore *(VP-Sls)*
Daniel Schlegel *(VP-Ops)*
Paul Antor *(VP-Product Support)*
David Brown *(Dir-HR)*
Ben Lee *(Dir-Key Acct Sls)*
Jeff Peterson *(Dir-Mfg)*
Christian Loew *(VP-Product Dev)*
Julie Richardson *(Dir-Inside Sls)*
Rick Schiel *(Dir-Dealer Sls)*

Subsidiary (Non-US):

**Linde (China) Forklift Truck Corp.,
Ltd.**   (3)
No 89 Jinshang Rd, PO Box 0956, Xiamen,
361009, China
Tel.: (86) 5925533800
Web Site: http://www.linde-china.com
Sales Range: $125-149.9 Million
Forklifts & Industrial Trucks Mfr
N.A.I.C.S.: 333924

Linde Fordertechnik GmbH   (3)
Franzosenhausweg 35, 4030, Linz, Austria
Tel.: (43) 50389510
Web Site: https://www.linde-mh.at
Sales Range: $75-99.9 Million
Emp.: 160
Forklifts, Industrial Trucks & Hydraulic
Equipment Mfr
N.A.I.C.S.: 333924

Linde Heavy Truck Division Ltd.   (3)
Linde Industrial Park, Merthyr Tydfil, CF48
4LA, United Kingdom
Tel.: (44) 1443624200
Web Site: http://www.linde-htd.com
Sales Range: $125-149.9 Million
Large Forklifts & Industrial Trucks Mfr
N.A.I.C.S.: 333924

Linde High Lift Chile S.A.   (3)
Avenida El Retiro 1251 Centro Industrial El
Montijo, Complejo Megacentro, Renca,
8640000, Chile
Tel.: (56) 24398100
Web Site: http://www.lindehighlift.cl
Sales Range: $50-74.9 Million
Emp.: 150
Forklifts & Industrial Trucks Mfr
N.A.I.C.S.: 333924

Linde Lansing Fordertechnik AG   (3)
Alte Dubendorferstrasse 20, 8305, Dietlikon,
Switzerland
Tel.: (41) 448352300
Web Site: https://www.linde-mh.ch
Sales Range: $50-74.9 Million
Emp.: 170
Forklifts & Industrial Trucks Mfr
N.A.I.C.S.: 333924

**Linde Material Handling (Australia)
Pty, Ltd.**   (3)
3 Healey Circuit, Huntingwood, 2148, Aus-
tralia
Tel.: (61) 1300 454 633
Web Site: http://www.lindemh.com.au
Sales Range: $75-99.9 Million
Emp.: 220
Forklifts & Industrial Trucks Mfr
N.A.I.C.S.: 333924

**Linde Material Handling (Pty)
Ltd.**   (3)
Milkway & Newton Road Linbro Park, PO
Box 1101, Cnr Milkyway & Neutron Ave,
2001, Johannesburg, South Africa
Tel.: (27) 0117237000
Web Site: http://www.linde.co.za
Sales Range: $75-99.9 Million
Emp.: 185
Forklifts & Industrial Trucks Mfr
N.A.I.C.S.: 333924
Branton Alexander *(Mng Dir)*

**Linde Material Handling (UK)
Ltd.**   (3)
Kingsclere Road, Basingstoke, RG21 6XJ,
Hampshire, United Kingdom
Tel.: (44) 1256 342 000
Web Site: http://www.linde-mh.co.uk
Sales Range: $200-249.9 Million
Emp.: 300
Fork Lifts & Industrial Trucks Mfr
N.A.I.C.S.: 333924
Ulrike Just *(Mng Dir)*

**Linde Material Handling Ceska repu-
blica s.r.o.**   (3)
Polygraficka 622/2, Prague, 108 00, Czech
Republic
Tel.: (420) 271078111
Web Site: http://www.linde-mh.cz
Sales Range: $75-99.9 Million
Emp.: 200
Forklifts & Industrial Trucks Mfr
N.A.I.C.S.: 333924

**Linde Material Handling Iberica
S.A.**   (3)
Avenida Prat de la Riba 181, Palleja,
08780, Spain
Tel.: (34) 936633232
Web Site: http://www.linde-mh.es
Sales Range: $75-99.9 Million
Emp.: 400
Forklifts & Industrial Trucks Mfr
N.A.I.C.S.: 333924
Paul F. Drumm *(Mng Dir)*

**Linde Material Handling Italia
S.p.A.**   (3)
Via Luguzzone Zona Industriale, Brunello,
Buguggiate, 21020, Varese, Italy
Tel.: (39) 0332877111
Web Site: http://www.linde-mh.it
Sales Range: $25-49.9 Million
Emp.: 96
Forklifts & Industrial Trucks Mfr
N.A.I.C.S.: 333924

**Linde Material Handling do Brasil
Ltda.**   (3)
Rua Victorino 134, Barueri, 06230-110, SP,
Brazil
Tel.: (55) 1136044755
Web Site: http://www.linde-mh.com.br
Sales Range: $25-49.9 Million
Emp.: 80
Forklifts & Industrial Trucks Distr, Sales &
Service
N.A.I.C.S.: 333924

Linde Vilicari Hrvatska d.o.o.   (3)
Novoselska 25, 10040, Zagreb, Croatia
Tel.: (385) 12991111
Web Site: http://www.linde.hr
Sales Range: $25-49.9 Million
Emp.: 100
Forklifts & Industrial Trucks Mfr
N.A.I.C.S.: 333924

**Motocar Service Company
(MSC)**   (3)
Komatevsko shouse Str 26, 4007, Plovdiv,
Bulgaria
Tel.: (359) 32625051
Web Site: http://www.motocarservice.com
Sales Range: $25-49.9 Million
Emp.: 94
Forklifts & Industrial Trucks Mfr
N.A.I.C.S.: 333924
George Terzeiv *(Chm & Gen Mgr-Sls)*

**Motrac Handling & Cleaning
n.v.-s.a.**   (3)
Noorderlaan 612, 2030, Antwerp, Belgium
Tel.: (32) 33601111
Web Site: http://www.motrac.be
Sales Range: $75-99.9 Million
Emp.: 150

Parts Distr & Maintenance Services for
Forklifts & Industrial Trucks
N.A.I.C.S.: 811198

Subsidiary (Non-US):

OM Carrelli Elevatori S.p.A.   (2)
Viale A de Gasperi 7, 20020, Lainate, Milan,
Italy
Tel.: (39) 02937651
Web Site: http://www.om-still.it
Sales Range: $350-399.9 Million
Emp.: 1,232
Forklifts & Industrial Trucks Mfr
N.A.I.C.S.: 333924
Angelo Zanotti *(CEO-Sls & Svc)*

Subsidiary (Non-US):

Ibercarretillas OM Espana S.A.   (3)
Pol Ind Pratense - Calle 111 s/n, 8820, El
Prat de Llobregat, Spain
Tel.: (34) 934798500
Sales Range: $25-49.9 Million
Emp.: 70
Forklifts & Industrial Trucks Mfr
N.A.I.C.S.: 333924

Subsidiary (Domestic):

STILL GmbH   (2)
Berzeliusstrasse 10, PO Box 740720,
D-22113, Hamburg, Germany
Tel.: (49) 4073390
Web Site: http://www.still.de
Sales Range: $1-4.9 Billion
Emp.: 6,258
Forklifts & Industrial Trucks Mfr
N.A.I.C.S.: 333924
Henry Puhl *(Chm-Mgmt Bd, Pres & Mng
Dir)*
Frank Muller *(Sr VP)*

Subsidiary (Non-US):

STILL AG   (3)
Industrie strasse 50, 8112, Otelfingen, Swit-
zerland
Tel.: (41) 448465111
Web Site: http://www.still.ch
Sales Range: $25-49.9 Million
Emp.: 60
Forklifts & Industrial Trucks Mfr
N.A.I.C.S.: 333924

STILL CR, spol. s r.o.   (3)
Sterboholska 102 10 Hostivar, 102 19,
Prague, Czech Republic
Tel.: (420) 274001411
Web Site: https://www.still.cz
Sales Range: $50-74.9 Million
Emp.: 130
Forklifts & Industrial Trucks Mfr
N.A.I.C.S.: 333924

STILL Danmark A/S   (3)
Essen 1, 6000, Kolding, Denmark
Tel.: (45) 76319800
Web Site: https://www.still.dk
Sales Range: $25-49.9 Million
Emp.: 100
Forklifts & Industrial Trucks Mfr
N.A.I.C.S.: 333924

STILL Gesellschaft m.b.H.   (3)
Industriezentrum No Sud Strabe 3 Objekt 6,
2351, Wiener Neudorf, Austria
Tel.: (43) 2236615010
Web Site: http://www.still.at
Sales Range: $25-49.9 Million
Emp.: 102
Forklifts & Industrial Trucks Mfr
N.A.I.C.S.: 333924

STILL Intern Transport B.V.   (3)
Nijverheidsweg 5, PO Box 150, 3340 AD,
Hendrik-Ido-Ambacht, Netherlands
Tel.: (31) 786845200
Web Site: https://www.still.nl
Sales Range: $75-99.9 Million
Emp.: 200
Forklifts & Industrial Trucks Mfr
N.A.I.C.S.: 333924

STILL Italia S.p.A.   (3)
Corso Europa 5, 20020, Lainate, Italy
Tel.: (39) 0293 5761
Web Site: http://www.still.it
Sales Range: $25-49.9 Million
Emp.: 85
Forklifts & Industrial Trucks Mfr

N.A.I.C.S.: 333924

STILL Materials Handling Ltd.   (3)
Aston Way Moss Side, Leyland, PR26 7UX,
Lancashire, United Kingdom
Tel.: (44) 1772644300
Web Site: http://www.still.co.uk
Sales Range: $25-49.9 Million
Emp.: 55
Forklifts & Industrial Trucks Mfr
N.A.I.C.S.: 333924
Gillian Reed *(Mng Dir)*

STILL N.V.   (3)
Vosveld 9, 2110, Wijnegem, Belgium
Tel.: (32) 33606200
Web Site: http://www.still.be
Sales Range: $50-74.9 Million
Emp.: 125
Forklifts & Industrial Trucks Mfr
N.A.I.C.S.: 333924
Jean-Paul DuBois *(Mng Dir)*

STILL S.A.   (3)
Calle Primer De Maig-Pg Ind Gran Via Sud
38 - 48 L hospitalet de, Llobregat, 08908,
Barcelona, Spain
Tel.: (34) 933946000
Web Site: http://www.still.es
Sales Range: $50-74.9 Million
Emp.: 150
Forklifts & Industrial Trucks Mfr
N.A.I.C.S.: 333924

STILL S.A.S.   (3)
6 Bd Michael Faraday Serris, 77716,
Marne-la-Vallee, France
Tel.: (33) 164174000
Web Site: http://www.still-fr.com
Sales Range: $200-249.9 Million
Emp.: 700
Forklifts & Industrial Trucks Mfr
N.A.I.C.S.: 333924

Subsidiary (Domestic):

STILL Wagner GmbH & Co. KG   (3)
Ernst Wagner Weg 1-5, PO Box 2943,
D-72766, Reutlingen, Germany
Tel.: (49) 7127815541
Web Site: http://www.kiongroup.com
Sales Range: $125-149.9 Million
Emp.: 500
Forklifts & Industrial Trucks Mfr
N.A.I.C.S.: 333924

KJR Management   (1)
7 3 Marunouchi 2 Chome, Chiyoda-ku, To-
kyo, 100-6420, Japan
Tel.: (81) 3 5293 7000
Web Site: https://www.kjrm.co.jp
Emp.: 161
Real Estate Investment Services
N.A.I.C.S.: 531390

KKR & Co. L.P. - Menlo Park   (1)
2800 Sand Hill Rd Ste 200, Menlo Park, CA
94025-7055
Tel.: (650) 233-6560
Web Site: http://www.kkr.com
Sales Range: $50-74.9 Million
Emp.: 75
Private Equity Services
N.A.I.C.S.: 523910

KKR 2006 Fund (GDG) L.P.   (1)
9 W 57th St Ste 4200, New York, NY 10019
Tel.: (212) 230-9742
Trust, Fiduciary & Custody Services
N.A.I.C.S.: 523991

**KKR Alternative Investment
Management**   (1)
75 St Stephens Green, Dublin, Ireland
Tel.: (353) 1 475 7499
Web Site: http://www.kkr.com
Investment Management Service
N.A.I.C.S.: 523940

KKR Asia Limited   (1)
Level 56 Cheung Kong Center 2 Queen's
Road, Central, Hong Kong, China (Hong
Kong)
Tel.: (852) 36027300
Investment Management Service
N.A.I.C.S.: 523999
Ralph F. Rosenberg *(Head-Real Estate)*
John Pattar *(Head-Real Estate Bus)*

KKR Australia Pty Limited   (1)
Level 42 Gateway Building 1 Macquarie

KKR & Co. Inc.—(Continued)

Place, Sydney, 2000, NSW, Australia
Tel.: (61) 28 298 5500
Web Site: http://www.kkr.com
Emp.: 25
Investment Management Service
N.A.I.C.S.: 523940
Tony Schultz *(Mng Dir)*

Subsidiary (Domestic):

KKR Australia Investment Management Pty. Limited (2)
Level 39 Gateway Building 1 Macquarie
Place, Sydney, 2000, NSW, Australia
Tel.: (61) 28 298 5500
Web Site: http://www.kkr.com
Investment Management Service
N.A.I.C.S.: 523940

KKR Canada ULC (1)
850-335 8 Ave SW, Calgary, T2P 1C9, AB,
Canada
Tel.: (403) 775-9244
Investment Management Service
N.A.I.C.S.: 523940

KKR Capital Markets India Private Limited (1)
2nd Floor Piramal Tower, Peninsula Corporate Park Ganpatrao Kadam Marg Lower
Parel West, Mumbai, 400 013, India
Tel.: (91) 224 355 1300
Web Site: http://www.kkr.com
Investment Management Service
N.A.I.C.S.: 523940
Arun Gupta *(Principal-Global Risk Strategies)*

KKR Capital Markets LLC (1)
9 W 57 St, New York, NY 10019
Tel.: (212) 230-9433
Web Site: https://www.kkr.com
Emp.: 600
Security Brokerage Services
N.A.I.C.S.: 523150

KKR Credit Advisors (EMEA) LLP (1)
18 Hanover Sqaure, London, W1S 1JY,
United Kingdom
Tel.: (44) 2078399800
Financial Investment Services
N.A.I.C.S.: 523999

KKR Credit Advisors (Ireland) (1)
75 St Stephens Green, Dublin, Ireland
Tel.: (353) 1 475 7499
Web Site: http://www.kkr.com
Emp.: 50
Investment Management Service
N.A.I.C.S.: 523940

KKR Credit Advisors (US) LLC (1)
555 California St 50th Fl, New York, NY
94104
Tel.: (415) 315-3620
Web Site: http://www.kkr.com
Investment Management Service
N.A.I.C.S.: 523940

Joint Venture (Domestic):

Cengage Learning Holdings II, Inc. (2)
3 Ctr Plz Ste 700, Boston, MA 02108
Tel.: (513) 229-1000
Web Site: https://www.cengagegroup.com
Rev.: $1,502,700,000
Assets: $2,600,400,000
Liabilities: $2,485,700,000
Net Worth: ($389,400,000)
Earnings: ($80,900,000)
Emp.: 4,400
Fiscal Year-end: 03/31/2024
Holding Company; Library Reference &
Educational Materials Publishing & Learning
Solutions
N.A.I.C.S.: 551112
Michael E. Hansen *(CEO)*
Jim Chilton *(CTO)*
Darren Person *(Chief Digital Officer)*
Michael E. Hansen *(CEO)*
Bob Munro *(CFO)*
Alexander Broich *(Pres-Cengage Select & Gen Mgr-English Language Teaching & Cengage Work)*
Jeri Herman *(Chief People Officer)*
Brooke Carey *(Chief Comm Officer)*

Dawn Ehlers *(Gen Counsel)*
Morgan Wolbe *(Exec VP-Ops-Global & Chief Transformation Officer)*

Subsidiary (Domestic):

Cengage Learning, Inc. (3)
3 Ctr Plz Ste 700, Boston, MA 2108
Tel.: (513) 229-1000
Web Site: http://www.cengage.com
Library Reference & Educational Materials
Publishing & Learning Solutions
N.A.I.C.S.: 513130
Michael E. Hansen *(CEO)*
Sean Chamberland *(Sr Dir-Mktg-Cengage Canada)*
Julianne Isaac *(Gen Mgr)*

Subsidiary (Domestic):

Advanced Instructional Systems, Inc. (4)
1791 Varsity Dr Ste 200, Raleigh, NC
27606
Tel.: (919) 829-8181
Web Site: https://www.webassign.com
Sales Range: $1-9.9 Million
Emp.: 25
Online Software Solutions Services
N.A.I.C.S.: 513210
Rob Simora *(CTO)*

Division (Domestic):

Cengage Higher Education (4)
20 Davis Dr, Belmont, CA 94002
Tel.: (650) 595-2350
Web Site:
http://www.academic.cengage.com
Educational Book Publishing
N.A.I.C.S.: 513130

Unit (Domestic):

South-Western Cengage Learning (5)
5191 Natorp Blvd, Mason, OH 45040
Tel.: (513) 229-1000
Web Site: http://www.cengagelearning.com
Sales Range: $200-249.9 Million
Accounting, Marketing & Management Education Book Publisher
N.A.I.C.S.: 513130

Wadsworth Cengage Learning (5)
10 Davis Dr, Belmont, CA 94002-3002
Tel.: (650) 595-2350
Web Site:
http://www.academic.cengage.com
Educational Software & Textbook Publisher
N.A.I.C.S.: 513130

Subsidiary (Non-US):

Cengage Learning Asia (4)
30A Kallang Place 12-06, UIC Bldg, Singapore, 339213, Singapore
Tel.: (65) 64101200
Web Site: https://www.cengageasia.com
Sales Range: $50-74.9 Million
Emp.: 70
Educational & Reference Book Publisher
N.A.I.C.S.: 513130

Cengage Learning Australia Pty. Limited (4)
80 Dorcas St Level 7, Victoria, 3205, VIC,
Australia
Tel.: (61) 396854111
Web Site: http://www.cengage.com.au
Sales Range: $50-74.9 Million
Emp.: 200
Educational & Reference Book Publishing
N.A.I.C.S.: 513130
Tamara Silver *(Mgr-HR)*
Paul Petrulis *(VP-Higher Education)*
Nicole McCarten *(VP-Schools Div)*
John Durow *(Fin Dir & COO)*
Paul Brady *(Dir-Technologies)*
Nigel Matai *(Head-Production)*

Subsidiary (Domestic):

Delmar Cengage Learning (4)
5 Maxwell Dr Executive Woods, Clifton
Park, NY 12065-2919
Tel.: (518) 348-2300
Web Site: http://www.cengage.com
Sales Range: $100-124.9 Million
Emp.: 294

Educational, Technical & Vocational Publishers
N.A.I.C.S.: 513130

Subsidiary (Non-US):

Gale Group Inc. (4)
Tel.: (248) 699-4253
Web Site: http://www.gale.com
Sales Range: $300-349.9 Million
Reference Book & Electronic Reference
Materials Publisher
N.A.I.C.S.: 513140
Paul Gazzolo *(Sr VP & Gen Mgr)*
Brian McDonough *(Sr VP-Sls-North America)*
Terry Robinson *(Mng Dir-Intl & Sr VP)*

Division (Domestic):

Macmillan Reference USA (5)
12 Lunar Dr, Woodbridge, CT 06525-2322
Tel.: (203) 397-2600
Web Site: http://gale.cengage.com
Sales Range: $25-49.9 Million
Emp.: 55
Publisher of Academic & Professional Reference Materials, Newspapers & U.S. &
Foreign Patents
N.A.I.C.S.: 513130

Subsidiary (Domestic):

Learning Objects, Inc. (4)
1528 Connecticut Ave NW, Washington, DC
20036
Tel.: (202) 265-3276
Web Site: https://www.learningobjects.com
Education Technology Software Publisher
N.A.I.C.S.: 513210

Subsidiary (Non-US):

Nelson Education Ltd. (4)
1120 Birchmount Rd, Scarborough, M1K
5G4, ON, Canada
Tel.: (416) 752-9448
Web Site: http://www.nelson.com
Sales Range: $100-124.9 Million
Education & Reference Book Publisher
N.A.I.C.S.: 513130
Steve Brown *(Pres & CEO)*
Claudine O'Donnell *(Sr VP)*
Ryan Anklesaria *(Sr VP)*

KKR Credit Advisory (UK) LLP (1)
100 Pall Mall, London, SW1Y 5NQ, United
Kingdom
Tel.: (44) 2078399800
Web Site: http://www.kkr.com
Investment Management Service
N.A.I.C.S.: 523940

KKR Financial Holdings LLC (1)
555 California St 50th Fl, San Francisco,
CA 94104-1701
Tel.: (415) 315-3620
Rev.: $292,072,000
Assets: $5,851,057,000
Liabilities: $3,982,872,000
Net Worth: $1,868,185,000
Earnings: $33,160,000
Emp.: 150
Fiscal Year-end: 12/31/2016
Holding Company
N.A.I.C.S.: 551112
William J. Janetschek *(Pres & CEO)*

KKR India Advisors Private Limited (1)
2nd Floor Piramal Tower Peninsula Corporate Park, Ganpatrao Kadam Marg Lower
Parel West, Mumbai, 400 013, India
Tel.: (91) 22 4355 1300
Web Site: http://www.kkr.com
Emp.: 30
Financial Advisory Services
N.A.I.C.S.: 523940

KKR India Financial Services Private Limited (1)
2nd floor Piramal Tower, Peninsula Corporate Park Ganpatrao Kadam Marg Lower
Parel W, Mumbai, 400 013, India
Tel.: (91) 224 355 1300
Web Site: https://www.kkr.com
Emp.: 45
Financial Management Services
N.A.I.C.S.: 523999
Kapil Singhal *(Mng Dir)*

KKR Japan Limited (1)
11F Meiji Yasuda Seimei Building 2-1-1
Marunouchi, Chiyoda-ku, Tokyo, 100-0005,
Japan
Tel.: (81) 36 268 6000
Web Site: http://www.kkr.com
Emp.: 30
Asset Management Services
N.A.I.C.S.: 523940
Hirofumi Hirano *(Pres)*
Kazuyuki Kido *(Mng Dir-Private Equity)*

Subsidiary (Domestic):

KKR Capital Markets Japan Limited (2)
11F Meiji Yasuda Seimei Building 2-1-1,
Marunouchi Chiyoda-ku, Tokyo, 100-0005,
Japan
Tel.: (81) 362686666
Web Site: http://japan.kkr.com
Emp.: 10
Investment Management Service
N.A.I.C.S.: 523940

KKR Luxembourg S.a r.l. (1)
2 Rue Edward Steichen, 2540, Luxembourg, Luxembourg
Tel.: (352) 270243100
Financial Investment Services
N.A.I.C.S.: 523999

KKR MENA Limited (1)
Gate Village 4 Levels 5 and 6 DIFC, PO
Box 506804, Dubai, United Arab Emirates
Tel.: (971) 43781500
Financial Management Services
N.A.I.C.S.: 523999

KKR Saudi Limited (1)
Faisaliah Tower Floor 18, PO Box 54995,
Olaya District, Riyadh, 11524, Saudi Arabia
Tel.: (966) 114903767
Web Site: https://www.kkrsaudi.com
Financial Investment Services
N.A.I.C.S.: 523999

Kerridge Commercial Systems Limited (1)
Unit 2A Herongate Charnham Park, Hungerford, RG17 0YU, Berkshire, United Kingdom
Tel.: (44) 1488662000
Web Site: https://www.kerridgecs.com
Specialist Software, Services & Support
N.A.I.C.S.: 541511

Subsidiary (Domestic):

EAGLE BIDCO 2018 LIMITED (2)
Herongate Charnham Park, Hungerford,
RG17 0YU, United Kingdom
Tel.: (44) 1488662000
Dormant Company
N.A.I.C.S.: 551114

Subsidiary (Domestic):

Kerridge Commercial Systems (KSH) Limited (3)
Unit 2A Herongate Charnham Park, Hungerford, RG17 0YU, Berks, United Kingdom
Tel.: (44) 1142622000
Web Site: http://www.kerridgecs.com
Electronic Data Processing Services
N.A.I.C.S.: 334610
Ian Bendelow *(CEO)*

Subsidiary (US):

MAM Software Group, Inc. (4)
2 Valley Sq Ste 220 512 Township Line Rd,
Blue Bell, PA 19422
Tel.: (010) 000-9045
Web Site: http://www.mamsoftware.com
Rev.: $37,714,000
Assets: $32,519,000
Liabilities: $14,982,000
Net Worth: $17,537,000
Earnings: $3,713,000
Emp.: 249
Fiscal Year-end: 06/30/2019
Automotive Aftermarket Business Management Systems, Information Products & Online Services
N.A.I.C.S.: 513210
Michael G. Jamieson *(Pres & CEO)*
Brian H. Callahan *(CFO & Exec VP)*

Subsidiary (Non-US):

MAM Software Ltd. (5)

Maple Park Maple Court, Tankersley, Barnsley, S75 3DP, South Yorkshire, United Kingdom
Tel.: (44) 1226352900
Web Site: https://www.mamsoftware.com
Computer Peripheral Equipment Whslr
N.A.I.C.S.: 423430

Subsidiary (Domestic):

MAM Software, Inc. (5)
512 Township Line Rd, Blue Bell, PA 19422
Tel.: (610) 336-9045
Web Site: http://www.mamsoftware.com
Software Development Services
N.A.I.C.S.: 541511

Subsidiary (Non-US):

Origin Solutions, Ltd. (5)
4 The Cottages Deva Centre Trinity Way, Manchester, M3 7BE, United Kingdom
Tel.: (44) 1618060868
Web Site: https://origin-solutions.uk
Web Development Services
N.A.I.C.S.: 541511

Subsidiary (Non-US):

Infomat N.V. (2)
Garden Sq Bloc AB, Laarstraat 16B, Wilrijk, Belgium
Tel.: (32) 38206000
Web Site: http://www.infomat.eu
Business Services
N.A.I.C.S.: 561439

Kohlberg Kravis Roberts & Co. Limited (1)
7 Carlton Gardens, London, SW1Y 5AD, United Kingdom
Tel.: (44) 2078399800
Financial Investment Services
N.A.I.C.S.: 523999

Kohlberg Kravis Roberts & Co. Partners LLP (1)
18 Hanover Sqaure, London, W1S 1JY, United Kingdom
Tel.: (44) 2078399800
Financial Investment Services
N.A.I.C.S.: 523999
Stephen Shanley *(Executives)*

Kohlberg Kravis Roberts & Co. SAS (1)
42 Avenue Montaigne, 75008, Paris, France
Tel.: (33) 1 53 53 96 00
Web Site: http://www.kkr.com
Investment Management Service
N.A.I.C.S.: 523999

Kohlberg Kravis Roberts (Espana) Asesores SL
Edificio Beatriz Calle de Jose Ortega y Gasset 29, 28006, Madrid, Spain
Tel.: (34) 911980004
Investment Management Service
N.A.I.C.S.: 523940

Kohlberg Kravis Roberts GmbH (1)
OpernTurm 18th floor Bockenheimer Landstrasse 2-4, 60306, Frankfurt am Main, Germany
Tel.: (49) 69222293900
Investment Intermediation Services
N.A.I.C.S.: 523150

Koki Holdings Co., Ltd. (1)
Shinigawa Intercity A Building 2 15 1 Konan, Minato-ku, Tokyo, 108-6018, Japan
Tel.: (81) 357830601
Web Site: https://www.koki-holdings.co.jp
Emp.: 6,604
Power Tools & Life Science Equipment Mfr
N.A.I.C.S.: 333991
Yoichiro Tanaka *(Chief Admin Officer, COO-APAC & Mng Exec Officer)*
Mutsue Harada *(CTO & Mng Exec Officer)*
Hiroshi Teraguchi *(Pres)*
Osamu Kawanobe *(Chief Production Officer)*

Subsidiary (Non-US):

HiKoki Power Tools Italia SpA (2)
Via Piave 35, 36077, Altavilla Vicentina, Italy
Tel.: (39) 0444548111
Web Site: https://www.hikoki-powertools.it
Power Tool Distr

N.A.I.C.S.: 423830

Hikoki Power Tools (Malaysia) Sdn. Bhd. (2)
Wisma Sumber Lot 558 Jalan Subang 3 Off Persiaran Subang, Sungai Penaga Industrial Park, 81400, Senai, Johor Darul Takzim, Malaysia
Tel.: (60) 3 56241833
Web Site: http://www.hikoki-powertools.my
Power Driven Tool Mfr
N.A.I.C.S.: 333991

Hikoki Power Tools (Singapore) Pte.Ltd. (2)
No 31 Jurong Port Road Level 1M2 01-11M Jurong Logistics Hub, Singapore, 619115, Singapore
Tel.: (65) 64103355
Web Site: https://www.hikoki-powertools.sg
Electric Power Tool Mfr
N.A.I.C.S.: 333991

Hikoki Power Tools (Thailand) Co.,Ltd. (2)
899/17 Moo 21 Soi Jongsiri Bangphli-Tamru Road, Bangphli-yai Subdistrict Bangphli District, Samut Prakan, 10540, Thailand
Tel.: (66) 23160975
Web Site: https://www.hikoki-powertools.co.th
Power Tool Mfr & Distr
N.A.I.C.S.: 333991

Hikoki Power Tools (U.K.) Ltd. (2)
Precedent Drive, Rooklsey, Milton Keynes, MK13 8PJ, Buckinghamshire, United Kingdom
Tel.: (44) 1908660663
Web Site: https://www.hikoki-powertools.co.uk
Power Tool Distr
N.A.I.C.S.: 423830

Hikoki Power Tools Asia Co., Ltd. (2)
Workshop 01-05 on 10th Floor King Palace Plaza No 52A Sha Tsui Road, New Territories, Tsuen Wan, China (Hong Kong)
Tel.: (852) 24379291
Web Site: http://www.hitachi.com.hk
Electric Power Tools, Line Printers & Scientific Instruments Dist
N.A.I.C.S.: 423830

Hikoki Power Tools Belgium N.V./S.A. (2)
Koningin Astridlaan 51, 1780, Wemmel, Belgium
Tel.: (32) 24601720
Web Site: https://www.hikoki-powertools.be
Power Tool Mfr
N.A.I.C.S.: 333991

Hikoki Power Tools Deutschland GmbH (2)
Siemensring 34, 47877, Willich, Germany
Tel.: (49) 215449930
Web Site: https://hikoki-powertools.eu
Power Tool Mfr
N.A.I.C.S.: 333517

Hikoki Power Tools France S.A.S. (2)
Parc de l Eglantier -22 rue des Cerisiers, 91090, Lisses, France
Tel.: (33) 169474949
Web Site: https://www.hikoki-powertools.fr
Power Tool Distr
N.A.I.C.S.: 423830

Hikoki Power Tools Hungary Kft. (2)
Bogancsvirag Utca 5-7, 1106, Budapest, Hungary
Tel.: (36) 12643433
Web Site: http://www.hikoki-powertools.hu
Electric Power Tool Mfr
N.A.I.C.S.: 333991

Hikoki Power Tools Iberica, S.A. (2)
C Puigbarral 26 28 Pol Ind Can Petit, 08227, Terrassa, Spain
Tel.: (34) 937356722
Web Site: https://hikoki-powertools.es
Industrial Machinery Whslr
N.A.I.C.S.: 423830

Hikoki Power Tools India Private Ltd. (2)
Plot No 9A 1st Phase, Peenya Industrial

Area, Bengaluru, 560058, India
Tel.: (91) 8041170777
Web Site: https://www.koki-holdings.com
Electric Power Tools, Line Printers & Scientific Instruments Sales
N.A.I.C.S.: 423830

Hikoki Power Tools Netherlands B.V. (2)
Brabanthaven 11, 3433 PJ; Nieuwegein, Netherlands
Tel.: (31) 306084040
Web Site: https://www.hikoki-powertools.nl
Power-Driven Hand Tools Mfr
N.A.I.C.S.: 333991

Hikoki Power Tools Norway AS (2)
Kjeller Vest 7, PO Box 124, 2027, Kjeller, Norway
Tel.: (47) 66926600
Web Site: http://www.hikoki-powertools.no
Power & Hand Tool Whslr
N.A.I.C.S.: 423830

Hikoki Power Tools Osterreich GmbH (2)
Str 7 Objekt 58/A6 Industriezentrum No Sud, 2355, Wiener Neudorf, Austria
Tel.: (43) 2236646730
Web Site: https://hikoki-powertools.eu
Power Tool Mfr & Distr
N.A.I.C.S.: 333991

Hikoki Power Tools RUS L.L.C. (2)
Kashirskoe Shosse 41 bldg 2, 115409, Moscow, Russia
Tel.: (7) 4957274460
Web Site: http://www.hikoki-powertools.ru
Power Tool Distr
N.A.I.C.S.: 423830

Hikoki Power Tools Romania S.R.L. (2)
Ring Road No 66 Mustang Traco Warehouses, Warehouse No 1, 77145, Pantelimon, Ilfov, Romania
Tel.: (40) 371135109
Web Site: https://www.hikoki-powertools.ro
Power Tool Mfr & Distr
N.A.I.C.S.: 333991

Hikoki Power Tools Sweden AB (2)
Rotebergsvagen 2B, 192 78, Sollentuna, Sweden
Tel.: (46) 859899900
Web Site: http://www.hikoki-powertools.se
Power Tool Whslr
N.A.I.C.S.: 423830

Subsidiary (US):

Koki Holdings America Ltd. (2)
1111 Broadway Ave, Braselton, GA 30517
Tel.: (770) 925-1774
Web Site: http://www.metabo-hpt.com
Electric Power Tools, Line Printers & Scientific Instruments Dist
N.A.I.C.S.: 423830

Subsidiary (Non-US):

Koki Holdings America Ltd. - Canada (2)
3450 American Drive Suite 09, Mississauga, L4V 1T6, ON, Canada
Tel.: (905) 564-9477
Web Site: http://www.metabo-hpt.com
Power Tool Mfr & Distr
N.A.I.C.S.: 423830

Subsidiary (Domestic):

Koki Sales Co., Ltd. (2)
5th Floor Heiwajima Distribution Center 5-5-36, Heiwajima Ota-ku, Tokyo, 143-0006, Japan
Tel.: (81) 357537700
Web Site: http://www.koki-hanbai.co.jp
Electric Power Tools, Line Printers & Scientific Instruments Dist
N.A.I.C.S.: 333991

Kokusai Electric Corporation (1)
5th floor oak Kanda Kajicho Bldg 3-4 Kanda Kaji-cho, Chiyoda-ku, Tokyo, 101-0045, Japan **(100%)**
Tel.: (81) 352978530
Web Site: https://www.kokusai-electric.com
Holding Company
N.A.I.C.S.: 551112

Subsidiary (Domestic):

Hitachi Kokusai Electric, Inc. (2)
Hitachi Atago Bldg 6F 2-15-12, Nishishimbashi Minato-ku, Tokyo, 105-8039, Japan **(60%)**
Tel.: (81) 355105931
Web Site: https://www.hitachi-kokusai.co.jp
Emp.: 1,496
Mobile Phones, Other Wireless Communications Equipment & Semiconductors Mfr
N.A.I.C.S.: 517112
Akio Ito *(Exec Officer & Exec VP)*
Kaichiro Sakuma *(Pres & CEO)*
Mikio Kobayashi *(Exec Officer & VP)*
Masao Ichikawa *(Exec Officer)*
Takashi Onodera *(Exec Officer)*
Kiyoshi Inoue *(Auditor)*
Koichi Okabe *(Exec Officer)*

Subsidiary (US):

Hitachi Kokusai Electric America, Ltd. (3)
150 Crossways Park Dr, Woodbury, NY 11797
Tel.: (516) 921-7200
Web Site: https://www.hitachikokusai.us
Sales Range: $25-49.9 Million
Emp.: 30
Broadcasting & Video Equipment Sales, Maintenance & Installation Services
N.A.I.C.S.: 512120

Subsidiary (Domestic):

Kokusai Semiconductor Equipment Corporation (4)
Ste 290 2460 N 1st St, San Jose, CA 95131-1024
Tel.: (408) 456-2750
Web Site: http://www.ksec.com
Sales Range: $25-49.9 Million
Mfr of Semiconductors
N.A.I.C.S.: 423690
Ray McFarland *(Mgr-Matls & Pur)*

Subsidiary (Non-US):

Hitachi Kokusai Electric Canada, Ltd. (3)
1 Select Avenue Unit No 12, Scarborough, M1V 5J3, ON, Canada
Tel.: (416) 299-5900
Web Site: http://www.hitachikokusai.ca
Sales Range: $25-49.9 Million
Emp.: 4
Broadcasting & Video Equipment Sales, Maintenance & Installation Services
N.A.I.C.S.: 334220

Hitachi Kokusai Electric Europe GmbH (3)
Siemensstrasse 9, Neu-Isenburg, 63263, Frankfurt am Main, Germany
Tel.: (49) 610283320
Web Site: https://www.hitachi-keu.com
Sales Range: $25-49.9 Million
Emp.: 11
Broadcasting & Video Equipment Sales, Maintenance & Installation
N.A.I.C.S.: 517112
Hirofumi Suzuki *(Mng Dir)*

Subsidiary (Domestic):

Hitachi Kokusai Electric Services Inc. (3)
Akihabara Udx Bldg 4-14-1 Sotokanda, Chiyoda-ku, Tokyo, 101-8980, Japan
Tel.: (81) 352095931
Web Site: http://www.hitachi-kokusai.co.jp
Sales Range: $75-99.9 Million
Emp.: 400
Wireless Communication Equipment
N.A.I.C.S.: 334220

Subsidiary (Non-US):

KOOKJE ELECTRIC KOREA Co., Ltd. (3)
46 2gongdan 8-gil, Seobuk-gu, Cheonan, Chungcheongnam-do, Korea (South)
Tel.: (82) 415591705
Web Site: https://www.kekorea.co.kr
Sales Range: $125-149.9 Million
Electronic Components Mfr
N.A.I.C.S.: 334419
Masanari Nagai *(CEO)*

KKR & Co. Inc.—(Continued)

Kokusai Electric Asia Pacific Co., Ltd. (3)
9F 10F No 282 Beida Road, Hsin-chu, 300, Taiwan
Tel.: (886) 35285788
Semiconductor Production Equipment Installation & Maintenance Services
N.A.I.C.S.: 334413
Ken Chen *(Gen Mgr)*

Kokusai Electric Europe GmbH (3)
Gruitener Strasse 3, 40699, Erkrath, Germany
Tel.: (49) 210496550
Web Site: http://www.hitachi-keu.com
Sales Range: $25-49.9 Million
Emp.: 10
Semiconductor Manufacturing Equipment Sales & Maintenance
N.A.I.C.S.: 334413
Mark Blythe *(Mng Dir)*

Subsidiary (Domestic):

Kokusai Electric Semiconductor Service Inc. (3)
2-1 Honai, Yaocho, Toyama, 939-2393, Japan
Tel.: (81) 764545931
Web Site: https://www.kokusai-electric.com
Sales Range: $25-49.9 Million
Emp.: 179
Semiconductor Equipment Mfr, Installation & Sales
N.A.I.C.S.: 333242

Yagi Antenna Inc (3)
2-28-7 Kami-ochiai Shinjuku-ku, 161-0034, Tokyo, Japan
Tel.: (81) 353378681
Web Site: http://www.yagi-antenna.co.jp
Electrical Communication Equipment Mfr & Sales
N.A.I.C.S.: 335929

LCY Chemical Corp. (1)
No 3 Jhonglin Rd Xiaogang Dist, Kaohsiung, 812, Taiwan   **(100%)**
Tel.: (886) 227631611
Web Site: http://www.lcygroup.com
Rev.: $1,516,585,949
Assets: $1,590,299,000
Liabilities: $658,544,297
Net Worth: $931,754,704
Earnings: $123,585,110
Fiscal Year-end: 12/31/2017
Chemical Product Mfr & Distr
N.A.I.C.S.: 325998
T. H. Hong *(Chm & VP-Thermoplastic Elastomers BU)*
Vincent Liu *(CEO)*
C. J. Lee *(COO)*
Gavin Song *(Sr VP-Performance Plastics BU)*
Charles Wei *(Sr VP-Fin Center)*
Joey Lin *(VP-Thermoplastic Elastomers BU)*
Nova Fan *(Asst VP-Environmental Risk Mgmt Div)*
Terry Hu *(CTO)*
Wen Chiang *(Assoc VP-Methanol BU)*
Roger Chen *(Assoc VP-Electronic Material BU)*

Subsidiary (Non-US):

Huizhou LCY Elastomers Corp. (2)
299 Shihua Dadaozhong Dayawan Economic, Technological Development Zone, Huizhou, 516082, Guangdong, China
Tel.: (86) 7525599000
Petrochemical Mfr
N.A.I.C.S.: 325110

Subsidiary (US):

LCY Elastomers LP (2)
4803 Decker Dr, Baytown, TX 77520
Tel.: (281) 424-6100
Petrochemical Mfr
N.A.I.C.S.: 325110

Subsidiary (Domestic):

Lee Chang Yung Technology Corporation (2)
5F No 83 Sec 4 Bade Rd Songshan Dist, Taipei, 105, Taiwan
Tel.: (886) 227631611

Petrochemical Mfr
N.A.I.C.S.: 325110

Subsidiary (Non-US):

Zhenjiang LCY Warehousing & Storage Co., Ltd. (2)
Dantu Economic Development Zone, Zhenjiang, Jiangsu, China
Tel.: (86) 51185680337
Petrochemical Mfr
N.A.I.C.S.: 325110

Zhenjiang Lee Chang Yung General Chemical Co., Ltd. (2)
No 226 Erzhong Road Gaozi Street, Dantu District, Zhenjiang, Jiangsu, China
Tel.: (86) 51185680337
Petrochemical Products Mfr
N.A.I.C.S.: 325998

LGC Limited (1)
Queens Road, Teddington, TW11 0LY, Middlesex, United Kingdom
Tel.: (44) 2089437000
Web Site: http://www.lgcgroup.com
Laboratory Services, Measurement Standards, Reference Materials & Proficiency Testing Services
N.A.I.C.S.: 621511
Simon Parsons *(CFO)*
Tim Robinson *(CEO)*
Derek Craston *(Chief Scientific Officer)*
Euan O'Sullivan *(Pres & COO)*
Manjeet Aujla *(Chief Digital & Information Officer)*
Greer McMullen *(Gen Counsel & Sec)*
Sanjeev Rana *(Sr VP-Corp Strategy, Dev, and Comm)*
Julie Cormack *(Chief People Officer)*
Lee Maw *(Chief Digital Officer)*
Vivid Sehgal *(CFO)*

Subsidiary (US):

LGC Biosearch Technologies (2)
2199 S McDowell Blvd, Petaluma, CA 94954-6904
Tel.: (415) 883-8400
Web Site: http://www.biosearchtech.com
Emp.: 170
Genomic Chemicals & Reagent Products Mfr
N.A.I.C.S.: 325998
Ronald M. Cook *(Pres & CEO)*

Lucigen Corp. (2)
2905 Parmenter St, Middleton, WI 53562
Tel.: (608) 831-9011
Web Site: http://www.lucigen.com
Adhesives And Sealants
N.A.I.C.S.: 325520

SeraCare Life Sciences, Inc. (2)
37 Birch St, Milford, MA 01757
Tel.: (508) 244-6400
Web Site: http://www.seracare.com
Plasma Collection Services
N.A.I.C.S.: 325412
Bharathi Anekella *(Sr VP-Product Dev & Technical Ops)*
Russell Garlick *(Chief Scientific Officer)*
Todd Anderson *(VP-Supply Chain)*
Heather Buckley *(VP-Quality & Regulatory Affairs)*
Daniel Lamendola *(Sr VP-Ops)*
John Krawczynski *(Sr VP-Fin)*
Greg Ballish *(Sr VP-Comml)*
Michael Sweatt *(Exec VP & Gen Mgr)*
Jonathan Baldwin *(Controller)*

LOGISTEED, Ltd. (1)
2-9-2 Kyobashi, Chuo-ku, Tokyo, 104-8350, Japan   **(51.1%)**
Tel.: (81) 362632800
Web Site: https://www.logisteed.com
Rev.: $6,315,038,400
Assets: $7,627,220,480
Liabilities: $6,058,024,720
Net Worth: $1,569,195,760
Earnings: $221,410,640
Emp.: 43,729
Fiscal Year-end: 03/31/2021
Logistic Services
N.A.I.C.S.: 541614
Yasuo Nakatani *(Pres & CEO)*
Takashi Jinguji *(Exec Officer & Exec VP)*
Kunio Iida *(Exec Officer & Sr VP)*
Kazuhisa Hatakeyama *(Exec Officer & VP)*

Nobukazu Hayashi *(Exec Officer, Sr VP & Gen Mgr-Fin Strategy Office)*
Hiromoto Fujitani *(Exec Officer, VP & Gen Mgr-Bus Mgmt & Project Mgmt)*
Hiroaki Takagi *(Exec Officer)*
Kiyoshi Nagao *(Exec Officer)*
Yasushi Hagiwara *(Exec Officer, VP & Gen Mgr-HR & Bus Support Office)*
Seiki Sato *(Exec Officer, Sr VP & Gen Mgr-Corp Strategy Office)*
Kazuhiro Nishikawa *(Exec Officer)*
Ichiro Iino *(Exec Officer, VP & Gen Mgr-Bus Mgmt, AEO & Corp Export-Global)*
Koji Tanaka *(Chm)*
Yuichi Kuroume *(Exec Officer)*
Riichiro Hirano *(Exec Officer)*
Kazuhisa Sakaguchi *(Exec Officer)*
Hitoshi Honda *(Exec Officer & Deputy Gen Mgr-Fin Strategy Office)*
Tetsuji Mimura *(Exec Officer & Gen Mgr-Bus Dev & Bus Mgmt Headquarters)*

Subsidiary (US):

Carter Logistics, LLC (2)
4020 W 73rd St, Anderson, IN 46011
Tel.: (800) 738-7705
Web Site: http://www.carterexpress.com
Logistic Services
N.A.I.C.S.: 541614
Richard DeBoer *(Sr VP-Sls & Mktg)*
Ted Bowley *(Supvr)*
Jessica Paugh *(Asst Dir-Mktg)*
Sandra Martinez *(Dir-Logistics Ops)*
Jessica Warnke *(CEO)*
Nick Geesaman *(COO)*

Subsidiary (Non-US):

Dahang International Transportation Co., Ltd. (2)
6F Manpo Plaza, 500 West Yan'an Road, Shanghai, 200050, China
Tel.: (86) 21 23 25 9588
Web Site: http://www.hitachitransport.com.cn
Logistic Services
N.A.I.C.S.: 541614
Shima Hiroki *(Mgr)*

EHB Logistics Co., Ltd. (2)
L 25F Pacific Trade Building 4028 Jiabin Road, Shenzhen, 518001, Guangdong, China
Tel.: (86) 755 2586 3666
Logistic Services
N.A.I.C.S.: 541614

ESA s.r.o. (2)
Oldrichova 158 272 03, Kladno, Czech Republic
Logistic Services
N.A.I.C.S.: 541614

Eternity Grand Logistics Public Company Limited (2)
18/8 Moo4 Bangna-Trad Road, Bangsaothong, Tambol, 10540, Samutprakan, Thailand
Tel.: (66) 2 315 7333
Logistic Services
N.A.I.C.S.: 541614

Fine Chemical Logistics Hong Kong Co., Ltd. (2)
Flat A G/F Tung Chun Ind Bldg Stage 1 9-11 Cheong Wing Rd, Berth 1, Kwai Chung, New Territories, China (Hong Kong)   **(90%)**
Tel.: (852) 2429 7333
Web Site: http://www.hitachi-hb.co.jp
Sales Range: $25-49.9 Million
Emp.: 29
Logistics Services & Transport & Storage of Chemicals
N.A.I.C.S.: 541614

Subsidiary (Non-US):

Fine Chemical Logisitics China Company Limited (3)
Room 703 Manpo Plaza 500 West Yan'an Road, Shanghai, 200050, China
Tel.: (86) 21 6240 1616
Web Site: http://www.hitachi-hb.co.jp
Logistics Services & Transport & Storage of Chemicals
N.A.I.C.S.: 541614

Subsidiary (Non-US):

Flyjac Logistics Pvt. Ltd. (2)

102 Awas Apartments Sahar Pipe Line Road, Andheri E, Mumbai, 400 059, Andheri, India
Tel.: (91) 223 090 4900
Web Site: http://www.flyjaclogistics.com
Emp.: 1,500
Logistic Services
N.A.I.C.S.: 541614
Prem Kumar *(Gen Mgr-P&A)*
A. V. Ravikumar *(CEO & Mng Dir)*
Martin K. Eapen *(CFO)*
J. Shyam Sundar *(COO & Dir)*
Durga Thota *(Sec & Deputy Gen Mgr-Legal)*

HTS Forwarding Malaysia Sdn. Bhd. (2)
Lot 7 Jalan P/2 Bangi Industrial Estate, Selangor Darul Ehsan, Petaling Jaya, 43650, Malaysia
Tel.: (60) 3 8926 8122
Logistic Services
N.A.I.C.S.: 541614

Hitachi Collabonext Transport System Co., Ltd. (2)
Packing, Transport & Storage of Cosmetics
N.A.I.C.S.: 541614

Hitachi Distribution Software (Shanghai) Co., Ltd. (2)
Rm.2901Raffles City Office Tower, 268 Xizang Central Road, Shanghai, China
Tel.: (86) 21 6340 3730
Logistic Services
N.A.I.C.S.: 541614

Hitachi Sistema de Transporte Mexico, S.A. de C.V. (2)
Tel.: (52) 6649737460
Emp.: 4
Logistic Services
N.A.I.C.S.: 541614

Hitachi Transport Systeem (Nederland) BV (2)
Achterweg 29, 4181 AD, Waardenburg, Netherlands
Tel.: (31) 418 65 7654
Web Site: http://www.hitachitransport-eu.com
Logistics Consulting Servies
N.A.I.C.S.: 541614

Hitachi Transport System (Asia) Pte. Ltd. (2)
Logistic Services
N.A.I.C.S.: 541614

Hitachi Transport System (Australia) Pty. Ltd. (2)
Tel.: (61) 385238000
Logistic Services
N.A.I.C.S.: 541614

Hitachi Transport System (Europe) B.V. (2)
Achterweg 29, 4181, Waardenburg, Netherlands
Logistic Services
N.A.I.C.S.: 541614

Hitachi Transport System (Europe) GmbH (2)
Frankenstrasse 3, 20097, Hamburg, Germany
Tel.: (49) 40 2361 290
Sales Range: $25-49.9 Million
Emp.: 15
Logistics Consulting Servies
N.A.I.C.S.: 541614

Hitachi Transport System (Hong Kong) Ltd. (2)
10/F Ever Gain Bldg, No 22 On Sum Street, Sha Tin, China (Hong Kong)
Tel.: (852) 2783 0099
Logistic Services
N.A.I.C.S.: 541614

Hitachi Transport System (Korea), Ltd. (2)
Tel.: (82) 27557201
Logistic Services
N.A.I.C.S.: 541614

Hitachi Transport System (M) Sdn. Bhd. (2)
Logistic Services

N.A.I.C.S.: 541614

Hitachi Transport System (Shanghai), Ltd (2)
No 62 of Lane 379, Debao Road, Shanghai, China
Tel.: (86) 21 6393 0315
Logistic Services
N.A.I.C.S.: 541614

Hitachi Transport System (Taiwan) Ltd. (2)
10595 14F-4 No 1nFu Hsing N Rd, Taipei, Songshan, Taiwan
Tel.: (886) 2 2775 1551
Logistic Services
N.A.I.C.S.: 541614

Hitachi Transport System (Thailand), Ltd. (2)
2002 Moo 9 Sukhumvit Road, Theparak Muang Samutprakarn, Tambol, 10270, Thailand
Tel.: (66) 2 757 6088
Logistic Services
N.A.I.C.S.: 541614

Hitachi Transport System (UK) Ltd. (2)
Units 14-17 Bilton Road, Kingsland Business Park, Basingstoke, RG24 8LJ, Hampshire, United Kingdom
Tel.: (44) 1256365670
Web Site: http://www.hitachitransport-eu.com
Sales Range: $25-49.9 Million
Emp.: 7
Logistics Consulting Servies
N.A.I.C.S.: 541614

Hitachi Transport System India Pvt. Ltd. (2)
116&117 1st Floor Rectangle, D-4 District Centre, New Delhi, 110017, India
Tel.: (91) 11 40525200
Logistic Services
N.A.I.C.S.: 541614

Hitachi Transport Systems (France) S.A.R.L. (2)
Parc De Limere Zone Industrielle, 45160, Ardon, France
Tel.: (33) 238698700
Sales Range: $25-49.9 Million
Emp.: 12
Logistics Consulting Servies
N.A.I.C.S.: 541614
Yokoi Masasumi (Mng Dir)

Hitachi Transport Systems Ltd. (2)
Sucursal En Espana Ronda Shimuzu 1 Pol Ind Can Torrella, Vacarisses, Barcelona, Spain
Tel.: (34) 93 828 0959
Logistics Consulting Servies
N.A.I.C.S.: 541614

Hitachi Transport Systems S.A.R.L. (2)
ZI De La Feuchere 16 Rue Jean Mermoz, 77290, Compans, France
Tel.: (33) 1 60 94 95 50
Sales Range: $25-49.9 Million
Emp.: 8
Logistics Consulting Servies
N.A.I.C.S.: 541614
Matsumoto Atsuo (Gen Mgr)

Hitachi Travel Bureau Shanghai Co., Ltd. (2)
Rm 2605 Floor Rui Jin Building No 205 Maoming Road, Shanghai, 200020, China
Tel.: (86) 21 6472 7770
Logistic Services
N.A.I.C.S.: 541614

Hitachi Xinxin Global Logistics (Henan) Co., Ltd (2)
Room B 17th Floor No 1 Building, Jingsan Road, Fortune Plaza No 32, Zhengzhou, Heana, China
Tel.: (86) 371 6906 7766
Logistic Services
N.A.I.C.S.: 541614

Manila International Freight Forwarders, Inc. (2)
3rd floor Kingsland Bldg Dr A Santos Ave Brgy, San Isidro Sucat, Paranaque, 1709,

Metro Manila, Philippines
Tel.: (63) 288253182
Web Site: http://www.miffi.com.ph
Sales Range: $25-49.9 Million
Emp.: 60
Logistics Consulting Servies
N.A.I.C.S.: 541614

Miffi Logistics, Co. Inc. (2)
Logistic Services
N.A.I.C.S.: 541614

Nisshin Transportation (Qingdao) Co., Ltd. (2)
Flat B 21nd Story of Futai Bldg, No 18 Hong Kong Zhong Road, Qingdao, China
Tel.: (86) 532 8577 1025
Logistic Services
N.A.I.C.S.: 541614

Nisshin Transportation (Shanghai) Co., Ltd. (2)
19/F Jian-Ai Bldg 8 Changyang Road, Shanghai, China
Tel.: (86) 21 6545 8800
Logistic Services
N.A.I.C.S.: 541614

Nisshin Unyu (SHANGHAI) Co., Ltd. (2)
RM 1109 Tomson Commercial Bldg, 710 Dong Fang Road Pudong, Shanghai, China
Tel.: (86) 21 5830 3208
Logistic Services
N.A.I.C.S.: 541614

PT. Nisshin Kuwahara Indonesia (2)
Graha Mustika Ratu 4th Floor Ji Jend, Gatot Subroto Kav 74-75, Jakarta, 12870, Indonesia
Tel.: (62) 22 779 2246
Web Site: http://www.nitran.co.jp
Emp.: 115
Logistic Services
N.A.I.C.S.: 541614
Hidenobu Itami (Dir)

Shanghai Bondex Nisshin Logistics Co., Ltd. (2)
No 255 Tianyu Road, Lingang Industrial Area, Shanghai, Nanhui, China
Tel.: (86) 21 6828 0297
Logistic Services
N.A.I.C.S.: 541614

Shanghai Xiexin Customs Declaration Co., Ltd. (2)
19/F Jian-Ai Bldg 8 Changyang Road, Shanghai, China
Tel.: (86) 21 6545 1707
Logistic Services
N.A.I.C.S.: 541614

Suzhou Bondex Nisshin Logistic Co., Ltd. (2)
2/F C4/ Depot No 88 XianDai Ave, Suzhou Logistics Center Suzhou, Suzhou, Jiangsu, China
Tel.: (86) 512 6258 8233
Logistic Services
N.A.I.C.S.: 541614

TST Sunrise Service, Ltd. (2)
Logistic Services
N.A.I.C.S.: 541614

Subsidiary (Domestic):

Vantec Corporation (2)
4F Minatomirai Center Building 3-6-1 Minatomirai, Nishi-ku, Yokohama, 220-0012, Kanagawa, Japan
Tel.: (81) 45 306 5221
Web Site: https://www.vantec-gl.com
Emp.: 5,291
Holding Company
N.A.I.C.S.: 551112
Yukinobu Kodama (Pres)
Masaaki Nishizawa (Exec VP)
Kazuya Fukumoto (Mng Exec Officer)
Shuji Ueno (Mng Exec Officer)
Nobuyuki Arai (Exec Officer)
Kazuhiro Konba (Exec Officer)
Hirotaka Takada (Exec Officer)
Masayuki Kojima (Exec Officer)
Shouji Suzuki (Exec Officer)

Subsidiary (Domestic):

Ikeda Unyu Company Limited (3)

527 Nase-cho Totsuka-ku, Yokohama, 245-0051, Kanagawa, Japan
Tel.: (81) 458111421
Freight Forwarding Services
N.A.I.C.S.: 488510

LITI Research & Development Inc. (3)
Maruito Sapporo Bldg Kita2-jo Nishi 1-1, Chuo-ku, Sapporo, 060-0002, Japan
Tel.: (81) 112618877
RFID Technology Services
N.A.I.C.S.: 334413

Sakae Unyu Company Limited (3)
1-22-56 Mizumoto, Katsushika, Tokyo, 125-0032, Japan
Tel.: (81) 336092840
Web Site: https://www.sakaeunyu.com
Emp.: 81
Freight Trucking, Storage, Packaging & Equipment Maintenance Services
N.A.I.C.S.: 484121

Shonan Vantec Corporation (3)
2F Green Copo Yatsuzaka, 5-1 Horiguchi Kanazawa-ku, Yokohama, 236-0054, Kanagawa, Japan
Tel.: (81) 45785 9721
Freight Trucking & Warehousing Services
N.A.I.C.S.: 484121
Hideo Nobuo (Dir-Ops)

TCC Service Company Limited (3)
Daikyu-chuo Bldg, 4-9-11 Nihonbashi-honcho, Tokyo, 103-0023, Japan
Tel.: (81) 35642 3671
Temporary Staffing Services
N.A.I.C.S.: 561320

Tokiwa Kaiun Company Limited (3)
1 Honmoku-futo, Naka-ku, Yokohama, 231-0811, Kanagawa, Japan
Tel.: (81) 456228772
Sales Range: $25-49.9 Million
Emp.: 22
Freight Trucking & Warehousing Services
N.A.I.C.S.: 484121
Mitsuyuki Kitahara (Mgr-Sls)

VZ Butsuryu Corporation (3)
305 Kamishinden Kumagaya, Saitama, 360-0117, Japan
Tel.: (81) 48 536 7500
Equipment Maintenance Services
N.A.I.C.S.: 811111
Sachio Nieda (Dir-Ops)

Vantec Central Corporation (3)
3-13-1 Moriya-cho, Kanagawa-ku, Yokohama, 221-0022, Kanagawa, Japan
Tel.: (81) 454400951
Web Site: http://www.vantec-gl.com
Freight Trucking, Transport, Storage, Packaging & Insurance Services
N.A.I.C.S.: 484121

Vantec Central Logistics Corporation (3)
3-13-1 Moriya-cho, Kanagawa-ku, Yokohama, 221-0022, Kanagawa, Japan
Tel.: (81) 45 440 0951
Web Site: http://www.vantec-gl.com
Emp.: 30
Freight Trucking, Freight Forwarding & Waste Disposal Services
N.A.I.C.S.: 484121

Vantec East Logistics Corporation (3)
3-2 Hanamidai Hikigun Ranzanmachi, Saitama, 355-0204, Japan
Tel.: (81) 493 61 0065
Web Site: http://www.vantec-gl.com
Emp.: 800
Freight Trucking, Packaging Services & Waste Disposal
N.A.I.C.S.: 484121
Yuji Murakami (Pres)

Subsidiary (Non-US):

Vantec Europe Limited (3)
3 Infiniti Drive, Hillthorn Business Park, Washington, NE37 3HG, Tyne & Wear, United Kingdom
Tel.: (44) 191 416 1133
Web Site: https://www.vantec-gl.com
Automobile Material Handling Operations
N.A.I.C.S.: 562920

Martin Kendall (Mng Dir)

Subsidiary (Domestic):

Vantec RF Solutions Corporation (3)
Asahi Bldg 5-29-19 Shiba, Minato-ku, Tokyo, 108-0014, Japan
Tel.: (81) 364005225
RFID Software Development Services
N.A.I.C.S.: 513210

Vantec Tokai Logistics Corporation (3)
2-21-33 Hachiban Atsuta-ku, Nagoya, Aichi, Japan
Tel.: (81) 52651 3461
Freight Trucking & Warehousing Services
N.A.I.C.S.: 484121
Kenichi Osaki (Pres)

LRG Investor LLC (1)
477 9th Ave Ste 100, San Mateo, CA 94402
Tel.: (650) 692-3400
Web Site: http://www.lrginvestors.com
Investment Management Service
N.A.I.C.S.: 523940
Ryan Nickelson (Partner)
Kirk Declark (Dir-Acquisitions)
Julia Shuman (Controller)
Steve Cutter (Co-Founder)
Josh Amoroso (Co-Founder)

Laureate Education, Inc. (1)
1000 Brickell Ave Ste 715, Miami, FL 33131
Tel.: (786) 209-3368
Web Site: https://www.laureate.net
Rev.: $1,484,288,000
Assets: $2,125,616,000,000
Liabilities: $1,176,478,000,000
Net Worth: $949,138,000,000
Earnings: $107,590,000
Emp.: 28,900
Fiscal Year-end: 12/31/2023
Colleges, Universities & Professional Schools
N.A.I.C.S.: 611310
Marcelo Barbalho Cardoso (COO & Exec VP)
Richard M. Buskirk (CFO & Sr VP)
Gerard M. Knauer (Principal Acctg Officer, VP & Controller)
Adam Smith (Sr VP)
Andrew Booke Cohen (Vice Chm)
Eilif Serck-Hanssen (Pres & CEO)

Subsidiary (Non-US):

Think: Education Group Pty Limited (2)
17-51 Foveaux Street Surry Hills, Sydney, 2010, NSW, Australia (20%)
Tel.: (61) 300575803
Web Site: http://www.think.edu.au
Private Education & Training Services
N.A.I.C.S.: 611710
Linda Brown (CEO)
Alwyn Louw (Dir-Academic)
Michael Mann (Chm)
Scott Luckett (CFO)

Subsidiary (Domestic):

Think: Education Services Pty Limited (3)
171 Pacific Hwy, N Sydney, Sydney, 2060, Australia
Tel.: (61) 299551122
Education Management Services
N.A.I.C.S.: 611710

MMI Holdings Limited (1)
10 Kaki Bukit Avenue 1 07-04 Kaki Bukit Industrial Estate, 01-16 Lobby 3 Northtech Bldg, Singapore, 417942, Singapore
Tel.: (65) 68307333
Web Site: https://www.mmi.com.sg
Sales Range: $500-549.9 Million
Emp.: 12,000
Holding Company; Precision Engineered Electro-Mechanical Components & Assemblies Mfr
N.A.I.C.S.: 551112
Shermin Fock (CFO)
Teh Bong Lim (Founder)
Koh Tong Ho (CEO)

MYOB Group Limited (1)
Level 3 235 Springvale Road, Glen Waverley, 3150, VIC, Australia (100%)
Tel.: (61) 392229992

KKR & Co. Inc.—(Continued)

Web Site: http://www.myob.com
Rev.: $325,060,817
Assets: $1,092,582,195
Liabilities: $433,520,049
Net Worth: $659,062,146
Earnings: $47,360,133
Emp.: 1,500
Fiscal Year-end: 12/31/2017
Software Development Services
N.A.I.C.S.: 513210
Natalie Feehan (Gen Mgr-Mktg)
David Weickhardt (Gen Mgr-Product)
John Moss (Chief Strategy Officer)
Helen Lea (Chief Employee Experience Officer)
Blake Collins (Gen Mgr-Partners)
Greg Ellis (CEO)
Darren Smith (CTO)

Marelli Holdings Co., Ltd. (1)
2-1917 Nisshin-cho, Kita-ku, Saitama, 331-8501, Japan
Tel.: (81) 486602111
Web Site: https://www.marelli.com
Sales Range: $5-14.9 Billion
Emp.: 50,000
Holding Company; Automotive Components Mfr & Whslr
N.A.I.C.S.: 551112
David Slump (CEO)
Dinesh Paliwal (Chm)
Joachim Fetzer (CTO)
Alanna Abrahamson (CFO)

Subsidiary (Domestic):

Marelli Corporation (2)
2-1917 Nisshin-cho, Kita-ku, Saitama, 331-8501, Japan
Tel.: (81) 486602111
Web Site: https://marelli.com
Automotive Parts & Electronics Mfr
N.A.I.C.S.: 336390
Beda Borsenius (Pres & CEO)
David Slump (Pres)
Joachim Fetzer (CTO)
Alanna Abrahamson (CFO)

Subsidiary (Non-US):

CALSONIC KANSEI MOTHERSON AUTO PRODUCTS Private Limited (3)
194 Sector4 IMT Manesar, Gurgaon, 122 050, India
Tel.: (91) 124 4365513
Web Site: http://www.marelli-corporation.com
Electronic Components Mfr
N.A.I.C.S.: 334419

Calsonic Kansei (Guangzhou) Corp. (3)
18 Qichacheng Donfeng Dadao, Guangzhou, 510800, China
Tel.: (86) 2086733188
Web Site: http://www.marelli-corporation.com
Electronic Components Mfr
N.A.I.C.S.: 334419

Calsonic Kansei (Haimen) Car Air-Conditioning Compressor Corporation (3)
353Zhuhai Road Binjiang District, Haimen, 226110, Jiangsu, China
Tel.: (86) 513 8123 2323
Web Site: http://www.marelli-corporation.com
Electronic Components Mfr
N.A.I.C.S.: 334419

Calsonic Kansei (Malaysia) Sdn.Bhd. (3)
PLO 673 Jalan Keluli 3 Pasir Gudang Industrial Estate, 81700, Pasir Gudang, Johor, Malaysia
Tel.: (60) 72562288
Web Site: https://www.highly-marelli.com.my
Emp.: 300
Electronic Components Mfr
N.A.I.C.S.: 334419

Calsonic Kansei (Shanghai) Corp. (3)
Room 1325 No 345 Jinxiang Road, Pilot Free Trade Zone, Shanghai, 200336, China

Tel.: (86) 2152080707
Web Site: http://www.marelli-corporation.com
Electronic Components Mfr
N.A.I.C.S.: 334419

Calsonic Kansei (Wuxi) Corporation (3)
No J4 Wuxi Export Process District, Nanjing, 214028, China
Tel.: (86) 510 6661 7200
Web Site: http://www.marelli-corporation.com
Electronic Components Mfr
N.A.I.C.S.: 334419

Calsonic Kansei Korea Corporation (3)
800 Gomo-ro Hallim-myeon, Gimhae, 50850, Gyeongsangnam-do, Korea (South)
Tel.: (82) 553458888
Web Site: http://www.marelli-corporation.com
Electronic Components Mfr
N.A.I.C.S.: 334419

Calsonic Kansei Mexicana, S.A. de R.L. de C.V. (3)
Circuito Aguascalientes Oriente 127 Parque Ind Del Valle de, 20300, Aguascalientes, Mexico
Tel.: (52) 4499100100
Web Site: http://www.marelli-corporation.com
Electronic Components Mfr
N.A.I.C.S.: 334419

Subsidiary (Domestic):

ITEC Corporation (3)
387-7 Miho, Shimizu-ku, Shizuoka, 424-8510, Japan
Tel.: (81) 54 337 2000
Web Site: http://www.iteo-c.co.jp
Rev.: $818,715,040
Assets: $740,810,400
Liabilities: $408,602,480
Net Worth: $332,207,920
Earnings: $41,401,360
Emp.: 431
Fiscal Year-end: 03/31/2022
Steel Product Mfr & Distr
N.A.I.C.S.: 331221

Subsidiary (Non-US):

Marelli (Thailand) Co., Ltd (3)
Amata Nakorn Industrial Estate 700/641, Moo 3 Tambol Bankao Amphur Panthong, Bangkok, 20160, Chonburi, Thailand
Tel.: (66) 38210129
Web Site: http://www.marelli-corporation.com
Electronic Components Mfr
N.A.I.C.S.: 334419

Marelli (Xiang Yang) Corporation (3)
Xinxing Rd Automotive Industry Development Area, Xiangyang, 441004, China
Tel.: (86) 7103314388
Web Site: http://www.marelli-corporation.com
Electronic Components Mfr
N.A.I.C.S.: 334419

Marelli Automotive Components (Guangzhou) Corporation (3)
West Dongfeng Road Autombile city, Huadu District, Guangzhou, 510800, China
Tel.: (86) 2066852899
Web Site: http://www.marelli-corporation.com
Electronic Components Mfr
N.A.I.C.S.: 334419

Marelli Automotive Components (Wuxi) Corporation (3)
17 Xinrong Road Wuxi National Hi-tech Industrial Development Zone, Jiangsu, 214112, China
Tel.: (86) 51066612666
Web Site: http://www.marelli-corporation.com
Electronic Components Mfr
N.A.I.C.S.: 334419

Marelli Automotive Systems Europe plc (3)
Llethri Road Llanelli, Carmarthen, SA14 8HU, United Kingdom

Tel.: (44) 1554747000
Web Site: http://www.marelli-corporation.com
Electronic Components Mfr
N.A.I.C.S.: 334419

Marelli Automotive Systems Europe plc - France Branch Office (3)
Immeuble START 15 bis avenue du Centre, 78280, Guyancourt, France
Tel.: (33) 139305180
Web Site: http://www.marelli-corporation.com
Electronic Components Mfr
N.A.I.C.S.: 334419

Marelli Automotive Systems UK Limited (3)
Llethri Road Llanelli, Carmarthen, SA14 8HU, United Kingdom
Tel.: (44) 1554747000
Web Site: http://www.marelli-corporation.com
Electronic Components Mfr
N.A.I.C.S.: 334419

Marelli Barcelona Espana S.A.U. (3)
Ronda de Collsabadell 1-3 Poligono Industrial G-2 Llinars del Valles, Casa Nova, 08450, Barcelona, Spain
Tel.: (34) 938642000
Web Site: http://www.marelli-corporation.com
Electronic Components Mfr
N.A.I.C.S.: 334419

Marelli China Holding Company (3)
Room 1808 18th floor Shanghai International Trade Center, west Yan'an road, Shanghai, 2201, China
Tel.: (86) 2152080707
Web Site: http://www.marelli-corporation.com
Electronic Components Mfr
N.A.I.C.S.: 334419

Subsidiary (US):

Marelli North America, Inc. (3)
1 Calsonic Way, Shelbyville, TN 37160
Tel.: (931) 684-4490
Web Site: http://www.marelli-corporation.com
Automobile Parts Mfr
N.A.I.C.S.: 336390

Subsidiary (Non-US):

Marelli Ploiesti Romania S.R.L. (3)
Industrial Park Ploiesti, Conului Street No 7, Ploiesti, 100213, Romania
Tel.: (40) 244402000
Web Site: http://www.marelli-corporation.com
Electronic Components Mfr
N.A.I.C.S.: 334419

Marelli R&D Co., Limited (3)
Shanghai Euromate City Industrial Park Bid No 6, Yuanshan Road Lane 88 Xinzhuang, Shanghai, 201108, China
Tel.: (86) 2164897868
Web Site: http://www.marelli-corporation.com
Electronic Components Mfr
N.A.I.C.S.: 334419

Marelli Tooling (Guangzhou) Corporation (3)
West Dongfeng Road Autombile city, Huadu District, Guangzhou, 510800, China
Tel.: (86) 2086733128
Web Site: http://www.marelli-corporation.com
Electronic Components Mfr
N.A.I.C.S.: 334419

Marelli do Brasil Industria e Comercio Ltda (3)
Nissan Avenue 1500 Main gate 3 -TRIM build, Resende, Rio de Janeiro, 27537-800, Brazil
Tel.: (55) 2421080400
Web Site: http://www.marelli-corporation.com
Electronic Components Mfr
N.A.I.C.S.: 334419

Siam Calsonic Co., Limited. (3)

Amata Nakom Industrial Estate 700/342 Moo 6, Tambol Nongmaidaeng Amphur Muang, Bangkok, 20000, Chonburi, Thailand
Tel.: (66) 38214357
Web Site: http://www.marelli-corporation.com
Electronic Components Mfr
N.A.I.C.S.: 334419

Subsidiary (Non-US):

Marelli Europe S.p.A. (2)
Viale Aldo Borletti 61 63, 20011, Corbetta, MI, Italy
Tel.: (39) 0297227111
Web Site: https://www.magnetimarelli.com
Automotive Lighting, Powertrain Components, Electronic Systems, Exhaust Systems, Suspension Systems & Shock Absorbers Mfr
N.A.I.C.S.: 336330

Joint Venture (Domestic):

DTR VMS Italy S.r.l. (3)
Sede Legale e Stabilimento Via S Antonio 59, 25050, Passirano, BS, Italy
Tel.: (39) 030 6855 1
Emp.: 1,900
Automobile Parts Mfr
N.A.I.C.S.: 336390
Luca Olivetti (VP-Bus Dev)
Simone Calvi (Dir-Quality)
Andrea Giunta (Plant Mgr)
Gabriele Ravasi (Dir-Sls)

Subsidiary (Domestic):

Magneti Marelli After Market Parts and Services S.p.A. (3)
Viale Aldo Borletti 61/63, Corbetta, Milan, 20011, Italy
Tel.: (39) 0297227454
Web Site: http://www.magnetimarelli.com
Automobile Parts Distr
N.A.I.C.S.: 423120
Alberto Dall'Osso (Grp Product Mgr)

Subsidiary (Non-US):

Magneti Marelli Aftermarket GmbH (4)
Heinz-Nixdorf-Strasse 4, 74172, Neckarsulm, Germany
Tel.: (49) 71312910
Web Site: https://www.magnetimarelli-parts-and-services.de
Automobile Parts Distr
N.A.I.C.S.: 423120

Magneti Marelli Aftermarket Sp. z o.o. (4)
Plac Pod Lipami 5, 40-476, Katowice, Poland
Tel.: (48) 326036107
Web Site: https://www.magnetimarelli-checkstar.pl
Automobile Mfr & Distr
N.A.I.C.S.: 336110

Magneti Marelli Repuestos S.A. (4)
1035 Andonaegui, C1427BEC, Buenos Aires, Argentina
Tel.: (54) 11 4523 6612
Web Site: http://www.marellicofap.com.ar
Automobile Parts Distr
N.A.I.C.S.: 423120

Subsidiary (Non-US):

Magneti Marelli Automotive Components (WUHU) Co. Ltd. (3)
No 5 Shangzha Rd Qiaobei Industry Park Economic Technology, Development Zone, Wuhu, 241009, Anhui, China
Tel.: (86) 5535716808
Web Site: http://www.magnetimarelli.com
Automobile Parts Mfr
N.A.I.C.S.: 336390

Magneti Marelli Exhaust Systems Polska Sp. zo.o. (3)
ul Zaruskiego 11, 41-219, Sosnowiec, Poland
Tel.: (48) 323642863
Web Site: http://www.magnetimarelli.com
Automobile Parts Mfr
N.A.I.C.S.: 336390

Magneti Marelli France S.a.s. (3)
5-7 Rue Albert Einstein ZA de Trappes
Elancourt, 78190, Trappes, France
Tel.: (33) 1 30 16 69 60
Web Site: http://www.magnetimarelli.com
Automobile Parts Mfr
N.A.I.C.S.: 336390

Subsidiary (US):

**Magneti Marelli Holding U.S.A.
Inc.** (3)
3900 Automation Ave, Auburn Hills, MI
48326
Tel.: (248) 418-3000
Web Site: http://www.magnetimarelli-
checkstar.com
Investment Management Service
N.A.I.C.S.: 523999

Subsidiary (Domestic):

Marelli North Carolina USA LLC (4)
2101 Nash St, Sanford, NC 27330
Tel.: (919) 776-4111
Web Site: http://www.magnetimarelli.com
Powertrain Mfr
N.A.I.C.S.: 336110

Marelli Tennessee USA LLC (4)
181 Bennett Dr, Pulaski, TN 38478
Tel.: (931) 363-4535
Web Site: http://www.magnetimarelli.com
Motor Vehicle Parts Mfr
N.A.I.C.S.: 336390

Subsidiary (Non-US):

Magneti Marelli Japan K.K. (3)
3-17-5 Shin-Yokohama, Kohoku-Ku, Yoko-
hama, 222-0033, Kanagawa, Japan
Tel.: (81) 454780045
Web Site: http://www.magnetimarelli.com
Automobile Parts Mfr
N.A.I.C.S.: 336390

**Magneti Marelli Motopropulsion
France SAS** (3)
9 Rue Maurice Ravel, Argentan, 61200,
France
Tel.: (33) 2 33 67 71 71
Web Site: http://www.magnetimarelli.com
Automobile Parts Distr
N.A.I.C.S.: 423120

**Magneti Marelli Powertrain (Shang-
hai) Co. Ltd.** (3)
No 168 Taigu Road, Shanghai, 200131,
China
Tel.: (86) 2158669090
Web Site: http://www.magnetimarelli.com
Automobile Parts Mfr
N.A.I.C.S.: 336390

**Magneti Marelli Powertrain Slovakia
s.r.o.** (3)
275 Kechnec 275, Kosice, 044 58, Slovakia
Tel.: (421) 903 921 759
Web Site: http://www.magnetimarelli.com
Automotive Engine Mfr
N.A.I.C.S.: 336390

Magneti Marelli Slovakia s.r.o. (3)
275 Kechnec 275, Kosice, 044 58, Slovakia
Tel.: (421) 903 921 759
Web Site: http://www.magnetimarelli.com
Automobile Parts Mfr
N.A.I.C.S.: 336390

**Magneti Marelli Suspension Systems
Bielsko Sp. z.o.o.** (3)
ul M Grazynskiego 141, Bielsko-Biala, 43-
300, Poland
Tel.: (48) 33 813 21 99
Web Site: http://www.magnetimarelli.com
Automobile Parts Mfr
N.A.I.C.S.: 336390

**Magneti Marelli do Brasil Industria e
Comercio SA** (3)
Rua Manoel Da Nobrega 350 Maua, Sao
Paulo, 09380-120, Brazil
Tel.: (55) 11 3289 1284
Web Site: http://www.magnetimarelli.com
Automobile Parts Distr
N.A.I.C.S.: 423120

Marmic Fire & Safety Co., Inc. (1)
1014 S Wall Ave, Joplin, MO 64801
Tel.: (417) 624-6117

Web Site: http://www.marmicfire.com
Miscellaneous Durable Goods Merchant
Whslr
N.A.I.C.S.: 423990
Charles Teeter *(Pres)*
Greg Bochicchio *(CEO)*

Maxeda B.V. (1)
De entree 500, PO Box 268, Amsterdam,
1101 EE, Netherlands
Tel.: (31) 205490500
Web Site: http://www.maxeda.com
Sales Range: $1-4.9 Billion
Emp.: 37,410
Holding Company; Department Stores,
Home Furnishings & Fashion Design
N.A.I.C.S.: 551112

Affiliate (Domestic):

AudioSonic (2)
Tijnmuiden 15 19, 1046 AK, Amsterdam,
Netherlands
Tel.: (31) 205854900
Sales Range: $25-49.9 Million
Emp.: 50
Consumer Electronics
N.A.I.C.S.: 441330

Subsidiary (Domestic):

Dixons B.V. (2)
Goudenheuvel 47, 5234 GA, 's-
Hertogenbosch, Netherlands
Tel.: (31) 853034876
Web Site: https://www.dixons.nl
Sales Range: $25-49.9 Million
Emp.: 120
Photography, Consumer Electronics & Elec-
tric Household Appliances
N.A.I.C.S.: 335220

Formido B.V. (2)
Watergoorweg 65, Nijkerk, 3861 MA, Neth-
erlands
Tel.: (31) 332474547
Web Site: http://www.formido.nl
Sales Range: $10-24.9 Million
Emp.: 60
Do-It-Yourself Stores
N.A.I.C.S.: 811198

Praxis (2)
Eekholt 54, 1112 XH, Diemen, Netherlands
Tel.: (31) 203983333
Web Site: http://www.praxis.nl
Sales Range: $25-49.9 Million
Emp.: 250
Do-It-Yourself Stores
N.A.I.C.S.: 811198

Schaap & Citroen (2)
Van Baerlestraat 27, 1071 AN, Amsterdam,
Netherlands
Tel.: (31) 202384790
Web Site: https://www.schaapcitroen.nl
Sales Range: $25-49.9 Million
Emp.: 100
Jewelry
N.A.I.C.S.: 339910

de Bijenkorf (2)
Dam 1, 1012 JS, Amsterdam, Netherlands
Tel.: (31) 8089333
Web Site: https://www.debijenkorf.nl
Sales Range: $650-699.9 Million
Emp.: 2,500
Department Stores
N.A.I.C.S.: 455110

Merchant Capital Solutions LLC (1)
147 W35th St Ste 805, New York, NY
10001
Tel.: (212) 213-5680
Web Site: http://www.efundex.com
Financial Planning Advice Services
N.A.I.C.S.: 523940

**Merchants Mortgage & Trust Corpo-
ration, LLC** (1)
7400 E Crestline Cir # 250, Englewood, CO
80111
Tel.: (303) 773-3000
Web Site: http://www.merchantsmtg.com
Real Estate Credit
N.A.I.C.S.: 522292
Dana Reynolds *(VP-Ops)*
Kim Hubbard *(Exec VP-Loan Production)*
Susan Aubin *(Officer-Loan & VP)*
Jack Keane *(CFO & Sec)*

Bo Seamands *(Officer-Loan & VP)*
Boris Shmit *(VP & Mgr-Improvement Es-
crows)*
Mark Steinbeck *(Officer-Loan & VP)*
Mary Pawlowski *(VP & Controller)*
Max Miller *(Officer-Loan)*
Justin Land *(CEO)*

National Vision, Inc. (1)
2435 Commerce Ave Bldg 2200, Duluth,
GA 30096
Tel.: (770) 822-3600
Web Site: https://www.nationalvision.com
Sales Range: $200-249.9 Million
Emp.: 7,000
Optical Retailer
N.A.I.C.S.: 456130

Unit (Domestic):

**America's Best Contacts &
Eyeglasses** (2)
2435 Commerce Ave Bldg 2200, Duluth,
GA 30096
Tel.: (770) 822-3600
Web Site: http://www.americasbest.com
Sales Range: $50-74.9 Million
Emp.: 300
Optical Goods Stores
N.A.I.C.S.: 456130

Eyeglass World (2)
2000 Newpoint Pkwy, Lawrenceville, GA
30043
Tel.: (470) 321-7603
Web Site: https://www.eyeglassworld.com
Optical Goods Stores
N.A.I.C.S.: 456130

Branch (Domestic):

**National Vision - St. Cloud Optical
Laboartory** (2)
3400 Energy Dr, Saint Cloud, MN 56304
Tel.: (320) 252-6006
Web Site: http://www.nationalvision.com
Optical Goods Mfr
N.A.I.C.S.: 333310

Ness Technologies, Inc. (1)
300 Frank W Burr Blvd 7th Fl, Teaneck, NJ
07666
Tel.: (201) 488-7222
Web Site: http://www.ness.com
Information Technology Services
N.A.I.C.S.: 541511
Pete Rogers *(Mng Dir-Western Europe)*
Ed Galati *(Co-Pres & CFO)*
Joe Burke *(Pres-Global Cloud & Data Svcs)*
Vinay RajadHyaksha *(Co-Pres & COO)*
Shashank Samant *(Founder)*
Ranjit Tinaikar *(CEO)*
Narayanan Nair *(Chief People Officer)*
David Mahoney *(Head-M&A)*
Drew Naukam *(Chief Growth Officer-North
America)*
Mark Shwartz *(Chief Legal Officer)*
Carla Deisenroth *(Head-Global Mktg)*
Rajul Rana *(Chief Solutions Officer)*

Subsidiary (Domestic):

Intricity, LLC (2)
244 5th Ave, New York, NY 10001
Tel.: (212) 461-1100
Web Site: http://www.intricity.com
Rev.: $5,100,000
Emp.: 41
Data Processing, Hosting & Related Ser-
vices
N.A.I.C.S.: 518210
Adrian Boerstra *(Dir-Bus Intelligence & Sls)*
Troy Clemente *(Co-Founder & Principal)*
Arkady Kleyner *(Co-Founder & Principal)*
Paul Maiella *(Principal)*

Subsidiary (Non-US):

Ness Canada Inc (2)
2 Robert Speck Parkway Suite 753, Missis-
sauga, L5R 3K6, ON, Canada
Tel.: (905) 272-0370
Web Site: http://www.ness.com
IT Services
N.A.I.C.S.: 541512

Ness Czech s.r.o (2)
V Parku 2335/20, 148 00, Prague, Czech
Republic (100%)
Tel.: (420) 244026400

Web Site: http://www.ness.cz
Sales Range: $150-199.9 Million
Emp.: 4,000
Software Development Services
N.A.I.C.S.: 541512
Petr Mytina *(Mng Dir)*

Branch (Domestic):

Ness Czech s.r.o. - Brno (3)
Londynske Namesti 1, 63900, Brno, Czech
Republic (100%)
Tel.: (420) 533429222
Web Site: http://www.ness.com
Information Technology Solutions
N.A.I.C.S.: 541512
Mirko Kalous *(Mng Dir)*

Ness Czech s.r.o. - Ostrava (3)
Ul 30 Dubna 635, 70200, Ostrava, Morav-
ska, Czech Republic (100%)
Tel.: (420) 597350332
Web Site: http://www.ness.com
Information Technology Solutions
N.A.I.C.S.: 541512

Subsidiary (Non-US):

Ness Hungary Ltd. (3)
Bartok Bela Street 105 113, Budapest,
1115, Hungary (100%)
Tel.: (36) 14814550
Web Site: http://www.ness.com
Sales Range: $25-49.9 Million
Information Technology Solutions & Ser-
vices
N.A.I.C.S.: 541512

Ness KDC s.r.o. (3)
10 B Moldavska Cesta, 040 11, Kosice,
Slovakia (100%)
Tel.: (421) 557235111
Web Site: http://www.ness.com
Sales Range: $75-99.9 Million
Emp.: 300
Information Technology Services
N.A.I.C.S.: 541512

Ness Romania (3)
Bucharest Bus Pk 23 Menuetului St, En-
trance D 5th Fl District 1, 013713, Bucha-
rest, Romania (100%)
Tel.: (40) 213005518
Web Site: http://www.ness.com
Sales Range: $25-49.9 Million
Emp.: 73
Information Technology Solutions
N.A.I.C.S.: 541512

Ness S.A. (3)
Rue De Lausanne 65, Geneva, Switzerland
Tel.: (41) 229080680
Web Site: http://www.ness.com
Computer Related Services
N.A.I.C.S.: 541519

Ness Slovensko a.s. (3)
Galvaniho Business Centrum III, Galvaniho
15/C, 821 04, Bratislava, Slovakia (100%)
Tel.: (421) 258261000
Web Site: http://www.ness.com
Information Technology Solutions
N.A.I.C.S.: 541512
Petr Mytina *(Mng Dir)*

S.C. Ness Romania S.r.l (3)
United Business Center 2 Strada Palas 5B
Palas, Iasi, 700032, Romania (100%)
Tel.: (40) 372805800
Web Site: http://www.ness.com
Sales Range: $25-49.9 Million
Emp.: 44
Software Development Services
N.A.I.C.S.: 541512
Yoav Armony *(Country Mgr)*

Subsidiary (Non-US):

Ness Global Services Ltd. (2)
No 1 Bell Street, Maidenhead, SL6 1BU,
Berkshire, United Kingdom (100%)
Tel.: (44) 1628 421 840
Web Site: http://www.ness.com
Sales Range: $25-49.9 Million
Emp.: 15
IT Services
N.A.I.C.S.: 541512
James Shearer *(Dir-Bus Dev)*

**Ness Technologies (India) Pvt.
Ltd.** (2)

KKR & Co. Inc.—(Continued)

No 33 6th Block 17th H Main Road, Kora-
mangala, Bengaluru, 560095,
India   **(100%)**
Tel.: (91) 8041961000
Web Site: http://www.ness.com
Sales Range: $450-499.9 Million
Information Technology Products & Services
N.A.I.C.S.: 541512
Satyajit Bandyopadhyay (Pres)

Branch (Domestic):

**Ness Technologies (India) Pvt. Ltd. -
Hyderabad**   **(3)**
Hitech City IT Rehaja Park Mindspace
Maximas 2A Building, Hyderabad, 500 052,
India
Tel.: (91) 4067 262 000
Web Site: http://www.ness.com
Sales Range: $150-199.9 Million
Emp.: 1,000
Information Technology Development Ser-
vices
N.A.I.C.S.: 541512
N. GopaKumar (CEO)

Branch (Non-US):

**Ness Technologies, Inc. - Technology
Innovation Center**   **(2)**
Ness Tower Atidim High-Tech Industrial
Park Building 10, Tel Aviv, 61580, Israel
Tel.: (972) 3 766 6800
Web Site: http://www.ness.com
Information Technology Services & Solu-
tions
N.A.I.C.S.: 541519

Subsidiary (Domestic):

Ness USA, Inc.   **(2)**
300 Frank W Burr Blvd, Teaneck, NJ 17666
Tel.: (201) 488-7222
Web Site: http://www.ness.com
Computer System Design Services
N.A.I.C.S.: 541512

Novaria Holdings LLC   **(1)**
6625 Iron Horse Blvd, North Richland Hills,
TX 76180
Tel.: (817) 381-3810
Web Site: http://www.novariagroup.com
Investment Holding Company; Precision
Components Mfr
N.A.I.C.S.: 551112
Bryan Perkins (CEO)
Mike Wagner (Exec VP-Ops)
Justin Tucker (CFO)
Jed Burmahln (Gen Mgr)

Subsidiary (Domestic):

Anillo Industries, Inc.   **(2)**
2090 N Glassell St, Orange, CA 92865
Tel.: (714) 637-7000
Web Site: http://www.anilloinc.com
Sales Range: $1-9.9 Million
Emp.: 28
Bolt, Nut, Screw, Rivet & Washer Mfr
N.A.I.C.S.: 332722
Kurt Koch (Pres)
Ben Omidwar (Dir-Quality)
Paula Wasper (Mgr-Sls)
David Hultquist (Mgr-Matls)
Mark Koch (VP)
Tom Horne (Mgr-Ops)
Bhupesh Aminb (Mgr-Plating)

**Elastic Stop Nut Corporation of
America**   **(2)**
611 Country Club Rd, Pocahontas, AR
72455
Tel.: (870) 892-5201
Web Site: https://www.esnaproducts.com
Emp.: 200
Fasteners & Nuts Mfr & Whslr
N.A.I.C.S.: 332722

Branch (Domestic):

ESNA - Texas   **(3)**
6625 Iron Horse Blvd, North Richland Hills,
TX 76180
Tel.: (817) 281-8816
Web Site: http://www.esnaproducts.com
Sales Range: $1-9.9 Million
Emp.: 55
Precision Aerospace Components Mfr

N.A.I.C.S.: 336413

Subsidiary (Domestic):

GK Mechanical Systems LLC   **(2)**
934 Federal Rd, Brookfield, CT 06804-1125
Tel.: (203) 775-4970
Web Site: http://www.gkmechanical.com
Mfg Locks
N.A.I.C.S.: 332510
Michael Barnes (Gen Mgr)

**Hohman Plating & Manufacturing,
LLC**   **(2)**
814 Hillrose Ave, Dayton, OH 45404-1132
Tel.: (937) 228-2191
Web Site: http://www.hohmanplating.com
Electroplating, Plating, Polishing, Anodizing
& Coloring
N.A.I.C.S.: 332813
Dave Fulton (Gen Mgr)
Brad Kremer (Pres)

**Hydro Fitting Manufacturing
Corp.**   **(2)**
733 E Edna Pl, Covina, CA 91723
Tel.: (626) 967-5151
Web Site: http://www.hydrofitting.com
Mfg High Pressure Valves & Fittings
N.A.I.C.S.: 336310
Johanne Schwartz (Controller)
Seth Schwartz (Pres)

John Hassall, LLC   **(2)**
609-1 Cantiague Rock Rd, Westbury, NY
11590
Tel.: (516) 334-6200
Web Site: http://www.hassall.com
Custom Pins, Rivets & Threaded Fasteners
Mfr
N.A.I.C.S.: 332722

Long-Lok Fasteners Corporation   **(2)**
10630 Chester Rd, Cincinnati, OH 45215
Tel.: (513) 772-1880
Web Site: http://www.longlok.com
Sales Range: $10-24.9 Million
Emp.: 75
Self-Locking & Self-Sealing Fasteners Mfr &
Distr
N.A.I.C.S.: 332722
Bob Bennett (CEO)

Division (Domestic):

**Long-Lok Fasteners Corporation -
Locking Division West**   **(3)**
20531 Belshaw Ave, Carson, CA 90746-
3505
Tel.: (424) 213-4570
Web Site: http://www.longlok.com
Self-Locking & Self-Sealing Fastener Mfr
N.A.I.C.S.: 332722

Subsidiary (Domestic):

Space-Lok, Inc.   **(2)**
13306 Halldale Ave, Gardena, CA 90249
Tel.: (310) 527-6150
Web Site: https://spacelok.com
Fasteners & Multiple Component Mecha-
nisms Mfr
N.A.I.C.S.: 336413

The Young Engineers, Inc.   **(2)**
25841 Commercentre Dr, Lake Forest, CA
92630
Tel.: (949) 581-9411
Web Site: http://www.youngengineers.com
Sales Range: $10-24.9 Million
Emp.: 50
Hardware Mfr
N.A.I.C.S.: 332510
Miki Young (CEO)
John Pumphrey (Mgr-Sls-Natl)
Pat Wells (Pres)
Sam Frias (Mgr-Engrg)
Terry Litwinski (Mgr-Inside Sls)
David Eshleman (Mgr-Quality Assurance)
Richard Switzer (Mgr-Territory & Engr-Sls)
Tim Till (Mgr-Mfg)

Weatherford Aerospace, Inc.   **(2)**
1020 E Columbia St, Weatherford, TX
76086
Tel.: (817) 594-5464
Web Site:
    http://www.weatherfordaerospace.com
Sales Range: $1-9.9 Million
Emp.: 101

Chemical Treatment of Materials for Aerospace Industry
N.A.I.C.S.: 325510

Ocean Yield ASA   **(1)**
Oksenoyveien 10, 1366, Lysaker,
Norway   **(94.3%)**
Tel.: (47) 41742000
Web Site: http://www.oceanyield.no
Rev.: $237,000,000
Assets: $2,311,700,000
Liabilities: $1,659,900,000
Net Worth: $651,800,000
Earnings: $92,500,000
Emp.: 8
Fiscal Year-end: 12/31/2023
Oil-Service & Industrial Shipping Investment
Services
N.A.I.C.S.: 213112
Frank Ove Reite (Chm)
Lars Solbakken (CEO)
Eirik Eide (CFO)
Marius Magelie (Sr VP-Fin & IR)
Kristine Kosi (Chief Acctg Officer)
Andreas Reklev (Sr VP-Investments)
Erik Hiller Holom (VP-Investments)
Andreas Rode (Head-Bus Dev & M&A)

Subsidiary (Domestic):

Aker Floating Production ASA   **(2)**
Fjordalleen 16, 250, Oslo, Norway
Tel.: (47) 24 13 00 00
Web Site:
    http://www.akerfloatingproduction.com
Oil & Gas Drilling Services
N.A.I.C.S.: 213111
Havard Garseth (Mng Dir)
Lars Oddvar Aulesjord (VP-Ops & Produc-
tion)

Optiv Security, Inc.   **(1)**
1144 15th St Ste 2900, Denver, CO 80202
Tel.: (303) 298-0600
Web Site: https://www.optiv.com
Sales Range: Less than $1 Million
Computer & Internet Security Services
N.A.I.C.S.: 541519
John Ihn Park (Chm)
Dan Burns (Founder)
Nate Brady (CFO)
Kevin Lynch (CEO)
Heather Rim (CMO)
Heather Allen Strbiak (Chief HR Officer)
Rocky DeStefano (CTO)
Jason Lewkowicz (Exec VP)
Josh Locker (Exec VP)
Cheryl Van Voorhees (Exec VP)
William H. Croutch (Gen Counsel & Exec
VP)
William H. Croutch (Gen Counsel & Exec
VP)

Subsidiary (Domestic):

ClearShark LLC   **(2)**
7030 Dorsey Rd Ste 102, Hanover, MD
21076
Tel.: (443) 853-1900
Web Site: http://www.clearshark.com
Information Technology Consulting Services
N.A.I.C.S.: 541512
Jason Miller (Exec VP)
Marshall Bailey (Pres)

OverDrive, Inc.   **(1)**
1 OverDrive Way, Cleveland, OH 44125
Tel.: (216) 573-6886
Web Site: http://www.overdrive.com
Digital Publishing Services
N.A.I.C.S.: 513199
David Burleigh (Dir-Brand & Comm)
Steve Potash (Founder, Pres & CEO)
Lori Franklin (COO)
Jeff Sterling (CTO)
Greg Farmer (CFO)
Erica Lazzaro (Gen Counsel & Exec VP-
Publr Svcs)
Ryan Fish (Exec VP-Product Mgmt, UI &
UX)

Pepper Group Limited   **(1)**
Level 27 177 Pacific Highway, North Syd-
ney, 2060, NSW, Australia
Tel.: (61) 137377
Web Site: https://www.peppermoney.com.au
Sales Range: $550-599.9 Million
Fiscal Year-end: 12/31/2016
Financial Lending Services
N.A.I.C.S.: 522291

John Williams (Gen Counsel & Sec)
Neil Culkin (Head-Credit & Settlements-
Mortgages & Personal Loans)
Ken Spellacy (Gen Mgr-Asset Fin)
Sue Kent (Chief VP Officer)
Michael Vainauskas (Chief Risk Officer)
Anthony Moir (Treas)
Steven Meek (CIO)

Pets at Home Ltd.   **(1)**
Handforth Dean Shopping Park Long Marl
Drive, Stanley Green Trading Estate, Hand-
forth, SK9 3TJ, Cheshire, United Kingdom
Tel.: (44) 3452668522
Web Site: http://www.petsathome.com
Sales Range: $700-749.9 Million
Emp.: 4,300
Pet & Pet Supplies Stores Operator
N.A.I.C.S.: 459910
Peter Pritchard (CEO)
Ian Burke (Chm)

PharMerica Corporation   **(1)**
805 N Whittington Pkwy, Louisville, KY
40222
Web Site: https://www.pharmerica.com
Institutional & Long Term Care Pharmacies
Operator & Support Services
N.A.I.C.S.: 456110
Jon Rousseau (CEO)
Jennifer Yowler (Pres)
T. J. Griffin (Sr VP)
Bill Deane (Sr VP)
Lisa Bowen (VP)

Subsidiary (Domestic):

Amerita, Inc.   **(2)**
5299 DTC Blvd Ste 900, Greenwood Vil-
lage, CO 80111
Tel.: (720) 282-5325
Web Site: https://www.ameritaiv.com
Home Infusion Therapy Services
N.A.I.C.S.: 621610
Richard Iriye (Pres)
Kathi Costello (Sr VP-Ops)
Scott Danitz (CFO & Sr VP)
Stacie Robertson (VP-HR)

Res-Care, Inc.   **(2)**
805 N Whittington Pkwy, Louisville, KY
40222
Tel.: (502) 394-2100
Web Site: http://www.brightspringhealth.com
Long-Term Residential Care, Training &
Support Services
N.A.I.C.S.: 623990
Steven S. Reed (Chief Legal Officer)
Jon B. Rousseau (Pres & CEO)
Laurie Babin (Chief Revenue & Innovation
Officer)
Jim Mattingly (CFO & Exec VP)
Steven Zeller (Chief Dev Officer)
Hachael Kurzer Givens (Chief Compliance
Officer)
Bob Barnes (Pres-ResCare Community Liv-
ing)
Rexanne Domico (Pres-Home Health Care
& Rehabilitation Svcs)
Joydeep Mutsuddi (Chief HR Officer)
Susan Sender (Chief Clinical Officer)
William Mills (Sr VP-Medical Affairs)
Mark Douglass (Pres-ResCare Workforce
Svcs)
Lisa Nalley (Sr VP-HR)
Stephen Myers (Sr VP-Tech Svcs)

Subsidiary (Domestic):

A Place To Call Home, Inc.   **(3)**
1255 W Baseline Rd Ste B-258, Mesa, AZ
85202
Tel.: (480) 456-0549
Web Site: https://www.tocallhome.com
Foster Care Licensing, Certifying, Training
& Placement Services
N.A.I.C.S.: 812199

**Children & Family Services,
Corp.**   **(3)**
2290 Theobald Ln, Vincennes Industrial
Park, Vincennes, IN 47591
Tel.: (812) 886-3000
Youth Services
N.A.I.C.S.: 624110
Angel Padilla (Sec)

**Southern Home Care Services,
Inc.**   **(3)**
2318 N Patterson ST, Valdosta, GA 31602

Tel.: (229) 588-8024
Web Site: http://www.rescare.com
Nursing & Personal Care Services
N.A.I.C.S.: 621610

Subsidiary (Domestic):

Southern Home Care Services, Inc.-Michigan (4)
2766 W 11 Mile Rd Ste 3, Berkley, MI 48076
Tel.: (248) 572-3458
Web Site: http://www.allwayscaring.com
Residential & Intellectual & Developmental Disabilities Support Services & Provides Education, Vocational Training, Job Placement & In-Home Assistance Services
N.A.I.C.S.: 621610

Subsidiary (Domestic):

Sorkin's Rx, Ltd. (2)
1981 Marcus Ave Ste 225, New Hyde Park, NY 11042
Tel.: (877) 227-3405
Pharmacies & Drug Stores
N.A.I.C.S.: 456110

Pillarstone Europe LLP (1)
13 Hanover Square, London, W1S 1HN, United Kingdom
Tel.: (44) 203 897 6371
Web Site: http://www.pillarstone.com
Debt Equity Investment Firm
N.A.I.C.S.: 523999
Jens Martin Jensen (Partner-Shipping Portfolio Investment)

Subsidiary (Non-US):

Pillarstone Greece (2)
Othonos 6, 10557, Athens, Greece
Tel.: (30) 216 3000 700
Web Site: http://www.pillarstone.com
Debt Equity Investment Firm
N.A.I.C.S.: 523999

Pillarstone Italy S.p.A. (2)
Piazza Affari 2, 20123, Milan, Italy
Tel.: (39) 0282823900
Web Site: https://www.pillarstone.com
Debt Equity Investment Firm
N.A.I.C.S.: 523999

Holding (Non-US):

Premuda S.p.a. (2)
Via Ceccardi 4/28, 16121, Genoa, Italy
Tel.: (39) 01054441
Web Site: https://www.premuda.net
Cargo Vessels Owner & Operator
N.A.I.C.S.: 488320
Marco Fiori (CEO)
Enrico Barbieri (CFO)
Luca Benzi (Head-Chartering & Ops)
Andrea Berlingieri (Gen Counsel)
Gaudenzio Bonaldo Gregori (VP)

Subsidiary (Non-US):

Premuda (Monaco) Sam (3)
Le Metropole 1 Ave des Citronniers, Monte Carlo, 98000, Monaco
Tel.: (377) 93101090
Web Site: http://www.premuda.net
Navigational Shipping Services
N.A.I.C.S.: 488330

Potter Electric Signal Company, LLC (1)
2081 Craig Rd, Saint Louis, MO 63146-4161
Tel.: (314) 878-4321
Web Site: http://www.pottersignal.com
Communication Equipment Mfr
N.A.I.C.S.: 334290
Bernie Lears (Vice Chm)
Kelly A. Romano (Co-Chm)

Quadion LLC (1)
1100 Xenium Ln N, Minneapolis, MN 55441-4405
Tel.: (952) 927-1400
Web Site: https://www.mnrubber.com
Sales Range: $300-349.9 Million
Emp.: 105
Custom Molded Rubber & Plastic Components Mfr
N.A.I.C.S.: 326299
John Hale (Chm)
Jay Ward (CEO)

Subsidiary (Non-US):

Minnesota Rubber & Plastics Asia Pacific Pte. Ltd. (2)
75 Bukit Batok Crescent, Singapore, 658065, Singapore (100%)
Tel.: (65) 6795 6725
Sales Range: $1-9.9 Million
Emp.: 55
Custom Molded Rubber & Plastic Components Distr
N.A.I.C.S.: 424610

Plant (Domestic):

Quadion LLC - River Falls Plant (2)
434 Highland Dr, River Falls, WI 54022
Tel.: (715) 426-4700
Web Site: http://www.quadion.com
Emp.: 100
Custom Molded Rubber & Plastic Components Mfr
N.A.I.C.S.: 326199

Re Sustainability Limited (1)
Level 11B Aurobindo Galaxy Hyderabad Knowledge City Hitech City Road, Hyderabad, 500081, India (60%)
Tel.: (91) 4024446000
Web Site:
    http://www.ramkyenviroengineers.com
Environmental & Waste Management Services
N.A.I.C.S.: 562998
Alla Ayodhya Rami Reddy (Chm)
Rama Mohan Rao (Head-Municipal Solid Waste Mgmt)
M. Goutham Reddy (CEO & Co-Mng Dir)
Satya Adamala (Head-Bio Medical Waste Mgmt)
Sanjiv Kumar (Head-Industrial Waste Mgmt)
B. S. Shantharaju (Chm)
Masood Mallick (Co-Mng Dir)
Anil Khandelwal (Co-Mng Dir)
Sujiv Nair (Chief HR Officer & Chief Transformation Officer)
Shujath Ali (Chief Compliance Officer & Gen Counsel)
Sathish Cheeti (CEO-Recycling)
Rahul Dua (Head-Middle East)
Bobby Kurien (Head-Integrated Environmental Svcs)
Pankaj Maharaj (Sr VP-Fin & Accounts)

Subsidiary (Non-US):

Entech Industries Pty. Limited (2)
Unit 10 Cnr Union & Merewether Streets, Merewether, Newcastle, 2291, NSW, Australia
Tel.: (61) 2 4963 1626
Web Site: http://www.entech-industries.com.au
Environmental, Chemical & Waste Management Consulting Services; Hazardous Waste & Contaminated Soil Treatment Services
N.A.I.C.S.: 541620

Ramky Cleantech Services Pte. Ltd. (2)
16 Jalan Kilang 02-01 Hoi Hup Building, Singapore, 159416, Singapore
Tel.: (65) 68765400
Web Site: http://www.ramky.com.sg
Hazardous Waste Collection Services
N.A.I.C.S.: 562112

Ramky Enviro Engineers Middle East FZLLC (2)
Unit: 206 Ibn Sina Building No 27, PO Box 505175, Dubai Health Care City, Dubai, United Arab Emirates
Tel.: (971) 44408904
Hazardous Waste Collection Services
N.A.I.C.S.: 562112
Anagha Borkar (Mgr-Fin & Acct)

Re Sustainability International (Singapore) Pte. Ltd. (2)
16 Jalan Kilang #02-01 Hoi Hup Building, 159416, Singapore, Singapore
Tel.: (65) 68765400
Web Site: https://resustainability.com.sg
Environmental & Waste Management Services
N.A.I.C.S.: 541620

Refresco Group N.V. (1)

Fascinatio Boulevard 270 Brainpark III, The Mark 9th Floor, 3065 WB, Rotterdam, Netherlands
Tel.: (31) 10 440 51 00
Web Site: http://www.refresco.com
Rev.: $4,363,758,462
Assets: $5,568,279,878
Liabilities: $4,666,120,662
Net Worth: $902,159,216
Earnings: ($17,917,760)
Emp.: 9,181
Fiscal Year-end: 12/31/2019
Holding Company; Soft Drink Mfr & Whslr
N.A.I.C.S.: 551112
Hans Roelofs (CEO & Member-Exec Bd)
Aart Duijzer (CFO & Member-Exec Bd)
Vincent Deloziere (Chief Comml Officer)
Brad Goist (COO-North America)
Luis Bach (Chm-Supervisory Bd)

Subsidiary (Domestic):

Refresco B.V. (2)
Fascinatio Boulevard 270 Brainpark III, The Mark 8th Floor, 3065 WB, Rotterdam, Netherlands
Tel.: (31) 104405100
Web Site: https://www.refresco.com
Soft Drink Mfr & Whslr
N.A.I.C.S.: 312111
Hans Roelofs (CEO)
Vincent Deloziere (COO-Europe)
Brad Goist (COO-North America)
Christoph Hausler (CMO)
Bill McFarland (CFO)
Martha Zandbergen (Chief Legal Officer)

Subsidiary (US):

Refresco Beverages US Inc. (2)
Corp Ctr III 8112 Woodland Ctr Blvd, Tampa, FL 33614
Tel.: (813) 313-1800
Bottled & Canned Soft Drinks & Water Mfr
N.A.I.C.S.: 312111
Brad Goist (Pres & CEO)

Joint Venture (Non-US):

Cott Beverages Canada (3)
6525 Viscount Rd, Mississauga, L4V1H6, ON, Canada
Tel.: (905) 672-1900
Sales Range: $25-49.9 Million
Emp.: 150
Soda Mfr
N.A.I.C.S.: 312112
Jerry S. G. Fowden (CEO)

Joint Venture (Domestic):

Refresco Beverages US Inc. - San Antonio (3)
4238 Director Dr, San Antonio, TX 78219
Tel.: (210) 333-4310
Bottled & Canned Soft Drinks & Water Mfr
N.A.I.C.S.: 312111

Refresco Beverages US Inc. - Sikeston (3)
301 Larcel Dr, Sikeston, MO 63801-9380
Tel.: (573) 471-4445
Bottled & Canned Soft Drinks & Water Mfr
N.A.I.C.S.: 312111

Subsidiary (Non-US):

Refresco Drinks UK Ltd. (2)
Citrus Grove Side Ley, Kegworth, DE74 2FJ, Derbs, United Kingdom
Tel.: (44) 1509674915
Beverages Whslr
N.A.I.C.S.: 312111

Joint Venture (Domestic):

Calypso Soft Drinks Limited (3)
Refresco Kegworth Derby, Derby, DE74 2FJ, United Kingdom
Tel.: (44) 1978668400
Web Site: http://www.calypso.co.uk
Soft Drinks Mfr
N.A.I.C.S.: 312111
John Piddock (Mgr-Ops)

Refresco (Nelson) Limited (3)
Citrus Grove Sideley Kegworth, Derby, DE74 2FJ, United Kingdom
Tel.: (44) 1509 674915
Soft Drinks Mfr
N.A.I.C.S.: 312111

Subsidiary (US):

Varni Brothers Corporation (2)
400 Hosmer Ave, Modesto, CA 95351
Tel.: (209) 521-1777
Web Site: http://www.noahs7up.com
Rev.: $17,200,000
Emp.: 60
Carbonated Beverages, Nonalcoholic: Pkged, In Cans, Bottles
N.A.I.C.S.: 312111
Tony Varni (Pres)

Resource Environmental Solutions, LLC (1)
6575 W Loop S Ste 300, Bellaire, TX 77401
Tel.: (713) 520-5400
Web Site: https://res.us
Facilities Support Services
N.A.I.C.S.: 561210
Michael Hare (Dir-Govt Affairs, Bus Dev & Comm)
Tim Moritz (Reg Mgr-Client Solutions-Midwest & Gulf Coast)
Michael Sachs (Gen Mgr-Northeast)
Heather Haynes-Long (Dir-Sls Ops)
Matt Stahman (Dir-Regulatory)
Gaye Denley (Dir-Mktg)
Lorne Phillips (CFO)
Russell Bzoza (VP)
Ben Eubanks (VP)

Subsidiary (Domestic):

Applied Ecological Services, Inc. (2)
17921 W Smith Rd, Brodhead, WI 53520
Tel.: (608) 897-8641
Web Site: http://www.appliedeco.com
Rev.: $10,500,000
Emp.: 60
Ecological Consulting Contracting & Restoration Services
N.A.I.C.S.: 541620
Josh Lapointe (Project Mgr)
Tara Hering (Mgr-Plant Production)
Todd A. Polacek (Mgr-Project Dev)
Mathew Stone (Mgr-Construction)
Thomas Hunt (Dir-Science-Wisconsin)
Steve Dischler (Pres & CEO)

Lecon, Inc. (2)
4302 Creekmont Dr, Houston, TX 77091-5330
Tel.: (713) 681-4366
Web Site: http://www.leconinc.com
Heavy & Civil Engineering Construction Services
N.A.I.C.S.: 237990
Dan Lloyd (Founder & CEO)

Redwing Ecological Service Inc. (2)
129 S 6th St, Louisville, KY 40202
Tel.: (502) 625-3009
Web Site: http://www.redwingeco.com
Rev.: $1,584,000
Emp.: 9
Research & Development in Biotechnology
N.A.I.C.S.: 541714
Kiersten Fuchs (Co-Owner)
Ron Thomas (Co-Owner)

Sara Lee Frozen Bakery, LLC (1)
1 Tower Ln Ste 600, Oakbrook Terrace, IL 60181
Tel.: (630) 282-9900
Web Site: https://saraleefrozenbakery.com
Pastries & Bakery Shops
N.A.I.C.S.: 311812

Subsidiary (Domestic):

Superior Cake Products, Inc. (2)
105 Ashland Ave, Southbridge, MA 01550
Tel.: (800) 483-7253
Web Site: http://www.superiorcake.com
Commercial Bakeries
N.A.I.C.S.: 311812

Simon & Schuster, Inc. (1)
1230 Avenue of the Americas, New York, NY 10020
Tel.: (212) 698-7000
Web Site: http://www.simonandschuster.com
Sales Range: $750-799.9 Million
Emp.: 1,500
Book, Audio Book & Visual Media Publisher
N.A.I.C.S.: 513130
Gary Urda (Sr VP-Sls)
Dennis Eulau (CFO & Exec VP-Ops)
Adam Rothberg (Sr VP-Corp Comm)

KKR & Co. Inc.—(Continued)

Carolyn Connolly *(Sr VP-HR)*
Nita Pronovost *(Dir-Editorial-Canada)*
Patricia Ocampo *(Mng Dir-Canada)*
Amy Cormier *(Dir-Publicity)*
Hazel Ann-Mayers *(Gen Counsel & Exec VP)*
Tara Parsons *(Editor-in-Chief-Touchstone Imprint)*
Tracy Nelson *(Dir-Field Sls)*
Liz Perl *(Chief Mktg Officer & Exec VP)*
Karen Cooper *(Publr & VP)*
Ian Chapman *(Publr)*
Jonathan Karp *(Pres & CEO)*
Dana Canedy *(Publr & Sr VP)*
Aminda Marques Gonzalez *(VP & Exec Editor)*

Division (Domestic):

Simon & Schuster Children's Publishing **(2)**
1230 Ave of the Americas, New York, NY 10020
Tel.: (212) 698-2809
Web Site: http://www.simonandschuster.com
Juvenile Picture Books, Fiction & Non-Fiction Publisher
N.A.I.C.S.: 513130
Mara Anastas *(Publr-Aladdin Books & Simon Pulse)*
Jon Anderson *(Pres & Publr)*
Jodie Hockensmith *(Assoc Dir-Publicity)*
Jason Wells *(VP-Mktg & Publicity)*
Chrissy Noh *(Dir-Mktg)*
Matt Pantoliano *(Assoc Dir-Digital Mktg)*
Carolyn Swerdloff *(Assoc Dir-Mktg)*
Katy Hershberger *(Assoc Dir-Publicity)*
Jennifer Ung *(Editor)*
Sarah Jane Abbott *(Asst Editor)*
Amy Beaudoin *(Mgr-Mktg)*
Alexa Pastor *(Editor-Atheneum Books)*
Rebecca Vitkus *(Editor-Production)*
Lisa Lauria *(Editor-Simon Spotlight)*
Cassie Malmo *(Mgr-Publicity)*
Annika Voss *(Coord-Digital & Social Mktg)*
Alissa Nigro *(Mktg Mgr-Aladdin & Simon Pulse)*
Amelia Jenkins *(Coord-Production)*

Spur Energy Partners LLC **(1)**
9655 Katy Fwy Ste 500, Houston, TX 77024
Tel.: (832) 930-8502
Web Site: https://www.spurenergy.com
Petroleum Lubricating Oil & Greese Mfr
N.A.I.C.S.: 324191
Jay Graham *(CEO)*
Kyle Roane *(Exec VP-Bus Dev)*
Buddy Clarke *(CFO & Exec VP)*
Mike R. Sherwood *(Exec VP-Exploration & Dev)*
Paul R. Eschete *(Exec VP-Land)*
Todd R. Mucha *(Exec VP-Ops)*
John M. Nabors *(Sr VP-Ops)*
Norm M. Pennington *(Sr VP-Subsurface)*
Nash Bell *(VP)*
Brad Coffey *(VP)*
Courtney Damm *(VP)*
Mark Hicks *(VP)*
Seth Ireland *(VP)*
Donald John *(VP)*
C. J. Lipinski *(VP)*
Matt van Wie *(VP)*

The Bay Clubs Company. LLC **(1)**
1 Lombard St, San Francisco, CA 94111
Tel.: (415) 781-1874
Web Site: https://www.bayclubs.com
Sales Range: $100-124.9 Million
Luxury Fitness & Recreational Sports Centers Operator
N.A.I.C.S.: 713940

Subsidiary (Domestic):

Bay Club America, Inc. **(2)**
555 California St Concourse Level, San Francisco, CA 94104
Tel.: (415) 362-7800
Sales Range: $10-24.9 Million
Luxury Fitness & Recreational Sports Center Operator
N.A.I.C.S.: 713940

Bay Club Golden Gateway, Inc. **(2)**
370 Drumm St, San Francisco, CA 94111
Tel.: (415) 616-8800
Web Site: http://www.bayclubs.com

Sales Range: $10-24.9 Million
Luxury Fitness & Recreational Sports Center Operator
N.A.I.C.S.: 713940
Alan Skelton *(Dir-Tennis)*

Bay Club Marin **(2)**
220 Corte Madera Town Ctr, Corte Madera, CA 94925
Tel.: (415) 945-3000
Web Site: http://www.bayclubmarin.com
Sales Range: $25-49.9 Million
Luxury Fitness & Recreational Sports Resort Operator
N.A.I.C.S.: 713940
Linda Morello *(Dir-Grp Exercise)*
Libby Majors *(Dir-Childcare)*
Larry Krieger *(VP-Raquet Sports)*
Annie Appel *(Exec VP-Mktg)*
Lisa Graf *(Exec VP-Ops)*
Victor Woo *(Exec VP-Ops)*

Courtside Club **(2)**
14675 Winchester Blvd at Hwy 85, Los Gatos, CA 95032
Tel.: (408) 395-7111
Web Site: http://www.bayclubs.com
Sales Range: $25-49.9 Million
Luxury Fitness & Recreational Sports Resort Operator
N.A.I.C.S.: 713940
Gordon Collins *(Dir-Tennis)*
Lisa Graf *(Gen Mgr)*
Grace Avila *(Dir-Food & Beverage)*
Gina Raiola *(Dir-Spa Svcs)*
Lesieli Tavake *(Dir-Membership & Acctg)*

Decathlon Club **(2)**
3250 Central Expy, Santa Clara, CA 95051
Tel.: (408) 738-2582
Web Site: http://www.decathlon-club.com
Sales Range: $25-49.9 Million
Emp.: 100
Luxury Fitness & Recreational Sports Resort Operator
N.A.I.C.S.: 713940
Patty Beacher *(Gen Mgr)*

Pacific Athletic Club **(2)**
200 Redwood Shores Pkwy, Redwood City, CA 94065
Tel.: (650) 593-4900
Web Site: http://www.pacclub.com
Sales Range: $25-49.9 Million
Luxury Fitness & Recreational Sports Resort Operator
N.A.I.C.S.: 713940
Terry Romero *(Gen Mgr)*
Shelly Alifano *(Mgr-Ops)*
Robin McDonald *(Dir-Grp Exercise)*
Leigh Anne Dennis *(Dir-Aquatics)*

Pacific Athletic Club - San Diego **(2)**
12000 Carmel Country Rd, San Diego, CA 92130
Tel.: (858) 509-9933
Web Site: http://www.pacsandiego.com
Sales Range: $25-49.9 Million
Luxury Fitness & Recreational Sports Resort Operator
N.A.I.C.S.: 713940
Chris Lakey *(Dir-Food & Beverage)*
Amanda Erhardt *(Dir-Childcare)*
Tom Shea *(Dir-Tennis)*
Sam Berry *(Dir-Grp Exercise)*

Professional Recreation Organization Inc. **(2)**
4455 148th Ave NE, Bellevue, WA 98007
Tel.: (425) 885-5566
Web Site: http://www.proclub.com
Sales Range: $10-24.9 Million
Emp.: 650
Fitness & Recreational Sports Centers
N.A.I.C.S.: 713940

San Francisco Bay Club, Inc. **(2)**
150 Greenwich St, San Francisco, CA 94111 **(100%)**
Tel.: (415) 433-2200
Web Site: http://www.sfbayclub.com
Sales Range: $25-49.9 Million
Luxury Fitness & Recreational Sports Center Operator
N.A.I.C.S.: 713940

The Bountiful Company **(1)**
2100 Smithtown Ave, Ronkonkoma, NY 11779
Tel.: (631) 200-2000

Web Site: http://www.bountifulcompany.com
Rev.: $2,069,075,000
Assets: $3,845,412,000
Liabilities: $2,794,888,000
Net Worth: $1,050,524,000
Earnings: $69,930,000
Emp.: 4,150
Fiscal Year-end: 09/30/2020
Natural Vitamins, Food Supplements & Cosmetics Mfr & Distr
N.A.I.C.S.: 325411
Paul L. Sturman *(Pres & CEO)*
Mark Gelbert *(Chief Scientific Officer)*
Don Kerrigan *(Pres-North America)*
Stratis Philippis *(Chief Compliance Officer & Gen Counsel)*
Amy von Walter *(Chief Admin Officer)*
Edward McCormick *(CFO)*
Jay Jones *(Chief Supply Chain Officer)*

Subsidiary (Non-US);

Holland & Barrett Retail Limited **(2)**
Samuel Ryder House Barling Way Eliot Park, Nuneaton, CV10 7RH, Wacks, United Kingdom
Tel.: (44) 3300582025
Web Site:
    https://www.hollandandbarrett.com
Vitamins, Minerals & Nutritional & Herbal Supplements Retailer
N.A.I.C.S.: 424210
John Walden *(Chm)*

Subsidiary (Domestic):

NBTY Acquisition, LLC **(2)**
90 Orville Dr, Bohemia, NY 11716
Tel.: (631) 567-9500
Vitamins, Food Supplements, Hair & Skin Products Mfr & Retailer
N.A.I.C.S.: 325412
Silvia Bonilla *(Coordinator-Receiving)*

Puritan's Pride, Inc. **(2)**
1233 Montauk Hwy, Oakdale, NY 11769-9001 **(100%)**
Tel.: (631) 567-9500
Web Site: https://www.puritan.com
Vitamin Mfr; Catalog & Mail-Order Houses
N.A.I.C.S.: 325411

Rexall Sundom, Inc. **(2)**
851 Broken Sound Pkwy, Boca Raton, FL 33487-3693
Tel.: (561) 241-9400
Web Site: http://www.sundownnutrition.com
Vitamins, Nutritional Supplements & Consumer Health Products Mfr & Distr
N.A.I.C.S.: 424210
Stratis Philippis *(Sec)*

Solgar, Inc. **(2)**
500 Willow Tree Rd, Leonia, NJ 07605
Tel.: (201) 944-2311
Web Site: https://www.solgar.com
Vitamins Mfr & Distr, Minerals & Herbal Products
N.A.I.C.S.: 325411

The Ester-C Company **(2)**
4320 Veterans Memorial Hwy, Holbrook, NY 11741
Tel.: (928) 445-8063
Web Site: https://www.esterc.com
Vitamin Mfr
N.A.I.C.S.: 325411
Edward W. McCormick *(Sec)*

Subsidiary (Non-US):

Vita Health Products, Inc. **(2)**
150 Beghin Avenue, Winnipeg, R2J 3W2, MB, Canada
Tel.: (204) 661-8386
Web Site: http://www.vitahealth.ca
Natural Health Products
N.A.I.C.S.: 456191

The Crosby Group LLC **(1)**
2801 Dawson Rd, Tulsa, OK 74110
Tel.: (918) 834-4611
Web Site: http://www.thecrosbygroup.com
Sales Range: $100-124.9 Million
Emp.: 300
Hardware & Fittings for Wire Rope & Chain Mfr
N.A.I.C.S.: 332510
Jared Knudson *(Pres)*

Subsidiary (Non-US):

Crosby Europe N.V. **(2)**
Industriepark Zone B Nr 26, 2220, Heist-op-den-Berg, Belgium
Tel.: (32) 15757125
Web Site: http://www.thecrosbygroup.com
Sales Range: $25-49.9 Million
Emp.: 5
Electric Cable & Accessories Mfr
N.A.I.C.S.: 334419

Subsidiary (Domestic):

Crosby-National Swage Co. **(2)**
2511 W Main, Jacksonville, AR 72076
Tel.: (501) 982-3112
Web Site: http://www.thecrosbygroup.com
Sales Range: $25-49.9 Million
Emp.: 65
Wire Rope Fittings Mfr
N.A.I.C.S.: 332919

Lebus Manufacturing Co. **(2)**
900 Fisher Rd, Longview, TX 75604-4709
Tel.: (903) 759-4424
Web Site: http://www.thecrosbygroup.com
Sales Range: $100-124.9 Million
Emp.: 275
Forged Steel Mfr
N.A.I.C.S.: 332111

McKissick Products Co. **(2)**
2857 Dawson Rd, Tulsa, OK 74110-5042
Tel.: (918) 834-4611
Web Site: http://www.thecrosbygroup.com
Sales Range: $125-149.9 Million
Emp.: 300
Steel Block Mfr
N.A.I.C.S.: 332510
Jared Knudson *(Pres)*

The Global Atlantic Financial Group LLC **(1)**
19 Par-La-Ville Rd Second Floor, Hamilton, HM 11, Bermuda
Tel.: (441) 8774628992
Life Insurance & Pension Services
N.A.I.C.S.: 524113

USI Holdings Corporation **(1)**
100 Summit Lake Dr Ste 400, Valhalla, NY 10595
Tel.: (914) 749-8500
Web Site: http://www.usi.com
Holding Company; Insurance Agencies & Services
N.A.I.C.S.: 551112
Edward J. Bowler *(CFO & Sr VP-Corp Dev)*

Subsidiary (Domestic):

USI Insurance Services LLC **(2)**
100 Summit Lk Dr Ste 400, Valhalla, NY 10595
Tel.: (866) 657-0861
Web Site: https://www.usi.com
Insurance Services
N.A.I.C.S.: 524210
Kimberly Cheung *(VP-Comml)*
Ralph A. Sepe *(Sr VP)*
Jennifer Ditaranto *(VP)*
Frank J. Aiosa *(Exec VP-Managing Consultant)*
Christine McCarton *(Sr VP-Employee Benefits)*
Michael J. Sicard *(Chm & Pres)*
Sanford Ware *(VP)*
James O'Hara *(Pres & CEO)*

Subsidiary (Domestic):

Accelerated Benefits **(3)**
5880 Venture Dr, Dublin, OH 43017
Tel.: (614) 791-1143
Web Site: http://www.accben.com
Insurance & Benefits Brokerage Firm
N.A.I.C.S.: 524210

Associated Financial Group, LLC **(3)**
12600 Whitewater Dr Ste 100, Minnetonka, MN 55343-9437
Tel.: (952) 945-0200
Web Site: http://www.associatedbrc.com
Emp.: 400
Insurance Agency; Human Resource Consulting, Risk & Employee Benefits Management Services
N.A.I.C.S.: 524210
Mardi Burns *(Sr VP)*

Branch (Domestic):

Associated Financial Group, LLC - Waukesha Office (4)
N16 W23250 Stone Rdg Dr Ste 5, Waukesha, WI 53188
Tel.: (262) 542-8822
Web Site:
http://www.associatedfinancialgroup.com
Sales Range: $25-49.9 Million
Emp.: 30
Financial Services
N.A.I.C.S.: 523999

Subsidiary (Domestic):

Financial Resource Management Group, Inc. (4)
6000 Clearwater Dr, Minnetonka, MN 55343-9437
Tel.: (952) 945-0200
Sales Range: $50-74.9 Million
Emp.: 1
Insurance & Pension Fund Management Services
N.A.I.C.S.: 524292
Rick Thill (Gen Mgr)

Subsidiary (Domestic):

BOK Financial Insurance, Inc. (3)
821 17th St, Denver, CO 80202
Tel.: (303) 988-0446
Web Site: http://www.cobizins.com
Business Insurance & Employee Benefit Consulting Services
N.A.I.C.S.: 525110

Beneficial Insurance Services, LLC (3)
1818 Market St Ste 2100, Philadelphia, PA 19103
Tel.: (215) 925-7656
Sales Range: $1-9.9 Million
Emp.: 40
Insurance Services
N.A.I.C.S.: 524298
Joe Robinson (Pres)

Cavanah Associates, Inc. (3)
1100 Alakea St Ste 2600, Honolulu, HI 96813
Tel.: (808) 537-1970
Web Site: http://www.cavanah.com
Sales Range: $1-9.9 Million
Emp.: 19
Insurance Brokerage Services
N.A.I.C.S.: 524210

Chernoff Diamond & Co, LLC (3)
725 RXR Plaza E Tower, Uniondale, NY 11556
Tel.: (516) 683-6100
Human Resources & Executive Search Consulting Services
N.A.I.C.S.: 541612
Frank J. Aiosa (Partner-Transaction Services)

Cohen-Seltzer, Inc. (3)
520 W Pennsylvania Ave, Fort Washington, PA 19034
Tel.: (215) 542-0600
Web Site: http://www.cosel.com
Insurance, Risk Management & Financial Services
N.A.I.C.S.: 524210

Daul Insurance Agency, Inc. (3)
94 Westbank Expy Ste A, Gretna, LA 70054
Tel.: (504) 362-0667
Web Site: http://www.daulinsurance.com
Insurance Agencies & Brokerages
N.A.I.C.S.: 524210
Jerry Daul (Owner & Pres)

Full Service Insurance, Inc. (3)
903 Murfreesboro Rd, Franklin, TN 37064-3002
Tel.: (615) 790-0990
Web Site: http://www.fullserviceins.com
Insurance Brokerage Services
N.A.I.C.S.: 524210
Eddie Fly (Mgr-Comml Lines Mktg)
Pam Marshall (Mgr-Claims)
Blake Lambert (VP-Personal Lines)
David Kardokus (VP-Life & Health)
Justin Forton (VP-Employee Benefits)
Patrick Baggett (VP-Comml Lines)
John Pratt Jr. (Pres)

Gaudreau Group Inc. (3)
2377 Boston Road, Wilbraham, MA 01095
Tel.: (413) 543-3534
Web Site: http://www.gaudreaugroup.com
Insurance Related Activities
N.A.I.C.S.: 524298
Jules O. Gaudreau (Pres)

Hildi Incorporated (3)
14852 Scenic Heights R Ste 205, Minneapolis, MN 55344
Tel.: (952) 934-5554
Web Site: http://www.hildiinc.com
Professional, Scientific & Technical Services
N.A.I.C.S.: 541990
Roxane Gilje (Office Mgr)
Jill Urdahl (Pres)

Marcotte Insurance Agency, Inc. (3)
9394 W Dodge Rd #250, Omaha, NE 68114
Tel.: (402) 398-9009
Insurance Agencies & Brokerages
N.A.I.C.S.: 524210
Amy Fredrickson (Acct Mgr)
Cathi Gage (Acct Mgr)

Ritman & Associates, Inc. (3)
1154 Conner St, Noblesville, IN 46060-2808
Tel.: (317) 770-3000
Web Site: http://www.ritmanassoc.com
Insurance Agents
N.A.I.C.S.: 524210
Jennifer Ritman (Pres)

Scheetz & Hogan Insurance Agency, Inc. (3)
1000 E North St, Greenville, SC 29601
Tel.: (864) 232-5162
Web Site: http://www.shfpins.com
Insurance Agencies & Brokerages
N.A.I.C.S.: 524210
Ronald D. Scheetz (Pres & CEO)
Wanda Smith (Acct Mgr)
David Rich (Sr VP-Insurance)
Mark S. Miller (Sr VP)
Roy Phillips (Partner)
Tracy Freeman (Exec VP)

The Bert Company (3)
3645 W Lk Rd, Erie, PA 16505-3450
Tel.: (814) 838-0000
Insurance Brokerage & Consulting Services
N.A.I.C.S.: 524210

The Colburn Corp. (3)
3001 W Big Beaver Rd, Troy, MI 48084
Tel.: (248) 643-4800
Web Site: http://www.colburngroup.com
Sales Range: $1-9.9 Million
Emp.: 20
Insurance Agencies & Brokerages
N.A.I.C.S.: 524210
Harry S. Colburn (Principal)

U.S. Risk Insurance Group, Inc. (3)
8401 North Central Expy Ste 1000, Dallas, TX 75225
Tel.: (214) 265-7090
Web Site: http://www.usrisk.com
Holding Company; Insurance Services
N.A.I.C.S.: 551112
Randall Goss (CEO)
Ron Price (VP & Branch Mgr)
Matthew McCampbell (Exec VP-Corp Strategy & Dev)
George Ahn (CIO & Exec VP-Corp Shared Svcs)
Beth Boisseau-Coots (VP-Sls)
Peter Stanislaw (VP & Mgr-StaffPak Program)
Dutch Phillips (VP & Branch Mgr)
Sheila Boatman (VP)
Cason Burdett (VP)
Aaron Cardwell (VP)
Chris Chiodetti (VP)
Chris Christian (VP)
Quinton Goss (VP)
Tony Greer (VP)
Andy Hightower (VP)
Crystal Jacobs (VP)
Tammy Morgan (VP)
Marcus Paxton (VP)
Patricia Sutton (VP)
Jody Travis (VP)
Leslie Craft (Sr VP)
Bill Rinker (Mgr-TCAP Program)
Stephen Vallender (Exec VP-Brokerage)
Gary Atkins (Exec VP & Reg Dir)

Scott T. Carroll (Exec VP & Dir-Program)
Gus Kontogianis (Dir-Bus Dev)
George Gorney (CIO & Exec VP-Corp Shared Svcs)
Theresa Drago (Asst VP)
Travis Reynolds (Asst VP)

Subsidiary (Domestic):

Continental Risk Insurance Services (4)
330 S Fairmont Ave Ste 2, Lodi, CA 95240-3843
Tel.: (209) 365-6130
Web Site:
https://www.continentalriskins.com
Emp.: 100
Insurance Agencies & Brokerages
N.A.I.C.S.: 524210
Jeana Ramos (VP)
Ed Bordenave (Pres)

Gumtree Wholesale Insurance Brokers, Inc. (4)
2616 Lakeward Dr Ste 120, Jackson, MS 39216
Tel.: (601) 983-4005
Web Site: http://www.gumtree-ins.com
Insurance Brokerage Services
N.A.I.C.S.: 524210
Nick Myers (Dir-Mktg & Underwriting)

U.S. Risk, LLC (4)
8401 N Central Expy Ste 1000, Dallas, TX 75225
Tel.: (214) 265-7090
Web Site: http://www.usrisk.com
Sales Range: $100-124.9 Million
Emp.: 500
Provider of Insurance Services
N.A.I.C.S.: 524210
Randall G. Goss (CEO)

Subsidiary (Domestic):

KRB Management, Inc. (5)
365 Miron Dr Ste D, Southlake, TX 76092
Tel.: (817) 424-1996
Web Site: http://www.auminsur.com
Insurance Agent/Broker
N.A.I.C.S.: 524210
Kenneth Boyd (Chm, Pres & CEO)
Nena Boyd (Exec VP)
Tammy Tabor (Dir-Mktg)
Tom Moyer (VP)
Leslie Craft (Dir-Underwriting)
Andrew Hightower (VP)
Ed Collinsworth (CFO & Sr VP)

U.S. Risk Brokers, Inc. (5)
201 Rue Iberville Ste 725, Lafayette, LA 70508-8521
Tel.: (337) 235-7745
Web Site: https://www.usrisk.com
Insurance Brokerage Services
N.A.I.C.S.: 524210

Subsidiary (Domestic):

Regency Insurance Brokerage Services, Inc. (6)
217 E Hallandale Bch Blvd, Hallandale, FL 33009
Tel.: (954) 458-6323
Insurance Agencies & Brokerages
N.A.I.C.S.: 524210
Paul A. Riemer (CEO)

Subsidiary (Domestic):

U.S. Risk Financial Services, Inc. (5)
2550 Meridian Ste 200, Franklin, TN 37067
Tel.: (214) 265-7090
Web Site: http://www.usrisk.com
Sales Range: $25-49.9 Million
Emp.: 7
Provider of Insurance Services
N.A.I.C.S.: 524210

U.S. Risk Management, Inc. (5)
10210 N Central Expy Ste 500, Dallas, TX 75231-3425
Tel.: (214) 696-4700
Web Site: http://www.usrisk.com
Sales Range: $50-74.9 Million
Emp.: 250
Insurance Services
N.A.I.C.S.: 524298

George Gorney (CIO & Exec VP-Corp Shared Svcs)
Peter Stanislaw (VP & Mgr-StaffPak Program)

US E & O Brokers (5)
820 Gessner Ste 1680, Houston, TX 77024
Tel.: (713) 984-1370
Web Site: http://www.useo.com
Insurance Agencies & Brokerages
N.A.I.C.S.: 524210
Susan Kirby (Branch Mgr)
Angela T. Schroder (Pres)
Lori Williams (VP)
Terry Tomlinson (CFO)

Subsidiary (Domestic):

U.S.I. Insurance Services of Massachusetts, Inc. (3)
12 Gill St Ste 5500, Woburn, MA 01801
Tel.: (781) 938-7500
Web Site: http://www.usi.com
Insurance Services
N.A.I.C.S.: 524210

Unit (Domestic):

USI Affinity (3)
3805 W Chester Pike Ste 200, Newtown Square, PA 19073
Tel.: (610) 833-1800
Web Site: http://www.usiaffinity.com
Insurance & Financial Risk Management Services
N.A.I.C.S.: 524298

Subsidiary (Domestic):

USI Colorado LLC (3)
6501 S Fiddlers Green Cir Ste 100, Greenwood Village, CO 80111
Tel.: (303) 837-8500
Web Site: http://www.usi.com
Insurance Brokers
N.A.I.C.S.: 524210

Unit (Domestic):

USI Consulting Group (3)
95 Glastonbury Blvd Ste 102, Glastonbury, CT 06033-6503
Tel.: (860) 633-5283
Web Site: https://www.usicg.com
Employee Benefit Consulting Services
N.A.I.C.S.: 541612
Christopher J. Martin (Sr VP-Defined Contribution)
William M. Tremko (Pres & CEO)
Timothy Ryor (Sr VP)
Robert R. Cross (Pres-Central Reg)
Paul W. Denu (Pres-NY & Mid-Atlantic Reg)
Susan M. Fullwood (CFO)
Michael Sullivan (Sr VP & Reg Dir-Sls)
Karen McDonough (Chief Legal Officer)
Bart Ballinger (Sr VP & Reg Dir-Sls)

Subsidiary (Domestic):

Hooker & Holcombe, Inc. (4)
65 Lasalle Road Ste 402, West Hartford, CT 06107
Tel.: (860) 521-8400
Web Site: http://www.hhconsultants.com
Rev.: $7,000,000
Emp.: 60
Employee Benefit Consulting Services
N.A.I.C.S.: 541611
Richard S. Sych (Pres)
Rodger K. Metzger (Pres/Chief Investment Officer-Investment Advisory Grp & Chm)
Timothy A. Ryor (Sr VP)
Barry Bonetti (Mng Dir-Client Services)
Jonathan S. Gruber (Dir-Wealth Mgmt)
Jonida M. Papajani (Mgr-Operations)

Branch (Domestic):

USI Insurance Services LLC - Austin (3)
7600 C N Capital of Texas Hwy Ste 200, Austin, TX 78731-1184
Tel.: (512) 451-7555
Web Site: http://www.usi.com
Insurance Agent Broker & Service
N.A.I.C.S.: 524210

USI Insurance Services LLC - Dallas (3)
14241 Dallas Pkwy, Dallas, TX 75254
Tel.: (214) 443-3100

KKR & Co. Inc.—(Continued)

Web Site: http://www.usi.com
Insurance Agents, Brokers & Service
N.A.I.C.S.: 524210

USI Insurance Services LLC - Fort Lauderdale (3)
2400 E Commercial Blvd Ste 600, Fort Lauderdale, FL 33309-2185
Tel.: (954) 607-4000
Web Site: http://www.usi.com
Commercial Property & Casualty Insurance,
Retirement Planning & Employee Benefit
Services
N.A.I.C.S.: 524126

USI Insurance Services LLC - Houston (3)
9811 Katy Fwy Ste 500, Houston, TX 77024
Tel.: (713) 490-4600
Web Site: http://www.usi.com
Insurance Agents, Brokers & Service
N.A.I.C.S.: 524210

USI Insurance Services LLC - Phoenix (3)
2375 E Camelback Rd Ste 250, Phoenix, AZ 85016
Tel.: (602) 395-9111
Web Site: http://www.usi.com
Insurance Brokers
N.A.I.C.S.: 524210

USI Insurance Services LLC - San Angelo (3)
133 W Concho Ave Ste 109, San Angelo, TX 76903
Tel.: (325) 486-5143
Web Site: http://www.usi.com
Insurance Agents, Brokers & Service
N.A.I.C.S.: 524210

USI Insurance Services LLC - South Portland (3)
75 John Roberts Rd, South Portland, ME 04106
Tel.: (855) 874-0123
Web Site: http://www.usi.com
Personal Insurance Brokerage Services
N.A.I.C.S.: 524210

Subsidiary (Domestic):

USI Insurance Services of Connecticut, LLC (3)
530 Preston Ave, Meriden, CT 06450-1040
Tel.: (203) 634-5700
Web Site: http://www.usi.com
Insurance Services
N.A.I.C.S.: 524298

Venneberg Insurance, Inc. (3)
225 Harbor Dr, Sitka, AK 99835-0199
Tel.: (907) 747-8625
Web Site:
http://www.venneberginsurance.com
Insurance Agencies & Brokerages
N.A.I.C.S.: 524210

Vista Insurance Partners of Illinois, Inc. (3)
6 W Hubbard St 4 Fl, Chicago, IL 60654
Tel.: (312) 755-0084
Web Site: http://www.ajrenner.com
Insurance Brokers
N.A.I.C.S.: 512110
Alison J. Renner (CEO)
Angela Mancari-Pickert (VP)
Patrick M. Nolan (VP)
Tracy A. Boss (COO & VP)
Lana D. Wagener (Controller)
Janice M. Duda (Asst VP-Broker)

Universum Film GmbH (1)
Neumarkter Str 28, 81673, Munich, Germany
Tel.: (49) 89 4136 9600
Web Site: http://www.universumfilm.de
Film & Television Production Services
N.A.I.C.S.: 512110
Bernhard zu Castell (CEO)

Vantage Towers AG (1)
Prinzenallee 11-13, 40549, Dusseldorf, Germany
Tel.: (49) 211617120
Web Site: https://www.vantagetowers.com
Telecommunication Tower Services
N.A.I.C.S.: 237130

Rudiger Grube (Co-Chm)
Vivek Badrinath (Co-Chm)

Virescent Renewable Energy Trust (1)
Piramal Tower Peninsula Corporate Park
2nd Floor, Lower Parel Mumbai, Maharashtra, 400013, India
Tel.: (91) 858 6808 337
Web Site: https://virescent.co.in
Investment Services
N.A.I.C.S.: 523999

Subsidiary (Domestic):

Godawari Green Energy Limited (2)
Hira Arcade 2nd Floor Near Bus Stand,
Pandri, Raipur, 492 004, Chattisgarh, India
Tel.: (91) 7714082751
Web Site: http://www.ggelindia.com
Wind Electric Power Generation Services
N.A.I.C.S.: 221115

Viridor Limited (1)
Viridor House Priory Bridge Road, Somerset, Taunton, TA1 1AP, Somersetshire, United Kingdom
Tel.: (44) 1823 721 400
Web Site: http://www.viridor.co.uk
Sales Range: $25-49.9 Million
Emp.: 70
Waste Treatment & Disposal Services
N.A.I.C.S.: 562211
Paul Ringham (Dir-Comml)
Phillip Piddington (Mng Dir)
Kevin Bradshaw (CEO)

Subsidiary (Domestic):

Viridor Waste Limited (2)
Priory Bridge Road, Taunton, TA1 1AP, United Kingdom
Tel.: (44) 1823 721 400
Waste Management Services
N.A.I.C.S.: 562998

Subsidiary (Domestic):

Viridor Waste Exeter Limited (3)
Great Western House, Station Approach,
Taunton, TA1 1QW, Somerset, United Kingdom (100%)
Tel.: (44) 1823721400
Web Site: http://www.viridor.co.uk
Water Supply & Irrigation Systems
N.A.I.C.S.: 221310

Viridor Waste Management Ltd. (3)
Viridor House Youngman Place Priory
Bridge Road, Taunton, TA1 1AP, Sonerset, United Kingdom (100%)
Tel.: (44) 823721400
Rev.: $276,244,800
Emp.: 70
Waste Management Services
N.A.I.C.S.: 562998
Mike Hellings (Mng Dir)

Subsidiary (Domestic):

Parkwood Group Limited (4)
Salmon Pastures Attercliffe Road, Sheffield,
S4 7WT, South Yorkshire, United Kingdom
Tel.: (44) 114 241 4140
Waste Water Treatment & Disposal Services
N.A.I.C.S.: 221310

Subsidiary (Domestic):

Viridor Waste (Sheffield) Limited (5)
Parkwood Road, Neepsend, Sheffield, S3 8AG, United Kingdom
Tel.: (44) 114 272 8347
Waste Management Services
N.A.I.C.S.: 562998

Subsidiary (Domestic):

Viridor (Martock) Limited (4)
Martock Business Park Unit 25 Great Western Road, Martock, TA12 6HB, Somerset, United Kingdom
Tel.: (44) 1935 823101
Scrap & Waste Recycling Materials Distr
N.A.I.C.S.: 423930

Viridor EnviroScot Limited (4)
Langmuir Way Bargeddie, Glasgow, G69 7RW, United Kingdom
Tel.: (44) 7071224955

Web Site: http://www.viridor.co.uk
Sales Range: $25-49.9 Million
Management Consulting Services
N.A.I.C.S.: 541618

Viridor Glass Recycling Limited (4)
Lancots La, Saint Helens, WA93 EX, United Kingdom (100%)
Tel.: (44) 1744454444
Web Site: http://www.viridor.co.uk
Sales Range: $25-49.9 Million
Emp.: 70
Pressed & Blown Glass & Glassware Mfr
N.A.I.C.S.: 327212

Viridor London Recycling Limited (4)
11B South Crescent Cody Road, London, E16 4TL, United Kingdom
Tel.: (44) 20 7511 8000
Web Site: http://www.viridor.co.uk
Sales Range: $25-49.9 Million
Emp.: 80
Waste Treatment & Disposal Services
N.A.I.C.S.: 562219

Viridor Polymer Recycling Limited (4)
Gerrard Place East Gillibrands, Skelmersdale, WN8 9SF, United Kingdom
Tel.: (44) 1695 731915
Web Site: http://www.viridor.co.uk
Sales Range: $10-24.9 Million
Emp.: 50
Plastic Waste Recycling Services
N.A.I.C.S.: 562920

Viridor Resource Management Limited (4)
Viridor House Youngman Place Priory
Bridge Road, Taunton, TA1 1AP, Somerset, United Kingdom
Tel.: (44) 1732 229200
Sales Range: $25-49.9 Million
Emp.: 70
Waste Recovery Services
N.A.I.C.S.: 562920
Ian McAulay (Mng Dir)

Viridor Waste (Bristol Holdings) Limited (4)
Northway Gloucester Rd N Filton, Bristol, BS347QG, United Kingdom (100%)
Tel.: (44) 1179695460
Web Site: http://www.viridor.co.uk
Sales Range: $10-24.9 Million
Emp.: 40
Waste Management Services
N.A.I.C.S.: 562998

Viridor Waste (Bristol) Limited (4)
Northway Gloucester Road North Filton, Bristol, BS347QG, United Kingdom (100%)
Tel.: (44) 1179695460
Sales Range: $10-24.9 Million
Emp.: 40
Waste Management Services
N.A.I.C.S.: 562998

Viridor Waste (Greater Manchester) Limited (4)
Reliance St, Manchester, M40 3EZ, United Kingdom
Tel.: (44) 161 688 5611
Web Site: http://www.viridor.co.uk
Sales Range: $10-24.9 Million
Emp.: 30
Waste Treatment & Disposal Services
N.A.I.C.S.: 562219

Viridor Waste (Landfill Restoration) Limited (4)
Great Western House Station Approach,
Taunton, TA1 1QW, Somerset, United Kingdom
Tel.: (44) 1823721400
Web Site: http://www.viridor.com
Emp.: 200
Waste Treatment & Disposal Services
N.A.I.C.S.: 562219

Viridor Waste (Somerset) Limited (4)
Youngman Place Priory Bridge Rd, Taunton, TA11AP, Somerset, United Kingdom (100%)
Tel.: (44) 1823721400
Web Site: http://www.viridor.co.uk
Sales Range: $75-99.9 Million
Emp.: 70
Water Supply & Irrigation Systems

N.A.I.C.S.: 221310

Viridor Waste (Suffolk) Limited (4)
2 The Sq, Ipswich, United Kingdom
Tel.: (44) 1473620110
Water Supply & Irrigation Systems
N.A.I.C.S.: 221310

Viridor Waste (Thames) Limited (4)
Thames House Wood Lane, Slough, SL19EB, United Kingdom
Tel.: (44) 1753512832
Web Site: http://www.viridor.co.uk
Sales Range: $50-74.9 Million
Emp.: 13
Water Supply & Irrigation Systems
N.A.I.C.S.: 221310

Viridor Waste (West Sussex) Limited (4)
Viridor House Young Man Pl, Taunton, TA1 1AP, Somerset, United Kingdom
Tel.: (44) 1823721400
Web Site: http://www.viridor.co.uk
Sales Range: $25-49.9 Million
Emp.: 80
Waste Treatment & Disposal Services
N.A.I.C.S.: 562219

Viridor Waste Disposal Limited (4)
42 Kings Hill Avenue, West Malling, ME19 4AJ, United Kingdom
Tel.: (44) 1732229200
Sales Range: $25-49.9 Million
Waste Management Services
N.A.I.C.S.: 562998

Viridor Waste Kent Limited (4)
Reclamation House Canterbury Industrial Park, Island Road Hersden, Canterbury, CT3 4HQ, Kent, United Kingdom
Tel.: (44) 1227712364
Web Site: http://www.viridor.co.uk
Waste Management Services
N.A.I.C.S.: 562998

Visma AS (1)
Karenlyst Alle 56, 0277, Oslo, Norway (31.3%)
Tel.: (47) 46404000
Web Site: http://www.visma.com
Rev.: $1,706,404,419
Assets: $4,273,388,164
Liabilities: $2,705,806,114
Net Worth: $1,567,582,050
Earnings: $112,499,095
Emp.: 11,175
Fiscal Year-end: 12/31/2019
Business Software Developer
N.A.I.C.S.: 513210
Oystein Moan (Chm & Co-CEO)
Steffen Torp (Chief Comml Officer)
Stian Grindheim (CFO)
Ellen Furru (COO)
Kasper Lyhr (Dir-Pub segment-Nordic)
Lars Ottersen (Chief Risk Officer)
Alexander Lystad (CTO)

Subsidiary (Domestic):

Visma Mamut AS (2)
Karenslyst Alle 56, 0277, Oslo, Norway
Tel.: (47) 46404000
Web Site: http://www.visma.no
Integrated Customer Relationship Management Accounting Personnel & E-commerce Software Mfr
N.A.I.C.S.: 513210
Kenneth Lovold (Mng Dir)
Marius Andersen (Mktg Dir)

Subsidiary (Non-US):

Mamut AB (3)
Kungsgatan 24, Stockholm, Sweden
Tel.: (46) 084116190
Sales Range: $25-49.9 Million
Emp.: 30
Software Reproducing
N.A.I.C.S.: 334610

Mamut Aps (3)
Arne Jacobsens Alle 15, 2300, Copenhagen, Denmark
Tel.: (45) 80390002
Web Site: http://www.mamut.dk
Sales Range: $25-49.9 Million
Emp.: 15
Computer & Computer Peripheral Equipment & Software Merchant Whslr
N.A.I.C.S.: 423430

Michael Brahe *(Pres)*

Subsidiary (Domestic):

Mamut Norge AS **(3)**
Pilestredet 75 C, Oslo, Norway
Tel.: (47) 23203500
Web Site: http://www.mamut.com
Computer & Computer Peripheral Equipment & Software Merchant Whslr
N.A.I.C.S.: 423430

Subsidiary (Non-US):

Mamut Software Ltd. **(3)**
90 Long Acre Covent Garden, London,
WC2E 9RZ, United Kingdom
Tel.: (44) 2071530900
Web Site: http://www.visma.co.uk
Computer & Computer Peripheral Equipment & Software Merchant Whslr
N.A.I.C.S.: 423430

Wal-Mart Japan Holdings K.K. **(1)**
1-1 Akabane 2-chome, Kita-ku, Tokyo, 115-0045, Japan **(65%)**
Tel.: (81) 335987000
Web Site: http://www.seiyu.co.jp
Sales Range: $5-14.9 Billion
Emp.: 32,643
Operation of Retail Chain Stores
N.A.I.C.S.: 455219
Tsuneo Okubo *(CEO)*

Yayoi Co., Ltd. **(1)**
21F Akihabara UDX 4-14-1 Sotokanda,
Chiyoda-ku, Tokyo, 101-0021, Japan
Tel.: (81) 3 5207 8841
Web Site: http://www.yayoi-kk.co.jp
Emp.: 599
Accounting Software Publisher
N.A.I.C.S.: 513210
Koichiro Okamoto *(Pres)*

mdf commerce, inc. **(1)**
1111 St-Charles Street West East Tower
Suite 255, Longueuil, J4K 5G4, QC,
Canada
Tel.: (450) 449-0102
Web Site: https://www.mdfcommerce.com
Rev.: $84,688,851
Assets: $363,643,640
Liabilities: $114,142,475
Net Worth: $249,501,165
Earnings: ($18,726,219)
Emp.: 800
Fiscal Year-end: 03/31/2022
E-Business Networks & Solutions Whslr
N.A.I.C.S.: 425120
Helene Hallak *(VP-Corporate Development)*
Jean-Michel Stam *(Pres-Marketplaces)*
Philippe Duval *(COO-Grp & First VP-Grp)*
Luc Filiatreault *(Pres & CEO)*
Nicolas Vanasse *(Chief Legal Officer, Sec & VP)*
Andreanne Simon *(Pres-Supply Chain)*
Pascal Cardinal *(Pres-ECommerce)*
Julie Belanger *(VP)*
Patrick Boisvert *(VP)*

Subsidiary (Domestic):

Carrus Technologies Inc. **(2)**
1111 St-Charles W East Tower Suite 255,
Longueuil, J4K 5G4, QC, Canada
Tel.: (450) 449-8720
Auto Parts Whslr
N.A.I.C.S.: 423120
Mario Comtois *(Gen Mgr)*

Subsidiary (US):

EcoInteractive, LLC **(2)**
508 2nd St Ste 208, Davis, CA 95616-4664
Tel.: (530) 750-1736
Web Site: http://www.ecoInteractive.com
Custom Computer Programming Services
N.A.I.C.S.: 541511
Kevin Peterson *(Pres)*

Subsidiary (Domestic):

InterTrade Systems Inc. **(2)**
3224 Jean-Beraud Avenue Suite 270, Laval,
H7T 2S4, QC, Canada
Web Site: https://intertrade.com
Information Technology Services
N.A.I.C.S.: 541511

KCentric Technologies, Inc. **(2)**
666 St-Martin W Boulevard Suite 330, La-

val, H7M 5G4, QC, Canada
Tel.: (514) 973-2510
Web Site: http://www.k-ecommerce.com
E-Commerce Software Solutions
N.A.I.C.S.: 513210
Richard Brossoit *(Sr VP)*
Laurent Allaidin *(Mgr)*

Subsidiary (US):

k-eCommerce **(3)**
45550 Helm St, Plymouth, MI 48170
Tel.: (734) 928-6010
Web Site: http://www.azox.com
Emp.: 20
E-Commerce Software Solutions
N.A.I.C.S.: 513210
Bernie Huang *(Pres)*

Subsidiary (US):

Market Velocity, Inc. **(2)**
1305 Mall of Georgia Blvd Ste 190, Buford,
GA 30519
Tel.: (770) 325-6300
Web Site: http://www.marketvelocity.com
Sales Range: $25-49.9 Million
Emp.: 25
E-Commerce Software
N.A.I.C.S.: 513210
Mark Eigenbauer *(Pres)*

Subsidiary (Domestic):

Orckestra Technologies Inc. **(2)**
1111 St-Charles Street West Suite 255,
Longueuil, J4K 5G4, QC, Canada
Tel.: (514) 398-0999
Web Site: https://www.orckestra.com
Information Technology Services
N.A.I.C.S.: 541511
Frank Kouretas *(Chief Product Officer)*
Eric Gagnon *(VP)*
Bertrand Guignat *(VP-Marketing-ECommerce)*
Andre Mainville *(VP-Sales)*
Tolu Sodeyi *(VP-Customer Support)*

Subsidiary (US):

Periscope Holdings Inc. **(2)**
5000 Plaza on the Lake Ste 100, Austin, TX
78746
Web Site:
    https://www.periscopeholdings.com
Procurement Software Publisher
N.A.I.C.S.: 513210
Brian Utley *(Pres & CEO)*
Chris Kennedy *(COO)*
Cesar Gonzalez *(CTO)*
David English *(CFO)*
Jean A. Clark *(Pres-NIGP Commodity & Svcs Code)*
David Landsman *(Sr VP)*

Subsidiary (Domestic):

BidSync Inc. **(3)**
629 Quality Dr Ste 101, American Fork, UT
84003
Tel.: (801) 765-9245
Web Site: http://www.bidsync.com
Software for Bid Requests & Quotes
N.A.I.C.S.: 513210
Jake Pollman *(Dir-IT)*

Subsidiary (US):

Periscope Intermediate Corp. **(2)**
15 British American Blvd, Latham, NY
12110
Web Site:
    https://www.periscopeholdings.com
Software Development Services
N.A.I.C.S.: 541810

Subsidiary (Domestic):

The Broker Forum Inc. **(2)**
1111 St-Charles Street West East Tower
Suite 255, Longueuil, J4K 5G4, QC,
Canada
Tel.: (450) 449-8713
Web Site: https://www.brokerforum.com
Electronic Components Distr
N.A.I.C.S.: 423690

KKR REAL ESTATE FINANCE TRUST INC.

30 Hudson Yards, New York, NY
10001
Tel.: (212) 750-8300   MD
Web Site: https://www.kkrreit.com
Year Founded: 2014
KREF—(NYSE)
Rev.: $181,610,000
Assets: $7,547,618,000
Liabilities: $6,143,436,000
Net Worth: $1,404,182,000
Earnings: ($53,919,000)
Fiscal Year-end: 12/31/23
Commerciall Real Estate Asset Management Services
N.A.I.C.S.: 531210
Kendra L. Decious *(CFO & Treas)*
Christen E. J. Lee *(Vice Chm)*
Matthew A. Salem *(CEO)*
W. Patrick Mattson *(Pres & COO)*
Vincent J. Napolitano *(Mgr, Sec & Gen Counsel)*
Joel Traut *(Partner & Head)*
Julia Butler *(Mng Dir-Real Estate)*
Paul Fine *(Mng Dir-Real Estate)*
Adam Simon *(Dir-Real Estate)*
Ian McConnell *(Dir-Real Estate)*
Christine Patterson *(Head-Asset Mgmt)*
Robert Elson *(Principal-Real Estate)*
Julian Hodgeman *(Principal-Real Estate)*
Jackie Lee *(Principal-Real Estate)*
Duncan Chalfant *(Principal)*
Celine Comeau *(Principal)*
Andrew Egan *(Principal)*
Tommie Maxie *(Principal)*
Andrew Palmieri *(Principal)*
Eric Smith *(Principal)*
Turner Trapp *(Principal)*
Matt Vargo *(Principal)*
Jackie Goodison *(Principal)*
Francesco Cariati *(Principal)*
Saurav Chakraborti *(Principal)*
Leo Michalakos *(Principal)*

KL ACQUISITION CORP.

111 W 33rd St Ste 1910, New York,
NY 10120
Tel.: (212) 782-3482   DE
Year Founded: 2020
KLAQ—(NASDAQ)
Rev.: $10,727,087
Assets: $288,424,610
Liabilities: $305,660,704
Net Worth: ($17,236,094)
Earnings: $9,894,031
Emp.: 3
Fiscal Year-end: 12/31/21
Investment Services
N.A.I.C.S.: 523999
Doug Logigian *(Chm & CEO)*
Richard Gumer *(CFO & Sec)*
David Kho *(COO)*

KLA CORPORATION

3 Technology Dr, Milpitas, CA 95035
Tel.: (408) 875-3000   DE
Web Site: https://www.kla.com
Year Founded: 1975
KLAC—(NASDAQ)
Rev.: $9,812,247,000
Assets: $15,433,566,000
Liabilities: $12,065,238,000
Net Worth: $3,368,328,000
Earnings: $2,761,896,000
Emp.: 15,000
Fiscal Year-end: 06/30/24
Semiconductor Product Mfr
N.A.I.C.S.: 334515
Robert M. Calderoni *(Chm)*
Ben Bin-Ming Tsai *(Chief Technical Officer & Exec VP-Corp Alliances)*
Lena Nicolaides *(Sr VP/Gen Mgr-pattern inspection process control division)*
Virendra A. Kirloskar *(Chief Acctg Officer & Sr VP)*

Bobby R. Bell *(Chief Strategy Officer & Exec VP)*
Ahmad Khan *(Pres-Semiconductor Process Control)*
Oreste Donzella *(Exec VP-Electronics-Packaging-Components)*
Brian Lorig *(Exec VP & Gen Mgr-Svcs & Support-Global)*
John Van Camp *(Chief HR Officer & Exec VP)*
Kevin Kessel *(VP-Investor Relations)*
MaryBeth Wilkinson *(Chief Legal Officer, Sec & Exec VP)*
Richard P. Wallace *(Pres & CEO)*

Subsidiaries:

Air Bearing Technology, Inc. **(1)**
2260 American Ave Ste 1, Hayward, CA
94545-1815
Tel.: (510) 887-2647
Web Site:
    https://www.airbearingtechnology.com
Sales Range: $1-9.9 Million
Emp.: 25
Mechanical Power Transmission Equipment
Mfr
N.A.I.C.S.: 333613
David S. Peters *(Dir-Ops)*

Anchor (Shanghai) Semiconductor Inc. **(1)**
668 East Beijing Road East Building Floor
28B, Shanghai, 200001, China
Tel.: (86) 2153082801
Software Development Services
N.A.I.C.S.: 541511

Anchor Semiconductor, Inc. **(1)**
3235 Kifer Rd Ste 200, Santa Clara, CA
95051
Tel.: (408) 986-8969
Web Site: https://anchorsemi.com
Semiconductor Mfr
N.A.I.C.S.: 334413

Capres A/S **(1)**
Diplomvej 373, 2800, Kongens Lyngby,
Denmark
Tel.: (45) 88821470
Web Site: http://www.capres.com
Industrial Equipment Mfr
N.A.I.C.S.: 334413
Bo Svarrer Hansen *(CEO)*
Peter F. Nielsen *(Co-Founder)*
Christian Leth Petersen *(Co-Founder)*
Ulrik Quade *(Co-Founder)*
Lars Norregaard *(Engr-R&D)*

ECI Technology International, Inc. **(1)**
60 Gordon Dr, Totowa, NJ 07512
Tel.: (973) 773-8686
Web Site: https://www.ecitechnology.com
Emp.: 200
Semiconductor Device Mfr & Distr
N.A.I.C.S.: 334413

Filmetrics, Inc. **(1)**
10655 Roselle St, San Diego, CA 92121
Tel.: (858) 573-9300
Web Site: https://www.filmetrics.com
Thickness Measurement Mfr
N.A.I.C.S.: 334519
Scott Chalmers *(Pres)*

ICOS Vision Systems (Shenzhen) Co. Ltd. **(1)**
2F & 3F Block 2 King Wing Tat Technology
Ind Park, Gangtou Bantian Buji, Shenzhen,
518129, China
Tel.: (86) 75589747468
Sales Range: $25-49.9 Million
Emp.: 70
Semiconductor Testing Equipment Mfr
N.A.I.C.S.: 334515

ICOS Vision Systems Corporation N.V. **(1)**
Research Pk Haasrode Zone 1 Esperanto-laan 8, 3001, Heverlee, Belgium
Tel.: (32) 016398220
Web Site: http://www.icos.be
Sales Range: Less than $1 Million
Emp.: 100
Semiconductor & Electronic Assembly Inspection System Developer & Mfr
N.A.I.C.S.: 334515

KLA Corporation—(Continued)

Carl Smets *(Pres)*

Subsidiary (Non-US):

ICOS Vision Systems Ltd. (2)
1stFloor Yokohama Nishiguchi KN Building, 2 8 4 Kitasaiwai Nishi Ku, Yokohama, 220 0004, Japan
Tel.: (81) 453160123
Web Site: http://www.icos.de
Semiconductor & Electronic Assembly Inspection System Developer & Mfr
N.A.I.C.S.: 334515

ICOS Vision Systems NV (1)
Research Park Haasrode Zone 1 Esperantolaan 8C, 3001, Leuven, Belgium
Tel.: (32) 16398220
Sales Range: $75-99.9 Million
Emp.: 90
Semiconductor Testing Equipment Mfr
N.A.I.C.S.: 334515
Carl Smets *(Gen Mgr)*

InnerSense (1)
19 Hartom St ByNet Building, Har-Hotzvim, Jerusalem, 97775, Israel
Tel.: (972) 25619631
Web Site: https://www.innersense-semi.com
Semiconductor Mfr
N.A.I.C.S.: 334413

KLA-Tencor (Singapore) Pte. Ltd. (1)
4 Serangoon North Avenue 5, Singapore, 554532, Singapore
Tel.: (65) 63676788
Semiconductor Testing Equipment Mfr
N.A.I.C.S.: 334515

KLA-Tencor Asia-Pac Distribution Corporation (1)
3 Technology Dr, Milpitas, CA 95035-7916
Tel.: (408) 875-3000
Web Site: http://www.kla-tencor.com
Semiconductor Testing Equipment Mfr
N.A.I.C.S.: 334413

KLA-Tencor China Corporation (1)
1st Floor No 71-72 1st floor No 79-80 and 5th floor No 88 Lane 887, Zu ChongZhi Road Zhangjiang High-Tech Park, Shanghai, 201203, China
Tel.: (86) 2138619788
Web Site: http://www.klatencor.com
Sales Range: $25-49.9 Million
Emp.: 100
Semiconductor Testing Equipment Mfr
N.A.I.C.S.: 334515

KLA-Tencor Corp. - Texas-Finle Division (1)
8834 N Capital of Texas Hwy Ste 301, Austin, TX 78759
Tel.: (512) 231-4200
Web Site: http://www.klatencor.com
Emp.: 50
Semiconductor Testing Equipment Mfr
N.A.I.C.S.: 334515

KLA-Tencor GmbH (1)
Moritzburger Weg 67 D-01109/ME No B, 01109, Dresden, Germany
Tel.: (49) 351828020
Web Site: http://www.kla-tencor.com
Sales Range: $25-49.9 Million
Emp.: 100
Semiconductor Testing Equipment Mfr
N.A.I.C.S.: 334515

KLA-Tencor Italy S.R.L. (1)
Via Paracelso 22, 20864, Agrate Brianza, MB, Italy
Tel.: (39) 0396112900
Web Site: http://www.kla-tencor.com
Semiconductor Testing Equipment Mfr
N.A.I.C.S.: 334515

KLA-Tencor MIE GmbH (1)
Kubacher Weg 4, 35781, Weilburg, Germany
Tel.: (49) 64719100
Web Site: http://www.kla-tencor.com
Sales Range: $25-49.9 Million
Emp.: 120
Semiconductor Testing Equipment Mfr
N.A.I.C.S.: 334515

KLA-Tencor MIE India Private Limited (1)

Prince Infocity Towers 286/1 & 286/2 Old Mahabalipuram Road, Kottivakkam Village, Chennai, 600 096, Tamil Nadu, India
Tel.: (91) 4443964000
Web Site: http://www.kla-tencor.com
Sales Range: $50-74.9 Million
Emp.: 250
Semiconductor Testing Equipment Mfr
N.A.I.C.S.: 334515

KLA-Tencor Massachusetts (1)
60 Glacier Dr, Westwood, MA 02090
Tel.: (781) 467-3500
Web Site: http://www.kla-tencor.com
Sales Range: $25-49.9 Million
Emp.: 100
Electron Optical Scanners & X-Ray Equipment Mfr
N.A.I.C.S.: 334516

KLA-Tencor Software India Private Limited (1)
Prince Infocity Towers 286/1 & 286/2 Old Mahabalipuram Road, Kottivakkam Village Kandanchavadi, Chennai, 600 096, India
Tel.: (91) 4443964000
Web Site: http://www.kla-tencor.com
Emp.: 250
Software Development Services
N.A.I.C.S.: 541512
Dominic David *(Mng Dir)*

Microsense, LLC (1)
205 Industrial Ave E, Lowell, MA 01852
Tel.: (978) 843-7670
Web Site: https://www.microsense.net
Sensor Module Mfr
N.A.I.C.S.: 334413
Tom McNabb *(Pres & CEO)*
Peter Bagley *(Dir-Wafer Geometry Metrology Bus)*
David Kallus *(Dir-Wafer Dimensional Metrology Bus)*
Erik Samwel *(Dir-VSM Bus)*
Ferenc Vajda *(Dir-Magnetic Metrology Bus)*

Nanomechanics Inc. (1)
105 Meco Ln Ste 100, Oak Ridge, TN 37830
Web Site:
    http://www.nanomechanicsinc.com
Analytical Laboratory Mfr
N.A.I.C.S.: 334516
John Swindeman *(Bus Mgr-Unit)*
Kermit Parks *(Mgr-Product)*
Bob Hirche *(Sls Mgr)*

Orbotech Asia Ltd. (1)
Orbotech Asia Limited 30/F Tower 5 The Gateway Harbour City, 15 Canton Road Tsim Sha Tsui, Kowloon, China (Hong Kong)
Tel.: (852) 28276688
Electric Equipment Mfr
N.A.I.C.S.: 334111
Avihou Barkay *(Pres)*
Yuval Ronen *(Head-Fin & Bus Svcs-Asia Pacific)*

Orbotech Electronics (Shenzhen) Co., Ltd. (1)
3/F Nanshan Building Nanhai Road 1065 Shenzhen Road 1065, Nanshan District, Shenzhen, China
Tel.: (86) 75526021777
Electric Equipment Mfr
N.A.I.C.S.: 334111

Orbotech Electronics (Suzhou) Co., Ltd. (1)
Unit F No 1 Kezhi Road, Suzhou Industry Park, Suzhou, 215121, Jiangsu, China
Tel.: (00) 51205500000
Electric Equipment Mfr
N.A.I.C.S.: 334111

Orbotech LT Solar, LLC (1)
5970 Optical Ct, San Jose, CA 95138
Tel.: (408) 226-9900
Photovoltaic Cell Mfr
N.A.I.C.S.: 334413
Craig Stevens *(VP-Total Product Ops)*

Orbotech Ltd. (1)
7 Sanhedrin Boulevard North Industrial Zone, PO Box 215, Yavne, 8110101, Israel
Tel.: (972) 89423533
Web Site: http://www.orbotech.com
Sales Range: $900-999.9 Million
Automated Optical Inspection Systems Developer

N.A.I.C.S.: 334513
Shmulik Perez *(VP-Ops)*
Yochai Richter *(Chm-Acting)*
Abraham Gross *(Sr VP-Tech)*
Dolev Rafaeli *(Founder)*
Gil Oron *(Pres)*
Roni Romm *(VP-HR)*
Shay Levy *(VP-Fin)*

Subsidiary (Domestic):

Orbograph Ltd. (2)
PO Box 215, Yavne, 81102, Israel
Tel.: (972) 89322257
Web Site: http://www.orbograph.com
Sales Range: $25-49.9 Million
Emp.: 40
Data Processing & Preparation Services; Software Developer
N.A.I.C.S.: 518210
Avikam Baltsan *(Co-Pres & CTO)*
Barry Cohen *(Co-Pres)*
Stewart H. Levine *(VP-Client Svcs)*
Andy Leonhardt *(VP-Sls)*
Jeffrey Buechler *(VP-Fin)*
Arik Elimelech *(VP-R&D)*

Subsidiary (US):

Orbotech Inc. (2)
44 Manning Rd, Billerica, MA 01821-3931 (100%)
Tel.: (978) 667-6037
Web Site: http://www.orbotech.com
Sales Range: $50-74.9 Million
Emp.: 70
Instruments & Control Equipment Distr
N.A.I.C.S.: 423690

Subsidiary (Domestic):

Photon Dynamics, Inc. (3)
5970 Optical Ct, San Jose, CA 95138
Tel.: (408) 226-9900
Web Site: http://www.orbotech.com
Sales Range: $25-49.9 Million
Electronic Components Mfr
N.A.I.C.S.: 334419

Subsidiary (Non-US):

Orbotech Japan Co., Ltd. (2)
6F Sumitomo Aobadai Hills 4-7-7 Aobadai, Meguro-ku, Tokyo, 153-0042, Japan (100%)
Tel.: (81) 363672500
Web Site: http://www.orbotech.com
Sales Range: $25-49.9 Million
Emp.: 100
N.A.I.C.S.: 541511
Chiharu Aono *(Pres)*

Orbotech Pacific Ltd. (2)
Orbotech Asia Limited 30/F Tower 5 The Gateway Harbour City, 15 Canton Road Tsim Sha Tsui, Kowloon, China (Hong Kong) (100%)
Tel.: (852) 28276688
Electric Optic Systems Distr
N.A.I.C.S.: 238210
Kathy Hui *(Dir-HR)*

Orbotech S.A., Europe (2)
64 Rue de la Fusee, 1130, Brussels, Belgium (100%)
Tel.: (32) 27274811
Sales Range: $25-49.9 Million
Emp.: 15
Distr of Electric Optic Systems to the Print Circuit Board Industries
N.A.I.C.S.: 238210

Subsidiary (Non-US):

Laser Imaging Systems GmbH & Co. KG (3)
Friedrich-Hund-Str 3, 07745, Jena, Germany
Tel.: (49) 36418761800
Sales Range: $25-49.9 Million
Electronic Component Mfr & Whslr
N.A.I.C.S.: 334419

New System s.r.l. (3)
Via Monte Hermada 5, 34170, Gorizia, Italy
Tel.: (39) 0481520810
Web Site: http://www.new-system.com
Circuit Board Tester Mfr
N.A.I.C.S.: 334519

Subsidiary (Non-US):

Orbotech Singapore Corporation Pte. Ltd. (2)
20 Science Park Rd 03-25 TeleTech Park Singapore Science Park 2, Singapore, 117674, Singapore
Tel.: (65) 65675657
Web Site: http://www.orbotech.com
Sales Range: $25-49.9 Million
Emp.: 15
Electronic Component Mfr & Distr
N.A.I.C.S.: 334419

SPTS Technologies Ltd. (2)
Ringland Way, Newport, NP18 2TA, United Kingdom
Tel.: (44) 1633414000
Web Site: https://www.spts.com
Sales Range: $200-249.9 Million
Etch, Deposition Process & Machinery Equipment Mfr
N.A.I.C.S.: 333242

Subsidiary (Non-US):

SPTS K.K. (3)
8F Office Tower Y, 1-9-11 Harumi Chuo-ku, 104-6108, Tokyo, Japan
Tel.: (81) 3 6220 0729
Web Site: http://www.spts.com
Sales Range: $100-124.9 Million
Semiconductor Production Equipment Mfr
N.A.I.C.S.: 333242

SPTS Technologies (Shanghai) Inc. (3)
Room 403C 4th Floor Building 5 No 3000 Long Dong Ave, Pudong, Shanghai, 201203, China
Tel.: (86) 2138683705
Web Site: http://www.spts.com
Sales Range: $10-24.9 Million
Semiconductor Production Equipment Mfr
N.A.I.C.S.: 333242

SPTS Technologies - Korea (3)
14 15th Fl SK V1 Center 830 Dongtansunhwan-daero, Bundang-gu, Hwaseong, 18468, Gyeonggi-do, Korea (South)
Tel.: (82) 312881199
Web Site: http://www.spts.com
Sales Range: $10-24.9 Million
Semiconductor Production Equipment Mfr
N.A.I.C.S.: 333242

SPTS Technologies - Malaysia (3)
21 1F Techno Centre Kulim Hi-Tech Park, 09000, Kulim, Kedah Darul Aman, Malaysia
Tel.: (60) 44062328
Web Site: http://www.spts.com
Semiconductor Production Equipment Mfr
N.A.I.C.S.: 333242

SPTS Technologies - Taiwan (3)
10F-1 No 120 Sec 2 Gong Dao Wu Rd, Hsin-chu, 30072, Taiwan
Tel.: (886) 35753105
Web Site: http://www.spts.com
Sales Range: $25-49.9 Million
Semiconductor Production Equipment Mfr
N.A.I.C.S.: 333242

SPTS Technologies GmbH (3)
Provianthofstrasse 1, D-01099, Dresden, Germany
Tel.: (49) 3512606510
Web Site: http://www.spts.com
Sales Range: $25-49.9 Million
Emp.: 21
Semiconductor Production Equipment Mfr
N.A.I.C.S.: 333242

SPTS Technologies Pte. Ltd. (3)
10 Ang Mo Kio St 65 05-11 Techpoint, Singapore, 569059, Singapore
Tel.: (65) 65562327
Web Site: http://www.spts.com
Sales Range: $25-49.9 Million
Emp.: 11
Semiconductor Production Equipment Mfr
N.A.I.C.S.: 333242

Subsidiary (US):

SPTS Technologies, Inc. (3)
1150 Ringwood Ct, San Jose, CA 95131-1726
Tel.: (408) 571-1400

Web Site: http://www.spts.com
Semiconductor Production Equipment Mfr
N.A.I.C.S.: 333242

PixCell Medical Technologies Ltd. (1)
Hayezira St, PO Box 1136, South Industrial Zone, Yoqne'am Illit, 2069202, Israel
Tel.: (972) 495935167
Web Site: http://www.pixcell-medical.com
Medical Diagnostic Product Mfr
N.A.I.C.S.: 325412
Avishay Bransky (Co-Founder & CEO)
Max Herzberg (Co-Founder)
Hanan Ben-Asher (COO)
Yaara Ben-Yosef (Dir-RA & Clinical Affairs)
David Stein (Chm)

Qoniac GmbH (1)
Dr Kuelz-Ring 15, 01067, Dresden, Germany
Tel.: (49) 35141893340
Web Site: http://www.qoniac.com
Semiconductor Lithography Distr
N.A.I.C.S.: 423690
Adwin Timmer (CEO)

Qoniac Japan Ltd. (1)
1029 Fujisawa, Fujisawa, 251-0052, Kanagawa-ken, Japan
Tel.: (81) 466291361
Semiconductor Lithography Distr
N.A.I.C.S.: 423690

Qoniac Korea Ltd. (1)
1004 of the Geumgang IT Tower 557 Dongtangiheung-ro, Hwaseong, Gyeonggi-do, Korea (South)
Tel.: (82) 1050391586
Semiconductor Lithography Distr
N.A.I.C.S.: 423690

SPTS Technologies Ltd. (1)
10F 1 No 120 Sec 2 Gong Dao Wu Rd, Hsinchu, Taiwan
Tel.: (886) 35753105
Electric Equipment Mfr
N.A.I.C.S.: 334111

SPTS Technologies SAS (1)
387 Avenue Jean Kuntzmann, 38330, Montbonnot-Saint-Martin, France
Tel.: (33) 476181430
Electric Equipment Mfr
N.A.I.C.S.: 334111

VLSI Standards, Inc. (1)
5 Technology Dr, Milpitas, CA 95035-7916
Tel.: (408) 428-1800
Web Site: https://www.vlsistandards.com
Semiconductor Testing Equipment Mfr
N.A.I.C.S.: 334515

Zeta Instruments (Shanghai) Co., Ltd. (1)
518 Bibo Road Suite 210, Pudong District, Shanghai, 201203, China
Tel.: (86) 2120231266
Semiconductor Machinery Mfr
N.A.I.C.S.: 333242
Zhen Hou (Gen Mgr)

Zeta Instruments, Inc. (1)
1 Technology Dr, Milpitas, CA 95035
Tel.: (408) 875-0692
Web Site: http://www.kla-tencor.com
Optical Instrument & Lens Mfr
N.A.I.C.S.: 333310

KLAUS TECH, INC.
101 E Park Blvd Ste 600, Plano, TX 75074
Tel.: (505) 470-6990
Web Site: http://www.klaustech.com
Year Founded: 1998
KLTI—(OTCIQ)
Software Publishing Services
N.A.I.C.S.: 513210
Claudio Scola (Founder, Chm, Pres & CEO)
Luigi Cramico (COO)
Lawrence A. Gress (CFO)

KLAVIYO, INC.
125 Summer St Fl 6, Boston, MA 02111
Tel.: (617) 213-1788   DE

Web Site: https://www.klaviyo.com
Year Founded: 2012
KVYO—(NYSE)
Marketing Consulting Services
N.A.I.C.S.: 541613
Amanda Whalen (CFO)
Andrew Bialecki (Co-Founder, Chm & CEO)
Ed Hallen (Co-Founder & Chief Product Officer)

KLEGG ELECTRONICS, INC.
6320 McLeod Dr Ste 3, Las Vegas, NV 89120
Tel.: (702) 530-9417   NV
Year Founded: 2003
KLGG—(OTCIQ)
Electronic Wellness Equipment Distr
N.A.I.C.S.: 423690
Dennis Gentles (Pres)

KLX ENERGY SERVICES HOLDINGS, INC.
3040 Post Oak Blvd 15th Fl, Houston, TX 77056
Tel.: (832) 844-1015   DE
Web Site: https://www.klxenergy.com
Year Founded: 2018
KLXE—(NASDAQ)
Rev.: $781,600,000
Assets: $465,900,000
Liabilities: $481,700,000
Net Worth: ($15,800,000)
Earnings: ($3,100,000)
Emp.: 1,779
Fiscal Year-end: 12/31/22
Holding Company
N.A.I.C.S.: 551112
Christopher J. Baker (Pres & CEO)
Keefer M. Lehner (CFO & Exec VP)
Max L. Bouthillette (Chief Compliance Officer, Gen Counsel & Exec VP)
Geoffrey C. Stanford (Chief Acctg Officer)

KM WEDDING EVENTS MANAGEMENT, INC.
11501 Dublin Blvd Ste 200, Dublin, CA 94568
Tel.: (925) 891-8029   DE
Web Site:
http://www.kmmatrimony.com
Year Founded: 2012
KMWE—(OTCIQ)
Wedding Events Management Services
N.A.I.C.S.: 812990
Meera Nagarajan (CEO & Mng Dir)

KMA HOLDING, INC.
1420 NW 23rd Ave, Fort Lauderdale, FL 33311
Tel.: (954) 465-1642   WY
Year Founded: 2009
MCDA—(OTCIQ)
Medical & Cosmetic Mfr
N.A.I.C.S.: 339112
Ron Ritter (CEO)
Steven Cohen (Pres)

KNIGHT-SWIFT TRANSPORTATION HOLDINGS INC.
2002 W Wahalla Ln, Phoenix, AZ 85027
Tel.: (602) 269-2000   DE
Web Site:
https://www.knighttrans.com
Year Founded: 2010
KNX—(NYSE)
Rev.: $7,141,766,000
Assets: $12,870,765,000
Liabilities: $5,766,684,000
Net Worth: $7,104,081,000
Earnings: $217,149,000
Emp.: 34,300
Fiscal Year-end: 12/31/23

Holding Company; Freight Trucking & Logistics Services
N.A.I.C.S.: 551112
Kevin P. Knight (Chm)
Adam W. Miller (CEO)
Gary J. Knight (Vice Chm)
Cary M. Flanagan (Chief Acctg Officer)

Subsidiaries:

AAA Cooper Transportation, Inc. (1)
1751 Kinsey Rd, Dothan, AL 36303-5877
Tel.: (334) 793-2284
Web Site: http://www.aaacooper.com
Sales Range: $350-399.9 Million
Emp.: 4,500
Trucking Service
N.A.I.C.S.: 484121
Reid B. Dove (CEO)
G. Mack Dove (Chm)
Charlie Prickett (COO & Exec VP)
Jerry Hill (Mgr-Claims)
Joe Hanks (Acct Mgr-Natl)
Ronnie Cole (Dir-Network Support)
Scott Thomley (Dir-Pricing Analysis)
Tammy Garner (Coord-Ops)
Valerie Shelton (Mgr-Benefit)
Josh Coleman (Sr Mgr-Pricing & Design)
John Hammons (VP-Enterprise Dev)
Tim Kinnaird (Dir-Ops Dedicated Svcs)
Ruby Lee (Mgr-Dev & Comm)
Kristen Morgan (Project Coord)
Larry Turvin (Mgr-Traffic)
Joanne Weathers (Project Mgr)
Joya Cheriogotis (Supvr-Environmental & Safety)
Eric Middleton (Mgr-Sys)
Peter Petrillo (Mgr-Web Applications)
Eddie Yance (Supvr-Safety)

Abilene Motor Express, LLC (1)
1700 Willis Rd, Richmond, VA 23237
Tel.: (804) 275-0224
Web Site: https://www.abilenemotor.com
Railroad & Trucking Services
N.A.I.C.S.: 484230

Knight Transportation, Inc. (1)
20002 N 19th Ave, Phoenix, AZ 85027
Tel.: (602) 269-2000
Web Site: https://www.knighttrans.com
Sales Range: $1-4.9 Billion
Short-Haul Cargo Transport Services
N.A.I.C.S.: 484110
David A. Jackson (Pres)

Subsidiary (Domestic):

Barr-Nunn Transportation, Inc. (2)
1803 Burr Oak Blvd, Granger, IA 50109
Tel.: (515) 999-2525
Web Site: http://www.barr-nunn.com
Trucking Service
N.A.I.C.S.: 484121

Knight Truck & Trailer Sales, LLC (2)
5601 W Buckeye Rd, Phoenix, AZ 85043
Tel.: (559) 759-0952
Web Site: http://www.knighttrucksales.com
Container & Trucking Services
N.A.I.C.S.: 484110
J. D. Drigotas (Acct Mgr-Sls)

Kold Trans, LLC (2)
1980 S 900 W, Salt Lake City, UT 84104
Tel.: (801) 907-4600
Web Site: http://koldtrans.com
Transportation Services
N.A.I.C.S.: 488999

Strehl, LLC (1)
15957 N 81st St Ste 102, Scottsdale, AZ 85260
Web Site: http://www.trailerblade.com
Motor Vehicle Parts Distr
N.A.I.C.S.: 423120

Swift Logistics, LLC (1)
2200 S 75th Ave, Phoenix, AZ 85043
Tel.: (602) 272-1500
Web Site: https://www.swiftlogistics.com
Truck Transportation Services
N.A.I.C.S.: 484121
Will Allen (Acct Mgr)
Matt Duran (Dir-Accounts)
Donna Vaughn (VP-Logistics Systems)

Swift Refrigerated Service, LLC (1)
2200 S 75th Ave, Phoenix, AZ 85043
Tel.: (801) 924-7000
Web Site: http://www.swifttrans.com
Temperature-Controlled Transportation Services
N.A.I.C.S.: 484230

Swift Transportation Co., LLC (1)
2200 S 75th Ave, Phoenix, AZ 85043
Tel.: (602) 269-9700
Web Site: http://www.swifttrans.com
Freight Trucking & Logistics Services
N.A.I.C.S.: 484121

Subsidiary (Domestic):

Swift Leasing Co., LLC (2)
2200 S 75th Ave, Phoenix, AZ 85043
Tel.: (602) 269-9700
Web Site: http://www.swifttrans.com
Cargo Truck Leasing Services
N.A.I.C.S.: 532120

Swift Transportation Services, LLC (2)
2200 S 75th Ave, Phoenix, AZ 85043-7410
Tel.: (602) 269-9700
Web Site: http://www.swifttrans.com
Freight Trucking Support Services
N.A.I.C.S.: 488490

U.S. Xpress Enterprises, Inc. (1)
4080 Jenkins Rd, Chattanooga, TN 37421
Tel.: (423) 510-3000
Web Site: https://www.usxpress.com
Rev.: $2,161,170,000
Assets: $1,381,465,000
Liabilities: $1,139,400,000
Net Worth: $242,065,000
Earnings: ($42,394,000)
Emp.: 9,397
Fiscal Year-end: 12/31/2022
Holding Company; Freight Transportation & Logistics Services
N.A.I.C.S.: 551112
Nathan Harwell (Chief Legal Officer)
Julie Van de Kamp (Pres)

Subsidiary (Domestic):

Total Transportation of Mississippi LLC (2)
125 Riverview Dr Ste 4401, Richland, MS 39218   (80%)
Tel.: (601) 936-2104
Web Site: https://www.totalms.com
Sales Range: $25-49.9 Million
Emp.: 1,350
Dry Freight Truck Transportation Services
N.A.I.C.S.: 484121
Tony Wallace (VP-Operations)
Stormie Janzen (VP-Safety &)
Micah Peagler (VP-Strategy)
Trip Wiygul (VP-Sales)

U.S. Xpress, Inc. (2)
4080 Jenkins Rd, Chattanooga, TN 37421-1174
Tel.: (423) 510-3815
Web Site: https://www.usxpress.com
Freight Transportation & Logistics Services
N.A.I.C.S.: 484121

UTXL, Inc. (1)
12200 N Ambassador Dr Ste 103, Kansas City, MO 64163
Tel.: (816) 891-7770
Web Site: https://www.utxl.com
Sales Range: $10-24.9 Million
Emp.: 30
Nationwide Transportation Services
N.A.I.C.S.: 488510
Paul Schultz (CEO)

KNIGHTSCOPE, INC.
1070 Terra Bella Ave, Mountain View, CA 94043
Tel.: (650) 924-1025   DE
Web Site:
https://www.knightscope.com
Year Founded: 2013
KSCP—(NASDAQ)
Rev.: $5,631,000
Assets: $22,082,000
Liabilities: $65,668,000
Net Worth: ($43,586,000)
Earnings: ($25,643,000)

Knightscope, Inc.—(Continued)

Emp.: 92
Fiscal Year-end: 12/31/22
All Other Miscellaneous General Purpose Machinery Manufacturing
N.A.I.C.S.: 333998
William Santana Li *(Co-Founder, Chm, Pres & CEO)*
Stacy Dean Stephens *(Co-Founder, Chief Client Officer & Exec VP)*
Mercedes Soria *(Chief Intelligence Officer & Exec VP)*
Aaron J. Lehnhardt *(Chief Design Officer & Exec VP)*
Apoorv S. Dwivedi *(CFO, Principal Acctg Officer & Exec VP)*

KNIGHTSWAN ACQUISITION CORPORATION

99 Wall St Ste 460, New York, NY 10005
Tel.: (301) 613-8632   DE
Year Founded: 2021
KNSW—(NYSE)
Rev.: $3,399,497
Assets: $240,824,366
Liabilities: $247,682,590
Net Worth: ($6,858,224)
Earnings: ($564,499)
Emp.: 1
Fiscal Year-end: 12/31/22
Investment Services
N.A.I.C.S.: 523999
Matthew McElroy *(CFO)*

KNOW LABS, INC.

619 Western Ave Ste 610, Seattle, WA 98104
Tel.: (206) 903-1351   NV
Web Site: https://www.knowlabs.co
Year Founded: 1998
KNW—(NYSEAMEX)
Rev.: $155,248
Assets: $3,664,428
Liabilities: $5,820,629
Net Worth: ($2,156,201)
Earnings: ($16,581,558)
Emp.: 12
Fiscal Year-end: 09/30/24
Security & Quality Control Solutions for Use in Homeland Security, Anti-Counterfeiting, Forgery Prevention, Fraud Prevention, Brand Protection & Process Control Applications
N.A.I.C.S.: 561621
Ronald P. Erickson *(Co-Founder, Chm & Treas)*
James Anderson *(Chief Medical Officer)*
Peter Conley *(CFO & Sr VP-Intellectual Property)*
Leo Trautwein *(CTO)*
Jessica English *(Co-Founder, CEO, CMO & Chief Sls Officer)*

KNOWLES CORPORATION

1151 Maplewood Dr, Itasca, IL 60143
Tel.: (630) 250-5100   DE
Web Site: https://www.knowles.com
Year Founded: 1946
KN—(NYSE)
Rev.: $764,700,000
Assets: $1,183,900,000
Liabilities: $191,000,000
Net Worth: $992,900,000
Earnings: ($430,100,000)
Emp.: 7,000
Fiscal Year-end: 12/31/22
Electronic Components Mfr
N.A.I.C.S.: 334419
Jeffrey S. Niew *(Pres & CEO)*
Raymond D. Cabrera *(Chief Admin Officer & Sr VP-HR)*
Daniel J. Giesecke *(COO & Sr VP)*
John S. Anderson *(CFO & Sr VP)*

Michael J. Knapp *(VP-Investor Relations)*
Chris Dugan *(Pres-Precision Devices)*
Brian Crannell *(Sr VP-Corp Dev)*
Robert J. Perna *(Gen Counsel, Sec & Sr VP)*
Air A. Bastarrica Jr. *(VP & Controller)*

Subsidiaries:

Cornell Dubilier Electronics, Inc.   (1)
140 Technology Pl, Liberty, SC 29657-3300
Tel.: (864) 843-2626
Web Site: https://www.cde.com
Emp.: 200
Mfr of Electronic Capacitors
N.A.I.C.S.: 334416
James P. Kaplan *(Pres)*
Laird Macomber *(Mgr-Tech)*
Rex Easterly *(Mgr-Production)*
Mike McGeachie *(Mgr-Tech Support)*
Victor Whitworth *(CFO)*

Subsidiary (Non-US):

C.D. Electronica de Mexico, S.A. de C.V.   (2)
Blvd Benito Juarez s/n Colonia Sanchez Taboada, 21360, Mexicali, Baja California, Mexico
Tel.: (52) 6865617031
Emp.: 450
Capacitor Mfr
N.A.I.C.S.: 334416

Subsidiary (Domestic):

Cornell Dubilier Marketing, Inc.   (2)
140 Technology Pl, Liberty, SC 29657
Tel.: (864) 843-2277
Sales Range: $25-49.9 Million
Capacitor Mfr
N.A.I.C.S.: 334416

Cornell Dubilier Property Corp.   (1)
140 Technology Pl, Liberty, SC 29657
Tel.: (864) 843-2626
Web Site: https://www.cde.com
Electronic Product Mfr & Distr
N.A.I.C.S.: 334419

Integrated Microwave Corporation   (1)
11353 Sorrento Valley Rd, San Diego, CA 92121
Tel.: (858) 259-2600
Web Site: http://www.imcsd.com
Mfg Electronic Components Mfg Semiconductors/Related Devices Mfg Porcelain Electrical Suppplies
N.A.I.C.S.: 334419
Allon Hobba *(VP)*

Knowles Cazenovia Inc.   (1)
2777 Hwy 20, Cazenovia, NY 13035
Tel.: (315) 655-8710
Web Site: https://www.knowles.com
Electronic Capacitor Mfr
N.A.I.C.S.: 334416

Knowles Electronics Austria GmbH   (1)
Gutheil-Schoder-Gasse 8-12, 1100, Vienna, Austria
Tel.: (43) 1608700
Semiconductor Equipment Mfr
N.A.I.C.S.: 334413
Gordon Schriefer *(Sr Mgr-AME)*

Knowles Electronics Holdings, Inc.   (1)
1151 Maplewood Dr, Itasca, IL 60143-2058
Tel.: (630) 250-5100
Web Site: https://www.knowles.com
Holding Company
N.A.I.C.S.: 551112

Subsidiary (Non-US):

Knowles (UK) Ltd   (2)
Hethel Engineering Centre Chapman Way Hethel, Norwich, NR14 8FB, United Kingdom
Tel.: (44) 1603723300
Web Site:
    http://www.knowlescapacitors.com
Ceramic Capacitor Mfr
N.A.I.C.S.: 334416

Subsidiary (Domestic):

Knowles Cazenovia   (2)
2777 Route 20 E, Cazenovia, NY 13035
Tel.: (315) 655-8710
Web Site: http://www.knowles.com
Ceramic Dielectric Heating Equipment Mfr
N.A.I.C.S.: 334416

Subsidiary (Non-US):

Knowles Electronics (Malaysia) Sdn. Bhd.   (2)
Plot 104 Lebuhraya Kg Jawa, Bayan Lepas Industrial Estate, 11900, Penang, Malaysia
Tel.: (60) 46147466
Acoustic Component Mfr
N.A.I.C.S.: 334419

Knowles Electronics Denmark ApS   (2)
Tel.: (45) 70253570
Web Site: https://www.knowles.com
Sales Range: $10-24.9 Million
Electronic Components Mfr
N.A.I.C.S.: 334419

Knowles Electronics Taiwan, Ltd.   (2)
5F No 129 Ln 235 Baoqiao Road, Xindian Dist, New Taipei City, 23145, Taiwan
Tel.: (886) 289191799
Web Site: https://www.knowles.com
Electronic Components Mfr
N.A.I.C.S.: 334419

Subsidiary (Domestic):

Knowles Electronics, LLC   (2)
1151 Maplewood Dr, Itasca, IL 60143-2071
Tel.: (630) 250-5100
Web Site: https://www.knowles.com
Sales Range: $25-49.9 Million
Electronic Components Mfr
N.A.I.C.S.: 334419

KODIAK SCIENCES INC.

1200 Page Mill Rd, Palo Alto, CA 94304
Tel.: (650) 281-0850   DE
Web Site: https://www.kodiak.com
Year Founded: 2009
KOD—(NASDAQ)
Rev.: $7,071,000
Assets: $666,628,000
Liabilities: $230,461,000
Net Worth: $436,167,000
Earnings: ($333,823,000)
Emp.: 112
Fiscal Year-end: 12/31/22
Biopharmaceutical Product Research & Development Services
N.A.I.C.S.: 325412
John Borgeson *(CFO & Sr.VP)*
Hong Liang *(Sr VP-Discovery Medicine)*
Joel Naor *(VP-Clinical Science & Dev Ops)*
Almas Qudrat *(Sr VP-Quality Ops)*
Stephen Raillard *(VP-Chemical Dev & Mfg)*
Pablo Velazquez-Martin *(VP-Clinical Res & Translational Medicine)*
Stephen A. Charles *(Founder)*
Laurent Ducry *(VP-Biologics Dev & Mfg)*
Sinette Heys *(VP & Head-Clinical Ops)*
Victor Perlroth *(Co-Founder, Chm & CEO)*

KOHL'S CORPORATION

N56 W17000 Ridgewood Dr, Menomonee Falls, WI 53051
Tel.: (262) 703-7000   WI
Web Site: https://corporate.kohls.com
Year Founded: 1962
KSS—(NYSE)
Rev.: $17,476,000,000
Assets: $14,009,000,000
Liabilities: $10,116,000,000
Net Worth: $3,893,000,000
Earnings: $317,000,000

Emp.: 36,000
Fiscal Year-end: 02/03/24
Department Store Retailer
N.A.I.C.S.: 455110
Jennifer J. Kent *(Chief Legal Officer)*
Thomas A. Kingsbury *(CEO)*
Marc Chini *(Chief People Officer & Sr Exec VP)*
Jill Timm *(CFO & Sr Exec VP)*
Nick Jones *(Chief Mdsg & Digital Officer)*
Jason Kelroy *(Gen Counsel, Sec & Sr Exec VP)*
Michelle A. Banks *(Chief Diversity & Inclusion Officer)*
Siobhan Mc Feeney *(CTO)*
Christie Raymond *(CMO & Sr Exec VP)*
Nick Jones *(Chief Mdsg & Digital Officer)*

Subsidiaries:

Kohl's Department Stores   (1)
N95W18000 Appleton Ave, Menomonee Falls, WI 53051
Tel.: (262) 251-9075
Web Site: http://www.kohls.com
Sales Range: $100-124.9 Million
Emp.: 143
Departmental Store Operator
N.A.I.C.S.: 455110

Subsidiary (Domestic):

Kohl's Indiana Inc   (2)
3722 National Rd E, Richmond, IN 47374
Tel.: (765) 935-1507
Department Stores
N.A.I.C.S.: 455110

KOIL ENERGY SOLUTIONS, INC.

1310 Rankin Rd, Houston, TX 77073
Tel.: (281) 862-2201
Web Site: https://www.koilenergy.com
KLNG—(OTCQB)
Rev.: $15,343,000
Assets: $17,062,000
Liabilities: $11,444,000
Net Worth: $5,618,000
Earnings: ($1,554,000)
Emp.: 51
Fiscal Year-end: 12/31/23
Oil Field Services
N.A.I.C.S.: 213112
Erik Wiik *(Pres & CEO)*
Ronald E. Smith *(Foundor)*
Mark Carden *(Chm)*

KOLON TISSUEGENE, INC.

9713 Key Ave W Ste 300, Rockville, MD 20850
Tel.: (301) 921-6000
Web Site:
    https://www.tissuegene.com
Year Founded: 1999
950160—(KRS)
Rev.: $7,319,202
Assets: $86,711,825
Liabilities: $14,519,975
Net Worth: $72,191,850
Earnings: ($8,619,693)
Emp.: 48
Fiscal Year-end: 12/31/22
Pharmaceuticals Product Mfr
N.A.I.C.S.: 325412
Moon J. Noh *(CEO)*
Soon-Wook Kweon *(VP)*
Jung In Kim *(CFO)*
Sun-Jin Kim *(Chief Medical Officer)*
Diana M. Halim *(VP-Clinical & Regulatory Affairs)*

KOLORFUSION INTERNATIONAL, INC.

5401 Oswego St Unit C, Denver, CO 80239
Tel.: (303) 340-9994

Web Site:
https://www.kolorfusion.com
Year Founded: 1995
KOLR—(NASDAQ)
Develops & Markets Color Transfer-ring Processes
N.A.I.C.S.: 323111

KONARED CORPORATION
1101 Via Callejon Ste 200, San Clemente, CA 92673
Tel.: (808) 212-1553   NV
Web Site: http://www.konared.com
Year Founded: 2010
KRED—(OTCIQ)
Beverages Mfr
N.A.I.C.S.: 312111
James S. Tonkin *(Chm & Pres)*
Kyle Redfield *(CEO & CFO)*
Shaun Roberts *(Vice Chm)*

KONATEL, INC.
500 N Central Expy Ste 202, Plano, TX 75074
Tel.: (214) 323-8410   DE
Web Site: https://www.konatel.com
Year Founded: 1986
KTEL—(OTCQB)
Rev.: $18,223,745
Assets: $4,809,684
Liabilities: $7,823,089
Net Worth: ($3,013,405)
Earnings: ($3,940,827)
Emp.: 34
Fiscal Year-end: 12/31/23
Wireless Telecommunications Carri-ers (except Satellite)
N.A.I.C.S.: 551112
D. Sean McEwen *(Founder, Chm, Pres & CEO)*
Brian R. Riffle *(CFO)*
B. Todd Murcer *(Sec & Exec VP-Fin)*

Subsidiaries:

Apeiron Systems, Inc.   (1)
2629 Manhattan Ave 166, Hermosa Beach, CA 90254
Web Site: https://www.apeiron.io
Business Communications Services
N.A.I.C.S.: 561499

IM Telecom, LLC   (1)
500 N Central Expressway Ste 202, Plano, TX 75074
Web Site: https://infinitimobile.com
Wireless Telecommunication Services
N.A.I.C.S.: 517121

KonaTel Inc.   (1)
500 N Central Expressway Ste 202, Plano, TX 75074
Tel.: (214) 323-8410
Web Site: https://konatel.com
Wireless Telecommunications Reseller
N.A.I.C.S.: 517121

KONTOOR BRANDS, INC.
400 N Elm, Greensboro, NC 27401
Tel.: (336) 332-3400   NC
Web Site:
https://www.kontoorbrands.com
Year Founded: 2018
KTB—(NYSE)
Rev.: $2,475,916,000
Assets: $1,533,024,000
Liabilities: $1,384,886,000
Net Worth: $148,138,000
Earnings: $195,423,000
Emp.: 14,000
Fiscal Year-end: 01/01/22
Holding Company
N.A.I.C.S.: 551112
Joseph A. Alkire *(CFO & Exec VP)*
Scott Shoener *(Chief HR Officer-Corp Comm & Exec VP)*
Thomas E. Waldron *(COO & Exec VP)*
Denise Sumner *(Chief Acctg Officer & VP)*

Karen Smith *(Exec VP-Supply Chain)*
Eric Tracy *(VP-Fin & IR)*
Julia Burge *(Dir-External Comm)*
Mame Annan-Brown *(Head-Environmental, Social & Governance-Global)*
Vanessa McCutchen *(VP-Comm)*
Ezio Garciamendez *(Chief Supply Chain Officer & Exec VP)*
Pete Kidd *(Chief HR Officer & Exec VP)*
Scott H. Baxter *(Chm, Pres & CEO)*

Subsidiaries:

Lee Jeans   (1)
400 N Elm St, Greensboro, NC 27401
Tel.: (913) 384-4000
Web Site: http://www.lee.com
Clothing Mfr
N.A.I.C.S.: 315210
Chris Waldeck *(Pres)*

VF Jeanswear Limited Partnership   (1)
400 N Elm St, Greensboro, NC 27401
Tel.: (336) 332-3400
Men's, Women's & Children's Clothing Mfr.
N.A.I.C.S.: 315250

Subsidiary (Non-US):

VF (J) France, S.A.   (2)
31-33 rue Du Louvre, 75002, Paris, France
Tel.: (33) 148176220
Apparels Mfr
N.A.I.C.S.: 315250

Plant (Domestic):

VF Jeanswear - El Paso   (2)
12173 Rojas Dr, El Paso, TX 79936
Tel.: (915) 858-8700
Apparels Mfr
N.A.I.C.S.: 315250
Kevin Simank *(Sr Dir-Distr Ops)*

VF Jeanswear - Seminole   (2)
1400 W Wrangler Blvd, Seminole, OK 74868
Tel.: (405) 382-7447
Apparels Mfr
N.A.I.C.S.: 315250

Subsidiary (Non-US):

VF Jeanswear Espana S.L.   (2)
Calle Moll Barcelona S/N, Barcelona, 08039, Spain
Tel.: (34) 935088620
Clothing Stores
N.A.I.C.S.: 455219

Subsidiary (Domestic):

VF Jeanswear Sales, Inc.   (2)
2626 Glenwood Ave, Raleigh, NC 27608
Tel.: (336) 424-6211
Apparel & Accessory Retailer
N.A.I.C.S.: 458110

Subsidiary (Non-US):

VF Jeanswear de Mexico SA de CV   (2)
Av Paseo De La Reforma No 2620 PiLo-mas Altas, Miguel Hidalgo, Mexico, 11950, Mexico
Tel.: (52) 5550811500
Clothing Mfr
N.A.I.C.S.: 315250

Subsidiary (Domestic):

VF Outlet Inc.   (2)
739 Reading Ave Ste 200 W, Reading, PA 19611
Tel.: (610) 373-2159
Web Site: http://www.vfoutlet.com
Clothing Retailer
N.A.I.C.S.: 458110

KOPIN CORPORATION
125 N Dr, Westborough, MA 01581
Tel.: (508) 870-5959   DE
Web Site: https://www.kopin.com
Year Founded: 1984

KOPN—(NASDAQ)
Rev.: $47,401,190
Assets: $43,752,172
Liabilities: $19,761,557
Net Worth: $23,990,615
Earnings: ($19,325,917)
Emp.: 177
Fiscal Year-end: 12/31/22
Lightweight, Power Efficient, Ultra-Small Liquid Crystal Displays (LCDs) & Heterojunction Bipolar Transistors (HBTs) Mfr
N.A.I.C.S.: 334413
Michael Murray *(Pres & CEO)*
John C. C. Fan *(Founder)*
Richard A. Sneider *(CFO & Treas)*
James K. Brewington *(Chm)*
Raymond Schubnel *(Dir-Quality)*

Subsidiaries:

Forth Dimension Displays   (1)
7 St David's Drive, Dalgety Bay, KY11 9NB, Fife, United Kingdom
Tel.: (44) 138 382 7950
Web Site: https://www.forthdd.com
Sales Range: $25-49.9 Million
Emp.: 3
Electronic Components Mfr
N.A.I.C.S.: 334419
Greg Truman *(CEO)*
Calum Dewar *(Dir-Product Design)*
Henning Molsen *(VP-Sls & Mktg)*
Andrew McCue *(VP-Ops)*
Michael Hay *(Controller-Fin)*

Fourth Dimension Display Ltd.   (1)
7 Street Davids Drive Saint Davids Busi-ness Park Dalgety Bay, Dunfermline, KY11 9NB, Fife, United Kingdom
Tel.: (44) 1383827950
Sales Range: $25-49.9 Million
Emp.: 50
Holding Company
N.A.I.C.S.: 551112

Intoware Ltd.   (1)
The Ingenuity Centre Jubilee Campus Uni-versity of Nottingham, West Bridgford, Not-tingham, NG7 2TU, United Kingdom
Tel.: (44) 1159778969
Web Site: https://www.intoware.com
Technology Solution Provider
N.A.I.C.S.: 561110

eMDT America Inc.   (1)
2338 Walsh Ave, Santa Clara, CA 95051-1301
Tel.: (408) 986-0400
Electronic Components Mfr
N.A.I.C.S.: 334419

KOPP GLASS, INC.
2108 Palmer St, Pittsburgh, PA 15218
Tel.: (412) 271-0190   PA
Web Site: https://www.koppglass.com
KOGL—(OTCIQ)
Glass Product Manufacturing Made of Purchased Glass
N.A.I.C.S.: 327215
Rob Diana *(VP-Ops)*

KOPPERS HOLDINGS INC.
436 7th Ave, Pittsburgh, PA 15219-1800
Tel.: (412) 227-2001   PA
Web Site: https://www.koppers.com
Year Founded: 2004
KOP—(NYSE)
Rev.: $1,980,500,000
Assets: $1,711,400,000
Liabilities: $1,308,400,000
Net Worth: $403,000,000
Earnings: $63,400,000
Emp.: 961
Fiscal Year-end: 12/31/22
Holding Company: Integrated Pro-ducer of Chemicals, Carbon Com-pounds & Treated Wood Products for Various Industries
N.A.I.C.S.: 325180

Leslie S. Hyde *(Chief Sustainability & Officer/Sr VP-Koppers Inc)*
James A. Sullivan *(Pres & COO)*
Leroy M. Ball Jr. *(CEO)*
Stephen R. Tritch *(Chm)*
Jimmi Sue Smith *(CFO)*
Bradley A. Pearce *(Chief Acctg Offi-cer)*
Stephanie L. Apostolou *(Gen Counsel & Sec)*
Tushar Lovalekar *(VP)*
Quynh McGuire *(VP)*
Kevin Washington *(VP)*
Douglas Fenwick *(Pres)*
Travis Gross *(VP)*
Christian Nielsen *(Sr VP)*

Subsidiaries:

Cox Recovery Services, LLC   (1)
128 Millport Cir Ste 200, Greenville, SC 29607
Web Site: http://www.coxrecovery.com
Biomass Fuel Generation Services
N.A.I.C.S.: 221117

Koppers (Tianjin) Trading Co., Ltd.   (1)
No 1702 C3 Tower TEDA MSD No 79, 1st Ave Binhai Area, Tianjin, 300457, China
Tel.: (86) 13917631238
Wood Preservation Services
N.A.I.C.S.: 321114

Koppers Ashcroft Inc.   (1)
1425 Evans Road, PO Box 1510, Ashcroft, Thompson, V0K 1A0, BC, Canada
Tel.: (250) 453-2221
Cyclic Crude & Intermediate Mfr
N.A.I.C.S.: 325194

Koppers Deutschland GmbH   (1)
Am Sagewerk 26, 68526, Ladenburg, Ger-many
Tel.: (49) 6203954310
Wood Preservation Services
N.A.I.C.S.: 321114

Koppers Inc.   (1)
436 7th Ave, Pittsburgh, PA 15219-1800
Tel.: (412) 227-2001
Web Site: https://www.koppers.com
Sales Range: $125-149.9 Million
Emp.: 1,800
Chemicals, Carbon Compounds & Wood Treatment Products Mfr
N.A.I.C.S.: 321113
Leslie S. Hyde *(Chief Sustainability Officer & Sr VP)*
James A. Sullivan *(Pres & COO)*
Leroy M. Ball Jr. *(CEO)*
Joseph P. Dowd *(VP-Zero Harm)*
Christian Nielsen *(Sr VP-Global Carbon Ma-terials & Chemicals)*
Quynh T. McGuire *(Dir-IR)*
Stephanie L. Apostolou *(Gen Counsel & Sec)*
James J. Healey *(VP-Utility & Industrial Products)*
Quynh McGuire *(VP-Investor Relations)*
Tushar Lovalekar *(VP-Information Technol-ogy)*
Stephen G. Lucas *(VP-Culture & Engage-ment)*
Daniel J. Skrovanek *(VP-Growth & Innova-tion)*
Jimmi Sue Smith *(CFO)*
Kevin Washington *(VP-External Relations)*
Stephen Tritch *(Chm)*

Subsidiary (Domestic):

Gross & Janes Co.   (2)
102 N Clay Ave, Kirkwood, MO 63122
Tel.: (636) 343-8484
Web Site: http://www.grossjanes.com
Sales Range: $1-9.9 Million
Emp.: 30
Miscellaneous Durable Goods Merchant Whslr
N.A.I.C.S.: 423990
David Maple *(Mgr-Tie Pur-Doniphan)*
Gene Willard *(Plant Mgr-Williamsville)*
Jeff Peterson *(Mgr-Yard)*
Mike DiRaimondo *(CFO)*
Paula Rogers *(Mgr-Northern Territory-Nixa)*
Scott McBride *(VP-Procurement)*
Bill Behan *(Pres)*

Koppers Holdings Inc.—(Continued)

Koppers Performance Chemicals Inc. (2)
1016 Everee Inn Rd, Griffin, GA 30224-4733
Tel.: (770) 233-4200
Web Site:
https://www.koppersperformancechemicals.com
Sales Range: $50-74.9 Million
Emp.: 100
Wood Preservatives Mfr & Distr
N.A.I.C.S.: 321114
Leroy M. Ball Jr. *(Pres & CEO)*

Subsidiary (Non-US):

Koppers Performance Chemicals New Zealand (3)
14 Mayo Road Wiri, Auckland, 2104, New Zealand
Tel.: (64) 9 277 7770
Web Site: https://www.kopperspc.co.nz
Sales Range: $10-24.9 Million
Emp.: 17
Timber Preservatives, Antisapstains & Associated Timber Protection Chemicals Mfr & Marketer
N.A.I.C.S.: 321114

Protim Solignum Ltd. (3)
Fieldhouse Lane, Marlow, SL7 1LS, Buckinghamshire, United Kingdom
Tel.: (44) 162 848 6644
Web Site: http://www.kopperspc.eu
Wood Preservative Chemicals Mfr
N.A.I.C.S.: 325998
Sarah Macaulay *(Ops Mgr)*
Thomas Christensen *(Mng Dir-Europe)*
Stuart Jepson *(Comml Dir-Intl)*
Martin Kolaszynski *(Dir-Ops)*
Matthew Hempson *(Dir-Bus Dev-Europe)*
Steve Uphill *(Head-Dev)*
Lars Nyborg *(Dir-Technical-OCE-Nordic & CE)*
Graham Mackie *(Bus Mgr-Scotland)*
Simon Brookes *(Mgr-Customer Svc)*
Terry Wentworth *(Mgr-Technical)*
Paul Cave *(Mgr-Sls)*
Michael Boe *(Reg Mgr-Bus)*

Subsidiary (Domestic):

Koppers Railroad Structures Inc. (2)
4546 Tompkins Dr, Madison, WI 53716
Tel.: (608) 395-6600
Web Site: https://www.koppersrs.com
Rail Infrastructure Inspection, Maintenance & Rehabilitation Services
N.A.I.C.S.: 488210

Koppers Latvia SIA (1)
Aizputes 1 k-1, Riga, 1046, Latvia
Tel.: (371) 67344220
Wood Preservation Services
N.A.I.C.S.: 321114

Koppers Norway AS (1)
Sagtomta, Tangen, 2337, Stange, Norway
Tel.: (47) 62582400
Wood Preservation Services
N.A.I.C.S.: 321114

Koppers Performance Chemicals Australia Pty Ltd (1)
Level 5 53 Walker Street, North Sydney, 2060, NSW, Australia
Tel.: (61) 887231399
Web Site: https://www.kopperspc.com.au
Wood Preservative Distr
N.A.I.C.S.: 424690

Koppers Specialty Chemicals Limited (1)
Normanby Gateway Lysaghts Way, Lysaghts Way, Scunthorpe, DN15 9YG, United Kingdom
Tel.: (44) 1724281555
Wood Preservation Services
N.A.I.C.S.: 321114

Koppers Sweden AB (1)
Lilla Garnisonsgatan 39, 254 67, Helsingborg, Sweden
Tel.: (46) 42262580
Wood Preservation Services
N.A.I.C.S.: 321114

Koppers UK Limited (1)

---

1 Park Row, Leeds, LS1 5AB, South Humberside, United Kingdom
Tel.: (44) 1724281555
Wood treating Chemicals Whslr
N.A.I.C.S.: 424690
Markus Spiess *(VP-Global Sls & Mktg)*

Koppers Utility & Industrial Products Inc. (1)
237 Forestry Rd, Eutawville, SC 29048
Web Site: https://www.koppersuip.com
Wood Pole Mfr
N.A.I.C.S.: 321114

Subsidiary (Domestic):

Brown Wood Preserving Company Inc. (2)
6201 Camp Ground Rd, Louisville, KY 40216
Tel.: (502) 448-2337
Web Site: http://www.brownwoodpoles.com
Sales Range: $50-74.9 Million
Emp.: 60
Mfr of Preserved Wood Utility Poles
N.A.I.C.S.: 321114

Koppers WorldWide Ventures Corporation (1)
Two Grennville Crossing, Greenville, DE 19807
Tel.: (302) 421-2245
Gum & Wood Chemical Mfr
N.A.I.C.S.: 325194

Osmose Chile Limitada (1)
Av Americo Vespucio Norte 2680 Office 62 El Cortijo, 8551378, Santiago, Chile
Tel.: (56) 226242800
Web Site: https://www.osmose.cl
Wood Preservation Services
N.A.I.C.S.: 321114
Roberto Wilkendorf *(Gen Mgr)*

Oy Koppers Finland Ab (1)
Mannerheiminkatu 20 A, 06100, Porvoo, Finland
Tel.: (358) 19581177
Wood Preservation Services
N.A.I.C.S.: 321114

Protim Ltd. (1)
Jamestown Road, Finglas, Dublin, 11, Ireland
Tel.: (353) 18068648
Wood Preservation Services
N.A.I.C.S.: 321114

Timber Specialties Co. (1)
35 Crawford Crescent, PO Box 520, Campbellville, L0P 1B0, ON, Canada
Tel.: (905) 854-2244
Web Site: https://www.timberspecialties.com
Wood Preservation Services
N.A.I.C.S.: 321114

Wood Protection LP (1)
5151 South Loop E, Houston, TX 77033-0376
Tel.: (713) 733-7421
Wood Preservation Services
N.A.I.C.S.: 321114

KORN FERRY
1900 Ave of the Stars Ste 1500, Los Angeles, CA 90067
Tel.: (310) 552-1834   DE
Web Site: https://www.kornferry.com
Year Founded: 1969
KFY—(NYSE)
Rev.: $2,795,505,000
Assets: $3,678,869,000
Liabilities: $1,941,544,000
Net Worth: $1,737,325,000
Earnings: $169,154,000
Emp.: 9,076
Fiscal Year-end: 04/30/24
Holding Company; Executive & Professional Search, Recruitment, Leadership Development Products & Consulting Services
N.A.I.C.S.: 551112
Bryan Ackermann *(Mng Partner-Assessment-Succession-Leadership-Professional Dev)*
Michael Distefano *(Chm-Asia Pacific)*

Joseph E. Griesedieck *(Vice Chm, Mng Dir & CEO-Svcs-San Francisco)*
Linda Hyman *(Exec VP-HR-Global)*
Jeanne MacDonald *(CEO-RPO)*
Alan C. Guarino *(Vice Chm)*
Robert Wesselkamper *(Vice Chm-Rewards,Benefits Solutions)*
Jeanne MacDonald *(CEO-Recruitment Process Outsourcing)*
Mathias Herzog *(Pres-Global Tech)*
Gary D. Burnison *(Pres & CEO)*
Alex Martin *(Board of Directors & Sr Partner-Client)*
Jaime Massar *(Sr Partner-Client & Legal Centre for Excellence-Legal Practice,Global)*
Brandon Johnson *(CIO & Sr VP-Los Angeles)*
Jill Wiltfong *(CMO)*
J. T. Saunders *(Chief Diversity Officer)*
Jay Kizer *(Pres-Life Sciences-Dallas)*
Jean-Marc Laouchez *(Pres-Korn Ferry Institute-New York)*
Greg Button *(Pres-Global Healthcare Svcs-Philadelphia)*
Dominique Virchaux *(Pres-South America)*
Sonamara Jeffreys *(Pres-EMEA)*
Esther Colwill *(Pres-Asia Pacific)*
Mark Arian *(CEO-Consulting)*
Jonathan Kuai *(Gen Counsel, Sec & Mng Dir-ESG & Bus Affairs)*
Addy Chulef *(Assoc Partner-Client)*
Alexandra Blakeslee Hartwell *(Principal-Food & Agribusiness)*
Brian Bloom *(VP-Global Benefits & Mobility Ops)*
Robert P. Rozek *(CFO, Chief Corp Officer & Exec VP)*

Subsidiaries:

Agensi Pekerjaan Korn Ferry Sdn. Bhd. (1)
Ste 15.4 Level 15 Menara IMC 8 Jalan Sultan Ismail, 50250, Kuala Lumpur, Malaysia   (49%)
Tel.: (60) 320781655
Web Site: http://www.kornferry.com
Rev.: $500,000
Emp.: 10
Executive Search Service
N.A.I.C.S.: 541612
Mary Chua *(Sr Partner-Client)*
Shahril Ariffin *(Assoc Partner-Client)*

Boca Enterprise Management (Shanghai) Co., Ltd. (1)
2215 22/F Centro International Tower No 568 Hengfeng Road, Shanghai, 200070, China
Tel.: (86) 2122265020
Educational Support Services
N.A.I.C.S.: 611710

Futurestep (Shanghai) Talent Consulting Company Limited (1)
Unit 1018 China World Tower 2 No 1 Jian Guo Men Wai Avenue, ChaoYang, Beijing, 100004, China
Tel.: (86) 1065359600
Web Site: http://www.futurestep.com
Executive Search & Global Recruitment Services
N.A.I.C.S.: 541612

Guangzhou Korn/Ferry Human Capital Company Ltd. (1)
Unit 3601-02 China Shine Plaza No 9 Linhe Road West, Tianhe District, Guangzhou, 510610, Guangdong, China
Tel.: (86) 2038116000
Executive Search & Global Recruitment Services
N.A.I.C.S.: 541612

Hay Group LLC (1)
Qatar Financial Centre Tower 1 1st Floor Business Centre Office 6, PO Box 23245, West Bay, Doha, Qatar
Tel.: (974) 44967692
Organization Development Consulting Services

N.A.I.C.S.: 541612

Hay Group UAB (1)
Seimyniskiu St 1A, Vilnius, 09312, Lithuania
Tel.: (370) 52757022
Organization Development Consulting Services
N.A.I.C.S.: 541612

Hay Group s.r.o. (1)
Lakeside Park Tomasikova 64, 831 04, Bratislava, Slovakia
Tel.: (421) 249114901
Organization Development Consulting Services
N.A.I.C.S.: 541612

Infinity Consulting Solutions, Inc. (1)
462 7th Ave 2nd Fl, New York, NY 10018
Tel.: (212) 593-9797
Web Site: http://www.infinity-cs.com
Sales Range: $10-24.9 Million
Emp.: 132
Staffing & Consulting Solutions Services
N.A.I.C.S.: 561311
Douglas Klares *(Pres)*
Elisa Emeritz *(Mgr-Talent Acq)*
John Liberatore *(Dir-South Florida)*
Gary Pfennig *(Dir-Houston)*

Korn Ferry (AT) GmbH (1)
Johannesgasse 18, 1010, Vienna, Austria   (100%)
Tel.: (43) 1531030
Web Site: https://www.kornferry.com
Executive Search Service
N.A.I.C.S.: 541612

Korn Ferry (AU) Pty. Ltd. (1)
Level 18 Aurora Place 88 Phillip Street, Sydney, 2000, NSW, Australia   (100%)
Tel.: (61) 290063400
Web Site: https://www.kornferry.com
Executive Search Service
N.A.I.C.S.: 541612

Branch (Domestic):

Korn Ferry (AU) Pty. Ltd. - Melbourne (2)
Level 20 120 Collins Street, Melbourne, 3000, VIC, Australia
Tel.: (61) 396310300
Web Site: http://www.kornferry.com
Executive Search Service
N.A.I.C.S.: 541612
Katie Lahey *(Mng Dir)*
Cassy Schulz *(Principal)*
Colin Couzin-Wood *(Dir-Assessment & Succession-ANZ)*
Stephanie Edwards *(Mng Dir-ANZ Solutions RPO & Projects)*
Tim Nelson *(Mng Dir)*
Cyrus Cavina *(Partner)*
Emily Voigt *(Principal)*
Lan Qiu *(Sr Principal)*
Louise Hogan *(Sr Partner)*
May Tang *(Principal)*
Mithran Doraisamy *(Sr Partner)*
Therese Doupe *(Sr Partner)*
Trevor Warden *(Sr Partner)*

Korn Ferry (BE) BVBA (1)
Rue aux Laines 70, 1000, Brussels, Belgium   (100%)
Tel.: (32) 23323304
Human Resource Management Services
N.A.I.C.S.: 541612

Korn Ferry (BR) Consultores Ltda. (1)
    (100%)
Tel.: (55) 1121142222
Web Site: https://www.kornferry.com
Executive Search Service
N.A.I.C.S.: 541612

Branch (Domestic):

Korn Ferry (BR) Consultores Ltda. - Rio de Janeiro (2)
Avenida Rio Branco 311 Sala 303, Edificio Brasilia Centro 20040-903, Rio de Janeiro, 22250-040, Brazil
Tel.: (55) 21 2588 8279
Web Site: http://www.kornferry.com

Executive Search, Leadership & Talent Consulting, Leadership Consultant, Coaching, Talent Management & Executive Recruiting Services
N.A.I.C.S.: 541612

Korn Ferry (CA) Ltd. (1)
Brookfield Place Bay Wellington Tower, Box 763, 181 Bay Street Suite 3810, Toronto, M5J 2T3, ON, Canada (100%)
Tel.: (416) 365-1841
Web Site: http://www.kornferry.com
Executive Search & Consulting Services
N.A.I.C.S.: 541612

Branch (Domestic):

Korn Ferry (CA) Ltd. - Calgary (2)
Home Oil Tower Suite 1550 324-8th Ave SW, Calgary, T2P 2Z2, AB, Canada
Tel.: (403) 269-3277
Web Site: http://www.kornferry.com
Executive Search Service
N.A.I.C.S.: 541612
Robert Sutton (Sr Partner-Client)
Kevin Libin (Mng Partner)
T. J. van Schalkwyk (Assoc Partner-Client)

Korn Ferry (CA) Ltd. - Vancouver (2)
1021 West Hastings Street Suite 3000, PO Box 49206, Vancouver, V6E 0C3, BC, Canada
Tel.: (604) 684-1834
Web Site: http://www.kornferry.com
Executive Search Service
N.A.I.C.S.: 541612

Subsidiary (Domestic):

TwentyEighty Strategy Execution, Inc. (2)
36 King Street East 4th Floor, Toronto, M5C 3B2, ON, Canada
Tel.: (905) 963-0645
Educational Support Services
N.A.I.C.S.: 611710
Art White (Sr Dir-Bus Dev)

Korn Ferry (DE) GmbH (1)
Barckhausstrasse 12-14, 60325, Frankfurt, Germany (100%)
Tel.: (49) 69716700
Web Site: https://www.kornferry.com
Executive Search Service
N.A.I.C.S.: 541612
Oliver Dange (Sr Partner-Client)
Alexander Wink (Sr Partner-Client & Head-Digital Speciality Practice)
Holger Winzer (Assoc Partner-Client)
Thomas Piecha (Principal)
Birgit Korf (Sr Principal)
Carsten Kroehl (Sr Partner)
Christian Rodermund (Sr Partner)
Christiane Sauer (Sr Partner)
Dominik Dreyer (Sr Partner)
Gilbert Plugowski (Principal)
Holger Jahn (Sr Partner)
Magdalena Daberkow (Principal)
Mathias Kesting (Sr Partner)
Sassan Yussefi (Sr Partner)
Steffen Graff (Sr Partner)
Stephan Frettlohr (Sr Partner)
Thomas Faltin (Sr Principal)
Torsten Holstad (Sr Principal)
Ulrike Simon (Sr Partner)

Subsidiary (Domestic):

TwentyEighty Strategy Execution (Germany) GmbH (2)
Prinzenallee 3, 40549, Dusseldorf, Germany
Tel.: (49) 692443273795
Web Site: http://www.strategyex.de
Educational Support Services
N.A.I.C.S.: 611710

Korn Ferry (DK) A/S (1)
Kongens Nytorv 8 4 Floor, 1050, Copenhagen, Denmark
Tel.: (45) 33288500
Web Site: http://www.kornferry.com
Executive Search & Global Recruitment Services
N.A.I.C.S.: 541612

Korn Ferry (FR) SARL (1)
12-14 Rond-point des Champs Elysees, 75008, Paris, France
Tel.: (33) 178407300

Web Site: http://www.kornferry.com
Executive Search Service
N.A.I.C.S.: 541612
Paul Navratil (Sr Partner-Client-Energy & Natural Resources Industry)
Alice Risetti (Assoc Partner-Client)
Anne-Flavie Abbott (Principal)
Caroline Chantereau (Principal)
Francois Godin (Head-Industry & HR)
Noemie Lefort (Principal)
Olivier Chanal (Principal)

Korn Ferry (HK) Limited (1)
15/FSt George's Building 2 Ice House Street, Central, China (Hong Kong) (100%)
Tel.: (852) 29712700
Web Site: https://www.kornferry.com
Executive Search Service
N.A.I.C.S.: 541612
Andrew Tsui (Chm)
Tim Wiseman (Assoc Partner-Client)

Subsidiary (Domestic):

Korn Ferry RPOPS (Hong Kong) Ltd. (2)
15/F St George's Building 2 Ice House Street, Central, China (Hong Kong)
Tel.: (852) 29712700
Web Site: http://www.kornferry.com
Executive Search & Global Recruitment Services
N.A.I.C.S.: 541612
Andrew Tsui (Chm)
Harriet Holbrook-Lui (Principal)
Lam Hang Ching (Assoc Partner-Client)
Merissa Yeow (Dir-Global Client Solutions)
Tim Wiseman (Assoc Partner-Client)

Korn Ferry (IT) S.R.L. (1)
Via Broletto 35, 20121, Milan, Italy (100%)
Tel.: (39) 02806001
Web Site: https://www.kornferry.com
Executive Search Service
N.A.I.C.S.: 541612
Giuseppina Gentili (Principal)
Michele Annovazzi (Assoc Partner-Client)

Branch (Domestic):

Korn Ferry (IT) S.R.L. - Rome (2)
Via Leonida Bissolati 54, 00187, Rome, Italy
Tel.: (39) 02 77166 10
Web Site: http://www.kornferry.com
Executive Search Service
N.A.I.C.S.: 541612

Korn Ferry (Japan) Ltd. (1)
Marunouchi Trust Tower N14F 1-8-1 Marunouchi, Chiyoda-ku, Tokyo, 100-0005, Japan
Tel.: (81) 362673333
Web Site: https://ww.kornferry.com
Executive Search Service
N.A.I.C.S.: 541612

Korn Ferry (Luxembourg) S.a.r.l. (1)
19 Cote D Eich, L 1450, Luxembourg, Luxembourg
Tel.: (352) 4643421
Web Site: http://www.kornferry.com
Sales Range: $1-9.9 Million
Emp.: 6
Executive Search Service
N.A.I.C.S.: 541612

Korn Ferry (NL) B.V. (1)
Piet Hein Buildings Piet Heinkade 93, 1019 GM, Amsterdam, Netherlands
Tel.: (31) 207999000
Executive Search & Human Resource Consultancy Services
N.A.I.C.S.: 541612
Eric Engesaeth (Sr Partner-Client & Head-Executive Pay & Governance-Netherlands)

Korn Ferry (NZ) (1)
Tel.: (64) 99215900
Web Site: https://www.kornferry.com
Executive Search & Global Recruitment Services
N.A.I.C.S.: 541612

Korn Ferry (PL) Sp. z o.o. (1)
ul J Hoene-Wronskiego 7, 00-434, Warsaw, Poland (100%)
Tel.: (48) 226222829
Executive Search Service

N.A.I.C.S.: 541612
Krzysztof Nowakowski (Mng Dir-Warsaw-Fin)

Korn Ferry (SG) Pte. Ltd. (1)
3 Temasek Avenue Centennial Tower 12-01, Singapore, 039190, Singapore (100%)
Tel.: (65) 62243111
Executive Search Service
N.A.I.C.S.: 541612
Jasbir Singh (Principal)
Zann Lee (Principal)
Alvin T. J. Ng (Principal)
Andrew Yap (Sr Principal)
Casey Kelly (Sr Partner)
Chandana Shukla (Sr Partner)
Daniel Cheng (Vice Chm)
Elektra Mararian (Sr Partner)
Eugene Chang (Sr Partner)
Gareth McIlroy (Reg Mng Dir)
Handan Aribas Toker (Sr Principal)
John Stewart (Sr Partner)
Jonathan Zhu (Mng Partner)
Karen Chiew (Sr Principal)
Kartikey Singh (Sr Partner)
Lee Yen Chin (Assoc Partner)
Manisha Dahiya (Principal)
Melvin Lee (Principal)
Michael Di Cicco (Sr Partner)
Mike Ferns (Sr Principal)
Natalie Chan (Sr Principal)
Pip Eastman (Mng Dir)
Rajen Makhijani (Assoc Partner)
Robert Cho (Sr Partner)
Scott Hensarling (Sr Partner)
Seiyi Goh (Sr Partner)
Shirley Costa (Sr VP)
Steve Stine (Sr Partner)
Tamara Sigerhall (Principal)
Vanessa San (Principal)

Subsidiary (Domestic):

Korn Ferry RPOPS (SG) Pte. Ltd. (2)
3 Temasek Avenue Centennial Tower 09-01, Singapore, 039190, Singapore
Tel.: (65) 62243111
Web Site: http://www.futurestep.com
Executive Search & Global Recruitment Services
N.A.I.C.S.: 541612

Korn Ferry (SK) s.r.o. (1)
Lakeside Park Phase 1 Tomisikova 64, 831 04, Bratislava, Slovakia
Tel.: (421) 249114901
Educational Support Services
N.A.I.C.S.: 611710

Korn Ferry (Schweiz) GmbH (1)
Prime Tower Hardstrasse 201, 8005, Zurich, Switzerland (100%)
Tel.: (41) 433667788
Web Site: https://www.kornferry.com
Executive Search & Global Recruitment Services
N.A.I.C.S.: 541612

Korn Ferry (Sweden) AB (1)
Tel.: (46) 86115015
Management Consulting Services
N.A.I.C.S.: 561312
David Stromwall (Mng Dir)
Charlotte Wetterlundh (Principal)

Korn Ferry (US) (1)
33 S 6th St Ste 4900, Minneapolis, MN 55402
Tel.: (612) 339-0927
Executive Search & Recruitment Services & Leadership Development Products & Services
N.A.I.C.S.: 541612
Carol Skube (Principal)
R. J. Heckman (Vice Chm)
Tanya Just (Principal)
RJ Heckman (Vice Chm)
Anna Waters (Sr Principal)
Ashley Bowes Johnson (Principal)
Barbara Lubinski (Principal)
Dave Cotter (Principal)
Dee Gaeddert (Sr Partner)
Dina Rauker (Sr Partner)

Subsidiary (Domestic):

Korn Ferry Leadership Consulting Corporation (2)

33 S 6th St Ste 4900, Minneapolis, MN 55402
Tel.: (612) 339-0927
Executive Placement Services
N.A.I.C.S.: 561312

Pivot Learning, LLC (2)
500 12th St Ste 350, Oakland, CA 94607
Tel.: (510) 250-2543
Web Site: http://www.pivotlearning.org
Education Reform
N.A.I.C.S.: 611710
Arun Ramanathan (CEO)
Allison Carter (VP-Curriculum Adoption & Implementation)
Johannah Kaplan (Chief Talent & Culture Officer)
Nadya Chinoy Dabby (Chief Growth Officer)
Arielle Davies (Dir-Product Dev)
Nicodemus Ford (Sr Program Mgr)
Amy Fourrier (Program Mgr)
Sophie Green (Sr Program Mgr-Dev & External Rels)
Leah Guevara (Sr Program Mgr-District & School Partnerships)
Erick Harrison (Mgr-IT)
Joyce Highhouse (Sr Dir-Education Programs)
Maryia Krivoruchko (Program Mgr-Curriculum Adoption & Implementation)
Jamahr McDaniel (Dir-Curriculum Adoption & Implementation)
Hannah Melnicoe (Sr Program Mgr)
Monica Ng (VP-Education Programs)
Jignasha Pandya (Sr Program Mgr-Curriculum Adoption & Implementation)
Randy Westbrook (Accountant)

Subsidiary (Domestic):

Consortium on Reaching Excellence in Education, Inc. (3)
1300 Clay tS Ste 600, Oakland, CA 94612
Tel.: (888) 249-6155
Web Site: http://www.corelearn.com
Educational Support Services
N.A.I.C.S.: 611710

Subsidiary (Domestic):

Sensa Solutions, Inc. (2)
2000 Corporate Ridge Ste 1095, McLean, VA 22102
Tel.: (703) 547-0500
Web Site: http://www.sensasolutions.com
Sales Range: $25-49.9 Million
Emp.: 50
Administrative Management & Consulting Services
N.A.I.C.S.: 541611

Korn Ferry A/S (1)
Vika Atrium Munkedamsveien 45, N-0250, Oslo, Norway (100%)
Tel.: (47) 22823900
Web Site: https://www.kornferry.com
Executive Search Service
N.A.I.C.S.: 541612

Korn Ferry CR S.R.L. (1)
Ruta 27 Avenida Escazu Edificio 101 6to piso Torre Lexus, 1560-100, San Jose, Costa Rica
Tel.: (506) 22956630
Educational Support Services
N.A.I.C.S.: 611710

Korn Ferry Futurestep (The Philippines) Inc. (1)
12F units 1-3 Arthaland Century Pacific Tower 5th Ave cor 30th Street, Taguig, 1634, Manila, Philippines
Tel.: (63) 28807900
Educational Support Services
N.A.I.C.S.: 611710

Korn Ferry International S.A. (1)
Avenida del Libertador 498 Piso 7N, Ciudad Autonoma de Buenos Aires, C1001, Buenos Aires, Argentina (100%)
Tel.: (54) 1141140000
Web Site: http://www.kornferry.com
Executive Search Service
N.A.I.C.S.: 541612

Korn Ferry International S.A. (1)
Alcala 44 2nd Fl B, 28014, Madrid, Spain
Tel.: (34) 917014380
Web Site: http://www.kornferry.com

Korn Ferry—(Continued)

Sales Range: $10-24.9 Million
Emp.: 15
Executive Recruitment & Leadership Development Programs
N.A.I.C.S.: 541612
Dominique Virchaux (Pres-South America)
Barbara Ramos (Sr Partner-Client)
Julio Moreno (Sr Partner)
Ivan Oterino (Mng Dir & Sr Partner-Client)
Loreto Gonzalez (Sr Partner-Client)

Subsidiary (Domestic):

Futurestep (Espana), S.L.   (2)
c/Alcala 44 - 2B, Madrid, 28014, Spain
Tel.: (34) 917453205
Sales Range: $25-49.9 Million
Emp.: 5
Executive Search & Global Recruitment
Services
N.A.I.C.S.: 541612

Branch (Domestic):

Korn/Ferry International S.A.   (2)
Plaza Europa 21-23 9a Planta Hospitalet de
Llobregat, Barcelona, 28046, Spain
Tel.: (34) 932092744
Web Site: http://www.kornferry.com
Executive Search, Leadership & Talent
Consulting Services
N.A.I.C.S.: 561312

Korn Ferry International S.A.   (1)
Av Apoquindo 3885 Piso 13, Las Condes,
Santiago, Chile   (100%)
Tel.: (56) 2 2387 8200
Web Site: http://www.kornferry.com
Executive Search Service
N.A.I.C.S.: 541612

Subsidiary (Domestic):

Hay Group Limitada   (2)
Calle Enrique Foster Sur 20 Piso 8 801,
Las Condes, Santiago, Chile
Tel.: (56) 223213000
Management Consulting Services
N.A.I.C.S.: 541611

Korn Ferry LLC   (1)
4 Mytropolyta Andrea Sheptytskogo Str
Floor 14, 2002, Kiev, Ukraine
Tel.: (380) 444997101
Management Consulting Services
N.A.I.C.S.: 561312

Korn Ferry Limited   (1)
22 - 24 Lower Mount Street Newmount
House, Dublin, Ireland
Tel.: (353) 12344300
Organization Development Consulting Services
N.A.I.C.S.: 541612

Korn Ferry RPO (Sweden) AB   (1)
Norrlandsgatan 18, 111 43, Stockholm,
Sweden
Tel.: (46) 86115015
Recruitment Process Outsourcing Services
N.A.I.C.S.: 561311

**Korn Ferry Recruitment (Thailand)
Ltd.**   (1)
1 South Sathorn Road 18th Floor Unit 3 Q
House Lumpini Thung, Mahamek, Bangkok,
10120, Thailand
Tel.: (66) 26777515
Management Consulting Services
N.A.I.C.S.: 561312
Mana Lohatepanont (Mng Dir)

Korn Ferry S.A.   (1)
Edificio Atlantis Av D Joao II 44C Piso 7 1 e
7 2, 1990-095, Lisbon, Portugal
Tel.: (351) 213152170
Organization Development Consulting Services
N.A.I.C.S.: 541612

Korn Ferry SP LLC   (1)
4000 Ponce De Leon Blvd Ste 410, Coral
Gables, FL 33146
Tel.: (305) 377-4121
Management Consulting Services
N.A.I.C.S.: 541612

Korn Ferry s.r.o.   (1)
City Tower Hvezdova 1716/2b, Nusle, 140

00, Prague, Czech Republic
Tel.: (420) 222753430
Human Resource Consulting Services
N.A.I.C.S.: 541612
Gabriela Nemcova (Sr Mgr-Client Relationship)

**Korn/Ferry (Shanghai) Human Capital
Consulting Co., Ltd.**   (1)
21/F Link Square 1 222 Hubin Road,
Huangpu District, Shanghai, 200021, China
Tel.: (86) 2123068500
Executive Search & Global Recruitment
Services
N.A.I.C.S.: 541612
Bill Gu (Head-Office)

Korn/Ferry (Thailand) Limited   (1)
1 South Sathorn Road 18th floor Unit 3 Q
House Lumpini, Thung Mahamek, Bangkok,
10120, Thailand
Tel.: (66) 26777515
Web Site: http://www.kornferry.com
Sales Range: $1-9.9 Million
Emp.: 3
Executive Search Service
N.A.I.C.S.: 541612
Mana Lohatepanont (Mng Dir)

**Korn/Ferry International (Korea)
Limited**   (1)
11th Fl Young-Poong Bldg 41
Cheonggyecheon-ro, Jongno-gu, Seoul,
3188, Korea (South)   (100%)
Tel.: (82) 220036700
Executive Search Service
N.A.I.C.S.: 541612
Eun-Joo Chae (Mng Dir)
Harry Chung (Gen Mgr-Advisory)

**Korn/Ferry International (Taiwan) Co.
Limited**   (1)
Room D-1 27F Taipei 101 Building No 7
Xin-Yi Road Sec 5, Taipei, 110, Taiwan
Tel.: (886) 287221600
Web Site: http://www.kornferry.com
Sales Range: $25-49.9 Million
Emp.: 7
Executive Search & Global Recruitment
Services
N.A.I.C.S.: 541612
Peter Yuan (Mng Dir)

**Korn/Ferry International -
Colombia**   (1)
Avenida Carrera 7 #113-43 Oficina 902,
Samsung Tower PH Cudinamarca, Bogota,
Colombia   (100%)
Tel.: (57) 1 313 1400
Web Site: http://www.kornferry.com
Executive Search Service
N.A.I.C.S.: 541612

Korn/Ferry International AB   (1)
Sveavagen 20, 11120, Stockholm,
Sweden   (100%)
Tel.: (46) 86115015
Web Site: http://www.kornferry.com
Executive Search Service
N.A.I.C.S.: 541612
Marcus Pokorny (Principal)

Branch (Domestic):

**Korn/Ferry International AB -
Gothenburg**   (2)
Rosenlundsgatan 3, 411 20, Gothenburg,
Sweden
Tel.: (46) 317402020
Web Site: http://www.kornferry.com
Executive Search Service
N.A.I.C.S.: 541612

Subsidiary (Domestic):

**Personnel Decisions International
Scandinavia A.B.**   (2)
Vasagatan 36, Stockholm, 111 20, Sweden
Tel.: (46) 86115015
Executive Placement Services
N.A.I.C.S.: 561312

**Korn/Ferry International Budapest
Individual Consulting & Service
Ltd.**   (1)
Bimbo Ut 77, 1022, Budapest,
Hungary   (100%)
Tel.: (36) 13460600
Web Site: http://www.kornferry.com

Executive Search Service
N.A.I.C.S.: 541612
Vilmos Szabo (Mng Dir)

**Korn/Ferry International Consultores
Asociados, C.A.**   (1)
Edificio Parque Cristal Torre Este Piso 8
Oficina 8-12, Los Palos Grandes Apartado,
Caracas, 1060, Venezuela   (100%)
Tel.: (58) 2122850067
Web Site: http://www.kornferry.com
Executive Search Service
N.A.I.C.S.: 541612

Korn/Ferry International Limited   (1)
Ryder Court 14 Ryder St, London, SW1Y
6QB, United Kingdom   (100%)
Tel.: (44) 2070249000
Web Site: https://www.kornferry.com
Executive Search Service
N.A.I.C.S.: 541612
Lesley Uren (Sr Partner-Client)
Suzannah Conway (Assoc Partner-Client)

Subsidiary (Domestic):

AchieveForum (UK) Limited   (2)
7-11 Bishopsgate, London, EC2N 3AR,
United Kingdom
Tel.: (44) 2037432950
Educational Support Services
N.A.I.C.S.: 611710

Futurestep (UK) Limited   (2)
Ryder Court 14 Ryder St, London, SW1Y
6QB, United Kingdom
Tel.: (44) 2070249000
Web Site: http://futurestep.co.uk
Emp.: 50
Executive Search & Global Recruitment
Services
N.A.I.C.S.: 541612
Jonathan Brown (Mng Dir-Solutions-
RPO,Projects & Consulting Svcs-EMEA)

**TwentyEighty Strategy Execution
(UK) Ltd.**   (2)
2nd Floor, 7 Bishopsgate, London, EC2N
3AR, United Kingdom
Tel.: (44) 2037432910
Web Site: http://www.strategyex.co.uk
Educational Support Services
N.A.I.C.S.: 611710
Matthew Ansbro (Chief Comml Officer)

**Korn/Ferry International Musavirlik
Limited Sirketi**   (1)
191 Buysukcaddesecad, 34330, Istanbul,
Turkiye
Tel.: (90) 2122313949
Web Site: http://www.kornferry.com
Sales Range: $10-24.9 Million
Emp.: 12
Executive Search Service
N.A.I.C.S.: 541612

Korn/Ferry International Oy   (1)
Urho Kekkosen katu 3 B 8th floor, 00100,
Helsinki, Finland   (100%)
Tel.: (358) 941336626
Web Site: http://www.kornferry.com
Sales Range: $1-9.9 Million
Emp.: 5
Executive Search Service
N.A.I.C.S.: 541612
Johan Blomqvist (Gen Mgr)
Juhani Ruuskanen (Assoc Partner-Client)

Subsidiary (Domestic):

Hay Group Oy   (2)
Urho Kekkosen katu 3 B 8th floor, 00100,
Helsinki, Finland
Tel.: (358) 941336626
Human Resource Consulting Services
N.A.I.C.S.: 541612

**Korn/Ferry International Private
Limited**   (1)
Two Horizon Center 2nd Floor Golf Course
Road, DLF Phase V, Gurgaon, 122002,
Haryana, India   (100%)
Tel.: (91) 1244321000
Executive Search Service
N.A.I.C.S.: 541612
Madhav Sharan (Mng Dir-New Delhi)
Navnit Singh (Mng Dir-India)
Rajiv Krishnan (Mng Dir-Korn Ferry Hay
Grp)
Sharad Vishvanath (Head-Transformation &
Transaction Merger & Acq Practice)

Subsidiary (Domestic):

Futurestep Recruitment Services Private Ltd.   (2)
1st Floor Prestige Nebula-II, Infantry Road,
Bengaluru, 560-001, Karnataka, India
Tel.: (91) 8040198282
Web Site: http://www.kornferryasia.com
Emp.: 35
Executive Search & Global Recruitment
Services
N.A.I.C.S.: 541612

Korn/Ferry International S.A.   (1)
                                               (100%)
Tel.: (30) 2107228000
Web Site: https://www.kornferry.com
Executive Search Service
N.A.I.C.S.: 541612

Subsidiary (Domestic):

Hay Group S.A.   (2)
27 Vas Sofias Avenue, 106 74, Athens,
Greece
Tel.: (30) 2107228000
Human Resource Consulting Services
N.A.I.C.S.: 541612

**Korn/Ferry International S.A. de
C.V.**   (1)
Montes Urales 505 3rd Floor Lomas de
Chapultepec, Del Miguel Hidalgo, 11000,
Mexico, Mexico   (100%)
Tel.: (52) 5550959500
Web Site: http://www.kornferry.com
Sales Range: $10-24.9 Million
Emp.: 40
Executive Search Service
N.A.I.C.S.: 541612

Subsidiary (Domestic):

**Korn/Ferry International Belnorde
S.A. de C.V.**   (2)
Padre Mier 1675 Pte Col Obispado, Monterrey, 64060, Nuevo Leon, Mexico   (100%)
Tel.: (52) 8182205959
Web Site: http://www.kornferry.com
Sales Range: $500-549.9 Million
Emp.: 1,894
Executive Search Service
N.A.I.C.S.: 541612

Korn/Ferry International-Peru Sociedad Anonima   (1)
Av Santo Toribio 173 Via Central 125 Edificio Real Ocho Oficina 1202, San Isidro,
Lima, 27, Peru   (100%)
Tel.: (51) 1 7000 600
Web Site: http://www.kornferry.com
Executive Search Service
N.A.I.C.S.: 541612

Miller Heiman Group, Inc.   (1)
10901 W Toller Dr Ste 203, Littleton, CO
80127
Tel.: (877) 678-3380
Web Site:
    http://www.millerheimangroup.com
Sales Performance Consulting Services
N.A.I.C.S.: 541613
Martin Sparkes (Mng Dir-ANZ)
Tom Werle (Chief Strategy Officer)

Subsidiary (Domestic):

AchieveGlobal Inc.   (2)
8875 Hidden River Pkwy Ste 400, Tampa,
FL 33637
Tel.: (813) 631-5799
Web Site: http://www.achieveglobal.com
Sales Range: $350-399.9 Million
Emp.: 1,600
Training & Consulting Services
N.A.I.C.S.: 541618

Subsidiary (Non-US):

Miller Heiman Europe GmbH   (2)
Fleurystrasse 7, Amberg, 92224, Germany
Tel.: (49) 9621 91770 0
Web Site:
    http://www.millerheimangroup.com
Emp.: 10
Sales Performance Consulting Services
N.A.I.C.S.: 541613

Subsidiary (Non-US):

**Miller Heiman Group (UK)
Limited**   (3)

Ryder Court 14 Ryder St, London, SW1Y 6QB, United Kingdom
Tel.: (44) 2070249000
Web Site:
http://www.millerheimangroup.com
Emp.: 300
Sales Performance Consulting Services
N.A.I.C.S.: 541613

Subsidiary (Non-US):

Miller Heiman Group (Asia) Pte. Ltd.   (2)
3 Temasek Avenue Centennial Tower 10-01, Singapore, 391901, Singapore
Tel.: (65) 62316159
Educational Support Services
N.A.I.C.S.: 611710
Yvonne Fock (Mgr-Customer Success)

OOO Hay Group   (1)
17-23 Taganskaya St Block C 5th Floor, Moscow, 109147, Russia
Tel.: (7) 4953636630
Organization Development Consulting Services
N.A.I.C.S.: 541612

PT Korn/Ferry International   (1)
DBS Bank Tower 25th Floor Suite 2501 Ciputra World 1, Jl Prof Dr Satrio Kav 3-5, Jakarta, 12940, Indonesia   (100%)
Tel.: (62) 2180861800
Sales Range: $1-9.9 Million
Emp.: 60
Executive Search Service
N.A.I.C.S.: 541612

Patina Solutions Group Inc.   (1)
13890 Bishops Dr Ste 320, Brookfield, WI 53005
Tel.: (262) 797-5700
Web Site: http://www.patinasolutions.com
Sales Range: $25-49.9 Million
Emp.: 75
Employment Services
N.A.I.C.S.: 561311
Mike Harris (CEO)
Debbie Seeger (Founder & Sr VP)
Michael Jalbert (Mng Dir)
Barbara Haith (Mng Dir)
Jodi Brendel (Mng Partner)
Sharon Aho (Mng Dir)
Bob Carlson (Pres & COO)
Kate McLellan (Mng Partner)

Division (Domestic):

Patina Solutions Group Inc.   (2)
253 Summer St 3rd Fl, Boston, MA 02210
Tel.: (617) 933-0900
Web Site: http://www.patinasolutions.com
Emp.: 17
Employment Services
N.A.I.C.S.: 561311
Kate McLellan (Mng Partner)

Patina Solutions Group Inc.   (2)
1016 W Jackson Blvd, Chicago, IL 60607
Tel.: (312) 447-0900
Employment Services
N.A.I.C.S.: 561311

Patina Solutions Group Inc.   (2)
2001 Crocker Rd Ste 510, Cleveland, OH 44145
Tel.: (440) 925-2810
Employment Services
N.A.I.C.S.: 561311

Patina Solutions Group Inc.   (2)
4200 Regent St Ste 200, Columbus, OH 43219
Tel.: (614) 944-5202
Emp.: 3
Employment Services
N.A.I.C.S.: 561311
Shawn McGrath (Mng Dir)

Patina Solutions Group Inc.   (2)
14 W Mifflin St Ste 300, Madison, WI 53703
Tel.: (608) 233-3377
Employment Services
N.A.I.C.S.: 561311

Patina Solutions Group Inc.   (2)
1270 Northland Dr, Mendota Heights, MN 55120
Tel.: (651) 688-7300
Employment Services
N.A.I.C.S.: 561311

Jodi Brendel (Mng Partner)

Patina Solutions Group Inc.   (2)
4511 N Himes Ave Ste 200, Tampa, FL 33614
Tel.: (813) 449-4339
Employment Services
N.A.I.C.S.: 561311

Salo, LLC   (1)
20 S 13th St Ste 200, Minneapolis, MN 55403
Tel.: (612) 230-7256
Web Site: http://www.salollc.com
Accounting & Finance Services
N.A.I.C.S.: 541219
John Folkestad (Co-Founder)
Amy Langer (Co-Founder)
Katie Brothers (Sr Dir-Bus Dev, Fin & Acctg-Minneapolis)
Elisabeth Kraft Dittmann (Dir-Bus Dev)
Lois Depiesse (Dir-Bus Dev)
Erica Eggers (Dir-Bus Dev)
Jessica Lukensow (Dir-Bus Dev)
Cory Johnson (Dir-Bus Dev)
Nicole Reid (Dir-Bus Dev)
Sheryl Caspers (Dir-Bus Dev)
Matt Berra (Dir-Bus Dev-Chicago)
Nick Stokes (Dir-Bus Dev)
Angie Holsen (Principal)
Seema Malveaux (Sr Principal-Fin & Acctg-Chicago)
Russ Testa (Chief Talent Officer)
Jon Cermak (Mgr-Talent Connection)
Ryan Jeffery (Dir-Bus Dev)
Jessica Schmidt (Coord-Bus Dev)
Marie Petrangelo (Coord-Bus Dev)
Susan Smith (Mgr-Total Rewards)
Nick Gust (Sr Mng Dir-Bus Dev Strategy)
Dave Rust (CFO)
Loralee Wick (Mng Dir-Fin)
Danielle Ringwelski (Dir-Bus Dev-HR)
Anne Loughery (Dir-Bus Dev-Fin)
Nick Marvin (Dir-Bus Dev-Chicago)
Jeff Donnay (Gen Mgr)

Shanghai Korn/Ferry Human Capital Consulting Co., Ltd.   (1)
21/F Link Square 1 222 Hubin Road, Huangpu District, Shanghai, 200021, China
Tel.: (86) 2123068500
Web Site: http://www.kornferry.com
Business Consulting Services
N.A.I.C.S.: 541611
Bill Gu (Dir)
Claudia Wu (Sr Partner)
Frank Xu (Assoc Partner)
Henry Sheng (Sr Partner)
Joanne Yu (Sr Partner)

WOFE Korn/Ferry International Human Capital Consulting (Beijing) Limited   (1)
41/F Fortune Financial Center 5 Dong San Huan Central Road, Chaoyang District, Beijing, 100020, China   (100%)
Tel.: (86) 1058163100
Web Site: http://www.kornferry.com
Executive Search & Global Recruitment Services
N.A.I.C.S.: 541612
Bill Gu (Mng Dir-Shanghai)

KORU MEDICAL SYSTEMS, INC.
100 Corporate Dr, Mahwah, NJ 07430
Tel.: (845) 469-2042   NY
Web Site:
https://www.korumedical.com
Year Founded: 1980
KRMD—(NASDAQ)
Rev.: $27,896,037
Assets: $42,332,443
Liabilities: $11,006,480
Net Worth: $31,325,963
Earnings: ($8,661,142)
Emp.: 85
Fiscal Year-end: 12/31/22
Surgical & Medical Instrument Manufacturing
N.A.I.C.S.: 339112
Thomas Adams (CFO)
Linda M. Tharby (Pres & CEO)

KORVER CORP.

1660 S Highway 100 Ste 500, Saint Louis Park, MN 55416
Tel.: (612) 287-5842
KOVR—(OTCIQ)
Medical Cannabis Product Mfr
N.A.I.C.S.: 325411
Sang-Ho Kim (CEO)

KOSMOS ENERGY LTD.
8176 Park Ln Ste 500, Dallas, TX 75231
Tel.: (214) 445-9600   BM
Web Site:
https://www.kosmosenergy.com
Year Founded: 2003
KOS—(NYSE)
Rev.: $2,299,775,000
Assets: $4,579,988,000
Liabilities: $3,792,140,000
Net Worth: $787,848,000
Earnings: $226,551,000
Emp.: 236
Fiscal Year-end: 12/31/22
Crude Petroleum Extraction Services
N.A.I.C.S.: 211120
Christopher James Ball (Chief Comml Officer & Sr VP)
Neal D. Shah (CFO & Sr VP)
Paul Tooms (Sr VP-Technical Functions)
Joe Mensah (Sr VP & Head-Ghana Bus Unit)
Ronald Glass (Chief Acctg Officer & VP)
Todd Neibregge (Sr VP & Head--Senegal Bus Unit)
Mike Anderson (Sr VP)
Tim Nicholson (Sr VP)
Andrew G. Inglis (Chm & CEO)

Subsidiaries:

Hess Equatorial Guinea Inc.   (1)
Triton House Calle Acasio, Mane, Malabo, 90726, Equatorial Guinea
Tel.: (240) 24090728
Oil & Gas Exploration Services
N.A.I.C.S.: 213111

Kosmos Energy Ghana HC   (1)
D Anchor House 12 First Osu Badu Street, West Airport Res Area, Accra, Ghana
Tel.: (233) 302740888
Oil & Gas Exploration Services
N.A.I.C.S.: 211120

Kosmos Energy Offshore Morocco HC   (1)
BP 8172 Rabat Nations Unies, 10102, Rabat, Morocco
Tel.: (212) 537778628
Oil & Gas Exploration Services
N.A.I.C.S.: 211120

Kosmos Energy, LLC   (1)
8176 Park Ln Ste 500, Dallas, TX 75231
Tel.: (214) 445-9600
Web Site: http://www.kosmosenergy.com
Oil & Gas Exploration Services
N.A.I.C.S.: 211120
Andrew Inglis (CEO)

KOSS CORPORATION
4129 N Port Washington Ave, Milwaukee, WI 53212
Tel.: (414) 964-5000   DE
Web Site: https://www.koss.com
Year Founded: 1953
KOSS—(NASDAQ)
Rev.: $12,265,069
Assets: $37,199,479
Liabilities: $6,052,303
Net Worth: $31,147,176
Earnings: ($950,911)
Emp.: 28
Fiscal Year-end: 06/30/24
Stereo Headphones & Accessories Designer, Mfr & Retailer
N.A.I.C.S.: 334310
Michael J. Koss (Chm, Pres & CEO)
Kim M. Schulte (CFO & Sec)

Subsidiaries:

Koss Europe S.A.   (1)
Centro Commerciale, CH 6855, Stabio, Switzerland   (100%)
Tel.: (41) 916416120
Web Site: http://www.koss.com
Sales Range: $10-24.9 Million
Mfr of High Fidelity Stereophones, Computer Headsets, Telecommunication Headsets, Active Noise Cancelling Stereophones & Wireless Stereophones of American Orchestras
N.A.I.C.S.: 334310
Michael J. Koss (Chm, Pres, CEO & COO)

KRAIG BIOCRAFT LABORATORIES, INC.
2723 S State St Ste 150, Ann Arbor, MI 48104
Tel.: (734) 619-8066   WY
Web Site: https://www.kraiglabs.com
Year Founded: 2006
KBLB—(OTCQB)
Assets: $4,570,920
Liabilities: $8,092,780
Net Worth: ($3,521,860)
Earnings: ($3,842,014)
Emp.: 6
Fiscal Year-end: 12/31/22
Polymers & High Performance Fibers Developer & Researcher
N.A.I.C.S.: 541715
Kim K. Thompson (Founder, Pres, CEO & CFO)
Jonathan R. Rice (COO)

KRATOS DEFENSE & SECURITY SOLUTIONS, INC.
10680 Treena St 6th Fl, San Diego, CA 92131
Tel.: (858) 812-7300   DE
Web Site:
https://www.kratosdefense.com
Year Founded: 1994
KTOS—(NASDAQ)
Rev.: $1,037,100,000
Assets: $1,632,500,000
Liabilities: $656,500,000
Net Worth: $976,000,000)
Earnings: ($8,900,000)
Emp.: 3,900
Fiscal Year-end: 12/31/23
Holding Company; Military Command, Control, Communications, Weapon Systems, Intelligence, Surveillance & IT Products Mfr & Support Services
N.A.I.C.S.: 551112
Yonah Adelman (Pres-Microwave Electronics Div)
Phil Carrai (Pres-Space & Trng Cyber Div)
Steven S. Fendley (Pres-Unmanned Sys Div)
Eric M. DeMarco (Pres & CEO)
Deanna Hom Lund (CFO & Exec VP)
David Carter (Pres-Defense & Rocket Support Svcs Div)
Maria Cervantes de Burgreen (VP & Controller)
Stacey Rock (Pres-Turbine Tech Div)
Thomas Mills (Pres-C5ISR Systems Div)
Greg Caicedo (VP-Space Domain Awareness & Space Superiority)

Subsidiaries:

ASC Signal Division, Inc.   (1)
1120 Jupiter Rd Ste 102, Plano, TX 75074
Tel.: (214) 291-7654
Web Site: http://www.cpii.com
Enterprise & Consumer Antenna RF Electronic & Satellite Communication Application Services
N.A.I.C.S.: 517410

Subsidiary (Non-US):

ASC Signal Division - Manufacturing   (2)

Kratos Defense & Security Solutions, Inc.—(Continued)

606 Beech Street West, Whitby, L1N 7T8, ON, Canada
Tel.: (905) 665-4300
Web Site: http://www.cpii.com
Antenna & Transmission Line Mfr
N.A.I.C.S.: 334220
Jennifer Trainor *(VP-Ops)*

Ai Metrix, Inc. **(1)**
100 Shockoe Slip Fl 2, Richmond, VA 23219-4100
Tel.: (703) 254-2000
Management Consulting Services
N.A.I.C.S.: 541618

Avtec Systems, Inc. **(1)**
100 Innovation Pl, Lexington, SC 29072
Tel.: (803) 358-3601
Web Site: http://www.avtecinc.com
Management Consulting Services
N.A.I.C.S.: 541618

Carlsbad ISI, Inc. **(1)**
1630 Faraday Ave, Carlsbad, CA 92008
Tel.: (760) 929-6700
Web Site: http://www.interiorspecialists.com
Interior Design Services
N.A.I.C.S.: 541410

Composite Engineering, Inc. **(1)**
5381 Raley Blvd, Sacramento, CA 95838 **(100%)**
Tel.: (916) 991-1990
Web Site: http://www.compositeeng.com
Sales Range: $75-99.9 Million
Emp.: 400
Aerial Target Drone Systems & Composite Structures Designer & Mfr
N.A.I.C.S.: 336411

Consolidated Turbine Specialists Canada, LLP **(1)**
Hangar 7 - 5333 216th St, Langley, V2Y 2N3, BC, Canada
Tel.: (778) 294-8182
Aircraft Repair Services
N.A.I.C.S.: 488190

Consolidated Turbine Specialists, LLC **(1)**
24323 S 385th W Ave, Bristow, OK 74010
Tel.: (918) 367-9665
Web Site: https://ctsturbines.com
Aircraft Maintenance Services
N.A.I.C.S.: 488190
Johnny Bump Grant *(VP)*
Rich Kasabula *(Mgr)*
Jennifer Pitts *(Mgr-Customer Support)*
Thad Wages *(Mgr-Logistics)*
Johnny Johnson *(Production Mgr)*

DEI Services Corporation **(1)**
7213 Sandscove Ct Ste 1, Winter Park, FL 32792
Tel.: (407) 678-3388
Web Site: http://www.deicorp.net
Sales Range: $50-74.9 Million
Emp.: 300
Flight & Military Vehicle Simulator Mfr
N.A.I.C.S.: 611512

Defense Systems, Inc. **(1)**
8251 Greensboro Dr Ste 510, McLean, VA 22102
Tel.: (703) 876-5100
Web Site: http://www.defensesystems.com
Fiscal Year-end: 12/31/2006
Computer Related Services
N.A.I.C.S.: 541519

Digital Fusion Inc. **(1)**
5030 Bradford Dr NW Ste 210, Huntsville, AL 35805-1923
Tel.: (256) 327-0000
Sales Range: $25-49.9 Million
Emp.: 284
Computer Related Consulting Services
N.A.I.C.S.: 541511
Dave Carter *(Pres & COO)*

Diversified Security Solutions, Inc. **(1)**
17 Battery Pl Ste 701, New York, NY 10004
Tel.: (212) 240-9500
Web Site: http://www.dssinyc.com
Sales Range: $10-24.9 Million
Emp.: 6

Emergency Action Plan & Fire Safety Services
N.A.I.C.S.: 624230
Bruce DeBon *(Mng Dir)*

FTT Deutschland GmbH **(1)**
Ludwig-Witthoft-Strasse 14, 15745, Wildau, Germany
Tel.: (49) 3375497200
Web Site: https://www.fttgmbh.de
Engineering Consulting Services
N.A.I.C.S.: 541330
Brian Owen *(Acct Mgr)*

Florida Turbine Technologies Inc. **(1)**
1701 Military Trl Ste 110, Jupiter, FL 33458 **(80.1%)**
Tel.: (561) 427-6400
Web Site: http://www.fttjobs.com
Industrial Gas Turbine Design & Analysis
N.A.I.C.S.: 333611

General Microwave Corporation **(1)**
10680 Treena St 6th Fl, San Diego, CA 92131
Tel.: (516) 802-0900
Microwave Component Mfr
N.A.I.C.S.: 334419

Gichner Holdings, Inc. **(1)**
490 E Locust St, Dallastown, PA 17313
Tel.: (717) 244-7611
Web Site: http://www.gichner.us
Emp.: 350
Holding Company
N.A.I.C.S.: 551112

Gichner Systems Group Inc. **(1)**
490 E Locust St, Dallastown, PA 17313-1902 **(100%)**
Tel.: (717) 246-5453
Web Site: http://www.gichnersystemsgroup.com
Sales Range: $250-299.9 Million
Emp.: 500
Designer & Mfr of Tactical Shelters, Containers & Specialized Truck Bodies
N.A.I.C.S.: 332311
Bill Wilson *(CFO & Exec VP)*

Gichner Systems International, Inc. **(1)**
10680 Treena St 6th Fl, San Diego, CA 92131
Tel.: (717) 244-7611
Emp.: 3
Prefabricated Metal Building & Component Mfr
N.A.I.C.S.: 332311

HGS Holdings, Inc. **(1)**
11405 N Pennsylvania St, Carmel, IN 46032
Tel.: (317) 843-0186
Holding Company
N.A.I.C.S.: 551112

Haverstick Consulting, Inc. **(1)**
6270 Corporate Dr, Indianapolis, IN 46278
Tel.: (317) 218-1700
Computer Systems Integration Services; Computer Related Consulting Services
N.A.I.C.S.: 541512

Henry Bros. Electronics, Inc. **(1)**
1511 E Orangethorpe Ave Ste A, Fullerton, CA 92831
Tel.: (714) 525-4350
Computer System Design Services
N.A.I.C.S.: 541512

Henry Bros. Electronics, Inc. **(1)**
4710 E Elwood St, Phoenix, AZ 85040
Tel.: (480) 894-2826
Computer System Design Services
N.A.I.C.S.: 541512

Henry Bros. Electronics, Inc. **(1)**
1701 Pollitt Dr Ste 5, Fair Lawn, NJ 07410
Tel.: (201) 794-6500
Emp.: 205
Computer System Design Services
N.A.I.C.S.: 541512

Herley GMI Eyal Ltd. **(1)**
Pierre Koenig 20, PO BOX 53278, Talpiot Industrial Center, Jerusalem, 91531, Israel
Tel.: (972) 25689444
Emp.: 150
Microwave Component Mfr
N.A.I.C.S.: 334419

Integral Systems Europe Ltd. **(1)**
Unit 8 Queens Court North Third Avenue, Gateshead, NE11 0BU, Tyne & Wear, United Kingdom
Tel.: (44) 1914977760
Web Site: http://www.integ.uk.com
Satellite Telecommunication Services
N.A.I.C.S.: 517410

KPSS Government Solutions, Inc. **(1)**
251 Little Falls Dr, Wilmington, DE 19808
Tel.: (858) 812-7300
Weapon System Mfr
N.A.I.C.S.: 336419

Kratos Arabia, Ltd. **(1)**
The Business Gate Level 1 Building 7 Zone A Airport Road, PO Box 93597, Riyadh, 11683, Saudi Arabia
Tel.: (966) 112611403
Web Site: https://www.kratosarabia.com
National Security Services
N.A.I.C.S.: 928110

Kratos Communications Ltd. **(1)**
17 Princes Park Fourth Avenue, Gateshead, NE11 0LQ, Tyne & Wear, United Kingdom
Tel.: (44) 1914977760
Communication Service
N.A.I.C.S.: 517410

Kratos Defense & Rocket Support Services, Inc. **(1)**
4820 Eastgate Mall Ste 200, San Diego, CA 92121
Tel.: (858) 812-7300
Web Site: http://www.kratospss.com
Engineeering Services
N.A.I.C.S.: 541330

Kratos Defense Engineering Solutions, Inc. **(1)**
4457 Indian Head Hwy, Indian Head, MD 20640
Tel.: (301) 753-5737
Computer System Design Services
N.A.I.C.S.: 541512

Kratos Integral Systems Europe S.A.S. **(1)**
57 Rue Marco Polo, Labege, 31670, France
Tel.: (33) 899868244
Web Site: http://www.integeurope.com
Satellite Telecommunication Services
N.A.I.C.S.: 517410

Kratos Integral Systems International, Inc. **(1)**
5200 Philadelphia Way Ste G, Lanham, MD 20706
Tel.: (443) 539-5008
Web Site: http://www.kratosdefense.com
Satellite Telecommunication Services
N.A.I.C.S.: 517410

Kratos Mid-Atlantic, Inc. **(1)**
1100 First State Blvd, Newport, DE 19804
Tel.: (302) 992-7950
Web Site: http://www.kratosdefense.com
Sales Range: $25-49.9 Million
Emp.: 100
Security Training & Software Publisher
N.A.I.C.S.: 561612

Kratos Networks, Inc. **(1)**
10680 Treena St 6th Fl, San Diego, CA 92131
Tel.: (703) 254-2000
Web Site: http://www.kratosnetworks.com
Custom Computer Programming Services
N.A.I.C.S.: 541511

Kratos Norway AS **(1)**
Martin Linges Vei 25, 1364, Fornebu, Norway
Tel.: (47) 91770902
Communication Service
N.A.I.C.S.: 517410
Petter Amundsen *(Gen Mgr)*

Kratos Southwest, L.P. **(1)**
9203 Emmott Rd, Houston, TX 77040
Tel.: (713) 937-8506
Security Surveillance Installation Services
N.A.I.C.S.: 238210

Kratos Space & Missile Defense Systems, Inc. **(1)**

2409 Peppermill Dr Ste A, Glen Burnie, MD 21061
Tel.: (443) 572-0002
Weapon System Mfr
N.A.I.C.S.: 336419

Kratos Technology & Training Solutions, Inc. **(1)**
4820 Eastgate Mall Ste 200, San Diego, CA 92121
Tel.: (858) 715-5500
Web Site: http://www.kratostts.com
Custom Computer Programming Services
N.A.I.C.S.: 541511

Kratos Unmanned Systems Solutions, Inc. **(1)**
5381 Raley Blvd, Sacramento, CA 95838
Tel.: (916) 991-1990
Web Site: http://www.kratosusd.com
Custom Computer Programming Services
N.A.I.C.S.: 541511

Subsidiary (Domestic):

5-D Systems, Inc. **(2)**
1 Chisholm Trl Ste 3200, Round Rock, TX 78681
Tel.: (512) 238-9840
Web Site: https://www.5dsystems.com
Sales Range: $1-9.9 Million
Emp.: 25
Engineeering Services
N.A.I.C.S.: 541330
Steve Fendley *(Chm & Pres-Unnamed Sys Div)*
Kimberly Karnes *(Sr VP & VP-Bus Ops)*

Kratos-General Microwave Israel **(1)**
Pierre Koenig 20 Ground Floor, PO Box 53278, Jerusalem, 91531, Israel
Tel.: (972) 25689444
Web Site: http://www.kratosmed.com
Microwave Components, Assemblies & Sub-Systems Design & Mfr
N.A.I.C.S.: 334220

Kratos-Integral Systems, Inc. **(1)**
5200 Philadelphia Way Ste G, Lanham, MD 20706
Tel.: (703) 254-2000
Web Site: http://www.kratos-isi.com
Satellite Ground Systems for Satellite Command & Control, Payload Processing & Integration & Testing Services
N.A.I.C.S.: 334112
James B. Kramer *(Sr VP & Gen Mgr)*

Madison Research Corporation **(1)**
4904 Research Dr, Huntsville, AL 35805
Tel.: (256) 327-8100
Sales Range: $50-74.9 Million
Emp.: 650
Provider of Engineering & Information Technology Services
N.A.I.C.S.: 541511

Micro Systems, Inc. **(1)**
10680 Treena St Ste 600, San Diego, CA 92131 **(100%)**
Tel.: (850) 244-2332
Web Site: http://www.kratos-msi.com
Aerospace Defense Application Design, Development & Mfr
N.A.I.C.S.: 334511

Real Time Logic, Inc. **(1)**
12515 Academy Ridge Vw, Colorado Springs, CO 80921
Tel.: (719) 598-2801
Web Site: http://www.rtlogic.com
Sales Range: $50-74.9 Million
Emp.: 250
Communication Equipment Distr
N.A.I.C.S.: 423690

RealTime Logic, Inc. **(1)**
14130 Sullyfield Cir Ste E1, Chantilly, VA 20151
Tel.: (703) 488-2500
Web Site: http://www.rtlogic.com
Information Technology Services
N.A.I.C.S.: 519290

Rocket Support Services, LLC **(1)**
2409 Peppermill Dr Ste A, Glen Burnie, MD 21061-3267
Tel.: (443) 572-0002
Engineeering Services
N.A.I.C.S.: 541330

SAT Corporation (1)
321 Soquel Way, Sunnyvale, CA 94085
Tel.: (408) 220-9200
Web Site: http://www.sat.com
Communication Equipment Installation Services
N.A.I.C.S.: 238210

SCT Acquisition, LLC (1)
843 Mount Carmel Rd, Walterboro, SC 29488
Tel.: (843) 538-8859
Web Site:
    http://www.southsidecontainer.com
Sales Range: $25-49.9 Million
Emp.: 30
Modified Container Building System Mfr
N.A.I.C.S.: 332439

SYS Technologies, Inc. (1)
4820 E Gate Mall, San Diego, CA 92121 (100%)
Tel.: (858) 715-5500
Sales Range: $75-99.9 Million
Emp.: 404
Technical Professional Services To Government Agencies
N.A.I.C.S.: 541512

Subsidiary (Domestic):

SYS - Enterprise Solutions Division (2)
1721 Pacific Ave Ste 210, Oxnard, CA 93033
Tel.: (805) 486-4444
Sales Range: $25-49.9 Million
Emp.: 120
Technical Professional Services
N.A.I.C.S.: 541611

SYS - Integrated & Information Solutions Group (2)
4820 Eastgate Mall Ste 200, San Diego, CA 92121
Tel.: (858) 812-7300
Web Site: http://www.kratosdefense.com
Sales Range: $75-99.9 Million
Technical Professional Services
N.A.I.C.S.: 541611

SYS - Systems Engineering & Management Division (2)
2711 Jefferson Davis Hwy Airport Plz 1 Ste 200, Arlington, VA 22202
Tel.: (703) 418-4627
Web Site: http://www.kratosdefense.com
Sales Range: $75-99.9 Million
Technical Professional Services
N.A.I.C.S.: 541611

SecureInfo Corporation (1)
14432 Albemarle Point Pl, Chantilly, VA 20151
Tel.: (703) 488-2500
Web Site: http://www.secureinfo.com
Cybersecurity & Security Management System Services
N.A.I.C.S.: 561621

Stapor Research, Inc. (1)
4511 Daly Dr Ste A, Chantilly, VA 20151
Tel.: (703) 378-9505
Web Site: http://www.staporresearch.com
Unique Consulting & Engineering Services
N.A.I.C.S.: 541618

WFI NMC Corp. (1)
4820 Eastgate Mall, San Diego, CA 92121-1993
Tel.: (858) 812-7300
Real Estate Development Services
N.A.I.C.S.: 531390

KRISPY KREME, INC.
2116 Hawkins St, Charlotte, NC 28203 DE
Web Site:
    https://www.krispykreme.com
Year Founded: 2012
DNUT—(NASDAQ)
Rev.: $1,529,898,000
Assets: $3,148,537,000
Liabilities: $1,849,662,000
Net Worth: $1,298,875,000
Earnings: ($15,622,000)
Emp.: 23,500
Fiscal Year-end: 01/01/23

Holding Company; Doughnut Shops Owner & Operator
N.A.I.C.S.: 551112
Michael J. Tattersfield (Pres & CEO)
Kelly P. McBride (Chief Acctg Officer)
Jeremiah Ashukian (CFO & Exec VP)
Atiba Adams (Chief Legal Officer & Sec)
Raphael Duvivier (Chief Dev Officer)
Javier Rancano (Pres-US)
Sherif Riad (Chief Supply Chain Officer)
Angela Yochem (CIO)
David Skena (CMO & Chief Brand Officer)
Terri Zandhuis (Chief People Officer)
Matthew Spanjers (Chief Growth Officer)
Paul Michaels (Vice Chm)

Subsidiaries:

Krispy Kreme Doughnuts, Inc. (1)
370 Knollwood St, Winston Salem, NC 27103
Tel.: (336) 725-2981
Web Site: http://www.krispykreme.com
Sales Range: $500-549.9 Million
Holding Company; Doughnut Shops Owner & Operator
N.A.I.C.S.: 551112
Anthony N. Thompson (Pres & CEO)

Subsidiary (Domestic):

Krispy Kreme Doughnut Corporation (2)
259 S Stratford Rd, Winston Salem, NC 27103
Tel.: (336) 724-2484
Web Site: http://www.krispykreme.com
Bakery Products Whslr
N.A.I.C.S.: 311811
Niren Chaudhary (COO & Pres-Intl)

KRONOS BIO, INC.
1300 So El Camino Real Ste 400, San Mateo, CA 94402
Tel.: (650) 781-5200 DE
Web Site: https://www.kronosbio.com
Year Founded: 2017
KRON—(NASDAQ)
Rev.: $3,911,000
Assets: $294,938,000
Liabilities: $50,439,000
Net Worth: $244,499,000
Earnings: ($133,204,000)
Emp.: 97
Fiscal Year-end: 12/31/22
Biotechnology Research & Development Services
N.A.I.C.S.: 541714
Norbert W. Bischofberger (Pres & CEO)
Norbert Bischofberger (Pres & CEO)
Christopher Lee (VP-Program Mgmt)
Jennifer Nicholson (VP-Regulatory Affairs)
Douglas C. Saffran (VP-Pharmacology)
Zung To (VP-Clinical Ops)
Wes Trotter (VP-Chemistry)
Arie Belldegrun (Chm)
Anders Vinther (VP-Quality)
Sarah Connors (VP-IR & Corp Comm)
Brendan Strong (Mng Dir)
Deborah Knobelman (CFO, COO & Principal Acctg Officer)
Joshua A. Kazam (Founder)

KRYSTAL BIOTECH, INC.
2100 Wharton St Ste 310, Pittsburgh, PA 15203
Tel.: (412) 586-5830 CA
Web Site: https://www.krystalbio.com
Year Founded: 2015
KRYS—(NASDAQ)
Rev.: $5,221,000
Assets: $558,450,000

Liabilities: $36,219,000
Net Worth: $522,231,000
Earnings: ($139,975,000)
Emp.: 210
Fiscal Year-end: 12/31/22
Biopharmaceutical Research & Development Services
N.A.I.C.S.: 325412
Krish S. Krishnan (Chm, Pres & CEO)
Suma M. Krishnan (Founder & Pres-R&D)
Adam Tarabay (Coord-Materials)
Hubert Chen (Sr VP)
David Chien (Sr VP)
Meg Dodge (VP)
John Garcia (Sr VP)
David Glynn (Gen Counsel)
Laurent Goux (Sr VP)
Ram Kamineni (Sr VP)
Stephane Paquette (VP)
John Thomas (Gen Counsel)
Andy Orth (Chief Comml Officer)

KS BANCORP INC.
1031 N Brightleaf Blvd, Smithfield, NC 27577
Tel.: (919) 938-3101
Web Site: https://www.ksbankinc.com
KSBI—(OTCIQ)
Rev.: $23,679,000
Assets: $546,350,000
Liabilities: $514,115
Net Worth: $32,235
Earnings: $7,557,000
Emp.: 87
Fiscal Year-end: 12/31/22
Bank Holding Company
N.A.I.C.S.: 551111
Harold T. Keen (Pres & CEO)
Regina Smith (CFO)

Subsidiaries:

KS Bank, Inc. (1)
1031 N Brightleaf Blvd, Smithfield, NC 27577
Tel.: (919) 938-3119
Web Site: http://www.ksbankinc.com
Rev.: $11,800,000
Emp.: 90
Banking Services
N.A.I.C.S.: 521110
Deb Pattison (Mgr-HR)
Harold T. Keen (Pres & CEO)
Regina Smith (CFO)
H. Geoffrey Kokiko (Chief Banking Officer)

KS INTERNATIONAL HOLDINGS CORP.
750 Coronado Center Dr Ste 120, Henderson, NV 89052
Tel.: (702) 966-5968
Year Founded: 2003
KSIH—(OTCIQ)
Liabilities: $175,000
Net Worth: ($175,000)
Earnings: ($21,000)
Fiscal Year-end: 11/30/19
Network Broadcasting Services
N.A.I.C.S.: 515120
Lu Ying-Pi (Pres & CEO)

KUBIENT, INC.
500 7th Ave 8th Fl, New York, NY 10018 DE
Web Site: https://www.kubient.com
Year Founded: 2017
KBNT—(NASDAQ)
Rev.: $2,403,408
Assets: $15,232,077
Liabilities: $2,427,639
Net Worth: $12,804,438
Earnings: ($13,619,884)
Emp.: 16
Fiscal Year-end: 12/31/22
Software Development Services
N.A.I.C.S.: 541511

Elisabeth H. DeMarse III (Pres & Interim CEO)

KUBOO, INC.
1820 State Rd 13 Unit 11-43, Saint Johns, FL 32259
Tel.: (480) 385-3893 TX
Year Founded: 2002
SGTB—(OTCIQ)
Media Advertising Services
N.A.I.C.S.: 541840
David R. Olund (Pres & CEO)
Chuck Ragland (Treas & Sec)

KULR TECHNOLOGY GROUP, INC.
4863 Shawline St Ste B, San Diego, CA 92111
Tel.: (408) 663-5247 DE
Web Site:
    https://www.kulrtechnology.com
Year Founded: 2015
KULR—(NYSEAMEX)
Rev.: $3,994,634
Assets: $23,625,930
Liabilities: $13,132,197
Net Worth: $10,493,733
Earnings: ($19,436,479)
Emp.: 62
Fiscal Year-end: 12/31/22
Technology Product Distr
N.A.I.C.S.: 423430
Shawn Canter (CFO)
Michael Mo (Founder, Chm & CEO)
William Walker (CTO)
Michael G. Carpenter (VP-Engrg)
Ted Krupp (VP-Sales & Marketing)

KURA ONCOLOGY, INC.
12730 High Bluff Dr Ste 400, San Diego, CA 92130
Tel.: (858) 500-8800 DE
Web Site:
    https://www.kuraoncology.com
Year Founded: 2014
KURA—(NASDAQ)
Rev.: $4,025,000
Assets: $456,306,000
Liabilities: $36,028,000
Net Worth: $420,278,000
Earnings: ($135,840,000)
Emp.: 133
Fiscal Year-end: 12/31/22
Biopharmaceutical Mfr
N.A.I.C.S.: 325412
Troy E. Wilson (Founder, Chm, Pres & CEO)
Kathleen Ford (COO)
Stephen Dale (Chief Medical Officer)
Thomas Doyle (Principal Acctg Officer & Sr VP-Fin & Acctg)
Brian Powl (Chief Comml Officer)
Alexandra Weingarten (Sr Mgr-Corp Comm)

KVH INDUSTRIES INC
50 Enterprise Ctr, Middletown, RI 02842
Tel.: (401) 847-3327 DE
Web Site: https://www.kvh.com
Year Founded: 1981
KVHI—(NASDAQ)
Rev.: $138,878,000
Assets: $200,530,000
Liabilities: $43,874,000
Net Worth: $156,656,000
Earnings: $24,101,000
Emp.: 351
Fiscal Year-end: 12/31/22
Mobile Satellite Communications Products Developer, Mfr & Marketer
N.A.I.C.S.: 334220
Roger A. Kuebel (Principal Acctg Officer)
Cielo M. Hernandez (Dir)
Robert W. B. Kits van Heyningen

KVH Industries Inc—(Continued)

(Founder)
Brent C. Bruun *(Pres & CEO)*
Elizabeth Jackson *(CMO & Exec VP-Strategy)*
Cathy-Ann Martine-Dolecki *(Chm)*
Martin A. Kits van Heyningen *(Co-Founder)*

Subsidiaries:

KVH Europe A/S   **(1)**
Birkerod Kongevej 150B, 3460, Birkerod, Denmark
Tel.: (45) 45160180
Web Site: http://www.kvh.com
Sales Range: $10-24.9 Million
Emp.: 20
Mfr of Mobile Satellite Communications & Navigation Systems
N.A.I.C.S.: 517410

KVH Industries A/S   **(1)**
Birkeroed Kongevej 150B, Birkeroed, 3460, Copenhagen, Denmark
Tel.: (45) 45160180
Emp.: 25
Satellite Communication Equipment Mfr
N.A.I.C.S.: 517410

KVH Industries Japan Co. Ltd.   **(1)**
TSR Bldg 3F 20-9 Nishishimbashi 1-chome, Minato-ku, Tokyo, 105-0003, Japan
Tel.: (81) 362808811
Satellite Telecommunication Services
N.A.I.C.S.: 517410

KVH Industries Norway A/S   **(1)**
4th Floor Raveien 205, Borre, 3184, Horten, Norway
Tel.: (47) 33030530
Satellite Communication Equipment Mfr
N.A.I.C.S.: 517410

KVH Media Group Ltd.   **(1)**
Omonoias 52 Troodos Court 1st Floor Flat/Office 3, Lemesos, 3052, Limassol, Cyprus
Tel.: (357) 25340360
Satellite Telecommunication Services
N.A.I.C.S.: 517410
Barbara Jakunik *(Mgr-Admin)*

KVH Media Group Ltd.   **(1)**
78 Wellington Street, Leeds, LS1 2EQ, United Kingdom
Tel.: (44) 1132337832
Web Site: http://www.kvhmediagroup.com
Satellite Telecommunication Services
N.A.I.C.S.: 517410

KWIKCLICK, INC.
585 W 500 S Ste 130, Bountiful, UT 84010
Tel.: (801) 243-4840   **DE**
Web Site: https://kwik.com
Year Founded: 1993
KWIK—(OTCQB)
Rev.: $606,835
Assets: $1,221,670
Liabilities: $795,716
Net Worth: $425,954
Earnings: ($3,946,791)
Fiscal Year-end: 12/31/22
Software Development Services
N.A.I.C.S.: 541511
Matt Williams *(Pres)*
Jeffrey Yates *(CFO)*

KYMERA THERAPEUTICS, INC.
500 N Beacon St 4th Fl, Watertown, MA 02472
Tel.: (857) 285-5300   **DE**
Web Site: https://www.kymeratx.com
Year Founded: 2015
KYMR—(NASDAQ)
Rev.: $78,592,000
Assets: $575,759,000
Liabilities: $180,788,000
Net Worth: $394,971,000
Earnings: ($146,962,000)
Emp.: 187

Fiscal Year-end: 12/31/23
Biotechnology Research & Development Services
N.A.I.C.S.: 541714
Jeremy G. Chadwick *(COO)*
Jared Gollob *(Chief Medical Officer)*
Bruce Jacobs *(CFO)*
Ellen Chiniara *(Chief Legal Officer & Gen Counsel)*
Juliet Williams *(Sr VP & Head-Res)*
Bruce Booth *(Co-Founder & Chm)*
Bruce L. Booth *(Co-Founder & Chm)*
Nello Mainolfi *(Co-Founder, Pres & CEO)*

KYN CAPITAL GROUP, INC.
11321 Trade Ctr Dr Ste 255, Rancho Cordova, CA 95742
Tel.: (650) 222-2863
Web Site: https://www.kyncap.com
KYNC—(OTCIQ)
Sales Range: Less than $1 Million
Emp.: 10
Equipment Leasing & Asset-Based Lending
N.A.I.C.S.: 532412
Rick Wilson *(CEO)*

KYNDRYL HOLDINGS INC.
1 Vanderbilt Ave 15th Fl, New York, NY 10017
Tel.: (212) 896-2100   **DE**
Web Site: https://www.kyndryl.com
Year Founded: 2021
KD—(NYSE)
Rev.: $16,052,000,000
Assets: $10,590,000,000
Liabilities: $9,468,000,000
Net Worth: $1,122,000,000
Earnings: ($340,000,000)
Emp.: 80,000
Fiscal Year-end: 03/31/24
Holding Company
N.A.I.C.S.: 551112
David Wyshner *(CFO)*
Elly Keinan *(Pres)*
Harsh Chugh *(COO)*
Martin Schroeter *(Chm)*
Maryjo Charbonnier *(Chief HR Officer)*

Subsidiaries:

Skytap, Inc.   **(1)**
710 2nd Ave Ste 1130, Seattle, WA 98104
Tel.: (206) 866-1162
Web Site: http://www.skytap.com
Self-Service Cloud Automation Solutions
N.A.I.C.S.: 513210
Brian White *(VP-Products)*
Wayne H. Monk *(VP-Bus Dev & Alliances)*
Jill Domanico *(VP-Talent)*
David Frost *(VP-Customer Success)*
Virginia Wei *(Chief Legal Officer)*
Jeffry Dyer *(Sr VP-Worldwide Sls)*
Roger Frey *(VP-Bus Dev)*
Lucas Welch *(Dir-Comm)*
Neil Holloway *(Sr VP-Bus Dev)*
Rahul Tripathi *(Chief Product & Tech Officer)*

KYTO TECHNOLOGY & LIFE SCIENCE, INC.
305 Lytton Ave, Palo Alto, CA 94301
Tel.: (650) 843-2743   **FL**
Web Site: https://k2x.capital
Year Founded: 1999
KBPH—(OTCIQ)
Assets: $8,429,166
Liabilities: $1,436,003
Net Worth: $6,993,163
Earnings: ($768,842)
Fiscal Year-end: 03/31/21
Other Financial Vehicles
N.A.I.C.S.: 525990
Paul M. Russo *(Chm & CEO)*
Simon Westbrook *(CFO)*
John Ricci *(Dir-Portfolio Mgmt)*
Tom Vogelsong *(Dir-Deal Flow)*

KYVERNA THERAPEUTICS, INC.
5980 Horton St Ste 550, Emeryville, CA 94608
Tel.: (510) 925-2492   **DE**
Web Site: https://www.kyvernatx.com
Year Founded: 2018
KYTX—(NASDAQ)
Rev.: $2,282,000
Assets: $75,195,000
Liabilities: $206,592,000
Net Worth: ($131,397,000)
Earnings: ($60,366,000)
Emp.: 96
Fiscal Year-end: 12/31/23
Biotechnology Research & Development Services
N.A.I.C.S.: 541714
Warner Biddle *(CEO)*

L CATTERTON LATIN AMERICA ACQUISITION CORP.
599 West Putnam Ave, Greenwich, CT 06830
Tel.: (203) 629-4901   **Ky**
Year Founded: 2021
LCLAU—(NYSE)
Investment Services
N.A.I.C.S.: 523999
Ian Friedman *(Partner, Mng Dir & Co-Head-Tech)*
Dirk Donath *(Chm)*
Ricardo Salmon *(CEO)*
Rebecca Franco *(Controller)*

L.B. FOSTER COMPANY
415 Holiday Dr Ste 100, Pittsburgh, PA 15220
Tel.: (412) 928-3400   **PA**
Web Site: https://www.lbfoster.com
Year Founded: 1902
FSTR—(NASDAQ)
Rev.: $497,497,000
Assets: $365,313,000
Liabilities: $227,712,000
Net Worth: $137,598,000
Earnings: ($45,564,000)
Emp.: 604
Fiscal Year-end: 12/31/22
Products & Services for Rail, Construction, Energy & Utility Markets
Mfr, Fabricator & Distr
N.A.I.C.S.: 332111
Sean M. Reilly *(Principal Acctg Officer & Controller)*
John F. Kasel *(Pres & CEO)*
Brian H. Kelly *(Sr VP-HR & Admin)*
Peter Jones *(Mng Dir-European Ops)*
Patrick J. Guinee *(Gen Counsel, Sec & Exec VP)*
Peter D. V. Jones *(VP)*
Robert A. Ness *(VP)*
Brian H. Friedman *(Chief Growth Officer & Sr VP)*

Subsidiaries:

Allegheny Rail Products   **(1)**
415 Holiday Dr, Pittsburgh, PA 15220
Tel.: (412) 928-3505
Sales Range: $300-349.9 Million
Emp.: 800
Engineers & Markets Insulated Rail Joints & Related Products for Rail & Mass Transit Industries
N.A.I.C.S.: 423860
Sidney A. Shue *(Gen Mgr-Engineered Products)*

Ball Winch, LLC   **(1)**
15786 N Hwy 75, Willis, TX 77378
Tel.: (936) 228-0077
Web Site: http://www.ballwinch.com
Emp.: 35
Water & Sewer Line & Related Structures Construction
N.A.I.C.S.: 237110

CXT, Inc.   **(1)**
Tel.: (509) 921-8766

Web Site: http://www.cxtinc.com
Precast Concrete Products Mfr
N.A.I.C.S.: 327390

Chemtec Energy Services, LLC   **(1)**
11745 Cude Cemetery Rd, Willis, TX 77318
Tel.: (936) 856-1704
Web Site: http://www.chemtecenergy.com
Oil & Gas Machinery Mfr
N.A.I.C.S.: 333132
Ed Segovis *(Acct Mgr)*
Jeb Williams *(Sls Mgr)*
Zane Bullock *(Mgr-Bus Dev)*
Andrew Mahon *(Mgr-Bus Dev)*
Shawn Laughlin *(Dir-Ops)*

IOS Acquisitions, Inc.   **(1)**
501 Madison Ave 5th Fl, New York, NY 10022-3410
Tel.: (972) 991-9596
Web Site: http://www.iosstaffing.com
Energy Equipment Distr
N.A.I.C.S.: 423830

IOS Holdings, Inc.   **(1)**
3306 Magnolia Blvd, Temple, TX 76502
Tel.: (254) 773-4128
Holding Company
N.A.I.C.S.: 551112

IOS/PCI, LLC   **(1)**
7814 Miller Rd 3, Houston, TX 77049
Tel.: (281) 452-4300
Web Site: https://www.iosinspection.com
Drill Tool Product Distr
N.A.I.C.S.: 423830

L B Pipe & Coupling Products, LLC   **(1)**
21220 FM 1488, Magnolia, TX 77355
Tel.: (832) 934-1850
Web Site: http://www.lbpipeandcouplingproducts.com
Manufactures, Markets & Sells Products for Energy, Utility & Construction Markets
N.A.I.C.S.: 331210

L. B. Foster Rail Technologies, Inc.   **(1)**
415 Holiday Dr Ste 100, Pittsburgh, PA 15220
Tel.: (412) 928-3400
Web Site: http://www.lbfoster.com
Railroad Track & Maintenance Products Mfr
N.A.I.C.S.: 332999

Subsidiary (Non-US):

L.B. Foster Rail Technologies (UK) Ltd.   **(2)**
Stamford Street, Sheffield, S9 2TX, United Kingdom
Tel.: (44) 1142562225
Web Site: https://www.lbfoctor.ou
Emp.: 500
Railway Track Components Mfr & Supplier
N.A.I.C.S.: 336510
Mike Hull *(Gen Mgr)*

L.B. Foster Rail Technologies Canada Ltd   **(2)**
4041 Remi Place, Burnaby, V5A 4J8, BC, Canada   **(100%)**
Tel.: (514) 695-8500
Web Site: http://www.lbfoster-railproducts.com
Sales Range: $25-49.9 Million
Emp.: 29
Suppliers of Railway Track Components
N.A.I.C.S.: 332999

Subsidiary (Domestic):

Salient Systems, Inc.   **(2)**
4393 K Tuller Rd, Dublin, OH 43017
Tel.: (614) 792-5800
Web Site: http://www.salientsystems.com
Emp.: 19
Railroad Track & Equipment Failure Detection Technology Solutions
N.A.I.C.S.: 334610

L.B. Foster Ball Winch, Inc.   **(1)**
15786 St Hwy 75 N, Willis, TX 77378
Tel.: (936) 228-0077
Web Site: http://www.lbfoster-ballwinch.com
Metal Plating Services
N.A.I.C.S.: 332812

L.B. Foster Co. - Bedford   **(1)**
202 Weber Ln, Bedford, PA 15522

Tel.: (814) 623-6101
Web Site: http://www.lbfoster.com
Sales Range: $50-74.9 Million
Emp.: 60
Mfr of Steel for Pipes
N.A.I.C.S.: 332312

L.B. Foster Rail Technologies, Inc. (1)
415 Holiday Dr, Pittsburgh, PA 15220
Tel.: (412) 928-3400
Industrial Machinery Mfr & Whslr
N.A.I.C.S.: 333248
Walt Mizia (Gen Mgr-Technical Rail Sls-E Mississippi & Eastern Canada)
Mark Hammons (Gen Mgr-Technical Rail Sls-W Mississippi & Eastern Canada)
Bill Zimmer (Dir-Class I Rail Sls-Kansas City Southern Reg)
Stacy Borkofsky (Mgr-Class I Sls-Canadian Pacific Reg)
David Sprinkle (Mgr-Class I Sls-Norfolk Southern Reg)
Kyley Holmstrom (Mgr-Class I Sls-Union Pacific Reg)
Mike Yared (Mgr-Sls & Mktg)
Victor Gonzalez (Mgr-Sls)
Robinson Gedra (Gen Mgr)
Hector Herrera (Mgr-Intl Dist)

L.B. Foster UK Ltd. (1)
Stamford Street, Sheffield, S9 2TX, United Kingdom
Tel.: (44) 1142562225
Web Site: http://www.lbfoster.co.uk
Industrial Machinery Mfr
N.A.I.C.S.: 333248

OTI Operating, Inc. (1)
205659 E County Rd 43, Woodward, OK 73801
Tel.: (580) 256-6939
Site Preparation Contractor Services
N.A.I.C.S.: 238910

TEW Engineering Limited (1)
The Midway Lenton, Nottingham, NG7 2TS, United Kingdom
Tel.: (44) 1159354354
Web Site: http://www.tew.co.uk
Electric Equipment Mfr
N.A.I.C.S.: 336320

TEW Plus Limited (1)
6 The Midway Lenton, Nottingham, NG7 2TS, United Kingdom
Tel.: (44) 1158400500
Web Site: http://www.tewplus.com
Telecommunication Servicesb
N.A.I.C.S.: 517810

L3HARRIS TECHNOLOGIES, INC.

1025 W NASA Blvd, Melbourne, FL 32919
Tel.: (321) 727-9100   DE
Web Site: https://www.l3harris.com
Year Founded: 2019
LHX—(NYSE)
Rev.: $19,419,000,000
Assets: $41,687,000,000
Liabilities: $22,858,000,000
Net Worth: $18,829,000,000
Earnings: $1,227,000,000
Emp.: 50,000
Fiscal Year-end: 12/29/23
Holding Company; Electronic Systems & Communications Products Mfr
N.A.I.C.S.: 551112
Christopher E. Kubasik (Chm & CEO)
Edward J. Zoiss (Pres-Space & Airborne Sys)
Jacqueline Nevils (CIO & VP)
Jon Rambeau (Pres-Integrated Missions Sys)
Samir Mehta (Pres-Comm Sys)
John Tierney (VP-Surface & C5 Sys & Gen Mgr-Surface & C5 Sys)
Mark Kratz (VP)
Quinlan Lyte (VP/Gen Mgr-Space & Sensors)

Subsidiaries:

Aerojet Rocketdyne Holdings, Inc. (1)

222 N Pacific Coast Hwy Ste 500, El Segundo, CA 90245
Tel.: (310) 252-8100
Web Site:
https://www.aerojetrocketdyne.com
Rev.: $2,237,600,000
Assets: $2,371,800,000
Liabilities: $1,830,500,000
Net Worth: $541,300,000
Earnings: $74,000,000
Emp.: 5,283
Fiscal Year-end: 12/31/2022
Industrial, Space & Missile Defense Systems
N.A.I.C.S.: 336415
Scott T. Mikuen (Sec & VP)
Ross Niebergall (Pres)
Gregory A. Jones (Sr VP-Strategy & Bus Dev)
Joseph Chontos (Gen Counsel, Sec & VP)

Subsidiary (Domestic):

Aerojet Rocketdyne, Inc. (2)
2001 Aerojet Rd, Rancho Cordova, CA 95742-6418
Tel.: (916) 355-4000
Sales Range: $450-499.9 Million
Emp.: 3,000
Aerospace & Defence Services
N.A.I.C.S.: 336415
Tyler Evans (VP-Defense Advanced Programs)

Subsidiary (Domestic):

Aerojet International, Inc. (3)
2001 Aerojet Rd, Rancho Cordova, CA 95742-6418
Tel.: (916) 355-4000
Web Site: https://www.rocket.com
Holding Company
N.A.I.C.S.: 551112

Aerojet Ordnance Tennessee, Inc. (3)
1367 Old State Route 34, Jonesborough, TN 37659
Tel.: (423) 753-1344
Web Site: https://www.rocket.com
Sales Range: $100-124.9 Million
Aerospace & Defence Services
N.A.I.C.S.: 336415
Kel Smalley (CEO)

Aerojet Rocketdyne of DE, Inc. (3)
8900 De Soto Ave, Canoga Park, CA 91304
Tel.: (818) 586-1000
Web Site: https://www.rocket.com
Aerospace Propulsion Systems Designer, Developer & Mfr
N.A.I.C.S.: 336415

Subsidiary (Domestic):

Arde, Inc. (4)
875 Washington Ave, Carlstadt, NJ 07072
Tel.: (201) 270-5800
Web Site: https://www.ardeinc.com
Sales Range: $1-9.9 Million
Sheet Metal Installation Services
N.A.I.C.S.: 238160

Subsidiary (Domestic):

Arde-Barinco, Inc. (5)
875 Washington Ave, Carlstadt, NJ 07072
Tel.: (201) 970-7297
Web Site: https://www.arde-barinco.com
Mixer Mfr
N.A.I.C.S.: 333241

Plant (Domestic):

Aerojet Rocketdyne, Inc. - Camden (3)
14160 W AR 274 Hwy, Camden, AR 71701
Tel.: (870) 574-0610
Web Site: http://www.rocket.com
Sales Range: $200-249.9 Million
Emp.: 560
Mfr of Rocket Motors & Energetic Packages For Air Bags
N.A.I.C.S.: 336415

Aerojet Rocketdyne, Inc. - Gainesville (3)
8050 Piney Branch Ln, Bristow, VA 20136
Tel.: (703) 754-5000
Web Site: http://www.rocket.com

Sales Range: $200-249.9 Million
Emp.: 475
Mfr of Propulsion Products
N.A.I.C.S.: 336415

Subsidiary (Non-US):

European Space Propulsion Limited (3)
9 Alanbrooke Road, Castlereagh, Belfast, BT6 9PQ, United Kingdom
Tel.: (44) 2890707962
Space Propulsion Equipment Mfr
N.A.I.C.S.: 336419

Flight Data Services Limited (1)
1600 Parkway, Whiteley, PO15 7AH, Hampshire, United Kingdom
Tel.: (44) 1329223663
Web Site: http://www.flightdataservices.com
Aircraft Data Processing Services
N.A.I.C.S.: 518210
Dave Jesse (Founder & CEO)

Harris Asia Pacific (M) Sdn. Bhd (1)
Unit 803 Level 8 Menara Amcorp, Amcorp Trade Center, No 18 Jalan Persiaran Barat, 46050, Petaling Jaya, Selangor, Malaysia   (100%)
Tel.: (60) 379598915
Web Site: https://www.harris.com
Sales Range: $1-9.9 Million
Holding Company; Regional Managing Office
N.A.I.C.S.: 551112

Harris Canada, Inc. (1)
6727 9th St NE, Calgary, T2E 8R9, AB, Canada   (100%)
Tel.: (403) 295-4770
Emp.: 60
Holding Company; Communications Equipment Mfr & Distr
N.A.I.C.S.: 551112

Subsidiary (Domestic):

Harris Canada Holdings Inc. (2)
6727 9 St Ne, Calgary, T2E 8R9, AB, Canada
Tel.: (403) 295-4770
Computer Programming Services
N.A.I.C.S.: 541511

Harris Canada Systems, Inc. (2)
6727 9th Street NE, Calgary, T2E 8R9, AB, Canada   (100%)
Tel.: (403) 295-4770
Sales Range: $25-49.9 Million
Emp.: 50
Communications Equipment Mfr & Distr
N.A.I.C.S.: 334290

Harris Communications (Australia) Pty. Ltd. (1)
Level 2 Limestore 33 Longland Street, Newstead, 4006, QLD, Australia
Tel.: (61) 732532000
Emp.: 150
Communication System Mfr & Distr
N.A.I.C.S.: 334220
Damien Berglas (Reg Mgr-HR)

Harris Communications Egypt, LLC (1)
25 Misr Helwan Road El Zeiny Tower, Flat no 86, Maadi, Egypt
Tel.: (20) 1003431279
Wireless Communication Equipment Mfr
N.A.I.C.S.: 334220

Harris Communications FZCO (1)
A24-A26 Marina Park Offices, PO Box 63309, Abu Dhabi, United Arab Emirates
Tel.: (971) 26167010
Wireless Communication Equipment Mfr
N.A.I.C.S.: 334220

Harris Comunicacoes Participacoes do Brasil Ltda. (1)
Avenue Eng Luiz Carlos Berrini, 1511/8 andar Conj 82 Brooklin, Sao Paulo, 04571-011, Brazil
Tel.: (55) 1135384150
Wireless Communication Equipment Mfr
N.A.I.C.S.: 334220

Harris Corp. - Communications Division (1)

1680 University Ave, Rochester, NY 14610-1839
Tel.: (585) 244-5830
Web Site: http://www.harris.com
Sales Range: $500-549.9 Million
Tactical & Airborne Radios, Night Vision Technology & Defense & Public Safety Networks Developer & Mfr
N.A.I.C.S.: 334220

Unit (Domestic):

Harris Corp. - Night Vision & Communications Solutions Division (2)
1919 W Cook Rd, Fort Wayne, IN 46818
Tel.: (260) 451-6000
Sales Range: $1-4.9 Billion
Emp.: 2,000
Military Night Vision & Tactical Communications Equipment Designer, Mfr & Whslr
N.A.I.C.S.: 334511
Nick Kreigh (Dir-Design & Mfg)
Steve Derickson (Mgr-Ops Test Engrg)

Harris Corp. - Electronic Systems Division (1)
100 Charles J. Herbert Dr, Palm Bay, FL 32905
Tel.: (321) 729-2289
Web Site: http://www.harris.com
Integrated Electronic Warfare, Avionics, Radar, Sonar, Reconnaissance Systems & Robotics & Satellite Communications Developer & Mfr for Government & Commercial Markets
N.A.I.C.S.: 334419

Subsidiary (Domestic):

EDO Western Corp. (2)
2645 S 300 W, Salt Lake City, UT 84115-2910
Tel.: (801) 486-7481
Web Site: http://www.harris.com
Sales Range: $50-74.9 Million
Emp.: 300
Piezoelectric Ceramic Products Mfr
N.A.I.C.S.: 334419

Subsidiary (Non-US):

Exelis C4i Pty Ltd. (2)
380 St Kilda Road, Melbourne, 3004, VIC, Australia
Tel.: (61) 3 9926 1100
Web Site: http://www.c4i.com
Sales Range: $25-49.9 Million
Emp.: 45
Secure Military & Government Communication Equipment Developer, Mfr & Whslr
N.A.I.C.S.: 334290

Unit (Domestic):

Harris Corp. - Electronic Systems Division - Amityville (2)
1500 New Horizons Blvd, Amityville, NY 11701-1130
Tel.: (631) 630-4000
Military & Government Marine & Aircraft Electronic Systems Developer, Mfr & Whslr
N.A.I.C.S.: 334511
Peter Martin (VP-Release Sys & Antenna Products)
James Ryan (Sr Mgr-Bus Dev-Suspension & Release Sys)

Harris Corp. - Electronic Systems Division - Electronic Warfare Systems - Clifton (2)
77 River Rd, Clifton, NJ 07014
Tel.: (973) 284-0123
Emp.: 1,000
Defense, Intelligence & Information Assurance Electronic Systems Developer, Mfr & Whslr
N.A.I.C.S.: 423690
Joseph Rambala (VP & Gen Mgr-Integrated Electronic Warfare Sys)
Richard D. Sorelle (Pres-Electronic Warfare Sys)
Andrew Dunn (VP-Bus Dev-Electronic Warfare Sys)
Henry Bourne (Dir-Engrg-Electronic Warfare)
Chris Winkler (Dir-Supply Chain-Integrated Electronic Warfare Sys)

Harris Corp. - Electronic Systems Division - Radar & Reconnaissance

L3Harris Technologies, Inc.—(Continued)

Systems - Van Nuys (2)
7821 Orion Ave, Van Nuys, CA 91406-2027
Tel.: (818) 988-2600
Sales Range: $125-149.9 Million
Emp.: 500
Radar, Reconnaissance & Other Military
Electronic Equipment Developer, Mfr &
Whslr
N.A.I.C.S.: 334511
Dennis Miller (Dir-Bus Dev-Radar & Reconnaissance)

Harris Corp. - Electronic Systems Division - Reconnaissance & Surveillance Systems - Morgan Hill (2)
18705 Madrone Pkwy, Morgan Hill, CA
95037-2876
Tel.: (408) 201-8000
Emp.: 80
Military & Government Reconnaissance &
Surveillance Equipment Developer, Mfr &
Whslr
N.A.I.C.S.: 334511
Brian Murphy (Sr Mgr-Bus Dev)

Harris Corp. - Electronic Systems Division - Sonar & Command Systems - Chesapeake (2)
1801-L Sara Dr, Chesapeake, VA 23320-
2647
Tel.: (757) 424-1004
Sales Range: $10-24.9 Million
Emp.: 40
Military Sonar & Other Subsea Electronic
Systems Developer, Mfr & Whslr
N.A.I.C.S.: 334511
Rich Krasinski (Mgr)

Subsidiary (Domestic):

Impact Science & Technology, Inc. (2)
85 Northwest Blvd, Nashua, NH 03063
Tel.: (603) 459-2200
Sales Range: $50-74.9 Million
Emp.: 200
Designs, Tests & Manufactures Electronic
Systems for Commercial & Military Use
N.A.I.C.S.: 334419

Harris Corp. - Space & Intelligence Systems Division (1)
2400 Palm Bay Rd NE, Palm Bay, FL
32905
Tel.: (321) 727-9100
Web Site: http://www.harris.com
Sales Range: $800-899.9 Million
Earth Observation, Weather, Geospatial,
Space Protection & Intelligence Solutions
N.A.I.C.S.: 334419

Subsidiary (Domestic):

Exelis Visual Information Solutions, Inc. (2)
385 Interlocken Crescent Ste 300, Broom-
field, CO 80021
Tel.: (303) 786-9900
Web Site: http://www.harrisgeospatial.com
Sales Range: $50-74.9 Million
Emp.: 210
Geospatial Imagery Software Developer,
Publisher & Whslr
N.A.I.C.S.: 513210

Subsidiary (Non-US):

Exelis VIS KK (3)
Nakayama Bldg 3F 1-20-3, Hongo Bunkyo-
ku, Tokyo, 113-0033, Japan (100%)
Tel.: (81) 3 6801 6147
Web Site: http://www.exelisvis.co.jp
Emp.: 7
Geospatial Imagery Software Whslr
N.A.I.C.S.: 423430
Mitsujiro Okawa (Gen Mgr)

Exelis Visual Information Solutions B.V. (3)
Nassauplein 30, 2585 EC, Hague, Nether-
lands
Tel.: (31) 70 311 4171
Web Site: http://www.harrisgeospatial.com
Geospatial Imagery Software Whslr
N.A.I.C.S.: 423430

Exelis Visual Information Solutions France SARL (3)

Tour de l'Horloge 4 Place Louis Armand,
75603, Paris, Cedex 12, France
Tel.: (33) 1 7302 4620
Web Site: http://www.harrisgeospatial.fr
Emp.: 12
Geospatial Imagery Software Whslr
N.A.I.C.S.: 423430

Exelis Visual Information Solutions GmbH (3)
Talhofstrasse 32A, 82205, Gilching, Ger-
many
Tel.: (49) 81 05378 0
Web Site: http://www.harrisgeospatial.de
Emp.: 10
Geospatial Imagery Software Whslr
N.A.I.C.S.: 423430

Exelis Visual Information Solutions SRL (3)
Via Salvo D'Acquisto 31, 20864, Concor-
ezzo, Italy
Tel.: (39) 039 605 8605
Web Site: http://www.harrisgeospatial.it
Emp.: 8
Geospatial Imagery Software Whslr
N.A.I.C.S.: 423430

Exelis Visual Information Solutions UK Limited (3)
1010 Eskdale Road, Winnersh, Wokingham,
RG41 5TS, Berks, United Kingdom
Tel.: (44) 1189641500
Web Site: http://www.harrisgeospatial.co.uk
Sales Range: $25-49.9 Million
Emp.: 10
Geospatial Imagery Software Whslr
N.A.I.C.S.: 423430

Unit (Domestic):

Harris Corp. - Geospatial Systems Division (2)
400 Initiative Dr, Rochester, NY 14606
Tel.: (585) 269-5600
Emp.: 300
Remote Sensing & Navigation Technologies
Designer, Mfr & Whslr
N.A.I.C.S.: 334511
Thomas Thompson (Mgr-Contracts)
Larry Wilkinson (Sr Program Mgr)
Dwight Greenlee (Dir-Strategy-
Environmental Solutions)
Stephanie Dickman (VP-Strategy-Space &
Intelligence Sys)

Harris Corp. - Washington Operations (1)
600 Maryland Ave SW, Ste 850E, Washing-
ton, DC 20024
Tel.: (202) 729-3700
Web Site: http://www.harris.com
Systems Engineering & Technical Assis-
tance for the Government
Information/Technology Market
N.A.I.C.S.: 541512

Harris Geospatial Solutions GmbH (1)
Talhofstrasse 32A, 82205, Gilching, Ger-
many
Tel.: (49) 81053780
Software Development Services
N.A.I.C.S.: 513210

Harris Geospatial Solutions Italia SRL (1)
Via Centro Colleoni 3, 20864, Agrate Bri-
anza, Monza and Brianza, Italy
Tel.: (39) 0396058605
Software Development Services
N.A.I.C.S.: 513210

Harris Geospatial Solutions SARL (1)
Tour de l'Horloge 4 Place Louis Armand,
Paris, Cedex, France
Tel.: (33) 173024620
Software Publishing Services
N.A.I.C.S.: 513210

Harris Geospatial Solutions UK Limited (1)
1010 Eskdale Road Winnersh, Berkshire,
Wokingham, RG41 5TS, United Kingdom
Tel.: (44) 1189641500
Web Site: http://harrisgeospatial.co.uk
Software Development Services
N.A.I.C.S.: 513210

Harris Geospatial Solutions, Inc. (1)
385 Interlocken Crescent Ste 300, Broom-
field, CO 80021
Tel.: (303) 786-9900
Software Development Services
N.A.I.C.S.: 513210

Harris Norge AS (1)
Maskinveien 13, Stavanger, 4033, Norway
Tel.: (47) 51222026
Sales Range: $25-49.9 Million
Emp.: 40
Satellite Telecommunications
N.A.I.C.S.: 517410
Rolf Derge (Gen Mgr)

Harris Orthogon GmbH (1)
Hastedter Osterdeich 222, 28207, Bremen,
Germany
Tel.: (49) 421201220
Web Site: http://www.harris-orthogon.com
Emp.: 60
Air Traffic Management Software Developer
N.A.I.C.S.: 541511

Harris Software Systems Pty. Ltd. (1)
Level 2 Limestore 33 Longland Street, New-
stead, 4006, QLD, Australia
Tel.: (61) 732532000
Wireless Communication Equipment Mfr
N.A.I.C.S.: 334220

Harris Systems Limited (1)
1010 Eskdale Road, Winnersh, RG41 5TS,
United Kingdom (100%)
Tel.: (44) 118 964 1500
Web Site: http://www.harris.com
Emp.: 600
Broadcast, Government & Radio Frequency
Communications Equipment & Information
Systems Mfr & Support Services; Regional
Managing Office
N.A.I.C.S.: 334290

Subsidiary (Domestic):

Applied Kilovolts Limited (2)
A Harris Company Woods Way Goring by
Sea, Worthing, BN12 4QY, West Sussex,
United Kingdom
Tel.: (44) 1903 708850
Web Site: http://www.appliedkilovolts.com
Sales Range: $10-24.9 Million
Emp.: 60
Power Supply Equipment Designer & Mfr
N.A.I.C.S.: 335311

Imagine Communications Corp. - Germany (1)
Carl-Zeiss Ring 19a, 85737, Ismaning, Ger-
many
Tel.: (49) 89 149 0490
Web Site:
http://www.imaginecommunications.com
Graphic Design Services
N.A.I.C.S.: 541430

Jariet Technologies, Inc. (1)
103 W Torrance Blvd, Redondo Beach, CA
90277
Tel.: (310) 698-1009
Web Site: http://www.jariettech.com
Digital Microwave Integrated Circuit Mfr
N.A.I.C.S.: 334290
Charles Harper (Co-Founder & CEO)
Craig Hornbuckle (Co-Founder & CTO)
David Clark (VP-Program Mgmt)
Monica Gilbert (VP-Strategic Programs)
Matthew Hoppe (VP-Mfg)
Thomas Krawczyk (Sr Dir-Application En-
grg)

L-3 Communications Korea Co., Ltd. (1)
Hancom Building 12th Floor, Jung-Gu 21
Sogong-dong, Seoul, 100-070, Korea
(South)
Tel.: (82) 27734361
Communication Product Mfr
N.A.I.C.S.: 334220

L3 Technologies, Inc. (1)
600 3rd Ave, New York, NY 10016
Tel.: (212) 697-1111
Web Site: http://www.l3t.com
Rev.: $10,244,000,000
Assets: $13,518,000,000
Liabilities: $7,611,000,000
Net Worth: $5,907,000,000

Earnings: $1,005,000,000
Emp.: 31,000
Fiscal Year-end: 12/31/2018
Military Electronics & Communications
Equipment Mfr
N.A.I.C.S.: 334220

Subsidiary (Non-US):

APSS S.r.l. (2)
Via S Sebastiano 16, Cuneo, Cuneo, Italy
Tel.: (39) 0173468468
Web Site: http://www.apss.it
Sales Range: $25-49.9 Million
Emp.: 60
Marine Automation Systems Services
N.A.I.C.S.: 334511

Advanced New Technologies Ltd (2)
1000 Lakeside North Harbour Western
Road, Portsmouth, PO6 3EZ, United King-
dom
Tel.: (44) 23 9280 8300
Web Site: http://www.a-n-t.net
Sales Range: $10-24.9 Million
Emp.: 35
Software Services
N.A.I.C.S.: 513210

AeroElite Limited (2)
88 Condor Close, Woolsbridge Industrial
Park, Wimborne, BH21 6SU, United King-
dom
Tel.: (44) 7375674754
Web Site: https://aeroelite.co.uk
Wireless Telecommunication Services
N.A.I.C.S.: 334511

Subsidiary (Domestic):

Aerosim Technologies, Inc. (2)
351 Cliff Rd, Burnsville, MN 55337
Tel.: (952) 894-4694
Web Site: https://www.aerospace-
technology.com
Logistic Services
N.A.I.C.S.: 541614

Subsidiary (Non-US):

Amplidan A/S (2)
Lyngso Alle 2, Horsholm, Denmark
Tel.: (45) 166200
Web Site:
http://www.amplidan.equip4ship.com
Emp.: 60
Communication Equipment Mfr
N.A.I.C.S.: 334220

Subsidiary (Domestic):

Applied Defense Solutions, Inc. (2)
10440 Little Patuxent Pkwy Ste 600, Co-
lumbia, MD 21044
Tel.: (410) 715-0005
Web Site: http://www.applieddefense.com
Software Development Services
N.A.I.C.S.: 541511
Thomas Kubancik (Gen Mgr-Comml, Civil &
Intl Space)
Robert MacMillian (CEO)
Elaine Brown (CFO)
Tiom Craychee (Reg Mgr-Virginia)
Kirk Carter (Reg Mgr-West)
John Earp (Dir-Engrg)
Gene Richardson (VP-IT, Security & Facili-
ties)

Army Fleet Support LLC (2)
902 Quarter Master Rd, Fort Rucker, AL
36362
Tel.: (334) 598-0400
Web Site: http://www.armyfleetsupport.com
Aircraft Equipment Mfr
N.A.I.C.S.: 336413
Lowell A. Green (VP & Gen Mgr)

Subsidiary (Non-US):

Asian Aviation Training Centre Ltd. (2)
Bangkok Airways Bldg 3 3rd Floor 999 Moo
4 Bangna-Trat Rd, Bangchalong, Bang Phli,
10540, Samut Prakan, Thailand
Tel.: (66) 2316062224
Web Site: https://www.l3harris.com
Aviation Training Services
N.A.I.C.S.: 611710

Autonomous Surface Vehicles Limited (2)

Unit 12 Murrills Estate Southampton Road, Portchester, PO16 9RD, United Kingdom
Tel.: (44) 2392382573
Web Site: http://www.asvglobal.com
Emp.: 159
Control Systems Mfr
N.A.I.C.S.: 334511

Joint Venture (Domestic):

Aviation Communication & Surveillance Systems, LLC (2)
19810 N 7th Ave, Phoenix, AZ 85027-4400
Tel.: (623) 445-7000
Web Site: http://www.acss.com
Sales Range: $100-124.9 Million
Emp.: 300
Safety Avionics Systems Mfr
N.A.I.C.S.: 334111
Kris Ganase (Pres)
Dena Cunningham (CFO)

Subsidiary (Non-US):

Beijing MAPPS-SERI Technology Company Ltd. (2)
2/F Tower A No 4 Xing Huo Road Fengtai District, Beijing, 100070, China
Tel.: (86) 1056654797
Web Site: http://www.mappseri.com
Marine Software Development Services
N.A.I.C.S.: 541511
Michael Chow (Gen Mgr)
Chao Sun (Deputy Gen Mgr)
Laura Shi (Controller-Fin)

C.K. Industrial Engineers Limited (2)
Unit 4-8 Enterprise Way Wickford Business Park, Wickford, SS11 8DH, Essex, United Kingdom
Tel.: (44) 1268561471
Web Site: http://www.ck-ind.com
Industrial Machinery Distr
N.A.I.C.S.: 423830

Subsidiary (Domestic):

C3-ilex LLC (2)
47009 Benicia St, Fremont, CA 94538
Tel.: (510) 659-8300
Web Site: http://www.c3ilex.com
Emp.: 169
Supervisory Control & Data Acquisition Systems Mfr
N.A.I.C.S.: 334419

Subsidiary (Non-US):

CTC Aviation Group Limited (2)
Mauretania Road, Southampton, SO16 0YS, United Kingdom
Tel.: (44) 2380742400
Web Site: http://www.ctcaviation.com
Pilot & Crew Training & Resourcing Services
N.A.I.C.S.: 541612

Subsidiary (Domestic):

Combat Advanced Propulsion, LLC (2)
76 S Getty St, Muskegon, MI 49442-1242
Tel.: (231) 724-2100
Internal Combustion Engine Mfr
N.A.I.C.S.: 336412

Doss Aviation, Inc. (2)
3670 Rebecca Ln, Colorado Springs, CO 80917
Tel.: (719) 570-9804
Web Site: http://www.dossaviation.com
Aircraft Maintenance Services
N.A.I.C.S.: 488190
Randy Davis (CEO)

Subsidiary (Non-US):

ESSCO Collins Limited (2)
Kilkishen Nnnis, Shannon, Co Clare, Ireland
Tel.: (353) 6 136 7244
Web Site: http://www.l-3com.com
Emp.: 50
Electronic Equipment Whslr
N.A.I.C.S.: 423690

Subsidiary (Domestic):

Electrodynamics Inc (2)
3975 McMann Rd, Cincinnati, OH 45245
Tel.: (513) 943-2000
Communication Equipment Mfr

N.A.I.C.S.: 335999
Maritza Rivera (Coord-Export Compliance)

Subsidiary (Non-US):

EuroAtlas Gesellschaft fur Leistungselektronik GmbH (2)
Zum Panrepel 2, 28307, Bremen, Germany
Tel.: (49) 421486930
Web Site: http://www.euroatlas.de
Communication Equipment Mfr
N.A.I.C.S.: 334220

Exmac Automation Limited (2)
Unit 105 Pointon Way Hampton Lovett, Droitwich, WR9 0LW, Worcestershire, United Kingdom
Tel.: (44) 1905773851
Web Site: http://www.exmac.co.uk
Conveyor Mfr & Distr
N.A.I.C.S.: 333922

Subsidiary (Domestic):

Forcex Inc. (2)
1001 Progress Dr, Clarksville, TN 37040-5359
Tel.: (931) 368-0111
Web Site: http://www.forcextech.com
Custom Computer Programming Services
N.A.I.C.S.: 541511
Luke Savoie (Sr VP-Bus Dev)
Ian Young (Sr Dir-Programs)

Forfeiture Support Associates LLC (2)
20110 Ashbrook Pl Ste 220, Ashburn, VA 20147
Tel.: (571) 291-8900
Web Site: http://www.fsafederal.com
Sales Range: $25-49.9 Million
Emp.: 40
Human Resource Consulting Services
N.A.I.C.S.: 541612
Peter Nunez (Dir-West Reg)
George Mendiola (Pres)
Steven Derr (VP-Ops-DOJ)
Tim Prange (VP-Ops-Federal Programs)
Sarah Geroulo (Chief Admin Officer & VP)
Chandler Terry (VP-Fin Acctg)
Neil Desousa (Dir-South Reg)
Ruth Porter-Whipple (Dir-North Central)
Kevin L. Lane (Reg Dir-Northeast)
Russell Harrington (Project Dir-Drug Enforcement Admin)
Steven Hooten (Mgr-Agency-Federal Bureau-Investigation Asset Forfeiture)
Summer Jones (Mgr-Agency-Federal Bureau-Investigation Non-Asset Forfeiture)
Madeam Lee (Mgr-Agency-Bureau-Alcohol, Tobacco, Firearms & Explosives)
Darrin Sachs (Mgr-Agency-Organized Crime Drug Enforcement Task Force)
Todd Smith (Dir-Project-Money Laundering & Asset Recovery Section)

Subsidiary (Non-US):

Funa GmbH Nachrichtentechnik (2)
Offentlichkeitsarbeit Stedinger Strasse 11, Emden, 26723, Germany
Tel.: (49) 4921 967 0
Web Site: http://www.funa-marine.com
Communication Service
N.A.I.C.S.: 517810

Funa International B.V. (2)
Zernikepark 12, 9747 AN, Groningen, Netherlands
Tel.: (31) 50 750 2002
Web Site: http://www.funa.com
Engineeering Services
N.A.I.C.S.: 541330

Funa International Oy (2)
Vaskikatu 5 G, 20380, Turku, Finland
Tel.: (358) 22405000
Web Site: http://www.funa-international-oy.rakentajalle.fi
Communication Equipment Mfr & Distr
N.A.I.C.S.: 334220

Funa International Srl (2)
Via Macaggi 18/22-23-24-25, 16121, Genoa, Italy
Tel.: (39) 0108978447
Communication Equipment Mfr & Distr
N.A.I.C.S.: 334220

Subsidiary (Domestic):

Honeywell TCAS Inc. (2)

21111 N 19th Ave, Phoenix, AZ 85027-2700
Tel.: (602) 436-1234
Communication Equipment Mfr
N.A.I.C.S.: 334220

Insight Technology Incorporated (2)
9 Akira Way, Londonderry, NH 03053
Tel.: (603) 628-4800
Web Site: http://www.insighttechgear.com
Sales Range: $200-249.9 Million
Emp.: 1,100
Night Vision & Electro-Optical Equipment Mfr
N.A.I.C.S.: 333310

Interstate Electronics Corporation (2)
602 E Vermont Ave, Anaheim, CA 92803-3117
Tel.: (714) 758-0500
Web Site: http://www2.l-3com.com
Communication Equipment Mfr
N.A.I.C.S.: 334220

Kigre, Inc. (2)
100 Marshland Rd, Hilton Head Island, SC 29926
Tel.: (843) 681-5800
Web Site: http://www.kigre.com
Laser Mfr
N.A.I.C.S.: 334510

Kollmorgen Electro-Optical (2)
50 Prince St, Northampton, MA 01060
Tel.: (413) 586-2330
Web Site: http://www.l-3com.com
Sales Range: $125-149.9 Million
Emp.: 350
Electro-Optical Defense Technology Mfr
N.A.I.C.S.: 334517

Unit (Domestic):

L-3 AVISYS (2)
8601 Wall St Bldg 8-800, Austin, TX 78754-4528
Tel.: (512) 339-0031
Web Site: http://www.l-3com.com
Sales Range: $100-124.9 Million
Defense Technology Products
N.A.I.C.S.: 561621

Subsidiary (Domestic):

L-3 Advanced Laser Systems Technology (2)
2500 N Orange Blossom Trl, Orlando, FL 32804
Tel.: (407) 295-5878
Emp.: 40
Lasers & Laser Range-Finding Systems Mfr
N.A.I.C.S.: 561621

Unit (Domestic):

L-3 Applied Signal & Image Technology (2)
613 Global Way, Linthicum Heights, MD 21090-2258
Tel.: (443) 457-1111
Web Site: http://www.asitinc.com
Sales Range: $25-49.9 Million
Emp.: 70
Signal Processing Systems
N.A.I.C.S.: 561621
Bob Biller (Pres)

Subsidiary (Domestic):

L-3 Applied Technologies, Inc. (2)
600 3rd Ave 34th Fl, New York, NY 10016
Tel.: (212) 697-1111
Communication Equipment Mfr
N.A.I.C.S.: 334220

Unit (Domestic):

L-3 Aviation Recorders (2)
100 Cattleman Rd, Sarasota, FL 34232
Tel.: (941) 371-0811
Web Site: http://www.l-3ar.com
Sales Range: $50-74.9 Million
Emp.: 201
Telemetry, Signal Processing Systems, Instrumentation & Tape Recorders Mfr
N.A.I.C.S.: 334220

Subsidiary (Domestic):

L-3 Avionics Systems, Inc. (2)
5353 52nd St SE, Grand Rapids, MI 49512

Tel.: (616) 949-6600
Web Site: http://www.as.l-3com.com
Sales Range: $75-99.9 Million
Emp.: 45,000
Cockpit Avionics Designer & Mfr
N.A.I.C.S.: 334511

L-3 Chesapeake Sciences Corporation (2)
1121H Benfield Blvd, Millersville, MD 21108
Tel.: (410) 923-1300
Sales Range: $50-74.9 Million
Emp.: 100
Anti-Submarine Warfare Systems Developer & Mfr
N.A.I.C.S.: 334511
John McDaris (CEO)

Unit (Domestic):

L-3 Cincinnati Electronics (2)
7500 Innovation Way, Mason, OH 45040-9699
Tel.: (513) 573-6100
Web Site: http://www.cinele.com
Sales Range: $10-24.9 Million
Emp.: 660
Infrared Sensors, Hybrid Microelectronics & Cryogenics for Autonomous Guidance, Situational Awareness, Threat Warning & Targeting
N.A.I.C.S.: 561621

L-3 Command & Control Systems and Software (2)
246 Industrial Way W, Eatontown, NJ 07724
Tel.: (732) 380-9400
Sales Range: $100-124.9 Million
Communication Software Support Services to Military & Government Intelligence Markets
N.A.I.C.S.: 541519
John V. Medea (Pres)

L-3 Communication Applied Technologies/Jaycor (2)
10770 Wateridge Cir Ste 200, San Diego, CA 92121
Tel.: (858) 404-7817
Sales Range: $25-49.9 Million
Emp.: 85
National Defense Systems
N.A.I.C.S.: 928110

L-3 Communications (2)
300 Concord Rd Ste 400, Billerica, MA 01821
Tel.: (978) 663-6600
Sales Range: $150-199.9 Million
Emp.: 64,000
Engineering Systems & Software Development
N.A.I.C.S.: 541511

Subsidiary (Non-US):

L-3 Communications ASA Limited (2)
Rusint House Harvest Crescent, Fleet, GU51 2QS, Hampshire, United Kingdom
Tel.: (44) 1252775700
Web Site: http://www.l-3asa.com
Emp.: 60
Communication Equipment Mfr
N.A.I.C.S.: 334220

Subsidiary (Domestic):

L-3 Communications Advanced Laser Systems Technology Inc (2)
2500 N Orange Blossom Trl, Orlando, FL 32804
Tel.: (407) 295-5878
Web Site: http://www2.l3t.com
Emp.: 80
Laser Product Mfr
N.A.I.C.S.: 335999

L-3 Communications Aeromet, Inc. (2)
6501 E Apache St, Tulsa, OK 74115-3640
Tel.: (918) 832-6300
Web Site: http://www.l-3com.com
Sales Range: $100-124.9 Million
Airborne Electronic Systems
N.A.I.C.S.: 334419

Subsidiary (Non-US):

L-3 Communications Australia Group Pty Ltd (2)

L3Harris Technologies, Inc.—(Continued)

Level 1 97 Northbourne Avenue, Turner,
2612, ACT, Australia
Tel.: (61) 262484400
Emp.: 4
Communication Equipment Mfr
N.A.I.C.S.: 334220
Racheil Clarkson (Office Mgr)

Unit (Domestic):

L-3 Communications Brashear (2)
615 Epsilon Dr, Pittsburgh, PA 15238
Tel.: (412) 967-7700
Sales Range: $50-74.9 Million
Emp.: 200
Optics Technology Services
N.A.I.C.S.: 333310

Subsidiary (Domestic):

**L-3 Communications Cincinnati Elec-
tronics Corporation** (2)
7500 Innovation Way, Mason, OH 45040
Tel.: (513) 573-6100
Web Site: http://www.cinele.com
Electric Equipment Mfr
N.A.I.C.S.: 334419

Unit (Domestic):

L-3 Communications ComCept (2)
1700 Science Pl, Rockwall, TX 75032
Tel.: (972) 772-7501
Web Site: http://www.l3com.com
Sales Range: $100-124.9 Million
System Engineering Services
N.A.I.C.S.: 541511

**L-3 Communications Combat Propul-
sion Systems** (2)
76 Getty St, Muskegon, MI 49442-1238
Tel.: (231) 724-2151
Web Site: http://www.l3t.com
Sales Range: $300-349.9 Million
Propulsion & Mobility Systems for Military
Combat
N.A.I.C.S.: 336390
Don Rodrigues (Pres)

**L-3 Communications Communication
Systems-East** (2)
1 Federal St, Camden, NJ 08103 **(100%)**
Tel.: (856) 338-3000
Web Site: http://www.l-3t.com
Sales Range: $350-399.9 Million
Emp.: 650
Intelligence, Surveillance & Reconnaissance
Systems
N.A.I.C.S.: 561621
David Micha (Pres)
Donald Hairston (Pres)

**L-3 Communications Communication
Systems-West** (2)
640 N 2200 W, Salt Lake City, UT 84116-
0850
Tel.: (801) 594-2000
Web Site: http://www.l-
3communications.com
Sales Range: $500-549.9 Million
Emp.: 2,000
Intelligence, Surveillance & Reconnaissance
Systems
N.A.I.C.S.: 561621

Unit (Domestic):

L-3 Photonics (3)
5957 Landau Ct, Carlsbad, CA 92008
Tel.: (760) 431-6800
Web Site: http://www.l-3.com
Sales Range: $10-24.9 Million
Emp.: 40
Advanced Photonic Systems & Compo-
nents Mfr
N.A.I.C.S.: 561621

Subsidiary (Domestic):

**L-3 Communications CyTerra
Corporation** (2)
7558 Southland Blvd Ste 130, Orlando, FL
32809
Tel.: (407) 926-1900
Web Site: http://www.cyterracorp.com
Sales Range: $25-49.9 Million
Emp.: 80
Security Detection Equipment Mfr

N.A.I.C.S.: 334419

Unit (Domestic):

L-3 Communications Datron (2)
200 W Los Angeles Ave, Simi Valley, CA
93065-1650
Tel.: (805) 584-1717
Web Site: http://www.l-3com.com
Sales Range: $50-74.9 Million
Emp.: 131
Design, Develop & Mfr Remote Sensing
Ground Stations & Antenna Systems for
Research, Government & Commercial Inter-
ests
N.A.I.C.S.: 517410
John J. Di Gioia Jr. (Pres)

Subsidiary (Non-US):

**L-3 Communications ELAC Nautik
GmbH** (2)
Neufeldtstrasse 10, 24118, Kiel, Germany
Tel.: (49) 4318830
Web Site: https://www.elac-sonar.de
Communication Equipment Mfr
N.A.I.C.S.: 334220

Subsidiary (Domestic):

L-3 Communications EO/IR Inc (2)
420 Aviation Blvd Ste 101, Santa Rosa, CA
95403-1039
Tel.: (707) 236-1077
Communication Equipment Mfr
N.A.I.C.S.: 334290

Unit (Domestic):

**L-3 Communications Electron
Devices** (2)
960 Industrial Rd, San Carlos, CA 94070
Tel.: (650) 591-8411
Web Site: http://www.l-3com.com
Sales Range: $100-124.9 Million
Microwave Vacuum Devices Mfr
N.A.I.C.S.: 334419

Branch (Domestic):

**L-3 Communications Electron
Devices** (3)
1035 Westminster Dr, Williamsport, PA
17701
Tel.: (570) 326-3561
Web Site: http://www.l-3com.com
Sales Range: $75-99.9 Million
Emp.: 200
Microwave Vacuum Devices Mfr
N.A.I.C.S.: 334220

Subsidiary (Domestic):

**L-3 Communications Electron Tech-
nologies Inc** (2)
3100 W Lomita Blvd, Torrance, CA 90505
Tel.: (310) 517-6000
Web Site: http://www.l-3com.com
Space & Military Electronic Equipment Mfr
N.A.I.C.S.: 334419

Subsidiary (Non-US):

**L-3 Communications Electronic
Systems** (2)
25 City View Drive, Toronto, M9W 5A7, ON,
Canada
Tel.: (416) 249-1231
Web Site: http://www.l-3com.com
Rev.: $95,000,000
Emp.: 750
Aviation Systems
N.A.I.C.S.: 334511

Subsidiary (Domestic):

**L-3 Communications Flight Interna-
tional Aviation LLC** (2)
1 Lear Dr, Newport News, VA 23602
Tel.: (757) 886-5500
Web Site: http://www.l-3com.com
Sales Range: $25-49.9 Million
Emp.: 170
Aviation Services
N.A.I.C.S.: 481219

Unit (Domestic):

**L-3 Communications Global Network
Solutions** (2)
1519 Grundys Ln, Bristol, PA 19007

Tel.: (215) 957-3719
Web Site: http://www.gns.l3com.com
Sales Range: $10-24.9 Million
Emp.: 50
Network Solutions for Commercial Commu-
nications
N.A.I.C.S.: 517112

**L-3 Communications Infrared
Products** (2)
3414 Herrmann Dr, Garland, TX 75041
Tel.: (972) 840-5600
Web Site: http://www.thermal-eye.com
Sales Range: $100-124.9 Million
Emp.: 200
Thermal Imaging Products Designer & Mfr
N.A.I.C.S.: 561621

**L-3 Communications Integrated Sys-
tems Group** (2)
10001 Jack Finney Blvd, Greenville, TX
75402
Tel.: (903) 455-3450
Web Site: http://www.l-3com.com
Sales Range: $150-199.9 Million
Emp.: 23,000
Advanced Avionic System Developer
N.A.I.C.S.: 336412
Gordon Walsh (CFO & Sr VP-Fin)

Branch (Domestic):

**L-3 Communications Integrated
Systems** (3)
7500 Maehr Rd M/S 1130, Waco, TX
76705 **(100%)**
Tel.: (254) 799-5533
Web Site: http://www.l-3com.com
Sales Range: $450-499.9 Million
Emp.: 1,000
Aircraft Modification & Maintenance Ser-
vices
N.A.I.C.S.: 336413

Subsidiary (Domestic):

**L-3 Communications Integrated Sys-
tems L.P.** (2)
1309 Rdg Rd Ste 401, Rockwall, TX 75087
Tel.: (903) 455-3450
Emp.: 5
Aircraft Maintenance Services
N.A.I.C.S.: 488190
John C. McNellis (Pres)

**L-3 Communications Klein Associ-
ates, Inc.** (2)
11 Klein Dr, Salem, NH 03079-1249
Tel.: (603) 893-6131
Web Site: http://www.l-3klein.com
Sales Range: $1-9.9 Million
Emp.: 70
Side Scan Sonar, Sub-Bottom Profilers &
Related Instruments & Accessories Devel-
oper & Mfr
N.A.I.C.S.: 334511
Roberta Dickey (CFO)

Subsidiary (Non-US):

**L-3 Communications MAPPS
Inc.** (2)
8565 Cote-de-Liesse, Saint Laurent, H4T
1G5, QC, Canada
Tel.: (514) 787-5000
Web Site: http://www.mapps.l-3com.com
Sales Range: $50-74.9 Million
Emp.: 200
Integrated Marine Control Systems & Prod-
ucts
N.A.I.C.S.: 561621
Rangesh Kasturi (Pres)

**L-3 Communications MAS (Canada)
Inc.** (2)
10000 Helen-Bristol Street, Montreal Inter-
national Airport, Mirabel, J7N 1H3, QC,
Canada
Tel.: (450) 476-4000
Web Site: http://www.mas.l-3com.com
Emp.: 800
Aviation Training Services
N.A.I.C.S.: 611710

**L-3 Communications Magnet-Motor
GmbH** (2)
Petersbrunner Strasse 2, D-82319, Starn-
berg, Germany
Tel.: (49) 81512620

Web Site: https://www.magnet-motor.de
Emp.: 45
Electric Propulsion & Energy Storage Sys-
tems Mfr
N.A.I.C.S.: 335999

Subsidiary (Domestic):

L-3 Communications MariPro Inc (2)
1522 Cook Pl, Goleta, CA 93117
Tel.: (805) 683-3881
Web Site: http://www.l-3com.com
Emp.: 100
Sensor System Mfr
N.A.I.C.S.: 335999

Subsidiary (Non-US):

**L-3 Communications Marine Holdings
AS** (2)
Buskerud Road 129, Drammen, 3027, Nor-
way
Tel.: (47) 32218100
Web Site: http://www.valmarine.com
Emp.: 70
Marine Communication & Navigation Equip-
ment Mfr
N.A.I.C.S.: 334511

**L-3 Communications Marine Systems
UK Ltd** (2)
Unit 2 Clayton Manor Victoria Gardens,
Burgess Hill, RH15 9NB, West Sussex,
United Kingdom
Tel.: (44) 1444480100
Web Site: http://www.l-
3marinesystems.co.uk
Sales Range: $25-49.9 Million
Emp.: 80
Marine Navigation & Communication Equip-
ments Mfr
N.A.I.C.S.: 334511

Subsidiary (Domestic):

**L-3 Communications Mobile-Vision,
Inc.** (2)
400 Commons Way, Rockaway, NJ 07866
Tel.: (800) 336-8475
Web Site: http://www.mobile-vision.com
Communication Equipment Mfr
N.A.I.C.S.: 334290

Unit (Domestic):

**L-3 Communications Narda
Microwave-East** (2)
435 Moreland Rd, Hauppauge, NY 11788
Tel.: (631) 231-1700
Web Site: http://www.nardamicrowave.com
Sales Range: $100-124.9 Million
Emp.: 331
Microwave & Ultra High Frequency Elec-
tronic Test Equipment, Components & Sub
systems Mfr
N.A.I.C.S.: 334220

**L-3 Communications Narda
Microwave-West** (2)
107 Woodmere Rd, Folsom, CA 95630
Tel.: (916) 351-4500
Web Site: http://www.nardamicrowave.com
Sales Range: $25-49.9 Million
Emp.: 148
Microwave & Electronic Components Mfr
N.A.I.C.S.: 334419

**L-3 Communications Narda Satellite
Networks** (2)
435 Moreland Rd, Hauppauge, NY
11788 **(100%)**
Tel.: (631) 231-1700
Web Site: http://nardamiteo.com
Sales Range: $50-74.9 Million
Emp.: 300
Satellite Communication Equipment Mfr
N.A.I.C.S.: 334220

Subsidiary (Domestic):

**L-3 Communications Nova Engineer-
ing, Inc.** (2)
4393 Digital Way, Mason, OH 45040-7604
Tel.: (513) 642-3000
Web Site: http://www.nova-eng.com
Sales Range: $10-24.9 Million
Emp.: 100
Communication System Design & Engineer-
ing Services
N.A.I.C.S.: 541512

Mark Fischer (Pres)

Unit (Domestic):

L-3 Communications Ocean Systems (2)
15825 Roxford St, Sylmar, CA 91392-9212
Tel.: (805) 879-0138
Web Site: http://www2.l3t.com
Sales Range: $100-124.9 Million
Acoustic Undersea Warfare Systems
N.A.I.C.S.: 561621

Subsidiary (Non-US):

L-3 Communications Oceania Pty Limited (2)
108 Marine Terrace, Fremantle, 6160, WA, Australia
Tel.: (61) 894310000
Web Site: http://www2.l3t.com
Maritime Communication Systems & Equipment Mfr
N.A.I.C.S.: 334220

Unit (Domestic):

L-3 Communications Randtron Antenna Systems (2)
130 Constitution Dr, Menlo Park, CA 94025-1141
Tel.: (650) 326-9500
Web Site: http://www.l3com.com
Sales Range: $25-49.9 Million
Emp.: 200
Antenna Mfr
N.A.I.C.S.: 334220

L-3 Communications SSG-Tinsley (2)
65 Jonspin Rd, Wilmington, MA 01887
Tel.: (978) 694-9991
Web Site: http://www.l3com.com
Sales Range: $10-24.9 Million
Emp.: 175
Optical Instrument Mfr
N.A.I.C.S.: 333310

Subsidiary (Domestic):

L-3 Communications Security and Detection Systems, Inc. (2)
10E Commerce Way, Woburn, MA 01801
Tel.: (781) 939-3800
Web Site: http://www.sds.l3com.com
Emp.: 108
Security Equipment Mfr
N.A.I.C.S.: 334290

Subsidiary (Non-US):

L-3 Communications Singapore Pte Ltd (2)
300 Tampines Avenue 5 Unit 05-04 Tampines Junction, Singapore, 529653, Singapore
Tel.: (65) 67870118
Web Site: http://www.l3t.com
Sales Range: $25-49.9 Million
Emp.: 50
Communication Equipment Mfr
N.A.I.C.S.: 334290

Subsidiary (Domestic):

L-3 Communications Sonoma EO Inc (2)
428 Aviation Blvd, Santa Rosa, CA 95403
Tel.: (707) 568-3000
Web Site: http://www2.l3t.com
Emp.: 110
Infrared Imaging Systems Mfr
N.A.I.C.S.: 334419

Subsidiary (Non-US):

L-3 Communications Targa Systems (2)
2081 Merivale Road, Ottawa, K2G 1G9, ON, Canada
Tel.: (613) 727-9876
Sales Range: $10-24.9 Million
Emp.: 11
Data Storage Products for Military & Aerospace Applications
N.A.I.C.S.: 518210
Dave Saunders (Gen Mgr)

Unit (Domestic):

L-3 Communications Telemetry-West (2)

9020 Balboa Ave, San Diego, CA 92123-3507
Tel.: (858) 694-7500
Web Site: http://www.tw.l-3com.com
Sales Range: $75-99.9 Million
Emp.: 450
Satellite Transponders, Transmitters, Receivers, Encoders, Video Compression Systems & Telemetry Systems Mfr
N.A.I.C.S.: 334220

Subsidiary (Non-US):

L-3 Communications UK Ltd (2)
Astro Ho Brant Bridge Way, Bracknell, RG12 9HW, Berkshire, United Kingdom
Tel.: (44) 1344477900
Web Site: http://www.l-3com.com
Communication Equipment Mfr
N.A.I.C.S.: 334290

L-3 Communications Valmarine AS (2)
Buskerudveien 129, 3027, Drammen, Norway
Tel.: (47) 32218100
Web Site: http://www.valmarine.com
Sales Range: $25-49.9 Million
Emp.: 80
Automation & Navigation Systems Distr
N.A.I.C.S.: 423690

Unit (Domestic):

L-3 Communications-Display Systems (2)
1355 Bluegrass Lakes Pkwy, Alpharetta, GA 30004
Tel.: (770) 752-7000
Web Site: http://www.l-3com.com
Sales Range: $75-99.9 Million
Emp.: 300
Display Systems for Air, Sea & Ground-Based Military Applications
N.A.I.C.S.: 334513

Subsidiary (Domestic):

L-3 D.P. Associates Inc. (2)
2961 W California Ave, Salt Lake City, UT 84104
Tel.: (801) 983-9900
Web Site: http://www.l-3training.com
Sales Range: $10-24.9 Million
Emp.: 70
Simulation Technology Services
N.A.I.C.S.: 541690

L-3 EOTech, Inc. (2)
1201 E Ellsworth Rd, Ann Arbor, MI 48108
Tel.: (734) 741-8868
Web Site: http://www.eotech-inc.com
Sales Range: $100-124.9 Million
Emp.: 300
Electro-Optics Products & Systems
N.A.I.C.S.: 333310

L-3 Electron Technologies, Inc. (2)
3100 W Lomita Blvd Bldg 230 Rm 2129A, Torrance, CA 90509
Tel.: (310) 517-6000
Web Site: http://www.l-3com.com
Sales Range: $100-124.9 Million
Electron Technology Services
N.A.I.C.S.: 561621

Unit (Domestic):

L-3 Fuzing & Ordnance Systems (2)
1650 Manheim Pike Ste 201, Lancaster, PA 17601-3088
Tel.: (717) 735-0300
Web Site: http://www2.l-3com.com
Sales Range: $10-24.9 Million
Emp.: 25
Ordnance Fuzing Products for Military & Government Agencies
N.A.I.C.S.: 561621

Subsidiary (Domestic):

L-3 G.A. International, Inc. (2)
5553 Ravenswood Rd Ste 102, Fort Lauderdale, FL 33312
Tel.: (954) 524-9107
Web Site: http://www.l-3mps.com
Marine Electronics Whslr
N.A.I.C.S.: 423690
Gunter Olbrich (Pres)

L-3 Interstate Electronics Corporation (2)
602 E Vermont Ave, Anaheim, CA 92803-3117
Tel.: (714) 758-4011
Web Site: http://www.l2.l3t.com
Sales Range: $50-74.9 Million
Emp.: 600
Instrumentation & Missile Tracking Systems, Network Information Systems & Global Positioning System Technologies Mfr
N.A.I.C.S.: 334511

Subsidiary (Non-US):

L-3 MAS Canada (2)
10000 Helen Bristol St, Mirabel, J7N 1H3, QC, Canada **(100%)**
Tel.: (450) 476-4000
Web Site: http://www.mas.l-3com.com
Rev.: $400,000,000
Emp.: 1,200
Airplane & Internal Combustion Engines Maintenance
N.A.I.C.S.: 333618

Unit (Domestic):

L-3 Marine Systems (2)
750 Miller Dr SE Ste 100, Leesburg, VA 20175-8916
Tel.: (703) 443-1700
Web Site: http://www.mapps.l-3
Sales Range: $25-49.9 Million
Emp.: 85
Marine Control Systems
N.A.I.C.S.: 541512

Subsidiary (Domestic):

L-3 Microdyne Outsourcing, Inc. (2)
3120 Lomita Blvd, Torrance, CA 90505 **(100%)**
Tel.: (310) 257-2600
Sales Range: $450-499.9 Million
Emp.: 1,600
Outsourcing Services
N.A.I.C.S.: 561990

Unit (Domestic):

L-3 Mustang Technology (2)
6900 K Ave, Plano, TX 75074-2527
Tel.: (972) 747-0707
Web Site: http://www.mustangtechnology.com
Sales Range: $25-49.9 Million
Emp.: 115
Designer & Developer of Radar Solutions
N.A.I.C.S.: 334511

L-3 Narda-MITEQ (2)
435 Moreland Rd, Hauppauge, NY 11788
Tel.: (631) 231-1700
Web Site: http://www.nardamiteq.com
Microwave Components, Assemblies & Subsystems Design & Mfr
N.A.I.C.S.: 334220

Subsidiary (Domestic):

L-3 Power & Control Systems Group (2)
600 3rd Ave, New York, NY 10016
Tel.: (212) 697-1111
Web Site: http://www.l-3.com
Sales Range: $200-249.9 Million
Secure Communications Systems & Products
N.A.I.C.S.: 517112

Division (Domestic):

L-3 Communications Westwood Corporation (3)
12402 E 60th St, Tulsa, OK 74146-6920
Tel.: (918) 317-4564
Web Site: http://www.l-3mps.com
Rev.: $52,100,000
Emp.: 211
Electrical Distribution & Control Equipment Mfr
N.A.I.C.S.: 333613

Division (Domestic):

L-3 Communications Westwood Corporation-NMP Division (4)
12402 E 60th St, Tulsa, OK 74146 **(100%)**
Tel.: (918) 317-4564
Web Site: http://www.l-3.com

Sales Range: $25-49.9 Million
Emp.: 130
Shipboard Equipment Designer & Mfr
N.A.I.C.S.: 335313

L-3 Communications Westwood Corporation-Tano Division (4)
5700 Citrus Blvd Ste E, New Orleans, LA 70123 **(100%)**
Tel.: (504) 733-4777
Web Site: http://www.l-3com.com
Sales Range: $1-9.9 Million
Emp.: 32
Marine Automation Systems Mfr
N.A.I.C.S.: 333310

Unit (Domestic):

L-3 SPD Electrical Systems, Inc. (3)
13500 Roosevelt Blvd, Philadelphia, PA 19116
Tel.: (215) 677-4900
Web Site: http://www.l-3mps.com
Sales Range: $50-74.9 Million
Emp.: 400
Military Circuit Breakers & Electrical Protection Equipment Mfr
N.A.I.C.S.: 335311
Jerome Ozovek (Pres)

Subsidiary (Domestic):

L-3 Maritime Systems (4)
90 Nemco Way, Ayer, MA 01432 **(100%)**
Tel.: (978) 784-1999
Web Site: http://www.henschel.com
Sales Range: $10-24.9 Million
Emp.: 120
Designer, Mfr & Sales of Marine Platform Control Systems & Training Solutions for U.S. Navy
N.A.I.C.S.: 488330

Division (Domestic):

Power Paragon (3)
901 E Ball Rd, Anaheim, CA 92805
Tel.: (714) 956-9200
Web Site: http://www.l-3com.com
Sales Range: $75-99.9 Million
Emp.: 300
Power Conversion & Distribution Systems Mfr
N.A.I.C.S.: 335311

Unit (Domestic):

L-3 Sonoma EO (2)
428 Aviation Blvd, Santa Rosa, CA 95403
Tel.: (707) 568-3000
Sales Range: $100-124.9 Million
Electro-Optical & Infrared Image Systems for Military Use
N.A.I.C.S.: 333310

L-3 Systems & Imagery (2)
1200 Woody Burke Rd, Melbourne, FL 32901
Tel.: (321) 727-0660
Web Site: http://www.l-3com.com
Sales Range: $50-74.9 Million
Emp.: 331
Defense Electronics, Digital Communications, Computer Science & Satellite Tracking
N.A.I.C.S.: 334511

L-3 Unidyne (2)
3835 E Princess Anne Rd, Norfolk, VA 23502
Tel.: (757) 855-8037
Web Site: http://www.l3.com
Sales Range: $75-99.9 Million
Engineering, Analytical, Technical & Industrial Services to Department of Defense & Commercial Businesses
N.A.I.C.S.: 541330

L-3 Unmanned Systems (2)
6900 K Ave, Plano, TX 75074-2527
Tel.: (469) 568-2376
Web Site: http://www2.l3t.com
Sales Range: $10-24.9 Million
Emp.: 6
Unmanned Aircraft System Mfr
N.A.I.C.S.: 336411

Subsidiary (Non-US):

L-3 Wescam Inc. (2)
649 North Service Rd West, Burlington, L7P

L3Harris Technologies, Inc.—(Continued)

5B9, ON, Canada
Tel.: (905) 633-4000
Web Site: http://www.wescam.com
Sales Range: $100-124.9 Million
Emp.: 500
Visual Information Systems Mfr & Designer
N.A.I.C.S.: 333310

Unit (Domestic):

L-3 Wolf Coach (2)
90 Nemco Way, Ayer, MA 01432
Tel.: (978) 568-5100
Web Site: http://www.l-3com.com
Sales Range: $25-49.9 Million
Emp.: 170
Mobile Telecommunications Systems
N.A.I.C.S.: 517810

Subsidiary (Domestic):

L3 Adaptive Methods (2)
5860 Trinity Pkwy Ste 200, Centreville, VA 20120
Tel.: (703) 968-8040
Web Site: http://www.adaptivemethods.com
Sensor Systems Mfr
N.A.I.C.S.: 334419
Walt Allensworth (VP-Tech)
David Goffe (VP-Sensor Sys)
John Heaton (VP & Gen Mgr)
Sarah Cronin (Dir-Specialized Sys)
Shauna Fox (Dir-Mission Sys)

L3 Aviation Products, Inc. (2)
5353 52nd St SE, Grand Rapids, MI 49512-9704
Tel.: (616) 949-6600
Web Site: http://www.l3aviationproducts.com
Electronic Component Mfr & Distr
N.A.I.C.S.: 334419

Subsidiary (Non-US):

L3 CTS Airline Academy (NZ) Limited (2)
131 Boyd Road RD2 Hamilton Airport Wai-kato, Hamilton, 3282, New Zealand
Tel.: (64) 78439118
Communication Equipment Distr
N.A.I.C.S.: 423690

L3 Commercial Training Solutions Limited (2)
L3Harris London Training Centre 2-3 Gat-wick Road, Crawley, RH10 9BG, West Sussex, United Kingdom
Tel.: (44) 1293491402
Web Site: http://www.l3cts.com
Airline Training Services
N.A.I.C.S.: 611512

Unit (Domestic):

L3 Communications Corp. - Pulse Sciences (2)
2700 Merced St, San Leandro, CA 94577-5602
Tel.: (510) 357-4610
Web Site:
   http://www.L3communications.com
Sales Range: $50-74.9 Million
Emp.: 100
Electron Beam Pulsed Power Machines Developer & Mfr
N.A.I.C.S.: 334220

Subsidiary (Domestic):

L3 Electron Devices, Inc. (2)
3100 W Lomita Blvd, Torrance, CA 90505
Tel.: (310) 517-6000
Semiconductor Device Mfr & Distr
N.A.I.C.S.: 334413
Scott Dunbar (VP-Ops)

L3 Fuzing & Ordnance Systems, Inc. (2)
3975 McMann Rd, Cincinnati, OH 45245-2395
Tel.: (513) 943-2000
Arming Device Mfr
N.A.I.C.S.: 332993
Stephen Schmidt (Dir-Bus Dev)

L3 Latitude, LLC (2)
744 S Euclid Ave, Tucson, AZ 85719
Tel.: (520) 792-2006

Web Site:
   http://www.latitudeengineering.com
Communication Equipment Mfr
N.A.I.C.S.: 334290

L3 MariPro, Inc. (2)
1522 Cook Pl, Goleta, CA 93117
Tel.: (805) 683-3881
Sensor Mfr & Distr
N.A.I.C.S.: 334511

Subsidiary (Non-US):

L3 Micreo Pty Limited (2)
7 Hi-Tech Court Brisbane Technology Park, Eight Mile Plains, 4113, QLD, Australia
Tel.: (61) 733406200
Web Site: http://www.micreo.com
Semiconductor Device Mfr & Distr
N.A.I.C.S.: 334413

Subsidiary (Domestic):

L3 OceanServer, Inc. (2)
275 Martine St, Fall River, MA 02723
Tel.: (508) 678-0550
Web Site: http://www.ocean-server.com
Submarine Vehicle Mfr
N.A.I.C.S.: 333998

Subsidiary (Non-US):

L3 Oceania Pty Limited (2)
108 Marine Terrace, Fremantle, 6160, WA, Australia
Tel.: (61) 894310000
Web Site: http://www.l3t.com
Marine Acoustic Equipment Mfr
N.A.I.C.S.: 334511
Scott Elson (CTO)

Unit (Domestic):

L3 Security & Detection Systems, Inc. (2)
10E Commerce Way, Woburn, MA 01801
Tel.: (781) 939-3800
Web Site: http://www.sds.l-3com.com
X-Ray Security Screening & Metal Detectors
N.A.I.C.S.: 561621

Subsidiary (Non-US):

L3 Technologies Canada Inc. (2)
255 Albert Street Suite 804, Ottawa, K1P 6A9, ON, Canada
Tel.: (613) 569-5257
Communication Equipment Distr
N.A.I.C.S.: 423690

L3 Technologies MAS Inc. (2)
10000 Helen-Bristol Street, Mirabel, J7N 1H3, QC, Canada
Tel.: (450) 476 4000
Web Site: http://www.mas.l-3com.com
Logistic Services
N.A.I.C.S.: 541614

Subsidiary (Domestic):

L3 Unidyne, Inc. (2)
3835 E Princess Anne Rd, Norfolk, VA 23502
Tel.: (757) 855-8037
Web Site: http://www.l-3mps.com
Communication Equipment Mfr & Distr
N.A.I.C.S.: 334220

L3 Westwood Corporation (2)
12402 E 60th St, Tulsa, OK 74146
Tel.: (918) 317-4564
Web Site: http://www.l-3mps.com
Communication Equipment Mfr & Distr
N.A.I.C.S.: 334220

Subsidiary (Non-US):

Lyngso Marine A/S (2)
Lyngso Alle 2, 2970, Horsholm, Denmark
Tel.: (45) 45166200
Web Site: http://www.lyngsoe.com
Emp.: 60
Marine Electronic Equipments Mfr
N.A.I.C.S.: 334511

MHA-Stopford Limited (2)
Custom House Merseyton Road, Ellesmere Port, CH65 3AD, Cheshire, United Kingdom
Tel.: (44) 1513574480
Web Site: http://www.mha-stopford.co.uk
Emp.: 170

Engineeering Services
N.A.I.C.S.: 541330

MacDonald Humfrey (Automation) Limited (2)
Electronic Component Mfr & Distr

Subsidiary (Non-US):

MacDonald Humfrey (Automation) SEA PTE. Ltd. (3)
Tel.: (65) 68446223
Communication Equipment Distr
N.A.I.C.S.: 423690

Subsidiary (Non-US):

Narda Safety Test Solutions GmbH (2)
Sandwiesenstr 7, 72793, Pfullingen, Germany
Tel.: (49) 7121 97 32 0
Web Site: http://www.narda-sts.com
Sales Range: $25-49.9 Million
Emp.: 90
Measuring Equipment Mfr
N.A.I.C.S.: 334519

Narda Safety Test Solutions S.r.l. (2)
Via Rimini 22, 20142, Milan, Italy
Tel.: (39) 02581881
Web Site: http://www.narda-sts.it
Emp.: 90
Measuring Equipment Mfr
N.A.I.C.S.: 334519

SAM Electronics GmbH (2)
Behringstrasse 120, 22763, Hamburg, Germany
Tel.: (49) 40 88 25 0000
Web Site: http://www.sam-electronics.de
Sales Range: $250-299.9 Million
Emp.: 1,450
Maritime Electrical & Electronic Mfr
N.A.I.C.S.: 334511

SAM Electronics Nederland B.V. (2)
IJzerwerkerkade 36, 3077 MC, Rotterdam, Netherlands
Tel.: (31) 104795444
Web Site: http://www.wartsila.nl
Sales Range: $25-49.9 Million
Emp.: 60
Ships Communication Systems Mfr
N.A.I.C.S.: 334419

SAM Taihang Electronics Co Ltd (2)
No 6 TaiHe Road Hailing Industrial Park, Taizhou, 225300, China
Tel.: (86) 52386998520
Communication Equipment Mfr
N.A.I.C.S.: 334290

STN Schiffselektrik Verwaltungs GmbH (2)
Gewerbeallee 13, Elmenhorst, Rostock, 18107, Germany
Tel.: (49) 381776360
Web Site: http://www.stn-schiffselektrik.de
Sales Range: $25-49.9 Million
Emp.: 70
Communication Equipment Mfr
N.A.I.C.S.: 334290

Subsidiary (Domestic):

TCS, Inc. (2)
324 Corder Rd, Warner Robins, GA 31088-3606
Tel.: (478) 328-8537
Web Site: http://www.tcsdesign.com
Sales Range: $25-49.9 Million
Emp.: 100
Aircraft & Avionics Systems Hardware & Software Integration, Development, Production, Modification, Test & Documentation Services
N.A.I.C.S.: 541519

Subsidiary (Non-US):

TRL Technology Limited (2)
Unit 19 Miller Court Severn Drive Tewkesbury Business Park, Tewkesbury, GL20 8ND, Gloucestershire, United Kingdom
Tel.: (44) 1684278700
Web Site: http://www.trltech.co.uk
Sales Range: $75-99.9 Million
Emp.: 230
Electronic Warfare & Communication Systems Mfr

N.A.I.C.S.: 334290

Wartsila Jovyatlas Euroatlas GmbH (2)
Zum Panrepel 2, 28307, Bremen, Germany
Tel.: (49) 49160020
Web Site: http://www.jovyatlas.de
Emp.: 20
Eleectric Equipments Mfr
N.A.I.C.S.: 333613

Wartsila Marine Systems Korea Co. Ltd. (2)
8th Floor Saesam Building 1485-1 Jwa-dong, Haeundae-gu, Busan, 612-030, Korea (South)
Tel.: (82) 51 704 9270
Communication Equipment Mfr
N.A.I.C.S.: 334290

Wescam Inc. (2)
649 North Service Rd West, Burlington, L7P 5B9, ON, Canada
Tel.: (905) 633-4000
Web Site: https://www.2.l-3com.com

L3Harris MAS Inc. (1)
10000 Helen-Bristol Street, Mirabel, J7N 1H3, QC, Canada
Tel.: (450) 476-4000
Web Site: https://mas-suppliers.l3harris.com
Aircraft Component Distr
N.A.I.C.S.: 423860

Patriot Technologies, Inc. (1)
5108 Pegasus Ct Ste F, Frederick, MD 21704-8326
Tel.: (301) 695-4711
Web Site: http://www.patriot-tech.com
Computer & Computer Peripheral Equipment & Software Merchant Whslr
N.A.I.C.S.: 423430
Steve Keefe (Pres & CEO)

Subsidiary (Domestic):

Clearcomm Technologies, LLC (2)
600 Beam St, Salisbury, MD 21801
Tel.: (410) 860-0500
Web Site: https://www.clearcommtech.com
Wired Telecommunications Carriers
N.A.I.C.S.: 517111

Peak Nano Optics, LLC (1)
8951 Cypress Waters Blvd Ste 140, Coppell, TX 75019
Tel.: (469) 464-4504
Web Site: https://www.peaknano.com
Electronic Components Mfr
N.A.I.C.S.: 334290
Jim Welsh (Co-Founder & CEO)
Chad Lewis (Co-Founder & Pres)
Mike Ponting (CTO)
Casey Fisher (COO)
Wendy Hoenig (Chief Mktg & Sls Officer)
Suzanne Vinzant (Dir-HR)
Mike Hus (Sr VP-Engrg)
Alan Longshore (Sr VP-Mfg)
Rich Lepkowicz (Sr VP-Optical Engrg)
John Mark Prewitt (CFO)
Jim Olson (VP)
Adin Pfeuffer (VP)

LA-Z-BOY INCORPORATED
21320 Signal Hill Plz, Sterling, VA 20164
Tel.: (734) 242-1444   MI
Web Site: https://www.la-z-boy.com
Year Founded: 1927
LZB—(NYSE)
Rev.: $2,047,027,000
Assets: $1,913,442,000
Liabilities: $900,082,000
Net Worth: $1,013,360,000
Earnings: $124,636,000
Emp.: 10,200
Fiscal Year-end: 04/27/24
Furniture Mfr
N.A.I.C.S.: 337121
Michael T. Lawton (Chm)
Melinda D. Whittington (Pres & CEO)
Katie Vanderjagt (Chief HR Officer & VP)
Tj Linz (Pres-Portfolio Brands)
Robert Sundy (Chief Comml Officer & Pres-La-Z-Boy)

Robert G. Lucian (CFO & Sr VP)
Jennifer L. McCurry (Chief Acctg Officer, VP & Controller)
Raphael Z. Richmond (Chief Compliance Officer, Gen Counsel & VP)
Rebecca Reeder (Pres-Retail-La-Z-Boy Furniture Galleries)

Subsidiaries:

American Drew   (1)
240 Pleasant Hill Rd, Hudson, NC 28638
Tel.: (336) 294-5233
Web Site: http://www.americandrew.com
Emp.: 39
Bedroom & Dining Room Furniture Mfr
N.A.I.C.S.: 337215

England, Inc.   (1)
402 Old Knoxville Hwy, New Tazewell, TN
37825   (100%)
Tel.: (423) 626-5211
Web Site: http://www.lzb.com
Sales Range: $350-399.9 Million
Emp.: 1,100
Upholstered Furniture Mfr
N.A.I.C.S.: 337121
Tery England (Pres)

Kincaid Furniture Company, Inc. (1)
240 Pleasant Hill Rd, Hudson, NC
28638-2244   (100%)
Tel.: (828) 728-3261
Web Site: http://www.kincaidfurniture.com
Sales Range: $450-499.9 Million
Emp.: 1,700
Furniture Mfr
N.A.I.C.S.: 337121

Division (Domestic):

Kincaid Upholstery   (2)
Hwy 90 E, Taylorsville, NC 28681
Tel.: (828) 632-9774
Sales Range: $75-99.9 Million
Emp.: 250
Furniture Mfr
N.A.I.C.S.: 337121
Steven M. Kincaid (Pres)

LZB Furniture Galleries of Paramus,
Inc.   (1)
3050 Berlin Tpke, Newington, CT 06111
Tel.: (860) 665-0249
Web Site: https://www.la-z-boy.com
Furniture Retailer
N.A.I.C.S.: 449110

LZB Furniture Galleries of St. Louis,
Inc.   (1)
14177 Manchester Rd, Ballwin, MO 63011
Tel.: (636) 394-7447
Web Site: http://www.la-z-boy.com
Sales Range: $10-24.9 Million
Emp.: 10
Furniture Mfr
N.A.I.C.S.: 337121

La-Z-Boy (Thailand) Ltd.   (1)
2991/12 Ladprao 101/3 Road Klongjan,
Bangkapi, Bangkok, 10240, Thailand
Tel.: (66) 23760118
Web Site: https://www.lazboythailand.com
Furniture Distr
N.A.I.C.S.: 423210

La-Z-Boy Logistics, Inc.   (1)
402 Old Knoxville Hwy, New Tazewell, TN
37825
Tel.: (423) 626-6182
Web Site: http://www.llitn.com
Freight Transportation Services
N.A.I.C.S.: 488510

La-Z-Boy Residential   (1)
La-Z-Boy Dr 4162, Monroe, MI
48162-5138   (100%)
Tel.: (734) 242-1444
Web Site: http://www.lazboy.com
Sales Range: $125-149.9 Million
Emp.: 400
Reclining Chairs & Upholstered Furniture
Mfr
N.A.I.C.S.: 337121

La-Z-Boy South   (1)
133 Scanlan St, Newton, MS
39345   (100%)
Tel.: (601) 683-3354
Web Site: http://www.la-z-boy.com

Sales Range: $200-249.9 Million
Emp.: 650
Furniture Mfr
N.A.I.C.S.: 337121

La-Z-Boy Tennessee   (1)
500 Walnut Grove Rd, Dayton, TN
37321   (100%)
Tel.: (423) 775-3900
Web Site: http://www.la-z-boy.com
Sales Range: $500-549.9 Million
Emp.: 2,000
Furniture Mfr
N.A.I.C.S.: 337121

La-Z-Boy West   (1)
301 Tennessee St, Redlands, CA
92373-8125   (100%)
Tel.: (909) 793-3204
Web Site: http://www.la-z-boy.com
Sales Range: $100-124.9 Million
Emp.: 370
Furniture Mfr
N.A.I.C.S.: 337121

LABOR SMART INC.
Tel.: (770) 800-3728   NV
Web Site:
  https://www.laborsmart.com
Year Founded: 2011
LTNC—(OTCIQ)
Temporary Staffing
N.A.I.C.S.: 561320
Toby McBride (CEO-Takeover Industries)
Michael Costello (CEO)
Jason Tucker (Pres-Takeover Industries)
Michael Holley (COO-Takeover Industries)
Joe Pavlik (Chief Science Officer-Takeover Industries)

Subsidiaries:

Kwik Jobs, Inc.   (1)
1034 3rd Ave W, Birmingham, AL 35204
Tel.: (205) 785-4950
Web Site: http://www.kwikjobsinc.com
Sales Range: $1-9.9 Million
Emp.: 204
Employment Placement Agencies
N.A.I.C.S.: 561311
John Hall (Pres)

LABORATORY CORPORATION
OF AMERICA HOLDINGS
358 S Main St, Burlington, NC 27215
Tel.: (336) 229-1127   DE
Web Site: https://www.labcorp.com
Year Founded: 1971
LH—(NYSE)
Rev.: $12,161,600,000
Assets: $16,725,100,000
Liabilities: $8,850,100,000
Net Worth: $7,875,000,000
Earnings: $418,000,000
Emp.: 67,000
Fiscal Year-end: 12/31/23
Holding Company
N.A.I.C.S.: 551112
Lance V. Berberian (CIO, CTO & Exec VP)
Thomas H. Pike (Pres/CEO-Drug & Clinical Dev Bus)
Paul R. N. Kirchgraber (CEO-Early Dev, Central Laboratories & Global Oncology & Exec VP)
Adam H. Schechter (Chm, Pres & CEO)
Glenn A. Eisenberg (CFO & Exec VP)
Peter J. Wilkinson (Chief Acctg Officer & Sr VP)
Sandra D. van der Vaart (Chief Legal Officer, Chief Compliance Officer, Sec & Exec VP)
Brian J. Caveney (Chief Medical & Scientific Officer, Pres-Early Dev & Exec VP)

Mark S. Schroeder (COO, Pres-Diagnostics Laboratory Ops & Global Supply Chain & Exec VP)
Amy B. Summy (CMO & Exec VP)
Chas Cook (VP-IR)
Mark S. Schroeder (COO, Pres-Diagnostics & Exec VP)

Subsidiaries:

Bode Cellmark Forensics, Inc.   (1)
10430 Furnace Rd Ste 107, Lorton, VA
22079
Tel.: (703) 646-9740
Web Site: https://www.bodetech.com
DNA Analysis, Collection & Forensic Research Services
N.A.I.C.S.: 541715
Manzar Ahmed (VP-Global Products & Intl Bus)
Jon Davoren (Dir-Applied Res)

CannAmm Limited Partnership   (1)
Suite 200 9636-51 Avenue, Edmonton, T6E
6A5, AB, Canada
Tel.: (780) 454-7373
Web Site: https://www.cannamm.com
Testing Laboratory
N.A.I.C.S.: 621511

Center For Disease Detection,
LLC   (1)
11603 Crosswinds Way Ste 100, San Antonio, TX 78233-6003
Tel.: (210) 590-3033
Web Site: https://www.cddmedical.com
Diagnostic Laboratory Services
N.A.I.C.S.: 621511
Dean Skelley (Dir-Medical-Laboratory)
Mohammad Al-Ghoul (Dir-Technical)
Karen Rodman (Mgr-Billing)
Mike Kossman (Sls Mgr)

Clearstone Central Laboratories
(Canada) Inc.   (1)
1980 Matheson Boulevard E Ste A, Mississauga, L4W 5N3, ON, Canada
Tel.: (905) 206-8887
Testing Laboratory
N.A.I.C.S.: 621511
Maureen Marentette (Dir-Global)

Correlagen Diagnostics, Inc.   (1)
307 Waverley Oaks Rd Ste 101, Waltham,
MA 02452
Tel.: (781) 647-0604
Web Site: http://www.correlagen.com
Genetic Testing Services
N.A.I.C.S.: 541380

Covance, Inc.   (1)
100 Mettlers Rd, Somerset, NJ 08873
Tel.: (732) 873-2550
Sales Range: $1-4.9 Billion
Emp.: 12,000
Contract Research Organization & Drug
Development
N.A.I.C.S.: 541715
Barry J. Goldstein (VP-Clinical Dev Svcs Bus & Head-Global Therapeutic Area)
Steven M. Anderson (Chief Scientific Officer)

Subsidiary (Domestic):

CJB Inc.   (2)
210 Carnegie Ctr, Princeton, NJ 08540-6233
Tel.: (609) 452-4440
Clinical Research Services
N.A.I.C.S.: 541715

Subsidiary (Non-US):

Chiltern International Limited   (2)
171 Bath Rd, Slough, SL1 4AA, Berks,
United Kingdom
Tel.: (44) 1753512000
Web Site: http://www.chiltern.com
Emp.: 4,200
Data Management, Medical Writing & Clinical Research
N.A.I.C.S.: 541715

Subsidiary (Non-US):

Chiltern Clinical Research India Private Ltd.   (3)
No 99/100 6th & 7th Floor Prestige Towers

Residency Road, Bengaluru, 560025, Karnataka, India
Tel.: (91) 8040640400
Biomedical Research & Development Services
N.A.I.C.S.: 541715
Anil Kumar (Mgr-IT Ops)

Subsidiary (Domestic):

Chiltern International Holdings
Limited   (3)
171 Bath Road, Slough, SL1 4AA, Berkshire, United Kingdom
Tel.: (44) 1753512000
Research & Development Services
N.A.I.C.S.: 541714

Subsidiary (US):

Chiltern International Inc.   (3)
3147 S 17th St Ste #300, Wilmington, NC
28412
Tel.: (910) 338-4760
Clinical Research & Development Services
N.A.I.C.S.: 541714

Subsidiary (Non-US):

Chiltern International Kft   (3)
Ganz utca 12-14 4 em, Budapest, 1027,
Hungary
Tel.: (36) 12099019
Research & Development Services
N.A.I.C.S.: 541714

Chiltern International Portugal
LDA   (3)
Av das Descobertas N 59-3 - Alto, da Barra
Galleries, Oeiras, 2780-053, Portugal
Tel.: (351) 211543980
Research & Development Services
N.A.I.C.S.: 541714

Chiltern International Sro   (3)
Pod Visnovkou 1661/31, 14000, Prague,
Czech Republic
Tel.: (420) 234708911
Research & Development Services
N.A.I.C.S.: 541713

Subsidiary (Non-US):

Covance (Asia) Pte. Ltd.   (2)
1 International Business Park 02-13 The
Synergy, Singapore, 609917,
Singapore   (100%)
Tel.: (65) 65686588
Sales Range: $10-24.9 Million
Emp.: 30
Provider of Drug Research & Development
N.A.I.C.S.: 541715

Subsidiary (Domestic):

Covance Bioanalytical Services
LLC   (2)
8211 Scicor Dr Ste B, Indianapolis, IN
46214-2942
Tel.: (317) 271-1200
Commercial Physical Research
N.A.I.C.S.: 541715

Subsidiary (Non-US):

Covance Central Laboratory Services
SA   (2)
7 rue Moise-Marcinhes, 1217, Geneva,
Switzerland   (100%)
Tel.: (41) 588227000
Sales Range: $50-74.9 Million
Emp.: 45
Research & Drug Development Services
N.A.I.C.S.: 541715

Subsidiary (Domestic):

Covance Central Laboratory Services, Inc.   (2)
100 Perimeter Park Dr Ste C, Morrisville,
NC 27560   (100%)
Tel.: (919) 388-5540
Sales Range: $10-24.9 Million
Emp.: 30
Laboratory Tests & Data Management Services
N.A.I.C.S.: 621511

Subsidiary (Non-US):

Covance Chile Services Limitada (2)

Laboratory Corporation of America
Holdings—(Continued)

Av Apoquindo 4700 11th Floor Office 1101,
Las Condes, 7560969, Santiago, Chile
Tel.: (56) 228820120
Health Care Srvices
N.A.I.C.S.: 622110

Subsidiary (Domestic):

Covance Classic Laboratory Services
Inc. **(2)**
8211 SciCor Dr, Indianapolis, IN 46214
Tel.: (317) 271-1200
Health Care Srvices
N.A.I.C.S.: 622110

Subsidiary (Non-US):

Covance Clinical & Periapproval Ser-
vices S.A. **(2)**
Avenue Marcel Thiry 77 B, 1200, Brussels,
Belgium **(100%)**
Tel.: (32) 27732911
Sales Range: $25-49.9 Million
Emp.: 75
Contract Research & Drug Development
Services
N.A.I.C.S.: 541715
Griet Goddemaer (Dir-Global)

Covance Clinical Product Develop-
ments Ltd. **(2)**
Sti Barbaros Mah Cigdem Sok Agaoglu, No
1 Kat 4/18 Atasehir, Istanbul, 34746, Tur-
kiye
Tel.: (90) 2162506077
Health Care Srvices
N.A.I.C.S.: 622110

Covance Clinical Research Unit
Ltd. **(2)**
Springfield House Hyde Street, Leeds, LS2
9LH, West Yorkshire, United Kingdom
Tel.: (44) 1133013500
Physical & Biological Research Services
N.A.I.C.S.: 541714

Subsidiary (Domestic):

Covance Clinical Research Unit,
Inc. **(2)**
3402 Kinsman Blvd, Madison, WI
53704-2526 **(100%)**
Tel.: (608) 443-1478
Web Site: http://www.covance.com
Sales Range: $50-74.9 Million
Medical Laboratory Testing Services
N.A.I.C.S.: 621511

Subsidiary (Non-US):

Covance Clinical and Periapproval
Services Limited **(2)**
Osprey House Westacott Way Littlewick
Green, Maidenhead, SL6 3QH, United King-
dom
Tel.: (44) 1628548000
Sales Range: $150-199.9 Million
Emp.: 700
Physical & Biological Research Services
N.A.I.C.S.: 541714

Covance Clinical and Periapproval
Services SARL **(2)**
Immeuble Ariane 2 Rue Jacques Daguerre,
92565, Rueil-Malmaison, Cedex, France
Tel.: (33) 147168200
Web Site: http://www.covance.com
Emp.: 200
Scientific Research Centers & Laboratories
N.A.I.C.S.: 541715
Mohamed Elziky (CEO)

Covance GmbH **(2)**
Rosenkavalierplatz 10 Bogenhausen,
81925, Munich, Germany **(100%)**
Tel.: (49) 899210930
Web Site: http://www.covance.com
Sales Range: $10-24.9 Million
Emp.: 30
Contract Research Organization & Drug
Development
N.A.I.C.S.: 541715

Subsidiary (Domestic):

Covance Health Economics & Outcome Services, Inc. **(2)**

9801 Washingtonian Blvd Fl 9, Gaithers-
burg, MD 20878 **(100%)**
Tel.: (240) 632-3000
Web Site: http://www.covance.com
Sales Range: $50-74.9 Million
Emp.: 200
Provider of Research Services
N.A.I.C.S.: 541618

Subsidiary (Non-US):

Covance Hong Kong Services
Limited **(2)**
Rm4703a 47/F Central Plaza 18 Harbour
Road, Wan Chai, Hong Kong, China (Hong
Kong)
Tel.: (852) 25886816
Health Care Srvices
N.A.I.C.S.: 622110

Covance India Pharmaceutical Ser-
vices Private Limited **(2)**
Building No 1 UNIT No 601 Raheja Mind-
space Plot Nos Gen/2/1/D, Gen 2/1/E
Gen/2/1/F AT MIDC Trans Thane Creek In-
dustrial Area, Mumbai, 400 706, Maharash-
tra, India
Tel.: (91) 2268221500
Health Care Srvices
N.A.I.C.S.: 622110

Covance Japan Co. Ltd. **(2)**
Tokyo Tatemono Umeda Bldg 13F 1-12-12
Umeda, Kita-ku, Osaka, 530-0001, Japan
Tel.: (81) 676388688
Web Site: http://www.covance.asia
Physical & Biological Research Services
N.A.I.C.S.: 541714

Covance Korea Services Limited **(2)**
13th Floor POBA Gangnam Tower 343,
Hakdong-ro Gangnam-gu, Seoul, 135-820,
Korea (South)
Tel.: (82) 260043500
Medical Testing Laboratory
N.A.I.C.S.: 621511

Covance Laboratories GmbH **(2)**
Kesselfeld 29, 48163, Munster, Germany
Tel.: (49) 25197980
Emp.: 13
Scientific Research Centre & Laboratory
N.A.I.C.S.: 541715

Subsidiary (Domestic):

Covance Laboratories Inc. **(2)**
3301 Kinsman Blvd, Madison, WI 53704-
2523
Tel.: (608) 241-4471
Biopharmaceutical Drug Development Services
N.A.I.C.S.: 541714

Subsidiary (Non-US):

Covance Laboratories Korea Com-
pany Limited **(2)**
13th Floor POBA Gangnam Tower 343,
Hakdong-ro Gangnam-gu, Seoul, 135-820,
Korea (South)
Tel.: (82) 260043500
Medical Testing Laboratory
N.A.I.C.S.: 621511

Covance Laboratories Limited **(2)**
Otley Road, Harrogate, HG3 1PY, North
Yorkshire, United Kingdom
Tel.: (44) 1423500011
Sales Range: $200-249.9 Million
Emp.: 1,500
Clinical Research Services
N.A.I.C.S.: 541715

Covance Limited **(2)**
Osprey House Westacott Way Littlewick
Green, Maidenhead, SL6 3QH, United King-
dom
Tel.: (44) 1628548000
Web Site: http://www.covance.com
Clinical Research Services
N.A.I.C.S.: 541715

Covance Mexico Services, S. DE R.
L. De C.V. **(2)**
Orre Altiva Blvd Manuel Avila Camacho 138
Piso 10, Lomas De Chapultepec, 11000,
Mexico, Mexico
Tel.: (52) 5583101600
Medical Testing Laboratory

N.A.I.C.S.: 621511

Covance Peru Services S.A. **(2)**
Av El Derby 055 Edifficio Cronos Torrei Piso
7, Santiago De Surco, Lima, Peru
Tel.: (51) 17162612
Medical Laboratory Testing Services
N.A.I.C.S.: 621511

Covance Preclinical Services
GmbH **(2)**
Kesselfeld 29, 48163, Munster, Germany
Tel.: (49) 25197980
Medical Laboratory Services
N.A.I.C.S.: 621511
Florian Timo Ludwig (Dir-Study)

Covance Pty. Ltd. **(2)**
Suite 3 02 Level 3 Building A 97 Waterloo
Road, Macquarie Corporate Centre, Mac-
quarie Park, 2113, NSW, Australia **(100%)**
Tel.: (61) 288792000
Sales Range: $10-24.9 Million
Emp.: 70
Provider of Research & Drug Development
Services
N.A.I.C.S.: 541715

Subsidiary (Domestic):

Covance Research Products Inc. **(2)**
310 Swamp Bridge Rd, Denver, PA 17517-
8723
Tel.: (717) 336-4921
Web Site: http://www.covance.com
Scientific & Technical Consulting Services
N.A.I.C.S.: 541690

Subsidiary (Non-US):

Covance Services (Thailand)
Limited **(2)**
1 Q House Lumpini Level 27th South
Sathorn Road, TungMahamek Sathorn,
Bangkok, 10120, Thailand
Tel.: (66) 26103669
Medical Testing Laboratory
N.A.I.C.S.: 621511

Covance Taiwan Services
Limited **(2)**
18F No 1 Song Kao Rd, Taipei, 11071, Tai-
wan
Tel.: (886) 287580888
Medical Testing Laboratory
N.A.I.C.S.: 621511

International Food Network Ltd. **(2)**
319 Al Nasr Office building Oud Mehta,
Dubai, United Arab Emirates
Tel.: (971) 43547748
Farm Management Services
N.A.I.C.S.: 115110

Diagnostic Services, Inc. **(1)**
220 Mountain Ave, Middlesex, NJ 08846
Tel.: (732) 271-9199
Web Site: https://www.diagnostic-services-
inc.com
Testing & Clinical Laboratory Services
N.A.I.C.S.: 423450

Dianon Systems, Inc. **(1)**
2440 S Sepulveda Blvd Ste 235, Los Ange-
les, CA 90064
Web Site: http://www.dianon.com
Diagnostic Pathology Laboratory
N.A.I.C.S.: 621511
Jonathan Klein (Dir-Medical-Connecticut)
Honggang Shen (Dir-Laboratory)

Branch (Domestic):

Dianon Systems, Inc. **(1)**
5610 W LaSalle St, Tampa, FL 33607
Tel.: (813) 289-5227
Web Site: http://www.dianon.com
Sales Range: $25-49.9 Million
Emp.: 100
Diagnostic Anatomic Laboratory Services
N.A.I.C.S.: 621511

Subsidiary (Domestic):

Dianon Systems, Inc. **(1)**
51 Charles Lindberg Blvd, Uniondale, NY
11553
Tel.: (516) 794-4646
Web Site: http://www.dianon.com

Sales Range: $10-24.9 Million
Emp.: 25
Diagnostic Pathology Laboratory
N.A.I.C.S.: 621511

Dynacare Canada Inc. **(1)**
115 Midair Court, Brampton, L6T 5M3, ON,
Canada
Tel.: (905) 790-3055
Web Site: http://www.dynacare.ca
Medical Laboratory Services
N.A.I.C.S.: 621511
Vito Ciciretto (CEO)
Jenisa Naidoo (Chief Scientific Officer)
Arun Thomas (CIO & VP-IT Solutions &
Svcs)
Paolo Maggiotto (CFO & VP)
Brad Neufeld (Chief Privacy Officer & VP-
Legal)

Dynacare Company **(1)**
3885 boul Industriel, Laval, H7L 4S3, QC,
Canada
Web Site: https://www.dynacare.ca
Drug Testing Services
N.A.I.C.S.: 621511

Dynacare Inc. **(1)**
115 Midair Court, Brampton, L6T 5M3, ON,
Canada **(100%)**
Tel.: (905) 790-3055
Web Site: https://www.dynacare.ca
Sales Range: $400-449.9 Million
Emp.: 6,400
Holding Company; Medical & Testing Labo-
ratories
N.A.I.C.S.: 551112

Subsidiary (Domestic):

DynaLifeDX **(2)**
200 10150 - 102 Street, Edmonton, T5J
5E2, AB, Canada
Tel.: (780) 451-3702
Web Site: https://www.dynalife.ca
Medical Laboratories Services
N.A.I.C.S.: 621511
Roxanne Bunyan (VP-Scientific & Regula-
tory Affairs)
Raymond Lai (Dir-Medical)
Roland Maier (Mgr-Science & Tech)

Subsidiary (US):

Dynacare Northwest Inc. **(2)**
James Tower 550 17th Ave Ste 200, Se-
attle, WA 98122
Tel.: (206) 861-7000
Web Site: http://www.dynacare.com
Sales Range: $10-24.9 Million
Emp.: 80
Medical Laboratory
N.A.I.C.S.: 621511

Endpoint Clinical **(1)**
701 Edgewater Dr Ste 320, Wakefield, MA
01880
Tel.: (415) 970-5546
Web Site: https://www.endpointclinical.com
Medical Device Mfr
N.A.I.C.S.: 334510
Christine Oliver (CEO)
Sri Kadari (VP-APAC Ops)
Adam Brand (Sr Acct Dir)
Jeff Rubesin (Dir-Product Strategy)
Beth Sawyer (Sr Dir-HR)
Michael Tober (VP)

Esoterix Genetic Counseling,
LLC **(1)**
833 Chestnut Ste, Philadelphia, PA 19107-
4414
Tel.: (215) 351-2331
Testing Laboratory
N.A.I.C.S.: 621511

Esoterix, Inc. **(1)**
4509 Freidrich Ln Bldg 1 Ste 100, Austin,
TX 78744 **(100%)**
Tel.: (512) 225-1100
Web Site: http://www.esoterix.com
Sales Range: $100-124.9 Million
Emp.: 750
Clinical Testing Laboratories
N.A.I.C.S.: 541380

Subsidiary (Domestic):

Esoterix Genetic Laboratories,
LLC **(2)**

3400 Computer Dr, Westborough, MA 01581 **(100%)**
Tel.: (508) 898-9001
Web Site: http://www.genzymegenetics.com
Medical Laboratory Testing Services
N.A.I.C.S.: 621511

Subsidiary (Non-US):

LabCorp Clinical Trials **(2)**
Zandvoortstraat 2, Mechelen, Belgium
Tel.: (32) 15787000
Clinical Trial Laboratory Services
N.A.I.C.S.: 621511

FirstSource Laboratory Solutions, Inc. **(1)**
10022 Lantern Rd Ste 600, Fishers, IN 46037
Tel.: (317) 566-9846
Medical Information Services
N.A.I.C.S.: 519290

Global Specimen Solutions Inc **(1)**
8 Moore Dr, Durham, NC 27709
Tel.: (919) 741-5008
Research & Development Services
N.A.I.C.S.: 541713

Health Testing Centers, Inc. **(1)**
3115 NW 10th Ter Ste 113, Fort Lauderdale, FL 33309
Tel.: (954) 485-3322
Web Site:
   http://www.healthtestingcenters.com
Testing Laboratory Services
N.A.I.C.S.: 541380

Home Healthcare Laboratory of America, LLC **(1)**
320 Premier Ct S Ste 220, Franklin, TN 37067-8248
Tel.: (800) 522-4452
Web Site: http://www.hhla.com
Laboratory Testing Services
N.A.I.C.S.: 541380

IDX Pathology, Inc. **(1)**
1151 W Miller St, Boise, ID 83702
Tel.: (208) 377-1969
Medical Laboratories
N.A.I.C.S.: 621511

Impact Genetics Corporation **(1)**
10880 Wilshire Blvd Ste 1101, Los Angeles, CA 90024-4112
Tel.: (647) 478-4902
Medical Laboratory Services
N.A.I.C.S.: 621511

Impact Genetics, Inc. **(1)**
115 Midair Court, Brampton, L6T 5M3, ON, Canada
Tel.: (647) 478-4902
Web Site: https://impactgenetics.com
Medical Testing Laboratory
N.A.I.C.S.: 621511
Brenda L. Gallie *(Founder & Dir-Retinoblastoma Program)*

Integrated Development Associates Co., Ltd. **(1)**
Kasumigaseki Building 6F 3-2-5 Kasumigaseki, Chiyoda-ku, Tokyo, 100-6006, Japan
Tel.: (81) 368112323
Web Site: http://www.i-d-a.com
Medical Research & Development Services
N.A.I.C.S.: 541715

Integrated Development Associates Philippines, Inc. **(1)**
2011-2012 20th Floor Entrata Urban Complex Condominium Corp, 2609 Civic Drive Filinvest City Alabang Muntinlupa City, Manila, 1781, Philippines
Tel.: (63) 27773375
Medical Research & Development Services
N.A.I.C.S.: 541715

LabCorp - Baton Rouge **(1)**
11441 Industriplex Blvd Ste 140, Baton Rouge, LA 70809
Tel.: (225) 298-8209
Web Site: https://locations.labcorp.com
Sales Range: $10-24.9 Million
Emp.: 60
Provider of Laboratory Services
N.A.I.C.S.: 621512
Nancy Day *(Mgr-Lab)*

LabCorp - Cheyenne **(1)**
2301 House Ave Ste 105, Cheyenne, WY 82001-3859
Tel.: (307) 635-7931
Medical Laboratory Legal Services
N.A.I.C.S.: 541199

LabCorp BVBA **(1)**
Zandvoortstraat 2, 2800, Mechelen, Belgium
Tel.: (32) 15342111
Medical Testing Laboratory
N.A.I.C.S.: 621511
Kurt M. Peeters *(Mng Dir & VP-Global Logistics Ops)*

LabCorp Employer Services, Inc. **(1)**
7617 Arlington Rd, Bethesda, MD 20814
Web Site: http://www.wellnesscorporatesolutions.com
Health Screening Services
N.A.I.C.S.: 621999
Emily Roberts *(Pres)*
Jeffrey Taylor *(CFO)*
John Wall *(COO)*
Jared Rice *(VP-Tech)*
Daniel Clevenger *(VP-Screening Svcs)*

LabCorp Japan, G.K. **(1)**
Tsukiji 2-11-9 RBM Tsukiji Station Building Second Floor, Chuo, 104-0045, Japan
Tel.: (81) 362260880
Emp.: 21
Health Care Srvices
N.A.I.C.S.: 621511

LipoScience, Inc. **(1)**
2500 Sumner Blvd, Raleigh, NC 27616
Tel.: (919) 212-1999
Sales Range: $50-74.9 Million
Emp.: 239
Nuclear Magnetic Resonance Clinical Diagnostic Products Developer & Marketer
N.A.I.C.S.: 325413
Thomas Clement *(VP-Regulatory & Quality Affairs)*

Litholink Corporation **(1)**
2250 W Campbell Park Dr, Chicago, IL 60612
Tel.: (312) 243-0600
Web Site: http://www.litholink.com
Medical Laboratories
N.A.I.C.S.: 541380

MEDTOX Scientific, Inc. **(1)**
402 W County Rd D, Saint Paul, MN 55112
Tel.: (651) 636-7466
Web Site: http://www.medtox.com
Sales Range: $100-124.9 Million
Emp.: 667
Laboratory Services & Onsite Point of Collection Devices
N.A.I.C.S.: 621511

Division (Domestic):

MEDTOX Diagnostics, Inc. **(2)**
1238 Anthony Rd, Burlington, NC 27215-8936
Tel.: (336) 226-6311
Web Site:
   https://www.medtoxdiagnostics.com
Sales Range: $50-74.9 Million
Emp.: 70
Mfr of Drug & Other Toxin Analysis Services For Hospitals & Laboratories
N.A.I.C.S.: 334516
B. Mitchell Owens *(COO & VP)*

MEDTOX Laboratories, Inc. **(2)**
402 W County Road D, Saint Paul, MN 55112
Tel.: (651) 636-7466
Web Site: http://www.medtox.com
Sales Range: $25-49.9 Million
Emp.: 600
Forensic & Clinical Laboratory Services
N.A.I.C.S.: 541380

Subsidiary (Domestic):

New Brighton Business Center, LLC **(2)**
402 County Rd D W, New Brighton, MN 55112-3522
Tel.: (651) 636-7466
Medical Laboratories
N.A.I.C.S.: 621511

MedAxio Insurance Medical Services LP **(1)**
500 Sherbrooke St W 11th Fl, Montreal, H3A 3C6, QC, Canada
Tel.: (514) 845-1211
Health Care Services
N.A.I.C.S.: 622110

Monogram Biosciences, Inc. **(1)**
345 Oyster Point Blvd, South San Francisco, CA 94080-1913
Tel.: (650) 635-1100
Web Site: http://www.monogrambio.com
Biological Test Products Mfr
N.A.I.C.S.: 325414

National Genetics Institute **(1)**
2440 S Sepulveda Blvd Ste 235, Los Angeles, CA 90064
Tel.: (310) 996-0036
Web Site: http://www.ngi.com
Medical Testing Laboratories
N.A.I.C.S.: 541380

Orchid Cellmark Ltd. **(1)**
16 Blacklands Way, Abingdon, OX14 1DY, Oxon, United Kingdom **(100%)**
Tel.: (44) 1235528609
Web Site:
   https://www.cellmarkforensics.co.uk
Sales Range: $25-49.9 Million
Emp.: 400
DNA Testing Services
N.A.I.C.S.: 541715

Orchid Cellmark ULC **(1)**
635 Columbia St, New Westminster, V3M 1A7, BC, Canada
Tel.: (604) 523-2945
Emp.: 6
Medical Testing Laboratory
N.A.I.C.S.: 621511

Ovuline, Inc. **(1)**
76 Summer St, Boston, MA 02111
Tel.: (415) 830-2865
Web Site: http://www.ovuline.com
Research & Development in Biotechnology
N.A.I.C.S.: 541714

PMD Properties, LLC **(1)**
178 E 205th St, Bronx, NY 10458
Tel.: (718) 295-4534
Real Estate Services
N.A.I.C.S.: 531210

Pee Dee Pathology Associates, Inc, **(1)**
805 Pamplico Hwy Ste B-210, Florence, SC 29505
Tel.: (843) 664-4314
Web Site: https://www.pdpathology.com
Medical Laboratory Services
N.A.I.C.S.: 621511

Protedyne Corporation **(1)**
1000 Day Hill Rd, Windsor, CT 06095
Tel.: (860) 683-1860
Web Site: https://www.protedyne.com
Emp.: 70
Automation System Mfr
N.A.I.C.S.: 339999
Rolf A. Classon *(Chm)*
Rolf A. Classon *(Chm)*

Sciformix Corporation **(1)**
206 Carnegie Ctr, Princeton, NJ 08540
Web Site: http://www.sciformix.com
Biopharmaceutical Product Research & Development Services
N.A.I.C.S.: 325412
Manish Soman *(Sr VP)*
Ajit Nagral *(Founder)*
Chitra Lele *(Chief Scientific Officer)*
Warun Nayar *(COO)*
David Balderson *(VP-Safety Ops-Global)*

Sciformix Philippines, Inc. **(1)**
12/F One Corporate Centre Bldg Julia Vargas Ave, Cor Meralco Ave Ortigas Business Center Pasig, Manila, Philippines
Tel.: (63) 24221700
Biopharmaceutical Product Research & Development Services
N.A.I.C.S.: 325412

Sciformix Technologies Private Limited **(1)**
Akruti Softech Park 2nd Floor Road No 21 MIDC Andheri East, Mumbai, 400 093, India

Tel.: (91) 2267304300
Biopharmaceutical Product Research & Development Services
N.A.I.C.S.: 325412

Sequenom, Inc. **(1)**
3595 John Hopkins Ct, San Diego, CA 92121-1121
Tel.: (858) 202-9000
Genomic & Genetic Analytical Products Mfr & Whslr; Molecular Diagnostics Laboratories Operator
N.A.I.C.S.: 334516

Subsidiary (Domestic):

Sequenom Center for Molecular Medicine, LLC **(2)**
3595 John Hopkins Ct, San Diego, CA 92121-1121 **(100%)**
Tel.: (858) 202-9051
Web Site: http://www.sequenom.com
Molecular Diagnostics Laboratory
N.A.I.C.S.: 621511
Phillip M. Cacheris *(Dir-Laboratory)*

Southern Idaho Regional Laboratory **(1)**
5475 Bethel St, Boise, ID 83706
Tel.: (208) 367-6392
Web Site: https://www.treasurevalleylab.com
Healthcare Services
N.A.I.C.S.: 621999

St. Joseph's Health Centre **(1)**
30 The Queensway, Toronto, M6R 1B5, ON, Canada
Tel.: (416) 530-6000
Web Site: http://www.stjoestoronto.ca
Healthcare Services
N.A.I.C.S.: 621610
Rod Hochman *(Pres & CEO)*
Rodney F. Hochman *(Pres & CEO)*
Andre Michael Canezal *(Mgr)*

Tandem Labs, Inc. **(1)**
1121 E 3900 S Ste Bldg C Ste 105, Salt Lake City, UT 84124
Tel.: (801) 293-2400
Bioanalytical Laboratory Testing Services to the Pharmaceutical Industry
N.A.I.C.S.: 541380

Toxikon Corporation **(1)**
15 Wiggins Ave, Bedford, MA 01730
Tel.: (781) 275-3330
Web Site: http://www.toxikon.com
Sales Range: $10-24.9 Million
Emp.: 100
Provider of Product Testing Services
N.A.I.C.S.: 541380
Nancy DiGiulio *(VP)*

Tri-Cities Laboratory, LLC **(1)**
7131 West Grandridge Blvd, Kennewick, WA 99336
Tel.: (509) 736-0100
Web Site: http://www.tricitieslab.com
Medical Laboratory Services
N.A.I.C.S.: 621511
Jean Lewis *(Mgr-Laboratory)*

Viro-Med Laboratories, Inc. **(1)**
1447 York Ct, Burlington, NC 27215
Tel.: (800) 582-0077
Web Site: http://www.viromed.com
Laboratory Testing Services
N.A.I.C.S.: 541380
Kristen L. Smith *(Dir-Laboratory)*
Brandon Allen *(Dir-Quality)*

LABWIRE, INC.
6015 N 43rd Ave, Phoenix, AZ 85019
Tel.: (281) 934-3153 NV
Web Site: https://labwire.co
Year Founded: 2004
LBWR—(OTCIQ)
Holding Company; Occupational Laboratory Testing Services
N.A.I.C.S.: 551112
Dexter Morris *(Chm)*

LADDER CAPITAL CORP.
320 Park Ave 15th Fl, New York, NY 10022
Tel.: (212) 715-3170 DE

Ladder Capital Corp.—(Continued)

Web Site:
https://www.laddercapital.com
Year Founded: 2013
LADR—(NYSE)
Rev.: $407,284,000
Assets: $5,512,677,000
Liabilities: $3,980,479,000
Net Worth: $1,532,198,000
Earnings: $101,125,000
Emp.: 59
Fiscal Year-end: 12/31/23
Commercial Real Estate Financial
Services
N.A.I.C.S.: 522310
Brian R. Harris *(Co-Founder & CEO)*
Robert M. Perelman *(Co-Founder & Head-Asset Mgmt)*
Greta Guggenheim *(Co-Founder)*
Paul J. Miceli *(CFO)*
Michael Scarola *(Chief Credit Officer)*
Craig Robertson *(Head-Underwriting & Portfolio Mgr-Loan)*
Matthew Fitzgerald *(Treas)*
Michelle Wallach *(Chief Compliance Officer)*
Mark Ableman *(Head-Transaction Mgmt)*
David Traitel *(Head-Legal Structuring)*
Ed Peterson *(Head-CMBS Trading & Co-Head-Securitization)*
Adam Siper *(Head-Origination)*
Anthony V. Esposito *(Chief Acctg Officer)*
Michael Cafaro *(CTO)*
Pamela L. McCormack *(Co-Founder & Pres)*

Subsidiaries:

Ladder Capital Adviser LLC   **(1)**
345 Park Ave, New York, NY 10154
Tel.: (212) 715-3170
Investment Advisory Services
N.A.I.C.S.: 523940
Robert Perelman *(Head-Asset Mgmt)*

Ladder Capital Asset Management
LLC   **(1)**
345 Park Ave 8th Fl, New York, NY 10154
Tel.: (212) 715-3170
Web Site: http://www.ladderfunds.com
Asset Management Services
N.A.I.C.S.: 531390
Craig Sedmak *(Mng Dir & Portfolio Mgr)*

Ladder Capital Finance Holdings
LLLP   **(1)**
345 Park Ave 8th Fl, New York, NY 10154
Tel.: (212) 715-3170
Web Site: http://www.laddercapital.com
Holding Company
N.A.I.C.S.: 551112

Ladder Capital Securities LLC   **(1)**
345 Park Ave 8th Fl, New York, NY 10154
Tel.: (212) 715-3170
Web Site: http://www.laddercapital.com
Brokerage Services for Equity Market
N.A.I.C.S.: 523150

Lingerfelt Office Properties LLC   **(1)**
4121 Cox Rd, Glen Allen, VA 23060-3321
Tel.: (804) 270-4249
Real Estate Services
N.A.I.C.S.: 531210

ONP Owner LLC   **(1)**
28411 Northwestern Hwy, Southfield, MI
48034
Tel.: (248) 353-2990
Brokerage Services
N.A.I.C.S.: 523150

LADRX CORPORATION

11726 San Vicente Blvd Ste 650, Los
Angeles, CA 90049
Tel.: (310) 826-5648   DE
Web Site: https://www.ladrxcorp.com
Year Founded: 1985
LADX—(OTCQB)
Rev.: $11,689
Assets: $2,246,772

Liabilities: $3,564,736
Net Worth: ($1,317,964)
Earnings: ($4,761,954)
Emp.: 3
Fiscal Year-end: 12/31/22
Biological Product (except Diagnostic)
Manufacturing
N.A.I.C.S.: 325414
John Y. Caloz *(CFO & Sr VP)*
Stephen Snowdy *(CEO)*

LADYBUG RESOURCE GROUP, INC.

1408 S Denver Ave, Tulsa, OK 74119
Tel.: (918) 727-7137   OK
Year Founded: 2007
LBRG—(OTCIQ)
Information Technology Services
N.A.I.C.S.: 541512
James P. Kurko *(Pres, CEO & CFO)*

LAIRD SUPERFOOD, INC.

5303 Spine Rd Ste 204, Boulder, CO
80301
Tel.: (541) 588-3600   DE
Web Site:
https://www.lairdsuperfood.com
Year Founded: 2015
LSF—(NYSEAMEX)
Rev.: $35,828,392
Assets: $30,039,340
Liabilities: $7,528,328
Net Worth: $22,511,012
Earnings: ($40,337,318)
Emp.: 35
Fiscal Year-end: 12/31/22
Food Product Mfr & Distr
N.A.I.C.S.: 311999
Anna Kochetova Hamill *(Interim CFO)*
Geoffrey T. Barker *(Chm)*
Jason Vieth *(Pres & CEO)*
Laird Hamilton *(Co-Founder)*
Gabby Reece *(Co-Founder)*
Andrew Judd *(Chief Comml Officer)*

LAKE SHORE BANCORP, INC.

128 E 4th St, Dunkirk, NY 14048
Tel.: (716) 366-4070   NY
Web Site:
https://www.lakeshoresavings.com
Year Founded: 1891
LSBK—(NASDAQ)
Rev.: $29,458,000
Assets: $699,914,000
Liabilities: $618,730,000
Net Worth: $81,184,000
Earnings: $5,708,000
Emp.: 113
Fiscal Year-end: 12/31/22
Bank Holding Company; Federally-
Chartered Savings & Loan Services
N.A.I.C.S.: 551111
Susan C. Ballard *(Exec VP-Retail, Sls, and Mktg)*
Taylor Gilden *(CFO, CFO/Treas-Lake Shore, MHC & Treas)*
Jeffrey M. Werdein *(Interim Principal Exec Officer & Exec VP-Comml Division)*
Sharon E. Brautigam *(Vice Chm)*
Kim C. Liddoll *(Proc & CEO)*
Dylan P. Rubadeaux *(Officer-Comml Loan, Sr VP & Asst VP)*
Adam J. Dimitri *(VP-Retail Banking, Asst VP & Reg Mgr-Sls)*
Amy Harding *(Officer-Reg Sls, VP, Asst VP & Reg Mgr-Sls)*
Melissa Sprague *(COO)*
Robert V. Cortellucci *(CTO)*
Tamara Bellanti *(Sr VP-Human Resources)*
Benjamin Pietak *(Controller)*
Tyler Pendleton *(Officer-Comml Loan & Asst VP)*
Christina Schwindler *(Officer-Reg Sls & VP)*

Subsidiaries:

Lake Shore Savings Bank   **(1)**
128 E 4th St, Dunkirk, NY 14048   **(100%)**
Tel.: (716) 366-4070
Web Site:
https://www.lakeshoresavings.com
Sales Range: $25-49.9 Million
Commericial Banking
N.A.I.C.S.: 522110
Jeffrey M. Werdein *(Exec VP-Comml Div)*
Dylan P. Rubadeaux *(Officer-Comml Loan & VP)*
Mike Noville *(VP)*
Tyler Pendleton *(Asst VP)*

LAKELAND FINANCIAL CORPORATION

202 E Ctr St, Warsaw, IN 46580
Tel.: (574) 267-6144   IN
Web Site:
https://www.lakecitybank.com
Year Founded: 1983
LKFN—(NASDAQ)
Rev.: $281,429,000
Assets: $6,432,371,000
Liabilities: $5,863,484,000
Net Worth: $568,887,000
Earnings: $103,817,000
Emp.: 610
Fiscal Year-end: 12/31/22
Bank Holding Company
N.A.I.C.S.: 551111
David M. Findlay *(CEO)*
Donald J. Robinson-Gay *(Chief Credit Officer & Sr VP)*
Kristin L. Pruitt *(Pres)*
Lisa M. O'Neill *(CFO & Exec VP)*
Brok A. Lahrman *(Chief Acctg Officer & Sr VP-Fin)*
Kyra E. Clark *(Chief HR Officer)*
J. Rickard Donovan *(Gen Counsel)*
Stephanie J. Leniski *(Chief Retail Banking Officer)*
Jonathan P. Steiner *(Chief Wealth Advisory Officer)*

Subsidiaries:

Lake City Bank   **(1)**
202 E Ctr St, Warsaw, IN 46580
Tel.: (574) 267-6144
Web Site: https://www.lakecitybank.com
Sales Range: $150-199.9 Million
Emp.: 500
Provider of Financial Services
N.A.I.C.S.: 522110
David M. Findlay *(CEO)*
Donald J. Robinson-Gay *(Chief Credit Officer & Sr VP)*
Kristin L. Pruitt *(Pres)*
Stephanie R. Leniski *(Chief Retail Banking Officer & Sr VP)*
Lisa M. O'Neill *(CFO & Exec VP)*
Jill A. DeBatty *(Dir & Sr VP)*
Eric H. Ottinger *(Chief Banking Officer & Exec VP)*
Mary Horan *(Dir-Mktg & PR)*
Kristin L. Pruitt *(Chief Admin Officer & Exec VP)*
Jonathan P. Steiner *(Chief Wealth Advisory Officer & Sr VP)*
Rick Donovan *(Gen Counsel & Sr VP)*
Scott B. Bucher *(Mgr & VP)*
Kyra E. Clark *(Chief HR Officer & Sr VP)*
Kevin Hampton *(VP)*

Subsidiary (Domestic):

Lake City Bank Investments
Limited   **(2)**
202 E Ctr St, Warsaw, IN 46581
Tel.: (574) 267-6144
Web Site: http://www.lakecitybank.com
Sales Range: $10-24.9 Million
Emp.: 50
Provider of Financial services
N.A.I.C.S.: 522110

LAKELAND INDUSTRIES, INC.

1525 Perimeter Pkwy Ste 325, Huntsville, AL 35806
Tel.: (256) 350-3873   DE

Web Site: https://www.lakeland.com
Year Founded: 1982
LAKE—(NASDAQ)
Rev.: $112,846,000
Assets: $142,327,000
Liabilities: $22,337,000
Net Worth: $119,990,000
Earnings: $1,873,000
Emp.: 1,550
Fiscal Year-end: 01/31/23
Industrial Safety Garments & Accessories Mfr & Whslr
N.A.I.C.S.: 339113
James M. Jenkins *(Chm, Pres & CEO)*
Roger D. Shannon *(CFO & Sec)*
Hui An *(COO)*

Subsidiaries:

Chemland Industries, Inc.   **(1)**
202 Pride Ln SW, Decatur, AL
35603   **(100%)**
Tel.: (256) 353-9395
Web Site: http://www.lakeland.com
Sales Range: $50-74.9 Million
Emp.: 200
Mfr of Protective Clothing
N.A.I.C.S.: 339113

Industrias Lakeland S.A. de C.V. **(1)**
Tomas Urbinia 1 Colonia Villa Flavia,
99340, Jerez de Garcia Salinas, Zacatecas,
Mexico
Tel.: (52) 4949454961
Web Site: http://www.lakeland.com
Emp.: 300
Safety Glove & Apparel Mfr
N.A.I.C.S.: 316990

LHD Group Deutschland GmbH   **(1)**
Herseler Str. 20-40, 50389, Wesseling, Germany
Tel.: (49) 2236 3307100
Web Site: https://www.lhd-group.com
Emp.: 160
Textile Mfr
N.A.I.C.S.: 315990

Subsidiary (US):

BullEx, Inc.   **(2)**
20 Corporate Cir, Albany, NY 12203
Tel.: (518) 833-0432
Web Site: http://www.bullex.com
Emp.: 80
Fire, Safety & Hazmat Training Tools Mfr
N.A.I.C.S.: 333998
Steve Schwartz *(CEO)*

Lion Group, Inc   **(2)**
7200 Poe Avenue, Suite 400, Dayton, OH
45414
Tel.: (800) 421-2926
Web Site: http://www.lionprotects.com
Emergency Services; Law Enforcement &
Military Apparel & Equipment Mfr
N.A.I.C.S.: 315250

Subsidiary (Domestic):

Elbeco Incorporated   **(3)**
4418 Pottsville Pike, Reading, PA 19605-
1205
Tel.: (610) 921-0651
Web Site: http://www.elbeco.com
Sales Range: $150-199.9 Million
Emp.: 600
Mfr of Professional Uniform Apparel
N.A.I.C.S.: 315250

Lion Apparel, Inc.   **(3)**
7200 Poe Ave Ste 400, Dayton, OH 45414-
2547
Tel.: (937) 898-1949
Web Site: http://www.lionprotects.com
Sales Range: $100-124.9 Million
Emp.: 1,000
Emergency Services, Law Enforcement &
Military Apparel & Equipment Mfr
N.A.I.C.S.: 315250
Steve Schwartz *(CEO)*
Jim DiSanto *(CFO)*

Lakeland (Beijing) Safety Products,
Co., Ltd.   **(1)**
Unit 503 Bldg B Sinolight Plaza No 4
Wangjing Qi Yang Road, Chaoyang District,

Beijing, 100102, China
Tel.: (86) 1064379226
Web Site: http://www.lakeland.com
Emp.: 50
Safety Glove & Apparel Mfr
N.A.I.C.S.: 316990

Lakeland Argentina, SRL (1)
Calle Cuba Calle 130 No 4870, Parque Industrial Newton Villa Ballester San Martin,
B1653KBN, Buenos Aires, Argentina
Tel.: (54) 1147679484
Web Site: http://global.lakeland.com
Safety Glove & Apparel Mfr
N.A.I.C.S.: 316990

Lakeland Gloves and Safety Apparel Private Ltd. (1)
B-42 sector- 2, Noida, 201301, Uttar Pradesh, India
Tel.: (91) 9725213499
Safety Glove & Apparel Mfr
N.A.I.C.S.: 316990
Anil Thomas *(Gen mgr-Ops)*
Mayank Arora *(Head-Ops)*

Lakeland India Private Limited (1)
A-29 Sector 83, G B Nagar District, Noida,
201305, Uttar Pradesh, India
Tel.: (91) 1204249261
Protective Cloth Mfr
N.A.I.C.S.: 315990

Lakeland Industries Europe Ltd. (1)
Unit 9-10 Jet Park Jet Park Way 244 Main Road, Newport, HU15 2JU, East Yorkshire,
United Kingdom
Tel.: (44) 1430478140
Web Site: http://www.lakeland.com
Emp.: 15
Safety Glove & Apparel Mfr
N.A.I.C.S.: 316990

Lakeland Industries, Inc. Agencia en Chile (1)
Camino del Cerro 290, Modulo G3, 123,
Santiago, Chile
Tel.: (56) 229980545
Web Site: http://global.lakeland.com
Safety Glove & Apparel Mfr
N.A.I.C.S.: 316990

Lakeland Protective Wear, Inc. (1)
59 Bury Court, Brantford, N3S 0A9, ON,
Canada (100%)
Tel.: (519) 757-0700
Web Site: http://www.lakeland.com
Sales Range: $1-9.9 Million
Emp.: 10
Mfr of Industrial Safety Apparel
N.A.I.C.S.: 315990

Migliara S.A. (1)
Avda Brasil 2633 Apto 203, Montevideo,
Uruguay
Tel.: (598) 11147679484
Protective Cloth Mfr
N.A.I.C.S.: 315990

SAL Commercial Venture One, S.A. de C.V. (1)
Tomas Urbinia 1 Colonia Villa Flavia, Jerez de Garcia Salinas, 99340, Zacatecas,
Mexico
Tel.: (52) 4949454961
Protective Cloth Mfr
N.A.I.C.S.: 315990

Weifang Lakeland Safety Products Co., Ltd. (1)
No 61 South Huaan Road, Anqing, 262100,
Shandong, China
Tel.: (86) 5364264990
Safety Glove & Apparel Mfr
N.A.I.C.S.: 316990

Weifang Meiyang Protective Products Co., Ltd. (1)
Hua An Road Zhongduan, Anqing, 262100,
Shandong, China
Tel.: (86) 53285269999
Web Site: http://www.lakeland.com
Safety Glove & Apparel Mfr
N.A.I.C.S.: 316990

LAKESIDE BANCSHARES, INC.
4735 Nelson Rd, Lake Charles, LA
70606-4140

Tel.: (337) 474-3766   LA
Web Site: https://mylksb.bank
Year Founded: 2018
LKSB—(OTCIQ)
Sales Range: $1-9.9 Million
Offices of Bank Holding Companies
N.A.I.C.S.: 551111
Roy Raftery *(Pres & CEO)*
Shively Verrette *(CFO)*

Subsidiaries:

Lakeside Bank (1)
4735 Nelson Rd, Lake Charles, LA 70605
Tel.: (337) 474-3766
Web Site: http://mylksb.bank
Sales Range: $1-9.9 Million
Emp.: 42
Commercial Banking
N.A.I.C.S.: 522110
Roy Raftery *(Pres & CEO)*
Shively Verrette *(CFO & Exec VP)*

LAKEVIEW ACQUISITION CORPORATION
155 Vlg Blvd Ste 205, Princeton, NJ
08540
Tel.: (609) 342-2088   DE
Year Founded: 2021
LKVA.U—(NYSE)
Investment Services
N.A.I.C.S.: 523999
Jeffrey Hayman *(Chm & CEO)*
George Perrotta *(CFO)*

LAM RESEARCH CORPORATION
4650 Cushing Pkwy, Fremont, CA
94538
Tel.: (510) 572-0200   CA
Web Site:
    https://www.lamresearch.com
Year Founded: 1980
LRCX—(NASDAQ)
Rev.: $14,905,386,000
Assets: $18,744,728,000
Liabilities: $10,205,274,000
Net Worth: $8,539,454,000
Earnings: $3,827,772,000
Emp.: 17,450
Fiscal Year-end: 06/30/24
Semiconductor Processing Equipment Used in the Fabrication of Integrated Circuits
N.A.I.C.S.: 333242
Douglas R. Bettinger *(CFO & Exec VP)*
Abhijit Y. Talwalkar *(Chm)*
Richard A. Gottscho *(Exec VP)*
Patrick J. Lord *(COO & Exec VP)*
Vahid Vahedi *(CTO & Sr VP)*
Seshasayee Varadarajan *(Sr VP-Global Products Gp)*
Audrey Charles *(Sr VP-Corporate Strategy)*
Rob Hawthorne *(CIO)*
Karsten Theess *(VP-Security, Transformation & Resilience-Global)*
Ava M. Hahn *(Chief Legal Officer, Sec & Sr VP)*
Mary Hassett *(Chief HR Officer)*
Stacey MacNeil *(Chief Comm Officer)*
Neil Fernandes *(Sr VP-Global Customer Ops)*
Christina C. Correia *(Chief Acctg Officer & VP-Corp Fin & IR)*
Timothy M. Archer *(Pres & CEO)*

Subsidiaries:

Corus Manufacturing Ltd. (1)
14-9 Gajangsaneopdong-ro, Osan, 18103,
Gyeonggi-do, Korea (South)
Tel.: (82) 3180554900
Web Site: http://www.corusmfg.com
Semiconductor Mfr
N.A.I.C.S.: 334413

Coventor Korea Limited (1)
Mffice Dongtan Center Room No 704 7F 61

Dongtanmunhwasenteo-ro, Hwaseong,
Gyeonggi-do, Korea (South)
Tel.: (82) 1090313392
Semiconductor Machinery Mfr
N.A.I.C.S.: 333242

Coventor Sarl (1)
3 avenue du Quebec, ZI de Courtaboeuf,
91140, Villebon-sur-Yvette, France
Tel.: (33) 169298494
Semiconductor Machinery Mfr
N.A.I.C.S.: 333242

Coventor, Inc. (1)
135 Beaver St Ste 205, Waltham, MA
02452
Tel.: (617) 648-8388
Web Site: http://www.coventor.com
Software Publishers; Automated Solutions
N.A.I.C.S.: 513210
Michael J. Jamiolkowski *(Founder, VP & Gen Mgr)*
David Fried *(VP-Computational Products)*
Kenneth B. Greiner *(Sr Dir-Semiconductor Product Dev)*

Lam Research (India) Private Ltd. (1)
Krishnappa Garden, CV Raman Nagar,
Bengaluru, 560071, India (100%)
Tel.: (91) 8041500126
Semiconductor Equipment Mfr & Sales
N.A.I.C.S.: 333242

Lam Research (Ireland) Limited (1)
Part First Floor Bewley's House Northern Cross Bewley's House, Dublin, 17, Ireland
Tel.: (353) 187748000
Sales Range: $100-124.9 Million
Mfr of Semiconductors
N.A.I.C.S.: 334413

Lam Research (Israel) Ltd. (1)
17 Tzoran Street, Gat Industrial Park,
Qiryat-Gat, 8258121, Israel
Tel.: (972) 89576622
Sales Range: $100-124.9 Million
Emp.: 50
Semiconductor Mfr & Testing Services
N.A.I.C.S.: 334413

Lam Research (Shanghai) Co., Ltd. (1)
Area B 2F No 177 Bibo Road, Zhang Jiang Hi Tech Park Pudong, Shanghai, 201203,
China (100%)
Tel.: (86) 2120371500
Sales Range: $10-24.9 Million
Emp.: 15
Mfr of Electronic Components
N.A.I.C.S.: 334419
Daniel Liao *(Executives)*

Lam Research B.V. (1)
Fokkerweg 300, 1438, Oude Meer,
Netherlands (100%)
Tel.: (31) 205000541
Web Site: http://www.lamresearch.com
Sales Range: $10-24.9 Million
Emp.: 11
Mfr of Semiconductors
N.A.I.C.S.: 334413
P. Ruijter *(Mng Dir)*

Lam Research Co., Ltd. (1)
Yusen Shinyokohama 1-Chome Bldg 7F
1-7-9 Shinyokohama, Kohoku-ku, Yoko-hama, 222-0033, Kanagawa, Japan
Tel.: (81) 454780300
Web Site: http://www.lamresearch.com
Emp.: 240
Semiconductor Manufacturing Equipment Sales & Service
N.A.I.C.S.: 423690
Yoshida Yukimasa *(Pres)*

Branch (Domestic):

Lam Research Co., Ltd. (2)
Block M5-7 Wing-Wing Takaoka Bldg 5F
1-8 Suehiro-cho, Takaoka-shi, Toyama, 933-0023, Japan (100%)
Tel.: (81) 766282101
Sales Range: $100-124.9 Million
Emp.: 6
Semiconductor Mfr
N.A.I.C.S.: 334413

Lam Research Co., Ltd. (2)
Sakura Bldg 2C, 6-15 Harashin-machi, Oita,

870-0912, Japan
Tel.: (81) 975514761
Sales Range: $1-9.9 Million
Emp.: 7
Mfr of Semiconductors
N.A.I.C.S.: 334413

Lam Research Co., Ltd. - Hiroshima Service Center (2)
Sakaemachi Bldg 1F 10-27 Saijosakae-machi Higashi, Hiroshima, 739-0015, Japan
Tel.: (81) 824982330
Web Site: http://www.lamresearch.com
Sales Range: $100-124.9 Million
Emp.: 100
Mfr of Semiconductors
N.A.I.C.S.: 334413

Lam Research Co., Ltd. (1)
1F No 22 R&D Rd II Hsinchu Science Park,
Hsinchu, 300092, Taiwan (100%)
Tel.: (886) 35798666
Sales Range: $25-49.9 Million
Emp.: 300
Computers & Software
N.A.I.C.S.: 423430

Lam Research Corporation (1)
60 Merritt Blvd Ste 100, Fishkill, NY 12524-2236
Tel.: (845) 897-1300
Sales Range: $25-49.9 Million
Emp.: 35
Mfr of Semiconductors
N.A.I.C.S.: 332216

Lam Research Corporation (1)
6401 S Eisenman Rd Ste 109, Boise, ID
83716 (100%)
Tel.: (208) 373-7400
Sales Range: $25-49.9 Million
Emp.: 30
Mfr of Semiconductors
N.A.I.C.S.: 333242

Lam Research Corporation (1)
12345 N Lamar Blvd Ste 150, Austin, TX
78753
Tel.: (512) 652-5200
Sales Range: $100-124.9 Million
Mfr of Semiconductor Processing Equipment
N.A.I.C.S.: 334413

Lam Research Corporation (1)
222 NE Park Plz Dr Ste 130, Vancouver,
WA 98684-5878
Tel.: (360) 260-9600
Sales Range: $10-24.9 Million
Emp.: 12
Supplier of Semiconductors
N.A.I.C.S.: 333242

Lam Research GmbH (1)
Manfred-von-Ardenne-Ring 20 Haus A,
01099, Dresden, Germany (100%)
Tel.: (49) 3518966164
Sales Range: $100-124.9 Million
Mfr of Semiconductors
N.A.I.C.S.: 334413

Lam Research Holding GmbH (1)
Leutschenbachstr 95, 8050, Zurich, Switzerland
Tel.: (41) 13083948
Sales Range: $250-299.9 Million
Emp.: 880
Wet Water Surface Conditioning Mfr
N.A.I.C.S.: 333414

Subsidiary (Non-US):

Lam Research AG (2)
Sez-Strasse 1, 9500, Villach,
Austria (100%)
Tel.: (43) 42422040
Web Site: http://www.lamresearch.com
Sales Range: $100-124.9 Million
Emp.: 450
Semiconductor Mfr Equipment
N.A.I.C.S.: 333242

Lam Research Management GmbH (2)
Sez-Strasse 1, 9500, Villach,
Austria (100%)
Tel.: (43) 42422040
Web Site: http://www.lamresearch.com

Lam Research Corporation—(Continued)

Sales Range: $75-99.9 Million
Emp.: 600
Administrative Management & General
Management Consulting Services
N.A.I.C.S.: 541611
Bulson Christian (Mng Dir)

SEZ Korea Ltd. (2)
4F 28 Pangyo-ro 255beon-gil, Bundang-gu,
Seongnam, Gyeonggi-do, Korea
(South) (100%)
Tel.: (82) 317106600
Sales Range: $75-99.9 Million
Marketing Consulting Services
N.A.I.C.S.: 541613

Lam Research Illinois IAG, Inc. (1)
509 N 3rd Ave, Des Plaines, IL 60016-1196
Tel.: (847) 803-3200
High Precision Processing Machine Mfr
N.A.I.C.S.: 333248

**Lam Research International Holding
Company** (1)
4650 Cushing Pkwy, Fremont, CA 94538
Tel.: (510) 572-0200
Holding Company
N.A.I.C.S.: 551112

Lam Research International Sarl (1)
Avenue Edouard-Dubois 20, 2000, Neucha-
tel, Switzerland
Tel.: (41) 329242999
Web Site: http://www.lamresearch.com
Sales Range: $25-49.9 Million
Emp.: 30
Semiconductor & Related Device Mfr
N.A.I.C.S.: 334413

Lam Research Korea Ltd. (1)
4F 28 Pangyo-ro 255beon-gil, Bundang-gu,
Songnam, Gyeonggi, Korea (South)
Tel.: (82) 317106600
Web Site: http://www.lamresearch.com
Mfr of Semiconductors
N.A.I.C.S.: 334413

**Lam Research Malaysia Sdn.
Bhd.** (1)
Suite 1 050 1st Floor Business Center, Ku-
lim Hi-Tech Park, 09000, Kulim, Kedah,
Malaysia (100%)
Tel.: (60) 44023100
Web Site: http://www.lamresearch.com
Sales Range: $10-24.9 Million
Emp.: 12
Semiconductor Equipment Sales
N.A.I.C.S.: 423690

**Lam Research Manufacturing Korea,
LLC** (1)
14-9 Gajangsaneopdong-ro, Osan, 18103,
Gyeonggi, Korea (South)
Tel.: (82) 3180554900
Electronic Parts & Equipment Whslr
N.A.I.C.S.: 423690

Lam Research SAS (1)
31 Old Oak Road, 38240, Meylan,
France (100%)
Tel.: (33) 476614900
Sales Range: $10-24.9 Million
Emp.: 37
Semiconductor Mfr
N.A.I.C.S.: 334413

Branch (Domestic):

Lam Research SAS (2)
Essonne Nanopole 224 Boulevard John
Kennedy, 91105, Corbeil-Essonnes, Cedex,
France (100%)
Tel.: (33) 164937400
Sales Range: $10-24.9 Million
Mfr of Semiconductors
N.A.I.C.S.: 334413

Lam Research Service Co., Ltd. (1)
Room 302 No 6 Building No 89 Xingchuang
4Th Road, Wuxi New District, Wuxi,
214028, JiangSu, China
Tel.: (86) 51081903880
Emp.: 200
Semiconductor Processing Equipment Mfr
N.A.I.C.S.: 334413
Liu Ghu (Mgr)

Lam Research Services Ltd. (1)
17 Tzoran Street, Gat Industrial Park,

Qiryat-Gat, 8258121, Israel (100%)
Tel.: (972) 89576622
Semiconductor Equipment Mfr & Sales
N.A.I.C.S.: 333242

**Lam Research Singapore Pte.
Ltd.** (1)
67 Ubi Avenue 1 06-12 Starhub Green, Sin-
gapore, 408942, Singapore (100%)
Tel.: (65) 63476888
Sales Range: $25-49.9 Million
Emp.: 95
Mfr of Industrial Machinery & Equipment
N.A.I.C.S.: 425120

Lam Research Srl (1)
Centro Direzionale Colleoni Viale Colleoni
11 Palazzo Sirio 3, 20864, Agrate Brianza,
MB, Italy (100%)
Tel.: (39) 039657041
Web Site: http://www.lamresearch.com
Sales Range: $100-124.9 Million
Mfr of Semiconductors
N.A.I.C.S.: 334413

Metryx, Ltd. (1)
1230/1240/1255 Park Avenue Aztec West,
Almondsbury, BS32 4SH, United Kingdom
Tel.: (44) 1454456370
Web Site: http://www.metryx.net
Semiconductor Mfr
N.A.I.C.S.: 334413
Alistair Smith (Chm)

**Novellus Systems International Trad-
ing (Shanghai) Co. Ltd.** (1)
439 Chun Xiao Rd Unit 10, Pudong New
Area, Shanghai, 201203, China (100%)
Tel.: (86) 2150802056
Sales Range: $125-149.9 Million
Semiconductor Equipment Sales
N.A.I.C.S.: 423690

Novellus Systems Italy SRL (1)
Via Fratelli Ruffini 10, 20123, Milan,
Italy (100%)
Tel.: (39) 0396058624
Sales Range: $10-24.9 Million
Emp.: 4
Semiconductor Equipment Sales & Service
N.A.I.C.S.: 423690

**Novellus Systems Semiconductor
Equipment Shanghai Co. Ltd.** (1)
Unit 10 SOHO Bldg 439 Chun Xiao Rd, Pu-
dong New Area, Shanghai, 201203,
China (100%)
Tel.: (86) 2150802056
Sales Range: $25-49.9 Million
Emp.: 30
Semiconductor Equipment Mfr
N.A.I.C.S.: 333242

Semsysco GmbH (1)
Karolingerstrasse 7C, 5020, Salzburg, Aus-
tria
Tel.: (43) 66222210
Web Site: https://www.semsysco.com
Emp.: 200
Semiconductor Processing Solution Ser-
vices
N.A.I.C.S.: 541380

Semsysco Singapore Pte. Ltd. (1)
5 Simei St 3 05-04, Singapore, 5298792,
Singapore
Tel.: (65) 67820229
Semiconductor Processing Solution Ser-
vices
N.A.I.C.S.: 541380

Silfex, Incorporated (1)
950 S Franklin St, Eaton, OH 45320
Tel.: (937) 472-3311
Web Site: https://www.silfex.com
Custom Silicon Component Mfr
N.A.I.C.S.: 334413

SolMateS B.V. (1)
Auke Vleerstraat 3, 7521 PE, Enschede,
Netherlands
Tel.: (31) 537009709
Web Site: https://www.solmates-pld.com
Semiconductor Device Distr
N.A.I.C.S.: 423690
Arjen Janssens (CEO)
Matthijn Dekkers (CTO)
Kristiaan Bohm (COO)
Rob Jansen (CFO)
Bart Berenbak (Chief Business Develop-
ment Officer)

Talus Manufacturing, Ltd. (1)
No 3 Ziqiang 3rd Rd, Zhongli Dist, Taoyuan,
320023, Taiwan
Tel.: (886) 34518123
Web Site: https://www.talusmfg.com
Semiconductor Product Mfr
N.A.I.C.S.: 334413
Shahriar Shaghafi (Chm, VP-Ops & Strate-
gic Plng & Gen Mgr)
Wyman Fang (COO)
Evan Edward Patton (VP-CSBG & Reliant
Sys)
George Milford Schisler (Vice Chm & VP-
Legal & Corp Legal Svcs)
Odette Marie Go (VP-Treasury-Global)

LAMAR ADVERTISING COMPANY
5321 Corp Blvd, Baton Rouge, LA
70808
Tel.: (225) 926-1000 DE
Web Site: https://www.lamar.com
Year Founded: 1902
LAMR—(NASDAQ)
Rev.: $2,110,987,000
Assets: $6,563,622,000
Liabilities: $5,346,834,000
Net Worth: $1,216,788,000
Earnings: $495,398,000
Emp.: 3,550
Fiscal Year-end: 12/31/23
Outdoor Advertising Real Estate In-
vestment Trust
N.A.I.C.S.: 525990
Jay L. Johnson (CFO, Treas & Exec
VP)
Sean E. Reilly (Pres & CEO)

Subsidiaries:

Ashby Street Outdoor LLC (1)
1830 Shelby Ln, Fayetteville, AR 72704-
5255
Tel.: (479) 442-0300
Web Site: http://www.ashbystoutdoor.com
Outdoor Advertising
N.A.I.C.S.: 541850
Jim Matalone (Founder & CEO)

Canadian TODS Limited (1)
120 Whitmore Rd Unit 8 Suite 200, Wood-
bridge, L4L 6A3, ON, Canada
Tel.: (905) 851-1322
Web Site: http://www.canadatods.com
Emp.: 16
Advertising Services
N.A.I.C.S.: 541850

Colorado Logos, Inc. (1)
7717 W 6th Ave Ste A, Lakewood, CO
80214
Tel.: (303) 462-2320
Web Site:
https://colorado.interstatelogos.com
Advertising Services
N.A.I.C.S.: 541850

Delaware Logos, L.L.C. (1)
1230 Parkway Ave Ste 100, West Trenton,
NJ 08628
Web Site:
https://www.delaware.interstatelogos.com
Advertising Services
N.A.I.C.S.: 541850

Georgia Logos, L.L.C. (1)
6597 Peachtree Industrial Blvd Ste A,
Peachtree Corners, GA 30092
Tel.: (770) 447-6399
Web Site:
https://georgia.interstatelogos.com
Advertising Services
N.A.I.C.S.: 541850

Interstate Logos, L.L.C. (1)
6696 Exchequer Dr, Baton Rouge, LA
70809
Tel.: (225) 927-9408
Web Site: https://www.interstatelogos.com
N.A.I.C.S.: 541810

Kansas Logos, Inc. (1)
2231 SW Wanamaker Rd Ste 200, Topeka,
KS 66614
Tel.: (785) 272-1771
Web Site: https://kansas.interstatelogos.com
Emp.: 2
Advertising Services

Display Advertising Services
N.A.I.C.S.: 541850

Kentucky Logos, LLC (1)
2129 Commercial Dr Ste C, Frankfort, KY
40601
Tel.: (502) 227-0802
Web Site:
https://kentucky.interstatelogos.com
Emp.: 3
Logo Sign & Tourist-Oriented Directional
Signing Services
N.A.I.C.S.: 541850

**Lamar Advertising Co. - Richmond
Branch** (1)
700 Southlake Blvd, Richmond, VA 23236
Tel.: (804) 794-7000
Web Site: https://www.lamar.com
Sales Range: $10-24.9 Million
Emp.: 35
Provid
N.A.I.C.S.: 513110

**Lamar Alliance Airport Advertising
Co.** (1)
8945 W Russell Rd Ste 150, Las Vegas,
NV 89148-1228
Tel.: (702) 362-4777
Web Site:
https://www.allianceairportadvertising.com
Emp.: 11
Advertising Services at Airports
N.A.I.C.S.: 541890
Shauna Forsythe (Pres & CEO)

Lamar Corporation (1)
5321 Corporate Blvd, Baton Rouge, LA
70808
Tel.: (225) 926-1000
Web Site: http://www.lamar.com
Sales Range: $25-49.9 Million
Emp.: 130
Real Estate Owner, Manager & Outdoor
Advertising
N.A.I.C.S.: 541850
Kevin P. Reilly Jr. (Chm, Pres & Co-CEO)

Subsidiary (Domestic):

**Lamar Advertising of Colorado
Springs, Inc.** (2)
2110 Naegele Rd, Colorado Springs, CO
80904
Tel.: (719) 473-4747
Web Site: https://www.lamar.com
Display Advertising Services
N.A.I.C.S.: 541810
Tara Winterfeld (Office Mgr)
Trevin Wecks (Gen Mgr)

**Lamar Advertising of Michigan,
Inc.** (2)
6405 N Hix Rd, Westland, MI 48185
Tel.: (734) 729-6430
Web Site: http://www.lamar.com
Emp.: 21
Advertising Services
N.A.I.C.S.: 541850
Richard Rickert (Mgr-Territory)

**Lamar Advertising of Oklahoma,
Inc.** (2)
123 NW 50th St, Oklahoma City, OK 73118
Tel.: (405) 528-2683
Web Site: https://www.lamar.com
Advertising Services
N.A.I.C.S.: 541850

Lamar Advertising of Penn, LLC (2)
437 5th Ave 3rd Fl, New York, NY 10016
Tel.: (212) 644-6147
Advertising Services
N.A.I.C.S.: 541850

**Lamar Advertising of South Dakota,
Inc.** (2)
3839 Sturgis Rd, Rapid City, SD 57702
Tel.: (605) 787-6688
Web Site: https://www.lamar.com
Advertising Services
N.A.I.C.S.: 541850

**Lamar Advertising of Youngstown,
Inc.** (2)
1063 Trumbull Ave, Girard, OH 44420
Tel.: (330) 759-8200
Web Site: http://www.lamar.com
Emp.: 20
Advertising Services

N.A.I.C.S.: 541850
Bob Schneider *(Gen Mgr)*
Ann Beeson *(Office Mgr)*
Hannah Heinl Ashbaugh *(Coord-Sls & Campaign)*
Jon Hunt *(Mgr-Sls)*
Michael Basile *(Mgr-Real Estate)*
Shannon Morrall *(Coord-Sls & Campaign)*

Lamar Central Outdoor, LLC (2)
77-583 El Duna Ct Ste J, Palm Desert, CA 92211
Tel.: (760) 327-4500
Advertising Services
N.A.I.C.S.: 541810

Lamar Obie Corporation (2)
1600 Valley River Dr Ste 390, Eugene, OR 97401
Tel.: (541) 686-8400
Display Advertising Services
N.A.I.C.S.: 541850

Lamar Pensacola Transit, Inc. (2)
1401 N Tarragona St, Pensacola, FL 32501-2661
Tel.: (850) 433-0024
Web Site: http://www.lamar.com
Advertising Services
N.A.I.C.S.: 541850

Lamar Tennessee, L.L.C. (2)
1993 Southerland Dr, Nashville, TN 37207
Tel.: (615) 228-5500
Advertising Services
N.A.I.C.S.: 541850

Lamar Texas Limited Partnership (2)
5521 Corporate Blvd, Baton Rouge, LA 70808-2567
Tel.: (804) 794-7000
Advertising Services
N.A.I.C.S.: 541850

Subsidiary (Non-US):

Lamar Transit Advertising Canada Ltd. (2)
3280 Production Way, Burnaby, V5A 4R4, BC, Canada
Web Site: https://www.lamar.com
Advertising Services
N.A.I.C.S.: 541850

Lamar Investments, LLC (1)
5321 Corporate Blvd, Baton Rouge, LA 70808
Tel.: (225) 926-1000
Advertising Services
N.A.I.C.S.: 541810

Lamar Media Corp. (1)
5321 Corporate Blvd, Baton Rouge, LA 70808
Tel.: (225) 926-1000
Web Site: https://www.lamar.com
Rev.: $2,110,986,999
Assets: $6,546,880,000
Liabilities: $5,337,103,000
Net Worth: $1,209,777,000
Earnings: $497,333,000
Emp.: 3,549
Fiscal Year-end: 12/31/2023
Digital Advertising Services
N.A.I.C.S.: 541850
Sean E. Reilly *(Pres & CEO)*
C. Brent McCoy *(Exec VP-Bus Dev)*
Kevin P. Reilly Jr. *(Chm)*

Louisiana Interstate Logos, L.L.C. (1)
6696 Exchequer Dr, Baton Rouge, LA 70809
Tel.: (225) 752-8640
Web Site: https://www.louisiana.interstatelogos.com
Emp.: 6
Display Advertising Services
N.A.I.C.S.: 541850

Michigan Logos, Inc. (1)
5030 Northwind Dr Ste 103, East Lansing, MI 48823
Tel.: (517) 337-2267
Web Site: https://www.michigan.interstatelogos.com
Emp.: 5
Advertising Services
N.A.I.C.S.: 541850

Minnesota Logos, Inc. (1)

7373 W 147th St Ste 107, Apple Valley, MN 55124
Tel.: (952) 895-8079
Web Site: https://www.minnesota.interstatelogos.com
Advertising Services
N.A.I.C.S.: 541850

Mississippi Logos, L.L.C. (1)
113 Village Blvd Ste C, Madison, MS 39110
Tel.: (601) 853-7100
Web Site: https://www.mississippi.interstatelogos.com
Sales Range: $25-49.9 Million
Emp.: 3
Display Advertising Services
N.A.I.C.S.: 541850

Missouri Logos, LLC (1)
4742-A Country Club Dr, Jefferson City, MO 65109
Tel.: (573) 893-6662
Web Site: https://www.missouri.interstatelogos.com
Sales Range: $25-49.9 Million
Emp.: 6
Advertising Services
N.A.I.C.S.: 541850

Montana Logos, L.L.C. (1)
70 W Custer Ave Ste A, Helena, MT 59602
Tel.: (406) 443-5646
Web Site: https://montana.interstatelogos.com
Advertising Services
N.A.I.C.S.: 541850

Nebraska Logos, Inc. (1)
315 S 9th St Ste 207, Lincoln, NE 68508
Tel.: (402) 435-5646
Web Site: https://nebraska.interstatelogos.com
Advertising Services
N.A.I.C.S.: 541850

Nevada Logos, Inc. (1)
4945 Joule St, Reno, NV 89502
Tel.: (775) 323-8787
Web Site: https://nevada.interstatelogos.com
Display Advertising Services
N.A.I.C.S.: 541850

New Mexico Logos, Inc. (1)
8601-C Washington NE, Albuquerque, NM 87113
Tel.: (505) 836-5170
Web Site: https://newmexico.interstatelogos.com
Emp.: 2
Advertising Services
N.A.I.C.S.: 541850

Ohio Logos, Inc. (1)
4384 Tuller Rd, Dublin, OH 43017
Tel.: (614) 717-0833
Web Site: http://ohio.interstatelogos.com
Sales Range: $25-49.9 Million
Emp.: 7
Advertising Services
N.A.I.C.S.: 541850

Oklahoma Logos, L.L.C. (1)
4334 NW Expy Ste 169, Oklahoma City, OK 73116
Tel.: (405) 840-1550
Web Site: https://oklahoma.interstatelogos.com
Advertising Services
N.A.I.C.S.: 541850

South Carolina Logos, Inc. (1)
1221 Atlas Rd, Columbia, SC 29209
Tel.: (803) 783-1288
Web Site: https://southcarolina.interstatelogos.com
Emp.: 2
Advertising Services
N.A.I.C.S.: 541850

Utah Logos, Inc. (1)
1226 WS Jordan Pkwy Ste C1, South Jordan, UT 84095
Tel.: (801) 263-2263
Web Site: https://utah.interstatelogos.com
Advertising Services
N.A.I.C.S.: 541850

Virginia Logos, LLC (1)

700 Southlake Blvd, Richmond, VA 23236
Tel.: (804) 229-7398
Web Site: https://virginia.interstatelogos.com
Advertising Services
N.A.I.C.S.: 541850

LAMB WESTON HOLDINGS, INC.

599 S Rivershore Ln, Eagle, ID 83616
Tel.: (208) 938-1047   OR
Web Site:
   https://www.lambweston.com
Year Founded: 1950
LW—(NYSE)
Rev.: $6,467,600,000
Assets: $7,367,000,000
Liabilities: $5,579,200,000
Net Worth: $1,787,800,000
Earnings: $725,500,000
Emp.: 10,700
Fiscal Year-end: 05/26/24
Holding Company; Frozen Potato Food Products Mfr & Whslr
N.A.I.C.S.: 551112
Bernadette M. Madarieta *(CFO & Sr VP)*
Eryk J. Spytek *(Gen Counsel, Sec & Sr VP)*
Sharon L. Miller *(Pres-North America)*
Gerardo Scheufler *(Chief Supply Chain Officer & Sr VP)*
Gregory W. Jones *(VP & Controller)*
Sukshma Rajagopalan *(Chief Information & Digital Officer)*
Marc Schroeder *(Pres-International)*
William G. Jurgensen *(Chm)*
Thomas P. Werner *(Executives)*
Michael J. Smith *(Pres & CEO)*

Subsidiaries:

Harvest Choice Australia Pty. Ltd. (1)
25 Abbott Road, Hallam, 3803, VIC, Australia
Tel.: (61) 387863322
Web Site: http://www.harvestchoice.com.au
Food Products Distr
N.A.I.C.S.: 424490
Alex Bromidis *(Ops Mgr)*

Lamb Weston, Inc. (1)
599 S Rivershore Ln, Eagle, ID 83616
Tel.: (208) 938-1047
Web Site: http://www.lambweston.com
Frozen Potato & Frozen Food Products Mfr & Distr
N.A.I.C.S.: 311412

Affiliate (Domestic):

Lamb Weston BSW, LLC (2)
300 Deschutes Way SW Ste 304, Tumwater, WA 98501
Tel.: (509) 349-2210
Frozen Potato Products Mfr
N.A.I.C.S.: 311412

Subsidiary (Non-US):

Lamb Weston Canada ULC (2)
Range Road 153 Purple Springs, Taber, T0K 1X0, AB, Canada
Tel.: (403) 223-3088
Frozen Food Mfr
N.A.I.C.S.: 311412

Subsidiary (Domestic):

Lamb Weston Sales, Inc. (2)
300 Deschutes Way SW Ste 304, Tumwater, WA 98501
Tel.: (509) 349-2210
Frozen Food Product Distr
N.A.I.C.S.: 424420

Marvel Packers Pty. Ltd. (1)
24-36 OGrady Rd, Hallam, VIC, Australia
Tel.: (61) 397032566
Web Site: http://www.marvelpackers.com.au
Frozen Specialty Food Mfr
N.A.I.C.S.: 311412

LANCASTER COLONY CORPORATION

380 Polaris Pkwy Ste 400, Westerville, OH 43082
Tel.: (614) 224-7141   OH
Web Site:
   https://www.lancastercolony.com
Year Founded: 1961
LANC—(NASDAQ)
Rev.: $1,871,759,000
Assets: $1,206,931,000
Liabilities: $281,159,000
Net Worth: $925,772,000
Earnings: $158,613,000
Emp.: 3,400
Fiscal Year-end: 06/30/24
Holding Company; Specialty Foods, Candles & Glassware & Automotive Products
N.A.I.C.S.: 551112
John B. Gerlach Jr. *(Chm)*
David A. Ciesinski *(Pres & CEO)*
Matthew R. Shurte *(Chief Ethics Officer, Gen Counsel & Sec)*
Richard W. Gentil *(Asst Treas)*
Dale N. Ganobsik *(Treas & VP-Corp Fin & Corp Fin)*
Thomas K. Pigott *(CFO, VP & Asst Sec)*

Subsidiaries:

Bantam Bagels, LLC (1)
283 Bleecker St, New York, NY 10014
Tel.: (646) 852-6320
Web Site: http://www.bantambagels.com
Food & Beverage Distr
N.A.I.C.S.: 424490

Candle-Lite (1)
10521 Millington Ct, Cincinnati, OH 45242
Tel.: (513) 563-1113
Web Site: http://www.candle-lite.com
Sales Range: $25-49.9 Million
Emp.: 160
Candle Mfr
N.A.I.C.S.: 339999

Jackson Plastics Operations Inc (1)
270 S Bennett Ave, Jackson, OH 45640-8656   **(100%)**
Tel.: (740) 286-5081
Sales Range: $25-49.9 Million
Emp.: 35
Mfr of Dish Drainers, Plastic Boxes & Buckets
N.A.I.C.S.: 331511
David Howard *(Plant Mgr)*

Lancaster Colony Commercial Products, Inc. (1)
3902 Indianola Ave, Columbus, OH 43214   **(100%)**
Tel.: (614) 263-2850
Web Site: http://www.lccpinc.com
Sales Range: $10-24.9 Million
Emp.: 20
Marketer of Commerical & Institutional Nonfood Items
N.A.I.C.S.: 425120

T. Marzetti Company (1)
380 Polaris Pkwy Ste 400, Westerville, OH 43082   **(100%)**
Tel.: (614) 846-2232
Web Site: https://www.marzetti.com
Sales Range: Less than $1 Million
Emp.: 175
Salad Dressings, Frozen Pies, Frozen Bread & Refrigerated Chip Dips Mfr
N.A.I.C.S.: 311941
David A. Ciesinski *(Pres & CEO)*
Alysa Spittle *(Dir-Comm)*

Unit (Domestic):

Marzetti Frozen Pasta (2)
803 8th St SW, Altoona, IA 50009
Tel.: (515) 967-4254
Web Site: http://www.marzetti.com
Emp.: 250
Mfr of Frozen Egg Noodles & Dumplings
N.A.I.C.S.: 311412

New York Frozen Foods Inc. (2)
380 Polaris Pkwy Ste 400, Westerville, OH 43082
Tel.: (216) 292-5655

Lancaster Colony Corporation—(Continued)

Web Site: https://nybakery.com
Partially Baked & Frozen Bread Mfr
N.A.I.C.S.: 311812
Vince Tripodi (Supvr-Production)

Sister Schubert's Homemade Rolls, Inc. (2)
100 Crenshaw Pkwy, Luverne, AL 36049
Tel.: (334) 335-2232
Web Site: http://www.ssrolls.com
Bakery Products Mfr
N.A.I.C.S.: 311812

T. Marzetti Company - West (2)
876 Yosemite Dr, Milpitas, CA 95035-5437
Tel.: (408) 263-7540
Web Site: http://www.marzetti.com
Mfr of Salad Dressings
N.A.I.C.S.: 311941

The Quality Bakery Co., Inc. (1)
50 N Glenwood Ave, Columbus, OH 43222 (100%)
Tel.: (614) 224-1424
Web Site: http://www.qualitybakery.com
Sales Range: $25-49.9 Million
Emp.: 45
Mfr of Frozen Pies
N.A.I.C.S.: 311812

LANCER ORTHODONTICS INC.
2726 Loker Ave W, Carlsbad, CA 92010
Tel.: (760) 744-5585   **CA**
Web Site:
https://www.lancerortho.com
Year Founded: 1967
LANZ—(OTCIQ)
Sales Range: $1-9.9 Million
Emp.: 40
Dental Equipment & Supplies Manufacturing
N.A.I.C.S.: 339114
Laura Abbiate (Mgr-Sls)

LANDMARK BANCORP, INC.
Tel.: (785) 565-2000   **DE**
Web Site:
https://www.landmarkbancorpinc.com
LARK—(NASDAQ)
Rev.: $56,926,000
Assets: $1,502,867,000
Liabilities: $1,391,434,000
Net Worth: $111,433,000
Earnings: $9,878,000
Emp.: 276
Fiscal Year-end: 12/31/22
Holding Company
N.A.I.C.S.: 551111
Mark A. Herpich (CFO, Treas, Sec & VP)
Patrick L. Alexander (Chm)
Abigail M. Wendel (Pres & CEO)

Subsidiaries:

Landmark National Bank (1)
701 Poyntz Ave, Manhattan, KS 66502-6052 (100%)
Tel.: (785) 565-2000
Web Site: https://www.banklandmark.com
Sales Range: $10-24.9 Million
Emp.: 50
Banking Services
N.A.I.C.S.: 522110
Mark A. Herpich (CFO)
Patrick L. Alexander (Chm)

LANDS' END, INC.
1 Lands'End Ln, Dodgeville, WI 53595
Tel.: (608) 935-6170   **DE**
Web Site: https://www.landsend.com
Year Founded: 1963
LE—(NASDAQ)
Rev.: $1,555,429,000
Assets: $1,082,148,000
Liabilities: $701,396,000
Net Worth: $380,752,000

Earnings: ($12,530,000)
Emp.: 5,000
Fiscal Year-end: 01/27/23
Holding Company; Family Clothing, Home Furnishings & Luggage Retailer & Whslr
N.A.I.C.S.: 551112
Kelly A. Ritchie (Sr VP-Employee Svcs)
Andrew J. McLean (CEO)
Bernard Louis McCracken (CFO, Principal Acctg Officer & Treas)
Jerome Squire Griffith (Vice Chm)
Angela S. Rieger (Chief Transformation Officer & Exec VP)
Peter L. Gray (Chief Admin Officer, Gen Counsel, Sec & Exec VP)
Claudia Mazo (Sr VP-Retail & Outfitters)
Luciana Marsicano (Sr VP-Sourcing-Global)
Matt Trainor (Sr VP-Brand Creative)
Andrew J. McLean (CEO)
Scott Heise (CIO & Sr VP)
Rob Gagnon (Sr VP-Mdsg)

Subsidiaries:

Lands' End Direct Merchants, Inc. (1)
820 W 78th St, Richfield, MN 55423
Tel.: (612) 861-4100
Web Site: http://www.landsend.com
Emp.: 20
Family Clothing, Bedding & Luggage Stores Operator
N.A.I.C.S.: 458110
Mark R. Pickart (Pres)

Lands' End Europe Limited (1)
Lands' End Way, Rutland, Oakham, LE15 6US, United Kingdom (100%)
Tel.: (44) 157 275 8070
Web Site: https://www.landsend.co.uk
Sales Range: $400-449.9 Million
Emp.: 550
Family Clothing, Home Furnishings & Luggage Retailer & Distr
N.A.I.C.S.: 423220

Lands' End GmbH (1)
In der Langwiese, 66693, Mettlach, Germany (100%)
Tel.: (49) 6 864 9210
Web Site: https://www.landsend.de
Sales Range: $150-199.9 Million
Emp.: 350
Family Clothing, Home Furnishings & Luggage Retailer & Distr
N.A.I.C.S.: 423220

Lands' End Japan, K.K. (1)
1-19-20 Shin-Yokohama, Kohoku Ward, Yokohama, 222-8585, Kanagawa, Japan (100%)
Tel.: (81) 45 476 0830
Web Site: https://www.landsend.co.jp
Emp.: 210
Family Clothing, Home Furnishings & Luggage Retailer & Distr
N.A.I.C.S.: 423990

LANDSEA HOMES CORP.
3130 Crow Canyon Pl Ste 325, San Ramon, CA 94583
Tel.: (949) 345-8080   **DE**
Web Site:
https://www.landseahomes.com
Year Founded: 2017
LSEA—(NASDAQ)
Rev.: $1,446,449,000
Assets: $1,440,496,000
Liabilities: $730,177,000
Net Worth: $710,319,000
Earnings: $73,551,000
Emp.: 454
Fiscal Year-end: 12/31/22
Residential Property Managers
N.A.I.C.S.: 531311
Dilliana Stewart (Chief Acctg Officer & Sr VP-Acctg)
John Ho (CEO)
Mike Forsum (Pres & COO)

Christopher Porter (CFO)
Trenton Schreiner (Sr VP-Divisional Financing)
Bruce Frank (Interim Chm)
Ming Tian (Founder)

Subsidiaries:

Antares Homes, Ltd. (1)
840 Interstate 20 E, Arlington, TX 76018
Tel.: (817) 478-6336
Sales Range: $1-9.9 Million
Emp.: 25
Management Consulting Services
N.A.I.C.S.: 541611

LANDSTAR SYSTEM, INC.
13410 Sutton Park Dr S, Jacksonville, FL 32224
Tel.: (904) 398-9400   **DE**
Web Site: https://www.landstar.com
Year Founded: 1991
LSTR—(NASDAQ)
Rev.: $5,303,322,000
Assets: $1,801,846,000
Liabilities: $817,923,000
Net Worth: $983,923,000
Earnings: $264,394,000
Emp.: 1,468
Fiscal Year-end: 12/30/23
Holding Company; Freight Transportation & Logistics Services
N.A.I.C.S.: 551112
Michael Kneller (Gen Counsel, Sec & VP)
Joe Beacom (Chief Safety & Ops Officer & VP)
Rick Coro (CIO & VP)
Frank A. Lonegro (Pres & CEO)
Aimee Cooper (Chief Admin Officer)

Subsidiaries:

Landstar Blue LLC (1)
10234 Centurian Pkwy Ste 260, Jacksonville, FL 32256
Tel.: (904) 900-5778
Web Site: https://www.landstarblue.com
Logistic Services
N.A.I.C.S.: 541614
Kim Mastronardi (Dir-Ops)
Katie MacDonald (Exec VP)
Darren Reid (VP)

Landstar System Holdings, Inc. (1)
13410 Sutton Park Dr S, Jacksonville, FL 32224 (100%)
Tel.: (904) 398-9400
Holding Company
N.A.I.C.S.: 551112
Henry H. Gerkens (Chm)
Michael L. Harvey (Sec)

Subsidiary (Domestic):

Landstar Global Logistics, Inc. (2)
840 N 3rd St, Philadelphia, PA 19123
Tel.: (917) 819-0090
Web Site: https://www.landstarbkn.com
Trucking Service
N.A.I.C.S.: 488510

Subsidiary (Domestic):

Landstar Express America, Inc. (3)
13410 Sutton Park Dr S, Jacksonville, FL 32224-5270
Tel.: (904) 398-9400
Sales Range: $200-249.9 Million
Emp.: 900
Emergency & Expedited Ground & Air Freight Transportation
N.A.I.C.S.: 488510

Subsidiary (Domestic):

Landstar Inway, Inc. (2)
13410 Sutton Park Dr S, Jacksonville, FL 32224
Tel.: (904) 398-9400
Oversized Specialty Freight Transportation Services
N.A.I.C.S.: 484230

Landstar Ligon, Inc. (2)

13410 Sutton Park Dr S, Jacksonville, FL 32224-5270
Tel.: (904) 306-2440
Trucking Service
N.A.I.C.S.: 484121

Landstar Ranger, Inc. (2)
13410 Sutton Park Dr S, Jacksonville, FL 32224-5270
Tel.: (904) 398-9400
Emp.: 900
Provider of Trucking Services
N.A.I.C.S.: 484121

Subsidiary (Domestic):

Landstar Gemini, Inc. (3)
13410 Sutton Park Dr S, Jacksonville, FL 32224-5270 (100%)
Tel.: (904) 390-4800
Emp.: 1,000
Less-Than-Truckload Freight Transportation Services
N.A.I.C.S.: 484122

Unit (Domestic):

Landstar System, Inc. - Rockford Service Center (2)
1000 Simpson Rd, Rockford, IL 61102
Tel.: (815) 972-5000
Web Site: http://www.landstar.com
Freight Transportation Arrangement Services
N.A.I.C.S.: 488510

Subsidiary (Domestic):

Landstar Transportation Logistics, Inc. (2)
13410 Sutton Park Dr S, Jacksonville, FL 32224
Tel.: (904) 398-9400
Transportation & Logistics Services
N.A.I.C.S.: 484121

Risk Management Claim Services (2)
13410 Sutton Park Dr S, Jacksonville, FL 32224-5270
Tel.: (904) 398-9400
Web Site: http://www.landstar.com
Rev.: $723,000
Emp.: 928
Insurance Claims Processing
N.A.I.C.S.: 524292
Robert C Larose (VP)
Dennis Owen (VP)

LANNETT COMPANY, INC.
1150 Northbrook Dr Ste 155, Trevose, PA 19053
Tel.: (215) 333 0000   **DE**
Web Site: http://www.lannett.com
Year Founded: 1942
LCI—(NYSE)
Rev.: $340,579,000
Assets: $484,435,000
Liabilities: $735,498,000
Net Worth: ($251,063,000)
Earnings: ($231,620,000)
Emp.: 560
Fiscal Year-end: 06/30/22
Generic Pharmaceutical Products Mfr
N.A.I.C.S.: 325412
Patrick G. LePore (Chm)
Kristie Stephens (VP-Regulatory Affairs)
Samuel H. Israel (Chief Legal Officer & Gen Counsel)
Timothy C. Crew (CEO)
Maureen M. Cavanaugh (Chief Comml Ops Officer & Sr VP)
John M. Abt (Chief Quality & Ops Officer & VP)
Grant Brock (VP-Operations)
Michael Block (VP-Business Development)

Subsidiaries:

Cody Laboratories, Inc. (1)
601 Yellowstone Ave, Cody, WY 82414
Tel.: (307) 587-7099
Pharmaceuticals Product Mfr
N.A.I.C.S.: 325412

Lannett Holdings, Inc. (1)
13200 Townsend Rd, Philadelphia, PA
19154-1014
Tel.: (215) 333-9000
Web Site: http://www.lannett.com
Sales Range: $250-299.9 Million
Emp.: 250
Holding Company
N.A.I.C.S.: 551112
Arthur P. Bedrosian (CEO)

Silarx Pharmaceuticals, Inc. (1)
1033 Stoneleigh Ave, Carmel, NY 10512
Tel.: (845) 352-4020
Web Site: http://www.silarx.com
Sales Range: $10-24.9 Million
Emp.: 37
Generic Liquid Pharmaceutical Products Mfr
N.A.I.C.S.: 325412

LANS HOLDINGS, INC.
801 Brickell, Miami, FL 33133
Tel.: (305) 755-7451   NV
Web Site:
   http://www.lansholdings.com
Year Founded: 2007
LAHO—(OTCIQ)
Sales Range: Less than $1 Million
Hoding Company; Online Payment
Processing Software
N.A.I.C.S.: 551112
Trevor Allen (CEO)
Anthony Ribas (Pres)
Ritesh Mitra (CTO)
David Christensen (Chief Strategy
Officer)

LANTERN PHARMA INC.
1920 McKinney Ave 7th Fl, Dallas,
TX 75201
Tel.: (972) 277-1136   DE
Web Site:
   https://www.lanternpharma.com
Year Founded: 2013
LTRN—(NASDAQ)
Rev.: $204,355
Assets: $58,836,321
Liabilities: $2,798,297
Net Worth: $56,038,024
Earnings: ($14,259,946)
Emp.: 22
Fiscal Year-end: 12/31/22
Biotechnology Research & Development Services
N.A.I.C.S.: 541714
Panna Sharma (Pres & CEO)
David R. Margrave (CFO & Sec)
Kishor G. Bhatia (Chief Scientific Officer)
Peter Nara (Founder)
Donald Jeff Keyser (Chm)
Reggie Ewesuedo (VP-Clinical Dev)
Ernest Kitt (Head-Clinical Ops)
Annum Zhara (Sr Project Mgr-Clinical Trial)

LANTRONIX, INC.
48 Discovery Ste 250, Irvine, CA
92618
Tel.: (949) 453-3990   DE
Web Site: https://www.lantronix.com
Year Founded: 1989
LTRX—(NASDAQ)
Rev.: $129,655,000
Assets: $137,374,000
Liabilities: $57,478,000
Net Worth: $79,896,000
Earnings: ($5,362,000)
Emp.: 335
Fiscal Year-end: 06/30/22
Other Communications Equipment
Manufacturing
N.A.I.C.S.: 334290
Bernhard Bruscha (Founder)
Saleel Aware (Pres & CEO)
Gail Kathryn Miller (Mgr-Corp Mktg &
Comm)
David Goren (Sec & VP-Bus Affairs)

Subsidiaries:

**Intrinsyc Technologies
Corporation** (1)
885 Dunsmuir Street 3rd Floor, Vancouver,
V6C 1N5, BC, Canada
Tel.: (604) 801-6461
Web Site: http://www.intrinsyc.com
Mobility Software & Services
N.A.I.C.S.: 513210

Subsidiary (Non-US):

**Intrinsyc Software (Barbados)
Inc.** (2)
The Business Ctr, Upton, Saint Michael,
BB11103, Barbados
Tel.: (246) 246 435 8600
Sales Range: $25-49.9 Million
Emp.: 15
Software Development Services
N.A.I.C.S.: 513210
Sherene Blackett (Pres)

Japan Lantronix K.K. (1)
2 4 19 105 Sekiguchi, Bunkyo-ku, Tokyo,
112-0014, Japan
Tel.: (81) 339466031
Sales Range: $125-149.9 Million
Developer of Network Management Technology
N.A.I.C.S.: 334112

Lantronix Hong Kong Ltd. (1)
Unit 2116 22/F One Pacific Centre 414
Kwun Tong Road, Hong Kong, China (Hong
Kong)
Tel.: (852) 39550218
Software Integration Services
N.A.I.C.S.: 541512

Lantronix Japan K.K. (1)
7F Akasaka Tango-Building 4-7-15, Akasaka
Minato-ku, Tokyo, 1070052, Japan
Tel.: (81) 362778802
Web Site: http://www.lantronix.com
Information Services
N.A.I.C.S.: 519290

Lantronix Netherlands B.V. (1)
Neerloopweg 25, 4814 RS, Breda, Netherlands
Tel.: (31) 765236744
Web Site: http://www.lantronix.com
Information Services
N.A.I.C.S.: 519290

Uplogix, Inc. (1)
823 Congress Ave Ste 1200, Austin, TX
78701
Tel.: (512) 857-7000
Web Site: http://www.uplogix.com
Sales Range: $1-9.9 Million
Emp.: 20
Prepackaged Software
N.A.I.C.S.: 513210
Drew Schaal (CFO)
Lisa Frankovitch (CEO)

LANZATECH GLOBAL, INC.
8045 Lamon Ave Ste 400, Skokie, IL
60077
Tel.: (847) 324-2400   DE
Web Site: https://lanzatech.com
Year Founded: 2005
LNZA—(NASDAQ)
Emp.: 390
All Other Miscellaneous Chemical
Product & Preparation Manufacturing
N.A.I.C.S.: 325998
Jennifer Holmgren (CEO)

LAREDO OIL, INC.
2021 Guadalupe St Ste 260, Austin,
TX 78705
Tel.: (512) 337-1199   DE
Web Site: https://www.laredo-oil.com
Year Founded: 2008
LRDC—(OTCIQ)
Rev.: $74,225
Assets: $5,126,127
Liabilities: $10,207,466
Net Worth: ($5,081,339)
Earnings: ($3,112,051)
Emp.: 10
Fiscal Year-end: 05/31/23

Crude Petroleum Extraction Services
N.A.I.C.S.: 211120
Bradley E. Sparks (CFO & Treas)
Mark S. See (Founder, Chm, CEO &
Sec)

**LARIMAR THERAPEUTICS,
INC.**
3 Bala Plz E Ste 506, Bala Cynwyd,
PA 19004   DE
Web Site: https://www.larimartx.com
Year Founded: 2005
LRMR—(NASDAQ)
Rev.: $1,171,000
Assets: $126,405,000
Liabilities: $15,502,000
Net Worth: $110,903,000
Earnings: ($35,355,000)
Emp.: 26
Fiscal Year-end: 12/31/22
Pharmaceutical Preparation Manufacturing
N.A.I.C.S.: 325412
Carole S. Ben-Maimon (Pres & CEO)
Michael Celano (CFO)
John Berman (VP-Fin & Ops)
Frances Michael Conway (VP & Controller)
Noreen Scherer (VP-Clinical Ops)
Joe Truitt (Chm)
Gopi Shankar (Chief Dev Officer)
Russell Clayton (Chief Medical Officer)
Jennifer Johansson (VP)
Keith E. Lynch Jr. (VP)
Mohamed Hamdani (VP)

**LARIS MEDIA ACQUISITION
CORP.**
14918 S Figueroa St, Gardena, CA
90248
Tel.: (213) 510-6240   Ky
Year Founded: 2021
LRISU—(NASDAQ)
Investment Services
N.A.I.C.S.: 523999
Darren Throop (Chm)
Yoon Onn Ho (CEO)
Clemens Dornemann (CFO)
Simon Katz (COO)

LAS VEGAS SANDS CORP.
3355 Las Vegas Blvd S, Las Vegas,
NV 89109
Tel.: (702) 923-9000   NV
Web Site: https://www.sands.com
LVS—(NYSE)
Rev.: $10,372,000,000
Assets: $21,778,000,000
Liabilities: $17,674,000,000
Net Worth: $4,104,000,000
Earnings: $1,221,000,000
Emp.: 38,400
Fiscal Year-end: 12/31/23
Casinos, Hotels, Resorts & Convention Space Owner & Operator
N.A.I.C.S.: 721120
Robert G. Goldstein (Chm & CEO)
Patrick Dumont (Pres & COO)
Randy A. Hyzak (CFO, Chief Acctg
Officer & Exec VP)
Daniel J. Briggs (Sr VP-IR)
Alistair Scobie (VP-IR)
D. Zachary Hudson (Gen Counsel-
Global & Exec VP)

Subsidiaries:

Carlo's Bakery Las Vegas LLC (1)
3327 S Las Vegas Blvd, Las Vegas, NV
89109
Tel.: (702) 430-2625
Web Site: http://www.carlosbakery.com
Commercial Bakery Operating Services
N.A.I.C.S.: 311812

LVCUT Associates, LLC (1)
6430 Arville St, Las Vegas, NV 89118-4322

Tel.: (702) 737-9600
Web Site: http://www.wolfgangpuck.com
Hotels & Motels Services
N.A.I.C.S.: 721110

Las Vegas Sands, LLC (1)
501 Bay Ave, Somers Point, NJ 08244
Tel.: (609) 926-0905
Hotels Motels Service
N.A.I.C.S.: 721110
Robert G. Goldstein (Pres & COO)

Marina Bay Sands Pte. Ltd. (1)
10 Bayfront Avenue, Singapore, 018956,
Singapore
Tel.: (65) 66888868
Web Site: http://www.marinabaysands.com
Sales Range: $750-799.9 Million
Hotels & Motels Services
N.A.I.C.S.: 721110

Sands China Ltd. (1)
17th Floor Hopewell Centre 183 Queen s
Road East Wanchai, Hong Kong, China
(Hong Kong)
Tel.: (852) 28901888
Web Site: https://www.sandschina.com
Rev.: $1,605,000,000
Assets: $10,562,000,000
Liabilities: $11,262,000,000
Net Worth: ($700,000,000)
Earnings: ($1,582,000,000)
Emp.: 24,000
Fiscal Year-end: 12/31/2022
Holding Company; Hotel Resorts & Casinos
Development, Operation & Management
N.A.I.C.S.: 551112
Robert G. Goldstein (Chm & CEO)
Dylan James Williams (Gen Counsel & Sec)
Ying Wai Wong (Pres)
Dave Minqi Sun (CFO & Sr VP)
Grant Chum Kwan Lock (COO)

**Sands Expo & Convention Center,
Inc.** (1)
201 Sands Ave, Las Vegas, NV 89169
Tel.: (702) 733-5556
Web Site:
   https://www.sandsexpolasvegas.com
Convention Center Operating Services
N.A.I.C.S.: 531120
Julia M. Brown (Executives)

TK Las Vegas, LLC (1)
3355 Las Vegas Blvd S, Las Vegas, NV
89109-8941
Tel.: (702) 414-6200
Restaurant Operating Services
N.A.I.C.S.: 722511

Two Roads Las Vegas, LLC (1)
206 Spring St, New York, NY 10012
Tel.: (212) 529-0900
Restaurant Operating Services
N.A.I.C.S.: 722511

Venetian Casino Resort, LLC (1)
3355 Las Vegas Blvd S, Las Vegas, NV
89109
Tel.: (702) 414-1000
Web Site:
   https://www.venetianlasvegas.com
Emp.: 10,000
Hotels & Restaurant Services
N.A.I.C.S.: 721110

**Venetian Marketing Services
Limited** (1)
3105 B 27 31/F Shun Tak Ctr China Merchants Twr, Sheung Wan, Hong Kong,
China (Hong Kong)
Tel.: (852) 39873988
Web Site: http://www.sands.com
Sales Range: $10-24.9 Million
Emp.: 60
Home Management Services
N.A.I.C.S.: 721110

LASER ENERGETICS, INC.
3535 Quakerbridge Rd Ste 700, Mercerville, NJ 08619
Tel.: (609) 587-8250   OK
Year Founded: 1991
LNGT—(OTCIQ)
Water Equipment Mfr
N.A.I.C.S.: 335999
Robert D. Battis (Pres & CEO)

Laser Photonics Corporation—(Continued)

LASER PHOTONICS CORPORATION
1101 N Keller Rd Ste G2, Orlando, FL 32810
Tel.: (407) 804-1000   DE
Web Site:
https://www.laserphotonics.com
Year Founded: 2019
LASE—(NASDAQ)
Rev.: $4,954,689
Assets: $19,694,592
Liabilities: $2,203,459
Net Worth: $17,491,133
Earnings: ($997,461)
Emp.: 23
Fiscal Year-end: 12/31/22
Electrical Apparatus & Equipment, Wiring Supplies & Related Equipment Merchant Wholesalers
N.A.I.C.S.: 423610
Wayne Tupuola *(Chm & CEO)*
Miller Cordeiro *(Mgr-Content)*
Seth Bush *(Mktg Dir)*

Subsidiaries:

Control Micro Systems, Inc.   (1)
4420 Metric Dr, Winter Park, FL 32792
Tel.: (407) 679-9716
Web Site: http://www.cmslaser.com
Laser Machinery & Equipment Mfr & Whslr
N.A.I.C.S.: 335999
Don Haselton *(Pres)*
Trevor Laurence *(Dir-Sls & Bus Dev)*
Tony Kochell *(Ops Mgr)*
Ivan Musin *(Production Mgr)*
Richard Reilly *(Dir-Global Sls)*
Jim Merkel *(Sls Mgr)*
Sergio Eckhardt *(Sls Mgr)*
Greg McDaniel *(Reg Sls Mgr-Southeast)*
Tom Walsh *(Sls Mgr-New England)*

LASERMASTER INTERNATIONAL
1000 1st St, Harrison, NJ 07029
Tel.: (973) 482-7200   NY
Web Site: http://www.flexocraft.com
LMTI—(OTCIQ)
Gift Wrap Paper
N.A.I.C.S.: 323111
Leah Leah *(Sec)*
Mendel Klein *(Pres)*

LATCH, INC.
1220 N Price Rd Ste 2, Olivette, MO 63132
Tel.: (314) 200-5218   DE
Web Site: https://www.latch.com
Year Founded: 2020
LTCH—(OTCEM)
Rev.: $42,955,000
Assets: $316,662,000
Liabilities: $75,907,000
Net Worth: $240,755,000
Earnings: ($162,336,000)
Emp.: 75
Fiscal Year-end: 12/31/22
Investment Services
N.A.I.C.S.: 523999
Paul A. Galiano *(COO)*
Jenny Wong *(Chief Investment Officer)*
Jason Keyes *(Interim CEO)*
Marc Landy *(Interim CFO)*
David Lillis *(Sr VP-Fin)*
Luciano Panaro *(CTO)*
Claire Duval *(VP-Ops)*
Eugenia Adjigogovic *(Head-People)*
Chris Peckham *(Head-Sls)*

LATHAM GROUP, INC.
787 Watervliet Shaker Rd, Latham, NY 12110
Tel.:   DE
Web Site: https://ir.lathampool.com
Year Founded: 2018
SWIM—(NASDAQ)
Rev.: $695,736,000

Assets: $869,683,000
Liabilities: $486,893,000
Net Worth: $382,790,000
Earnings: ($5,694,000)
Emp.: 2,198
Fiscal Year-end: 12/31/22
Holding Company
N.A.I.C.S.: 551112
Mark P. Laven *(Vice Chm)*
Scott M. Rajeski *(Pres & CEO)*
Oliver C. Gloe *(CFO)*
James E. Cline *(Chm)*
Sanjeev Bahl *(COO)*
Kaushal B. Dhruv *(CIO)*

Subsidiaries:

Radiant Pools   (1)
440 N Pearl St, Menands, NY 12204
Web Site: http://www.radiantpools.com
Sheet Metal Work Mfg
N.A.I.C.S.: 332322
James Beaudoin *(Owner)*

LATTICE BIOLOGICS LTD.
16701 N 90th St Ste 101, Scottsdale, AZ 85260
Tel.: (480) 563-0800   BC
Year Founded: 1989
LBLTF—(OTCIQ)
Sales Range: Less than $1 Million
Biologic Products Developer & Mfr
N.A.I.C.S.: 325414
Guy Cook *(CEO)*
Cheryl A. Farmer *(CFO)*

LATTICE INC.
7150 N Park Dr Ste 500, Pennsauken, NJ 08109
Tel.: (856) 910-1166   DE
Web Site: https://www.latticeinc.com
Year Founded: 1973
LTTC—(NASDAQ)
Telephone Operating & Telecommunications Services
N.A.I.C.S.: 517810
Paul Burgess *(Chm & CEO)*
Terry Whiteside *(COO)*

LATTICE SEMICONDUCTOR CORPORATION
5555 NE Moore Ct, Hillsboro, OR 97124-6421
Tel.: (503) 268-8000   DE
Web Site:
https://www.latticesemi.com
Year Founded: 1983
LSCC—(NASDAQ)
Rev.: $737,154,000
Assets: $840,894,000
Liabilities: $148,874,000
Net Worth: $692,020,000
Earnings: $259,061,000
Emp.: 1,156
Fiscal Year-end: 12/30/23
Programmable Logic Devices Mfr
N.A.I.C.S.: 334413
Jerry Xu *(Pres-APAC)*
Esam Elashmawi *(CMO & Chief Strategy Officer)*
Esam Elashmawi *(Chief Mktg & Strategy Officer)*
Sherri Luther *(CFO)*
Tracy Feanny *(Gen Counsel)*
Denis Lavallee *(Sr VP)*
Ford Tamer *(Pres & CEO)*

Subsidiaries:

DVDO, Inc.   (1)
3350 Scott Blvd Bldg 49, Santa Clara, CA 95054
Tel.: (408) 213-6680
Web Site: https://www.dvdo.com
Video Processing Equipment Mfr
N.A.I.C.S.: 334419
Doug Fealtman *(CEO)*
Bill Herz *(Chief Innovation Officer & Chief Innovation Officer)*

Lattice SG Pte. Ltd.   (1)
150 Beach Road The Gateway West Level 35, Singapore, 189720, Singapore
Tel.: (65) 67274704
Semiconductor Mfr.
N.A.I.C.S.: 334413

Lattice Semiconducteurs SARL   (1)
37 Avenue Ledru Rollin, 75012, Paris, France
Tel.: (33) 156951806
Web Site: http://www.latticesemi.com
Sales Range: $100-124.9 Million
Emp.: 3
Semiconductor Components Mfr
N.A.I.C.S.: 334413

Lattice Semiconductor (PH) Corporation   (1)
11/F Aeon Centre Lot 2-3 Blk 45 Filinvest Ctr Alabang Zapote Road cor, Northbridgeway, Muntinlupa, 1780, Philippines
Tel.: (63) 27 717 6600
Web Site: https://www.latticesemi.com
Emp.: 300
Semiconductor Mfr.
N.A.I.C.S.: 334413

Lattice Semiconductor (Shanghai) Co. Ltd.   (1)
55 W Huaihai Rd 16th Fl, Shen Tong Infoport Plz, Shanghai, 200030, China
Tel.: (86) 21 5298 9999
Sales Range: $100-124.9 Million
Semiconductor Components Mfr
N.A.I.C.S.: 334413

Lattice Semiconductor GmbH   (1)
Lilienthal Strasse 27, Hallbergmoos, 85399, Germany
Tel.: (49) 70015288423
Web Site: http://www.latticesemi.com
Sales Range: $10-24.9 Million
Emp.: 10
Semiconductor Component Sales
N.A.I.C.S.: 334413

Lattice Semiconductor Japan KK   (1)
TOC Osaki Building 15F 1-6-1, Osaki Shinagawa-ku, Tokyo, 141-0032, Japan
Tel.: (81) 354352379
Semiconductor Devices Mfr
N.A.I.C.S.: 334413

Lattice Semiconductor K.K.   (1)
TOC Osaki Building 15F 1-6-1 Osaki, Shinagawa-ku, Tokyo, 141-0032, Japan
Tel.: (81) 35 435 2379
Web Site: https://www.latticesemi.com
Semiconductor Components Mfr.
N.A.I.C.S.: 334413

Lattice Semiconductor S.R.I.   (1)
Centro Direzionale Milanofiori, Strada 1 - Palazzo F2, 20090, Rozzano, Italy
Tel.: (39) 0235990370
Web Site: http://www.latticesemi.com
Sales Range: $100-124.9 Million
Semiconductor Components Mfr
N.A.I.C.S.: 334413

Lattice Semiconductor UK Limited   (1)
1st Fl Rivermead House Hamm Moor Ln, Addlestone, KT15 2SF, United Kingdom
Tel.: (44) 1932825700
Web Site: http://www.latticesemi.com
Sales Range: $1-9.9 Million
Emp.: 5
Semiconductor Components Mfr
N.A.I.C.S.: 334413

Qterics, Inc.   (1)
3140 Harbor Ln Ste 240, Plymouth, MN 55447
Tel.: (612) 594-7530
Web Site: https://www.qterics.com
Electronic Products Mfr.
N.A.I.C.S.: 334419

Silicon Image India Research and Development Private Ltd.   (1)
3rd Floor Building No 21 Raheja Mindspace Hitec City, Madhapur, Hyderabad, 500081, India
Tel.: (91) 4066584444
Wireless Communication Services
N.A.I.C.S.: 517112
Nitin Kumar *(Gen Mgr)*

LAVA MEDTECH ACQUISITION CORP.
303 Wyman St Ste 300, Waltham, MA 02451
Tel.: (781) 530-3868   DE
Year Founded: 2021
LVAC—(NASDAQ)
Rev.: $6,370,050
Assets: $120,666,593
Liabilities: $123,676,328
Net Worth: ($3,009,735)
Earnings: $4,504,994
Emp.: 5
Fiscal Year-end: 12/31/22
Investment Services
N.A.I.C.S.: 523999
Anthony Natale *(CEO)*
Richard Emmitt *(Chm)*
Gerry Brunk *(Pres)*
Daniel Hetu *(Exec VP)*
Vasco Larcina *(CFO)*

LAZYDAYS HOLDINGS, INC.
6130 Lazy Days Blvd, Tampa, FL 33584
Tel.: (813) 246-4999
Web Site: https://www.lazydays.com
GORV—(NASDAQ)
Rev.: $1,326,961,000
Assets: $830,718,000
Liabilities: $593,706,000
Net Worth: $237,012,000
Earnings: $61,592,000
Emp.: 1,400
Fiscal Year-end: 12/31/22
Bus & Other Motor Vehicle Transit Systems
N.A.I.C.S.: 485113
Ron Fleming *(VP & Gen Mgr-Natl)*
Linda Stephens *(VP-Customer Experience)*
Srinivas Kuchipudi *(VP-Ops & Supply Chain Mgmt)*
Keith Foerster *(VP-Svc)*
Tom Peterson *(CMO)*
Harsh Uchariya *(CIO)*
John F. North *(CEO)*

Subsidiaries:

Alliance Coach Inc.   (1)
4505 Monaco Way, Wildwood, FL 34785
Tel.: (352) 280-3444
Web Site: https://www.lazydays.com
Motor Vehicle Parts Mfr
N.A.I.C.S.: 336390

Buddy Gregg Motor Homes Inc.   (1)
11730 Snyder Rd, Knoxville, TN 37932-2957
Tel.: (865) 675-1986
Web Site: https://www.buddygregg.com
Sales Range: $25-49.9 Million
Emp.: 150
Recreational Vehicle Services
N.A.I.C.S.: 441210
Buddy Gregg *(Pres)*

Century RV, Inc.   (1)
10400 E I25 Frontage Rd, Longmont, CO 80504
Tel.: (720) 652-7000
Web Site: http://www.centuryrv.com
Sales Range: $1-9.9 Million
Emp.: 35
Recreational Vehicle Dealers
N.A.I.C.S.: 441210
Steve Hata *(VP)*

Chilhowee Trailer Sales, Inc.   (1)
4037 Airport Hwy, Alcoa, TN 37701
Tel.: (865) 970-4085
Web Site: http://www.chilhoweerv.com
Sales Range: $10-24.9 Million
Emp.: 45
Recreational Vehicle Whslr
N.A.I.C.S.: 441210
Fred Waggoner Sr. *(Owner)*

Dave's Claremore RV Inc.   (1)
PO Box 1620, Catoosa, OK 74015
Tel.: (918) 341-0114
Web Site: http://www.davesrv.com

Sporting & Recreational Goods & Supplies
Merchant Whslr
N.A.I.C.S.: 423910
Bryan O'Steen *(Office Mgr-Bus)*

Hohl-Findlay, LLC   **(1)**
4530 Boulder Hwy, Las Vegas, NV 89121
Tel.: (702) 435-2500
Recreational Vehicle Dealers
N.A.I.C.S.: 441210
Edward Findlay *(Principal)*

Korges Enterprises, Inc.   **(1)**
2260 E Main St, Mesa, AZ 85213
Tel.: (480) 964-2277
Web Site: http://www.desertautoplex.com
Passenger Car Rental
N.A.I.C.S.: 532111

Lazy Days' R.V. Center, Inc.   **(1)**
6130 Lazy Days Blvd, Seffner, FL 33584-
2968
Tel.: (813) 246-4333
Web Site: http://www.lazydays.com
Sales Range: $400-449.9 Million
Emp.: 600
Recreational Vehicle Retailer & Camp-
ground Operator
N.A.I.C.S.: 441210
Linda Stephens *(VP-Customer Experience)*
William P. Murnane *(Chm & CEO)*
Scott Caylor *(Mgr-Sls)*
Steve Adams *(Dir-Mktg)*
Andy Glogower *(Mgr-Fin)*
Ron Fleming *(VP & Gen Mgr-Natl)*
Jeff Dillard *(Gen Mgr-Tampa)*
Maura L. Berney *(CFO)*
Victor J. Doran *(VP-Svc)*
Tony Bruce *(Gen Mgr-Tucson)*
Jason Rees *(Gen Mgr-Dealership-Knoxville)*
Robert Brooke *(Gen Mgr-Minneapolis Deal-
ership)*
Keith A. Foerster *(VP-Svc Ops)*
Tom Peterson *(CMO)*

LCI INDUSTRIES

3501 County Rd 6 E, Elkhart, IN
46514
Tel.: (574) 535-1125   DE
Web Site: https://www.lci1.com
Year Founded: 1962
LCII—(NYSE)
Rev.: $5,207,143,000
Assets: $3,246,912,000
Liabilities: $1,865,904,000
Net Worth: $1,381,008,000
Earnings: $394,974,000
Emp.: 12,900
Fiscal Year-end: 12/31/22
Holding Company; Recreational Ve-
hicle & Manufactured Home Compo-
nents & Products Mfr
N.A.I.C.S.: 551112
Jason D. Lippert *(Pres & CEO)*
Ryan Smith *(Sr VP-Ops)*
Lillian D. Etzkorn *(CFO & Exec VP)*
Jamie Schnur *(Pres)*
Andrew J. Namenye *(Chief Legal Of-
ficer, Sec & Exec VP)*

Subsidiaries:

Ciesse S.p.A.   **(1)**
Via G Di Vittorio 66, Rignano sull Arno,
50067, Florence, FI, Italy
Tel.: (39) 055696417
Web Site: http://www.ciessespa.it
Railway Interior Product Mfr
N.A.I.C.S.: 336510
Vieri Passarelli *(Dir-Project Mgmt)*

Delta Glass B.V.   **(1)**
Deltaweg 4, 4691 RX, Tholen, Netherlands
Tel.: (31) 166603456
Web Site: https://www.deltaglass.nl
Emp.: 24
Plastic & Sheet Mfr
N.A.I.C.S.: 326113

Femto Engineering S.r.l.   **(1)**
Via Etruria, San Casciano In Val Di Pesa,
50026, Florence, Italy
Tel.: (39) 055 822 8381
Web Site: https://www.femto.it
Polymer Component Mfr
N.A.I.C.S.: 325211

Haulgauge, Inc.   **(1)**
3000 Sierra Vista Way, Provo, UT 84606
Tel.: (801) 692-7224
Web Site: http://www.haulgauge.com
Automotive Towing Product Mfr
N.A.I.C.S.: 336211
Melanie Hall *(VP)*

Lavet S.r.l.   **(1)**
Zona Ind Ie II fase-viale 11 n 12, 97100,
Ragusa, RG, Italy
Tel.: (39) 093 266 7329
Web Site: https://www.lavet.it
Glass Products Mfr
N.A.I.C.S.: 327215

Lippert Components, Inc.   **(1)**
3501 County Road 6 E, Elkhart, IN
46514   **(100%)**
Tel.: (574) 535-1125
Web Site: http://www.lci1.com
Recreational Vehicle & Manufactured Home
Components & Products Mfr
N.A.I.C.S.: 332999
Jamie M. Schnur *(Grp Pres)*
Jason D. Lippert *(Pres & CEO)*
Ryan Smith *(Sr VP-Sls & Ops)*
Marc Grimes *(Sr VP-Product Strategy)*
Jim Menefee *(Grp Pres-Europe)*
Rob Ford *(CTO)*
Andrew Pocock *(Exec VP-Building & Trans-
portation Products)*
Nicole Sult *(Sr VP-Customer Experience)*
Carlos Navarro *(CFO-Europe, Middle East
& Africa)*

Subsidiary (Domestic):

CURT Manufacturing LLC   **(2)**
6208 Industrial Dr, Eau Claire, WI 54701
Tel.: (715) 831-8713
Web Site: https://www.curtmfg.com
Trailer Hitches, Towing Products & Automo-
tive Accessories Mfr
N.A.I.C.S.: 336390

Subsidiary (Domestic):

**Aries Automotive Accessories,
Inc.**   **(3)**
23935 Madison St Unit B, Torrance, CA
90505
Tel.: (310) 784-1011
Web Site: http://www.ariesautomotive.com
Sales Range: $1-9.9 Million
Emp.: 10
Motor Vehicle Supplies & New Parts Mer-
chant Whslr
N.A.I.C.S.: 423120

Luverne Truck Equipment Inc.   **(3)**
1200 E Birch St, Brandon, SD 57005
Tel.: (605) 582-7200
Web Site: http://www.luvernetruck.com
Motor Vehicle Parts & Accessories Design
& Mfr
N.A.I.C.S.: 336390
John Schulzetenberg *(Pres)*

Subsidiary (Domestic):

Challenger Door, LLC   **(2)**
PO Box 67, Nappanee, IN 46550-0067
Tel.: (574) 773-0470
Web Site: http://www.challengerdoor.com
Motor Vehicle Parts Mfr
N.A.I.C.S.: 336390
Ian Becker *(Dir-Pur)*

Duncan Systems Inc.   **(2)**
29391 Old US Hwy 33, Elkhart, IN 46516
Tel.: (574) 294-6852
Web Site: http://www.duncansys.com
Automobile Glass Sales & Service
N.A.I.C.S.: 423120

Extreme Engineering, Inc.   **(2)**
168 S Spruce Ave, Rialto, CA 92376
Tel.: (909) 546-4129
Web Site: http://www.extremetrailers.com
Sales Range: $10-24.9 Million
Emp.: 50
Specialty Boat & Watercraft Trailer Designer
& Mfr
N.A.I.C.S.: 333924

Hehr International Inc.   **(2)**
3333 Casitas Ave, Los Angeles, CA 90039-
0160
Tel.: (909) 628-5557

Windows & Accessories for Mobile Homes,
Recreational Vehicles, Vans, Toppers,
Buses, Alternators, Generators, Battery
Isolators
N.A.I.C.S.: 332321

Subsidiary (Domestic):

Hehr Glass Company Inc.   **(3)**
200 S 1st St, Chesaning, MI 48616-0388
Tel.: (989) 845-7292
Custom-tempered Glass & Laminated Glass
for Automotive & Architectural Use
N.A.I.C.S.: 327215

Plant (Domestic):

**Hehr International Inc. - Indiana Win-
dow Plant**   **(3)**
1101 N Oak Rd, Plymouth, IN 46563-0219
Tel.: (574) 935-5122
Web Site: http://www.hehrintl.com
Wood Window & Door Mfr
N.A.I.C.S.: 321911

**Hehr International Inc. - Kansas
Glass Plant**   **(3)**
1050 S Meridian, Newton, KS 67114-0846
Tel.: (316) 283-0627
Glass Products Mfr
N.A.I.C.S.: 327215

**Hehr International Inc. - Kansas Win-
dow Plant**   **(3)**
600 W 24th St, Newton, KS 67114-0189
Tel.: (316) 283-0627
Glass Window Mfr
N.A.I.C.S.: 321911

**Hehr International Inc. - Michigan
Window Plant**   **(3)**
1103 W Pearl St, Chesaning, MI 48616-
0217
Tel.: (989) 845-3061
Wood Window & Door Mfr
N.A.I.C.S.: 321911

Subsidiary (Domestic):

Innovative Design Solutions, Inc.   **(2)**
6801 15 Mile Rd, Sterling Heights, MI
48312-4517
Tel.: (248) 583-1010
Web Site: http://www.idselectronics.com
Sales Range: $10-24.9 Million
Emp.: 100
Designer, Developer & Mfr of Electronic
Systems
N.A.I.C.S.: 334419

Subsidiary (Non-US):

Lewmar Marine Ltd.   **(2)**
Southmoor Ln, Havant, PO9 1JJ, Hamp-
shire, United Kingdom
Tel.: (44) 2392471841
Web Site: https://www.lewmar.com
Marine Equipment Mfr
N.A.I.C.S.: 334220

Subsidiary (US):

Lewmar Inc.   **(3)**
351 New Whitfield St, Guilford, CT 06437-
0388
Tel.: (203) 458-6200
Web Site: http://www.lewmar.com
Sales Range: $50-74.9 Million
Emp.: 60
Marine Equipment Mfr
N.A.I.C.S.: 423860

Subsidiary (Domestic):

Lewmar Ltd.   **(3)**
Southmoor Lane, Havant, PO9 1JJ, Hamp-
shire, United Kingdom
Tel.: (44) 2392471841
Web Site: https://www.lewmar.com
Sales Range: $25-49.9 Million
Marine Equipment Mfr
N.A.I.C.S.: 333618

Subsidiary (Non-US):

Lewmar North Europe Ltd.   **(3)**
Popovstraat 12, 8013 RK, Zwolle, Nether-
lands
Tel.: (31) 384273490

Sales Range: $25-49.9 Million
Emp.: 5
Marine Equipment Mfr
N.A.I.C.S.: 333618

Subsidiary (Domestic):

Taylor Made Group, LLC   **(2)**
65 Harrison St, Gloversville, NY 12078
Tel.: (518) 725-0681
Web Site:
https://www.taylormadeproducts.com
Accessories for Boats, Windshields, Mirrors,
Flags, Tempered Glass, Portable Toilets for
RVs & Marine Vehicles, Air Conditioning &
Refrigeration for Boats & Awnings Mfr
N.A.I.C.S.: 314910

Unit (Domestic):

Ameritex Fabric Systems   **(3)**
1900 47th Ter E, Bradenton, FL 34203
Tel.: (941) 747-1900
Web Site: http://www.ameritexfabrics.com
Fabric Enclosures (for Recreation Boats)
Mfr
N.A.I.C.S.: 441222

Taylor Made Custom Products   **(3)**
10 W 9th Ave, Gloversville, NY 12078
Tel.: (518) 725-2624
Web Site:
http://www.taylormadecustomproducts.com
Awning Mfr
N.A.I.C.S.: 332323

Subsidiary (Non-US):

**Taylor Made Glass & Systems
Limited**   **(3)**
Railway Road, Templemore, Tipperary, Ire-
land
Tel.: (353) 50431411
Web Site: http://www.taylormadeglass.com
Glass Products Mfr
N.A.I.C.S.: 327215

Subsidiary (Domestic):

Taylor Made Glass Ohio, Inc.   **(3)**
407 N Maple St, Payne, OH 45880-0077
Tel.: (419) 263-2313
Web Site: http://www.taylormadeglass.com
Glass Tempering
N.A.I.C.S.: 327215

Unit (Domestic):

Taylor Made Products   **(3)**
65 Harrison St, Gloversville, NY 12078-
4738
Tel.: (518) 773-9400
Web Site:
http://www.taylormadeproducts.com
Custom Awnings Mfr
N.A.I.C.S.: 423910

Taylor Made Systems   **(3)**
93 S Blvd, Gloversville, NY 12078-4730
Tel.: (518) 773-0636
Web Site:
http://www.taylormadesystems.com
Windshields & Tops (for Boats) Mfr
N.A.I.C.S.: 423860

Plant (Domestic):

**Taylor Made Systems - Indiana
Facility**   **(4)**
1101 Stonebreaker Dr, Kendallville, IN
46755
Tel.: (941) 713-1635
Web Site:
http://www.taylormadesystems.com
Windshield Mfr
N.A.I.C.S.: 336390

Subsidiary (Non-US):

Trend Marine Products Limited   **(3)**
Sutton Road, Catfield, Great Yarmouth,
NR29 5BG, Norfolk, United Kingdom
Tel.: (44) 1692581307
Web Site: https://www.trendmarine.com
Emp.: 170
Safety Glass Mfr
N.A.I.C.S.: 327215

Subsidiary (Domestic):

Zieman Manufacturing Company   **(2)**

LCI Industries—(Continued)

168 S Spruce, Rialto, CA 92376
Tel.: (909) 873-0061
Web Site: https://www.zieman.com
Sales Range: $75-99.9 Million
Emp.: 200
Chassis & Steel Parts for the Manufactured
Housing & Recreational Vehicle Industry,
Equipment Trailers, Personal Water Craft,
Custom Boat, Motorcycle & Snowmobile
Trailers Mfr
N.A.I.C.S.: 336212

Polyplastic B.V. (1)
Thurledeweg 5, 3044 EN, Rotterdam, Netherlands
Tel.: (31) 104461100
Web Site: https://www.polyplastic.nl
Emp.: 200
Cast Acrylic Mfr
N.A.I.C.S.: 325211

Project 2000 S.r.l. (1)
Via della speranza 44, Castronno, 04100, Latina, Italy
Tel.: (39) 0558825239
Recreational Vehicle Accessory Mfr
N.A.I.C.S.: 336999
Roberto Belvisi (Founder)
Giovanni Onori (Chief Bus Officer)

ST.LA. S.r.l. (1)
Via Marche 5/7, 56025, Pontedera, Pisa, Italy
Tel.: (39) 0587292625
Web Site: http://www.stla.it
Aluminium Products Mfr
N.A.I.C.S.: 332812

Sessa Klein S.p.A. (1)
Via Cavour 8, Castronno, 21040, Varese, Italy
Tel.: (39) 0332896811
Window Mfr
N.A.I.C.S.: 332321

doubleCOOL B.V. (1)
Thurledeweg 5, 3044 EN, Rotterdam, Netherlands
Tel.: (31) 10 446 1100
Web Site: https://www.doublecool.com
Acrylic Cabinet Door Distr
N.A.I.C.S.: 444180

LCNB CORP.

2 N Broadway, Lebanon, OH 45036
Tel.: (513) 932-1414　　　　　OH
Web Site: https://www.lcnb.com
Year Founded: 1998
LCNB—(NASDAQ)
Rev.: $95,010,000
Assets: $2,291,592,000
Liabilities: $2,056,289,000
Net Worth: $235,303,000
Earnings: $12,628,000
Emp.: 345
Fiscal Year-end: 12/31/23
Bank Holding Company
N.A.I.C.S.: 551111
Eric J. Meilstrup (Pres & CEO)
Lawrence P. Mulligan Jr. (COO & Exec VP)
Anne E. Krehbiel (Sec)
Bradley Austin Ruppert (Chief Investment Officer & Exec VP)
Matthew P. Layer (Exec VP)
Robert C. Haines II (CFO, Chief Acctg Officer & Exec VP)

Subsidiaries:

Cincinnati Bancorp, Inc. (1)
6581 Harrison Ave, Cincinnati, OH 45247
Tel.: (513) 574-3025
Web Site: http://www.cincinnatifederal.com
Rev.: $17,765,575
Assets: $251,464,039
Liabilities: $208,564,321
Net Worth: $42,899,718
Earnings: $1,648,544
Emp.: 73
Fiscal Year-end: 12/31/2021
Holding Company
N.A.I.C.S.: 551112

Eagle Financial Bancorp, Inc. (1)

6415 Bridgetown Rd, Cincinnati, OH 45248
Tel.: (513) 574-0700
Web Site: http://www.eaglesavings.com
Rev.: $5,403,000
Assets: $142,788,000
Liabilities: $114,885,000
Net Worth: $27,903,000
Earnings: $658,000
Emp.: 37
Fiscal Year-end: 12/31/2019
Bank Holding Company
N.A.I.C.S.: 551111
Kevin R. Schramm (CFO, Treas & VP)
Patricia L. Walter (Pres)
Ray W. McCleese (VP-Comml Lending-Bank)

LCNB National Bank (1)
2 N Broadway, Lebanon, OH 45036-1789
Tel.: (513) 932-1414
Web Site: https://www.lcnb.com
Retail & Commercial Banking
N.A.I.C.S.: 522110
Steve P. Foster (Founder-IT Dept)
Eric J. Meilstrup (Pres & CEO)

LCTI LOW CARBON TECHNOLOGIES INTERNATIONAL INC.

4010 Bluebonnet Ste 209, Houston, TX 77025
Tel.: (832) 267-8424　　　　　BC
Web Site: http://www.lctiinc.com
Year Founded: 2008
LWCTF—(TSXV)
Oil & Gas Related Services; Real Estate; Banking
N.A.I.C.S.: 213112
Bryan Scott Jarnagin (Chm & CEO)
Michael P. Lege (CFO, Treas & Sec)
Brandon S. Jarnagin (VP)
Gary Bush (Head-Engrg)
Gerardo Hubard (Head-Project Mgmt)

LEAD EDGE GROWTH OPPORTUNITIES, LTD.

96 Spring St 5th Fl, New York, NY 10012
Tel.: (212) 984-2421　　　　　Ky
Year Founded: 2020
LEGAU—(NASDAQ)
Rev.: $9,706,331
Assets: $346,186,302
Liabilities: $366,979,083
Net Worth: ($20,792,781)
Earnings: $8,756,054
Fiscal Year-end: 12/31/21
Investment Services
N.A.I.C.S.: 523999
Mitchell H. Green (Founder, Chm & CEO)
Nimay Mehta (Pres & CFO)
Brian Neider (COO)

LEAF OF FAITH BEVERAGE INC.

110 Spring Hill Dr Ste 16, Grass Valley, CA 95945
Tel.: (530) 648-1333　　　　　OK
LOFB—(OTCIQ)
Financial Investment Services
N.A.I.C.S.: 523999
Justin Gonzalez (Pres, Treas & Sec)

LEAFBUYER TECHNOLOGIES, INC.

6888 S Clinton St Ste 301, Greenwood Village, CO 80112
Tel.: (720) 235-0099　　　　　NV
Web Site: https://www.leafbuyer.com
Year Founded: 2014
LBUY—(OTCIQ)
Rev.: $5,601,357
Assets: $873,694
Liabilities: $2,555,228
Net Worth: ($1,681,534)
Earnings: ($709,430)
Emp.: 12
Fiscal Year-end: 06/30/24

Online Information Services
N.A.I.C.S.: 513140
Mark Breen (Co-Founder, CFO, COO & VP-Bus Dev)
Kurt Rossner (Co-Founder, Chm, Pres & CEO)
Michael Goerner (Co-Founder, CTO & Treas)

Subsidiaries:

LB Media Group, LLC (1)
6888 S Clinton St Ste 300, Greenwood Village, CO 80112
Tel.: (720) 235-0099
Web Site: https://lbmediagroupllc.com
Digital Transformation Services
N.A.I.C.S.: 518210

LEAP THERAPEUTICS, INC.

47 Thorndike St Ste B1-1, Cambridge, MA 02141
Tel.: (617) 714-0360
Web Site: https://www.leaptx.com
LPTX—(NASDAQ)
Rev.: $925,000
Assets: $70,353,000
Liabilities: $11,487,000
Net Worth: $58,866,000
Earnings: ($54,596,000)
Emp.: 44
Fiscal Year-end: 12/31/22
Therapeutics
N.A.I.C.S.: 621340
Augustine J. Lawlor (COO)
Christopher K. Mirabelli (Chm)
Cynthia Sirard (Chief Medical Officer)
Mark O'Mahony (Chief Mfg Officer)
Jason S. Baum (VP & Head-Translational Medicine)
Christine M. Granfield (VP & Head-Regulatory Affairs & Quality)
Kevin Lloyd (VP-Program & Alliance Mgmt)
Douglas E. Onsi (Pres & CEO)

Subsidiaries:

Leap Therapeutics Ltd. (1)
47 Thorndike St Ste B1-1, Cambridge, MA 02141 (100%)
Tel.: (617) 714-0360
Web Site: https://www.leaptx.com
Pharmaceuticals Mfr
N.A.I.C.S.: 325412

LEAR CORPORATION

21557 Telegraph Rd, Southfield, MI 48033
Tel.: (248) 447-1500　　　　　DE
Web Site: https://www.lear.com
Year Founded: 1917
LEA—(NYSE)
Rev.: $23,466,900,000
Assets: $14,695,500,000
Liabilities: $9,634,900,000
Net Worth: $5,060,600,000
Earnings: $572,500,000
Emp.: 186,600
Fiscal Year-end: 12/31/23
Automobile & Truck Seating & Electrical Systems Mfr
N.A.I.C.S.: 336360
Frank C. Orsini (Pres-Seating & Exec VP)
Raymond E. Scott (Pres & CEO)
Amy A. Doyle (Chief Acctg Officer & VP)
Alicia J. Davis (Chief Strategy Officer)
Harry A. Kemp (Gen Counsel, Sec & Sr VP)
John P. Absmeier (CTO)
Carl A. Esposito (Sr VP-IDEA)
Derrick Mitchell (VP-Diversity, Equity, Inclusion & Non-Production Pur)
Todd Kennedy (VP-Global)
Marianne Vidershain (Treas & VP)
Jason M. Cardew (CFO & Sr VP)

Subsidiaries:

AccuMED Corporation (1)
155 Boyce Dr, Mocksville, NC 27028-4187
Tel.: (336) 936-8400
Web Site: http://www.accumedtech.com
Medical Device Mfr
N.A.I.C.S.: 339112

Bauerhin-Elektro-Warme GmbH (1)
Falkensteiner Str 40, 08239, Trieb, Germany
Tel.: (49) 37463780
Heating Element Mfr & Distr
N.A.I.C.S.: 333414

Consorcio Industrial Mexicano de Autopartes S. de R.L. de C.V. (1)
Avenida Ejercito Nacional 6525, 32390, Ciudad Juarez, Mexico
Tel.: (52) 6566881100
Car Parts & Accessory Mfr
N.A.I.C.S.: 336390

Eagle Ottawa (Thailand) Co., Ltd. (1)
140 Moo 4 Huay Prab-Pluak Daeng Rd Mabyangporn, Pluak Daeng, Rayong, 21140, Thailand
Tel.: (66) 38929800
Automotive Leather Mfr & Distr
N.A.I.C.S.: 316990
Nuttaphong Chaowanothai (Mgr-Engrg)

Eagle Ottawa Brasil Industria e Beneficiamento de Couros Ltda. (1)
Rodovia Celso Garcia Cid n 15 830 Gleba 3 Bocas, PO Box 7041, Londrina, 86010-990, Brazil
Tel.: (55) 4333054800
Automotive Leather Mfr
N.A.I.C.S.: 316990
Helena Yuhara (Controller-Plant & Fin)

Eagle Ottawa China Ltd. (1)
No 2999 Huaning Road, Minhang District, Shanghai, 201108, China
Tel.: (86) 2133572000
Automotive Leather Mfr
N.A.I.C.S.: 316990
Adam Jin (Dir-Asia Launch)

Eagle Ottawa Hungary Kft. (1)
Piroskai ut 12, 5000, Szolnok, Hungary
Tel.: (36) 56887400
Web Site: http://www.eagleottawa.com
Automotive Leather Mfr
N.A.I.C.S.: 316990

Eagle Ottawa LLC (1)
1885 Pond Run, Auburn Hills, MI 48326
Tel.: (248) 364-7400
Web Site: http://www.eagleottawa.com
Automotive Leather Supplier
N.A.I.C.S.: 316110
Jerry Sumpter (CEO)

Eagle Ottawa North America, LLC (1)
21557 Telegraph Rd, Southfield, MI 48033
Tel.: (248) 447-1500
Automotive Leather Mfr & Distr
N.A.I.C.S.: 316990

Eagle Ottawa U.K. Ltd. (1)
2 Coventry Innovation Village Coventry University Technology Park, Cheetah Road, Coventry, CV1 2TL, United Kingdom
Tel.: (44) 2476234160
Automotive Seat Leather Distr
N.A.I.C.S.: 424990
Gavin Pearce (Engr-Global Cutting Ops)

Guilford Mills Automotive (Czech Republic) Limited (1)
Somercotes, Alfreton, DE55 4NJ, Derbyshire, United Kingdom
Tel.: (44) 1773841267
Automobile Parts Mfr
N.A.I.C.S.: 336390
Michel Key (Mng Dir)

Guilford Mills Automotive (Portugal) Limited (1)
Birchwood Way Somercotes, Alfreton, DE55 4NJ, Derbyshire, United Kingdom
Tel.: (44) 1773547200
Web Site: http://www.guilfordproduct.co.uk
Emp.: 400
Textile Goods Distr

N.A.I.C.S.: 314999

Guilford Mills Europe Limited (1)
Cotes Park, Alfreton, DE55 4NJ, United Kingdom
Tel.: (44) 1773607401
Textile Finishing Services
N.A.I.C.S.: 313310

Guilford Mills, Inc. (1)
1001 Military Cutoff Rd Ste 300, Wilmington, NC 28405
Tel.: (910) 794-5810
Emp.: 2,600
Fabric & Textile Product Mfr & Distr
N.A.I.C.S.: 313310
Chan W. Galbato (Chm)

Guilford Performance Textiles, Inc. (1)
1001 Military Cutoff Rd Ste 300, Wilmington, NC 28405
Tel.: (910) 794-5810
Web Site: http://www.guilfordtextiles.com
Sales Range: $400-449.9 Million
Emp.: 1,600
Automotive & Household Textile Products Designer & Mfr
N.A.I.C.S.: 314999

Subsidiary (Non-US):

Guilford Europe Ltd. (2)
Cotes Park Lane, Somercotes, Alfreton, DE55 4NJ, Derbys, United Kingdom
Tel.: (44) 1773547200
Web Site: http://www.guilfordtextiles.com
Sales Range: $25-49.9 Million
Emp.: 350
Textiles Mfr & Marketer
N.A.I.C.S.: 314999

Subsidiary (Non-US):

Guilford Automocion Iberica, S.L. (3)
c/Filadors 25 Fl 9, 08208, Sabadell, Gerona, Spain
Tel.: (34) 937243670
Web Site: http://www.guilfordtextiles.com
Sales Range: $25-49.9 Million
Emp.: 1
Automotive Fabrics Distr
N.A.I.C.S.: 423990

Guilford Deutschland GmbH (3)
Hanns Martin Schleyer Strasse 18A, Willich, 47877, Germany
Tel.: (49) 215494050
Web Site: http://www.guilfordtextiles.com
Sales Range: $25-49.9 Million
Emp.: 10
Automotive Textile Products Whslr
N.A.I.C.S.: 423990

Subsidiary (Non-US):

Guilford France (2)
14 Rue De La Sotiere, Trois-Villes, 59980, France
Tel.: (33) 327765062
Web Site: http://www.guilfordtextiles.com
Sales Range: $25-49.9 Million
Emp.: 50
Textile Mill
N.A.I.C.S.: 313310

Plant (Domestic):

Guilford Mills - Automotive & Upholstery Fabrics (2)
1754 N Carolina Hwy 903, Kenansville, NC 28349
Tel.: (910) 296-5200
Web Site: http://www.guilfordproducts.com
Sales Range: $150-199.9 Million
Emp.: 600
Textile Mill
N.A.I.C.S.: 313310
Eddie Whithord (Dir-Site Ops)

Guilford Shanghai Trading Co., Ltd. (1)
Room 1203 Tower A City Center of Shanghai No 100 ZunYi Road, ChangNing District, Shanghai, 200051, China
Tel.: (86) 2162350376
Web Site: http://www.lear.com
Textile Goods Distr
N.A.I.C.S.: 314999
Jay Kunkel (Pres)

IGB Automotive Ltd. (1)
3090 Marentette Ave, Windsor, N8X 4G2, ON, Canada
Tel.: (519) 250-5777
Automotive Electronic Mfr & Distr
N.A.I.C.S.: 334515

IGB Automotive Vietnam Co., Ltd. (1)
Song Than 3 Industrial Park LotCN16 No 2A Crossroad Road 4, 820000, Thu Dau Mot, Binh Duong, Vietnam
Tel.: (84) 2747303039
Automotive Electronic Mfr & Distr
N.A.I.C.S.: 334515

IGB Automotriz S. de R.L. de C.V. (1)
Avenida Rio Sononra No 100 Parque Industrial El Rio, CP 84279, Agua Prieta, Sonora, Mexico
Tel.: (52) 6333388065
Steering Heating Wheel Mfr & Distr
N.A.I.C.S.: 336330

Intouch Automation, Inc. (1)
46615 Ryan Ct, Novi, MI 48377
Tel.: (248) 669-4185
Web Site: https://intouchautomation.com
Sales Range: $10-24.9 Million
Emp.: 30
Engineeering Services
N.A.I.C.S.: 541330
Mark Marentic (Pres)

Lear Automotive India Private Limited (1)
Gat No 427 Hissa No 6 To 9 Chakan Talegaon Road, Pune, 410501, Maharashtra, India
Tel.: (91) 9545255559
Interior Motor Equipment Mfr
N.A.I.C.S.: 336360
Bhavesh Dave (Mgr-Sls)

Lear Automotive Morocco SAS (1)
Lot 102 B/2 Zone Franche D'exportation Route De Rabat, Tangiers, 90000, Morocco
Tel.: (212) 539949702
Web Site: http://www.lear.com
Sales Range: $25-49.9 Million
Emp.: 100
Automotive Components Mfr
N.A.I.C.S.: 336390

Lear Canada Investments Ltd. (1)
530 Manitou Dr, Kitchener, N2G 4C2, ON, Canada
Tel.: (519) 895-1600
Emp.: 3
Bank Holding Company
N.A.I.C.S.: 551111

Lear Corporation (Shanghai) Limited (1)
Bldg 3 No 509 Renqing Rd Pudong New Area, Shanghai, 233941, China
Tel.: (86) 2138527800
Motor Vehicle Body Mfr
N.A.I.C.S.: 336211

Lear Corporation (UK) Limited (1)
20 Black Friars Lane, Coventry, EC4V 6HD, West Midlands, United Kingdom
Tel.: (44) 2476867200
Motor Vehicle Body Mfr
N.A.I.C.S.: 336211

Lear Corporation Asientos S.L. (1)
Camino El Sabinar S/n Pol Ind Valdemuel, Epila, Zaragoza, 50290, Spain
Tel.: (34) 976816100
Web Site: http://www.lear.com
Emp.: 300
Textile Goods Distr
N.A.I.C.S.: 314999

Lear Corporation Belgium CVA (1)
Mondeolaan 1, Genk, 3600, Limburg, Belgium
Tel.: (32) 89 32 86 11
Emp.: 15
Motor Vehicle Body Mfr
N.A.I.C.S.: 336211
Pascal Hermans (Gen Mgr)

Lear Corporation Beteiligungs GmbH (1)
Vor Der Schanz 1-15, Ginsheim-

Gustavsburg, Gross-Gerau, 65462, Germany
Tel.: (49) 61345860
Financial Holding Company
N.A.I.C.S.: 551112

Lear Corporation Changchun Automotive Interior Systems Co., Ltd. (1)
No 270 Suzhou North Street Economic Technology Development Zon, Changchun, 130033, China
Tel.: (86) 43184699020
Motor Vehicle Body Mfr
N.A.I.C.S.: 336211

Lear Corporation Czech Republic s.r.o. (1)
Tovarni 735/10, Vyskov, 68201, Czech Republic
Tel.: (420) 517577711
Web Site: http://www.lear.com
Emp.: 500
Automotive Electrical Parts
N.A.I.C.S.: 336320

Lear Corporation GmbH & Co. KG (1)
Schlosserstrasse 4, 42899, Remscheid, Germany
Tel.: (49) 2191464309719
Web Site: http://www.lear.com
Sales Range: $75-99.9 Million
Automotive Electrical Components Mfr
N.A.I.C.S.: 336320

Lear Corporation Hungary Automotive Manufacturing Kft. (1)
Haraszti Street 4, 2100, Godollo, Hungary
Tel.: (36) 28520300
Web Site: http://www.lear.com
Emp.: 1,500
Automotive Components Mfr
N.A.I.C.S.: 336390

Lear Corporation Italia S.r.l. (1)
Corso Canonico Giuseppe Allamano 32, 10095, Grugliasco, Italy
Tel.: (39) 0114016111
Web Site: http://www.lear.com
Emp.: 1,000
Automotive Seating & Components Mfr
N.A.I.C.S.: 336360

Lear Corporation Jarny, S.A.S. (1)
Rue Gustave Eiffel Zac Jarny Giraumont, 54800, Jarny, France
Tel.: (33) 382475440
Automotive Seat Distr
N.A.I.C.S.: 423120

Lear Corporation Poland II Sp. z o.o. (1)
ul Serdeczna 40, 43-100, Tychy, Poland
Tel.: (48) 32 218 5900
Web Site: https://www.lear.pl
Automotive Components Mfr
N.A.I.C.S.: 336390

Lear Corporation Pontevedra, S.A.U. (1)
Poligono Industrial As Gandaras Parc R Mitad Norte, 36412, Pontevedra, O Porrino Galicia, Spain
Tel.: (34) 986823800
Automotive Seat Distr
N.A.I.C.S.: 423120
Marga Mendoza (Engr-Process)

Lear Corporation Portugal - Componentes Para Automoveis S.A. (1)
Lt 134 Melgacos Setubal, 2950-066, Palmela, Portugal
Tel.: (351) 212334019
Automotive Components Mfr
N.A.I.C.S.: 336390
Francisco Tepello (Gen Mgr)

Lear Corporation Romania S.r.L. (1)
Str George Cosbuc nr 33, Pitesti, 110103, Arges, Romania
Tel.: (40) 248207444
Electric Equipment Mfr
N.A.I.C.S.: 335999
Cristina Rotariu (Gen Mgr)

Lear Corporation Seating France Feignies SAS (1)
Zi De Greveaux Les Guides Cite De L entreprise, 59750, Feignies, France
Tel.: (33) 327533330

Automobile Parts Mfr
N.A.I.C.S.: 336390

Lear Corporation Seating France SAS (1)
Parc d'Activite des Bellevues Gare au Nord Batiment 1 Bis, BP 297, Rue de Patelle, Herblay, 95617, Cergy Pontoise, France
Tel.: (33) 134404500
Automobile Seating Mfr
N.A.I.C.S.: 336360

Lear Corporation Sweden AB (1)
Celsiusgatan 10, 417 63, Gothenburg, Sweden
Tel.: (46) 520485100
Web Site: http://www.lear.com
Automobile & Truck Product Mfr
N.A.I.C.S.: 811121

Lear Corporation Vigo, S.A.U. (1)
C Fusters 54 Poligono Industrial, Valls, 36312, Spain
Tel.: (34) 986829700
Automotive Seat Distr
N.A.I.C.S.: 423120
Lucia Vila Concejo (Mgr-Plant Quality)

Lear European Holding S.L. (1)
Calle Fusters Pg Industrial 54, Valls, 43800, Spain
Tel.: (34) 977617108
Web Site: http://www.lear.com
Motor Vehicle Body Mfr
N.A.I.C.S.: 336211

Lear Holdings (Hungary) Kft. (1)
Haraszti Ut 4, Godollo, 2100, Hungary
Tel.: (36) 28520300
Web Site: http://www.lear.com
Automobile Parts Mfr
N.A.I.C.S.: 441330
Bela Szabo (Pres)

Lear Mexican Seating Corporation (1)
950 Loma Verde Dr, El Paso, TX 79936-7899
Tel.: (915) 787-3610
Plastics Product Mfr
N.A.I.C.S.: 326199

Lear Mexican Trim Operations, S. de R.L. de C.V. (1)
Rio Bravo No 1181 Independencia 1, Ciudad Juarez, 32640, Mexico
Tel.: (52) 6566290922
Textile Goods Distr
N.A.I.C.S.: 314999

Lear North European Operations GmbH (1)
Rue du Plebiscite 5, L-2341, Luxembourg, Luxembourg
Tel.: (352) 24831220
Motor Vehicle Body Mfr
N.A.I.C.S.: 336211

Lear Sewing (Pty.) Ltd. (1)
1 Penkop Road, East London, 5201, Eastern Cape, South Africa
Tel.: (27) 437033600
Leather Goods Mfr
N.A.I.C.S.: 316990
Luaan Sedras (CEO)

Lear Shanghai Automotive Metals Co., Ltd. (1)
No 1 Building 1588 Xintian Industry Park Li An Road, Shanghai, 201100, China
Tel.: (86) 2154880606
Motor Vehicle Parts Mfr
N.A.I.C.S.: 336211

Lear Teknik Oto Yan Sanayi Ltd. Sirket (67%)
Demirtas Organize Sanayi Bolgesi, PO Box 13, 16369, Bursa, Turkiye
Tel.: (90) 2242610718
Sales Range: $550-599.9 Million
Emp.: 1,800
Automobile Parts Mfr
N.A.I.C.S.: 336390

NHK Seating of America, Inc. (1)
2298 W State Rd 28, Frankfort, IN 46041-9185
Tel.: (765) 659-4781
Web Site: http://www.nhkseating.com
Automobile Seats Mfr

Lear Corporation—(Continued)
N.A.I.C.S.: 336360
Rich Reck (Gen Mgr)

Shanghai Lear Automotive Systems Co., Ltd.
No 568 Wangqiao Road, Pudong New District, Shanghai, 201201, China
Tel.: (86) 2158385980
Web Site: http://www.lear.com
Emp.: 50
Motor Vehicle Body Mfr
N.A.I.C.S.: 336211

Shenyang Lear Automotive Seating and Interior Systems Co., Ltd. **(1)**
No 2 6a Kafa Rd Economic & Technological Development Zone, Shenyang, 110141, China **(60%)**
Tel.: (86) 2425375808
Web Site: http://www.lear.com
Automotive Interior Parts Distr
N.A.I.C.S.: 423120

TS-Lear Automotive (Malaysia) Sdn. Bhd. **(1)**
Lot 6695 Batu 7 Jalan Kebun, Klang, 42450, Malaysia
Tel.: (60) 351612922
Emp.: 100
Household Furniture Mfr
N.A.I.C.S.: 337126
Hasni Abdulaziz (Gen Mgr)

Tacle Automotive India Private Limited **(1)**
Plot No E-15 Cmda Industrial Complex Maramalai Nagar, Chenglepet Taluk, Kanchipuram, Tamil Nadu, India
Tel.: (91) 4447408600
Motor Vehicle Body Mfr
N.A.I.C.S.: 336211

Xevo Inc. **(1)**
10900 NE 8th St Ste 800, Bellevue, WA 98004
Web Site: https://www.xevo.com
Software Developer Services
N.A.I.C.S.: 541511
Shaun Smiley (Mgr-Dev & Ops)

LEARN CW INVESTMENT CORP.
11755 Wilshire Blvd Ste 2320, Los Angeles, CA 90025
Tel.: (424) 324-2990   **Ky**
Web Site:
    https://www.learncwinvestment corp.com
Year Founded: 2021
LCW—(NYSE)
Rev.: $3,274,564
Assets: $236,908,540
Liabilities: $248,569,311
Net Worth: ($11,660,771)
Earnings: $9,891,490
Emp.: 3
Fiscal Year-end: 12/31/22
Investment Services
N.A.I.C.S.: 523999
Adam Fisher (Pres)
Robert Hutter (CEO)

LEARNING TREE INTERNATIONAL, INC.
13650 Dulles Technology Dr Ste 400, Herndon, VA 20171-6150
Tel.: (703) 709-9119   **DE**
Web Site:
    https://www.learningtree.com
LTRE—(OTCIQ)
Sales Range: $50-74.9 Million
Emp.: 248
Computer Training
N.A.I.C.S.: 611420
Magnus Nylund (COO)
Igor Lima (CFO)
David Brown (CEO)
Tricia Sacchetti (VP-Worldwide Mktg)
Tim Vatne (CIO)

Subsidiaries:

Learning Tree International AB **(1)**

Lindhagensgatan 126, Stockholm, 112 51, Sweden
Tel.: (46) 850666800
Web Site: http://www.learningtree.se
Sales Range: $10-24.9 Million
Emp.: 14
Education & Training to Information Technology Professionals in Business & Government Organizations
N.A.I.C.S.: 611430
Staffan Windrup (Gen Mgr)

Learning Tree International Inc. **(1)**
150 Elgin Street Suite 1000, Ottawa, K2P 1L4, ON, Canada **(100%)**
Web Site: https://www.learningtree.ca
Education & Training to Information Technology Professionals in Business & Government Organizations Services
N.A.I.C.S.: 611430

Learning Tree International Ltd. **(1)**
24 Eversholt St Euston House, London, NW1 1AD, United Kingdom
Tel.: (44) 2078745000
Web Site: http://www.learningtree.co.uk
Sales Range: $25-49.9 Million
Emp.: 90
Provider of Education & Training to Information Technology Professionals in Business & Government Organizations
N.A.I.C.S.: 611430

Learning Tree International USA, Inc. **(1)**
400 N Continental Blvd Ste 100, El Segundo, CA 90245
Tel.: (310) 417-9700
Sales Range: $10-24.9 Million
Emp.: 50
Provider of Education & Training to Information Technology Professionals in Business & Government Organizations
N.A.I.C.S.: 611519

Learning Tree International, K.K. **(1)**
Kyoritsu Building 3-10-2, Kandajinbocho, Chiyoda-ku, Chiyoda-Ku, Tokyo, 1010051, Japan
Tel.: (81) 352263004
Web Site: http://www.learningtree.co.jp
Sales Range: $1-9.9 Million
Emp.: 7
Provider of Education & Training to Information Technology Professionals in Business & Government Organizations
N.A.I.C.S.: 611430
Yoko Segawa (Gen Mgr)

LEDYARD FINANCIAL GROUP, INC.
38 S Main St, Hanover, NH 03755
Tel.: (603) 643-2244   **NH**
Web Site:
    https://www.ledyardbank.com
Year Founded: 1991
LFGP—(OTCIQ)
Rev.: $17,906,582
Assets: $500,391,005
Liabilities: $444,256,576
Net Worth: $56,134,429
Earnings: $5,816,161
Fiscal Year-end: 12/31/19
Banking Holding Company
N.A.I.C.S.: 551111
Dennis E. Logue (Branch Mgr)
Josephine Moran (Pres & CEO)
Gregory D. Steverson (CFO, COO & Exoo VP)
Barbara S. Graf (Sr VP & Dir-HR)
Bruce King (Chm)

LEE ENTERPRISES, INCORPORATED
4600 E 53rd St, Davenport, IA 52807   **DE**
Web Site: https://lee.net
Year Founded: 1890
LEE—(NASDAQ)
Rev.: $780,969,000
Assets: $744,042,000
Liabilities: $726,805,000
Net Worth: $17,237,000
Earnings: ($2,017,000)

Emp.: 3,577
Fiscal Year-end: 09/25/22
Holding Company; Newspaper Publisher
N.A.I.C.S.: 551112
Kevin D. Mowbray (Pres & CEO)
James A. Green (VP-Digital)
Astrid J. Garcia (VP)
Nathan E. Bekke (VP-Marketing)
Timothy R. Millage (Treas & VP)
Joseph J. Battistoni (VP-Sales & Marketing)
Jolene Sherman (VP-Business Development & Market Strategies)
Jason Adrians (VP)
Mary E. Junck (Chm)

Subsidiaries:

Amplified Digital, LLC **(1)**
900 N Tucker Blvd 4th Fl, Saint Louis, MO 63101
Tel.: (314) 884-2080
Web Site: http://www.amplifieddigitalstl.com
Emp.: 30
Digital Media Marketing Services
N.A.I.C.S.: 541613

Arizona Daily Sun **(1)**
1300 W University Ste 100, Flagstaff, AZ 86001-8716
Tel.: (928) 774-4545
Web Site: https://www.azdailysun.com
Sales Range: $25-49.9 Million
Emp.: 100
Community Newspaper
N.A.I.C.S.: 513110

BH Media Group Inc. **(1)**
300 E Franklin St, Richmond, VA 23219-2214
Tel.: (804) 649-6000
Holding Company; Newspaper Publisher
N.A.I.C.S.: 551112

Subsidiary (Domestic):

BH Media Group **(2)**
300 E Franklin St, Richmond, VA 23219-2214
Tel.: (804) 649-6000
Newspaper Publishers
N.A.I.C.S.: 513110
Doug Kastrup (Exec VP)

Subsidiary (Domestic):

Bristol Herald Courier **(3)**
320 Bob Morrison Blvd, Bristol, VA 24201 **(100%)**
Tel.: (276) 669-2181
Web Site: https://www.tricities.com
Sales Range: $50-74.9 Million
Emp.: 150
Daily Newspaper Publisher
N.A.I.C.S.: 513110
Ruby Michele Guffey (Supvr-Classified & Recruitment)

Culpeper Star-Exponent **(3)**
122 W Spencer St, Culpeper, VA 22701 **(100%)**
Tel.: (540) 829-5496
Web Site: https://www.starexponent.com
Sales Range: $25-49.9 Million
Emp.: 45
Daily Newspaper Publisher
N.A.I.C.S.: 513110

Danville Register & Bee **(3)**
700 Monument St, Danville, VA 24541 **(100%)**
Tel.: (434) 793-2311
Web Site: https://godanriver.com
Daily Newspaper Publisher
N.A.I.C.S.: 513110

Hickory Daily Record **(3)**
1100 11th Ave Blvd SE, Hickory, NC 28602-0968 **(100%)**
Tel.: (828) 304-6979
Web Site: https://www.hickoryrecord.com
Sales Range: $25-49.9 Million
Emp.: 100
Daily Newspaper Publication & Distr
N.A.I.C.S.: 513110
Rita Bolick (Office Mgr-Circulation)
Tiffany Hovis (Dir-Adv)

Morning News **(3)**
310 S Dargan St, Florence, SC 29506 **(100%)**
Tel.: (843) 317-6397
Web Site:
    http://www.morningnewsonline.com
Sales Range: $100-124.9 Million
Emp.: 300
Publishing Daily Newspaper
N.A.I.C.S.: 513110

Omaha World Herald Company **(3)**
1314 Douglas St Ste 1500, Omaha, NE 68102-1138
Tel.: (402) 444-1000
Web Site: https://www.omaha.com
Sales Range: $400-449.9 Million
Emp.: 2,200
Newspaper Publishers
N.A.I.C.S.: 513110
Bryan Slimp (Mgr-Circulation Consumer Rels)
Ava Thomas (Pres)
Scott Carr (VP)

Joint Venture (Domestic):

Election Systems & Software Inc. **(4)**
11208 John Galt Blvd, Omaha, NE 68137-2320
Tel.: (402) 593-0101
Web Site: http://www.essvote.com
Sales Range: $75-99.9 Million
Computer Peripheral Equipment Mfr
N.A.I.C.S.: 334118

Subsidiary (Domestic):

Premier Election Solutions, Inc. **(5)**
1611 Wilmeth Rd, McKinney, TX 75069-8250
Tel.: (972) 542-6000
Web Site: http://www.premierelections.com
Sales Range: $200-249.9 Million
Electronic Voting Systems Mfr
N.A.I.C.S.: 541512

Subsidiary (Domestic):

Kearney Hub Publishing Company Inc. **(4)**
13 E 22nd St, Kearney, NE 68847-5404
Tel.: (308) 237-2152
Web Site: https://www.kearneyhub.com
Rev.: $5,000,000
Emp.: 80
Publisher of Daily Newspapers
N.A.I.C.S.: 513110

The Grand Island Daily Independent **(4)**
422 W 1st St, Grand Island, NE 68801
Tel.: (308) 382-1000
Web Site: http://www.theindependent.com
Sales Range: $25-49.9 Million
Emp.: 100
Newspaper Publishers
N.A.I.C.S.: 513110
John Lilly (Dir-Ops)
Pat Bell (Coord-Adv Sls & Special Events)
Jim Faddis (Mng Editor)
Terrie Baker (Publr)
David Haines (Supvr-Distr)
Bette Pore (Sr Editor)
Beth Thompson (Dir-Circulation)
Tosha Brown (District Mgr)
Shon Barenklau (Mng Editor)
Maddie Elder (Dir-Digital)

The York News-Times **(4)**
327 Platte Ave, York, NE 68467
Tel.: (402) 362-4478
Web Site: https://www.yorknewstimes.com
Sales Range: $10-24.9 Million
Emp.: 22
Newspaper Publishers
N.A.I.C.S.: 513110
Carrie Colburn (Publr)
Melanie Wilkinson (Mng Editor-News)
Rick Pfeifer (Mgr-Circulation)

Subsidiary (Domestic):

Opelika-Auburn News **(3)**
204 S 8th St, Opelika, AL 36801 **(100%)**
Tel.: (334) 749-6271
Web Site: https://www.oanow.com
Sales Range: $75-99.9 Million
Emp.: 75
Daily Newspaper

N.A.I.C.S.: 513110
Teila Drake *(Coord-Customer Rels)*
Dimon Kendrick-Holmes *(Editor)*

Richmond Times-Dispatch   (3)
300 E Franklin St, Richmond, VA
23219   **(100%)**
Tel.: (804) 649-6000
Web Site: https://www.richmond.com
Sales Range: $350-399.9 Million
Emp.: 1,100
Newspaper Publishers
N.A.I.C.S.: 513110

The Daily Progress   (3)
685 W Rio Rd, Charlottesville, VA
22901-1413   **(100%)**
Tel.: (434) 978-7200
Web Site: https://www.dailyprogress.com
Sales Range: $100-124.9 Million
Daily Newspaper Publisher
N.A.I.C.S.: 513110

The Dothan Eagle   (3)
2999 Ross Clark Cir Ste 300, Dothan, AL
36301   **(100%)**
Tel.: (334) 792-3141
Web Site: http://www.dothaneagle.com
Sales Range: $10-24.9 Million
Emp.: 50
Daily Newspaper Publisher
N.A.I.C.S.: 513110
Robert Jesswein *(Gen Mgr & Controller)*

The News Virginian   (3)
201 C Rosser Ave, Waynesboro, VA
22980   **(100%)**
Tel.: (540) 949-8213
Web Site: https://newsvirginian.com
Sales Range: $25-49.9 Million
Emp.: 30
Daily Newspaper Publisher
N.A.I.C.S.: 513110

Winston-Salem Journal   (3)
418 N Marshall St, Winston Salem, NC
27101-2815   **(100%)**
Tel.: (336) 727-7211
Web Site: https://www.journalnow.com
Sales Range: $100-124.9 Million
Emp.: 300
Newspaper Publishers
N.A.I.C.S.: 513110

Unit (Domestic):

Eden Daily News   (2)
1921 Vance St, Reidsville, NC
27320   **(100%)**
Tel.: (336) 623-2155
Web Site: http://www.rockinghamnow.com
Sales Range: $10-24.9 Million
Emp.: 15
Newspaper Publishers
N.A.I.C.S.: 513110

Enterprise Ledger   (2)
1110 Boll Weevil Cir Ste E, Enterprise, AL
36330-2524   **(100%)**
Tel.: (334) 347-9533
Web Site: http://www.dothaneagle.com
Sales Range: $10-24.9 Million
Emp.: 10
Daily Newspaper Publisher
N.A.I.C.S.: 513110

Independent Tribune   (2)
363 Church St N Ste 140, Concord, NC
28025
Tel.: (828) 304-6905
Web Site:
  https://www.independenttribune.com
Sales Range: $25-49.9 Million
Emp.: 45
Newspapers
N.A.I.C.S.: 513110
Mark Plemmons *(Editor)*

Jackson County Floridan   (2)
4403 Constitution Ln, Marianna, FL
32448-4472   **(100%)**
Tel.: (850) 526-3614
Web Site: https://dothaneagle.com
Sales Range: $10-24.9 Million
Emp.: 20
Newspaper Publishing
N.A.I.C.S.: 513110

Subsidiary (Domestic):

Stockton Newspapers Inc.   (2)

530 E Market St, Stockton, CA 95202
Tel.: (209) 943-6568
Web Site: http://www.recoodnet.com
Sales Range: $75-99.9 Million
Emp.: 340
Newspapers
N.A.I.C.S.: 513110

Unit (Domestic):

The News & Advance   (2)
101 Wyndale Dr, Lynchburg, VA
24501-6710   **(100%)**
Tel.: (434) 385-5440
Web Site: https://www.newsadvance.com
Sales Range: $25-49.9 Million
Emp.: 80
Daily Newspaper
N.A.I.C.S.: 513110

The Reidsville Review   (2)
1921 Vance St, Reidsville, NC
27320   **(100%)**
Tel.: (336) 361-4002
Web Site: http://www.rockhinghamlow.com
Sales Range: $25-49.9 Million
Emp.: 15
Daily Newspaper
N.A.I.C.S.: 513110

Virginia Business Magazine   (2)
1207 E Main St, Richmond, VA
23219   **(100%)**
Tel.: (804) 225-1366
Web Site: http://www.virginiabusiness.com
Business Publication
N.A.I.C.S.: 513130
Bernard A. Niemeier *(Pres & Publr)*
Karen Chenault *(Mgr-Circulation)*
Joel Smith *(Dir-Art)*
Lori Collier Waran *(VP-Sls & Mktg)*
Lynn Williams *(Mgr-Sls-Roanoke)*

Corvallis Gazette-Times   (1)
600 Lyon St SW, Albany, OR
97321   **(100%)**
Tel.: (541) 926-2211
Web Site: https://www.gazettetimes.com
Sales Range: $25-49.9 Million
Emp.: 20
Newspaper Publishers
N.A.I.C.S.: 513110

Democrat News   (1)
131 S Main St, Fredericktown, MO 63645-
1451
Tel.: (573) 783-3366
Web Site:
  http://www.democratnewsonline.com
Sales Range: $10-24.9 Million
Emp.: 5
Daily Newspaper
N.A.I.C.S.: 513110
Alan Kopitsky *(Mng Editor)*

Flagstaff Publishing Co.   (1)
1751 S Thompson St, Flagstaff, AZ 86001-
8716
Tel.: (928) 774-4545
Web Site: http://www.azdailysun.com
Newspaper Publishing Services
N.A.I.C.S.: 513110

Globe-Gazette   (1)
687 S Taft Ave Ste 2, Mason City, IA
50401-3222
Tel.: (641) 421-0500
Web Site: https://www.globegazette.com
Sales Range: $50-74.9 Million
Emp.: 120
Newspaper Publishers
N.A.I.C.S.: 513110
Linda Halfman *(Controller)*
Greg Wilderman *(Dir-Circulation)*
Olivia Stalker *(Mgr-Digital & Coord-Adv)*
John Frels *(Mgr-Circulation Ops)*
Tricia Wilderman *(Mgr-Classified)*

Hanford Sentinel, Inc.   (1)
300 W 6th St, Hanford, CA 93230 **(100%)**
Tel.: (559) 582-0471
Web Site: https://hanfordsentinel.com
Community Newspaper
N.A.I.C.S.: 513110
Davis Taylor *(Publr)*
Ron Walker *(Dir-IT)*
Chris Aguirre *(Editor)*
Mark Daniel *(Mgr-Adv)*
Rusty Williamson *(Coord-Adv)*

Herald & Review   (1)

225 S Main St No 200, Decatur, IL
62523-1142   **(100%)**
Tel.: (217) 429-5151
Web Site: https://www.herald-review.com
Sales Range: $75-99.9 Million
Emp.: 275
Newspaper Publishers
N.A.I.C.S.: 513110
Josh Harmon *(Dir-Audience)*
Randy Terwilliger *(Mgr-Home Delivery)*
Katie McShane *(Mgr-Circulation Svcs)*
Angela Stewart *(Mgr-Multimedia Sls)*
Chris Coates *(Editor-Central Illinois)*
Julie Gerke *(Editor-Local News)*
Randy Kindred *(Editor-Sports)*
Dan McNeile *(Editor-Night)*
Nick Keeley *(Editor-Copy)*
Jane Pickering *(Editor-Copy)*
Barry Winterland *(Gen Mgr-Central Illinois)*

INN Partners, L.C.   (1)
1033 7th St Ste 200, East Moline, IL
61244   **(82.5%)**
Tel.: (309) 743-0800
Web Site: http://www.townnews.com
Sales Range: $25-49.9 Million
Online News Publisher
N.A.I.C.S.: 513110
Marc Wilson *(Founder)*
Brad Ward *(CEO)*
Rick Rogers *(Chief Revenue Officer)*
Roger Lee *(Sr Mgr-Reg Sls)*
Sinead Steele *(VP-Ops)*
Aaron Gillette *(Dir-Mktg)*
Carol Grubbe *(Exec Mgr-Media Sls)*
John Montgomery *(Exec Mgr-Media Sls)*
Steve Parrott *(Sr Mgr-Brdcst Sls)*
Jessica Reinert *(Sr Mgr-Brdcst Sls)*
Jerry Lyles *(Dir-Sls-New Ventures)*
Phil Pracht *(Reg Mgr-Sls)*
Derek Gebler *(VP-Brdcst & Video)*
Betsy Davison *(Dir-Quality Assurance)*
David Hantz *(Dir-Client Svcs)*
Christine Masters *(Dir-Product Mgmt)*
Chris Murley *(Dir-Network Ops)*
Patrick O'Lone *(Dir-Software Dev)*
Brian Sandrock *(Dir-Online Production)*
Tim Turner *(Dir-Content & Data Svcs)*
Ryan Ingersoll *(Mgr-Program)*
Stevie Longwith *(Program Mgr-Ad Ops)*
Susan Bell *(Sr Mgr-Product)*
Joe Hansen *(Sr Mgr-Product)*
Rich Griffin *(Product Mgr)*
Michael Worringer *(Product Mgr)*
Doug Green *(Product Mgr)*
John Jordan *(VP-Partner Success)*
Edwina Umphrey *(Dir-Adv Svcs)*
Susan Inglis *(Product Mgr)*
Rodney Blaukat *(Reg Sls Mgr)*

Iowa Farmer Today   (1)
1625 Boyson Rd Ste 106, Hiawatha, IA
52233
Tel.: (319) 398-2640
Web Site: https://agupdate.com
Sales Range: $25-49.9 Million
Emp.: 33
Specialty Newspaper Publisher
N.A.I.C.S.: 513110
Terry Reilly *(Publr & Mgr-Sls)*

Journal-Star Printing Co.   (1)
926 P St, Lincoln, NE 68508-3615 **(100%)**
Tel.: (402) 475-4200
Web Site: http://www.journalstar.com
Sales Range: $50-74.9 Million
Newspaper Publishers
N.A.I.C.S.: 513110

Unit (Domestic):

Columbus Telegram   (2)
1254 27th Ave, Columbus, NE
68601-5656   **(100%)**
Tel.: (402) 564-2741
Web Site:
  https://www.columbustelegram.com
Rev: $3,100,000
Emp.: 35
Newspaper Publishers
N.A.I.C.S.: 513110

Lincoln Journal-Star   (2)
926 P St, Lincoln, NE 68508-3615
Tel.: (402) 475-4200
Web Site: https://www.journalstar.com
Sales Range: $50-74.9 Million
Emp.: 250
Newspaper Publishers

N.A.I.C.S.: 513110

Subsidiary (Domestic):

The Plattsmouth Journal   (2)
410 Main St, Plattsmouth, NE 68048-1960
Tel.: (402) 296-2141
Web Site: http://www.cass-news.com
Sales Range: $10-24.9 Million
Emp.: 15
Newspapers
N.A.I.C.S.: 513110

La Crosse Tribune   (1)
1407 St Andrew St Ste A100, La Crosse,
WI 54603
Tel.: (608) 782-9710
Web Site: https://www.lacrossetribune.com
Sales Range: $100-124.9 Million
Emp.: 300
Newspaper Publishers
N.A.I.C.S.: 513110
Sandy Powell *(Mgr-Circulation)*
Scott Rada *(Editor-Digital News)*
Allan Swift *(Supvr-Copy Desk)*
Avery Wehrs *(Editor-News Copy)*
Eric Lee *(Editor-News Copy)*
Russell Cunningham Jr. *(Exec Editor)*

Lake Geneva Regional News   (1)
315 Broad St, Lake Geneva, WI 53147-
1884
Tel.: (262) 248-4444
Web Site: http://www.lakegenevanews.net
Printing
N.A.I.C.S.: 513110
Doug Bearder *(Mgr)*

Lebanon Express   (1)
90 E Grant St, Lebanon, OR 97355-0459
Tel.: (541) 258-3151
Web Site: http://www.lebanon-express.com
Sales Range: $10-24.9 Million
Emp.: 6
Newspaper Publishers
N.A.I.C.S.: 513110

Lee Foundation   (1)
201 N Harrison St Ste 600, Davenport, IA
52801   **(100%)**
Tel.: (563) 383-2100
Web Site: http://www.lee.net
Newspaper Publishing Services
N.A.I.C.S.: 513110

Lee Procurement Solutions Co.   (1)
201 N Harrison Ste 600, Davenport, IA
52801-1924   **(100%)**
Tel.: (563) 383-2100
Web Site: http://www.lee.net
Sales Range: $100-124.9 Million
Emp.: 100
Newspaper Publishing Services
N.A.I.C.S.: 513110

Lee Publications, Inc.   (1)
6113 State Hwy 5, Palatine Bridge, NY
13428   **(100%)**
Tel.: (518) 673-3237
Web Site: https://www.leepub.com
Sales Range: $25-49.9 Million
Newspaper Publishers
N.A.I.C.S.: 513110

Madison Newspapers, Inc.   (1)
1901 Fish Hatchery Rd, Madison, WI
53713-1248   **(50%)**
Tel.: (608) 252-6200
Web Site: http://www.madison.com
Sales Range: $50-74.9 Million
Emp.: 500
Newspaper Publishers
N.A.I.C.S.: 513110

Unit (Domestic):

The Capital Times   (2)
1901 Fish Hatchery Rd, Madison, WI
53713-1297
Tel.: (608) 252-6400
Web Site: https://captimes.com
Sales Range: $100-124.9 Million
Emp.: 300
Online Newspaper Publisher
N.A.I.C.S.: 513110

Wisconsin State Journal   (2)
1901 Fish Hatchery Rd, Madison, WI
53713-1248
Tel.: (608) 252-6200
Web Site: https://www.madison.com

Lee Enterprises, Incorporated—(Continued)

Sales Range: $75-99.9 Million
Emp.: 400
Newspaper Publishers
N.A.I.C.S.: 513110

Moline Dispatch Publishing Co. LLC (1)
1033 7th St Ste 101, East Moline, IL 61244
Tel.: (309) 764-4344
Web Site: http://www.qconline.com
Provider of Newspaper Services
N.A.I.C.S.: 513110

Muscatine Journal (1)
301 E 3rd St, Muscatine, IA 52761-4116
Tel.: (563) 263-2331
Web Site: https://www.muscatinejournal.com
Sales Range: $25-49.9 Million
Emp.: 10
Newspaper Publishers
N.A.I.C.S.: 513110

Napa Valley Publishing Co. (1)
1615 Soscol Ave, Napa, CA 94559-2818 (100%)
Tel.: (707) 226-3711
Sales Range: $25-49.9 Million
Emp.: 132
Newspaper Publishers
N.A.I.C.S.: 513110
Kevin Courtney (Editor-City)
Samie Hartley (Editor-Online & Calendar)
Kelly Doren (Editor-Copy Desk & Wire)
Jennifer Huffman (Editor-Bus)
Davis Taylor (Publr)
Annabelle Anopol (Mgr-Campaign-Real Estate & Auto)
Jacob Alexander (Mgr-Campaign)
Glen Tabangcura (Mgr-Amplified Digital)
Norma Kostecka (Dir-Adv)
Tim Yagle (Editor-Copy)
Sasha Paulsen (Editor-Features)

Pantagraph Publishing Co. (1)
205 N Main St, Bloomington, IL 61701
Tel.: (309) 829-9000
Sales Range: $100-124.9 Million
Emp.: 280
Newspaper Publishers
N.A.I.C.S.: 513110

Pulitzer Inc. (1)
900 N Tucker Blvd, Saint Louis, MO 63101-1069
Tel.: (314) 340-8000
Newspaper Publishing Services
N.A.I.C.S.: 513110

Quad-City Times (1)
500 E 3rd St, Davenport, IA 52801-1502
Tel.: (563) 383-2200
Web Site: https://www.qctimes.com
Sales Range: $100-124.9 Million
Emp.: 300
Newspaper Publishers
N.A.I.C.S.: 513110
David Zorich (Controller)
Liz Boardman (Editor-City)
Ed Tibbetts (Editor-Editorial Page)
Kevin Schmidt (Editor-Photo)
Matt Coss (Editor-Sports)
Alex Valentine (Editor-Enterprise)
Jim Holm (Mgr-Adv Sls)

Rapid City Journal (1)
507 Main St, Rapid City, SD 57701-2733
Tel.: (605) 394-8300
Web Site: https://www.rapidcityjournal.com
Sales Range: $50-74.9 Million
Emp.: 145
Newspaper Publishing Services
N.A.I.C.S.: 513110
Richard Anderson (Editor-Sports)
Josh Hart (Dir-Ops & Circulation)
Holly Edmiston (Editor-Copy)

Ravalli Republic (1)
232 W Main St, Hamilton, MT 59840-2552
Tel.: (406) 523-5290
Web Site: https://www.ravallirepublic.com
Sales Range: $10-24.9 Million
Emp.: 12
Community Newspaper
N.A.I.C.S.: 513110
Jim Strauss (Publr)

Santa Maria Times, Inc. (1)
3200 Skyway Dr, Santa Maria, CA 93455 (100%)

Tel.: (805) 925-2691
Web Site: https://santamariatimes.com
Sales Range: $25-49.9 Million
Emp.: 80
Community Newspaper
N.A.I.C.S.: 513110
Braxton Carroll (Mgr-Sys)
George Fischer (Mgr-Production)
Joe Bailey (Editor-Sports)
Mike Hodgson (Assoc Editor)
Marga Cooley (Mng Editor)
Davis Taylor (Publr)
Guillermo Tamayo (Mgr-Circulation)

Sioux City Newspapers, Inc. (1)
515 Pavonia St, Sioux City, IA 51102 (100%)
Tel.: (712) 293-4250
Web Site: https://www.siouxcityjournal.com
Sales Range: $50-74.9 Million
Newspaper Publishers
N.A.I.C.S.: 513110

Southwestern Oregon Publishing Co. (1)
172 Anderson Ave, Coos Bay, OR 97420-0147 (100%)
Tel.: (541) 266-6047
Web Site: http://www.theworldlink.com
Sales Range: $25-49.9 Million
Emp.: 50
Newspaper & Periodical Publisher
N.A.I.C.S.: 513110
David Thornberry (Publr)

Unit (Domestic):

The World Newspaper (2)
172 Anderson Ave, Coos Bay, OR 97420
Tel.: (541) 266-6047
Web Site: http://www.theworldlink.com
Newspaper Publishers
N.A.I.C.S.: 513110

St. Louis Post-Dispatch LLC (1)
901 N 10th St, Saint Louis, MO 63101 (95%)
Tel.: (314) 340-8000
Sales Range: $300-349.9 Million
Emp.: 850
Daily Newspaper
N.A.I.C.S.: 513110

Star Publishing Company (1)
4850 S Park Ave, Tucson, AZ 85714-1637
Tel.: (520) 618-9393
Newspaper Publishing Services
N.A.I.C.S.: 513110

Suburban Journals of Greater St. Louis LLC (1)
900 N Tucker Blvd, Saint Louis, MO 63101
Tel.: (314) 340-8000
Web Site: http://www.stltoday.com
Emp.: 550
Newspaper & Online Publishing Services
N.A.I.C.S.: 513110

Suburban Newspapers of Greater St. Louis (1)
14522 S Outer 40 Dr 3rd Fl, Town and Country, MO 63017 (100%)
Tel.: (314) 821-1110
Web Site: http://www.stltoday.com
Sales Range: $25-49.9 Million
Emp.: 65
Newspaper Publishers
N.A.I.C.S.: 513110

TNI Partners (1)
4850 S Park Ave, Tucson, AZ 85714
Tel.: (520) 573-4427
Web Site: https://tucson.com
Sales Range: $300-349.9 Million
Emp.: 750
Newspaper Publisher Services
N.A.I.C.S.: 513110
Mark Henschen (Pres & Publr)

Unit (Domestic):

The Arizona Daily Star (2)
4850 S Park Ave, Tucson, AZ 85714-1637
Tel.: (520) 573-4366
Web Site: https://www.tucson.com
Sales Range: $50-74.9 Million
Emp.: 170
Newspaper Publishing
N.A.I.C.S.: 513110
John F. Lundgren (Dir-Print Ops)

The Albany Democrat-Herald (1)
600 Lyon St SW, Albany, OR 97321-2919 (100%)
Tel.: (541) 926-2211
Web Site: https://www.democratherald.com
Sales Range: $50-74.9 Million
Emp.: 160
Newspaper Publishers
N.A.I.C.S.: 513110

The Avenal Progress (1)
524 E Merced St, Avenal, CA 93204
Tel.: (559) 386-9385
Sales Range: $1-9.9 Million
Emp.: 2
Community Newspaper; Central California Weeklies
N.A.I.C.S.: 921110

The Billings Gazette (1)
401 N Broadway, Billings, MT 59101-1243 (100%)
Tel.: (406) 657-1200
Web Site: https://www.billingsgazette.com
Sales Range: $75-99.9 Million
Emp.: 250
Newspaper Publishers
N.A.I.C.S.: 513110
Brett French (Editor-Montana Untamed)
Lindsay Rossmiller (Editor-Digital Sports)
Larry Mayer (Editor-Photo)

The Bismarck Tribune (1)
707 E Front Ave, Bismarck, ND 58504-5646 (100%)
Tel.: (701) 223-2500
Web Site: https://www.bismarktribune.com
Sales Range: $50-74.9 Million
Emp.: 210
Newspaper Publishers
N.A.I.C.S.: 513110
Blake Nicholson (Editor-News)
Dave Selvig (Editor-Sports)

The Buffalo News (1)
1 News Plz, Buffalo, NY 14240 (100%)
Tel.: (716) 842-1111
Sales Range: $350-399.9 Million
Emp.: 850
Daily & Sunday Newspaper
N.A.I.C.S.: 513110
Warren Todd Colville (VP-Sls)
Brian Connolly (VP-Bus Dev & Innovation)
Cindy Colello (Dir-Retail Sls & Adv)
Linda Moskal (Mgr-Real Estate)
Margaret Kenny (Deputy Mng Editor)
Kevin Walter (Editor-Editorial Page)
Rod Watson (Editor-Urban Affairs)
Patrick Lakamp (Editor-Enterprise)
Mike McAndrew (Editor-Watchdog Team)
Toni Ruberto (Editor-Gusto)
Scott Scanlon (Editor-Refresh)
Barb Juzwiak (Mgr-Credit)
Sheila Hayam (Exec Editor)
Tom Wiley (Pres & Publr)
Katie Mulligan (VP)

The Coalinga Record (1)
192 E Elm Ave, Coalinga, CA 93210-2832
Tel.: (559) 935-2906
Sales Range: $10-24.9 Million
Emp.: 4
Community Newspaper
N.A.I.C.S.: 513110

The Daily Herald (1)
1200 Towne Ctr Blvd Ste 1058, Provo, UT 84601
Tel.: (801) 373-5050
Web Site: https://www.heraldextra.com
Sales Range: $75-99.9 Million
Emp.: 220
Community Newspaper
N.A.I.C.S.: 513110

The Daily Journal (1)
1513 S Saint Joe Dr, Park Hills, MO 63601-2402
Tel.: (573) 431-2010
Web Site: https://www.dailyjournalonline.com
Sales Range: $25-49.9 Million
Emp.: 50
Community Newspaper
N.A.I.C.S.: 513110
Matt King (Editor-Sports)
Kevin Jenkins (Mng Editor)

The Independent Record (1)
317 Cruz Ave 59601, Helena, MT 59601 (100%)

Tel.: (406) 447-4000
Web Site: https://www.helenair.com
Sales Range: $25-49.9 Million
Emp.: 25
Newspaper Publishers
N.A.I.C.S.: 513110
Anita Fasbender (Publr)
Steve Biere (Mgr-Circulation)
Eric Seidle (Editor-Digital)
Jeff Welsch (Exec Editor-Sports)
Chris Peterson (Editor-Sports)

The Journal Times (1)
212 4th St, Racine, WI 53403-1005
Tel.: (262) 634-3322
Web Site: https://www.journaltimes.com
Sales Range: $25-49.9 Million
Emp.: 100
Newspaper Publishers
N.A.I.C.S.: 513110
Tom Farley (Editor-News)
Clint Wiedholz (Mgr-Online & Classified Sls)
Loreen Mohr (Coord-Community)
Brenda Wishau (Coord-Digital Content)
Becky Girard (Mgr-Front Counter)
Sandra Johnsrud (Dir-Circulation)
Dave Chvilcek (Mgr-Pkg & Maintenance)

The Missoulian (1)
2291 W Broadway, Missoula, MT 59808
Tel.: (406) 523-5200
Web Site: https://www.missoulian.com
Sales Range: $50-74.9 Million
Emp.: 200
Newspaper Publishers
N.A.I.C.S.: 513110
Jim Strauss (Publr)
Keila Szpaller (Editor-City)
Tyler Christensen (Editor-Opinion)
Anne Cruikshank (Editor-Digital)
Jeff Welsch (Exec Editor-Sports)

The Montana Standard (1)
25 W Granite St, Butte, MT 59701-9213
Tel.: (406) 496-5500
Web Site: https://www.mtstandard.com
Sales Range: $25-49.9 Million
Emp.: 115
Newspaper Publishers
N.A.I.C.S.: 513110
David McCumber (Editor)
Jenean Kujawa (Mgr-Adv Sls)
Eric Seidle (Editor-Digital)
Kristie Constantine (Editor-City)
Jeff Welsch (Exec Editor-Sports)
Beth Walsh (Coord-Majors-Natl)

Winona Daily News (1)
279 E 3rd St Ste 370, Winona, MN 55987 (100%)
Tel.: (507) 453-3500
Web Site: https://www.winonadailynews.com
Sales Range: $25-49.9 Million
Emp.: 80
Newspaper Publishers
N.A.I.C.S.: 513110
John Casper (Coord-Comm)

LEE PHARMACEUTICALS
1434 Santa Anita Ave, South El Monte, CA 91733-3312
Tel.: (626) 442-3141   CA
Year Founded: 1971
LPHM—(OTCIQ)
Polymeric Biomaterials & Consumer Products Developer, Mfr & Marketer
N.A.I.C.S.: 325412
Ronald G. Lee (Chm & Pres)
Michael Agresti (Treas, Sec & VP-Fin)

Subsidiaries:

Lee Consumer Products Division (1)
1434 Santa Anita Ave, South El Monte, CA 91733-3312 (100%)
Tel.: (626) 442-3141
Web Site: http://leepharmaceuticals.com
Mfr & Market Cosmetics & Consumer Products
N.A.I.C.S.: 445230
Mike Agresti (VP)

Lee Dental & Orthodontics Division (1)
1434 Santa Anita Ave, South El Monte, CA 91733-3312 (100%)
Tel.: (626) 442-3141

Mfr & Market Dental Products
N.A.I.C.S.: 325620

LEEP INC
255 Blue Lakes Blvd N Ste 516, Twin Falls, ID 83301
Tel.: (208) 320-8786
Web Site: https://leepinc.com
Year Founded: 1998
LPPI—(OTCEM)
Mineral Products Mfr
N.A.I.C.S.: 327332

LEFTERIS ACQUISITION CORP.
292 Newbury St Ste 293, Boston, MA 02115
Tel.: (617) 510-1991   DE
Year Founded: 2020
LFTRU—(NASDAQ)
Rev.: $15,288,859
Assets: $207,379,545
Liabilities: $225,994,626
Net Worth: ($18,615,081)
Earnings: $11,657,463
Emp.: 5
Fiscal Year-end: 12/31/21
Investment Services
N.A.I.C.S.: 523999
Mark S. Casady *(Chm)*
Karl Roessner *(Vice Chm)*
Jon Isaacson *(CEO, CFO, COO & Chief Corp Dev Officer)*
David Bergers *(Gen Counsel)*

LEGACY EDUCATION ALLI-ANCE, INC.
1490 NE Pine Island Rd Ste 5D, Cape Coral, FL 33909
Tel.: (239) 542-0643   NV
Web Site:
  https://www.legacyeducationalli
  ance.com
Year Founded: 2010
LEAI—(OTCQB)
Rev.: $7,710,000
Assets: $1,921,000
Liabilities: $24,104,000
Net Worth: ($22,183,000)
Earnings: ($566,000)
Emp.: 19
Fiscal Year-end: 12/31/21
Educational Support Services
N.A.I.C.S.: 611710
Barry M. Kostiner *(Chm & CEO)*

Subsidiaries:

Elite Legacy Education Ltd.   (1)
Parkshot House 5 Kew Road, Richmond, TW9 2PR, Surrey, United Kingdom
Tel.: (44) 2089966700
Web Site: https://store.legacyeducation.com
Education Services
N.A.I.C.S.: 611710

Rich Dad Education Ltd.   (1)
Suite 302 - 2233 Argentia Rd, Mississauga, L5N 2X7, ON, Canada
Tel.: (905) 264-2114
Web Site: http://www.richdadeducation.com
Education Services
N.A.I.C.S.: 611710

LEGACY EDUCATION INC.
701 W Ave K Ste 123, Lancaster, CA 93534
Tel.: (661) 940-9300   NV
Web Site: https://www.legacyed.com
Year Founded: 2009
LGCY—(NYSEAMEX)
Rev.: $46,000,316
Assets: $35,173,050
Liabilities: $12,754,038
Net Worth: $22,419,012
Earnings: $5,114,852
Emp.: 68
Fiscal Year-end: 06/30/24
Educational Support Services

N.A.I.C.S.: 611710

LEGACY HOUSING CORPO-RATION
4801 Mark IV Pkwy, Fort Worth, TX 76106
Tel.: (817) 799-4900   DE
Web Site: https://legacyhousing.com
Year Founded: 2005
LEGH—(NASDAQ)
Rev.: $189,144,000
Assets: $506,742,000
Liabilities: $70,007,000
Net Worth: $436,735,000
Earnings: $54,460,000
Emp.: 572
Fiscal Year-end: 12/31/23
Residential Property Managers
N.A.I.C.S.: 531311
Curtis D. Hodgson *(Co-Founder & Chm)*
Kenneth E. Shipley *(Co-Founder & Exec VP)*
Robert Duncan Bates *(Pres & CEO)*
Shane Allred *(Dir-Fin Reporting)*
Max M. Africk *(Gen Counsel & Sec)*
Jeff Fiedelman *(CFO)*

LEGALZOOM.COM, INC.
101 N Brand Blvd 11th Fl, Glendale, CA 91203
Tel.: (323) 962-8600   DE
Web Site:
  https://www.legalzoom.com
Year Founded: 1999
LZ—(NASDAQ)
Rev.: $660,727,000
Assets: $447,818,000
Liabilities: $278,984,000
Net Worth: $168,834,000
Earnings: $13,953,000
Emp.: 1,190
Fiscal Year-end: 12/31/23
Law firm
N.A.I.C.S.: 541199
Noel Watson *(CFO)*
Sheily Panchal *(Chief People Officer)*
Nicole Miller *(Gen Counsel)*
Kathy Tsitovich *(Chief Partnership Officer)*
Noel B. Watson Jr. *(CFO & COO)*
Daniel Lysaught *(CMO)*
Jeffrey Stibel *(Chm & CEO)*

Subsidiaries:

Earth Class Mail, Inc.   (1)
9450 SW Gemini Dr Ste 101, Beaverton, OR 97008
Tel.: (971) 250-5000
Web Site: http://www.earthclassmail.com
Private Mail Centers
N.A.I.C.S.: 561431

LEGATO MERGER CORP.
777 3rd Ave 37th Fl, New York, NY 10017
Tel.: (212) 319-7676   DE
Year Founded: 2020
LEGOU—(NASDAQ)
Investment Services
N.A.I.C.S.: 523999
Adam Jaffe *(CFO & Sec)*
Eric S. Rosenfeld *(Chief Space Officer)*

LEGEND BIOTECH CORPORA-TION
2101 Cottontail Ln, Somerset, NJ 08873
Tel.: (732) 317-5050   Ky
Web Site: https://legendbiotech.com
Year Founded: 2015
LEGN—(NASDAQ)
Rev.: $117,005,000
Assets: $1,330,963,000
Liabilities: $586,651,000
Net Worth: $744,312,000

Earnings: ($446,349,000)
Emp.: 1,390
Fiscal Year-end: 12/31/22
Research & Development in Biotech-nology (except Nanobiotechnology)
N.A.I.C.S.: 541714
Ying Huang *(CEO)*
Lori Macomber *(CFO)*
Guowei Fang *(Chief Scientific Officer & Head-Bus Dev)*
Mythili Koneru *(Chief Medical Officer)*
Jim Pepin *(Gen Counsel)*
Frank Zhang *(Chm)*

Subsidiaries:

Legend Biotech USA
Incorporated   (1)
2101 Cottontail Ln, Somerset, NJ 08873
Tel.: (732) 317-5050
Web Site: https://legendbiotech.com
Life Science Research & Development Services
N.A.I.C.S.: 541715
Tonia Nesheiwat *(Exec Dir-Medical Affairs)*
Surabhi Verma *(Mgr-IR & Corp Comm)*
Jessie Yeung *(Head-Corp Fin & IR)*
Ye Wang *(Chm)*
Ying Huang *(CEO & CFO)*
Meeta Chatterjee *(Sr VP-Bus Dev-Global)*

LEGEND OIL AND GAS, LTD.
555 N Point Ctr E Ste 410, Al-pharetta, GA 30022
Tel.: (678) 366-4587   CO
Web Site: http://www.midconoil.com
Year Founded: 2000
LOGL—(OTCEM)
Sales Range: $1-9.9 Million
Emp.: 18
Oil & Gas Exploration
N.A.I.C.S.: 211120
Warren S. Binderman *(Pres, CFO, Exec VP, Treas & Sec)*
James Vandeberg *(CFO, Sec & VP)*

Subsidiaries:

Black Diamond Energy Holdings
LLC   (1)
5445 DTC Pkwy PH 4, Greenwood Village, CO 80111
Tel.: (720) 709-4713
Web Site: http://www.maxxonenergy.com
Holding Company
N.A.I.C.S.: 551112
Warren S. Binderman *(Pres, Interim CEO & CFO)*
Ian Sylvester *(COO & Gen Mgr)*
April Walker *(Supvr-Dispatch)*

Maxxon Logistics LLC   (1)
129104 South Ave SW, Killdeer, ND 58640
Tel.: (701) 300-3446
General Freight Trucking Services
N.A.I.C.S.: 484110

Treeline Diesel Center LLC   (1)
129 104S Ave SW, Killdeer, ND 58640
Tel.: (701) 764-6710
Web Site:
  http://www.treelinedieselcenter.com
Truck Repair Services
N.A.I.C.S.: 811111

LEGGETT & PLATT, INCORPO-RATED
No 1 Leggett Rd, Carthage, MO 64836
Tel.: (417) 358-8131   MO
Web Site: https://www.leggett.com
Year Founded: 1883
LEG—(NYSE)
Rev.: $4,725,300,000
Assets: $4,634,500,000
Liabilities: $3,300,500,000
Net Worth: $1,334,000,000
Earnings: ($136,800,000)
Emp.: 19,300
Fiscal Year-end: 12/31/23
Bedding & Furniture Components,
Finished Furniture & Carpet Cushion-

ing; Products Made from Steel, Steel Wire, Aluminum, Foam & Plastic Chemicals, Textile Scrap & Various Woods Mfr & Sales
N.A.I.C.S.: 321211
Matthew C. Flanigan *(CFO & Sr VP)*
Karl G. Glassman *(Chm, Pres & CEO)*
R. Samuel Smith III *(Pres-Furniture, Flooring, and Textile Products & Sr VP)*
Michael W. Blinzler *(CIO & VP)*
Scott S. Douglas *(Gen Counsel, Sec & Sr VP)*
Susan R. McCoy *(Sr VP-IR)*
Tammy M. Trent *(Chief Acctg Officer & Sr VP)*
Benjamin M. Burns *(CFO & Exec VP)*
Lindsey N. Odaffer *(VP-Internal Audit & Due Diligence)*
Marcus T. Olsen *(VP-Procurement)*
Charles P. Hutchins *(Chief Tax Officer & VP)*
Andrew C. Bender *(Treas & VP)*
Jennifer J. Coleman *(VP & Deputy Gen Counsel)*
Darrel E. Wild *(Chief Credit Officer & VP)*
Cassie J. Branscum *(Sr Dir-IR)*
Kolina A. Talbert *(Mgr-IR)*
Christina Ptasinski *(Chief HR Officer)*

Subsidiaries:

Bergen Cable Technology, LLC   (1)
343 Kaplan Dr, Fairfield, NJ 07004
Tel.: (973) 276-9596
Web Site: https://www.bergencable.com
Sales Range: $25-49.9 Million
Emp.: 25
Mfr of Miniature Cable Assemblies for Com-puter Printer Drives & Other Office Product Applications; Cables & Cable Assemblies for Aircraft Controls; Push-Pull Cable Con-trols
N.A.I.C.S.: 331222

Buffalo Batt & Felt, LLC   (1)
3307 Walden Ave, Depew, NY 14043
Tel.: (716) 683-4100
Web Site: http://www.buffalobatt.com
Polyster Fiber Product Mfr
N.A.I.C.S.: 325220

Capitol Hardware, Inc.   (1)
402 N Main St, Middlebury, IN 46540
Tel.: (269) 683-9585
Web Site:
  http://www.capitolhardwareinc.com
Sales Range: $25-49.9 Million
Emp.: 10
Distr Of Store Fixtures
N.A.I.C.S.: 423440

Chieng Yeng Ent. Co., Ltd.   (1)
Hui Long Industrial Area Nan Hai Area, Yan Bu Town, Foshan, 528247, Guangdong, China
Tel.: (86) 75785701858
Web Site: https://www.chiengyeng.com
Hardware Product Mfr
N.A.I.C.S.: 332510

Crest-Foam Corp.   (1)
521 Sunfield Ave, Edison, NJ
08837-3898   (100%)
Tel.: (732) 225-2440
Web Site: http://www.griffinserv.com
Sales Range: $25-49.9 Million
Emp.: 100
Mfr of Polyurethane Foam
N.A.I.C.S.: 326150

DHAP Ltd   (1)
The Headlands Downton, Salisbury, SP5 3HT, United Kingdom
Tel.: (44) 1725513639
Aerospace Product Distr
N.A.I.C.S.: 423860

David Hart Aerospace Pipes
Limited   (1)
Long Close, Downton, Salisbury, SP5 3HG,

Leggett & Platt, Incorporated—(Continued)

Wiltshire, United Kingdom
Tel.: (44) 1725513639
Web Site: https://leggettaerospace.com
Emp.: 90
Metal Pipe Fabrication Services
N.A.I.C.S.: 332996
Mark Gossington (Mgr-Sales)
Al Houde (VP-Sales-Aerospace Grp)
Roland Wheeler (Sls Dir)
Al Houde (VP-Sales-Aerospace Grp)
Roland Wheeler (Sls Dir)

Eagan Products, LLC (1)
205 W Wacker Dr Ste 1000, Chicago, IL 60606
Web Site: https://www.drifttr.com
Mattress Mfr & Distr
N.A.I.C.S.: 337910

Elite Foam, LLC (1)
76 Sprayberry Rd, Newnan, GA 30263-1054
Tel.: (501) 269-5039
Web Site: https://www.elitefoamllc.com
Polyurethane Foam Mfr
N.A.I.C.S.: 326150

Fashion Bed Group (1)
5950 W 51st St, Chicago, IL 60638 (100%)
Tel.: (708) 458-1800
Web Site: http://www.fashionbedgroup.com
Sales Range: $25-49.9 Million
Emp.: 100
Mfr of Metal, Wood, Rattan Furniture
N.A.I.C.S.: 337126
Ron Ainsworth (Pres)

Flex-O-Lators, Incorporated (1)
1460 Jackson Dr, Carthage, MO 64836
Tel.: (417) 358-4095
Web Site: http://www.leggettandplatt.com
Sales Range: $100-124.9 Million
Emp.: 200
Automotive Seating Component Mfr
N.A.I.C.S.: 336360

Galkin Automated Products Corp. (1)
1129 W Fairview, Carthage, MO 64836
Tel.: (417) 237-6254
Web Site: http://www.gsgcompanies.com
Industrial Sewing Machines & Parts Mfr
N.A.I.C.S.: 333248

Garcy Piedmont (1)
1000 Garcy Blvd, Piedmont, AL 36272-1488
Tel.: (256) 447-9016
Web Site: http://www.pwpl.com
Sales Range: $75-99.9 Million
Emp.: 130
Wood Store & Display Fixtures Mfr
N.A.I.C.S.: 321999
Sam Tunstall (Owner)

Gateway (Textiles) Limited (1)
Unit 3 Northgate Terrace Northern Road Industrial Estate, Newark, NG24 2EU, Notts, United Kingdom
Tel.: (44) 01636676194
Web Site: http://www.gsgcompanies.com
Sales Range: $10-24.9 Million
Emp.: 8
Industrial Machinery Mfr
N.A.I.C.S.: 333248
David Elsdon (Mng Dir)

Gribetz International, Inc. (1)
13800 NW 4th St, Sunrise, FL 33325
Tel.: (954) 846-0300
Web Site: http://www.gribetz.com
Sales Range: $25-49.9 Million
Emp.: 55
Quilting & Stitching Machines & Parts Mfr & Distr
N.A.I.C.S.: 337121
David Elsdon (Mgr-Sales)

Guangdong Zhaoqing L&V Co. Ltd. (1)
Yingbin Road 21 Zhaoqing Hi-Tech Zone, Zhaoqing, 526238, China
Tel.: (86) 7583623917
Automobile Parts Mfr
N.A.I.C.S.: 336390

Hanes Companies - New Jersey, LLC (1)

104 Sunfield Ave, Edison, NJ 08837-3845
Tel.: (732) 343-7740
Web Site: http://www.hanesindustries.com
Textile Converter Product Distr
N.A.I.C.S.: 313310

Hanes Companies, Inc. (1)
500 N McLin Creek Rd, Conover, NC 28613
Tel.: (828) 464-4673
Web Site: http://www.hanesindustries.com
Sales Range: $400-449.9 Million
Emp.: 1,100
Nonwoven Material & Woven Fabric Mfr
N.A.I.C.S.: 313310
Jerry Greene (Pres)

Subsidiary (Domestic):

Hanes Dye & Finishing (2)
600 Northwest Blvd, Winston Salem, NC 27101
Tel.: (336) 725-1391
Web Site: https://hanescompanies.com
Sales Range: $125-149.9 Million
Emp.: 200
Processor & Converter of Textile Products
N.A.I.C.S.: 424310

Branch (Domestic):

Hanes Industries (3)
3401 Etiwanda Ave Bldg 1011D, Mira Loma, CA 91752
Tel.: (562) 926-0441
Web Site: http://www.hanesindustries.com
Sales Range: $75-99.9 Million
Emp.: 80
Mfr & Sales of Residential Furniture Upholstery Materials
N.A.I.C.S.: 424310

Subsidiary (Domestic):

Hanes Geo Components (2)
815 Buxton St, Winston-Salem, NC 27101-1310
Tel.: (336) 747-1600
Web Site: http://www.hanesgeo.com
Woven & Non-Woven Fabric Mfr
N.A.I.C.S.: 313310

Indiana Chair Frame (1)
330 N Greensboro St, Liberty, NC 27298 (100%)
Tel.: (336) 622-0121
Web Site: http://www.lp-icf.com
Sales Range: $10-24.9 Million
Emp.: 50
Office Chair Mfr & Distr
N.A.I.C.S.: 337121

Japenamelac Corp. (1)
25 Katrina Rd, Chelmsford, MA 01824
Tel.: (978) 256-2212
Web Site: http://www.japenamelac.com
Sales Range: $25-49.9 Million
Emp.: 80
Metal Painting Services
N.A.I.C.S.: 238320

Jentschmann AG (1)
Feldstrasse 2, 8194, Huntwangen, Switzerland
Tel.: (41) 447358383
Web Site: https://jentschmann.ch
Sales Range: $10-24.9 Million
Emp.: 15
Special Sewing Machines, Ultrasonic Welding & Cutting Machines Mfr
N.A.I.C.S.: 333248

Kintec-Solution GmbH (1)
Bokeler Str 100, 33397, Rietberg, Germany
Tel.: (49) 5244907950
Web Site: https://www.kintec-solution.com
Furniture Mfr & Distr
N.A.I.C.S.: 337214
Michael L. Carter (Mng Dir)
Tyson Hagale (Mng Dir)
Shonna L. Koch (Mng Dir)
Markus Rohr (Mng Dir)

L and C Windsor Cables Ltd. (1)
2005 Blackacre Drive, Old Castle, N0R 1L0, ON, Canada
Tel.: (519) 737-1497
Sales Range: $25-49.9 Million
Emp.: 40
Insulated Wire Product Mfr
N.A.I.C.S.: 335999

L&C Changsha Cable Industries Ltd. (1)
No 38 Yingxia Road, Quantang Industrial Park, Changsha, 410100, Hunan, China (100%)
Tel.: (86) 73182967988
Sales Range: $150-199.9 Million
Mfr of Cables for Automotive Industry
N.A.I.C.S.: 332618

L&P Aerospace Acquisition Company, LLC (1)
1 Leggett Rd, Carthage, MO 64836
Tel.: (417) 358-8131
Emp.: 96
Aircraft Engine & Engine Parts Mfr
N.A.I.C.S.: 336412

L&P Automotive Europe Headquarters GmbH (1)
Frankenstrasse 150A, 90461, Nuremberg, Germany
Tel.: (49) 9117104031002
Web Site: http://www.leggett-automotive.com
Engineering & Design of Automotive Lumbars
N.A.I.C.S.: 336110

Subsidiary (Non-US):

Schukra Berndorf Ges.m.b.H. (2)
Leobersdorfer Strasse 26, 2560, Berndorf, Austria (100%)
Tel.: (43) 2672835400
Car Seat Lumbar Support Mfr
N.A.I.C.S.: 336110

L&P Denmark ApS (1)
Larkevej 6, Tistrup Stationsby, 6862, Denmark
Tel.: (45) 76981800
Mattress & Upholstery Spring Units Mfr
N.A.I.C.S.: 332613

L&P Financial Services Co. (1)
2015 N Macarthur Dr, Tracy, CA 95376
Tel.: (209) 839-8230
Emp.: 99
Financial Investment Services
N.A.I.C.S.: 523999
Eugene Buettner (CTO)

L&P International Holdings Company (1)
1 Leggett Rd, Carthage, MO 64836-0757 (100%)
Tel.: (417) 358-8131
Web Site: http://www.lagett.com
Sales Range: $10-24.9 Million
Emp.: 560
Bedding Mfr
N.A.I.C.S.: 337121

L&P Materials Manufacturing, Inc. (1)
925 Ln Ave N, Jacksonville, FL 32254-2828 (100%)
Tel.: (904) 786-0750
Sales Range: $50-74.9 Million
Emp.: 103
Mfr of Wire
N.A.I.C.S.: 493190
Steve Tecker (Mgr)

L&P Property Management Company (1)
1 Leggett Rd, Carthage, MO 64836-9649
Tel.: (417) 358-8131
Web Site: http://www.leggett.com
Sales Range: $10-24.9 Million
Emp.: 500
Bedding Mfr
N.A.I.C.S.: 337121

L&P Somappa Comfort Systems (India) Private Limited (1)
C-13 Ambattur Industrial Estate, Ambattur, Chennai, 600 053, India
Tel.: (91) 4426350511
Sales Range: $50-74.9 Million
Emp.: 300
Electrical Component Mfr
N.A.I.C.S.: 335999
S. Balachander (Gen Mgr)

L&P Springs Denmark A/S (1)
Vardevej 34, Tistrup Stationsby, 6862, Denmark
Tel.: (45) 76981800

Web Site: http://www.lpeurope.com
Emp.: 100
Carpet Product Mfr
N.A.I.C.S.: 314110
Niels Albaek (Mng Dir)

L&P Springs Italia S.r.l. (1)
Via Ferravilla Edoardo 70, 20033, Desio, Italy
Tel.: (39) 0362625441
Web Site: http://www.beddingcomponents.com
Sales Range: $25-49.9 Million
Emp.: 4
Bedding Springs Importer & Exporter
N.A.I.C.S.: 332613

L&P Swiss Holding Gmbh (1)
Gruntalstrasse 23, Kronbuhl, 9300, Wittenbach, Switzerland (100%)
Tel.: (41) 712921288
Holding Company
N.A.I.C.S.: 551112

L&P Transportation, LLC (1)
309 N McGregor, Carthage, MO 64836
Tel.: (417) 358-8131
Web Site: http://www.leggett.com
Trucking Service
N.A.I.C.S.: 484121
Brian Arterburn (Dir-Logistics)

L&P tehnologije d.o.o. (1)
Hrupine 4, 40323, Prelog, 40323, Croatia
Tel.: (385) 40650500
Web Site: http://www.lpt.hr
Sales Range: $50-74.9 Million
Emp.: 405
Business Services
N.A.I.C.S.: 561499

LPT d.o.o. (1)
Hrupine 4, 40323, Prelog, 40323, Croatia
Tel.: (385) 40650500
Web Site: http://www.lpt.hr
Emp.: 405
Spring Mfr
N.A.I.C.S.: 332613
Davor Gecic (Pres-Bus Unit)

Landmark Earth Solutions, Inc. (1)
1275 Shiloh Rd NW Ste 2020, Kennesaw, GA 30144
Tel.: (888) 574-6473
Web Site: http://www.erosion-management.com
Industrial Machinery Mfr
N.A.I.C.S.: 333248

Leggett & Platt (Guangzhou) Co. Ltd. (1)
Northern Chaotian Industry zone Shilou town, Panyu, Guangzhou, 511447, China
Tel.: (86) 203485200
Web Site: http://www.leggett-china.com
Sales Range: $25-49.9 Million
Emp.: 180
Furniture Product Mfr
N.A.I.C.S.: 337211

Leggett & Platt (Jiaxing) Co. Ltd. (1)
No 21 Zongsan Road Wangjiangjin Development Zone, Jiaxing, 314016, Zhejiang, China
Tel.: (86) 5732282766
Mattress Mfr
N.A.I.C.S.: 337910

Leggett & Platt (Shanghai) Co. Ltd. (1)
No 378 North Mei Gui Road Wai Gai Qiao Free Trade Zone, Shanghai, 200131, China
Tel.: (86) 2150462285
Hardware Merchant Whslr
N.A.I.C.S.: 423710

Leggett & Platt (Shanghai) Machinery Technology Co. Ltd (1)
No 1051 Zhang Xiang Road Anting Town, Jia Ding District, Shanghai, 201814, China
Tel.: (86) 2159508600
Web Site: http://www.leggett-china.com
Needle Machinery Mfr
N.A.I.C.S.: 333248

Leggett & Platt (Taizhou) Co. Ltd. (1)
No 2 Zhengyu E Rd Private Econom, Jiangyan, Taizhou, 225500, China
Tel.: (86) 52382071

Household Furniture Mfr
N.A.I.C.S.: 337122

Leggett & Platt - Amco Division (1)
11230 Harland Dr, Covington, GA
30014 **(100%)**
Tel.: (770) 787-9830
Sales Range: $100-124.9 Million
Emp.: 200
Mfr of Shelving System
N.A.I.C.S.: 337126

Leggett & Platt Administradora, S.A. de C.V. (1)
Montes Aconcagua 325 Lomas 2a Secc,
78210, San Luis Potosi, Mexico
Tel.: (52) 4448341400
Emp.: 1,000
Hardware Merchant Whslr
N.A.I.C.S.: 423710
Tammy Trent (Office Mgr)

Leggett & Platt Aerospace Middletown, LLC (1)
422 Timber Ridge Rd, Middletown, CT
06457
Tel.: (860) 635-8811
Fabricated Tube & Pipe Assembly Mfr
N.A.I.C.S.: 332996
Chris DiPentima (Pres-Tube Div)

Leggett & Platt Asia Limited (1)
1610 Evergain Plaza Tower One 88 Container Port Road, Kwai Chung, New Territories, China (Hong Kong)
Tel.: (852) 37582656
Hardware Merchant Whslr
N.A.I.C.S.: 423710
Kenmin Alex Qu (Mgr-Ops)

Leggett & Platt Canada Co. (1)
1959 Upper Water Street Suite 900, Halifax,
B3J 2X2, NS, Canada
Tel.: (417) 358-8131
Hardware Merchant Whslr
N.A.I.C.S.: 423710

Leggett & Platt Commercial Vehicle Products, Inc. (1)
905 Memorial Dr SE, Atlanta, GA 30316
Tel.: (404) 218-8335
Web Site: http://www.commercialvehicle-products.com
Emp.: 100
Hardware Product Mfr
N.A.I.C.S.: 332510

Leggett & Platt Components Company, Inc. (1)
241 Jamie Whitten Blvd, Saltillo, MS 38866-8701
Tel.: (662) 869-1060
Hardware Merchant Whslr
N.A.I.C.S.: 423710

Leggett & Platt Components Europe Limited (1)
C/O Bracher Rawlins Llp 16 High Holborn,
Grimethorpe, London, WC1V 6BX, S Yorkshire, United Kingdom
Tel.: (44) 1226707550
Web Site: http://www.lpeurope.com
Sales Range: $25-49.9 Million
Emp.: 200
Mattress Springs Mfr
N.A.I.C.S.: 337910

Leggett & Platt France S.A.S. (1)
Z A de l'Orriere, 72800, Aubigne-Racan,
France
Tel.: (33) 243462940
Web Site: http://www.lpeurope.com
Emp.: 7
Bedsprings & Mattress Mfr
N.A.I.C.S.: 337910
Max Acdarian (Mng Dir)

Leggett & Platt Industry (Huizhou) Co Ltd (1)
West Area Industrial Park Factory Along
The River, Dayawan Huiyan, 516000, Huizhou, China
Tel.: (86) 7525206351
Web Site: http://www.leggettmotion-intl.com
Emp.: 125
Household Furniture Mfr
N.A.I.C.S.: 337122

Leggett & Platt International Development Co. (1)

1 Leggett Rd, Carthage, MO 64836-9649
Tel.: (417) 358-8131
Web Site: http://www.leggett.com
Sales Range: $250-299.9 Million
Emp.: 800
Bedding Mfr
N.A.I.C.S.: 337121

Leggett & Platt International Service Corporation (1)
1 Leggett Rd, Carthage, MO
64836 **(100%)**
Tel.: (417) 358-8131
Web Site: http://www.leggett.com
Sales Range: $10-24.9 Million
Distribution of Furniture
N.A.I.C.S.: 337910

Leggett & Platt Office Components International S.r.l. (1)
1/3 2l, 31055, Quinto di Treviso, Italy
Tel.: (39) 04220470098
Web Site: http://www.lpoci.it
Sales Range: $10-24.9 Million
Emp.: 14
Furniture Product Mfr
N.A.I.C.S.: 337214

Leggett & Platt Office Components, LLC (1)
1640 Blandwood Dr 330 N Ringsboro, High
Point, NC 27298
Tel.: (336) 885-4000
Web Site: http://www.legett.com
Emp.: 35
Furniture Product Mfr
N.A.I.C.S.: 337214

Leggett & Platt Residencial, S. de R.L. de C.V. (1)
Avenida de la Luz No 90 LT 22 23, Parque
Industrial la Luz, 54716, Mexico, DF,
Mexico
Tel.: (52) 4448341400
Web Site:
http://www.leggettlatinamerica.com
Bedding & Furniture Components & Products Mfr
N.A.I.C.S.: 337126

Leggett & Platt de Mexico, S. de R.L. de C.V. (1)
Montes Aconcagua 325 Lomas 2nd Secc,
Tangamanga District, 78210, San Luis Potosi, 78210, Mexico **(100%)**
Tel.: (52) 4448341400
Web Site:
http://www.leggettlatinamerica.com
Emp.: 350
Hardware Merchant Whslr
N.A.I.C.S.: 423710

Leggett & Platt do Brasil Ltda. (1)
Av Genesio Vargas 1425, Camanducaia,
37650-000, MG, Brazil
Tel.: (55) 3534338600
Web Site: https://www.leggett.com.br
Sales Range: $50-74.9 Million
Emp.: 120
Bedsprings Mfr
N.A.I.C.S.: 332613

Leggett & Platt, Inc. - Chicago (1)
6755 W 65th St, Bedford Park, IL 60638
Tel.: (708) 594-0045
Web Site: http://www.lpcpg.com
Sales Range: $50-74.9 Million
Emp.: 210
Fashion Bed Distr
N.A.I.C.S.: 337126
John Case (Pres-Consumer Products Grp)

Leggett & Platt, Inc. - Oxford (1)
23 Dana Rd, Oxford, MA 01540-1767
Tel.: (508) 987-8706
Web Site:
http://www.beddingcomponents.com
Sales Range: $50-74.9 Million
Emp.: 19
Mfr of General Spring & Wire
N.A.I.C.S.: 332613

MPI, Inc. (1)
165 Smith St, Poughkeepsie, NY 12601
Tel.: (845) 471-7630
Web Site: https://www.mpi-systems.com
Sales Range: $10-24.9 Million
Emp.: 7
Grinding Company
N.A.I.C.S.: 337910

Mary Ann Industries Inc. (1)
34 E Industrial Ct, Villa Rica, GA 30180
Tel.: (770) 459-3653
Sales Range: $10-24.9 Million
Emp.: 75
Nonwoven Fabric Mfr
N.A.I.C.S.: 313310
Tim Rodman (Mgr-Fin)

MasterRackCrown (1)
7315 E Lincoln Way, Apple Creek, OH
44606 **(100%)**
Tel.: (330) 262-6010
Web Site: http://www.crown-na.com
Sales Range: $600-649.9 Million
Emp.: 420
Special Vehicle Bodies & Interiors
N.A.I.C.S.: 811111

No-Sag Products Division (1)
2225 Production Rd, Kendallville, IN 46755
Tel.: (260) 347-2600
Web Site: https://www.nosagproducts.com
Sales Range: $75-99.9 Million
Emp.: 80
Mfr of Furniture Springs
N.A.I.C.S.: 332613

Northfield Metal Products Ltd. (1)
195 Bathurst Drive, PO Box 214, Waterloo,
N2V 2B2, ON, Canada **(100%)**
Tel.: (519) 884-1860
Web Site:
https://www.northfieldmetalproducts.com
Sales Range: $125-149.9 Million
Emp.: 500
Mfr of Chair Components
N.A.I.C.S.: 337121
Bob Doerner (Pres)

Precision Hydraulic Cylinders (UK) Limited (1)
Bassington Lane, Bassington Industrial Estate, Cramlington, NE23 8AE, Northumberland, United Kingdom
Tel.: (44) 1670707203
Web Site: http://www.phc-global.com
Industrial Equipment Mfr
N.A.I.C.S.: 334513

Precision Hydraulic Cylinders Inc. (1)
196 N 41 Hwy, Beulaville, NC 28518
Tel.: (910) 298-0100
Web Site: http://www.phc-global.com
Fluid Power Cylinder & Actuator Mfr
N.A.I.C.S.: 333995

Precision Hydraulics Private Limited (1)
No 83 84 and 117 Sipcot Industrial Complex, Gummidipoondi, 601 201, Chennai,
601201, India
Tel.: (91) 4427921298
Web Site: http://www.phc-global.com
Industrial Equipment Mfr
N.A.I.C.S.: 334513

Pullmaflex Benelux N.V. (1)
Kortrijkstraat 343, 8560, Wevelgem, Belgium
Tel.: (32) 56438130
Web Site: http://www.pullmaflex.com
Sales Range: $75-99.9 Million
Emp.: 180
Automobile Seating Components Mfr
N.A.I.C.S.: 336110
Stefaan Deceuninck (Plant Mgr)

Pullmaflex U.K. Limited (1)
C/O Bracher Rawlins Llp 16 High Holborn,
Ammanford, London, WC1V 6BX, United
Kingdom
Tel.: (44) 1269592301
Web Site: http://www.lpautomotive.com
Sales Range: $25-49.9 Million
Emp.: 65
Car Seat Suspension Units Mfr
N.A.I.C.S.: 333310

SCHUKRA Geratebau GmbH (1)
Leobersdorfer Strasse 26, 2560, Berndorf,
Lower Austria, Austria
Tel.: (43) 267283540
Web Site: http://www.leggett-automotive.com
Furniture Product Mfr
N.A.I.C.S.: 337214

Sackner Products Inc. (1)

178 Orbit Rd, Statesville, NC 28677
Tel.: (704) 873-1086
Sales Range: $50-74.9 Million
Emp.: 78
Mfr & Sale of Furniture Supplies for the Furniture Industry
N.A.I.C.S.: 314999
Bob Montle (Product Mgr)
Joe Dishman (Branch Mgr)

Schukra of North America Ltd. (1)
360 Silver Creek Industrial Dr RR 1, Tecumseh, N8N 4Y3, ON, Canada
Tel.: (519) 727-7000
Web Site: http://www.schukra.com
Sales Range: $200-249.9 Million
Emp.: 400
Seating Component Mfr
N.A.I.C.S.: 336360

Solon Specialty Wire Co. (1)
30000 Solon Rd, Cleveland, OH 44139
Tel.: (440) 248-7600
Web Site: http://www.leggett.com
Sales Range: $50-74.9 Million
Emp.: 74
Steel Pole Mfr
N.A.I.C.S.: 332618

Spartan Showcase, Inc. (1)
124 S Seymour St, Saint James, MO 65559
Tel.: (636) 583-4050
Web Site:
https://www.spartanshowcase.com
Sales Range: $100-124.9 Million
Emp.: 147
Mfr Of Showcase & Store Fixtures
N.A.I.C.S.: 337215

Specitubes SAS (1)
Parc de l'ile 17 rue du Port, 92022, Nanterre, France
Tel.: (33) 141209430
Web Site: http://www.specitubes.com
Tube Mfr
N.A.I.C.S.: 331210

Sponge-Cushion, Inc. (1)
902 Armstrong St, Morris, IL 60450
Tel.: (815) 942-2300
Web Site: http://www.commercial-carpetcushion.com
Sponge Rubber Product Mfr
N.A.I.C.S.: 326299

Spuhl AG (1)
Gruntalstrasse 23, Truenserasse 23, 9300,
Wittenbach, Switzerland
Tel.: (41) 712921375
Web Site: http://www.spuhi.ch
Sales Range: $100-124.9 Million
Emp.: 250
Coiling Machines & Digital Printing Machines Mfr
N.A.I.C.S.: 333310

Spuhl GmbH (1)
Gruntalstrasse 23, 9300, Wittenbach, Switzerland
Tel.: (41) 712921111
Web Site: https://www.spuhl.com
Emp.: 180
Spring Mfr
N.A.I.C.S.: 332613

Sterling Steel Company, LLC (1)
101 Ave K, Sterling, IL 61081
Tel.: (815) 548-7000
Web Site: http://www.leggett.com
Steel Mfrs
N.A.I.C.S.: 332999

TAG Environmental Inc. (1)
23 Trueman Rd, Barrie, L4N 6E7, ON,
Canada
Tel.: (705) 725-1938
Emp.: 18
Industrial Equipment Mfr
N.A.I.C.S.: 334513

Talbot Industries, Inc. (1)
1211 W Harmony St, Neosho, MO 64850-1636
Tel.: (417) 451-5900
Web Site: http://www.talbotindustries.com
Sales Range: $25-49.9 Million
Emp.: 75
Wire Fabrication
N.A.I.C.S.: 332618

Terrafix Geosynthetics Inc. (1)

Leggett & Platt, Incorporated—(Continued)

455 Horner Avenue, Toronto, M8W 4W9, ON, Canada
Tel.: (416) 674-0363
Web Site: https://www.terrafixgeo.com
System Installation Services
N.A.I.C.S.: 238210

Valley Metals, LLC (1)
13125 Gregg St, Poway, CA 92064
Tel.: (858) 513-1300
Web Site: https://www.leggettaerospace.com
Tubing & Tubular Component Supplier
N.A.I.C.S.: 313220

Vertex Fasteners, Inc. (1)
1798 Sherwin Ave, Des Plaines, IL 60018
Tel.: (847) 768-6139
Web Site: https://www.vertexfasteners.com
Sales Range: $25-49.9 Million
Emp.: 45
Mfr of Specialty Fasteners
N.A.I.C.S.: 333519
Don Ayres (Pres)

Walk-On Products, Inc. (1)
1170 Chuck Taylor Ln, Salisbury, NC 28147
Tel.: (866) 592-5566
Web Site: https://www.walkonproducts.com
Industrial Automation Equipments Mfr
N.A.I.C.S.: 334513

Western Pneumatic Tube Company, LLC (1)
835 6th St S, Kirkland, WA 98033-6759
Tel.: (425) 822-8271
Web Site: https://leggettaerospace.com
Welding Tube Mfr
N.A.I.C.S.: 333992

Wuxi Leggett & Platt-Huaguang Auto-mobile Parts Co. Ltd. (1)
No 18 Ouyang Road, Luoshe, Wuxi, 214154, Jiangsu, China (70%)
Tel.: (86) 51083558541
Automobile Parts Mfr
N.A.I.C.S.: 336390
Zhiwei Du (Supvr-Product)

LEIDOS HOLDINGS, INC.
1750 Presidents St, Reston, VA 20190
Tel.: (571) 526-6000   DE
Web Site: https://www.leidos.com
Year Founded: 1969
LDOS—(NYSE)
Rev.: $15,438,000,000
Assets: $12,695,000,000
Liabilities: $8,437,000,000
Net Worth: $4,258,000,000
Earnings: $199,000,000
Emp.: 47,000
Fiscal Year-end: 12/29/23
National Security, Health & Engineer-ing Solutions
N.A.I.C.S.: 541511
Thomas A. Bell (CEO)
Gerard A. Fasano (Chief Growth Offi-cer & Exec VP)
Gerard A. Fasano (Pres-Defense Grp)
Michele M. Brown (Chief Ethics & Compliance Officer)
Jason Albanese (Sr VP-Bus Dev & Strategy)
Paul Engola (Deputy Pres-Dynetics Grp & Exec VP-Natl Security Space)
Carly E. Kimball (Chief Performance Officer & Exec VP)
Carly E. Kimball (Chief Acctg Officer)
Maureen Waterston (Chief HR Offi-cer)
Debbie Opiekun (Chief Bus Dev Offi-cer)
Steve Cook (Pres)
Andrew Campbell (VP-Bus Dev-Australia)
Hans Tench (VP-Bus Dev-Asia Pa-cific & VP-Strategy-Australia)
Ryan Leo (VP-Bus Dev & Strategy)

Subsidiaries:

1901 Group, LLC (1)

2003 Edmund Halley Dr Ste 102, Reston, VA 20191
Tel.: (703) 773-6240
Web Site: https://www.1901group.com
Electrical Contractor
N.A.I.C.S.: 238210
Brian Lubin (Sr VP-Svc Mgmt)
Paul Wilkinson (Exec VP-Bus Dev)
James Christopher (Exec VP-Ops & Engrg)
Sonu Singh (CEO & Founder)
George Batsakis (Chief Strategy Officer & Exec VP)
Brendan Walsh (Sr VP-Partner Rels)
Tom Pugliese (Sr VP-Enterprise Solutions)
Dana Pittman (Sr VP-Talent Strategy & HR)
Don Hirsch (Sr VP-Svc Delivery)
Sheri Neely (VP-Operational Performance)
Tricia Long (VP-Mktg Comm & PR)
Wayne Whitlock (Sr VP-Enterprise IT Ops Center)

Dynetics Inc. (1)
1002 Explorer Blvd, Huntsville, AL 35806-2806
Tel.: (256) 964-4000
Web Site: http://www.dynetics.com
Sales Range: $25-49.9 Million
Emp.: 1,500
Scientific, IT & Engineering Services
N.A.I.C.S.: 541715
David King (Pres-Grp)
Steve Cook (Deputy Pres-Grp & Mgr-Ops-Leidos Innovations Center)
Mike Moody (COO)
Ronnie Chronister (Sr VP-Weapons Tech & Mfg)
Tim Barton (CTO)
Jonathan Pettus (Sr VP-Aerospace, De-fense & Civil)
Matt Bender (VP-Product Dev & Mfg)
Mike Durboraw (VP-Threat Exploitation & Spectrum Warfare)
Kay Gray (VP-HR & Mgr-Bus Team)
Keith McCollum (VP-Integrated Sys Tech-nologies)
Mark Miller (VP-Missile & Aviation Sys)
Steve Thomas (VP-Fin Plng & Analysis)
Barry Byrd (Dir-Contracts)
Elizabeth Robertson (VP)
Charlie Pelham (Dir-Bus Dev)

Gibbs & Cox Inc. (1)
2711 Richmond Hwy, Arlington, VA 22202
Tel.: (703) 416-3627
Web Site: https://www.gibbscox.com
Sales Range: $10-24.9 Million
Emp.: 525
Naval Architecture & Marine Engineering Services
N.A.I.C.S.: 541330
Keith Harper (VP)
Ray Sheldon (COO)
Chris Deegan (Pres & CEO)
Matthew Hans (VP)
Thomas A. Schubert (Chief Engrg Officer & Chief Engrg Officer)
Benedict P. Capuco (VP)
Kevin White (VP-Finance-Administration)
Jonathan Applequist (Mgr & VP)
Edward Daffan (Chm)
Kevin Prince (VP)
Brian Hobbs (CIO)

Subsidiary (Domestic):

Donald L. Blount & Associates, Inc. (2)
860 Greenbrier Cir Ste 201, Chesapeake, VA 23320-6343
Tel.: (757) 545-3700
Web Site: https://www.dlba-inc.com
Naval Architecture & Marine Engineering Services
N.A.I.C.S.: 541310
Don Rickerson (Mgr-Engineering)

Leidos Canada (1)
60 Queen St Ste 1516, Ottawa, K1P 5Y7, ON, Canada (100%)
Tel.: (613) 563-7242
Web Site: http://www.leidos.com
Sales Range: $10-24.9 Million
Emp.: 20
Engineeering Services
N.A.I.C.S.: 541330

Leidos, Inc. (1)
11951 Freedom Dr Ste 500, Reston, VA 20190 (100%)

Tel.: (571) 526-6000
Web Site: http://www.leidos.com
Sales Range: $5-14.9 Billion
National Security, Health & Engineering Solutions
N.A.I.C.S.: 541511
Thomas A. Bell (CEO)
Kirk Riggs (VP-Strategy & Bus Dev Ops-Intelligence Grp)
Frank Pandolfe (VP-Navy & Marine Corps & Acct Exec-Strategic-Navy & Marine Corps)
Bobby Saxon (VP)

Subsidiary (Domestic):

Leidos Biomedical Research, Inc. (2)
1050 Boyles St, Frederick, MD 21702
Tel.: (301) 846-5031
Web Site: http://www.saic-frederick.com
Sales Range: $250-299.9 Million
Emp.: 1,500
Research & Development Services
N.A.I.C.S.: 541715

Unit (Domestic):

Leidos Engineering (2)
7 Wells Ave, Newton, MA 02459-3247
Tel.: (617) 964-7070
Rev.: $70,000,000
Emp.: 480
Provider of Research & Product Develop-ment Services
N.A.I.C.S.: 541715

Leidos Engineering (2)
3800 Watt Ave Ste 210, Sacramento, CA 95821-2622 (100%)
Tel.: (916) 974-8800
Sales Range: $10-24.9 Million
Emp.: 50
Software Develoment
N.A.I.C.S.: 541512

Leidos Engineering (2)
6310 Allentown Blvd, Harrisburg, PA 17112-3377 (100%)
Tel.: (717) 901-8100
Sales Range: $25-49.9 Million
Emp.: 98
Remediation Services
N.A.I.C.S.: 541330

Leidos Engineering (2)
6565 Arlington Blvd Ste 101, Falls Church, VA 22042-3000
Tel.: (703) 676-4300
Sales Range: $50-74.9 Million
Emp.: 150
Integrator of Information Technology Sys-tems
N.A.I.C.S.: 541715

Subsidiary (Domestic):

Leidos Engineering of North Carolina, Inc. (2)
15800 John J Delaney Dr Ste 175, Char-lotte, NC 28277
Tel.: (704) 542-2908
Construction Engineering Services
N.A.I.C.S.: 541330

Unit (Domestic):

SAIC (1)
3375 Koapaka St, Honolulu, HI 96819-1800
Tel.: (808) 836-6898
Sales Range: $25-49.9 Million
Emp.: 11
Materials Ordering Services
N.A.I.C.S.: 423860

Science, Engineering, and Technol-ogy Associates Corporation (1)
1005 N Glebe Rd 4th Flr, Arlington, VA 22201
Tel.: (703) 738-6200
Web Site: http://www.setcorp.com
Commercial & Institutional Building Con-struction
N.A.I.C.S.: 236220

LEISURE ACQUISITION CORP.
250 W 57th St Ste 415, New York, NY 10107
Tel.: (646) 565-6940   DE
Web Site: http://www.leisureacq.com

Year Founded: 2017
LACQ—(NASDAQ)
Rev.: $4,017,853
Assets: $12,854,634
Liabilities: $7,854,627
Net Worth: $5,000,007
Earnings: $2,404,519
Emp.: 4
Fiscal Year-end: 12/31/20
Investment Services
N.A.I.C.S.: 523999
Eric Carrera (Sr VP-Fin & Bus Dev)
George Peng (CFO, Treas & Sec)

LEMAITRE VASCULAR, INC.
63 2nd Ave, Burlington, MA 01803
Tel.: (781) 221-2266   DE
Web Site: https://www.lemaitre.com
Year Founded: 1983
LMAT—(NASDAQ)
Rev.: $161,651,000
Assets: $310,476,000
Liabilities: $42,275,000
Net Worth: $268,201,000
Earnings: $20,636,000
Emp.: 591
Fiscal Year-end: 12/31/22
Surgical & Medical Instrument Manu-facturing
N.A.I.C.S.: 339112
George W. Lemaitre (Chm & CEO)
David B. Roberts (Pres)
Andrew Hodgkinson (Sr VP-Clinical, Regulatory & Quality Affairs)
Giovanella Deiure (VP-Sls-Southern Europe)
Roli Kumar-Choudhury (VP-Quality Affairs)
Stephane Maier (Sr VP-Ops-EMEA)
James Russell (VP-Production & Supply Chain)
Xiang Zhang (VP-Regulatory Affairs)
Chance Kriesel (VP-Sls-The Ameri-cas)
Jacob Petersen (VP-Asia Pacific)
Helen Goulding (Dir-Sls-Northern Eu-rope)
Daniel J. Mumford (Dir-HR)
Ina Leininger (Sls Dir)
Christopher D. Minnett (Mgr)
Joseph P. Pellegrino Jr. (CFO)

Subsidiaries:

Artegraft Inc (1)
220 N Center Dr, North Brunswick, NJ 08902
Tel.: (732) 422-8333
Web Site: http://www.artegraft.com
Surgical Appliance & Supplies Mfr
N.A.I.C.S.: 339113
Richard A. Gibson (Pres & CEO)
Norris J. Horn (CFO)
Cathleen VanDerVeer (VP-Ops)
Warren Kirschbaum (VP-Sls)
Laurence A. Potter (VP-Scientific Affairs)

LeMaitre Medical Technology (Shang-hai) Co., Ltd. (1)
Room 809 Shangguang Xuhui Center Jin Block No 407 YiShan Road, Xuhui District, Shanghai, 200030, China
Tel.: (86) 2164696919
Medical Equipment Mfr
N.A.I.C.S.: 339113

LeMaitre Vascular AS (1)
Dronning Eufemiasgate 16, 0191, Oslo, Norway
Tel.: (47) 40627382
Medical Equipment Mfr
N.A.I.C.S.: 339113

LeMaitre Vascular GK (1)
1F Kyodo Bldg Ichibancho 16-1 Ichibancho, Chiyoda-ku, Tokyo, 102-0082, Japan
Tel.: (81) 352155681
Surgical & Medical Instrument Mfr
N.A.I.C.S.: 339112

LeMaitre Vascular GmbH (1)
Otto-Volger-Str 5a/b, Taunus, 65843, Sulz-

bach, Germany
Tel.: (49) 6196659230
Sales Range: $50-74.9 Million
Emp.: 30
Surgical & Medical Instrument Mfr
N.A.I.C.S.: 339112

LeMaitre Vascular Pty Ltd (1)
49 Stubbs Street, Kensington, 3031, VIC,
Australia
Tel.: (61) 393304775
Emp.: 15
Medical Equipment Mfr
N.A.I.C.S.: 339113

**LeMaitre Vascular Switzerland
GmbH** (1)
Neuhofstrasse 5A, CH-6340, Baar, Switzer-
land
Tel.: (41) 800561761
Medical Equipment Mfr
N.A.I.C.S.: 339113

LeMaitre Vascular ULC (1)
9135 Keele Street Suite B6, Vaughan, L4K
0J4, ON, Canada
Tel.: (905) 832-8077
Web Site: http://www.lemaitre.com
Medical Equipment Mfr
N.A.I.C.S.: 339113

LeMaitre Vascular, Ltd (1)
Stirling House Centenary Park, Skylon Cen-
tral, Hereford, HR2 6FJ, United Kingdom
Tel.: (44) 1432513125
Medical Equipment Mfr & Distr
N.A.I.C.S.: 339112

LEMONADE, INC.
5 Crosby St 3rd Fl, New York, NY
10013   DE
Web Site: https://www.lemonade.com
Year Founded: 2015
LMND—(NYSE)
Rev.: $429,800,000
Assets: $1,633,300,000
Liabilities: $924,400,000
Net Worth: $708,900,000
Earnings: ($236,900,000)
Emp.: 1,258
Fiscal Year-end: 12/31/23
Holding Company
N.A.I.C.S.: 551112
Tim Bixby (CFO)
Daniel Schreiber (Co-Founder, Chm
& CEO)
Shai Wininger (Pres, CTO, Treas &
Sec)

LENDINGCLUB CORPORA-
TION
595 Market St Ste 200, San Fran-
cisco, CA 94105
Tel.: (415) 632-5600   DE
Web Site:
  https://www.lendingclub.com
Year Founded: 2006
LC—(NYSE)
Rev.: $1,135,411,000
Assets: $8,827,463,000
Liabilities: $7,575,641,000
Net Worth: $1,251,822,000
Earnings: $38,939,000
Emp.: 1,025
Fiscal Year-end: 12/31/23
Online Lending Services
N.A.I.C.S.: 522310
Annie Armstrong (Chief Risk Officer)
Andrew LaBenne (CFO)
Tina Wilson (Chief People Officer)
Drew LaBenne (COO)
Balaji Thiagarajan (CTO)
John C. Morris (Chm)
Scott C. Sanborn (CEO)

Subsidiaries:

Radius Bancorp Inc. (1)
1 Harbor St Ste 201, Boston, MA 02210
Tel.: (617) 482-4000
Web Site: http://www.radiusbank.com
Bank Holding Company
N.A.I.C.S.: 551111

Michael A. Butler (Pres & CEO)

Subsidiary (Domestic):

Radius Bank (2)
1 Harbor St Ste 200, Boston, MA 02210
Tel.: (617) 482-4000
Web Site: https://www.lendingclub.com
Sales Range: $25-49.9 Million
Emp.: 73
Federal Savings Bank
N.A.I.C.S.: 522180
Michael A. Butler (Pres & CEO)
Chris Tremont (Exec VP-Virtual Banking)
Kathleen Barrett (VP-Mktg)
Grant Skeens (Exec VP & Natl Dir-Govt
Guaranteed Lending-Chicago)
Louise Sorrentino (VP-Acq)
Alain Glanzman (VP-Small Bus Banking)
Tyler Mensick (VP-Reg Sls & Mgr-
Relationship-Escrow Sls)
John Relyea (Sr VP-Comml API Banking)
Joey Miranda (VP-Cash Mgmt Sls)
Phil Peters (COO & Exec VP)
Stephen Hunt (Exec VP-Equipment Fin)
Brenda Mackey (Exec VP-Institutional
Banking & Cash Mgmt)

LENDINGTREE, INC.
1415 Vantage Park Dr Ste 700, Char-
lotte, NC 28203
Tel.: (704) 541-5351   DE
Web Site:
  https://www.lendingtree.com
Year Founded: 1998
TREE—(NASDAQ)
Rev.: $984,992,000
Assets: $1,199,313,000
Liabilities: $991,373,000
Net Worth: $207,940,000
Earnings: ($187,952,000)
Emp.: 1,240
Fiscal Year-end: 12/31/22
Online Lending & Financial Services
N.A.I.C.S.: 522310
Scott Peyree (Pres-Insurance)
Douglas R. Lebda (Founder, Chm &
CEO)
Carla Shumate (Chief Acctg Officer &
Sr VP)
Shiv Singh (Chief Marketing & Cus-
tomer Experience Officer)
Lisa Young (Gen Counsel)
Jorge De Castro (Sr VP)
Scott Totman (CTO)
Jill Olmstead (Chief HR Officer)

Subsidiaries:

Iron Horse Holdings Inc. (1)
Cigar Factory 701 East Bay St, Charleston,
SC 29401-3184
Tel.: (843) 952-7003
Offices of Other Holding Companies
N.A.I.C.S.: 551112

LendingTree, LLC (1)
1415 Vantage Park Dr Ste 700, Charlotte,
NC 28203
Tel.: (866) 501-2397
Online Lending & Financial Services
N.A.I.C.S.: 522310
Doug Lebda (Founder & CEO)
Scott Peyree (Pres)
Trent Ziegler (CFO)
Jill Olmstead (Chief HR Officer)
Scott Totman (CTO)
Heather Enlow-Novitsky (Gen Counsel)
Arun Sankaran (Chief Information Security
Officer)

Subsidiary (Domestic):

QuoteWizard.com LLC (2)
157 Yesler Way Ste 400, Seattle, WA 98104
Tel.: (866) 224-2194
Web Site: http://www.quotewizard.com
Sales Range: $1-9.9 Million
Emp.: 130
Insurance Matching Services for Consum-
ers
N.A.I.C.S.: 524298
Scott Peyree (CEO)

Ovation Credit Services, Inc. (1)

9143 Philips Hwy Ste 560, Jacksonville, FL
32256
Web Site: https://ovationcredit.com
Credit Management Services
N.A.I.C.S.: 541990

LENDWAY, INC.
212 3rd Ave N, Minneapolis, MN
55401
Tel.: (763) 392-6200   MN
Web Site:
  https://www.insigniasystems.com
Year Founded: 1990
LDWY—(NASDAQ)
Rev.: $18,800,000
Assets: $20,968,000
Liabilities: $7,567,000
Net Worth: $13,401,000
Earnings: $10,046,000
Emp.: 30
Fiscal Year-end: 12/31/22
In-Store Advertising Products, Pro-
grams & Services
N.A.I.C.S.: 541870
Jacob J. Berning (Chm)
Adam D. May (Chief Growth Officer)
Alison Nelson (Sr VP-Sls)
Erika Rahm (Sls Dir)
Kelly Hagglund (Dir-HR)
Caroline Zack (Sr Dir-Sls Execution)
Katie Woods (Assoc Dir-Creative)
Brian Bothwell (Sr Dir-Ops & Strate-
gic Relationships)
Marty Bloom (Dir-Client Success)
Dan Moldenhauer (Controller)
Chrissy Hawkins (Mgr)
Brady Witt (VP)
Bryan Perry (Dir)
Sarai Konerza (Dir)
Danielle Derethik (Mgr)
Lydia Johnson (Assoc Mgr)
Tanya Loosbrock (Sr Mgr)
Carey Welch (Mgr)
Hailey Thompson (Mgr)
Katie McDonald (Mgr)
Martha Hedstrom (Mgr)
Sara Rantapaa (Mgr)
Greg Knight (Mgr)
Rochelle Sweeney (Mgr)
Tamarre Kelly-Bedford (Coord)
Kelly Rogers (Coord)
Evan Anderson (Designer)
Jessica Roberts (Designer)
Mark R. Jundt (Vice Chm & CEO)

LENNAR CORPORATION
5505 Waterford District Dr, Miami, FL
33126
Tel.: (305) 559-4000   FL
Web Site: https://www.lennar.com
Year Founded: 1954
LEN—(NYSE)
Rev.: $34,233,366,000
Assets: $39,234,303,000
Liabilities: $12,532,337,000
Net Worth: $26,701,966,000
Earnings: $3,938,511,000
Emp.: 12,284
Fiscal Year-end: 11/30/23
Single-Family Home Development &
Construction Services
N.A.I.C.S.: 236115
Jonathan M. Jaffe (Pres & Co-CEO)
Diane J. Bessette (CFO, Treas & VP)
Kay Howard (Chief Mktg & Comm
Officer)
Michael Petrolino (VP-Taxation)
David M. Collins (Principal Acctg Offi-
cer, VP & Controller)
Fred Rothman (COO)
Greg McGuff (Reg Pres-Lennar
Homebuilding & Land)
Ed Easley (Pres-Dev-Lennar Multi-
family Communities)
Chris Marlin (Founder)
Jeff J. McCall (Exec VP)

Jim Parker (Reg Pres-Lennar Home-
building & Land)
JoAnn Blaylock (Pres-LMC Living)
Cristina Pardo (Pres-Title)
Laura Escobar (Pres-Mortgage)
David Grove (Reg Pres-Texas)
Stuart A. Miller (Chm & Co-CEO)
Mark Sustana (Gen Counsel, Sec &
VP)

Subsidiaries:

Alliance Financial Services, Inc. (1)
1311 SE Cardinal Ct Ste 100, Vancouver,
WA 98683
Tel.: (360) 448-6077
Web Site: http://www.alliancefs.net
Financial Services
N.A.I.C.S.: 523999
Ryan Holtcamp (Gen Mgr)

BCI Properties, LLC (1)
9702 S Tacoma Way Ste 106, Lakewood,
WA 98499
Tel.: (253) 531-1010
Web Site: http://www.bci-properties.com
Property Management Services
N.A.I.C.S.: 531390
Lynn Robertson (Co-Owner)
Patrick Schatz (Co-Owner)
Tanisha White (Asst Mgr-Property)
Naomi Burke (Office Mgr & Mgr-Property)

CalAtlantic Group, Inc. (1)
1100 Wilson Blvd Ste 2100, Arlington, VA
22209
Tel.: (240) 532-3800
Sales Range: $5-14.9 Billion
Holding Company; Single-Family Home
Construction & Mortgage Services
N.A.I.C.S.: 551112
John Babel (Gen Counsel & Exec VP)
Budnek Christopher (Mgr-Construction)

Subsidiary (Domestic):

CalAtlantic Homes of Texas, Inc. (2)
13620 N FM 620 Bldg B Ste 150, Austin,
TX 78717
Tel.: (512) 506-4000
Housing Construction Services
N.A.I.C.S.: 236115

Lennar Homes of Utah, Inc. (2)
1099 W S Jordan Pkwy, South Jordan, UT
84095-8809
Tel.: (801) 495-3420
Housing Construction Services
N.A.I.C.S.: 236116

Ryland Homes of California, Inc. (2)
3011 Townsgate Rd Ste 200, Westlake Vil-
lage, CA 91361
Tel.: (818) 223-7500
Housing Construction Services
N.A.I.C.S.: 236117

Standard Pacific of Colorado,
Inc. (2)
7800 E Dorado Pl Ste 220, Greenwood Vil-
lage, CO 80111
Tel.: (303) 486-5000
New Housing Construction Services
N.A.I.C.S.: 236117

Standard Pacific of the Carolinas,
LLC (2)
1100 Perimeter Park Dr, Morrisville, NC
27560
Tel.: (919) 465-5900
Residential Building Construction Services
N.A.I.C.S.: 236115

Streetman Homes Corp. (2)
4407 Bee Caves Rd Ste 212, Austin, TX
78746
Tel.: (888) 448-4053
Housing Services
N.A.I.C.S.: 236115

T2 Construction, LLC (2)
611 136th Ave Ste 5, Holland, MI 49424
Tel.: (616) 738-1600
Web Site:
  http://www.t2constructionmanagement.com

Lennar Corporation—(Continued)

Residential & Commercial Building Construction Services
N.A.I.C.S.: 236116

The Ryland Corporation (2)
6075 14th St S, Fargo, ND 58104
Tel.: (701) 219-0765
Web Site: http://therylandcorp.com
Housing Construction Services
N.A.I.C.S.: 236115

Westfield Homes USA, Inc. (2)
5100 W Lemon St Ste 312, Tampa, FL 33609
Tel.: (813) 288-7600
Residential Real Estate Development & Construction Services
N.A.I.C.S.: 236117

CalAtlantic Title Agency, LLC (1)
20709 N Main St, Cornelius, NC 28031
Tel.: (704) 896-3991
Real Estate Manangement Services
N.A.I.C.S.: 531210

Cedar Pointe Club, LLC (1)
28805 SW 163 Ct, Miami, FL 33033
Real Estate & Financial Services
N.A.I.C.S.: 531390

Fidelity Guaranty and Acceptance Corp. (1)
700 NW 107th Ave, Miami, FL 33172
Tel.: (305) 599-4000
Insurance Brokerage Services
N.A.I.C.S.: 524210

Friendswood Development Company, LLC (1)
681 Greens Pkwy Ste 220, Houston, TX 77067
Tel.: (281) 875-1552
Web Site:
  https://friendswooddevelopment.com
Residential Building Construction Services
N.A.I.C.S.: 531110

Greywall Club L.L.C. (1)
Caton Farm Rd, Joliet, IL 60435
Tel.: (815) 609-2467
Web Site: https://www.greywallclub.net
Residential Building Construction Services
N.A.I.C.S.: 531110

Kentuckiana Medical Center, LLC (1)
4601 Medical Plz Way, Clarksville, IN 47129
Tel.: (812) 284-6100
Web Site: http://www.kmchospital.com
Health Care Srvices
N.A.I.C.S.: 622110
Michael Phillips (CEO)

LMC Construction, LLC (1)
19200 SW Teton Ave, Tualatin, OR 97062
Tel.: (503) 646-0521
Web Site: http://www.lmcconstruction.com
Sales Range: $1-9.9 Million
Emp.: 16
Construction Services
N.A.I.C.S.: 236220
Kyle Anderson (VP)
Aaron Maguire (Project Mgr)
Andriel Langston (Assoc Mgr-Project)
April O'Neal (Engr-Project)
Chris Duffin (Pres)
Clyde Zahn (Sr Project Mgr)
Gavin Nakamura (Supvr-Warranty)
Ken Bello (Project Mgr)
Richard Reese (VP-Construction)
J. P. Mickelsen (VP-Acctg & Fin)
Art O'Leary (Superintendent)
Bo Wilkie (Superintendent)
Casey Doyle (Superintendent)
Chris Maas (Superintendent)
Chris Smith (Superintendent)
Dylan Dalton (Superintendent)
Eric Sparks (Superintendent)
Jake Yamanoha (Superintendent)
Vaughn Kessler (Superintendent)
Al Wallace (Project Mgr)
Allen Murray (Project Mgr)
Iris O'Neal (Project Mgr)
Noel Southard (Project Mgr)
Derik White (Mgr-Special Projects & Warranty)
Tom Michie (Mgr-Quality Control)

Scott Dekker (Dir-Pre-Construction Svcs)
Bryan Bilicke (Dir-IT)
Sara Hamlet (Dir-HR)
Heather Brown (Assoc Mgr-Project)

LMC East Village I Holdings, LLC (1)
95 Enterprise Ste 200, Aliso Viejo, CA 92656
Tel.: (949) 448-1600
Holding Company
N.A.I.C.S.: 551112

LMC Living, LLC (1)
500 E Morehead St Ste 300, Charlotte, NC 28202
Tel.: (704) 998-0363
Web Site: https://livelmc.com
Building Construction Services
N.A.I.C.S.: 236118
Alex Burris (Sr VP-Ops)
Lee Bradford (VP-Ops & Trng)
Simon Andrew (VP-Ops)
Josh Purkeypile (VP-Ops)
Amy Bui (VP-Ops)
Beth Tuttle (VP-Mktg)
Lucy Simone (Sr VP-Assoc Dev)
JoAnn Blaylock (Pres)
Tim O'Keefe (Controller)

LMF Commercial, LLC (1)
590 Madison Ave Fl 9, New York, NY 10022
Tel.: (212) 894-4567
Web Site: https://www.lmfcommercial.com
Residential Building Construction Services
N.A.I.C.S.: 531110

LMI Contractors, LLC (1)
201 S Tryon Ste 1050, Charlotte, NC 28202
Tel.: (704) 998-0368
Residential Construction Services
N.A.I.C.S.: 236115
Stewart Miller (Pres)

Lennar Arizona Construction, Inc. (1)
1665 W Alameda Dr, Tempe, AZ 85282
Tel.: (480) 476-8400
Web Site: http://www.lennar.com
Residential Building Rental & Leasing Services
N.A.I.C.S.: 531110

Lennar Chicago, Inc. (1)
1760 Newberry Ln, Hoffman Estates, IL 60192
Tel.: (630) 507-9197
Web Site: http://www.lennar.com
New Home Builder
N.A.I.C.S.: 236115

Lennar Colorado, LLC (1)
9781 S Meridian Blvd Ste 120, Englewood, CO 80112
Tel.: (303) 754-0600
Real Estate Brokerage Services
N.A.I.C.S.: 531210

Lennar Communities, Inc. (1)
25 Enterprise ste 400, Aliso Viejo, CA 92656
Tel.: (949) 349-8000
Land Subdivision Services
N.A.I.C.S.: 237210
Stewart Miller (CEO)

Lennar Financial Services, Inc. (1)
700 NW 107th Ave 3rd Fl, Miami, FL 33172-3139
Tel.: (305) 485-2038
Web Site: http://www.lennar.com
Sales Range: $50-74.9 Million
Emp.: 100
Holding Company for Mortgage Subsidiaries
N.A.I.C.S.: 522292
Bruce E. Gross (CEO)

Subsidiary (Domestic):

Eagle Home Mortgage LLC (2)
301 116th Ave SE Ste 400, Bellevue, WA 98004 (100%)
Tel.: (425) 822-6733
Web Site: http://eaglehm.com
Emp.: 75
Residential Mortgage Services
N.A.I.C.S.: 522292
Laura Escobar (Pres)
Kirk Park (Exec VP)
David Todd (Exec VP)
Monte Murdock (VP-Mortgage Tech)

Lennar Homes of Tennessee, LLC (1)
381 Mallory Sta Rd Ste 200, Franklin, TN 37067-8264
Tel.: (615) 465-4328
Residential Construction Services
N.A.I.C.S.: 236115
Mike Zakrzewski (Pres-Div)
Josh Thacker (Mgr-Pur)

Lennar Homes of Texas Land and Construction, Ltd. (1)
681 Greens Pkwy Ste 220, Houston, TX 77067
Tel.: (281) 875-1552
Residential Building Construction Services
N.A.I.C.S.: 531110

Lennar Homes, Inc. (1)
550 Greens Pkwy Ste 200, Houston, TX 77067-4526
Tel.: (281) 875-1000
Web Site: http://www.lennar.com
Sales Range: $1-4.9 Billion
Emp.: 6,053
Residential Construction Services
N.A.I.C.S.: 236115

Division (Domestic):

Lennar (2)
10211 Wincopin Cir Ste 300, Columbia, MD 21044-3429 (100%)
Tel.: (410) 997-5522
Web Site: http://www.lennar.com
Residential Construction
N.A.I.C.S.: 236115

Lennar Design Studio Home (2)
2490 Paseo Verde Pkwy Ste 120, Henderson, NV 89074-7121
Tel.: (702) 877-9600
Sales Range: $50-74.9 Million
Emp.: 80
Residential Construction
N.A.I.C.S.: 236115

Lennar Homes, Colorado Div (2)
9781 S Meridian Blvd Ste 120, Englewood, CO 80112-5935
Tel.: (303) 754-0600
Web Site: http://www.lennarhome.com
Sales Range: $75-99.9 Million
Emp.: 230
Residential Construction
N.A.I.C.S.: 236115

Lennar Homes, Inc. (2)
1707 Marketplace Blvd Ste 250, Irving, TX 75063 (100%)
Tel.: (469) 587-5300
Web Site: http://www.lennar.com
Sales Range: $50-74.9 Million
Emp.: 61
Residential Construction
N.A.I.C.S.: 236115

Lennar Homes, Inc. (2)
9 10471 Bn C Prtt Sx, Fort Myers, FL 33916
Tel.: (239) 561-6522
Sales Range: $50-74.9 Million
Emp.: 101
Residential Construction
N.A.I.C.S.: 236115
Darin McMurray (Pres)

Lennar Homes, Inc. (2)
800 W Main St, Freehold, NJ 07728 (100%)
Tel.: (732) 625-2314
Web Site: http://www.lennar.com
Sales Range: $50-74.9 Million
Emp.: 50
Residential Construction
N.A.I.C.S.: 236115

Lennar Homes, Inc. (2)
1922 Dry Creek Way Ste 101, San Antonio, TX 78259
Tel.: (210) 403-6200
Web Site: http://www.lennar.com
Sales Range: $50-74.9 Million
Emp.: 120
Residential Construction
N.A.I.C.S.: 236115
David Grove (Pres)

Lennar Homes, Inc. - Orlando (2)
898 Suffolk Pl, Davenport, FL 33896-5108

Tel.: (863) 420-2337
Sales Range: $50-74.9 Million
Emp.: 150
Residential Construction
N.A.I.C.S.: 236115
Brock Nicholas (Pres)
Stacy Sanders (VP-Mktg)

Lennar US Homes (2)
3275 W Ina Rd Ste 275, Tucson, AZ 85741
Tel.: (520) 747-0997
Web Site: http://www.lennar.com
Sales Range: $25-49.9 Million
Emp.: 20
Single Family Home Builder
N.A.I.C.S.: 236115

Tampa Lennar Division (2)
600 NW Shore Blvd Ste 600, Tampa, FL 33609 (100%)
Tel.: (813) 769-5277
Web Site: http://www.lennar.com
Sales Range: $50-74.9 Million
Emp.: 134
Residential Construction
N.A.I.C.S.: 236115

Lennar Homes, Inc. (1)
700 NW 107th Ave Ste 400, Miami, FL 33172-3139 (100%)
Tel.: (305) 559-4000
Web Site: http://www.lennar.com
Sales Range: $400-449.9 Million
Emp.: 600
Residential Construction
N.A.I.C.S.: 236220

Lennar Mare Island, LLC (1)
690 Walnut Ave Ste 100 Mare Island, Vallejo, CA 94592
Tel.: (707) 562-3553
Web Site:
  http://www.discovermareisland.com
Land Redevelopment Agency
N.A.I.C.S.: 327910

Lennar Mortgage, LLC (1)
140 Fountain Pkwy N Ste 250, Saint Petersburg, FL 33716
Web Site: https://www.lennarmortgage.com
Residential Building Construction Services
N.A.I.C.S.: 531110

Lennar Multifamily Communities, LLC (1)
95 Enterprise Ste 200, Aliso Viejo, CA 92656
Tel.: (949) 448-1600
Web Site: http://livelmc.com
Multifamily Housing Development, Construction & Management Services
N.A.I.C.S.: 236116

Lennar Sacramento, Inc. (1)
4048 Wyman Way, Roseville, CA 95747
Tel.: (916) 905-1620
Residential Building Construction Services
N.A.I.C.S.: 236115

Lennar Title, Inc. (1)
7035 Albert Einstein Dr Ste 200A, Columbia, MD 21046
Tel.: (410) 423-3567
Residential Building Construction Services
N.A.I.C.S.: 531110

Lennar Title, LLC (1)
20709 N Main St, Cornelius, NC 28031
Tel.: (704) 896-3991
Residential Building Construction Services
N.A.I.C.S.: 531110

Lennar Winncrest, LLC (1)
1075 Creekside Rdg Dr Ste 110, Roseville, CA 95678
Tel.: (916) 783-3224
Land Subdivision & Development Services
N.A.I.C.S.: 237210

Majestic Woods, LLC (1)
207 Sparks Ave Ste 104, Jeffersonville, IN 47130
Tel.: (502) 262-7808
Web Site:
  http://www.majesticwoodsestates.com
Residential Building Construction Services
N.A.I.C.S.: 236115

NASSA LLC (1)
851 Trafalgar Ct Ste 132E, Maitland, FL 32751

Tel.: (407) 869-5200
Residential Building Construction Services
N.A.I.C.S.: 236115

North American National Title Solutions, LLC (1)
760 NW 107th Ave Ste 400, Miami, FL 33172
Web Site: http://www.nants.com
Home Construction Services
N.A.I.C.S.: 236115
John B. Shafer (Dir-Natl Comml Division)
Jill Anderson Blanco (VP)

North American Real Estate Group, LLC (1)
27 N Green St, Chicago, IL 60607
Tel.: (847) 882-0471
Web Site: https://www.naregroup.com
Real Estate & Financial Services
N.A.I.C.S.: 531390

POMAC, LLC (1)
365-C New Albany Rd, Moorestown, NJ 08057-1117
Tel.: (856) 273-9636
Web Site: http://www.pomacnetwork.com
Nursing Care Services
N.A.I.C.S.: 623110

Raintree Village, L.L.C. (1)
2125 Tremont Ave, Yorkville, IL 60560
Tel.: (224) 802-5645
Residential Building Construction Services
N.A.I.C.S.: 531110

Rialto Holdings, LLC (1)
200 Central Ave, White Plains, NY 10606
Tel.: (914) 681-1952
Holding Company
N.A.I.C.S.: 551112

Rialto Management Group, LLC (1)
790 NW 107th Ave Ste 400, Miami, FL 33172
Tel.: (305) 485-2077
Web Site: http://www.rialtocapital.com
Emp.: 200
Real Estate Investment Services
N.A.I.C.S.: 523940
Jeffrey Krasnoff (CEO)

SimplyTitle Company (1)
330 Himmarshee St Ste111, Fort Lauderdale, FL 33312
Tel.: (954) 766-8364
Web Site: http://www.simplytitle.com
Emp.: 2
Real Estate Services
N.A.I.C.S.: 531120
Jared Fletcher (Pres)

Stoneybrook Golf Club, Inc. (1)
8000 Stone Harbour Loop, Bradenton, FL 34212
Tel.: (941) 749-1842
Web Site: http://www.golfstoneybrook.com
Golf Course & Country Club Services
N.A.I.C.S.: 713910

Storey Park Club, LLC (1)
11650 Biography Way, Orlando, FL 32832
Tel.: (407) 867-5903
Web Site: https://www.storeyparkclub.com
Residential Building Construction Services
N.A.I.C.S.: 531110

Strategic Holdings, Inc. (1)
4550 E Thousand Oaks Blvd Ste 200, Westlake Village, CA 91362
Tel.: (805) 410-4622
Web Site: https://www.strategicholdings.com
Residential Building Construction Services
N.A.I.C.S.: 531110

The Bridges at Rancho Santa Fe Sales Company, Inc. (1)
18550 Seven Bridges Rd, Rancho Santa Fe, CA 92091
Tel.: (858) 759-7200
Web Site: http://www.thebridgesrsf.com
Sports & Recreation Clubs Services
N.A.I.C.S.: 713940

The Newhall Land & Farming Company, Inc. (1)
25124 Springfield Ct Ste 300, Valencia, CA 91355 (17%)
Tel.: (661) 255-4000
Land Developer
N.A.I.C.S.: 237210

The Shipyard Communities Retail Operator, LLC (1)
69 W 23rd St, New York, NY 10010
Tel.: (212) 243-8898
Web Site: http://www.thestorehousenyc.com
Pub Operator
N.A.I.C.S.: 722511

Titlezoom Company (1)
400 Sawgrass Corporate Pkwy Ste 100, Sunrise, FL 33325
Tel.: (954) 607-1192
Web Site: http://www.titlezoom.com
Real Estate Manangement Services
N.A.I.C.S.: 531390

Treasure Island Community Development, LLC (1)
1 Ave of the Palms Ste 212, San Francisco, CA 94130
Web Site: https://tisf.com
Physical Construction Services
N.A.I.C.S.: 236220

U.S. Home of Arizona Construction Co. (1)
1150 W Grove Pkwy Ste 110, Tempe, AZ 85283-4487
Tel.: (480) 345-0077
Sales Range: $25-49.9 Million
Emp.: 30
Residential Building Construction Services
N.A.I.C.S.: 236115
Gail Woelsel (Gen Mgr)

Universal American Mortgage Company-Lennar (1)
730 NW 107th Ave Fl 4, Miami, FL 33172-3104 (100%)
Tel.: (305) 229-6500
Web Site: http://www.uamc.com
Sales Range: $25-49.9 Million
Emp.: 14
Builder-Affiliated Mortgage Services
N.A.I.C.S.: 522292

Subsidiary (Domestic):

Universal American Mortgage Company (2)
15550 Lightwave Dr Ste 200, Clearwater, FL 33760 (100%)
Tel.: (727) 791-2111
Web Site: http://www.uamc.com
Sales Range: $1-9.9 Million
Mortgage Lending Services
N.A.I.C.S.: 522292
Ginny Casagrande (CFO)

Universal American Mortgage Company of California (2)
620 Ave 1, San Jose, CA 95123
Tel.: (408) 409-8965
Web Site: http://www.uamc.com
Real Estate & Financial Services
N.A.I.C.S.: 531390

Valencia at Doral, LLC (1)
10000 NW 45th Ter, Doral, FL 33178
Tel.: (305) 599-2122
Sales Range: $25-49.9 Million
Emp.: 7
Residential Building Construction Services
N.A.I.C.S.: 236115
Augusgo Taylhargad (Mgr)

WCI Communities, Inc. (1)
24301 Walden Center Dr, Bonita Springs, FL 34134
Tel.: (239) 498-8200
Web Site: http://www.wcicommunities.com
Sales Range: $600-649.9 Million
Single Family Homes & Retirement Communities Developer; Real Estate Services
N.A.I.C.S.: 236115
Jerry Starkey (Principal)
Jon Rapaport (Sr VP-Dev)

Subsidiary (Domestic):

Pelican Marsh Golf Club (2)
1810 Persimmon Dr, Naples, FL 34109
Tel.: (239) 597-3000
Web Site: http://www.pelicanmarshgc.com
Golf Club Operations
N.A.I.C.S.: 713910
Ron Parris (COO & Gen Mgr)
Karen Gross (Controller)
Shea Brower (Dir-Membership & Comm)
Phil Pellerito (Dir-PGA-Golf)

Nick Baumhart (Head-PGA-Golf Professional)
Brook Maxwell (Dir-Golf Course Ops)
Carlos Garcia (Engr-Facilities)
Amy Warner (Dir-Food & Beverage)
Jessi Jordan (Asst Dir-Food & Beverage)

Waterview at Hanover, LLC (1)
406 Waterview Ct, Cedar Knolls, NJ 07927
Tel.: (908) 516-4790
Web Site:
https://www.waterviewathanover.com
Residential Building Construction Services
N.A.I.C.S.: 531110

LENNOX INTERNATIONAL INC.
2140 Lake Park Blvd, Richardson, TX 75080
Tel.: (972) 497-5000   DE
Web Site: https://www.lennox.com
Year Founded: 1895
LII—(NYSE)
Rev.: $4,981,900,000
Assets: $2,798,300,000
Liabilities: $2,513,000,000
Net Worth: $285,300,000
Earnings: $590,100,000
Emp.: 12,600
Fiscal Year-end: 12/31/23
Climate Control Solutions
N.A.I.C.S.: 333415
Daniel M. Sessa (Chief HR Officer & Exec VP)
Prakash Bedapudi (CTO & Exec VP)
Mary Ellen Mondi (VP)
Alok Maskara (CEO)
John D. Torres (Chief Legal Officer, Sec & Exec VP)

Subsidiaries:

AES Industries, Inc. (1)
2171 Alabama Hwy 229, Tallassee, AL 36078
Tel.: (334) 283-6578
Web Site: https://www.aescurb.com
Sales Range: $25-49.9 Million
Emp.: 100
Sheet Metal Work Mfg
N.A.I.C.S.: 332322
Jason Benton (Pres)
Dean Cleondis (VP-Ops & Sourcing)
Chad Ledbetter (VP-Mfg & Recycling)
Cliff Jones (VP-Logistics)
Chad Burt (Sr Acct Mgr-Wal Mart)
Paul Ledbetter (Mgr-Engrg)
Glenda Parker (Comptroller)
Joe Chaffin (Engr-Design)
Rachel Cunningham (Mgr-Customer Svc & Scheduling)
Karsten Reinhardt (Engr-Design)
Gary Tew (Engr-Design)

Advanced Distributor Products LLC (1)
2175 W Park Place Blvd, Stone Mountain, GA 30087
Tel.: (662) 229-3000
Web Site: https://www.adpnow.com
Emp.: 20
Evaporator Coils Mfr
N.A.I.C.S.: 333415

Allied Air Enterprises Inc. (1)
215 Metropolitan Dr, West Columbia, SC 29170 (100%)
Tel.: (803) 738-4000
Web Site: https://www.alliedair.com
Sales Range: $125-149.9 Million
Emp.: 130
Mfr Heating & Cooling
N.A.I.C.S.: 333415

Etablissements Brancher S.A.S. (1)
6 Rue Des Albatros, Mions, 69780, France
Tel.: (33) 472232070
Sales Range: $25-49.9 Million
Emp.: 100
Air-Conditioning & Heating Equipment Mfr
N.A.I.C.S.: 333415
Heree Martimo (Mng Dir)

Freschi Service Experts (1)
2440 Sprig Ct, Concord, CA 94520
Tel.: (925) 384-1303

Web Site:
https://www.freschiserviceexperts.com
Appliance Repair & Maintenance
N.A.I.C.S.: 811412

Heatcraft Geelong Pty Ltd (1)
Unit 2&3 38 Autumn St, Geelong, 3218, VIC, Australia
Tel.: (61) 352484533
Web Site: http://www.heatcraft.com.au
Sales Range: $25-49.9 Million
Emp.: 2
Air Conditioning & Refrigeration Whslr
N.A.I.C.S.: 423740

Heatcraft Refrigeration (Wuxi) Co. Ltd. (1)
No 12 Xindu Rd, Wuxi, 214028, Jiangsu, China
Tel.: (86) 51085282020
Air-Conditioning & Warm Air Heating Equipment Mfr
N.A.I.C.S.: 333415

Heatcraft Tasmania Pty Ltd (1)
Unit 2/225 Wellington St, Launceston, 7250, TAS, Australia
Tel.: (61) 363346969
Web Site: http://www.heatcraft.com.au
Emp.: 7
Air-Conditioning & Warm Air Heating Equipment Mfr
N.A.I.C.S.: 333415

Kysor/Warren de Mexico, S. de R.L. de C.V. (1)
Centro Industrial 1027 Los Reyes, Fracc Industrial Alce Blanco, 54073, Tlalnepantla, Mexico
Tel.: (52) 5553339790
Web Site: http://www.kysorwarren.com
Sales Range: $25-49.9 Million
Emp.: 50
Refrigeration System Mfr
N.A.I.C.S.: 333415

LGL Germany GmbH (1)
Industriepark 54, 56593, Altenkirchen, Germany
Tel.: (49) 26878980
Air-Conditioning & Warm Air Heating Equipment Mfr
N.A.I.C.S.: 333415

Lennox France S.A.S. (1)
Rue des Albatros, 69780, Mions, France
Tel.: (33) 472232020
Web Site: https://www.lennoxemea.com
Emp.: 800
Air-Conditioning & Warm Air Heating Equipment Mfr
N.A.I.C.S.: 333415

Lennox Industries Inc. (1)
2100 Lake Park Blvd, Richardson, TX 75080 (100%)
Tel.: (972) 497-5000
Web Site: http://www.lennoxinternationl.com
Sales Range: $250-299.9 Million
Emp.: 850
Mfr of Residential & Commercial Heating & Air Conditioning Equipment
N.A.I.C.S.: 333415
Tamme Gaddis (Partner-HR Bus)
David Pataky (Supvr-Tactical Pricing)
Keith Mowery (VP-Controls Engrg)
Steve Pitlik (Dir-Sourcing-Heatcraft Worldwide Refrigeration)

Subsidiary (Non-US):

Cheminees Securite International Ltee (2)
2125 Monterey, Laval, H7L 3T6, QC, Canada
Tel.: (450) 973-9999
Web Site: http://www.securitychimneys.com
Emp.: 120
Residential & Industrial Chimneys Mfr
N.A.I.C.S.: 238110

Subsidiary (Domestic):

Lennox National Account Services Inc. (2)
3511 NE 22nd Ave Ste 100, Fort Lauderdale, FL 33308
Tel.: (954) 537-5544

LENNOX INTERNATIONAL INC.

Lennox International Inc.—(Continued)
Web Site: https://www.lennoxnas.com
HVAC Contractors
N.A.I.C.S.: 238220

Subsidiary (Non-US):

Securite Cheminees International
Ltee **(2)**
2125 Monterey, Laval, H7L 3T6, QC,
Canada **(100%)**
Tel.: (450) 973-9999
Web Site: http://www.securitychimneys.com
Sales Range: $25-49.9 Million
Emp.: 200
Mfr Of Chimneys & Fireplaces
N.A.I.C.S.: 333414

Lennox Polska sp. z o.o. **(1)**
Wybrzeze Gdynskie 6a, PO Box 01531,
01-531, Warsaw, Poland
Tel.: (48) 225848610
Web Site: https://lennoxemea.com
Air-Conditioning & Warm Air Heating Equipment Mfr
N.A.I.C.S.: 333415
Pawel Gruchalski (Mng Dir)

LENSAR, INC.

2800 Discovery Dr, Orlando, FL
32826
Tel.: (407) 641-4889 **DE**
Web Site: https://www.lensar.com
LNSR—(NASDAQ)
Rev.: $35,358,000
Assets: $55,844,000
Liabilities: $13,860,000
Net Worth: $41,984,000
Earnings: ($19,914,000)
Emp.: 110
Fiscal Year-end: 12/31/22
Ocular Laser Technologies Developer
& Mfr
N.A.I.C.S.: 334510
Nicholas T. Curtis (CEO)
Alan Connaughton (COO)
Kendra W. Wong (Principal Acctg Officer)
Thomas R. Staab II (CFO)

LENZ THERAPEUTICS, INC.

201 Lomas Santa Fe Dr Ste 300, Solana Beach, CA 92075
Tel.: (858) 925-7000 **DE**
Web Site: https://lenz-tx.com
Year Founded: 2019
LENZ—(NASDAQ)
Rev.: $10,919,000
Assets: $188,456,000
Liabilities: $4,874,000
Net Worth: $183,582,000
Earnings: ($124,651,000)
Fiscal Year-end: 12/31/23
Research & Development in Biotechnology (except Nanobiotechnology)
N.A.I.C.S.: 541714
Josh Lehrer (Pres & CEO)
Philip P. Gutry (Chief Bus Officer)
Perry Karsen (Chm)

Subsidiaries:

LENZ Therapeutics Operations,
Inc. **(1)**
445 MARINE View Ave., Ste #320, Del Mar,
CA 92014
Tel.: (619) 890-5125
Biopharmaceutical Company
N.A.I.C.S.: 541714

LEONE ASSET MANAGEMENT, INC.

801 West Bay Dr Ste 715, Largo, FL
33770
Tel.: (727) 581-1500 **NV**
Web Site: http://www.leoneasset.com
Year Founded: 2005
LEON—(OTCIQ)
Sales Range: Less than $1 Million
Asset Management Services
N.A.I.C.S.: 523999

James Martin Price (Chm & CEO)
Troy Fort (Controller)

Subsidiaries:

Go Epic Health, Inc. **(1)**
801 West Bay Dr Ste 715 and 206, Largo,
FL 33770
Tel.: (727) 581-1500
Web Site: http://www.goepichealth.com
Nutritional Product Mfr
N.A.I.C.S.: 456191
James Price (Founder & CEO)
Woody Junot (Pres)

Subsidiary (Domestic):

American Retail Alliance Corp. **(2)**
1723 Commerece, Belleair Bluffs, FL 33716
Tel.: (727) 581-1500
Web Site:
http://www.americanretailalliance.com
Consumer Non-Durable & Durable Products
Distr
N.A.I.C.S.: 423990
Brett Phillips (Pres & CEO)
John Tsakos (Acct Mgr)
Kayla Gelanoy (Mgr-Sls)

LERER HIPPEAU ACQUISITION CORP.

100 Crosby St Ste 201, New York,
NY 10012
Tel.: (646) 237-4837 **DE**
Web Site:
http://www.lererhippeauacquisition.com
Year Founded: 2021
LHAA—(NASDAQ)
Investment Services
N.A.I.C.S.: 523999
Kenneth B. Lerer (Founder & Mng
Partner)
Eric C. Hippeau (Mng Partner)
Kenneth Lerer (Chm)
Eric Hippeau (CEO)
Ben Lerer (Pres)
Joe Medved (COO)
Dan Rochkind (CFO, Sec & Treas)

LESCARDEN, INC.

420 Lexington Ave, New York, NY
10170
Tel.: (212) 687-1050 **NY**
Web Site: http://www.catrix.com
Year Founded: 1960
LCAR—(OTCIQ)
Sales Range: Less than $1 Million
Emp.: 1
Pharmaceutical Preparation Mfr
N.A.I.C.S.: 325412
William E. Luther (Pres, CEO & CFO)

LESLIE'S, INC.

2005 E Indian School Rd, Phoenix,
AZ 85016
Tel.: (602) 366-3999 **DE**
Web Site:
https://www.lesliespool.com
Year Founded: 1963
LESL—(NASDAQ)
Rev.: $1,330,121,000
Assets: $1,050,325,000
Liabilities: $1,227,474,000
Net Worth: ($177,149,000)
Earnings: ($23,379,000)
Emp.: 3,850
Fiscal Year-end: 09/28/24
Swimming Pool Products Distr
N.A.I.C.S.: 423910
Scott J. Bowman (CFO & Treas)
Moyo LaBode (Chief Mdsg Officer)
Jason B. McDonell (CEO)

LEVELBLOX, INC.

6371 Business Blvd Ste 200, Sarasota, FL 34240
Tel.: (941) 907-8822 **DE**
Web Site: http://www.levelblox.com
Year Founded: 2008

LVBX—(OTCIQ)
Sales Range: Less than $1 Million
Visual Modeling IT Asset Management Software
N.A.I.C.S.: 513210
Gary W. Macleod (Chm & CEO)
Barry Friedman (VP-SAM Solutions)
Chris Jackson (VP-Bus Dev)

Subsidiaries:

Strategy to Revenue Inc. **(1)**
6371 Business Blvd Ste 200, Sarasota, FL
34240
Tel.: (941) 907-8822
Web Site: http://www.strategytorevenue.com
Software Consulting Services
N.A.I.C.S.: 541611
Dominic Jones (CEO)
Matt Downes (Sr VP-Intl Ops)
Robert Fox (VP-Sls & Mktg)
Martin Dean (Head-Innovation)
Mark Savinson (Sr VP-Customer Experience)

LEVI STRAUSS & CO.

1155 Battery St, San Francisco, CA
94111
Tel.: (415) 501-6000 **DE**
Web Site:
https://www.levistrauss.com
Year Founded: 1853
LEVI—(NYSE)
Rev.: $5,763,936,000
Assets: $5,900,069,000
Liabilities: $4,234,408,000
Net Worth: $1,665,661,000
Earnings: $553,541,000
Emp.: 16,600
Fiscal Year-end: 11/28/21
Jeans & Apparel Mfr & Marketer
N.A.I.C.S.: 315250
Harmit J. Singh (Chief Fin & Growth
Officer & Exec VP)
Michelle Gass (Pres & CEO)
Gianluca Flore (Chief Comml Officer
& Exec VP)
Katia Walsh (Chief Strategy & Artificial Intelligence Officer & Sr VP)
Lisa Stirling (Principal Accounting Officer, Principal Accounting Officer &
Principal Accounting Officer)
Jason Gowans (Chief Digital Officer
& Sr VP)
Elizabeth O'Neill (COO & Exec VP)
Kelly McGinnis (Chief Comm Officer
& Sr VP)
Karyn Hillman (Chief Product Officer
& Sr VP)
David Jedrzejek (Gen Counsel & Sr
VP)
Dawn Vitale (Chief Mdsg Officer)

Subsidiaries:

Dockers Brand **(1)**
1155 Battery St, San Francisco, CA 94111-
1230
Tel.: (415) 501-6000
Web Site: http://www.dockers.com
Sales Range: $650-699.9 Million
Emp.: 10,000
Men's & Women's Apparel Mfr
N.A.I.C.S.: 458110

Levi Strauss & Co. **(1)**
3350 Sw 148th Ave Ste 202, Miramar, FL
33027-3239
Tel.: (954) 885-3300
Web Site: http://www.levis.com
Sales Range: $50-74.9 Million
Emp.: 25
Denim Clothing Whslr
N.A.I.C.S.: 458110

Levi Strauss & Co. **(1)**
3750 N Bend Rd, Hebron, KY 41048-8465
Tel.: (859) 334-6200
Web Site: http://www.levistrauss.com
Sales Range: $50-74.9 Million
Emp.: 500
Clothing Distr
N.A.I.C.S.: 315250

Levi Strauss & Co. **(1)**
955 Hamilton Ridge Ln, Knoxville, TN
37922-5150
Tel.: (865) 692-3956
Web Site: http://www.levi.com
Men's & Boys' Jeans Wear Mfr
N.A.I.C.S.: 315250

Levi Strauss & Co. **(1)**
501 Executive Airport Dr, Henderson, NV
89052
Tel.: (702) 269-8700
Sales Range: $25-49.9 Million
Emp.: 250
Denim Clothing Distr
N.A.I.C.S.: 424350
Larry Howard (Mgr-Transportation)
Linda Jones (Coord-Consumer Returns)
Mike Wheelock (Supvr-Tech Svc)

Levi Strauss & Co. **(1)**
15000 Panatela Pkwy, Little Rock, AR
72206
Tel.: (501) 897-5100
Sales Range: $50-74.9 Million
Emp.: 400
Clothing Distr
N.A.I.C.S.: 424350

Levi Strauss & Co. **(1)**
1411 Broadway Fl 11, New York, NY
10018-3411 **(100%)**
Tel.: (212) 704-3200
Web Site: http://www.levi.com
Sales Range: $25-49.9 Million
Emp.: 40
Clothing Retailer
N.A.I.C.S.: 424350

Levi Strauss & Co. **(1)**
501 Denim Way, Canton, MS
39046-8664 **(100%)**
Tel.: (601) 856-3003
Web Site: http://www.levistrauss.com
Sales Range: $25-49.9 Million
Emp.: 245
Clothing Mfr
N.A.I.C.S.: 458110

Levi Strauss & Co. **(1)**
1725 16th Avenue Suite 200, Richmond
Hill, L4B 4C6, ON, Canada
Tel.: (905) 763-4400
Web Site: http://www.levi.com
Sales Range: $10-24.9 Million
Emp.: 60
Men's, Boys' & Ladies' Clothing Distr
N.A.I.C.S.: 315210
Diana Dimitian (Mng Dir)

Levi Strauss & Co. APD **(1)**
11 North Buona Vista Drive 14-08 Metropolis Tower 2, Great World City East Tower,
Singapore, 138589, Singapore
Tel.: (65) 67359303
Sales Range: $25-49.9 Million
Emp.: 200
Jeans & Apparel Mfr & Distr
N.A.I.C.S.: 315250

Levi Strauss (Australia) Pty. Ltd. **(1)**
Level 4 52 York Street, South Melbourne,
3205, VIC, Australia
Sales Range: $10-24.9 Million
Emp.: 45
Apparel Mfr & Distr
N.A.I.C.S.: 315250

Levi Strauss (Hong Kong)
Limited **(1)**
22/F Standard Chartered Tower Millennium
City 1 388 Kwun Tong Road, Kowloon,
China (Hong Kong)
Tel.: (852) 24119900
Web Site: http://www.levi.com.hk
Jeans & Apparel Mfr & Marketer
N.A.I.C.S.: 315250

Levi Strauss (Malaysia) Sdn Bhd **(1)**
Uptown 1 Unit 501A Level 5 1 Jalan SS21,
Damansara Utama, 47400, Petaling Jaya,
Selangor, Malaysia
Web Site: http://www.levi.com.my
Jeans & Apparel Mfr & Marketer
N.A.I.C.S.: 315250

Levi-Strauss (Philippines) Inc. **(1)**
Tel.: (63) 288899301
Web Site: http://www.levi.com.ph
Jeans & Apparel Mfr & Marketer

N.A.I.C.S.: 315250

Levi Strauss (Suisse) SA (1)
Klosterstrasse 40, CH-5430, Wettingen,
Switzerland
Tel.: (41) 216952490
Web Site: http://www.levi.com
Jeans & Apparel Mfr & Marketer
N.A.I.C.S.: 315250

Levi Strauss (UK) Limited (1)
Swan Valley, Northampton, NN4 9BA,
United Kingdom
Tel.: (44) 1604581501
Web Site: http://www.levi.com
Jeans & Apparel Mfr & Marketer
N.A.I.C.S.: 315250

Levi Strauss Europe (1)
Airport Plaza Leonardo da Vincilaan 19,
1050, Zaventem, Belgium
Tel.: (32) 26416011
Web Site: http://www.levi.com
Sales Range: $50-74.9 Million
Emp.: 600
Jeans & Apparel Mfr & Marketer
N.A.I.C.S.: 315250

Levi Strauss Germany GmbH (1)
18 Levi-Strauss-Allee, D-63 150, Heusen-
stamm, Germany
Tel.: (49) 61046010
Jeans & Apparel Mfr & Marketer
N.A.I.C.S.: 315250

**Levi Strauss Global Trading Com-
pany II, Limited** (1)
22/F Standard Chartered Tower Millennium
City 1 388 Kwun Tong Road, Kwun Tong,
China (Hong Kong)
Tel.: (852) 24119900
Web Site: http://www.levi.com.hk
Apparel Distr
N.A.I.C.S.: 458110

Levi Strauss Hellas SA (1)
2 Kalavryton Kaiafa & Amaliados, 145 64,
Kifissia, Greece
Tel.: (30) 2106873501
Jeans & Apparel Mfr & Marketer
N.A.I.C.S.: 315250

Levi Strauss International Inc. (1)
675 Factory Stores Dr, Napa, CA 94558-
5630
Tel.: (707) 252-6926
Web Site: http://www.levistrauss.com
Sales Range: $25-49.9 Million
Emp.: 11
Clothing Retailer
N.A.I.C.S.: 458110

Levi Strauss International, Inc. (1)
1155 Battery St, San Francisco, CA 94111-
1203
Tel.: (415) 501-6000
Web Site: http://www.levi.com
Jeans & Casual Wear Mfr
N.A.I.C.S.: 315250
Charles V. Bergh (Pres & CEO)
David Love (Pres-Asia, Middle East & Af-
rica)

**Levi Strauss Istanbul Konfeksiyon
Sanayi ve Ticaret A.S.** (1)
Buyukdere Cad Yapi Kredi Plaza C Block,
Levent, 80620, Istanbul, Turkiye
Tel.: (90) 2122798465
Web Site: http://www.levistrauss.com
Sales Range: $10-24.9 Million
Emp.: 80
Jeans & Apparel Mfr & Marketer
N.A.I.C.S.: 315250

Levi Strauss Italia srl (1)
Tel.: (39) 02290231
Sales Range: $25-49.9 Million
Emp.: 140
Jeans & Apparel Mfr & Marketer
N.A.I.C.S.: 315250

Levi Strauss Japan K.K. (1)
Tel.: (81) 357740501
Emp.: 75
Jeans & Apparel Mfr & Marketer
N.A.I.C.S.: 315250

Levi Strauss Lisbon (1)
Rua Dr Eduardo Neves 9-1, Lisbon,
P-1050-077, Portugal
Tel.: (351) 1795 8150

Jeans & Apparel Mfr & Marketer
N.A.I.C.S.: 315250

**Levi Strauss New Zealand
Limited** (1)
7 Windsor St, 1101, Auckland, Parnell, New
Zealand
Tel.: (64) 93090319
Web Site: http://www.levis.co.nz
Jeans & Apparel Mfr & Marketer
N.A.I.C.S.: 315250

Levi Strauss Norway A/S (1)
Nedre Vaskegang 2, PO Box 9156, Groen-
land, 0134, Oslo, Norway
Tel.: (47) 23326900
Jeans & Apparel Mfr & Marketer
N.A.I.C.S.: 315250

Levi Strauss Poland Sp z.o.o. (1)
Otolinska 8, 09407, Plock, Poland
Tel.: (48) 24 264 03 93
Web Site: http://www.levi.com
Jeans & Apparel Mfr & Marketer
N.A.I.C.S.: 315210

Levi Strauss Praha, spol s.r.o. (1)
Na Porici 10, 110 00, Prague, 1, Czech
Republic
Tel.: (420) 221899360
Jeans & Apparel Mfr & Marketer
N.A.I.C.S.: 315250

Levi Strauss SA (Pty) Ltd. (1)
17th Floor Portside 4 Bree Street, Cape
Town, 8001, South Africa
Tel.: (27) 214039400
Web Site: http://www.levis.co.za
Sales Range: $10-24.9 Million
Emp.: 400
Apparel Mfr & Distr
N.A.I.C.S.: 327910

Levi Strauss Trading Kft (1)
62 Andrassy 100, Budapest, 1062, Hungary
Tel.: (36) 13277600
Web Site: http://www.levi.com
Sales Range: $10-24.9 Million
Emp.: 11
Jeans & Apparel Mfr & Marketer
N.A.I.C.S.: 315250

Levi Strauss de Espana S.A. (1)
Ave Diagonal 605 3rd Fl, 8028, Barcelona,
Spain
Tel.: (34) 932276900
Jeans & Apparel Mfr & Marketer
N.A.I.C.S.: 315250

**Levi Strauss de Mexico SA de
CV** (1)
Boulevard Miguel de Cervantes Saavedra
301 Torre Norte Piso 7, Colonia Ampliacion
Granada Alcadia Miguel Hidalgo, CP 11529,
Mexico, Mexico
Tel.: (52) 55 8438 1818
Web Site: http://www.levi.com.mx
Apparel Mfr & Distr
N.A.I.C.S.: 315250

**Levi Strauss do Brasil Industria e Co-
mercio Ltda.** (1)
Tel.: (55) 1144964700
Web Site: http://www.levi.com.br
Jeans & Apparel Mfr & Marketer
N.A.I.C.S.: 315250

Levi's Brand (1)
1155 Battery St, San Francisco, CA 94111-
1230
Tel.: (415) 501-6000
Web Site: http://www.levistrauss.com
Men's & Women's Sportswear & Jeans Mfr
N.A.I.C.S.: 458110

**Levi's Footwear & Accessories (Swit-
zerland) S.A.** (1)
Tel.: (41) 916115171
Apparel Distr
N.A.I.C.S.: 458110

**Levi's Footwear & Accessories Spain
S.A.** (1)
Tel.: (34) 933325416
Apparel Distr
N.A.I.C.S.: 458110

d-Scan Inc. (1)
2195 Philipott Rd, South Boston, VA 24592
Tel.: (434) 575-0900
Web Site: http://www.tvilum.com

Sales Range: $10-24.9 Million
Emp.: 20
Home, Office & Bedroom Ready-to-
Assemble Product Mfr
N.A.I.C.S.: 449110

LEWIS & CLARK BANK
15960 S Agnes Ave, Oregon City, OR
97045
Tel.: (503) 212-3200 OR
Web Site:
http://www.lewisandclarkbank.com
Year Founded: 2006
LWCL—(OTCIQ)
Commericial Banking
N.A.I.C.S.: 522110
Karen York (Treas, Sr VP & Control-
ler)
Trey Maust (Exec Vice Chm)
William Reiling (Chief Credit Officer)
Jeffrey Sumpter (Pres & CEO)
Mark Ellingson (VP & Mgr-Portfolio)
Kirk Hansen (VP & Mgr-Relationship)
Adam Hiatt (VP & Mgr-Potfolio)
Heather Anderson (VP & Mgr-Loan
Ops)
John Davis (Sr VP & Dir-IT)
Barb Erickson (VP, HR & Compli-
ance)
Dave Takata (Sr VP & Mgr-Loan
Dept)
Tessah Danel (VP & Mgr-Customer
Rels-Comml Banking)
Lorianne Fiedler (VP & Ops Mgr)
Ben Durdel (VP & Mgr-Relationship)

Subsidiaries:

Clatsop Community Bank (1)
1150 N Roosevelt Dr Ste 101, Seaside, OR
97138
Tel.: (503) 738-8000
Web Site: http://www.clatsopbank.com
Banking Services
N.A.I.C.S.: 522110
Derith Andrew (VP-IT & Compliance Admin)
Jack Ficken (Bus Dev & Loan Officer-
Astoria)
Steve McCoy (CFO)
Mallory Litehiser (VP-Ops)
Cindy Trask (Chief Credit Officer)

LEXEO THERAPEUTICS, INC.
345 Park Ave S Fl 6, New York, NY
10010
Tel.: (212) 547-9879 DE
Web Site: https://www.lexeotx.com
Year Founded: 2017
LXEO—(NASDAQ)
Rev.: $2,867,000
Assets: $139,807,000
Liabilities: $26,272,000
Net Worth: $113,535,000
Earnings: ($66,394,000)
Emp.: 58
Fiscal Year-end: 12/31/23
Biotechnology Research & Develop-
ment Services
N.A.I.C.S.: 541714

LEXICON PHARMACEUTI-
CALS, INC.
2445 Technology Forest Blvd 11th Fl,
The Woodlands, TX 77381
Tel.: (281) 863-3000 DE
Web Site:
https://www.lexpharma.com
Year Founded: 1995
LXRX—(NASDAQ)
Rev.: $139,000
Assets: $194,299,000
Liabilities: $77,175,000
Net Worth: $117,124,000
Earnings: ($101,944,000)
Emp.: 135
Fiscal Year-end: 12/31/22
Pharmaceutical Preparation Manufac-
turing
N.A.I.C.S.: 325412

Alan J. Main (Exec VP-Innovation &
Chemical Sciences)
Craig B. Granowitz (Chief Medical
Officer & Sr VP)
Brian T. Crum (Gen Counsel & VP)
Kristen L. Alexander (VP-Acctg & Fin)
Wendy E. McDermott (VP)
Tom Garner (Chief Comml Officer &
Sr VP)
Jeffrey L. Wade (Pres & COO)

Subsidiaries:

Lexicon Pharmaceuticals, Inc. (1)
100 Somerset Corporate Blvd Ste 4000,
Bridgewater, NJ 08807
Tel.: (908) 360-4600
Web Site: https://www.lexpharma.com
Sales Range: $25-49.9 Million
Emp.: 100
Pharmaceuticals Research & Development
N.A.I.C.S.: 325412

LFTD PARTNERS INC.
14155 Pine Isl Dr, Jacksonville, FL
32224
Tel.: (847) 915-2446 NV
Web Site:
https://www.lftdpartners.com
Year Founded: 1986
LIFD—(OTCQB)
Rev.: $51,560,562
Assets: $51,346,651
Liabilities: $12,528,640
Net Worth: $38,818,011
Earnings: $2,159,007
Emp.: 166
Fiscal Year-end: 12/31/23
Investment Services
N.A.I.C.S.: 523999
Gerard M. Jacobs (Chm, CEO & Sec)
William C. Jacobs (Pres, CFO &
Treas)
Nicholas S. Warrender (Founder, Vice
Chm & COO)

LGA HOLDINGS, INC.
3380 N El Paso St Ste G, Colorado
Springs, CO 80917
Tel.: (719) 630-3800 CO
LGAH—(OTCIQ)
Holding Company
N.A.I.C.S.: 551112
Marty Williams (Pres & CEO)

LGBTQ LOYALTY HOLDINGS,
INC.
2435 Dixie Hwy, Wilton, FL 33305
Tel.: (954) 947-6133 DE
Web Site:
http://www.lifeappsbrands.com
Year Founded: 2010
LFAP—(OTCIQ)
Assets: $138,516
Liabilities: $7,087,152
Net Worth: ($6,948,636)
Earnings: ($6,612,679)
Emp.: 3
Fiscal Year-end: 12/31/21
Mobile Application Developer
N.A.I.C.S.: 513210
Robert A. Blair (Chm & CEO)
Eric Sherb (CFO)
Jeffrey Sterling (COO)
Lawrence Patrick Roan (Exec Dir)
John Rochard (Chief Strategy Officer)

LGI HOMES, INC.
1450 Lake Robbins Dr Ste 430, The
Woodlands, TX 77380
Tel.: (281) 362-8998 DE
Web Site: https://www.lgihomes.com
LGIH—(NASDAQ)
Rev.: $2,358,580,000
Assets: $3,407,851,000
Liabilities: $1,551,820,000
Net Worth: $1,856,031,000
Earnings: $199,227,000

LGI Homes, Inc.—(Continued)

Emp.: 1,089
Fiscal Year-end: 12/31/23
Residential Construction
N.A.I.C.S.: 236115
Charles Merdian *(CFO & Treas)*
Eric Thomas Lipar *(Founder, Chm & CEO)*
Jack Lipar *(Exec VP-Acquisitions)*
Rachel Eaton *(CMO)*
Scott Garber *(Gen Counsel & Sec)*
Mike Snider *(Pres)*
Subsidiaries:

LGI HOMES - ARIZONA, LLC   **(1)**
10520 E Wallflower Ln, Florence, AZ 85132
Tel.: (520) 518-5120
Real Estate Services
N.A.I.C.S.: 531210

LGI HOMES - DEER CREEK, LLC   **(1)**
504 Noble Grove Ln, Fort Worth, TX 76140
Tel.: (817) 551-2998
Real Estate Services
N.A.I.C.S.: 531210

LGI HOMES - E SAN ANTONIO, LLC   **(1)**
6115 Still Meadow, San Antonio, TX 78222
Tel.: (210) 236-5766
Emp.: 6
Real Estate Services
N.A.I.C.S.: 531210
Erica Torres *(Office Mgr)*
Jesse Torres *(Mgr-Sls)*

LGI HOMES - FLORIDA, LLC   **(1)**
3603 Chiquita Blvd S, Cape Coral, FL 33914
Tel.: (239) 257-1086
Emp.: 7
Real Estate Services
N.A.I.C.S.: 531210
Todd Fitzgerald *(Pres-Florida Div)*

LGI HOMES - FW, LLC   **(1)**
539 Bailer Dr, Crowley, TX 76036
Tel.: (817) 297-3016
Real Estate Services
N.A.I.C.S.: 531210

LGI HOMES - LUCKEY RANCH, LLC   **(1)**
6215 Luckey Ranch, San Antonio, TX 78252
Tel.: (210) 677-8200
Real Estate Services
N.A.I.C.S.: 531210

LGI HOMES - MAPLE PARK, LLC   **(1)**
4107 Pearhaven Ln, Gainesville, GA 30504
Housing Construction Services
N.A.I.C.S.: 236115

LGI HOMES - NC, LLC   **(1)**
721 Governor Morrison St, Charlotte, NC 28211
Tel.: (803) 738-6375
Real Estate Services
N.A.I.C.S.: 531210
Scott Sterling *(VP-Construction)*

LGI HOMES - OAK HOLLOW, LLC   **(1)**
1913 Pin Oak Trl, Anna, TX 75409
Tel.: (972) 924-7209
Emp.: 10
Real Estate Services
N.A.I.C.S.: 531210
Sal Aceves *(Mgr-Sls)*

LGI HOMES - PRESIDENTIAL GLEN, LLC   **(1)**
19501 Per Lange Pass, Manor, TX 78653
Tel.: (512) 358-1618
Real Estate Services
N.A.I.C.S.: 531210

LGI HOMES - SC, LLC   **(1)**
3037 Sherman Rd, Lancaster, SC 29720
Tel.: (803) 286-0064
Housing Construction Services
N.A.I.C.S.: 236115

LGI HOMES - SONTERRA, LLC   **(1)**

300 Sonterra Blvd, Jarrell, TX 76537
Tel.: (512) 746-6740
Real Estate Services
N.A.I.C.S.: 531210

LGI HOMES - STERLING LAKES PARTNERS, LLC   **(1)**
9446 Calm Amber Dr, Rosharon, TX 77583
Tel.: (281) 778-1940
Housing Construction Services
N.A.I.C.S.: 236115

LGI HOMES - WINDMILL FARMS, LLC   **(1)**
3001 Spyglass Dr, Forney, TX 75126
Tel.: (469) 355-0690
Residential Construction
N.A.I.C.S.: 236116
Drew Dallard *(Mgr)*

LGI HOMES AVONDALE, LLC   **(1)**
121 Avondale Blvd, Conyers, GA 30013
Tel.: (770) 761-0224
Housing Construction Services
N.A.I.C.S.: 236115

LGI HOMES AZ SALES, LLC   **(1)**
11445 E Viaduct Linda Ste 21, Scottsdale, AZ 85259
Tel.: (480) 703-2250
Housing Construction Services
N.A.I.C.S.: 236115

LGI HOMES GROUP, LLC   **(1)**
1450 Lake Robbins Dr Ste 430, The Woodlands, TX 77380
Tel.: (281) 362-8998
Real Estate Services
N.A.I.C.S.: 531210

LGI HOMES REALTY LLC   **(1)**
695 Mansell Rd Ste 220, Roswell, GA 30076
Tel.: (678) 604-7165
Housing Construction Services
N.A.I.C.S.: 236115

LIANBIO

103 Carnegie Ctr Dr Ste 309, Princeton, NJ 08540
Tel.: (609) 486-2308   Ky
Web Site: https://www.lianbio.com
Year Founded: 2019
LIAN—(NASDAQ)
Rev.: $4,321,000
Assets: $319,960,000
Liabilities: $26,313,000
Net Worth: $293,647,000
Earnings: ($110,290,000)
Emp.: 163
Fiscal Year-end: 12/31/22
Biotechnology Research & Development Services
N.A.I.C.S.: 541714
Adam Stone *(Interim CEO)*
Konstantin Poukalov *(Chm)*

LIBERATED SYNDICATION INC.

5001 Baum Blvd Ste 770, Pittsburgh, PA 15213
Tel.: (412) 621-0902   NV
Web Site: http://www.libsyn.com
Year Founded: 2015
LSYN—(OTCIQ)
Rev.: $24,201,629
Assets: $44,602,006
Liabilities: $14,509,264
Net Worth: $30,092,742
Earnings: $2,833,841
Emp.: 87
Fiscal Year-end: 12/31/19
Podcast Hosting Services
N.A.I.C.S.: 518210
Laurie A. Sims *(Pres & COO)*
Jonathan M. Charak *(CFO & Treas)*
Bradley M. Tirpak *(CEO)*
Rob Greenlee *(VP-Content & Partnership)*
Rob Walch *(VP-Podcaster Rels)*
Elsie Escobar *(Mgr-Community)*

Gabriel J. Mosey *(Controller)*
Brian Kibby *(Chm)*
Jonathan Charak *(CFO)*
Subsidiaries:

Pair Networks, Inc.   **(1)**
2403 Sidney St Ste 210, Pittsburgh, PA 15203-2168
Tel.: (412) 381-7247
Web Site: http://www.pair.com
Data Hosting Services
N.A.I.C.S.: 518210

LIBERTY ALL-STAR EQUITY FUND

1290 Broadway Ste 1000, Denver, CO 80203
Web Site: https://www.all-starfunds.com
Year Founded: 1986
USA—(NYSE)
Rev.: $22,944,169
Assets: $1,477,196,883
Liabilities: $36,910,001
Net Worth: $1,440,286,882
Earnings: $9,709,918
Fiscal Year-end: 12/31/19
Investment Management Service
N.A.I.C.S.: 525990
Craig C. Blum *(Mgr-Fund)*

LIBERTY BROADBAND CORPORATION

12300 Liberty Blvd, Englewood, CO 80112
Tel.: (720) 875-5700   DE
Web Site:
   https://www.libertybroadband.com
Year Founded: 2014
LBRDA—(NASDAQ)
Rev.: $981,000,000
Assets: $15,641,000,000
Liabilities: $6,618,000,000
Net Worth: $9,023,000,000
Earnings: $688,000,000
Emp.: 1,900
Fiscal Year-end: 12/31/23
Broadband Services
N.A.I.C.S.: 517810
John C. Malone *(Chm & Interim CEO)*
Richard N. Baer *(Chief Legal Officer)*
Brian J. Wendling *(Sr VP & Controller)*
Ben Oren *(Treas)*
Subsidiaries:

GCI Liberty, Inc.   **(1)**
12300 Liberty Blvd, Englewood, CO 80112
Tel.: (720) 875-5900
Web Site: http://www.gciliberty.com
Rev.: $3,780,519,000
Assets: $11,933,445,000
Liabilities: $5,723,161,000
Net Worth: $6,210,284,000
Earnings: $1,938,690,000
Emp.: 2,051
Fiscal Year-end: 12/31/2019
Telecommunication Servicesb
N.A.I.C.S.: 517111
Courtnee Alice Chun *(Chief Portfolio Officer & Sr VP-IR)*
Albert E. Rosenthaler *(Chief Corp Dev Officer)*
John C. Malone *(Principal)*
Brian J. Wendling *(CFO, Chief Acctg Officer, Sr VP & Controller)*
Subsidiary (Domestic):

Alaska United Fiber System Partnership   **(2)**
5151A Fairbanks St, Anchorage, AK 99503
Tel.: (907) 868-5555
Fiber Optic Communication Services
N.A.I.C.S.: 237130

Bortek, LLC   **(2)**
2550 Denali St Ste 1000, Anchorage, AK 99503   **(100%)**
Tel.: (907) 748-2913

Telecommunication Servicesb
N.A.I.C.S.: 517810

Cycle30, Inc.   **(2)**
710 2nd Ave Suite 1260, Seattle, WA 98104
Hosted, Order-to-Cash Billing Services for Telecom, Cable, Utility & M2M Industries
N.A.I.C.S.: 522390

Denali Media Holdings, Corp.   **(2)**
1001 Northway Dr, Anchorage, AK 99508
Tel.: (907) 274-1111
Web Site: https://denalimedia.business.site
Holding Company
N.A.I.C.S.: 551112
Subsidiary (Domestic):

Denali Media Anchorage, Corp.   **(3)**
2550 Denali St Ste 1000, Anchorage, AK 99503   **(100%)**
Tel.: (907) 868-5615
Television Broadcasting
N.A.I.C.S.: 516120
Unit (Domestic):

KTVA-TV   **(4)**
1001 Northway Dr St 202, Anchorage, AK 99508
Tel.: (907) 929-9700
Web Site: http://www.ktva.com
Television Station
N.A.I.C.S.: 516120
Cyd Terhune *(Dir-Programming)*
Monica Bouvier-Walker *(Mgr-Traffic & PSA)*
Rick Boots *(Dir-Sls)*
Erik Kuhlman *(Dir-Broadcast Engrg & Ops)*
Jes Stugelmayer *(Mgr-Digital Content)*
Janis Harper *(Dir-News)*
Gina Romero *(Asst Dir-News)*
Steve Quinn *(Mgr-News Content)*
Subsidiary (Domestic):

Denali Media Juneau, Corp.   **(3)**
2550 Denali St Ste 1000, Anchorage, AK 99503
Tel.: (907) 929-9700
Telecommunication Servicesb
N.A.I.C.S.: 517810

Denali Media Southeast, Corp.   **(3)**
2550 Denali St Ste 1000, Anchorage, AK 99503
Tel.: (907) 868-5615
Television Broadcasting
N.A.I.C.S.: 516120
Subsidiary (Domestic):

GCI Cable, Inc.   **(2)**
5151 Fairbanks St, Anchorage, AK 99503   **(100%)**
Tol.: (907) 868 6154
Web Site: http://www.gci.com
Cable & Entertainment Mfr
N.A.I.C.S.: 516210

GCI Communication Corp.   **(2)**
2550 Denali St Ste 1000, Anchorage, AK 99503
Tel.: (907) 265-5600
Web Site: https://www.gci.com
Emp.: 1,800
Telecommunication Servicesb
N.A.I.C.S.: 517810

GCI, LLC   **(2)**
12300 Liberty Blvd, Englewood, CO 80112
Tel.: (720) 875-5900
Rev.: $3,182,788,000
Assets: $11,356,020,000
Liabilities: $4,849,951,000
Net Worth: $6,506,069,000
Earnings: $2,186,168,000
Fiscal Year-end: 12/31/2019
Telecommunication Support Services
N.A.I.C.S.: 517810
Brian J. Wendling *(CFO & Chief Acctg Officer)*

Global Cooling, Inc.   **(2)**
6000 Poston Rd, Athens, OH 45701
Tel.: (740) 592-2655
Web Site: http://www.globalcooling.com
Rev.: $2,000,000
Emp.: 18
Ultra Low Temperature Freezers Mfr
N.A.I.C.S.: 423740

United Utilities, Inc.   **(2)**

5450 A St, Anchorage, AK 99518
Tel.: (907) 561-1674
Web Site: https://www.uui-alaska.com
Telephone Communications
N.A.I.C.S.: 517111
Steve Hamlen (CEO)

United-KUC, Inc. (2)
5450 A St, Anchorage, AK 99518
Tel.: (907) 561-1674
Web Site: http://www.uui-alaska.com
Telecommunication Servicesb
N.A.I.C.S.: 517810

TruePosition, Inc. (1)
1000 Chesterbrook Blvd Ste 200, Berwyn, PA 19312 (100%)
Tel.: (610) 680-1000
Web Site: http://www.truepositions.com
Sales Range: $75-99.9 Million
Emp.: 350
Satellite Geospatial Positioning Systems Developer & Mfr
N.A.I.C.S.: 334511
Robert Anderson (CTO & Sr VP-Tech/Engrg)
Craig Waggy (CEO)
Michael Hoppman (CFO & Sr VP)

Subsidiary (Domestic):

Skyhook Wireless, Inc. (2)
12 Thomson Pl Fl 4, Boston, MA 02210
Tel.: (617) 314-9802
Web Site: http://www.skyhook.com
Location Identification Software Developer
N.A.I.C.S.: 541511
Robert Anderson (CTO)
Craig Waggy (CEO)
Michael Hoppman (CFO)
Steve Solari (Sr VP-Strategic Accounts)
Karl Holzthum (Chief Mktg Officer & Chief Sls Officer)
Dan Gill (Sr VP-AdTech Sls)
David Bairstow (VP-Product Mgmt)
Matt Kojalo (VP-AdTech)
Rodman K. Forter Jr. (Gen Counsel & Sr VP-Licensing & Strategy)

LIBERTY ENERGY INC.
950 17th St Ste 2400, Denver, CO 80202
Tel.: (303) 515-2800   DE
Web Site: https://libertyenergy.com
Year Founded: 2016
LBRT—(NYSE)
Rev.: $4,149,228,000
Assets: $2,575,932,000
Liabilities: $1,078,626,000
Net Worth: $1,497,306,000
Earnings: $399,602,000
Emp.: 4,580
Fiscal Year-end: 12/31/22
Holding Company; Oil & Gas Hydraulic Fracturing & Engineering Services
N.A.I.C.S.: 551112
Christopher A. Wright (Founder, Chm & CEO)
Ron Gusek (Pres)
Ryan T. Gosney (Chief Acctg Officer)
Michael Stock (CFO & Treas)
R. Sean Elliott (Chief Legal Officer, Gen Counsel, Sec & VP)
Jim Brady (Sr VP-Operations & VP-Ops)
Leen Weijers (Sr VP-Engineering & VP-Engrg)
Jack Amant (VP-HSEQ & Training)
Mike Machovoe (VP-Business Development)
Greg McKee (VP-Supply Chain)
Tracee Quinnell (VP-Human Resources)

Subsidiaries:

Liberty Oilfield Services LLC (1)
950 17th St Fl 24, Denver, CO 80202
Tel.: (303) 515-2800
Web Site: https://www.libertyenergy.com
Oil & Gas Hydraulic Fracturing & Engineering Services
N.A.I.C.S.: 213112

Christopher A. Wright (CEO)
Michael Stock (CFO)
Ron Gusek (Pres)
Sean Elliott (VP & Gen Counsel)
Ryan Gosney (Chief Acctg Officer)
Mike Machovoe (Dir-Business Development)
Mike Machovoe (Dir-Business Development)
Jim Brady (VP)
Tracee Quinnell (VP)
Lean Weijers (VP)
Greg McKee (VP)

LIBERTY MEDIA ACQUISITION CORPORATION
12300 Liberty Blvd, Englewood, CO 80112
Tel.: (720) 875-5800   DE
Year Founded: 2020
LMACU—(NASDAQ)
Rev.: $53,412
Assets: $576,084,867
Liabilities: $650,719,444
Net Worth: ($74,634,577)
Earnings: ($23,956,566)
Emp.: 4
Fiscal Year-end: 12/31/21
Investment Services
N.A.I.C.S.: 523999
Gregory B. Maffei (Pres & CEO)
Albert E. Rosenthaler (Chief Corp Dev Officer)
Brian J. Wendling (Chief Acctg Officer)
Renee L. Wilm (Chief Legal Officer)

LIBERTY MEDIA CORPORATION
12300 Liberty Blvd, Englewood, CO 80112
Tel.: (720) 875-5400   DE
Web Site: https://www.libertymedia.com
Year Founded: 2012
LSXMA—(NASDAQ)
Rev.: $12,525,000,000
Assets: $41,168,000,000
Liabilities: $21,723,000,000
Net Worth: $19,445,000,000
Earnings: $761,000,000
Emp.: 6,486
Fiscal Year-end: 12/31/23
Holding Company
N.A.I.C.S.: 551112
Gregory B. Maffei (Senior Advisor)
John C. Malone (Chm & Interim CEO)
Brian J. Wendling (CFO & Chief Acctg Officer)
Renee L. Wilm (Chief Legal Officer & Chief Admin Officer)
Robert R. Bennett (Founder)

Subsidiaries:

Formula One Administration Limited (1)
6 Princes Gate, Knightsbridge, London, SW7 1QJ, United Kingdom
Tel.: (44) 2039849372
Media & Entertainment Business Services
N.A.I.C.S.: 517810

QuintEvents LLC (1)
9335 Harris Corners Pkwy Ste 500, Charlotte, NC 28269
Web Site: http://www.quintevents.com
Event & Hospitality Packages
N.A.I.C.S.: 711310
Nickolas Cardinale (COO)
John Langbein (Partner)
Kim Lankford (Sr VP-Product Dev)
Brian Ruede (CEO)
Aaron Odom (VP-Tech)
Keith Bruce (Pres-Intl)
Andrew Bruce (CFO)
Neil Goldman (Chief Travel Officer)
Nick Bisho (Sr VP-Sls)
Francis Dharmai (Sr VP-MEASA)
Tom Schneider (Sr VP-Rooms)

Subsidiary (Domestic):

Hotels for Hope, Inc. (2)
336 S Congress Ave Ste 512, Austin, TX 78704
Tel.: (512) 691-9555
Web Site: http://www.hotelsforhope.com
Sales Range: $1-9.9 Million
Hotel Operator
N.A.I.C.S.: 721110
Neil Goldman (Founder & CEO)
Kyle Sorensen (Dir-Mktg & Tech)
Nicole Watson (Dir-Mktg & Giving)
Marenna Chulick (Dir-Success)
Tommy Belton (Dir-Groups Div)
Ricky Robichaud (Dir-Hotel Rels)
Sarah Maloney (Dir-Groups Div)
Lamar Humphreys (Dir-Guest Rels)
Natalie Meyersick (Mgr-Groups & Brokerage Div)
Laura Celestino (Mgr-Guest Rels)
Jonathan Pollard (Dir-Tech & Data)
Kerri Morgan (Mgr-Acct-Global)
Veronica Lee (Dir-Hotel Brokerage)
Olivia Shea (Mgr-Acct-Global)
Steven Macias (Coord-Guest Rels)
Danielle Crespo (Acct Dir-Nascar)
Craig Karus (Dir-Corp Ops)

Sirius XM Holdings Inc. (1)
1221 Ave of the Americas 35th Fl, New York, NY 10020
Tel.: (212) 584-5100
Web Site: http://www.siriusxm.com
Rev.: $9,003,000,000
Assets: $10,022,000,000
Liabilities: $13,373,000,000
Net Worth: ($3,351,000,000)
Earnings: $1,213,000,000
Emp.: 5,869
Fiscal Year-end: 12/31/2022
Holding Company; Satellite Radio Broadcasting Services
N.A.I.C.S.: 551112
Jennifer C. Witz (CEO)
James E. Meyer (Vice Chm)
Scott A. Greenstein (Pres & Chief Content Officer)
Joseph Inzerillo (Chief Product & Tech Officer)
Patrick L. Donnelly (Gen Counsel, Sec & Exec VP)
Thomas D. Barry (CFO, Chief Acctg Officer & Exec VP)
Joseph A. Verbrugge (Chief Comml Officer)
Joe Inzerillo (Chief Product & Tech Officer)
Richard Beatty (Chief Subscription Revenue Officer)
Jessica Casano-Antonellis (Sr VP)
Hooper Stevens (Sr VP)
John Trimble (Chief Advertising Revenue Officer)
Joe Verbrugge (Chief Comml Officer)
Suzi Watford (Chief Growth Officer)

Subsidiary (Domestic):

Pandora Media, LLC (2)
2100 Franklin St Ste 700, Oakland, CA 94612
Tel.: (510) 451-4100
Web Site: https://www.pandora.com
Internet Radio Services
N.A.I.C.S.: 516110

Subsidiary (Domestic):

Adswizz Inc. (3)
487A S El Camino Real, San Mateo, CA 94402
Tel.: (650) 931-4575
Web Site: https://www.adswizz.com
Computer System Design Services
N.A.I.C.S.: 541512

Subsidiary (Domestic):

Sirius XM Radio Inc. (2)
1221 Ave of the Americas, New York, NY 10020
Tel.: (212) 584-5100
Web Site: https://www.siriusxm.com
Satellite Radio Broadcasting Services
N.A.I.C.S.: 516110
Jennifer C. Witz (Pres-Sls & Ops)
Joseph Inzerillo (Chief Product & Tech Officer)
Richard Beatty (Sr VP)
Jessica Casano-Antonellis (Sr VP)

Scott Greenstein (Pres)
Nicole Hughey (Sr VP)
Hooper Stevens (Sr VP)
John Trimble (Exec VP)
Faye Tylee (Chief People Officer)
Suzi Watford (Sr VP)

Unit (Domestic):

Sirius XM Innovation Center (3)
3161 SW 10th St, Deerfield Beach, FL 33442
Tel.: (954) 571-4300
Web Site: http://www.xmradio.com
Sales Range: $10-24.9 Million
Emp.: 60
Satellite Radio Technology Research & Development
N.A.I.C.S.: 541715

Subsidiary (Domestic):

XM 1500 Eckington LLC (3)
1500 Eckington Pl NE, Washington, DC 20002
Tel.: (202) 380-4000
Radio Broadcasting Services
N.A.I.C.S.: 516110

Subsidiary (Domestic):

Stitcher Inc. (2)
250 Montgomery St 15th Fl, San Francisco, CA 94105
Tel.: (415) 956-1801
Web Site: http://www.stitcher.com
Podcast & Radio Streaming Application Provider
N.A.I.C.S.: 334220

LIBERTY RESOURCES ACQUISITION CORP.
10 E 53rd St Ste 3001, New York, NY 10022
Tel.: (305) 809-7217   DE
Year Founded: 2021
LIBY—(NASDAQ)
Rev.: $1,690,069
Assets: $119,670,332
Liabilities: $124,082,234
Net Worth: ($4,411,902)
Earnings: $400,163
Fiscal Year-end: 12/31/22
Investment Services
N.A.I.C.S.: 523999
Khalid Ahmad (CFO & Sec)

LIBERTY STAR URANIUM & METALS CORP.
2 E Congress St Ste 900, Tucson, AZ 85701
Tel.: (520) 425-1433   NV
Web Site: https://www.libertystaruranium.com
Year Founded: 2001
LBSR—(OTCQB)
Rev.: $3,941
Assets: $104,099
Liabilities: $3,166,898
Net Worth: ($3,062,799)
Earnings: ($4,080,258)
Fiscal Year-end: 01/31/24
Uranium & Other Metal Mining Services
N.A.I.C.S.: 212290
Peter O'Heeron (Chm, Treas & Sec)
Patricia Madaris (CFO & VP-Fin)
Jay Crawford (Mgr-Field Ops)
Tracy Myers (Mgr-IR)

LICT CORPORATION
401 Theodore Fremd Ave, Rye, NY 10580
Tel.: (914) 921-8821   DE
Web Site: https://www.lictcorp.com
Year Founded: 1999
LICT—(OTCIQ)
Rev.: $124,174,000
Assets: $283,376,000
Liabilities: $102,781,000

LICT Corporation—(Continued)

Net Worth: $180,595,000
Earnings: $37,268,000
Emp.: 343
Fiscal Year-end: 12/31/20
Telecommunications, Security, Cable
Television & Broadcasting Services
N.A.I.C.S.: 517111
Evelyn C. Jerden *(Sr VP-Regulatory Dynamics)*
Robert E. Dolan *(Co-CFO)*
Stephen J. Moore *(VP-Fin)*
John M. Aoki *(Controller)*
Mario J. Gabelli *(Chm & CEO)*
Kevin Errity *(COO)*
Alexander Dominguez *(Asst Controller)*
Mario J. Gabelli *(Chm & CEO)*

Subsidiaries:

Central Scott Telephone   (1)
125 N Second St, Eldridge, IA
52748   **(100%)**
Tel.: (563) 285-9611
Web Site: http://www.centralscott.com
Sales Range: $10-24.9 Million
Emp.: 19
Provider of Telecommunications Products &
Services
N.A.I.C.S.: 517121
Bruce R. Duling *(Mgr-Mktg & PR)*
Julie Anderson *(Office Mgr-Billing)*
Donn Wilmott *(Pres & COO)*

Central Utah Telephone, Inc.   (1)
35 S State, Fairview, UT 84629   **(100%)**
Tel.: (435) 427-3331
Sales Range: $10-24.9 Million
Emp.: 40
Provider of Telecommunication Products &
Services
N.A.I.C.S.: 517121
Eddie Cox *(Gen Mgr)*

Cuba City Telephone Exchange
Co.   (1)
121 N Washington St, Cuba City, WI 53807
Tel.: (608) 744-2154
Web Site: http://www.cstech.com
Sales Range: $200-249.9 Million
Emp.: 6
Telephone Company
N.A.I.C.S.: 517121
Debbie Egli *(Gen Mgr)*

Giant Communications, Inc.   (1)
418 West 5th St Ste B, Holton, KS
66436   **(100%)**
Tel.: (785) 362-2532
Web Site: http://www.giantcomm.net
Sales Range: $10-24.9 Million
Emp.: 17
Provider of Telecommunication Products &
Services
N.A.I.C.S.: 516210
Gene Morris *(Gen Mgr)*

Haviland Telephone Company,
Inc.   (1)
104 N Main St, Haviland, KS 67059-9500
Tel.: (620) 862-5211
Web Site: http://www.havilandtelco.com
Sales Range: $10-24.9 Million
Emp.: 25
Telephone Communications
N.A.I.C.S.: 517121
Gene Morris *(Pres)*
Mark Wade *(Gen Mgr)*

Inter-Community Telephone
Company   (1)
556 Main St, Nome, ND 58062
Tel.: (701) 924-8815
Web Site: http://www.ictc.com
Sales Range: $10-24.9 Million
Emp.: 15
Telephone Communication, Except Radio
N.A.I.C.S.: 517121
Mark Jhonson *(Gen Mgr)*

J.B.N. Telephone Co.   (1)
418 W 5th St Ste A, Holton, KS 66436
Tel.: (785) 866-2310
Web Site: http://www.jbntelco.com
Sales Range: $10-24.9 Million
Emp.: 15
Telephone Company

N.A.I.C.S.: 517121
Eugene Morris *(Gen Mgr)*

WNM Communications   (1)
314 W Yankie St, Silver City, NM 88061-4938
Tel.: (505) 388-2549
Web Site: http://www.wnmt.com
Sales Range: $10-24.9 Million
Emp.: 15
Phone & Internet Telecommunications
N.A.I.C.S.: 517121

LIFE CLIPS, INC.

18851 NE 29th Ave Ste 700, Aventura, FL 33180   **WY**
Web Site: http://www.lifeclips.com
Year Founded: 2013
LCLP—(OTCIQ)
Rev.: $50,000
Assets: $303,378
Liabilities: $7,827,665
Net Worth: ($7,524,287)
Earnings: ($3,479,037)
Emp.: 534
Fiscal Year-end: 06/30/21
Investment Services
N.A.I.C.S.: 523999
Victoria Diana Rudman *(CFO, Treas & Sec)*
Robert Grinberg *(Chm & CEO)*

LIFE DESIGN STATION INTERNATIONAL, INC.

660 S Figueroa St Ste No 1820, Los
Angeles, CA 90017
Tel.: (213) 624-1800
LDSI—(OTCIQ)
Financial Consulting Services
N.A.I.C.S.: 541611
Eiichiro Hemmi *(Pres, CEO, Treas & Sec)*

LIFE ON EARTH, INC.

575 Lexington Ave 4th Fl, New York,
NY 10022
Tel.: (646) 844-9897   **DE**
Web Site:
  http://www.lifeonearthinc.com
Year Founded: 2013
LFER—(OTCIQ)
Assets: $5,219,344
Liabilities: $9,881,135
Net Worth: ($4,661,791)
Earnings: ($1,434,073)
Emp.: 3
Fiscal Year-end: 05/31/21
Food & Beverage Distr
N.A.I.C.S.: 424490
Jerry Gruenbaum *(Co-Founder)*
Fernando Oswaldo Leonzo *(Co-Founder & Chm)*
Robert Gunther *(Co-Founder, COO, Treas & Sec)*
John Carlos Romagosa *(Co-Founder & Pres)*
Mahmood Alam Khan *(CEO)*

LIFE TIME GROUP HOLDINGS, INC.

2902 Corporate Pl, Chanhassen, MN
55317   **DE**
Tel.: (952) 947-0000
Year Founded: 1992
LTH—(NYSE)
Rev.: $1,822,557,000
Assets: $6,625,363,000
Liabilities: $4,501,102,000
Net Worth: $2,124,261,000
Earnings: ($1,793,000)
Emp.: 34,000
Fiscal Year-end: 12/31/22
Holding Company
N.A.I.C.S.: 551112
Bahram Akradi *(Founder, Chm & CEO)*

Bahram Akradi *(Founder, Chm & CEO)*
Erik Weaver *(CFO & Exec VP)*

LIFE'S TIME CAPSULE SERVICES, INC.

401 Continental Dr Ste 401-703,
Newark, DE 19713   **NV**
Web Site: http://ltcpservices.com
Year Founded: 2008
LTCP—(OTCIQ)
Emp.: 4
Clinic Management Software Developer & Video Equipment Mfr
N.A.I.C.S.: 513210
Edward Taylor Gibstein *(Chm)*

Subsidiaries:

CPU, LLC   (1)
2901 Houma Blvd Ste 5, Metairie, LA 70006
Tel.: (504) 456-7446
Web Site: http://www.cpullc.com
Measurement Software Services
N.A.I.C.S.: 513210
Robert Phillpott *(Owner)*

LIFE360, INC.

1900 S Norfolk St Ste 310, San Mateo, CA 94403   **DE**
Tel.: (415) 484-5244
Web Site: https://www.life360.com
360—(ASX)
Rev.: $228,305,000
Assets: $339,630,000
Liabilities: $95,092,000
Net Worth: $244,538,000
Earnings: ($91,629,000)
Emp.: 400
Fiscal Year-end: 12/31/22
Custom Computer Programming Services
N.A.I.C.S.: 541511
Russell Burke *(CFO)*
Charles Prober *(Pres)*
Alex Haro *(Co-Founder)*
Heather Houston *(Chief People Officer)*
James Selby *(Chief Product Officer)*
Chris Hulls *(Co-Founder & CEO)*
Lauren Antonoff *(COO)*
David Rice *(Chief Strategy Officer & Gen Mgr-Intl)*
Susan Stick *(Gen Counsel)*
Mike Zeman *(CMO)*
Justin Moore *(CTO)*

LIFECORE BIOMEDICAL, INC.

3515 Lyman Blvd, Chaska, MN 55318
Tel.: (952) 368-4300   **DE**
Web Site: https://www.lifecore.com
Year Founded: 1986
LFCR—(NASDAQ)
Rev.: $185,786,000
Assets: $295,160,000
Liabilities: $187,215,000
Net Worth: $107,945,000
Earnings: ($97,431,000)
Emp.: 689
Fiscal Year-end: 05/29/22
Temperature-Activated & Other Specialty Polymer Products Designer,
Developer, Mfr & Retailer
N.A.I.C.S.: 325211
Katrina L. Houde *(Chm)*
Paul Josephs *(Pres & CEO)*
Jackie Q. Klecker *(Exec VP & Gen Mgr)*
Darren M. Hieber *(Sr VP-Corporate Development & Partnerships)*
Brikkelle Thompson *(Sr VP-Human Resources)*
Matt Augustson *(Sr VP-Information Technology)*
Kipling Thacker *(VP)*

Scott J. Collins *(VP-Finance)*
Phil Sticha *(VP-Bus Ops)*
Ryan D. Lake *(CFO & Sec)*

Subsidiaries:

Curation Foods, Inc.   (1)
2811 Air Park Drive, Santa Maria, CA
93455   **(100%)**
Tel.: (805) 343-2835
Web Site: http://www.apioinc.com
Produce Harvester, Packer & Marketer;
Specialty Processed Food Retailer
N.A.I.C.S.: 115114

Dock Resins Corporation   (1)
76 Porcupine Rd, Pedricktown, NJ 08067-3509
Tel.: (908) 862-2351
Sales Range: $10-24.9 Million
Emp.: 55
Mfr & Marketer of Specialty Acrylics & Other
Polymers
N.A.I.C.S.: 325211

Landec AG   (1)
306 N Main St, Monticello, IN 47960
Tel.: (574) 583-2741
Web Site:
  http://www.fielderschoicedirect.com
Sales Range: $25-49.9 Million
Emp.: 75
Polymer Based Seed Coating
N.A.I.C.S.: 325320

Lifecore Biomedical, Inc.   (1)
3515 Lyman Blvd, Chaska, MN 55318-3050
Tel.: (952) 368-4300
Web Site: http://www.lifecore.com
Rev.: $128,261,000
Assets: $253,960,000
Liabilities: $200,058,000
Net Worth: $53,902,000
Earnings: $9,331,000
Emp.: 524
Fiscal Year-end: 05/26/2024
Hyaluronan Mfr
N.A.I.C.S.: 325414
Kipling Thacker *(Chief Scientific Officer & VP)*
Paul Josephs *(Pres & CEO)*
Scott J. Collins *(VP-Fin)*
Jackie Q. Klecker *(VP & Gen Mgr)*
Rick Sitarz *(VP-Comm Dev)*
Steve W. Laninga *(VP-Ops)*

O Olive Oil, LLC   (1)
1997 S McDowell Blvd Ste A, Petaluma, CA
94954
Tel.: (707) 766-1755
Web Site: http://www.ooliveoil.com
Ambulatory Health Care Services
N.A.I.C.S.: 621999

LIFELINE BIOTECHNOLOGIES, INC.

1325 Airmotive Way Ste 175L, Reno,
NV 89502
Tel.: (775) 852-3222   **NV**
Web Site: http://www.lbti.com
Year Founded: 1981
LLBO—(OTCIQ)
Sales Range: Less than $1 Million
Breast Cancer Early Detection System
N.A.I.C.S.: 339112
Jim Holmes *(Chm, Pres & CEO)*
Fred V. Schiemann *(Sec)*

LIFELOC TECHNOLOGIES, INC.

12441 W 49th Ave Ste 4, Wheat
Ridge, CO 80033
Tel.: (303) 431-9500   **CO**
Web Site: https://www.lifeloc.com
Year Founded: 1983
LCTC—(OTCIQ)
Rev.: $8,481,993
Assets: $8,517,761
Liabilities: $2,362,550
Net Worth: $6,155,211
Earnings: ($455,757)
Emp.: 35
Fiscal Year-end: 12/31/22

Portable Hand-Held Breathalyzers & Related Supplies Developer, Mfr & Marketer
N.A.I.C.S.: 339112
Michelle Heim (Controller)
Wayne R. Willkomm (Pres & CEO)
Vern D. Kornelsen (Chm, CFO & Sec)

LIFEMD, INC.
236 Fifth Ave Ste 400, New York, NY 10001
DE
Web Site: https://lifemd.com
Year Founded: 1987
LFMD—(NASDAQ)
Rev.: $152,547,006
Assets: $58,480,709
Liabilities: $52,914,550
Net Worth: $5,566,159
Earnings: ($17,839,057)
Emp.: 207
Fiscal Year-end: 12/31/23
Natural Immune Support Products Mfr & Sales
N.A.I.C.S.: 325412
Stefan Galluppi (Chief Innovation & Mktg Officer)
Justin Schreiber (Chm & CEO)
Nicholas Alvarez (Chief Acquisition Officer)
Eric H. Yecies (Chief Compliance Officer & Gen Counsel)
Brad Roberts (COO)
Marc Benathen (CFO)
Dennis Wijnker (CTO)
Garett Hunter (Sr VP/Gen Mgr-LifeMD Primary Care)
Maria Stan (Principal Acctg Officer & Controller)
Anthony D. Puopolo II (Pres)
James Porte (Sr VP)

LIFEQUEST WORLD CORP.
100 Challenger Rd 8th Fl, Ridgefield Park, NJ 07660
Tel.: (646) 201-5242
MN
Web Site: https://www.lifequestcorp.com
LQWC—(OTCIQ)
Sewage Treatment Facilities
N.A.I.C.S.: 221320
Max Khan (Pres & CEO)

Subsidiaries:

Abrimix (Pty) Ltd. (1)
Unit 30 22 Elsecar Street, Kya Sand Industrial Village, Johannesburg, South Africa
Tel.: (27) 114637244
Web Site: http://www.abrimix.co.za
Waste Treatment Services
N.A.I.C.S.: 221310

LIFESTANCE HEALTH GROUP, INC.
4800 N Scottsdale Rd Ste 2300, Scottsdale, AZ 85251
Tel.: (602) 767-2100
DE
Web Site: https://www.lifestance.com
Year Founded: 2021
LFST—(NASDAQ)
Rev.: $859,542,000
Assets: $2,173,871,000
Liabilities: $655,148,000
Net Worth: $1,518,723,000
Earnings: ($215,564,000)
Emp.: 7,830
Fiscal Year-end: 12/31/22
Holding Company
N.A.I.C.S.: 551112
David Bourdon (CFO & Treas)
Ryan Pardo (Chief Legal Officer & Sec)
Pablo Pantaleoni (Chief Digital Officer)
Anisha Patel-Dunn (Trustee & Chief Medical Officer)

Ujjwal Ramtekkar (Chief Medical Officer)
Ann Varanakis (Chief People Officer)
Kenneth A. Burdick (Chm & CEO)

LIFESTORE FINANCIAL GROUP
21 E Ashe St, West Jefferson, NC 28694
Tel.: (336) 246-4344
NC
Web Site: http://www.golifestore.com
Year Founded: 1939
LSFG—(OTCIQ)
Rev.: $22,383,000
Assets: $347,201,000
Liabilities: $311,322,000
Net Worth: $35,879,000
Earnings: $4,173,000
Emp.: 117
Fiscal Year-end: 06/30/20
Bank Holding Company
N.A.I.C.S.: 551111
Robert E. Washburn (Pres & CEO)
Melanie Paisley Miller (CFO, Sec & Exec VP)

LIFESTYLE MEDICAL NETWORK INC.
121 S Orange Ave Ste 1500, Orlando, FL 32801
Tel.: (407) 514-1260
NV
LMNK—(OTCIQ)
Sales Range: $1-9.9 Million
Emp.: 1
Investment Services
N.A.I.C.S.: 523999
Christopher P. Smith (Pres, CEO & CFO)
Adam Sachs (Sec)

LIFETIME BRANDS, INC.
1000 Stewart Ave, Garden City, NY 11530
Tel.: (516) 683-6000
DE
Web Site: https://www.lifetimebrands.com
Year Founded: 1983
LCUT—(NASDAQ)
Rev.: $727,662,000
Assets: $725,888,000
Liabilities: $485,800,000
Net Worth: $240,088,000
Earnings: ($6,166,000)
Emp.: 1,260
Fiscal Year-end: 12/31/22
Household Cutlery, Kitchenware, Cutting Board, Pantryware & Bakeware Designer, Marketer & Distr
N.A.I.C.S.: 332215
Robert Bruce Kay (CEO)
Daniel T. Siegel (Pres)

Subsidiaries:

Can't Live Without It, LLC (1)
28 W 23rd St Fl 5, New York, NY 10010
Tel.: (844) 607-9355
Web Site: http://www.swellbottle.com
Sales Range: $75-99.9 Million
Emp.: 75
Bottle Mfr & Distr
N.A.I.C.S.: 332439
Sarah Kauss (Founder & CEO)

Creative Tops Limited (1)
The Hub Nobel Way, Birmingham, B6 7EU, United Kingdom
Tel.: (44) 1216041111
Kitchen Utensil Pot & Pan Mfr
N.A.I.C.S.: 332215
Katrinea Lawton (Mktg Mgr-Europe)

Empire Silver Co., Inc. (1)
6520 New Utrecht Ave, Brooklyn, NY 11219
Tel.: (718) 232-3389
Sales Range: $1-9.9 Million
Emp.: 50
Silverware & Hollowware Mfr
N.A.I.C.S.: 339910
Dennis Otranto (Pres)

Fitz & Floyd, Inc. (1)
22 Blake St, Medford, MA 02155
Web Site: http://www.fitzandfloyd.com
Gifts, Dinnerware & Collectibles Mfr & Distr
N.A.I.C.S.: 424990

La Cafetiere (UK) Limited (1)
Coast Road Greenfield, Holywell, CH8 9DP, Flintshire, United Kingdom
Tel.: (44) 1352717555
Web Site: http://www.lacafetiere.com
Kitchenware & Tableware Distr
N.A.I.C.S.: 321999

Lifetime Brands Global Limited (1)
38th Floor 9 Wing Hong Street, Lai Chi Kok, Hong Kong, China (Hong Kong)
Tel.: (852) 35650107
Home Furnishings Services
N.A.I.C.S.: 449129

Lifetime Brands Global Trading (Shanghai) Company Limited (1)
Shanghai Company Limited 8f No 40 East Tower, City Of Elit No 1888 Xinjinqiao Rd Pudong, Shanghai, China
Tel.: (86) 862151088765
Kitchenware & Tableware Distr
N.A.I.C.S.: 321999

Lifetime Brands, Inc. - BUILT Division (1)
41 Madison Ave, New York, NY 10010
Tel.: (212) 227-2044
Web Site: http://www.builtny.com
Sales Range: $10-24.9 Million
Emp.: 45
Neoprene Bag & Case Mfr
N.A.I.C.S.: 423990

Taylor Precision Products, Inc. (1)
2311 W 22nd St Ste 200, Oak Brook, IL 60523-1246
Web Site: http://www.taylorusa.com
Measuring Scales & Thermometers Mfr
N.A.I.C.S.: 334519

Plant (Domestic):

Taylor Precision Products, Inc. - Las Cruces (2)
2220 Entrada Del Sol, Las Cruces, NM 88001-3971
Tel.: (575) 526-0944
Web Site: http://www.taylorusa.com
Mfr of Scales & Balances
N.A.I.C.S.: 334519
Ajit Shanbhag (Dir-Ops)

Thomas Plant (Birmingham) Limited (1)
Plumbob House Valepits Road Garretts Green, Birmingham, B33 0TD, United Kingdom
Tel.: (44) 1216046000
Web Site: http://www.kitchencraft.co.uk
Sales Range: $50-74.9 Million
Emp.: 75
Kitchenware Mfr
N.A.I.C.S.: 332215

Wilton Armetale Inc. (1)
Plumb & Square St, Mount Joy, PA 17552 (100%)
Tel.: (717) 653-4444
Web Site: http://www.armetale.com
Emp.: 100
Mfr of Metal, Grillware & Glassware Products
N.A.I.C.S.: 332312

LIFEVANTAGE CORPORATION
3300 N Triumph Blvd Ste 700, Lehi, UT 84043
Tel.: (801) 432-9000
CO
Web Site: https://www.lifevantage.com
LFVN—(NASDAQ)
Rev.: $200,164,000
Assets: $60,299,000
Liabilities: $34,308,000
Net Worth: $25,991,000
Earnings: $2,937,000
Emp.: 217
Fiscal Year-end: 06/30/24
Nutritional Supplements Mfr
N.A.I.C.S.: 325412

Michelle Oborn (Sr VP-HR)
Eric Marchant (VP-Compliance)
Steven R. Fife (Pres & CEO)
Raymond B. Greer (Chm)
Kristen Cunningham (Chief Sls Officer)
Alissa Neufeld (Gen Counsel & Sec)
Garry M. Mauro (Executives)
Rob Harris (Chief Digital Officer)
Julie Boyster (CMO)

Subsidiaries:

Dinng Creative, Inc. (1)
48 W Market St Ste 220, Salt Lake City, UT 84101
Tel.: (801) 432-9181
Web Site: http://www.dinng.com
Hospitality & Dining Management Services
N.A.I.C.S.: 722511
Ryan Goodwin (Creative Dir)
Stephen Chai (Dir-Design)
Jacey Bills (Acct Mgr)
Adaline Strong (Project Mgr)

LifeVantage Canada Ltd. (1)
1959 Upper Water Street Suite 900, Halifax, B3J 3N2, NS, Canada
Web Site: https://www.lifevantage.com
Nutrition Product Distr
N.A.I.C.S.: 424490

LifeVantage Hong Kong Limited (1)
22/F Empress Plaza 17-19 Chatham Road South, Tsim Sha Tsui, Kowloon, China (Hong Kong)
Tel.: (852) 69772993
Web Site: https://www.lifevantage.com
Nutrition Product Distr
N.A.I.C.S.: 424490

LifeVantage Thailand Company Limited (1)
33/4 The Nine Tower Grand Pharam 9 Floors 14, Room TNB01-03 Pharam 9 Road Huay-Khwang District, Bangkok, 10310, Thailand
Tel.: (66) 20181999
Web Site: https://www.lifevantage.com
Nutrition Product Distr
N.A.I.C.S.: 424490

LIFEWAY FOODS, INC.
6431 W Oakton St, Morton Grove, IL 60053
Tel.: (847) 967-1010
IL
Web Site: https://lifewaykefir.com
Year Founded: 1986
LWAY—(NASDAQ)
Rev.: $141,568,000
Assets: $68,999,000
Liabilities: $21,429,000
Net Worth: $47,570,000
Earnings: $924,000
Emp.: 289
Fiscal Year-end: 12/31/22
Specialty Dairy Products Mfr
N.A.I.C.S.: 112120
Julie Smolyansky (Pres & CEO)
Eric A. Hanson (Chief Acctg Officer & Treas)
Amy Feldman (Sr Exec VP-Sls)

Subsidiaries:

Fresh Made, Inc. (1)
810-20 Bleigh Ave, Philadelphia, PA 19111-3016
Tel.: (215) 725-9013
Web Site: https://www.freshmadedairy.com
Dairy Products Mfr
N.A.I.C.S.: 424490

GlenOaks Farms, Inc. (1)
1100 S Coast Hwy Ste 317, Laguna Beach, CA 92651-2971
Tel.: (949) 497-5400
Web Site: http://www.glenoaksyogurt.com
Yogurt Products Mfr & Distr
N.A.I.C.S.: 445298
Neil B. Donavan (Pres)

The Lifeway Kefir Shop (1)
1745 W Division St, Chicago, IL 60622
Tel.: (773) 395-9300
Web Site: http://www.lifewaykefirshop.com

Lifeway Foods, Inc.—(Continued)
Dairy Products Mfr
N.A.I.C.S.: 424490

LIG ASSETS, INC.
118 3rd Ave S No 4-164, Nashville,
TN 37203
Tel.: (615) 394-0890   NV
Web Site:
  http://www.leadingreenassets.com
LIGA—(OTCIQ)
Rev.: $4,198,000
Assets: $2,385,000
Liabilities: $2,973,000
Net Worth: ($588,000)
Earnings: ($218,000)
Fiscal Year-end: 12/31/19
Real Estate Investment Services
N.A.I.C.S.: 525990
Marvin Baker (Pres)
Alan Gillis (CEO)

LIGAND PHARMACEUTICALS INCORPORATED
3911 Sorrento Vly Blvd Ste 110, San
Diego, CA 92121
Tel.: (858) 550-7500   DE
Web Site: https://www.ligand.com
Year Founded: 1987
LGND—(NASDAQ)
Rev.: $196,245,000
Assets: $762,668,000
Liabilities: $165,183,000
Net Worth: $597,485,000
Earnings: ($33,361,000)
Emp.: 76
Fiscal Year-end: 12/31/22
Pharmaceutical Developer & Mfr
N.A.I.C.S.: 325412
James Pipkin (VP-New Product Dev-
Captisol)
Keith Marschke (Sr VP-Biology & Sci-
entific Affairs-Res)
Vince Antle (Sr VP-Technical Ops &
Quality Assurance-Captisol)
Octavio Espinoza (CFO)
Andrew Reardon (Chief Legal Officer)
Todd C. Davis (CEO)
John W. Kozarich (Chm)

Subsidiaries:

Crystal   (1)
1850 Atlanta Ave, Riverside, CA 92507
Tel.: (951) 779-9300
Crystal Door & Window Mfr
N.A.I.C.S.: 327215

Crystal Bioscience, Inc.   (1)
5980 Horton St Ste 405, Emeryville, CA
94608
Tel.: (510) 250-7800
Web Site: http://www.crystalbioscience.com
Chemicals Mfr
N.A.I.C.S.: 325414
Rob Etches (Founder)

CyDex Pharmaceuticals, Inc.   (1)
10513 W 84th Ter, Lenexa, KS
66214   (100%)
Tel.: (913) 685-8850
Web Site: http://www.cydexpharma.com
Sales Range: $10-24.9 Million
Emp.: 27
Drug Delivery Technology Developer
N.A.I.C.S.: 325412

Pelican Expression Technology   (1)
10790 Roselle St, San Diego, CA 92121
Tel.: (858) 352-4400
Web Site:
  https://www.pelicanexpression.com
Biotechnology Mfr, Developer & Researcher
N.A.I.C.S.: 325414

Vernalis plc   (1)
100 Berkshire Place Wharfedale Road,
Winnersh, RG41 5RD, United Kingdom
Tel.: (44) 1189380000
Web Site: http://www.vernalis.com
Pharmaceuticals Mfr
N.A.I.C.S.: 325412

Subsidiary (Domestic):

Cita NeuroPharmaceuticals Inc   (2)
Oakdene Court, 613 Reading Road, Win-
nersh, RG41 5UA, Berkshire, United King-
dom
Tel.: (44) 1189773133
Pharmaceuticals Mfr
N.A.I.C.S.: 325412

Vernalis (R&D) Ltd   (2)
Granta Park, Great Abington, Cambridge,
CB21 6GB, Berkshire, United Kingdom
Tel.: (44) 1223895555
Web Site: http://www.vernalis.com
Pharmaceuticals Mfr
N.A.I.C.S.: 325412
Mike Wood (Mng Dir)

Vernalis Development Limited   (2)
Granta Park Great Abington, Cambridge,
CB21 6GB, United Kingdom
Tel.: (44) 1223895555
Web Site: http://www.vernalis.com
Pharmaceuticals Mfr
N.A.I.C.S.: 325412

LIGATT SECURITY INTERNATIONAL, INC.
6050 Peachtree Pkwy Ste 240 147,
Norcross, GA 30092   CA
Year Founded: 2003
LGTT—(OTCIQ)
Information Technology Services
N.A.I.C.S.: 541519
Gregory Evans (Chm & Pres)

LIGHT & WONDER, INC.
6601 Bermuda Rd, Las Vegas, NV
89119
Tel.: (702) 532-7700   NV
Web Site: https://www.lnw.com
Year Founded: 1973
LNW—(NASDAQ)
Rev.: $2,512,000,000
Assets: $6,009,000,000
Liabilities: $4,848,000,000
Net Worth: $1,161,000,000
Earnings: $3,675,000,000
Emp.: 6,100
Fiscal Year-end: 12/31/22
Computerized Wagering Systems Mfr
& Retailer for Horse & Greyhound
Racetracks, Jai Alai Frontons & Off-
Track Wagering Facilities
N.A.I.C.S.: 541511
Jordan E. Levin (CEO-Digital-Grp &
Exec VP)
Oliver Chow (CFO, Treas & Exec VP)
Andy Fouche (VP-Corp Comm)
Nick Zangari (Sr VP-IR)
James Sottile (Chief Legal Officer &
Exec VP)
Vanja Kalabic (Chief Acctg Officer, Sr
VP & Controller)
Roxane Lukas (Chief People Capabil-
ity Officer)
Victor Blanco (CTO & Exec VP)
Rich Schneider (Chief Product Officer
& Exec VP)
Jamie R. Odell (Chm)
Matthew Wilson (Pres & CEO)
Antonia Korsanos (Vice Chm)

Subsidiaries:

Bally Technologies Australia Holdings
I Pty Ltd   (1)
1 Sheridan Close, Milperra, 2214, NSW,
Australia
Tel.: (61) 297730299
Holding Company
N.A.I.C.S.: 551112

Bally Technologies, Inc.   (1)
6601 S Bermuda Rd, Las Vegas, NV 89119
Tel.: (702) 532-7700
Web Site: http://www.sggaming.com
Casino Game Machines Designer, Mfr &
Whslr
N.A.I.C.S.: 334118
Shiv Shankar (Dir-Tech)

Subsidiary (Non-US):

Bally Technologies India Private
Limited   (2)
Unit 1 4 11th Floor Crest Building Interna-
tional Tech Park, Taramani CSIR Road,
Chennai, 600 113, India
Tel.: (91) 44 4221 2000
Web Site: http://ballytech.com
Gambling Equipment Technology Services
N.A.I.C.S.: 713290

Subsidiary (Domestic):

NYX Gaming Group LLC   (2)
400 S Rampart Blvd Ste 220, Las Vegas,
NV 89145
Tel.: (702) 586-8428
Web Site: http://www.sgdigital.com
Gaming Software
N.A.I.C.S.: 513210

Barcrest Group Ltd.   (1)
Margaret Street, Ashton under Lyne, OL7
0QQ, Lancashire, United Kingdom (100%)
Tel.: (44) 16834100
Web Site: http://www.barcrest.com
Sales Range: $50-74.9 Million
Emp.: 400
Mfr & Retailer of Gaming Content & Ma-
chines; Online Gaming Services
N.A.I.C.S.: 334118

Betdigital Ltd.   (1)
Unit 3B Radley Place, Oxfordshire, Abing-
don, OX14 3RY, United Kingdom
Tel.: (44) 1235797228
Web Site: https://www.betdigital.net
Software Development Services
N.A.I.C.S.: 541511

Cryptologic Inc.   (1)
5 Hazelton Avenue Suite 300, Toronto, M5R
2E1, ON, Canada
Tel.: (647) 715-3707
Web Site: http://www.cryptologic.com
Fiscal Year-end: 12/31/2005
Cryptocurrency Mining Services
N.A.I.C.S.: 518210
John Kennedy FitzGerald (Pres & CEO)
Jordan Greenberg (CFO)
Paul Leggett (COO)
Dale Johnson (Chm)

Don Best Sports Corporation   (1)
3120 S Durango Dr Ste 305, Las Vegas,
NV 89117
Tel.: (702) 579-7900
Web Site: https://www.donbest.com
Online Sports Betting & Gaming Services
N.A.I.C.S.: 713290

Dragonplay Ltd   (1)
19 Toshia St, Tel Aviv, 67218, Israel
Tel.: (972) 775592178
Web Site: http://www.dragonplay.com
Game Design & Creating Services
N.A.I.C.S.: 541512

Global Draw Limited   (1)
1 Dukes Green Avenue, Feltham, TW14
0LR, United Kingdom
Tel.: (44) 2085806000
Web Site: http://www.theglobaldraw.com
Sales Range: $50-74.9 Million
Emp.: 300
Server Based Gaming Machines Provider
N.A.I.C.S.: 339999
Phil Horne (CEO-SG Gaming)
Lee Morton (Dir-Comml Ops)
Justin Raymond (Dir-Field Ops)
Gareth Phillips (Mng Dir-Intl)

Lapis Software Associates LLC   (1)
Ste 1000 935 Jefferson Blvd, Warwick, RI
02886-2263
Tel.: (973) 884-4006
Web Site: http://www.lapis.com
Software Development Services
N.A.I.C.S.: 513210
Jean Lombard (Pres)

MDI Entertainment LLC   (1)
1500 Bluegrass Lakes Pkwy, Alpharetta,
GA 30004   (100%)
Tel.: (770) 664-3700
Web Site: http://www.scientificgames.com
Sales Range: $10-24.9 Million
Emp.: 22
Marketer of State Lottery Games

N.A.I.C.S.: 541512

Regal Amusement Machine Sales
Ltd.   (1)
139 Brookfield Place Walton Summit, Bam-
ber Bridge, Preston, PR5 8BF, United King-
dom
Tel.: (44) 1772694242
Web Site: https://www.regalgaming.co.uk
Emp.: 450
Amusement Machine Operator
N.A.I.C.S.: 713120
Andrew Bell (Mng Dir-Fin)
Matthew Bicknell (Mng Dir-Ops)
Stephen Palin (Dir-IT)
Richard Briggs (Acct Dir)
John Silkstone (Dir-Svc)
Roger Lawton (Mgr-Natl Svc)
Debbie O'Sullivan (Mgr-Natl Collections)
Carla Jackson (Mgr-Logistics)
Julie Hinds (Mgr-Data Input)
Claire Sawyer (Mgr-Customer Admin)

SG Gaming Asia Limited   (1)
Unit B 1/f Cam Office Toweravenida Wai
Longtaipamacau, Macau, China (Macau)
Tel.: (853) 28722539
Software Development Services
N.A.I.C.S.: 541511

SG Gaming Australia Holdings I Pty
Ltd   (1)
4 Newington Road Silverwater, Sydney,
2128, NSW, Australia
Tel.: (61) 287076300
Software Development Services
N.A.I.C.S.: 541511

SG Gaming UK Limited   (1)
SG House 1 Howarth Court Gateway Cres-
cent, Oldham, OL9 9XB, United Kingdom
Tel.: (44) 1616834100
Software Development Services
N.A.I.C.S.: 513210

SHFL entertainment (Argentina)
S.R.L.   (1)
Av Sucre 2425, PB 1, San Isidro, Buenos
Aires, B1643AQF, Argentina
Tel.: (54) 1143173200
Game Design & Creating Services
N.A.I.C.S.: 541512

SciPlay Corporation   (1)
6601 Bermuda Rd, Las Vegas, NV 89119
Tel.: (702) 897-7150
Web Site: https://www.sciplay.com
Rev.: $671,000,000
Assets: $765,700,000
Liabilities: $150,100,000
Net Worth: $615,600,000
Earnings: $22,400,000
Emp.: 855
Fiscal Year-end: 12/31/2022
Software Development Services
N.A.I.C.S.: 541511

Scientific Games (China) Company
Limited   (1)
West Building 4 No 28 Jinghai Second
Road, Beijing Economic and Technolog,
Beijing, 100176, China
Tel.: (86) 1085797199
Web Site: http://www.scientificgames.com
Emp.: 30
Lottery Systems & Games Operator
N.A.I.C.S.: 713290

Scientific Games Deutschland
GmbH   (1)
Albert Einstein Ring 17, Hamburg, 22761,
Germany
Tel.: (49) 40898020
Sales Range: $10-24.9 Million
Emp.: 20
Gaming Software Developer
N.A.I.C.S.: 513210
Christian Kometer (Mng Dir)

Scientific Games Germany
GmbH   (1)
Max-Stromeyer-Str 116, 78467, Konstanz,
Germany
Tel.: (49) 7531942260
Lottery Systems & Games Operator
N.A.I.C.S.: 713290

Scientific Games Holdings (Canada)
ULC   (1)
3000 Boul De L'assomption, Montreal, H1N

3V5, QC, Canada
Tel.: (514) 254-3000
Web Site: https://www.scientificgames.com
Sales Range: $100-124.9 Million
Emp.: 300
Investment Management Services & Gaming Solutions
N.A.I.C.S.: 523940
Raymond Goudreault *(Gen Mgr)*

Scientific Games International **(1)**
1500 Bluegrass Lakes Pkwy, Alpharetta, GA 30004-7712
Tel.: (770) 664-3700
Web Site: https://www.scientificgames.com
Sales Range: $450-499.9 Million
Emp.: 1,200
Provider of Lottery Products, Services & Systems
N.A.I.C.S.: 323111

Scientific Games Kft. **(1)**
Fo utca 14-18 5 em, 1011, Budapest, Hungary
Tel.: (36) 13464300
Game Design & Creating Services
N.A.I.C.S.: 541512
Sandor Kopanyi *(Sr Engr-Software Dev)*

Scientific Games Lottery Services KFT **(1)**
Pala House 5th floor, Fo u14, Budapest, 1011, Hungary
Tel.: (36) 13464300
Web Site: http://www.scientificgames.se
Sales Range: $10-24.9 Million
Emp.: 100
Gaming Software Developer
N.A.I.C.S.: 513210

Scientific Games New Jersey, LLC **(1)**
6601 S Bermuda Rd, Las Vegas, NV 89119
Tel.: (702) 532-7700
Game Design & Creating Services
N.A.I.C.S.: 541512

Scientific Games Puerto Rico, LLC **(1)**
255 Canals St, San Juan, PR 00907
Tel.: (787) 725-7777
Lottery Products & Game Desigs Printing Services
N.A.I.C.S.: 323111
James Bunsitky *(VP-Finance)*

Scientific Games Sweden AB **(1)**
Hammarby Kajvag 18, Stockholm, 120 06, Sweden
Tel.: (46) 87025700
Sales Range: $75-99.9 Million
Emp.: 12
Gaming Software Developer
N.A.I.C.S.: 513210

Scientific Games Worldwide Limited **(1)**
Athlone Road, Ballymahon, Longford, N39 AX63, Ireland
Tel.: (353) 906432666
Web Site: http://www.scientificgames.com
Sales Range: $25-49.9 Million
Emp.: 50
Lottery Systems & Racing Games Operator
N.A.I.C.S.: 713290
James Gilmore *(Mng Dir)*

Stargames Australia Pty Limited **(1)**
2 Wiblen St, Silverwater, 2128, NSW, Australia
Tel.: (61) 297481177
Emp.: 30
Holding Company
N.A.I.C.S.: 551112

WMS Industries Inc. **(1)**
800 S Northpoint Blvd, Waukegan, IL 60085
Tel.: (847) 785-3000
Web Site: http://www.wms.com
Rev.: $697,300,000
Assets: $1,224,600,000
Liabilities: $295,600,000
Net Worth: $929,000,000
Earnings: $34,600,000
Emp.: 1,894
Fiscal Year-end: 06/30/2013
Holding Company; Commercial Videogames & Video Lottery Terminals Designer, Mfr & Distr
N.A.I.C.S.: 334118

Subsidiary (Non-US):

Jadestone Group AB **(2)**
Ostgotagatan 16, 116 25, Stockholm, Sweden
Tel.: (46) 8240501
Web Site: http://www.jadestone.se
Sales Range: $1-9.9 Million
Emp.: 45
Internet Gaming Software Developer
N.A.I.C.S.: 513210

Subsidiary (Domestic):

Phantom EFX, LLC **(2)**
900 Technology Pkwy Ste 300, Cedar Falls, IA 50613-3101
Tel.: (319) 266-3656
Web Site: http://www.phantomefx.com
Game Development Services
N.A.I.C.S.: 513210

Subsidiary (Non-US):

WMS Gaming Inc. **(2)**
(100%)
Tel.: (773) 961-1620
Sales Range: $150-199.9 Million
Emp.: 800
Commercial Videogames & Video Lottery Terminals Designer, Mfr & Distr
N.A.I.C.S.: 333310

Subsidiary (Non-US):

WMS Gaming Africa (Pty) Ltd. **(3)**
Tel.: (27) 115422760
Web Site: http://www.wms.com
Sales Range: $25-49.9 Million
Retailer & Servicer of Coin-Operated Amusement Games & Video Lottery Terminals
N.A.I.C.S.: 713120

WMS Gaming Australia PTY Ltd. **(3)**
Tel.: (61) 292118920
Sales Range: $10-24.9 Million
Emp.: 55
Retailer & Servicer of Coin-Operated Amusement Games & Video Lottery Terminals
N.A.I.C.S.: 713120

WMS Gaming International, S.L. **(3)**
Tel.: (34) 935948720
Sales Range: $10-24.9 Million
Emp.: 35
Retailer & Servicer of Coin-Operated Amusement Games & Video Lottery Terminals
N.A.I.C.S.: 713120

WMS Gaming Mexico, S. de R.L. de C.V. **(3)**
Tel.: (52) 5552913837
Electronic & Digital Gaming Entertainment & Gaming Machines Mfr & Distr
N.A.I.C.S.: 713120

WMS Gaming Services Europe, S.L. **(3)**
Tel.: (34) 935948720
Web Site: http://www.wms.com
Sales Range: $25-49.9 Million
Emp.: 50
Electronic & Digital Gaming Entertainment & Gaming Machines Mfr & Distr
N.A.I.C.S.: 713120

Subsidiary (Non-US):

WMS International (Macau) Limited **(2)**
No 235-287 Alameda Dr Carlos d Assumpcao, Macau, China (Macau)
Tel.: (853) 28575235
Web Site: http://www.wms.com
Sales Range: $25-49.9 Million
Emp.: 6
Electronic & Digital Gaming Machines Mfr & Distr
N.A.I.C.S.: 423920

Subsidiary (Domestic):

Williams Interactive LLC **(2)**
15 Laurel Crest Dr, Burlington, CT 06013
Tel.: (860) 930-4893
Web Site: https://www.kevinmwilliams.com
Emp.: 2
Marketing Consulting Services

N.A.I.C.S.: 541613

LIGHT ENGINE DESIGN CORP.
8180 E Shea Blvd Ste 1033, Scottsdale, AZ 85260
Web Site: http://www.ledesigncorp.com
TLED—(OTCIQ)
Rev.: $40,000
Assets: $1,820,000
Liabilities: $876,000
Net Worth: $944,000
Earnings: ($187,000)
Emp.: 6
Fiscal Year-end: 12/31/19
Lighting Product Mfr
N.A.I.C.S.: 335132
Paul O. Williams *(Chm & CFO)*

LIGHT MEDIA HOLDINGS, INC.
2365 Wall St, Conyers, GA 30013
Tel.: (404) 585-8267   DE
Year Founded: 2006
LGMH—(OTCIQ)
Rev.: $1,000
Assets: $169,000
Liabilities: $67,000
Net Worth: $102,000
Earnings: ($16,000)
Fiscal Year-end: 12/31/19
Online Shopping Retailer
N.A.I.C.S.: 519290
Deirdre Phillips *(CFO)*
Danny Wilson *(CEO)*

LIGHTBRIDGE CORPORATION
11710 Plz Dr Ste 2000, Reston, VA 20190
Tel.: (571) 730-1200   NV
Web Site: https://www.ltbridge.com
Year Founded: 1999
LTBR—(NASDAQ)
Rev.: $289,435
Assets: $29,468,486
Liabilities: $350,331
Net Worth: $29,118,155
Earnings: ($7,497,857)
Emp.: 5
Fiscal Year-end: 12/31/22
Nuclear Power Generation & Nuclear Advisory Services
N.A.I.C.S.: 221113
Seth Grae *(Pres & CEO)*
Andrey Mushakov *(Exec VP-Nuclear Ops)*
James D. Fornof *(VP-Nuclear Program Mgmt)*
Sherrie Holloway *(Mgr-Acctg)*
Darla M. Bond *(Mgr-HR)*
Larry Goldman *(CFO, Treas & Sec)*

LIGHTHOUSE GLOBAL HOLDINGS, INC.
4100 W. Flamingo Rd. 1488, Las Vegas, NV 89103
Tel.: (725) 999-5888   NV
Web Site: http://www.lhgincorp.com
LHGI—(OTCIQ)
Real Estate Manangement Services
N.A.I.C.S.: 531390
Danny Lim *(Chm & CEO)*

LIGHTNING EMOTORS, INC.
815 14th St SW Ste A100, Loveland, CO 80537   DE
Web Site: https://lightningemotors.com
Year Founded: 2020
ZEV—(NYSE)
Rev.: $24,413,000
Assets: $143,559,000
Liabilities: $89,001,000
Net Worth: $54,558,000
Earnings: $15,170,000
Emp.: 268
Fiscal Year-end: 12/31/22

Other Motor Vehicle Parts Manufacturing
N.A.I.C.S.: 336390

LIGHTPATH TECHNOLOGIES, INC.
2603 Challenger Tech Ct Ste 100, Orlando, FL 32826
Tel.: (407) 382-4003   DE
Web Site: https://www.lightpath.com
Year Founded: 1992
LPTH—(NASDAQ)
Rev.: $31,726,192
Assets: $48,086,964
Liabilities: $17,887,299
Net Worth: $30,199,665
Earnings: ($8,007,346)
Emp.: 304
Fiscal Year-end: 06/30/24
Optoelectronics Products Mfr
N.A.I.C.S.: 334413
Shmuel Rubin *(Pres & CEO)*
Mark Palvino *(VP-Mktg & Sls-Global)*
Albert Miranda *(CFO)*
Peter Greif *(VP-Operations)*
M. Scott Faris *(Chm)*

Subsidiaries:

ISP Optics Corp. **(1)**
2603 Challenger Tech Ct, Orlando, FL 32826 **(100%)**
Tel.: (914) 591-3070
Optical Instruments & Lenses Mfr
N.A.I.C.S.: 333310
Shmuel Rubin *(CEO)*
Joseph Menaker *(Founder & Pres)*

ISP Optics Latvia, SIA **(1)**
24A Ganibu Dambis Street, Riga, Latvia
Tel.: (371) 67323779
Optical Lens Machinery Mfr
N.A.I.C.S.: 333248

LIGHTWAVE LOGIC, INC.
369 Inverness Pkwy Ste 350, Englewood, CO 80112-6039
Tel.: (720) 340-4949   NV
Web Site: https://www.lightwavelogic.com
Year Founded: 1997
LWLG—(NASDAQ)
Rev.: $40,502
Assets: $41,783,585
Liabilities: $5,349,771
Net Worth: $36,433,814
Earnings: ($21,038,032)
Emp.: 33
Fiscal Year-end: 12/31/23
Electro-Optic Polymers
N.A.I.C.S.: 325998
James S. Marcelli *(Pres, COO & Sec)*
Michael S. Lebby *(CEO)*

LIMBACH HOLDINGS, INC.
797 Commonwealth Dr, Warrendale, PA 15086
Tel.: (412) 359-2100   DE
Web Site: https://www.limbachinc.com
Year Founded: 2014
LMB—(NASDAQ)
Rev.: $516,350,000
Assets: $304,439,000
Liabilities: $183,524,000
Net Worth: $120,915,000
Earnings: $20,754,000
Emp.: 400
Fiscal Year-end: 12/31/23
Investment Services
N.A.I.C.S.: 523999
Charles A. Bacon III *(Pres)*
Michael M. McCann *(CEO)*
Scott Wright *(Exec VP-Legal & Risk Mgmt)*
Jayme L. Brooks *(CFO & Exec VP)*
Melissa DiMuro *(Chief People, Culture & Mktg Officer)*

Limbach Holdings, Inc.—(Continued)

Shawan Murphy *(Pres-Limbach Engrg & Design Svcs)*
Christos Ruci *(CIO)*
Dominick Traina *(Exec VP-Shared Svcs)*
S. Matthew Katz *(Exec VP)*
Dennis Sacco Jr. *(Sr VP)*
Rob Sudz *(Dir)*
Dan Murtha *(Controller)*
Katie Mistry *(VP)*
Brent Sobieralski *(Dir)*
Ron Turner *(VP)*
Jody Reilly *(VP)*
Katie Massie *(Mktg Mgr)*
Andy Wiegand *(Mgr)*
Thom Brazel *(Mgr)*
David Strobino *(Mgr)*
Ian Switalski *(Mgr)*
Brian Groark *(Mgr)*
Tom Roche *(Mgr)*
Ron Wilburn *(Mgr)*
Erich Muensterman *(Mgr)*
Billy Brockenbrough *(Mgr)*
Holt Hamilton *(Mgr)*

Subsidiaries:

ACME Industrial Piping, LLC **(1)**
4301 Rossville Blvd, Chattanooga, TN 37407
Tel.: (423) 867-1001
Web Site: http://www.acmeindustrialpiping.com
Rev.: $8,350,000
Emp.: 50
Industrial Maintenance Services
N.A.I.C.S.: 541330

Consolidated Mechanical, Inc. **(1)**
3110 Fairview Dr, Owensboro, KY 42303
Tel.: (270) 685-0148
Web Site: https://www.conmechinc.com
Rev.: $7,500,000
Emp.: 10
Site Preparation Contractor
N.A.I.C.S.: 238910
Phillip Altman *(CFO)*
Michael Koger *(CEO)*

Industrial Air Inc. **(1)**
PO Box 8769, Greensboro, NC 27419-0769
Tel.: (336) 292-1030
Motor Vehicle Parts Mfr
N.A.I.C.S.: 336390
Allen Hunter *(Pres)*

Limbach Facility Services LLC **(1)**
31-35th St, Pittsburgh, PA 15201
Tel.: (412) 359-2100
Web Site: http://www.limbachinc.com
Sales Range: $350-399.9 Million
Emp.: 40
Plumbing, Heating & Air-Conditioning Contracting Services
N.A.I.C.S.: 238210

Subsidiary (Non-US):

Harper Limbach LLC **(2)**
Tel.: (407) 321-8100
Web Site: https://www.harperlimbach.com
Sales Range: $25-49.9 Million
Mechanical Contractor
N.A.I.C.S.: 238220
Nick Angerosa *(Pres)*
Holt Hamilton *(VP)*

Subsidiary (Domestic):

Limbach Company LLC **(2)**
822 Cleveland Ave, Columbus, OH 43201
Tel.: (614) 299-2175
Web Site: http://www.limbachinc.com
Construction Services
N.A.I.C.S.: 236220
Jay Sharp *(Pres)*

Limbach Engineering & Design Services (LEDS) **(2)**
5401 Benchmark Ln, Sanford, FL 32773-6433
Tel.: (407) 321-8100
Web Site: http://www.limbachinc.com
Rev.: $980,000
Emp.: 35

Engineeering Services
N.A.I.C.S.: 541330
Shawn Murphy *(Pres)*
Steve McClurg *(Sr Engr)*
Brian Graham *(Engr-Mechanical)*
Lumin Abraham *(Mgr-BIM Estimating)*
Richard Davis *(Mgr-Leap Program)*
Daniel Koehler *(Engr-Mechanical)*
Ron Turner *(VP & Dir-Branch Rels)*
Caton Cook *(Sr Engr-Mechanical)*
Craig Turner *(Sr Engr-Electrical)*
Eugene San Diego *(Engr-Construction Admin)*

LIMITLESS VENTURE GROUP, INC.
121 E 35th St, Tulsa, OK 74105
Tel.: (918) 671-9935
Web Site: http://www.lvginc.com
Year Founded: 2007
LVGI—(OTCIQ)
Health & Wellness Organic Product Mfr
N.A.I.C.S.: 325411
Joseph Francella *(Pres & CEO)*
Devon Diaz *(COO)*

LIMITLESS X HOLDINGS INC.
9454 Wilshire Blvd Ste 300, Beverly Hills, CA 90212
Tel.: (720) 273-0433 **DE**
Web Site: https://www.limitlessx.com
VYBE—(OTCQB)
Rev.: $58,688,296
Assets: $11,841,226
Liabilities: $18,893,962
Net Worth: ($7,052,736)
Earnings: ($10,024,006)
Emp.: 12
Fiscal Year-end: 12/31/22
Advertising Agencies
N.A.I.C.S.: 541810
W. Edward Nichols *(CEO)*
Darrell Avey *(CFO & VP)*

LIMONEIRA COMPANY
1141 Cummings Rd, Santa Paula, CA 93060
Tel.: (805) 525-5541 **DE**
Web Site: https://www.limoneira.com
Year Founded: 1893
LMNR—(NASDAQ)
Rev.: $179,901,000
Assets: $301,210,000
Liabilities: $111,523,000
Net Worth: $189,687,000
Earnings: $9,400,000
Emp.: 257
Fiscal Year-end: 10/31/23
Agribusiness, Real Estate, Energy & Resource Management Services
N.A.I.C.S.: 111998
Robert M. Sawyer *(Executives)*
John Carter *(VP-Sls)*
Mark Palamountain *(CFO & Treas)*
Susan Jones-Ng *(Dir-Bus Dev-Intl)*
John Caragliano *(Dir-Sls-Eastern)*
Rick Goodside *(Mgr-Domestic Sls-Ops)*
Stephen Sheldon *(Mgr)*
Maria Vargas *(Coord-Sls)*
Vince Giacolone *(Dir-Southern Farming)*
Stewart Lockwood *(Dir-Field Ops)*
Anthony Ecuyer *(VP-Packing Ops)*
Eric Tovias *(Dir-Information Sys)*
Greg Hamm *(VP & Controller)*
Kathleen Thompson *(Dir-Human Resources)*
Rosie Castillo *(Dir-Housing & Comml Ops)*
Ryan Nasalroad *(Mgr-Svc Ops)*
Tomas Gonzalez *(Dir-Global Food Safety & Compliance)*
Edgar Gutierrez *(VP-Farming Ops)*
Amy Fukutomi *(Sec & VP-Compliance)*
Brett Johnson *(Dir-Sls-Western)*

Jocelyn Hernandez *(Coord)*
Michael Gonzales *(Mktg Mgr)*
Michael Burn *(Mgr-Global)*
Dyson Schneider *(Dir)*
Debra Walker *(Dir-Human Resources)*
Kevin Poindexter *(Gen Mgr)*
John Chamberlain *(Mktg Dir)*
John Mills *(Mng Partner)*
Harold S. Edwards *(Pres & CEO)*

Subsidiaries:

Associated Citrus Packers, Inc. **(1)**
635 S Main St, Yuma, AZ 85364
Tel.: (928) 782-3794
Fruit Farming & Distr
N.A.I.C.S.: 111336

Limoneira International Division, LLC **(1)**
1141 Cummings Rd, Santa Paula, CA 93060
Tel.: (805) 525-5541
Credit Union Management Services
N.A.I.C.S.: 522130

Limoneira Lewis Community Builders, LLC **(1)**
1156 N Mountain Ave, Upland, CA 91786 **(50%)**
Tel.: (909) 270-4369
Web Site: http://www.harvestatlimoneira.com
Real Estate Services
N.A.I.C.S.: 531390

Rockville Enterprises LLC **(1)**
720 Harrington Rd, Rockville, MD 20852
Tel.: (202) 412-4787
Legal Consulting Services
N.A.I.C.S.: 541110

Templeton Santa Barbara, LLC **(1)**
1141 Cummings Rd, Santa Paula, CA 93060
Tel.: (805) 525-5541
Real Estate Management Services
N.A.I.C.S.: 531390

Windfall Investors, LLC **(1)**
895 Prairie St, Prairie Du Sac, WI 53578
Tel.: (608) 643-0521
Real Estate Energy & Resource Management Services
N.A.I.C.S.: 111998

LINCOLN EDUCATIONAL SERVICES CORPORATION
14 Sylvan Way Ste A, Parsippany, NJ 07054
Tel.: (973) 736-9340 **NJ**
Web Site: https://www.lincolntech.edu
Year Founded: 1946
LINC—(NASDAQ)
Rev.: $348,287,000
Assets: $291,566,000
Liabilities: $146,689,000
Net Worth: $144,877,000
Earnings: $12,634,000
Emp.: 1,688
Fiscal Year-end: 12/31/22
Career Education & Training Services
N.A.I.C.S.: 611699
Scott M. Shaw *(Pres & CEO)*
Alexandra M. Luster *(Gen Counsel, Soo & Sr VP)*
Brian K. Meyers *(CFO, Treas & Exec VP)*
Stephen Ace *(Sr VP-HR)*
Valerian J. Thomas *(CIO & Sr VP)*
Peter Tahinos *(Sr VP-Mktg)*
Chad Nyce *(Chief Innovation Officer)*
Susan English *(Sr VP)*
Francis S. Giglio *(Sr VP)*
James Rasmussen *(Sr VP)*

Subsidiaries:

Euphoria Acquisition, LLC **(1)**
9340 W Sahara Ave - Ste 205, Las Vegas, NV 89117
Tel.: (702) 341-8111

Web Site: http://www.euphoriainstitute-usa.com
Cosmetology Educational Services
N.A.I.C.S.: 611511

Lincoln College of Technology **(1)**
2410 Metrocentre Blvd, West Palm Beach, FL 33407 **(100%)**
Tel.: (561) 842-8324
Web Site: http://www.lincolnedu.com
Sales Range: $75-99.9 Million
Vocational Education
N.A.I.C.S.: 611210

NN Acquisition, LLC **(1)**
85 Sigourney St, Hartford, CT 06105
Tel.: (860) 560-0781
Educational Support Services
N.A.I.C.S.: 611699

LINCOLN ELECTRIC HOLDINGS, INC.
22801 St Clair Ave, Cleveland, OH 44117
Tel.: (216) 481-8100 **OH**
Web Site: http://www.lincolnelectric.com
Year Founded: 1895
LECO—(NASDAQ)
Rev.: $4,191,636,000
Assets: $3,377,297,000
Liabilities: $2,068,445,000
Net Worth: $1,308,852,000
Earnings: $545,248,000
Emp.: 12,000
Fiscal Year-end: 12/31/23
Electrodes & Welding Supplies Mfr; Flux Cored Wire & Solid Core Wire for Mig & Submerged Arc Welding
N.A.I.C.S.: 333992
Gabriel Bruno *(CFO, Principal Acctg Officer, Treas & Exec VP)*
Michele R. Kuhrt *(Chief Transformation Officer & Exec VP)*
Thomas A. Flohn *(Pres-Intl & Sr VP)*
Peter Pletcher *(Pres-Intl & Sr VP)*
Steven B. Hedlund *(Pres & CEO)*
Christopher L. Mapes *(Exec Chm)*
Jennifer I. Ansberry *(Gen Counsel, Sec & Exec VP)*
Geoffrey P. Allman *(Sr VP-Strategy & Bus Dev)*
Amanda Butler *(VP-IR & Comm)*
Michael J. Whitehead *(Pres-Automation, Cutting & Additive Bus-Global & Sr VP)*
Lisa A. Dietrich *(CIO)*

Subsidiaries:

Air Liquide Welding (Thailand) LTD **(1)**
Vorawat Building 14th floor Unit 1401-1402 849 Silom Road Bangrak, Bangkok, 10500, Thailand
Tel.: (66) 26351600
Emp.: 240
Industrial & Medical Gas Distr
N.A.I.C.S.: 424690

Air Liquide Welding Central Europe S.R.O. **(1)**
Prievozska 4/A, 821 09, Bratislava, Slovakia
Tel.: (421) 258101051
Industrial Gas Distr
N.A.I.C.S.: 424690
Hastislav Porubsky *(CFO & Country Mgr)*

Air Liquide Welding Luxembourg S.A. **(1)**
Zoning PED - BP4, 4801, Rodange, Luxembourg
Tel.: (352) 5062631
Industrial & Medical Gas Distr
N.A.I.C.S.: 424690

Air Liquide Welding Middle East FZE **(1)**
Plot No B34B02A Jebel Ali Free Zone Authority, PO Box 16848, Jebel Ali, United Arab Emirates
Tel.: (971) 48816001
Industrial & Medical Gas Distr
N.A.I.C.S.: 424690

Joji Samuel *(Head-Logistics)*

Air Liquide Welding Polska Spolka Zograniczona Odpowiedzialnoscia (1)
Ul Jasnogorska 9, 31-358, Krakow, Poland
Tel.: (48) 126279300
Natural Gas Distr
N.A.I.C.S.: 221210
Tomasz Juda *(Mgr-Production)*

Arc Products, Inc. (1)
4010 La Reunion Pkwy Ste 160, Dallas, TX 75212
Tel.: (214) 638-2468
Web Site: https://www.arcproductsinc.com
Chemical Product Merchant Whslr
N.A.I.C.S.: 424690
Bobby Viteaux *(Co-Owner & Pres)*
Sandra Melendez *(Mgr-Customer Svc)*
Michael Heath *(Co-Owner & CEO)*
Barbara Viteaux *(Gen Mgr)*

Baker Industries, Inc. (1)
16936 Enterprise Dr, Macomb, MI 48044
Tel.: (586) 286-4900
Web Site: http://www.bakerindustriesinc.com
Sales Range: $1-9.9 Million
Emp.: 19
Special Die & Tool, Die Set, Jig & Fixture Mfr
N.A.I.C.S.: 333514

Burlington Automation Corporation (1)
63 Innovation Drive, Hamilton, L9H 7L8, ON, Canada
Tel.: (905) 689-7771
Web Site: http://www.burlingtonautomation.com
Emp.: 50
CNC Metal Fabrication Machinery Mfr
N.A.I.C.S.: 333248

Coldwater Machine Company, LLC (1)
911 N 2nd St, Coldwater, OH 45828-8736
Tel.: (419) 678-4877
Web Site: http://www.coldwatermachine.com
Emp.: 75
Felxible Automation Integrator & Precision Machining & Assembly Mfr
N.A.I.C.S.: 333310

Easom Automation Systems, Inc. (1)
32471 Industrial Dr, Madison Heights, MI 48071
Tel.: (248) 307-0650
Web Site: http://www.easomeng.com
Emp.: 80
Automation System Design & Installation Services
N.A.I.C.S.: 333514

Electro-Arco S.A. (1)
Estrada Espanhois, Venda Alcaide, 2955-020, Pinhal Novo, Portugal
Tel.: (351) 210482374
Web Site: https://www.electro-arco.com.pt
Welding Equipment & Accessories Mfr
N.A.I.C.S.: 333992

Fori Automation LLC (1)
50955 Wing Dr, Shelby, MI 48315-8315
Tel.: (586) 247-2336
Web Site: http://www.foriauto.com
Machine Tools Mfr
N.A.I.C.S.: 333517
Marshall McMaster *(Gen Mgr-Ops-Oakville-Automodular Corp)*

Harris Calorific GmbH (1)
Beethovenstrasse 9, 88450, Berkheim, Germany
Tel.: (49) 8395912800
Web Site: http://eu.harrisproductsgroup.com
Gas Welding & Cutting Equipment Mfr
N.A.I.C.S.: 333992
Carlos Benseler *(Mgr-Austria & Switzerland Branch)*

Harris Calorific International Sp. z o.o. (1)
Ul Strefowa 8, 58-200, Dzierzoniow, Poland
Tel.: (48) 746462352
Welding Equipment Mfr
N.A.I.C.S.: 333992

Harris Calorific S.r.l. (1)
Via Ronco Maruni 34, 40068, San Lazzaro di Savena, Bologna, Italy
Tel.: (39) 0513766227
Welding Equipment Mfr
N.A.I.C.S.: 333992

Harris Euro S.L. (1)
C/ Arq Ricard Giralt s/n Nave 6, 17600, Figueres, Girona, Spain
Tel.: (34) 972678826
Sales Range: $10-24.9 Million
Emp.: 9
Welding Product Mfr
N.A.I.C.S.: 333992
Raul Guridi *(Gen Mgr)*

Harris Soldas Especiais S.A. (1)
Rua Rosa Kasinski 525, Sao Paulo Cap-uava, Maua, 09371-220, Brazil
Tel.: (55) 1149938111
Web Site: https://www.harrisproductsgroup.com
Sales Range: $25-49.9 Million
Emp.: 80
Nonferrous Product Mfr & Distr
N.A.I.C.S.: 331529

ISAF Drahtwerk GMBH (1)
Kiefernweg 4 Beetzsee Ot Brielow, 14778, Brandenburg, Germany
Tel.: (49) 3381715010
Welding Wire Whslr
N.A.I.C.S.: 423840

Inovatech Engineering Corporation (1)
101 Steve Fonyo Dr, PO Box 479, Vankleek Hill, Ottawa, K0B 1R0, ON, Canada
Tel.: (613) 809-3614
Web Site: http://inovatechengineering.com
Fabricated Structural Metal Mfr
N.A.I.C.S.: 332312

J.W. Harris Co., Inc. (1)
4501 Quality Pl, Mason, OH 45040-1971
Tel.: (513) 234-2000
Sales Range: $50-74.9 Million
Welding Equipment Whslr
N.A.I.C.S.: 423830

Kaynak Teknigi Sanayi ve Ticaret A.S. (1)
2 Cadde No 5 Sekerpinar, 41420, Cayirova, Kocaeli, Turkiye **(99.6%)**
Tel.: (90) 850 228 8288
Web Site: https://www.askaynak.com.tr
Emp.: 500
Welding Consumables Whslr
N.A.I.C.S.: 423830

Lincoln Canada Holdings ULC (1)
179 Wicksteed Avenue, Toronto, M4G 2B9, ON, Canada
Tel.: (416) 421-2600
Welding Consumables Mfr
N.A.I.C.S.: 333992
Adel Amir *(Pres)*

Lincoln Electric (Thailand) Ltd. (1)
25 Pandan Crescent Tic Tec Centre 06-13, Singapore, 128477, Singapore
Tel.: (65) 66855548376
Welding Product Mfr
N.A.I.C.S.: 333992
Wasu Sraubol *(Mng Dir)*

Lincoln Electric (U.K.) Ltd. (1)
Aston House Mansfield Road, Aston, Sheffield, S26 2BS, United Kingdom **(100%)**
Tel.: (44) 1142872401
Web Site: https://www.lincolnelectric.co.uk
Sales Range: $50-74.9 Million
Welding Equipment Mfr & Sales
N.A.I.C.S.: 333992

Lincoln Electric Bester Sp. z o.o. (1)
ul Jana III Sobieskiego 19A, 58-260, Bielawa, Poland
Tel.: (48) 746461000
Web Site: https://www.lincolnelectric.com
Welding Equipment Mfr
N.A.I.C.S.: 333992

Lincoln Electric CZ s.r.o. (1)
Pod brizkami 800, 530 02, Pardubice, Czech Republic
Tel.: (420) 466303210
Web Site: https://www.czweld.cz
Welding Product Mfr
N.A.I.C.S.: 333992

Lincoln Electric Company (India) Private Limited (1)
Plot No P40 Central Avenue Domestic Tariff Area Mahindra World City, Mahindra World City Post Office Kancheepuram District, Chengalpattu, 603 004, Tamil Nadu, India
Tel.: (91) 4447424999
Web Site: https://www.lincolnelectric.in
Sales Range: $25-49.9 Million
Emp.: 125
Welding Product Mfr
N.A.I.C.S.: 333992
S. Sundarram *(Mng Dir)*
Lajpat Yadav *(Gen Mgr-Sales-Marketing)*

Lincoln Electric Deutschland (1)
Christinenstrasse 2a, Ratingen, 40880, Germany
Tel.: (49) 2102713960
Web Site: http://de.lincolnelectric.com
Sales Range: $25-49.9 Million
Emp.: 30
Welding Products & Systems Mfr
N.A.I.C.S.: 333992

Lincoln Electric Europe B.V. (1)
Nieuwe Dukenburgseweg 20, PO Box 253, 6534 AD, Nijmegen, Netherlands
Tel.: (31) 248080328
Web Site: http://www.lincolnelectric.com
Sales Range: $25-49.9 Million
Emp.: 150
Welding Equipment Mfr
N.A.I.C.S.: 333992

Lincoln Electric Europe S.L. (1)
Balmes 89 - 8 2a, 08008, Barcelona, Spain
Tel.: (34) 93 492 20 00
Web Site: http://www.lincolnelectric.com
Welding Equipment Mfr & Sales
N.A.I.C.S.: 333992

Lincoln Electric France S.A.S. (1)
Avenue Franklin Roosevelt, PO Box 214, 76120, Le Grand-Quevilly, France **(100%)**
Tel.: (33) 255030551
Web Site: https://www.lincolnelectric.com
Sales Range: $50-74.9 Million
Welding Equipment Mfr & Sales
N.A.I.C.S.: 333992

Subsidiary (Non-US):

Lincoln Electric Belgium (2)
ZI West Grijpen, Grijpenlaan 5, Tienen, Belgium
Tel.: (32) 16804820
Web Site: http://www.oerlikon-welding.com
Design & Mfr of Welding Equipment
N.A.I.C.S.: 333992

Oerlikon Scandinavia AB (2)
Trans Fargo Starragen 100, 23261, Arlov, Sweden
Tel.: (46) 406701500
Web Site: http://www.oerlikon-welding.com
Design & Mfr of Welding Equipment
N.A.I.C.S.: 333992

Oerlikon Schweisstechnik AG (2)
Hauptstrasse 23, 5737, Menziken, Switzerland
Tel.: (41) 627718305
Web Site: https://www.iso-oerlikon.ch
Design & Mfr of Welding Equipment
N.A.I.C.S.: 333992

Oerlikon Schweisstechnik GmbH (2)
Industriestrasse 12, Pfalz, 67304, Eisenberg, Germany
Tel.: (49) 20143890932
Design & Mfr of Welding Equipment
N.A.I.C.S.: 333992

Oerlikon Soldadura SA (2)
Poligono Industrial La Noria Carretera de Castellon Km 15 500, 50730, Zaragoza, Spain
Tel.: (34) 976104700
Web Site: http://www.oerlikon-welding.com
Welding Machinery & Equipment Whslr
N.A.I.C.S.: 423830

Lincoln Electric Heli (Zhengzhou) Welding Materials Company Ltd. (1)
No 60 Dengfeng South Road, Shang Jie District, Zhengzhou, 450041, Henan, China
Tel.: (86) 37167316888
Web Site: http://www.lincolnelectric.com.cn
Welding Consumables Mfr
N.A.I.C.S.: 333992

Lincoln Electric Iberia, S.L. (1)
Crta Laurea Miro 396-398 P I El Pla, 08980, San Feliu de Llobregat, Spain
Tel.: (34) 936859643
Welding Consumables Mfr
N.A.I.C.S.: 333992

Lincoln Electric Italia S.r.l. (1)
Loc Casalmenini 3, Rivoli Veronese, 37010, Verona, Italy **(100%)**
Tel.: (39) 0458130232
Web Site: https://www.lincolnelectric.com
Sales Range: $25-49.9 Million
Emp.: 100
Sales of Arc Welding Machines & Electrodes
N.A.I.C.S.: 423830

Lincoln Electric Japan K.K. (1)
424-5 Nippacho, Kohoku Ward, Yokohama, 223-0057, Kanagawa, Japan **(100%)**
Tel.: (81) 458349651
Web Site: https://www.lincolnelectric.co.jp
Sales Range: $25-49.9 Million
Mfr of Ideal-Arc & Shield-Arc Welders; Fleetweld & Jetweld Electrodes & Welding Supplies; Flux Cored Wire & Solid Core Wire
N.A.I.C.S.: 333992

Lincoln Electric Luxembourg S.ar.l. (1)
41 Avenue de la Gare, 1611, Luxembourg, Luxembourg
Tel.: (352) 26203608
Welding Equipment Mfr
N.A.I.C.S.: 333992

Lincoln Electric Malaysia Sdn. Bhd. (1)
No 7F-3 7th Floor Tower 1 PFCC Jalan Puteri 1/2, Bandar Puteri, 47100, Puchong, Selangor, Malaysia
Tel.: (60) 380608638
Welding & Cutting Equipment Mfr
N.A.I.C.S.: 333992

Lincoln Electric Maquinas, S. de R.L. de C.V. (1)
Blvd San Pedro 80 Desarrollo Industrial Mieleras, Coahuila, 27400, Torreon, Mexico
Tel.: (52) 8717290900
Welding Equipment Mfr
N.A.I.C.S.: 333992

Lincoln Electric Mexicana S.A. de C.V. (1)
Calz Azcapotzalco La Villa No 869 Colonia Industrial Vallejo, Delegacion Azcapotzal, 02300, Mexico, Mexico **(100%)**
Tel.: (52) 55 50 630 030
Web Site: http://www.lincolnelectric.com
Sales Range: $100-124.9 Million
Mfr & Sales of Arc Welding & Electrodes
N.A.I.C.S.: 333992
Joaquin Guerra *(Mng Dir)*

Lincoln Electric Middle East FZE (1)
RA08 AA04 Jafza, PO Box 17117, Dubai, United Arab Emirates
Tel.: (971) 48833317
Welding Consumables Mfr
N.A.I.C.S.: 333992

Lincoln Electric Portugal, S.A. (1)
Rua Salgueiro Maia 29 RC Dto, Pinhal Novo, 2955-028, Portugal
Tel.: (351) 212387300
Welding Product Mfr
N.A.I.C.S.: 333992

Lincoln Electric S.A. (1)
Pje Father Montes Carballo 1651, C14071XC, Buenos Aires, Argentina
Tel.: (54) 1146833259
Web Site: http://www.lincoln-argentina.com.ar
Welding Equipment Mfr
N.A.I.C.S.: 333992
Gabriel de Benedetti *(Pres)*

Lincoln Electric Spain, S.L. (1)
Ctra Laurea Miro 396-398, San Feliu de Llobregat, 08980, Spain
Tel.: (34) 936859600
Web Site: http://www.lincolnelectric.es
Sales Range: $25-49.9 Million
Emp.: 40
Welding Equipment Mfr
N.A.I.C.S.: 333992

Lincoln Electric Holdings, Inc.—(Continued)

Lincoln Electric Sverige   **(1)**
Nynasvagen 31, 51156, Kinna,
Sweden   **(100%)**
Tel.: (46) 320211710
Web Site: http://www.lincolnelectric.se
Sales Range: $25-49.9 Million
Emp.: 12
Welding Equipment Sales
N.A.I.C.S.: 423830

Lincoln Electric do Brasil Industria e
Comercio Ltda.   **(1)**
Av Papa Joao Paulo I N 1818 Cumbica,
Guarulhos, 07170-350, SP, Brazil
Tel.: (55) 112 431 4700
Web Site: https://www.lincolnelectric.com.br
Arc Welding Machines & Electrodes Mfr &
Sales
N.A.I.C.S.: 333992

Lincoln Smitweld Belgium S.A.   **(1)**
Grijpenlaan 5, Tienen, 3300, Belgium
Tel.: (32) 16804841
Web Site: http://www.lincolnelectric.com
Welding Equipment Mfr
N.A.I.C.S.: 333992

Oerlikon Skandinavien AB   **(1)**
Starrvagen 100, 232 61, Arlov, Sweden
Tel.: (46) 406701500
Web Site: http://www.oerlikon-welding.com
Welding Product Whslr
N.A.I.C.S.: 423840

Orion Custom Metal Fabrication
Corporation   **(1)**
101 Steve Fonyo Dr, PO Box 479, Vankleek
Hill, Ottawa, K0B 1R0, ON, Canada
Tel.: (613) 448-9191
Web Site: http://ocmf.ca
Metal Fabrication Product Mfr
N.A.I.C.S.: 332312

Overstreet-Hughes Co., Inc.   **(1)**
131 Frogs Landing, Carthage, TN 37030
Tel.: (615) 735-3201
Sales Range: $25-49.9 Million
Emp.: 120
Mfr of Copper Tube & Wrought Copper Fit-
tings; Brass Alloy Rod; Commercial Tube;
Forgings; Impact Extrusions; Refrigeration &
Air Conditioning Products
N.A.I.C.S.: 331410

PT Lincoln Electric Indonesia   **(1)**
Jl Inti Raya Blok C 10/12A, Bekasi Interna-
tional Industrial Estate, Lippo Cikarang,
17550, West Java, Indonesia
Tel.: (62) 2189907629
Web Site: http://www.lincolnelectric.com
Welding Equipment Mfr
N.A.I.C.S.: 333992

PT Lincoln Indoweld   **(1)**
Komp Golden Plaza B/26 Jl RS Fatmawati
No 15 Gandaria Selatan, Jakarta Selatan,
Jakarta, Indonesia
Tel.: (62) 2175909515
Welding Product Mfr
N.A.I.C.S.: 333992
Agus Priyambodo *(Mgr-Factory)*

Pro Systems, LLC   **(1)**
6235 N 650 E, Churubusco, IN 46723
Tel.: (260) 693-0303
Web Site: http://www.pro-systems.com
Automated Machines & Systems Mfr
N.A.I.C.S.: 333922

Rimrock Corporation   **(1)**
1700 Jetway Blvd, Columbus, OH 43219
Tel.: (614) 471-5926
Web Site: https://www.rimrockcorp.com
Die Casting, Forging & Foundry Automation
Solutions
N.A.I.C.S.: 333248

Division (Domestic):

Wolf Robotics, LLC   **(2)**
4600 Innovation Dr, Fort Collins, CO 80525
Tel.: (970) 225-7600
Web Site: https://www.wolfrobotics.com
Robotic Arc Welding Services
N.A.I.C.S.: 333992
Jeremiah King *(Gen Mgr)*

Rimrock Holdings Corporation   **(1)**

1700 Jetway Blvd, Columbus, OH 43219-
1675
Tel.: (970) 225-7600
Holding Company
N.A.I.C.S.: 551112

Robolution GmbH   **(1)**
Dammstrasse 14, Grafenhausen, 64331,
Weiterstadt, Germany
Tel.: (49) 6150 591 9830
Web Site: https://www.robolution.de
Welding Consumables Mfr
N.A.I.C.S.: 333992
Patrick Haber *(Gen Mgr)*
Torsten Sebelka *(Dir-Technical)*
Thomas Buttner *(Head-Sls)*
Andreas Hajek *(Sls Mgr)*
Sahin Kavak *(Sls Mgr)*
Georg Ruth *(Sls Mgr)*
Andreas Wagner *(Sls Mgr)*
Alexander Gessler *(Sls Mgr)*
Alexander Hein *(Head-Project Mgmt, After*
Sales & Doku)
Stefan Fleckenstein *(Head-Pur Dept)*

SAF-Oerlikon Malaysia Swdn
Bhd   **(1)**
No 10 Jalan TPP 5/1 Taman Perindustrian,
Puchong, 47100, Malaysia
Tel.: (60) 380608638
Welding Product Mfr
N.A.I.C.S.: 333992
Cheah Chee Ming *(Mgr-Technical)*

SSCO Manufacturing, Inc.   **(1)**
1245 30th St, San Diego, CA 92154
Tel.: (619) 628-1022
Web Site: http://www.arc-products.com
Sales Range: $1-9.9 Million
Emp.: 40
Welding Apparatus Mfr
N.A.I.C.S.: 333992

SWP N.Z. Limited   **(1)**
16A Saltash Street, PO Box 8140, Upper
Vogeltown, New Plymouth, 4310, New Zea-
land
Tel.: (64) 67538044
Web Site: https://aus.swp.com.au
Industrial Machinery & Equipment Merchant
Whslr
N.A.I.C.S.: 423830

Specialised Welding Products Pty.
Ltd.   **(1)**
Unit D7 2A Westall Road, Springvale, Mel-
bourne, 3171, VIC, Australia
Tel.: (61) 39 583 0488
Web Site: https://aus.swp.com.au
Welding Product Whslr
N.A.I.C.S.: 423840

Superior Controls, Inc.   **(1)**
46247 Five Mile Rd, Plymouth, MI 48170
Tel.: (734) 454-0500
Web Site: http://www.redviking.com
Emp.: 200
Custom Industrial Manufacturing & Testing
Equipment Designer & Mfr
N.A.I.C.S.: 333248
Randall E. Brodzik *(Pres & CEO)*
Chris Lake *(VP-Engrg)*
Rod Emery *(VP-Assembly Sys & Integra-*
tion)
Greg Cameron *(VP)*
Mark Sobkow *(VP-Mfg Sys)*
Greg Giles *(Dir-Mfg Execution Sys)*
Jason Stefanski *(Dir-Engrg-Dynamic Test*
Sys)
Chuck Fulk *(Dir-Project Mgmt)*
Brooke Notton Elliott *(Dir-Mktg & Comm)*

Subsidiary (Domestic):

RedViking Group, LLC   **(2)**
46247 Five Mile Rd, Plymouth, MI 48170
Tel.: (734) 454-0500
Web Site: http://www.redviking.com
Custom Industrial Manufacturing & Testing
Equipment Designer & Mfr
N.A.I.C.S.: 333248
Randall E. Brodzik *(Pres & CEO)*
Brooke Notton Elliott *(Dir-Mktg & Comm)*

Plant (Domestic):

RedViking - Research Triangle Engi-
neering Center   **(3)**
7208 ACC Blvd, Raleigh, NC 27617-8736
Tel.: (919) 398-6441

Web Site: http://www.redviking.com
Custom Industrial Manufacturing & Testing
Equipment Designer & Mfr
N.A.I.C.S.: 333248
Kevin Harris *(Dir-Engrg-Dynamic Test Sys)*

Techalloy Co., Inc.   **(1)**
8015 Corporate Dr Ste 1, Baltimore, MD
21236
Tel.: (410) 931-2724
Web Site: http://www.techalloy.com
Sales Range: $50-74.9 Million
Emp.: 250
Stainless Steel & Nickel Alloys in Wire &
Rod; Welding Wire, Rod, Coated Electrodes
Mfr
N.A.I.C.S.: 331222

Tennessee Rand, Inc.   **(1)**
702 Moccasin Bend Rd, Chattanooga, TN
37405
Tel.: (423) 664-7263
Web Site: https://www.tennrand.com
Emp.: 200
Welding Design Services
N.A.I.C.S.: 541490
Dobie Kilgore *(Gen Mgr)*

The Lincoln Electric Company (Asia
Pacific) Pte. Ltd.   **(1)**
25 Pandan Crescent Tic Tech Centre 06-13,
Singapore, 128477, Singapore   **(100%)**
Tel.: (65) 68545360
Web Site: https://www.lincolnelectric.com
Sales Range: $10-24.9 Million
Emp.: 15
Electric Arc Welding & Cutting Sales
N.A.I.C.S.: 333992

The Lincoln Electric Company (New
Zealand) Limited   **(1)**
Patrick Wahlen 7B 761 Great Sough Rd,
PO Box 12574, Penrose, 1061, New
Zealand   **(100%)**
Tel.: (64) 95804008
Web Site: http://www.lincolnelectric.com
Welding Equipment Sales
N.A.I.C.S.: 423830

The Lincoln Electric Company Austra-
lia Pty. Ltd.   **(1)**
35 Bryant Street, Padstow, 2211, NSW,
Australia   **(100%)**
Tel.: (61) 297727222
Web Site: http://www.lincolnelectric.com.au
Sales Range: $100-124.9 Million
Emp.: 300
Mfr & Sales of Arc Welding Equipment
N.A.I.C.S.: 333992
Patrick Wahlen *(Mng Dir)*

The Lincoln Electric Company of
Canada LP   **(1)**
179 Wicksteed Ave, Toronto, M4G 2B9, ON,
Canada   **(100%)**
Tel.: (416) 421-2600
Web Site: http://www.lincolnelectric.ca
Sales Range: $50-74.9 Million
Emp.: 100
Sales of Electric Welding Machines
N.A.I.C.S.: 423830

The Lincoln Electric Company of
South Africa (Pty) Ltd.   **(1)**
Route 21 Office Park 43 Regency Drive
Building C1, Irene, Johannesburg, 0174,
Gauteng, South Africa   **(100%)**
Tel.: (27) 113120601
Web Site: http://www.lincolnelectric.eu
Sales Range: $25-49.9 Million
Welding Equipment Whslr
N.A.I.C.S.: 423830
Benoit Limotte *(Mng Dir)*

The Nanjing Lincoln Electric Co.,
Ltd.   **(1)**
No 18 Baoxiang Road, Riverside Economic
Development Zone Jiangning District, Nan-
jing, 211161, Jiangsu, China
Tel.: (86) 258 418 8377
Web Site: https://www.lincolnelectric.com.cn
Sales Range: $25-49.9 Million
Welding Product Mfr
N.A.I.C.S.: 333992

The Shanghai Lincoln Electric Co.,
Ltd.   **(1)**
No 195 Lane 5008 Hu Tai Road, Shanghai,
201907, China   **(100%)**

Tel.: (86) 2166734530
Web Site: http://www.lincolnelectric.com.cn
Welding Equipment Mfr & Sales
N.A.I.C.S.: 333992

Torchmate, Inc.   **(1)**
1170 Trademark Dr Ste 101, Reno, NV
89521
Tel.: (775) 673-2200
Web Site: https://www.torchmate.com
Emp.: 4,800
Cutting Machine Mfr
N.A.I.C.S.: 333515

Uhrhan & Schwill Schweisstechnik
GmbH   **(1)**
Max-Keith-Strasse 39 D, 45136, Essen,
Germany   **(100%)**
Tel.: (49) 201266946
Web Site: http://www.uhrhan-schwill.de
Sales Range: $25-49.9 Million
Emp.: 40
Mfr of Welding Systems for Pipe Production
N.A.I.C.S.: 333992
Ingo Schwill *(Mng Dir)*
Jeannine Melis *(Dir-Bus Unit Pipe Mills)*

Uhrhan & Schwill Schweisstechnik
GmbH   **(1)**
Max-Keith-Strasse 39 D, 45136, Essen,
Germany
Tel.: (49) 201266946
Web Site: http://www.uhrhan-schwill.de
Welding Consumables Mfr
N.A.I.C.S.: 333992

Vernon Tool Company, Ltd.   **(1)**
1170 Trademark Dr Ste 101, Reno, NV
89521
Tel.: (775) 673-2200
Web Site: https://www.vernontool.com
Sales Range: $25-49.9 Million
Emp.: 30
Metal Valve & Pipe Fitting Mfr
N.A.I.C.S.: 332919

Vizient Manufacturing Solutions,
Inc.   **(1)**
3129 State St, Bettendorf, IA 52722
Tel.: (563) 355-4812
Web Site: http://www.vizient.com
Robotic Arc Welding Services
N.A.I.C.S.: 333992

Wayne Trail Technologies, Inc.   **(1)**
407 S Main St, Fort Loramie, OH 45845
Tel.: (937) 295-2120
Web Site: https://www.waynetrail.com
Sales Range: $50-74.9 Million
Metal Tooling & Automated Systems Mfr
N.A.I.C.S.: 333248

Weartech International Limited   **(1)**
Moor Road, Baglan Industrial Estate, Port
Talbot, SA12 7BJ, United Kingdom
Tel.: (44) 163 981 2900
Web Site: https://www.weartech.eu
Welding Consumables Mfr
N.A.I.C.S.: 333992

Weartech International, Inc.   **(1)**
1177 N Grove St, Anaheim, CA 92806
Tel.: (714) 683-2430
Web Site: http://www.weartech.net
Alloy Consumables Mfr
N.A.I.C.S.: 331110

LINCOLN NATIONAL CORPO-
RATION
150 N Radnor-Chester Rd Ste A305,
Radnor, PA 19087
Tel.: (484) 583-1400   **IN**
Web Site:
    https://www.lincolnfinancial.com
Year Founded: 1905
LNC—(NYSE)
Rev.: $11,645,000,000
Assets: $372,413,000,000
Liabilities: $365,520,000,000
Net Worth: $6,893,000,000
Earnings: ($752,000,000)
Emp.: 11,024
Fiscal Year-end: 12/31/23
Diversified Financial, Investment, Re-
tirement Planning & Insurance Ser-
vices
N.A.I.C.S.: 524130

Jayson Bronchetti *(Chief Investment Officer, Exec VP & Head-Risk & Sustainability)*
Craig T. Beazer *(Gen Counsel & Exec VP)*
Christopher Neczypor *(CFO & Exec VP)*
John Kennedy *(Chief Distr & Brand Officer & Exec VP)*
Ellen G. Cooper *(Chm, Pres & CEO)*

Subsidiaries:

First Penn-Pacific Life Insurance
Company **(1)**
1300 S Clinton St, Fort Wayne, IN 46802
Tel.: (847) 466-8000
Fire Insurance Services
N.A.I.C.S.: 524113

Lincoln Financial Advisors
Corporation **(1)**
1301 S Harrison St, Fort Wayne, IN 46802
Tel.: (260) 455-2562
Web Site: https://www.lincolnfinancial.com
Investment Advisory Services
N.A.I.C.S.: 524298

Lincoln Financial Benefit
Partners **(1)**
8801 Indian Hills Dr, Omaha, NE 68114
Tel.: (402) 361-7300
Web Site: http://www.lfg.com
Sales Range: $50-74.9 Million
Emp.: 1,000
Employee Life, Disability & Dental Insurance Services
N.A.I.C.S.: 524210

Lincoln Financial Distributors,
Inc. **(1)**
130 N Radnor Chester Rd, Radnor, PA 19087
Tel.: (484) 583-6000
Investment Management Service
N.A.I.C.S.: 523940
Tim Seifert *(VP & Mgr-Natl Sls-Intermediary Retirement Plan Svcs)*
Richard Aneser *(CMO)*
Chris Somers *(Dir-Sls)*
Michael Hall *(Dir-Natl Sls)*
Kathy Kavanaugh *(VP-Strategic Solutions & Partner Mktg)*
Beth O'Brien *(Sr VP & Head-Fin & Strategy)*
Michele Wyatt *(Reg Dir-Sls-Intermediary Retirement Plan Sls Force)*
Mathew Abraham *(Reg Dir-Sls-Intermediary Retirement Plan Sls Force)*
Thomas O'Connell *(Reg Dir-Sls-Intermediary Retirement Plan Sls Force)*
Jim McCrory *(Div Mgr-Sls)*
Drew Disher *(Div Mgr-Sls)*
Peter Sims *(Head-Intermediary Retirement Plan Sls)*
LuJean Smith *(VP-Comm)*
Kathy Leckey *(VP & Head-Strategy-Retirement Solutions Distr)*
James Christie *(VP & Head-Competitive Market Solutions-Insurance Solutions Distr)*
Joe Mrozek *(Mgr-Sls-Intermediary Retirement Plan Svcs Div-Natl)*
John Kennedy *(Sr VP & Head-Retirement Solutions Distr)*

Lincoln Financial Limited Liability
Company I **(1)**
1300 S Clinton St, Fort Wayne, IN 46802-3506
Tel.: (260) 455-6588
Insurance Management Services
N.A.I.C.S.: 524298

Lincoln Financial Media
Company **(1)**
3340 Peachtree Rd NE Ste 1430, Atlanta, GA 30326
Tel.: (404) 239-7211
Web Site:
http://www.lincolnfinancialmedia.com
Radio Broadcasting Services
N.A.I.C.S.: 516110

Lincoln Financial Securities
Corporation **(1)**
1 Granite Pl, Concord, NH 03301-3258
Tel.: (603) 224-7741

Web Site: https://www.lfsecurities.com
Sales Range: $1-4.9 Billion
Emp.: 700
Investment Services
N.A.I.C.S.: 523150

Lincoln Variable Insurance Products
Trust **(1)**
1 Granite Pl, Concord, NH 03301
Tel.: (603) 226-5457
Web Site: http://www.lfg.com
Emp.: 9,000
Investment Management Service
N.A.I.C.S.: 523940
Jayson Bronchetti *(Chm)*

The Lincoln National Life Insurance
Co. **(1)**
1301 S Harrison St, Fort Wayne, IN 46802
Tel.: (260) 455-2000
Web Site: https://www.lincolnfinancial.com
Rev.: $17,785,000,000
Assets: $338,594,000,000
Liabilities: $330,796,000,000
Net Worth: $7,798,000,000
Earnings: ($1,273,000,000)
Emp.: 11,261
Fiscal Year-end: 12/31/2022
Life Insurance & Financial Services
N.A.I.C.S.: 524113
Craig T. Beazer *(Gen Counsel)*
Jayson R. Bronchetti *(Exec VP)*
John C. Kennedy *(Chief Brand Officer)*
Brian Kroll *(Exec VP)*
Andrew D. Rallis *(Exec VP)*
James W. Reid *(Exec VP)*
Kenneth S. Solon *(Exec VP)*
Sean N. Woodroffe *(Chief Culture Officer)*

Subsidiary (Domestic):

California Fringe Benefit and Insurance Marketing Corporation **(2)**
3000 Executive Pkwy Ste 400, San Ramon, CA 94583-4335
Tel.: (925) 659-0300
Insurance Broker Services
N.A.I.C.S.: 524298
Bob Dineen *(CEO)*

Lincoln Life & Annuity Company of
New York **(2)**
120 Madison St Ste 1700, Syracuse, NY 13202-2802
Tel.: (315) 428-8400
Insurance Management Services
N.A.I.C.S.: 524298
Robert Sheppard *(Gen Counsel)*

LINDBLAD EXPEDITIONS HOLDINGS, INC.
1625 N Market Blvd, Sacramento, CA 95834
Tel.: (916) 445-1254 DE
Web Site:
https://www.expeditions.com
Year Founded: 2010
LIND—(NASDAQ)
Rev.: $421,500,000
Assets: $787,975,000
Liabilities: $970,650,000
Net Worth: ($182,675,000)
Earnings: ($111,381,000)
Emp.: 870
Fiscal Year-end: 12/31/22
Holding Company; Specialty Sea & Land Excursion Travel Services
N.A.I.C.S.: 551112
Sven-Olof Lindblad *(Founder, Pres & CEO)*
Alexis Freeman *(Gen Counsel)*
Leo Chang *(VP-Strategic Fin)*
Noah Brodsky *(Chief Comml Officer)*
David Lorber *(Chief Medical Officer)*
Lesa Bain *(VP)*
Rachel Woodward *(VP)*
Christine Robinson *(VP)*
Vanessa Picariello *(VP)*
Amy Berquist *(VP)*
Bertha Espinosa *(VP)*
Ana Esteves *(VP)*
Dean Byus III *(Chief Expedition Officer)*

Subsidiaries:

Classic Journeys, LLC **(1)**
7855 Ivanhoe Ave Ste 220, La Jolla, CA 92037-4508 **(80%)**
Tel.: (858) 454-5004
Web Site: https://www.classicjourneys.com
Tour Operator
N.A.I.C.S.: 561520
Edward Piegza *(Founder)*

Duvine Adventures, Inc. **(1)**
667 Somerville Ave, Somerville, MA 02143
Tel.: (617) 776-4441
Web Site: http://www.duvine.com
Golf Courses & Country Clubs
N.A.I.C.S.: 713910

Lindblad Expeditions, LLC **(1)**
96 Morton St, New York, NY 11201
Tel.: (212) 261-9000
Web Site: http://www.expeditions.com
Sales Range: $200-249.9 Million
Specialty Sea & Land Excursion Travel Services
N.A.I.C.S.: 487210
Trey Byus *(Chief Expedition Officer)*
Leo Chang *(VP-Strategic Fin)*
Alexis Freeman *(Gen Counsel)*
Craig Felenstein *(CFO)*
David Lorber *(Chief Medical Officer)*
Dolf Berle *(CEO)*
Noah Brodsky *(Chief Comml Officer)*

Off The Beaten Path, LLC **(1)**
7 E Beall St Ste 200, Bozeman, MT 59715
Tel.: (406) 586-1311
Web Site: https://www.offthebeatenpath.com
Sales Range: $1-9.9 Million
Emp.: 17
Travel Agencies
N.A.I.C.S.: 561510
Cory Lawrence *(Pres)*

LINDSAY CORPORATION
18135 Burke St Ste 100, Omaha, NE 68022
Tel.: (402) 829-6800 DE
Web Site: https://www.lindsay.com
Year Founded: 1955
LNN—(NYSE)
Rev.: $607,074,000
Assets: $760,232,000
Liabilities: $279,339,000
Net Worth: $480,893,000
Earnings: $66,257,000
Emp.: 1,280
Fiscal Year-end: 08/31/24
Irrigation Equipment Mfr
N.A.I.C.S.: 325120
Robert E. Brunner *(Chm)*
Eric R. Arneson *(Gen Counsel, Sec & Sr VP)*
Brian L. Ketcham *(CFO & Sr VP)*
Randy A. Wood *(Pres & CEO)*
J. Scott Marion *(Pres-Infrastructure)*
Kelly M. Staup *(Chief Diversity Officer & Sr VP-HR)*
P. David Salen *(Sr VP-Ops-Global)*
Gustavo E. Oberto *(Pres-Irrigation)*
Melissa G. Moreno *(CIO & Sr VP)*
Brian Magnusson *(Sr VP-Strategy & Bus Dev)*
Richard A. Harold *(Sr VP)*

Subsidiaries:

Claude Laval Corporation **(1)**
1365 N Clovis Ave, Fresno, CA 93727-2282
Tel.: (559) 255-1601
Web Site: https://www.lakos.com
Sales Range: $25-49.9 Million
Emp.: 125
Filtration Equipment Mfr
N.A.I.C.S.: 333914
Kathy Colby *(Gen Mgr)*

Elecsys Corporation **(1)**
846 N Mart-Way Ct, Olathe, KS 66061
Tel.: (913) 647-0158
Web Site: http://www.elecsyscorp.com
Sales Range: $25-49.9 Million
Communication Technology Solutions & Data Acquisition; Industrial Electronic Equipment Mfr & Sales

N.A.I.C.S.: 334511
Michael D. Morgan *(Pres)*

FieldWise, LLC **(1)**
3607 Bradford Ave, Norfolk, NE 68701
Tel.: (713) 300-0472
Irrigation Infrastructure Equipment Mfr & Distr
N.A.I.C.S.: 333111

Irz Consulting LLC **(1)**
2800 NW 29th Ave, Portland, OR 97210
Tel.: (503) 222-0241
Web Site: http://www.irzconsulting.com
Sales Range: $25-49.9 Million
Emp.: 12
Irrigation Management Services
N.A.I.C.S.: 221310
Fred A. Ziari *(Founder)*

Lindsay (Tianjin) Industry Co.,
Ltd. **(1)**
169 Huanhenan Road, Tianjin Airport Economic Area, Tianjin, 300308, China
Tel.: (86) 2258679198
Farm Machinery & Equipment Mfr
N.A.I.C.S.: 333111

Lindsay America do Sul Ltda. **(1)**
Rua Gustavo Amburst No 36 CONJ 1103 E 1104, PO Box 1001, Mogi Mirim, Sao Paulo, 13092-106, Brazil **(100%)**
Tel.: (55) 1938141100
Web Site: http://www.lindsaybrazil.com
Sales Range: $10-24.9 Million
Emp.: 41
Irrigation Systems Services
N.A.I.C.S.: 221310

Lindsay Europe SA **(1)**
L'Epinglerie, 72300, La Chapelle-d'Aligne, France **(100%)**
Tel.: (33) 243480202
Web Site: http://www.lindsay.com
Sales Range: $10-24.9 Million
Emp.: 40
Irrigation Systems Services
N.A.I.C.S.: 221310
Olivier Debart *(Chm)*

Lindsay International (ANZ) Pty
Ltd. **(1)**
19 Spencer Street, Toowoomba, 4350, QLD, Australia
Tel.: (61) 746135000
Agricultural Equipment Mfr
N.A.I.C.S.: 333998

Branch (Non-US):

Lindsay International (ANZ) Pty
Ltd. **(2)**
581 Taonui Road, Feilding, 4775, New Zealand
Tel.: (64) 62120550
Web Site: http://www.gpsfarmmap.com
Sales Range: $10-24.9 Million
Emp.: 6
Global Positioning System Equipment Mfr
N.A.I.C.S.: 334220

Lindsay Manufacturing Africa Pty.
Ltd. **(1)**
6 Talana Close Sacks Circle, Bellville South, Bellville, 7530, South Africa **(100%)**
Tel.: (27) 219868900
Web Site: https://www.lindsay.com
Irrigation Systems Services
N.A.I.C.S.: 221310

Lindsay Manufacturing Company **(1)**
214 E 2nd St, Lindsay, NE 68644-4620
Tel.: (402) 428-2131
Web Site: http://www.zimmatic.com
Sales Range: $25-49.9 Million
Emp.: 25
Mfr of Farm & Garden Machinery
N.A.I.C.S.: 333111
Richard W. Parod *(Pres & CEO)*

Lindsay Sulama ve Altyapi Sanayi ve
Ticarct A.S. **(1)**
Karamehmet Mh Avrupa Serbest Bolgesi 4 Cadde No 3, Ergene, Corlu, Tekirdag, Turkiye
Tel.: (90) 5422940174
Farm Machinery & Equipment Distr
N.A.I.C.S.: 423820

Lindsay Transportation Solutions,
Inc. **(1)**

Lindsay Corporation—(Continued)

180 River Rd, Rio Vista, CA 94571
Tel.: (707) 374-6800
Web Site: http://www.barriersystemsinc.com
Agricultural Equipment Mfr
N.A.I.C.S.: 333998

Lindsay Transportation, Inc. **(1)**
214 E 2nd St Hwy 91, Lindsay, NE 68644
Tel.: (402) 428-2131
Web Site: http://www.lindsay.com
Emp.: 4
General Freight Trucking Services
N.A.I.C.S.: 484110

SPF Water Engineering, LLC **(1)**
300 E Mallard Dr Ste 350, Boise, ID 83706
Tel.: (208) 383-4140
Web Site: http://www.spfwater.com
Water Resource Engineering & Construction Services
N.A.I.C.S.: 238320
Crystal Jensen (Gen Mgr)
Terry Scanlan (Founder)
Kalli Everhart (Coord-Mktg)
Mike Kettner (Project Mgr)
Steve Hannula (Sr Project Mgr)
Scott King (Project Mgr)
Justin Lerari (Project Mgr)
Matt Rasmusson (Sr Project Mgr)

Safe Technologies, Inc. **(1)**
170 River Rd, Rio Vista, CA 94571
Tel.: (707) 374-6158
Road Infrastructure Management Services
N.A.I.C.S.: 488490

Snoline S.p.A. **(1)**
Via Francesco Baracca 23, 20056, Trezzo-sull Adda, Milan, Italy
Tel.: (39) 02909961
Web Site: http://www.snoline.com
Traffic Safety Products Mfr
N.A.I.C.S.: 488490

Watertronics, LLC **(1)**
525 E Industrial Dr, Hartland, WI 53029
Tel.: (262) 367-5000
Web Site: http://www.watertronics.com
Custom Water Pump Mfr
N.A.I.C.S.: 333914

LINEAGE CELL THERAPEUTICS, INC.

2173 Salk Ave Ste 200, Carlsbad, CA 92008
Tel.: (442) 287-8990 CA
Web Site:
  https://www.lineagecell.com
Year Founded: 1990
LCTX—(NYSEAMEX)
Rev.: $14,703,000
Assets: $123,664,000
Liabilities: $51,728,000
Net Worth: $71,936,000
Earnings: ($26,273,000)
Emp.: 70
Fiscal Year-end: 12/31/22
Medical Biotechnology Products Mfr
N.A.I.C.S.: 325414
Alfred D. Kingsley (Chm)
Ronald S. Barkin (Pres & COO)
Gary S. Hogge (Sr VP-Clinical & Medical Affairs)
Brian M. Culley (CEO)
Derek Kelaita (VP-Bus Dev)
Rami Skaliter (CFO-Cell Cure Neurosciences)
Jill Ann Howe (CFO)
Aleksandra J. Poole (VP)
Jennifer Bahr-Davidson (Exec Dir)
George A. Samuel III (Gen Counsel & Sec)

Subsidiaries:

Asterias Biotherapeutics, Inc. **(1)**
6300 Dumbarton Cir, Fremont, CA 94555 **(100%)**
Tel.: (510) 456-3800
Web Site: http://www.biotimeinc.com
Sales Range: $1-9.9 Million
Biopharmaceutical Mfr
N.A.I.C.S.: 325412

Michael H. Mulroy (Pres)

Cell Cure Neurosciences, Ltd. **(1)**
Jerusalem BioPark, POB 12247, Jerusalem, 91121, Israel
Tel.: (972) 5722000
Web Site:
  http://www.cellcureneurosciences.com
Sales Range: $25-49.9 Million
Emp.: 30
Biotechnology Research & Development
N.A.I.C.S.: 541714
Benjamin Reubinoff (Chief Scientific Officer)
Moshe Hukaylo (CFO)
Rami Skaliter (CEO)
Sara Altman (Fin Mgr)
David Schlachet (Chm)

Embryome Sciences, Inc. **(1)**
1301 Harbor Bay Pkwy, Alameda, CA 94502
Tel.: (510) 521-3390
Web Site: http://www.biotimeinc.net
Sales Range: $75-99.9 Million
Emp.: 43
Embryonic Stem Cell Research Services
N.A.I.C.S.: 541715

LifeMap Sciences, Ltd. **(1)**
3 Hanehoshet St Building B 7th floor, Tel Aviv, 69710, Israel
Tel.: (972) 36420429
Biomedical Research & Development Services
N.A.I.C.S.: 541715

ReCyte Therapeutics, Inc. **(1)**
1301 Harbor Bay Pkwy Ste 100, Alameda, CA 94502
Tel.: (510) 521-3390
Web Site: http://www.recyte.com
Biotechnology Research & Development
N.A.I.C.S.: 541714
David Larocca (VP-R&D)

LINGERIE FIGHTING CHAMPIONSHIPS, INC.

6955 N Durango Dr Ste 1115-129, Las Vegas, NV 89149
Tel.: (702) 527-2942 NV
Web Site: https://www.lingeriefc.com
Year Founded: 2006
BOTY—(OTCIQ)
Rev.: $117,722
Assets: $5,295
Liabilities: $4,204,402
Net Worth: ($4,199,107)
Earnings: $308,452
Emp.: 1
Fiscal Year-end: 12/31/23
Investment Services
N.A.I.C.S.: 523999
Shaun Edward Donnelly (Chm, CEO & CFO)

LINKBANCORP, INC.

3045 Market St, Camp Hill, PA 17011 PA
Web Site: https://ir.linkbancorp.com
Year Founded: 2018
LNKB—(NASDAQ)
Rev.: $43,221,000
Assets: $1,163,654,000
Liabilities: $1,025,101,000
Net Worth: $138,553,000
Earnings: $5,598,000
Emp.: 132
Fiscal Year-end: 12/31/22
Bank Holding Company
N.A.I.C.S.: 551111
Brent Smith (Pres)
Kris Paul (CFO)
Andrew S. Samuel (Bd of Dirs, Executives)

Subsidiaries:

LINKBANK **(1)**
3045 Market St, Camp Hill, PA 17011
Tel.: (717) 458-9095
Web Site: https://www.linkbank.com
Commercial Banking
N.A.I.C.S.: 522110

Joseph C. Michetti Jr. (Chm)
Wesley M. Weymers (Pres & CEO)

Subsidiary (Domestic):

Johnson Mortgage Company, LLC **(2)**
739 Thimble Shoals Blvd Ste 507, Newport News, VA 23606-3562
Tel.: (757) 873-1287
Web Site: https://www.johnson-mortgage.com
Sales Range: $1-9.9 Million
Mortgage Lending Services
N.A.I.C.S.: 522292
R. Allen Barber III (Pres)

LIPELLA PHARMACEUTICALS INC.

7800 Susquehanna St Ste 505, Pittsburgh, PA 15208-2573
Tel.: (412) 894-1853
Web Site: https://www.lipella.com
Year Founded: 2005
LIPO—(NASDAQ)
Emp.: 5
Research & Development in Biotechnology
N.A.I.C.S.: 541714
Jonathan Kaufman (Chm, Pres & CEO)
Michael Chancellor (Chief Medical Officer)
Douglas Johnston (CFO)
Michele Gruber (Dir-Operations)
Janet Okonski (Dir-Clinical Ops)
Katie Johnston (Controller)

LIPOCINE INC.

675 Arapeen Dr Ste 202, Salt Lake City, UT 84108
Tel.: (801) 994-7383 DE
Web Site: https://www.lipocine.com
Year Founded: 2011
LPCN—(NASDAQ)
Rev.: $500,000
Assets: $37,542,922
Liabilities: $1,907,982
Net Worth: $35,634,940
Earnings: ($10,758,636)
Emp.: 17
Fiscal Year-end: 12/31/22
Specialty Pharmaceutical Developer & Mfr
N.A.I.C.S.: 325412
Chidu Chidambaram (VP)
Mahesh V. Patel (Pres & CEO)

Subsidiaries:

Lipocine Operating Inc. **(1)**
675 S Arapeen Dr, Salt Lake City, UT 84108
Tel.: (801) 994-7383
Pharmaceutical Preparation Mfr
N.A.I.C.S.: 325412

LIQUIDIA TECHNOLOGIES, INC.

419 Davis Dr Ste 100, Morrisville, NC 27560
Tel.: (919) 328-4400 DE
Web Site: https://www.liquidia.com
Year Founded: 2004
LQDA—(NASDAQ)
Rev.: $8,072,120
Assets: $68,842,067
Liabilities: $33,894,520
Net Worth: $34,947,547
Earnings: ($47,583,455)
Emp.: 64
Fiscal Year-end: 12/31/19
Biopharmaceutical Product Development Services
N.A.I.C.S.: 541715
Robert A. Lippe (COO)
Benjamin Maynor (Sr VP-R&D)
Stephen D. Bloch (Chm)
Robert Roscigno (Sr VP-Product Dev)

Jeri Thomas (Sr VP-Comml)
Jason Adair (VP-Corp Dev & Strategy)
Florina Gordon-Krawchick (Sr VP-HR)
Tushar Shah (Chief Medical Officer)
Steven Bariahtaris (Interim CFO)
Roger Jeffs (CEO)

LIQUIDITY SERVICES, INC.

6931 Arlington Rd Ste 460, Bethesda, MD 20814
Tel.: (202) 467-6868 DE
Web Site:
  https://www.liquidityservices.com
Year Founded: 1999
LQDT—(NASDAQ)
Rev.: $257,531,000
Assets: $255,576,000
Liabilities: $120,561,000
Net Worth: $135,015,000
Earnings: $50,949,000
Emp.: 614
Fiscal Year-end: 09/30/21
Holding Company; Wholesale, Salvage & Surplus Assets Online Auction Services
N.A.I.C.S.: 551112
Jaime Mateus-Tique (Co-Founder)
Jorge A. Celaya (CFO, Chief Acctg Officer & Exec VP)
Mark A. Shaffer (Chief Legal Officer & Sec)
John Daunt (Chief Comml Officer)
Steven J. Weiskircher (CTO)
Novelette Murray (Chief HR Officer)
Anthony Long (VP-Mktg)
William P. Angrick III (Co-Founder, Chm & CEO)

Subsidiaries:

GoIndustry-DoveBid Limited **(1)**
1 Alie St, London, E1 8DE, United Kingdom
Tel.: (44) 2070983700
Web Site: http://www.go-dove.com
Emp.: 312
Holding Company; Industrial Machinery Appraisal & Auction Services
N.A.I.C.S.: 551112

Subsidiary (Non-US):

GoIndustry DoveBid (S) Pte. Ltd **(2)**
100 Beach Road 12-04 Shaw Tower, Singapore, 189702, Singapore
Tel.: (65) 68203828
Sales Range: $25-49.9 Million
Emp.: 7
Surplus Asset Management, Valuation & Disposition Services
N.A.I.C.S.: 423830
B. C. Lee (Gen Mgr)

GoIndustry-DoveBid (Australia) Pty. Ltd. **(2)**
Level 27 101 Collins Street, Melbourne, 3000, VIC, Australia
Tel.: (61) 396539385
Web Site: http://www.go-dove.com
Surplus Asset Management, Valuation & Disposition Services
N.A.I.C.S.: 423830

GoIndustry-DoveBid (Hong Kong) Ltd **(2)**
Flat 1104 11 Floor Chinachem Leighton Plaza, 43-59 Queens Road East, Causeway Bay, China (Hong Kong)
Tel.: (852) 25289313
Web Site: http://www.goindustry.com
Emp.: 5
Surplus Asset Management, Valuation & Disposition Services
N.A.I.C.S.: 423830

Subsidiary (Domestic):

GoIndustry DoveBid Asset Management (H.K.) Ltd. **(3)**
Room 1104 ChinaChem Leighton Plaza, 29 Leighton Road, Causeway Bay, China (Hong Kong)
Tel.: (852) 25289313

Surplus Asset Management, Valuation & Disposition Services
N.A.I.C.S.: 493110

Subsidiary (Non-US):

GoIndustry-DoveBid (Malaysia) Sdn. Bhd. (2)
Unit 11-07 11th Floor Heritage House, Jalan Yap Ah Shak, Kuala Lumpur, 50300, Malaysia (70%)
Tel.: (60) 326917704
Web Site: http://www.go-dove.com
Sales Range: $25-49.9 Million
Emp.: 8
Surplus Asset Management, Valuation & Disposition Services
N.A.I.C.S.: 423830

GoIndustry-DoveBid (Shanghai) Co., Ltd. (2)
Unit 4311 Nanzheng Building, No 580 Nanjing Road West, Shanghai, 200041, China
Tel.: (86) 2162726246
Emp.: 15
Surplus Asset Management, Valuation & Disposition Services
N.A.I.C.S.: 423830

GoIndustry-DoveBid Mexico SA de CV (2)
Libertad 16 Colonia Jurica, Queretaro, 76100, Mexico (100%)
Tel.: (52) 4422452304
Surplus Asset Management, Valuation & Disposition Services
N.A.I.C.S.: 423830

GoIndustry-DoveBid Philippines, Inc. (2)
Unit 6B 6th Floor 1100 Citibank-Frabelle Builidng, Madrigal Business Park, Alabang-Zapote Road, Muntinlupa, 1770, Philippines
Tel.: (63) 24785555
Web Site: http://www.go-dove.com
Sales Range: $25-49.9 Million
Emp.: 20
Surplus Asset Management, Valuation & Disposition Services
N.A.I.C.S.: 423830

Liquidity Services UK Ltd (1)
1 Alie Street, 18-20 St Andrew Street, London, E1 8DE, United Kingdom
Tel.: (44) 2070983700
Web Site: http://www.liquidityservices.com
Emp.: 50
Industrial Machinery Appraisal & Auction Services
N.A.I.C.S.: 541990

Machinio Corp. (1)
2045 W Grand Ave Ste B PMB 19483, Chicago, IL 60612
Web Site: https://www.machinio.com
Transportation Equipment Distr
N.A.I.C.S.: 423860

Network International Inc. (1)
3555 Timmons Ln Ste 1200, Houston, TX 77027
Tel.: (713) 659-7500
Web Site: http://www.networkintl.com
Sales Range: $25-49.9 Million
Emp.: 35
Oil Well Machinery, Equipment & Supplies
N.A.I.C.S.: 423830

Sierra Auction Management, Inc. (1)
3570 Grand Ave, Phoenix, AZ 85019-3413
Tel.: (602) 242-7121
Web Site: http://sierraauction.com
Rev.: $1,200,000
Emp.: 9
Business Services, Nec, Nsk
N.A.I.C.S.: 459420
Dan White (CEO)
Nick Carr (Dir-Ops)
Robert J. Glovitz (Exec VP)
Sherri Jones (Mgr-Mktg)

Surplus Acquisition Venture, LLC (1)
15051 N Kierland Blvd, Scottsdale, AZ 85254
Tel.: (480) 367-1100
Web Site: http://www.go-dove.com
Asset Management Services
N.A.I.C.S.: 531390

Subsidiary (Domestic):

Government Liquidation.com, LLC (2)

15051 N Kierland Blvd, Scottsdale, AZ 85254
Tel.: (480) 367-1300
Web Site: http://www.govliquidation.com
Asset Management & Disposition Services
N.A.I.C.S.: 531390

JTC Prison Industries, LLC (2)
445 S Munsterman St, Appleton, MN 56208-2608
Tel.: (320) 289-2052
Miscellaneous Product Mfr
N.A.I.C.S.: 339999

TruckCenter.com, LLC (1)
1121 Cantrell Sansom Rd, Fort Worth, TX 76131
Tel.: (404) 627-5346
Web Site: http://www.go-dove.com
Automobile Auction Services
N.A.I.C.S.: 425120

LIQUIDMETAL TECHNOLOGIES, INC.

20321 Valencia Cir, Lake Forest, CA 92630
Tel.: (949) 635-2100   DE
Web Site:
https://www.liquidmetal.com
Year Founded: 1987
LQMT—(OTCQB)
Rev.: $383,000
Assets: $33,335,000
Liabilities: $1,296,000
Net Worth: $32,039,000
Earnings: ($2,393,000)
Emp.: 7
Fiscal Year-end: 12/31/22
Research, Development & Commercialization of Amorphous Metals
N.A.I.C.S.: 332999
Tony Chung (CEO)
Abdi Mahamedi (Vice Chm)
Yeung Tak Lugee Li (Chm)
Isaac Bresnick (Pres)

LITHIA MOTORS, INC.

150 N Bartlett St, Medford, OR 97501
Tel.: (541) 776-6401   OR
Web Site:
https://www.lithiainvestorrelations.com
Year Founded: 1946
LAD—(NYSE)
Rev.: $31,042,300,000
Assets: $19,632,500,000
Liabilities: $13,393,600,000
Net Worth: $6,238,900,000
Earnings: $1,000,800,000
Emp.: 27,446
Fiscal Year-end: 12/31/23
Holding Company; New & Used Automobile Dealerships Owner & Operator
N.A.I.C.S.: 551112
Sidney B. DeBoer (Founder & Chm)
Bryan B. DeBoer (Pres & CEO)
Tina Miller (CFO, Principal Acctg Officer & Sr VP)
George Hines (Chief Innovation & Tech Officer & Sr VP)
Chuck Lietz (VP-Fin)
Marguerite Celeste (CMO & Sr VP)
Gary Glandon (Chief People Officer)
Tom Naso (Pres)
Adam Chamberlain (Pres)
Carol Deacon (Sr VP)
Adam Chamberlain (COO & Exec VP)
Christopher Holzshu (Exec VP)

Subsidiaries:

Arden Maidstone Limited (1)
736 London Road, Larkfield, ME20 6BG, United Kingdom
Tel.: (44) 1622295657
Web Site:
https://www.ardenmaidstonemini.co.uk
New & Used Car Distr
N.A.I.C.S.: 441120

Arden Tunbridge Wells Limited (1)
Longfield Rd, Royal Tunbridge Wells, TN2 3UE, Kent, United Kingdom
Tel.: (44) 1892349650
Web Site: https://www.ardentunbridgewells bmw.co.uk
Motor Vehicle Distr
N.A.I.C.S.: 423110

Audi Coral Springs (1)
5555 N State Rd 7, Coral Springs, FL 33073
Web Site: https://www.audicoralsprings.com
Auto Body Repair Services
N.A.I.C.S.: 811111

Audi Farmington Hills (1)
37911 Grand River Ave, Farmington Hills, MI 48335
Tel.: (248) 471-0800
Web Site:
https://www.audifarmingtonhills.com
Car Dealing Services
N.A.I.C.S.: 441110

Autoworks Markham, LP (1)
189 Bullock Dr, Markham, L3P 1W4, ON, Canada
Tel.: (289) 661-1591
Web Site: https://www.pfaffautoworks.com
Car Repair Services
N.A.I.C.S.: 811198

Baierl Automotive Corporation (1)
11410 Perry Hwy, Wexford, PA 15090-9241
Tel.: (724) 940-2197
Web Site: https://www.baierlacura.com
Holding Company; Automobile Dealerships Owner & Operator
N.A.I.C.S.: 551112

Subsidiary (Domestic):

Baierl Chevrolet, Inc. (2)
10430 Perry Hwy, Wexford, PA 15090
Tel.: (878) 332-7300
Web Site: https://www.baierlchevrolet.com
New & Used Automobile Dealer
N.A.I.C.S.: 441110
Bob Helsel (Mgr)
Jeff Nock (Gen Mgr-Sls)
Brett Gardner (Bus Mgr)
Larry Sano (Mgr-Bus Dev Center)
Melody Bursick (Office Mgr)
Allison Cricks (Coord-Appointment)
Hepburn Walker (Mgr-Parts)
Alex Riederer (Mgr)
Kevin Covert (Mgr)
Kevin Katchmark (Mgr)
Tim Golden (Mgr)
Alex Riederer (Mgr)
Kevin Covert (Mgr)
Kevin Katchmark (Mgr)
Tim Golden (Mgr)

Unit (Domestic):

Baierl Toyota (3)
19045 Perry Hwy, Mars, PA 16046
Tel.: (724) 453-4103
Web Site: https://www.baierltoyota.com
New & Used Car Dealer
N.A.I.C.S.: 441110
Alex Smith (Fin Mgr)
Marcus Dominish (Fin Mgr)
Timothy Boyd (Sls Mgr)
Shawn Crow (Mgr)
Joe McMahon (Mgr-BDC)
Ian Renter (Sls Mgr)
Dawn Stewart (Office Mgr)
Brad Pavlik (Gen Mgr)

Bellevue-S, LLC (1)
15150 SE Eastgate Way, Bellevue, WA 98007
Tel.: (425) 406-1158
Web Site: https://www.michaelssubaru.com
Automobile Mfr
N.A.I.C.S.: 336110

Bellevue-T, LLC (1)
3080 148th Ave SE, Bellevue, WA 98007
Tel.: (425) 230-2799
Web Site: https://www.toyotaofbellevue.com
Automobile Mfr
N.A.I.C.S.: 336110

Bend-CDJR, LLC (1)
1865 NE Hwy 20, Bend, OR 97701
Tel.: (541) 306-4090

Web Site: http://www.lithiacdjrbend.com
Car Dealing Services
N.A.I.C.S.: 441110
Steve Burnett (Gen Mgr)

Buick GMC of Beaverton (1)
9155 SW Canyon Rd, Portland, OR 97225
Tel.: (503) 292-8801
Web Site: https://www.beavertongmc.com
Sales Range: $50-74.9 Million
Emp.: 80
New & Used Car Sales
N.A.I.C.S.: 441110
Charles Brown (Gen Mgr)

Cadillac of Portland Lloyd Center, LLC (1)
9141 SW Canyon Rd, Portland, OR 97225-3518
Tel.: (503) 300-7150
Web Site: https://www.cadillacportland.com
Automobile Dealers
N.A.I.C.S.: 441110

Caldwell-Air, LLC (1)
1705 Industrial Way, Caldwell, ID 83605
Tel.: (208) 400-9324
Web Site: https://www.boiseairstream.com
New & Used Car Distr
N.A.I.C.S.: 441120

Camp Automotive, Inc. (1)
101 E Montgomery Ave, Spokane, WA 99207
Web Site: https://www.campchevrolet.com
Sales Range: $125-149.9 Million
Emp.: 150
New & Used Car Dealers
N.A.I.C.S.: 441110
James Baughman (Gen Mgr)
Elizabeth Freter (Asst Mgr)
Justin Robidoux (Mgr)

Carbone Automotive Group (1)
5194 Commercial Dr, Yorkville, NY 13495
Tel.: (315) 724-4216
Web Site: http://www.carbonecars.com
Automobile Insurance Agency
N.A.I.C.S.: 524210
Alexander Carbone (Pres)

Chesapeake-H, LLC (1)
621 N Battlefield Blvd, Chesapeake, VA 23320
Tel.: (757) 213-6600
Web Site:
https://www.priorityhondachesapeake.com
New & Used Car Distr
N.A.I.C.S.: 441120

Clackamas Ultimate Airstreams, LLC (1)
16250 SE Evelyn St, Clackamas, OR 97015
Tel.: (503) 570-9001
Web Site:
https://www.ultimateairstreams.com
Interior Airstream Mfr & Distr
N.A.I.C.S.: 336213

Clear Lake-I, Inc. (1)
14705 Gulf Freeway, Houston, TX 77034
Tel.: (832) 553-1792
Web Site: https://www.clearlakeinfiniti.com
New & Used Car Distr
N.A.I.C.S.: 441120

Curry Honda (1)
5525 Peachtree Industrial Blvd, Chamblee, GA 30341
Tel.: (770) 451-2700
Web Site: http://www.curryhondaga.com
Sales Range: $50-74.9 Million
Automobile Dealers
N.A.I.C.S.: 441110
Bill Clark (Dir)
Brian Dominick (Gen Mgr-Sls)
Misty Smith (Mgr-BDC)
Chuck Hayden (Mgr-Finance)
Reed Waldman (Mgr-Internet Sls)
Jason Yi (Mgr)
T. J. Toreno (Mgr-Ops)
Brian Baty (Mgr-Production)
Bruce Smith (Dir-Sls)
Junior Coker (Dir-Fixed Ops)
Adam Zukerman (Pres)
Calvin Barnes (Sls Mgr)
George Amini (Mgr)
James Keller (Sls Mgr)
Adon Haas (Fin Mgr)
Sanober Nichols (Fin Mgr)

Lithia Motors, Inc.—(Continued)

V. P. Patel *(Fin Mgr)*
Karen Silva *(Mgr)*
Sarah Stewart *(Mgr)*
Jay Brown *(Mgr)*
Quyen Chau *(Asst Mgr)*
Trisha Saha *(Coord)*
Adam Zukerman *(Pres)*
Calvin Barnes *(Sls Mgr)*
George Amini *(Mgr)*
James Keller *(Sls Mgr)*
Adon Haas *(Fin Mgr)*
Sanober Nichols *(Fin Mgr)*
V. P. Patel *(Fin Mgr)*
Karen Silva *(Mgr)*
Sarah Stewart *(Mgr)*
Jay Brown *(Mgr)*
Quyen Chau *(Asst Mgr)*
Trisha Saha *(Coord)*

DCH (Oxnard) Inc. (1)
1500 E Ventura Blvd, Oxnard, CA 93036
Tel.: (805) 790-9344
Web Site: https://www.hondaofoxnard.com
Automotive Retailer
N.A.I.C.S.: 441120
Masood Zamani *(Mgr-Sls)*
Alex Lopez *(Dir-Parts)*
Claudia Coronado *(Dir-Internet)*

DCH Auto Group (USA) Inc. (1)
955 Rte 9 N, South Amboy, NJ 08879
Tel.: (732) 727-9168
Web Site: https://www.dchauto.com
New & Used Car Dealerships Owner & Operator
N.A.I.C.S.: 551112

Subsidiary (Domestic):

DCH Ford of Thousand Oaks (2)
3810 Thousand Oaks Blvd, Thousand
Oaks, CA 91362
Tel.: (805) 719-6384
Web Site:
https://www.dchfordofthousandoaks.com
New & Used Car Dealer
N.A.I.C.S.: 441110
D. J. Donoho *(Mgr-Parts)*
Charles Zeidman *(Mgr-Sls)*

DCH Honda of Nanuet (2)
10 Route 304, Nanuet, NY 10954
Tel.: (845) 367-7050
Web Site:
https://www.dchhondaofnanuet.com
New & Used Car Dealer
N.A.I.C.S.: 441110
Thomas Muradian *(Sls Mgr)*
Dominick Garretson *(Mgr)*
Gloria Amaro *(Mgr-Svc BDC)*
John Puglisi *(Gen Mgr)*
Darren Makofsky *(Mgr-Pre-Owned)*
Dhimitri Robo *(Mgr-Sls)*
Greg Brandford *(Mgr-Sls)*
Mike Ehirim *(Mgr-Fin)*
Kamu Foggie *(Mgr-Fin)*
Zakir Hussain *(Gen Sls Mgr)*
Haleema Asif *(Sls Mgr-Internet)*
James Torres *(Fin Mgr)*
Joseph Modica *(Mgr-Svc)*
Wilbert Myles *(Asst Mgr-Svc)*
Darwish Mustafa *(Fin Mgr)*

DCH Management Services Inc. (2)
955 US Hwy 9, South Amboy, NJ 08879
Tel.: (732) 727-9168
Emp.: 40
Business Consulting Services
N.A.I.C.S.: 541611
William Owusu *(Mgr)*
Rehab Attia *(Project Mgr-Design & Construction Mgmt)*

DCH Paramus Honda (2)
120 NJ-4, Paramus, NJ 07652
Tel.: (201) 351-2669
Web Site:
https://www.dchparamushonda.com
New & Used Car Dealer
N.A.I.C.S.: 441110
Jose Hernandez *(Dir-Used Car)*
Robert Tranquilli *(Mgr-F&I)*
John Medrano *(Mgr-F&I)*
Kelvin Rodriguez *(Mgr-F&I)*
Jerrod Hurley *(Mgr-F&I)*
Stacy Sorrentino *(Acct Mgr)*
Hamad Deeb *(Specialist-)*
Ariel Argueta *(Coord)*

Breana Manderson *(Coord)*
Brianna Faranesh *(Coord)*
Chelsea Hernandez *(Coord)*
Jada Hester *(Coord)*
Matthew Sampayo *(Coord)*
Mixeal Veras *(Coord)*
Tarik Aldakhlallah *(Coord)*
Russell Kent *(Mgr-Body Shop)*
Donna Mazzaro *(Mgr)*
Alberto Cabrera *(Mgr)*
Carlos Gonzalez *(Mgr-F&I)*
Darwish Mustafa *(Mgr)*
Shadi Saadeh *(Mgr-F&I)*
Paul Park *(Mgr-F&I)*
Mike Lee *(Dir-New Car Sls)*
Lenny Ramos *(Mgr-Desk)*
Bruce Laga *(Dir-Svc & Parts)*
Chet Forbes *(Mgr-)*
Daniel Talbot *(Mgr-Parts)*
Kristal Stanislawczyk *(Sls Dir)*
Lisa Williams *(Acct Mgr)*
Bill Sutera *(Portfolio Mgr)*
Cindy Espinosa *(Acct Mgr)*
Kimberly Graney *(Acct Mgr)*
Isam Adawi *(Acct Mgr-)*
Barbara Caeser *(Head-)*
Martha Batista *(Fin Dir)*
Sunil Patel *(Mgr-)*
Freddy Francisco *(Mgr-)*
Robert Kibbler *(Gen Mgr)*
Michael DeAngelis *(Mgr)*

DCH Bloomfield LLC (1)
425 Bloomfield Ave, Bloomfield, NJ 07003
Web Site: https://www.bmwofbloomfield.com
Automobile Mfr
N.A.I.C.S.: 336110

DCH CA LLC (1)
26705 Ynez Rd, Temecula, CA 92591
Tel.: (951) 699-1515
Web Site:
https://www.ohacuraoftemecula.com
Automotive Retailer
N.A.I.C.S.: 441120

DCH California Motors Inc. (1)
1631 Auto Center Dr, Oxnard, CA 93036
Tel.: (805) 988-7900
Web Site: https://www.toyotaofoxnard.com
Automotive Retailer
N.A.I.C.S.: 441120
John Hautman *(Gen Mgr)*
Jasmin Lawson *(Asst Mgr-Svc)*
Bob Cobos *(Asst Mgr-Svc)*
Andres Santander *(Mgr-Fin)*
Jerry Durazo *(Asst Mgr-Parts)*
Oscar Gutierrez *(Gen Mgr-Sls)*

DCH Del Norte, INC. (1)
1640 Auto Center Dr, Oxnard, CA 93036
Tel.: (805) 764-1866
Web Site: http://www.dchlexusofoxnard.com
Automotive Retailer
N.A.I.C.S.: 441120

DCH Delaware LLC (1)
Concord Mall, Wilmington, DE 19803
Tel.: (302) 478-4600
Automobile Dealers
N.A.I.C.S.: 441110

DCH Freehold LLC (1)
4268 Route 9 S, Freehold, NJ 07728
Web Site:
https://www.dchfreeholdtoyota.com
Automobile Mfr
N.A.I.C.S.: 336110

DCH Holdings LLC (1)
201 Diplomat Dr, Philadelphia, PA 19113
Tel.: (610) 362-2422
Emp.: 6
Holding Company
N.A.I.C.S.: 551112
David Henderson *(Principal)*

DCH Investments Inc. (1)
4268 Us Hwy 9, Freehold, NJ 07728
Tel.: (732) 409-0904
Automobile Dealers
N.A.I.C.S.: 441110

DCH Korean Imports LLC (1)
26799 Ynez Rd, Temecula, CA 92591
Web Site:
https://www.dchkiaoftemecula.com
Automotive Part Whslr
N.A.I.C.S.: 441120
Joseph Yanni *(Mgr-Sls)*
Brian Norstedt *(Mgr-Parts)*

DCH Mamaroneck LLC (1)
1305 E Boston Post Rd, Mamaroneck, NY
10543
Automotive Distr
N.A.I.C.S.: 423110

DCH Mission Valley LLC (1)
5812 Mission Gorge Rd, San Diego, CA
92120
Tel.: (619) 521-6000
Web Site:
https://www.dchhondaofmissionvalley.com
Automotive Retailer
N.A.I.C.S.: 441120
Marty Meador *(Gen Mgr)*
Jeff Chapin *(Gen Sls Mgr)*
Brian Haywood *(Mgr-Sls)*
Scott Bada *(Mgr-Svc)*
Daniel Meador *(Sls Mgr)*
Jonathan Orellana *(Fin Mgr)*
Isella Salazar *(Coord-Appointment)*
Mayra Cajica *(Coord-Appointment)*

DCH Montclair LLC (1)
100 Bloomfield Ave, Verona, NJ 07044
Tel.: (862) 292-2604
Web Site:
https://www.dchmontclairacura.com
Automobile Mfr
N.A.I.C.S.: 336110

DCH Motors LLC (1)
200 NJ-36, Eatontown, NJ 07724
Automotive Distr
N.A.I.C.S.: 423110

DCH Oxnard 1521 Imports Inc. (1)
1600 E Ventura Blvd, Oxnard, CA 93036
Tel.: (805) 228-4921
Web Site: https://www.dchaudioxnard.com
Automotive Retailer
N.A.I.C.S.: 441120
Steve Handler *(Gen Mgr)*
Yixin Tong *(Mgr-Lease Retention & Inventory)*
Cesar Rojas *(Mgr-Svc)*
Heather Massey *(Fin Mgr)*

DCH Simi Valley Inc. (1)
2380 1st St, Simi Valley, CA 93065
Tel.: (805) 526-7500
Web Site: https://www.simivalleytoyota.com
Automotive Distr
N.A.I.C.S.: 423110

DCH Temecula Imports LLC (1)
26755 Ynez Rd, Temecula, CA 92591
Web Site:
https://www.dchhondaoftemecula.com
Automotive Retailer
N.A.I.C.S.: 441120
Corbin Higgins *(Mgr-Fin)*
Chris Johnson *(Mgr-Svc)*
Daniel Galal *(Gen Mgr-Sls)*
William Tiedmond *(Mgr-Sls)*
Kelly Zala *(Mgr-Customer Rels)*
Peter Shehata *(Sls Mgr)*
Teresa Cabanillas *(Mgr-Client Care)*
Russ Capuano *(Asst Mgr-Svc)*

DCH Temecula Motors LLC (1)
26845 Ynez Rd, Temecula, CA 92591
Tel.: (951) 404-1884
Web Site:
https://www.dchchryslerjeepdodgeofte
mecula.com
Emp.: 3
Automotive Retailer
N.A.I.C.S.: 441120
Marty Striano *(Mgr-Internet Sls)*
Greg Carey *(Mgr-Internet Sls)*
Dennis Shoup *(Mgr-Internet Sls)*
John Holmbeck *(Gen Mgr)*
Ted Rapp *(Sls Mgr)*
Jack Szanto *(Mgr-Parts)*
Ryan Mistak *(Mgr-Fin)*
Robert Traver *(Mgr-Internet Sls)*
John Mendoza *(Mgr-Internet Sls)*

DCH Torrance Imports Inc. (1)
2909 Pacific Coast Hwy, Torrance, CA
90505
Tel.: (424) 319-7174
Web Site: https://www.torrancetoyota.com
Automotive Retailer
N.A.I.C.S.: 441120
Clara Serna *(Dir-Svc)*
Amy Rodriguez *(Asst Mgr-Svc)*
Manny Pena *(Mgr-Parts)*
Keith White *(Dir-Internet)*

Dallas-H, Inc. (1)
5311 Lemmon Ave, Dallas, TX 75209
Tel.: (214) 646-1564
Web Site:
https://www.johneaglehondaofdallas.com
Car Dealing Services
N.A.I.C.S.: 441110

Dallas-T, Inc. (1)
12650 Lyndon B Johnson Fwy, Dallas, TX
75228
Web Site: https://www.sportcitytoyota.com
Car Dealing Services
N.A.I.C.S.: 441110
Gary Gray *(Gen Mgr)*
Charles Cooley *(Mgr-New Vehicle)*
Jesus Alcala *(Mgr-Used Vehicle)*

Daron Motors LLC (1)
1101 US 9, Old Bridge, NJ 08857
Web Site:
https://www.dchacademyhonda.com
Automobile Mfr
N.A.I.C.S.: 336110

Doral-Hy, LLC (1)
10285 NW 12th St, Doral, FL 33172
Tel.: (305) 722-6094
Web Site: https://www.doralhyundai.com
Motor Vehicle Mfr & Distr
N.A.I.C.S.: 336211

Doral-VW, LLC (1)
10455 NW 12th St Ste C, Doral, FL 33172
Tel.: (786) 567-3498
Web Site: https://www.doralvw.com
Motor Vehicle Distr
N.A.I.C.S.: 423110

Driveway Finance Corporation (1)
150 N Bartlett St, Medford, OR 97501
Web Site:
https://www.drivewayfinancecorp.com
Automobile Finance Services
N.A.I.C.S.: 522220

Driveway Motors, LLC (1)
8929 E Independence Blvd, Matthews, NC
28105
Tel.: (704) 274-1748
Web Site: https://www.drivewaymotor.com
Used Car Distr
N.A.I.C.S.: 441120

Ferndale Collision, LLC (1)
1600 Bonner St, Ferndale, MI 48220
Auto Body Repair Services
N.A.I.C.S.: 811111

Garden City-CJD, LLC (1)
32850 Ford Rd, Garden City, MI 48135-
1570
Tel.: (734) 338-8824
Web Site:
https://www.suburbanchryslerdodgejeep
ramofgardencity.com
New & Used Car Distr
N.A.I.C.S.: 441120

Guelph-S, LP (1)
12 Wilbert St, Guelph, N1K 0A4, ON,
Canada
Tel.: (226) 299-0770
Web Site: https://www.pfaffsubaru.com
New & Used Car Distr
N.A.I.C.S.: 441120

Henderson-Hy, LLC (1)
460 N Boulder Hwy, Henderson, NV 89015
Tel.: (725) 228-3195
Web Site:
https://www.hendersonhyundai.com
Motor Vehicle Distr
N.A.I.C.S.: 423110

Honda of Ames (1)
220 Kitty Hawk Dr, Ames, IA 50010
Web Site: https://www.ameshonda.com
New & Used Car Dealership
N.A.I.C.S.: 441110
Mike Gougherty *(Gen Mgr)*
Tom Albers *(Mgr-Parts)*
Doug Krogman *(Mgr)*
Tom Wishman *(Sls Mgr)*
Lindy Ellett *(Mgr--Honda)*
Jason Reece *(Sls Mgr)*
Melvin Gawley *(Mgr)*

Honolulu Ford, Inc. (1)
1370 N King St, Honolulu, HI 96817
Tel.: (808) 824-3973
Web Site: https://www.honoluluford.com

Sales Range: $75-99.9 Million
New & Used Car Dealer
N.A.I.C.S.: 441110
Angela Wong (Gen Mgr)
Mark Sherlock (Gen Sls Mgr)
John Holmes (Sls Mgr)
Stuart Alsup (Fin Mgr)
Art Tsukamoto (Mgr-Fleet)
John Le (Mgr-Svc)

Hutchins Eugene Nissan, Inc. (1)
2060 Martin Luther King Jr Blvd, Eugene,
OR 97401
Web Site:
    https://www.lithianissaneugene.com
Automobile Dealers
N.A.I.C.S.: 441110
Aaron Bingham (Gen Mgr)
Kristina Spurgeon (Office Mgr)
Mickey McKinney (Mgr)
Jesse Kinney (Mgr)
Jordan McCray (Mgr-Finance)

Hutchins Imported Motors, Inc. (1)
163 S 9th St, Springfield, OR 97477
Tel.: (541) 225-5452
Web Site:
    https://www.lithiatoyotaspringfield.com
Sales Range: $25-49.9 Million
Emp.: 70
Automobile Dealers
N.A.I.C.S.: 441110
Sam Jones (Mgr-Sls)
Rodney Kellum (Mgr-Internet Sls)
Keith Moreck (Mgr-Internet Sls)
Chris Vann (Mgr-Internet Sls)
Michael Hawkins (Mgr-Parts)
Dennis Dietrich (Mgr-Fin)
Samantha Howell (Mgr-Bus)
J. J. Lawson (Mgr)
Dianne Yrigollen (Asst Office Mgr)
Steve Bennett (Fin Mgr)
Blake Bleisch (Gen Sls Mgr)
Zamir Marquez (Mgr-)
Tony Owings (Fin Mgr)

Jackson-T, LLC (1)
6100 I-55 N Frontage Rd, Jackson, MS
39211
Tel.: (601) 351-9635
Web Site: https://www.toyotaofjackson.com
Automobile Mfr
N.A.I.C.S.: 336110

**Jaguar Land Rover North America,
LLC** (1)
28701 Marguerite Pkwy, Mission Viejo, CA
92692
Tel.: (949) 973-8900
Web Site:
    http://www.jaguarmissionviejo.com
Sales Range: $25-49.9 Million
Emp.: 50
Car Dealership
N.A.I.C.S.: 441110
Chris Crinion (Mgr)
Marcio Barrancas (Asst Mgr)
Adam Partridge (Sls Mgr)
Brian Smith (Sls Mgr)
Matt Goodwin (Mgr)
Steven Rudkin (Gen Mgr)
Robert Davis (Mgr)
Jeff Assad (Fin Mgr)
Pablo Hojberg (Fin Mgr)

**Jardine Motors Group UK
Limited** (1)
770 The Crescent, Colchester Business
Park, Colchester, CO4 9YQ, Essex, United
Kingdom
Tel.: (44) 1206838788
Web Site: http://www.jardinemotors.co.uk
Sales Range: $25-49.9 Million
Emp.: 30
Automotive Retailer
N.A.I.C.S.: 441110

Subsidiary (Domestic):

Colliers of Birmingham Limited (2)
884 Warwick Rd, Acocks Green, Birming-
ham, B11 2ES, W Midlands, United King-
dom
Tel.: (44) 1215147980
Web Site: http://www.colliers.co.uk
New & Used Car Dealer
N.A.I.C.S.: 441110
Phil Mountford (Principal-Dealer)
Nick Bailey (Sls Mgr)
Sean Walley (Bus Mgr)

Lancaster plc (2)
770 The Crescent, Colchester Business
Park, Colchester, CO4 9YQ, Essex, United
Kingdom
Tel.: (44) 1206 838 788
Web Site: http://www.jardinemotors.co.uk
Sales Range: $25-49.9 Million
Emp.: 20
Holding Company; New & Used Car Dealer-
ships Operator
N.A.I.C.S.: 551112
New Williams (CEO)

Subsidiary (Domestic):

**Lancaster Motor Company
Limited** (3)
770 The Crescent, Colchester Business
Park, Colchester, CO4 9YQ, Essex, United
Kingdom
Tel.: (44) 1206838788
Web Site: http://www.jardinemotors.co.uk
New & Used Car Dealer
N.A.I.C.S.: 441110
Mark Herbert (CEO)

Subsidiary (Domestic):

Lancaster Cars Limited (4)
770 The Crescent, Colchester Business
Park, Colchester, CO4 9YQ, United King-
dom
Tel.: (44) 1206 838 788
New & Used Car Dealerships Operator
N.A.I.C.S.: 441110

**Lancaster Specialist Cars
Limited** (4)
770 The Crescent, Colchester, CO4 9YQ,
Essex, United Kingdom
Tel.: (44) 1206 838788
Web Site: http://www.jardinemotors.co.uk
Emp.: 25
New & Used Car Dealerships Operator
N.A.I.C.S.: 441110
Stuart Lee (Gen Mgr)

Lancaster Sports Cars Limited (4)
770 The Crescent, Colchester Business
Park, Colchester, CO4 9YQ, Essex, United
Kingdom
Tel.: (44) 1206 838 788
New & Used Car Dealerships Operator
N.A.I.C.S.: 441110

Jim Cogdill Company (1)
8544 Kingston Pike, Knoxville, TN 37919
Tel.: (865) 690-1611
Web Site: http://www.jimcogdill.com
Automobiles, New & Used
N.A.I.C.S.: 441110
James T. Cogdill (Pres)
Bradley Rayfield (Gen Sls Mgr)
Eric Isenberg (Mgr)

Jim Smolich Motors, Inc. (1)
1865 NE Hwy 20, Bend, OR 97701
Tel.: (541) 312-6802
Web Site: http://www.smolichmotors.com
Credit Bureaus
N.A.I.C.S.: 561040
Steve Burnett (Gen Mgr)
Michael Dipasquale (Gen Sls Mgr)
Matt Paden (Mgr-Used Car)
Chris Anderson (Fin Mgr)
Shannon Gasper (Fin Mgr)
Delissa Kinsey (Fin Mgr)
Jared Jordan (Mgr-Svc)
Kate Kraft-Couraud (Office Mgr)

Katy-H, Inc. (1)
21001 Katy Fwy, Katy, TX 77450
Tel.: (281) 616-8830
Web Site: https://www.hondacarsofkaty.com
Car Dealing Services
N.A.I.C.S.: 441110

Knoxville-CJD, LLC (1)
8544 Kingston Pike, Knoxville, TN 37919-
5353
Tel.: (865) 270-4243
Web Site: https://www.jimcogdilldodge.com
Car Dealing Services
N.A.I.C.S.: 441110

LBMP, LLC (1)
2001 SW Jefferson St, Portland, OR 97201-
2464
Web Site: https://www.bmwportland.com
Automobile Dealers

N.A.I.C.S.: 441110

LDLC, LLC (1)
860 N Tel Shor Blvd, Las Cruces, NM
88011
Tel.: (575) 556-2400
Web Site: http://www.lascrucesdodge.com
Automobile Dealers
N.A.I.C.S.: 441110

LFKF, LLC (1)
2833 Washburn Way, Klamath Falls, OR
97603
Tel.: (541) 205-0292
Web Site:
    https://www.lithiafordklamathfalls.com
Emp.: 50
Automobile Dealers
N.A.I.C.S.: 441110
Kirby Gordon (Gen Mgr)
Charles Whitmore (Sls Mgr-Finance)
Dylan Smith (Sls Mgr-Fin)

LGPAC, Inc. (1)
1421 NE 6th St, Grants Pass, OR 97526-
1253
Tel.: (541) 293-1112
Web Site: https://www.lithiagrantspass.com
Sales Range: $75-99.9 Million
Emp.: 47
New & Used Automobile Dealer
N.A.I.C.S.: 441110

LLL Sales CO LLC (1)
15541 S Western Ave, Gardena, CA 90249
Tel.: (424) 216-9226
Web Site: https://www.gardenahonda.com
Automobile Dealers
N.A.I.C.S.: 441110

LMBB, LLC (1)
9275 SW Canyon Rd, Portland, OR 97225
Tel.: (503) 296-1700
Web Site:
    https://www.mercedesbenzbeaverton.com
Automobile Dealers
N.A.I.C.S.: 441110
Chris Walters (Mgr-Svc)
Mejra Berisa (Fin Mgr)

LMBP, LLC (1)
1605 SW Naito Pkwy, Portland, OR 97201
Tel.: (971) 270-3860
Web Site:
    https://www.mercedesbenzportland.com
Sales Range: $25-49.9 Million
Emp.: 60
Automobile Dealers
N.A.I.C.S.: 441110

Latham Ford-F, LLC (1)
702 Troy Schenectady Rd, Latham, NY
12110
Tel.: (518) 328-3387
Web Site:
    https://www.lathamfordmotors.com
Car Dealing Services
N.A.I.C.S.: 441110

League City-H, Inc. (1)
2205 Gulf Fwy S, League City, TX 77573
Tel.: (281) 724-5111
Web Site:
    https://www.hondaofclearlake.com
Car Dealing Services
N.A.I.C.S.: 441110

**Lehman Dealership Enterprises,
Inc.** (1)
21400 NW 2nd Ave, Miami, FL 33169
Tel.: (305) 653-7111
Web Site: http://www.lehmanautoworld.com
New & Used Car Dealer
N.A.I.C.S.: 441110

Subsidiary (Domestic):

William Lehman & Associates (2)
21200 NW 2nd Ave, Miami, FL 33169
Tel.: (305) 652-5252
Web Site: http://www.lehmanmitsubishi.com
Automobile New & Used Distr
N.A.I.C.S.: 441110

William Lehman Buick Inc. (2)
21400 NW 2nd Ave, Miami, FL 33169
Tel.: (305) 306-1637
Web Site: https://www.lehmanhyundai.com
Automobiles, New & Used
N.A.I.C.S.: 441110
William Lehman Jr. (Pres)

William Lehman Leasing Corp. (2)
21400 NW 2nd Ave, Miami, FL 33169
Tel.: (305) 654-6300
Rev.: $4,500,000
Emp.: 10
Passenger Car Leasing
N.A.I.C.S.: 532112
Ted Mccarthy (Pres)

Lexington-CJD, LLC (1)
1560 E New Circle Rd, Lexington, KY
40509
Tel.: (859) 519-3147
Web Site:
    https://www.freedomcdjroflexington.com
New & Used Car Distr
N.A.I.C.S.: 441120

Lithia ACDM, Inc. (1)
5138 Merle Hay Rd, Johnston, IA 50131
Tel.: (515) 446-3581
Web Site: https://www.acuraofjohnston.com
Sales Range: $10-24.9 Million
Emp.: 70
New & Used Car Dealer
N.A.I.C.S.: 441110

Lithia BNM, Inc. (1)
4560 Grumman Dr, Medford, OR 97504
Tel.: (541) 774-8440
Web Site:
    https://www.lithianissanmedford.com
Emp.: 35
Automobile Dealers
N.A.I.C.S.: 441110

Lithia Bryan Texas, Inc. (1)
301 N Earl Rudder Fwy, Bryan, TX 77802
Tel.: (979) 977-1427
Web Site:
    https://www.bryanchryslerdodgejeep.com
Sales Range: $25-49.9 Million
Emp.: 60
Automobile Dealers
N.A.I.C.S.: 441110
Coy Alexander (Gen Mgr)
Jessica Foster (Office Mgr)
Mitchel Scoggins (Mgr)
Steven Emert (Mgr-Mdsg)
Archie Clary (Fin Mgr)
Nick Munoz (Sls Mgr)
Sonny Easley (Fin Mgr)
Rizwan Ahmad (Asst Mgr)

Lithia CDH, Inc. (1)
3401 E US Hwy 12, Helena, MT 59601-
9708
Tel.: (406) 430-3528
Web Site:
    https://www.lithiachryslerhelena.com
Sales Range: $25-49.9 Million
Emp.: 50
Automobile Dealers
N.A.I.C.S.: 441110
Tom Blunn (Mgr-Parts)

Lithia CJDO, Inc. (1)
2510 E 8th St, Odessa, TX 79761-4904
Tel.: (432) 231-0733
Web Site: https://www.allamericanchryslero
    dessa.com
Sales Range: $25-49.9 Million
Emp.: 100
Car Dealership
N.A.I.C.S.: 441110
Larry Hook (Gen Mgr)
Carlos Bueno (Sls Mgr)

Lithia CJDSA, Inc. (1)
4310 Sherwood Way, San Angelo, TX
76901-5615
Tel.: (325) 777-3122
Web Site:
    https://www.allamericanchryslersanan
    gelo.com
Automobile Dealers
N.A.I.C.S.: 441110
Mary Kendall (Mgr-Bus)
Coy Carney (Mgr-Insurance & Fin)
Julie Rainey (Accountant-Dealership)
Sherry Welch (Accountant-Dealership-I)

Lithia CJDSF, Inc. (1)
7401 Cerrillos Rd, Santa Fe, NM 87507-
8076
Web Site: https://www.lithiasantafe.com
Automobile Dealers
N.A.I.C.S.: 441110
Joselle Martinez (Office Mgr)
David Custred (Sls Mgr)
Richard Gonzales (Gen Sls Mgr)

Lithia Motors, Inc.—(Continued)

Crystal Baca (*Mgr-Internet*)
Alex Mineo (*Fin Mgr*)
Isidro Lopez (*Mgr-Inventory*)

Lithia Chrysler Jeep Dodge of Billings   **(1)**
2229 King Ave W, Billings, MT 59102-6421
Web Site:
  https://www.lithiadodgebillings.com
Automobile Dealers
N.A.I.C.S.: 441110

Lithia DE, Inc.   **(1)**
2121 Martin Luther King Jr Blvd, Eugene, OR 97401-2470
Tel.: (541) 632-8610
Web Site:
  https://www.lithiadodgeeugene.com
Automobile Dealers
N.A.I.C.S.: 441110
Rob Bennett (*Gen Mgr*)
Devin Pratt (*Mgr-Fin*)
Michele Strunk (*Office Mgr*)
Matt Sidman (*Mgr*)
Brian Fisher (*Mgr-Internet Sls*)
Guy Germann (*Mgr-Sls*)
Robert Monia (*Mgr-Fin*)
Javier Mendoza (*Mgr-Mdsg*)
Ryan Brown (*Gen Sls Mgr*)

Lithia DM, Inc.   **(1)**
4540 Grumman Dr, Medford, OR 97504
Tel.: (541) 776-6400
Web Site:
  http://www.lithiachryslermedford.com
Sales Range: $25-49.9 Million
Emp.: 3
New & Used Automobile Dealer
N.A.I.C.S.: 441110

Lithia DMID, Inc.   **(1)**
3801 W Wall St, Midland, TX 79703-7711
Tel.: (432) 315-2773
Web Site: https://www.allamericandodgemidland.com
Automobile Dealers
N.A.I.C.S.: 441110
Cathy Day (*Office Mgr*)
Ladonna Wilson (*Gen Mgr*)
Carlos Bueno (*Gen Sls Mgr*)
Toby Nock (*Mgr-Svc*)
Kylie Yonts (*Sls Mgr*)
Freddie San Miguel (*Mgr*)
Gabe Vasquez (*Fin Mgr*)
Zak Owen (*Fin Mgr*)
Kevin Tavarez (*Fin Mgr*)
Patrick Vasquez (*Fin Mgr*)
Mike Duarte (*Mgr-Fleet*)
Karla Esparza (*Asst Mgr-Parts*)
Samantha Tvrdy (*Asst Office Mgr*)
Melissa Gaston (*Coord-Personnel*)
Jeff Slaughter (*Gen Sls Mgr*)
Winston Lewis (*Sls Mgr*)

Lithia Des Moines-VW, LLC   **(1)**
5200 Merle Hay Rd, Johnston, IA 50131
Tel.: (515) 727-7064
Web Site:
  https://www.volkswagenofdesmoines.com
Used Car Retailer
N.A.I.C.S.: 441120
Jeremy Lester (*Sls Mgr*)
Midhat Efendic (*Fin Mgr*)
Ron Anderko (*Gen Mgr*)
Austin Berkes (*Mgr*)

Lithia Dodge of Tri-Cities, Inc.   **(1)**
7171 W Canal Dr, Kennewick, WA 99336-7660
Tel.: (509) 870-3760
Web Site:
  https://www.lithiadodgetricities.com
Automobile Dealers
N.A.I.C.S.: 441110

Lithia FMF, Inc.   **(1)**
195 E Auto Center Dr, Fresno, CA 93710
Tel.: (559) 761-1500
Web Site: http://www.lithiafordoffresno.com
Automobile Dealers
N.A.I.C.S.: 441110
Dean Payne (*Mgr-Fleet*)
Mike Chavez (*Mgr-Parts*)

Lithia Financial Corporation   **(1)**
2611 Biddle Rd, Medford, OR 97501-5825
Tel.: (541) 776-6400
Web Site: https://www.lithia.com

Passenger Car Leasing
N.A.I.C.S.: 532112

Lithia Ford of Boise, Inc.   **(1)**
8853 W Fairview Ave, Boise, ID 83704
Web Site: https://www.lithiafordboise.com
Automobile Dealers
N.A.I.C.S.: 441110
Jim Sterk (*Gen Mgr--Store*)
Dave Schultz (*Mgr-Gen Sls*)
Jim Gentle (*Mgr*)
Shannon Pike (*Mgr-*)
Logan Bird (*Mgr-*)
Aron Anderson (*Mgr-Body Shop*)
Gennadiy Barbin (*Mgr-F&I*)
Ryan Curran (*Mgr*)
Tom Smith (*Mgr*)
Rod Bradley (*Mgr*)
Cristian Szentanai (*Mgr*)
Lucy Lechuga (*Asst Office Mgr*)
Allen Oltman (*Mgr*)
Ted Wesler (*Mgr*)
Rhett Sheeder (*Mgr-*)
Neris Saric (*Mgr-*)
Steven Dougherty (*Mgr-*)
Aaron Wagner (*Mgr-*)
Anthony Laughlin (*Mgr-*)
Brian Sucher (*Mgr-*)
Chris Young (*Asst Mgr*)

Lithia HGF   **(1)**
4900 10th Ave S, Great Falls, MT 59405
Tel.: (406) 564-1296
Web Site: http://www.greatfallshonda.com
Sales Range: $25-49.9 Million
Emp.: 50
Automobile Dealers
N.A.I.C.S.: 441110

Lithia HMID, Inc.   **(1)**
5000 John Ben Shepperd Pkwy, Odessa, TX 79762
Tel.: (432) 614-9404
Web Site: https://www.hyundaiofodessa.com
Sales Range: $25-49.9 Million
Emp.: 100
Automobile Dealers
N.A.I.C.S.: 441110
Joe Jordan (*Mgr-Parts*)

Lithia Idaho Falls-F, Inc.   **(1)**
980 W Broadway, Idaho Falls, ID 83402
Web Site:
  https://www.lithiafordidahofalls.com
Used Car Retailer
N.A.I.C.S.: 441120

Lithia JEF, Inc.   **(1)**
5590 N Blackstone, Fresno, CA 93710
Tel.: (559) 899-3257
Automotive Distr
N.A.I.C.S.: 423110
Ash Desai (*Gen Mgr*)
Stephanie Roberts (*Office Mgr*)
Victor Ochoa (*Gen Sls Mgr*)
Al Pacheco (*Sls Mgr*)
Ruben Castano (*Mgr-Used Car*)
Stan Ivy (*Sls Mgr*)
Eric Taylor (*Mgr-Parts*)
Matt Calderone (*Mgr-Svc*)

Lithia Klamath, Inc.   **(1)**
2675 Washburn Way, Klamath Falls, OR 97603-4515
Tel.: (541) 539-4494
Web Site: https://www.lithiaklamathfalls.com
Sales Range: $25-49.9 Million
Emp.: 50
Automobile Dealers
N.A.I.C.S.: 441110

Lithia MBDM, Inc.   **(1)**
9993 Hickman Rd, Urbandale, IA 50322
Web Site: https://www.mercedesbenzdesmoines.com
Automobile Dealers
N.A.I.C.S.: 441110
Christopher Cashen (*Mgr-Parts*)
Anthony Gladney (*Gen Mgr*)
John Rowold (*Mgr-Sls*)

Lithia MMF, Inc.   **(1)**
5200 N Blackstone Ave, Fresno, CA 93710
Tel.: (599) 540-7196
Web Site: http://www.fresnomazda.com
Automobile Mfr
N.A.I.C.S.: 336110

Lithia MTLM, LLC   **(1)**

1420 N Riverside Ave, Medford, OR 97501
Tel.: (541) 716-0200
Web Site:
  https://www.lithiatoyotamedford.com
Automobile Dealers
N.A.I.C.S.: 441110

Lithia Medford Hon, Inc.   **(1)**
4095 Crater Lake Hwy, Medford, OR 97504
Web Site:
  http://www.lithiahondamedford.com
Sales Range: $25-49.9 Million
Emp.: 50
Automobile Dealers
N.A.I.C.S.: 441110
Travis Hawes (*Gen Mgr*)
Nate Mould (*Mgr*)
Stephen Ferris (*Mgr*)
Jared Tiedemann (*Mgr*)
Paul Ouelette (*Coord*)

Lithia Monroeville-F, LLC   **(1)**
3696 William Penn Hwy, Monroeville, PA 15146
Tel.: (412) 856-0600
Web Site: https://www.fordmonroeville.com
Automotive Distr
N.A.I.C.S.: 423110

Lithia Moon-S, LLC   **(1)**
5450 University Blvd, Moon Township, PA 15108
Tel.: (724) 782-3268
Web Site:
  https://www.drivewaysubarumoon.com
Automobile Mfr
N.A.I.C.S.: 336110

Lithia Moon-V, LLC   **(1)**
5252 University Blvd, Moon Township, PA 15108
Web Site: https://www.vwmoon.com
Automobile Mfr
N.A.I.C.S.: 336110

Lithia NA, Inc.   **(1)**
730 E 5th Ave, Anchorage, AK 99501
Web Site:
  https://www.bmwofanchorage.com
Sales Range: $25-49.9 Million
Emp.: 50
Automobile Dealers
N.A.I.C.S.: 441110
David Billman (*Gen Mgr*)
Tessa Copeland (*Office Mgr*)
Larry Pace (*Mgr-Finance*)
Travis Palmer (*Sls Mgr*)
Brian Erickson (*Mgr*)

Lithia ND Acquisition Corp. #3   **(1)**
2373 32nd Ave S, Grand Forks, ND 58201-6546
Tel.: (701) 746-9444
Web Site:
  https://www.chryslerjeepdodgeofgrandforks.com
Sales Range: $10-24.9 Million
Emp.: 60
New & Used Car Dealer
N.A.I.C.S.: 441110
Grady Eastman (*Fin Mgr*)

Lithia NF, Inc.   **(1)**
5580 N Blackstone Ave, Fresno, CA 93710
Tel.: (559) 358-2985
Web Site:
  https://www.lithianissanfresno.com
Automobile Dealers
N.A.I.C.S.: 441110
Jason Lowery (*Mgr*)
Larry Kirby (*Mgr*)
Eric Taylor (*Mgr-Parts*)
Henee Homero (*Mgr-BDC*)
Ruben Castano (*Mgr*)
Abraham Santaolalla (*Mgr*)
Frank Aldaz (*Mgr*)
Jimmy Mendoza (*Assoc Mgr-Sales*)
Robert Tucker (*Assoc Mgr-Sales*)
Roberto Moreno (*Assoc Mgr-Sales*)
Victor Ochoa (*Gen Sls Mgr*)

Lithia NSA, Inc.   **(1)**
5130 W Houston Harte Expy, San Angelo, TX 76901
Tel.: (325) 610-6499
Web Site:
  https://www.brownhondasanangelo.com
Emp.: 25
Automobile Dealers
N.A.I.C.S.: 441110

Lithia Nissan of Ames   **(1)**
2901 S Duff Ave, Ames, IA 50010
Tel.: (515) 620-4099
Web Site: https://www.amesnissan.com
Car Dealership
N.A.I.C.S.: 441110
Mike Gougherty (*Gen Mgr*)

Lithia Paramus-M, LLC   **(1)**
755 Route 17, Paramus, NJ 07652
Web Site:
  https://www.mercedesbenzparamus.com
Automotive Distr
N.A.I.C.S.: 423110

Lithia Ramsey-B, LLC   **(1)**
985 State Route 17, Ramsey, NJ 07446
Tel.: (201) 258-6000
Web Site: https://www.bmwramsey.com
Automotive Distr
N.A.I.C.S.: 423110

Lithia Ramsey-L, LLC   **(1)**
1000 Route 17 N, Ramsey, NJ 07446
Web Site: https://www.prestigelexus.com
Automotive Distr
N.A.I.C.S.: 423110

Lithia Ramsey-M, LLC   **(1)**
925 Route 17 S, Ramsey, NJ 07446
Web Site: https://www.miniramsey.com
Automotive Distr
N.A.I.C.S.: 423110

Lithia Reno Sub-Hyun, Inc.   **(1)**
2270 Kietzke Ln, Reno, NV 89502
Tel.: (775) 624-5369
Web Site: https://www.lithiasubarureno.com
Automobile Dealers
N.A.I.C.S.: 441110
Randy Goldman (*Gen Mgr*)
Ciprian Ciciovan (*Mgr-Gen Sls*)
Jozsef Szuhai (*Mgr-Sls*)
Jesse Watkins (*Mgr-Fin*)
Cindy Costello (*Office Mgr*)

Lithia Reno-CJ, LLC   **(1)**
1050 E Plumb Ln, Reno, NV 89502-3652
Tel.: (775) 328-7069
Web Site: https://www.lithiachryslerreno.com
Car Dealing Services
N.A.I.C.S.: 441110
Scott Williford (*Gen Mgr*)
Joe Green (*Gen Sls Mgr*)
Aaron Lauer (*Mgr-New Car*)
Tony Moore (*Sls Mgr*)

Lithia Reno-VW, LLC   **(1)**
1050 E Plumb Ln Ste 110, Reno, NV 89502
Tel.: (775) 312-9579
Web Site: https://www.lithiarenovw.com
Car Dealing Services
N.A.I.C.S.: 441110
S. David Wolpe (*Gen Mgr*)
Corey Wild (*Mgr-Svc*)

Lithia Rose-FT, Inc.   **(1)**
1650 NE Stephens St, Roseburg, OR 97470
Web Site: http://www.lithiafordroseburg.com
Automobile Dealers
N.A.I.C.S.: 441110
Wayne Knowles (*Gen Mgr*)
Dennis Dietrich (*Mgr*)
Tanner Dougherty (*Sls Mgr*)

Lithia SALMIR, Inc.   **(1)**
2620 Kietzke Ln, Reno, NV 89502
Tel.: (775) 800-5703
Web Site: https://www.lithiahyundaireno.com
Sales Range: Less than $1 Million
Emp.: 50
New & Used Automobile Dealer
N.A.I.C.S.: 441110

Lithia SOC, Inc.   **(1)**
1404 Main St, Oregon City, OR 97045
Web Site:
  https://www.oregoncitysubaru.com
Sales Range: $25-49.9 Million
Emp.: 50
Automobile Dealers
N.A.I.C.S.: 441110
Ryan Vaughan (*Mgr*)
Cory Fay (*Gen Sls Mgr*)
Gene Rude (*Mgr*)
William Grenier (*Mgr*)
Lea Jewell (*Mgr-Parts*)
Diana Watson (*Office Mgr*)
Val Brown (*Mgr-Sales*)
Geoff Eades (*Mgr-Fin*)
Nick Bocarius (*Mgr-Fin*)

Tobias Ray *(Mgr-Fin)*
Aaron Macy *(Mgr-Finance)*
Andrea Cook *(Mgr)*
Austin Koehler *(Mgr-Merchandising)*
Ira Jones *(Gen Mgr)*
Annie Barnes *(Mgr-)*
Michael Haley *(Fin Mgr)*
Brandi Hughes *(Office Mgr)*

Lithia Sea P, Inc.   (1)
1781 Del Monte Blvd, Seaside, CA 93955
Web Site:
   https://www.porschemonterey.com
Automobile Dealers
N.A.I.C.S.: 441110

Lithia Seaside, Inc.   (1)
1 Geary Plz, Seaside, CA 93955-3612
Tel.: (831) 920-3444
Web Site: https://www.bmwmonterey.com
Emp.: 70
Automobile Dealers
N.A.I.C.S.: 441110
Michael Crnkovic *(Fin Mgr)*
Edgar García *(Mgr-Mdse)*
Amir Mohsin *(Mgr-Pre-Owned)*
Monika Parzych *(Office Mgr)*
Jimmy Cahill *(Gen Sls Mgr)*

Lithia Subaru Hyundai GMC Buick   (1)
800 Central Ave, Great Falls, MT 59401
Tel.: (406) 205-3357
Sales Range: $10-24.9 Million
Emp.: 47
New Car Dealers
N.A.I.C.S.: 441110
Brian Belderrain *(Gen Mgr)*

Lithia TA, Inc.   (1)
4449 Southwest Dr, Abilene, TX 79606
Tel.: (325) 550-2122
Web Site: http://www.toyotaabilene.com
Automobile Dealers
N.A.I.C.S.: 441110
Kenan Pyeatt *(Gen Mgr)*
Jim Buckner *(Mgr-Sls Desk)*
Trip Gollihar *(Mgr-Svc)*
Aaron Coker *(Fin Mgr)*
Mike Mizikar IV *(Mgr-Fin)*

Lithia TR, Inc.   (1)
250 E Cypress Ave, Redding, CA 96002
Web Site:
   https://www.lithiatoyotaredding.com
Emp.: 96
Automobile Dealers
N.A.I.C.S.: 441110
Corey Kersten *(Gen Sls Mgr)*
Jason Beeman *(Mgr-Sls)*
Scott Brown *(Mgr-Parts)*
Jeff Franklin *(Asst Mgr-Parts)*

Lithia Uniontown-C, LLC   (1)
5209 Pittsburgh Rd, Uniontown, PA 15401
Tel.: (724) 438-2577
Automotive Distr
N.A.I.C.S.: 423110

Lithia VF, Inc.   (1)
5212 N Blackstone Ave, Fresno, CA 93710
Tel.: (559) 540-7193
Web Site: http://www.volvooffresno.com
Automobile Dealers
N.A.I.C.S.: 441110
Julian Marquez *(Gen Mgr)*
Avi Brah *(Mgr-Sls)*
Kevin Bunton *(Mgr-Sls)*
Joel Ohnstad *(Dir-Internet)*
Nettie Johnson *(Mgr-Fin)*

Lithia of Abilene, Inc.   (1)
4449 Southwest Dr, Abilene, TX 79606
Tel.: (325) 603-4229
Web Site: https://www.toyotaabilene.com
Sales Range: $25-49.9 Million
Emp.: 50
Automobile Dealers
N.A.I.C.S.: 441110

Lithia of Bellingham, LLC   (1)
3891 Northwest Ave, Bellingham, WA 98226
Tel.: (360) 419-5139
Web Site: http://www.bellinghamchevy.com
Automobile Dealers
N.A.I.C.S.: 441110
Michael Bowthorpe *(Mgr-Svc)*
Heather Stocking *(Office Mgr)*
Jeffery Tolsma *(Mgr-Sls)*

Xavier Cortes *(Owner)*
Brian Cortes *(Gen Mgr)*
Nelson Cruz *(Sls Mgr)*
Kelly Queen *(Fin Dir)*
Stephanie Akers-Pash *(Dir-Internet Sls)*
Ty Davis *(Mgr-Parts)*
Leo Renteria *(Mgr-Detail Dept)*
Hope Dell *(Mgr-Inventory)*

Lithia of Bennington - 1, LLC   (1)
897 N Bennington Rd, Bennington, VT 05201
Tel.: (877) 369-2006
Automotive Distr
N.A.I.C.S.: 423110

Lithia of Casper, LLC   (1)
3333 Cy Ave, Casper, WY 82604
Tel.: (307) 266-1680
Web Site: https://www.greinerford.com
Automotive Distr
N.A.I.C.S.: 423110

Lithia of Clear Lake, LLC   (1)
15121 Gulf Fwy, Houston, TX 77034
Automotive Distr
N.A.I.C.S.: 423110

Lithia of Concord I, Inc.   (1)
4901 Marsh Dr, Concord, CA 94520
Tel.: (925) 246-2295
Automotive Distr
N.A.I.C.S.: 423110

Lithia of Concord II, Inc.   (1)
4905 Marsh Dr, Concord, CA 94520
Tel.: (925) 246-2296
Automotive Distr
N.A.I.C.S.: 423110

Lithia of Corpus Christi, Inc.   (1)
4313 S Staples St, Corpus Christi, TX 78411-2703
Web Site:
   https://www.lithiadodgeofcorpuschristi.com
Automobile Dealers
N.A.I.C.S.: 441110

Lithia of Des Moines, Inc.   (1)
9631 Hickman Rd, Urbandale, IA 50322-5323
Tel.: (515) 461-2724
Web Site: https://www.bmwdesmoines.com
Automobile Dealers
N.A.I.C.S.: 441110
Scott Long *(Gen Mgr)*
Jamie Arend *(Office Mgr)*
Waye Terry *(Gen Sls Mgr)*
Jamie Carlson *(Mgr-Parts)*
Tyler Van Weelden *(Gen Mgr)*
Kiera Harris *(Mgr)*
Greg Pingel *(Mgr-Finance)*

Lithia of Eugene, LLC   (1)
2121 Martin Luther King Jr Blvd, Eugene, OR 97401
Tel.: (541) 334-3100
Web Site:
   http://www.lithiadodgeeugene.com
Automobile Dealers
N.A.I.C.S.: 441110

Lithia of Eureka, Inc.   (1)
4320 Broadway, Eureka, CA 95503-5740
Tel.: (707) 382-3208
Web Site: https://www.driveeureka.com
Automobile Dealers
N.A.I.C.S.: 441110
Tim Call *(Gen Mgr)*
Scott Krause *(Mgr)*
Jackie Eldridge *(Office Mgr)*
Michael Kubala *(Mgr)*
Becki Bean *(Office Mgr)*

Lithia of Great Falls, Inc.   (1)
4025 10th Ave S, Great Falls, MT 59405-5617
Web Site:
   http://www.lithiachryslergreatfalls.com
Automobile Dealers
N.A.I.C.S.: 441110
Brian Belderrain *(Gen Mgr)*

Lithia of HonoluluBGMCC, LLC   (1)
2945 N Nimitz Hwy, Honolulu, HI 96819
Tel.: (808) 836-7007
Web Site: https://www.honolulugmc.com
Automobile Dealers
N.A.I.C.S.: 441110

Justen Chilcoat *(Gen Sls Mgr)*
Kalai Mukawa *(Mgr-Sls)*
Thomas Pokorny *(Mgr-Parts)*

Lithia of HonoluluV, LLC   (1)
2881 N Nimitz Hwy, Honolulu, HI 96819
Tel.: (808) 369-9016
Web Site: https://www.honoluluvw.com
Automobile Dealers
N.A.I.C.S.: 441110

Lithia of Killeen, LLC   (1)
1802 E Central Texas Expy, Killeen, TX 76541-9113
Tel.: (254) 200-4600
Web Site: https://www.killeenchevrolet.com
Automobile Dealers
N.A.I.C.S.: 441110

Lithia of Maui-H, LLC   (1)
110 Hana Hwy, Kahului, HI 96732
Tel.: (808) 727-1987
Web Site: https://www.islandhonda.com
New & Used Car Dealer
N.A.I.C.S.: 441110

Lithia of Missoula, Inc.   (1)
5001 Grizzly Ct, Missoula, MT 59802
Web Site:
   http://www.lithiachryslermissoula.com
Sales Range: $25-49.9 Million
Emp.: 30
Automobile Dealers
N.A.I.C.S.: 441110
Ryan Tuttle *(Gen Mgr)*

Lithia of Portland, LLC   (1)
9155 Sw Canyon Rd, Portland, OR 97225
Tel.: (503) 292-8801
Automotive Distr
N.A.I.C.S.: 423110

Lithia of Roseburg, Inc.   (1)
1600 NE Airport Rd, Roseburg, OR 97470-1555
Tel.: (541) 378-4627
Web Site:
   https://www.lithiadogeroseburg.com
New & Used Car Dealer
N.A.I.C.S.: 441110
Shawn Penny *(Mgr-Internet & Sls)*
James Pearson *(Mgr-Parts)*

Lithia of Santa Rosa, Inc.   (1)
2727 Dowd Dr, Santa Rosa, CA 95407-7818
Web Site:
   https://www.lithiadodgesantarosa.com
Emp.: 40
Automobile Dealers
N.A.I.C.S.: 441110
Steve Fox *(Gen Mgr)*
David Crawford *(Mgr-Svc)*
Josh Svihula *(Mgr-Sls)*
Jarret Garrigan *(Mgr-Sales)*
David Henderson *(Mgr)*
Sam Keller *(Mgr-F&I)*
Melody Menefee *(Office Mgr)*
Devin Doree *(Mgr-Parts)*
Ryan Pullara *(Gen Mgr)*

Lithia of Seattle, Inc.   (1)
1002 Airport Way S, Seattle, WA 98134
Web Site: https://www.bmwseattle.com
Emp.: 200
Automobile Dealers
N.A.I.C.S.: 441110

Lithia of South Central AK, Inc.   (1)
3700 E Parks Hwy, Wasilla, AK 99654
Tel.: (907) 268-2499
Web Site: https://www.wasillachevrolet.com
Sales Range: $25-49.9 Million
Emp.: 45
New & Used Car Dealer
N.A.I.C.S.: 441110
Richard Smith *(Gen Mgr)*
Denise Moss *(Mgr-Bus)*
Christopher Bills *(Mgr-Parts)*
Roderick O'Neill *(Mgr-Svc)*
Matthew Hallman *(Mgr-F&I)*
James Horine *(Mgr-Sls Desk)*
Richard Locher *(Mgr-F&I)*

Lithia of Spokane, Inc.   (1)
21802 E George Gee Ave, Liberty Lake, WA 99019
Tel.: (509) 455-9100
Web Site:
   http://www.spokanemercedes.com
Automobile Dealers

N.A.I.C.S.: 441110
Scott Murphy *(Mgr-Svc)*

Lithia of Stockton-V, Inc.   (1)
6215 Holman Rd, Stockton, CA 95212
Tel.: (209) 644-8500
Web Site: http://www.vwofstockton.com
Emp.: 30
New & Used Car Dealer
N.A.I.C.S.: 441110

Lithia of TF, Inc.   (1)
1310 Poleline Rd E, Twin Falls, ID 83301
Tel.: (208) 738-9517
Web Site: https://www.twinfallsdodge.com
Automobile Dealers
N.A.I.C.S.: 441110
Jose Guevara *(Gen Mgr)*
Jorge Leon *(Mgr-Finance)*

Lithia of Utica-1, LLC   (1)
5712 Horatio st, Utica, NY 13502
Automotive Distr
N.A.I.C.S.: 423110

Lithia of Walnut Creek, Inc.   (1)
2646 N Main St, Walnut Creek, CA 94597
Tel.: (925) 448-3021
Web Site: https://www.diablosubaru.com
New & Used Car Dealer
N.A.I.C.S.: 441110

Lithia of Wasilla, LLC   (1)
2891 E Sun Mountain Ave, Wasilla, AK 99654-7348
Tel.: (907) 631-7000
Web Site: https://www.wasilladodge.com
Automotive Retailer
N.A.I.C.S.: 441120
Eva Marple *(Office Mgr)*

Lithia of Yorkville-1, LLC   (1)
5043 Commercial Dr, Yorkville, NY 13495
Tel.: (315) 736-0811
Automotive Distr
N.A.I.C.S.: 423110

Lithia of Yorkville-3, LLC   (1)
5009 Commercial Dr, Yorkville, NJ 13495
Tel.: (315) 736-7310
Automotive Distr
N.A.I.C.S.: 423110

Markham-B, LP   (1)
8111 Kennedy Road, Markham, L3R 5M2, ON, Canada
Tel.: (905) 513-8900
Web Site: https://www.minimarkham.ca
New & Used Car Distr
N.A.I.C.S.: 441120

Markham-P, LP   (1)
8590 McCowan Road, Markham, L3P 3M2, ON, Canada
Tel.: (289) 661-1588
Web Site:
   https://www.porschecentremarkham.com
New & Used Car Distr
N.A.I.C.S.: 441120

Miami Gardens-S, LLC   (1)
21300 NW 2nd Ave, Miami, FL 33169
Tel.: (786) 946-9516
Web Site:
   https://www.subaruofnorthmiami.com
New & Used Car Distr
N.A.I.C.S.: 441120

Mission Hills-H, Inc.   (1)
10240 Sepulveda Blvd, Mission Hills, CA 91345
Web Site: https://www.mhhyundai.com
Car Dealing Services
N.A.I.C.S.: 441110

New Port Richey-H, LLC   (1)
3936 US Hwy 19, New Port Richey, FL 34652
Tel.: (727) 312-1290
Web Site:
   https://www.hyundaiofnewportrichey.com
Car Dealing Services
N.A.I.C.S.: 441110
Mike Morris *(Sls Mgr)*
Warren Blackburn *(Sls Mgr)*

New Port Richey-V, LLC   (1)
4727 US Hwy 19, New Port Richey, FL 34652
Tel.: (727) 732-4639
Web Site: https://www.vwofnpr.com

Lithia Motors, Inc.—(Continued)
Car Dealing Services
N.A.I.C.S.: 441110

Phoenix-T, Inc. (1)
2020 W Bell Rd, Phoenix, AZ 85023
Tel.: (480) 795-5886
Web Site: http://www.bellroadtoyota.com
Car Dealing Services
N.A.I.C.S.: 441110
Rafeh Talas (Gen Mgr)

Planet Honda (1)
2285 US Hwy 22 W, Union, NJ 07083
Tel.: (908) 964-1600
Web Site: http://www.planethondanj.com
Sales of New & Used Automobiles
N.A.I.C.S.: 441110
William Feinstein (Dealer Principal)
Tamara Twitty (Asst Mgr)
Kelsey Moore (Dir-Finance)
Alessandra Vilarinho (Asst Mgr)
Bob Dockery (Dir-Finance)
Erin Watson (Mgr)
Victor Kavanach (Mgr-Finance)
Luke Cwiek (Mgr-Sales)
Sue Lerch (Dir-Customer Svc)
Paul Ferreira (Dir)
Eddie Amorin (Gen Sls Mgr)
Joe Messina (Mgr)
Kero Rofail (Mgr)
Luis Astudillo (Mgr)
Danny Odoiboye (Mgr)
Edward Gorham (Mgr)
Steve Saunders (Mgr)
Delia Mensch (Dir)
Jose Velez (Dir)
John Falihee (Dir)
Ray Gambino (Fin Dir)
Kero Rofail (Mgr)
Luis Astudillo (Mgr)
Danny Odoiboye (Mgr)
Edward Gorham (Mgr)
Steve Saunders (Mgr)
Delia Mensch (Dir)
Jose Velez (Dir)
John Falihee (Dir)
Ray Gambino (Fin Dir)

Richmond Hill-H, LP (1)
8885 Jane St, Vaughan, L4K 2M6, ON,
Canada
Tel.: (905) 709-1340
Web Site: https://www.pfaffharley.com
New & Used Car Distr
N.A.I.C.S.: 441120

Rockwall-H, Inc. (1)
1550 I-30 Frontage Rd, Rockwall, TX 75087
Tel.: (469) 772-0595
Web Site:
   https://www.hondacarsofrockwall.com
Car Dealing Services
N.A.I.C.S.: 441110
John Frazier (Gen Mgr)
David Tunnell (Dir-Fixed Ops)
Tanner Maxwell (Dir-New Car)
Jarrett Watson (Dir-Used Car)
John Martinez (Fin Dir)

Roseville-C, Inc. (1)
311 Vernon St, Roseville, CA 95678
Tel.: (916) 774-5362
Web Site: https://www.roseville.ca.us
Automobile Maintenance Services
N.A.I.C.S.: 811111

Salem-V, LLC (1)
3335 Del Webb Ave NE, Salem, OR 97301
Tel.: (503) 400-6307
Automotive Distr
N.A.I.C.S.: 423110

San Francisco-B, Inc. (1)
1675 Howard St, San Francisco, CA 94103
Tel.: (415) 814-1780
Web Site: https://www.bmwsf.com
Car Dealing Services
N.A.I.C.S.: 441110

Sharlene Realty LLC (1)
1504 US Rt 1 North Brunswick Township,
New Brunswick, NJ 08902
Tel.: (732) 798-7936
Automotive Distr
N.A.I.C.S.: 423110

Sherman Oaks-A, Inc. (1)
5239 Van Nuys Blvd, Sherman Oaks, CA
91401

Web Site: https://www.audivannuys.com
Car Dealing Services
N.A.I.C.S.: 441110
Sam Dajani (Sls Mgr)
Sam Salehi (Sls Mgr)

Smyrna-F, LLC (1)
3860 S Cobb Dr, Smyrna, GA 30080-5537
Tel.: (770) 764-2121
Web Site: https://www.wadeford.com
New & Used Car Distr
N.A.I.C.S.: 441120

**Southern Cascades Finance
Corporation** (1)
150 N Bartlett St, Medford, OR 97501-6015
Tel.: (541) 618-5749
Automobile Dealers
N.A.I.C.S.: 441110

Sterling-BM, LLC (1)
21710 Auto World Cir, Sterling, VA 20166
Tel.: (571) 789-2306
Web Site: https://www.bmwofsterling.com
Car Dealing Services
N.A.I.C.S.: 441110

Sterling-RLM, LLC (1)
21826 Pacific Blvd, Sterling, VA 20166
Tel.: (571) 620-6226
Web Site: https://www.rolls-
   roycemotorcarswashington.com
Car Dealing Services
N.A.I.C.S.: 441110
Amir Hadzimehmedovic (Gen Mgr)
Tina Grossman (Brand Mgr-Rolls-Royce)
Luke Huntington (Brand Mgr-McLaren)

Stewart's Classics, Inc. (1)
1480 E County Line Rd, Littleton, CO
80126
Tel.: (303) 730-7340
Emp.: 100
Holding Company; New & Used Car Dealer-
ships Operator
N.A.I.C.S.: 551112

Subsidiary (Domestic):

**Stewart's Classics of Colorado
LLC** (2)
1480 E County Line Rd, Littleton, CO
80126
Tel.: (303) 730-7340
Web Site: https://www.ferrariofdenver.com
New & Used Car Dealerships Operator
N.A.I.C.S.: 441110
Mike Parmecan (Mgr-Fin)

Thousand Oaks-S, Inc. (1)
3725 Auto Mall Dr, Thousand Oaks, CA
91362
Tel.: (805) 263-7620
Web Site:
   https://www.dchsubaruthousandoaks.com
Automobile Maintenance Services
N.A.I.C.S.: 811111

Troy Collision, LLC (1)
1759 Maplelawn Dr, Troy, MI 48084
Tel.: (248) 859-7950
Car Repair Services
N.A.I.C.S.: 811198

Troy-CJD, LLC (1)
1790 Maplelawn Dr, Troy, MI 48084-4611
Tel.: (248) 206-3435
Web Site:
   https://www.suburbanchryslerdodgejeep
   ramoftroy.com
Automobile Maintenance Services
N.A.I.C.S.: 811111

Troy-I, LLC (1)
1816 Maplelawn, Troy, MI 48084
Tel.: (248) 430-9650
Web Site:
   https://www.suburbaninfinitioftroy.com
New & Used Car Distr
N.A.I.C.S.: 441120

Tustin Motors Inc. (1)
9 Auto Center Dr, Tustin, CA 92782
Tel.: (657) 221-2726
Web Site: https://www.dchtustinacura.com
Automobile Dealers
N.A.I.C.S.: 441110

Urbandale-S, LLC (1)
9625 Hickman Rd, Urbandale, IA 50322
Web Site: https://www.ramseysubaru.com

Car Dealing Services
N.A.I.C.S.: 441110
Pat Klinefelter (Sls Mgr)

Valencia-A, Inc. (1)
23923 Creekside Rd, Valencia, CA 91355
Web Site: http://www.audivalencia.com
Car Dealing Services
N.A.I.C.S.: 441110
Mazy Hassanpour (Gen Mgr)

Van Nuys-H, LLC (1)
5746 Van Nuys Blvd, Van Nuys, CA 91401
Web Site: https://www.keyeshyundai.com
Car Dealing Services
N.A.I.C.S.: 441110
Brian Sobel (Gen Mgr)
Darin Lawrence (Gen Sls Mgr)
Taimur Amin (Sls Mgr)
Eddie Fefer (Sls Mgr)
Jason Jhee (Sls Mgr)

Vaughan-P, LP (1)
105 Four Valley Drive, Vaughan, L4K 4V8,
ON, Canada
Tel.: (905) 851-0852
Web Site: https://dealer.porsche.com
New & Used Car Distr
N.A.I.C.S.: 441120

Waukesha-CJD, Inc. (1)
1710 Hwy 164 S, Waukesha, WI 53186-
3937
Web Site: https://www.wildedodge.com
New & Used Car Distr
N.A.I.C.S.: 441120

Wesley Chapel-C, LLC (1)
26922 Wesley Chapel Blvd, Wesley Chapel,
FL 33544
Tel.: (813) 906-8004
Web Site:
   https://www.chevyofwesleychapel.com
Car Dealing Services
N.A.I.C.S.: 441110

Wesley Chapel-Hy, LLC (1)
27000 Wesley Chapel Blvd, Wesley Chapel,
FL 33544
Tel.: (813) 279-7400
Web Site:
   https://www.hyundaiofwesleychapel.com
New & Used Car Distr
N.A.I.C.S.: 441120

Wesley Chapel-M, LLC (1)
26944 Wesley Chapel Blvd, Wesley Chapel,
FL 33544
Tel.: (813) 279-7509
Web Site:
   https://www.mazdaofwesleychapel.com
Car Dealing Services
N.A.I.C.S.: 441110

Wesley Chapel-Moto, LLC (1)
25245 Wesley Chapel Blvd, Lutz, FL 33559
Tel.: (813) 213-3415
Web Site: https://wesleychapelhd.com
New & Used Car Distr
N.A.I.C.S.: 441120

West Allis-T, Inc. (1)
3225 S 108th St, West Allis, WI 53227
Tel.: (414) 310-6794
Web Site: https://www.wildetoyota.com
New & Used Car Distr
N.A.I.C.S.: 441120

Yuba City-CJD, Inc. (1)
950 Harter Pkwy, Yuba City, CA 95993-
9457
Tel.: (916) 790-5143
Web Site:
   https://www.johnsullivandodgechrys
   ler.com
Automobile Maintenance Services
N.A.I.C.S.: 811111

LITHIUM CORPORATION
1031 RailRd St Ste 102B, Elko, NV
89801
Tel.: (775) 410-5287   NV
Web Site:
   https://www.lithiumcorporation.com
Year Founded: 2007
LTUM—(OTCQB)
Rev.: $75,327
Assets: $4,044,235
Liabilities: $2,225,977

Net Worth: $1,818,258
Earnings: ($618,193)
Fiscal Year-end: 12/31/23
Lithium Exploration & Mining Services
N.A.I.C.S.: 212290
Tom Lewis (Pres, Treas & Sec)

LITTELFUSE, INC.
8755 W Higgins Rd Ste 500, Chi-
cago, IL 60631
Tel.: (773) 628-1000   DE
Web Site: https://www.littelfuse.com
Year Founded: 1927
LFUS—(NASDAQ)
Rev.: $2,362,657,000
Assets: $3,995,275,000
Liabilities: $1,514,794,000
Net Worth: $2,480,481,000
Earnings: $259,485,000
Emp.: 17,000
Fiscal Year-end: 12/30/23
Electronic, Automotive & Power
Fuses & Other Circuit Protection De-
vices Mfr & Distr
N.A.I.C.S.: 335313
David W. Heinzmann (Pres & CEO)
Ryan K. Stafford (Chief Legal & HR
Officer, Sec & Exec VP)
Deepak Nayar (Sr VP & Gen Mgr-
Electronics Bus)
Matthew J. Cole (Sr VP-eMobility &
Strategy)
Meenal A. Sethna (CFO & Exec VP)
Trisha Tuntland (Head-IR)
Alexander Conrad (Sr VP & Gen Mgr-
Passenger Vehicle Bus)
Eyal Altman (Chief Digital & IT Officer
& VP)
Maggie Chu (Chief HR Officer & Sr
VP)

Subsidiaries:

Accel AB (1)
Norra Vallgatan 70, 211 22, Malmo, Swe-
den
Tel.: (46) 107502616
Web Site: https://www.accelaktiebolag.com
Electronic Equipment Whslr
N.A.I.C.S.: 423690
Magnus Nilsson (Mng Dir)

Accel Elektronika UAB (1)
Savanoriu pr 271, 50131, Kaunas, Lithuania
Tel.: (370) 37311018
Web Site: http://www.accel.lt
Emp.: 347
Electronic Components Mfr
N.A.I.C.S.: 334110

C&K Components, Inc. (1)
15 Riverdale Ave, Newton, MA 02458
Tel.: (617) 969-3700
Web Site: http://www.ckswitches.com
Electronic Switchgear & Connectors Mfr
N.A.I.C.S.: 335313
John Boucher (CEO)
Tom Schultz (CFO)
Doug Williams (CMO)
Phillip Gerard (Gen Mgr-Americas)
William Xu (Gen Mgr-Asia)
Bruno Prevot (Gen Mgr-Europe)
Jeremy Hebras (Dir-Worldwide R&D)
Jerome Brochot (Dir-Global Quality)

Cole Hersee Company (1)
20 Old Colony Ave, Boston, MA 02127
Tel.: (617) 268-2100
Web Site: http://www.colehersee.com
Sales Range: $50-74.9 Million
Emp.: 212
Mfr of Vehicle Electrical Components, Digi-
tal Switches, Connectors & Related Elec-
tronic Products
N.A.I.C.S.: 335931

E.I.S. Electronics GmbH (1)
Rudloffstrasse 47, D-27568, Bremerhaven,
Germany
Tel.: (49) 47194550
Web Site: https://www.eis-electronics.de
Electrical Product Mfr & Distr
N.A.I.C.S.: 335999

Embed Limited (1)
Viscount Centre D Millburn Hill Road, University of Warwick Science Park, Coventry,

CV4 7HS, United Kingdom
Tel.: (44) 2476323250
Web Site: https://www.embeduk.com
Automotive Parts Mfr & Distr
N.A.I.C.S.: 336390

Hamlin, Inc. (1)
612 E Lake St, Lake Mills, WI 53551
Tel.: (920) 648-3000
Web Site: http://www.hamlin.com
Sales Range: $200-249.9 Million
Emp.: 900
Electronic Sensor Components Mfr
N.A.I.C.S.: 334513

Subsidiary (Non-US):

Hamlin Electronics (Suzhou) Limited (2)
1A No 1 Workshop No 55 Weixi Road Weiting Town, Suzhou Industrial, Suzhou, 215121, China
Tel.: (86) 512 69365800
Emp.: 140
Electronic Components Mfr & Distr
N.A.I.C.S.: 334419
Cai Hong (Gen Mgr)

Hamlin Electronics Europe Ltd. (2)
Lakeside 200 Old Chapel Way Broadland Business Park, Norwich, NR7 0WG, United Kingdom
Tel.: (44) 1603 257700
Web Site: http://www.hamlin.com
Sales Range: $25-49.9 Million
Emp.: 35
Reed Switches, Magnetic Position Sensors, Reed Relays & Other Electronic Components Mfr & Supplier
N.A.I.C.S.: 335314

Hartland Controls LLC (1)
807 Antec Rd, Rock Falls, IL 61071
Tel.: (815) 626-5170
Web Site: https://hartlandcontrols.com
Rev.: $3,275,100
Emp.: 30
Site Preparation Contractor
N.A.I.C.S.: 238910
Ahmed Abed (Mgr-Sls-Reg)

IXYS Corporation (1)
1590 Buckeye Dr, Milpitas, CA 95035-7418
Tel.: (408) 457-9000
Web Site: http://www.ixys.com
Power Semiconductors & Power Modules Mfr
N.A.I.C.S.: 334413
Meenal A. Sethna (CFO & Exec VP)
David Heinzmann (Pres & CEO)
Ryan K. Stafford (Chief Legal & HR Officer, Chief Legal & HR Officer & Chief Legal & HR Officer)
Matthew J. Cole (Sr VP-Business Development-Strategy)
Alexander Conrad (Sr VP & Gen Mgr)
Deepak Nayar (Sr VP & Gen Mgr)
Michael P. Rutz (Sr VP & Gen Mgr)

Subsidiary (Domestic):

Clare Instruments US, Inc. (2)
6304 Benjamin Rd, Tampa, FL 33634-5128
Tel.: (813) 886-2775
Web Site: http://www.seaward-groupusa.com
Test Instruments (for Electrical Safety) Mfr
N.A.I.C.S.: 541350

Subsidiary (Non-US):

IXYS Global Services GmbH (2)
Edisonstrasse 15, 68623, Lampertheim, Germany
Tel.: (49) 62065030
Semiconductor Devices Mfr
N.A.I.C.S.: 334413

Subsidiary (Domestic):

IXYS Integrated Circuits Division Inc. (2)
78 Cherry Hill Dr, Beverly, MA 01915-1048 (100%)
Tel.: (978) 524-6700
Web Site: http://www.clare.com
Semiconductor & Electromagnetic Relays & Switches, Surge Arresters & Applied Magnetic Products Mfr
N.A.I.C.S.: 335314

Mark F. Heisig (VP & Gen Mgr)
Nicole Gibbons (Founder)

IXYS Long Beach Inc. (2)
2500 Mira Mar Ave, Long Beach, CA 90815 (100%)
Tel.: (562) 296-6584
Semiconductor Mfr
N.A.I.C.S.: 334413
Ray Segall (Gen Mgr)

Subsidiary (Non-US):

IXYS Semiconductors GmbH (2)
Edisonstrasse 15, Lampertheim, 68623, Germany (100%)
Tel.: (49) 62065030
Mfr of Semiconductors
N.A.I.C.S.: 334413

IXYS UK Westcode Limited (2)
Langley Park Way, Langley Park, Chippenham, SN15 1GE, United Kingdom
Tel.: (44) 1249455500
Web Site: http://www.ixysuk.com
Optoelectronic Device Mfr
N.A.I.C.S.: 334413
Karen Read (Mgr-Human Resources)

Subsidiary (Domestic):

Zilog Inc. (2)
1590 Buckeye Dr, Milpitas, CA 95035-7418
Tel.: (408) 457-9000
Web Site: http://www.zilog.com
Semiconductor Product Mfr
N.A.I.C.S.: 334413

IXYS Semiconductor GmbH (1)
Edisonstrasse 15, 68623, Lampertheim, Germany
Tel.: (49) 6 206 5030
Web Site: https://www.ixys.de
Power Semiconductor Mfr
N.A.I.C.S.: 334413

Littelfuse Asia Sales B.V. (1)
Prins bernhardplein 200, 1097 JB, Amsterdam, Netherlands
Tel.: (31) 205214777
Electric Equipment Mfr
N.A.I.C.S.: 335313

Littelfuse Far East, Pte. Ltd. (1)
Science Park II 41 Science Park Rd #03-17 The Gemini, Singapore, 117610, Singapore (100%)
Tel.: (65) 6885 9185
Web Site: http://www.littelfuse.com
Electronic Part & Equipment Whslr
N.A.I.C.S.: 423690

Littelfuse GmbH (1)
Bonsiepen 6-8, 45136, Essen, Germany
Tel.: (49) 20110227810
Investment Management Service
N.A.I.C.S.: 523940

Littelfuse HK Ltd. (1)
Unit 1305 13/F Tower 2 Metroplaza 223 Hing Fong, Kwai Fong, 999077, China (Hong Kong)
Tel.: (852) 28105099
Web Site: http://www.littelfuse.com.hk
Mfr & Seller of Electronic, Automotive & Power Fuses & Other Circuit Protection Devices
N.A.I.C.S.: 336320

Littelfuse Italy S.r.l. (1)
Via Faulenta 12 Ozegna, 10080, Turin, Italy
Tel.: (39) 0124425819
Web Site: http://www.sigmar.com
Electric Equipment Mfr
N.A.I.C.S.: 335313

Littelfuse Japan LLC (1)
Shiba Exage Bldg 5 F3-24-7 Shiba, Minato-ku, Tokyo, 105-0014, Japan (100%)
Tel.: (81) 364350750
Web Site: https://www.littelfuse.co.jp
Electronic, Automotive & Power Fuses & Other Circuit Protection Devices Mfr
N.A.I.C.S.: 336320

Littelfuse LT, UAB (1)
Draugystes g 14, 51259, Kaunas, Lithuania
Tel.: (370) 37311018
Emp.: 757
Electronics Product Mfr & Distr
N.A.I.C.S.: 334419

Littelfuse Mexico Holding LLC (1)
612 E Lake St, Lake Mills, WI 53551
Tel.: (920) 648-3000
Emp.: 187
Holding Company
N.A.I.C.S.: 551112

Littelfuse S. de R.L. de C.V. (1)
Venustiano Carranza 2501 Col Lomas de la Villa, 26090, Piedras Negras, Mexico
Tel.: (52) 8787826222
Electronic Product Distr
N.A.I.C.S.: 423690
Raul Uribe (Mgr-Quality)

Littelfuse Semiconductor (Wuxi) Company (1)
3 Zhenfa 6 Road Shuofang Industrial Zone, Wuxi, 214242, China
Tel.: (86) 51085277701
Electronic Components Mfr
N.A.I.C.S.: 334511

Littelfuse Startco (1)
3714 Kinnear Place, Saskatoon, S7P 0A6, SK, Canada
Tel.: (306) 373-5505
Web Site: http://www.littelfuse.com
Electrical Products & Protective Relays Mfr
N.A.I.C.S.: 334513

Littelfuse Triad, Inc. (1)
Rm 202 Korea Trade Tower 159-1, Samsung-Dong Kangnam-Ku, Seoul, 135-729, Korea (South)
Tel.: (82) 260008621
Web Site: http://www.littelfusetriad.en.ec21.com
Emp.: 50
Electronic Circuit Protection Devices Mfr & Distr
N.A.I.C.S.: 335313

Littelfuse do Brasil (1)
av Jose Caballero 283 Conj 83 Vila Bastos, Santo Andre, Sao Paulo, 09040 210, SP, Brazil (100%)
Tel.: (55) 11 4432 1338
Web Site: http://www.littelfuse.com
Sales Range: Less than $1 Million
Emp.: 6
Mfr & Seller of Electronic, Automotive & Power Fuses & Other Circuit Protection Devices
N.A.I.C.S.: 336320

RadioPulse, Inc. (1)
1106 U-Space 1a 660 Daewangpangyo-Ro, Bundang-gu, Seongnam, 463-400, Gyeonggi-do, Korea (South)
Tel.: (82) 27071130913
Web Site: http://www.radiopulse.co.kr
Software Development Services
N.A.I.C.S.: 541511
Tae Hwi Kwon (CEO)

Reaction Technology Epi, LLC (1)
301 Ridgemont Dr, Allen, TX 75002
Tel.: (972) 747-8607
Web Site: https://www.reactiontechnologyepi.com
Semiconductor Product Mfr
N.A.I.C.S.: 334413

SSAC LLC (1)
222 Disk Dr, Rapid City, SD 57701
Tel.: (605) 348-5580
Web Site: http://www.ssac.com
Electronic Components Mfr
N.A.I.C.S.: 334419

Selco AS (1)
Betonvej 11, 4000, Roskilde, Denmark
Tel.: (45) 70261122
Web Site: https://www.selco.com
Sales Range: $25-49.9 Million
Emp.: 10
Electronic Circuit Protection Devices Mfr & Distr
N.A.I.C.S.: 336320

U.S. Sensor Corp. (1)
1832 W Collins Ave, Orange, CA 92867
Tel.: (714) 639-1000
Web Site: http://www.ussensor.com
Thermistors Mfr
N.A.I.C.S.: 334416

Western Automation Research & Development Limited (1)

2 Atreus Place Poolboy, Co Galway, Ballinasloe, H53 TD 78, Ireland
Tel.: (353) 909643359
Electronic Equipment Mfr & Distr
N.A.I.C.S.: 335311

LITTLE SIOUX CORN PROCESSORS, L.L.C.
4808 F Ave, Marcus, IA 51035
Tel.: (712) 376-2800
LTUU—(NASDAQ)
Chemicals Mfr
N.A.I.C.S.: 325998
Gary Grotjohn (CFO)

LITTLEFIELD CORPORATION
2501 N Lamar Blvd, Austin, TX 78705
Tel.: (512) 476-5141 DE
Web Site: http://www.littlefield.com
Year Founded: 1994
LTFD—(OTCIQ)
Sales Range: $1-9.9 Million
Emp.: 33
Charitable Bingo Halls, Gaming & Amusement Arcades
N.A.I.C.S.: 713990
James D. Recks (Pres & CEO)
Richard K. Bunkley (COO)

Subsidiaries:

Littlefield Entertainment (1)
4547 Lake Shore Dr, Waco, TX 76702 (100%)
Tel.: (512) 476-5141
Web Site: http://www.littlefieldhospitality.com
Sales Range: $1-9.9 Million
Emp.: 12
Operators of Charitable Bingo Halls
N.A.I.C.S.: 713990
James Recks (CEO)

LIVE CURRENT MEDIA INC.
10801 Thornmint Rd Ste 200, San Diego, CA 92127
Tel.: (604) 648-0500 NV
Web Site: https://www.livecurrent.com
Year Founded: 1995
LIVC—(OTCQB)
Rev.: $488,018
Assets: $498,814
Liabilities: $3,135,174
Net Worth: ($2,636,360)
Earnings: ($15,731,697)
Emp.: 15
Fiscal Year-end: 12/31/22
Internet & Website Services
N.A.I.C.S.: 518210
David M. Jeffs (Pres)
Mark Ollila (CEO)
Steve Smith (CFO)

LIVE MICROSYSTEMS, INC.
1 Broadway 14th Fl, Cambridge, MA 02142
Tel.: (617) 401-2104
Year Founded: 1983
LMSC—(OTCEM)
Medical Device Mfr
N.A.I.C.S.: 339112
Matthew A. Gerritsen (Pres)

LIVE NATION ENTERTAINMENT, INC.
9348 Civic Ctr Dr, Beverly Hills, CA 90210
Tel.: (310) 867-7000 DE
Web Site: https://www.livenationentertainment.com
Year Founded: 2005
LYV—(NYSE)
Rev.: $22,749,073,000
Assets: $19,074,045,000
Liabilities: $18,486,888,000
Net Worth: $587,157,000
Earnings: $563,280,000

Live Nation Entertainment, Inc.—(Continued)

Emp.: 14,700
Fiscal Year-end: 12/31/23
Holding Company; Live Entertainment Production, Promotion, Ticketing & Artist Management Services
N.A.I.C.S.: 551112
Michael Rapino *(CEO)*
Arthur Fogel *(Chm-Music-Global & Pres-Touring-Global)*
John Hopmans *(Exec VP-Mergers & Acquisitions & Strategic Fin)*
Joe Berchtold *(Co-Pres & CFO)*
Jacqueline Beato *(Exec VP)*
Johnel Evans *(Head)*
Lucy August-Perna *(Head)*

Subsidiaries:

AC Entertainment, LLC (1)
900 S Gay St 1001, Knoxville, TN 37902
Tel.: (865) 523-2665
Artist Management Services
N.A.I.C.S.: 713990
Tim Burns *(Dir-Technical)*

Antwerps Sportpaleis N.V. (1)
Schijnpoortweg 119, Merksem, 2170, Antwerp, Belgium
Tel.: (32) 3 400 4040
Web Site: https://www.sportpaleis.be
Concert & Sporting Event Operator
N.A.I.C.S.: 711320
Jan Vereecke *(Mng Dir)*

Aragon Entertainment Center, Inc. (1)
1106 W Lawrence, Chicago, IL 60640
Tel.: (773) 561-9500
Fitness & Recreational Sports Center Operator
N.A.I.C.S.: 713940

Artist & Business Transport Group B.V. (1)
Krommewetering 21, 3543 AP, Utrecht, Netherlands
Tel.: (31) 854868833
Web Site: https://abtgroup.nl
Travel Agency Services
N.A.I.C.S.: 561510

August Hall, LLC (1)
420 Mason St, San Francisco, CA 94102
Tel.: (415) 872-5745
Web Site: https://www.augusthallsf.com
Event Hall Rental Services
N.A.I.C.S.: 532310

B.V. Exploitatiemaatschappij GelreDome (1)
Batavierenweg 25, 6841 HN, Arnhem, Netherlands
Tel.: (31) 268807888
Web Site: https://gelredome.nl
Convention & Trade Show Organizing Services
N.A.I.C.S.: 561920
Harald Vandebunt *(Gen Mgr)*

Be-At Venues N.V. (1)
Schijnpoortweg 119, 2170, Antwerp, Belgium
Tel.: (32) 34004040
Web Site: https://beatvenues.be
Event Management Services
N.A.I.C.S.: 711310

Beats at Sea, LLC (1)
105 E Atlantic Ave Ste 200, Delray Beach, FL 33444
Tel.: (561) 368-8922
Web Site: https://beatsatsea.com
Event Management Services
N.A.I.C.S.: 711310

Bergen Live AS (1)
Bergenhus 13, 5003, Bergen, 5003, Norway
Tel.: (47) 55215060
Web Site: https://www.bergenlive.no
Concert Promoter Services
N.A.I.C.S.: 711310

Biletix Bilet Dagitim Basim ve Ticaret AS (1)
Ayazaga Mah Azerbaycan Cad Blok 1B No 3B lc kapi 2, Sariyer, Istanbul, 34396, Turkiye

Tel.: (90) 850 755 5555
Web Site: https://www.biletix.com
Convention & Trade Show Organizing Services
N.A.I.C.S.: 561920

Black Page Concessions, LLC (1)
4 S Market St, Boston, MA 02109
Tel.: (617) 371-3985
Web Site:
    https://blackpageconcessions.com
Event Management Services
N.A.I.C.S.: 711310

Brag FZ-LLC (1)
Design Quarter Building 7 Office 408B, Dubai Design District Business Bay, Dubai, United Arab Emirates
Tel.: (971) 44327844
Web Site: https://brag.world
Event Management Services
N.A.I.C.S.: 711310

Brand New Live BV (1)
Mozartlaan 25C, 1217 CM, Hilversum, 1217 CM, Netherlands
Tel.: (31) 356222080
Web Site: https://www.brandnewlive.nl
Sales Range: $25-49.9 Million
Emp.: 1
Convention Trade Show Organizers
N.A.I.C.S.: 561920

Brooklyn Bowl Las Vegas, LLC (1)
3545 Las Vegas Blvd S, Las Vegas, NV 89109
Tel.: (702) 862-2695
Web Site: https://www.brooklynbowl.com
Concert & Sporting Event Services
N.A.I.C.S.: 711320
Ashley Cavalli *(Sr Mgr-Sales-Events)*

C I (Events) Limited (1)
30 St John Street, London, EC1M 4AY, United Kingdom
Tel.: (44) 2083365283
Convention & Trade Show Organizing Services
N.A.I.C.S.: 561920

C3 Presents, LLC (1)
1645 E 6th St Ste 150, Austin, TX 78702 (51%)
Tel.: (512) 478-7211
Web Site: https://www.c3concerts.com
Concert & Event Production & Promotion Services
N.A.I.C.S.: 711320

Comcerto Srl (1)
Via Del Commercio 21/D, 60127, Ancona, Italy
Tel.: (39) 0712900711
Web Site: https://www.comcerto.it
Concert & Sporting Event Services
N.A.I.C.S.: 711320

Concert Supplies Sp. z o.o. (1)
ul Kurpinskiego 55 B, 2733, Warsaw, Mazovia, Poland
Tel.: (48) 225497662
Convention & Trade Show Organizing Services
N.A.I.C.S.: 561920

Cosmopop Gmbh (1)
Unteres Rheinufer 39, 67061, Ludwigshafen, Germany
Tel.: (49) 62118191919
Web Site: https://www.cosmopop.biz
Event & Festival Management Services
N.A.I.C.S.: 711310

Cream Holdings Limited (1)
5-6 Argyll Street Cream Group, London, W1F 7TE, United Kingdom
Tel.: (44) 1517071309
Holding Company
N.A.I.C.S.: 551112

Crowdcare B.V. (1)
Krommewetering 21, 2543 AP, Utrecht, Netherlands
Tel.: (31) 683714816
Web Site: https://www.crowdcare.nl
Concert & Sporting Event Services
N.A.I.C.S.: 711320

Cuffe and Taylor Limited (1)
Unit 13 Bartle Court Business Centre Rosemary Lane Bartle, Preston, PR4 0HF, Lan-

cashire, United Kingdom
Tel.: (44) 8448440444
Web Site: https://cuffeandtaylor.com
Event Management Services
N.A.I.C.S.: 711310

D.F. Concerts Limited (1)
272 St Vincent St, Glasgow, G2 5RL, United Kingdom
Tel.: (44) 1415664999
Web Site:
    http://www.dfconcertsandevents.com
Sales Range: $25-49.9 Million
Emp.: 40
Convention Trade Show Organizers
N.A.I.C.S.: 561920
Geoff Ellis *(CEO)*

DG Medios SpA (1)
Alonso de Cordova 4294 local 5, Vitacura, Santiago, Chile
Tel.: (56) 223525900
Web Site: http://www.dgmedios.com
Amusement & Recreation Services
N.A.I.C.S.: 713990
Carlos Geniso Lopez *(Founder & CEO)*

Delmar Hall, LLC (1)
6133 Delmar Blvd, Saint Louis, MO 63112
Tel.: (314) 726-6161
Web Site: https://www.thepageant.com
Concert Hall Rental Services
N.A.I.C.S.: 531120
Sean Pierce *(Sys Engr-Audio)*

Diversified Production Services, LLC (1)
1801 Willow Ave Ste 101, Weehawken, NJ 07086
Tel.: (646) 386-2100
Web Site: https://www.dps-us.com
Convention & Trade Show Organizing Services
N.A.I.C.S.: 561920
Michael Ferrante *(Mgr-Production-Touring)*
Darian Reynolds *(Production Mgr)*

ESM Productions, LLC (1)
2 Penn Ctr 1500 John F Kennedy Blvd Ste 600, Philadelphia, PA 19102
Tel.: (215) 925-2566
Web Site: https://www.esmproductions.com
Event Management Services
N.A.I.C.S.: 711130

EXMO, Inc. (1)
3030 N Rocky Point Dr W Ste 150, Tampa, FL 33607
Tel.: (321) 209-3966
Custom Computer Programming Services
N.A.I.C.S.: 541511

Eagles Personal Management Company (1)
28465 SW Meadows Loop, Wilsonville, OR 97070
Tel.: (503) 570-9837
Financial Investment Services
N.A.I.C.S.: 523999

Emporium Presents, LLC (1)
2221 E St Ste 20, Golden, CO 80401
Tel.: (303) 835-6951
Web Site:
    https://www.emporiumpresents.com
Online Booking Services
N.A.I.C.S.: 512199

Equity Distribution LLC (1)
9348 Civic Ctr Dr, Beverly Hills, CA 90210
Tel.: (310) 867-7000
Web Site: https://www.equitydistro.com
Concert & Sporting Event Services
N.A.I.C.S.: 711320

EventInventory.com, Inc. (1)
38100 Golf Rd Ste 125, Rolling Meadows, IL 60008
Tel.: (877) 800-3434
Web Site: http://www.eventinventory.com
Emp.: 100
Software Publisher
N.A.I.C.S.: 513210

F and F Concessions, Inc. (1)
1106 W Lawrence Ave, Chicago, IL 60640
Tel.: (312) 561-9500
Limited-Service Restaurant Operator
N.A.I.C.S.: 722513

FRHUG Festival GmbH & Co. KG (1)

Pfuelstrasse 5, 10997, Berlin, Germany
Tel.: (49) 3040367050
Web Site: http://www.lollapaloozade.com
Amusement & Recreation Services
N.A.I.C.S.: 713990

Faculty Productions, LLC (1)
835 Seward St, Los Angeles, CA 90038
Tel.: (747) 476-5580
Web Site: https://www.facultyinc.com
Tour Guide Services
N.A.I.C.S.: 713990

Festival Hall Venue Management Pty. Ltd. (1)
300 Dudley St, Melbourhe, 3003, VIC, Australia
Tel.: (61) 386322178
Web Site: https://www.festivalhall.com.au
Live Music Concert Services
N.A.I.C.S.: 711310

Festivals Limburg B.V. (1)
Mauritslaan 25, 6161 HP, Geleen, Netherlands
Tel.: (31) 464752500
Convention & Trade Show Organizing Services
N.A.I.C.S.: 561920

Fifty Fifty Antwerpen B.V. (1)
Ahoyweg 10, 3084 BA, Rotterdam, Netherlands
Tel.: (31) 102933300
Convention & Trade Show Organizing Services
N.A.I.C.S.: 561920

First Fleet Concerts, LLC (1)
504 E Locust St, Des Moines, IA 50309
Tel.: (515) 244-0550
Web Site: https://www.firstfleetconcerts.com
Event Management Services
N.A.I.C.S.: 711310

Founders Entertainment, LLC (1)
430 W 15th St Fl 2, New York, NY 10011
Tel.: (917) 591-6376
Web Site: https://www.foundersent.com
Musical Event Production Services
N.A.I.C.S.: 711310
Jordan Wolowitz *(Co-Founder & Partner)*

Frank Productions, Inc. (1)
29 S Livingston St, Madison, WI 53703-3703
Tel.: (608) 234-5923
Web Site: https://www.frankproductions.com
Advertising Services
N.A.I.C.S.: 541870

Front Gate Holdings, LLC (1)
615 Camp Comfort Rd, Spearfish, SD 57783
Tel.: (605) 641-0574
Holding Company
N.A.I.C.S.: 551112

Full Production Oy (1)
Lintulahdenkatu 2, 00500, Helsinki, Finland
Tel.: (358) 407378995
Event Production Consulting Services
N.A.I.C.S.: 711310

Fundacion OCESA Entretenimiento, A.C. (1)
Av Industria Militar S/N Puerta 2 Acceso A Piso 2, Hipodromo de Las Americas Col Lomas De Sotelo Alcaldia Miguel Hidalgo, 11200, Mexico, Mexico
Tel.: (52) 5592620177
Web Site: https://fundacionocesa.org
Live Music Concert Services
N.A.I.C.S.: 711310

Gellman Management LLC (1)
22917 Pacific Coast Hwy, Malibu, CA 90265
Tel.: (310) 456-2620
Recording Studio
N.A.I.C.S.: 512240

Gigtech B.V. (1)
Dijkgraaf 9a, Duiven, 6921 RL, Lochem, Netherlands
Tel.: (31) 859020848
Web Site: https://www.gigtech.nl
Convention & Trade Show Organizing Services
N.A.I.C.S.: 561920

Glow Events, LLC (1)
3675 Sacramento St, San Francisco, CA
94118
Tel.: (707) 652-9881
Web Site: https://glowevents.com
Events Organizer Services
N.A.I.C.S.: 561920

Goodlive Artists GmbH & Co. KG (1)
Pfuelstr 5, 10997, Berlin, Germany
Tel.: (49) 3040367050
Web Site: https://goodliveartists.com
Event & Festival Management Services
N.A.I.C.S.: 711310

Goodlive GmbH (1)
Pfuelstr 5, 10997, Berlin, Germany
Tel.: (49) 3040367050
Web Site: https://www.goodlive.ag
Live Music Concert Services
N.A.I.C.S.: 711310

Gota Lejon Live AB (1)
Gotgatan 55, 116 21, Stockholm, Sweden
Tel.: (46) 850529000
Web Site: https://www.gotalejon.se
Live Music Concert Services
N.A.I.C.S.: 711310

**Greenlight Media & Marketing,
LLC** (1)
8439 W Sunset Blvd 4th Fl, West Holly-
wood, CA 90069
Tel.: (323) 802-2783
Artist & Entertainer Management Agency
Services
N.A.I.C.S.: 711410
Dominic Sandifer (Pres)
Nick Davidge (Creative Dir)
Bruce Flohr (Partner)
Tom Williams (Acct Dir)

**Greenstone Entertainment GP
Limited** (1)
PO Box 522, Warkworth, 0941, New Zea-
land
Tel.: (64) 73789542
Web Site: https://www.greenstoneentertain
ment.co.nz
Amusement & Recreation Services
N.A.I.C.S.: 713990
Amanda Calvert (CEO)

Groot Hospitality LLC (1)
1680 Meridian Ave Ste 200, Miami Beach,
FL 33139
Tel.: (305) 534-7101
Web Site: https://www.groothospitality.com
Hospitality Management Services
N.A.I.C.S.: 722511
David Grutman (Founder)

Guyo Entertainment, Inc. (1)
2850 Ocean Park Blvd Ste 300, Santa
Monica, CA 90405
Tel.: (310) 282-0477
Convention & Trade Show Organizing Ser-
vices
N.A.I.C.S.: 561920

HOB Entertainment, Inc. (1)
7060 Holywood Blvd, Los Angeles, CA
90028
Tel.: (323) 769-4600
Web Site: http://www.houseofblues.com
Sales Range: $25-49.9 Million
Emp.: 125
Holding Company; Live Entertainment &
Restaurant Properties Operator; Concert
Promotion Services
N.A.I.C.S.: 551112

Subsidiary (Domestic):

House of Blues Concerts, Inc. (2)
6255 W Sunset Blvd 16th Fl, Los Angeles,
CA 90028
Tel.: (323) 769-4977
Web Site: http://www.hob.com
Rev.: $8,600,000
Emp.: 150
Concert Promotion & Management Services
N.A.I.C.S.: 711310

**House of Blues Dallas Restaurant
Corp.** (2)
2200 N Lamar St, Dallas, TX 75202
Tel.: (214) 978-2583
Web Site: http://www.houseofblues.com
Convention Trade Show Organizers

N.A.I.C.S.: 561920

**House of Blues Houston Restaurant
Corp.** (2)
1204 Caroline St, Houston, TX 77002
Web Site: https://www.houseofblues.com
Trade Show Organizing Services
N.A.I.C.S.: 561920

**House of Blues Las Vegas Restau-
rant Corp.** (2)
3950 Las Vegas Blvd, Las Vegas, NV
89119
Tel.: (702) 632-7600
Web Site: https://www.houseofblues.com
Trade Show Organizer
N.A.I.C.S.: 561920

**House of Blues Myrtle Beach Restau-
rant Corp.** (2)
4640 Hwy 17, North Myrtle Beach, SC
29582
Tel.: (843) 272-3000
Web Site: https://www.houseofblues.com
Live Entertainment, Eating & Drinking
Places
N.A.I.C.S.: 722410

**House of Blues New Orleans Restau-
rant Corp.** (2)
225 Decatur, New Orleans, LA 70130
Tel.: (504) 310-4999
Web Site: https://www.houseofblues.com
Restaurant & Club Services
N.A.I.C.S.: 722511

**House of Blues Orlando Restaurant
Corp.** (2)
1490 E Buena Vista Dr, Orlando, FL 32830
Tel.: (407) 934-2583
Web Site: https://www.houseofblues.com
Restaurant Services
N.A.I.C.S.: 722513

Hard Events LLC (1)
820 Seward St, Los Angeles, CA 90038
Tel.: (323) 836-0282
Convention & Trade Show Organizing Ser-
vices
N.A.I.C.S.: 561920

High Noon Saloon LLC (1)
701A E Washington Ave, Madison, WI
53703
Tel.: (608) 268-1122
Web Site: https://www.high-noon.com
Live Music Venue Operator
N.A.I.C.S.: 711130
Lindberg Chambliss (Mgr)

IO Media, Inc. (1)
640 W 28th St 9th Fl, New York, NY 10001
Tel.: (212) 352-1115
Web Site: https://www.io-media.com
Media Graphic Design Services
N.A.I.C.S.: 541430
Peter Korian (Founder & Pres)
Steven Korian (Exec VP)
Ashwan Wadhwa (Mng Dir-India)
John Leone (Sr VP-Analytics & Strategy)
Eugene Carroll (VP-IT Svcs & Infrastruc-
ture)

Insomniac Holdings, LLC (1)
5023 Pkwy, Calabasas, CA 91302
Tel.: (323) 874-7020
Web Site: https://www.insomniac.com
Holding Company
N.A.I.C.S.: 551112

Key Club Miami LLC (1)
3015 Grand Ave, Coconut Grove, FL 33133
Tel.: (305) 521-4969
Web Site: https://thekeyclub.com
Restaurant & Hotel Services
N.A.I.C.S.: 721110

Kingdom of Mind, LLC (1)
9348 Civic Ctr Dr, Beverly Hills, CA 90210
Tel.: (310) 878-4802
Web Site: https://www.kingdomofmind.co
Concert & Sporting Event Services
N.A.I.C.S.: 711320

Laffitte Management Group LLC (1)
1100 Glendon Ave Ste 2000, Los Angeles,
CA 90024
Tel.: (310) 209-6460
Convention & Trade Show Organizing Ser-
vices

N.A.I.C.S.: 561920

Live Nation (HK) Limited (1)
Unit 4105-06 Hopewell Center, Wan Chai,
Hong Kong, China (Hong Kong)
Tel.: (852) 29899239
Web Site: https://www.livenation.hk
Trade Show Organizer
N.A.I.C.S.: 561920

Live Nation (Music) UK Limited (1)
30 St John Street, London, EC1M 4AY,
United Kingdom
Tel.: (44) 2070093333
Web Site: https://www.livenation.co.uk
Sales Range: $50-74.9 Million
Emp.: 250

Live Nation - Midwest Division (1)
44 N Main St, Chagrin Falls, OH 44022
Tel.: (440) 247-2722
Web Site: http://www.livenation.com
Sales Range: $10-24.9 Million
Emp.: 20
Live Entertainment Producer & Promoter
N.A.I.C.S.: 711310

Live Nation - Southern Division (1)
2000 W Loop S, Houston, TX 77027-3513
Tel.: (713) 693-8600
Web Site: http://www.livenation.com
Sales Range: $75-99.9 Million
Emp.: 130
Live Entertainment Producer & Promoter
N.A.I.C.S.: 711320
Brian Capo (Chief Acctg Officer)

Live Nation Australia Pty Ltd (1)
Level 2 11 Newton St, Cremorne, 3121,
VIC, Australia
Tel.: (61) 395097666
Web Site: https://www.livenation.com.au
Sales Range: $25-49.9 Million
Emp.: 5
Convention Trade Show Organizers
N.A.I.C.S.: 561920

**Live Nation BEC-Tero Entertainment
Co., Ltd** (1)
3199 Maleenont Tower 21st-22nd Floor
25th-28th Floor Rama IV Road, Khlongton
Khlongtoey, Bangkok, 10110, Thailand
Tel.: (66) 22623800
Live Musical Entertainment Services
N.A.I.C.S.: 711130
Blue Satittammanoon (Mgr-Project)

Live Nation Baltics OU (1)
Estonia pst 9, 10143, Tallinn, Estonia
Tel.: (372) 6155100
Web Site: https://www.fbi.ee
Convention & Trade Show Organizing Ser-
vices
N.A.I.C.S.: 561920

**Live Nation Brand Partnership & Me-
dia GmbH** (1)
Kohlbrandtreppe 2, 22767, Hamburg, Ger-
many
Tel.: (49) 404117260
Event Management Services
N.A.I.C.S.: 711320
Katrin Adolph (Head-Ops)

Live Nation Denmark Aps (1)
Frederiksberg Alle 3 2, 1621, Copenhagen,
Denmark
Tel.: (45) 35254100
Web Site: https://www.livenation.dk
Convention Trade Show Organizers
N.A.I.C.S.: 561920

Subsidiary (Domestic):

BILLETnet AS (2)
Gammel Kongevej 60 5th floor, 1850, Fred-
eriksberg, Denmark
Tel.: (45) 20309474
Web Site: https://www.ticketmaster.dk
Sales Range: $25-49.9 Million
Emp.: 7
Convention Trade Show Organizers
N.A.I.C.S.: 561920

**Live Nation Denmark Management
Aps** (2)
Frederiksberg Alle 3, 1790, Copenhagen,
Denmark
Tel.: (45) 35254100
Web Site: http://www.livenation.dk

Sales Range: $25-49.9 Million
Emp.: 25
Convention Trade Show Organizers
N.A.I.C.S.: 561920

**Live Nation Entertainment, Inc. -
Times Square Office** (1)
220 W 42nd St 1, New York, NY 10036
Tel.: (917) 421-4000
Producer & Promoter of Live Entertainment
Events
N.A.I.C.S.: 711320
Greg Hagglund (Exec VP-Mktg)

Live Nation Espana SAU (1)
Paseo San Juan 104 6 2, 08037, Barce-
lona, Spain
Tel.: (34) 934592362
Web Site: https://www.livenation.es
Sales Range: $25-49.9 Million
Emp.: 30
Convention Trade Show Organizers
N.A.I.C.S.: 561920

Subsidiary (Domestic):

**Madrid Deportes y Espectaculos
SA** (2)
Avenida Felipe Ii S/N, Madrid, 28009, Spain
Tel.: (34) 914449949
Convention Trade Show Organizers
N.A.I.C.S.: 561920

Rock in Rio Madrid SA (2)
Calle General Rodrigo Cuerpo Alto 8 6, Ma-
drid, 28003, Spain
Tel.: (34) 902406088
Web Site: https://www.rockinrio.com
Sales Range: $25-49.9 Million
Emp.: 1
Convention Trade Show Organizers
N.A.I.C.S.: 561920

Live Nation Italia S.r.l. (1)
Via Francesco Valori 7, 50132, Florence, Fi,
Italy
Tel.: (39) 055 552 0575
Web Site: http://www.livenation.it
Convention Trade Show Organizers
N.A.I.C.S.: 561920

Subsidiary (Domestic):

Live Nation LGTours (USA), LLC (1)
Asesores De Flete Palau Sant Jordi Paseo,
Olimpico 5 7 Es, 08038, Barcelona, Spain
Tel.: (34) 934262089
Convention & Trade Show Organizing Ser-
vices
N.A.I.C.S.: 561920

**Live Nation Lushington (Hong Kong)
Limited** (1)
3/F The Rays 71 Hung To Road, Kwun
Tong, Hong Kong, Kowloon, China (Hong
Kong)
Tel.: (852) 26296248
Convention & Trade Show Organizing Ser-
vices
N.A.I.C.S.: 561920
Cissy So (Mgr-Mktg & Promos)

Live Nation Merchandise Inc. (1)
450 mis St 300, San Francisco, CA 94105
Tel.: (415) 247-7400
Web Site: http://www.livenation.com
Sales Range: $25-49.9 Million
Emp.: 70
Music Merchandise Licensing Services
N.A.I.C.S.: 533110

Live Nation Middle East FZ-LLC (1)
G01 Dubai Islamic Bank Bldg, PO Box
502699, Dubai Internet City, Dubai, United
Arab Emirates
Tel.: (971) 44278166
Web Site: https://www.livenation.me
Emp.: 8
Convention Trade Show Organizers
N.A.I.C.S.: 561920

Live Nation Nordic AB (1)
Linnegatan 89, Stockholm, Sweden
Tel.: (46) 86650100
Web Site: https://www.livenation.com
Sales Range: $25-49.9 Million
Emp.: 60
Convention Trade Show Organizers
N.A.I.C.S.: 561920

Subsidiary (Non-US):

Live Nation Finland OY (2)

Live Nation Entertainment, Inc.—(Continued)

Tyopajankatu 13a, 00580, Helsinki, Finland
Tel.: (358) 985673400
Web Site: https://www.livenation.fi
Sales Range: $25-49.9 Million
Emp.: 5
Live Concerts
N.A.I.C.S.: 711130

Subsidiary (Domestic):

Events Club OY (3)
Hameentie 15 7 krs, 00500, Helsinki, Finland
Tel.: (358) 985673456
Web Site: https://www.eventsclub.fi
Sales Range: $25-49.9 Million
Emp.: 3
Convention Trade Show Organizers
N.A.I.C.S.: 561920

Ticketmaster Suomi Oy (3)
Keskuskatu 6, 00100, Helsinki, Finland
Tel.: (358) 60010800
Web Site: https://www.ticketmaster.fi
Convention Trade Show Organizers
N.A.I.C.S.: 561920

Welldone LR OY (3)
Sorvaajankatu 11 A 5th floor, 00880, Helsinki, Finland
Tel.: (358) 934871100
Web Site: https://www.wdlr.fi
Emp.: 5
Convention Trade Show Organizers
N.A.I.C.S.: 561920
Markku Pesonen (Partner & Dir-Production)
Petra Riissanen (Coord-Admin)
Joona Nyman (Acct Mgr)

Subsidiary (Non-US):

Live Nation Norway AS (2)
Sonja Henies Plass 2, Oslo, 0185, Norway
Tel.: (47) 23163260
Web Site: https://www.livenation.no
Lite Music Services
N.A.I.C.S.: 561920

Subsidiary (Domestic):

Billettservice AS (3)
Grensen 16, 0159, Oslo, Norway
Tel.: (47) 22828100
Web Site: https://www.ticketmaster.no
Ticket Sales & Distribution
N.A.I.C.S.: 561920

Subsidiary (Domestic):

Live Nation Sweden AB (2)
Folkungagatan 44, PO Box 24151, 118 26, Stockholm, Sweden
Tel.: (46) 86650100
Web Site: https://www.livenation.se
Sales Range: $25-49.9 Million
Emp.: 80
Convention Trade Show Organizers
N.A.I.C.S.: 561920

Subsidiary (Non-US):

Lugerinc AB (3)
Tel.: (46) 86650100
Web Site: https://www.luger.se
Convention Trade Show Organizers
N.A.I.C.S.: 561920

Subsidiary (Domestic):

Moondog Entertainment AB (3)
Linnegatan 89, 115 23, Stockholm, Sweden
Tel.: (46) 86650100
Convention Trade Show Organizers
N.A.I.C.S.: 561920

Live Nation Sp. z.o.o. (1)
Ul Pilicka 4, 02-629, Warsaw, Poland
Tel.: (48) 226460649
Web Site: https://www.livenation.pl
Convention Trade Show Organizers
N.A.I.C.S.: 561920
Hubert Stajniak (Mng Dir)

Live Nation Venues (Netherlands) BV (1)
Johan Cruijff Boulevard 590, 1101 DS, Amsterdam, Netherlands
Tel.: (31) 9006874242
Web Site: https://www.afaslive.nl
Convention & Trade Show Organizer

N.A.I.C.S.: 561920

Logjam Presents, LLC (1)
134 W Front St, Missoula, MT 59802
Tel.: (406) 830-4640
Web Site: https://www.logjampresents.com
Event Hall Entertainment Services
N.A.I.C.S.: 531120

Lollapalooza, LLC (1)
590 Reinante Ave, Coral Gables, FL 33156-2344
Tel.: (305) 200-3736
Convention & Trade Show Organizing Services
N.A.I.C.S.: 561920
Berkeley Reinhold (Gen Counsel)

MAMA & Company Limited (1)
30 St John Street, London, EC1M 4AY, United Kingdom
Tel.: (44) 2076889000
Emp.: 538
Artist Management Services
N.A.I.C.S.: 713990

MCD Productions Limited (1)
7 Park Road, Dun Laoghiare, Dublin, Ireland
Tel.: (353) 15169056
Web Site: https://www.mcd.ie
Concert Promoter Services
N.A.I.C.S.: 711320

MMM Studio Limited (1)
Unit 1015 10/F Wing On Plaza 62 Mody Rd Tsim Sha Tsui East, Hong Kong, China (Hong Kong)
Tel.: (852) 64115922
Web Site: https://mmminterior.com
Residential & Restaurant Interior Design Services
N.A.I.C.S.: 541410

MOJO Concerts B.V. (1)
Noordeinde 19-21, PO Box 3121, 2611 KE, Delft, Netherlands
Tel.: (31) 27223030
Web Site: https://www.mojo.nl
Convention Trade Show Organizers
N.A.I.C.S.: 561920

Mainland Music AG (1)
Elias-Canetti-Strasse 7, 8050, Zurich, Switzerland
Tel.: (41) 445159000
Web Site: https://www.mainlandmusic.com
Concert & Live Music Operator
N.A.I.C.S.: 711320

Mojo Concerts BV (2)
Noordeinde 19-21, Delft, 2611 KE, Netherlands
Tel · (31) 152121980
Web Site: http://www.mojo.nl
Emp.: 85
Music Concerts
N.A.I.C.S.: 711130

Mojo Works B.V. (1)
Noordeinde 19, 2611 KE, Delft, Netherlands
Tel.: (31) 152121980
Largest Concert Promoting Services
N.A.I.C.S.: 711320
Cees Muurling (COO)

Music Marketing Sp. z.o.o. (1)
Ul Pilicka 4, 02-629, Warsaw, Poland
Tel.: (48) 22 646 0649
Web Site: https://www.musicmarketing.pl
Live Music Entertainment
N.A.I.C.S.: 561920

New Era Farms, LLC (1)
1720 Wire Rd, Aiken, SC 29805
Tel.: (803) 262-5434
Web Site: https://newerafarm.com
Horse Riding Instruction Services
N.A.I.C.S.: 611620

PDH Music A/S (1)
Frederiksberg Alle 3, 1790, Copenhagen, Denmark
Tel.: (45) 33112200
Web Site: https://www.pdh.dk
Concert & Live Music Services
N.A.I.C.S.: 711320

Planet Events S.A. (1)
Gran via 32 bis 6a planta, 28013, Madrid, Spain

Tel.: (34) 917817983
Web Site: https://www.planetevents.es
Event Management Services
N.A.I.C.S.: 541870

Quietus Management Limited (1)
14 Ivor Place, London, NW1 6HS, United Kingdom
Tel.: (44) 2032200310
Web Site:
https://www.quietusmanagement.com
Convention & Trade Show Organizing Services
N.A.I.C.S.: 561920

Red Mountain Entertainment, LLC (1)
2107 5th Ave N Ste 501, Birmingham, AL 35203
Tel.: (205) 714-5933
Web Site: https://www.redmountainentertainment.com
Performing Arts Companies
N.A.I.C.S.: 711190

Revival Event Venue Inc. (1)
783 College Street, Toronto, M6G-1C5, ON, Canada
Tel.: (613) 294-6409
Web Site: https://www.revivaleventvenue.ca
Live Music Concert Services
N.A.I.C.S.: 711310

Rival Labs, Inc. (1)
2225 E Belt Line Rd Ste 105, Carrollton, TX 75006
Tel.: (972) 788-0808
Web Site: http://www.rivallabs.com
Laboratory Testing Services
N.A.I.C.S.: 541380
Jeff Randol (Founder)

Rock World Lisboa S.A. (1)
Edificio LACS Cais da Rocha de Conde D Obidos, 1350-352, Lisbon, Portugal
Tel.: (351) 210913500
Web Site: https://rockinriolisboa.pt
Event Management Services
N.A.I.C.S.: 711310

Roseclaim Limited (1)
Lancashire Gate 21 Tiviot Dale, Stockport, SK1 1TD, United Kingdom
Tel.: (44) 288582214
Convention & Trade Show Organizing Services
N.A.I.C.S.: 561920

Scheme Engine, LLC (1)
8275 Beverly Blvd, Beverly Hills, CA 90048
Tel.: (310) 612-0025
Event & Media Network Services
N.A.I.C.S.: 711320
Devin Chanda (Chief Creative Officer)
Charles Todd (COO)
Matt Mitchener (Creative Dir)
Alex Kaplan (CEO)

Seatwave Nederland B.V. (1)
4 Pentonville Road, London, N1 9HF, United Kingdom
Tel.: (44) 207948593
Ticket Agency Services
N.A.I.C.S.: 561599

Secret Sounds Group Services Pty Ltd (1)
6/59 Centennial Circuit, Byron Bay, 2481, NSW, Australia
Tel.: (61) 266857900
Web Site: https://www.secretsounds.com
Event Management Services
N.A.I.C.S.: 711310

Subsidiary (Domestic):

Secret Sounds Group Pty Ltd (2)
55 Anderson Street, Fortitude Valley, 4006, QLD, Australia
Tel.: (61) 736200200
Web Site: https://www.secretsounds.com
Artist Management Services
N.A.I.C.S.: 713990

Security Company Security B.V. (1)
Bouwerij 30, Amstelveen, Netherlands
Tel.: (31) 204562222
Security Services
N.A.I.C.S.: 561612
Jackques Ddoes (Mng Dir)

Seitrack USA, LLC (1)
1680 Meridian Ave Ste 301, Miami Beach, FL 33139
Tel.: (305) 535-8337
Web Site: https://seitrackus.com
Artist Management Services
N.A.I.C.S.: 711410

Sensible Events Limited (1)
14 Haringey Park, London, N8 9HY, United Kingdom
Tel.: (44) 2034689490
Web Site: https://www.sensibleevents.com
Sales Range: $25-49.9 Million
Emp.: 3
Music Agents
N.A.I.C.S.: 561920

Sherpa.be SA (1)
Avenue du port 86c B 202, 1000, Brussels, Belgium
Tel.: (32) 90084100
Web Site: http://www.sherpa.be
Convention & Trade Show Organizing Services
N.A.I.C.S.: 561920

Shoreline Amphitheatre, Ltd. (1)
1 Amphitheatre Pkwy, Mountain View, CA 94043
Tel.: (650) 967-4040
Convention Trade Show Organizers
N.A.I.C.S.: 561920

Showsec International Limited (1)
Motorpoint Arena Cardiff Mary Ann Street, Cardiff, CF10 2EQ, United Kingdom
Tel.: (44) 1162043333
Web Site: https://www.showsec.co.uk
Sales Range: $25-49.9 Million
Emp.: 2
Convention Trade Show Organizers
N.A.I.C.S.: 561920

Singer's Getranke Shop GmbH & Co. KG (1)
Meinersdorferstrasse 3, 09390, Gornsdorf, Germany
Tel.: (49) 372186696
Web Site: https://www.singers-getraenkeshop.de
Emp.: 20
Event & Catering Services
N.A.I.C.S.: 722320

Soundcheck, LLC (1)
28715 Greenfield Rd, Southfield, MI 48076
Tel.: (248) 440-5996
Web Site: https://soundcheckllc.com
Home Theater Mfr
N.A.I.C.S.: 334310

Southern Promotions, Inc. (1)
146 Volunteer Dr Unit B, Hendersonville, TN 37075
Tel.: (615) 826-0003
Web Site:
https://www.southernpromotionsinc.com
Sales Range: $10-24.9 Million
Emp.: 20
Radio & Television Employment Agency
N.A.I.C.S.: 561311

Straight International Security BV (1)
Krommewetering 21, PO Box 1025, 3543 AP, Utrecht, Netherlands
Tel.: (31) 303031903
Web Site: https://www.tsc.nl
Sales Range: $100-124.9 Million
Emp.: 1,000
Convention Trade Show Organizers
N.A.I.C.S.: 561920

Stubb's Austin Restaurant Company, LC (1)
801 Red River St, Austin, TX 78701
Tel.: (737) 465-1218
Web Site: https://www.stubbsaustin.com
Restaurant & Hotel Services
N.A.I.C.S.: 721110
Ryan Garrett (Gen Mgr)
Misael Barrera (Mgr-)
Dany Carbajal (Mgr-)
John Mickan (Production Mgr)
Carol Amador (Dir-)

Superbloom Festival GmbH & Co. KG (1)
Pfuelstrasse 5, 10997, Berlin, Germany
Tel.: (49) 3040367050

Web Site: https://superbloom.de
Live Music Concert Services
N.A.I.C.S.: 711310

Sweden Rock Festival AB   **(1)**
Nygatan 27, 294 34, Solvesborg, Sweden
Tel.: (46) 45631795
Web Site: https://www.swedenrock.com
Largest Live Concert Organizing Services
N.A.I.C.S.: 711320
Jon Bergsjo *(Mgr-Comml)*

T Shirt Printers Pty Limited   **(1)**
14 McGill Street, Lewisham, Sydney, 2049, NSW, Australia
Tel.: (61) 295181488
Textile & Fabric Finishing Mill Operator
N.A.I.C.S.: 313310

The Event Support Company BV   **(1)**
Bouweri 30, 1185 XX, Amstelveen, Netherlands
Tel.: (31) 204562222
Web Site: https://www.events.nl
Convention Trade Show Organizers
N.A.I.C.S.: 561920

The Opera House Inc.   **(1)**
735 Queen Street East, Toronto, M4M 1H1, ON, Canada
Tel.: (416) 466-0313
Web Site: https://theoperahousetoronto.com
Live Music Concert Services
N.A.I.C.S.: 711310

The Security Company Utrecht Holland Holding BV   **(1)**
Curve law 21, 3543 AP, Utrecht, Netherlands
Tel.: (31) 204562222
Convention Trade Show Organizers
N.A.I.C.S.: 561920

The Triffid Pty. Ltd.   **(1)**
7-9 Stratton Street, Newstead, 4006, QLD, Australia
Tel.: (61) 731713001
Web Site: https://thetriffid.com.au
Live Music Concert Services
N.A.I.C.S.: 711310

The Wolf Bookings B.V.   **(1)**
Noordeinde 19, 2611 KE, Delft, Netherlands
Tel.: (31) 367112740
Artist Management Services
N.A.I.C.S.: 713990

Three Six Zero Group, Inc.   **(1)**
7175 Willoughby Ave, Los Angeles, CA 90046
Tel.: (323) 802-0812
Emp.: 3
Artist Management Services
N.A.I.C.S.: 713990
Carly Mann *(Mgr-Artist)*

Three Six Zero Grp Limited   **(1)**
C/O Hillier Hopkins Llp Ground Floor 45 Pall Mall, London, SW1Y 5JG, United Kingdom
Tel.: (44) 1732462110
Web Site: http://www.threesixzerogroup.com
Sales Range: $25-49.9 Million
Emp.: 5
Convention Trade Show Organizers
N.A.I.C.S.: 561920

Ticketmaster B.V.   **(1)**
Regulusweg 5, 2516 AC, Hague, Netherlands
Tel.: (31) 704169333
Artist Management Services
N.A.I.C.S.: 713990

Ticketmaster Entertainment LLC   **(1)**
9348 Civic Center Dr, Beverly Hills, CA 90210
Tel.: (310) 867-7000
Web Site: http://www.ticketmaster.com
Sales Range: $1-4.9 Billion
Emp.: 3,900
Holding Company; Live Entertainment Ticketing & Marketing Services
N.A.I.C.S.: 551112
Jared Smith *(Pres-North America)*

Subsidiary (Non-US):

GET ME IN! Ltd.   **(2)**
2nd Floor Regent Arcade House 19-25 Argyll Street, PO Box 68685, London, W1F

7TS, United Kingdom
Tel.: (44) 2033686939
Web Site: http://www.getmein.com
Sales Range: $100-124.9 Million
Event Ticketing Services
N.A.I.C.S.: 711310

Kartenhaus Ticketservice GmbH   **(2)**
Stresemannstrasse 29, 22769, Hamburg, Germany
Tel.: (49) 40808197500
Web Site: http://www.ticketmaster.de
Sales Range: $100-124.9 Million
Event Ticketing Services
N.A.I.C.S.: 561599

Subsidiary (Domestic):

TicketWeb LLC   **(2)**
807 S Jackson Rd, Pharr, TX 78577
Tel.: (415) 901-0210
Web Site: https://info.ticketweb.com
Online Ticket Sales
N.A.I.C.S.: 561599

Subsidiary (Non-US):

Ticketmaster Canada Ltd.   **(2)**
1304 Hornby St, Vancouver, V6Z 1W6, BC, Canada
Tel.: (604) 682-8455
Web Site: https://www.ticketmaster.ca
Sales Range: $25-49.9 Million
Emp.: 60
Ticketing Services
N.A.I.C.S.: 561599

Ticketmaster GmbH   **(2)**
Spree Forum Alt-Moabit 60, D-10555, Berlin, Germany
Tel.: (49) 18059690000
Web Site: https://www.ticketmaster.de
Convention Trade Show Organizers
N.A.I.C.S.: 561920
Klaus Zemke *(Mng Dir)*

Subsidiary (Domestic):

Ticketmaster LLC   **(2)**
9348 Civic Center Dr, Beverly Hills, CA 90210-3624
Tel.: (800) 653-8000
Web Site: http://www.ticketmaster.com
Sales Range: $25-49.9 Million
Emp.: 5,000
Ticket Reservation Services
N.A.I.C.S.: 561599
Amy Howe *(Pres/COO-Ticketmaster-North America)*

Subsidiary (Non-US):

Ticketmaster NZ Limited   **(2)**
Stace Hammond Level 15 34 Shortland Street, Auckland, 1010, New Zealand
Tel.: (64) 99709700
Web Site: https://www.ticketmaster.co.nz
Convention Trade Show Organizers
N.A.I.C.S.: 561920
David Nicholas Hamilton *(Dir)*

Ticketmaster Systems Limited   **(2)**
West Coast Riverside Off Park, Campbell Rd, Stoke-on-Trent, ST4 4DA, Staffordshire, United Kingdom
Tel.: (44) 8448440099
Web Site: http://www.ticketmaster.co.uk
Sales Range: $25-49.9 Million
Emp.: 50
Convention Trade Show Organizers
N.A.I.C.S.: 561920

Ticketmaster UK Limited   **(2)**
30 St John Street, London, EC1M 4AY, United Kingdom
Tel.: (44) 3333219999
Web Site: https://www.ticketmaster.co.uk
Music Tickets
N.A.I.C.S.: 561920
Dan Pearce *(Sr VP-)*

Subsidiary (Domestic):

TicketsNow.com, Inc.   **(2)**
3800 Golf Rd Ste 125, Rolling Meadows, IL 60008
Tel.: (815) 444-9800
Web Site: http://www.ticketsnow.com
Entertainment Ticketing Services
N.A.I.C.S.: 561599

Ticketmaster Israel Ltd   **(1)**
Sderot Yitzhak Rabin 7, Rishon le Zion, Israel
Tel.: (972) 35007000
Web Site: https://www.tmisrael.co.il
Ticket Reservation Services
N.A.I.C.S.: 561599

Ticketmaster Poland Sp. z.o.o.   **(1)**
ul Bukowinska 22b, 02-703, Warsaw, Poland
Tel.: (48) 223958700
Web Site: https://www.ticketmaster.pl
Convention & Trade Show Organizing Services
N.A.I.C.S.: 561920

Ticketmaster Schweiz AG   **(1)**
Zurichstrasse 125, 8600, Dubendorf, Switzerland
Tel.: (41) 900091091
Web Site: https://www.ticketmaster.ch
Event Ticket Seller Services
N.A.I.C.S.: 561599

Ticketmaster-Singapore Pte. Ltd.   **(1)**
2 Stadium Walk Kallang Indoor Stadium, Singapore, 397691, Singapore
Tel.: (65) 31588588
Web Site: https://www.ticketmaster.sg
Event Ticket Seller Services
N.A.I.C.S.: 561599

Ticketpro Polska sp zoo   **(1)**
Ul Osikowa 45, 40-181, Katowice, Poland
Tel.: (48) 323520004
Amusement Ticket Reservation Services
N.A.I.C.S.: 561599

TimeOut Agency & Concerts AS   **(1)**
Fred Olsen gate 1, 0152, Oslo, Norway
Tel.: (47) 21422500
Web Site: https://www.timeout.no
Convention & Trade Show Organizing Services
N.A.I.C.S.: 561920
Kristine Kamsvaag *(Production Mgr)*

Veeps Inc.   **(1)**
269 S Beverly Dr Ste 1672, Beverly Hills, CA 90212
Web Site: https://www.veeps.com
Concert Promoter Services
N.A.I.C.S.: 711320

WE Fest Holdings, LLC   **(1)**
900 Wayzata Blvd E Ste 130, Wayzata, MN 55391
Web Site: http://www.wefest.com
Show Organizer Services
N.A.I.C.S.: 561920

Wolfson Entertainment, Inc.   **(1)**
2659 Townsgate Rd Ste 119, Westlake Village, CA 91361
Tel.: (805) 494-9600
Web Site: http://wolfsonent.com
Entertainment Services
N.A.I.C.S.: 711130

Yourtrove, Inc.   **(1)**
156 2nd St, San Francisco, CA 94105
Tel.: (415) 894-2724
Convention & Trade Show Organizing Services
N.A.I.C.S.: 561920

LIVE OAK BANCSHARES, INC.
1757 Tiburon Dr, Wilmington, NC 28403
Tel.: (910) 790-5867   NC
Web Site:
  https://www.liveoakbank.com
LOB—(NYSE)
Rev.: $800,008,000
Assets: $11,271,423,000
Liabilities: $10,368,757,000
Net Worth: $902,666,000
Earnings: $73,898,000
Emp.: 943
Fiscal Year-end: 12/31/23
Bank Holding Company
N.A.I.C.S.: 551111
William Lee Williams III *(Vice Chm & Exec VP)*
Steven J. Smits *(Chief Credit Officer-Live Oak Bank)*

William C. Losch III *(Pres & CFO)*
Claire Parker *(Sr VP-Corp Comm)*
James S. Mahan III *(Founder, Chm & CEO)*
J. Wesley Sutherland *(Chief Acctg Officer)*

Subsidiaries:

Government Loan Solutions, Inc.   **(1)**
1741 Tiburon Dr, Wilmington, NC 28403
Tel.: (216) 456-2480
Web Site: https://glsolutions.us
Financial Consulting Services
N.A.I.C.S.: 541611
Scott Evans *(Co-Founder & Principal)*
Rob Herrick *(Co-Founder)*

Live Oak Banking Company   **(1)**
1757 Tiburon Dr, Wilmington, NC 28403
Tel.: (910) 790-5867
Web Site: https://www.liveoakbank.com
Banking Services
N.A.I.C.S.: 522110
Angus McDonald *(Exec VP-Specialty Fin)*
Mike McGinley *(Exec VP-Small Bus Banking)*
Dawn Thompson *(Sr VP-Govt Rels)*
Renato Derraik *(Chief Info & Digital Officer)*
Steve Smits *(Chief Credit Officer)*
Courtney Spencer *(Chief Experience Officer)*
Micah Davis *(Chief Comm Officer)*
Walt J. Phifer *(CFO)*
James S. Mahan III *(Chm & CEO)*

Live Oak Private Wealth, LLC   **(1)**
1741 Tiburon Dr, Wilmington, NC 28403
Web Site:
  https://www.liveoakprivatewealth.com
Wealth Management Services
N.A.I.C.S.: 523940
Andy Basinger *(Mng Dir)*
Bill Coleman *(Mng Dir)*
Connor Keller *(Mng Dir)*
Amy Bennett *(Mgr-Client Relationship)*
Frank Jolley *(Mng Dir)*
Missy Musser *(Mgr-Client Relationship)*
Jan Robillard *(Mgr-Client Relationship)*
Terry Sapp *(Dir-Ops)*

RELTCO, Inc.   **(1)**
12886 Commodity Pl, Tampa, FL 33626
Tel.: (813) 855-0009
Web Site: https://www.reltco.com
Company Holding Services
N.A.I.C.S.: 551111
Paula L. Woodring *(Founder & CEO)*

LIVE OAK CRESTVIEW CLIMATE ACQUISITION CORP.
40 S Main St Ste 2550, Memphis, TN 38103
Tel.: (901) 685-2865   DE
Web Site:
  https://www.liveoakacq.com
Year Founded: 2021
LOCC—(NYSE)
Rev.: $2,882,855
Assets: $203,350,253
Liabilities: $210,295,315
Net Worth: ($6,945,062)
Earnings: ($488,988)
Emp.: 3
Fiscal Year-end: 12/31/22
Investment Services
N.A.I.C.S.: 523999
Richard J. Hendrix *(CEO)*
John P. Amboian *(Chm)*
Adam J. Fishman *(COO)*
Gary K. Wunderlich Jr. *(Pres, CFO & Sec)*

LIVE OAK MOBILITY ACQUISITION CORP.
4921 William Arnold Rd, Memphis, TN 38117
Tel.: (901) 685-2865   DE
Web Site: http://www.liveoakacq.com
Year Founded: 2021

Live Oak Mobility Acquisition Corp.—(Continued)
LOKM—(NYSE)
Emp.: 3
Investment Services
N.A.I.C.S.: 523999
Richard J. Hendrix (CEO)
Adam J. Fishman (COO)
Gary K. Wunderlich Jr. (Pres & CFO)

LIVE VENTURES INCORPORATED

325 E Warm Springs Rd Ste 102,
Las Vegas, NV 89119
Tel.: (702) 997-5968   NV
Web Site: https://www.live-
ventures.com
Year Founded: 1968
LIVE—(NASDAQ)
Rev.: $472,840,000
Assets: $407,547,000
Liabilities: $334,658,000
Net Worth: $72,889,000
Earnings: ($26,685,000)
Emp.: 1,429
Fiscal Year-end: 09/30/24
Online Directory Publisher
N.A.I.C.S.: 513140
Jon Isaac (Pres & CEO)
Wayne R. Ipsen (Chief Legal Officer
& Sec)
Michael J. Stein (Gen Counsel & Sr
VP)
David Verret (CFO & Chief Acctg Of-
ficer)
Eric Althofer (Mng Dir-Fin)
Tony Isaac (Strategist)

Subsidiaries:

ApplianceSmart Holdings LLC (1)
325 E Warm Springs Rd Ste 102, Las Ve-
gas, NV 89119
Tel.: (702) 939-0231
Investment Services
N.A.I.C.S.: 523999

ApplianceSmart, Inc. (1)
325 E Warm Springs Rd Ste 105, Las Ve-
gas, NV 89119
Tel.: (702) 939-0231
Web Site: http://www.appliancesmart.com
Appliance Whslr
N.A.I.C.S.: 449210

Branch (Domestic):

ApplianceSmart (2)
8900 109th Ave N, Champlin, MN
55316   (100%)
Tel.: (763) 712-1052
Appliance Retail Store
N.A.I.C.S.: 449210

ApplianceSmart (2)
6080 E Main St, Columbus, OH
43231   (100%)
Tel.: (614) 816-2994
Web Site: http://www.appliancesmart.com
Appliance Retail Store
N.A.I.C.S.: 449210

Astro Carpet Mills LLC (1)
PO Box 1308, Chatsworth, GA 30705
Web Site: http://www.astrocarpetmills.com
Carpet Mfr
N.A.I.C.S.: 314110

Central Steel Fabricators Inc. (1)
2100 Parkes Dr, Broadview, IL 60155
Tel.: (708) 652-2037
Web Site: https://www.centralsteelfab.com
Sales Range: $25-49.9 Million
Emp.: 45
Miscellaneous Metalwork
N.A.I.C.S.: 332322
Gregory D. Johnston (Pres)
David Antrim (Mgr-Pur)

Elite Builder Services, Inc. (1)
1903 Rutan Dr, Livermore, CA 94551
Tel.: (925) 932-4101
Web Site: https://elitebuilderservices.com
Interior Design Services
N.A.I.C.S.: 541410

Floorable, LLC (1)
1581-B Cummins Dr, Modesto, CA 95358
Tel.: (916) 396-5277
Web Site: https://floorable.com
Cabinet Mfr & Distr
N.A.I.C.S.: 337110

Flooring Liquidators, Inc. (1)
1328 N Carpenter Rd, Modesto, CA 95351
Tel.: (209) 341-0123
Web Site: http://www.flooringliquidators.net
Emp.: 625
Floor Covering Stores
N.A.I.C.S.: 449121
Steven Kellogg (Pres)

Subsidiary (Domestic):

Cal Coast Carpet Warehouse,
Inc (2)
1570 W Branch St, Arroyo Grande, CA
93420
Tel.: (805) 481-5559
Web Site: http://www.calcoastcarpet.net
Floor Covering Stores
N.A.I.C.S.: 449121
Debbie Fastlaben (Owner)

Live Ventures Incorporated (1)
325 E Warm Springs Rd Ste 102, Las Ve-
gas, NV 89119
Web Site: http://www.livedeal.com
Restaurant Services
N.A.I.C.S.: 722511

Marquis Industries, Inc. (1)
2743 Hwy 76, Chatsworth, GA 30705
Web Site: http://www.marquisind.com
Wood Products Mfr
N.A.I.C.S.: 321999
Wes Godfrey (CEO)

Modern Everyday, Inc. (1)
614 S Date Ave, Alhambra, CA 91803
Tel.: (888) 980-9963
Web Site: http://www.moderneveryday.com
Sales Range: $1-9.9 Million
Emp.: 24
Retailer & Online Sales of Home Products,
Toys & Sporting Goods
N.A.I.C.S.: 459110
Byron Hsu (Pres, CEO & CTO)

Precision Industries Inc. (1)
99 Berry Rd, Washington, PA 15301
Tel.: (724) 222-2100
Web Site: http://www.pmsteel.com
Process Steel
N.A.I.C.S.: 331221
Thomas R. Sedlak (CEO)
Michael Valeri (CFO)
Michele Miles (Sls Mgr)
Adam Helphenstine (Ops Mgr)
Luis Longoria (Mgr-Distr Sys)

SW Financial (1)
1295 Walt Whitman Rd Ste A, Melville, NY
11747
Tel.: (631) 482-1150
Web Site: https://www.sw-financial.com
Financial Investment Services
N.A.I.C.S.: 523999

The Kinetic Co., Inc. (1)
6775 W Loomis Rd, Greendale, WI 53129
Tel.: (414) 425-8221
Web Site: https://www.knifemaker.com
Industrial Knive Mfr & Distr
N.A.I.C.S.: 332216

Velocity Local, Inc. (1)
15456 Ventura Blvd, Sherman Oaks, CA
91403
Tel.: (919) 528-3670
Web Site: http://www.velocitylocal.com
Advertising Services
N.A.I.C.S.: 541810

Velocity Marketing Concepts, Inc (1)
16045 Stevensburg Rd Brandy Station, Cul-
peper, VA 22714
Tel.: (540) 760-4873
Marketing Consulting Services
N.A.I.C.S.: 541613

Vintage Stock, Inc. (1)
202 E 32nd St, Joplin, MO 64804 (100%)
Tel.: (417) 623-1550
Web Site: https://www.vintagestock.com
Music, Movies, Video Games, Sports Col-
lectibles, Trading Cards, Games & Comics
Retailer

N.A.I.C.S.: 459420
Ken Caviness (CFO)

Division (Domestic):

Movie Trading Company (2)
5809 Greenville Ave, Dallas, TX 75206
Tel.: (214) 361-8287
Web Site: http://www.vintagestock.com
Video Tape & Disc Rental Services
N.A.I.C.S.: 532282

LIVENT CORPORATION

1818 Market St, Philadelphia, PA
19103
Tel.: (215) 299-5900
Web Site: https://www.livent.com
LTHM—(NYSE)
Rev.: $813,200,000
Assets: $2,074,200,000
Liabilities: $631,200,000
Net Worth: $1,443,000,000
Earnings: $273,500,000
Emp.: 1,350
Fiscal Year-end: 12/31/22
Lithium Chemical Mfr
N.A.I.C.S.: 325180
Paul W. Graves (Pres & CEO)
Alicia Markmann (Chief HR Officer)
Walter Czarnecki (Chief Comml Offi-
cer)
Sara Ponessa (Gen Counsel, Sec &
VP)
Barbara Fochtman (Chief Ops & En-
grg Officer)
Juan Carlos Cruz (Chief Comm Offi-
cer & Head-Pub Affairs-Global)
Gilberto Antoniazzi (CFO & VP)
Ronald Stark (Chief Acctg Officer)

LIVENTO GROUP, INC.

555 W 5th St, Los Angeles, CA
90013
Tel.: (714) 641-2640   NV
Web Site:
https://www.liventogroup.com
Year Founded: 2013
NUGN—(OTCIQ)
Rev.: $2,005,789
Assets: $46,860,003
Liabilities: $3,838,005
Net Worth: $43,021,998
Earnings: ($6,546,152)
Emp.: 11
Fiscal Year-end: 12/31/23
Investment Holding Company
N.A.I.C.S.: 523999
Mohammed Ali Kharazmi (Founder)
Mohammed Saeed Kharazmi (Chm,
Acting CFO, Treas & Sec)

LIVEONE, INC.

269 S Beverly Dr Ste 1450, Beverly
Hills, CA 90212
Tel.: (310) 601-2500   DE
Web Site: https://www.liveone.com
Year Founded: 2009
LVO—(NASDAQ)
Rev.: $118,440,000
Assets: $63,863,000
Liabilities: $57,000,000
Net Worth: $6,557,000
Earnings: ($11,966,000)
Emp.: 140
Fiscal Year-end: 03/31/24
Holding Company; Music-Related
Streaming & Video Content Services
N.A.I.C.S.: 551112
Aaron Sullivan (CFO, Treas & Sec)
Robert L. Ellin (Founder, Chm &
CEO)
David Schulhof (Chief Dev Officer)
Dermot A. McCormack (Pres)
Jason Miller (Head-Sls &
Partnerships-Global)
Jackie Stone (CMO)

Subsidiaries:

PodcastOne, Inc. (1)
335 N Maple Dr Ste 127, Beverly Hills, CA
90210   (74%)
Tel.: (310) 858-0888
Web Site: https://www.podcastone.com
Rev.: $43,302,000
Assets: $24,125,000
Liabilities: $7,784,000
Net Worth: $16,341,000
Earnings: ($14,732,000)
Emp.: 40
Fiscal Year-end: 03/31/2024
Podcast Platform Developer & Publisher
N.A.I.C.S.: 518210
Aaron Sullivan (CFO, Treas & Sec)

Slacker, Inc. (1)
16935 W Bernardo Dr Ste 270, San Diego,
CA 92127
Tel.: (858) 943-5000
Web Site: http://www.slacker.com
Music Streaming Services
N.A.I.C.S.: 518210
Aaron Sullivan (CFO, Treas & Sec)

LIVEPERSON, INC.

530 7th Ave Fl M1, New York, NY
10018
Tel.: (212) 609-4200   DE
Web Site:
https://www.liveperson.com
Year Founded: 1995
LPSN—(NASDAQ)
Rev.: $514,800,000
Assets: $1,088,940,000
Liabilities: $1,020,852,000
Net Worth: $68,088,000
Earnings: ($225,747,000)
Emp.: 1,301
Fiscal Year-end: 12/31/22
Online Internet Sales & Customer
Service Solutions
N.A.I.C.S.: 513210
Robert P. LoCascio (Founder)
Monica Greenberg (Gen Counsel &
Exec VP-Corp Dev & Strategic Alli-
ances)
Jill Layfield (Chm)
John D. Collins (CFO & COO)
Anthony John Sabino (CEO)
Ruth Zive (CMO)
Alex Kroman (CTO, Chief Product
Officer & Exec VP)
Jeff Ford (Chief Acctg Officer)
Sandy Hogan (Chief Revenue Offi-
cer)
Dan Sincavage (Sr VP-Global Part-
nerships)
Nirali Amin (Sr VP-Solutions)
Christian Thum (Sr VP-Software Dev)

Subsidiaries:

Contact At Once!, LLC (1)
11720 Amber Park Dr Ste 500, Alpharetta,
GA 30009
Web Site: http://www.contactatonce.com
Website Chat Software Developer & Mar-
keter
N.A.I.C.S.: 518210

Engage Pty Ltd. (1)
Level 3 80 Dorcas Street, South Melbourne,
3205, VIC, Australia
Tel.: (61) 390400000
Software Development Services
N.A.I.C.S.: 541511

Subsidiary (US):

Kasamba, Inc. (2)
475 10th Ave 5th FL, New York, NY 10018
Tel.: (916) 571-1310
Web Site: http://www.kasamba.com
Online Consulting Services
N.A.I.C.S.: 541618

LivePerson Netherlands B.V. (1)
Herengracht 124, 1015 BT, Amsterdam,
Netherlands
Tel.: (31) 852100987
Software Development Services
N.A.I.C.S.: 541511

LIVERAMP HOLDINGS, INC.

225 Bush St 17th Fl, San Francisco,
CA 94104   DE
Web Site: https://www.liveramp.com
Year Founded: 1969
RAMP—(NYSE)
Rev.: $659,661,000
Assets: $1,231,443,000
Liabilities: $282,308,000
Net Worth: $949,135,000
Earnings: $11,881,000
Emp.: 1,400
Fiscal Year-end: 03/31/24
Data Services & Technology Products
Mfr
N.A.I.C.S.: 518210
Lauren Dillard *(CFO & Exec VP)*
Scott E. Howe *(CEO)*
Travis Clinger *(Sr VP-Addressability
& Ecosystem)*
Amy Lee Stewart *(Chief Data Ethics
Officer-Global, Gen Counsel & Sr VP)*
Daniella Harkins *(Gen Mgr-Agencies)*
Mohsin Hussain *(CTO)*
Jerry C. Jones *(Chief Ethics & Legal
Officer, Exec VP & Asst Sec)*
Jessica Shapiro *(CMO)*
David Eisenberg *(Chief Strategy Offi-
cer)*
Sharawn Tipton *(Chief People Offi-
cer)*
Vihan Sharma *(Chief Revenue Offi-
cer, Exec VP-Global Revenue & Mng
Dir-Europe)*
Kimberly Bloomston *(Chief Product
Officer)*
Joe Glass *(Sr VP & Gen Mgr-Sales &
Marketing-Global)*
Josh Abdulla *(Chief Customer Officer)*

Subsidiaries:

LiveRamp UK Ltd.   (1)
1st Floor Imperial House 8 Kean Street,
London, WC2B 4AS, United Kingdom
Tel.: (44) 2039664150
Marketing & Advertising Services
N.A.I.C.S.: 541810
Eleanor Bulleid *(Office Mgr)*

LiveRamp, Inc.   (1)
225 Bush St 17th Fl, San Francisco, CA
94104
Tel.: (415) 363-6555
Web Site: http://disaster.liveramp.com
Information Technology Consulting Services
N.A.I.C.S.: 541512
Anneka Gupta *(Pres)*
Lauren Dillard *(CFO)*
Scott Howe *(CEO)*

LIVETOBEHAPPY, INC.

6000 Fairview Rd, Charlotte, NC
28210
Tel.: (704) 564-2372   NV
Web Site:
    https://www.livetobehappy.com
Year Founded: 1995
CAVR—(OTCIQ)
Rev.: $10,522,000
Assets: $7,544,000
Liabilities: $255,000
Net Worth: $7,289,000
Earnings: $1,135,000
Emp.: 5
Fiscal Year-end: 12/31/20
Natural Gas & Energy Services
N.A.I.C.S.: 213112
Robert E. Silver *(Chm)*
Toi Hershman *(Pres-Growing To-
gether Academy)*
Shaun Fuller *(Pres-Soku)*
Kevin Vincent Cox *(CEO)*
R. Grant Edwards *(CFO)*
Michael Murphy *(CTO)*
Joe Caprino *(Pres & Chief Comml
Officer)*

LIVEWIRE ERGOGENICS, INC.

1600 N Kraemer Blvd, ANAHEIM, CA
92806
Tel.: (714) 740-5144   NV
Web Site:
    https://livewireergogenics.com
Year Founded: 2008
LVVV—(OTCIQ)
Property Management Services
N.A.I.C.S.: 531311

LIVEWIRE GROUP, INC.

3700 W Juneau Ave, Milwaukee, WI
53208
Tel.: (650) 447-8424   DE
Web Site: https://www.livewire.group
Year Founded: 2021
LVWR—(NYSE)
Rev.: $46,833,000
Assets: $351,805,000
Liabilities: $45,005,000
Net Worth: $306,800,000
Earnings: ($78,938,000)
Emp.: 225
Fiscal Year-end: 12/31/22
Automobile Parts Mfr
N.A.I.C.S.: 336110
Tralisa Maraj *(CFO & Chief Acctg
Officer)*
Jon Carter *(Chief Acctg Officer)*
Karim Donnez *(CEO)*

LIVEWORLD, INC.

2105 S Bascom Ave Ste 159, Camp-
bell, CA 95008
Tel.: (408) 871-5200   DE
Web Site: https://www.liveworld.com
Year Founded: 1996
LVWD—(OTCIQ)
Rev.: $7,374,000
Assets: $1,773,000
Liabilities: $994,000
Net Worth: $779,000
Earnings: ($449,000)
Emp.: 73
Fiscal Year-end: 12/31/19
Internet Marketing & Support Ser-
vices
N.A.I.C.S.: 491110
Peter H. Friedman *(Founder, Chm &
CEO)*
Martin Bishop *(VP-Client Svcs)*
Rishi Kadiwar *(VP-Strategy & Dir-
Consumer)*
Serina Morris *(Assoc Dir-Creative)*

LIXTE BIOTECHNOLOGY
HOLDINGS, INC.

680 E Colorado Blvd Ste 180, Pasa-
dena, CA 91101
Tel.: (631) 830-7092   DE
Web Site: https://www.lixte.com
LIXT—(NASDAQ)
Rev.: $11,195
Assets: $5,560,013
Liabilities: $394,786
Net Worth: $5,165,227
Earnings: ($6,312,535)
Emp.: 3
Fiscal Year-end: 12/31/22
Biotechnology Mfr
N.A.I.C.S.: 325412
John S. Kovach *(Founder, Exec Chm
& Chief Scientific Officer)*
Robert Neal Weingarten *(CFO & VP)*
Bastiaan van der Baan *(Vice Chm,
Pres & CEO)*

LKA GOLD, INC.

3724 47th St Ct NW, Gig Harbor, WA
98335
Tel.: (253) 514-6661   DE
Web Site: http://www.lkagold.com
Year Founded: 1988
LKAI—(OTCIQ)
Sales Range: Less than $1 Million
Gold & Silver Mining

N.A.I.C.S.: 212220
Kye A. Abraham *(Chm & Pres)*
Nanette K. Abraham *(Treas & Sec)*

LKQ CORPORATION

500 W Madison St Ste 2800, Chi-
cago, IL 60661
Tel.: (312) 621-1950   DE
Web Site: https://www.lkqcorp.com
Year Founded: 1998
LKQ—(NASDAQ)
Rev.: $13,866,000,000
Assets: $15,079,000,000
Liabilities: $8,898,000,000
Net Worth: $6,181,000,000
Earnings: $938,000,000
Emp.: 49,000
Fiscal Year-end: 12/31/23
Automobile Parts Distr
N.A.I.C.S.: 423140
Walter P. Hanley *(Sr VP-Dev)*
Michael S. Clark *(Sr VP-Policy & Ad-
min)*
Joseph P. Boutross *(VP-IR)*
Michael T. Brooks *(CIO-Global & Sr
VP)*
Matthew J. McKay *(Gen Counsel,
Sec & Sr VP)*
Genevieve L. Dombrowski *(Sr VP-
HR)*
Rick Galloway *(CFO & Sr VP)*
Justin L. Jude *(Pres, CEO, COO &
Exec VP)*

Subsidiaries:

A-Reliable Auto Parts & Wreckers,
Inc.   (1)
2247 139th St, Blue Island, IL 60406
Tel.: (708) 385-5595
Used Motor Vehicle Parts Whslr
N.A.I.C.S.: 423140

A.S.A.P. Supplies Limited   (1)
Reed House, Ellough Industrial Estate,
Beccles, NR34 7TD, Suffolk, United King-
dom
Tel.: (44) 1502716993
Web Site: https://www.asap-supplies.com
Automotive Part Whslr
N.A.I.C.S.: 441330
Kyle Baker *(Supvr-Goods Out)*

APM Automotive s.r.o.   (1)
Nadrazni 104, Kdyne, 345 06, Plzen, Czech
Republic
Tel.: (420) 379302911
Web Site: http://www.apm.cz
Automobile Parts Distr
N.A.I.C.S.: 441330
Tomas Raiser *(Dir-Product Mgmt)*

APS B.V.   (1)
Nobelstraat 10, 7903 BH, Hoogeveen,
Netherlands
Tel.: (31) 528274641
Web Site: https://www.apsbv.com
Automotive Part Whslr
N.A.I.C.S.: 441330

AeroVision International, LLC   (1)
620 E Ellis Rd, Muskegon, MI 49441
Tel.: (231) 799-9000
Web Site: https://aerovi.com
Automotive Equipment Whslr
N.A.I.C.S.: 441330
Greg Vanboxel *(CEO)*
Victor Gallegos *(Sr VP)*

Alfa Paints B.V.   (1)
Gewandeweg 5, 6161 DJ, Geleen, Nether-
lands
Tel.: (31) 89480600
Web Site: https://www.alfapaints.com
Car Accessory Whslr
N.A.I.C.S.: 423120

Annex-Technik GmbH   (1)
Friedrich-Hagemann-Str 58-60, 33719,
Bielefeld, Germany
Tel.: (49) 5213052050
Web Site: http://www.annex-technik.de
Pumps Mfr
N.A.I.C.S.: 333914
Friedhelm Glormann *(Mng Dir)*

Aquafax Limited   (1)
Sundon Business Park Unit 1 Dencora
Way, Luton, LU3 3HP, Bedfordshire, United
Kingdom
Tel.: (44) 1582568700
Web Site: https://www.aquafax.co.uk
Emp.: 70
Marine & Industrial Equipment Distr
N.A.I.C.S.: 441222

Arleigh International Limited   (1)
Century Park Ballin Road, Nuneaton, CV10
9GA, Warwickshire, United Kingdom
Tel.: (44) 2476390100
Web Site: https://www.arleigh.co.uk
Automobile Parts Mfr
N.A.I.C.S.: 333618

Assured Quality Testing Services,
LLC   (1)
1870 Riverfork Dr, Huntington, IN 46750
Tel.: (260) 359-7443
Web Site: https://www.aqtslabs.com
Automotive Parts Testing Services
N.A.I.C.S.: 811198

Atracco Auto AB   (1)
Ljungadalsgatan 6B, 352 46, Vaxjo, Swe-
den
Tel.: (46) 470771100
Web Site: https://atraccoauto.se
Automotive & Truck Repair Services
N.A.I.C.S.: 811111

Auto Electra Naaldwijk B.V.   (1)
Verspycklaan 74, 2671 CS, Naaldwijk,
Netherlands
Tel.: (31) 174626746
Automotive Part Whslr
N.A.I.C.S.: 441330

Auto Kelly Slovakia s.r.o.   (1)
Stara Vajnorska 15, 831 04, Bratislava,
Slovakia
Tel.: (421) 326595305
Web Site: https://www.autokelly.sk
Automotive Equipment Whslr
N.A.I.C.S.: 441330
Karol Tisoncik *(CEO)*

Auto Kelly a.s.   (1)
Ocelarska 16, 190 00, Prague, Czech Re-
public
Tel.: (420) 266100245
Web Site: http://www.autokelly.cz
Automotive Part Whslr
N.A.I.C.S.: 441330

Auto Wessel B.V.   (1)
Franciscusweg 17/A, 1216 SK, Hilversum,
Netherlands
Tel.: (31) 355825184
Automotive Equipment Whslr
N.A.I.C.S.: 441330

Autodistribution Benelux B.V.   (1)
20 Darwin Street, 6718XR, Ede, Nether-
lands
Tel.: (31) 162497497
Web Site: http://www.adbenelux.com
Automotive Accessory Retailer
N.A.I.C.S.: 441330

Automotive Academy B.V.   (1)
Jan van Riebeeckweg 27, 3125 AL,
Schiedam, Netherlands
Tel.: (31) 880044123
Web Site: https://automotiveacademy.nl
Car Parts Whslr
N.A.I.C.S.: 423110

Automotive Data Services
Limited   (1)
Unit 3 Bewick House, Horsley Business
Centre, Horsley, NE15 0NY, Northumber-
land, United Kingdom
Tel.: (44) 166 185 4731
Web Site:
    https://www.automotivedataservices.com
Emp.: 20
Used Motor Vehicle Parts Whslr
N.A.I.C.S.: 423140
Mike Spelding *(Mng Dir)*

Autoparts Prosec NV   (1)
Dendermondesteenweg 50, 9070, Destel-
bergen, Belgium
Tel.: (32) 92189220
Automotive Part Whslr

LKQ Corporation—(Continued)
N.A.I.C.S.: 441330

Autosport Willy SA (1)
Rue Jules Vanthieghem 1, 7711, Dottignies,
Belgium
Tel.: (32) 56856565
Automotive Part Whslr
N.A.I.C.S.: 441330

Autostop Leuven NV (1)
Kareelveld 8A, 3000, Leuven, Belgium
Tel.: (32) 16292920
Web Site: http://www.autostop.be
Car Parts Whslr
N.A.I.C.S.: 423110

Autoteile Supermarkt GmbH (1)
Bodenseestr 275, 81249, Munich, Germany
Tel.: (49) 8989770099
Web Site: http://www.autoteile-
supermarkt.de
Car Dealing Services
N.A.I.C.S.: 441120

BRUNN GmbH (1)
Bendenweg 107, 53121, Bonn, Germany
Tel.: (49) 2286682209
Web Site: http://www.autoland-brunn.de
Automotive Car Repair Shop Services
N.A.I.C.S.: 811198

Bertolotti S.p.A. (1)
Localita' Sant'antonio, 50064, Incisa in Val
d'Arno, FI, Italy
Tel.: (39) 055833171
Web Site: https://www.bertolottispa.com
Automotive Equipment Whslr
N.A.I.C.S.: 441330

Bildemontering i Helsingborg AV (1)
Lagergatan 22, 254 64, Helsingborg, Swe-
den
Tel.: (46) 42158840
Web Site:
https://dev.bildelonline.advisoryhosting.se
Automotive Equipment Whslr
N.A.I.C.S.: 441330

Bols Motoren B.V. (1)
N C B -Laan 109, 5462 GC, Veghel, Neth-
erlands
Tel.: (31) 135058400
Web Site: https://www.bols-motorrevisie.nl
Engine Rebuilding Services
N.A.I.C.S.: 811198

Budget Auto Parts U-Pull-It, Inc. (1)
4007 Interstate 10, Port Allen, LA 70767
Tel.: (225) 377-2000
Used Motor Vehicle Parts Whslr
N.A.I.C.S.: 423140

Car Systems B.V. (1)
Kloosterweg 24, 6412 CN, Heerlen, Nether-
lands
Tel.: (31) 885600080
Web Site: https://www.carsys.online
Packaged Car Software Publisher
N.A.I.C.S.: 513210

**Cartal Rijsbergen Automotive
B.V.** (1)
Berchvliet 20, 1046 CA, Amsterdam, Neth-
erlands
Tel.: (31) 888809000
Web Site: http://www.rijsbergen.nl
Automotive Accessory Retailer
N.A.I.C.S.: 441330

Caruso GmbH (1)
Steinheilstrasse 10, 85737, Ismaning, Ger-
many
Tel.: (49) 893212160
Web Site: https://www.caruso-
dataplace.com
Automotive Mfr & Distr
N.A.I.C.S.: 336211

DCM Tools NV (1)
Tisseltsesteenweg 49, 2830, Willebroek,
Belgium
Tel.: (32) 38600240
Web Site: https://www.lkqcorp.com
Tire Repair Services
N.A.I.C.S.: 811198

**De Bruyn Professional Coatings
NV** (1)

Antoon Van Osslaan 1-10, 1120, Brussels,
Belgium
Tel.: (32) 24262105
Automotive Equipment Whslr
N.A.I.C.S.: 441330

De Maesschalck H N.V. (1)
Watermolenstraat 17, 9320, Erembodegem,
Belgium
Tel.: (32) 53662270
Web Site: http://www.verven-
demaesschalck.be
Car & Wall Painting Services
N.A.I.C.S.: 238320

**Digraph Transport Supplies (Telford)
Limited** (1)
Unit 2 Chewton Street, Eastwood, NG16
3HB, Nottinghamshire, United Kingdom
Tel.: (44) 1773537701
Web Site: https://www.digraph.co.uk
Automobile Parts Mfr
N.A.I.C.S.: 336390

**Digraph Transport Supplies
Limited** (1)
Unit 2 Chewton Street, Eastwood, NG16
3HB, Nottinghamshire, United Kingdom
Tel.: (44) 1773537701
Web Site: https://www.digraph.co.uk
Automotive Truck & Bus Mfr
N.A.I.C.S.: 336340
James Rawson *(Founder)*

ELIT CZ, Spol s.r.o. (1)
Jeremiasova 1283/18 Stodulky, 155 00,
Prague, Czech Republic
Tel.: (420) 271022222
Web Site: http://www.elit.cz
Emp.: 500
Automotive Equipment Whslr
N.A.I.C.S.: 441330

ELIT Polska sp. z o.o. (1)
Ul Makuszynskiego 24, 31-752, Krakow,
Poland
Tel.: (48) 126838800
Web Site: https://www.elitpolska.pl
Automotive Parts & Accessory Whslr
N.A.I.C.S.: 441330

ELIT Slovakia s.r.o. (1)
Kolma 4, 851 01, Bratislava, Slovakia
Tel.: (421) 263535353
Web Site: http://www.elit.sk
Automotive Equipment Whslr
N.A.I.C.S.: 441330

ELIT Ukraine LLC (1)
Str 135 Pirogivskyi Shlyach, 03026, Kiev,
Ukraine
Tel.: (380) 443894433
Web Site: https://elit.ua
Automotive Part Whslr
N.A.I.C.S.: 441330
Oleg Varvarskyi *(CEO)*

ERA S.r.l. (1)
Via F Santi 15, 10024, Moncalieri, TO, Italy
Tel.: (39) 0116891511
Web Site: https://www.eraspares.com
Automotive Spare Parts Distr
N.A.I.C.S.: 441330

Elit Group GmbH (1)
Hinterhostattstrasse 6, 6376, Emmetten,
Switzerland
Tel.: (41) 585109401
Web Site: https://elitegroup.ch
Financial Investment Services
N.A.I.C.S.: 523999

Era S.p.A. (1)
Via F Santi 15, 10024, Moncalieri, TO, Italy
Tel.: (39) 011 689 1511
Web Site: https://www.eraspares.com
Automotive Part Whslr
N.A.I.C.S.: 441330

**Euro Car Parts (Northern Ireland)
Limited** (1)
Unit 8 Adelaide Business Park Falcon Road
Boucher Road, Belfast, BT12 6RD, United
Kingdom
Tel.: (44) 2890689700
Sales Range: $25-49.9 Million
Emp.: 52
Recycled Motor Vehicle Parts Provider
N.A.I.C.S.: 423140
Michael O'Neil *(Gen Mgr)*

Euro Garage Solutions Ltd (1)
Euro House Fulton Road, Wembley, HA9
0TF, Middlesex, United Kingdom
Tel.: (44) 8456022570
Web Site:
http://www.eurogaragesolutions.com
Emp.: 500
Garage & Diagnostic Equipment Services
N.A.I.C.S.: 811198

Gearhead Engines Inc. (1)
23191 La Cadena Dr Ste 103, Laguna Hills,
CA 92656
Web Site: https://gearheadengines.com
Remanufactured Engines Distr
N.A.I.C.S.: 423120

Global Trade Alliance Inc. (1)
5830 Green Pointe Dr S A, Groveport, OH
43125
Tel.: (614) 751-3100
Rev.: $13,500,000
Emp.: 3
Automotive Supplies & Parts
N.A.I.C.S.: 423120

Greenleaf Auto Recyclers, LLC (1)
904 S Interstate 45 Service Rd, Hutchins,
TX 75141-4195
Tel.: (817) 804-1781
Web Site: http://www.greenleafauto.com
Rev.: $60,000,000
Emp.: 800
Recycled Automotive Parts Whslr
N.A.I.C.S.: 423930

Harrems Tools B.V. (1)
Hogebrinkerweg 18, 3871 KN, Hoevelaken,
Netherlands
Tel.: (31) 302650311
Automotive Part Whslr
N.A.I.C.S.: 441330

Havam Automotive B.V. (1)
Tjalkkade 25, 5928 PZ, Venlo, Netherlands
Tel.: (31) 773879500
Automotive Accessory Retailer
N.A.I.C.S.: 441330

Heuts Handel B.V. (1)
De Koumen 38 40, 6433KD, Heerlen, Neth-
erlands
Tel.: (31) 455222525
Web Site: http://www.heuts.nl
Emp.: 400
Automotive Equipment Whslr
N.A.I.C.S.: 441330

IPAR Industrial Partners B.V. (1)
Columbusweg 33, 5928 LA, Venlo, Nether-
lands
Tel.: (31) 773879629
Web Site: https://www.ipar.nl
Automotive Equipment Whslr
N.A.I.C.S.: 441330

Karstorp Bildemontering AB (1)
Bjorkebergavagen, Box 13075, 605 95,
Norrkoping, Sweden
Tel.: (46) 114954000
Web Site:
https://www.karstorpsbildemontering.se
Automobile Parts Distr
N.A.I.C.S.: 441330

**Keystone Automotive Industries ON,
Inc.** (1)
1230 Old Innes Road 401, Ottawa, K1B
3V3, ON, Canada
Tel.: (613) 296-3731
Web Site: https://www.orderkeystone.ca
Automotive Replacement Collision Parts
Supplier
N.A.I.C.S.: 441330

**Keystone Automotive Industries,
Inc.** (1)
700 E Bonita Ave, Pomona, CA 91767
Tel.: (909) 624-8041
Sales Range: $700-749.9 Million
Emp.: 4,000
Auto Parts Distr
N.A.I.C.S.: 423120

Unit (Domestic):

**Keystone Automotive Industries -
Atlanta** (1)
777A Wharton Dr SW, Atlanta, GA 30336-
2123
Tel.: (404) 691-6930

Web Site: http://www.keystone.com
Sales Range: $50-74.9 Million
Emp.: 140
Automotive Crash Parts & Bumpers to Auto
Body Shops
N.A.I.C.S.: 423120

**Keystone Automotive Industries -
Bethlehem** (2)
Route 378, Bethlehem, PA 18015
Tel.: (610) 866-0313
Web Site: http://www.keystone-auto.com
Sales Range: $25-49.9 Million
Emp.: 50
Automotive Crash Parts & Bumpers to Auto
Body Shops
N.A.I.C.S.: 423120

**Keystone Automotive Industries -
Buffalo** (2)
485 Ludwig Ave 2871 Broadway Ste 3500,
Buffalo, NY 14227-1014
Tel.: (716) 894-6262
Web Site: http://www.keystone-auto.com
Sales Range: $25-49.9 Million
Emp.: 40
Automotive Crash Parts & Bumpers to Auto
Body Shops
N.A.I.C.S.: 441330

**Keystone Automotive Industries -
Nashville** (2)
85 B Cleveland St, Brentwood, TN 37027-
3225
Tel.: (615) 226-9090
Web Site: http://www.lkq.com
Sales Range: $25-49.9 Million
Emp.: 30
Automotive Replacement Parts Distr
N.A.I.C.S.: 423120

**Keystone Automotive Industries -
Stockton** (2)
1627 Army Ct Ste 7, Stockton, CA 95206
Tel.: (209) 948-1101
Web Site: http://www.keystone-auto.com
Sales Range: $150-199.9 Million
Automotive Crash Parts & Bumpers to Auto
Body Shops
N.A.I.C.S.: 332813

**Keystone Automotive Operations,
Inc.** (1)
44 Tunkhannock Ave, Exeter, PA 18643
Tel.: (570) 655-4514
Web Site:
https://www.keystoneautomotive.com
Sales Range: $450-499.9 Million
Emp.: 1,500
Holding Company; Automotive Parts & Sup-
plies Whslr & Retailer
N.A.I.C.S.: 551112

Subsidiary (Domestic):

A&A Auto Parts Stores, Inc. (2)
1575 Wyoming Ave, Exeter, PA 18643
Tel.: (570) 654-3331
Web Site: https://www.aaautostores.com
Sales Range: $25-49.9 Million
Emp.: 200
Automotive Parts & Supplies Store Retailer
N.A.I.C.S.: 441330

**Keystone Automotive Distributors
Company, LLC** (2)
44 Tunkhannock Ave, Exeter, PA 18643
Tel.: (570) 655-4514
Web Site:
http://www.keystoneautomotive.com
Sales Range: $25-49.9 Million
Emp.: 100
Automotive Parts & Supplies Wholesale
Distr
N.A.I.C.S.: 423120

Division (Domestic):

NTP Distribution (2)
27150 SW Kinsman Rd, Wilsonville, OR
97070
Tel.: (503) 570-0171
Web Site: http://www.ntpdistribution.com
Sales Range: $25-49.9 Million
Emp.: 200
Distr of Aftermarket Products, Parts & Ac-
cessories for Recreational Vehicles
N.A.I.C.S.: 423120

Kwik Auto Body Supplies, Inc. (1)

163 Mystic Ave, Medford, MA 02155
Tel.: (781) 395-2176
Auto Body Shop Supplies & Whslr
N.A.I.C.S.: 423120

LKQ 1st Choice Auto Parts, LLC (1)
3124 N Peoria, Tulsa, OK 74106
Tel.: (918) 241-3800
Web Site: https://www.lkqcorp.com
Used Motor Vehicle Parts Whslr
N.A.I.C.S.: 423140

LKQ 250 Auto, Inc. (1)
152 State Route 250, Harrison, OH 43974
Tel.: (740) 546-3521
Recycled Original Equipment Mfr & Distr
N.A.I.C.S.: 423140

LKQ All Models Corp. (1)
3024 S 40th St, Phoenix, AZ 85040-1621
Tel.: (602) 437-0194
Web Site: http://www.lkq.com
Recycled Motor Vehicle Parts Whslr
N.A.I.C.S.: 423930

LKQ Apex Auto Parts, Inc. (1)
3124 N Peoria, Tulsa, OK 74106
Tel.: (918) 428-3835
Used Motor Vehicle Parts Whslr
N.A.I.C.S.: 423140

LKQ Atlanta, L.P. (1)
2401 Hwy 42 N, Jenkinsburg, GA 30234-2316
Tel.: (770) 775-2700
Used Motor Vehicle Parts Whslr
N.A.I.C.S.: 423140

**LKQ Auto Parts of North Texas,
L.P.** (1)
904 Interstate 45 S, Hutchins, TX 75141-4195
Tel.: (972) 225-1600
Automobile Parts Dealer
N.A.I.C.S.: 441330
Grant Allen *(Gen Mgr)*

LKQ Auto Parts of Orlando, LLC (1)
9205 E Colonial Dr, Orlando, FL 32817
Tel.: (407) 382-2727
Web Site:
  https://locations.lkqpickyourpart.com
Used Motor Vehicle Parts Whslr
N.A.I.C.S.: 423140

LKQ Belgium BVBA (1)
Havendoklaan 14, 1800, Vilvoorde, Belgium
Tel.: (32) 693786956
Web Site: https://www.lkqbelgium.be
Automobile Parts Distr
N.A.I.C.S.: 441330

LKQ Best Automotive Corp. (1)
1710 W Mount Houston Rd, Houston, TX 77038
Tel.: (281) 820-9184
Sales Range: $50-74.9 Million
Emp.: 100
Used Auto Parts Supplier
N.A.I.C.S.: 423140

LKQ CZ s.r.o. (1)
Ocelarska 16, Vysocany, 190 00, Prague, 9, Czech Republic
Tel.: (420) 266100245
Web Site: https://www.lkq.cz
Automotive Spare Parts Distr
N.A.I.C.S.: 423120

LKQ Canada Auto Parts Inc. (1)
1765 Pension Lane, London, N5W 6C7, ON, Canada
Tel.: (519) 455-1200
Web Site: https://www.lkq.com
Emp.: 35
Used Motor Vehicle Parts Whslr
N.A.I.C.S.: 423140

LKQ Central, Inc. (1)
2115 S Union Ave, Bakersfield, CA 93307
Automobile Parts Distr
N.A.I.C.S.: 441330

**LKQ Copher Self Service Auto Parts-
Bradenton Inc.** (1)
1880 63rd Ave E, Bradenton, FL 34203-5011
Tel.: (941) 753-2887
Web Site:
  https://locations.lkqpickyourpart.com
Used Motor Vehicle Whslr

N.A.I.C.S.: 423140

**LKQ Copher Self Service Auto Parts-
St. Petersburg Inc.** (1)
5105 64th St N, Saint Petersburg, FL 33709
Tel.: (727) 546-9224
Web Site: http://www.lkqselfserve.com
Used Motor Vehicle Parts Whslr
N.A.I.C.S.: 423140

LKQ Crystal River, Inc. (1)
4950 W Hwy 486, Crystal River, FL 34429-5731
Tel.: (352) 746-3011
Automotive Parts & Accessories Distr
N.A.I.C.S.: 441330

LKQ Foster Auto Parts, Inc. (1)
10355 SE Foster Rd, Portland, OR 97266
Tel.: (503) 445-7200
Web Site: https://www.fosterauto.com
Rebuildable Vehicles & Motorcycles Supplier
N.A.I.C.S.: 423140

LKQ Gorham Auto Parts Corp. (1)
192 Narragansett St, Gorham, ME 04038
Tel.: (207) 839-3080
Web Site: https://www.lkqcorp.com
Used Motor Vehicle Parts Whslr
N.A.I.C.S.: 423140

LKQ Great Lakes Corp. (1)
728 W US Hwy 20, Michigan City, IN 46360
Tel.: (219) 872-5567
Web Site: http://www.lkqcorp.com
Used Motor Vehicle Parts Whslr
N.A.I.C.S.: 423140

**LKQ Heavy Truck-Texas Best Diesel,
L.P.** (1)
1020 Rankin Rd, Houston, TX 77073
Tel.: (713) 673-9191
Web Site: http://www.texasbestdiesel.com
Used Diesel Trucks & Parts Whslr
N.A.I.C.S.: 423140

**LKQ Hunts Point Auto Parts
Corp.** (1)
1480 Sheridan Expy, Bronx, NY 10459
Tel.: (718) 589-4444
Web Site: http://www.lkqcorp.com
Used Motor Vehicle Parts Whslr
N.A.I.C.S.: 423140

**LKQ Lakenor Auto & Truck Salvage,
Inc.** (1)
13603 Foster Rd, Santa Fe Springs, CA 90670
Tel.: (562) 944-6422
Used Motor Vehicle Parts Whslr
N.A.I.C.S.: 423140

LKQ Metro, Inc. (1)
2450 Black Ln, Caseyville, IL 62232
Tel.: (618) 345-9659
Web Site: http://www.lkqcorp.com
Used Motor Vehicle Parts Whslr
N.A.I.C.S.: 423140

LKQ Midwest, Inc. (1)
8901 Irvington Rd, Omaha, NE 68122
Tel.: (402) 571-4424
Web Site: https://www.lkqcorp.com
Automobile Parts Distr
N.A.I.C.S.: 441330

LKQ Online Corp. (1)
4955 Kalamath St, Denver, CO 80221
Web Site: http://www.lkqonline.com
Sales Range: $25-49.9 Million
Emp.: 12
Remanufactured Auto Parts Online Retailer
N.A.I.C.S.: 441330
Joseph M. Holsten *(Chm)*

LKQ Penn-Mar, Inc. (1)
269 River Rd, York Haven, PA 17370
Tel.: (717) 266-9500
Sales Range: $50-74.9 Million
Emp.: 100
Used Motor Vehicle Parts Whslr
N.A.I.C.S.: 423140

**LKQ Plunks Truck Parts &
Equipment-Jackson, Inc.** (1)
4100 I-55 S E Frontage Rd, Jackson, MS 39272
Tel.: (601) 939-3000
Web Site: http://www.lkqcorp.com

Sales Range: $25-49.9 Million
Emp.: 25
Used Truck Parts & Salvage Dealer
N.A.I.C.S.: 423140

LKQ Precious Metals, Inc. (1)
500 W Madison St Ste 2800, Chicago, IL 60661
Tel.: (312) 621-1950
Automotive Accessory Retailer
N.A.I.C.S.: 441330

LKQ Raleigh Auto Parts Corp. (1)
2928 US 70 E, Clayton, NC 27520
Tel.: (919) 553-5900
Sales Range: $50-74.9 Million
Emp.: 40
Used Motor Vehicle Parts Whslr
N.A.I.C.S.: 423140
Shelley Smith *(Gen Mgr)*

LKQ SK s.r.o. (1)
Stara Vajnorska 15, Nove Mesto District, 831 04, Bratislava, Slovakia
Tel.: (421) 326595305
Web Site: https://www.lkq.sk
Emp.: 26,000
Automotive Spare Parts Distr
N.A.I.C.S.: 423110

**LKQ Self Service Auto Parts-Holland,
Inc.** (1)
11475 Chicago Dr, Holland, MI 49424-9613
Tel.: (616) 396-3551
Web Site: http://www.lkqselfserve.com
Used Motor Vehicle Parts Whslr
N.A.I.C.S.: 423140

**LKQ Self Service Auto Parts-
Kalamazoo, Inc.** (1)
2707 E Michigan Ave, Kalamazoo, MI 49048
Tel.: (269) 345-1183
Web Site: http://www.lkqselfserve.com
Used Motor Vehicle Whslr
N.A.I.C.S.: 423140

**LKQ Self Service Auto Parts-
Memphis LLC** (1)
966 W Mitchell Rd, Memphis, TN 38109-3568
Tel.: (901) 785-6666
Web Site: http://www.lkqselfserve.com
Sales Range: $25-49.9 Million
Emp.: 14
Used Motor Vehicle Whslr
N.A.I.C.S.: 423140

**LKQ Self Service Auto Parts-Tulsa,
Inc.** (1)
3i12 N Peoria Ave, Tulsa, OK 74145
Tel.: (918) 794-7846
Web Site: http://www.lkqselfserve.com
Sales Range: $25-49.9 Million
Emp.: 20
Used Motor Vehicle Whslr
N.A.I.C.S.: 423140

LKQ Smart Parts, Inc. (1)
N4079 County Rd E, Hustisford, WI 53034
Tel.: (920) 349-3236
Used Motor Vehicle Parts Whslr
N.A.I.C.S.: 423140

LKQ Southwick LLC (1)
58 Sam W Rd, Southwick, MA 01077
Tel.: (413) 569-1266
Used Motor Vehicle Parts Whslr
N.A.I.C.S.: 423140
Mike Salovan *(Plant Mgr)*

LKQ Triplett ASAP, Inc. (1)
1435 Triplett Blvd, Akron, OH 44306
Tel.: (330) 733-6333
Web Site: http://www.triplettasap.com
Auto Recycling Service Provider
N.A.I.C.S.: 423140

**LKQ U-Pull-It Auto Damascus,
Inc.** (1)
19510 SE Sunnyside Rd, Boring, OR 97301
Tel.: (612) 706-5321
Used Motor Vehicle Whslr
N.A.I.C.S.: 423140

LKQ of Michigan, Inc. (1)
41247 E Huron River, Belleville, MI 48111-2879
Tel.: (734) 699-6709
Web Site: http://www.laq.com

Used Motor Vehicle Parts Whslr
N.A.I.C.S.: 423140

LKQ of Nevada, Inc. (1)
3370 E Lone Mtn Rd, North Las Vegas, NV 89081
Tel.: (702) 642-1333
Web Site: http://www.lkqcorp.com
Sales Range: $50-74.9 Million
Emp.: 105
Used Motor Vehicle Parts Whslr
N.A.I.C.S.: 423140

LKQ of Tennessee, Inc. (1)
3055 Hillsboro Hwy, Manchester, TN 37355
Tel.: (931) 728-6900
Used Motor Vehicle Parts Whslr
N.A.I.C.S.: 423140

Lang Kft. (1)
Vaci Ut 156, 1138, Budapest, Hungary
Tel.: (36) 145196666
Web Site: http://www.langauto.hu
Automotive Equipment Whslr
N.A.I.C.S.: 441330

Leaseservice Partner B.V. (1)
Melkrijder 15, 3861SG, Nijkerk, Netherlands
Tel.: (31) 857605975
Web Site: https://www.leaseservicepartner.nl
Electric Vehicle Mfr & Distr
N.A.I.C.S.: 336211

**M.P.M. International Oil Company
B.V.** (1)
Cyclotronweg 1, 2629 HN, Delft, Netherlands
Tel.: (31) 152514030
Web Site: https://www.mpmoil.nl
Car Mfr
N.A.I.C.S.: 336110

M.R.T. Polska Sp. z o.o. (1)
Ul Ostrowiecka 21, 27-200, Starachowice, Poland
Tel.: (48) 412733897
Web Site: https://mrtpolska.pl
Emp.: 50
Engine Rebuilding Services
N.A.I.C.S.: 811198

MRT-Engines B.V. (1)
Pater v d Elsenlaan 6, Postbus 252, 5462 GG, Veghel, Netherlands
Tel.: (31) 413342014
Web Site: https://www.motor-revisie.nl
Engine Rebuilding Services
N.A.I.C.S.: 811198

Matorit Data AB (1)
Druveforsvagen 32, 504 33, Boras, Sweden
Tel.: (46) 184770560
Web Site: https://www.matorit.se
Software Development Services
N.A.I.C.S.: 513210

Messmer GmbH (1)
Klingwiesen 10, 71409, Schwaikheim, Germany
Tel.: (49) 719551033
Web Site: http://www.stuckateur-messmer.de
Automotive Equipment Repair Services
N.A.I.C.S.: 811111

Michael Auto Parts, Incorporated (1)
1301 S Orange Blossom Trl, Orlando, FL 32805
Tel.: (407) 423-1695
Recycled Motor Vehicle Parts Provider
N.A.I.C.S.: 423140

Midland Chandlers Limited (1)
Units 1-5 Century Park Ballin Rd, Nuneaton, CV10 9GA, Warwickshire, United Kingdom
Tel.: (44) 2476390111
Web Site:
  https://www.midlandchandlers.co.uk
Water Treatment Equipment Whslr
N.A.I.C.S.: 423830

MotorXchange S.A.R.L. (1)
320 Av Berthelot, 69008, Lyon, France
Tel.: (33) 825899099
Web Site: http://www.motorxchange.fr
Automotive Car Repair Shop Services
N.A.I.C.S.: 811198

**Nya Christianstads Billackering
AB** (1)

LKQ Corporation—(Continued)

Sjohemsvagen 2, 291 54, Kristianstad, Sweden
Tel.: (46) 44211088
Web Site: http://billack.nu
Automotive Equipment Whslr
N.A.I.C.S.: 441330

Optimal AG & Co. KG (1)
Alfred-Kuhne-Strasse 3, Langenbach, 85416, Freising, Germany
Tel.: (49) 876172060
Web Site: https://www.optimal-germany.com
Motor Vehicle Parts Mfr
N.A.I.C.S.: 336390
Helge Schongarth (Member-Mgmt Bd)
Florian Herrmann (Chm-Supervisory Bd)

Subsidiary (Non-US):

I4B Sp. z o.o. (2)
Biskupa Czeslawa Domina 12, 75-065, Koszalin, Poland
Tel.: (48) 947173672
Web Site: https://i4b.pl
Engineering Construction Services
N.A.I.C.S.: 541330

Optimal Benelux Bvba (2)
Zuunstraat 124, 1070, Anderlecht, Belgium
Tel.: (32) 23322131
Web Site: http://www.optimal-benelux.be
Motor Vehicle Parts & Supply Merchant Whslr
N.A.I.C.S.: 423120

Optimal Polska Sp. z o.o. (2)
Ul Lwowska 15, 78-106, Kolo, Poland
Tel.: (48) 943542493
Web Site: https://www.optimalpolska.pl
Motor Vehicle Parts Mfr
N.A.I.C.S.: 336390

Optimal UK Distribution Limited (2)
Unit 12 Hereward Rise Halesowen, West Midlands, Halesowen, B62 8AW, United Kingdom
Tel.: (44) 1215502317
Web Site: https://www.uksdistribution.com
Motor Vehicle Parts Whslr
N.A.I.C.S.: 423120

Subsidiary (Domestic):

Q-Parts24 GmbH & Co. KG (2)
Ludwigstrasse 47, 85399, Hallbergmoos, Germany
Tel.: (49) 81129993232
Web Site: https://www.qp24.de
High Quality Car Parts & Replacement Parts Retailer
N.A.I.C.S.: 441330
Grzegorz Sztefic (Mng Dir)

Subsidiary (Non-US):

Starmann Sp. z o.o. (2)
Ul Lwowska 15, 78-106, Kolo, Poland
Tel.: (48) 943543459
Web Site: http://www.sgparts.pl
Automotive Spare Parts Whslr
N.A.I.C.S.: 423120

Orebro Bidemontering AB (1)
Maskingatan 1, 702 86, Orebro, Sweden
Tel.: (46) 196701200
Web Site: http://orebrobildemo.se
Truck Tires & Tubes Whslr
N.A.I.C.S.: 423130

Orebro Bildemontering AB (1)
Stortorp 560, PO Box 6032, 705 95, Orebro, Sweden
Tel.: (46) 196701200
Web Site: https://www.orebrobildemo.se
Emp.: 2
Used Car & Spare Parts Services
N.A.I.C.S.: 423140
Johan Himberg (CEO)
Stefan Johansson (Sls Mgr)
Olov Nilsson (Mgr-Car Handling & Sls)

Pala Holding, B.V. (1)
Waldorpstraat 327, 2521 CJ, Hague, Netherlands
Tel.: (31) 402647637
Automotive Part Whslr
N.A.I.C.S.: 441330

Pick-Your-Part Auto Wrecking Inc. (1)

1235 S Beach Blvd, Anaheim, CA 92804
Tel.: (714) 385-1200
Web Site: https://www.lkqpickyourpart.com
Sales Range: $100-124.9 Million
Emp.: 70
Auto Part Salvage
N.A.I.C.S.: 441330

Pika Autoteile GmbH (1)
Raiffeisenstrasse 10, D-61169, Friedberg, Germany
Tel.: (49) 603172120
Web Site: https://www.pika.de
Automotive Equipment Whslr
N.A.I.C.S.: 441330
Don Wittkopp (Mng Dir)
Ralf Stuth (Mng Dir)
Justin Fabbro (Mng Dir)

Plastique Royal Inc. (1)
2809 Etienne-Lenoir Street, Laval, H7R 6J4, QC, Canada
Tel.: (450) 661-8250
Web Site: https://plastiqueroyal.com
Automotive Refinish Product Distr
N.A.I.C.S.: 424950

Potomac German Auto, Inc. (1)
4305 Lime Kiln Rd, Frederick, MD 21703
Tel.: (301) 831-1111
Web Site: https://www.pgauto.com
Sales Range: $25-49.9 Million
Emp.: 25
Recycled Motor Vehicle Parts Provider
N.A.I.C.S.: 423140

Recopart AB (1)
Druveforsvagen 32, SE-504 33, Boras, Sweden
Tel.: (46) 333484300
Web Site: https://www.recopart.com
Automotive Equipment Whslr
N.A.I.C.S.: 441330

Rhenoy Onderdelen B.V. (1)
Holweistraat 10, 4181 CC, Waardenburg, Netherlands
Tel.: (31) 418657474
Web Site: https://www.rhenoy.nl
Automobile Parts Mfr
N.A.I.C.S.: 336390

Rhiag Group Ltd. (1)
Oberneuhofstrasse 6, 6340, Baar, Switzerland
Tel.: (41) 417695555
Web Site: https://www.rhiag.ch
Emp.: 110
Automotive Equipment Whslr
N.A.I.C.S.: 441330

STAHLGRUBER Ges. m.b.H (1)
Am Romerstein 17, 5071, Wals, Austria
Tel.: (43) 662856666
Web Site: https://www.stahlgruber.at
Tire Repair Services
N.A.I.C.S.: 811198

Sator Holding B.V. (1)
S-Gravelandseweg 379, 3125 BJ, Schiedam, Netherlands
Tel.: (31) 104469600
Web Site: https://www.fource.nl
Emp.: 2,700
Automotive Equipment Whslr
N.A.I.C.S.: 441330
Jelena Stevanovic (CEO)

Sergoyne Car-Parts BVBA (1)
Veilinglaan 18, 1861, Wolvertem, Belgium
Tel.: (32) 22693545
Automotive Part Whslr
N.A.I.C.S.: 441330

SiM Impex d.o.o. (1)
Poslovna zona Ramici bb, 78000, Banja Luka, Bosnia & Herzegovina
Tel.: (387) 51389520
Web Site: https://simimpex.ba
Automotive Equipment Whslr
N.A.I.C.S.: 441330

Signalen AB (1)
Vastra Oknebacksvagen 7, 383 36, Monsteras, Sweden
Tel.: (46) 49949000
Web Site: https://www.mdmonsteras.se
Automotive Part Whslr
N.A.I.C.S.: 441330

Spectrum Verf B.V. (1)

Kapitein Hatterasstraat 46, PO Box 4090, 5015 BB, Tilburg, Netherlands
Tel.: (31) 297230999
Web Site: http://www.spectrumverf.nl
Car Body Repair & Paint Services
N.A.I.C.S.: 811121

Stahlgruber CZ s.r.o. (1)
Prumyslova 1385 Areal Tulipan Park, 253 01, Hostivice, Czech Republic
Tel.: (420) 225983200
Web Site: http://www.stahlgruber.cz
Automobile Parts Distr
N.A.I.C.S.: 441330
Hana Korenkova (Mgr-Bus Dev)

Stahlgruber GmbH (1)
Gruber Strasse 65, 85586, Poing, Germany
Tel.: (49) 81217070
Web Site: https://www.stahlgruber.de
Emp.: 5,489
Vehicle Accessory Retailer & Whslr
N.A.I.C.S.: 441330
Frank Scholler (Chm, CEO & Mng Dir)
Timothy Grygotis (Mng Dir)

Stahlgruber d.o.o. (1)
Prosinacka 14 Kerestinec, 10431, Sveta Nedelja, Croatia
Tel.: (385) 13887705
Web Site: https://www.stahlgruber.hr
Car Spare Parts Retailer
N.A.I.C.S.: 441330

Stahlgruber trgovina d.o.o. (1)
Ob Zeleznici 18, 1000, Ljubljana, Slovenia
Tel.: (386) 15873130
Web Site: https://www.stahlgruber.si
Vehicle Accessory Retailer & Whslr
N.A.I.C.S.: 441330

Technisch Service Centrum Rhenoy B.V. (1)
Holweistraat 10, 4181 CC, Waardenburg, Netherlands
Tel.: (31) 418657477
Automobile Parts Mfr
N.A.I.C.S.: 336390

Thomassons.nu Grupp AB (1)
Lagergatan 24, 254 64, Helsingborg, Sweden
Tel.: (46) 42168280
Web Site: http://www.thomassons.nu
Automotive Equipment Whslr
N.A.I.C.S.: 441330

Troms Bildelsenter AS (1)
Ringveien 90, 9018, Tromso, Norway
Tel.: (47) 77600700
Web Site: http://www.tromsbildelsenter.no
Automotive Equipment Whslr
N.A.I.C.S.: 441330

Tubize Parts Service S.r.l. (1)
Chaussee de Mons 329, 1480, Tubize, Belgium
Tel.: (32) 23554078
Automotive Spare Parts Distr
N.A.I.C.S.: 441330

Uni-Select Inc. (1)
170 Industriel Blvd, Boucherville, J4B 2X3, QC, Canada
Tel.: (450) 641-2440
Web Site: http://www.uniselect.com
Rev.: $1,471,816,000
Assets: $1,375,272,000
Liabilities: $901,217,000
Net Worth: $474,055,000
Earnings: ($31,531,000)
Emp.: 4,781
Fiscal Year-end: 12/31/2020
Motor Vehicle Parts & Accessories Distr
N.A.I.C.S.: 423120
Me Louis Juneau (Chief Legal & Admin Officer & Sec)
Emilie Gaudet (Pres-Canadian Automotive Grp & COO-Canadian Automotive Grp)
Brian McManus (Chm & CEO)
Anthony Pagano (CFO)
Max Rogan (Chief Legal Officer)
Michael Sylvester (Pres)

Subsidiary (US):

FinishMaster, Inc.
Ste 800 54 Monument Cir, Indianapolis, IN 46204-2949 (100%)
Tel.: (317) 237-3678
Web Site: https://www.finishmaster.com

Sales Range: $400-449.9 Million
Emp.: 1,400
Automotive Paint Distr
N.A.I.C.S.: 424950
Travis N. Trott (VP-Fin)
David Zelner (VP-Natl Ops)
Zach Wickler (VP-HR)
Bart Chambers (VP-IT)
Craig Stevenson (VP-Mergers & Acquisitions)
Joseph E. McCorry (Pres & COO)

Subsidiary (Domestic):

Autobody Supply Company, Inc. (3)
115 West Washington St Ste 700, Columbus, OH 46204
Tel.: (614) 228-4328
Web Site: http://www.finishmaster.com
Sales Range: $1-9.9 Million
Emp.: 16
Motor Vehicle Supplies
N.A.I.C.S.: 423120
James Volpe (Pres)

Blaise of Color (3)
2208 Hamilton Blvd Ste A, South Plainfield, NJ 07080-3142
Tel.: (908) 757-1205
Web Site: http://www.blaiseofcolor.com
Motor Vehicle Supplies & New Parts Merchant Whslr
N.A.I.C.S.: 423120

Gladwin Paint Company Austin, Ltd. (3)
2000 Broadway, San Antonio, TX 78215
Tel.: (210) 223-2695
Web Site: http://www.gladwinpaint.com
Sales Range: $1-9.9 Million
Emp.: 47
Paint, Varnish & Supplies Merchant Whslr
N.A.I.C.S.: 424950

Magnuson - Hagopian Enterprises, Inc. (3)
836 Livernois, Ferndale, MI 48220 (100%)
Tel.: (248) 541-3053
Web Site: http://www.finishmaster.com
Sales Range: $1-9.9 Million
Emp.: 20
Automotive Coatings
N.A.I.C.S.: 424950
Steve Arndt (Pres & COO)
Tony Miller (Branch Mgr)

Subsidiary (Non-US):

GSF Car Parts Limited (2)
15th Floor 6 Bevis Marks Bury Court, London, EC3A 7BA, United Kingdom
Tel.: (44) 1216267971
Web Site: https://www.gsfcarparts.com
Automobile Parts Mfr
N.A.I.C.S.: 336390

Subsidiary (Domestic):

Maslack Supply Ltd. (2)
488 Falconbridge Road, Sudbury, P3A 4S4, ON, Canada
Tel.: (705) 566-1270
Web Site: http://www.maslack.com
Automotive Suppliers
N.A.I.C.S.: 441330
Pino Vocaturo (Gen Mgr)
Guy Legault (Mgr-Pur)
Carolanne Campeau (Office Mgr)
Sylvain Gauthier (Supvr-Branch)
Curtis Roy (Mgr-Refinish)
Don Pilon (Gen Mgr-Nordic Bearnngs)

Subsidiary (Non-US):

Parts Alliance Group Limited (2)
The Parts Alliance Unit 105 Midpoint Park Kingsbury Road, Minworth, Sutton Coldfield, B76 1AF, West Midlands, United Kingdom
Tel.: (44) 1215656100
Web Site: http://www.thepartsalliance.com
Automobile Parts Distr
N.A.I.C.S.: 423140
Neil Croxson (COO)

Van Heck Interpieces N.V. (1)
Havendklaan 14, 1800, Vilvoorde, Belgium
Tel.: (32) 22558450
Web Site: http://www.vhip.be

Automotive Equipment Whslr
N.A.I.C.S.: 441330

Vanesch Verf Groep B.V. (1)
Kapitein Hatterasstraat 46, 5015 BB, Til-
burg, Netherlands
Tel.: (31) 135715770
Web Site: https://vaneschverf.nl
Automotive & Industrial Paint Whslr
N.A.I.C.S.: 424950

Vaxjo Lackcenter AB (1)
Sjouddevagen 4A, 352 46, Vaxjo, Sweden
Tel.: (46) 47066530
Web Site: https://vaxjolackcenter.se
Emp.: 10
Automotive Part Whslr
N.A.I.C.S.: 441330

Vege Automotive Spain, S.L.U. (1)
Dels Hostalers Avenue 11, Ribarroja del
Turia, 46394, Valencia, Spain
Tel.: (34) 960225342
Web Site: https://www.vege.es
Automobile Parts Distr
N.A.I.C.S.: 441330

Vehicle Data Services Limited (1)
Unit 10 Stephenson House, Horsley Busi-
ness Centre, Horsley, NE15 0NY, Northum-
berland, United Kingdom
Tel.: (44) 166 185 4388
Web Site:
   https://www.vehicledataservices.co.uk
Automotive Parts Services
N.A.I.C.S.: 811111

Widells Bilplat Eftr AB (1)
Branthovdagatan 7, 721 35, Vasteras, Swe-
den
Tel.: (46) 2 112 2855
Web Site: https://widells.se
Automotive Equipment Repair Services
N.A.I.C.S.: 811111

LL FLOORING HOLDINGS, INC.
4901 Bakers Mill Ln, Richmond, VA
23230
Tel.: (804) 463-2000   DE
Web Site: https://www.llflooring.com
Year Founded: 1994
LL—(NYSE)
Rev.: $1,110,679,000
Assets: $613,953,000
Liabilities: $357,872,000
Net Worth: $256,081,000
Earnings: ($12,081,000)
Emp.: 2,300
Fiscal Year-end: 12/31/22
Hardwood Flooring Products Retailer
N.A.I.C.S.: 444110
Robert L. Madore Jr. *(CFO & Exec VP)*
Nancy M. Taylor *(Chm)*
Charles E. Tyson *(Pres & CEO)*
Jennifer S. Bohaty *(Chief Ethics & Compliance Officer)*
Andrew W. Wadhams *(Sr VP-Retail & Comml Sls)*
Laura Massaro *(CMO & Sr VP)*
Douglas Clark *(Sr VP)*
Alice Givens *(Chief Legal Officer)*
Kristian Lesher *(CTO)*

Subsidiaries:

Lumber Liquidators Services, LLC (1)
3000 John Deere Rd, Toano, VA 23168
Tel.: (757) 259-4280
Emp.: 27
Building Materials Whslr
N.A.I.C.S.: 444110

LM FUNDING AMERICA, INC.
1200 W Platt St Ste 100, Tampa, FL
33606
Tel.: (813) 222-8996   DE
Web Site: https://www.lmfunding.com
LMFA—(NASDAQ)
Rev.: $1,733,951
Assets: $53,189,618
Liabilities: $2,392,389

Net Worth: $50,797,229
Earnings: ($29,240,201)
Emp.: 8
Fiscal Year-end: 12/31/22
Other Financial Vehicles
N.A.I.C.S.: 525990
Bruce M. Rodgers *(Chm, Pres & CEO)*
Carollinn Gould *(Founder)*
Richard D. Russell *(CFO)*
Ryan H. Duran *(VP-Ops)*

Subsidiaries:

Wallach & Company (1)
107 W Federal St, Middleburg, VA 20118-0480
Tel.: (540) 687-3166
Web Site: https://www.wallach.com
Health Care Insurance Services
N.A.I.C.S.: 524114

LMP AUTOMOTIVE HOLDINGS, INC.
500 E Broward Blvd Ste 1900, Fort
Lauderdale, FL 33394
Tel.: (954) 895-0352   DE
Web Site: http://lmpmotors.com
Year Founded: 2017
LMPX—(NASDAQ)
Rev.: $30,442,617
Assets: $34,413,055
Liabilities: $5,268,566
Net Worth: $29,144,489
Earnings: ($4,815,793)
Emp.: 17
Fiscal Year-end: 12/31/20
Holding Company
N.A.I.C.S.: 551112

LMP CAPITAL & INCOME FUND, INC.
620 8th Ave 47th Fl, New York, NY
10018
Tel.: (212) 601-6000   MD
SCD—(NYSE)
Fund Management Services
N.A.I.C.S.: 523940
Jane E. Trust *(Chm, Pres & CEO)*

LOANDEPOT, INC.
6561 Irvine Ctr Dr, Irvine, CA 92618
Tel.: (949) 434-5964   DE
Web Site:
   https://investors.loandepot.com
Year Founded: 2020
LDI—(NYSE)
Rev.: $1,255,796,000
Assets: $6,609,934,000
Liabilities: $5,688,461,000
Net Worth: $921,473,000
Earnings: ($273,020,000)
Emp.: 5,194
Fiscal Year-end: 12/31/22
Holding Company
N.A.I.C.S.: 551112
Melanie Graper *(Chief HR Officer)*
David R. Hayes *(CFO & Principal Acctg Officer)*
George Brady *(Chief Digital Officer & Exec VP)*
Sudhir Nair *(CIO)*
Gerhard Erdelji *(Sr VP-IR)*
Rebecca Anderson *(Sr VP-Comm & PR)*
Karin Lockovitch *(Chief Risk Officer & Exec VP)*
Jeff DerGurahian *(Chief Capital Markets Officer & Exec VP)*
Jeff Walsh *(Pres-Mortgage)*
Alec Hanson *(CMO)*
Jonathan Fine *(VP-PR)*
David Smith *(VP-Natl VA Lending)*
Anthony Hsieh *(Founder)*
Frank Martell *(Pres & CEO)*

LOANS4LESS.COM, INC.

22409 Susana Ave, Torrance, CA
90505
Tel.: (310) 540-0157
Web Site:
   https://www.loans4less.com
Year Founded: 1993
LFLS—(OTCIQ)
Mortgage & Nonmortgage Loan Bro-
kers
N.A.I.C.S.: 522310
Steven M. Hershman *(Chm, Pres, CFO & Treas)*
Daniela Haynie *(Exec VP)*

LOCAL BOUNTI CORPORATION
490 Foley Ln, Hamilton, MT 59840 DE
Web Site:
   https://www.localbounti.com
Year Founded: 2018
LOCL—(NYSE)
Rev.: $19,474,000
Assets: $278,740,000
Liabilities: $157,407,000
Net Worth: $121,333,000
Earnings: ($111,071,000)
Emp.: 289
Fiscal Year-end: 12/31/22
Computer System Design Services
N.A.I.C.S.: 541512
Kathleen Valiasek *(Pres & CFO)*
Craig M. Hurlbert *(Founder, Chm & CEO)*

LOCAL CORPORATION
7555 Irvine Ctr Dr, Irvine, CA 92618
Tel.: (949) 784-0800   DE
Web Site: http://www.local.com
Year Founded: 1999
LOCM—(OTCIQ)
Sales Range: $75-99.9 Million
Emp.: 70
Local Search Engine; Advertising
Network Services
N.A.I.C.S.: 425120
Scott Reinke *(Chief Legal Officer)*

Subsidiaries:

Krillion, Inc. (1)
607A W Dana St, Mountain View, CA 94041
Tel.: (650) 965-0222
Web Site: http://www.krillion.com
Sales Range: $10-24.9 Million
Emp.: 9
Product Search Technology Developer
N.A.I.C.S.: 519290

LOCATION BASED TECHNOLOGIES INC.
7545 Irvine Ctr Dr Ste 200, Irvine, CA
92618   NV
Web Site:
   https://www.locationbasedtech.com
Year Founded: 2006
LBAS—(OTCIQ)
Sales Range: $1-9.9 Million
Emp.: 6
Wireless Location Tracking Systems
Mfr
N.A.I.C.S.: 334220
Joseph F. Scalisi *(Founder)*
David M. Morse *(Chm, Pres & CEO)*
Desiree Mejia *(COO & Sec)*

LOCKHEED MARTIN CORPORATION
6801 Rockledge Dr, Bethesda, MD
20817-1877
Tel.: (301) 897-6000   MD
Web Site:
   https://www.lockheedmartin.com
Year Founded: 1995
LMT—(NYSE)
Rev.: $67,571,000,000
Assets: $52,456,000,000
Liabilities: $45,621,000,000
Net Worth: $6,835,000,000

Earnings: $6,920,000,000
Emp.: 122,000
Fiscal Year-end: 12/31/23
Space, Defense, Electronics, Com-
munications, Information Systems,
Data Management & Energy Prod-
ucts Designer, Developer, Mfr & Inte-
grator
N.A.I.C.S.: 334511
Gregory M. Ulmer *(Exec VP-Aeronautics)*
Stephanie C. Hill *(Exec VP-Rotary & Mission Sys)*
Leo S. Mackay Jr. *(Sr VP-Ethics & Enterprise Assurance)*
James D. Taiclet Jr. *(Chm, Pres & CEO)*
Frank A. St. John *(COO)*
Robert E. Mullins *(Sr VP-Corp Strategy & Dev)*
Dean Acosta *(Chief Comm Officer & Sr VP)*
Jesus Jay Malave Jr. *(CFO)*
David Weston *(Dir-IR)*
Tim Cahill *(Exec VP-Missiles & Fire Control)*
Yvonne O. Hodge *(CIO-Enterprise Bus & Digital Transformation & Sr VP)*
Christian Marrone *(Sr VP-Govt Affairs)*
Robert Lightfoot *(Exec VP-Space)*
Evan T. Scott *(Treas & VP)*
H. Edward Paul III *(VP & Controller)*
Michael Williamson *(Sr VP-Global Bus Dev & Strategy)*
Linda O'Brien *(VP & Chief Engr)*
Ryan D. McCarthy *(VP)*
Jason Hopkins *(VP-Strategy & Bus Dev-Crescent Space)*
Maryanne R. Lavan *(Gen Counsel, Sec & Sr VP)*

Subsidiaries:

Lockheed Martin Advanced
Projects (1)
9500 Godwin Dr Bldg 400, Manassas, VA
20110-4166
Tel.: (703) 367-2121
Sales Range: $10-24.9 Million
Emp.: 10
Aircraft Self-Protection, Antisubmarine War-
fare & Weapon & Guidance Control Prod-
ucts
N.A.I.C.S.: 336414

Lockheed Martin Aeronautics
Company (1)
PO Box 748, Fort Worth, TX 76101-0748
Tel.: (817) 777-2000
Web Site: http://www.lockheedmartin.com
Sales Range: $5-14.9 Billion
Emp.: 28,000
Military Aircraft Designer, Developer, Sys-
tems Integrator, Producer & Support Ser-
vices
N.A.I.C.S.: 336411

Subsidiary (Domestic):

Deposition Sciences, Inc. (2)
3300 Coffey Ln, Santa Rosa, CA 95403
Tel.: (707) 573-6700
Web Site: http://www.depsci.com
Sales Range: $10-24.9 Million
Emp.: 85
Optical Thin Film & Magnetic Coatings Mfr
N.A.I.C.S.: 325998
James Johnson *(Mgr-Quality Assurance)*
Jim Giacobazzi *(Pres)*
Eric Kurman *(CTO)*

Lockheed Martin AeroParts, Inc. (2)
211 Industrial Park Rd, Johnstown, PA
15904-1961
Tel.: (814) 262-3000
Sales Range: $50-74.9 Million
Emp.: 100
Aircraft Engines & Engine Parts
N.A.I.C.S.: 336412

Lockheed Martin Corporation—(Continued)

Plant (Domestic):

Lockheed Martin Aeronautics Company (2)
1011 Lockheed Way, Palmdale, CA 93599-0001
Tel.: (661) 572-2974
Sales Range: $250-299.9 Million
Military Aircraft Designer, Developer, Systems Integrator, Producer & Support Services
N.A.I.C.S.: 336411

Lockheed Martin Aeronautics Company (2)
86 S Cobb Dr Se, Marietta, GA 30063
Tel.: (770) 494-4411
Sales Range: $25-49.9 Million
Military Aircraft Designer, Developer, Systems Integrator, Producer & Support Services
N.A.I.C.S.: 811310
Jeff Babione (VP & Deputy Mgr-F 35 Lightning II Program)

Lockheed Martin Business Technology Solutions Limited (1)
Greenock Road India of Inchinnan Inchinnan, Renfrew, PA4 9LH, United Kingdom
Tel.: (44) 1418143700
Information Technology Consulting Services
N.A.I.C.S.: 541511

Lockheed Martin Desktop Solutions, Inc. (1)
2700 Prosperity Ave, Fairfax, VA 22031
Tel.: (703) 206-0030
Sales Range: $25-49.9 Million
Emp.: 170
Computers Peripherals & Software
N.A.I.C.S.: 541511

Lockheed Martin Engine Investments, LLC (1)
3510 Silverside Rd, Wilmington, DE 19810
Tel.: (302) 478-1583
Aerospace, Defense & Information Systems Product Designer & Mfr
N.A.I.C.S.: 334511

Lockheed Martin Global, Inc. (1)
8033 Sunset Blvd 1017, Los Angeles, CA 90046
Tel.: (310) 967-2007
Web Site: http://locationmanagers.org
Emp.: 3,000
Holding Company
N.A.I.C.S.: 551112

Subsidiary (Non-US):

Lockheed Martin Australia Pty. Limited (2)
Lockheed Martin Australia House 8 Brisbane Avenue, Barton, 2600, ACT, Australia (100%)
Tel.: (61) 261506500
Web Site: http://www.lockheedmartin.com
Sales Range: $10-24.9 Million
Guided Missiles & Space Vehicles
N.A.I.C.S.: 336414

Lockheed Martin Canada Inc. (2)
501 Palladium Drive, Ottawa, K2V 0A2, ON, Canada
Tel.: (613) 599-3270
Web Site: https://www.lockheedmartin.com
Sales Range: $100-124.9 Million
Air Traffic Control, Space, Defense, Electronics, Information & Communication Systems Designer, Mfr & Systems Integrator
N.A.I.C.S.: 541512

Unit (Domestic):

Lockheed Martin Canada (3)
7171 Cote-Vertu Ouest, Montreal, H4S 1Z3, QC, Canada (100%)
Tel.: (514) 340-8310
Web Site: https://www.lockheedmartin.com
Sales Range: $25-49.9 Million
Emp.: 150
Software Development & Research Services
N.A.I.C.S.: 334610

Representative Office (Non-US):

Lockheed Martin Global, Inc. - Belgium Office (2)

Ave Louise 480, Brussels, 1050, Belgium
Tel.: (32) 26753380
Sales Range: $10-24.9 Million
Emp.: 10
Aircraft Marketing Services
N.A.I.C.S.: 336411

Lockheed Martin Global, Inc. - Turkey Office (2)
Cinnah Caddesi 45 2 Cankaya, Ankara, Turkiye
Tel.: (90) 3124415647
Sales Range: $10-24.9 Million
Emp.: 5
Aircraft Marketing Services
N.A.I.C.S.: 336411

Subsidiary (Non-US):

Lockheed Martin International S.A. (2)
1 Pl Longemalle, 1204, Geneva, Switzerland
Tel.: (41) 223184040
Web Site: http://www.lockheed.com
Sales Range: $50-74.9 Million
Emp.: 20
Aircraft Marketing Services
N.A.I.C.S.: 336411
Marillyn A. Hewson (Chrm, Pres & CEO)
Timothy Cahill (Sr VP-Bus Dev-Global)

Lockheed Martin UK Ltd. (2)
Solent Business Park 2nd Floor Building 3000C, Whiteley, Fareham, PO15 7FX, United Kingdom
Tel.: (44) 7989 395856
Web Site: http://www.lockheedmartin.co.uk
Emp.: 1,800
Advanced Technology Systems, Products & Services
N.A.I.C.S.: 541512

Subsidiary (Domestic):

Lockheed Martin UK Ampthill Limited (3)
Reddings Wood, Ampthill, MK45 2HD, Bedford, United Kingdom (100%)
Tel.: (44) 1525841000
Emp.: 900
Aerospace, Defense & Information Systems Design & Development Services
N.A.I.C.S.: 927110

Subsidiary (Non-US):

Lockheed Middle East Services (2)
PO Box 2811, Riyadh, Saudi Arabia (100%)
Tel.: (966) 4630726
Web Site: http://www.lockheedmartin.com
Sales Range: $200-249.9 Million
Emp.: 500
Aircraft Management & Technical Support Services
N.A.I.C.S.: 488119

Lockheed Martin Integrated Systems, Inc. (1)
3935 NW Aloclek Pl Ste A100, Hillsboro, OR 97124
Tel.: (503) 466-6800
Aerospace, Defense & Information Systems Product Designer & Mfr
N.A.I.C.S.: 334511

Lockheed Martin Integrated Technology, LLC (1)
5290 Shawnee Rd, Alexandria, VA 22312
Tel.: (703) 916-7358
Aerospace, Defense & Information Systems Product Designer & Mfr
N.A.I.C.S.: 334511

Lockheed Martin Investments Inc. (1)
3510 Silverside Rd Ste 3, Wilmington, DE 19810
Tel.: (302) 478-1583
Aircraft Mfr
N.A.I.C.S.: 336411

Lockheed Martin Missiles & Fire Control (1)
1902 W Freeway, Grand Prairie, TX 75051-3601
Tel.: (972) 603-1000
Web Site: http://www.lockheedmartin.com
Emp.: 2,809

Combat, Missile, Rocket & Space Systems Developer & Mfr
N.A.I.C.S.: 336411

Plant (Domestic):

Lockheed Martin Missiles & Fire Control - Orlando (2)
5600 Sand Lake Rd, Orlando, FL 32819
Tel.: (407) 356-2000
Web Site: http://www.lmco.com
Emp.: 4,043
Defense Systems
N.A.I.C.S.: 488999

Lockheed Martin Operations Support, Inc. (1)
6801 Rockledge Dr, Bethesda, MD 20817-1803
Tel.: (301) 897-6000
Web Site: http://www.lockheedmartincorporation.com
Aerospace, Defense & Information Systems Product Designer & Mfr
N.A.I.C.S.: 334511

Lockheed Martin Services, Inc. (1)
6801 Rockledge Dr, Bethesda, MD 20817-1877
Tel.: (301) 897-6000
Web Site: http://www.lmco.com
Office Administrative Services
N.A.I.C.S.: 561110

Lockheed Martin Simulation, Training & Support (1)
4000 Memorial Pkwy SW, Huntsville, AL 35802-1326
Tel.: (256) 880-5500
Sales Range: $25-49.9 Million
Emp.: 100
Training Solutions
N.A.I.C.S.: 611430
Lee Chandler (Gen Mgr)

Lockheed Martin Simulation, Training & Support (1)
12506 Lake Underhill Rd, Orlando, FL 32825-5002
Tel.: (407) 306-1000
Military & Aerospace Training Solutions
N.A.I.C.S.: 611430

Lockheed Martin Sippican, Inc. (1)
7 Barnabas Rd, Marion, MA 02738-1421
Tel.: (508) 748-1160
Web Site: http://www.sippican.com
Sales Range: $50-74.9 Million
Emp.: 350
Defense Electronics Contractor
N.A.I.C.S.: 334511

Unit (Domestic):

Lockheed Martin Government Electronic Systems (2)
199 Borton Landing Rd, Moorestown, NJ 08057-3054
Tel.: (856) 722-5000
Government Electronic Systems
N.A.I.C.S.: 336414

Lockheed Martin Management & Data Systems (2)
7000 Geerdes Blvd, King of Prussia, PA 19406-1525
Tel.: (610) 531-7400
Web Site: http://www.lockheed.com
Systems Integration, Engineering, Software Development & Program Management Services
N.A.I.C.S.: 812990

Lockheed Martin Maritime Systems & Sensors (2)
PO Box 4840, Syracuse, NY 13221-4840
Tel.: (315) 456-0123
Systems & Sensors
N.A.I.C.S.: 336414

Lockheed Martin Maritime Systems & Sensors (2)
199 Borton Landing Rd, Moorestown, NJ 08057-0927
Tel.: (856) 722-4100
Surface, Air & Undersea Military Applications
N.A.I.C.S.: 336414

Lockheed Martin Naval & Electronic Systems (2)

2323 Eastern Blvd, Baltimore, MD 21220-4207 (100%)
Tel.: (410) 682-1000
Shipboard Electronic Warfare Systems
N.A.I.C.S.: 336414

Lockheed Martin Sippican Countermeasure Systems (2)
7 Barnabas Rd, Marion, MA 02738
Tel.: (508) 748-1160
Web Site: http://www.sippican.com
Sales Range: $75-99.9 Million
Defense Electronics Contractor
N.A.I.C.S.: 334511

Lockheed Martin Systems Integration - Owego (2)
1801 State Route 17C, Owego, NY 13827-3900 (100%)
Tel.: (607) 751-2000
Advanced Technology Products, Services & Systems Integration Solutions
N.A.I.C.S.: 334118

Lockheed Martin Tactical Defense Systems (2)
1210 Massillon Rd, Akron, OH 44315-0001
Tel.: (330) 796-2800
Simulation & Training Services
N.A.I.C.S.: 541611

Subsidiary (Domestic):

Polaris Contract Manufacturing, Inc. (2)
15 Barnabas Rd, Marion, MA 02738
Tel.: (508) 748-3399
Sales Range: $25-49.9 Million
Emp.: 150
Provider of Electronic Manufacturing
N.A.I.C.S.: 561499
William Stark (Mgr)

Lockheed Martin Space Systems Company (1)
8000 Southpark Way Bldg 2, Littleton, CO 80120
Tel.: (720) 344-1037
Web Site: http://www.lockheedmartin.com
Sales Range: $1-4.9 Billion
Emp.: 8,000
Launch Vehicles & Systems, Spacecraft Telecommunications, Remote Sensing, Space Science & Defensive & Strategic Missile Systems Designer, Producer & Integrator
N.A.I.C.S.: 336411
Kay N. Sears (VP & Gen Mgr-Military Space line of Bus)

Subsidiary (Domestic):

Astrotech Space Operations, LLC (2)
1515 Chaffee Dr, Titusville, FL 32780
Tel.: (321) 268-3830
Web Site: http://www.astrotechspaceoperations.com
Spacecraft Launch Site Facilities Processing & Related Services
N.A.I.C.S.: 488999

Unit (Domestic):

Astrotech Space Operations, Inc. - Vandenberg Air Force Base (3)
Bldg 1036 Tangair Rd & Red Rd, Vandenberg AFB, CA 93437
Tel.: (805) 875-6400
Web Site: http://www.astrotechspaceoperations.com
Spacecraft Launch Site Facilities Processing & Related Services
N.A.I.C.S.: 488999

Unit (Domestic):

Lockheed Martin Commercial Space Systems (2)
100 Campus Dr, Newton, PA 18940
Tel.: (215) 497-1100
Sales Range: $75-99.9 Million
Satellite Communications Payload Mfr
N.A.I.C.S.: 517410

Lockheed Martin Space Systems Co. - El Paso (2)
Chaffee Rd Bldg 2488, El Paso, TX 79916-7011
Tel.: (915) 568-4257

Temporary Help Service
N.A.I.C.S.: 561320

Lockheed Martin Space Systems Co. - New Orleans (2)
13800 Old Gentilly Rd, New Orleans, LA 70129-2215
Tel.: (504) 257-3311
Space Shuttle External Tanks Mfr
N.A.I.C.S.: 332420

Lockheed Martin Space Systems Co. - Sunnyvale (2)
1111 Lockheed Martin Way, Sunnyvale, CA 94089
Tel.: (408) 742-4321
Emp.: 5,000
Launch Vehicles & Systems, Spacecraft Telecommunications, Remote Sensing, Space Science & Defensive & Strategic Missile Systems Designer, Producer & Integrator
N.A.I.C.S.: 336411

Subsidiary (Domestic):

Sandia Corporation (2)
1515 Eubank Blvd SE, Albuquerque, NM 87123-3453
Tel.: (505) 845-0011
Web Site: http://www.sandia.gov
Sales Range: $1-4.9 Billion
Emp.: 8,722
National Security Research & Development
N.A.I.C.S.: 541715

QTC Management, Inc. (1)
924 Overland Ct, San Dimas, CA 91773
Tel.: (909) 859-2100
Web Site: http://www.qtcm.com
Healthcare Training Services
N.A.I.C.S.: 621111
Jamshid Tamiry (Dir-Medical)
Grant Kim (CEO)
Nader Nemati (CIO)
Carla Abramcheck (VP-Bus Capture)
Larry Schaefer (COO)
Frenorgin Ubungen (VP-Clinical Quality)
Virginia Mao (VP-Corp Admin)
Valma Kwong (VP-Fin & Acctg)
Tony Buratti (VP-Corp Dev)
Patricia Dantzler (VP-HR)
John Mitchell (VP-Comml Div)
Bessie Green (Dir-Quality Compliance-VA Svcs)
Joe O'Brien (Dir-Program Mgmt)
Daniel Highland (Dir-Bus Ops)

Systems Made Simple, Inc. (1)
149 Northern Concourse, Syracuse, NY 13212
Tel.: (315) 455-3200
Web Site:
    http://www.systemsmadesimple.com
Sales Range: $25-49.9 Million
Emp.: 114
Information Technology Services for Healthcare Industry
N.A.I.C.S.: 541511
Christopher Roberts (CFO)

Terran Orbital Corporation (1)
6800 Broken Sound Pkwy NW Ste 200, Boca Raton, FL 33487
Tel.: (561) 988-1704
Web Site: https://www.terranorbital.com
Rev.: $94,237,000
Assets: $182,654,000
Liabilities: $274,075,000
Net Worth: ($91,421,000)
Earnings: ($163,980,000)
Emp.: 480
Fiscal Year-end: 12/31/2022
Radio & Television Broadcasting & Wireless Communications Equipment Manufacturing
N.A.I.C.S.: 334220

Zeta Associates, Inc. (1)
10302 Eaton Pl Ste 500, Fairfax, VA 22030
Tel.: (703) 385-7050
Web Site: http://www.zai.com
Computer Programming Services
N.A.I.C.S.: 541511

LOCUST WALK ACQUISITION CORP.
2 Commerce Sq 2001 Market St Ste 3400, Philadelphia, PA 19103
Tel.: (215) 731-9450   DE

Year Founded: 2020
LWACU—(NASDAQ)
Investment Services
N.A.I.C.S.: 523999
Chris Ehrlich (CEO)
Daniel Geffken (CFO)

LODE-STAR MINING INC.
1 E Liberty St Ste 600, Reno, NV 89501
Tel.: (775) 234-5443   NV
Year Founded: 2004
LSMG—(OTCQB)
Assets: $2,474
Liabilities: $91,924
Net Worth: ($89,450)
Earnings: $62,940
Fiscal Year-end: 12/31/23
Gold Mining Services
N.A.I.C.S.: 212220
Mark Walmesley (CEO, CFO, Interim Treas & Interim Sec)

LOEWS CORPORATION
9 W 57th St, New York, NY 10019-2714
Tel.: (212) 521-2000   DE
Web Site: https://www.loews.com
Year Founded: 1959
L—(NYSE)
Rev.: $15,901,000,000
Assets: $79,197,000,000
Liabilities: $62,672,000,000
Net Worth: $16,525,000,000
Earnings: $1,434,000,000
Emp.: 12,280
Fiscal Year-end: 12/31/23
Holding Company
N.A.I.C.S.: 551112
Kenneth I. Siegel (Sr VP-Merger, Acq, Energy Subsidiaries, and Strategic Plng)
Jane J. Wang (CFO & Sr VP)
Benjamin J. Tisch (Pres & CEO)
Susan Becker (VP-Tax)
Mark S. Schwartz (Chief Acctg Officer, Treas & VP)
Richard Waldo Scott (Chief Investment Officer & Sr VP)
Marc A. Alpert (Gen Counsel, Sec & Sr VP)
Herb E. Hofmann (VP-IT)
Glenn Robertson (VP-Internal Audit)
Brandon Holder (VP-Tax)
Alexander H. Tisch (VP)

Subsidiaries:

Altium Packaging LP (1)
2500 Windy Rdg Pkwy SE Ste 1400, Atlanta, GA 30339
Tel.: (678) 742-4600
Web Site: https://altiumpkg.com
Blow Molder of Plastic Packaging Services
N.A.I.C.S.: 326150
Sean Fallmann (Pres & CEO)

Subsidiary (Domestic):

Altium Healthcare (2)
600 Vista Dr, Sparta, TN 38583
Web Site: https://www.altiumhealthcare.com
Plastic Mfr
N.A.I.C.S.: 326130
Jim Daus (Mgr-Sls)

Altium Packaging Canada (2)
2500 Windy Rdg Pkwy SE Ste 1400, Atlanta, GA 30339
Tel.: (678) 742-4600
Web Site: https://altiumpkg.ca
Plastic Packaging Mfr
N.A.I.C.S.: 326199

Subsidiary (Non-US):

Plastique Micron Inc. (3)
21 Boulevard Begin, Sainte-Claire, G0R 2V0, QC, Canada
Tel.: (418) 883-3333
Web Site: http://www.plastiquemicron.com
Emp.: 200

Plastic Container Mfr
N.A.I.C.S.: 326160
Bernard Poitras (Pres)
Jean-Sebastien Blais (Fin Dir & VP)
Jolyane Pare (Dir-HR)
Laurier Lapointe (Dir-IT)
Ghyslain Drolet (Dir-Production)

Subsidiary (Domestic):

Envision Plastics Industries, LLC (2)
606B Walters St, Reidsville, NC 27320
Tel.: (336) 342-4749
Web Site: http://www.envisionplastics.com
Plastics Product Mfr
N.A.I.C.S.: 326199

Boardwalk Pipeline Partners, LP (1)
9 Greenway Plz Ste 2800, Houston, TX 77046   (100%)
Web Site: http://www.bwpipelines.com
Rev.: $1,617,700,000
Assets: $9,696,400,000
Liabilities: $3,905,300,000
Net Worth: $5,791,100,000
Earnings: $386,000,000
Emp.: 1,260
Fiscal Year-end: 12/31/2023
Natural Gas Transportation, Gathering & Storage Services
N.A.I.C.S.: 486910
Kenneth I. Siegel (Chm)
Michael E. McMahon (Gen Counsel, Sec & Sr VP)
Jamie L. Buskill (Chief Financial & Admin Officer, Treas & Sr VP)
Richard Keyser (Sr VP-Operations-Engineering)
Mercy Kamps (Sr VP-HR, Corp Comm & IR)
Stanley C. Horton (Pres & CEO)

Subsidiary (Domestic):

Boardwalk Acquisition Company, LLC (2)
4470 Bluebonnet Blvd, Baton Rouge, LA 70809
Tel.: (225) 706-2239
Liquid & Natural Gas Transportation & Processing Services
N.A.I.C.S.: 213112

Boardwalk Field Services, LLC (2)
9 Greenway Plz ste 2800, Houston, TX 77046-0926
Tel.: (713) 479-8134
Web Site: http://www.boardwalkfs.com
Natural Gas Pipeline Transportation Services
N.A.I.C.S.: 486210

Boardwalk Operating GP, LLC (2)
9 Greenway Plz Ste 2800, Houston, TX 77046-0926
Tel.: (713) 479-8000
Liquid & Natural Gas Transportation & Processing Services
N.A.I.C.S.: 213112

Boardwalk Pipelines, LP (2)
610 W 2nd St, Owensboro, KY 42301
Tel.: (270) 926-8686
Web Site: http://www.bwpmlp.com
Sales Range: $75-99.9 Million
Emp.: 250
Insurance Service Provider
N.A.I.C.S.: 524126

Boardwalk Storage Company, LLC (2)
60825 Hwy 1148, Plaquemine, LA 70764
Tel.: (225) 685-1400
Web Site: http://www.bwpmmp.com
Liquid & Natural Gas Transportation & Processing Services
N.A.I.C.S.: 213112
Riz St.Germain (Mgr-Ops)

Gulf South Pipeline Company, LP (2)
9 Greenway Plz Ste 2800, Houston, TX 77046
Tel.: (713) 479-8000
Rev.: $467,300,000
Assets: $3,050,300,000
Liabilities: $968,800,000
Net Worth: $2,081,500,000
Earnings: $59,900,000
Emp.: 600

Fiscal Year-end: 12/31/2014
Natural Gas Pipeline System Operator
N.A.I.C.S.: 486210

Texas Gas Transmission, LLC (2)
610 W 2nd St, Owensboro, KY 42301
Tel.: (270) 926-8686
Web Site: http://www.txgt.com
Sales Range: $250-299.9 Million
Emp.: 275
Natural Gas Distribution
N.A.I.C.S.: 486210

CNA Financial Corporation (1)
151 N Franklin, Chicago, IL 60606   (91%)
Tel.: (312) 822-5000
Web Site: https://www.cna.com
Rev.: $13,299,000,000
Assets: $64,711,000,000
Liabilities: $54,818,000,000
Net Worth: $9,893,000,000
Earnings: $1,205,000,000
Emp.: 6,300
Fiscal Year-end: 12/31/2023
Holding Company; Property, Casualty & Life Insurance Products & Services
N.A.I.C.S.: 551112
Elizabeth A. Aguinaga (Chief HR Officer & Exec VP)
Dino E. Robusto (Chm & CEO)
Douglas M. Worman (Chief Underwriting Officer & Exec VP)
Michael Costonis (Chief Ops Officer & Chief Ops Officer-Marketing-Strategy-Global)
Jose Ramon Gonzalez (Gen Counsel & Gen Counsel)
Bob Hopper (Chief Actuary & Exec VP)
Daniel Franzetti (Exec VP-Worldwide Claim)
Scott R. Lindquist (CFO & Exec VP)
Amy M. Smith (Chief Acctg Officer)
Gary Haase (COO & Exec VP)

Group (Domestic):

CNA Insurance Companies (2)
CNA Ctr 333 S Wabash Ave, Chicago, IL 60604-0001
Tel.: (312) 822-5000
Web Site: http://www.cna.com
Sales Range: $1-4.9 Billion
Insurance
N.A.I.C.S.: 524128
Thomas Firouz Motamed (Chm & CEO)

Subsidiary (Domestic):

American Casualty Company of Reading, Pennsylvania (3)
333 S Wabash Ave, Chicago, IL 60604
Tel.: (312) 822-5000
Web Site: http://www.cna.com
Insurance Service Provider
N.A.I.C.S.: 524126

CNA Financial Corporation - Chicago Branch (3)
151 N Franklin St Fl 9, Chicago, IL 60606
Tel.: (312) 822-5000
Web Site: http://www.cna.com
Property & Casualty Insurance, Reinsurance, Financial & Insurance Services
N.A.I.C.S.: 524210

Branch (Domestic):

CNA Insurance - New York City Branch (3)
125 Broad St 7th & 8th Fl, New York, NY 10004
Tel.: (212) 440-7070
Web Site: http://www.cna.com
Insurance Agents Brokers & Service
N.A.I.C.S.: 524298

CNA Insurance - Ohio Branch (3)
550 Polaris Pkwy Ste 100, Westerville, OH 43082
Tel.: (614) 516-2000
Web Site: http://www.cna.com
Sales Range: $25-49.9 Million
Emp.: 35
Fire Marine & Casualty Insurance
N.A.I.C.S.: 524126
David G. Moyer (Dir-Small Bus Sls)
George Moore (Branch Mgr)
Rich Rivera (Mgr-Small Bus Sls)
Ryan Macke (Mgr-Comml)
Brian Knight (Mgr-Claim Client Svcs)
John Bielak (Dir-Risk Control)

Loews Corporation—(Continued)

CNA Insurance - Reading Branch **(3)**
401 Penn St, Reading, PA 19601
Tel.: (610) 320-4000
Web Site: http://www.cna.com
Insurance Agents & Brokerage Services
N.A.I.C.S.: 524210

Subsidiary (Domestic):

CNA National Warranty Corporation **(3)**
4150 N Drinkwater Blvd, Scottsdale, AZ 85251-3611
Tel.: (480) 941-1626
Web Site: https://www.cnanational.com
Sales Range: $200-249.9 Million
Third Party Insurance Administrator
N.A.I.C.S.: 524210
Joe Becker (Pres & CEO)

CNA Surety Corporation **(3)**
151 N Franklin St 17th Fl, Chicago, IL 60606 **(100%)**
Tel.: (312) 822-5000
Web Site: http://www.cnasurety.com
Sales Range: $450-499.9 Million
Emp.: 720
Surety & Fidelity Bonds
N.A.I.C.S.: 524126
John F. Welch (Pres)

Subsidiary (Domestic):

CNA Surety Corporation **(4)**
Small Commercial Service Center 101 S Reid St Ste 300, Sioux Falls, SD 57103
Tel.: (605) 336-0850
Web Site: http://www.cnasurety.com
Property & Casualty Insurance Services
N.A.I.C.S.: 524126

Subsidiary (Non-US):

Western Surety Company **(4)**
(100%)
Tel.: (605) 336-0850
Web Site: http://www.cnasurety.com
Sales Range: $450-499.9 Million
Emp.: 400
Small Fidelity & Non-Contract Surety Bonds; Fidelity, Surety & Casualty Insurance
N.A.I.C.S.: 524126

Subsidiary (Domestic):

Troy Fain Insurance Inc. **(5)**
5524 Apalachee Pkwy, Tallahassee, FL 32311
Tel.: (850) 224-3156
Web Site: http://www.troyfaininsurance.com
Sales Range: Less than $1 Million
Emp.: 5
Insurance Agents
N.A.I.C.S.: 524210

Subsidiary (Domestic):

Columbia Casualty Company **(3)**
333 S Wabash Ave, Chicago, IL 60604
Tel.: (312) 822-5000
Web Site: http://www.cna.com
Sales Range: $650-699.9 Million
Emp.: 4,000
Fire Marine & Casualty Insurance & Carriers
N.A.I.C.S.: 524126

Continental Casualty Company **(3)**
333 S Wabash Ave CNA Ctr, Chicago, IL 60604
Tel.: (312) 822-5000
Web Site: http://www.cna.com
Sales Range: $700-749.9 Million
Emp.: 1,000
Casualty Insurance Carrier
N.A.I.C.S.: 524126

Subsidiary (Non-US):

Hardy Underwriting Bermuda Limited **(3)**
4th Floor Park Place 55 Par-la-ville Road, Hamilton, HM 11, Bermuda
Tel.: (441) 295 0382
Web Site: http://www.hardygroup.bm
Emp.: 121

Holding Company; General Insurance & Reinsurance Services
N.A.I.C.S.: 551112
Jamie MacDiarmid (Dir-Fin)
David Carson (Head-Property Treaty)

Subsidiary (Non-US):

Hardy Guernsey Limited **(4)**
Mill Court La Charroterie, PO Box 155, Saint Peter Port, GY1 4ET, Guernsey
Tel.: (44) 1481719292
Web Site: http://www.hardygroup.co.uk
Property & Casualty Reinsurance Services
N.A.I.C.S.: 524130
Jonathan Beck (Mng Dir)

Hardy Underwriting Limited **(4)**
1st Floor Fitzwilliam House, 10 St Mary Axe, London, EC3A 8NA, United Kingdom
Tel.: (44) 2076260382
Web Site: http://www.hardygroup.co.uk
Sales Range: $50-74.9 Million
Insurance Agents & Underwriters
N.A.I.C.S.: 524298

Subsidiary (Domestic):

The Continental Insurance Company of New Jersey **(3)**
333 S Wabash Ave, Chicago, IL 60604
Tel.: (312) 822-5000
Web Site: http://www.cna.com
Insurance Products & Services
N.A.I.C.S.: 524128

Subsidiary (Non-US):

CNA Insurance Company Limited **(2)**
Tel.: (44) 2077436800
Emp.: 140
Property & Liability Insurance Services
N.A.I.C.S.: 524126
Tina Booth (Asst VP-Professional Indemnity)
Carl Anthony Kearney (Chief Actuary & Chief Risk Officer)
Rhonda Buege (VP-Underwriting)
Mark Armstrong (Mgr-Underwriting-Tech & Cyber Risk)
Callum English (Mgr-Underwriting-Southern Reg)
Phil Robey (Mgr-Underwriting-Marine)
Justin Godman (Mgr-Underwriting)
Dave Sewell (Mgr-Underwriting)
Asha Patel (Mgr-Underwriting)
Natalie Boardman (Mgr-Underwriting)
Ingrid Woodward (Head-IT & Ops)
Lisa Skeels (Head-HH)
Matthew Bunting (Head-Claims-Intl)
Raphael Borrel (Dir-Risks-Hardy)

Subsidiary (Domestic):

Surety Bonding Company of America **(2)**
101 S Reid St Ste 300, Sioux Falls, SD 57103-7030
Tel.: (605) 336-0850
Property & Casualty Insurance Services
N.A.I.C.S.: 524126

The Continental Insurance Company **(2)**
8049 W Chester Pike, Upper Darby, PA 19082-1317
Tel.: (610) 853-2100
Web Site: http://www.continentalins.com
Fire Insurance Services
N.A.I.C.S.: 524113

Transportation Insurance Company **(2)**
333 S Wabash Ave, Chicago, IL 60685-4107
Tel.: (312) 822-5000
Fire & Casualty Insurance Services
N.A.I.C.S.: 524126

Diamond Offshore Development Company **(1)**
15415 Katy Fwy Ste 100, Houston, TX 77094
Tel.: (281) 492-5300
Web Site: http://www.diamondoffshore.com
Emp.: 300
Drilling Oil & Gas Wells Services
N.A.I.C.S.: 213111

Loews Hotels Holding Corporation **(1)**
667 Madison Ave, New York, NY 10065 **(100%)**
Tel.: (212) 521-2000
Web Site: https://www.loewshotels.com
Sales Range: $200-249.9 Million
Emp.: 2,000
Hotel & Resort Operator
N.A.I.C.S.: 721110
Jonathan M. Tisch (Exec Chm)
Alexander H. Tisch (Pres & CEO)
Alex Tisch (Pres)

Subsidiary (Domestic):

Don CeSar Resort Hotel Ltd. **(2)**
3400 Gulf Blvd, Saint Pete Beach, FL 33706
Tel.: (727) 360-1881
Web Site: http://www.doncesar.com
Sales Range: $25-49.9 Million
Emp.: 300
Hotel & Motel Services
N.A.I.C.S.: 721110

Subsidiary (Non-US):

LJC Development Corp. **(2)**
1425 Rue De La Montagne, Montreal, H3G 1Z3, QC, Canada **(100%)**
Tel.: (514) 285-5555
Web Site: http://www.loewshotel.com
Sales Range: $1-9.9 Million
Emp.: 115
Hotels & Motels
N.A.I.C.S.: 721110
Mathew Larochelle (Mng Dir)

Unit (Domestic):

Loews Santa Monica Beach Hotel **(2)**
1700 Ocean Ave, Santa Monica, CA 90401
Tel.: (310) 458-6700
Web Site: http://www.loewshotels.com
Emp.: 250
Hotel Operator
N.A.I.C.S.: 721110

Loews Vanderbilt Plaza Hotel **(2)**
2100 W End Ave, Nashville, TN 37203 **(100%)**
Tel.: (615) 320-1700
Web Site: http://www.loewshotels.com
Sales Range: $10-24.9 Million
Emp.: 400
Hotels & Motels
N.A.I.C.S.: 721110

The Regency Hotel **(2)**
540 Park Ave & 61st St, New York, NY 10065 **(100%)**
Tel.: (212) 759-4100
Web Site: http://www.loewshotels.com
Sales Range: $1-9.9 Million
Emp.: 100
Hotel
N.A.I.C.S.: 721199
Simon Mais (Mng Dir)

LOGAN CLAY PRODUCTS CO.
201 S Walnut St, Logan, OH 43138
Tel.: (740) 385-2184   **OH**
Web Site:
  https://www.loganclaypipe.com
LGNC—(OTCIQ)
Clay Products Mfr
N.A.I.C.S.: 327120
Barton A. Hall (Chm)

LOGAN RIDGE FINANCE CORPORATION
650 Madison Ave 3rd Fl, New York, NY 10022
Tel.: (212) 891-2880   **MD**
Web Site:
  https://www.loganridgefinance.com
Year Founded: 2013
LRFC—(NASDAQ)
Rev.: $14,927,000
Assets: $214,710,000
Liabilities: $119,705,000
Net Worth: $95,005,000
Earnings: ($1,162,000)
Fiscal Year-end: 12/31/22

Investment Services
N.A.I.C.S.: 523999
Patrick Schafer (Chief Investment Officer)
David Held (Chief Compliance Officer)
Brandon Satoren (CFO, Chief Acctg Officer, Treas & Sec)
Ted Goldthorpe (Pres & CEO)

Subsidiaries:

Source Support Services, Inc. **(1)**
3505 Newpoint Pl Ste 450, Lawrenceville, GA 30043
Tel.: (678) 835-6100
Web Site: http://www.sourcesupport.com
Research & Development in Biotechnology
N.A.I.C.S.: 541713
Christina Bowden (Sr Dir-HR)
Mark Oldfield (Founder)
John Trautwein (Chief Customer Officer)
Steve Snyder (CFO)
Mike Stolz (CEO)
Eric Lomascolo (Sr VP-Tech & Product Mgmt)
Jeff Nesler (Sr VP-Svcs Delivery)
Regina Caudle (VP-Logistics)
Angie Sligh (VP-Quality)
Uriel Bowdre (Sr Dir-Fin & Sls Ops)
Ivan Ruyle (Dir-Customer Success)

LOGANSPORT FINANCIAL CORP.
723 E Broadway, Logansport, IN 46947
Tel.: (574) 722-3855   **IN**
Web Site:
  https://www.logansportsavings.com
Year Founded: 1925
LOGN—(OTCQB)
Bank Holding Company
N.A.I.C.S.: 551111
Chad Higgins (CEO)
Brian J. Morrill (Bd of Dirs & Chm)
Kristie Richey (CFO)
Deion Rennewanz (Controller)

Subsidiaries:

Logansport Savings Bank **(1)**
723 E Broadway, Logansport, IN 46947
Tel.: (574) 722-3855
Web Site: http://www.logansportsavings.com
Sales Range: $10-24.9 Million
Bank
N.A.I.C.S.: 522180
Chad R. Geer (Exec VP)
Chad Higgins (CEO)
Brian J. Morrill (Chm)

LOGICMARK, INC.
2801 Diode Ln, Louisville, KY 40299
Tel.: (502) 442-7911   **DE**
Web Site: https://www.logicmark.com
Year Founded: 2011
LGMK—(NASDAQ)
Rev.: $11,916,482
Assets: $25,641,124
Liabilities: $4,661,105
Net Worth: $20,980,019
Earnings: ($7,253,421)
Emp.: 25
Fiscal Year-end: 12/31/22
Biometric-Based Mobile Security Software Publisher
N.A.I.C.S.: 513210
Chia-Lin Simmons (CEO)
Mark Archer (Interim CFO)

Subsidiaries:

3D-ID, LLC **(1)**
1721 Winding Rdg Cir SE, Palm Bay, FL 32909
Tel.: (203) 305-3568
Software Publishing Services
N.A.I.C.S.: 561621

LogicMark, LLC **(1)**
2801 Diode Ln, Louisville, KY 40299
Tel.: (703) 934-7934
Web Site: https://www.logicmark.com

Emp.: 15
Personal Emergency Response Systems
Mfr
N.A.I.C.S.: 423450
Kevin O'Connor *(Pres)*

LOGIQ, INC.
85 Broad St 16-079, New York, NY
10004
Tel.: (659) 366-2322   DE
Web Site: http://www.logiq.com
LGIQ—(OTCIQ)
Rev.: $37,346,859
Assets: $34,186,409
Liabilities: $4,611,088
Net Worth: $29,575,321
Earnings: ($20,126,787)
Emp.: 37
Fiscal Year-end: 12/31/21
E-commerce Software Services; Mobile Application Developer
N.A.I.C.S.: 513210
Brent Y. Suen *(Co-Founder, Chm & CEO)*
Lionel Khuat Leok Choong *(CFO)*

Subsidiaries:

Push Interactive, LLC   (1)
225 Thomas Ave N, Minneapolis, MN
55405
Web Site: https://www.pushint.com
Consumer Offering Services
N.A.I.C.S.: 812990
Chris Jahnke *(Co-Founder)*

LOGISTICS INNOVATION TECHNOLOGIES CORP.
3348 Peachtree Rd Ste 700, Atlanta,
GA 30326
Tel.: (678) 954-4822   DE
Year Founded: 2021
LITT—(NASDAQ)
Rev.: $19,111,200
Assets: $345,498,604
Liabilities: $357,896,311
Net Worth: ($12,397,707)
Earnings: $16,588,089
Emp.: 2
Fiscal Year-end: 12/31/22
Investment Services
N.A.I.C.S.: 523999
Alan Gershenhorn *(Chm & CEO)*
Isaac Applbaum *(CFO)*

LOGITECH INTERNATIONAL S.A.
3930 N 1st St, San Jose, CA 95134
Tel.: (510) 795-8500   CA
Web Site: http://www.logitech.com
Year Founded: 1981
LOGI—(NASDAQ)
Rev.: $4,298,467,000
Assets: $3,604,704,000
Liabilities: $1,371,051,000
Net Worth: $2,233,653,000
Earnings: $612,143,000
Emp.: 7,300
Fiscal Year-end: 03/31/24
Computer Peripherals Designer, Mfr
& Marketer
N.A.I.C.S.: 334118
Wendy Becker *(Chm)*
Hanneke Faber *(CEO)*
Samantha Harnett *(Gen Counsel)*
Nate Melihercik *(Head-Global IR)*
Nicole Kenyon *(Head-Global Corp & Internal Comm)*
Hanneke Faber *(CEO)*
Erin M. Chin *(CMO-Streamers & Creators Bus)*
Prakash Arunkundrum *(COO)*
Matteo Anversa *(CFO)*

Subsidiaries:

Liminal Collective, Inc.   (1)
7700 Gateway Blvd, Newark, CA 94560
Tel.: (646) 454-3200

Web Site: http://www.liminalcollective.co
Event Management Services
N.A.I.C.S.: 561920
Andy Walshe *(Partner & Chief Performance Officer)*
Hoby Darling *(Partner)*
Jurgen Heitmann *(Partner)*
Coleman Ruiz *(Partner)*

Logicool Co., Ltd.   (1)
4-3-1 Toranomon Shiroyama Trust Tower
14f, Minato-ku, Tokyo, 105-0001, Japan
Tel.: (81) 363857100
Web Site: http://www.logicool.co.jp
Computer Peripheral Equipment Mfr
N.A.I.C.S.: 334118

Logitech Asia Pacific Limited   (1)
18/F Cambridge House Taikoo Place 979
Kings Road, Quarry Bay, China (Hong Kong)
Tel.: (852) 28215900
Holding Company; Regional Managing Office; Computer Peripheral Equipment Mfr
N.A.I.C.S.: 551112

Subsidiary (Non-US):

Logitech Australia Computer Peripherals Pty, Limited   (2)
103 Alexander St Crows Nest, Sydney,
Sydney, 2065, NSW, Australia
Tel.: (61) 297648300
Web Site: http://www.logitech.com
Computer Peripheral Equipment Mfr
N.A.I.C.S.: 334118

Logitech Engineering & Designs India
Private Limited   (2)
Olympia Tech Park 01 SIDCO Industrial Estate 10th Floor Level 11, Fortius Block
Guindy, Chennai, 600032, India
Tel.: (91) 4442432000
Web Site: https://www.logitech.com
Sales Range: $50-74.9 Million
Emp.: 200
Computer Peripheral Equipment Mfr
N.A.I.C.S.: 334118

Logitech Far East Ltd.   (2)
2 Creation Road IV Science Based Industrial Park, Hsin-chu, 300, Taiwan   (100%)
Tel.: (886) 35778241
Sales Range: $100-124.9 Million
Emp.: 500
N.A.I.C.S.: 334111
Louis Kuo *(Gen Mgr)*

Subsidiary (Domestic):

Logitech Hong Kong, Limited   (2)
Unit 2907-A 29/F Cable TV Tower 9 Hoi
Shing Road, Tsuen Wan, China (Hong Kong)
Tel.: (852) 38984910
Web Site: https://www.logitech.com
Computer Peripheral Equipment Mfr
N.A.I.C.S.: 334118

Subsidiary (Non-US):

Logitech Korea Ltd.   (2)
402B CCMM B/D 12, Yeoido-Dong Young
Deung Po-Ku, Seoul, Korea (South)
Tel.: (82) 27611207
Computer Peripheral Equipment Mfr
N.A.I.C.S.: 334118

Logitech Technology (Suzhou) Co.,
Ltd.   (2)
3 Songshan Road High Technology, High
New District, Suzhou, 215129, China
Tel.: (86) 51266622666
Computer Peripheral Equipment Mfr
N.A.I.C.S.: 334118
Guerrino De Luca *(Chm)*

Logitech Europe SA   (1)
EPFL - Quartier de l'Innovation Daniel Borel
Innovation Center, 1015, Lausanne, Switzerland
Tel.: (41) 218635111
Web Site: https://www.logitech.com
Sales Range: $100-124.9 Million
Emp.: 250
Holding Company; Regional Managing Office; Computer Peripheral Developer & Mfr
N.A.I.C.S.: 551112
Preisig Antoine *(Gen Mgr)*

Subsidiary (US):

JayBird, LLC   (2)
2700 Rasmussen Rd Ste 100, Park City,
UT 84098
Tel.: (800) 601-1372
Web Site: http://jaybirdsport.com
Bluetooth Devices
N.A.I.C.S.: 517810
Judd Armstrong *(Founder)*

Subsidiary (Domestic):

Logitech (Streaming Media) SA   (2)
Quartier de l innovation, 1015, Lausanne,
Vaud, Switzerland
Tel.: (41) 218635111
Electric Equipment Mfr
N.A.I.C.S.: 334416

Subsidiary (Non-US):

Logitech France SAS   (2)
168 Bis - 170 Rue Raymond, Losserand,
75014, Paris, France
Tel.: (33) 144589898
Web Site: http://www.logitech.fr
Computer Peripheral Equipment Whslr
N.A.I.C.S.: 423430

Logitech GmbH   (2)
Clarita-Bernhard-Str 18, 81289, Munich,
Germany
Tel.: (49) 89894670
Web Site: http://www.logitech.de
Sales Range: $25-49.9 Million
Emp.: 30
Computer Peripheral Developer & Mfr
N.A.I.C.S.: 334118

Logitech Hellas MEPE   (2)
Everest Eos 2, Neo Psychiko, Athens,
Greece
Tel.: (30) 210 6774512
Web Site: http://www.logitech.com
Emp.: 2
Computer Peripheral Equipment Whslr
N.A.I.C.S.: 423430

Subsidiary (Non-US):

Logitech Ireland Services Limited   (3)
3400 Airport Business Park Kinsale Road,
Cork, Ireland
Tel.: (353) 214620800
Computer Peripheral Equipment Mfr
N.A.I.C.S.: 334118

Subsidiary (Non-US):

Logitech Italia SRL   (2)
Via dei Carracci 5, 20149, Milan, Italy
Tel.: (39) 026693872
Web Site: https://www.logitechsrl.com
Electronic Data Processing Services
N.A.I.C.S.: 518210

Logitech Nordic AB   (2)
Torsgatan 8, 111 23, Stockholm, Sweden
Tel.: (46) 850163283
Web Site: http://www.logitech.com
Emp.: 11
Information Technology Consulting Services
N.A.I.C.S.: 541512

Subsidiary (Domestic):

Logitech Schweiz AG   (2)
Baendliweg 20, 8048, Zurich, Switzerland
Tel.: (41) 433117770
Web Site: http://www.logitech.com
Sales Range: $25-49.9 Million
Emp.: 11
Computer Peripheral Equipment Distr
N.A.I.C.S.: 423430

Subsidiary (Non-US):

Logitech UK Ltd   (2)
Erskine Ferry Road, Old Kilpatrick, Glasgow, G60 5EU, United Kingdom   (100%)
Tel.: (44) 1389875444
Web Site: https://www.logitech.uk.com
Sales Range: $25-49.9 Million
Emp.: 15
N.A.I.C.S.: 334111

Logitech Inc.   (1)
7700 Gateway Blvd, Newark, CA
94560   (100%)
Tel.: (646) 454-3200

Web Site: https://www.logitech.com
Sales Range: $1-4.9 Billion
Computer Peripheral Developer, Servicer &
Marketer
N.A.I.C.S.: 334118

Subsidiary (Domestic):

3Dconnexion Inc.   (2)
6505 Kaiser Dr, Fremont, CA 94555
Tel.: (510) 713-6000
Web Site: http://www.3dconnexion.com
Sales Range: $25-49.9 Million
Emp.: 20
Computer Peripheral Developer & Mfr
N.A.I.C.S.: 334118

Subsidiary (Non-US):

3Dconnexion GmbH   (3)
Clarita-Bernhard-Strasse 18, 81249, Munich, Germany
Tel.: (49) 8989745420
Web Site: https://www.3dconnexion.de
Sales Range: $25-49.9 Million
Computer Peripheral Developer & Mfr
N.A.I.C.S.: 334118

Subsidiary (Domestic):

Astro Gaming, Inc.   (2)
348 6th St, San Francisco, CA 94103
Tel.: (415) 354-6300
Web Site: http://www.astrogaming.com
Emp.: 25
Children Toys Mfr
N.A.I.C.S.: 339930
Gordon Rubenstein *(Co-Founder)*

LifeSize Communications, Inc.   (2)
1601 S Mopac Expy Ste 100, Austin, TX
78746
Tel.: (512) 347-9300
Web Site: https://www.lifesize.com
Sales Range: $75-99.9 Million
Videoconferencing Equipment Mfr
N.A.I.C.S.: 334310

Subsidiary (Non-US):

LifeSize Communications Limited   (3)
The Gherkin Building 28th Floor 30 St
Mary's Axe, London, EC3A 8BF, United
Kingdom
Tel.: (44) 2073376016
Web Site: http://www.lifesize.com
Computer Peripheral Equipment Mfr
N.A.I.C.S.: 334118

LifeSize Communications, GmbH   (3)
Nymphenburgerstr, 80335, Munich, Germany
Tel.: (49) 8912228990
Web Site: http://www.lifesize.com
Sales Range: $25-49.9 Million
Emp.: 25
Computer Peripheral Equipment Mfr
N.A.I.C.S.: 334118

Logitech Middle East FZ-LLC   (1)
Office 305 Dubai Internet City 3, Dubai,
United Arab Emirates
Tel.: (971) 43636886
Web Site: https://www.logitechg.com
Emp.: 4
Computer Peripheral Equipment Distr
N.A.I.C.S.: 423430

Meetio AB   (1)
Tel.: (46) 101019560
Web Site: https://www.meetio.com
Information Technology Consulting Services
N.A.I.C.S.: 541690

Meetio Inc.   (1)
700 Sw 5th Ave, Portland, OR 97204-2000
Tel.: (971) 205-6170
Information Technology Consulting Services
N.A.I.C.S.: 541690

LONGBOARD PHARMACEUTICALS, INC.
4275 Executive Sq Ste 950, La Jolla,
CA 92037
Tel.: (619) 592-9775   DE
Web Site:
https://www.longboardpharma.com
Year Founded: 2020

Longboard Pharmaceuticals, Inc.—(Continued)

LBPH—(NASDAQ)
Rev.: $837,000
Assets: $70,616,000
Liabilities: $9,146,000
Net Worth: $61,470,000
Earnings: ($43,945,000)
Emp.: 32
Fiscal Year-end: 12/31/22
Research & Development in Biotechnology (except Nanobiotechnology)
N.A.I.C.S.: 541714
Randall E. Kaye (Chief Medical Officer)
Kevin R. Lind (Pres & CEO)
Brandi L. Roberts (CFO)
Anne Danks (VP & Head-Preclinical Dev)
Chad Orevillo (VP & Head-Ops)
Dolly Parasrampuria (VP & Head-Clinical Pharmacology)
Jodi Parsons (VP & Head-Regulatory Affairs)
Steven W. Spector (Gen Counsel)

LONGEVERON INC.

1951 NW 7th Ave Ste 520, Miami, FL 33136
Tel.: (305) 909-0840   DE
Web Site:
   https://www.longeveron.com
Year Founded: 2014
LGVN—(NASDAQ)
Rev.: $1,222,000
Assets: $27,413,000
Liabilities: $6,910,000
Net Worth: $20,503,000
Earnings: ($18,835,000)
Emp.: 19
Fiscal Year-end: 12/31/22
Biotechnology Research & Development Services
N.A.I.C.S.: 541714
Wa'el Hashad (CEO)
Joshua M. Hare (Founder, Chm & Chief Science Officer)
Paul Lehr (Gen Counsel & Sec)
Lisa McClain-Moss (Sr Dir-Mfg)
Anthony Oliva (Sr. VP-Scientific Affairs)
Donald M. Soffer (Co-Founder)
Jerome Bailey (VP-Bus Ops)
Nataliya Agafonova (Chief Medical Officer)
Lisa Locklear (CFO, Principal Acctg Officer & Exec VP)

LONGFIN CORP.

16-017 85 Broad St, New York, NY 10004
Tel.: (646) 202-9550   DE
Web Site:
   https://www.longfincorp.com
Year Founded: 2017
LFIN—(NASDAQ)
Rev.: $75,048,000
Assets: $178,259,000
Liabilities: $39,293,000
Net Worth: $138,966,000
Earnings: ($26,369,000)
Emp.: 10
Fiscal Year-end: 12/31/17
Financial Technology Services
N.A.I.C.S.: 523160

LONGWEN GROUP CORP.

7702 E Doubletree Ranch Rd Ste 300, Scottsdale, AZ 85258
Tel.: (480) 607-4393   NV
Year Founded: 1980
LWLW—(OTCQB)
Rev.: $41,137
Assets: $405,661
Liabilities: $134,706
Net Worth: $270,955
Earnings: ($746,426)

Emp.: 10
Fiscal Year-end: 12/31/22
Investment Services
N.A.I.C.S.: 523999
Xi Zhen Ye (Chm, Pres, CEO & CFO)

LOOKSMART GROUP, INC.

2850 W Horizon Ridge Pkwy Ste 200, Henderson, NV 89052
Tel.: (646) 236-4638   NV
Web Site: http://www.looksmart.com
Year Founded: 1995
LKST—(OTCIQ)
Advertising Solutions Services
N.A.I.C.S.: 541810
Michael Onghai (CEO, Treas & Sec)

Subsidiaries:

LookSmart Canada Ltd   (1)
305 King St W 7th Fl, Kitchener, N2G 1B8, ON, Canada
Tel.: (415) 348-7435
Sales Range: $10-24.9 Million
Data Processing & Related Services
N.A.I.C.S.: 518210

LOOP MEDIA, INC.

2600 W Olive Ave Ste 5470, Burbank, CA 91505
Tel.: (213) 436-2100   NV
Web Site: https://www.loop.tv
Year Founded: 2015
LPTV—(OTCIQ)
Rev.: $22,254,959
Assets: $7,511,437
Liabilities: $25,295,600
Net Worth: ($17,784,163)
Earnings: ($24,495,602)
Emp.: 40
Fiscal Year-end: 09/30/24
Multichannel Streaming Platform
N.A.I.C.S.: 512199
Neil T. Watanabe (CFO)
Jon M. Nierman (Chm & CEO)
Liam McCallum (Co-Founder)
Andy Schoun (Head-Loop Media Studios)
Andy Schuon (Head)
Patrick Sheil (Corp Counsel & Head)
James J. Cerna Jr. (Head)
Shawn Driscoll (Co-Founder)
Bob Gruters (Chief Revenue Officer)
Jon M. Nierman (Co-Founder)
James J. Cerna Jr. (CFO)

LORD GLOBAL CORPORATION

318 N Carson St Ste 208, Carson City, NV 89701
Tel.: (816) 304-2686   NV
Year Founded: 2011
LRDG—(OTCEM)
Rev.: $888
Assets: $1,666
Liabilities: $1,214,370
Net Worth: ($1,212,704)
Earnings: ($490,715)
Fiscal Year-end: 07/31/19
Motion Pictures, Television Programs & DVDs Production
N.A.I.C.S.: 512110
Joseph Frontiere (CEO)
Carmine Thomas Biscardi III (Pres)

LORDSTOWN MOTORS CORP.

2300 Hallock Young Rd, Lordstown, OH 44481
Tel.: (234) 285-4001   DE
Web Site:
   https://www.lordstownmotors.com
Year Founded: 2018
RIDE—(NASDAQ)
Rev.: $194,000
Assets: $452,312,000
Liabilities: $100,541,000
Net Worth: $351,771,000
Earnings: ($282,665,000)

Emp.: 260
Fiscal Year-end: 12/31/22
Electric Pickup Trucks Mfr
N.A.I.C.S.: 336110
Daniel A. Ninivaggi (Chm)
Mary Ann Sicafuse (VP-HR)
Shane Brown (Chief Production Officer)
Carter Driscoll (VP-Dev, Capital Markets & IR)
Adam B. Kroll (CFO, Principal Acctg Officer & Exec VP)
Edward T. Hightower (Pres & CEO)
Donna Bell (Exec VP-Product Creation, Engrg & Supply Chain)
Andrew Reyntjes (Sr VP-Sls, Service & Mktg)
Jill Coniglio-Kirk (VP-People & Culture)
Shea Burns (Sr VP-Ops)
Melissa Leonard (Gen Counsel, Sec & Exec VP)

LOTTERY.COM INC.

20808 State Hwy 71 W Unit B, Spicewood, TX 78669   DE
Year Founded: 2016
LTRY—(NASDAQ)
Rev.: $6,779,057
Assets: $79,380,253
Liabilities: $17,563,768
Net Worth: $61,816,485
Earnings: ($60,383,265)
Emp.: 10
Fiscal Year-end: 12/31/22
Lottery Ticket Management Services
N.A.I.C.S.: 713290
Robert J. Stubblefield (CFO)
Gregory Potts (COO)
Matthew McGahan (Chm, Pres, CEO & Sec)

LOUD TECHNOLOGIES INC.

16220 Wood-Red Rd NE, Woodinville, WA 98072
Tel.: (425) 487-4333   WA
Web Site:
   http://www.loudtechinc.com
Year Founded: 1988
LTEC—(OTCIQ)
Sales Range: $200-249.9 Million
Emp.: 533
Professional Audio Equipment Mfr
N.A.I.C.S.: 334220
Case Kuehn (CFO & Sr VP)
Mark Graham (Chm, Pres & CEO)
Jeff Rocha (VP & Gen Mgr)
Alex Nelson (Pres-Music Gear Grp)
Larry Pendergrass (Sr VP-Engrg-Music Gear Grp)
Matt Redmon (Dir-Channel Mktg-MG Brands)
Don Young (VP-Mktg-MG Brands)
Loren Robinson (Dir-Sls & Independent Accts-Mackie & Ampeg Brands)
Henri Cohen (VP-Worldwide Sls)
Kelsea Robson (Dir-Sls-US Natl Accts)
Jamie Engen (CEO)

Subsidiaries:

Mackie Designs S.P.A.   (1)
Via Serraris 2C, 42029, Maurizio, Reggio Nell Emilia, Italy   (100%)
Tel.: (39) 0522354111
Web Site: http://www.mackie.com
Sales Range: $100-124.9 Million
Mfr of Professional Audio Equipment
N.A.I.C.S.: 334310

LOUISIANA FOOD COMPANY

17485 Opportunity Dr Ste E, Baton Rouge, LA 70817   NV
Year Founded: 2010
LUSI—(OTCIQ)

Specialty Food Products, Sauces & Coffee Producer
N.A.I.C.S.: 311999
David Loflin (Pres & CEO)
Waddell D. Loflin (CFO, Sec & VP)

LOUISIANA-PACIFIC CORPORATION

1610 W End Ave Ste 200, Nashville, TN 37203
Tel.: (615) 986-5600   DE
Web Site: https://www.lpcorp.com
Year Founded: 1973
LPX—(NYSE)
Rev.: $2,581,000,000
Assets: $2,437,000,000
Liabilities: $880,000,000
Net Worth: $1,557,000,000
Earnings: $178,000,000
Emp.: 4,100
Fiscal Year-end: 12/31/23
Building Products; Lumber, OSB, Wood, Aluminum, Panel Products, Engineered I-Joists, Cellulose Insulation
N.A.I.C.S.: 321113
William Bradley Southern (Chm & CEO)
Mike Blosser (Sr VP-Mfg Svcs)
Jason Ringblom (Exec VP & Gen Mgr-Siding)
Craig Sichling (VP-Specialty Sls & Mktg)
Alan J. M. Haughie (CFO & Exec VP)
Jimmy Mason (Exec VP & Gen Mgr-OSB)
Robin Hirsch Everhart (Chief HR & Transformation Officer & Sr VP)
Nicole C. Daniel (Gen Counsel, Corp Sec & Sr VP)
Derek Doyle (Chief Acctg Officer, VP & Controller)
Frederick Price (Gen Mgr-South America)
Libby Berman (VP)
Bob Hopkins (Treas)
Craig Miles (VP)
Jeff Sweet (VP)
Jeff Yelle (CIO)

Subsidiaries:

Entekra, LLC   (1)
945 E Whitmore Ave, Modesto, CA 95358
Tel.: (209) 624-1630
Web Site: https://www.entekra.com
Construction Materials Mfr
N.A.I.C.S.: 333120
Gerard McCaughey (Chm, CEO & Sr VP-Supply Chain)
Bran Keogh (COO)
April Murray (CFO)
Alan Fannin (Sr VP-Engrg)

LPS Corporation   (1)
250 State Rte 23, Butler, NJ 07405
Tel.: (973) 838-1200
Web Site: https://www.lpscorpsecure.com
Security & Fire System Installation Services
N.A.I.C.S.: 238210

Louisiana-Pacific Argentina S.R.L.   (1)
Web Site: https://lpargentina.com.ar
Construction Services
N.A.I.C.S.: 236220

Louisiana-Pacific Chile S.A.   (1)
Av Santa Clara 085 8th floor City Park 2 Building Huechuraba, Santiago, Chile
Tel.: (56) 224142200
Web Site: https://lpchile.cl
Wood Engineering Product Mfr & Distr
N.A.I.C.S.: 321219

Louisiana-Pacific Colombia S.A.S.   (1)
Calle 100 N 7-33 piso 14 Edificio Capital

Tower Torre 1, Bogota, Colombia
Web Site: http://lpcolombia.com.co
Construction Services
N.A.I.C.S.: 236220

Louisiana-Pacific Paraguay S.A. **(1)**
Pope John XXIII Corner John Max Boettner
Office 9C Park Plaza Building, Park Square
Building, Asuncion, Paraguay
Tel.: (595) 985729946
Web Site: https://lpparaguay.com.py
Construction Wood Product Mfr
N.A.I.C.S.: 321992

Louisiana-Pacific Southern Div. **(1)**
100 Interstate 45 N, Conroe, TX 77301-
2890
Tel.: (936) 756-0541
Sales Range: $50-74.9 Million
Emp.: 30
Produces Building Products; Lumber, OSB,
Wood & Aluminum Doors, Wood, Aluminum
& Vinyl Windows, Pulp, Panel Products,
Plywood, Engineered I-Joists, Fiber Gyp-
sum, Wallboard, Cellulose Insulation
N.A.I.C.S.: 321918

Prefinished Staining Products
Inc. **(1)**
4575 Anston Rd, Green Bay, WI 54313
Tel.: (920) 865-1144
Web Site:
  http://www.prefinishedstaining.com
Exterior Siding Product Distr
N.A.I.C.S.: 423330
Aaron Matuszewski *(Pres)*

LOWE'S COMPANIES, INC.
1000 Lowes Blvd, Mooresville, NC
28117
Tel.: (704) 758-1000   NC
Web Site: https://www.lowes.com
Year Founded: 1946
LOW—(NYSE)
Rev.: $86,377,000,000
Assets: $41,795,000,000
Liabilities: $56,845,000,000
Net Worth: ($15,050,000,000)
Earnings: $7,726,000,000
Emp.: 168,000
Fiscal Year-end: 02/02/24
Household Products Mfr
N.A.I.C.S.: 551112
J. Todd Bleckley *(Sr VP & Gen Mgr-
Mdsg-Hardlines)*
Donald E. Frieson *(Exec VP-Supply
Chain)*
Jeff R. Vining *(Chief Compliance Offi-
cer, Sr VP & Deputy Gen Counsel)*
William P. Boltz *(Exec VP-Mdsg)*
Seemantini Godbole *(Chief Digital &
Info Officer & Exec VP)*
Anthony T. Hurst *(Sr VP-Pro Svcs &
Intl)*
Vincent Scalese *(Sr VP-Store Ops)*
Margi Vagell *(Sr VP & Gen Mgr-
Mdsg-Home Decor)*
Bryan G. Audiss *(Pres-North Div)*
Janice Dupre Little *(Exec VP-HR)*
Neelima V. Sharma *(Sr VP-Tech,
E-Commerce, Mktg & Mdsg)*
David L. Shoop *(Sr VP-Tech Stores,
Corp Svcs, Pro & Svcs)*
Quonta D. Vance *(Sr VP & Gen Mgr-
Mdsg & Building Products)*
Juliette W. Pryor *(Chief Legal Officer,
Sec & Exec VP)*
Sarah Dodd *(Sr VP-Mdsg-Global)*
Ankur Mittal *(Sr VP-Tech)*
Mike Sablowski *(Sr VP-Inventory, Re-
plenishment & Plng)*
Brandon J. Sink *(CFO & Exec VP)*
Amaresh Siva *(Sr VP-Innovation,
Data & Supply Chain Tech)*
Jennifer E. Wilson *(Sr VP-Enterprise
Brand & Mktg)*
Joseph Michael McFarland III *(Exec
VP-Stores)*
Dan Clayton Griggs Jr. *(Chief Acctg
Officer & VP)*
Marvin R. Ellison *(Chm, Pres & CEO)*

Subsidiaries:

Boomerang Commerce, Inc. **(1)**
2100 Geng Rd Ste 210, Palo Alto, CA
94303
Tel.: (415) 475-9745
Web Site: https://www.commerceiq.ai
Ecommerce Channel Services
N.A.I.C.S.: 423440
Guru Hariharan *(CEO)*
Prasun Kumar *(VP-Engrg)*
Adrian Seet *(VP-Fin)*
Nate Palafox-Just *(VP-Customer Success)*

Lowe's Home Centers, LLC **(1)**
509 River Hwy, Mooresville, NC 28117
Tel.: (704) 660-7177
Web Site: http://www.lowes.com
Home Center Operator
N.A.I.C.S.: 444110

Subsidiary (Non-US):

Lowe's Home Centres (Canada)
Inc. **(2)**
5160 Yonge Street Suite 200, North York,
M2N 6L9, ON, Canada
Web Site: http://www.lowes.ca
Home Center Operator
N.A.I.C.S.: 444110

Subsidiary (Domestic):

RONA Inc. **(3)**
220 chemin du Tremblay, Boucherville, J4B
8H7, QC, Canada
Tel.: (514) 599-5900
Web Site: https://www.rona.ca
Hardware, Home Improvement & Gardening
Products Retailer
N.A.I.C.S.: 444110

Subsidiary (Domestic):

Maintenance Supply Headquarters,
LP **(2)**
6910 Brasada Dr, Houston, TX 77085
Tel.: (281) 983-6300
Web Site: https://www.lowesprosupply.com
Emp.: 570
Maintenance Equipment & Supplies Mer-
chant Whslr
N.A.I.C.S.: 423850

Orchard Supply Company, LLC **(2)**
6450 Via Del Oro, San Jose, CA
95119   **(100%)**
Tel.: (408) 281-3500
Web Site: http://www.osh.com
Sales Range: $650-699.9 Million
Emp.: 5,000
Hardware & Garden Supplies Stores Opera-
tor
N.A.I.C.S.: 444140
David I. Bogage *(Sr VP-HR)*

LOWELL FARMS INC.
19 Quail Run Cir Ste B, Salinas, CA
93907
Tel.: (831) 998-8214
Web Site: https://lowellfarms.com
Year Founded: 2005
LOWLF—(OTCQB)
Rev.: $43,535,000
Assets: $118,823,000
Liabilities: $70,706,000
Net Worth: $48,117,000
Earnings: ($24,564,000)
Emp.: 123
Fiscal Year-end: 12/31/22
Mineral Exploration Services
N.A.I.C.S.: 212290
Mark Ainsworth *(Founder & CEO)*
Ann Lawrence *(Chm)*

LPL FINANCIAL HOLDINGS INC.
4707 Executive Dr, San Diego, CA
92121
Tel.: (617) 897-4574   DE
Web Site: https://www.lpl.com
Year Founded: 1989
LPLA—(NASDAQ)
Rev.: $10,052,848,000
Assets: $10,385,480,000

Liabilities: $8,306,501,000
Net Worth: $2,078,979,000
Earnings: $1,066,250,000
Emp.: 8,400
Fiscal Year-end: 12/31/23
Holding Company; Investment Advi-
sory, Brokerage & Asset Management
Services
N.A.I.C.S.: 551112
Sallie R. Larsen *(Mng Dir & Chief
Human Capital Officer)*
George Burt White *(Chief Investment
Officer & Mng Dir-Investor & Invest-
ment Solution)*
Michelle Oroschakoff *(Mng Dir &
Chief Legal Officer)*
Matthew J. Audette *(Mng Dir, CFO,
Principal Acctg Officer & Head-Bus
Ops)*
Brent B. Simonich *(Chief Risk Officer,
Treas & Exec VP)*
Matthew Enyedi *(Mng Dir-Bus Solu-
tions)*
Cathrine Cotman *(Sr VP-Corporate
Real Estate)*
Greg Gates *(Mng Dir)*
Aneri Jambusaria *(Mng Dir)*
Richard Steinmeier *(CEO)*

Subsidiaries:

Allen & Company of Florida, Inc. **(1)**
1401 S Florida Ave, Lakeland, FL 33803
Tel.: (863) 688-9000
Web Site: http://www.alleninvestments.com
Investment Banking & Advisory Services
N.A.I.C.S.: 523150
Keith Albritton *(VP)*
Laura J. Hawley *(Sr VP)*
Michael H. Wright *(Sr VP)*
Ralph C. Allen *(Chm & VP)*
Carol M. Zitzelberger *(VP)*
Bill Sassano *(Mgr-Operations)*
Terry Tolbert *(VP)*
Lorin Bice *(VP)*
Chris Hammond *(Portfolio Mgr)*
Cynthia Marotz *(VP)*
Fred Lopez *(Mng Dir)*
Ginny Houghton *(VP)*
Isaac Hartmann *(Mng Dir)*
Kurt Elmhorst *(Sr VP)*
Souri Vongvirat *(Sr VP)*
Steve McTaggart *(Mng Dir & VP)*
Thomas Bixby *(VP)*
William Slover *(VP)*
Diane Burr *(VP)*
Kyle Cobia *(VP)*
John Campbell *(VP)*
Eric Greenhow *(Sr VP)*
Brad Stainsby *(VP)*
Michael Walker *(VP)*
Bob Sullivan *(VP)*
Dana Hurley *(VP)*

Blaze Portfolio Systems LLC **(1)**
4619 N Ravenswood Ave Ste 302C, Chi-
cago, IL 60640
Tel.: (773) 935-2470
Web Site: https://www.blazeportfolio.com
Portfolio Management Services
N.A.I.C.S.: 523940
Bryson Pouw *(Founder & CEO)*
Joe Tabak *(COO)*
Raymond Frost *(Engr-Software)*

Crown Capital Securities LP **(1)**
725 Town & Country Rd Ste 530, Orange,
CA 92868
Tel.: (949) 588-0399
Web Site:
  http://www.crowncapitalsecurities.com
Investment Advice
N.A.I.C.S.: 523940

Fortigent Holdings Company,
Inc. **(1)**
2600 Tower Oaks Blvd Ste 500, Rockville,
MD 20852
Tel.: (301) 816-1200
Investment Management Service
N.A.I.C.S.: 523999

Subsidiary (Domestic):

Fortigent, LLC **(2)**

2600 Tower Oaks Blvd Ste 300, Rockville,
MD 20852
Tel.: (301) 816-1200
Web Site: http://www.fortigent.com
Sales Range: $75-99.9 Million
Emp.: 100
Wealth Management Services
N.A.I.C.S.: 523940

LPL Financial LLC **(1)**
75 State St 22nd Fl, Boston, MA 02109
Tel.: (617) 423-3644
Web Site: http://www.lpl.com
Securities Brokerage
N.A.I.C.S.: 523150
James S. Putnam *(Bd of Dirs, Executives)*
Dan H. Arnold *(Pres & CEO)*
Sallie R. Larsen *(Mng Dir & Chief Human
Capital Officer)*
Kabir Sethi *(Mng Dir & Chief Product Offi-
cer)*
Matthew J. Audette *(CFO)*
Rich Steinmeier *(Mng Dir & Pres-Business
Development)*
Edward Fandrey *(Mng Dir & Pres-Advisor
Solutions)*
Greg Gates *(Mng Dir & Chief Tech & Info
Officer)*
Brett H. Goodman *(Exec VP-Corp Bus Dev
& IR)*
Bill Sappington *(Exec VP-Banking & Lend-
ing Solutions)*
Kabir Sethi *(Mng Dir & Chief Product Offi-
cer)*
Amy Philbrook *(Exec VP & Head-Svc)*
John O'Neill *(Exec VP-Svc & Supervision)*

Subsidiary (Domestic):

Advisoryworld **(2)**
21241 Ventura Blvd Ste 290, Woodland
Hills, CA 91364
Tel.: (818) 999-0015
Web Site: https://www.advisoryworld.com
Computer & Software Stores
N.A.I.C.S.: 449210
Philip S. Wilson *(Founder)*

E.K. Riley Investments, LLC **(2)**
1420 5th Ave Ste 3300, Seattle, WA 98101
Tel.: (206) 832-1527
Web Site: http://www.ekriley.com
Investment Banking & Securities Dealing
N.A.I.C.S.: 523150
Edward Riley *(Chm & CEO)*
Brian Bertsch *(Pres)*

LPL Insurance Associates, Inc. **(1)**
4707 Executive Dr, San Diego, CA 92121-
3091
Tel.: (858) 450-9606
Emp.: 1,200
Investment Brokerage Services
N.A.I.C.S.: 523150
Maisha Mahone *(Mgr-Insurance Ops)*

The Private Trust Company, N.A. **(1)**
1422 Euclid Ave Ste 1130, Cleveland, OH
44115-2068
Tel.: (858) 779-5053
Web Site:
  https://theprivatetrustcompany.com
Sales Range: $25-49.9 Million
Emp.: 18
Trust Administrative Services
N.A.I.C.S.: 561110
Danielle Gutter *(VP-Ops)*
Jack Keane *(CFO & VP)*
Dan Allen *(COO)*
Tristan McCormick *(Chief Fiduciary Officer)*
Nate Brent *(VP-Business Development)*
Dianne Harmata *(VP-)*

LQR HOUSE INC.
6800 Indian Creek Dr Ste 1E, Miami
Beach, FL 33141
Tel.: (786) 389-9771   NV
Web Site: https://www.lqrhouse.com
Year Founded: 2021
LQR—(NASDAQ)
Rev.: $601,131
Assets: $2,630,356
Liabilities: $590,715
Net Worth: $2,039,641
Earnings: ($1,842,175)
Emp.: 3
Fiscal Year-end: 12/31/22

LQR House Inc.—(Continued)

Alcoholic Beverage Distr
N.A.I.C.S.: 424820
Kumar Abhishek *(CFO)*
Sean Dollinger *(CEO)*
Jaclyn Hoffman *(CMO)*

LSB INDUSTRIES, INC.

3503 NW 63rd St Ste 500, Oklahoma
City, OK 73116-2238
Tel.: (405) 235-4546   **DE**
Web Site:
  https://www.lsbindustries.com
Year Founded: 1968
LXU—(NYSE)
Rev.: $901,711,000
Assets: $1,439,819,000
Liabilities: $923,946,000
Net Worth: $515,873,000
Earnings: $230,347,000
Emp.: 571
Fiscal Year-end: 12/31/22
Diversified Holding Company; Mfr &
Marketer of Chemicals, Pumps & Cli-
mate Control Products
N.A.I.C.S.: 551112
Kristy Carver *(Treas & Sr VP)*
Mark T. Behrman *(Chm, Pres & CEO)*
Michael J. Foster *(Gen Counsel, Sec*
& Exec VP)
Cheryl A. Maguire *(CFO & Exec VP)*
Damien Renwick *(Chief Comml Offi-*
cer & Exec VP)
Harold L. Rieker Jr. *(Principal Acctg*
Officer & VP-Financial Reporting)

Subsidiaries:

LSB Chemical LLC   **(1)**
       (100%)
Tel.: (281) 383-5020
Web Site: http://www.lsb-okc.com
Sales Range: $50-74.9 Million
Emp.: 60
Mfr of Chemicals
N.A.I.C.S.: 325998
Jack E. Golsen *(Chm)*

Subsidiary (Domestic):

Cherokee Nitrogen Holdings, Inc.   **(2)**
1080 Industrial Dr, Cherokee, AL 35616
Tel.: (256) 359-7000
Web Site: http://www.cherokeenitrogen.com
Emp.: 100
Nitrogenous Fertilizer Mfr
N.A.I.C.S.: 325311

Cherokee Nitrogen LLC   **(2)**
1080 Industrial Dr, Cherokee, AL 35616
Tel.: (256) 359-7222
Emp.: 99
Nitrogenous Fertilizer Mfr
N.A.I.C.S.: 325311

El Dorado Chemical Company   **(2)**
16 S Pennsylvania Ave, Oklahoma City, OK
73107   **(100%)**
Tel.: (405) 235-4546
Web Site: http://www.eldoradochemical.com
Sales Range: $50-74.9 Million
Emp.: 30
Fertilizer Mfr & Marketer
N.A.I.C.S.: 325998

Subsidiary (Domestic):

El Dorado Ammonia L.L.C.   **(3)**
16 S Pennsylvania Ave, Oklahoma City, OK
73107
Tel.: (405) 235-4546
Web Site: http://www.lsbindustries.com
Emp.: 58
Chemical Products Mfr
N.A.I.C.S.: 325199

Subsidiary (Domestic):

El Dorado Nitric LLC   **(2)**
8490 W Bay Rd, Baytown, TX 77523
Tel.: (281) 383-1807
Chemical Products & Fertilizer Mfr
N.A.I.C.S.: 325311

Pryor Chemical Company   **(2)**

4463 Hunt St Mid America Industrial Park,
Pryor, OK 74361
Tel.: (918) 825-9000
Web Site: http://www.pryorchemical.com
Agricultural, Industrial & Mining Chemicals
Mfr
N.A.I.C.S.: 325180

Summit Machine Tool Manufacturing
LLC   **(1)**
518 N Indiana Ave, Oklahoma City, OK
73106-2607   **(100%)**
Tel.: (405) 235-2075
Web Site: https://www.summitmt.com
Sales Range: $25-49.9 Million
Emp.: 25
Distribution of Machine Tools
N.A.I.C.S.: 333517

TRISON Construction, Inc.   **(1)**
1115 E 30th St, Baltimore, MD 21218
Tel.: (301) 441-8844
Web Site: https://www.trisoninc.com
Construction Support Services
N.A.I.C.S.: 541330

LSEB CREATIVE CORP.

30 N Gould St Ste 4000, Sheridan,
WY 82801   **WY**
Web Site:
  https://www.lsebcreative.com
Year Founded: 2019
LSEB—(OTCIQ)
Rev.: $3,989
Assets: $154,734
Liabilities: $89,228
Net Worth: $65,506
Earnings: ($163,553)
Emp.: 1
Fiscal Year-end: 03/31/24
Apparel Mfr & Distr
N.A.I.C.S.: 315990
Jordan Starkman *(CFO)*
Lauren Bentley *(Founder)*

LSI INDUSTRIES INC.

10000 Alliance Rd, Cincinnati, OH
45242
Tel.: (513) 793-3200   **OH**
Web Site: https://www.lsicorp.com
Year Founded: 1976
LYTS—(NASDAQ)
Rev.: $469,638,000
Assets: $348,800,000
Liabilities: $144,445,000
Net Worth: $204,355,000
Earnings: $24,977,000
Emp.: 1,900
Fiscal Year-end: 06/30/24
Lighting, Graphics & Menu Board
Systems Mfr
N.A.I.C.S.: 335139
Wilfred T. O'Gara *(Chm)*
Jeffery S. Bastian *(Chief Acctg Officer*
& VP)
James E. Galeese *(CFO & Exec VP)*
James A. Clark *(Pres & CEO)*
Thomas A. Caneris *(Gen Counsel &*
Sr VP-HR)
Michael A. Prachar *(CMO)*

Subsidiaries:

Atlas Lighting Products, Inc.   **(1)**
1406 S Mebane St, Burlington, NC 27215
Tel.: (336) 222-9258
Web Site:
  https://www.atlaslightingproducts.com
Residential Electric Lighting Fixture Mfr
N.A.I.C.S.: 335131
Seth Walters *(Pres)*

JSI Store Fixtures, Inc.   **(1)**
140 Park St, Milo, ME 04463
Tel.: (207) 943-7400
Web Site: https://www.jsi.corp.com
Sales Range: $25-49.9 Million
Display Fixture Mfr
N.A.I.C.S.: 337215
Sam Civiello *(Natl Mgr-Accounts)*
Bill Rothwell *(Natl Mgr-Accounts)*
Jeremy West *(VP-Bus Dev)*
Mark Awalt *(Pres)*

Gretel Seeley *(Exec VP-Sls & Mktg)*
Dan Cassier *(Dir-Design & Dev)*
Brad Awalt *(Reg Sls Mgr)*
Duane A. Hallowell *(VP-Refrigeration)*

LSI ADL Technology Inc.   **(1)**
2727 Scioto Pkwy, Columbus, OH 43221
Tel.: (614) 345-9040
Web Site: https://lsicorp.com
Emp.: 170
Electronic Components Mfr
N.A.I.C.S.: 334419

LSI Adapt Inc.   **(1)**
9260 Pleasantwood Ave NW, North Canton,
OH 44720   **(100%)**
Tel.: (330) 494-9444
Rev.: $75,000,000
Emp.: 100
Engineeering Services
N.A.I.C.S.: 541330

LSI Graphic Solutions Plus   **(1)**
14902 Sommermeyer St Ste 120, Houston,
TX 77041-5308   **(100%)**
Tel.: (713) 744-4100
Web Site: http://www.lsiindustries.com
Sales Range: $50-74.9 Million
Emp.: 190
Screen Printing & Architectural Graphic
Products Serving Corporate Image Needs
N.A.I.C.S.: 323113

LSI Graphic Solutions Plus   **(1)**
9260 Pleasantwood Ave NW, North Canton,
OH 44720-9006   **(100%)**
Tel.: (330) 494-9444
Web Site: http://www.lsi-gsp.com
Sales Range: $25-49.9 Million
Emp.: 60
Interior Graphics, Signage & Point of Pur-
chase Displays
N.A.I.C.S.: 323113

LSI Integrated Graphics L.P.   **(1)**
14902 Sommermeyer Ste 120, Houston, TX
77041   **(100%)**
Tel.: (713) 744-4100
Sales Range: $75-99.9 Million
Emp.: 250
Mfr of Signs & Commercial Printing
N.A.I.C.S.: 323113

LSI Kentucky LLC   **(1)**
3871 Turkeyfoot Rd, Erlanger, KY
41018   **(100%)**
Tel.: (859) 342-9944
Sales Range: $50-74.9 Million
Emp.: 90
Mfr of Metal Stampings & Fabricator of
Sheet Metal
N.A.I.C.S.: 332119

LSI Lightron Inc.   **(1)**
500 Hudson Vly Ave, New Windsor, NY
12553-5506   **(100%)**
Tel.: (845) 220-3200
Sales Range: $100-124.9 Million
Commercial, Industrial & Institutional Elec-
tric Lighting
N.A.I.C.S.: 335132

LSI MidWest Lighting Inc.   **(1)**
100 Funston Rd, Kansas City, KS 66115
Tel.: (913) 281-1100
Lighting Fixture Mfr
N.A.I.C.S.: 335131
Cris Walkinshaw *(Mgr-Quality Control)*

LSI Retail Graphics Inc.   **(1)**
811 Park E Dr, Woonsocket, RI
02895-6112   **(100%)**
Tel.: (401) 766-7446
Web Site: http://www.lsi.com
Sales Range: $10-24.9 Million
Emp.: 50
Mfr & Design of Interior Signage & Graphics
N.A.I.C.S.: 339950

LSI Saco Technologies, Inc.   **(1)**
7809 Trans Canada Hwy, Montreal, H4S
1L3, QC, Canada
Tel.: (514) 745-0310
Web Site: http://www.smartvision.com
Sales Range: $10-24.9 Million
Emp.: 35
Light Engines & Large-Format LED Video
Screens Designer & Mfr
N.A.I.C.S.: 334310
Fred D. Jalbout *(Chm & CEO)*

LTC PROPERTIES, INC.

3011 Townsgate Rd Ste 220, West-
lake Village, CA 91361
Tel.: (805) 981-8655   **MD**
Web Site: https://www.ltcreit.com
Year Founded: 1992
LTC—(NYSE)
Rev.: $175,153,000
Assets: $1,656,103,000
Liabilities: $805,796,000
Net Worth: $850,307,000
Earnings: $100,024,000
Emp.: 24
Fiscal Year-end: 12/31/22
Healthcare Real Estate Investment
Trust
N.A.I.C.S.: 525990
Wendy L. Simpson *(Chm & CEO)*
Clint B. Malin *(Co-Pres & Chief In-*
vestment Officer)
Pamela J. Shelley-Kessler *(Co-Pres,*
CFO & Sec)
Peter G. Lyew *(VP & Dir-Tax)*
Doug Korey *(Mng Dir-Bus Dev &*
Exec VP)
Caroline L. Chikhale *(Chief Acctg Of-*
ficer, Treas & Exec VP)
Gibson Satterwhite *(Sr VP-Asset*
Mgmt)
Michael Bowden *(VP-Investments)*
Rachel Son *(VP & Controller)*
Eric Smith *(VP)*

Subsidiaries:

Coronado Corporation   **(1)**
1730 E 156th St, Carmel, IN 46033
Tel.: (317) 867-4800
Web Site:
  http://www.coronadocorporation.com
Residential Construction
N.A.I.C.S.: 236115
Larry Brown *(Pres)*

JVC Holdings, Inc.   **(1)**
PO Box 391, Smithfield, VA 23430
Tel.: (757) 897-0185
Web Site: http://www.jvcholdingsllc.com
Holding Company
N.A.I.C.S.: 551112

Juniper Assisted Living Residence I,
LLC   **(1)**
400 Broadacres Dr, Bloomfield, NJ 07003
Tel.: (973) 661-8300
Web Site:
  https://www.junipercommunities.com
Orphanage Services
N.A.I.C.S.: 633000
Donald F. Breneman *(VP-Risk Mgmt & Bus*
Ops)
Linda Donato *(Sec, VP-Ops & Dir-Long*
Term Care Acctg)
Lynne S. Katzmann *(Founder & CEO)*
Cindy Longfellow *(VP-Bus Dev, Sls, and*
Mktg)
Anne Campbell *(Natl Dir-Special Projects)*
Diane Byrne *(VP)*
Charles Hastings *(VP)*

LUBY'S, INC.

13111 Northwest Fwy Ste 600, Hous-
ton, TX 77040
Tel.: (713) 329-6800   **DE**
Web Site: http://www.lubysinc.com
Year Founded: 1947
LUB—(NYSE)
Rev.: $214,022,000
Assets: $177,403,000
Liabilities: $103,804,000
Net Worth: $73,599,000
Earnings: ($29,450,000)
Emp.: 3,074
Fiscal Year-end: 08/26/20
Cafeteria & Restaurant Owner & Op-
erator
N.A.I.C.S.: 722511
Christopher J. Pappas *(Pres & CEO)*
Jill Griffin *(Vice Chm)*
Paulette Gerukos *(VP-HR)*
Bill Gordon *(VP-Real Estate)*

Gerald W. Bodzy *(Chm)*
Trent Taylor *(VP-Ops)*
Shan Peters *(VP-Fuddruckers Ops)*
David Greenberg *(VP-Brand & Mktg Strategy)*
John Holzem *(VP-IT)*
Philip J. Rider *(Chief Acctg Officer & Controller)*
Eric Montague *(CFO-Interim)*
Michael A. Racusin *(Gen Counsel & Sec)*

Subsidiaries:

Cheeseburger in Paradise of Anne Arundel County, Inc. **(1)**
8026 Ritchie Hwy Ste B, Pasadena, MD 21122
Tel.: (410) 761-1003
Web Site:
http://www.cheeseburgerinparadise.com
Emp.: 60
Restaurant Operators
N.A.I.C.S.: 722511

Cheeseburger of Southport, LLC **(1)**
4670 Southport Crossings, Indianapolis, IN 46237
Tel.: (317) 883-4386
Emp.: 50
Restaurant Operators
N.A.I.C.S.: 722511
Peter Tripoli *(CEO)*

Fuddruckers of Annapolis, LLC **(1)**
175 Jennifer Rd, Annapolis, MD 21401
Tel.: (410) 266-8030
Web Site: http://www.fuddruckers.com
Fast Food Restaurant Operator
N.A.I.C.S.: 424420

LUBCO, Inc. **(1)**
103 Foulk Rd, Wilmington, DE 19803
Tel.: (302) 657-0260
Restaurant Operating Services
N.A.I.C.S.: 722511

Luby's Bevco, Inc. **(1)**
2200 S 10th St, McAllen, TX 78503-5437
Tel.: (956) 928-1853
Restaurant Operating Services
N.A.I.C.S.: 722511

Luby's Holdings, Inc. **(1)**
13111 NW Fwy, Houston, TX 77040
Tel.: (713) 329-6800
Web Site: http://www.lubys.com
Sales Range: $250-299.9 Million
Restaurant Services
N.A.I.C.S.: 551112

Luby's Limited Partner, Inc. **(1)**
13111 NW Fwy Ste 600, Houston, TX 77040
Tel.: (713) 329-6800
Web Site: http://www.lubys.com
Sales Range: $50-74.9 Million
Restaurant Services
N.A.I.C.S.: 722511

Luby's Management, Inc. **(1)**
13111 NW Fwy Ste 600, Houston, TX 77040
Tel.: (713) 329-6800
Web Site: http://www.lubys.com
Sales Range: $50-74.9 Million
Restaurant Management Services
N.A.I.C.S.: 722511

LUCID GROUP, INC.
7373 Gateway Blvd, Newark, CA 94560
Tel.: (510) 648-3553　　　　**DE**
Web Site: https://lucidmotors.com
Year Founded: 2020
LCID—(NASDAQ)
Rev.: $595,271,000
Assets: $8,512,718,000
Liabilities: $3,661,026,000
Net Worth: $4,851,692,000
Earnings: ($2,828,420,000)
Emp.: 6,500
Fiscal Year-end: 12/31/23
Holding Company; Motor Vehicle Mfr & Whslr
N.A.I.C.S.: 551112

Gagan Dhingra *(Interim CFO)*
Peter Rawlinson *(CEO & CTO)*

Subsidiaries:

Atieva, Inc. **(1)**
7373 Gateway Blvd, Newark, CA 94560
Tel.: (510) 648-3553
Web Site: https://lucidmotors.com
Automobile Mfr & Whslr
N.A.I.C.S.: 336110

LUCID, INC.
50 Methodist Hill Dr Ste 1000, Rochester, NY 14623
Tel.: (585) 239-9800　　　　**NY**
LCDX—(OTCIQ)
Medical Equipment Mfr
N.A.I.C.S.: 339112

LUCIRA HEALTH, INC.
1412 62nd St, Emeryville, CA 94608
Tel.: (510) 350-8071　　　　**DE**
Web Site:
http://www.lucirahealth.com
Year Founded: 2013
LHDX—(NASDAQ)
Rev.: $93,055,000
Assets: $240,354,000
Liabilities: $51,551,000
Net Worth: $188,803,000
Earnings: ($64,827,000)
Emp.: 141
Fiscal Year-end: 12/31/21
Medical Equipment Mfr & Distr
N.A.I.C.S.: 339112
Erik T. Engelson *(Pres & CEO)*
Daniel George *(CFO & Treas)*
Debkishore Mitra *(CTO)*
Tamanna Prashar *(VP-Global Supply Chain, Ops & Quality)*
Tony Allen *(COO)*
Richard Narido *(CFO & Principal Acctg Officer)*

LUCKY FRIDAY EXTENSION MINING CO.
905 N Pines Rd Ste A, Spokane Valley, WA 99206
Tel.: (509) 922-3035
LFEX—(OTCIQ)
Metal Mining Services
N.A.I.C.S.: 213114
W. A. Campbell *(Pres)*

LUDWIG ENTERPRISES, INC.
1749 Victorian Ave C 350, Sparks, NV 89431
Tel.: (786) 235-9026
Web Site: https://www.ludwigent.com
LUDG—(OTCIQ)
Sales Range: Less than $1 Million
Radio Broadcasting Network
N.A.I.C.S.: 516210
Bodhan Stryzak *(Project Mgr)*
Jean Cherubin *(Chm)*
Scott J. Silverman *(CFO)*
Marvin S. Hausman *(CEO)*
Patrick Greenish Jr. *(Pres)*
Marvin S. Hausman *(Chief Science Officer)*

LULU'S FASHION LOUNGE HOLDINGS, INC.
195 Humboldt Ave, Chico, CA 95928
Tel.: (530) 343-3545　　　　**DE**
Web Site: https://www.lulus.com
Year Founded: 1996
LVLU—(NASDAQ)
Rev.: $248,656,000
Assets: $105,076,000
Liabilities: $274,077,000
Net Worth: ($169,001,000)
Earnings: ($19,808,000)
Emp.: 689
Fiscal Year-end: 01/03/21
Holding Company

N.A.I.C.S.: 551112
David McCreight *(CEO)*
Crystal Landsem *(COO)*
Mark Vos *(Pres & CIO)*
Naomi Beckman-Straus *(Gen Counsel & Sec)*
Tiffany R. Smith *(CFO)*

LUMBEE GUARANTY BANK
403 E 3rd St, Pembroke, NC 28372
Tel.: (910) 521-9707　　　　**NC**
Web Site:
https://www.lumbeeguaranty
bank.com
Year Founded: 1971
LUMB—(OTCQX)
Rev.: $22,961,218
Assets: $519,656,155
Liabilities: $477,375,090
Net Worth: $42,281,065
Earnings: $5,957,400
Emp.: 97
Fiscal Year-end: 12/31/23
Commercial Banking Services
N.A.I.C.S.: 522110
Sybil J. Bullard *(Chm)*
James Gore *(Chief Credit Officer & Exec VP)*
Tre Bell *(Sr VP & Dir-Information Technology)*
Jessica Jones *(Controller & Asst VP)*
Katie B. Smith *(VP-Legal Counsel)*
Arnold Locklear *(Vice Chm)*
Bryan Maynor *(Pres & COO)*
Kyle R. Chavis *(CEO)*
Thresia Locklear *(Sr VP-Ops)*

LUMEN TECHNOLOGIES, INC.
100 CenturyLink Dr, Monroe, LA 71203
Tel.: (318) 388-9000　　　　**LA**
Web Site: https://www.lumen.com
LUMN—(NYSE)
Rev.: $14,557,000,000
Assets: $34,018,000,000
Liabilities: $33,601,000,000
Net Worth: $417,000,000
Earnings: ($10,298,000,000)
Emp.: 28,000
Fiscal Year-end: 12/31/23
Telecommunication Servicesb
N.A.I.C.S.: 517111
Chadwick Ho *(Chief Legal Officer & Exec VP)*
Laurinda Pang *(Pres-Global Customer Success)*
Sham Chotai *(Exec VP-Tech & Product)*
Kate E. Johnson *(Pres & CEO)*
Ashley Haynes-Gaspar *(Customer Experience Officer & Exec VP-Intl & Wholesale)*

Subsidiaries:

AppFog, Inc. **(1)**
319 SW Washington St Ste 700, Portland, OR 97204
Tel.: (503) 206-6179
Telecommunication & Wireless Services
N.A.I.C.S.: 517112

Cascade Autovon Company **(1)**
805 Broadway Ste 800, Vancouver, WA 98660
Tel.: (360) 905-6839
Telecommunication & Wireless Services
N.A.I.C.S.: 517112

Century Cellunet International, Inc. **(1)**
100 CenturyLink Dr, Monroe, LA 71203
Tel.: (913) 345-6387
Telecommunication & Wireless Services
N.A.I.C.S.: 517112

Century Marketing Solutions, LLC **(1)**
3000 Cameron St, Monroe, LA 71201-3716
Tel.: (318) 387-4621
Commercial Printing & Marketing Services

N.A.I.C.S.: 323111

CenturyLink Australia Pty. Ltd. **(1)**
Level 20 201 Sussex St, Sydney, 2000, NSW, Australia
Tel.: (61) 290061101
Information Technology Consulting Services
N.A.I.C.S.: 541512

CenturyLink Canada, Inc. **(1)**
6800 Millcreek Dr, Mississauga, L5N 4J9, ON, Canada
Tel.: (905) 363-3737
Telecommunication Servicesb
N.A.I.C.S.: 517810
Chris Jones *(Sr Project Mgr)*

CenturyLink Chile S.A. **(1)**
Av Presidente Kennedy 5735 Edificio Marriott Torre Poniente Of 802, Las Condes, 7560356, Santiago, Chile
Tel.: (56) 224225900
Telecommunication Servicesb
N.A.I.C.S.: 517810
Juan Mardones *(Mgr-Svc Client)*

CenturyLink Colombia S.A. **(1)**
Calle 185 Suite 45-03/Centro Comercial Santa Fe Torre Empresarial, Pisos 4 y 5, Bogota, Colombia
Tel.: (57) 16119000
Network Security Services
N.A.I.C.S.: 518210
Juan Manuel Sarmiento *(Sr Mgr-Acct)*

CenturyLink Communications (IMPSAT) Nederland B.V. **(1)**
Stekkenbergweg 4, 1105 AJ, Amsterdam, Netherlands
Tel.: (31) 20 808 3900
Telecommunication Servicesb
N.A.I.C.S.: 517121

CenturyLink Communications Belgium SA **(1)**
Avenue Leon Grosjean 2, Evere, Belgium
Tel.: (32) 25887500
Telecommunication Servicesb
N.A.I.C.S.: 517810

CenturyLink Communications Italia Srl **(1)**
Via Mengoni 4, 20121, Milan, Italy
Tel.: (39) 0 294 754 936
Telecommunication Servicesb
N.A.I.C.S.: 517121

CenturyLink Comunicacoes do Brasil Ltda. **(1)**
Av Eid Mansur 666 Rod Raposo Tavares Km 25, Cotia, 6708070, Sao Paulo, Brazil
Tel.: (55) 11 3957 2200
Telecommunication Servicesb
N.A.I.C.S.: 517121

CenturyLink Corporation Japan **(1)**
Atago Green Hills Mori Tower 17th Floor 2-5-1 Atago, Minato-ku, Tokyo, 105-6217, Japan
Tel.: (81) 364359658
Network Security Services
N.A.I.C.S.: 518210
Motoki Kai *(Dir-Acct)*

CenturyLink Costa Rica, S.R.L. **(1)**
Torre la Sabana-Piso 7, San Jose, Costa Rica
Tel.: (506) 722907220
Network Security Services
N.A.I.C.S.: 518210

CenturyLink Germany GmbH **(1)**
Eschenheimer Anlage 1 Stadt - Hessen, 60316, Frankfurt am Main, Germany
Tel.: (49) 69710456156
Data Analysis & Processing Services
N.A.I.C.S.: 518210

CenturyLink Investment Management Company **(1)**
1801 California St Ste 3800, Denver, CO 80202-2028
Tel.: (303) 382-0608
Emp.: 18
Investment & Welfare Fund Services
N.A.I.C.S.: 525120

CenturyLink Japan, Ltd **(1)**
Atago Green Hills Mori Tower 17th Floor 2-5-1 Atago, Minato-ku, Tokyo, 105-6217, Japan
Tel.: (81) 364359658

Lumen Technologies, Inc.—(Continued)

Information Technology Consulting Services
N.A.I.C.S.: 541512

CenturyLink Limited (1)
260-266 Goswell Road, London, EC1V
7EB, United Kingdom
Tel.: (44) 2074005600
Wired Telecommunication Services
N.A.I.C.S.: 517111

CenturyLink Panama (1)
0851 Av Arnulfo Arias y Calle Remon Levy,
Amador, Panama, Panama
Tel.: (507) 314 0324
Telecommunication Servicesb
N.A.I.C.S.: 517121

CenturyLink Peru S.A. (1)
Av Manuel Olguin 395, Santiago de Surco,
Lima, 33, Peru
Tel.: (51) 1 705 5700
Telecommunication Servicesb
N.A.I.C.S.: 517121

**CenturyLink Public Communications,
Inc.** (1)
2200 Danbury St, San Antonio, TX 78217
Tel.: (850) 599-1379
Telecommunication & Wireless Services
N.A.I.C.S.: 517112

CenturyLink Singapore Pte. Ltd. (1)
50 Raffles Place 36-01 Singapore Land
Tower, Singapore, 048623, Singapore
Tel.: (65) 67688000
Information Technology Consulting Services
N.A.I.C.S.: 541512
Adhika Widjaya (Sr Engr-Database)

**CenturyLink Technologies India Pri-
vate Limited** (1)
Plot No 9a Green Boulevard 5th Floor Block
B Noida Sector 62, Noida, 201301, India
Tel.: (91) 1206681801
Web Site: http://www.centurylinkindia.com
Information Technology Consulting Services
N.A.I.C.S.: 541512

**CenturyLink Technology Australia Pty.
Limited** (1)
8th Floor 34 Queen Street, Melbourne,
3000, VIC, Australia
Tel.: (61) 1300240161
Network Security Services
N.A.I.C.S.: 518210

**CenturyLink Technology Hong Kong
Limited** (1)
Unit 5007-12 50/F Hopewell Centre 183
Queen's Road East, Wan Chai, Hong Kong,
China (Hong Kong)
Tel.: (852) 21908798
Web Site: http://www.centurylink.hk
Information Technology Consulting Services
N.A.I.C.S.: 541512

**CenturyLink Technology Singapore
Pte Ltd.** (1)
50 Raffles Place Suite 36-01 Singapore
Land Tower, Singapore, 048623, Singapore
Tel.: (65) 67688000
Network Security Services
N.A.I.C.S.: 518210
Joanna Lee (Mgr-HR)

**CenturyLink Technology UK
Limited** (1)
230 Wharfedale Road Winnersh Triangle,
Wokingham, RG41 5TP, Berkshire, United
Kingdom
Tel.: (44) 2074005600
Web Site: http://www.centurylink.co.uk
Emp.: 400
Information Technology Consulting Services
N.A.I.C.S.: 541512

**CenturyLink Telecomunicaciones
S.A.** (1)
La Urbina Calle 7, Caracas, 1070, Venezu-
ela
Tel.: (58) 2122049275
Network Security Services
N.A.I.C.S.: 518210

CenturyLink of Adamsville, Inc. (1)
116 N Oak St, Adamsville, TN
38310-0405 (100%)
Tel.: (731) 632-3313

Sales Range: $200-249.9 Million
Rural & Small-Town Telecommunications
Services
N.A.I.C.S.: 517111

**CenturyLink of Monroe County,
LLC** (1)
311 S Court St, Sparta, WI
54656-1716 (100%)
Tel.: (608) 269-0820
Web Site: http://www.centurytel.com
Sales Range: $10-24.9 Million
Emp.: 50
Rural & Small-Town Telecommunications
Services
N.A.I.C.S.: 517111

**CenturyLink of North Louisiana,
LLC** (1)
119 N Lynch St, Plain Dealing, LA 71064-
0428
Tel.: (318) 326-5868
Web Site: http://www.centurylink.com
Sales Range: $10-24.9 Million
Emp.: 29
Telecommunication Servicesb
N.A.I.C.S.: 517111

**CenturyLink of the Southwest,
Inc.** (1)
3 S Main St, Pecos, NM
87552-0488 (100%)
Tel.: (505) 757-8826
Web Site: http://www.centurylink.com
Sales Range: $1-9.9 Million
Emp.: 2
Rural & Small-Town Telecommunications
Services
N.A.I.C.S.: 517111

CenturyLinkEcuador S.A. (1)
Urbanizacion Inaquito Alto Calle Juan Diaz
No 37-111, Quito, Ecuador
Tel.: (593) 2 400 4040
Telecommunication Servicesb
N.A.I.C.S.: 517121

CenturyTel Acquisition LLC (1)
100 Centurylink Dr, Monroe, LA 71203
Tel.: (318) 388-9000
Web Site: http://www.centurylink.com
Telecommunication & Wireless Services
N.A.I.C.S.: 517112

**CenturyTel Arkansas Holdings,
Inc.** (1)
100 Centurylink Dr, Monroe, LA 71203-
2041
Tel.: (318) 388-9000
Telecommunication Servicesb
N.A.I.C.S.: 517810

**CenturyTel Broadband Wireless,
LLC** (1)
805 Broadway Ste 800, Vancouver, WA
98660
Tel.: (360) 905-6839
Telecommunication Servicesb
N.A.I.C.S.: 517810

**CenturyTel Holdings Missouri,
Inc.** (1)
1151 Centurytel Dr, Wentzville, MO 63385-
1941
Tel.: (636) 332-3011
Sales Range: $75-99.9 Million
Emp.: 300
Rural & Small-Town Telecommunications
Services
N.A.I.C.S.: 517111

CenturyTel Interactive Company (1)
103 Current Dr, Monroe, LA 71203
Tel.: (318) 388-9000
Telecommunication & Wireless Services
N.A.I.C.S.: 517112

CenturyTel SM Telecorp, Inc. (1)
133 W San Antonio St, San Marcos, TX
78666
Tel.: (512) 396-2411
Emp.: 35
Telecommunication & Wireless Services
N.A.I.C.S.: 517112

CenturyTel TeleVideo, Inc. (1)
405 N Washington St, Thorp, WI 54771-
9538
Tel.: (715) 669-5304
Telecommunication Servicesb

N.A.I.C.S.: 517810

**CenturyTel of Central Arkansas,
LLC** (1)
2616 W Main St, Jacksonville, AR
72076 (100%)
Tel.: (501) 241-6401
Sales Range: $25-49.9 Million
Emp.: 150
Rural & Small-Town Telecommunications
Services
N.A.I.C.S.: 517111

**CenturyTel of Central Indiana,
Inc.** (1)
601 S South St, Brookston, IN 47923-8311
Tel.: (800) 201-4099
Telecommunication Servicesb
N.A.I.C.S.: 517810

CenturyTel of Claiborne, Inc. (1)
507 Main St, New Tazewell, TN 37825
Tel.: (423) 626-2233
Web Site: http://www.centurytel.com
Rural & Small-Town Telecommunications
Services
N.A.I.C.S.: 517111

CenturyTel of Colorado, Inc. (1)
421 Lewis St, Pagosa Springs, CO 81147
Tel.: (970) 264-2240
Telecommunication & Wireless Services
N.A.I.C.S.: 517112

CenturyTel of Inter Island, Inc. (1)
8102 Skansie Ave, Gig Harbor, WA 98332
Tel.: (253) 851-1450
Emp.: 15
Telecommunication & Wireless Services
N.A.I.C.S.: 517112

CenturyTel of Lake Dallas, Inc. (1)
450 Main St, Lake Dallas, TX 75065-2724
Tel.: (940) 321-1900
Sales Range: $10-24.9 Million
Emp.: 20
Rural & Small-Town Telecommunications
Services
N.A.I.C.S.: 517111

**CenturyTel of Northern Wisconsin,
LLC** (1)
425 Ellingson Ave, Hawkins, WI
54530-9513 (100%)
Tel.: (715) 585-6388
Sales Range: $25-49.9 Million
Emp.: 80
Rural & Small-Town Telecommunications
Services
N.A.I.C.S.: 517111

**CenturyTel of Northwest Louisiana,
Inc.** (1)
157 Clarke Williams Dr, Marion, LA 71260
Tel.: (318) 292-6300
Web Site: http://www.centurylink.com
Sales Range: $10-24.9 Million
Emp.: 30
Telecommunication Servicesb
N.A.I.C.S.: 517810

**CenturyTel of Northwest Wisconsin,
LLC** (1)
PO Box 547, Frederic, WI 54837
Tel.: (715) 327-8100
Web Site: http://www.centurylink.com
Emp.: 2
Telecommunication & Wireless Services
N.A.I.C.S.: 517112

CenturyTel of Ohio, Inc. (1)
203 W 9th St, Lorain, OH 44052
Tel.: (440) 244-8400
Emp.: 2,008
Telecommunication & Wireless Services
N.A.I.C.S.: 517112

**CenturyTel of Ooltewah-Collegedale,
Inc.** (1)
5616 Main St, Ooltewah, TN 37363
Tel.: (423) 238-6872
Telecommunication & Wireless Services
N.A.I.C.S.: 517112

CenturyTel of Wisconsin, LLC (1)
333 N Front St, La Crosse, WI
54601-4003 (100%)
Tel.: (608) 796-5051
Web Site: http://www.centurylink.com

Sales Range: $200-249.9 Million
Emp.: 800
Telephone Communication Services
N.A.I.C.S.: 517121

CenturyTel of Wyoming, Inc. (1)
620 Red Table Dr, Gypsum, CO 81637
Tel.: (913) 345-6387
Web Site: https://www.centurylink.com
Sales Range: $10-24.9 Million
Emp.: 25
Telecommunication Servicesb
N.A.I.C.S.: 517121

CenturyTel of the Northwest, Inc. (1)
805 Broadway St, Vancouver, WA 98660-
3213
Tel.: (360) 256-4040
Web Site: https://www.centurylink.com
Rural & Small-Town Telecommunications
Services
N.A.I.C.S.: 517111

**CenturyTel/Teleview of Wisconsin,
Inc.** (1)
201 Stark St, Randolph, WI 53956
Tel.: (920) 326-2226
Telecommunication & Wireless Services
N.A.I.C.S.: 517112

Coastal Communications, Inc. (1)
15218 Lemoyne Blvd, Biloxi, MS 39532
Tel.: (228) 354-0355
Web Site: http://www.coastalcomm.net
Sales Range: $1-9.9 Million
Emp.: 19
Telecommunication & Wireless Services
N.A.I.C.S.: 517112
Roy Reaux (Pres)

DataGardens, Inc. (1)
14956-121 A Avenue, Edmonton, T5V
1A3C, AB, Canada
Tel.: (780) 784-5000
Web Site: http://www.datagardens.com
Wireless Telecommunication Services
N.A.I.C.S.: 517112

ElasticBox Inc. (1)
620 Folsom St, San Francisco, CA 94107
Tel.: (415) 766-0907
Web Site: http://www.elasticbox.com
Software Publisher
N.A.I.C.S.: 513210

Embarq Communications, Inc. (1)
5454 W 110th St, Overland Park, KS
66211-1204
Tel.: (913) 345-7859
Telecommunication & Wireless Services
N.A.I.C.S.: 517112

Subsidiary (Domestic):

**Embarq Mid-Atlantic Management
Services Company** (2)
160 Mine Lk Ct Ste 200, Raleigh, NC
27615-6417
Tel.: (919) 729-6869
Telecommunication Servicesb
N.A.I.C.S.: 517112
Kay Buchart (Sec)

Embarq Minnesota, Inc. (2)
164 Pioneer Trl, Chaska, MN 55318
Tel.: (952) 556-5679
Telecommunication & Wireless Services
N.A.I.C.S.: 517112

GulfTel Communications (1)
19812 Underwood Rd, Foley, AL 36536
Tel.: (251) 952-5100
Web Site: http://www.gulftelephone.com
Sales Range: $75-99.9 Million
Emp.: 365
Provider of Telephone Communication, Ex-
cept Radio
N.A.I.C.S.: 517810

**Hillsboro Telephone Company,
Inc.** (1)
121 Mill St, Hillsboro, WI 54634
Tel.: (608) 489-3230
Web Site: https://hillsborotel.net
Wired Telecommunication Services
N.A.I.C.S.: 517111

Level 3 Argentina, S.A. (1)
Alferez Pareja 256, Buenos Aires,
C1107BJD, Argentina
Tel.: (54) 1151700000

Wired Telecommunication Services
N.A.I.C.S.: 517111

Level 3 Communications Hong Kong Limited (1)
2801 Tower 2 Times Square 1 Matheson Street, Causeway Bay, China (Hong Kong)
Tel.: (852) 35125838
Wired Telecommunication Services
N.A.I.C.S.: 517111

Level 3 Communications PEC Ireland Limited (1)
Second Floor Marconi House Digges Lane, Dublin, Ireland
Tel.: (353) 851114251
Wired Telecommunication Services
N.A.I.C.S.: 517111

Level 3 Mexico Landing S. de R.L. (1)
Lago Zurich 96 Ampliacion Granada, Mexico, 11529, Mexico
Tel.: (52) 5525816270
Wired Telecommunication Services
N.A.I.C.S.: 517111

Level 3 Parent, LLC (1)
1025 Eldorado Blvd, Broomfield, CO 80021-8869
Tel.: (720) 888-1000
Rev.: $7,037,000,000
Assets: $17,253,000,000
Liabilities: $13,637,000,000
Net Worth: $3,616,000,000
Earnings: ($2,004,000,000)
Emp.: 8,000
Fiscal Year-end: 12/31/2023
Holding Company; Internet Protocol & Communications Services
N.A.I.C.S.: 551112
Eric J. Mortensen (Sr VP & Controller)
Stacey W. Goff (Gen Counsel & Exec VP)

Subsidiary (Domestic):

HQ Realty, Inc. (2)
848 Brickell Ave Ste 1210, Miami, FL 33131
Tel.: (305) 724-4091
Web Site: https://www.hqrealty.com
Wired Telecommunication Services
N.A.I.C.S.: 517111

Subsidiary (Non-US):

Level 3 Chile S.A. (2)
Av Presidente Kennedy 5735 Edificio Marriott, Torre Poniente of 802, Las Condes, Santiago, Chile
Tel.: (56) 22 422 5900
Telecommunication Servicesb
N.A.I.C.S.: 517121

Level 3 Colombia S.A. (2)
Calle 185 45-03 Centro Comercial Santa Fe, Torre Empresarial Pisos 4 y 5, Bogota, Colombia
Tel.: (57) 16119000
Telecommunication Servicesb
N.A.I.C.S.: 517121

Level 3 Communications (Asia Pacific) Limited (2)
Room 2801 28/F Tower Two Times Square 1 Matheson Street, Causeway Bay, Hong Kong, China (Hong Kong)
Tel.: (852) 3512 5855
Telecommunication Servicesb
N.A.I.C.S.: 517121

Level 3 Communications Austria GmbH (2)
Nottendorfer G 11, 1030, Vienna, Austria
Tel.: (43) 1 947 5995
Telecommunication Servicesb
N.A.I.C.S.: 517121

Level 3 Communications Japan KK (2)
2-5-1 Atago Green Hills Mori Tower 17th Floor, Minato-ku, Tokyo, 105-6217, Japan
Tel.: (81) 3 6435 9658
Telecommunication Servicesb
N.A.I.C.S.: 517121

Level 3 Communications Limited (2)
260-266 Goswell Road, London, EC1V 7EB, United Kingdom
Tel.: (44) 8450001000
Internet Service Provider

N.A.I.C.S.: 517111

Level 3 Communications PEC Luxembourg II S.a.r.l. (2)
208 Val des Bons-Malades, 2121, Luxembourg, Luxembourg
Tel.: (352) 26 47 07
Telecommunication Servicesb
N.A.I.C.S.: 517121

Level 3 Communications Singapore Pte. Ltd. (2)
3 Irving Road 06-01 Tai Seng Centre, Singapore, 369522, Singapore
Tel.: (65) 6768 8000
Telecommunication Servicesb
N.A.I.C.S.: 517121

Subsidiary (Domestic):

Level 3 Communications, LLC (2)
1025 Eldorado Blvd, Broomfield, CO 80021
Tel.: (720) 888-1000
Telecommunication Servicesb
N.A.I.C.S.: 517810

Branch (Domestic):

Level 3 Communications, LLC - Pittsburgh (2)
200 Technology Dr, Pittsburgh, PA 15219
Tel.: (610) 572-4887
Telecommunications Products & Services
N.A.I.C.S.: 516210

Subsidiary (Non-US):

Level 3 Mexico II, S. de R.L. de C.V. (2)
Lago Zurich 96 Colonia Ampliacion Granada, Del Miguel Hidalgo, 11529, Mexico, Mexico
Tel.: (52) 55 2581 6270
Telecommunication Servicesb
N.A.I.C.S.: 517121

Subsidiary (Domestic):

Level 3 Telecom of Arizona, LLC (2)
120 E Van Buren St, Phoenix, AZ 85004
Tel.: (602) 258-3144
Telecommunication Servicesb
N.A.I.C.S.: 517121

Level 3 Telecom of Georgia, LP (2)
180 Peachtree St, Atlanta, GA 30303
Tel.: (404) 382-7784
Telecommunication Servicesb
N.A.I.C.S.: 517121

Level 3 Telecom of Oregon, LLC (2)
520 SW 6th Ave Ste 300, Portland, OR 97204
Tel.: (503) 416-1926
Telecommunication Servicesb
N.A.I.C.S.: 517121

Level 3 Telecom of South Carolina, LLC (2)
1401 Main St Ste 202, Columbia, SC 29201
Telecommunication Servicesb
N.A.I.C.S.: 517121

Level 3 Telecom of Texas, LLC (2)
2821 W 7th St Ste 500, Fort Worth, TX 76107
Tel.: (682) 708-6094
Telecommunication Servicesb
N.A.I.C.S.: 517121

Subsidiary (Non-US):

Level 3 telekomunikacijski storitve d.o.o. (2)
Bleiweisova cesta 30, 1000, Ljubljana, Slovenia
Tel.: (386) 41706517
Telecommunication Servicesb
N.A.I.C.S.: 517121

Lumen Technologies Europe Limited (1)
260-266 Goswell Road, London, EC1V 7EB, United Kingdom
Tel.: (44) 8450001000
Telecommunication Servicesb
N.A.I.C.S.: 517121

Lumen Technologies Germany GmbH (1)
Russelsheimer Strasse 22, 60326, Frank-

furt, Germany
Tel.: (49) 6950608000
Wired Telecommunication & Internet Services
N.A.I.C.S.: 517111

Lumen Technologies Poland SP. Z o.o. (1)
Aleje Jerozolimskie 181B, 02-222, Warsaw, Poland
Tel.: (48) 664714040
Telecommunication Servicesb
N.A.I.C.S.: 517121

Lumen Technologies Switzerland AG (1)
Aargauerstrasse 10, 8048, Zurich, Switzerland
Tel.: (41) 435085790
Telecommunication Servicesb
N.A.I.C.S.: 517121

Lumen Technologies UK Limited (1)
260-266 Goswell Road, London, EC1V 7EB, United Kingdom
Tel.: (44) 8450001000
Telecommunication Servicesb
N.A.I.C.S.: 517111

Madison River Communications, LLC (1)
1615 Poydras St Ste 1050, New Orleans, LA 70112
Tel.: (504) 200-2000
Telecommunication & Wireless Services
N.A.I.C.S.: 517112

Madison River Holdings LLC (1)
9436 S Union Sq, Sandy, UT 84070
Tel.: (801) 571-6377
Holding Company
N.A.I.C.S.: 551112

Mebtel, Inc. (1)
103 S 7thaSt, Mebane, NC 27302
Tel.: (919) 563-2224
Telecommunication & Wireless Services
N.A.I.C.S.: 517112

OOO Level 3 Communications (1)
4-th Lesnoy Pereulok 4, Moscow, 125047, Russia
Tel.: (7) 4956413789
Wired Telecommunication Services
N.A.I.C.S.: 517111

PTI Communications of Ketchikan, Inc. (1)
3940 Arctic Blvd, Anchorage, AK 99503
Tel.: (907) 562-1231
Telecommunication & Wireless Services
N.A.I.C.S.: 517112

Qwest Broadband Services, Inc. (1)
555 17th St Ste 1, Denver, CO 80202
Tel.: (303) 992-1400
Wireless Telecommunication Services
N.A.I.C.S.: 517112

Qwest Communications International Inc. (1)
1801 California St, Denver, CO 80202
Tel.: (303) 992-1400
Rev.: $11,730,000,000
Assets: $17,220,000,000
Liabilities: $18,875,000,000
Net Worth: ($1,655,000,000)
Earnings: ($55,000,000)
Emp.: 28,343
Fiscal Year-end: 12/31/2010
Holding Company; Wired Data, Internet, Video & Voice Telecommunications Carrier
N.A.I.C.S.: 551112

Subsidiary (Domestic):

Qwest Services Corporation (2)
1801 California St, Denver, CO 80202
Tel.: (303) 992-1400
Web Site: http://www.qwest.com
Wired Data, Internet, Video & Voice Telecommunications Services
N.A.I.C.S.: 517810

Subsidiary (Domestic):

CenturyLink Communications, LLC (3)
1801 California St, Denver, CO 80202
Tel.: (303) 922-1400

Data Integration & Hosting, Internet Access, Voice-over Internet Protocol & Other Fiber Optic Telecommunications Services
N.A.I.C.S.: 517810

Qwest Corporation (3)
100 CenturyLink Dr, Monroe, LA 71203
Tel.: (318) 388-9000
Web Site: https://www.centurylink.com
Telecommunications Products & Services
N.A.I.C.S.: 517112

RiskSense, Inc.(1) (1)
4200 Osuna Rd Ne Ste 3-300, Albuquerque, NM 87109
Tel.: (505) 217-9422
Web Site: https://www.risksense.com
Cyber Security Services
N.A.I.C.S.: 923130
Srinivas Mukkamala (Founder & CEO)
Frank Brown (CFO)
Alok Damireddy (VP-Engrg)
Chris Kenworthy (Chief Revenue Officer)
Christopher Acton (VP-Security Svcs & Customer Success)

SAVVIS, Inc (1)
1 Savvis Pkwy, Town and Country, MO 63017
Tel.: (314) 628-7000
Web Site: http://www.savvis.com
Sales Range: $900-999.9 Million
Emp.: 2,440
Information Technology Services
N.A.I.C.S.: 541511

Subsidiary (Non-US):

SAVVIS Communications K.K. (2)
Atago Green Hills Mori Tower 17th Floor 2-5-1 Atago, Minato-ku, Tokyo, 105-6217, Japan
Tel.: (81) 364359658
Telecommunication & Wireless Services
N.A.I.C.S.: 517112

Subsidiary (Domestic):

SAVVIS Federal Systems, Inc. (2)
12851 Worldgate Dr, Herndon, VA 20170
Tel.: (703) 667-6000
Internet Host Services
N.A.I.C.S.: 517112

Subsidiary (Non-US):

SAVVIS Germany GmbH (2)
Russelsheimer Strasse 22, 60326, Frankfurt am Main, Germany
Tel.: (49) 69710456156
Telecommunication & Wireless Services
N.A.I.C.S.: 517112

SAVVIS Hong Kong Limited (2)
Unit 5007-12 50/F Hopewell Centre 183 Queen's Road East, Wan Chai, Hong Kong, 999, China (Hong Kong)
Tel.: (852) 31612889
Computer Networking Services
N.A.I.C.S.: 541513

SAVVIS Singapore (2)
80 Raffles Place 32-01 Uob Plaza, Singapore, 048624, Singapore
Tel.: (65) 67688000
Sales Range: $25-49.9 Million
Emp.: 100
Computer Networking Services
N.A.I.C.S.: 541513

SAVVIS Singapore Company Pte. Ltd. (2)
50 Raffles Place No 13-01/04 Singapore Land Tower, Singapore, 048623, Singapore
Tel.: (65) 67688000
Web Site: http://www.savvis.com
Information Technology Consulting Services
N.A.I.C.S.: 541512

SAVVIS United Kingdom (2)
Eskdale Rd Winnersh Triangle Wokingham Berkshire, Reading, RG415TS, United Kingdom
Tel.: (44) 183226000
Web Site: http://www.savvis.co.uk
Sales Range: $100-124.9 Million
Computer Networking Services
N.A.I.C.S.: 541513

SEAL Consulting, Inc. (1)

Lumen Technologies, Inc.—(Continued)

105 Fieldcrest Ave 4th Fl Raritan Plz III,
Edison, NJ 08837
Tel.: (732) 417-9595
Web Site: https://www.sealconsult.net
Wireless Telecommunication Services
N.A.I.C.S.: 517112

Seal Infotech Private Limited   (1)
56l Bason Futura IT Park Venkata Naray-
ana Road, Chennai, 600 017, India
Tel.: (91) 4466187000
Web Site: https://www.in.sealconsult.com
Software Development Services
N.A.I.C.S.: 541511

Telephone USA of Wisconsin,
LLC   (1)
333 Front St N, La Crosse, WI 54601
Tel.: (608) 796-5000
Telecommunication & Wireless Services
N.A.I.C.S.: 517112

United Telephone Company of Penn-
sylvania LLC, The   (1)
317 S Richard St, Bedford, PA 15522
Tel.: (814) 623-5121
Telecommunication & Wireless Services
N.A.I.C.S.: 517112

United Telephone Southeast LLC   (1)
1060 W Main St Ste 1-1, Abingdon, VA
24210-4736
Tel.: (276) 676-0515
Telecommunication Servicesb
N.A.I.C.S.: 517810

Valley Network Partnership   (1)
1 Lumos Plz, Waynesboro, VA 22980
Tel.: (540) 946-3525
Web Site: https://www.valleynet.com
Wired Telecommunication Services
N.A.I.C.S.: 517111

centurytel.com, LLC   (1)
100 CenturyLink Dr, Monroe, LA 71203
Tel.: (318) 388-9500
Emp.: 20,300
Telecommunication & Wireless Services
N.A.I.C.S.: 517112

LUMENT FINANCE TRUST, INC.

230 Park Ave 20th Fl, New York, NY
10169
Tel.: (212) 317-5700   MD
Web Site:
   https://www.lumentfinancetrust.com
Year Founded: 2012
LFT—(NYSE)
Rev.: $23,874,804
Assets: $1,127,965,537
Liabilities: $884,964,040
Net Worth: $243,001,497
Earnings: $5,123,660
Emp.: 600
Fiscal Year-end: 12/31/22
Real Estate Investment Services
N.A.I.C.S.: 523999
James J. Henson (Pres)
James Peter Flynn (Chm)
Stephanie G. Culpepper (Sec)

LUMENTUM HOLDINGS INC.

1001 Ridder Park Dr, San Jose, CA
95131
Tel.: (408) 546-5483   DE
Web Site: https://www.lumentum.com
LITE—(NASDAQ)
Rev.: $1,359,200,000
Assets: $3,931,900,000
Liabilities: $2,974,600,000
Net Worth: $957,300,000
Earnings: ($546,500,000)
Emp.: 7,257
Fiscal Year-end: 06/29/24
Optical & Photonic Products Mfr &
Sales
N.A.I.C.S.: 333310
Alan S. Lowe (CEO & Pres)
Penelope A. Herscher (Chm)
Matthew Sepe (Chief Acctg Officer)
Wajid Ali (CFO & Exec VP)

Grace Lee (Chief HR Officer & Sr
VP)
Caroline Pan (CMO & Sr VP)

Subsidiaries:

CCOP International (Thailand) Co.
Ltd.   (1)
75/10 CCOP Building Rama 6 Road, Thung
Phaya Thai Khet Ratchathewi, Bangkok,
10400, Thailand
Tel.: (66) 26445468
Web Site: https://ccop.asia
Communication Equipment Mfr
N.A.I.C.S.: 334290

Lumentum International (Thailand)
Co., Ltd.   (1)
60/129 Moo 19 Klongnueng Klongluang,
Pathumthani, 12120, Thailand
Tel.: (66) 21091678
Software Development Services
N.A.I.C.S.: 513210

Lumentum Operations LLC   (1)
1001 Ridder Park Dr, San Jose, CA 95131
Tel.: (408) 546-5483
Industrial Machinery Product Mfr & Distr
N.A.I.C.S.: 333515
Judy G. Hamel (Gen Counsel, Sec & Sr
VP)
Alan Lowe (Pres & CEO)
Ralph Loura (CIO & Sr VP-IT)
Misha Rozenberg (Chief Quality Officer &
Sr VP-Global Ops)

Lumentum Switzerland AG   (1)
Rutistrasse 12 and 14 3rd Floor, 8952,
Schlieren, Zurich, Switzerland
Tel.: (41) 445011000
Software Development Services
N.A.I.C.S.: 513210

Lumentum Taiwan Co., Ltd.   (1)
No 16 Xinzhan Road 32nd Floor, Banqiao
District, New Taipei City, 220, Taiwan
Tel.: (886) 7010150368
Software Development Services
N.A.I.C.S.: 513210

NeoPhotonics Corporation   (1)
3081 Zanker Rd, San Jose, CA 95134
Tel.: (408) 232-9200
Web Site: http://www.neophotonics.com
Rev.: $290,289,000
Assets: $305,567,000
Liabilities: $152,606,000
Net Worth: $152,961,000
Earnings: ($40,719,000)
Emp.: 1,157
Fiscal Year-end: 12/31/2021
Photonic Integrated Circuit-Based Module,
Component & Subsystem Mfr
N.A.I.C.S.: 334418
Raymond Cheung (COO & Sr VP)
Timothy Storrs Jenks (Chm, Pres & CEO)
Wupen Yuen (Chief Product Officer, Sr VP
& Gen Mgr)
G. Ferris Lipscomb (VP-Mktg)
Mona Taylor (Sr VP-HR)
Winston Way (CTO & VP)
Barbara Rogan (Gen Counsel & Sr VP)
Bradford W. Wright (Sr VP-Sls-Global)

Subsidiary (Non-US):

NeoPhotonics (China) Co., Ltd.   (2)
NeoPhotonics Building No 8 12th South Keji
Rd, South Hi-Tech Industry Park, Shen-
zhen, 518057, Guangdong, China
Tel.: (86) 75526748181
Web Site: http://www.neophotonics.com
Optical Component Mfr
N.A.I.C.S.: 456130

Oclaro, Inc.   (1)
225 Charcot Ave, San Jose, CA 95131
Tel.: (408) 383-1400
Web Site: http://www.oclaro.com
Rev.: $543,170,000
Assets: $720,799,000
Liabilities: $128,783,000
Net Worth: $592,016,000
Earnings: $62,453,000
Emp.: 1,701
Fiscal Year-end: 06/30/2018
Holding Company; Communication Optical
Components, Modules & Subsystems De-
signer, Mfr & Marketer
N.A.I.C.S.: 551112

Subsidiary (Non-US):

Oclaro Japan K.K.   (2)
Takagi Building 3F Iwamoto-cho 1-3-9,
Chiyoda-ku, Tokyo, 101-0032, Japan
Tel.: (81) 3 3865 5591
Web Site: http://www.oclaro.com
Communication Optical Components, Mod-
ules & Subsystems Marketer & Distr
N.A.I.C.S.: 423690
Tadayuki Kanno (Pres)

Oclaro Japan, Inc.   (2)
4-1-55 Oyama Chuo, Sagamihara, 252-
5250, Kanagawa, Japan
Tel.: (81) 427707011
Web Site: http://www.oclaro.com
Optical Instrument Mfr
N.A.I.C.S.: 237130
Tadayuki Kanno (Pres)

Subsidiary (Domestic):

Oclaro Photonics, Inc.   (2)
3640 Westwind Blvd, Santa Rosa, CA
95403-1037
Tel.: (408) 919-2728
Optical Instrument & Lens Mfr
N.A.I.C.S.: 333310

Subsidiary (Non-US):

Oclaro Technology (Shenzhen) Co.,
Ltd.   (2)
1/F 3/F 4/F 6/F 7/F of Wanli Industrial Build-
ing 2 Phoenix Road, Futian Free Trade
Zone, Shenzhen, 518038, Guangdong,
China
Tel.: (86) 75533305888
Electronic Components Mfr
N.A.I.C.S.: 334419

Oclaro Technology Limited   (2)
Caswell, Towcester, NN12 8EQ, Northants,
United Kingdom
Tel.: (44) 1327350581
Web Site: http://www.oclaro.com
Sales Range: $50-74.9 Million
Emp.: 200
Optical Components, Modules & Subsys-
tems Designer, Mfr & Marketer
N.A.I.C.S.: 333310

Subsidiary (Domestic):

Oclaro Technology, Inc.   (2)
3640 Westwind Blvd, Santa Rosa, CA
95403
Tel.: (707) 636-1227
Sales Range: $25-49.9 Million
Emp.: 60
Optical Instrument & Lens Mfr
N.A.I.C.S.: 333310

LUMINAR TECHNOLOGIES, INC.

2603 Discovery Dr Ste 100, Orlando,
FL 32826
Tel.: (407) 900-5259   DE
Web Site:
   https://www.luminartech.com
Year Founded: 2012
LAZR—(NASDAQ)
Rev.: $40,698,000
Assets: $687,327,000
Liabilities: $713,732,000
Net Worth: ($26,405,000)
Earnings: ($445,939,000)
Emp.: 600
Fiscal Year-end: 12/31/22
Driving Technology Solutions & Ser-
vices
N.A.I.C.S.: 441330
Tom Fennimore (CFO)
Allan Prescott (Chief Legal Officer)
Jason Elchenholz (Co-Founder &
CTO)
Austin Russell (Co-Founder, Chm,
Pres & CEO)

LUMOS PHARMA, INC.

4200 Marathon Blvd Ste 200, Austin,
TX 78756
Tel.: (512) 215-2630   DE

Web Site: https://www.lumos-
pharma.com
Year Founded: 1999
LUMO—(NASDAQ)
Rev.: $1,523,000
Assets: $72,292,000
Liabilities: $12,708,000
Net Worth: $59,584,000
Earnings: ($31,062,000)
Emp.: 32
Fiscal Year-end: 12/31/22
Pharmaceutical Preparation Manufac-
turing
N.A.I.C.S.: 325412
Charles J. Link Jr. (Founder)
Lori Lawley (CFO, Chief Acctg Offi-
cer, Sr VP-Fin & Controller)
Lisa Miller (Dir-IR & Media Rels)
Pisit Pitukcheewanont (Chief Medical
Officer)
Aaron Schuchart (Chief Bus Officer)
Chris Bemben (VP)
Michael Thorner (VP)
Ed Varnado (VP)
Richard J. Hawkins (Chm & CEO)

Subsidiaries:

BioProtection Systems
Corporation   (1)
2901 S Loop Dr Ste 3360, Ames, IA 50010
Tel.: (515) 598-2932
Biotechnology Research Services
N.A.I.C.S.: 541714

LUNA INNOVATIONS INCOR- PORATED

301 1st St SW Ste 200, Roanoke, VA
24011
Tel.: (540) 769-8400   DE
Web Site: https://www.lunainc.com
Year Founded: 1990
LUNA—(NASDAQ)
Rev.: $109,497,000
Assets: $151,007,000
Liabilities: $57,605,000
Net Worth: $93,402,000
Earnings: $9,279,000
Emp.: 337
Fiscal Year-end: 12/31/22
Innovative Technologies Research &
Development
N.A.I.C.S.: 541715
John C. Roiko (CFO & Principal
Acctg Officer)
Eva Hartmann (Sr VP-HR)
Thomas Oldemeyer (Sr VP & Mng
Dir-Europe, Middle East & Africa)
Salvan Farooqui (Sr VP)
Jackie Kline (Sr VP)
David Blaker (VP)
Melanie Singleton (VP)
Andy Brown (VP)
Allison L. Woody (Sr Dir)

Subsidiaries:

Advanced Photonix, Inc.   (1)
2925 Boardwalk, Ann Arbor, MI 48104
Tel.: (734) 864-5600
Web Site:
   https://www.advancedphotonix.com
Sales Range: $25-49.9 Million
Emp.: 122
Optoelectronic Devices, Systems & Sub-
Systems Developer & Mfr
N.A.I.C.S.: 334413

General Photonics Corporation   (1)
14351 Pipeline Ave, Chino, CA 91710
Tel.: (909) 590-5473
Web Site: http://www.generalphotonics.com
Rev.: $3,000,000
Emp.: 50
Fiscal Year-end: 12/31/2006
Automated Controller Distr
N.A.I.C.S.: 423610

Luna Technologies, Inc.   (1)
301 1st St SW Ste 200, Roanoke, VA
24011
Tel.: (540) 769-8400

Web Site: http://www.lunatechnologies.com
Sales Range: $75-99.9 Million
Emp.: 400
Optical Testing Device Mfr
N.A.I.C.S.: 335931

OptaSense Canada Ltd. (1)
57 Ave NE Bay 140-999, Calgary, T2E 8X9,
AB, Canada
Tel.: (403) 265-6165
Oilfield Monitoring Equipment Mfr & Distr
N.A.I.C.S.: 333132

Picometrix, LLC (1)
2925 Boardwalk, Ann Arbor, MI 48104
Tel.: (734) 864-5600
Web Site: http://lunainc.com
Ultra-High-Speed Optical Receivers & In-
strumentation Mfr
N.A.I.C.S.: 334290

LUVU BRANDS, INC.
2745 Bankers Industrial Dr, Atlanta,
GA 30360
Tel.: (770) 246-6400   FL
Web Site:
   https://www.luvubrands.com
Year Founded: 1999
LUVU—(OTCQB)
Rev.: $24,574,000
Assets: $9,131,000
Liabilities: $6,301,000
Net Worth: $2,830,000
Earnings: ($399,000)
Emp.: 192
Fiscal Year-end: 06/30/24
Investment Services
N.A.I.C.S.: 339999
Christopher Knauf (CFO & Controller)
Manuel Munoz (Dir-Info Sys)
Louis S. Friedman (Chm)

Subsidiaries:

One Up Innovations, Inc. (1)
2745 Bankers Industrial Dr, Atlanta, GA
30360
Tel.: (770) 246-6400
Web Site:
   https://www.oneupinnovations.com
Metal Products Mfr
N.A.I.C.S.: 331313

LUXURBAN HOTELS INC.
2125 Biscayne Blvd Ste 253, Miami,
FL 33137   DE
Web Site: https://luxurbanhotels.com
Year Founded: 2017
LUXH—(NASDAQ)
Rev.: $43,825,424
Assets: $107,963,021
Liabilities: $111,255,145
Net Worth: ($3,292,124)
Earnings: ($9,390,353)
Emp.: 213
Fiscal Year-end: 12/31/22
Apartment Rental Services
N.A.I.C.S.: 531110
Brian Ferdinand (Founder)
Michael C. James (CFO)
Karl Rothman (Chief Acctg Officer)
Rob Arigo (CEO)

LXP INDUSTRIAL TRUST
1 Penn Plz Ste 4015, New York, NY
10119-4015
Tel.: (212) 692-7200   MD
Web Site: https://www.lxp.com
Year Founded: 1993
LXP—(NYSE)
Rev.: $321,245,000
Assets: $4,053,847,000
Liabilities: $1,662,844,000
Net Worth: $2,391,003,000
Earnings: $113,783,000
Emp.: 66
Fiscal Year-end: 12/31/22
Real Estate Investment Trust
N.A.I.C.S.: 525990

T. Wilson Eglin (Chm, Pres & CEO)
Patrick Carroll (Chief Risk Officer &
Exec VP)
Natasha Roberts (Exec VP & Dir-
Acq)
Brendan P. Mullinix (Chief Investment
Officer & Exec VP)
Lara Sweeney Johnson (Exec VP-
Strategic Transactions)
Joseph S. Bonventre (COO, Gen
Counsel, Sec & Exec VP)
Nabil Andrawis (Exec VP & Dir-
Taxation)
Beth Boulerice (CFO, Treas & Exec
VP)
James Dudley (Exec VP & Dir-Asset
Mgmt)
Mark Cherone (Chief Acctg Officer)

Subsidiaries:

LEX DALLAS L.P. (1)
9701 W Ferris Branch Blvd, Dallas, TX
75243
Tel.: (214) 343-3832
Web Site: https://www.thelexdallas.com
Apartment Rental Services
N.A.I.C.S.: 531311

LEX PHOENIX L.P. (1)
1 Penn Plz Ste 4015, New York, NY 10119-
4015
Tel.: (212) 692-7200
Residential Building & Dwelling Leasing
Services
N.A.I.C.S.: 531110

LEXINGTON KNOXVILLE LLC (1)
10630 Lexington Dr, Knoxville, TN, 37932
Tel.: (865) 238-4356
Residential Building & Dwelling Leasing
Services
N.A.I.C.S.: 531110

LEXINGTON LAC LENEXA L.P. (1)
1 Penn Plz Ste 4015, New York, NY 10119-
4015
Tel.: (212) 692-7200
Emp.: 10
Commercial Building Rental & Leasing Ser-
vices
N.A.I.C.S.: 531120

**LEXINGTON OLIVE BRANCH MAN-
AGER LLC** (1)
1 Penn Plz Ste 4015, New York, NY 10119-
4015
Tel.: (212) 692-7200
Web Site: http://www.lxp.com
Real Estate Investment Services
N.A.I.C.S.: 525990

LRA MKP TRS L.P. (1)
2000 W Loop S Ste 1920, Houston, TX
77027-3529
Tel.: (212) 692-7200
Web Site: http://www.lxp.com
Real Estate Brokerage Services
N.A.I.C.S.: 525990

Lexington Finance (1)
1 Penn Plz Ste 4015, New York, NY 10119
Tel.: (212) 692-7200
Web Site: http://www.lxp.com
Sales Range: $25-49.9 Million
Real Estate Investment Trust
N.A.I.C.S.: 525990

Lexington ISS Holdings (1)
1 Penn Plz Ste 4015, New York, NY 10119
Tel.: (212) 692-7200
Sales Range: $250-299.9 Million
Real Estate Investment Trust
N.A.I.C.S.: 525990

**Lexington Real Estate Income
Trust** (1)
1 Penn Plz Ste 4015, New York, NY 10119
Tel.: (212) 692-7200
Web Site: http://www.lxp.com
Sales Range: $25-49.9 Million
Real Estate Investment Trust
N.A.I.C.S.: 525990

MLP UNIT PLEDGE L.P. (1)
2711 Centerville Rd Ste 400, Wilmington,
DE 19808

Tel.: (302) 636-5401
Real Estate Investment Services
N.A.I.C.S.: 525990

**PGA Professional Center Property
Owners Association** (1)
7100 Fairway Dr Ste 29, West Palm Beach,
FL 33418
Tel.: (561) 627-2800
Web Site: https://www.pga-poa.com
Sales Range: $250-299.9 Million
Emp.: 4
Real Estate Investment Trust
N.A.I.C.S.: 525990

LYDALL, INC.
1 Colonial Rd, Manchester, CT 06042
Tel.: (860) 646-1233   DE
Web Site: http://www.lydall.com
Year Founded: 1969
LDL—(NYSE)
Rev.: $764,041,000
Assets: $775,462,000
Liabilities: $517,766,000
Net Worth: $257,696,000
Earnings: ($73,725,000)
Emp.: 3,500
Fiscal Year-end: 12/31/20
Thermal & Acoustical Barriers, Auto-
motive Heat Shields & Insulation
Products Mfr
N.A.I.C.S.: 423330
Ashish Diwanji (Pres-Performance
Materials)
Marc T. Giles (Chm)
Paul G. Igoe (Gen Counsel, Sec &
VP)
Chad A. McDaniel (Chief Admin Offi-
cer, Gen Counsel & Exec VP)
Robert B. Junker (Pres-Technical
Nonwovens)

Subsidiaries:

**Andrew Industrial Textile Manufactur-
ing Company (Wuxi) Limited** (1)
500 Zhongtong Road Shuofang Town, Wuxi
New District, Wuxi, 214143, Jiangsu, China
Tel.: (86) 51085277300
Textile Products Mfr
N.A.I.C.S.: 314999

**Gutsche Environmental Technology
(Yixing) Co. Ltd.** (1)
Nanhuan Road Dingshan, Yixing, 214221,
Jiangsu, China
Tel.: (86) 51080723600
Industrial Equipment Distr
N.A.I.C.S.: 423830

**Interface Performance Materials In-
dia, LLP** (1)
I1 Maxis Presidium New no 2 Old no 63/1 L
Block 24th Street, Anna Nagar East, Chen-
nai, 600 102, India
Tel.: (91) 9962420700
Oil Seal Molded Packing & Coaxial Me-
chanical Face Seal Mfr
N.A.I.C.S.: 339991

**Interface Performance Materials,
Inc.** (1)
216 Wohlsen Way, Lancaster, PA 17603
Tel.: (800) 942-7538
Web Site: http://www.interfacematerials.com
Designer & Mfr of Sealing Systems; Gas-
kets, Fibreboard & Fibre Composites Mfr
N.A.I.C.S.: 339991
Bob Rathsam (CFO & Exec VP)

Unit (Domestic):

Interface Sealing Solutions (2)
410 S First Ave, Marshalltown, IA 50158
Tel.: (641) 752-6736
Web Site:
   http://www.interfacesealingsolutions.com
Sales Range: $10-24.9 Million
Gasket Seal Mfr
N.A.I.C.S.: 339991

**Interface Sealing Solutions, Europe
SARL** (1)
Maison Lilipean, Bonloc, Hasparren, 64240,
France
Tel.: (33) 559291220

Industrial Equipment Distr
N.A.I.C.S.: 423830

**Lydall Filtration Separation
S.A.S.** (1)
Saint Rivalain Operation Saint Rivalain, PO
Box 9, 56310, Melrand, France   (100%)
Tel.: (33) 297285300
Web Site: http://www.lydallfiltration.com
Sales Range: $25-49.9 Million
Emp.: 70
Provider of High Performance Engineered
Solutions for Air & Liquid Filtration Applica-
tions
N.A.I.C.S.: 313230

Lydall Filtration, Inc. (1)
68 Geore St, Green Island, NY 12183
Tel.: (518) 273-6320
Web Site: http://www.lydallthermal.com
Sales Range: $50-74.9 Million
Emp.: 100
Industrial Filtration Products
N.A.I.C.S.: 236210

**Lydall Filtration/Separation, Inc.
Rochester Operation** (1)
PO Box 1960, Rochester, NH
03866-1960   (100%)
Tel.: (603) 332-4600
Web Site: http://www.lydallfiltration.com
Sales Range: $50-74.9 Million
Emp.: 120
High-Performance Engineered Solutions for
Demanding Air & Liquid Filtration Applica-
tions
N.A.I.C.S.: 313230

Lydall Gutsche GmbH & Co. KG (1)
Hermann-Muth-Strasse 8, 36039, Fulda,
Germany
Tel.: (49) 66183840
Web Site: http://www.lydall-gutsche.com
Industrial Equipment Mfr & Distr
N.A.I.C.S.: 333413

**Lydall Industrial Filtration (EMEA)
Limited** (1)
Bycars Road, PO Box 1, Burslem, ST6
4SH, Stoke on Trent, United Kingdom
Tel.: (44) 1782838591
Web Site: http://www.lydallif.com
Emp.: 80
Engineeering Services
N.A.I.C.S.: 541330

**Lydall Industrial Filtration Textile
Manufacturing (EMEA) Limited** (1)
Hareholme Mill Bacup Road, Rossendale,
Rawtenstall, BB4 7JL, Lancashire, United
Kingdom
Tel.: (44) 1706214001
Textile Products Mfr
N.A.I.C.S.: 314999

**Lydall Industrial Textile Manufacturing
Company (Shanghai) Limited** (1)
Building 6 No1855 Tianchen Road, Qingpu,
Shanghai, 201712, China
Tel.: (86) 2159227025
Web Site: http://www.lydallif.com
Emp.: 150
Textile Products Mfr
N.A.I.C.S.: 314999

**Lydall Industrial Textile Manufacturing
Company (Wuxi) Limited** (1)
No 8 Zhongtong Road, Shuofang Town
Wuxi New District, Wuxi, 214143, Jiangsu,
China
Tel.: (86) 51085277300
Industrial Equipment Distr
N.A.I.C.S.: 423830

**Lydall Performance Materials
B.V.** (1)
Eisterweg 4, 6422 PN, Heerlen, Nether-
lands
Tel.: (31) 457515212
Engineeering Services
N.A.I.C.S.: 541330

**Lydall Performance Materials
S.A.S.** (1)
Saint Rivalain Operation Saint Rivalain,
56310, Melrand, France
Tel.: (33) 297285300
Web Site: http://www.lydallpm.com
Emp.: 95

Lydall, Inc.—(Continued)

Engineeering Services
N.A.I.C.S.: 541330

Lydall Performance Materials, Inc. (1)
134 Chestnut Hill Rd, Rochester, NH 03867
Tel.: (603) 332-4600
Engineeering Services
N.A.I.C.S.: 541330
Ashish Diwanji (Pres)

Lydall Solutech B.V. (1)
Eisterweg 4, 6422 PN, Heerlen, Netherlands
Tel.: (31) 457515212
Industrial Filtration & Thermal Insulation Products Mfr
N.A.I.C.S.: 313230

Lydall Thermal/Acoustical (1)
Brooks Crossroads 1241 Buck Shoals Rd, Hamptonville, NC 27020 (100%)
Tel.: (336) 468-8522
Web Site: http://www.lydall.com
Sales Range: $125-149.9 Million
Emp.: 700
Thermo & Automotive Parts Mfr
N.A.I.C.S.: 326299

Lydall Thermal/Acoustical Company Limited (Taicang) (1)
No 210 East Qingdao Road Loudong Street, Taicang, 215413, Jiangsu, China
Tel.: (86) 51282787830
Engineeering Services
N.A.I.C.S.: 541330

Lydall Thermal/Acoustical Sales, LLC (1)
39500 Mackenzie Dr Ste 300, Novi, MI 48377
Tel.: (248) 457-8101
Web Site: http://www.lydallautomotive.com
Emp.: 25
Thermal & Acoustical Insulation Products Mfr & Distr
N.A.I.C.S.: 238310

Lydall Thermique/Acoustique S.A.S. (1)
1 rue Alfred Kastler Z I de Brais BP 332, 44615, Saint-Nazaire, Cedex, France
Tel.: (33) 228541900
Web Site: http://www.lydall.com
Emp.: 100
Industrial Filtration & Thermal Insulation Products Mfr
N.A.I.C.S.: 313230

Southern Felt Company, Inc. (1)
1695 Edgefield Rd, North Augusta, SC 29860
Tel.: (803) 663-6693
Web Site: http://www.lydall.com
Emp.: 300
Automotive Products Mfr
N.A.I.C.S.: 336390

Texel Geosol Inc. (1)
1300 2e Rue Parc Industriel, Sainte-Marie, G6E 1G8, QC, Canada
Tel.: (418) 387-5910
Construction Equipment Installtion Services
N.A.I.C.S.: 237990
Francois Thivierge (Dir-Construction)

Texel Technical Materials, Inc. (1)
485 rue des Erables, Saint-Elzear, G0S 2J1, QC, Canada
Tel.: (418) 387-5910
Web Site: http://www.texel.ca
Nonwoven Material Mfr
N.A.I.C.S.: 339999

LYELL IMMUNOPHARMA, INC.
201 Haskins Way Ste 101, South San Francisco, CA 94080
Tel.: (650) 695-0677   DE
Web Site: https://www.lyell.com
Year Founded: 2018
LYEL—(NASDAQ)
Rev.: $84,683,000
Assets: $937,561,000
Liabilities: $104,309,000
Net Worth: $833,252,000
Earnings: ($183,118,000)

Emp.: 274
Fiscal Year-end: 12/31/22
Research & Development in Biotechnology (except Nanobiotechnology)
N.A.I.C.S.: 541714
Charles W. Newton (CFO)
Matthew Lang (Chief Bus Officer)
Tina Albertston (Chief Medical Officer & Head-Dev)
Richard Goold (CIO)
Lisa Ryan (Chief People Officer)
Elaine Cheung (Sr VP-Corp Strategy & Bus Dev)
Krys Corbett (Sr VP-Alliance Mgmt)
Nick Restifo (Exec VP-Research)
Ellen Rose (Sr VP-Comm & IR)
Richard Klausner (Founder & Chm)
Lynn Seely (Pres & CEO)

LYFT, INC.
185 Berry St Ste 400, San Francisco, CA 94107   DE
Web Site: https://www.lyft.com
Year Founded: 2007
LYFT—(NASDAQ)
Rev.: $4,403,589,000
Assets: $4,564,467,000
Liabilities: $4,022,949,000
Net Worth: $541,518,000
Earnings: ($340,320,000)
Emp.: 2,945
Fiscal Year-end: 12/31/23
Ride-Sharing Application Developer
N.A.I.C.S.: 513210
Lisa Blackwood-Kapral (Chief Acctg Officer)
Dominic Carr (Exec VP-Comm & Mktg)
Sona Iliffe-Moon (VP-External Comm)
Denise Bertuccelli (Sr Dir-Internal Comm)
Erin Brewer (CFO)
John Zimmer (Co-Founder & Vice Chm)
John David Risher (CEO)
Logan D. Green (Co-Founder)

LYONS BANCORP, INC.
35 William St, Lyons, NY 14489
Tel.: (315) 946-4871
Web Site: https://bankwithlnb.com
LYBC—(OTCQX)
Rev.: $86,880,000
Assets: $1,848,564,000
Liabilities: $1,744,904,000
Net Worth: $103,660,000
Earnings: $17,359,000
Emp.: 250
Fiscal Year-end: 12/31/23
Executive Office
N.A.I.C.S.: 921110
Robert A. Schick (Chm & CEO)
Thomas L. Kime (Pres)

Subsidiaries:

The Lyons National Bank (1)
470 Exchange St, Geneva, NY 14456
Tel.: (315) 946-4871
Sales Range: $25-49.9 Million
Emp.: 30
Provider of Banking Services
N.A.I.C.S.: 522110
Robert A. Schick (Chm & CEO)
Darrin Brentnall (VP-Macedon)
Michael Colacino (Asst VP)
Jeffrey Friend (Sr VP)
Todd Juffs (VP)
Tara Rago (VP & Branch Mgr-Canandaigua)
Tom Kime (Pres)
Charles Parkhurst (Asst VP & Branch Mgr-Farmington)
Angelo Battoglia (Asst Branch Mgr-Farmington)

LYRA THERAPEUTICS, INC.
480 Arsenal way, Watertown, MA 02472
Tel.: (617) 393-4600   DE

Web Site:
https://lyratherapeutics.com
Year Founded: 2005
LYRA—(NASDAQ)
Rev.: $1,558,000
Assets: $142,600,000
Liabilities: $53,180,000
Net Worth: $89,420,000
Earnings: ($62,680,000)
Emp.: 88
Fiscal Year-end: 12/31/23
Biotechnology Research & Development Services
N.A.I.C.S.: 541714
Maria Palasis (Pres & CEO)
Corinne Noyes (Sr VP-Comml Strategy & Market Dev)
Vineeta Belanger (Sr VP-Clinical Affairs)
John E. Bishop (CTO)
Robert Richard (Sr VP-Technical Ops & R&D)
Jason Cavalier (CFO)
Richard Nieman (Chief Medical Officer)

M&F BANCORP, INC.
2634 Durham-Chapel Hill Blvd Ste 101, Durham, NC 27707-2800
Tel.: (919) 687-7800   NC
Web Site: http://www.mfbonline.com
Year Founded: 1907
MFBP—(OTCIQ)
Sales Range: $10-24.9 Million
Emp.: 67
Bank Holding Company
N.A.I.C.S.: 551111
James H. Sills III (Pres & CEO)
Connie J. White (Vice Chm)
Kathy E. Fox (Sr VP & Controller)
James A. Stewart (Chm)

Subsidiaries:

M&F Bank (1)
2634 Durham Chapel Hill Blvd, Durham, NC 27707
Tel.: (919) 687-7800
Web Site: http://www.mfbonline.com
Sales Range: $50-74.9 Million
Emp.: 80
Commericial Banking
N.A.I.C.S.: 522110
Valerie M. Quiett (Sec)
Randall C. Hall (CFO)
James H. Sills III (Pres & CEO)
James Edward Sansom (Chief Lending Officer)
Cristina Velasquez (Asst VP & Mgr-HR)

M&T BANK CORPORATION
1 M&T Plz, Buffalo, NY 14203
Tel.: (716) 635-4000   NY
Web Site: https://www.mtb.com
Year Founded: 1969
MTB—(NYSE)
Rev.: $10,224,000,000
Assets: $208,264,000,000
Liabilities: $181,307,000,000
Net Worth: $26,957,000,000
Earnings: $2,741,000,000
Emp.: 22,223
Fiscal Year-end: 12/31/23
Bank Holding Company
N.A.I.C.S.: 551111
Marie King (Sec & Grp VP)
Kevin J. Pearson (Vice Chm)
D. Scott N. Warman (Treas & Exec VP)
Richard S. Gold (Pres & COO)
Rene F. Jones (Chm & CEO)
Michael R. Spychala (Sr Dir-Fin)
William J. Farrell II (Exec VP-Wealth & Institutional Svcs)
Matthew Petrula (Head-Reg Real Estate)
Michael J. Todaro (Exec VP-Enterprise Transformation)

Christopher E. Kay (Exec VP-Consumer Banking, Bus Banking & Mktg)
Francesco Lagutaine (Chief Mktg & Comm Officer)
John R. Taylor (Controller)
Tim Gallagher (Head-Comml Real Estate)
Hugh Giorgio (Head-Investment Banking)
Jeff Carpenter (Head-Corp Banking)
Michelle Brett (Head-Comml Risk)
Jennifer Warren (Sr Exec VP)
Julie Urban (Sr Exec VP)
Laura O'Hara (Gen Counsel)
Michael T. Keegan (Sr Exec VP)
Michael A. Wisler (Sr Exec VP)
Peter G. D'Arcy (Sr Exec VP)

Subsidiaries:

Manufacturers & Traders Trust Company (1)
1 M&T Plz, Buffalo, NY 14203 (100%)
Tel.: (716) 842-5445
Web Site: http://www.mtb.com
Commercial Banking & Diversified Financial Services
N.A.I.C.S.: 522110

Subsidiary (Domestic):

Highland Lease Corporation (2)
1 M&T Plz, Buffalo, NY 14203-2309 (100%)
Tel.: (716) 842-5445
Web Site: http://www.mntbank.com
Sales Range: $1-4.9 Billion
Consumer Lending
N.A.I.C.S.: 522291

M&T Credit Corporation (2)
1 M & T Plz, Buffalo, NY 14203-2309 (100%)
Tel.: (716) 842-5445
Web Site: http://www.mandtbank.com
Rev.: $30,177,000
Consumer Lending
N.A.I.C.S.: 522291

M&T Insurance Agency, Inc (2)
285 Delaware Ave Ste 4000, Buffalo, NY 14202
Tel.: (716) 853-7960
Web Site: http://www.mtb.com
Sales Range: $1-9.9 Million
Emp.: 70
Property & Casualty Insurance Services
N.A.I.C.S.: 524126
John Rumschik (Vice Chm)

M&T Mortgage Corp. (2)
1 Fountain Plz M T Ctr Fl 5, Buffalo, NY 14203-2399 (100%)
Tel.: (716) 848-4848
Web Site: http://www.mandtbank.com
Rev.: $112,676,000
Emp.: 150
Residential Mortgage Lending
N.A.I.C.S.: 522292

M&T Realty Capital Corporation (2)
25 S Charles St 17th Fl, Baltimore, MD 21201 (100%)
Tel.: (410) 545-2411
Web Site: https://www.mtrcc.com
Commercial Real Estate Financing Services
N.A.I.C.S.: 522292
Joe McFarland (CFO)
Steven Muth (Mng Dir)
Michael Edelman (Mgr-Agency Program-Fannie Mae & Freddie Mac)
Wendy Leblanc (Chief Closing & Delivery Officer)

Subsidiary (Domestic):

Carey, Kramer, Pettit, Panichelli & Associates, Inc. (3)
460 E Swedesford Rd Ste 1000, Wayne, PA 19087
Tel.: (610) 341-0200

Web Site: http://www.ckpp.com
Rev.: $2,700,000,000
Emp.: 15
Commercial Real Estate Financing Services
N.A.I.C.S.: 522292

Subsidiary (Domestic):

M&T Securities, Inc. **(2)**
1 M&T Plz, Buffalo, NY
14203-2309 **(100%)**
Tel.: (716) 635-9308
Rev.: $21,589,000
Securities Brokerage & Investment Advisory
Services
N.A.I.C.S.: 523150

People's United Financial, Inc. **(1)**
850 Main St, Bridgeport, CT 06604
Tel.: (203) 338-7171
Web Site: http://www.peoples.com
Rev.: $1,994,900,000
Assets: $64,642,400,000
Liabilities: $56,740,600,000
Net Worth: $7,901,800,000
Earnings: $604,900,000
Emp.: 5,193
Fiscal Year-end: 12/31/2021
Bank Holding Company
N.A.I.C.S.: 551111
Marie King (Sec)
D. Scott N. Warman (Treas)
Richard S. Gold (Pres)
Jeffrey A. Hoyt (Chief Acctg Officer & Sr
VP)
Lee C. Powlus (Chief Admin Officer & Sr
Exec VP)
Stephen T. Wilson (Asst Sec)

Subsidiary (Domestic):

People's United Bank, N.A. **(2)**
850 Main St, Bridgeport, CT
06604-4917 **(100%)**
Tel.: (203) 338-7001
Web Site: http://branches.peoples.com
Sales Range: $1-4.9 Billion
Emp.: 5,000
Commericial Banking
N.A.I.C.S.: 522110
Kirk W. Walters (Sr Exec VP-Corp Dev &
Strategic Plng)
Michael J. Casparino (Reg Pres-Retail
Banking-Northern Connecticut)
Patrick J. Sullivan (Pres-Massachusetts &
Exec VP-Comml Banking)
Dianne M. Mercier (Reg Pres-New Hamp-
shire)

Subsidiary (Domestic):

LEAF Commercial Capital, Inc. **(3)**
1 Commerce Sq 2005 Market St 14th Fl,
Philadelphia, PA 19103
Web Site: https://www.leafnow.com
Equipment Finance Leasing Services
N.A.I.C.S.: 522220

MSB Real Estate Corp. **(3)**
850 Main St, Bridgeport, CT 06604
Tel.: (203) 338-7171
Web Site: http://www.peoples.com
Rev.: $390,000
Emp.: 6
Real Estate Financial/Management Services
N.A.I.C.S.: 531120

People's Capital & Leasing Corp. **(3)**
207-235 Bank St, Waterbury, CT 06702-
2213
Tel.: (203) 754-9000
Web Site: http://www.peoples.com
Sales Range: $10-24.9 Million
Emp.: 35
Equipment Rental & Leasing
N.A.I.C.S.: 532490
Ray Shilling (VP-Northeast)
Ray McGowan (Sr VP-Equipment Grp)

People's United Advisors, Inc. **(3)**
850 Main St, Bridgeport, CT
06604 **(100%)**
Tel.: (203) 338-7001
Web Site: http://www.peoples.com
Investment Advisory & Wealth Management
Services
N.A.I.C.S.: 523940

Division (Domestic):

Gerstein, Fisher & Associates,
Inc. **(4)**

565 5th Ave 27th Fl Entrance on E 46th St,
New York, NY 10017-2478
Tel.: (212) 968-0707
Web Site: http://www.gersteinfisher.com
Investment Management Service
N.A.I.C.S.: 523940
Gregg S. Fisher (Founder & Head-
Quantitative Res & Portfolio Strategy)

Subsidiary (Domestic):

Olson Mobeck Investment Advisors
Inc. **(4)**
1310 Silas Deane Hwy Ste 201, Wethers-
field, CT 06109 **(100%)**
Tel.: (860) 563-2368
Web Site: http://www.peoplesbank.com
Rev.: $2,000,000
Emp.: 26
Investment Advice
N.A.I.C.S.: 523940

Subsidiary (Domestic):

People's United Equipment Finance
Corp. **(3)**
1300 Post Oak Blvd Ste 1300, Houston, TX
77056-3028
Tel.: (713) 439-1177
Web Site: http://www.puefc.com
Sales Range: $25-49.9 Million
Emp.: 30
Commercial Equipment Sales Financing
Services
N.A.I.C.S.: 522220
Paul Sinsheimer (Pres)

Wilmington Trust Corporation **(1)**
1100 N Market St Ste 1300, Wilmington, DE
19890-0001
Tel.: (302) 651-1000
Web Site: http://www.wilmingtontrust.com
Sales Range: $750-799.9 Million
Emp.: 2,793
Holding Company; Wealth Advisory, Corpo-
rate Client & Regional Banking Services
N.A.I.C.S.: 551111
William Marder (Mng Dir)
Rick D'Emilia (Mng Dir)
Caroline Magee (Mng Dir)
Mike Orendorf (VP-Capital Markets Insur-
ance)
W. Chris Sponenberg (VP)
Tom Strauss (VP)
Dominick D'Eramo (Head-Fixed Income)
Tony Lunger (Mng Dir & VP)
Alex Pashley (Head-Structured Fin-UK)
Medita Vucic (VP)
Laron Galea (Head-M&A Admin)
Fiona Boger (Head-M&A Shareholder Rep
Bus)
Stephen A. Seivold (VP)
Bob Bockrath (VP-Capital Market Insur-
ance)
Rob Weiss (VP)
Jim Deitrick (VP)
John Jorlin (VP)
Donald P. Dicarlo Jr. (Chief People Officer)

Subsidiary (Domestic):

Wilmington Trust Company **(2)**
1100 N Market St Ste 1300, Wilmington, DE
19890-0001
Tel.: (302) 651-1000
Web Site: http://www.wilmingtontrust.com
Financial Services
N.A.I.C.S.: 523999
Tony Roth (Chief Investment Officer)
Dominick D'Eramo (Head-Fixed Income)
Mary Alice Avery (VP)
Meghan Shue (Head-Investment Strategy)
Phil Ravenscroft (Head-Portfolio Construc-
tion)
Matt Glaser (Head-Equities & Nontraditional
Investments)
Andrew Hopkins (Head-Equity Res)
Mark D. Horst (Sr Portfolio Mgr)
Clement Miller (Sr Portfolio Mgr)
Steve Norcini (Sr Portfolio Mgr-Equity)
Tom Pierce (Head-Fixed Income Res &
Strategy)
Jordan Strauss (Sr Portfolio Mgr)
James Hannan (Sr Portfolio Mgr)
Jason Hannon (Head-Municipal Strategy)
Dan Scholl (Head-Municipal Fixed Income)
Karleen Strayer (Head-Municipal Res)
Patrick Tadie (VP)
Tom Strauss (VP)
Pat Schulze (VP)

M-TRON INDUSTRIES, INC.
2525 Shader Rd, Orlando, FL 32804
Tel.: (407) 298-2000 SD
Web Site: https://www.mtronpti.com
Year Founded: 1976
MPTI—(NYSEAMEX)
Rev.: $31,845,000
Assets: $19,273,000
Liabilities: $4,932,000
Net Worth: $14,341,000
Earnings: $1,798,000
Emp.: 161
Fiscal Year-end: 12/31/22
Other Electronic Parts & Equipment
Merchant Wholesalers
N.A.I.C.S.: 423690
Michael J. Ferrantino Jr. (CEO)

Subsidiaries:

M-tron Industries, Ltd. **(1)**
Unit 2004 20th Floor Aitken Vanson Centre
No 61 Hoi Yuen Road, Kwun Tong, Kow-
loon, China (Hong Kong)
Tel.: (852) 2 866 8023
Web Site: http://www.mtronpti.com
Emp.: 1
Electronic Components Mfr
N.A.I.C.S.: 334419

M/I HOMES, INC.
4131 Worth Ave Ste 500, Columbus,
OH 43219
Tel.: (614) 418-8000 OH
Web Site: https://www.mihomes.com
Year Founded: 1976
MHO—(NYSE)
Rev.: $4,033,502,000
Assets: $4,022,440,000
Liabilities: $1,505,501,000
Net Worth: $2,516,939,000
Earnings: $465,365,000
Emp.: 1,607
Fiscal Year-end: 12/31/23
Homebuilders
N.A.I.C.S.: 236220
Robert H. Schottenstein (Chm, Pres
& CEO)
Phillip G. Creek (CFO & Exec VP)
Susan E. Krohne (Chief Legal Officer,
Sec & Sr VP)

Subsidiaries:

M/I Financial Corp. **(1)**
3 Easton Oval Ste 540, Columbus, OH
43219
Tel.: (614) 418-8650
Web Site: http://www.mihomes.com
Sales Range: $150-199.9 Million
Emp.: 85
Mortgage Services
N.A.I.C.S.: 522292
Robert H. Schottenstein (Pres)

Subsidiary (Domestic):

M/I Title Agency Ltd. **(2)**
400 International Pkwy, Lake Mary, FL
32746
Tel.: (407) 531-5215
Emp.: 3
Residential Construction
N.A.I.C.S.: 236115
Tracey Kelley (Gen Mgr)

M/I Homes of Austin, LLC **(1)**
7600 N Capital of Texas Hwy Bldg C Ste
250, Austin, TX 78731
Tel.: (512) 368-8420
Real Estate Related Services
N.A.I.C.S.: 531390
James Blamey (Mgr-Construction)

M/I Homes of Charlotte, LLC **(1)**
5350 77 Center Dr Ste 150, Charlotte, NC
28217
Tel.: (704) 228-3892
Web Site: http://www.mihomes.com
Emp.: 40
Residential Construction
N.A.I.C.S.: 236115

M/I Homes of Indiana, L.P. **(1)**

8500 Keystone Crossing Ste 590, India-
napolis, IN 46240
Tel.: (317) 255-9600
Residential Construction
N.A.I.C.S.: 236115

M/I Homes of Raleigh, LLC **(1)**
1511 Sunday Dr Ste 100, Raleigh, NC
27607-5195
Tel.: (919) 205-9980
Web Site: https://www.mihomes.com
Emp.: 28
Residential Construction
N.A.I.C.S.: 236115

M/I Insurance Agency, LLC **(1)**
3 Easton Oval Ste 220, Columbus, OH
43219
Tel.: (614) 418-8719
Sales Range: $1-9.9 Million
Emp.: 72
Insurance Services
N.A.I.C.S.: 524210
Robert H. Schottenstein (Pres)

M/I Properties, LLC **(1)**
3 Easton Oval Ste 500, Columbus, OH
43219-6011
Tel.: (614) 418-8300
Residential Construction
N.A.I.C.S.: 236115

MI Homes of Michigan, LLC **(1)**
40950 Woodward Ave Ste 203, Bloomfield
Hills, MI 48304
Tel.: (248) 221-5000
Housing Construction Services
N.A.I.C.S.: 236116
Joe FontanaPres- (Pres-Sarasota)

MI Homes of MinneapolisSt. Paul,
LLC **(1)**
5354 Parkdale Dr Ste 100, Saint Louis
Park, MN 55416
Tel.: (763) 586-7279
Emp.: 22
Housing Construction Services
N.A.I.C.S.: 236116
Eric Wiseman (Superintendent-
Construction)

TransOhio Residential Title Agency,
Ltd. **(1)**
3 Easton Oval, Columbus, OH 43219
Tel.: (614) 418-8999
Real Estate Title Insurance Carriers
N.A.I.C.S.: 524127

**M3-BRIGADE ACQUISITION V
CORP.**
1700 Broadway 19th Fl, New York,
NY 10019
Tel.: (212) 202-2200 Ky
Web Site: https://www.m3-
brigade.com
Year Founded: 2024
MBAV—(NYSE)
Investment Holding Company
N.A.I.C.S.: 551111

**MACAU CAPITAL INVEST-
MENTS, INC.**
1001 Texas Ave Ste 1400, Houston,
TX 77002
Tel.: (832) 859-3678 DE
Year Founded: 1990
MCIM—(OTCIQ)
Waste Management Services
N.A.I.C.S.: 562998
Hershell Hayes (CEO)
Monique Hayes (Pres & CFO)

**MACE SECURITY INTERNA-
TIONAL, INC.**
4400 Carnegie Ave, Cleveland, OH
44103
Tel.: (440) 424-5321 DE
Web Site: https://www.mace.com
Year Founded: 1987
MACE—(OTCIQ)
Rev.: $15,391,000
Assets: $11,389,000
Liabilities: $3,000,000
Net Worth: $8,389,000

Mace Security International, Inc.—(Continued)

Earnings: $1,701,000
Emp.: 42
Fiscal Year-end: 12/31/20
Personal Defense & Security Products Mfr, Marketer & Online Retailer
N.A.I.C.S.: 334290
Gary Medved *(Pres & CEO)*
Sanjay Singh *(Chm)*
Michael Weisbarth *(CFO)*
Dan Brass *(Dir-Channel Sls)*

Subsidiaries:

Washington Laboratories, Ltd. **(1)**
7560 Lindbergh Dr, Gaithersburg, MD 20879-5414
Tel.: (301) 216-1500
Web Site: http://www.wll.com
Testing Laboratory & Engineering Services
N.A.I.C.S.: 541380
Michael Violette *(CEO)*

MACH NATURAL RESOURCES LP

14201 Wireless Way Ste 300, Oklahoma City, OK 73134
Tel.: (405) 252-8100   **DE**
Web Site: https://www.machnr.com
Year Founded: 2017
MNR—(NYSE)
Rev.: $762,309,000
Assets: $2,304,515,000
Liabilities: $1,112,791,000
Net Worth: $1,191,724,000
Earnings: $68,518,000
Emp.: 442
Fiscal Year-end: 12/31/23
Natural Gas Extraction Services
N.A.I.C.S.: 211130

MACH7 TECHNOLOGIES LIMITED

120 Kimball Ave Ste 210, South Burlington, VT 05403
Tel.: (802) 861-7745   **AU**
Web Site: https://www.mach7t.com
Year Founded: 2007
M7T—(ASX)
Rev.: $45,663,624
Assets: $125,072,178
Liabilities: $34,680,799
Net Worth: $90,391,379
Earnings: ($1,592,711)
Fiscal Year-end: 06/30/23
Holding Company; Medical Specific Imaging Solutions & Data Management Software Developer & Publisher
N.A.I.C.S.: 511112

Subsidiaries:

Mach7 Technologies, Inc. **(1)**
120 Kimball Ave Ste 210, South Burlington, VT 05403
Tel.: (802) 861-7745
Web Site: http://www.mach7t.com
Medical Specific Imaging Solutions & Data Management Software Developer & Publisher
N.A.I.C.S.: 513210

MACHTEN, INC.

1516 Barlow St Ste D, Traverse City, MI 49686
Tel.: (855) 642-4227   **DE**
Web Site: https://www.machteninc.com
Year Founded: 2022
MACT—(OTCIQ)
Offices of Other Holding Companies
N.A.I.C.S.: 551112

MACKENZIE REALTY CAPITAL, INC.

89 Davis Rd Ste 100, Orinda, CA 94563
Tel.: (925) 631-9100   **MD**

Web Site:
   https://www.mackenzierealty.com
Year Founded: 2012
MKZR—(OTCQX)
Rev.: $15,736,103
Assets: $233,087,768
Liabilities: $125,138,676
Net Worth: $107,949,092
Earnings: ($11,223,832)
Fiscal Year-end: 06/30/24
Real Estate Investment Services
N.A.I.C.S.: 531210
Robert E. Dixon *(Pres & CEO)*
Paul Koslosky *(CFO & Treas)*
Glen W. Fuller *(COO)*
Jeri Bluth *(Chief Compliance Officer)*
Charles Patterson *(Owner, Chm, Gen Partner, Mng Dir, Exec Officer, Gen Counsel-Advisers & Mgr, Sec & Sr VP-Advisers & Mgr)*

MACKINAC FINANCIAL CORPORATION

130 S Cedar St, Manistique, MI 49854   **MI**
Web Site:
   http://www.bankmbank.com
Year Founded: 1974
MFNC—(NASDAQ)
Rev.: $62,029,000
Assets: $1,501,730,000
Liabilities: $1,333,866,000
Net Worth: $167,864,000
Earnings: $13,473,000
Emp.: 315
Fiscal Year-end: 12/31/20
Bank Holding Company
N.A.I.C.S.: 551111
Kelly W. George *(Pres)*

Subsidiaries:

First Manistique Agency, Inc. **(1)**
130 S Cedar St, Manistique, MI 49854-1438   **(100%)**
Tel.: (906) 341-8401
Insurance Agencies & Brokerage Services
N.A.I.C.S.: 524210
Kelly George *(CEO)*

mBank **(1)**
130 S Cedar St, Manistique, MI 49854   **(100%)**
Tel.: (906) 341-8401
Web Site: http://www.bankmbank.com
Emp.: 320
Commericial Banking
N.A.I.C.S.: 522110
Kelly W. George *(Pres & CEO)*
Paul D. Tobias *(Chm)*
Jesse A. Deering *(CFO & Exec VP)*
Tammy R. McDowell *(Exec VP & Mng Dir-Credit Admin & Ops)*
Gregory Schuetter *(Sr VP-Eastern UP & Mgr-Comml Lending)*
Joanna B. Slaght *(Exec VP & Mng Dir-Compliance & Regulatory Risk)*
Clay V. Peterson *(Exec VP & Mng Dir-Retail Banking)*
Boris Martysz *(Officer-Comml Banking & Sr VP)*
Erin McCormick *(Officer-Sls & Sr VP-Admin Branch)*
Sherry Arnold *(Sr VP-Admin & Dir-Talent)*
Jerome W. Tracey *(Sr VP-Comml Banking & Alpena Market)*
Rick Demers *(Officer-Comml Banking & VP)*
Magan Peterson *(VP)*

MACOM TECHNOLOGY SOLUTIONS HOLDINGS, INC.

100 Chelmsford St, Lowell, MA 01851
Tel.: (978) 656-2500   **DE**
Web Site: https://www.macom.com
MTSI—(NASDAQ)
Rev.: $729,578,000
Assets: $1,755,640,000
Liabilities: $629,297,000
Net Worth: $1,126,343,000
Earnings: $76,859,000
Emp.: 1,700

Fiscal Year-end: 09/27/24
Holding Company; Integrated Circuit, Power Transistor & Diode Segment Products Mfr
N.A.I.C.S.: 551112
John L. Ocampo *(Chm)*
Robert Dennehy *(Sr VP-Ops)*
Stephen G. Daly *(Chm, Pres & CEO)*
Donghyun Thomas Hwang *(Sr VP-Sls-Global)*
John F. Kober III *(CFO & Sr VP)*
Ambra Roth *(Gen Counsel-HR, Sec & Sr VP)*
Stephen Ferranti *(VP-Strategic Initiatives & IR)*

Subsidiaries:

Applied Micro Circuits Corporation **(1)**
4555 Great America Pkwy Ste 6th, Santa Clara, CA 95054
Tel.: (408) 542-8600
Web Site: http://www.apm.com
High-Performance, High-Bandwidth Silicon Connectivity Products for the Telecommunications Industry
N.A.I.C.S.: 334413

Subsidiary (Non-US):

AMCC Japan Co. Ltd. **(2)**
Regus Center W22F Shibuya Mark City 1-12-1 Dogenzaka, Shibuya-ku, Tokyo, 150-0043, Japan
Tel.: (81) 343605386
Web Site: http://www.appliedmicro.com
Marketer of High-Performance, High-Bandwidth Silicon Connectivity for the Telecommunications Industry
N.A.I.C.S.: 423430

Applied Micro Circuits Corporation Canada **(2)**
62 Steacle Drive #102, Kanata, K2K 2A9, ON, Canada
Tel.: (613) 254-6700
Web Site: http://www.apm.com
Microprocessor Chip Mfr
N.A.I.C.S.: 334413

BinOptics Corp. **(1)**
9 Brown Rd, Ithaca, NY 14850
Tel.: (607) 257-3200
Web Site: http://www.binoptics.com
Sales Range: $1-9.9 Million
Emp.: 35
Optical Instrument & Lens Mfr
N.A.I.C.S.: 333310
Alex Behfar *(Founder)*

Linear Space Technology, LLC **(1)**
3 Nami Ln Ste 9, Hamilton, NJ 08619
Tel.: (609) 584-8424
Solid State Amplifier Mfr
N.A.I.C.S.: 335999

Linearizer Technology, Inc. **(1)**
3 Nami Ln, Trenton, NJ 08619
Tel.: (609) 584-8424
Web Site: http://www.lintech.com
Sales Range: $1-9.9 Million
Emp.: 32
Electron Tube Mfr
N.A.I.C.S.: 334419
Allen Katz *(Pres)*
Allan Guida *(CFO)*
Elizabeth Klepner *(Mgr-Mktg)*
Roger Dorval *(VP)*
Therese D. Ulrich *(Mgr)*
Victor Belanger *(VP-Engrg)*
Eugene Hoffman *(VP-Quality-Production Assembly MEA Ops)*
John A. MacDonald *(VP & Gen Mgr)*
Michelle Rybinski *(Comptroller)*

M/A-COM Technology Solutions (UK) Limited **(1)**
Unit 2 Bridgewood House, Belfast, BT9 5NW, United Kingdom
Tel.: (44) 2890662878
Semiconductor Devices Mfr
N.A.I.C.S.: 334413

M/A-COM Technology Solutions Inc. **(1)**
100 Chelmsford St, Lowell, MA 01851
Tel.: (978) 656-2500

Semiconductors, Active & Passive Components & Sub-assemblies for use in Radio Frequency, Microwave & Millimeter Wave Applications Mfr
N.A.I.C.S.: 334413

Subsidiary (Domestic):

Mimix Broadband, Inc. **(2)**
100 Chelmsford St, Lowell, MA 01851-2620
Tel.: (281) 988-4600
Web Site: http://www.mimixbroadband.com
Sales Range: $75-99.9 Million
Emp.: 110
Semiconductor Designer, Developer & Distr
N.A.I.C.S.: 334413
Alden Lofquist *(VP-Sls)*

M/ACOM Technology Solutions (Cork) Limited **(1)**
4 EastGate Road, Little Island, Cork, Ireland
Tel.: (353) 212446400
Emp.: 70
Semiconductor Devices Mfr
N.A.I.C.S.: 334413

MACOM Japan Limited **(1)**
9F Palazzo Siena 2-4-6, Higashi-shinbashi Minato-ku, Tokyo, 105-0021, Japan
Tel.: (81) 354721609
Semiconductor Mfr
N.A.I.C.S.: 334413

MACOM Technology Solutions (Bangalore) Private Limited **(1)**
Prestige Atrium Unit 404 3rd Floor Level 4 Central Street, Bengaluru, 560001, India
Tel.: (91) 8043537383
Semiconductor Devices Mfr
N.A.I.C.S.: 334413

MACOM Technology Solutions Canada Inc. **(1)**
5045 South Service Road Suite 202, Burlington, L7L 5Y7, ON, Canada
Tel.: (905) 633-3650
Semiconductor Mfr
N.A.I.C.S.: 334413

Mindspeed Technologies India Private Ltd. **(1)**
Ascendas IT Park Software Units Layout, Madhapur, Hyderabad, 500081, India
Tel.: (91) 40207081
Software Publishing Services
N.A.I.C.S.: 513210

Mindspeed Technologies, Inc. **(1)**
4000 MacArthur Blvd East Tower, Newport Beach, CA 92660-3095
Tel.: (949) 579-3000
Web Site: http://www.mindspeed.com
Rev.: $161,401,000
Assets: $91,324,000
Liabilities: $87,566,000
Net Worth: $3,758,000
Earnings: ($89,148,000)
Emp.: 478
Fiscal Year-end: 09/27/2013
Semiconductor Mfr
N.A.I.C.S.: 334413
John R. Croteau *(Pres & CEO)*

Subsidiary (Non-US):

Mindspeed Technologies (K.K.) **(2)**
15F Shiba NBF Tower 1-1 -30 Shibadaimon, Minato-ku, Tokyo, 105-0012, Tokyo, Japan
Tel.: (81) 354721601
Emp.: 4
Computer Terminal Mfr
N.A.I.C.S.: 334118
Nigel Goward *(Gen Mgr)*

MACQUARIE GLOBAL INFRASTRUCTURE TOTAL RETURN FUND INC.

125 W 55th St, New York, NY 10019
MGU—(NYSE)
Investment Management Service
N.A.I.C.S.: 525990
Brad L. Frishberg *(Mgr-Fund)*
Thomas W. Hunersen *(Chm)*
John C. Leonard *(Pres & CEO)*

MACQUARIE/FIRST TRUST

GLOBAL INFRASTRUCTURE/UTILITIES DIVIDEND & INCOME FUND
120 E Liberty Dr Ste 400, Wheaton, IL 60187
Tel.: (630) 765-8000   **MA**
MFD—(NYSE)
Closed-End Investment Fund
N.A.I.C.S.: 525990

MACREPORT.NET, INC.
1603 Capitol Ave Ste 310 A278, Cheyenne, WY 82001
Tel.: (315) 567-6946   **WY**
Year Founded: 2000
MRPT—(OTCIQ)
Media Services
N.A.I.C.S.: 541840
V. William Lucchetti *(Pres & CEO)*

MACROGENICS, INC.
9704 Medical Center Dr, Rockville, MD 20850
Tel.: (301) 251-5172   **DE**
Web Site:
   https://www.macrogenics.com
Year Founded: 2000
MGNX—(NASDAQ)
Rev.: $151,941,000
Assets: $280,468,000
Liabilities: $138,455,000
Net Worth: $142,013,000
Earnings: ($119,758,000)
Emp.: 357
Fiscal Year-end: 12/31/22
Pharmaceutical Mfr, Researcher & Developer
N.A.I.C.S.: 325412
James Karrels *(CFO, Sec & Sr VP)*
Ezio Bonvini *(Chief Scientific Officer & Sr VP-Res)*
Lynn Cilinski *(Treas, VP & Controller)*
Scott Koenig *(Founder, Pres & CEO)*
Stephen Eck *(Chief Medical Officer & Sr VP-Clinical Dev)*

MACY'S, INC.
151 W 34th St, New York, NY 10001
Tel.: (212) 494-1621   **DE**
Web Site: https://www.macysinc.com
Year Founded: 1929
M—(NYSE)
Rev.: $23,866,000,000
Assets: $16,246,000,000
Liabilities: $12,109,000,000
Net Worth: $4,137,000,000
Earnings: $105,000,000
Emp.: 85,581
Fiscal Year-end: 02/03/24
Department Store Retailer
N.A.I.C.S.: 455110
Tony Spring *(CEO)*
Antony Spring *(Chm & CEO)*
Sharon Otterman *(CMO)*
Danielle L. Kirgan *(Chief Transformation & HR Officer)*
Dennis Mullahy *(Chief Supply Chain Officer)*
Marc Mastronardi *(Chief Stores Officer)*
Paul Griscom *(Sr VP & Controller)*
Adrian V. Mitchell *(CFO & COO)*
Malek Robert Amirshahi *(Sr VP-Corp Comm)*
Nata Dvir *(Chief Mdsg Officer)*
Emily Erusha-Hilleque *(Sr VP-Private Brands)*
Julie Walsh *(Sr VP & Gen Mgr-Center Core & Beauty)*

Subsidiaries:

Advertex Communications Inc.   **(1)**
151 W 34th St, New York, NY 10001-2101
Tel.: (212) 695-4400
Web Site: http://www.macys.com

Sales Range: $25-49.9 Million
Emp.: 150
Advertising Agencies
N.A.I.C.S.: 541810

Bloomingdale's, Inc.   **(1)**
1000 3rd Ave, New York, NY 10022   **(100%)**
Tel.: (212) 705-2000
Web Site: https://www.bloomingdales.com
Department Stores & Mail Order Catalog Sales
N.A.I.C.S.: 455110

Division (Domestic):

bloomingdales.com   **(2)**
1000 3rd Ave 59th St Lexington Ave, New York, NY 10022   **(100%)**
Tel.: (212) 705-2000
Web Site: http://www.bloomingdales.com
Sales Range: $1-9.9 Million
Internet Retail Services
N.A.I.C.S.: 518210

Bluemercury, Inc.   **(1)**
3059 M St NW, Washington, DC 20007
Tel.: (202) 965-1300
Web Site: http://www.bluemercury.com
Beauty Products Whslr & Distr
N.A.I.C.S.: 456120
Marla Malcolm Beck *(Co-Founder & CEO-Macy's)*
Barry Beck *(Co-Founder)*
Maly Bernstein *(CEO)*

FDS Bank   **(1)**
9111 Duke Blvd Ste 100, Mason, OH 45040
Tel.: (513) 573-2265
Personal & Commercial Banking Services
N.A.I.C.S.: 522110

Leadville Insurance Company   **(1)**
84 Pine St 450, Burlington, VT 05401
Tel.: (802) 864-2300
Sales Range: Less than $1 Million
Emp.: 4
Insurance Services
N.A.I.C.S.: 524210
William M. Goddard *(Pres)*

Macy's Corporate Services, Inc. **(1)**
7 W 7th St, Cincinnati, OH 45202
Tel.: (513) 579-7000
Departmental Stores Operating Services
N.A.I.C.S.: 445110
Gerry Lundgren *(CEO)*

Macy's Credit and Customer Services, Inc.   **(1)**
9111 Duke Blvd, Mason, OH 45040
Tel.: (513) 398-5221
Credit Card Processing Services
N.A.I.C.S.: 522210
Michael J. Gatio *(Pres)*

Macy's Florida Stores, LLC   **(1)**
7 W 7th St Fl 8, Cincinnati, OH 45202-2468
Tel.: (513) 579-7000
Departmental Store Operator
N.A.I.C.S.: 445110

Macy's Logistics & Operations   **(1)**
500 Meadowlands Pkwy, Secaucus, NJ 07094-1805
Tel.: (201) 863-3250
Web Site: http://www.macys.com
Sales Range: $50-74.9 Million
Emp.: 200
Coordinates Key Operational Areas of Department Stores
N.A.I.C.S.: 488999

Division (Domestic):

Macy's Logistics & Operations   **(2)**
475 Knotter Dr, Cheshire, CT 06410-1120   **(100%)**
Tel.: (203) 271-5300
Web Site: http://www.macys.com
Mail Order Warehouse
N.A.I.C.S.: 541614

Macy's Merchandising Group, Inc.   **(1)**
11 Penn Plz, New York, NY 10001
Tel.: (646) 429-6000
Sales Range: $100-124.9 Million
Merchandising & Product Development
N.A.I.C.S.: 561499
Harry Frenkel *(CFO)*

Macy's Systems and Technology, Inc.   **(1)**
5985 State Bridge Rd, Duluth, GA 30097
Tel.: (678) 474-2000
Emp.: 1,700
Information Technology Services
N.A.I.C.S.: 519290

Macy's West Stores, Inc.   **(1)**
701 State St, Santa Barbara, CA 93101-3329
Tel.: (805) 963-4566
Web Site: http://www1.macys.com
Emp.: 120
Grocery Products Retailer
N.A.I.C.S.: 445110

Unit (Domestic):

Macy's West Stores, Inc. - Hawaii   **(2)**
1450 Ala Moana Blvd, Honolulu, HI 96814
Tel.: (808) 941-2345
Web Site: http://www.macys.com
Sales Range: $100-124.9 Million
Retail Mdsg.
N.A.I.C.S.: 455110

Macy's West Stores, Inc.   **(1)**
7 W 7th St, Cincinnati, OH 45202
Tel.: (678) 474-2518
Departmental Store Operator
N.A.I.C.S.: 445110

Macy's, Inc. - Financial, Administrative & Credit Services Group **(1)**
9111 Duke Blvd, Mason, OH 45040
Tel.: (513) 398-5221
Web Site: http://www.macys.com
Emp.: 50
Credit & Customer Services
N.A.I.C.S.: 522320

Macys Backstage, Inc.   **(1)**
5001 Monroe St Ste D100, Toledo, OH 43623
Tel.: (419) 479-2300
Web Site:
   https://stores.macysbackstage.com
Shopping Store Retailer
N.A.I.C.S.: 455110

Macys.com, Inc.   **(1)**
170 Ofarrell St, San Francisco, CA 94102
Tel.: (415) 397-3333
Web Site: http://www.macys.com
Sales Range: $100-124.9 Million
E-Commerce Operation
N.A.I.C.S.: 455110

MADISON COUNTY FINANCIAL, INC.
111 W 3rd St, Madison, NE 68748
Tel.: (402) 454-6511   **MD**
Web Site:
   https://www.madisoncounty
   bank.com
MCBK—(OTCIQ)
Rev.: $17,967,000
Assets: $450,339,000
Liabilities: $368,812,000
Net Worth: $81,527,000
Earnings: $6,736,000
Emp.: 51
Fiscal Year-end: 12/31/20
Bank Holding Company
N.A.I.C.S.: 551111
David J. Warnemunde *(Chm, Pres & CEO)*
Brenda L. Borchers *(VP)*
Warren R. Blank *(Sec)*

Subsidiaries:

Madison County Bank   **(1)**
111 W 3rd St, Madison, NE 68748
Tel.: (402) 454-6511
Web Site:
   http://www.madisoncountybank.com
Federal Savings Institutions
N.A.I.C.S.: 522180
David J. Warnemunde *(Chm, Pres & CEO)*
Daniel A. Fullner *(Gen Counsel & Sr VP)*
Brenda L. Borchers *(CFO)*

Subsidary (Domestic):

Bush and Roe Financial, Inc.   **(2)**

402 W Locust Ave, Plainview, NE 68769
Tel.: (402) 582-4952
Insurance Agencies & Brokerage Services
N.A.I.C.S.: 524210

MADISON SQUARE GARDEN ENTERTAINMENT CORP.
2 Pennsylvania Plz, New York, NY 10121
Tel.: (212) 465-6000   **DE**
Web Site:
   https://www.msgentertainment.com
Year Founded: 2022
MSGE—(NYSE)
Rev.: $959,265,000
Assets: $1,552,707,000
Liabilities: $1,575,872,000
Net Worth: ($23,165,000)
Earnings: $144,300,000
Emp.: 1,200
Fiscal Year-end: 06/30/24
Holding Company
N.A.I.C.S.: 551112
James L. Dolan *(Chm & CEO)*
Philip G. D'Ambrosio *(Treas & Exec VP)*
Michael J. Grau *(Interim Principal Acctg Officer)*
James J. Claffey Jr. *(Exec VP-Venue Mgmt)*
Richard Constable *(Exec VP & Head-Govt Affairs & Social Impact-Global)*
Joel Fisher *(Exec VP-Marquee Events & Ops)*
Sandra Kapell *(Chief Admin Officer & Exec VP)*
Josephine Vaccarello *(Exec VP-Live)*
Layth Taki *(Principal Acctg Officer, Sr VP & Controller)*

Subsidiaries:

Radio City Productions LLC   **(1)**
1260 6th Ave, New York, NY 10020
Tel.: (212) 465-6741
Producer of Entertainment
N.A.I.C.S.: 711211

MADISON SQUARE GARDEN SPORTS CORP.
2 Pennsylvania Plz, New York, NY 10121
Tel.: (212) 465-4111   **DE**
Web Site:
   https://www.msgsports.com
MSGS—(NYSE)
Rev.: $1,027,149,000
Assets: $1,346,292,000
Liabilities: $1,612,602,000
Net Worth: ($266,310,000)
Earnings: $58,771,000
Emp.: 533
Fiscal Year-end: 06/30/24
Holding Company; Sports Teams & Entertainment Properties Owner & Operator
N.A.I.C.S.: 551112
James L. Dolan *(Chm)*
Philip G. D'Ambrosio *(Interim Principal Fin Officer, Treas & Exec VP)*
Victoria M. Mink *(CFO, Treas & Exec VP)*
Alexander Shvartsman *(Principal Acctg Officer, Sr VP & Controller)*
Ari Danes *(Sr VP-Investor Relations)*
David Hopkinson *(Pres-Team Bus Ops & Exec VP)*
David Hopkinson *(Pres & COO)*
Quentin F. Dolan *(Dir-Investment)*
Jamaal Lesane *(Interim Pres & Interim COO)*

Subsidiaries:

MSG Sports & Entertainment, LLC   **(1)**
2 Pennsylvania Plz, New York, NY 10121
Tel.: (212) 465-6000

Madison Square Garden Sports Corp.—(Continued)

Web Site:
https://www.msgentertainment.com
Entertainment Services
N.A.I.C.S.: 713940
Neal Kirschner *(Chief Info Security Officer)*

Joint Venture (Domestic):

Azoff MSG Entertainment LLC **(2)**
1100 Glendon Ave Ste 2000, Los Angeles,
CA 90024 **(50%)**
Tel.: (310) 209-3100
Entertainment Services
N.A.I.C.S.: 711310
Irving L. Azoff *(Chm & CEO)*
Shelli Azoff *(CMO)*

Subsidiary (Domestic):

Hartford Wolfpack, LLC **(2)**
1 Civic Ctr Plz, Hartford, CT 06103
Tel.: (860) 722-9425
Web Site: https://www.hartfordwolfpack.com
Entertainment Services
N.A.I.C.S.: 713940

Madison Square Garden, L.P. **(2)**
2 Penn Plz, New York, NY 10121-0091
Tel.: (212) 465-6000
Web Site: https://www.msg.com
Sales Range: $800-899.9 Million
Emp.: 200
Sports & Entertainment Programmer
N.A.I.C.S.: 711211

New York Knicks, LLC **(2)**
Madison Sq Garden 2 Pennsylvania Plz,
New York, NY 10121-0091
Tel.: (212) 465-6471
Sales Range: $350-399.9 Million
Professional Basketball Team
N.A.I.C.S.: 711211
Scott Perry *(Gen Mgr)*
Leon Rose *(Pres)*
James Dolan *(Owner)*
Brock Aller *(VP-Basketball & Strategic Plng)*
Walt Perrin *(Asst Gen Mgr-College Scouting)*
Frank Zanin *(Asst Gen Mgr-Pro Scouting)*

New York Liberty, LLC **(2)**
Madison Square Garden 2 Pennsylvania
Plz 14th Fl, New York, NY 10121
Tel.: (212) 465-6073
Entertainment Services
N.A.I.C.S.: 713940
Vincent Novicki *(Dir-Comm)*
Daakeia Clarke *(Dir-Mktg)*
Brett Tessler *(Mgr-Fan Dev & Social Responsibility)*

New York Rangers, LLC **(2)**
2 Pennsylvania Plz, New York, NY 10121
Tel.: (212) 465-6000
Web Site: https://www.nhl.com
Emp.: 500
Professional Hockey Team
N.A.I.C.S.: 711211
Rod Gilbert *(Dir-Special Projects)*

Westchester Knicks, LLC **(2)**
198 Central Ave, White Plains, NY 10606
Tel.: (914) 559-6889
Entertainment Services
N.A.I.C.S.: 713940
Kevin Bovet *(VP-Sls & Bus Ops)*
Katie Hatch *(Dir-Mktg & Bus Rels)*
Marc Miller *(Dir-Mktg Partnership)*
Max Finley *(Mgr-Ticket Sls)*
Alexis Kalchbrenner *(Mgr-Ticket Ops)*

MADISON TECHNOLOGIES INC.

450 Park Ave 30th Fl, New York, NY
10022
Tel.: (212) 257-4193 **NV**
Web Site: http://www.madisontech.io
Year Founded: 1998
MDEX—(OTCEM)
Rev.: $1,374
Assets: $510,616
Liabilities: $668,516
Net Worth: ($157,900)
Earnings: ($910,163)
Fiscal Year-end: 12/31/20

Investment Holding Company
N.A.I.C.S.: 551112
Philip A. Falcone *(CEO)*
Jeffrey Michael Canouse *(Chief Compliance Officer, Chief Comml Officer & Sec)*

MADRIGAL PHARMACEUTICALS, INC.

200 Barr Harbor Dr Ste 200, West
Conshohocken, PA 19428
Tel.: (267) 824-2827 **DE**
Web Site:
https://www.madrigalpharma.com
Year Founded: 1992
MDGL—(NASDAQ)
Rev.: $2,185,000
Assets: $362,572,000
Liabilities: $165,183,000
Net Worth: $197,389,000
Earnings: ($295,350,000)
Emp.: 92
Fiscal Year-end: 12/31/22
Immune, Metabolic Disorders & Cancer Drugs Mfr
N.A.I.C.S.: 325412
William Sibold *(Pres & CEO)*
Rebecca Taub *(Pres-R&D)*
Carole Huntsman *(Chief Comml Officer)*
Mardi C. Dier *(CFO & Sr VP)*
Robert Waltermire *(Chief Pharmaceutical Dev Officer)*
Stephen Dodge *(Sr VP)*
Kai Motesharei *(Sr VP)*
Thomas Hare *(Sr VP)*
Edward Chiang *(Sr VP)*
Ronald Filippo *(CIO)*

MAGELLAN GOLD CORPORATION

602 Cedar St Ste 205, Wallace, ID
83873
Tel.: (208) 556-1600 **NV**
Web Site:
http://www.magellangoldcorp.com
Year Founded: 2010
MAGE—(OTCIQ)
Assets: $100,099
Liabilities: $1,784,770
Net Worth: ($1,684,671)
Earnings: ($1,464,036)
Fiscal Year-end: 12/31/23
Gold Mining Services
N.A.I.C.S.: 212220
Michael B. Lavigne *(Pres, CEO & Principal Acctg Officer)*

MAGNITE, INC.

1250 Broadway 9th Fl, New York, NY
10001
Tel.: (212) 243-2769 **DE**
Web Site: https://www.magnite.com
Year Founded: 2007
MGNI—(NASDAQ)
Rev.: $577,069,000
Assets: $2,712,213,000
Liabilities: $1,920,915,000
Net Worth: $791,298,000
Earnings: ($130,323,000)
Emp.: 947
Fiscal Year-end: 12/31/22
Online Advertising Services
N.A.I.C.S.: 541890
Michael G. Barrett *(Pres & CEO)*
Erik Michael Hovanec *(Chief Strategy Officer)*
Shawna Hughes *(Chief People Officer)*
Brian Gephart *(Chief Acctg Officer)*
Rebecca Ackers *(Mng Dir-UK & Nordics)*
Aaron Saltz *(Chief Legal Officer)*
Katie Evans *(COO)*
David Buonasera *(CTO)*
David Day *(CFO)*

Sean Buckley *(Chief Revenue Officer)*
Erik Brydges *(Head-Political Demand)*

Subsidiaries:

Magnite Singapore Pte. Ltd. **(1)**
1 Tampines North Drive 1 07-29, Singapore,
528559, Singapore
Tel.: (65) 91895575
Web Site: https://magnetite.com.sg
Construction Services
N.A.I.C.S.: 236220

RTK.io, Inc. **(1)**
530 7th Ave Fl M1, New York, NY 10018
Tel.: (347) 557-8128
Web Site: http://www.rtk.io
Online Advertising Services
N.A.I.C.S.: 541810

Rubicon Project Servicos De Internet
LTDA. **(1)**
Av Doutor Cardoso De Melo 1460 Andar 12
Edif Pilar, Sao Paulo, 04548-005, Brazil
Tel.: (55) 1130776520
Internet Advertising Services
N.A.I.C.S.: 541810

Telaria, Inc. **(1)**
222 Broadway 16th Fl, New York, NY
10038
Tel.: (646) 723-5300
Web Site: http://www.telaria.com
Rev.: $68,038,000
Assets: $256,850,000
Liabilities: $200,073,000
Net Worth: $56,777,000
Earnings: ($9,007,000)
Emp.: 179
Fiscal Year-end: 12/31/2019
Software Company; Technology-Driven
Video Advertising Solutions
N.A.I.C.S.: 541890
Andrew Posen *(VP-Investor Relations)*
Katie Evans *(COO)*
Jennifer Catto *(CMO)*
Adam Lowy *(Chief Comml Officer)*
Doug Campbell *(Chief Strategy Officer)*
Aaron Saltz *(Gen Counsel)*
Tiffany Francis *(Chief HR Officer)*
Bill Swanson *(VP)*
William Jones *(Head-Europe,Middle East-,Africa)*

Subsidiary (Non-US):

Telaria Brazil Publicidade Ltda. **(2)**
Av Faria Lima 4509 8 andar cj 825, Sao
Paulo, 04538-133, Brazil
Tel.: (55) 1138180897
Software Publisher
N.A.I.C.S.: 513210

The Rubicon Project Ltd. **(1)**
Walmar House 5th Floor 296 Regent Street,
London, W1B 3AP, United Kingdom
Tel.: (44) 2032062400
Web Site: http://www.rubiconproject.com
Emp.: 65
Internet Advertising Services
N.A.I.C.S.: 541810

MAGNOLIA OIL & GAS CORPORATION

9 Greenway Plz Ste 1300, Houston,
TX 77046
Tel.: (713) 842-9050 **DE**
Web Site:
https://www.magnoliaoilgas.com
Year Founded: 2017
MGY—(NYSE)
Rev.: $1,694,493,000
Assets: $2,572,585,000
Liabilities: $832,394,000
Net Worth: $1,740,191,000
Earnings: $1,050,249,000
Emp.: 213
Fiscal Year-end: 12/31/22
Holding Company;Investment Services
N.A.I.C.S.: 523999
Christopher G. Stavros *(Pres & CEO)*
Timothy D. Yang *(Gen Counsel, Sec & Exec VP)*

Steve F. Millican *(Sr VP-Ops)*
Brian M. Corales *(CFO, Principal Acctg Officer & Sr VP)*

Subsidiaries:

Highlander Oil & Gas Asset LLC **(1)**
9 Greenway Plz Ste 1400, Houston, TX
77046
Tel.: (281) 849-9758
Web Site: https://highlanderog.com
Oil & Natural Gas Exploration Services
N.A.I.C.S.: 213112

MAIA BIOTECHNOLOGY, INC.

444 W Lake St Ste 1700, Chicago, IL
60606
Tel.: (312) 416-8592 **DE**
Web Site: https://maiabiotech.com
Year Founded: 2018
MAIA—(NYSEAMEX)
Rev.: $1,870
Assets: $12,022,040
Liabilities: $3,514,247
Net Worth: $8,507,793
Earnings: ($16,219,857)
Emp.: 18
Fiscal Year-end: 12/31/22
Biotechnology Research & Development Services
N.A.I.C.S.: 541714
Vlad Vitoc *(Founder, Chm, Pres & CEO)*
Sergei M. Gryaznov *(Chief Scientific Officer)*
Jeffrey C. Himmelreich *(Head-Finance)*

MAIN STREET CAPITAL CORPORATION

1300 Post Oak Blvd 8th Fl, Houston,
TX 77056
Tel.: (713) 350-6000
Web Site:
https://www.mainstcapital.com
Year Founded: 2002
MAIN—(NYSE)
Rev.: $376,860,000
Assets: $4,241,885,000
Liabilities: $2,133,299,000
Net Worth: $2,108,586,000
Earnings: $245,327,000
Emp.: 91
Fiscal Year-end: 12/31/22
Private Equity Firm
N.A.I.C.S.: 523999
Vincent D. Foster *(Co-Founder & Chm)*
Dwayne Louis Hyzak *(Co-Founder & CEO)*
David L. Magdol *(Pres & Chief Investment Officer)*
Charles P. Rosenstein *(Controller)*
Brent D. Smith *(CFO & Treas)*
Katherine S. Silva *(VP & Asst Treas)*
Paul Marlow *(VP-Tax)*
Adam Park *(Asst Gen Counsel)*

Subsidiaries:

Gamber-Johnson, LLC **(1)**
5001 Joerns Dr, Stevens Point, WI 54481
Tel.: (715) 344-3482
Web Site: https://www.gamberjohnson.com
Hardware Product Mfr
N.A.I.C.S.: 332510
Brian Wagner *(Pres & CEO)*

Subsidiary (Domestic):

Lind Electronics, Inc. **(2)**
6414 Cambridge St, Minneapolis, MN
55426
Tel.: (952) 927-6303
Web Site: http://www.lindelectronics.com
Sales Range: $10-24.9 Million
Emp.: 50
Portable Power Supplies, Adapters & Accessories Mfr for Laptop Computers
N.A.I.C.S.: 335999

Leroy R. Lind *(Pres)*
David Murphy *(VP-Sls & Mktg)*
Karen Dong *(VP-Procurement)*

Progressive Marketing Products, Inc. (2)
2620 Palisades Dr, Corona, CA 92882
Tel.: (714) 528-2072
Web Site: http://www.premiermounts.com
Sales Range: $1-9.9 Million
Emp.: 40
Flat Panel & Projector Mounts Mfr
N.A.I.C.S.: 331110
Leonard Dozier *(Founder & CEO)*
Curtis Rose *(Dir-Mktg)*
Brent Henderson *(Gen Mgr)*

Gulf Publishing Company (1)
2 Greenway Plz Ste 1020, Houston, TX 77046
Tel.: (713) 529-4301
Web Site: https://store.gulfenergyinfo.com
Magazine, Catalog & Trade Journal Publishers
N.A.I.C.S.: 513120
Sheryl Stone *(VP-Production)*
John T. Royall *(Pres & CEO)*
Andy McDowell *(Publr-World Oil)*
Catherine Watkins *(Publr-Hydrocarbon & Gas Processing)*
Pamela Harvey *(CFO)*
Brian Nessen *(Grp Publr)*

Subsidiary (Non-US):

The Petroleum Economist Limited (2)
27 Furnival Street, London, EC4A 1JQ, United Kingdom
Tel.: (44) 2034092240
Web Site: https://www.pemedianetwork.com
Online & Print Energy Trade Journal Publisher
N.A.I.C.S.: 513120
Rachel McGhie *(Mgr-Events)*

MAIN STREET FINANCIAL SERVICES CORP.
2001 Main St Celoron Plz on the ground fl, Wheeling, WV 26003
Tel.: (304) 232-2001
Web Site: https://www.mymainstreetbank.bank
MSWV—(OTCQX)
Holding Company
N.A.I.C.S.: 551111

Subsidiaries:

Main Street Bank Corp. (1)
2001 Main St Ste 100, Wheeling, WV 26003
Tel.: (304) 232-2001
Sales Range: $1-9.9 Million
Emp.: 13
Commericial Banking
N.A.I.C.S.: 522110

Wayne Savings Bancshares, Inc. (1)
151 N Market St, Wooster, OH 44691
Tel.: (330) 264-5767
Web Site: http://www.waynesavings.com
Rev.: $23,390,000
Assets: $591,591,000
Liabilities: $539,476,000
Net Worth: $52,115,000
Earnings: $6,690,000
Emp.: 104
Fiscal Year-end: 12/31/2020
Bank Holding Company
N.A.I.C.S.: 551111
James R. VanSickle II *(Pres & CEO)*
Debra A. Marthey *(Treas & Sec)*
Mark Witmer *(Chm)*
Joel D. Beckler *(Officer-Loan & Sr VP)*
Myron L. Swartzentrube *(CFO, Treas & Sr VP)*
A. Fitzsimmons Lee *(VP)*
Matthew L. Hartzler *(Chief Risk Officer & Officer-Ops & VP)*
Jennifer D. Winter *(VP)*
Amberly M. Wolf *(Chief Retail Officer & VP)*

Subsidiary (Domestic):

Wayne Savings Community Bank (2)
151 N Market St, Wooster, OH 44691

Tel.: (330) 264-5767
Web Site: http://www.waynesavings.com
Sales Range: $125-149.9 Million
Emp.: 109
Commercial Banking Services
N.A.I.C.S.: 522110
Myron L. Swartzentruber *(CFO & Sr VP)*
Jonathan Ciccotelli *(Dir-Board)*
Glenn W. Miller *(Dir-Board)*
James R. VanSickle II *(Pres & CEO)*

MAINSTAY MACKAY DEFINED-TERM MUNICIPAL OPPORTU-NITIES FUND
Tel.: (212) 576-7000
Web Site: http://www.nylinvestments.com
MMD—(NYSE)
Rev.: $41,451,524
Assets: $895,659,560
Liabilities: $332,561,069
Net Worth: $563,098,491
Earnings: $27,777,432
Emp.: 20,000
Fiscal Year-end: 05/31/19
Investment Services
N.A.I.C.S.: 523999
Jack R. Benintende *(Treas)*
J. Kevin Gao *(Chief Legal Officer & Sec)*
Scott T. Harrington *(VP-Admin)*
Robert DiMella *(Exec Mng Dir & Portfolio Mgr)*
John M. Loffredo *(Exec Mng Dir & Portfolio Mgr)*
W. Michael Petty *(Sr Mng Dir)*
Scott Sprauer *(Mng Dir & Portfolio Mgr)*
David M. Dowden *(Mng Dir & Portfolio Mgr)*
Susan B. Kerley *(Chm)*

MAINSTREET BANCSHARES, INC.
10089 Fairfax Blvd, Fairfax, VA 22030
Tel.: (703) 481-4567   VA
Web Site: https://mstreetbank.com
Year Founded: 2016
MNSB—(NASDAQ)
Rev.: $88,679,000
Assets: $1,925,751,000
Liabilities: $1,727,469,000
Net Worth: $198,282,000
Earnings: $26,674,000
Emp.: 168
Fiscal Year-end: 12/31/22
Bank Holding Company
N.A.I.C.S.: 551111
Jeff W. Dick *(Chm & CEO)*
Thomas J. Chmelik *(CFO, Sec & Sr Exec VP)*
Abdul Hersiburane *(Pres)*

Subsidiaries:

MainStreet Bank (1)
10089 Fairfax Blvd, Fairfax, VA 22030
Tel.: (703) 481-4567
Web Site: http://www.mstreetbank.com
Rev.: $29,231,144
Assets: $807,951,483
Liabilities: $739,150,301
Net Worth: $68,801,182
Earnings: $3,882,210
Emp.: 104
Fiscal Year-end: 12/31/2017
Banking Services
N.A.I.C.S.: 522110
Jeff W. Dick *(Chm & CEO)*
Thomas J. Chmelik *(CFO, Sec & Sr Exec VP)*
Abdul Hersiburane *(Pres)*
Todd Youngren *(Pres-Avenu)*
Thomas Cary *(Dir-Bus Banking)*
Todd Youngren *(Pres-Avenu)*

MAISON SOLUTIONS INC.
127 N Garfield Ave, Monterey Park, CA 91754

Tel.: (626) 737-5888   DE
Web Site: https://www.maisonsolutionsinc.com
Year Founded: 2019
MSS—(NYSE)
Rev.: $58,043,161
Assets: $82,397,143
Liabilities: $71,678,023
Net Worth: $10,719,120
Earnings: ($3,387,029)
Emp.: 355
Fiscal Year-end: 04/30/24
Grocery Retailer
N.A.I.C.S.: 424490
Alexandria M. Lopez *(CFO)*
Chris Zhang *(VP)*

MAJOR LEAGUE FOOTBALL, INC.
15515 Lemon Fish Dr, Lakewood Ranch, FL 34202
Tel.: (847) 924-4332   DE
Web Site: http://www.mlfb.com
Year Founded: 2004
MLFB—(OTCIQ)
Assets: $1,257,391
Liabilities: $4,916,306
Net Worth: ($3,658,915)
Earnings: ($1,669,699)
Fiscal Year-end: 04/30/22
Professional Spring Football League Operator
N.A.I.C.S.: 711211
Frank J. Murtha *(Pres & CEO)*
Greg Francis Campbell *(CFO)*
Mike Paul McCarthy *(Sr VP-Operations)*
Steve Videtich *(VP)*
Scott Miller *(VP)*
Bill George Lyons *(CMO)*
Todd Worly *(Sls Dir)*
John Joseph Coyne *(Exec VP)*

MAKAMER HOLDINGS, INC.
2934 N Beverly Glen Cir Ste 338, Los Angeles, CA 90077
Tel.: (310) 692-4121   NV
Year Founded: 1904
HWIN—(OTCIQ)
Rev.: $25,004
Assets: $1,161,075
Liabilities: $75,265
Net Worth: $1,085,810
Earnings: ($481,287)
Emp.: 1
Fiscal Year-end: 12/31/21
Restaurant Management Services
N.A.I.C.S.: 722511
Alex Mond *(CEO)*
Karen Mond *(CFO)*

MALAGA FINANCIAL CORP.
2514 Via Tejon, Palos Verdes Estates, CA 90274
Tel.: (310) 375-9000
Web Site: https://www.malagabank.com
MLGF—(OTCIQ)
Rev.: $48,309,248
Assets: $1,312,293,562
Liabilities: $1,155,913,223
Net Worth: $156,380,339
Earnings: $18,334,501
Emp.: 73
Fiscal Year-end: 12/31/20
Bank Holding Company
N.A.I.C.S.: 551111
Randy C. Bowers *(Chm, Pres & CEO)*
Jasna Penich *(CFO & Exec VP)*
Jerry A. Donahue *(Sec)*
Mark Bustamante *(Sr VP-Income Property Lending)*
Nina Brister *(VP & Mgr-Loan Svc & Funding)*

Gayle CdeBaca *(Asst VP & Mgr-Facilities)*
Carmela Carroll *(Asst VP)*
Cathy Jaramillo *(VP & Mgr-Loan Processing)*
Sacha Ohara *(Officer-Bus Dev & Sr VP)*
Naher Elramly *(VP & Mgr-Branch Svcs)*
Kristina Keys *(Mgr-Retail Banking)*
Donald Lee *(Officer-Risk & BSA & Sr VP)*
Rafael Vargas *(VP & Mgr-IT)*
Maureen Bray *(Asst VP & Creative Dir-Mktg)*
Sheree Carroll *(Officer-Security, Asst VP & Project Mgr)*
Julia Parton *(Officer-Bus Dev & VP)*
Helen Stoddart *(Asst VP & Mgr-Retail Banking)*
Ana Straser *(Asst VP & Mgr-Retail Banking)*
John Tellenbach *(Chief Credit Officer & Sr VP)*
John Erikson *(VP)*
Susan Pengelly *(Asst VP-Income Property Lending)*
Mario Navarrete *(Asst VP-Income Property Lending)*
Andrea Lastimosa *(Asst VP & Mgr-Retail Banking-Rolling Hills Estates)*
Ivette Matienzo-Marin *(Asst VP & Mgr-Retail Banking)*
David Iwasaka *(VP & Controller)*
Bryan Grageda *(Asst VP & Mgr-Trng)*

Subsidiaries:

Malaga Bank FSB (1)
2514 Via Tejon, Palos Verdes Estates, CA 90274
Tel.: (310) 375-9000
Web Site: http://www.malagabank.com
Sales Range: $100-124.9 Million
Emp.: 200
Retail & Commercial Banking
N.A.I.C.S.: 522180
Randy C. Bowers *(Chm, Pres & CEO)*
Jasna Penich *(CFO & Exec VP)*

MALIBU BOATS, INC.
5075 Kimberly Way, Loudon, TN 37774
Tel.: (865) 458-5478   DE
Web Site: https://www.malibuboats.com
Year Founded: 1982
MBUU—(NASDAQ)
Rev.: $829,035,000
Assets: $739,624,000
Liabilities: $204,905,000
Net Worth: $534,719,000
Earnings: ($56,443,000)
Emp.: 2,250
Fiscal Year-end: 06/30/24
Boat Mfr
N.A.I.C.S.: 336612
Ritchie L. Anderson *(Pres)*
Deborah S. Kent *(VP-Human Resources)*
Bruce W. Beckman *(CFO)*
Eric K. Bondy *(VP-Sales)*
David S. Black *(VP-Fin)*
Steven D. Menneto *(CEO)*

Subsidiaries:

Cobalt Boats, LLC (1)
1715 N 8th St, Neodesha, KS 66757-1283
Tel.: (620) 325-2653
Web Site: https://www.cobaltboats.com
Boatbuilding & Repairing
N.A.I.C.S.: 336612
Shane Stanfill *(Pres)*

Cobalt Sportswear, LLC (1)
1715 N 8th St, Neodesha, KS 66757
Tel.: (620) 325-2653
Web Site: https://www.cobaltsports.com
Apparel Accessory Distr
N.A.I.C.S.: 458110

Malibu Boats, Inc.—(Continued)

Malibu Boats Holdings, LLC (1)
5075 Kimberly Way, Loudon, TN 37774
Tel.: (865) 458-5478
Sport Boat Mfr
N.A.I.C.S.: 336612

Malibu Boats Pty Ltd. (1)
813 Hope Court, Albury, 2640, NSW, Australia
Tel.: (61) 260401174
Web Site: https://www.malibuboats.com.au
Sport Boat Mfr
N.A.I.C.S.: 336612

Maverick Boat Group, Inc. (1)
3207 Industrial 29th St, Fort Pierce, FL 34946
Tel.: (772) 465-0631
Web Site:
https://www.maverickboatgroup.com
Boat Building Services
N.A.I.C.S.: 532411

MALLARD ACQUISITION CORP.
19701 Bethel Church Rd Ste 302, Cornelius, NC 28031
Tel.: (813) 407-0444   DE
Year Founded: 2020
MACUU—(NASDAQ)
Investment Services
N.A.I.C.S.: 523999
P. Jeffrey Leck (Pres & CEO)
John F. Kirtley (CFO, Treas & Sec)

MAMA'S CREATIONS, INC.
25 Branca Rd, East Rutherford, NJ 07073
Tel.: (201) 531-1212   NV
Web Site:
https://www.mamamancinis.com
Year Founded: 2009
MAMA—(NASDAQ)
Rev.: $93,187,621
Assets: $34,585,195
Liabilities: $22,070,117
Net Worth: $12,515,078
Earnings: $2,302,674
Emp.: 1
Fiscal Year-end: 01/31/23
Pre-Prepared, Frozen & Refrigerated Foods Distr
N.A.I.C.S.: 424420
Dan Dougherty (Co-Founder)
Daniel Mancini (Co-Founder)
Scott Shaffer (Sr VP-Sls)
Adam L. Michaels (Chm & CEO)
Anthony J. Gruber (CFO)
Steven Burns (Chief Admin Officer)

MANATI INDUSTRIES, INC.
PO Box 56-5264, Miami, FL 33256
Tel.: (305) 661-1080   NY
MNII—(OTCIQ)
Agricultural Production Services
N.A.I.C.S.: 111998
Carlos Zarraluqui (Pres & CEO)

MANGOCEUTICALS, INC.
15110 N Dallas Pkwy Ste 600, Dallas, TX 75248
Tel.: (214) 242-9619   TX
Web Site: https://www.mangorx.com
Year Founded: 2021
MGRX—(NASDAQ)
Health Care Srvices
N.A.I.C.S.: 621610
Jacob D. Cohen (Chm)
Eugene M. Johnston (CFO)
Amanda Hammer (COO)

MANHATTAN ASSOCIATES, INC.
2300 Windy Rdg Pkwy 10th Fl, Atlanta, GA 30339
Tel.: (770) 955-7070   GA
Web Site: http://www.manh.com

Year Founded: 1990
MANH—(NASDAQ)
Rev.: $928,725,000
Assets: $673,353,000
Liabilities: $395,075,000
Net Worth: $278,278,000
Earnings: $176,568,000
Emp.: 4,580
Fiscal Year-end: 12/31/23
Supply Chain Management Products & Services
N.A.I.C.S.: 513210
Deepak Raghavan (Co-Founder)
Eddie Capel (Pres & CEO)
Bruce S. Richards (Chief Legal Officer & Sr VP)
Sanjeev Siotia (CTO & Sr VP)
Henri Seroux (Sr VP-EMEA)
Brian Kinsella (Sr VP-Product Mgmt)
Ann Sung Ruckstuhl (CMO & Sr VP)
Suzanne Hough (Chief HR Officer)
Deep Sharma (Sr VP)

Subsidiaries:

Manhattan Associates (India) Development Centre Private Limited (1)
Brigade Tech Gardens 5th & 6th floor B1 Block, Whitefield Road, Bengaluru, 560037, India
Tel.: (91) 804 041 8080
Web Site: http://www.manh.com
Sales Range: $200-249.9 Million
Custom Computer Programming Services
N.A.I.C.S.: 541511
Ushasri Tirumala (Sr VP & Gen Mgr)

Manhattan Associates Europe B.V. (1)
Buizerdlaan 2, 3435 SB, Nieuwegein, Netherlands
Tel.: (31) 302143000
Web Site: http://www.manh.com
Supply Chain Software Services
N.A.I.C.S.: 541618
Pieter Zan Den Broecke (Mng Dir)

Manhattan Associates France SARL (1)
11-13 Cours Valmy, 92977, Paris, Cedex, France
Tel.: (33) 170150391
Web Site: https://www.manh.com
Supply Chain Software Services
N.A.I.C.S.: 541618

Manhattan Associates KK (1)
Toranomon Jitsugyo-Kaikan Bldg 2Fl 1-1-20 Toranomon, Minato-Ku, Tokyo, 105-0001, Japan
Tel.: (81) 362057400
Web Site: http://www.manh.com
Custom Computer Programming Services
N.A.I.C.S.: 541511

Manhattan Associates Limited (1)
e2 Eskdale Road Winnersh Triangle, Wokingham, RG41 5TS, Berkshire, United Kingdom
Tel.: (44) 118 922 8000
Web Site: https://www.manh.com
Supply Chain Software Services
N.A.I.C.S.: 541618

Manhattan Associates Pty Ltd (1)
Suite 2 01 10 Barrack St, Sydney, 2000, NSW, Australia
Tel.: (61) 294545400
Web Site: http://www.manh.com
Supply Chain Management Products & Services
N.A.I.C.S.: 513210

Manhattan Associates Software (Shanghai), Co. Ltd. (1)
Room 4303 Hong Kong New World Building No 300 Huaihai Middle Road, Huangpu District, Shanghai, 200021, China
Tel.: (86) 2160573500
Web Site: http://www.manh.com
Custom Computer Programming Services
N.A.I.C.S.: 541511

Manhattan Associates Software Pte Ltd. (1)
133 Cecil Street 09 02A Keck Seng Tower, 07-04 China Square Central, Singapore,

069535, Singapore
Tel.: (65) 63063600
Web Site: https://www.manh.com
Emp.: 10
Supply Chain Software Services
N.A.I.C.S.: 513210
Amanda Pang (Office Mgr)

MANHATTAN BRIDGE CAPITAL, INC.
60 Cutter Mill Rd Ste 205, Great Neck, NY 11021
Tel.: (516) 444-3400   NY
Web Site:
https://www.manhattanbridgecapital.com
LOAN—(NASDAQ)
Rev.: $8,570,964
Assets: $76,280,001
Liabilities: $33,416,428
Net Worth: $42,863,573
Earnings: $5,211,738
Emp.: 5
Fiscal Year-end: 12/31/22
Real Estate Lending Services
N.A.I.C.S.: 522292
Assaf Ran (Founder, Chm, Pres & CEO)
Vanessa Kao (CFO, Treas, Sec & VP)
Hong Zhu (Controller)

MANHATTAN SCIENTIFICS, INC.
244 5th Ave Ste 2341, New York, NY 10001
Tel.: (646) 300-2765   DE
Web Site: https://www.mhtx.com
MHTX—(OTCQB)
Assets: $316,000
Liabilities: $3,176,000
Net Worth: ($2,860,000)
Earnings: ($1,165,000)
Fiscal Year-end: 12/31/23
Nanotechnology Investment Services
N.A.I.C.S.: 523999
Emmanuel Tsoupanarias (Pres & CEO)

MANIFESTSEVEN HOLDINGS CORPORATION
111 Pacifica Ste 100, Irvine, CA 92618
Tel.: (604) 609-6155
Web Site: http://www.manifest7.com
MSVN—(CNSX)
Rev.: $17,131
Assets: $913,437
Liabilities: $751,663
Net Worth: $161,774
Earnings: ($137,106)
Fiscal Year-end: 12/31/19
Cannabis Product Mfr & Distr
N.A.I.C.S.: 325412
Sturges Karban (CEO)
Urban Smedeby (Pres)
Pierre Rouleau (COO)
Jordan Gerber (CFO)
Dmitry Gordeychev (Chief Investment Officer)

MANITEX INTERNATIONAL, INC.
9725 Industrial Dr, Bridgeview, IL 60455
Tel.: (708) 430-7500   MI
Web Site:
https://www.manitexinternational.com
MNTX—(NASDAQ)
Rev.: $273,854,000
Assets: $236,603,000
Liabilities: $168,642,000
Net Worth: $67,961,000
Earnings: ($4,901,000)
Emp.: 601
Fiscal Year-end: 12/31/22

Engineered Lifting Equipment Mfr & Distr
N.A.I.C.S.: 333923
David J. Langevin (Chm)
Steve Filipov (CEO)
Joseph Doolan (CFO)

Subsidiaries:

Badger Equipment Company (1)
217 Patenaude Dr, Winona, MN 55987
Tel.: (507) 454-1563
Web Site: http://www.badgerequipment.com
Sales Range: $25-49.9 Million
Emp.: 50
Excavating Equipment, Hydraulic RT Cranes, Burro R.R. Locomotive Cranes & C-F Under Hook Lifters Mfr
N.A.I.C.S.: 333120

Manitex Valla S.r.L. (1)
Via Verdi 22, San Cesario sul Panaro, 41018, Modena, Italy
Tel.: (39) 059936811
Web Site: https://www.valla.com
Automotive Equipment Whslr
N.A.I.C.S.: 441330

Manitex, Inc. (1)
3000 S Austin Ave, Georgetown, TX 78626
Tel.: (512) 942-3000
Web Site: https://www.manitex.com
Sales Range: $50-74.9 Million
Emp.: 140
Industrial Truck Machinery Mfr & Distr
N.A.I.C.S.: 333924
Randy Robertson (Dir-Sls & Mktg & Bus Mgr-Western & South Central Reg)
Eric Lau (Mgr-Product Support)
David McDaniel (Dir-Sls & Sls-Articulating Cranes)
Richard Mills (Pres)
Jeff Long (VP-Sales)

PM Argentina Sistemas De Elevacion S.A. (1)
Predio Industrial La Papelera Intendente Neyer 1133 Unid 15, PO Box 1643, Beccar, CP 1643, Buenos Aires, Argentina
Tel.: (54) 1147329008
Industrial Truck & Crane Mfr
N.A.I.C.S.: 333924

PM Chile S.P.A. (1)
Alcalde Guzman N 0121 Galpon Pyme 3, Quilicura, Santiago, Chile
Tel.: (56) 227630300
Industrial Truck & Crane Mfr
N.A.I.C.S.: 333924

PM Equipment Trading FZE (1)
Business Centres World FZE Jafza one - Tower A 11th floor, PO Box 26376, Jebel Ali Free Zone, Dubai, United Arab Emirates
Tel.: (971) 43207913
Industrial Truck & Crane Mfr
N.A.I.C.S.: 333924

PM Oil & Steel Iberica S.L. (1)
Ctra Nacional III 339, Riba-Roja del Turia, 46190, Valencia, Spain
Tel.: (34) 902636778
Industrial Truck & Crane Mfr
N.A.I.C.S.: 333924

PM Oil & Steel S.p.A. (1)
Via G Verdi 22, San Cesario sul Panaro, 41018, San Felice sul Panaro, Modena, Italy
Tel.: (39) 059936811
Web Site: https://www.pm-group.eu
Industrial Truck & Crane Mfr
N.A.I.C.S.: 333924

Rabern Rentals, LP (1)
4807 S Washington St, Amarillo, TX 79110
Tel.: (806) 379-6444
Web Site: http://www.rabernrental.com
Sales Range: $1-9.9 Million
Emp.: 18
Construction, Mining & Forestry Machinery & Equipment Rental & Leasing
N.A.I.C.S.: 532412
Gene Rahll (Principal)

MANNATECH, INCORPORATED
1410 Lakeside Pkwy Ste 200, Flower Mound, TX 75028

Tel.: (972) 471-7400　　　　　　　　TX
Web Site: https://us.mannatech.com
Year Founded: 1993
MTEX—(NASDAQ)
Rev.: $137,208,000
Assets: $49,128,000
Liabilities: $34,952,000
Net Worth: $14,176,000
Earnings: ($4,490,000)
Emp.: 228
Fiscal Year-end: 12/31/22
Proprietary Nutritional Supplements &
Topical Products
N.A.I.C.S.: 325411
James Clavijo *(CFO & Principal Acctg Officer)*
Landen Fredrick *(Pres & CEO)*
Tyler Rameson *(Officer)*
Steve Nugent *(Chief Health & Science Officer)*
J. Stanley Fredrick *(Chm)*
James Clavijo *(CFO)*

Subsidiaries:

Mannatech Australia Pty Limited　(1)
Locked Bag 5000, Saint Leonards, 2065, NSW, Australia
Tel.: (61) 130 036 1878
Web Site: https://www.au.mannatech.com
Glyconutrition & Food Supplements Mfr
N.A.I.C.S.: 456191

Mannatech Japan, Inc.　(1)
Star Zen Shinagawa Building 3rd Floor
2-4-13 Konan, Minato-ku, Tokyo, 108-0075, Japan
Tel.: (81) 357808050
Web Site: http://www.mannatech.co.jp
Sales Range: $10-24.9 Million
Emp.: 41
Nutritional Supplements
N.A.I.C.S.: 325411

Mannatech Taiwan Corporation　(1)
10th Floor 333 Tun Hua S Rd Sec 2, Taipei, 10669, Taiwan
Tel.: (886) 281761200
Web Site: http://www.mannatech.com.tw
Sales Range: $10-24.9 Million
Emp.: 20
Nutritional Supplements
N.A.I.C.S.: 325411
Patrick Park *(Pres-Asia)*

MANNKIND CORPORATION
1 Casper St, Danbury, CT 06810
Tel.: (818) 661-5000　　　　　　　DE
Web Site:
　　https://www.mannkindcorp.com
Year Founded: 1991
MNKD—(NASDAQ)
Rev.: $99,770,000
Assets: $295,282,000
Liabilities: $545,820,000
Net Worth: ($250,538,000)
Earnings: ($87,400,000)
Emp.: 391
Fiscal Year-end: 12/31/22
Pharmaceutical Preparation Manufacturing
N.A.I.C.S.: 325412
David B. Thomson *(Gen Counsel & Sec)*
Lauren M. Sabella *(COO & Exec VP)*
Burkhard Blank *(Chief Medical Officer & Exec VP-R&D)*
Michael E. Castagna *(CEO)*
Stuart A. Tross *(Chief People & Workplace Officer)*
Christopher B. Prentiss *(CFO & Principal Acctg Officer)*
Lauren Sabella *(COO & Exec VP)*
Thomas Hofmann *(Chief Scientific Officer)*
Karen Jaffe *(VP)*
Kevin Kaiserman *(VP)*
Matthew Nguyen *(Sr VP)*
Arpan Patel *(VP)*
Sanjay Singh *(Exec VP)*
Steven B. Binder *(Exec VP-Special Projects)*

Subsidiaries:

MannKind BioPharmaceuticals　(1)
1 Casper St, Danbury, CT 06810
Tel.: (203) 798-8000
Web Site: http://www.mannkindcorp.com
Sales Range: $25-49.9 Million
Emp.: 125
Insulin Research, Development & Manufacturing
N.A.I.C.S.: 541715

MANOR NATIONAL BANK
83 Race St, Manor, PA 15665-0627
Tel.: (724) 863-5510
MANR—(OTCIQ)
Banking Services
N.A.I.C.S.: 522110
Wayne S. Whitehead *(Pres & CEO)*

MANPOWERGROUP INC.
100 Manpower Pl, Milwaukee, WI 53212
Tel.: (414) 961-1000　　　　　　　WI
Web Site:
　　https://www.manpowergroup.com
Year Founded: 1948
MAN—(NYSE)
Rev.: $18,914,500,000
Assets: $8,830,200,000
Liabilities: $6,596,100,000
Net Worth: $2,234,100,000
Earnings: $88,800,000
Emp.: 27,900
Fiscal Year-end: 12/31/23
Human Resource Consultancy Services
N.A.I.C.S.: 561311
Jonas Prising *(CEO)*
Richard D. Buchband *(Gen Counsel, Sec & Sr VP)*
John T. McGinnis *(CFO & Exec VP)*
Diane W. Strong-Treister *(Owner-Franchise & Pres)*
Monica Flores *(Pres-Latin America)*
Alain Roumilhac *(Pres-France)*
Michelle Nettles *(Chief People & Culture Officer)*
Randy Herold *(Chief Information Security & Privacy Officer)*
Tomas Chamorro-Premuzic *(Chief Innovation Officer)*
Frits Scholte *(Sr VP)*

Subsidiaries:

Anyhelp Brasil Assessoria E Servicos em Sistemas de Informacao Ltda.　(1)
Av Das Nacoes Unidas 17891 7th Floor, Birmann Building South Zone, Sao Paulo, 04795-100, Brazil
Tel.: (55) 1121553900
Web Site:
　　http://www.manpowergroup.com.br
Training & Development Services
N.A.I.C.S.: 541612

Anyhelp International, S.L.U.　(1)
Lagasca 88, Madrid, 28001, Spain
Tel.: (34) 913788147
Web Site:
　　http://www.anyhelpinternational.com
Employee Consultancy Services
N.A.I.C.S.: 561320

Arcqus GmbH　(1)
Steindamm 96, 20099, Hamburg, Germany
Tel.: (49) 6142 835 5672
Web Site: https://www.arcqus.com
Emp.: 100
Automobile Mfr
N.A.I.C.S.: 336211

Avan AS　(1)
Lakkegata 55, 0187, Oslo, Norway
Tel.: (47) 97707994
Web Site: http://www.avan.no
Employee Consultancy Services
N.A.I.C.S.: 561320
Jan Erik Moberg *(Dir-Sales)*
Bodil Bjanes *(Mng Dir)*
Elizabeth Svensson *(Sr Project Mgr)*

AviationPower Technical Services GmbH　(1)
Hessenring 15g, 64546, Morfelden-Walldorf, Germany
Tel.: (49) 692740050
Web Site: http://www.aviationpowergroup.de
Air Aviation Management Services
N.A.I.C.S.: 488190
Michael Kluge *(Mgr-MRO)*

AviationPower UK Ltd.　(1)
Regus House Heronsway, Chester, CH4 9QR, United Kingdom
Tel.: (44) 1244455410
Web Site: http://www.aviationpower.co.uk
Aircraft Maintenance Services
N.A.I.C.S.: 488190

AviationStaff Management　(1)
Obenhauptstrasse 5, 22335, Hamburg, Germany
Tel.: (49) 40386386200
Web Site:
　　http://www.aviationstaffmanagement.de
Aviation Staffing Services
N.A.I.C.S.: 561320
Gunter Host *(Mng Dir)*

AviationStaffManagement GmbH　(1)
Obenhauptstrasse 5, 22335, Hamburg, Germany
Tel.: (49) 40507061675
Web Site: https://www.aviationpower.de
Temporary Staffing Services
N.A.I.C.S.: 561320

Bankpower GmbH Personaldienstleistungen　(1)
Grosse Gallusstrasse 1-7, 60311, Frankfurt, Germany
Tel.: (49) 692 999 0060
Web Site: https://www.bankpower.de
Emp.: 15
Management Consulting Services
N.A.I.C.S.: 541611

Benefits S.A.　(1)
Maipu 942-Piso 23, C1006ACN, Buenos Aires, Argentina
Tel.: (54) 1155506698
Recruitment & Staffing Services
N.A.I.C.S.: 561320

ByManpower, S.L.U.　(1)
Calle Corsega 418, Barcelona, 8037, Spain
Tel.: (34) 934591819
Web Site: http://www.manpower.es
Emp.: 100
Management Consulting Services
N.A.I.C.S.: 541611

Career Harmony, Ltd　(1)
90 Yigal Alon St, Tel Aviv, 4951763, Israel
Tel.: (972) 39780100
Web Site: http://www.careerharmony.com
Sales Range: $25-49.9 Million
Management Consulting Services
N.A.I.C.S.: 541611

Dubai Airport Free Zone　(1)
PO Box 491, Dubai, United Arab Emirates
Tel.: (971) 600532392
Web Site: http://www.dafz.ae
Staffing & Recruitment Services
N.A.I.C.S.: 561320

Elan Group Ltd.　(1)
Elan House 5-11 Fetter Ln, London, EC4A 1QX, United Kingdom
Tel.: (44) 2078301300
Web Site: http://www.elanit.com
Sales Range: $50-74.9 Million
Emp.: 870
Provider of Labor Services
N.A.I.C.S.: 561320

Subsidiary (Non-US):

Elan I.T. Resource SAS　(2)
Buropolis 1 1240 Route Des Dolines Les Bouillides, Valbonne, 06560, France
Tel.: (33) 489874000
Web Site: http://www.experis-it.fr
Information Technology Consulting Services
N.A.I.C.S.: 541512

Elan IT Resource A/S　(2)
Nonnesetergaten 4, Bergen, 5806, Norway
Tel.: (47) 22 01 83 00
Management Consulting Services
N.A.I.C.S.: 541611

Elan IT Services GmbH　(2)
Lise Meitner Str 1, Dietzenbach, 63128, Germany
Tel.: (49) 6074842800
Sales Range: $25-49.9 Million
Emp.: 13
Management Consulting Services
N.A.I.C.S.: 541611
Brant Wechleering *(Gen Mgr)*

Event Elite Production and Promotion Limited　(1)
Block H 12/F Phase 4 Kwun Tong Industrial Centre, 436-446 Kwun Tong Road, Kowloon, China (Hong Kong)
Tel.: (852) 27702370
Web Site: https://www.eventelite.com
Marketing Consulting Services
N.A.I.C.S.: 541613

Experis (M) Sdn Bhd　(1)
Suite 20 01 Level 20 Centrepoint South The Boulevard, Mid Valley City, 59200, Kuala Lumpur, Malaysia
Tel.: (60) 320870000
Web Site: https://experis.com.my
Staffing & Recruitment Services
N.A.I.C.S.: 561320

Experis A/S　(1)
Oldenburg Alle 3 2 TV, 2630, Taastrup, Denmark
Tel.: (45) 45902800
Web Site: http://www.experis.dk
Human Resource Consulting Services
N.A.I.C.S.: 541612

Experis AB　(1)
Sodermalmsallen 36, 111 81, Stockholm, Sweden
Tel.: (46) 77 155 9920
Web Site: https://www.experis.se
Human Resource Consulting Services
N.A.I.C.S.: 541612

Experis AG　(1)
Wasserwerkstrasse 10, 8006, Zurich, Switzerland
Tel.: (41) 44 229 9999
Web Site: https://www.experis.ch
Information Technology Consulting Services
N.A.I.C.S.: 541512
Nigel Lindsey-Noble *(Sls Mgr)*
Mike McGinty *(Dir-Country)*

Experis AS　(1)
Lakkegata 53, Solli, 0187, Oslo, Norway
Tel.: (47) 22018100
Web Site: http://www.experis.no
Human Resource Consulting Services
N.A.I.C.S.: 541612

Experis Belgium SA　(1)
Avenue Des Communautes 110, Woluwe-St Lambert, 1200, Brussels, Belgium
Tel.: (32) 2 588 9728
Web Site: https://www.experis.be
Recruitment & Staffing Services
N.A.I.C.S.: 561320

Experis Ciber B.V.　(1)
Vredeoord 105, Eindhoven, 5621, Netherlands
Tel.: (31) 402329090
Management Consultancy Services
N.A.I.C.S.: 541611

Experis Cyber Ltd.　(1)
Yigal Alon 90 Entrance B 3rd Floor Ashdar Center, Tel Aviv, Israel
Tel.: (972) 35686400
Web Site: http://www.experis-cyber.com
Emp.: 40,000
Cyber Security Services
N.A.I.C.S.: 541512

Experis Executive Co. Ltd.　(1)
Tamachi Station Tower North 30F 3-1-1, Shibaura Minato, Tokyo, 108-0023, Japan
Tel.: (81) 345312971
Web Site: https://www.experis-executive.jp
Human Resouce Services
N.A.I.C.S.: 561312
Pema Chhophyel *(Dir-Consumer)*
Steve Skrysak *(CEO)*

ManpowerGroup Inc.—(Continued)

Experis Executive France (1)
89/91 rue du Faubourg Saint-Honore,
78008, Paris, France
Tel.: (33) 145645454
Web Site: http://www.experis-executive.fr
Recruitment & Staffing Services
N.A.I.C.S.: 561320

Experis Executive France SAS (1)
89/91 Rue Du Faubourg Saint Honore,
Paris, 75008, France
Tel.: (33) 145645454
Executive Recruitment Services
N.A.I.C.S.: 541612

Experis Executive Lyon SAS (1)
Immeuble Le Rhone-Alpes 235 Cours La-
fayette, 69006, Lyon, France
Tel.: (33) 482536581
Recruitment & Staffing Services
N.A.I.C.S.: 561320

Experis GmbH (1)
Lassallestrasse 7a, 1020, Vienna, Austria
Tel.: (43) 1516767000
Web Site: http://www.experis.at
Emp.: 200
Recruitment & Staffing Services
N.A.I.C.S.: 561320

Experis GmbH (1)
Dusseldorfer Strasse 9, 65760, Eschborn,
Germany
Tel.: (49) 69153030
Web Site: http://www.experis.de
Human Resource Consulting Services
N.A.I.C.S.: 541612

Experis IT Private Limited (1)
Block GP Plot J3 Sector V Salt Lake City,
Kolkata, 700091, West Bengal, India
Tel.: (91) 334 038 1111
Web Site: https://www.experisindia.com
Human Resource Consulting Services
N.A.I.C.S.: 541612

Experis Limited (1)
8 Harcourt St, Dublin, Ireland
Tel.: (353) 16455250
Web Site: http://www.experis.ie
Human Resource Consulting Services
N.A.I.C.S.: 541612
John Galvin (Mng Dir)

Experis Limited (1)
6 New Bridge Street, London, EC4V 6AB,
United Kingdom
Tel.: (44) 2031220200
Web Site: http://www.experis.co.uk
Human Resource Consulting Services
N.A.I.C.S.: 541612

Experis ManpowerGroup, S.L. (1)
Lagasca 88 30, Madrid, Spain
Tel.: (34) 911213550
Web Site: http://www.candidate.experis.com
Sales Range: $25-49.9 Million
Emp.: 30
Employment Placement Services
N.A.I.C.S.: 561311

Experis Nederland B.V. (1)
Tel.: (31) 2879379
Web Site: http://www.experis.nl
Human Resource Consulting Services
N.A.I.C.S.: 541612

Experis S.r.l. (1)
Piazza Zanellato 5, 35131, Padua, PD, Italy
Tel.: (39) 049 778 0601
Web Site: https://www.experis.it
Recruitment & Staffing Services
N.A.I.C.S.: 561320

Experis Software (1)
90 Yigal Alon, Tel Aviv, Israel
Tel.: (972) 35686400
Web Site: https://www.experis.co.il
Software Development Services, Consulting
& Custom-Tailored Training
N.A.I.C.S.: 541511

**Experis Technology Futures Co.
Ltd.** (1)
World Trade Center 19f 241 Hamamatsu-
cho, Minatoku, Tokyo, 105-6119, Japan
Tel.: (81) 368606028
Employee Consultancy Services
N.A.I.C.S.: 561320

FAO Office GmbH (1)
Strahlenberger Weg 6, 60599, Frankfurt,
Germany
Tel.: (49) 692108480
Management & Consulting Services
N.A.I.C.S.: 541611

**Factoria y Manufactura S.A. de
C.V.** (1)
Insurgentes Sur 688 Fl 3, Benito Jurez Dis-
trito Federal, 03100, Mexico, Mexico
Tel.: (52) 5553404315
Web Site: http://www.manpower.com.mx
Sales Range: $200-249.9 Million
Emp.: 120
Management Consulting Services
N.A.I.C.S.: 541611

Flexservice Solutions BV (1)
Julianalaan 1, 1213 AP, Hilversum, Nether-
lands
Tel.: (31) 356464400
Web Site: http://www.flexservice.com
Emp.: 50
Management Consulting Services
N.A.I.C.S.: 541611

Greythorn Pty Ltd. (1)
Level 22 Darling Park Tower 2 201 Sussex
Street, Sydney, 2000, NSW, Australia
Tel.: (61) 292498000
Web Site: http://www.greythorn.com.au
Information Technology Recruitment Ser-
vices
N.A.I.C.S.: 541612

**Integral Search & Selection
Limited** (1)
5 Chancery Lane, Holborn, London, EC4A
1BL, United Kingdom
Tel.: (44) 203 195 1936
Web Site: https://www.integralsearch.com
Employee Consultancy Services
N.A.I.C.S.: 561320
Toby Danos (Mng Dir)
Michelle Taylor (Dir-Professional Svcs &
Tax)
Phil Jolley (Dir-Fin Svcs)
Sarah Ford (Dir-Professional Svcs)
Ben Thrower (Assoc Dir)
Pam Skeates (Mgr-Fin)

**Jefferson Wells International,
Inc.** (1)
100 Manpower Pl 4th Fl, Milwaukee, WI
53212
Tel.: (262) 957-3400
Web Site: http://www.jeffersonwells.com
Sales Range: $25-49.9 Million
Emp.: 90
Tax, Technology Risk Management, Internal
Audit & Control & Finance & Accounting
Professional Services
N.A.I.C.S.: 561499

**MBS (Manpower Business Solutions)
Ltd.** (1)
90 Igal Alon, Tel Aviv, 67891, Israel
Tel.: (972) 35639999
Web Site: http://www.manpower-bs.co.il
Sales Range: $25-49.9 Million
Emp.: 80
Management Consulting Services
N.A.I.C.S.: 541611

MGS Language Services (1)
17 Hemelsim St, Petah Tiqwa, 49514, Israel
Tel.: (972) 39244410
Web Site: https://manpowerlanguage.com
Language Translation Services
N.A.I.C.S.: 541930
Tali Mazor (Mgr-Language & Quality)
Shulamit Gilan (CEO)
Tzvi Gordon (Head-DTP-Engineering)
Shai Haviv (Mgr-Localization-Translation
Ops)
Hilla Yovel (Head-Documentation Dept-
Talent Engagement-Content Solutions)
Yair Avishur (Head-Interpretation)
Hadar Musael (Mgr-Bus Dev-Pharma &
Medical)

MNPM SOLUTIONS LTD (1)
110 Alon Igal, Tel Aviv, 67891, Israel
Tel.: (972) 36259101
Logistics Management Services
N.A.I.C.S.: 541614

MP Services Sp. z o.o. (1)
Wilcza 66 /68, 006-79, Warsaw, Poland

Tel.: (48) 606248603
Human Resource Consulting Services
N.A.I.C.S.: 541612

**Manpower (Ireland) Group
Limited** (1)
The Greenway Block C Ardilaun Court 112-
114 St, Stephen's Green, Dublin, 2, Ireland
Tel.: (353) 16455200
Web Site: https://www.manpowergroup.ie
Staffing & Recruitment Services
N.A.I.C.S.: 561320

Manpower (Ireland) Limited (1)
The Greenway Block C Ardilaun Court 112-
114 St, Dublin, Ireland
Tel.: (353) 16455200
Web Site: https://www.manpower.ie
Sales Range: $50-74.9 Million
Emp.: 30
Staffing
N.A.I.C.S.: 561320
Jonny Edgar (Dir-Ops)
Paul Howard (Mktg Mgr)
Olivia Kehoe (Head-HR)
John Galvin (Mng Dir)

Manpower (Israel) Ltd. (1)
Yigal Alon 110, Tel Aviv, 6789149, Israel
Tel.: (972) 3 563 9999
Web Site: https://www.manpower.co.il
Sales Range: $10-24.9 Million
Staffing
N.A.I.C.S.: 561311
Amnon Reder (Chrm)
Michal Dan-Harel (CEO)
Hanni Yaacov (VP)
Sharon Stelman-Gal (CFO)
Roni Zuberi (CTO)
Orit Dahbash-Yeheskel (VP-KA Div)
Lilach Ron-Himelman (VP-Mktg)
Keren Bar-Dror Cohen (VP-HR)
Meital Brami (VP-Southern Div)
Ran Konstantin (VP-Procurement & Core
Div)

Manpower A/S (Denmark) (1)
Gyldenlovesgade 11, 1600, Copenhagen,
Denmark
Tel.: (45) 70201000
Web Site: http://www.manpower.dk
Sales Range: $25-49.9 Million
Emp.: 3
Management Consulting Services
N.A.I.C.S.: 541611

Manpower B.V. (1)
Diemerhof 16-18, 1112 XN, Diemen, Neth-
erlands
Tel.: (31) 206602222
Web Site: https://www.manpower.nl
Staffing & Recruitment Services
N.A.I.C.S.: 561320

Manpower Bulgaria OOD (1)
33 Nikola Mirchev Str office no 3, Sofia,
1113, Bulgaria
Tel.: (359) 29426811
Web Site: https://www.manpower.bg
Sales Range: $25-49.9 Million
Emp.: 50
Management Consulting Services
N.A.I.C.S.: 541611

**Manpower Business Consulting
(Shanghai) Co. Ltd.** (1)
36/F Xin Mei Union Square No 999 Pudong
Road S Pudong, Shanghai, 200120, China
Tel.: (86) 02158782618
Web Site: http://www.manpower.com.cn
Sales Range: $100-124.9 Million
Staffing
N.A.I.C.S.: 561311

**Manpower Business Solutions
GmbH** (1)
Dusseldorfer Str 9, Eschborn, 65760, Ger-
many
Tel.: (49) 69153030
Web Site:
http://www.manpowergroupsolutions.de
Emp.: 10
Management Consulting Services
N.A.I.C.S.: 541611

**Manpower Business Solutions
Kft** (1)
Capital Square Office Building Vaci ut 76 V
Torony, 1133, Budapest, Hungary
Tel.: (36) 14111590

Web Site: https://www.manpower.hu
Management Consulting Services
N.A.I.C.S.: 541611

**Manpower Business Solutions
SA** (1)
Avenue des Communes 110 - 1200, 1050,
Brussels, Belgium
Tel.: (32) 26391070
Web Site: https://www.manpower.be
Management Consulting Services
N.A.I.C.S.: 541611
Philippe Lacroix (Mng Dir)

**Manpower Business Solutions,
S.L.U** (1)
Corcega 418, 08037, Barcelona, Spain
Tel.: (34) 934591819
Management Consulting Services
N.A.I.C.S.: 541611

Manpower Caden China Co Ltd (1)
36F Building A Xin Mei Union Square No
999 Pudong Road, Shanghai, 200120,
China
Tel.: (86) 4008200711
Management Consulting Services
N.A.I.C.S.: 541611

Manpower Care Ltd. (1)
62 Sokolov St, Ramat HaSharon, Israel
Tel.: (972) 35404533
Web Site: https://manpowercare.co.il
Staffing & Recruitment Services
N.A.I.C.S.: 561320

Manpower Deutschland GmbH (1)
Dusseldorfer Strasse 9, 65760, Eschborn,
Germany
Tel.: (49) 69153030
Web Site: http://www.manpower.de
Sales Range: $50-74.9 Million
Emp.: 190
Staffing
N.A.I.C.S.: 561311

Manpower Europe Holdings, Aps (1)
Hoje Taastrup Boulev 20 Taastrup, 2360,
Arhus, Denmark
Tel.: (45) 70201000
Web Site: http://www.manpower.dk
Sales Range: $25-49.9 Million
Emp.: 4
Management Consulting Services
N.A.I.C.S.: 541611

**Manpower Framnaes Installasjon
AS** (1)
Gneisveien 12, 3221, Sandefjord, Norway
Tel.: (47) 33428600
Web Site: https://framnes-installasjon.no
Emp.: 11,000
Staffing & Mechanical Services
N.A.I.C.S.: 541330

**Manpower GmbH & Co. KG
Personaldienstleistungen** (1)
Kounprinz St 24, Stuttgart, 70173, Germany
Tel.: (49) 711239810
Web Site: http://www.manpower.de
Management Consulting Services
N.A.I.C.S.: 541611

Manpower Guatemala S.A. (1)
7a Avenida 7-07 zona 9 Oficina 1-B, Guate-
mala, Guatemala
Tel.: (502) 23760000
Staffing & Recruitment Services
N.A.I.C.S.: 561320

Manpower HR Management S.A, (1)
Rue Arnold Winkelried 46, Geneva, 1201,
Switzerland
Tel.: (41) 229082121
Sales Range: $50-74.9 Million
Emp.: 150
Management Consulting Services
N.A.I.C.S.: 541611
Willy Mumenthaler (Gen Mgr)

Manpower HR SRL (1)
Str Izvor Nr 80 Et 2b Amerele 1 Si 2 Sector
5, Bucharest, Romania
Tel.: (40) 213177919
Employment Placement Agency Services
N.A.I.C.S.:

Manpower Holding AG (1)
Bahnhofstrasse 7, Zug, 6300, Switzerland
Tel.: (41) 443139070
Web Site: http://www.manpower.ch

Sales Range: $25-49.9 Million
Emp.: 6
Management Consulting Services
N.A.I.C.S.: 541611

Manpower Honduras, S.A. (1)
Torre II Metropolis 21 Piso Local 10507
Boulevard Suyapa, Tegucigalpa, Honduras
Tel.: (504) 22161800
Staffing & Recruitment Services
N.A.I.C.S.: 561311

Manpower Inc. - San Diego (1)
1855 1St Ave Ste 300, San Diego, CA
92101
Tel.: (619) 237-9900
Web Site:
 https://www.manpowersandiego.com
Sales Range: $10-24.9 Million
Emp.: 18
Help Supply Services
N.A.I.C.S.: 561320

**Manpower Insan Kaynaklari Limited
Sirketi** (1)
Mecidiyekoy Mah Oguz Sok Ronesans Me-
cidiyekoy Plaza No 4 K 1 Sisli, Istanbul,
Turkiye
Tel.: (90) 2122136777
Web Site: http://www.manpower.com.tr
Human Resource Consulting Services
N.A.I.C.S.: 541612

Manpower Kaz LLC (1)
Nauryzbai batyra st 31 office 44 6th floor,
50000, Almaty, Kazakhstan
Tel.: (7) 7273131373
Web Site: https://manpower.kz
Staffing & Recruitment Services
N.A.I.C.S.: 561320

Manpower Korea, Inc, (1)
9F 15F Dongshin Bldg 141-28 Samsung-
dong Gangnam-gu, Seoul, 006-162,
Gangnam-gu, Korea (South) (100%)
Tel.: (82) 266779900
Web Site: http://www.manpower.co.kr
Sales Range: $25-49.9 Million
Staffing
N.A.I.C.S.: 561311
Yong Ki Moon (CEO)

Manpower Lit UAB (1)
Seimyniskiu g 1 A IBC verslo centras 7 auk-
stas, LT-09312, Vilnius, Lithuania
Tel.: (370) 5 211 3270
Web Site: https://www.manpower.lt
Sales Range: $25-49.9 Million
Management Consulting Services
N.A.I.C.S.: 541611
Zivile Svezauskiene (CEO)

Manpower Luxembourg S.A. (1)
33 rue de Gasperich, 5826, Hesperange,
Luxembourg
Tel.: (352) 2 712 7800
Web Site: https://www.manpower.lu
Recruitment & Staffing Services
N.A.I.C.S.: 561320

**Manpower Mensajeria, S.A. de
C.V.** (1)
Av Insurgentes Sur No 688 Del Valle Benito
Juarez, Mexico, 3100, Mexico
Tel.: (52) 5554481400
Web Site: http://www.manpower.com.mx
Emp.: 100
Management Consulting Services
N.A.I.C.S.: 541611

Manpower Middle East FZ-LLC (1)
Dubai Internet City Building 1 Office 204,
PO Box 26359, Dubai, United Arab Emir-
ates
Tel.: (971) 4 391 0460
Web Site: https://www.manpowergroup.ae
Emp.: 40
Human Resource Consulting Services
N.A.I.C.S.: 541612
Jonas Prising (CEO)
Filip Rideau (Mng Dir)
Francois Lancon (Reg Pres)

Manpower Monaco SAM (1)
9 Rue Princesse Florestine, 98000, Mo-
naco, Monaco
Tel.: (377) 93501307
Staffing & Recruitment Services
N.A.I.C.S.: 561320

Manpower Nicaruagua S.A. (1)

Km 4 5 Carretera a Masaya del Restau-
rante Tip Top, 75 metros al oeste Ed Park
Plaza, Managua, Nicaragua
Tel.: (505) 22708304
Staffing & Recruitment Services
N.A.I.C.S.: 561320

Manpower Norway Holdings AS (1)
Lakkegata 53, 0187, Oslo, Norway
Tel.: (47) 22018000
Web Site: http://www.manpower.no
Sales Range: $50-74.9 Million
Emp.: 34
Management Consulting Services
N.A.I.C.S.: 541611
Maalfrid Brath (CEO)
Sven Fossum (Head)

Manpower OY (1)
Kaivokatu 6A 8 krs, Helsinki, 00100, Finland
Tel.: (358) 201700100
Sales Range: $100-124.9 Million
Emp.: 100
Staffing
N.A.I.C.S.: 561311
Iikka Lindroos (Mng Dir)

**Manpower Outsourcing Services
Inc.** (1)
21F Strata 2000 F Ortigas Jr Road Ortigas
Center, Pasig, 1600, Metro Manila, Philip-
pines
Tel.: (63) 2 737 0123
Web Site:
 https://www.manpowergroup.com.ph
Sales Range: $25-49.9 Million
Management Consulting Services
N.A.I.C.S.: 541611

Manpower Panama S.A. (1)
San Francisco calle 74 Este Edificio Mid-
town piso 11 oficina 11-02, Panama,
Panama
Tel.: (507) 3775300
Staffing & Recruitment Services
N.A.I.C.S.: 561320

Manpower Panama S.A. (1)
San Francisco calle 74 Este Edificio Mid-
town piso 11 oficina 11-02, Panama,
Panama
Tel.: (507) 3775300
Web Site: https://www.manpowergroup.com
Human Resource Consulting Services
N.A.I.C.S.: 541612

Manpower Paraguay S.R.L. (1)
Av Espana 888 Esq Padre Pucheu, Asun-
cion, Paraguay
Tel.: (595) 21213229
Staffing & Recruitment Services
N.A.I.C.S.: 561320

Manpower Peru S.A. (1)
Calle Monte Rosa 233 Piso 11 Urb, Chaca-
rilla del Estanque Santiago de Surco, Lima,
33, Peru
Tel.: (51) 1 212 5454
Web Site: http://www.manpower.pe
Management Consulting Services
N.A.I.C.S.: 541611

Manpower Polska SP. ZO. O (1)
ul Prosta 68, 00-838, Warsaw, Mazow-
ieckie, Poland
Tel.: (48) 225040715
Web Site: https://www.manpower.pl
Sales Range: $25-49.9 Million
Management Consulting Services
N.A.I.C.S.: 541611

**Manpower Portugal Empresa de Tra-
balho Temporario S.A.** (1)
Rua Carlos Alberto Mota Pinto Edificio
Amoreiras Plaza 9 5 B 2, 1070-374, Lisbon,
Portugal
Tel.: (351) 300014602
Web Site: http://paginasamarelas.pai.pt
Web Marketing Services
N.A.I.C.S.: 541810

Manpower Romania SRL (1)
Blvd Iuliu Maniu 10th floor, 061103, Bucha-
rest, Romania
Tel.: (40) 213121898
Staffing & Recruitment Services
N.A.I.C.S.: 561320

Manpower S.A. (1)
7a Avenida 7-07 Zona 9 Oficina 1-B, Guatemala, Guatemala

Tel.: (502) 23760000
Personnel Finding & Training Services
N.A.I.C.S.: 561311

Manpower S.A. de C.V. (1)
Insurgentes Sur 688 Col Del Valle, Mexico,
03100, Mexico (100%)
Tel.: (52) 5554481400
Web Site: http://www.manpower.com.mx
Sales Range: $450-499.9 Million
Emp.: 3,500
Staffing Services
N.A.I.C.S.: 561311
Monica Floris (Mng Dir)

Manpower S.r.l (1)
Via Rossini 6/8, 20122, Milan, Italy
Tel.: (39) 0223 0031
Web Site: https://www.manpower.it
Recruitment & Staffing Services
N.A.I.C.S.: 561320

Manpower SA (Pty) Ltd. (1)
Corner Leslie Road and Sparrow Drive
Fourways, Johannesburg, 2055, Gauteng,
South Africa
Tel.: (27) 114656020
Web Site: https://www.manpowergroup.com
Sales Range: $25-49.9 Million
Emp.: 3
Management Consulting Services
N.A.I.C.S.: 541612

Manpower Savjetovanje DOO (1)
Avenija Dubrovnik 16, 10020, Zagreb, Croa-
tia
Tel.: (385) 15565700
Web Site: https://manpower.hr
Emp.: 90
Staffing & Recruitment Services
N.A.I.C.S.: 561320

Manpower Service Inc. (1)
1133 Dunsan 2 Dong Seo Gu, Taejon,
302708, Korea (South)
Tel.: (82) 424716634
Management Consulting Services
N.A.I.C.S.: 541611

**Manpower Services (Australia) Pty.
Ltd.** (1)
Level 22 Darling Pk 2 201 Sussex St, Syd-
ney, 2000, NSW, Australia
Tel.: (61) 292638500
Web Site: http://www.manpower.com.au
Sales Range: $25-49.9 Million
Staffing Services
N.A.I.C.S.: 561311

**Manpower Services (Hong Kong)
Limited** (1)
Rooms 2303-04 9 Chong Yip Street, Kwun
Tong, Hong Kong, China (Hong Kong)
Tel.: (852) 25253513
Web Site: https://www.manpowergrc.hk
Sales Range: $100-124.9 Million
Staffing
N.A.I.C.S.: 561311

**Manpower Services (Macau)
Limited** (1)
Rm E 15 F Central Plz 61 Avenida Almeida
Ribereiro, Macau, China (Macau)
Tel.: (853) 28355513
Web Site: http://www.manpower.mo
Sales Range: $25-49.9 Million
Emp.: 4
Management Consulting Services
N.A.I.C.S.: 541611

**Manpower Services (Taiwan) Co.,
Ltd.** (1)
106 10th and 13th floors No 105 Section 2
Dunhua South Road, Daan District, Taipei,
Taiwan
Tel.: (886) 227845352
Web Site: http://www.manpower.com.tw
Emp.: 100
Business Consulting Services
N.A.I.C.S.: 541618

**Manpower Services Canada
Limited** (1)
4950 Yonge Street Suite 700, Toronto, M2N
6K1, ON, Canada
Tel.: (416) 225-4455
Web Site: http://www.manpower.ca
Sales Range: $25-49.9 Million
Emp.: 2
Management Consulting Services

N.A.I.C.S.: 541511

Manpower Slovakia SRO (1)
Lazaretska 8, 810 00, Bratislava, Slovakia
Tel.: (421) 257103407
Web Site: https://www.manpowergroup.com
Emp.: 50
Management Consulting Services
N.A.I.C.S.: 541511
Silvia Kovacsova (Mgr-HR)
Juraj Polak (Head)

**Manpower Staffing (Australia) Pty
Limited** (1)
Level 9 201 Kent Street, Sydney, 2000,
NSW, Australia
Tel.: (61) 292638500
Staffing Service Provider
N.A.I.C.S.: 561311

**Manpower Staffing Services (Malay-
sia) Sdn Bhd** (1)
Suite 20 01 Level 20 Centrepoint South The
Boulevard Mid Valley City, Lingkaran Syed
Putra, 59200, Kuala Lumpur, Malaysia
Tel.: (60) 320870000
Web Site: https://www.manpower.com.my
Emp.: 100
Management Consulting Services
N.A.I.C.S.: 541611
Jescinta Kumari Joseph (Head)
Christine Leem (Dir-Operations)
Vishnu Jeevapragasan (Dir-)
Kelly Lim (Fin Dir)
Betty Lee (Dir)
Dalvinder Kaur (Dir-)
Nitin Anthony (Head)

**Manpower Staffing Services (Singa-
pore) Pte. Ltd.** (1)
1 Wallich Street 09-02 Guoco Tower, Singa-
pore, 078881, Singapore
Tel.: (65) 6 232 8811
Web Site: https://www.manpower.com.sg
Recruitment & Staffing Services
N.A.I.C.S.: 561311

Manpower Student AB (1)
PO Box 20092, 161 02, Bromma, Sweden
Tel.: (46) 87361900
Employment Placement Agency Services
N.A.I.C.S.: 561311

**Manpower Tunisie International
SARL** (1)
Kaffel Building rue du lac Lochness The
Banks of the Lake, 1053, Tunis, Tunisia
Tel.: (216) 71656230
Management Consulting Services
N.A.I.C.S.: 541611

Manpower UK Limited (1)
Capital Court Windsor Street, Uxbridge,
UB8 1AB, Middlesex, United Kingdom
Tel.: (44) 189 520 5407
Web Site: https://www.manpower.co.uk
Sales Range: $25-49.9 Million
Recruitment Services
N.A.I.C.S.: 541611

Subsidiary (Domestic):

Brook Street (UK) Limited (2)
34 George Street, Luton, LU1 2AZ, Beds,
United Kingdom
Tel.: (44) 172 781 3000
Web Site: https://www.brookstreet.co.uk
Recruitment Agency Services
N.A.I.C.S.: 561311

Brook Street Bureau PLC (2)
34 George Street, Luton, LU1 2AZ, Beds,
United Kingdom
Tel.: (44) 1727848292
Web Site: http://www.brookstreet.co.uk
Management Consulting Services
N.A.I.C.S.: 541611

**Juice Resource Solutions
Limited** (2)
3 Soothouse Spring, Saint Albans, AL3 6PF,
Hertfordshire, United Kingdom
Tel.: (44) 1727867772
Web Site:
 http://www.juiceresourcesolutions.com
Emp.: 12
Human Resource Consulting Services
N.A.I.C.S.: 541612

Nicholas Andrews Limited (2)

ManpowerGroup Inc.—(Continued)

Brook Street Bureau Plc, Saint Albans, AL1
4JB, Hertfordshire, United Kingdom
Tel.: (44) 1727370051
Human Resource Consulting Services
N.A.I.C.S.: 541612

SJB Corporate Limited (2)
2nd Floor 6 New Bridge Street, London,
EC4V 6AB, United Kingdom
Tel.: (44) 207 832 1960
Web Site: https://www.thesjbgroup.com
Executive Search Service
N.A.I.C.S.: 561312
Nick Gaztelua *(Partner-Client)*
Tim Lewis *(Chief Comml Officer & Member-
Mgmt Bd)*
Anna Marshall *(Mgr-Delivery Ops)*
Sandip Sanyal *(Partner-Client)*

SJB Services UK Limited (2)
45 Ludgate Hill, London, EC4M 7JU, United
Kingdom
Tel.: (44) 2076536930
Human Resource Consulting Services
N.A.I.C.S.: 541612

Manpower d.o.o. (1)
Vodovodna 101, 1000, Ljubljana, Slovenia
Tel.: (386) 12429100
Web Site: https://www.manpower.si
Human Resource Consulting Services
N.A.I.C.S.: 541612

Manpower de Venezuela C.A. (1)
Edificio Torre Delta Piso 3 Av Francisco Mi-
randa, Altamira, Caracas, Venezuela
Tel.: (58) 2122614459
Web Site: http://www.manpower-
venezuela.com
Human Resource Consulting Services
N.A.I.C.S.: 541612

**Manpower, Inc. / California
Peninsula** (1)
3180 Newberry Dr, San Jose, CA 95118
Tel.: (408) 264-5200
Recruitment & Staffing Services
N.A.I.C.S.: 561320
Marlin S. Krebs *(Chm & CEO)*
Jan Sonneman *(VP & Gen Mgr-Westcoast)*
Donna Long *(Dir-HR)*
Christine Marzouk *(Controller & Dir-Fin)*
Linda Crane *(Dir-Mktg & Ops)*
Martin Wieczorkowski *(Dir-IT)*
Priscilla Azcueta *(Reg Dir-Onsite & Man-
aged Svcs Program)*

Manpower, S.A. de C.V. (1)
Insurgentes Sur 688 Col Del Valle, 3er Piso
Col Del Valle Benito Juarez, Mexico, 03100,
Mexico
Tel.: (52) 5554481400
Employee Consultancy Services
N.A.I.C.S.: 561320

**ManpowerGroup (Ireland)
Limited** (1)
2nd Floor 8 Harcourt Street, Dublin, Ireland
Tel.: (353) 16455200
Web Site: http://www.manpower.ie
Recruitment Services
N.A.I.C.S.: 561312

ManpowerGroup AB (1)
Sodermalmsallen 36, Box 1125, 118 28,
Stockholm, Sweden
Tel.: (46) 77 155 9900
Web Site: https://www.manpowergroup.se
Human Resource Consulting Services
N.A.I.C.S.: 541612
Daniel Johansson *(CFO)*

Subsidiary (Domestic):

Manpower AB (2)
Klarabergsgatan 29 1 tr, Box 1125, 111 81,
Stockholm, Sweden
Tel.: (46) 87361900
Web Site: http://www.manpower.se
Human Resource Consulting Services
N.A.I.C.S.: 541612

**Manpower Business Solutions Ser-
vice Center AB** (2)
Klarabergsgatan 29, Stockholm, 111 81,
Sweden
Tel.: (46) 87361900
Web Site: http://www.manpower.se

Sales Range: $25-49.9 Million
Emp.: 1
Management Consulting Services
N.A.I.C.S.: 541611

Manpower EL & Tele AB (2)
Lilla Bommen 5, PO Box 11112, 411 04,
Gothenburg, Sweden
Tel.: (46) 31631540
Recruitment & Staffing Services
N.A.I.C.S.: 561320

ManpowerGroup Solutions IT AB (2)
Sodermalmsallen 36, 118 28, Stockholm,
Sweden
Tel.: (46) 77 155 9920
Web Site: https://www.manpower.se
Human Resource Consulting Services
N.A.I.C.S.: 541612

Nordic Talent Professionals (2)
Klarabergsviadukten 70 Section D Floor 4
World Trade Center, Box 70396, 107 24,
Stockholm, Sweden
Tel.: (46) 87918080
Web Site: http://www.talentprofessionals.se
Recruitment & Staffing Services
N.A.I.C.S.: 561320

ManpowerGroup AS (1)
Lakkegata 53, 0187, Oslo, Norway
Tel.: (47) 2 201 8000
Web Site: https://www.manpowergroup.no
Emp.: 67
Human Resource Consulting Services
N.A.I.C.S.: 541612
Maalfrid Brath *(CEO)*

Subsidiary (Domestic):

Alubar A/S (2)
Nygardsveien 80, N-3221, Sandefjord, Nor-
way
Tel.: (47) 46802801
Web Site: http://www.alubar.no
Management Consulting Services
N.A.I.C.S.: 541611
Bjorn Ragnar Olsen *(Mng Dir)*
John Terje Johansen *(Project Engr)*

CIBER Norge AS (2)
Sentrum, PO Box 417, 0103, Oslo, Norway
Tel.: (47) 22348000
Web Site: http://www.ciber.no
Emp.: 150
Computer System Design Services
N.A.I.C.S.: 541512

Manpower A/S (2)
Lakkegata 53, 0187, Oslo, Norway
Tel.: (47) 22018000
Web Site: https://www.manpower.no
Emp.: 5
Management Consulting Services
N.A.I.C.S.: 541611
Sven Fossum *(Head)*
Solvi Spilde Monsen *(Mng Dir)*

**Manpower Business Solutions -Retail
AS** (2)
Tordenskiolds Gate 2, Oslo, 160, Norway
Tel.: (47) 22018000
Web Site: http://www.manpower.com
Sales Range: $75-99.9 Million
Emp.: 35
Management Consulting Services
N.A.I.C.S.: 541511

**Manpower Professional Engineering
AS** (2)
Forusbeen 78, 4033, Stavanger, Norway
Tel.: (47) 22018000
Web Site: http://www.manpower.no
Sales Range: $25-49.9 Million
Emp.: 5
Management Consulting Services
N.A.I.C.S.: 541611

Manpower Staffing Services AS (2)
Skomvaergata 1, Porsgrunn, 3921, Norway
Tel.: (47) 22018000
Management Consulting Services
N.A.I.C.S.: 541611

**ManpowerGroup Business Solutions
Ltd.** (1)
20 Strovolos Avenue, 2011, Strovolos, Nico-
sia, Cyprus
Tel.: (357) 22710000
Staffing & Recruitment Services
N.A.I.C.S.: 561320

ManpowerGroup Co. Limited (1)
3-1-1 Shibaura Tamachi Station Tower N
30th floor, Minato-ku, Tokyo, 108-0023, Ja-
pan
Tel.: (81) 12 085 0074
Web Site: https://www.manpowergroup.jp
Emp.: 3,770
Recruitment & Staffing Services
N.A.I.C.S.: 561320

ManpowerGroup Co., Ltd. (1)
Tamachi Station Tower N 30th Floor 3-1-1
Shibaura, Minato-ku, Tokyo, 108-0023, Ja-
pan
Tel.: (81) 120850074
Web Site: https://www.manpowergroup.jp
Emp.: 3,772
Staffing Service Provider
N.A.I.C.S.: 561311

**ManpowerGroup Deutschland
GmbH** (1)
Dusseldorfer Strasse 9, 65760, Eschborn,
Germany
Tel.: (49) 6 915 3030
Web Site: https://www.manpowergroup.de
Human Resouce Services
N.A.I.C.S.: 541612

ManpowerGroup France Sas (1)
13 rue Ernest Renan, 92729, Nanterre,
France
Tel.: (33) 15 766 1040
Web Site: http://www.manpowergroup.fr
Human Resource Consulting Services
N.A.I.C.S.: 541612

Subsidiary (Domestic):

EABI Consulting Sas (2)
129 avenue Charles De Gaulle, 92200,
Neuilly-sur-Seine, France
Tel.: (33) 175848280
Information Technology Consulting Services
N.A.I.C.S.: 541512

Manpower France SAS (2)
13 Rue Ernest Renan, 92723, Nanterre,
Cedex, France
Tel.: (33) 15 766 1000
Web Site: https://www.manpowergroup.fr
Workforce Solutions; Manpower Services
N.A.I.C.S.: 561311

Pixid S.N.C. (2)
53-55 rue du Capitaine Guynemer, 92400,
Courbevoie, France
Tel.: (33) 141163400
Web Site: https://www.pixid.fr
Management Consulting Services
N.A.I.C.S.: 541611

Proservia SA (2)
15 rue Christian Pauc, CS 40822, 44308,
Nantes, Cedex, France
Tel.: (33) 244211111
Web Site: http://www.proservia.fr
Emp.: 858
Information Technology Consulting Services
N.A.I.C.S.: 541512

Spirit Search SAS (2)
89 R Du Faubourg Saint Honore, 75008,
Paris, France
Tel.: (33) 145645454
Management Consulting Services
N.A.I.C.S.: 541611

Supplay SAS (2)
2 Rue Gaston Boyer, Reims, 51100, France
Tel.: (33) 326484370
Management Consulting Services
N.A.I.C.S.: 541611

Syfadis SAS (2)
35 Bd Solferino, 35000, Rennes, France
Tel.: (33) 223203000
Software Development Services
N.A.I.C.S.: 541511
Pierre Berthu *(Mng Dir)*

Tapfin SARL (2)
11 rue de la Vistule, 75013, Paris, France
Tel.: (33) 153205230
Web Site: http://www.tapfin.com
Human Resource Consulting Services
N.A.I.C.S.: 541612

ManpowerGroup GmbH (1)
Lassallestrasse 7a, 1020, Vienna, Austria
Tel.: (43) 151 676 7000

Web Site: https://www.manpowergroup.at
Recruitment & Staffing Services
N.A.I.C.S.: 561320

ManpowerGroup Holding GmbH (1)
Lassallestrasse 7a, 1020, Vienna, Austria
Tel.: (43) 151 676 7000
Web Site: https://www.manpower.at
Holding Company
N.A.I.C.S.: 551112

ManpowerGroup Korea, Inc. (1)
141-28 Samseong-dong Dongshin Building
409 Teheran-ro, Gangnam-gu, Seoul,
06162, Korea (South)
Tel.: (82) 26 677 9900
Web Site: https://www.manpower.co.kr
Employment Placement Agency Services
N.A.I.C.S.: 561311

**ManpowerGroup Netherlands
B.V.** (1)
Diemerhof 16-18, 1112 XN, Diemen, Neth-
erlands
Tel.: (31) 20 660 2222
Web Site: https://www.manpowergroup.nl
Human Resource Consulting Services
N.A.I.C.S.: 541612

Subsidiary (Domestic):

Manpower B.V. (2)
Diemerhof 16-18, 1112 XN, Diemen, Neth-
erlands
Tel.: (31) 206602222
Web Site: http://www.manpower.nl
Human Resource Consulting Services
N.A.I.C.S.: 541612

ManpowerGroup Solutions B.V. (2)
Pastoriestraat 147, Eindhoven, 5612 EK,
Noord-Brabant, Netherlands
Tel.: (31) 882555250
Business Consulting Services
N.A.I.C.S.: 541618

ManpowerGroup OY (1)
Keskuskatu 1b 3 krs, 00100, Helsinki, Fin-
land
Tel.: (358) 20 170 0100
Web Site: https://www.manpower.fi
Human Resource Consulting Services
N.A.I.C.S.: 541612

**ManpowerGroup Polska Sp. z
o.o.** (1)
ul Prosta 68, 00-838, Warsaw, Poland
Tel.: (48) 225040715
Web Site: https://www.manpowergroup.pl
Human Resource Consulting Services
N.A.I.C.S.: 541612

**ManpowerGroup Portugal - SGPS,
S.A.** (1)
Centro Empresarial Torres de Lisboa Rua
Tomas da Fonseca, Torre G Piso 15, 1600-
209, Lisbon, Portugal
Tel.: (351) 30 003 2623
Web Site: https://www.manpowergroup.pt
Human Resource Consulting Services
N.A.I.C.S.: 541612

Subsidiary (Domestic):

ManpowerGroup Solutions LDA (2)
Centro Empresarial Torres De Lisboa Rua
Tomas Da Fonseca, Torre G Piso 3B, 1600-
209, Lisbon, Portugal
Tel.: (351) 300032628
Emp.: 50
Human Resource Consulting Services
N.A.I.C.S.: 541612
Nuno Gameyro *(Pres)*

**ManpowerGroup Public Sector
Inc.** (1)
6400 Arlington Blvd Ste 300, Falls Church,
VA 22042
Tel.: (703) 245-9400
Language Translation Services
N.A.I.C.S.: 541930

ManpowerGroup S.A. (1)
128-130 Alexandras Avenue, 114 71, Ath-
ens, Greece
Tel.: (30) 210 692 7400
Web Site: https://www.manpowergroup.gr
Recruitment & Staffing Services
N.A.I.C.S.: 561320

Subsidiary (Domestic):

Project Solutions S.A.   (2)
Mesogion 2-4 Pyrgos Athenon Building, PO
Box 11527, 115 27, Athens, Greece
Tel.: (30) 210 331 9220
Web Site: https://www.projectsolutions.gr
Management Consulting Services
N.A.I.C.S.: 541611

**ManpowerGroup Services India Pvt.
Ltd.**   (1)
First Floor DLF Building No 10-B DLF Cy-
ber City, Gurgaon, 122002, India
Tel.: (91) 1246795400
Temporary Employment Services
N.A.I.C.S.: 561320

ManpowerGroup Slovensko s.r.o. (1)
Lazaretska 8, 811 08, Bratislava, Slovakia
Tel.: (421) 800600100
Web Site: http://www.manpower.sk
Temporary Staffing Services
N.A.I.C.S.: 541612

ManpowerGroup Solutions AS   (1)
Tordenskiolds gate 2, 0160, Oslo, Norway
Tel.: (47) 22018000
Human Resource Consulting Services
N.A.I.C.S.: 541612

ManpowerGroup Solutions SRL   (1)
Via Rossini 6/8, 20122, Milan, Italy
Tel.: (39) 02230031
Web Site: http://www.manpower.it
Information Technology Consulting Services
N.A.I.C.S.: 541512

**ManpowerGroup Solutions,
S.L.U**   (1)
Calle San Francisco Javier no 20 bajo, Se-
ville, 41018, Spain
Tel.: (34) 954926498
Human Resource Consulting Services
N.A.I.C.S.: 541612

ManpowerGroup Sp. z o.o.   (1)
Ul Prosta 68, 00-838, Warsaw, Poland
Tel.: (48) 225040715
Web Site: https://www.manpowergroup.pl
Employment Recruitment Services
N.A.I.C.S.: 561311

ManpowerGroup UK Limited   (1)
Capital Court Windsor Street, Uxbridge,
UB8 1AB, United Kingdom
Tel.: (44) 1895205200
IT Management Services
N.A.I.C.S.: 541618
Lee Graham (Head-Comml Mgmt)

ManpowerGroup s r.o.   (1)
Na Florenci 2116/15, 110 00, Prague,
Czech Republic
Tel.: (420) 24 249 9370
Web Site: https://www.manpower.cz
Recruitment & Staffing Services
N.A.I.C.S.: 561320

**Marks Sattin (Australia) Pty
Limited**   (1)
Level 22 Darling Park Tower 2 201 Sussex
Street, Sydney, 2000, NSW, Australia
Tel.: (61) 292475655
Web Site: http://www.markssattin.com.au
Employment Placement Agency Services
N.A.I.C.S.: 561311

Montaplan GmbH   (1)
Luxemburger Str 79 83, 50354, Hurth, Ger-
many
Tel.: (49) 2236943590
Web Site: http://www.montaplan.com
Employment Placement Agency Services
N.A.I.C.S.: 561311

Netmagic II Sarl   (1)
Rue Louis Thys 7, Brussels, 1150, Belgium
Tel.: (32) 27629535
Business Consulting Services
N.A.I.C.S.: 541618

**P.T. Manpower Business Solutions
Indonesia**
Level 30 South Tower Sampoerna Strategic
Square, Jalan Jendral Sudirman Kav 45 46,
Jakarta, 12930, Indonesia
Tel.: (62) 2129930901
Employment Placement Agency Services
N.A.I.C.S.: 561311

**People Source Consulting
Limited**   (1)
1 Georges Square Bath Street, Bristol, BS1
6BA, United Kingdom
Tel.: (44) 117 922 7000
Web Site: https://www.peoplesource.co.uk
Recruitment Services
N.A.I.C.S.: 561311
Nick Snelling (Assoc Dir)
Tim Allen (Mng Dir)
Noel O'Sullivan (Comml Dir)

**Prime Manpower Resources Devel-
opment Inc.**   (1)
21st Floor Strata 2000 F Ortigas Jr Road,
Ortigas Center, Pasig, 1600, Philippines
Tel.: (63) 287370123
Web Site:
    https://www.primemanpower.com.ph
Staffing & Recruitment Services
N.A.I.C.S.: 561320

Proservia GmbH   (1)
Dusseldorfer Strasse 9, 65760, Eschborn,
Germany
Tel.: (49) 69 153 03 0
Web Site: http://www.proservia.de
Management Consulting Services
N.A.I.C.S.: 541611
Alexander Wurdack (Mng Dir)
Frederikus Scholte (Mng Dir)
Helmut Cerveny (Sls Dir)

Right Czech Republic   (1)
Spalena 108/51, 110 00, Prague, Czech
Republic
Tel.: (420) 242406994
Human Resource Consulting Services
N.A.I.C.S.: 541612

**Right Management Argentina
S.A.**   (1)
Av Corrientes 800 piso 31 CABA, Buenos
Aires, C1006AAD, Argentina
Tel.: (54) 1153658500
Employment Placement Agency Services
N.A.I.C.S.: 561311

Right Management Canada   (1)
2 Sheppard Ave East 20th Floor, Toronto,
M2N 7E7, ON, Canada
Tel.: (416) 926-1324
Web Site: http://www.rightmanagement.ca
Human Resource Consulting Services
N.A.I.C.S.: 541612

Right Management China   (1)
2037 Rm 24 West Tower Fortune plaza No
116-118 East Tiyu Road, Guangzhou,
510620, Tianhe, China
Tel.: (86) 2085160291
Web Site: http://www.right.com
Emp.: 5
Management Consulting Services
N.A.I.C.S.: 541611

**Right Management Consultants Inter-
national Pty Ltd**   (1)
Level 8 307 Queen Street, Brisbane, 4000,
QLD, Australia
Tel.: (61) 734073188
Web Site:
    http://www.rightmanagement.com.au
Management Consulting Services
N.A.I.C.S.: 541611

**Right Management Consultants Pty
Ltd**   (1)
L 6 312 St Kilda Road, Melbourne, 3004,
VIC, Australia
Tel.: (61) 385542200
Web Site:
    http://www.rightmanagement.com.au
Sales Range: $25-49.9 Million
Emp.: 50
Management Consulting Services
N.A.I.C.S.: 541611
Tim Roche (Sr VP-)
Aman Syed (Partner-Bus & Fin Mgr)
Lindsay Thorrington (Mng Principal)
Lizzie Allen (Acct Dir)
Niveen Soliman (Head--North & Acct Dir)
Louise Miller (Head--South & Acct Dir)

**Right Management Consultants,
Inc.**   (1)
1818 Market St Fl 33, Philadelphia, PA
19103-3655
Tel.: (215) 988-1588

Web Site: http://www.right.com
Sales Range: $10-24.9 Million
Emp.: 62
Developer & Marketer of Career Manage-
ment & Human Resource Consulting Ser-
vices
N.A.I.C.S.: 561311

Subsidiary (Non-US):

**Right Management Singapore Pte.
Ltd.**   (2)
1 Wallich Street 09-02 Guoco Tower, Singapore, 078881, Singapore
Tel.: (65) 6 532 4100
Developer & Marketer of Career Management & Human Resource Consulting Services
N.A.I.C.S.: 541612

**Right Management Consulting
(Shanghai) Co., Ltd**   (1)
37f Tower A Shinmay Union Square 999
Pudong Road, Shanghai, 200120, China
Tel.: (86) 2180181820
Employment Placement Agency Services
N.A.I.C.S.: 561311

Right Management Denmark A/S (1)
Thistedgade 10, 2630, Taastrup, Denmark
Tel.: (45) 70110505
Web Site: http://www.manpower.dk
Emp.: 5
Management Consulting Services
N.A.I.C.S.: 541511

**Right Management Korea Co.
Ltd.**   (1)
Samsung-dong Coex Trade Tower 3704
Yeongdong-daero 511, Gangnam-gu, Seoul,
Korea (South)
Tel.: (82) 220516660
Staffing & Recruitment Services
N.A.I.C.S.: 561320

Right Management Limited   (1)
The Northern Trust Building 50 Bank Street,
Canary Wharf, London, E14 5NS, United
Kingdom
Tel.: (44) 2074696660
Web Site:
    https://www.rightmanagement.co.uk
Staffing & Recruitment Services
N.A.I.C.S.: 561320

**Right Management Luxembourg
SA**   (1)
28 rue de Strasbourg, 2560, Luxembourg,
Luxembourg
Tel.: (352) 264971
Recruitment & Staffing Services
N.A.I.C.S.: 561320

**Right Management Mexico, S.A. de
C.V.**   (1)
Revolucion 725 piso 4 Col Santa Maria
Nonoalco, 03700, Mexico, Mexico
Tel.: (52) 5526294400
Web Site:
    https://www.rightmanagement.com.mx
Staffing & Recruitment Services
N.A.I.C.S.: 561320

**Right Management Nederland
B.V.**   (1)
Gebouw Athena Diemerhof 16-18, 1112 XN,
Diemen, Netherlands
Tel.: (31) 205840000
Web Site: https://www.rightmanagement.nl
Staffing & Recruitment Services
N.A.I.C.S.: 561320

**Right Management Nordic Holding
A/S**   (1)
hoje taastrup blvd 23, 2360, Copenhagen,
Denmark
Tel.: (45) 70110505
Web Site: http://www.rightmanagement.com
Management Consulting Services
N.A.I.C.S.: 541611

Right Management Norway A/S (1)
Lakkegata 53, Oslo, 160, Norway
Tel.: (47) 40002495
Web Site: http://www.rightmanagement.no
Sales Range: $25-49.9 Million
Emp.: 3
Management Consulting Services
N.A.I.C.S.: 541611

Right Management Peru S.A.C.   (1)
Ca Monterosa 233 Piso 11 Urb Chacarilla
del Estanque, Santiago de Surco, Lima, 27,
Peru
Tel.: (51) 98 148 1214
Web Site: https://www.right.pe
Sales Range: $25-49.9 Million
Management Consulting Services
N.A.I.C.S.: 541611

Right Management S.A.   (1)
Av Corrientes 800 piso 31 CABA, C1008,
Buenos Aires, Argentina
Tel.: (54) 1153658500
Web Site:
    https://www.rightmanagement.com.ar
Staffing & Recruitment Services
N.A.I.C.S.: 561320

Right Management Spain, S.L.U. (1)
Avda de Burgos 18 Planta 10 Talent Tower,
28036, Madrid, Spain
Tel.: (34) 914364260
Web Site: https://www.rightmanagement.es
Staffing & Recruitment Services
N.A.I.C.S.: 561320

Right Management Spain, S.L.U. (1)
Avda De Burgos 18 Planta 10 Talent Tower,
Madrid, 28036, Spain
Tel.: (34) 914364260
Web Site: http://www.rightmanagement.es
Emp.: 30
Human Resource Consulting Services
N.A.I.C.S.: 541612

Right Management Sweden AB (1)
Klarabergsgatan 29, 111 81, Stockholm,
Sweden
Tel.: (46) 850885900
Web Site: https://www.rightmanagement.se
Recruitment & Staffing Services
N.A.I.C.S.: 561320

**Right Management Switzerland
AG**   (1)
Elias-Canetti-Strasse 2, 8050, Zurich, Swit-
zerland
Tel.: (41) 442688844
Web Site: http://www.rightmanagement.ch
Management Consulting Services
N.A.I.C.S.: 541611
Gilbert Bapst (Acct Dir)
Marina Cereghetti (Mgr-Finance-
Administration)
Patricia Morganti (Project Mgr & Mgr-Client
Service-Western Reg)
Maria Langhard (Mgr-Client Service-
Eastern,Central Reg)
Johanna Domine (Mgr-Client Service-
Western)

**Right Management Taiwan Co.,
Ltd.**   (1)
7F No 142 Sec 4 Zhong Xiao East Road
Da-An, Da'an Dist, Taipei, 106, Taiwan
Tel.: (886) 2 2781 1266
Emp.: 10
Employment Consulting Agency Services
N.A.I.C.S.: 561311
Josephine Lee (Gen Mgr)

Right Sinova AB   (1)
Torsgatan 10, Stockholm, 111 23, Sweden
Tel.: (46) 850885900
Management Consulting Services
N.A.I.C.S.: 541611

Right do Brasil Ltda   (1)
Olimpaadas 66 3a Andar Cjs 31 E 32, Sao
Paulo, 04551, Brazil
Tel.: (55) 1130273636
Management Consulting Services
N.A.I.C.S.: 541611

Rotostat Services Private Limited (1)
505 The Summit-Business Bay Off Andheri-
Kurla Road, Near Western Express High-
way Andheri East, 400093, Mumbai, India
Tel.: (91) 2226040647
Web Site: http://rotostat.in
Oil & Gas Field Services
N.A.I.C.S.: 213112
Probal Mukherjee (CEO & Mng Dir)
Hatim Rampurawala (Sec & Exec Dir)
Lulu Khandeshi (Chief HR Officer)
Avneesh Makkar (Fin Dir)
Prashant Pandey (Pres)
Shreyash Tripathi (Sr Mgr-Engineering)
Sandeep Gulati (Mng Dir)
Ratish Kumar (CFO)

ManpowerGroup Inc.—(Continued)

S.A. Manpower (Belgium) N.V. (1)
Gemeenschappenlaan 110, 1200, Brussels, Belgium
Tel.: (32) 2 639 1070
Web Site: https://www.manpower.be
Sales Range: $150-199.9 Million
Emp.: 700
Staffing
N.A.I.C.S.: 561311

Subsidiary (Domestic):

ManpowerGroup Solutions Belgium SA (2)
Avenue des Communautes 110, 1200, Brussels, Belgium
Tel.: (32) 2 639 1070
Web Site: https://www.manpowergroup.be
Emp.: 100
Human Resource Consulting Services
N.A.I.C.S.: 541612

Network Computing Technology & Services SARL (2)
Avenue de la Couronne no 311, 1050, Brussels, Belgium
Tel.: (32) 25244950
Web Site: http://www.ncts-be.com
Information Technology Consulting Services
N.A.I.C.S.: 541512

SC Manpower Romania SRL (1)
Blvd Iuliu Maniu 10th floor, 061103, Bucharest, Romania
Tel.: (40) 21 312 1898
Web Site: http://www.manpower.ro
Human Resource Consulting Services
N.A.I.C.S.: 541612

Safesearch Pty Limited (1)
Level 7 180 Flinders Street, Melbourne, 3000, VIC, Australia
Tel.: (61) 396635513
Web Site: https://www.safesearch.com.au
Recruitment & Staffing Services
N.A.I.C.S.: 561320

Salarisprofs B.V. (1)
Hoofdveste 19, 3992 DH, Houten, Netherlands
Tel.: (31) 880909010
Web Site: http://www.salarisprofs.nl
Employee Consultancy Services
N.A.I.C.S.: 561320

Shoga GmbH (1)
Huyssenallee 3, 45128, Essen, Germany
Tel.: (49) 20179984
Web Site: http://www.shoga-personal.de
Emp.: 700
Food & Catering Services
N.A.I.C.S.: 722320

Siebenlist, Grey & Partner GmbH (1)
Uerdinger Strasse 5, 40474, Dusseldorf, Germany
Tel.: (49) 211470560
Web Site: http://www.siebenlist.de
Employment Placement Agency Services
N.A.I.C.S.: 561311

Skillpower Services (Thailand) Co. Ltd. (1)
177 1 Soi Anumanrachathon 1 Surawongse Road, 2nd Floor BUI Building, Bangkok, 10500, Thailand
Tel.: (66) 26347273
Web Site: http://www.manpowerthailand.com
Emp.: 230
Management Consulting Services
N.A.I.C.S.: 541611

Splu Experts GmbH (1)
Dalbergstr 29, 36037, Fulda, Germany
Tel.: (49) 6613 809 6100
Web Site: https://www.splu-engineers.com
Emp.: 300
Engineering Consulting Services
N.A.I.C.S.: 541330
Terry Cade (Mng Dir)

StegPlus Personal GmbH (1)
Ludwigsstrasse 11, 55116, Mainz, Germany
Tel.: (49) 61315844488
Web Site: http://www.stegplus.de
Holistic Personnel Services

N.A.I.C.S.: 561312
Kathrin Hess (Mng Dir)
Petra Kogler (Head-Hospitality & Healthcare)

Stegdoc GmbH (1)
Walther Von Cronberg Platz 6, 60594, Frankfurt, Germany
Tel.: (49) 8007834362
Web Site: http://www.stegdoc.de
Doctor Recruitment Services
N.A.I.C.S.: 561330

Stegmann Personaldienstleistung GmbH (1)
Ludwigsstrasse 11, 55116, Mainz, Germany
Tel.: (49) 61315844480
Web Site: https://www.stegmann-personal.de
Emp.: 4,000
Staffing & Recruitment Services
N.A.I.C.S.: 561320

Stowe Group Healthcare, LLC (1)
500 Edgewater Dr Ste 570, Wakefield, MA 01880-6232
Tel.: (617) 440-2020
Web Site: http://www.stowegroup.com
Employment Placement Agency Services
N.A.I.C.S.: 561311

TAPFIN LLC (1)
2050 E Asu Cir Ste 120, Tempe, AZ 85284-1839
Tel.: (414) 961-1000
Web Site: http://www.tapfin.com
Management Consulting Services
N.A.I.C.S.: 541611

Techno5, Inc. (1)
759 Carre Victoria Bureau 222, Montreal, H2Y 2J7, QC, Canada
Tel.: (514) 843-4343
Data Preparation & Processing Services
N.A.I.C.S.: 518210

VIS GmbH (1)
Bahnstrasse 1 - 3, 08233, Treuen, Germany
Tel.: (49) 374686660
Web Site: https://www.visgmbh.eu
Conveyor Belts Mfr
N.A.I.C.S.: 333922

Vivento Interim Services GmbH (1)
Riemenschneiderstr 11, 53175, Bonn, Germany
Tel.: (49) 2289379970
Web Site: http://www.vis-connect.de
Management Consulting Services
N.A.I.C.S.: 541611

Volaris Exec Recruitment Limited (1)
1 Georges Square Bath Street, Bristol, BS1 6BA, United Kingdom
Tel.: (44) 1173254200
Web Site: http://www.volarisexec.com
Employment Placement Agency Services
N.A.I.C.S.: 561311
Sarah Wilton (Mng Partner)

Workshop Bemanning og Kompetanse AS (1)
Ostensjoveien 43, 0667, Oslo, Norway
Tel.: (47) 21503090
Web Site: http://www.workshop.no
Emp.: 40
Human Resource Consulting Services
N.A.I.C.S.: 541612

Workshop Holding AS (1)
Ostensjoveien 43, 0667, Oslo, Norway
Tel.: (47) 55301980
Holding Company
N.A.I.C.S.: 551112

ettain group Inc. (1)
127 W Worthington Ave Ste 100, Charlotte, NC 28203
Tel.: (704) 525-5499
Web Site: http://www.ettaingroup.com
Recruitment & Managed Services
N.A.I.C.S.: 561311
Brian Deblitz (Co-Founder)
Dan Royle (VP)
Jeff Harris (Co-Founder)
Jon Olin (Co-Founder)
John Walker (CFO)
Trent Beekman (CEO)
Scott Freidheim (Co-Chm)
Michael McGowan (Co-Chm)

Steve Brady (Chief Revenue Officer)
Scott Forester (CFO)
Harold Russell (COO)
Davin Juckett (Pres)
Frank Waite (Exec VP)
Caroline Weitzel (Exec VP-People-Marketing)
Patrick Reddin (Exec VP)
Sam McClure (Exec VP)
Margaret Ptacek (VP)
Mark Dermott (VP-Live Solutions)
Ben Llewellyn (VP-Information Technology)
Paula Sanders (VP-Human Resources)
Karissa Phillips (Mktg Dir)

Subsidiary (Domestic):

Bradford & Galt Inc. (2)
11457 Olde Cabin Rd Ste 200, Saint Louis, MO 63141
Tel.: (314) 997-4644
Web Site: http://www.bradfordandgalt.com
Employment Services
N.A.I.C.S.: 541612
Bradford Craig Layton (CEO)
Derek Hoppe (VP-Ops)

Global Employment Solutions, Inc. (2)
10375 Park Meadows Dr Ste 475, Littleton, CO 80124
Tel.: (303) 216-9500
Web Site: http://www.gesnetwork.com
Sales Range: $10-24.9 Million
Employment Placement Agencies
N.A.I.C.S.: 561311
Diana Rudolph (Dir-Marketing)
Shawn Mckinstrie (VP)
Kevin LeCompte (Pres & CEO)
Ashley Notthoff (VP-Operations)
Theresa McDannald (CFO)

INT Technologies LLC (2)
4862 E Baseline Rs Ste 104, Mesa, AZ 85206
Tel.: (602) 508-6177
Web Site: http://www.inttechnologies.com
Sales Range: $50-74.9 Million
Emp.: 40
Staff Recruiting Services
N.A.I.C.S.: 561311
Christopher Knott (Pres & Founder)
Rhonda Rutledge (Dir & VP)
James Moloney (VP-Business Development)
Richard Krause (VP-Operations)
Tamara Moloney (VP)

Leidos Health, LLC (2)
705 E Main St, Westfield, IN 46074
Tel.: (317) 867-2682
Web Site: http://www.leidoshealth.com
Health Care Srvices
N.A.I.C.S.: 621610

Timberhorn, LLC. (2)
3000 Internet Blvd Ste 100, Frisco, TX 75034
Tel.: (469) 238-0000
Web Site: http://www.timberhorn.com
Sales Range: $10-24.9 Million
Emp.: 150
Information Technology Consulting Services
N.A.I.C.S.: 541512
Jayson Spaits (Mgr-Recruiting)

iJobs B.V. (1)
Zuidelijk Halfrond 11, 2801 DD, Gouda, Netherlands
Tel.: (31) 182692020
Employee Consultancy Services
N.A.I.C.S.: 561320

iSense & B.V. (1)
Zuidelijk Halfrond 11, 2801, Gouda, Netherlands
Tel.: (31) 182692020
Information Technology Recruitment Services
N.A.I.C.S.: 541612
Marco Berkhout (Mng Dir)
Richard Tanga (Mng Dir)

iSense Eindhoven B.V. (1)
Vredeoord 105 Building Vs, 5621 CX, Eindhoven, Netherlands
Tel.: (31) 408002240
Information Technology Recruitment Services
N.A.I.C.S.: 541612

jenovation GmbH (1)
Leutragraben 2-4 B 59 2nd Floor, 07743, Jena, Germany
Tel.: (49) 36414821525
Web Site: http://www.jenovation.de
Human Resource Staffing Services
N.A.I.C.S.: 541612

MANUFACTURED HOUSING PROPERTIES INC.
4037 E Independence Blvd Ste 200, Charlotte, NC 28205
Tel.: (980) 273-1702 NV
Web Site:
https://www.mhproperties.com
Year Founded: 2003
MHPC—(OTCIQ)
Rev.: $14,202,273
Assets: $103,593,153
Liabilities: $123,189,372
Net Worth: ($19,596,219)
Earnings: ($7,847,665)
Emp.: 58
Fiscal Year-end: 12/31/22
Administration of Housing Programs
N.A.I.C.S.: 925110
Raymond M. Gee (Chm, CEO & CFO)
Adam A. Martin (Chief Investment Officer)
Mollie L. Boyce (Dir-Capital Markets)
John P. Gee (VP)
Jay Wardlaw (Pres)

Subsidiaries:

B&D MHP LLC (1)
2706 Dove Ln, Chester, SC 29706
Web Site: https://mhproperties.com
Property Development Services
N.A.I.C.S.: 531390

Chatham Pines MHP LLC (1)
71 Barn Dr, Chapel Hill, NC 27517
Tel.: (919) 525-3050
Web Site: https://mhproperties.com
Property Development Services
N.A.I.C.S.: 531390

Holly Faye MHP LLC (1)
100 Brian Cir, Gastonia, NC 28056
Tel.: (704) 815-3767
Web Site: https://mhproperties.com
Property Development Services
N.A.I.C.S.: 531390

Hunt Club MHP LLC (1)
7201 Hunt Club Rd, Columbia, SC 29223
Tel.: (336) 792-5343
Web Site: https://mhproperties.com
Property Development Services
N.A.I.C.S.: 531390

Palm Shadows Mobile Home & RV Resort (1)
200 N Val Verde Rd, Donna, TX 30276-1895
Tel.: (956) 464-3324
Web Site: https://palmshadowsrvpark.com
Lessors of Other Real Estate Property
N.A.I.C.S.: 531190
Judy Mason (Mgr)

MAPLEBEAR INC
50 Beale St Ste 600, San Francisco, CA 94105
Tel.: (910) 817-2278 DE
Web Site: http://www.instacart.com
Year Founded: 2012
CART—(NASDAQ)
Rev.: $3,042,000,000
Assets: $4,727,000,000
Liabilities: $977,000,000
Net Worth: $3,750,000,000
Earnings: ($1,622,000,000)
Emp.: 3,380
Fiscal Year-end: 12/31/23
Grocery Delivery Services
N.A.I.C.S.: 492110
Sarah Mastrorocco (VP-Bus Dev)
Karney Li (VP-Engrg-Toronto)
Chris Rogers (Chief Bus Officer)
Christina Hall (Chief HR Officer)

Ariel Bardin *(Sr VP-Product)*
Fidji Simo *(Chm, Pres & CEO)*
Nikila Srinivasan *(VP-Product-Intl)*
David McIntosh *(VP-Product-Retail)*
Max Eulenstein *(VP-Product-Instacart App)*
Ryan Mayward *(VP-Ad Sls)*
Rama Katkar *(VP-Fin)*
Casey Aden-Wansbury *(VP-Policy & Govt Affairs)*
Vik Gupta *(VP-Engrg-Adv)*
Varouj Chitilian *(CTO)*
Dan Danker *(Chief Product Officer)*
Laura Jones *(CMO)*

MAPTELLIGENT INC.

2831 St Rose Pkwy Ste 297, Henderson, NV 89052
Tel.: (415) 990-8141   NV
Web Site:
   https://www.maptelligent.com
Year Founded: 1974
MAPT—(OTCIQ)
Rev.: $2,833,270
Assets: $452,774
Liabilities: $2,987,958
Net Worth: ($2,535,184)
Earnings: $2,182,100
Emp.: 3
Fiscal Year-end: 12/31/22
Railway Transportation Services
N.A.I.C.S.: 482112
Joseph A. Cosio-Barron *(Pres, CEO & Dir-Compliance)*
Glenn Corso *(Chm)*
Richard Ziccardi *(CFO)*
Joel Rothschild *(CTO)*

MAQUIA CAPITAL ACQUISITION CORPORATION

50 Biscayne Blvd Ste 2406, Miami, FL 33132
Tel.: (305) 608-1395   DE
Year Founded: 2020
MAQC—(NASDAQ)
Rev.: $8,543,314
Assets: $37,703,500
Liabilities: $44,836,670
Net Worth: ($7,133,170)
Earnings: $7,193,270
Emp.: 4
Fiscal Year-end: 12/31/22
Investment Holding Company
N.A.I.C.S.: 551112
Jeff Ransdell *(CEO)*
Guillermo Cruz *(COO)*
Jeronimo Peralta *(CFO)*
Maggie Vo *(Chief Investment Officer)*

MARANI BRANDS, INC.

6490 W Desert Inn Rd, Las Vegas, NV 91706
Tel.: (914) 361-9877   NV
Web Site:
   http://www.maranibrands.com
MRIB—(OTCIQ)
Sales Range: Less than $1 Million
Spirits & Wine Mfr & Distr
N.A.I.C.S.: 312140
Kevin Elder *(CFO & COO)*

MARATHON BANCORP, INC.

Tel.: (715) 845-7331   MD
Web Site:
   https://www.marathonbancorp.com
Year Founded: 2020
MBBC—(OTCIQ)
Rev.: $10,156,605
Assets: $219,234,013
Liabilities: $187,939,229
Net Worth: $31,294,784
Earnings: ($186,994)
Emp.: 35
Fiscal Year-end: 06/30/24
Bank Holding Company
N.A.I.C.S.: 551111

Nicholas W. Zillges *(Pres & CEO)*
Terry Cornish *(Chief Credit Officer & VP)*
Joy Selting-Buchberger *(CFO & Sr VP)*
Nora Spatz *(Chief Admin Officer & Exec VP)*
Michelle Knopf *(Officer-Loan, Exec VP, Sr VP & Dir-Mortgage Svcs)*
Timothy R. Wimmer *(Vice Chm)*

MARATHON DIGITAL HOLDINGS, INC.

101 NE 3rd Ave Ste 1200, Fort Lauderdale, FL 33301
Tel.: (703) 997-7320   NV
Web Site: https://www.mara.com
Year Founded: 2010
MARA—(NASDAQ)
Rev.: $387,508,000
Assets: $1,990,973,000
Liabilities: $375,052,000
Net Worth: $1,615,921,000
Earnings: $259,052,000
Emp.: 60
Fiscal Year-end: 12/31/23
Intellectual Property Related Services
N.A.I.C.S.: 561499
Frederick G. Thiel *(Chm & CEO)*
James G. Crawford *(COO)*
Ashu Swami *(CTO)*
John Lee *(Chief Acctg Officer)*
Salman Khan *(CFO)*
Peter Benz *(VP-Corp Dev)*

Subsidiaries:

Sampo IP, LLC   **(1)**
2331 Mill Rd Ste 100, Alexandria, VA 22314
Tel.: (703) 626-4984
Commercial Sector Regulation, Licensing & Inspection Services
N.A.I.C.S.: 561320

MARATHON PETROLEUM CORPORATION

539 S Main St, Findlay, OH 45840-3229
Tel.: (419) 422-2121   DE
Web Site:
   https://www.marathonpetroleum.com
Year Founded: 1887
MPC—(NYSE)
Rev.: $150,307,000,000
Assets: $85,987,000,000
Liabilities: $55,483,000,000
Net Worth: $30,504,000,000
Earnings: $9,681,000,000
Emp.: 18,200
Fiscal Year-end: 12/31/23
Refined Petroleum Mfr & Distr
N.A.I.C.S.: 324110
James R. Wilkins III *(Sr VP-Health, Environment, Safety, and Security)*
John J. Quaid *(CFO & Exec VP)*
Molly R. Benson *(Chief Legal Officer & Sec)*
C. Kristopher Hagedorn *(Principal Acctg Officer, Sr VP & Controller)*
Fiona C. Laird *(Chief HR Officer & Sr VP-Comm)*
Michael J. Hennigan *(Exec Chm)*
James R. Wilkins Jr. *(Sr VP-Health, Environment, Safety, and Security)*
Maryann T. Mannen *(Pres & CEO)*
Ehren D. Powell *(Chief Digital Officer & Sr VP)*
Timothy J. Aydt *(Exec VP-Refining)*
Brian K. Partee *(Chief Global Optimization Officer & Sr VP-Global-Clean Products)*
David R. Heppner *(Chief Strategy Officer & Sr VP-Strategy)*
Rick D. Hessling *(Chief Comml Officer & Sr VP-Global Feedstocks)*
Erin M. Brzezinski *(VP & Controller)*

Subsidiaries:

Andeavor LLC   **(1)**
19100 Ridgewood Pkwy, San Antonio, TX 78259
Tel.: (210) 626-6000
Holding Company; Petroleum Refining & Marketing Services
N.A.I.C.S.: 551112
Blane W. Peery *(VP & Controller)*
Phillip M. Anderson *(Sr VP-North Area Value Chain)*
Michael J. Morrison *(Sr VP-Mktg)*
Nate Weeks *(Sr VP-Strategy & Bus Dev)*
Don Sorensen *(Sr VP-Logistcis)*
Paul Carlson *(Sr VP-Southern Area Value Chain)*

Subsidiary (Domestic):

Alon Asphalt Company   **(2)**
10090 Waterman Rd, Elk Grove, CA 95624
Tel.: (562) 633-4332
Web Site:
   http://www.alonasphaltcompany.com
Asphalt Mfr
N.A.I.C.S.: 324121
Mark Wells *(Mgr-Environmental)*

Affiliate (Domestic):

Paramount-Nevada Asphalt Company, LLC   **(3)**
425 S Logan Ln, Fernley, NV 89408   **(50%)**
Tel.: (775) 835-6366
Asphalt Mfr
N.A.I.C.S.: 324121

Subsidiary (Domestic):

BakkenLink Pipeline LLC   **(2)**
19100 Ridgewood Pkwy, San Antonio, TX 78259
Tel.: (701) 250-1963
Web Site: http://www.bakkenlink.com
Emp.: 6
Crude Oil Pipeline Transportation Services
N.A.I.C.S.: 486110

Marathon Martinez Refinery   **(2)**
150 Solano Way Pacheco, Martinez, CA 94553
Tel.: (925) 228-1220
Web Site:
   http://www.marathonpetroleum.com
Oil Refinery
N.A.I.C.S.: 213112

Tesoro Alaska Co LLC   **(2)**
539 South Main Street, Findlay, OH 45840-3229   **(100%)**
Tel.: (907) 561-5521
Refining & Marketing of Petroleum Products
N.A.I.C.S.: 445131

Branch (Domestic):

Tesoro Alaska Pipeline Co. LLC   **(3)**
PO Box 3369, Kenai, AK 99611-3369
Tel.: (907) 776-8191
Petroleum Refining
N.A.I.C.S.: 457120

Subsidiary (Domestic):

Tesoro Companies, Inc.   **(2)**
19100 Richwood Pkwy, San Antonio, TX 78259
Tel.: (210) 828-8484
Web Site: http://www.andeavor.com
Business Support Services
N.A.I.C.S.: 211120

Subsidiary (Domestic):

Virent, Inc.   **(3)**
3571 Anderson St, Madison, WI 53704
Tel.: (608) 663-0228
Web Site: https://www.virent.com
Biofuel Technology
N.A.I.C.S.: 541715
David Kettner *(Pres & Gen Counsel)*
Andrew Held *(VP-Engineering-Operations)*
Bob Rozmiarek *(VP-Strategy & Bus Analysis)*
Edgar Steenwinkel *(Sr VP-Technology)*
Dana Hatch *(Mgr-Res)*
Brice Dally *(Mgr-Production)*

Shelly Norris *(Office Mgr)*
David Runnels *(Mgr-Facilities)*
Ned Smith *(Controller)*

Subsidiary (Domestic):

Tesoro Refining & Marketing Company LLC   **(2)**
1999 Bryan St. Suite 900, Dallas, Texas 75201
Tel.: (210) 626-6000
Oil Refinery & Marketing Services
N.A.I.C.S.: 211120

Western Refining Southwest, Inc.   **(2)**
92 Giant Crossing Rd, Gallup, NM 87301
Tel.: (505) 722-3833
Petroleum Refining Services
N.A.I.C.S.: 324110

Western Refining, Inc.   **(2)**
1999 Bryan St. Suite 900, Dallas, TX 75201
Tel.: (915) 775-3319
Web Site:
   http://www.marathonpetroleum.com
Crude Oil Refining Services
N.A.I.C.S.: 324110

Subsidiary (Domestic):

Empire Oil Co.   **(3)**
2756 S Riverside Ave, Bloomington, CA 92316-3248
Tel.: (909) 877-0226
Web Site: http://www.wandr.com
Sales Range: $25-49.9 Million
Emp.: 30
Petroleum Product Distr
N.A.I.C.S.: 424720

Northern Tier Energy GP LLC   **(3)**
1250 W Washington St Ste 300, Tempe, AZ 85281
Tel.: (602) 302-5450
Petroleum Refining Assets Manager
N.A.I.C.S.: 523940

Subsidiary (Domestic):

Northern Tier Energy LLC   **(4)**
1250 W Washington St Ste 300, Tempe, AZ 85281
Tel.: (602) 302-5450
Holding Company; Petroleum Refining, Transportation & Marketing Services
N.A.I.C.S.: 551112
Brock Hayes *(Mgr)*

Subsidiary (Domestic):

Northern Tier Energy LLC   **(5)**
38C Grove St Ste 100, Ridgefield, CT 06877
Tel.: (203) 244-6550
Web Site: http://www.ntenergy.com
Petroleum Refining, Transportation & Marketing Services
N.A.I.C.S.: 324110

Subsidiary (Domestic):

Northern Tier Bakery LLC   **(6)**
625 2nd St, Saint Paul Park, MN 55071
Tel.: (651) 459-2253
Web Site: http://www.superamerica.com
Convenience Store Baked Goods & Perishable Foods Mfr & Distr
N.A.I.C.S.: 311812

Northern Tier Oil Transport LLC   **(6)**
8116 S 61st St, Stanley, ND 58784
Tel.: (651) 458-2777
Refined Petroleum Products Pipeline Transportation Services
N.A.I.C.S.: 486910

Northern Tier Retail LLC   **(6)**
576 Bielenberg Dr Ste 200, Woodbury, MN 55125
Web Site: http://www.superamerica.com
Gas Stations with Convenience Stores Operator & Franchisor
N.A.I.C.S.: 457110

St. Paul Park Refining Co. LLC   **(6)**
301 Saint Paul Park Rd, Saint Paul, MN 55071
Tel.: (651) 459-9771

Marathon Petroleum Corporation—(Continued)

Sales Range: $250-299.9 Million
Emp.: 302
Petroleum Refinery Operator
N.A.I.C.S.: 324110
Greg Mullins (Pres)
Jason Akey (Mgr-Comml Ops)

Subsidiary (Domestic):

Western Refining Company, L.P. (3)
6500 Trowbridge Dr, El Paso, TX 79905
Tel.: (915) 775-3300
Web Site: http://www.wnr.com
Sales Range: $250-299.9 Million
Emp.: 450
Crude Oil Refining
N.A.I.C.S.: 486110

Plant (Domestic):

**Western Refining Co. - Gallup
Refinery** (4)
I-40 Exit 39, Jamestown, NM 87347
Tel.: (505) 722-3833
Web Site: http://www.wnr.com
Sales Range: $25-49.9 Million
Emp.: 110
Petroleum Refiner
N.A.I.C.S.: 324110

Cincinnati BioRefining Corp. (1)
470 Este Ave, Cincinnati, OH 45232
Tel.: (513) 482-8800
Emp.: 75
Crude Oil & Petroleum Product Whslr
N.A.I.C.S.: 486110

Enchi Corporation (1)
67 Etna Rd Ste 200, Lebanon, NH 03766
Tel.: (603) 676-3320
Web Site: http://www.mascoma.com
Fuel Distr
N.A.I.C.S.: 424720

Green Bay Terminal Corporation (1)
1031 Hurlbut St, Green Bay, WI 54303-
3736
Tel.: (920) 432-7793
Sales Range: $150-199.9 Million
Gas Whslr
N.A.I.C.S.: 424710

MPLX LP (1)
200 E Hardin St, Findlay, OH
45840-3229 (63.6%)
Tel.: (419) 422-2121
Web Site: https://www.mplx.com
Rev.: $11,281,000,000
Assets: $36,529,000,000
Liabilities: $23,840,000,000
Net Worth: $12,689,000,000
Earnings: $3,928,000,000
Emp.: 5,810
Fiscal Year-end: 12/31/2023
Pipeline Operations
N.A.I.C.S.: 486110
Michael J. Hennigan (Chm, Pres & CEO)
C. Kristopher Hagedorn (CFO & Exec VP)
Gregory S. Floerke (COO & Exec VP)
David R. Heppner (Sr VP)
Rick D. Hessling (Sr VP)
Kristina A. Kazarian (VP-Finance & Human
Resources)
Shawn M. Lyon (Sr VP-Logistics & Storage)
Brian K. Partee (Sr VP)
Kelly D. Wright (VP & Controller)

Subsidiary (Domestic):

Andeavor Logistics LP (2)
200 E Hardin St, Findlay, OH
45840 (63.6%)
Tel.: (419) 421-2414
Web Site: http://www.andeavorlogistics.com
Rev.: $2,380,000,000
Assets: $10,295,000,000
Liabilities: $5,621,000,000
Net Worth: $4,674,000,000
Earnings: $600,000,000
Fiscal Year-end: 12/31/2018
Crude Oil & Refined Product Logistics Ser-
vices
N.A.I.C.S.: 541614

Subsidiary (Domestic):

**Tesoro High Plains Pipeline Company
LLC** (3)
11071 32nd St SW, Dickinson, ND 58601

Tel.: (701) 483-7944
Crude Oil & Refined Product Transportation
Services
N.A.I.C.S.: 488999

Tesoro Logistics Operations LLC (3)
19100 Ridgewood Pkwy, San Antonio, TX
78259
Tel.: (210) 626-4280
Web Site: http://www.tsocorp.com
Crude Oil & Refined Product Transportation
Services
N.A.I.C.S.: 484121

Western Refining Logistics, LP (3)
212 N Clark Dr, El Paso, TX 79905
Tel.: (915) 775-3300
Terminals, Storage Tanks, Pipelines & Other
Logistics Assets Owner, Operator, Devel-
oper & Acquirer
N.A.I.C.S.: 213112

Subsidiary (Domestic):

MarkWest Energy Partners, L.P. (2)
1515 Arapahoe St Tower 1 Ste 1600, Den-
ver, CO 80202 (100%)
Tel.: (303) 925-9200
Web Site: https://www.markwest.com
Emp.: 1,404
Natural Gas Services
N.A.I.C.S.: 211130

Plant (Domestic):

**MarkWest Energy Partners, L.P. -
Carthage Processing Facility** (4)
3239 SW Loop, Carthage, TX 75633
Tel.: (903) 694-2225
Web Site: http://www.markwest.com
Petroleum Refiner
N.A.I.C.S.: 324110

Subsidiary (Domestic):

**MarkWest Michigan Pipeline Com-
pany, L.L.C.** (3)
1515 Thomas Road Driveway Ste 6, Ka-
lkaska, MI 49646
Tel.: (231) 258-4614
Web Site: http://www.markwest.com
Petroleum Pipeline Construction Services
N.A.I.C.S.: 486110

MarkWest Power Tex, L.L.C. (3)
3417 73rd St Ste I, Lubbock, TX 79423
Tel.: (806) 799-0569
Web Site: http://www.markwest.com
Natural Gas Liquid Extraction Services
N.A.I.C.S.: 211130

**Marathon Petroleum Company
Canada Ltd** (1)
2400 440 2nd Ave SW, Calgary, T2P 5E9,
AB, Canada (100%)
Tel.: (403) 233-1700
Web Site: http://www.marathon.com
Sales Range: $10-24.9 Million
Emp.: 6
Marketer of Petroleum Products
N.A.I.C.S.: 541613

**Marathon Petroleum Company
LLC** (1)
Hwy 61 Marathon Ave, Garyville, LA 70051
Tel.: (985) 535-2241
Petroleum Refiner
N.A.I.C.S.: 324110

**Marathon Petroleum Company
LLC** (1)
502 10th St S, Texas City, TX 77590-8560
Tel.: (713) 945-2331
Sales Range: $200-249.9 Million
Emp.: 245
Petroleum Refiner
N.A.I.C.S.: 324110

**Marathon Petroleum Company
LLC** (1)
1001 Oakwood, Detroit, MI 48217
Tel.: (313) 297-6000
Sales Range: $200-249.9 Million
Emp.: 300
Petroleum Refiner
N.A.I.C.S.: 324110

**Marathon Petroleum Company
LLC** (1)

4131 Seaman Rd, Oregon, OH
43616-2448 (100%)
Tel.: (419) 691-4605
Sales Range: $10-24.9 Million
Emp.: 4
Petroleum Terminal
N.A.I.C.S.: 486910

Marathon Pipe Line LLC (1)
539 S Main St, Findlay, OH 45840 (100%)
Tel.: (419) 422-2121
Web Site:
https://www.marathonpipeline.com
Sales Range: $700-749.9 Million
Emp.: 1,500
Operator of Pipelines for Transport of Crude
Oil & Refined Petroleum Products
N.A.I.C.S.: 486110

Subsidiary (Domestic):

LOOP, LLC (2)
137 Northpark Blvd, Covington, LA
70433 (51%)
Tel.: (985) 276-6100
Web Site: https://www.loopllc.com
Rev.: $147,439,292
Emp.: 140
Deepwater Port Services for Petroleum
Transport Vessels; Owned by Marathon
Pipe Line LLC, Murphy Oil Corporation &
Shell Oil Company
N.A.I.C.S.: 488310
Terrance Coleman (Pres)

**MarkWest Texas LPG Pipeline,
L.L.C.** (1)
1515 Arapahoe St 1, Denver, CO 80202
Tel.: (800) 730-8388
Emp.: 4
Crude Oil & Petroleum Product Whslr
N.A.I.C.S.: 486110

**Minnesota Pipe Line Company,
LLC** (1)
PO Box 3696, Saint Paul, MN 55101
Tel.: (651) 438-1556
Web Site:
https://www.minnesotapipeline.com
Pipeline Rehabilitation Services
N.A.I.C.S.: 237120

**Port Everglades Environmental
Corp.** (1)
2550 Eisenhower Blvd, Fort Lauderdale, FL
33316
Tel.: (954) 467-0000
Natural Gas Extraction Services
N.A.I.C.S.: 211130

Speedway Prepaid Card LLC (1)
500 Speedway Dr, Enon, OH 45323
Petroleum Product Distr
N.A.I.C.S.: 424710

Starvin Marvin, Inc. (1)
1028 Shelton Beach Rd, Saraland, AL
36571-3099
Tel.: (251) 675-5011
Crude Petroleum Natural Gas Extraction
N.A.I.C.S.: 211120

Wilco Transportation LLC (1)
5446 University Pkwy, Winston Salem, NC
27105
Tel.: (336) 767-6280
Natural Gas Transmission Services
N.A.I.C.S.: 486210

**MARAVAI LIFESCIENCES
HOLDINGS, INC.**
10770 Wateridge Cir Ste 200, San
Diego, CA 92121
Tel.: (858) 546-0004 DE
Web Site: https://www.maravai.com
Year Founded: 2020
MRVI—(NASDAQ)
Rev.: $288,945,000
Assets: $1,487,450,000
Liabilities: $697,566,000
Net Worth: $789,884,000
Earnings: ($119,029,000)
Emp.: 570
Fiscal Year-end: 12/31/23
Holding Company
N.A.I.C.S.: 551112

Carl Hull (CEO)
Andrew Burch (Exec VP & Gen Mgr-
Nucleic Acid Products Operating Div)
William Martin III (CEO)

Subsidiaries:

Trilink Biotechnologies, Inc. (1)
10770 Wateridge Cir Ste 200, San Diego,
CA 92121
Tel.: (858) 546-0004
Web Site: https://www.trilinkbiotech.com
Emp.: 160
Fiscal Year-end: 12/31/2006
Medical Equipment Mfr
N.A.I.C.S.: 339112
Brian Neel (COO)
Michael Houston (Chief Scientific Officer)
Jeff Whitmore (VP-Comml Ops)

**MARBLEGATE ACQUISITION
CORP.**
411 Theodore Fremd Ave Ste 206s,
Rye, NY 10580
Tel.: (212) 370-1300 DE
Web Site:
https://marblegateacquisition.com
Year Founded: 2020
GATE—(NASDAQ)
Rev.: $3,539,635
Assets: $11,219,899
Liabilities: $27,005,138
Net Worth: ($15,785,239)
Earnings: $1,230,338
Emp.: 3
Fiscal Year-end: 12/31/22
Investment Services
N.A.I.C.S.: 523999
Jeffrey Kravetz (CFO & Principal
Acctg Officer)
Andrew Milgram (CEO)
Paul Arrouet (Pres)
Harvey Golub (Chm)

MARCHEX, INC.
1200 5th Ave Ste 1300, Seattle, WA
98101
Tel.: (206) 331-3300 DE
Web Site: https://www.marchex.com
Year Founded: 2003
MCHX—(NASDAQ)
Rev.: $52,170,000
Assets: $56,794,000
Liabilities: $12,682,000
Net Worth: $44,112,000
Earnings: ($8,245,000)
Emp.: 193
Fiscal Year-end: 12/31/22
Internet/Web Design
N.A.I.C.S.: 541490
Russell C. Horowitz (Founder & Chm)
Michael A. Arends (Vice Chm)
Trevor Caldwell (Sr VP-IR & Strategic
Initiatives)
Travis Fairchild (Exec VP-Bus Dev &
Solution Consulting)
Edwin A. Miller (CEO)
William Li (VP-Engrg)
Troy W. Hartless (Chief Revenue Of-
ficer)
Julie Warner (Dir-People Svcs)
Francis J. Feeney (Chief Corp &
Strategic Affairs Officer)
Holly A. Aglio (CFO)

Subsidiaries:

Archeo, Inc. (1)
520 Pike St Ste 2000, Seattle, WA 98101
Tel.: (206) 331-3300
Computer Related Services
N.A.I.C.S.: 541519

Archonic, LLC (1)
244 5th Ave Ste D151, New York, NY
10001
Tel.: (646) 793-4124
Web Site: http://www.agrinos.com.ua
Agriculture Product Distr
N.A.I.C.S.: 424910

Marchex Sales, LLC (1)
520 Pike St Ste 2000, Seattle, WA 98101
Tel.: (206) 331-3300
Web Site: http://www.marchex.com
Emp.: 200
Owns & Operates Domains; Web Based
Advertising Services
N.A.I.C.S.: 541890

SITA Laboratories, Inc. (1)
125 N Emporia Ste 201, Wichita, KS 67202
Tel.: (844) 815-3455
Web Site: http://www.callcap.com
Call Tracking & Monitoring Services
N.A.I.C.S.: 517810

Telmetrics Corporation (1)
2645 Skymark Avenue Suite 202, Missis-
sauga, L4W 4H2, ON, Canada
Web Site: http://telmetrics.com
Marketing Services
N.A.I.C.S.: 541613
Rami Michael (CTO)
Emely Sabandal (VP-Fin)
Catherine Caplice (VP-Customer Success)

MARCUS & MILLICHAP, INC.
23975 Park Sorrento Ste 400, Cala-
basas, CA 91302
Tel.: (818) 212-2250   DE
Web Site:
    https://www.marcusmillichap.com
Year Founded: 1971
MMI—(NYSE)
Rev.: $1,301,710,000
Assets: $1,003,708,000
Liabilities: $290,199,000
Net Worth: $713,509,000
Earnings: $104,225,000
Emp.: 887
Fiscal Year-end: 12/31/22
Holding Company; Commercial Real
Estate Brokerage & Property Man-
agement Services
N.A.I.C.S.: 551112
George M. Marcus (Founder & Co-
Chm)
Hessam Nadji (Pres & CEO)
Kurt H. Schwarz (Chief Acctg Officer
& First VP-Fin)
Gregory A. LaBerge (Chief Admin
Officer & Sr VP)
Rick Puttkammer (VP-Investments-
San Diego)
Jordan Klink (Sr VP-Investments-
Indianapolis)
Brett R. Hatcher (Sr Mng Dir-
Investments-Columbus)
Josh Caruana (First VP & Mgr-
Indianapolis)
Lisa A. Sickinger (First VP-
Investments-Cincinnati)
Ethan H. Pintard (First VP-
Investments-Oakland)
Todd Lindblom (VP, Natl Dir-Seniors
Housing Div & Reg Mgr)
Mark Ruble (Exec Mng Dir-
Investments-Phoenix)
Clayton Primm (First VP-Investments-
Denver)
Drew Babcock (First VP-Investments-
Columbia)
Kevin J. King (Sr Mng Dir-
Investments-Long Beach)
Steve Bogie Bogoyevac (Sr Mng Dir-
Investments-South Bay)
Earle J. Hyman (Sr Mng Dir-
Investments-Encino)
Gregory A. Mills (Sr Mng Dir-
Investments-Encino)
Jeff Louks (Exec Mng Dir-
Investments-Encino)
Lior Regenstreif (Sr Mng Dir-
Investments-Encino)
Matthew Ziegler (Sr Mng Dir-
Investments-Encino)
Gordon Reese (Sr VP-Investments-
Newport Beach)
Jack C. Hopkins (Sr VP-Investments-
Newport Beach)

Joseph R. Berkson (Sr VP-
Investments-Newport Beach)
Tony Azzi (Exec Mng Dir-
Investments-West Los Angeles)
Kevin Turner (Sr Mng Dir-
Investments-Oakland)
Rick E. Raymundo (Sr Mng Dir-
Investments-Los Angeles)
Matthew E. Whiteside (Sr Mng Dir-
Investments-Milwaukee)
Phil Sambazis (Exec Mng Dir-
Investments-San Diego)
Will Stone (First VP-Investments-
Portland)
Charles LeClaire (Exec Mng Dir-
Investments-Denver)
Brad Nathanson (Sr Mng Dir-
Investments)
Anthony Palladino (VP-Investments)
Giovanni Napoli (Sr Mng Dir-
Investments)
Philip E. Assouad (Sr Mng Dir-
Investments-Seattle)
Steven F. DeGennaro (CFO & Exec
VP)
Mark Cortell (Chief Legal Officer & Sr
VP)
Tyler Theobald (Chief Compliance
Officer, Gen Counsel & First VP)
Biran Patel (Sr VP & Dir-Natl-
Hospitality Div)
Andrew Strockis (CMO)
John Horowitz (Sr VP)
Brian Hosey (Sr VP)
John P. Manning (Sr VP)
Jim Palmer (Sr VP)

Subsidiaries:

**Marcus & Millichap Capital
Corporation** (1)
23975 Park Sorrento Ste 400, Calabasas,
CA 91302
Tel.: (818) 212-2250
Web Site:
    http://www.marcusandmillichap.com
Emp.: 200
Real Estate Investment Credit
N.A.I.C.S.: 522292

Subsidiary (Domestic):

LMI Capital, Inc. (2)
520 Post Oak Blvd, Houston, TX 77027-
9481
Tel.: (713) 239-0500
Web Site: http://www.lmicapital.com
Real Estate Advisory Services
N.A.I.C.S.: 522292

Mission Capital Advisors, LLC (2)
41 Madison Ave 35th Fl, New York, NY
10010
Tel.: (212) 925-6692
Web Site: http://www.missioncap.com
Sales Range: $1-9.9 Million
Emp.: 26
Investment Advice
N.A.I.C.S.: 523940
William David Tobin (Sr Mng Dir)
Chad Coluccio (Mng Dir-Sls & Trading)
Debbie Johnston (VP-Loan Sale Ops)
Dwight Bostic (Mng Dir-Sls & Trading)
Jordan Ray (Sr Mng Dir-Capital Markets)
Mimi Grotto (Partner)
Julia Blewitt (VP-Compliance & HR)
Steven Buchwald (Sr Mng Dir-Capital Mar-
kets)
Alex Draganiuk (Mng Dir)
April Kennedy (VP-Collateral Cures & Title)
Jamie Matheny (Dir-Capital Markets)
Spencer Kirsch (VP)
Jonathan More (Sr VP-Capital Markets)
Philip Justiss (Sr VP-Capital Markets)
Matthew Polci (Sr VP-Capital Markets)
Jordana Stanhope (Dir-Design)
Raymond Salameh (Dir-Capital Markets)
Janice Francis (Mgr-Sls Force Program)
Cameron Coker (VP)
Patryk Braganza-Gallagher (Mgr-IT Ops)
Joseph A. Runk Jr. (Sr Mng Dir)

**Marcus & Millichap REIS of Atlanta,
Inc.** (1)

1100 Abernathy Rd NE Bldg 500 Ste 600,
Atlanta, GA 30328
Tel.: (678) 808-2700
Web Site:
    http://www.marcusandmillichap.com
Real Estate Services
N.A.I.C.S.: 531390

**Marcus & Millichap REIS of Chicago,
Inc.** (1)
333 W Wacker Dr Ste 200, Chicago, IL
60606
Tel.: (312) 327-5400
Web Site: http://www.marcusmillichap.com
Emp.: 55
Real Estate Manangement Services
N.A.I.C.S.: 531390

**Marcus & Millichap REIS of Florida,
Inc.** (1)
5900 N Andrews Ave Ste 100, Fort Lauder-
dale, FL 33309
Tel.: (954) 245-3400
Web Site: http://www.marcusmillichap.com
Emp.: 80
Real Estate Services
N.A.I.C.S.: 531390

**Marcus & Millichap REIS of Nevada,
Inc.** (1)
3800 Howard Hughes Pkwy Ste 1550, Las
Vegas, NV 89169
Tel.: (702) 215-7100
Web Site: http://www.marcusmillichap.com
Real Estate Services
N.A.I.C.S.: 531390
Justin Forman (Reg Mgr)

**Marcus & Millichap REIS of North
Carolina, Inc.** (1)
201 S Tryon St Ste 1220, Charlotte, NC
28202
Tel.: (704) 831-4600
Web Site: http://www.marcusmillichap.com
Real Estate Services
N.A.I.C.S.: 531390

**Marcus & Millichap REIS of Seattle,
Inc.** (1)
601 Union St Ste 2710, Seattle, WA 98101
Tel.: (206) 826-5700
Web Site:
    http://www.marcusandmillichap.com
Emp.: 60
Real Estate Services
N.A.I.C.S.: 531390

**Marcus & Millichap Real Estate In-
vestment Services, Inc.** (1)
23975 Park Sorrento Ste 400, Calabasas,
CA 91302
Tel.: (818) 212-2250
Web Site: https://www.marcusmillichap.com
Sales Range: $600-649.9 Million
Emp.: 1,900
Real Estate Services
N.A.I.C.S.: 531390
George M. Marcus (Founder & Chm)
Hessam Nadji (Pres & CEO)

Subsidiary (Domestic):

**Marcus & Millichap Real Estate In-
vestment Brokerage Company** (2)
2626 Hanover St, Palo Alto, CA 94304
Tel.: (650) 391-1700
Web Site: http://www.marcusmillichap.com
Sales Range: $25-49.9 Million
Emp.: 50
Real Estate Credit
N.A.I.C.S.: 522292
Ronald Z. Harris (Exec Mng Dir-
Investments)
Steven J. Seligman (First VP & Mgr)
Bill Allen (First VP-Investments)
Carlos Azucena (First VP-Investments)
Jacob Becher (First VP-Investments)
David Campbell (First VP-Capital Markets)
David Cutler (VP-Investments)
David J. Dematteis (Sr Mng Dir-
Investments)
Tom Doglio (Sr VP-Investments)
Michael Henshaw (Sr VP-Investments)
Joshua Johnson (VP-Investments)
Robert Johnston (Sr Mng Dir-Investments)
Stanford W. Jones (Exec Mng Dir-
Investments)
Ted Kokernak (Sr Mng Dir-Investments)
Adam Levin (Exec Mng Dir-Investments)

Robert Mallett (First VP-Capital Markets)
Russ Panowicz (First VP-Investments)
Richard Reisman (First VP-Investments)
Raymond Rodriguez (VP-Investments)
Philip A. Saglimbeni (Sr Mng Dir-
Investments)
Salvatore S. Saglimbeni (Sr Mng Dir-
Investments)
Fabio Sangiorgi (First VP-Investments)
Steve Sauter (Sr Mng Dir-Investments)
Yuri Sergunin (First VP-Investments)
Fred Rubio III (VP-Investments)

Mark One Capital, Inc. (1)
5001 Spring Vly Ste 100W, Dallas, TX
75244
Tel.: (972) 755-5200
Web Site: https://www.marcusmillichap.com
Emp.: 7
Real Estate Services
N.A.I.C.S.: 531390
Josh Sciotto (VP-Capital Markets)
Tim Speck (First VP & District Mgr)

**Metropolitan Capital Advisors,
Ltd.** (1)
18111 Preston Rd Ste 650, Dallas, TX
75252
Tel.: (972) 267-0600
Web Site: http://www.metcapital.com
Miscellaneous Business Credit Institution
N.A.I.C.S.: 522299

MARGO CARIBE, INC.
10501 Cold Storage Rd Bldg 100,
Vega Alta, PR 32218
Tel.: (904) 309-5707   PR
Year Founded: 1993
MRGO—(OTCIQ)
Sales Range: $1-9.9 Million
Tropical & Flowering Plants; Lawn &
Garden Products Seller & Distr
N.A.I.C.S.: 111421
Michael J. Spector Miller (Pres)
George Christopher Kelly (VP-
Marketing)
Gregory Boyd Carrier (VP)
Miguel Rivera Delgado (VP)
Steve George Morrill (CFO & Sr VP)

Subsidiaries:

Margo Garden Products, Inc. (1)
Carr 690 km 5.8, Vega Alta, PR 00646-
1370
Tel.: (787) 883-2570
Tree & Nursery Services
N.A.I.C.S.: 111421
Michael J. Spector Miller (Pres)

Margo Nursery Farms, Inc. (1)
Carr 690 km 5.8, Vega Alta, PR 00692
Tel.: (787) 883-2570
Tree & Nursery Farm
N.A.I.C.S.: 111421
Michael J. Spector Miller (Pres)

MARIJUANA COMPANY OF
AMERICA, INC.
633 W 5th St Ste 2826, Los Angeles,
CA 90071   UT
Web Site:
    http://www.marijuanacompanyof
    america.com
Year Founded: 1985
MCOA—(OTCIQ)
Rev.: $1,030,249
Assets: $7,959,899
Liabilities: $7,729,010
Net Worth: $230,889
Earnings: ($10,191,450)
Emp.: 7
Fiscal Year-end: 12/31/21
Cannabis Growth, Cultivation, Har-
vesting, Distribution Research & De-
velopment
N.A.I.C.S.: 111419
Jesus M. Quintero (Chm, CEO, CFO,
Principal Acctg Officer & Treas)

MARIMED INC.
10 Oceana Way Fl 2, Norwood, MA
02062

MariMed Inc.—(Continued)

Tel.: (781) 277-0007   **DE**
Web Site:
  https://www.marimedinc.com
Year Founded: 2011
MRMD—(OTCQX)
Rev.: $134,010,000
Assets: $152,202,000
Liabilities: $57,167,000
Net Worth: $95,035,000
Earnings: $13,468,000
Emp.: 592
Fiscal Year-end: 12/31/22
Offices of Other Holding Companies
N.A.I.C.S.: 551112
Edward J. Gildea (Chm)
Jon R. Levine (Co-Founder & Pres)
Timothy Shaw (COO)
Howard Schacter (Chief Comm Officer)
Jon R. Levine (Co-Founder, Pres & CEO)

MARIN SOFTWARE INC.
149 New Montgomery St 4 th Fl, San Francisco, CA 94105
Tel.: (415) 399-2580   **DE**
Web Site:
  https://www.marinsoftware.com
Year Founded: 2006
MRIN—(NASDAQ)
Rev.: $20,019,000
Assets: $42,084,000
Liabilities: $9,370,000
Net Worth: $32,714,000
Earnings: ($18,227,000)
Emp.: 177
Fiscal Year-end: 12/31/22
Online Advertising Management Software Developer
N.A.I.C.S.: 513210
Christopher A. Lien (Co-Founder, Chm & CEO)
Wister Walcott (Co-Founder & Exec VP-Product & Tech)
Doug Pan (Sr VP-Engrg)
Robert Bertz (CFO & Principal Acctg Officer)
Marie Boivent (Sr VP-Revenue)

Subsidiaries:

Marin Software (Shanghai) Co., Ltd.   (1)
Room 05/06 Level 29 Chonghing Finance Centre No 288 Nanjing Road West, Huang'pu District, Shanghai, 200003, China
Tel.: (86) 2180259000
Web Site: http://www.marinsoftware.com
Software Development Services
N.A.I.C.S.: 541511

Marin Software GmbH   (1)
Neuer Wall 63, 20354, Hamburg, Germany
Tel.: (49) 40808074232
Web Site: http://www.marinsoftware.com
Software Development Services
N.A.I.C.S.: 541511

Marin Software K.K.   (1)
16th Floor Ark Hills Front Tower, 2-23-1 Akasaka Minato-ku, Tokyo, 107-0052, Japan
Tel.: (81) 362305400
Web Site: http://www.marinsoftware.com
Software Development Services
N.A.I.C.S.: 541511

Marin Software Limited(UK)   (1)
18 Soho Square, London, W1D 3QL, United Kingdom
Tel.: (44) 2039209405
Web Site: http://www.marinsoftware.com
Emp.: 60
Software Development Services
N.A.I.C.S.: 541511

NowSpots, Inc.   (1)
210 W Hill St Ste 3, Chicago, IL 60610
Tel.: (269) 861-5280
Media Streaming Services
N.A.I.C.S.: 518210

Brad Flora (Founder)

MARINE BANCORP OF FLORIDA, INC.
571 Beachland Blvd, Vero Beach, FL 32963
Tel.: (772) 231-6611
Web Site:
  https://www.marinebankandtrust.bank.com
MBOF—(OTCIQ)
Bank Holding Company
N.A.I.C.S.: 551111
William J. Penney (Pres & CEO)

Subsidiaries:

Marine Bank & Trust Company   (1)
571 Beachland Blvd, Vero Beach, FL 32963
Tel.: (772) 231-6611
Web Site:
  http://www.marinebankandtrust.com
Sales Range: $1-9.9 Million
Emp.: 31
Commericial Banking
N.A.I.C.S.: 522110
William J. Penney (Pres & CEO)
Brian C. Fowler (Chief Credit Officer & Sr VP)
George R. Slater (Founder)
Kim Prado (Asst VP & Branch Mgr)
Kristine M. Martin (Asst VP & Mgr-Deposit Ops)
Deric R. Meadows (Asst VP-IT)
Gloria Taylor (Asst VP-Residential Loans)
Georgia L. Irish (VP-Client Svcs & New Bus Dev)
J. Cary Allen (VP-Credit Admin)
Jo-Ann L. Copeland (Chief Compliance Officer & Sr VP)
Karl L. Williams (Officer-Comml Loan & VP)
Malak M. Hammad (VP & Mgr-Melbourne)
Mary A. Cone (VP & Mgr-Residential Mortgage)
Rebekah E. Refford (VP-Loan Admin)
Robert A. Morgan (VP-Residential Mortgage Lending)
Stephen D. Shields (Sr VP & Mgr-Residential Lending)
William C. Koehne (Sr VP & Mgr-Comml Lending)
Charlie J. Gisler Jr. (CFO, COO & Exec VP)

MARINE PETROLEUM TRUST
3838 Oak Lawn Ave Ste 1720, Dallas, TX 75219   **TX**
Web Site: https://marps-marine.com
MARPS—(NASDAQ)
Rev.: $1,044,997
Assets: $965,220
Net Worth: $965,220
Earnings: $713,165
Fiscal Year-end: 06/30/24
Investment Services
N.A.I.C.S.: 525910
Ron E. Hooper (Sr VP)

MARINE PRODUCTS CORPORATION
2801 Buford Hwy NE Ste 300, Atlanta, GA 30329
Tel.: (404) 321-7910   **DE**
Web Site:
  https://www.marineproductscorp.com
MPX—(NYSE)
Rev.: $380,995,000
Assets: $163,715,000
Liabilities: $39,334,000
Net Worth: $124,381,000
Earnings: $40,347,000
Emp.: 935
Fiscal Year-end: 12/31/22
Fiberglass Boat Building & Repairing
N.A.I.C.S.: 336612
Richard A. Hubbell (Chm)
Ben M. Palmer (Pres & CEO)
Michael L. Schmit (CFO, Treas, Sec & VP)

Subsidiaries:

Chaparral Boats, Inc.   (1)
300 Industrial Park Blvd, Nashville, GA 31639
Tel.: (229) 686-7481
Web Site: https://www.chaparralboats.com
Sales Range: $350-399.9 Million
Boat Mfr
N.A.I.C.S.: 336612

MARINEMAX, INC.
501 Brooker Creek Blvd, Oldsmar, FL 34677
Tel.: (727) 531-1700   **DE**
Web Site:
  https://www.marinemax.com
Year Founded: 1998
HZO—(NYSE)
Rev.: $2,431,008,000
Assets: $2,605,068,000
Liabilities: $1,618,819,000
Net Worth: $986,249,000
Earnings: $38,738,000
Emp.: 4,050
Fiscal Year-end: 09/30/24
Recreational Boat Retailer
N.A.I.C.S.: 441222
Michael H. McLamb (CFO, Sec & Exec VP)
William Brett McGill (Pres & CEO)
Shawn Berg (Chief Digital Officer)
Kyle Langbehn (Pres-Retail Ops)
Manny Alvare (VP)
Beth Garland (Sr VP)
Anthony E. Cassella Jr. (Chief Acctg Officer & VP-Fin)

Subsidiaries:

Boatzon Holdings, LLC   (1)
1909 Tyler St Ste 301, Hollywood, FL 33009
Web Site: https://boatzon.com
Holding Company
N.A.I.C.S.: 551112

Fraser Yachts Limited   (1)
Berkeley Square House Berkeley Square, St Jamess, London, W1J 6BD, United Kingdom
Tel.: (44) 2070164480
Yacht Brokerage Services
N.A.I.C.S.: 441222

Fraser Yachts Management & Services LLC   (1)
Suhaim Bin Hamad / C Ring Rd Suhaim Tower Office No 407, Al Sadd, Doha, Qatar
Tel.: (974) 44319799
Boat Retailer
N.A.I.C.S.: 441222

Global Marine Brokerage, LLC   (1)
6810 Gulfport Blvd S Ste 200, South Pasadena, FL 33707
Tel.: (727) 498-6477
Web Site:
  https://www.globalmarineboats.com
Boat Distr
N.A.I.C.S.: 441222
Joe Lieser (Founder)

IGY Malaga Marina   (1)
Paseo de la Farola S/N, 29016, Malaga, Spain
Tel.: (34) 628492362
Boat Rental Services
N.A.I.C.S.: 532284

KCS International, Inc.   (1)
804 Pecor St, Oconto, WI 54153
Tel.: (920) 834-2211
Web Site: http://www.cruisersyachts.com
Boat Building & Repairing
N.A.I.C.S.: 336612
Mark Pedersen (Pres)

MarineMax East, Inc.   (1)
5800 Holiday Rd, Buford, GA 30518-1582
Tel.: (770) 781-9370
Web Site: http://www.marinemax.com
Sales Range: $25-49.9 Million
Emp.: 20
Recreational Boat Retailer
N.A.I.C.S.: 441222

Subsidiary (Domestic):

Boating Gear Center, LLC   (2)
18167 US Hwy 19 N Ste 300, Clearwater, FL 33764
Tel.: (888) 268-2402
Web Site: http://www.boatinggearcenter.com
Boat Accessories & Parts Retailer
N.A.I.C.S.: 441222

Fraser Yachts Florida, Inc.   (2)
1800 SE 10th Ave Ste 400, Fort Lauderdale, FL 33316
Tel.: (954) 463-0600
Web Site: http://www.fraseryachts.com
Yacht Brokerage & Services
N.A.I.C.S.: 532411
Eric Turoff (Superintendent-Technical)
Eugene Parfyonov (Superintendent-Technical)
Fathima Jameel (Mgr-HR)
Jeanne Bruss (Controller)
Jessica Althoff (Mgr-Charter)
Michael Busacca (COO)
Peter Selivanoff (Mgr-Svcs)

Subsidiary (Domestic):

Fraser Yachts California   (3)
4960 N Harbor Dr Ste 100, San Diego, CA 92106
Tel.: (619) 225-4800
Yacht Brokerage & Management Services
N.A.I.C.S.: 532284
Megan Day (Office Mgr)

Subsidiary (Non-US):

Fraser Yachts Spain SLU   (3)
C/ Porto Pi 4A, Palma de Mallorca, Spain
Tel.: (34) 971700445
Yacht Brokerage Services
N.A.I.C.S.: 441222
Arancha Garcia (Office Mgr)

Subsidiary (Domestic):

MarineMax Services, Inc.   (2)
18167 US Hwy 19 N Ste 300, Clearwater, FL 33764
Tel.: (727) 531-1700
Sales Range: $250-299.9 Million
Emp.: 90
Recreational Boat Retailer
N.A.I.C.S.: 441222

MarineMax Vacations, LTD   (2)
2600 McCormick Dr Ste 130, Clearwater, FL 33759
Tel.: (813) 644-8071
Web Site: https://www.marinemax.com
Emp.: 6
Recreational Boat Retailer
N.A.I.C.S.: 441222
Raul Bermudez (VP-Charter Div)
Dave Rigge (VP)
Clarence Malone (Dir-Ops-BVI Charter Base)

MarineMax of Minnesota, Inc.   (1)
20300 County Rd 81, Rogers, MN 55374
Tel.: (763) 428-4126
Web Site: http://www.marinemax.com
Sales Range: $10-24.9 Million
Emp.: 40
Recreational Boat Retailer
N.A.I.C.S.: 441222

MarineMax of New Jersey Holdings, Inc.   (1)
1500 Riverside, Brick, NJ 08724
Tel.: (732) 840-2100
Web Site: http://www.marinmax.com
Sales Range: $50-74.9 Million
Emp.: 60
Recreational Boat Retailer
N.A.I.C.S.: 441222

Subsidiary (Domestic):

MarineMax NJ Partners, Inc.   (2)
1500 Riverside, Brick, NJ 08724
Tel.: (732) 840-2100
Web Site: http://www.marinemax.com
Sales Range: $200-249.9 Million
Emp.: 30
Recreational Boat Retailer
N.A.I.C.S.: 441222

MarineMax of North Carolina, Inc.   (1)
130 Short St, Wrightsville Beach, NC 28480-1764
Tel.: (910) 256-8100

Web Site: http://www.marinemax.com
Sales Range: $50-74.9 Million
Emp.: 40
Recreational Boat Retailer
N.A.I.C.S.: 441222
Bill McGill *(Pres & CEO)*

MarineMax of Ohio, Inc. (1)
1991 NE Catawba Rd, Port Clinton, OH
43452
Tel.: (419) 797-4492
Web Site: http://www.marinemax.com
Sales Range: $50-74.9 Million
Emp.: 40
Recreational Boat Retailer
N.A.I.C.S.: 441222

Midcoast Marine Group LLC (1)
1078 Island Ave, Tarpon Springs, FL 34689
Tel.: (727) 800-5512
Web Site: https://midcoastllc.com
Marine Construction Services
N.A.I.C.S.: 237990

New Wave Innovations, LLC (1)
502 N School St, Lodi, CA 95240
Web Site:
    https://newwaveinnovationsinc.com
Car Washing Equipment Mfr
N.A.I.C.S.: 334310

**Newcoast Financial Services,
Inc.** (1)
2600 McCormick Dr Ste 100, Clearwater,
FL 33759
Tel.: (727) 450-1160
Web Site: http://www.newcoast.com
Sales Range: $10-24.9 Million
Emp.: 15
Financial Services for Marine & RV's
N.A.I.C.S.: 561499
Jim Kelaita *(Pres)*

Nisswa Marine, LLC (1)
24238 Smiley Rd, Nisswa, MN 56468
Tel.: (218) 963-2292
Web Site: https://www.nisswamarine.com
Sales Range: $1-9.9 Million
Emp.: 25
Boat Distr
N.A.I.C.S.: 441222
Donna Wiczek *(Gen Mgr)*

**Northrop & Johnson Monaco
S.A.M.** (1)
Le Panorama 57 Rue Grimaldi Bloc A/B 7e
etage, Monaco, Monaco
Tel.: (377) 97772720
Yacht Brokerage Services
N.A.I.C.S.: 441222
Patrick Coote *(Mng Dir)*

**Northrop & Johnson Yachts-Ships
LLC** (1)
2015 SW 20th St Ste 200, Fort Lauderdale,
FL 33315
Tel.: (954) 522-3344
Web Site:
    http://www.northropandjohnson.com
Retail Boats
N.A.I.C.S.: 441222
Kevin Merrigan *(Chm)*
Daniel Ziriakus *(Pres & COO)*
Maria Giovanniello *(Dir-Fin & HR)*
Crom Littlejohn *(Chief Comml Officer)*
Vanessa Jiron *(Dir-Admin)*
Adam Fitzmaurice *(Sr Mgr-Charter)*
Marcy Williams *(Dir-Crew Svcs)*
Alberto Carrillo *(Art Dir)*
Alfredo Lopez *(Mktg Dir)*
Mark Erlewine *(Project Mgr-Mktg & Tech)*
Janine Stdenis *(Mgr-Mktg & Comm)*
Ramone Wilson *(Mgr-IT)*
Miriam Cain *(Dir-Editorial)*

Orbeth, Inc. (1)
36448 County Rd 66, Crosslake, MN
56442-2506
Tel.: (218) 692-3570
Web Site: http://www.ccboatworks.com
Rev.: $3,000,000
Emp.: 4
Boat Dealers
N.A.I.C.S.: 441222
Deborah Nelson *(VP)*
Brad Nelson *(CEO)*

**Silver Seas Yachts of California,
Inc.** (1)
300 Harbor Dr, Sausalito, CA 94965

Tel.: (415) 367-4022
Web Site: http://www.silverseasyachts.com
Boat Distr
N.A.I.C.S.: 441222

Super Yacht Management S.A.S. (1)
B51 La Capitainerie Port Camille Rayon,
06220, Golfe-Juan, France
Tel.: (33) 493341394
Web Site: https://sym.eu
Super Yacht Management Services
N.A.I.C.S.: 713930

TCN Antibes S.A.R.L. (1)
12 Avenue Pasteur, 06600, Antibes, France
Tel.: (33) 497211313
Yacht Brokerage Services
N.A.I.C.S.: 441222

US Liquidators, LLC (1)
2605 N 43rd St, Tampa, FL 33605-3216
Tel.: (813) 627-0172
Web Site:
    http://www.usliquidatorsonline.com
Boat Dealers
N.A.I.C.S.: 441222

MARINUS PHARMACEUTI-CALS INC.

5 Radnor Corporate Ctr Ste 500 100
Matsonford Rd, Radnor, PA 19087
Tel.: (484) 801-4670   DE
Web Site:
    https://www.marinuspharma.com
Year Founded: 2003
MRNS—(NASDAQ)
Rev.: $30,989,000
Assets: $170,908,000
Liabilities: $154,143,000
Net Worth: $16,765,000
Earnings: ($141,405,000)
Emp.: 165
Fiscal Year-end: 12/31/23
Pharmaceuticals Mfr
N.A.I.C.S.: 325412
Joseph Hulihan *(Chief Medical Offi-cer)*
Christy Shafer *(Chief Comml Officer)*
Molly Cameron *(Dir-Communications
& Investor Relations)*
Scott Braunstein *(Chm, Pres & CEO)*
David A. Czekai *(Officer-Chemistry,
Manufacturing, and Controls & Sr VP-Chemistry, Mfg, and Controls)*
Sonya Weigle *(Chief People Officer,
Chief IR Officer & Sr VP)*

MARIZYME, INC.

555 Heritage Dr Ste 205, Jupiter, FL
33458
Tel.: (561) 935-9955   NV
Web Site: https://www.marizyme.com
MRZM—(OTCQB)
Rev.: $645,810
Assets: $22,015,075
Liabilities: $26,675,711
Net Worth: ($4,660,636)
Earnings: ($65,346,916)
Emp.: 11
Fiscal Year-end: 12/31/23
Pharmaceuticals Product Mfr
N.A.I.C.S.: 325412
Vithalbhai D. Dhaduk *(Chm)*
David Barthel *(CEO & Sec)*
George Kovalyov *(CFO)*
Harrison Ross *(VP-Fin)*
Claudio Rigatto *(Chief Medical
Officer-My Health Logic)*

Subsidiaries:

Somaceutica, Inc. (1)
225 Chimney Corner Ln Ste 2021, Jupiter,
FL 33458
Web Site: http://www.somaceutica.com
Pharmaceutical Preparation Mfr
N.A.I.C.S.: 325412

Somahlution, Inc. (1)
225 Chimney Corner Ln Ste 2001, Jupiter,
FL 33458
Tel.: (561) 935-9955

Web Site: http://www.somahlution.com
Pharmaceutical Preparation Mfr
N.A.I.C.S.: 325412

MARKEL GROUP INC.

4521 Highwoods Pkwy, Glen Allen,
VA 23060
Tel.: (804) 747-0136   VA
Web Site: https://www.markel.com
Year Founded: 1930
MKL—(NYSE)
Rev.: $15,803,630,000
Assets: $55,045,710,000
Liabilities: $39,519,817,000
Net Worth: $15,525,893,000
Earnings: $1,960,060,000
Emp.: 21,600
Fiscal Year-end: 12/31/23
Financial Investment Services
N.A.I.C.S.: 551112
Thomas Sinnickson Gayner *(CEO)*
Richard R. Grinnan *(Chief Legal Offi-cer, Sec & Sr VP)*
Brian C. Tkacz *(Sr Dir-IT Managed
Services-Global)*
Jeremy Andrew Noble *(Pres-Insurance Ops)*
Sue Davies *(Chief HR Officer)*
Andrew G. Crowley *(Pres)*
Teresa S. Gendron *(CFO)*

Subsidiaries:

**AMF Automation Technologies,
LLC** (1)
2115 W Laburnum Ave, Richmond, VA
23227
Tel.: (804) 355-7961
Web Site: https://www.amfbakery.com
Bakery Equipment Mfr
N.A.I.C.S.: 333241
Larry Gore *(Dir-Sls Admin)*
Gary McDonald *(Reg Mgr-Acct)*
Dave Pedro *(Reg Mgr-Acct)*
Kenneth R. Newsome *(Chm, Pres & CEO)*
Jonathan Edrich *(Reg Mgr-Acct)*
Charles Schulze *(Reg Mgr-Acct)*
Brandon Brilliant *(Reg Mgr-Acct)*

Subsidiary (Domestic):

Baking Technology Systems, Inc. (2)
5359 Royal Woods Pkwy, Tucker, GA
30084
Tel.: (770) 270-5911
Insurance Services
N.A.I.C.S.: 524127

Abbey Protection plc (1)
Minories House 2-5 Minories, London,
EC3N 1BJ, United Kingdom
Tel.: (44) 8452178293
Web Site:
    https://www.abbeyprotectionplc.com
Sales Range: $50-74.9 Million
Emp.: 275
Holding Company; Insurance Agencies &
Brokerages
N.A.I.C.S.: 551112

Subsidiary (Domestic):

Abbey Protection Group Limited (2)
11th Floor 82 King St, 2-5 Minories, Man-chester, M2 4WQ, United Kingdom
Tel.: (44) 8450762288
Insurance Agents & Brokers
N.A.I.C.S.: 524210

Division (Domestic):

Abbey HR Services (3)
Suite 5 Bloxam Court Corporation Street,
Rugby, CV21 2DU, Warwickshire, United
Kingdom
Tel.: (44) 3450762288
Web Site: https://ahrconsultants.co.uk
Human Resource Consulting Services
N.A.I.C.S.: 541612

Subsidiary (Domestic):

Abbey Legal Protection Limited (3)
Minories House 2-5 Minories, London,
EC3N 1BJ, United Kingdom
Tel.: (44) 8706001480

Insurance Related Services
N.A.I.C.S.: 524210
Robert Nicholls *(Dir-Sls)*

**Abbey Tax & Consultancy Services
Limited** (3)
Minories House 2-5 Minories, London,
EC3N 1BJ, United Kingdom
Tel.: (44) 8452232727
Insurance Related Services
N.A.I.C.S.: 524210

Accountax Consulting Limited (3)
One Mitchell Court Castle Mound Way,
Rugby, CV23 0UY, Warwickshire, United
Kingdom
Tel.: (44) 3450660035
Web Site:
    http://www.accountaxconsulting.com
Tax Consulting Services
N.A.I.C.S.: 541213

Subsidiary (Non-US):

**Ibex Reinsurance Company
Limited** (3)
Polygon Hall Le Marchant St, Saint Peter
Port, GY1 4HY, Guernsey
Tel.: (44) 1481716000
Reinsurance Services
N.A.I.C.S.: 524130

Subsidiary (Domestic):

**Lewis Hymanson Small Solicitors
LLP** (3)
3rd Floor Corinthian House 17 Lansdowne
Road, Croydon, CR0 2BX, United Kingdom
Tel.: (44) 3453134143
Web Site: http://www.lhsolicitors.com
Insurance Related Services
N.A.I.C.S.: 524210
Alex Gurr *(Mgr-Bus Dev)*
Andrew Forrest *(Head-IT)*

Brahmin Leather Works, LLC (1)
77 Alden Rd, Fairhaven, MA 02719
Tel.: (508) 994-4000
Web Site: https://www.brahmin.com
Leather Handbag & Accessories Mfr
N.A.I.C.S.: 316990

Buckner Heavylift Cranes, LLC (1)
4732 NC Hwy 54 E, Graham, NC 27253
Tel.: (336) 376-8888
Web Site:
    https://www.bucknercompanies.com
Crane Operator
N.A.I.C.S.: 532412

**Caunce O'Hara & Company
Limited** (1)
82 King Street, Manchester, M2 4WQ,
United Kingdom
Tel.: (44) 3333211403
Web Site: https://www.caunceohara.co.uk
Insurance Services
N.A.I.C.S.: 524210
Fernanda Lima *(Mgr)*

Cottrell, Inc. (1)
2125 Candler Rd, Gainesville, GA 30507
Tel.: (770) 532-7251
Web Site: https://www.cottrelltrailers.com
Automobile Parts Mfr
N.A.I.C.S.: 336211

**Eagle Commercial Construction,
LLC** (1)
2250 Old Brick Rd Ste 220, Glen Allen, VA
23060
Tel.: (804) 741-4663
Web Site:
    https://www.eaglecomconstruction.com
Commercial Building Construction Services
N.A.I.C.S.: 236220

Eagle Commercial Realty, LLC (1)
8100 Harford Rd, Parkville, MD 21234
Tel.: (410) 426-2700
Web Site:
    http://www.eaglecommercialrealty.com
Real Estate Broking Services
N.A.I.C.S.: 531210

Eagle Construction of Va., LLC (1)
10618 Patterson Ave, Henrico, VA 23238
Tel.: (804) 741-4663
Web Site: https://www.eagleofva.com

Markel Group Inc.—(Continued)
Insurance Related Services
N.A.I.C.S.: 524210

Subsidiary (Domestic):

Eagle Realty of Virginia, LLC (2)
2250 Old Brick Rd Ste 220, Glen Allen, VA
23060-6008
Tel.: (804) 741-4663
General Insurance Services
N.A.I.C.S.: 524210

Innslake Title Agency, LLC (2)
10618 Patterson Ave, Henrico, VA 23238
Tel.: (804) 217-6911
Web Site: https://www.innslaketitle.com
Insurance Related Services
N.A.I.C.S.: 524210

Precision Realty, LLC (2)
778 S Main St, Plantsville, CT 06479
Tel.: (860) 785-3634
Web Site: https://www.precisionrealtyct.com
Real Estate Agency Services
N.A.I.C.S.: 531390
Jeffrey Kornblau (Pres)

Elliott Special Risks LP (1)
200 Wellington Street West Suite 800, To-
ronto, M5V 3C7, ON, Canada
Tel.: (416) 601-1133
Web Site:
https://www.markelinternational.ca
Insurance Brokerage Services
N.A.I.C.S.: 524210

Essentia Insurance Company (1)
1 Beacon Ln, Canton, MA 02021-1030
Tel.: (781) 332-7000
Insurance Related Services
N.A.I.C.S.: 524210

FSB Insurance Service Limited (1)
5th Floor Interchange 81-85 Station Road,
Croydon, CR0 2RD, United Kingdom
Tel.: (44) 2038837976
Web Site: https://www.fsb-insurance-
service.com
Insurance Agency Services
N.A.I.C.S.: 524210
Katie Freemantle (Mng Dir)

**FirstComp Underwriters Group,
Inc.** (1)
222 S 15th St Central Park Plz N Ste 1500,
Omaha, NE 68102-1680
Tel.: (402) 926-0099
Web Site: http://www.markelfirstcomp.com
Insurance Services
N.A.I.C.S.: 524298

IDRECO B.V. (1)
Nijverheidsstraat 12A, s-Heerenberg, 7041
GE, Netherlands
Tel.: (31) 314667001
Insurance Services
N.A.I.C.S.: 524127

**Investors Underwriting Managers,
Inc.** (1)
310 Hwy 35 S, Red Bank, NJ
07701 **(100%)**
Tel.: (732) 224-0500
Web Site: http://www.markelcorp.com
Sales Range: $50-74.9 Million
Emp.: 170
N.A.I.C.S.: 524298

**Lodgepine Capital Management
Limited** (1)
8th Floor East 141 Front Street, Hamilton,
Bermuda
Tel.: (441) 5049178
Web Site: https://www.lodgepine.com
Insurance Agency Services
N.A.I.C.S.: 524210
Brenton Slade (Pres)

Markel (UK) Limited (1)
2nd Floor Verity House 6 Canal Wharf,
Leeds, LS11 5AS, United Kingdom
Tel.: (44) 3308223558
Web Site: https://www.markeluk.com
Insurance Services
N.A.I.C.S.: 524210

**Markel American Insurance
Company** (1)

N 14 W 23800 Stone Rdg Dr, Waukesha,
WI 53188
Tel.: (262) 548-9880
Underwriter of Marine, Sport Vehicle & Spe-
cialty Property Insurance
N.A.I.C.S.: 524130

**Markel CATCo Investment Manage-
ment Ltd.** (1)
8th Floor East 141 Front Street, Hamilton,
HM 19, Bermuda
Tel.: (441) 5049178
Web Site: https://www.markelcatco.com
Investment Management Service
N.A.I.C.S.: 523940

Markel Canada Limited (1)
200 Wellington St W Ste 800, Toronto, M5V
3C7, ON, Canada
Tel.: (416) 601-1133
Web Site: https://www.markel.ca
Insurance Services
N.A.I.C.S.: 524127
David Crozier (Pres)
Jennifer Devereaux (Sr VP-Underwriting)
Jeff Smith (Sr VP- & Operations)
Jeff Sutton (Sr VP-Sales & Marketing)
Maureen Tomlinson (Sr VP-Operations)
Kathryn Britnell (VP-)
Christopher Kelen (VP-)
Andrew Poulton (VP-)
Michael Kearney (VP-)

**Markel Consultancy Services
Limited** (1)
20 Fenchurch Street, London, EC3M 3AZ,
United Kingdom
Tel.: (44) 2079536000
Web Site: https://www.markeltax.co.uk
Emp.: 2,500
Tax Consulting Services
N.A.I.C.S.: 541213

Markel Corp. - Woodland Hills (1)
21600 Oxnard St Ste 900, Woodland Hills,
CA 91367-6476
Tel.: (818) 595-0600
Web Site: http://www.markelcorp.com
Sales Range: $1-9.9 Million
Emp.: 70
Provider of Fire Marine & Casualty Insur-
ance
N.A.I.C.S.: 524210

Markel Insurance Company (1)
4521 Highwoods Pkwy, Glen Allen, VA
23060 **(100%)**
Tel.: (804) 527-2700
Web Site: https://www.markelinsurance.com
Sales Range: $200-249.9 Million
Emp.: 350
Specialty Insurance Services
N.A.I.C.S.: 524126

Subsidiary (Domestic):

Deerfield Insurance Company (2)
420 Lk Cook Rd Ste 111, Deerfield, IL
60015-2526
Tel.: (847) 945-0155
Web Site: http://www.markelcorp.com
Emp.: 107
Insurance Brokerage Services
N.A.I.C.S.: 524210
Mimi Siske (Pres)

Markel Service, Inc. (2)
4521 Highwoods Pkwy Ste 2009-10, Glen
Allen, VA 23060-6148
Tel.: (804) 747-0136
Web Site: https://www.markelcorp.com
Independent Agent Services
N.A.I.C.S.: 524126

Subsidiary (Domestic):

**Thompson Insurance Enterprises,
LLC** (3)
3380 Chastain Meadows Pkwy Ste 100,
Kennesaw, GA 30144
Tel.: (678) 290-2100
Insurance Related Services
N.A.I.C.S.: 524210

Markel Insurance S.E. (1)
Sophienstr 26, 80333, Munich, Germany
Tel.: (49) 89890831650
Insurance Services
N.A.I.C.S.: 524128

**Markel International (Dubai)
Limited** (1)
Gate Village 8 5th Floor, PO Box 506914,
Dubai, United Arab Emirates
Tel.: (971) 45906777
Reinsurance Services
N.A.I.C.S.: 524130
Leroy Almeida (Sr Exec Officer & Head-
Ops-Middle East)
Eman Arafat (Office Mgr-Support)

Markel International Limited (1)
20 Fenchurch Street, London, EC3M 3AZ,
United Kingdom **(100%)**
Tel.: (44) 2079536000
Web Site:
http://www.markelinternational.com
Sales Range: $125-149.9 Million
Emp.: 600
Holding Company
N.A.I.C.S.: 551112
Andy Davies (COO)
William Stovin (Pres)
Simon Barrett (Fin Dir)
Nick Line (Chief Underwriting Officer)
Thomas Upton (Mgr-Claims-Energy, Liability
& Terrorism)
Andrew Green (Head-Underwriting Risk)
Emma Higgins (Head-Catastrophe Mgmt)
Guenter Kryszon (Officer-Underwriting-
Global)

**Markel International Singapore Pte.
Limited** (1)
138 Market Street 04-02 CapitaGreen, Sin-
gapore, 048946, Singapore
Tel.: (65) 63883000
Reinsurance Services
N.A.I.C.S.: 524130
Christian Stobbs (Mng Dir-Asia)
Nicole Lee (Office Mgr)
Simon Moi (Head-Professional & Fin Risks)
Vera Low (Mgr-Fin & Ops-Asia)
Suriyani Yang (Asst Mgr-Fin & Ops)

Markel Law LLP (1)
11th floor 82 King Street, Manchester, M2
4WQ, United Kingdom
Tel.: (44) 3453510025
Web Site: https://www.markellaw.co.uk
Insurance Agency Services
N.A.I.C.S.: 524210
Beverley Bates (Dir)
Chris Burns (Partner)
Deborah Nicholson (Partner)
Laura Hoyle (Ops Mgr-Compliance-
Operations-Manchester)
Mark Rankin (Partner)
Craig McCracken (Partner)

Markel Midwest (1)
Ten Pkwy N, Deerfield, IL 60015 **(100%)**
Tel.: (847) 572-6000
Web Site: http://www.markelcorp.com
Rev.: $104,907,000
Emp.: 107
Medical Malpractice, Professional Products,
Errors & Omissions Liability Insurance
N.A.I.C.S.: 524126

Subsidiary (Domestic):

Evanston Insurance Company (2)
10 Pkwy N, Deerfield, IL 60015 **(100%)**
Tel.: (847) 572-6000
Web Site: http://www.markelcorporation.com
Sales Range: $100-124.9 Million
Emp.: 107
Professional & Product Liability Insurance
N.A.I.C.S.: 524126

Markel Seguradora do Brasil SA (1)
Av Rio Branco 1 Conjunto 806 Centro, Rio
de Janeiro, 20090 003, Brazil
Tel.: (55) 2135595900
Web Site: http://www.markelseguros.com.br
Insurance Services
N.A.I.C.S.: 524127

Markel Surety Corporation (1)
9500 Arboretum Blvd Ste 400, Austin, TX
78759
Tel.: (512) 732-0099
Web Site: https://www.suretec.com
Insurance Services
N.A.I.C.S.: 524127

Markel Ventures, Inc. (1)
4521 Highwoods Pkwy, Glen Allen, VA
23060 **(100%)**

Tel.: (804) 747-0136
Web Site: https://www.markelventures.com
Privater Equity Firm
N.A.I.C.S.: 523999

Holding (Domestic):

AMF Bakery Systems (2)
2115 W Laburnum Ave, Richmond, VA
23227-4315
Tel.: (804) 355-7961
Web Site: http://www.amfbakery.com
Sales Range: $25-49.9 Million
Emp.: 145
Industrial Bakery Equipment Mfr & Marketer
N.A.I.C.S.: 333241
Larry Gore (Dir-Sls Admin)
Jason Ward (Pres & Dir-Interim-Sls)
Guillaume Joly (Dir-Sls-Canada)

Subsidiary (Domestic):

AMF Bake-Tech (3)
5359 Royal Woods Pkwy, Tucker, GA
30084
Tel.: (770) 270-5911
Bakery Equipment Mfr
N.A.I.C.S.: 335220

Subsidiary (Domestic):

Diamond Healthcare Corporation (2)
Federal Reserve Bank Bldg 701 E Byrd St
15th Fl, Richmond, VA 23219
Tel.: (804) 649-9340
Web Site: http://www.diamondhealth.com
Healthcare Services
N.A.I.C.S.: 621610
Richard I. Feldman (Pres & CEO)
Rebekah M. Stewart (Chief Ethics & Com-
pliance Officer)
James M. Stevenson (Chief Medical Officer)
Sheila Butler (Chief Engagement Officer)
Jane Odberg (VP-Comm)
Mike Raisig (VP-Ops)
Donna Tidwell (VP-Ops)
Trey Steckline (VP-Ops)
Carmen Leschuk (VP-Bus Dev)
Neil Konitzer (VP-IT)
Ann Belvin (VP-Talent & Employee Engage-
ment)
Patricia Scalfari (VP)
Donald Lovelace (CFO)
Stephen Merz (Exec VP-Operations)
Jane Piechocki (VP-Bus Dev)
Jerry G. Browder (CEO & Chm)
Joy G. Figarsky (Pres & COO)
Blake K. Browder (CFO)
Tish C. Anderson (Exec VP)
Pat Doyle (Chief Dev Officer & Exec VP)

Holding (Domestic):

Ellicott Dredge Enterprisoc, LLC (2)
1611 Bush St, Baltimore, MD 21230
Tel.: (410) 625-0808
Web Site: https://www.dredge.com
Dredging Equipment Mfr
N.A.I.C.S.: 333120

Subsidiary (Domestic):

Ellicott Dredges, LLC (3)
1611 Bush St, Baltimore, MD 21230
Tel.: (410) 545-0232
Web Site: https://www.dredge.com
Rev.: $16,000,000
Emp.: 150
Mfr & Distr of Dredges & Dredging Machin-
ery; Contract Machining, Fabrication & As-
sembly Services
N.A.I.C.S.: 333120

Rohr Dredge NA, LLC (3)
1611 Bush St, Baltimore, MD 21230
Tel.: (410) 625-0808
Web Site: https://www.dredge.com
Dredge Equipment Mfr & Distr
N.A.I.C.S.: 333120

Subsidiary (Domestic):

P2, Inc. (2)
14839 Pioneer Trl, Eden Prairie, MN 55347
Tel.: (952) 472-2577
Web Site: http://www.p2inc.com
Aircraft Maintenance Services
N.A.I.C.S.: 488119

Subsidiary (Domestic):

Gardenvision, LLC (3)

3377 Bethel Rd SE Ste 107, Port Orchard, WA 98366
Tel.: (360) 908-5887
Web Site: https://www.gardenvisioninc.com
Garden Maintenance Services
N.A.I.C.S.: 561730

Holding (Domestic):

Reading Pretzel Machinery Corporation (2)
380 Old W Penn Ave, Robesonia, PA 19551-8903
Tel.: (610) 693-5816
Web Site: https://www.readingbakery.com
Bakery Equipment Mfr
N.A.I.C.S.: 333241

Division (Domestic):

Thomas L. Green & Company, Inc. (3)
7802 Moller Rd, Indianapolis, IN 46268
Tel.: (317) 263-6935
Web Site: http://www.tlgreen.com
Sales Range: $10-24.9 Million
Emp.: 16
Mfr of Bakery Machinery
N.A.I.C.S.: 333310

Holding (Domestic):

Weldship Corporation (2)
225 W 2nd St, Bethlehem, PA 18015-1274
Tel.: (610) 861-7330
Web Site: http://www.weldship.com
Sales Range: $25-49.9 Million
Emp.: 90
Mfr of Tube & Tank Trailers & ISO Containers for Industrial Gas & Specialty Chemical Markets
N.A.I.C.S.: 333924
Robert F. Arcieri (Pres)
Arthur Sakzenian (Mgr-Sls-South America)
Bill Angus (VP-Operations)
Paul Horrigan (VP-Bus Dev)
Dwight Ernst (Plant Mgr)
Michael Arcieri (Sls Mgr-Northeast, Central & Southeast)
Jim Cielinski (Gen Mgr-Sales)
Hector Guerrero (Mgr-Tech Svcs-PA)
Kent Mansker (Dir-Engrg & Mgr-Ops)
Ray Williams (Mgr-Quality Control-TX)
Roy Leidy (Dir-Quality)
Rocky Chunko (Mgr-Quality Control)
Scott Greisen (Mgr-Sls-Southwestern & Western)
Eric Liskanich (Mgr-Inside Sls)
Jeff Burrichter (Mgr-Tech & Asst Mgr-Ops)

Subsidiary (Domestic):

Texas Trailer Corp. (3)
1310 Hwy 82 W, Gainesville, TX 76240
Tel.: (940) 668-1777
Web Site: http://www.texastrailercorp.com
Sales Range: $25-49.9 Million
Emp.: 40
Metal Tanks & Specialty Trailer Mfr
N.A.I.C.S.: 332420

Nephila Capital Ltd. (1)
Victoria Place 3rd Floor West 31 Victoria Street, Hamilton, HM10, Bermuda
Tel.: (441) 296 3626
Web Site: https://www.nephila.com
Reinsurance Services
N.A.I.C.S.: 524130
Frank Majors (Co-Founder)
Greg Hagood (Co-Founder)

Nephila Syndicate Management Ltd. (1)
Walsingham House 4th Floor 35 Seething Lane, London, EC3N 4AH, United Kingdom
Tel.: (44) 2038083120
Reinsurance Services
N.A.I.C.S.: 524130
Charity Bare (Dir-Risk & Compliance)

Panel Specialists Inc. (1)
3115 Range Rd, Temple, TX 76504
Tel.: (254) 774-9800
Web Site: https://www.panelspec.com
Sales Range: $10-24.9 Million
Public Building & Related Furniture
N.A.I.C.S.: 337127
Elliot Germany (Pres & CEO)

PartnerMD, LLC (1)

7001 Forest Ave Ste 302, Richmond, VA 23230
Tel.: (804) 237-8282
Web Site: https://www.partnermd.com
Concierge Medicine Service Provider
N.A.I.C.S.: 621999
James Mumper (Founder & Chief Medical Officer)
Zack Smith (CEO)
Kristin P. Richardson (CMO & Chief Sls Officer)
Josephine Rick (Chief Culture Officer)
Jack Bretcher (COO)
Joseph Lasher (CFO)
Bonnie Reeves (Chief Practice Officer)

Reading Bakery Systems, Inc. (1)
380 Old W Penn Ave, Robesonia, PA 19551
Tel.: (610) 693-5816
Web Site: https://www.readingbakery.com
Snack Food Equipment Mfr
N.A.I.C.S.: 311919
Mark Priar (Dir-Parts & Svc Sls)
Gary Shollenberger (Coord-Spare Parts & Die Sls)
Tom Purkiss (Dir-Parts & Svc Sls)
Steve Mull (Coord-Svc & Parts Project)
Joseph Zaleski (Pres)
David Kuipers (Sr VP-Sls & Mktg)
Chip Czulada (CFO & Exec VP)
Travis Getz (VP-Ops)
Dulcie Freymoyer (Dir-HR)
Shawn Moye (VP-Sls)
Jim Warren (VP-Exact Mixing)
Roseann Reinhold (Dir-HR)
Sam Pallottini (Dir-Cookie, Cracker & Pet Food Sls)
Cameron Johnston (Dir-Engrg)
Shane Hanlon (Dir)
Matt Risser (Mgr-)
Joshua Derrer (Project Mgr)
Andrew Rosenthal (Project Mgr)
Michael Snarski (Mgr)
Ken Zvoncheck (Dir-Process Tech)
Mike Johnson (VP)
Donald Smith (Sys Engr)
Vardan Upadhyaya (Project Mgr)
Dan Garrison (Project Mgr)
Michael Manley (Project Mgr)
Michael McDermott (Project Mgr)
Steve Moya (Mgr)
Mike Johnson (VP)
Donald Smith (Sys Engr)
Vardan Upadhyaya (Project Mgr)
Dan Garrison (Project Mgr)
Michael Manley (Project Mgr)
Michael McDermott (Project Mgr)
Steve Moya (Mgr)

Retail Data, LLC (1)
11013 W Broad St Ste 300, Glen Allen, VA 23060
Tel.: (804) 678-7500
Web Site: https://www.retaildatallc.com
Sales Range: $25-49.9 Million
Retail Intelligence Data Service Provider
N.A.I.C.S.: 518210

Rohr Bagger GmbH (1)
Rotterdamer Str 15, 68219, Mannheim, Germany
Tel.: (49) 621845590
Web Site: http://www.rohrbagger.de
Emp.: 40
Sand & Gravel Extraction Equipment Mfr
N.A.I.C.S.: 333248

Solbern LLC (1)
8 Kulick Rd, Fairfield, NJ 07004
Tel.: (973) 227-3030
Web Site: https://www.solbern.com
Sales Range: $1-9.9 Million
Emp.: 37
Food Processing Equipment Mfr
N.A.I.C.S.: 333241

State National Companies, Inc. (1)
1900 L Don Dodson Dr, Bedford, TX 76021
Tel.: (817) 265-2000
Web Site: https://www.statenational.com
Property & Casualty Insurance
N.A.I.C.S.: 524126
Terry Ledbetter (Co-Founder)
Garry Ledbetter (Co-Founder)

Subsidiary (Domestic):

Independent Specialty Insurance Company (2)

1900 L Don Dodson Dr, Bedford, TX 76021
Tel.: (817) 265-2000
Insurance Services
N.A.I.C.S.: 524126

Tromp Group Americas, LLC (1)
677 River Cove Ct, Dacula, GA 30019
Tel.: (770) 682-9282
Insurance Services
N.A.I.C.S.: 524127

Tromp Group B.V. (1)
Edisonweg 9, 3752 LV, Bunschoten, Netherlands
Tel.: (31) 332994373
Web Site: http://www.trompgroup.nl
Food Processing Equipment Mfr
N.A.I.C.S.: 333241
Richard van Heukelum (Pres)
Pieter Doornbos (Acct Mgr)
Pieter Doornbos (Acct Mgr)

Weldship Industries, Inc. (1)
225 W 2nd St, Bethlehem, PA 18015-1274
Tel.: (610) 861-7330
Web Site: http://www.weldship.com
Sales Range: $50-74.9 Million
Emp.: 150
Industrial Gas Mfr
N.A.I.C.S.: 325120
Roy Leidy (Dir-Quality)
Paul Horrigan (VP-Business Development)
Eric Liskanich (Mgr)
Hector Guerrero (Mgr)
Kent Mansker (Dir-Engineering)
Jeff Burrichter (Mgr & Asst Mgr-Operations)
Ray Williams (Mgr-Quality Control)

MARKER THERAPEUTICS, INC.
2450 Holcombe Blvd Ste BCM-A MS BCM251, Houston, TX 77021
Tel.: (713) 400-6400   NV
Web Site:
   https://www.markertherapeutics.com
Year Founded: 1991
MRKR—(NASDAQ)
Rev.: $9,013,544
Assets: $34,422,184
Liabilities: $14,821,147
Net Worth: $19,601,037
Earnings: ($29,930,694)
Emp.: 67
Fiscal Year-end: 12/31/22
Cancer & Infectious Disease Pharmaceuticals Researcher, Developer & Mfr
N.A.I.C.S.: 325412
Edmund Cheung (VP-HR)
Monic Stuart (Chief Medical Officer)
Patricia Allison (Head-Clinical Operations)
Mary Newman (Head-Regulatory Affairs)
Juan F. Vera (Co-Founder, Pres, CEO, Principal Fin & Acctg Officer & Principal Executive Officer)
John R. Wilson (Co-Founder)

MARKETAXESS HOLDINGS INC.
55 Hudson Yards, New York, NY 10001
Tel.: (212) 813-6000   DE
Web Site:
   https://www.marketaxess.com
Year Founded: 2000
MKTX—(NASDAQ)
Rev.: $752,547,000
Assets: $2,015,067,000
Liabilities: $722,104,000
Net Worth: $1,292,963,000
Earnings: $258,055,000
Emp.: 881
Fiscal Year-end: 12/31/23
Holding Company; Financial Transaction Processing & Securities Trading Services
N.A.I.C.S.: 551112
Richard M. McVey (Founder & Chm)
Stephen Davidson (Head-Comm & IR)

Kevin M. McPherson (Head-Sls-Global)
Ilene Fiszel Bieler (CFO)
Christopher R. Concannon (CEO)
Oliver Huggins (Chief Risk Officer-Global)
Julie Sheffet (Chief HR Officer)
Raj Paranandi (COO-EMEA & APAC)
Nash Panchal (CIO)
Christophe Roupie (Head)

Subsidiaries:

MarketAxess Corporation (1)
55 Hudson Yards Fl 15, New York, NY 10001
Tel.: (212) 813-6000
Web Site: https://www.marketaxess.com
Sales Range: $50-74.9 Million
Emp.: 200
Computerized Financial Trading & Information Services
N.A.I.C.S.: 522320

Subsidiary (Non-US):

MarketAxess Europe Ltd (2)
5 Aldermanbury Square, London, EC2V 7HR, United Kingdom
Tel.: (44) 2077093100
Web Site: http://www.marketaxess.com
Sales Range: $1-9.9 Million
Emp.: 40
Credit Product Trading & Research Services
N.A.I.C.S.: 522320

MarketAxess NL B.V. (1)
Herengracht 280, 1016 BX, Amsterdam, Netherlands
Tel.: (31) 208888010
Financial Services
N.A.I.C.S.: 523940

MarketAxess Post-Trade B.V. (1)
Herengracht 280, 1016BX, Amsterdam, Netherlands
Tel.: (31) 208888010
Data Analytics & Trading Services
N.A.I.C.S.: 518210

MarketAxess Post-Trade Limited (1)
5 Aldermanbury Square, London, EC2V 7HR, United Kingdom
Tel.: (44) 2077093100
Data Analytics & Trading Services
N.A.I.C.S.: 518210

MARKETWISE, INC.
1125 N Charles St, Baltimore, MD 21201
Tel.: (212) 209-6126   Ky
Web Site:
   https://corporate.marketwise.com
Year Founded: 2020
MKTW—(NASDAQ)
Rev.: $512,403,000
Assets: $442,508,000
Liabilities: $740,891,000
Net Worth: ($298,383,000)
Earnings: $17,990,000
Emp.: 732
Fiscal Year-end: 12/31/22
Investment Services
N.A.I.C.S.: 523999
Erik Mickels (CFO)
Frank Porter Stansberry (Founder)
Michael Palmer (Mng Dir & Copywriter)
David Eifrig (CEO)

MARKFORGED HOLDING CORPORATION
60 Tower Rd, Waltham, MA 02451
Tel.: (415) 480-1752   Ky
Web Site:
   https://www.markforged.com
MKFG—(NYSE)
Rev.: $100,958,000

Markforged Holding Corporation—(Continued)

Assets: $345,941,000
Liabilities: $93,387,000
Net Worth: $252,554,000
Earnings: ($25,388,000)
Emp.: 428
Fiscal Year-end: 12/31/22
Investment Services
N.A.I.C.S.: 523999
Kevin Hartz *(Founder & CEO)*
Assaf Zipori *(CFO & Principal Acctg Officer)*
Shai Terem *(Pres & COO)*

MARKRAY CORP.
2515 E Broadway Rd Ste 101, Mesa, AZ 85202
Tel.: (602) 818-5030
Year Founded: 1998
RVBR—(OTCIQ)
Metal Mining Services
N.A.I.C.S.: 213114
Jonathan Andre Bliven *(CEO)*

MARLIN TECHNOLOGY CORPORATION
338 Pier Ave, Hermosa Beach, CA 90254
Tel.: (310) 364-0110 **Ky**
Year Founded: 2020
FINMU—(NASDAQ)
Rev.: $16,690,333
Assets: $414,777,497
Liabilities: $443,611,452
Net Worth: ($28,833,955)
Earnings: $13,815,195
Emp.: 2
Fiscal Year-end: 12/31/21
Investment Services
N.A.I.C.S.: 523999
Pete Spasov *(Chm)*
Nick Kaiser *(CEO)*
Doug Bayerd *(CFO)*
Michael Nutting *(CTO)*

MARPAI, INC
615 Channelside Dr Ste 207, Tampa, FL 33602
Tel.: (646) 303-3483 **DE**
Web Site:
https://www.marpaihealth.com
Year Founded: 2021
MRAI—(NASDAQ)
Rev.: $24,341,874
Assets: $49,949,620
Liabilities: $43,815,295
Net Worth: $6,134,325
Earnings: ($26,468,390)
Emp.: 303
Fiscal Year-end: 12/31/22
Health Care Srvices
N.A.I.C.S.: 621610
Edmundo Gonzalez *(Co-Founder)*
Mordechai Geva *(CTO)*
Yaron Eitan *(Co-Founder & Chm)*
Damien Lamendola *(CEO)*
Arthur Hoath IV *(Chief Revenue Officer)*

Subsidiaries:

Maestro Health, Inc. **(1)**
500 W Madison Ste 1250, Chicago, IL 60661
Tel.: (312) 517-3500
Web Site: http://www.maestrohealth.com
Healthcare Technology Services
N.A.I.C.S.: 923130
Nancy Reardon *(Chief Strategy Officer & Chief Product Officer)*
Florian Bezault *(CFO)*
Brandon Wood *(CEO)*
Kathleen Sweitzer *(Gen Counsel)*
Pete Murphy *(CTO)*
Joe Meyer *(Sr VP-Sls & Mktg)*
Kim Howe *(Sr VP-HR)*
Franck Brice *(Chief Dev Officer)*

Subsidiary (Domestic):

Group Associates, Inc. **(2)**
30800 Telegraph Rd Ste 3800, Bingham Farms, MI 48025
Tel.: (248) 593-2000
Web Site: http://www.groupassociates.com
Sales Range: $1-9.9 Million
Emp.: 40
Insurance Agencies & Brokerages
N.A.I.C.S.: 524210
David G. Zick *(Pres)*
John Briskey *(Dir-Fin)*
Sheryl Simmons *(Dir-HR)*
Carol Rita *(Chief Compliance Officer)*
Ann Brcka *(Dir-Client Svcs)*
Joyce Zick *(Dir-Benefits Admin)*
Carol Rito *(Officer-Compliance)*

MARQETA, INC.
180 Grand Ave 6th Fl, Oakland, CA 94612 **DE**
Web Site: https://www.marqeta.com
Year Founded: 2010
MQ—(NASDAQ)
Rev.: $748,206,000
Assets: $1,770,346,000
Liabilities: $297,390,000
Net Worth: $1,472,956,000
Earnings: ($184,780,000)
Emp.: 958
Fiscal Year-end: 12/31/22
Computer System Design Services
N.A.I.C.S.: 541512
Barbie Brewer *(Chief People Officer)*
Heather Gantt-Evans *(Chief Info Security Officer)*
Randy Kern *(CTO)*
Brian Kieley *(Sr VP-Program Mgmt)*
Renata Caine *(Sr VP-Intl, Strategy & Plng)*
Crystal Sumner *(Chief Legal Officer)*
Mike Milotich *(CFO)*
Todd Pollack *(Chief Revenue Officer)*
Karna Crawford *(CMO)*
Jason Gardner *(Founder)*
Simon Khalaf *(CEO)*

MARQUETTE NATIONAL CORPORATION
6316 S Wern Ave, Chicago, IL 60636
Tel.: (708) 226-8026 **DE**
Web Site:
https://www.emarquettebank.com
MNAT—(OTCIQ)
Rev.: $58,169,000
Assets: $1,070,029,000
Liabilities: $1,506,552,000
Net Worth: $163,477,000
Earnings: $15,717,000
Fiscal Year-end: 12/31/19
Offices of Bank Holding Companies
N.A.I.C.S.: 551111
George S. Moncada *(Pres & CEO)*

Subsidiaries:

Marquette Bank **(1)**
5700 159th St, Oak Forest, IL 60452
Tel.: (708) 687-9400
Web Site: http://www.emarquettebank.com
Sales Range: $10-24.9 Million
Emp.: 112
Banking Services
N.A.I.C.S.: 522100
Paul M. McCarthy *(Chm)*

MARRIOTT INTERNATIONAL, INC.
7750 Wisconsin Ave, Bethesda, MD 20814
Tel.: (301) 380-3000 **DE**
Web Site: https://www.marriott.com
Year Founded: 1927
MAR—(NASDAQ)
Rev.: $23,713,000,000
Assets: $25,674,000,000
Liabilities: $26,356,000,000
Net Worth: ($682,000,000)
Earnings: $3,083,000,000

Emp.: 411,000
Fiscal Year-end: 12/31/23
Hotels & Related Lodging Facilities Operation & Franchise Services
N.A.I.C.S.: 721110
Tina Edmundson *(Pres-Luxury)*
Anthony G. Capuano *(Pres & CEO)*
Brian King *(Pres-Caribbean & Latin America)*
Rajeev Menon *(Pres-Asia Pacific)*
Tricia Primrose *(Chief Comm & Pub Affairs Officer-Global & Exec VP)*
Kathleen K. Oberg *(CFO & Exec VP)*
Rena Hozore Reiss *(Gen Counsel & Exec VP)*
Eiko Yasui *(Sr Mgr-Japan)*
Ivan Widarmana *(VP-Indonesia)*
Gianleo Bosticco *(Sr Dir-Italy, Greece, Cyprus & Malta)*
Tim Walton *(VP-Western Europe)*
Jim Scholefield *(Chief Info & Digital Officer-Global)*
Felitia Lee *(Chief Acctg Officer & Controller)*
Satya Anand *(Pres-Europe, Middle East and Africa)*
Erika Alexander *(Chief Global Officer-Global Ops)*
Raymond Bennett *(Pres-Canada, Franchising & MxM MSB)*
Carla J. Murray *(Pres-Full Svc-Western Reg)*
Ty Breland *(Chief HR Officer & Exec VP)*
Peggy Fang Roe *(Global Officer-Customer Experience-Loyalty & New Ventures-Global, Chief Customer Officer & Exec VP)*
Anthony G. Capuano *(CEO)*
Jennifer Mason *(Treas & Global Officer)*
Karen Finberg *(Chief Franchise Officer)*
Bob Boulle *(VP)*
William P. Brown *(Pres-Grp-U.S. & Canada)*

Subsidiaries:

Beijing International Club Co. Ltd. **(1)**
No 21 Jianguomenwai Street, Chaoyang District, Beijing, 100020, China
Tel.: (86) 1085321710
Luxury Hotel Operator
N.A.I.C.S.: 721110
Zhang Lijian *(Chm & Gen Mgr)*

Bulgari Hotels and Resorts Milano, S.r.l. **(1)**
Via Privata Fratelli Gabba 7B, 20121, Milan, Italy
Tel.: (39) 028058051
Web Site: https://www.bulgarihotels.com
Emp.: 140
Hotel & Motel Services
N.A.I.C.S.: 721110

Camelback Country Club Inc. **(1)**
7847 N Mockingbird Ln, Scottsdale, AZ 85253 **(100%)**
Tel.: (480) 596-7050
Sales Range: $75-99.9 Million
Emp.: 1,000
Operators of Hotels & Resorts
N.A.I.C.S.: 721110

City Center Annex Tenant Corporation **(1)**
21 N Juniper St, Philadelphia, PA 19107
Tel.: (215) 496-3200
Restaurant Operating Services
N.A.I.C.S.: 722511
Dan Croutch *(Gen Mgr)*

Cologne MH Operating Company GmbH **(1)**
Johannisstrasse 76-80, 50668, Cologne, Germany
Tel.: (49) 221942220
Web Site: http://www.colognemarriott.com
Hotel & Motel Services

N.A.I.C.S.: 721110

Courtyard Marriott-Vacaville Inc. **(1)**
120 Nut Tree Pkwy, Vacaville, CA 95687-3251
Tel.: (707) 451-9000
Web Site: http://www.mariott.com
Hotels & Motels
N.A.I.C.S.: 721110

East Side Hotel Services, Inc. **(1)**
525 Lexington Ave At 49th St, New York, NY 10017
Tel.: (212) 755-4000
Hotels & Motels Services
N.A.I.C.S.: 721110
Joe Genbek *(Pres)*

Fairfield FMC, LLC **(1)**
10400 Fernwood Rd, Bethesda, MD 20817
Tel.: (301) 380-3000
Web Site: http://www.mariot.com
Sales Range: $125-149.9 Million
Emp.: 3,000
Hotels And Motels
N.A.I.C.S.: 721110

Frankfurt Marriott Hotelmanagement GmbH **(1)**
Hamburger Allee 2, 60486, Frankfurt, Germany
Tel.: (49) 6979550
Web Site: http://www.marriott.com
Hotel & Motel Services
N.A.I.C.S.: 721110

Frankfurt RH Operating Company GmbH **(1)**
Inge-Beisheim-Platz 1, Berlin, 10785, Germany
Tel.: (49) 30220000
Restaurant Operating Services
N.A.I.C.S.: 722511

Globair Hungary Kft. **(1)**
Piarista u 4 Millennium Center 8 em, 1052, Budapest, Hungary
Tel.: (36) 12356000
Web Site: http://www.globairgroup.com
Hotel Operator
N.A.I.C.S.: 721199

Hamburg Marriott Hotelmanagement GmbH **(1)**
ABC Strasse 52, 20354, Hamburg, Germany
Tel.: (49) 4035050
Hotel & Motel Services
N.A.I.C.S.: 721110

Hunt Valley Courtyard, Inc. **(1)**
221 International Cir, Hunt Valley, MD 21030
Tel.: (410) 584-7070
Hotels & Motels Services
N.A.I.C.S.: 721110

International Hotel Licensing Company S.a.r.l. Luxembourg **(1)**
Bahnhofplatz 14, 8001, Zurich, Switzerland
Tel.: (41) 447235100
Restaurant Operating Services
N.A.I.C.S.: 722511
Carlton Eievn *(Chief Dev Officer)*

Limited Liability Company "CY Griboedova Hotel Leasing" **(1)**
Kanonerskaya 33 Gridoegovas, Saint Petersburg, 190121, Russia
Tel.: (7) 8126105000
Hotel & Motel Services
N.A.I.C.S.: 721110

Limited Liability Company CYBM Voznesenkiy Hotel Leasing **(1)**
Voznesenskiy Pereulok 7, Tsentralnyy Federalnyy Okrug, 125009, Moscow, Russia
Tel.: (7) 4959813300
Hotel Operator
N.A.I.C.S.: 721110
Olga Nikitina *(Gen Mgr)*

Luxury Hotel Management of Czech Republic s.r.o. **(1)**
V celnici 1028/8, 11000, Prague, Czech Republic
Tel.: (420) 222888888
Web Site: https://marriott.sluzby.cz

Restaurant Operating Services
N.A.I.C.S.: 722511

Luxury Hotels International of Spain S.L.U. (1)
Calle Marina 19 - 21 Barcelona, Barcelona, 8005, Spain
Tel.: (34) 932211000
Emp.: 300
Hotel Operator
N.A.I.C.S.: 721110
Raul Salcido *(Gen Mgr)*

Unit (Domestic):

Hotel Arts Barcelona (2)
Marina 19-21, 08005, Barcelona, Spain
Tel.: (34) 932211000
Web Site:
　https://www.hotelartsbarcelona.com
Hotel Operator
N.A.I.C.S.: 721110

MI Fulfillment Services, LLC (1)
10400 Fernwood Rd, Bethesda, MD 20817-1102
Tel.: (301) 634-5100
Financial Management Services
N.A.I.C.S.: 541611

MIF, L.L.C. (1)
5665 Meadows Rd 160, Lake Oswego, OR 97035
Tel.: (503) 639-7364
Civic & Social Trust Services
N.A.I.C.S.: 813410

Marriott Curacao N.V. (1)
John F Kennedy Boulevard, Piscadera Bay, Willemstad, Curacao
Tel.: (599) 97368800
Restaurant Operating Services
N.A.I.C.S.: 722511

Marriott European Hotel Operating Company Limited (1)
111 Glasgow Road, Edinburgh, EH12 8NF, United Kingdom
Tel.: (44) 1313147501
Restaurant Operating Services
N.A.I.C.S.: 722511

Marriott Hotel Holding GmbH (1)
Mannheimer Strasse 1, Eschborn, 65760, Germany
Tel.: (49) 61967853009
Emp.: 200
Hotel Accounting & HR Services
N.A.I.C.S.: 721110
Rainer Fathau *(COO)*

Marriott Hotel Services, Inc. (1)
69-275 Waikoloa Beach Dr, Waikoloa, HI 96738
Tel.: (808) 886-6789
Web Site: http://www.marriotthawaii.com
Hotel Operator
N.A.I.C.S.: 721110
Bill Marriott *(Pres)*

Marriott Hotel-Betriebsgesellschaft, mbH (1)
Parking ring 12a, Vienna, 1010, Austria
Tel.: (43) 1515180
Web Site: http://www.viennamarriott.at
Emp.: 200
Hotel & Motel Services
N.A.I.C.S.: 721110

Marriott Hotelmanagement Cologne GmbH (1)
Johannisstrasse 76-80, North Rhine-Westphalia, 50668, Cologne, Germany
Tel.: (49) 221942220
Home Management Services
N.A.I.C.S.: 561110

Marriott Hotelmanagement GmbH (1)
Berliner Strasse 93, Munich, 80805, Germany
Tel.: (49) 89360020
Restaurant Operating Services
N.A.I.C.S.: 722511

Marriott Hotels International B.V. (1)
Naritaweg 165 Telestone 8, Amsterdam, 1043 BW, Netherlands
Tel.: (31) 205722300
Hotels & Motels Services
N.A.I.C.S.: 721110

Marriott Hotels International Limited (1)
Barnards Inn 86 Fetter Lane, London, EC4A 1EN, United Kingdom
Tel.: (44) 2070127000
Web Site: http://www.marriott.co.uk
Emp.: 250
Hotesl & Motels Services
N.A.I.C.S.: 721110
Amy C. McPherson *(Pres & Mng Dir)*

Marriott Hotels Limited (1)
Airport Way, Parkland Sq Capablility Green, Luton, LU2 9LF, United Kingdom
Tel.: (44) 7500102156
Hotel & Motel Services
N.A.I.C.S.: 721110

Marriott Hotels Management France SAS (1)
70 Avenue des Champs-Elysees, 75008, Paris, France
Tel.: (33) 153935500
Hotel & Motel Services
N.A.I.C.S.: 721110

Marriott Hotels and Resorts of Canada (1)
2425 Matherson Boulevard East Suite 100, Mississauga, L4W 5K4, ON, Canada (100%)
Tel.: (905) 366-5208
Sales Range: Less than $1 Million
Emp.: 50
Hotels & Motels
N.A.I.C.S.: 721110

Marriott Hotels of Amsterdam, B.V. (1)
Stadhouderskade 12, 1054 ES, Amsterdam, Netherlands
Tel.: (31) 206075555
Hotel & Motel Services
N.A.I.C.S.: 721110

Marriott Hotels of Canada Ltd. (1)
2425 Matheson Blvd E Ste 100, Mississauga, ON, Canada
Tel.: (905) 366-5200
Restaurant Operating Services
N.A.I.C.S.: 722511

Marriott International Capital Corporation (1)
10400 Fernwood Rd, Bethesda, MD 20817
Tel.: (301) 380-3000
Hotel Operating Services
N.A.I.C.S.: 722511
Soren Son *(COO)*

Marriott International Hotels (1)
1 Marriott Dr, Washington, DC 20058-0001
Tel.: (301) 380-9000
Sales Range: $1-4.9 Billion
Emp.: 15,296
Hotel or Motel Management
N.A.I.C.S.: 541211

Marriott Peru Licensing Company SAC (1)
Cal Guillermo Marconi Nro 451 Urb San Felipe, San Isidro, Lima, Peru
Tel.: (51) 2118585
Licensure Agency Services
N.A.I.C.S.: 926150

Munich Airport Marriott Hotelmanagement GmbH (1)
Alois Steinecker Strasse 20, 85354, Freising, Germany
Tel.: (49) 81619660
Emp.: 5
Hotel & Motel Services
N.A.I.C.S.: 721110

PH Victoria Junction (Pty) Ltd (1)
Corner Somerset Road & Ebenezer Road, Green Point, Cape Town, 8002, South Africa
Tel.: (27) 214181234
Restaurant Operating Services
N.A.I.C.S.: 722511
Dinie Smith *(Gen Mgr)*

Plan One (Pty) Ltd (1)
18 Arthurs Rd, Sea Point, Cape Town, Western Cape, South Africa
Tel.: (27) 214342204
Soft & Upholstered Furnishing Services
N.A.I.C.S.: 449129

Procurement International (Pty) Limited (1)
Cnr Arthur s Rd Main Rd, PO Box 675, Sea Point, Cape Town, 8060, South Africa
Tel.: (27) 214305258
Web Site:
　https://www.procurementint.weebly.com
Hospitality Management Services
N.A.I.C.S.: 611519

R-C Spain, S.L. (1)
C Marina 19 21, 8005, Barcelona, Spain
Tel.: (34) 932211000
Web Site:
　http://www.hotelartsbarcelona.com
Emp.: 70
Hotel & Motel Services
N.A.I.C.S.: 721110

Renaissance Dusseldorf Hotemmanagment GmbH (1)
Nordlicher Zubringer 6, 40470, Dusseldorf, Germany
Tel.: (49) 21162160
Home Management Services
N.A.I.C.S.: 561110

Renaissance Hamburg Hotelmanagement GmbH (1)
Grosse Bleichen, 20354, Hamburg, Germany
Tel.: (49) 40349180
Web Site: http://www.renaissance-hamburg.com
Restaurant Operating Services
N.A.I.C.S.: 722511

Renaissance Hotel Group N.V. (1)
24h Fl Fortis Ctr 1063 King's Rd, Quarry Bay, China (Hong Kong) (100%)
Tel.: (852) 21926000
Web Site: http://www.marriotthotels.com
Sales Range: $25-49.9 Million
Emp.: 70
Real Estate Investment, Hotels
N.A.I.C.S.: 237210
Craig Smith *(COO)*

Renaissance do Brasil Hoteleria Ltda. (1)
Alameda Santos 2233, Sao Paulo, 01419-002, Brazil
Tel.: (55) 1130692233
Hotel Operations
N.A.I.C.S.: 721110

Residence Inn by Marriott, LLC (1)
7335 Wisconsin Ave, Bethesda, MD 20814
Tel.: (301) 718-0200
Web Site:
　http://www.residenceinn.marriot.com
Hotel Franchisor & Operator
N.A.I.C.S.: 721110
Samira Clarke *(Dir-Sales-Long Island Garden City)*

Unit (Domestic):

Residence Inn Dallas Richardson (2)
1705 E President George Bush Hwy, Plano, TX 75074
Tel.: (972) 424-9101
Sales Range: $1-9.9 Million
Emp.: 50
Hotel Operator
N.A.I.C.S.: 721110

San Fernando Sheraton Corporation (1)
333 Universal Hollywood Dr, Universal City, CA 91608
Tel.: (818) 980-1212
Web Site: http://www.marriott.com
Hotel & Motel Management Services
N.A.I.C.S.: 721110

Sheraton Grand Phoenix LLC (1)
340 N 3rd St, Phoenix, AZ 85004
Tel.: (602) 262-2500
Hotel Services
N.A.I.C.S.: 721110
Debbi See *(Dir-Sls)*

Sheraton Operating Corporation (1)
5594 W Wild Horse Pass Blvd, Phoenix, AZ 85260
Tel.: (602) 225-0100
Web Site: http://www.marriott.com
Hotel & Motel Management Services

N.A.I.C.S.: 721110

SpringHill SMC, LLC (1)
2363 Stemmons Trl, Dallas, TX 75220-5328
Tel.: (214) 350-2300
Emp.: 25
Restaurant Operating Services
N.A.I.C.S.: 722511

SpringHill Suites (by Marriott) - Convention Center/International Drive Area (1)
8840 Universal Blvd, Orlando, FL 32819
Tel.: (407) 345-9073
Web Site: http://www.marriott.com
Hotel Operator
N.A.I.C.S.: 721110

SpringHill Suites (by Marriott) - Tarrytown Greenburgh (1)
480 White Plains Rd, Tarrytown, NY 10591
Tel.: (914) 366-4600
Web Site: http://www.marriott.com
Hotel Operator
N.A.I.C.S.: 721110

St. Regis San Francisco Hotel LLC (1)
125 3rd St, San Francisco, CA 94103
Tel.: (415) 284-4000
Hotel & Accommodation Services
N.A.I.C.S.: 721110
Jacqueline Volkart *(Gen Mgr)*

Starwood Hotels & Resorts Worldwide, LLC (1)
One StarPoint, Stamford, CT 06902
Tel.: (203) 964-6000
Web Site: http://www.starwoodhotels.com
Holding Company; Hotel & Resort Operator
N.A.I.C.S.: 551112
Brian McGuinness *(Sr VP-Specialty Select Brands)*
Barry Stuart Sternlicht *(Founder)*

Subsidiary (Domestic):

Capitol Hill Hotel (2)
200 C St SE, Washington, DC 20003-1909
Tel.: (202) 543-6000
Web Site: https://www.capitolhillhotel-dc.com
Hotel Operations
N.A.I.C.S.: 721110

Subsidiary (Non-US):

Design Hotels AG (2)
Stralauer Allee 2c, 10245, Berlin, Germany
Tel.: (49) 30884940000
Web Site: http://www.designhotels.com
Hotels & Resorts Marketing Services
N.A.I.C.S.: 541890
Claus Sendlinger *(Founder)*
Sascha Wolff *(CFO)*
Allison Barclay *(Sls Mgr)*
Jinou Park *(VP)*
Markus Schreyer *(Sr VP-Americas)*

Subsidiary (Domestic):

Galaxy Hotel Systems LLC (2)
5 Peters Canyon Ste 375, Irvine, CA 92606
Tel.: (714) 258-5800
Computer Software Solutions for the Hotel Industry
N.A.I.C.S.: 721110

Subsidiary (Non-US):

Imperial Hotels Austria AG (2)
Kaerntner Ring 16, 1015, Vienna, 1015, Austria (100%)
Tel.: (43) 1501100
Web Site: http://www.luxurycollection.com
Hotel Operations
N.A.I.C.S.: 721110

Subsidiary (Domestic):

Le Meridien Atlanta Perimeter (2)
111 Perimeter Ctr W, Atlanta, GA 30346
Tel.: (770) 396-6800
Hotel Operations
N.A.I.C.S.: 721110

Subsidiary (Non-US):

Starwood Asia Pacific Hotels & Resorts Pte Ltd. (2)
6 Temasek Boulevard Suite 40-01, Singa-

Marriott International, Inc.—(Continued)

pore, 38986, Singapore
Tel.: (65) 63338878
Home Management Services
N.A.I.C.S.: 721110
Francis Tan *(VP-Fin)*

Starwood Italia S.r.l. **(2)**
Piazza Della Repubblica 24, 20124, Milan,
Italy
Tel.: (39) 026266100
Management Consulting Services
N.A.I.C.S.: 541611

Subsidiary (Domestic):

The Sheraton Corporation **(2)**
700 E Main St, Stamford, CT 06901
Tel.: (203) 358-8400
Web Site: http://www.sheraton.com
Hotels & Inns
N.A.I.C.S.: 721110

Unit (Domestic):

Element Lexington **(3)**
727 Marrett Rd - B, Lexington, MA 02421
Tel.: (781) 761-1750
Web Site: http://www.marriott.com
Hotel Operations
N.A.I.C.S.: 721110

Division (Domestic):

Four Points by Sheraton **(3)**
1201 Race St, Philadelphia, PA 19107
Tel.: (215) 496-2700
Web Site: http://www.marriott.com
Hotel
N.A.I.C.S.: 721110

Unit (Domestic):

**Four Points by Sheraton Philadelphia
Airport** **(4)**
4101A Island Ave, Philadelphia, PA 19153
Tel.: (215) 492-0400
Hotel Operations
N.A.I.C.S.: 721110

**Four Points by Sheraton Portland
East** **(4)**
1919 NE 181st Ave, Portland, OR 97230
Tel.: (503) 491-1818
Hotel Operations
N.A.I.C.S.: 721110

Unit (Domestic):

**Four Points by Sheraton Suites
Tampa Airport Westshore** **(3)**
4400 W Cypress St, Tampa, FL 33607
Tel.: (813) 873-8675
Hotel Operator
N.A.I.C.S.: 721110

**Four Points by Sheraton Wakefield
Boston Hotel & Conference
Center** **(3)**
1 Audubon Rd, Wakefield, MA 01880
Tel.: (781) 245-9300
Web Site: http://www.marriott.com
Hotel Operations
N.A.I.C.S.: 721110

**Sheraton Baltimore Washington Air-
port Hotel - BWI** **(3)**
1100 Old Elkridge Landing Rd, Linthicum
Heights, MD 21090
Tel.: (443) 577-2100
Web Site: http://www.marriott.com
Hotel Operations
N.A.I.C.S.: 721110
Dianne Watkins *(Mgr-Human Resources)*

Subsidiary (Domestic):

Sheraton Boston Hotel **(3)**
39 Dalton St, Boston, MA 02199-3901
Tel.: (617) 236-2000
Hotel Services
N.A.I.C.S.: 721199

Unit (Domestic):

**Sheraton College Park North
Hotel** **(3)**
4095 Powder Mill Rd, Beltsville, MD 20705
Tel.: (301) 937-4422
Web Site: http://www.sheraton.com

Hotel Operations
N.A.I.C.S.: 721110

**Sheraton Denver Tech Center
Hotel** **(3)**
7007 S Clinton St, Greenwood Village, CO
80112
Tel.: (303) 799-6200
Hotel Operations
N.A.I.C.S.: 721110

Sheraton Detroit Novi **(3)**
21111 Haggerty Rd, Novi, MI 48375
Tel.: (248) 349-4000
Hotel Operations
N.A.I.C.S.: 812990

Sheraton Edison Hotel **(3)**
125 Raritan Center Pkwy, Edison, NJ
08837-3614
Tel.: (732) 225-8300
Hotel Operations
N.A.I.C.S.: 721110

Sheraton Indianapolis Hotel **(3)**
8787 Keystone Crossing, Indianapolis, IN
46240
Tel.: (317) 846-2700
Hotel Operations
N.A.I.C.S.: 721110

Subsidiary (Domestic):

Sheraton International, LLC **(3)**
1111 Westchester Ave, White Plains, NY
10604
Tel.: (800) 328-6242
Web Site: http://www.sheraton.com
Sales Range: $150-199.9 Million
Owner & Operator of Hotels
N.A.I.C.S.: 721110

Unit (Non-US):

Sheraton Centre Toronto Hotel **(4)**
123 Queen Street West, Toronto, M5H 2M9,
ON, Canada **(100%)**
Tel.: (416) 361-1000
Web Site: http://www.sheratontoronto.com
Hotel & Resort Services
N.A.I.C.S.: 721110

**Sheraton Skyline Hotel London
Heathrow** **(4)**
Heathrow Airport Bath Road, Hayes, UB3
5BP, Middlesex, United Kingdom
Tel.: (44) 2087592535
Web Site: http://www.sheraton.com
Operator of Hotels
N.A.I.C.S.: 721110

Unit (Domestic):

**Sheraton Milwaukee Brookfield
Hotel** **(3)**
375 S Moorland Rd, Brookfield, WI 53005
Tel.: (262) 364-1100
Hotel Services
N.A.I.C.S.: 721110

Subsidiary (Domestic):

**Sheraton Overseas Management
Corporation** **(3)**
1111 Westchester Ave, White Plains, NY
10604
Tel.: (914) 640-8100
Owner & Operator of Hotels
N.A.I.C.S.: 721110

Unit (Domestic):

**Sheraton Providence Airport
Hotel** **(3)**
1850 Post Rd, Warwick, RI 02886
Tel.: (401) 738-4000
Hotel Operations
N.A.I.C.S.: 721110

**Sheraton San Diego Hotel &
Marina** **(3)**
1380 Harbor Island Dr, San Diego, CA
92101
Tel.: (619) 291-2900
Web Site:
http://www.sheratonsandiegohotel.com
Hotel Services
N.A.I.C.S.: 721110

Unit (Domestic):

**Sheraton Suites Philadelphia
Airport** **(3)**

4101 B Island Ave, Philadelphia, PA 19153
Tel.: (215) 365-6600
Hotel Operations
N.A.I.C.S.: 721199

**Sheraton Suites Wilmington
Downtown** **(3)**
422 Delaware Ave, Wilmington, DE 19801
Tel.: (302) 654-8300
Web Site:
http://www.sheratonsuiteswilmington.com
Hotel Operator
N.A.I.C.S.: 721110

Sheraton Tucson Hotel & Suites **(3)**
5151 E Grant Rd, Tucson, AZ 85712
Tel.: (520) 323-6262
Hotel Operations
N.A.I.C.S.: 561110

Sheraton Tysons Hotel **(3)**
8661 Leesburg Pike, Vienna, VA 22182
Tel.: (703) 448-1234
Web Site: http://www.sheratontysons.com
Hotel Operations
N.A.I.C.S.: 721110

Subsidiary (Domestic):

The Phoenician **(3)**
6000 E Camelback Rd, Scottsdale, AZ
85251-1949
Tel.: (480) 941-8200
Web Site: https://www.thephoenician.com
Resort Hotel
N.A.I.C.S.: 721110

Unit (Domestic):

The St. Regis - New York **(2)**
2 E 55th St at 5th Ave, New York, NY
10022
Tel.: (212) 753-4500
Hotel Operations
N.A.I.C.S.: 721110

The St. Regis Aspen Resort **(2)**
315 E Dean St, Aspen, CO 81611
Tel.: (970) 920-3300
Web Site: http://www.stregisaspen.com
Hotel Operations
N.A.I.C.S.: 721110

The St. Regis Hotel - Houston **(3)**
1919 Briar Oaks Ln, Houston, TX 77027-
3408
Tel.: (713) 840-7600
Hotel Operating Services
N.A.I.C.S.: 721110

Subsidiary (Domestic):

Vistana Vacation Ownership, Inc. **(2)**
9002 San Marco Ct, Orlando, FL 32819
Tel.: (407) 303-4640
Web Site: http://www.vistana.com
Resort Time-Share & Property Services
N.A.I.C.S.: 531390

Subsidiary (Domestic):

SVO Management, Inc. **(3)**
9002 San Marco Ct, Orlando, FL 32819
Tel.: (407) 903-4670
Web Site: http://www.vistana.com
Third-Party Homeowner Association Admin-
istrative & Business Affair Management
Services
N.A.I.C.S.: 541611

Unit (Domestic):

Sheraton Vistana Resort **(4)**
8800 Vistana Centre Dr, Orlando, FL 32821
Tel.: (407) 239-3100
Web Site: http://www.vistana.com
Hotel & Resort Services
N.A.I.C.S.: 721110

Subsidiary (Domestic):

Vistana Development, Inc. **(3)**
9002 San Marco Ct, Orlando, FL
32819 **(100%)**
Tel.: (407) 239-3000
Web Site: http://www.vistana.com
Resort Real Estate Development
N.A.I.C.S.: 237210
Sergio D. Rivera *(Pres & Mng Dir)*

Vistana Portfolio Services, Inc. **(3)**
9002 San Marco Ct, Orlando, FL 32819

Tel.: (407) 206-6000
Web Site: http://www.vistana.com
Resort Property Portfolio Management Ser-
vices
N.A.I.C.S.: 523940
Sergio D. Rivera *(CEO)*

Subsidiary (Domestic):

W Hotels Real Estate, LLC **(2)**
8 Albany St, New York, NY 10005
Tel.: (646) 826-8600
Web Site: http://www.w-hotels.marriott.com
Hotel Operator
N.A.I.C.S.: 721110
Gregory Polino *(Gen Mgr-W Miami)*
Leah Chisholm *(Dir-Music-North America)*

Unit (Domestic):

Le Meridien New Orleans **(3)**
333 Poydras St, New Orleans, LA 70130
Tel.: (504) 525-9444
Hotel Operations
N.A.I.C.S.: 721110

W Atlanta - Downtown Hotel **(3)**
45 Ivan Allen Jr Blvd, Atlanta, GA 30308
Tel.: (404) 582-5800
Hotel Operator
N.A.I.C.S.: 721110

W Chicago - City Center Hotel **(3)**
172 W Adams St, Chicago, IL 60603-3604
Tel.: (312) 332-1200
Hotel Services
N.A.I.C.S.: 721110

**W New Orleans - French Quarter
Hotel** **(3)**
316 Chartres St, New Orleans, LA 70130
Tel.: (504) 581-1200
Hotel Operations
N.A.I.C.S.: 721110

W Seattle Hotel **(3)**
1112 4th Ave, Seattle, WA 98101
Tel.: (206) 264-6000
Web Site: http://www.marriott.com
Hotel Operations
N.A.I.C.S.: 721110

Subsidiary (Domestic):

Westin Hotel Management, LP **(2)**
1111 Westchester Ave, White Plains, NY
10604
Tel.: (617) 532-4600
Web Site: http://www.westin.com
Emp.: 1,500
Hotel Operations
N.A.I.C.S.: 721199

Unit (Domestic):

The Westin Denver Downtown **(3)**
1672 Lawrence St, Denver, CO 80202
Tel.: (303) 572-9100
Web Site:
http://www.westindenverdowntown.com
Hotel Services
N.A.I.C.S.: 721110

The Westin Fort Lauderdale **(3)**
400 Corporate Dr, Fort Lauderdale, FL
33334
Tel.: (954) 772-1331
Web Site:
http://www.westinfortlauderdalehotel.com
Hotel Services
N.A.I.C.S.: 721199

The Westin Galleria Houston **(3)**
5000 W Alabama, Houston, TX 77056
Tel.: (713) 960-8100
Emp.: 60
Hotel Operations
N.A.I.C.S.: 721110

The Westin Indianapolis **(3)**
241 W Washington St, Indianapolis, IN
46204
Tel.: (317) 262-8100
Hotel Services
N.A.I.C.S.: 721110

The Westin Long Beach **(3)**
333 E Ocean Blvd, Long Beach, CA 90802
Tel.: (562) 436-3000
Web Site:
http://www.westinlongbeachhotel.com
Hotel Operations

N.A.I.C.S.: 722511

The Westin Los Angeles Airport (3)
5400 W Century Blvd, Los Angeles, CA 90045
Tel.: (310) 216-5858
Web Site:
    http://www.westinlosangelesairport.com
Hotel Services
N.A.I.C.S.: 721110

The Westin New York at Times Square (3)
270 W 43rd St, New York, NY 10036
Tel.: (212) 201-2700
Web Site: http://www.westinny.com
Hotel Operator
N.A.I.C.S.: 721110

The Westin Philadelphia (3)
99 S 17th St at Liberty Pl, Philadelphia, PA 19103
Tel.: (215) 563-1600
Web Site: http://www.marriott.com
Hotel Operations
N.A.I.C.S.: 721110

The Westin Princeton at Forrestal Village Hotel (3)
201 Village Blvd, Princeton, NJ 08540
Tel.: (609) 452-7900
Web Site: http://www.westinprinceton.com
Hotel Operations
N.A.I.C.S.: 721110

The Westin San Francisco Airport (3)
1 Old Bayshore Hwy, Millbrae, CA 94030
Tel.: (650) 692-3500
Hotel Operator
N.A.I.C.S.: 721110

The Westin Seattle (3)
1900 5th Ave, Seattle, WA 98101
Tel.: (206) 728-1000
Web Site: http://www.westinseattle.com
Hotel Operations
N.A.I.C.S.: 721110

The Westin South Coast Plaza, Costa Mesa (3)
686 Anton Blvd, Costa Mesa, CA 92626
Tel.: (714) 540-2500
Web Site:
    http://www.westinsouthcoastplaza.com
Hotel Operations
N.A.I.C.S.: 721110

The Westin Southfield Detroit (3)
1500 Town Ctr, Southfield, MI 48075
Tel.: (248) 827-4000
Web Site:
    http://www.westinsouthfielddetroit.com
Hotel Operations
N.A.I.C.S.: 812990

The Westin St. Francis San Francisco on Union Square (3)
335 Powell St, San Francisco, CA 94102
Tel.: (415) 397-7000
Web Site: http://www.marriott.com
Hotel Operator
N.A.I.C.S.: 721110

The Westin St. John Resort Villas (3)
300B Chocolate Hole, Cruz Bay, VI 00830
Tel.: (340) 693-8000
Web Site: http://www.westinresortstjohn.com
Resort Hotel
N.A.I.C.S.: 721110

The Westin Waltham Boston (3)
70 3rd Ave, Waltham, MA 02451-7523
Tel.: (781) 290-5600
Web Site: http://www.marriott.com
Hotel Operations
N.A.I.C.S.: 721110

The Renaissance Wailea Beach Resort (1)
3700 Wailea Alanui Dr, Kihei, HI 96753-8347
Tel.: (808) 879-4900
Web Site: http://www.renaissancehotels.com
Sales Range: $1-9.9 Million
Emp.: 400
Hotel
N.A.I.C.S.: 721110

The Ritz-Carlton Hotel Company of Qatar Limited (1)
PO Box 23400, West Bay Lagoon, Doha, Qatar
Tel.: (974) 44848000
Traveler Accommodation Services
N.A.I.C.S.: 721199
Maria Vazoura (Mktg Dir)

The Vinoy Renaissance St. Petersburg Resort & Golf Club (1)
501 5th Ave NE, Saint Petersburg, FL 33701
Tel.: (727) 894-1000
Web Site:
    http://www.vinoyrenaissanceresort.com
Hotel & Resort Operator
N.A.I.C.S.: 721110
Tabish Siddiquie (Gen Mgr)

Toronto Marriott Downtown Centre Hotel (1)
525 Bay Street, Toronto, M5G 2L2, ON, Canada (100%)
Tel.: (416) 597-9200
Web Site:
    http://www.marriotteatoncentre.com
Sales Range: $25-49.9 Million
Emp.: 268
Hotels & Motels
N.A.I.C.S.: 721110

W Atlanta Buckhead Beverage LLC (1)
3377 Peachtree Rd NE, Atlanta, GA 30326
Tel.: (678) 500-3100
Hotel Services
N.A.I.C.S.: 721110
Amanda Wright (Sr Mgr-Event)

W Leicester Square Ltd. (1)
10 Wardour Street, London, W1D 6QF, United Kingdom
Tel.: (44) 2077581000
Hotel Services
N.A.I.C.S.: 721110
Martijn Mulder (Gen Mgr)

Westin International (Malta) Ltd. (1)
Dragonara Road, Saint Julian's, STJ 3143, Malta
Tel.: (356) 21381000
Hotel & Resort Services
N.A.I.C.S.: 721110
Edward Bonello (Dir-Sls & Mktg)

Westin San Antonio Resort Company (1)
420 W Market St, San Antonio, TX 78205
Tel.: (210) 224-6500
Hotel & Resort Services
N.A.I.C.S.: 721110
Lori Thiemann (Dir-Sls & Mktg)

Westin Savannah Holdings, LLC (1)
1 Resort Dr, Savannah, GA 31421
Tel.: (912) 201-2000
Hotel & Resort Services
N.A.I.C.S.: 721110
Kristyn Clark (Mgr-HR)

MARRIOTT VACATIONS WORLDWIDE CORPORATION
9002 San Marco Ct, Orlando, FL 32819
Tel.: (407) 206-6000   DE
Web Site:
    https://www.marriottvacationsworld
    wide.com
Year Founded: 2011
VAC—(NYSE)
Rev.: $4,727,000,000
Assets: $9,680,000,000
Liabilities: $7,298,000,000
Net Worth: $2,382,000,000
Earnings: $252,000,000
Emp.: 22,000
Fiscal Year-end: 12/31/23
Holding Company; Resort Property Developer, Marketer, Time-Sharing Sales & Leasing Services
N.A.I.C.S.: 551112
R. Lee Cunningham (COO-Vacation Ownership & Exec VP)
John E. Geller Jr. (Pres & CEO)

Dwight D. Smith (CIO & Exec VP)
Michael E. Yonker (Chief HR Officer & Exec VP)
James H. Hunter IV (Gen Counsel & Exec VP)
Lizabeth Kane-Hanan (Chief Dev & Product Officer & Exec VP)
Brian E. Miller (Pres-Vacation Ownership)
Lori Gustafson (Chief Brand & Digital Strategy Officer & Exec VP)
Kathleen Pighini (Chief Acctg Officer, Sr VP & Controller)
Stephanie Sobeck Butera (Exec VP)

Subsidiaries:

Fortyseven Park Street Limited (1)
47 Park Street, London, W1K 7EB, Mayfair, United Kingdom
Tel.: (44) 2074917282
Web Site: https://www.47parkstreet.com
Emp.: 80
Home Management Services
N.A.I.C.S.: 721110

Great Destinations, Inc. (1)
627 S Tillotson Ave, Muncie, IN 47304
Tel.: (765) 284-6316
Web Site:
    http://www.greatdestinationstravel.com
Travel Agency Services
N.A.I.C.S.: 561510

ILG, LLC (1)
9002 San Marco Ct, Orlando, FL 32819
Tel.: (407) 206-6000
Rev.: $1,786,000,000
Assets: $3,671,000,000
Liabilities: $1,968,000,000
Net Worth: $1,703,000,000
Earnings: $168,000,000
Emp.: 11,600
Fiscal Year-end: 12/31/2017
Vacation Exchange Network & Travel & Leisure Services
N.A.I.C.S.: 561599

Subsidiary (Domestic):

Aqua Hospitality LLC (2)
820 Mililani St Ste 600, Honolulu, HI 96813
Tel.: (808) 931-1400
Home Management Services
N.A.I.C.S.: 561110

Aqua Luana Operator LLC (2)
2045 Kalakaua Ave, Honolulu, HI 96815
Tel.: (808) 955-6000
Travel Arrangement & Reservation Services
N.A.I.C.S.: 561599

Aqua-Aston Hospitality, LLC (2)
820 Mililani St Ste 600, Honolulu, HI 96813
Tel.: (808) 931-1400
Web Site: https://www.aquaaston.com
Home Management Services
N.A.I.C.S.: 721110
Janice Wakatsuki (Sr VP-HR)
Chris Port (Chief Dev Officer)
Lesli Reynolds (Sr VP-Ops)
Andrea Mue (Sr VP)
Marivic Senkow (Mgr-Contracting)

Subsidiary (Non-US):

Great Destinations, Inc. (2)
Tel.: (855) 438-7000
Travel Management Services
N.A.I.C.S.: 561510

Subsidiary (Domestic):

HV Global Group, Inc. (2)
9002 San Marco Ct, Orlando, FL 32819
Tel.: (727) 803-9400
Web Site: https://www.hvocareers.com
Owns, Operates, Manages & Franchises Hotels & Resorts
N.A.I.C.S.: 721110

Subsidiary (Non-US):

Hoteles Cancun K20, S. de R.L. de C.V. (2)
Boulevard Kukulkan 20, Cancun, Quintana Roo, Mexico
Tel.: (52) 9988487400
Travel Arrangement & Reservation Services

N.A.I.C.S.: 561599

Interval International Argentina S.A. (2)
Tel.: (54) 1150789470
Web Site: https://www.intervalworld.com
Membership & Leisure Services
N.A.I.C.S.: 813410

Interval International Egypt Ltd. (2)
8 Khaled Ibn El Waleed Street 3rd Floor Apartment 5, Masaken Sheraton Heliopolis, Cairo, Egypt
Tel.: (20) 8000060491
Web Site: https://www.intervalworld.com
Membership & Leisure Services
N.A.I.C.S.: 813410

Interval International Finland Oy (2)
Kappelikuja 6A, 02200, Espoo, Finland
Tel.: (358) 942726944
Web Site: https://www.intervalworld.com
Membership & Leisure Services
N.A.I.C.S.: 813410

Interval International GmbH (2)
PO Box 10 24 19, Postfach 10 24 19, D-70020, Stuttgart, Germany
Tel.: (49) 711224080
Hotel & Motel Services
N.A.I.C.S.: 721110

Interval International Italia SRL (2)
Via Dante 12 5 Piano, Milan, 20121, Italy
Tel.: (39) 0272536333
Web Site: https://www.intervalworld.com
Membership & Leisure Services
N.A.I.C.S.: 813410

Interval International Limited (2)
Mitre House 1 Canbury Park Road, Kingston upon Thames, KT2 6JX, Surrey, United Kingdom
Tel.: (44) 3447014444
Membership & Leisure Services
N.A.I.C.S.: 813410

Interval International Singapore (Pte) Ltd. (2)
Triple One Somerset 111 Somerset Road 03-09, Singapore, 238164, Singapore
Tel.: (65) 31051540
Membership & Leisure Services
N.A.I.C.S.: 813410

Subsidiary (Domestic):

Interval Software Services, LLC (2)
6262 Sunset Dr, Miami, FL 33143
Tel.: (305) 666-1884
Web Site: https://www.intervalworld.com
Applications Software Programming Services
N.A.I.C.S.: 541511

Kai Management Services, LLC (2)
4331 Kauai Beach Dr, Lihue, HI 96766
Tel.: (808) 245-1955
Travel Arrangement & Reservation Services
N.A.I.C.S.: 561599

Meridian Financial Services, Inc. (2)
1636 Hendersonville Rd Ste 135, Asheville, NC 28803
Tel.: (828) 575-9564
Web Site: https://www.merid.com
Financial Management Services
N.A.I.C.S.: 541611
Gregory B. Sheperd (Pres)
Zaida Smith (VP-Intl Sls)
Karen Green (Dir-Client Svcs)

Meridian Financial Services, Inc. (2)
1636 Hendersonville Rd Ste 135, Asheville, NC 28803
Tel.: (828) 575-9564
Web Site: https://www.merid.com
Financial Management Services
N.A.I.C.S.: 541611
Gregory B. Sheperd (Pres)
Zaida Smith (VP-Intl Sls)
Karen Green (Dir-Client Svcs)

Meridian Financial Services, Inc. (2)
1636 Hendersonville Rd Ste 135, Asheville, NC 28803
Tel.: (828) 575-9564
Web Site: https://www.merid.com
Financial Management Services
N.A.I.C.S.: 541611
Gregory B. Sheperd (Pres)
Zaida Smith (VP-Intl Sls)
Karen Green (Dir-Client Svcs)

Marriott Vacations Worldwide Corporation—(Continued)

Meridian Financial Services, Inc. (2)
1636 Hendersonville Rd Ste 135, Asheville, NC 28803
Tel.: (828) 575-9564
Web Site: https://www.merid.com
Financial Management Services
N.A.I.C.S.: 541611
Gregory B. Sheperd (Pres)
Zaida Smith (VP-Intl Sls)
Karen Green (Dir-Client Svcs)

Paradise Vacation Adventures, LLC (2)
4260 L Honoapiilani Rd, Lahaina, HI 96761
Tel.: (808) 669-2814
Travel Arrangement & Reservation Services
N.A.I.C.S.: 561599

Points of Colorado, Inc. (2)
9002 San Marco Ct, Orlando, FL 32819
Tel.: (407) 206-6000
Travel Arrangement & Reservation Services
N.A.I.C.S.: 561599

Subsidiary (Non-US):

Resort Solutions Limited (2)
St Mary's House St Mary's Road, Market Harborough, LE16 7DS, Leicestershire, United Kingdom
Tel.: (44) 1858431160
Web Site: http://www.resort-solutions.co.uk
Hotels & Resort Operator
N.A.I.C.S.: 721120

Subsidiary (Domestic):

Trading Places International, LLC (2)
25510 Commerce Ctr Dr Ste 100, Lake Forest, CA 92630
Tel.: (949) 448-5150
Web Site: http://www.tradingplaces.com
Emp.: 250
Travel Agencies
N.A.I.C.S.: 561510

Vacation Resorts International, LLC (2)
25510 Commercentre Dr Ste 100, Lake Forest, CA 92630
Tel.: (949) 587-2299
Web Site: http://www.vriresorts.com
Vacation Home Rentals Services
N.A.I.C.S.: 721199
Roy I. Fraser (Founder)
Jan Samson (Sr VP-Corp Dev & Bus)
Richard Muller (Exec VP-Resort Ops)
Royce Pennington (Reg VP-Resort Ops-Central)

Vistana Signature Experiences, Inc. (2)
7812 Palm Pkwy, Orlando, FL 32836
Tel.: (407) 903-4640
Web Site: https://www.vistana.com
Professional Vacation Services
N.A.I.C.S.: 531311

MVW International Finance Company LLC (1)
6649 W Wood Blvd Ste 500, Orlando, FL 32821
Tel.: (407) 206-6000
Emp.: 18
Financial Management Services
N.A.I.C.S.: 541611

Marriott Ownership Resorts, Inc. (1)
9002 San Marco Ct, Orlando, FL 32819
Tel.: (407) 206-6000
Web Site: http://www.marriottvacationclub.com
Resort Property Time-Sharing Sales & Leasing Services
N.A.I.C.S.: 531210
Stephen P. Weisz (Pres & CEO)

Division (Domestic):

Grand Residences by Marriott (2)
6649 Westwood Blvd Ste 500, Orlando, FL 32821-6044
Tel.: (407) 206-6278
Web Site: https://www.grandresidenceclub.com

Resort Property Time-Sharing Sales & Leasing Services
N.A.I.C.S.: 531210

Subsidiary (Non-US):

MVCI Asia Pacific Pte. Ltd. (2)
75 Bukit Timah Road Unit 02-03 Boon Siew Building, Singapore, 229833, Singapore
Tel.: (65) 68776088
Web Site: http://www.vacationclubap.com
Emp.: 50
Home Management Services
N.A.I.C.S.: 721110

MVCI Holidays, S.L. (2)
Carretera De Cadiz, Marbella, 29604, Spain
Tel.: (34) 952769622
Home Management Services
N.A.I.C.S.: 721110

Promociones Marriott, S.A. de C.V. (1)
Boulevard Manuel Avila Camacho 24 piso 7 Lomas de Chapultepec, 11000, Mexico, Mexico
Tel.: (52) 50892502
Hotels & Motels Services
N.A.I.C.S.: 721110

MARS ACQUISITION CORP.
1177 Ave Of The Americas Ste 5100, New York, NY 10036   Ky
Year Founded: 2021
MARX—(NASDAQ)
Rev.: $2,207,820
Assets: $72,915,777
Liabilities: $72,604,183
Net Worth: $311,594
Earnings: $1,686,238
Emp.: 3
Fiscal Year-end: 09/30/23
Investment Services
N.A.I.C.S.: 523999
Karl Brenza (CEO & CFO)
Xiaochen Zhao (COO)
Shanchun Huang (Chm)

MARSH & MCLENNAN COMPANIES, INC.
1166 Avenue of the Americas, New York, NY 10036-2774
Tel.: (212) 345-5000   DE
Web Site: https://www.marshmclennan.com
Year Founded: 1871
MMC—(NYSE)
Rev.: $22,736,000,000
Assets: $48,030,000,000
Liabilities: $35,660,000,000
Net Worth: $12,370,000,000
Earnings: $3,756,000,000
Emp.: 85,000
Fiscal Year-end: 12/31/23
Holding Company; Risk Management, Insurance, Investment, Human Resource & Consulting Services
N.A.I.C.S.: 551112
H. Edward Hanway (Chm)
Martine Ferland (Vice Chm)
Carmen Fernandez (Chief People Officer & Sr VP)
Paul Beswick (CIO & Sr VP)
Amelia Woltering (Dir-Media Rels-Global)
Alex Moczarski (Chm-Intl)
Patrick Tomlinson (Vice Chm, Pres & CEO)
Mark C. McGivney (CFO)
Keith Walsh (CTO)

Subsidiaries:

8Works Ltd. (1)
7 Heddon Street, London, W1B 4BD, United Kingdom
Tel.: (44) 8458724888
Web Site: http://www.8works.com
Management Consulting Services
N.A.I.C.S.: 541618

Alpha Consultants Limited (1)

Level 1 35 Grey Street, Tauranga, 3110, New Zealand
Tel.: (64) 75790520
Web Site: https://www.alphaconsultants.co.nz
Reinsurance Services
N.A.I.C.S.: 524130

Anda Insurance Agencies Pte. Ltd. (1)
1 King Georges Avenue 06-00 Rehau Building, Singapore, 208557, Singapore
Tel.: (65) 65342288
Web Site: https://www.anda.com.sg
General Insurance Services
N.A.I.C.S.: 524113
Belinda Lee (Mng Dir)

Argyll Insurance Services Limited (1)
The Courtyard, Gillingham, ME8 0NZ, United Kingdom
Tel.: (44) 1634360000
Insurance Agency & Brokerage Services
N.A.I.C.S.: 524210

Assurance Services Corporation (1)
PO Box 11047, Richmond, VA 23230
Tel.: (804) 643-5061
Third Party Administration of Insurance Services
N.A.I.C.S.: 524292
Tom Brown (CEO)

Beaumonts Insurance Brokers Limited (1)
12 Trevor Foster Way, Bradford, BD5 8HB, United Kingdom
Tel.: (44) 3450400002
Web Site: http://www.beaumonts-insurance.co.uk
Insurance Agency & Brokerage Services
N.A.I.C.S.: 524210

Beneficios Integrales Oportunos SA (1)
Calle 77B 57 - 103 Edificio Green Towers Oficina 2301, Barranquilla, Colombia
Tel.: (57) 6053227150
Web Site: https://www.bio.sa.com
Reinsurance Services
N.A.I.C.S.: 524130

Bluefin Underwriting Limited (1)
Tower Place East, London, EC3R 5BU, United Kingdom
Tel.: (44) 3330100300
Web Site: http://www.victorinsurance.co.uk
Management Consulting Services
N.A.I.C.S.: 541618

Bowring Marsh (Bermuda) Ltd. (1)
Power House 7 Par-la-Ville Rd, PO Box HM 11, Hamilton, HM JX, Bermuda
Tel.: (441) 4412953454
Emp.: 50
Insurance Management Services
N.A.I.C.S.: 524298
Christopher Reeves (Pres & CEO)
Mark Simons (Sr VP-Fin & Pro Liability Placement)
Lindsay Roos (Mng Dir-Healthcare Placement)
Laura Norman (Sr VP)
Kyla Evans (VP)

Bowring Marsh (Dublin) Limited (1)
25-28 Adelaide Rd Ranelagh, 25-28 Adelaide Rd, Dublin, 2, Ireland
Tel.: (353) 1 605 3000
Web Site: http://www.marsh.com
Sales Range: $10-24.9 Million
Emp.: 6
Financial Services
N.A.I.C.S.: 921130
Chris Lay (CEO)
Eileen Mercer (Mgr-Media Rels)

Bowring Marsh Limited (1)
1 Tower Place West, London, EC3R 5BU, United Kingdom
Tel.: (44) 2073571000
Insurance Management Services
N.A.I.C.S.: 524298

BuildPay LLC (1)
105 Jordan Rd, Troy, NY 12180
Tel.: (518) 567-9882
Web Site: https://www.buildpay.com
Software Development Services

N.A.I.C.S.: 541512
Steve Wightman (Founder & CEO)

Castle Cairn (Insurance Brokers) Limited (1)
15 Northumberland Street, Edinburgh, EH3 6LL, United Kingdom
Tel.: (44) 1315576868
Insurance Services
N.A.I.C.S.: 524210

Clark Thomson Insurance Brokers Limited (1)
24 Whitefriars Street, Perth, PH1 1PP, United Kingdom
Tel.: (44) 1738639777
Web Site: http://www.clarkthomson.co.uk
Management Consulting Services
N.A.I.C.S.: 541618

DVA - Deutsche Verkehrs-Assekuranz-Vermittlungs GmbH (1)
Marienbader Platz 1, 61348, Bad Homburg, Germany
Tel.: (49) 617248680
Web Site: https://www.dva.net
Reinsurance Services
N.A.I.C.S.: 524130

Darwin Technologies S.R.L. (1)
Building The Office 21 Decembrie 1989 Blvd no 77 penthouse floor, room F 6 1, 400124, Cluj-Napoca, Romania
Tel.: (40) 364135000
Software Development Services
N.A.I.C.S.: 541511

Darwin Technologies SG Pte. Ltd. (1)
83 Clemenceau Avenue 18-01 UE Square, Singapore, 239920, Singapore
Tel.: (65) 63831700
Software Development Services
N.A.I.C.S.: 541511

Dovetail Insurance Corp. (1)
1333 Main St Ste 600, Columbia, SC 29201
Tel.: (803) 255-8891
Web Site: http://www.dovetailinsurance.com
Insurance Management Services
N.A.I.C.S.: 524298
Michael M. Ferber (CEO)
Dan Bradley (Mgr-Fin)

Dovetail Managing General Agency Corporation (1)
1333 Main St Ste 600, Columbia, SC 29201-3262
Tel.: (212) 345-9680
Insurance Agency & Brokerage Services
N.A.I.C.S.: 524210

Draw Connect Limited (1)
The Leathermarket Unit 3 2 Weston Street, London, SE1 3ER, United Kingdom
Tel.: (44) 2074077666
Management Consulting Services
N.A.I.C.S.: 541618

Draw Create Limited (1)
The Leathermarket Unit 3 2 Weston Street, London, SE1 3ER, United Kingdom
Tel.: (44) 2074077666
Management Consulting Services
N.A.I.C.S.: 541618

Echelon Australia Pty Limited (1)
One International Towers Sydney 100 Barangaroo Avenue, Sydney, 2000, NSW, Australia
Tel.: (61) 288646555
Insurance Claims Management Services
N.A.I.C.S.: 524292

Encon Group Inc. (1)
500-1400 Blair Towers Place, Ottawa, K1J 9B8, ON, Canada
Tel.: (613) 786-2000
Web Site: https://www.victorinsurance.ca
Sales Range: $25-49.9 Million
Emp.: 172
Insurance Services
N.A.I.C.S.: 524210
Mark Reszel (Sr VP-Insurance)
David Cook (Pres)
Michael McNeill (VP)
Stefanie McKay (Mng Dir & Chief Underwriting Officer)
Tara McGuire (Sr VP)

Tanya Banfield *(Sr VP)*
Rhonda Sommerville *(Mng Dir)*
Stefanie McKay *(Mng Dir & Chief Underwriting Officer)*
Tara McGuire *(Sr VP)*
Tanya Banfield *(Sr VP)*
Rhonda Sommerville *(Mng Dir)*

Faulkner & Flynn, Inc. **(1)**
1 S Jefferson St, Roanoke, VA 24011
Tel.: (540) 985-9540
Computer Mfr
N.A.I.C.S.: 423430
Tamela Evans *(Sr VP-HR)*

Freedom Trust Services Limited **(1)**
Charlotte House Charlemont St, Dublin, Ireland
Tel.: (353) 16362700
Trust Services
N.A.I.C.S.: 523991

GCube Insurance Services Inc. **(1)**
100 Bayview Cir Ste 505, Newport Beach, CA 92660
Tel.: (949) 515-9981
Web Site: http://www.gcube-insurance.com
Insurance Services
N.A.I.C.S.: 524210
Jatin Sharma *(Pres)*
Anthony Micallef *(Controller-Finance)*
Kristina Williams *(Head-North America)*

GCube Underwriting Limited **(1)**
20 Fenchurch St, London, EC3M 3BY, United Kingdom
Tel.: (44) 2079770200
Web Site: http://www.gcube-insurance.com
Renewable Energy Insurance Services
N.A.I.C.S.: 524298
Fraser McLachlan *(CEO)*
Roy Munoz *(Head-Claims-Global)*
Alan Rand *(Fin Dir)*
Matthew Snelling *(COO)*
Joshua Cantwell *(Head)*

Gama Consultores Associados Ltda. **(1)**
Brasilia Shopping and Towers Torre Norte Sala 118, Brasilia, 70715-900, Brazil
Tel.: (55) 6132039690
Web Site: http://www.gama-ca.com.br
Management Consulting Services
N.A.I.C.S.: 541611

Global Premium Finance Company **(1)**
One S Jefferson St, Roanoke, VA 24011
Tel.: (540) 982-3511
Finance Services
N.A.I.C.S.: 921130

GrECo International Holding AG **(1)**
Elmargasse 2-4, 1190, Vienna, Austria
Tel.: (43) 504040
Web Site: https://greco.services
Reinsurance Services
N.A.I.C.S.: 524130
Georg Neubrand *(CFO-Fin & Admin)*
Ante Banovac *(COO)*

Guian S.A. **(1)**
Espace Caillard 3 rue Louis Eudier, 76600, Le Havre, France
Tel.: (33) 235192100
Web Site: https://www.guian.com
Insurance Brokerage Services
N.A.I.C.S.: 524210

Guy Carpenter & Co. Labuan Ltd. **(1)**
Level 42-01 West Wing Q Sentral 2A Jalan Stesen Sentral 2 KL Sentral, 50470, Kuala Lumpur, Malaysia
Tel.: (60) 327768188
Reinsurance Broking Services
N.A.I.C.S.: 524210

Guy Carpenter & Company, LLC **(1)**
1166 Avenue of the Americas, New York, NY 10036 **(100%)**
Tel.: (917) 937-3000
Web Site: https://www.guycarp.com
Emp.: 3,200
Reinsurance Services
N.A.I.C.S.: 524130
David Priebe *(Chm)*
Kevin Fisher *(Chm-UK)*
Peter Hearn *(CEO)*
John Trace *(CFO)*

James Boyce *(CEO-Global Specialties)*
Michael Sevi *(Chief Compliance Officer & Gen Counsel)*
Vijaya Singh *(Head-Marketing-Communications-Global)*
John Ehinger *(Head-Operations-Global)*
Frank Achtert *(Head-Europe,the Middle East,Africa)*
Ronnie Carroll *(Mng Dir-Global)*
Ed Hochberg *(Head-Global)*
Andrea Piatti *(Mng Dir-Global)*
Dean Klisura *(Pres & CEO)*
Melissa Hartshorn *(Chief HR Officer)*
Victoria Carter *(Chm-Global Capital Solutions-Intl)*
Rob Bentley *(CEO-Global Strategic Advisory)*
Neil Mayer *(COO)*
John Crichton *(CIO)*
Lara Mowery *(Head-Distr-Global)*
Jeffrey Livingston *(Head-Sls-Global)*
Miles Shephard *(Mng Dir & Head-GC Access-Intl)*

Subsidiary (Non-US):

Carpenter Turner SA **(2)**
7 Granikou Street, Maroussi, 15125, Athens, Greece
Tel.: (30) 2130119000
Web Site: https://www.carpenterturner.com
Insurance Brokerage Services
N.A.I.C.S.: 524210
Alexander Turner *(CEO)*
George Amerikanos *(Dir-Non-Life Treaty)*
Marios Apergis *(Dir-Life, Accident & Health)*
Petros Mazarakis *(Dir-Property Facultative)*
Eleni Kallia *(Dir-Liability Facultative)*
Walid Abdo *(Dir-Corp Facultative)*
Lia Preventa *(Mgr-Corp Facultative)*
Nopi Togia *(Mgr-Corp Facultative Acct)*
George Kritikos *(CFO)*
Setrak Aivazian *(Dir-IT)*
Effie Bertsia *(Mgr-Non-Life Treaty)*

Guy Carpenter & Cia., S.A. **(2)**
Paseo de la Castellana 216, 28046, Madrid, Spain
Tel.: (34) 15 676 4800
Web Site: http://www.guycarp.com
Sales Range: $10-24.9 Million
Reinsurance Services
N.A.I.C.S.: 524130

Guy Carpenter & Co. Labuan Ltd. **(2)**
18 Cross Street 14 05 12, Marsh & McLennan Ctr, Singapore, Singapore
Tel.: (65) 63273133
Web Site: http://www.guycarp.com
Sales Range: $25-49.9 Million
Emp.: 5
General Insurance Services
N.A.I.C.S.: 524298

Guy Carpenter & Company (Pty) Limited **(2)**
11 Alice Lane, Johannesburg, 2196, Sandton, South Africa
Tel.: (27) 110607600
Web Site: http://www.guycarp.com
Reinsurance Services
N.A.I.C.S.: 524130

Guy Carpenter & Company AB **(2)**
Torsgatan 26, 113 21, Stockholm, Sweden
Tel.: (46) 85 057 3500
Web Site: http://www.guycarp.com
Sales Range: $10-24.9 Million
Reinsurance Services
N.A.I.C.S.: 524130

Guy Carpenter & Company B.V. **(2)**
Groothandelsgebouw E5 157, Conradstraat 18, 3013 AP, Rotterdam, Netherlands
Tel.: (31) 104060010
Web Site: http://www.guycarp.com
Sales Range: $10-24.9 Million
Emp.: 2
Reinsurance Services
N.A.I.C.S.: 524130

Guy Carpenter & Company Corredores de Reaseguros Ltda **(2)**
Avda Americo Vespucio Sur N 100 3rd Floor, Los Condes, Santiago, Chile
Tel.: (56) 24286600
Web Site: http://www.guycarp.com
Sales Range: $10-24.9 Million
Reinsurance Services
N.A.I.C.S.: 524130

Guy Carpenter & Company Corretora de Resseguros Ltda. **(2)**
Rua da Quitanda 86 - 2 Andar Sala 202 Centro, Rio de Janeiro, 20091-005, Brazil
Tel.: (55) 2121030800
Insurance Management Services
N.A.I.C.S.: 524298

Guy Carpenter & Company GmbH **(2)**
Muellerstrasse 3, 80469, Munich, Germany
Tel.: (49) 89 286 6030
Web Site: http://www.guycarp.com
Reinsurance Services
N.A.I.C.S.: 524130

Subsidiary (Domestic):

Guy Carpenter & Company Inc. of Pennsylvania **(2)**
3 Logan Sq Fl 8, Philadelphia, PA 19103-2707
Tel.: (215) 864-3600
Web Site: http://www.guycarp.com
Sales Range: $25-49.9 Million
Emp.: 150
Reinsurance Services
N.A.I.C.S.: 524210

Subsidiary (Non-US):

Guy Carpenter & Company Limited **(2)**
Tower Place West, London, EC3R 5BT, United Kingdom
Tel.: (44) 207 357 1000
Web Site: http://www.guycarp.com
Reinsurance Services
N.A.I.C.S.: 524130

Guy Carpenter & Company Limited **(2)**
Tower Place West, London, EC3R 5BT, United Kingdom
Tel.: (44) 2073571000
Reinsurance Services
N.A.I.C.S.: 524130

Guy Carpenter & Company Peru Corredores de Reaseguros S.A. **(2)**
Amador Merino Reyna 285 Piso 9, San Isidro, Lima, 27, Peru
Tel.: (51) 1 611 8900
Web Site: http://www.guycarp.com
Reinsurance Services
N.A.I.C.S.: 524130

Guy Carpenter & Company Private Limited **(2)**
8 Marina View 09-06 Asian Square Tower 1, Marsh & McLennan Ctr, Singapore, 018960, Singapore
Tel.: (65) 69221900
General Insurance Services
N.A.I.C.S.: 524298
James Nash *(Pres-Intl)*

Guy Carpenter & Company Pty. Limited **(2)**
727 Collins Street, Melbourne, 3000, VIC, Australia
Tel.: (61) 396032222
Reinsurance Services
N.A.I.C.S.: 524130

Guy Carpenter & Company S.A. **(2)**
Conradstraat 18, 3013 AP, Rotterdam, Netherlands
Tel.: (31) 104060600
Reinsurance Services
N.A.I.C.S.: 524130

Guy Carpenter & Company S.r.l. **(2)**
Corso Italia 8, 20122, Milan, Italy
Tel.: (39) 02 332 2131
Web Site: http://www.guycarp.com
Sales Range: $150-199.9 Million
Reinsurance Services
N.A.I.C.S.: 524130

Guy Carpenter & Company, Limited **(2)**
Suite 3402-3406 34th Floor One Taikoo Place 979 King's Road, Quarry Bay, China (Hong Kong)
Tel.: (852) 25823500
Reinsurance Services
N.A.I.C.S.: 524130

Guy Carpenter & Company, Limited **(2)**
Suite 3402-3406 34th Floor One Taikoo Place 979 King's Road, Quarry Bay, China (Hong Kong)
Tel.: (852) 25823500
Insurance Management Services
N.A.I.C.S.: 524298
Tony Gallagher *(CEO-Asia Pacific)*

Guy Carpenter & Company, Ltd. **(2)**
120 Bremner Boulevard Suite 800, Toronto, M5J 0A8, ON, Canada
Tel.: (416) 979-0123
Web Site: http://www.guycarp.com
Sales Range: $10-24.9 Million
Reinsurance Services
N.A.I.C.S.: 524130
Peter Askew *(Pres & CEO)*

Guy Carpenter & Company, Ltda. **(2)**
Rua da Quitanda 86-2 Andar Sala 202 Centro, Rio de Janeiro, 20091-005, Brazil
Tel.: (55) 2121030800
Web Site: http://www.guycarp.com
Reinsurance Services
N.A.I.C.S.: 524130

Guy Carpenter & Company, S.A. **(2)**
Avenue Herrmann-Debroux 2, 1160, Brussels, Belgium
Tel.: (32) 2 674 9810
Web Site: http://www.guycarp.com
Sales Range: $10-24.9 Million
Reinsurance Services
N.A.I.C.S.: 524130

Guy Carpenter & Company, S.A. **(2)**
Tour Ariane 5 place de la Pyramide, 92088, Paris, France
Tel.: (33) 156764800
Web Site: http://www.guycarp.com
Sales Range: $150-199.9 Million
Emp.: 30
Reinsurance Services
N.A.I.C.S.: 524130

Guy Carpenter & Company, S.A. **(2)**
Florida 234 Floor 4, Buenos Aires, C1005AAF, Argentina
Tel.: (54) 115 671 3000
Web Site: http://www.guycarp.com
Sales Range: $10-24.9 Million
Reinsurance, Capital & Strategic Services
N.A.I.C.S.: 524130

Guy Carpenter & Company, S.A.S. **(2)**
5 Place des Pyramides, 92088, Paris, France
Tel.: (33) 156764800
Web Site: http://www.guycarp.com
Insurance Management Services
N.A.I.C.S.: 524298

Guy Carpenter (Middle East) Limited **(2)**
Gate Village 7 Level 3 Office No 301 DIFC, PO Box 506572, Dubai, United Arab Emirates
Tel.: (971) 45203999
Reinsurance Services
N.A.I.C.S.: 524130

Guy Carpenter Bermuda Ltd. **(2)**
Overbay 106 Pitts Bay Road, Pembroke, HM 08, Bermuda
Tel.: (441) 4892277
Reinsurance Services
N.A.I.C.S.: 524130

Guy Carpenter Colombia Ltda. **(2)**
Avenida el Dorado No 69B-45 Piso 9, Bogota, Colombia
Tel.: (57) 14235690
Web Site: http://www.guycarp.com
Reinsurance Broking Expertise & Strategic Advisory Services
N.A.I.C.S.: 524130

Guy Carpenter Insurance Brokers (Beijing) Co. Ltd. **(2)**
Suite 1109 Office Tower E3 Oriental Plaza 1

Marsh & McLennan Companies, Inc.—(Continued)

East Chang An Avenue, Beijing, 100738, China
Tel.: (86) 1065334100
Insurance Brokerage Services
N.A.I.C.S.: 524210

Guy Carpenter Japan, Inc. (2)
Midtown Tower 17th Floor 9-7-1, Akasaka
Minato-ku, Tokyo, 107-6216, Japan
Tel.: (81) 367756800
Reinsurance Services
N.A.I.C.S.: 524130

Guy Carpenter Mexico Intermediario de Reaseguro, S.A. de C.V. (2)
Av Insurgentes Sur 1898 Piso 9, Mexico, 01030, Mexico
Tel.: (52) 5591407000
Insurance Management Services
N.A.I.C.S.: 524298

Guy Carpenter Mexico, Intermediaro de Reasuguro, S.A. de C.V. (2)
Av Insurgentes Sur 1898 Piso 9, Mexico, 01030, Mexico
Tel.: (52) 5591407000
Web Site: http://www.guycarp.com
Sales Range: $25-49.9 Million
Emp.: 50
Reinsurance Services
N.A.I.C.S.: 524130

Subsidiary (Domestic):

Reinsurance Solutions International, L.L.C. (2)
2 Logan Sq Ste 600, Philadelphia, PA 19103
Tel.: (276) 675-3333
Web Site: http://www.rsi-solutions.com
Sales Range: $200-249.9 Million
Emp.: 350
Reinsurance Services
N.A.I.C.S.: 524130

HAE Insurance Services Limited (1)
Partnership House Priory Park East, Hull, HU4 7DY, United Kingdom
Tel.: (44) 1482388552
Web Site: http://www.insurance-partnership.com
Insurance Agency & Brokerage Services
N.A.I.C.S.: 524210

Hamilton Bond Limited (1)
Apex House Apex Park Wainwright Road, Worcester, WR4 9FN, United Kingdom
Tel.: (44) 1905726407
Web Site: https://www.hamilton-bond.co.uk
Management Consulting Services
N.A.I.C.S.: 541611
Andrew Holmes (Dir-Technical)
David Homer (Mng Dir)
Hayley Phillips (Mgr-Bus Dev)
Natalie Price (Ops Mgr)

Hansen International Inc. (1)
130 Zenker Rd, Lexington, SC 29072
Tel.: (803) 695-1500
Web Site: https://www.hansenint.com
Vehicle Components Mfr
N.A.I.C.S.: 336390
Lisa Beebe (Pres)
Michael Coggins (COO)
Fanny Leung (Controller)
Jennifer Hollis (Mgr-Key Acct)

Subsidiary (Domestic):

Salem Vent International, Inc. (2)
3993 Daugherty Rd, Salem, VA 24153
Tel.: (540) 387-0217
Web Site: http://www.salemvent.com
Furniture Merchant Whslr
N.A.I.C.S.: 423210

Howell Shone Insurance Brokers Limited (1)
Station Walk House King Street, Newcastle-under-Lyme, ST5 1EH, United Kingdom
Tel.: (44) 1782629211
Insurance Agency & Brokerage Services
N.A.I.C.S.: 524210

INSIA Europe SE (1)
Atrium Flora Vinohradska 2828/151, 130 00, Prague, Czech Republic
Tel.: (420) 245003111
Web Site: http://www.insia.eu

Insurance Management Services
N.A.I.C.S.: 524298

INSIA SK s.r.o. (1)
Laurinska 3, 811 01, Bratislava, Slovakia
Tel.: (421) 22 057 0714
Web Site: https://www.insia.sk
Emp.: 1,700
Insurance Management Services
N.A.I.C.S.: 524298
Monika Vlckova (Mng Dir-West,Central,Northern Slovakia)

INSIA a.s. (1)
Atrium Flora vchod A Vinohradska 2828/151, Vinohrady, 130 00, Prague, 3, Czech Republic
Tel.: (420) 245003111
Web Site: https://www.insia.cz
Insurance Management Services
N.A.I.C.S.: 524298

Industrial Risks Protection Consultants (1)
4 Ilabere Avenue, Ikoyi, Lagos, Nigeria
Tel.: (234) 8022252906
Web Site: https://irpc.com.ng
Reinsurance Services
N.A.I.C.S.: 524130

Insurance Brokers of Nigeria Limited (1)
4 Ilabere Ave Ikoyi, GPO Box 2010, Lagos, Nigeria
Tel.: (234) 14615234
Web Site: https://www.ibn.com.ng
Sales Range: $1-9.9 Million
Insurance Services
N.A.I.C.S.: 524210

Irish Pensions Trust Limited (1)
Oyster Point Temple Road, Blackrock, Dublin, Ireland
Tel.: (353) 12799620
Pension Fund Management Services
N.A.I.C.S.: 525110

JL Marine Insurance-Brokers GmbH & Co. KG (1)
Morgan Haus Grosse Backerstrasse 9, 20095, Hamburg, Germany
Tel.: (49) 40369179266
Web Site: http://www.jlmarine.eu
Insurance Brokerage Services
N.A.I.C.S.: 524210

JLM Verwaltungs GmbH (1)
Am Strom 58, Warnemunde, 18119, Rostock, Germany
Tel.: (49) 381519690
Web Site: https://www.belvedere-warnemuende.de
Hotel Operator
N.A.I.C.S.: 721110

JLT Independent Insurance Brokers Private Limited (1)
A Wing 1st Floor Unit no 103 and 104 Peninsula Corporate Park, Ganpat Rao Kadam Marg Off Senapati Bapat Marg Lower Parel, Mumbai, 400013, India
Tel.: (91) 2245105000
Web Site: http://www.jltindependent.com
Reinsurance Services
N.A.I.C.S.: 524130
Namrata Shukla (Mgr)

Jardine Lloyd Thompson Group plc (1)
The St Botolph Building, 138 Houndsditch, London, EC3A 7AW, United Kingdom
Tel.: (44) 2075284444
Web Site: http://www.jlt.com
Sales Range: $1-4.9 Billion
Insurance Services
N.A.I.C.S.: 524298

Subsidiary (Domestic):

Expacare Limited (2)
Bracknell Enterprise Centre Easthampstead Road, Bracknell, RG12 1NF, Berkshire, United Kingdom
Tel.: (44) 1344233950
Web Site: https://www.expacare.com
Sales Range: $50-74.9 Million
Emp.: 15
General Insurance Services
N.A.I.C.S.: 524114

JLT Benefit Solutions Limited (2)
100 Greystoke Business Centre Victoria Street, Avon, Bristol, BS1 6HZ, United Kingdom
Tel.: (44) 11 7968 9600
General Insurance Services
N.A.I.C.S.: 525110

Subsidiary (Non-US):

JLT Bermuda Ltd. (2)
Cedar House 41 Cedar Avenue, Hamilton, HM 12, Bermuda
Tel.: (441) 292 4364
Web Site: http://www.jlt.com
Insurance Brokerage Services
N.A.I.C.S.: 524210

JLT Insurance Brokers Ireland Limited (2)
Friends First House Cherrywood Business Park Loughlinstown, Crescent, Dublin, 18, Leinster, Ireland
Tel.: (353) 12026000
Web Site: http://www.jlt.ie
Sales Range: $75-99.9 Million
Emp.: 100
General Insurance Services
N.A.I.C.S.: 524114
Tara Keenan (Acct Exec)
Patrick Howett (Mng Dir)

Subsidiary (Domestic):

FBD Insurance Brokers Limited (3)
Friends First House Cherrywood Business Park Loughlinstown, Bluebell, Dublin, 18, Ireland (100%)
Tel.: (353) 14093201
Web Site: http://www.jltonline.ie
Sales Range: $75-99.9 Million
Emp.: 80
Risk Management & Insurance Brokerage Services
N.A.I.C.S.: 524210

Subsidiary (Non-US):

JLT Insurance Management (Bermuda) Limited (2)
Cedar House 41 Cedar Avenue, Hamilton, HM 12, Bermuda
Tel.: (441) 292 4364
Sales Range: $50-74.9 Million
Emp.: 18
Insurance Brokerage & Consulting Services
N.A.I.C.S.: 524210

Subsidiary (Domestic):

JLT Investment Management Limited (2)
St James House 7 Charlotte Street, Manchester, M1 4DZ, United Kingdom
Tel.: (44) 1619314400
Web Site: http://www.jardinelloydthompson.com
Emp.: 400
Investment Management Service
N.A.I.C.S.: 523999

JLT Re Limited (2)
The St Botolph Building, 138 Houndsditch, London, EC3A 7AG, United Kingdom
Tel.: (44) 2074661300
Web Site: http://www.jltre.com
Insurance Brokerage Services
N.A.I.C.S.: 524210

JLT Reinsurance Brokers Limited (2)
St Botolph Building 138 Houndsditch, London, EC3A 7AW, United Kingdom
Tel.: (44) 2074661300
Web Site: http://www.jltre.com
Emp.: 1,100
General Insurance Services
N.A.I.C.S.: 524130

Subsidiary (Domestic):

JLT Advisory Limited (3)
The St Botolph Building 138 Houndsditch, London, EC3A 7AW, United Kingdom
Tel.: (44) 20 7466 5280
Web Site: http://www.jltadvisory.com
Emp.: 6
General Insurance Services
N.A.I.C.S.: 524130

Subsidiary (Non-US):

JLT Risk Solutions AB (2)
Jakobsbergsgatan 7, Stockholm, 111 44, Sweden
Tel.: (46) 8 442 57 30
Web Site: http://www.jltrisk.se
Sales Range: $50-74.9 Million
Emp.: 20
Investment Management & Consulting Services
N.A.I.C.S.: 523999

Subsidiary (Non-US):

Tripol AS (3)
Strandveien 35, 1366, Lysaker, Akershus, Norway
Tel.: (47) 98266444
Web Site: https://www.tripol.no
General Insurance Services
N.A.I.C.S.: 524210

Subsidiary (Domestic):

JLT Specialty Limited (2)
St Botolph Building 138 Houndsditch, London, EC3A7AW, United Kingdom
Tel.: (44) 2075284000
Web Site: http://www.jltgroup.com
Insurance Brokerages & Consulting Services
N.A.I.C.S.: 524210

JLT Wealth Management Limited (2)
35 Richmond Hill, Bournemouth, BH2 6HT, Dorset, United Kingdom
Tel.: (44) 1202446400
Web Site: http://jltwm.com
Sales Range: $50-74.9 Million
Emp.: 25
Investment Management Service
N.A.I.C.S.: 523999

Subsidiary (Non-US):

JMIB Holdings BV (2)
Diepenbrockstraat 19, Amsterdam, North Holland, Netherlands
Tel.: (31) 204700258
Insurance Brokerages & Consulting Services
N.A.I.C.S.: 524210

Subsidiary (Domestic):

Jardine Lloyd Thompson (2)
The St Botolph Building 138 Houndsditch, Boar Lane, London, EC3A 7AW, United Kingdom
Tel.: (44) 1132035800
Web Site: http://www.jltgroup.com
Sales Range: $75-99.9 Million
Emp.: 50
Insurance Services
N.A.I.C.S.: 524298

Subsidiary (Non-US):

Jardine Lloyd Thompson Asia Private Limited (2)
5th Floor Cityplaza Four 12 Taikoo Wan Road, Taikoo Shing, Island East, China (Hong Kong)
Tel.: (852) 28645333
Web Site: http://www.jltasia.com
Sales Range: $400-449.9 Million
Emp.: 300
Insurance Brokerages & Consulting Services
N.A.I.C.S.: 524210

Subsidiary (Non-US):

JLT Holdings Japan Limited (3)
Halifax Bldg 4F 16-26 Roppongi 3 Chome, Minato-ku, Tokyo, 106-0032, Japan
Tel.: (81) 367303500
Web Site: http://www.jltasia.com
Emp.: 6
Insurance Brokerages & Consulting Services
N.A.I.C.S.: 524210

Subsidiary (Domestic):

JLT Japan Limited (4)
Halifax Building 4F 16-26 Roppongi 3 Chome, Minato-ku, Tokyo, 106-0032, Japan
Tel.: (81) 367303530
Web Site: http://www.jltasia.com

Sales Range: $75-99.9 Million
Emp.: 2
Insurance Brokerages & Consulting Services
N.A.I.C.S.: 524210

JLT Risk Services Japan Limited (4)
Halifax Building 4F 16-26 Roppongi 3
Chome, Minato-ku, Tokyo, 106-0032, Japan
Tel.: (81) 3 6730 3510
Web Site: http://www.jltasia.com
Sales Range: $50-74.9 Million
Emp.: 20
Insurance Brokerages & Consulting Services
N.A.I.C.S.: 524210

Subsidiary (Non-US):

JLT Insurance Management (Singapore) Pte Ltd (3)
1 Raffles Quay 27-01 One Raffles Quay
North Tower, Singapore, 48583, Singapore
Tel.: (65) 6333 6311
Web Site: http://www.jltasia.com
Insurance Brokerages & Consulting Services
N.A.I.C.S.: 524210

JLT Interactive Pte Ltd (3)
8 Marina View 09-02 Asia Square Tower 1,
Singapore, 018960, Singapore
Tel.: (65) 65000495
Web Site: https://www.jltinteractive.com
Sales Range: $25-49.9 Million
Insurance Administration Software Development & Training Services
N.A.I.C.S.: 541511

JLT Risk Solutions Asia Pte Limited (3)
138 Market Street Unit 07-01, Singapore,
048960, Singapore
Tel.: (65) 63336006
Emp.: 410
Insurance Brokerage Services
N.A.I.C.S.: 524210

Jardine Lloyd Thompson Korea Limited (3)
22 Floor Olive Tower 135 Seosomun-dong,
Jung-gu, Seoul, 100-737, Korea (South)
Tel.: (82) 23978100
Sales Range: $75-99.9 Million
Emp.: 25
Insurance Brokeragea & Advisory Services
N.A.I.C.S.: 524210

Jardine Lloyd Thompson Limited (3)
13th Floor World Trade Building 50 Hsin
Sheng South Road Section 1, Taipei,
10059, Taiwan
Tel.: (886) 2 2395 4611
Web Site: http://www.jltasia.com
Sales Range: $50-74.9 Million
Emp.: 23
Reinsurance Services
N.A.I.C.S.: 524130

Jardine Lloyd Thompson Limited (3)
Floor 29 Vanit Building II 1126/2 New
Petchburi Road Makkasan, Rachthevee,
Bangkok, 10400, Thailand
Tel.: (66) 26262500
Sales Range: $50-74.9 Million
Emp.: 50
Insurance Brokerages & Consulting Services
N.A.I.C.S.: 524210
Andrew Minnitt (Mng Dir)

Jardine Lloyd Thompson Limited (3)
Gemadept Building 6 Le Thanh Ton Street
District 1, Ben Nghe Ward District 1, Ho Chi
Minh City, Vietnam
Tel.: (84) 8 3822 2340
Web Site: http://www.jltasia.com
Sales Range: $50-74.9 Million
Emp.: 15
Insurance Brokerages & Consulting Services
N.A.I.C.S.: 524210

Jardine Lloyd Thompson Pte Limited (3)
8 Marina View 09-02 Asia Square Tower 1,
Singapore, 18960, Singapore
Tel.: (65) 63336311
Insurance Brokerages & Consulting Services

N.A.I.C.S.: 524210

Jardine Lloyd Thompson Sdn Bhd (3)
Suite 10.2 10th Floor Faber Imperial Court
21A Jalan Sultan Ismail, 50250, Kuala Lumpur, Federal Territory, Malaysia
Tel.: (60) 3 2723 3388
Web Site: http://www.jltasia.com
Sales Range: $75-99.9 Million
Emp.: 100
Insurance Brokerage Services
N.A.I.C.S.: 524210

Subsidiary (Non-US):

Jardine Lloyd Thompson Australia Pty Limited (2)
Level 11 66 Clarence Street, Sydney, 2000,
NSW, Australia
Tel.: (61) 292908000
Web Site: http://www.jlta.com.au
General Insurance & Advisory Services
N.A.I.C.S.: 524298

Subsidiary (Domestic):

The Recovre Group Pty Limited (3)
One International Towers 100 Barangaroo
Avenue, Sydney, 2000, NSW, Australia
Tel.: (61) 1300550276
Web Site: http://www.recovre.com.au
Workplace Health, Safety, Rehabilitation &
Training Solutions
N.A.I.C.S.: 561499

Subsidiary (Non-US):

Jardine Lloyd Thompson Limited (2)
Level 11 PwC Tower 15 Customs Street
West, PO Box 2221, Shortland Street,
Auckland, 1140, New Zealand
Tel.: (64) 99283000
General Insurance Services
N.A.I.C.S.: 524210

Subsidiary (Domestic):

Jardine Lloyd Thompson Risk & Insurance Group (2)
138 Houndfditch, London, EC3A 7AW,
United Kingdom
Tel.: (44) 2075284444
Web Site: http://www.jltgroup.com
Insurance Brokers
N.A.I.C.S.: 524298

Subsidiary (Non-US):

Jardine Lloyd Thompson S.p.A. (2)
Via San Gregorio 34, 20124, Milan, Italy
Tel.: (39) 02303191
Web Site: http://www.jltitalia.com
General Insurance & Consulting Services
N.A.I.C.S.: 524210

Subsidiary (Domestic):

Lloyd & Partners Limited (2)
One America Square, London, EC3N 2JL,
United Kingdom
Tel.: (44) 2074666500
Web Site: http://www.lloydandpartners.com
Sales Range: $200-249.9 Million
Emp.: 270
General Insurance Services
N.A.I.C.S.: 524114

Profund Solutions Limited (2)
100 Victoria Street, Bristol, BS1 6HZ,
United Kingdom
Tel.: (44) 1179278400
Web Site: http://www.profund.com
Sales Range: $25-49.9 Million
Pension Administration Software Development & Training Services
N.A.I.C.S.: 541511

Kepler Associates Limited (1)
1 Tower Place West, London, EC3R 5BU,
United Kingdom
Tel.: (44) 2071785112
Management Consulting Services
N.A.I.C.S.: 541611

Kessler & Co AG (1)
ForchStrasse 95, 8032, Zurich, Switzerland
Tel.: (41) 44 387 8711
Web Site: https://www.kessler.ch

Sales Range: $50-74.9 Million
Insurance Services
N.A.I.C.S.: 524210

Subsidiary (Domestic):

Kessler Prevoyance SA (2)
Rue Pepinet 1, PO Box 6648, 1002, Lausanne, Switzerland
Tel.: (41) 213216030
Web Site: https://www.kessler.ch
Sales Range: $75-99.9 Million
Insurance Services
N.A.I.C.S.: 524210

Kessler Consulting, Inc. (1)
14620 N Nebraska Ave Bldg D, Tampa, FL
33613
Tel.: (813) 971-8333
Web Site: https://www.kesconsult.com
Consulting Services
N.A.I.C.S.: 541620
Mitch Kessler (Principal)
Nikki McNew (Fin Mgr)

Lavaretus Underwriting AB (1)
Pieni Roobertinkatu / Lilla Robertsgatan 11
4 Bhelsingfors, 00130, Helsinki, Finland
Tel.: (358) 103229909
Web Site: https://www.lavaretus.com
Insurance Services
N.A.I.C.S.: 524128
Henrik Jensen (Chief Technical Officer)
Jens Ostrup Olsen (Chief Nautical Officer)
Niklas Ohman (Controller-Finance)
Victor Forsten (Officer)

Libra Insurance Services Limited (1)
Harrison House 140-142 High Street, Watford, Bushey, WD23 3DH, Hertfordshire,
United Kingdom
Tel.: (44) 2089500404
Web Site: http://www.jelf.com
Insurance Service Provider
N.A.I.C.S.: 524128
Shailain H. H. Shah (Mng Dir)

Lynch Insurance Brokers Limited (1)
Sky Mall Haggatt Hall St Michael, PO Box
140, Bridgetown, BB11000, Barbados
Tel.: (246) 426 5062
Web Site: https://www.lynchbrokers.com
Sales Range: $10-24.9 Million
Reinsurance Services
N.A.I.C.S.: 524130

MAG JLT SpA (1)
via Delle Tre Madonne 12, 00197, Rome,
Italy
Tel.: (39) 0685306540
Web Site: http://www.magjlt.com
Insurance Brokerage Services
N.A.I.C.S.: 524210
Pierluca Impronta (CEO & Chm)

MAG SpA (1)
Via Delle Tre Madonne 12, 00197, Rome,
Italy
Tel.: (39) 0685306540
Web Site: https://www.magitaliagroup.com
Reinsurance Services
N.A.I.C.S.: 524130

MHBT, Inc. (1)
4411 98th St Ste 200, Lubbock, TX 79424
Tel.: (806) 798-9050
Web Site: https://www.marshmma.com
Insurance Brokers
N.A.I.C.S.: 524210

MMA Securities LLC (1)
1166 Avenue of the Americas, New York,
NY 10036
Tel.: (212) 345-5000
Portfolio Management Services
N.A.I.C.S.: 523940
Craig J. Reid (Pres)

MMC Securities Corp. (1)
1166 Ave of the Americas, New York, NY
10036
Tel.: (212) 345-5000
Investment Management Service
N.A.I.C.S.: 523940

MRC Marsh Risk Consulting GmbH (1)
Calwer Str 7, 70173, Stuttgart, Germany
Tel.: (49) 71123800
Insurance Services
N.A.I.C.S.: 524298

Georg Brauchle (Mgr)

Manson Warner Healthcare Limited (1)
Finance House 55 Mosley Street, Manchester, M2 3HY, United Kingdom
Tel.: (44) 1612451234
Emp.: 20
Health Insurance Services
N.A.I.C.S.: 524114

Marine, Aviation & General (London) Limited (1)
1 Minster Court Mincing Lane, London,
EC3R 7AA, United Kingdom
Tel.: (44) 2073984010
Web Site: https://maglondon.com
Insurance Brokerage Services
N.A.I.C.S.: 524210
Ivo Impronta (Vice Chm)
Guy Wilson (Fin Dir)
Elda Boccia (Dir & Head)
Alessandro Iobbi (CFO)
Matthew Fosh (Chm)

Marsh (1)
Avenue Herrmann-Debroux / Herrmann-Debrouxlaan 2, 1160, Brussels, Belgium
Tel.: (32) 26749611
Web Site: https://www.marsh.com
Insurance Brokerage Services
N.A.I.C.S.: 524210

Marsh & McLennan Agencies AS (1)
Karenslyst Alle 20, Oslo, Norway
Tel.: (47) 22 01 10 00
Web Site: http://www.marsh.com
Emp.: 120
Insurance Agencies & Brokerage Services
N.A.I.C.S.: 524210
David L. Eslick (Chm & CEO)

Marsh & McLennan Agency AB (1)
Klara Norra Kyrkogatan 29, 111 22, Stockholm, Sweden
Tel.: (46) 84124239
Web Site: http://www.se.mercer.com
Emp.: 50
Insurance Management Services
N.A.I.C.S.: 524298

Marsh & McLennan Agency Pty Ltd. (1)
100 Barangaroo Ave Tower One International Towers, Sydney, 2000, NSW, Australia
Tel.: (61) 288647688
Web Site: https://online.ap.marsh.com
Insurance Management Services
N.A.I.C.S.: 524298
Tim Atkins (Dir)

Marsh & McLennan Companies UK Limited (1)
Tower Place, London, EC3R 5BU, United
Kingdom
Tel.: (44) 2073571000
Web Site: http://www.marsh.com
Insurance Brokers
N.A.I.C.S.: 524210

Subsidiary (Domestic):

InSolutions Limited (2)
Willow House Peachman Way, Broadland
Business Park, Norwich, NR7 0WF, United
Kingdom
Tel.: (44) 1603207648
Web Site:
https://insolutionsworld.marsh.com
Sales Range: $50-74.9 Million
Insurance Agents
N.A.I.C.S.: 524210
Kellin Plham (Mng Dir)

Jelf Group plc (2)
Hillside Court Bowling Hill, Chipping Sodbury, Bristol, BS37 6JX, United Kingdom
Tel.: (44) 1454272727
Web Site: http://www.jelfgroup.com
Emp.: 1,200
Insurance, Healthcare, Employee Benefits,
Commercial Finance & Wealth Management
Services

Marsh & McLennan Companies, Inc.—(Continued)

N.A.I.C.S.: 523940
Christopher Jelf *(Founder)*

Subsidiary (Domestic):

Jelf Clarke Roxburgh (3)
2 Clarburgh House 32 Church Street,
Malvern, WR14 2AZ, Worcs, United King-
dom
Tel.: (44) 1684565333
Web Site: http://www.jelfgroup.com
Emp.: 3,000
Insurance Brokers
N.A.I.C.S.: 524210

Jelf Financial Planning Limited (3)
80-86 Bath Road, Westmoreland House,
Cheltenham, GL53 7JT, Gloucestershire,
United Kingdom
Tel.: (44) 1242 225860
Web Site: http://www.jelfgroup.com
Wealth Management Services
N.A.I.C.S.: 541611
Phil Barton *(CEO)*

Jelf Financial Planning Limited (3)
Ground Floor West 300 TVP2 Thames Val-
ley Park Drive, Reading, RG6 1PT, United
Kingdom
Tel.: (44) 118 983 9800
Web Site: http://www.jelfgroup.com
Wealth Management Services
N.A.I.C.S.: 541611

Jelf Insurance Brokers Limited (3)
1st Floor 3 Liverpool Gardens, Worthing,
BN11 1TF, West Sussex, United Kingdom
Tel.: (44) 1903205753
Web Site: http://www.jelfgroup.com
Insurance Brokers
N.A.I.C.S.: 524210

Jelf Lampier (3)
Edgecombe Hall, Richmond Hill, Bristol,
BS8 1AT, Avon, United Kingdom
Tel.: (44) 117 240 2000
Web Site: http://www.jelfgroup.com
Insurance Brokers
N.A.I.C.S.: 524210

Jelf Manson (3)
Kabel House 15 Quay Street, Manchester,
M3 3HY, Lancs, United Kingdom
Tel.: (44) 161 228 0444
Web Site: http://www.jelfgroup.com
Emp.: 45
Insurance Brokers
N.A.I.C.S.: 524210

Jelf Wellbeing Limited (3)
Endeavour House Crow Arch Lane, Ring-
wood, BH24 1HP, United Kingdom
Tel.: (44) 1425471452
Web Site: http://www.jelfgroup.com
Emp.: 50
Healthcare & Employee Benefits Manage-
ment Services
N.A.I.C.S.: 621610

Subsidiary (Domestic):

MMC UK Group Limited (2)
39 Kings Hill Avenue Kings Hill, Maidstone
Kent, West Malling, ME19 4ER, United
Kingdom
Tel.: (44) 1732 877 500
Web Site: http://www.marsh.com
Insurance Services
N.A.I.C.S.: 524298

MMC UK Pension Fund Trustee
Limited (2)
Westgate House 52 Westgate, PO Box 476,
Chichester, PO19 3HF, United Kingdom
Tel.: (44) 1243532000
Web Site: http://www.pensions.uk.mmc.com
Insurance Services
N.A.I.C.S.: 524298

Marsh & McLennan Deutschland
GmbH (1)
Mullerstrasse 3, Munich, Germany
Tel.: (49) 89290560
Web Site: http://www.marsh.com
Insurance Management Services
N.A.I.C.S.: 524298

Marsh & McLennan Real Estate Advi-
sors Inc. (1)

1166 Avenue of the Americas, New York,
NY 10036-2708 **(100%)**
Tel.: (212) 345-5000
Web Site: http://www.mmc.com
Sales Range: $50-74.9 Million
Emp.: 5,000
Real Estate Services
N.A.I.C.S.: 531210

Marsh & McLennan Servicios, S.A.
De C.V. (1)
Torre Mayor Paseo de la Reforma No 505
Pisos 10 al 15, Cuauhtemoc, 06500,
Mexico, Mexico
Tel.: (52) 5596287000
Insurance Management Services
N.A.I.C.S.: 524298

Marsh & McLennan Sweden AB (1)
Klara norra kyrkogata 29, 111 22, Stock-
holm, 11122, Sweden
Tel.: (46) 850530800
Web Site: http://www.sweden.marsh.com
Emp.: 65
Insurance Services
N.A.I.C.S.: 524298
Anders Lindgren *(Head-RM)*

Marsh & McLennan,
Incorporated (1)
1166 Avenue Of The Americas, New York,
NY 10036
Tel.: (212) 345-5000
Investment Management Service
N.A.I.C.S.: 523999

Marsh (Beijing) Insurance Brokers
Co., Ltd. (1)
Suite 30-022 Hang Seng Bank Tower No
1000 Lujiazui Ring Road, Pudong New
Area, Shanghai, 200120, China
Tel.: (86) 2160965819
Web Site: http://www.marshcargo.com
Risk Managemeng Srvices
N.A.I.C.S.: 524298
Michael Li *(CEO)*

Marsh (China) Insurance Brokers
Co., Ltd. (1)
Unit 1506 North Tower Beijing Kerry Center
1 Guanghua Road, Chao Yang District, Bei-
jing, 100020, China
Tel.: (86) 1065334000
Web Site: https://www.marsh.com
Insurance Agency & Brokerage Services
N.A.I.C.S.: 524210

Marsh (Malawi) Limited (1)
Ground Floor MDC House Glyn Jones
Road, PO Box 2913, Blantyre, Malawi
Tel.: (265) 1820044
Web Site: http://www.marsh.com
Emp.: 24
Insurance Services
N.A.I.C.S.: 524210

Marsh (QLD) Pty Ltd. (1)
One International Towers Sydney 100 Ba-
rangaroo Avenue, 201 Sussex St, Sydney,
2000, NSW, Australia
Tel.: (61) 288648888
Web Site: http://www.marsh.com.au
Sales Range: $450-499.9 Million
Emp.: 150
Insurance Services
N.A.I.C.S.: 524298
Peter S. Zaffino *(Pres & CEO)*

Marsh AS (1)
Karenslyst Alle 20, Oslo, Vika, Norway
Tel.: (47) 21011000
Web Site: http://www.marsh.com
Emp.: 80
Insurance Services
N.A.I.C.S.: 524298
Jan-Tore Undersaker *(Mng Dir)*

Marsh Advantage Insurance Pty
Ltd. (1)
Tower 1 727 Collins Street, PO Box 1229,
Melbourne, 3000, VIC, Australia
Tel.: (61) 396032222
Web Site:
    http://www.marshadvantage.com.au
Insurance Brokerage Services
N.A.I.C.S.: 524210
Lorna Molam *(Exec Dir)*
Samantha Dell *(Natl Mgr)*
Stuart Munro *(Natl Mgr)*
Stephen Jones *(Natl Mgr)*

Leah Douglas *(Natl Mgr-Comml,Consumer)*
Mark Borthwick *(Natl Sls Mgr-Commercial)*
Travis Kemp *(Exec Dir)*
Kirsten Mills *(Head-Australia)*

Marsh Botswana (Proprietary)
Limited (1)
Samora Machel Drive Plot 50363 Show-
grounds, Gaborone, Botswana
Tel.: (267) 3993100
Insurance Agency & Brokerage Services
N.A.I.C.S.: 524210

Marsh Brockman y Schuh Agente de
Seguros y de Fianzas, S.A. de
C.V. (1)
Torre Mayor Paseo de la Reforma No 505
Pisos 10 al 15, Col Cuauhtemoc, 06500,
Mexico, Distrito Federal, Mexico
Tel.: (52) 5596287000
Web Site: http://www.marsh.com
Insurance Management Services
N.A.I.C.S.: 524298

Marsh Broker de Asigurare-
Reasigurare S.R.L. (1)
Floreasca Business Park Calea Floreasca
169A Building A Floor 3, Sector 1, Bucha-
rest, 300011, Romania
Tel.: (40) 256437843
Web Site: http://www.marsh.com
Sales Range: $50-74.9 Million
Insurance Services
N.A.I.C.S.: 524298

Marsh Brokers (Hong Kong)
Limited (1)
Suite 3402-3406 One Taikoo Place 979
King's Road, Hong Kong, China (Hong
Kong)
Tel.: (852) 23017000
Web Site: http://www.marsh.com
Insurance Services
N.A.I.C.S.: 524298

Marsh Corretora de Seguros
Ltda. (1)
Av Maria Coelho Aguiar 215 - Bloco F - 1
andar, Sao Paulo, 05804900, Brazil
Tel.: (55) 1138782000
Web Site: http://www.marsh.com
Emp.: 1,500
Insurance Services
N.A.I.C.S.: 524298
Flavio Piccolomini *(Pres-Intl)*

Marsh EOOD (1)
90 Tsarigradsko Shouse Boulevard Capital
Fort Body A Floor 11, Sofia, 1784, Bulgaria
Tel.: (359) 24020000
Web Site: https://www.marsh.com
Sales Range: $25-49.9 Million
Insurance Services
N.A.I.C.S.: 524298

Marsh Eurofinance B.V. (1)
Conradstraat 18, Groot Handelsgebouw E5
167, 3013 AP, Rotterdam, Netherlands
Tel.: (31) 104060600
Web Site: http://www.marsh.com
Sales Range: $75-99.9 Million
Insurance Services
N.A.I.C.S.: 524298

Marsh Finance B.V. (1)
Adres Conradstraat 18, Groot Handelsge-
bouw E5 167, 3013 AP, Rotterdam, Nether-
lands
Tel.: (31) 104060030
Web Site: https://victorinsurance.nl
Sales Range: $75-99.9 Million
Emp.: 250
Insurance Services
N.A.I.C.S.: 524298

Marsh For Insurance Services (1)
Nile City Towers - North Tower 17th Floor
2005 C Cornish ElNile, Mohandiseen Area,
Cairo, 12411, Egypt
Tel.: (20) 233053881
Web Site: https://www.marsh.com
Sales Range: $25-49.9 Million
Emp.: 16
Insurance Services
N.A.I.C.S.: 524298

Marsh GSC Administracao e Correta-
gem de Seguros Ltda. (1)
Av Maria Coelho Aguiar, 215-Bloco F-1 andar, CEP 05804-900, Sao Paulo, Brazil

Tel.: (55) 1137411441
Web Site: http://www.brasil.marsh.com
Insurance Brokerage Services
N.A.I.C.S.: 524210

Marsh Holding AB (1)
Klara Norra Kyrkogata 29, 111 22, Stock-
holm, Sweden
Tel.: (46) 84124200
Web Site: http://www.marsh.com
Emp.: 55
Holding Company
N.A.I.C.S.: 551112
Bjorn Henrik Gunnar Gunolf *(CEO)*

Marsh Holdings B.V. (1)
Conrad Street 18, 3019 AP, Rotterdam,
Netherlands
Tel.: (31) 10406 09 22
Web Site: http://www.marsh.nl
Emp.: 25
Insurance Services
N.A.I.C.S.: 524298

Marsh IAS Management Services
(Bermuda) Ltd. (1)
Power house 7 Par-la-ville Rd, Hamilton,
HM11, Bermuda
Tel.: (441) 2924402
Web Site: http://www.marsh.com
Emp.: 70
Management Consulting Services
N.A.I.C.S.: 541611
Jill Husbands *(Mng Dir & Head-Office)*

Marsh Inc. (1)
1166 Avenue of the Americas, New York,
NY 10036 **(100%)**
Tel.: (212) 345-5000
Web Site: http://www.marsh.com
Risk Management, Insurance & Financial
Services
N.A.I.C.S.: 524210

Subsidiary (Non-US):

DeLima Marsh S.A. - Los Corredores
de Seguros S.A. (2)
Calle 67 Norte No 6N-85, Interior 1, Cali,
Colombia
Tel.: (57) 114269999
Sales Range: $75-99.9 Million
Insurance Services
N.A.I.C.S.: 524210

Marsh (Bahrain) Company SPC (2)
Unitag House - 4th Floor 150 Government
Avenue, 3237, Manama, Bahrain
Tel.: (973) 17226002
Web Site: http://www.marsh.com
Sales Range: $10-24.9 Million
Insurance Services
N.A.I.C.S.: 524210
Abed Qassas *(CEO)*
Paul Tolfrey *(CEO)*

Marsh (Hong Kong) Limited (2)
Suite 3402-3406 One Taikoo Place 979
King's Road, Hong Kong, China (Hong
Kong)
Tel.: (852) 23017000
Web Site: https://www.marsh.com
Sales Range: $10-24.9 Million
Insurance & Risk Management Services
N.A.I.C.S.: 524210

Marsh (Insurance Brokers) LLP (2)
17 Mitin Boulevard, 50020, Almaty, Kazakh-
stan
Tel.: (7) 273560051
Sales Range: $75-99.9 Million
Insurance Services
N.A.I.C.S.: 524210

Marsh (Namibia) (Proprietary)
Limited (2)
Unit 17G, PO Box 1011, Tenbergen Village,
Windhoek, Namibia
Tel.: (264) 612704000
Sales Range: $10-24.9 Million
Insurance Services
N.A.I.C.S.: 524210

Marsh A/S (2)
Teknikerbyen 1, 2830, Virum, Denmark
Tel.: (45) 45959595
Web Site: https://www.marsh.com
Sales Range: $100-124.9 Million
Insurance & Risk Management Services
N.A.I.C.S.: 524210

Marsh AB (2)
Klara Norra Kyrkogata 29, Stockholm, Sweden
Tel.: (46) 84124200
Web Site: http://www.marsh.com.se
Sales Range: $10-24.9 Million
Insurance Services
N.A.I.C.S.: 524210

Marsh AG (2)
Tessinerplatz 5, PO Box 8027, 8002, Zurich, Switzerland
Tel.: (41) 442859300
Sales Range: $1-9.9 Million
Insurance Services
N.A.I.C.S.: 524210
Elaine Casaprima (CEO)

Marsh Austria G.m.b.H. (2)
Handelskai 94-96, 1200, Vienna, Austria
Tel.: (43) 15864983
Web Site: https://www.marsh.com
Sales Range: $1-9.9 Million
Insurance Services
N.A.I.C.S.: 524210
Lukas Herrmanns (CEO-Central & Eastern Europe)
Christian Berger (Mng Dir)

Marsh B.V. (2)
Conradstraat 18 Groot Handelsgebouw
E5167, Zuid-Holland, 3013 AP, Rotterdam, Netherlands
Tel.: (31) 104060600
Web Site: https://www.marsh.com
Sales Range: $100-124.9 Million
Insurance & Risk Management Services
N.A.I.C.S.: 524210

Marsh Canada Limited (2)
120 Bremner Boulevard Suite 800, Toronto, M5J 0A8, ON, Canada (100%)
Tel.: (416) 868-2600
Web Site: http://www.mmc.com
Sales Range: $800-899.9 Million
Insurance Services
N.A.I.C.S.: 524298

Marsh Europe - Organizacna zlozka Slovensko (2)
Laurinska 3, 811 01, Bratislava, Slovakia
Tel.: (421) 259205411
Web Site: http://slovakia.marsh.com
Insurance Brokerage & Risk Management Services
N.A.I.C.S.: 524210

Marsh Europe S.A. (2)
Avenue Herrmann-Debroux / Herrmann-Debrouxlaan 2, Vorstlaan 2, Brussels, Belgium (100%)
Tel.: (32) 26749611
Web Site: http://www.marsh.com
Sales Range: $100-124.9 Million
Insurance Services
N.A.I.C.S.: 524298

Marsh GmbH (2)
Calwer Strasse 7, Kronprinzbau, Stuttgart, Germany (100%)
Tel.: (49) 71123800
Web Site: http://www.marsh.com
Sales Range: $25-49.9 Million
Insurance Services
N.A.I.C.S.: 524298
Erwin Lehmann (Officer-Relationship)

Joint Venture (Domestic):

DVA - Deutsche Verkehrs-Assekuranz-Vermittlungs GmbH (3)
Marienbader Platz 1, 61348, Bad Homburg, Germany
Tel.: (49) 617248680
Web Site: http://www.dva-assekuranz.de
Sales Range: $10-24.9 Million
Emp.: 120
Insurance Agency Services
N.A.I.C.S.: 524210
Christian Heidersdorf (Mng Dir & Member-Mgmt Bd)
Holger Schafer (Mng Dir & Member-Mgmt Bd)

Subsidiary (Domestic):

Marsh GmbH (3)
Leonarstrasse 36, 60528, Frankfurt, Germany
Tel.: (49) 6966760

Web Site: http://www.marsh.com
Sales Range: $75-99.9 Million
Emp.: 200
Insurance Services
N.A.I.C.S.: 524210
Oliver Dobner (Mng Dir)
Bernd Eiser (Officer-Relationship)
Markus Groth (Head-Advisory)
Sebastian Linck (Head-Stuttgart)
Stefan Pleyer (Head-Frankfurt)
Mirela Radoncic (Head-Corp Customers)
Karolin Black (Head-Legal & Compliance)
Nico Stehr (Head-Berlin & Leipzig)
Nicolas Wettstein (Head-Dusseldorf)
Christoph Aicher (Chief HR Officer)
Ingo Gurcke (Mng Dir-Medical Consulting)

Subsidiary (Non-US):

Marsh INSCO LLC (2)
Ground & 16th Floors Al Gurg Tower 3, Dubai, United Arab Emirates
Tel.: (971) 42237700
Web Site: http://www.marsh.com
Sales Range: $10-24.9 Million
Emp.: 130
Insurance Services
N.A.I.C.S.: 524210

Marsh Insurance and Risk Management Consultants Ltd. (2)
1506 North Tower Kerry Center, Guanghua Road No 1, Beijing, 100020, China
Tel.: (86) 1065334000
Web Site: http://www.marsh.com
Sales Range: $100-124.9 Million
Emp.: 100
Insurance & Risk Management Services
N.A.I.C.S.: 524210
Michael Li (CEO)

Marsh Ireland Limited (2)
25-28 Adelaide Rd, Dublin, 2, Ireland
Tel.: (353) 16048100
Web Site: http://www.marsh.com
Sales Range: $50-74.9 Million
Emp.: 200
Insurance Services
N.A.I.C.S.: 524210

Marsh Israel Insurance Agency Ltd. (2)
12 A Abba Hillel St, Ramat Gan, 52506, Israel
Tel.: (972) 36383030
Sales Range: $1-9.9 Million
Insurance Services
N.A.I.C.S.: 524210

Marsh Japan, Inc. (2)
Midtown Tower 9-7-1 Akasaka, Minato-ku, Tokyo, 107-6216, Japan
Tel.: (81) 367756397
Web Site: https://www.marsh.com
Sales Range: $25-49.9 Million
Emp.: 220
Insurance & Risk Management Services
N.A.I.C.S.: 524210
Chikara Nakanishi (Pres)

Subsidiary (Domestic):

Marsh Broker Japan, Inc. (3)
Midtown Tower 9-7-1 Akasaka, Minato-ku, Tokyo, 107-6216, Japan (100%)
Tel.: (81) 367756100
Sales Range: $10-24.9 Million
Emp.: 65
Risk Managemeng Srvices
N.A.I.C.S.: 541611

Subsidiary (Non-US):

Marsh Kindlustusmaakler AS (2)
Tartu mnt 18, 10115, Tallinn, Estonia
Tel.: (372) 6811000
Web Site: https://www.marsh.com
Sales Range: $1-9.9 Million
Insurance & Risk Management Services
N.A.I.C.S.: 524210

Marsh LLC (2)
Forum Business City 13 Pymonenko Street, Entrance 5B 2nd Floor, Kiev, Ukraine
Tel.: (380) 444906363
Web Site: http://www.marsh.com
Sales Range: $1-9.9 Million
Insurance & Risk Management Services
N.A.I.C.S.: 524210

Christos Adamantiadis (CEO-Middle East & Africa)
Liz Cole (Chief HR Officer)
Mark Drummond Brady (Vice Chm)
Patricia Hagemann (Chief Admin Officer)
John Jones (CMO & Chief Comm Officer)
Louis Piliego (COO)
Susan A. Stone (Gen Counsel)
Martin South (Pres & CEO)
Katherine Brennan (Gen Counsel)
Linda Foppiano (Chief HR Officer)
Tamara Simpkins Franklin (Chief Digital Data & Analytics Officer)
Martin South (Pres & CEO)
Katherine Brennan (Gen Counsel)
Linda Foppiano (Chief HR Officer)
Tamara Simpkins Franklin (Chief Digital Data & Analytics Officer)
Keith Walsh (CFO)

Marsh LLC Insurance Brokers (2)
8-10 Sorou Street and Dimitsanas, Maroussi, 15125, Athens, Greece
Tel.: (30) 2108176000
Web Site: https://www.marsh.com
Sales Range: $1-9.9 Million
Insurance Services
N.A.I.C.S.: 524210

Marsh Limited (2)
Level 11 PwC Tower 15 Customs Street East, Auckland, New Zealand
Tel.: (64) 800627744
Web Site: https://www.marsh.com
Sales Range: $10-24.9 Million
Insurance Services
N.A.I.C.S.: 524210
Steven Hills (Reg Mgr-)
Tony Bridgman (CFO)
Steve Walsh (Chief Client Officer)
Matthew Riddle (Chm)
Deborah Fisher (Head-)
Josh Roach (Head-)
Martyn Sinclair (Head-)
Josh Roach (Head-)
Martyn Sinclair (Head-)
Toni Ferrier (CEO)
Jon Griffiths (Sr VP)

Marsh Ltd. Taiwan Branch (2)
3F No 2 Sec 3 Minquan East Road, Taipei, 10477, Taiwan
Tel.: (886) 221837777
Web Site: http://www.taiwan.marsh.com
Sales Range: $100-124.9 Million
Emp.: 140
Insurance & Risk Management Services
N.A.I.C.S.: 524210
Jerry Mao (CEO)

Marsh Luxembourg SA (2)
16 Rue Robert Stimper, Luxembourg, 2557, Luxembourg
Tel.: (352) 495238
Web Site: http://www.marsh.com
Sales Range: Less than $1 Million
Emp.: 8
Insurance & Risk Management Services
N.A.I.C.S.: 524210
Francois Thomas (CFO)

Marsh Management Services (Barbados) Ltd. (2)
White Park House White Park Road, Bridgetown, Barbados
Tel.: (246) 4369929
Web Site: http://www.marsh.com
Sales Range: $100-124.9 Million
Insurance & Management Services
N.A.I.C.S.: 524210

Marsh Management Services (Bermuda) Ltd. (2)
Power House 7 Par-la-Ville Road, Hamilton, HM11, Bermuda (100%)
Tel.: (441) 2924402
Web Site: http://www.marsh.com
Sales Range: $150-199.9 Million
Insurance Management Services
N.A.I.C.S.: 524128

Marsh Management Services (Cayman) Ltd. (2)
Governors Square Building 4 2nd Fl, PO Box 1051, 23 Lime Tree Bay Ave, Georgetown, KY1 1102, Grand Cayman, Cayman Islands (100%)
Tel.: (345) 9145722
Web Site: http://www.marsh.com

Sales Range: $150-199.9 Million
Insurance Management Services
N.A.I.C.S.: 524128
John Ramsey (Sr VP)

Marsh Management Services (Luxembourg) SA (2)
74 rue de Merl, 2146, Luxembourg, Luxembourg
Tel.: (352) 496951
Web Site: http://www.marsh.com
Sales Range: $10-24.9 Million
Management Consulting Services
N.A.I.C.S.: 541611

Marsh Marine & Energy AS (2)
Karenslyst Alle 20, Oslo, 278, Norway
Web Site: http://www.marsh.com
Sales Range: $10-24.9 Million
Emp.: 100
Insurance Services
N.A.I.C.S.: 524210

Marsh Norway AS (2)
Munkedamsvn 45, PO Box 1623, 0119, Oslo, Norway
Tel.: (47) 22011100
Web Site: http://www.marsh.com
Sales Range: $25-49.9 Million
Emp.: 120
Insurance Services
N.A.I.C.S.: 524210

Marsh PB Co., Ltd. (2)
88 The Parq 6th Floor West Wing Ratchadapisek Road, Klongtoey, Bangkok, 10110, Thailand
Tel.: (66) 26957100
Sales Range: $100-124.9 Million
Insurance & Risk Management Services
N.A.I.C.S.: 524210

Marsh Peru SA Corredores de Seguros (2)
Edifico Targa, Amador Merino Reyna 285, Lima, 27, Peru
Tel.: (51) 12159500
Web Site: http://www.marsh.com
Sales Range: $75-99.9 Million
Emp.: 200
Insurance Services
N.A.I.C.S.: 524210

Marsh Philippines, Inc. (2)
20/F Net Lima Building 5th Avenue corner 26th Street, Bonifacio Global City, Taguig, 1634, Philippines (100%)
Tel.: (63) 29023000
Sales Range: $100-124.9 Million
Insurance & Risk Management Services
N.A.I.C.S.: 524210

Marsh Pty Ltd (2)
100 Barangaroo Ave Tower One International Towers, Sydney, 2000, NSW, Australia (100%)
Tel.: (61) 88648888
Web Site: https://www.marsh.com
Sales Range: $750-799.9 Million
Risk Management & Insurance Services
N.A.I.C.S.: 524128

Subsidiary (Non-US):

Marsh Limited (3)
Level 9 BSP Suva Central Renwick Road, PO Box 1333, Suva, Fiji
Tel.: (679) 3327300
Web Site: https://www.marsh.com
Insurance Broking & Risk Management Services
N.A.I.C.S.: 524298

Marsh Limited (3)
Level 8 Deloitte Tower, Douglas Street, Port Moresby, Papua New Guinea
Tel.: (675) 3211811
Web Site: http://www.marsh.com.pg
Sales Range: $75-99.9 Million
Insurance Services
N.A.I.C.S.: 524210

Subsidiary (Non-US):

Marsh S.A. (2)
Ariane 9, 92088, Paris, France
Tel.: (33) 141345000
Web Site: http://www.marsh.fr

Marsh & McLennan Companies, Inc.—(Continued)

Sales Range: $50-74.9 Million
Emp.: 1,000
Insurance & Risk Management Services
N.A.I.C.S.: 524210
Fabrice Domange *(CEO)*
Cyrille Brand *(Dir-Key Accounts)*
Valentine Studer *(Dir-Bus & SME)*
Christophe Pardessus *(Dir-Claims)*
Philippe Maraux *(Dir-Retail Placement)*
Jean-Christophe Tessier *(Dir-RC & Fin Lines)*
Bruno Bajard *(Dir-Specialties)*
Julien Alzounies *(Dir-Ops & Customer Svc)*
Isabelle Benat *(CFO)*
France Vagner *(Dir-HR & Gen Svcs)*

Marsh S.A. Corredores De Seguros **(2)**
Los Militares 4611 Piso 3 y 4 Comuna, Las Condes, Santiago, Chile
Tel.: (56) 229292300
Web Site: http://www.marsh.com
Sales Range: $10-24.9 Million
Insurance Services
N.A.I.C.S.: 524298

Marsh S.p.A. **(2)**
Viale Bodio 33, Milan, Italy
Tel.: (39) 02485381
Web Site: https://www.marsh.com
Sales Range: $100-124.9 Million
Insurance & Risk Management Services
N.A.I.C.S.: 524210

Marsh SA **(2)**
Av Cordova 111, Piso 16, Buenos Aires, Argentina
Tel.: (54) 1143205800
Sales Range: $10-24.9 Million
Insurance Services
N.A.I.C.S.: 524210

Marsh SIA **(2)**
Dzirnavu iela 37-13, Riga, 1010, Latvia
Tel.: (371) 67095095
Web Site: https://www.marsh.com
Insurance & Risk Management Services
N.A.I.C.S.: 524210

Marsh Sigorta ve Reasurans Broker-ligi A.S. **(2)**
Maya Akar Center Buyukdere Cd No 100 Kat 4, 34394, Istanbul, Turkiye
Tel.: (90) 2123554300
Web Site: http://www.marsh.com
Sales Range: $50-74.9 Million
Insurance Services
N.A.I.C.S.: 524210

Marsh Singapore Pte Ltd. **(2)**
8 Marina View 09-02 Asia Square Tower 1, Singapore, 018960, Singapore
Tel.: (65) 69228388
Sales Range: $50-74.9 Million
Insurance & Risk Management Services
N.A.I.C.S.: 524210
James Addington-Smith *(CEO-South Asia)*

Marsh Spolka z.o.o. **(2)**
Al Jerozolimskie 98, 00-807, Warsaw, Poland
Tel.: (48) 224564200
Web Site: https://www.marsh.com
Sales Range: $100-124.9 Million
Insurance & Risk Management Services
N.A.I.C.S.: 524210
Artur Grzeskowiak *(Pres & Member-Mgmt Bd)*

Marsh UK Limited **(2)**
Tower Place, Lower Thames Street, London, EC3R 5BU, United Kingdom **(100%)**
Tel.: (44) 2073571000
Web Site: http://www.marsh.com
Sales Range: $1-4.9 Billion
Emp.: 6,500
Insurance Broker & Risk Management Services
N.A.I.C.S.: 524128
Chris Lay *(CEO)*

Subsidiary (Non-US):

Marsh (Isle of Man) Limited **(3)**
51-59 Circular Road, Douglas, IM1 1RE, Isle of Man
Tel.: (44) 1624691900
Web Site: http://www.marsh.co.uk

Sales Range: $75-99.9 Million
Emp.: 6
Insurance Services
N.A.I.C.S.: 524210

Subsidiary (Domestic):

Marsh Brokers Limited **(3)**
1 Tower Place West, Tower Place, London, EC3R 5BU, United Kingdom **(100%)**
Tel.: (44) 2072475433
Web Site: http://www.marsh.com
Insurance Brokerage Services
N.A.I.C.S.: 524210

Marsh UK Holdings Limited **(3)**
1 Tower Place West, London, EC3R 5BU, United Kingdom
Tel.: (44) 02073571000
Web Site: http://www.marsh.com
Sales Range: $350-399.9 Million
Emp.: 100
Insurance Services
N.A.I.C.S.: 524298

Subsidiary (Domestic):

Marsh USA Inc. **(2)**
1166 Avenue of the Americas, New York, NY 10036-2708 **(100%)**
Tel.: (212) 345-5000
Web Site: http://www.mmc.com
Sales Range: $5-14.9 Billion
Insurance Services
N.A.I.C.S.: 524210

Subsidiary (Domestic):

Border Insurance Services, Inc. **(3)**
2004 Dairy Mart Rd Ste 114, San Ysidro, CA 92173
Tel.: (619) 428-0095
Web Site: http://www.mexborder.com
Sales Range: $10-24.9 Million
Emp.: 7
Insurance Services
N.A.I.C.S.: 524210

CS Stars LLC **(3)**
540 W Madison Ste 1200, Chicago, IL 60661-3630
Tel.: (312) 627-6000
Web Site: http://www.march.com
Risk Management Technology Software & Services
N.A.I.C.S.: 513210
Yuri Pinsker *(Gen Counsel)*

Marsh & McLennan Agency LLC **(3)**
360 HamiltonAve Ste 930, White Plains, NY 10601
Tel.: (212) 345-5000
Web Site: http://www.marshmma.com
Insurance Brokerage Services
N.A.I.C.S.: 524210
David L. Eslick *(Chm & CEO)*
John C. Stanchina *(CEO-Mid-Atlantic)*
Timothy Fleming *(CEO-Upper Midwest)*
Bill Jeatran *(Pres)*
Christina Mott *(COO)*
Stephane Massie *(CEO-Canada)*
Jerry Alderman *(Pres-New England & Northeast)*
Denise Perlman *(Pres-Natl Bus Insurance)*
Nathan Rasmussen *(Mng Dir-Retirement Svcs-New England)*
Nathan Durham *(Exec VP & Mng Dir-Johns Creek)*
Paul Hering *(Vice Chm)*
Ben Newman *(CFO)*
Sharon Werner *(Chief HR Officer)*
Steven Handmaker *(CMO)*
Trindl Reeves *(Chief Sls Officer)*
Kate Moher *(Pres-Natl Employee Health & Benefits)*
Jim Maza *(CIO)*
Alexandra von Ferstel *(Gen Counsel)*
Richard DeSanctis *(Chief Compliance Officer)*
Kira Kimball *(Chief Diversity, Equity, & Inclusion Officer)*
Pete Walther *(Pres-Private Client Svcs)*
Shannon P. Alfonso *(CEO-Florida)*
Doug Bishop *(CEO-Bouchard)*
Tony Chimino *(CEO-Midwest)*
Matt Stadler *(CEO-Southwest)*
Peter Krause *(Pres-Southeast)*
Kyle Lingscheit *(CEO-Northwest)*
Andrew Neary *(CEO-East)*
Chris Williams *(CEO-West)*

Jess Brown *(CFO-Southeast)*
Christie Conley *(Sr VP-Southeast)*
Angela Lee *(Sr VP-Southeast & Dir-Regional Claims-Southeast)*

Subsidiary (Domestic):

Ameristar Agency, Inc. **(4)**
800 E Wayzata Blvd Ste 250, Wayzata, MN 55391
Tel.: (763) 542-8377
Web Site: http://www.ameristaragency.com
Rev.: $1,200,000
Emp.: 8
Fiscal Year-end: 12/31/2009
Insurance Agencies & Brokerages
N.A.I.C.S.: 524210
Mark Schadow *(CEO)*
Melody Wolter *(Mgr-Personal Lines)*

Aviation Solutions, LLC **(4)**
7015 College Boulevard Suite 750 Overland Park, Overland Park, KS 66211
Tel.: (816) 353-1047
Web Site: http://www.aviationsolutionsllc.com
Emp.: 7
Insurance Agencies & Brokerages
N.A.I.C.S.: 524210

Barney & Barney, Inc. **(4)**
9171 Towne Centre Dr Ste 500, San Diego, CA 92122
Tel.: (858) 457-3414
Web Site: http://www.barneyandbarney.com
Sales Range: $10-24.9 Million
Emp.: 420
Insurance Brokerage Services
N.A.I.C.S.: 524210

Benefits Advisory Group LLC **(4)**
3715 Northside Pkwy Bldg 200 Ste 400, Atlanta, GA 30327
Tel.: (770) 859-0189
Web Site: http://www.benefitsadvisorygroup.biz
Employee & Executive Benefits Consulting Services
N.A.I.C.S.: 541612

Bradley Insurance Agency. **(4)**
5210-B Schubert Rd, Knoxville, TN 37912
Tel.: (865) 531-7722
Web Site: https://www.bradley-ins.com
Insurance Agencies & Brokerages
N.A.I.C.S.: 524210

Cline Wood Agency, Inc. **(4)**
4300 W 133rd St, Leawood, KS 66209
Tel.: (913) 451-3900
Web Site: http://www.clinewood.com
Sales Range: $10-24.9 Million
Emp.: 73
Casualty Insurance Services
N.A.I.C.S.: 524126

Compass Financial Partners, LLC **(4)**
701 Green Vly Rd Ste 308, Greensboro, NC 27408
Tel.: (336) 510-1550
Web Site: http://www.compassfp.com
Investment Advice
N.A.I.C.S.: 523940
Kathleen Kelly *(Mng Partner)*
George Hoyle *(Mng Partner)*

Corporate Consulting Services **(4)**
605 3rd Ave, New York, NY 10158
Tel.: (212) 808-5577
Web Site: http://www.ccsstrategies.com
Sales Range: $1-9.9 Million
Emp.: 21
Insurance Related Activities
N.A.I.C.S.: 524298

Elsey & Associates Surety Insurance Agency, Inc. **(4)**
21755 I45 N Bldg 8, Spring, TX 77388
Tel.: (281) 651-0002
Web Site: http://www.elseyagency.com
Sales Range: $1-9.9 Million
Emp.: 23
Insurance Services
N.A.I.C.S.: 524128
David Groppell *(Sr VP)*
Sharen Groppell *(Sr VP)*
Ned Moore *(VP)*
Brett Baker *(VP)*
Rachel Thayer *(VP)*

Terry Mann *(VP)*
Cindy Lou Wilson *(Mktg Dir)*
Cindy Chandler *(Acct Mgr)*
Gay Lynn Goss *(Acct Mgr)*
Jacke Siegel *(Acct Mgr)*
Jessica Hanson *(Acct Mgr)*
Melinda Drevojanek *(Acct Mgr)*
Terri Galleymore *(Acct Mgr)*
Misty Amaya *(Coord--Comml Lines)*
Beverly Ireland *(Acct Mgr)*
Lori Ellis *(Acct Mgr)*
Mary Rifaat *(Acct Mgr)*
Roxanne Hebert *(Acct Mgr)*
Christy Baker *(Acct Mgr-Benefits)*
Jeanne Eggers *(Mgr)*

Fisher Brown Bottrell Insurance, Inc. **(4)**
248 E Capitol St Ste 1200, Jackson, MS 39201-0291
Tel.: (601) 960-8200
Web Site: http://www.fbbins.com
Insurance Agency & Risk Management Services
N.A.I.C.S.: 524210

Co-Headquarters (Domestic):

Fisher Brown Bottrell Insurance, Inc. - Pensacola Office **(5)**
19 W Garden St Ste 300, Pensacola, FL 32502
Tel.: (850) 432-7474
Web Site: http://www.fbbins.com
Insurance Agency & Risk Management Services
N.A.I.C.S.: 524210

Subsidiary (Domestic):

HMS Insurance Associates, Inc. **(4)**
20 Wight Av Ste 300, Cockeysville, MD 21030-2003
Tel.: (410) 584-7600
Web Site: http://www.hmsia.com
Insurance Brokerage Services
N.A.I.C.S.: 524210
Angela Vecchioni *(Sr Mgr-Acct)*
Harry Trostle *(Mgr)*
Jessica Causey *(Sr Mgr-Acct)*
Joy Davidson *(Sr Mgr-Acct)*
Magnus Turesson *(Dir-Risk Control)*
Michael Sutherland *(VP-Risk Control & Captive Ops)*
Stephanie Fairley *(Mgr-Acct)*
Gary L. Berger *(Pres)*

Heritage Insurance Service Inc. **(4)**
20 Lily Creek Rd Ste 201, Louisville, KY 40243
Tel.: (502) 650-8920
Web Site: http://www.heritageinsuranceservice.com
Insurance Agencies & Brokerages
N.A.I.C.S.: 524210
Steven L. Turner *(Founder)*

Inspro, Inc. **(4)**
100 East 6th St, Fremont, NE 68026
Tel.: (402) 721-9707
Web Site: http://www.insproins.com
Sales Range: $1-9.9 Million
Emp.: 10
Direct Life Insurance Carriers
N.A.I.C.S.: 524113
Michael J. Chvatal *(Exec VP)*
Rick G. Wimer *(Sr VP)*
Samuel Gifford *(Pres)*
Jeffrey Jorgensen *(COO)*
Randall Eikmeier *(Chm & CEO)*
Loren D. Sweigard *(Exec VP)*
Dan Chvatal *(VP)*
Jan Kirkner *(Sr Acct Mgr-Employee Health & Benefits)*
Jennifer Batenhorst *(Mgr-Claims)*
Allyson Mary *(Sr Acct Mgr)*
Lori L. Fitz *(Sr Acct Mgr)*
Doris A. Nickolaison *(Sr Acct Mgr)*
Andrea Millet *(Accountant)*
Mitchell Walker *(VP)*
Allyson Perry *(Sr Acct Mgr)*
Lindsey Nelson *(Acct Mgr)*
Amanda Christian *(Acct Mgr)*
Shelly Jensen *(Comptroller)*
Mitchell Walker *(VP)*
Allyson Perry *(Sr Acct Mgr)*
Lindsey Nelson *(Acct Mgr)*
Amanda Christian *(Acct Mgr)*
Shelly Jensen *(Comptroller)*

Mitchell Walker *(VP)*
Allyson Perry *(Sr Acct Mgr)*
Lindsey Nelson *(Acct Mgr)*
Amanda Christian *(Acct Mgr)*
Shelly Jensen *(Comptroller)*

Insurance Partners of Texas **(4)**
2230 Industrial Blvd, Abilene, TX 79602-7857
Tel.: (325) 437-0900
Web Site: http://www.ipot.net
Health & Benefits-related Services
N.A.I.C.S.: 524210

Ironwood Insurance Services LLC **(4)**
4401 Northside Pkwy Ste 800, Atlanta, GA 30327
Tel.: (404) 503-9100
Web Site: http://www.ironwoodins.com
Insurance Agencies & Brokerages
N.A.I.C.S.: 524210
Mark R. Conner *(Sr VP)*
Matthew R. Hene *(Co-Pres)*
Mike M. Trammell *(Sr VP-)*
Matthew Lovein *(Co-Pres)*
William E. Underwood III *(Founding PArtner)*

J. Smith Lanier & Co. **(4)**
300 W 10th St, West Point, GA 31833
Tel.: (706) 645-2211
Web Site: http://www.jsmithlanier.com
Insurance Agency, Employee Benefits & Financial Services
N.A.I.C.S.: 524210
David Gaines Lanier *(CEO)*
Gary E. Ivey *(COO)*
Lynn Yarborough *(Mng Dir)*

Klein Agency, Inc. **(4)**
3570 Lexington Ave N, Saint Paul, MN 55126-8049
Tel.: (651) 484-6461
Web Site: http://www.marshmma.com
Direct Property & Casualty Insurance Carriers
N.A.I.C.S.: 524126

LA/Beach Strategic Alliance, LLC **(4)**
1800 Bering Dr Ste 900, Houston, TX 77057
Tel.: (713) 425-6700
Web Site: http://www.focusins.com
Insurance Agencies & Brokerages
N.A.I.C.S.: 524210
John Murphy *(Mgr-IT)*

Lovitt & Touche, Inc. **(4)**
7202 E Rosewood St Ste 200, Tucson, AZ 85710
Tel.: (520) 722-3000
Web Site: http://www.lovitt-touche.com
Emp.: 200
Insurance Agents
N.A.I.C.S.: 524210
David Wilder *(VP)*
Jody Sarchett *(Exec VP-Sls)*
Lisa Heppler *(VP-Comml Lines)*
Anthony Sylvester *(Sr Acct Exec)*
Charles Touche *(CEO)*
Steven Touche *(Pres)*
Will Spong *(Exec VP-Benefits)*
Jessica Huber *(CFO)*
Dawn Parker *(Dir)*
Sue Espinoza *(VP-Mktg & Placement)*
Shawn Ellis *(VP-HR)*
Melissa Lykins *(VP-Claims)*
Kirk Welch *(Dir-Bonds)*
Andrea Windish *(Mgr)*
Brian Owens *(Mgr)*
Doug Adelberg *(Sr VP)*
Bill Charles *(VP)*
Michael Cody *(Sr VP)*
Julie Friedly *(VP)*
Lisa LaVoie *(VP)*
David Passey *(Sr VP)*
Ryan Passey *(VP)*
Scott Ragland *(VP)*
R. J. Riley *(VP)*
Elise Thorpe *(VP)*
Dennis Tsonis *(Sr VP)*
Brian Wilder *(VP)*
Charles S. Touche *(VP)*

Mariners Insurance Agency Inc. **(4)**
77 N Water St, New Bedford, MA 02740-6244
Tel.: (508) 993-7411
Web Site: http://www.smithwick-ins.com

Sales Range: $10-24.9 Million
Emp.: 8
Insurance Services
N.A.I.C.S.: 524126

Subsidiary (Non-US):

Marsh & McLennan Agency A/S **(4)**
Teknikerbyen 1, 2830, Virum, Denmark
Tel.: (45) 45959595
Web Site: https://www.marsh.com
Human Resource Consulting Services
N.A.I.C.S.: 541612

Subsidiary (US):

Integrity HR, Inc. **(5)**
109 Daventry Ln, Louisville, KY 40223
Tel.: (502) 753-0970
Web Site: https://www.integrityhr.com
Human Resource Consulting Services
N.A.I.C.S.: 541612
Christina Reising *(Mgr-Consulting Svcs)*
Kristy Rowan *(Mgr-Consulting Svcs)*
Linda Hundley *(Coord-Acctg & Billing)*
Mark Hardy *(Mgr-Talent Acquisition)*
Mary Mitchell *(Mgr-Consulting Svcs)*
Tonya Smith *(Mgr-Consulting Svcs)*

Branch (Domestic):

Marsh & McLennan Agency LLC - Midwest Region **(4)**
309 E Monument Ave Ste 400, Dayton, OH 45402-1795
Tel.: (937) 228-4135
Web Site: http://www.marshmma.com
Insurance Services
N.A.I.C.S.: 524210
Jeff Lightner *(Pres & CEO)*
Bob Bair *(Sr VP)*
Timothy J. Antil *(VP)*
John Barron *(Sr VP)*
Nick Bertke *(Exec VP-Bus Insurance Carrier & Client Rels)*
Tyler Bertke *(Sr VP)*
J. Norman Eckstein *(Sr VP)*
Edward Gallagher *(Sr VP)*
Stephen Gallagher *(VP)*
David Griffin *(Sr VP)*
Marc Reynolds *(Sr VP)*
Jeff Sammons *(Sr VP)*
Ken Smith *(VP)*
Kevin Svarda *(VP-Voluntary Benefits)*
Kevin Aston *(Pres-Property & Casualty & Reg)*
Nick Dattilo *(Pres-Employee Health & Benefits & Reg)*
Joe Woods *(Sr VP)*
Andrew Watson *(Sr VP)*
Sam Tuten *(Sr VP)*
Greg Schweppe *(Sr VP)*
Jeffrey Orlando *(Sr VP)*
Brendan Murray *(Sr VP)*
Carroll Leonard *(Sr VP)*
Ann Larimer *(Sr VP-Coverage & Claims Consulting)*
Rhonda Hess *(Sr VP-HR Consulting)*
Jim Gray *(Sr VP)*
Sarah Goodwin *(Sr VP)*
Kathleen Bogenschutz *(Sr VP)*
David Eveleigh *(Sr VP-Mktg)*
Scott Egbers *(Sr VP & Coord-Mktg)*
Justin Thomas *(VP-Employee Health & Benefits)*
Grant Powers *(VP-Bus Insurance)*
Nick Maronde *(VP-Employee Health & Benefits)*
Dwayne Henderson *(VP-Employee Health & Benefits)*
Dana Gore *(VP-Employee Health & Benefits)*
John Clark *(Exec VP-Sls)*
Charlie Filisko *(VP-Property & Casualty)*
Aliou Diouf *(VP-Employee Health & Benefits)*
Kevin Crail *(VP-Bus Insurance)*

Subsidiary (Domestic):

Mcdonald Zaring Insurance, Inc. **(4)**
22 E Main St, Walla Walla, WA 99362
Tel.: (509) 525-5730
Web Site: http://www.mcdonaldzaring.com
Insurance Agents, Brokers, And Service, N
N.A.I.C.S.: 524210
Dan Bassney *(Pres)*

Momentous Insurance Brokerage, Inc. **(4)**

5990 Sepulveda Blvd Ste 550, Van Nuys, CA 91411-2536
Tel.: (818) 933-2700
Web Site: http://www.momentousins.com
Insurance Agencies & Brokerages
N.A.I.C.S.: 524210

Nico Insurance Services, Inc. **(4)**
7290 Navajo Rd Ste 111, San Diego, CA 92119
Tel.: (619) 667-2111
Web Site: http://www.nicoins.com
Sales Range: $1-9.9 Million
Emp.: 11
Benefit Brokerage Firm
N.A.I.C.S.: 524210
Phillip Nico *(Pres)*

Otis-Magie Insurance Agency, Inc. **(4)**
332 W Superior St Ste 700, Duluth, MN 55802
Tel.: (218) 722-7753
Insurance Agencies & Brokerages
N.A.I.C.S.: 524210

PayneWest Insurance, Inc. **(4)**
3289 Gabel Rd, Billings, MT 59102
Tel.: (406) 238-1900
Web Site: http://www.paynewest.com
Sales Range: $50-74.9 Million
Emp.: 700
Insurance Agency Services
N.A.I.C.S.: 524210
Kyle Lingscheit *(CEO)*
Terry Payne *(Founder & Chm)*
Pat McCutcheon *(Sr VP)*
Craig Stahlberg *(VP-Finance)*
Stephen Smelley *(COO)*
Mindy Carver *(Gen Counsel)*
Katie Shaver *(Dir)*
Troy Kane *(Mng Dir-Benefits)*
Kerry Heine *(VP-Finance)*
Allison Johnston *(CFO)*
Dan Antonietti *(Mng Dir-Admin)*
Ryan Bramlette *(Mng Dir)*
Kyle Brucker *(Mng Dir-Tech-IT)*
Karen Diehl *(Mng Dir)*
Ed Heine *(Mng Dir-)*
Chris Huwaldt *(Mng Dir-)*
Scott Simmons *(Mng Dir-)*
Mark Theriault *(Mng Dir- & Exec)*
Jeremy Vannatta *(Mng Dir-Mktg & Comm)*
Sarah Walsh *(Co-COO)*
Amber Bauer *(Controller-Accounting)*
Steven Bauer *(Mgr-)*
Sue Bynum *(Dir--Agribusiness Practice)*
Sue Craig *(Assoc Dir-Accounting)*
Brian Daubert *(Sls Dir-)*
Nate Fulton *(Dir--Bus Insurance)*
Leif Ergeson *(Dir--Bus Insurance)*
Wendy Dieziger *(Dir--Small Bus)*
Tammy Dedrick *(Assoc Dir--Small Bus)*
Joe Gandolfi *(Assoc Dir--Bus Insurance)*
Kari Glennon *(Mng Dir-Sales & Business Development-Admin)*
Jenel Harju *(Sr Dir--Comml Practices)*
Brad Huse *(Sr Dir-Sales-Bus Insurance)*
Candice Hyer *(Assoc Dir--Bus Insurance)*
Peggy Kerins *(Dir-Human Resources)*
Renee King *(Dir-Human Resources)*
Jaci Kruse *(Dir--Bus Insurance)*
Debbie Mills *(Dir--Bus Insurance)*
Jean Merkel *(Dir--Personal Insurance)*
Brooke Laaber *(Dir--Bus Insurance)*
Rhonda Nowak *(Dir-Benefits-Employee Health)*
Colt Palmer *(Sls Dir--Bus Insurance)*
Lauren Patti *(Dir--Admin)*
Carol Williams *(Dir-Development-Admin)*
Shawn Petrie *(Sls Dir-)*
Amber Bauer *(Controller-Accounting)*
Steven Bauer *(Mgr-)*
Sue Bynum *(Dir--Agribusiness Practice)*
Sue Craig *(Assoc Dir-Accounting)*
Brian Daubert *(Sls Dir-)*
Nate Fulton *(Dir--Bus Insurance)*
Leif Ergeson *(Dir--Bus Insurance)*
Wendy Dieziger *(Dir--Small Bus)*
Tammy Dedrick *(Assoc Dir--Small Bus)*
Joe Gandolfi *(Assoc Dir--Bus Insurance)*
Kari Glennon *(Mng Dir-Sales & Business Development-Admin)*
Jenel Harju *(Sr Dir--Comml Practices)*
Brad Huse *(Sr Dir-Sales-Bus Insurance)*
Candice Hyer *(Assoc Dir--Bus Insurance)*
Peggy Kerins *(Dir-Human Resources)*
Renee King *(Dir-Human Resources)*
Jaci Kruse *(Dir--Bus Insurance)*

Debbie Mills *(Dir--Bus Insurance)*
Jean Merkel *(Dir--Personal Insurance)*
Brooke Laaber *(Dir--Bus Insurance)*
Rhonda Nowak *(Dir-Benefits-Employee Health)*
Colt Palmer *(Sls Dir--Bus Insurance)*
Lauren Patti *(Dir--Admin)*
Carol Williams *(Dir-Development-Admin)*
Shawn Petrie *(Sls Dir-)*
Amber Bauer *(Controller-Accounting)*
Steven Bauer *(Mgr-)*
Sue Bynum *(Dir--Agribusiness Practice)*
Sue Craig *(Assoc Dir-Accounting)*
Brian Daubert *(Sls Dir-)*
Nate Fulton *(Dir--Bus Insurance)*
Leif Ergeson *(Dir--Bus Insurance)*
Wendy Dieziger *(Dir--Small Bus)*
Tammy Dedrick *(Assoc Dir--Small Bus)*
Joe Gandolfi *(Assoc Dir--Bus Insurance)*
Kari Glennon *(Mng Dir-Sales & Business Development-Admin)*
Jenel Harju *(Sr Dir--Comml Practices)*
Brad Huse *(Sr Dir-Sales-Bus Insurance)*
Candice Hyer *(Assoc Dir--Bus Insurance)*
Peggy Kerins *(Dir-Human Resources)*
Renee King *(Dir-Human Resources)*
Jaci Kruse *(Dir--Bus Insurance)*
Debbie Mills *(Dir--Bus Insurance)*
Jean Merkel *(Dir--Personal Insurance)*
Brooke Laaber *(Dir--Bus Insurance)*
Rhonda Nowak *(Dir-Benefits-Employee Health)*
Colt Palmer *(Sls Dir--Bus Insurance)*
Lauren Patti *(Dir--Admin)*
Carol Williams *(Dir-Development-Admin)*
Shawn Petrie *(Sls Dir-)*

Co-Headquarters (Domestic):

PayneWest Insurance, Inc. - Missoula (Palmer Street) Corporate Office **(5)**
2925 Palmer St, Missoula, MT 59808-1658
Tel.: (406) 721-1000
Web Site: http://www.paynewest.com
Emp.: 115
Insurance Agents
N.A.I.C.S.: 524210
Kyle Lingscheit *(CEO)*
Mindy Carver *(Gen Counsel)*
Karen Diehl *(Mng Dir-Helena)*
Ed Heine *(Mng Dir-Surety)*
Chris Huwaldt *(Mng Dir-Personal Insurance-McMinnville)*
Allison Johnston *(CFO-Accounting)*
Troy Kane *(Mng Dir-Benefits-Billings)*
Craig Stahlberg *(VP-Finance)*
Sarah Walsh *(COO-Helena)*

Branch (Domestic):

PayneWest Insurance, Inc. - Helena, Cedar Street **(6)**
1300 Cedar St, Helena, MT 59601-0900
Tel.: (406) 442-8010
Web Site: http://www.paynewest.com
Sales Range: $25-49.9 Million
Emp.: 30
Insurance Agents
N.A.I.C.S.: 524210
Sarah Walsh Kelly *(Co-COO)*
Deanna Hoffman *(Sr Acct Mgr)*
Kim Rasmussen *(Mgr-)*
Karen Rimestad *(Acct Mgr)*
Jennifer Sorheim *(Acct Mgr)*
Amanda Bartsch *(Acct Mgr)*
Kathy Burt *(Mgr-)*
Dianne Centrella *(Mgr-)*
Lisa Duncan *(Sr Acct Mgr)*
Ange Furlong *(Acct Mgr)*
Brandy Garber *(Asst Mgr-)*
Kelsey Langemo *(Acct Mgr)*
David Lyons *(Acct Mgr)*
Shelley Oliver *(Acct Mgr)*
Sherry Sauer *(Sr Acct Mgr)*
Cheryl Wignot *(Acct Mgr)*
Peter Wipf *(Acct Mgr)*
Shelly Batista *(Mgr-)*
Sarah Bunton *(Mgr-)*
Meghan Larsen *(Mgr-)*
Melissa Mazurek *(Sr Acct Mgr)*
Teri Palmer *(Acct Mgr)*
Kris Schmaus *(Acct Mgr)*
Peggy Kerins *(Dir-Human Resources)*
Mary Ternes *(Coord-Human Resources)*
Deanna Hoffman *(Sr Acct Mgr)*
Kim Rasmussen *(Mgr-)*

Marsh & McLennan Companies, Inc.—(Continued)

Karen Rimestad *(Acct Mgr)*
Jennifer Sorheim *(Acct Mgr)*
Amanda Bartsch *(Acct Mgr)*
Kathy Burt *(Mgr-)*
Dianne Centrella *(Mgr-)*
Lisa Duncan *(Sr Acct Mgr)*
Ange Furlong *(Acct Mgr)*
Brandy Garber *(Asst Mgr-)*
Kelsey Langemo *(Acct Mgr)*
David Lyons *(Acct Mgr)*
Shelley Oliver *(Acct Mgr)*
Sherry Sauer *(Sr Acct Mgr)*
Cheryl Wignot *(Acct Mgr)*
Peter Wipf *(Acct Mgr)*
Shelly Batista *(Mgr-)*
Sarah Bunton *(Mgr-)*
Meghan Larsen *(Mgr-)*
Melissa Mazurek *(Sr Acct Mgr)*
Teri Palmer *(Acct Mgr)*
Kris Schmaus *(Acct Mgr)*
Peggy Kerins *(Dir-Human Resources)*
Mary Ternes *(Coord-Human Resources)*

**PayneWest Insurance, Inc. -
Kalispell** **(6)**
33 Village Loop Rd, Kalispell, MT 59901-
2859
Tel.: (406) 758-4200
Web Site: http://www.paynewest.com
Sales Range: $25-49.9 Million
Emp.: 25
Insurance Agents
N.A.I.C.S.: 524210
Kimberley Thomas *(Acct Coord)*
Dan Antonietti *(Mng Dir-Administration)*
Amber Bauer *(Controller-Accounting)*
Steven Bauer *(Mgr-)*
Kyle Brucker *(Mng Dir-Technology-IT)*
Sue Bynum *(Dir--Agribusiness Practice, Bus
Insurance)*
Sue Craig *(Assoc Dir-Accounting)*
Brian Daubert *(Sls Dir-)*
Tammy Dedrick *(Assoc Dir--Small Bus)*
Wendy Dieziger *(Dir--Small Bus)*
Leif Ergeson *(Dir--Bus Insurance)*
Nate Fulton *(Dir--Bus Insurance)*
Joe Gandolfi *(Assoc Dir--Bus Insurance)*
Kari Glennon *(Mng Dir-Sales & Business
Development-Admin)*
Jenel Harju *(Sr Dir--Comml Practices, Bus
Insurance)*
Brad Huse *(Sr Dir-Sales-Bus Insurance)*
Candice Hyer *(Assoc Dir--Bus Insurance)*
Peggy Kerins *(Dir-Human Resources)*
Renee King *(Dir-Human Resources)*
Jaci Kruse *(Dir--Bus Insurance)*
Brooke Laaber *(Dir--Bus Insurance)*
Jean Merkel *(Dir--Personal Insurance)*
Debbie Mills *(Dir--Bus Insurance)*
Shawn Petrie *(Sls Dir-)*
Rhonda Nowak *(Dir-Benefits-Employee
Health)*
Jeff Wallace *(Mng Dir--Admin)*
Dan Antonietti *(Mng Dir-Administration)*
Amber Bauer *(Controller-Accounting)*
Steven Bauer *(Mgr-)*
Kyle Brucker *(Mng Dir-Technology-IT)*
Sue Bynum *(Dir--Agribusiness Practice, Bus
Insurance)*
Sue Craig *(Assoc Dir-Accounting)*
Brian Daubert *(Sls Dir-)*
Tammy Dedrick *(Assoc Dir--Small Bus)*
Wendy Dieziger *(Dir--Small Bus)*
Leif Ergeson *(Dir--Bus Insurance)*
Nate Fulton *(Dir--Bus Insurance)*
Joe Gandolfi *(Assoc Dir--Bus Insurance)*
Kari Glennon *(Mng Dir-Sales & Business
Development-Admin)*
Jenel Harju *(Sr Dir--Comml Practices, Bus
Insurance)*
Brad Huse *(Sr Dir-Sales-Bus Insurance)*
Candice Hyer *(Assoc Dir--Bus Insurance)*
Peggy Kerins *(Dir-Human Resources)*
Renee King *(Dir-Human Resources)*
Jaci Kruse *(Dir--Bus Insurance)*
Brooke Laaber *(Dir--Bus Insurance)*
Jean Merkel *(Dir--Personal Insurance)*
Debbie Mills *(Dir--Bus Insurance)*
Shawn Petrie *(Sls Dir-)*
Rhonda Nowak *(Dir-Benefits-Employee
Health)*
Jeff Wallace *(Mng Dir--Admin)*

**PayneWest Insurance, Inc. - Mis-
soula, Front Street** **(6)**
2925 Palmer St, Missoula, MT 59808
Tel.: (406) 728-2910

Web Site: http://www.paynewest.com
Emp.: 21
Insurance Agents
N.A.I.C.S.: 524210

Subsidiary (Domestic):

Presidio Benefits Group, Inc. **(4)**
142 Sansome St 4th Fl, San Francisco, CA
94104
Tel.: (415) 315-9717
Web Site: http://www.presidiobenefits.com
Insurance Agencies
N.A.I.C.S.: 524210
Matthew Coan *(Founder & Principal)*

Roger Bouchard Insurance, Inc. **(4)**
101 N Starcrest Dr, Clearwater, FL 33765
Tel.: (727) 447-6481
Web Site:
http://www.bouchardinsurance.com
Full-Service Retail Insurance Agency
N.A.I.C.S.: 524210
Doug Bishop *(Pres & CEO)*
Matt Elsey *(CFO)*
Jeff L. Welch *(Partner)*
Andy Davis *(COO)*
Adam Bouchard *(Partner)*
Eric Beck *(Partner)*
Ileane Altamura *(Partner)*
Nick Amaro *(Partner)*
Todd McWhirter *(Partner)*
Matt Shemwell *(Exec VP-Sales)*
Taylor Devine *(Coord-)*
Matt Shemwell *(Exec VP-Sales)*
Taylor Devine *(Coord-)*

**Rosenfeld Einstein & Associates,
Inc.** **(4)**
870 S Pleasantburg Dr, Greenville, SC
29607
Tel.: (864) 271-6336
Web Site: http://www.rosenfeldeinstein.com
Sales Range: $10-24.9 Million
Emp.: 50
Insurance Agents
N.A.I.C.S.: 524210

**The Bostonian Group Insurance
Agency, Inc.** **(4)**
101 Huntington Ave Suite 401, Boston, MA
02199
Tel.: (617) 587-2300
Web Site: http://www.mma-newengland.com
Emp.: 75
Insurance Agencies Brokerages
N.A.I.C.S.: 524210

The Centurion Group, Inc. **(4)**
6062 Hollow Tree Ct, Colorado Springs, CO
80918
Tel.: (719) 268-2953
Web Site: http://www.tcgiteam.com
Facilities Maintenance & Repair Services
N.A.I.C.S.: 561210
Oscar T. Valdez *(Pres & CEO)*
David Valdez *(Mgr-Safety & Quality Control)*

The Horton Group Inc. **(4)**
10320 Orland Pkwy, Orland Park, IL 60467
Tel.: (708) 845-3000
Web Site: http://www.thehortongroup.com
Emp.: 225
Insurance Agents, Brokers & Service
N.A.I.C.S.: 524210
Glenn M. Horton *(Chm & CEO)*
Bob DeChene *(Sr VP)*
Mike Gleason *(Sr VP)*
Fred Garfield *(Sr VP)*
John Hamer *(Dir-Ops)*
Rich Kauzlarich *(VP)*
Ken Olson *(Pres-Div)*
Paul A. Sabatino *(VP)*
Rick Klein *(Sr VP)*
Tom Palmer *(VP)*
Doug Henderson *(VP)*
John Naso *(VP)*
Mike Madey *(Sr VP)*
Mike Wojcik *(Sr VP)*
Ed Young *(Sr VP)*
Paul Shaheen *(VP)*
Kelly Kehoe *(Chief Client Officer)*
Gregg Brasseur *(VP)*
Todd Adams *(VP)*
George Daly *(COO)*
Tim Deaton *(VP)*
Gary Glader *(Pres-Safety Consultants)*
Kevin Herman *(VP)*
Tony Hopkins *(VP)*

Dan Horton *(Pres)*
Tom R. Housand *(VP)*
Paul Johnson *(Sr VP)*
Jeff Kaminski *(Sr VP)*
David Kleifield *(VP)*
Kristine Lambert *(Mgr-Ops)*
Kevin Palmer *(VP & Atty)*
Les Peach *(VP)*
Ryan Smale *(Pres-Waukesha)*
Penny Solski *(Dir-Claims Mgmt Svcs)*
Michelle Strauss *(Sr Mgr-Acct)*
Ken Tidwell *(VP)*
Dave Valentine *(VP)*
Michael Zoladz *(Sr VP)*
Tricia Pucek *(CFO)*
Michael J. Fox *(Sr VP)*
Sean Dauber *(Sr VP)*
William Holler *(Sr VP)*
Chris Pfeiffer *(VP)*
Debbie Lorsch *(VP)*
Tim Walsh *(VP)*
Luis Paz III *(Sr VP)*

Division (Domestic):

**Marsh Risk & Insurance
Services** **(3)**
777 S Figueroa St Ste 2200, Los Angeles,
CA 90017-5820
Tel.: (213) 624-5555
Web Site: http://www.marsh.com
Rev.: $47,000,000
Emp.: 375
Insurance Brokers
N.A.I.C.S.: 524298

Subsidiary (Domestic):

Marsh Saldana Inc. **(3)**
City View Plz Ste 700 48 Rd 165 Km 1-2,
Guaynabo, PR 00968
Tel.: (787) 721-2600
Web Site: http://www.marshsaldana.com
Sales Range: $25-49.9 Million
Insurance Services
N.A.I.C.S.: 524210

Branch (Domestic):

Marsh USA Inc. - Alabama **(3)**
1500 Urban Center Dr, Birmingham, AL
35242
Tel.: (205) 262-2300
Web Site: http://www.marsh.com
Insurance & Risk Management Services
N.A.I.C.S.: 524210

Marsh USA Inc. - Alaska **(3)**
1031 W 4th Ave Ste 400, Anchorage, AK
99501
Tel.: (907) 276-5617
Web Site: http://www.marsh.com
Sales Range: $10-24.9 Million
Emp.: 60
Insurance & Risk Management Services
N.A.I.C.S.: 524210

Marsh USA Inc. - Connecticut **(3)**
20 Church St, Hartford, CT 06103
Tel.: (860) 723-5600
Web Site: http://www.marsh.com
Sales Range: $1-9.9 Million
Emp.: 30
Insurance & Risk Management Services
N.A.I.C.S.: 524210

Marsh USA Inc. - Idaho **(3)**
225 N 9th St, Boise, ID 83702
Tel.: (208) 342-6573
Web Site: http://www.marsh.com
Sales Range: $1-9.9 Million
Emp.: 35
Insurance & Risk Management Services
N.A.I.C.S.: 524210

Marsh USA Inc. - Illinois **(3)**
540 W Madison St, Chicago, IL 60661
Tel.: (312) 627-6000
Web Site: http://www.marsh.com
Sales Range: $100-124.9 Million
Emp.: 700
Insurance & Risk Management Services
N.A.I.C.S.: 524210

Marsh USA Inc. - Indiana **(3)**
111 Monument Cir Fl 43, Indianapolis, IN
46204
Tel.: (317) 261-9300
Web Site: http://www.marsh.com

Sales Range: $1-9.9 Million
Emp.: 50
Insurance & Risk Management Services
N.A.I.C.S.: 524210

Marsh USA Inc. - Kentucky **(3)**
260 Crossfield Dr Ste 1, Versailles, KY
40383
Tel.: (859) 879-0278
Web Site: http://www.marsh.com
Sales Range: Less than $1 Million
Emp.: 4
Insurance & Risk Management Services
N.A.I.C.S.: 524210

Marsh USA Inc. - Michigan **(3)**
200 Ottawa Ave Ste 700, Grand Rapids, MI
49503
Tel.: (616) 233-4200
Web Site: http://www.marsh.com
Sales Range: $100-124.9 Million
Emp.: 30
Insurance & Risk Management Services
N.A.I.C.S.: 524210

Marsh USA Inc. - Nevada **(3)**
7251 W Lk Mead Blvd Ste 401, Las Vegas,
NV 89128-8351
Tel.: (702) 804-7200
Web Site: http://www.marsh.com
Rev.: $6,300,000
Emp.: 150
Insurance Services
N.A.I.C.S.: 524210

Marsh USA Inc. - Pennsylvania **(3)**
Two Logan Sq, Philadelphia, PA 19103-
2797
Tel.: (215) 246-1000
Web Site: http://www.marsh.com
Sales Range: $50-74.9 Million
Emp.: 200
Insurance & Risk Management Services
N.A.I.C.S.: 524210

Marsh USA Inc. - Tennessee **(3)**
1000 Ridgeway Loop Rd, Memphis, TN
38120-4045
Tel.: (901) 761-1550
Web Site: http://www.marsh.com
Sales Range: $75-99.9 Million
Emp.: 282
Risk Management Consulting & Insurance
Services
N.A.I.C.S.: 524210

Marsh USA Inc. - Texas **(3)**
500 Dallas St Ste 1500, Houston, TX 77002
Tel.: (713) 276-8000
Web Site: http://www.marsh.com
Sales Range: $75-99.9 Million
Emp.: 250
Insurance Services
N.A.I.C.S.: 524210

Marsh USA Inc. - Utah **(3)**
15 W S Temple, Salt Lake City, UT 84101
Tel.: (801) 533-3600
Web Site: http://www.marsh.com
Sales Range: $1-9.9 Million
Emp.: 35
Insurance & Risk Management Services
N.A.I.C.S.: 524210

Marsh USA Inc. - Virginia **(3)**
1051 E Cary St Ste 900, Richmond, VA
23219-4044
Tel.: (212) 345-7000
Web Site: http://www.marsh.com
Sales Range: $10-24.9 Million
Emp.: 300
Insurance & Risk Management Services
N.A.I.C.S.: 524210

**Marsh USA Inc. - Washington,
D.C.** **(3)**
1050 Connecticut Ave NW Ste 700, Wash-
ington, DC 20036
Tel.: (202) 263-7600
Web Site: http://www.marsh.com
Rev.: $500,000
Emp.: 300
Security Brokers
N.A.I.C.S.: 523910

Division (Domestic):

Marsh Wortham **(3)**
1717 Main St Ste 4400, Dallas, TX 75201
Tel.: (214) 303-8000
Web Site: http://wortham.marsh.com

Business Support Services
N.A.I.C.S.: 561499

Subsidiary (Domestic):

John L. Wortham & Son LLP (4)
2727 Allen Pkwy 24th Fl, Houston, TX
77019
Tel.: (713) 526-3366
Web Site: http://www.jwortham.com
Rev.: $48,341,000
Emp.: 250
Insurance Agents, Brokers & Service
N.A.I.C.S.: 524210
Scott Howard (Mng Dir)

Subsidiary (Domestic):

**Second Opinion Insurance
Services** (3)
20750 Ventura Blvd Ste 300, Woodland
Hills, CA 91364
Tel.: (818) 348-3775
Sales Range: $75-99.9 Million
Insurance Services
N.A.I.C.S.: 524210

Subsidiary (Non-US):

Marsh d.o.o. Beograd (2)
Omladinskih Brigada 88b, 11070, Belgrade,
Serbia
Tel.: (381) 113130409
Web Site: https://www.marsh.com
Iindustry-focused Consulting, Brokerage &
Claims Advocacy Services
N.A.I.C.S.: 524210

**Marsh d.o.o. za posredovanje u
osiguranju** (2)
Ul grada Vukovara 271, Zagreb, Croatia
Tel.: (385) 16060400
Web Site: http://www.marsh.com
Sales Range: Less than $1 Million
Insurance & Risk Management Services
N.A.I.C.S.: 524210

Marsh s.r.o. (2)
Vinohradska 2828/151, 130 00, Prague,
Czech Republic
Tel.: (420) 221418111
Web Site: https://www.marsh.com
Sales Range: $1-9.9 Million
Insurance & Risk Management Services
N.A.I.C.S.: 524210
Petr Bany (Mng Dir & Head-Comml & Sls)
Marek Kalbac (Sr Mgr-Client Relationship
Mgmt)
Artur Grzeskowiak (CEO & Interim & Head-
North Sub-Reg)

**Marsh, S.A. Mediadores de
Seguros** (2)
Paseo de la castellana n 216, 28046, Ma-
drid, Spain
Tel.: (34) 914569400
Web Site: https://www.marsh.com
Sales Range: $100-124.9 Million
Insurance & Risk Management Services
N.A.I.C.S.: 524210
Alvaro Milans del Bosch (CEO)

PT. Marsh Indonesia (2)
World Trade Center 3 16-17 Floor Jl Jen-
deral Sudirman Kavling 29-31, Jl Asia Afrika
8, Jakarta, 12920, Indonesia
Tel.: (62) 2157978100
Web Site: https://www.marsh.com
Sales Range: $100-124.9 Million
Insurance & Risk Management Services
N.A.I.C.S.: 524210

Subsidiary (Domestic):

**Victor O. Schinnerer & Company,
Inc.** (2)
2 Wisconsin Cir Ste 1100, Chevy Chase,
MD 20815-7003 (100%)
Tel.: (301) 961-9800
Web Site: http://www.schinnerer.com
Sales Range: $100-124.9 Million
Emp.: 300
Insurance Underwriting Services
N.A.I.C.S.: 541611

Branch (Domestic):

**Victor O. Schinnerer & Company,
Inc.** (3)

160 Spears St Ste 1620, San Francisco,
CA 94105
Tel.: (301) 961-9800
Web Site: http://www.schinnerer.com
Sales Range: Less than $1 Million
Emp.: 18
Insurance Services
N.A.I.C.S.: 524210

**Marsh Insurance Brokers (Malaysia)
Sdn Bhd**
Level 42-01 West Wing Q Sentral 2A Jalan
Stesen Sentral 2, Kuala Lumpur Sentral,
50470, Kuala Lumpur, Malaysia
Tel.: (60) 40652825
Web Site: https://asia.marsh.com
Sales Range: $50-74.9 Million
Emp.: 80
Insurance & Risk Management Services
N.A.I.C.S.: 524298
C. B. Lim (Chief Client Officer)
Chou Sean Chong (CEO)

**Marsh Insurance and Reinsurance
Brokers LLC** (1)
45A Khagani Street 3rd floor Landmark II,
Baku, AZ1010, Azerbaijan
Tel.: (994) 124659920
Web Site: https://www.marsh.com
Sales Range: $25-49.9 Million
Insurance Services
N.A.I.C.S.: 524298

**Marsh International Holdings,
Inc.** (1)
125 Broad St Ste 38, New York, NY 10004
Tel.: (212) 345-5000
Web Site: http://www.marsh.com
Insurance Services
N.A.I.C.S.: 524210
Flavio Piccolomini (Pres)

Subsidiary (Non-US):

**Marsh India Insurance Brokers Pvt.
Limited** (2)
1201-02 Tower 2 One World Center Plot-
841, Jupiter Textile Compound Mills Sena-
pati Bapat Marg Elphinstone Road W,
Mumbai, 400 013, India (92%)
Tel.: (91) 2266512900
Web Site: http://www.marsh.co.in
Sales Range: $100-124.9 Million
Insurance & Risk Management Services
N.A.I.C.S.: 524210

Marsh Investment B.V. (1)
Conradstraat 18, Groot Handelsgebouw E5
167, Rotterdam, 3013AP, Netherlands
Tel.: (31) 10 4060600
Web Site: http://www.marsh.com
Insurance Services
N.A.I.C.S.: 524298
David Sanderse (CEO)

Marsh Israel (Holdings) Ltd. (1)
12 A Abba Hillel Street, Ramat Gan,
5250606, Israel
Tel.: (972) 36383030
Web Site: http://usa.marsh.com
Sales Range: $25-49.9 Million
Emp.: 30
Investment Services
N.A.I.C.S.: 523999

Marsh Israel Consultants Ltd. (1)
12 A Abba Hillel St, Ramat Gan, 52506,
Israel
Tel.: (972) 3 6383030
Web Site: http://www.marsh.com
Sales Range: $25-49.9 Million
Insurance Services
N.A.I.C.S.: 524298
Elad Nave (Mng Dir & Head-Country)

Marsh JCS Inc. (1)
65 Broadway 21st Fl, New York, NY 10006
Tel.: (212) 709-3360
Web Site: http://www.cosmosame.com
General Insurance Services
N.A.I.C.S.: 524210

Marsh Korea, Inc. (1)
38F Three IFC 10 Gukjegeumyung-ro,
Yeongdeungpo-gu, Seoul, 07326, Korea
(South)
Tel.: (82) 220959394
Web Site: https://www.marsh.com
Reinsurance Services
N.A.I.C.S.: 524130

Marsh Korea, Inc. (1)
38F Three IFC 10 Gukjegeumyung-ro,
Yeongdeungpo-gu, Seoul, Korea (South)
Tel.: (82) 220959394
Web Site: https://www.marsh.com
Insurance Management Services
N.A.I.C.S.: 524298
HyungKoo Lee (CEO)

Marsh LLC (1)
1166 Ave of the Americas, New York, NY
10036
Tel.: (212) 345-5000
Web Site: http://www.marsh.com
Insurance Brokerage Services
N.A.I.C.S.: 524210
Keith Walsh (CFO)
Keith Walsh (CFO)
John Q. Doyle (Pres & CEO)
Liz Cole (Chief Human Resources Officer)
Mark Drummond Brady (Vice Chm)
Patricia Hagemann (Chief Admin Officer)
Louis Piliego (COO)
Lucy Clarke (Pres)
Flavia Piccolomini (Pres-International)
Martin South (Pres & CEO)
Katherine Brennan (Gen Cousel)
Linda Foppiano (Chief HR Officer)
John Jones (Chief Mktg & Comm Officer)
Keith Walsh (CFO)
Katherine Brennan (Gen Cousel)
Linda Foppiano (Chief HR Officer)
John Jones (Chief Mktg & Comm Officer)
Keith Walsh (CFO)

Marsh Limited (1)
Ground Floor MDC House Glyn Jones
Road, Blantyre, Malawi
Tel.: (265) 1820044
Web Site: http://www.marsh.com
Emp.: 19
Insurance Management Services
N.A.I.C.S.: 524298

**Marsh Lorant Agente de Seguros y
de Fianzas, S.A. de C.V.** (1)
Av Parque Chapultepec 56 Floor 4 Col The
Park, 53398, Naucalpan, Estado de Mexico,
Mexico
Tel.: (52) 5590000000
Web Site: http://lorant.marsh.com
Insurance Broking Services
N.A.I.C.S.: 524210

Marsh Ltd. (1)
1166 Ave of Americas, New York, NY 10036
Tel.: (212) 345-5000
Web Site: https://www.marsh.com
Insurance Services
N.A.I.C.S.: 524298

**Marsh Management Services (Dubai)
Limited** (1)
Dubai International Financial Centre Level
5, PO Box 506770, Office 01 B Precinct
Building 2, Dubai, United Arab Emirates
Tel.: (971) 45080403
Web Site: http://www.marsh.com
Emp.: 14
Management Consulting Services
N.A.I.C.S.: 541611

**Marsh Management Services (Dublin)
Limited** (1)
4th Floor 25-28 Adelaide Road, Dublin, 2,
Ireland
Tel.: (353) 16048100
Emp.: 40
Management Consulting Services
N.A.I.C.S.: 541611
Ian Clancy (Office Head)

**Marsh Management Services
(Labuan) Limited** (1)
Whitepark House White Park Road St Mi-
chael, Barbados, Bridgetown, Malaysia
Tel.: (60) 87417672
Sales Range: $25-49.9 Million
Emp.: 1
Management Services
N.A.I.C.S.: 327910
Nazri Wong (Mgr-Insurance)

**Marsh Management Services
Inc.** (1)
PO Box 530, Burlington, VT 05402
Tel.: (802) 864-5599
Insurance Management Services
N.A.I.C.S.: 524298

**Marsh Management Services Isle of
Man Limited** (1)
1st Floor Goldie House 1-4 Goldie Terrace
Upper Church Street, PO Box 305, Doug-
las, IM1 1EB, Isle of Man
Tel.: (44) 1624630500
Web Site: http://www.marsh.com
Sales Range: $25-49.9 Million
Emp.: 15
Insurance Services
N.A.I.C.S.: 524298
Derek Patience (Head-Office)

**Marsh Management Services Malta
Limited** (1)
The Hedge Business Center - Level 3 Triq
ir-Rampa Ta San Giljan, Balluta Bay, Saint
Julian's, STJ 1062, Malta
Tel.: (356) 23423000
Insurance Services
N.A.I.C.S.: 524298
William Thomas-Ferrand (Sr VP)

**Marsh Management Services Swe-
den AB** (1)
Torsgatan 26, S-113 21, Stockholm, Swe-
den
Tel.: (46) 84124200
Web Site: http://www.marsh.se
Insurance Services
N.A.I.C.S.: 524298

Marsh Marine & Energy AB (1)
Stora Nygatan 29, Box 3047, 400 10, Goth-
enburg, Sweden
Tel.: (46) 317550300
Marine & Energy Services
N.A.I.C.S.: 488320
Bengt Anderson (Mgr)

Marsh Marine Nederland B.V. (1)
Conradstraat 18 Groot Handelsgebouw E5
167, 3013 AP, Rotterdam, Netherlands
Tel.: (31) 104060600
Web Site: http://www.nederland.marsh.com
Emp.: 300
Insurance Brokerage Services
N.A.I.C.S.: 524210
Focke Dorhoutmees (CEO)

Marsh Medical Consulting GmbH (1)
Bismarckstrasse 2, 32756, Detmold, Ger-
many
Tel.: (49) 5231308190
Emp.: 10
Insurance Brokerage Services
N.A.I.C.S.: 524210
Ingo Gurcke (Gen Mgr)

**Marsh Mercer Holdings (Australia)
Pty Ltd** (1)
Darling Park Tower 3 201 Sussex St, Syd-
ney, 2000, NSW, Australia
Tel.: (61) 288648888
Emp.: 2,400
Financial Services
N.A.I.C.S.: 551112

Marsh Oman LLC (1)
220 Hatat House Mina Al Fahal-116, PO
Box 197, Muscat, Oman
Tel.: (968) 24659001
Web Site: https://www.marsh.com
Insurance Management Services
N.A.I.C.S.: 524298

Marsh Oy (1)
Keilaranta 10 E, 02150, Espoo, Finland
Tel.: (358) 986774200
Web Site: https://www.marsh.com
Sales Range: $25-49.9 Million
Insurance Services
N.A.I.C.S.: 524298

**Marsh Private Client Life Insurance
Services** (1)
20750 Ventura Blvd Ste 300, Woodland
Hills, CA 91364
Tel.: (949) 224-8400
Web Site: http://www.marsh.com
Insurance Services
N.A.I.C.S.: 524298
Martin South (Pres-US & Canada Div)

Marsh Resolutions Pty Limited (1)
One International Towers Sydney 100 Ba-
rangaroo Avenue, Barangaroo, 2000, NSW,
Australia
Tel.: (61) 288648888
Web Site: http://www.australia.marsh.com

Marsh & McLennan Companies, Inc.—(Continued)
Emp.: 650
Insurance Brokerage Services
N.A.I.C.S.: 524210
Stephen Brough *(Sr VP & Gen Mgr-Reg)*

Marsh Risk Consulting Limitada **(1)**
Paseo de la Castellana 216, 28046, Madrid, Spain
Tel.: (34) 914569400
Web Site: http://www.marsh.es
Sales Range: $100-124.9 Million
Emp.: 30
Insurance Services
N.A.I.C.S.: 524298

Marsh Risk Consulting, S.L. **(1)**
Po Castellana 216, 28046, Madrid, Spain
Tel.: (34) 914569400
Insurance Services
N.A.I.C.S.: 524298

Marsh S.A.S. **(1)**
Tour Ariane, La Defense, 92088, Paris, Cedex, France
Tel.: (33) 141345000
Web Site: https://www.marsh.com
Insurance Management Services
N.A.I.C.S.: 524298

Marsh SA **(1)**
Plaza Independencia 721 P 7, Montevideo, Uruguay
Tel.: (598) 29021135
Insurance Agency & Brokerage Services
N.A.I.C.S.: 524210

Marsh SA **(1)**
5-7 rue Leon Laval, 3372, Leudelange, Luxembourg
Tel.: (352) 495238
Web Site: https://www.marsh.com
Insurance Management Services
N.A.I.C.S.: 524298

Marsh Saudi Arabia Insurance & Reinsurance Brokers **(1)**
Al Morouj Tower 7th Floor Olaya Street North, Riyadh, 11583, Saudi Arabia
Tel.: (966) 114347500
Insurance Brokerage Services
N.A.I.C.S.: 524210

Marsh Services Spolka z.o.o. **(1)**
Aleje Jerozolimskie 98, 00-807, Warsaw, Poland
Tel.: (48) 224564200
Web Site: https://marshservices.pl
Reinsurance Services
N.A.I.C.S.: 524130

Marsh Treasury Services (Dublin) Limited **(1)**
5th Floor 25/28 Adelaide Road, Dublin, Ireland
Tel.: (353) 16053000
Treasury Management Services
N.A.I.C.S.: 921130

Marsh Uganda Limited **(1)**
UAP Nakawa Business Park Block A 3rd Floor Plot 3-5 Portbell Road, PO Box 24712, Kampala, 3190, Uganda
Tel.: (256) 312302851
Insurance Management Services
N.A.I.C.S.: 524298

Marsh Zambia Limited **(1)**
Kwacha Pension House 2nd Floor Corner Tito Church Roads Rhodes Park, PO Box 34139, Fairview, Lusaka, Zambia
Tel.: (260) 211374889
Insurance Management Services
N.A.I.C.S.: 524298

Marsh, Lda. **(1)**
Apartado 1373, PO Box 1072, EC Arroios, 1001-000, Lisbon, Portugal
Tel.: (351) 213113700
Web Site: https://www.marsh.com
Insurance Management Services
N.A.I.C.S.: 524298

Matthiessen Assurans AB **(1)**
Last Makar Gatan 22, 11489, Stockholm, Sweden
Tel.: (46) 08 613 02 00
Web Site: http://www.matthiessen.com

Sales Range: $75-99.9 Million
Emp.: 250
Insurance Services
N.A.I.C.S.: 524298

Mercer (China) Limited **(1)**
Youhao Mansion Room 712-715 Youhao Road 15B, Dalian, 116001, China
Tel.: (86) 41182530280
Reinsurance Services
N.A.I.C.S.: 524130

Mercer Consulting Group, Inc. **(1)**
1166 Avenue of the Americas, New York, NY 10036
Tel.: (212) 345-7000
Web Site: http://www.mercer.us
Financial Services
N.A.I.C.S.: 523999

Mercer Consulting, S.L.U. **(1)**
Puerta Europa Paseo de la Castellana 216, 28046, Madrid, Spain
Tel.: (34) 914569400
Web Site: http://www.mercer.es
Insurance Agency & Brokerage Services
N.A.I.C.S.: 524210

Mercer Health & Benefits (Singapore) Pte. Ltd. **(1)**
8 Marina View No 09 08 Asia Square Tower 1, Singapore, 018960, Singapore
Tel.: (65) 63982800
Web Site: https://www.mercer.com.sg
Insurance Agency & Brokerage Services
N.A.I.C.S.: 524210

Mercer LLC **(1)**
1166 6th Ave, New York, NY 10036 **(100%)**
Tel.: (212) 345-7000
Web Site: https://www.mercer.com
Emp.: 25,000
Human Resource Consulting Services
N.A.I.C.S.: 541612
Patrick Tomlinson *(Pres & CEO)*
David Anderson *(Chief Comml Officer)*
Ilya Bonic *(Pres-Career & Head-Mercer Strategy)*
Bala Viswanathan *(COO)*
Rich Nuzum *(Pres-Investments & Retirement Bus)*
Gail Evans *(Chief Digital Officer-Global)*
Achim Luder *(Chief HR Officer)*
Pat Tomlinson *(Pres)*
Rian Miller *(VP & Gen Counsel)*
Mark Elliott *(CFO)*
Herve Balzano *(Pres-Health & Pres-)*
Rian Miller *(VP & Gen Counsel)*
Mark Elliott *(CFO)*
Herve Balzano *(Pres-)*
Nina Chen-Langenmayr *(Partner-Client Relationship Mgmt Gp)*

Subsidiary (Non-US):

Cardano Risk Management Ltd **(2)**
6 Bevis Marks 9th Floor, EC3A 7BA, London, United Kingdom - England
Tel.: (44) 2031705910
Web Site: http://www.cardano.co.uk
Investment Company
N.A.I.C.S.: 523999
Kerrin Rosenberg *(CEO)*
Harold Naus *(CEO-Cardano NL)*

Subsidiary (Domestic):

NOW: Pensions Ltd. **(3)**
3rd Floor 164 Bishopsgate, London, EC2M 4LX, United Kingdom
Tel.: (44) 333 33 222 22
Web Site: http://www.nowpensions.com
Pension Fund Management Services
N.A.I.C.S.: 525110
Charlotte Obahiagbon *(Head-Fin-Nottingham)*
Troy Clutterbuck *(Interim CEO)*
Nigel Waterson *(Chm)*

Subsidiary (Non-US):

Mercer **(2)**
Charlotte House Charlemont St, Dublin, Ireland
Tel.: (353) 16039700
Web Site: http://www.mercer.com
Sales Range: $125-149.9 Million
Emp.: 500
Human Resource Consulting Services

N.A.I.C.S.: 541612

Mercer (Argentina) S.A. **(2)**
Av Cordoba 111 Floor 16, C1054AAA, Buenos Aires, Argentina
Tel.: (54) 91140000900
Sales Range: $75-99.9 Million
Human Resource Consulting Services
N.A.I.C.S.: 541612
Daniel Nadborny *(CEO-Chile)*

Mercer (Australia) Pty Ltd **(2)**
One International Towers Sydney 100 Barangaroo Avenue, Sydney, 2000, NSW, Australia
Tel.: (61) 288646800
Web Site: http://www.mercer.com.au
Consulting Services
N.A.I.C.S.: 541611
Ben Walsh *(CEO & Mng Dir)*
David Bryant *(CEO)*
Tim Barber *(Head)*

Subsidiary (Domestic):

Advance Asset Management Limited **(3)**
Level 5 182 George Street, 2000, Sydney, NSW, Australia **(100%)**
Tel.: (61) 894155655
Web Site: http://www.advance.com.au
Open-End Investment Funds
N.A.I.C.S.: 525910

Subsidiary (Non-US):

Mercer (Austria) GmbH **(2)**
Handelskai 94-96, 1200, Vienna, Austria
Tel.: (43) 15339766
Web Site: https://www.mercer.at
Business Consulting Services
N.A.I.C.S.: 541611

Mercer (Belgium) SA-NV **(2)**
Avenue Herrmann-Debrouxlaan 2, Vorstlaan 24, 1160, Brussels, Belgium
Tel.: (32) 26748911
Web Site: http://www.mercer.be
Insurance Services
N.A.I.C.S.: 524298

Mercer (Canada) Limited **(2)**
120 Bremner Boulevard Suite 800, Toronto, M5J 0A8, ON, Canada
Tel.: (416) 868-2000
Web Site: http://www.mercer.ca
Insurance Services
N.A.I.C.S.: 524298
Jaqui Parchment *(CEO)*
Brian Goldslager *(Dir-Fin)*
Susannah Crabtree *(Partner)*
Angelita Graham *(Partner)*
Kevin Hendershot *(Partner)*

Mercer (Colombia) Ltda. **(2)**
Avenida el Dorado 69B - 45 Piso 9, Bogota, Colombia
Tel.: (57) 6015146300
Reinsurance Services
N.A.I.C.S.: 524130

Mercer (Czech) a.s. **(2)**
Trianon Building Budejovicka 1518 13b, 14000, Prague, Czech Republic
Tel.: (420) 277 003 151
Web Site: http://www.mercer.com
Sales Range: $25-49.9 Million
Emp.: 20
Insurance Services
N.A.I.C.S.: 524298

Mercer (Danmark) A/S **(2)**
Teknikerbyen 1 2, 2830, Virum, Denmark
Tel.: (45) 45959668
Web Site: https://www.mercer.dk
Consulting Services
N.A.I.C.S.: 541611

Mercer (France) SAS **(2)**
Tour Ariane La Defense 9, La Defense, 92088, Paris, Cedex, France
Tel.: (33) 155213500
Web Site: https://www.mercer.fr
Consulting Services
N.A.I.C.S.: 541611

Mercer (Hong Kong) Limited **(2)**
28/F Devon House Taikoo Place 979 Kings Road, 18 Harbour Rd, Quarry Bay, China (Hong Kong)
Tel.: (852) 34763800

Web Site: https://www.mercer.com.hk
Sales Range: $25-49.9 Million
Consulting Services
N.A.I.C.S.: 541611

Mercer (Ireland) Limited **(2)**
Charlotte House Charlemont St, Dublin, 2, Ireland
Tel.: (353) 16039700
Web Site: http://www.mercer.ie
Consulting Services
N.A.I.C.S.: 541611

Mercer (Malaysia) Sdn. Bhd. **(2)**
Level 42-01 West Wing Q Sentral No 2A Jalan Stesen Sentral 2, 50470, Kuala Lumpur, Malaysia
Tel.: (60) 323028575
Web Site: http://www.mercer.com
Consulting Investment Services
N.A.I.C.S.: 541611

Mercer (N.Z.) Limited **(2)**
Level 11 PwC Tower 15 Customs Street, West Auckland Central, Auckland, 1010, New Zealand
Tel.: (64) 99843500
Web Site: http://www.mercer.co.nz
Consulting Services
N.A.I.C.S.: 541611

Mercer (Nederland) B.V. **(2)**
Startbaan 6, 1185 XR, Amstelveen, Netherlands
Tel.: (31) 204313700
Reinsurance Services
N.A.I.C.S.: 524130

Mercer (Nederland) B.V. **(2)**
Startbaan 6, 1185 XR, Amstelveen, Netherlands
Tel.: (31) 20 431 3700
Web Site: https://www.mercer.nl
Insurance Management Services
N.A.I.C.S.: 524298

Mercer (Norge) AS **(2)**
Karenslyst Alle 20, 0123, Oslo, Norway
Tel.: (47) 21011000
Web Site: https://www.mercer.no
Consulting Services
N.A.I.C.S.: 541611

Mercer (Polska) Sp.z o.o. **(2)**
Al Jerozolimskie 98, 00-807, Warsaw, Poland
Tel.: (48) 224564020
Web Site: https://www.mercer.com.pl
Sales Range: $50-74.9 Million
Consulting Services
N.A.I.C.S.: 541611

Mercer (Portugal) Lda **(2)**
Hua Antonio Pedro n 111, 1150-045, Lisbon, Portugal
Tel.: (351) 213113770
Reinsurance Services
N.A.I.C.S.: 524130

Mercer (Portugal) Lda **(2)**
Rua Antonio Pedro 111, Lisbon, 1150-045, Portugal
Tel.: (351) 213113770
Web Site: http://www.mercer.pt
Emp.: 250
Insurance Management Services
N.A.I.C.S.: 524298

Mercer (Singapore) Pte Ltd **(2)**
8 Marina View 09-08 Asia Square Tower 1, Singapore, 018960, Singapore
Tel.: (65) 63982800
Consulting Services
N.A.I.C.S.: 541611
Kulshaan Singh *(Head-Sls-Asia & IMETA)*
Davin Wong *(CEO)*
Anubhav Bhushan *(CEO)*

Mercer (Sweden) AB **(2)**
Torsgatan 22, 113 21, Stockholm, Sweden
Tel.: (46) 850530800
Web Site: https://se.mercer.com
Consulting Services
N.A.I.C.S.: 541611

Mercer (Switzerland) SA **(2)**
Tessinerplatz 5, 8027, Zurich, Switzerland
Tel.: (41) 44200450
Reinsurance Services
N.A.I.C.S.: 524130

Mercer (Switzerland) SA (2)
Tessinerplatz 5, 8027, Zurich, Switzerland
Tel.: (41) 442004500
Web Site: https://www.mercer.ch
Insurance Management Services
N.A.I.C.S.: 524298

Mercer (Taiwan) Ltd. (2)
4F No 2 Sec 3, Minquan East Road, Taipei,
10059, Taiwan
Tel.: (886) 221837900
Web Site: https://www.mercer.com.tw
Consulting Services
N.A.I.C.S.: 541611

Mercer (Thailand) Ltd. (2)
Q House Lumpini Building 11th Floor Rm
1102, 1 South Sathorn Road Tungmahamek
Sathorn, Bangkok, 10120, Thailand
Tel.: (66) 26268300
Web Site: http://www.mercer.com
Business Consultancy Services
N.A.I.C.S.: 541618

Subsidiary (Domestic):

Mercer (US) Inc. (2)
1166 Avenue of the Americas, New York,
NY 10036-2708
Tel.: (212) 345-7000
Web Site: http://www.mercer.com
Sales Range: $1-4.9 Billion
Emp.: 500
Human Resource Consulting Services
N.A.I.C.S.: 541612

Subsidiary (Domestic):

CPSG Partners LLC (3)
1717 Main St, Dallas, TX 75201-4612
Tel.: (214) 220-3500
Web Site: http://www.cpsgpartners.com
Sales Range: $10-24.9 Million
Emp.: 200
Information Technology Consulting Services
N.A.I.C.S.: 541519
Rohit Mehrotra *(Founder)*

Mercer Health & Benefits Administration LLC (3)
800 W Main St 1250, Boise, ID 83702
Tel.: (208) 342-6573
Insurance Management Services
N.A.I.C.S.: 524298

Mercer Health & Benefits LLC (3)
601 W Main Ste 810, Spokane, WA 99201
Tel.: (509) 358-3900
Web Site: http://www.mercer.com
Emp.: 14
Insurance Management Services
N.A.I.C.S.: 524298
Amy Robbins *(Principal)*

Mercer Human Resource Consulting of Kentucky, Inc. (3)
400 W Market St Ste 700, Louisville, KY
40202
Tel.: (502) 561-4500
Web Site: http://www.mercer.com
Sales Range: $150-199.9 Million
Human Resource Consulting Services
N.A.I.C.S.: 541612

Mercer Human Resource Consulting of Massachusetts, Inc. (3)
99 High St, Boston, MA 02110
Tel.: (617) 747-9500
Web Site: http://www.mercerhr.com
Sales Range: $10-24.9 Million
Emp.: 50
Human Resource Consulting Services
N.A.I.C.S.: 541612

Mercer Human Resource Consulting of Texas, Inc. (3)
Bank 1 Ctr 1717 Main St Ste 4400, Dallas,
TX 75201
Tel.: (972) 720-2000
Web Site: http://www.mercer.com
Sales Range: $75-99.9 Million
Emp.: 500
Human Resource Management Services
N.A.I.C.S.: 541612

Mercer Human Resource Consulting of Virginia, Inc. (3)
1051 E Cary St Ste 900, Richmond, VA
23219
Tel.: (804) 344-2600

Web Site: http://www.mercer.com
Sales Range: $75-99.9 Million
Human Resource Consulting Services
N.A.I.C.S.: 541612

Mercer Investment Consulting, Inc. (3)
1166 Avenue of the Americas, New York,
NY 10036
Tel.: (212) 345-7000
Investment Management Service
N.A.I.C.S.: 523940

Mercer Investment Management, Inc. (3)
99 High St, Boston, MA 02110
Tel.: (617) 747-9500
Investment Management Service
N.A.I.C.S.: 523940

Sirota Consulting LLC (3)
1 Manhattanville Rd Ste 202, Purchase, NY
10577-2100
Tel.: (914) 696-4700
Web Site: http://www.sirota.com
General Management Consulting Services
N.A.I.C.S.: 541611

Subsidiary (Non-US):

Mercer Benefit Services Pty Ltd (2)
727 Collins Street, Melbourne, 3008, VIC,
Australia
Tel.: (61) 396235555
Human Resource Consulting Services
N.A.I.C.S.: 541611

Mercer Certificering B.V. (2)
Startbaan 6, 1185 XR, Amstelveen, Netherlands
Tel.: (31) 20 4313700
Web Site: http://www.mercer.nl
Emp.: 20
Consulting Services
N.A.I.C.S.: 541611

Mercer Consulting (Australia) Pty Ltd (2)
727 Collins Street, Docklands, Melbourne,
3008, VIC, Australia
Tel.: (61) 396235555
Web Site: http://www.mercer.com.au
Management Consulting Services
N.A.I.C.S.: 541611

Mercer Consulting (Chile) Ltda. (2)
Avenida Americo Vespucio Sur 100 Piso 3
Building 302 Floor 4, Las Condes, Santiago, Chile
Tel.: (56) 24206000
Web Site: http://www.mercer.com
Emp.: 100
Human Resource Consulting Services
N.A.I.C.S.: 541612

Mercer Consulting (China) Ltd. (2)
Rm 3601 Hong Kong New World Tower,
300 Huaihai Zhong Rd, Shanghai, 200021,
China
Tel.: (86) 21 6335 3358
Human Resource Consulting Services
N.A.I.C.S.: 541611

Mercer Consulting (France) SAS (2)
Tour Ariane La Defense 9, 92800, Puteaux,
Cedex, France
Tel.: (33) 155213500
Consulting Services
N.A.I.C.S.: 541611

Mercer Consulting (India) Private Ltd. (2)
Unit No C-401 4th Floor Tower C1 The Millennia No 1 & 2, Murphy Road Ulsoor, Bengaluru, 560008, Karnataka, India
Tel.: (91) 80 41857700
Web Site: http://www.mercer.co.in
Human Resource Consulting Services
N.A.I.C.S.: 541611
Pradeep Mukerjee *(CEO)*

Mercer Consulting B.V. (2)
Startbaan 6, 1185 XR, Amstelveen, Netherlands
Tel.: (31) 204313700
Web Site: http://www.mercer.nl
Management Consulting Services
N.A.I.C.S.: 541611
David Sanderse *(CEO)*

Mercer Consulting Limited (2)

120 Bremner Blvd Ste 800, PO Box 501,
Toronto, M5J 0A8, ON, Canada
Tel.: (416) 868-2000
Web Site: http://www.mercer.ca
Sales Range: $200-249.9 Million
Employee Benefits & Compensation Consulting Services
N.A.I.C.S.: 541612

Mercer Corredores de Seguros Ltda. (2)
Los Militares 4611 Offices 5th & 6th Comuna, Las Condes, 7550000, Santiago,
Chile
Tel.: (56) 229292300
Emp.: 50
Human Resource Consulting Services
N.A.I.C.S.: 541612

Mercer Deutschland GmbH (2)
Platz der Einheit 1, 60327, Frankfurt, Germany
Tel.: (49) 6897780
Web Site: https://www.mercer.com
Sales Range: $25-49.9 Million
Human Resource Consulting Services
N.A.I.C.S.: 541612

Mercer Employee Benefits - Mediacao de Seguros, Lda. (2)
Edificio Monumental Av Fontes Pereira de
Melo 51-3 A-E, 1050-120, Lisbon, Portugal
Tel.: (351) 213113775
Web Site: http://www.mercer.com
Emp.: 12
Consulting Services
N.A.I.C.S.: 541611
Tiago Pimentel *(Mgr-Marketing)*

Mercer Employee Benefits Limited (2)
G1 Building 5 George Square, Glasgow, G2
1AR, United Kingdom
Tel.: (44) 1412485511
Web Site: http://www.uk.mercer.com
Investment Services
N.A.I.C.S.: 523150

Mercer Employee Benefits OY (2)
Keilaranta 10, 2150, Espoo, Finland
Tel.: (358) 9 8677 4300
Web Site: http://www.Mercer.fi
Consulting Services
N.A.I.C.S.: 541611

Mercer Financial Advice (Australia) Pty Ltd (2)
Level 6 225 St Georges Tce, Perth, 6000,
WA, Australia
Tel.: (61) 892893700
Financial Advisory Services
N.A.I.C.S.: 523940

Mercer Finland (2)
Keilaranta 10, 02150, Espoo, Finland
Tel.: (358) 986774300
Web Site: https://www.mercer.com
Sales Range: $10-24.9 Million
Human Resource Consulting Services
N.A.I.C.S.: 541612

Mercer Human Resource Consulting (2)
Maya Akar Center Buyukdere Cad No 100 -
102 Kat 2, Esentepe, 34394, Istanbul, Turkiye
Tel.: (90) 2123554593
Web Site: http://www.mercer.com
Human Resource Consulting Services
N.A.I.C.S.: 541612

Mercer Human Resource Consulting (S) Pte Ltd (2)
8 Marina View 09-08 Asia Square Tower 1,
Singapore, 018960, Singapore
Tel.: (65) 63982800
Web Site: https://www.asean.mercer.com
Sales Range: $10-24.9 Million
Emp.: 50
Human Resource Consulting Services
N.A.I.C.S.: 541612

Mercer Human Resource Consulting A/S (2)
Teknikerbyen 1 2, 2830, Virum, Denmark
Tel.: (45) 45959668
Human Resource Consulting Services
N.A.I.C.S.: 541612

Mercer Human Resource Consulting AS (2)

Karenslyst Alle 20, Oslo, 0278, Norway
Tel.: (47) 21011000
Web Site: http://www.mercer.com
Human Resource Consulting Services
N.A.I.C.S.: 541612

Mercer Human Resource Consulting GmbH (2)
Handelskae 94-96, 1200, Vienna, Austria
Tel.: (43) 15339766
Web Site: http://www.mercer.com
Sales Range: $25-49.9 Million
Emp.: 12
Human Resource Consulting Services
N.A.I.C.S.: 813311

Mercer Human Resource Consulting Limited (2)
1 Tower Place West, Tower Place, London,
EC3R 5BU, United Kingdom
Tel.: (44) 2076266000
Web Site: http://www.mercer.com
Sales Range: $200-249.9 Million
Emp.: 300
Human Resource Consulting Services
N.A.I.C.S.: 541612

Mercer Human Resource Consulting Ltd. (2)
4F No 2 Sec 3 Minquan East Road, Taipei,
10059, Taiwan
Tel.: (886) 221837900
Web Site: http://www.mercer.com
Sales Range: $10-24.9 Million
Emp.: 40
Human Resource Consulting Services
N.A.I.C.S.: 561311

Mercer Human Resource Consulting Ltda (2)
Avenida Americo Vespucio Sur 100 Fl 4,
Las Condes, Santiago, 7550188, Chile
Tel.: (56) 24206000
Web Site: http://www.mercer.cl
Sales Range: $25-49.9 Million
Emp.: 130
Human Resource Consulting Services
N.A.I.C.S.: 541612

Mercer Human Resource Consulting Pty Ltd (2)
727 Collins St, Melbourne, 3000, VIC, Australia
Tel.: (61) 392455555
Sales Range: $125-149.9 Million
Emp.: 900
Human Resource Consulting Services
N.A.I.C.S.: 541612

Mercer Human Resource Consulting S.A. (2)
Tour Ariane La Defense 9, 92088, Paris,
Cedex, France (100%)
Tel.: (33) 155213500
Web Site: http://www.mercerhr.com
Sales Range: $450-499.9 Million
Human Resource Consulting Services
N.A.I.C.S.: 541612

Mercer Human Resource Consulting S.A. de C.V. (2)
Paseo de la Reforma 505 Torre Mayor
Floors 11 - 12, Cuauhtemoc, Mexico, Distrito Federal, Mexico
Tel.: (52) 5596287300
Emp.: 260
Human Resource Consulting Services
N.A.I.C.S.: 541612

Mercer Human Resource Consulting SA (2)
Rue Francois Perreard 22, Geneva, CH-
1225, Switzerland
Tel.: (41) 228693000
Web Site: http://www.mercer.com
Sales Range: $10-24.9 Million
Emp.: 50
Human Resource Consulting Services
N.A.I.C.S.: 541612

Mercer Human Resource Consulting Srl (2)
Viale Bodio 33, 20158, Milan, Italy
Tel.: (39) 02 724131
Web Site: http://www.mercer.com
Sales Range: $75-99.9 Million
Human Resource Consulting Services
N.A.I.C.S.: 561311

Mercer Human Resource Consulting and Insurance Brokers Limited (2)

Marsh & McLennan Companies, Inc.—(Continued)

Futo St 47 53, 1082, Budapest, Hungary
Tel.: (36) 18882100
Web Site: http://www.mercerhr.com
Sales Range: $75-99.9 Million
Human Resource Consulting Services
N.A.I.C.S.: 541612

Mercer Human Resource Consulting, S.L. (2)
Paseo de la Castellana 216, 28046, Madrid, Spain
Tel.: (34) 914569400
Web Site: http://www.mercerhr.es
Sales Range: $25-49.9 Million
Emp.: 150
Human Resource Consulting Services
N.A.I.C.S.: 561311

Mercer India Private Limited (2)
13th UF Raheja Tower M G Road, Bengaluru, 560 001, India
Tel.: (91) 8041857700
Reinsurance Services
N.A.I.C.S.: 524130

Mercer Investments (Korea) Co., Ltd. (2)
27th Floor West Center Center 1 Building 67, Suha-dong Jung-gu, Seoul, 100 210, Korea (South)
Tel.: (82) 260308753
Investment Management Service
N.A.I.C.S.: 523940

Mercer Italia Srl (2)
Via Montebello 2, Bologna, Italy
Tel.: (39) 0510500830
Reinsurance Services
N.A.I.C.S.: 524130

Mercer Italia Srl (2)
Viale Bodio 33, Milan, Italy
Tel.: (39) 02724131
Insurance Management Services
N.A.I.C.S.: 524298

Mercer Japan Ltd (2)
9-7-1 Akasaka Midtown Tower, Minato-ku, Tokyo, 107-6216, Japan
Tel.: (81) 367756500
Reinsurance Services
N.A.I.C.S.: 524130

Mercer Japan Ltd. (2)
9-7-1 Akasaka Midtown Tower, Minato-ku, Tokyo, 107-6216, Japan
Tel.: (81) 367756500
Web Site: http://www.mercer.co.jp
Asset Management Services
N.A.I.C.S.: 531390

Mercer Korea Co. Ltd. (2)
38F Three IFC 10 Gukjegeumyung-ro, Yeongdeungpo-gu, Seoul, 07326, Korea (South)
Tel.: (82) 220958100
Reinsurance Services
N.A.I.C.S.: 524130

Mercer LLC (2)
9-7-1 Akasaka Midtown Tower, Minato-ku, Tokyo, 107-6216, Japan
Tel.: (81) 367756500
Web Site: http://www.mercer.co.jp
Sales Range: $50-74.9 Million
Emp.: 160
Human Resource Consulting Services
N.A.I.C.S.: 541612

Mercer Limited (2)
Four Brindley Place, Birmingham, B1 2JQ United Kingdom
Tel.: (44) 1216313343
Reinsurance Services
N.A.I.C.S.: 524130

Mercer Philippines, Inc. (2)
Six/NEO Building 5th Ave Corner 26th Street, Bonifacio Global City, Taguig, 1634, Philippines
Tel.: (63) 279023000
Reinsurance Services
N.A.I.C.S.: 524130

Mercer Philippines, Inc. (2)
20th Floor Six/NEO Building 26th Street, Bonifacio Global City, Taguig, 1634, Philippines
Tel.: (63) 29023000

Insurance Management Services
N.A.I.C.S.: 524298

Mercer Sigorta Brokerligi Anonim Sirketi (2)
Maya Akar Center Buyukdere Cad No 100 - 102 Kat 2, 34394, Esentepe, Istanbul, Turkiye
Tel.: (90) 2123554593
Web Site: http://www.mercer.com
Insurance Management Services
N.A.I.C.S.: 524298

Mercer Superannuation (Australia) Limited (2)
727 Collins St, Docklands, Melbourne, 3001, VIC, Australia
Tel.: (61) 396235555
Investment Management Service
N.A.I.C.S.: 523940

Mercer Treuhand GmbH (2)
Lyoner Str 36, 60528, Frankfurt, Hessen, Germany
Tel.: (49) 696897780
Insurance Management Services
N.A.I.C.S.: 524298

Mercer, Agente de Seguros, S.A. de C.V. (2)
Avenida Paseo de La Reforma 505 Piso 11 Y 12, Cuauhtemoc, 06500, Mexico, Mexico
Tel.: (52) 5559991900
Insurance Management Services
N.A.I.C.S.: 524298

Thomsons Online Benefits Ltd. (2)
Gordon House 10 Greencoat Place, London, SW1P 1PH, United Kingdom
Tel.: (44) 2033284000
Web Site: http://www.thomsons.com
Benefits Administration Services
N.A.I.C.S.: 923130
Pete Craghill *(CTO)*
Chris Bruce *(Co-Founder & Mng Dir)*
Stephen Read *(CEO)*
Tina Shah *(CFO)*
Chris Nowell *(COO)*
Matt Cockett *(Chief Comml Officer)*
James Akers *(Dir-Product Mgmt)*
Jonathan Day *(Dir-Enterprise Consulting)*

Mercer Lestisharat Alamal LP (1)
Level 6 Building 2 Karadsheh Tower Mecca Street, PO Box 3898, 13C, Amman, 11821, Jordan
Tel.: (962) 65528382
Financial Consulting Services
N.A.I.C.S.: 523940

Mercer Private Markets AG (1)
Tessinerplatz 5, 8027, Zurich, Switzerland
Tel.: (41) 44200450
Web Site:
http://www.mercerprivatemarkets.com
Investment Funding Services
N.A.I.C.S.: 525910
Christoph Bigger *(CEO)*
Benjamin Baumann *(CIO)*
Peter Zollinger *(Head-Legal & Compliance)*

Mercer South Africa (Pty) Ltd. (1)
Marsh Building 1 Entrance 1 11 Alice Lane Precinct, Sandton, South Africa
Tel.: (27) 110607393
Reinsurance Services
N.A.I.C.S.: 524130

Moola Systems Limited (1)
The St Botolph Building 138 Houndsditch, London, EC3A 7AW, United Kingdom
Tel.: (44) 3308083258
Web Site: http://www.moo.la
Financial Investment Services
N.A.I.C.S.: 523999

NetComp Insurance Corp. (1)
1333 Main St Ste 600, Columbia, SC 29201-3262
Tel.: (803) 454-6800
Web Site:
http://www.netcompinsurance.com
Insurance Service Provider
N.A.I.C.S.: 524128

OWL Marine Insurance-Brokers GmbH & Co. KG (1)
Neuer Dovenhof Brandstwiete 1, 20457, Hamburg, Germany
Tel.: (49) 40376920

Web Site: https://www.owl-marine.com
Insurance Brokerage Services
N.A.I.C.S.: 524210
Henrik Oel *(Mng Dir)*
Nicolas Wolff *(Mng Dir)*
Ulf Lixfeld *(Mng Dir)*

Oliver Wyman (Hong Kong) Limited (1)
Level 34 Unit 01 Central Plaza 18 Harbor Road, Wanchai, China (Hong Kong)
Tel.: (852) 22011700
Management Consulting Services
N.A.I.C.S.: 541611

Oliver Wyman (Pty) Ltd. (1)
Cnr 5th Street and Fredman Drive Building 1 Entrance 1 Alice Lane, Sandton, 2196, Johannesburg, South Africa
Tel.: (27) 110607100
Management Consulting Services
N.A.I.C.S.: 541618

Oliver Wyman Consulting (Shanghai) Ltd (1)
Room 3708 10 The Center 989 Changle Rd, Xuhui District, Shanghai, 200031, China
Tel.: (86) 2180369300
Management Consulting Services
N.A.I.C.S.: 541611
Hunter Williams *(Partner)*

Oliver Wyman Limited Liability Company (1)
1 Filellinon & Othonos Street, 10557, Athens, Greece
Tel.: (30) 2128090100
Reinsurance Services
N.A.I.C.S.: 524130

Oliver Wyman S.A.S. (1)
Av El Dorado No 69B - 45 piso 10, Bogota, Colombia
Tel.: (57) 14269999
Management Consulting Services
N.A.I.C.S.: 541618

Oliver Wyman SAS (1)
1 Rue Euler, 75008, Paris, France
Tel.: (33) 145023000
Management Consulting Services
N.A.I.C.S.: 541611

Oliver Wyman, Inc. (1)
1166 Avenue of the Americas, New York, NY 10036-2708
Tel.: (212) 345-8000
Web Site: http://www.oliverwyman.com
Sales Range: $50-74.9 Million
Management Consulting Services
N.A.I.C.S.: 541611
Simon Harris *(Chief Strategy Officer)*
Scott McDonald *(Pres & CEO)*
Nicola Dingemans *(Chief Human Capital Officer)*
Paula McGlarry *(Gen Counsel)*
Terry Stone *(Mng Partner)*
Abhimanyu Bhuchar *(Head--South East Asia, Energy, Asia Pacific)*
Margarita Economides *(Principal)*
Andreas Niehaus *(Partner)*
Claire Negiar *(Mgr-Engagement)*
Christian Edelmann *(Partner & Head-Europe)*
Rafa Asensio *(Partner & Head-Comm, Media, and Tech-Global)*
Martin Schulte *(Partner-Retail & Consumer Products)*
Vadim Kosin *(Partner)*
Martina Weimert *(Partner-Fin Svcs Practice-European)*
Xavier Nougues *(Partner & Head-Value Sourcing-Global)*
Ana Carla Abrao Costa *(Partner-Fin, Risk, and Pub Policy)*
Alban Pyanet *(Principal-Fin Svcs)*
Ted Moynihan *(Mng Partner & Head-Fin Svcs-Global)*
Shivani Shah *(Principal-Health & Life Sciences)*
David Gillespie *(Partner & Head-UK & Ireland)*
Beatriz Lacave *(Partner)*
Saahil Malik *(Partner-Communications-Media-Technology)*
Amanda Evison *(Partner-)*
Vivian Meker *(Partner-Financial Services)*
Abdulkarim Alyousef *(Partner-)*
Dan Jones *(Partner-)*

Antonio Pimentel *(Principal)*
Mark Kremers *(Partner)*
Alex Shutter *(Partner-Retail & Consumer Goods)*
Christine Oumansour *(Partner)*
Jacob Hook *(Partner & Head-)*
Wei Ying Cheah *(Partner)*
Hang Qian *(Partner-Fin)*
Aarti Nihalani *(Partner)*
Andrea Federico *(Partner)*
Claudia Wang *(Partner)*
Andrew Chien *(Partner)*
Kristina Gerteiser *(Partner)*
Xingyu Wu *(Sr Mgr)*
Elizabeth Hoyler *(Mgr-)*
Chip Greene *(Partner-)*
Raji Souag *(Partner)*
Heinz Pley *(Partner)*
Randall Sargent *(Principal)*
Tim Hoyland *(Partner & Head--America)*
Dylan Walsh *(Partner & Head--Global)*
Ilya Khaykin *(Partner & Head--America)*
Varun Ratta *(Partner)*
Tony Simpson *(Partner)*
Ken Aso *(Partner)*
Sumati Sharma *(Partner)*
Rebecca Emerson *(Partner)*
Thomas Fritz *(Partner)*
Rupal Kantaria *(Partner)*
Ethan Murray *(Partner)*
Karina Swette *(Partner)*
Patrick Daoust *(Partner)*
Chaitra Chandrasekhar *(Partner)*
Ilana Hechter *(Partner)*
Srinath Rengarajan *(Head--Global)*
Jill Labbadia *(Principal)*

Subsidiary (Domestic):

Avascent Group (2)
1615 L St NW Ste 1200, Washington, DC 20036
Tel.: (202) 452-6990
Web Site: https://www.avascent.com
Sales Range: $10-24.9 Million
Emp.: 95
Business Consulting Services
N.A.I.C.S.: 541611
Steve Irwin *(Pres)*
Douglas Berenson *(Mng Dir)*
Timothy R. Garnett *(Mng Dir)*
Jay Korman *(Mng Dir)*
Mark Shields *(Partner)*
Timothy Wickham *(Mng Dir)*
Timothy S. Stanos *(Mng Dir)*
James Tinsley *(Mng Dir)*
Stephen Ganote *(Mng Dir)*
Aleksandar Jovovic *(Principal)*
Joshua Pavluk *(Principal)*
James Thompson *(Principal)*
Matt Caris *(Principal)*
Vanda de la Mata *(Principal)*
Stephen Ganyard *(Principal)*
Rachel Jenkins *(Principal)*
Christopher Meissner *(Principal)*
Mimi Shieh *(Chief HR Officer)*
Brian Sweeney *(Principal)*

Subsidiary (Domestic):

Formtek, Inc. (3)
2190 Meridian Park Blvd Ste G, Concord, CA 94520
Tel.: (925) 459-0482
Web Site: http://www.formtek.com
Sales Range: $10-24.9 Million
Emp.: 25
IT Infrastructure Management Solutions for Content Management Systems
N.A.I.C.S.: 541512
Dennis M. Scanlon *(Pres & COO)*
Gary D. Mann *(Chm & CEO)*
Dick Weisinger *(VP)*
Victor Malespina *(VP-Bus Dev)*

Division (Domestic):

CAVOK (2)
720 Whitley Rd, Keller, TX 76248
Tel.: (817) 380-2817
Web Site: http://www.cavokgroup.com
Aviation Industry Technical Support & Consulting Services
N.A.I.C.S.: 541990
Tom Cooper *(VP)*
David Marcontell *(Sr VP & Gen Mgr)*
Mary Zobrak *(VP)*
Oksana Bardygula *(VP)*
Steve Douglas *(VP)*
Scott Whittaker *(VP-)*

Lippincott (2)
499 Park Ave, New York, NY 10022-1240
Tel.: (212) 521-0000
Web Site: http://www.lippincott.com
Sales Range: $25-49.9 Million
Emp.: 110
Corporate Identity & Communication Consulting Services
N.A.I.C.S.: 541820
Connie Birdsall (Sr Partner & Dir-Creative-Global)
Rodney Abbot (Sr Partner-Design)
Michael D'Esopo (Sr Partner & Dir-Brand Strategy)
Stefan Fillip (Sr Partner & Dir-Asia Pacific)
Simon Glynn (Sr Partner)
Richard Wilke (Sr Partner)
Rick Wise (CEO)
Dylan Stuart (Sr Partner--San Francisco)
Tim Cunningham (Sr Partner-Brand Strategy & Dir-West)
Heather Stern (CMO)
Fabian Diaz (Sr Partner-Innovation)
Allen Gove (Sr Partner--Boston)
Adam Stringer (Partner-Design)
Alissa Tribelli (Partner--New York)
Amit Sabharwal (Sr Partner-Brand Strategy)
Daniel Johnston (Partner--New York)
David Stein (Sr Partner-Brand Strategy)
Erika Rosenberg (Partner-Administrative Services)
James Yamada (Partner-Innovation)
Jenifer Lehker (Partner--New York)
Mark Scragg (Partner-Design-London)
Nital Patel (Sr Partner--New York)
Rose Baki (Sr Partner--New York)
Vincenzo Perri (Partner & Creative Dir-Asia)
Wendy Tsang (Partner-)
Cory Cruser (Sr Partner-Innovation-London)
George Bigden (Partner-Brand Strategy-London)
Dan Clay (Partner-Innovation)
Sean Doh (Sr Partner--Seoul)
Jim Forsyth (Partner-Fin)
Bogdan Geana (Partner-Design)
Liz Greene (Partner-Brand Strategy)
Michael Guerin (Partner-Design)
Emily Guilmette (Partner-Brand Strategy)
Taddy Hall (Sr Partner-Innovation)
Jake Hancock (Sr Partner--Boston)
Graham Harvey (Sr Partner--Hong Kong)
Shelby Hawker (Sr Partner-Brand Strategy)
Aline Kim (Partner--San Francisco)
Greg Handrick (Sr Partner & Dir-)
Vilmundur Sveinsson (Sr Dir--London)
Winston Thomas (Partner)
Bethany Lesko (Partner-Design)
Alicia Chiu (Sr Dir--Hong Kong)
Chris Pross (Sr Dir-)
James Atkins (Sr Dir-)
Helen Chow (Partner-)
Emma Cofer (Partner-)
Siobhan Cooper (Partner-Strategy)
Justin D'Onofrio (Sr Dir-)
Katie Danon (Dir-Human Capital)
Aurelio Saiz (Partner-)
Lizzie Harris (Partner-)
Tyler Holden (Partner-)
Jung Kwon (Sr Dir-)
Ben Le (Partner-)
Jessica Lee (Sr Dir-)
Rui Maekawa (Sr Dir-)
David Pianin (Partner-)
Brian Rosenberg (Partner-)
Jennifer Rosenbloom (Partner-)
Mario Samayoa (Partner-Business Development)
Alexandra Samet (Partner-)
Clemens Schrenk (Partner-)
Jeroen Sikma (Sr Dir-)
Melissa Tait (Partner-Engineering)
Pascale Tam (Partner-)
Hannah Viviano (Dir-)
James Atkins (Sr Dir-)
Helen Chow (Partner-)
Emma Cofer (Partner-)
Siobhan Cooper (Partner-Strategy)
Justin D'Onofrio (Sr Dir-)
Katie Danon (Dir-Human Capital)
Aurelio Saiz (Partner-)
Lizzie Harris (Partner-)
Tyler Holden (Partner-)
Jung Kwon (Sr Dir-)
Ben Le (Partner-)
Jessica Lee (Sr Dir-)
Rui Maekawa (Sr Dir-)
David Pianin (Partner-)
Brian Rosenberg (Partner-)

Jennifer Rosenbloom (Partner-)
Mario Samayoa (Partner-Business Development)
Alexandra Samet (Partner-)
Clemens Schrenk (Partner-)
Jeroen Sikma (Sr Dir-)
Melissa Tait (Partner-Engineering)
Pascale Tam (Partner-)
Hannah Viviano (Dir-)
Graham Garvie (Partner)
Louise Cantrill (Partner)
Renee Jung (Partner)
Alex Paine (Partner)
Julius Roberge (Partner)
Harriet Scheiner (Partner)
Eric Tsytsylin (Partner)
Dan Vasconcelos (Partner)
Gardenia Willoughby (Partner)

Subsidiary (Domestic):

Lippincott - San Francisco (3)
577 2nd St Ste 200, San Francisco, CA 94107
Tel.: (415) 597-9930
Web Site: http://www.lippincott.com
Management Consulting Services
N.A.I.C.S.: 541611

Subsidiary (Domestic):

National Economic Research Associates, Inc. (2)
360 Hamilton Ave 10 Fl, White Plains, NY 10601
Tel.: (914) 448-4000
Web Site: http://www.nera.com
Sales Range: $100-124.9 Million
Economic Consulting
N.A.I.C.S.: 611710
Lawrence Wu (Pres-San Francisco)

Subsidiary (Non-US):

NERA Australia Pty Limited (3)
One International Towers, 100 Barangaroo Avenue, Sydney, 2000, NSW, Australia
Tel.: (61) 288646500
Web Site: http://www.nera.com
Economic Analysis & Research Services
N.A.I.C.S.: 541611
James Mellsop (Mng Dir)

Subsidiary (Domestic):

NERA Economic Consulting (3)
360 Hamilton Ave, White Plains, NY 10606
Tel.: (914) 448-4000
Web Site: http://www.nera.com
Emp.: 70
Economic Consulting Services
N.A.I.C.S.: 541618
Vinita Juneja (Mng Dir-New York City)
Lauren Stiroh (Mng Dir)
Lawrence Wu (Pres)
Graeme Hunter (Mng Dir-New York City)
Richard Marsden (Mng Dir-New York City)
Christine Siegwarth Meyer (Mng Dir)
Sandra Ringelstetter Ennis (Mng Dir & COO-Chicago)
Lucy P. Allen (Mng Dir)
Denise Neumann Martin (Mng Dir)
Ramsey Shehadeh (Mng Dir)
David Tabak (Mng Dir)
Ling Ling Ang (Assoc Dir)
Airat Chanyshev (Assoc Dir)
Drew Claxton (Assoc Dir)
Alan Grant (Assoc Dir)
Bryan Ray (Assoc Dir)
Sheng Li (Assoc Dir)

Subsidiary (Non-US):

NERA S.R.L. (3)
Viale di Villa Grazioli 23, 00198, Rome, Italy
Tel.: (39) 0696708200
Web Site: http://www.nera.com
Sales Range: $10-24.9 Million
Emp.: 10
Economic Analysis & Research Consulting Services
N.A.I.C.S.: 541611

NERA UK Limited (3)
Marble Arch House 66 Seymour Street, London, W1H 5BT, United Kingdom
Tel.: (44) 2076598500
Web Site: http://www.nera.com
Sales Range: $25-49.9 Million
Economic Analysis & Research Consulting Services

N.A.I.C.S.: 541611
Richard Hern (Mng Dir)

National Economic Research Associates KK (3)
The Imperial Hotel Tower 14F 1-1-1 Uchisaiwai-cho, Chiyoda-ku, Tokyo, 100-0011, Japan
Tel.: (81) 335003290
Web Site: http://www.nera.jp
Sales Range: $10-24.9 Million
Emp.: 7
Economic Analysis & Research Consulting Services
N.A.I.C.S.: 541611
Hiroaki Ishigaki (Mng Dir)
Hans-Martin Ihle (Assoc Dir)
Naoya Kaneko (Assoc Dir)
Yuko Saito (Assoc Dir)

Subsidiary (Non-US):

Oliver Wyman AB (2)
Birger Jarlsgatan 4, 114 34, Stockholm, Sweden
Tel.: (46) 854624070
Web Site: http://www.oliverwyman.com
Insurance Services
N.A.I.C.S.: 524298

Oliver Wyman AG (2)
Tessinerplatz 5, 8027, Zurich, Switzerland
Tel.: (41) 445533333
Web Site: https://www.oliverwyman.com
Sales Range: $10-24.9 Million
Management Consulting Services
N.A.I.C.S.: 541611
Joris D'Inca (Partner)

Subsidiary (Domestic):

Oliver Wyman Actuarial Consulting, Inc. (2)
1166 Ave of the Americas, New York, NY 10036-2708
Tel.: (212) 345-8900
Sales Range: $25-49.9 Million
Emp.: 100
Actuarial Consulting Services
N.A.I.C.S.: 541611

Subsidiary (Non-US):

Oliver Wyman Consulting Limited (2)
55 Baker St, London, W1U 8EW, United Kingdom
Tel.: (44) 2072355444
Web Site: http://www.oliverwyman.com
Sales Range: $75-99.9 Million
Emp.: 700
Management Consulting Services
N.A.I.C.S.: 541611

Oliver Wyman Consulting SARL (2)
1 Rue Euler, 75008, Paris, France (100%)
Tel.: (33) 145023000
Web Site: http://www.oliverwyman.com
Sales Range: $75-99.9 Million
Emp.: 200
Management Consulting Services
N.A.I.C.S.: 541611

Oliver Wyman Consulting SL (2)
Paseo de la Castellana 13, Madrid, 28046, Spain (100%)
Tel.: (34) 914328400
Web Site: http://www.oliverwyman.com
Sales Range: $10-24.9 Million
Emp.: 15
Management Consulting Services
N.A.I.C.S.: 541611
Pablo Tompos (Mng Dir)

Oliver Wyman Consultoria em Estrategia de Negocios Ltda. (2)
Street Architect Olavo Redig de Campos 105 EZ Tower, Tower B - 26th floor, Sao Paulo, 04711-904, Alto de Pinheiros, Brazil
Tel.: (55) 1138782000
Consulting Services
N.A.I.C.S.: 541618
Mariana Paes (Office Mgr)

Oliver Wyman Energy Consulting Limited (2)
55 Baker Street, London, W1U 8EW, United Kingdom
Tel.: (44) 2073338333
Web Site: http://www.oliverwyman.com

Management Consulting Services
N.A.I.C.S.: 541611

Oliver Wyman FZ-LLC (2)
Arjaan Offices 11th Floor, PO Box 500525, Dubai, United Arab Emirates
Tel.: (971) 44257000
Web Site: http://www.oliverwyman.com
Management Consulting
N.A.I.C.S.: 523150

Oliver Wyman Germany GmbH (2)
Friedrich Ebert Anlage 49, 60313, Frankfurt am Main, Germany (100%)
Tel.: (49) 699551200
Web Site: http://www.oliverwyman.com
Sales Range: $10-24.9 Million
Emp.: 70
Management Consulting Services
N.A.I.C.S.: 541611
Johan Peppel (Mng Dir)

Subsidiary (Domestic):

Oliver Wyman Consulting GmbH (3)
The Seven Office Mullerstrasse 3, Munich, 80469, Germany
Tel.: (49) 89939490
Web Site: http://www.oliverwyman.de
Management Consulting Services
N.A.I.C.S.: 541611

Subsidiary (Non-US):

Oliver Wyman GmbH (2)
The Seven Office Mullerstrasse 3, 80469, Munich, Germany
Tel.: (49) 89939490
Web Site: http://www.oliverwyman.de
Human Resource Consulting Services
N.A.I.C.S.: 541612

Oliver Wyman Group KK (2)
Midtown Tower 16F 9-7-1, Akasaka Minato-ku, Tokyo, 107-6216, Japan
Tel.: (81) 368717008
Web Site: http://www.oliverwyman.com
Management Consulting Services
N.A.I.C.S.: 541611

Oliver Wyman Limited (2)
120 Bremner Boulevard Suite 800, Toronto, M5J 0A8, ON, Canada (100%)
Tel.: (416) 868-2200
Web Site: http://www.oliverwyman.com
Sales Range: $25-49.9 Million
Management Consulting Services
N.A.I.C.S.: 541611

Oliver Wyman Ltd. (2)
22F Youngpoong Building 41 Cheonggyecheon-ro, Seoul, 03188, Jongno-gu, Korea (South)
Tel.: (82) 23995400
Investment Services
N.A.I.C.S.: 523150

Oliver Wyman Pte. Ltd. (2)
8 Marina View Asia Square Tower 1 09-07, Singapore, 018960, Singapore (100%)
Tel.: (65) 65109700
Sales Range: $10-24.9 Million
Management Consulting Services
N.A.I.C.S.: 541611

Oliver Wyman Pty. Ltd. (2)
1 International Towers Sydney 100 Barangaroo Avenue, Sydney, 2000, NSW, Australia
Tel.: (61) 288646555
Sales Range: $25-49.9 Million
Emp.: 25
Financial Services
N.A.I.C.S.: 541611

Oliver Wyman Pty. Ltd. (2)
1 International Tower 100 Brig Avenue, Sydney, 2000, Australia
Tel.: (61) 288646555
Management Consulting Services
N.A.I.C.S.: 541611

Oliver Wyman S.L. (2)
Paseo de la Castellana 216 Pl 13, 28046, Madrid, Spain
Tel.: (34) 915317900
Web Site: http://www.oliverwyman.es
Investment Services
N.A.I.C.S.: 523999

Oliver Wyman SNC (2)

Marsh & McLennan Companies, Inc.—(Continued)

1 rue Euler, 75008, Paris, France
Tel.: (33) 145023000
Web Site: http://www.oliverwyman.fr
Investment Services
N.A.I.C.S.: 523150

Oliver Wyman Sdn. Bhd. (2)
Level 42-01 West Wing Q Sentral 2A Jalan
Stesen Sentral 2 KL Sentral, 50470, Kuala
Lumpur, Malaysia
Tel.: (60) 323028488
Web Site: https://www.oliverwyman.com
Insurance Brokerage Services
N.A.I.C.S.: 524210

Oliver Wyman sp. z o.o. (2)
Nimbus Al Jerozolimskie 98, 00-807, War-
saw, Poland
Tel.: (48) 224564020
Web Site: http://www.oliverwyman.com
Insurance Brokerage Services
N.A.I.C.S.: 524210

Oliver Wyman, S. de R.L. de (2)
C.V.
Torre Mayor Paseo de la Reforma No 505,
Col Cuauhtemoc, 06500, Mexico, DF,
Mexico
Tel.: (52) 5596287500
Management Consulting Services
N.A.I.C.S.: 541611

Subsidiary (Domestic):

Veritas Total Solutions, LLC (2)
258 Cape Jasmine Ct, The Woodlands, TX
77381
Tel.: (281) 384-5650
Web Site: https://www.veritasts.com
General Management Consulting Services
N.A.I.C.S.: 541611
Matt Schuetz (Partner)
Delfina Govia (Partner)

Organizacion Brockman y Schuh S.A. (1)
de C.V.
Avenida Paseo de la Reforma 505 Piso 10,
Cuauhtemoc, 06500, Mexico, Mexico
Tel.: (52) 5559991900
Insurance Management Services
N.A.I.C.S.: 524298

Orizon Underwriters SL (1)
Calle Goya 29, 28001, Madrid, Spain
Tel.: (34) 919023299
Web Site: https://www.orizonunderwriters.es
Insurance Services
N.A.I.C.S.: 524210

PT Marsh Reinsurance Brokers (1)
Indonesia
World Trade Center 16-17 Floor Jalan Jen-
dral Sudirman Kavling 29-31, Tanah Abang,
Jakarta, 12920, Indonesia
Tel.: (62) 2157900110
Web Site: http://www.mmc.com
Insurance Brokerage Services
N.A.I.C.S.: 524210

PT Mercer Indonesia (1)
World Trade Center WTC 3 JI Gen
Sudirman Cav 29-31 Floor 16, Jalan Asia
Afrika No 8, Jakarta, 12920, Indonesia
Tel.: (62) 2129758000
Web Site: https://www.mercer.com
Emp.: 25
Insurance Services
N.A.I.C.S.: 524298

Peart Insurance Brokers Limited (1)
79 Stricklandgate, Kendal, LA9 4LT, United
Kingdom
Tel.: (44) 1539730666
Web Site: http://www.peart.co.uk
Insurance Brokerage Services
N.A.I.C.S.: 524210

Perils AG (1)
Marktgasse 3, 8001, Zurich, Switzerland
Tel.: (41) 442568100
Web Site: https://www.perils.org
Emp.: 4
Marketing Consulting Services
N.A.I.C.S.: 541613
Luzi Hitz (CEO)
Martin Bisping (Chm)
Sibylle Steimen (Chm)

Pillar Capital Management
Limited (1)

Chevron House 11 Church Street, PO Box
HM 2261, HM 11, Hamilton, Bermuda
Tel.: (441) 2788560
Web Site: https://www.pillar-capital.com
Investment Management Service
N.A.I.C.S.: 523940
Stephen A. Velotti (CEO & CIO)
Tara L. Railton (CFO & COO)
Jeff Franklin (Chief Underwriting Officer &
Chief Underwriting Officer)
Stewart Foster (Sr VP & Head-Catastrophe
Modeling)
Judith Howe Tucker (Sr VP-Operations)
Tom Cosenza (Chief Actuary)

Private Client Services by Mercer
China Limited (1)
R 5001 Hong Kong New World Tower No
300 Huaihai Zhong Road, Shanghai,
200021, China
Tel.: (86) 2160582000
Reinsurance Broking Services
N.A.I.C.S.: 524210

Private Client Services by Mercer
Limited (1)
28/F Devon House Taikoo Place 979 King's
Road, Quarry Bay, China (Hong Kong)
Tel.: (852) 28645333
Reinsurance Broking Services
N.A.I.C.S.: 524210

Private Client Services by Mercer
Pte. Ltd. (1)
8 Marina View 09-12 Asia Square Tower 1,
Singapore, 018960, Singapore
Tel.: (65) 63336311
Reinsurance Broking Services
N.A.I.C.S.: 524210

Private Client Services by Mercer
SA (1)
Dreikonigsstrasse 31a, 8002, Zurich, Swit-
zerland
Tel.: (41) 796015800
Web Site: https://www.mercer.com
Reinsurance Broking Services
N.A.I.C.S.: 524210

R. Mees & Zoonen Assuradeuren (1)
B.V.
Conradstraat 18 Groot Handelsgebouw E5
167, 3013 AP, Rotterdam, Netherlands
Tel.: (31) 104060030
Web Site: http://www.meesenzoonen.nl
Insurance Management Services
N.A.I.C.S.: 524298

RRB Beratungsgesellschaft fur Alters-
versorgung mbH (1)
Baedekerstrasse 5, 45128, Essen, Ger-
many
Tel.: (49) 20124517
Investment Services
N.A.I.C.S.: 523150

Renewable Energy Loss Adjusters
Limited (1)
3rd Floor 70 Gracechurch Street, London,
EC3V 0HR, United Kingdom
Tel.: (44) 2039687845
Web Site: http://www.re-lossadjusters.com
Insurance Claim Investigation Services
N.A.I.C.S.: 524291

Rivers Group Limited (1)
Garden Floor 16 Connaught Place, London,
W2 2ES, United Kingdom
Tel.: (44) 2074207000
Web Site: https://www.therivergroup.co.uk
Reinsurance Services
N.A.I.C.S.: 524130

SCM Strategic Capital Management
Asia Ltd (1)
3 F Three Pacific Place 1 Queen's Road
East, Hong Kong, China (Hong Kong)
Tel.: (852) 28556930
Investment Funding Services
N.A.I.C.S.: 525910

SME Insurance Services Limited (1)
1 Whitehall Quay Whitehall Road, Leeds,
LS1 4HR, West Yorkshire, United Kingdom
Tel.: (44) 3301620965
Web Site: https://www.smeinsurance.com
Insurance Agency & Brokerage Services
N.A.I.C.S.: 524210

Seabury & Smith, Inc. (1)

1255 23rd St NW Ste 400, Washington, DC
20037
Tel.: (202) 367-5035
Web Site:
http://www.brokerdealercoverage.com
Insurance Brokerage Services
N.A.I.C.S.: 524210

Sedgwick (Deutschland) GmbH (1)
Gladbecker Strasse 1, 40472, Dusseldorf,
Germany
Tel.: (49) 21154014237
Reinsurance Services
N.A.I.C.S.: 524130

Sedgwick Internationaal B.V. (1)
Westerstraat 21, PO Box 23212, 3001 KE,
Rotterdam, Netherlands
Tel.: (31) 882866464
Web Site: http://www.sedgwick.com
Insurance Services
N.A.I.C.S.: 524298

Sedgwick Limited (1)
30 Fenchurch Street, London, EC3M 3BD,
United Kingdom
Tel.: (44) 3456049826
Reinsurance Services
N.A.I.C.S.: 524130

Sedgwick Noble Lowndes Group
Limited (1)
1 Tower Place West Tower Place, London,
EC3R 5BU, United Kingdom
Tel.: (44) 2073571000
Web Site: http://www.marsh.co.uk
Emp.: 1,000
Investment Management Service
N.A.I.C.S.: 523940

Sedgwick Pte Ltd (1)
30 Cecil Street Level 12 Prudential Tower,
Singapore, 049712, Singapore
Tel.: (65) 62232008
Reinsurance Services
N.A.I.C.S.: 524130

Shorewest Insurance Associates,
LLC (1)
17450 W N Ave, Brookfield, WI 53045-4365
Tel.: (262) 827-0200
Insurance Brokerage Services
N.A.I.C.S.: 524210

Sirota Asia Pacific Pte. Ltd. (1)
8 Marina View 09-08 Asia Square Tower 1,
Singapore, 18960, Singapore
Tel.: (65) 64071199
Web Site: http://www.sirota.com
Management Consulting Services
N.A.I.C.S.: 541618

Sirota Consulting UK Limited (1)
Premier House 15-19 Church Street West,
Woking, GU21 6DJ, Surrey, United King-
dom
Tel.: (44) 1483717980
Web Site: http://www.sirota.com
Management Consulting Services
N.A.I.C.S.: 541618

The Insurance Partnership Holdings
Limited (1)
Priory Park East, Hull, HU4 7DY, United
Kingdom
Tel.: (44) 1482213215
Holding Company
N.A.I.C.S.: 551112

The Schinnerer Group, Inc. (1)
2 Wisconsin Cir, Chevy Chase, MD 20815
Tel.: (301) 961-9800
Insurance Agencies Brokerages
N.A.I.C.S.: 524210
Christopher Schaper (CEO-Mng Gen Agent
Bus-Bermuda)

Thomas Rutherfoord Inc. (1)
1 S Jefferson St, Roanoke, VA 24011
Tel.: (540) 982-3511
Web Site: http://www.rutherfoord.com
Sales Range: $10-24.9 Million
Emp.: 300
Surety Insurance Bonding
N.A.I.C.S.: 524126

Torrent Government Contracting Ser-
vices, LLC (1)
8400 Corporate Dr Ste 350, Hyattsville, MD
20785
Tel.: (301) 577-4104

Insurance Brokerage Services
N.A.I.C.S.: 524210

Torrent Technologies, Inc. (1)
165 Timberwolf Pkwy, Kalispell, MT 59901
Web Site: https://www.torrentcorp.com
Management Consulting Services
N.A.I.C.S.: 541618
Mel Hodges (VP-Compliance)
Tanya Astle (Sr VP-Ops)
Dianne Peterson (Sr VP-Ops)
Mark Damico (COO)

UAD BB Marsh Lietuva (1)
Olimpieciu st 1 -56, 09235, Vilnius, Lithu-
ania
Tel.: (370) 61613048
Web Site: https://www.marsh.com
Insurance Management Services
N.A.I.C.S.: 524298

Vezina Assurances Inc. (1)
4374 avenue Pierre-De Coubertin, Mon-
treal, H1V 1A6, QC, Canada
Tel.: (514) 253-5221
Web Site: http://www.vezinainc.com
Insurance Agency & Brokerage Services
N.A.I.C.S.: 524210
Stephane Massie (Co-Pres & CEO)
Pierre Vezina (Chm, Co-Pres & CEO-Sls &
Mktg)

Victor Deutschland GmbH (1)
Hohenzollernring 79-83, 50672, Cologne,
Germany
Tel.: (49) 22196750200
Web Site: https://www.victordeutschland.de
Reinsurance Services
N.A.I.C.S.: 524130

Victor Insurance Europe B.V. (1)
Conradstraat 18 Groot Handelsgebouw E5
167, 3013 AP, Rotterdam, Netherlands
Tel.: (31) 104060030
Web Site: https://victorinsurance.nl
Management Consulting Services
N.A.I.C.S.: 541618
Fred Willemze (Mng Dir)

Victor Insurance Italia S.r.l. (1)
Via Calabria 31, 20158, Milan, Italy
Tel.: (39) 0248538714
Web Site: https://victorinsurance.it
Management Consulting Services
N.A.I.C.S.: 541618

Victor Insurance Managers Inc. (1)
7700 Wisconsin Ave Ste 400, Bethesda,
MD 20814
Tel.: (301) 961-9800
Web Site:
https://www.victorinsuranceus.com
Disability Insurance Services
N.A.I.C.S.: 524126
Brian Cropp (Mgr-Bus Dev)
Richard Turner (Head-Intl)
Anthony Stevens (Pres-International)
Brian Hanuschak (Pres)
Brian Pierce (Chief Underwriting Officer)
Bill Balderston (Head-Sales-Distribution)
Jillian Glover (Head-Marketing)
Frank DiCicca (Head-Information Technol-
ogy)
Brian Hanuschak (Pres)
Brian Pierce (Chief Underwriting Officer)
Bill Balderston (Head-Sales-Distribution)
Jillian Glover (Head-Marketing)
Frank DiCicca (Head-Information Technol-
ogy)

Wellnz Limited (1)
Level 11 PwC Tower 15 Customs Street
West, Auckland, 1010, New Zealand
Tel.: (64) 93090502
Web Site: https://www.wellnz.co.nz
Compensation Insurance Services
N.A.I.C.S.: 525190
Kath Lynch (Gen Mgr-Ops)
Fergus Rolston (Mgr)
Lorraine Siemsen (Branch Mgr)
Denise Stuart (Project Mgr)

MARTEN TRANSPORT, LTD.
129 Marten St, Mondovi, WI 54755
Tel.: (715) 214-2110   DE
Web Site: https://www.marten.com
Year Founded: 1946
MRTN—(NASDAQ)
Rev.: $1,263,878,000

Assets: $965,679,000
Liabilities: $261,760,000
Net Worth: $703,919,000
Earnings: $110,354,000
Emp.: 4,575
Fiscal Year-end: 12/31/22
Time & Temperature-Sensitive Cargo
Carrier Services
N.A.I.C.S.: 484230
Randolph L. Marten *(Exec Chm)*
James J. Hinnendael *(CFO & Exec VP)*
Timothy M. Kohl *(CEO)*
Patrick J. Pazderka *(Sec)*
Doug Petit *(Pres)*
Adam D. Phillips *(COO & Exec VP)*

MARTI TECHNOLOGIES, INC.

2001 S St NW Ste 320, Washington, DC 20009
Tel.: (202) 866-0901   Ky
Web Site: https://www.marti.tech
Year Founded: 2021
MRT—(NYSEAMEX)
Rev.: $20,029,552
Assets: $40,211,169
Liabilities: $72,908,827
Net Worth: ($32,697,658)
Earnings: ($33,814,719)
Emp.: 553
Fiscal Year-end: 12/31/23
Transportation Services
N.A.I.C.S.: 488999
Cankut Durgun *(Co-Founder & Pres)*
Oguz Alper Oktem *(Co-Founder & CEO)*

Subsidiaries:

Marti Ileri Teknoloji A.S.   **(1)**
Maslak Mah Buyukdere Cad Noramin Is Merkezi Sitesi No 237 Ic Kapi No 5, Sariyer, Istanbul, Turkiye
Tel.: (90) 8503083419
Information Technology Services
N.A.I.C.S.: 541519

MARTIN MARIETTA MATERIALS, INC.

4123 Parklake Ave, Raleigh, NC 27612
Tel.: (919) 781-4550   NC
Web Site:
  https://www.martinmarietta.com
Year Founded: 1993
MLM—(NYSE)
Rev.: $6,777,200,000
Assets: $15,124,900,000
Liabilities: $7,089,300,000
Net Worth: $8,035,600,000
Earnings: $1,168,900,000
Emp.: 9,400
Fiscal Year-end: 12/31/23
Building Materials Distr
N.A.I.C.S.: 444180
C. Howard Nye *(Chm, Pres & CEO)*
Roselyn R. Bar *(Gen Counsel, Sec & Exec VP)*
James A. J. Nickolas *(CFO & Sr VP)*
John P. Mohr *(CIO & Sr VP)*
Robert J. Cardin *(Chief Acctg Officer, Sr VP & Controller)*

Subsidiaries:

Albert Frei & Sons Inc.   **(1)**
PO Box 700, Henderson, CO 80640
Tel.: (303) 289-1837
Web Site: http://www.albertfreiandsons.com
Sales Range: $10-24.9 Million
Emp.: 60
Construction Sand Mining
N.A.I.C.S.: 212321
Aaron Harrington *(Controller)*

Bluegrass Materials Company, LLC   **(1)**
200 W Forsyth St Ste 1200, Jacksonville, FL 32202
Tel.: (904) 701-6500

Aggregate Quarrying & Distr
N.A.I.C.S.: 212319

Guernsey Stone Company   **(1)**
49 Quarry Rd, Guernsey, WY 82214   **(100%)**
Tel.: (307) 836-2514
Sales Range: $50-74.9 Million
Emp.: 20
Crushed & Broken Granite Mining & Quarrying
N.A.I.C.S.: 212313

Martin Marietta Aggregates   **(1)**
6028 Triangle Dr, Raleigh, NC 27617   **(100%)**
Tel.: (919) 788-4392
Web Site: https://www.martinmarietta.com
Sales Range: $50-74.9 Million
Emp.: 300
Crushed Stone, Sand & Gravel
N.A.I.C.S.: 212313

Martin Marietta Magnesia Specialties, Inc.   **(1)**
8140 Corporate Dr Ste 220, Baltimore, MD 21236   **(100%)**
Tel.: (410) 780-5500
Web Site:
  https://www.magnesiaspecialties.com
Sales Range: $100-124.9 Million
Emp.: 325
Producer of Refractory Materials, Chemical Magnesia & Fuel Additives
N.A.I.C.S.: 327992
John Harman *(Pres)*
Douglas Bopst *(VP-Sls & Sls Mgr-Africa, Europe, Middle East & Russia)*

Martin Marietta Materials Southwest, Inc.   **(1)**
5710 W Hausman Rd Ste 121, San Antonio, TX 78249
Tel.: (210) 208-4400
Web Site: http://www.martinmarietta.com
Construction Materials Whslr
N.A.I.C.S.: 423320
Ron Kopplin *(Pres-East Div)*
Kirk Light *(Pres)*

Subsidiary (Domestic):

Alamo Gulf Coast Railroad Company   **(2)**
5710 W Hausman Rd Ste 121, San Antonio, TX 78249   **(99.5%)**
Tel.: (210) 696-8500
Sales Range: $25-49.9 Million
Emp.: 5
Construction Materials Supply Whslr
N.A.I.C.S.: 423320

Monroe Ready Mix   **(1)**
4919 Construction Ave, Monroe, LA 71203
Tel.: (318) 387-5831
Web Site: http://www.martinmarietta.com
Sales Range: $25-49.9 Million
Emp.: 35
Readymix Concrete Mfr
N.A.I.C.S.: 327320

Powderly Transportation, Inc.   **(1)**
2710 Wycliff Rd, Raleigh, NC 27607-3033
Tel.: (903) 732-3124
Freight Transportation Services
N.A.I.C.S.: 488999

Rock & Rail LLC   **(1)**
501 S 9th St, Canon City, CO 81212
Tel.: (719) 276-2042
Web Site: https://www.rockandrail.com
Railroad Operator
N.A.I.C.S.: 482111

St. Marys Sand Company, LLC   **(1)**
6700 Stokes Rd C R 3, Saint George, GA 31562
Tel.: (912) 843-2049
Building Materials Distr
N.A.I.C.S.: 444180

Texas Industries, Inc.   **(1)**
1503 Lyndon B Johnson Fwy Ste 400, Dallas, TX 75234-6007
Tel.: (972) 647-6700
Producer of Steel & Construction Materials, Including Cement, Aggregates & Concrete; Real Estate
N.A.I.C.S.: 324199

Subsidiary (Domestic):

Brookhollow Corporation   **(2)**
2710 Wycliff Rd, Raleigh, NC 27607-3033   **(100%)**
Tel.: (919) 781-4550
Holding Company; Real Estate Property
N.A.I.C.S.: 551112

Greenville Ready Mix   **(2)**
6500 N FM 1570 N, Greenville, TX 75402
Tel.: (903) 439-1500
Cement Whslr
N.A.I.C.S.: 423320
Jack Brown *(Mgr-Sls)*

Plant (Domestic):

Midlothian Cement Plant   **(2)**
610 Eastgate Rd, Midlothian, TX 76065-9645
Tel.: (254) 981-7795
Web Site: https://www.martinmarietta.com
Sales Range: $75-99.9 Million
Emp.: 200
Cement Mfr & Distr
N.A.I.C.S.: 327331

Subsidiary (Domestic):

TXI Riverside Inc.   **(2)**
1500 Rubidoux Blvd, Riverside, CA 92509   **(100%)**
Tel.: (951) 774-2500
Cement Mfr & Distr
N.A.I.C.S.: 327310

Tiller Corp.   **(1)**
7200 Hemlock Ln Ste 200, Maple Grove, MN 55369
Tel.: (763) 425-4191
Web Site: https://www.tillercorp.com
Emp.: 225
Construction Sand & Gravel Mining
N.A.I.C.S.: 212321
Matt Schulenberg *(Dir-Aggregate Sls)*
Todd Judge *(Mgr-Plant)*

MARTIN MIDSTREAM PARTNERS LP

Tel.: (903) 983-6200   DE
Web Site: https://www.mmlp.com
Year Founded: 2002
MMLP—(NASDAQ)
Rev.: $797,963,000
Assets: $509,375,000
Liabilities: $573,999,000
Net Worth: ($64,624,000)
Earnings: ($4,549,000)
Emp.: 1,619
Fiscal Year-end: 12/31/23
Petroleum Products & Fertilizers Mfr & Liquefied Petroleum Gas Transportation Services
N.A.I.C.S.: 457210
Sharon Taylor *(CFO)*
Melanie Mathews *(VP)*
Johnnie Murry *(Sr VP)*
William Posey *(VP)*
Scot Shoup *(Sr VP)*
Karen Yost *(VP)*
Matt Yost *(Sr VP)*
Ruben S. Martin III *(Chm)*

Subsidiaries:

Cardinal Gas Storage Partners LLC   **(1)**
Three Riverway Ste 1250, Houston, TX 77056
Tel.: (713) 350-2500
Web Site: http://www.cardinalgs.com
Sales Range: $25-49.9 Million
Emp.: 100
Natural Gas Storage & Consulting Services
N.A.I.C.S.: 457110

Martin Midstream Finance Corp   **(1)**
4200 B Stone Rd, Kilgore, TX 75662
Tel.: (903) 983-6200
Natural Gas Extraction Services
N.A.I.C.S.: 211130

Martin Operating Partnership L.P.   **(1)**
4200 Stone Rd, Kilgore, TX 75662

Tel.: (903) 983-6250
Sales Range: $50-74.9 Million
Emp.: 175
Oil & Gas Logistics Services
N.A.I.C.S.: 213112
Matt A. Yost *(Sr VP-Terminalling & Engrg)*
Chris Booth *(VP, Sec & Gen Counsel)*
Jeff Posey *(Mgr-Sls)*
Joel Herrington *(Mgr)*
Randy Tauscher *(Gen Mgr)*
Robert D. Bondurant *(Exec VP & CFO)*
Ruben S. Martin *(Pres & CEO)*
Tom Redd *(VP-Sls)*

MARVION INC.

736 E Braeburn Dr, Phoenix, AZ 85022
Tel.: (928) 251-4044   NV
Web Site: https://www.marvion.media
Year Founded: 2008
MVNC—(OTCIQ)
Rev.: $11,482,606
Assets: $4,824,774
Liabilities: $6,823,919
Net Worth: ($1,999,145)
Earnings: ($10,047,662)
Emp.: 1
Fiscal Year-end: 12/31/22
Gold Mining & Exploration Services
N.A.I.C.S.: 212220

MASCO CORPORATION

17450 College Pkwy, Livonia, MI 48152
Tel.: (313) 274-7400   DE
Web Site: https://www.masco.com
Year Founded: 1929
MAS—(NYSE)
Rev.: $7,967,000,000
Assets: $5,363,000,000
Liabilities: $5,265,000,000
Net Worth: $98,000,000
Earnings: $908,000,000
Emp.: 18,000
Fiscal Year-end: 12/31/23
Home Improvement Products Mfr
N.A.I.C.S.: 337126
Jai Shah *(Executives)*
John P. Lindow *(Chief Acctg Officer, VP & Controller)*
Keith J. Allman *(Pres & CEO)*
Kenneth G. Cole *(Gen Counsel, Sec & VP)*
Renee Straber *(Chief HR Officer)*
Richard Westenberg *(CFO & VP)*
David A. Chaika *(Treas-IR & VP)*
Robin L. Zondervan *(Chief Acctg Officer, VP & Controller)*
Robin Zondervan *(Chief Acctg Officer, VP & Controller)*
Jai Shah *(Grp Pres-Plumbing Products)*
Richard Westenberg *(CFO & VP)*
Sue Sabo *(Dir-Corp Comm)*

Subsidiaries:

Arrow Fastener Co., LLC   **(1)**
271 Mayhill St, Saddle Brook, NJ 07663-5303
Tel.: (201) 843-6900
Web Site: http://www.arrowfastener.com
Sales Range: $200-249.9 Million
Emp.: 600
Hand Tools & Related Products
N.A.I.C.S.: 333991

Behr Holdings Corporation   **(1)**
PO Box 1287, Santa Ana, CA 92702
Tel.: (714) 545-7101
Web Site: http://www.behr.com
Sales Range: $75-99.9 Million
Emp.: 200
Holding Company
N.A.I.C.S.: 551112

Subsidiary (Domestic):

Behr Process Corporation   **(2)**
1801 E St Andrew Pl, Santa Ana, CA 92705
Tel.: (714) 545-7101
Web Site: http://www.behr.com

Masco Corporation—(Continued)

Sales Range: $50-74.9 Million
Paint Product Mfr
N.A.I.C.S.: 424690
Jeff Filley *(Pres)*

Subsidiary (Non-US):

Behr Process Canada Ltd. **(3)**
(100%)
Web Site: https://www.behr.ca
Sales Range: $25-49.9 Million
Emp.: 25
Paints
N.A.I.C.S.: 425120

Plant (Domestic):

Behr Process Corporation **(3)**
270 State St, Chicago Heights, IL 60411-1263
Tel.: (708) 757-6350
Web Site: http://www.behr.com
Sales Range: $25-49.9 Million
Paints & Paint Additives
N.A.I.C.S.: 325510

Behr Process Paints (India) Private Limited **(1)**
236 & 237 Taco Rd Opp Tata Auto Comp System Ltd Phase 1, Taluka Mulshi Hinjewadi, Pune, 411057, India
Tel.: (91) 2066750650
Paint & Coating Mfr
N.A.I.C.S.: 325510

BrassCraft Manufacturing Company **(1)**
39600 Orchard Hill Pl, Novi, MI 48375-5331
Tel.: (248) 305-6000
Web Site: http://www.brasscraft.com
Sales Range: $75-99.9 Million
Emp.: 160
Water Supplies & Gas Plumbing Products Mfr & Distr
N.A.I.C.S.: 332919
Thomas Assante *(Pres)*
Robert Zell *(Founder)*

Subsidiary (Non-US):

BrassCraft Canada Ltd. **(2)**
35 Currah Rd, Saint Thomas, N5P 3R2, ON, Canada **(100%)**
Tel.: (519) 633-0340
Web Site: http://www.mascocanada.com
Sales Range: $50-74.9 Million
Water Supply Products
N.A.I.C.S.: 325612

Plant (Domestic):

BrassCraft Manufacturing Company **(2)**
39600 Orchard Hill Pl, Novi, MI 48375-5331
Tel.: (248) 305-6000
Web Site: https://www.brasscraft.com
Sales Range: $75-99.9 Million
Water & Gas Connector Products
N.A.I.C.S.: 332919

BrassCraft Manufacturing Company **(2)**
17450 College Pkwy, Livonia, MI 48152
Tel.: (313) 274-7400
Web Site: http://www.brasscraft.com
Sales Range: $100-124.9 Million
Water Supply & Gas Connector Products
N.A.I.C.S.: 332919

Subsidiary (Non-US):

Masco Canada Limited **(2)**
6990 Creditview Road Unit 5, Mississauga, L5N 8R9, ON, Canada
Tel.: (905) 712-3030
Web Site: https://www.mascocanada.com
Sales Range: $25-49.9 Million
Emp.: 38
Home Improvement & Construction Products Mfr
N.A.I.C.S.: 332913
Imran Ahmad *(Pres)*

Brasstech, Inc. **(1)**
2001 Carnegie Ave, Santa Ana, CA 92705-5531
Tel.: (949) 417-5207
Web Site: https://www.brasstech.com

Sales Range: $100-124.9 Million
Emp.: 500
Plumbing Products Mfr
N.A.I.C.S.: 332913

Delta Faucet Company India Private Limited **(1)**
Unit Nos 15-17 10th Floor Tower B Emaar Digital Greens, Golf Course Extn Road Sector 61, Gurgaon, 122102, India
Tel.: (91) 1244066109
Home Accessory Mfr
N.A.I.C.S.: 332999

Delta Faucet Company Mexico, S. de R.L. de C.V. **(1)**
Edificio Prisma IZA BC Avenida Insurgentes Sur 1647 Piso 1 oficina 111, Colonia San Jose Insurgentes Delegacion Benito Juarez, 03900, Mexico, Mexico
Tel.: (52) 5580008118
Bathroom Accessories Whslr
N.A.I.C.S.: 423220

Diversified Cabinet Distributors **(1)**
5250 Brook Hollow Pkwy, Norcross, GA 30071
Tel.: (770) 447-6363
Web Site: http://www.dcdcabinate.com
Sales Range: $25-49.9 Million
Emp.: 100
Cabinet & Counter Top Installer & Distr
N.A.I.C.S.: 449110
John Winfree *(Branch Mgr)*

ESS GmbH **(1)**
Steinkueppel 6, 35041, Marburg, Germany
Tel.: (49) 642141040
Web Site: https://www.e-s-s.com
Medical Equipment Mfr & Distr
N.A.I.C.S.: 339112

Erickson Building Components, LLC **(1)**
250 N Beck Ave, Chandler, AZ 85226-1701
Tel.: (480) 627-1140
Building Components Mfr
N.A.I.C.S.: 327120

Erickson Building Components, a California Limited Partnership **(1)**
8350 Industrial Ave, Roseville, CA 95678-5946
Tel.: (916) 774-1115
Building Framing Contractors
N.A.I.C.S.: 238130
Mark Scanlon *(Mgr)*

Erickson Construction, LP **(1)**
8350 Industrial Ave, Roseville, CA 95678-6239
Tel.: (916) 774-1100
Web Site: http://www.ericksoncompanies.com
Emp.: 125
Plumbing Products Mfr
N.A.I.C.S.: 332913
Tony D'Aptomo *(CFO)*

Hansgrohe SE7 **(1)**
Auestr 5-9, 77761, Schiltach, Germany
Tel.: (49) 7836510
Web Site: https://www.hansgrohe.com
Bathroom Accessory Mfr & Distr
N.A.I.C.S.: 327110

Huppe S.L. **(1)**
Av de la Via Augusta 85 - 87 4a Planta, Sant Cugat del Valles, 08174, Barcelona, Spain
Tel.: (34) 935632920
Bathroom Accessory Distr
N.A.I.C.S.: 423220

Kraus USA Plumbing LLC **(1)**
12 Harbor Park Dr, Port Washington, NY 11050
Tel.: (631) 212-0703
Web Site: https://www.kraususa.com
Kitchen & Bathroom Fixture Mfr
N.A.I.C.S.: 327110

Liberty Hardware Manufacturing Corporation **(1)**
140 Business Park Dr, Winston Salem, NC 27107
Tel.: (336) 769-4077
Web Site: http://www.libertyhardware.com
Sales Range: $200-249.9 Million
Emp.: 450
Hardware Whslr

N.A.I.C.S.: 423710
Mark Stull *(Pres)*

Subsidiary (Domestic):

General Accessory Manufacturing Company **(2)**
1 Gamco Pl, Durant, OK 74701-1910
Tel.: (580) 924-8066
Web Site: http://www.gamcousa.com
Rev.: $9,431,876
Emp.: 80
Commercial Bath Accessories
N.A.I.C.S.: 327110

Subsidiary (Non-US):

Masco Asia (Shenzhen) Co. Ltd. **(2)**
Suite 7-202 Dong PU Seasight Garden Jin Rong Road Sha Tou Jia, Shenzhen, 518081, China
Tel.: (86) 75582127146
Office Supplies Whslr
N.A.I.C.S.: 424120
Xia Summer *(Supvr-Advanced Pur)*

Masco Bath Corporation **(1)**
540 Glen Ave, Moorestown, NJ 08057-1746
Tel.: (856) 235-7700
Web Site: http://www.mascobath.com
Sales Range: $25-49.9 Million
Emp.: 100
Shower Enclosure Systems
N.A.I.C.S.: 326191

Branch (Domestic):

Masco Bath **(2)**
693 South Ct, Lapeer, MI 48446-0398
Tel.: (810) 664-8501
Web Site: http://www.mascobath.com
Sales Range: $50-74.9 Million
Bath & Shower Products
N.A.I.C.S.: 326191

Masco Beteiligungsgesellschaft mbH **(1)**
Hinterm Haag 10, 69207, Sandhausen, Baden-Wurttemberg, Germany
Tel.: (49) 622493090
Household Accessory Whslr
N.A.I.C.S.: 423220

Subsidiary (Domestic):

Hansgrohe SE **(2)**
Auestr 5-9, 77761, Schiltach, Germany
Tel.: (49) 7836510
Web Site: https://www.hansgrohe.com
Bathroom Accessories Whslr
N.A.I.C.S.: 423220

Subsidiary (Domestic):

Hansgrohe Deutschland Vertrlebs GmbH **(3)**
Auestr 5-9, 77761, Schiltach, Germany
Tel.: (49) 7836510
Web Site: https://www.hansgrohe.de
Emp.: 100
Sanitary Fitting Distr
N.A.I.C.S.: 423720

Hansgrohe International Gmbh **(3)**
Auestr 5-9, 77761, Schiltach, Germany
Tel.: (49) 7836510
Web Site: http://www.hansgrohe.com
Emp.: 2,000
Plumbing Products Mfr
N.A.I.C.S.: 332913

Subsidiary (Non-US):

Cleopatra Holding B.V. **(4)**
Oostzijde 295, Zaandam, 1508EN, Netherlands
Tel.: (31) 756478200
Web Site: https://cleopatra.nl
Holding Company
N.A.I.C.S.: 551112

Hansgrohe A.B. **(4)**
Ridspogatan 10, Malmo, 21377, Sweden
Tel.: (46) 40519150
Plumbing Products Mfr
N.A.I.C.S.: 332913

Hansgrohe Armatur Sanayi ve Ticaret Limited Sirketi **(4)**
Fulya Mh Ortaklar Cd Bahceler Sk No 17 K 2, Sisli, Istanbul, 34387, Turkiye

Tel.: (90) 2122730730
Web Site: http://www.hansgrohe.com.tr
Emp.: 20
Bathroom Accessories Whslr
N.A.I.C.S.: 423220
Albert Emlek *(Mng Dir)*

Hansgrohe Brasil Metals Santitarios Ltda. **(4)**
Alameda Joaquim Eugenio de Lima 61 - Bela Vista, Sao Paulo, 01403-002, Brazil
Tel.: (55) 1131497070
Web Site: http://www.hansgrohe.com.br
Bathroom Accessories Whslr
N.A.I.C.S.: 423220

Hansgrohe Handelsges.mbH **(4)**
Industriezentrum NO Sud Strasse 2d/Objekt M18, 2355, Wiener Neudorf, Austria
Tel.: (43) 223662830
Web Site: https://www.hansgrohe.at
Emp.: 30
Plumbing Products Mfr
N.A.I.C.S.: 332913

Hansgrohe Japan, KK **(4)**
Tennozu First Tower 3F 2-2-4 Higashi Shinagawa, Shinagawa-ku, Tokyo, 1080074, Japan
Tel.: (81) 357153054
Web Site: http://www.hansgrohe.co.jp
Plumbing Products Mfr
N.A.I.C.S.: 332913

Hansgrohe Limited **(4)**
Units D1 and D2, Sandown Park Industrial Estate Royal Mills, Esher, KT10 8BL, Surrey, United Kingdom
Tel.: (44) 1372465655
Web Site: http://www.hansgrohe.co.uk
Emp.: 90
Sanitary Ware Mfr
N.A.I.C.S.: 332999
Christopher Gourlan *(Member-Exec Bd)*
Hans-Jurgen Kalmbach *(Chm-Exec Bd)*
Reinhard Mayer *(Member-Exec Bd)*
Frank Semling *(Member-Exec Bd)*
Klaus F. Jaenecke *(Chm-Supervisory Bd)*
Jay Phillips *(Mng Dir)*

Hansgrohe N.V. **(4)**
Tel.: (32) 25430140
Web Site: https://www.hansgrohe.be
Emp.: 34
Bathroom Product Mfr
N.A.I.C.S.: 327110

Hansgrohe Pty Ltd **(4)**
Unit 4/71 Victoria Crescent, East Hawthorn, Abbotsford, 3067, VIC, Australia
Tel.: (61) 383195753
Web Site: https://www.hansgrohe.com.au
Emp.: 4
Bathroom Accessories Whslr
N.A.I.C.S.: 423220
Frank Semling *(Member-Exec Bd)*
K. C. Lee *(Mng Dir)*
Hans-Jurgen Kalmbach *(Chm-Exec Bd)*
Christophe Gourlan *(Member-Exec Bd)*

Hansgrohe S.A. **(4)**
Av Del Libertador 2451 14th Floor, Olivos, B1636DSE, Buenos Aires, Argentina
Tel.: (54) 1153655050
Web Site: http://www.hansgrohe-la.com
Emp.: 4
Plumbing Products Mfr
N.A.I.C.S.: 332913

Hansgrohe S.A.U. **(4)**
Riera Can Pahissa 26, 08750, Molins de Rei, Spain
Tel.: (34) 936803900
Web Site: http://www.hansgrohe.es
Bathroom Accessories Whslr
N.A.I.C.S.: 423220

Hansgrohe SA (Pty) Ltd. **(4)**
30 Archimedes Street, Kramerville, Johannesburg, South Africa
Tel.: (27) 114450000
Web Site: https://www.hansgrohe.co.za
Bathroom Accessories Whslr
N.A.I.C.S.: 423220

Hansgrohe Sp. z.o.o. **(4)**
Sowia 12, 62-080, Tarnowo Podgorne, Poland
Tel.: (48) 618168600
Plumbing Products Mfr

N.A.I.C.S.: 332913

Hansgrohe d.o.o. (4)
Oreskoviceva 6h / 1, 10010, Zagreb, Croatia
Tel.: (385) 15630800
Web Site: https://www.hansgrohe.hr
Sanitary Fitting Mfr & Distr
N.A.I.C.S.: 332913

Hansgrohe ooo (4)
Semenovskaya sq 1a BC Sokolinaya Gora
21st floor, 107023, Moscow, Russia
Tel.: (7) 4956470735
Web Site: https://www.hansgrohe.ru
Emp.: 30
Plumbing Products Mfr
N.A.I.C.S.: 332913
Mikhael Igmatyev (Gen Dir)

Masco Chile Limitada (1)
Avenida Cristobal Colon, 7682, Las Condes, Santiago, Chile (99.99%)
Tel.: (56) 223421738
Construction Materials Whslr
N.A.I.C.S.: 444180

Masco Corporation Limited (1)
The Lodge, Old Warren Farm, Camp Rd, London, SW19 4UR, United Kingdom
Tel.: (44) 20 8947 9484
Sales Range: $300-349.9 Million
Mfr of Plumbing Fittings & Brass Goods, Wood Kitchen Cabinets & Cabinetwork; Builders Hardware, Home Furnishings & Specialty Consumer Products
N.A.I.C.S.: 337110

Subsidiary (Domestic):

Arrow Fastener (U.K.) Limited (2)
Fifth Floor 23 Commerce Way, London, W1W 8AQ, United Kingdom
Tel.: (44) 2086 86 91 80
Sales Range: $10-24.9 Million
Emp.: 5
Plumbing Products Mfr
N.A.I.C.S.: 332913

Bristan Group Ltd. (2)
Birch Coppice Business Park, Dordon, Tamworth, B78 1SG, Staffordshire, United Kingdom
Tel.: (44) 3300266273
Web Site: http://www.bristan.com
Sales Range: $75-99.9 Million
Bathroom & Kitchen Faucet Distr
N.A.I.C.S.: 327110
Ian Hansell (Gen Mgr)
Joanne Hatton (Dir-HR & Customer Contact)

Duraflex Ltd. (2)
6400 Severn Dr, Tewkesbury Business Park, Tewkesbury, GL20 8SF, Gloucestershire, United Kingdom
Tel.: (44) 1684852600
Web Site: http://www.duraflex.co.uk
Sales Range: $100-124.9 Million
Emp.: 200
Window Frame Extruders
N.A.I.C.S.: 332321

Masco UK Window Group Limited (2)
Western Industrial Estate, Lon-y-Llyn, Caerphilly, CF83 1BQF, United Kingdom
Tel.: (44) 2920854428
Web Site: http://www.ukwg.co.uk
Sales Range: $75-99.9 Million
Emp.: 400
Fabricators of Polyvinylchloride Windows, Doors, Sunrooms & Greenhouses
N.A.I.C.S.: 332311

Subsidiary (Domestic):

Phoenix Door Panels Limited (3)
Lola House 18 Glebe Rd, Huntingdon, PE29 7DL, Cambridgeshire, United Kingdom
Tel.: (44) 1487740469
Web Site: http://www.phoenixdoorpanels.co.uk
Emp.: 150
Wood Panel Mfr
N.A.I.C.S.: 321211

Subsidiary (Domestic):

Moores Furniture Group Ltd. (2)

Thorp Arch Estate, Wetherby, LS23 7DD, West Yorkshire, United Kingdom (100%)
Tel.: (44) 1937842394
Web Site: http://www.moores.co.uk
Sales Range: $250-299.9 Million
Emp.: 600
Cabinets
N.A.I.C.S.: 337110

Premier Trade Frames Ltd. (2)
Premier Trade House Western Industrial Estate, Caerphilly, CF83 1BQ, Cardiff, United Kingdom
Tel.: (44) 2920881200
Web Site: http://www.premier-trade.co.uk
Sales Range: $125-149.9 Million
Emp.: 300
Vinyl Window Frames, Door Frames & Conservatories Fabricator
N.A.I.C.S.: 326199

Watkins Distribution UK Limited (2)
HotSpring House Little Boyton Hall, Roxwell, Chelmsford, CM1 4LN, Essex, United Kingdom
Tel.: (44) 124 549 0056
Web Site: https://www.hotspringworld.co.uk
Hot Tubs, Swim Spas & Accessories Mfr & Distr
N.A.I.C.S.: 332999

Masco Corporation of Indiana (1)
55 E 111th St, Indianapolis, IN 46280
Tel.: (317) 848-1812
Holding Company; Faucets & Other Plumbing Accessories Mfr
N.A.I.C.S.: 551112
Rick Burkman (VP & Controller)
Ken Roberts (VP-Intl Bus Dev)

Subsidiary (Domestic):

Delta Faucet Company (2)
55 E 111th St, Indianapolis, IN 46280-1071
Tel.: (317) 848-1812
Web Site: http://www.deltafaucet.com
Sales Range: $125-149.9 Million
Emp.: 300
Faucet Mfr
N.A.I.C.S.: 332913

Subsidiary (Non-US):

Delta Faucet Company (3)
350 S Edgeware Rd, Saint Thomas, N5P 4L1, ON, Canada (100%)
Tel.: (519) 659-3626
Web Site: http://www.mascocanada.com
Sales Range: $125-149.9 Million
Emp.: 300
Faucets & Fittings
N.A.I.C.S.: 332913

Plant (Domestic):

Delta Faucet Company (3)
55 E 111th st, Indianapolis, IN 46280
Tel.: (812) 663-4433
Web Site: http://www.deltafaucet.com
Emp.: 280
Faucets
N.A.I.C.S.: 332913
Jill Ehnes (Pres)

Delta Faucet Company (3)
3441 Ridgecrest Rd Ext, Jackson, TN 38305-7500
Tel.: (731) 427-8228
Web Site: http://www.deltafaucet.com
Faucets
N.A.I.C.S.: 423720

Subsidiary (Domestic):

Delta Faucet of Oklahoma, Inc. (3)
2500 Hwy 62 W, Chickasha, OK 73023-0905
Tel.: (405) 224-4827
Web Site: http://www.deltafaucet.com
Sales Range: $100-124.9 Million
Faucets
N.A.I.C.S.: 332913

Peerless Faucet Corporation (3)
55 E 111th St, Indianapolis, IN 46280-0980
Tel.: (317) 848-1812
Web Site: http://www.peerlessfaucet.com
Emp.: 400
Faucets Mfr & Marketer
N.A.I.C.S.: 332913

Masco Europe S.a.r.l. (1)
Parc d Activite Syrdall 22, Munsbach, 5365, Luxembourg
Tel.: (352) 3056301
Sales Range: $250-299.9 Million
Emp.: 16
Holding Company
N.A.I.C.S.: 551112
Darius Padler (Pres)

Subsidiary (Non-US):

Aran World s.r.l. (2)
Zona Industriale, Casoli, 64032, Teramo, Italy
Tel.: (39) 08587941
Web Site: http://www.aran.it
Sales Range: $125-149.9 Million
Emp.: 250
Kitchen Cabinets
N.A.I.C.S.: 337110

Glass Idromassaggio SRL (2)
Via Baite 12 EZ I, 31046, Oderzo, Italy
Tel.: (39) 04227146
Web Site: http://www.masco.com
Sales Range: $50-74.9 Million
Emp.: 150
Hydromassage Systems Distr
N.A.I.C.S.: 335210

Tvilum (2)
Egeon Kristiansens Alle 2, 8882, Farvang, Denmark
Tel.: (45) 87573600
Web Site: https://www.tvilum.com
Sales Range: $400-449.9 Million
Emp.: 900
Ready-to-Assemble Home Furniture Mfr
N.A.I.C.S.: 337126

XEY Corp. Empresarial, S.L. (2)
Barrio de Quina S/N, Zumaya, 20750, Spain
Tel.: (34) 943865010
Web Site: http://www.xey.es
Sales Range: $150-199.9 Million
Kitchen Cabinet Mfr
N.A.I.C.S.: 337110

Masco Germany Holding GmbH (1)
Hinterham Haag 10, Sandhausen, 69207, Germany
Tel.: (49) 622493090
Web Site: http://www.masco.com
Sales Range: $250-299.9 Million
Holding Company
N.A.I.C.S.: 551112

Subsidiary (Domestic):

Huppe GmbH (2)
Industriestrasse 3, 26160, Bad Zwischenahn, Germany (100%)
Tel.: (49) 4403670
Web Site: http://www.hueppe.com
Sales Range: $100-124.9 Million
Bathroom Fixture Mfr
N.A.I.C.S.: 327110

Subsidiary (Non-US):

Huppe (Shanghai) Co., Ltd. (3)
B1 Factory No 303 Xinke Rd, Qingpu Town Qingpu District, Shanghai, 201700, China
Tel.: (86) 2122139091
Bathroom Accessories Whslr
N.A.I.C.S.: 423220

Huppe B.V. (3)
Kelvinring 1, 2952 BG, Alblasserdam, Netherlands
Tel.: (31) 78 610 2022
Web Site: http://www.hueppe.com
Bathroom Fixtures & Accessories Mfr & Distr
N.A.I.C.S.: 332913

Huppe Belgium N.V./S.A. (3)
Leuvensesteenweg 49, St Stevens Woluwe, 1932, Zaventem, Belgium
Tel.: (32) 27260030
Web Site: http://www.hueppe.com
Shower Enclosures, Shower Trays, Design & Sanitary Products Mfr (Shower Enclosures, Shower Trays, Design)
N.A.I.C.S.: 332913

Huppe Insaat Sanayi ve Ticaret A.S. (3)
Cerkezkoy Organize Sanayi Bolgesi Ataturk

Caddesi 4 Sokak No 2, Cerkezkoy, Tekirdag, 59500, Turkiye
Tel.: (90) 2827581511
Web Site: http://www.hueppe.com.tr
Emp.: 150
Bathroom Accessories Whslr
N.A.I.C.S.: 423220
Omer Kalender (Gen Mgr)

Huppe SARL (3)
Zl du Ried 13 rue du Ried, 67590, Schweighouse, France
Tel.: (33) 368920010
Web Site: http://www.hueppe.com
Sales Range: $25-49.9 Million
Emp.: 22
Mfrs. of Bathroom Appliances, Tubs, Whirlpools & Spas
N.A.I.C.S.: 327110

Huppe Sp. z.o.o. (3)
ul Malwowa 154, Skorzewo, 60-185, Poznan, Poland
Tel.: (48) 618945080
Web Site: http://www.hueppe.com
Emp.: 23
Plumbing Products Mfr
N.A.I.C.S.: 332913

Huppe Spain, S.L.U. (3)
C/ De la Quimica 9-23 Poligono Industrial A7-Llinars Park, Llinars del Valles, 8450, Barcelona, Spain
Tel.: (34) 938476100
Web Site: http://www.huppe.es
Plumbing Products Mfr
N.A.I.C.S.: 332913

Masco Product Design, Inc. (1)
1021 W Adams St Ste 101, Chicago, IL 60607-2935
Tel.: (312) 324-0925
Web Site: http://www.mascodesign.com
Sales Range: $25-49.9 Million
Emp.: 24
Scientific & Technical Services
N.A.I.C.S.: 541990

Masco Retail Cabinet Group, LLC (1)
15535 S State Ave, Middlefield, OH 44062
Tel.: (440) 632-5333
Web Site: http://www.kraftmais.com
Cabinetry Mfr
N.A.I.C.S.: 337110
Joe Gross (Pres)

Masco Retail Sales Support, Inc. (1)
141 Byers Creek Rd, Mooresville, NC 28117-4376
Tel.: (704) 660-7240
Web Site: http://www.masco.com
Emp.: 35
Plumbing Products Mfr
N.A.I.C.S.: 332913

Masco Services Group Corp. (1)
16910 59th Ave NE Ste 100, Arlington, WA 98223-3725
Tel.: (360) 676-9969
Web Site: http://www.mascocs.com
Plumbing Products Mfr
N.A.I.C.S.: 332913

Subsidiary (Domestic):

Blow in Blanket, LLC (2)
14100 E 35th Pl Ste 104, Aurora, CO 80011
Tel.: (303) 733-0405
Web Site: http://www.bibs.com
Insulation System Mfr
N.A.I.C.S.: 238310

Lilienthal Insulation Company, LLC (2)
22 W Reserve Dr, Kalispell, MT 59901
Tel.: (406) 752-4756
Web Site: http://www.lilienthalinsulation.com
Sales Range: $25-49.9 Million
Emp.: 21
Building Insulation Services
N.A.I.C.S.: 238310
Gene Riffle (Project Mgr)

Masco Services, Inc. (1)
375 Longwood Ave, Boston, MA 02215
Tel.: (617) 632-2349
Web Site: http://www.masco.org
Emp.: 100
Telecommunication Servicesb

Masco Corporation—(Continued)

N.A.I.C.S.: 517810
Gary J. Dupont *(Dir-Telecom & Call Center Ops)*
Holli Roth *(Treas)*

Mascomex S.A. de C.V. (1)
Blvd Adolfo Ruiz Cortinez 3642-501, Col Jardines del Pedregal, Mexico, 01900, Mexico
Tel.: (52) 5555687950
Web Site: http://www.mascomex.com.mx
Plumbing Products Mfr
N.A.I.C.S.: 332913

Masterchem Industries, LLC (1)
1801 E St Andrew Pl, Santa Ana, CA 92705
Tel.: (714) 545-7101
Web Site: https://www.kilz.com
Sales Range: $50-74.9 Million
Emp.: 125
Primers & Paints Mfr
N.A.I.C.S.: 325510

Plumb Shop (1)
39600 Orchard Hill Pl, Novi, MI 48375-5331
Tel.: (248) 305-6000
Web Site: http://www.plumbshop.com
Sales Range: $75-99.9 Million
Emp.: 150
Plumbing Product Distr
N.A.I.C.S.: 332913

Sauna360 Group Oy (1)
Pl 15, FI-10901, Hanko, Finland
Tel.: (358) 207560300
Web Site: https://sauna360.com
Electric Heater Mfr & Distr
N.A.I.C.S.: 333415

Service Partners of Florida, LLC (1)
8999 Western Way Ste 100, Jacksonville, FL 32256
Tel.: (904) 519-7792
Web Site: http://www.service-partners.com
Building Material Dealers
N.A.I.C.S.: 444180

Tempered Products, Inc. (1)
10F-2 631 Chung Teh Rd Sec 1, Taichung, Taiwan
Tel.: (886) 422327002
Plumbing Products Mfr
N.A.I.C.S.: 332913

Vapor Technologies, Inc. (1)
6400 Dry Creek Pkwy, Longmont, CO 80503 **(100%)**
Tel.: (303) 652-8500
Web Site: https://vaportech.com
Sales Range: $50-74.9 Million
Emp.: 28
Coatings & Finishing Equipment
N.A.I.C.S.: 332812

Watkins Manufacturing Corporation (1)
1280 Park Ctr Dr, Vista, CA 92081
Tel.: (760) 598-6464
Web Site: http://www.hotspring.com
Sales Range: $250-299.9 Million
Spas
N.A.I.C.S.: 326191

Subsidiary (Domestic):

Endless Pools, Inc. (2)
1601 Dutton Mill Rd, Aston, PA 19014
Tel.: (484) 768-1865
Web Site: http://www.endlesspools.com
Swimming Pools Mfr & Distr
N.A.I.C.S.: 339920
James Murdock *(Founder)*

Subsidiary (Non-US):

Hot Spring Spa Australasia Pty Ltd (2)
U2 7 Hoyle Ave Castle hill, Bella Vista, 2154, Australia
Tel.: (61) 288243992
Web Site: http://www.hotspring.com.au
Emp.: 1
Bathroom Accessories Whslr
N.A.I.C.S.: 423220

Hot Spring Spas New Zealand (2)
35 William Pickering Drive, Albany, 0632, Auckland, New Zealand
Tel.: (64) 94154722

Web Site: https://www.hotspring.co.nz
Emp.: 15
Spa Pool Products Mfr
N.A.I.C.S.: 332913

Wellness Marketing Corporation (1)
1601 Dutton Mill Rd, Aston, PA 19014
Tel.: (484) 768-1865
Web Site: https://www.endlesspools.com
Swimming Pool Construction Services
N.A.I.C.S.: 238990

MASIMO CORPORATION

52 Discovery, Irvine, CA 92618
Tel.: (949) 297-7000   DE
Web Site: https://www.masimo.com
Year Founded: 1989
MASI—(NASDAQ)
Rev.: $2,048,100,000
Assets: $3,041,500,000
Liabilities: $1,676,700,000
Net Worth: $1,364,800,000
Earnings: $81,500,000
Emp.: 3,800
Fiscal Year-end: 12/30/23
Motion & Low Perfusion Tolerant Pulse Oximetry Mfr
N.A.I.C.S.: 334517
Tom McClenahan *(Gen Counsel & Exec VP)*
Micah Young *(CFO & Exec VP)*
Tao Levy *(Exec VP-Bus Dev)*
Bilal Muhsin *(COO)*
Blair Tripodi *(COO-Consumer)*
Paul Hataishi *(Chief Acctg Officer & Sr VP)*
Joe E. Kiani *(Founder)*
Michelle M. Brennan *(Interim CEO)*

Subsidiaries:

B&W Group (Schweiz) GmbH (1)
Ifangstrasse 5, 8952, Schlieren, Switzerland
Tel.: (41) 434336150
Web Site: https://www.bwgroup.ch
Household Appliance Mfr & Distr
N.A.I.C.S.: 335220

D&M Premium Sound Solutions, LLC (1)
44099 Plymouth Oaks Blvd-ste 106, Plymouth, MI 48170
Tel.: (734) 259-6142
Electronic Audio & Video Equipment Mfr
N.A.I.C.S.: 334310

LiDCO Group Plc (1)
402-3 Salisbury House 29 Finsbury Circus, London, EC2M 5SQ, United Kingdom **(100%)**
Tel.: (44) 2077491500
Web Site: http://www.lidco.com
Sales Range: $1-9.9 Million
Emp.: 48
Cardiac Monitoring Systems Developer & Mfr
N.A.I.C.S.: 325412
Ji Hee Ko *(Mgr-Quality & Regulatory Affairs)*
John Hubbard *(Mgr-Operations)*
Tim Hall *(CFO & Sec)*
Bal Padam *(Ops Mgr)*

Subsidiary (Domestic):

LiDCO Limited (2)
16 Orsman Road, London, N1 5QJ, United Kingdom
Tel.: (44) 1223830666
Web Site: http://www.lidco.com
Sales Range: $25-49.9 Million
Emp.: 2
Cardiac Monitoring Equipment Mfr & Sales
N.A.I.C.S.: 334510
James Johnston *(Acct Mgr)*

Masimo Americas, Inc. (1)
40 Parker, Irvine, CA 92618
Tel.: (949) 297-7000
Web Site: http://www.masimo.com
Surgical & Medical Instrument Mfr
N.A.I.C.S.: 339112

Masimo Asia Pacific PTE. Ltd. (1)
31 Ubi Road 1 04-05, Singapore, 408694, Singapore

Tel.: (65) 65216700
Sales Range: $10-24.9 Million
Emp.: 1
Pulse Oximeters Mfr
N.A.I.C.S.: 334510

Masimo Europe Limited, Sucursal en Espana (1)
Ronda de Poniente 12 2F, Tres Cantos, 28760, Madrid, Spain
Tel.: (34) 918049734
Medical Device Mfr & Distr
N.A.I.C.S.: 339112

Masimo Europe Ltd. (1)
Lindberghstr 11, 82178, Puchheim, Germany
Tel.: (49) 89800658990
Web Site: http://www.masimo.com
Sales Range: $25-49.9 Million
Emp.: 25
Motion & Low Perfusion Tolerant Pulse Oximetry
N.A.I.C.S.: 423450

Masimo Gulf, LLC (1)
Shoumoukh Tower B 10th floor Office No 1047 C -Ring Road, PO Box 55896, Al Sadd, Doha, Qatar
Tel.: (974) 40075161
Medical Device Mfr & Distr
N.A.I.C.S.: 339112

Masimo International SARL - Dubai, U.A.E. (1)
DSO-DDP-Office-A4-401-407-408 Dubai Silicon Oasis, Dubai, United Arab Emirates
Tel.: (971) 45467498
Medical Device Mfr & Distr
N.A.I.C.S.: 339112

Masimo Korea, LLC (1)
BNK Digital Tower 2F Seochodae-ro 398, Seochu-gu, Seoul, Korea (South)
Tel.: (82) 25974900
Patient Monitoring Equipment Mfr
N.A.I.C.S.: 334510

Masimo Medikal Urunler Ticaret Limited Sirketi Istanbul Subesi (1)
Akat Mah Gul Sok No 2/7 Maya Park Tower 2, Akatlar Besiktas, 34335, Istanbul, Turkiye
Tel.: (90) 312 219 5438
Medical Device Mfr
N.A.I.C.S.: 339112

Masimo Semiconductor, Inc. (1)
25 Sagamore Park Rd, Hudson, NH 03051
Tel.: (603) 595-8900
Web Site: https://www.masimosemiconductor.com
Emp.: 30
Semiconductor Devices Mfr
N.A.I.C.S.: 334413

Masimo Sweden AB (1)
Svardvagen 15, 182 33, Danderyd, Sweden
Tel.: (46) 854498150
Web Site: http://www.masimosweden.com
Emp.: 25
Medical Device Mfr
N.A.I.C.S.: 339112

Masimo UK Ltd. (1)
Matrix House Basing View, Basingstoke, RG21 4DZ, Hampshire, United Kingdom
Tel.: (44) 1256479988
Sales Range: $25-49.9 Million
Emp.: 70
Motion & Low Perfusion Tolerant Pulse Oximetry
N.A.I.C.S.: 423450

TNI medical AG (1)
Hofmannstrasse 8, 97084, Wurzburg, Germany
Tel.: (49) 93120792902
Web Site: https://www.tni-medical.de
Therapy Services
N.A.I.C.S.: 621610
Ewald Anger *(CEO)*

MASON INDUSTRIAL TECH-NOLOGY, INC.

110 E 59th St, New York, NY 10022
Tel.: (212) 771-1206   DE
Web Site:
   http://www.masonitech.com
Year Founded: 2020

MIT—(NYSE)
Rev.: $19,240,926
Assets: $501,673,274
Liabilities: $534,709,255
Net Worth: ($33,035,981)
Earnings: $17,631,175
Emp.: 2
Fiscal Year-end: 12/31/21
Investment Services
N.A.I.C.S.: 523999
Derek Satzinger *(CFO)*
Michael E. Martino *(Chm)*
Phillip B. Whitehead *(Vice Chm)*
Edward A. Rose III *(CEO)*

MASS MEGAWATTS WIND POWER, INC.

119 Boston Turnpike Ste 290, Shrewsbury, MA 01545
Tel.: (508) 942-3531   MA
Web Site:
   https://www.massmegawatts.com
Year Founded: 1997
MMMW—(OTCIQ)
Assets: $2,829
Liabilities: $272,709
Net Worth: ($269,880)
Earnings: ($347,174)
Fiscal Year-end: 04/30/23
Wind Power Generation
N.A.I.C.S.: 221118
Jonathan C. Ricker *(Chm & CEO)*
Thomas M. Dill *(Dir-Consulting-Corp Svcs)*

MASSACHUSETTS BUSINESS DEVELOPMENT CORP.

500 Edgewater Dr Ste 555, Wakefield, MA 01880
Tel.: (781) 928-1100   MA
MBDC—(OTCIQ)
Financial Services
N.A.I.C.S.: 523999
Peter Forman *(CEO)*

MASSIMO GROUP

3101 W Miller Rd, Garland, TX 75041
Web Site:
   https://www.massimomotor.com   NV
Year Founded: 2020
MAMO—(NASDAQ)
Rev.: $115,037,544
Assets: $41,943,479
Liabilities: $27,455,673
Net Worth: $14,487,800
Earnings: $10,415,225
Emp.: 126
Fiscal Year-end: 12/31/23
Motor Vehicle Mfr & Distr
N.A.I.C.S.: 336991

MASTEC, INC.

800 S Douglas Rd 12th Fl, Coral Gables, FL 33134
Tel.: (305) 599-1800   FL
Web Site: https://www.mastec.com
Year Founded: 1929
MTZ—(NYSE)
Rev.: $11,995,934,000
Assets: $9,373,511,000
Liabilities: $6,652,250,000
Net Worth: $2,721,261,000
Earnings: ($49,949,000)
Emp.: 34,000
Fiscal Year-end: 12/31/23
Telecommunications & Energy Infrastructure Construction Services
N.A.I.C.S.: 237130
Robert E. Apple *(COO)*
Pablo Alvarez *(Exec VP-Merger & Acquisitions)*
Ben Gilbert *(VP-Bus Dev)*
Jose Ramon Mas *(Co-Founder & CEO)*
Sherina Maye Edwards *(Chief Strategy Officer)*
Paul DiMarco *(CFO & Exec VP)*

T. Michael Love *(Chief Acctg Officer)*
Alberto De Cardenas *(Exec VP)*
Jorge Mas *(Co-Founder)*

Subsidiaries:

EC Source Services, LLC (1)
1138 N Alma School Rd Ste 220, Mesa, AZ 85201
Tel.: (480) 245-7200
Web Site:
  https://www.ecsourceservices.com
Sales Range: $25-49.9 Million
Emp.: 30
Construction Engineering Services
N.A.I.C.S.: 541330
Steven Gilkey *(Exec VP-Ops)*
Howard Lewczyk *(VP-Ops)*
Glen Hartwig *(Exec VP)*
Paul Mackintire *(VP-Safety)*
Steve Luetkehans *(VP-Business Development)*
Tim Henry *(VP-Operations-Southern Region)*
Michael Childers *(VP-Operations)*
Thomas Tacconelli *(VP-Operations)*

Fabcor TargetCo Ltd. (1)
10202 74 Ave, Clairmont, Grande Prairie, T0H 0W0, AB, Canada
Tel.: (780) 532-3350
Sales Range: $25-49.9 Million
Emp.: 30
Construction Engineering Services
N.A.I.C.S.: 541330

Subsidiary (Domestic):

Fabcor 2001, Inc. (2)
10202 74 Ave, Clairmont, Grande Prairie, T0H 0W0, AB, Canada
Tel.: (780) 532-3350
Web Site: http://www.fabcor.ca
Sales Range: $75-99.9 Million
Emp.: 30
Pipeline Construction Services
N.A.I.C.S.: 237120

Henkels & McCoy, Inc. (1)
985 Jolly Rd, Blue Bell, PA 19422-0900
Tel.: (215) 283-7600
Web Site: https://www.henkels.com
Communications & Energy Utility Services; Engineering, Construction & Maintenance
N.A.I.C.S.: 237130

Subsidiary (Non-US):

Henkels & McCoy Canada, Inc. (2)
2525 Tedlo St Unit 1, Mississauga, L5A 4A8, ON, Canada
Tel.: (905) 848-2822
Sales Range: $10-24.9 Million
Emp.: 65
Construction Engineering Services
N.A.I.C.S.: 541330

Infrastructure & Energy Alternatives Inc. (1)
6325 Digital Way Ste 460, Indianapolis, IN 46278
Tel.: (765) 828-2580
Web Site: http://www.iea.net
Rev.: $2,078,420,000
Assets: $899,753,000
Liabilities: $862,496,000
Net Worth: $37,257,000
Earnings: ($85,316,000)
Emp.: 3,718
Fiscal Year-end: 12/31/2021
Investment Services
N.A.I.C.S.: 523999
Derek W. Glanvill *(Chm)*
Chris Hanson *(Exec VP-Renewable Energy)*
Brian Hummer *(Exec VP-Specialty Civil Ops)*
Chris Kahila *(Exec VP-Power Delivery)*
Kevin Turner *(Sr VP-Health & Safety)*
Michael Edward Stoecker *(COO)*
Alyson Hanson *(VP-Mktg & Comm)*
Peter J. Moerbeek *(CFO & Exec VP)*
Morayma Da Silva *(VP-Diversity & Inclusion)*
Angela Hudgins *(Sr VP-HR)*

Subsidiary (Domestic):

American Civil Constructors Holding Inc. (2)
4901 S Windermere St, Littleton, CO 80120

Tel.: (303) 795-2582
Web Site: http://www.accbuilt.com
Rev.: $42,100,000
Emp.: 1,500
Civil Engineering Services
N.A.I.C.S.: 237310
Randy Maher *(Pres & COO)*
Jeffrey Foerste *(Pres-West Coast)*
Jody Randall *(Chief Admin Officer)*
Ryan Evans *(CFO)*

Subsidiary (Domestic):

American Civil Constructors West Coast LLC (3)
2990 Bay Vista Ct Ste D, Benicia, CA 94510
Tel.: (707) 746-8028
Energy Construction Services
N.A.I.C.S.: 237130
Jeff Foerste *(Pres)*

Subsidiary (Domestic):

Infrastructure & Energy Alternatives, LLC (2)
6325 Digital Way Ste 460, Indianapolis, IN 46278
Tel.: (708) 375-3010
Web Site: http://www.iea.net
Energy & Water Infrastructure Services
N.A.I.C.S.: 237310
Michael Stoecker *(COO)*
Peter Moerbeek *(CFO)*
Erin Roth *(Exec VP)*
Chris Kahila *(Exec VP)*
Kevin Turner *(Sr VP)*

Subsidiary (Domestic):

White Construction Inc. (3)
3900 E White Ave, Clinton, IN 47842
Tel.: (765) 832-2075
Web Site: http://www.whiteconstruction.com
Heavy Civil Construction Contractor
N.A.I.C.S.: 237990

Subsidiary (Non-US):

H.B. White Canada Corp. (4)
70 Summerlea Rd, Brampton, L6T4X3, ON, Canada
Tel.: (905) 433-9333
Heavy Civil Construction Contractor
N.A.I.C.S.: 237130

Subsidiary (Domestic):

William Charles Construction Company, LLC (2)
833 Featherstone Rd, Rockford, IL 61107
Tel.: (815) 654-4700
Web Site:
  https://www.williamcharlesconstruction.com
Sales Range: $25-49.9 Million
Emp.: 100
Highway & Street Construction Services
N.A.I.C.S.: 237310

Subsidiary (Non-US):

Ragnar Benson, Inc. (3)
Tel.: (815) 654-4700
Web Site: https://www.rbic.com
General Contractors
N.A.I.C.S.: 236210

Division (Domestic):

William Charles Construction - Materials Division (3)
5290 Nimtz Rd, Loves Park, IL 61111-3932
Tel.: (815) 654-4700
Web Site:
  https://www.williamcharlesconstruction.com
Sales Range: $25-49.9 Million
Emp.: 40
Lumber & Other Building Materials
N.A.I.C.S.: 444180

Intren, Inc. (1)
18202 W Union Rd, Union, IL 60180-9710
Tel.: (815) 923-2300
Web Site: https://www.intren.com
Sales Range: $50-74.9 Million
Emp.: 1,000
Construction Engineering Services
N.A.I.C.S.: 237310

Sherina Maye Edwards *(Pres)*
Jon Arnopolin *(Sr Dir-Fin)*
Dennis Bednarski *(VP-Midwest)*
Brian Carlin *(Acct Mgr-Midwest East)*
Keith Garvey *(VP-Bus Dev-East Coast)*
Kelly Tomblin *(CEO)*
Matthew Turk *(Exec VP)*
Andy Carmean *(VP-Indianapolis & St. Louis)*

MasTec Canada, Inc. (1)
333 7 Ave SW Suite 2000, Calgary, T2P 2Z1, AB, Canada
Tel.: (403) 225-8867
Web Site: https://www.masteccanada.com
Pipeline & Facility Construction Services
N.A.I.C.S.: 237120
Greg Northcott *(Exec VP)*
Rory Vaselenak *(VP-Finance)*
Brad Chandler *(Dir-Construction Support Svcs)*
Rod Sobchishin *(Mng Dir-Business Development)*
Chris Stamp *(Mgr-Corporate HSE)*
Carlos Plazas *(Dir-Quality)*
Joanne Arthurs *(Mgr-Talent & Tech Svcs)*

MasTec North America, Inc. (1)
211 E 7th Ste 620, Austin, TX 78701   **(100%)**
Tel.: (512) 476-6777
Telephone Communication Services
N.A.I.C.S.: 237130

Subsidiary (Domestic):

Big Country Energy Services LLC. (2)
5241 142nd Dr NW, Williston, ND 58801
Tel.: (403) 529-6444
Oil & Gas Field Services
N.A.I.C.S.: 237120

Bottom Line Services, LLC (2)
900 Isom Rd Ste 200, San Antonio, TX 78284
Tel.: (210) 780-7130
Web Site:
  https://www.bottomlineservicesinc.com
Oil & Gas Well Drilling Services
N.A.I.C.S.: 213111

Cash Construction Company, Inc. (2)
217 Kingston Lacy Blvd, Pflugerville, TX 78660
Tel.: (512) 251-7872
Web Site: https://www.cashconstruction.com
Construction Management Services
N.A.I.C.S.: 237990

Globetec Construction, LLC (2)
4774 N Powerline Rd, Deerfield Beach, FL 33073
Tel.: (954) 590-3305
Web Site:
  http://www.globetecconstruction.com
Sales Range: $25-49.9 Million
Emp.: 10
Public Utility Construction Services
N.A.I.C.S.: 237990
Antonio Assenza *(Pres & CEO)*

Power Partners MasTec LLC (2)
9140 Arrowpoint Blvd Ste 200, Charlotte, NC 28273
Tel.: (704) 329-8277
Web Site: http://www.powerpartnersllc.com
Sales Range: $25-49.9 Million
Emp.: 6
Electric System Construction & Maintenance Services
N.A.I.C.S.: 238210
Ricardo Delfino *(Gen Mgr)*
Adolfo Valderrama *(Mgr-Div)*
Alex Carstens *(Mgr-Div)*

Pumpco, Inc. (2)
1209 S Main St, Giddings, TX 78942
Tel.: (979) 542-9054
Web Site: https://www.pumpco.cc
Oil & Gas Pipeline Construction Services
N.A.I.C.S.: 237120

SEFNCO Communications, Inc. (2)
1019 39th Ave SE Ste 200, Puyallup, WA 98374-2116
Tel.: (877) 385-2903
Web Site: http://www.sefnco.com

Communication Networks & Infrastructure Construction
N.A.I.C.S.: 237130

Master Canada Inc. - Fort St. John (1)
9929 Swanson St, Fort Saint John, V1J 4M6, BC, Canada
Tel.: (250) 787-0787
Web Site: http://www.mastedcanada.com
Energy Consulting Services
N.A.I.C.S.: 541690

Precision Pipeline LLC (1)
3314 56th St, Eau Claire, WI 54703
Tel.: (715) 874-4510
Web Site:
  https://www.precisionpipelinellc.com
Emp.: 50
Oil & Gas Pipeline Construction Services
N.A.I.C.S.: 237120

SEFNCO Communications, Inc. (1)
8615 Elder Creek Rd, Sacramento, CA 95828
Web Site: http://www.sefnco.com
Construction Engineering Services
N.A.I.C.S.: 541330
Scott Nall *(Founder & CEO)*

Three Phase Line Construction, Inc. (1)
35E Industrial Way Ste 202, Rochester, NH 03867
Tel.: (603) 755-9610
Web Site: https://www.threephaseline.com
Electrical Contracting Services
N.A.I.C.S.: 238210
Christina Magoon *(VP-Operations-Northeast)*
Eric Burkey *(Dir-Operations-Midwest)*
Rudolph Kunz *(Dir-Safety)*
Kevin Olsen *(Dir)*

Wanzek Construction Inc. (1)
2028 2nd Ave NW, West Fargo, ND 58078
Tel.: (701) 282-6171
Web Site: https://www.wanzek.com
Sales Range: $150-199.9 Million
Emp.: 1,000
Industrial Construction Services
N.A.I.C.S.: 236210
Rob Lee *(Exec VP)*
Travis Solberg *(CFO)*
Michael Miketa *(VP-Construction-Industrial)*
Troy Ochoa *(VP-Construction-Solar)*
Matt Tetrault *(VP-Wind Construction & Svcs)*
Travis Bennett *(VP-Corp Svcs)*
Timothy Palmer *(VP-Environmental, Health, Safety & Quality)*
Jack Lawrence *(VP-Information Svcs)*
Neal Detert *(VP-Project Svcs)*

WesTower Communications, LLC (1)
2460 Sandlake Rd, Orlando, FL 32809
Tel.: (321) 209-8800
Power & Communication Tower Construction Services
N.A.I.C.S.: 237130

MASTECH DIGITAL, INC.
1305 Cherrington Pkwy Bldg 210 Ste 400, Moon Township, PA 15108
Tel.: (412) 787-2100   **PA**
Web Site:
  https://www.mastechdigital.com
Year Founded: 1986
MHH—(NYSEAMEX)
Rev.: $242,238,000
Assets: $108,879,000
Liabilities: $22,876,000
Net Worth: $86,003,000
Earnings: $8,712,000
Emp.: 1,695
Fiscal Year-end: 12/31/22
Information Technology Services
N.A.I.C.S.: 541512
Jennifer Ford Lacey *(Gen Counsel & Head-Legal & Admin)*
Sunil Wadhwani *(Co-Founder & Co-Chm)*
Ashok K. Trivedi *(Co-Founder & Co-Chm)*
Vivek Gupta *(Pres & CEO)*
Vishwanath Shetty *(Head-HR)*
Michael Bryan *(Head-Enterprise Bus-IT Staffing)*

Mastech Digital, Inc.—(Continued)

Shipra Sharma *(Head-Recruiting-IT Staffing)*
Donna Kijowski *(Mgr-IR)*
John J. Cronin Jr. *(CFO)*

Subsidiaries:

Mastech InfoTrellis, Inc. **(1)**
1305 Cherrington Pkwy Bldg 210 Ste 400,
Moon Township, PA 15108
Tel.: (412) 746-1648
Web Site:
　　https://www.mastechinfotrellis.com
Data Management Services
N.A.I.C.S.: 541513
Kishalay Gangopadhyay *(VP-Ops)*
Mike Ashwell *(VP & Gen Mgr-Data Mgmt)*
Vicki Liu *(VP-Channels & Ops)*

Mastech Staffing Services Pvt.
Ltd. **(1)**
8th Floor B-07 Sector-132, Noida, 201301,
Uttar Pradesh, India
Tel.: (91) 1206494025
Human Resource Consulting Services
N.A.I.C.S.: 541612

MASTERBRAND, INC.
1 MasterBrand Cabinets Dr, Jasper,
IN 47547
Tel.: (812) 482-2527　　　**DE**
Web Site:
　　https://www.masterbrand.com
Year Founded: 2022
MBC—(NYSE)
Holding Company; Residential Cabinets & Related Products Mfr
N.A.I.C.S.: 551112
R. David Banyard Jr. *(Pres & CEO)*

Subsidiaries:

MasterBrand Cabinets LLC **(1)**
1 MasterBrand Cabinets Dr, Jasper, IN
47546
Tel.: (812) 481-7879
Web Site: http://www.masterbrand.com
Sales Range: $75-99.9 Million
Emp.: 420
Cabinetry Mfr
N.A.I.C.S.: 337110
David Banyard *(Pres)*

Division (Domestic):

MasterBrand Cabinets LLC - Decora
Cabinets **(2)**
1 MasterBrand Cabinets Dr, Jasper, IN
47547
Tel.: (812) 482-2527
Web Site: http://www.decoracabinets.com
Wood Cabinet & Vanities Mfr
N.A.I.C.S.: 337110

Subsidiary (Non-US):

Masterbrand Cabinet NHB Industries
Ltd. **(2)**
100 Jameson Dr, Peterborough, K9J 6X6,
ON, Canada　　　　　　　　　　**(100%)**
Tel.: (705) 749-1201
Web Site:
　　http://www.masterbrandcabinets.com
Sales Range: $25-49.9 Million
Emp.: 20
Wood Kitchen Cabinet Mfr
N.A.I.C.S.: 337110

Subsidiary (Domestic):

Omega Cabinets, Ltd. **(2)**
1205 Peters Dr, Waterloo, IA 50703
Tel.: (319) 833-2003
Web Site: http://www.omegacab.com
Wood Cabinet Mfr
N.A.I.C.S.: 337110

Subsidiary (Non-US):

Kitchen Craft of Canada **(3)**
1180 Springfield Road, Winnipeg, R2C 2Z2,
MB, Canada　　　　　　　　　　**(100%)**
Tel.: (204) 224-3211
Web Site: http://www.kitchencraft.com

Sales Range: $350-399.9 Million
Emp.: 1,500
Hardware Merchant Whslr
N.A.I.C.S.: 423710

Subsidiary (Domestic):

Woodcrafters Home Products,
LLC **(2)**
3700 Camino De Verdad, Weslaco, TX
78596
Tel.: (956) 647-8300
Web Site: http://www.woodcrafters-tx.com
Sales Range: $200-249.9 Million
Emp.: 2,000
Wood Kitchen Cabinet & Countertop Mfr
N.A.I.C.S.: 337110

Norcraft Companies, Inc. **(1)**
950 Blue Gentian Rd Ste 200, Eagan, MN
55121
Tel.: (651) 234-3300
Hardware Mfr
N.A.I.C.S.: 332510

Subsidiary (Domestic):

Mid Continent Cabinetry Inc. **(2)**
950 Blue Gentian Rd Ste 200, Eagan, MN
55121
Web Site:
　　http://www.midcontinentcabinetry.com
Kitchen Cabinet Mfr
N.A.I.C.S.: 337110

Subsidiary (Non-US):

Norcraft Canada Corporation **(2)**
1980 Springfield Road, Winnipeg, R2G 2Z2,
MB, Canada
Tel.: (204) 222-9888
Cabinetry Mfr
N.A.I.C.S.: 337110

Norcraft Holdings, L.P. **(2)**
Tel.: (651) 234-3300
Web Site:
　　http://www.norcraftcompanies.com
Sales Range: $250-299.9 Million
Emp.: 1,630
Holding Company; Wood Kitchen Cabinets
Mfr & Distr
N.A.I.C.S.: 551112

Subsidiary (Domestic):

Norcraft Companies, L.P. **(3)**
3020 Denmark Ave Ste 100, Eagan, MN
55121
Tel.: (800) 297-0661
Emp.: 1,892
Cabinetry Mfr
N.A.I.C.S.: 337110

Subsidiary (Domestic):

StarMark Cabinetry **(2)**
600 E 48th St N, Sioux Falls, SD 57104
Tel.: (800) 594-9444
Web Site: http://www.starmarkcabinetry.com
Wood Cabinet Mfr
N.A.I.C.S.: 337110

MASTERCARD INCORPORATED
2000 Purchase St, Purchase, NY
10577
Tel.: (914) 249-2000　　　**DE**
Web Site: https://www.mastercard.us
Year Founded: 1966
MA—(NYSE)
Rev.: $25,098,000,000
Assets: $42,448,000,000
Liabilities: $35,473,000,000
Net Worth: $6,975,000,000
Earnings: $11,195,000,000
Emp.: 33,400
Fiscal Year-end: 12/31/23
Holding Company; Credit Card Services
N.A.I.C.S.: 551112
Timothy H. Murphy *(Chief Admin Officer)*
Venkata Rajamannar Madabhushi
(Chief Comm Officer & Pres-Healthcare)
Sachin Mehra *(CFO)*

Venkata Rajamannar Madabhushi
(Chief Comm Officer & Pres-Healthcare)
Raj Seshadri *(Pres-Data & Svcs)*
Michael Miebach *(CEO)*
Craig E. Vosburg *(Chief Product Officer)*
Michael Fraccaro *(Chief People Officer)*
Ajay Bhalla *(Pres-Cyber & Intelligence Solutions)*
Carlo Enrico *(Pres-Latin America & Caribbean)*
Linda Kirkpatrick *(Pres-North America)*
Jorn Lambert *(Chief Digital Officer-Digital Consumer Solutions)*
Raja Rajamannar *(CMO, Chief Comm Officer & Pres-Healthcare)*
Jennifer Erickson *(Exec VP-Comm)*
Mark Barnett *(Pres-Europe)*
Greg Ulrich *(Exec VP-Strategy, Corp Dev & M&A)*
Karen Griffin *(Chief Risk Officer)*
Ken Moore *(Chief Innovation Officer)*
Michael Braverman G. Froman *(Vice Chm-Strategic Growth & Pres-Strategic Growth)*

Subsidiaries:

Brighterion, Inc. **(1)**
123 Mission St 17th Fl, San Francisco, CA
94105
Tel.: (415) 986-5600
Web Site: https://www.brighterion.com
Computer Software Development
N.A.I.C.S.: 541511
Sudhir Jha *(Sr VP & Head-Brighterion)*

Finicity Corporation **(1)**
434 W Ascension Way Ste 200, Salt Lake
City, UT 84123
Tel.: (801) 984-4200
Web Site: http://www.finicity.com
Software Publisher
N.A.I.C.S.: 513210
Steve Smith *(CEO)*

MasterCard International
Incorporated **(1)**
2000 Purchase St, Purchase, NY 10577
Tel.: (914) 249-2000
Web Site: http://www.mastercard.us
Sales Range: $650-699.9 Million
Emp.: 2,700
Credit Card & Financial Services
N.A.I.C.S.: 522320
Venkata Rajamannar Madabhushi *(Chief Comm Officer, Chief Mktg Officer & Pres-Healthcare)*
Venkata Rajamannar Madabhushi *(Chief Comm Officer, Chief Mktg Officer & Pres-Healthcare)*

Subsidiary (Domestic):

Applied Predictive Technologies,
Inc. **(2)**
4250 N Fairfax Dr 11th Fl, Arlington, VA
22203
Tel.: (703) 875-7700
Web Site:
　　http://www.predictivetechnologies.com
Emp.: 200
Analytic Software Developer
N.A.I.C.S.: 513210
Anthony Bruce *(Co-Founder & CEO)*

Subsidiary (Non-US):

Envoy Services Limited **(2)**
60 Charlotte Street, London, W1T 2NU,
United Kingdom
Tel.: (44) 2074367851
Web Site: http://www.envoyservices.com
Emp.: 60
Financial Payment Services
N.A.I.C.S.: 522320
Phillip McGriskin *(CEO)*
Paul Townsend *(COO)*
Jonathan Fisher *(CTO)*
Mark OBrien *(CFO)*

ExperCash GmbH **(2)**

Augustaanlage 59, Mannheim, 68165, Germany
Tel.: (49) 6217249380
Web Site: http://www.expercash.de
Payment Solutions & Services
N.A.I.C.S.: 541214

Gatekeeper Services Limited **(2)**
3 Studley Court Guildford Road, Woking,
GU24 8EB, Surrey, United Kingdom
Tel.: (44) 1276856444
Web Site: http://www.gatekeeper.co.uk
Online Security Networking Services
N.A.I.C.S.: 561621

MasterCard Asia/Pacific (Australia)
Pty. Ltd. **(2)**
72 Christie St, Saint Leonards, 2065, NSW,
Australia
Tel.: (61) 294663700
Web Site: http://www.mastercard.com
Payment Solutions & Services
N.A.I.C.S.: 541214

MasterCard Asia/Pacific Pte. Ltd. **(2)**
3 Fraser Street DUO Tower Level 17, Singapore, 189352, Singapore
Tel.: (65) 65332888
Web Site: http://www.mastercard.com
Sales Range: $50-74.9 Million
Payment Solutions & Services
N.A.I.C.S.: 541214

MasterCard Canada, Inc. **(2)**
121 Bloor Street East Suite 600, Toronto,
M4W 3M5, ON, Canada
Tel.: (416) 365-6655
Web Site: http://www.mastercard.com
Sales Range: $125-149.9 Million
Emp.: 70
Credit Card Issuing
N.A.I.C.S.: 522210

MasterCard Europe SA **(2)**
Chausee de Tervuren 198A, 1410, Waterloo, Belgium　　　　　　　　**(100%)**
Tel.: (32) 23525111
Web Site:
　　http://www.mastercardeurope.com
Sales Range: $250-299.9 Million
Provider of Credit & Debit Cards
N.A.I.C.S.: 522210
Regis Folbaum *(Gen Mgr-France)*
Roberto Tittarelli *(Pres-Western Europe)*
Mark Barnett *(Pres)*
Caroline Louveaux *(Chief Privacy Officer-Brussels)*

MasterCard International Incorporated
- Ireland **(2)**
Mountain View Central Park, Leopardstown,
Dublin, 18, Ireland
Tel.: (353) 12178600
Web Site: http://www.mastercard.us
Credit Cards Distr
N.A.I.C.S.: 522210

Mastercard Payment Gateway Services Ltd. **(2)**
10 Upper Bank Street, London, E14 5NP,
United Kingdom
Tel.: (44) 2074219280
Web Site: http://www.mastercard.com
Emp.: 362
Outsourced Payment Processing Services
N.A.I.C.S.: 522320
Andrea Scerch *(Pres)*

Trans Fast Remittance, Inc. **(1)**
44 Wall St, New York, NY 10005
Tel.: (888) 578-7267
Web Site: http://www.transfast.com
Remittance Services
N.A.I.C.S.: 522320

Transactis, Inc. **(1)**
1250 Broadway, New York, NY 10001
Tel.: (347) 474-7342
Web Site: http://www.transactis.com
Financial Services
N.A.I.C.S.: 522320
Bil Manes *(VP-Enterprise Strategy)*
John Mottola *(Dir-Infrastructure)*
Chris Russell *(Dir-Change Mgmt)*

MASTERCRAFT BOAT HOLDINGS, INC.
100 Cherokee Cove Dr, Vonore, TN
37885

Tel.: (423) 884-2221   DE
Web Site:
  https://www.mastercraft.com
Year Founded: 2000
MCFT—(NASDAQ)
Rev.: $366,588,000
Assets: $317,984,000
Liabilities: $134,105,000
Net Worth: $183,879,000
Earnings: $7,800,000
Emp.: 920
Fiscal Year-end: 06/30/24
Holding Company; Recreational
Boats Mfr
N.A.I.C.S.: 551112
Bradley M. Nelson *(CEO)*
Timothy M. Oxley *(Treas, Sec & VP)*
Dave Ekern *(Chief Product Officer)*
Mike Schmidt *(CIO)*
Charlene Hampton *(VP-Human Resources)*
Jim Brown *(VP-Operations)*
George Steinbarger *(Chief Revenue Officer)*
Matt McDevitt *(VP-Sls-Global)*
Jan Morton *(VP-Supply Chain)*

Subsidiaries:

Crest Marine, LLC   (1)
2710 S M 52, Owosso, MI 48867-9203
Tel.: (989) 725-5188
Web Site:
  https://www.crestpontoonboats.com
Sales Range: $10-24.9 Million
Emp.: 185
Boatbuilding & Repairing
N.A.I.C.S.: 336612
Joe Antonneau *(Pres)*

MasterCraft Boat Company, LLC   (1)
100 Cherokee Cove Dr, Vonore, TN 37885-2129
Tel.: (423) 884-7708
Web Site: http://www.mastercraft.com
Sales Range: $200-249.9 Million
Emp.: 560
Powerboats Mfr
N.A.I.C.S.: 336612

Nautic Star, LLC   (1)
500 Waterway Dr, Amory, MS 38821
Tel.: (662) 256-5636
Web Site: http://www.nauticstarboats.com
Sales Range: $50-74.9 Million
Emp.: 51
Boat Design & Building
N.A.I.C.S.: 336612
Scott Womack *(Pres)*

MATADOR RESOURCES COMPANY
5400 LBJ Fwy Ste 1500, Dallas, TX 75240
Tel.: (972) 371-5200   TX
Web Site:
  https://www.matadorresources.com
Year Founded: 2003
MTDR—(NYSE)
Rev.: $3,058,025,000
Assets: $5,554,505,000
Liabilities: $2,237,414,000
Net Worth: $3,317,091,000
Earnings: $1,214,206,000
Emp.: 360
Fiscal Year-end: 12/31/22
Crude Petroleum & Natural Gas Exploration Services
N.A.I.C.S.: 211120
G. Gregg Krug *(Exec VP-Mktg Midstream & Strategy)*
Brian J. Willey *(CFO, Pres-Midstream Ops & Exec VP)*
Ermund L. Frost III *(Exec VP)*
Christopher P. Calvert *(COO & Exec VP)*
Michael D. Frenzel *(Treas & Exec VP)*
Jonathan J. Filbert *(Exec VP/Sr VP-Land)*

Van H. Singleton II *(Pres-Land, Acquisitions, Divestitures, and Planning)*
Joseph William Foran *(Founder, Chm & CEO)*

Subsidiaries:

Delaware Water Management Company, LLC   (1)
5400 LBJ Fwy Ste 1500, Dallas, TX 75240
Tel.: (972) 371-5232
Waste Management Services
N.A.I.C.S.: 237110

Longwood Gathering & Disposal Systems, LP   (1)
One Lincoln Ctr 5400 LBJ Fwy Ste 1500, Dallas, TX 75240
Tel.: (972) 371-5200
Oil & Gas Exploration Services
N.A.I.C.S.: 213112
Joseph William Foran *(Chm, Pres & CEO)*
Matt Spicer *(Pres)*

Matador Production Company   (1)
5400 Lbj Freeway Ste 1500l, Dallas, TX 75240
Tel.: (972) 371-5200
Emp.: 20
Oil & Gas Exploration Services
N.A.I.C.S.: 213112

MATERION CORPORATION
6070 Parkland Blvd, Mayfield Heights, OH 44124
Tel.: (216) 486-4200   OH
Web Site: https://www.materion.com
Year Founded: 2000
MTRN—(NYSE)
Rev.: $1,757,109,000
Assets: $1,691,979,000
Liabilities: $891,989,000
Net Worth: $799,990,000
Earnings: $85,990,000
Emp.: 3,723
Fiscal Year-end: 12/31/22
Holding Company; Advanced Engineered Materials Mfr
N.A.I.C.S.: 551112
Gregory R. Chemnitz *(Gen Counsel, Sec & VP)*
Jugal K. Vijayvargiya *(Pres & CEO)*
Clive A. Grannum *(Pres-Performance Alloys & Composites)*
John M. Zaranec *(CFO-Performance Materials)*
Shelly M. Chadwick *(CFO, Principal Acctg Officer & VP-Fin)*

Subsidiaries:

Aerospace Metal Composites Limited   (1)
1 R A E Road, Farnborough, GU14 6XE, Hampshire, United Kingdom
Tel.: (44) 12063058837
Alloy Steel Mfr & Distr
N.A.I.C.S.: 331513

EIS Optics (Shanghai) Limited   (1)
33 No Building No 76 Fu Te Dong San Road, WGQ Free Trade Zone Pudong, Shanghai, 200131, China
Tel.: (86) 2150574646
Web Site: http://www.eisoptics.com
Sales Range: $75-99.9 Million
Emp.: 300
Optical Film Component Whslr
N.A.I.C.S.: 423460

EIS Optics Limited   (1)
1 R A E Road, 30 Buckingham Gate, Farnborough, GU14 6XE, Hampshire, United Kingdom
Tel.: (44) 1635223838
Web Site: http://www.eisoptics.com
Sales Range: $25-49.9 Million
Emp.: 10
Optical Film Component Whslr
N.A.I.C.S.: 423460

Egbert Corp.   (1)
No 6 Qingshan Road Licang District, Qingdao, 266000, Shandong, China
Tel.: (86) 53280913291

Web Site: http://www.egbertcorp.com
Chemical Mfr & Distr
N.A.I.C.S.: 335311

Materion Advanced Chemicals Inc.   (1)
407 N 13th St, Milwaukee, WI 53233
Tel.: (414) 289-9800
Web Site: http://www.materion.com
Sales Range: $25-49.9 Million
Inorganic Chemical Mfr
N.A.I.C.S.: 325180

Materion Advanced Materials Germany GmbH   (1)
Borsigstrasse 10, 63755, Alzenau, Germany
Tel.: (49) 602391820
Alloy Steel Distr
N.A.I.C.S.: 423510

Materion Advanced Materials Technologies & Services Far East Philippines Ptd Ltd.   (1)
Bldg 8365 Argonut Highway Cubi Pt Boton Area, Subic Bay Freeport Zone, Olongapo, Philippines
Tel.: (63) 472522640
Sheet Metal Mfr
N.A.I.C.S.: 332322

Materion Advanced Materials Technologies and Services (Suzhou) Ltd.   (1)
No 28 Sutong Road, Suzhou Industrial Park, Suzhou, 215021, China
Tel.: (86) 51267671018
Web Site: http://www.materion.com
Emp.: 30
Nonferrous Metal Refining Services
N.A.I.C.S.: 331410

Materion Advanced Materials Technologies and Services Inc.   (1)
2978 Main St, Buffalo, NY 14214
Tel.: (716) 837-1000
Web Site: http://www.materion.com
Thin Film Deposition Material Mfr & Distr
N.A.I.C.S.: 333242

Materion Brewster LLC   (1)
42 Mount Ebo Rd S, Brewster, NY 10509
Tel.: (845) 279-0900
Metal Ore Mining Services
N.A.I.C.S.: 212290
Mary Gregory *(Mgr-HR)*

Materion Brush (Japan) Ltd.   (1)
Dai-ichi Marusan Building 3-9 Kanda Jimbocho, Chiyoda-ku, Tokyo, 101-0051, Japan
Tel.: (81) 332302961
Web Site: http://www.materion.jp
Copper Beryllium Alloy Mfr & Distr
N.A.I.C.S.: 331420

Materion Brush (Singapore) PTE Ltd.   (1)
1008 Toa Payoh North No 04-12/14/15, Singapore, 318996, Singapore
Tel.: (65) 68424456
Web Site: http://www.materion.jp
Industrial Engineered Product Whslr
N.A.I.C.S.: 423840

Materion Brush GmbH   (1)
Motorstrasse 34, 70499, Stuttgart, Germany
Tel.: (49) 71 183 0930
Web Site: https://www.materion.de.com
Sales Range: $25-49.9 Million
Emp.: 30
Industrial Engineered Product Whslr
N.A.I.C.S.: 423840
Helena Furstenberg *(Mng Dir)*

Materion Brush International   (1)
11th FL-6 No 188 Section 5 Nanking East Road, Taipei, Taiwan
Tel.: (886) 227478800
Alloy Steel Distr
N.A.I.C.S.: 423510

Materion Brush International   (1)
Unit 1911B 19/F Skyline Tower 39 Wang Kwong Rd Kowloon, Kowloon Bay, China (Hong Kong)
Tel.: (852) 23181907
Alloy Steel Distr
N.A.I.C.S.: 423510

Materion Brush International, Inc. (1)

6070 Parkland Blvd, Mayfield Heights, OH 44124
Tel.: (216) 486-4200
Metal Product Distr
N.A.I.C.S.: 423510

Materion Brush Performance Alloys   (1)
6070 Parkland Blvd 2nd Fl, Mayfield Heights, OH 44124   (100%)
Tel.: (216) 383-6800
Web Site: http://www.materion.com
Sales Range: $50-74.9 Million
Emp.: 123
High Performance Engineered Materials
N.A.I.C.S.: 331420

Materion Brush Singapore Shanghai   (1)
Rm 2115 West Yan'an Road Longemont Building, Changning District, Shanghai, 200052, China
Tel.: (86) 2160574646
Alloy Steel Distr
N.A.I.C.S.: 423510

Materion Ceramics Inc.   (1)
6100 S Tucson Blvd, Tucson, AZ 85706-4520
Tel.: (520) 746-0699
Emp.: 52
Industrial Engineered Product Whslr
N.A.I.C.S.: 423840
Robert Napoles *(Mgr-HR)*

Materion Holdings Limited   (1)
Ballysimon Road, Limerick, Ireland
Tel.: (353) 61208182
Sales Range: $25-49.9 Million
Emp.: 32
Holding Company
N.A.I.C.S.: 551112
Eidan Gurack *(Mng Dir)*

Materion Ireland Ltd.   (1)
Ballysimon Road, Limerick, V94 E195, Ireland
Tel.: (353) 61208182
Alloy Steel Distr
N.A.I.C.S.: 423510

Materion Japan Ltd.   (1)
3-9 Kanda Jinbocho Koho Building, Chiyoda-ku, Tokyo, 101-0051, Japan
Tel.: (81) 332302961
Web Site: http://www.materion.jp
Metal Products Mfr
N.A.I.C.S.: 332999

Materion Korea Ltd.   (1)
303 3F Sejong Plaza 29 Dongnam-ro 75 gil, Seoul, 05269, Korea (South)
Tel.: (82) 234280070
Metal Product Distr
N.A.I.C.S.: 423510

Materion Precision Optics (Shanghai) Limited   (1)
33 Building No 76 Fu Te Dong San Rd WaiGaoQiao Free Trade Zone, Pudong, Shanghai, 200131, China
Tel.: (86) 2150574646
Metal Ore Mining Services
N.A.I.C.S.: 212290

Materion Precision Optics (U.K.) Limited   (1)
1st Floor Cayzer House 30 Buckingham Gate, London, SW1E 6NN, United Kingdom
Tel.: (44) 7789078648
Metal Ore Mining Services
N.A.I.C.S.: 212290
Stuart Lawson *(Dir-Global Sls)*

Materion Precision Optics and Thin Film Coatings Corporation   (1)
153 Industrial Way, Buellton, CA 93427
Tel.: (805) 688-4949
Web Site: http://www.materion.com
Thin Film Coatings & Optical Filters Mfr
N.A.I.C.S.: 334413

Materion Singapore Pte. Ltd.   (1)
28 Woodlands Loop 01-00, Singapore, 738308, Singapore
Tel.: (65) 65594450
Sheet Metal Work Mfg
N.A.I.C.S.: 332322

Materion Taiwan Co. Ltd.   (1)

Materion Corporation—(Continued)

1F No 6 Housheng Road, Luzhu District,
Taoyuan, 33855, Taiwan
Tel.: (886) 32226350
Sheet Metal Work Mfg
N.A.I.C.S.: 332322

Materion Technical Materials,
Inc. (1)
5 Wellington Rd, Lincoln, RI 02865
Tel.: (401) 333-1700
Web Site: http://www.materion.com
Sales Range: $25-49.9 Million
Emp.: 2,550
Specialty Strip Metal Products Mfr
N.A.I.C.S.: 332999

Materion UK Limited (1)
1 R A E Road, Farnborough, GU14 6XE,
Hampshire, United Kingdom
Tel.: (44) 1252375001
Packaging Material Mfr & Distr
N.A.I.C.S.: 326112

Optics Balzers AG (1)
Neugrut 35, 9496, Balzers, Liechtenstein
Tel.: (423) 3889200
Web Site: http://www.opticsbalzers.com
Optical Component Mfr
N.A.I.C.S.: 333310
Norman Korner (CFO)
Dirk von Frajer (CMO)
Stefan Pleier (Mng Dir)

Optics Balzers GmbH (1)
Mergenthalerallee 73-75, 65760, Eschborn,
Germany
Tel.: (49) 61969994144
Optical Component Mfr
N.A.I.C.S.: 333310

Optics Balzers Jena GmbH (1)
Otto-Eppenstein-Strasse 2, 07745, Jena,
Germany
Tel.: (49) 3641352930
Optical Component Mfr
N.A.I.C.S.: 333310
Stefan Jakobs (Mng Dir)

Optics Balzers Malaysia Sdn.
Bhd. (1)
Plot 574 Lorong Perusahaan 4, Prai Free
Industrial Zone, 13600, Penang, Malaysia
Tel.: (60) 43890000
Optical Component Mfr
N.A.I.C.S.: 333310
Leong Hooi Tan (Mng Dir)

Optics Balzers USA Inc. (1)
8379 Gasparilla Rd, Port Charlotte, FL
33981
Tel.: (303) 502-5401
Optical Component Mfr
N.A.I.C.S.: 333310

Technical Materials, Inc. (1)
5 Wellington Rd, Lincoln, RI
02865-4411 (100%)
Tel.: (401) 333-1700
Web Site: http://www.materion.com
Sales Range: $50-74.9 Million
Emp.: 200
Mfr Of Specialty Clad Metals
N.A.I.C.S.: 331410

Williams Advanced Materials Inc. (1)
2978 Main St, Buffalo, NY 14214 (100%)
Tel.: (716) 837-1000
Sales Range: $50-74.9 Million
Emp.: 200
Thin Film Deposition & Semiconductor
Packaging Components Mfr
N.A.I.C.S.: 334419

Subsidiary (Domestic):

Academy Corporation (2)
5520 Midway Park Pl Ne, Albuquerque, NM
87109-5800
Tel.: (505) 345-1805
Sales Range: $50-74.9 Million
Emp.: 150
Specialty Metal Refining & Manufacturing
Services
N.A.I.C.S.: 331492
Halleemah Nash (Chief Partnerships
Officer-Chicago)

Plant (Domestic):

Materion Microelectronics &
Services (2)

2080 Lockport Rd, Wheatfield, NY 14304-
1110
Tel.: (716) 837-1000
Web Site: http://www.materion.com
Sales Range: $10-24.9 Million
Emp.: 10
Mfr & Supplier of Thin Film Deposition Ma-
terials, Electronic Packaging Products &
High Purity & Specialty Materials
N.A.I.C.S.: 423510

Subsidiary (Domestic):

Materion Microelectronics &
Services (2)
22 Graf Rd, Newburyport, MA 01950
Tel.: (978) 463-6545
Web Site: http://www.materion.com
Sales Range: $50-74.9 Million
Emp.: 50
High Performance RF & Microwave Power
Packages & Other Electronic Components
Mfr
N.A.I.C.S.: 335311

Materion Precision Optics and Thin
Film Coatings Inc. (2)
155 Federal ST., Ste 700, Boston, MA
02110
Tel.: (978) 692-7513
Web Site: https://materion.com
Precision Thin Film Coatings & Optical Fil-
ters Mfr
N.A.I.C.S.: 333310

MATINAS BIOPHARMA HOLD-
INGS, INC.
1545 Rte 206 S Ste 302, Bedminster,
NJ 07921
Tel.: (908) 484-8805 DE
Web Site:
https://www.matinasbiopharma.com
Year Founded: 2011
MTNB—(NYSEAMEX)
Rev.: $1,096,000
Assets: $25,104,000
Liabilities: $5,858,000
Net Worth: $19,246,000
Earnings: ($22,942,000)
Emp.: 32
Fiscal Year-end: 12/31/23
Pharmaceuticals Mfr
N.A.I.C.S.: 325412
Thomas Hoover (Chief Bus Officer)
Jerome D. Jabbour (Pres & CEO)
Hui Liu (CTO)
Eric J. Ende (Chm)
Keith A. Kucinski (CFO)
Theresa Matkovits (Chief Dev Officer)
James J. Ferguson III (Chief Medical
Officer)

MATIV HOLDINGS, INC.
100 Kimball Pl Ste 600, Alpharetta,
GA 30009 DE
Web Site: https://www.mativ.com
Year Founded: 1994
MATV—(NYSE)
Rev.: $2,167,400,000
Assets: $3,669,200,000
Liabilities: $2,489,900,000
Net Worth: $1,179,300,000
Earnings: ($7,500,000)
Emp.: 7,500
Fiscal Year-end: 12/31/22
Cigarette Paper & Fine Paper Mfr
N.A.I.C.S.: 322120
Christoph Stenzel (Grp Pres-
Advanced Materials)
Julie A. Schertell (Pres & CEO)
Greg Weitzel (CFO-Global)
Mark W. Johnson Sr. (Chief Legal
Officer, Gen Counsel & Sec)
Cheryl Allegri (Chief Acctg Officer &
Controller)
Brendan Streich (VP-Global Comm &
Engagement)
Andrew Wamser (CFO)
Natalie Poteran (Chief Transformation
Officer)
Mike Rickheim (Chief HR Officer)
Rajeev Kapur (CIO)

Subsidiaries:

Argotec Deutschland GmBH (1)
Husarenhof 7b, 22043, Hamburg, Germany
Tel.: (49) 4035085133
Fine Paper Whslr
N.A.I.C.S.: 424110

China Tobacco Mauduit (Jiangmen)
Paper Industry Company Ltd. (1)
No 15 Baotang Road Tangxia Town, Pengji-
ang District, Jiangmen, 529085,
China (50%)
Tel.: (86) 750 3626262
Cigarette Paper Mfr
N.A.I.C.S.: 322120

DelStar International, Limited (1)
C/O Bishop Fleming Llp 10 Temple Back,
Bristol, BS1 6FL, United Kingdom
Tel.: (44) 1454613991
Health Care Equipment Mfr
N.A.I.C.S.: 339112

DelStar Technologies, Inc. (1)
601 Industrial Rd, Middletown, DE 19709
Tel.: (302) 378-8888
Plastic & Metal Components Mfr
N.A.I.C.S.: 326199

Subsidiary (Domestic):

Conwed Plastics LLC (2)
2810 Weeks Ave SE, Minneapolis, MN
55414
Tel.: (612) 623-1700
Emp.: 430
Plastic Netting & Other Plastic Products Mfr
N.A.I.C.S.: 326199

Subsidiary (Non-US):

Conwed Plastics N.V. (3)
Marcel Havetslaan 20, Industrial Zone 4
Genk N, 3600, Genk, Limburg, Belgium
Tel.: (32) 89848310
Plastic Nettings Mfr
N.A.I.C.S.: 326199
Berten Verbeeck (Gen Mgr)

Subsidiary (Domestic):

Filtrexx International, LLC (1)
61 N Cleveland Massillon Rd Ste E, Akron,
OH 44333
Tel.: (877) 542-7699
Web Site: http://www.filtrexx.com
Farm Management Services
N.A.I.C.S.: 115116

LTR Industries S.A. (1)
Kerisole, 29300, Quimperle,
France (100%)
Tel.: (33) 243474200
Cigarette Paper & Fine Paper Mfr
N.A.I.C.S.: 322120

Neenah, Inc. (1)
3460 Preston Ridge Rd, Alpharetta, GA
30005
Tel.: (678) 566-6500
Web Site: http://www.neenah.com
Rev.: $1,028,500,000
Assets: $1,081,700,000
Liabilities: $765,700,000
Net Worth: $316,000,000
Earnings: ($24,900,000)
Emp.: 2,493
Fiscal Year-end: 12/31/2021
Fine Paper & Packaging Mfr
N.A.I.C.S.: 322120
Noah S. Benz (Gen Counsel, Sec & Sr VP)
Paul F. DeSantis (CFO, Treas & Sr VP)
Michael W. Rickheim (Chief Admin Officer,
Chief HR Officer & Sr VP)
Kingsley E. Shannon (Pres-Fine Paper &
Packaging & Sr VP)
Jason T. Free (Exec VP-Ops-Global)
Kyle Anderson (VP-Strategy & IR)
Missy Elam (Dir-Comm)

Subsidiary (Non-US):

Neenah Coldenhove BV (2)
D W Van Vreeswijklaan 9, 6961 LG, Ee-
rbeek, Netherlands
Tel.: (31) 313670670
Web Site: https://www.coldenhove.com
Paper Mill Printing Product Mfr
N.A.I.C.S.: 322120

Neenah Gessner GmbH (2)
Otto-von-Steinbeis-Str 14b, 83052,
Bruckmuhl, Germany
Tel.: (49) 80627030
Web Site: https://www.neenah-gessner.de
Emp.: 660
Specialty Paper Mfr
N.A.I.C.S.: 322220

Subsidiary (Domestic):

Neenah Paper Michigan, Inc. (2)
501 E Munising Ave, Munising, MI 49862-
1490
Tel.: (906) 387-2700
Web Site: http://www.neenahpaper.com
Sales Range: $250-299.9 Million
Emp.: 350
Mfr of Paper Products
N.A.I.C.S.: 322120

Neenah Technical Materials, Inc. (2)
Ashuelot Park II 448 Hubbard Ave, Pitts-
field, MA 01201
Tel.: (413) 553-4302
Web Site: http://www.cranenonwovens.com
Nonwoven Product Mfr
N.A.I.C.S.: 313230

Papeteries de Malaucene S.A.S (1)
Avenue de Petrarque, Malaucène, 84340,
France (100%)
Tel.: (33) 490126400
Cigarette Paper Mfr
N.A.I.C.S.: 322120
Jean-Yves Klein (Gen Mgr)

Papeteries de Saint-Girons
S.A.S. (1)
Eycheil, 09200, Saint-Girons,
France (100%)
Tel.: (33) 534143500
Sales Range: $300-349.9 Million
Emp.: 300
Cigarette Paper & Fine Paper Mfr
N.A.I.C.S.: 322120
Marc Bernard (Dir-Sls & Mktg)
Andre Pavot (Dir-DP)

Subsidiary (Domestic):

Saint-Girons Industries S.N.C. (2)
Eycheil, 9200, Saint-Girons,
France (100%)
Tel.: (33) 534143500
Web Site: http://www.swmintl.com
Sales Range: $250-299.9 Million
Cigarette Paper & Fine Paper Mfr
N.A.I.C.S.: 322120

SWM International -
Massachusetts (1)
53 Silvio O Conte Dr, Greenfield, MA 01301
Tel.: (413) 772-2564
Web Site: http://www.swmintl.com
Plastic Film & Sheet Mfr
N.A.I.C.S.: 326113

Scapa Group plc (1)
Manchester Road, Ashton under Lyne, OL7
0ED, Greater Manchester, United Kingdom
Tel.: (44) 1613017400
Web Site: https://www.scapa.com
Technical Tapes, Adhesive Films & Cable
Products Mfr
N.A.I.C.S.: 325520
Heejae Richard Chae (CEO)
Wendy Baker (Gen Counsel & Sec)
Oskar Zahn (CFO)
Chris Brinsmead (Chm)
Brett Pollard (Mng Dir-Global Corp Dev &
Strategy)
John Petreanu (Pres-Healthcare)

Subsidiary (US):

BioMed Laboratories Inc. (2)
8181 Eastpoint Dr, Dallas, TX 75227-2071
Tel.: (972) 707-1210
Web Site: http://www.biomedlabs.com
Pharmaceutical, Medical Device, Wound
Care & Skin Care Products Mfr
N.A.I.C.S.: 325412

Euromed, Inc. (2)
25 Corporate Dr, Orangeburg, NY 10962
Tel.: (865) 246-4264
Web Site: https://www.scapahealthcare.com
Sales Range: $1-9.9 Million
Emp.: 60
Surgical Appliance & Supplies Mfr

N.A.I.C.S.: 339113
Lionel Bonte *(Pres-Healthcare & Wellness)*
Juan Toro *(VP-Global Sls & Marketing)*
Matt Ellison *(VP-Global Ops)*

Markel Industries, Inc.   **(2)**
135 Sheldon Rd, Manchester, CT 06042
Tel.: (860) 646-5303
Web Site: http://www.markelind.com
Sales Range: $1-9.9 Million
Plastics Product Mfr
N.A.I.C.S.: 326199
Robert W. Crichton *(Pres)*

Subsidiary (Non-US):

Scapa (HK) Holdings Ltd   **(2)**
Unit P 19th Floor Teda Building 87 Wing
Lok Street, Sheung Wan, New Territories,
China (Hong Kong)
Tel.: (852) 24394330
Investment Management Service
N.A.I.C.S.: 523999

Subsidiary (Domestic):

Scapa Hong Kong Ltd   **(3)**
Unit B 19/F Teda Building No 87 Wing Lok
St, Sheung Wan, China (Hong Kong)
Tel.: (852) 24394330
Adhesive Tape Mfr
N.A.I.C.S.: 325520

Subsidiary (Non-US):

Scapa (Schweiz) AG   **(2)**
Feldmuhlestrasse 37, 9400, Rorschach,
Switzerland
Tel.: (41) 71 844 56 56
Sales Range: $25-49.9 Million
Emp.: 10
Adhesive Tape Mfr
N.A.I.C.S.: 325520
Sandro Pellegrino *(Gen Mgr)*

**Scapa (Shanghai) International Trad-
ing Company Ltd**   **(2)**
1st Floor No 55 Hua Shen Road,
Waigaoqiao Free Trade Zone, Shanghai,
200131, China
Tel.: (86) 2150464750
Adhesive Tape Distr
N.A.I.C.S.: 424120

Scapa France S.A.   **(2)**
79 Allee Bernard Palissy, 26001, Valence,
France   **(100%)**
Tel.: (33) 475448000
Web Site: http://www.scapa.com
Sales Range: $50-74.9 Million
Emp.: 200
Specialist Tapes
N.A.I.C.S.: 325520

Scapa Holdings GmbH   **(2)**
Markircher Str 12a, Mannheim, 68829,
Baden-Wurttemberg, Germany
Tel.: (49) 621470910
Web Site: http://www.scapa.com
Sales Range: $25-49.9 Million
Emp.: 15
Adhesive Films & Tapes Mfr
N.A.I.C.S.: 325520
Sandro Pellegreno *(Mng Dir)*

Scapa Italia S.p.A.   **(2)**
Via Vittorio Emanuele 2nd 27, 13030, Ghis-
larengo, VC, Italy   **(100%)**
Tel.: (39) 0161867311
Sales Range: $50-74.9 Million
Emp.: 150
Specialist Tapes
N.A.I.C.S.: 325520

Subsidiary (US):

Scapa North America Inc.   **(2)**
111 Great Pond Dr, Windsor, CT
06095   **(100%)**
Tel.: (860) 688-8000
Web Site: https://www.scapa.com
Sales Range: $75-99.9 Million
Emp.: 300
Presurre Sensitive Tapes
N.A.I.C.S.: 322220

Subsidiary (Non-US):

Scapa Tapes (Korea) Co. Ltd   **(2)**
7th Floor Enhasu Building 410-7 Do Gok-
Dong, Kang Nam-Gu, Seoul, Korea (South)

Tel.: (82) 2 561 4511
Adhesive Product Mfr
N.A.I.C.S.: 325520

Scapa Tapes Malaysia Sdn Bhd   **(2)**
8 Jalan Kartunis U1/47 Temasya Industrial
Park, 40150, Shah Alam, Selangor Darul
Ehsan, Malaysia
Tel.: (60) 355692529
Sales Range: $25-49.9 Million
Emp.: 62
Adhesive Tape Mfr
N.A.I.C.S.: 322230

Scapa Tapes North America   **(2)**
609 Barnet Boulevard RR 3 Stn Main, Ren-
frew, K7V 0A9, ON, Canada   **(100%)**
Tel.: (613) 432-8545
Web Site: http://www.scapana.com
Sales Range: $25-49.9 Million
Emp.: 200
Dryer & Forming Fabrics
N.A.I.C.S.: 313230

Scapa Tapes North America Inc.   **(2)**
Tel.: (860) 688-8000
Sales Range: $1-9.9 Million
Emp.: 45
Converted Plastic Product Mfr
N.A.I.C.S.: 326199

Subsidiary (Domestic):

Scapa Tapes UK Ltd.   **(2)**
Manchester Road, Ashton under Lyne, OL7
0ED, Greater Manchester, United
Kingdom   **(100%)**
Tel.: (44) 161 301 7400
Web Site: http://www.scapa.com
Sales Range: $300-349.9 Million
Emp.: 100
Specialty Tapes & Coating Compounds
N.A.I.C.S.: 325520
Heejae Richard Chae *(CEO)*

Schweitzer-Mauduit Canada, Inc.   **(1)**
340 Airport Dr Main Station, PO Box 1039,
Winkler, R6W 4B1, MB, Canada   **(100%)**
Tel.: (204) 325-7986
Web Site: http://www.schweitzer-
      mauduit.com
Sales Range: $25-49.9 Million
Emp.: 56
Paper Fiber Processing Operations
N.A.I.C.S.: 322120

U.S. Netting, Inc.   **(1)**
1514 Veshecco Dr, Erie, PA 16501
Tel.: (814) 455-9400
Web Site: http://www.usnetting.com
Logistics Consulting Servies
N.A.I.C.S.: 541614
Paul Galla *(Pres)*

MATMOWN, INC.
800 N Rainbow Blvd Ste 208-029,
Las Vegas, NV 89107
Tel.: (702) 738-0016   NV
Web Site: http://www.matmown.com
Year Founded: 2008
MTMW—(OTCIQ)
Gold Exploration
N.A.I.C.S.: 212220
Michael Christopher Boyko *(Pres &
CEO)*
Alex Portelli *(Chm, Treas & Sec)*

MATRIX SERVICE COMPANY
15 E 5th St Ste 1100, Tulsa, OK
74103
Tel.: (918) 838-8822   DE
Web Site:
      https://www.matrixservicecom
      pany.com
Year Founded: 1984
MTRX—(NASDAQ)
Rev.: $795,020,000
Assets: $400,504,000
Liabilities: $219,020,000
Net Worth: $181,484,000
Earnings: ($52,361,000)
Emp.: 2,545
Fiscal Year-end: 06/30/23
Storage Tanks & Pressure Vessels;
Plant Services Including Turn-
Arounds & Turnkey Construction Ser-
vices

N.A.I.C.S.: 238910
Alan R. Updyke *(COO)*
Nancy E. Austin *(Chief Admin Officer
& VP)*
Jim W. Mogg *(Chm)*
Kevin S. Cavanah *(CFO & VP)*
John R. Hewitt *(CEO)*
D. Quinton Beasley *(VP-Acctg)*
Rick J. Bennett *(CIO & VP)*
Justin D. Sheets *(Gen Counsel, Sec
& VP)*
Kellie Smythe *(Sr Dir-IR)*
Melissa K. Gilliland *(VP-HR)*
Kevin A. Durkin *(Chief Bus Dev &
Strategy Officer & VP)*
Patrick M. Chambers *(VP-Bus Dev)*
John R. Hart *(VP-Bus Dev)*
Vikas V. Moharir *(VP-Bus Dev &
Strategy)*
John W. Zwack *(VP-Bus Dev)*
Camron Azadan *(Dir-Bus Dev)*
Mohamed Abdelaziz *(Dir-Bus Dev)*
Shawn Payne *(Co-Pres)*
Glyn A. Rodgers *(Co-Pres)*
Karen McDonald *(VP)*
Vicki R. Reese *(VP)*

Subsidiaries:

Allentech, Inc.   **(1)**
6350 Hedgewood Dr Ste 100, Allentown,
PA 18106
Tel.: (484) 664-7887
Web Site: http://www.allentech.com
Sales Range: $50-74.9 Million
Emp.: 70
Fabrication of Aluminum Floating Roofs;
Primary & Secondary Seals
N.A.I.C.S.: 238160

Matrix Applied Technologies, Ltd. **(1)**
90 Donyu-2 Ro, Paju-eup, Paju, 413-902,
Kyunggi-do, Korea (South)
Tel.: (82) 319496854
Oil & Gas Construction Services
N.A.I.C.S.: 237120

**Matrix Applied Technologies, Pty.
Ltd.**   **(1)**
191 Oriordan St Ste 5 02 Mascot, Sydney,
2020, NSW, Australia
Tel.: (61) 971561813631
Oil & Gas Construction Services
N.A.I.C.S.: 237120

**Matrix North American Construction,
Inc.**   **(1)**
1974 Sproul Rd Ste 300, Broomall, PA
19008-3402
Tel.: (610) 876-9292
Web Site: https://www.matrixnac.com
Construction Services
N.A.I.C.S.: 236210
Alan R. Updyke *(Interim Pres & COO)*
Terry D. Stewart *(Sr VP-Ops)*
Vicki R. Reese *(VP-Acctg & Fin)*
Diego Carducci *(VP-Ops)*
Jay Crilley *(VP-Bus Dev)*

Matrix PDM Engineering, Inc.   **(1)**
15 E 5th St Ste 1100, Tulsa, OK 74103
Tel.: (918) 838-8822
Web Site: https://www.matrixpdm.com
Engineering Services
N.A.I.C.S.: 541330
Glyn Rodgers *(Pres)*
Vikas Moharir *(VP-Bus Dev & Strategy)*

Matrix Service Canada ULC   **(1)**
3022 Calgary Trail South, Edmonton, T9E
0B3, AB, Canada
Tel.: (780) 986-4058
Web Site: http://www.matrixservice.ca
Sales Range: $25-49.9 Million
Emp.: 15
Industrial Service Contractor
N.A.I.C.S.: 238910

**Matrix Service Company - Fabrication
Division**   **(1)**
1109 W Main Pkwy, Catoosa, OK 74015-
3035
Tel.: (918) 379-6300
Web Site: http://www.matrixservice.com
Sales Range: $100-124.9 Million
Emp.: 220
Fabrication of Storage Tanks

N.A.I.C.S.: 332312

**Matrix Service Company - Tank Con-
struction Division**   **(1)**
1107 W Main Pkwy, Catoosa, OK 74015
Tel.: (918) 425-3106
Web Site: http://www.matrixservice.com
Sales Range: $75-99.9 Million
Emp.: 147
Construction Of Storage Tanks
N.A.I.C.S.: 332420

**Matrix Service Industrial Contractors
Inc.**   **(1)**
1510 Chester Pike Ste 500, Crum Lynne,
PA 19022
Tel.: (302) 453-8300
Web Site: http://www.matrixservice.com
Sales Range: $10-24.9 Million
Emp.: 34
Tank Welding Service
N.A.I.C.S.: 238220

Matrix Service, Inc.   **(1)**
1105 W Main Pkwy, Catoosa, OK 74015-
2333
Tel.: (918) 437-0240
Sales Range: $50-74.9 Million
Emp.: 72
N.A.I.C.S.: 213112
James P. Ryan *(VP)*
Kevin A. Durkin *(VP-Bus Dev)*
Shawn P. Payne *(Co-Pres)*
Shawn Payne *(Founder, Co-Pres, CEO,
CIO & VP)*

Branch (Domestic):

Matrix Service, Inc.   **(2)**
7021 Gregdale Rd, Houston, TX
77049-3406   **(100%)**
Tel.: (281) 458-8781
Web Site: http://www.matrixservice.com
Sales Range: $75-99.9 Million
N.A.I.C.S.: 213112

Branch (Non-US):

Matrix Service, Inc.   **(2)**
473 Scott Rd, Sarnia, N7T 7W1, ON,
Canada   **(100%)**
Tel.: (519) 336-5490
Web Site: http://www.matrixservice.ca
Sales Range: $25-49.9 Million
Emp.: 20
Metal Coatings & Industrial Painting Ser-
vices
N.A.I.C.S.: 332812

Branch (Domestic):

Matrix Service, Inc.   **(2)**
500 W Collins Ave, Orange, CA
92867   **(100%)**
Tel.: (714) 289-4419
Support Svcs
N.A.I.C.S.: 213112
David Cherek *(Mgr-QA & QC)*

Matrix Service, Inc.   **(2)**
3810 Bakerview Spur, Bellingham, WA
98226-8034   **(100%)**
Tel.: (360) 676-4905
Web Site: http://www.matrixservices.com
Provider of Oil Field Services
N.A.I.C.S.: 236220

MATSON, INC.
1411 Sand Island Pkwy, Honolulu, HI
96819
Tel.: (510) 628-4000   HI
Web Site: https://www.matson.com
Year Founded: 2011
MATX—(NYSE)
Rev.: $4,343,000,000
Assets: $4,330,000,000
Liabilities: $2,033,100,000
Net Worth: $2,296,900,000
Earnings: $1,063,900,000
Emp.: 4,288
Fiscal Year-end: 12/31/22
Holding Company; Freight Transpor-
tation & Marine Cargo Handling Ser-
vices
N.A.I.C.S.: 551112
Matthew J. Cox *(Chm & CEO)*
John P. Lauer *(Chief Comml Officer &
Exec VP)*

Matson, Inc.—(Continued)

Kevin L. Stuck *(Chief Acctg Officer, VP & Controller)*
Joel M. Wine *(CFO & Exec VP)*
Peter T. Heilmann *(Chief Admin Officer, Gen Counsel & Exec VP)*
Rusty K. Rolfe *(Pres-Logistics)*
Grace M. Cerocke *(Sr VP-Fin)*
Rich S. Kinney *(Sr VP-Network Ops)*
Laura L. Rascon *(Sr VP-Customer Experience)*
Chris A. Scott *(Sr VP-Transpacific Svcs)*
Jack W. Sullivan *(Sr VP-Vessel Ops & Engrg)*
Qiang Gao *(Sr VP)*
Leonard P. Isotoff *(Exec VP)*
Ku'uhaku T. Park *(Sr VP)*
Jason L. Taylor *(Sr VP)*

Subsidiaries:

ABHI-Crockett, Inc. **(1)**
822 Bishop St, Honolulu, HI 96813-3924
Tel.: (808) 525-6611
Real Estate Services
N.A.I.C.S.: 531210

Matson Navigation Company, Inc. **(1)**
555 12th St Ste 700, Oakland, CA 94607 **(100%)**
Tel.: (510) 628-4000
Sales Range: $1-4.9 Billion
Freight Transportation & Marine Cargo Handling Services
N.A.I.C.S.: 483111
Matthew J. Cox *(Chm & CEO)*

Subsidiary (Domestic):

Matson Alaska, Inc. **(2)**
1411 Sand Island Pkwy, Honolulu, HI 96819
Tel.: (808) 848-1211
Web Site: http://www.matson.com
Sales Range: $1-4.9 Billion
Emp.: 1,633
Holding Company; Freight Shipping Services
N.A.I.C.S.: 551112

Matson Logistics, Inc. **(2)**
1855 Gateway Blvd Ste 550, Concord, CA 94520 **(100%)**
Tel.: (925) 887-6200
Web Site: http://www.matson.com
Sales Range: $25-49.9 Million
Emp.: 86
Freight Transportation Arrangement Services
N.A.I.C.S.: 488510
Rusty K. Rolfe *(Pres)*

Subsidiary (Domestic):

Span Alaska Transportation, Inc. **(3)**
3815 W Valley Hwy N, Auburn, WA 98001
Tel.: (253) 395-7726
Web Site: http://www.spanalaska.com
Emp.: 200
Freight Transportation Arrangement
N.A.I.C.S.: 488510
Tom Souply *(Exec VP-Corporate Development)*

Subsidiary (Domestic):

Matson Terminals, Inc. **(2)**
1411 Sand Is pkwy, Honolulu, HI 96819 **(100%)**
Tel.: (808) 848-1211
Web Site: http://www.matson.com
Sales Range: $100-124.9 Million
Emp.: 300
Freight Shipping Services
N.A.I.C.S.: 483111

MATTEL, INC.
333 Continental Blvd, El Segundo, CA 90245-5012
Tel.: (310) 252-2000   **DE**
Web Site:
https://corporate.mattel.com
Year Founded: 1943

MAT—(NASDAQ)
Rev.: $5,441,219,000
Assets: $6,435,822,000
Liabilities: $4,286,609,000
Net Worth: $2,149,213,000
Earnings: $214,352,000
Emp.: 33,000
Fiscal Year-end: 12/31/23
Toy Products Marketer, Designer & Mfr.
N.A.I.C.S.: 339930
Robbie Brenner *(Pres-Films)*
Jonathan H. Anschell *(Chief legal Officer, Sec & Exec VP)*
Ynon Kreiz *(Chm & CEO)*
Sven Gerjets *(CTO & Exec VP)*
Amanda J. Thompson *(Chief People Officer & Exec VP)*
Steve Totzke *(Co-Pres & Chief Comml Officer)*
Yoon J. Hugh *(Principal Acctg Officer, Sr VP & Controller)*
Catherine Frymark *(Exec VP-Corp Comm)*
Roberto Isaias *(Chief Supply Chain Officer & Exec VP)*
Michelle Mendelovitz *(Head-Mattel Television Studios)*
Josh Silverman *(Chief Franchise Officer)*

Subsidiaries:

American Girl LLC **(1)**
 (100%)
Tel.: (608) 831-5210
Web Site: https://www.americangirl.com
Sales Range: $800-899.9 Million
Emp.: 1,500
Books, Dolls & Accessories Direct Mail Retailer, Publisher & Marketer
N.A.I.C.S.: 513130

Subsidiary (Domestic):

American Girl Brands, LLC **(2)**
8400 Fairway Pl, Middleton, WI 53562-0497 **(100%)**
Tel.: (608) 831-5210
Web Site: https://www.americangirl.com
Intellectual Property Holding Company
N.A.I.C.S.: 551112

American Girl Place Inc. **(2)**
835 N Michigan, Chicago, IL 60611-2010 **(100%)**
Tel.: (312) 943-9400
Web Site: https://www.americangirl.com
Sales Range: Less than $1 Million
Emp.: 3
Retailer & Direct Marketer Children's Publishers
N.A.I.C.S.: 423920

Fisher-Price, Inc. **(1)**
636 Girard Ave, East Aurora, NY 14052
Tel.: (716) 687-3000
Web Site: http://www.fisher-price.com
Sales Range: $400-449.9 Million
Emp.: 900
Toys & Juvenile Products Mfr
N.A.I.C.S.: 423920

MEGA Brands Inc. **(1)**
4505 Hickmore, Montreal, H4T 1K4, QC, Canada
Tel.: (514) 333-3339
Web Site: http://www.megabrands.com
Emp.: 1,600
Toys, Stationery & Board Games Mfr & Sales
N.A.I.C.S.: 339930
Thomas W. Prichard *(Pres-Stationery & Activities)*

Subsidiary (US):

Mega Brands America Inc. **(2)**
3 Ada Ste 200, Irvine, CA 92618
Tel.: (949) 727-9009
Web Site: http://www.megabrands.com
Emp.: 25
Arts & Craft Products Mfr
N.A.I.C.S.: 339930

Subsidiary (Non-US):

Mega Brands Australia Pty. Ltd. **(2)**

Se 4 Bldg 26 270 Ferntree Gully Rd, Notting Hill, Notting Hill, 3168, VIC, Australia
Tel.: (61) 395012030
Web Site: http://www.megabrands.com
Sales Range: $50-74.9 Million
Emp.: 6
Toy & Hobby Goods & Supplies Whslr
N.A.I.C.S.: 423920

Mega Brands Europe NV **(2)**
Laagstraat 14A, Temse, 9140, Belgium **(100%)**
Tel.: (32) 37109797
Web Site: http://www.megabrands.com
Sales Range: $25-49.9 Million
Emp.: 40
Toy & Hobby Goods & Supplies Whslr
N.A.I.C.S.: 423920

Mega Brands Italy SpA **(2)**
Via Balzella 83B, 47122, Forli, Italy **(100%)**
Tel.: (39) 0543 093651
Web Site: http://www.megabrands.com
Sales Range: $50-74.9 Million
Emp.: 4
Toy & Hobby Goods & Supplies Whslr
N.A.I.C.S.: 423920

Mega Brands Latinoamerica SA de CV **(2)**
Bosque De Radiatas No 26 Piso 6 Letra A Col Bosques De Las Lomas, Del Miguel Hidalgo C P, 11700, Mexico, Mexico
Tel.: (52) 5552768770
Sales Range: $25-49.9 Million
Emp.: 40
Toy & Hobby Goods & Supplies Whslr
N.A.I.C.S.: 423920

Mega Brands Spain & Portugal Srl **(2)**
CL Doctor Esquerdo 105, 28007, Madrid, Spain
Tel.: (34) 914009639
Web Site: http://www.megabrands.com
Sales Range: $25-49.9 Million
Emp.: 9
Doll & Stuffed Toy Mfr
N.A.I.C.S.: 339930

Mega Brands United Kingdom Ltd. **(2)**
Parkwood Stud Aston Rowant, Oxford, OX49 5SP, Oxfordshire, United Kingdom
Tel.: (44) 1844350033
Web Site: http://www.megabrands.com
Sales Range: $25-49.9 Million
Emp.: 18
Doll & Stuffed Toy Mfr
N.A.I.C.S.: 339930

Subsidiary (US):

Rose Moon Inc. **(2)**
1150 5th Ave N, Lewisburg, TN 37091-2108
Tel.: (931) 359-1501
Web Site: http://www.moonproducts.com
Stationery Product Mfr
N.A.I.C.S.: 322230

Mattel (Malaysia) SDN. BHD. **(1)**
Plot 206 Prai Free Trade Zone Prai Industrial Estate, Prai, 13600, Wellesley, Malaysia **(100%)**
Tel.: (60) 43907207
Web Site: http://www.corporate.mattel.com
Sales Range: $300-349.9 Million
Emp.: 2,008
Toy Mfr
N.A.I.C.S.: 339930

Mattel (UK) Ltd. **(1)**
Mattel House Vanwall Business Park, Vanwall Road, Maidenhead, SL6 4UB, Berkshire, United Kingdom **(100%)**
Tel.: (44) 1628500303
Web Site: http://www.mattel.com
Sales Range: $75-99.9 Million
Emp.: 150
Toys & Games Mfr
N.A.I.C.S.: 459120

Subsidiary (Domestic):

HIT Entertainment Ltd. **(2)**
Maple House, 149 Tottenham Court Rd, London, W1T 7NF, United Kingdom
Tel.: (44) 2075542500
Web Site: http://www.hitentertainment.com

Producer & Distr of Children's Television Programming
N.A.I.C.S.: 512110

Subsidiary (US):

HIT Entertainment, Inc. **(3)**
230 Park Ave S 13th Fl, New York, NY 10003-1547 **(100%)**
Tel.: (212) 463-9623
Web Site: http://www.hitentertainment.com
Sales Range: $25-49.9 Million
Emp.: 70
Producer & Distr of Children's Television Programming
N.A.I.C.S.: 512110

Mattel Asia Ltd. **(1)**
11-4 South Tower World Finance Centre Harbour City, Tsimshatsui, Kowloon, China (Hong Kong) **(100%)**
Tel.: (852) 31855000
Web Site: http://www.mattel.com
Sales Range: $150-199.9 Million
Sales & Marketing of Toys
N.A.I.C.S.: 459120

Mattel Australia Pty. Ltd. **(1)**
658 Church Street, PO Box 870, Richmond, 3121, VIC, Australia **(75%)**
Tel.: (61) 300135312
Web Site: http://www.mattel.com
Sales Range: $50-74.9 Million
Emp.: 120
Toys Marketer & Supplier
N.A.I.C.S.: 459120

Mattel B.V. (Netherlands) **(1)**
Gondel 1, Amstelveen, 1186MG, Netherlands **(100%)**
Tel.: (31) 205030503
Web Site: http://www.mattel.com
Sales Range: $75-99.9 Million
Emp.: 130
Toy Mfr
N.A.I.C.S.: 459120

Mattel Canada, Inc. **(1)**
6155 Freemont Blvd, Mississauga, L5R 3W2, ON, Canada
Tel.: (800) 567-7724
Web Site: http://www.mattel.com
Sales Range: $150-199.9 Million
Toys Wholesale Distr
N.A.I.C.S.: 459120

Mattel Espana, S.A. **(1)**
Aribau 200-210 10 planta, Barcelona, 8036, Spain **(100%)**
Tel.: (34) 933067900
Web Site: http://www.mattel.com
Sales Range: $125-149.9 Million
Emp.: 90
Toy Retailer
N.A.I.C.S.: 339930

Mattel Europa BV **(1)**
Gondel 1, 1186 MJ, Amstelveen, Netherlands
Tel.: (31) 6088364848
Toy Products Marketer, Designer & Mfr
N.A.I.C.S.: 339930

Mattel Europe Holdings B.V. **(1)**
Gondel 1 2hg, 1186 MJ, Amstelveen, Netherlands
Tel.: (31) 205030550
Holding Company
N.A.I.C.S.: 551112

Mattel Foreign Holdings, Ltd. **(1)**
333 Continental Blvd, El Segundo, CA 90245
Tel.: (310) 252-2000
Sales Range: $250-299.9 Million
Holding Company
N.A.I.C.S.: 551112

Mattel Games/Puzzles **(1)**
333 Continental Blvd, El Segundo, CA 90245-5012 **(100%)**
Tel.: (310) 252-5548
Web Site: http://www.mattel.com
Sales Range: $10-24.9 Million
Emp.: 18
Card, Board, Travel & Action Games Mfr
N.A.I.C.S.: 339930

Mattel GmbH **(1)**
Solmsstr 4, 60486, Frankfurt am Main, Germany

Tel.: (49) 697953300
Web Site: http://www.mattel.de
Toy Mfr
N.A.I.C.S.: 339930

Mattel GmbH (1)
Haupt St 82, A 2384, Vienna, Breitenfurt, Austria (100%)
Tel.: (43) 2236311029
Web Site: http://www.matchbox.com
Sales Range: $25-49.9 Million
Emp.: 3
Sales
N.A.I.C.S.: 459120

Mattel Holding, Inc. (1)
333 Continental Blvd, El Segundo, CA 90245-5032 (100%)
Tel.: (310) 252-2000
Sales Range: $75-99.9 Million
Holding Company
N.A.I.C.S.: 339930

Mattel International Finance B.V. (1)
Gondel 1/2EETAGE, 1186 MJ, Amstelveen, 1186MJ, Netherlands
Tel.: (31) 205030503
Toy Product & Accessories Mfr
N.A.I.C.S.: 459120

Mattel Overseas, Inc. (1)
333 Continental Blvd, El Segundo, CA 90245-5012 (100%)
Tel.: (310) 252-2000
Web Site: http://www.corporate.mattel.com
Holding Company
N.A.I.C.S.: 551112

Mattel Pty. Ltd. (1)
658 Church St, Richmond, 3121, VIC, Australia (100%)
Tel.: (61) 394255222
Web Site: http://www.mattel.com
Sales Range: $10-24.9 Million
Emp.: 80
Toys Mfr & Distr
N.A.I.C.S.: 339930

Mattel S.R.L. (1)
Via Vittorio Veneto 119, 28040, Novara, Oleggio Castell, Italy (100%)
Tel.: (39) 02699631
Web Site: http://www.mattel.com
Sales Range: $75-99.9 Million
Emp.: 150
Toys Marketer & Distr
N.A.I.C.S.: 336991

Mattel Toys (H.K.) Ltd. (1)
Len Shing Industrial Building 4A Kung Ngam Village Road, Shau Kei Wan, China (Hong Kong)
Tel.: (852) 28867688
Sales Range: $75-99.9 Million
Mfr of Toys
N.A.I.C.S.: 339930

Precision Moulds, Ltd. (1)
Lower Ground Floor Wah Shun Industrial Bldg 4 Cho Yuen St, Yau Tong, Kowloon, China (Hong Kong) (100%)
Tel.: (852) 37755264
Sales Range: $125-149.9 Million
Mfr of Die Cast Molds, Injection Molds, Berylium Copper Inserts Molds
N.A.I.C.S.: 333511

MATTERPORT, INC.
352 E Java Dr, Sunnyvale, CA 94089
Tel.: (650) 641-2241   DE
Web Site:
   https://www.matterport.com
MTTR—(NASDAQ)
Rev.: $136,125,000
Assets: $640,395,000
Liabilities: $56,484,000
Net Worth: $583,911,000
Earnings: ($111,339,000)
Emp.: 590
Fiscal Year-end: 12/31/22
Investment Services
N.A.I.C.S.: 523999
James Daniel Fay *(CFO)*
Peter Presunka *(Chief Acctg Officer)*
Lou Marzano *(Chief Hardware Officer)*
Jay Remley *(Chief Revenue Officer)*

Jean Barbagelata *(Chief People Officer)*
Dave Gausebeck *(Founder & Chief Scientist Officer)*
Japjit Tulsi *(CTO)*
Tom Klein *(CMO)*
Matthew Zinn *(Chief Legal Officer)*
R. J. Pittman *(Chm & CEO)*

Subsidiaries:

Matterport Operating, LLC (1)
140 S Whisman Rd Ste A, Mountain View, CA 94041
Tel.: (650) 400-6288
Web Site: http://www.matterport.com
Custom Computer Programming Services
N.A.I.C.S.: 541511
Dave Gausebeck *(CTO)*
R. J. Pittman *(CEO)*
J. D. Fay *(CFO)*
Jay Remley *(Chief Revenue Officer)*

MATTHEWS INTERNATIONAL CORPORATION
2 N Shore Ctr, Pittsburgh, PA 15212
Tel.: (412) 442-8200   PA
Web Site: https://www.matw.com
Year Founded: 1850
MATW—(NASDAQ)
Rev.: $1,795,737,000
Assets: $1,834,890,000
Liabilities: $1,397,684,000
Net Worth: $437,206,000
Earnings: ($59,660,000)
Emp.: 11,000
Fiscal Year-end: 09/30/24
Industrial Marking Products, Bronze, Aluminum & Plastic Tablets, Signs & Memorials, Rubber Printing Plates, Rubber Stamps & Projects, Machinery for Product Identification & Cutting Dies Mfr
N.A.I.C.S.: 331523
Joseph C. Bartolacci *(Pres & CEO)*
Steven F. Nicola *(CFO & Sec)*
Brian J. Dunn *(Exec VP-Strategy & Corp Dev)*
Brian D. Walters *(Gen Counsel & Exec VP)*
Alvaro Garcia-Tunon *(Chm)*
Gregory S. Babe *(Grp Pres-Industrial Technologies segment, CTO & Head-Engrg)*
Steven D. Gackenbach *(Memorialization Grp)*
Davor Brkovich *(CIO)*
Reena Gurtner *(Sr VP-HR)*
Ronald C. Awenowicz *(Sr VP-HR)*

Subsidiaries:

5flow GmbH (1)
Helmholzstr 35, 52428, Julich, Germany
Tel.: (49) 246197770
Web Site: http://www.5flow.eu
Information Technology Consulting Services
N.A.I.C.S.: 541512
Robert Mertens *(CEO)*

Aurora Casket Company, LLC (1)
10944 Marsh Rd, Aurora, IN 47001
Tel.: (812) 926-1111
Web Site: http://www.auroracasket.com
Burial Caskets, Cremation & Memorial Products Mfr & Distr
N.A.I.C.S.: 339995

C. Morello, Pty. Ltd. (1)
Unit 1 33-35 Commercial Drive, Thomastown, 3074, VIC, Australia
Tel.: (61) 394704313
Web Site: http://www.cmorello.net.au
Emp.: 3
Monumental & Mausoleum Product Distr
N.A.I.C.S.: 424990

Equator Design, Inc. (1)
Civic Opera Bldg 20 N Wacker Ste 2200, Chicago, IL 60606
Tel.: (847) 212-3231
Web Site: http://www.equator-design.com
Building Architectural Services

N.A.I.C.S.: 541310

Freeman Metal Products Inc. (1)
2124 United States Hwy 13 S, Ahoskie, NC 27910
Tel.: (252) 332-5390
Web Site: http://www.freemanmetal.com
Sales Range: $25-49.9 Million
Emp.: 120
Burial Caskets
N.A.I.C.S.: 339995
Morris Freeman *(Founder & Pres)*

Subsidiary (Domestic):

Southern Heritage Casket Co. (2)
175 Sherman Dr, Oxford, AL 36203
Tel.: (256) 835-2771
Web Site:
   http://www.southernheritagecasket.com
Sales Range: $25-49.9 Million
Emp.: 25
Casket Mfr
N.A.I.C.S.: 339995

Frost Converting Systems, Inc. (1)
2056 Willow Springs Ln, Burlington, NC 27215
Tel.: (336) 395-6200
Rotary Dies & Converting Equipment Mfr & Distr
N.A.I.C.S.: 333514

Furnace Construction Cremators Limited (1)
Mill Street Newton Moor Industrial Estate, Hyde, SK14 4LF, United Kingdom
Tel.: (44) 1613688419
Web Site: http://www.fccremators.com
Industrial Furnace Mfr
N.A.I.C.S.: 333413

Greenbrier Pet Loss Services, LLC (1)
3703 W Kelly Park Rd, Apopka, FL 32712
Tel.: (407) 886-2620
Web Site: http://www.greenbrierpets.com
Pet Cemetery & Memorial Garden Services
N.A.I.C.S.: 812220

Guidance Automation Limited (1)
Unit 2 Meridian South Meridian Business Park, Leicester, LE19 1WY, United Kingdom
Tel.: (44) 1162436250
Web Site:
   https://www.guidanceautomation.com
Robotic Automobile Mfr
N.A.I.C.S.: 336110

IDL Worldwide, Inc. (1)
6515 Penn Ave, Pittsburgh, PA 15206
Web Site: http://www.idlww.com
Consumer Research & Strategy; Point of Purchase Displays
N.A.I.C.S.: 339950

IDL Worldwide, Inc. (1)
500 Grand Ave, East Butler, PA 16029
Tel.: (724) 431-4700
Web Site: http://www.idlww.com
Sales Range: $75-99.9 Million
Emp.: 300
Retail Brand Design Services
N.A.I.C.S.: 541490
C. Michael Dempe *(COO)*

Klischeewerkstatt Scholler GmbH (1)
Andernacher Str 21 A, Nuremberg, 90411, Germany
Tel.: (49) 91195233
Web Site: http://www.scholler-prepress.com
Sales Range: $25-49.9 Million
Emp.: 90
Printing Machinery & Equipment Mfr
N.A.I.C.S.: 561910

Matthews Bronze Pty. Ltd. (1)
22-24 Elliott Road, Dandenong South, 3175, VIC, Australia
Tel.: (61) 397942922
Web Site: https://www.arrowbronze.com.au
Sales Range: $25-49.9 Million
Emp.: 60
Bronze Product Distr
N.A.I.C.S.: 423510

Matthews Environmental Solutions Limited (1)

Units 2 and 3 Hyde Point Dunkirk Lane, Hyde, SK14 4NL, Cheshire, United Kingdom
Tel.: (44) 1613374488
Web Site:
   https://matthewsenvironmentalsolutions.com
Incinerator Installation Services
N.A.I.C.S.: 238290

Matthews Europe GmbH (1)
Schifferstrasse 196, 47059, Duisburg, Germany
Tel.: (49) 2564120
Holding Company
N.A.I.C.S.: 551112

Matthews Gibraltar Mausoleum & Construction Company (1)
252 RIDC Park W Dr, Pittsburgh, PA 15275
Web Site:
   https://www.matthewsgibraltarmausoleum.com
Construction Services
N.A.I.C.S.: 236220
Paul Rauch *(Mgr-Sls)*
Timothy Gorgas *(Mgr-Pre-Construction)*
Jim Landon *(Mgr-Construction)*
Ed Faux *(Mgr-Construction)*

Matthews International (EFN) GmbH (1)
Rudolf-Diesel Str 16, D-52428, Julich, Germany (100%)
Tel.: (49) 2461935310
Web Site: http://www.matw-eu.com
Sales Range: $25-49.9 Million
Emp.: 5
Provider of Engraving & Pre-Press Services
N.A.I.C.S.: 332812

Subsidiary (Non-US):

Repro-Busek GmbH & Co. KG (2)
Europlatz No 2, 1120, Vienna, Austria (75%)
Tel.: (43) 161507350
Web Site: http://www.schawk.com
Sales Range: $25-49.9 Million
Mfr of Printing Plates
N.A.I.C.S.: 323120

Subsidiary (Domestic):

Reproservice Eurodigital GmbH (2)
Dalanstrasse 73 Plant no 21A 1st Fl, 81541, Munich, Germany (100%)
Tel.: (49) 899610060
Web Site: http://www.reproservice.net
Sales Range: $10-24.9 Million
Emp.: 40
Mfr of Digital Plates
N.A.I.C.S.: 323120

Rudolf Reproflex GmbH & Co. KG (2)
Magdenburger Kamp 5, Goslar, 38644, Germany (75%)
Tel.: (49) 532137150
Web Site: http://www.schawk.eu
Sales Range: $25-49.9 Million
Emp.: 155
Mfr of Printing Plates
N.A.I.C.S.: 323120
Lars Mentgen *(Mng Dir)*

Subsidiary (Domestic):

Matthews Instore Solutions Europe GmbH (3)
Magde Burger Kamp 3, 38644, Goslar, Germany
Tel.: (49) 53216866220
Web Site: http://www.idlww.de
Emp.: 100
Motion Picture Animation Services
N.A.I.C.S.: 512191

Reproflex GmbH Leipzig (3)
Petersstrasse 39/41, 4109, Leipzig, Germany
Tel.: (49) 3418603790
Web Site: http://www.reproflex.de
Commercial Printing Services
N.A.I.C.S.: 323111

Subsidiary (Domestic):

S+T GmbH & Co. KG (2)
Helmholtzstrasse 35, 52428, Julich, Germany (50%)
Tel.: (49) 246197770

Matthews International
Corporation—(Continued)

Web Site: http://www.st-packline.de
Sales Range: $50-74.9 Million
Provider of Engraving & Pre-Press Services
N.A.I.C.S.: 332812

Scholler GmbH & Co. KG (2)
Andernacher Strasse 21a, 90411, Nuremberg, Germany (75%)
Tel.: (49) 91195233
Web Site: http://www.scholler-prepress.com
Sales Range: $10-24.9 Million
Emp.: 100
Mfr of Printing Plates
N.A.I.C.S.: 323120

Matthews International Corp. - Bronze (1)
1315 W Liberty Ave, Pittsburgh, PA 15226-1040 (100%)
Tel.: (412) 571-5500
Web Site: http://www.matthewsbronze.com
Sales Range: $200-249.9 Million
Emp.: 325
Bronze Markers, Memorials & Signage
N.A.I.C.S.: 331529

Matthews International Corp. - Casket Division Distribution Center (1)
534 Union St, Brooklyn, NY 11215-1021
Tel.: (718) 852-6606
Sales Range: $50-74.9 Million
Emp.: 150
Mfr & Distributor of Caskets
N.A.I.C.S.: 423850
Thomas Pontone *(Pres-Matthews Funeral Products)*

Matthews International Corp. - Graphics Imaging (1)
252 Parkwest Dr, Pittsburgh, PA 15275-1002 (100%)
Tel.: (412) 788-2111
Web Site: http://www.matthewsgsd.com
Sales Range: $25-49.9 Million
Emp.: 110
Printing Plates for the Corrugated Industry
N.A.I.C.S.: 323120

Plant (Domestic):

Matthews Packaging Graphics (2)
10866 Indianhead Industrial Blvd, Saint Louis, MO 63132
Tel.: (314) 423-9800
Web Site:
http://www.matthewsinternational.com
Sales Range: $25-49.9 Million
Emp.: 25
Printing Plates for the Corrugated Industry
N.A.I.C.S.: 323120
Rondall Peek *(Gen Mgr)*

Matthews Packaging Graphics & Design (2)
1851 Harbor Bay Pkwy Ste 1000, Alameda, CA 94502 (100%)
Tel.: (510) 263-1840
Web Site:
http://www.matthewsbrandsolutions.com
Sales Range: $10-24.9 Million
Emp.: 41
Prepress Services & Analog Flexoplates Mfr
N.A.I.C.S.: 323120

Matthews International Corp. - Marking Products (1)
6515 Penn Ave, Pittsburgh, PA 15206-4407
Tel.: (412) 665-2500
Web Site: http://www.matthewsmarking.com
Sales Range: $25-49.9 Million
Emp.: 100
Industrial Marking Equipment Mfr
N.A.I.C.S.: 339940

Subsidiary (Domestic):

Holjeron Corporation (2)
9524 SW Tualatin Sherwood Rd, Tualatin, OR 97062-8586
Tel.: (503) 582-0820
Web Site: http://www.holjeron.com
Sales Range: $50-74.9 Million
Emp.: 17
Network Based Input Output Products for Industrial Applications
N.A.I.C.S.: 334220

Subsidiary (Non-US):

Matthews Canada Ltd. (2)
810 Nipissing Rd Unit 200, Milton, L9T 4Z9, ON, Canada (100%)
Tel.: (905) 878-2358
Web Site: http://www.matthewsbronze.net
Sales Range: $10-24.9 Million
Emp.: 4
Industrial Marking Devices Mfr
N.A.I.C.S.: 339940

Matthews International GmbH (1)
Gutenbergstrasse 1-3, 48691, Vreden, Germany
Tel.: (49) 2564120
Holding Company
N.A.I.C.S.: 551112

Subsidiary (Domestic):

Ungricht GmbH + Co KG (2)
Karstrasse 90, 41068, Monchengladbach, Germany
Tel.: (49) 21613590
Burial Casket Mfr
N.A.I.C.S.: 339995

Matthews International S.p.A. (1)
Via Martiri Della Liberta 71, 43052, Parma, Italy (100%)
Tel.: (39) 05215208
Web Site: http://www.caggiati.it
Sales Range: $50-74.9 Million
Emp.: 115
Foundry for Bronze Items
N.A.I.C.S.: 332812
Sorrentino Nazzareno *(Mng Dir)*

Subsidiary (Non-US):

Caggiati France SARL (2)
Chem Du Favier, 69230, Saint Genis Laval, France
Tel.: (33) 478564956
Funeral Monuments Mfr
N.A.I.C.S.: 327991

Subsidiary (Domestic):

Gem Matthews International s.r.l. (2)
Via Zanussi 315 - Z I U, 33100, Udine, Italy
Tel.: (39) 0432524374
Emp.: 30
Energy Recovery Services
N.A.I.C.S.: 221118
Fabrizio Giust *(Mng Dir)*

Matthews International Sarl (2)
Via Martiri della Liberta 71, Colomo, 43052, Parma, Italy
Tel.: (39) 05215208
Web Site: http://www.caggiati.it
Casket Services
N.A.I.C.S.: 812210

Subsidiary (Non-US):

Rottenecker-Caggiati GmbH (2)
Gewerbestr 9a, Niederschopfheim, 77749, Hohberg, Germany
Tel.: (49) 7808914460
Web Site: https://www.rottenecker.de
Grave Decoration Product Mfr
N.A.I.C.S.: 327991

Subsidiary (Domestic):

Tyche SpA (2)
Corso Filippo Turati 11/C, 10128, Turin, Italy
Tel.: (39) 0115812302
Web Site: http://www.tyche-spa.com
Crematory Services
N.A.I.C.S.: 812220

Matthews Marking Systems Sweden AB (1)
Mobelgatan 4, 431 33, Molndal, Sweden
Tel.: (46) 313387900
Web Site: http://www.matthewsmarking.se
Industrial Equipment Whsr
N.A.I.C.S.: 423830
Lisa Almgren *(Mgr-Mktg-EMEA & APAC)*

Matthews Swedot AB (1)
Mobelgakan 4, SE 431 22, Molndal, Sweden (100%)
Tel.: (46) 313387900
Web Site:
http://www.matthewsmorkang.com

Sales Range: $25-49.9 Million
Emp.: 56
Mfr, Developer & Marketer of Printing Machinery
N.A.I.C.S.: 333248

Subsidiary (Non-US):

Matthews Kodiersysteme GmbH (2)
Kampenwandstrasse 77C, Aschau, 83229, Germany
Tel.: (49) 805295110
Web Site: http://www.matthews.de
Sales Range: $25-49.9 Million
Emp.: 13
Printing System Distr
N.A.I.C.S.: 423830

Melton Company, Inc. (1)
5900 Patterson Rd, Little Rock, AR 72209
Tel.: (501) 565-2400
Web Site:
http://www.meltoncompanyinc.com
Burial Casket Distr
N.A.I.C.S.: 423850

OLBRICH GmbH (1)
Teutonenstr 2-10, 46395, Bocholt, Germany
Tel.: (49) 28712830
Web Site: https://www.olbrich.com
Floor Covering Mfr
N.A.I.C.S.: 326199

Subsidiary (Domestic):

R+S Technik GmbH (2)
Am Kreuzstein 80, 63477, Maintal, Germany
Tel.: (49) 6109 7123 0
Web Site: http://www.rstechnik.de
Emp.: 15
Automobile Parts Mfr
N.A.I.C.S.: 336330
Thimo van Gessel *(Dir-Sls)*

Repro Busek Druckvorstufentechnick GmbH & Co. KG (1)
Grossmarktstrasse 22, 1230, Vienna, Austria
Tel.: (43) 161507350
Web Site: http://www.reprobusek.at
Emp.: 40
Product Packaging Services
N.A.I.C.S.: 561910

Subsidiary (Domestic):

Rasterpunkt-Druckvorstufeurverpakungen GmbH (2)
Ferdinandstrasse 5/5, 1020, Vienna, Austria
Tel.: (43) 12123838
Web Site: http://www.rasterpunkt.at
Industrial Machinery & Furnace Mfr
N.A.I.C.S.: 333413

Reproflex Vietnam Limited Company (1)
DTC Building 5th Floor 99A1 Cong Hoa Street Ward 4, Ho Chi Minh City, Vietnam
Tel.: (84) 917651478
Commercial Printing Services
N.A.I.C.S.: 323113

SGK LLC (1)
1 N Dearborn, Chicago, IL 60602
Tel.: (312) 666-9200
Web Site: http://www.sgkinc.com
Sales Range: $400-449.9 Million
Emp.: 3,600
Holding Company; Advertising & Printing Services
N.A.I.C.S.: 551112

Subsidiary (Non-US):

Brandimage Desgrippes and LAGA SAS (2)
39 Rue Saint-Sabin, 75011, Paris, France
Tel.: (33) 1 4418 4418
Web Site: http://www.brand-image.com
Sales Range: $25-49.9 Million
Emp.: 40
Brand Image Design Services
N.A.I.C.S.: 541430
Alain Dore *(Exec Dir-Creative)*
Delphine Dauge *(Dir-Agency)*

Subsidiary (Non-US):

Brandimage Belgique Holdings SA (3)

Brand Wheclock St 87, Brussels, 1200, Belgium
Tel.: (32) 22153400
Emp.: 5
Holding Company
N.A.I.C.S.: 551112
Nike Stellamans *(Gen Mgr)*

Subsidiary (Non-US):

Brandmark International Holding B.V. (2)
Marathon 5 C, 1213 PC, Hilversum, Netherlands
Tel.: (31) 355393793
Holding Company
N.A.I.C.S.: 551112

Equator (Scotland) Ltd. (2)
Equator Building 58 Elliot Street, Glasgow, G3 8DZ, United Kingdom
Tel.: (44) 141 229 1800
Web Site: http://www.eqtr.com
Emp.: 170
Digital Advertising & Marketing Agency
N.A.I.C.S.: 541810
James Jefferson *(Co-Founder & Chief Creative Officer)*
Garry Hamilton *(Co-Founder & Dir-Bus Dev)*
John McLeish *(Co-Founder & Mng Dir)*

Subsidiary (Domestic):

999 Design Group Ltd. (3)
The Mews 42 Elliot Street, Glasgow, G3 8DZ, United Kingdom
Tel.: (44) 141 332 2684
Web Site: http://www.999design.com
Branding & Digital Design Services
N.A.I.C.S.: 541810
Richard Bissland *(Co-Founder)*
Bill Gaughan *(Co-Founder)*

Subsidiary (Non-US):

Schawk Asia Pacific Pte. Ltd. (2)
241 River Valley Road Gianum Building Level 4, Singapore, 238298, Singapore
Tel.: (65) 62582622
Web Site: http://www.schawk.com
Emp.: 100
Digital Imaging Prepress Services
N.A.I.C.S.: 323120
Adam Ransom *(Mng Dir)*

Subsidiary (Non-US):

Schawk Holdings Australia Pty. Ltd. (3)
Level 17 99 Walker St, North Sydney, 2060, NSW, Australia (100%)
Tel.: (61) 298157777
Sales Range: $25-49.9 Million
Emp.: 50
Holding Company
N.A.I.C.S.: 551112
Adam Ransom *(Mng Dir-APAC)*

Subsidiary (Domestic):

Anthem! Design Pty. Ltd. (4)
Level 17 99 Walker Street, North Sydney, 2060, NSW, Australia
Tel.: (61) 2 9463 6600
Web Site: http://www.anthemww.com
Emp.: 10
Graphic Design Services
N.A.I.C.S.: 541430
Simon MacDonald *(Mng Dir)*

Subsidiary (Non-US):

Schawk India Ltd. (3)
RMZ Millenia Business Park Campus 2 5th Fl No 143 Dr MGR Road, Kandanchavdi, Chennai, 600096, India (100%)
Tel.: (91) 44 4213 7777
Web Site: http://www.schawk.com
Sales Range: $50-74.9 Million
Emp.: 550
Artwork Management, Pre-Media & Print Media Services
N.A.I.C.S.: 323120

Schawk India Pvt. Ltd. (3)
RMZ Millenia Business Park Campus-2 5th Floor No 143 Dr M G R Road, Kandanchavdi, Chennai, 600 096, India
Tel.: (91) 4442137777
Web Site: http://www.schawk.com

Media Production Services
N.A.I.C.S.: 323111

Subsidiary (Non-US):

Schawk Canada Inc.   (2)
1620 Tech Ave, Mississauga, L4W 5S7,
ON, Canada
Tel.: (905) 219-1600
Web Site: http://www.schawk.com
Sales Range: $25-49.9 Million
Emp.: 145
Digital Imaging Services
N.A.I.C.S.: 541430

Subsidiary (Domestic):

Schawk Digital Solutions, Inc.   (2)
1600 E Sherwin Ave, Des Plaines, IL 60018
Tel.: (847) 827-8424
Web Site: http://www.schawk.com
Sales Range: $10-24.9 Million
Emp.: 40
Content-Centric Technology & Digital Solutions
N.A.I.C.S.: 513210

Subsidiary (Non-US):

Schawk Imaging (Shanghai) Co.
Ltd.   (2)
2nd Fl T52-1 General Bldg South 3079
Shen Jiang Rd, Jin Qiao Export Process
Area, Pudong, Shanghai, 201206, China
Tel.: (86) 2158545475
Web Site: http://www.schawk.com
Graphic Design Services
N.A.I.C.S.: 541430

Schawk Imaging Sdn. Bhd.   (2)
Plot 39 Jalan Perindustrian Bukit Minyak,
Kaw Perindustrian Bukit Minyak, Simpang
Empat, 14100, Palau Penang,
Malaysia   (100%)
Tel.: (60) 4501 3001
Web Site: http://www.schawk.com
Sales Range: $50-74.9 Million
Emp.: 205
Comprehensive Brand Point Management
Services
N.A.I.C.S.: 541430

Schawk Japan, Ltd.   (2)
IK Building 4F Kamiosaki 2-24-9,
Shinagawa-ku, Tokyo, 141-0021, Japan
Tel.: (81) 357596170
Web Site: http://www.schawk.com
Emp.: 30
Branding & Strategic Design Services
N.A.I.C.S.: 541430

Subsidiary (Domestic):

Schawk USA, Inc.   (2)
1918 W Walnut St, Chicago, IL 60612
Tel.: (312) 542-4400
Web Site: http://www.schawk.com
Advetising Agency
N.A.I.C.S.: 541810

Unit (Domestic):

Anthem Worldwide   (3)
77 Maiden Ln 4th Fl, San Francisco, CA
94108
Tel.: (415) 896-9399
Sales Range: $25-49.9 Million
Emp.: 45
Advetising Agency
N.A.I.C.S.: 541810
Rob Hollands *(Mng Dir)*

Branch (Domestic):

Anthem Worldwide - Cincinnati   (4)
537 E Pete Rose Way Ste 100, Cincinnati,
OH 45202-3378
Tel.: (513) 784-0066
Advertising Agencies
N.A.I.C.S.: 541810

Anthem Worldwide - New York   (4)
135 Spring St 3rd Fl, New York, NY 10012
Tel.: (646) 344-4821
Emp.: 30
Advetising Agency
N.A.I.C.S.: 541810
Janice Jaworski *(Mng Dir)*

Branch (Non-US):

Anthem Worldwide - Toronto   (4)

1620 Tech Avenue, Mississauga, L4W 5P4,
ON, Canada
Tel.: (905) 219-1700
Web Site: http://www.anthemww.com
Sales Range: $10-24.9 Million
Emp.: 25
Art & Graphic Design
N.A.I.C.S.: 541430

Unit (Domestic):

Schawk Retail Marketing   (3)
1 N Dearborn Ste 700, Chicago, IL 60602
Tel.: (312) 666-9200
Advetising Agency
N.A.I.C.S.: 541430
Lynne Smith Obiala *(VP-Client Svcs)*
Lou Bart *(Sr VP-Acct Svcs)*

Branch (Domestic):

Schawk USA, Inc. - Atlanta   (3)
1100 Circle 75 Pkwy SE Ste 300, Atlanta,
GA 30339
Tel.: (770) 333-9432
Web Site: http://www.schawk.com
Emp.: 45
Advetising Agency
N.A.I.C.S.: 541810
Bill Farrisee *(Mng Dir-Latin America & VP)*

Schawk USA, Inc. - Kalamazoo   (3)
2325 N Burdick St, Kalamazoo, MI 49007-
1876
Tel.: (269) 381-3820
Web Site: http://www.schawk.com
Emp.: 80
Advetising Agency
N.A.I.C.S.: 541810

Schawk USA, Inc. - Minneapolis   (3)
2626 2nd St NE, Minneapolis, MN 55418
Tel.: (612) 789-8514
Web Site: http://www.schawk.com
Emp.: 55
Advetising Agency
N.A.I.C.S.: 541810

Schawk USA, Inc. - Redmond   (3)
18211 NE 68th St Ste E120, Redmond, WA
98052
Tel.: (425) 881-5454
Web Site: http://www.schawk.com
Emp.: 40
Advetising Agency
N.A.I.C.S.: 541810
Marcel Ceballos *(Mng Dir)*

Subsidiary (Non-US):

Schawk de Mexico SRL de CV   (3)
Avenida de las Fuentes 5A Parque Indus-
trial Bernardo Quintana, El Marques, Que-
retaro, 72646, Mexico   (100%)
Tel.: (52) 4422900700
Web Site: http://www.schawk.com
Emp.: 40
Graphic Design Services
N.A.I.C.S.: 541430

Saueressig Baski Oncesi Hazirlik
Sistemier Sanaji ve Tricarct Amonin
Sirketi   (1)
10036 Sokak No 8 A O S B Cigli, Izmir,
Turkiye
Tel.: (90) 2323282666
Die Casting & Metal Distr
N.A.I.C.S.: 423510

Saueressig GmbH & Co. KG   (1)
Gutenbergstrasse 1-3, 48691, Ger-
many
Tel.: (49) 2564120
Web Site: http://www.saueressig.com
Printing Equipment Mfr
N.A.I.C.S.: 333248
Tomas Sterkenburgh *(Mng Dir)*

Subsidiary (Domestic):

Saueressig Design Studio GmbH   (2)
Krefelder Str 660, Monchengladbach,
41066, Germany
Tel.: (49) 2161965920
Web Site: http://www.designstudiomg.de
Emp.: 38
Printing Plate & Other Product Mfr
N.A.I.C.S.: 333248

Saueressig Flexo GmbH   (2)

Gutenbergstrasse 1-3, D-48691, Vreden,
Germany
Tel.: (49) 2564120
Web Site: http://www.saueressig.de
Industrial Machinery Mfr
N.A.I.C.S.: 333248

Subsidiary (Non-US):

Saueressig Ltd.   (2)
405 Central Park Petherton Road, Bristol,
BS14 9BZ, United Kingdom
Tel.: (44) 1275894400
Web Site: http://www.saueressig.com
Emp.: 40
Printing Forms Mfr
N.A.I.C.S.: 333248

Saueressig Polska Sp. z.o.o.   (2)
Ul Krucza 4, 62-080, Tarnowo Podgorne,
Poland
Tel.: (48) 618167040
Web Site: http://www.saueressig.de
Emp.: 120
Printing Equipment Mfr
N.A.I.C.S.: 333248

Saueressig ooo   (2)
10 Tikhvinskaya Street, 173003, Velikiy
Novgorod, Russia
Tel.: (7) 8162974400
Web Site: http://www.Saueressig.ru
Emp.: 38
Printing Equipment Mfr
N.A.I.C.S.: 333248

Star Granite Co., Inc.   (1)
1311 Bowman Highway, Elberton, GA
30635
Tel.: (706) 283-2836
Web Site: http://www.stargranite.com
Granite Mfr & Distr
N.A.I.C.S.: 327991

Tact Group Limited   (1)
21/F 9 Chong Yip Street, Kwun Tong, Kow-
loon, China (Hong Kong)
Tel.: (852) 28513200
Web Site: http://www.tacthk.com
Emp.: 30
Retail Packing Services
N.A.I.C.S.: 561910

The InTouch Group Ltd   (1)
Intouch House Riverside Drive, Cleck-
heaton, BD19 4DH, W Yorkshire, United
Kingdom
Tel.: (44) 1274848000
Web Site: http://www.theintouchgroup.com
Sales Range: $50-74.9 Million
Emp.: 250
Brand Implementation Services Ranging
from Creative Design, Artwork, Reprograph-
ics & Printing Plate Production to Workflow
Systems Solutions
N.A.I.C.S.: 541430
David Lloyd *(Chm)*

Subsidiary (US):

Marketing by Design, LLC   (2)
500 Cummings Center Ste 2500, Beverly,
MA 01915
Tel.: (978) 998-6600
Web Site: http://www.mbdesign.com
Rev.: $2,000,000
Emp.: 32
Graphic Design & Brand Marketing Services
N.A.I.C.S.: 541430

The York Group, Inc.   (1)
2 Northshore Ctr, Pittsburgh, PA
15212-5851   (100%)
Tel.: (412) 995-1600
Sales Range: $150-199.9 Million
Emp.: 600
Holding Company; Burial Casket Mfr & Distr
N.A.I.C.S.: 551112

Subsidiary (Domestic):

Milso Industries Corporation   (2)
534 Union St, Brooklyn, NY 11215
Tel.: (718) 624-4593
Web Site: http://www.mitw.com
Sales Range: $25-49.9 Million
Emp.: 30
Metal & Hardwood Product Mfr
N.A.I.C.S.: 321211

York Casket Development Company,
Inc.   (2)

2 N Shore Ctr, Pittsburgh, PA
15212-5851   (100%)
Tel.: (412) 995-1600
Web Site: http://www.yorkgrp.com
Sales Range: $10-24.9 Million
Emp.: 55
Burial Casket Mfr
N.A.I.C.S.: 339995

TodaySure Matthews Limited   (1)
Units 2 and 3 Hyde Point Dunkirk Lane,
Hyde, SK14 4NL, Cheshire, United King-
dom
Tel.: (44) 1613374488
Web Site: http://www.todaysure.com
Combustion System Installation & Mfr
N.A.I.C.S.: 336310

VCG (Holdings) Limited   (1)
1 Europa ParkCroft Way, Witham, CM8
2FN, Essex, United Kingdom
Tel.: (44) 1376533055
Web Site: http://www.vcg-group.com
Art Graphic Design Services
N.A.I.C.S.: 541430

Wetzel GmbH   (1)
Solvaystrasse 31, 79639, Grenzach-
Wyhlen, Germany
Tel.: (49) 76243010
Web Site: http://www.wetzel.co
Emp.: 300
Commercial Printing Services
N.A.I.C.S.: 323113

Subsidiary (Domestic):

Wetzel Academy GmbH   (2)
Solvaystr 31, Grenzach-Wyhlen, 79639,
Baden-Wurttemberg, Germany
Tel.: (49) 610669070
Industrial Products Mfr
N.A.I.C.S.: 331523

Subsidiary (Non-US):

Wetzel Sp. z.o.o.   (2)
ul Krucza 4 Pl, Duchnow, 05-462, Masovian
Voivodeship, Poland
Tel.: (48) 227802000
Web Site: http://www.wetzel.pl
Steel Engraving Services
N.A.I.C.S.: 332812

Wetzel Holding AG   (1)
Frankfurt-Strasse 66, 4142, Munchenstein,
Switzerland
Tel.: (41) 619732030
Web Site: http://www.wetzel.co
Holding Company
N.A.I.C.S.: 551112

Subsidiary (Domestic):

Wetzel Service AG   (2)
Frankfurt-Strasse 66, Basel-Land,
Munchenstein, 4142, Switzerland
Tel.: (41) 619732030
Industrial Products Mfr
N.A.I.C.S.: 331523

York Agency, Inc.   (1)
9127 Dickey Dr, Mechanicsville, VA 23116
Tel.: (804) 569-6033
Web Site: https://www.yorkeagency.com
Insurance Services
N.A.I.C.S.: 524210
Jeffrey O. Yorke *(Founder & Pres)*
Jeremy O. Yorke *(VP)*

**MAUI LAND & PINEAPPLE
COMPANY, INC.**
500 Office Rd, Lahaina, HI 96761
Tel.: (808) 877-3351   HI
Web Site: https://www.mauiland.com
Year Founded: 1909
MLP—(NYSE)
Rev.: $20,960,000
Assets: $42,406,000
Liabilities: $8,634,000
Net Worth: $33,772,000
Earnings: $1,787,000
Emp.: 9
Fiscal Year-end: 12/31/22
Land Holding & Operating Services
for Agriculture & Resort Operations;
Pineapple Production
N.A.I.C.S.: 311421

Wade K. Kodama *(CFO & Principal Acctg Officer)*
Race Randle *(CEO)*
Ashley Takitani Leahey *(VP)*

Subsidiaries:

Kapalua Land Company, Ltd. **(1)**
200 Village Rd, Lahaina, HI 96761 **(100%)**
Tel.: (808) 877-1667
Web Site: http://mauiland.com
Resort Development Company Services
N.A.I.C.S.: 237210

Subsidiary (Domestic):

Kapalua Realty Company, Ltd. **(2)**
700 Office Rd, Lahaina, HI 96761
Tel.: (808) 665-5454
Web Site: http://www.kapaluarealty.com
Real Estate Services
N.A.I.C.S.: 531210

Maui Pineapple Company, Ltd. **(1)**
120 W Kane St, Kahului, HI 96732 **(100%)**
Tel.: (808) 877-3805
Web Site: http://www.pineapplehawaii.com
Sales Range: $250-299.9 Million
Grower & Canner of Pineapple; Plants Located at Kahului & Maui; Plantations at Honolua & Haliimaile, Maui
N.A.I.C.S.: 311421

MAVERICK ENERGY GROUP, LTD.
135 Jenkins St Ste 105B-356, Saint Augustine, FL 32086
Tel.: (210) 705-1740   NV
Web Site: http://www.maverick-energy.com
MKGP—(OTCIQ)
Oil & Gas Exploration Services
N.A.I.C.S.: 213112
Christiane Lopez *(Sec)*
Reed Morgan *(CFO)*
J. David LaPrade *(COO & Dir-Horizontal Drilling)*
James W. McCabe Jr. *(Pres & CEO)*

MAX SOUND CORPORATION
8861 Villa La Jolla Drive Unit 12109, La Jolla, CA 92039   DE
Web Site: https://www.maxd.audio
Year Founded: 2005
MAXD—(OTCIQ)
Rev.: $288,000
Liabilities: $13,767,821
Net Worth: ($13,767,821)
Earnings: ($1,394,826)
Emp.: 1
Fiscal Year-end: 12/31/21
Audio Systems Mfr
N.A.I.C.S.: 334310
Gregory J. Halpern *(Founder, Chm, Pres, CEO & CFO)*

MAXCYTE, INC.
9713 Key W Ave Ste 400, Rockville, MD 20850
Tel.: (301) 944-1700   DE
Web Site: https://www.maxcyte.com
Year Founded: 1998
MXCT—(NASDAQ)
Rev.: $44,261,500
Assets: $286,653,400
Liabilities: $32,686,200
Net Worth: $253,967,200
Earnings: ($23,570,800)
Emp.: 125
Fiscal Year-end: 12/31/22
Pharmaceutical Preparation Manufacturing
N.A.I.C.S.: 325412
Ron Holtz *(Exec VP-Administration)*
Thomas M. Ross *(Exec VP-Global Sls & Mktg)*
James Brady *(Sr VP-Technical Applications & Customer Support)*

Sarah Haecker Meeks *(Sr VP-Bus Dev)*
James Lovgren *(Sr VP-Global Mktg)*
Gene Zhu *(VP)*
Jill Mayer *(VP)*
Jessica McClure *(VP)*
Jay Gelfman *(VP)*
Douglas J. Swirsky *(CFO & Principal Acctg Officer)*
Maher Masoud *(Pres & CEO)*

MAXIMUS, INC.
1600 Tysons Blvd Ste 1400, McLean, VA 22102
Tel.: (703) 251-8500   VA
Web Site: https://www.maximus.com
Year Founded: 1975
MMS—(NYSE)
Rev.: $5,306,197,000
Assets: $4,131,508,000
Liabilities: $2,288,693,000
Net Worth: $1,842,815,000
Earnings: $306,914,000
Emp.: 41,100
Fiscal Year-end: 09/30/24
Government Consulting & Support Services
N.A.I.C.S.: 921190
David Casey *(Sr VP-Govt Rels & Bus Dev)*
Bruce L. Caswell *(Pres & CEO)*
John Lambeth *(CIO)*
Michael S. Weiner *(Chief Medical Officer)*
Jericho Seguin *(Sr VP-Corp Dev)*
Ilene Baylinson *(Gen Mgr-Svcs Segment-US)*
Michelle F. Link *(Chief HR Officer)*
Kevin Reilly *(Gen Mgr-Outside US Segment)*
James Francis *(Sr Dir-IR)*
Madison West *(Sr Dir-Corp Responsibility & IR)*
Theresa Golinvaux *(Sr VP & Controller)*
Rebecca Kenawell *(Sr VP-HR)*
David Mutryn *(CFO & Treas)*
Bruce Perkins *(Deputy Gen Counsel)*
Marie Russell *(VP-Federal Alliances)*
Jennifer Ferreira *(VP-Bus Dev-Dept of Homeland Security)*
John Mandell *(Mng Dir-Natl Security)*
Scott Barr *(Sr VP-Tech & Consulting Svcs)*
Craig Shinn *(VP-Digital Govt Solutions)*
John MacMillan *(VP-Future Market Dev)*
Elisabeth Schmidt *(Sr VP-Tech & Consulting Svcs)*
Jessica Batt *(VP)*
Julia Bailey *(Sr VP)*
Frank Aiello *(Chief Information Security Officer)*
Jennifer Lazenby *(Sr VP)*
Eileen Cassidy Rivera *(VP)*
Keely Wilson *(Sr VP)*
Lou W. Shields *(Interim Gen Mgr-Federal Svcs)*
Christian Gingras *(Mng Dir)*
Darren Hooper *(Country Mgr)*
Gursel Mehmet *(Mng Dir)*
John Martinez *(Gen Counsel)*
Anne K. Altman *(Vice Chm)*

Subsidiaries:

Cheviot Recruitment Ltd **(1)**
18 Spice Court Ivory Square, Plantation Wharf, London, SW11 3UE, United Kingdom
Tel.: (44) 8455215521
Professional & Management Development Training
N.A.I.C.S.: 611430

Connect Assist Limited **(1)**
Unit 3 Cefn Coed Parc, Nantgarw, Cardiff,

CF15 7QQ, United Kingdom
Tel.: (44) 1443827600
Outsourced Call Center Services
N.A.I.C.S.: 561422

GT Hiring Solutions (2005) Inc. **(1)**
400 1207 Douglas Street, Victoria, V8W 2E7, BC, Canada
Tel.: (250) 382-3303
Web Site: http://www.gthiringsolutions.ca
Employment Services
N.A.I.C.S.: 561311

Health Management Limited **(1)**
Ash House The Broyle, Ringmer, BN8 5NN, East Sussex, United Kingdom
Tel.: (44) 1273818000
Web Site: http://healthmanagement.co.uk
Emp.: 300
Health Care Srvices
N.A.I.C.S.: 621610
Matt Wood *(Mng Dir)*
John Devlin *(Dir-IT)*
Claire Herne *(Dir-Client Svcs)*
Mary Rafferty *(Dir-Clinical Ops)*
Jonathan Sammut *(Dir-Bus Intelligence)*
Mark Simpson *(Chief Medical Officer)*
Peter Swann *(Dir-Fin)*
Alice Morton *(Deputy Dir-Client Svcs)*
Michaela Oliver *(Sr Mgr-Customer Svcs)*
Paul Keller *(Mgr-Ops)*
Richard Beasley *(Mgr-Recruitment)*
Alexandra Harkins *(Dir-Medical-Primary Care)*

ITSolutions Net Inc. **(1)**
3130 Frview Park Dr 800, Falls Church, VA 22042
Tel.: (703) 712-4000
Administrative Management Consulting Services
N.A.I.C.S.: 541611

InSysCo, Inc. **(1)**
1340 Central Park Blvd Ste 206, Fredericksburg, VA 22401
Tel.: (540) 785-9600
Information Technology Consulting Services
N.A.I.C.S.: 541512
Danielle Johnson *(Pres)*
Randy Phillips *(VP)*
Frank Nigro *(VP-Treasury Programs)*
Shelbi Potter *(VP-Bus Ops)*

Index Root Co., Ltd. **(1)**
19th Floor 503 Nonhyeon-ro, Yeoksam-dong Gangnam-gu, Seoul, Korea (South)
Tel.: (82) 16668219
Web Site: http://indexroot.co.kr
Employment Services
N.A.I.C.S.: 561311

Injury Net Australia Pty Ltd **(1)**
Level 1 173 Burke Road, Glen Iris, 3146, VIC, Australia
Tel.: (61) 395009968
Web Site: http://www.injurynet.au
Medical Advisory Services
N.A.I.C.S.: 541611

MAX Solutions Pty Limited **(1)**
111 Macquarie Road, PO Box 1164, Springwood, 2777, NSW, Australia
Tel.: (61) 1800603503
Web Site: http://www.maxsolutions.com.au
Health Care Srvices
N.A.I.C.S.: 621610
Richard Spurrell *(Exec Gen Mgr-Quality, Performance Analytics & Facilities)*
Adam Heilbron *(Exec Gen Mgr-Tech)*
Cameron Taylor *(Exec Gen Mgr-Fin)*
Rachel Chapman-McGowan *(Exec Gen Mgr-HR)*
Karen Massier *(Exec Gen Mgr-Strategy)*

MAXIMUS Asia Pte. Ltd. **(1)**
1 Gateway Drive 11-02 Westgate Tower, Singapore, 608531, Singapore
Tel.: (65) 68176049
Web Site: http://www.maximussingapore.sg
General Government Support Services
N.A.I.C.S.: 541512

MAXIMUS Canada, Inc. **(1)**
716 Yates Street, Victoria, V8W 1L4, BC, Canada
Tel.: (250) 405-3700
Web Site: http://www.maximuscanada.ca
Emp.: 1,360
Management Consulting Services

N.A.I.C.S.: 541611

MAXIMUS Employment & Training Limited **(1)**
MAXIMUS House Pynes Hill, Exeter, EX2 5AZ, Devon, United Kingdom
Tel.: (44) 1392330100
Web Site: http://www.maximusuk.co.uk
Emp.: 5
Employment Placement Services
N.A.I.C.S.: 561311

MAXIMUS Federal Services, Inc. **(1)**
3750 Monroe Ave Ste 702, Pittsford, NY 14534-1302
Tel.: (585) 348-3300
Web Site: http://www.medicareappeal.com
Emp.: 18,000
Process & Logistics Consulting Services
N.A.I.C.S.: 541614
Roland Scott *(Sr Dir-Accounts)*

Subsidiary (Domestic):

Acentia, LLC **(2)**
3130 Fairview Park Dr Ste 800, Falls Church, VA 22042
Tel.: (703) 712-4000
Web Site: http://www.acentia.com
Emp.: 1,000
Information Technology Services
N.A.I.C.S.: 541519

MAXIMUS Health & Human Services Limited **(1)**
Maximus House Pynes Hill, Exeter, EX2 5AZ, Devon, United Kingdom
Tel.: (44) 1392330100
Web Site: http://www.maximusuk.co.uk
Health Care Srvices
N.A.I.C.S.: 621610

MAXIMUS Health Services, Inc. **(1)**
1891 Metro Ctr Dr, Reston, VA 20190-5287
Tel.: (703) 251-8500
Management Consulting Services
N.A.I.C.S.: 541611

MAXIMUS Properties LLC **(1)**
1214 Blvd, Colonial Heights, VA 23834-3002
Tel.: (804) 526-1214
Real Estate Property Management Services
N.A.I.C.S.: 531311

Optimos LLC **(1)**
6290 Abbotts Bridge Rd Ste 103, Johns Creek, GA 30097
Web Site: http://www.optimosinternational.com
Computer Related Services
N.A.I.C.S.: 541519

Remploy Limited **(1)**
18c Meridian East Meridian Business Park, Leicester, LE19 1WZ, Leicestershire, United Kingdom
Tel.: (44) 3004568119
Web Site: http://www.remploy.co.uk
Employment Service Provider
N.A.I.C.S.: 561311
Gareth Parry *(CEO)*

Revitalised Limited **(1)**
Room 913 Spaces Peter House, Manchester, M1 5AN, United Kingdom
Tel.: (44) 1612404557
Web Site: http://www.revitalised.co.uk
Software Development Services
N.A.I.C.S.: 513210

Stirling Institute of Australia Pty. Ltd. **(1)**
Ground Floor 99 Queensbridge Street, Southbank, 3006, VIC, Australia
Tel.: (61) 1300790265
Web Site: https://sia.edu.au
Education Training Services
N.A.I.C.S.: 621399

The Centre for Health & Disability Assessments Ltd. **(1)**
Ash House The Broyle Ringmer, Lewes, BN8 5NN, East Sussex, United Kingdom
Tel.: (44) 8002888777
Web Site: http://www.chdauk.co.uk
Health & Welfare Fund Services
N.A.I.C.S.: 525120

MAXLINEAR, INC.

5966 La Pl Ct Ste 100, Carlsbad, CA 92008
Tel.: (760) 692-0711   DE
Web Site: https://www.maxlinear.com
Year Founded: 2003
MXL—(NASDAQ)
Rev.: $693,263,000
Assets: $1,080,257,000
Liabilities: $393,992,000
Net Worth: $686,265,000
Earnings: ($73,147,000)
Emp.: 1,759
Fiscal Year-end: 12/31/23
Radio Frequency Analog & Mixed Signal Semiconductor Solutions for Broadband Communications Applications
N.A.I.C.S.: 334413
Kishore Seendripu *(Co-Founder, Chm, Pres & CEO)*
Curtis Ling *(Co-Founder & Chief Technical Officer)*
Madhukar Reddy *(VP-IC & RF Sys Engrg)*
William G. Torgerson *(VP & Gen Mgr-Broadband Grp)*
Kathi Guiney *(VP-HR)*
James Lougheed *(VP-Mktg & High Performance Analog)*
Michael Bollesen *(VP-Sls)*
Connie Kwong *(Controller)*
Kelly Jones *(VP-Ops-Worldwide)*
Steven G. Litchfield *(CFO & Chief Corp Strategy Officer)*

Subsidiaries:

MaxLinear Asia Singapore Pte. Ltd.   (1)
20 Bendemeer Road 07-01 BS Bendemeer Centre, Singapore, 339914, Singapore
Tel.: (65) 69892720
Network Equipment Distr
N.A.I.C.S.: 423690

MaxLinear Hispania, S.L.   (1)
Ronda Narciso Monturiol 11d, Paterna, 46980, Valencia, Spain
Tel.: (34) 961366004
Web Site: http://www.maxlinear.com
Integrated Circuits Mfr
N.A.I.C.S.: 334413

MaxLinear Japan GK   (1)
Kanou Building 7F 1-26-7 Nishigotanda, Shinagawa-ku, Tokyo, 141-0031, Japan
Tel.: (81) 364170578
Semiconductor & Related Device Mfr
N.A.I.C.S.: 334413

MaxLinear Shanghai Limited   (1)
R303 Tower A Lane 2889 Jinke Road, Pudong New District, Shanghai, 201203, China
Tel.: (86) 2168822066
Semiconductor & Related Device Mfr
N.A.I.C.S.: 334413

MaxLinear Technologies Private Limited   (1)
Umiya Business Bay Tower 1 4th Floor Cessna Business Park, Embassy Tech Square Main Road KadubeesanahalliKaverappa Layout, Bengaluru, 560103, Karnataka, India
Tel.: (91) 8042405000
Semiconductor & Related Device Mfr
N.A.I.C.S.: 334413

Physpeed, LLC   (1)
4055 Mission Oaks Blvd Ste B, Camarillo, CA 93012
Tel.: (805) 259-3100
Web Site: http://www.physpeed.com
Emp.: 6
Integrated Circuits Mfr
N.A.I.C.S.: 334412

MAXUS REALTY TRUST, INC.
104 Armour Rd, Kansas City, MO 64116
Tel.: (816) 303-4500   MO
Web Site: http://www.mrti.com
Year Founded: 1984

MRTI—(OTCIQ)
Rev.: $120,262,000
Assets: $1,094,034,000
Liabilities: $952,878,000
Net Worth: $141,156,000
Earnings: $11,348,000
Fiscal Year-end: 12/31/20
Real Estate Investment Trust
N.A.I.C.S.: 525990
DeAnn M. Totta *(Sec & VP)*
David L. Johnson *(Chm, Pres & CEO)*
Ryan Snyder *(CFO, Treas & VP)*
Cheryl Marshall *(VP-Ops)*

MAYVILLE ENGINEERING COMPANY, INC.
715 South St, Mayville, WI 53050
Tel.: (414) 381-2860   WI
Web Site: https://www.mecinc.com
Year Founded: 1945
MEC—(NYSE)
Rev.: $539,392,000
Assets: $440,581,000
Liabilities: $222,714,000
Net Worth: $217,867,000
Earnings: $18,727,000
Emp.: 2,300
Fiscal Year-end: 12/31/22
Shotshell Reloaders & Aerial Work Platforms Mfr; Contract Engineering & Manufacturing Services
N.A.I.C.S.: 332119
Todd M. Butz *(CFO)*
Jagadeesh A. Reddy *(Pres & CEO)*
Rachele M. Lehr *(Chief HR Officer)*
Sean P. Leuba *(Gen Counsel & Sr VP-Corporate Development)*
Ryan F. Raber *(Exec VP-Strategy, Sls, and Mktg)*

Subsidiaries:

Defiance Metal Products Co.   (1)
21 Seneca St, Defiance, OH 43512-2274
Tel.: (419) 784-5332
Web Site: http://www.defiancemetal.com
Sales Range: $25-49.9 Million
Emp.: 975
Mfr of Automotive Stampings
N.A.I.C.S.: 336370

Plant (Non-US):

Defiance Metal Products Co. Inc. - China Plant   (2)
No 88 Jinghua Rd Shipai Bacheng Town, Kunshan, 215312, Jiangsu, China
Tel.: (86) 512 5033 3300
Fabricated Structural Metal Mfr
N.A.I.C.S.: 332312

Plant (Domestic):

Defiance Metal Products Co. Inc. - Defiance North Plant   (2)
06728 State Route 66 N, Defiance, OH 43512
Tel.: (419) 784-5332
Fabricated Structural Metal Mfr
N.A.I.C.S.: 332312

Defiance Metal Products Co. Inc. - Oshkosh Plant   (2)
2840 Bradley St, Oshkosh, WI 54902
Tel.: (920) 426-9207
Fabricated Structural Metal Mfr
N.A.I.C.S.: 332312
Dan Deker *(Gen Mgr)*

Subsidiary (Domestic):

Defiance Metal Products of Arkansas Inc.   (2)
944 Bypass Rd, Heber Springs, AR 72543
Tel.: (501) 362-1919
Web Site: http://www.defiancemetalproducts.com
Sales Range: $25-49.9 Million
Emp.: 200
Mfr of Automotive Stampings
N.A.I.C.S.: 336370

Defiance Metal Products, Inc.   (2)

550 Sunnyside Rd Ste 101, Bedford, PA 15522
Tel.: (814) 623-1104
Web Site: http://www.defiancemetal.com
Sales Range: $10-24.9 Million
Emp.: 30
Metal Stamping
N.A.I.C.S.: 332119

Fabricating Specialists, LLC   (1)
1506 Industrial Park Dr, Neillsville, WI 54456
Tel.: (715) 743-3090
Web Site: http://www.fsmec.com
Sales Range: $10-24.9 Million
Emp.: 20
Fabricated Structural Metal Mfr
N.A.I.C.S.: 332312

Mayville Engineering Company, Inc. - Byron Center   (1)
990 84th St SW, Byron Center, MI 49315
Tel.: (616) 878-3324
Web Site: http://www.mecinc.com
Welded Tubular Assembly Mfr
N.A.I.C.S.: 331210

Mid-States Aluminum Corp.   (1)
132 Trowbridge Dr, Fond Du Lac, WI 54937-9177
Tel.: (920) 922-7207
Web Site: http://www.midstal.com
Aluminum Rolling, Drawing & Extruding Services
N.A.I.C.S.: 331318
Joseph P. Colwin *(Pres)*

MBG HOLDINGS, INC.
4301 W Bank Dr Ste 110B, Austin, TX 78746
Tel.: (512) 360-0459   NV
Year Founded: 2009
MBGH—(OTCEM)
Assets: $138
Liabilities: $99,263
Net Worth: ($99,125)
Earnings: ($47,797)
Emp.: 300
Fiscal Year-end: 12/31/21
Metal Recycling Services
N.A.I.C.S.: 562998
Gordon Muir *(Founder)*
Bob Kirk *(VP-Fin)*
Bret Boster *(Dir-North American Ops)*
Joseph O'Bell *(Chief Legal Officer)*
Samantha Sondrup *(Sr VP & Head-Staff)*
James Frinzi *(CEO)*

MBIA INC.
1 Manhattanville Rd Ste 301, Purchase, NY 10577
Tel.: (914) 273-4545   CT
Web Site: https://www.mbia.com
Year Founded: 1973
MBI—(NYSE)
Rev.: $154,000,000
Assets: $3,375,000,000
Liabilities: $4,251,000,000
Net Worth: ($876,000,000)
Earnings: ($195,000,000)
Emp.: 75
Fiscal Year-end: 12/31/22
Municipal & Corporate Bond Insurance
N.A.I.C.S.: 524126
Joseph R. Schachinger *(CFO & Exec VP)*
William Charles Fallon *(CEO)*
Greg Diamond *(Mng Dir & Head-Investor & Media Rels)*
Jonathan C. Harris *(Gen Counsel & Sec)*
Daniel M. Avitabile *(Asst VP)*
Adam T. Bergonzi *(Chief Risk Officer-Natl & Asst VP)*
Christopher H. Young *(CFO-Natl & Asst VP)*

Subsidiaries:

MBIA   (1)

1700 S Broadway, Denver, CO 80202
Tel.: (303) 864-7400
Web Site: http://www.mbia.com
Sales Range: $25-49.9 Million
Emp.: 20
Portfolio Management
N.A.I.C.S.: 523940

MBIA Insurance Corporation   (1)
1 Manhattanville Rd Ste 301, Purchase, NY 10577
Tel.: (914) 273-4545
Emp.: 97
Municipal Bond & Asset Securities Insurance Services
N.A.I.C.S.: 524126
Joseph R. Schachinger *(Chm & CFO)*

Joint Venture (Domestic):

MD Helicopters, Inc.   (2)
4555 E McDowell Rd, Mesa, AZ 85215
Tel.: (480) 346-6344
Web Site: http://www.mdhelicopters.com
Sales Range: $25-49.9 Million
Helicopter Mfr
N.A.I.C.S.: 336411
Lynn Tilton *(CEO)*
Edward P. Dolanski *(Chm)*

MBIA Mexico, S.A. de C.V.   (1)
Insurgentes Sur 1898 Floor 12 Office 01, Col Florida, 01020, Mexico, Distrito Federal, Mexico
Tel.: (52) 5591710267
Bond Insurance Services
N.A.I.C.S.: 524126

MC ENDEAVORS, INC.
14752 Crenshaw Blvd Ste 128, Gardena, CA 90249
Tel.: (310) 349-9570   NV
Web Site:
http://www.mcendeavors.com
Year Founded: 2001
MSMY—(OTCIQ)
Natural Disaster Resistant Services
N.A.I.C.S.: 624230
Wilson Ndubueze Anaekwe *(Pres, CEO & Sec)*

MCCORMICK & COMPANY, INCORPORATED
24 Schilling Rd, Hunt Valley, MD 21031
Tel.: (410) 527-6189   MD
Web Site:
https://www.mccormickcorporation.com
Year Founded: 1889
MKC—(NYSE)
Rev.: $6,662,200,000
Assets: $12,862,300,000
Liabilities: $7,778,800,000
Net Worth: $5,083,500,000
Earnings: $680,600,000
Emp.: 13,800
Fiscal Year-end: 11/30/23
Specialty Food Products, Seasonings & Flavorings & Baking Products Mfr
N.A.I.C.S.: 311999
Brendan M. Foley *(Pres & CEO)*
Jeffery D. Schwartz *(Gen Counsel, Sec & VP)*
Michael Okoroafor *(VP)*
Michael R. Smith *(CFO & Exec VP)*
Gregory P. Repas *(Chief Acctg Officer, VP & Controller)*
Gregory P. Repas *(VP & Controller)*
Sarah Piper *(Chief Human Rels Officer)*
Lawrence E. Kurzius *(Exec Chm)*

Subsidiaries:

AVT McCormick Ingredients Pvt Ltd.   (1)
Marampilly PO, Aluva, 683107, Kerala, India   (50%)
Tel.: (91) 4842677262
Web Site: http://www.avtmccormick.com
Sales Range: $150-199.9 Million
Emp.: 370

McCormick & Company, Incorporated—(Continued)

Specialty Food Products, Seasonings, Flavorings & Food Decorations Mfr
N.A.I.C.S.: 311942
Sushama Srikandath (Mng Dir)

Botanical Food Company Pty. Ltd. (1)
80 Palmwoods Montville Road, Palmwoods, Sunshine Coast, 4555, QLD, Australia
Tel.: (61) 754532500
Web Site: http://www.gourmetgarden.com
Spice & Extract Mfr & Whslr
N.A.I.C.S.: 311942

Botanical Food Company, Inc. (1)
1843 Iron Point Rd Ste 140, Folsom, CA 95630
Tel.: (888) 878-3663
Spice & Extract Mfr & Whslr
N.A.I.C.S.: 311942

Dessert Products International (1)
315 Rue Marcel Demonque, Avignon, 849173, France (100%)
Tel.: (33) 432736565
Web Site: http://www.gucros.com
Sales Range: $25-49.9 Million
Emp.: 250
Dessert Products
N.A.I.C.S.: 311942

Drogheria E Alimentari SPA (1)
V le Nilde Iotti 23/25, 50038, San Piero a Sieve, Florence, Italy
Tel.: (39) 05 584 3251
Web Site: https://www.drogheria.com
Food Flavor Mfr & Distr
N.A.I.C.S.: 311942

Enrico Giotti SPA (1)
Via Pisana 592, 50018, Scandicci, Florence, Italy
Tel.: (39) 05572091
Web Site: https://www.enrico-giotti.it
Natural & Organic Flavor Mfr
N.A.I.C.S.: 311930

FONA International, LLC (1)
1900 Averill Rd, Geneva, IL 60134-1601
Tel.: (630) 578-8600
Web Site: https://www.fona.com
Extracts & Flavoring Products Developer
N.A.I.C.S.: 311942
Joseph James Slawek (Founder)
T. J. Widuch (Exec VP)
Robert Sobel (VP-Res & Innovation)
Manon Daoust (Exec VP)
Jeremy Thompson (Pres & COO)

La Cie McCormick Canada Co. (1)
600 Clarke Rd, London, N5V 3K5, ON, Canada
Tel.: (519) 432-7311
Specialty Food Products, Seasonings, Flavorings & Food Decorations Mfr & Distr
N.A.I.C.S.: 311942

McCormick (Guangzhou) Food Company Limited (1)
No 183 Binhe Road, Dongji Industrial District, Economic Development Zone, 510730, Guangzhou, China
Tel.: (86) 2082220832
Web Site: http://en.mccormick.com.cn
Flavorings, Seasonings & Spices Mfr
N.A.I.C.S.: 311930

McCormick Flavor Division (1)
226 Schilling Cir, Hunt Valley, MD 21031 (100%)
Tel.: (410) 771-7500
Web Site: http://www.mccormickflavor.com
Sales Range: $250-299.9 Million
Emp.: 350
Flavors, Food Colors, Seasonings & Spices Mfr
N.A.I.C.S.: 311423

Plant (Domestic):

McCormick Company-South Bend (2)
3425 Lathrop St, South Bend, IN 46628
Tel.: (574) 234-8101
Web Site: http://www.mccormick.com
Sales Range: $75-99.9 Million
Emp.: 130
Food Products Mfr
N.A.I.C.S.: 311999

Allen Wilson (Chm, Pres & CEO)

McCormick Condiment Plant (2)
10950 Beaver Dam at Gilroy Rd, Hunt Valley, MD 21031
Tel.: (410) 771-7744
Sales Range: $50-74.9 Million
Emp.: 119
Food Products Mfr
N.A.I.C.S.: 311999

McCormick Spice Mill (2)
10901 Gilroy Rd, Hunt Valley, MD 21031 (100%)
Tel.: (410) 771-5073
Web Site: http://www.mccormickflavor.com
Sales Range: $75-99.9 Million
Emp.: 180
Spice Products
N.A.I.C.S.: 311942

McCormick Food Service Division (1)
226 Schilling Cir, Hunt Valley, MD 21031-8647
Tel.: (410) 771-7500
Web Site: http://www.mccormick.com
Sales Range: $150-199.9 Million
Emp.: 300
Food Products for Food Service Installations
N.A.I.C.S.: 311942

Plant (Domestic):

McCormick-Hunt Valley Plant (2)
11100 McCormick Rd, Hunt Valley, MD 21031
Tel.: (410) 771-7778
Web Site: http://www.mccormick.com
Sales Range: $25-49.9 Million
Mfr of Foil-Packed Seasoning, Seasoning Blends, Gravy, Sauce Mixes & Dips, Flavoring Extracts & Tea
N.A.I.C.S.: 493110

McCormick-Salinas Plant (2)
1311 Schilling Pl, Salinas, CA 93901
Tel.: (831) 758-2411
Web Site: http://www.stange.co.jp
Sales Range: $150-199.9 Million
Food Products Mfr
N.A.I.C.S.: 311423

McCormick Foods Australia Pty. Ltd. (1)
Private Bag 31, Clayton, 3169, VIC, Australia
Web Site: http://www.mccormick.com.au
Specialty Food Products, Seasonings, Flavorings & Food Decorations Mfr
N.A.I.C.S.: 311930

McCormick France, S.A.S. (1)
315 Rue Marcel Demonque, 84917, Avignon, Cedex 9, France
Tel.: (33) 800600662
Web Site: https://www.ducros.com
Sales Range: $300-349.9 Million
Frozen Food Mfr & Whslr
N.A.I.C.S.: 424420

McCormick Glentham (Proprietary) Limited (1)
317 16th Road, Midrand, 1685, South Africa (100%)
Tel.: (27) 116900300
Sales Range: $50-74.9 Million
Emp.: 150
Flavorings, Seasonings & Spices
N.A.I.C.S.: 311930

McCormick Ingredients Southeast Asia Private Limited (1)
21 Bipolis Road McCormick #05-10 Nucleos North Tower, Singapore, 138567, Singapore
Tel.: (65) 62653433
Web Site: http://www.mccormickflavor.com
Food Products Mfr
N.A.I.C.S.: 311942

McCormick International Holdings Ltd. (1)
Haddenham Business Park Pegasus Way, Haddenham, Aylesbury, HP17 8LB, Bucks, United Kingdom
Tel.: (44) 1844292930
Holding Company
N.A.I.C.S.: 551112

Subsidiary (Domestic):

McCormick (UK) Ltd. (2)
Haddenham Business Park Pegasus Way, Haddenham, Aylesbury, HP17 8LB, United Kingdom (100%)
Tel.: (44) 808 100 0363
Web Site: https://www.mccormickflavoursolutions.co.uk
Spices, Seasonings & Relishes Distr
N.A.I.C.S.: 445298

McCormick Europe Ltd. (2)
Haddenham Business Park Pegasus Way, Haddenham, Aylesbury, HP17 8LB, United Kingdom
Tel.: (44) 1844292930
Holding Company
N.A.I.C.S.: 551112

McCormick Pesa, S.A. de C.V. (1)
Antigua Carretera Mexico-cuautitlan Km 31 5 #31, 54879, Cuautitlan, Mexico
Tel.: (52) 5558997900
Web Site: http://www.mccormickpesa.com
Sales Range: $125-149.9 Million
Emp.: 300
Flavorings, Seasonings & Spices
N.A.I.C.S.: 311930

McCormick Philippines, Inc. (1)
SYSU Centre 145 Panay Avenue, Quezon City, 1103, Philippines
Tel.: (63) 29205291
Web Site: http://www.mccormick.com.ph
Sales Range: $125-149.9 Million
Emp.: 300
Flavorings, Seasonings & Spices
N.A.I.C.S.: 311930
Steven Sy (Gen Mgr)

McCormick Polska S.A. (1)
Stefanowo ul Malinowa 18/20, 05-552, Wolka Kosowska, Poland
Tel.: (48) 227171900
Web Site: https://www.kamis.pl
Spices Farming Services
N.A.I.C.S.: 111998

McCormick South Africa Pty Limited (1)
317 16th Road Halfway House, Midrand, Johannesburg, 1682, South Africa
Tel.: (27) 116900300
Web Site: http://www.mccormick.com
Spice & Extract Whslr
N.A.I.C.S.: 424490

McCormick Switzerland GmbH (1)
Steinackerstrasse 9, 8700, Kusnacht, Switzerland (100%)
Tel.: (41) 449911365
Web Site: http://www.mccormick.com
Sales Range: $100-124.9 Million
Emp.: 7
Investment Services
N.A.I.C.S.: 523999
Petrus Gerardus van Tol (Chm)

McCormick de Centro America, S.A. de C.V. (1)
Bulevar Deininger y Avenida Las Palmera, La Libertad, El Salvador
Tel.: (503) 22128500
Web Site: http://www.mccormick.com.sv
Specialty Food Products, Seasonings, Flavorings & Food Decorations Mfr
N.A.I.C.S.: 311930

McCormick de Mexico, S.A. de C.V. (1)
Calzada de San Bartolo Naucalpan 360 Col Argentina Pte, Delegacion Miguel Hidalgo, 11230, Mexico, Mexico
Tel.: (52) 5550494280
Web Site: http://www.mccormick.com.mx
Sales Range: $200-249.9 Million
Emp.: 460
Specialty Food Products, Seasonings, Flavorings & Food Decorations; Owned 50% by McCormick & Company, Incorporated & 50% by Grupo Herdez, S.A. de C.V.
N.A.I.C.S.: 311930

Mojave Foods Corporation (1)
6200 E Slauson Ave, Commerce, CA 90040
Tel.: (323) 890-8900
Web Site: http://www.mojavefoods.com
Food Products Mfr
N.A.I.C.S.: 311423

Shanghai McCormick Foods Company Limited (1)
701 Hong Mei Rd S, Shanghai, 200237, China (90%)
Tel.: (86) 2164761589
Web Site: http://www.McCormick.com.cn
Sales Range: $150-199.9 Million
Emp.: 400
Specialty Food Products, Seasonings, Flavorings & Food Decorations Mfr
N.A.I.C.S.: 311930

Stange (Japan) K.K. (1)
7 Kanda-Mitoshirocho, Chiyoda-ku, Tokyo, 101-0053, Japan
Tel.: (81) 332336300
Web Site: http://www.stange.co.jp
Emp.: 130
Spices, Salad Dressings & Specialties Mfr
N.A.I.C.S.: 311942

The French's Food Company LLC (1)
PO Box 224, Parsippany, NJ 07054-0224
Web Site: http://www.frenchs.com
Condiments, Salad Toppers & Snacks Mfr
N.A.I.C.S.: 311941

Zatarain's Brands, Inc. (1)
82 1st St, Gretna, LA 70053
Tel.: (504) 367-2950
Web Site: http://www.zatarain.com
New Orleans-Style Foods Mfr
N.A.I.C.S.: 311999

MCDERMOTT INTERNATIONAL, INC.
915 N Eldridge Pkwy, Houston, TX 77079
Tel.: (281) 588-6600 Pa
Web Site: https://www.mcdermott.com
Year Founded: 1946
MCDIF—(OTCEM)
Rev.: $8,431,000,000
Assets: $8,737,000,000
Liabilities: $10,880,000,000
Net Worth: ($2,143,000,000)
Earnings: ($2,909,000,000)
Emp.: 42,600
Fiscal Year-end: 12/31/19
Boiler Mfr
N.A.I.C.S.: 332410
Scott Munro (Officer-Corp Dev & Sr VP)
John Mark Freeman (Chief Legal Officer, Sec & Exec VP)
Ian Prescott (Sr VP-Asia Pacific)
Brian McLaughlin (Chief Comml Officer & Sr VP)
Linh Austin (Sr VP-Middle East & North Africa)
Christopher A. Krummel (CFO & Exec VP)
Samik Mukherjee (COO & Exec VP)
Daniel M. McCarthy (Exec VP-Lummus Tech)
Neil Gunnion (Sr VP-Project Execution & Delivery)
Tareq F. Kawash (Sr VP-Europe, Africa, Russia & Caspian)
Gentry Brann (Sr VP)
John Staurt (Mgr)
Dale Suderman (Chief Acctg Officer & VP)
Kevin Hargrove (Treas & VP)
Reba Reid (Sr Dir-Global Comm & Mktg)
Nils Larsen (Chm)
Michael McKelvy (Pres & CEO)

Subsidiaries:

Chicago Bridge & Iron Company N.V. (1)
Prinses Beatrixlaan 35, 2595 AK, Hague, Netherlands
Tel.: (31) 703732010
Rev.: $6,673,330,000
Assets: $5,971,582,000
Liabilities: $5,753,218,000
Net Worth: $218,364,000

Earnings: ($1,458,193,000)
Emp.: 26,400
Fiscal Year-end: 12/31/2017
Holding Company; Process Technology Licensing, Specialty Engineering & Construction Services
N.A.I.C.S.: 551112

Subsidiary (Non-US):

CB&I Singapore Pte Ltd. (2)
3A International Business Park 09-01/09
icon ibp - Tower A, 609935, Singapore
Tel.: (65) 62436868
Engineeering Services
N.A.I.C.S.: 541330

CBI Eastern Anstalt (2)
10th Floor Standard Charter Tower Downtown, PO Box 2750, Dubai, United Arab
Emirates   (100%)
Tel.: (971) 42609111
Web Site: http://www.cbi.com
Sales Range: $50-74.9 Million
Emp.: 120
N.A.I.C.S.: 562910
Tom Boshoff (Mng Dir)

Subsidiary (US):

Chicago Bridge & Iron Company (2)
2103 Research Forest Dr, The Woodlands,
TX 77380-1123
Tel.: (832) 513-1600
Sales Range: $1-4.9 Billion
Emp.: 300
Holding Company; Corporate Administrative Office
N.A.I.C.S.: 551112

Subsidiary (Domestic):

**Aptim Government Solutions,
LLC** (3)
1200 Brickyard Ln, Ste 202, Baton Rouge,
LA 70802
Tel.: (833) 862-7846
Web Site: https://www.aptim.com
Design-Build Infrastructure Projects for Federal, State & Local Governments
N.A.I.C.S.: 236220

CB&I Inc. (3)
2103 Research Forrest Dr, The Woodlands,
TX 77380
Tel.: (832) 513-1000
Construction of Plate Steel Structures
N.A.I.C.S.: 238120

Branch (Domestic):

CB&I - Alpharetta (4)
11560 Great Oaks Wy, Ste 500, Alpharetta,
GA 30022-2424   (100%)
Tel.: (770) 521-6545
Structural Steel Erectors
N.A.I.C.S.: 332410

CB&I - Clive (4)
9600 Hickman Rd, Clive, IA 50325
Tel.: (515) 270-8712
Metal & Fabricated Mfg.
N.A.I.C.S.: 332312

Subsidiary (Non-US):

CB&I London (3)
2 New Square, Bedfont Lakes Business
Park, Feltham, TW14 8HA, Middlesex,
United Kingdom
Tel.: (44) 2070533000
Oil & Gas Pipeline Construction Services
N.A.I.C.S.: 237120

CB&I Paddington Limited (3)
2 New Square Bedfont Lakes Business
Park Feltham, Mddx, TW14 8HA, United
Kingdom
Tel.: (44) 2070533000
Oil & Gas Pipeline Construction Services
N.A.I.C.S.: 237120

Subsidiary (Domestic):

CBI Services, Inc. (New Castle) (3)
24 Reads Way, New Castle, DE
19720   (100%)
Tel.: (302) 325-8420
Steel Construction
N.A.I.C.S.: 236210

Chicago Bridge & Iron Company (3)

14105 S Rte 59, Plainfield, IL 60544-8984
Tel.: (815) 439-6000
Construction Engineering Services
N.A.I.C.S.: 541330

Lummus Technology, Inc. (3)
1515 Broad St, Bloomfield, NJ 07003-3096
Tel.: (973) 893-1515
Web Site: http://www.cbi.com
Process Technology, Engineering & Industrial Construction Services
N.A.I.C.S.: 541330
Daniel M. McCarthy (Exec VP)

Division (Domestic):

**Lummus Technology - Heat
Transfer** (4)
1515 Broad St, Bloomfield, NJ 07003-3002
Tel.: (973) 893-1515
Web Site:
     https://www.lummustechnology.com
Heat Transfer Equipment Supplier & Mfr
N.A.I.C.S.: 541330

Subsidiary (Domestic):

**Chicago Bridge & Iron Company
B.V.** (2)
Prinses Beatrixlaan 35, Hague, 2595 AK,
Netherlands   (100%)
Tel.: (31) 703732010
Process Technology Licensing, Specialty
Engineering & Construction Services
N.A.I.C.S.: 541330

Subsidiary (Non-US):

Arabian CBI Ltd. (3)
5th Floor, Sumou Tower, Al Khobar, 31431,
Saudi Arabia   (75%)
Tel.: (966) 138453100
Fabricated Metal & Mfg.
N.A.I.C.S.: 332410

CB&I (3)
20th Floor Equitable Bank Tower 8751
Paseo de Roxas Ave, Makati, 1226, Manila,
Philippines
Tel.: (63) 22386911
Web Site: http://www.cbi.com
Sales Range: $25-49.9 Million
Emp.: 77
Engineering & Construction Services
N.A.I.C.S.: 562910

Subsidiary (Domestic):

CB&I Lummus B.V. (3)
Oostduinlaan 75, 2596 JJ, Hague, Netherlands
Tel.: (31) 703732010
Engineeering Services
N.A.I.C.S.: 541330

Subsidiary (Non-US):

CB&I Lummus GmbH (3)
Lorenz Schott Strasse 4, 55252, Mainz-Kastel, Germany
Tel.: (49) 61347120
Web Site: http://www.lummusonline.com
Engineering Services
N.A.I.C.S.: 541330

Subsidiary (Domestic):

**Lummus Novolen Technology
GmbH** (4)
Gottlieb Daimler Strasse 8, Mannheim,
68165, Germany
Tel.: (49) 6214949400
Engineering & Construction Services
N.A.I.C.S.: 541330
Fred Follmer (Mng Dir)

Subsidiary (Domestic):

CB&I Oil & Gas Europe B.V. (3)
Prinses Beatrixlaan 35, Hague, 2595AK,
Netherlands
Tel.: (31) 703732010
Oil & Gas Exploration Services
N.A.I.C.S.: 213112

Subsidiary (Non-US):

CB&I Lummus s.r.o. (4)
Holandska 8, Brno, 639 00, Czech Republic
Tel.: (420) 545517111
Construction Engineering Services

N.A.I.C.S.: 541330

Subsidiary (Domestic):

CB&I Nederland B.V. (4)
Prinses Beatrixlaan 35, Hague, 2595AK,
Netherlands
Construction Engineering Services
N.A.I.C.S.: 541330

Subsidiary (Non-US):

CB&I s.r.o. (4)
Holandska 8, 639 00, Brno, Czech Republic
Tel.: (420) 545517111
Engineeering Services
N.A.I.C.S.: 541330

Subsidiary (Domestic):

**Lummus Technology Heat Transfer
B.V.** (4)
Prinses Beatrixlaan 35, Hague, 2595, Netherlands
Tel.: (31) 703733010
Heat Transfer Equipment Distr
N.A.I.C.S.: 423720

Subsidiary (Non-US):

CB&I UK Limited (3)
40 Eastbourne Terrace, London, W2 6LG,
United Kingdom
Tel.: (44) 2070533000
Civil Engineering Construction Services
N.A.I.C.S.: 237990

CBI Constructors Pty. Ltd (3)
Suite 2.12, 371 MacArthur Terrace, Hamilton, 4007, QLD, Australia   (100%)
Tel.: (61) 894881578
Engineeering Services
N.A.I.C.S.: 541330

Branch (Domestic):

**CBI Constructors Pty. Ltd.
(Perth)** (4)
Level 4/15-17 William St,, Perth, 6000, WA,
Australia   (100%)
Tel.: (61) 893245555
Engineeering Services
N.A.I.C.S.: 541330

Subsidiary (Non-US):

CBI Venezolana, S.A. (3)
2 Da Av De Campo Alegre Torre Credival
9th Floor, 1010, Caracas,
Venezuela   (100%)
Tel.: (58) 2122634011
Web Site: http://www.cbi.com
Remediation Services
N.A.I.C.S.: 562910

Subsidiary (Domestic):

CMP Holdings B.V. (3)
Oostduinlaan 75, Hague, 2596 JJ, Netherlands
Tel.: (31) 703732010
Investment Management Service
N.A.I.C.S.: 523999

Subsidiary (Domestic):

CB&I Europe B.V. (4)
Prinses Beatrixlaan 35, 2596 JJ, Hague,
Netherlands
Tel.: (31) 703732010
Oil & Gas Exploration Services
N.A.I.C.S.: 213112

Subsidiary (Domestic):

Cojafex B.V. (3)
Boompjes 40, 3011 XB, Rotterdam,
Netherlands   (100%)
Tel.: (31) 102068080
Web Site: http://www.cojafex.com
Mfr & Supplier of Induction Pipe Bending
Equipment & Induction Structural Shape
Bending Machines
N.A.I.C.S.: 333248

Subsidiary (Non-US):

Horton CBI, Limited (3)
103 B 9816 Hardin Street, Fort McMurray,
T9H 4K3, AB, Canada
Tel.: (780) 743-0114

Construction, Repair & Maintenance of Engineered Plate Metal Structures
N.A.I.C.S.: 237990

Branch (Domestic):

Horton CBI, Limited (4)
55116 Hwy. 825 Sturgeon Industrial, Park
Sturgeon County, T8L 5C1, AB,
Canada   (100%)
Tel.: (780) 998-2800
Web Site: https://www.mcdermott.com
Sales Range: $50-74.9 Million
Emp.: 36
Construction, Repair & Maintenance of Engineered Plate Metal Structures
N.A.I.C.S.: 237990

Horton CBI, Limited (4)
700 6th Ave SW Ste 1920, Calgary, T2P
0T8, AB, Canada   (100%)
Tel.: (403) 718-0187
Construction, Repair & Maintenance of Engineered Plate Metal Structures
N.A.I.C.S.: 237990

Horton CBI, Limited (4)
101 Lampman Ct Ste 302, Niagara Falls,
L0S 1J0, ON, Canada   (100%)
Tel.: (905) 684-0012
Web Site: https://www.mcdermott.com
Structural Steel Erection
N.A.I.C.S.: 237990

Affiliate (Non-US):

P.T. Chicago Bridge & Iron (3)
Wisma Korindo Lantai 2 - Jl. MT Haryono
Kav. 62, Jakarta, 12780, Indonesia
Tel.: (62) 0217976209
Blast Furnace & Steel Mills
N.A.I.C.S.: 331110

**J. Ray McDermott (Aust.) Holding Pty
Limited** (1)
220 St Georges Tce, Perth, 6000, WA, Australia
Tel.: (61) 894881988
Web Site: http://www.mcdermott.com
Investment Management Service
N.A.I.C.S.: 551112

**J. Ray McDermott de Mexico, S.A. de
C.V.** (1)
Paseo De La Reforma 505 Cuauhtemoc
Distrito Federal, Mexico, 06500, Mexico
Tel.: (52) 5511021260
Emp.: 145
Construction Engineering Services
N.A.I.C.S.: 541330

**McDermott Marine Construction
Limited** (1)
Global House 1 Ashley Avenue, Epsom,
KT18 5AD, Surrey, United Kingdom
Tel.: (44) 1372741448
Oil Field Engineering Services
N.A.I.C.S.: 213112
Adrian Wylde (Project Dir)

MCDONALD'S CORPORATION

110 N Carpenter St, Chicago, IL
60607
**Tel.: (630) 623-3000   DE
Web Site:**
     https://corporate.mcdonalds.com
Year Founded: 1955
MCD—(NYSE)
Rev.: $25,493,700,000
Assets: $56,146,800,000
Liabilities: $60,853,500,000
Net Worth: ($4,706,700,000)
Earnings: $8,468,800,000
Emp.: 150,000
Fiscal Year-end: 12/31/23
Fast Food Restaurants
N.A.I.C.S.: 722513
Jon Banner (Chief Impact Officer-Global & Exec VP)
Christopher J. Kempczinski (Pres & CEO)
Ian Frederick Borden (CFO & Exec VP)
Heidi Capozzi (Chief People Officer-Global & Exec VP)
Mahrukh Hussain (Sec)

McDonald's Corporation—(Continued)

Brian Rice *(CIO-Global & Exec VP)*
Morgan Flatley *(CMO)*
Marion Gross *(Exec VP)*
Kevin Ozan *(Sr Exec VP)*
Manu Steijaert *(Exec VP)*
Lauren B. Elting *(Principal Acctg Officer, VP & Controller)*
Christopher J. Kempczinski *(Chm, Pres & CEO)*

Subsidiaries:

Golden Arches Restaurants Sdn. Bhd. (1)
Level 11 Menara Luxor 6 Jalan Persiaran, Tropicana, Petaling Jaya, 47410, Selangor Darul Ehsan, Malaysia
Tel.: (60) 37118888
Web Site: http://www.mcdonalds.com.my
Restaurant Services
N.A.I.C.S.: 722511

HanGook McDonald's Co. Ltd. (1)
70 Gongpyeong-dong, Jongno-gu, Seoul, Korea (South)
Tel.: (82) 16005252
Web Site: https://www.mcdonalds.co.kr
Restaurant Operators
N.A.I.C.S.: 722511
Kiwon Kim *(CEO)*

McDonald's Australia Limited (1)
21-29 Central Ave, Thornleigh, 2120, NSW, Australia (100%)
Tel.: (61) 298756666
Web Site: https://www.mcdonalds.com.au
Sales Range: $125-149.9 Million
Emp.: 400
Restaurant
N.A.I.C.S.: 722511
Antoni Martinez *(CEO)*
Brad McMullen *(CFO)*
Emma Napoli-Hala *(Chief People Officer)*
Cameron Newlands *(Chief Restaurant Officer)*
Skye Baker *(Chief Dev Officer)*

McDonald's Deutschland GmbH (1)
Drygalski Alee 51, 81477, Munich, Germany (100%)
Tel.: (49) 89785940
Web Site: http://www.mcdonalds.de
Sales Range: $50-74.9 Million
Emp.: 350
Restaurant
N.A.I.C.S.: 722511
Holger Beeck *(CEO)*

McDonald's France SA (1)
1 Rue Gustave Eiffel, 78045, Guyancourt, Cedex, France (100%)
Tel.: (33) 130486000
Web Site: https://www.mcdonalds.fr
Fast Food Restaurants
N.A.I.C.S.: 722511
Jacques Mignault *(Pres)*
Aglae Strachwitz *(Chief Restaurant Officer)*
Amelie Duclos *(Chief People Officer)*
Romain Girard *(CFO)*
Jean-Guillaume Bertola *(CMO)*

McDonald's France Services SARL (1)
1 rue Gustave Eiffel, 78045, Guyancourt, France
Tel.: (33) 130486000
Web Site: https://www.mcdonalds.fr
Restaurant Operators
N.A.I.C.S.: 722511

McDonald's Franchise GmbH (Austria) (1)
Campus 21 Liebermannstrasse AO1601, 2345, Brunn am Gebirge, Austria
Tel.: (43) 223630700
Web Site: https://www.mcdonalds.at
Sales Range: $50-74.9 Million
Emp.: 80
Fast Food Restaurants
N.A.I.C.S.: 722511

McDonald's GmbH (1)
Industriestrasse 64, 56218, Mulheim-Karlich, Germany
Tel.: (49) 26304218
Limited-Service Restaurants
N.A.I.C.S.: 722513

McDonald's Holdings Co. (Japan), Ltd. (1)
Shinjuku i-Land Tower 6-5-1 Nishi Shinjuku, Shinjuku-ku, Tokyo, 163-1339, Japan (50%)
Tel.: (81) 333458223
Web Site: https://www.mcd-holdings.co.jp
Rev.: $2,708,302,010
Assets: $2,207,776,370
Liabilities: $600,664,800
Net Worth: $1,607,111,570
Earnings: $178,405,670
Emp.: 2,644
Fiscal Year-end: 12/31/2023
Holding Company
N.A.I.C.S.: 551112
Hitoshi Sato *(Sr VP)*
Sarah L. Casanova *(Pres & CEO)*
Takaaki Ishii *(Auditor)*
Robert D. Larson *(Chm)*
Atsuo Shimodaira *(COO & Exec VP)*
Kenji Miyashita *(VP)*

Subsidiary (Domestic):

EveryD Mc, Inc. (2)
Ogishima Bldg 8F 3-9 Moto-Akasaka 1, Chomeminato-ku, Tokyo, Japan (100%)
Tel.: (81) 357725115
Sales Range: $1-9.9 Million
Emp.: 11
Advetising Agency
N.A.I.C.S.: 541810

McDonald's Company (Japan), Ltd. (2)
Shinjuku I-Land Tower 6 5 1 Nishi Shinjuku, Shinjuku-Ku, Tokyo, 163-1339, Japan (100%)
Tel.: (81) 369115000
Web Site: http://www.mcd-holdings.co.jp
Hamburger Restaurant Chain Operator
N.A.I.C.S.: 722511

McDonald's Immobilien GmbH (1)
Drygalski Allee 51, 81477, Munich, Germany
Tel.: (49) 89785940
Limited-Service Restaurants
N.A.I.C.S.: 722513

McDonald's International (1)
2111 Midwest Rd, Oak Brook, IL 60523 (100%)
Tel.: (630) 620-0457
Web Site: http://www.mcdonalds.com
Sales Range: $800-899.9 Million
Emp.: 3,000
Public Relations Services
N.A.I.C.S.: 533110

McDonald's Italia S.r.l. (1)
Via Del Bosco Rinnovato 6 Assago, 20090, Milan, Italy (100%)
Tel.: (39) 02748181
Web Site: http://www.mcdonalds.it
Sales Range: $25-49.9 Million
Emp.: 200
Restaurant
N.A.I.C.S.: 722511

McDonald's Liegenschaftsverwaltungs Gesellschaft m.b.H. (1)
Campus 21 Liebermannstrasse A01601, 2345, Brunn am Gebirge, Austria
Tel.: (43) 223630700
Web Site: http://www.mcdonalds.at
Restaurant Services
N.A.I.C.S.: 722511

McDonald's Nederland B.V. (1)
Paashuevelweg 14, 1105 BH, Amsterdam, Netherlands
Tel.: (31) 202254037
Web Site: http://www.mcdonalds.nl
Sales Range: $10-24.9 Million
Emp.: 70
Fast Food Restaurants
N.A.I.C.S.: 722511

McDonald's Panama (1)
Edificio Evergreen Piso 8 5B Avenida Sur y Calle 78, PO Box 0833-0210, San Francisco, Panama, Panama
Tel.: (507) 5072706700
Web Site: http://www.mcdonalds.com.pa
Sales Range: $10-24.9 Million
Emp.: 68
Fast Food Restaurant Operator
N.A.I.C.S.: 722511

McDonald's Polska Sp. z o.o (1)
ul Marynarska 15, 02-674, Warsaw, Poland
Tel.: (48) 222115800
Web Site: https://mcdonalds.pl
Emp.: 100
Restaurant Services
N.A.I.C.S.: 722511

McDonald's Restaurants (Hong Kong) Ltd. (1)
36/F Dorset House Taikoo Place, 979 Kings Road, Quarry Bay, China (Hong Kong) (100%)
Tel.: (852) 28807300
Web Site: https://mcdonalds.com.hk
Sales Range: $300-349.9 Million
Emp.: 11,000
Fast Food Restaurants
N.A.I.C.S.: 722511

McDonald's Restaurants (New Zealand) Limited (1)
302 Great South Road, Greenlane, Auckland, 1051, New Zealand
Tel.: (64) 95394300
Web Site: https://www.mcdonalds.co.nz
Emp.: 9,000
Restaurant Services
N.A.I.C.S.: 722511
Kylie Freeland *(Mng Dir)*

McDonald's Restaurants (New Zealand) Limited (1)
302 Great South Road, Greenlane, Auckland, 1051, New Zealand
Tel.: (64) 95394300
Web Site: https://mcdonalds.co.nz
Restaurant Operators
N.A.I.C.S.: 722511

McDonald's Restaurants Limited (1)
11-59 High Road, East Finchley, London, N2 8AW, United Kingdom
Tel.: (44) 3705244622
Web Site: https://www.mcdonalds.co.uk
Fast Food Restaurant Operator
N.A.I.C.S.: 722513

McDonald's Restaurants Pte. Ltd. (1)
10 Kallang Avenue 04-10 Aperia Tower 2, Singapore, 339510, Singapore
Tel.: (65) 64620800
Web Site: https://www.mcdonalds.com.sg
Sales Range: $450-499.9 Million
Emp.: 6,000
Fast Food Restaurants
N.A.I.C.S.: 722511

McDonald's Restaurants of Canada Ltd. (1)
1 McDonalds Pl, Toronto, M3C 3L4, ON, Canada (100%)
Tel.: (416) 443-1000
Web Site: https://www.mcdonalds.com
Sales Range: $1-4.9 Billion
Emp.: 90,000
Fast Food Restaurants
N.A.I.C.S.: 722511
Alyssa Buetikofer *(CMO)*
Rod Halladay *(Chief Restaurant Officer)*
Denise Hansen *(Sr VP)*
David McMullen *(CTO)*
Alex Snelling *(Chief People Officer)*

McDonald's Restaurants of Illinois, Inc. (1)
445 Roosevelt Rd, Glen Ellyn, IL 60137-5622
Tel.: (630) 858-1114
Limited-Service Restaurants
N.A.I.C.S.: 722513

McDonald's Restaurants of Ireland Limited (Ireland) (1)
7 Richview Office Park, Clonskeagh, Dublin, Ireland
Tel.: (353) 15138100
Web Site: http://www.mcdonalds.ie
Restaurant Services
N.A.I.C.S.: 722511

McDonald's Restaurants of Maryland, Inc. (1)
9450 Crain Hwy, Upper Marlboro, MD 20772-5427
Tel.: (301) 856-1329
Emp.: 56
Limited-Service Restaurants

N.A.I.C.S.: 722513
Alex Caceres *(Mgr-Store)*

McDonald's Suisse Franchise Sarl (1)
Rue De Morges 23, 1023, Crissier, Switzerland
Tel.: (41) 21 631 1150
Web Site: https://www.mcdonalds.ch
Limited-Service Restaurants
N.A.I.C.S.: 722513

McDonald's USA, LLC (1)
2111 Midwest Rd, Oak Brook, IL 60523
Tel.: (630) 620-0457
Web Site: https://www.mcdonalds.com
Restaurant Services
N.A.I.C.S.: 722511
Joseph M. Erlinger *(Pres)*
Chris Kempczinski *(CEO)*
Tiffanie Boyd *(Chief People Officer)*
Tom Dillon *(CFO)*
Myra Doria *(Pres-)*
Michael Gonda *(Chief Impact Officer-)*
Jami Guthrie *(VP- &)*
Tariq Hassan *(Chief Customer Experience Officer)*
Whitney McGinnis *(CIO)*
Mason Smoot *(Chief Restaurant Officer)*
Angela Steele *(Gen Counsel)*
Bob Stewart *(Chief Supply Chain Officer-)*
Tabassum Zalotrawala *(Chief Dev Officer)*

McThai Company Ltd. (1)
97/11 Big C Rajdamri Building Office Room 1 5th Floor Rajdamri Road, Lumpini Pathumwan, Bangkok, 10330, Thailand
Tel.: (66) 26964900
Web Site: https://www.mcdonalds.co.th
Sales Range: $50-74.9 Million
Fast Food Restaurants
N.A.I.C.S.: 722513
Hester Chew *(Owner)*

Restaurantes McDonald's S.A. (1)
C/ Basauri 17 Edificio Oasis Module B - 1st Floor Plan, Urbanizacion La Florida, 28023, Madrid, Spain (100%)
Tel.: (34) 910213500
Web Site: https://www.mcdonalds.es
Sales Range: $25-49.9 Million
Emp.: 150
Fast Food Restaurant Operator
N.A.I.C.S.: 722511

Ronald McDonald House Charities, Inc. (1)
1 Kroc Dr, Oak Brook, IL 60523
Tel.: (630) 623-7048
Web Site: http://www.rmhc.org
Sales Range: $75-99.9 Million
Emp.: 3,000
Charity Involved in Creating, Finding & Supporting Programs that Directly Improve the Health & Well-Being of Children
N.A.I.C.S.: 624110
Mahrukh Hussain *(Co-Sec)*
Katie Fitzgerald *(Pres & CEO)*
Ginger Hardage *(Chm)*
Spero Droulias *(Treas)*
Stacey Bifero *(CFO)*
Janet Burton *(Chief Field Ops Officer)*
Joanna Sabato *(Chief Mktg & Dev Officer)*
Manish Yadav *(Co-Sec)*
Jon Banner *(Global Chief Impact Officer & Exec VP)*

Sistemas McDonald's Portugal Lda (1)
Building 7-Floor 2, 2740-244, Porto Salvo, Portugal
Tel.: (351) 214405300
Web Site: http://www.mcdonalds.pt
Emp.: 6,000
Restaurant Services
N.A.I.C.S.: 722511
Sofia Mendoca *(Dir-HR)*
Vitor Oliveira *(CFO)*

Svenska McDonald's AB (1)
Lindvretsvagen 9, Skarholmen, Stockholm, 127 85, Sweden
Tel.: (46) 87408500
Web Site: https://www.mcdonalds.se
Limited-Service Restaurants
N.A.I.C.S.: 722513
Anne Nordberg *(CFO)*

MCGRATH RENTCORP.

5700 Las Positas Rd, Livermore, CA
94551-7800
Tel.: (925) 606-9200   **CA**
Web Site: https://www.mgrc.com
Year Founded: 1979
MGRC—(NASDAQ)
Rev.: $831,842,000
Assets: $2,217,283,000
Liabilities: $1,283,481,000
Net Worth: $933,802,000
Earnings: $174,621,000
Emp.: 1,204
Fiscal Year-end: 12/31/23
Relocatable Modular Office & Class-
room Space & Electronic Test Equip-
ment Mfr, Retailer & Renter
N.A.I.C.S.: 532490
Joseph F. Hanna *(Pres & CEO)*
Keith E. Pratt *(CFO & Exec VP)*
David M. Whitney *(Chief Acctg Offi-
cer, VP & Controller)*
Bradley Mize Shuster *(Chm)*
John P. Lieffrig *(VP & Mgr-Mobile
Modular Portable Storage)*

Subsidiaries:

Design Space Modular Buildings
PNW, LP   **(1)**
26020 Acero Ste 100, Mission Viejo, CA
92691
Tel.: (909) 349-2100
Web Site:
    http://www.designspacemodular.com
Building Material Dealers
N.A.I.C.S.: 444180
Danie McGregor *(CFO & VP)*
Paul McShane *(CEO)*
Tony Esernia *(Founder)*

Enviroplex, Inc   **(1)**
4777 E Carpenter Rd, Stockton, CA
95215   **(100%)**
Tel.: (209) 466-8000
Web Site: https://www.enviroplex.com
Sales Range: $100-124.9 Million
Emp.: 75
Mfr Steelframe Modular School Facilities
N.A.I.C.S.: 332311

Jerald R. Brekke, Inc.   **(1)**
105 3rd Ave, Longmont, CO 80501
Tel.: (303) 776-2610
Web Site: http://www.brekkestorage.com
Rev.: $1,272,000
Emp.: 8
General Warehousing & Storage
N.A.I.C.S.: 493110
Shauna Brekke *(Office Mgr)*

Mobile Modular Management
Corporation   **(1)**
5700 Las Positas Rd, Livermore, CA 94551
Tel.: (925) 269-7420
Web Site: http://www.mgrc.com
Real Estate Property Management Services
N.A.I.C.S.: 531311

TRS-RenTelco Inc.   **(1)**
1830 W Airfield Dr DFW Airport, Dallas, TX
75261
Tel.: (972) 456-4000
Web Site: https://www.trsrentelco.com
Commercial & Industrial Machinery Equip-
ment Rental & Leasing Services
N.A.I.C.S.: 532490

Vesta Housing Solutions LLC   **(1)**
1000 Town Ctr Ste 975, Southfield, MI
48075
Tel.: (817) 663-8527
Web Site: http://www.vestamodular.com
Building Services
N.A.I.C.S.: 236220
Daniel McMurtrie *(Founder & CEO)*
Billy Hall *(Founder & COO)*
Chris Mattina *(CFO)*
Pat Carmody *(Pres-Ops)*

Subsidiary (Domestic):

Innovative Modular Solutions,
Inc.   **(2)**
155 Kirkland Cir Ste 500, Oswego, IL
60543
Tel.: (630) 972-0500
Web Site: http://www.innovativemodular.com

Temporary & Permanent Modular Building
Construction Services
N.A.I.C.S.: 236210
Gary Hahn *(Dir-Building & Grounds)*

MCHENRY BANCORP, INC.
353 Bank Dr, McHenry, IL 60050
Tel.: (815) 385-3000   **IL**
Year Founded: 1955
MCHN—(OTCIQ)
Bank Holding Company
N.A.I.C.S.: 551111
Don Wilson *(Chm, Pres & CEO)*
Douglas Howe *(CFO & Exec VP)*
Robert Ollech *(Chief Compliance Offi-
cer, Chief Credit Officer & Exec VP)*
Peter G. Sesin *(VP)*
Jennifer Osborn *(Mgr-Shareholder
Rels)*

Subsidiaries:

McHenry Savings Bank   **(1)**
353 Bank Dr, McHenry, IL 60050
Tel.: (815) 385-3000
Web Site: http://www.mchenrysavings.com
Sales Range: $10-24.9 Million
Emp.: 100
Provider of Banking Services
N.A.I.C.S.: 522180
Brian T. Nash *(Sr VP-IT)*
Donald H. Wilson *(Chm, Pres & CEO)*

MCHENRY METALS GOLF
CORP.
5430 Links Ln, Zephyrhills, FL 33541
Tel.: (813) 900-8472   **NV**
Web Site:
    https://mchenrymetalsgolf.com
GLFN—(OTCIQ)
Golf Club Operator
N.A.I.C.S.: 713910
Theodore Aroney *(Chm & Sec)*
Gary V. Adams *(CEO)*
Bradley J. Wilhite *(Pres)*
G. L. Moles *(COO)*
Douglas Willford *(CFO)*

MCKESSON CORPORATION
6555 State Hwy 161, Irving, TX
75039
Tel.: (972) 446-4800   **DE**
Web Site: https://www.mckesson.com
Year Founded: 1833
MCK—(NYSE)
Rev.: $276,711,000,000
Assets: $62,320,000,000
Liabilities: $63,810,000,000
Net Worth: ($1,490,000,000)
Earnings: $3,560,000,000
Emp.: 45,000
Fiscal Year-end: 03/31/23
Pharmaceutical Products Distr
N.A.I.C.S.: 424210
Brian Scott Tyler *(Pres & CEO)*
Donald R. Knauss *(Chm)*
Napoleon B. Rutledge Jr. *(Chief
Acctg Officer & Controller)*
Lori A. Schechter *(Chief Legal Officer,
Gen Counsel & Exec VP)*
Tom Rodgers *(Chief Strategy & Bus
Dev Officer & Exec VP)*
Britt J. Vitalone *(CFO & Exec VP)*
C. Lyn Fitzgerald *(VP-Sls)*
Dave Schulte *(Mng Dir-Ventures & Sr
VP)*
Jennifer M. Carter *(Partner & VP-
Venture Operations)*
Carrie Hurwitz Williams *(Partner-
McKesson Ventures & VP)*
Kelvin A. Baggett *(Chief Impact Offi-
cer & Exec VP)*
Michelle Snyder *(Partner-McKesson
Ventures)*
Nancy Flores *(Executives)*
Kevin W. Emerson *(Sr VP-Fin Ops)*

LeAnn B. Smith *(Chief HR Officer &
Exec VP)*
Francisco Fraga *(CIO & Exec VP)*

Subsidiaries:

Biologics, Inc.   **(1)**
11800 Weston Pkwy, Cary, NC 27513
Tel.: (800) 856-1984
Web Site: http://www.biologicsinc.com
Cancer Treatment Services
N.A.I.C.S.: 622310

Change Healthcare Holdings,
Inc.   **(1)**
3055 Lebanon Pike Ste 1000, Nashville, TN
37214
Tel.: (615) 932-3000
Web Site: http://changehealthcare.com
Rev.: $1,477,083,000
Assets: $4,573,534,000
Liabilities: $3,597,845,000
Net Worth: $975,689,000
Earnings: ($96,069,000)
Emp.: 5,000
Fiscal Year-end: 12/31/2015
Revenue & Payment Cycle Management
Services
N.A.I.C.S.: 518210
Neil E. de Crescenzo *(CEO)*
Steven Martin *(Exec VP-Enterprise Tech)*
Ryan Miller *(Sr VP-Corp Dev)*

Subsidiary (Domestic):

Capario, Inc.   **(2)**
1901 E Alton Ave Ste 100, Santa Ana, CA
92705
Tel.: (949) 852-3400
Web Site: http://www.capario.com
Sales Range: $25-49.9 Million
Emp.: 50
Remote Communication & Service Devices
for the Clinical Laboratory Industry
N.A.I.C.S.: 423430

Chamberlin Edmonds & Associates,
Inc.   **(2)**
14 Piedmont Ctr NE 3535 Piedmont Rd Ste
800, Atlanta, GA 30305-1618
Tel.: (800) 255-0953
Web Site:
    http://www.chamberlinedmonds.com
Patient Eligibility & Enrollment Services
N.A.I.C.S.: 561499

Change Healthcare Corporation   **(2)**
216 Centerview Dr Ste 300, Brentwood, TN
37027
Tel.: (615) 775-9441
Web Site: http://www.changehealthcare.com
Healthcare Cost Transparency Solutions
N.A.I.C.S.: 513210
Mark Vachon *(Pres-Sls, Ops & Tech En-
abled Svcs & Exec VP)*
Neil E. de Crescenzo *(Pres & CEO)*
Kris Joshi *(Pres-Network Solutions & Exec
VP)*
Linda Whitley-Taylor *(Chief People Officer &
Exec VP)*
Loretta Cecil *(Gen Counsel & Exec VP)*
Rod O'Reilly *(Pres-Software & Analytics &
Exec VP)*
W. Thomas McEnery *(CMO & Exec VP-
Corp Affairs)*
August Calhoun *(Pres-Sls & Ops & Exec
VP)*
Thomas Laur *(Pres-Tech Enabled Svcs &
Exec VP)*
Steven Martin *(Exec VP-Enterprise Tech)*

Emdeon Business Services LLC   **(2)**
3055 Lebanon Pike Ste 1000, Nashville, TN
37214-2230
Tel.: (615) 932-3000
Sales Range: $800-899.9 Million
Emp.: 3,000
Revenue Cycle Management & Clinical
Communication Services
N.A.I.C.S.: 522320

Branch (Domestic):

Emdeon Business Services   **(3)**
100 N Byrne Rd, Toledo, OH 43607
Tel.: (419) 324-8000
Medical Billing Services, Revenue Cycle
Management & Clinical Communication
Services
N.A.I.C.S.: 518210

Emdeon Business Services   **(3)**
7130 Minstrel Way Ste 130, Columbia, MD
21045
Tel.: (410) 381-3113
Sales Range: $750-799.9 Million
Emp.: 80
Imaging & Data Capture Services
N.A.I.C.S.: 518210

Subsidiary (Domestic):

Goold Health Systems   **(2)**
45 Commerce Dr Ste 5, Augusta, ME
04330
Tel.: (207) 622-7153
Web Site: http://www.ghsinc.com
Sales Range: $1-9.9 Million
Emp.: 63
Healthcare Management, Data Processing
& Administration Services
N.A.I.C.S.: 541519
James Clair *(Pres)*
Chad Bissell *(Dir-Clinical Svcs)*
Jason Hargrove *(Sr Dir-Admin)*
Marcia Pykare *(Dir-Data Svcs)*
Michael Ouellette *(Mgr-Pharmacy Acct)*
Rossi Rowe *(Mgr-Rebate Svcs)*
Tina M. Hisel *(Mgr-Pharmacy Acct)*
Miklos Van Halen *(Sr Dir-Product Engrg)*
John Grotton *(Sr Dir-Medicaid Pharmacy
Ops)*
Laureen Biczak *(Dir-Medical)*
Jeffrey Barkin *(Assoc Dir-Medical)*
Steve Liles *(Sr Dir-Pharmacy Svcs)*
Brian Erickson *(Mgr-IT)*
Eliza Mathias *(Mgr-Bus Dev)*
Kerri Powell *(Dir-Pharmacy Svcs)*
Shelagh Harvard *(Mgr-Community Assess-
ment Program Ops)*
Aurelie Allen *(Supvr-Data Capture & Mail-
room)*
Douglas Martin *(Mgr-Acct-Georgia Rebate
Program)*
Erin Halverson *(Mgr-Pharmacy Acct)*
Sara Howe *(Mgr-Wyoming Acct)*

PokitDok, Inc.   **(2)**
281 E 3rd Ave Ste 300, San Mateo, CA
94401
Tel.: (650) 503-3793
Web Site: http://www.pokitdok.com
Software Publisher; Healthcare
N.A.I.C.S.: 513210
Theodore Tanner *(Co-Founder & CTO)*

TC3 Health, Inc.   **(2)**
19732 MacArthur Blvd Ste 100, Irvine, CA
92612
Tel.: (714) 689-1900
Web Site: http://www.tc3health.com
Healthcare Claims Management Solutions
N.A.I.C.S.: 541519

Conscia Enterprise Systems
Limited   **(1)**
280 St Vincent St, Glasgow, G2 5RL, Scot-
land, United Kingdom
Tel.: (44) 1412215522
Web Site: http://www.conscia.co.uk
Sales Range: $100-124.9 Million
Emp.: 20
Software Design & Development & Hosting
Services
N.A.I.C.S.: 518210

CoverMyMeds LLC   **(1)**
2 Miranova Pl, Columbus, OH 43215
Tel.: (614) 360-1732
Web Site: http://www.covermymeds.com
Electronic Medication Prior Authorization
Services
N.A.I.C.S.: 518210
Sam Rajan *(Co-Founder)*

MED3000 Group, Inc.   **(1)**
Foster Plz 10 680 Andersen Dr, Pittsburgh,
PA 15220
Tel.: (412) 937-8887
Web Site: http://www.med3000.com
Sales Range: $800-899.9 Million
Emp.: 2,000
Healthcare Management & Technology So-
lutions
N.A.I.C.S.: 513210
John Wallace *(Sr VP, Pres/COO & Practice
Resources)*

Branch (Domestic):

MED3000 Group, Inc. - Oldsmar   **(2)**

McKesson Corporation—(Continued)

4033 Tampa Rd Ste 101, Oldsmar, FL 34677
Tel.: (813) 855-6880
Sales Range: $25-49.9 Million
Emp.: 100
Medical Management Software Solutions
N.A.I.C.S.: 513210

MED3000 Group, Inc. - (2)
Scottsdale
9060 E Via Linda Ste 120, Scottsdale, AZ 85258
Tel.: (480) 778-1000
Sales Range: $25-49.9 Million
Emp.: 33
Browser-Based Electronic Health Record Systems for Physician Group Practices
N.A.I.C.S.: 541511

McKesson Canada (1)
4705 Dobrin Street, Saint Laurent, H4R 2P7, QC, Canada
Tel.: (514) 745-2100
Web Site: http://www.mckesson.ca
Emp.: 3,500
Distr of Pharmaceutical Products
N.A.I.C.S.: 325412
Dimitris Polygenis (Pres-Pharmaceutical Solutions & Specialty Health)
Jennifer Zerczy (Sr VP-Legal & Regulatory Affairs)
Loris Zancan (CFO & Sr VP)
Rebecca McKillican (CEO)
Jean-Philippe Blouin (Sr VP-Pharmaceutical Distr & Ops)
Nicolas Caprio (Pres-Rexall Pharmacy Grp)
Lora Haak (Sr VP-HR)
Manasi Kulkarni (Sr VP-Corp Strategy, Bus Dev & Comm)
Andrea Polatos (CIO & Sr VP)
Tim Smith (Sr VP-Bus Dev & Customer Partnerships)
Erin Young (Chief Mktg & Mdsg Officer)

Subsidiary (Domestic):

McKesson Medical Imaging
Group (2)
10711 Cambie Road, Richmond, V6X 3G5, BC, Canada
Tel.: (604) 279-5422
Web Site: http://www.alitech.com
Rev.: $21,231,686
Emp.: 200
Provider of Medical Imaging System Services
N.A.I.C.S.: 621512

Medicine Shoppe Canada, Inc. (2)
10104 103rd Avenue Bell Tower Suite 1600, Edmonton, T5J 0H8, AB, Canada (100%)
Tel.: (780) 424-3096
Web Site: http://www.medicineshoppe.ca
Sales Range: $25-49.9 Million
Emp.: 50
Provider of Retail Drug Services
N.A.I.C.S.: 456110

Uniprix Inc. (2)
5000 Metropolitain Boulevard East, Montreal, H1S 3G7, QC, Canada
Tel.: (514) 725-1212
Web Site: http://www.uniprix.com
Drug Store Operator
N.A.I.C.S.: 456110
Richard Williamson (Dir-Recruitment)

McKesson Europe AG (1)
Stockholmer Platz 1, 70173, Stuttgart, Germany
Tel.: (49) 711500100
Web Site: http://www.mckesson.eu
Rev.: $20,570,686,344
Assets: $8,655,775,752
Liabilities: $6,321,505,632
Net Worth: $2,334,270,120
Earnings: ($8,966,152)
Emp.: 21,192
Fiscal Year-end: 03/31/2021
Pharmaceutical Wholesaling, Research & Retailing
N.A.I.C.S.: 325412
Brian Scott Tyler (Chm)
W. M. Henning Rehder (Deputy Chm-Supervisory Bd)
Tilo Koster (Member-Mgmt Bd)
Kevin Kettler (Chm-Mgmt Bd)
Ihno Goldenstein (Deputy Chm-Supervisory Bd)
Holger Landauer (Member-Mgmt Bd)

Subsidiary (Non-US):

AAH Pharmaceuticals Ltd. (2)
Sapphire Court Walsgrave Triangle, Coventry, CV2 2TX, United Kingdom
Tel.: (44) 3445618899
Web Site: http://www.aah.co.uk
Emp.: 1,200
Pharmaceutical & Healthcare Products Distr
N.A.I.C.S.: 423450

Subsidiary (Domestic):

Statim Finance Limited (3)
Sapphire Court Paradise Way Coventry Walsgrave Triangle West Midlands, Coventry, CV2 2TX, United Kingdom (100%)
Tel.: (44) 2476432500
Web Site: http://www.aah.co.uk
Sales Range: $350-399.9 Million
Emp.: 1,100
Guarantor of Pharmacy Loans
N.A.I.C.S.: 522299

Subsidiary (Non-US):

Herba Chemosan Apotheker-AG (2)
Haidestrasse 4, 1110, Vienna, Austria
Tel.: (43) 1 401 04 0
Web Site: http://www.herba-chemosan.at
Emp.: 750
Pharmaceuticals Whslr
N.A.I.C.S.: 424210

Lloyds Pharmacy Clinical Homecare
Limited (2)
Scimitar Park Roydon Road, Essex, Harlow, CM19 5GU, United Kingdom
Tel.: (44) 3452636123
Web Site:
http://www.lpclinicalhomecare.co.uk
Health Care Srvices
N.A.I.C.S.: 621999
Steve Spencer (Mgr-Bus Dev)

Norsk Medisinaldepot AS (2)
Alf Bjerckes vei 28, 0596, Oslo, Norway
Tel.: (47) 24 05 30 00
Web Site: http://www.nmd.no
Emp.: 2,500
Pharmaceuticals Whslr
N.A.I.C.S.: 424210

Pharma Belgium SA (2)
Rue Carli 17/19, 1140, Brussels, Belgium
Tel.: (32) 2 244 16 03
Web Site: http://www.pharmabelgium.be
Pharmaceuticals Whslr
N.A.I.C.S.: 424210

Division (Domestic):

Pharma Belgium Flandria (3)
Nederzwijnaarde 4, 9052, Zwijnaarde, Belgium
Tel.: (32) 92400811
Web Site: http://www.pharmabelgium.be
Emp.: 180
Pharmaceuticals Whslr
N.A.I.C.S.: 424210

McKesson Europe AG (1)
Stockholmer Platz 1, 70173, Stuttgart, Germany
Tel.: (49) 711500100
Web Site: http://www.mckesson.eu
Emp.: 38,000
Pharmaceutical Products Distr
N.A.I.C.S.: 424210
Ronan Brett (Dir-Pub Affairs)
Kevin Kettler (Chm-Mgmt Bd & Dir-Labour Rels)
Tilo Koster (Member-Mgmt Bd)

McKesson Health Solutions LLC (1)
275 Grove St Ste 1-210, Auburndale, MA 02466
Tel.: (617) 273-2800
Web Site: http://www.mckesson.com
Sales Range: $50-74.9 Million
Emp.: 200
Medical Management Products
N.A.I.C.S.: 513210

McKesson Information Solutions
Holdings Limited (1)
3300 Cork Airport Business Park Kinsale Rd, Cork, T12 XN72, Ireland
Tel.: (353) 214548200
Web Site: http://www.mckesson.com

Sales Range: $50-74.9 Million
Emp.: 110
Healthcare Products & Information Systems
N.A.I.C.S.: 456199

McKesson Medical-Surgical (1)
9954 Mayland Dr, Henrico, VA 23233
Tel.: (804) 264-7500
Web Site: http://www.mckesson.com
Rev.: $1,700,000,000
Emp.: 500
Distribution of Medical Equipment
N.A.I.C.S.: 456199

McKesson Medical-Surgical Inc. (1)
9954 Mayland Dr Ste 4000, Richmond, VA 23233
Web Site: http://mms.mckesson.com
Pharmaceuticals Distr
N.A.I.C.S.: 424210

McKesson Pharmaceutical (1)
1 Post St, San Francisco, CA 94104-5203
Tel.: (415) 983-8300
Web Site: http://www.mckesson.com
Sales Range: $50-74.9 Million
Emp.: 35
Pharmaceutical Equipment & Supplies Distr
N.A.I.C.S.: 424210

McKesson Pharmacy Systems (1)
30881 Schoolcraft Rd, Livonia, MI 48150 (100%)
Tel.: (734) 427-2000
Web Site: http://www.mckesson.com
Sales Range: $75-99.9 Million
Emp.: 400
Pharmacy Management Systems & Services Supplier
N.A.I.C.S.: 541511

McKesson Plasma and Biologics,
LLC (1)
2615 Medical Center Pkwy Ste 1580, Murfreesboro, TN 37129
Web Site: http://www.mckesson.com
Plasma Supplier
N.A.I.C.S.: 423450

McKesson Provider Technologies (1)
5995 Windward Pkwy, Alpharetta, GA 30005
Tel.: (404) 338-6000
Web Site: http://www.mckesson.com
Sales Range: $500-549.9 Million
Emp.: 6,286
Information Solutions to the Healthcare Industry
N.A.I.C.S.: 541512

Branch (Domestic):

McKesson Provider Technologies (2)
220 Davidson Ave, Somerset, NJ 08873-4149
Tel.: (732) 764-9898
Sales Range: $300-349.9 Million
Emp.: 250
Business Management Services & Information Systems for Physicians & Physician Delivery Systems & Ambulatory Department/Centers of Hospitals
N.A.I.C.S.: 531210

McKesson Specialty Health (1)
10101 Woodloch Forest, The Woodlands, TX 77380
Tel.: (281) 863-1000
Web Site: http://www.usoncology.com
Emp.: 800
Specialty Drugs Distr
N.A.I.C.S.: 424210

Medical Specialties Distributors
LLC (1)
800 Technology Center Dr, Stoughton, MA 02072
Tel.: (781) 344-6000
Medical Supplies & Equipment Distr
N.A.I.C.S.: 423450
Jim Beck (Chm)
Peter Huie (Sr VP-Facilities & Transportation)
Richard Worthen (Exec VP-Sls & Strategic Rels)
Paula A. Hardy (Dir-Natl Accts)
Larry Ovian (Dir-Natl Accts)
Mark Steele (Exec VP-Sls & Mktg)
Simon Smith (Dir-Mktg)
John Dunne (CIO)
Tom Burke (CEO)
Mike Rossi (CFO)

Subsidiary (Domestic):

Outpatient Infusion Systems, Inc. (2)
5950 Shiloh Rd E, Alpharetta, GA 30005
Tel.: (678) 513-3849
Ambulatory Infustion Solution Operating Services
N.A.I.C.S.: 423450

Oncology Therapeutic Network
Corporation (1)
395 Oyster Point Blvd Ste 500, South San Francisco, CA 94080-1995
Tel.: (650) 952-8400
Physician Oriented Technology Solutions
N.A.I.C.S.: 541990
Chuck Dowling (Head-Oncology Network & Physician Services)

Portico Systems, Inc. (1)
518 E Township Line Rd Ste 100, Blue Bell, PA 19422
Tel.: (215) 358-3800
Web Site: http://www.porticosys.com
Sales Range: $10-24.9 Million
Healthcare Provider Management Solutions
N.A.I.C.S.: 513210

RXC Acquisition Company (1)
6535 N State Hwy 161, Irving, TX 75039
Web Site: http://www.mckesson.com
Pharmaceutical Business Management & Product Support Services
N.A.I.C.S.: 541611
Michelle Lau (Sec & Dir)
Todd E. Baldanzi (Treas & Dir)

RelayHealth (1)
1564 NorthEast Expy, Atlanta, GA 30329
Tel.: (404) 728-2000
Web Site: http://www.relayhealth.com
Sales Range: $100-124.9 Million
Emp.: 31
Clinical Communication & Care Delivery Services
N.A.I.C.S.: 541512

Subsidiary (Domestic):

RelayHealth (2)
8720 Orion Pl Ste 300, Columbus, OH 43240
Tel.: (614) 885-1272
Web Site: http://www.relayhealth.com
Sales Range: $1-9.9 Million
Emp.: 55
Healthcare Management Solutions
N.A.I.C.S.: 513210

Rexall Pharmacy Group Ltd. (1)
5965 Coopers Avenue, Mississauga, L4Z 1R9, ON, Canada (100%)
Tel.: (905) 502-5965
Web Site: http://www.rexall.ca
Holding Company; Retail Pharmacies & Drug Stores Operator
N.A.I.C.S.: 551112
Nicolas Caprio (Pres)
Joyce Lee (CFO & Sr VP)
Frank Monteleone (Chief People Officer & Sr VP)
Paul Chidley (Sr VP-Store Ops)
Mona Sabharwal (Sr VP-Pharmacy Svcs)

Division (Domestic):

MediTrust Pharmacy (2)
9625 Yonge Street, Richmond Hill, L4C 5T2, ON, Canada
Tel.: (888) 792-3667
Web Site: http://www.meditrust.ca
Pharmaceutical Home Delivery Services
N.A.I.C.S.: 102210

Subsidiary (Domestic):

ProPharm Ltd. (2)
131 McNabb St, Markham, L3R 5V7, ON, Canada
Tel.: (905) 943-9736
Web Site: http://www.propharm.com
Pharmacy Technology Products & Services
N.A.I.C.S.: 513210

US Oncology, Inc. (1)
10101 Woodloch Forrest, The Woodlands, TX 77380
Tel.: (281) 863-1000
Web Site: http://www.usoncology.com
Emp.: 4,800
Cancer-Care Services

N.A.I.C.S.: 622310
Claire Crye (Mgr-PR)

United Drug Wholesale Limited (1)
Magna Drive Magna Business Park City-
west Road 24, Dublin, D24 XKE5, Ireland
Tel.: (353) 14632300
Web Site: http://www.united-drug.com
Pharmaceutical Products Distr
N.A.I.C.S.: 424210
Paul Reilly (Mng Dir)
Christy Canavan (Dir-Consumer)
Catherine Cummins (Dir-Ops)
David Keyes (Dir-Distr & Hospitals)
Stephen O'Donoghue (Dir-Procurement)
Jim McAuliffe (Dir-Fin)
Sharon Moyles (Mgr-Customer Svc)
Mary Magner (Mgr-Category)
Graham Dowling (Head-Legal & Compli-
ance)
Hazel Sullivan (Dir-HR)
Ronelle Wyngaard (Head-Customer Care
Svcs)
David Lawless (Officer-Data Protection)

Well.ca LLC (1)
935-B Southgate Drive, 935-B Southgate
Drive Guelph, ON, N1L 0B9, CA, Guelph,
N1L 0B9, ON, Canada
Tel.: (519) 489-7185
Web Site: https://well.ca
Health and Wellness Products Retailers
N.A.I.C.S.: 456199

MCLAREN TECHNOLOGY AC-QUISITION CORP.
2600 Michelson Dr Ste 2700, Irvine,
CA 92612
Tel.: (949) 989-4638   DE
Year Founded: 2021
MLAIU—(NASDAQ)
Investment Services
N.A.I.C.S.: 523999
Sajan Pillai (Chm & CEO)
John Vilina (Pres & Sec)
Rajeev Nair (CFO)
Murali Gopalan (COO)

MCNB BANKS, INC.
Tel.: (304) 436-4112
Web Site:
  https://www.mcnbbanks.com
MKIN—(OTCIQ)
Bank Holding Company
N.A.I.C.S.: 551111
John Reed (CEO)

Subsidiaries:

MCNB Bank and Trust Co. (1)
75 Wyoming St, Welch, WV 24801
Tel.: (304) 436-4112
Web Site: http://www.mcnbbanks.com
Emp.: 50
Banking Services
N.A.I.C.S.: 522110
Lee Ellis (Pres)

MCRAE INDUSTRIES, INC.
400 N Main St, Mount Gilead, NC
27306
Tel.: (910) 439-6147   DE
Web Site:
  https://www.mcraeindustries.com
Year Founded: 1959
MCRAA—(OTCIQ)
Rev.: $82,191,000
Assets: $77,885,000
Liabilities: $5,639,000
Net Worth: $72,246,000
Earnings: $3,352,000
Emp.: 398
Fiscal Year-end: 07/31/21
Footwear Manufacturing
N.A.I.C.S.: 316210
D. Gary McRae (Chm, Pres, CEO &
Treas)
James W. McRae (Sec & VP)
Charles E. Covatch (Pres-Footwear)

Subsidiaries:

Dan Post Boot Co. (1)

601 East Railroad St, Waverly, TN
37185   **(100%)**
Tel.: (931) 296-2288
Web Site: http://www.danpostboot.com
Rev.: $6,402,000
Emp.: 18
Mfr of Boots
N.A.I.C.S.: 316210

McRae Footwear Division (1)
400 N Main St, Mount Gilead, NC 27306-
9038
Tel.: (910) 439-6147
Web Site: http://www.mcraeindustries.com
Rev.: $7,365,000
Emp.: 150
Mfr of Direct Molded Sole (DMS) Combat
Boots
N.A.I.C.S.: 316210
Victor A. Karam (Pres-Footwear)

MCX TECHNOLOGIES COR-PORATION
176 S Capital Blvd, Boise, ID 83702
Tel.: (208) 863-6243   CA
Web Site: https://www.mcorpcx.com
Year Founded: 2001
MCCX—(OTCEM)
Rev.: $101,409
Assets: $270,854
Liabilities: $116,497
Net Worth: $154,357
Earnings: ($465,552)
Emp.: 6
Fiscal Year-end: 12/31/22
Software Developer
N.A.I.C.S.: 513210
Lynn Davison (COO)
Stephen Shay (VP)
Gregg Raymond Budoi (Chm & CFO)
Graham Clark (VP-Market Dev)

MDB CAPITAL HOLDINGS, LLC
14135 Midway Rd Ste G-150, Addi-
son, TX 75001
Tel.: (945) 262-9010   DE
Web Site: https://www.mdb.com
Year Founded: 1997
MDBH—(NASDAQ)
Holding Company
N.A.I.C.S.: 551112
Christopher Marlett (Founder, Chm &
CEO)
George Brandon (Pres & Head-
Community Development)
Jeremy James (CFO & Chief Acctg
Officer)
Anthony Digiandomenico (Founder &
Head-New Venture Discovery)
Mo Hayat (Chief Legal Officer &
Head-Corporate Development)
Lou Basenese (Pres)
Gary Schuman (CFO & Head-
Compliance)
Tony Dammicci (Officer)
Kevin Cotter (Head-Capital Markets)
Dave Byrne (CTO)
Alex Zapanta (VP-Trading Opera-
tions)
Derek Page (VP-Brokerage Opera-
tions)
Edgardo Rayo (Dir-Investment Analy-
sis)
Ivonne Bordas (Mgr-Investment
Analysis)

MDECHEM, INC.
923 10th St Ste PMB101, Floresville,
TX 78114
Tel.: (830) 393-5293   TX
Web Site: http://www.mdechem.com
Year Founded: 1996
MDKM—(OTCIQ)
Biotechnology Research & Develop-
ment Services
N.A.I.C.S.: 541715
Paul W. Sack (Pres)

MDH ACQUISITION CORP.
600 N Carroll Ave Ste 100, South-
lake, TX 76092
Tel.: (415) 968-4444   DE
Year Founded: 2020
MDH—(NYSE)
Rev.: $8,794,487
Assets: $276,235,006
Liabilities: $298,206,629
Net Worth: ($21,971,623)
Earnings: $5,258,009
Emp.: 4
Fiscal Year-end: 12/31/21
Investment Services
N.A.I.C.S.: 523999
Franklin McLarty (Chm)
Jim Wilkinson (Vice Chm)
Donald Blair (CEO)
Brent Whittington (CFO)

MDM PERMIAN, INC.
2122 Kidwell St Ste 210, Dallas, TX
75214
Tel.: (469) 252-3600
Web Site:
  https://www.mdmpermian.com
Year Founded: 1981
MDMP—(OTCIQ)
Oil & Gas Field Drilling Services
N.A.I.C.S.: 213112
Michael Rafael (Chm & Pres)

MDU RESOURCES GROUP, INC.
1200 W Century Ave, Bismarck, ND
58503
Tel.: (701) 530-1000   DE
Web Site: http://www.mdu.com
Year Founded: 1924
MDU—(NYSE)
Rev.: $4,657,340,000
Assets: $7,833,159,000
Liabilities: $4,927,926,000
Net Worth: $2,905,233,000
Earnings: $414,707,000
Emp.: 9,145
Fiscal Year-end: 12/31/23
Holding Company; Energy Resource
Production, Utility Distribution, Con-
struction Materials & Contracting Ser-
vices
N.A.I.C.S.: 551112
Jason L. Vollmer (VP)
Nicole A. Kivisto (Pres & CEO)
Peggy A. Link (CIO & VP)
Stephanie A. Barth (Chief Acctg Offi-
cer, VP & Controller)
Laura Lueder (Mgr-Comm & PR)
Brent Miller (Asst Treas)
Paul R. Sanderson (Chief Legal Offi-
cer, Sec & VP)
Garret Senger (Chief Utilities Officer)

Subsidiaries:

Ames Sand & Gravel, Inc. (1)
2702 1st Ave N, Fargo, ND 58102
Tel.: (701) 232-2594
Concrete Ready Mix Mfr
N.A.I.C.S.: 327320

Arc Fabricators, LLC (1)
3500 W Teem Dr, Sioux Falls, SD 57107
Tel.: (605) 338-1321
Web Site: https://www.arcfabricators.com
Engineeering Services
N.A.I.C.S.: 541330

Bombard Electric, LLC (1)
4380 W Post Rd, Las Vegas, NV 89118
Tel.: (702) 263-3570
Web Site: https://www.bombardelectric.com
Electrical Engineering Services
N.A.I.C.S.: 541330
Kenneth A. Kefalas (Pres)
Dick Pendleton (Sr Project Mgr)

Subsidiary (Domestic):

CNGC Energy Corp. (2)

222 Fairview Ave N, Seattle, WA 98109-
5312
Tel.: (206) 624-3900
Web Site: http://www.cngc.com
Sales Range: $10-24.9 Million
Emp.: 5
Natural Gas Services
N.A.I.C.S.: 211130

Bombard Mechanical, LLC (1)
3933 W Ali Baba Ln, Las Vegas, NV 89118
Tel.: (702) 940-4822
Web Site:
  https://www.bombardmechanical.com
Pipeline Transportation Services
N.A.I.C.S.: 486990

Cascade Natural Gas
Corporation (1)
8113 W Grandridge Blvd, Kennewick, WA
99336-7166
Web Site: https://www.cngc.com
Natural Gas Distr
N.A.I.C.S.: 221210
Nicole A. Kivisto (Pres & CEO)
Mark Chiles (VP-Regulatory Affairs & Cus-
tomer Svc)

Centennial Energy Holdings, Inc. (1)
1200 W Century Ave, Bismarck, ND
58503   **(100%)**
Tel.: (701) 530-1000
Sales Range: $1-4.9 Billion
Emp.: 8,200
Holding Company
N.A.I.C.S.: 551112

Subsidiary (Domestic):

Knife River Corporation (2)
1150 W Century Ave, Bismarck, ND 58506
Tel.: (701) 530-1400
Web Site: https://www.kniferiver.com
Rev.: $2,534,729,000
Assets: $2,294,319,000
Liabilities: $1,265,730,000
Net Worth: $1,028,589,000
Earnings: $116,220,000
Emp.: 5,710
Fiscal Year-end: 12/31/2022
Holding Company; Construction Sand &
Gravel Mining, Construction Materials Mfr &
Construction Contractor Services
N.A.I.C.S.: 212321
Nathan W. Ring (CFO & VP)
Karl A. Liepitz (Chief Legal Officer, Sec &
VP)
Nancy K. Christenson (VP-Admin)
Trevor J. Hastings (COO & VP)
Brian R. Gray (Pres & CEO)
Tony Spilde (Sr Dir-Comm)
Glenn R. Pladson (VP-Support Svcs)
Marney L. Kadrmas (Chief Acctg Officer)
Robert Van Til (Pres-South)
Zane Karimi (Dir-IR)

Subsidiary (Domestic):

Alaska Basic Industries, Inc. (3)
1300 Ocean Dock Rd, Anchorage, AK
99515
Tel.: (907) 348-6780
Web Site: https://www.anchsand.com
Sales Range: $25-49.9 Million
Emp.: 100
Holding Company; Cement, Concrete &
Other Construction Materials Whslr
N.A.I.C.S.: 551112
Chris Taylor (Pres)

Division (Domestic):

Anchorage Sand & Gravel Company,
Inc. (4)
1040 O'Malley Rd, Anchorage, AK 99515
Tel.: (907) 348-6700
Web Site: https://www.anchsand.com
Sales Range: $100-124.9 Million
Construction Materials Mining, Cement &
Concrete Mfr & Building Materials Whslr
N.A.I.C.S.: 423320

Unit (Domestic):

Dimond Fabricators (5)
11400 Lang St, Anchorage, AK 99515
Tel.: (907) 348-6750
Web Site: http://www.anchsand.com
Sales Range: $100-124.9 Million
Emp.: 2
Construction Rebar Mfr

MDU Resources Group, Inc.—(Continued)

N.A.I.C.S.: 332312

Subsidiary (Domestic):

Baldwin Contracting Company, Inc. (3)
1764 Skyway Dr, Chico, CA 95928
Tel.: (530) 891-6555
Sales Range: $25-49.9 Million
Emp.: 5,600
Highway & Street Construction
N.A.I.C.S.: 237310

Central Oregon Redi-Mix, LLC (3)
64500 O B Riley Rd, Bend, OR 97701
Tel.: (541) 693-5900
Web Site: http://www.kniferiver.com
Sales Range: $25-49.9 Million
Ready Mixed Concrete
N.A.I.C.S.: 327320

Concrete, Inc. (3)
400 S Lincoln St, Stockton, CA 95203
Tel.: (209) 933-6980
Sales Range: $50-74.9 Million
Ready Mixed Concrete
N.A.I.C.S.: 327320
David Barney (Pres)

Connolly-Pacific Company (3)
1925 W Pier D St, Long Beach, CA 90802
Tel.: (562) 437-2831
Web Site: http://www.conpaco.com
Sales Range: $50-74.9 Million
Marine Construction Contractors
N.A.I.C.S.: 236220

Hawaiian Cement (3)
99-1300 Halawa Valley St, Aiea, HI 96701-3289
Tel.: (808) 532-3400
Web Site: https://hawaiiancement.com
Sales Range: $100-124.9 Million
Emp.: 200
Hydraulic Cement Mfr
N.A.I.C.S.: 327310
John L. Delong (Pres)
Jonathan Esperanza (Gen Mgr)
Jonathan Esperanza (Gen Mgr)

Knife River - East Texas Division (3)
4825 Romeda Rd, Beaumont, TX 77705
Tel.: (409) 842-2100
Web Site: http://www.kniferiver.com
Sales Range: $25-49.9 Million
Ready Mixed Concrete
N.A.I.C.S.: 327320

Knife River Corporation - Sauk Rapids (3)
4787 Shadow Wood Dr NE, Sauk Rapids, MN 56379
Tel.: (320) 251-9472
Web Site: http://www.kniferiver.com
Sales Range: $800-899.9 Million
Highway & Street Construction
N.A.I.C.S.: 237310

Knife River Materials (3)
4787 Shadow Wood Dr NE, Sauk Rapids, MN 56379 (100%)
Tel.: (320) 251-9472
Web Site: http://www.kniferiver.com
Sales Range: $50-74.9 Million
Ready-Mixed Concrete Products
N.A.I.C.S.: 327320

Knife River Materials (3)
4101 Bemidji Ave N, Bemidji, MN 56601
Tel.: (218) 751-5413
Web Site: http://www.kniferiver.com
Sales Range: $25-40.0 Million
Road Construction
N.A.I.C.S.: 237310
Doug Muyres (Pres)

Knife River Materials - Medford (3)
3959 Hamrick Rd, Central Point, OR 97502
Tel.: (541) 770-2960
Web Site: http://www.kniferiver.com
Readymix Concrete Mfr
N.A.I.C.S.: 327320

Knife River-Medford (3)
3770 Kirtland Rd, Central Point, OR 97502
Tel.: (541) 664-4155
Web Site: http://www.kniferiver.com
Sales Range: $25-49.9 Million
Aggregate Mining
N.A.I.C.S.: 212319

Plant (Domestic):

Knife River-Waco Ready Mix Plant (3)
2901 Marlin Hwy 6, Waco, TX 76705
Tel.: (254) 761-2600
Web Site: http://www.mduresources.com
Sales Range: $150-199.9 Million
Concrete Products Mfr
N.A.I.C.S.: 327390

Subsidiary (Domestic):

McMurry Ready Mix Co. (3)
5684 Old W Yellowstone, Casper, WY 82604-9215
Tel.: (307) 473-9581
Web Site: http://www.mcmurryreadymix.com
General Contractor, Highway & Street Construction, Paving & Resurfacing, Concrete Mix
N.A.I.C.S.: 237310

Subsidiary (Domestic):

MDU Construction Services Group, Inc. (2)
1150 W Century Ave, Bismarck, ND 58503 (100%)
Tel.: (701) 530-1353
Web Site: https://www.mducsg.com
Sales Range: $1-4.9 Billion
Holding Company; Electric & Telecommunication Lines, Natural Gas Pipelines, Fire Protection Systems, External Lighting & Traffic Signalization Equipment Construction & Maintenance Services
N.A.I.C.S.: 551112
Jeff Thiede (Pres & CEO)

Subsidiary (Domestic):

Bell Electrical Contractors, Inc. (3)
128 Millwell Dr, Saint Louis, MO 63043
Tel.: (314) 739-7744
Web Site: https://www.bellelectrical.com
Sales Range: $25-49.9 Million
Emp.: 50
Electrical Contractor
N.A.I.C.S.: 517111

Capital Electric Construction Company, Inc. (3)
2801 Fairfax Trey, Kansas City, KS 66115
Tel.: (816) 472-9500
Web Site: https://www.capitalelectric.com
Sales Range: $10-24.9 Million
Electrical Contractor
N.A.I.C.S.: 238210

Capital Electric Line Builders, Inc. (3)
4400 NW Mattox Rd, Riverside, MO 64150
Tel.: (816) 389-4000
Web Site: https://www.celbinc.com
Sales Range: $25-49.9 Million
Power Line Construction
N.A.I.C.S.: 237130
Greg Darkenwald (Pres)
Adam Bundy (VP- & Distribution)
Kevin Minor (VP- &)

ESI, Inc. (3)
4696 Devitt Dr, Cincinnati, OH 45246 (100%)
Tel.: (513) 454-3741
Web Site: https://www.esielectrical.com
Sales Range: $25-49.9 Million
Emp.: 100
Electrical Contractor
N.A.I.C.S.: 238210

Branch (Domestic):

ESI Dayton (4)
3400 Kettering Blvd, Dayton, OH 45439
Tel.: (937) 293-6138
Sales Range: $50-74.9 Million
Electrical Contractor
N.A.I.C.S.: 238210
Mathew Hartshorn (VP)

Subsidiary (Domestic):

Loy Clark Pipeline Co. (3)
19020A SW Cipole Rd, Tualatin, OR 97062
Tel.: (503) 644-2137
Web Site: https://www.loyclark.com

Sales Range: $150-199.9 Million
Pipeline Contracting
N.A.I.C.S.: 237110

OEG, Inc. (3)
3200 NW Yeon Ave, Portland, OR 97210
Tel.: (503) 234-9900
Web Site: https://www.oeg.us.com
Electrical & Telecommunications Contractor
N.A.I.C.S.: 238210
Gary Blaser (VP-Acct & Fin)
Brad Brandenburg (VP)
Sean Cox (VP)

Division (Domestic):

Pride Electric, Inc. (4)
18133 NE 68th St Ste D120, Redmond, WA 98052
Tel.: (425) 454-3665
Web Site: http://www.prideelectric.com
Commercial Electrical Services
N.A.I.C.S.: 238210
David L. Goodin (Pres & CEO)

Subsidiary (Domestic):

Rocky Mountain Contractors, Inc. (3)
PO Box 8688, Kalispell, MT 59904
Tel.: (406) 752-4277
Web Site: https://www.rockymountaincontractors.com
Sales Range: $1-9.9 Million
Utility Contractor
N.A.I.C.S.: 237130

The Wagner-Smith Company (3)
3201 Encrete Ln, Dayton, OH 45401
Tel.: (937) 298-7481
Web Site: https://www.wagnersmith.com
Sales Range: $75-99.9 Million
Emp.: 200
Electrical Contractor
N.A.I.C.S.: 238210

Subsidiary (Domestic):

WBI Holdings, Inc. (2)
1250 W Century Ave, Bismarck, ND 58503-0911 (100%)
Tel.: (701) 530-1500
Web Site: https://www.wbip.com
Sales Range: $300-349.9 Million
Emp.: 609
Holding Company; Petroleum & Natural Gas Exploration, Property Acquisition, Development & Production
N.A.I.C.S.: 551112

Subsidiary (Domestic):

Bitter Creek Pipelines, LLC (3)
PO Box 5601, Bismarck, ND 58506-5601
Tel.: (701) 530-1585
Web Site:
  http://www.bittercreekpipelines.com
Sales Range: $200-249.9 Million
Natural Gas Pipeline Transportation Services
N.A.I.C.S.: 486210

WBI Energy Transmission, Inc. (3)
1250 W Century Ave, Bismarck, ND 58503
Tel.: (701) 530-1630
Web Site:
  https://transmission.wbienergy.com
Transmission & Corrosion Services
N.A.I.C.S.: 486210

Connolly-Pacific Co. (1)
1925 Pier D St, Long Beach, CA 90802
Tel.: (562) 437-2831
Web Site: https://www.connollypacific.com
Rock Quarrying Services
N.A.I.C.S.: 212319
Laura Saldana-Machado (Office Mgr-Quarry)
Steven Schryver (VP & Gen Mgr)

D S S Company (1)
655 W Clay St, Stockton, CA 95206
Tel.: (209) 948-0302
Civil Engineering Services
N.A.I.C.S.: 541330

Desert Fire Holdings, Inc. (1)
505 Vly Rd, Reno, NV 89512
Tel.: (775) 329-1926
Investment Management Service

N.A.I.C.S.: 551112

Desert Fire Protection, Inc. (1)
505 Valley Rd, Reno, NV 89512
Tel.: (775) 329-1926
Web Site: https://www.desertfire.com
Fire Protection Equipment Installation Services
N.A.I.C.S.: 238210
Bob Audenried (VP-Operations)

Duro Electric, LLC (1)
2271 W Yale Ave, Englewood, CO 80110
Tel.: (303) 934-3303
Web Site: https://www.duroelectric.com
Electrical Contracting Services
N.A.I.C.S.: 238210
Marty Lund (Controller)
Dave Nordini (Mgr-Project)
Jake Jacobson (Mgr-Project)
Johnny Guyton Jr. (Dir-HR)

Ellis & Eastern Company (1)
1500 N Sweetman Pl, Sioux Falls, SD 57118-4140
Tel.: (605) 357-6000
Construction Materials Distr
N.A.I.C.S.: 423320

Fairbanks Materials, Inc. (1)
1122 Bradway Rd, North Pole, AK 99705
Tel.: (907) 459-4820
Web Site:
  https://www.fairbanksmaterials.com
Sales Range: $25-49.9 Million
Concrete Products Mfr
N.A.I.C.S.: 327390
Ryan Johnson (Mgr-Precast)
Adam Garber (Mgr-Rebar)

InterSource Insurance Company (1)
7 Burlington Sq Fl 5, Burlington, VT 05401
Tel.: (802) 864-5599
Emp.: 2
Insurance Brokerage Services
N.A.I.C.S.: 524298

Intermountain Gas Company (1)
555 S Cole Rd, Boise, ID 83709
Tel.: (208) 377-6840
Web Site: https://www.intgas.com
Sales Range: $350-399.9 Million
Natural Gas Distr
N.A.I.C.S.: 221210
Nicole A. Kivisto (Pres & CEO)

International Line Builders, Inc. (1)
19020 A SW Cipole Rd, Tualatin, OR 97062
Tel.: (503) 692-0193
Web Site: https://www.ilbinc.com
Sales Range: $25-49.9 Million
Construction Engineering Services
N.A.I.C.S.: 237990

Jebro Incorporated (1)
2303 Bridgeport Dr, Sioux City, IA 51111
Tel.: (712) 277-8859
Web Site: https://www.jebro.com
Oil Exploration Services
N.A.I.C.S.: 213112

Kent's Oil Service (1)
3310 E Miner Ave, Stockton, CA 95205
Tel.: (209) 463-4762
Asphalt Emulsion & Dust Control Product Mfr
N.A.I.C.S.: 324122
David Barney (Office Mgr)

Kents Oil Service (1)
3310 E Miner Ave, Stockton, CA 95205
Tel.: (209) 463-4762
Asphalt Emulsion Product Mfr
N.A.I.C.S.: 324110

Knife River Corporation - North Central (1)
4787 Shadow Wood Dr NE, Sauk Rapids, MN 56379
Tel.: (320) 251-9472
Web Site: https://www.kniferiver.com
Concrete Ready Mix Mfr
N.A.I.C.S.: 327320
Jackie Schaefer (Office Mgr)

Knife River Corporation - Northwest (1)
12222 NW Marina Way, Portland, OR 97231
Tel.: (503) 944-3500
Web Site: https://www.kniferiver.com
Emp.: 100

Construction Engineering Services
N.A.I.C.S.: 237990

Knife River Corporation - South (1)
2901 Marlin Hwy 6, Waco, TX 76705
Tel.: (254) 761-2600
Web Site: https://www.kniferiver.com
Construction Engineering Services
N.A.I.C.S.: 237990

Knife River Hawaii, Inc. (1)
67-2399 Mamalahoa Hwy, Kamuela, HI
96743
Tel.: (808) 885-7307
Concrete Ready Mix Mfr
N.A.I.C.S.: 327320

**Lone Mountain Excavation & Utilities,
LLC** (1)
7350 Dean Martin Dr Ste 310, Las Vegas,
NV 89118-4434
Tel.: (702) 474-4216
Web Site: https://www.lmxlv.com
Sales Range: $25-49.9 Million
Construction Engineering Services
N.A.I.C.S.: 237990
Stefan Hoffman (Pres)

Midland Technical Crafts, Inc. (1)
9522-B E 47th Pl, Tulsa, OK 74145
Tel.: (918) 622-3036
Web Site: http://www.midland-tech.com
Emp.: 4
Construction Engineering Services
N.A.I.C.S.: 237990

Montana-Dakota Utilities Co. (1)
400 N 4th St, Bismarck, ND
58501-4092 (100%)
Tel.: (701) 222-7900
Web Site: https://www.montana-dakota.com
Natural Gas & Electric Distribution Services
N.A.I.C.S.: 221210

Nevada Solar Solutions, LLC (1)
1200 W Century Ave, Bismarck, ND 58503
Tel.: (701) 530-1022
Eletric Power Generation Services
N.A.I.C.S.: 221118

PerLectric, Inc. (1)
2711 Prosperity Ave Ste 300, Fairfax, VA
22031-4308
Tel.: (703) 352-5151
Web Site: http://www.perlectric.com
Electrical Construction Company
N.A.I.C.S.: 238210

Rail to Road, Inc. (1)
3520 E Rice St, Sioux Falls, SD 57103
Tel.: (605) 336-5855
Web Site: https://www.railtoroad.com
Railroad Construction Services
N.A.I.C.S.: 237990
Clark Meyer (Pres)

Sweetman Construction Co. (1)
1500 N Sweetman Pl, Sioux Falls, SD
57107
Tel.: (605) 357-6000
Web Site:
http://www.concretematerialscompa
ny.com
Ready Mixed Concrete
N.A.I.C.S.: 212321

WBI Energy Midstream, LLC (1)
1250 W Century Ave, Bismarck, ND 58503
Tel.: (701) 530-1500
Web Site: https://www.wbienergy.com
Oil & Gas Operating Services
N.A.I.C.S.: 213112

WBI Energy Services, Inc. (1)
1250 W Century Ave, Bismarck, ND 58503
Tel.: (701) 530-1095
Web Site: http://www.wbienergy.com
Pipeline Transportation Services
N.A.I.C.S.: 486990

**WBI Energy Wind Ridge Pipeline,
LLC** (1)
1250 W Century Ave, Bismarck, ND 58503
Tel.: (877) 924-4677
Web Site: http://www.wbienergy.com
Natural Gas & Energy Services
N.A.I.C.S.: 238210

Wagner Industrial Electric, Inc. (1)
3178 Encrete Ln, Dayton, OH 45439
Tel.: (937) 298-7481

Web Site: https://esielectrical.com
Sales Range: $10-24.9 Million
Emp.: 20
Electric Equipment Mfr
N.A.I.C.S.: 335999
Jim Fortkamp (Pres)

Wagner-Smith Equipment Co. (1)
5701 Highpoint Pkwy, Burleson, TX 76028
Tel.: (817) 447-8085
Web Site: https://www.wagnersmith.com
Conductor Stringing Equipment Distr
N.A.I.C.S.: 423810

MDWERKS, INC.
411 Walnut St Ste 20125, Green
Cove Springs, FL 32043
Tel.: (252) 501-0019   DE
Web Site: https://mdwerksinc.com
Year Founded: 2003
MDWK—(OTCIQ)
Rev.: $104,066
Assets: $3,233,068
Liabilities: $2,072,851
Net Worth: $1,160,217
Earnings: ($291,672)
Emp.: 12
Fiscal Year-end: 12/31/23
Software Development Services
N.A.I.C.S.: 541511
Steven Laker (CEO)
George Glackin (Sr Dir-Intellectual
Property & Patent Strategy)
Jim Cassidy (Exec Chm)

MEDALIST DIVERSIFIED REIT, INC.
Tel.: (804) 338-7708   MD
Web Site:
https://www.medalistreit.com
Year Founded: 2015
MDRR—(NASDAQ)
Rev.: $11,091,325
Assets: $87,915,404
Liabilities: $69,222,965
Net Worth: $18,692,439
Earnings: ($4,769,241)
Emp.: 9,993
Fiscal Year-end: 12/31/22
Real Estate Investment Services
N.A.I.C.S.: 531210
Francis P. Kavanaugh (Interim Pres &
Interim CEO)
Colin Elliott (VP)
Francis P. Kavanaugh (Chm, Pres,
CEO & Sec)
C. Brent Winn Jr. (CFO)

MEDALLION FINANCIAL CORP.
437 Madison Ave 38th Fl, New York,
NY 10022
Tel.: (212) 328-2100   DE
Web Site: https://www.medallion.com
Year Founded: 1996
MFIN—(NASDAQ)
Rev.: $196,621,000
Assets: $2,259,879,000
Liabilities: $1,889,355,000
Net Worth: $370,524,000
Earnings: $43,840,000
Emp.: 158
Fiscal Year-end: 12/31/22
Specialty Finance Services
N.A.I.C.S.: 525990
Alvin Murstein (Chm & CEO)
Andrew M. Murstein (Pres & COO)
Thomas J. Munson (Chief Credit Offi-
cer & Exec VP)
Anthony N. Cutrone (CFO & Exec
VP)

Subsidiaries:

Medallion Bank (1)
1100 E 6600 S Ste 510, Salt Lake City, UT
84121
Web Site: https://www.medallionbank.com

Sales Range: $25-49.9 Million
Emp.: 30
Commercial Banking Services
N.A.I.C.S.: 522110
Steve Hannay (Chief Lending Officer &
Exec VP)
Donald S. Poulton (Pres & CEO)
Justin Haley (COO & Sr VP)
John Taylor (Sr VP-Strategic Partnerships &
Bus Dev)
Vikki Hawke (Sr VP-Consumer Lending
Ops)
Sean Baird (VP & Mgr-Credit)
Thomas Riddle (Mgr-Customer Svc)
Timothy Thiel (Mgr-Sls-North Central Reg)
Robin Lane (Mgr-Sls-Southeast Reg)
Trent E. Hudson (CFO & Sr VP)
Jon Allen (Chief Compliance Officer & Sr
VP)
Melanie Bird (Asst Mgr-Credit)
Aaron Heaps (CIO)

Medallion Business Credit, LLC (1)
437 Madison Ave 38th Fl, New York, NY
10022-7001 (100%)
Tel.: (212) 328-2100
Web Site: http://www.medallionfinancial.com
Sales Range: $25-49.9 Million
Emp.: 12
Commercial Finance Company
N.A.I.C.S.: 522299

Medallion Capital, Inc. (1)
3000 W County Rd 42 Ste 301, Burnsville,
MN 55337-4827
Tel.: (952) 831-2025
Web Site: https://www.medallioncapital.com
Sales Range: $50-74.9 Million
Emp.: 7
Loan Brokerage Firm
N.A.I.C.S.: 523999
Aaron Price (VP)

Medallion Funding LLC (1)
(100%)
Tel.: (973) 565-0200
Web Site: http://www.medallionfinancial.com
Small Business Investment Services
N.A.I.C.S.: 525990

Medallion Sports Media, Inc. (1)
437 Madison Ave, New York, NY 10022
Tel.: (212) 328-2100
Advetising Agency
N.A.I.C.S.: 541810

MEDIA PAL HOLDINGS, CORP.
1700 Prospect St, Sarasota, FL
34239
Tel.: (301) 460-5818   FL
Year Founded: 1936
MPHD—(OTCEM)
Holding Company
N.A.I.C.S.: 551112

MEDIA SENTIMENT, INC.
529 Buchanan St, San Francisco, CA
94102-5527
Tel.: (415) 861-3421   NV
Web Site:
http://www.mediasentiment.com
Year Founded: 2006
MSEZ—(OTCIQ)
Online Business Information & News
N.A.I.C.S.: 513210

MEDIAALPHA, INC.
700 S Flower St Ste 640, Los Ange-
les, CA 90017
Tel.: (213) 316-6256   DE
Web Site:
https://www.mediaalpha.com
Year Founded: 2020
MAX—(NYSE)
Rev.: $388,149,000
Assets: $153,925,000
Liabilities: $248,350,000
Net Worth: ($94,425,000)
Earnings: ($40,420,000)
Emp.: 137
Fiscal Year-end: 12/31/23
Holding Company
N.A.I.C.S.: 551112

Steven M. Yi (Co-Founder, Pres &
CEO)
Ambrose Wang (Co-Founder)
Jeff Coyne (Gen Counsel)
Keith Cramer (Sr VP-Supply Partner-
ships)
Brian Mikalis (Sr VP-Demand Part-
nerships)
Amy Yeh (Sr VP-Tech)
Patrick R. Thompson (CFO & Treas)
Eugene Nonko (Co-Founder)

MEDIACO HOLDING INC.
48 W 25th St 3 Fl, New York, NY
10010
Tel.: (212) 229-9797   IN
Year Founded: 2019
MDIA—(NASDAQ)
Rev.: $38,595,000
Assets: $96,705,000
Liabilities: $49,729,000
Net Worth: $46,976,000
Earnings: $27,584,000
Emp.: 141
Fiscal Year-end: 12/31/22
Holding Company
N.A.I.C.S.: 551112
Kristin Roderick (VP-Sls-HOT 97 &
WBLS)
Kudjo Sogadzi (COO)
James A. Fagan (CEO)
Michael Grujicich (CFO)
Ann C. Beemish (Treas & Exec VP)
J. Scott Enright (Gen Counsel, Sec &
Exec VP)
Patrick M. Walsh (Pres)

MEDIAG3, INC.
1 Almaden Blvd Ste 310, San Jose,
CA 95113
Tel.: (408) 260-5000   DE
Web Site: http://www.mediag3.com
Year Founded: 2005
MDGC—(OTCIQ)
Software Development Services
N.A.I.C.S.: 541511
Val Westergard (Chm)
Byron Ryals (CEO)
Stephan Moynihan (CFO)

MEDICAL CONNECTIONS HOLDINGS, INC.
4800 T Rex Ave Ste 310, Boca Ra-
ton, FL 33431-4479
Tel.: (561) 221-1853   FL
Web Site:
http://www.medicalconnections.com
Year Founded: 1999
MCTH—(OTCEM)
Sales Range: $1-9.9 Million
Emp.: 36
Medical Recruitment & Staffing Ser-
vices
N.A.I.C.S.: 541612
Anthony Nicolosi (Pres)

MEDICAL IMAGING CORP.
848 N Rainbow Blvd Ste 2494, Las
Vegas, NV 89107   NV
Web Site:
http://www.medimagingcorp.com
Year Founded: 2000
MEDD—(OTCEM)
Sales Range: $1-9.9 Million
Emp.: 40
Diagnostic Imaging Centers
N.A.I.C.S.: 621512
Mitchell Geisler (Chm, Pres & CEO)

Subsidiaries:

**Partners Imaging Center of Charlotte,
LLC** (1)
4161 Tamiami Trl Ste 204, Port Charlotte,
FL 33952
Tel.: (941) 255-5151

Medical Imaging Corp.—(Continued)

Web Site:
http://www.portcharlottemedical.com
Diagnostic Imaging Center Operator
N.A.I.C.S.: 621512

Partners Imaging Center of Naples, LLC (1)
730 Goodlette Rd N Ste 101, Naples, FL 34102
Tel.: (239) 262-5151
Web Site:
http://www.naplesmedicalimaging.com
Diagnostic Imaging Center Operator
N.A.I.C.S.: 621512
Christy Bostwick (Mgr-Center)

Partners Imaging Center of Venice, LLC (1)
842 Sunset Lake Blvd Ste 301, Venice, FL 34292
Tel.: (941) 441-0060
Web Site:
http://www.venicemedicalimaging.com
Diagnostic Imaging Center Operator
N.A.I.C.S.: 621512

Schuylkill Open MRI, Inc. (1)
48 Tunnel Rd Ste 102, Pottsville, PA 17901
Tel.: (570) 622-6206
Web Site: http://www.schuylkillmedical.com
Diagnostic Imaging Center Operator
N.A.I.C.S.: 621512
Shelley Tomey (Mgr-Center)

MEDICAL MARIJUANA INC.
2384 La Mirada Dr, Vista, CA 92081
Tel.: (858) 283-4016
Web Site:
https://www.medicalmarijuana
inc.com
Year Founded: 2009
MJNA—(OTCIQ)
Sales Range: $75-99.9 Million
Medical Marijuana Mfr
N.A.I.C.S.: 325411
Timothy R. Scott (Chm & CEO)

MEDICAL PROPERTIES TRUST, INC.
1000 Urban Ctr Dr Ste 501, Birmingham, AL 35242
Tel.: (205) 969-3755   MD
Web Site:
https://www.medicalproperties
trust.com
Year Founded: 2003
MPW—(NYSE)
Rev.: $871,799,000
Assets: $18,304,844,000
Liabilities: $10,670,979,000
Net Worth: $7,633,865,000
Earnings: ($556,476,000)
Emp.: 121
Fiscal Year-end: 12/31/23
Real Estate Manangement Services
N.A.I.C.S.: 531390
R. Steven Hamner (Co-Founder)
Emmett E. McLean (Co-Founder)
J. Kevin Hanna (Chief Acctg Officer, Sr VP & Controller)
Rosa H. Hooper (Sr VP-Ops & Asst Sec)
Charles R. Lambert (Mng Dir-Capital Markets, Treas & VP)
R. Lucas Savage (VP & Head-Global Acquisitions)
Edward K. Aldag Jr. (Co-Founder, Chm, Chm, Pres, Pres, CEO & CEO)
Edward K. Aldag Jr. (Co-Founder, Chm, Pres & CEO)

Subsidiaries:

MPT Operating Partnership, L.P. (1)
1000 Urban Center Dr Ste 501, Birmingham, AL 35242
Tel.: (205) 969-3755
Rev.: $871,798,999
Assets: $18,304,843,999
Liabilities: $10,670,588,999
Net Worth: $7,634,254,999

Earnings: ($556,475,999)
Emp.: 120
Fiscal Year-end: 12/31/2023
Real Estate Investment Services
N.A.I.C.S.: 531210
Edward K. Aldag Jr. (Chm, Pres & CEO)

MPT of Allen FCER, LLC (1)
1000 Urban Center Dr Ste 501, Birmingham, AL 35242
Tel.: (205) 969-3755
Emp.: 50
Real Estate Investment Services
N.A.I.C.S.: 525990
Ed Aldag (Pres)

MPT of Dallas, LLC (1)
1000 Urban Center Dr Ste 501, Birmingham, AL 35242
Tel.: (205) 397-8564
Real Estate Investment Services
N.A.I.C.S.: 525990

MPT of St Vincent Avon, LLC (1)
9613 E US Hwy 36, Avon, IN 46123
Tel.: (317) 613-5300
Healtcare Services
N.A.I.C.S.: 621999

MPT of St Vincent Brownsburg, LLC (1)
590 Pit Rd, Brownsburg, IN 46112
Tel.: (317) 415-6040
Healtcare Services
N.A.I.C.S.: 621999

MPT of St Vincent Castleton, LLC (1)
8602 Allisonville Rd, Indianapolis, IN 46250
Tel.: (317) 703-1970
Healtcare Services
N.A.I.C.S.: 621999

MPT of St Vincent Indianapolis South, LLC (1)
8451 S Emerson Ave, Indianapolis, IN 46237
Tel.: (317) 884-7540
Healtcare Services
N.A.I.C.S.: 621999

MPT of St Vincent Noblesville South, LLC (1)
9460 E 146th St, Noblesville, IN 46060
Tel.: (317) 703-1999
Healtcare Services
N.A.I.C.S.: 621999

MPT of St Vincent Plainfield, LLC (1)
2412 E Main St, Plainfield, IN 46168
Tel.: (317) 204-6910
Healtcare Services
N.A.I.C.O.: 021999

MPT of St. Luke's Leawood, LLC (1)
13200 State Line Rd, Leawood, KS 66209
Tel.: (913) 222-8380
Healtcare Services
N.A.I.C.S.: 621999

MPT of St. Luke's Olathe, LLC (1)
13405 S Black Bob Rd, Olathe, KS 66062
Tel.: (913) 222-8390
Healtcare Services
N.A.I.C.S.: 621999

MPT of St. Luke's Parallel Parkway, LLC (1)
10544 Parallel Pkwy, Kansas City, KS 66109
Tel.: (913) 222-8325
Healtcare Services
N.A.I.C.S.: 621999

MPT of St. Luke's Roeland Park, LLC (1)
4720 Johnson Dr, Roeland Park, KS 66205
Tel.: (913) 222-8399
Healtcare Services
N.A.I.C.S.: 621999

MPT of St. Luke's Shawnee, LLC (1)
14950 W 67th St, Shawnee, KS 66216
Tel.: (913) 222-8404
Healtcare Services
N.A.I.C.S.: 621999

MEDICAL SUPPLY INTERNA-

TIONAL USA, INC.
10-34 44th Dr, Long Island City, NY 10968   NV
Year Founded: 2001
MSIU—(OTCIQ)
Financial Investment Services
N.A.I.C.S.: 523999
Christopher Ginas (CEO)
Troy A. Alix (Treas)

MEDICAN ENTERPRISES, INC.
265 Kitts Way, Reno, NV 89521   NV
Year Founded: 1988
MDCN—(OTCEM)
Holding Company; Medical Marijuana Developer, Distr & Marketer
N.A.I.C.S.: 551112
Wayne Arthur Hansen (CFO)

MEDICINE MAN TECHNOLO-GIES, INC.
4880 Havana St Ste 201, Denver, CO 80239
Tel.: (303) 371-0387   NV
Web Site: https://www.schwazze.com
Year Founded: 2014
SHWZ—(OTCQX)
Rev.: $159,379,219
Assets: $322,882,733
Liabilities: $190,719,362
Net Worth: $132,163,371
Earnings: ($26,270,424)
Emp.: 651
Fiscal Year-end: 12/31/22
Business Consulting Services
N.A.I.C.S.: 541613
Andrew Williams (Founder)
Forrest Hoffmaster (Interim CEO & CFO)
Dan Pabon (Chief Policy & Regulatory Affairs Officer)
Julie Suntrup (VP-Mktg & Mdsg)
Jeremy Bullock (VP-Comml Sls)
Christine Jones (Chief Legal Officer)

MEDICINOVA, INC.
4275 Executive Sq Ste 300, La Jolla, CA 92037
Tel.: (858) 373-1500   DE
Web Site:
https://www.medicinova.com
MNOV—(NASDAQ)
Rev.: $809,673
Assets: $74,154,905
Liabilities: $3,912,870
Net Worth: $70,242,035
Earnings: ($14,069,083)
Emp.: 13
Fiscal Year-end: 12/31/22
Pharmaceutical Mfr, Researcher & Developer
N.A.I.C.S.: 325412
David H. Crean (Chief Bus Officer)
Yuichi Iwaki (Founder, Pres & Acting CEO)
Jason J. Kruger (CFO)
Kazuko Matsuda (Chief Medical Officer & Chief Medical Officer)

MEDICUS SCIENCES ACQUISI-TION CORP.
152 W 57th St Fl 20, New York, NY 10019
Tel.: (212) 259-8400   Ky
Year Founded: 2020
MSAC—(NASDAQ)
Rev.: $2,512,552
Assets: $93,624,429
Liabilities: $100,267,336
Net Worth: ($6,642,907)
Earnings: $1,897,877
Emp.: 4
Fiscal Year-end: 12/31/21
Investment Services
N.A.I.C.S.: 523999

Jacob Gottlieb (Chm)
Michael Castor (CEO)
Judah Drillick (CFO)
Neil Puri (Chief Bus Officer)

MEDIFAST, INC.
100 International Dr 18th Fl, Baltimore, MD 21202
Tel.: (410) 581-8042   DE
Web Site: https://ir.medifastinc.com
Year Founded: 1981
MED—(NYSE)
Rev.: $1,072,054,000
Assets: $309,908,000
Liabilities: $108,427,000
Net Worth: $201,481,000
Earnings: $99,415,000
Emp.: 634
Fiscal Year-end: 12/31/23
Holding Company; Weight & Disease Management Products Mfr & Distr
N.A.I.C.S.: 551112
James P. Maloney (CFO)
Steve Zenker (VP-IR)
Daniel R. Chard (Chm & CEO)

Subsidiaries:

OPTAVIA (Hong Kong) Limited (1)
9/F V Point 18 Tang Lung Street, Prince Edward Road West Mongkok, Causeway Bay, China (Hong Kong)
Tel.: (852) 800931717
Web Site: https://www.optavia.com
Health Care Srvices
N.A.I.C.S.: 621610

OPTAVIA (Singapore) Pte. Ltd. (1)
6 Raffles Boulevard 03-308 Marina Square, Singapore, 039594, Singapore
Tel.: (65) 8003211188
Web Site: https://www.optavia.com
Health Care Srvices
N.A.I.C.S.: 621610

OPTAVIA, LLC (1)
100 International Dr 18th Fl, Baltimore, MD 21202
Web Site: https://www.optavia.com
Health Care Srvices
N.A.I.C.S.: 621610
Wayne Andersen (Founder)

Take Shape For Life, Inc (1)
11444 Cronhill Dr, Owings Mills, MD 21117
Tel.: (800) 572-4417
Web Site: http://www.tsfl.com
Food Supplement Whslr
N.A.I.C.S.: 456191
Wayne S. Andersen (Founder)

MEDIFIRST SOLUTIONS, INC.
4400 Rte 9 S Ste 1000, Freehold, NJ 07728
Tel.: (732) 786-8044   NV
Web Site:
http://www.medifirstsolutions.com
Year Founded: 2010
MFST—(OTCIQ)
Sales Range: Less than $1 Million
Emp.: 1
Light Therapy, Water Generation & Laser Technology Products Sales
N.A.I.C.S.: 423450
Jonathan Cross (Interim CEO)

MEDIFOCUS, INC.
10240 Old Columbia Rd Ste G, Columbia, MD 21046
Tel.: (410) 290-5734   ON
Web Site:
http://www.medifocusinc.com
MFS—(OTCIQ)
Rev.: $2,766,740
Assets: $1,765,754
Liabilities: $12,638,250
Net Worth: ($10,872,496)
Earnings: ($1,470,532)
Emp.: 7
Fiscal Year-end: 03/31/19

Cancer Heat Treatment Systems Mfr
N.A.I.C.S.: 339112
Grant B. Walsh *(Chm)*
Douglas Liu *(VP-Fin & Gen Mgr)*
William W. Jow *(Pres, CEO & Dir-Medical)*
Stuart E. Katz *(VP-Ops)*
John Mon *(VP-Regulatory Affairs & Product Dev)*
John Mon *(VP-Regulatory Affairs & Product Dev)*

MEDINAH MINERALS, INC.
9449PriorityWayWDr, Indianapolis, IN 46240
Tel.: (702) 366-1883   NV
Web Site: http://www.medinah-minerals.com
MDMN—(OTCIQ)
Metal Mining Services
N.A.I.C.S.: 213114
Gary P. Goodin *(Pres & CEO)*
Raul Matias Del Solar *(Pres & Treas)*
Italo Volante *(Sec)*

MEDIRECT LATINO, INC.
2101 W Atl Blvd Ste No 101, Pompano Beach, FL 33069
Tel.: (954) 321-3540   FL
Web Site: https://www.medirectlatino.org
Year Founded: 2005
MLTO—(OTCEM)
Sales Range: $1-9.9 Million
Emp.: 98
Medical, Dental & Hospital Equipment & Supplies Merchant Whslr
N.A.I.C.S.: 423450
Jim Legates *(CFO)*

MEDITE CANCER DIAGNOS-TICS INC.
10524 Moss Park Rd Ste 204-357, Orlando, FL 32832
Tel.: (407) 996-9630   DE
Web Site: http://www.medite-group.com
Year Founded: 1998
MDIT—(OTCIQ)
Sales Range: $1-9.9 Million
Emp.: 71
Biomolecular Diagnostic Cancer Screening Systems Mfr & Marketer
N.A.I.C.S.: 339112
Stephen Von Rump *(CEO)*
Antoinette Torres *(Controller)*
William Austin Lewis IV *(Chm)*

MEDIZONE INTERNATIONAL, INC.
350 East Michigan Ave Ste 500, Kalamazoo, MI 49007
Tel.: (269) 202-5020   NV
Web Site: http://www.medizoneint.com
Year Founded: 1986
MZEI—(OTCIQ)
Rev.: $31
Assets: $463,422
Liabilities: $5,010,076
Net Worth: ($4,546,654)
Earnings: ($2,013,799)
Emp.: 7
Fiscal Year-end: 12/31/17
Sterilization Products Mfr
N.A.I.C.S.: 325998
Michael E. Shannon *(Pres)*
David Alan Dodd *(CEO)*
David A. Esposito *(Chm)*
Stephanie Lynn Sorensen *(CFO)*
Jude Dinges *(Chief Comml Officer & Exec VP)*
Philip A. Theodore *(Gen Counsel, Sec & Exec VP-Ops & Admin)*
Philip A. Theodore *(Gen Counsel, Sec & Exec VP-Ops & Admin)*

MEDLEY LLC
280 Park Ave 6th Fl E, New York, NY 10017
Tel.: (212) 759-0777   DE
Year Founded: 2010
MDLQ—(NYSE)
Rev.: $33,252,000
Assets: $32,197,000
Liabilities: $166,814,000
Net Worth: ($134,617,000)
Earnings: ($19,614,000)
Emp.: 40
Fiscal Year-end: 12/31/20
Asset Management Services
N.A.I.C.S.: 531390
Seth Taube *(Co-Chm & Co-CEO)*
Brook Taube *(Co-Chm, Co-CEO & Chief Investment Officer)*
Richard T. Allorto Jr. *(CFO)*

MEDLEY MANAGEMENT INC.
280 Park Ave 6th Fl E, New York, NY 10017
Tel.: (212) 759-0777   DE
Web Site: http://www.mdly.com
MDLM—(OTCQB)
Rev.: $33,252,000
Assets: $35,553,000
Liabilities: $169,223,000
Net Worth: ($133,670,000)
Earnings: ($2,664,000)
Emp.: 40
Fiscal Year-end: 12/31/20
Holding Company; Investment Advisory Services
N.A.I.C.S.: 551112
Seth Taube *(Co-Chm)*
Brook Taube *(Co-Chm)*
Samuel Anderson *(Head-Capital Markets & Risk Mgmt)*
Brett Barra *(Principal)*
Min Kim *(Principal & Controller-Fin Dept)*
Sal Jeraci *(Principal)*
Paul Sohn *(Principal)*
Joshua Coleman *(Principal)*
Bojan Bajic *(VP)*
Manuel Sandigo *(VP)*
Christopher B. Taube *(Sr Mng Dir & Head-Institutional Fundraising)*
Victor Dessis *(Mng Dir & Controller)*
Eric Nortman *(Principal)*
Elio Espinal *(VP & Mgr-IT)*

MEDNAX, INC.
1301 Concord Ter, Sunrise, FL 33323
Tel.: (954) 384-0175   FL
Web Site: http://www.mednax.com
Year Founded: 1979
MD—(NYSE)
Rev.: $1,911,191,000
Assets: $2,722,546,000
Liabilities: $1,825,854,000
Net Worth: $896,692,000
Earnings: $130,964,000
Emp.: 2,725
Fiscal Year-end: 12/31/21
Contract Management Services for Hospital-Based Neonatal & Pediatric Intensive Care Units
N.A.I.C.S.: 621111
Mark S. Ordan *(CEO)*
Guy P. Sansone *(Chm)*
James D. Swift *(COO & Exec VP)*
Dominic J. Andreano *(Gen Counsel, Sec & Exec VP)*
Charles Lynch *(VP-Strategy & IR)*
John C. Pepia *(Chief Accounting Officer & Sr VP)*
Claire Fair *(Chief HR Officer & Sr VP)*
Curtis B. Pickert *(Pres-Clinical Svcs Div)*
Mary Ann E. Moore *(Chief Enterprise Risk & Legal Ops Officer & Exec VP)*
C. Marc Richards *(CFO & Exec VP)*

Subsidiaries:

American Anesthesiology of Naples, Inc.   (1)
6101 Pine Rdg Rd, Naples, FL 34119-3900
Tel.: (239) 304-4862
Ambulatory Surgery & Anesthesia Services
N.A.I.C.S.: 621111

MedData, Inc.   (1)
6880 W Snowville Rd Ste 210, Brecksville, OH 44141
Tel.: (440) 717-6600
Web Site: http://www.meddata.com
Medical Billing Services
N.A.I.C.S.: 541219
Emily Fisher *(Pres & COO)*
Frank Stellato *(CFO)*
Michael Shea *(Chm & CEO)*
Tony Briggs *(CIO)*
Tom Watters *(Sr VP-Corp Dev & Strategy)*
Tom Birchfield *(Gen Counsel & VP)*
Nicole Guido *(Sr VP-Natl Sls)*
Edward Beitle *(Exec VP-Ops)*
Matt Blackner *(Exec VP-Ops)*
Lisa Almaraz *(Exec VP-Ops)*
Emily Arias *(Exec VP-Ops)*
Lynn Musselwhite *(Exec VP-Ops, A/R Recovery & Resolution)*
Jack Tindal *(Sr VP-Human Resources)*
Barb Astler *(Sr VP)*

Subsidiary (Domestic):

Alegis Revenue Group LLC   (2)
25227 Grogans Mill Rd Ste 100, The Woodlands, TX 77380
Tel.: (281) 719-7000
Web Site: http://meddata.com
Eligibility & Enrollment Solution Services
N.A.I.C.S.: 513210

Mednax Services, Inc.   (1)
1301 Concord Ter, Sunrise, FL 33323
Tel.: (954) 384-0175
Web Site: https://www.mednax.com
Sales Range: $50-74.9 Million
Emp.: 700
Physician Subspecialty Services
N.A.I.C.S.: 621111

Midwest Perinatal Associates, P.A.   (1)
12200 W 106th St Ste 110, Overland Park, KS 66215
Tel.: (913) 599-1396
Web Site: http://www.perinatalmd.com
Offices of Physicians (except Mental Health Specialists)
N.A.I.C.S.: 621111

Obstetrix Medical Group   (1)
1301 Concord Ter, Sunrise, FL 33333   (100%)
Tel.: (954) 384-0175
Web Site: http://www.obstetrix.com
Sales Range: $75-99.9 Million
Emp.: 700
Maternal-Fetal Medical Specialists
N.A.I.C.S.: 622110

Pediatrix Medical Group, Inc.   (1)
1301 Concord Ter, Sunrise, FL 33323
Tel.: (954) 384-0175
Web Site: https://www.pediatrix.com
Rev.: $1,994,640,000
Assets: $2,219,810,000
Liabilities: $1,370,749,000
Net Worth: $849,061,000
Earnings: ($60,408,000)
Emp.: 2,900
Fiscal Year-end: 12/31/2023
Health Care Srvices
N.A.I.C.S.: 621111
Roger J. Medel *(Co-Founder)*
James D. Swift *(CEO)*

South Dade Neonatology, LLC   (1)
215 Grand Ave, Coral Gables, FL 33133
Tel.: (305) 441-7179
Web Site: http://www.southdadeneonatology.com
Perinatal/Neonatal Health Services; Physician, Nursing & Medical Student Practice Company
N.A.I.C.S.: 621399
Bernardo Pimentel *(Partner)*
Manuel Campo *(Partner)*
Omar Costa-Cruz *(Partner)*

Gisela Diaz-Monroig *(Partner)*
Alex Koetzle *(Partner)*
Ernesto Valdes *(Partner)*

Surgical Directions, LLC   (1)
80 N Stetson Ave Ste 1610, Chicago, IL 60611
Tel.: (312) 870-5600
Web Site: http://www.surgicaldirections.com
Management Consulting Services
N.A.I.C.S.: 541618
Alecia Torrance *(Sr VP)*
Jeffry Peters *(Founder & Chm)*
Leslie Meyer Basham *(CEO)*
Lee Hedman *(Exec VP)*
Brian Watha *(Sr VP)*
Mark O'Connor *(Chief Growth Officer)*
Anne Cole *(Sr VP)*
Christopher Drevalas *(Asst VP-Operations)*
Tom Blasco *(Sr Mng Dir)*
David Young *(Mng Dir)*
Josh Miller *(Mng Dir)*
Casey Harper *(Dir)*
Patricia May *(Dir)*
Barbara McClenathan *(Dir)*
Michael Besedick *(Dir)*
Audrey Coppola *(Dir)*
Amanda Kieser *(Mgr)*
Kartik Bhatt *(Mgr)*

Synergy Radiology Associates, P.A.   (1)
4223 Richmond Ave, Houston, TX 77027
Tel.: (713) 351-0630
Web Site: http://www.synergyrad.org
Offices of All Other Miscellaneous Health Practitioners
N.A.I.C.S.: 621399
Lauren McKee *(Dir)*
Maegan Moore *(Dir-Marketing)*
Kim Marriott *(Sr Mgr-Accounting)*
Loay Wahbeh *(Fin Dir)*
Walid Adham *(Chm)*
John Loucks *(Dir-Information Technology)*
Michael Rodriguez *(Pres)*
Scott Allison *(Chm-Information Technology-Interventional, Vascular)*
Nan Garrett *(Chm-Body Imaging,Breast Imaging)*
Sunny Mittal *(Chm-Finance-Musculoskeletal)*
Chris Newton *(Chm-Musculoskeletal)*
Keyur Patel *(Chm-Musculoskeletal)*
Arif Rahman *(Chm-Interventional,Vascular)*
Ram K. Rao *(Chm-Operations-Musculoskeletal)*
Sendasaperumal N. Sendos *(Chm-Investor Relations-Interventional, Vascular)*
Justin Tholany *(Chm-Body Imaging)*
Sasidhar Yallampalli *(Chm-Interventional, Vascular)*
Stephen Wong *(Chm-Musculoskeletal)*

Virtual Radiologic Corporation   (1)
11995 Singletree Ln Ste 500, Eden Prairie, MN 55344
Tel.: (952) 595-0610
Web Site: http://www.vrad.com
Sales Range: $150-199.9 Million
Emp.: 350
Remote Digital Diagnostic Imaging Services
N.A.I.C.S.: 621512
Benjamin W. Strong *(Chief Medical Officer)*
Ryan Check *(Chief Admin Officer & Gen Counsel)*
Gerry Fitterer *(CFO & COO)*
Imad B. Nijim *(CIO)*
Michelle Torkelson *(VP-Human Resources)*
Joe Schmugge *(Sr VP-Operations)*
Evan Ebner *(Sr VP-Sales-Marketing)*
Raymond Montecalvo *(Sr Dir-Medical)*
Arlene Sussman *(Dir-Medical-Mammography)*
Edward Callaway *(Dir-Medical)*
Christina Geatrakas *(Dir-Medical)*
Scott Baginski *(Dir-Medical)*
Sloan Miller *(Dir-Medical)*
Scott Baginski *(Dir-Medical)*
Sloan Miller *(Dir-Medical)*

Subsidiary (Domestic):

Nighthawk Radiology, Inc.   (2)
5944 Coral Ridge Dr Ste 276, Coral Springs, FL 33076
Tel.: (818) 206-1622
Web Site: http://www.nighthawkradiology.com

MEDNAX, Inc.—(Continued)

Radiology & Cardiology Medical Services
N.A.I.C.S.: 621512
Richard Steinman *(CEO & Chief Medical Officer)*
Mela Sandler *(Dir-Ops)*
Christina Brower *(Dir-Bus Dev)*

Subsidiary (Domestic):

American Telemedicine, Inc.　　(3)
4972 NW 120th Ave, Coral Springs, FL 33076
Tel.: (818) 206-1622
Web Site:
　http://www.americantelemedicine.com
Telemedicine Infrastructure & Medical Record Data Storage Services
N.A.I.C.S.: 518210

MEDPACE HOLDINGS, INC.
5375 Medpace Way, Cincinnati, OH 45227
Tel.: (513) 579-9911　　　　DE
Web Site: https://www.medpace.com
Year Founded: 1992
MEDP—(NASDAQ)
Rev.: $1,885,842,000
Assets: $1,656,828,000
Liabilities: $1,097,878,000
Net Worth: $558,950,000
Earnings: $282,810,000
Emp.: 5,900
Fiscal Year-end: 12/31/23
Biotechnology Research & Development Services
N.A.I.C.S.: 541714
August James Troendle *(Founder, Chm & CEO)*
Jesse J. Geiger *(Pres)*
Susan E. Burwig *(Exec VP-Ops)*
Jonathan L. Isaacsohn *(Exec VP)*
Weimin Gai *(Sr VP-Biometrics)*
Daniel O'Leary *(Sr VP-Medical Dept)*
Traci Turner *(VP-MRL Ops & MARC)*
Stephen P. Ewald *(Chief Compliance Officer, Gen Counsel & Sec)*
Todd Meyers *(VP-Bus Dev & Mktg)*
John T. Wynne *(Sr VP-Comml Ops & Clinical Pharmacology Unit)*
Reinilde Heyrman *(VP-Medical Dept)*
Brandon Ebken *(CIO)*

Subsidiaries:

Medpace Clinical Pharmacology LLC　　　　　　　　　　(1)
5355 Medpace Way, Cincinnati, OH 45227
Tel.: (513) 366-3220
Biotechnology Research & Development Services
N.A.I.C.S.: 541714

MEEMEE MEDIA INC.
6630 W Sunset Blvd, Los Angeles, CA 90027
Tel.: (416) 903-6691　　　　NV
Year Founded: 2005
MEME—(OTCIQ)
Sales Range: Less than $1 Million
Emp.: 2
Women Apparel Mfr & Whslr
N.A.I.C.S.: 315250
Paul Amsellem *(CEO)*
Martin Jeffrey Doane *(Chm, Pres, CFO, Treas & Sec)*

MEET GROUP, INC.
100 Union Sq Dr, New Hope, PA 18938
Tel.: (215) 862-1162　　　　NV
Web Site: http://www.meetme.com
MEET—(NASDAQ)
Rev.: $211,701,000
Assets: $272,721,000
Liabilities: $75,481,000
Net Worth: $197,240,000
Earnings: $11,334,000
Emp.: 330

Fiscal Year-end: 12/31/19
Latino Social Networking Websites & Search Engine
N.A.I.C.S.: 516210
Frederic Beckley *(Gen Counsel & Exec VP-Bus Affairs)*
Geoffrey Cook *(Co-Founder)*
Spencer Garrett Rhodes *(Chm)*
Jeremy Zorn *(Sr VP-Product)*
James E. Bugden *(Chief Acctg Officer)*
Florian Braunschweig *(Gen Mgr-Europe)*
Leslie Arena *(Sr VP-IR)*
Nick Hermansader *(Sr VP-Adv)*
Catherine Connelly *(Sr VP-Mktg)*
Blake Kuhre *(Sr VP-Corp Dev)*

MEGA MATRIX CORP.
3000 El Camino Real Bldg 4 Ste 200, Palo Alto, CA 94306
Tel.: (650) 340-1888　　　　DE
Web Site: https://www.megamatrix.io
Year Founded: 1997
MPU—(NYSEAMEX)
Rev.: $1,927,400
Assets: $12,551,800
Liabilities: $5,589,900
Net Worth: $6,961,900
Earnings: ($8,466,000)
Emp.: 4
Fiscal Year-end: 12/31/22
Airplane Leasing & Financial Services
N.A.I.C.S.: 532411
Harold M. Lyons *(CFO, Treas, Sec & Sr VP-Fin)*
Yucheng Hu *(Chm, Pres & CEO)*
Qin Wang *(CFO, Treas & Sec)*

MEGANET CORPORATION
2510 E Sunset Rd Unit 5-777, Las Vegas, NV 89120
Tel.: (702) 987-0087　　　　NV
Web Site: http://www.meganet.com
Year Founded: 2009
MGNT—(OTCIQ)
Data Security, Intelligence/Counter-Intelligence & Military Operational Devices
N.A.I.C.S.: 561621
Saul Backal *(Chm, CEO & CFO)*
Orna Mizrahi *(Treas)*
Merav Backal *(VP)*

MEGATECH CORPORATION
525 Woburn St Ste 3, Tewksbury, MA 01876
Tel.: (978) 937-9600　　　　MA
Web Site:
　https://www.megatechcorp.com
MGTC—(OTCIQ)
All Other Industrial Machinery Manufacturing
N.A.I.C.S.: 333248
Vahan A. Basmajian *(Pres)*

MEI PHARMA, INC.
11455 El Camino Real Ste 250, San Diego, CA 92130
Tel.: (858) 369-7100　　　　DE
Web Site:
　https://www.meipharma.com
Year Founded: 2000
MEIP—(NASDAQ)
Rev.: $65,297,000
Assets: $41,375,000
Liabilities: $8,355,000
Net Worth: $33,020,000
Earnings: $17,778,000
Emp.: 28
Fiscal Year-end: 06/30/24
Anti-Cancer Therapies & Pharmaceuticals Mfr, Researcher & Developer
N.A.I.C.S.: 325411
Justin J. File *(Acting CEO, CFO & Sec)*

Ofir Moreno *(Sr VP-Pharmaceutical Sciences)*
Karen E. Potts *(Sr VP-Regulatory Affairs)*
David A. Walsey *(Sr VP-Corp Affairs)*
Tina C. Beamon *(Chief Compliance Officer)*
Ben Cadieux *(VP-Medical Affairs)*
Staci Ellis *(VP-Regulatory Affairs)*
Eugene Park *(VP-Mktg)*
Brian T. Powl *(Sr VP-Mktg)*
Virginia Sankey *(VP-Fin)*
Peter K. Smith *(VP-Program & Alliance Mgmt)*
Jamie A. Tereschuck *(VP-HR)*

MEIRAGTX HOLDINGS PLC
450 E 29th St 14th Fl, New York, NY 10016
Tel.: (646) 860-7985　　　　Ky
Web Site: https://www.meiragtx.com
Year Founded: 2018
MGTX—(NASDAQ)
Rev.: $15,920,000
Assets: $318,237,000
Liabilities: $200,499,000
Net Worth: $117,738,000
Earnings: ($129,615,000)
Emp.: 343
Fiscal Year-end: 12/31/22
Holding Company
N.A.I.C.S.: 551112
Stuart Naylor *(Chief Dev Officer)*
Richard Giroux *(CFO & COO)*
Robert K. Zeldin *(Chief Medical Officer)*
Robert Wollin *(Gen Counsel & Sec)*
Alastair Leighton *(Sr VP-Mfg & Supply Chain)*
Christine Sheehy *(Sr VP-Integration Global)*
Joel Brooks *(Sr VP-Fin)*
Tim Randall *(Sr VP-Risk & Internal Controls)*
Michel Michaelides *(Head-Clinical Ophthalmology)*
Alexandria Forbes *(Pres & CEO)*
Joel S. Marcus *(Executives)*

Subsidiaries:

Arthrogen B.V.　　　　　　　(1)
Meibergdreef 45, 1105 BA, Amsterdam, Netherlands
Tel.: (31) 205662648
Web Site: http://www.arthrogen.nl
Biotechnology Research Services
N.A.I.C.S.: 541714
Janneke Meulenberg *(Mng Dir)*
Paul Peter Tak *(Founder)*

MELI KASZEK PIONEER CORP.
78 SW 7th St Individual Office No 07-156, Miami, FL 33130
Tel.: (598) 292-7277　　　　Ky
Web Site:
　https://www.melikaszek.com
Year Founded: 2021
MEKA—(NASDAQ)
Rev.: $1,467,906
Assets: $293,002,456
Liabilities: $205,162,306
Net Worth: ($2,159,850)
Earnings: $83,515,124
Emp.: 3
Fiscal Year-end: 12/31/22
Investment Services
N.A.I.C.S.: 523999
Pedro Arnt *(Co-CEO)*
Hernan Kazah *(Chm & Co-CEO)*
Angel Uribe *(Chief Investment Officer)*

MELTRONIX, INC.
9577 Chesapeake Dr, San Diego, CA 92123
Tel.: (858) 292-7000　　　　CA

MTNX—(OTCIQ)
Electric Equipment Mfr
N.A.I.C.S.: 335999
Denis J. Trafecanty *(CFO)*
Timothy da Silva *(Pres & CEO)*

MENTOR CAPITAL, INC.
5964 Campus Ct, Plano, TX 75093
Tel.: (760) 788-4700　　　　CA
Web Site:
　https://www.mentorcapital.com
MNTR—(OTCQB)
Rev.: $7,705,715
Assets: $4,993,892
Liabilities: $3,267,793
Net Worth: $1,726,099
Earnings: ($471,386)
Emp.: 91
Fiscal Year-end: 12/31/22
Cannabis Industry Investments
N.A.I.C.S.: 525990
Chester Billingsley *(Chm, CEO & Principal Fin Officer)*
Lori J. Stansfield *(Treas)*
Robert Bernhard Meyer *(Sec)*
Sara Billingsley *(Dir-Bus Ops & Asst Sec)*

MERCANTILE BANK CORPORATION
310 Leonard St NW, Grand Rapids, MI 49504
Tel.: (616) 406-3000　　　　MI
Web Site: https://www.mercbank.com
MBWM—(NASDAQ)
Rev.: $213,916,000
Assets: $4,872,619,000
Liabilities: $4,431,211,000
Net Worth: $441,408,000
Earnings: $61,063,000
Emp.: 601
Fiscal Year-end: 12/31/22
Bank Holding Company
N.A.I.C.S.: 551111
Robert B. Kaminski Jr. *(Founder)*
Charles E. Christmas *(CFO, Treas & Exec VP)*
Raymond E. Reitsma *(Pres & CEO)*
Brett Hoover *(Sr VP & Dir-HR)*

Subsidiaries:

Keystone Community Bank　　(1)
235 N Drake Rd, Kalamazoo, MI 49009-1103
Tel.: (269) 544-9100
Web Site: http://www.keystonebank.com
Commercial Banking
N.A.I.C.S.: 522110

Mercantile Bank of Michigan　(1)
310 Leonard St NW, Grand Rapids, MI 49504
Tel.: (616) 242-7760
Web Site: https://www.mercbank.com
Emp.: 150
Commercial Banking
N.A.I.C.S.: 522110
Raymond E. Reitsma *(Pres & CEO)*
Raymond E. Reitsma *(Pres)*
Todd Dood *(Sr VP)*
Mark Augustyn *(Chief Lending Officer)*
Doug Holtrop *(Sr VP)*
Justin Karl *(Sr VP)*
Thomas Kelly *(Sr VP)*
Tim Ladd *(Officer-Treasury Sls & VP)*
Andrew Meyers *(Officer-Treasury Sls)*
Mike Siminski *(Sr VP)*
Michael Stapleton *(Sr VP)*
Holly Williams *(Officer-Treasury Sls & VP)*
Robert T. Worthington *(Sr VP)*
Mike Bishop *(Sr VP)*
Jeannie Hammer *(VP)*
Kyle Cochran *(Officer)*
Emily Postema *(Officer)*
Matt Zimmerman *(Sr VP)*
Dan Zink *(VP)*

MERCATO PARTNERS ACQUISITION CORP.

2750 E Cottonwood Pkwy Ste 500,
Cottonwood Heights, UT 84121
Tel.: (801) 220-0055   DE
Year Founded: 2021
MPRA—(NASDAQ)
Rev.: $3,490,614
Assets: $237,097,060
Liabilities: $238,360,568
Net Worth: ($1,263,508)
Earnings: $13,731,763
Emp.: 2
Fiscal Year-end: 12/31/22
Investment Services
N.A.I.C.S.: 523999
Greg Warnock (CEO & Chm)
Scott Klossner (CFO & Sec)

MERCER BANCORP, INC.

1100 Irmscher Blvd, Celina, OH
45822
Tel.: (419) 586-5158   MD
Year Founded: 2023
MSBB—(OTCQB)
Rev.: $6,647,868
Assets: $159,046,613
Liabilities: $136,261,988
Net Worth: $22,784,625
Earnings: $769,558
Emp.: 29
Fiscal Year-end: 09/30/23
Bank Holding Company
N.A.I.C.S.: 551111
Barry Parmiter (Pres & CEO)
Sherman Crum (CFO, Principal Acctg
Officer & Controller)

MERCHANTS & MARINE BAN-CORP, INC.

3118 Pascagoula St, Pascagoula, MS
39567
Web Site: https://mandmbank.com
Year Founded: 1899
MNMB—(OTCQX)
Offices of Bank Holding Companies
N.A.I.C.S.: 551111
Lisa Works (COO)
Michael M. Bush (Division Pres &
Divisional CEO-Mississippi River
Bank)

Subsidiaries:

Merchants & Marine Bank   (1)
3118 Pascagoula St, Pascagoula, MS
39567
Tel.: (228) 762-3311
Web Site: http://www.mandmbank.com
Provider of Banking Services
N.A.I.C.S.: 522110
Marty Regan (Sr VP-Ops)
Clayton Legear (Pres & CEO)
Lisa Adams (Mgr-Loan Dept)
Debbie Dixon (Mgr-Branch Ops)
Casey Hill (CFO)
Grant Walker (Pres-Pine Belt Market)
Greg Hodges (Chief Banking Officer)

Mississippi River Bank   (1)
8435 Hwy 23, Belle Chasse, LA 70037
Tel.: (504) 392-1111
Web Site:
   http://www.mississippiriverbank.net
Rev.: $9,700,000
Emp.: 43
Commericial Banking
N.A.I.C.S.: 522110
Michael O'Connor (VP)
Jeffrey J. Ramos (VP)
Gina Roberts (Officer-Banking)
Jessica Williams (Officer-Banking)
Susan Pavon (Officer-Banking)
Stacy Burke (Officer-Banking)
Sue Pelas (VP-Port Sulphur)

MERCHANTS BANCORP

410 Monon Blvd, Carmel, IN 46032
Tel.: (317) 324-4660   IN
Web Site:
   https://www.merchantsbancorp.com
MBIN—(NASDAQ)
Rev.: $606,769,000

Assets: $12,615,227,000
Liabilities: $11,155,488,000
Net Worth: $1,459,739,000
Earnings: $219,721,000
Emp.: 556
Fiscal Year-end: 12/31/22
Bank Holding Company
N.A.I.C.S.: 551111
Michael F. Petrie (Founder, Chm &
CEO)
Randall D. Rogers (Vice Chm)
Michael J. Dunlap (Pres & COO)

Subsidiaries:

Farmers-Merchants Bank of
Illinois   (1)
101 W Main St, Joy, IL 61260
Tel.: (309) 584-4146
Web Site: https://www.fmbankil.com
Banking Services
N.A.I.C.S.: 522110

Merchants Bank of Indiana   (1)
11590 N Meridian St Ste 120, Carmel, IN
46032-6906
Tel.: (317) 805-4303
Web Site: http://www.merchantscapital.com
Other Activities Related to Credit Interme-
diation
N.A.I.C.S.: 522390
Michael Petrie (Owner)

PR Mortgage Investment Manage-
ment, LLC   (1)
2000 Midlantic Dr Ste 220, Mount Laurel,
NJ 08054
Tel.: (215) 360-3800
Web Site:
   https://www.prmortgageinvestment.com
Mortgage Investment Services
N.A.I.C.S.: 525990
Barry Bier (Pres & Co-Chief Investment Of-
ficer)
Sanford Blitzer (Co-Chief Investment Offi-
cer)
Brad Brautigam (CFO)

MERCK & CO., INC.

126 E Lincoln Ave, Rahway, NJ
07065
Tel.: (908) 740-4000   NJ
Web Site: https://www.merck.com
Year Founded: 1891
MRK—(NYSE)
Rev.: $60,115,000,000
Assets: $106,675,000,000
Liabilities: $69,040,000,000
Net Worth: $37,635,000,000
Earnings: $365,000,000
Emp.: 70,000
Fiscal Year-end: 12/31/23
Pharmaceutical Products Distr
N.A.I.C.S.: 424210
Steven C. Mizell (Chief HR Officer &
Exec VP)
Sanat Chattopadhyay (Pres-Mfg Div
& Exec VP)
Y. Li (Pres-Res Laboratories & Exec
VP)
Dave Williams (Chief Information &
Digital Officer)
Michael W. Fleming (Chief Ethics &
Compliance Officer & Sr VP)
Michael A. Klobuchar (Chief Strategy
Officer & Exec VP)
Caroline Litchfield (CFO & Exec VP)
Michael A. Klobuchar (Chief Strategy
Officer)
Cristal N. Downing (Exec VP)
Chirfi Guindo (CMO)
Jannie Oosthuizen (Pres)
Joseph Romanelli (Pres)
Richard R. DeLuca Jr. (Pres-Animal
Health & Exec VP)
Robert M. Davis (Chm, Pres & CEO)

Subsidiaries:

Acceleron Pharma Inc.   (1)
128 Sidney St, Cambridge, MA 02139
Tel.: (617) 649-9200

Web Site: http://www.acceleronpharma.com
Rev.: $92,523,000
Assets: $932,337,000
Liabilities: $77,230,000
Net Worth: $855,107,000
Earnings: ($166,030,000)
Emp.: 312
Fiscal Year-end: 12/31/2020
Pharmaceuticals Mfr
N.A.I.C.S.: 325412
Ravindra Kumar (Chief Scientific Officer &
Sr VP)
James Desiderio (Sr VP-Regulatory & Qual-
ity)
Todd James (Sr VP-Corp Affairs & IR)
Tracey Sacco (Sr VP-Strategic Mktg-Global)
Matt Fearer (Sr Dir-Corp Comm)
Kevin McManus (Chief HR Officer)
Lisa Wyman (Sr VP-Technical Ops)
Adam Veness (Gen Counsel, Sec & Sr VP)
Jamie Bernard (Assoc Dir-IR)
Jasbir S. Seehra (Co-Founder)

Afferent Pharmaceuticals, Inc.   (1)
2929 Campus Dr Ste 230, San Mateo, CA
94403   (100%)
Tel.: (650) 286-1276
Web Site: http://www.afferentpharma.com
Biopharmaceutical Research & Develop-
ment Services
N.A.I.C.S.: 541715

Agrident GmbH   (1)
Steinklippenstrasse 10, 30890, Barsing-
hausen, Germany
Tel.: (49) 510558257310
Web Site: http://www.agrident.com
Measuring & Testing Electricity Product Mfr
N.A.I.C.S.: 334515
Benjamin Seichter (Sls Mgr)

Aleis Pty Ltd   (1)
37 Neumann Road, Capalaba, 4157, QLD,
Australia
Tel.: (61) 732459100
Web Site: http://www.aleis.com
Electronic Component Mfr & Distr
N.A.I.C.S.: 334419

Allflex Argentia S.A.   (1)
Luis Saenz Pena 2002, 1035, Buenos Ai-
res, Argentina
Tel.: (54) 941164870
Industrial Machinery Mfr
N.A.I.C.S.: 333248

Allflex Australia Pty Ltd   (1)
185 Queensport Road North, Murarrie,
4172, QLD, Australia
Tel.: (61) 732459100
Web Site: https://www.allflex.com.au
Industrial Machinery Mfr
N.A.I.C.S.: 333248
Mark Mckay (Reg Mgr-Sales)
Neil Rogers (Sls Mgr)
Sam Henry (Sls Mgr)
Scott Bullock (Sls Mgr)
Paddy Ryan (Acct Mgr)

Allflex Dan-mark ApS   (1)
Rugmarken 31, 7620, Lemvig, Denmark
Tel.: (45) 9 781 1555
Web Site: https://www.allflex.dk
Industrial Machinery Mfr
N.A.I.C.S.: 333248

Allflex Group Germany GmbH   (1)
Luxemburgerstrasse 1, 48455, Bad Ben-
theim, Germany
Tel.: (49) 592 444 8980
Web Site: https://www.allflex.global
Industrial Machinery Mfr
N.A.I.C.S.: 333248
Christian Vogelsberg (Comml Dir-DACH &
Attorney)

Allflex India Private Limited   (1)
Plot No 76 Sector - 8 IMT Manesar, Gur-
gaon, 122 051, Haryana, India
Tel.: (91) 1244800030
Web Site: https://www.allflex.global
Pharmaceutical Drugs & Medicines Mfr
N.A.I.C.S.: 325412

Allflex International do Brasil
Ltda   (1)
Rua Dona Francisca 8 300, Distrito Indus-
trial Perini Business Park, Joinville, 89239-
270, Santa Catarina, Brazil
Tel.: (55) 4734510500

Livestock Tag Mfr & Distr
N.A.I.C.S.: 332999

Allflex New Zealand Limited   (1)
17 El Prado Drive, PB 11003, Palmerston
North, 4470, New Zealand
Tel.: (64) 6 356 7199
Web Site: https://www.allflex.global
Industrial Machinery Mfr
N.A.I.C.S.: 333248

Allflex Polska Sp z o.o.   (1)
Psary Male ul Nekielska 11G, 62-300, Wrz-
esnia, Poland
Tel.: (48) 61 895 2010
Web Site: https://www.allflex.global
Industrial Machinery Mfr
N.A.I.C.S.: 333248
Michal Kubiatowicz (Dir-Ops)

Allflex SCR Vostok   (1)
103-36B School St, Stan Korolyov Village,
Minsk, 223027, Belarus
Tel.: (375) 175115068
Web Site: http://www.allflex.by
Livestock Tag Mfr & Distr
N.A.I.C.S.: 332999

Allflex UK Group   (1)
1 Greencroft Industrial Park Stanley, Dur-
ham, DH9 7YA, United Kingdom
Tel.: (44) 1207523175
Web Site: http://www.allflex.co.uk
Industrial Machinery Mfr
N.A.I.C.S.: 333248

Aptus Health International
France   (1)
Tour Ariane 22nd floor 5 place de la Pyra-
mide, La Defense, 92800, Puteaux, France
Tel.: (33) 173140000
Software Development Services
N.A.I.C.S.: 541511
Sven Awege (VP-Intl Strategic Acct Mgmt)

Beijing Allflex Plastic Products Co.,
Ltd.   (1)
Santaishan Xiaohongmen, Chaoyang Dis-
trict, Beijing, 100176, China
Tel.: (86) 1087605808
Web Site: http://www.allflex.com.cn
Livestock Tag Mfr & Distr
N.A.I.C.S.: 332999

Burgwedel Biotech GmbH   (1)
Im Langen Felde 5, 30938, Burgwedel, Ha-
nover, Germany
Tel.: (49) 51398970
Pharmaceuticals Product Mfr
N.A.I.C.S.: 325412

C3i Support Services Private
Limited   (1)
Orion Block 5th Floor The V Plot No 17
Software Units Layout, Madhapur, Hydera-
bad, 500 081, India
Tel.: (91) 4066564600
Pharmaceuticals Product Mfr
N.A.I.C.S.: 325412
Lavanya Surabi (Coord-HR)

Chevillot S.A.S.   (1)
Zone Industrielle St Antoine, BP 216,
81011, Albi, Cedex 9, France
Tel.: (33) 563782222
Web Site: https://www.chevillot.com
Electronic Component Mfr & Distr
N.A.I.C.S.: 334419

Chibret pharmazeutische Gesellschaft
mit beschrankter Haftung   (1)
Lindenplatz 1, 85540, Haar, Germany
Tel.: (49) 89456110
Pharmaceuticals Product Mfr
N.A.I.C.S.: 456110

Comsort, Inc.   (1)
200 W Butler Ave 686, Ambler, PA 19002-
0686
Tel.: (410) 785-4853
Web Site: http://comsort.com
Pharmaceutical Preparation Mfr
N.A.I.C.S.: 325412
Brian Massouda (Dir-IT)
Nick Privalov (Engr-Software)
Marshall Hawks (Dir-Analytics)
Michael Marcucci (Sr Engr-Software)
Danny Luchan (Engr-Data)

Destron Fearing Corporation   (1)

Merck & Co., Inc.—(Continued)

2805 E 14th St DFW Airport, Dallas, TX 75261
Web Site: https://www.destronfearing.com
Livestock Tag Mfr & Distr
N.A.I.C.S.: 332999
Andrew Dorn (Mgr-Beef Bus Dev)
Steve Bretey (Mgr-Swine Bus Dev)
Brandt Kreuscher (Mgr-Dairy Bus Dev)
Scott Holt (Mktg Mgr-North America)
Jesse Odom (Reg Mgr-Northwest)

Dieckmann Arzneimittel GmbH (1)
Lindenplatz 1, 85540, Haar, Germany
Tel.: (49) 89 456.10
Web Site: http://www.msd.de
Sales Range: $150-199.9 Million
Emp.: 500
Pharmaceutical Preparation Mfr
N.A.I.C.S.: 325412

Diosynth Produtos Farmo-quimicos Ltda. (1)
Av Marginal Esquerda do Rio Tiete 5 101
Aldeia Velha, Barueri, 0641, Sao Paulo, Brazil
Tel.: (55) 112 176 8900
Web Site: https://www.3296-br.all.biz
Pharmaceutical Products Distr
N.A.I.C.S.: 456110

Drovers ID Pty Ltd (1)
Level 1 37 Neumann Road, Capalaba, 4157, QLD, Australia
Tel.: (61) 1300138247
Web Site: http://www.drovers.com.au
Livestock Tag Mfr & Distr
N.A.I.C.S.: 332999

Elastec S.R.L (1)
Boqueron 145 Lomas de Zamora, 1832, Buenos Aires, Argentina
Tel.: (54) 1142831833
Vaccines Merchant Whslr
N.A.I.C.S.: 424210

Essex Chemie AG (1)
Weystrasse 20 Luzern 6, Lucerne, 6000, Switzerland
Tel.: (41) 4181616
Web Site: http://www.merc.ch
Sales Range: $25-49.9 Million
Emp.: 120
Pharmaceuticals Mfr
N.A.I.C.S.: 325412

Subsidiary (Domestic):

Werthenstein BioPharma GmbH (2)
Industrie Nord 1 Schachen, 6105, Lucerne, Switzerland
Tel.: (41) 4149997979
Web Site: http://www.msd.ch
Biotechnological & Pharmaceutical Development
N.A.I.C.S.: 541714

Farmasix-Produtos Farmaceuticos, Lda (1)
Qta Supply No 19 Edif Vasco DaGama, Porto Salvo, 2770-192, Portugal
Tel.: (351) 21 4465700
Web Site: http://www.merck.com
Emp.: 30
Pharmaceutical Preparation Mfr
N.A.I.C.S.: 325412

Harpoon Therapeutics, Inc. (1)
131 Oyster Point Blvd Ste 300, South San Francisco, CA 94080
Tel.: (650) 443-7400
Web Site: https://www.harpoontx.com
Rev.: $31,915,000
Assets: $73,720,000
Liabilities: $68,330,000
Net Worth: $5,399,000
Earnings: ($67,731,000)
Emp.: 50
Fiscal Year-end: 12/31/2022
Biotechnology Research & Development Services
N.A.I.C.S.: 541714

Horus B.V. (1)
Handwerkerszijde 35, 9201 CJ, Drachten, Netherlands
Tel.: (31) 206375251
Pharmaceutical Preparation Mfr
N.A.I.C.S.: 325412

IHSM B.V. (1)
Daltonlaan 400, 3584 BK, Utrecht, Netherlands
Tel.: (31) 412661222
Web Site: http://www.hethuisartslab.nl
Laboratory Testing Services
N.A.I.C.S.: 541380

Idenix Pharmaceuticals, Inc. (1)
Tel.: (617) 995-9800
Sales Range: Less than $1 Million
Emp.: 84
Biopharmaceutical Mfr
N.A.I.C.S.: 325412

IdentiGEN Limited (1)
Block 2 Blackrock Business Park Carysfort Avenue, Dublin, A94 H2X4, Ireland
Tel.: (353) 16770221
Web Site: https://www.identigen.com
Deoxyribonucleic Acid Traceability Services
N.A.I.C.S.: 561611

IdentiGEN North America Inc. (1)
2033 Becker Dr Ste 301, Lawrence, KS 66047
Tel.: (785) 856-8800
Deoxyribonucleic Acid Traceability Services
N.A.I.C.S.: 561611

IdentiGEN Switzerland AG (1)
Brandstr 24, Schlieren, 8952, Zurich, Switzerland
Tel.: (41) 447337000
Deoxyribonucleic Acid Traceability Services
N.A.I.C.S.: 561611

Imago BioSciences, Inc. (1)
329 Oyster Point Blvd 3rd Fl, South San Francisco, CA 94080
Tel.: (415) 529-5055
Web Site: http://www.imagobio.com
Rev.: $314,000
Assets: $224,786,000
Liabilities: $10,092,000
Net Worth: $214,694,000
Earnings: ($42,311,000)
Emp.: 27
Fiscal Year-end: 12/31/2021
Biotechnology Research & Development Services
N.A.I.C.S.: 541714
Michael H. Arenberg (Chief Operating & Bus Officer)
Hugh Y. Rienhoff (CEO)
Laura G. Eichorn (CFO)
Wan-Jen Hong (Chief Medical Officer)
Jennifer Peppe (Sr VP-Clinical Ops)
Amy Tapper (Sr VP-Non Clinical & CMC)
Dennis Henner (Chm)
Hsiangyi Chiang (Principal Acctg Officer)

Immune Design Corp. (1)
1616 Eastlake Ave E Ste 310, Seattle, WA 98102
Tel.: (206) 682-0645
Web Site: http://www.immunedesign.com
Rev.: $2,196,000
Assets: $100,960,000
Liabilities: $8,955,000
Net Worth: $92,005,000
Earnings: ($54,758,000)
Emp.: 48
Fiscal Year-end: 12/31/2018
Biopharmaceutical Mfr
N.A.I.C.S.: 325412
Wayne R. Gombotz (Chief Dev Officer)
Jan Henrik Ter Meulen (Chief Scientific Officer)
Frank J. Hsu (VP & Head-Oncology)
Heidi Petersen (VP-Regulatory Affairs)
Sergey Yurasov (Chief Medical Officer & Sr VP-Clinical Dev)
Sandy Mohan (VP-Quality & Compliance)
Fred Kerwood (VP-Clinical Ops & Project Mgmt)
Edward Etienne Penhoet (Chm)

International Indemnity Ltd. (1)
26 Victoria St, Hamilton, HM 11, Bermuda
Tel.: (441) 2941550
Web Site: http://www.merck.com
Emp.: 9
Pharmaceutical Products Distr
N.A.I.C.S.: 424210

Intervet (Ireland) Limited (1)
Red Oak North, South County Business Park Leopardstown, Dublin, Ireland
Tel.: (353) 1 297 0220

Web Site: https://www.msd-animal-health.ie
Emp.: 30
Veterinary Drug Product Distr
N.A.I.C.S.: 424210

Intervet (Proprietary) Limited (1)
20 Spartan Road Spartan Ext 20, Kempton Park, 1619, South Africa
Tel.: (27) 11 923 9300
Web Site: https://www.msd-animal-health.co.za
Veterinary Drug Product Distr
N.A.I.C.S.: 424210

Intervet AB (1)
Gavlegatan 22 B4, 113 30, Stockholm, Sweden
Tel.: (46) 85 222 1660
Web Site: https://www.msd-animal-health.se
Veterinary Drug Product Mfr
N.A.I.C.S.: 325412

Intervet Colombia Ltda (1)
Calle 127A 53 A-45 Piso 8 complejo empresarial colpatrua Torre 3, Bogota, Colombia
Tel.: (57) 15924400
Web Site: http://www.msd-salud-animal.com.co
Veterinary Drug Product Mfr
N.A.I.C.S.: 325412

Intervet Hellas A.E. (1)
3 Paparigopoulou St, Athens, Greece
Tel.: (30) 16846814
Veterinary Drug Distr
N.A.I.C.S.: 424210

Intervet Inc. (1)
556 Morris Ave, Summit, NJ 07901
Tel.: (908) 473-4000
Web Site: http://www.merck-animal-health-usa.com
Sales Range: $300-349.9 Million
Emp.: 6,000
Veterinary Pharmaceutical Mfr
N.A.I.C.S.: 325412

Subsidiary (Domestic):

Global Animal Management, Inc. (2)
556 Morris Ave, Summit, NJ 07901-1330
Tel.: (908) 473-3423
Web Site: http://devweb.mygamonline.com
Pharmaceutical Preparation Mfr
N.A.I.C.S.: 325412

Harrisvaccines, Inc. (2)
1102 Southern Hills Dr Ste 101, Ames, IA 50010-8225
Tel.: (515) 296-3930
Animal Vaccines Developer & Mfr
N.A.I.C.S.: 325412
Patrick Jennings (Assoc Dir-Process Dev)

Subsidiary (Non-US):

Intervet (M) Sdn Bhd (2)
29-1 Jalan USJ 9/5Q Subang Business Centre, Subang Jaya, 47620, Selangor, Malaysia
Tel.: (60) 3 8024 6467
Web Site: http://www.merck.com
Pharmaceuticals Product Mfr
N.A.I.C.S.: 325412

Intervet (Thailand) Ltd. (2)
183 South Sathorn Road, Sathon, Bangkok, 10120, Thailand
Tel.: (66) 22879555
Web Site: http://www.intervet.co.th
Sales Range: $25-49.9 Million
Emp.: 42
Animal Health Product Distr
N.A.I.C.S.: 325412

Intervet Agencies B.V. (2)
Wim De Korverstraat 35, 5831 AN, Boxmeer, 5831 AN, Netherlands
Tel.: (31) 485587600
Pharmaceuticals Product Mfr
N.A.I.C.S.: 325412

Intervet Argentina S.A. (2)
Complejo Urbana Cazadores de Coquimbo 2841 Piso 4 - 1605, Munro, Argentina
Tel.: (54) 116 090 7200
Web Site: https://www.msd-salud-animal.com.ar
Veterinary Pharmaceuticals Mfr & Marketer
N.A.I.C.S.: 325412

Intervet Australia Pty Ltd (2)
91-105 Harpin St, Bendigo, 3550, VIC, Australia
Tel.: (61) 1800033461
Web Site: http://www.msd-animal-health.com.au
Animal Health Product Distr
N.A.I.C.S.: 325412

Intervet Canada Corp. (2)
16750 route Transcanadienne, Kirkland, H9H 4M7, QC, Canada
Tel.: (514) 428-7013
Web Site: https://www.merck-animal-health.ca
Sales Range: $10-24.9 Million
Emp.: 22
Animal Pharmaceutical & Healthcare Products Mfr
N.A.I.C.S.: 325412

Intervet Denmark A/S (2)
Lautrupbjerg 4, 2750, Ballerup, Denmark
Tel.: (45) 44 82 42 00
Web Site: http://www.msd-animal-health.dk
Emp.: 35
Pharmaceuticals Product Mfr
N.A.I.C.S.: 325412

Intervet Deutschland GmbH (2)
Feldstrasse 1a, 85716, Unterschleissheim, Germany
Tel.: (49) 894 561 4100
Web Site: https://www.msd-tiergesundheit.de
Emp.: 130
Veterinary Pharmaceuticals Sales
N.A.I.C.S.: 424210

Intervet Egypt for Animal Health SAE (2)
46 Farid Street, Cairo, Heliopolis, 11341, Egypt
Tel.: (20) 226145100
Web Site: http://www.intervet.com.eg
Sales Range: $25-49.9 Million
Emp.: 30
Animal Health Care Services
N.A.I.C.S.: 541940
Mamdouh Mahfouz (Gen Mgr)
Nibal Khafagy (Mgr-Regulatory Affairs)
Yasser El-Moursy (Mgr-Poultry Bus Unit)
Murad Selim (Mgr-Large Animal & Companions Bus Unit)
Abdel Salam Farouk (Mgr-Production & Warehouse)
Sahar El-Azhary (Fin Mgr)
Ehab Mourice (Mgr-Large Animal & Companions Technical)
Ahmed Adel (Mgr-Poultry Technical)

Intervet Ges mbH (2)
Siemensstrasse 107, Floridsdorf, 1210, Vienna, Austria
Tel.: (43) 1 256 8787
Web Site: https://www.msd-tiergesundheit.at
Pharmaceuticals Product Mfr
N.A.I.C.S.: 325412

Intervet Hungaria Kft (2)
Lechner Odon fasor 10/b, 1095, Budapest, Hungary
Tel.: (36) 14563090
Pharmaceuticals Product Mfr
N.A.I.C.S.: 325412

Plant (Domestic):

Intervet Inc. - Elkhorn (2)
21401 W Ctr Rd, Elkhorn, NE 68022-2202
Tel.: (402) 331-3900
Web Site: http://www.merck.com
Sales Range: $50-74.9 Million
Emp.: 250
Veterinary Pharmaceutical Mfr
N.A.I.C.S.: 325412

Intervet Inc. - Millsboro (2)
29160 Intervet Ln, Millsboro, DE 19966
Tel.: (302) 934-8051
Emp.: 300
Animal Vaccine Researcher, Mfr & Marketer
N.A.I.C.S.: 325412
Brett Whitehead (Dir-Equine & Retail Bus)

Subsidiary (Non-US):

Intervet K.K. (2)
27 14 Hamamatsucho 1-chome, Minato-ku Chiyoda-Ku, Tokyo, 102-0073, Japan

Tel.: (81) 354730640
Veterinary Medicine Services
N.A.I.C.S.: 541940

Intervet Middle East Ltd (2)
Alpha Building Suite 01 Ground Floor Dubai
Internet City, PO Box 502947, Dubai Inter-
net City, Dubai, United Arab Emirates
Tel.: (971) 44468001
Web Site: http://secure.merck-animal-
health.com
Veterinary Medicine Services
N.A.I.C.S.: 541940

Intervet Nederland B.V. (2)
PD001 1 018, Postbus 50, 5830 AB, Box-
meer, Netherlands
Tel.: (31) 485587600
Web Site: http://www.msd-animal-health.nl
Sales Range: $1-4.9 Billion
Emp.: 1,500
Veterinary Medicines Researcher, Devel-
oper, Mfr & Marketer
N.A.I.C.S.: 325412

Intervet Norbio A.S. (2)
Thormahlens Gate 55, Bergen, 5008, Nor-
way
Tel.: (47) 55543750
Web Site: http://www.msdanimalhealth.com
Sales Range: $25-49.9 Million
Emp.: 35
Veterinary Medicine Services
N.A.I.C.S.: 541940

**Intervet Norbio Singapore Pte
Ltd** (2)
1 Perahu Road, Singapore, 718847, Singa-
pore
Tel.: (65) 63971121
Veterinary Medicine Services
N.A.I.C.S.: 541940

Intervet Norge AS (2)
Thormahlensgate 55, 5006, Bergen, Nor-
way
Tel.: (47) 55 54 37 35
Web Site: http://www.msdanimalhealth.com
Sales Range: $25-49.9 Million
Emp.: 37
Veterinary Medicine Services
N.A.I.C.S.: 541940

Intervet Oy (2)
Keilaranta 3, PO Box 86, 02150, Espoo,
Finland
Tel.: (358) 102310750
Web Site: http://www.msd-animal-health.fi
Sales Range: $25-49.9 Million
Emp.: 10
Veterinary Medicine Services
N.A.I.C.S.: 541940

**Intervet Schering-Plough Animal
Health Pty Ltd** (2)
91-105 Harpin Street, Bendigo, 3550, VIC,
Australia
Tel.: (61) 3 5440 9888
Web Site: http://www.msd-animal-
health.com.au
Emp.: 75
Animal Pharmaceutical Product Mfr
N.A.I.C.S.: 325412

Intervet U.K. Ltd. (2)
Walton Manor, Milton Keynes, MK7 7AJ,
Bucks, United Kingdom
Tel.: (44) 1908685685
Web Site: https://www.msd-animal-health-
hub.co.uk
Sales Range: $125-149.9 Million
Emp.: 400
Veterinary Pharmaceuticals Developer &
Mfr
N.A.I.C.S.: 325412

Intervet Veterinaria Chile Ltda (2)
Mariano Sanchez Fontecilla 310 Piso 5, Las
Condes, 7550296, Santiago, Chile
Tel.: (56) 226558940
Pharmaceuticals Product Mfr
N.A.I.C.S.: 325412

Laboratorios Intervet S.A. (2)
Poligono El Montalvo 39, Carbajosa de la
Sagrada, 37080, Salamanca, Spain
Tel.: (34) 923190345
Web Site: http://www.msd.es
Sales Range: $75-99.9 Million
Emp.: 300
Veterinary Products Mfr & Marketer

N.A.I.C.S.: 325412

MSD Animal Health BVBA (2)
Lynx Binnenhof 5, 1200, Brussels, Belgium
Tel.: (32) 23709401
Web Site: http://nl.msd-animal-health.be
Emp.: 40
Animal Health Pharmaceuticals Developer,
Mfr & Whslr
N.A.I.C.S.: 325412

Intervet India Pvt. Ltd (1)
6th Floor Tower 5 World Trade Center Sur-
vey No 1, Kharadi, Pune, 411 014, India
Tel.: (91) 2066294700
Pharmaceutical Drugs & Medicines Mfr
N.A.I.C.S.: 325412

Intervet India Pvt. Ltd (1)
Briahnagar Off Pune-Nagar Road, Wagholi,
412 207, Pune, India
Tel.: (91) 2066207800
Web Site: http://www.msd-animal-
health.co.in
Emp.: 90
Veterinary Drug Product Mfr
N.A.I.C.S.: 325412

Intervet LLC (1)
Naro-fominskiy r-n d Yakovlevskoe d 21,
Moscow, 143340, Russia
Tel.: (7) 4963420334
Veterinary Drug Distr
N.A.I.C.S.: 424210

Intervet Mexico S.A. de C.V. (1)
Av San Jeronimo No 369, Col La Otra
Banda Alvaro Obregon, 01090, Mexico,
Mexico, Mexico
Tel.: (52) 54819600
Web Site: http://www.msd-salud-animal.mx
Veterinary Drug Product Mfr
N.A.I.C.S.: 325412

Intervet Philippines, Inc. (1)
28th Floor Philamlife Tower Paseo de
Roxas, Makati, 8767, Philippines
Tel.: (63) 2 784 4800
Web Site: https://www.msd-animal-health.ph
Veterinary Drug Product Mfr
N.A.I.C.S.: 325412

Intervet Romania SRL (1)
Sos de Centura nr 13A Sat Chiajna,
Chiajna, 077040, Jud Ilfov, Romania
Tel.: (40) 21 311 8311
Web Site: https://www.msd-animal-health.ro
Veterinary Drug Product Mfr
N.A.I.C.S.: 325412

Intervet S.A.S (1)
7 Rue Olivier De Serres-Angers Techno-
pole, CS 17144, 49071, Beaucouze, Cedex,
France
Tel.: (33) 24 122 8383
Web Site: https://www.msd-sante-animale.fr
Veterinary Drug Product Distr
N.A.I.C.S.: 424210

**Intervet South Africa (Proprietary)
Limited** (1)
Spartanweg 20, Spartan, Kempton Park,
1619, South Africa
Tel.: (27) 11 923 9300
Web Site: http://www.msd-animal-
health.co.za
Animal Health Production Services
N.A.I.C.S.: 115210

Intervet Sp. z o.o. (1)
ul Chlodna 51, 00-867, Warsaw, Poland
Tel.: (48) 221832200
Pharmaceutical Drugs & Medicines Mfr
N.A.I.C.S.: 325412

Intervet Sp. z o.o. (1)
ul Chlodna 51, 00-867, Warsaw, Poland
Tel.: (48) 22 183 2200
Web Site: https://www.msd-animal-health.pl
Veterinary Drug Product Mfr
N.A.I.C.S.: 325412

Intervet Venezolana SA (1)
Calle Altagracia Edif P&G Piso 2 Local
Torre Sur Urb Sorokaima, Caracas, 1080,
Miranda, Venezuela
Tel.: (58) 2125405
Web Site: http://www.msd-salud-
animal.com.ve
Veterinary Drug Product Mfr
N.A.I.C.S.: 325412

Intervet Vietnam Co., Ltd. (1)
37 Ton Duc Thang Street District 1, Ho Chi
Minh City, Vietnam
Tel.: (84) 839109845
Web Site: http://www.msd-animal-health.vn
Veterinary Drug Product Mfr
N.A.I.C.S.: 325412

Intervet, s.r.o. (1)
Na Valentine 3336/4, Smichov, 150 00,
Prague, 5, Czech Republic
Tel.: (420) 233010242
Veterinary Drug Distr
N.A.I.C.S.: 424210

**Istituto Di Richerche Di Biologia Mo-
lecolare S.p.A.** (1)
Via Vitorchiano 151, Rome, 0189, Italy
Tel.: (39) 06910931
Pharmaceuticals Product Mfr
N.A.I.C.S.: 325412

KBI-E Inc. (1)
5307 Limestone Rd, Wilmington, DE 19808-
1268
Tel.: (302) 235-2701
Pharmaceuticals Product Mfr
N.A.I.C.S.: 325412

Koneksa Health LLC (1)
1 World Trade Ctr 285 Fulton St 77th Fl,
New York, NY 10007
Web Site: https://www.koneksahealth.com
Pharmaceutical Drugs & Medicines Mfr
N.A.I.C.S.: 325412

**Laboratoires Merck Sharp & Dohme-
Chibret SNC** (1)
Mirabel Plant / Research Center Route de
Marsat - Riom, 63963, Clermont-Ferrand,
Cedex, France
Tel.: (33) 473675000
Web Site: http://www.msd-france.com
Sales Range: $75-99.9 Million
Emp.: 250
Pharmaceuticals Clinical Research, Market-
ing & Administrative Services
N.A.I.C.S.: 424210

Laboratorios Frosst, S.A. (1)
Julian Camarillo 35, 28037, Madrid, Spain
Tel.: (34) 911190818
Web Site: http://www.roviservices.com
Pharmaceuticals Product Mfr
N.A.I.C.S.: 325412

MCM Vaccine B.V.1 (1)
Robert Boyleweg 4, 2333 CG, Leiden,
Netherlands
Tel.: (31) 713322412
Web Site: https://www.mcmbv.eu
Pharmaceutical Drugs & Medicines Mfr
N.A.I.C.S.: 325412

MSD (Italia) s.r.l. (1)
Via Vitorchiano 151, Rome, Italy
Tel.: (39) 03472867642
Web Site: https://www.msd-italia.it
Emp.: 850
Pharmaceutical Drugs & Medicines Mfr
N.A.I.C.S.: 325412

**MSD (L-SP) Unterstutzungskasse
GmbH** (1)
Lindenplatz 1, 85540, Haar, Germany
Tel.: (49) 8945610
Web Site: http://www.msd.de
Pharmaceutical Products Distr
N.A.I.C.S.: 456110

MSD (Norge) A/S (1)
Gronland 51, 3045, Drammen,
Norway (100%)
Tel.: (47) 32207300
Web Site: http://www.msd.no
Sales Range: $150-199.9 Million
Emp.: 160
Pharmaceuticals Distr
N.A.I.C.S.: 424210
Kari Haugli (Dir-HR)

MSD (Pty) Ltd (1)
117 16th Road, PO Box X3, Halfway
House, Midrand, 1685, South Africa
Tel.: (27) 11 655 3000
Web Site: https://www.msd.co.za
Sales Range: $75-99.9 Million
Emp.: 300
Pharmaceuticals Mfr & Marketer
N.A.I.C.S.: 325412

MSD (Thailand) Ltd. (1)
999/9 The Offices at CentralWorld Floor
37th Unit OFMH 3707-3712, Rama I Road
Pathumwan Sub-district Pathumwan Dis-
trict, Bangkok, 10330, Thailand
Tel.: (66) 2 262 5700
Web Site: https://www.msd-thailand.com
Sales Range: $75-99.9 Million
Emp.: 300
Pharmaceuticals Marketing & Sales
N.A.I.C.S.: 424210

MSD Animal Health (Phils.), Inc. (1)
28th Floor Philamlife Tower Paseo de
Roxas, Makati, 8767, Philippines
Tel.: (63) 27844800
Web Site: https://www.msd-animal-health.ph
Animal Health Products Mfr
N.A.I.C.S.: 325412

**MSD Animal Health (Shanghai) Trad-
ing Co., Ltd.** (1)
Building A Headquarters Park Phase 2
1582 Gumei Road, Xuhui District, Shang-
hai, 200233, China
Tel.: (86) 2122118888
Web Site: http://www.msd-animal-
health.com.cn
Veterinary Drug Product Distr
N.A.I.C.S.: 424210

MSD Animal Health A/S (1)
Havneholmen 25, 1561, Copenhagen, Den-
mark
Tel.: (45) 4 482 4200
Web Site: https://www.msd-animal-health.dk
Vaccines Merchant Whslr
N.A.I.C.S.: 424210

MSD Animal Health BVBA (1)
Lynx Binnenhof 5, 1200, Brussels, Belgium
Tel.: (32) 2 370 9401
Web Site: https://www.nl.msd-animal-
health.be
Veterinary Drug Product Distr
N.A.I.C.S.: 424210

**MSD Animal Health Danube Biotech
GmbH** (1)
Brennaustrasse 1, 3500, Krems an der
Donau, Austria
Tel.: (43) 720205116002
Pharmaceutical Drugs & Medicines Mfr
N.A.I.C.S.: 325412

MSD Animal Health FZ-LLC (1)
Alpha Building Suite 01 Ground Floor Dubai
Internet City, PO Box 502947, Dubai,
United Arab Emirates
Tel.: (971) 4 446 8001
Web Site: https://www.msd-animal-health-
me.com
Emp.: 30
Veterinary Drug Distr
N.A.I.C.S.: 424210
Jaime Feced (Mng Dir)

MSD Animal Health GmbH (1)
Weystrasse 20, 6006, Lucerne, Switzerland
Tel.: (41) 586181414
Web Site: http://www.msd-animal-health.ch
Emp.: 28
Veterinary Drug Product Mfr
N.A.I.C.S.: 325412

**MSD Animal Health Innovation
AS** (1)
Thormohlensgate 55, 5006, Bergen, Horda-
land, Norway
Tel.: (47) 55543735
Web Site: http://www.msd-animal-health.no
Emp.: 35
Veterinary Drug Mfr
N.A.I.C.S.: 325412

MSD Animal Health K.K. (1)
Kitanomaru Square 1-13-12, Kudankita
Chiyoda-ku, Tokyo, 102-8667, Japan
Tel.: (81) 36 272 1099
Web Site: https://www.msd-animal-health.jp
Animal Health Care Services
N.A.I.C.S.: 541940

MSD Animal Health Korea Ltd. (1)
Hannam-dong Yongsan-way 13 to 20 Han-
nam Building 4th Floor, 140-886, Seoul,
Korea (South)
Tel.: (82) 27697500
Web Site: http://www.msd-animal-
health.co.kr

Merck & Co., Inc.—(Continued)

Veterinary Drug Product Mfr
N.A.I.C.S.: 325412

MSD Animal Health Limited (1)
Walton Manor, Walton, Milton Keynes, MK7
7AJ, Buckinghamshire, United Kingdom
Tel.: (44) 3700603380
Web Site: https://www.msd-animal-
health.co.uk
Veterinary Drug Product Mfr
N.A.I.C.S.: 325412

MSD Animal Health Norge AS (1)
Thormohlensgate 55, 5006, Bergen, Nor-
way
Tel.: (47) 5 554 3735
Web Site: https://www.msd-animal-health.no
Animal Health Production Services
N.A.I.C.S.: 115210
Eric Flanagan (Gen Mgr)

MSD Animal Health S.r.l. (1)
Strada di Olgia Vecchia snc Centro Direzi-
onale, Milano Due Palazzo Canova, 20054,
Segrate, MI, Italy
Tel.: (39) 0251 6861
Web Site: https://www.msd-animal-health.it
Veterinary Drug Product Mfr
N.A.I.C.S.: 325412

MSD Animal Health Vietnam Co.
Ltd. (1)
16th Floor MPlaza SaiGon 39 Le Duan
Street, District 1, Ho Chi Minh City, Vietnam
Tel.: (84) 2839155800
Vaccines Merchant Whslr
N.A.I.C.S.: 424210

MSD Animal Health, Lda. (1)
Quinta da Fonte Edificio Vasco da Gama
19, 2770-192, Paco d'Arcos, Portugal
Tel.: (351) 214465700
Web Site: http://www.msd-animal-health.pt
Veterinary Drug Product Mfr
N.A.I.C.S.: 325412

MSD Argentina SRL (1)
Complejo Urbana Cazadores de Coquimbo
2841 Piso 4, Vicente Lopez, 1605, Munro,
Argentina
Tel.: (54) 116 090 7200
Web Site: https://www.msd-salud-
animal.com.ar
Veterinary Drug Product Mfr
N.A.I.C.S.: 325412

MSD Australia (1)
Building 8 Level 1 26 Talavera Road, Mac-
quarie, 2113, NSW, Australia
Tel.: (61) 2 8988 8000
Web Site: http://www.merck.com
Sales Range: $50-74.9 Million
Emp.: 200
Pharmaceutical Products Mfr & Marketer
N.A.I.C.S.: 325412

Plant (Domestic):

MSD Australia - Manufacturing
Division (2)
54-68 Ferndell Street, Sydney, 2142, NSW,
Australia
Tel.: (61) 2 9795 9500
Web Site: http://www.msd-australia.com.au
Pharmaceuticals Mfr
N.A.I.C.S.: 325412

MSD BV Haarlem (1)
Waarderweg 39, 2031 BN, Haarlem, Neth-
erlands
Tel.: (31) 235153153
Web Site: http://www.msd.nl
Pharmaceuticals Product Mfr
N.A.I.C.S.: 325412

MSD Belgium BVBA/SPRL (1)
Clos du Lynx Binnenhof 5, 1200, Brussels,
Belgium
Tel.: (32) 27766211
Web Site: https://www.msd-belgium.be
Emp.: 1,400
Pharmaceuticals Product Mfr
N.A.I.C.S.: 325412
Brecht Vanneste (Mng Dir)

MSD Chibropharm GmbH (1)
Lindenplatz 1, Haar, 85540, Germany
Tel.: (49) 8945610
Web Site: http://www.msd.de

Pharmaceuticals Product Mfr
N.A.I.C.S.: 325412

MSD Danmark ApS (1)
Havneholmen 25 2, 1561, Copenhagen,
Denmark
Tel.: (45) 4 482 4000
Web Site: https://www.msd.dk
Emp.: 200
Pharmaceuticals Mfr
N.A.I.C.S.: 325412
Sanat Chattopadhyay (Pres/Exec VP-MSD
Mfr Div)

MSD Finland Oy (1)
Keilaranta 3, 02150, Espoo,
Finland (100%)
Tel.: (358) 9804650
Web Site: https://www.msd.fi
Sales Range: $75-99.9 Million
Emp.: 130
Pharmaceuticals Distr
N.A.I.C.S.: 424210

MSD France S.A.S. (1)
10-12 Cours Michelet, 92800, Puteaux,
France
Tel.: (33) 18 046 4000
Web Site: https://www.msd-france.com
Sales Range: $50-74.9 Million
Emp.: 200
Pharmaceuticals Product Mfr
N.A.I.C.S.: 325412

MSD Greece (1)
Agiou Dimitriou 63 Alimos, 174 55, Athens,
Greece
Tel.: (30) 2109897300
Web Site: http://www.msd.gr
Sales Range: $25-49.9 Million
Emp.: 200
Pharmaceutical Marketing & Sales
N.A.I.C.S.: 424210

MSD Human Health Holding B.V. (1)
Molenstraat 110, Oss, 5342 CC, Nether-
lands
Tel.: (31) 412661222
Web Site: http://www.msd.nl
Emp.: 3
Holding Company
N.A.I.C.S.: 551112

MSD IT Global Innovation Center
s.r.o. (1)
Svornosti 3321/2, 150 00, Prague, 150 00,
Czech Republic
Tel.: (420) 277026000
Web Site: https://www.msd.cz
Vaccines Merchant Whslr
N.A.I.C.S.: 424210
Klara Curdova (Program Mgr)

MSD International Holdings
GmbH (1)
Weystrasse 20, Lucerne, 6006, Switzerland
Tel.: (41) 414181616
Web Site: http://www.msd.ch
Holding Company
N.A.I.C.S.: 551112

MSD Italia s.r.l. (1)
Via Vitorchiano 151, Rome, 00189, Italy
Tel.: (39) 06361911
Web Site: http://www.msd-italia.it
Dermatological Product Mfr
N.A.I.C.S.: 325412

MSD K.K. (1)
Kitanomaru Square 1-13-12, Kudankita
Chiyoda-ku, Tokyo, 102-8667,
Japan (100%)
Tel.: (81) 362720088
Web Site: http://www.msd.co.jp
Sales Range: $1-4.9 Billion
Emp.: 4,400
Pharmaceuticals Research & Development,
Manufacturing, Sales & Marketing
N.A.I.C.S.: 325412
Tony Alvarez (Pres)

MSD Korea Ltd. (1)
SK Life Insurance Building 168, Gongduk-
dong Mapo-ku, Seoul, Korea (South)
Tel.: (82) 2 331 2000
Web Site: http://www.msd-korea.com
Pharmaceuticals Marketing & Sales
N.A.I.C.S.: 424210

MSD Magyarorszag Kereskedelmi es
Szolgaltato Korlatolt Felelossegu

Tarsasag (1)
Lechner Odon fasor 8, Budapest, 1095,
Hungary
Tel.: (36) 18885300
Animal Health Production Services
N.A.I.C.S.: 115210

MSD Merck Sharp & Dohme AG (1)
Werftestrasse 4, 6005, Lucerne, Switzer-
land
Tel.: (41) 586183030
Web Site: https://www.msd.ch
Pharmaceuticals Product Mfr
N.A.I.C.S.: 325412

MSD Panama (1)
Avenida Paseo del Mar Torre MMG piso 15,
Costa del Este, Panama, 63798, Panama
Tel.: (507) 2827200
Sales Range: $10-24.9 Million
Emp.: 50
Pharmaceuticals Marketing & Sales
N.A.I.C.S.: 424210

MSD Pharma (Singapore) Pte.
Ltd. (1)
150 Beach Road 31-00 Gateway West, Sin-
gapore, 189720, Singapore
Tel.: (65) 6 508 8400
Web Site: https://www.msd-singapore.com
Ambulatory Health Care Services
N.A.I.C.S.: 621493

MSD Pharma Hungary Korlatolt Felel-
ossegu Tarsasag (1)
Lechner Odon fasor 8, 1095, Budapest,
Hungary
Tel.: (36) 1 888 5300
Web Site: https://www.msd.hu
Pharmaceuticals Product Mfr
N.A.I.C.S.: 325412

MSD Pharmaceuticals LLC (1)
St Timur Frunze 11 building 1, BC Demidov,
Moscow, Russia
Tel.: (7) 4959167100
Web Site: http://www.msd.ru
Sales Range: $150-199.9 Million
Emp.: 400
Pharmaceuticals Marketing & Sales
N.A.I.C.S.: 424210

MSD Pharmaceuticals Private
Limited (1)
Platina 8th Floor C 59 G Block Bandra
Kurla Complex Bandra East, Mumbai, 400
098, India
Tel.: (91) 2267898888
Web Site: http://www.msdindia.in
Emp.: 600
Pharmaceuticals Research & Development
N.A.I.C.S.: 541715
Neelima Dwivedi (Sr Dir-Pub Policy, Corp
Comm & Market Access)
Tanzeem Siddiqui (Dir-Comml Ops & Pub
Markets)
Alok Kumar Sengupta (Dir)

Unit (Domestic):

MSD Pharmaceuticals (2)
6th Floor Tower B Vatika Towers, Section
54, Gurgaon, 122 002, India
Tel.: (91) 1244647300
Web Site: http://www.msdindia.in
Rev.: $200,000,000
Emp.: 165
Pharmaceutical Mfr, Marketer & Whslr
N.A.I.C.S.: 325412

MSD Philippines (1)
26/F Philamlife Tower, 8767 Paseo de
Roxas, Makati, Philippines
Tel.: (63) 28850700
Web Site: http://www.msd.com.ph
Pharmaceuticals Marketing & Sales
N.A.I.C.S.: 424210

MSD Polska Dystrybucja Sp.
Z.o.o. (1)
Ul Chlodna 51, 00-867, Warsaw, Poland
Tel.: (48) 228908050
Marketing Research Service
N.A.I.C.S.: 541910

MSD Polska Sp. z o.o. (1)
ul Chlodna 51, 00-867, Warsaw, Poland
Tel.: (48) 22 549 5100
Web Site: https://www.msd.pl

Clinical Research, Marketing & Sales of
Pharmaceuticals
N.A.I.C.S.: 424210
Lukasz Zybaczynski (CEO)

MSD Sharp & Dohme Gesellschaft
mit beschrankter Haftung (1)
Lindenplatz 1, 85540, Haar, Germany
Tel.: (49) 8945610
Web Site: http://www.msd.de
Emp.: 2,500
Pharmaceuticals Product Mfr
N.A.I.C.S.: 325412
Chantal Friebertshauser (Mng Dir)
Gertraud Polz-Heyrman (Mng Dir)

MSD Sharp & Dohme GmbH (1)
Lindenplatz 1, 85540, Haar, Germany
Tel.: (49) 89 45 61 0
Web Site: http://www.msd.de
Sales Range: $400-449.9 Million
Emp.: 1,600
Pharmaceuticals Mfr & Marketer
N.A.I.C.S.: 325412

MSD Swords (1)
2 Dublin Landings North Wall Quay - North
Dock, PO Box 2857, Dublin, D01 V4A3,
Ireland
Tel.: (353) 15828250
Sales Range: $250-299.9 Million
Emp.: 540
Pharmaceutical Developer & Mfr
N.A.I.C.S.: 325412

MSD Ukraine Limited Liability
Company (1)
3rd Floor Horizon Business Park 12
Amosova Street, Kiev, 03680, Ukraine
Tel.: (380) 44 393 7480
Web Site: https://www.msd.ua
Pharmaceuticals Product Mfr
N.A.I.C.S.: 325412

MSD Vaccins (1)
162 Avenue Jean Jaures CS 50712, Lyon,
69367 Cedex 07, France
Tel.: (33) 437284000
Vaccines Merchant Whslr
N.A.I.C.S.: 424210
Marion Vincent (Dir-Comm)

MSD Verwaltungs GmbH (1)
Lindenplatz 1, Haar, 85540, Bayern, Ger-
many
Tel.: (49) 8962731526
Web Site: http://www.msd.de
Emp.: 40
Pharmaceuticals Product Mfr
N.A.I.C.S.: 325412

MSD-SP Ltd. (1)
Hertford Road, Hoddesdon, EN11 9BU,
Hertfordshire, United Kingdom
Tel.: (44) 1992467272
Web Site: http://www.msd-uk.com
Emp.: 70
Pharmaceuticals Product Mfr
N.A.I.C.S.: 325412

Mavec Corporation (1)
Horizonte II, Lima, 15112, Peru
Tel.: (51) 980649609
Health Care Srvices
N.A.I.C.S.: 621610

Merck & Co. Inc. (1)
126 E Lincoln Ave, Rahway, NJ 07065
Tel.: (908) 740-4000
Sales Range: $10-24.9 Million
Emp.: 20
Policy & Government Relations
N.A.I.C.S.: 541820

Merck & Co. Inc. (1)
33 Ave Louis Pasteur, Boston, MA
02115 (100%)
Tel.: (617) 992-2000
Web Site: http://www.merck.com
Sales Range: $25-49.9 Million
Emp.: 450
Pharmaceuticals Distr
N.A.I.C.S.: 424210

Merck & Co. Inc. (1)
4633 Merck Rd W, Wilson, NC 27893
Tel.: (252) 243-3261
Web Site: http://www.merck.com
Sales Range: $250-299.9 Million
Emp.: 600
Mfr of Pharmaceutical Preparations

N.A.I.C.S.: 325412
Cristal N. Downing (Chief Comm & Pub Affairs Officer)

Merck & Co. Inc. (1)
200 Mansell Ct E Ste 200, Roswell, GA
30076 (100%)
Tel.: (770) 643-4600
Web Site: http://www.merck.com
Sales Range: $10-24.9 Million
Emp.: 35
Pharmaceutical Products
N.A.I.C.S.: 325412

Merck & Co. Inc. (1)
2778 SE Side Hwy, Elkton, VA 22827
Tel.: (540) 298-1211
Web Site: http://www.merck.com
Sales Range: $350-399.9 Million
Emp.: 766
Industrial Inorganic Chemical Mfr
N.A.I.C.S.: 325180

**Merck & Co., Inc. - Manufacturing
Division** (1)
126 E Lincoln Ave, Rahway, NJ 07065
Tel.: (732) 594-5301
Web Site: http://www.merck.com
Sales Range: $25-49.9 Billion
Emp.: 90,000
Pharmaceuticals Mfr
N.A.I.C.S.: 325412
Sanat Chattopadhyay (Pres)
Cristal N. Downing (Exec VP)
Michael A. Klobuchar (Chief Strategy Officer)

Merck & Co., Inc. - Springfield (1)
50 Lawrence Rd, Springfield, NJ 07081
Tel.: (973) 921-7100
Emp.: 400
Pharmaceuticals Product Mfr
N.A.I.C.S.: 325412

**Merck & Co., Inc. - Vaccine
Division** (1)
770 Sumneytown Pike, West Point, PA
19486
Tel.: (215) 652-5000
Web Site: http://www.merck.com
Vaccines Mfr
N.A.I.C.S.: 325412

Merck Canada (1)
16750 Trans Canada Hwy, Kirkland, H9H
4M7, QC, Canada (100%)
Tel.: (514) 428-7920
Web Site: http://www.merck.ca
Sales Range: $200-249.9 Million
Emp.: 500
Pharmaceuticals Product Mfr
N.A.I.C.S.: 325412

Merck Canada Inc. (1)
16750 Trans-Canada Highway, Kirkland,
H9H 4M7, QC, Canada
Tel.: (514) 428-7920
Web Site: https://www.merck.ca
Health Care Srvices
N.A.I.C.S.: 621610

Merck Healthcare Products (1)
4207 Michigan Ave, Cleveland, TN 37311
Tel.: (423) 476-2201
Sales Range: $150-199.9 Million
Emp.: 400
Consumer Healthcare Products Distr
N.A.I.C.S.: 339999
Jeff Allar (Gen Mgr)

**Merck Lumira Biosciences Fund
L.P.** (1)
141 Adelaide Street West Suite 770, Toronto, M5H 3L5, ON, Canada
Tel.: (416) 213-4223
Capital Market Investment Services
N.A.I.C.S.: 523940

Merck Research Laboratories (1)
1 Merck Dr, Whitehouse Station, NJ 08889
Tel.: (215) 652-5000
Web Site: http://www.merck.com
Sales Range: $75-99.9 Million
Emp.: 4,000
Medical Research Services
N.A.I.C.S.: 541715
Roy D. Baynes (Sr VP & Head-Clinical Dev-Global)

Branch (Domestic):

**Merck & Co. Research &
Development** (2)

975 California Ave, Palo Alto, CA
94304-1104 (100%)
Tel.: (650) 493-0124
Web Site: http://www.merck.com
Rev.: $35,036,000
Emp.: 110
Pharmaceutical Research & Development;
Biologics Medicines
N.A.I.C.S.: 541714

**Merck & Co. Research &
Development** (2)
90 E Scott Ave, Rahway, NJ
07065-0900 (100%)
Tel.: (732) 594-4000
Web Site: http://www.merck.com
Pharmaceuticals Research & Development
N.A.I.C.S.: 325412

Unit (Domestic):

**Merck Biologics Research
Center** (2)
2000 Galloping Hill Rd, Kenilworth, NJ
07033-1310 (100%)
Tel.: (908) 298-4000
Sales Range: $75-99.9 Million
Emp.: 350
Pharmaceutical Research & Development
Services
N.A.I.C.S.: 541715

**Merck Sharp & Dohme (Argentina)
Inc.**
Cazadores de Coquimbo 2841/57 Piso 4
Munro, Vicente Lopez, B1638BGN, Buenos
Aires, Argentina
Tel.: (54) 1160907200
Web Site:
http://www.corporativo.msd.com.ar
Pharmaceuticals Mfr
N.A.I.C.S.: 325412

**Merck Sharp & Dohme (Australia)
Pty. Limited** (1)
Level 1 26 Talavera Road, Macquarie Park,
2113, NSW, Australia
Tel.: (61) 289888000
Web Site: https://www.msd-australia.com.au
Health Care Srvices
N.A.I.C.S.: 621610

**Merck Sharp & Dohme (Chile)
Ltda.** (1)
Avenida Mariano Sanchez Fontecilla 310
Piso 5, Las Condes, 6761641, Santiago,
Chile
Tel.: (56) 22 655 8800
Web Site:
https://www.corporativo.msdchile.cl
Pharmaceutical Products Distr
N.A.I.C.S.: 456110

**Merck Sharp & Dohme (China)
Ltd.** (1)
1582 Headquarters Park II Building A Chinese Cuban-American Road, Xuhui District,
Shanghai, 200233, China
Tel.: (86) 21 2211 8888
Web Site: http://www.msdchina.com.cn
Sales Range: $1-4.9 Billion
Emp.: 4,500
Pharmaceuticals Mfr & Marketer
N.A.I.C.S.: 325412

**Merck Sharp & Dohme (Europe)
Inc.** (1)
Clos du Lynx Binnenhof 5, 1200, Brussels,
Belgium
Tel.: (32) 27766211
Web Site: http://www.msd-belgium.be
Emp.: 500
N.A.I.C.S.: 518210

**Merck Sharp & Dohme (Holdings)
Limited** (1)
120 Moorgate, London, EC2M 6UR, Hertfordshire, United Kingdom
Tel.: (44) 2081548000
Web Site: https://www.msd-uk.com
Sales Range: $200-249.9 Million
Emp.: 1,387
Pharmaceuticals Product Mfr
N.A.I.C.S.: 325412

**Merck Sharp & Dohme (Holdings) Pty
Ltd** (1)
Level 1 26 Talavera Road, Macquarie Park,
2113, NSW, Australia

Tel.: (61) 28 988 8000
Web Site: https://www.msd-australia.com.au
Holding Company
N.A.I.C.S.: 551112

Subsidiary (Domestic):

Viralytics Limited (2)
305/66 Hunter Street, Sydney, 2000, NSW,
Australia
Tel.: (61) 299884000
Anti Cancer Biotechnology Services
N.A.I.C.S.: 541714

**Merck Sharp & Dohme (I.A.)
Corp.** (1)
1 Merck Dr, Whitehouse Station, NJ 08889-
3400
Tel.: (908) 423-1000
Sales Range: $50-74.9 Million
Emp.: 10
Pharmaceuticals Marketing & Sales
N.A.I.C.S.: 424210

Subsidiary (Domestic):

ArQule, Inc. (2)
1 Wall St, Burlington, MA 01803
Tel.: (781) 994-0300
Web Site: http://www.arqule.com
Rev.: $25,764,000
Assets: $106,676,000
Liabilities: $27,708,000
Net Worth: $78,968,000
Earnings: ($15,482,000)
Emp.: 36
Fiscal Year-end: 12/31/2018
Clinical Stage Biotechnology Services
N.A.I.C.S.: 325412
Remi Barbier (Founder)
Patrick J. Zenner (Chm & Dir)

Inspire Pharmaceuticals, Inc. (2)
8081 Arco Corporate Dr Ste 400, Raleigh,
NC 27617
Tel.: (919) 941-9777
Sales Range: $100-124.9 Million
Emp.: 240
Drugs for the Treatment of Respiratory &
Ocular Diseases Developer & Researcher
N.A.I.C.S.: 325412
Terrance McGuire (Co-Founder)
Terrance G. McGuire (Co-Founder)
Reza Haque (VP-Clinical Ophthalmology &
Medical Affairs)

Representative Office (Non-US):

**Merck Sharp & Dohme (I.A.)
Corp.** (2)
Mariano Sanchez Fontecilla 310 Floor 8
Las Condes, Las Condes, Santiago,
7550296, Chile
Tel.: (56) 26558800
Web Site: http://www.msdchile.cl
Sales Range: $50-74.9 Million
Pharmaceuticals Distribution, Marketing,
Sales & Clinical Research
N.A.I.C.S.: 424210

**Merck Sharp & Dohme (I.A.)
Corp.** (2)
T2-9 Jaya 33 No 3 Jalan Semangat
Seksyen 13, 46200, Petaling Jaya, Selangor Darul Ehsan, Malaysia
Tel.: (60) 3 7718 1600
Web Site: http://www.msd-malaysia.com
Sales Range: $75-99.9 Million
Pharmaceutical Marketing & Sales
N.A.I.C.S.: 424210

**Merck Sharp & Dohme (I.A.)
Corp.** (2)
150 Beach Road #31-00 Gateway West,
Singapore, 189720, Singapore
Tel.: (65) 65088400
Web Site: http://www.msd-singapore-ia.com
Sales Range: $25-49.9 Million
Pharmaceuticals Marketing & Sales
N.A.I.C.S.: 424210

Branch (Domestic):

**Merck Sharp & Dohme (I.A.)
Corp.** (2)
Puerto Rico Industrial Park 370, Carolina,
PR 00987
Tel.: (787) 474-8200
Web Site: http://www.msd.com.pr

Sales Range: $25-49.9 Million
Marketing & Sales for Merck Products
N.A.I.C.S.: 424210

Subsidiary (Domestic):

**Merck Sharp & Dohme Quimica de
Puerto Rico, Inc.** (3)
State Rd No 183 Pridco Industrial Zone
KM-2.6, Las Piedras, PR 00771
Tel.: (787) 623-7777
Web Site: http://www.msd.com.pr
Pharmaceuticals Mfr
N.A.I.C.S.: 325412

**Merck Sharp & Dohme (I.A.)
LLC** (1)
126 E Lincoln Ave, Rahway, NJ 07065
Tel.: (908) 740-4000
Web Site: https://www.msd.com
Emp.: 72,000
Pharmaceuticals Product Mfr
N.A.I.C.S.: 325412

**Merck Sharp & Dohme (Ireland)
Ltd.** (1)
Ballydine, Kilsheelan, Clonmel, Co Tipperary, Ireland
Tel.: (353) 51601000
Web Site: http://www.msd-ireland.com
Sales Range: $150-199.9 Million
Emp.: 480
Pharmaceuticals Mfr
N.A.I.C.S.: 325412

**Merck Sharp & Dohme (Italia)
S.p.A.** (1)
Vitorchiano 151, 00191, Rome, Italy
Tel.: (39) 06361911
Web Site: http://www.msd-italia.it
Pharmaceuticals Mfr & Marketer
N.A.I.C.S.: 325412

**Merck Sharp & Dohme (Malaysia)
SDN. BHD.** (1)
B-22-1 B-22-2 The Ascent Paradigm No 1
Jalan SS 7/26A, Kelana Jaya, 47301, Petaling Jaya, Selangor Darul Ehsan, Malaysia
Tel.: (60) 37 499 1600
Web Site: https://www.msd-malaysia.com
Emp.: 300
Pharmaceutical Products Distr
N.A.I.C.S.: 456110
Ashish Pal (Mng Dir)

Merck Sharp & Dohme (New Zealand) Limited (1)
Level 3 123 Carlton Gore Road, Newmarket, Auckland, 1023, New Zealand
Tel.: (64) 9 523 6000
Web Site: https://www.msd-newzealand.com
Sales Range: $50-74.9 Million
Emp.: 50
Pharmaceuticals Clinical Research, Marketing & Sales
N.A.I.C.S.: 424210

**Merck Sharp & Dohme (Sweden)
AB** (1)
Gavlegatan 22, 113 30, Stockholm, Sweden
Tel.: (46) 85 781 3500
Web Site: https://www.msd.se
Sales Range: $25-49.9 Million
Emp.: 250
Pharmaceutical Products Marketer; Clinical
Trials
N.A.I.C.S.: 424210
Marc Gailhardou (Mng Dir)

**Merck Sharp & Dohme Animal
Health, S.L.** (1)
C/ Josefa Valcarcel 38, 28027, Madrid,
Spain
Tel.: (34) 923190345
Web Site: http://www.msd-animal-health.es
Veterinary Drug Product Distr
N.A.I.C.S.: 424210

**Merck Sharp & Dohme Asia Pacific
Services Pte. Ltd.** (1)
21 Tuas South Avenue 6, Singapore,
637766, Singapore
Tel.: (65) 63472084
Web Site: http://www.msd-singapore.com
Pharmaceuticals Product Mfr
N.A.I.C.S.: 325412

Merck Sharp & Dohme BV (1)
Waarderweg 39, 2031 BN, Haarlem, Netherlands

Merck & Co., Inc.—(Continued)

Tel.: (31) 23 515 3153
Web Site: http://www.msd.nl
Emp.: 2,000
Pharmaceutical Research & Marketing
N.A.I.C.S.: 551112

Unit (Domestic):

MSD Oss (2)
Molenstraat 110, 5342 CC, Oss, Netherlands
Tel.: (31) 880140888
Web Site: http://www.msd.nl
Sales Range: $100-124.9 Million
Emp.: 486
Pharmaceuticals Research & Development
N.A.I.C.S.: 541715

Merck Sharp & Dohme BV (1)
Lynx Binnenhof 5, Woluwe-Saint-Lambert, 1200, Brussels, Belgium
Tel.: (32) 23734211
Web Site: http://www.msd-belgium.be
Medical Research, Marketing & Sale of Pharmaceuticals
N.A.I.C.S.: 424210

Merck Sharp & Dohme Colombia S.A.S. (1)
Calle 127A No 53A - 45 Torre 3 Piso 8
Complejo empresarial Colpatria, Bogota, Colombia
Tel.: (57) 15924400
Web Site:
http://www.corporativo.msd.com.co
Pharmaceutical Products Distr
N.A.I.C.S.: 456110

Merck Sharp & Dohme Cyprus Limited (1)
Riverside Forum 2A Chilonos Street, 1101, Nicosia, Cyprus
Tel.: (357) 22866700
Web Site: https://www.msd-cyprus.com.cy
Pharmaceutical Drugs & Medicines Mfr
N.A.I.C.S.: 325412

Merck Sharp & Dohme Farmaceutica Ltda (1)
Rua Alexandre Dumas 2510, PO Box 3734, Chacara Santo Antonio, Sao Paulo, 04717-004, Brazil
Tel.: (55) 1151897700
Web Site: http://www.msdonline.com.br
Sales Range: $250-299.9 Million
Emp.: 750
Pharmaceuticals Research & Development, Mfr & Marketer
N.A.I.C.S.: 325412

Plant (Domestic):

MSD Brazil (2)
Av Doutor Chucri Zaidan 246 96 Vila Cordeiro, Sao Paulo, Brazil
Tel.: (55) 1151897700
Web Site: http://www.msd.com
Sales Range: $200-249.9 Million
Pharmaceutical Developer & Mfr
N.A.I.C.S.: 325412

Merck Sharp & Dohme Gesellschaft m.b.H. (1)
The Icon Vienna Wiedner Gurtel 9-13, 1100, Vienna, Austria
Tel.: (43) 126 0440
Web Site: https://www.msd.at
Emp.: 800
Pharmaceuticals Product Mfr
N.A.I.C.S.: 325412

Merck Sharp & Dohme Ilaclari Limited Sirketi (1)
Mah Buyukdere Cad No 199 Levent 199 Ofis Blogu Kat 13, Levent, 34394, Istanbul, Turkiye
Tel.: (90) 2123361000
Web Site: https://www.msd.com.tr
Emp.: 200
Pharmaceuticals Marketing & Sales
N.A.I.C.S.: 424210

Merck Sharp & Dohme Ireland (Human Health) Ltd (1)
South County Business Park, Leopardstown, Dublin, Ireland
Tel.: (353) 1 299 8700
Web Site: http://www.msd-ireland.com

Sales Range: $50-74.9 Million
Emp.: 123
Sales, Marketing & Clinical Research of Pharmaceutical Products
N.A.I.C.S.: 424210

Merck Sharp & Dohme Latvija (1)
Skanstes Iela 50A, Riga, 1013, Latvia
Tel.: (371) 67025300
Web Site: https://www.msd.lv
Pharmaceutical Drugs & Medicines Mfr
N.A.I.C.S.: 325412

Merck Sharp & Dohme Limited (1)
120 Moorgate, London, EC2M 6UR, Hertfordshire, United Kingdom
Tel.: (44) 2081548000
Web Site: https://www.msd-uk.com
Emp.: 1,400
Pharmaceutical Research & Development
N.A.I.C.S.: 541715

Merck Sharp & Dohme OU (1)
A H Tammsaare Tee 47, Tallinn, 11316, Estonia
Tel.: (372) 614 4200
Web Site: https://www.msd.ee
Pharmaceuticals Product Mfr
N.A.I.C.S.: 325412

Merck Sharp & Dohme Peru SRL (1)
Ave Circunvalacion del Club Golf Los Incas 134 Tower 2 Office 1901, Urbanization Club Golf Los Incas, Lima, 15023, Peru
Tel.: (51) 14115100
Web Site: http://www.msd.com.pe
Sales Range: $50-74.9 Million
Emp.: 160
Pharmaceuticals Distribution, Marketing, Sales & Clinical Research
N.A.I.C.S.: 424210

Merck Sharp & Dohme Research GmbH (1)
Tribschenstrasse 60, 6005, Lucerne, Switzerland
Tel.: (41) 586181616
Pharmaceutical Products Distr
N.A.I.C.S.: 456110

Merck Sharp & Dohme Romania SRL (1)
Soseaua Bucuresti - Ploiesti Nr 1 A Bucuresti Business Park, Cladirea C Etaj 3 Sector 1, Bucharest, 13681, Romania
Tel.: (40) 215292900
Web Site: http://www.msd.ro
Pharmaceuticals Product Mfr
N.A.I.C.S.: 325412
Kostas Papagiannis (Gen Mgr)

Merck Sharp & Dohme S. de R.L. de C.V. (1)
Av San Jeronimo No 369 piso 7, Col La Otra Banda, 01090, Mexico, Mexico
Tel.: (52) 54819600
Web Site:
https://www.corporativo.msd.com.mx
Pharmaceutical Drugs & Medicines Mfr
N.A.I.C.S.: 325412

Merck Sharp & Dohme Saude Animal Ltda. (1)
Avenida Doutor Chucri Zaidan 296 12 Andar, Sao Paulo, 04583-110, Brazil
Tel.: (55) 8007070512
Web Site: https://www.msd-saude-animal.com.br
Pharmaceutical Drugs & Medicines Mfr
N.A.I.C.S.: 325412

Merck Sharp & Dohme d.o.o. (1)
Ivana Lucica 2a, 10000, Zagreb, Croatia
Tel.: (385) 16611333
Web Site: https://www.msd.hr
Pharmaceutical Drugs & Medicines Mfr
N.A.I.C.S.: 325412

Merck Sharp & Dohme d.o.o. (1)
Ivana Lucica 2a, 10000, Zagreb, Croatia
Tel.: (385) 1 661 1333
Web Site: https://www.msd.hr
Pharmaceutical Products Distr
N.A.I.C.S.: 456110

Merck Sharp & Dohme d.o.o. Belgrade (1)
Omladinskih Brigada 90a, 11070, Belgrade, Serbia

Tel.: (381) 112257200
Web Site: http://www.msd.rs
Pharmaceutical Products Distr
N.A.I.C.S.: 456110

Merck Sharp & Dohme de Espana SAU (1)
Poligono Industrial El Montalvo C/ Zeppelin 6 - Parcela 38, Carbajosa de La Sagrada, 37008, Salamanca, Spain
Tel.: (34) 923190345
Web Site: http://www.msd.es
Health Care Srvices
N.A.I.C.S.: 621610

Merck Sharp & Dohme de Espana, S.A. (1)
Josefa Valcarcel 38, 28027, Madrid, Spain (100%)
Tel.: (34) 913210600
Web Site: https://www.msd.es
Sales Range: $150-199.9 Million
Emp.: 1,300
Pharmaceuticals Mfr & Marketer
N.A.I.C.S.: 325412

Merck Sharp & Dohme de Mexico S.A. de C.V. (1)
Av San Jeronimo 369-Piso 8, Col Tizapan San Angel, 01090, Mexico, Mexico
Tel.: (52) 5554819600
Web Site: http://www.msd.com.mx
Pharmaceuticals Mfr, Marketer & Distr
N.A.I.C.S.: 325412

Plant (Domestic):

MSD Mexico (2)
Av San Jeronimo No 369 piso 7, Col La Otra Banda, 01090, Mexico, Mexico
Tel.: (52) 54819600
Web Site:
https://www.corporativo.msd.com.mx
Pharmaceuticals Product Mfr
N.A.I.C.S.: 325412

Plant (Non-US):

Merck Sharp & Dohme-Chibret - Mirabel (2)
Route de Marsat, Riom, 63963, Clermont-Ferrand, Cedex 9, France
Tel.: (33) 4 73 67 50 00
Web Site: http://www.msd-france.com
Sales Range: $250-299.9 Million
Emp.: 800
Pharmaceuticals Mfr
N.A.I.C.S.: 325412

Merck Sharp & Dohme de Venezuela SRL (1)
Avenida Principal De Los Cortijos De Lourdes-Centro, Empresarial Senderos - Piso 1 Los Cortijos De Lourdes, 1080, Caracas, Venezuela
Tel.: (58) 2 122 025500
Web Site: http://www.msd.com.ve
Sales Range: $50-74.9 Million
Emp.: 200
Pharmaceuticals Marketing & Sales
N.A.I.C.S.: 424210

Merck Sharp & Dohme inovativna zdravila d.o.o. (1)
Smartinska Cesta 140, 1000, Ljubljana, Slovenia
Tel.: (386) 15204201
Web Site: http://www.msd.si
Emp.: 50
Pharmaceuticals Product Mfr
N.A.I.C.S.: 325412
Pirr Paert (Mng Dir)

Merck Sharp & Dohme s.r.o. (1)
Na Valentine 3336/4, 150 00, Prague, Czech Republic
Tel.: (420) 277050000
Web Site: http://www.msd.cz
Emp.: 1,200
Animal Health Products Mfr
N.A.I.C.S.: 325412

Merck Sharp & Dohme, Limitada (1)
Quinta da Fonte Edificio Vasco da Gama 19, 2770-192, Paco d'Arcos, Portugal
Tel.: (351) 21 446 5700
Web Site: https://www.msd.pt
Emp.: 100
Medical Chemicals & Botanical Products Mfr

N.A.I.C.S.: 325411

Merck Sharp & Dohme, s.r.o. (1)
Apollo Business Center A3 Mlynske Nivy 43, 821 09, Bratislava, Slovakia
Tel.: (421) 258282010
Web Site: http://www.elobase.sk
Pharmaceutical Product Mfr & Distr
N.A.I.C.S.: 325412

Merck Sharp & Dohme-Chibret AG (1)
Schaffhauserstrasse 136, CH 8152, Opfikon, Switzerland
Tel.: (41) 44 828 71 11
Web Site: http://www.msd.ch
Sales Range: $50-74.9 Million
Emp.: 130
Pharmaceuticals Mfr & Marketer
N.A.I.C.S.: 325412

Merck Sharp Dohme Ilaclari Limited Sirketi (1)
Buyukdere Caddesi No 199 Levent 199 Office Blog Kat 13, Levent, 34394, Istanbul, Turkiye
Tel.: (90) 212 336 1000
Web Site: https://www.msd.com.tr
Emp.: 200
Pharmaceutical Products Distr
N.A.I.C.S.: 456110
Erdogan Betul (Dir-Clinical Res-Turkey, Middle East & Egypt)

Merko B.V. (1)
PO Box 424, 7570 AK, Oldenzaal, Netherlands
Tel.: (31) 164671414
Web Site: http://www.merkodalton.nl
Pet Supply Distr
N.A.I.C.S.: 459910

Merko NV (1)
Britselei 36, 2000, Antwerp, Belgium
Tel.: (32) 3 360 2670
Web Site: https://www.merko.be
Pet Supply Retail
N.A.I.C.S.: 459910

P.T. Merck Sharp & Dohme Indonesia (1)
Wisma BNI 46 27th Floor Jl Jend Sudirman Kav 1, Jakarta, 10220, Indonesia
Tel.: (62) 215 789 7000
Web Site: https://www.msd-indonesia.com
Sales Range: $100-124.9 Million
Emp.: 293
Pharmaceuticals Product Mfr
N.A.I.C.S.: 325412

Subsidiary (Domestic):

P.T. Merck Sharp & Dohme Indonesia (2)
27th Floor Wisma BNI 46 Jalan Jendral Sudirman Kav 1, Jakarta, 10220, Indonesia
Tel.: (62) 2157897000
Web Site: http://www.msd-indonesia.com
Pharmaceuticals Research & Marketing
N.A.I.C.S.: 325412

PT Merck Sharp Dohme Pharma Tbk (1)
Wisma BNI 46 27th floor Jl Jend Sudirman Kav 1, Jakarta, 10220, Indonesia
Tel.: (62) 2157897000
Web Site: http://www.msd-indonesia.com
Pharmaceuticals Product Mfr
N.A.I.C.S.: 325412

Pandion Therapeutics, Inc. (1)
134 Coolidge Ave, Watertown, MA 02472
Tel.: (617) 393-5925
Web Site: http://www.pandiontx.com
Biotechnology Research & Development Services
N.A.I.C.S.: 541714
Joanne Viney (Co-Founder, Pres & Chief Scientific Officer)
Gregg Beloff (CFO-Interim)
Edward Freedman (COO)
Vikas Goyal (Sr VP-Bus Dev)
John Sundy (Chief Medical Officer)
Eric Larson (VP-Fin)

Pharmavet Maroc S.A. (1)
Route 110 Km 10 300 Boulevard Chefchaouni, Casablanca, 20000, Morocco
Tel.: (212) 522341088
Web Site: http://www.pharmavetmaroc.com

Veterinary Drug Product Distr
N.A.I.C.S.: 424210

Physicians Interactive India Private Limited (1)
Unit 802 801-B and 801-A 8th Floor Liberty Tower Plot No K10, Kalwa Industrial Area Village Airoli, Navi Mumbai, 400 708, India
Tel.: (91) 2261509300
Software Development Services
N.A.I.C.S.: 541511

Polnet ID Spolka z ograniczona odpowiedzialnoscia (1)
ul Nekielska 11G, Psary Male, 62-300, Wrzesnia, Poland
Tel.: (48) 616280400
Web Site: https://www.polnet-kolczyki.pl
Pediatric Vaccine Mfr
N.A.I.C.S.: 325412

Prometheus Biosciences, Inc. (1)
3050 Science Park Rd, San Diego, CA 92121
Tel.: (858) 422-4300
Web Site:
  https://www.prometheusbiosciences.com
Rev.: $3,129,000
Assets: $267,801,000
Liabilities: $32,646,000
Net Worth: $235,155,000
Earnings: ($90,195,000)
Emp.: 72
Fiscal Year-end: 12/31/2021
Pharmaceuticals Product Mfr
N.A.I.C.S.: 325412
Allison Luo *(Chief Medical Officer)*
Timothy K. Andrews *(Gen Counsel & Sec)*
Laurens Kruidenier *(Chief Scientific Officer)*
Olivier Laurent *(CTO)*
Chris Doughty *(Chief Bus Officer)*
Noel Kurdi *(VP-IR & Comm)*
Evan McClure *(VP-Bus Ops)*
Vika Brough *(Sr VP-Fin)*
Nori Ebersole *(Chief People Officer)*

Subsidiary (Domestic):

Prometheus Laboratories, Inc. (2)
9410 Carrol Park Dr, San Diego, CA 92121-4203
Tel.: (858) 824-0895
Web Site: http://www.prometheuslabs.com
Emp.: 400
Pharmaceuticals Product Mfr
N.A.I.C.S.: 325412

Prondil S.A. (1)
Barros Arana 5402, Montevideo, Uruguay
Tel.: (598) 25133254
Vaccines Merchant Whslr
N.A.I.C.S.: 424210

Prondil Sociedad Anonina (1)
Barros Arana 5402, Montevideo, Uruguay
Tel.: (598) 25133254
Animal Health Product Mfr & Distr
N.A.I.C.S.: 325412

Rigontec GmbH (1)
Levelingstrasse 4a, 81673, Munich, Germany
Tel.: (49) 89200066411
Gene Therapy Preparation Mfr
N.A.I.C.S.: 325414
Christian Schetter *(CEO)*

S.C. Allflex Romania S.R.L. (1)
Calea Sagului 235, Timisoara, Romania
Tel.: (40) 75 404 7922
Web Site: http://www.allflex.ro
Industrial Machinery Mfr
N.A.I.C.S.: 333248

SCR Europe SRL (1)
Via Mattei 2 Loc-Gariga, 29027, Podenzano, PC, Italy
Tel.: (39) 05231867200
Industrial Machinery & Equipment Whslr
N.A.I.C.S.: 423830

Sanofi Pasteur MSD, SNC (1)
8 rue Jonas Salk, 69367, Lyon, France
Tel.: (33) 437284000
Web Site: http://www.sanofi.com
Vaccine Mfr & Distr; Joint Venture of Sanofi-Aventis (50%) & Merck & Co. Inc. (50%)
N.A.I.C.S.: 325414

Subsidiary (Non-US):

Sanofi Pasteur MSD (2)

Hemvarnsgatan 15, 171 54, Solna, Sweden
Tel.: (46) 856488860
Web Site: http://www.spmsd.se
Sales Range: $25-49.9 Million
Emp.: 21
Vaccine Mfr & Distr; Joint Venture of Sanofi-Aventis (50%) & Merck & Co. Inc. (50%)
N.A.I.C.S.: 325412

Sanofi Pasteur MSD AG (2)
Gulmmatt, Baar, 6340, Switzerland
Tel.: (41) 417615665
Sales Range: $25-49.9 Million
Emp.: 10
Mfr of Vaccines & Immunology Products; Joint Venture of Sanofi-Aventis (50%) & Merck & Co. Inc. (50%)
N.A.I.C.S.: 325414
Monthtny Andree *(Mgr)*

Sanofi Pasteur MSD GmbH (2)
Alexanderufer Str 3, 69181, Berlin, Germany
Tel.: (49) 62245940
Web Site: http://www.spmsd.de
Sales Range: $50-74.9 Million
Emp.: 200
Mfr of Vaccines & Immunology Products; Joint Venture of Sanofi-Aventis (50%) & Merck & Co. Inc. (50%)
N.A.I.C.S.: 325414

Sanofi Pasteur MSD GmbH (2)
Campus 21 Europaring F11/402, Brunn am Gebirge, A 2345, Vienna, Austria
Tel.: (43) 18667022200
Web Site: http://www.spmsd.at
Mfr of Vaccines & Immunology Products; Joint Venture of Sanofi-Aventis (50%) & Merck & Co. Inc. (50%)
N.A.I.C.S.: 325414

Sanofi Pasteur MSD N.V. (2)
Taurusavenue 31a, 2132 LS, Hoofddorp, Netherlands
Tel.: (31) 235679600
Mfr of Vaccines & Immunology Products; Joint Venture of Sanofi-Aventis (50%) & Merck & Co. Inc. (50%)
N.A.I.C.S.: 325414

Sanofi Pasteur MSD Oy (2)
Keilaranda 3, 00810, Espoo, Finland
Tel.: (358) 95658830
Web Site: http://www.spmsd.fi
Mfr of Vaccines & Immunology Products; Joint Venture of Sanofi-Aventis (50%) & Merck & Co. Inc. (50%)
N.A.I.C.S.: 325414

Sanofi Pasteur MSD SpA (2)
Via degli Aldobrandeschi 15, 00163, Rome, Italy
Tel.: (39) 0666409211
Mfr of Vaccines & Immunology Products; Joint Venture of Sanofi-Aventis (50%) & Merck & Co. Inc. (50%)
N.A.I.C.S.: 325414

Sanofi Pasteur MSD, SA (2)
Avenida el Partenon 4-6 2nd Floor, Paseo de la Castellana 141- 2, 28046, Madrid, Spain
Tel.: (34) 913717800
Web Site: http://www.spmsd.com
Sales Range: $50-74.9 Million
Emp.: 100
Mfr of Vaccines & Immunology Products; Joint Venture of Sanofi-Aventis (50%) & Merck & Co. Inc. (50%)
N.A.I.C.S.: 325414

Schering-Plough Canada Inc. (1)
3535 Trans-Canada Highway, Pointe-Claire, Montreal, 10220, QC, Canada
Tel.: (514) 426-7300
Pharmaceuticals Product Mfr
N.A.I.C.S.: 325412

Schering-Plough Sante Animale (1)
Allee De La Grindoliere, 49500, Segre, France
Tel.: (33) 241947220
Web Site: http://www.merck.com
Emp.: 100
Pharmaceuticals Product Mfr
N.A.I.C.S.: 325412

Stallmastaren AB (1)
Skaragatan 110, 531 40, Lidkoping, Sweden

Tel.: (46) 5 102 0445
Web Site: https://www.stallmastaren.se
Agricultural Services
N.A.I.C.S.: 115116

Themis Bioscience NV (1)
Muthgasse 11/2, 1190, Vienna, Austria
Tel.: (43) 12367151
Web Site: http://www.themisbio.com
Biotechnology Research & Development Services
N.A.I.C.S.: 541714
Erich Tauber *(Founder & CEO)*

UAB Merck Sharp & Dohme (1)
Kestucio g 59/27, LT-08124, Vilnius, Lithuania
Tel.: (370) 52780247
Web Site: https://www.msd.lt
Sales Range: $25-49.9 Million
Emp.: 6
Pharmaceuticals Product Mfr
N.A.I.C.S.: 325412

Venco Farmaceutica S.A. (1)
Crta Nacional Guarenas Guatire, Caracas, Distrito Federal, Venezuela
Tel.: (58) 2122125481
Emp.: 5
Pharmaceuticals Product Mfr
N.A.I.C.S.: 325412

Vet Pharma Friesoythe GmbH (1)
Sedelsberger Str 2, 26169, Friesoythe, Germany
Tel.: (49) 4 491 2940
Web Site: https://www.msd-tiergesundheit.de
Pharmaceuticals Product Mfr
N.A.I.C.S.: 325412

MERCURY GENERAL CORPORATION

555 W Imperial Hwy, Brea, CA 92821-4802
Tel.: (323) 937-1060   CA
Web Site:
  https://www.mercuryinsurance.com
Year Founded: 1961
MCY—(NYSE)
Rev.: $4,629,631,000
Assets: $7,103,397,000
Liabilities: $5,555,252,000
Net Worth: $1,548,145,000
Earnings: $96,336,000
Emp.: 4,100
Fiscal Year-end: 12/31/23
Direct Property & Casualty Insurance Carriers
N.A.I.C.S.: 524126
George Joseph *(Founder & Chm)*
Gabriel Tirador *(CEO)*
Judy A. Walters *(Sec & VP-Corp Affairs)*
Theodore R. Stalick *(CFO & Sr VP)*
Charles Toney *(Chief Actuary & VP)*
Victor G. Joseph *(Pres & COO)*
Randall R. Petro *(Chief Claims Officer & VP)*
Heidi C. Sullivan *(Chief Human Capital Officer & VP)*
Jeffrey M, Schroeder *(Chief Product Officer & VP)*
Christopher Graves *(Chief Investment Officer & VP)*

Subsidiaries:

AIS Management LLC (1)
999 N Sepulveda Blvd, El Segundo, CA 90245
Tel.: (310) 606-4247
Web Site: http://www.aisinsurance.com
Emp.: 999
Insurance Management Services
N.A.I.C.S.: 524298

American Mercury Insurance Company (1)
7301 NW Expy, Oklahoma City, OK 73172
Tel.: (405) 621-6585
Emp.: 200
Automobile Insurance Services
N.A.I.C.S.: 524126

American Mercury Lloyds Insurance Company (1)
4484 Wilshire Blvd, Los Angeles, CA 90010
Tel.: (323) 937-1060
Web Site: http://www.mercuryinsurance.com
Sales Range: $75-99.9 Million
Emp.: 200
Insurance Services
N.A.I.C.S.: 524298

American Mercury MGA, Inc. (1)
4484 Wilshire Blvd, Los Angeles, CA 90010
Tel.: (323) 937-1060
Web Site: http://www.mercuryinsurance.com
Sales Range: $50-74.9 Million
Emp.: 110
Provider of Insurance Services
N.A.I.C.S.: 524126

Auto Insurance Specialists, LLC (1)
999 N Sepulveda Blvd Ste 800, El Segundo, CA 90245
Tel.: (310) 606-4247
Web Site: http://www.aisinsurance.com
Sales Range: Less than $1 Million
Emp.: 20
Insurance Agents
N.A.I.C.S.: 524210

Branch (Domestic):

Auto Insurance Specialists (2)
5000 E Spring St Ste 100, Long Beach, CA 90815-5217
Insurance Agents Brokers & Service
N.A.I.C.S.: 524210

California Automobile Insurance Company (1)
4484 Wilshire Blvd, Los Angeles, CA 90010
Tel.: (323) 937-1060
Web Site: http://www.mercuryinsurance.com
Sales Range: $150-199.9 Million
Emp.: 100
Automobile Insurance Services
N.A.I.C.S.: 524126

California General Underwriters Insurance Company, Inc. (1)
4484 Wilshire Blvd, Los Angeles, CA 90010
Tel.: (323) 937-1060
Sales Range: $150-199.9 Million
Emp.: 100
Insurance Services
N.A.I.C.S.: 524126
Gab Tirador *(CEO)*

Mercury Casualty Company (1)
4484 Wilshire Blvd, Los Angeles, CA 90010
Tel.: (323) 937-1060
Web Site: http://www.mercuryinsurance.com
Sales Range: $650-699.9 Million
Emp.: 150
Casualty Insurance Products & Services
N.A.I.C.S.: 524126
Gabriel Tirador *(Pres & CEO)*

Mercury County Mutual Insurance Company (1)
4484 Wilshire Blvd, Los Angeles, CA 90010
Tel.: (323) 937-1060
Sales Range: $125-149.9 Million
Emp.: 100
Provider of Insurance Services
N.A.I.C.S.: 524126
Gabriel Tirador *(Pres & CEO)*

Mercury Indemnity Company of America (1)
1901 Ulmerton Rd 6th Fl, Clearwater, FL 33762-2307
Tel.: (727) 561-4000
Insurance Management Services
N.A.I.C.S.: 524298

Mercury Insurance Company (1)
4484 Wilshire Blvd, Los Angeles, CA 90010
Tel.: (323) 937-1060
Web Site: http://www.mercuryinsurance.com
Sales Range: $25-49.9 Million
Emp.: 150
Provider of Automobile Insurance Services
N.A.I.C.S.: 541110
George Joseph *(Chm)*
Gabriel Tirador *(Pres & CEO)*

Mercury Insurance Services, LLC (1)
555 W Imperial Hwy, Brea, CA 92821-4802
Tel.: (323) 937-1060

Mercury General Corporation—(Continued)

Web Site:
https://www.mercuryinsurance.com
Sales Range: $50-74.9 Million
Emp.: 100
Provider of Insurance Services
N.A.I.C.S.: 524126
Gabriel Tirador (Pres & CEO)

PoliSeek AIS Insurance Solutions, Inc. (1)
17785 Ctr Ct Dr Ste 250, Cerritos, CA 90703
Tel.: (562) 345-6262
Insurance Management Services
N.A.I.C.S.: 524298

Workmen's Auto Insurance Company (1)
4484 Wilshire Blvd, Los Angeles, CA 90010   **(100%)**
Tel.: (213) 747-4699
Web Site: http://www.waic.com
Art Insurance Services
N.A.I.C.S.: 524126
Shana Horonetz (Pres & COO)

MERCURY SYSTEMS, INC.
50 Minuteman Rd, Andover, MA 01810
Tel.: (978) 256-1300   **MA**
Web Site: https://www.mrcy.com
Year Founded: 1981
MRCY—(NASDAQ)
Rev.: $835,275,000
Assets: $2,378,905,000
Liabilities: $906,130,000
Net Worth: $1,472,775,000
Earnings: ($137,640,000)
Emp.: 2,364
Fiscal Year-end: 06/28/24
Commercially Developed Open Sensor & Big Data Processing Systems, Software & Services
N.A.I.C.S.: 334111
David E. Farnsworth (CFO, Treas & Exec VP)
Brian E. Perry (Pres-Processing Div & Exec VP)
Christopher C. Cambria (Gen Counsel, Sec & Exec VP)
William Conley (CTO)
William L. Ballhaus (Interim Pres & Interim CEO)
Stephanie Georges (CMO & Sr VP)
Jeffrey Eason (CIO & Sr VP)
Charles Roger Wells IV (COO & Exec VP)
Roger Wells (Pres-Microelectronics Div & Exec VP)
Nelson Erickson (Sr VP-Strategy & Corp Dev)
Turner Brinton (Sr Dir-Corp Comm)
David Farnsworth (CFO)
William L. Ballhaus (Chm & CEO)

Subsidiaries:

American Panel Corporation (1)
6675 Shiloh Rd E, Alpharetta, GA 30005
Tel.: (770) 205-9546
Aerospace Products Mfr
N.A.I.C.S.: 336413

Lewis Innovative Technologies, Inc. (1)
534 Lawrence St, Moulton, AL 35650
Tel.: (256) 905-0775
Web Site: http://www.lewisinnovative.com
Sales Range: $1-9.9 Million
Emp.: 34
Engineeering Services
N.A.I.C.S.: 541330
Elizabeth Lewis (Pres)
Justin LouAllen (Engr-Electrical)
Eddie McAbee (COO)
Jim Crosslin (Engr-Electrical)
Brooks Slayton (Engr-Mechanical)
Dane Walther (Engr-Electrical Design)

Mercury Commercial Electronics, Inc. (1)
267 Lowell Rd, Hudson, NH 03051

Tel.: (603) 883-2900
Web Site: http://www.mrcy.com
Microwave & Radio Frequency Subsystems & Components Designer & Mfr
N.A.I.C.S.: 334419

Mercury Computer Systems Ltd. (1)
Unit 1 Easter Park Benyon Road, Silchester, Reading, RG7 SPQ, United Kingdom
Tel.: (44) 1189702050
Web Site: http://www.mrcy.com
Realtime Digital Signal, Images Processing System, Specialized Software Mfr; Commercial Computing Markets
N.A.I.C.S.: 334118

Mercury Defense Systems, Inc. (1)
10855 Business Center Dr Bldg A, Cypress, CA 90630
Tel.: (714) 898-8200
Electronic Components Mfr
N.A.I.C.S.: 335999
Chris Michalski (Dir-ISR Technical)

Mercury Intelligence Systems, Inc. (1)
3025 S Parker Rd Tower II Ste 1000, Aurora, CO 80014
Tel.: (303) 597-5200
Electronic Components Mfr
N.A.I.C.S.: 335999

Subsidiary (Domestic):

Paragon Dynamics Inc. (2)
3025 S Parker Rd Tower II Ste 1000, Aurora, CO 80014
Tel.: (303) 597-5200
Web Site: http://www.paragondynamics.com
Rev.: $5,020,220
Emp.: 37
Custom Computer Programming Services
N.A.I.C.S.: 541511

Mercury Mission Systems International, SA (1)
Avenue Eugene-Lance 38 Grand-Lancy 1, PO Box 584, CH-1212, Geneva, Switzerland
Tel.: (41) 228845100
Electronic Equipment Whslr
N.A.I.C.S.: 423490

Mercury Mission Systems Spain, SL (1)
Miguel Faraday 20 Offices B105-106, Getafe, 28906, Madrid, Spain
Tel.: (34) 914916536
Electronic Equipment Whslr
N.A.I.C.S.: 423490

Mercury Systems - Trusted Mission Solutions, Inc. (1)
47200 Bayside Pkwy, Fremont, CA 94538-6567
Tel.: (510) 252-0870
Web Site: http://www.mrcy.com
Electronic Computers
N.A.I.C.S.: 334111

Mercury Systems SARL (1)
Centre Regus 26 Avenue Jean Kuntzmann, 38330, Montbonnot-Saint-Martin, France
Tel.: (33) 608419949
Aircraft Electronic Product Mfr
N.A.I.C.S.: 334418

Mercury Systems, Inc. - RF Integrated Solutions (1)
1000 Avenida Acaso, Camarillo, CA 93012
Tel.: (805) 388-1345
Wireless Communication Amplifier Mfr
N.A.I.C.S.: 334290

Nihon Mercury Computer Systems K.K. (1)
Gotanda No 2 Hanatani Bldg 6F 5-28-10 Higashi Gotanda, Shinagawa-ku, Tokyo, 141-0022, Japan
Tel.: (81) 334730140
Web Site: http://www.mc.com
Sales Range: $10-24.9 Million
Emp.: 4
Supplier of Realtime, Multicomputer Systems for Time-Critical & Computer-Intensive Applications
N.A.I.C.S.: 334118

Pentek Systems, Inc. (1)

1 Park Way, Upper Saddle River, NJ 07458
Tel.: (201) 818-5900
Web Site: http://www.pentek.com
Embedded Computer Board Mfr
N.A.I.C.S.: 334418
Rodger Hosking (VP)

Physical Optics Corporation (1)
20701 Manhattan Pl, Torrance, CA 90501-1510
Tel.: (310) 320-3088
Web Site: http://www.poc.com
Provider of Commercial Physical Research Optoelectronics
N.A.I.C.S.: 541715
Joanna Jannson (Founder)
Rick Shie (Vice Chm & Chief Strategic Officer)
Gajendra Savant (COO)
Andrew Kostrzewski (CTO)
Kevin Walter (Pres & CEO)
Yun Kim (CFO)
Robert Waldo (Chief Bus Dev Officer)
Keith Baker (Chief Admin Officer)

Subsidiary (Domestic):

Broadata Communications Inc (2)
2545 W 237th St, Torrance, CA 90505
Tel.: (310) 530-1416
Web Site: http://www.broadatacom.com
Rev.: $1,300,000
Emp.: 20
Scientific Research Agency
N.A.I.C.S.: 541715

Intelligent Optical Systems (2)
19601 Mariner Ave, Torrance, CA 90503
Tel.: (424) 263-6300
Web Site: https://www.intopsys.com
Rev.: $4,639,746
Emp.: 50
Fiber Optics Communications Equipment
N.A.I.C.S.: 541910
Reuben Sandler (CEO)
Manal Beshay (COO)

Waveband Corporation (2)
Ste 100 15245 Alton Pkwy, Irvine, CA 92618-2618
Tel.: (949) 253-4019
Web Site: http://www.waveband.com
Rev.: $1,393,133
Emp.: 25
Antennas, Receiving
N.A.I.C.S.: 238990

MEREDITH CORPORATION
1716 Locust St, Des Moines, IA 50309-3023
Tel.: (515) 284-3000   **IA**
Web Site: http://www.meredith.com
Year Founded: 1902
MDP—(NYSE)
Rev.: $2,977,400,000
Assets: $5,565,800,000
Liabilities: $4,913,700,000
Net Worth: $652,100,000
Earnings: $306,600,000
Emp.: 5,050
Fiscal Year-end: 06/30/21
Publishing & Broadcasting Services
N.A.I.C.S.: 513120
Patrick J. McCreery (Pres-Local Media Grp)
John S. Zieser (Chief Dev Officer, Gen Counsel & Sec)
Dianna Mell Meredith Frazier (Vice Chm)
Thomas H. Harty (Chm, Pres & CEO)
Doug Olson (Pres-Magazines)
Dina Nathanson (Sr VP-HR)
Catherine A. Levene (Pres-Natl Media Grp)
Jason M. Frierott (CFO)
Daphne Kwon (Chief Strategy Officer)
Erica Jensen (Chief Comm Officer & Sr VP)
Jenny McCoy (Exec Dir-ESG)
Alysia Borsa (Pres-Digital)
Thomas Witschi (Pres-Consumer Products-Natl Media Grp)

Subsidiaries:

Allrecipes.com, Inc. (1)

413 Pine St Ste 500, Seattle, WA 98101-3669
Tel.: (206) 436-7466
Web Site: http://www.allrecipes.com
Sales Range: $25-49.9 Million
Emp.: 200
Website Offering Recipes, Cooking Techniques, Menu Ideas & Other Culinary Products & Services
N.A.I.C.S.: 513140
Esmee Williams (VP-Brand Mktg)

American Baby Magazine (1)
805 3rd Ave, New York, NY 10022-5529
Tel.: (212) 499-2000
Web Site: http://www.americanbaby.com
Sales Range: $10-24.9 Million
Emp.: 50
Magazine Publisher
N.A.I.C.S.: 513120
Chuck Hajj (Mng Dir)

Better Homes & Gardens Books (1)
1716 Locust St, Des Moines, IA 50309-3023
Tel.: (515) 284-3000
Web Site: http://www.bhg.com
Sales Range: $25-49.9 Million
Emp.: 90
Magazine Publisher
N.A.I.C.S.: 513120

Bizrate Insights Inc. (1)
12200 W Olympic Blvd Ste 300, Los Angeles, CA 90064
Tel.: (310) 571-1235
Web Site: http://www.bizrateinsights.com
Customer Feedback Analysis Services
N.A.I.C.S.: 541910

Country Home Magazine (1)
1716 Locust St, Des Moines, IA 50309-3023
Tel.: (515) 284-2015
Web Site: http://www.countryhome.com
Sales Range: $100-124.9 Million
Magazine Publisher
N.A.I.C.S.: 513120

Cozi Group Inc. (1)
506 2nd Ave Ste 800, Seattle, WA 98104-2328
Tel.: (206) 957-8447
Web Site: http://www.cozi.com
Custom Computer Programming Services
N.A.I.C.S.: 541511

Departures Magazine (1)
1120 Avenue of the Americas 11th Fl, New York, NY 10036
Tel.: (212) 827-6437
Web Site: http://www.departures.com
Sales Range: $1-9.9 Million
Emp.: 20
Trade Magazine Publisher
N.A.I.C.S.: 513120

Entertainment Weekly Inc. (1)
135 W 50th St 3 Fl, New York, NY 10020
Tel.: (212) 522-5600
Web Site: http://www.ew.com
Weekly Magazine Publisher
N.A.I.C.S.: 513120
Ellie Duque (Publr & Sr VP)
Mary Margaret (Editor-in-Chief)

Fitness Magazine (1)
805 3rd Ave, New York, NY 10022-5514
Tel.: (212) 499-2000
Web Site: http://www.fitnessmagazine.com
Sales Range: $10-24.9 Million
Emp.: 30
Magazine Publisher
N.A.I.C.S.: 513120

Food & Wine (1)
225 Liberty St, New York, NY 10281
Tel.: (212) 522-1639
Web Site: http://www.foodandwine.com
Magazine Publisher
N.A.I.C.S.: 513120
Winslow Taft (Creative Dir)
Meg Clark (Sr Editor-Social Media)
Elsa Saatela (Editor-Digital Ops)
Abby Hocking (Editor-Digital Photo)
Hunter Lewis (Editor-in-Chief)

Health Media Ventures Inc. (1)
1271 Avenue of the Americas 20th Fl, New York, NY 10020-1300
Tel.: (212) 522-9400

Web Site: http://www.health.com
Sales Range: $25-49.9 Million
Publishing
N.A.I.C.S.: 513120

Branch (Domestic):

**Health Media Ventures Inc. - Los
Angeles** (2)
11766 Wilshire Blvd 18th Fl, Los Angeles,
CA 90025-6538
Tel.: (310) 268-7560
Web Site: http://www.health.com
Sales Range: $10-24.9 Million
Emp.: 2
Magazine Publisher
N.A.I.C.S.: 513120

IPC Media Limited (1)
Blue Fin Bldg 110 Southwark St, London,
SE1 0SU, United Kingdom
Tel.: (44) 2031485000
Web Site: http://www.ipcmedia.com
Sales Range: $450-499.9 Million
Emp.: 1,898
Publisher of Consumer Magazines
N.A.I.C.S.: 513120

Subsidiary (Domestic):

IPC Inspire (2)
The Blue Fin Bldg 110 Southwark St, London, SE1 0SU, United Kingdom (100%)
Tel.: (44) 2031485000
Web Site: http://www.ipcmedia.com
Sales Range: $25-49.9 Million
Emp.: 65
Leisure Interest Publisher
N.A.I.C.S.: 513120

Marie Claire Magazine (2)
Blue Fin Building 110 Southwark St, London, SE1 0SU, United Kingdom (100%)
Tel.: (44) 20 3148 5000
Web Site: http://www.marieclaire.com
Consumer Magazine Publishing
N.A.I.C.S.: 513120

Marketforce (UK) Limited (2)
110 Southwark St, Blue Finance Bldg, London, SE1 9LS, United Kingdom (100%)
Tel.: (44) 2031483300
Web Site: http://www.marketforce.co.uk
Sales Range: $50-74.9 Million
Emp.: 200
Magazine Marketing & Distribution
N.A.I.C.S.: 513120

InStyle Magazine (1)
1271 Ave of the Americas Ste 18-38B2,
New York, NY 10020
Tel.: (212) 522-4455
Web Site: http://www.instyle.com
Sales Range: $100-124.9 Million
Magazine
N.A.I.C.S.: 513120
Molly Stout (Exec Editor)
Kelly Chiello (Editor-Photo)
Peyton Dix (Editor-Special Projects)
Sam Reed (Sr Editor)
Kayla Greaves (Sr Editor-Beauty)
Alyssa Hardy (Sr Editor-News)
Kylie Gilbert (Sr Editor-Lifestyle)
Samantha Sutton (Editor-Fashion)
Erin Lukas (Editor-Beauty)
Kate Guarino (Sr Editor-Social Media)
Jackie Frere (Editor-Social Media)
Erin Glover (Assoc Editor-Photo)

KCTV-TV (1)
4500 Shawnee Mission Pkwy, Fairway, KS
66205
Tel.: (913) 677-5555
Web Site: http://www.kctv5.com
Sales Range: $50-74.9 Million
Emp.: 162
Television Broadcasting Services
N.A.I.C.S.: 516120
Mike Sulzman (Dir-Engrg)
Seth Rosenthal (Sls Dir)

Unit (Domestic):

KSMO-TV (2)
4500 Shawnee Mission Pkwy, Fairway, KS
66205
Tel.: (913) 621-6262
Web Site: http://www.kctv5.com
TV Station
N.A.I.C.S.: 516120

Seth Rosenthal (Sls Dir)

KMOV-TV, Inc. (1)
1 Memorial Dr, Saint Louis, MO 63102
Tel.: (314) 621-4444
Web Site: http://www.kmov.com
Sales Range: $25-49.9 Million
Emp.: 155
Television Broadcasting
N.A.I.C.S.: 516120

KPDX-TV (1)
14975 NW Greenbrier Pkwy, Beaverton,
OR 97006
Tel.: (503) 906-1249
Web Site: http://www.kptv.com
Sales Range: $50-74.9 Million
Emp.: 150
Television Broadcasting Station
N.A.I.C.S.: 516120
Chris Passon (Dir-News)
Mark Handwerger (Sls Mgr-Local)
Tamara Voremberg (Gen Sls Mgr)
Corey Hanson (VP & Gen Mgr)

KPHO Broadcasting Corporation (1)
5555 N 7th Ave, Phoenix, AZ 85013
Tel.: (602) 207-3333
Web Site: http://www.azfamily.com
Media Streaming Services
N.A.I.C.S.: 518210
Raymond Rios (Sls Mgr)

KPHO-TV (1)
4016 N Black Canyon Hwy, Phoenix, AZ
85017
Tel.: (602) 650-0712
Web Site: http://www.kpho.com
Sales Range: $50-74.9 Million
Emp.: 200
Television Broadcasting Station
N.A.I.C.S.: 516120
Bridget Fairchild (Sls Mgr-Local)

KTVK, Inc. (1)
5555 N 7th Ave, Phoenix, AZ 85013
Tel.: (602) 207-3333
Web Site: http://www.azfamily.com
Emp.: 320
Television Broadcasting Station
N.A.I.C.S.: 516120
Dennis Welch (Editor-Political)
Jon Thorwaldson (Coord-Captioning)

Unit (Domestic):

KTVK-3TV (2)
5555 N 7th Ave, Phoenix, AZ 85013-1701
Tel.: (602) 207-3333
Web Site: http://www.azfamily.com
Emp.: 200
Television Broadcasting Station
N.A.I.C.S.: 516120
Donald F. Cass Jr. (Pres & Gen Mgr)

KVVU-TV (1)
25 TV 5 Dr, Henderson, NV 89014
Tel.: (702) 435-5555
Web Site: http://www.fox5vegas.com
Sales Range: $25-49.9 Million
Emp.: 120
Television Broadcasting Station
N.A.I.C.S.: 516120
Ashley Casper (Dir-Content)
Crissie Bown (Sls Mgr-Local)
Natalia Claytor (Dir-HR)
Tom Baker (Gen Sls Mgr)
Yvette Rodriguez (Mkt Mgr)
Dan Schwarz (Sls Mgr-Local)
Rose Burbach (Coord-Captioning)

MNI Targeted Media Inc (1)
225 High Ridge Rd, Stamford, CT 06905
Tel.: (800) 225-3457
Web Site: http://www.mni.com
Produce & Sell Ads for National Magazines
For Distribution on Basis of Locale
N.A.I.C.S.: 541810
Matthew Fanelli (Sr VP-Digital)
Klarn DePalma (Exec VP)
Mark Glatzhofer (VP & Gen Mgr)
Vicki Brakl (Sr VP-Mktg, Trng & Dev)
Laura West (VP-Sls-Eastern)
Brooke Willcox (Dir-Digital Bus Dev &
Emerging Media)
Kevin Whitlow (VP-Sls-Southwestern)
Karen Brown (Dir-Sls, Mktg & Integration)
Aron Caruso (Dir-Sls & Magazines)
Beth Dwyer (Dir-Sls-Atlantic)
Melissa McGrath (Dir-Mktg Strategy & In-
sights)

Janine Pollack (Dir-Integrated Mktg)
Stefanie Sena (Dir-Digital Acct Ops)
Aaron Toye (VP-Sls-Northwestern)
Drew Pedersen (Sls Dir-Northwest)
Sue Williams (Dir-Production)
Meghan Aubert (Dir-Product Mktg)
Glenn Dolce (VP-Bus Dev)
Cristina Maida (Dir-HR)
Kathryn Marshall (Dir-Media Plng & Strat-
egy)

Meredith Exelerated Marketing (1)
800 Corporate Pointe Ste 100, Culver City,
CA 90230
Tel.: (424) 672-9500
Web Site:
http://www.meredithxceleratedmarke
ting.com
Rev.: $11,500,000
Emp.: 150
Advetising Agency
N.A.I.C.S.: 541810
Kristi VandenBosch (Chief Digital Officer)

Meredith Integrated Marketing (1)
11766 Wilshire Blvd Ste 260, Los Angeles,
CA 90025-6538
Tel.: (310) 689-1800
Web Site: http://www.meredith.com
Sales Range: $10-24.9 Million
Emp.: 80
Holding Company; Advertising Agencies
N.A.I.C.S.: 551112

Meredith List Marketing (1)
1716 Locust St, Des Moines, IA 50309-
3023
Tel.: (515) 284-3000
Web Site: http://www.meredith.com
Sales Range: $50-74.9 Million
Emp.: 300
Consumer Mailing List Services
N.A.I.C.S.: 541910

Midwest Living Magazine (1)
805 3rd Ave 27th Fl, New York, NY 10022
Tel.: (212) 557-6600
Web Site: http://www.midwestliving.com
Sales Range: $100-124.9 Million
Magazine Publisher
N.A.I.C.S.: 513120

Natural Health Magazine (1)
21100 Erwin St, Woodland Hills, CA 91367
Tel.: (212) 545-4800
Sales Range: $10-24.9 Million
Emp.: 20
Magazine
N.A.I.C.S.: 513120

New Media Strategies (1)
1100 Wilson Blvd Ste 1400, Arlington, VA
22209
Tel.: (703) 253-0050
Web Site: http://www.meredith.com
Rev.: $20,000,000
Emp.: 36
Advetising Agency
N.A.I.C.S.: 541810

Parents Magazine (1)
805 3rd Ave, New York, NY 10022-7541
Tel.: (212) 499-2000
Web Site: http://www.parents.com
Sales Range: $50-74.9 Million
Emp.: 200
Magazine Publisher
N.A.I.C.S.: 513120

People Magazine (1)
Time Life Bldg Rockefeller Ctr, New York,
NY 10020
Tel.: (212) 522-2028
Web Site: http://www.people.com
Sales Range: $100-124.9 Million
Weekly News & Features Magazine
N.A.I.C.S.: 513120
Cece Ryan (Sr VP & Publr)
Rebecca Hanley (Assoc Publr)
Maria Jakubek (Exec Dir)
Meredith Waltman (Exec Dir-Ad)

Readymade Magazine (1)
1716 Locust St, Des Moines, IA 50309
Tel.: (515) 284-3000
Web Site: http://www.bhg.com
Magazine
N.A.I.C.S.: 513120

Sports Illustrated (1)
225 Liberty St, New York, NY 10281

Tel.: (212) 522-1212
Web Site: http://www.si.com
Sales Range: $100-124.9 Million
Publisher of Weekly Magazine Devoted To
Sports, Recreation & Active Leisure
N.A.I.C.S.: 513120
Ryan Hunt (Editor-in-Chief)
Ross B. Levinsohn (CEO)

Unit (Domestic):

Golf Magazine (2)
1 Time Warner Ctr 33rd Fl, New York, NY
10019
Tel.: (212) 522-9890
Web Site: http://www.golf.com
Sales Range: $25-49.9 Million
Emp.: 20
Golf Magazine
N.A.I.C.S.: 513120

Successful Farming Magazine (1)
1716 Locust St, Des Moines, IA 50309-
3023
Tel.: (515) 284-2903
Web Site: http://www.agriculture.com
Sales Range: $100-124.9 Million
Magazine Publisher
N.A.I.C.S.: 513120

Synapse Group, Inc. (1)
225 High Ridge Rd, Stamford, CT 06905-
1325
Tel.: (203) 595-8255
Web Site: http://www.synapsegroupinc.com
Emp.: 170
Management Services for Publishers of
Consumer Magazines; Online Magazine
Retailer
N.A.I.C.S.: 541618
Eileen Peacock (Sr VP-Partnership Mktg &
Sls)
Scott Macon (Pres-Bizrate)
Silas Abraham (VP-Products, Svcs & Publr
Rels)

TI Inc. Affluent Media Group (1)
1120 Ave Of The Americas, New York, NY
10036-6700 (100%)
Tel.: (212) 382-5600
Web Site: http://www.departures.com
Sales Range: $25-49.9 Million
Emp.: 350
Magazine Publisher
N.A.I.C.S.: 513120

Time USA, LLC (1)
1271 Ave of the Americas, New York, NY
10020 (100%)
Tel.: (212) 522-4200
Web Site: http://www.time.com
Weekly Magazine Publisher
N.A.I.C.S.: 513120
Edward Felsenthal (CEO & Editor-in-Chief)
Lynne Benioff (Co-Chm)

Traditional Home (1)
805 3rd Ave, New York, NY 10022
Tel.: (212) 557-6600
Web Site: http://www.traditionalhome.com
Magazine Publisher
N.A.I.C.S.: 513120

WALA-TV (1)
1501 Satchel Paige Dr, Mobile, AL 36606-
2532
Tel.: (251) 434-1010
Web Site: http://www.fox10tv.com
Emp.: 125
Television Station
N.A.I.C.S.: 516120
Michael Strickler (Sls Dir)
Faye Olensky (Sls Mgr-Local)

WFSB-TV (1)
333 Capital Blvd, Rocky Hill, CT 06067
Tel.: (860) 728-3333
Web Site: http://www.wfsb.com
Sales Range: $50-74.9 Million
Emp.: 211
Television Broadcasting Station
N.A.I.C.S.: 516120
Victor Zarrilli (Coord-Captioning)

WNEM-TV (1)
107 N Franklin St, Saginaw, MI 48607
Tel.: (989) 755-8191
Web Site: http://www.wnem.com
Sales Range: $25-49.9 Million
Emp.: 130
Television Broadcasting Station

Meredith Corporation—(Continued)

N.A.I.C.S.: 516120
Mike Terry (Coord-Captioning)

WSMV-TV (1)
5700 Knob Rd, Nashville, TN 37209
Tel.: (615) 353-4444
Web Site: http://www.wsmv.com
Rev.: $38,083,000
Emp.: 175
Television Broadcasting Station
N.A.I.C.S.: 516120

MERGENCE CORP.
1 Technology Dr Bldg H, Irvine, CA
92618
Tel.: (949) 753-0593   **DE**
Year Founded: 1998
MRGN—(OTCIQ)
Media Entertainment Services
N.A.I.C.S.: 541840

MERGER MINES CORP.
3129 W Kings Ridge Dr, Coeur
D'Alene, ID 83814
Tel.: (208) 691-4881
Web Site:
 https://www.mergerminescorp.com
Year Founded: 1929
MERG—(OTCIQ)
Assets: $73,000
Liabilities: $690,000
Net Worth: ($617,000)
Earnings: ($192,000)
Fiscal Year-end: 12/31/19
Mining Machinery & Equipment
Manufacturing
N.A.I.C.S.: 333131
Lex Smith (Pres)

MERIDIAN BANCORP, INC.
67 Prospect St, Peabody, MA 01960
Tel.: (617) 567-1500   **MD**
Web Site: http://www.ebsb.com
Year Founded: 2014
EBSB—(NASDAQ)
Rev.: $269,379,000
Assets: $6,619,848,000
Liabilities: $5,850,963,000
Net Worth: $768,885,000
Earnings: $65,051,000
Emp.: 501
Fiscal Year-end: 12/31/20
Bank Holding Company
N.A.I.C.S.: 551111
Richard J. Gavegnano (Chm, Pres &
CEO)

Subsidiaries:

East Boston Savings Bank (1)
10 Meridian St, East Boston, MA 02128-
0997
Tel.: (617) 567-1500
Web Site: http://www.ebsb.com
Sales Range: $200-249.9 Million
Commericial Banking
N.A.I.C.S.: 522110
John A. Carroll (COO & Exec VP)
Richard J. Gavegnano (res & CEO)
Edward J. Merritt (Sec & Exec VP-Bus Dev
& Community Rels)
Eric M. Heath (Sr VP-HR)
John Migliozzi (Exec VP-Lending)
Frank P. Romano (Exec VP Corp Banking)
Keith D. Armstrong (Sr VP-Admin)
Paula Cotter (Sr VP-Ops)
Mary Hagen (Sr VP-Electronic Banking &
Customer Support)
David Lahive (Chief Credit Officer & Sr VP)
Ronald F. Mauriello (Sr VP-Compliance &
Risk Mgmt)
Joseph Nash (Sr VP-Residential Lending)

MERIDIAN BIOSCIENCE INC.
3471 River Hills Dr, Cincinnati, OH
45244
Tel.: (513) 271-3700   **OH**
Web Site:
 http://www.meridianbioscience.com
Year Founded: 1977

VIVO—(NASDAQ)
Rev.: $317,896,000
Assets: $449,722,000
Liabilities: $121,420,000
Net Worth: $328,302,000
Earnings: $71,407,000
Emp.: 702
Fiscal Year-end: 09/30/21
Diagnostic Test Kits, Purified Re-
agents & Related Products, Enabling
Early Diagnosis & Treatment of Gas-
trointestinal, Viral, Urinary Tract &
Respiratory Infections Mfr, Developer
& Marketer
N.A.I.C.S.: 325412
David C. Phillips (Chm)
Lourdes G. Weltzien (Exec VP-Life
Science)
Melissa McCarey (VP-HR-Global)
Andrew S. Kitzmiller (CFO)
Charlie Wood (VP-IR)
Tony Serafini-Lamanna (Exec VP-
Diagnostics)
Julie Smith (Principal Acctg Officer,
Sr VP & Controller)
Emerson C. Moser (Corp Counsel)

Subsidiaries:

Bioline GmbH (1)
Im Biotechnologiepark 3, 14943, Lucken-
walde, Germany
Tel.: (49) 33716022200
Sales Range: $25-49.9 Million
Emp.: 25
Pharmaceutical Preparation Mfr
N.A.I.C.S.: 325412
Marco J. Calzavara (Pres)

Bioline Ltd. (1)
Unit 16 The Edge Business Centre, Humber
Road, London, NW2 6EW, United Kingdom
Tel.: (44) 2088305300
Web Site: http://www.bioline.com
Emp.: 70
Pharmaceutical Preparation Mfr
N.A.I.C.S.: 325412
Marco J. Calzavara (Pres)

Bioline Reagents Ltd. (1)
Unit 16 The Edge Business Centre Humber
Road, London, NW2 6EW, United Kingdom
Tel.: (44) 2088305300
Web Site: http://www.bioline.com
Pharmaceutical Preparation Mfr
N.A.I.C.S.: 325412
Marco J. Calzavara (Pres)

Exalenz Bioscience Ltd. (1)
4 Ha'maayan St, Modi'in-Maccabim-Re'ut,
7177872, Israel
Tel.: (972) 89737500
Web Site: http://www.exalenz.com
Rev.: $13,144,000
Assets: $13,859,000
Liabilities: $17,110,000
Net Worth: ($3,251,000)
Earnings: ($5,498,000)
Emp.: 53
Fiscal Year-end: 12/31/2018
Medical Equipment Mfr
N.A.I.C.S.: 334510
Uri Geiger (Chm)

Subsidiary (US):

Exalenz Bioscience Inc. (2)
35 Colby Ave Ste 9, Manasquan, NJ 08736
Medical Equipment Mfr
N.A.I.C.S.: 334510

Magellan Diagnostics, Inc. (1)
3471 River Hills Dr, Cincinnati, OH 45244
Tel.: (978) 856-2345
Web Site: http://www.magellandx.com
Medical Diagnostic Equipment Developer &
Mfr
N.A.I.C.S.: 334510

Meridian Bioscience Corporation (1)
3471 River Hills Dr, Cincinnati, OH
45244 (100%)
Tel.: (513) 271-3700
Sales Range: $100-124.9 Million
Medical Laboratories
N.A.I.C.S.: 339112

Meridian Bioscience Europe B.V. (1)
PO Box 256, 5480 AG, Schijndel,
Netherlands (100%)
Tel.: (31) 411621166
Web Site: http://www.mdeur.com
Sales Range: $1-9.9 Million
Emp.: 2
Mfr, Developer & Marketer of Diagnostic
Test Kits, Purified Reagents & Related
Products, Enabling Early Diagnosis & Treat-
ment of Gastrointestinal, Viral, Urinary Tract
& Respiratory Infections
N.A.I.C.S.: 325413
Marco Calzavara (Pres)

Meridian Bioscience Europe
France (1)
455 Promenade Des Anglais Le Quadra,
6299, Nice, Cedex, France (100%)
Tel.: (33) 493187210
Web Site: http://www.meridianbioscience.eu
Sales Range: $10-24.9 Million
Emp.: 8
Mfr, Developer & Marketer of Diagnostic
Test Kits, Purified Reagents & Related
Products, Enabling Early Diagnosis & Treat-
ment of Gastrointestinal, Viral, Urinary Tract
& Respiratory Infections
N.A.I.C.S.: 325413

Meridian Bioscience Europe S.A. (1)
2 Avenue du Japon, 1420, Braine-l'Alleud,
Belgium
Tel.: (32) 67895959
Web Site: http://www.meridianbioscience.eu
Sales Range: $1-9.9 Million
Emp.: 5
Mfr, Developer & Marketer of Diagnostic
Test Kits, Purified Reagents & Related
Products, Enabling Early Diagnosis & Treat-
ment of Gastrointestinal, Viral, Urinary Tract
& Respiratory Infections
N.A.I.C.S.: 325413

Meridian Bioscience Europe s.r.l. (1)
Via dell Industria 7, Villa Cortese, 20035,
Milan, Italy (100%)
Tel.: (39) 0331433636
Web Site: http://www.meridianbioscience.eu
Sales Range: $10-24.9 Million
Emp.: 21
Retailer of Immunodiagnostic Products
N.A.I.C.S.: 423450
Marco G. Calzavara (Pres)

Meridian Bioscience Israel Holding
Ltd. (1)
4 Ha'maayan St, Modi'in-Maccabim-Re'ut,
Israel
Tel.: (972) 89737500
Medical Device Mfr
N.A.I.C.S.: 339112

Meridian Bioscience S.A. (1)
2 Avenue du Japon, 1420, Braine-l'Alleud,
Belgium (100%)
Tel.: (32) 67895959
Web Site: http://www.meridianbioscience.eu
Sales Range: $1-9.9 Million
Emp.: 5
Holding Company
N.A.I.C.S.: 551112

Meridian Bioscience UK Ltd. (1)
Unit 16 The Edge Business Centre Humber
Road, London, NW2 6EW, United Kingdom
Tel.: (44) 2084537970
Web Site: http://www.bioline.com
Emp.: 60
Pharmaceutical Mfr & Distr
N.A.I.C.S.: 325412

Meridian Life Science, Inc. (1)
60 Ind Park Rd, Saco, ME 04072-1840
Tel.: (207) 283-6500
Web Site:
 https://www.meridianbioscience.com
Sales Range: $10-24.9 Million
Emp.: 24
Supplier of Monoclonal & Polyclonal Anti-
bodies, Purified Reagents & Assay Devel-
opment; Reagents for Industry & Research
N.A.I.C.S.: 325411

Subsidiary (Domestic):

Bioline USA Inc. (2)
305 Constitution Dr, Taunton, MA 02780
Tel.: (508) 880-8990
Web Site: http://www.bioline.com

Sales Range: $25-49.9 Million
Emp.: 6
Pharmaceutical Preparation Mfr
N.A.I.C.S.: 325412

MERIDIAN CORPORATION
9 Old Lincoln Hwy, Malvern, PA
19355
Tel.: (484) 568-5000   **PA**
Web Site:
 https://www.meridianbanker.com
Year Founded: 2009
MRBK—(NASDAQ)
Rev.: $130,445,000
Assets: $2,062,228,000
Liabilities: $1,908,948,000
Net Worth: $153,280,000
Earnings: $21,829,000
Emp.: 366
Fiscal Year-end: 12/31/22
Bank Holding Company
N.A.I.C.S.: 551111
Christopher J. Annas (Founder, Chm,
Pres & CEO)
Denise Lindsay (CFO & Exec VP)

Subsidiaries:

Meridian Bank (1)
9 Old Lincoln Hwy, Malvern, PA 19355
Tel.: (484) 568-5000
Web Site: https://www.meridianbanker.com
Sales Range: $50-74.9 Million
Commericial Banking
N.A.I.C.S.: 522110
Christopher J. Annas (Founder, Chm, Pres
& CEO)
Denise Lindsay (CFO & Exec VP)
Kim Arnold (VP-Comml Lending)

Meridian Land Settlement Services,
LLC (1)
9 Old Lincoln Hwy, Malvern, PA 19355
Tel.: (484) 586-3521
Web Site: https://www.meridian-land.com
Insurance Services
N.A.I.C.S.: 524127

Meridian Wealth Partners, LLC (1)
653 Skippack Pike Ste 210, Blue Bell, PA
19422
Tel.: (610) 272-4700
Web Site:
 https://www.meridianwealthpartners.com
Financial Services
N.A.I.C.S.: 523940
Jay L. Heller (Mng Dir)
Brian Kohute (Mng Dir)
Heather Tracey (Dir-Client Svc)

MERIT MEDICAL SYSTEMS,
INC.
1600 W Merit Pkwy, South Jordan,
UT 84095
Tel.: (801) 253-1600   **UT**
Web Site: https://www.merit.com
Year Founded: 1987
MMSI—(NASDAQ)
Rev.: $1,150,981,000
Assets: $1,663,966,000
Liabilities: $519,569,000
Net Worth: $1,144,397,000
Earnings: $74,516,000
Emp.: 6,846
Fiscal Year-end: 12/31/22
Developer, Mfr & Marketer of Medical
Products for Cardiology & Radiology
N.A.I.C.S.: 339113
Fred P. Lampropoulos (Founder, Chm
& CEO)
Joseph C. Wright (Pres)
Joseph Pierce (CIO)
John Knorpp (Chief Regulatory Affairs
Officer)
Jason Treft (CTO)
Brian G. Lloyd (Chief Legal Officer &
Sec)
Nicole Priest (Chief Wellness Officer)
Mike Voigt (Chief HR Officer)
Neil Peterson (COO)
Raul Parra Jr. (CFO & Treas)

Subsidiaries:

BioSphere Medical, Inc. **(1)**
1050 Hingham St, Rockland, MA 02370
Tel.: (781) 681-7900
Web Site: http://www.biospace.com
Research in Bio-Engineered Microspheres
in Embolotherapy
N.A.I.C.S.: 339112
Fred P. Lampropoulos *(Pres)*

Division (Non-US):

**BioSphere Medical EMEA &
India** **(2)**
Bat A Parc des Nations Paris Nord 2, BP
54289, Charles de Gaulle, Cedex, France
Tel.: (33) 148172525
Web Site: http://www.biospheremed.com
Sales Range: $10-24.9 Million
Emp.: 35
Research in Bio-Engineered Microspheres
in Embolotherapy
N.A.I.C.S.: 339112

Dfine, Inc. **(1)**
3047 Orchard Pkwy, San Jose, CA 95134
Tel.: (408) 321-9999
Web Site: http://www.dfineinc.com
Rev.: $2,600,000
Emp.: 32
Research & Development in Biotechnology
N.A.I.C.S.: 541714

ITL HealthCare Pty Limited **(1)**
63 Wells Rd, Chelsea Heights, 3196, VIC,
Australia
Tel.: (61) 1300133804
Medical Devices Design & Mfr
N.A.I.C.S.: 334510

MCTec B.V. **(1)**
Van Coehoornstraat 7, 5916 PH, Venlo,
Netherlands
Tel.: (31) 773559000
Web Site: https://www.medicaldevice-
network.com
Emp.: 34
Electrical Equipment & Component Mfr
N.A.I.C.S.: 335999

Merit Medical Canada Ltd. **(1)**
1 Valleywood Dr, Markham, L3R 5L9, ON,
Canada
Tel.: (905) 477-2600
Medical Equipment Mfr
N.A.I.C.S.: 339113

Merit Medical Denmark A/S **(1)**
Bygdoy Alle 2, 1826, Frederiksberg, Den-
mark
Tel.: (45) 80880024
Medical Device Mfr
N.A.I.C.S.: 339112

Merit Medical Ireland, Limited **(1)**
Parkmore Business Park West, Ballybrit,
Galway, Ireland
Tel.: (353) 1800553163
Emp.: 790
Disposable Medical Devices Mfr
N.A.I.C.S.: 339112

Merit Medical Korea Co., Ltd. **(1)**
Room 901 9F 289-22 Sungsu2ga,
Seongdong-gu, Seoul, Korea (South)
Tel.: (82) 222050707
Web Site: http://www.merit.com
Emp.: 50
Pharmaceuticals Product Mfr
N.A.I.C.S.: 325412

Merit Medical Malaysia Sdn. Bhd **(1)**
Suite 20-01 & 20-02B Level 20 The Pin-
nacle Persiaran Lagoon, 47500, Bandar
Sunway, Malaysia
Tel.: (60) 356244413
Pharmaceuticals Product Mfr
N.A.I.C.S.: 325412

Merit Medical Nederland B.V. **(1)**
Amerikalaan 18-28, 6199 AE, Maastricht,
Netherlands
Tel.: (31) 433588222
Sales Range: $10-24.9 Million
Emp.: 80
Medical Diagnostic & Interventional Equip-
ment Mfr
N.A.I.C.S.: 339112

Merit Medical Norway AS **(1)**

Bygdoy Avenue 2, 257, Oslo, Norway
Tel.: (47) 80011629
Medical Instrument Mfr
N.A.I.C.S.: 339112

**Merit Medical Systems India Private
Limited** **(1)**
206-207 HM Geneva House 14 Cunning-
ham Road, Bengaluru, 560052, India
Tel.: (91) 8041223376
Web Site: http://www.merid.com
Emp.: 4
Pharmaceuticals Product Mfr
N.A.I.C.S.: 325412

Merit Sensor Systems, Inc. **(1)**
1600 W Merit Pkwy, South Jordan, UT
84095
Tel.: (801) 208-4700
Web Site: https://www.meritsensor.com
Piezoresistive Pressure Sensors Mfr
N.A.I.C.S.: 334413

**STD Pharmaceutical Products
Limited** **(1)**
Plough Lane, Hereford, HR4 0EL, United
Kingdom
Tel.: (44) 143 237 3555
Web Site: https://www.stdpharm.co.uk
Pharmaceutical Products Distr
N.A.I.C.S.: 424210
Bruce Gardiner *(Mng Dir)*

Thomas Medical Products, Inc. **(1)**
65 Great Valley Pkwy, Malvern, PA 19355
Tel.: (610) 651-5000
Web Site: http://www.meritmedical.com
Sales Range: $100-124.9 Million
Emp.: 100
Designer, Developer & Mfr of Medical De-
vices
N.A.I.C.S.: 339112

MERITAGE HOMES CORPO-
RATION

18655 N Claret Dr Ste 400, Scotts-
dale, AZ 85255
Tel.: (480) 515-8100 MD
Web Site:
https://www.meritagehomes.com
Year Founded: 1988
MTH—(NYSE)
Rev.: $6,113,013,000
Assets: $6,353,134,000
Liabilities: $1,741,234,000
Net Worth: $4,611,900,000
Earnings: $738,748,000
Emp.: 1,838
Fiscal Year-end: 12/31/23
Residential Construction
N.A.I.C.S.: 236118
Hilla Sferruzza *(CFO & Exec VP)*
Steven J. Hilton *(Exec Chm)*
Phillippe Lord *(CEO)*
Malissia R. Clinton *(Gen Counsel,
Sec & Exec VP)*
Emily Tadano *(VP-IR & ESG)*
Clinton Szubinski *(COO & Exec VP)*
Javier Feliciano *(Chief People Officer
& Exec VP)*

Subsidiaries:

Meritage Homes of Arizona, Inc. **(1)**
8800 E Raintree Dr Ste 300, Scottsdale, AZ
85260
Tel.: (480) 515-8100
Web Site: http://www.meritagehomes.com
Housing Construction Services
N.A.I.C.S.: 236115

**Meritage Homes of Florida Realty
LLC** **(1)**
5337 Millenia Lakes Blvd Ste 235, Orlando,
FL 32839
Tel.: (407) 712-8640
Civil Engineering Services
N.A.I.C.S.: 541330
Polly Heard *(Mgr-Mktg)*

**Meritage Homes of the Carolinas,
Inc.** **(1)**
Tel.: (480) 515-8100
Web Site: http://www.meritagehomes.com
Civil Engineering Services

N.A.I.C.S.: 541330

MERITAGE HOSPITALITY
GROUP INC.

45 Ottawa Ave SW Ste 600, Grand
Rapids, MI 49503
Tel.: (616) 776-2600 MI
Web Site:
https://www.meritagehospitality.com
Year Founded: 1986
MHGU—(OTCIQ)
Rev.: $516,178,000
Assets: $689,926,000
Liabilities: $591,507,000
Net Worth: $98,419,000
Earnings: $15,755,000
Emp.: 10,400
Fiscal Year-end: 01/03/21
Limited-Service Restaurants
N.A.I.C.S.: 722513
Gary A. Rose *(Pres & COO)*
Tracey Smith *(CFO & VP)*
Doug Poland *(VP-Real Estate)*
Jeff VanHaitsma *(VP-HR)*
Greg Corr *(Exec VP-Wendy's Ops)*
Robert Potts *(Gen Counsel)*
Alex Rusticus *(Fin Dir)*
Jon Sykes *(Dir-IT)*
Robert E. Schermer Jr. *(CEO)*

MERRIMACK PHARMACEUTI-
CALS, INC.

1 Broadway 14th Fl, Cambridge, MA
02142
Tel.: (617) 720-8606 DE
Web Site:
https://www.merrimack.com
Year Founded: 1993
MACK—(NASDAQ)
Rev.: $188,000
Assets: $19,836,000
Liabilities: $589,000
Net Worth: $19,247,000
Earnings: ($1,544,000)
Emp.: 27
Fiscal Year-end: 12/31/22
Biotechnology Pharmaceutical Re-
searcher & Developer
N.A.I.C.S.: 541714
Gary L. Crocker *(Chm, Pres & CEO)*
Gavin MacBeath *(Co-Founder)*
Anthony J. Sinskey *(Co-Founder)*

Subsidiaries:

**Silver Creek Pharmaceuticals,
Inc.** **(1)**
409 Illinois St, San Francisco, CA 94158
Tel.: (415) 978-2178
Web Site:
https://www.silvercreekpharma.com
Emp.: 8
Pharmaceuticals Product Mfr
N.A.I.C.S.: 325412
Michael Fairbanks *(Chm)*
Kris Kuchenbecker *(CTO)*

MERSANA THERAPEUTICS,
INC

840 Memorial Dr, Cambridge, MA
02139
Tel.: (617) 498-0020 DE
Web Site: https://www.mersana.com
Year Founded: 2002
MRSN—(NASDAQ)
Rev.: $36,855,000
Assets: $226,060,000
Liabilities: $189,156,000
Net Worth: $36,904,000
Earnings: ($171,670,000)
Emp.: 123
Fiscal Year-end: 12/31/23
Biotechnology Research & Develop-
ment Services
N.A.I.C.S.: 541713
Martin H. Huber *(Pres & CEO)*
Alejandra Carvajal *(Chief Legal Offi-
cer & Sr VP)*

Chuck Miller *(Sr VP-Regulatory Af-
fairs)*
Mohan Bala *(Sr VP)*
Mohan Bala *(Chief Dev Officer & Sr
VP)*
Brian C. DeSchuytner *(CFO, COO &
Sr VP)*
Ashish Mandelia *(Chief Acctg Officer
& VP)*
Timothy B. Lowinger *(CTO, Chief Sci-
ence Officer, Chief Science & Tech
Officer & Sr VP)*
David M. Mott *(Chm)*

MESA AIR GROUP, INC.

410 N 44th St Ste 700, Phoenix, AZ
85008
Tel.: (602) 685-4000 NV
Web Site: https://www.mesa-air.com
Year Founded: 1982
MESA—(NASDAQ)
Rev.: $503,591,000
Assets: $1,456,597,000
Liabilities: $968,550,000
Net Worth: $488,047,000
Earnings: $16,588,000
Emp.: 3,241
Fiscal Year-end: 09/30/21
Holding Company
N.A.I.C.S.: 551112
Michael J. Lotz *(Pres & Interim CFO)*
Jonathan G. Ornstein *(Chm & CEO)*
Brian S. Gillman *(Gen Counsel, Sec
& Exec VP)*
Tyler J. Campbell *(VP-Safety & Secu-
rity)*
James E. Swigart *(Treas & VP)*
C. Cody Thomas *(VP-Ops Control &
Plng)*
Brad Holt *(Sr VP-Flight Ops)*
Amber Wansten *(VP-Inflight Svcs)*
Christian Toro *(VP-Maintenance &
Engrg)*
Danita Fulton *(VP-HR)*
Michael Ferverda *(Sr VP)*
Christian Daoud *(VP)*
Edward Faith Jr. *(VP)*
David Hopkins *(CIO)*
John Hornibrook *(Sr VP)*
John Bacon Jr. *(VP-Supply Chain)*

Subsidiaries:

CCAIR, Inc. **(1)**
410 N 44th St Ste 100, Phoenix, AZ 85008
Tel.: (602) 685-4000
Web Site: http://www.mesa-air.com
Sales Range: $300-349.9 Million
Emp.: 645
Regional Air Carrier Providing Passenger
Service
N.A.I.C.S.: 481111

**Mesa Airlines Pilot Development,
Inc.** **(1)**
410 N 44th St Ste 700, Phoenix, AZ
85008 **(100%)**
Tel.: (602) 685-4000
Web Site: http://www.mesanet.mesa-air.com
Sales Range: $350-399.9 Million
Emp.: 10
Airline Pilot Training Programs
N.A.I.C.S.: 923110

Mesa Airlines, Inc. **(1)**
2700 Farmington Ave Bldg K-2, Farmington,
NM 87401-4552 **(100%)**
Tel.: (505) 326-3338
Sales Range: $900-999.9 Million
N.A.I.C.S.: 481111

MESA LABORATORIES, INC.

12100 W 6th Ave, Lakewood, CO
80228
Tel.: (303) 987-8000 CO
Web Site: https://www.mesalabs.com
Year Founded: 1982
MLAB—(NASDAQ)
Rev.: $216,187,000
Assets: $446,796,000

Mesa Laboratories, Inc.—(Continued)

Liabilities: $301,403,000
Net Worth: $145,393,000
Earnings: ($254,246,000)
Emp.: 736
Fiscal Year-end: 03/31/24
Medical Products for Kidney Dialysis
& Sensor Products Used in Industrial
Processing & Transportation
N.A.I.C.S.: 334513
John J. Sullivan (Chm)
John V. Sakys (CFO, Chief Acctg Officer & Treas)
Gary M. Owens (Pres & CEO)
Brian Archbold (Sr VP-Continuous Improvement)
Peter Jung (VP & Gen Mgr-Sterilization & Disinfection Control Div)
Boden Larson (VP-Bus Information Svcs)

Subsidiaries:

Agena Bioscience, Inc.   (1)
4755 Eastgate Mall, San Diego, CA 92121
Tel.: (858) 202-9000
Web Site: https://www.agenabio.com
Bioscientific Technology & Research Products Developer, Mfr & Marketer
N.A.I.C.S.: 334516
John Lillig (Chm)
David Coorey (Mng Dir & VP-EMEA)

Gyros Protein Technologies AB   (1)
Uppsala Science Park Dag Hammarskjolds
Vag 54, 751 83, Uppsala, Sweden
Tel.: (46) 18 56 63 00
Web Site:
   http://www.gyrosproteintechnologies.com
Peptide Synthesizers & Reagents Mfr
N.A.I.C.S.: 339112

Gyros Protein Technology AB   (1)
Uppsala Science Park Dag Hammarskjolds
Vag 54, 751 83, Uppsala, Sweden
Tel.: (46) 18566300
Web Site:
   https://www.gyrosproteintechnologies.com
Biological Product Mfr
N.A.I.C.S.: 325414

Gyros U.S. Inc.   (1)
30 Technology Dr Ste 1F, Warren, NJ 07059
Tel.: (908) 755-0011
Web Site:
   https://www.gyrosproteintechnologies.com
Bio Therapeutic Product Mfr
N.A.I.C.S.: 325412

IBP Medical GmbH   (1)
Ikarusallee 15, 30179, Hannover, Germany
Tel.: (49) 5119573360
Web Site: https://www.ibpmt.com
Hemodialysis Testing Device Mfr
N.A.I.C.S.: 334510
Werner Pfingstmann (CEO)

Mesa Canada, Inc.   (1)
3075 14th Ave 1, Markham, L3R 0G9, ON, Canada
Medical Device Mfr
N.A.I.C.S.: 339113
Miray Yenokians (Project Mgr & Mgr-HR)

Mesa France SAS   (1)
2 Rue Auguste Fresnel, 69680, Chassieu, Cedex, France
Tel.: (33) 478905688
Web Site: https://mesalabs.com
Medical Device Mfr
N.A.I.C.S.: 339113

Mesa Germany GmbH   (1)
Sigmund Riefler-Bogen 19 Riem, 81829, Munich, Germany
Tel.: (49) 8995927120
Medical Device Mfr
N.A.I.C.S.: 339113

Mesa Laboratories, Inc. - Biological Indicator Facility   (1)
10 Evergreen Dr Ste E, Bozeman, MT 59715
Tel.: (406) 585-9535

Web Site:
   http://biologicalindicators.mesalabs.com
Sales Range: $1-9.9 Million
Emp.: 50
Biological Product Mfr
N.A.I.C.S.: 325414

Mesa Laboratories, Inc. - North Bay Bioscience   (1)
13606 S West Bay Shore Dr, Traverse City, MI 49684
Tel.: (231) 922-2211
Web Site: http://www.nbbs.com
Sales Range: $1-9.9 Million
Emp.: 25
Sterilizer Monitoring Solutions
N.A.I.C.S.: 339112

Mesa Omaha (OMF) Biological Indicator Manufacturing Facility   (1)
8607 Park Dr, Omaha, NE 68127
Tel.: (303) 987-8000
Web Site: http://mesalabs.com
Biological Indicator Mfr; Sterilization Validation Services
N.A.I.C.S.: 621511

Simicon GmbH   (1)
Sigmund-Riefler-Bogen 19, 81829, Munich, Germany
Tel.: (49) 896733660
Web Site: https://www.simicon.de
Medical Device Mfr
N.A.I.C.S.: 339113

MESA ROYALTY TRUST
601 Travis St 16th Fl, Houston, TX 77002   TX
Tel.: (713) 483-6020
Web Site: https://mtr.q4web.com
Year Founded: 1979
MTR—(NYSE)
Rev.: $4,119,378
Assets: $3,749,307
Liabilities: $1,058,842
Net Worth: $2,690,465
Earnings: $3,682,228
Fiscal Year-end: 12/31/22
Trusts, Estates & Agency Accounts
N.A.I.C.S.: 525920
Elaina Rodgers (Officer-Trust & VP)

MESABI TRUST
1 Columbus Cir 17th Fl, New York, NY 10019   NY
Tel.: (904) 271-2520
Web Site: https://www.mesabi-trust.com
Year Founded: 1961
MSB—(NYSE)
Rev.: $7,741,974
Assets: $14,117,298
Liabilities: $2,679,081
Net Worth: $11,438,217
Earnings: $5,309,085
Fiscal Year-end: 01/31/23
Iron Ore Mining Services
N.A.I.C.S.: 212210
Jeffrey Schoenfeld (VP)

MESO NUMISMATICS, INC.
433 Plaza Real Ste 275, Boca Raton, FL 33432   NV
Web Site:
   https://www.mesocoins.com
Year Founded: 2001
MSSV—(OTCIQ)
Rev.: $1,530,223
Assets: $8,080,273
Liabilities: $20,062,565
Net Worth: ($11,982,292)
Earnings: ($5,506,822)
Emp.: 1
Fiscal Year-end: 12/31/22
Investment Services
N.A.I.C.S.: 523999
David Christensen (Pres, CEO, CFO & Sec)

MESSAGE PROCESSING INTERNATIONAL, INC.

414 SE Washington Blvd PMB 366, Bartlesville, OK 74006
Tel.: (801) 399-3632
Year Founded: 1991
MPIN—(OTCIQ)
Telephone Apparatus Mfr
N.A.I.C.S.: 334210
David Lennox (Pres)

MESTEK, INC.
260 N Elm St, Westfield, MA 01085   PA
Tel.: (413) 568-9571
Web Site: https://www.mestek.com
Year Founded: 1946
MCCK—(OTCIQ)
Sales Range: $350-399.9 Million
Emp.: 2,600
Holding Company; Heating, Ventilation & Air Conditioning Products, Coil Handling Equipment, Extruded Aluminum Products & Computer Information Systems Mfr
N.A.I.C.S.: 551112
J. Nicholas Filler (Vice Chm & Sr VP-Corp & Legal)
Stephen M. Shea (CFO & Exec VP)
Steven F. Olearcek (Sec)
Stewart B. Reed (Chm & CEO)

Subsidiaries:

Anemostat Products   (1)
1220 E Watson Center Rd, Carson, CA 90745-4206   (100%)
Tel.: (310) 835-7500
Web Site: http://www.anemostat.com
Sales Range: $25-49.9 Million
Emp.: 40
Mfr of Air Terminal Boxes, Sound Traps, Grilles, Registers & Other Metal Products for Installation
N.A.I.C.S.: 333994
Dave Chipman (Pres)

Boyertown Foundry Company   (1)
9th & Rothermel Dr, New Berlinville, PA 19545
Tel.: (610) 473-1000
Sales Range: $75-99.9 Million
Emp.: 150
Foundry
N.A.I.C.S.: 333414

Embassy Industries, Inc.   (1)
315 Oser Ave, Hauppauge, NY 11788
Tel.: (631) 694-1800
Web Site: http://www.embassyind.com
Rev.: $12,000,000
Emp.: 6
Baseboard & Radiant Floor Heating Equipment Mfr
N.A.I.C.S.: 333414

Formtek, Inc.   (1)
4899 Commerce Pkwy, Warrensville Heights, OH 44128
Tel.: (216) 292-4460
Web Site: http://www.formtekinc.com
Sales Range: $125-149.9 Million
Metal Forming Solutions & Services
N.A.I.C.S.: 333517
Mary Jane Schroeder (Mgr-Admin)

Subsidiary (Non-US):

Formtek Asia-Pacific   (2)
Bei Qi Jia High-Tech Industrial Park, Changping, Beijing, 102209, China
Tel.: (86) 10 89751509
Web Site: http://www.formtek.com.cn
Sales Range: $125-149.9 Million
Emp.: 4
Metal Forming Machinery
N.A.I.C.S.: 333519
Le Yong (Gen Mgr)

Subsidiary (Domestic):

Hill Engineering, Inc.   (2)
373 Randy Rd, Carol Stream, IL 60188
Tel.: (630) 834-4430
Web Site: http://www.hillengr.com
Sales Range: $25-49.9 Million
Emp.: 18
Tooling & Special Machinery Builder
N.A.I.C.S.: 333514

Iowa Rebuilders, Inc.   (2)
5480 6th St SW, Cedar Rapids, IA 52404
Tel.: (319) 362-8020
Sales Range: $1-9.9 Million
Emp.: 4
Machinery Rebuilder & Sales
N.A.I.C.S.: 811210

Yoder - Formtek Metal Forming, Inc.   (2)
4899 Commerce Pkwy, Cleveland, OH 44128-5905
Tel.: (216) 292-6300
Web Site: http://www.yodermfg.com
Sales Range: $50-74.9 Million
Emp.: 100
Mfr of Mill Forming Tube & Pipe Mill Systems
N.A.I.C.S.: 333519

Lockformer Company   (1)
5480 6th St SW, Cedar Rapids, IA 52404   (100%)
Tel.: (319) 364-9181
Web Site: http://www.lockformer.com
Sales Range: $25-49.9 Million
Emp.: 50
Roll-Forming Machinery Mfr
N.A.I.C.S.: 333517

Mestek Canada Inc.   (1)
7555 Tranmere Dr, Mississauga, L5S 1L4, ON, Canada
Tel.: (905) 670-5888
Web Site: http://www.mestekcanada.com
Sales Range: $100-124.9 Million
Heating Equipment Mfr
N.A.I.C.S.: 333414
Manny DeSilva (Pres)

Reed National Company   (1)
7301 International Dr, Holland, OH 43528-9412   (100%)
Tel.: (419) 865-5000
Web Site: http://www.awv.com
Sales Range: $10-24.9 Million
Emp.: 40
Louvers & Dampers Mfr
N.A.I.C.S.: 334512

META PLATFORMS, INC.
1 Meta Way, Menlo Park, CA 94025
Tel.: (650) 543-4800   DE
Web Site: http://investor.fb.com
Year Founded: 2004
META—(NASDAQ)
Rev.: $134,902,000,000
Assets: $229,623,000,000
Liabilities: $76,455,000,000
Net Worth: $153,168,000,000
Earnings: $39,098,000,000
Emp.: 67,317
Fiscal Year-end: 12/31/23
Holding Company; Online Social Networking Site Operator
N.A.I.C.S.: 551112
Dustin Moskovitz (Co-Founder)
Kevin J. Martin Jr. (VP-US Public Policy)
Alvin Bowles Jr. (VP-Global Bus Grp-America)
Chris Hughes (Co-Founder)
Javier Olivan (COO)
Susan J. Li (CFO)
Nick Clegg (Pres-Global Affairs)
Jennifer G. Newstead (Chief Legal Officer)
Ime Archibong (VP-Product Management & Head-Product & Messenger)
Dawn Carfora (VP-Bus Plng, Ops, and Global Bus Grp)
Nick Clegg (Pres)
Maren Lau (Reg VP-Latin America)
Susan Li (CFO)
Mark Zuckerberg (Co-Founder, Chm & CEO)

Subsidiaries:

Atlas   (1)
315 5th Ave S 500, Seattle, WA 98104
Tel.: (206) 816-8000
Sales Range: $25-49.9 Million
Emp.: 130
Digital Advertising & Marketing Services

N.A.I.C.S.: 541870

Branch (Domestic):

Atlas (2)
1 Post St Ste 850, San Francisco, CA
94104-5266
Tel.: (415) 399-3820
Sales Range: $10-24.9 Million
Emp.: 15
Digital Advertising & Marketing Services
N.A.I.C.S.: 541870

Edge Network Services Limited (1)
32 Farm Avenue, Cricklewood, London,
NW2 2BH, United Kingdom
Tel.: (44) 2084501811
Web Site: http://www.edgenetservices.com
Social Networking Website Operator
N.A.I.C.S.: 516210

Instagram, Inc. (1)
181 S Park St Ste 2, San Francisco, CA
94107
Tel.: (415) 857-3369
Web Site: http://www.instagram.com
Internet Broadcasting Services
N.A.I.C.S.: 516210
Adam Mosseri (CEO)
Kaylie Smith (Head-Market Ops-
Asia,Pacific)
Justin Osofsky (COO)

Karma Science, Inc (1)
120 2nd St 4th Fl, San Francisco, CA
94105
Tel.: (415) 891-9141
Web Site: http://www.getkarma.com
Sales Range: $10-24.9 Million
Emp.: 16
Social Mobile Commerce Application Devel-
oper
N.A.I.C.S.: 513210

Kustomer, Inc. (1)
318 W 39th St 5th Flr, New York, NY 10018
Tel.: (212) 497-1188
Web Site: http://www.kustomer.com
Customer Service And Support
N.A.I.C.S.: 561421
Peter Johnson (VP-Product)
Vikas Bhambri (Sr VP-Sls & Customer Ex-
perience)
Amir Oren (Sr VP-Fin)
Gabe Larsen (VP-Mktg)
Mike Chapin (VP, Gen Counsel & Sec)
Tanya Livingstone (VP-People)
Abhishek Gupta (VP-Ops)

Oculus VR, LLC (1)
19800 MacArthur Blvd Ste 200, Irvine, CA
92612
Tel.: (949) 502-2070
Web Site: http://www.oculusvr.com
Virtual Reality Gaming Headset Mfr
N.A.I.C.S.: 334419
Rebecca Van Dyck (CMO)
Palmer Luckey (Founder)

Parse, LLC (1)
1601 Willow Rd, Menlo Park, CA 94025
Tel.: (650) 543-4800
Web Site: http://www.parse.com
Software Development & Application Ser-
vices
N.A.I.C.S.: 541512

Ready At Dawn Studios, LLC (1)
5271 California Ave, Irvine, CA 92617
Tel.: (949) 724-1234
Web Site: http://www.readyatdawn.com
Custom Computer Programming Services
N.A.I.C.S.: 541511

Vitesse, LLC (1)
735 SW Connect Way, Prineville, OR
97754
Tel.: (650) 644-8484
Data Processing Services
N.A.I.C.S.: 518210

WhatsApp Inc. (1)
650 Castro St Ste 120-219, Mountain View,
CA 94041
Tel.: (510) 494-1228
Web Site: http://www.whatsapp.com
Cross-Platform Mobile Messaging Applica-
tion Developer
N.A.I.C.S.: 541511
Brian Acton (Founder)

**META POWER INTERNA-
TIONAL, INC.**
5300 MacArthur Blvd Ste 201, Van-
couver, WA 98861
Tel.: (360) 450-4209   DE
Web Site:
   http://www.metapower.com.tw
Year Founded: 2007
MTPR—(OTCIQ)
Business Consulting Services
N.A.I.C.S.: 541618
John E. Prouty (Pres, CEO & VP-
Product Development)
Ed Gibson (Pres)
Stephen Ivy (VP-Finance)

METACRINE, INC.
3985 Sorrento Valley Blvd Ste C, San
Diego, CA 92121
Tel.: (858) 369-7800   DE
Web Site: http://www.metacrine.com
Year Founded: 2014
MTCR—(NASDAQ)
Rev.: $102,000
Assets: $79,989,000
Liabilities: $22,634,000
Net Worth: $57,355,000
Earnings: ($1,128,000)
Emp.: 17
Fiscal Year-end: 12/31/21
Biotechnology Research & Develop-
ment Services
N.A.I.C.S.: 541714
Richard A. Heyman (Co-Founder &
Exec Chm)
Michael York (Pres, CEO, Chief Bus
Officer, Treas, Sec & Principal Fin &
Acctg Officer)
Hubert Chen (Chief Medical Officer)
Theresa Lowry (VP-HR)
Ronald Evans (Co-Founder)
Brandee Wagner (VP-Biology)
Richard A. Heyman (Co-Founder &
Chm)

METAIRIE BANK & TRUST CO.
3344 Metairie Rd, Metairie, LA 70001
Tel.: (504) 834-6330
Web Site:
   https://www.metairiebank.com
MBKL—(OTCIQ)
State Commercial Banks
N.A.I.C.S.: 522110
Priscilla W. May (Asst VP)
Scott A. Schellhaas (VP-Mortgage
Loans)
Wendy M. Harness (Asst VP)
Gina Dodge (VP & Mgr-Electronic
Banking)
Karen Pelaez (Asst VP)
Elaine White (VP-Mortgage Loans)
Bruce Chapman (Asst VP-Consumer
Loans)
Robbin Hardee (VP)
Steven Sullivan (Asst VP-Acctg)
Edward J. Vollenweider (VP-
Mortgage Loans)
Dawn Farrell (VP-Auditing)
Mike Licali (VP-Credit Admin)
Tammie B. Taffi (Asst VP)
Richard C. Stanley (Chm)
Sam Fradella (VP-Bus & Pro)
Shane Smith (Asst VP-Credit Admin)
Charlene Forshee (Asst VP-Loan
Ops)
Erin M. DiZinno (VP-Bus & Pro Dept)
Brian Cook (VP-Bus & Pro Dept-
Mandeville)
John P. LeBlanc (CFO & Sr VP)
Reginald H. Smith Jr. (Pres)
Albert J. Aucoin Jr. (Asst VP & Mgr-
IT)
Paul A. Myers IV (VP-Mandeville)
Ronald E. Samford Jr. (Pres & CEO)

METAL ARTS COMPANY, INC.

420 Lexington Ave Ste 300, New
York, NY 10170
Tel.: (212) 479-2580   NY
Year Founded: 1976
MTRT—(OTCIQ)
Nickel & Aluminum Product Mfr
N.A.I.C.S.: 331491
Yongseok Kwon (CTO)
Pan Jong Kim (Pres & CEO)
Yunho Chung (CFO & Sec)

**METAL SKY STAR ACQUISI-
TION CORPORATION**
132 W 31st St 9th FL, New York, NY
10001
Tel.: (332) 237-6141   Ky
Year Founded: 2021
MSSA—(NASDAQ)
Rev.: $2,950,668
Assets: $35,360,963
Liabilities: $5,721,517
Net Worth: $29,639,446
Earnings: $2,152,160
Fiscal Year-end: 12/31/23
Investment Management Service
N.A.I.C.S.: 523999
Wenxi He (CEO & CFO)

METALERT INC.
117 W 9th St Ste 1214, Los Angeles,
CA 90015
Tel.: (213) 489-3019   NV
Web Site: https://www.metalert.com
Year Founded: 2006
MLRT—(OTCIQ)
Rev.: $334,606
Assets: $163,762
Liabilities: $3,476,639
Net Worth: ($3,312,877)
Earnings: ($1,503,087)
Emp.: 8
Fiscal Year-end: 12/31/22
Wireless Telecommunications Carri-
ers (except Satellite)
N.A.I.C.S.: 517112
Patrick E. Bertagna (Co-Founder,
Chm, Pres & CEO)
Louis Rosenbaum (Co-Founder &
VP-Ops & Fin)
Andrew Duncan (Pres-Bus Dev,
Treas & Sec)
Alex G. McKean (CFO)
Li Wang (Sr Engr-Product Dev)
Jose Monroy (Head-Customer Sup-
port)
Sagorika Parvin (Project Mgr-Engrg)

Subsidiaries:

LOCiMobile, Inc. (1)
117 W 9th St Ste 1214, Los Angeles, CA 90015
Tel.: (213) 489-3019
Web Site: https://www.locimobile.com
Online Dating Services
N.A.I.C.S.: 812990

**METALINE CONTACT MINES
CO.**
W 3848 Turtle Patch Rd, Pine River,
WI 54965
Tel.: (920) 987-5105   WA
Year Founded: 1928
MTLI—(OTCIQ)
Metal Mining Services
N.A.I.C.S.: 212290
John W. Beasley (CFO, Treas & Sec)

METALLUS INC.
1835 Dueber Ave SW, Canton, OH
44706
Tel.: (330) 471-7000   OH
Web Site: https://metallus.com
Year Founded: 1917
MTUS—(NYSE)
Rev.: $1,362,400,000
Assets: $1,175,300,000
Liabilities: $443,700,000

Net Worth: $731,600,000
Earnings: $69,400,000
Emp.: 1,840
Fiscal Year-end: 12/31/23
All Other Miscellaneous Fabricated
Metal Product Manufacturing
N.A.I.C.S.: 332999
Joseph A. Carrabba (Founder)
Donald T. Misheff (Founder)
Randall A. Wotring (Founder)
Kristopher R. Westbrooks (CFO &
Exec VP)
Michael S. Williams (Pres & CEO)

Subsidiaries:

EDC, Inc. (1)
1500 W 33rd Ave Unit 100, Anchorage, AK
99503
Tel.: (907) 276-7933
Web Site: https://www.edc-alaska.com
Emp.: 10
Roller Bearing Mfr
N.A.I.C.S.: 332991
John Faschan (Pres & Engr-Electrical)
John Pepe (VP & Engr-Electrical)
Cory Wardrope (Engr-Electrical-Staff)
Craig Freedeen (Sr Engr-Mechanical)
Zach Boldrick (Engr-Electrical)

**TimkenSteel (Shanghai) Corporation
Limited** (1)
RM302 Building A China Fortune Universe
No 200 Tianlin Road, Shanghai, China
Tel.: (86) 2160231080
Metal Product Distr
N.A.I.C.S.: 423510

TimkenSteel UK Limited (1)
The Old Rectory Main Street, Glenfield, LE3
8DG, Leicestershire, United Kingdom
Tel.: (44) 1162325186
Metal Product Distr
N.A.I.C.S.: 423510

METALS ACQUISITION CORP.
425 Houston St Ste 400, Fort Worth,
TX 76102
Tel.: (817) 698-9901   Ky
Year Founded: 2021
MTAL—(NYSE)
Rev.: $5,224,466
Assets: $270,191,265
Liabilities: $294,584,352
Net Worth: ($24,393,087)
Earnings: ($4,742,618)
Emp.: 3
Fiscal Year-end: 12/31/22
Investment Services
N.A.I.C.S.: 523999
Neville Joseph Power (Chm)

METATRON APPS, INC.
160 Greentree Dr Ste 101, Dover, DE
19904
Tel.: (302) 489-4016   DE
Web Site: https://metatronapps.com
MRNJ—(OTCIQ)
Mobile Application Development Ser-
vices
N.A.I.C.S.: 541511
Joe Riehl (Pres & CEO)
Denis Sluka (COO)

**METAURUS EQUITY COMPO-
NENT TRUST**
589 5th Ave Ste 808, New York, NY
10017
Tel.: (212) 634-4250   DE
Year Founded: 2016
IDIV—(NYSA)
Rev.: $171,791
Assets: $19,985,408
Liabilities: $271,655
Net Worth: $19,713,753
Earnings: ($1,970)
Fiscal Year-end: 12/31/20
Investment Services
N.A.I.C.S.: 523999
Richard Sandulli (CEO)

Metaurus Equity Component Trust—(Continued)

METAVESCO, INC.
410 Peachtree Pkwy Ste 4245, Cumming, GA 30041
Tel.: (678) 341-5898 **VA**
Web Site:
https://www.metavesco.com
Year Founded: 1993
MVCO—(OTCIQ)
Rev.: $127,087
Assets: $336,326
Liabilities: $329,925
Net Worth: $6,401
Earnings: ($572,845)
Emp.: 1
Fiscal Year-end: 06/30/23
Small Business Investments & Venture Capital Funding
N.A.I.C.S.: 525910
Ryan Schadel (CEO)

METAWORKS PLATFORMS, INC.
3250 Oakland Hls Ct, Fairfield, CA 94534
Tel.: (424) 570-9446 **NV**
Web Site: https://www.metaworks.ai
Year Founded: 2010
MWRK—(OTCQB)
Rev.: $415,082
Assets: $1,682,134
Liabilities: $2,580,767
Net Worth: ($898,633)
Earnings: ($5,664,278)
Emp.: 2
Fiscal Year-end: 12/31/23
Literary Representation Services
N.A.I.C.S.: 711410
Cameron Chell (Founder & Chm)
Scott Gallagher (Pres)

METHES ENERGIES INTERNATIONAL LTD.
14160 McCormick Dr, Tampa, FL 33626
Tel.: (321) 214-4039 **NV**
Web Site: https://www.methes.com
Year Founded: 2007
MEIL—(OTCIQ)
Sales Range: $1-9.9 Million
Emp.: 23
Biodiesel Production Services
N.A.I.C.S.: 324191
David A. Hoeft (CFO)
Johann Loewen (Co-Founder & VP-Ops)
Michael Hallman (VP-Project Mgmt)
Steven Anthony (VP-Sls & Mktg)
Afrin Shams (Chief Acctg Officer)
Pat Reid (Officer-Logistics)
Doug Taylor (Mgr-Sombra Plant)
Nicholas Ng (Co-Founder & Pres)

METHODE ELECTRONICS, INC.
8750 W Bryn Mawr Ave Ste 1000, Chicago, IL 60631
Tel.: (708) 867-6777 **DE**
Web Site: https://www.methode.com
Year Founded: 1946
MEI—(NYSE)
Rev.: $1,114,500,000
Assets: $1,403,500,000
Liabilities: $637,500,000
Net Worth: $766,000,000
Earnings: ($123,300,000)
Emp.: 7,500
Fiscal Year-end: 04/27/24
Electronic Connectors, Controls & Power Distribution Systems Mfr
N.A.I.C.S.: 334417
Walter J. Aspatore (Chm)
Mark D. Schwabero (Vice Chm)
Timothy R. Glandon (VP)
Andrea J. Barry (Chief HR Officer)

Amit N. Patel (Chief Acctg Officer)
Anil V. Shetty (VP)
Robert K. Cherry (VP-IR)
Kevin M. Martin (VP)
Jonathan B. DeGaynor (Pres & CEO)
Laura Kowalchik (CFO)

Subsidiaries:

Alsentis LLC **(1)**
1261 S Waverly Rd, Holland, MI 49423
Tel.: (616) 582-3160
Web Site: https://www.alsentis.com
Mobile Panel Mfr
N.A.I.C.S.: 334413

Automotive Electronic Controls **(1)**
111 W Buchanan St, Carthage, IL 62321 **(100%)**
Tel.: (217) 357-3941
Web Site: http://www.methode.com
Sales Range: $300-349.9 Million
Emp.: 500
Mfr of Switches & Controls for the Automotive Industry
N.A.I.C.S.: 334417

BMAC Limited **(1)**
Units 13 & 14 South Shepley Road, Shepley Industrial Estate, Audenshaw, M34 5DW, United Kingdom
Tel.: (44) 1613373070
Web Site: https://www.bmac.ltd.uk
Light & Electrical Product Mfr
N.A.I.C.S.: 327212

Connectivity Technologies **(1)**
1111 Digital Dr Ste 150, Richardson, TX 75081
Tel.: (972) 406-0000
Web Site: http://www.contech1.com
Sales Range: $10-24.9 Million
Emp.: 25
Designer of Products & Services for Data Center & LAN Cabling Environments
N.A.I.C.S.: 541512

DataMate Division **(1)**
7401 W Wilson Ave, Chicago, IL 60706-4548 **(100%)**
Tel.: (708) 867-6777
Web Site: http://www.methode.com
Sales Range: $10-24.9 Million
Emp.: 3,500
Mfr of Computerized Circuits
N.A.I.C.S.: 334417

DataMate Products Group **(1)**
7401 W Wilson Ave, Chicago, IL 60706-4548
Tel.: (708) 867-6777
Web Site: http://www.methode.com
Sales Range: $75-99.9 Million
Emp.: 250
Mfr of Electronic Connectors & Controls; Power Distribution Systems
N.A.I.C.S.: 334417

Grakon, LLC **(1)**
1911 S 218th St, Seattle, WA 98198
Tel.: (206) 824-6000
Web Site: https://www.grakon.com
Motor Vehicle Lighting Systems & Engineered Trim Components Mfr
N.A.I.C.S.: 336320

Subsidiary (Non-US):

Hamsar Diversco Inc. **(2)**
5320 Downey Street, Burlington, L7L 6M2, ON, Canada
Tel.: (905) 332-4094
Web Site: https://www.hamsar.com
Sales Range: $10-24.9 Million
Lighting & Electronic Products Mfr
N.A.I.C.S.: 335139
K. Douglas Mann (Dir-Ops)

Hetronic Asia **(1)**
121 East Main Avenue Laguna Technopark, Binan, 4024, Laguna, Philippines
Tel.: (63) 495440004
Web Site: http://www.hetronic.com
Electronic Parts & Equipment Mfr, Warehousing & Logistics Center
N.A.I.C.S.: 334419

Hetronic International, Inc. **(1)**
3905 NW 36th St, Oklahoma City, OK 73112

Tel.: (405) 946-3574
Web Site: https://www.hetronic.com
Emp.: 60
Radio Remote Control System Mfr
N.A.I.C.S.: 334290

Hetronic Italy S.R.L. **(1)**
PTB Polo Technologico Brianza Via Lavoratori Dell Autobianchi, n 1 lotto n 24 Desio, Milan, 20832, MI, Italy
Tel.: (39) 026993361
Software Development Services
N.A.I.C.S.: 541511

Hetronic Midwest, LLC **(1)**
765 N Hague Ave, Columbus, OH 43204
Tel.: (614) 308-3120
Software Development Services
N.A.I.C.S.: 541511

Hetronic Swiss AG **(1)**
Altgraben 23, 4624, Harkingen, Switzerland
Tel.: (41) 623889920
Web Site: http://www.hetronic.ch
Sales Range: $10-24.9 Million
Emp.: 7
Safety Radio Remote Control Mfr
N.A.I.C.S.: 334290
Pascal Cretin (Mng Dir)

Hetronic USA, Inc. **(1)**
3905 NW 36th St, Oklahoma City, OK 73112
Tel.: (405) 946-3574
Web Site: https://www.hetronic.com
Radio Remote Control System Mfr
N.A.I.C.S.: 334290

Interconnect Products Division **(1)**
1700 Hicks Rd, Rolling Meadows, IL 60008-1229
Tel.: (847) 392-3500
Web Site: http://www.methode.com
Sales Range: $150-199.9 Million
Mfr of Connectors
N.A.I.C.S.: 424690

Magna-Lastic Devices **(1)**
7401 W Wilson Ave, Harwood Heights, IL 60706
Tel.: (708) 867-6777
Web Site: http://www.mdi-sensor.com
Sales Range: $25-49.9 Million
Emp.: 100
Non-contact Torque Sensors Mfr
N.A.I.C.S.: 334519

Methode Development Company **(1)**
7401 W Wilson Ave, Chicago, IL 60706-4548
Tel.: (708) 867-6777
Web Site: http://www.methode.com
Sales Range: $100-124.9 Million
Emp.: 300
Mfr of Resistive & Conductive Pastes
N.A.I.C.S.: 334417

Methode Electronics **(1)**
1700 Hicks Rd, Rolling Meadows, IL 60008
Tel.: (847) 577-9545
Sales Range: $50-74.9 Million
Emp.: 200
Power Connection Systems Mfr
N.A.I.C.S.: 334417
Andy Urda (Gen Mgr)

Methode Electronics (Shanghai) Co. Ltd. **(1)**
N40B T40B-7 No 1765 Chuan Qiao Road, Jin Qiao Export Processing Zone Pudong, Shanghai, 201206, China
Tel.: (86) 215 899 6570
Web Site: http://www.methode.com
Electronic Connectors, Controls & Power Distribution Systems Mfr
N.A.I.C.S.: 334417

Methode Electronics Asia Pte, Ltd. **(1)**
10 Jln Kilang Unit 03-02 Sime Darby Enterprise Centre, Singapore, 159410, Singapore
Tel.: (65) 64933000
Web Site: http://www.methode.com
Sales Range: $10-24.9 Million
Emp.: 5
Electronic Connector & Power Distribution System Design, Engineering, Sales & Support
N.A.I.C.S.: 334417

Methode Electronics Connectivity Technologies, Inc. **(1)**

1111 Digital Dr Ste 150, Richardson, TX 75081
Tel.: (972) 406-0000
Web Site: http://www.methode.com
Emp.: 40
Fiber Optic & Copper Infrastructure System Installation Services, Sales & Support
N.A.I.C.S.: 238210

Methode Electronics Europe Ltd. **(1)**
Vale of Leven Industrial Estate, West Dunbartonshire, Dumbarton, G82 3PD, Scotland, United Kingdom
Tel.: (44) 1389732123
Sales Range: $100-124.9 Million
Electronic & Mechatronic Parts Mfr
N.A.I.C.S.: 334419

Methode Electronics Far East Pte., Ltd. **(1)**
10 Jalan Kilang 03-02 Sime Darby Enterprise Centre, Singapore, 159410, Singapore **(100%)**
Tel.: (65) 64933000
Web Site: http://www.methode.com
Sales Range: $10-24.9 Million
Emp.: 5
Discrete Wire, Flat Cable & Printed Circuit Connectors & Microcircuit Sockets Mfr
N.A.I.C.S.: 335313
Ronald Liew (Dir-Fin)

Methode Electronics India, Private Ltd. **(1)**
Raj Driva 99/A 3rd Floor 5th Block KHB Colony, Koramangala, Bengaluru, 560095, India
Tel.: (91) 8043500700
Web Site: http://www.methode.com
Sales Range: $25-49.9 Million
Emp.: 120
Electronic Connector & Power Distribution System Mfr
N.A.I.C.S.: 334417
Anand Shetty (Mng Dir)

Methode Electronics International GmbH **(1)**
Rheinstrasse 40, 55435, Gau-Algesheim, Germany
Tel.: (49) 672553095120
Sales Range: $10-24.9 Million
Emp.: 23
Electrical Connection Parts Mfr & Whslr
N.A.I.C.S.: 335999
Dack Koman (Mng Dir)

Methode Electronics Ireland, Ltd. **(1)**
Unit H Crossagalla Business Park, Limerick, Ireland **(100%)**
Tel.: (353) 61401222
Web Site: http://www.methode.com
Sales Range: $10-24.9 Million
Emp.: 6
Electronic Connectors & Controls & Power Distribution Systems Mfr
N.A.I.C.S.: 334417

Methode Electronics Malta Holdings Ltd. **(1)**
Methode Buildings Mriehel Industrial Estate, Mriehel, BKR 3000, Malta
Tel.: (356) 21484184
Web Site: http://www.methode.com
Sales Range: $250-299.9 Million
Emp.: 1,000
Holding Company
N.A.I.C.S.: 551112

Subsidiary (Domestic):

Methode Electronics Malta Ltd. **(2)**
Triq I-Awdituri Zone 4, Central Business District, Birkirkara, CBD 4070, Malta **(100%)**
Tel.: (356) 23892300
Automotive Switches Mfr
N.A.I.C.S.: 335313

Methode Mexico, S.A. de C.V. **(1)**
Calle Spectrum 200 Ste D, Parque Industrial FINSA Monterrey, Apodaca, 66600, Mexico
Tel.: (52) 8181450312
Web Site: http://www.methode.com
Weight Sensor Bladder Mfr
N.A.I.C.S.: 334513

Methode Power Solutions Group **(1)**

1700 Hicks Rd, Rolling Meadows, IL 60008-1229
Tel.: (847) 577-9545
Web Site: http://www.methode.com
Sales Range: $100-124.9 Million
Design, Engineering & Manufacturing of Power Cables & Bus Bars
N.A.I.C.S.: 334417

Methode dataMate Products (1)
7401 W Wilson Ave, Chicago, IL 60706
Tel.: (708) 867-6777
Web Site: http://www.methode.com
Emp.: 200
Electronic Parts Mfr
N.A.I.C.S.: 334419

Network Business Products (1)
1700 Hicks Rd, Rolling Meadows, IL 60008-1025
Tel.: (847) 577-9546
Web Site: http://www.methode.com
Sales Range: $100-124.9 Million
Mfr of Bus Bars
N.A.I.C.S.: 334417

Nordic Lights Oy (1)
Bennasvagen 155, PO Box 36, 68601, Jakobstad, Finland
Tel.: (358) 8618121588923
Web Site: https://www.nordiclights.com
Automotive Light Mfr & Distr
N.A.I.C.S.: 332119

Optokon Co. Ltd. (1)
Cerveny Kriz 250, 58601, Jihlava, Czech Republic (75%)
Tel.: (420) 564040111
Web Site: http://www.optokon.com
Sales Range: $50-74.9 Million
Emp.: 160
Fiber Optic Cable Mfr
N.A.I.C.S.: 335921

Optokon Polska Sp. z o.o. (1)
Ul Kopuszanska 53, 02-232, Warsaw, Poland
Tel.: (48) 600490493
Web Site: http://www.optokon.pl
Sales Range: $10-24.9 Million
Emp.: 6
Electronic Connectors, Controls & Power Distribution Systems Mfr
N.A.I.C.S.: 334417

Optokon d.o.o. (1)
Trzaska 215, 1000, Ljubljana, Slovenia
Tel.: (386) 142282978
Sales Range: $10-24.9 Million
Emp.: 1
Electronic Connectors, Controls & Power Distribution Systems Mfr
N.A.I.C.S.: 334417
Grohar Marko (Mng Dir)

Pacific Insight Electronics Corp. (1)
1155 Insight Drive, Nelson, V1L 5P5, BC, Canada
Tel.: (250) 354-1155
Web Site: http://www.pacificinsight.com
Sales Range: $75-99.9 Million
Electronic Products Designer, Mfr & Supplier
N.A.I.C.S.: 334419

Procoplast S.A. (1)
Zenobe Gramme Strasse 9-11, Lontzen, 4710, Liege, Belgium
Tel.: (32) 87595090
Web Site: https://www.procoplast.be
Electronic Materials Mfr
N.A.I.C.S.: 327110

SIA Optokon Baltic (1)
Maza Kandavas iela 9, Riga, LV-1083, Latvia
Tel.: (371) 67802594
Web Site: http://www.optokon.lv
Sales Range: $10-24.9 Million
Emp.: 5
Electronic Connectors, Controls & Power Distribution Systems Mfr
N.A.I.C.S.: 334417

TouchSensor Technologies, L.L.C. (1)
203 N Gables Blvd, Wheaton, IL 60187
Tel.: (630) 221-9000
Web Site: https://www.touchsensor.com
Electronic & Mechatronic Parts Mfr

N.A.I.C.S.: 334419

Trace Laboratories Chicago (1)
1150 W Euclid Ave, Palatine, IL 60067-7368 (100%)
Tel.: (847) 934-5300
Web Site: http://www.tracelabs.com
Sales Range: $10-24.9 Million
Emp.: 20
Laboratory & Testing Consulting Services
N.A.I.C.S.: 541715

Trace Laboratories East (1)
5 N Park Dr Hunt Vly, Baltimore, MD 21030-1813 (100%)
Tel.: (410) 584-9099
Web Site: http://www.tracelabs.com
Sales Range: $10-24.9 Million
Emp.: 30
Testing Laboratory
N.A.I.C.S.: 541380

Translec Limited (1)
Saddleworth Business Park Huddersfield Road Delph, Oldham, OL3 5DF, Lancashire, United Kingdom
Tel.: (44) 1457878888
Web Site: https://www.translec.co.uk
Light & Electrical Product Mfr
N.A.I.C.S.: 327212

METLIFE, INC.
200 Park Ave, New York, NY 10166-0188
Tel.: (212) 578-9500 DE
Web Site: https://www.metlife.com
Year Founded: 1868
MET—(NYSE)
Rev.: $66,905,000,000
Assets: $687,584,000,000
Liabilities: $657,331,000,000
Net Worth: $30,253,000,000
Earnings: $1,578,000,000
Emp.: 45,000
Fiscal Year-end: 12/31/23
Holding Company; Insurance & Financial Services
N.A.I.C.S.: 551112
Ramy Tadros (Pres-Bus)
Catherine R. Kinney (Executives, Bd of Dirs)
Marlene Debel (Chief Risk Officer, Exec VP & Head-Insurance Investments)
Robert Glenn Hubbard (Chm)
Michael A. Zarcone (Exec VP & Head-Affairs)
Susan Podlogar (Chief HR Officer & Exec VP)
Stephen W. Gauster (Gen Counsel & Exec VP)
Tamara L. Schock (Chief Acctg Officer & Exec VP)
Bill Pappas (Exec VP & Head-Global Tech & Ops)
Robin Gordon (Chief Data & Analytics Officer)
Ben Cushman (Head-Regulatory Policy-Global)
Steven J. Goulart (Chief Investment Officer)
Nuria Garcia (Pres)
Lyndon Oliver (Pres)
Michael Roberts (CMO)
Cynthia F. Smith (Sr VP-Reg Bus & Distr Dev)
Michel A. Khalaf (Pres & CEO)

Subsidiaries:

1075 PEACHTREE, LLC (1)
1075 Peachtree St Ne, Atlanta, GA 30309-3911
Tel.: (404) 920-2350
Web Site: https://www.1075peachtree.com
Fire Insurance Services
N.A.I.C.S.: 524113

655 WEST BROADWAY, LLC (1)
655 W Broadway, San Diego, CA 92101
Tel.: (619) 702-0655
Web Site: https://www.655westbroadway.com

Fire Insurance Services
N.A.I.C.S.: 524113

ALICO ASIGURARI ROMANIA S.A (1)
47 53 Lascar Catargiu Bd Sector 1, Bucharest, 10665, Romania
Tel.: (40) 212084100
Web Site: http://www.alico.ro
Life Insurance Products & Services
N.A.I.C.S.: 524113

ALICO ITALIA S.P.A. (1)
Viale Castro Pretorio 124, Rome, 185, Italy
Tel.: (39) 06492161
Insurance Services
N.A.I.C.S.: 524113

ALPHA PROPERTIES, INC. (1)
224 Market Ave, Boerne, TX 78006
Tel.: (210) 764-2600
Web Site: https://alpha-properties.com
Fire Insurance Services
N.A.I.C.S.: 524113

AMMETLIFE INSURANCE BERHAD (1)
Level 24 Menara 1 Sentrum No 201 Jalan Tun Sambanthan, 50470, Kuala Lumpur, Malaysia
Tel.: (60) 32 271 8000
Web Site: https://www.ammetlife.com
General Insurance Services
N.A.I.C.S.: 524210
Horng Fatt Cho (Chm)

Administradora de Fondos de Pensiones Provida S.A. (1)
Av Pedro de Valdivia 100, Providencia, Santiago, Chile (91.38%)
Tel.: (56) 6002010150
Web Site: http://www.provida.cl
Rev.: $348,431,010
Assets: $672,495,270
Liabilities: $187,251,120
Net Worth: $485,244,150
Earnings: $149,698,500
Emp.: 2,195
Fiscal Year-end: 12/31/2014
Pension Fund Management Services
N.A.I.C.S.: 524292

Subsidiary (Non-US):

AFP Genesis Administradora de Fondos y Fideicomisos S.A. (2)
Av Rodrigo Chavez Parque Empresarial Colon Bldg Pacific Plaza, PB Offices 3 and 4, Guayaquil, Ecuador (100%)
Tel.: (593) 7200200
Web Site: https://www.fondosgenesis.com
Pension Fund Administration Services
N.A.I.C.S.: 524292

Affirmative Investment Management Partners Ltd. (1)
8th Floor One Angel Lane, London, EC4R 3AB, United Kingdom
Tel.: (44) 2039496900
Web Site: http://www.affirmativeim.com
Financial Management Services
N.A.I.C.S.: 541611

Alico Cia de Seguros S.A. (1)
18 de Julio 1738, Montevideo, Uruguay
Tel.: (598) 24033939
Insurance Services
N.A.I.C.S.: 524113

American Life Insurance Company (1)
Corporation Trust Ctr 1209 Orange St, Wilmington, DE 19801 (100%)
Tel.: (302) 594-2000
Life Insurance
N.A.I.C.S.: 524128

Subsidiary (Non-US):

ALICO Bulgaria (2)
Building B 51 Bulgaria Blvd, 1404, Sofia, Bulgaria (100%)
Tel.: (359) 28186200
Web Site: http://www.metlife.bg
Sales Range: $1-9.9 Million
Emp.: 60
Insurance Services
N.A.I.C.S.: 524210

Alico AIG Life Ukraine (2)

Kominterna St 14, 02132, Kiev, Ukraine (100%)
Tel.: (380) 444941343
Web Site: http://www.metlifealico.com.ua
Sales Range: $1-9.9 Million
Insurance Services
N.A.I.C.S.: 524210

Alico a.s (2)
Hviezdoslavovo Nam 20, 81102, Bratislava, Slovakia (100%)
Tel.: (421) 259363111
Web Site: http://www.metlife.sk
Sales Range: $1-9.9 Million
Insurance Services
N.A.I.C.S.: 524210

Amcico Pojistovna A.S. (2)
Londynska 41, V Celnici 1028 10, Prague, 120 21, Czech Republic (100%)
Tel.: (420) 227111000
Web Site: http://www.metlifeamcico.cz
Sales Range: $100-124.9 Million
Insurance Services
N.A.I.C.S.: 524210
Christos Mistillioglou (Chm)

MetLife Alico Cyprus (2)
38 Kennedy Ave, PO Box 21383, 1507, Nicosia, Cyprus (100%)
Tel.: (357) 22845845
Web Site: http://www.metlife.com.cy
Sales Range: $1-9.9 Million
Emp.: 55
Life, Pensions, Accident & Health Insurance Coverages
N.A.I.C.S.: 524210

MetLife India Insurance Company Private Limited (2)
Unit No 701 702 703 7th Floor West Wing Raheja Towers 26/27 M G Road, Bengaluru, 560 001, Karnataka, India (26%)
Tel.: (91) 2241790000
Web Site: https://www.pnbmetlife.com
Sales Range: $100-124.9 Million
Insurance & Financial Services
N.A.I.C.S.: 524298
Ashish Kumar Srivastava (CEO)
Asha Murali (Chief Actuary Officer)
Samrat Das (COO)
Sanjay Kumar (Chief Investment Officer)
Sarang Cheema (Chief Risk Officer)
Shishir Agarwal (Chief HR Officer)
Vineet Maheshwari (Chief Strategy Officer)
Motty John (Chief Legal Officer)
Yagya Turker (Sec)

Metlife Alico Mutual Funds Company (2)
119 Kifissia Avenue, Maroussi, 151 24, Greece (100%)
Tel.: (30) 210 878 7000
Web Site: http://www.metlifemfc.gr
Sales Range: $75-99.9 Million
Financial, Mutual Funds & Insurance Services
N.A.I.C.S.: 524210

Ammetlife Takaful Berhad (1)
Level 23 Menara 1 Sentrum No 201 Jalan Tun Sambanthan, 50470, Kuala Lumpur, Malaysia
Tel.: (60) 322718000
Web Site: https://www.ammetlifetakaful.com
Insurance Claims Services
N.A.I.C.S.: 524291
Mohd Tarmidzi Ahmad Nordin (Chm)
Azilah Ayup (Head-Ops)
Azam Mohd Yusof (CEO)
Haslinda Ahmad (Head-Risk Mgmt)

BIDV METLIFE LIFE INSURANCE LIMITED LIABILITY COMPANY (1)
10th floor Tower A Vincom City Towers 191 Ba Trieu, Hai Ba Trung District, Hanoi, Vietnam
Tel.: (84) 246 282 0808
Web Site: https://www.bidvmetlife.com.vn
Emp.: 100
Medical Insurance Services
N.A.I.C.S.: 524114
Nguyen Thi Quynh Giao (Chm)

BOULEVARD RESIDENTIAL, LLC (1)
4080 Campbell Ave, Menlo Park, CA 94025
Tel.: (650) 328-5050
Web Site: https://www.blvdresidential.com

MetLife, Inc.—(Continued)

Fire Insurance Services
N.A.I.C.S.: 524113

Borderland Investments Limited (1)
700 Montana Ave, El Paso, TX 79902
Tel.: (915) 533-0765
Web Site:
   https://www.borderlandinvestments.com
Fire Insurance Services
N.A.I.C.S.: 524113

Brighthouse Life Insurance
Company (1)
11225 N Community House Rd, Charlotte,
NC 28277 (100%)
Tel.: (980) 365-7100
Rev.: $7,832,000,000
Assets: $216,151,000,000
Liabilities: $209,287,000,000
Net Worth: $6,864,000,000
Earnings: ($63,000,000)
Fiscal Year-end: 12/31/2022
General Insurance Services
N.A.I.C.S.: 524210
Eric T. Steigerwalt *(Chm, Pres & CEO)*
Myles J. Lambert *(Chief Distr & Mktg Offi-*
cer & Exec VP)
John L. Rosenthal *(CIO & Exec VP)*
Conor E. Murphy *(COO & Exec VP)*
Edward A. Spehar *(CFO & Exec VP)*
Vonda Huss *(Exec VP)*
Kristine H. Toscano *(Chief Acctg Officer)*

CHESTNUT FLATS WIND, LLC (1)
1801 Market St Ste 2700, Philadelphia, PA
19103-1628
Tel.: (215) 665-9810
Eletric Power Generation Services
N.A.I.C.S.: 221115

DEWEY SQUARE TOWER ASSOCI-
ATES, LLC (1)
100 Cambridge St Ste 1301, Boston, MA
02114
Tel.: (617) 367-9929
Web Site: http://www.deweysquare.com
Emp.: 10
Real Estate Property Lessor Services
N.A.I.C.S.: 531190

EL CONQUISTADOR MAH II
LLC (1)
10000 N Oracle Rd, Tucson, AZ 85704-
7644
Tel.: (520) 544-5000
Hotel & Motel Operating Services
N.A.I.C.S.: 721110

FEDERAL FLOOD CERTIFICATION
LLC (1)
1555 W Walnut Hill Ln, Irving, TX 75038
Tel.: (214) 492-7075
Professional Services
N.A.I.C.S.: 813920

Fortissimo Co., Ltd. (1)
1-27-13 Takadanobaba 3rd floor Plums
Building, Shinjuku-ku, Tokyo, 169-0075,
Japan
Tel.: (81) 35 291 5234
Web Site: https://www.fortissimo-japan.com
Fire Insurance Services
N.A.I.C.S.: 524113

GBN,LLC (1)
275 Cherry St Apt 26c, New York, NY
10002
Tel.: (718) 986-5175
Business Support Services
N.A.I.C.S.: 561990

Hyatt Legal Plans, Inc. (1)
1111 Superior Ave Ste 800, Cleveland, OH
44114-2527 (100%)
Tel.: (216) 241-0022
Web Site: https://www.legalplans.com
Sales Range: $1-9.9 Million
Emp.: 90
Prepaid Group Legal Plan Services
N.A.I.C.S.: 524210
David Seed *(Dir-Marketing)*
Felicia Surtel *(CFO)*
Ingrid Tolentino *(CEO)*
Roger Elder *(Gen Counsel)*
Claire Godlewski *(Asst VP-Ops & Reg Mar-*
ket Admin)

LEGAL CHILE S.A. (1)

Presidente Riesco 5335 Of 302, Las Con-
des, Chile
Tel.: (56) 228874000
Web Site: https://www.legalchile.cl
Fire Insurance Services
N.A.I.C.S.: 524113

Logan Circle Partners, L.P. (1)
1717 Arch St Fl 15, Philadelphia, PA 19103
Tel.: (267) 330-0000
Web Site:
   http://www.logancirclepartners.com
Rev.: $38,000,000,000
Financial Investment Services
N.A.I.C.S.: 523999

Lumenlab Malaysia Sdn. Bhd. (1)
Unit 32-01 Level 32 Tower B The Vertical
Corporate Towers Avenue 10, Bangsar
South No 8 Jalan Kerinchi, 59200, Kuala
Lumpur, Malaysia
Tel.: (60) 327863530
Web Site:
   http://www.dev.lumenlab.my.dottylabs.com
Insurance Services
N.A.I.C.S.: 524126

MCP Property Management,
LLC (1)
120 E Chestnut St, Burlington, WI 53105
Tel.: (262) 661-4284
Web Site: http://www.mpcpm.com
Property Management Services
N.A.I.C.S.: 531311

MET II OFFICE LLC (1)
355 SE 2nd Ave, Miami, FL 33131
Tel.: (305) 350-0726
Emp.: 9
Real Estate Services
N.A.I.C.S.: 531210
Maggie Vassilaros *(Gen Mgr)*

METLIFE ADMINISTRADORA DE
FUNDOS MULTIPATROCINADOS
LTDA. (1)
Rua Florida 1595 4 Andar, Brooklin Novo,
Sao Paulo, 04565-001, Brazil
Tel.: (55) 1155019700
Fire Insurance Services
N.A.I.C.S.: 524113

METLIFE AMERICAN INTERNA-
TIONAL GROUP AND ARAB NA-
TIONAL BANK COOPERATIVE IN-
SURANCE COMPANY (1)
Al-ebdaa Tower - King Fahd Road - Olaya
District, PO Box 56437, Riyadh, 11554,
Saudi Arabia
Tel.: (966) 115109300
Insurance & Financial Services
N.A.I.C.S.: 524210

METLIFE COLOMBIA SEGUROS de
VIDA S.A. (1)
Carrera 7 No 99-53 Piso 17, Bogota, Co-
lombia
Tel.: (57) 307 7049
Web Site: https://www.metlife.com.co
Fire Insurance Services
N.A.I.C.S.: 524210

METLIFE COMMERCIAL MORT-
GAGE INCOME FUND GP, LLC (1)
10 Park Ave, Morristown, NJ 07960
Tel.: (973) 355-4000
Fire Insurance Services
N.A.I.C.S.: 524113

METLIFE CORE PROPERTY REIT,
LLC (1)
10 Park Ave, Morristown, NJ 07962
Tel.: (973) 355-4077
Fire Insurance Services
N.A.I.C.S.: 524210

METLIFE EUROPE INSURANCE
LIMITED (1)
20 on Hatch Lower Hatch Street, Dublin,
DO2 HC8O, Ireland
Tel.: (353) 12650700
Fire Insurance Services
N.A.I.C.S.: 524210
Keith Ryne *(Mng Dir)*

METLIFE GENERAL INSURANCE
LIMITED (1)
Level 9 2 Park Street, PO Box 3319, Syd-
ney, 2000, NSW, Australia

Tel.: (61) 1300555625
Web Site: http://www.metlife.com.au
Sales Range: $100-124.9 Million
Emp.: 250
Insurance Services
N.A.I.C.S.: 524113

METLIFE INSURANCE K.K. (1)
4-1-3 Taihei Olinas Tower, Sumida-ku, To-
kyo, 130-0012, Japan
Tel.: (81) 332844111
General Insurance Services
N.A.I.C.S.: 524210

METLIFE INSURANCE LIMITED (1)
PO Box 3319, Sydney, 2001, NSW, Austra-
lia
Tel.: (61) 1300555625
Web Site: https://www.metlife.com.au
Fire Insurance Services
N.A.I.C.S.: 524113

METLIFE INVESTMENT MANAGE-
MENT LIMITED (1)
8th Floor 1 Angel Lane, London, EC4R
3AB, United Kingdom
Tel.: (44) 2077152000
Fire Insurance Services
N.A.I.C.S.: 524113

METLIFE INVESTMENT MANAGE-
MENT, LLC (1)
200 Park Ave, New York, NY 10166
Tel.: (212) 578-7531
Investment Management Service
N.A.I.C.S.: 523940
Amy Cummings *(Mng Dir-San Francisco)*
Jason Funk *(Head-Bus Dev-Institutional Cli-*
ent Grp-EMEA)
Joseph Pollaro *(COO)*
Thomas Metzler *(Mng Dir-Institutional Client*
Grp)
David J. Rothenberg *(Mng Dir & Head-*
Institutional Client Grp-Global)
Maya Kiyokawa *(Dir-Institutional Client Grp-*
Tokyo)
Esther Rulli *(Dir-Institutional Sls-United*
Kingdom & Netherlands)
Matthew Mosca *(Head-Institutional Client*
Grp-Global)
Steve Goulart *(Pres)*
Robert Merck *(Sr Mng Dir & Head-Real Es-*
tate & Agriculture-Global)
Sara Queen *(Mng Dir & Head-Real Estate*
Equity)

Subsidiary (Domestic):

Raven Capital Management LLC (2)
110 Greene St Ste 9G, New York, NY
10012
Tel.: (212) 966-7926
Web Site: http://www.ravencm.com
Private Equity Firm & Investment Adviser
N.A.I.C.S.: 523999
Josh Green *(Pres & CIO)*
Brandon Doerr *(Mng Dir)*
Chris Felice *(CFO)*

Subsidiary (Domestic):

Open Road Films, LLC (3)
12301 Wilshire Blvd Ste 600, Los Angeles,
CA 90025 (100%)
Tel.: (310) 696-7575
Web Site: http://www.openroadfilms.com
Film Distribution Services
N.A.I.C.S.: 512120
Elliott Kleinberg *(COO)*
Steven Andriuzzo *(CFO)*
Jason Cassidy *(Pres-Mktg)*
Elliot Slutzky *(Exec VP-Distr)*
Sophie Cassidy *(Sr VP-Production)*
Lejo Pet *(Sr VP-Acq)*

METLIFE INVESTMENTS ASIA.
LIMITED (1)
9/F One Taikoo Place 979 King's Road,
Quarry Bay, China (Hong Kong)
Tel.: (852) 22774411
Fire Insurance Services
N.A.I.C.S.: 524113

METLIFE MAS, S.A. DE C.V. (1)
Avenida Insurgentes Sur No 1457 piso 11,
Colonia Insurgentes Mixcoac alcaldia benito
juarez, 03920, Mexico, Mexico
Tel.: (52) 5552794542
Web Site: https://www.metlifemas.com.mx
Fire Insurance Services

N.A.I.C.S.: 524113

METLIFE POJISTOVNA A.S. (1)
Londynska 41, Prague, 12021, Czech Re-
public
Tel.: (420) 221416111
Web Site: http://www.metlife.cz
Fire Insurance Services
N.A.I.C.S.: 524210

METLIFE PROPERTIES VEN-
TURES, LLC (1)
200 Pk Ave, New York, NY 10166
Tel.: (212) 578-2211
Web Site: http://www.metlife.com
Insurance Services
N.A.I.C.S.: 524210

METLIFE SEGUROS S.A. (1)
Gral Peron 646 6th Floor, 1038, Buenos
Aires, Argentina
Tel.: (54) 43487500
Web Site: http://www.metlife.com.ar
Fire Insurance Services
N.A.I.C.S.: 524210

METLIFE SEGUROS S.A. (1)
Yaguaron 1407 4th Floor of 401, CP 11100,
Montevideo, Uruguay
Tel.: (598) 29033030
Web Site: http://www.metlife.com.uy
Fire Insurance Services
N.A.I.C.S.: 524210

METLIFE SERVICES CYPRUS
LIMITED (1)
38 Kennedy Avenue, PO Box 21383, 1507,
Nicosia, Cyprus
Tel.: (357) 22845845
Insurance & Financial Services
N.A.I.C.S.: 524210

METLIFE SLOVAKIA S.R.O. (1)
Budova Eurovea vchod Central 3 Pribinova
10, 811 09, Bratislava, Slovakia
Tel.: (421) 259363111
Web Site: https://www.metlife.sk
Fire Insurance Services
N.A.I.C.S.: 524113

METLIFE WORLDWIDE HOLDINGS,
INC. (1)
200 Pk Ave, New York, NY 10166-0188
Tel.: (212) 578-2211
Web Site: http://www.metlif.com
Insurance Products & Services
N.A.I.C.S.: 524113

METLIFE, LIFE INSURANCE
COMPANY (1)
75 Road 90 Cairo, 11835, New Cairo, Egypt
Tel.: (20) 224619020
Insuranoo Sorvicoo
N.A.I.C.S.: 524114

METROPOLITAN LIFE SOCIETATE
de ADMINISTRARE a UNUI FOND
de PENSII ADMINISTRAT PRIVAT
S (1)
B-dul Lascar Catargiu 47-53 Unit 4B Floor 4
Sector 1, 010665, Bucharest, Romania
Tel.: (40) 212084444
Web Site: http://www.metropolitanlife.ro
Emp.: 150
General Insurance Services
N.A.I.C.S.: 524210

MTL LEASING, LLC (1)
119 Legend Dale, San Antonio, TX 78260
Tel.: (210) 460-9700
Web Site: https://mtleasingllc.com
Fire Insurance Services
N.A.I.C.S.: 524113

Maxis GBN S.A.S. (1)
Terrasse 4 7 Boulevard Des Bouvets,
92000, Nanterre, France (50%)
Tel.: (33) 157321864
Web Site: http://www.maxis-gbn.com
Sales Range: $75-99.9 Million
Employee Benefits Services
N.A.I.C.S.: 524298

MetLife Auto & Home Insurance
Agency, Inc. (1)
500 Economy Ct, Freeport, IL
61032-5065 (100%)
Tel.: (815) 233-2000
Web Site: http://www.metlife.com

Sales Range: $550-599.9 Million
Emp.: 600
Fire, Marine & Casualty Insurance Services
N.A.I.C.S.: 524126

MetLife International Holdings, LLC (1)
200 Park Ave, New York, NY 10166-0188
Tel.: (212) 578-2211
Web Site: http://www.metlife.com
Holding Company
N.A.I.C.S.: 551112

Affiliate (Non-US):

MetLife Direct Co., Ltd. (2)
12th Floor Yurakucho ITOCiA 2-7-1 Yurakucho, Chiyoda-ku 2-3-14 Higashi-shinagawa Shinagawa-ku, Tokyo, 100-0006, Japan
Tel.: (81) 368604585
Web Site: http://www.metlife.co.jp
Sales Range: $75-99.9 Million
Insurance & Financial Services
N.A.I.C.S.: 524298

Subsidiary (Non-US):

MetLife Insurance Limited (2)
2 Park St Level 9, Sydney, 2000, NSW, Australia
Tel.: (61) 1300555625
Web Site: http://www.metlife.com.au
Insurance & Financial Services
N.A.I.C.S.: 524298
Richard Nunn *(CEO)*
Brad Brandenburg *(Chief Compliance Officer & Chief Risk Officer)*
Gerard McDermott *(Chief Strategy Officer & Chief Data Officer)*
Meary El-Khoury *(Chief Retail Insurance Officer)*
Michael Mulholland *(Chief Distr Officer)*
David Curry *(CIO)*
Keiren McKinnon *(CFO)*
Olivia Sarah-Le Lacheur *(COO)*

MetLife Limited (2)
Beacon House 27 Clarendon Road, Belfast, BT1 3PR, United Kingdom
Tel.: (44) 8009170100
Web Site: https://www.metlife.co.uk
Sales Range: $1-9.9 Million
Emp.: 50,
Insurance & Financial Services
N.A.I.C.S.: 524298
Dominic Grinstead *(Mng Dir)*

MetLife Saengmyoung Insurance Co. Ltd. (2)
MetLife Tower 316 Teheran-ro, Gangnam-gu, Seoul, Korea (South) **(100%)**
Tel.: (82) 220176700
Web Site: http://www.metlife.co.kr
Sales Range: $250-299.9 Million
Emp.: 360
Personal Whole Life, Health & Endowment Insurance & Annuities & Group Life Insurance & Pension Services
N.A.I.C.S.: 524113

Metropolitan Life Seguros de Vida, S.A. (2)
Tte General Peron 646 3 piso, Buenos Aires, 1038, Argentina **(100%)**
Tel.: (54) 11 4340 3500
Web Site: http://www.metlife.com.ar
Sales Range: $25-49.9 Million
Emp.: 150
Seller of Individual Life Insurance & Disability Products
N.A.I.C.S.: 524298

Metropolitan Life Seguros e Previdencia Privada S.A. (2)
Avenue Engenheiro Luis Carlos Berrini 1253, Brooklin, Sao Paulo, 04571-010, SP, Brazil
Tel.: (55) 115 501 9700
Web Site: https://www.metlife.com.br
Individual & Group Life Insurance & Retirement Savings Services
N.A.I.C.S.: 524298

MetLife Mexico S.A. (2)
Avenida Insurgentes Sur numero 1457 del piso 11 al 14, Colonia Insurgentes Mixcoac Alcaldia Benito Juarez, 03920, Mexico, Mexico
Tel.: (52) 555 328 7000
Web Site: https://www.metlife.com.mx

Sales Range: $450-499.9 Million
Emp.: 1,150
Life Insurance & Retirement Savings Services
N.A.I.C.S.: 524298

MetLife Policyholder Trust (1)
Rodney Sq N 1100 N Market St, Wilmington, DE 19890
Tel.: (302) 651-1000
Assets: $9,027,725,000
Liabilities: $82,347,000
Net Worth: $8,945,378,000
Earnings: $250,340,000
Fiscal Year-end: 12/31/2022
Insurance Support Services
N.A.I.C.S.: 524298
Beth Andrews *(VP)*

MetLife Securities, Inc. (1)
1095 Ave of the Americas, New York, NY 10036
Tel.: (212) 578-2211
Web Site: http://www.metlife.com
Sales Range: $200-249.9 Million
Emp.: 25
Financing & Investment Services
N.A.I.C.S.: 523999

Metlife Insurance Company of Connecticut (1)
1300 Hall Blvd, Bloomfield, CT 06002
Tel.: (860) 656-3000
Rev.: $3,405,000,000
Assets: $226,204,000,000
Liabilities: $220,263,000,000
Net Worth: $5,941,000,000
Earnings: ($1,124,000,000)
Fiscal Year-end: 12/31/2023
Fire Insurance Services
N.A.I.C.S.: 524113

Metlife Investors Distribution Company (1)
1 Met Life Plz, Long Island City, NY 11101
Tel.: (212) 578-2211
Emp.: 8
Insurance Management Services
N.A.I.C.S.: 524298

Metlife Uk Limited (1)
PO Box 1411, Sunderland, SR5 9RB, United Kingdom
Tel.: (44) 8009170100
Web Site: https://www.metlife.co.uk
Life Insurance Provider
N.A.I.C.S.: 524210

Metropolitan Casualty Insurance Co. (1)
700 Quaker Ln, Warwick, RI 02886
Tel.: (401) 827-2400
Web Site: http://www.metlife.com
Automobile Insurance Services
N.A.I.C.S.: 524126

Metropolitan General Insurance Co. (1)
700 Quaker Ln, Warwick, RI 02886
Tel.: (401) 827-2400
Web Site: http://www.metlife.com
Emp.: 32
Automobile Insurance Services
N.A.I.C.S.: 524126

New England Life Insurance Co. (1)
501 Boylston St, Boston, MA 02117 **(100%)**
Tel.: (212) 578-2211
Web Site: http://www.nefn.com
Sales Range: $650-699.9 Million
Emp.: 2,400
Life & Health Insurance Services
N.A.I.C.S.: 524113

OBS REIT, LLC (1)
10 Park Ave, Morristown, NJ 07962
Tel.: (973) 355-4077
General Insurance Services
N.A.I.C.S.: 524210

PNB METLIFE INDIA INSURANCE COMPANY LIMITED (1)
Unit No 701 702 703 7th Floor West Wing Raheja Towers 26/27 M G Road, Bengaluru, 560001, Karnataka, India
Tel.: (91) 2241790000
Web Site: https://www.pnbmetlife.com
Life Insurance Agency Services
N.A.I.C.S.: 524210

Reynolds Plantation, Inc. (1)
1341 Linger Longer Rd, Greensboro, GA 30642
Tel.: (706) 467-1676
Web Site: https://www.reynoldslakeoconee.com
Emp.: 500
Golf Courses, Marinas & Vacation Resort Operator
N.A.I.C.S.: 713910
Lee Arberg *(Sr VP)*

SEGUROS VENEZUELA C.A. (1)
Av Francisco de Miranda Edif Seguros Venezuela pisos 8 y 9, Urb Campo Alegre, Caracas, Estado Miranda, Venezuela
Tel.: (58) 2129017111
Web Site: http://www.segurosvenezuela.com
Insurance Services
N.A.I.C.S.: 524113

SINO-US UNITED METLIFE INSURANCE CO (1)
Central Plz 15f No 227 N Huang Pi Rd, Shanghai, 200003, China
Tel.: (86) 2123103636
Insurance & Financial Services
N.A.I.C.S.: 524210

SafeGuard Health Enterprises, Inc. (1)
95 Enterprise Ste 200, Aliso Viejo, CA 92656-2065
Tel.: (949) 425-4300
Web Site: http://www.safeguard.net
Sales Range: $100-124.9 Million
Emp.: 360
Dental Insurance Benefits
N.A.I.C.S.: 524114

Subsidiary (Domestic):

SafeGuard Health Plans, Inc. (2)
95 Enterprise Ste 200, Aliso Viejo, CA 92656
Tel.: (949) 425-4300
Web Site: https://www.metlife.com
Sales Range: $75-99.9 Million
Emp.: 150
Dental Insurance Benefits
N.A.I.C.S.: 524114

Superior Vision of New Jersey, Inc. (1)
PO Box 1416, Latham, NY 12110
Fire Insurance Services
N.A.I.C.S.: 524113

Versant Health Holdco, Inc. (1)
PO Box 1416, Latham, NY 12110
Web Site: https://versanthealth.com
Fire Insurance Services
N.A.I.C.S.: 524113

METRO ONE TELECOMMUNICATIONS, INC.
30 N Gould St Ste 5953, Sheridan, WY 82801
Tel.: (646) 831-6244   DE
Web Site:
   https://metro1telecomm.com
Year Founded: 1989
WOWI—(OTCIQ)
Rev.: $17,888,000
Assets: $19,567,000
Liabilities: $13,900,000
Net Worth: $5,667,000
Earnings: ($14,417,000)
Emp.: 632
Fiscal Year-end: 12/31/07
Contact Services, Data & Analytics for Consumer & Business Marketers
N.A.I.C.S.: 561499

METRO PHOENIX BANK
4686 E Van Buren St Ste 190, Phoenix, AZ 85008
Tel.: (602) 346-1800
Web Site:
   http://www.metrophoenixbank.com
Year Founded: 2007
MPHX—(OTCIQ)
Commercial Banking Services
N.A.I.C.S.: 522110

Stephen P. Haggard *(Pres & CEO)*
Jack W. Hilton *(Chm)*
James R. Barrons *(Vice Chm)*
Helen C. DeFusco *(CFO & Exec VP)*
Michael S. Morano *(Chief Credit Officer & Exec VP)*

METROCITY BANKSHARES, INC.
5114 Buford Hwy, Doraville, GA 30340
Tel.: (770) 455-4989   GA
Web Site:
   https://www.metrocitybank.bank
Year Founded: 2014
MCBS—(NASDAQ)
Rev.: $166,424,000
Assets: $3,427,239,000
Liabilities: $3,077,818,000
Net Worth: $349,421,000
Earnings: $62,602,000
Emp.: 216
Fiscal Year-end: 12/31/22
Bank Holding Company
N.A.I.C.S.: 551111
Nack Y. Paek *(Chm & CEO)*
Farid Tan *(Pres)*
Howard Hwasaeng Kim *(COO, Chief Lending Officer & Exec VP)*
Don T. P. Leung *(Vice Chm)*
Lucas Stewart *(CFO & Exec VP)*

Subsidiaries:

Metro City Bank (1)
5114 Buford Hwy, Doraville, GA 30340
Tel.: (770) 455-4989
Web Site: http://www.metrocitybank.com
Commercial Banking Services
N.A.I.C.S.: 522110
Nack Y. Paek *(Founder, Exec Chm & CEO)*
Farid Tan *(CEO)*
Howard Hwasaeng Kim *(Pres, COO & Exec VP)*
Don T. P. Leung *(Vice Chm)*

METROPOLITAN BANK HOLDING CORP.
99 Park Ave, New York, NY 10016
Tel.: (212) 659-0600   NY
Web Site: https://www.mcbankny.com
Year Founded: 1999
MCB—(NYSE)
Rev.: $287,332,000
Assets: $6,267,337,000
Liabilities: $5,691,440,000
Net Worth: $575,897,000
Earnings: $59,425,000
Emp.: 239
Fiscal Year-end: 12/31/22
Commercial Banking Services
N.A.I.C.S.: 522110
Daniel F. Dougherty *(CFO & Exec VP)*
Nick R. Rosenberg *(Exec VP & Head-Payments Grp-Global)*
Michael A. Guarino *(Sr VP)*
Scott Lublin *(Chief Lending Officer & Exec VP)*
Dixiana M. Berrios *(COO & Exec VP)*
Jean-Philippe Gerbi *(Chief Digital Officer-Metropolitan Comml Bank & Sr VP-Metropolitan Comml Bank)*
Laura Capra *(Exec VP)*
Frederik F. Erikson *(Gen Counsel & Exec VP)*
Mark R. DeFazio *(Pres & CEO)*

METROSPACES, INC.
12 Ford St Fl 14, Brooklyn, NY 11213
Tel.: (646) 850-3374   FL
Web Site:
   http://www.metrospaces.com
MSPC—(OTCIQ)
Real Estate Manangement Services
N.A.I.C.S.: 531190
Carlos Daniel Silva *(CEO)*

METROSPACES, INC.—(Continued)

METTLER-TOLEDO INTERNATIONAL, INC.
1900 Polaris Pkwy, Columbus, OH 43240
Tel.: (614) 438-4794   DE
Web Site: https://www.mt.com
Year Founded: 1945
MTD—(NYSE)
Rev.: $3,788,309,000
Assets: $3,355,555,000
Liabilities: ($3,505,493,000)
Net Worth: ($149,938,000)
Earnings: $788,778,000
Emp.: 16,000
Fiscal Year-end: 12/31/23
Precision Instruments Mfr & Marketer
N.A.I.C.S.: 334516
Christian Magloth (Head-HR)
Shawn P. Vadala (CFO)
Oliver Wittorf (Head-Supply Chain & IT)
Gerry Keller (Head-Process Analytics Div)
Michelle Roe (Gen Counsel)
Elena Markwalder (Head-Industrial Div)
Jonas Greutert (Head-Product Inspection Div)

Subsidiaries:

Accurate Poly Services APS (1)
210 Rue Geiler de Kaysersberg Parc dinnovation, PO Box 10160, 67404, Illkirch-Graffenstaden, Cedex, France
Tel.: (33) 388654280
Web Site: http://www.aps-metrologie.fr
Laboratory Instrument Mfr
N.A.I.C.S.: 334516

Anachem Limited (1)
64 Boston Road Beaumont Leys, Leicester, LE4 1AW, Bedfordshire, United Kingdom   (100%)
Tel.: (44) 1162357070
Web Site: http://www.anachem.co.uk
Sales Range: $25-49.9 Million
Emp.: 40
Scientific Laboratory Supplies Distr
N.A.I.C.S.: 423450
Mark Pearle (Mng Dir)

CargoScan AS (1)
Ulvenveien 92 B, Oslo, 0581, Norway   (100%)
Tel.: (47) 23067777
Web Site: https://www.mt.com
Sales Range: $10-24.9 Million
Emp.: 50
Producer, Developer & Marketer of Equipment for Automating the Sorting of Packaging Waste
N.A.I.C.S.: 333993

Eagle Product Inspection LLC (1)
1571 Northpointe Pkwy, Lutz, FL 33558
Web Site: https://www.eaglepi.com
Industrial Machinery Mfr
N.A.I.C.S.: 333310

Eagle Product Inspection Limited (1)
Royston Business Park, Royston, SG8 5HN, Hertfordshire, United Kingdom
Tel.: (44) 1763244858
X-Ray Machine Mfr
N.A.I.C.S.: 334517

Gelan Detectiesystemen B.V. (1)
Kievitsven 30, 5249 JJ, Rosmalen, Netherlands
Tel.: (31) 738905020
Web Site: https://www.gelan.nl
Sales Range: $25-49.9 Million
Emp.: 50
Metal Detector Mfr
N.A.I.C.S.: 334519

Henry Troemner LLC (1)
201 Wolf Dr, Thorofare, NJ 08086-2245
Tel.: (856) 686-1600
Web Site: https://www.troemner.com
Laboratory Equipment Mfr
N.A.I.C.S.: 334516
Mark Kline (Exec VP)

Melibokus Industrie-Elektronik GmbH (1)
Gernsheimer Strasse 2, 64673, Zwingenberg, Germany
Tel.: (49) 6251854400
Web Site: http://www.melibokus.com
Analytical Laboratory Instrument Mfr
N.A.I.C.S.: 334516

Mettler Toledo Analyse Industrielle S.a.r.l.
30 Bd de Douaumont, BP 949, 75829, Paris, Cedex, France   (100%)
Tel.: (33) 147370600
Web Site: http://www.mtpro.com
Sales Range: $1-9.9 Million
Emp.: 30
Provider of Precision Instruments
N.A.I.C.S.: 333310

Mettler Toledo Instruments (Shanghai) Ltd. (1)
589 Gui Ping Rd, Cao He Jing Hi Tech Park, Shanghai, 200233, China   (100%)
Tel.: (86) 2161209633
Web Site: http://www.mtchina.com
Provider of Precision Instruments
N.A.I.C.S.: 333310

Mettler-Toledo (Albstadt) GmbH (1)
Unter Dem Malesfelsen 34, PO Box 250, Albstadt, 72458, Germany   (100%)
Tel.: (49) 7431140
Web Site: http://www.mt.com
Precision Instruments Mfr
N.A.I.C.S.: 811210

Mettler-Toledo (Changzhou) Precision Instruments Ltd. (1)
No 111 Taihu West Road, Xinbei District, Changzhou, 213125, Jiangsu, China
Tel.: (86) 51986642040
Web Site: https://www.mt.com
Emp.: 1,300
Analytical Laboratory Instrument Mfr
N.A.I.C.S.: 334516
Mary T. Finnegan (Mng Dir)

Mettler-Toledo (Changzhou) Scale & System Ltd. (1)
No 111 Changxi Road, Xinbei District, Changzhou, 213001, Jiangsu, China
Tel.: (86) 5196642040
Web Site: http://www.met.com
Emp.: 2,000
Analytical Laboratory Instrument Whslr
N.A.I.C.S.: 423490

Mettler-Toledo (HK) Ltd. (1)
Unit 503-504 5th Floor Fashion Centre 51-53 Wing Hong Street, Cheung Sha Wan, Kowloon, China (Hong Kong)
Tel · (852) 2 744 1221
Web Site: https://www.mt.com
Analytical Laboratory Instrument Mfr
N.A.I.C.S.: 334516

Mettler-Toledo (Korea) Ltd. (1)
5th floor 155 Songpa-daero, Songpa-gu, Seoul, 05855, Korea (South)
Tel.: (82) 234983566
Web Site: https://www.mt.com
Analytical Laboratory Instrument Mfr
N.A.I.C.S.: 334516

Mettler-Toledo (M) Sdn. Bhd. (1)
Unit 1-01 1st Floor Lot 8 Jalan Astaka U8/84 Seksyen U8, Bukit Jelutong, 40150, Shah Alam, Selangor, Malaysia
Tel.: (60) 378445888
Web Site: https://www.mt.com
Sales Range: $25-49.9 Million
Analytical Laboratory Instrument Mfr
N.A.I.C.S.: 334516

Mettler-Toledo (S) Pte Ltd. (1)
2 International Business Park 06-03/07, Strategy Tower 1, Singapore, 609930, Singapore   (100%)
Tel.: (65) 68900011
Web Site: https://www.mt.com
Sales Range: $25-49.9 Million
Provider of Precision Instruments
N.A.I.C.S.: 334519

Mettler-Toledo (Schweiz) GmbH (1)
Im Langacher 44, 8606, Greifensee, Switzerland   (100%)
Tel.: (41) 449444747
Web Site: https://www.mt.com

Sales Range: $150-199.9 Million
Provider of Precision Instruments
N.A.I.C.S.: 334519

Mettler-Toledo (Thailand) Ltd. (1)
846/4 - 846/5 Lasalle Road, Bangna Tai Subdistrict Bangna District, 10260, Bangkok, 10260, Thailand
Tel.: (66) 27230300
Web Site: https://www.mt.com
Analytical Laboratory Instrument Mfr
N.A.I.C.S.: 334516

Mettler-Toledo (Xinjiang) Electronic Scale Ltd. (1)
No 16 Xiamen Road Economic Technology Development Zone, Wulumuqi, Xinjiang, 830026, China
Tel.: (86) 9913736253
Analytical Laboratory Instrument Mfr
N.A.I.C.S.: 334516

Mettler-Toledo - Product Inspection (1)
6005 Benjamin Rd, Tampa, FL 33634-5103
Tel.: (813) 889-9500
Controlling Instruments & Accessories
N.A.I.C.S.: 423830
Viggo Nielsen (Gen Mgr)
Harry D. Seibert (Head-Sls)

Mettler-Toledo A/S (1)
Naverland 8, 2600, Glostrup, Denmark
Tel.: (45) 43270800
Web Site: http://www.mt.com
Precision Instruments Mfr
N.A.I.C.S.: 333310

Mettler-Toledo A/S (1)
Ulvenveien 92B, 0581, Oslo, Norway   (100%)
Tel.: (47) 22304490
Web Site: https://www.mt.com
Sales Range: $10-24.9 Million
Provider of Precision Instruments
N.A.I.C.S.: 333310

Mettler-Toledo AB (1)
Virkesvagen 10 Hammarby Sjostad, PO Box 92161, 120 08, Stockholm, Sweden   (100%)
Tel.: (46) 87025000
Web Site: https://www.mt.com
Sales Range: $25-49.9 Million
Provider of Precision Instruments
N.A.I.C.S.: 334519

Mettler-Toledo AG (1)
Im Langacher 44, 8606, Greifensee, Switzerland
Tel.: (41) 449444747
Web Site: http://www.mttro.com
Sales Range: $25-49.9 Million
Emp.: 200
Development, Production & Sales of Electrodes & Sensors for PH-Values
N.A.I.C.S.: 334513

Mettler-Toledo AG-Analytical Instruments (1)
Sonnenbergstrasse 74, CH-8603, Schwerzenbach, Switzerland   (100%)
Tel.: (41) 18067711
Sales Range: $25-49.9 Million
Emp.: 200
Provider of Analytical Instruments
N.A.I.C.S.: 334516

Mettler-Toledo AutoChem, Inc. (1)
6708 Alexander Bell Dr, Columbia, MD 21046
Tel.: (410) 910-8500
Web Site: https://www.mt.com
Emp.: 60
Analytical Laboratory Instrument Mfr
N.A.I.C.S.: 334516

Mettler-Toledo B.V. (1)
Franklinstraat 5, 4004 JK, Tiel, Netherlands   (100%)
Tel.: (31) 344638363
Web Site: https://www.mt.com
Sales Range: $50-74.9 Million
Sale of Instruments
N.A.I.C.S.: 423490

Mettler-Toledo Cargoscan AS (1)
Ulvenveien 92B, 0581, Oslo, Norway
Tel.: (47) 22304490
Web Site: https://www.mt.com

Analytical Laboratory Instrument Mfr
N.A.I.C.S.: 334516

Mettler-Toledo Garvens GmbH (1)
Kampstrasse 7, 31180, Giesen, Germany
Tel.: (49) 51219330
Web Site: http://www.mt.com
Dynamic Weighing System Provider
N.A.I.C.S.: 423830

Mettler-Toledo Ges.m.b.H. (1)
Laxenburger Strasse 252/2, 1230, Vienna, Austria   (100%)
Tel.: (43) 16041980
Web Site: http://www.mt.com
Sales Range: $10-24.9 Million
Provider of Precision Instruments
N.A.I.C.S.: 811210

Mettler-Toledo GmbH (1)
Ockerweg 3, 35353, Giessen, Germany   (100%)
Tel.: (49) 641507444
Web Site: http://www.mt.com
Sales Range: $25-49.9 Million
Provider of Precision Instruments
N.A.I.C.S.: 811210

Mettler-Toledo Holding AG (1)
Im Langacher 44, 8606, Greifensee, Switzerland
Tel.: (41) 449444545
Web Site: http://www.mt.com
Investment Management Service
N.A.I.C.S.: 551112

Mettler-Toledo Inc. (1)
1900 Polaris Pkwy, Columbus, OH 43240   (100%)
Tel.: (614) 438-4511
Web Site: http://www.mt.com
Sales Range: $25-49.9 Million
Electronic Scales, Industrial Software & Weighing Systems Mfr
N.A.I.C.S.: 333998

Mettler-Toledo Inc. (1)
2915 Argentia Road Unit 6, Mississauga, L5N 8G6, ON, Canada
Web Site: http://www.mt.com
Analytical Laboratory Instrument Mfr
N.A.I.C.S.: 334516

Mettler-Toledo Ind. E Com. Ltda. (1)
Avenida Tambore 418, Sao Paulo, Barueri, 06460-000, SP, Brazil   (100%)
Tel.: (55) 1141667400
Web Site: http://www.mt.com
Sales Range: $1-9.9 Million
Emp.: 70
Mfr Precision Instruments
N.A.I.C.S.: 333310

Mettler-Toledo India Private Limited (1)
Prima Bay Tower B 2nd Floor Saki Naka Vihar Road, Powai, Mumbai, 400 072, India
Tel.: (91) 8001028460
Web Site: https://www.mt.com
Analytical Laboratory Instrument Mfr
N.A.I.C.S.: 334516
Sanjeev Dhar (Mng Dir)

Mettler-Toledo Ingold Inc. (1)
900 Middlesex Tpke 8-1, Billerica, MA 01821
Tel.: (781) 301-8800
Web Site: http://www.mt.com
Sales Range: $25-49.9 Million
Emp.: 100
Process Analysis Technology Mfr
N.A.I.C.S.: 334513

Mettler-Toledo Ingold, Inc. (1)
36 Middlesex Tpke, Bedford, MA 01730
Tel.: (781) 301-8800
Scale & Balance Instrument Mfr
N.A.I.C.S.: 333998

Mettler-Toledo International Finance, Inc. (1)
1900 Polaris Pkwy, Columbus, OH 43240-4035
Tel.: (614) 438-4511
Investment Management Service
N.A.I.C.S.: 523940
Suresh Kumar (Mgr-Global Plng)

Mettler-Toledo International Trading (Shanghai) Co., Ltd. (1)

589 Guiping Road, Shanghai, 200233, China
Tel.: (86) 4008878788
Web Site: http://www.mt.com
Analytical Laboratory Instrument Mfr
N.A.I.C.S.: 334516

Mettler-Toledo Logistik GmbH (1)
Buchbergstrasse 4, Uznach, 8730, Switzerland (100%)
Tel.: (41) 552859585
Web Site: http://www.mt.com
Industrial Instrument Mfr
N.A.I.C.S.: 334519

Mettler-Toledo Ltd. (1)
220 Turner Street, PO Box 173, Port Melbourne, 3207, VIC, Australia (100%)
Tel.: (61) 1300659761
Web Site: http://www.mt.com
Provider of Precision Instruments
N.A.I.C.S.: 811210

Mettler-Toledo Ltd. (1)
64 Boston Road, Beaumont Leys, Leicester, LE4 1AW, United Kingdom (100%)
Tel.: (44) 1162357070
Web Site: https://www.mt.com
Sales Range: $25-49.9 Million
Provider of Precision Instruments
N.A.I.C.S.: 811210

Mettler-Toledo Management Holding Deutschland GmbH (1)
Unter dem Malesfelsen 34, Albstadt, D-72458, Germany
Tel.: (49) 7431140
Web Site: http://www.mt.com
Investment Management Service
N.A.I.C.S.: 551112

Mettler-Toledo OnLine GmbH (1)
Im Langacher 44, 8606, Greifensee, Switzerland
Tel.: (41) 449442211
Web Site: http://www.mt.com
Analytical Laboratory Instrument Mfr
N.A.I.C.S.: 334516

Mettler-Toledo Philippines Inc. (1)
6/F JD Tower formerly NOL Towers Commerce Ave, Madrigal Business Park Ayala Alabang, Muntinlupa, 1780, Philippines
Tel.: (63) 285288900
Web Site: https://www.mt.com
Industrial Electronic & Precision Equipment Maintenance Services
N.A.I.C.S.: 811210
Emerson Baldesco (Engr-Sls)

Mettler-Toledo Process Analytics, Inc. (1)
900 Middlesex Tpke Bldg 8, Billerica, MA 01821
Industrial Electronic & Precision Equipment Maintenance Services
N.A.I.C.S.: 811210
Paul Bray (Head-Fin & Control)

Mettler-Toledo Product Inspection B.V. (1)
Het Sterrenbeeld 48, 5215 ML, s-Hertogenbosch, 5215, Netherlands
Tel.: (31) 735481188
Web Site: https://www.mt.com
Sales Range: $25-49.9 Million
Emp.: 50
Analytical Laboratory Instrument Mfr
N.A.I.C.S.: 334516

Mettler-Toledo S.A. de C.V. (1)
Amores 1322-Building A Colonia del Valle Benito Juarez, 03104, Mexico, Mexico (100%)
Tel.: (52) 5519462720
Web Site: https://www.mt.com
Sales Range: $25-49.9 Million
Provider of Precision Instruments
N.A.I.C.S.: 333310

Mettler-Toledo S.A.S. (1)
18/20 avenue de la Pepiniere, 78220, Viroflay, France
Tel.: (33) 130971717
Web Site: https://www.mt.com
Precision Instruments Mfr
N.A.I.C.S.: 811210

Mettler-Toledo S.p.A. (1)
Via Anna Maria Mozzoni 2/1, 20152, Milan,

MI, Italy (100%)
Tel.: (39) 02333321
Web Site: https://www.mt.com
Sales Range: $25-49.9 Million
Provider of Precision Instruments
N.A.I.C.S.: 811210

Mettler-Toledo SAE (1)
Carrer del Segria 7-9, Cornella del Llobregat, 08940, Barcelona, Spain (100%)
Tel.: (34) 900922550
Web Site: https://www.mt.com
Sales Range: $25-49.9 Million
Provider of Precision Instruments
N.A.I.C.S.: 334519

Mettler-Toledo Safeline Limited (1)
Montford Street, Salford, M50 2XD, Lancashire, United Kingdom
Tel.: (44) 1618488636
Web Site: https://www.mt.com
Sales Range: $50-74.9 Million
Metal Detection System Mfr
N.A.I.C.S.: 334516
Allen Purvis (Mng Dir)

Mettler-Toledo Safeline X-Ray Limited (1)
Greenfield Royston Business Park, Herts, Royston, SG8 5HN, United Kingdom
Tel.: (44) 1763257900
Emp.: 150
Analytical Laboratory Instrument Mfr
N.A.I.C.S.: 334516

Mettler-Toledo Sales International GmbH (1)
Im Langacher, PO Box VI 400, 8606, Greifensee, Switzerland
Tel.: (41) 449442211
Web Site: https://www.mt.com
Scale & Balance Instrument Mfr
N.A.I.C.S.: 333998

Mettler-Toledo Sp. z.o.o. (1)
ul Poleczki 21, 02-822, Warsaw, Poland (100%)
Tel.: (48) 224406700
Web Site: https://www.mt.com
Sales Range: $25-49.9 Million
Provider of Precision Instruments
N.A.I.C.S.: 333310

Mettler-Toledo TR Olcum Aletleri Ticaret Satis vs Servis Hizmetleri Anonim Sirketi (1)
Haluk Turksoy Sokak No 6, Uskudar, 34662, Istanbul, Turkiye
Tel.: (90) 2164002020
Web Site: https://www.mt.com
Sales Range: $25-49.9 Million
Analytical Laboratory Instrument Mfr
N.A.I.C.S.: 334516

Mettler-Toledo Technologies (China) Co., Ltd. (1)
No 589 Guiping Road, Shanghai, 200233, China
Tel.: (86) 4008878788
Web Site: https://www.mt.com
Laboratory Equipment Mfr
N.A.I.C.S.: 334516

Mettler-Toledo Thornton Inc. (1)
36 Middlesex Tpke, Bedford, MA 01730
Tel.: (781) 301-8600
Analytical Laboratory Instrument Mfr
N.A.I.C.S.: 334516

Mettler-Toledo UK Holdings Limited (1)
64 Boston Road Beaumont Leys, Leicester, LE4 1AW, United Kingdom
Tel.: (44) 1162357070
Web Site: http://www.mt.com
Sales Range: $25-49.9 Million
Emp.: 100
Investment Management Service
N.A.I.C.S.: 551112

Mettler-Toledo d.o.o. (1)
Jure Kastelana 19, 10000, Zagreb, Croatia
Tel.: (385) 12958131
Hospital Equipment Distr
N.A.I.C.S.: 423450

Mettler-Toledo s.r.o. (1)
Hattalova 12/A, 831 03, Bratislava, Slovakia
Tel.: (421) 244441220
Web Site: https://www.mt.com

Analytical Laboratory Instrument Mfr
N.A.I.C.S.: 334516

Mettler-Toledo spol. s.r.o. (1)
Trebohosticka 2283/2, 100 00, Prague, 10, Czech Republic
Tel.: (420) 226808150
Web Site: http://www.mt.com
Analytical Laboratory Instrument Mfr
N.A.I.C.S.: 334516

N.V. Mettler-Toledo S.A. (1)
Leuvensesteenweg 384 Kleine Lozenberg, 1932, Zaventem, Belgium (100%)
Tel.: (32) 23340211
Web Site: http://www.mt.com
Sales Range: $25-49.9 Million
Provider of Precision Instruments
N.A.I.C.S.: 811210

Ohaus Australia Pty. Ltd. (1)
Level 1 191 Salmon Street, PO Box 173, Port Melbourne, 3207, VIC, Australia
Tel.: (61) 1300464287
Web Site: https://oceania.ohaus.com
Laboratory Scale & Balance Mfr & Distr
N.A.I.C.S.: 423490

Ohaus Corporation (1)
7 Campus Dr Ste 310, Parsippany, NJ 07054 (100%)
Tel.: (973) 377-9000
Web Site: https://us.ohaus.com
Sales Range: $50-74.9 Million
Emp.: 130
Weighing Industry Logistical & Technical Support Services
N.A.I.C.S.: 333998

Ohaus Europe GmbH (1)
Heuwinkelstrasse 3, Greifensee, 8606, Zurich, Switzerland
Tel.: (41) 449443366
Analytical Laboratory Instrument Mfr
N.A.I.C.S.: 334516

Ohaus Indochina Limited (1)
284 A4 Building Soi Soonvijai 4 Rama 9 Road, Bangkapi Huay Kwang, Bangkok, 10320, Thailand
Tel.: (66) 271964189
Analytical Laboratory Instrument Mfr
N.A.I.C.S.: 334516

Ohaus Instruments (Shanghai) Co. Ltd. (1)
7F Block 33 680 Guiping Road, Shanghai, 200233, China
Tel.: (86) 4008217188
Analytical Laboratory Instrument Mfr
N.A.I.C.S.: 334516

Ohaus de Mexico S.A. de C.V. (1)
Managua 697 Despacho 404, Col Lindavista, 07300, Mexico, Mexico
Tel.: (52) 5557525746
Web Site: https://mx.ohaus.com
Sales Range: $10-24.9 Million
Analytical Laboratory Instrument Mfr
N.A.I.C.S.: 334516

PT Mettler-Toledo Indonesia (1)
Grha Persada 3rd Floor D1 Jl K H Noer Ali No 3A, Bekasi, 17144, Indonesia
Tel.: (62) 2129453919
Web Site: https://www.mt.com
Scale & Balance Instrument Mfr
N.A.I.C.S.: 333998

Panzhihua Toledo Electronic Scale Ltd. (1)
Mianshawan Renhe, Panzhihua, 617061, Sichuan, China
Tel.: (86) 8122903348
Analytical Laboratory Instrument Mfr
N.A.I.C.S.: 334516

Pharmacontrol Electronic GmbH (1)
Harzstrasse 1, 64646, Heppenheim, Germany
Tel.: (49) 625267360
Web Site: http://www.pharmacontrol.de
Optical Inspection System Provider
N.A.I.C.S.: 334516

Pipette Calibration Services, Inc. (1)
150 Wells Ave, Newton, MA 02459
Web Site: http://www.pipettecal.com
Pipette Calibration & Repair Services
N.A.I.C.S.: 811210

Rainin Instrument LLC (1)
7500 Edgewater Dr, Oakland, CA 94621
Tel.: (510) 564-1600
Web Site: http://www.rainin.com
Rev.: $26,200,000
Emp.: 100
Laboratory Apparatus & Furniture
N.A.I.C.S.: 541715

Scale-up Systems Limited (1)
23 Shelbourne Road, Dublin, 4, Ireland
Tel.: (353) 16675232
Web Site: https://www.scale-up.com
Software Development Services
N.A.I.C.S.: 541511

METWOOD, INC.
819 Naff Rd, Boones Mill, VA 24065
Tel.: (540) 334-4294   NV
Web Site: http://www.metwood.com
Year Founded: 1993
MTWD—(OTCIQ)
Sales Range: $1-9.9 Million
Emp.: 14
Construction Materials Mfr & Whlsr
N.A.I.C.S.: 332312

MEXCO ENERGY CORPORATION
415 W Wall Ste 475, Midland, TX 79701
Tel.: (432) 682-1119   CO
Web Site:
https://www.mexcoenergy.com
Year Founded: 1972
MXC—(NYSEAMEX)
Rev.: $6,604,884
Assets: $19,058,854
Liabilities: $1,430,589
Net Worth: $17,628,265
Earnings: $1,344,952
Emp.: 3
Fiscal Year-end: 03/31/24
Crude Petroleum Extraction Services
N.A.I.C.S.: 211120
Tamala L. McComic (Pres, CFO, Treas & Asst Sec)
Nicholas C. Taylor (Chm & CEO)
Donna Gail Yanko (Sec & VP)

Subsidiaries:

TBO Oil & Gas, LLC (1)
4505 Mockingbird Ln, Midland, TX 79707
Tel.: (432) 697-2179
Oil & Gas Field Services
N.A.I.C.S.: 213112

MEXUS GOLD US
1805 N Carson St Ste 150, Carson City, NV 89701
Tel.: (775) 721-9960   CO
Web Site:
https://www.mexusgoldus.com
MXSG—(OTCEM)
Assets: $294,357
Liabilities: $2,725,680
Net Worth: ($2,431,323)
Earnings: ($1,796,728)
Emp.: 1
Fiscal Year-end: 03/31/23
Gold, Silver & Copper Exploration
N.A.I.C.S.: 212220
Paul D. Thompson Sr. (Pres, CEO, CFO, Principal Acctg Officer & Sec)

MFA FINANCIAL, INC.
1 Vanderbilt Ave 48th FL, New York, NY 10017
Tel.: (212) 207-6400   MD
Web Site:
https://www.mfafinancial.com
Year Founded: 1997
MFA—(NYSE)
Rev.: $47,289,000
Assets: $10,772,690,000
Liabilities: $8,872,775,000
Net Worth: $1,899,915,000
Earnings: $80,164,000

MFA FINANCIAL, INC.—(Continued)

Emp.: 377
Fiscal Year-end: 12/31/23
Financial Services
N.A.I.C.S.: 525990
Harold E. Schwartz *(Gen Counsel, Sec & Sr VP)*
Michael C. Roper *(CFO & Sr VP)*
Michael Roper *(CFO)*
Bryan Doran *(Chief Acctg Officer & Sr VP)*
Lori Samuels *(Chief Loan Ops Officer)*
Craig L. Knutson *(CEO)*
Bryan Wulfsohn *(Pres & Chief Investment Officer)*

Subsidiaries:

Lima One Capital, LLC **(1)**
201 E McBee Ave Ste 300, Greenville, SC 29601 **(100%)**
Web Site: https://www.limaone.com
Sales Range: $25-49.9 Million
Emp.: 130
Real Estate Investment Services
N.A.I.C.S.: 531390
Jeff Tennyson *(Pres & CEO)*
John Thompson *(COO)*
Josh Woodward *(CFO)*
Josh Craig *(Chief Revenue Officer)*
Justin Thompson *(Dir & CMO)*
Rankin Blair *(Mng Dir & Head-Operations)*
Nate Trunfio *(Mng Dir & Head-Sales)*
Annmarie Higgins *(Chief HR Officer)*
Vinod Thomas *(Mng Dir & Head)*
Brian Cauthen *(Dir)*
Brandy Cogsdill *(Dir)*
John Della Bella *(Dir)*
Kim Deter *(Dir-Term Fin)*
Dalton Elliott *(Dir)*
Kevin Holliday *(Dir)*
Shahin Ilbeig *(Dir)*
Tim Lawhorne *(Dir)*
Bill McDonald *(Dir)*
Taylor Owens *(CMO)*
Rob Parsley *(Dir)*
Diane Sugrue *(Dir)*
Lucas Whaley *(Sr Dir-Technology)*
Abigail Williams *(Sr Dir-Compliance)*
Rankin Blair *(Mng Dir & Head-Operations)*
Nate Trunfio *(Mng Dir & Head-Sales)*
Annmarie Higgins *(Chief HR Officer)*
Vinod Thomas *(Mng Dir & Head)*
Brian Cauthen *(Dir)*
Brandy Cogsdill *(Dir)*
John Della Bella *(Dir)*
Kim Deter *(Dir-Term Fin)*
Dalton Elliott *(Dir)*
Kevin Holliday *(Dir)*
Shahin Ilbeig *(Dir)*
Tim Lawhorne *(Dir)*
Bill McDonald *(Dir)*
Taylor Owens *(CMO)*
Rob Parsley *(Dir)*
Diane Sugrue *(Dir)*
Lucas Whaley *(Sr Dir-Technology)*
Abigail Williams *(Sr Dir-Compliance)*

MFS CHARTER INCOME TRUST

111 Huntington Ave 24th Fl, Boston, MA 02119
Tel.: (617) 954-5000 **MA**
MCR—(NYSE)
Rev.: $22,118,659
Assets: $510,263,880
Liabilities: $107,018,432
Net Worth: $403,245,448
Earnings: $16,482,434
Fiscal Year-end: 11/30/19
Investment Management Service
N.A.I.C.S.: 525990

MFS GOVERNMENT MARKETS INCOME TRUST

111 Huntington Ave 24th Fl, Boston, MA 02119
Tel.: (617) 954-5000 **MA**
MGF—(NYSE)
Rev.: $4,938,869
Assets: $165,581,038

Liabilities: $10,744,715
Net Worth: $154,836,323
Earnings: $3,789,080
Fiscal Year-end: 11/30/19
Investment Management Service
N.A.I.C.S.: 525990

MFS HIGH INCOME MUNICIPAL TRUST

111 Huntington Ave 24th Fl, Boston, MA 02119
Tel.: (617) 954-5000 **MA**
CXE—(NYSE)
Rev.: $12,995,548
Assets: $269,520,989
Liabilities: $98,042,399
Net Worth: $171,478,590
Earnings: $8,233,423
Fiscal Year-end: 11/30/19
Investment Management Service
N.A.I.C.S.: 525990

MFS HIGH YIELD MUNICIPAL TRUST

111 Huntington Ave 24th Fl, Boston, MA 02119
Tel.: (617) 954-5000 **MA**
CMU—(NYSE)
Rev.: $10,291,685
Assets: $214,527,594
Liabilities: $75,485,941
Net Worth: $139,041,653
Earnings: $6,555,285
Fiscal Year-end: 11/30/19
Investment Management Service
N.A.I.C.S.: 525990

MFS INTERMEDIATE HIGH INCOME FUND

111 Huntington Ave 24th Fl, Boston, MA 02119
Tel.: (617) 954-5000 **MA**
CIF—(NYSE)
Rev.: $3,939,127
Assets: $71,923,539
Liabilities: $21,536,712
Net Worth: $50,386,827
Earnings: $2,700,692
Fiscal Year-end: 11/30/19
Investment Management Service
N.A.I.C.S.: 525990

MFS INTERMEDIATE INCOME TRUST

111 Huntington Ave 24th Fl, Boston, MA 02119
Tel.: (617) 954-5000 **MA**
MIN—(NYSE)
Rev.: $15,301,777
Assets: $472,756,352
Liabilities: $334,186
Net Worth: $472,422,166
Earnings: $12,212,459
Fiscal Year-end: 10/31/19
Investment Management Service
N.A.I.C.S.: 525990

MFS INVESTMENT GRADE MUNICIPAL TRUST

111 Huntington Ave 24th Fl, Boston, MA 02119
Tel.: (617) 954-5000 **MA**
CXH—(NYSE)
Rev.: $6,664,267
Assets: $152,351,066
Liabilities: $54,518,578
Net Worth: $97,832,488
Earnings: $4,077,801
Fiscal Year-end: 11/30/19
Investment Management Service
N.A.I.C.S.: 525990

MFS MULTIMARKET INCOME TRUST

111 Huntington Ave 24th Fl, Boston, MA 02119
Tel.: (617) 954-5000 **MA**
MMT—(NYSE)
Rev.: $24,708,363
Assets: $519,488,274
Liabilities: $111,628,949
Net Worth: $407,859,325
Earnings: $18,396,387
Fiscal Year-end: 10/31/19
Investment Management Service
N.A.I.C.S.: 525990

MFS MUNICIPAL INCOME TRUST

111 Huntington Ave 24th Fl, Boston, MA 02119
Tel.: (617) 954-5000 **MA**
MFM—(NYSE)
Rev.: $20,615,719
Assets: $428,042,956
Liabilities: $121,391,231
Net Worth: $306,651,725
Earnings: $14,184,666
Fiscal Year-end: 10/31/19
Investment Management Service
N.A.I.C.S.: 525990

MFS SPECIAL VALUE TRUST

500 Boylston St, Boston, MA 02116
Tel.: (617) 954-5000 **MA**
MFV—(NYSE)
Rev.: $1,687,964
Assets: $40,863,386
Liabilities: $605,520
Net Worth: $40,257,866
Earnings: $1,133,601
Fiscal Year-end: 10/31/19
Investment Management Service
N.A.I.C.S.: 525990
Matthew W. Ryan *(Mgr-Fund)*

MGE ENERGY, INC.

133 S Blair St, Madison, WI 53788
Tel.: (608) 252-7000 **WI**
Web Site:
https://www.mgeenergy.com
Year Founded: 1896
MGEE—(NASDAQ)
Rev.: $714,519,000
Assets: $2,517,600,000
Liabilities: $850,680,000
Net Worth: $1,666,920,000
Earnings: $110,952,000
Emp.: 701
Fiscal Year-end: 12/31/22
Electricity & Natural Gas Distr
N.A.I.C.S.: 221118
Lynn K. Hobbie *(Exec VP-Mktg & Comm)*
Jeffrey M. Keebler *(Chm, Pres & CEO)*
Cari Anne Renlund *(Gen Counsel, Sec & VP)*
Melissa T. Garner *(VP)*
John A. Jicha *(VP)*
Bryan R. Sullivan *(CIO)*

Subsidiaries:

Central Wisconsin Development Corporation **(1)**
PO Box 1231, Madison, WI 53701-1231 **(100%)**
Tel.: (608) 252-7000
Web Site: http://www.mge.com
Sales Range: $1-4.9 Billion
Emp.: 700
Economic Development & Investment Services
N.A.I.C.S.: 523999

MGE Power LLC **(1)**
133 S Blair St, Madison, WI 53703-3432
Tel.: (608) 252-5647
Eletric Power Generation Services
N.A.I.C.S.: 221118

Madison Gas & Electric Company **(1)**

133 S Blair St, Madison, WI 53788 **(100%)**
Tel.: (608) 252-7000
Web Site: https://www.mge.com
Rev.: $714,518,999
Assets: $2,404,639,000
Liabilities: $817,007,000
Net Worth: $1,587,632,000
Earnings: $83,916,000
Emp.: 700
Fiscal Year-end: 12/31/2022
Electricity & Natural Gas Distr
N.A.I.C.S.: 221122
Jeffrey M. Keebler *(Chm, Pres & CEO)*
Cari Anne Renlund *(Gen Counsel, Sec & VP)*
Jared J. Bushek *(CFO, CIO, Treas & VP-Fin)*
Lynn K. Hobbie *(Exec VP-Mktg & Comm)*
Melissa T. Garner *(VP)*
John A. Jicha *(VP)*
Bryan R. Sullivan *(VP)*

MGIC INVESTMENT CORPORATION

250 E Kilbourn Ave, Milwaukee, WI 53202
Tel.: (414) 347-6480 **WI**
Web Site: https://www.mgic.com
Year Founded: 1985
MTG—(NYSE)
Rev.: $1,155,102,000
Assets: $6,538,380,000
Liabilities: $1,466,363,000
Net Worth: $5,072,017,000
Earnings: $712,949,000
Emp.: 627
Fiscal Year-end: 12/31/23
Holding Company; Mortgage Insurance Services
N.A.I.C.S.: 524126
Salvatore A. Miosi *(Pres & COO)*
Timothy J. Mattke *(CEO)*
Nathaniel H. Colson *(CFO & Exec VP)*
Julie K. Sperber *(Chief Acctg Officer, VP & Controller)*
James J. Hughes *(Exec VP-Sls & Bus Dev)*
Paula C. Maggio *(Gen Counsel, Sec & Exec VP)*
Steven Thompson *(Chief Risk Officer & Exec VP)*

Subsidiaries:

MGIC Assurance Corporation **(1)**
250 E Kilbourn Ave, Milwaukee, WI 53201
Tel.: (414) 347-2770
Direct Property & Casualty Insurance Services
N.A.I.C.S.: 524126

MGIC Credit Assurance Corporation **(1)**
270 E Kilbourn Ave, Milwaukee, WI 53202
Web Site: https://www.mgic.com
Property Insurance Services
N.A.I.C.S.: 524126

Mortgage Guaranty Insurance Corporation **(1)**
MGIC Plz 250 E Kilbourn Ave, Milwaukee, WI 53202
Tel.: (414) 347-6480
Web Site: https://www.mgic.com
Sales Range: $700-749.9 Million
Mortgage Insurance Services
N.A.I.C.S.: 524126
Salvatore A. Miosi *(Pres & COO)*
Robert J. Candelmo *(CIO & Sr VP)*
Margaret M. Crowley *(VP-Marketing)*
Nathaniel H. Colson *(CFO)*
Tara E. Radmann *(VP-Bus Automation)*
Steven M. Thompson *(Chief Risk Officer & Exec VP)*
Terry A. Aikin *(Mng Dir & VP)*
Jane S. Coleman *(VP-Natl Accounts)*
Luis A. Contreras *(VP-Natl Accounts)*
Dean D. Dardzinski *(Mng Dir & VP)*
Mary L. Elkins *(VP-Sys Dev)*
Daniel J. Garcia-Velez *(VP-Bus Dev)*
Heidi A. Heyrman *(VP, Asst Sec & Asst Gen Counsel)*
Dianna L. Higgins *(VP-Internal Audit)*

Gary J. Johnson (VP-Data Science)
Mark J. Krauter (VP-Natl Accounts)
Michael L. Kull (Mng Dir)
Elyse M. Mitchell (VP-Natl Accounts)
Stacey B. Murphy (VP-Talent & Total Rewards)
Christopher T. Perry (VP-Sls)

eMagic.com LLC (1)
250 E Kilbourn Ave, Milwaukee, WI 53202
Web Site: http://www.emagic.com
Mortgage Industry Business-to-Business
E-commerce Services
N.A.I.C.S.: 561499

MGM RESORTS INTERNATIONAL
3600 Las Vegas Blvd S, Las Vegas, NV 89109
Tel.: (702) 693-7120 **DE**
Web Site:
https://www.mgmresorts.com
Year Founded: 1986
MGM—(NYSE)
Rev.: $16,164,249,000
Assets: $42,368,548,000
Liabilities: $38,034,403,000
Net Worth: $4,334,145,000
Earnings: $1,142,180,000
Emp.: 45,000
Fiscal Year-end: 12/31/23
Hotel Operator
N.A.I.C.S.: 551112
William Joseph Hornbuckle IV (Pres, CEO & Chief Customer Development Officer)
Jonathan S. Halkyard (CFO & Treas)
Jyoti Chopra (Chief People Officer, Chief Sustainability Officer, Chief Inclusion Officer & Sr VP)
Ayesha Molino (Sr VP-Pub Affairs)
Corey Sanders (COO)

Subsidiaries:

Circus Circus Casinos, Inc. (1)
2880 S Las Vegas Blvd, Las Vegas, NV 89109-1138
Tel.: (702) 734-0410
Web Site: https://www.circuscircus.com
Sales Range: $200-249.9 Million
Emp.: 4,500
Gambling Casino & Hotel
N.A.I.C.S.: 721120

Jean Development Company, LLC (1)
1 Main St, Jean, NV 89109 (100%)
Tel.: (702) 477-5000
Web Site: http://www.stopatjean.com
Sales Range: $10-24.9 Million
Emp.: 500
Hotel & Casino
N.A.I.C.S.: 721120

Las Vegas Arena Management, LLC (1)
3950 Las Vegas Blvd S, Las Vegas, NV 89119
Tel.: (702) 632-9800
Casino Hotels
N.A.I.C.S.: 721120

MGM China Holdings Limited (1)
Suite 1402 China Merchants Tower 200 Connaught Road, Central, China (Hong Kong)
Tel.: (852) 36982288
Web Site:
http://www.mgmchinaholdings.com
Rev.: $657,279,887
Assets: $3,826,675,891
Liabilities: $3,179,497,588
Net Worth: $647,178,303
Earnings: ($670,893,468)
Emp.: 10,364
Fiscal Year-end: 12/31/2020
Casino Hotel Operator
N.A.I.C.S.: 721120
James Joseph Murren (Co-Chm)
William Joseph Hornbuckle IV (Co-Chm)
Pansy Catilina Chiu King Ho (Co-Chm)
Yau Wong Chen (Exec Dir)
Antonio Jose Menano (Gen Counsel, Gen Counsel & Gen Counsel)

Hubert Qi Wang Zhi (CFO & Pres)
Wendy Ying Yu Yuen (Exec VP-Human Resources)
Holubowskyj G. Michael (Sr VP-Security-Safety)
John M. McManus (Exec Dir)
Tian Han (Sr VP-Strategic Marketing)
Catarina Kei Lio Weng (VP)

MGM Finance Corp. (1)
1531 E Main St, Duncan, SC 29334
Tel.: (864) 486-8000
Casino Hotel Operator
N.A.I.C.S.: 721120

MGM Grand (International), Pte (1)
1 Scotts Road 22-03, Shaw Centre, Singapore, 228208, Singapore
Tel.: (65) 67341812
Hotel & Motel Services
N.A.I.C.S.: 721110

MGM Grand (Macao) Limited (1)
Edf Mgm 1101 Avenida Dr Sun Yat Sen, Macau, 00853, China (Macau)
Tel.: (853) 88028888
Home Management Services
N.A.I.C.S.: 721110

MGM Grand Detroit, LLC (1)
1777 3rd St, Detroit, MI 48226-2414 (97%)
Tel.: (313) 393-7777
Web Site:
http://mgmgranddetroit.mgmresorts.com
Sales Range: $150-199.9 Million
Emp.: 3,000
Hotel & Casino
N.A.I.C.S.: 721120
George P. Corchis Jr. (Pres/COO-Reg Ops)

MGM Grand Hotel, LLC (1)
3799 S Las Vegas Blvd, Las Vegas, NV 89109
Tel.: (702) 891-1111
Web Site: http://mgmgrand.mgmresorts.com
Sales Range: $700-749.9 Million
Emp.: 9,300
Hotel, Casino & Entertainment
N.A.I.C.S.: 721120

Subsidiary (Domestic):

Grand Laundry, Inc. (2)
4225 Arcata Way, North Las Vegas, NV 89030
Tel.: (702) 657-6363
Emp.: 150
Dry Cleaning & Laundry Services
N.A.I.C.S.: 812320

MGM International, LLC (1)
3950 Las Vegas Blvd S, Las Vegas, NV 89119 (100%)
Tel.: (702) 632-7777
Management Consulting Services
N.A.I.C.S.: 541611

MGM MIRAGE Advertising, Inc. (1)
3400 Las Vegas Blvd, Las Vegas, NV 89109-1132
Tel.: (702) 791-7111
Web Site: http://www.mirage.com
Sales Range: $25-49.9 Million
Emp.: 130
House Agencies
N.A.I.C.S.: 541810

MGM National Harbor, LLC (1)
101 MGM National Ave, Oxon Hill, MD 20745
Tel.: (301) 971-5000
Web Site: https://mgmnationalharbor.mgmresorts.com
Casino Hotels
N.A.I.C.S.: 721120

Subsidiary (Domestic):

NH Cigars, LLC (2)
297 S Willow St, Manchester, NH 03103
Tel.: (603) 623-3337
Web Site: https://www.nhcigars.com
E Cigarette & Vapor Whslr
N.A.I.C.S.: 424940

MGM Resorts International Marketing, LTD (1)
Rm 1902 19/F Hutchison Hse 10 Harcourt Rd, Hong Kong, China (Hong Kong)
Tel.: (852) 23752818

Hotel & Motel Services
N.A.I.C.S.: 721110

MGM Springfield, LLC (1)
1 MGM Way, Springfield, MA 01103
Tel.: (413) 273-5000
Casino Hotels
N.A.I.C.S.: 721120
Sarah Moore (VP-Mktg, Adv, and Retail)

Mandalay Corp. (1)
3950 S Las Vegas Blvd, Las Vegas, NV 89119
Tel.: (702) 632-7777
Web Site:
https://mandalaybay.mgmresorts.com
Sales Range: $350-399.9 Million
Emp.: 7,000
Hotel & Casino Operator
N.A.I.C.S.: 721120
Renee West (Pres & COO)

Mandalay Place (1)
3950 S Las Vegas Blvd, Las Vegas, NV 89119
Tel.: (702) 632-7447
Web Site:
http://mandalaybay.mgmresorts.com
Shopping Arcade & Restaurants
N.A.I.C.S.: 455219

Marina District Development Holding Co., LLC (1)
8025 Black Horse Pike Ste 200, Atlantic City, NJ 08232-2960 (100%)
Tel.: (609) 677-1000
Holding Company
N.A.I.C.S.: 551112

Subsidiary (Domestic):

Borgata Hotel Casino & Spa, LLC (2)
1 Borgata Way, Atlantic City, NJ 08401
Tel.: (609) 317-1000
Web Site: https://borgata.mgmresorts.com
Sales Range: $200-249.9 Million
Emp.: 6,000
Hotel & Casino; Owned by Boyd Gaming Corporation & Tracinda Corporation
N.A.I.C.S.: 721120
Travis Lunn (Pres & COO)
Chris Rynkiewicz (CFO & VP)

Mirage Resorts Incorporated (1)
3400 Las Vegas Blvd S, Las Vegas, NV 89109-8923
Tel.: (702) 791-7111
Web Site: http://www.mirage.com
Sales Range: $300-349.9 Million
Emp.: 7,000
Gaming Casinos & Resorts
N.A.I.C.S.: 721120
Scott Sibella (Pres)

Subsidiary (Domestic):

Aria Resort & Casino, LLC (2)
3730 S Las Vegas Blvd, Las Vegas, NV 89158-4300
Tel.: (702) 590-7111
Web Site: https://aria.mgmresorts.com
Sales Range: $750-799.9 Million
Hotel & Motel Services
N.A.I.C.S.: 721110

Beau Rivage Resorts, Inc (2)
875 Beach Blvd, Biloxi, MS 39530
Tel.: (228) 386-7111
Web Site:
https://beaurivage.mgmresorts.com
Hotel & Motel Services
N.A.I.C.S.: 721110
Travis Lunn (Pres)

Bellagio, LLC (2)
3600 S Las Vegas Blvd, Las Vegas, NV 89109
Tel.: (702) 693-7111
Web Site: https://bellagio.mgmresorts.com
Hotel & Casino
N.A.I.C.S.: 721120

Vdara Condo Hotel, LLC (2)
2600 W Harmon Ave, Las Vegas, NV 89158
Tel.: (702) 590-2111
Web Site: https://vdara.mgmresorts.com
Hotel & Motel Services
N.A.I.C.S.: 721110

New Castle Corp. (1)

3850 Las Vegas Blvd S, Las Vegas, NV 89109-4324 (100%)
Tel.: (702) 597-7777
Web Site: http://www.excalibur.com
Sales Range: $125-149.9 Million
Emp.: 4,000
Hotel & Casino Operator
N.A.I.C.S.: 721120

New York-New York Hotel & Casino, LLC (1)
3790 S Las Vegas Blvd, Las Vegas, NV 89109-4338
Tel.: (702) 740-3311
Web Site:
https://newyorknewyork.mgmresorts.com
Sales Range: $250-299.9 Million
Emp.: 2,300
Hotel & Casino
N.A.I.C.S.: 721120

Northfield Park Associates LLC (1)
10777 Northfield Rd, Northfield, OH 44067-0374
Tel.: (330) 908-7625
Web Site:
https://mgmnorthfieldpark.mgmresorts.com
Event Management Services
N.A.I.C.S.: 711310

Railroad Pass Investment Group (1)
1500 Railroad Pass Casino Rd, Henderson, NV 89002
Tel.: (702) 294-5000
Web Site: https://www.railroadpass.com
Sales Range: $75-99.9 Million
Emp.: 1,000
Casino
N.A.I.C.S.: 721120

Yonkers Racing Corporation (1)
810 Yonkers Ave, Yonkers, NY 10704
Tel.: (914) 968-4200
Web Site: http://www.yonkersraceway.com
Gambling Industries
N.A.I.C.S.: 713290
Helena Ferreira (Mgr-Pur)

MGO GLOBAL INC.
1515 S E 17th St Ste 121, Fort Lauderdale, FL 33346
Tel.: (347) 913-3316 **DE**
Web Site:
https://www.mgoglobalinc.com
Year Founded: 2018
MGOL—(NASDAQ)
Rev.: $1,048,012
Assets: $440,968
Liabilities: $1,635,529
Net Worth: ($1,194,561)
Earnings: ($2,582,946)
Emp.: 7
Fiscal Year-end: 12/31/22
Apparel Product Mfr & Distr
N.A.I.C.S.: 316210
Dana Eschenburg Perez (CFO)

MGP INGREDIENTS, INC.
100 Commercial St, Atchison, KS 66002
Tel.: (913) 367-1480 **KS**
Web Site:
https://www.mgpingredients.com
Year Founded: 1941
MGPI—(NASDAQ)
Rev.: $836,523,000
Assets: $1,392,348,000
Liabilities: $543,281,000
Net Worth: $849,067,000
Earnings: $106,401,000
Emp.: 705
Fiscal Year-end: 12/31/23
Flour, Vital Wheat Gluten, Wheat Starch & Food Grade Alcohol Mfr & Distr
N.A.I.C.S.: 311211
David S. Bratcher (Pres & CEO)
Brandon Gall (CFO & VP-Fin)
Erika Lapish (Chief HR Officer)
Amel Pasagic (Chief Comml Officer)
Matt Krusemark (VP)
Ryan Earey (VP)
Fletcher Buchman (VP)

MGP Ingredients, Inc.—(Continued)

Subsidiaries:

Luxco, Inc.　　　　　　　　**(1)**
5050 Kemper Ave, Saint Louis, MO 63139-1106
Tel.: (314) 772-2626
Web Site: http://www.luxco.com
Sales Range: $200-249.9 Million
Emp.: 200
Distilled & Blended Liquors Mfr
N.A.I.C.S.: 312140
Donn S. Lux (Chm & CEO)
David S. Bratcher (Pres)
Greg Mefford (Dir-Sls-Intl)
Jon Capozzoli (Mgr-Commonwealth Div)

Division (Domestic):

Luxco Cleveland Division - Bottling & Blending Facility　　**(2)**
3116 Berea Rd, Cleveland, OH 44111
Tel.: (216) 671-6300
Web Site: http://www.luxco.com
Distilled & Blended Liquors Distr
N.A.I.C.S.: 424820

Subsidiary (Domestic):

Meier's Wine Cellars, Inc.　　**(2)**
6955 Plainfield Rd, Cincinnati, OH 45236-3733
Tel.: (513) 891-2900
Web Site:
https://www.meierswinecellars.com
Wines, Champagnes & Vermouth Producer
N.A.I.C.S.: 312130
Paul Lux (Pres)
Barbara Boyd (Controller)
Rich Hubsch (Mgr-Maintenance)
Gaulin Ivy (Accountant)
Stephanie Moore (Mgr-Retail Store)

MGT CAPITAL INVESTMENTS, INC.
150 Fayetteville St Ste 1110, Raleigh, NC 27601
Tel.: (914) 630-7430　　DE
Web Site: https://www.mgtci.com
Year Founded: 1977
MGTI—(OTCIQ)
Rev.: $809,000
Assets: $1,654,000
Liabilities: $5,388,000
Net Worth: ($3,734,000)
Earnings: ($5,978,000)
Emp.: 2
Fiscal Year-end: 12/31/22
Offices of Other Holding Companies
N.A.I.C.S.: 551112

Subsidiaries:

MGT Sweden AB　　**(1)**
Skeppsbron 18, PO Box 2094, 11130, Stockholm, Sweden
Tel.: (46) 856200050
Broadcasting Services
N.A.I.C.S.: 516210
Maria Redin (CFO)

MHHC ENTERPRISES INC
400 Union Ave SE Ste 200, Olympia, WA 98501
Tel.: (253) 336-6442　　NV
Web Site: https://www.mhhcco.com
MHHC—(OTCIQ)
Holding Company
N.A.I.C.S.: 551112
Frank Hawley (Chm, Pres & CEO)

Subsidiaries:

McCusker & Company, Inc.　　**(1)**
400 Union Ave SE Ste 200, Olympia, WA 98501
Tel.: (800) 743-7480
Web Site: http://www.mccuskerco.com
Business & Warranty Service Contract Consulting Services
N.A.I.C.S.: 541611
Kelly Brands (VP)
Frank Hawley (CEO)

MIAMI BREEZE CAR CARE, INC.
848 Brickell Ave PH 5, Miami, FL 33131
Tel.: (786) 743-3017　　FL
Web Site: https://miami-breeze.us
Year Founded: 2021
MIBE—(OTCIQ)
Rev.: $16,850
Assets: $199,847
Liabilities: $23,809
Net Worth: $176,038
Earnings: ($850,912)
Fiscal Year-end: 12/31/23
Automobile Product Distr
N.A.I.C.S.: 441330

MICRO IMAGING TECHNOLOGY, INC.
970 Calle Amanecer Ste F, San Clemente, CA 92673
Tel.: (949) 388-4546　　CA
Web Site: https://www.micro-identification.com
Year Founded: 1979
MMTC—(NASDAQ)
Sales Range: Less than $1 Million
Emp.: 5
Imaging Technology Products Mfr
N.A.I.C.S.: 333248
David L. Haavig (VP)
Jeffrey G. Nunez (Chm & Pres)
Victor A. Hollander (CFO)

MICROBOT MEDICAL INC.
25 Recreation Park Dr Unit 108, Hingham, MA 02043
Tel.: (781) 875-3605　　DE
Web Site:
https://www.microbotmedical.com
Year Founded: 1988
MBOT—(NASDAQ)
Rev.: $118,000
Assets: $9,537,000
Liabilities: $2,248,000
Net Worth: $7,289,000
Earnings: ($13,168,000)
Emp.: 18
Fiscal Year-end: 12/31/22
Research & Development in the Physical, Engineering & Life Sciences (except Nanotechnology & Biotechnology)
N.A.I.C.S.: 541715
Harel Gadot (Founder, Chm, Pres & CEO)
Eran Cohen (Sr Dir-Bus Dev)
Noa Ofer (Mgr-Intellectual Property)
Rachel Vaknin (CFO)
Juan Diaz-Cartelle (Chief Medical Officer)

MICROCHIP TECHNOLOGY INCORPORATED
2355 W Chandler Blvd, Chandler, AZ 85224-6199
Tel.: (480) 792-7200　　DE
Web Site: https://www.microchip.com
Year Founded: 1989
MCHP—(NASDAQ)
Rev.: $7,634,400,000
Assets: $15,873,200,000
Liabilities: $9,215,400,000
Net Worth: $6,657,800,000
Earnings: $1,906,900,000
Emp.: 22,300
Fiscal Year-end: 03/31/24
Semiconductor Mfr & Distr
N.A.I.C.S.: 334413
Randall L. Drwinga (VP-Memory Products Bus Unit)
Mitchel Obolsky (Sr VP-Networking-Data Center Bus Units)
Michael A. Finley (Sr VP-Fab Ops)
Fanie Duvenhage (VP-Human Machine Interface Bus Unit)

Sumit K. Mitra (Sr VP-32-bit MCU,MPU,Wireless Bus Units)
James Eric Bjornholt (CFO & Sr VP)
Lauren A. Carr (Sr VP-HR-Global)
Thomas J. Grune (VP-Sls-Americas)
Mathew B. Bunker (Sr VP-Back-End Ops)
Mark W. Reiten (VP-Licensing)
Stephen T. Caldwell (VP-Wireless Products Bus Div)
Ian F. Harris (VP-Computing Products Bus Unit)
Patrick Johnson (Sr VP-Mixed Signal, Timing & FPGA Bus Units)
Nawaz Sharif (VP-Finance-Europe)
Joseph Thomsen (VP-MCU16 Bus Unit)
Robert Williams (VP-Information Svcs-Global)
Nuri Dagdeviren (VP-Security Products Bus Unit)
Rod Drake (VP-MCU32 Bus Unit)
Matthias Kaestner (VP-Automative)
Rami Kanama (VP-Timing-Comm Bus Unit)
Charles Forni (VP-UNG & Networking Bus Unit)
Dan Malinaric (VP-Fab 5 Ops)
Greg Perzanowski (VP-Quality & Reliability Sys)
Randy Brudzinski (VP-Frequency & Time Sys Bus Unit)
John Costello (VP-Govt Affairs)
Leon Gross (VP-Discrete Products Bus Unit)
Pete Hazen (VP-Data Center Solutions Bus Unit)
Suresh Menon (VP-Engineering-FPGA)
Bruce Weyer (VP-FPGA Bus Unit)
Richard J. Simoncic (COO & Exec VP)
Steve Sanghi (Chm, Interim Pres & Interim CEO)

Subsidiaries:

K2L GmbH　　**(1)**
Emmy-Noether-Strasse 14, 76131, Karlsruhe, Germany
Tel.: (49) 721 62537 0
Web Site: http://www.k2l.de
Software Development Services
N.A.I.C.S.: 541511

Microchip Technology (Thailand) Co., Ltd.　　**(1)**
Tel.: (66) 26941351
Sales Range: $150-199.9 Million
Emp.: 2,000
Mfr Semiconductors & Other Electronic Components
N.A.I.C.S.: 334413

Microsemi Corporation　　**(1)**
1 Enterprise, Aliso Viejo, CA 92656
Tel.: (949) 380-6100
Web Site: http://www.microsemi.com
Rev.: $1,811,800,000
Assets: $4,323,100,000
Liabilities: $2,328,800,000
Net Worth: $1,994,300,000
Earnings: $176,300,000
Emp.: 4,500
Fiscal Year-end: 10/01/2017
Holding Company; Analog & Mixed Signal Integrated Circuits & Discrete Semiconductors Mfr
N.A.I.C.S.: 551112
Ganesh Moorthy (Pres)

Subsidiary (Domestic):

Microsemi Communications, Inc.　**(2)**
4721 Calle Carga, Camarillo, CA 93012
Tel.: (805) 388-3700
Web Site: http://www.microsemi.com
Integrated Circuits Mfr
N.A.I.C.S.: 334413

Subsidiary (Non-US):

Microsemi Semiconductor Corporation A/S　　**(3)**

Horkaer 16-18, 2730, Herlev, Denmark
Tel.: (45) 44855900
Web Site: http://www.microsemi.com
Semiconductor Equipment Mfr
N.A.I.C.S.: 333242

Microsemi Semiconductor GmbH & Co. KG　　**(3)**
Borussiastr 112, Dortmund, 44149, Germany
Tel.: (49) 231656010
Web Site: http://www.microsemi.com
Semiconductor Equipment Mfr
N.A.I.C.S.: 333242

Subsidiary (Domestic):

Microsemi Corp. - Analog Mixed Signal Group　　**(2)**
11861 Western Ave, Garden Grove, CA 92841　　**(100%)**
Tel.: (714) 898-8121
Web Site: http://www.microsemi.com
Linear & Mixed Signal Integrated Circuits Mfr
N.A.I.C.S.: 334413

Microsemi Corp. - Massachusetts　**(2)**
75 Technology Dr, Lowell, MA 01851
Tel.: (978) 442-5600
Web Site: http://www.microsemi.com
Semiconductors & Related Devices Mfr
N.A.I.C.S.: 334413

Microsemi Corp. - Power Management Group　　**(2)**
11861 Western Ave, Garden Grove, CA 92841
Tel.: (714) 994-6500
Web Site: http://www.microsemi.com
Miscellaneous Electrical Equipment & Component Mfr
N.A.I.C.S.: 335999

Microsemi Corp. - Power Products Group　　**(2)**
405 SW Columbia St, Bend, OR 97702
Tel.: (541) 382-8028
Web Site: http://www.microsemi.com
Mfr of Switching Power Semiconductors
N.A.I.C.S.: 334413

Subsidiary (Domestic):

Microsemi Corp. - RF Power Products　　**(3)**
3000 Oakmead Vlg Dr Ste 100, Santa Clara, CA 95051
Tel.: (408) 986-8031
Web Site: http://www.microsemi.com
Radio Frequency Transistors & Amplifiers Mfr
N.A.I.C.S.: 334413

Subsidiary (Domestic):

Microsemi Corp. - Scottsdale　**(2)**
8700 E Thomas Rd, Scottsdale, AZ 85252　　**(100%)**
Tel.: (480) 941-6300
Web Site: http://www.microsemi.com
Electronic Components Mfr
N.A.I.C.S.: 334413

Microsemi Frequency & Time Corporation　　**(2)**
3870 N 1st St, San Jose, CA 95134
Tel.: (408) 433-0910
Rev.: $210,990,000
Assets: $230,928,000
Liabilities: $41,146,000
Net Worth: $189,782,000
Earnings: ($2,705,000)
Emp.: 544
Fiscal Year-end: 06/30/2013
Telecommunications Equipment & Linear & Mixed Signal Integrated Circuits Mfr & Sales
N.A.I.C.S.: 334210
Scott Davis (VP-Sls-America)

Subsidiary (Non-US):

Microsemi Frequency & Time GmbH　　**(3)**
Altlaufstrasse 42, 85635, Hohenkirchen, Germany　　**(100%)**
Tel.: (49) 8102896150
Web Site: https://www.microsemi.com

Telecommunications Equipment Mfr
N.A.I.C.S.: 334210

Subsidiary (Non-US):

Microsemi Ireland, Ltd. **(2)**
Bay 3 Gort Road Industrial Estates, Ennis,
County Clare, Ireland **(100%)**
Tel.: (353) 656840044
Web Site: http://www.microsemi.com
Electronic Component Sales
N.A.I.C.S.: 423690

Microsemi Israel, Ltd. **(2)**
1 Hanagar, Neve Neeman Industrial Zone,
Hod Hasharon, 4501305, Israel
Tel.: (972) 97755100
Web Site: http://www.microsemi.com
Integrated Circuits, Modules & Systems Mfr
N.A.I.C.S.: 334418

Subsidiary (Domestic):

Microsemi Semiconductor (U.S.)
Inc. **(2)**
4509 Freidrichh Ln Ste 200, Austin, TX
78744
Tel.: (512) 228-5438
Web Site: https://www.microsemi.com
Semiconductor Devices Mfr
N.A.I.C.S.: 334413

Subsidiary (Non-US):

Microsemi Semiconductor ULC **(2)**
400 March Road, Ottawa, K2K 3H4, ON,
Canada
Tel.: (613) 592-0200
Web Site: http://www.microsemi.com
Semiconductor & Related Device Mfr
N.A.I.C.S.: 334413

Subsidiary (Domestic):

Microsemi Storage Solutions,
Inc. **(2)**
1380 Bordeaux Dr, Sunnyvale, CA 94089
Tel.: (408) 239-8000
Web Site: https://www.microsemi.com
Processors, Chips & Semiconductor Sys-
tems Solutions
N.A.I.C.S.: 334413

SMC Japan **(1)**
Akihabara UDX15F 4-14-1 Sotokanda,
Chiyoda-ku 1014 Hamamatsu-cho 1
Chome, Tokyo, 101-0021, Japan **(100%)**
Tel.: (81) 352078271
Sales Range: $10-24.9 Million
Emp.: 39
Integrated Circuits Mfr
N.A.I.C.S.: 334413
Yosuke Yoshida *(Pres)*

Silicon Storage Technology Inc. **(1)**
2355 W Chandler Blvd, Chandler, AZ 85224
Tel.: (480) 792-7200
Web Site: https://www.sst.com
Semiconductor Product Mfr
N.A.I.C.S.: 334413

MICROCLOUD HOLOGRAM INC.
100 Park Ave, New York, NY 10017
Tel.: (212) 599-3322   Ky
Year Founded: 2018
HOLO—(NASDAQ)
Rev.: $28,182,876
Assets: $22,230,727
Liabilities: $2,680,032
Net Worth: $19,550,695
Earnings: ($11,296,522)
Emp.: 46
Fiscal Year-end: 12/31/23
Investment Services
N.A.I.C.S.: 523999

Subsidiaries:

MC Hologram Inc. **(1)**
Unit 03, 10/F T-PARK SZ-HK Film & TV
Creative Park 2001 Binhe Ave, Nanyuan St,
Futian Shenzhen, Guangdong, 518036,
China
Tel.: (86) 18680332608
Holographic Technology
N.A.I.C.S.: 513210

Ocean Cloud Technology Co.,
Limited **(1)**
Rm 707 7/F Fortress Tower 250 King's
Road, North Point, China (Hong Kong)
Tel.: (852) 95379263
Software Development Services
N.A.I.C.S.: 541511

MICROMOBILITY.COM INC.
1 Penn Plz 36th Fl, New York, NY
10019
Tel.: (212) 786-7429   DE
Year Founded: 2019
MCOM—(NASDAQ)
Rev.: $342,949
Assets: $58,413,629
Liabilities: $53,413,625
Net Worth: $5,000,004
Earnings: ($509,907)
Emp.: 2
Fiscal Year-end: 12/31/20
Investment Services
N.A.I.C.S.: 523999
Zhigeng Fu *(Chm)*
Qi Ye *(Treas & Sec)*
Salvatore Palella *(CEO)*

MICRON SOLUTIONS, INC.
25 Sawyer Passway, Fitchburg, MA
01420
Tel.: (978) 345-5000   DE
Web Site:
   https://www.micronsolutions.com
Year Founded: 1982
MICRD—(OTCIQ)
Rev.: $20,410,000
Assets: $11,919,000
Liabilities: $6,210,000
Net Worth: $5,709,000
Earnings: $1,726,000
Emp.: 116
Fiscal Year-end: 12/31/21
Electrocardiographic Software for the
Detection of Arrhythmias
N.A.I.C.S.: 334510
Andrei Soran *(Chm)*
Michael Simmons *(COO)*
Jerry O'connor *(Sr VP-Business De-
velopment)*
Mike Marcinkiewicz *(Controller)*

Subsidiaries:

Micron Products, Inc. **(1)**
25 Sawyer Passway, Fitchburg, MA
01420-5769 **(100%)**
Tel.: (978) 345-5000
Web Site: http://www.micronproducts.com
Sales Range: $10-24.9 Million
Emp.: 80
Sensors Mfr for Electrocardiographic Equip-
ment
N.A.I.C.S.: 334510
Mark LaViolette *(VP-Sls)*
Daniel White *(VP-Bus Dev)*
Michael Simmons *(Sr VP-Ops)*
Ann Mangold *(Controller)*
Drew Santin *(VP-Engrg)*
Helen Bibeau *(Dir-NPL & B&P)*
Lori Maronne *(Dir-HR)*

MICRON TECHNOLOGY, INC.
6360 S Federal Way, Boise, ID
83716-9632
Tel.: (208) 368-4555   DE
Web Site: https://www.micron.com
Year Founded: 1978
MU—(NASDAQ)
Rev.: $25,111,000,000
Assets: $69,416,000,000
Liabilities: $24,285,000,000
Net Worth: $45,131,000,000
Earnings: $778,000,000
Emp.: 48,000
Fiscal Year-end: 08/29/24
Memory, Storage & Imaging Semi-
conductor Mfr & Distr
N.A.I.C.S.: 334413

Robert E. Switz *(Chm)*
Michael W. Bokan *(Sr VP-Worldwide
Sls)*
Scott J. DeBoer *(Exec VP-Tech &
Products)*
Sumit Sadana *(Chief Bus Officer &
Exec VP)*
Mark J. Murphy *(CFO & Exec VP)*
April S. Arnzen *(Chief People Officer
& Sr VP)*
Sharawn Connors *(Chief Diversity &
Inclusion Officer)*
Scott Allen *(Chief Acctg Officer & VP)*
Mark J. Murphy *(CFO & Exec VP)*
Rob Beard *(Corp Counsel & Exec
VP)*
Sanjay Mehrotra *(Pres & CEO)*

Subsidiaries:

IM Flash Technologies, LLC **(1)**
4000 N Flash Dr, Lehi, UT 84043
Tel.: (801) 767-4000
Web Site: http://www.imftech.com
Electronic Components Mfr
N.A.I.C.S.: 334419

MEL Micron Europe Ltd. **(1)**
12 Redwood Crescent, Peel Park Campus,
East Kilbride, G74 5PA, Scotland, United
Kingdom
Tel.: (44) 1355586000
Web Site: http://www.uk.micron.com
Sales Range: $100-124.9 Million
Emp.: 150
Memory Module Assembly & Testing Facility
N.A.I.C.S.: 334419

Micron Consumer Products Group,
Inc. **(1)**
47300 Bayside Pkwy, Fremont, CA 94538
Tel.: (510) 413-1200
Web Site: http://www.micron.com
Sales Range: $800-899.9 Million
Emp.: 160
Designer, Marketer & Licensor of Remov-
able Flash-Based Digital Storage Media &
Card Readers for the Digital Photography,
Consumer Electronics, Industrial & Commu-
nications Markets
N.A.I.C.S.: 325992

Branch (Non-US):

Micron Consumer Products **(2)**
Sumitomo Fudosan Mita Twin Building East
Wing 12F 4-2-8 Shibaura, Minato-ku, Tokyo,
108-0023, Japan
Tel.: (81) 3 5439 3400
Web Site: http://www.lexar.com
Sales Range: $50-74.9 Million
Emp.: 8
Designer, Marketer & Licensor of Remov-
able Flash-Based Digital Storage Media &
Card Readers for the Digital Photography,
Consumer Electronics, Industrial & Commu-
nications Markets
N.A.I.C.S.: 541512

Micron Consumer Products
Group **(2)**
12 Redwood Crescent Peel Park Campus,
East Kilbride, G74 5PA, Surrey, United
Kingdom
Tel.: (44) 1355 586033
Web Site: http://www.lexar.com
Sales Range: $25-49.9 Million
Emp.: 100
Designer, Marketer & Licensor of Remov-
able Flash-Based Digital Storage Media &
Card Readers for the Digital Photography,
Consumer Electronics, Industrial & Commu-
nications Markets
N.A.I.C.S.: 541512

Micron Europe Limited **(1)**
Greenwood House London Road, Bracknell,
RG12 2AA, Berkshire, United Kingdom
Tel.: (44) 1344383400
Mfr of Computer Memory Modules & Chips
N.A.I.C.S.: 541512

Micron Japan, Ltd. **(1)**
302-2 Hirano Cho, Nishiwaki, 677 0063,
Hyogo, Japan **(100%)**
Tel.: (81) 795236601
Sales Range: $400-449.9 Million
Emp.: 1,500
Flash Memory Mfr

N.A.I.C.S.: 334413

Micron Memory Japan, Inc. **(1)**
Shinagawa Season Terrace 8F 1-2-70 Ko-
nan, Minato-ku, Tokyo, 108-0075, Japan
Tel.: (81) 5035053200
Sales Range: $5-14.9 Billion
Emp.: 5,585
Development, Design, Manufacture & Sale
of Semiconductor Products
N.A.I.C.S.: 334413

Subsidiary (Non-US):

Elpida Memory (Europe) Sarl **(2)**
Avenue Eugene-Lance 38 bis, Grand-
Lancy, 1212, Lancy, Switzerland
Tel.: (41) 228845860
Web Site: http://www.elpida.com
Integrated Circuits Mfr
N.A.I.C.S.: 334413

Elpida Memory (Hong Kong) Co.,
Ltd. **(2)**
Unit 11-12 33/F Standard Chartered Tower
Millennium City 1, 388 Kwun Tong Road,
Kowloon, China (Hong Kong) **(100%)**
Tel.: (852) 2902 7200
Web Site: http://www.elpida.com
Sales Range: $25-49.9 Million
Emp.: 10
Semiconductors & Computer Peripheral
Equipment Whslr
N.A.I.C.S.: 423430

Elpida Memory (Korea) Co., Ltd. **(2)**
11th Floor Seo Young Bldg 13 Teheran-ro
87 gil, Gangnam-Gu, Seoul, 135-090, Ko-
rea (South)
Tel.: (82) 2 2051 7793
Web Site: http://www.elpida.com
Integrated Circuits Mfr
N.A.I.C.S.: 334413

Elpida Memory (Taiwan) Co.,
Ltd. **(2)**
4F No 66 Nanjing W Rd, Datong Dist, Tai-
pei, 10352, Taiwan **(100%)**
Tel.: (886) 2 2558 5955
Web Site: http://www.elpida.com
Semiconductors & Computer Peripheral
Equipment Whslr
N.A.I.C.S.: 423430

Subsidiary (US):

Elpida Memory (USA) Inc. **(2)**
1175 Sonora Ct, Sunnyvale, CA
94086 **(100%)**
Tel.: (408) 542-7000
Web Site: http://www.elpida.com
Rev.: $500,000,000
Emp.: 30
Semiconductors & Computer Peripheral
Equipment Whslr
N.A.I.C.S.: 423430

Subsidiary (Domestic):

Micron Akita, Inc. **(2)**
89-2 Yamada Yuwaishida, Akita, 010-1222,
Japan **(100%)**
Tel.: (81) 18 886 2011
Web Site: http://www.a-elpida.com
Sales Range: $75-99.9 Million
Emp.: 400
Semiconductor Mfr
N.A.I.C.S.: 334413

Plant (Domestic):

Micron Memory Japan - Hiroshima
Plant **(2)**
7-10 Yoshikawa Kogyo Danchi, Higashi-
hiroshima, 739-0198, Japan
Tel.: (81) 82 429 3333
Web Site: http://www.jp.micron.com
Integrated Circuits Mfr
N.A.I.C.S.: 334412

Micron Memory Taiwan Co., Ltd. **(1)**
No 369 Sec 4 Sanfeng Rd, Houli Dist, Taic-
hung, 42152, Taiwan
Tel.: (886) 425218000
Emp.: 2,017
Semiconductor Equipment Mfr
N.A.I.C.S.: 334413

Micron Semiconductor (Deutschland)
GmbH **(1)**

Micron Technology, Inc.—(Continued)

Sternstrasse 20, D 85609, Aschheim,
Germany　　　　　　　　　　　**(100%)**
Tel.: (49) 899048720
Web Site: http://www.micron.com
Sales Range: $25-49.9 Million
Emp.: 10
Semiconductors & Components Support
Services
N.A.I.C.S.: 423690

**Micron Semiconductor (Xi'an) Co.,
Ltd.**　　　　　　　　　　　　　**(1)**
Zone B of Shaanxi Xi'an Export Processing
Zone 28 XinXi Avenue, Xi'an, 710119,
China
Tel.: (86) 2968916666
Semiconductor Devices Mfr
N.A.I.C.S.: 334413

**Micron Semiconductor (Xiamen) Co.,
Ltd.**　　　　　　　　　　　　　**(1)**
Rm 202 2/F Administration Committee
Building, Xiangyu Free Trade Zone, Xia-
men, 361006, China
Tel.: (86) 925651088
Web Site: http://www.micron.com
Sales Range: $100-124.9 Million
Semiconductors & Flash Memory Distr
N.A.I.C.S.: 334413

**Micron Semiconductor Asia Opera-
tions Pte. Ltd.**　　　　　　　　**(1)**
990 Bendemeer Road, Singapore, 339942,
Singapore
Tel.: (65) 62903000
Mobile Device Mfr
N.A.I.C.S.: 321991

**Micron Semiconductor Asia Pte.
Ltd.**　　　　　　　　　　　　　**(1)**
990 Bendemeer Road, Singapore, 339942,
Singapore
Tel.: (65) 62903000
Web Site: http://sg.micron.com
Flash Memory & Modules Assembly & Test-
ing
N.A.I.C.S.: 423690

Micron Semiconductor Italia S.r.l.　**(1)**
La Cittadella - Torre 2 Sottopassaggio M
Saggin 2, 35131, Padova, Italy
Tel.: (39) 0863456001
Mobile Device Mfr
N.A.I.C.S.: 321991

**Micron Semiconductor Korea Co.,
Ltd.**　　　　　　　　　　　　　**(1)**
5th Floor Glass Tower Bldg 534 Teheran-ro,
Gangnam-gu, Seoul, 6181, Korea (South)
Tel.: (82) 25307800
Web Site: http://www.micron.com
Sales Range: $100-124.9 Million
Semiconductor Distr
N.A.I.C.S.: 334413

**Micron Semiconductor Malaysia Sdn.
Bhd.**　　　　　　　　　　　　　**(1)**
Tanjung Agas Industrial Area, PO Box 62,
Muar, 84000, Johor, Malaysia
Tel.: (60) 69562600
Mobile Device Mfr
N.A.I.C.S.: 321991

**Micron Semiconductor Products,
Inc.**　　　　　　　　　　　　　**(1)**
8000 S Federal Way, Boise, ID 83707-0006
Tel.: (208) 368-4000
Semiconductor Devices Mfr
N.A.I.C.S.: 333242

Micron Systems Integration, Inc.　**(1)**
7560 S Federal Way, Boise, ID 83716-9605
Tel.: (208) 368-2200
Web Site: http://www.micron.com
Sales Range: $100-124.9 Million
Emp.: 5,000
Mfr & Designer of Semiconductor Testing
Equipment
N.A.I.C.S.: 334111

**Micron Technology Asia Pacific,
Inc.**　　　　　　　　　　　　　**(1)**
23F 24F No 170 Jingmao 1st Rd, Nangang
Dist, Taipei, 11568, Taiwan　　　**(100%)**
Tel.: (886) 227576622
Sales Range: $25-49.9 Million
Emp.: 35
Semiconductor Products Sales

N.A.I.C.S.: 423690

Micron Technology Services, Inc.　**(1)**
8000 S Federal Way, Boise, ID 83716
Tel.: (208) 368-3900
Sales Range: $1-4.9 Billion
Emp.: 9,000
Mfr of Semiconductor Components
N.A.I.C.S.: 334413

Micron Technology Taiwan, Inc.　**(1)**
No 667 Fuhsing 3rd Rd, Hwa-Ya Technol-
ogy Park Guishan District, Taoyuan, 33383,
Taiwan
Tel.: (886) 33272988
Mobile Device Mfr
N.A.I.C.S.: 321991

Micron Technology Texas, LLC　**(1)**
950 W Bethany Dr Ste 120, Allen, TX
75013-8010
Tel.: (972) 521-5200
Sales Range: $1-4.9 Billion
Emp.: 90
Developer of Semiconductors
N.A.I.C.S.: 334413

Micron Technology of Virginia　**(1)**
9600 Godwin Dr, Manassas, VA 20110-
4162
Tel.: (703) 396-1000
Web Site: http://www.micron.com
Sales Range: $400-449.9 Million
Emp.: 1,600
Mfr of Semiconductors
N.A.I.C.S.: 334118

**Micron Technology, Inc. - Crucial
Division**　　　　　　　　　　　**(1)**
3475 E Commercial Ct, Meridian, ID
83642-6041
Tel.: (208) 363-5790
Web Site: http://www.crucial.com
Sales Range: $125-149.9 Million
Emp.: 300
Flash Memory Distr
N.A.I.C.S.: 423690

MICROPAC INDUSTRIES INC.
1655 State Hwy 66, Garland, TX
75040
Tel.: (972) 272-3571　　　　　**DE**
Web Site: https://www.micropac.com
Year Founded: 1969
MPAD—(OTCIQ)
Rev.: $30,639,000
Assets: $55,307,000
Liabilities: $20,039,000
Net Worth: $35,268,000
Earnings: $632,000
Emp.: 143
Fiscal Year-end: 11/30/23
Integrated Microcircuits Distr
N.A.I.C.S.: 334413
Patrick S. Cefalu (CFO & Exec VP)
Mark W. King (Pres & CEO)

MICROPHONICS, INC.
1 Vantage Way Ste B-130, Nashville,
TN 37228
Tel.: (615) 871-4000　　　　　**NY**
MRPS—(OTCIQ)
Health Care Srvices
N.A.I.C.S.: 621999
Jerome Mariam (Sec)
Joel Heffron (Pres, CEO, CFO &
Treas)
Courtney Dawson (Asst VP & Asst
Sec)

MICROSOFT CORPORATION
1 Microsoft Way, Redmond, WA
98052-6399
Tel.: (425) 882-8080　　　　　**WA**
Web Site: https://www.microsoft.com
Year Founded: 1975
MSFT—(NASDAQ)
Rev.: $245,122,000,000
Assets: $512,163,000,000
Liabilities: $243,686,000,000
Net Worth: $268,477,000,000
Earnings: $88,136,000,000
Emp.: 228,000

Fiscal Year-end: 06/30/24
Software Development Services
N.A.I.C.S.: 513210
Angela L. Heise (VP-Public Sector-
Worldwide)
Jean-Philippe Courtois (Pres-National
Transformation Partnerships & Exec
VP)
Christopher C. Capossela (CMO &
Exec VP-Mktg & Consumer Bus)
Rajesh Jha (Exec VP-Experiences &
Devices)
Scott Guthrie (Exec VP-Cloud & AI
Grp)
Judson B. Althoff (Chief Comml Offi-
cer & Exec VP)
Judson Althoff (Chief Comml Officer
& Exec VP)
Amy E. Hood (CFO & Exec VP)
Bradford L. Smith (Pres & Chief Le-
gal Officer)
Charlotte B. Yarkoni (Pres-
Commerce, Ecosystems, and Cloud
& AI)
Kevin Scott (CTO & Exec VP-Tech &
Res)
Vasumati P. Jakkal (VP-Security,
Compliance, Identity & Privacy)
Yusuf I. Mehdi (CMO-Consumer &
Exec VP)
Darryl K. Willis (VP-Energy Industry)
Jack Ngare (Mng Dir-Africa Dev
Centre-Kenya)
Kathleen T. Hogan (Chief People Offi-
cer & Exec VP-HR)
Deb Cupp (Pres-North America)
Shirin S. O'Connor (VP-Engrg, Pro-
curement, and Construction)
Lila Tretikov (Deputy CTO & VP)
Alice L. Jolla (Chief Acctg Officer &
VP)
Rani N. Borkar (VP-Azure Hardware
Sys & Infrastructure)
Patricia Obermaier (VP-Health & Life
Sciences)
Julia Liuson (Pres-Developer Divi-
sion)
Lakecia N. Gunter (VP/Gen Mgr-
Device Partner Solution Sales Grp)
John McNiff (VP-Federal Bus)
Gayle Sheppard (CTO-Asia & VP)
Parul Bhandari (Dir-Partner Strategy-
Worldwide Media & Comm)
Jason Roszak (Chief Product Officer)
Jair Clarke (CTO-Commercial
Systems-Global)
William A. Borden (Executives)
Nick Pinheiro (Principal-Azure Cloud
& Artificial Intelligence)
Edna Conway (Officer-Security &
Risk-Cloud Infrastructure & VP-Cloud
Infrastructure)
Charlie Bell (Exec VP-Security, Com-
pliance, Identity & Mgmt)
Julia Denman (VP & Head-Internal
Audit-Enterprise Risk & Compliance)
Martin Taylor (Executives)
Jaime Teevan (Chief Scientist)
Satya Nadella (Bd of Dirs, Bd of Dirs,
Chm, CEO, Pres-Server & Tools,
Exec VP-Cloud & Enterprise Grp, Sr
VP-Search, Portal & Advertising, Sr
VP-Online Svcs Div, VP-Bus Div-
Microsoft & Program Mgr-Windows
Developer Rels Grp)
Christopher David Young (Exec VP-
Bus Dev, Strategy, and Ventures)
Mala Anand (Executives)
Renee Wonlai Lo (Chm-
Women@Asia Grp & Gen Mgr)
Aparna Chennapragada (VP-
Generative AI)

Subsidiaries:

Activision Blizzard, Inc.　　　　　**(1)**

2701 Olympic Blvd Bldg B, Santa Monica,
CA 90404
Tel.: (310) 255-2000
Web Site: https://www.activisionblizzard.com
Rev.: $7,528,000,000
Assets: $27,383,000,000
Liabilities: $8,140,000,000
Net Worth: $19,243,000,000
Earnings: $1,513,000,000
Emp.: 13,000
Fiscal Year-end: 12/31/2022
Video Game Publisher
N.A.I.C.S.: 541511
Frances Fragos Townsend (Exec VP-
Corporate Affairs)
Kelvin Liu (Dir-Corp Comm)
Kristen Hines (Chief Diversity Officer, Chief
Equity Officer & Chief Inclusion Officer)
Ann Lundy (Sr VP-Corp Fin & Internal Au-
dit)

Subsidiary (Non-US):

**Activision Blizzard Deutschland
GmbH**　　　　　　　　　　　　**(2)**
Tec-Park 1 Fraunhoferstr 7, 85737, Isman-
ing, Germany
Tel.: (49) 899998170
Telecommunication Servicesb
N.A.I.C.S.: 517810

Activision Blizzard Pty Limited　**(2)**
51 Rawson Street Level 5, Epping, Sydney,
2121, NSW, Australia
Tel.: (61) 298690955
Gaming Software Development Services
N.A.I.C.S.: 541511

Activision Blizzard UK Limited　**(2)**
Ditton Park Riding Court Road, Datchet,
SL3 9LL, Slough Berkshire, United Kingdom
Tel.: (44) 20 3060 1000
Web Site: http://www.activisionblizzard.com
Sales Range: $50-74.9 Million
Emp.: 120
Gaming Software Publisher
N.A.I.C.S.: 513210

Subsidiary (Domestic):

**Activision Publishing Minneapolis,
Inc**　　　　　　　　　　　　　**(2)**
5600 W 83rd St, Minneapolis, MN 55437
Tel.: (952) 918-9400
Web Site: http://www.activision.com
Emp.: 4,000
Computer Software Developer & Publisher
N.A.I.C.S.: 513210

Activision Publishing, Inc.　　　**(2)**
3100 Ocean Park Blvd, Santa Monica, CA
90405
Tel.: (310) 255-2000
Web Site: http://www.activisionblizzard.com
Computer Game Publisher
N.A.I.C.S.: 399930
Robert Kostich (Pres)
Dave Stohl (Exec VP)
Josh Taub (COO)
Rob Schonfeld (Officer)
Suzie Carr (Officer)
Terri Durham (Corp Counsel)

Subsidiary (Domestic):

RedOctane, Inc.　　　　　　　**(3)**
444 Castro St Ste 140, Mountain View, CA
94041
Tel.: (408) 481-9121
Sales Range: $1-9.9 Million
Emp.: 20
Video Game Controller & Accessory Mfr &
Video Game Publishing
N.A.I.C.S.: 334118

Unit (Domestic):

Blizzard Entertainment　　　　**(2)**
16215 Alton Pkwy, Irvine, CA 92618-3616
Tel.: (949) 955-0283
Web Site: http://www.blizzard.com
Sales Range: $1-4.9 Billion
Entertainment Software Publisher
N.A.I.C.S.: 513210

Subsidiary (Non-US):

Blizzard Entertainment S.A.S.　**(2)**
145 Rue Yves le Coz, 78000, Versailles,
France
Tel.: (33) 1 30679000

Web Site: http://eu.blizzard.com
Computer Gaming Software Development
Services
N.A.I.C.S.: 541511

Cooperatie Activision Blizzard International U.A (2)
Beechavenue 131d, Schiphol-Rijk, 1119 RB,
Netherlands
Tel.: (31) 207157700
Web Site: http://www.activision.com
Computer Software Developer & Publisher
N.A.I.C.S.: 513210

Cooperatie Activision Blizzard International U.A. (2)
Beechavenue 131, 1119 RB, Schiphol-Rijk,
Netherlands
Tel.: (31) 207157700
Web Site: http://www.activision.com
Emp.: 50
Gaming Software Development Services
N.A.I.C.S.: 541511

Subsidiary (Domestic):

Infinity Ward, Inc. (2)
15821 Ventura Blvd Ste 220, Encino, CA
91436
Tel.: (818) 386-0072
Web Site: http://www.infinityward.com
Gaming Software Development Services
N.A.I.C.S.: 541511

Subsidiary (Non-US):

King.com Limited (2)
Aragon House Business Centre Level 4
Dragonara Road St Julians, Saint Julians,
STJ3140, Malta
Tel.: (356) 493056837111
Web Site: http://www.king.com
Game Software Publisher
N.A.I.C.S.: 513210
Riccardo Zacconi (Co-Founder & Chm)
Sebastian Knutsson (Co-Founder)

Midasplayer AB (2)
Sveavagen 44, Stockholm, 111 34, Sweden
Tel.: (46) 854570430
Gaming Console Whslr
N.A.I.C.S.: 423920

Subsidiary (Domestic):

Neversoft Entertainment, Inc (2)
20335 Ventura Blvd Ste 320, Woodland
Hills, CA 91364
Tel.: (818) 610-4100
Computer Software Developer & Publisher
N.A.I.C.S.: 513210

Overwatch League, LLC (2)
1 Blizzard Way, Irvine, CA 92618-3616
Tel.: (949) 955-1380
Web Site: https://www.overwatchleague.com
Online Game Development Services
N.A.I.C.S.: 532282

Sierra Entertainment, Inc. (2)
3060 139th Ave Ste 500, Bellevue, WA
98005
Tel.: (425) 557-1146
Sales Range: $150-199.9 Million
Emp.: 629
Entertainment Software Publisher
N.A.I.C.S.: 513210

Sledgehammer Games, Inc (2)
1001 E Hillsdale Blvd Ste 610, Foster City,
CA 94404
Tel.: (650) 581-4800
Web Site:
    https://www.sledgehammergames.com
Gaming Software Publisher
N.A.I.C.S.: 513210

Sledghammer Games, Inc (2)
1001 E Hillsdale Blvd Ste 610, Foster City,
CA 94404
Tel.: (650) 581-4800
Web Site:
    http://www.sledgehammergames.com
Computer Software Developer & Publisher
N.A.I.C.S.: 513210

Treyarch Corporation (2)
3420 Ocean Park Blvd, Santa Monica, CA
90405
Tel.: (310) 581-4700
Web Site: http://www.treyarch.com

Computer Software Developer & Publisher
N.A.I.C.S.: 513210

Vicarious Visions, Inc. (2)
150 Broadway Ste 205, Albany, NY 12204
Tel.: (518) 701-2500
Web Site: http://www.vvisions.com
Sales Range: $25-49.9 Million
Emp.: 150
Video Game Software Development Services
N.A.I.C.S.: 541511
Aaron Ondek (CTO)

Avere Systems, Inc. (1)
910 River Ave, Pittsburgh, PA 15212
Tel.: (412) 894-2570
Web Site: http://www.microsoft.com
Computer Storage Device Mfr
N.A.I.C.S.: 334112

Double Fine Productions (1)
525 Brannan St Ste 200, San Francisco,
CA 94107
Tel.: (415) 896-1110
Web Site: http://www.doublefine.com
Video Games Publisher & Developer
N.A.I.C.S.: 513210
Lee Petty (Art Dir)

Equivio Inc. (1)
155 Gibbs St Ste 536, Rockville, MD 20850
Tel.: (800) 851-1965
Web Site: http://www.equivio.com
Software Publisher
N.A.I.C.S.: 513210
Amir Milo (Co-Founder & CEO)
Yiftach Ravid (Co-Founder & VP-Engrg)
Warwick Sharp (Co-Founder & VP-Mktg &
Bus Dev)

Geneed, Inc. (1)
135 Main St, San Francisco, CA 94105
Tel.: (415) 856-0097
Sales Range: $1-9.9 Million
Emp.: 20
Miscellaneous Schools & Instruction
N.A.I.C.S.: 611699
Paul M. Eisele (CEO & Dir)

GitHub, Inc. (1)
88 Colin P Kelly Jr St, San Francisco, CA
94107
Tel.: (877) 448-4820
Web Site: http://www.github.com
Software Development Hosting Services
N.A.I.C.S.: 518210
Jason Warner (CTO)
Carrie Olesen (Chief HR Officer)
Tyler Fuller (Gen Counsel)
Laura Heisman (VP-Comm & Corp Mktg)
Mike Taylor (CFO)
Erica Anderson (Sr VP-Revenue)
Keith Ballinger (Sr VP-Engrg)
Erica Brescia (COO)
Thomas Dohmke (CEO)
Shanku Niyogi (Sr VP-Product)
Sharryn Napier (VP-Sls-Asia Pacific)

Intentional Software Corporation (1)
3075 112th Ave NE Ste 100, Bellevue, WA
98004-8011
Tel.: (425) 822-0700
Web Site: http://www.intentsoft.com
Custom Computer Programming Services
N.A.I.C.S.: 541511

Microsoft (China) Co., Ltd. (1)
No 5 Danling St, Haidian District, Beijing,
100080, China (100%)
Tel.: (86) 1059178888
Web Site: http://www.microsoft.com
Sales Range: $75-99.9 Million
Emp.: 300
Software Platform Mfr & Services
N.A.I.C.S.: 513210
Alain Crozier (Chm & CEO)

Microsoft (Malaysia) Sdn. Bhd. (1)
Level 17 & 18 Menara Shell No 211 Jalan
Tun Sambanthan, 50470, Kuala Lumpur,
Malaysia
Tel.: (60) 327778888
Web Site: http://www.microsoft.com
Sales Range: $25-49.9 Million
Emp.: 150
Software Products & Services
N.A.I.C.S.: 334610
Raman K. (Mng Dir)

Microsoft (Thailand) Limited (1)

FI 37-38 CRC Tower All Seasons Place,
87/2 wireless Lumpini Pathumwan, Bangkok, 10330, Thailand (100%)
Tel.: (66) 22574999
Web Site: http://www.microsoft.com
Sales Range: $50-74.9 Million
Emp.: 200
Software Products & Services
N.A.I.C.S.: 334610
Haresh Khoobchandani (Mng Dir)

Microsoft Business Division (1)
1 Microsoft Way, Redmond, WA 98052-
6399
Tel.: (425) 882-8080
Web Site: http://www.microsoft.com
Sales Range: $75-99.9 Million
Business Software Mfr & Services
N.A.I.C.S.: 513210

Subsidiary (Non-US):

FAST (2)
Torggata 2-4-6, Oslo, NO-0181, Norway
Tel.: (47) 23011200
Web Site: http://www.fastsearch.com
Enterprise Search Software Developer,
Sales & Services
N.A.I.C.S.: 513210
Bjorn Olstad (CTO)

Microsoft Dynamics Danmark (2)
Tuborg Blvd 12, Hellerup, 2900, Denmark
Tel.: (45) 44890100
Sales Range: $25-49.9 Million
Emp.: 400
Financial & Business Management Software
Mfr
N.A.I.C.S.: 334610
Niels Soelberg (Gen Mgr)

Microsoft Canada Co. (1)
1950 Meadowvale Blvd, Mississauga, L5N
8L9, ON, Canada
Tel.: (905) 568-0434
Web Site: http://www.microsoft.com
Sales Range: $150-199.9 Million
Emp.: 650
Software Platform Mfr & Services
N.A.I.C.S.: 513210
Kevin Peesker (Pres)
Emma Da Silva (VP-Mktg & Ops)
Linda Sampson (CFO)
Lisa Gibson (Head-Comm & Bus Mgr-Mktg
& Ops)
Nadine Letson (Asst Gen Counsel-Corp,
External & Legal Affairs)
Travis Ames (VP-Consumer & Device Sls)
Sumeet Khanna (VP-Bus Transformation &
Strategic Initiatives)
Harp Girn (VP-Small Medium Corp Div)

Microsoft Co., Ltd. (1)
Shinagawa Grand Central Tower 2-16-3 Konan Minato-ku, Tokyo, 108-0075,
Japan (100%)
Tel.: (81) 343325300
Web Site: http://www.microsoft.com
Sales Range: $450-499.9 Million
Emp.: 1,560
Software Platform Mfr & Services
N.A.I.C.S.: 513210
Yasuyuki Higuchi (Pres)
Yasuyuki Higuchi (Pres)

Microsoft Corp. - Boise Office (1)
401 W Front St Ste 600, Boise, ID 83702
Tel.: (208) 344-1630
Web Site: http://www.microsoft.com
Sales Range: $10-24.9 Million
Emp.: 120
Business Analytic Services & Software Mfr
N.A.I.C.S.: 541511

Microsoft Corp. - Denver Office (1)
7595 Technology Way Ste 400, Denver, CO
80237-3007
Tel.: (720) 528-1700
Web Site: http://www.microsoft.com
Sales Range: $25-49.9 Million
Emp.: 150
Financial Analytics Software Mfr
N.A.I.C.S.: 513210

Microsoft Corp. - Fargo Office (1)
3900 Great Plains Dr S, Fargo, ND 58104-
3911
Tel.: (701) 281-6500
Web Site: http://www.microsoft.com
Business Management Software Mfr

N.A.I.C.S.: 513210

Microsoft Corporation (I) Pvt. Ltd. (1)
10th Floor Tower B C DLF Building No 5,
Cyber City DLF Phase III, Gurgaon, 122
002, India (100%)
Tel.: (91) 1244158000
Web Site: http://www.microsoft.com
Sales Range: $100-124.9 Million
Emp.: 450
Software Platform Mfr & Services
N.A.I.C.S.: 513210
Anant Maheshwari (Pres)
Keshav Dhakad (Head-Grp & Asst Gen
Counsel-Corp, External & Legal Affairs)
Ira Gupta (Head-HR)
Rajiv Kumar (Mng Dir-Microsoft IDC & VP-
Experiences & Devices-India-Grp)
Sriram Rajamani (Mng Dir-Res Lab)
Sundar Srinivasan (Gen Mgr-AI & Res)

Microsoft EMEA (1)
39 Quai du President Roosevelt, 92130,
Issy-les-Moulineaux, France
Tel.: (33) 157751000
Web Site: http://www.microsoft.com
Sales Range: $1-4.9 Billion
Emp.: 12,000
Holding Company; Software Platform &
Services
N.A.I.C.S.: 551112

Subsidiary (Non-US):

MS Portugal (2)
Rua do Fogo Go de Santelmo 2 07 02 Edificio
Qualidade C1 C2, Tagus Pk, 2744-010, Lisbon, Portugal
Tel.: (351) 214409200
Web Site: http://www.microsoft.com
Sales Range: $100-124.9 Million
Emp.: 400
Software Platform Mfr & Services
N.A.I.C.S.: 513210
Joao Couto (Partner & Mgr-Enablement)

Microsoft AB (2)
Regeringsgatan 25, PO Box 27, 111 53,
Stockholm, Sweden (100%)
Tel.: (46) 87525600
Web Site: https://www.microsoft.com
Software Platform Mfr & Services
N.A.I.C.S.: 513210
Per Adolfsson (Mng Dir)

Microsoft B.V. (2)
Evert van de Beekstraat 354, 1118 CZ,
Schiphol, Netherlands (100%)
Tel.: (31) 205001500
Web Site: https://www.microsoft.com
Sales Range: $125-149.9 Million
Emp.: 460
Software Platform Mfr & Services
N.A.I.C.S.: 513210

Microsoft Belgium & Luxembourg (2)
Dacinci, Zaventem, 1935, Belgium
Tel.: (32) 27043000
Web Site: http://www.microsoft.com
Sales Range: $100-124.9 Million
Emp.: 400
Software Platform Mfr & Services
N.A.I.C.S.: 513210

Microsoft Bilgisayar Yazilim Hizmetleri Limited Sirketi (2)
Bellevue Residences Aydin Sokak No 7
Levent, Levent District, 34340, Istanbul,
Turkiye
Tel.: (90) 2123705555
Web Site: https://www.microsoft.com
Sales Range: $25-49.9 Million
Emp.: 100
Software Platform Mfr & Services
N.A.I.C.S.: 513210

Microsoft Danmark ApS (2)
Kanalvej 7, Kongens, 2800, Lyngby, Denmark
Tel.: (45) 45678000
Web Site: https://www.microsoft.com
Sales Range: $75-99.9 Million
Emp.: 8
Software Platform Mfr & Services
N.A.I.C.S.: 513210

Microsoft Deutschland GmbH (2)
Walter-Gropius-Strasse 5, 80807, Munich,
Germany

Microsoft Corporation—(Continued)

Tel.: (49) 8931760
Web Site: https://news.microsoft.com
Sales Range: $450-499.9 Million
Emp.: 1,500
Software Platform Mfr & Services
N.A.I.C.S.: 513210

Subsidiary (Domestic):

Microsoft France S.A.R.L. (2)
39 President Roosevelt Wharf, Moulineaux,
92130, Issy-les-Moulineaux, France
Tel.: (33) 970019090
Web Site: https://www.microsoft.com
Sales Range: $400-449.9 Million
Emp.: 1,000
Software Platform Mfr & Services
N.A.I.C.S.: 513210

Subsidiary (Non-US):

Microsoft Gulf FZ LLC (2)
Dubai Internet City Building 8, Sheikh
Zayed Road, Dubai, United Arab Emirates
Tel.: (971) 43917000
Web Site: https://www.microsoft.com
Sales Range: $100-124.9 Million
Emp.: 500
Software Products & Services
N.A.I.C.S.: 334610

Microsoft Hellas S.A. (2)
221 Kifisias Ave, 151 24, Athens, Greece
Tel.: (30) 2111206000
Web Site: http://www.microsoft.com
Sales Range: $25-49.9 Million
Emp.: 100
Software Platform Mfr & Services
N.A.I.C.S.: 513210
Peggy Antonakou (CEO-Malta & Cyprus)

Microsoft Hungary (2)
Graphisoft Park 3 Zahony U, 1031, Buda-
pest, Hungary (100%)
Tel.: (36) 14372800
Web Site: http://www.microsoft.com
Sales Range: $25-49.9 Million
Emp.: 100
Software Platform Mfr & Services
N.A.I.C.S.: 513210

Microsoft Iberica S.R.L. (2)
Sports Club Promenade 1 La Finca Busi-
ness Center - Building 1, 28223, Madrid,
Spain (100%)
Tel.: (34) 913919000
Web Site: http://www.microsoft.com
Sales Range: $100-124.9 Million
Emp.: 400
Software Platform Mfr & Services
N.A.I.C.S.: 513210

**Microsoft Ireland Operations
Limited**
Building 3 Atrium B Carmanhall Road, San-
dyford Industrial Estate, Dublin, 18,
Ireland (100%)
Tel.: (353) 1850 940 940
Web Site: http://www.microsoft.com
Sales Range: $75-99.9 Million
Emp.: 300
Software Platform Mfr & Services
N.A.I.C.S.: 513210
Simon Fullerton (Sr Partner-HR Bus)

Microsoft Israel Ltd. (2)
2 Pearl St, Ra'anana, 43107, Israel
Tel.: (972) 97625400
Web Site: http://www.microsoft.com
Software Platform Mfr & Services
N.A.I.C.S.: 513210

Unit (Domestic):

**Microsoft - Herzliyya R&D
Center** (3)
13 Shenkar Street, Gav-Yam Building No 5,
Herzliyya, 46725, Israel
Tel.: (972) 7471111000
Web Site: http://www.microsoft.com
Sales Range: $75-99.9 Million
Product Research & Development
N.A.I.C.S.: 541715
Ariella Shina (Country Mgr-HR)
Michal Braverman-Blumenstyk (Gen Mgr)
Efim Hudis (CTO)

Unit (Domestic):
Microsoft - Haifa R&D Center (4)

Building No 25 Matam, Haifa, 3190501,
Israel
Tel.: (972) 9396000
Web Site: https://www.microsoftrnd.co.il
Product Research & Development
N.A.I.C.S.: 541715

Subsidiary (Non-US):

Microsoft Limited (2)
Microsoft Campus Thames Valley Park,
Reading, RG6 1WG, Berkshire, United
Kingdom
Tel.: (44) 8002400
Software Publisher
N.A.I.C.S.: 513210
Kostas Loukas (Gen Mgr-Pub Sector-
Central & Eastern Europe)
Ian Fordham (Dir-Education)
Derrick McCourt (Gen Mgr-Public Sector)

Microsoft Norge AS (2)
Lysaker Torg 45, PO Box 274, 1326, Ly-
saker, Norway (100%)
Tel.: (47) 22022500
Web Site: http://www.microsoft.com
Sales Range: $25-49.9 Million
Emp.: 350
Software Platform Mfr & Services
N.A.I.C.S.: 513210

Microsoft Osterreich GmbH (2)
Am Euro Platz 3, 1120, Vienna,
Austria (100%)
Tel.: (43) 1610640
Sales Range: $75-99.9 Million
Emp.: 300
Software Platform Mfr & Services
N.A.I.C.S.: 513210
Georg Obermeier (Gen Mgr)

Microsoft Oy Suomi (2)
Keilalahdentie 2-4, 02150, Espoo, Suomi,
Finland (100%)
Tel.: (358) 81710400
Web Site: http://www.microsoft.com
Sales Range: $75-99.9 Million
Emp.: 270
Software Platform Mfr & Services
N.A.I.C.S.: 513210
Ari Rahkonan (Mng Dir)

Microsoft Russia (2)
17 Ul Krylatskaya, Moscow, 121614,
Russia (100%)
Tel.: (7) 4959678585
Web Site: http://www.microsoft.com
Sales Range: $100-124.9 Million
Software Products & Services
N.A.I.C.S.: 334610
Pavel Betsis (Pres)

Microsoft S.R.L. (2)
Centro Direzionale San Felice, Via Rivol-
tana 13 Palazzo A, 20090, Segrate, MI,
Italy
Tel.: (39) 0270398398
Web Site: http://www.microsoft.com
Sales Range: $100-124.9 Million
Emp.: 375
Software Platform Mfr & Services
N.A.I.C.S.: 513210

Microsoft Schweiz GmbH (2)
The Circle, Flughafen, 8058, Zurich,
Switzerland (100%)
Tel.: (41) 848224488
Web Site: http://www.microsoft.com
Sales Range: $100-124.9 Million
Emp.: 500
Software Platform Mfr & Services
N.A.I.C.S.: 513210
Marianne Janik (CEO)

Microsoft Slovakia s.r.o. (2)
Pradiaren 1900 Svatoplukova 2A, 821 08,
Bratislava, Slovakia
Tel.: (421) 259295111
Web Site: http://www.microsoft.com
Sales Range: $25-49.9 Million
Emp.: 100
Software Platform Mfr & Services
N.A.I.C.S.: 513210

Microsoft South Africa (2)
3012 William Nicol Drive, Bryanston, Johan-
nesburg, 2191, South Africa (100%)
Tel.: (27) 113619000
Web Site: http://www.microsoft.com
Sales Range: $50-74.9 Million
Emp.: 200
Software Products & Services

N.A.I.C.S.: 334610
Samer Abu-Ltaif (Pres-Middle East & Africa)

Microsoft Sp. z o.o. (2)
Al Jerozolimskie 195a, 02-222, Warsaw,
Poland (100%)
Tel.: (48) 225941000
Web Site: http://www.microsoft.com
Sales Range: $100-124.9 Million
Emp.: 400
Software Platform Mfr & Services
N.A.I.C.S.: 513210

Microsoft d.o.o., Ljubljana (2)
Spinnery 1900 Svatoplukova 2A, 821 08,
Bratislava, Slovenia (100%)
Tel.: (386) 259295111
Web Site: https://www.microsoft.com
Software Platform Whslr
N.A.I.C.S.: 334610

Microsoft s.r.o. (2)
140 00 Prague 4, Vyskocilova 1561-4A, 140
00, Prague, Czech Republic (100%)
Tel.: (420) 261197665
Web Site: http://www.microsoft.com
Sales Range: $50-74.9 Million
Emp.: 200
Software Products & Services
N.A.I.C.S.: 334610

**Microsoft Entertainment & Devices
Division** (1)
1 Microsoft Way, Redmond, WA 98052-
6399
Tel.: (425) 882-8080
Web Site: http://www.microsoft.com
Sales Range: $100-124.9 Million
Entertainment Devices Mfr & Services
N.A.I.C.S.: 334118

Subsidiary (Domestic):

Danger Inc. (2)
3101 Park Blvd, Palo Alto, CA 94306
Tel.: (650) 289-5000
Sales Range: $25-49.9 Million
Emp.: 100
Mobile Phone Software Developer
N.A.I.C.S.: 513210

Subsidiary (Non-US):

Mojang AB (2)
Maria Skolgata 83 BV, 118 53, Stockholm,
Sweden
Tel.: (46) 850164225
Web Site: http://www.mojang.com
Video Game Developer & Publisher
N.A.I.C.S.: 513210
Karin Severinson (CFO)
Vu Bui (Chief Media Officer)
Henrik Pettersson (Dir-Game)
Marina Kostesic (Fin Dir)
Rikard Herlitz (CTO)
Mikaela Prim (Office Mgr)
Olof Carlson Sandvik (Chief Product Offi-
cer)
Owen Jones (Dir-Creative Comm)
Patrick Geuder (Dir-Bus Dev)
Ulrika Hojgard (Head-Stockholm Ops)
Jonas Martensson (CEO)
Jens Bergensten (Chief Creative Officer-
Design)
Saxs Persson (Chief Creative Officer-
Design)
Agnes Larsson (Dir-Game)
Jesse Merriam (Creative Dir)
Torfi Frans Olafsson (Dir-Creative)
Craig Leigh (Dir-Principal Design)
Michael W. Weilbacher (CTO-Programming)
Vince Curley (Head-Svcs & Ops Engrg)
Mike Carlson (Head-Stockholm Engrg)
Matthew Ng (Dir-Franchise Quality)
Christopher Ostlund (Dir-Technical)
Jason Cahill (Dir-Technical)
Jason Major (Dir-Technical)
Michael J. Ott (Dir-Technical)
Nathan Adams (Dir-Technical)
Andy Zibits (Art Dir-Visual Arts)
Deanna Hearns (Head-Creator & Produc-
tion)
John Thornton (Head-Platform Engrg)
Ryan B. Cooper (Head-Bus Engrg)
Aaron J. Buckley (Head-Creator Market-
place)
Patrick Liu (Head-Games)
Gama Aguilar-Gamez (Production Mgr)
Joel Alveroth (Coord-Office)
Lawrence M. Sanchez II (Dir-Technical)

Multimap Australasia (2)
Level 2 36 Carrington St, Sydney, 2000,
NSW, Australia
Tel.: (61) 292626551
Web Site: http://www.multimap.com
Mapping & Location-Based Information Ser-
vices
N.A.I.C.S.: 541360

Subsidiary (Domestic):

Xbox (2)
1 Microsoft Way, Redmond, WA 98052-
6399
Tel.: (425) 882-8080
Web Site: http://www.xbox.com
Sales Range: $50-74.9 Million
Video Game Console Mfr & Magazine Pub-
lisher
N.A.I.C.S.: 339930
Elan Lee (Chief Design Officer-
Entertainment Studios)

Xbox Game Studios (2)
1 Microsoft Way, Redmond, WA 98052-
6399
Tel.: (425) 882-8080
Web Site: https://www.xbox.com
Sales Range: $50-74.9 Million
Video Games Publisher & Developer
N.A.I.C.S.: 339930

Subsidiary (Domestic):

Obsidian Entertainment, Inc. (3)
8105 Irvine Ctr Dr Ste 200, Irvine, CA
92681
Tel.: (949) 379-3300
Web Site: http://www.obsidianent.com
Sales Range: $10-24.9 Million
Emp.: 100
Entertainment Software Developer
N.A.I.C.S.: 541511
Chris Jones (Founder & CTO)

inXile entertainment, Inc. (3)
2727 Newport Blvd Ste 100, Newport
Beach, CA 92663
Tel.: (949) 675-3690
Web Site: http://www.inxile-
entertainment.com
Software Publisher
N.A.I.C.S.: 513210
Elene Campbell (VP-People)

Microsoft Korea (1)
50 Jongno 1-gil, Jongno-gu, Seoul, Korea
(South) (100%)
Tel.: (82) 25314500
Web Site: http://www.microsoft.com
Sales Range: $125-149.9 Million
Emp.: 500
Software Platform Mfr & Services
N.A.I.C.S.: 513210

Microsoft Latin America (1)
6750 N Andrews Ave Ste 400, Fort Lauder-
dale, FL 33309
Tel.: (954) 489-4800
Web Site: http://www.mslatam.com
Sales Range: $75-99.9 Million
Emp.: 350
Software Platform Mfr & Services
N.A.I.C.S.: 513210

Subsidiary (Non-US):

**Corporacion Microsoft Del Ecuador
S.A.** (2)
Av Naciones Unidas 1014 Y Av Amazonas
Esquina, Edif La Previsora Torre Of 1001,
Quito, Ecuador
Tel.: (593) 22460453
Web Site: http://www.microsoft.com
Software Products Mfr & Services
N.A.I.C.S.: 513210

Microsoft Chile S.A. (2)
Av Vitacura 6844 Vitacura, Piso 6 Edificio
Briman 24, Santiago, 6760441,
Chile (100%)
Tel.: (56) 23306000
Web Site: https://www.microsoft.com
Sales Range: $25-49.9 Million
Emp.: 60
Software Platform Mfr & Services
N.A.I.C.S.: 513210

Microsoft Costa Rica (2)
universal tower Floor 1 Ave 12 Calle 42,

South Sabana, 10108, San Jose, Costa
Rica **(100%)**
Tel.: (506) 2011100
Web Site: https://www.microsoft.com
Sales Range: $75-99.9 Million
Emp.: 67
Software Platform Mfr & Services
N.A.I.C.S.: 513210

Microsoft Informatica Ltda. **(2)**
Av Presidente Juscelino Kubitscheck 1 909
- Torre Sul - 16th floor, 27 Andar, Sao
Paulo, 04551-065, SP, Brazil
Tel.: (55) 1155042155
Web Site: https://www.microsoft.com
Software Platform Mfr & Services
N.A.I.C.S.: 513210
Tania Cosentino (Pres)

Microsoft Mexico, S.A. de C.V. **(2)**
Av Vasco de Quiroga 3200 Floor 7 Col
Santa Fe City Center, From Alvaro Obre-
gon, 01210, Mexico, Mexico
Tel.: (52) 5552672000
Web Site: https://www.microsoft.com
Sales Range: $75-99.9 Million
Emp.: 280
Software Platform Mfr & Services
N.A.I.C.S.: 513210

Subsidiary (Domestic):

Microsoft Puerto Rico S.A. **(2)**
City View Plz Ste 107 48 State Rd, Guay-
nabo, PR 00968
Tel.: (787) 273-3600
Web Site: https://www.microsoft.com
Sales Range: $10-24.9 Million
Emp.: 75
Software Products Mfr & Services
N.A.I.C.S.: 513210

Subsidiary (Non-US):

Microsoft Venezuela S.A. **(2)**
Main Avenue of La Castellana Latvia center
ING Bank Tower 8th Floor, Caracas, Ven-
ezuela
Tel.: (58) 2122760500
Web Site: https://www.microsoft.com
Sales Range: $25-49.9 Million
Emp.: 120
Software Products & Services
N.A.I.C.S.: 334610

Microsoft Mobile Oy **(1)**
Kagelstranden 7, 02150, Espoo, Finland
Tel.: (358) 981710400
Sales Range: $50-74.9 Million
Emp.: 250
Cellular Mobile Telephones & Accessories;
Wide Area Pagers & Components; Data
Transmission Products
N.A.I.C.S.: 517112
Jo Harlow (Exec VP-Smart Devices)

Subsidiary (Non-US):

**Microsoft Mobile Deutschland
GmbH** **(2)**
Balcke-Durr-Allee 2, 40882, Ratingen, Ger-
many
Tel.: (49) 210289280
Communication Equipment Mfr & Whslr
N.A.I.C.S.: 334210

Unit (Domestic):

**Microsoft Mobile Deutschland GmbH
- Dusseldorf** **(3)**
Heltorstra Strasse 1, D 40472, Dusseldorf,
Germany
Tel.: (49) 21194120
Telecommunication Servicesb
N.A.I.C.S.: 517810

Subsidiary (US):

Microsoft Mobile Inc. **(1)**
16620 W Bernardo Dr, San Diego, CA
92127
Tel.: (858) 769-1220
Cellular Data Products Mfr
N.A.I.C.S.: 334310

Subsidiary (Non-US):

Nokia Mobile Phones **(2)**
20 F Philamlife Tower Paseo de Roxas,
Makati, 8767, Manila, Philippines **(100%)**
Tel.: (63) 27541600

Sales Range: $25-49.9 Million
Emp.: 100
Wireless Telecommunications
N.A.I.C.S.: 517112

Nokia Mobile Phones **(2)**
Jalan Stesen Sentral 5, Kuala Lumpur,
50470, Malaysia **(100%)**
Tel.: (60) 327868888
Wireless Telecommunications
N.A.I.C.S.: 334418

Nokia Mobile Phones **(2)**
District 1 The Metropolitan Bldg Ste 909
235 Dong Khoi St, Ho Chi Minh City,
Vietnam **(100%)**
Tel.: (84) 88245123
Wireless Telecommunications
N.A.I.C.S.: 334418

**Nokia Mobile Phones (Korea)
Ltd.** **(2)**
825-2 Yeoksam-dong Gangnam-gu, Seoul,
135080, Korea (South) **(100%)**
Tel.: (82) 221865000
Sales Range: $25-49.9 Million
Emp.: 35
Cellular Telecommunications
N.A.I.C.S.: 517112

**Nokia Mobile Phones (SEA) Pte
Ltd.** **(2)**
108 Thai Tower Rangnam Road Khwaeng
Thanon Phyathai Khet, Bangkok, 10400,
Rajthevee, Thailand
Tel.: (66) 26738888
Web Site: http://www.nokia.co.th
Sales Range: $25-49.9 Million
Emp.: 60
Telecommunications Equipment Mfr
N.A.I.C.S.: 238210

Unit (Domestic):

**Nokia Mobile Phones Wireless
Data** **(2)**
Visiokatu 4, PO Box 226, 00045, Tampere,
Finland **(100%)**
Tel.: (358) 718008000
Sales Range: $25-49.9 Million
Emp.: 250
Cellular Data Products Mfr
N.A.I.C.S.: 334310

Microsoft New Zealand Limited **(1)**
Level 5 22 Viaduct Harbour Ave, Auckland,
1010, New Zealand
Tel.: (64) 800800004
Web Site: http://www.microsoft.com
Sales Range: $25-49.9 Million
Emp.: 170
Software Products & Services
N.A.I.C.S.: 334610

Microsoft Nigeria Limited **(1)**
6th Floor Civic Towers Ozumba Mbadiwe
Road, beside Caverton Helicopters, Lagos,
Nigeria
Tel.: (234) 14621100
Web Site: http://www.microsoft.com
Software & Computer Related Services
N.A.I.C.S.: 513210
Rimini Haraya Makama (Dir-Intl Market
Expansion-Xbox Cloud Gaming)

**Microsoft Online Services
Division** **(1)**
1 Microsoft Way, Redmond, WA 98052-
6399
Tel.: (425) 882-8080
Web Site: http://www.microsoft.com
Sales Range: $75-99.9 Million
Software Platform Mfr & Services
N.A.I.C.S.: 513210
Qi Lu (Pres)

Subsidiary (Domestic):

Jellyfish.com, Inc. **(2)**
1 Microsoft Way, Redmond, WA 98052-
8300
Tel.: (608) 827-5385
Web Site: http://www.jellyfish.com
Sales Range: $75-99.9 Million
Shopping Search Engine Operator
N.A.I.C.S.: 519290
Paramjeet Sanghera (CTO)
Rob Pierre (CEO)
Mario Schiappacasse (Exec VP-Display)
Cory Hudson (VP-Creative)

Andrew Burakov (Sr Mgr-Paid Social)
Biney Singh (Dir-Paid Social)
Daniel Catelli (Acct Mgr)
Gina Ferrari (Sr Acct Mgr)
Kate Mezzanotte (Sr Dir-Display)
Julia Clark (Sr Mgr-PPC)
Larry Hannon (Dir-Paid Search)
Michael Verni (VP-Paid Media Ops)
Ryan McNamara (Dir-Paid Social)
Stefanie Seet (Sr Acct Mgr)
Stephanie Tom (Dir-Display)
Will Phung (Partner-Client)

LinkedIn Corporation **(2)**
1000 W Maude Ave, Sunnyvale, CA 94085
Tel.: (650) 687-3600
Web Site: http://www.linkedin.com
Emp.: 19,000
Online Social Networking Publisher
N.A.I.C.S.: 516210
Reid G. Hoffman (Co-Founder & Chm)
Allen Blue (Co-Founder & VP-Product
Mgmt)
Penry W. Price (VP-Mktg Solutions)
Jeffrey Weiner (Chm)
Catherine Fisher (Sr Dir-Content, Media &
Experiences-San Francisco)
Melissa Selcher (Chief Mktg & Comm Offi-
cer, Chief Comm Officer & Sr VP)
Matt Tindale (Mng Dir-ANZ, Head-
Enterprise-APAC-Mktg Solutions & Sr Dir)
Blair Decembrele Heitmann (Sr Dir-Comm
& Mktg)
Suzi Owens (Sr Dir-Corp Comm)
Dan Shapero (COO & Sr VP)
Ryan Roslansky (CEO)
Mohak Shroff (Sr VP-Engrg)
Adrienne M. Everett (Dir-Enterprise Ac-
count)

Subsidiary (Non-US):

ScreenTonic S.A. **(2)**
4 bis rue Saint Sauveur, 75002, Paris,
France
Tel.: (33) 144768901
Web Site: http://www.screentonic.com
Sales Range: $100-124.9 Million
Mobile Advertising Services
N.A.I.C.S.: 541890

Subsidiary (Domestic):

Stratature, Inc. **(2)**
11625 Rainwater Dr, Alpharetta, GA 30004
Tel.: (678) 353-2150
Web Site: http://www.stratature.com
Sales Range: $100-124.9 Million
Master Data Management Software Devel-
oper & Publisher
N.A.I.C.S.: 513210

Yammer, Inc. **(2)**
410 Townsend St, San Francisco, CA
94107
Tel.: (415) 796-7400
Web Site: http://www.yammer.com
Sales Range: $75-99.9 Million
Emp.: 350
Social Media Platform for Businesses
N.A.I.C.S.: 516210
David O. Sacks (Founder & CEO)
David Sacks (Founder & CEO)

Joint Venture (Non-US):

ninemsn Pty. Ltd. **(2)**
Level 7 Tower Building Australia Square,
264-278 George Street, Sydney, 2000,
NSW, Australia **(50%)**
Tel.: (61) 293836000
Web Site: http://www.ninemsn.com.au
Sales Range: $50-74.9 Million
Emp.: 200
Online Media Publishing & Broadcasting
Services
N.A.I.C.S.: 516210

Microsoft Online, Inc. **(1)**
6100 Neil Rd Ste 100, Reno, NV 89511-
1137
Tel.: (425) 882-8080
Online Software Support Services
N.A.I.C.S.: 541519

Microsoft Operations Pte Ltd **(1)**
438B Alexandra Rd Ste 04-09/12 Alexandra
Technopark, Singapore, 119968, Singapore
Tel.: (65) 63709000
Software Distr

N.A.I.C.S.: 423430
Colin Cheng (Dir-Consumer Channel Grp)
Bradley Hopkinson (Gen Mgr-Retail Sls &
Mktg-Greater Asia)
Kevin Wo (Mng Dir)
Wendy Johnstone (Gen Mgr-Mktg & Ops-
Asia Pacific)

Microsoft Philippines, Inc. **(1)**
11F One Ayala West Tower, Ayala Avenue
cor Edsa San Lorenzo, Makati, 1223,
Philippines **(100%)**
Tel.: (63) 288608989
Web Site: http://www.microsoft.com
Sales Range: $10-24.9 Million
Emp.: 30
Software Products & Services
N.A.I.C.S.: 334610
Karrie Ilagan (Mng Dir)

Microsoft Pty. Limited **(1)**
1 Denison Street, North Sydney, 2060,
NSW, Australia **(100%)**
Tel.: (61) 288707510
Web Site: http://www.microsoft.com
Sales Range: $150-199.9 Million
Emp.: 600
Software Products & Services
N.A.I.C.S.: 334610
Jo Dooley (Dir-Enterprise Comml)
Mark Leigh (Gen Mgr-Pub Sector)
Rachel Bondi (Dir-One Comml Partner)
Tom Daemen (Dir-Corp, External & Legal
Affairs)
Soraya Scott (COO-UK)
Peter Stanski (Dir-Customer Success Unit)
Elena Wise (Dir-Specialist Tech Unit)

Microsoft Server & Tools Division **(1)**
1 Microsoft Way, Redmond, WA 98052-
6399
Tel.: (425) 882-8080
Web Site: http://www.microsoft.com
Information Technology Product & Content
Licensing & Services
N.A.I.C.S.: 533110

Subsidiary (Domestic):

Microsoft Licensing, GP **(2)**
6100 Neil Rd Ste 100, Reno, NV 89511-
1137
Tel.: (775) 823-5600
Web Site: http://www.microsoft.com
Sales Range: $25-49.9 Million
Emp.: 165
Software Licensing Services
N.A.I.C.S.: 533110

Microsoft Taiwan Corporation **(1)**
18th Floor No 68 Section 5 Zhongxiao East
Road, Xinyi District, Taipei, 11065,
Taiwan **(100%)**
Tel.: (886) 237253888
Web Site: http://www.microsoft.com
Sales Range: $100-124.9 Million
Emp.: 500
Software Products & Services
N.A.I.C.S.: 334610

**Microsoft Windows & Windows Live
Division** **(1)**
1 Microsoft Way, Redmond, WA 98052-
6399
Tel.: (425) 882-8080
Web Site: http://www.microsoft.com
Sales Range: $100-124.9 Million
Computer Software & Services
N.A.I.C.S.: 513210
John DeVaan (Sr VP)

Music Choice **(1)**
650 Dresher Rd, Horsham, PA 19044
Tel.: (215) 784-5840
Web Site: http://www.musicchoice.com
Emp.: 60
Music Video Cable Television Programming,
Online & Mobile Publishing Services
N.A.I.C.S.: 516210
David Del Beccaro (Founder, Co-Pres &
CEO)
Christina Tancredi (Co-Pres & COO)
Jeremy Rosenberg (Co-Founder)

Nuance Communications, Inc. **(1)**
1 Wayside Rd, Burlington, MA 01803
Tel.: (781) 565-5000
Web Site: http://www.nuance.com
Rev.: $1,478,899,000
Assets: $3,593,332,000

Microsoft Corporation—(Continued)

Liabilities: $2,449,399,000
Net Worth: $1,143,933,000
Earnings: $21,396,000
Emp.: 7,100
Fiscal Year-end: 09/30/2020
Document Management, Digital Imaging &
Speech Recognition Software Developer
N.A.I.C.S.: 334610
Robert J. Weideman *(Exec VP & Gen Mgr-
Enterprise Div)*
Daniel D. Tempesta *(CFO & Exec VP)*
Alvaro J. Monserrat *(Exec VP & Gen Mgr-
Document Imaging Div)*
Arthur Giterman *(Chief Acctg Officer, Sr VP
& Controller)*
Wendy Cassity *(Chief Legal Officer & Exec
VP)*
Joe Petro *(CTO & Exec VP)*
Mark Sherwood *(CIO & Sr VP)*
Beth Conway *(Chief People Officer & Exec
VP)*
Robert Dahdah *(Chief Revenue Officer &
Exec VP)*
David Garfinkel *(Sr VP-Corp Dev)*
Diana L. Nole *(Exec VP & Gen Mgr-
Healthcare Div)*

Subsidiary (Non-US):

Accentus Inc. (2)
2430 Don Reid Drive Suite 202, Ottawa,
K1H 1E1, ON, Canada
Tel.: (613) 739-0808
Web Site: http://www.accentusinc.com
Transcription Document Imaging & Coding
Services
N.A.I.C.S.: 561410

BlueStar Options Inc. (2)
Wickhams Cay, Road Town, Tortola, Virgin
Islands (British)
Tel.: (284) 2844942204
Information Technology Consulting Services
N.A.I.C.S.: 541512

Subsidiary (Domestic):

Cerence Inc. (2)
25 Burlington Mall Rd Ste 416, Burlington,
MA 01803
Tel.: (857) 362-7300
Web Site: https://www.cerence.com
Rev.: $294,475,000
Assets: $1,297,590,000
Liabilities: $602,715,000
Net Worth: $694,875,000
Earnings: ($56,254,000)
Emp.: 1,700
Fiscal Year-end: 09/30/2023
Information Technology & Services
N.A.I.C.S.: 541511
Stefan Ortmanns *(Pres & CEO)*
Antonio Rodriquez *(Interim CFO)*
Arun Sarin *(Chm)*
Rich Yerganian *(VP-IR)*
Bridget Collins *(CIO)*
Udo Haiber *(Sr VP-R&D & Svcs)*
Egon Jungheim *(Sr VP-Sls-Global)*
Charles Kuai *(Gen Mgr-Mobility Solutions &
Sr VP)*
Nils Lenke *(VP & Gen Mgr-Applications)*
Richard Mack *(CMO)*
Sachin Sahney *(Chief HR Officer)*
Sujal Shah *(VP & Gen Mgr-Professional
Svcs)*

Subsidiary (Non-US):

Cerence Deutschland GmbH (3)
Julicher Strasse 376, 52070, Aachen, Ger-
many
Tel.: (49) 24188710
Software Publisher
N.A.I.C.S.: 513210

Cerence GmbH (3)
Im Mediapark 5b, 50670, Cologne, Ger-
many
Tel.: (49) 221355590
Web Site: http://www.communology.com
Mobile Software Development Services
N.A.I.C.S.: 541511

Cerence Switzerland AG (3)
Baslerstrasse 30, 8048, Zurich, Switzerland
Tel.: (41) 435440600
Computer Aided Medical Transcription Ser-
vices

N.A.I.C.S.: 561410

Subsidiary (Domestic):

SVOX AG (4)
Baslerstrasse 30, 8048, Zurich, Switzerland
Tel.: (41) 435440600
Sales Range: $25-49.9 Million
Emp.: 100
Text-to-Speech Technology Mfr
N.A.I.C.S.: 541512

Subsidiary (Domestic):

Ditech Networks, Inc. (2)
1 Wayside Rd, Burlington, MA 01803
Tel.: (781) 565-5000
Web Site: http://www.nuance.com
Emp.: 63
Holding Company; Voice Network Telecom-
munications Equipment & Services
N.A.I.C.S.: 551112
Todd M. DuChene *(Sec)*
Thomas J. Beaudoin *(Pres & Treas)*

Equitrac Corporation (2)
1000 S Pine Is Rd Ste 900, Plantation, FL
33324
Tel.: (954) 888-7800
Web Site: http://www.equitrac.com
Sales Range: $100-124.9 Million
Emp.: 420
Computer System Solutions for Automated
Cost Recovery & Expense Management of
Office Equipment
N.A.I.C.S.: 513210

Subsidiary (Non-US):

ITA Services Pty Ltd. (2)
245-249 Lutwyche Rd, Windsor, 4030,
QLD, Australia
Tel.: (61) 736222200
Emp.: 50
Investment Management Service
N.A.I.C.S.: 523940

Subsidiary (Domestic):

J.A. Thomas & Associates, Inc. (2)
3715 Northside Pkwy NW Ste 1-200, At-
lanta, GA 30327
Tel.: (770) 438-8537
Web Site: http://www.jathomas.com
Clinical Data Documentation Management
Services
N.A.I.C.S.: 518210

Subsidiary (Non-US):

Loquendo S.p.A. (2)
Via Arrigo Olivetti 6, 10148, Turin, Italy
Tel.: (39) 0112913111
Web Site: http://www.loquendo.com
Sales Range: $25-49.9 Million
Emp.: 100
Speech-Interaction Software Developer
N.A.I.C.S.: 513210

Subsidiary (Domestic):

**Medical Transcription Education Cen-
ter, Inc.** (2)
3618 W Market St Ste 103, Fairlawn, OH
44333
Tel.: (330) 670-9333
Web Site: http://www.mtecinc.com
Transcription Education Support Services
N.A.I.C.S.: 611710

Subsidiary (Non-US):

NSi Europe GmbH (2)
Eohanzenfeldatr 12, 35578, Wetzlar, Ger-
many
Tel.: (49) 6441671380
Software Publishing Services
N.A.I.C.S.: 513210

Subsidiary (Domestic):

Neurostar Solutions, Inc. (2)
6 Concourse Pkwy NE Ste 1625, Atlanta,
GA 30328
Tel.: (404) 575-4222
Computer Aided Medical Transcription Ser-
vices
N.A.I.C.S.: 561410

Notable Solutions, Inc. (2)
1 Way Side Rd, Burlington, MA 20850
Tel.: (240) 683-8400

Web Site: http://www.notablesolutions.com
Software Publishing Services
N.A.I.C.S.: 513210

Subsidiary (Non-US):

**Novitech Technologia e Servicos
Ltda.** (2)
Rua Andre Capretz Filho, 46 - Ruge Ra-
mos, Sao Bernardo do Campo, 09626-120,
SP, Brazil
Tel.: (55) 1126774386
Web Site: https://www.novitech.ind.br
Software Publishing Services
N.A.I.C.S.: 513210

**Nuance Communications Australia
Pty Ltd.** (2)
530 Collins Street, Melbourne, 3000, NSW,
Australia
Tel.: (61) 282239582
Web Site: http://australia.nuance.com
Sales Range: $900-999.9 Million
Digital Imaging & Speech Technology Soft-
ware Solutions
N.A.I.C.S.: 541511

**Nuance Communications Austria
GmbH** (2)
Am Europlatz 3, 1120, Vienna, Austria
Tel.: (43) 1601190
Software Development Services
N.A.I.C.S.: 541511

**Nuance Communications Canada,
Inc.** (2)
1500 Robert Bourassa Suite 850, Montreal,
H3A 3S7, QC, Canada
Tel.: (514) 904-7800
Web Site: http://www.nuance.com
Software Development Services
N.A.I.C.S.: 541511

Nuance Communications GmbH (2)
Ehlbeek 3, 30938, Burgwedel, Germany
Tel.: (49) 513989790
Web Site: http://www.nuance.com
Information Technology Consulting Services
N.A.I.C.S.: 541512

**Nuance Communications Healthcare
Germany GmbH** (2)
Otto-Hahn-Str 9a, 25337, Elmshorn,
Schleswig-Holstein, Germany
Tel.: (49) 4121800480
Information Technology Consulting Services
N.A.I.C.S.: 541512

**Nuance Communications Hong Kong
Limited** (2)
Unit 2402-07 24F Berkshire House 25
Westlands Road, Quarry Bay, China (Hong
Kong)
Tel.: (852) 37198161
Web Site: http://www.nuance.com
Information Technology Consulting Services
N.A.I.C.S.: 541512

**Nuance Communications Hungary
Kft** (2)
Nuance-Recognita Zrt Vaci ut 141, 1138,
Budapest, Hungary
Tel.: (36) 14128700
Software Publisher
N.A.I.C.S.: 513210

**Nuance Communications Iberica
SA** (2)
Avenida De La Astronomia, 41015, Seville,
Spain
Tel.: (34) 912754439
Information Technology Consulting Services
N.A.I.C.S.: 541512

**Nuance Communications Interna-
tional BVBA** (2)
Guldensporenpark Building 32, 9820, Merel-
beke, Belgium
Tel.: (32) 92398000
Web Site: http://www.nuance.com
Digital Imaging & Speech Technology Soft-
ware
N.A.I.C.S.: 513210

**Nuance Communications Israel,
Ltd.** (2)
2 Hatidhar Street 9 floor, PO Box 58220,
Ra'anana, 4366504, Israel
Tel.: (972) 37685000

Sales Range: $100-124.9 Million
Emp.: 25
Document Management, Digital Imaging &
Speech Recognition Software Developer
N.A.I.C.S.: 513210

**Nuance Communications Japan
K.K.** (2)
Level 26 Kyobashi Edo Grand, 2-2-1 Kyo-
bashi Chuo-ku, Tokyo, 104-0031, Chiyoda-
ku, Japan (100%)
Tel.: (81) 355216011
Web Site: http://www.japan.nuance.com
Sales Range: $10-24.9 Million
Emp.: 30
Digital Imaging & Voice Recognition Soft-
ware Developer
N.A.I.C.S.: 541511

**Nuance Communications Korea
Ltd.** (2)
7th Floor Metro Building 1339-9 Seocho-
dong, Seocho-gu, Seoul, 137-860, Korea
(South)
Tel.: (82) 0234150800
Software Development Services
N.A.I.C.S.: 541511

**Nuance Communications UK
Ltd.** (2)
33 Soho Square, London, W1D 3QU,
United Kingdom (100%)
Tel.: (44) 1628491600
Web Site: http://www.nuance.co.uk
Sales Range: $25-49.9 Million
Emp.: 34
Digital Imaging & Speech Technology Soft-
ware
N.A.I.C.S.: 423430

**Nuance Communicatons Hong Kong
Limited** (2)
Room 1109-10 11th Floor, Nan Fung Tower,
173 Des Voeux Road, Central, China (Hong
Kong)
Tel.: (852) 3607 6366
Document Management, Digital Imaging &
Speech Recognition Software Developer
N.A.I.C.S.: 513210

Subsidiary (Domestic):

**Nuance Dictaphone Healthcare
Solutions** (2)
1 Wayside Rd, Burlington, MA 01803
Tel.: (203) 381-7000
Web Site: http://www.nuance.com
Rev.: $350,000,000
Emp.: 500
Medical Voice Recognition & Documenta-
tion Software Developer & Mfr
N.A.I.C.S.: 513210

Unit (Domestic):

**Nuance Document Imaging
Solutions** (2)
1 Oracle Dr, Nashua, NH 03062
Tel.: (603) 324-8500
Web Site: http://www.ecopy.com
Sales Range: $10-24.9 Million
Emp.: 250
Online Document Copying & Transfer Ser-
vices
N.A.I.C.S.: 541511

Subsidiary (Non-US):

Nuance Document Imaging ULC (2)
460 Phillip St, Waterloo, N2L 5J2, ON,
Canada
Tel.: (519) 885-2458
Emp.: 100
Document Imaging & Coding Services
N.A.I.C.S.: 561410
Mike Stuhl *(Gen Mgr)*

Subsidiary (Domestic):

**Nuance Enterprise Solutions & Ser-
vices Corporation** (2)
1111 MacArthur Blvd Ste 100, Mahwah, NJ
07430
Tel.: (201) 252-9100
Web Site: http://www.nuance.com
Computer Software Development & Applications
N.A.I.C.S.: 541511

Nuance Enterprise Solutions & Services Corporation (2)
821 Second Ave Ste 1000, Seattle, WA 98104
Tel.: (206) 902-3900
Software Publishing Services
N.A.I.C.S.: 513210

Subsidiary (Non-US):

Nuance France (2)
47/49 avenue Edouard vaillant 6 eme Etage, 92100, Boulogne, Billancourt, France
Tel.: (33) 1 73 001471
Web Site: http://www.nuance.fr
Sales Range: $10-24.9 Million
Emp.: 15
Document Management, Digital Imaging & Speech Recognition Software Developer
N.A.I.C.S.: 513210

Nuance India Pvt. Ltd. (2)
2nd Floor 23 100 FT Inner Ring Road, Koramangala, Bengaluru, 560095, India
Tel.: (91) 8067236130
Software Development Services
N.A.I.C.S.: 541511

Nuance Japan K.K. (2)
Hibiya U-1 Building 20F 1-1-7 Uchisaiwai-cho, Chiyoda-ku, Tokyo, 100-0011, Japan
Tel.: (81) 355216011
Software Publisher
N.A.I.C.S.: 513210

Nuance Recognita Corp. (2)
Vaci ut 141, Budapest, 1138, Hungary (100%)
Tel.: (36) 14128700
Web Site: http://www.nuance.com
Sales Range: $10-24.9 Million
Emp.: 130
Digital Imaging & Speech Technology Software
N.A.I.C.S.: 513210

Nuance Software Technology (Beijing) Co., Ltd. (2)
Unit A2/B 20/F Tower A Gateway Plaza 18 Xiaguangli E 3rd Ring North Rd, Chaoyang, Beijing, 100027, China
Tel.: (86) 1058262500
Software Development Services
N.A.I.C.S.: 541511

Subsidiary (Domestic):

Nuance Transcription Services, Inc. (2)
PO Box 232, Hunt Valley, MD 21030
Tel.: (410) 526-4949
Web Site: http://www.transcendservice.com
Computer Aided Medical Transcription Services
N.A.I.C.S.: 561410
Laurel Smith (Pres & CFO)
Rod Smith (COO)
Jon Nickey (VP-Sls-Natl)
James Jones (Mgr-Ops)

Subsidiary (Non-US):

SafeCom A/S (2)
Lautrupvang 12, Ballerup, DK-2750, Denmark
Tel.: (45) 44360240
Web Site: http://www.safecom.eu
Information Technology Consulting Services
N.A.I.C.S.: 541512

SafeCom GmbH (2)
Otto-Lilienthal-Strasse 36, 71034, Boblingen, Germany
Tel.: (49) 18057233266
Software Development Services
N.A.I.C.S.: 541511

SafeCom UK Limited (2)
Suite 5 Fulshaw Hall Alderley Road, Wilmslow, SK9 1RL, Cheshire, United Kingdom
Tel.: (44) 8458387023
Commercial Printing Services
N.A.I.C.S.: 323113

Subsidiary (Domestic):

Swype, Inc. (2)
71 Columbia St Ste 200, Seattle, WA 98104
Tel.: (206) 547-5250

Web Site: http://www.swypeinc.com
Software Development Services
N.A.I.C.S.: 541511

Subsidiary (Non-US):

Transcend Services, Inc. (2)
Tel.: (678) 808-0600
Web Site: http://www.transcendservices.com
Emp.: 2,277
Patient Information Services
N.A.I.C.S.: 561499

Subsidiary (Non-US):

Heartland Information Services, Inc. (3)
Tel.: (419) 578-6300
Web Site: http://www.heartlandis.com
Sales Range: $10-24.9 Million
Emp.: 35
Medical Transcription Services
N.A.I.C.S.: 519290

Subsidiary (Domestic):

Varolii Corporation (2)
821 2nd Ave Ste 1000 10th Fl, Seattle, WA 98104
Tel.: (206) 902-3900
Web Site: http://www.varolii.com
Sales Range: $50-74.9 Million
Enterprise Customer Communication Solutions
N.A.I.C.S.: 513210
John Pierson (Sr VP-Sls & Svcs)
Joel Chaplin (VP-Ops)
Will Cousins (Sr Dir-Product Mgmt)

Viecore Federal Systems Division, Inc. (2)
23 Chirstopher Way, Eatontown, NJ 07724-3335
Tel.: (732) 759-6300
Data Processing & Management Services
N.A.I.C.S.: 518210

Subsidiary (Non-US):

Voice Signal Ireland Limited (2)
20 Merrion Road, Ballsbridge, Dublin, 4, Ireland
Tel.: (353) 15132500
Computer Aided Medical Transcription Services
N.A.I.C.S.: 561410

Voice Signal K.K. (2)
3-7-1 Nishishinjuku, Shinjuku-Ku, Tokyo, 160-0023, Japan
Tel.: (81) 353263084
Software Development Services
N.A.I.C.S.: 541511

Webmedx Inc. (2)
Tel.: (770) 522-4881
Web Site: http://www.webmedx.com
Sales Range: $25-49.9 Million
Emp.: 215
Health & Allied Services
N.A.I.C.S.: 621610

Subsidiary (Non-US):

Webmedx Inc. (3)
Tel.: (412) 968-9244
Healthcare Application Solutions Provider
N.A.I.C.S.: 561492

Subsidiary (Non-US):

Winscribe Europe Ltd. (2)
85 Uxbridge Road Ealing Cross Ealing, London, W5 5TH, United Kingdom
Tel.: (44) 2074710100
Software Development Services
N.A.I.C.S.: 513210

Winscribe GmbH (2)
Zurcherstrasse 35, 8620, Wetzikon, Switzerland
Tel.: (41) 2074710100
Software Development Services
N.A.I.C.S.: 513210

Winscribe Inc Ltd. (2)
Level 2 95 Hurstmere Road Takapuna, PO Box 33178, Auckland, 0622, New Zealand
Tel.: (64) 94869010
Software Development Services
N.A.I.C.S.: 513210

Parature, Inc. (1)
13625 Ste B Dulles Technology Dr, Herndon, VA 20171
Tel.: (703) 564-7758
Web Site: http://www.parature.com
Sales Range: $10-24.9 Million
Emp.: 105
CRM Software
N.A.I.C.S.: 541511
Ching-Ho Fung (Founder & CEO)

Skype Communications S.a.r.l. (1)
23-29 Rives de Clausen, L-2165, Luxembourg, Luxembourg
Tel.: (352) 26639130
Web Site: http://www.skype.com
Sales Range: $700-749.9 Million
Emp.: 788
Software Developer for Internet Communications
N.A.I.C.S.: 513210

Xamarin Inc. (1)
1355 Market St 3rd Fl, San Francisco, CA 94103 (100%)
Tel.: (855) 926-2746
Web Site: http://www.xamarin.com
Emp.: 350
Software Publisher
N.A.I.C.S.: 513210
Nat Friedman (Founder & CEO)

ZeniMax Media, Inc. (1)
1370 Piccard Dr Ste 120, Rockville, MD 20850
Tel.: (301) 926-8300
Web Site: http://www.zenimax.com
Interactive Entertainment Products Developer
N.A.I.C.S.: 513210
Denise Kidd (Sr VP-Fin & Controller)

Subsidiary (Domestic):

Bethesda Softworks, LLC (2)
1370 Piccard Dr, Rockville, MD 20850
Tel.: (301) 926-8300
Rev.: $6,300,000
Emp.: 75
Video Game Studio
N.A.I.C.S.: 541511

id Software, Inc. (2)
1500 N Greenville Ave Ste 700, Richardson, TX 75081
Tel.: (972) 613-3589
Web Site: https://www.idsoftware.com
Sales Range: $10-24.9 Million
Emp.: 14
Video Game Studio
N.A.I.C.S.: 541511

MICROSTRATEGY, INC.

1850 Towers Crescent Plz, Tysons Corner, VA 22182
Tel.: (703) 848-8600   DE
Web Site:
  https://www.microstrategy.com
Year Founded: 1989
MSTR—(NASDAQ)
Rev.: $496,261,000
Assets: $4,762,528,000
Liabilities: $2,597,556,000
Net Worth: $2,164,972,000
Earnings: $429,121,000
Emp.: 1,934
Fiscal Year-end: 12/31/23
E-Business Software & Services
N.A.I.C.S.: 334610
Michael J. Saylor (Founder & Exec Chm)
Wei-Ming Shao (Gen Counsel & Sr Exec VP)
Jeanine J. Montgomery (Chief Acctg Officer & Sr VP)
Andrew Kang (CFO)
Ponna Arumugam (CIO)
Paul Green (Sr Exec VP)
Cezary Raczko (Exec VP)
Hugh Owen (CMO)
Joty Paparello (Chief HR Officer)
Phong Q. Le (Pres & CEO)

Subsidiaries:

MicroStrategy Austria GmbH (1)

Wienerbergstrasse 11/12A, 1100, Vienna, Austria
Tel.: (43) 22165088870
Web Site: http://www.microstrategy.com.at
Emp.: 10
Software Development Services
N.A.I.C.S.: 541511
Herwig Wandaller (Gen Mgr)

MicroStrategy Belgium BVBA (1)
Airport Plaza Stockholm Building Leonardo Da Vincilaan 19, Diegem, 1831, Belgium
Tel.: (32) 27190200
Web Site: http://www.microstrategy.com
Enterprise Software & Social Intelligence Applications Provider
N.A.I.C.S.: 541511

MicroStrategy Benelux B.V. (1)
Kosterijland 46, 3981 AJ, Bunnik, Netherlands
Tel.: (31) 302408111
Web Site: http://www.microstrategy.nl
Sales Range: $100-124.9 Million
Emp.: 25
Business Data Analysis & Reporting
N.A.I.C.S.: 518210

MicroStrategy Brasil Ltda. (1)
R Irma Gabriela 51, Cidade Moncoes, Sao Paulo, 04571-130, SP, Brazil
Tel.: (55) 1142106787
Web Site: http://www.microstrategy.com.br
Sales Range: $25-49.9 Million
Software Development Services
N.A.I.C.S.: 541511

MicroStrategy Canada Inc. (1)
150 York Street, Toronto, M5H 3S5, ON, Canada
Tel.: (416) 646-6778
Web Site: https://www.microstrategy.com
Business Data Analysis & Reporting Services
N.A.I.C.S.: 518210

MicroStrategy Deutschland GmbH (1)
Gustav-Heinemann-Ufer 56, 50968, Cologne, Germany
Tel.: (49) 22165085977
Web Site: http://www.microstrategy.com
Sales Range: $10-24.9 Million
Business Data Analysis & Reporting
N.A.I.C.S.: 518210

MicroStrategy France SARL (1)
92 avenue Charles de Gaulle, Neuilly-sur-Seine, 92200, Paris, Cedex, France
Tel.: (33) 188547990
Web Site: http://www.microstrategy.com
Sales Range: $10-24.9 Million
Business Data Analysis & Reporting
N.A.I.C.S.: 518210

MicroStrategy Iberica, S.L.U. (1)
Plaza Pablo Ruiz Picasso 1 Torre Picasso planta 15, 28020, Madrid, Spain
Tel.: (34) 917102790
Web Site: http://www.microstrategy.com
Emp.: 45
Enterprise Software & Social Intelligence Applications Provider
N.A.I.C.S.: 541511

MicroStrategy India Private Limited (1)
8B102 WeWork Enam Sambhav C - 20, G Block Rd BKC Bandra, Mumbai, 400 051, India
Tel.: (91) 2244451084
Web Site: http://www.microstrategy.com
Enterprise Software & Intelligence Applications Provider
N.A.I.C.S.: 541511

MicroStrategy Italy S.r.l. (1)
Corso Italia 13, 20122, Milan, Italy
Tel.: (39) 027222251
Web Site: http://www.microstrategy.com
Sales Range: $100-124.9 Million
Business Data Analysis & Reporting
N.A.I.C.S.: 518210

MicroStrategy Korea Co., Ltd. (1)
Suite 402 504 Teheran-ro, Gangnam-gu, Seoul, 06178, Korea (South)
Tel.: (82) 260041343
Web Site: http://www.microstrategy.com
Sales Range: $10-24.9 Million
Business Data Analysis & Reporting
N.A.I.C.S.: 518210

MicroStrategy, Inc.—(Continued)

MicroStrategy Limited (1)
Chiswick Park Building 4 3rd Floor 566
Chiswick High Road, Chiswick, London, W4
5YE, United Kingdom
Tel.: (44) 208 396 0000
Web Site: http://www.microstrategy.com
Software Development Services
N.A.I.C.S.: 541511

**MicroStrategy Middle East
FZ-LLC** (1)
Dubai Internet City Building 20 Floor 1 Office 106, PO Box 500490, Dubai, United
Arab Emirates
Tel.: (971) 43644846
Software Development Services
N.A.I.C.S.: 541511
Sridip Ganguli (Country Mgr)

MicroStrategy Poland sp. z o. o. (1)
Skyliner Prosta 67, 00-838, Warsaw, Poland
Tel.: (48) 224595200
Web Site: http://www.microstrategy.com
Sales Range: $75-99.9 Million
Enterprise Software & Intelligence Application Provider
N.A.I.C.S.: 541511

MicroStrategy Portugal, Lda. (1)
Av da Republica 50, Parque das Nacoes,
Lisbon, 1050-196, Portugal
Tel.: (351) 211229082
Web Site: http://www.microstrategy.com
Business Data Analysis & Reporting
N.A.I.C.S.: 518210

MicroStrategy Pty. Ltd. (1)
Level 4 68 York Street, Sydney, 2000,
NSW, Australia
Tel.: (61) 293336400
Web Site: http://www.microstrategy.com
Sales Range: $10-24.9 Million
Business Data Analysis
N.A.I.C.S.: 518210

MicroStrategy Schweiz AG (1)
Dreikonigstrasse 31A, 8002, Zurich, Switzerland
Tel.: (41) 22165088870
Web Site: http://www.microstrategy.ch
Sales Range: $1-9.9 Million
Emp.: 10
Business Data Analysis & Reporting
N.A.I.C.S.: 518210

**MicroStrategy Singapore Pte.
Ltd.** (1)
1 Harbourfront Avenue 03-02 Keppel Bay
Tower, Singapore, 098632, Singapore
Tel.: (65) 31638466
Web Site: http://www.microstrategy.co.jp
Sales Range: $10-24.9 Million
Business Data Analysis & Reporting
N.A.I.C.S.: 518210

MicroStrategy Sweden AB (1)
Stureplan 4c 4th floor, 114 35, Stockholm,
Sweden
Tel.: (46) 84631046
Web Site: http://www.microstrategy.com
Business Intelligence Software Publisher
N.A.I.C.S.: 513210

MicroStrategy Switzerland GmbH (1)
Dreikonigstrasse 31A, 8002, Zurich, Switzerland
Tel.: (41) 22165088870
Web Site: http://www.microstrategy.com
Software Development Services
N.A.I.C.S.: 541511

MicroStrategy UK Limited (1)
Chiswick Park Building 4 3rd Floor 566
Chiswick High Road, Chiswick, London, W4
5YE, United Kingdom
Tel.: (44) 2083960000
Web Site: http://www.microstrategy.co.uk
Sales Range: $25-49.9 Million
Emp.: 100
Business Data Analysis & Reporting
N.A.I.C.S.: 518210

**MicroStrategy Yazilim Hizmetleri Ve
Urunleri Limited Sirketi** (1)
Zincirlikuyu mah, Maslak, Istanbul, 34340,
Turkiye
Tel.: (90) 2123714667

Software Development Services
N.A.I.C.S.: 541511

**Microstrategy Japan Kabushiki
Kaisha** (1)
Shin-Hanzomon Building 2nd Floor 1-13-1
Ichiban-cho, Chiyoda-Ku, Tokyo, 102-0082,
Japan
Tel.: (81) 335116700
Web Site: http://www.microstrategy.com
Sales Range: $25-49.9 Million
Business Intelligence Software Publisher
N.A.I.C.S.: 513210

Usher Incorporated (1)
1850 Towers Crescent Plz, Tysons Corner,
VA 22182
Tel.: (703) 848-8600
Emp.: 78
Software Development Services
N.A.I.C.S.: 541511

MICROVAST HOLDINGS, INC.
12603 SW Fwy Ste 300, Stafford, TX
77477
Tel.: (281) 491-9505　　　　　　DE
Web Site: https://www.microvast.com
Year Founded: 2019
MVST—(NASDAQ)
Rev.: $204,495,000
Assets: $984,957,000
Liabilities: $371,980,000
Net Worth: $612,977,000
Earnings: ($158,200,000)
Emp.: 1,535
Fiscal Year-end: 12/31/22
Miscellaneous Financial Investment
Activities
N.A.I.C.S.: 523999
Yang Wu (Founder, Chm & CEO)
Shane Smith (Chief Procurement
Officer)

Subsidiaries:

**Microvast Power Systems Co.,
Ltd.** (1)
No 2198 Hongfeng Road, Chuzhou,
313000, Zhejiang, China
Tel.: (86) 13255720705
Battery Mfr & Distr
N.A.I.C.S.: 335312

MICROVISION, INC.
18390 NE 68th St, Redmond, WA
98052
Tel.: (425) 936-6847　　　　　　DE
Web Site:
　　https://www.microvision.com
MVIS—(NASDAQ)
Rev.: $664,000
Assets: $114,996,000
Liabilities: $25,255,000
Net Worth: $89,741,000
Earnings: ($53,091,000)
Emp.: 350
Fiscal Year-end: 12/31/22
Display & Imaging Products for Mobile Applications
N.A.I.C.S.: 334419
Brian V. Turner (Chm)
Robert Paul Carlile (Vice Chm)
Anubhav Verma (CFO)
Sumit Sharma (CEO)
Drew Markham (Gen Counsel)

MICROWAVE FILTER COMPANY, INC.
6743 Kinne St, East Syracuse, NY
13057
Tel.: (315) 438-4700　　　　　　NY
Web Site:
　　https://www.microwavefilter.com
MFCO—(OTCIQ)
Rev.: $3,107,610
Assets: $1,941,415
Liabilities: $863,913
Net Worth: $1,077,502
Earnings: ($292,637)
Emp.: 29

Fiscal Year-end: 09/30/20
Electronic Filters for Processing
Cable Televison, Radio & Other Signals
N.A.I.C.S.: 334419
Richard L. Jones (CFO)
Sam Fanizzi (VP-Mktg & Sls)
Robert Paul (VP-Engrg)
John Kennedy (Chm)
Carl F. Fahrenkrug Sr. (Vice Chm)

MID PENN BANCORP, INC.
2407 Park Dr, Harrisburg, PA 17110A
Web Site:
　　https://www.midpennbank.com
Year Founded: 1991
MPB—(NASDAQ)
Rev.: $189,257,000
Assets: $4,497,954,000
Liabilities: $3,985,855,000
Net Worth: $512,099,000
Earnings: $54,806,000
Emp.: 590
Fiscal Year-end: 12/31/22
Bank Holding Company
N.A.I.C.S.: 551111
Rory G. Ritrievi (Chm, Pres & CEO)
Justin T. Webb (CFO & Sr Exec VP)
Scott W. Micklewright (Chief Revenue
Officer)
Joseph L. Paese (Dir-Trust & Wealth
Mgmt)
Jordan D. Space (COO)

Subsidiaries:

Brunswick Bancorp (1)
439 Livingston Ave, New Brunswick, NJ
08901
Tel.: (732) 247-5800
Web Site: http://www.brunswickbank.com
Sales Range: $1-9.9 Million
Bank Holding Company
N.A.I.C.S.: 551111
Joanne Chek (VP)
Pearl Lin (Asst Treas)
David Gazerwitz (CFO, Treas, Sec & VP)
Teresa Gilligan (Chief Risk Officer & Sr VP)
Keith Rada (Chief Lending Officer & Sr VP)
Joseph S. Krieg (CIO & VP)
Timothy J. Caruso (Officer-Comml Lending
& VP)
Ed Van Valkenburgh (VP)
Carl Carabelli (VP & Ops Mgr-Loan)
Laurie Visokay (Asst Treas)
Nicholas A. Frungillo Jr. (Pres & COO)

Mid Penn Bank (1)
349 Union St, Millersburg, PA 17061-1611
Tel.: (717) 692-7100
Web Site: https://midpennbank.com
Sales Range: $25-49.9 Million
Commericial Banking
N.A.I.C.S.: 522110
Rory G. Ritrievi (Pres & CEO)
Justin T. Webb (COO & Sr Exec VP)
Allison S. Johnson (CFO & Sr Exec VP)
Joan Dickinson (Sr VP)
Scott W. Micklewright (Chief Revenue Officer & Sr Exec VP)
Kelly K. Neiderer (Sr VP & Sr Banking Officer)
Heather Hall (Exec VP)

Riverview Financial Corporation (1)
3901 N Front St, Harrisburg, PA 17110
Tel.: (717) 957-2196
Web Site: http://www.riverviewbankpa.com
Rev.: $54,819,000
Assets: $1,357,554,000
Liabilities: $1,260,122,000
Net Worth: $97,432,000
Earnings: ($21,211,000)
Emp.: 221
Fiscal Year-end: 12/31/2020
Bank Holding Company
N.A.I.C.S.: 551111
Scott A. Seasock (CFO & Sr Exec VP)
Ginger G. Kunkel (COO & Sr Exec VP)
Richard W. Ogden (Chief Risk Officer & Sr
Exec VP)

Subsidiary (Domestic):

Riverview Bank (2)

500 S State Rd, Marysville, PA 17053
Tel.: (717) 957-2114
Web Site: http://www.riverviewbankpa.com
Retail & Commercial Banking
N.A.I.C.S.: 522110
Wim Van Olden (Chief Credit Officer & Exec
VP)
Ronald Bednar (CIO & Exec VP)
LeeAnn Gephart (CMO & Exec VP)
Linda Spoon (Sr VP & Dir-HR)
B. Nicole Sherman (Pres & CEO)
Joseph Kelly Jr. (Sr VP)

MID-AMERICA APARTMENT COMMUNITIES, INC.
6815 Poplar Ave Ste 500, Germantown, TN 38138
Tel.: (901) 682-6600　　　　　　TN
Web Site: https://www.maac.com
Year Founded: 1977
MAA—(NYSE)
Rev.: $2,148,468,000
Assets: $11,484,503,000
Liabilities: $5,204,548,000
Net Worth: $6,279,955,000
Earnings: $549,118,000
Emp.: 2,427
Fiscal Year-end: 12/31/23
Real Estate Investment Trust
N.A.I.C.S.: 525990
H. Eric Bolton Jr. (Chm, Pres & CEO)
Leslie B. C. Wolfgang (Chief Compliance Officer, Chief Ethics Officer, Sec
& Sr VP)
Kim Banks (Sr VP-North Div)
Robert Donnelly (Sr VP-Coastal Div)
Timothy P. Argo (Chief Strategy &
Analysis Officer & Exec VP)
Amber Fairbanks (Exec VP-Property
Mgmt)
Melanie M. Carpenter (Chief HR Officer & Exec VP)
Jana Ellis (Sr VP-South Div)
Kylee Lambert (Sr VP-West Div)
Charles A. Konas (Exec VP & Dir-
New Construction)
David C. Ward (Exec VP-Dev)
Bart French (Sr VP-Dev)
Indrid Agaj (Sr VP-Construction)
Bryan Ellsberry (Sr VP-Ancillary
Svcs)
Brad Sill (Sr VP-Enterprise Program
Mgmt)
Dianne Slotnick (Sr VP-Comml)
Melanie Whitson (Sr VP-
Transactions)
Denise Davenport (Dir-Sls &
Revenue-Coastal Div)
Julie Noggle (Dir-Sls & Revenue-
South Div)
Whitney Pillow (Dir-Sls & Revenue-
East Div)
A. Clay Holder (CFO)
Albert M. Campbell III (Exec VP)

Subsidiaries:

MAA Arkansas REIT, LLC (1)
6584 Poplar Ave, Memphis, TN 38138
Tel.: (901) 435-5436
Real Estate Investment Services
N.A.I.C.S.: 531210

Mid-America Apartments, L.P. (1)
6815 Poplar Ave Ste 500, Germantown, TN
38138
Tel.: (901) 682-6600
Web Site: https://www.maac.com
Rev.: $2,148,467,909
Assets: $11,484,502,999
Liabilities: $5,204,566,999
Net Worth: $6,279,936,000
Earnings: $564,081,000
Emp.: 2,426
Fiscal Year-end: 12/31/2023
Real Estate Property Management Services
N.A.I.C.S.: 531110
H. Eric Bolton Jr. (Chm & CEO)
A. Clay Holder (Chief Acctg Officer & Sr
VP)
Albert M. Campbell III (CFO & Exec VP)

Post South End, L.P. (1)
222 E Bland St, Charlotte, NC 28203
Tel.: (704) 538-4790
Rental Apartment Services
N.A.I.C.S.: 531110

MID-ATLANTIC HOME HEALTH NETWORK, INC.
25 Winchester St, Warrenton, VA 20186
Tel.: (703) 335-1957 VA
Year Founded: 1985
MAHN—(OTCIQ)
Health Care Srvices
N.A.I.C.S.: 621999
Kate Warman-Day (Dir)

MID-SOUTHERN BANCORP, INC.
Tel.: (812) 883-2639 IN
Web Site: https://www.mid-southern.com
Year Founded: 2018
MSVB—(NASDAQ)
Rev.: $10,065,000
Assets: $269,218,000
Liabilities: $235,896,000
Net Worth: $33,322,000
Earnings: $1,881,000
Emp.: 40
Fiscal Year-end: 12/31/22
Bank Holding Company
N.A.I.C.S.: 551111
Alexander G. Babey (Pres & CEO)
Dana J. Dunbar (Chm)
Erica B. Schmidt (CFO & Exec VP-Mid-Southern Savings Bank)

Subsidiaries:

Mid-Southern Savings Bank, FSB (1)
300 N Water St, Salem, IN 47167
Tel.: (812) 883-2639
Web Site: https://www.mid-southern.com
Federal Savings Bank
N.A.I.C.S.: 522180
Dana J. Dunbar (Owner)
Kermit A. Lamb (Branch Mgr)

MIDDLEBURY NATIONAL CORP.
Tel.: (802) 388-4982 DE
Web Site: https://www.nbmvt.com
Year Founded: 1831
MDVT—(OTCIQ)
Sales Range: $1-9.9 Million
Bank Holding Company
N.A.I.C.S.: 551111
Caroline R. Carpenter (Pres, Pres-National Bank of Middlebury & Exec VP)
G. Kenneth Perine (Pres & Exec VP)
Lawrence W. Miller II (Sec)

Subsidiaries:

National Bank of Middlebury (1)
30 Main St, Middlebury, VT 05753
Tel.: (802) 388-4982
Web Site: http://www.nbmvt.com
Emp.: 100
Banking Services
N.A.I.C.S.: 522110
Caroline R. Carpenter (Pres)
Laura J. Adams (Sr VP)
Sarah A.P. Cowan (Sr VP)
Grover K. Usilton (VP)
Julie L. Heffernan (VP)
Kerry D. Bolduc (VP)
Stacey Brown (CFO)
Sarah Stahl (Chm)

MIDDLEFIELD BANC CORP.
15985 E High St, Middlefield, OH 44062
Tel.: (440) 632-1666 OH
Web Site:
https://www.middlefieldbank.bank
Year Founded: 1988

MBCN—(NASDAQ)
Rev.: $61,652,000
Assets: $1,687,682,000
Liabilities: $1,489,991,000
Net Worth: $197,691,000
Earnings: $15,673,000
Emp.: 238
Fiscal Year-end: 12/31/22
Bank Holding Company
N.A.I.C.S.: 551111
Ronald L. Zimmerly Jr. (Pres & CEO)
James J. McCaskey (Vice Chm)

Subsidiaries:

Liberty Bancshares Inc. (1)
118 S Main St, Ada, OH 45810
Tel.: (419) 634-5015
Rev.: $16,387,300
Assets: $337,449,710
Liabilities: $288,387,212
Net Worth: $49,062,498
Earnings: $3,746,798
Fiscal Year-end: 12/31/2019
Bank Holding Company
N.A.I.C.S.: 551111

The Middlefield Banking Company (1)
15985 E High St, Middlefield, OH 44062
Tel.: (440) 632-1666
Web Site: http://www.middlefieldbank.bank
Sales Range: $25-49.9 Million
Emp.: 140
Commericial Banking
N.A.I.C.S.: 522110
Ronald L. Zimmerly Jr. (Pres & CEO)
Michael L. Cheravitch (Chief Banking Officer)
Tom Neikirk (Sr VP)
Michael Allen (Exec VP)
Larry Maniche (Branch Mgr)
Kevin Mitchell (Asst VP)
Greg Yurco (Sr VP)
Sarah Winters (Chief HR Officer & Sr VP)
Rebecca Noblit (Chief Credit Officer)

MIDDLESEX WATER COMPANY
485C Rte 1 S Ste 400, Iselin, NJ 08830
Tel.: (732) 634-1500 NJ
Web Site:
https://www.middlesexwater.com
Year Founded: 1897
MSEX—(NASDAQ)
Rev.: $162,434,000
Assets: $1,074,450,000
Liabilities: $381,758,000
Net Worth: $692,692,000
Earnings: $42,429,000
Emp.: 350
Fiscal Year-end: 12/31/22
Water & Wastewater System
N.A.I.C.S.: 221310
Bernadette M. Sohler (VP-Corp Affairs)
Lorrie Beth Ginegaw (VP-HR)
Jay L. Kooper (Gen Counsel, Sec & VP)
G. Christian Andreasen (VP-Enterprise Engrg)
Robert K. Fullagar (VP-Ops)
Nadine Duchemin-Leslie (Pres & CEO)
Robert J. Capko (Chief Acctg Officer)
Mohammed Ghali Zerhouni (CFO, Treas & Sr VP)

Subsidiaries:

Pinelands Water Company (1)
485C US Hwy 1 S Ste 400, Iselin, NJ 08830-3037 (100%)
Tel.: (609) 859-2044
Web Site:
http://www.middlesexwatercompany.com
Sales Range: $1-9.9 Million
Emp.: 4
Water Supply
N.A.I.C.S.: 221310

Tidewater Utilities, Inc. (1)

1100 S Little Creek Rd, Dover, DE 19901 (100%)
Tel.: (302) 734-7500
Web Site: http://www.tuiwater.com
Sales Range: $25-49.9 Million
Emp.: 85
Water Supply & Sewage Treatment Services
N.A.I.C.S.: 221310

Utility Service Affiliates (Perth Amboy) Inc. (1)
1500 Ronson Rd, Iselin, NJ 08830-0167 (100%)
Tel.: (732) 826-0290
Sales Range: $350-399.9 Million
Emp.: 150
Water & Wastewater Operations
N.A.I.C.S.: 221310

Utility Service Affiliates, Inc. (1)
485C Rte 1 S Ste 400, Iselin, NJ 08830
Tel.: (732) 819-3788
Web Site: http://www.middlesexwater.com
System Operations & Maintenance Services; Water Utility, Sewer Utility & Storm Water System Operator
N.A.I.C.S.: 221310

MIDLAND STATES BANCORP, INC.
1201 Network Ctr Dr, Effingham, IL 62401
Tel.: (217) 342-7321 IL
Web Site:
https://www.midlandsb.com
Year Founded: 1988
MSBI—(NASDAQ)
Rev.: $381,646,000
Assets: $7,855,501,000
Liabilities: $7,096,927,000
Net Worth: $758,574,000
Earnings: $99,025,000
Emp.: 935
Fiscal Year-end: 12/31/22
Bank Holding Company
N.A.I.C.S.: 551111
Jeffrey S. Mefford (Exec VP)
Jeffrey G. Ludwig (Vice Chm, Pres & CEO)
Donald J. Spring (Chief Acctg Officer)
Douglas J. Tucker (Corp Counsel & Sr VP)
Eric T. Lemke (CFO)

Subsidiaries:

Heartland Business Credit Corporation (1)
390 Union Blvd Ste 600, Lakewood, CO 80228
Tel.: (303) 986-4885
Banking Services
N.A.I.C.S.: 522110

Midland Financial Advisors, Inc. (1)
524 Milwaukee St Ste 300, Delafield, WI 53018
Tel.: (262) 303-4503
Web Site: http://www.midlandfa.com
Financial Investment Services
N.A.I.C.S.: 523940
Heath Sorenson (Pres)
Drew Bender (Officer-Trust)
Linda Mahon (Officer-Trust)
Benjamin Malsch (Officer-Trust)
Deanna Haught (Officer-Trust)
Christine Addy (Officer-Trust)
Robin Khan (Officer-Trust)
Diane Olear (Officer-Trust)

Midland States Bank (1)
110 S 5th St, Effingham, IL 62401
Tel.: (217) 342-2141
Web Site: https://www.midlandsb.com
Sales Range: $75-99.9 Million
Commericial Banking
N.A.I.C.S.: 522110
Robert F. Schultz (Chm)
Douglas J. Tucker (Sr VP)
Eric T. Lemke (CFO)

Subsidiary (Domestic):

Midland Trust Company (2)

120 White Plains Rd Ste 135, Tarrytown, NY 10591
Tel.: (914) 580-7500
Web Site: https://www.midlandtc.com
Financial Investment Services
N.A.I.C.S.: 523940
Jayne Hladio (Sr VP)
Kris Duer (Officer)
Brandon Mendez (Officer)
Sara Gonzalez (Officer)
Peggy Sajdak (Officer)
Ashley Slane (Officer)
Oscar Veras (Officer)
David Drew (Officer)

Subsidiary (Domestic):

ATG Trust Company (3)
1 S Wacker Dr 24th Fl, Chicago, IL 60606
Tel.: (312) 338-7878
Web Site: http://www.atgtrust.com
Title Insurance
N.A.I.C.S.: 522110
Kathryn Van Eeuwen (Pres & CEO)
Christopher LaPorta (VP-Investments)
Christine Campbell (VP)

Midland Wealth Advisors LLP (1)
1201 Network Centre Dr, Effingham, IL 62401
Tel.: (217) 342-7302
Wealth Management Services
N.A.I.C.S.: 523940

MIDWEST ENERGY EMISSIONS CORP.
1810 Jester Dr, Corsicana, TX 75109-9593
Tel.: (614) 505-6115
Web Site:
https://www.me2cenvironmental.com
Year Founded: 1983
MEEC—(OTCQB)
Rev.: $13,012,049
Assets: $8,134,783
Liabilities: $18,374,259
Net Worth: ($10,239,476)
Earnings: ($3,632,683)
Emp.: 11
Fiscal Year-end: 12/31/21
Mercury Emission Control Product Developer
N.A.I.C.S.: 334519
Richard A. MacPherson (Pres & CEO)
Christopher Greenberg (Chm)
James Trettel (VP-Ops)
Nicholas Lentz (Mgr-Field Technical)
John Pavlish (CTO & Sr VP)
David M. Kaye (Sec)

MIDWESTONE FINANCIAL GROUP, INC.
102 S Clinton St, Iowa City, IA 52240
Tel.: (319) 356-5800 IA
Web Site:
https://www.midwestone.com
Year Founded: 1983
MOFG—(NASDAQ)
Rev.: $244,278,000
Assets: $6,577,876,000
Liabilities: $6,085,083,000
Net Worth: $492,793,000
Earnings: $60,835,000
Emp.: 811
Fiscal Year-end: 12/31/22
Bank Holding Company
N.A.I.C.S.: 551111
Charles N. Reeves (CEO)
James M. Cantrell (Chief Investment Officer, Treas & Sr Exec VP)
Barry S. Ray (CFO & Sr Exec VP)
Gary L. Sims (Chief Credit Officer & Sr VP)
Katie A. Lorenson (CIO)
Kenneth R. Urmie (Sec)
Len D. Devaisher (Pres & COO)
Susan M. Moore (Chief Risk Officer & Sr VP)

MidWestOne Financial Group, Inc.—(Continued)

John J. Ruppel *(Chief Acctg Officer)*
Chase L. Stafford *(VP)*
Timothy M. Heth *(Chief HR Officer)*

Subsidiaries:

Iowa First Bancshares Corp.   **(1)**
300 E 2nd St, Muscatine, IA 52761
Tel.: (563) 263-4221
Web Site: http://www.fnbmusc.com
Sales Range: $10-24.9 Million
Emp.: 130
Bank Holding Company
N.A.I.C.S.: 551111
D. Scott Ingstad *(CEO)*

Subsidiary (Domestic):

First National Bank In Fairfield   **(2)**
100 E Burlington Ave, Fairfield, IA 52556
Tel.: (641) 472-4121
Web Site: http://www.fnbfairfieldiowa.com
Rev.: $3,800,000
Emp.: 36
National Commercial Banks
N.A.I.C.S.: 522110
Jeff Johnston *(Sr VP)*
Deb Fritz *(Branch Mgr)*
Mark Smith *(Pres & CEO)*

First National Bank Muscatine   **(2)**
300 E 2nd St, Muscatine, IA 52761
Tel.: (563) 263-4221
Web Site: http://www.fnbmusc.com
Rev.: $9,500,000
Emp.: 60
National Commercial Banks
N.A.I.C.S.: 522110
D. Scott Ingstab *(Chm)*
Dee Gerdts *(VP-IT)*

MidWestOne Bank   **(1)**
102 S Clinton St, Iowa City, IA 52240
Tel.: (319) 356-5800
Web Site: http://www.midwestone.com
Commercial Banking
N.A.I.C.S.: 522110
Charles N. Reeves *(CEO)*
James M. Cantrell *(Chief Investment Officer, Treas & Sr Exec VP)*
Len D. Devaisher *(Pres & COO)*
John J. Ruppel *(Chief Acctg Officer & Sr VP)*
Travis Eagle *(Production Mgr-Mortgage)*

Unit (Domestic):

MidWestOne Insurance Services   **(2)**
124 S 1st St, Oskaloosa, IA 52577
Tel.: (641) 673-8603
Web Site:
   http://www.midwestoneinsurance.com
Emp.: 7
Insurance Brokerage & Wealth Management Services
N.A.I.C.S.: 524210
Margaret Ratcliff *(Pres)*

MidWestOne Insurance Services, Inc.   **(1)**
700 Main St Ste 100, Pella, IA 50219
Tel.: (641) 628-4356
Web Site:
   http://www.midwestoneinsurance.com
Insurance Management Services
N.A.I.C.S.: 524298

MIGOM GLOBAL CORP.
1185 5th Ave 3rd Fl, New York, NY 10036
Tel.: (767) 448-4297   **NV**
Web Site: https://www.mgom.co
Year Founded: 2016
MGOM—(OTCIQ)
Rev.: $20,980,435
Assets: $18,283,158
Liabilities: $3,059,799
Net Worth: $15,223,359
Earnings: $12,216,397
Emp.: 5
Fiscal Year-end: 12/31/21
Video Editing Services
N.A.I.C.S.: 512191
Thomas A. Schaetti *(Pres)*

MILAN LASER INC.
17645 Wright St Ste 300, Omaha, NE 68130   **DE**
Year Founded: 2021
MLAN—(NYSE)
Emp.: 700
Holding Company
N.A.I.C.S.: 551112
Shikhar Saxena *(CEO, Co-Founder & Co-Chm)*
Clint Weiler *(CFO)*
Elizabeth Allison *(Pres)*
Abram Schumacher *(Co-Founder & Co-Chm)*

MILESTONE SCIENTIFIC INC.
425 Eagle Rock Ave, Roseland, NJ 07068
Tel.: (973) 535-2717   **DE**
Web Site:
   https://www.milestonescientific.com
Year Founded: 1989
MLSS—(NYSEAMEX)
Rev.: $8,805,906
Assets: $13,702,086
Liabilities: $3,695,652
Net Worth: $10,006,434
Earnings: ($8,706,131)
Emp.: 20
Fiscal Year-end: 12/31/22
Disposable Medical & Dental Products Developer, Mfr & Marketer
N.A.I.C.S.: 339113
Jan Adriaan Haverhals *(Pres & CEO)*
Mark Hochman *(Dir-Clinical Affairs & R&D)*
Neal Ira Goldman *(Chm)*

Subsidiaries:

Milestone Education LLC   **(1)**
203 220 S Orange Ave, Livingston, NJ 07039
Tel.: (973) 535-2717
Web Site: http://www.medental-usa.com
Medical Instrument Mfr
N.A.I.C.S.: 339112

Milestone Medical Inc.   **(1)**
425 Eagle Rock Ave Ste 403, Roseland, NJ 07068
Tel.: (973) 535-2717
Web Site:
   https://www.medicalmilestone.com
Medical Equipment Mfr
N.A.I.C.S.: 339113

Wand Dental , Inc.   **(1)**
425 Eagle Rock Ave, Roseland, NJ 07068
Tel.: (973) 535-2717
Web Site: http://www.thewand.com
Medical Equipment Distr
N.A.I.C.S.: 423450
Jan Adriaan Haverhals *(Pres & CEO)*

MILL CITY VENTURES III, LTD.
1907 Wayzata Blvd Ste 205, Wayzata, MN 55391
Tel.: (952) 479-1921   **MN**
Web Site:
   https://www.millcityventures3.com
Year Founded: 2006
MCVT—(NASDAQ)
Rev.: $4,199,453
Assets: $18,565,569
Liabilities: $223,230
Net Worth: $18,342,339
Earnings: $1,440,576
Emp.: 3
Fiscal Year-end: 12/31/22
Investment Services
N.A.I.C.S.: 523999
Douglas Michael Polinsky *(Co-Founder, Chm, Pres & CEO)*
Daniel E. Ryweck *(Controller)*
Joseph A. Geraci II *(Co-Founder & CFO)*

MILLENNIUM CELL, INC.

1 Industrial Way W, Eatontown, NJ 07724
Tel.: (732) 542-4000
MCELQ—(OTCEM)
Electronic Part & Equipment Distr
N.A.I.C.S.: 423690
H. David Ramm *(CEO)*

MILLENNIUM ENERGY CORPORATION
401 Cooper Landing Rd C-21, Cherry Hill, NJ 08002
Tel.: (856) 667-4300
Web Site:
   http://www.millenniumenergy
   corp.com
MENC—(OTCIQ)
Oil & Gas Exploration & Production
N.A.I.C.S.: 211120
Irving Aronson *(Chm)*
Alexander Lightman *(CEO)*
Michael F. Fuoco *(Deputy Chm & CFO)*

MILLENNIUM PRIME, INC.
6538 Collins Ave Ste 382, Miami Beach, FL 33141
Tel.: (786) 309-5549   **DE**
Web Site:
   https://www.millenniumprime.com
Year Founded: 1968
MLMN—(OTCIQ)
Lifestyle Brands Including Alcohol, Apparel, Merchandise & Entertainment
N.A.I.C.S.: 312140
John Antonucci *(Chm & CEO)*

MILLENNIUM SUSTAINABLE VENTURES CORP.
301 Winding Rd, Old Bethpage, NY 11804
Tel.: (212) 750-0371   **DE**
Year Founded: 2006
MILC—(OTC)
N.A.I.C.S.: 523999
David H. Lesser *(CEO)*
Suhel Kanuga *(Pres)*

MILLER INDUSTRIES, INC.
8503 Hilltop Dr, Ooltewah, TN 37363
Tel.: (423) 238-4171   **TN**
Web Site: https://www.millerind.com
Year Founded: 1990
MLR—(NYSE)
Rev.: $848,456,000
Assets: $501,429,000
Liabilities: $207,972,000
Net Worth: $293,457,000
Earnings: $20,346,000
Emp.: 1,450
Fiscal Year-end: 12/31/22
Towing & Recovery Equipment Mfr
N.A.I.C.S.: 336211
Vince Tiano *(Chief Revenue Officer & VP)*
Jamison Linden *(Chief Mfg Officer & VP)*
Frank Madonia *(Exec VP)*
William G. Millor *(Founder & Exec Chm)*
William G. Miller II *(Pres & CEO)*
Deborah L. Whitmire *(CFO, Treas & Exec VP)*

Subsidiaries:

Boniface Engineering, Ltd.   **(1)**
42 Howlett Way, Fison Way Industrial Estate, Thetford, IP24 1HZ, Norfolk, United Kingdom
Tel.: (44) 1842754232
Web Site: https://www.boniface-eng.com
Sales Range: $10-24.9 Million
Emp.: 35
Vehicle Towing & Hauling
N.A.I.C.S.: 488410

Chevron, Inc.   **(1)**
6001 Bollinger Canyon Rd, San Ramon, CA 94583
Tel.: (925) 842-1000
Web Site: http://www.millerind.com
Petroleum Refinery Services
N.A.I.C.S.: 324110

MILLER/HOWARD HIGH INCOME EQUITY FUND
45 Pine Grove Ave Ste 301, Kingston, NY 12401
Tel.: (845) 679-9166   **DE**
Web Site: https://www.mhinvest.com
Year Founded: 2011
HIE—(NYSE)
Rev.: $11,540,407
Assets: $285,024,555
Liabilities: $98,119,573
Net Worth: $186,904,982
Earnings: $7,122,923
Emp.: 50
Fiscal Year-end: 10/31/19
Miscellaneous Financial Investment Activities
N.A.I.C.S.: 523999
Lowell Glaser Miller *(Chm & Pres)*
Helen Hamada *(CFO)*
Dana Troxell *(Sec)*
Charles Atkins *(Chief Compliance Officer)*
John E. Leslie III *(Portfolio Mgr)*

MILLERKNOLL, INC.
855 E Main Ave, Zeeland, MI 49464
Tel.: (786) 642-7714   **MI**
Web Site: https://www.millerknoll.com
Year Founded: 1905
MLKN—(NASDAQ)
Rev.: $3,628,400,000
Assets: $4,043,600,000
Liabilities: $2,658,500,000
Net Worth: $1,385,100,000
Earnings: $84,600,000
Emp.: 10,200
Fiscal Year-end: 06/01/24
Office Systems, Furnishings & Related Services
N.A.I.C.S.: 337211
Michael A. Volkema *(Chm)*
Jeffrey M. Stutz *(CFO)*
Jacqueline Hourigan Rice *(Gen Counsel & Sec)*
Andrea R. Owen *(Pres & CEO)*
Megan Lyon *(Chief Strategy Officer)*
Benjamin P. T. Groom *(Chief Digital Officer)*
Debbie Propst *(Pres-Retail)*
Tim Straker *(CMO)*
Richard Scott *(Chief Mfg & Ops Officer)*
John Michael *(Pres-The Americas)*
Jeffrey L. Kurburski *(Co-CTO)*
B. Ben Watson *(Chief Creative Officer, Chief Product Officer & Chief Creative Officer)*
Chris Baldwin *(Grp Pres)*
Chris Demuth *(Chief People Officer)*
Kris Marubio *(VP-Global Corp Comm)*
Robyn Hofmeyer *(Sr VP-Bus Transformation)*

Subsidiaries:

Colebrook Bosson & Saunders (Products) Limited   **(1)**
35 Union Street, London, SE1 1SD, United Kingdom
Tel.: (44) 2079404266
Web Site:
   https://www.colebrookbossonsaunders.com
Monitor Arm Mfr
N.A.I.C.S.: 332992

Colebrook Bosson Saunders, Ltd.   **(1)**
35 Union Street, London, SE1 1SD, United Kingdom
Tel.: (44) 2079404266

Web Site: https://www.colebrookbossonsaun
ders.com
Emp.: 50
Computer Stand Mfr & Distr
N.A.I.C.S.: 337126

Colebrook Bosson Saunders, Pty. Ltd. (1)
3 / 1 - 3 Newton St, Docklands, Cremorne, 3121, VIC, Australia
Tel.: (61) 1300931927
Web Site: https://www.colebrookbossonsaun
ders.com
Emp.: 5
Office Furniture Mfr & Distr
N.A.I.C.S.: 337214

Design Within Reach, Inc. (1)
4 Star Point Ste 301, Stamford, CT 06902
Tel.: (203) 614-0600
Web Site: https://www.dwr.com
Sales Range: $200-249.9 Million
Emp.: 450
European-Style Home Furnishings Distr
N.A.I.C.S.: 541410

Geiger International (1)
6095 Fulton Industrial Blvd SW, Atlanta, GA 30336 (100%)
Tel.: (404) 344-1100
Web Site: https://www.geigerfurniture.com
Sales Range: $100-124.9 Million
Emp.: 400
Wood Office Furniture
N.A.I.C.S.: 337211
John Fuller (VP-Sls)

HAR AS (1)
Josefines Gate 23, 0351, Oslo, Norway
Tel.: (47) 96099190
Web Site: https://hayshop.no
Household Furniture Mfr
N.A.I.C.S.: 337126

HAY ApS (1)
Havnen 1, 8700, Horsens, Denmark
Tel.: (45) 31646000
Web Site: https://www.hay.dk
Household Furniture Mfr
N.A.I.C.S.: 337126

HAY International DE GmBH B.V. (1)
Siegesstrasse 19, 80802, Munich, Germany
Tel.: (49) 15205731189
Household Furniture Mfr
N.A.I.C.S.: 337126

Herman Miller (Australia) Pty., Ltd. (1)
Suite 2 09 90-96 Bourke Road, Sydney, 2015, NSW, Australia
Tel.: (61) 282110480
Web Site: https://www.hermanmiller.com.au
Institutional Furniture Mfr
N.A.I.C.S.: 337127

Herman Miller Asia (Pte.) Ltd. (1)
3 Anson Road 10-02 Springleaf Tower, Singapore, 79909, Singapore (100%)
Tel.: (65) 63275488
Web Site: http://www.hermanmiller.com
Sales Range: $100-124.9 Million
Emp.: 10
Office Furniture Distr
N.A.I.C.S.: 337214

Herman Miller Canada (1)
462 Wellington St W Suite 200, Toronto, M5V 1E3, ON, Canada (100%)
Tel.: (416) 366-3300
Web Site: https://www.hermanmiller.com
Sales Range: $10-24.9 Million
Emp.: 15
Office Furniture Mfr
N.A.I.C.S.: 337214

Herman Miller Furniture (India) Pvt. Ltd. (1)
Prestige Ferozes Unit No 101 1st Floor No 74, Sampangi Rama Temple Road Vasanth Nagar, Bengaluru, 560052, Karnataka, India
Tel.: (91) 8066921333
Web Site: https://www.hermanmiller.com
Emp.: 170
Office Furniture Mfr & Distr
N.A.I.C.S.: 337214

Herman Miller Italia S.p.A. (1)
Corso Garibaldi 70, 20121, Milan, Italy
Tel.: (39) 0265531711

Web Site: https://www.hermanmiller.com
Sales Range: $10-24.9 Million
Emp.: 25
Office Furniture
N.A.I.C.S.: 337214

Herman Miller Japan, Ltd. (1)
Shin-Kokusai Building 2F 3-4-1 Marunouchi, Chiyoda-ku, Tokyo, 100-0005, Japan
Tel.: (81) 120889252
Web Site: https://www.hermanmiller.com
Office Furniture Mfr
N.A.I.C.S.: 337214

Herman Miller Mexico S.A. de C.V. (1)
Alfonso Reyes 5 Hipodromo Condesa Cuauhtemoc, 06170, Mexico, DF, Mexico
Tel.: (52) 5550639600
Web Site: https://www.hermanmiller.com.mx
Sales Range: $10-24.9 Million
Emp.: 20
Wood & Wood Laminated Office Furniture
N.A.I.C.S.: 337211

Herman Miller Mexico S.A. de C.V.-Monterrey (1)
Arboleda Park Avenida Roble 660 Local 108 East Valle del Campestre, San Pedro Garza Garcia, 66266, Monterrey, Nuevo Leon, Mexico (100%)
Tel.: (52) 8180004600
Web Site: http://www.hermanmiller.com.mx
Sales Range: $10-24.9 Million
Emp.: 20
Wood & Wood Laminated Office Furniture
N.A.I.C.S.: 337211

Herman Miller do Brasil, Ltda. (1)
Rua Joao Lourenco 35 Vila Nova Conceicao, Sao Paulo, 04508-030, Brazil
Tel.: (55) 11972750750
Web Site: https://www.hermanmiller.com
Office Furniture Whslr
N.A.I.C.S.: 423210

Herman Miller, Ltd. (1)
2 Kingsway, London, WC2B 6LH, United Kingdom (100%)
Tel.: (44) 1225794000
Web Site: https://www.hermanmiller.com
Sales Range: $25-49.9 Million
Emp.: 80
Office Furniture
N.A.I.C.S.: 337211

Knoll, Inc. (1)
1235 Water St, East Greenville, PA 18041
Tel.: (215) 679-7991
Web Site: http://www.knoll.com
Rev.: $1,236,400,000
Assets: $1,453,100,000
Liabilities: $1,005,300,000
Net Worth: $447,800,000
Earnings: $7,700,000
Emp.: 3,082
Fiscal Year-end: 12/31/2020
Office Furniture & Textiles Mfr
N.A.I.C.S.: 337127
David E. Bright (Sr VP-Comm)
Benjamin A. Pardo (Exec VP & Dir-Design)
Michael A. Pollner (Chief Admin Officer, Gen Counsel & Sr VP)
Charles W. Rayfield (CFO & Sr VP)
Roxanne B. Klein (Sr VP-HR)
Usman Waheed (Chief Information & Tech Officer)
Christopher M. Baldwin (Pres & COO)

Subsidiary (Domestic):

Dates Weiser Furniture Corp. (2)
1700 Broadway, Buffalo, NY 14212
Tel.: (716) 891-1700
Web Site: https://datesweiser.com
Wood Office Furniture Mfr
N.A.I.C.S.: 337211
Rob Walsh (Dir-Ops)

Edelman Leather, LLC (2)
30 Bridge St Ste 201, New Milford, CT 06776
Tel.: (860) 350-9600
Web Site: https://www.edelmanleather.com
Sales Range: $10-24.9 Million
Emp.: 36
Leather & Leather Furniture Mfr
N.A.I.C.S.: 316110
Catherine D'Alleva (VP-Sls)

FilzFelt Inc. (2)
425 CrossPoint Pkwy, Getzville, NY 14068
Tel.: (716) 446-2380
Web Site: https://filzfelt.com
Sales Range: $1-9.9 Million
Oil Distr
N.A.I.C.S.: 424990
Traci Roloff (Co-Founder)
Kelly Smith (Co-Founder)

Fully, LLC (2)
117 SE Taylor St Ste 301, Portland, OR 97214
Web Site: http://www.fully.com
Office Furniture Mfr & Distr
N.A.I.C.S.: 337211
David Kahl (Founder)

Subsidiary (Non-US):

Fully Europe BVBA (3)
Nieuwewandeling 62-10, 9000, Gent, Belgium
Tel.: (32) 92964483
Office Furniture Distr
N.A.I.C.S.: 449110
Nick Cornille (Gen Mgr)

Subsidiary (Domestic):

HH Ruseau, LLC (2)
13736 Beta Rd, Dallas, TX 75244
Tel.: (972) 387-4578
Web Site: http://hhruseau.com
Wood Office Furniture Mfr
N.A.I.C.S.: 337211

Subsidiary (Non-US):

Holly Hunt Do Brasil Importacao E Comercio De Mobiliarios LTDA (2)
Alameda Gabriel Monteiro Da Silva 663, Jardim America, Sao Paulo, 1441000, Brazil
Tel.: (55) 1130633189
Furniture Merchant Whslr
N.A.I.C.S.: 423210

Subsidiary (Domestic):

Holly Hunt Enterprises, Inc. (2)
222 Merchandise Mart Plz Ste 1428, Chicago, IL 60654
Tel.: (312) 661-1900
Web Site: https://www.hollyhunt.com
Sales Range: $75-99.9 Million
Emp.: 60
Home Furnishings Designer & Retailer
N.A.I.C.S.: 423210
Rick Kilmer (Pres)

Subsidiary (Non-US):

Knoll International S.A. (2)
268 Boulevard Saint-Germain, 75007, Paris, France
Tel.: (33) 144181999
Web Site: http://www.knoll-int.com
Emp.: 2
Office Furniture Mfr
N.A.I.C.S.: 337214

Knoll International S.A. (2)
Avenue du Port 86C, Brussels, 1000, Belgium
Tel.: (32) 27151300
Web Site: http://www.knoll.com
Emp.: 1
Office Furniture Mfr
N.A.I.C.S.: 337214

Knoll International U.K. Ltd. (2)
91 Goswell Road, London, EC1V 7EX, United Kingdom
Tel.: (44) 2072366655
Web Site: http://www.knoll-int.com
Sales Range: $25-49.9 Million
Emp.: 25
Office Furniture & Textiles Designer & Mfr
N.A.I.C.S.: 337214

Subsidiary (Domestic):

Knoll Overseas, Inc. (2)
1235 Water St, East Greenville, PA 18041-2202
Tel.: (215) 679-7991
Web Site: http://www.knoll.com
Emp.: 1,000
Investment Management Service
N.A.I.C.S.: 523940

Subsidiary (Non-US):

Muuto A/S (2)
Ostergade 36-38, 1100, Copenhagen, Denmark
Tel.: (45) 32969899
Web Site: http://muuto.com
Office Furniture Mfr
N.A.I.C.S.: 337211

Subsidiary (Domestic):

Richard Schultz Design, LLC (2)
806 Gravel Pike, Palm, PA 18070
Tel.: (215) 679-2222
Outdoor Household Furniture Designer, Mfr & Distr
N.A.I.C.S.: 337126
Jennifer Strobel (Mgr-Matls)

Spinneybeck Enterprises, Inc. (2)
425 CrossPoint Pkwy, Getzville, NY 14068
Tel.: (716) 446-2380
Web Site: https://www.spinneybeck.com
Emp.: 50
Upholstery Leather Mfr & Distr
N.A.I.C.S.: 316110

Subsidiary (Non-US):

Spinneybeck Ireland (3)
Suite 2 Morrison Chambers 32 Nassau Street, Dublin, 2, Ireland
Tel.: (353) 16336505
Web Site: http://www.spinneybeck.com
Emp.: 1
Upholstery Leather Distr
N.A.I.C.S.: 316110

Subsidiary (Non-US):

Spinneybeck Limited (2)
Suite 2 Morrison Chambers 32 Nassau Street, Dublin, 2, Ireland
Tel.: (353) 16336505
Web Site: http://www.spinneybeck.com
Wood Office Furniture Mfr
N.A.I.C.S.: 337211

Maharam Fabric Corporation (1)
979 3rd Ave Ste 1701, New York, NY 10022
Tel.: (212) 319-4789
Web Site: http://www.maharam.com
Sales Range: $100-124.9 Million
Emp.: 250
Textiles Designer & Whslr
N.A.I.C.S.: 541490

Naughtone Manufacturing Ltd. (1)
Lowfields Business Park Warhurst Road, Elland, HX5 9DF, United Kingdom
Tel.: (44) 1423816500
Web Site: https://www.naughtone.com
Household Furniture Mfr
N.A.I.C.S.: 337126

Nemschoff, Inc. (1)
2218 Julson Ct, Sheboygan, WI 53081
Tel.: (920) 459-1285
Web Site: http://www.nemschoff.com
Sales Range: $75-99.9 Million
Emp.: 300
Health Care Furniture Mfr
N.A.I.C.S.: 337127

Subsidiary (Domestic):

Nemschoff Chairs, Inc. (2)
909 N 8th St, Sheboygan, WI 53081
Tel.: (920) 457-7726
Web Site: http://www.nemschoff.com
Hospital Furniture Mfr
N.A.I.C.S.: 337127

POSH Office Systems (HK) Ltd. (1)
Rm 4707-13 47/F Hopewell Centre 183 Queens Road East, Hong Kong, China (Hong Kong)
Tel.: (852) 21699260
Web Site: https://www.posh.com.hk
Sales Range: $200-249.9 Million
Emp.: 1,000
Office Furniture Mfr & Retailer
N.A.I.C.S.: 337127
Alan Tse (Acct Mgr)
Giuseppe Tseng (Mgr-Shop)
Gwyneth Li (Acct Mgr)
Dennis Chan (Officer-Project)
Eddie Law (Dir-Sls)
Kenneth Cheng (Dir-Comml)
Ian Kwok (Mgr-Shop)

MillerKnoll, Inc.—(Continued)

Ivan Tse *(Acct Mgr)*
Ray Yung *(Project Mgr-PM & PMS)*
Ricky Chan *(Supvr-Project)*
William Li *(Sr Acct Mgr)*

Sun Hing POSH Holdings
Limited   (1)
Unit K Upper G/F Block 4 Yau Tong Industrial Building 18-20 Sze, Shan Street Yau Tong, Hong Kong, China (Hong Kong)
Tel.: (852) 23893989
Office Furniture Retailer
N.A.I.C.S.: 449110

MILLS MUSIC TRUST

66 Hudson Blvd E, New York, NY
10001
Tel.: (212) 525-1349   NY
Year Founded: 1964
MMTRS—(OTCIQ)
Trust Management Services
N.A.I.C.S.: 523940

MILLSTREET CAPITAL ACQUISITION CORP.

545 Boylston St 8th Fl, Boston, MA
02116
Tel.: (617) 939-0030   DE
Year Founded: 2020
MLSTU—(NASDAQ)
Investment Services
N.A.I.C.S.: 523999
Craig Kelleher *(Co-Chm & Co-CEO)*
Brian Connolly *(Co-Chm & Co-CEO)*
Christina Rosello *(CFO)*

MIMEDX GROUP, INC.

1775 W Oak Commons Ct NE, Marietta, GA 30062
Tel.: (770) 651-9100   FL
Web Site: https://www.mimedx.com
Year Founded: 2008
MDXG—(NASDAQ)
Rev.: $267,841,000
Assets: $171,430,000
Liabilities: $189,418,000
Net Worth: ($17,988,000)
Earnings: ($30,197,000)
Emp.: 867
Fiscal Year-end: 12/31/22
Biomaterial-Based Products for Musculoskeletal Applications
N.A.I.C.S.: 339112
Doug Rice *(CFO & Chief Acctg Officer)*
Kate Surdez *(Chief HR Officer)*
Joseph H. Capper *(CEO)*
John Harper *(CTO)*
Kim Moller *(Sr VP)*
Eric Smith *(Sr VP)*

Subsidiaries:

MiMedx Tissue Services, LLC   (1)
1775 W Oak Commons Ct NE, Marietta, GA 30062
Tel.: (404) 461-9265
Web Site:
    https://www.placentadonation.com
Biotechnology Research & Development
Services
N.A.I.C.S.: 541714

SpineMedica, LLC   (1)
1775 W Oak Commons Ct NE, Marietta, GA 30062
Tel.: (678) 384-6720
Sales Range: $25-49.9 Million
Emp.: 100
Developer of Orthopedic Reconstruction & General Surgery Products
N.A.I.C.S.: 339112

Stability Inc.   (1)
2910 Poston Ave, Nashville, TN 37203-1312
Tel.: (615) 921-5551
Web Site: http://www.stabilitybio.com
Human Tissue Products Distr
N.A.I.C.S.: 325414

Brian Martin *(CEO)*
Tom Johnston *(Pres)*
David Dorsey *(Exec VP)*
Terry Hill *(COO)*

MIND SOLUTIONS, INC.

3525 Del Mar Heights Rd Ste 802,
San Diego, CA 92130   NV
Year Founded: 2012
VOIS—(OTCIQ)
Hardware Mfr
N.A.I.C.S.: 332510
Thomas Allinder *(Pres)*

MIND TECHNOLOGY, INC.

2002 Timberloch Pl Ste 550, The
Woodlands, TX 77380
Tel.: (281) 353-4475   TX
Web Site: https://www.mind-technology.com
Year Founded: 1987
MIND—(NASDAQ)
Rev.: $35,091,000
Assets: $32,858,000
Liabilities: $9,806,000
Net Worth: $23,052,000
Earnings: ($12,620,000)
Emp.: 190
Fiscal Year-end: 01/31/23
Geophysical & Other Equipment
Leasing & Sales
N.A.I.C.S.: 541360
Mark Welker *(VP-Seamap)*
Dean Dennison *(VP-Leasing Ops)*
Peter H. Blum *(Chm)*
Mark Alan Cox *(CFO, Chief Acctg Officer & VP-Acctg & Fin)*

Subsidiaries:

Mitcham Canada Ltd.   (1)
2080 21 St NE, Calgary, T2E 6S5, AB,
Canada   (100%)
Tel.: (403) 250-8010
Web Site: http://www.mitchamindustries.com
Sales Range: $10-24.9 Million
Emp.: 12
Lease & Sales of Geophysical & Other
Equipment
N.A.I.C.S.: 541360
Dean Dennison *(Gen Mgr)*
Jim Brack *(Mgr-Sls & Support)*

Mitcham Canada ULC   (1)
946 55th Avenue NE, Calgary, T2E 6Y4,
AB, Canada
Tel.: (403) 250-8010
Geophysical Surveying & Mapping Services
N.A.I.C.S.: 541360

Mitcham Seismic Eurasia, LLC (1)
56 Aksakov Street, Ufa Bashkortostan,
Moscow, Russia
Tel.: (7) 3472469074
Web Site: http://www.mitchamindustries.com
Lease & Sales of Geophysical Equipment
N.A.I.C.S.: 541360

Seamap (UK) Ltd.   (1)
Unit 34 The Maltings Charlton Estate,
Shepton Mallet, BA4 5QE, Somerset,
United Kingdom
Tel.: (44) 1749342223
Geophysical Surveying & Mapping Services
N.A.I.C.S.: 541360

Seamap Limited   (1)
Unit 34 The Maltings Charlton Estate,
Shepton Mallet, Somerset, BA4 5QE,
United Kingdom   (100%)
Tel.: (44) 1749342223
Web Site: http://www.seamap.com
Sales Range: $75-99.9 Million
Emp.: 38
Lease & Sales of Geophysical Equipment
N.A.I.C.S.: 541360
Michael Zwick *(VP-Sls)*
Tim Pinnington *(Mgr-Sls)*

Seamap Pte. Ltd.   (1)
51 Changi North Crescent, Singapore,
499626, Singapore   (100%)
Tel.: (65) 65451054
Web Site: http://www.seamap.com

Sales Range: $25-49.9 Million
Emp.: 100
Lease & Sales of Geophysical Equipment
N.A.I.C.S.: 541360
Mark Welker *(Mng Dir & VP)*

Seismic Asia Pacific Pty. Ltd.   (1)
556 Tarragindi Road, Salisbury, 4107, QLD,
Australia   (100%)
Tel.: (61) 737193400
Web Site: http://www.seismic.com.au
Sales Range: $10-24.9 Million
Emp.: 8
Supplier of Geophysical, Hydrographic & Navigation Data Aquisition Systems
N.A.I.C.S.: 541360
Paul Duncan *(Mng Dir)*

MINERALS TECHNOLOGIES, INC.

622 3rd Ave 38th Fl, New York, NY
10017
Tel.: (212) 878-1840   DE
Web Site:
    https://www.mineralstech.com
Year Founded: 1968
MTX—(NYSE)
Rev.: $2,169,900,000
Assets: $3,346,600,000
Liabilities: $1,659,900,000
Net Worth: $1,686,700,000
Earnings: $84,100,000
Emp.: 4,027
Fiscal Year-end: 12/31/23
Specialty Minerals, Mineral-Based & Synthetic Mineral Products Developer, Producer & Marketer
N.A.I.C.S.: 327999
Douglas T. Dietrich *(Chm & CEO)*
Jonathan J. Hastings *(Pres-Performance Materials Grp & Grp)*
Jonathan J. Hastings *(Pres-Performance Materials Grp & Grp)*
Michael A. Cipolla *(Chief Acctg Officer, VP & Controller)*
Brett Argirakis *(Mng Dir/Sr VP-Global Supply Chain-Minteq International Inc)*
Erin N. Cutler *(VP-HR)*
Erik C. Aldag *(CFO & Sr VP-Fin & Treasury)*
Timothy J. Jordan *(Chief Compliance Officer, Gen Counsel, Sec & VP)*
Daniel Joseph Monagle III *(Pres)*

Subsidiaries:

AMCOL International
Corporation   (1)
2870 Forbs Ave, Hoffman Estates, IL 60192
Tel.: (847) 851-1500
Web Site: http://www.amcolhpc.com
Minerals Producer, Mfr & Marketer
N.A.I.C.S.: 212323

Subsidiary (Non-US):

AMCOL Australia Pty Ltd   (2)
50 Crowle St, Geelong, 3215, VIC, Australia
Tel.: (61) 352782555
Web Site: http://www.mineralstech.com.au
Emp.: 20
Bentonite Clay Mfr
N.A.I.C.S.: 212323
Dougal Scott *(Mng Dir)*

AMCOL Minerals Europe Limited (2)
Weaver Valley Road, Winsford, CW7 3BU,
Cheshire, United Kingdom
Tel.: (44) 1606868200
Web Site:
    http://www.amcolmineralseurope.com
Chemical Products Mfr
N.A.I.C.S.: 212323

Subsidiary (Domestic):

Ameri-Co Carriers, Inc.   (2)
1702 E Overland, Scottsbluff, NE 69361-7727
Web Site: http://www.americo-carriers.com
Full-Service Truck Line
N.A.I.C.S.: 488510

Americo Logistics, Inc.   (2)

1702 E Overland, Scottsbluff, NE 69361
Tel.: (308) 635-3157
Web Site: http://www.americo-carriers.com
Freight Brokerage Services
N.A.I.C.S.: 488510

Subsidiary (Non-US):

CETCO (Europe) Ltd.   (2)
Birkenhead Road, Wallasey, CH44 7BU,
United Kingdom
Tel.: (44) 1516065900
Web Site: https://www.cetco.co.uk
Clay Ceramic & Refractory Mineral Mining
N.A.I.C.S.: 212323
Andrew Dunn *(Sls Mgr-Tech)*
Russell Harper *(Mgr-Sls-Northern Europe)*
Amanda Browne *(Coord-Sls-Europe, Middle East & Africa)*
Stafford Leitch *(Sls Mgr-Technical-Northern Reg)*
Geoff Adamson *(Sls Mgr-South)*

Subsidiary (Domestic):

Colloid Environmental Technologies
Company (CETCO)   (2)
2870 Forbs Ave, Hoffman Estates, IL 60192
Tel.: (847) 851-1800
Web Site: https://www.mineralstech.com
Waste Impoundment Products; Groundwater Monitoring Wells Mfr & Environmental Consulting Services
N.A.I.C.S.: 212323

Amcol Mineral Madencilik Sanayi ve
Ticaret A.S.   (1)
Ataturk Mahallesi Atasehir Bulvari Gardenya
Plaza 3 No 20 Kat 13, Atasehir, 34758, Istanbul, Turkiye
Tel.: (90) 2164149616
Web Site: http://www.amcol.com.tr
Mineral Mining Services
N.A.I.C.S.: 213114

American Colloid Company   (1)
35 Highland Ave, Bethlehem, PA 18017
Tel.: (847) 851-1500
Web Site: http://www.colloid.com
Clay Product Mfr & Distr
N.A.I.C.S.: 325998

CETCO Energy Services (Malaysia)
Sdn. Bhd.   (1)
Suite 2-3-1 3rd Floor Tower 2 PFCC Jalan
Puteri 1/2, Bandar Puteri Puchong, 47100,
Puchong, 47100, Selangor Darul Ehsan,
Malaysia
Tel.: (60) 380635849
Energy Research & Development Services
N.A.I.C.S.: 926110

CETCO Energy Services Company
LLC   (1)
1001 Ochsner Blvd Ste 425, Covington, LA
70433
Tel.: (985) 871-4700
Web Site: http://cetcoenergyservices.com
Energy Research & Development Services
N.A.I.C.S.: 926110
Robert J. Trauger *(Pres)*

CETCO Energy Services Limited (1)
Badentoy Crescent Badentoy Park Portlethen, Aberdeen, AB12 4YD, United Kingdom
Tel.: (44) 1224787340
Energy Research & Development Services
N.A.I.C.S.: 926110

CETCO Energy Services de Mexico,
S.A. de C.V.   (1)
Av Paseo Tabasco 1203 Col Linda Vista
Torre Empresarial, 15th floor Suite 1503,
Villahermosa, 86050, Tabasco, Mexico
Tel.: (52) 9931879171
Web Site:
    http://www.cetcoenergyservices.com
Energy Research & Development Services
N.A.I.C.S.: 926110

CETCO Oilfield Services Company
Nigeria Limited   (1)
271 Trans Amadi Industrial Layout, Port
Harcourt, Rivers, Nigeria
Tel.: (234) 8072293661
Energy Research & Development Services
N.A.I.C.S.: 926110
Vivian Ogunwa *(Officer-Procurement & Logistics)*

CETCO Sp. Z o.o. (1)
ul Monopolowa 6, 51-501, Wroclaw, Poland
Tel.: (48) 717879802
Energy Research & Development Services
N.A.I.C.S.: 926110

CETCOPoland, Cetco Sp. Z o.o. S.K.A. (1)
Korpele 13A - Strefa, 12-100, Szczytno, Poland
Tel.: (48) 896247312
Web Site: http://www.cetco.pl
Energy Research & Development Services
N.A.I.C.S.: 926110
Grzegorz Kubicki *(Mng Dir)*

Minerals Technologies Europe N.V. (1)
Chaussee de Tubize 485 H, Ikaroslaan 3, 1420, Braine-l'Alleud, Belgium
Tel.: (32) 27255160
Web Site: http://www.mineraltechnologies.com
Emp.: 1
Inorganic Chemical Product Mfr
N.A.I.C.S.: 325180

Minerals Technologies Holdings Ltd. (1)
The Broadgate Tower Third Floor 20 Primrose Street, London, EC2A 2RS, United Kingdom
Tel.: (44) 1709528899
Emp.: 572
Holding Company
N.A.I.C.S.: 551112
Joe Muscari *(Gen Mgr)*

Minerals Technologies India Private Limited (1)
3rd Floor 4/5/6 Rosa Vista Waghbil Opp to Suraj Water Park, Ghodbunder Road, Thane, 400 615, Maharashtra, India
Tel.: (91) 996 793 3944
Web Site: https://www.mineralstech.com
Inorganic Chemical Product Mfr
N.A.I.C.S.: 325180
Ramanathan Chandran *(Mng Dir)*

Minteq Australia Pty Ltd. (1)
118 Industrial Rd, Oak Flats, Wollongong, 2529, Australia
Tel.: (61) 242573511
Emp.: 12
Refractory Lining Mfr
N.A.I.C.S.: 327120
Alan Honan *(Mng Dir)*

Minteq B.V. (1)
Kruisbergseweg 1, 7255AG, Hengelo, Gelderland, Netherlands
Tel.: (31) 575463440
Web Site: http://www.mintech.com
Emp.: 15
Refractory Lining Mfr
N.A.I.C.S.: 327120

Minteq Europe Limited. (1)
Tivoli Industrial Estate, Cork, Ireland
Tel.: (353) 214503241
Refractory Lining Mfr
N.A.I.C.S.: 327120

Minteq International GmbH (1)
Dr-Alfred-Herrhausen-Allee 24, 47228, Duisburg, Germany
Tel.: (49) 20654236720
Web Site: https://www.minteq.de
Emp.: 70
Refractory Lining Mfr
N.A.I.C.S.: 327120

Minteq International, Inc. (1)
35 Highland Ave, Bethlehem, PA 18017-9482 **(100%)**
Tel.: (484) 403-7917
Web Site: http://www.mineralstech.com
Sales Range: $25-49.9 Million
Emp.: 50
Metal Product Distr
N.A.I.C.S.: 332117
Brett Argirakis *(Mng Dir & VP)*

Minteq Italiana S.p.A. (1)
Via Creta 8, 25124, Brescia, Italy
Tel.: (39) 030245551
Web Site: http://www.mineraltechnologies.com
Sales Range: $25-49.9 Million
Emp.: 11
Refractory Lining Mfr

Minteq Shapes and Services Inc. (1)
1789 Schiller St, Portage, IN 46368
Tel.: (219) 762-4863
Emp.: 10
Clay Building Material & Refractory Mfr
N.A.I.C.S.: 327120

Minteq UK Limited. (1)
The Broadgate Tower Third Floor 20 Primrose Street, London, EC2A 2RS, South Yorkshire, United Kingdom
Tel.: (44) 1709528899
Refractory Lining Mfr
N.A.I.C.S.: 327120

Normerica Inc (1)
1599 Hurontario St Ste 203, Port Credit, Mississauga, L5G 4S1, ON, Canada
Tel.: (416) 626-0556
Web Site: https://www.mineralstech.com
Emp.: 320
Dog & Cat Food Products Mfr
N.A.I.C.S.: 311111
John Kimmel *(CEO)*

PT. CETCO Oilfield Services Indonesia (1)
Wisma Bisnis Indonesia 2nd Floor Zone B2 JL KH Mas Mansur 12A, Karet Tengsin Tanah Abang, Jakarta, 10220, Indonesia
Tel.: (62) 2157901175
Energy Research & Development Services
N.A.I.C.S.: 926110

REGOS s.r.o. (1)
Dubravska cesta 2, 841 04, Bratislava, Slovakia
Tel.: (421) 905487200
Web Site: https://regos.sk
Geological Survey Services
N.A.I.C.S.: 541360

ROMIN SLOVAKIA, spol. s.r.o. (1)
Kopernica 225, SK-96701, Kremnica, Slovakia
Tel.: (421) 456789061
Web Site: https://romin.sk
Emp.: 55
Bentonite Extract & Processing Services
N.A.I.C.S.: 212323

Sivomatic B.V. (1)
Appelweg 15, 4782 PX, Moerdijk, Netherlands
Tel.: (31) 168419191
Web Site: https://www.sivomatic.nl
Mineral Product Mfr & Distr
N.A.I.C.S.: 327999

Specialty Minerals France s.p.a.s. (1)
1 Rue Du Grand Meix, 88460, Docelles, France
Tel.: (33) 329663984
Sales Range: $25-49.9 Million
Emp.: 8
Inorganic Chemical Product Mfr
N.A.I.C.S.: 325180
Christophe Weber *(Gen Mgr)*

Specialty Minerals GmbH (1)
Dr Wilhelm Roelen Str 129a, 47179, Duisburg, Germany
Tel.: (49) 20328618100
Sales Range: $25-49.9 Million
Emp.: 2
Inorganic Chemical Product Mfr
N.A.I.C.S.: 325180
Johannes Schutt *(Gen Mgr)*

Specialty Minerals Nordic Oy Ab (1)
Hallimestarinkatu 17, 20780, Kaarina, Finland
Tel.: (358) 22844200
Sales Range: $25-49.9 Million
Emp.: 1
Inorganic Chemical Product Mfr
N.A.I.C.S.: 325180
Johan Karlsson *(Gen Mgr)*

Specialty Minerals, Inc. (1)
35 Highland Ave, Bethlehem, PA 18017-9482 **(100%)**
Tel.: (484) 403-7913
Web Site: http://www.specialtyminerals.com
Sales Range: $50-74.9 Million
Emp.: 65
Producer & Supplier of Precipitated Calcium Carbonate (PCC) to the Paper Industry; Mines & Produces Natural Mineral-Based Products, Including Ground Calcium Carbonate & Talc

N.A.I.C.S.: 212390

Volclay Japan Co., Ltd. (1)
No 301 Shimbashi Bldg 7F 1-9 Shimbashi 3-chome, Minato-ku, Tokyo, 105-0004, Japan
Tel.: (81) 335957511
Web Site: https://volclay.jp
Chemical Products Distr
N.A.I.C.S.: 424690
Yoshihiko Kaneko *(Mng Exec Officer)*
Kazutoshi Naka *(Exec Officer)*
Issei Watanabe *(Pres & CEO)*

MINERALYS THERAPEUTICS, INC.
150 N Radnor Chester Rd Ste F200, Radnor, PA 19087 DE
Web Site: https://www.mineralystx.com
Year Founded: 2019
MLYS—(NASDAQ)
Assets: $11,125,000
Liabilities: $34,050,000
Net Worth: ($22,925,000)
Earnings: ($19,408,000)
Emp.: 12
Fiscal Year-end: 12/31/21
Research & Development in Biotechnology (except Nanobiotechnology)
N.A.I.C.S.: 541714
Jon Congleton *(CEO)*
Brian Taylor Slingsby *(Founder)*

MINERVA NEUROSCIENCES, INC.
1500 District Ave, Burlington, MA 01803
Tel.: (617) 600-7373 DE
Web Site: https://www.minervaneurosciences.com
Year Founded: 2007
NERV—(NASDAQ)
Rev.: $1,437,405
Assets: $56,899,750
Liabilities: $85,357,240
Net Worth: ($28,457,490)
Earnings: ($30,005,353)
Emp.: 9
Fiscal Year-end: 12/31/23
Biopharmaceutical Mfr
N.A.I.C.S.: 325412
Geoffrey Race *(Pres)*
Joseph Reilly *(COO & Sr VP)*
Remy Luthringer *(Chm & CEO)*
Frederick W. Ahlholm *(CFO, Principal Acctg Officer & Sr VP-Fin)*
Michael Davidson *(Chief Medical Officer)*
Ramana Kuchibhatla *(Sr VP & Head-R&D)*

Subsidiaries:

Mind-NRG SA (1)
Rue De Jargonnant 2, Geneva, 1207, Switzerland
Tel.: (41) 227370000
Pharmaceutical Drug Mfr
N.A.I.C.S.: 325412

MINILUXE HOLDING CORP.
1 Faneuil Hall Sq Fl 7, Boston, MA 02109
Tel.: (617) 826-6192
Web Site: https://miniluxe.com
MNLX—(TSXV)
Sales Range: $1-9.9 Million
Emp.: 100
Holding Company
N.A.I.C.S.: 551112
Anthony Tjan *(Exec Chm & CEO)*

Subsidiaries:

MiniLuxe, Inc. (1)
21 Highland Cir, Needham, MA 02494
Tel.: (781) 235-7575
Web Site: http://www.miniluxe.com

Diet & Weight Reducing Centers
N.A.I.C.S.: 812191
Carol S. Thirlwall *(Mgr)*
Leslie Brunner *(Pres)*

MINIM, INC.
848 Elm St, Manchester, NH 03101
Tel.: (617) 423-1072 DE
Web Site: https://www.minim.com
Year Founded: 1993
MINM—(NASDAQ)
Rev.: $50,622,143
Assets: $30,960,006
Liabilities: $14,615,338
Net Worth: $16,344,668
Earnings: ($15,549,244)
Emp.: 93
Fiscal Year-end: 12/31/22
Modems, Speed Dialers & Other Communications Products Mfr & Marketer
N.A.I.C.S.: 334290
David E. Lazar *(CEO)*

MINK THERAPEUTICS, INC.
149 5th Ave Ste 500, New York, NY 10010
Tel.: (212) 994-8250 DE
Web Site: https://www.minktherapeutics.com
Year Founded: 2017
INKT—(NASDAQ)
Rev.: $2,704,743
Assets: $21,471,602
Liabilities: $21,872,905
Net Worth: ($401,303)
Earnings: ($27,991,212)
Emp.: 37
Fiscal Year-end: 12/31/22
Research & Development in Biotechnology (except Nanobiotechnology)
N.A.I.C.S.: 541714
Jennifer S. Buell *(Co-Chm, Pres & CEO)*
Marc Van Dijk *(CTO)*
Christine M. Klaskin *(Treas)*
Patrick Jordan *(VP-Bus Ops)*
Sonia De Munari *(Head-Portfolio Strategy & Program Mgmt)*
Sandra Craig *(Head-Mfg)*
Kimberly Ha *(Head-IR)*
Garo H. Armen *(Co-Chm)*
Jennifer S. Buell *(Co-Chm, Pres & CEO)*

MINORITY EQUALITY OPPORTUNITIES ACQUISITION INC.
100 Executive Ct, Waxahachie, TX 75165
Tel.: (214) 444-7321 DE
Web Site: https://www.meoaus.com
Year Founded: 2021
MEOA—(NASDAQ)
Rev.: $8,175,209
Assets: $10,937,119
Liabilities: $19,228,854
Net Worth: ($8,291,735)
Earnings: $5,940,296
Emp.: 2
Fiscal Year-end: 12/31/22
Investment Services
N.A.I.C.S.: 523999
Shawn Rochester *(Chm, Pres & CEO)*
Robin D. Watkins *(CFO, Treas & Sec)*

MIRA PHARMACEUTICALS, INC.
1200 Brickell Ave Ste 1950 1183, Miami, FL 33133
Tel.: (786) 432-9792 FL
Web Site: https://www.mirapharmaceuticals.com
Year Founded: 2020
MIRA—(NASDAQ)
Assets: $858,074

MIRA Pharmaceuticals, Inc.—(Continued)

Liabilities: $1,454,306
Net Worth: ($596,232)
Earnings: ($7,058,190)
Emp.: 1
Fiscal Year-end: 12/31/22
Pharmaceutical Product Mfr & Distr
N.A.I.C.S.: 325412
Adam Kaplin (Founder)
Erez Aminov (Chm & CEO)
Michelle Yanez (CFO)

MIRACLE ENTERTAINMENT, INC.

8730 Sunset Blvd W, Hollywood, CA 90069
Tel.: (310) 360-7490
MEMI—(OTCIQ)
Entertainment Services
N.A.I.C.S.: 711110
Jason Zelin (Pres)

MIRAGE ENERGY CORPORATION

900 Isom Rd Ste 306, San Antonio, TX 78216
Tel.: (210) 858-3970　　　NV
Web Site:
　https://www.mirageenergycorp.com
Year Founded: 2014
MRGE—(OTCIQ)
Assets: $156,498
Liabilities: $3,226,178
Net Worth: ($3,069,680)
Earnings: ($4,222,660)
Emp.: 5
Fiscal Year-end: 07/31/21
Modular Pool Covering System,
Landscape & Design Services
N.A.I.C.S.: 326199
Patrick C. Dosser (VP)
Michael R. Ward (Chm, Pres, CEO, CFO & Principal Acctg Officer)

MIRION TECHNOLOGIES, INC.

1218 Menko Dr, Atlanta, GA 30318
Tel.: (770) 432-2744　　　DE
Web Site: https://www.mirion.com
Year Founded: 2018
MIR—(NYSE)
Rev.: $800,900,000
Assets: $2,718,500,000
Liabilities: $1,168,500,000
Net Worth: $1,550,000,000
Earnings: ($96,900,000)
Emp.: 3,000
Fiscal Year-end: 12/31/23
Holding Company
N.A.I.C.S.: 551112
Loic Eloy (Pres-Indus Grp)
Shelia Webb (CTO)
James Cocks (Chief Product Officer)
Christopher Moore (Chief Acctg Officer)
Erin Schesny (CMO)
Alex Gaddy (Treas & Sr VP-Strategy & IR)
Thomas D. Logan (Founder & CEO)
Brian Schopfer (CFO & Exec VP)
Emmanuelle Lee (Chief Legal Officer)
Alison Ulrich (Chief HR Officer)

Subsidiaries:

Mirion Technologies (US), Inc.　(1)
1218 Menlo Dr, Atlanta, GA 30318
Tel.: (770) 432-2744
Web Site: https://www.mirion.com
Holding Company; Radiation Detection, Measurement, Analysis & Monitoring Products & Services
N.A.I.C.S.: 551112
Shelia Webb (Chief Digital Officer)
James Cocks (CTO)
Christopher Moore (Chief Acctg Officer)
Erin Schesny (CMO)

Lawrence D. Kingsley (Co-Chm)
Brian Schopfer (CFO)
Mark Siviter (Chief Revenue Officer)

Subsidiary (Domestic):

Biodex Medical Systems, Inc.　(2)
20 Ramsey Rd, Shirley, NY 11967-4704
Tel.: (631) 924-9000
Web Site: http://www.biodex.com
Sales Range: $25-49.9 Million
Surgical & Medical Products Mfr
N.A.I.C.S.: 339112
James Reese (CEO)
Kathy Weihberg (Coord-Employee Events)
Lila Corwin (VP-Mktg)
Mark Gorman (Mgr-Svc)
Michael O'Connell (Supvr-Shipping)
Peter Wojcik (Mgr-Sls)
Rick Prince (VP-Design Engrg)
Tom Giammanco (Mgr-Sls)
Eric J. Farabaugh Sr. (VP-Sls-Physical Medicine)

Capintec Inc.　(2)
7 Vreeland Rd, Florham Park, NJ 07932
Tel.: (201) 825-9500
Web Site: http://www.capintec.com
Mfr, Developer & Marketer of Radiation Measuring & Monitoring Instrumentation
N.A.I.C.S.: 334519
John Viscovic (CEO)

Mirion Technologies (Canberra), Inc.　(2)
800 Research Pkwy, Meriden, CT 06450
Tel.: (203) 238-2351
Web Site: http://www.canberra.com
Emp.: 5,000
Radiation Detection & Analysis Instruments Mfr
N.A.I.C.S.: 334413
Frederic Van Heems (Pres, CEO & Dir)

Subsidiary (Non-US):

Mirion Technologies (Canberra BNLS) NV/SA　(3)
ZI Research Park 80, 1731, Zellik, Belgium
Tel.: (32) 24818530
Web Site: http://www.canberra.com
Marketing of Radiation Detection & Analysis Instrumentation
N.A.I.C.S.: 334519
Luc De Baerdemaeker (Gen Mgr)

Mirion Technologies (Canberra UK) Limited　(3)
Bldg 528 10 Unit 1 Harwell International Business Centre, Didcot, OX11 0DF, Oxon, United Kingdom
Tel.: (44) 1235838300
Web Site: http://www.oanberra.com
Nuclear Measurement Consultancy; Nuclear Apparatus Mfr & Sales
N.A.I.C.S.: 334513

Mirion Technologies (Canberra) SAS　(3)
1 Rue Des Herons, 78182, Saint-Quentin-en-Yvelines, Cedex, France
Tel.: (33) 139485770
Web Site: http://www.canberra.fr
Emp.: 250
Radiation Detector & Analyzer Mfr
N.A.I.C.S.: 334519
Jose Castellote (CEO)

Subsidiary (Domestic):

Mirion Technologies (IST) Corporation　(2)
315 Daniel Zenker Dr 200 IST Ctr, Horseheads, NY 14845-2256
Tel.: (607) 562-4530
Web Site: http://www.mirion.com
Radiation-Tolerant Cameras & Closed Circuit Television System Mfr
N.A.I.C.S.: 335999

Subsidiary (Domestic):

Mirion Technologies (Conax Nuclear), Inc.　(3)
402 Sonwil Dr, Buffalo, NY 14225-5929
Tel.: (716) 681-1973
Web Site: http://www.mirion.com
Nuclear Components Mfr
N.A.I.C.S.: 334519

Mitch Staskiewicz (Mgr-Sls)
Thomas Logan (Chm & CEO)
Mike Freed (COO)
Mike Brumbaugh (CIO & Exec VP)
Anthony Rabb (CFO)

Subsidiary (Domestic):

Sun Nuclear Corporation　(2)
3275 Suntree Blvd, Melbourne, FL 32940
Tel.: (321) 259-6862
Web Site: http://www.sunnuclear.com
Sales Range: $1-9.9 Million
Emp.: 48
Measuring & Controlling Device Mfr
N.A.I.C.S.: 334519
Jeff Simon (CEO)

MIRUM PHARMACEUTICALS, INC.

989 E Hillsdale Blvd Ste 300, Foster City, CA 94404
Tel.: (650) 667-4085　　　DE
Web Site:
　https://www.mirumpharma.com
Year Founded: 2018
MIRM—(NASDAQ)
Rev.: $77,062,000
Assets: $352,906,000
Liabilities: $210,869,000
Net Worth: $142,037,000
Earnings: ($135,665,000)
Emp.: 196
Fiscal Year-end: 12/31/22
Biotechnology Research & Development Services
N.A.I.C.S.: 541714
Eric H. Bjerkholt (CFO)
Peter Radovich (Pres & COO)
Lara Longpre (Chief Dev Officer)
Pamela Vig (Chief Scientific Officer)
Peter Radovich (COO)
Paul Ross (Chief Compliance Officer)
Christopher Peetz (Co-Founder & CEO)
Michael G. Grey (Co-Founder & Chm)

Subsidiaries:

Satiogen Pharmaceuticals, Inc.　(1)
350 10th Ave Ste 820, San Diego, CA 92101
Tel.: (619) 291-2757
Web Site: http://www.satiogen.com
Research & Development in Biotechnology
N.A.I.C.S.: 541714
Bronislava Gedulin (Co-Founder & CTO)

MISSION ADVANCEMENT CORP.

2525 E Camelback Rd Ste 850, Phoenix, AZ 85016
Tel.: (609) 474-0600　　　DE
Web Site:
　http://www.missioncorp.com
Year Founded: 2020
MACC—(NYSE)
Rev.: $13,354,921
Assets: $346,078,271
Liabilities: $368,166,840
Net Worth: ($22,088,569)
Earnings: $11,066,748
Emp.: 3
Fiscal Year-end: 12/01/21
Investment Services
N.A.I.C.S.: 523999

MISSION BANCORP

1301 17th St, Bakersfield, CA 93301
Tel.: (661) 859-2500　　　CA
Web Site:
　https://www.missionbank.bank
Year Founded: 2002
MSBC—(OTCIQ)
Rev.: $48,264,591
Assets: $1,279,888,050
Liabilities: $1,177,757,784
Net Worth: $102,130,266
Earnings: $15,688,282

Fiscal Year-end: 12/31/20
Bank Holding Company
N.A.I.C.S.: 551111
A. J. Antongiovanni (Pres & CEO)
Richard E. Fanucchi (Exec VP)
Jason Castle (CFO & Sr VP-Mission Bank)
Bruce L. Beretta (Chm)
John Bidart (Vice Chm)
Sheldon Ralph (Chief Admin Officer & Sr VP-Mission Bank)
Michael S. Congdon (Chief Credit Officer, Chief Credit Officer & Sr VP-Mission Bank)
Rob Hallum (Sr VP & Mgr-Ag Division-Mission Bank)
Esmeralda Rivas (Chief Compliance Officer & Chief Audit Officer)
Ryan Alvord (Treas)
Dustin Della (Reg Pres-Visalia)
Karen Heisinger (Reg Pres-Bakersfield & Shafter)
Craig Howells (Mgr-SBA Division)
Rodney Maston (Controller)
Loni Olson (Mgr-Compensation & Benefits)
Austin Petty (Reg Pres-San Luis Obispo)
Christine Rice (Mgr-Note Dept)
Valerie Vickers (Officer-Credit Svc)
Miranda Whitworth (CMO)
Nathan Wilkerson (Mgr-Financial Reporting, FP, and A)

Subsidiaries:

Mission Bank　(1)
1330 Truxtun Ave, Bakersfield, CA 93301
Tel.: (661) 859-2500
Web Site: http://www.missionbank.com
Retail & Commercial Banking
N.A.I.C.S.: 522110
A. J. Antongiovanni (Pres & CEO)
John Bianchi (CFO & Sr VP)
Richard E. Fanucchi (Pres, CEO & Sec)
Stuart Annable (Sr VP, Mgr-Loans & Branch Mgr-Bakersfield)

MISSION PRODUCE, INC.

2710 Camino Del Sol, Oxnard, CA 93030
Tel.: (805) 981-3650　　　CA
Web Site:
　https://www.missionproduce.com
Year Founded: 1983
AVO—(NASDAQ)
Rev.: $1,234,700,000
Assets: $971,500,000
Liabilities: $394,400,000
Net Worth: $577,100,000
Earnings: $41,800,000
Emp.: 3,100
Fiscal Year-end: 10/31/24
Provider of Fresh Fruits & Vegetables
N.A.I.C.S.: 424480
Stephen J. Barnard (Founder & CEO)
Jenna Aguilera (Mgr-Mktg & Comm)
Bryan E. Giles (CFO)
Joanne Wu (Gen Counsel & Sec)
Anita Lemos (VP-HR)
John Pawlowski (Pres & COO)

Subsidiaries:

Mission Produce Europe B.V.　(1)
Hazeldonk 6548, 4836 LD, Breda, Netherlands
Tel.: (31) 850662808
Emp.: 10
Avocado Distr
N.A.I.C.S.: 424480
Ine Potting (Mgr-Export-Europe)
Astrid Claasz Coockson (Office Mgr)

MISTER CAR WASH, INC.

222 E 5th St, Tucson, AZ 85705
Tel.: (520) 615-4000　　　DE
Web Site:
　https://www.mistercarwash.com
Year Founded: 2014

MCW—(NYSE)
Rev.: $927,070,000
Assets: $2,881,536,000
Liabilities: $1,966,501,000
Net Worth: $915,035,000
Earnings: $80,130,000
Emp.: 6,600
Fiscal Year-end: 12/31/23
Car Wash Services
N.A.I.C.S.: 811192
John Lai *(Chm, Pres & CEO)*
Jedidiah Gold *(CFO)*
Joseph Matheny *(Sr VP-Ops)*
Luke Hartke *(VP-M&A)*

MISTRAS GROUP, INC.
195 Clarksville Rd, Princeton Junction, NJ 08550
Tel.: (609) 716-4000   DE
Web Site:
  https://www.mistrasgroup.com
Year Founded: 1978
MG—(NYSE)
Rev.: $687,373,000
Assets: $534,904,000
Liabilities: $336,155,000
Net Worth: $198,749,000
Earnings: $6,499,000
Emp.: 5,400
Fiscal Year-end: 12/31/22
Mechanical Integrity & Non-Destructive Testing Technology & Services
N.A.I.C.S.: 334519
Sotirios J. Vahaviolos *(Founder)*
Michael J. Lange *(Sr Exec VP-Bus Dev & Strategic Plng)*
Manuel N. Stamatakis *(Chm, Interim Pres & Interim CEO)*
Michael C. Keefe *(Gen Counsel, Sec & Exec VP)*
Nestor S. Makarigakis *(Grp VP-Mktg & Comm)*
Edward J. Prajzner *(CFO, Treas & Exec VP)*
John A. Smith *(Pres-Svcs & Exec VP)*
Gennaro D'Alterio *(Chief Comml Officer & Exec VP)*
Hani Hammad *(CTO & Exec VP)*

Subsidiaries:

Aetos Group, Inc.   (1)
4000 Underwood Rd, La Porte, TX 77571
Tel.: (281) 478-1600
Web Site: https://www.aetosgroup.com
Automotive Equipment Whslr
N.A.I.C.S.: 441330

Carmagen Engineering, Inc.   (1)
4 W Main St, Rockaway, NJ 07866
Tel.: (281) 478-1600
Web Site: https://www.carmagen.com
Sales Range: $1-9.9 Million
Emp.: 150
Engineering Services
N.A.I.C.S.: 541330

Controles Industriels de L'entang (1)
6 rue Volta - Z I Ecopolis Sud, 13500, Martigues, France
Tel.: (33) 442072690
Web Site: https://www.cietang.com
Emp.: 30
Industrial Equipment Distr
N.A.I.C.S.: 423830
Yves Galves *(CEO)*

GMA Holding B.V.   (1)
Enschedesestraat 218 A, 7552 CL, Hengelo, Netherlands
Tel.: (31) 747113603
Web Site: https://www.gma-group.com
Holding Company
N.A.I.C.S.: 551112

MISTRAS Canada, Inc.   (1)
265 MacAlpine Crescent, Fort McMurray, T9H 4Y4, AB, Canada
Tel.: (780) 743-1072
Web Site: http://www.mistrasgroup.ca

Mechanical Integrity & Non-Destructive Testing Technology & Services
N.A.I.C.S.: 334519

Mistras Group B.V.   (1)
Hofweg 15, Zuid-Holland, 3208 LE, Spijkenisse, Netherlands
Tel.: (31) 102450325
Web Site: https://www.mistrasgroup.nl
Sales Range: $25-49.9 Million
Emp.: 45
Measuring & Controlling Device Mfr
N.A.I.C.S.: 334519

Mistras Group BVBA   (1)
Koordekenshoef - Haven 83, 2030, Antwerp, Belgium
Tel.: (32) 35405680
Web Site: https://www.mistrasgroup.be
Asset Management Services
N.A.I.C.S.: 531390

Mistras Group GmbH   (1)
Hansaallee 321 / Building 20, 40549, Dusseldorf, Germany
Tel.: (49) 211730940
Measuring & Controlling Device Mfr
N.A.I.C.S.: 334519

Mistras Group Hellas A.B.E.E. (1)
Eleftheriios Venizelou 7 Delfon, Metamorphosis, 14452, Athens, Greece
Tel.: (30) 2102846801
Measuring & Controlling Device Mfr
N.A.I.C.S.: 334519
Dimitrios Kourousis *(Dir-Ops)*

Mistras Group Limited   (1)
Norman Way Industrial Estate, Over, CB24 5QE, Cambridgeshire, United Kingdom
Tel.: (44) 1954231612
Web Site: http://mistrasgroup.co.uk
Sales Range: $25-49.9 Million
Emp.: 20
Asset Protection Services
N.A.I.C.S.: 541380
Tim Bradshaw *(Dir-Technology)*
Jon Burns *(Mng Dir)*
Malcolm Hunter *(Head-Commercial)*
Barry Morris *(Mgr-Business Development)*
Tony Coppola *(Mgr-Delivery)*

Mistras Group SAS   (1)
27 Rue Magellan Zone D Amenagement Concerte Porte, 94370, Sucy-en-Brie, France
Tel.: (33) 149826040
Web Site: https://mistrasgroup.fr
Measuring & Controlling Device Mfr
N.A.I.C.S.: 334519
Max Le Blond *(Mgr-IT Support)*

Mistras Metaltec Inc.   (1)
765 rue de Saint-Romuald, Levis, G6W 5M6, QC, Canada
Tel.: (418) 837-4664
Measuring & Controlling Device Mfr
N.A.I.C.S.: 334519

Mistras Ropeworks Training Corp.   (1)
8587 White Fir St A3, Reno, NV 89523
Tel.: (775) 747-3377
Web Site: https://www.ropeworks.com
Information Technology Services
N.A.I.C.S.: 541519
Nathan Schuster *(Mgr-Rope Access Program)*

NDT do Brasil Ltd.   (1)
Rua Joaquim Antunes 574, Pinheiros, Sao Paulo, Brazil
Tel.: (55) 1130825111
Web Site: http://www.pasa.com.br
Measuring & Controlling Device Mfr
N.A.I.C.S.: 334519
Pedro Feres Filho *(Pres)*

New Century Software, Inc.   (1)
2627 Redwing Rd Ste 100, Fort Collins, CO 80526
Tel.: (970) 267-2000
Web Site:
  http://www.newcenturysoftware.com
Prepackaged Software
N.A.I.C.S.: 513210
Ron Brush *(Founder & Pres)*
Pat Westrick *(Dir-Integrity Mgmt)*
Ryan Huntley *(Mgr-Integrity Mgmt)*
Jeff Boyton *(Sr Mgr-Software Engrg)*
Sue Luczyk *(Mgr-Software Support)*
Courtney Adams *(Ops Mgr)*

Onstream Pipeline Inspection Services Inc.   (1)
Suite 120 7455 - 68th Street SE, Calgary, T2C 5R4, AB, Canada
Tel.: (403) 234-8345
Web Site: https://onstream-pipeline.com
Natural Gas Pipeline Transportation Services
N.A.I.C.S.: 486210
Mark Rudnicki *(Exec Dir-Ops & Bus Svcs)*
Stephen Westwood *(Sr Dir-Engrg & Tech)*
Tony Carrier *(Sr Dir-Ops)*
Mike Niosi *(VP-Divisional)*

Penn Non-Destructive Testing, LLC   (1)
1010 Industrial Blvd, New Kensington, PA 15068
Tel.: (724) 334-1900
Web Site: http://www.westpenntesting.com
Testing Laboratories
N.A.I.C.S.: 541380
Steven Petkovsek *(Specialist-Sls)*

Physical Acoustics Corp.   (1)
195 Clarksville Rd, Princeton Junction, NJ 08550
Tel.: (609) 716-4000
Web Site:
  https://www.physicalacoustics.com
Sales Range: $100-124.9 Million
Emp.: 100
Mechanical Integrity & Non-Destructive Testing Technology & Services
N.A.I.C.S.: 334519
Sotirios J. Vahaviolos *(Chm)*

Subsidiary (Non-US):

DIAPAC Ltd.   (2)
gadchevseovo st 5 bldg 1, 125367, Moscow, Russia
Tel.: (7) 4957894549
Web Site: http://www.diapac.ru
Sales Range: $100-124.9 Million
Emp.: 50
Mechanical Integrity & Non-Destructive Testing Technology & Services
N.A.I.C.S.: 334519
Victor Shemyakin *(Mng Dir)*

Euro-Physical Acoustics S.A.   (2)
27 Rue Magellan, ZAC des Portes de Sucy, 94370, Sucy-en-Brie, France
Tel.: (33) 149826040
Web Site: https://mistrasgroup.fr
Sales Range: $100-124.9 Million
Emp.: 50
Mechanical Integrity & Non-Destructive Testing Technology & Services
N.A.I.C.S.: 334519

Mistras Cambridge   (2)
Norman Way Industrial Estate, Over, CB24 5QE, Cambridgeshire, United Kingdom
Tel.: (44) 1954231612
Web Site: http://www.mistrasgroup.co.uk
Sales Range: $100-124.9 Million
Emp.: 35
Acoustic Emission (AE), Structural Monitoring & Advanced Automated NDT (Nondestructive Testing)
N.A.I.C.S.: 334519
Tim Walsh *(Mng Dir)*

Mistras Hellas A.B.E.E.   (2)
El Venizelou 7 Delfon, Metamorfosis, 14452, Athens, Greece
Tel.: (30) 2102846801
Web Site: http://www.mistrasgroup.gr
Sales Range: $100-124.9 Million
Mechanical Integrity & Non-Destructive Testing Technology & Services
N.A.I.C.S.: 334519

Nippon Physical Acoustics Ltd.   (2)
8F Okamoto LK, Building 2 17 10, Tokyo, 150, Japan
Tel.: (81) 334983570
Web Site: http://www.pacjapan.com
Sales Range: $100-124.9 Million
Emp.: 10
Mechanical Integrity & Non-Destructive Testing Technology & Services
N.A.I.C.S.: 334519

Physical Acoustics B.V.   (2)
Hofweg 15, 3208 LE, Spijkenisse, Netherlands
Tel.: (31) 102450325

Web Site: http://www.pacbv.nl
Sales Range: $100-124.9 Million
Emp.: 30
Mechanical Integrity & Non-Destructive Testing Technology & Services
N.A.I.C.S.: 334519
Michel Kramerfrecher *(Mng Dir)*

Physical Acoustics South America Ltda.   (2)
Rua Joaquim Antunes 574, Pinheiros, Sao Paulo, 05415-001, Brazil
Tel.: (55) 113 082 5111
Web Site: https://www.pasa.com.br
Sales Range: $100-124.9 Million
Emp.: 100
Mechanical Integrity & Non-Destructive Testing Technology & Services
N.A.I.C.S.: 334519
Andreas Wende *(Mng Dir)*

QSL Quebec Inc.   (1)
961 boul Champlain, Quebec, G1K 4J9, QC, Canada
Tel.: (418) 522-4701
Web Site: https://www.qsl.com
Emp.: 2,000
Port & Harbor Operation Services
N.A.I.C.S.: 488310
Denis Dupuis *(Chm & Co-Pres)*
Robert Bellisle *(Co/Co-Pres, CEO & Co-CEO)*
Steve Quenneville *(VP-Central Quebec & Western)*
Nathalie Rousseau *(VP-HR)*
Ivan Boileau *(Exec VP-Strategic Partnerships & Asset Mgmt)*
Eric Lapointe *(VP-Eastern Quebec)*
Dominic Picard *(Exec VP-Information Technology)*

R.A.C. Group Inc.   (1)
265 MacAlpine Crescent, Fort McMurray, T9H 4Y4, AB, Canada
Tel.: (403) 264-2023
Web Site: https://www.rac-int.com
Automotive Equipment Whslr
N.A.I.C.S.: 441330
Morgan Portet *(Founder & Owner)*

Rope Access Calgary, Inc.   (1)
701 3 Ave SW, Calgary, T2P 5R3, AB, Canada
Tel.: (403) 467-3495
Web Site: https://xtremeaxis.com
Automotive Equipment Whslr
N.A.I.C.S.: 441330
Morgan Portet *(Pres)*

The NACHER Corporation   (1)
111 E Angus Dr, Youngsville, LA 70592
Tel.: (337) 856-9144
Web Site: http://www.nacher.net
Sales Range: $25-49.9 Million
Emp.: 250
Remediation Services for Oil & Gas Industry
N.A.I.C.S.: 562910

Vibra-Metrics, Inc.   (1)
195 Clarksville Rd, Princeton Junction, NJ 08550   (100%)
Tel.: (609) 716-4000
Web Site: http://www.mistrasgroup.com
Sales Range: $10-24.9 Million
Emp.: 200
Mfg. of Vibration Accelerometers
N.A.I.C.S.: 334519

MITEK SYSTEMS, INC.
770 1st Ave Ste 425, San Diego, CA 92101
Tel.: (619) 269-6800   DE
Web Site:
  https://www.miteksystems.com
Year Founded: 1986
MITK—(NASDAQ)
Rev.: $172,083,000
Assets: $413,753,000
Liabilities: $198,952,000
Net Worth: $214,801,000
Earnings: $3,278,000
Emp.: 565
Fiscal Year-end: 09/30/24
Automatic Data Recognition Software Producer; Check Image Analytics Producer Used to Detect Check Fraud & Improve Customer Service

Mitek Systems, Inc.—(Continued)

N.A.I.C.S.: 334118
Michael E. Diamond *(Sr VP & Gen Mgr-Digital Banking)*
Scott Carter *(Chm & Interim CEO)*
Stephen Ritter *(CTO)*
Sanjay Gupta *(VP & Head-Products & Corp Dev-Global)*
Xavier Codo Grasa *(Gen Mgr-ICAR)*
David B. Lyle *(CFO, Principal Acctg Officer & Sr VP)*
Cindy White *(CMO)*
Angela M. Romei *(Dir-Comm)*
Kerry Cantley *(VP-Digital Banking Strategy)*

Subsidiaries:

A2iA SAS   (1)
39 rue de la Bienfaisance, 75008, Paris, France
Tel.: (33) 144420080
Web Site: http://www.a2ia.com
Software Services
N.A.I.C.S.: 541511

DSP Labs Limited   (1)
Gelsingforsskaya Street 2, Sampsonievsky district, Saint Petersburg, 194044, Russia
Tel.: (7) 8124588658
Web Site: https://dsplabs.pro
Telemarketing Services
N.A.I.C.S.: 561422

HooYu Ltd.   (1)
180 Borough High Street, London, SE1 1LB, United Kingdom
Tel.: (44) 2079092173
Web Site: https://www.hooyu.com
Identity Verification Services
N.A.I.C.S.: 561499

ICAR Vision Systems, S.L.   (1)
Ronda Can Fatjo 11 Edificio A1 Planta 1 Parc Tecnologic del Valles, Cerdanyola del Valles, 08290, Barcelona, Spain
Tel.: (34) 935942474
Web Site: http://www.icarvision.com
Software Services
N.A.I.C.S.: 541511

Mitek Systems B.V.   (1)
Motion Building Radarweg 60, 1043 NT, Amsterdam, Netherlands
Tel.: (31) 208886623
Software Services
N.A.I.C.S.: 541511

Mitek Systems Private Limited   (1)
Fora 180 Borough High Street, London, SE1 1LB, United Kingdom
Tel.: (44) 2038808068
Software Services
N.A.I.C.S.: 541511

MITESCO, INC.
505 Beachland Blvd Ste 1377, Vero Beach, FL 32963
Tel.: (404) 913-1802   UT
Web Site:
  https://www.mitescoinc.com
Year Founded: 1983
MITI—(OTCQB)
Rev.: $690,534
Assets: $2,601,980
Liabilities: $21,739,329
Net Worth: ($19,137,349)
Earnings: ($23,236,129)
Emp.: 27
Fiscal Year-end: 12/31/22
Investment Services
N.A.I.C.S.: 523999
Julie R. Smith *(Pres)*

Subsidiaries:

The Good Clinic, LLC   (1)
307 1st Ave NE, Minneapolis, MN 55413
Tel.: (612) 284-8206
Web Site: https://www.thegoodclinic.com
Hospital & Health Care Services
N.A.I.C.S.: 622110
Michael C. Howe *(CEO)*
Rebecca Hafner-Fogarty *(Chief Medical Officer)*
Bradley Case *(Pres)*

MIX 1 LIFE INC.
16000 N 80th St Ste E, Scottsdale, AZ 85260
Tel.: (480) 371-1100   NV
Web Site: http://www.mix1life.com
Year Founded: 2009
MIXX—(OTCIQ)
Sales Range: $1-9.9 Million
Emp.: 15
Nutritional Supplement Distr
N.A.I.C.S.: 424210
Steve Staehr *(CFO & Treas)*

MJ HARVEST, INC.
9205 W Russell Rd Ste 240, Las Vegas, NV 89139
Tel.: (954) 519-3115
Web Site:
  https://www.mjharvestinc.com
MJHI—(OTCIQ)
Rev.: $172,825
Assets: $3,791,023
Liabilities: $3,070,836
Net Worth: $720,187
Earnings: ($2,875,784)
Emp.: 15
Fiscal Year-end: 05/31/22
Commercial & Institutional Building Construction
N.A.I.C.S.: 236220
Patrick Bilton *(CEO, Interim Principal Acctg Officer & Interim Principal Financial Officer)*
Jerry Cornwell *(Pres)*

MJ HOLDINGS, INC.
2043 Joy View Ln, Las Vegas, NV 89012
Tel.: (312) 953-2723   NV
Web Site:
  https://www.mjholdingsinc.com
Year Founded: 2006
MJNE—(OTCIQ)
Rev.: $362,313
Assets: $5,130,580
Liabilities: $4,756,028
Net Worth: $374,552
Earnings: ($5,380,241)
Emp.: 9
Fiscal Year-end: 12/31/22
Licensed Marijuana Operators Real Estate Leasing Services
N.A.I.C.S.: 531120
John P. Gorst *(Interim CEO)*
Thomas Valenzuela *(Interim Chm)*
Patricia Chinnici *(Interim CFO)*
Albert Reasonover *(Pres)*

MJARDIN GROUP, INC.
3461 Ringsby Ct 350, Denver, CO 80216
Tel.: (720) 613-4019
Web Site: http://www.mjardin.com
Year Founded: 1978
MJAR—(CNSX)
Cannabis Product Mfr
N.A.I.C.S.: 325411
Patrick Witcher *(CEO)*
Adrian Montgomery *(Chm)*

MKS INSTRUMENTS, INC.
2 Tech Dr Ste 201, Andover, MA 01810
Tel.: (978) 645-5500   MA
Web Site: https://www.mks.com
Year Founded: 1961
MKSI—(NASDAQ)
Rev.: $3,622,000,000
Assets: $9,118,000,000
Liabilities: $6,646,000,000
Net Worth: $2,472,000,000
Earnings: ($1,841,000,000)
Emp.: 10,000
Fiscal Year-end: 12/31/23
Instruments, Subsystems & Process Control Solutions Mfr

N.A.I.C.S.: 334513
Michelle M. McCarthy *(Chief Acctg Officer & VP)*
Kathleen F. Burke *(Gen Counsel, Sec & Sr VP)*
John T. C. Lee *(Pres, CEO & Interim Principal Fin Officer)*
Mark M. Gitin *(Exec VP/Gen Mgr-Photonics Solutions Div)*
James A. Schreiner *(COO & Sr VP)*
David P. Henry *(Exec VP-Ops & Corp Mktg)*
Eric R. Taranto *(Sr VP & Gen Mgr-Vacuum & Analysis Div)*
Henry C. Chang *(Sr VP)*
Sally Ann Bouley *(Interim Chief HR Officer)*
Ramakumar Mayampurath *(CFO, Treas & Exec VP)*

Subsidiaries:

Alter S.r.l.   (1)
Via Imperia 3/B, 20132, Milan, Italy
Tel.: (39) 0284800198
Web Site: https://www.alter-srl.it
Electronic Instrument Distr
N.A.I.C.S.: 423690

Electro Scientific Industries, Inc.   (1)
14523 SW Millikan Way, Beaverton, OR 97005
Tel.: (503) 641-4141
Web Site: https://www.esi.com
Rev.: $367,884,000
Assets: $372,988,000
Liabilities: $106,630,000
Net Worth: $266,358,000
Earnings: $116,223,000
Emp.: 615
Fiscal Year-end: 03/31/2018
Electronic Manufacturing Equipment Mfr
N.A.I.C.S.: 423830

Subsidiary (Non-US):

ESI Electronic Equipment (Shanghai) Co., Ltd.   (2)
Room 107 Building E No 139 Fanghua Road, Pudong New District, Shanghai, 201204, China
Tel.: (86) 2133927070
Web Site: http://www.esi.com
Electronic Manufacturing Equipment Mfr & Distr
N.A.I.C.S.: 423830

ESI Korea Co. Ltd.   (2)
7th FL Leaders Tower 12 Wongomae-ro, Giheung-gu, Yongin, 17086, Gyeonggi-do, Korea (South)
Tel.: (82) 3280211600
Web Site: http://www.esi.com
Electronic Manufacturing Equipment Mfr & Supplier
N.A.I.C.S.: 335999

Branch (Non-US):

ESI Taiwan   (2)
2F No 26 Tai Yuen Street, Zhubei, 30288, Hsinchu, Taiwan
Tel.: (886) 35526788
Web Site: http://www.esi.com
Electronic Manufacturing Equipment Mfr & Distr
N.A.I.C.S.: 335999

Subsidiary (Non-US):

ESI-PyroPhotonics Lasers, Inc.   (2)
275 Kesmark St, Dollard des Ormeaux, H9B 3J1, QC, Canada
Tel.: (514) 684-0100
Laser Products Developer & Mfr
N.A.I.C.S.: 334419

Electro Scientific Industries Europe Ltd.   (2)
8 Avro Court, Ermine Business Park, Huntingdon, PE29 6XS, Cambs, United Kingdom
Tel.: (44) 1480456566
Web Site: http://www.esi.com
Electronic Manufacturing Equipment Distr
N.A.I.C.S.: 423690

Electro Scientific Industries Japan Co., Ltd.   (2)
Moriichi Building 2F 14-3 Takabashi, Koto-ku, Tokyo, 135-0005, Japan
Tel.: (81) 356255100
Web Site: http://www.esi.com
Electronic Manufacturing Equipment Mfr & Supplier
N.A.I.C.S.: 335999

Electro Scientific Industries Singapore Pte Ltd.   (2)
1 Kaki Bukit View 02-05/07 Techview, Singapore, 415941, Singapore
Tel.: (65) 66030199
Electronic Manufacturing Equipment Supplier
N.A.I.C.S.: 423830

Eolite Systems, SAS   (2)
11 Avenue de Canteranne, 33600, Pessac, France
Tel.: (33) 5 56 46 45 50
Laser Products Developer & Mfr
N.A.I.C.S.: 334419

Wuhan Topwin Optoelectronics Technology Co. Ltd.   (2)
Jiuyang Science and Technology Park Guanggu Avenue 108, Iong Yang Technology Park, Wuhan, 430000, China
Tel.: (86) 2781710885
Web Site: http://www.whtopwin.com
Water Equipment Mfr
N.A.I.C.S.: 333992

MKS ASTeX Products   (1)
90 Industrial Way, Wilmington, MA 01887-4610
Tel.: (978) 645-5500
Web Site: http://www.astex.com
Sales Range: $50-74.9 Million
Emp.: 300
Provider of Production Technology Used in the Manufacture of Semiconductor Devices & Range of Medical, Industrial & Synthetic Diamond Applications
N.A.I.C.S.: 334513

Subsidiary (Non-US):

ASTeX GmbH   (2)
Schatzbogen 43, 81829, Munich, Germany   (100%)
Tel.: (49) 894200080
Web Site: http://www.astex.de
Sales Range: $10-24.9 Million
Emp.: 40
Gas Management Instrumentation Retailer
N.A.I.C.S.: 334513

MKS Denmark APS   (1)
Nordre Strandvej 119 G, Hellebaek, 3150, Denmark
Tel.: (45) 44929299
Web Site: http://www.mksinst.com
Sales Range: $10-24.9 Million
Emp.: 12
Measuring & Controlling Device Mfr
N.A.I.C.S.: 334513

MKS ENI Products   (1)
100 High Power Rd, Rochester, NY 14623
Tel.: (585) 427-8300
Web Site: http://www.mksinst.com
Sales Range: $100-124.9 Million
Emp.: 350
Mfr of Radio Frequency Power Supply Products & Systems
N.A.I.C.S.: 334419

MKS German Holding GmbH   (1)
Schatzbogen 43, 81829, Munich, Germany
Tel.: (49) 894200080
Holding Company
N.A.I.C.S.: 551112

MKS Germany Holding GmbH   (1)
Schatzbogen 43, Trudering-Riem, 81829, Munich, Germany
Tel.: (49) 894200080
Sales Range: $25-49.9 Million
Emp.: 60
Investment Management Service
N.A.I.C.S.: 551112

MKS Instruments AB   (1)
Stortorget 21, 211 34, Malmo, Sweden
Tel.: (46) 406642580
Data Collection & Analysis Services

N.A.I.C.S.: 518210

MKS Instruments Deutschland GmbH (1)
Schatzbogen 43, 81829, Munich, Germany
Tel.: (49) 894200080
Web Site: http://www.mksinstruments.de
Sales Range: $10-24.9 Million
Emp.: 70
Gas Instrumentation Equipment Retailer & Servicer
N.A.I.C.S.: 334513

MKS Instruments UK Ltd. (1)
2 Cowley Way Weston Road, Crewe, CW1 6AE, Cheshire, United Kingdom
Tel.: (44) 1270253400
Sales Range: $100-124.9 Million
Emp.: 35
Gas Management Instrumentation Mfr, Retailer & Servicer
N.A.I.C.S.: 334513

MKS Ion Systems (1)
1141 Harbor Bay Pkwy Ste 201, Alameda, CA 94502
Tel.: (510) 217-0600
Web Site: https://technology-ionization.simco-ion.com
Sales Range: $25-49.9 Million
Emp.: 105
Ionization Technology Products Mfr
N.A.I.C.S.: 335999

MKS Japan, Inc. (1)
Kudan First Place 6F 4-1-28, Kudan-kita Chiyoda-ku, Tokyo, 102-0073, Japan
Tel.: (81) 335563293
Gas Instrumentation Equipment Retailer & Services
N.A.I.C.S.: 334513

MKS MSC, Inc. (1)
90 Industrial Way, Wilmington, MA 01887
Tel.: (978) 284-4000
Emp.: 700
Measuring & Controlling Device Mfr
N.A.I.C.S.: 334513
Leo Berlinghieri (CEO)

MKS Materials Delivery Products (1)
2 Tech Dr Ste 201, Andover, MA 01810 (100%)
Tel.: (978) 645-5500
Web Site: http://www.mksinst.com
Sales Range: $100-124.9 Million
Mfr of Vapor & Liquid Flow Meters & Controllers
N.A.I.C.S.: 334513

MKS Taiwan Technology Ltd. (1)
2F No 47 Lane 2 Section 2 Kuang Fu Road, Hsinchu, 30070, Taiwan
Tel.: (886) 35753040
Web Site: http://www.mksinst.com
Sales Range: $25-49.9 Million
Emp.: 50
Electric Equipment Mfr
N.A.I.C.S.: 335999

MKS Umetrics AB (1)
Tvistevagen 48, PO Box 7960, 907 36, Umea, Sweden
Tel.: (46) 90184800
Web Site: http://www.umetrics.com
Software Development Consulting Services
N.A.I.C.S.: 541512

Newport Corporation (1)
1791 Deere Ave, Irvine, CA 92606
Tel.: (949) 863-3144
Web Site: http://www.newport.com
Holding Company; Vibration Control Products, Precision Instruments, Laser Optics & Mechanical Components Mfr
N.A.I.C.S.: 551112

Subsidiary (Domestic):

ILX Lightwave Corporation (2)
31950 Frontage Rd, Bozeman, MT 59715
Tel.: (406) 586-1244
Laser Scientific & Engineering Instruments Mfr
N.A.I.C.S.: 334516

Subsidiary (Non-US):

Micro-Controle Spectra-Physics S.A.S. (2)
9 Rue Du Bois Sauvage, 91055, Evry, Ce-

dex, France
Tel.: (33) 160916868
Web Site: http://www.spectra-physics.com
Laser & Optic Instrument Mfr
N.A.I.C.S.: 334413

Subsidiary (Domestic):

New Focus (2)
3635 Peterson Way, Santa Clara, CA 95054
Tel.: (866) 683-6287
Optical Instruments & Lenses Mfr
N.A.I.C.S.: 333310

Division (Domestic):

Newport Corp. - Spectra-Physics Division (2)
1565 Barber Ln, Milpitas, CA 95035
Tel.: (408) 980-4300
Web Site: http://www.spectra-physics.com
Research & Scientific & Industrial Lasers Mfr
N.A.I.C.S.: 335999

Subsidiary (Non-US):

Beijing Newport Spectra-Physics Technologies Co., Ltd. (3)
Room 2305 Building B Tri-Tower No 66 Zhong Guan Cun East Road, Beijing, 100080, China
Tel.: (86) 1062670065
Web Site: http://www.spectra-physics.com
Laser Optics & Mechanical Components Mfr
N.A.I.C.S.: 333310

High Q Laser GmbH (3)
Feldgut 9, 6830, Rankweil, Austria
Tel.: (43) 552282646
Laser Diodes Mfr
N.A.I.C.S.: 334413
Juerg Aus-der-Au (CTO)

Newport Spectra-Physics GmbH (3)
Guerickeweg 7, 64291, Darmstadt, Germany
Tel.: (49) 61517080
Web Site: http://www.spectra-physics.com
Engineering Scientific, Optical Instruments & Communication Equipment Mfr
N.A.I.C.S.: 333310

Newport Spectra-Physics Ltd. (3)
Unit 7 Library Avenue, Harwell Oxford, Didcot, OX11 0SG, Oxfordshire, United Kingdom
Tel.: (44) 1235 432 710
Web Site: http://www.spectra-physics.com
Electro-Optic Lasers & Precision Instruments Distr
N.A.I.C.S.: 423830

Spectra-Physics, K.K. (3)
Kudan First Place 6F 4-1-28, Kudankita Chiyoda-Ku, Tokyo, 102-0073, Japan
Tel.: (81) 335562705
Web Site: https://www.spectra-physics.com
Engineering Scientific, Optical Instruments & Communication Equipments Mfr
N.A.I.C.S.: 333310

Subsidiary (Non-US):

Newport Opto-Electronics Technologies (Singapore) Pte. Ltd. (2)
1 Kaki Bukit View 04-05/07 Techview, Singapore, 415941, Singapore
Tel.: (65) 64511062
Web Site: http://www.newport.com
Precision Instruments & Mechanical Components Mfr
N.A.I.C.S.: 333310

Ophir Optronics Solutions Ltd. (2)
Science-Based Industrial Park Har Hotzvim, POB 45021, Jerusalem, 9145001, Israel
Tel.: (972) 25484444
Web Site: http://www.ophiropt.com
Infrared Optics & Laser Measurement Equipment Mfr
N.A.I.C.S.: 334510

Subsidiary (Non-US):

Ophir Japan Ltd. (3)
Kudan First Place 4-1-28, Kudan-Kita Chiyoda-ku, Tokyo, 102-0073, Japan
Tel.: (81) 335562781

Web Site: https://www.ophiropt.com
Laser Device Mfr
N.A.I.C.S.: 334510
Susumu Kitashiro (Pres)

Subsidiary (US):

Ophir Optics, LLC (3)
3050 N 300 W N, Logan, UT 84341
Tel.: (435) 753-3729
Web Site: http://www.ophiropt.com
Optical Instrument Mfr
N.A.I.C.S.: 333310

Subsidiary (Non-US):

Ophir Optronics GmbH (3)
Guerickeweg 7, 64291, Darmstadt, Germany
Tel.: (49) 61517080
Web Site: http://www.ophiropt.de
Ophthalmic Instruments Mfr
N.A.I.C.S.: 333310

Subsidiary (Domestic):

Ophir Optronics Solutions Ltd. (3)
Science-based industrial Park Har Hotzvim, PO Box 45021, Jerusalem, 9145001, Israel
Tel.: (972) 2 548 4444
Web Site: https://www.ophiropt.com
Laser Optics & Mechanical Components Mfr
N.A.I.C.S.: 333310

Subsidiary (US):

Ophir-Spiricon, LLC (3)
Ophir USA Calibration Team 3050 N 300 W N, Logan, UT 84341
Tel.: (435) 753-3729
Web Site: http://www.ophiropt.com
Laser Calibration Devices Mfr
N.A.I.C.S.: 334510

Subsidiary (Non-US):

Ophir Spiricon Europe GmbH (4)
Guerickeweg 7, 64291, Darmstadt, Germany
Tel.: (49) 80067447678
Web Site: https://www.ophiropt.com
Laser Device Mfr
N.A.I.C.S.: 334510
Juergen Reingruber (Mng Dir)

Subsidiary (Non-US):

V-Gen Ltd. (2)
120 Yigal Alon St, Tel Aviv, 6744326, Israel
Tel.: (972) 35755756
Laser Optics & Mechanical Components Mfr
N.A.I.C.S.: 333310

Photon Control Inc. (1)
130 - 13500 Verdun Place, Richmond, V6V 1V2, BC, Canada
Tel.: (604) 900-3155
Web Site: http://www.photon-control.com
Measurement Devices Mfr
N.A.I.C.S.: 334519
D. Neil McDonnell (Chm)
Damian Towns (CFO & Corp Sec)
Eva Valencia (VP-Sls-Semiconductor)
Phil Schick (VP-Ops & Tech)

Plasmart, Inc. (1)
543 Yongsan-dong, Yuseong-gu, Daejeon, 305-500, Korea (South)
Tel.: (82) 429342545
Web Site: http://www.plasmart.com
Semiconductor Product Mfr
N.A.I.C.S.: 334413

Spectra SensorTech, Ltd. (1)
Cowley Way, Crewe, CW1 6AG, Cheshire, United Kingdom (100%)
Tel.: (44) 1270250150
Web Site: http://www.mksinst.com
Sales Range: $25-49.9 Million
Emp.: 40
Gas Analyser Mfr
N.A.I.C.S.: 213112

Umetrics, Inc. (1)
134 W Rio Robles Dr, San Jose, CA 95134
Tel.: (408) 750-2889
Software Development Services
N.A.I.C.S.: 541511

MMEX RESOURCES CORPORATION

3600 W Dickinson, Fort Stockton, TX 79735 NV
Web Site:
https://www.mmexresources.com
Year Founded: 2005
MMEX—(OTCIQ)
Assets: $1,045,307
Liabilities: $4,859,061
Net Worth: ($3,813,754)
Earnings: ($2,464,533)
Fiscal Year-end: 04/30/24
Coal Mining Services
N.A.I.C.S.: 212115
Jack W. Hanks (Chm, Pres, CEO & CFO)

MN8 ENERGY, INC.
1155 Avenue of the Americas 27th Fl, New York, NY 10282
Tel.: (332) 245-4052 DE
Web Site:
https://www.mn8energy.com
Year Founded: 2022
MNX—(NYSE)
Renewable Energy Services
N.A.I.C.S.: 221210
Jon Yoder (Pres & CEO)
David Callen (CFO)
David Fernandez (COO)
Jordan Meer (Chief Strategy & Investment Officer)
Patrick McAlpine (Chief Admin Officer)

MNB HOLDINGS CORPORATION
3060 16th St, San Francisco, CA 94103
Tel.: (415) 826-3627 CA
Year Founded: 1982
MNBO—(OTCQB)
Rev.: $12,424,345
Assets: $201,907,131
Liabilities: $173,687,705
Net Worth: $28,219,426
Earnings: $662,131
Emp.: 36
Fiscal Year-end: 12/31/23
Banking Holding Company
N.A.I.C.S.: 551111
Ray Skinner (CEO)
Ming Chow (Pres & CFO)
Matthew Anderson (Exec VP & Head)
Michael Green (Chief Credit Officer & Exec VP)
Joanne Loughlin (Chm)

MOBILE INFRASTRUCTURE CORPORATION
6060 Ctr Dr Fl 10, Los Angeles, CA 90045
Tel.: (310) 853-8878 MD
Web Site: http://www.mobileit.com
BEEP—(NYSEAMEX)
Rev.: $2,936,654
Assets: $278,674,388
Liabilities: $283,285,813
Net Worth: ($4,611,425)
Earnings: $274,559
Emp.: 2
Fiscal Year-end: 12/31/22
Real Estate Services
N.A.I.C.S.: 523999

Subsidiaries:

Mobile Infrastructure Corporation (1)
30 W 4th St, Cincinnati, OH 45202
Tel.: (513) 834-5110
Web Site: https://www.mobileit.com
Rev.: $29,101,000
Assets: $436,113,000
Liabilities: $249,105,000
Net Worth: $187,008,000
Earnings: ($8,119,000)
Emp.: 14
Fiscal Year-end: 12/31/2022
Real Estate Investment Trust

Mobile Infrastructure Corporation—(Continued)

N.A.I.C.S.: 525990
Bill Burns (VP)
Grace Kaplan (Dir)
Leanne Stamper (Controller)
Rob Tracy (VP)
Stephanie Hogue (Pres, CFO, Treas & Sec-Corporate)
Manuel Chavez III (Chm & CEO)

MOBILE LADS CORP.

2616 Willow Wren Dr, Las Vegas, NV 89084
Tel.: (905) 829-5000
Year Founded: 2013
MOBO—(OTCEM)
Mobile Accessory Distr
N.A.I.C.S.: 423690
Michael Anthony Paul (Pres & CEO)

MOBILE MATCHMAKING, INC.

2880 Stevens Creek Blvd Ste 101, San Jose, CA 95128
Tel.: (408) 884-2021
MLOV—(OTCIQ)
Business Consulting Services
N.A.I.C.S.: 541611
Robert A. Rositano (CEO)

MOBILESMITH, INC.

5400 Trinity Rd Ste 208, Raleigh, NC 27607   DE
Web Site:
    http://www.mobilesmith.com
MOST—(OTCIQ)
Rev.: $1,572,884
Assets: $1,048,904
Liabilities: $6,154,795
Net Worth: ($5,105,891)
Earnings: ($34,474,576)
Emp.: 24
Fiscal Year-end: 12/31/21
Mobile Application Development Software
N.A.I.C.S.: 513210
Gleb Mikhailov (Interim CEO & CFO)
Robert L. Smith (Chm)

MOBIQUITY TECHNOLOGIES, INC.

35 Torrington Ln, Shoreham, NY 11786
Tel.: (516) 246-9422   NY
Web Site:
    https://www.mobiquitytechnologies.com
Year Founded: 1998
MOBQ—(NASDAQ)
Rev.: $4,167,272
Assets: $2,635,575
Liabilities: $2,646,405
Net Worth: ($10,830)
Earnings: ($8,062,328)
Emp.: 14
Fiscal Year-end: 12/31/22
Promotional Marketing & Distribution Services
N.A.I.C.S.: 541890
L. Julia (Founder, Pres, CEO & Treas)
Don Walker Barrett (Chief Ops & Strategy Officer)
Sean J. McDonnell (CFO)
Paul Bauersfeld (CTO)
Sean Trepeta (Co-Founder, Pres & Pres-Mobiquity Networks)

Subsidiaries:

Mobiquity Networks, Inc.   (1)
35 Torrington Ln, Shoreham, NY 11786
Tel.: (516) 246-9422
Web Site:
    https://www.mobiquitynetworks.com
Communication Network Services
N.A.I.C.S.: 541890

MOBIVITY HOLDINGS CORP.

3133 W Frye Rd Ste 215, Chandler, AZ 85226   NV
Web Site: https://www.mobivity.com
Year Founded: 2008
MFON—(OTCQB)
Rev.: $7,533,912
Assets: $3,017,525
Liabilities: $11,822,434
Net Worth: ($8,804,909)
Earnings: ($10,061,122)
Emp.: 38
Fiscal Year-end: 12/31/22
Mobile Applications
N.A.I.C.S.: 513210
Thomas Bruce Akin (Chm)
Jeff Griffith (Exec VP-Product & Dev)
Kim Carlson (COO)
Skye Fossey-Tomaske (Interim CFO & Controller)

MOBIX LABS, INC.

15420 Laguna Canyon Rd Ste 100, Irvine, CA 92618   Ky
Web Site: https://mobixlabs.com
Year Founded: 2021
MOBX—(NASDAQ)
Rev.: $483,935
Assets: $10,011,197
Liabilities: $12,156,203
Net Worth: ($2,145,006)
Earnings: ($776,129)
Emp.: 2
Fiscal Year-end: 12/31/22
Investment Services
N.A.I.C.S.: 523999
Andre-Jacques Auberton-Herve (Chm)
Michael Lee (CFO)

Subsidiaries:

Mobix Labs, Inc.   (1)
15420 Laguna Canyon Rd Ste 100, Irvine, CA 92618
Tel.: (949) 808-8888
Web Site: http://www.mobixlabs.com
Fabless Semiconductor Company
N.A.I.C.S.: 334413
Fabian Battaglia (CEO)
Keyvan Samini (CFO & Chief Corp Dev Officer)

Subsidiary (Domestic):

Cosemi Technologies Inc.   (2)
1370 Reynolds Ave Ste 100, Irvine, CA 92614
Tel.: (949) 623-9816
Web Site: http://www.cosemi.com
Global Fabless Optical Component Solutions
N.A.I.C.S.: 333999
N.X. Nguyen (CEO)

MODEL N, INC.

777 Mariners Island Blvd Ste 300, San Mateo, CA 94404
Tel.: (650) 610-4600   DE
Web Site: https://www.modeln.com
Year Founded: 1999
MODN—(NYSE)
Rev.: $249,463,000
Assets: $500,095,000
Liabilities: $384,632,000
Net Worth: $115,463,000
Earnings: ($33,922,000)
Emp.: 1,089
Fiscal Year-end: 09/30/23
Life Science & Technology Revenue Management Solutions
N.A.I.C.S.: 513210
Mark Albert Anderson (Chief Svcs Officer)
Jason Blessing (CEO)
Rehmann Rayani (Chief Strategy & Mktg Officer)
Chris Lyon (Chief Revenue Officer)
Suresh Kannan (Chief Product Officer)

Laura Selig (Chief People Officer & Sr VP)
John Ederer (CFO)

Subsidiaries:

Model N India Software Private Limited   (1)
Block-3 Office-1 8th Fl DLF Cyber City Plot No 129-132, APHB Colony Gachibowli, Hyderabad, 500019, Andhra Pradesh, India
Tel.: (91) 4045465555
Software Development Services
N.A.I.C.S.: 541511

Model N UK Limited   (1)
3000 Hillswood Drive Hillswood Business Park, Chertsey, KT16 0RS, Surrey, United Kingdom
Tel.: (44) 225480904
Software Development Services
N.A.I.C.S.: 541511

MODERN MEDIA ACQUISITION CORP.

3414 Peachtree Rd Ste 480, Atlanta, GA 30326
Tel.: (404) 443-1182   DE
Year Founded: 2014
MMDMU—(NASDAQ)
Rev.: $3,881,672
Assets: $152,577,706
Liabilities: $147,577,702
Net Worth: $5,000,004
Earnings: $648,100
Emp.: 3
Fiscal Year-end: 03/31/19
Business Management Services
N.A.I.C.S.: 541611
William Drewry (CFO)
Adam Kagan (Gen Counsel & Asst Sec)
Lewis W. Dickey Jr. (Chm, Pres & CEO)

MODERNA, INC.

200 Technology Sq, Cambridge, MA 02139
Tel.: (617) 714-6500   DE
Web Site:
    https://www.modernatx.com
Year Founded: 2010
MRNA—(NASDAQ)
Rev.: $6,848,000,000
Assets: $18,426,000,000
Liabilities: $4,572,000,000
Net Worth: $13,854,000,000
Earnings: ($4,714,000,000)
Emp.: 5,600
Fiscal Year-end: 12/31/23
Biotechnology Research & Development Services
N.A.I.C.S.: 541714
Noubar B. Afeyan (Founder)
Stephane A. Bancel (CEO)
Juan Andres (Chief Technical Ops & Quality Officer & Pres-Strategic Partnerships & Enterprise Expansion)
Shannon Thyme Klinger (Chief Legal Officer & Sec)
James M. Mock (CFO)
Marcello Damiani (Chief Digital & Operational Excellence Officer)
Stephen Hoge (Pres)
Lavina Talukdar (Sr VP & Head-IR)
Kate Cronin (Chief Brand Officer)
Jerh Collins (Chief Technical Ops & Quality Officer)
Brad Miller (CIO)

Subsidiaries:

Moderna France   (1)
Chasnais ZI Paul Cretegny Street, 85407, Lucon, Cedex, France
Tel.: (33) 251285128
Web Site: https://www.moderna.fr
Stainless Steel Kitchen Sink Mfr
N.A.I.C.S.: 332215

Moderna Germany GmbH   (1)

Rosenheimer Str 143c c/o Design Offices Atlas, 81671, Munich, Germany
Tel.: (49) 89262036030
Web Site: https://www.modernatx.com
Pharmaceutical & Medicine Mfr
N.A.I.C.S.: 325414

Moderna Italy S.r.l.   (1)
Via Fornace 1 Casazza, 24060, Bergamo, Italy
Tel.: (39) 0284980096
Web Site: https://modernasrl.it
Emp.: 35
Pharmaceutical & Medicine Mfr
N.A.I.C.S.: 325414

MODINE MANUFACTURING COMPANY

1500 De Koven Ave, Racine, WI 53403-2552
Tel.: (262) 636-1200   WI
Web Site: https://www.modine.com
Year Founded: 1916
MOD—(NYSE)
Rev.: $2,050,100,000
Assets: $1,427,000,000
Liabilities: $968,900,000
Net Worth: $458,100,000
Earnings: $85,200,000
Emp.: 11,100
Fiscal Year-end: 03/31/22
Other Motor Vehicle Parts Manufacturing
N.A.I.C.S.: 336390
Erin J. Roth (Gen Counsel, Sec & VP)
Marsha C. Williams (Chm)
Michael B. Lucareli (CFO & Exec VP)
Kathleen T. Powers (Treas & VP)
Mark D. Hudson (VP & Controller)
Brian J. Agen (VP-HR)
James R. Moise (VP-Supply Chain-Global)
Neil D. Brinker (Pres & CEO)
Jonathan Schlemmer (Gen Mgr-Heating)
Eric McGinnis (VP-Building HVAC)
Adrian I. Peace (VP-Comml & Indus Solutions)

Subsidiaries:

Airedale Group Limited   (1)
Leeds Road Rawdon, Leeds, LS19 6JY, West Yorkshire, United Kingdom
Tel.: (44) 1132391000
Web Site: http://www.airedale.com
Sales Range: $125-149.9 Million
Emp.: 550
Air Conditioning Product Mfr
N.A.I.C.S.: 333415

Subsidiary (Non-US):

Airedale Air Conditioning S.A. Pty Ltd   (2)
DC Mech Pty Ltd 154 Schooner Avenue, Honeydew, Johannesburg, 2040, South Africa
Tel.: (27) 795137051
Web Site: http://www.aiac.co.za
Sales Range: $25-49.9 Million
Emp.: 29
Designs & Manufactures Air Conditioning Products
N.A.I.C.S.: 333415

Subsidiary (US):

Airedale North America, Inc.   (2)
Bldg HVAC Modine Manufacturing Company 1500 DeKoven Ave, Racine, WI 53403-2552
Tel.: (262) 636-1244
Web Site: http://www.airedaleusa.com
Sales Range: $125-149.9 Million
Designs & Manufactures Air Conditioning Products
N.A.I.C.S.: 333415
Tom Burke (Pres)

Subsidiary (Domestic):

Airedale Sheet Metal Limited (2)
Leeds Road, Rawdon, Leeds, LS19 6JY, United Kingdom
Tel.: (44) 1132391000
Web Site: http://www.airedale.com
Sales Range: $100-124.9 Million
Emp.: 550
Structural Metalwork
N.A.I.C.S.: 332322

Barkell Limited (1)
Unit 22 No 1 Industrial Estate, Consett, DH8 6SZ, Durham, United Kingdom
Tel.: (44) 1207590575
Web Site: http://www.barkell.co.uk
Industrial Equipment Mfr
N.A.I.C.S.: 333415

Modine CIS Italy Srl (1)
Via Giulio Locatelli 22, Pocenia, 33050, Udine, Italy
Tel.: (39) 0432772001
Heat Transfer Component Distr
N.A.I.C.S.: 423830

Subsidiary (Non-US):

Modine Soderkoping AB (2)
Industrigatan 2, 61481, Soderkoping, Sweden
Tel.: (46) 12119100
Heat Transfer Component Distr
N.A.I.C.S.: 423830
Jimmy Lonnqvist (Mgr-IT)

Modine Holding GmbH (1)
Arthur B Modine Strasse 1, D 70794, Filderstadt, Germany
Tel.: (49) 711 70940
Web Site: http://www.modine.com
Sales Range: $50-74.9 Million
Emp.: 100
Holding Company; Refrigeration & Heating Equipment Manufacturing
N.A.I.C.S.: 551112

Subsidiary (Domestic):

Modine Automobiltechnik GmbH (2)
Daimlerstrasse 3, Pliezhausen, 72124, Germany
Tel.: (49) 712781050
Sales Range: $75-99.9 Million
Automotive Radiators, Oil Coolers & Charge Air Coolers Mfr
N.A.I.C.S.: 336390

Modine Europe GmbH (2)
Arthur-B-Modine Strasse 1, 70794, Filderstadt, Germany
Tel.: (49) 71170940
Sales Range: $25-49.9 Million
Emp.: 60
Motor Vehicle Parts Mfr
N.A.I.C.S.: 336390
Holger Schwab (VP)

Subsidiary (Non-US):

Modine Hungaria Kft. (2)
Gabor Denes uit 2, 3200, Gyongyos, Hungary
Tel.: (36) 37510100
Web Site: http://www.modine.com
Sales Range: $125-149.9 Million
Refrigeration Equipment & Supplies Mfr
N.A.I.C.S.: 336390

Subsidiary (Domestic):

Modine Neuenkirchen GmbH (2)
Burgsteinfurter Damm 92-98, 48485, Neuenkirchen, Germany
Tel.: (49) 5973200
Web Site: http://www.modine.com
Sales Range: $50-74.9 Million
Automotive & Truck EGR Coolers Mfr
N.A.I.C.S.: 336390
Klaus Feldmann (Mng Dir)

Modine Pliezhausen GmbH (2)
Daimlerstrasse 3, 72124, Pliezhausen, Germany
Tel.: (49) 712781050
Heat Transfer Products Designs & Mfr
N.A.I.C.S.: 333414

Subsidiary (Non-US):

Modine Pontevico S.r.l. (2)

Viale Europa 1, 25026, Pontevico, Italy
Tel.: (39) 0309931311
Sales Range: $50-74.9 Million
Motor Vehicle Parts Mfr
N.A.I.C.S.: 336340
Mannschatz Hermann (Mng Dir)

Modine Uden B.V. (2)
Kuiperstraat 2, 5405 BB, Uden, Netherlands
Tel.: (31) 413242424
Web Site: http://www.modine.nl
Sales Range: $100-124.9 Million
Emp.: 200
Refrigeration & Heating Equipment Mfr
N.A.I.C.S.: 333415

Modine Jacksonville Inc. (1)
224 Talley Nichols Dr, Jacksonville, TX 75766
Tel.: (903) 589-0009
Heat Transfer Component Mfr
N.A.I.C.S.: 333415

Modine, Inc. (1)
1500 De Koven Ave, Racine, WI 53403-2552
Tel.: (262) 636-1200
Web Site: https://www.modine.com
Heat Transfer Equipment, Sheet Metal Radiators & Replacement Radiator Cores Mfr
N.A.I.C.S.: 333415

Subsidiary (Non-US):

Modine Transferencia de Calor, S.A. de C.V. (2)
Avenida de Los Dos Laredos Parque Industrial, Los Dos Laredos, Nuevo Laredo, 88190, Mexico (99.6%)
Tel.: (52) 956 791 0475
Web Site: http://www.modine.com
Radiators & Cooling Modules, Battery Cooling & HeatingParallel Flow Condensers Mfr
N.A.I.C.S.: 423120

Nikkei Heat Exchanger Co., Ltd (1)
161 Kambara, Shimizu-ku, Shizuoka, 421-3297, Japan
Tel.: (81) 543852164
Web Site: http://group.nikkeikin.co.jp
Aluminum Heat Exchange Services
N.A.I.C.S.: 331315

Radiadores Visconde S/A (1)
Av Narain Singh 262, Guarulhos, 07250-000, SP, Brazil
Tel.: (55) 1124875002
Web Site: https://www.radiadoresvisconde.com.br
Sales Range: $300-349.9 Million
Motor Vehicle Parts Mfr
N.A.I.C.S.: 336390

MODIV INDUSTRIAL, INC.

75 McCabe Dr Ste 19626, Reno, NV 89511   MD
Web Site: https://www.modiv.com
Year Founded: 2015
MDV—(NYSE)
Rev.: $46,174,267
Assets: $456,026,046
Liabilities: $214,992,086
Net Worth: $241,033,960
Earnings: ($6,976,035)
Emp.: 12
Fiscal Year-end: 12/31/22
Offices of Real Estate Agents & Brokers
N.A.I.C.S.: 531210
Raymond E. Wirta (Chm)
Aaron S. Halfacre (Pres & CEO)
Raymond J. Pacini (CFO, Treas, Sec & Exec VP)
Sandra G. Sciutto (Chief Acctg Officer & Sr VP)
William Broms (Chief Investment Officer)
John Raney (Chief Legal Officer & Gen Counsel)
Jennifer Barber (COO)
Reginald Salanga (VP-Fin Reporting)
Jason Miller (VP-REIT Controller)
Cecilia Griffith (VP)

MODIVCARE, INC.

6900 Layton Ave Ste 1200, Denver, CO 80237
Tel.: (303) 728-7030   DE
Web Site:
https://www.modivcare.com
Year Founded: 1996
MODV—(NASDAQ)
Rev.: $2,504,393,000
Assets: $1,944,272,000
Liabilities: $1,589,716,000
Net Worth: $354,556,000
Earnings: ($31,806,000)
Emp.: 20,000
Fiscal Year-end: 12/31/22
Other Social Advocacy Organizations
N.A.I.C.S.: 813319
Barbara K. Gutierrez (CFO)
L. Heath Sampson (Pres & CEO)
Jody Kepler (Chief Compliance Officer)
Kate Zerone (Dir-Ombudsman & Comm)
Kevin Ellich (VP & Head-IR)
Rebecca Orcutt (Chief Acctg Officer)
Matt Snyder (Sr VP)
Seth Ravine (Sr VP)
Christopher Scott Shackelton (Chm)

Subsidiaries:

CCHN Group Holdings, Inc. (1)
9201 E Mountain View Ste 220, Scottsdale, AZ 85258 (46.8%)
Web Site: http://www.matrixforme.com
Holding Company; In-Home Health Assessment & Care Management Services
N.A.I.C.S.: 551112
Walter W. Cooper (CEO)

Subsidiary (Domestic):

Community Care Health Network, Inc. (2)
9201 E Mountain View Ste 220, Scottsdale, AZ 85258
Web Site:
https://www.matrixmedicalnetwork.com
Sales Range: $50-74.9 Million
Emp.: 650
In-Home Health Assessment & Care Management Services
N.A.I.C.S.: 621610
Catherine Tabaka (CEO)
Joseph Buchanan (Sr VP)
Sophia Kim (Chief Comml Officer)
Kevin O'Kelly-Lynch (CFO)
Thor Treadwell (COO)

Subsidiary (Domestic):

Matrix Medical Network of Arizona, L.L.C. (3)
9201 E Mountain View Ste 220, Scottsdale, AZ 85258
Tel.: (480) 862-1887
Web Site: http://www.matrixforme.com
In-Home Health Assessment & Care Management Services
N.A.I.C.S.: 621610
Brian Morfitt (Chm)

Camelot Community Care, Inc. (1)
4910-D Creekside Dr, Clearwater, FL 33760
Tel.: (727) 593-0003
Web Site:
https://www.camelotcommunitycare.org
Sales Range: $10-24.9 Million
Emp.: 70
Behavioral Health Services
N.A.I.C.S.: 621330
Jenny Mannion (Sec)
Ron Schultz (Chm)
Tammy Davis (Vice Chm)
Michael DiBrizzi (Pres & CEO)
Rebecca Payne (Chief Dev Officer)
Sandra Bowman (Mgr-Risk)
Karen Battle (Dir-HR)
Brenda Oakes (Dir-Programs)
Kimberly Perez (Treas)
Mark Connolly (Chief Legal Officer)

Dockside Services, Inc (1)
800 Post St, Saint Joseph, MI 49085
Tel.: (269) 983-0801
Web Site: http://www.provcorp.com

Sales Range: $50-74.9 Million
Behavioral Health Services
N.A.I.C.S.: 621330

Independence Healthcare Corporation (1)
146 W Boylston Dr Ste 203, Worcester, MA 01606
Tel.: (508) 767-1776
Web Site:
https://www.independencehealthcare.org
Health Care Srvices
N.A.I.C.S.: 622110

Ingeus AB (1)
Drottninggatan 68 4 tr, 111 21, Stockholm, Sweden
Tel.: (46) 841032800
Web Site: http://www.ingeus.se
Human Resource Consulting Services
N.A.I.C.S.: 541612

Ingeus AG (1)
Thurgauerstrasse 39, 8050, Zurich, Switzerland
Tel.: (41) 432996700
Web Site: https://www.ingeus.ch
Human Resource Consulting Services
N.A.I.C.S.: 541612
Michelle Lahert (CFO)
Anthony Allcock (CIO)

Ingeus GmBH (1)
Bahnhofstrasse 11 b, 90402, Nuremberg, Germany
Tel.: (49) 91121667115
Web Site: https://www.ingeus.de
Human Resource Consulting Services
N.A.I.C.S.: 541612

Ingeus LLC (1)
Al Imam Saud Ibn Abdul Aziz Rd, PO Box 9361, AlNakheel District, Riyadh, 11413, Saudi Arabia
Tel.: (966) 114744465
Human Resource Consulting Services
N.A.I.C.S.: 541612

Ingeus Sp z.o.o. (1)
ul Krolewska 65, 30-081, Krakow, Poland
Tel.: (48) 126222070
Web Site: http://www.ingeus.pl
Human Resource Consulting Services
N.A.I.C.S.: 541612

Ingeus UK Limited (1)
Second floor 66-68 East Smithfield Royal Pharmaceutical Building, London, E1W 1AW, United Kingdom
Tel.: (44) 2072653000
Web Site: https://www.ingeus.co.uk
Human Resource Consulting Services
N.A.I.C.S.: 541612
Lindsay Mann (Dir-Strategy & Bus Dev-Grp)
Alex Hayes (Dir-Health)
Fiona Monahan (CEO)
Juliet Mortiss (Dir-People & Culture)
Simon Smithson (Dir-Youth Svcs)

LogistiCare Solutions LLC (1)
1275 Peachtree St NE 6th Fl, Atlanta, GA 30309
Tel.: (404) 888-5800
Web Site: https://www.modivcare.com
Sales Range: $300-349.9 Million
Emp.: 550
Non-Emergency Medicaid Transportation Solutions & Services
N.A.I.C.S.: 485991
Kenneth W. Wilson (COO)
Jonathan Bush (VP & Deputy Gen Counsel)
Jody Kepler (Chief Compliance Officer)
Chris Echols (Exec VP-Contracts & Pricing)

Subsidiary (Domestic):

National MedTrans, LLC (2)
PO Box 740815, Atlanta, GA 30374-0815
Tel.: (516) 858-4110
Web Site: http://www.nationalmedtrans.com
Medical Transportation Services
N.A.I.C.S.: 621910
Andrew Winakor (CEO)

Multicultural Home Care, Inc. (1)
330 Lynnway Lynn, Lynn, MA 01901
Tel.: (781) 593-7174
Web Site: https://multiculturalhomecare.com
Health Care Srvices
N.A.I.C.S.: 622110

ModivCare, Inc.—(Continued)

Pinnacle Acquisitions LLC (1)
18 Tehama St, Brooklyn, NY 11218
Tel.: (480) 285-9079
Emp.: 4
Securities Brokerage Services
N.A.I.C.S.: 523150
Raymond Shanahan (Dir-Acq)

Rio Grande Management Company, LLC (1)
425 S Telshor Blvd Ste C201, Las Cruces, NM 88011-8212
Tel.: (575) 532-2500
Investment Management Service
N.A.I.C.S.: 523940

Subsidiary (Domestic):

Rio Grande Behavioral Health Services, Inc (2)
1720 S Telshor Blvd, Las Cruces, NM 88011
Tel.: (575) 532-2500
Behavioral Health Services
N.A.I.C.S.: 621330
Roque Garcia (CEO)

Ross Innovative Employment Solutions Corp. (1)
7800 W Brown Deer Rd Ste 200, Milwaukee, WI 53223
Tel.: (414) 760-6060
Web Site: https://www.rossworks.com
Job Counseling & Training Services
N.A.I.C.S.: 624310

The Derbyshire Leicestershire Nottinghamshire & Rutland Community Rehabilitation Company Limited (1)
Second Floor 66-68 East Smithfield Royal Pharmaceutical Building, London, E1W 1AW, United Kingdom
Tel.: (44) 1162516008
Web Site: http://www.dlnrcrc.co.uk
Psychiatric & Rehabilitation Services
N.A.I.C.S.: 622210
Jack Sawyer (Chm)

The Staffordshire and West Midlands Community Rehabilitation Company Limited (1)
Second Floor 66-68 East Smithfield Royal Pharmaceutical Building, London, E1W 1AW, United Kingdom
Tel.: (44) 1212735500
Web Site: http://www.swmcrc.co.uk
Emp.: 660
Psychiatric & Rehabilitation Services
N.A.I.C.S.: 622210

WCG International Consultants Ltd. (1)
5 - 915 Fort St, Victoria, V8V 3K3, BC, Canada
Tel.: (250) 389-0699
Web Site: http://www.wcgservices.com
Sales Range: $25-49.9 Million
Emp.: 37
Employment Placement Agency Services
N.A.I.C.S.: 561311
Tania Bennett (CEO)
Rise Bulmer (VP-Bus Dev & Risk Mgmt)
Gillian Blair (VP)
Robin Thompson (VP)
Vanessa Corbett (COO)

MODULAR MEDICAL, INC.
10740 Thornmint Rd, San Diego, CA 92127
Tel.: (858) 800-3500   NV
Web Site: https://www.modular-medical.com
Year Founded: 1998
MODD—(NASDAQ)
Rev.: $975
Assets: $7,245,248
Liabilities: $2,169,272
Net Worth: $5,075,976
Earnings: ($13,878,936)
Emp.: 37
Fiscal Year-end: 03/31/23
Development Stage Medical Device Company
N.A.I.C.S.: 339112

Paul M. DiPerna (Founder, Chm, Pres, CFO & Treas)
James Besser (CEO)

MOELIS & COMPANY
399 Park Ave 4th Fl, New York, NY 10022
Tel.: (212) 883-3800   DE
Web Site: https://www.moelis.com
Year Founded: 2014
MC—(NYSE)
Rev.: $854,748,000
Assets: $1,179,759,000
Liabilities: $817,297,000
Net Worth: $362,462,000
Earnings: ($27,516,000)
Emp.: 1,161
Fiscal Year-end: 12/31/23
Holding Company; Investment Advisory Services
N.A.I.C.S.: 551112
Navid Mahmoodzadegan (Co-Pres & Mng Dir)
Jeffrey Raich (Co-Pres & Mng Dir)
Joseph W. Simon (Mng Dir & CFO)
Martin Houston (Chm-Global Energy Grp-Houston)
Ted Ferguson (Mng Dir)
Thane Carlston (Mng Dir & Co-Head-Recapitalization & Restructuring Grp)
Alan Aberg (Mng Dir)
Chrystalle Anstett (Mng Dir)
Georgi Balinov (Mng Dir)
Amy Chen (Mng Dir)
Michael Cortese (Mng Dir)
Justin Craig (Mng Dir)
Dennis Crandall (Mng Dir)
Brad Davis (Mng Dir)
Eliot Freeston (Mng Dir)
William Goodman (Mng Dir)
Sloan Harris (Mng Dir)
Robert Jackman (Mng Dir)
Grant Kassel (Mng Dir)
John Kimm (Mng Dir)
Roger Knight (Mng Dir)
Arek Kurkciyan (Mng Dir)
Tiffany Lundquist (Mng Dir)
Jane Ma (Mng Dir)
Mike McKeever (Mng Dir)
Kate Pilcher Ciafone (Co-Founder & COO)
Perry Hall (Mng Dir)
Jay Finney (Mng Dir)
John Colella (Mng Dir)
Ashish Contractor (Mng Dir)
Francesco Del Vecchio (Mng Dir)
Jared J. Dermont (Mng Dir)
Michael DiYanni (Mng Dir & Head-Risk Advisory)
David P. Faris (Mng Dir)
Ben Axelrod (Mng Dir)
Azad Badakhsh (Mng Dir)
Andrew Haber (Mng Dir)
Zul Jamal (Mng Dir)
Adam Keil (Mng Dir)
Barak Klein (Mng Dir)
Lawrence Kwon (Mng Dir)
Mark Laoun (Mng Dir)
Vincent Lima (Mng Dir)
Glenn Muscosky (Mng Dir)
William Nook (Mng Dir)
Dominick Petrosino (Mng Dir)
Anthony Rokovich (Mng Dir)
Alexander S. Rubin (Mng Dir)
Greg Starkins (Mng Dir)
Adam Steinberg (Mng Dir)
Nik Dampier (Mng Dir & Head-Global Bus Tech)
Steven Halperin (Mng Dir & Head-Equity Public Markets)
Gina Jowett (Mng Dir & Head-Human Capital Mgmt)
Melissa Mariaschin (Mng Dir & Head-Distribution & Capital Markets)
Bruno Brandao (Mng Dir)

Yatin Choksey (Mng Dir & Chief Info Security Officer)
Ankit Dalal (Mng Dir)
Jugjeev Duggal (Mng Dir)
Matt Hughes (Mng Dir)
Matt Janukowicz (Mng Dir)
Rob Mendelson (Mng Dir)
Rachel Murray (Mng Dir)
Subash Parameswaran (Mng Dir)
Douglas Pierson (Mng Dir)
Margot Shoshan (Mng Dir & Head-Marketing & Communications)
Brian Tichenor (Mng Dir)
Carl Torrillo (Mng Dir)
Osamu Watanabe (Gen Counsel)
Ryan Bell (Mng Dir)
Martin Houston (Chm-Global Energy Grp-Houston)
Elizabeth A. Crain (Co-Founder)
Kenneth D. Moelis (Founder, Chm & CEO)
Eric Cantor (Vice Chm, Mng Dir & Washington)

Subsidiaries:

Acure Asset Management Ltd (1)
140 St Georges Terrace, Perth, 6000, WA, Australia
Tel.: (61) 893225448
Web Site: https://acuream.com.au
Asset Management Services
N.A.I.C.S.: 531390
Angelo Del Borrello (Mng Dir)
Marco Marramiero (Gen Mgr)
Aaron Wong (CFO)
Michael Walden (Mgr-Asset)
Peter Isaksson (Sr Mgr-Asset-Distr,Acquisitions)

Moelis & Company Asia Limited (1)
Suite 1203-10 Two Pacific Place 88 Queensway, Admiralty, Hong Kong, China (Hong Kong)
Tel.: (852) 31801000
Investment Advisory Services
N.A.I.C.S.: 523940

Moelis & Company Consulting (Beijing) Company Limited (1)
China World Tower B Unit 5212 No 1 Jian Guo Men Wai Avenue, Chao Yang District, Beijing, 100004, China
Tel.: (86) 1056501700
Investment Advisory Services
N.A.I.C.S.: 523940

Moelis & Company Europe Limited (1)
8th Floor Office TaunusTurm Neue Mainzer Strasse 33- 37 Taunustor 1- 3, 60310, Frankfurt am Main, 60310, Germany
Tel.: (49) 69667787900
Investment Advisory Services
N.A.I.C.S.: 523940

Moelis & Company France SAS (1)
119-121 avenue des Champs-Elysees, Paris, 75008, France
Tel.: (33) 183790610
Web Site: http://www.moelis.com
Investment Advisory Services
N.A.I.C.S.: 523940

Moelis & Company Germany GmbH (1)
Neue Mainzer Strasse 52-58, 60311, Frankfurt, Germany
Tel.: (49) 69667787913
Investment Banking Services
N.A.I.C.S.: 523150
Stefan Gockeln (Exec Dir)

Moelis & Company India Private Limited (1)
1501-A Tower 1 One World Centre Senapati Bapat Marg, Elphinstone Road West, Mumbai, 400 013, India
Tel.: (91) 2261741300
Investment Advisory Services
N.A.I.C.S.: 523940

Moelis & Company Netherlands BV (1)
Zuidplein 158 World Trade Center Tower H - 19th Floor, 1077 XV, Amsterdam, Netherlands

Tel.: (31) 208088120
Investment Banking Services
N.A.I.C.S.: 523150

Moelis & Company UK LLP (1)
121 Avenue Des Champs-Elysees, 75008, Paris, 75008, France
Tel.: (33) 183790610
Financial Advisory Services
N.A.I.C.S.: 523940

Moelis & Company UK LLP (1)
Dubai International Financial Centre Gate Village 1 Level 2, PO Box 506777, Suite 202-205, Dubai, United Arab Emirates
Tel.: (971) 43045000
Financial Advisory Services
N.A.I.C.S.: 523940
Karim Wazni (VP)

Moelis & Company UK LLP (1)
Dubai International Financial Centre Gate Village 1 Level 2, PO Box 506777, Suite 203/204, Dubai, United Arab Emirates
Tel.: (971) 43045000
Financial Advisory Services
N.A.I.C.S.: 523940
Karim Wazni (VP)

Moelis & Company UK LLP (1)
121 avenue des Champs-Elysees 3rd Floor, 75008, Paris, 75008, France
Tel.: (33) 183790610
Financial Advisory Services
N.A.I.C.S.: 523940

Moelis Australia Asset Management Ltd (1)
Level 27 Governor Phillip Tower One Farrer Place, Sydney, 2000, NSW, Australia
Tel.: (61) 282885555
Web Site: http://www.moelisaustralia.com
Emp.: 70
Asset Management Services
N.A.I.C.S.: 531390
Andrew Martin (Head-Asset Mgmt)
Andrew Pridham (Vice Chm-Grp)
Paul Rathborne (Mng Dir)
Colin Richardson (Mng Dir)
Simon Scott (Mng Dir)
Hugh Thomson (Mng Dir)
Ben Wong (Mng Dir)
Chris Wyke (Co-CEO)
Jaron Yuen (Mng Dir)
Steve Bennett (Mng Dir)
Julian Biggins (Co-CEO)
Drew Bowie (Mng Dir)
John Garrett (Mng Dir)
Amelia Hill (Mng Dir)
Graham Lello (CFO)
Rebecca Ong (Gen Counsel & Sec)
Janna Robertson (COO)
Alice Tang (COO-Asset Mgmt)
Alan Reid (Mng Dir)
Enda Stankard (Mng Dir)
Susan Wang (Mng Dir)
Hayes Lee (Mng Dir)
Ross Victor (Mng Dir)
Richard Germain (Mng Dir)
John Sheffield (Mng Dir)
Matt Lane (Mng Dir)

Moelis UK LLP (1)
1st Floor Condor House 10 St Paul's Churchyard, London, EC4M 8AL, United Kingdom
Tel.: (44) 2076343500
Web Site: http://www.moelis.com
Emp.: 100
Investment Advisory Services
N.A.I.C.S.: 523940

MOGUL ENERGY INTERNATIONAL, INC.
3400 NW 74th Ave Unit 1, Miami, FL 33122
Tel.: (305) 503-2553   DE
Web Site: http://www.mogulenergy.com
Year Founded: 2005
MGUY—(OTCIQ)
Sales Range: Less than $1 Million
Emp.: 4
Oil & Gas Exploration
N.A.I.C.S.: 211120
Ronen Koubi (Pres & CEO)

Subsidiaries:

Florida Beauty Flora, Inc.　(1)
3100 NW 74th Ave, Miami, FL 33122
Tel.: (305) 503-1200
Web Site: http://www.floridabeauty.com
Transit & Ground Passenger Transportation
N.A.I.C.S.: 485999
Mike Fernandez *(Acct Exec)*

MOHAWK INDUSTRIES, INC.
160 S Industrial Blvd, Calhoun, GA
30701
Tel.: (706) 629-7721　　DE
Web Site:
　https://www.mohawkind.com
Year Founded: 1988
MHK—(NYSE)
Rev.: $11,135,115,000
Assets: $13,559,869,000
Liabilities: $5,930,733,000
Net Worth: $7,629,136,000
Earnings: ($439,516,000)
Emp.: 43,300
Fiscal Year-end: 12/31/23
Flooring Product Mfr
N.A.I.C.S.: 314110
Jeffrey S. Lorberbaum *(Chm & CEO)*
James F. Brunk *(CFO)*
Rodney David Patton *(Gen Counsel,
Sec & VP-Bus Strategy)*
Wim Messiaen *(Pres-Flooring Rest of
the World)*
William W. Harkins *(Chief Acctg Offi-
cer & Controller)*
W. Christopher Wellborn *(Pres &
COO)*

Subsidiaries:

Aladdin Manufacturing of Alabama,
LLC　(1)
202 Jacobs Ave, Bridgeport, AL 35740
Tel.: (800) 554-6637
Emp.: 190
Floor Covering Product Whslr
N.A.I.C.S.: 449121

B&M NV　(1)
Brusselsesteenweg 149b, 1785, Merchtem,
Belgium
Tel.: (32) 52343306
Web Site: http://www.b-m.be
Carpet & Rug Mill Operator
N.A.I.C.S.: 314110

Berghoef GmbH　(1)
Hardrain 3, Bischweier, 76476, Rastatt,
Germany
Tel.: (49) 7222406560
Floor Product Whslr
N.A.I.C.S.: 423850

Berghoef-Hout B.V.　(1)
Bolstoen 11, 1046 AS, Amsterdam, Nether-
lands
Tel.: (31) 205061777
Floor Product Whslr
N.A.I.C.S.: 423850

Cevotrans BV　(1)
Beneluxstraat 1, 5061 KD, Oisterwijk, Neth-
erlands
Tel.: (31) 135284551
Web Site: https://www.cevotrans.nl
N.A.I.C.S.: 485999

Dal-Tile Group, Inc　(1)
7834 C F Hawn Fwy, Dallas, TX 75217-
6544
Tel.: (214) 398-1411
Emp.: 800
Tiles Mfr
N.A.I.C.S.: 327120
Matthew Kahny *(CMO)*

Subsidiary (Domestic):

Dal-Tile Corporation　(2)
7834 C F Hawn Fwy, Dallas, TX
75217-6529　　(100%)
Tel.: (214) 398-1411
Web Site: http://www.daltile.com
Sales Range: $1-4.9 Billion
Emp.: 650
Mfr of Ceramic Wall & Floor Tile

N.A.I.C.S.: 327120

Subsidiary (Domestic):

Dal-Tile Distribution, Inc.　(3)
4801 Trademark Dr, Raleigh, NC 27610
Tel.: (919) 255-3510
Web Site: http://www.daltile.com
Emp.: 15
Tiles Mfr
N.A.I.C.S.: 327120

Dal-Tile International Inc.　(3)
7834 Hawn Freeway Ste 1704, Dallas, TX
75217
Tel.: (214) 398-1411
Web Site: http://www.daltile.com
Sales Range: $150-199.9 Million
Emp.: 600
Holding Company; Tiles Mfr & Distr
N.A.I.C.S.: 551112

Subsidiary (Non-US):

Dal-Tile Mexico S.A. de C.V.　(3)
Boulevard Diaz Ordaz Km 335, San Pedro,
66230, Garza Garcia, Nuevo Leon, Mexico
Tel.: (52) 818 124 8124
Web Site: http://www.daltile.com.mx
Sales Range: $150-199.9 Million
Emp.: 3,000
Ceramic Products Mfr
N.A.I.C.S.: 327120

Subsidiary (Domestic):

Dal-Tile Services, Inc.　(3)
160 S Industrial Blvd, Calhoun, GA 30701
Tel.: (706) 629-7721
Emp.: 7,524
Tiles Mfr
N.A.I.C.S.: 327120
Jeff Lorberbaun *(CEO)*

Subsidiary (Non-US):

Dal-Tile of Canada Inc　(3)
40 Graniteridge Rd Unit 1, Concord, L4K
5M8, ON, Canada
Tel.: (905) 738-2099
Web Site: http://locations.daltile.com
Construction Materials Mfr
N.A.I.C.S.: 423320

Feltex Carpets Ltd.　(3)
142 Kerrs Rd Wiri, Manukau, 2104, New
Zealand
Tel.: (64) 800100008
Carpet Product Mfr
N.A.I.C.S.: 314110
Kevin Potter *(Acct Mgr)*

Eliane S/A - Revestimentos
Ceramicos　(1)
Rua Maximiliano Gaidzinski 245, Cocal Do
Sul, 88845-000, Criciuma, Santa Catarina,
Brazil
Tel.: (55) 4834477777
Web Site: http://www.eliane.com
Porcelain Tile Product Mfr
N.A.I.C.S.: 327120

Emilamerica, Inc.　(1)
22701 Dulles Summit Ct, Dulles, VA 20166
Tel.: (703) 481-1150
Web Site: http://www.emilamerica.com
Floor Covering Product Whslr
N.A.I.C.S.: 449121

Emilceramica S.r.l　(1)
Via Ghiarola Nuova 29, 41042, Fiorano-
Modenese, MO, Italy
Tel.: (39) 053 683 5111
Web Site: https://www.emilgroup.it
Floor Covering Product Whslr
N.A.I.C.S.: 449121

Emilgermany GmbH　(1)
Borselstrasse 22 b, 22765, Hamburg, Ger-
many
Tel.: (49) 4052477730
Web Site: http://www.emilgroup.de
Stone Product Mfr
N.A.I.C.S.: 327991

Everel　(1)
Trebetice 102, 769 01, Holesov, Czech
Republic
Tel.: (420) 577941646
Web Site: http://www.everel.cz
Floor Covering Distr

N.A.I.C.S.: 423220

Explorer S.r.l.　(1)
Via Matteotti 16 Varese, Buguggiate, 21020,
Italy
Tel.: (39) 0332744980
Floor Covering Product Whslr
N.A.I.C.S.: 449121

Feltex Carpets Pty. Ltd.　(1)
7 Factories Road, PO Box 93, Geelong,
3220, VIC, Australia
Tel.: (61) 300130239
Web Site: http://www.feltex.com
Carpet Product Mfr
N.A.I.C.S.: 314110

Flooring Industries Ltd.　(1)
10B rue des Merovingiens, 8070, Ber-
trange, Luxembourg
Tel.: (352) 27004181
Construction Materials Merchant Whslr
N.A.I.C.S.: 423610

Flooring XL B.V.　(1)
Beneluxstraat 1, 5061 KD, Oisterwijk, Neth-
erlands
Tel.: (31) 135231313
Floor Covering Product Whslr
N.A.I.C.S.: 449121

Floorscape Limited　(1)
221A Bush Road, Albany, Auckland, 0632,
New Zealand
Tel.: (64) 9 476 0428
Web Site: https://www.floorscape.co.nz
Flooring Product Distr
N.A.I.C.S.: 423310

Godfrey Hirst (Singapore) Pte.
Ltd.　(1)
200 Jalan Sultan 10-07 Textile Centre, Sin-
gapore, 199018, Singapore
Tel.: (65) 568415529
Carpet Product Mfr & Distr
N.A.I.C.S.: 313110

Godfrey Hirst Australia Pty. Ltd.　(1)
7 Factories Road, Geelong, 3220, VIC,
Australia
Tel.: (61) 352250222
Web Site: https://www.godfreyhirst.com
Woolen Mill & Carpet Mfr
N.A.I.C.S.: 314110

Godfrey Hirst NZ Ltd.　(1)
142 Kerrs Road Wiri, Manukau, 2241, New
Zealand
Tel.: (64) 800500210
Carpet Product Mfr & Distr
N.A.I.C.S.: 313110

IVC Group Limited　(1)
Unit 5 Westside Park Raynesway, Derby,
DE21 7AZ, United Kingdom
Tel.: (44) 1332851500
Flooring Product Mfr
N.A.I.C.S.: 326199

IVC Luxembourg S.a r.l.　(1)
Route de Winseler 26, 9577, Wiltz, Luxem-
bourg
Tel.: (352) 26955211
Floor Covering Product Whslr
N.A.I.C.S.: 449121

IVC US, Inc.　(1)
101 IVC Dr, Dalton, GA 30721
Tel.: (706) 529-2600
Web Site: http://www.ivcfloors.com
Floor Covering Product Whslr
N.A.I.C.S.: 449121

KAI Group　(1)
1 Ahinora Str, Isperih, Bulgaria
Tel.: (359) 84312683
Web Site: http://www.kai.bg
Ceramic Tile Mfr
N.A.I.C.S.: 327110

KAI Mining EOOD　(1)
1 Ahinora Street, 7400, Isperih, Bulgaria
Tel.: (359) 84312577
Floor Covering Product Whslr
N.A.I.C.S.: 449121

Kerama Marazzi Ukraine OOO　(1)
Prospect Stepan Banderi 9 BC Forum Park
Plaza of 4-501, Kiev, Ukraine
Tel.: (380) 445935001
Web Site: http://www.kerama-
marazzi.com.ua

Ceramic Tile Mfr
N.A.I.C.S.: 327120

Khan Asparuh AD　(1)
1 Ahinora Street, 7400, Isperih, Bulgaria
Tel.: (359) 84312577
Floor Covering Product Whslr
N.A.I.C.S.: 449121
Lilia Kosseva *(Dir-Export)*

Koninklijke Peitsman B.V.　(1)
Boterdiep 36, 3077 AW, Rotterdam, Nether-
lands
Tel.: (31) 102921455
Web Site: http://www.peitsman.nl
Home Furnishings Products Whslr
N.A.I.C.S.: 449129

MG China Trading Ltd.　(1)
Rm 2003-04 20/Fl Tung Chiu Commercial
Centre, 193 Lockhart Road, Wanchai,
China (Hong Kong)
Tel.: (852) 25290812
Construction Materials Merchant Whslr
N.A.I.C.S.: 423610

Marazzi Group S.r.l.　(1)
Viale Regina Pacis 39, 41049, Sassuolo,
MO, Italy
Tel.: (39) 053 686 0800
Web Site: https://www.marazzi.it
Sales Range: $1-4.9 Billion
Emp.: 6,000
Ceramic Floor & Wall Tile Mfr & Distr
N.A.I.C.S.: 327120

Subsidiary (US):

American Marazzi Tile, Inc.　(2)
359 Clay Rd E Sunnyvale, Dallas, TX
75182
Tel.: (972) 232-3801
Web Site: http://www.marazziusa.com
Sales Range: $200-249.9 Million
Emp.: 650
Ceramic Floor & Wall Tile Mfr & Distr
N.A.I.C.S.: 327120
Hector Narvaez *(Exec VP-Sls & Mktg)*

Subsidiary (Domestic):

Marazzi Distribution, Inc.　(3)
359 Clay Rd, Sunnyvale, TX 75182
Tel.: (702) 248-3040
Construction Materials Merchant Whslr
N.A.I.C.S.: 423610

Monarch Ceramic Tiles　(3)
834 Rickwood Rd, Florence, AL 35630-
1368
Tel.: (256) 764-6181
Emp.: 200
Ceramic Wall & Floor Tiles Mfr & Distr
N.A.I.C.S.: 327120

Subsidiary (Non-US):

Kerama Marazzi　(2)
15/4 Leningradsky prospect Business cen-
ter Bolshevik building 4 and 6, Moscow,
Russia
Tel.: (7) 4957950045
Web Site: https://www.kerama-marazzi.com
Ceramic Tile Mfr & Distr
N.A.I.C.S.: 327120

Marazzi Deutschland G.m.b.H.　(2)
Lindwurmstr 114, 80337, Munich, Germany
Tel.: (49) 892109900
Construction Materials Merchant Whslr
N.A.I.C.S.: 423610

Marazzi Group F.Z.E.　(2)
Dafza 6W Building 15 Al Quds Street, 3
Floor Block A Office 327 Dubai International
Airport, Dubai, United Arab Emirates
Tel.: (971) 46091900
Construction Materials Merchant Whslr
N.A.I.C.S.: 423610

Marazzi Group Trading (Shanghai)
Co. Ltd.　(2)
Units 802-809 8F Tower A The Place No
100 Zunyi Road, Changning District, Shang-
hai, 200051, China
Tel.: (86) 2180267068
Web Site: http://www.marazzigroup.com
Construction Materials Merchant Whslr
N.A.I.C.S.: 423610

Marazzi Iberia S.A.　(2)

Mohawk Industries, Inc.—(Continued)

Avda Enrique Gimeno N 317, 12006, Castellon de la Plana, Spain
Tel.: (34) 96 434 9000
Web Site: https://www.marazzi.es
Sales Range: $25-49.9 Million
Emp.: 8
Ceramic Wall & Floor Tile Mfr & Distr
N.A.I.C.S.: 327120

Marazzi Japan Co., Ltd. (2)
Tokaidoginza Bldg 6F 6-4-1 Ginza, Chuou-ku, Tokyo, 104-0061, Japan
Tel.: (81) 352831355
Web Site: http://www.marazzijapan.com
Sales Range: $25-49.9 Million
Emp.: 7
Ceramic Tiles Distr
N.A.I.C.S.: 423320
Masayo Tamaoko (Mng Dir)

Moduleo GmbH (1)
Reisholzer Werftstr 33, 40589, Dusseldorf, Germany
Tel.: (49) 21159893000
Floor Covering Product Whslr
N.A.I.C.S.: 449121

Mohawk Factoring, Inc. (1)
160 S Industrial Blvd, Calhoun, GA 30701-3030
Tel.: (706) 629-7721
Residential & Commercial Flooring Products Whslr
N.A.I.C.S.: 238330

Mohawk Home (1)
3090 Sugar Valley Rd NW, Sugar Valley, GA 30746-5166 (100%)
Tel.: (706) 629-7916
Web Site: http://www.mohawkhome.com
Rev.: $15,000,000
Emp.: 800
Mfr of Rugs & Mats
N.A.I.C.S.: 314110

Mohawk Industries, Inc. - Dalton (1)
2001 Antioch Rd, Dalton, GA 30721-4622
Tel.: (706) 277-1100
Web Site: http://www.mohawkcarpet.com
Mfr of Carpets & Rugs
N.A.I.C.S.: 314110

Mohawk International Services BVBA (1)
Ooigemstraat 3, 8710, Wielsbeke, Belgium
Tel.: (32) 56675743
Floor Covering Product Whslr
N.A.I.C.S.: 449121
Hans de Ruysscher (Mgr-Procurement)

Mohawk Unilin International BV (1)
Eneluxstraat 1, 5061 KD, Oisterwijk, Netherlands
Tel.: (31) 135231313
Web Site: http://www.unilin.com
Carpet & Rug Mfr
N.A.I.C.S.: 314110

Mohawk/Columbia Flooring (1)
575 Kentuck Rd, Danville, VA 24540
Tel.: (434) 793-9842
Hardwood Veneer & Plywood Flooring
N.A.I.C.S.: 321211

Opstalan BV (1)
Beneluxstraat 1, 5061 KD, Oisterwijk, Netherlands
Tel.: (31) 135231313
Web Site: http://www.opstalan.nl
Roofing Installation Mfr
N.A.I.C.S.: 238160

Pergo (Europe) AB (1)
Persakersvagen 18, 231 25, Trelleborg, Sweden
Tel.: (46) 20476350
Web Site: http://www.pergogolv.se
Construction Materials Merchant Whslr
N.A.I.C.S.: 423610

Pergo AB (1)
Persakersvagen 18, PO Box 1010, 231 25, Trelleborg, Sweden
Tel.: (46) 20476350
Web Site: http://www.pergo.com
Sales Range: $300-349.9 Million
Emp.: 700
Laminate Flooring Mfr
N.A.I.C.S.: 326130

Subsidiary (Non-US):

Pergo (France) S. A. S. (2)
4 Passage Saint Antoine, Rueil-Malmaison, 92500, France
Tel.: (33) 141399712
Web Site: http://www.pergo.com
Sales Range: $25-49.9 Million
Emp.: 15
Laminated Flooring Material Mfr
N.A.I.C.S.: 326199

Pergo Asia Co. Ltd. (2)
139 / 7 Moo 7, Ratburana, Bangkok, 10140, Thailand
Tel.: (66) 2 8182530
Flooring Materials Distr
N.A.I.C.S.: 423310

Pergo GmbH (2)
Stralauer Allee 2 c, 10245, Berlin, Germany
Tel.: (49) 30 8321 939 39
Flooring Materials Mfr
N.A.I.C.S.: 327120

Pergo Holding B. V. (2)
Bruistensingel 166, 's-Hertogenbosch, 5232 AC, Netherlands
Tel.: (31) 736408610
Investment Management Service
N.A.I.C.S.: 523999

Subsidiary (US):

Pergo Inc. (2)
3128 Highwoods Blvd Ste 100, Raleigh, NC 27604
Tel.: (919) 773-6000
Web Site: http://www.pergo.com
Sales Range: $150-199.9 Million
Emp.: 550
Laminated Flooring
N.A.I.C.S.: 326199

Premium Floors Australia Pty Limited (1)
81-87 South Park Drive, Dandenong South, 3175, VIC, Australia
Tel.: (61) 39 798 0808
Web Site: https://www.premiumfloors.com.au
Construction Materials Merchant Whslr
N.A.I.C.S.: 423610

Sharikat Malaysia Wood Industries Sdn Bhd (1)
2126 Jln Raya Batu 1 3/4 Bakar Arang, Sungai Petani, 08000, Kedah, Malaysia
Tel.: (60) 44212761
Sales Range: $125-149.9 Million
Emp.: 700
Wood Equipment Mfr
N.A.I.C.S.: 333243

Spanolux SPRL (1)
Rue de la Foret 2, 6690, Vielsalm, Belgium
Tel.: (32) 80292710
Web Site: http://www.spanolux.com
Saws Product Mfr
N.A.I.C.S.: 333243

Unilin BVBA-Division Systems (1)
Waregemstraat 112, 8792, Desselgem, Belgium
Tel.: (32) 56735091
Web Site: http://www.unilin.com
Prefabricated Roofing Element Developer & Mfr
N.A.I.C.S.: 423330

Unilin Flooring NC, LLC (1)
550 Cloniger Dr, Thomasville, NC 27360-4960
Tel.: (336) 313-4000
Wood Products Mfr
N.A.I.C.S.: 321999

Unilin Industries BVBA (1)
Ooigemstraat 3, 8710, Wielsbeke, Belgium
Tel.: (32) 56 67 52 11
Web Site: http://www.unilin.com
Wooden Flooring Products Mfr
N.A.I.C.S.: 321918

Unilin Italia S.R.L. (1)
Via Linussio 52, 33100, Udine, Italy
Tel.: (39) 0432522727
Web Site: http://www.unilinitalia.it
Wood & Flooring Product Mfr & Distr
N.A.I.C.S.: 321114

Unilin North America, LLC (1)
7834 C F Hawn Freeway, Dallas, TX 75217-6529
Tel.: (214) 398-1411
Emp.: 100
Construction Materials Merchant Whslr
N.A.I.C.S.: 423610
David Anderson (VP)

Unilin Norway AS (1)
Veritasveien 16, 1363, Hovik, Akershus, Norway
Tel.: (47) 67803390
Construction Materials Merchant Whslr
N.A.I.C.S.: 423610

Unilin Poland Sp.z o.o. (1)
ul Batalionow Chlopskich 14, 83-000, Pruszcz Gdanski, woj pomorskie, Poland
Tel.: (48) 587732640
Construction Materials Merchant Whslr
N.A.I.C.S.: 423610
Szymon Lemanski (Mgr-Area Sls & Coord-Mktg)

Unilin Swiss GmbH (1)
Tannengutweg 10, 5600, Lenzburg, Switzerland
Tel.: (41) 628880066
Web Site: https://unilinswiss.ch
Wood & Flooring Product Mfr & Distr
N.A.I.C.S.: 321114

Xtratherm Limited (1)
Liscarton Industrial Estate Kells Road, Meath, Navan, C15 NP79, Ireland
Tel.: (353) 46 906 6000
Web Site: http://www.xtratherm.com
Insulation Product Mfr & Distr
N.A.I.C.S.: 327993

Xtratherm UK Limited (1)
Park Road Holmewood, Chesterfield, S42 5UY, Derbyshire, United Kingdom
Tel.: (44) 3712221033
Web Site: http://www.xtratherm.ie
Building Materials Mfr
N.A.I.C.S.: 333120

MOJO DIGITAL ASSETS INC.
URB Dorado Reef, Dorado, PR 00646
Tel.: (631) 360-3400 NV
Web Site: https://www.mojotags.com
Year Founded: 2010
MJDS—(OTCIQ)
Sales Range: Less than $1 Million
Emp.: 2
Investment Services
N.A.I.C.S.: 523999

MOLECULAR TEMPLATES INC.
9301 Amberglen Blvd Ste 100, Austin, TX 78729
Tel.: (512) 869-1555 DE
Web Site: https://www.mtem.com
Year Founded: 2001
MTEM—(NASDAQ)
Rev.: $19,754,000
Assets: $97,548,000
Liabilities: $112,680,000
Net Worth: ($15,132,000)
Earnings: $92,718,000
Emp.: 222
Fiscal Year-end: 12/31/22
Cancer Treatment Developer & Mfr
N.A.I.C.S.: 541715
Eric E. Poma (CEO & Chief Scientific Officer)
Jason S. Kim (Pres & CFO)
Ryan Hawkins (Sr VP & Head-Mfg)
Dennis Jones (Sr VP-Quality)
Joseph Phillips (Sr VP & Head-CMC Dev)
Kristen Quigley (COO)
Grace Kim (Chief Strategy Officer & Head-IR)
Harold E. Selick (Chm)

MOLECULIN BIOTECH, INC.
5300 Memorial Dr Ste 950, Houston, TX 77007

Tel.: (713) 300-5160 DE
Web Site: https://www.moleculin.com
Year Founded: 2015
MBRX—(NASDAQ)
Rev.: $240,000
Assets: $57,422,000
Liabilities: $5,231,000
Net Worth: $52,191,000
Earnings: ($29,025,000)
Emp.: 15
Fiscal Year-end: 12/31/22
Biopharmaceutical Product Research & Development Services
N.A.I.C.S.: 541715
Donald H. Picker (Chief Scientific Officer)
Sandra Silberman (Chief Medical Officer-New Products)
Walter V. Klemp (Chm, Pres & CEO)
Jonathan Foster (CFO & Exec VP)
John Paul Waymack (Chief Medical Officer)
Jonathan P. Foster (CFO, CFO, Exec VP & Exec VP)

MOLEKULE GROUP, INC.
10455 Riverside Dr, Palm Beach Gardens, FL 33410 DE
Web Site: https://molekule.com
Year Founded: 2011
MKUL—(NASDAQ)
Rev.: $227,186
Assets: $29,158,886
Liabilities: $9,455,684
Net Worth: $19,703,202
Earnings: ($6,168,931)
Emp.: 91
Fiscal Year-end: 12/31/22
Air Purification Products Mfr
N.A.I.C.S.: 333413
Jason DiBona (CEO)
Ryan Tyler (CFO)

MOLINA HEALTHCARE, INC.
200 Oceangate Ste 100, Long Beach, CA 90802
Tel.: (562) 435-3666 DE
Web Site: https://www.molinahealthcare.com
Year Founded: 2002
MOH—(NYSE)
Rev.: $34,072,000,000
Assets: $14,892,000,000
Liabilities: $10,677,000,000
Net Worth: $4,215,000,000
Earnings: $1,091,000,000
Emp.: 18,000
Fiscal Year-end: 12/31/23
Healthcare Services
N.A.I.C.S.: 551112
Ronna E. Romney (Vice Chm)
Joseph M. Zubretsky (Pres & CEO)
Mark L. Keim (CFO & Sr Exec VP)
Maurice S. Hebert (Chief Acctg Officer)
Mark L. Keim (CFO)

Subsidiaries:

Central Health Plan of California, Inc. (1)
Tel.: (866) 314-2427
Web Site: https://www.centralhealthplan.com
Health Care Srvices
N.A.I.C.S.: 621999

Molina Center LLC (1)
200 300 Oceangate, Long Beach, CA 90802
Tel.: (562) 435-8200
Web Site: http://www.molinacenter.com
Health Plans & Healthcare Services
N.A.I.C.S.: 621491

Molina Healthcare of California (1)
200 Oceangate Ste 100, Long Beach, CA 90802
Tel.: (562) 499-6191
Healtcare Services

N.A.I.C.S.: 621610

Molina Healthcare of Florida, Inc. **(1)**
8300 NW 33rd St Ste 400, Miami, FL 33122
Web Site:
   https://www.molinahealthcare.com
Sales Range: $450-499.9 Million
Emp.: 250
Health Care Srvices
N.A.I.C.S.: 621610

Molina Healthcare of Kentucky, Inc. **(1)**
5100 Commerce Crossings Dr, Louisville, KY 40229
Healtcare Services
N.A.I.C.S.: 621610

Molina Healthcare of Michigan, Inc. **(1)**
880 W Long Lk Rd, Troy, MI 48098
Tel.: (248) 925-1700
Web Site: http://www.molinahealthcare.com
Sales Range: $25-49.9 Million
Mental Health Care Services
N.A.I.C.S.: 524114

Molina Healthcare of Mississippi, Inc. **(1)**
188 E Capitol St Ste 700, Jackson, MS 39201
Healtcare Services
N.A.I.C.S.: 621610

Molina Healthcare of Nevada, Inc. **(1)**
8329 W Sunset Rd Ste 100, Las Vegas, NV 89113
Healtcare Services
N.A.I.C.S.: 621610

Molina Healthcare of New Mexico, Inc. **(1)**
400 Tijeras Ave NW Ste 200, Albuquerque, NM 87102
Tel.: (505) 342-4660
Web Site: http://www.molinahealthcare.com
Sales Range: $50-74.9 Million
Managed Healthcare Insurance Carrier
N.A.I.C.S.: 524114

Molina Healthcare of New York, Inc. **(1)**
5232 Witz Dr, North Syracuse, NY 13212
Health Insurance Carrier Services
N.A.I.C.S.: 524114

Molina Healthcare of Ohio, Inc. **(1)**
3000 Corporate Exchange Dr, Columbus, OH 43231
Sales Range: $125-149.9 Million
Emp.: 400
Managed Healthcare Insurance Carrier
N.A.I.C.S.: 524114
Jeffrey Hunter *(Chief Medical Officer)*

Molina Healthcare of Puerto Rico, Inc. **(1)**
654 Plz Ste 1600 654 Avenida Munoz Rivera, San Juan, PR 00918
Health Care Srvices
N.A.I.C.S.: 524114

Molina Healthcare of South Carolina, LLC **(1)**
4105 Faber Pl Dr Ste 120, North Charleston, SC 29405
Health Insurance Carrier Services
N.A.I.C.S.: 524114

Molina Healthcare of Texas, Inc. **(1)**
1660 Westridge Cir N, Irving, TX 75038
Web Site: http://www.molinahealthcare.com
Sales Range: $150-199.9 Million
Managed Healthcare Insurance Carrier Services
N.A.I.C.S.: 524114

Subsidiary (Domestic):

Molina Healthcare of Texas Insurance Company **(2)**
84 N E Loop 410 Ste 200, San Antonio, TX 78216
Tel.: (210) 366-6500
Healtcare Services
N.A.I.C.S.: 621610

Molina Healthcare of Utah, Inc. **(1)**

7050 Union Park Ct Ste 200, Midvale, UT 84047
Tel.: (801) 858-0400
Web Site: http://www.molinahealthcare.com
Sales Range: $100-124.9 Million
Managed Healthcare Insurance Carrier
N.A.I.C.S.: 524114

Molina Healthcare of Virginia, Inc. **(1)**
3829 Gaskins Rd, Glen Allen, VA 23233
Healtcare Services
N.A.I.C.S.: 621610

Molina Healthcare of Washington, Inc. **(1)**
21540 30th Dr SE Ste 400, Bothell, WA 98021
Tel.: (425) 424-1100
Web Site: http://www.molinahealthcare.com
Sales Range: $150-199.9 Million
Managed Healthcare Insurance Carrier
N.A.I.C.S.: 524114
Peter Adler *(Pres)*

Molina Healthcare of Wisconsin, Inc. **(1)**
11002 W Park Pl, Milwaukee, WI 53224
Tel.: (414) 847-1776
Healtcare Services
N.A.I.C.S.: 621610
Brian Maddy *(Pres-Plan)*

Universal Care, Inc. **(1)**
Tel.: (866) 255-4795
Web Site: https://www.bndhmo.com
Health Care Srvices
N.A.I.C.S.: 621999

MOLSON COORS BEVERAGE COMPANY

PO Box 4030, Golden, CO 80401
Tel.: (514) 521-1786   **CO**
Web Site:
   https://www.molsoncoors.com
Year Founded: 1786
TAP—(NYSE)
Rev.: $12,807,500,000
Assets: $25,868,300,000
Liabilities: $12,953,100,000
Net Worth: $12,915,200,000
Earnings: ($1,753,000,000)
Emp.: 16,600
Fiscal Year-end: 12/31/22
Holding Company
N.A.I.C.S.: 551112
Gavin D. K. Hattersley *(Pres & CEO)*
Tracey I. Joubert *(CFO)*
Michelle St. Jacques *(Chief Comml Officer)*
Roxanne Stelter *(Chief Acctg Officer, VP & Controller)*
Adam Collins *(Chief Comm & Corp Affairs Officer)*
Rahul Goyal *(Chief Strategy Officer)*
Michelle St. Jacques *(CMO)*
Dave Osswald *(Chief People & Diversity Officer)*
David S. Coors *(VP-Full Strength Spirits)*
Anne-Marie W. D'Angelo *(Chief Legal & Govt Affairs Officer)*

Subsidiaries:

Boulder Ionics Corporation **(1)**
18300 W Hwy 72, Arvada, CO 80007-8201
Tel.: (303) 432-1400
Web Site: http://www.boulderionics.com
Chemicals Mfr
N.A.I.C.S.: 325199
Jerry Martin *(CEO)*

MillerCoors LLC **(1)**
250 S Wacker Dr Ste 800, Chicago, IL 60606   **(100%)**
Tel.: (312) 496-2700
Web Site: http://www.millercoors.com
Beer Brewer & Distr
N.A.I.C.S.: 312120

Subsidiary (Domestic):

Coors Brewing Company **(2)**
311 Tenth St, Golden, CO 80401

Brewery
N.A.I.C.S.: 312120
Mauricio Cardenas *(Chief Officer-Latin America & US Multi-Cultural)*

Subsidiary (Domestic):

Coors Distributing Company **(3)**
5400 N Pecos St, Denver, CO 80221
Tel.: (303) 433-6541
Web Site: https://www.cdccoors.com
Emp.: 400
Beer Distributor
N.A.I.C.S.: 424810

Subsidiary (Domestic):

Jacob Leinenkugel Brewing Company **(2)**
124 E Elm St, Chippewa Falls, WI 54729
Tel.: (715) 723-5557
Web Site: https://www.leinie.com
Brewery
N.A.I.C.S.: 312120

Miller Brewing Company **(2)**
4251 W State St, Milwaukee, WI 53208
Tel.: (414) 931-2337
Brewery
N.A.I.C.S.: 312120

Division (Domestic):

Watertown Hops Company **(3)**
1224 American Way, Watertown, WI 53094
Tel.: (920) 261-0963
Web Site: https://www.watertownhops.com
Brewery
N.A.I.C.S.: 312120

Subsidiary (Domestic):

Tenth & Blake Beer Company **(2)**
250 S Wacker Dr, Chicago, IL 60606
Tel.: (312) 496-2700
Web Site: http://www.millercoors.com
Craft Beer Producer & Distr
N.A.I.C.S.: 312120

Molson Canada 2005 **(1)**
33 Carlingview Drive Etobicoke, Toronto, M9W 5E4, ON, Canada
Tel.: (416) 679-7629
Web Site: https://www.molson.com
Alcoholic Beverages Whslr
N.A.I.C.S.: 424810

Molson Coors (UK) Holdings LLP **(1)**
137 High Street, Burton-on-Trent, DE141JZ, Staffordshire, United Kingdom
Tel.: (44) 1283511000
Web Site: https://www.molsoncoors.co.uk
Holding Company; Beer & Other Beverage Products Mfr
N.A.I.C.S.: 551112

Molson Coors Brewing Company (UK) Ltd. **(1)**
137 High Street, Burton-on-Trent, DE14 1JZ, Staffs, United Kingdom
Tel.: (44) 3457112244
Web Site: https://www.coorsbrewers.com
Sales Range: $600-649.9 Million
Emp.: 2,010
Beer Brewers & Packers
N.A.I.C.S.: 312120

Molson Coors Canada **(1)**
131 Circular Road, PO Box 5308, Saint John's, A1C 5W1, NL, Canada
Tel.: (709) 726-1786
Beer & Other Beverage Products Mfr
N.A.I.C.S.: 312120

Molson Coors Canada Inc. **(1)**
33 Carlingview Drive, Toronto, M9W 5E4, ON, Canada   **(100%)**
Tel.: (303) 927-2337
Web Site: https://www.molson.com
Sales Range: $900-999.9 Million
Emp.: 3,000
Brewing & Beer & Ale Distribution
N.A.I.C.S.: 312120

Subsidiary (Domestic):

Molson Inc. **(2)**
1555 Notre Dame St, Montreal, H2L 2R5, QC, Canada
Tel.: (514) 521-1786

Web Site: http://www.Molson.com
Sales Range: $50-74.9 Million
Emp.: 150
Breweries, Sports & Entertainment
N.A.I.C.S.: 312120

Plant (Domestic):

Molson Brewery - British Columbia **(3)**
1550 Burrard St, Vancouver, V6J 3G5, BC, Canada
Tel.: (604) 664-1786
Web Site:
   http://www.molsoncoorscanada.com
Sales Range: $25-49.9 Million
Emp.: 50
Brewery
N.A.I.C.S.: 312120

Molson Brewery - Ontario **(3)**
1 Carlingview Dr, Etobicoke, M9W 5E4, ON, Canada
Tel.: (416) 675-1786
Web Site: http://www.molsoncoors.com
Emp.: 300
Brewery
N.A.I.C.S.: 312120

Molson Coors Central Europe s.r.o. **(1)**
Nadrazni 84 Prague 5, 150 54, Prague, Czech Republic
Tel.: (420) 257191814
Web Site: http://www.molsoncoors.com
Sales Range: $900-999.9 Million
Emp.: 4,100
Holding Company; Brewery Operator & Beer Whslr
N.A.I.C.S.: 551112

Subsidiary (Non-US):

Bergenbier S.A. **(2)**
Bucharest North Road No 10 Building O1 Floor 5, Ilfov County, 20335, Voluntari, Romania
Tel.: (40) 372207109
Web Site: https://www.bergenbiersa.ro
Sales Range: $150-199.9 Million
Emp.: 730
Brewery Operator
N.A.I.C.S.: 312120
Jens Hoesel *(Pres)*

Borsodi Sorgyar Zrt. **(2)**
Rakoczi utca 81, 3574, Bocs, Hungary
Tel.: (36) 46529600
Web Site: https://www.borsodisorgyar.hu
Sales Range: $100-124.9 Million
Emp.: 500
Brewery Operator
N.A.I.C.S.: 312120
Judit Veres *(Fin Dir)*

Zagrebacka Pivovara d.d. **(2)**
Ilica 224, 10000, Zagreb, Croatia   **(70%)**
Tel.: (385) 13900199
Web Site: https://www.ozujsko.com
Brewery Operator
N.A.I.C.S.: 312120
Miroslav Holjevac *(Pres & Dir-Sls & Comml Excellence)*
Slavica Kozina *(Member-Mgmt Bd & Dir-Fin)*
Alina Ruzic *(Dir-Legal & Corporate Affairs & Member-Mgmt Bd)*
Jadranka Sakoman *(Dir-HR)*
Dubravko Tome *(Dir-Prod & Logistics Ops)*
Ana Stebih Pinjuh *(Dir-Mktg)*

Molson Coors Netherlands BV **(1)**
Naritaweg 165, 1043 BW, Amsterdam, Netherlands
Tel.: (31) 205722300
Financial Services
N.A.I.C.S.: 551112

Subsidiary (Domestic):

Starbev Netherlands BV **(2)**
Naritaweg 165, 1043 BW, Amsterdam, Netherlands
Tel.: (31) 205722461
Asset Management Services
N.A.I.C.S.: 531390

Subsidiary (Non-US):

Borsodi Sorgyar Korlatolt Felelossegu Tarsasag **(3)**

Molson Coors Beverage Company—(Continued)

Rakoczi utca 81, Bocs, 3574, Hungary
Tel.: (36) 17786000
Web Site: http://www.borsodisorgyar.hu
Emp.: 420
Alcoholic Beverages Mfr
N.A.I.C.S.: 312120
Vuleta Zsolt (Exec Dir & Comml Dir)

Pivovary Staropramen a.s. (1)
Nadrazni 43/84, 150 00, Prague, 5, Czech
Republic
Tel.: (420) 257191111
Web Site: https://www.pivovary-
staropramen.cz
Emp.: 600
Alcoholic Beverages Mfr
N.A.I.C.S.: 312120

MOMENTUS INC.
1345 Abbot Kinney Blvd, Venice, CA
90291
Tel.: (650) 564-7820 DE
Web Site: https://momentus.space
Year Founded: 2017
MNTS—(NASDAQ)
Rev.: $2,234,000
Assets: $20,649,000
Liabilities: $17,462,000
Net Worth: $3,187,000
Earnings: $68,920,000
Fiscal Year-end: 12/31/23
Space Equipment Services
N.A.I.C.S.: 927110
John C. Rood (Chm & CEO)
Rob Schwarz (CTO)
Eric Williams (CFO)
Chris Kinman (Chief Comml Officer)
Paul Ney (Chief Legal Officer & Sec)

MONARCH CASINO & RE-SORT, INC.
3800 S Virginia St, Reno, NV 89502
Tel.: (775) 335-4600 NV
Web Site:
https://www.monarchcasino.com
Year Founded: 1993
MCRI—(NASDAQ)
Rev.: $477,870,000
Assets: $692,942,000
Liabilities: $153,988,000
Net Worth: $538,954,000
Earnings: $87,479,000
Emp.: 2,700
Fiscal Year-end: 12/31/22
Holding Company; Casino Hotels
Owner & Operator
N.A.I.C.S.: 721120
John Farahi (Co-Chm, CEO & Sec)
Bahram Farahi (Co-Chm & Pres)
Michelle Shriver (VP-Ops)
Darlyne Sullivan (Chief Product &
Svc Officer)
Edwin S. Koenig (Chief Acctg Officer)
Michelle Shriver (VP-Ops)
Cheraz Ecker (Gen Mgr)

Subsidiaries:

Golden Road Motor Inn, Inc. (1)
3800 S Virginia St, Reno, NV
89502-6005 (100%)
Tel.: (775) 825-4700
Web Site: http://www.atlantiscasino.com
Sales Range: $10-24.9 Million
Emp.: 250
Casino Hotels Owner & Operator
N.A.I.C.S.: 721120

Monarch Black Hawk, Inc. (1)
488 Main St, Black Hawk, CO 80422
Tel.: (303) 582-1000
Web Site:
https://www.monarchblackhawk.com
Hotel Operator
N.A.I.C.S.: 721120
Craig Pleva (Gen Mgr)

MONARCH CEMENT COM-PANY
449 1200 St, Humboldt, KS 66748

Tel.: (620) 473-2222 KS
Web Site:
https://www.monarchcement.com
Year Founded: 1908
MCEM—(OTCIQ)
Rev.: $188,825,253
Assets: $257,769,908
Liabilities: $45,208,754
Net Worth: $212,561,154
Earnings: $33,874,712
Emp.: 500
Fiscal Year-end: 12/31/20
Cement Mfr
N.A.I.C.S.: 327320
Robert M. Kissick (Vice Chm & VP)
N. Joan Perez (VP-Mktg)
Kent A. Webber (Pres)
Tony Kasten (CFO, Treas & Sec)
Douglas W. Sommers (VP-Sls)
Justin R. Tucker (Ops Mgr-
Subsidiary)
Walter H. Wulf Jr. (Chm & CEO)

Subsidiaries:

Kay Concrete Materials, Co. (1)
501 Kay Dr, Monett, MO 65708
Tel.: (417) 235-3628
Web Site: http://www.kayconcrete.com
Sales Range: $25-49.9 Million
Emp.: 60
Concrete Mfr
N.A.I.C.S.: 327320

MONARCH SERVICES, INC.
4517 Harford Rd, Baltimore, MD
21214
Tel.: (410) 254-9200 MD
Year Founded: 1958
MAHI—(OTCIQ)
Holding Company; Magazine Pub-lisher
N.A.I.C.S.: 551112
Marshall Chadwell (CFO)
Steven A. Szekely (Sec)

Subsidiaries:

Girls' Life, Inc. (1)
4529 Harford Rd, Baltimore, MD 21214-
3122
Tel.: (410) 254-9200
Web Site: http://www.girlslife.com
Magazine Publisher
N.A.I.C.S.: 513120
Jessica D'Argenio (Mgr-Ops & Assoc Edi-
tor)

MONDEE HOLDINGS, INC.
10800 Pecan Park Blvd Ste 400,
Austin, TX 78750
Tel.: (650) 646-3320 DE
Web Site: https://www.mondee.com
Year Founded: 2020
MOND—(NASDAQ)
Rev.: $159,484,000
Assets: $258,097,000
Liabilities: $287,419,000
Net Worth: ($29,322,000)
Earnings: ($90,238,000)
Emp.: 927
Fiscal Year-end: 12/31/22
Investment Services
N.A.I.C.S.: 523999
Prasad Gundumogula (Founder, Chm
& CEO)

Subsidiaries:

Mondee Inc. (1)
4000 E 3rd Ave Ste 650, Foster City, CA
94404
Tel.: (650) 646-3320
Web Site: http://www.mondee.com
Software Mfr
N.A.I.C.S.: 513210
Prasad Gundumogula (Founder & CEO)
Orestes Fintiklis (Vice Chm & Chief Corp
Strategy & Bus Dev Officer)

Skypass Travel, Inc (1)

2730 N Stemmons Freeway Ste 310, Dal-
las, TX 75207-2290
Tel.: (214) 634-8687
Web Site: http://www.skypasstravel.com
Travel Agencies
N.A.I.C.S.: 561510
Victor Abraham (Owner)

MONDELEZ INTERNATIONAL, INC.
905 W Fulton Market Ste 200, Chi-
cago, IL 60607
Tel.: (847) 943-4000 VA
Web Site:
https://www.mondelezinternatio
nal.com
MDLZ—(NASDAQ)
Rev.: $36,016,000,000
Assets: $71,391,000,000
Liabilities: $43,025,000,000
Net Worth: $28,366,000,000
Earnings: $4,959,000,000
Emp.: 91,000
Fiscal Year-end: 12/31/23
Holding Company; Packaged Grocery
Products Mfr
N.A.I.C.S.: 551112
Dirk Van de Put (Chm & CEO)
Luca Zaramella (CFO & Exec VP)
Gerhard W. Pleuhs (Gen Counsel &
Gen Counsel)
Paulette Alviti (Chief People Officer &
Exec VP)
Sandra F. MacQuillan (Chief Supply
Chain Officer & Exec VP)
Vinzenz P. Gruber (Pres-Europe &
Exec VP)
Minsok Pak (Chief Strategy & Trans-
formation Officer & Exec VP)
Gustavo C. Valle (Pres-North America
& Exec VP)
Laura Stein (Gen Counsel & Exec
VP-Corp & Legal Affairs)
Javier Polit (CIO & Chief Integrated
Bus Svcs Officer)
Michael Call (Chief Acctg Officer, Sr
VP & Controller)
Frank Cervi (Chief Supply Chain Ops
Officer)

Subsidiaries:

Cadbury Limited (1)
Cadbury House Sanderson Rd Uxbridge
Business Park, Uxbridge, UB8 1DH, Middle-
sex, United Kingdom
Tel.: (44) 1895615000
Web Site: http://www.kraftfoods.com
Sales Range: $5-14.9 Billion
Emp.: 54,744
Holding Company; Chocolate & Other Con-
fectionery Mfr & Distr
N.A.I.C.S.: 551112
Marcos Grasso (Pres-South America)

Subsidiary (Non-US):

Cadbury (Swaziland) (Pty)
Limited (2)
Industrial Sites, Matsapha, Eswatini
Tel.: (268) 25186030
Confectionery Product Mfr
N.A.I.C.S.: 311340

Cadbury Adams (Thailand)
Limited (2)
Ladkrabang Industrial Estate 102/1 Moo 4
Chalongkrung Rd Lamplatiew, Lat Krabang,
10520, Thailand
Tel.: (66) 23263000
Web Site: http://www.kraftfoods.com
Sales Range: $50-74.9 Million
Emp.: 100
Mobile Food Services
N.A.I.C.S.: 722330

Cadbury Adams Mexico, S. de R.L.
de C.V. (2)
Ave Santa Fe 485 Col Cruz Manca, Mexico,
05349, Mexico
Tel.: (52) 5553268300
Web Site: http://www.kraftfoods.mx
Mobile Food Services

N.A.I.C.S.: 722330

Cadbury Adams Middle East
S.A.L. (2)
Cadbury Adams Bldg Property Number 880,
Zahle, Lebanon
Tel.: (961) 0009211818
Mobile Food Services
N.A.I.C.S.: 722330

Cadbury Confectionery Malaysia Sdn
Bhd (2)
Persiaran Raja Muda Section 16, PO Box
7043, 40700, Shah Alam, Malaysia (100%)
Tel.: (60) 355191440
Web Site:
http://www.mondelezinternational.com
Sales Range: $75-99.9 Million
Emp.: 250
Confectionery Mfr
N.A.I.C.S.: 311351

Subsidiary (Domestic):

Cadbury Confectionery Sales (M)
Sdn. Bhd. (3)
Persiaran Raja Muda Section 16, Shah
Alam, 40700, Malaysia
Tel.: (60) 355191192
Web Site: http://www.kraftfoods.com
Food Mfr Services
N.A.I.C.S.: 722330

Subsidiary (Domestic):

Cadbury Eight LLP (2)
Cadbury House Sanderson Road, Uxbridge,
UB8 1DH, United Kingdom
Tel.: (44) 1895615000
Confectionery Product Mfr
N.A.I.C.S.: 311340

Subsidiary (Non-US):

Cadbury Enterprises Pte. Ltd. (2)
346 Jalan Boon Lay, Singapore, 619528,
Singapore
Tel.: (65) 62665646
Web Site:
http://www.kraftfoodscompany.com
Mobile Food Services
N.A.I.C.S.: 722330

Cadbury Food Co. Ltd. (2)
No 24 Wudian Rd, Beijing, 100076, China
Tel.: (86) 1087964384
Confectionery Mfr
N.A.I.C.S.: 311351

Cadbury France SAS (2)
143 Boulevard Romain Rolland, Paris,
75685, France
Tel.: (33) 158076250
Confectionery Product Distr
N.A.I.C.S.: 311340

Cadbury Ghana Ltd. (2)
20/6 Collins Ave, PO Box 49, Accra,
Ghana (100%)
Tel.: (233) 312025051
Sales Range: $75-99.9 Million
Emp.: 270
Confectionery Mfr
N.A.I.C.S.: 311351

Cadbury India Limited (2)
Mondelez House Unit 2001 20th Floor
Tower 3, One International Centre, Mumbai,
400 013, Maharashtra, India
Tel.: (91) 2233963100
Web Site:
https://www.mondelezinternational.com
Confectionery Mfr
N.A.I.C.S.: 311351
Manu Anand (Mng Dir & Pres-India & South
Asia)

Cadbury Ireland Ltd. (2)
Malahide Road, Coolock, Dublin,
Ireland (100%)
Tel.: (353) 1800678708
Web Site: http://www.cadbury.ie
Sales Range: $125-149.9 Million
Emp.: 500
Confectionery Mfr
N.A.I.C.S.: 311351

Cadbury Japan Ltd. (2)
5th Floor IK Building 24-9 Kamiosaki
2-chome, Shinagawa-ku, Tokyo, 141 8656,
Japan (100%)

Tel.: (81) 352835678
Confectionery Mfr
N.A.I.C.S.: 311351

Cadbury Kenya Limited (2)
Ol Kalou Rd Industrial area, PO Box 45466,
100, Nairobi, Kenya (100%)
Tel.: (254) 20530001
Web Site: http://www.cadbury.com
Confectionery Mfr
N.A.I.C.S.: 311351

Cadbury Ltd. (2)
494 Rosebank Road, Avondale, 1026,
Auckland, New Zealand (100%)
Tel.: (64) 98202600
Web Site: http://www.cadbury.co.nz
Sales Range: $50-74.9 Million
Emp.: 200
Confectionery Mfr
N.A.I.C.S.: 311351

**Cadbury Marketing Services Pty
Limited** (2)
Level 6 South Wharf Tower, 30 Convention
Centre Place, Melbourne, 3006, VIC, Aus-
tralia
Tel.: (61) 396765555
Food Service
N.A.I.C.S.: 722330

Cadbury Nigeria Plc (2)
Lateef Jakande Way Agidingbi Ikeja, Lagos,
Nigeria (74.99%)
Tel.: (234) 12717777
Web Site:
https://www.mondelezinternational.com
Confectionery & Bottled Drink Mfr & Distr
N.A.I.C.S.: 311352
Muhammad Amir Shamsi (Mng Dir)

Cadbury Pakistan Limited (2)
4th Floor Tower-B World Trade Centre, Clif-
ton Khayaban-e-Roomi, Karachi, 75600,
Pakistan
Tel.: (92) 215865281
Sales Range: $50-74.9 Million
Emp.: 140
Confectionery Mfr
N.A.I.C.S.: 311351

Cadbury Singapore Pte. Ltd. (2)
346 Jalan Boon Lay Jurong, Singapore,
619528, Singapore (100%)
Tel.: (65) 63038333
Web Site:
http://www.mondelezinternational.com
Sales Range: $25-49.9 Million
Emp.: 40
Confectionery Mfr
N.A.I.C.S.: 311351

Cadbury South Africa (Pty) Ltd. (2)
Woodmead Estate Building 6 1, Wood-
mead, Sandton, South Africa
Tel.: (27) 112534000
Web Site: http://www.cadbury.co.za
Sales Range: $75-99.9 Million
Emp.: 200
Confectionery Mfr
N.A.I.C.S.: 311351
Joost Vlaanderen (Mng Dir)

**Cadbury Stani Adams Argentina
S.A.** (2)
Uruguay 3911 1646 Victoria, B16448QE,
Buenos Aires, Argentina (100%)
Tel.: (54) 1145490062
Web Site: http://www.cadbury.com.ar
Sales Range: $125-149.9 Million
Emp.: 600
Confectionery Mfr
N.A.I.C.S.: 311351

Cadbury Trading Hong Kong Ltd. (2)
24/F Cambridge Hse Quarry Bay, Hong
Kong, China (Hong Kong)
Tel.: (852) 27917711
Confectionery Product Distr
N.A.I.C.S.: 424450

Subsidiary (Domestic):

Cadbury UK Limited (2)
Bournville, PO Box 12, Birmingham, B30
2LU, United Kingdom (100%)
Tel.: (44) 1214582000
Web Site: http://www.cadbury.co.uk
Sales Range: $800-899.9 Million
Confectionery Mfr
N.A.I.C.S.: 311352

Subsidiary (Domestic):

**Mondelez UK Confectionery Produc-
tion Limited** (3)
Bournville Lane, PO Box 12, Bournville, Bir-
mingham, B30 2LU, United Kingdom
Tel.: (44) 1923483483
Sales Range: $100-124.9 Million
Emp.: 500
Confectionery Mfr
N.A.I.C.S.: 311352

Subsidiary (Non-US):

Crystal Candy (Private) Ltd. (2)
12 Burnley Rd Workington, PO Box 2380,
Harare, Mashonaland, Zimbabwe (49%)
Tel.: (263) 4753822
Sales Range: $75-99.9 Million
Emp.: 400
Confectionery Mfr
N.A.I.C.S.: 311352
Jimmy Psillos (Gen Mgr)

Subsidiary (Domestic):

Green & Black's Limited (2)
25 Berkeley Square, London, W1J 6HN,
United Kingdom
Tel.: (44) 2076335900
Web Site: http://www.greenandblacks.com
Sales Range: $25-49.9 Million
Emp.: 45
Confectionery Mfr
N.A.I.C.S.: 311351
Craig Sams (Co-Founder)
Jo Fairley (Co-Founder)

Subsidiary (Non-US):

La Pie Qui Chante SA (2)
Marcq En Baroeul, Rue de la Chocolaterie,
59706, Lille, France
Tel.: (33) 320183525
Web Site: http://www.cadburyfrance.com
Sales Range: $50-74.9 Million
Emp.: 200
Confectionery Mfr
N.A.I.C.S.: 311352

Subsidiary (Domestic):

Reading Scientific Services Ltd. (2)
Reading Science Centre Whiteknights Cam-
pus Pepper Lane, Reading, RG6 6LA,
Berkshire, United Kingdom (100%)
Tel.: (44) 1189184000
Web Site: http://www.rssl.com
Sales Range: $75-99.9 Million
Confectionery Research Services
N.A.I.C.S.: 541990

Subsidiary (Non-US):

Trebor Bassett Sharps GmbH (2)
Gruner Deich 15, 20097, Hamburg,
Germany (100%)
Tel.: (49) 4046002680
Sales Range: $25-49.9 Million
Emp.: 6
Confectionery Mfr
N.A.I.C.S.: 311352
Michael Holtz (Mng Dir)

Cadbury South Africa (1)
No 18 Harrowdene Office Park Kelvin Dr,
Woodmead Sandton, Johannesburg, South
Africa
Tel.: (27) 112534000
Web Site: http://www.cadbury.co.za
Food Products Mfr
N.A.I.C.S.: 311999

Clif Bar & Company (1)
1451 66th St, Emeryville, CA 94608-1004
Tel.: (510) 596-6300
Web Site: http://www.clifbar.com
Sales Range: $25-49.9 Million
Emp.: 215
Energy & Nutritional Foods Mfr
N.A.I.C.S.: 311999
Shaunte D. Mears-Watkins (Chief Comml
Officer)
Dean Mayer (Mgr-Comm)
Gary Erickson (Co-Founder)
Kit Crawford (Co-Founder)
Geoff Showers (Sr Mgr-Customer-
Convenience Stores)
Sally Grimes (CEO)

Rizal Hamdallah (Chief Innovation Officer)
Hari K. Avula (Chief Financial & Strategic
Officer)

Daesung Machinery (1)
26 Hakgam-daero 192 beon-gil, Sasang-gu,
Busan, 47021, Korea (South)
Tel.: (82) 513245658
Web Site: https://www.dscardmc.com
Snack Food Mfr
N.A.I.C.S.: 311919

EPTA America LLC (1)
50 Morton St Unit A, East Rutherford, NJ
07073
Tel.: (973) 779-9900
Web Site: https://eptaamerica.com
Baked Snack Distr
N.A.I.C.S.: 424490

Enjoy Life Natural Brands, LLC (1)
8770 W Bryn Mawr Ave Ste 1100, Chicago,
IL 60631
Tel.: (847) 260-0300
Web Site: http://www.enjoylifefoods.com
Gluten-Free & Allergen-Free Food Mfr
N.A.I.C.S.: 311919
Nick Alex (CFO)

Fattorie Osella S.p.A. (1)
Via Bussolino 12, Caramagna Piemonte,
12030, Cuneo, Italy
Tel.: (39) 017289002
Web Site: https://www.fattorieosella.it
Snack Food Mfr
N.A.I.C.S.: 311919

Gourmet Food New Zealand Ltd. (1)
144 Birch Ave Judea, Tauranga, 3110, New
Zealand
Tel.: (64) 75779905
Web Site: https://gourmetfoodsltd.co.nz
Snack Food Mfr
N.A.I.C.S.: 311919

Grenade (UK) Ltd. (1)
Bournville Place, Bournville, Birmingham,
B30 2HP, United Kingdom
Tel.: (44) 2477170100
Web Site: https://www.grenade.com
Snack Food Mfr
N.A.I.C.S.: 311919

HUP Srl (1)
Via del Ronco 10, 22074, Lomazzo, CO,
Italy
Tel.: (39) 031563704
Web Site: https://hupdigital.it
Snack Food Mfr
N.A.I.C.S.: 311919

KF (Australia) Pty. Ltd. (1)
9 Garling Rd, Kings Park, 2148, NSW, Aus-
tralia
Tel.: (61) 296795800
Web Site:
http://www.kfspecialtyingredients.com
Emp.: 30
Confectionery Product Mfr
N.A.I.C.S.: 311340
Christine Giuliano (Mng Dir)

KJS India Private Limited (1)
Isnapur-Indira Karan Rd, Pashamylaram,
Hyderabad, 502 307, TS, India
Tel.: (91) 9703735666
Web Site: https://www.kjsindia.com
Snack Food Mfr
N.A.I.C.S.: 311919

**Kent Gida Maddeleri Sanayii ve Ti-
caret Anonim Sirketi** (1)
Cumhuriyet Mah 2253 Sok No 11, Gebze,
41400, Kocaeli, Turkiye
Tel.: (90) 2626487400
Web Site:
http://tr.mondelezinternational.com
Chocolate & Cocoa Product Mfr
N.A.I.C.S.: 311351

Kraft Foods (Puerto Rico), LLC (1)
Montehiedra Ofc Ctr 9615 Ave Los Rome-
ros Ste 801, San Juan, PR 00926-7037
Tel.: (787) 522-9810
Confectionary Product Mfr
N.A.I.C.S.: 311340

Kraft Foods Colombia Ltda. (1)
Av Cl 100 19-54 P-7, Bogota, Colombia
Tel.: (57) 16503000
Grocery Product Distr

N.A.I.C.S.: 492210

Kraft Foods Developing Markets (1)
3 Lakes Dr, Northfield, IL 60093-2753
Tel.: (847) 646-2000
Food Products Mfr & Distr
N.A.I.C.S.: 424410

Subsidiary (Non-US):

AGF Suzuka Co., Ltd. (2)
6410 Minamitamagakicho, Suzuka, 513-
0816, Japan
Tel.: (81) 593823181
Web Site: http://www.agf.co.jp
Emp.: 466
Coffee Product Mfr
N.A.I.C.S.: 722330

Joint Venture (Non-US):

Ajinomoto General Foods, Inc. (2)
3 20 2 Nishishinjuku Tokyo Opera City 40f,
Tokyo, 160-0023, Japan
Tel.: (81) 353027500
Mobile Food Services
N.A.I.C.S.: 722330

Subsidiary (Non-US):

Dong-Suh Foods Corporation (2)
324 Dokmak-ro Dongseo Building Dohwa-
dong, Mapo-gu, Seoul, 121040, Korea
(South)
Tel.: (82) 80 023 9114
Web Site: https://www.dongsuh.co.kr
Sales Range: $800-899.9 Million
Emp.: 1,700
Coffee & Tea Products Mfr
N.A.I.C.S.: 311920

Kraft Foods Costa Rica, S.A. (2)
300 Meter North Forum 2 Highway San-
tanabelen, San Jose, 10903, Costa Rica
Tel.: (506) 22046000
Emp.: 250
Food & Beverage Products Mfr
N.A.I.C.S.: 722330
Luis G. Rojas (Mgr-Journal)

Kraft Foods Egypt L.L.C. (2)
Ahmed Abd El-Kawy Street Block 1/8 Indus-
trial Zone A1, Cairo, Egypt
Tel.: (20) 15390000
Food & Beverage Products Mfr
N.A.I.C.S.: 722330

Kraft Foods de Nicaragua S.A. (2)
Km 5 Carretera Norte, Edificio Nabisco Crit-
sal de Nicaragua, Managua, Nicaragua
Tel.: (505) 22557389
Food & Beverage Products Mfr
N.A.I.C.S.: 722330

**Kraft Gida Sanayi Ve Ticaret A.
S.** (2)
11 Cumhuriyet Mahllesi 2253 Sokak, Istan-
bul, Turkiye
Tel.: (90) 2626487400
Web Site: http://www.kraftfoods.com
Food & Beverage Products Mfr
N.A.I.C.S.: 722330

Mondelez (Thailand) Co., Ltd. (2)
Q House Lumpini Bulding 1 35th Floor
South Sathorn Road, Tungmahamek
Sathorn, Bangkok, 10120, Thailand
Tel.: (66) 2 227 9000
Web Site:
https://www.mondelezinternational.com
Emp.: 800
Food & Beverage Products Mfr
N.A.I.C.S.: 311340

Mondelez Argentina S.A. (2)
Av Henry Ford 3200 Ricardo Rojas,
B1610BKW, Buenos Aires, Argentina
Tel.: (54) 3327456000
Sales Range: $650-699.9 Million
Emp.: 2,800
Food Products Mfr
N.A.I.C.S.: 311999

Mondelez Australia (Foods) Ltd. (2)
GPO Box 1673, Melbourne, 3001, VIC,
Australia
Tel.: (61) 383756051
Web Site:
http://au.mondelezinternational.com
Food & Beverage Products Mfr
N.A.I.C.S.: 311999

Mondelez International, Inc.—(Continued)

Mondelez Australia Pty. Ltd. **(2)**
Level 6 S Wharf Tower 30 Convention,
Centre Place, Melbourne, 3006, VIC, Australia
Tel.: (61) 396765555
Web Site:
http://www.mondelezinternational.com.au
Sales Range: $600-649.9 Million
Emp.: 3,500
Food Products Distr
N.A.I.C.S.: 424410

Subsidiary (Domestic):

Mondelez Australia Pty. Ltd. - Fishermans Bend **(3)**
PO Box 1673, South Melbourne, Victoria,
3001, Australia
Tel.: (61) 396765555
Web Site:
http://www.mondelezinternational.com
Sales Range: $150-199.9 Million
Emp.: 400
Food Products Mfr & Distr
N.A.I.C.S.: 311999

Subsidiary (Non-US):

Mondelez Bahrain W.L.L. **(2)**
Block 115 Building 1528 Road 1520 Hidd
Industrial Area Near H, PO Box 21701,
Hidd, Bahrain
Tel.: (973) 17464555
Sales Range: $25-49.9 Million
Emp.: 100
Food & Beverage Products Mfr
N.A.I.C.S.: 722330
Terry Denton (Dir-Plant)

Mondelez Chile S.A. **(2)**
Cerro Plomo no 5630 Off 603 Las Condes,
Santiago, 8550189, Chile
Tel.: (56) 22702400
Emp.: 50
Food & Beverage Products Mfr
N.A.I.C.S.: 311821
Martin Stigliano (Gen Mgr)
Martin Stigliamo (Gen Mgr)

Mondelez China Co., Ltd. **(2)**
10/F Kaide Mansion No 1 Building No 6a
Jianguomenwai St Cha, Beijing, 100022,
China
Tel.: (86) 1065690876
Emp.: 6,000
Food & Beverage Products Mfr
N.A.I.C.S.: 424410
Shawn Warren (Pres)

**Mondelez India Foods Private
Limited** **(2)**
Mondelez I Iouse Unit 2001 20th Floor
Tower 3 Wing C, One International Centre,
Mumbai, 400 013, Maharashtra, India
Tel.: (91) 2233963100
Web Site:
http://in.mondelezinternational.com
Food Products Mfr
N.A.I.C.S.: 311999
Deepak Iyer (Pres)

**Mondelez Jiangmen Food Co.,
Ltd.** **(2)**
47 JianShe Rd, Jiangmen, 529000, Guandong, China
Tel.: (86) 8008105536
Sales Range: $25-49.9 Million
Emp.: 50
Biscuit Mfr
N.A.I.C.S.: 311812

**Mondelez Malaysia Sales Sdn.
Bhd.** **(2)**
Lot 9 01 Level 9 1 First Avenue 2A Dataran
Bandar Utama, Bandar Utama Damansara,
47800, Petaling Jaya, Selangor, Malaysia
Tel.: (60) 378726688
Web Site:
https://www.mondelezinternational.com
Food & Beverage Products Distr
N.A.I.C.S.: 424410
Sunil Sethi (Mng Dir)
Peter Bingemann (Mng Dir)

Mondelez Malaysia Sdn Bhd. **(2)**
Lot 9 01 Level 9 1 First Avenue 2A Dataran
Bandar Utama, Bandar Utama Damansara,
47800, Petaling Jaya, Selangor, Malaysia

Tel.: (60) 37 872 6688
Web Site:
http://my.mondelezinternational.com
Sales Range: $250-299.9 Million
Snack Mfr
N.A.I.C.S.: 311812

Mondelez Philippines, Inc. **(2)**
8378 Dr A Santos Avenue, Sucat,
Paranaque, 1700, Metro Manila, Philippines
Tel.: (63) 288582500
Web Site:
http://ph.mondelezinternational.com
Sales Range: $200-249.9 Million
Food Products Mfr
N.A.I.C.S.: 311999

**Mondelez Shanghai Food Co.,
Ltd.** **(2)**
No 440 Caobao Road, Xuhui District,
Shanghai, 200233, China
Tel.: (86) 2161973188
Food & Beverage Products Mfr
N.A.I.C.S.: 311821

Mondelez Singapore Pte. Ltd. **(2)**
346 Jln Boon Lay, Jurong, Singapore,
619528, Singapore
Tel.: (65) 8005723874
Food & Beverage Products Distr
N.A.I.C.S.: 424410
Karen Poon (Country Mgr)

Mondelez Suzhou Food Co., Ltd. **(2)**
No 1 Songxiang Xinglong St Industrial Park,
Suzhou, 215126, China
Tel.: (86) 51262836266
Food & Beverage Products Mfr
N.A.I.C.S.: 311821

Mondelez Taiwan Limited **(2)**
4F No 392 Rueiguang Rd, Neithu District,
Taipei, 11492, Taiwan
Tel.: (886) 287982900
Food & Beverage Products Mfr
N.A.I.C.S.: 311821

Mondelez Uruguay S.A. **(2)**
Yaguaron 1407 Piso 16, Montevideo,
11800, Uruguay
Tel.: (598) 229003000
Web Site:
http://ar.mondelezinternational.com
Emp.: 60
Food & Beverage Products Mfr
N.A.I.C.S.: 311821

**Mondelez World Travel Retail
GmbH** **(2)**
Lindbergh-Allee 1, Glattpark, 8152, Opfikon,
Switzerland
Tel.: (41) 584404040
Food & Beverage Products Distr
N.A.I.C.S.: 424410

P.T. Kraft Ultrajaya Indonesia **(2)**
Jl Raya Cimareme No 131 Ngamprah Kab,
Bandung, 40552, Indonesia
Tel.: (62) 22662091618
Food & Beverage Products Mfr
N.A.I.C.S.: 722330

P.T. Mondelez Indonesia **(2)**
South Quarter B 2nd Floor Unit A-I JI R A
Kartini Kav 8, Cilandak, 12510, Jakarta,
Indonesia
Tel.: (62) 2179198822
Sales Range: $250-299.9 Million
Mfr of Biscuits
N.A.I.C.S.: 311812

**P.T. Mondelez Indonesia
Manufacturing** **(2)**
Jl Jababeka 7 Kav-K2 Cikarang, Bekasi,
17530, West Java, Indonesia
Tel.: (62) 218935340
Sales Range: $75-99.9 Million
Emp.: 800
Food & Beverage Products Mfr
N.A.I.C.S.: 311821
Arjun Bhowmik (Dir-Ops)

**Productos Kraft S. de R.L. de
C.V.** **(2)**
Av Santa Fe No 485 6th Fl Col Cruz
Manca, Mexico, 05349, DF, Mexico
Web Site:
http://mx.mondelezinternational.com
Snack Food & Beverage Products Mfr &
Distr

N.A.I.C.S.: 311999

**The Natural Confectionery Co. Pty
Ltd** **(2)**
Level 6 30 Convention Centre Place, Melbourne, 3006, VIC, Australia
Tel.: (61) 395207444
Sales Range: $10-24.9 Million
Emp.: 45
Food & Beverage Products Mfr
N.A.I.C.S.: 722330

Kraft Foods Entity Holdings B.V. **(1)**
Wilhelminakanaal Zuid 110, 4903 RA, Oosterhout, Netherlands
Tel.: (31) 162474000
Emp.: 120
Holding Company
N.A.I.C.S.: 551112

Kraft Foods Panama, S.A. **(1)**
Avenida Samuel Lewis y Calle 24 Torre
Generali Piso 26, Panama, Panama
Tel.: (507) 3002200
Confectionary Product Mfr
N.A.I.C.S.: 311340

Kraft Foods Sverige Holding AB **(1)**
Smedbyvagen 8, 194 86, Upplands Vasby,
Sweden
Tel.: (46) 86271000
Web Site:
http://www.mondelezinternational.com
Confectionary Product Mfr
N.A.I.C.S.: 311340
Jonas Majnusson (Mng Dir)

**Mondelez Australia Holdings Pty.
Ltd.** **(1)**
Level 3 1 Collins St, Melbourne, 3000, VIC,
Australia
Tel.: (61) 396553881
Web Site: http://www.ibisworld.com.au
Holding Company
N.A.I.C.S.: 551112

**Mondelez Belgium Manufacturing
Services BVBA** **(1)**
De Beukelaer-Pareinlaan 1, 2200, Herentals, Belgium
Tel.: (32) 15743500
Food Products Mfr
N.A.I.C.S.: 311999

Mondelez Brasil Ltda. **(1)**
Avenue Presidente Kennedy 2 511, Curitiba, 80610-404, Brazil
Tel.: (55) 4133144000
Packaged Food Mfr
N.A.I.C.S.: 311412

Mondelez Canada, Inc. **(1)**
277 Gladstone Ave, Toronto, M6J 3L9, ON,
Canada
Sales Range: $350-399.9 Million
Emp.: 3,000
In-house Corporate Services
N.A.I.C.S.: 561499

Subsidiary (Domestic):

Mondelez Canada, Inc.-Montreal **(2)**
2905 Place Louis-R Renaud suite 503, Laval, Montreal, H7V 0A3, QC, Canada
Tel.: (514) 259-6921
Sales Range: $300-349.9 Million
Emp.: 550
Snack Food Preparations Mfr
N.A.I.C.S.: 311999
Terenca Denton (Plant Mgr)

**Mondelez Canada,
Inc.-Scarborough** **(2)**
40 Bertrand Avenue, Scarborough, M1L
2P6, ON, Canada
Tel.: (416) 291-3713
Emp.: 190
Baked Goods Mfr
N.A.I.C.S.: 311812

Mondelez Deutschland Biscuits Production GmbH **(1)**
Gansler Joseph-Strasse 11 Worth, Erding,
86609, Germany
Tel.: (49) 90670040
Web Site:
http://www.mondelezinternational.com
Cookie & Cracker Whslr
N.A.I.C.S.: 424490

Mondelez Espana Confectionery Production, SLU **(1)**
Calle Eucalipto N 25, 28016, Madrid, Spain
Tel.: (34) 913254750
Coffee & Tea Product Mfr
N.A.I.C.S.: 311920

Mondelez Europe GmbH **(1)**
Lindbergh-Allee 1, Glattpark, 8152, Opfikon,
Switzerland
Tel.: (41) 584404040
Web Site:
http://www.mondelezinternational.eu
Emp.: 30,000
Food & Beverage Products Mfr
N.A.I.C.S.: 722330

Subsidiary (Non-US):

**Carlton Lebensmittel Vertriebs
GmbH** **(2)**
Langemarckstrasse 4 20, 28197, Bremen,
Germany
Tel.: (49) 42159901
Mobile Food Services
N.A.I.C.S.: 722330
Jorgen Leisse (Gen Mgr)

Ernest Jackson & Co Limited **(2)**
29 High Street, Crediton, EX17 3AP, Devon,
United Kingdom
Tel.: (44) 1363636000
Web Site: https://www.ejackson.co.uk
Emp.: 150
Food & Beverage Products Mfr
N.A.I.C.S.: 722330

**Kraft Foods (Middle East & Africa)
Ltd.** **(2)**
St Georges House Bayshill Rd, Cheltenham, GL50 3AE, Glos, United Kingdom
Tel.: (44) 1242236101
Food & Beverage Products Mfr
N.A.I.C.S.: 722330

Kraft Foods CEEMA GmbH **(2)**
Fohrenburgstr 1, Bludenz, 6700, Austria
Tel.: (43) 55526090
Web Site:
http://www.mondelezinternational.com
Food & Beverage Products Mfr
N.A.I.C.S.: 722330

Kraft Foods Eesti Osauhing **(2)**
Sopruse Pst 145, 13417, Tallinn, Estonia
Tel.: (372) 6755310
Food & Beverage Products Mfr
N.A.I.C.S.: 722330

**Kraft Foods Finland Production
Oy** **(2)**
Valimotie 5, 01510, Vantaa, Finland
Tel.: (358) 201427400
Web Site: http://www.kraftfoods.com
Food & Beverage Products Mfr
N.A.I.C.S.: 722330

Joint Venture (Non-US):

**Marsa Kraft Jacobs Suchard Sabanci
Gida Sanayi Ve Ticaret A.S** **(2)**
Kucukbakkalkoy Vedat Gunyol Cad Demir
Sok No 1A, Atasehir, Istanbul, Turkiye
Tel.: (90) 2165701400
Web Site: http://www.marsa.com.tr
Sales Range: $25-49.9 Million
Emp.: 100
Food Products Mfr; Owned 51% by Haci
Omer Sabanci Holding A.S. & 49% by Kraft
Foods Inc.
N.A.I.C.S.: 311224

Subsidiary (Non-US):

Mondelez Belgium BVBA **(2)**
Stationsstraat 100, 2800, Mechelen, Belgium
Tel.: (32) 15743500
Web Site:
http://www.mondelezinternational.be
Emp.: 350
Food & Beverage Products Mfr
N.A.I.C.S.: 424410

Subsidiary (Domestic):

Mondelez Belgium Biscuits Production NV **(3)**
De Beukelaer-Pareinlaan 1, 2200, Herentals, Belgium

Tel.: (32) 14241211
Sales Range: $50-74.9 Million
Emp.: 1,300
Food & Beverage Products Mfr
N.A.I.C.S.: 311999

Mondelez Belgium Production BVBA (3)
Montezumalaan 1, Herentals, 2200, Belgium
Tel.: (32) 14251211
Web Site:
   http://www.mondelezinternational.com
Emp.: 300
Food & Beverage Products Mfr
N.A.I.C.S.: 722330

Subsidiary (Non-US):

Mondelez Bulgaria AD (2)
Bldg 3 Fl 4 Business Park, Sofia, 1766, Bulgaria
Tel.: (359) 291011
Food & Beverage Products Mfr
N.A.I.C.S.: 424410
Svetla Lesova (Gen Mgr)

Mondelez Czech Republic s.r.o. (2)
Karolinska 661/4, 186 00, Prague, 8, Czech Republic
Tel.: (420) 296380111
Web Site: http://www.mondelez.jobs.cz
Sales Range: $25-49.9 Million
Emp.: 250
Food & Beverage Products Mfr
N.A.I.C.S.: 722330

Mondelez Czech Republic s.r.o. (2)
Karolinska 661 4, 18600, Prague, Czech Republic
Tel.: (420) 296380111
Web Site: http://mondelez.jobs.cz
Food & Beverage Products Mfr
N.A.I.C.S.: 722330

Mondelez Danmark ApS (2)
Ringager 2A 2 Sal, 2605, Brondby, Denmark
Tel.: (45) 43969622
Web Site:
   http://www.mondelezinternational.dk
Sales Range: $100-124.9 Million
Food Products Sales
N.A.I.C.S.: 424410

Mondelez Deutschland Professional GmbH (2)
Langemarckstrasse 4 20, 28199, Bremen, Germany
Tel.: (49) 42159901
Web Site:
   http://www.mondelezdeutschlandprofessional.de
Emp.: 50
Food & Beverage Products Mfr
N.A.I.C.S.: 311999

Mondelez Espana Biscuits Holdings y Campania S.C. (2)
Calle Del Raigue 12, Montornes del Valles, 08170, Barcelona, Spain
Tel.: (34) 913254750
Food & Beverage Products Mfr
N.A.I.C.S.: 311821

Mondelez Espana Galletas Production, S.L.U. (2)
C/Eucalipto 25, 28016, Madrid, Spain
Tel.: (34) 932272100
Sales Range: $25-49.9 Million
Emp.: 20
Food & Beverage Products Mfr
N.A.I.C.S.: 311821

Mondelez Espana Postres Production, S.A.U. (2)
C/Eucalipto 25, 28016, Madrid, Spain
Tel.: (34) 913254750
Packaged Snack Food Distr
N.A.I.C.S.: 424490

Mondelez Espana Services, S.L.U. (2)
C/Eucalipto 25, 28016, Madrid, Spain
Tel.: (34) 913254750
Mobile Food Services
N.A.I.C.S.: 722330

Mondelez European Business Services Centre s.r.o. (2)

Racianska 44, PO Box 400, 814 99, Bratislava, Slovakia
Tel.: (421) 49249243111
Food & Beverage Products Mfr
N.A.I.C.S.: 311821
Martin Hric (Mgr-Production)

Mondelez Finland Oy (2)
Tammiston kauppatie 7B, PO Box 1000, 1510, Vantaa, Finland
Tel.: (358) 201427400
Web Site:
   http://www.mondelezinternational.fi
Food & Beverage Products Mfr
N.A.I.C.S.: 722330

Mondelez France SAS (2)
6 avenue Reaumur, 92140, Clamart, France
Tel.: (33) 183113000
Web Site:
   http://www.mondelezinternational.fr
Sales Range: $400-449.9 Million
Food Preparation Mfr & Distr
N.A.I.C.S.: 311999

Subsidiary (Domestic):

Generale Biscuit SAS (3)
Batiment Saarinen 3 rue saarinen, Rungis, 94150, France
Tel.: (33) 156344000
Food & Beverage Products Mfr
N.A.I.C.S.: 722330

Kraft Foods France Intellectual Property S.A.S. (3)
13 Ave Morane Saulnier, 78140, Velizy-Villacoublay, France
Tel.: (33) 890210090
Food & Beverage Products Mfr
N.A.I.C.S.: 722330

Mondelez France Biscuits Production SAS (3)
3 rue Saarinen Batiment Saarinen Cedex, 94150, Rungis, France
Tel.: (33) 156344000
Web Site: http://www.lu-france.fr
Sales Range: $750-799.9 Million
Emp.: 3,077
Cookies, Biscuits & Snacks Mfr
N.A.I.C.S.: 311821

Branch (Non-US):

LU Biscuits-Barcelona (4)
Galileo Galilei 27-29 Industrial Area Coll De La Manya, 08403, Granollers, Spain
Tel.: (34) 932272100
Sales Range: $125-149.9 Million
Emp.: 300
Biscuits & Packaged Bread Products
N.A.I.C.S.: 311821

Subsidiary (Non-US):

LU General Biscuits Belgie N.V. (4)
De Beukelaer Pareinlaan 1, B 2200, Herentals, Belgium
Tel.: (32) 15 743888
Sales Range: $550-599.9 Million
Emp.: 1,300
Biscuits, Snacks, Packaged Bread Products Mfr
N.A.I.C.S.: 311821

LU General Biscuits Nederland B.V. (4)
Antwoordnummer 10036, 4903 RA, Oosterhout, Netherlands
Tel.: (31) 765231300
Web Site: http://www.lu.nl
Biscuits & Snacks Mfr
N.A.I.C.S.: 311821

LU Polska S.A. (4)
Domaniewska 49, 02-672, Warsaw, Poland
Tel.: (48) 228571000
Sales Range: $250-299.9 Million
Emp.: 300
Biscuit Mfr
N.A.I.C.S.: 311812
Agnieszka Kepinska (Gen Mgr)

Subsidiary (Non-US):

Saiwa S.r.l. (3)
Via Antonio Cecchi 6, IT-16129, Genoa, Italy
Tel.: (39) 01053921
Web Site: http://www.kraftfoods.com

Sales Range: $250-299.9 Million
Emp.: 60
Cracker Mfr
N.A.I.C.S.: 311821

Subsidiary (Non-US):

Mondelez Hellas S.A. (2)
Lamia National Road, 144 52, Metamorfosis, Greece
Tel.: (30) 2102889000
Web Site:
   http://www.mondelezinternational.gr
Sales Range: $150-199.9 Million
Prepared Food & Candy Mfr
N.A.I.C.S.: 311351

Mondelez Hungaria Kft (2)
Neumann Janos u 1/E, 1117, Budapest, Hungary
Tel.: (36) 13824242
Web Site:
   http://www.mondelezinternational.hu
Food & Beverage Products Distr
N.A.I.C.S.: 424410

Subsidiary (Domestic):

Mondelez International Finance AG (2)
Lindbergh-Allee 1, Glattpark, 8152, Opfikon, Switzerland
Tel.: (41) 417490440
Sales Range: $10-24.9 Million
Emp.: 12
Holding Company
N.A.I.C.S.: 522320

Subsidiary (Non-US):

Mondelez Ireland Limited (2)
Malahide Road, Coolock, Dublin, Ireland
Tel.: (353) 18480000
Food & Beverage Products Mfr
N.A.I.C.S.: 722330
Kieran Conway (Dir-Category Plng)
Eoin Kellett (Mng Dir)
Louise Stignant (Dir-Comml-Northern Europe)

Mondelez Italia S.r.l. (2)
Via Nizzoli 3, 20147, Milan, Italy
Tel.: (39) 0241351
Web Site:
   http://www.mondelezinternational.it
Food & Beverage Products Mfr
N.A.I.C.S.: 424410

Mondelez Namur Production SPRL (2)
Tel.: (32) 81563211
Web Site: http://www.mondelez.com
Food & Beverage Products Mfr
N.A.I.C.S.: 311821

Mondelez Nederland Services B.V. (2)
America Tower Wilhelminakanaal Zuid 110, 4903 RA, Oosterhout, Netherlands
Tel.: (31) 162474000
Sales Range: $25-49.9 Million
Emp.: 10
Food & Beverage Products Mfr
N.A.I.C.S.: 424410
Am Wheelan Balk (Gen Mgr)

Mondelez Norge AS (2)
Johan Throne Holsts plass 1, Pb 6658, Rodelokka, 0502, Oslo, Norway
Tel.: (47) 22044022
Web Site: https://www.freia.no
Food & Beverage Products Mfr
N.A.I.C.S.: 424410

Mondelez Osterreich GmbH (2)
Fohrenburgstrasse 1, 6700, Bludenz, Austria
Tel.: (43) 160544400
Web Site:
   http://www.mondelezinternational.at
Sales Range: $150-199.9 Million
Emp.: 342
Food Products Mfr & Distr
N.A.I.C.S.: 311999

Mondelez Polska S.A. (2)
Domaniewska 49 street, 02-672, Warsaw, Poland
Tel.: (48) 228571000
Web Site: http://www.karierakraftfoods.pl

Sales Range: $400-449.9 Million
Food Products Mfr
N.A.I.C.S.: 311999

Mondelez Portugal Iberia Production, S.A. (2)
Estr Alfragide Alfrapark Edif F Sul Piso 2 Bldg C Fl 3, 2720-000, Amadora, Portugal
Tel.: (351) 707200195
Web Site: http://www.mondelez.com
Emp.: 70
Food & Beverage Products Mfr
N.A.I.C.S.: 722330

Mondelez Portugal, Unipessoal, Lda. (2)
Alfrapark Estrada Do Seminario 4 Edificio C Piso 3, Alfragide, Amadora, 2610-171, Portugal
Tel.: (351) 219266700
Food & Beverage Products Mfr
N.A.I.C.S.: 424410

Mondelez Schweiz GmbH (2)
Tel.: (41) 584404040
Web Site:
   http://www.mondelezinternational.ch
Sales Range: $250-299.9 Million
Food Products Mfr
N.A.I.C.S.: 311999

Subsidiary (Domestic):

Mondelez Schweiz Production GmbH (3)
Riedbachstrasse 150-151, 3027, Bern, Switzerland
Tel.: (41) 795907997
Food & Beverage Products Mfr
N.A.I.C.S.: 311821

Taloca GmbH (3)
Chollerstrasse 4, 6301, Zug, Switzerland
Tel.: (41) 417490101
Web Site: http://www.kraftfoods.com
Sales Range: $25-49.9 Million
Emp.: 60
Food Whslr
N.A.I.C.S.: 722310

Subsidiary (Non-US):

Taloca Cafe Ltda. (4)
Fr Gaspar 24 26 1 & Cj 11 12, Santos, 11010-090, Brazil
Tel.: (55) 1321011700
Food & Beverage Products Mfr
N.A.I.C.S.: 722330

Subsidiary (Non-US):

Mondelez Slovakia s.r.o. (2)
Racianska 44, 832 42, Bratislava, Slovakia
Tel.: (421) 249243111
Web Site:
   http://eu.mondelezinternational.com
Food & Beverage Products Mfr
N.A.I.C.S.: 311821
Gabriela Bechynska (Mgr-Corp & Govt Affairs-CZ & SK)

Mondelez Strasbourg Production S.N.C. (2)
12 Route De La Federation, Strasbourg, 67100, France
Tel.: (33) 388319100
Web Site:
   http://www.mondelezinternational.com
Sales Range: $50-74.9 Million
Emp.: 200
Food & Beverage Products Mfr
N.A.I.C.S.: 722330

Mondelez Sverige AB (2)
Smedbyvagen 8, 194 86, Upplands Vasby, Sweden
Tel.: (46) 86271000
Web Site:
   http://eu.mondelezinternational.com
Emp.: 500
Food & Beverage Products Distr
N.A.I.C.S.: 424410

Mondelez UK Limited (2)
Sanderson Road, Uxbridge, UB8 1DH, Middlesex, United Kingdom
Tel.: (44) 1242236101
Sales Range: $400-449.9 Million
Emp.: 600

Mondelez International, Inc.—(Continued)

Chocolate & Confectionary Mfr; Chocolate Research & Development
N.A.I.C.S.: 311351
Jack Pipe *(Dir-Convenience Sls)*

Paddington   **(2)**
1 Rue Christian Moench, 54270, Nancy, France
Tel.: (33) 383295050
Food & Beverage Products Mfr
N.A.I.C.S.: 722330

Mondelez International (Thailand) Co., Ltd   **(1)**
35/F Q House Lumpini Tower 1 South Sathorn Road, Tungmahamek Sathorn, Bangkok, 10120, Thailand
Tel.: (66) 22279000
Web Site:
    http://th.mondelezinternational.com
Emp.: 1,300
Food Products Mfr
N.A.I.C.S.: 311999

Mondelez International Management Center-East Hanover   **(1)**
100 DeForest Ave, East Hanover, NJ 07936
Tel.: (973) 503-2000
Web Site:
    http://www.mondelezinternational.com
Food Production & Marketing Services
N.A.I.C.S.: 424490

Mondelez International Rus   **(1)**
Dolgorukovskaya Str 7, 127006, Moscow, Russia
Tel.: (7) 4959602480
Web Site:
    http://www.mondelezinternational.com
Emp.: 200
Confectionary Product Mfr
N.A.I.C.S.: 311340

Mondelez Ireland Production Limited   **(1)**
Malahide Road, Coolock, Dublin, Ireland
Tel.: (353) 18480000
Food Products Mfr
N.A.I.C.S.: 311999
Aodhan Breen *(Mgr-Safety, Sustainability & Facilities)*

Mondelez Japan Ltd   **(1)**
13th Floor Shinagawa Seaside East Tower 4-12-8 Higashi-Shinagawa, Shinagawa-ku, Tokyo, 140-0002, Fukuoka, Japan
Tel.: (81) 345106600
Confectionery Product Distr
N.A.I.C.S.: 424450

Mondelez Kinh Do Vietnam JSC (1)
Floor 8 Empress Tower 138-142 Hai Ba Trung Street, DaKao Ward District 1, Ho Chi Minh City, Vietnam
Tel.: (84) 283 827 0457
Web Site:
    https://www.mondelezinternational.com
Sales Range: Less than $1 Million
Emp.: 3,000
Food Products Mfr
N.A.I.C.S.: 311813

Mondelez Nederland B.V.   **(1)**
Verlengde Poolseweg 34, 4818 CL, Breda, Netherlands
Tel.: (31) 767998300
Snack Food Mfr
N.A.I.C.S.: 311919

Mondelez New Zealand   **(1)**
476 Rosebank Road, Avondale, Auckland, 1026, New Zealand
Tel.: (64) 800444045
Web Site:
    https://www.mondelezinternational.com
Cookie & Cracker Whslr
N.A.I.C.S.: 424490

Mondelez Oesterreich Production GmbH   **(1)**
Fohrenburgstrabe 1, Bludenz, 6700, Vorarlberg, Austria
Tel.: (43) 55526090
Web Site: http://www.mondelez.com
Chocolate & Cocoa Product Mfr
N.A.I.C.S.: 311351
Andreas Kutil *(Mng Dir-Sls)*

Mondelez Pakistan Limited   **(1)**

6th Floor Tower B World Trade Centre Main Khayaban-e-Roomi, Clifton, Karachi, 75600, Pakistan
Tel.: (92) 21358652815
Snack Food Mfr
N.A.I.C.S.: 311919

Mondelez Polska Production sp. z.o.o.   **(1)**
ul Domaniewska 49, 02-672, Warsaw, Poland
Tel.: (48) 228571000
Snack Food Mfr
N.A.I.C.S.: 311919

Mondelez Puerto Rico LLC   **(1)**
9615 Ave Los Romeros Ste 801 Montehiedra Office Ctr, San Juan, PR 00926
Tel.: (787) 522-9810
Food Products Mfr
N.A.I.C.S.: 311999

Mondelez South Africa (Pty) Ltd. (1)
6 Woodmead Estate Woodmead Drive, Johannesburg, 2196, Gauteng, South Africa
Tel.: (27) 112534000
Emp.: 1,000
Confectionary Product Mfr
N.A.I.C.S.: 311340
Joost Vlaanderen *(Mng Dir)*

Mondelez Turkey Gida Uretim A.S.   **(1)**
Cumhuriyet Mah 2253 Sok No 11, 41400, Gebze, Kocaeli, Türkiye
Tel.: (90) 8502104666
Bakery Product Mfr & Distr
N.A.I.C.S.: 311812

Mondelez d.o.o. Beograd   **(1)**
88b/III Omladinskih brigada Str, Belgrade, 11070, Serbia
Tel.: (381) 113530800
Web Site:
    http://www.mondelezinternational.com
Confectionary Product Mfr
N.A.I.C.S.: 311340

Opavia Lu s.r.o.   **(1)**
Kolonada factory Machova 272, 353 01, Marianske Lazne, Czech Republic
Tel.: (420) 553605102
Emp.: 400
Bakery Products Mfr
N.A.I.C.S.: 311821

Perfect Bar, LLC   **(1)**
Web Site: http://www.perfectsnacks.com
Nutrition Product Mfr & Distr
N.A.I.C.S.: 311911

Servicios Integrales Kraft, S. de R.L. de C.V.   **(1)**
Via Morelos 314, 55550, Mexico, Mexico
Tel.: (52) 5552588705
Confectionary Product Mfr
N.A.I.C.S.: 311340

Tate's Bake Shop   **(1)**
43 N Sea Rd, Southampton, NY 11968
Tel.: (631) 283-9830
Web Site: http://www.tatesbakeshop.com
Sweet & Cake Mfr
N.A.I.C.S.: 311811
Nancy Pak *(CEO)*

Thrive 365 LLC   **(1)**
9520 Ormsby Station Rd Ste 20, Louisville, KY 40223
Tel.: (502) 289-8020
Web Site: https://thrive365.com
Snack Food Mfr
N.A.I.C.S.: 311919

Tsimis S.A.   **(1)**
55 Pireos Str, Moschato, 183 46, Athens, Greece
Tel.: (30) 2104813707
Web Site: https://www.tsimis.gr
Printing & Packaging Product Mfr
N.A.I.C.S.: 326112

Xtrapack Limited   **(1)**
7 Bell Yard, London, WC2A 2JR, United Kingdom
Tel.: (44) 7718282346
Web Site: https://www.xtrapack.co.uk
Snack Food Mfr
N.A.I.C.S.: 311919

MONEYLION INC.

249 W 17 st St 4 th Fl, New York, NY 10011
Tel.: (212) 300-9865   **DE**
Web Site:
    https://www.moneylion.com
Year Founded: 2020
ML—(NYSE)
Rev.: $340,745,000
Assets: $596,342,000
Liabilities: $497,181,000
Net Worth: $99,161,000
Earnings: ($195,946,000)
Emp.: 677
Fiscal Year-end: 12/31/22
Investment Services
N.A.I.C.S.: 523999
Mark Torossian *(Chief Acctg Officer)*
John James *(CEO)*

Subsidiaries:

Malka Media Group LLC   **(1)**
75 Montgomery St, Jersey City, NJ 07302
Tel.: (201) 292-7897
Web Site: https://www.malkamedia.com
Sales Range: $1-9.9 Million
Media Advertising Services
N.A.I.C.S.: 541850
Louis Krubich *(Co-Founder & CEO)*
Jeff Frommer *(Co-Founder & Pres)*

MONEYONMOBILE, INC.

500 N Akard St Ste 2850, Dallas, TX 75201
Tel.: (214) 758-8600   **TX**
Web Site: http://www.money-on-mobile.com
Year Founded: 2006
MOMT—(OTCIQ)
Sales Range: $1-9.9 Million
Emp.: 7
Credit Card Processing Services
N.A.I.C.S.: 561499
Harold H. Montgomery *(Founder)*

MONGODB, INC.

1633 Broadway 38th Fl, New York, NY 10019
Tel.: (646) 727-4092   **DE**
Web Site: https://www.mongodb.com
Year Founded: 2007
MDB—(NASDAQ)
Rev.: $1,683,011,000
Assets: $2,869,642,000
Liabilities: $1,800,653,000
Net Worth: $1,068,989,000
Earnings: ($176,600,000)
Emp.: 5,037
Fiscal Year-end: 01/31/24
Database Management Software Developer
N.A.I.C.S.: 513210
Eliot Horowitz *(Founder)*
Dev C. Ittycheria *(Pres & CEO)*
Cailin Nelson *(Exec VP-Cloud & Engrg)*
Andrew Stephens *(Gen Counsel)*
Michael Lawrence Gordon *(CFO & COO)*
Sahir Azam *(Chief Product Officer)*
Cedric Pech *(Chief Revenue Officer)*
Lena Smart *(Chief Information Security Officer)*
Harsha Jalihal *(Chief People Officer)*
Peder Ulander *(CMO)*
Mindy Lieberman *(CIO)*

Subsidiaries:

MongoDB Limited   **(1)**
Building 2 Number 1 Ballsbridge Shellbourne Road, Ballsbridge, Dublin, D04 Y3X9, Ireland
Tel.: (353) 19014654
Software Development Services
N.A.I.C.S.: 541511
Eliot Horowitz *(Co-Founder & CTO)*

MONOLITHIC POWER SYSTEMS, INC.

5808 Lake Washington Blvd NE, Kirkland, WA 98033
Tel.: (425) 296-9956   **CA**
Web Site:
    https://www.monolithicpower.com
Year Founded: 1997
MPWR—(NASDAQ)
Rev.: $1,821,072,000
Assets: $2,434,353,000
Liabilities: $384,414,000
Net Worth: $2,049,939,000
Earnings: $427,374,000
Emp.: 3,564
Fiscal Year-end: 12/31/23
Analog & Mixed-Signal Semiconductor Designer & Marketer
N.A.I.C.S.: 334413
Maurice Sciammas *(Sr VP-Sls & Mktg-Worldwide)*
T. Bernie Blegen *(CFO & VP)*
Saria Tseng *(Gen Counsel, Sec & VP-Strategic Corp Dev)*
Michael R. Hsing *(Chm, Pres & CEO)*

Subsidiaries:

Chengdu Monolithic Power Systems Co., Ltd.   **(1)**
8 Kexin Road, West Park of Export Processing Zone West Hi-Tech Zone, Chengdu, 611731, Sichuan, China **(100%)**
Tel.: (86) 288 730 3000
Web Site: http://www.monolithicpower.com
Sales Range: $100-124.9 Million
Mfr of Semiconductors
N.A.I.C.S.: 334413

Hangzhou MPS Semiconductor Technology Ltd.   **(1)**
Floor6 Building A2 Xixi Center No 588 West Wenyi Road, Xihu District, Hangzhou, 310012, Zhejiang, China
Tel.: (86) 571 89818588
Semiconductor Mfr
N.A.I.C.S.: 334413

MPS Europe SARL   **(1)**
Alte Landstrasse 25, 1080 Chemin La Croix Verte, 85521, Ottobrunn, France **(100%)**
Tel.: (33) 8980913512
Web Site: http://www.monolithicpower.com
Sales Range: $100-124.9 Million
Emp.: 4
Semiconductor Mfr
N.A.I.C.S.: 334413

MPS International (Shanghai) Ltd.   **(1)**
Floor 27 Magnolia Plaza No 777 Hongqiao Road, Xuhui District, Shanghai, 20030, China   **(100%)**
Tel.: (86) 2122251700
Web Site: http://www.monolithicpower.com
Sales Range: $100-124.9 Million
Semiconductor Mfr
N.A.I.C.S.: 334413

MPS International (Taiwan) Ltd. **(1)**
29F No 97 Section 1 Xintai 5th Rd, Xizhi District, New Taipei City, 104, Taiwan   **(100%)**
Tel.: (886) 286911600
Web Site: http://www.monolithicpower.com
Sales Range: $100-124.9 Million
Emp.: 30
Semiconductor Mfr
N.A.I.C.S.: 334413

MPS International Korea Co., Ltd.   **(1)**
C 403 4F Pangyo Digital Center Sampyongdong 624 5pilgi, Bundang-gu, Seongnam, 13487, Kyunggi-do, Korea (South) **(100%)**
Tel.: (82) 7078309950
Web Site: http://www.monolithicpower.com
Sales Range: $10-24.9 Million
Emp.: 12
Mfr of Semiconductors
N.A.I.C.S.: 334413

MPS Japan K.K.   **(1)**
Shinjuku Sumitomo Bldg 31F 2-6-1, Nishishinjuku Shinjuku-ku, Tokyo, 163-0231, Japan   **(100%)**
Tel.: (81) 359890885
Web Site: http://www.monolithicpower.com

Sales Range: $1-9.9 Million
Emp.: 5
Mfr of Semiconductors
N.A.I.C.S.: 334413

MPS Tech Switzerland Sarl (1)
Route de Lully 5 A, 1131, Tolochenaz, Switzerland
Tel.: (41) 218050100
Semiconductor Devices Mfr
N.A.I.C.S.: 334413

Monolithic Power Spain, S.L. (1)
Av Josep Tarradellas 123 5-A, 08029, Barcelona, Spain
Tel.: (34) 931815400
Semiconductor Device & Related Product Mfr
N.A.I.C.S.: 334413
Enric Rodriguez (Mgr-Engrg Application)

MONOPAR THERAPEUTICS INC.
1000 Skokie Blvd Ste 350, Wilmette, IL 60091
Tel.: (847) 388-0349   DE
Web Site:
    https://www.monopartx.com
Year Founded: 2014
MNPR—(NASDAQ)
Rev.: $21,239
Assets: $13,226,954
Liabilities: $3,137,302
Net Worth: $10,089,652
Earnings: ($10,515,638)
Emp.: 11
Fiscal Year-end: 12/31/22
Immunotherapy Research & Development Services
N.A.I.C.S.: 541714
Chandler D. Robinson (Co-Founder & CEO)
Christopher M. Starr (Co/Co-Founder, Chm & Chm)
Andrew P. Mazar (Co-Founder)
Patrice Rioux (Chief Medical Acting Officer)
Andrew Cittadine (COO)

MONRO, INC.
200 Holleder Pkwy, Rochester, NY 14615
Tel.: (585) 647-6400   NY
Web Site: http://www.monro.com
Year Founded: 1966
MNRO—(NASDAQ)
Rev.: $1,359,328,000
Assets: $1,871,412,000
Liabilities: $1,088,506,000
Net Worth: $782,906,000
Earnings: $61,568,000
Emp.: 8,750
Fiscal Year-end: 03/26/22
Automotive Repair Services
N.A.I.C.S.: 811111
Robert E. Mellor (Chm)
Brian J. D'Ambrosia (CFO, Treas & Exec VP-Fin)
Gerald G. Alessia (Chief Mdsg Officer & Sr VP)
Maureen E. Mulholland (Gen Counsel, Sec & Sr VP)
Jack Heisman (VP-Business Development-Real Estate)
Robert Rajkowski (COO & Sr VP)
Cindy Donovan (VP-IT)
Karla Hock (VP-Risk-Safety Mgmt)
Michael T. Broderick (Pres & CEO)
Felix Veksler (Sr Dir-IR)

Subsidiaries:

Certified Tire & Service Centers, Inc. (1)
1875 Iowa Ave, Riverside, CA 92507-2507
Tel.: (510) 523-2900
Web Site: http://www.certifiedtire.com
Tire Dealers
N.A.I.C.S.: 441340

Monro Service Corporation (1)

200 Holldder Pkwy, Rochester, NY 14615
Tel.: (585) 647-6400
Web Site: http://www.monro.com
Sales Range: $500-549.9 Million
Emp.: 2,000
Automotive Exhaust System Repair
N.A.I.C.S.: 811114
Robert G. Gross (Chm)

Mr. Tire, Inc. (1)
200 Holleder Pkwy, Rochester, NY 14615
Web Site: http://www.mrtire.com
Tires & Tubes Whslr
N.A.I.C.S.: 423130

Tire Warehouse Central Inc. (1)
1042 W Swanzey Rd, Swanzey, NH 03446-3219
Tel.: (603) 352-7500
Web Site: http://www.tirewarehouse.net
Sales Range: $50-74.9 Million
Emp.: 250
Provider of Automotive Tires
N.A.I.C.S.: 441340

MONROE CAPITAL CORPORATION
311 S Wacker Dr 64th Fl, Chicago, IL 60606
Tel.: (312) 258-8300   MD
Web Site:
    https://www.monroebdc.com
Year Founded: 2011
MRCC—(NASDAQ)
Rev.: $56,566,000
Assets: $564,995,000
Liabilities: $339,976,000
Net Worth: $225,019,000
Earnings: $22,192,000
Fiscal Year-end: 12/31/22
Business Management Consulting Services
N.A.I.C.S.: 541611
Theodore L. Koenig (Founder, Chm & CEO)
David H. Jacobson (Chief Compliance Officer)
Lewis W. Solimene Jr. (CFO, Chief Investment Officer & Sec)

MONSTER ARTS, INC.
3565 S Las Vegas Blvd Ste 120, Las Vegas, NV 89109
Tel.: (725) 222-8281   NV
Year Founded: 2007
APPZ—(OTCEM)
Sales Range: Less than $1 Million
Emp.: 1
Software Developer for Mobile Devices, Smart TV & Set Top Boxes
N.A.I.C.S.: 513210
Wayne Irving II (Chm, Pres & CEO)

MONSTER BEVERAGE CORPORATION
1 Monster Way, Corona, CA 92879
Tel.: (951) 739-6200   DE
Web Site:
    https://www.monsterbevcorp.com
Year Founded: 2002
MNST—(NASDAQ)
Rev.: $7,140,027,000
Assets: $9,686,522,000
Liabilities: $1,457,778,000
Net Worth: $8,228,744,000
Earnings: $1,630,988,000
Emp.: 5,254
Fiscal Year-end: 12/31/23
Beverages Mfr
N.A.I.C.S.: 551112
Hilton H. Schlosberg (Vice Chm & Co-CEO)
Rodney C. Sacks (Chm & Co-CEO)
Thomas J. Kelly (CFO)

Subsidiaries:

American Fruits & Flavors LLC (1)
10725 Sutter Ave, Pacoima, CA 91331
Tel.: (818) 899-9574

Web Site: https://www.americanfruits-flavors.com
Juices & Food Products Mfr
N.A.I.C.S.: 311930

Division (Domestic):

American Fruits & Flavors LLC - Juice Division (2)
10725 Sutter Ave, Pacoima, CA 91331
Tel.: (818) 899-9574
Web Site: http://www.americanfruits-flavors.com
Fruit & Vegetable Canning Services
N.A.I.C.S.: 311421

Blue Sky Natural Beverage Co. (1)
550 Monica Cir Ste 201, Corona, CA 92880-5496
Tel.: (951) 739-6200
Web Site: http://www.drinkbluesky.com
Soft Drinks Mfr
N.A.I.C.S.: 312111
Rodney Sacks (Pres)

Energy Beverages LLC (1)
159 Concourse Dr, Pearl, MS 39208
Tel.: (601) 936-4606
Web Site:
    https://www.energybeveragemanage
    ment.com
Beverage Distr
N.A.I.C.S.: 424820

Fastest, LLC (1)
9909 Osuna Rd NE, Albuquerque, NM 87111-2255
Tel.: (505) 881-4274
Soft Drink Whslr
N.A.I.C.S.: 424490

Full Throttle Energy Company (1)
2390 Anselmo Dr, Corona, CA 92879
Tel.: (844) 538-7741
Web Site: http://www.drinkfullthrottle.com
Energy Drink Mfr
N.A.I.C.S.: 312111

Hansen Beverage Company (1)
1 Monsterway, Corona, CA 92879
Tel.: (951) 739-6200
Web Site: http://www.hansens.com
Fruit Juices, Natural Sodas & Energy Drinks Developer, Mfr & Marketer
N.A.I.C.S.: 312111
Hilton H. Schlosberg (COO & Sec)

Monster Energy Austria GmbH (1)
Teinfaltstrasse 8, 1010, Vienna, Austria
Tel.: (43) 15339630
Soft Drinks Mfr
N.A.I.C.S.: 312111

Monster Energy Company (1)
1 Monster Way Corona, Corona, CA 92879
Tel.: (678) 265-1580
Web Site: https://www.monsterenergy.com
Emp.: 6
Energy Drink Product Whslr
N.A.I.C.S.: 424490
Hilton H. Schlosberg (Vice Chm & CEO)
Rodney C. Sacks (Chm)

Monster Energy US LLC (1)
550 Monica Cir Ste 201, Corona, CA 92880
Tel.: (951) 739-6200
Energy Drink Product Whslr
N.A.I.C.S.: 424490

NOS Energy Company (1)
2390 Anselmo Dr, Corona, CA 92879
Web Site: https://www.drinknos.com
Energy Drink Mfr
N.A.I.C.S.: 312111

Reign Beverage Company LLC (1)
1547 N Knowles Ave, Los Angeles, CA 90063
Web Site: https://reignbodyfuel.com
Natural Caffeine & Electrolyte Mfr
N.A.I.C.S.: 325411

Vital Pharmaceuticals, Inc. (1)
1600 N Park Dr, Weston, FL 33326-3278
Tel.: (954) 641-0570
Web Site: http://www.vpxsports.com
Sales Range: $1-9.9 Million
Emp.: 110
Dietary Supplement Mfr & Marketer
N.A.I.C.S.: 325412

John H. Owoc (Founder)
Eric Hoult (Dir-Meltdown Diet-Natl)
Eugene Bukovi (COO)
Jose Rodriguez (Mgr-Processing)
John C. DiDonato (Interim CEO & Chief Transformation Officer)
Steve Panagos (Chm)

MONSTER DIGITAL, INC.
2655 Park Ctr Dr Unit C, Simi Valley, CA 93065
Tel.: (805) 955-4190   DE
Web Site:
    http://www.monsterdigital.com
MSDI—(NASDAQ)
Sales Range: $1-9.9 Million
Camera, Data Storage & Memory Products Developer, Mfr & Whslr
N.A.I.C.S.: 333310
David Howard Clarke (Chm & CEO)
David Olert (CFO)
Vivek Tandon (Dir-Bus Dev)
Neal Bobrick (Exec VP-Sls & Mktg)
Jawahar Lal Tandon (Founder)

MONTAGUE INTERNATIONAL HOLDING LTD.
1735 Market St Ste 3750, Philadelphia, PA 19103
Tel.: (267) 397-8039   OK
Year Founded: 2009
MIHL—(OTCIQ)
Financial Management Services
N.A.I.C.S.: 523999
Yossi Harel (VP)
Gregory Malits (VP-Technology)
Maureen Lerman-Gotli (VP)
Alexandr Kladchenko (VP)
Tony Pierce (VP)
Fredrik Sjodin (VP)
Robert Ringold (Chm)

MONTANA TECHNOLOGIES CORPORATION
34361 Innovation Dr, Ronan, MT 59864   DE
Web Site: https://mt.energy
Year Founded: 2021
AIRJ—(NASDAQ)
Rev.: $9,331,453
Assets: $114,700,694
Liabilities: $129,676,891
Net Worth: ($14,976,197)
Earnings: $1,242,993
Emp.: 18
Fiscal Year-end: 12/31/23
Renewable Energy Services
N.A.I.C.S.: 221210

MONTAUK HOLDINGS LIMITED
680 Andersen Dr Foster Plaza Ste 10 5th Floor, Pittsburgh, PA 15220
Tel.: (412) 747-8700
Web Site:
    http://www.montaukenergy.com
MNK—(JSE)
Rev.: $118,975,000
Assets: $262,973,000
Liabilities: $111,513,000
Net Worth: $151,460,000
Earnings: $20,125,000
Fiscal Year-end: 03/31/19
Gas Pipeline Production & Electric Power Generation Services
N.A.I.C.S.: 237120
Sean Fitzgerald McClain (CFO)
Martin Leonard Ryan (CEO)
Ira G. Pearl (COO)

MONTAUK RENEWABLES, INC.
5313 Campbells Run Rd Ste 200, Pittsburgh, PA 15205
Tel.: (412) 747-8700   DE
Web Site: https://montaukenergy.com
Year Founded: 2020

Montauk Renewables, Inc.—(Continued)

MNTK—(NASDAQ)
Rev.: $205,559,000
Assets: $332,316,000
Liabilities: $105,225,000
Net Worth: $227,091,000
Earnings: $35,194,000
Emp.: 137
Fiscal Year-end: 12/31/22
Renewable Energy Consulting Services
N.A.I.C.S.: 541690
Kevin A. Van Asdalan *(CFO)*
John Ciroli *(Chief Legal Officer, Gen Counsel, Sec & VP)*
James A. Shaw *(VP-Ops)*
Sharon R. Frank *(VP-Environmental, Health, and Safety)*
Sean Fitzgerald McClain *(Pres & CEO)*

MONTE ROSA THERAPEUTICS, INC.

321 Harrison Ave Ste 900, Boston, MA 02118
Tel.: (617) 949-2643   DE
Web Site:
   https://www.monterosatx.com
Year Founded: 2019
GLUE—(NASDAQ)
Rev.: $3,883,000
Assets: $342,389,000
Liabilities: $70,976,000
Net Worth: $271,413,000
Earnings: ($108,501,000)
Emp.: 123
Fiscal Year-end: 12/31/22
Biotechnology Research & Development Services
N.A.I.C.S.: 541714
Sharon Townson *(CTO & Chief Scientific Officer)*
Filip Janku *(Chief Medical Officer)*
Jullian Jones *(Sr VP & Head-Bus Dev)*
Silvia Buonamici *(Sr VP-Drug Discovery Biology)*
Phil Nickson *(Chief Legal Officer, Chief Bus Officer & Head-Legal Ops)*
Jennifer Champoux *(COO)*
Pamela Carey *(VP-Fin)*
Alexander Mayweg *(Chm)*
Markus Warmuth *(CEO)*

MONTEREY INNOVATION ACQUISITION CORP.

17 State St 21st Fl, New York, NY 10004
Tel.: (917) 267-0216   DE
Web Site:
   https://www.montereyinnova
   tion.com
Year Founded: 2020
MTRY—(NASDAQ)
Rev.: $881,092
Assets: $21,418,521
Liabilities: $22,559,948
Net Worth: ($1,141,427)
Earnings: ($1,273,875)
Emp.: 2
Fiscal Year-end: 12/31/22
Investment Services
N.A.I.C.S.: 523999
Sanjeev Satyal *(CEO)*
William McKeever *(CFO)*

MONTES ARCHIMEDES ACQUISITION CORP.

724 Oak Grove Ste 130, Menlo Park, CA 94025
Tel.: (650) 384-6558   DE
Web Site:
   http://www.montesarchimedesac
   quisitioncorp.com
Year Founded: 2020

MAACU—(NASDAQ)
Investment Services
N.A.I.C.S.: 523999
James C. Momtazee *(Chm, Pres & CEO)*

MONTROSE ENVIRONMENTAL GROUP, INC.

5120 Nshore Dr, North Little Rock, AR 72118
Tel.: (501) 900-6400
Web Site: https://www.montrose-
   env.com
MEG—(NYSE)
Rev.: $544,416,000
Assets: $791,914,000
Liabilities: $478,727,000
Net Worth: $313,187,000
Earnings: ($48,219,000)
Emp.: 2,900
Fiscal Year-end: 12/31/22
Environmental Consulting Services
N.A.I.C.S.: 541620
Vijay Manthripragada *(Pres & CEO)*
Joshua LeMaire *(COO)*
Allan Dicks *(CFO)*
Jose Revuelta *(Chief Strategy Officer)*
Nasym Afsari *(Gen Counsel & Sec)*
Scott Churbock *(Sr VP-Enterprise Risk & Regulatory Affairs)*
Kevin Gill *(Sr VP-HR)*
John Kemp *(VP-Tech)*
Todd Grosshandler *(Exec VP & Head-Commercialization)*
Mark Hall *(Sr VP-Advisory & Specialty Svcs)*
Sean Rome *(Sr VP)*
John Jackson *(CIO)*

Subsidiaries:

Air Water & Soil Laboratories, Inc.   (1)
1941 Reymet Rd, Richmond, VA 23237
Tel.: (804) 358-8295
Web Site: http://www.awslabs.com
Water Testing Services
N.A.I.C.S.: 541380

Analytical Environmental Services   (1)
1801 7th St Ste 100, Sacramento, CA 95811
Tel.: (916) 447-3479
Web Site: https://aes-montrose.com
Water Testing Services
N.A.I.C.S.: 541380

Environmental Alliance, Inc.   (1)
5341 Limestone Rd, Wilmington, DE 19808-1222
Web Site: http://www.envalliance.com
Environmental Consulting Services
N.A.I.C.S.: 541620
Laurie Mason *(Project Mgr)*
William Smith *(Pres)*

Environmental Chemistry, Inc.   (1)
2525 W Bellfort St, Houston, TX 77054
Tel.: (713) 666-0020
Web Site: http://www.envchem.com
Rev.: $1,200,000
Emp.: 12
Testing Laboratories
N.A.I.C.S.: 541380
Nan Thomey *(Pres)*
Gizela Batres *(Mgr-Quality Assurance)*
Clint David *(Mgr-Laboratory)*
Laura Dykstra *(Mgr-Bus)*
Deanna Jean Zeck *(CEO)*

Environmental Standards, Inc.   (1)
1140 Valley Forge Rd, Valley Forge, PA 19482
Tel.: (610) 935-5577
Web Site: https://www.envstd.com
Rev.: $8,700,000
Emp.: 80
Other Scientific & Technical Consulting Services
N.A.I.C.S.: 541690
Kevin Renninger *(Principal & Dir-Bus Dev)*
Rock Vitale *(Founder, CEO, Principal & Dir-Tech Chemistry)*

Michael R. Green *(Principal)*
Jennifer Gable *(Dir-Operations)*
Shaun M. Gilday *(Principal)*
Jacob Gruzalski *(Principal-Geoscientist)*

Huco Consulting Inc.   (1)
419 E 23rd St, Houston, TX 77008
Tel.: (713) 870-9073
Web Site: http://www.hucoconsulting.com
General Management Consulting Services
N.A.I.C.S.: 541611

MSE Group, LLC   (1)
5858 S Semoran Blvd, Orlando, FL 32822
Web Site: http://www.msegroup.com
Sales Range: $1-9.9 Million
Emp.: 25
Engineering Services
N.A.I.C.S.: 541330
Miyong Squire *(Pres & Sr Engr)*

PARS Environmental, Inc.   (1)
500 Horizon Dr Ste 540, Robbinsville, NJ 08691
Tel.: (609) 890-7277
Web Site: http://www.parsenviro.com
Environmental Consulting Services
N.A.I.C.S.: 541620

The Center for Toxicology & Environmental Health, LLC   (1)
5120 Northshore Dr, North Little Rock, AR 72118
Tel.: (501) 801-8500
Web Site: https://www.cteh.com
Environmental Consulting Services
N.A.I.C.S.: 541620
Ashley Reardon *(Mgr-Data Mgmt)*
April Steger *(VP)*
Brady Davis *(VP)*
Brendon Bailey *(Sr VP)*
Chase Selby *(Sr VP)*
Acob Fenske *(VP)*
Scott Skelton *(Principal)*

Triad Environmental Consultant   (1)
207 Donelson Pike Ste 200, Nashville, TN 37214-2931
Tel.: (615) 889-6888
Web Site: http://www.triadenv.com
Engineering Services
N.A.I.C.S.: 541330
Mark Hobbs *(Principal)*

MONUMENT CIRCLE ACQUISITION CORP.

1 Emmis Plz 40 Monument Cir Ste 700, Indianapolis, IN 46204
Tel.: (317) 266-0100   DE
Web Site:
   http://www.monumentcircleacquisi
   tion.com
Year Founded: 2020
MONCU—(NASDAQ)
Rev.: $7,663,431
Assets: $250,804,476
Liabilities: $269,166,342
Net Worth: ($18,361,866)
Earnings: $6,533,337
Emp.: 5
Fiscal Year-end: 12/31/21
Investment Services
N.A.I.C.S.: 523999
J. Scott Enright *(Gen Counsel, Sec & Exec VP)*
Jeffrey H. Smulyan *(Founder, Chm & CEO)*
Patrick Walsh *(Pres & COO)*
Ryan A. Hornaday *(CFO, Treas & Treas)*
Thomas J. Rupe *(Sr VP-Strategy & Corp Dev)*

MOODY'S CORPORATION

7 World Trade Ctr 250 Greenwich St, New York, NY 10007
Tel.: (212) 553-0300   DE
Web Site: https://www.moodys.com
Year Founded: 1990
MCO—(NYSE)
Rev.: $5,916,000,000
Assets: $14,622,000,000
Liabilities: $11,146,000,000

Net Worth: $3,476,000,000
Earnings: $1,607,000,000
Emp.: 15,151
Fiscal Year-end: 12/31/23
Holding Company; Credit Rating Information, Software & Research Services
N.A.I.C.S.: 551112
Richard Steele *(Gen Counsel)*
Michael West *(Pres-Investors Svc)*
Stephen Tulenko *(Pres-Analytics)*
Shivani Kak *(Head-IR)*
Noemie C. Heuland *(CFO & Sr VP)*
Tameka Alsop *(Chief Admin Officer)*
Robert Fauber *(Pres & CEO)*

Subsidiaries:

Acquire Media 1 UK Limited   (1)
28 Bruton Street, London, W1J 6QW, United Kingdom
Tel.: (44) 2036424160
Digital Media Services
N.A.I.C.S.: 541890

Amba Holdings Inc.   (1)
International Financial Services Limited IFS Court, TwentyEight Cybercity, Ebene, Mauritius
Tel.: (230) 4673000
Web Site: http://archive.is
Holding Company
N.A.I.C.S.: 551112

Amba Research (India) Private Limited   (1)
12th Floor Concorde Block UB City, Vittal Mallya Road, Bengaluru, 560 001, India
Tel.: (91) 8067788000
Investment Advisory Services
N.A.I.C.S.: 523940

Amba Research Costa Rica SA   (1)
3rd Floor West Tower Frente a Cenada Barreal de Heredia, Centro Ejecutivo de Negocios EuroCenter Diursa, San Jose, 935-1007, Costa Rica
Tel.: (506) 25092700
Investment Advisory Services
N.A.I.C.S.: 523940

Amba Research Lanka (Private) Limited   (1)
Level 32 Floor West Tower World Trade Center, Echelon Square, Colombo, Sri Lanka
Tel.: (94) 112356000
Investment Advisory Services
N.A.I.C.S.: 523940

Amba Research Singapore Pte. Ltd.   (1)
302 Orchard Road, 07-03 Tong Building Ste 706, Singapore, 238862, Singapore
Tel.: (65) 65213716
Investment Advisory Services
N.A.I.C.S.: 523940

Amba Research UK Limited   (1)
8th Floor, 1 Knightsbridge Green, London, SW1X 7NE, United Kingdom
Tel.: (44) 8453307209
Investment Advisory Services
N.A.I.C.S.: 523940

Amba Research USA Inc.   (1)
355 Lexington Ave 5th Fl, New York, NY 10017
Tel.: (646) 278-7290
Web Site: http://www.copalamba.com
Investment Advisory Services
N.A.I.C.S.: 523940

Barrie & Hibbert Ltd.   (1)
7 Exchange Crescent Conference Square, Edinburgh, EH3 8RD, United Kingdom
Tel.: (44) 1316250203
Web Site: http://www.moodysanalytics.com
Emp.: 100
Financial Management Consulting Services
N.A.I.C.S.: 541611
Andy Frepp *(CEO)*
Colin Holmes *(Dir-Technical Svcs)*

Bureau van Dijk E.P. DMCC   (1)
2708 JBC2 Tower Jumeirah Lakes Towers, PO Box 487995, Dubai, United Arab Emirates

Tel.: (971) 45039810
Credit Rating Agency Services
N.A.I.C.S.: 561450

Bureau van Dijk Editions Electroniques S.A. (1)
Avenue Louise 250, 1050, Brussels, Belgium
Tel.: (32) 26390606
Software Development Services
N.A.I.C.S.: 541511
Gert Jan Mattens (Acct Mgr)

Bureau van Dijk Editions Electroniques SAS (1)
7 Rue Drouot, 75009, Paris, France
Tel.: (33) 153454600
Credit Report Software Publisher
N.A.I.C.S.: 513210

Bureau van Dijk Edizioni Elettroniche SPA (1)
Via Bernardino Zenale 15, 20123, Milan, Italy
Tel.: (39) 0243982277
Web Site: http://www.bvdinfo.com
Credit Report Software Publisher
N.A.I.C.S.: 513210

Bureau van Dijk Electronic Publishing (Beijing) Co. Limited (1)
201 Tower W1 Oriental Plaza 1 East Chang An Avenue, Dong Cheng District, Beijing, 100738, China
Tel.: (86) 1085411200
Credit Report Software Publisher
N.A.I.C.S.: 513210

Bureau van Dijk Electronic Publishing AB (1)
Convendum Vasagatan 16, 111 20, Stockholm, Sweden
Tel.: (46) 851510480
Credit Report Software Publisher
N.A.I.C.S.: 513210

Bureau van Dijk Electronic Publishing Aps (1)
Ny Ostergade 7, 1101, Copenhagen, Denmark
Tel.: (45) 35152150
Credit Report Software Publisher
N.A.I.C.S.: 513210

Bureau van Dijk Electronic Publishing BV (1)
Hoogoorddreef 9, Zuidoost, 1101 BA, Amsterdam, Netherlands
Tel.: (31) 205400100
Web Site: https://www.bvdinfo.com
Business Information Publisher
N.A.I.C.S.: 513140

Bureau van Dijk Electronic Publishing GmbH (1)
Wienerbergstrasse 11/12a, 1100, Vienna, Austria
Tel.: (43) 160611960
Software Development Services
N.A.I.C.S.: 541511

Bureau van Dijk Electronic Publishing Hong Kong Limited (1)
Suite 5608 - 5610 56th Floor The Center 99 Queen's Road, Central, Hong Kong, China (Hong Kong)
Tel.: (852) 21543822
Credit Report Software Publisher
N.A.I.C.S.: 513210

Bureau van Dijk Electronic Publishing Inc. (1)
405 Howard St Ste 300, San Francisco, CA 94105
Tel.: (415) 773-1107
Credit Rating Information Services
N.A.I.C.S.: 561450

Bureau van Dijk Electronic Publishing KK (1)
20F Atago Greenhills MORI tower 2-5-1 Atago, Minato-ku, Tokyo, 105-6220, Japan
Tel.: (81) 354084280
Web Site: https://www.bvdinfo.com
Credit Report Software Publisher
N.A.I.C.S.: 513210

Bureau van Dijk Electronic Publishing LLC (1)

22F Two IFC 10 Gukjegeumyung-ro, Yeongdeungpo-gu, 07326, Seoul, 07326, Korea (South)
Tel.: (82) 261383753
Web Site: https://www.bvdinfo.com
Credit Report Software Publisher
N.A.I.C.S.: 513210

Bureau van Dijk Electronic Publishing Ltd (1)
The Alexandra 200-220 The Quays, Salford, M50 3SP, United Kingdom
Tel.: (44) 1799814000
Web Site: http://www.bvdinfo.com
Credit Report Software Publisher
N.A.I.C.S.: 513210

Bureau van Dijk Electronic Publishing PTY Limited (1)
Level 10 1 O'Connell Street, Sydney, 2000, NSW, Australia
Tel.: (61) 292701499
Credit Report Software Publisher
N.A.I.C.S.: 513210

Bureau van Dijk Electronic Publishing Pte Ltd (1)
6 Shenton Way, 14-08 OUE Downtown 2, Singapore, 068809, Singapore
Tel.: (65) 65114410
Credit Report Software Publisher
N.A.I.C.S.: 513210

Bureau van Dijk Electronic Publishing SA de CV (1)
Guillermo Gonzalez Camarena 1600 Piso 4-A Col Santa Fe, Alvaro Obregon, 01210, Mexico, Mexico
Tel.: (52) 5552842900
Credit Report Software Publisher
N.A.I.C.S.: 513210

Bureau van Dijk Electroniq Publishing SA (Pty) Ltd. (1)
Nelson Mandela Square 2nd Floor West Tower Maude Street, Sandton, 2196, Johannesburg, 2196, South Africa
Tel.: (27) 118815993
Credit Report Software Publisher
N.A.I.C.S.: 513210

Bureau van Dijk Publicacao Electronica LTDA (1)
Moody's Analytics Av Nacoes Unidas 12 551 16 andar-cj 1 601, 04578-903, Sao Paulo, 04578-903, Brazil
Tel.: (55) 1123485176
Credit Rating Agency Services
N.A.I.C.S.: 561450

Bureau van Dijk Publicaciones Electronicas SA (1)
C/ Marques de la Ensenada 2 5 Planta, 28004, Madrid, Spain
Tel.: (34) 913103804
Web Site: https://www.bvdinfo.com
Credit Rating Agency Services
N.A.I.C.S.: 561450

Copal Partners (US) Inc. (1)
355 Lexington Ave 5th Fl, New York, NY 10017
Tel.: (646) 286-6382
Web Site: http://www.copalamba.com
Emp.: 10
Financial Management Consulting Services
N.A.I.C.S.: 541611

Copal Partners UK Limited (1)
1 Poultry, London, EC2R 8EJ, United Kingdom
Tel.: (44) 2075504499
Web Site: http://www.copalpartners.com
Financial Research & Consulting Service Provider
N.A.I.C.S.: 541611

Copal Research India Private Limited (1)
4th Floor Plot No 267 Phase II Udyog Vihar, Gurgaon, 122015, Haryana, India
Tel.: (91) 1246430000
Web Site: https://www.moodys.com
Financial Research & Consulting Service Provider
N.A.I.C.S.: 541611

Copal Research Ltd. (Mauritius) (1)
4th Floor Amod Building 19 Poudriere Street, Port Louis, Mauritius

Tel.: (230) 2129855
Web Site: http://www.copalpartners.com
Financial Research & Consulting Service Provider
N.A.I.C.S.: 541611

Cortera, Inc. (1)
901 Yamato Rd Ste 210E, Boca Raton, FL 33431
Tel.: (561) 226-9000
Web Site: http://www.cortera.com
Sales Range: $10-24.9 Million
Emp.: 135
Credit Risk Management Software & Services for Credit & Collections Professionals
N.A.I.C.S.: 513210
Jim Swift (Pres & CEO)
Liz Devine (CIO)
Kevin Spendley (VP-Prof Svcs)
Michael J. Landis (CFO)
Greg Johnson (COO)

DVBS, Inc. (1)
5313 Steubenville Pike, McKees Rocks, PA 15136-1409
Tel.: (412) 787-5166
Credit Rating Information Services
N.A.I.C.S.: 561450

Equilibrium Calificadora de Riesgo S.A. (1)
Calle 50 y 54 Este Edificio Frontenac Local 5-A Bella Vista, Panama, Panama
Tel.: (507) 2143790
Credit Rating Agency Services
N.A.I.C.S.: 561450

Equilibrium Clasificadora de Riesgo S.A. (1)
Las Camelias 256 6th Floor Office 601 San Isidro, Lima, Peru
Tel.: (51) 16160400
Credit Rating Agency Services
N.A.I.C.S.: 561450

Exevo India Private Ltd. (1)
Unit No 216 Second Floor Square One C-2 District Centre Saket, New Delhi, 110017, India
Tel.: (91) 1141679440
Market Research & Outsourcing Services
N.A.I.C.S.: 541910

Fermat Private Ltd. (1)
3 Church Street 16/03, Singapore, 49483, Singapore
Tel.: (65) 63039360
Banking Sector Programming Services
N.A.I.C.S.: 541511

Four Twenty Seven, Inc. (1)
2000 Hearst Ave Ste 304, Berkeley, CA 94709
Tel.: (415) 930-9090
Web Site: http://www.427mt.com
Business Consulting Services
N.A.I.C.S.: 541618
Emilie Mazzacurati (Founder)
Colin Shaw (COO)
Frank Freitas (Chief Dev Officer)
Lisa Stanton (Chief Revenue Officer)
Klaus Fabian (VP-Engineering)

G.K. Four Twenty Seven Japan (1)
Minamomirai 3 Chome-7-1, Nishi Ward, Yokohama, 220-0012, Kanagawa, Japan
Tel.: (81) 8054264980
Climate Risk Disclosure Services
N.A.I.C.S.: 541620

Gilliland Gold Young Consulting Inc. (1)
5001 Yonge Street Suite 1300, Toronto, M2N 6P6, ON, Canada
Tel.: (416) 250-6777
Web Site: https://www.ggy.com
Software Development Services
N.A.I.C.S.: 513210

ICRA Global Capital, Inc. (1)
101 Merritt Blvd Ste 107, Trumbull, CT 06611
Tel.: (203) 375-8668
Investment Advisory Services
N.A.I.C.S.: 523940

ICRA Lanka Limited (1)
10-02 East Tower World Trade Center, Colombo, 00100, Sri Lanka
Tel.: (94) 114339907

Web Site: http://www.icralanka.com
Credit Rating Services
N.A.I.C.S.: 561450
W. Don Barnabas (CEO & Mng Dir)
Rasanga Weliwatta (Head-Fin Sector Ratings)
Lalinda Sugathadasa (Head-R&B Dev)

ICRA Limited (1)
B-710 Statesman House 148 Barakhamba Road, New Delhi, 110001, India
Tel.: (91) 1123357940
Web Site: https://www.icra.in
Rev.: $46,943,360
Assets: $122,305,788
Liabilities: $18,426,463
Net Worth: $103,879,326
Earnings: $11,286,284
Emp.: 419
Fiscal Year-end: 03/31/2021
Investment Information & Credit Rating Services
N.A.I.C.S.: 561450
Naresh Takkar (Grp CEO & Mng Dir)
Anjan Deb Ghosh (Chief Rating Officer & Exec VP)
Jayanta Chatterjee (Exec VP & Head-Strategic & Emerging Corp)
L. Shivakumar (Exec VP & Head-Institutional Corp Grp)
Vivek Mathur (Exec VP & Head-Rating Ops)
Subrata Ray (Sr VP)
Arun Duggal (Chm)
S. Shakeb Rahman (Officer-Compliance & Sec)
Amit Gupta (Gen Counsel)

Subsidiary (Domestic):

ICRA Management Consulting Services Limited (2)
4th Floor, Electric Mansion Appasaheb Marathe Marg, Prabhadevi, Mumbai, 400025, Maharashtra, India
Tel.: (91) 2261796300
Management Consulting Services
N.A.I.C.S.: 541618

ICRA Online Limited (2)
Infinity Benchmark 17th and 18th Floors Plot - G-1 Block GP, Sector V Salt Lake, Kolkata, 700 091, West Bengal, India
Tel.: (91) 3340170100
Web Site: http://www.icraonline.com
Emp.: 600
Investment Fund Management Services
N.A.I.C.S.: 523940
Sushmita Ghatak (CEO & Mng Dir)
N. Sivaraman (Chm)
Durgesh Jaiswal (CFO)

Subsidiary (US):

ICRA Sapphire Inc. (2)
101 Merritt Blvd Ste 107, Trumbull, CT 06611
Tel.: (203) 375-8668
Web Site: http://www.icteas.com
Sales Range: $50-74.9 Million
Emp.: 15
Financial Investment Services
N.A.I.C.S.: 523940
Prasad Vemuri (Pres)

ICRA Nepal Limited (1)
Sunrise Bizz Park 6th Floor Dillibazar, Kathmandu, Nepal
Tel.: (977) 14519910
Web Site: https://www.icranepal.com
Credit Rating Agency Services
N.A.I.C.S.: 561450

KIS Pricing (1)
4th floor Korea Fire Insurance Association Building, 38 Gukjegeumyung-ro 6-gil Yeongdeungpo-gu, Seoul, Korea (South)
Tel.: (82) 232151400
Web Site: https://www.bond.co.kr
Sales Range: $50-74.9 Million
Emp.: 93
Fixed Income Securities Service Provider
N.A.I.C.S.: 523150
Jeong Won Chang (CEO & Sr Mng Dir-Customer Svc & Strategy & Plng)

Korea Investors Service, Inc. (1)
48th/55F 50 63ro, Yeongdeungpo-gu, Seoul, 07345, Korea (South) **(100%)**
Tel.: (82) 27872200
Web Site: https://www.kisrating.com

Moody's Corporation—(Continued)

Emp.: 120
Credit Rating Information Services
N.A.I.C.S.: 561450
Jae-Hong Lee (CEO)

Lewtan Technologies Inc. (1)
410 Totten Pond Rd, Waltham, MA 02451-
8778
Tel.: (781) 895-9800
Web Site: http://www.lewtan.com
Data Processing, Hosting & Related Ser-
vices
N.A.I.C.S.: 518210

**MA Knowledge Services Research
(India) Private Limited** (1)
4th Floor Plot No 267 Udyog Vihar Phase
II, Gurgaon, 122015, Haryana, India
Tel.: (91) 1246609481
Credit Rating Agency Services
N.A.I.C.S.: 561450

MIS Quality Management Corp. (1)
501 Silverside Rd, Wilmington, DE 19809-
1374
Tel.: (302) 792-1223
Management Consulting Services
N.A.I.C.S.: 541611

Midroog Ltd. (1)
21 Ha'Arba'a st, Tel Aviv, 6473917, Israel
Tel.: (972) 36844700
Web Site: https://www.midroog.co.il
Credit Rating Information Services
N.A.I.C.S.: 561450
Ran Goldstein (VP & Head-Real Estate)
Avi Sternschuss (CEO)
Avi Ben-Noon (VP & Head)
Yishai Trieger (VP & Head)
Avigail Konikov-Livne (Chief Credit Officer)
Anat Erez (Officer-Compliance)
Moty Citrin (VP)
Eitan Zalewski (CFO)

Moody's America Latina Ltda. (1)
Av Nacoes Unidas 12551 - 16 andar-Cj
1601, 04578-903, Sao Paulo,
Brazil (100%)
Tel.: (55) 1130437300
Web Site: http://www.moodys.com.br
Sales Range: $75-99.9 Million
Emp.: 25
Credit Rating Information, Software & Re-
search Services
N.A.I.C.S.: 522390

Moody's Analytics (DIFC) Limited (1)
Al Fattan Currency House Office 209 -
Tower 1, PO Box 506845, Dubai Interna-
tional Financial Centre, Dubai, United Arab
Emirates
Tel.: (971) 2077725454
Credit Risk Management Services
N.A.I.C.S.: 541511

**Moody's Analytics Australia Pty.
Ltd.** (1)
Level 11 Suite 11 01 1 O'Connell Street,
Sydney, 2000, NSW, Australia
Tel.: (61) 292708100
Sales Range: $25-49.9 Million
Emp.: 55
Credit Rating Information Services
N.A.I.C.S.: 561450

**Moody's Analytics Czech Republic
s.r.o.** (1)
Pernerova 691/42 Bldg B, 186 00, Prague,
8, Czech Republic
Tel.: (420) 224106444
Sales Range: $25-49.9 Million
Emp.: 25
Credit Rating Information Services
N.A.I.C.S.: 561450

**Moody's Analytics Deutschland
GmbH** (1)
An der Welle 5, 60322, Frankfurt, Germany
Tel.: (49) 2077725454
Web Site: https://www.moodysanalytics.com
Credit Rating Information Services
N.A.I.C.S.: 561450

**Moody's Analytics Global Education
(Canada) Inc.** (1)
200 Wellington Street West 15th Floor, Toronto, M5V 3C7, ON, Canada
Tel.: (416) 364-9130

Web Site: https://www.csi.ca
Education Services
N.A.I.C.S.: 611710

Moody's Analytics Japan KK (1)
2-5-1 Atago, Minato-ku, Tokyo, 105-6220,
Japan
Tel.: (81) 354084100
Credit Rating Information Services
N.A.I.C.S.: 561450

Moody's Analytics SAS (1)
20 rue Lavoisier, Saint-Martin, 38330,
Grenoble, France
Tel.: (33) 170702229
Web Site: https://www.moodysanalytics.com
Emp.: 200
Credit Rating Information Services
N.A.I.C.S.: 561450

**Moody's Analytics Singapore Pte
Ltd.** (1)
5608 The Center 99 Queens Road, Central,
China (Hong Kong)
Tel.: (852) 35513084
Web Site: http://www.barrhibb.com
Analytical Risk Management Software De-
velopment
N.A.I.C.S.: 513210

Moody's Analytics, Inc. (1)
7 World Trade Ctr at 250 Greenwich St,
New York, NY 10007 (100%)
Tel.: (212) 553-1653
Web Site: https://www.moodys.com
Sales Range: $50-74.9 Million
Emp.: 27
Credit Analysis, Economic Research & Fi-
nancial Risk Management Information Distr,
Software Publisher, Investment Analysis &
Advisory Services
N.A.I.C.S.: 522390
Stephen Tulenko (Pres)
Keith Berry (Exec Dir)
Isabel Gomez Vidal (Exec Dir-Sls & Cus-
tomer Svc)
Nick Reed (Exec Dir)
Ari Lehavi (Exec Dir-Learning Solutions,
Mktg & Events)
Renee Reisel Tack (Chief Admin Officer,
Chief Risk Officer & Exec Dir)
Andy Frepp (Exec Dir-Enterprise Risk Solu-
tions)

Subsidiary (Domestic):

Catylist, Inc. (2)
444 N Wabash Ave, Chicago, IL 60611
Tel.: (312) 595-9209
Rev: $1,000,000
Emp.: 15
Custom Computer Programming Services
N.A.I.C.S.: 541511
Honald Marten (Founder, Pres & CEO)
Paul Brockmeyer (CTO)
Richard Maxson (Sr VP-Sls & Mktg)
Shane Hayes (VP-Sls)
Micah McCullough (Sec & Treas)
Peter Schork (CFO)

Subsidiary (Domestic):

**Catylist Real Estate Software,
Inc.** (3)
444 North Wabash Ave 400, Chicago, IL
60611
Tel.: (312) 321-4500
Web Site: http://www.catylist.com
Rev: $4,084,000
Emp.: 15
Custom Computer Programming Services
N.A.I.C.S.: 541511
Ronald D. Marten (Founder, Chm & CEO)
Richard Maxson (Sr VP-Sls & Mktg)
Shon Bendrey (COO)
Allen Benson (CIO)
Steve Golin (Sr VP-Natl Sls-Res)
Paul Brockmeyer (CTO)
Courtney Young (Sr VP & Mktg Dir)
Shane Hayes (Reg VP-Accounts)
Nancy Allen (Reg VP-Accounts)
Neal Marten (Reg VP-Accounts)
John Foster (VP-Res & Analytics)
Anna Winters (VP & Mktg Mgr)

Moody's Asia Pacific Ltd. (1)
24/F One Pacific Place 88 Queensway, Admiralty, Hong Kong, China (Hong
Kong) (100%)
Tel.: (852) 37581300

Sales Range: $125-149.9 Million
Emp.: 100
Holding Company; Regional Managing Of-
fice
N.A.I.C.S.: 551112

Subsidiary (Non-US):

Moody's Singapore Pte. Ltd. (2)
50 Raffles Place 23-06 Singapore Land
Tower, Singapore, 048623,
Singapore (100%)
Tel.: (65) 63988300
Web Site: http://www.moodys.com
Sales Range: $10-24.9 Million
Emp.: 30
Credit Rating Information, Software & Re-
search Services
N.A.I.C.S.: 522390

Moody's Canada, Inc. (1)
70 York Street Suite 1400, Toronto, M5J
1S9, ON, Canada (100%)
Tel.: (416) 214-1635
Web Site: http://www.moodys.com
Sales Range: $75-99.9 Million
Emp.: 30
Credit Rating Information, Software & Re-
search Services
N.A.I.C.S.: 522390
Donald Carter (Mng Dir)
Gavin Macfarlane (Officer-Credit-Utilities &
Pipelines & VP)

Moody's Deutschland GmbH (1)
An der Welle 5, 60322, Frankfurt am Main,
Germany (100%)
Tel.: (49) 6970730700
Sales Range: $25-49.9 Million
Credit Rating Information, Software & Re-
search Services
N.A.I.C.S.: 522390

Moody's Eastern Europe LLC (1)
7th Floor Four Winds Plaza 21 1st
Tverskaya-Yamskaya Street, 125047, Mos-
cow, Russia
Tel.: (7) 4952286060
Web Site: http://www.moodys.com
Sales Range: $25-49.9 Million
Emp.: 40
Credit Rating Information Services
N.A.I.C.S.: 561450

Moody's France S.A.S. (1)
21 boulevard Haussmann, 75009, Paris,
France (100%)
Tel.: (33) 153301020
Sales Range: $10-24.9 Million
Emp.: 45
Credit Rating Information, Software & Re-
search Services
N.A.I.C.S.: 522390

**Moody's Interfax Rating Agency
Ltd.** (1)
7th Floor Four Winds Plaza 21 1st
Tverskaya-Yamskaya Street, Moscow,
125047, Russia
Tel.: (7) 4952286060
Web Site: http://group.interfax.ru
Sales Range: $50-74.9 Million
Emp.: 500
Credit Rating Information Services
N.A.I.C.S.: 561450
Alexei Gorshkov Albertovich (Exec Dir)
Zakharov Vladimir Stepanovich (Dir-Admin
& Corp Affairs)
Roman Laba Miroslavovich (Deputy Gen
Dir)
Porshnev Igor Germanovich (Deputy Gen
Dir)
Ketko Mikhail Sergeevich (Gen Dir-Reg Svc
& Deputy Gen Dir)

**Moody's Investment Co. India Pvt.
Ltd.** (1)
Electric Mansion 3rd Floor Appasaheb
Marathe Marg, Prabhadevi, Mumbai, 400
025, Maharashtra, India
Tel.: (91) 2240046111
Web Site: http://www.moodys.co.in
Financial Management Consulting Services
N.A.I.C.S.: 541611

**Moody's Investors Service (Korea)
Inc.** (1)
55 Fl Hanwha Finance Center 63 50 63ro,
Youngdeungpo-gu, Seoul, Korea (South)
Tel.: (82) 27872277

Emp.: 4
Credit Rating Information Services
N.A.I.C.S.: 561450

**Moody's Investors Service (South
Africa) Pty. Ltd.** (1)
Regus at Nelson Mandela Square 2nd Floor
West Tower Maude Street, Sandton, 2196,
South Africa
Tel.: (27) 118815544
Emp.: 6
Credit Rating Information Services
N.A.I.C.S.: 561450

**Moody's Investors Service India Pri-
vate Limited** (1)
Electric Mansion 3rd Floor, Appasaheb
Marathe Marg Prabhadevi, Mumbai, 400
025, India
Tel.: (91) 2240046111
Investment Advisory Services
N.A.I.C.S.: 523940

**Moody's Investors Service Middle
East Limited** (1)
Dubai International Financial Centre Gate
Precinct Bldg 3 Level 3, PO Box 506845,
Dubai, United Arab Emirates
Tel.: (971) 42379500
Investment Advisory Services
N.A.I.C.S.: 523940

**Moody's Investors Service Pty
Limited** (1)
Level 10 1 O'Connell Street, Sydney, 2000,
NSW, Australia
Tel.: (61) 292708111
Investment Advisory Services
N.A.I.C.S.: 523940
Michael West (Pres)

Moody's Investors Service, Inc. (1)
7 World Trade Ctr at 250 Greenwich St,
New York, NY 10007 (100%)
Tel.: (212) 553-1653
Web Site: http://www.moodys.com
Credit Rating & Financial Research Ser-
vices
N.A.I.C.S.: 561450
Michael West (Pres)

Subsidiary (Non-US):

**Moody's Investors Service Cyprus
Ltd.** (2)
Porto Bello Building 1 Siafi Street, 3042,
Limassol, Cyprus (100%)
Tel.: (357) 2 558 6586
Web Site: https://www.moodys.com
Sales Range: $10-24.9 Million
Emp.: 20
Credit Rating & Financial Research Ser-
vices
N.A.I.C.S.: 561450
Mardig Haladjian (Country Mgr)

**Moody's Investors Service Espana,
S.A.** (2)
Calle Principe de Vergará 131 6 Planta,
28002, Madrid, Spain (100%)
Tel.: (34) 917688200
Sales Range: $10-24.9 Million
Emp.: 30
Credit Rating & Financial Research Ser-
vices
N.A.I.C.S.: 561450
Juan Pablo Soriano (Country Mgr)

Moody's Investors Service Ltd. (2)
One Canada Square Canary Wharf, Lon-
don, E14 5FA, United Kingdom (100%)
Tel.: (44) 2077721000
Web Site: http://www.moodys.com
Credit Rating Services
N.A.I.C.S.: 561450
Debbie Palmer (VP)
Benjamin Grout (Sr VP)
Anna Burel (VP)
John Paterson (VP)

**Moody's Investors Service Pty.
Ltd.** (2)
Level 10 1 O'Connell Street, Sydney, 2000,
NSW, Australia
Tel.: (61) 29 270 8111
Web Site: http://www.moodys.com.au
Sales Range: $25-49.9 Million
Emp.: 53
Credit Rating & Financial Research Ser-
vices

N.A.I.C.S.: 561450
Natalie Wells *(Mgr)*

Moody's Japan KK (1)
2-5-1 Atago, Minato-ku, Tokyo, 105-6220, Japan (100%)
Tel.: (81) 354084100
Sales Range: $10-24.9 Million
Emp.: 50
Credit Rating Information, Software & Research Services
N.A.I.C.S.: 522390

Moody's Latin America Agente de Calificacion de Riesgo SA (1)
Laminar Plaza Building 16th Floor, 240 Ing Butty Street, C1001AFB, Buenos Aires, Argentina
Tel.: (54) 1151292600
Investment Advisory Services
N.A.I.C.S.: 523940

Moodys France SAS (1)
96 boulevard Haussmann, 75008, Paris, France
Tel.: (33) 153301020
Credit Rating Agency Services
N.A.I.C.S.: 561450

Omega Performance Corporation (1)
7 World Trade Ctr at 250 Greenwich St, New York, NY 10007
Tel.: (646) 947-1800
Web Site: https://www.omega-performance.com
Financial Services Consulting
N.A.I.C.S.: 541618

PT ICRA Indonesia (1)
Menara Rajawali 6th Floor-Podium Jl DR Ide Anak Agung Gede Agung Lot, Suite 5 1, Jakarta, 12950, Indonesia
Tel.: (62) 215761516
Credit Rating Agency Services
N.A.I.C.S.: 561450

Passfort Limited (1)
1 Mark Square, London, EC2A 4EG, United Kingdom
Tel.: (44) 2036331761
Web Site: https://www.passfort.com
Financial Management Services
N.A.I.C.S.: 522291

Pragati Development Consulting Services Ltd. (1)
Logix Park 1st Floor, Tower A-4 & A-5 Sector 16, Noida, 201301, India
Tel.: (91) 120410337
Investment Advisory Services
N.A.I.C.S.: 523940

RealXData GmbH (1)
Oranienstrasse 185, 10999, Berlin, Germany
Tel.: (49) 3054909757
Web Site: https://www.realxdata.com
Real Estate Services
N.A.I.C.S.: 531210
Titus Albrecht *(Mng Dir & CEO-Business Development)*
Daniel Sprunker *(COO-Operations)*
Stefan Nusche *(Chief Sls Officer-Sales-Finance)*
Marie Ruf *(Sls Mgr)*

Regulatory DataCorp, Inc. (1)
211 S Gulph Rd Ste 125, King of Prussia, PA 19406
Tel.: (484) 688-5200
Web Site: http://www.rdc.com
Risk & Compliance Protection Information Services
N.A.I.C.S.: 561499
Rupert de Ruig *(Mng Dir-EMEA & APAC)*
Tom Walsh *(CEO)*
Adam Kupperman *(Head-Strategic Relationships & Channels-Global)*
Fabrizio Ferronato *(CFO)*
Jeff Sidell *(CTO)*
Don India *(Chief Revenue Officer)*
Alex Zuck *(Head-Product-Global)*
Dodie Reagan *(VP-Talent Mgmt)*

Reis, Inc. (1)
1185 Ave of the Americas, New York, NY 10036
Tel.: (212) 921-1122
Web Site: http://www.reis.com
Rev.: $48,189,687

Assets: $121,603,733
Liabilities: $33,130,383
Net Worth: $88,473,350
Earnings: ($3,158,363)
Emp.: 268
Fiscal Year-end: 12/31/2017
Commercial Real Estate Services
N.A.I.C.S.: 531390

Subsidiary (Domestic):

Red Canyon at Palomino Park L.L.C. (2)
6700 Palomino Pkwy, Highlands Ranch, CO 80130
Tel.: (303) 470-8400
Web Site: https://www.palominopark.com
Emp.: 50
Real Estate Manangement Services
N.A.I.C.S.: 531210

Silver Mesa at Palomino Park L.L.C. (2)
6402 Silver Mesa Dr, Highlands Ranch, CO 80130
Tel.: (303) 536-8941
Real Estate Manangement Services
N.A.I.C.S.: 531390

Risk Management Solutions, Inc. (1)
7575 Gateway Blvd, Newark, CA 94560-1152
Tel.: (510) 505-2500
Web Site: http://www.rms.com
Risk Management Solutions Provider
N.A.I.C.S.: 541618
Michael Steel *(Head-Bus Dev-Global)*
Karen White *(CEO)*
Cihan Biyikoglu *(Exec VP-Product)*
Moe Khosravy *(Exec VP-Software & Platform)*
Mohsen Rahnama *(Chief Risk Modeling Officer & Exec VP-Models & Data)*
Neil Isford *(Exec VP-Sales)*
Reed Birnbaum *(CFO)*
Marilyn Mersereau *(CMO)*
Alok Kumar *(Head-Global)*
Robert Muir-Wood *(Chief Res Officer)*
Mitch Parker *(Head-Customer Success-Global)*
Doug Solomon *(Chief Legal Officer)*
Diane Strohfus *(Chief HR Officer)*

Subsidiary (Non-US):

OYO RMS Corporation (2)
Nihon-Seimei Kasuga-Ekimae Bldg 3F 1-1-17, Koishikawa Bunkyo-ku, Tokyo, 112-0002, Japan (50%)
Tel.: (81) 364349801
Web Site: https://www.oyorms.co.jp
Sales Range: $25-49.9 Million
Emp.: 20
Risk Management Solutions Provider
N.A.I.C.S.: 541512

RMS Ltd. (2)
Peninsular House 30 Monument St, London, EC3R 8NB, United Kingdom (100%)
Tel.: (44) 2074447600
Web Site: http://www.rms.com
Risk Management Solutions Provider
N.A.I.C.S.: 541512

RMSI Private Limited (2)
A-8 Sector 16, Noida, 201 301, India (100%)
Tel.: (91) 1202511102
Web Site: http://www.rmsi.com
Geographic Information Services
N.A.I.C.S.: 541512

Branch (Domestic):

Risk Management Solutions - East Coast US (2)
433 Hackensack Ave Fl 5, Hackensack, NJ 07601
Tel.: (201) 498-8600
Web Site: http://www.rms.com
Sales Range: $25-49.9 Million
Emp.: 90
Risk Management Solution Providers
N.A.I.C.S.: 541618

Risk Management Solutions - Midwest US (2)
621 SW Commercial Ste D, Peoria, IL 61602
Tel.: (309) 637-6350

Web Site: http://www.rms.com
Risk Management Solutions
N.A.I.C.S.: 524210

Vigeo (1)
Les Mercuriales 40 rue Jean Jaures, 93170, Bagnolet, France
Tel.: (33) 155823240
Environmental Consulting Services
N.A.I.C.S.: 541620

Vigeo Belgium NV (1)
Rue du Progres 333/B7, 1030, Brussels, Belgium
Tel.: (32) 22066791
Environmental Consulting Services
N.A.I.C.S.: 541620

Vigeo Eiris Chile SpA (1)
Av Pedro de Valdivia 0193 Office 62, Providencia, Santiago, Chile
Tel.: (56) 232951362
Environmental Consulting Services
N.A.I.C.S.: 541620 *(Head-Markets-South America)*
Fanny Tora *(Head-Markets-South America)*

Vigeo Eiris Hong Kong Limited (1)
Unit 12124 12/F Mass Mutual Tower 33 Lockhart Road, Wanchai, China (Hong Kong)
Tel.: (852) 39054601
Environmental Consulting Services
N.A.I.C.S.: 541620

Vigeo Eiris USA, LLC (1)
18 W 18th St 6th Fl, New York, NY 10011
Tel.: (917) 318-2094
Environmental Consulting Services
N.A.I.C.S.: 541620

Vigeo Italia S.r.l (1)
Via Dell'Alpino 2, Bagnolo San Vito, 46031, Mantua, Italy
Tel.: (39) 037 644 9097
Web Site: https://www.vigeosrl.it
In-Vitro Diagnostic Substance Mfr
N.A.I.C.S.: 325413
Matteo Negrini *(CEO & Founder)*

Yellow Maple II B.V. (1)
Hoogoorddreef 9 Gebouw Afric, 1101 BA, Amsterdam, Netherlands
Tel.: (31) 205400100
Credit Rating Information Services
N.A.I.C.S.: 561450

ZM Financial Systems, LLC (1)
1020 Southhill Dr Ste 200, Cary, NC 27513
Tel.: (919) 493-0029
Web Site: http://www.w3.zmfs.com
Financial Services
N.A.I.C.S.: 523999
Tom Bowers *(Dir-Product Mgmt)*
Jerry Clark *(Sls Mgr)*
Michael Lau *(Dir-Product Mgmt)*

MOOG INC.

Tel.: (716) 652-2000 NY
Web Site: https://www.moog.com
Year Founded: 1951
MOG.A—(NYSE)
Rev.: $3,035,783,000
Assets: $3,431,841,000
Liabilities: $1,995,028,000
Net Worth: $1,436,813,000
Earnings: $155,177,000
Emp.: 14,000
Fiscal Year-end: 10/01/22
Search, Detection, Navigation, Guidance, Aeronautical & Nautical System & Instrument Manufacturing
N.A.I.C.S.: 334511
Mark J. Trabert *(COO & Exec VP)*
Jennifer Walter *(CFO & VP)*
Patrick J. Roche *(Pres & CEO)*
Paul Wilkinson *(Chief HR Officer & VP)*
Stuart Mclachlan *(Pres-Industrial Grp & VP)*
Joseph Alfieri *(Pres-Space & Defense & VP)*
Mark Graczyk *(Pres-Military Aircraft & VP)*
Michael Schaff *(Pres-Comml Aircraft & VP)*
Christopher A. Head *(Sec)*

Subsidiaries:

Animatics GmbH (1)
Allgaeustr 8a, 87766, Memmingen, Germany
Tel.: (49) 8331984800
Web Site: http://www.animatics.com
Emp.: 20
Fluid Control & Control System Design & Mfr
N.A.I.C.S.: 332911

Aston Photonic Technologies Limited (1)
6-7 Compass Point, Southampton, SO31 4RA, Hampshire, United Kingdom
Tel.: (44) 1212043390
Fluid Control & Control System Design & Mfr
N.A.I.C.S.: 332911

Flo-Tork Inc. (1)
1701 N Main St, Orrville, OH 44667-0068
Tel.: (330) 682-0010
Web Site: https://www.flo-tork.com
Sales Range: $10-24.9 Million
Emp.: 60
Mfr of Hydraulic & Pneumatic Rack & Pinion Rotary Actuators
N.A.I.C.S.: 335314

Insensys Holdings Ltd. (1)
No1-2 Kingdom Close, Fareham, PO15 5TJ, Hampshire, United Kingdom
Tel.: (44) 2380450550
Web Site: http://www.moog.com
Sales Range: $25-49.9 Million
Emp.: 15
Investment Management Service
N.A.I.C.S.: 551112

Subsidiary (Domestic):

Insensys Limited (2)
1-2 Kingdom Close, Fareham, PO15 5TJ, United Kingdom
Tel.: (44) 2380450550
Web Site: https://www.insensys.com
Emp.: 14
Fiber Optic Load Measurement Device Mfr
N.A.I.C.S.: 334513
Chris Knox *(CEO)*

MCG Kingsport, Inc. (1)
4545 W Stone Dr Bldg 135, Kingsport, TN 37660-1048
Tel.: (423) 578-7200
Sales Range: $10-24.9 Million
Emp.: 20
Semiconductor & Electronic Component Mfr
N.A.I.C.S.: 334413

Moog AG (1)
Neufeldstrasse 11, Worb, 3076, Switzerland
Tel.: (41) 318381919
Web Site: http://www.moog.ch
Emp.: 25
Aircraft & Missile Component Supplier
N.A.I.C.S.: 423860

Moog Aircraft Group (1)
Seneca St At Jamison Rd, East Aurora, NY 14052 (100%)
Tel.: (716) 652-2000
Web Site: http://www.moog.com
Rev.: $663,463,000
Emp.: 2,184
Servoactuator Mfr
N.A.I.C.S.: 334511
Mark J. Trabert *(Pres)*

Subsidiary (Domestic):

Crossbow Technology, Inc. (2)
421 McCarthy Blvd, Milpitas, CA 95035
Tel.: (408) 965-3300
Web Site: http://www.xbow.com
Sales Range: $10-24.9 Million
Emp.: 40
Measuring & Controlling Device Mfr
N.A.I.C.S.: 334519

Unit (Domestic):

Moog Aircraft Group - Torrance (2)
20263 Western Ave, Torrance, CA 90501-1310
Tel.: (310) 533-1178
Sales Range: $75-99.9 Million
Emp.: 450

Moog Inc.—(Continued)

Mechanical & Hydraulic Actuation Products for Use in Commercial & Military Aircraft Controls
N.A.I.C.S.: 334511

Moog Australia Pty. Ltd.   (1)
18 Corporate Drive, Heatherton, 3202, VIC, Australia   (100%)
Tel.: (61) 395616044
Web Site: http://www.moog.com.au
Sales Range: $10-24.9 Million
Emp.: 18
Precision Control Components Mfr
N.A.I.C.S.: 334514

Moog B.V.   (1)
Pesetaweg 53, 2153 PJ, Nieuw-Vennep, Netherlands
Tel.: (31) 252462000
Web Site: http://www.moognetherlands.nl
Sales Range: $25-49.9 Million
Emp.: 140
Motion Control System & Automation Design & Mfr
N.A.I.C.S.: 334519

Moog Brno s.r.o.   (1)
Linear Motor Mfr
N.A.I.C.S.: 335312

Moog Components Group   (1)
1213 N Main St, Blacksburg, VA 24060-3100
Tel.: (540) 552-3011
Sales Range: $200-249.9 Million
Emp.: 680
Motion Control & Electronic Components
N.A.I.C.S.: 334419

Subsidiary (Domestic):

Animatics Corp.   (2)
3200 Patrick Henry Dr, Santa Clara, CA 95054
Tel.: (408) 748-8721
Web Site: http://www.animatics.com
Sales Range: $10-24.9 Million
Emp.: 40
Relay & Industrial Control Mfr
N.A.I.C.S.: 335314

Moog Controls (India) Private Ltd.   (1)
No 683 15th Cross Road Sarakki 2nd Phase JP Nagar, Bengaluru, 560078, Karnataka, India
Tel.: (91) 8040576666
Web Site: http://www.moog.co.in
Sales Range: $25-49.9 Million
Emp.: 30
Fluid Control & Control System Design & Mfr
N.A.I.C.S.: 332911

Moog Controls Corp.-Philippines   (1)
BCEPZ Loakan Rd, Baguio, 2600, Philippines   (100%)
Tel.: (63) 744473355
Web Site: http://www.moog.com
Sales Range: $400-449.9 Million
Emp.: 1,200
Precision Control Components Mfr
N.A.I.C.S.: 334514

Moog Controls Hong Kong Ltd.   (1)
Ste 9 11th Fl Citimark 28 Yuen Shun Circuit, Siu Lek Yuen, Sha Tin, NT, China (Hong Kong)   (100%)
Tel.: (852) 26353200
Sales Range: $1-9.9 Million
Emp.: 5
Precision Control Components Mfr
N.A.I.C.S.: 334514
Morris Chan (Mgr-Sls)

Subsidiary (Non-US):

Moog Control Systems (Shanghai) Co., Ltd.   (2)
Factory No 68 No 96 Yiwei Road, Waigaoqiao Free Trade Zone Pudong New Area, Shanghai, 200131, China
Tel.: (86) 2128931600
Web Site: http://www.moog.com.cn
Aircraft & Missile Component Supplier
N.A.I.C.S.: 423860

Moog Controls Ltd.   (1)
Ashchurch, Tewkesbury, GL20 8NA,

Gloscestershire, United Kingdom   (100%)
Tel.: (44) 1684278223
Web Site: http://www.moog.co.uk
Sales Range: $75-99.9 Million
Emp.: 360
Development of Brushless Servomotors, Controllers & Servocontrols
N.A.I.C.S.: 335312

Subsidiary (Domestic):

Fernau Limited   (2)
Airport Executive Park President Way, Luton, LU2 9NY, Bedfordshire, United Kingdom
Tel.: (44) 1582483111
Web Site: http://www.moog.com
Emp.: 20
Air Navigation & Distance Measuring Equipment Supplier
N.A.I.C.S.: 334511
Paul Revell (Mng Dir)

Moog Fernau Limited   (2)
Airport Executive Park President Way, Luton, LU2 9NY, Bedfordshire, United Kingdom
Tel.: (44) 1582 483111
Web Site: http://www.moogfernau.com
Sales Range: $25-49.9 Million
Emp.: 20
Supplier of Ground-based Air Navigational Systems for Military Naval & Civil Aviation Applications
N.A.I.C.S.: 334511
Paul Revell (Mng Dir)

Moog Reading Limited   (2)
30 Sutton Industrial Estate Earley, Reading, RG6 1AW, Berkshire, United Kingdom
Tel.: (44) 1189666044
Emp.: 120
Aviation Services
N.A.I.C.S.: 334419
Steve Curtis (Mng Dir)

Moog Reading Limited   (2)
30 Sutton Industrial Estate Earley, Reading, RG6 1AW, Berkshire, United Kingdom
Tel.: (44) 118 966 6044
Motion Control Product Mfr & Distr
N.A.I.C.S.: 335314

Moog Dublin Ltd.   (1)
Unit 15 Northwest Business Park Ballycoolin, Dublin, 15, Ireland
Tel.: (353) 18610010
Web Site: http://www.moog.com
Emp.: 25
Aircraft Maintenance Services
N.A.I.C.S.: 488190

Moog GmbH   (1)
Hanns-Klemm-Str 28, 71034, Boblingen, Germany   (100%)
Tel.: (49) 70316220
Web Site: http://www.moog.de
Emp.: 521
Precision Control Components Mfr
N.A.I.C.S.: 334514
Johannes van den Dijssel (Mng Dir)
Thomas Czeppel (Mng Dir)

Subsidiary (Non-US):

Moog Italiana Srl   (2)
Via Avosso 94, 16015, Casella, GE, Italy   (100%)
Tel.: (39) 01096711
Web Site: http://www.moog.it
Sales Range: $25-49.9 Million
Emp.: 160
Electronic Components Mfr
N.A.I.C.S.: 334419

Subsidiary (Domestic):

Moog Rekofa GmbH   (2)
Bergstrasse 41, 53533, Antweiler, Germany
Tel.: (49) 2693 93330
Web Site: http://www.morgan-rekofa.de
Rotary Transfer System Mfr & Distr
N.A.I.C.S.: 335999
Lawrence J. Ball (Mng Dir)

Moog Ireland Ltd.   (1)
Ringaskiddy, Cork, Ireland
Tel.: (353) 214519000
Web Site: http://www.moog.com
Sales Range: $25-49.9 Million
Emp.: 100

Brushless Servomotors & Controllers, Servocontrols
N.A.I.C.S.: 335312

Moog Japan Ltd.   (1)
1-8-37 Nishishindo, Hiratsuka, 254-0019, Kanagawa, Japan   (100%)
Tel.: (81) 120609141
Web Site: http://www.moog.co.jp
Emp.: 180
Precision Control Components Mfr
N.A.I.C.S.: 334514
Takuman Furusawa (Pres)

Moog Korea Ltd.   (1)
24-49 Dunteor-ro, Majang-myeon, Icheon, Gyeonggi-do, Korea (South)   (100%)
Tel.: (82) 317646711
Web Site: http://www.moogkorea.com
Sales Range: $10-24.9 Million
Emp.: 28
Precision Control Components Mfr
N.A.I.C.S.: 334514

Moog Medical Devices Group   (1)
4314 Zevex Park Ln, Salt Lake City, UT 84123
Tel.: (801) 264-1001
Web Site: http://www.moog.com
Sales Range: $25-49.9 Million
Emp.: 158
Medical Equipment Sales & Mfr
N.A.I.C.S.: 339112

Subsidiary (Domestic):

Curlin Medical Inc.   (2)
15662 Commerce Ln, Huntington Beach, CA 92649-1604
Tel.: (714) 893-2200
Sales Range: $10-24.9 Million
Emp.: 70
Medical Tehnology Mfr
N.A.I.C.S.: 334510

Subsidiary (Domestic):

Moog Medical Devices Group   (3)
251 Seneca St, Buffalo, NY 14204
Tel.: (716) 842-4000
Mfr of Surgical & Medical Instruments
N.A.I.C.S.: 339112

Moog S.A.R.L.   (1)
1 Rue Camille Decauville, 91250, Tigery, France   (100%)
Tel.: (33) 145607000
Web Site: http://www.moog.com
Sales Range: $25-49.9 Million
Emp.: 28
Servovalves Mfr
N.A.I.C.S.: 332911

Moog Singapore Pte Ltd.   (1)
73 Science Park Drive 03-09 Cintech 1 Singapore Science Park 1, Singapore, 118254, Singapore   (100%)
Tel.: (65) 67736238
Web Site: http://www.moog.com.sg
Sales Range: $50-74.9 Million
Emp.: 20
Aircraft Part Mfr
N.A.I.C.S.: 336413

Subsidiary (Non-US):

Moog EM Solutions (India) Private Limited   (2)
AM2 Sublayout of Somapura, KIADB Industrial Area Nelamangala Taluk, Bengaluru, 562111, Karnataka, India
Tel.: (91) 802 852 7300
Servo Motor Mfr
N.A.I.C.S.: 335312

Moog Motion Controls Pvt. Ltd.   (2)
No 42 43, Doraisanipalya Village Bilekahalli Begur Hobli, Bengaluru, 560 076, India
Tel.: (91) 8040576600
Web Site: http://www.moog.co.in
Sales Range: Less than $1 Million
Emp.: 35
Aircraft Part Mfr
N.A.I.C.S.: 336413
Venkatesh R. (Mng Dir)

Moog Space & Defense Group   (1)
Plant 20 400 Jamison Rd, East Aurora, NY 14052
Tel.: (716) 652-2000
Web Site: http://www.moog.com

Emp.: 3,000
Liquid & Electronic Propulsion Systems, Thrust Vector Control Systems & Commercial & Military Electronics
N.A.I.C.S.: 927110

Subsidiary (Non-US):

Bradford Engineering B.V.   (2)
De Wijper 26, 4726 TG, Heerlen, Netherlands   (100%)
Tel.: (31) 165305100
Web Site: http://www.bradford-space.com
Sales Range: $10-24.9 Million
Emp.: 80
Developer & Mfr of Satellite Equipment for Spacecraft
N.A.I.C.S.: 336415

Subsidiary (Domestic):

Broad Reach Engineering Company   (2)
1113 Washington Ave Ste 200, Golden, CO 80401
Tel.: (303) 216-9777
Web Site: http://www.broadreachengineering.com
Sales Range: $10-24.9 Million
Emp.: 12
Spaceflight Hardware & Software Solutions
N.A.I.C.S.: 336413

Moog CSA Engineering   (2)
2565 Leghorn St, Mountain View, CA, 94043-1613
Tel.: (650) 210-9000
Web Site: http://www.csaengineering.com
Sales Range: $50-74.9 Million
Emp.: 45
Vibration Suppression & Precise Motion Control Systems Engineering
N.A.I.C.S.: 541330

Videolarm, Inc.   (2)
3650 Wood Head Dr North Brook, Northbrook, IL 60062
Tel.: (770) 987-7550
Web Site: http://www.videolarm.com
Sales Range: $25-49.9 Million
Emp.: 49
Security Products Mfr
N.A.I.C.S.: 326199

Moog Wolverhampton Limited   (1)
Valiant Way, Wolverhampton, WV9 5GB, United Kingdom
Tel.: (44) 1902397700
Web Site: http://www.moog.com
Sales Range: $150-199.9 Million
Emp.: 500
Flight Control Actuation Systems Mfr
N.A.I.C.S.: 336413

Moog do Brasil Controles Ltda.   (1)
Rua Prof Campos de Oliveira 338, Sao Paulo, 04675-100, Brazil
Tel.: (55) 1135720400
Web Site: http://www.moog.com.br
Precision Control Components Mfr
N.A.I.C.S.: 334419

Subsidiary (Non-US):

Moog de Argentina SRL   (2)
Av Roque Saenz Pena 740 Piso 9, 1035, Buenos Aires, Argentina
Tel.: (54) 1143265916
Aircraft & Missile Component Supplier
N.A.I.C.S.: 423860

Nammo (U.K.) Limited   (1)
Westcott Venture Park, Westcott, HP18 0XB, Buckinghamshire, United Kingdom
Tel.: (44) 1296652000
Emp.: 26
Motor & Generator Mfr
N.A.I.C.S.: 335312
Rob Salby (Gen Mgr)

Obshestwo s Ogranizennoi Otwetstwennostju Moog   (1)
Nizhegorodsky Filial Ul Chapaeva 43 kor 3 Pavlovo, Nizhegorodskaya Oblast, Nizhniy Novgorod, 606108, Russia
Tel.: (7) 8317131811
Web Site: http://www.moog.com
Emp.: 10
Motion Control System & Automation Design & Mfr

N.A.I.C.S.: 334519

Subsidiary (Non-US):

Focal Technologies Corporation (2)
77 Frazee Ave, Dartmouth, B3B 1Z4, NS,
Canada
Tel.: (902) 468-2263
Web Site: http://www.moog.com
Emp.: 100
Fibre Optic Rotary Joint & Multiplexer Mfr
N.A.I.C.S.: 335921

Moog Luxembourg (2)
421 Zone d'activites economiques Wolser
F, 3290, Bettembourg, Luxembourg
Tel.: (352) 4046401
Web Site: http://www.moog.lu
Motion Control System & Automation De-
sign & Mfr
N.A.I.C.S.: 334519

ProControl AG (2)
Degersheimerstrasse 40, 9230, Flawil, Swit-
zerland
Tel.: (41) 713945010
Web Site: http://www.procontrol.ch
Motion Control System & Automation De-
sign & Mfr
N.A.I.C.S.: 334519

Pieper GmbH (1)
Binnerheide 33, 58239, Schwerte, Germany
Tel.: (49) 230447010
Web Site: http://www.pieper-video.de
Sales Range: $10-24.9 Million
Video & Security Equipment Whslr
N.A.I.C.S.: 561621
Thorsten Wulff (Mng Dir)
Thomas Lampe (Mng Dir)
Ingo Maskos (Mgr-Quality)
Nandi Reinartz-Routh (Mgr-Mktg)
Christian Sommer (Mgr-Product)

Team Accessories Limited (1)
Ridgewell House, Hollywood Ballyboughal,
Dublin, A41 YV66, Ireland
Tel.: (353) 18433466
Web Site: https://team-accessories.aero
Aircraft Maintenance Services
N.A.I.C.S.: 488119

Tritech International Limited (1)
Peregrine Road, Westhill Business Park,
Westhill, AB32 6JL, Aberdeenshire, United
Kingdom
Tel.: (44) 1224744111
Web Site: http://www.tritech.co.uk
Sales Range: $10-24.9 Million
Emp.: 30
Sensor & Video Camera Mfr
N.A.I.C.S.: 333310
Jacqueline McCloy (Dir-Fin)
David Bradley (Mng Dir)
Mike Broadbent (Mgr-Sls)
Alastair Mitchell (Dir-Supply Chain)
Jo Mills (Production Mgr)
Phil Musker (Project Mgr)

Subsidiary (Non-US):

Moog Norden A.B. (2)
Berga Alle 3, 254 52, Helsingborg, Sweden
Tel.: (46) 31680060
Web Site: http://www.moog.se
Emp.: 3
Industrial Valve Mfr
N.A.I.C.S.: 332911

Viltechmeda UAB (1)
Mokslininku 6, 08412, Vilnius, Lithuania
Tel.: (370) 52776745
Web Site: http://www.aitecs.com
Emp.: 100
Syringe Infusion Pump Design & Mfr
N.A.I.C.S.: 339112

MOONLAKE IMMUNOTHERA-PEUTICS

200 Clarendon St 52nd Fl, Boston,
MA 02116
Tel.: (857) 702-0370   Ky
Year Founded: 2020
MLTX—(NASDAQ)
Rev.: $591,732
Assets: $76,843,301
Liabilities: $8,076,603
Net Worth: $68,766,698

Earnings: ($64,506,051)
Emp.: 20
Fiscal Year-end: 12/31/22
Investment Services
N.A.I.C.S.: 523999
Arnout Ploos van Amstel (Founder)

MORGAN GROUP HOLDING CO.

401 Theodore Fremd Ave, Rye, NY
10580
Tel.: (914) 921-5150
Web Site:
   https://www.morgangroupholding
   co.com
Year Founded: 2000
MGHL—(OTCIQ)
Rev.: $2,011,422
Assets: $3,417,716
Liabilities: $1,330,662
Net Worth: $2,087,054
Earnings: ($949,191)
Emp.: 4
Fiscal Year-end: 12/31/22
Holding Services
N.A.I.C.S.: 551112
Mario J. Gabelli (Founder)
Joseph L. Fernandez (Exec VP-Fin)
Vincent M. Amabile Jr. (Pres & CEO)

Subsidiaries:

G.research, LLC (1)
1 Corporate Ctr, Rye, NY 10580-1422
Tel.: (914) 921-5130
Investment Advisory Services
N.A.I.C.S.: 523940
Vincent M. Amabile (Pres)

MORGAN STANLEY

1585 Broadway, New York, NY 10036
Tel.: (212) 761-4000   DE
Web Site:
   https://www.morganstanley.com
Year Founded: 1935
MS—(NYSE)
Rev.: $54,143,000,000
Assets: $1,193,693,000,000
Liabilities: $1,093,711,000,000
Net Worth: $99,982,000,000
Earnings: $8,530,000,000
Emp.: 80,000
Fiscal Year-end: 12/31/23
Bank Holding Company; Institutional
Securities, Wealth & Asset Manage-
ment Services
N.A.I.C.S.: 551111
Andrew M. Saperstein (Co-Pres &
Head-Wealth & Investment Mgmt)
Dan Simkowitz (Co-Pres & Head-
Institutional Securities)
Jeffrey S. Brodsky (Co-Vice Chm)
Anish Shah (Mng Dir-Capital
Markets-Global & Co-Head-Global
Capital Markets & Global Head of
Acquisition Finance-Talent Dev)
Mandell Crawley (Chief HR Officer)
Edward N. Pick (CEO)

Subsidiaries:

APAC Realty Limited (1)
450 Lor 6 Toa Payoh ERA APAC Centre,
Singapore, 319394, Singapore   (64.8%)
Tel.: (65) 62262000
Web Site: https://www.apacrealty.com.sg
Rev.: $422,064,682
Assets: $259,539,498
Liabilities: $139,278,194
Net Worth: $120,261,304
Earnings: $8,029,236
Emp.: 281
Fiscal Year-end: 12/31/2023
Real Estate Manangement Services
N.A.I.C.S.: 531210
Khee Hak Chua (Chm & CEO)
Doris Ong (Co-COO)
Marcus Chu (Co-COO)
Chee Yong Poh (CFO)

Leong Yoke Leng (Exec VP-Admin & Corp
Sls)
Glen Hin (Sr VP-Bus Dev)
David Seah (Sr VP-IT)
Helen Ho (Sr VP-Fin)

Subsidiary (Domestic):

**Coldwell Banker Real Estate (S) Pte.
Ltd.** (2)
229 Mountbatten Road 03-26 Mounbatten
Square, Singapore, 398007, Singapore
Tel.: (65) 68055500
Web Site: http://www.coldwellbanker.com.sg
Real Estate Services
N.A.I.C.S.: 531390

ERA Realty Network Pte. Ltd. (2)
ERA APAC Centre 450 Lorong 6 Toa
Payoh, Singapore, 319394, Singapore
Tel.: (65) 62262000
Web Site: https://www.era.com.sg
Emp.: 7,400
Real Estate Services
N.A.I.C.S.: 531390
Poh Chee Yong (CFO)
Joy Koh (CMO)
Raymond Leong (CTO)

Subsidiary (Non-US):

PT Era Graharealty Tbk (2)
Tcc Batavia Tower One Lantai 8 Suite 3-5 Jl
Kh Mas Mansyur Kav 126, Jakarta Pusat,
10220, Indonesia   (84.98%)
Tel.: (62) 215708000
Web Site: https://eraindonesia.com
Rev.: $1,869,874
Assets: $2,893,492
Liabilities: $638,045
Net Worth: $2,255,447
Earnings: $185,267
Emp.: 31
Fiscal Year-end: 12/31/2023
Real Estate Services
N.A.I.C.S.: 531210
Darmadi Darmawangsa (Pres)

Subsidiary (Domestic):

**Realty International Associates Pte.
Ltd.** (2)
229 Mountbatten Rd, Singapore, 398007,
Singapore
Tel.: (65) 62497221
Web Site: https://www.riasg.com
Real Estate Services
N.A.I.C.S.: 531390

American Chemicals, LLC (1)
8082 W 24000 N, Portage, UT 84331
Tel.: (435) 227-5239
Web Site: https://www.americanchem.us
Investment Banking & Securities Dealing
Services
N.A.I.C.S.: 523150

Bayview Holding Ltd. (1)
2100 Travis St Ste 1555, Houston, TX
77002
Tel.: (713) 568-3055
Web Site: https://bayviewholdingsltd.com
Real Estate Investment Services
N.A.I.C.S.: 525990

**Bellevue Towers Condominiums,
LLC** (1)
700 112th Ave NE Ste 100, Bellevue, WA
98004
Tel.: (206) 391-2021
Web Site: http://www.thebellevueblock.com
Real Estate Services
N.A.I.C.S.: 531210

Ceres Managed Futures LLC (1)
522 Fifth Ave 14th Fl, New York, NY 10036
Tel.: (212) 296-1999
Investment Banking & Security Dealing Ser-
vices
N.A.I.C.S.: 523150
Patrick T. Egan (Chm & Pres)
Brooke Lambert (CFO, Principal & Treas)
Christopher P. Smock (Chief Compliance
Officer)

Cimarron Investments LLC (1)
430 Walnut St, Columbia, PA 17512
Tel.: (717) 278-7979
Web Site: https://cimarroninvestments.com

Investment Banking & Securities Dealing
Services
N.A.I.C.S.: 523150

Concept Petroleum, Inc. (1)
18207 Willow Ct, Spring, TX 77379
Tel.: (713) 826-2873
Fuel Oil Whslr
N.A.I.C.S.: 424720

D&Z Limited (1)
6th Floor Alapatt Heritage Mahatma Gandhi
Rd North, Kochi, 682 035, Kerala, India
Tel.: (91) 18004198150
Web Site: https://dzlimited.com
Investment Banking & Securities Dealing
Services
N.A.I.C.S.: 523150

Eaton Vance Corp. (1)
2 International Pl, Boston, MA 02110
Tel.: (617) 482-8260
Web Site: http://www.eatonvance.com
Rev.: $1,730,365,000
Assets: $4,949,298,000
Liabilities: $3,402,759,000
Net Worth: $1,546,539,000
Earnings: $138,516,000
Emp.: 1,983
Fiscal Year-end: 10/31/2020
Investment Adviser; Investment Company
Shares Distr
N.A.I.C.S.: 523940
Sebastiano Visentini (Pres, Treas & Sec)

Subsidiary (Domestic):

Eaton Vance Acquisitions (2)
2 International Pl, Boston, MA 02110
Tel.: (617) 482-8260
Web Site: http://www.eatonvance.com
Investment Advisory Services
N.A.I.C.S.: 523940

Subsidiary (Domestic):

**Atlanta Capital Management Com-
pany, LLC** (3)
1075 Peachtree St NE Ste 2100, Atlanta,
GA 30309
Tel.: (404) 876-9411
Web Site: https://www.atlcap.com
Sales Range: $25-49.9 Million
Emp.: 45
Investment Advisory & Management Ser-
vices
N.A.I.C.S.: 523940

Fox Asset Management LLC (3)
1040 Broad St Ste 203, Shrewsbury, NJ
07702
Tel.: (732) 747-6345
Web Site: http://www.foxasset.com
Investment Advisory Services
N.A.I.C.S.: 523940

**Parametric Portfolio Associates
LLC** (3)
800 5th Ave Ste 2800, Seattle, WA 98104
Tel.: (206) 694-5575
Web Site:
   https://www.parametricportfolio.com
Sales Range: $1-9.9 Million
Emp.: 230
Management Investment Companies
N.A.I.C.S.: 525910
Brian Dean Langstraat (CEO)
Melissa Fell (Mng Dir-HR)
Chris Powers (Dir-Bus Dev-Northeastern
Region & Canada)
Clint Talmo (Mng Dir)
Nisha Patel (Mng Dir)
Stephanie Nicolai (Mng Dir)

Subsidiary (Domestic):

Eaton Vance Distributors, Inc. (2)
2 Intl Pl, Boston, MA 02110   (100%)
Tel.: (617) 482-8260
Web Site:
   http://www.contact.eatonvance.com
Rev.: $3,089,210
Emp.: 570
Mutual Fund Distr
N.A.I.C.S.: 523940

**Eaton Vance Investment
Counsel** (2)
2 International Pl, Boston, MA 02110
Tel.: (617) 672-8151

Morgan Stanley—(Continued)

Web Site:
http://www.eatonvancecounsel.com
Emp.: 100
Investment Counseling Services
N.A.I.C.S.: 523940
Robert C. Quinn (VP)

Eaton Vance Management (2)
2 International Pl Ste 1400, Boston, MA
02110 (100%)
Tel.: (617) 482-8260.
Web Site: https://www.eatonvance.com
Sales Range: $1-4.9 Billion
Emp.: 1,400
Investment Management
N.A.I.C.S.: 523940
Thomas E. Faust Jr. (Pres & CEO)

Subsidiary (Domestic):

**Boston Management and
Research** (3)
40 Beach St Ste 200, Manchester, MA
01944
Tel.: (978) 526-9700
Web Site: https://bostonrm.com
Investment Banking & Securities Dealing
Services
N.A.I.C.S.: 523150

Subsidiary (Non-US):

**Eaton Vance Management (Interna-
tional) Limited** (3)
125 Old Broad Street, London, EC2N 1AR,
United Kingdom
Tel.: (44) 2032071900
Web Site: https://global.eatonvance.com
Investment Management Service
N.A.I.C.S.: 523940
David Miles (Dir-Bus Dev-Fin Institutions)

Affiliate (Domestic):

**Eaton Vance Municipal Income 2028
Term Trust** (2)
2 International Pl Ste 1400, Boston, MA
02110
Tel.: (617) 482-8260
Web Site: http://eatonvance.com
Rev.: $13,346,190
Assets: $367,439,335
Liabilities: $130,227,470
Net Worth: $237,211,865
Earnings: $8,265,106
Fiscal Year-end: 01/31/2020
Closed-End Investment Fund
N.A.I.C.S.: 525990
George J. Gorman (Chm)

Subsidiary (Domestic):

Eaton Vance WaterOak Advisors (2)
2 International Pl, Boston, MA 02110
Web Site: http://www.evwateroak.com
Financial Planning Services
N.A.I.C.S.: 523940
David C. McCabe (Pres)

**The Clifton Group Investment Man-
agement Company** (2)
3600 Minnesota Dr Ste 325, Minneapolis,
MN 55435
Tel.: (612) 870-8800
Web Site:
http://www.parametricportfolio.com
Sales Range: $25-49.9 Billion
Emp.: 98
Investment Advisory & Portfolio Manage-
ment Services
N.A.I.C.S.: 523940

Eaux Vives Water Inc. (1)
25 Adelaide Street East Suite 1000, To-
ronto, M5C 3A1, ON, Canada
Tel.: (416) 504-4888
Web Site: https://www.eskawater.com
Water Purification Services
N.A.I.C.S.: 312112

FrontPoint Management Inc. (1)
1600 Providence Hwy, Walpole, MA 02081
Tel.: (508) 404-1800
Web Site: https://frontpointllc.com
Investment Banking & Securities Dealing
Services
N.A.I.C.S.: 523150

**Global Equity High Yield Fund
B.V.** (1)
Weena 210, 3012 NJ, Rotterdam, Nether-
lands
Tel.: (31) 102013600
Securities Brokerage Services
N.A.I.C.S.: 523150

Hyas Group (1)
108 NW 9th Ave Ste 203, Portland, OR
90209-3318
Tel.: (971) 634-1504
Web Site: http://www.hyasgroup.com
Financial Investment Activities
N.A.I.C.S.: 523999
Jayson Davidson (Principal)

MS Solar Investments LLC (1)
2000 Westchester Ave, Purchase, NY
10577
Tel.: (914) 225-1593
Investment Banking Services
N.A.I.C.S.: 523150
Deborah Hart (CEO)

MSCP III, LLC (1)
1221 Ave of The Americas, New York, NY
10020
Tel.: (212) 762-8178
Investment Management Service
N.A.I.C.S.: 523940

MSREF Real Estate Advisor, Inc. (1)
1585 Broadway 30th Fl, New York, NY
10019
Tel.: (212) 761-7160
Real Estate Investment Services
N.A.I.C.S.: 525990

**Morgan Stanley & Co. International
plc** (1)
25 Cabot Square Canary Wharf, London,
E14 4QA, United Kingdom
Tel.: (44) 2074258000
Investment Banking Services
N.A.I.C.S.: 523150

Morgan Stanley & Co. LLC (1)
1300 Thames St, Baltimore, MD 21231
Tel.: (443) 627-6000
Investment Banking & Securities Dealing
Services
N.A.I.C.S.: 523150

Morgan Stanley & Co. LLC (1)
1585 Broadway Ave, New York, NY 10036
Tel.: (212) 761-4000
Web Site: http://www.msdwhomeloans.com
Retail Brokerage Services
N.A.I.C.S.: 523150
James P. Gorman (Exec Chm & CEO)

Division (Domestic):

**Morgan Stanley & Co.
Commodities** (2)
2000 Westchester Ave, Purchase, NY
10577
Tel.: (443) 627-6000
Web Site: http://www.morganstanley.com
Sales Range: $150-199.9 Million
Investment Transactions
N.A.I.C.S.: 523940

Branch (Domestic):

**Morgan Stanley & Co. LLC -
Brooklyn** (2)
1 Pierrepont Plz Fl 9, Brooklyn, NY 11201
Tel.: (718) 754-8950
Web Site: http://www.morganstanley.com
Securities Underwriting & Stock Market
Consulting Services
N.A.I.C.S.: 523150

**Morgan Stanley (China) Private Eq-
uity Investment Management Co.,
Ltd.** (1)
International Center Dikai 19th Street 38th
Floor, Chinese Osmanthus Jianggan Dis-
trict, Hangzhou, 310016, China
Tel.: (86) 57187216768
Web Site:
http://www.morganstanleypechina.com
Investment Banking Services
N.A.I.C.S.: 523150

Morgan Stanley (France) SAS (1)
61 Rue De Monceau, 75008, Paris, France
Tel.: (33) 142907000

Investment Banking Services
N.A.I.C.S.: 523150

Morgan Stanley (Israel) Ltd. (1)
Millennium Tower 19th Floor 17 HaArbaah
Street, South Kiryah, Tel Aviv, 64739, Israel
Tel.: (972) 36236300
Investment Banking Services
N.A.I.C.S.: 523150

**Morgan Stanley (Switzerland)
AG** (1)
Beethovenstrasse 33, 8002, Zurich, Swit-
zerland
Tel.: (41) 445881000
Web Site: http://www.morganstanley.com
Sales Range: $50-74.9 Million
Emp.: 150
Banking Services
N.A.I.C.S.: 522110

**Morgan Stanley (Thailand)
Limited** (1)
16/F Bhiraj Tower at EmQuartier 689
Sukhumvit Road, Vadhana, Bangkok,
10110, Thailand
Tel.: (66) 20369800
Investment Banking & Securities Dealing
Services
N.A.I.C.S.: 523150

Morgan Stanley AIP GP LP (1)
100 Front St Ste 400, Conshohocken, PA
19428-2881
Tel.: (610) 260-7600
Web Site: http://www.ms.com
Investment Advice Services
N.A.I.C.S.: 523940

**Morgan Stanley Asia (Singapore) Se-
curities Pte Ltd.** (1)
23 Church Street 16 01 Capital Square,
Singapore, 049481, Singapore
Tel.: (65) 68346888
Web Site: http://www.morganstanley.com
Emp.: 60
Security Services
N.A.I.C.S.: 523150

**Morgan Stanley Asia (Taiwan)
Ltd.** (1)
83F 83F-1 Taipei 101 No 7 Xinyi Rd Xinyi
District Sec 5, Taipei, 110, Taiwan
Tel.: (886) 227302800
Security Services
N.A.I.C.S.: 561621

Morgan Stanley Australia Limited (1)
Level 4 2 King William Street, Adelaide,
5000, SA, Australia
Tel.: (61) 1800812298
Web Site:
https://www.morganstanley.com.au
Investment Banking & Securities Dealing
Services
N.A.I.C.S.: 523150

Morgan Stanley B.V. (1)
Rembrandt Tower 11th Floor Amstelplein 1,
1096 HA, Amsterdam, Netherlands
Tel.: (31) 204621300
Investment Banking & Securities Dealing
Services
N.A.I.C.S.: 523150

**Morgan Stanley Bank Asia
Limited** (1)
31/F International Commerce Centre 1 Aus-
tin Road West, Kowloon, 999077, China
(Hong Kong)
Tel.: (852) 28488800
Financial Banking Services
N.A.I.C.S.: 522110

**Morgan Stanley Bank International
Limited** (1)
25 Cabot Square Canary Wharf, London,
E14 4QA, United Kingdom
Tel.: (44) 2074258000
Financial Services
N.A.I.C.S.: 522320

**Morgan Stanley Capital Management,
LLC** (1)
1585 Broadway, New York, NY 10036
Tel.: (212) 761-4000
Web Site: http://www.morganstanley.com
Sales Range: $250-299.9 Million
Holding Company
N.A.I.C.S.: 551112

Subsidiary (Domestic):

**Morgan Stanley Domestic Capital,
Inc.** (2)
1585 Broadway, New York, NY 10036
Tel.: (212) 761-4000
Web Site: http://www.morganstanley.com
Sales Range: $250-299.9 Million
Holding Company
N.A.I.C.S.: 551112

**Morgan Stanley Corporate
Trader** (1)
20 Bank Street, London, E14 4AD, United
Kingdom
Tel.: (44) 2074253875
Business Support Services
N.A.I.C.S.: 561990

Morgan Stanley Durango LLC (1)
940 Main Ave, Durango, CO 81301
Tel.: (970) 259-0937
Web Site: http://www.morganstanley.com
Emp.: 9
Securities Brokerage Services
N.A.I.C.S.: 561621

Morgan Stanley Elz GmbH (1)
Junghofstr 13 15, Frankfurt, 60311, Ger-
many
Tel.: (49) 6921660
Web Site: http://www.morganstanley.com
Investment Advice
N.A.I.C.S.: 523940

**Morgan Stanley Fund Services (Ire-
land) Limited** (1)
24-26 City Quay, Dublin Docklands, Dublin,
D02 NY19, Ireland
Tel.: (353) 5317998700
Investment Banking & Securities Dealing
Services
N.A.I.C.S.: 523150

**Morgan Stanley Hong Kong
Limited** (1)
Level 46 International Commerce Centre 1
Austin Road West, Kowloon, China (Hong
Kong)
Tel.: (852) 28485200
Investment Banking & Securities Dealing
Services
N.A.I.C.S.: 523150

**Morgan Stanley India Company Pri-
vate Limited** (1)
18th Floor Tower 2 One World Center Plot-
841, Jupiter Textile Mill Compound Senapati
Bapat Marg Lower Parel, Mumbai, 400 013,
India
Tel.: (91) 2261181000
Web Site: http://www.morganstanley.com
Research Sales Trading Service
N.A.I.C.S.: 522220

**Morgan Stanley Infrastructure,
Inc.** (1)
1585 Brdwy 39th fl, New York, NY 10036-
8200
Tel.: (212) 761-1278
Privater Equity Firm
N.A.I.C.S.: 523999
John V. Vich (Mng Dir & Chm)

Subsidiary (Domestic):

Seven Seas Water Corporation (2)
14400 Carlson Cir, Tampa, FL 33626
Tel.: (813) 855-8636
Web Site: http://www.sevenseaswater.com
Sales Range: $1-9.9 Million
Emp.: 195
Water Supply & Irrigation Systems
N.A.I.C.S.: 221310
John F. Curtis (Chm-Interim)
Brian Hernon (Sr VP-Global Engrg)
Lee S. Muller (Co-CFO)
Chad Schafer (Co-CFO)
Henry J. Charrabe (CEO)

Subsidiary (Non-US):

Seven Seas Water Corporation (3)
insurgentes Sur 1898 Piso 12 Col Florida,
Mexico, 01020, Mexico
Tel.: (52) 55 9171 1080
Water Supply & Irrigation Systems
N.A.I.C.S.: 221310

Subsidiary (Non-US):

Tele Columbus AG (2)

Kaiserin-Augusta-Allee 108, 10553, Berlin,
Germany   **(94.4%)**
Tel.: (49) 3025777777
Web Site: http://www.telecolumbus.com
Rev.: $589,432,376
Assets: $2,437,933,576
Liabilities: $2,288,948,064
Net Worth: $148,985,512
Earnings: ($231,154,768)
Emp.: 1,255
Fiscal Year-end: 12/31/2020
Cable Programming
N.A.I.C.S.: 516210
Roland Schneider *(COO & Member-Mgmt Bd)*
Tim Degenhardt *(Member-Exec Bd)*
Stefan Riedel *(Chief Consumer Officer & Member-Exec Bd)*
Daniel Ritz *(Chm-Exec Bd & CEO)*
Dietmar Poltl *(CTO & Member-Exec Bd)*
Rudiger Schmidt *(Member-Exec Bd)*
Eike Walters *(CFO & Member-Exec Bd)*
Volker Ruloff *(Chm-Supervisory Bd)*

Subsidiary (Domestic):

Antec Servicepool GmbH **(3)**
Berckhusenstr 25, 30625, Hannover, Germany
Tel.: (49) 51127090370
Web Site: https://www.antec-servicepool.de
Cable Television Connection Services
N.A.I.C.S.: 517111

Funk und Technik GmbH **(3)**
Sorauer Strasse 17-25, 03149, Forst, Germany
Tel.: (49) 356295900
Web Site: https://www.kabel-net.de
Emp.: 17
Cable Products Mfr
N.A.I.C.S.: 335921

HL komm Telekommunikations GmbH **(3)**
Nonnenmuhlgasse 1, 04107, Leipzig, Germany
Tel.: (49) 34186970
Web Site: https://www.an.de
Telecommunications Contracting Services
N.A.I.C.S.: 517810

KKG Kabelkommunikation Gustrow GmbH **(3)**
Goldberger Str 13, 18273, Rostock, Germany
Tel.: (49) 384382580
Web Site: http://www.gknetz.de
Cable Television Connection Services
N.A.I.C.S.: 517111

KSP-Kabelservice Prenzlau GmbH **(3)**
Freyschmidtstrasse 20, 17291, Prenzlau, Germany
Tel.: (49) 39848530
Web Site: https://www.ucker-net.de
Cable Television Connection Services
N.A.I.C.S.: 517111

Kabelcom Rheinhessen GmbH **(3)**
Dieselstrasse 1, 85774, Unterfohring, Germany
Tel.: (49) 6133578371
Web Site: http://www.kms.tv
Cable Television Distribution Services
N.A.I.C.S.: 517111

Kabelfernsehen Munchen Servicenter GmbH **(3)**
Dieselstrasse 1, 85774, Unterfohring, Germany
Tel.: (49) 8995083100
Cable Television Connection Services
N.A.I.C.S.: 517111

MDCC Magdeburg-City-Com GmbH **(3)**
Weitlingstrasse 22, 39104, Magdeburg, Germany
Tel.: (49) 3915874444
Web Site: https://www.mdcc.de
Cable Television Connection Services
N.A.I.C.S.: 517111

Mietho & Bar Kabelkom Kabelkommunikations-Betriebs GmbH **(3)**
Hegelstrasse 2, 03050, Cottbus, Germany
Tel.: (49) 3555800444

Web Site:
   http://www.mub.kabelkundenservice.de
Telecommunication Servicesb
N.A.I.C.S.: 517810

Pepcom GmbH **(3)**
Medienallee 24, 85774, Unterfohring, Germany
Tel.: (49) 89 710 4089 0
Web Site: http://www.pepcom.de
Cable Television Broadcasting, Broadband & Voice Telecommunications Services
N.A.I.C.S.: 517810
Rudiger Schmidt *(Co-Mng Dir)*
Frank Posnanski *(Co-Mng Dir)*
Ronny Verhelst *(Co-Mng Dir)*
Frank Hornberger *(Co-Mng Dir)*

PrimaCom Berlin GmbH **(3)**
Messe-Allee 2, 04356, Leipzig, Germany
Tel.: (49) 341 423 72 000
Web Site: http://www.primacom.de
Telecommunications Resellers
N.A.I.C.S.: 517121
Ronny Verhelst *(Mng Dir)*
Frank Posnanski *(Mng Dir)*

RFC Radio-, Fernseh- u. Computer-technik GmbH **(3)**
Winklhoferstrasse 15, 09116, Chemnitz, Germany
Tel.: (49) 371572920
Web Site: https://www.rfct.de
Emp.: 250
Cable Television Connection Services
N.A.I.C.S.: 517111

Tele-System Harz GmbH **(3)**
Muhlenstrasse 50A, 38889, Blankenburg, Germany
Tel.: (49) 3025777777
Web Site: https://www.ts-harz.de
Cable Television Connection Services
N.A.I.C.S.: 517111

Teleco GmbH Cottbus Telekommunikation **(3)**
Hegelstrasse 2, 3050, Cottbus, Germany
Tel.: (49) 3555800444
Web Site: https://www.teleco-gmbh.de
Telecommunication Servicesb
N.A.I.C.S.: 517810

WTC Wohnen & TeleCommunication GmbH & Co. KG **(3)**
Medienallee 24, 85774, Unterfohring, Germany
Tel.: (49) 899508530
Web Site: http://www.wtc.tv
Cable Television Connection Services
N.A.I.C.S.: 517111

Subsidiary (Non-US):

Valoriza Servicios Medioambientales SA **(2)**
C/ Juan Esplandiu 11-13 Planta 13, 28007, Madrid, Spain
Tel.: (34) 914434200
Web Site: http://www.valorizasm.com
Emp.: 8,367
Waste Management Services
N.A.I.C.S.: 562998

Morgan Stanley International Holdings Inc. **(1)**
1585 Broadway St, New York, NY 10036
Tel.: (212) 761-4000
Web Site: http://www.morganstanley.com
Global Financial Services
N.A.I.C.S.: 523999

Joint Venture (Non-US):

Mitsubishi UFJ Morgan Stanley Securities Co., Ltd. **(2)**
Otemachi Financial City Grand Cube 1-9-2, Otemachi Chiyoda-ku, Tokyo, 100-8127, Japan
Tel.: (81) 362138500
Web Site: https://www.sc.mufjg.jp
Sales Range: $1-4.9 Billion
Emp.: 5,630
Securities Brokerage Services
N.A.I.C.S.: 523150
Haruo Nakamura *(Deputy Pres)*
Kiyoshi Sato *(Deputy Pres)*
Akio Ninomiya *(Deputy Pres)*
Akihiro Sugimura *(Mng Exec Officer)*
Koshiro Tamura *(Chm)*

Masamichi Yasuda *(Deputy Pres)*
Naoki Isetani *(Mng Exec Officer)*
Nobuhiro Matsumoto *(Auditor)*
Saburo Araki *(Pres & CEO)*
Yasuhiro Kaga *(Mng Exec Officer)*
Naoyuki Hamada *(Deputy Pres)*
Hirochika Iwadare *(Mng Exec Officer)*
Hideyuki Sago *(Auditor)*
Masashi Kanematsu *(Deputy Pres)*
Hiroyuki Tomita *(Mng Exec Officer)*
Kazuki Tobimatsu *(Mng Exec Officer)*
Makoto Kobayashi *(Deputy Pres)*

Subsidiary (Non-US):

Morgan Stanley AB **(2)**
Hovslagargatan 5A, 111 48, Stockholm, Sweden **(100%)**
Tel.: (46) 86789600
Web Site: http://www.morganstanley.com
Sales Range: $75-99.9 Million
Emp.: 20
Security Brokerage Services
N.A.I.C.S.: 523150
Per Hillstrom *(Mng Dir)*

Morgan Stanley Asia Ltd. **(2)**
Level 46 International Commerce Centre, 1 Austin Road West, Kowloon, China (Hong Kong)
Tel.: (852) 28485200
Sales Range: $1-4.9 Billion
Emp.: 2,000
Private Wealth Management Services
N.A.I.C.S.: 523150
Ben Falloon *(Head-Fixed Income Markets-Asia Pacific)*

Subsidiary (Non-US):

Morgan Stanley Private Equity Asia Inc. **(2)**
Unit 02 29F China World Tower 2, 1 Jian-huomenwai Ave, 100004, Beijing, China
Tel.: (86) 65362800
Web Site: http://www.morganstanley.com
Sales Range: $650-699.9 Million
Private Equity Investments
N.A.I.C.S.: 523999

Subsidiary (Domestic):

Sihuan Pharmaceutical Holdings Group Ltd. **(4)**
Floor 22 Building 4 Zhubang 2000 Bal-izhuang xili, Chaoyang District, Beijing, 100025, China
Tel.: (86) 1057693700
Web Site: http://www.sihuanpharm.com
Rev.: $306,238,936
Assets: $1,704,533,360
Liabilities: $912,701,790
Net Worth: $791,831,570
Earnings: ($320,571,950)
Emp.: 3,313
Fiscal Year-end: 12/31/2022
Cardiocerebral Vascular Drug Mfr
N.A.I.C.S.: 325412
Fengsheng Che *(Co-Founder & Chm)*
Weicheng Guo *(Co-Founder, Deputy Chm & CEO)*

Subsidiary (Non-US):

Morgan Stanley Bank AG **(2)**
Grosse Gallusstrasse 18, 60312, Frankfurt am Main, Germany
Tel.: (49) 6921660
Web Site: http://www.morganstanley.com
Sales Range: $1-4.9 Billion
Emp.: 400
Investment Banking Services
N.A.I.C.S.: 523150

Morgan Stanley Canada Ltd. **(2)**
Brookfield Place 181 Bay Street Suite 3700, Toronto, M5J 2T3, ON, Canada
Tel.: (416) 943-8400
Web Site: http://www.morganstanley.com
Sales Range: $100-124.9 Million
Emp.: 50
Investment Services
N.A.I.C.S.: 523940

Morgan Stanley Dean Witter (Thailand) Ltd. **(2)**
16/F Bhiraj Tower at EmQuartier 689 Sukhumvit Road, Vadhana, Bangkok, 10110, Thailand
Tel.: (66) 20369800

Web Site: http://www.morganstanley.com
Securities Brokerage Services
N.A.I.C.S.: 523150

Morgan Stanley International Ltd. **(2)**
25 Cabot Square Canary Wharf, London, E14 4QA, United Kingdom
Tel.: (44) 2074258000
Web Site: http://www.morganstanley.co.uk
Sales Range: $100-124.9 Million
Emp.: 150
Financial Services for Europe, the Middle East & Africa
N.A.I.C.S.: 921130

Subsidiary (Domestic):

Morgan Stanley Latin America Incorporated **(2)**
1585 Broadway, New York, NY 10036
Tel.: (212) 761-4000
Web Site: http://www.morganstanley.com
Sales Range: $250-299.9 Million
Holding Company
N.A.I.C.S.: 551112

Subsidiary (Non-US):

Morgan Stanley Corretora de Titulos e Valores Mobiliarios S.A. **(3)**
Av Brigadeiro Faria Lima 3600 6 andar, Sao Paulo, 04543-000, Brazil
Tel.: (55) 1130486000
Web Site: http://www.morganstanley.com.br
Investment Banking Services
N.A.I.C.S.: 523150

Subsidiary (Non-US):

Morgan Stanley South Africa (Pty) Ltd. **(2)**
140 West Street Floor 10 South Tower, Jo-hannesburg, 2196, Sandton, South Africa **(100%)**
Tel.: (27) 115070800
Web Site: http://www.morganstanley.com
Sales Range: $25-49.9 Million
Emp.: 7
Global Financial Services
N.A.I.C.S.: 921130

Morgan Stanley Swiss Holdings GmbH **(2)**
Bahnofstrasse 92, Zurich, 8001, Switzerland
Tel.: (41) 442209111
Web Site: http://www.morganstanley.com
Sales Range: $50-74.9 Million
Emp.: 100
Bank Holding Company
N.A.I.C.S.: 551111

Morgan Stanley Wealth Management Australia Pty Ltd. **(2)**
101 Collins Street Level 53, Melbourne, 3000, VIC, Australia
Tel.: (61) 392568900
Web Site: http://www.morganstanley.com
Sales Range: $200-249.9 Million
Emp.: 200
Wealth Management Services
N.A.I.C.S.: 523150

Morgan Stanley, S.V.,S.A.U **(2)**
Serrano 55, Madrid, 28006, Spain
Tel.: (34) 914181200
Web Site: http://www.morganstanley.com
Investment Banking Services
N.A.I.C.S.: 523150

Morgan Stanley Investment Management (Australia) Pty Limited **(1)**
Level 53 101 Collins Street, Melbourne, 3000, VIC, Australia
Tel.: (61) 392568918
Investment Banking & Securities Dealing Services
N.A.I.C.S.: 523150

Morgan Stanley Investment Management (Japan) Co., Ltd. **(1)**
Otemachi Financial City South Tower 1-9-7 Otemachi, Chiyoda-ku, Tokyo, 100-8109, Japan
Tel.: (81) 368365100
Web Site: http://www.morganstanley.com
Emp.: 70
Financial Investment Services
N.A.I.C.S.: 523940

Morgan Stanley—(Continued)

Morgan Stanley Investment Management Limited (1)
25 Cabot Square Canary Wharf, London, E14 4QA, United Kingdom
Tel.: (44) 2074258000
Investment Advice
N.A.I.C.S.: 523940
Pepijn Heins (Head-Benelux Sls)

Morgan Stanley Investment Management, Inc. (1)
1221 Ave of the Americas, New York, NY 10020
Tel.: (212) 762-7100
Web Site: http://www.morganstanley.com
Sales Range: $1-4.9 Billion
Emp.: 440
Asset Management Services
N.A.I.C.S.: 523940
Thomas E. Faust Jr. (Executives, Bd of Dirs)
Seema R. Hingorani (Mng Dir)
Jeffrey Levin (Mng Dir, Head-Direct Lending & Portfolio Mgr)
David Kulakofsky (Mng Dir-Chicago)
David Pessah (Mng Dir)
John R. R. Klopp (Mng Dir & Head-Real Assets-Global)
Laurel Durkay (Head-Listed Real Assets-Global)
Anil Agarwal (Mng Dir)
Ted Eliopoulos (Vice Chm & Head-Strategic Partnerships)
Eric Kayne (Head-HR)
John Hagarty (COO)
Rui De Figueiredo (CIO & Head-Multi Asset-Grp)
Josh Balik-Klein (Head-HR)
Paresh Bhatt (Portfolio Mgr-AIP Hedge Fund Team)
Dan Callahan (VP)
Patrik Egan (Sr Portfolio Mgr)
Victoria Eckstein (Mng Dir & COO-Solutions)
Edward Cummings (VP & Exec Dir)

Joint Venture (Domestic):

Medical Area Total Energy Plant, LLC (2)
474 Brookline Ave, Boston, MA 02215
Tel.: (617) 598-2700
Web Site: https://www.matep.com
Cogeneration Power Facility Provides Heating, Chilled Water Services & Electricity to Hospitals
N.A.I.C.S.: 221118
Richard E. Kessel (Pres & CEO)
Kelly T. McCarthy (CFO & VP-Dev)

Subsidiary (Domestic):

Morgan Stanley Capital Partners (2)
1585 Broadway, New York, NY 10036
Tel.: (212) 761-4000
Web Site: http://www.morganstanley.com
Private Equity Investment Firm
N.A.I.C.S.: 523999
Steven E. Rodgers (Partner & Head-Healthcare Investing)
Aaron Sack (Head-Capital Partners & Consumer)
James Howland (Operating Partner & Mng Dir)
Jill Wight (Operating Partner & Mng Dir)
Sharveen Seebaluck (VP)
Alexander Roso (Exec Dir)
James R. Stewart (Exec Dir)
David M. Thompson (Exec Dir)
Geoff Laporte (Head-Bus Dev)
Harrison Grussmark (VP)
Maxwell Waterous (VP)
Patrick Whitehead (VP)
Brent Moore (CEO)
Steven E. Rodgers (Head-Healthcare Investing)
Eric Kanter (Mng Dir)

Holding (Non-US):

Access Cash General Partnership (3)
191 Attwell Drive Unit 4, Toronto, M9W 5Z2, ON, Canada
Tel.: (416) 247-0200
Web Site: https://www.access-cash.com
ATM Portfolio Management Services

N.A.I.C.S.: 525990

Subsidiary (Domestic):

GAB EZEE ATM LP (4)
191 Attwell Drive Unit 4, Toronto, M9M 5Z2, ON, Canada
Tel.: (416) 247-0200
Web Site: http://www.access-cash.ca
Emp.: 50
ATM Operator
N.A.I.C.S.: 522320
Chris Chandler (Pres & CEO)

Holding (Domestic):

Alliance Technical Group, LLC (3)
255 Grant St Ste 600, Decatur, AL 35601
Tel.: (256) 351-0121
Web Site: https://alliancetg.com
Emp.: 552
Environmental Services
N.A.I.C.S.: 541620
Chris LeMay (CEO)

Subsidiary (Domestic):

Chemtech Consulting Group, Inc. (4)
284 Sheffield St, Mountainside, NJ 07092
Tel.: (908) 789-8900
Web Site: http://www.chemtech.net
Management Consulting Services
N.A.I.C.S.: 541618
Emanuel Hedvat (Pres)

Fremont Analytical Inc. (4)
3600 Fremont Ave N, Seattle, WA 98103-8712
Tel.: (206) 352-3790
Web Site: http://www.fremontanalytical.com
Research & Development in Biotechnology
N.A.I.C.S.: 541714

Labcor, Inc. (4)
12242 SW Garden Pl, Tigard, OR 97223-8246
Tel.: (503) 624-2183
Web Site: http://www.chesterlab.net
Testing Laboratories
N.A.I.C.S.: 541380
Paul Duda (Pres, Mgr-Laboratory & Project Mgr)

Summit Environmental Technologies, Inc. (4)
3310 Win St, Cuyahoga Falls, OH 44223-3790
Tel.: (330) 253-8211
Web Site: http://www.summitlabs.com
Testing Laboratories
N.A.I.C.S.: 541380
Ron Gibas (Mgr-Quality)

Subsidiary (Domestic):

Educate 360 LLC (3)
1241 Cumberland Ave Ste A, West Lafayette, IN 47906-1304
Tel.: (877) 637-0450
Web Site: http://www.projectmanagementacademy.net
Project Management Training Services
N.A.I.C.S.: 611430
Jason Cassidy (CEO)
Michael McCay (CFO)
Russ Smith (CIO)
Amy Farber (VP-Strategy)
Mike Sweeney (Mktg Dir)

Subsidiary (Domestic):

Watermark Learning, Inc. (4)
8120 Penn Ave S Ste 470, Minneapolis, MN 55431
Tel.: (877) 202-5959
Web Site: http://www.watermarklearning.com
Professional & Management Development Training
N.A.I.C.S.: 611430
Chris Anderson (VP-Ops)
Andrea Brockmeier (Dir-Project Mgmt)
Susan Heidorn (Dir-Bus Solutions)

Holding (Domestic):

Impact Fitness (3)
1007 E Grand River Ave, Brighton, MI 48116

Tel.: (615) 532-2300
Fitness & Recreational Sports Centers
N.A.I.C.S.: 713940
Adam Willaeys (CEO)
Chris Klebba (Chm)

Subsidiary (Domestic):

Nivel Holdings, LLC (3)
3510 Port Jacksonville Pkwy, Jacksonville, FL 32226-2378
Tel.: (904) 741-6161
Web Site: http://www.nivelparts.com
Holding Company; Golf Cart Parts & Accessories Mfr & Distr
N.A.I.C.S.: 551112

Subsidiary (Domestic):

Nivel Parts & Manufacturing Company, LLC (4)
3510 Port Jacksonville Pkwy, Jacksonville, FL 32226-2378
Tel.: (904) 741-6161
Web Site: https://www.nivelparts.com
Golf & Industrial Vehicle Replacement Parts Mfr & Distr
N.A.I.C.S.: 336999
Brent Moore (CEO)

Subsidiary (Domestic):

High Lifter Products, Inc. (5)
780 Professional Dr N, Shreveport, LA 71105
Tel.: (318) 524-2270
Web Site: http://www.highlifter.com
Rev.: $9,600,000
Emp.: 32
Automobile & Other Motor Vehicle Merchant Whslr
N.A.I.C.S.: 423110
Tracie Engi (Coord-Event)
Scott Smith (Founder & CEO)
Mike Smith (Co-Owner)

Performance Plus Carts (5)
1051 US Highway 92 W, Auburndale, FL 33823
Tel.: (800) 539-3830
Web Site: http://www.performancepluscarts.com
Sales Range: $1-9.9 Million
Golf Cart & Accessory Distr
N.A.I.C.S.: 423910
Jessica Jouppi (Owner)

Holding (Domestic):

Sila Heating & Air Conditioning, Inc. (3)
722 2nd St, Annapolis, MD 21403
Tel.: (215) 464-1545
Web Site: http://www.sila.com
Plumbing, Heating & Air-Conditioning Contractors
N.A.I.C.S.: 238220
Evan Brodowski (Mgr)

Subsidiary (Domestic):

Astar Heating & Air, LLC (4)
36 Wes Warren Dr, Middletown, NY 10941
Tel.: (845) 986-4858
Web Site: http://www.astarheating.com
Site Preparation Contractor
N.A.I.C.S.: 238910
Jeremy Dunitz (Mgr-Ops)

Subsidiary (Domestic):

Petcosky & Sons Plumbing, Heating & A/C Inc. (5)
421 Commerce Rd, Vestal, NY 13850
Tel.: (607) 797-0160
Web Site: http://www.petcosky-sons.com
Plumbing, Heating & Air-Conditioning Contractors
N.A.I.C.S.: 238220

Subsidiary (Domestic):

Central Cooling & Heating Inc. (4)
9 N Maple St # 2, Woburn, MA 01801
Tel.: (781) 933-8288
Web Site: http://www.centralcooling.com
Site Preparation Contractor
N.A.I.C.S.: 238910

Jackson Comfort Systems, Inc. (4)
499 E Twinsburg Rd, Northfield, OH 44067

Tel.: (330) 655-5655
Web Site: http://www.jacksoncomfort.com
Sales Range: $1-9.9 Million
Emp.: 30
Plumbing, Heating & Air-Conditioning Contractors
N.A.I.C.S.: 238220
Gary Jackson (Mgr-Ops)

Sila Services, LLC (4)
290 Hansen Access Rd, King of Prussia 19406
Tel.: (610) 200-8070
Web Site: https://sila.com
HVAC, Plumbing & Electrical Services.
N.A.I.C.S.: 238220
Jason Rabbino (CEO)

Subsidiary (Domestic):

Burns & McBride Inc. (5)
240 S DuPont Hwy, New Castle, DE 19720
Tel.: (302) 656-5110
Web Site: http://www.burnsandmcbride.com
Sales Range: $10-24.9 Million
Emp.: 43
Fuel Oil Dealers
N.A.I.C.S.: 457210

Cleveland Air Comfort Corp. (5)
7575 Bond St, Cleveland, OH 44139
Tel.: (440) 232-1861
Web Site: http://www.clevelandaircomfort.com
Sales Range: $1-9.9 Million
Emp.: 20
Plumbing, Heating, Air-Conditioning, Nsk
N.A.I.C.S.: 238220

Subsidiary (Domestic):

Tri-State Home Services LLC (4)
82A Wormans Mill Court, Frederick, MD 21701
Tel.: (301) 969-9353
Web Site: http://www.tri-statehomeservices.com
Offices of Real Estate Agents & Brokers
N.A.I.C.S.: 531210

Subsidiary (Domestic):

Spendmend LLC (3)
2680 Horizon Drive SE, Grand Rapids, MI 49546
Tel.: (616) 257-6300
Web Site: http://www.spendmend.com
Management Consulting Services
N.A.I.C.S.: 541618
Teri Harkins (VP-Sls)

Holding (Domestic):

Triana Energy, LLC (3)
500 Lee St E Ste 401, Charleston, WV 25301
Tel.: (304) 380-0100
Web Site: https://www.trianaenergy.com
Sales Range: $125-149.9 Million
Holding Company; Oil & Gas Exploration & Production Services
N.A.I.C.S.: 333132

Trinity CO2 Investments LLC (3)
401 W Wall St, Midland, TX 79701-4403
Tel.: (432) 683-8262
Holding Company; Enhanced Oil Recovery Pipeline Operator & CO2 Supply Management Services
N.A.I.C.S.: 551112

Subsidiary (Domestic):

Trinity Pipeline, L.P. (4)
401 W Wall St, Midland, TX 79701
Tel.: (432) 683-8262
Web Site: https://www.trinitypipelinelp.com
Enhanced Oil Recovery Pipeline Operator
N.A.I.C.S.: 486110

Branch (Domestic):

Morgan Stanley Investment Management, Inc. - Philadelphia (2)
100 Front St Ste 400, West Conshohocken, PA 19428
Tel.: (610) 940-5000
Web Site: http://www.morganstanley.com
Emp.: 300
Asset Management Services
N.A.I.C.S.: 523940

Morgan Stanley Investment Management, Inc. - San Francisco (2)
555 California St 35th Fl, San Francisco, CA 94104
Tel.: (415) 984-6500
Web Site: http://www.morganstanley.com
Asset Management Services
N.A.I.C.S.: 523940

Subsidiary (Domestic):

Morgan Stanley Real Estate (2)
1585 Broadway, New York, NY 10036
Tel.: (212) 761-4000
Web Site: https://www.morganstanley.com
Sales Range: $25-49.9 Billion
Emp.: 817
Real Estate Management & Investment Services
N.A.I.C.S.: 531210
Christopher J. Niehaus (Executives)

Subsidiary (Domestic):

AMLI Residential Properties Trust (3)
141 W Jackson Blvd Ste 300, Chicago, IL 60604
Tel.: (312) 283-4700
Web Site: http://www.amli.com
Sales Range: $150-199.9 Million
Real Estate Development Services
N.A.I.C.S.: 525990

Morgan Stanley Japan Group Co., Ltd. (1)
Otemachi Financial City South Tower 1-9-7 Otemachi, Chiyoda-ku, Tokyo, 100-8109, Japan
Tel.: (81) 368365000
Investment Banking & Securities Dealing Services
N.A.I.C.S.: 523150

Morgan Stanley Japan Holdings Co., Ltd. (1)
Otemachi Financial City South Tower 1-9-7 Otemachi, Chiyoda-ku, Tokyo, 100-8109, Japan
Tel.: (81) 368365000
Investment Banking & Securities Dealing Services
N.A.I.C.S.: 523150
Alberto Tamura (CEO)

Morgan Stanley MUFG Securities Co., Ltd. (1)
Otemachi Financial City South Tower 1-9-7 Otemachi, Chiyoda-ku, Tokyo, 100-8104, Japan
Tel.: (81) 368365000
Investment Banking & Securities Dealing Services
N.A.I.C.S.: 523150
Masato Miyachi (Chm)
Alberto Tamura (CEO)

Morgan Stanley Menkul Degerler A.S. (1)
Esentepe Buyukdere Cad No 171 Metrocity is Merkezi, Metrocity Business Center A Block Floor 24, 34330, Istanbul, 34330, Turkiye
Tel.: (90) 2123980200
Web Site: http://www.morganstanley.com
Financial Services
N.A.I.C.S.: 523999

Morgan Stanley Realty Inc. (1)
1585 Broadway, New York, NY 10036
Tel.: (212) 761-4000
Web Site: http://www.morganstanley.com
Sales Range: $250-299.9 Million
Emp.: 230
Realty Services
N.A.I.C.S.: 531390

Subsidiary (Domestic):

Morgan Stanley Properties, Inc. (2)
1585 Broadway, New York, NY 10036
Tel.: (212) 761-4000 (100%)
Web Site: http://www.morganstanley.com
Sales Range: $250-299.9 Million
Holding Company
N.A.I.C.S.: 551112
Christopher J. Niehaus (Pres)

Subsidiary (Non-US):

Morgan Stanley Properties Corso Venezia S.r.l. (3)
Palazzo Serbelloni, Corso Venezia 16, 20121, Milan, Italy
Tel.: (39) 0276335502
Web Site: http://www.morganstanley.com
Sales Range: Less than $1 Million
Emp.: 10
Real Estate Services
N.A.I.C.S.: 531390

Morgan Stanley Properties France SAS (3)
61 rue de Monceau, 75008, Paris, France
Tel.: (33) 142907000
Web Site: http://www.morganstanley.com
Sales Range: Less than $1 Million
Emp.: 10
Real Estate Services
N.A.I.C.S.: 531390

Morgan Stanley Saudi Arabia (1)
Al Rashid Tower Floor 10 7931 King Saud Street, PO Box 66633, Al Sulimaniyah District, Riyadh, 12621, Saudi Arabia
Tel.: (966) 112187000
Investment Banking & Securities Dealing Services
N.A.I.C.S.: 523150

Morgan Stanley Services Canada Corp. (1)
700 Wellington Street Suite 2000, Montreal, H3C 3S4, QC, Canada
Tel.: (514) 413-3000
Investment Banking & Securities Dealing Services
N.A.I.C.S.: 523150

Morgan Stanley Services Pty Limited (1)
Level 39 Chifley Tower 2 Chifley Square, Sydney, 2000, NSW, Australia
Tel.: (61) 297701111
Web Site: http://www.morganstanley.com
Emp.: 400
Investment Banking Services
N.A.I.C.S.: 523150

Morgan Stanley Singapore Pte. Ltd. (1)
16-01 Capital Square 23 Church Street, Singapore, 049481, Singapore
Tel.: (65) 68346888
Investment Banking & Securities Dealing Services
N.A.I.C.S.: 523150

Morgan Stanley Smith Barney LLC (1)
1585 Broadway Ave, New York, NY 10036
Tel.: (212) 761-4000
Web Site:
   http://www.morganstanleysmithbarney.com
Sales Range: $1-4.9 Billion
Emp.: 12,400
Wealth Management Services; Owned by Morgan Stanley 51% & Citigroup Inc. 49%
N.A.I.C.S.: 523940

Morgan Stanley Solutions India Private Limited (1)
Nirlon Knowledge Park Bldg B2 Level 3 & 4 Bldg B4/5 Level 7 8 9, Bldg B7 Level 1 Off Western Express Highway Goregaon E, Mumbai, 400 063, India
Tel.: (91) 2266411000
Investment Banking Services
N.A.I.C.S.: 523150

Morgan Stanley Taiwan Limited (1)
83F 83F-1 Taipei 101 No 7 Xinyi Rd Xinyi District Sec 5, Taipei, 110, Taiwan
Tel.: (886) 227302888
Banking Services
N.A.I.C.S.: 522110

Morgan Stanley Trading Beteiligungs-GmbH (1)
Junghofstr 13 15, 60311, Frankfurt am Main, Germany
Tel.: (49) 6921660
Banking Services
N.A.I.C.S.: 522110

Morgan Stanley UK Limited (1)

122 Waterloo Street, Glasgow, G2 7DP, United Kingdom
Tel.: (44) 2074258000
Investment Banking & Securities Dealing Services
N.A.I.C.S.: 523150

Morgan Stanley Wealth Management Australia Pty Ltd (1)
Level 39 Chifley Tower 2 Chifley Square, Sydney, 2000, NSW, Australia
Tel.: (61) 297701111
Web Site: http://www.morganstanley.com.au
Investment Banking Services
N.A.I.C.S.: 523150

NaturEner Energy Canada Inc. (1)
Suite 910 517 - 10 Avenue SW, Calgary, T2R 0A8, AB, Canada
Tel.: (403) 699-9724
Wind Power Generation Services
N.A.I.C.S.: 221115
Jose Maria Sanchez Seara (Pres & CEO)
Erica Young (Gen Counsel, Sec & VP)
Chris Hodge (Sr VP-Comml Ops)
Greg Copeland (VP-Wind Energy Dev)
Gabriel Vaca (VP-Asset Mgmt)
Antonio Utrillas (Dir-Engrg)
Rosaura Velasquez (Dir-HR)
Tim Baumann (Dir-Environmental & Wildlife Conservation)

NaturEner USA, LLC (1)
435 Pacific Ave Ste 400, San Francisco, CA 94133
Tel.: (415) 217-5500
Web Site: http://www.naturener.us
Emp.: 35
Wind Power Generation Services
N.A.I.C.S.: 221115
Nancy Murray (Chief Compliance Officer & Chief Legal Officer)
Jim Kutey (Pres)
Walter H. Kamp III (CEO)

Subsidiary (Domestic):

NaturEner Rim Rock Wind Energy, LLC (2)
669 Rim Rd, Kevin, MT 59454
Tel.: (406) 937-0400
Web Site: http://www.naturener.us
Emp.: 20
Turbine Generator Mfr
N.A.I.C.S.: 333611

Olco Petroleum Group Inc. (1)
Battures de Beaubort, CP 2860, Quebec, G1J 5K3, QC, Canada
Tel.: (418) 660-6526
Sales Range: $25-49.9 Million
Emp.: 12
Petroleum Product Mfr
N.A.I.C.S.: 424720

Portland Natural Gas Transmission System (1)
1 Harbour Pl, Portsmouth, NH 03801
Tel.: (603) 559-5500
Web Site: http://www.pngts.com
Natural Gas Transmission & Power Services; Owned 62% by TransCanada Corporation & 38% by Northern New England Energy Corporation
N.A.I.C.S.: 486210

Realty Management Service Inc. (1)
300 H St, Bakersfield, CA 93304
Tel.: (661) 327-4496
Web Site:
   https://www.realtymanagement.com
Investment Banking & Securities Dealing Services
N.A.I.C.S.: 523150

Saxon Mortgage, Inc. (1)
4708 Mercantile Dr N, Fort Worth, TX 76137
Tel.: (804) 967-7400
Sales Range: $450-499.9 Million
Emp.: 550
Residential Mortgages & Services
N.A.I.C.S.: 522310
Richard A. Kraemer (Chm)

Solium Capital Inc. (1)
Suite 1500-600 3rd Avenue SW, Calgary, T2P 0G5, AB, Canada
Tel.: (403) 515-3910

Web Site: http://www.solium.com
Rev.: $86,502,000
Assets: $173,417,000
Liabilities: $25,746,000
Net Worth: $147,671,000
Earnings: $3,611,000
Emp.: 677
Fiscal Year-end: 12/31/2017
Web-Based Stock Plan Administration Technology & Services
N.A.I.C.S.: 541611

Subsidiary (US):

Solium Capital LLC (2)
60 E Rio Salado Pkwy Ste 510, Tempe, AZ 85281 (100%)
Tel.: (877) 380-7793
Web Site: http://www.solium.com
Web-Based Stock Plan Administration Technology & Services
N.A.I.C.S.: 541690

Subsidiary (Domestic):

Solium OptionEase, Inc. (3)
27201 Puerta Real Ste 200, Mission Viejo, CA 92691 (100%)
Tel.: (949) 542-3800
Web Site: http://www.solium.com
Sales Range: $1-9.9 Million
Emp.: 39
Accounting Compliance Software Solutions
N.A.I.C.S.: 513210

Subsidiary (Non-US):

Solium Capital UK Limited (2)
Corinthian House 4th Floor, 17 Lansdowne Road, London, CR0 2BX, United Kingdom
Tel.: (44) 20 8144 4668
Web Site: http://www.solium.com
Information Technology Services
N.A.I.C.S.: 541519

Subsidiary (Domestic):

StockVantage Inc. (2)
1500 6003 Ave SW, Calgary, T2P 0G5, AB, Canada
Tel.: (416) 618-7005
Financial Software Development Services
N.A.I.C.S.: 541511

South Eastern Electric Development Corporation (1)
230 Lee Rd 315, Smiths, AL 36877
Tel.: (334) 298-1148
Eletric Power Generation Services
N.A.I.C.S.: 221118

Southern Star Central Gas Pipeline, Inc. (1)
4700 State Route 56, Owensboro, KY 42301
Tel.: (270) 852-5000
Web Site: https://www.southernstar.com
Natural Gas Transmission Services
N.A.I.C.S.: 486210
Julie A. Dill (Chm)
Renaud Faucher (Vice Chm)

Third Planet Windpower, LLC (1)
4274 CR 446, Loraine, TX 79532
Tel.: (325) 737-2012
Web Site: http://www.thirdplanetwind.com
Eletric Power Generation Services
N.A.I.C.S.: 221118

TransMontaigne Marketing Canada Inc. (1)
1305 Pickering Parkway Suite 101, Pickering, L1V 3P2, ON, Canada
Tel.: (905) 420-2706
Fuel Products Whslr
N.A.I.C.S.: 424720

Ventura Property Management, LLC (1)
192 3rd St, Jersey City, NJ 07302
Tel.: (201) 656-4111
Property Management Services
N.A.I.C.S.: 531390

Warwick Holding GmbH (1)
Thurn-und Taxis-Platz 6, 60313, Frankfurt am Main, Germany
Web Site: http://www.warwickholding-angebot.de
Holding Company
N.A.I.C.S.: 551112

Morgan Stanley—(Continued)

Marc Maria van't Noordende *(Mng Dir)*
Christoph Oppenauer *(Mng Dir)*
Johannes Schonfeldt *(Mng Dir)*

Joint Venture (Domestic):

VTG Aktiengesellschaft (2)
Nagelsweg 34, D-20097, Hamburg, Germany
Tel.: (49) 4023540
Web Site: http://www.vtg.de
Rev.: $1,214,630,040
Assets: $3,695,997,030
Liabilities: $2,737,589,244
Net Worth: $958,407,786
Earnings: $81,574,266
Emp.: 1,527
Fiscal Year-end: 12/31/2017
Holding Company; Railway Freight &
Tanker Transportation Logistics & Railcar
Rental Services
N.A.I.C.S.: 551112
Heiko Fischer *(Chm-Exec Bd & CEO)*
Jost A. Massenberg *(Chm-Supervisory Bd)*
Mark Stevenson *(CFO & Member-Exec Bd)*
Oksana Janssen *(Member-Exec Bd)*
Sven Wellbrock *(Chief Safety Officer &
Member-Exec Bd)*
Marc van't Noordende *(Deputy Chm-
Supervisory Bd)*

Subsidiary (Non-US):

CIT Rail Holdings (Europe) SAS (3)
40 Rue La Boetie, 75008, Paris, France
Tel.: (33) 145615620
Holding Company
N.A.I.C.S.: 551112

Subsidiary (Domestic):

VOTG Tanktainer GmbH (3)
Nagelsweg 34, 20097, Hamburg,
Germany **(58.35%)**
Tel.: (49) 40280590
Sales Range: $50-74.9 Million
Emp.: 170
Tank Container Railcar Rental & Logistics
Services
N.A.I.C.S.: 532411

Subsidiary (US):

VOTG North America Inc. (4)
109 E Evans St, West Chester, PA
19380 **(100%)**
Tel.: (610) 429-5440
Emp.: 15
Tank Container Railcar Rental & Logistics
Services
N.A.I.C.S.: 532411
Lars Schuster *(Mng Dir)*

Representative Office (Non-US):

**VTG Deutschland GmbH - Belgium
Representative Office** (3)
Uitbreidingstraat 66, 2600, Berchem, Belgium
Tel.: (32) 32868430
Web Site: http://www.vtg.com
Sales Range: $25-49.9 Million
Emp.: 3
Freight Railcar Rental Services
N.A.I.C.S.: 532411

VTG Deutschland GmbH - Netherlands Representative Office (3)
Waalhaven Z z 19 Port City II 3rd Floor,
Port #2235, Rotterdam, 3089GH, Netherlands
Tel.: (31) 102642525
Web Site: http://www.vtg.com
Sales Range: $75-99.9 Million
Emp.: 4
Freight Railcar Rental Services
N.A.I.C.S.: 532411

Subsidiary (US):

VTG Rail (3)
103 W Vandalia Ste 200, Edwardsville, IL
62025
Tel.: (618) 343-0600
Web Site: http://www.vtg.com
Sales Range: $25-49.9 Million
Emp.: 13
Rail Cars Leasing Services
N.A.I.C.S.: 488210

Subsidiary (Non-US):

VTG Rail Espana S.L. (3)
C/ Acanto 22 - 7th floor, 28045, Madrid,
Spain
Tel.: (34) 915510804
Web Site: http://www.vtg.com
Sales Range: $25-49.9 Million
Emp.: 15
Railway Freight Transportation Logistics &
Railcar Rental Services
N.A.I.C.S.: 488510

Wellbore Capital, LLC (1)
5847 San Felipe Ste 2550, Houston, TX
77057
Tel.: (713) 974-0438
Web Site: http://www.wellborecapital.com
Oil & Gas Operators
N.A.I.C.S.: 213112
James Terracio *(Mng Dir)*
Stephen H. Hudson *(Mng Dir)*

MORINGA ACQUISITION CORP.

250 Park Ave 7th Fl, New York, NY
10177
Tel.: (212) 572-6395   **Ky**
Web Site:
   https://www.moringaac.com
Year Founded: 2020
MACA—(NASDAQ)
Rev.: $1,685,666
Assets: $116,795,605
Liabilities: $117,998,366
Net Worth: ($1,202,761)
Earnings: $584,025
Emp.: 3
Fiscal Year-end: 12/31/22
Investment Services
N.A.I.C.S.: 523999
Ilan Levin *(Co-Founder, Chm & CEO)*
Gil Maman *(CFO)*
Craig J. Marshak *(Co-Founder & Vice
Chm)*

MORNINGSTAR, INC.

22 W Washington St, Chicago, IL
60602
Tel.: (312) 696-6000   **IL**
Web Site:
   https://www.morningstar.com
Year Founded: 1984
MORN   (NASDAQ)
Rev.: $2,038,600,000
Assets: $3,403,400,000
Liabilities: $2,075,600,000
Net Worth: $1,327,800,000
Earnings: $141,100,000
Emp.: 11,334
Fiscal Year-end: 12/31/23
Investment Research & Software for
Individual & Professional Investors
N.A.I.C.S.: 523940
John Gabbert *(Co-Founder & CEO-
PitchBook Data Inc)*
Joe Mansueto *(Co-Founder & Exec
Chm)*
Kunal Kapoor *(CEO)*
Rob Pinkerton *(CMO)*
Jason Dubinsky *(CFO & Principal
Acctg Officer)*
Steve Bendt *(CIO)*
Ron Bundy *(Pres)*
Brock Johnson *(Pres)*
Marie Trzupek Lynch *(Chief People
Officer)*
Bob Mann *(Pres)*
Kathleen Peacock *(Chief Legal Officer)*
Detlef Scholz *(Pres)*

Subsidiaries:

ByAllAccounts, Inc. (1)
10 State St, Woburn, MA 01801-6820
Tel.: (781) 376-0801
Web Site: https://www.morningstar.com
Financial Management Services
N.A.I.C.S.: 541611

Ellen Dickau *(Founder, Pres & CEO)*

DBRS Limited (1)
DBRS Tower 181 University Avenue Suite
700, Toronto, M5H 3M7, ON, Canada
Tel.: (416) 593-5577
Web Site: https://www.dbrsmorningstar.com
Financial Services
N.A.I.C.S.: 327910
Larry J. White *(Mng Dir-Global Bus Dev)*
Doug Turnbull *(Vice Chm)*

DBRS Ratings GmbH (1)
Neue Mainzer Strasse 75, 60311, Frankfurt
am Main, Germany
Tel.: (49) 6980883500
Financial Services
N.A.I.C.S.: 541611

DBRS Ratings Limited (1)
20 Fenchurch Street 31st Floor, London,
EC3M 3BY, United Kingdom
Tel.: (44) 2078556600
Financial Services
N.A.I.C.S.: 541611
Rani Ryatt *(Asst VP)*

**Morningstar Associates Korea Co.,
Ltd.** (1)
Fourth Floor of Da Bo Building 140 Mapo-
Dong, Mapo-gu, Seoul, 121-714, Korea
(South) **(100%)**
Tel.: (82) 237710700
Web Site:
   http://associates.morningstar.co.kr
Investment Advisory Services
N.A.I.C.S.: 523940
James Kui-young Byun *(CEO & Chief In-
vestment Officer)*

Morningstar Canada Group, Inc. (1)
1 Toronto Street Suite 500, Toronto, M5C
2W4, ON, Canada
Tel.: (416) 489-7074
Web Site: https://www.morningstar.ca
Sales Range: $125-149.9 Million
Emp.: 100
Investment Services
N.A.I.C.S.: 523940

Morningstar Danmark A/S (1)
Gl Kongevej 60 18 sal, 1850, Frederiks-
berg, Denmark
Tel.: (45) 33186000
Web Site: https://www.morningstar.dk
Emp.: 10
Investment Advisory Services
N.A.I.C.S.: 523940

Morningstar Deutschland GmbH (1)
Junghofstrasse 24, 60311, Frankfurt am
Main, Germany
Tel.: (49) 69271377100
Web Site: https://www.morningstar.de
Sales Range: $25-49.9 Million
Emp.: 4
Investment Advisory Services
N.A.I.C.S.: 523940

Morningstar Europe, B.V. (1)
De Entree 246 11th Floor, 1101 EE, Am-
sterdam, Netherlands
Tel.: (31) 20 311 9090
Web Site: https://www.morningstar.nl
Sales Range: $25-49.9 Million
Emp.: 22
Investment Advisory Services
N.A.I.C.S.: 523940

**Morningstar France Fund Information
SARL** (1)
52 Rue De La Victoire, 75009, Paris,
France
Tel.: (33) 155501300
Web Site: https://www.morningstar.fr
Investment Advisory Services
N.A.I.C.S.: 523940

**Morningstar Group Australia Pty
Limited** (1)
Level 3 International Tower 1 100 Baranga-
roo Avenue, Barangaroo, Sydney, 2000,
NSW, Australia
Tel.: (61) 292764455
Web Site: http://www.morningstar.com.au
Investment Advisory Services
N.A.I.C.S.: 523940
Jamie Wickham *(Mng Dir)*

**Morningstar Investment Management
Australia Limited** (1)

Level 3 International Tower 1 100 Baranga-
roo Avenue, Barangaroo, 2000, NSW, Aus-
tralia
Tel.: (61) 800951999
Web Site:
   https://www.morningstarinvestments.com.au
Investment Services
N.A.I.C.S.: 525910

**Morningstar Investment Management
Europe Limited** (1)
1 Oliver's Yard 55-71 City Road, London,
EC1Y 1HQ, United Kingdom
Tel.: (44) 2031070000
Web Site: https://www.morningstar.co.uk
Investment Advisory Services
N.A.I.C.S.: 523940

**Morningstar Investment Management
South Africa (Pty) Limited** (1)
5th Floor 20 Vineyard Road, Claremont,
Cape Town, 7708, South Africa
Tel.: (27) 212014645
Investment Advisory Services
N.A.I.C.S.: 523940

Morningstar Italy, S.R.L. (1)
Via Pergolesi 25, 20124, Milan, Italy
Tel.: (39) 023030121
Web Site: https://www.morningstar.it
Investment Advisory Services
N.A.I.C.S.: 523940

Morningstar Research Limited (1)
Unit 2 Amuri Park cnr Bealey Avenue &
Churchill Road, Canterbury, Christchurch,
8013, New Zealand
Tel.: (64) 39615031
Investment Advisory Services
N.A.I.C.S.: 523940

**Morningstar Research Thailand
Limited** (1)
Office No S-06 37th Floor 98 Sathorn
Square Office Tower, North Sathorn Road,
Bangkok, 10500, Thailand
Tel.: (66) 21056373
Web Site:
   https://www.morningstarthailand.com
Sales Range: $25-49.9 Million
Emp.: 25
Investment Advisory Services
N.A.I.C.S.: 523940

Morningstar Sweden AB (1)
Birger Jarlsgatan 32B, 114 29, Stockholm,
Sweden
Tel.: (46) 856272950
Web Site: https://www.morningstar.se
Investment Advisory Services
N.A.I.C.S.: 523940

Morningstar Switzerland GmbH (1)
Josefstrasse 216, 8005, Zurich, Switzerland
Tel.: (41) 432102828
Web Site: https://www.morningstar.ch
Emp.: 20
Investment Advisory Services
N.A.I.C.S.: 523940

Pitchbook Data Inc. (1)
901 5th Ave Ste 1200, Seattle, WA 98164
Tel.: (206) 623-1986
Web Site: https://www.pitchbook.com
Financial Data Delivery & Research Ser-
vices
N.A.I.C.S.: 541690
John Gabbert *(Founder & CEO)*
Rod Diefendorf *(COO)*
Patrick Ross *(VP-Fin)*
Amy Whaley *(VP-People)*
Paul Santarelli *(VP-SIs)*
Brett Kaluza *(VP-Customer Success)*
Jason Marshall *(Chief Mktg Officer)*
Paul Jaeschke *(VP)*
Peter Escher *(VP)*
Silvina Aldeco Martinez *(VP)*

Pitchbook Data, Inc. (1)
901 5th Ave Ste 1200, Seattle, WA 98164
Tel.: (206) 623-1986
Web Site: https://www.pitchbook.com
Investment Advisory Services
N.A.I.C.S.: 523940
John Gabbert *(Founder & CEO)*
Rod Diefendorf *(COO)*

Paul Santarelli *(VP-Sls)*
Brett Kaluza *(VP-Customer Success)*
Joanna McGinley *(VP)*
Patrick Ross *(VP-Fin)*
Amy Whaley *(VP-People)*
Paul Jaeschke *(VP)*
Peter Escher *(VP)*
Silvina Aldeco-Martinez *(VP)*
Nizar Tarhuni *(VP)*
Paul Stoddart *(CMO)*

RequiSight, LLC (1)
22 W Washington St, Chicago, IL 60602
Tel.: (312) 696-6126
Web Site: http://www.rightpond.com
Data Processing Services
N.A.I.C.S.: 518210

Sustainalytics Japan Inc. (1)
Hibiya Building 6F 1-1-1, Shinbashi Minato-Ku, Tokyo, 105-0004, Japan
Tel.: (81) 345670198
Investment Management Service
N.A.I.C.S.: 523940

Sustainalytics U.S. Inc. (1)
Four World Trade Ctr 150 Greenwich St Fl 48, New York, NY 10007
Tel.: (347) 630-9308
Investment Management Service
N.A.I.C.S.: 523940

Sustainalytics UK Limited (1)
1 Oliver's Yard 55-71 City Road, London, EC1Y 1HQ, United Kingdom
Tel.: (44) 2045265640
Investment Management Service
N.A.I.C.S.: 523940

MORO CORP.
841 Worcester St Ste 511, Natick, MA 01760
Tel.: (484) 367-0300
Web Site: https://www.morocorp.com
MRCR—(OTCIQ)
Fabricated Structural Metal Mfr
N.A.I.C.S.: 332312
David W. Menard *(Chm, Pres, CEO, CFO & Principal Acctg Officer)*
Lawrence J. Corr *(Pres)*
Peter D. Menard *(VP-Corp Dev)*

MORRIS STATE BANCSHARES, INC.
301 Bellevue Ave, Dublin, GA 31021
Tel.: (478) 272-5202   GA
Web Site: https://www.morris.bank
MBLU—(OTCQX)
Rev.: $51,677,907
Assets: $1,006,947,971
Liabilities: $895,522,339
Net Worth: $111,425,632
Earnings: $13,620,954
Fiscal Year-end: 12/31/19
Bank Holding Company
N.A.I.C.S.: 551111
Spence Neil Mullis *(Pres & CEO)*
Christopher Mark Bond *(CFO & Exec VP)*
Susan Brandon *(Sec)*

Subsidiaries:

Morris Bank (1)
301 Bellevue Ave, Dublin, GA 31021
Tel.: (478) 272-5202
Web Site: http://www.morris.bank
Commericial Banking
N.A.I.C.S.: 522110
Spence Neil Mullis *(Pres & CEO)*
Roger W. Miller *(Pres-Laurens County/Exec VP)*
Christopher Mark Bond *(CFO & COO)*
Kelly Herrington *(Pres-Houston County & Sr VP-Comml Lending)*
Tracie Morgan *(Dir-Mktg)*

MORTGAGE OIL CORP.
915 Wilshire Blvd Ste 1760, Los Angeles, CA 90017
Tel.: (213) 483-3300   CA
Year Founded: 1948
MGAG—(OTCIQ)
Real Estate Manangement Services

N.A.I.C.S.: 531210
Kevin Kirkpatrick *(Treas)*
David Adams Jr. *(Pres, CEO & Sec)*

MOSAIC IMMUNOENGINEER-ING, INC.
9114 Adams Ave Ste 202, Huntington Beach, CA 92646
Tel.: (657) 208-0890   DE
Web Site: https://www.mosaicie.com
CPMV—(OTCQB)
Rev.: $249,052
Assets: $261,277
Liabilities: $5,146,035
Net Worth: ($4,884,758)
Earnings: ($2,380,870)
Emp.: 4
Fiscal Year-end: 12/31/22
Microprocessor Chips Intellectual Property Licensor
N.A.I.C.S.: 533110

MOTIVATING THE MASSES, INC.
300 Carlsbad Village Dr Ste 108A, Carlsbad, CA 92008
Tel.: (760) 931-9400   NV
Web Site:
    https://www.motivatingthemas
    ses.com
Year Founded: 1998
MNMT—(OTCIQ)
Sales Range: $1-9.9 Million
Emp.: 11
Professional & Management Development Training
N.A.I.C.S.: 611430
Lisa Nichols *(Founder & CEO)*
Susie Carder *(Pres & COO)*
Scott M. Ryder Jr. *(CFO)*

MOTOMOVA INC.
575 5th Ave Fl 15, New York, NY 10018
Tel.: (646) 257-4214   DE
Web Site: https://motomea.com
Year Founded: 2006
MTMV—(OTCIQ)
Offices of Other Holding Companies
N.A.I.C.S.: 551112

MOTOR CITY ACQUISITION CORP.
44225 Utica Rd, Utica, MI 48317
Tel.: (248) 294-0858   DE
Year Founded: 2021
MCTYU—(NASDAQ)
Investment Services
N.A.I.C.S.: 523999
Robert L. Wagman *(Chm & CEO)*
Eric S. Singer *(Pres & CFO)*

MOTORCAR PARTS OF AMERICA, INC.
2929 California St, Torrance, CA 90503
Tel.: (310) 212-7910   NY
Web Site:
    https://www.motorcarparts.com
Year Founded: 1968
MPAA—(NASDAQ)
Rev.: $717,684,000
Assets: $1,012,002,000
Liabilities: $726,892,000
Net Worth: $285,110,000
Earnings: ($49,244,000)
Emp.: 5,900
Fiscal Year-end: 03/31/24
Industrial Machinery & Equipment Merchant Wholesalers
N.A.I.C.S.: 423830
Selwyn H. Joffe *(Pres, CEO & Chm)*
David Lee *(CFO)*
Kamlesh Shah *(Chief Acctg Officer)*
Gary S. Maier *(VP-Corp Comm & IR)*
Ron Aparicio *(VP-Traditional Sls)*

Subsidiaries:

Central Auto Parts (Shanghai) Co., Ltd. (1)
No 665 Jinbi Road, Jinhui Town Fengxian District, Shanghai, China
Tel.: (86) 57570080
Web Site: https://www.centralautoparts.cn
Motor Vehicle Equipment Mfr
N.A.I.C.S.: 336320

D&V Electronic Technology (Shang-hai) Co., Ltd (1)
Room 5170 51/F Raffles City No 268 Xi Zang Middle Road, Huangpu, Shanghai, China
Tel.: (86) 18017268715
Laboratory Equipment Mfr & Distr
N.A.I.C.S.: 334515

D&V Electronics Ltd (1)
130 Zenway Boulevard, Woodbridge, L4H 2Y7, ON, Canada
Tel.: (905) 264-7646
Web Site: https://www.dvelectronics.com
Laboratory Equipment Mfr & Distr
N.A.I.C.S.: 334515

Dixie Electric Ltd. (1)
517 Basaltic Road, Concord, L4K 4W8, ON, Canada
Tel.: (905) 879-0533
Web Site: https://www.dixie-electric.com
Automotive Repair & Services
N.A.I.C.S.: 811114

Subsidiary (US):

Dixie Electric, Inc. (2)
5600 Pioneer Creek Dr Ste D, Maple Plain, MN 55359
Tel.: (763) 475-6629
Web Site: http://www.dixie-electric.com
Sales Range: $1-9.9 Million
Emp.: 21
Whol Auto Parts/Supplies
N.A.I.C.S.: 423120

MVR Products Pte. Limited (1)
322 Jalan Ahmad Ibrahim, Parvia Jala, Singapore, 629151, Singapore
Tel.: (65) 62613118
Motorcar Parts & Supplies Mfr
N.A.I.C.S.: 336320
Vincent Quek *(Mng Dir)*

OE Plus, Ltd. (1)
620 Spring St, North Dighton, MA 02764
Tel.: (508) 977-0020
Web Site: http://www.oeplus.com
Motor Vehicle Parts Mfr
N.A.I.C.S.: 336390
Peter Bourassa *(VP-Sls)*
Eric Roberts *(Pres & CEO)*
Andy Sampson *(VP-Ops)*
Eric Priestly *(Dir-Mktg)*
Brenda Ritz *(Mgr-Customer Svc)*

MOTOROLA SOLUTIONS, INC.
500 W Monroe St, Chicago, IL 60661
Tel.: (847) 576-5000   DE
Web Site:
    https://www.motorolasolutions.com
Year Founded: 1928
MSI—(NYSE)
Rev.: $9,978,000,000
Assets: $13,336,000,000
Liabilities: $12,597,000,000
Net Worth: $739,000,000
Earnings: $1,709,000,000
Emp.: 21,000
Fiscal Year-end: 12/31/23
Wireless & Broadband Telecommunications Equipment & Services
N.A.I.C.S.: 334220
John P. Molloy *(COO & Exec VP)*
Rajan Naik *(Chief Strategy Officer & Sr VP-Strategy & Ventures)*
Jason J. Winkler *(CFO & Exec VP)*
Katherine Maher *(Chief Acctg Officer & VP)*
James A. Niewiara *(Gen Counsel & Sr VP)*
Karen E. Dunning *(Sr VP-HR)*

Karen Dunning *(Sr VP)*
Jim Niewiara *(Gen Counsel)*
Gregory Q. Brown *(Chm & CEO)*

Subsidiaries:

Avigilon Corporation (1)
3rd Floor 555 Robson Street, Vancouver, V6B 1A6, BC, Canada
Tel.: (469) 599-4222
Web Site: https://www.avigilon.com
HD Surveillance Systems
N.A.I.C.S.: 334310

Dansk Beredsskabskommunikation A/S (1)
Sydvestvej 21, 2600, Glostrup, Denmark
Tel.: (45) 43488000
Web Site: https://dbkas.dk
Sales Range: $25-49.9 Million
Emp.: 200
Communications Products & Services
N.A.I.C.S.: 334220

Edesix Limited (1)
16 Forth Street, Edinburgh, EH1 3LH, United Kingdom
Tel.: (44) 1315100232
Web Site: http://www.edesix.com
Body Worn Camera Mfr
N.A.I.C.S.: 333310

Envysion, Inc. (1)
100 Superior Plaza Way Ste 260, Superior, CO 80027
Tel.: (303) 590-2350
Web Site: https://envysion.com
Custom Computer Programming Services
N.A.I.C.S.: 541511
W. Matthew Steinfort *(Founder)*
Michael Coar *(Sr VP-Operations)*
Christian Ellis *(VP-Engineering)*
Harry Hollines *(VP-Corporate Development)*
Calvin Quan *(CEO)*
Richard Scheig *(Sr VP-Sales-Marketing)*
Matt Umscheid *(CEO)*

Futurecom Systems Group Inc. (1)
3277 Langstaff Rd, Concord, L4K 5P8, ON, Canada
Tel.: (905) 660-5548
Web Site: http://www.futurecom.com
Rev.: $11,794,226
Emp.: 45
Extension Systems Mfr
N.A.I.C.S.: 334511
Paul Halinaty *(Pres & CEO)*

IPVideo Corporation (1)
1490 N Clinton Ave, Bay Shore, NY 11706
Tel.: (631) 969-2601
Web Site: https://ipvideocorp.com
Electronic Equipment Mfr & Distr
N.A.I.C.S.: 335999

IndigoVision Group plc (1)
Charles Darwin House The Edinburgh Technopole, Edinburgh, EH26 0PY, United Kingdom
Tel.: (44) 1314757200
Web Site: http://www.indigovision.com
Rev.: $50,184,000
Assets: $38,629,000
Liabilities: $20,495,000
Net Worth: $18,134,000
Earnings: $1,665,000
Emp.: 141
Fiscal Year-end: 12/31/2019
Video & Alarm Management Systems
N.A.I.C.S.: 561621
David Blair *(Head-Human Resources)*
Dean Brazenall *(Sls Dir-EMEA & VP-Sales-EMEA)*
Lim Then Poh *(VP-Sales-APAC)*
Alan Garland *(Head-Marketing)*
Martin McGreskin *(Head-Operations-Customer Care)*
Heather Robb *(Controller-Finance)*
Vincent Van Der Walt *(Head-Engineering)*
Andy Love *(Head)*

Subsidiary (Domestic):

IndigoVision Limited (2)
Darwin Building The Edinburgh Technopole, Bush Loan, Edinburgh, EH26 0PY, United Kingdom
Tel.: (44) 1314757200
Emp.: 80

Motorola Solutions, Inc.—(Continued)

Design, Development, Manufacture & Sale
of Software & Hardware Products
N.A.I.C.S.: 541512
Marcus Kneen *(CEO)*

Subsidiary (US):

IndigoVision Inc. **(3)**
29 Mayfield Ave Ste A, Edison, NJ 08837-
3820
Tel.: (908) 315-0288
Web Site: http://www.indigovision.com
Sales Range: $25-49.9 Million
Emp.: 3
Software & Hardware Products Sales
N.A.I.C.S.: 423430

Kodiak Networks, Inc. **(1)**
1501 10th St Ste 130, Plano, TX 75074
Tel.: (972) 665-0200
Web Site: http://kodiakptt.com
Telecommunication Servicesb
N.A.I.C.S.: 517112

Mobilink S.A.
5240 14th Floor Parque II Building, Las
Condes, Santiago, Chile
Tel.: (56) 22 240 6100
Web Site: https://www.mobilink.cl
Radio Communication Services
N.A.I.C.S.: 516210

Motorola AB **(1)**
Isafjordsgatan 35, Kista, 164 40,
Sweden **(100%)**
Tel.: (46) 87348800
Web Site: http://www.motorola.se
Sales Range: $25-49.9 Million
Emp.: 150
Wireless Communications Products
N.A.I.C.S.: 517112

Motorola Arabia, Inc. **(1)**
PO Box 51, King Fahad Street Olaya Dist,
Riyadh, 12211, Saudi Arabia
Tel.: (966) 112181100
Communications Products & Services
N.A.I.C.S.: 334220

Motorola Asia Limited **(1)**
18/F 2 Harbourfront 22 Tak Fung Street,
Kowloon, China (Hong Kong)
Tel.: (852) 29663000
Web Site: http://www.motorola.com.hk
Sales Range: $75-99.9 Million
Emp.: 280
Wireless Communications Mfr
N.A.I.C.S.: 517112

Subsidiary (Non-US):

Motorola (China) Electronics Ltd. **(2)**
No 108 Jian Guo Road 12th Floor, Chao
Yang District, Beijing, 100022,
China **(100%)**
Tel.: (86) 10 6564 2288
Mfr & Marketer of Wireless Communications
Products
N.A.I.C.S.: 334220
Ruey-Bin Kao *(Pres)*

Motorola Electronics Sdn. Bhd. **(2)**
Bayan Lepas Technoplex Industrial Park,
Bayan Lepas, 11900, Penang,
Malaysia **(100%)**
Tel.: (60) 46432511
Web Site: http://www.motorola.com
Sales Range: $25-49.9 Million
Emp.: 100
Wireless Communication Product Mfr
N.A.I.C.S.: 334220

**Motorola Solutions Singapore Pte
Ltd** **(2)**
80 Pasir Panjang Road 18-81, Singapore,
117372, Singapore **(100%)**
Tel.: (65) 68176800
Web Site: http://www.motorolasolutions.com
Electronic Wireless Communication Devices
N.A.I.C.S.: 334220

Subsidiary (Domestic):

**Motorola Trading Center Pte.
Ltd.** **(3)**
12 Ang Mo Kio Street 64, Ang Mo Kio Industrial Park 3, Singapore, 569088, Singapore
Tel.: (65) 64812000

Sales Range: $150-199.9 Million
Electonic Wireless Communications Equip-
ment Distr
N.A.I.C.S.: 423690

Subsidiary (Non-US):

Motorola Technology Sdn. Bhd. **(2)**
14th Floor Persoft Tower 6B Off Persiaran
Tropicana, 6B Off Persiaran Tropicana,
47410, Petaling Jaya, Selangor Darul Eh-
san, Malaysia
Tel.: (60) 340650700
Sales Range: $25-49.9 Million
Emp.: 100
Telecommunications Equipment & Services
N.A.I.C.S.: 334220

Motorola Australia Pty. Ltd. **(1)**
10 Wesley Court, Tally Ho Business Park,
Burwood East, 3151, VIC,
Australia **(100%)**
Tel.: (61) 398477500
Web Site: http://www.motorola.com.au
Sales Range: $25-49.9 Million
Emp.: 80
Wireless Communications
N.A.I.C.S.: 517112

Subsidiary (Non-US):

Motorola New Zealand Limited **(2)**
Penrose, PO Box 92820, New Market,
Auckland, New Zealand
Tel.: (64) 92590400
Wireless Communications
N.A.I.C.S.: 517112

Motorola B.V. **(1)**
Marconibaan 57, Nieuwegein, 3439,
Netherlands **(100%)**
Tel.: (31) 31 625 17 07
Web Site: http://www.motorola.com
Wireless Communications Products
N.A.I.C.S.: 517112

Motorola Chile S.A. **(1)**
Av Nueva Tajamar 481 Torre Sur, Edificio
World Trade Center Las Condes Of 1702,
Santiago, 7550099, Chile **(100%)**
Tel.: (56) 23389000
Web Site: http://www.motorola.com
Sales Range: $10-24.9 Million
Emp.: 25
Wireless Communications Distr
N.A.I.C.S.: 517112

Motorola GmbH **(1)**
Serviceware-Kreisel 1, 65510, Idstein,
Germany **(100%)**
Tel.: (49) 61269576030
Web Site: http://www.motorola.de
Sales Range: $100-124.9 Million
Emp.: 350
Components for Information & Communica-
tions Technology & for Industrial Electronic
Requirements; Mobile Telephones; Paging
Systems; Network Management Systems
Mfr & Whslr
N.A.I.C.S.: 334220

Subsidiary (Domestic):

Motorola Electronic GmbH **(2)**
Husumer Str 251, 24941, Flensburg,
Germany **(100%)**
Tel.: (49) 4618030
Web Site: http://www.motorola.de
Sales Range: $50-74.9 Million
Emp.: 200
Radio Communication Systems
N.A.I.C.S.: 334220

Division (Domestic):

Motorola GmbH **(2)**
Am Borsigturm 130, 13507, Berlin, Ger-
many
Tel.: (49) 3066860
Web Site: http://www.motorola.de
Sales Range: $75-99.9 Million
Communication Service
N.A.I.C.S.: 517112

Motorola Israel Limited **(1)**
Negev 2 Airport City, 70100, Haifa,
Israel **(100%)**
Tel.: (972) 35658888
Web Site: http://www.motorola.com

Sales Range: $200-249.9 Million
Emp.: 700
Wireless Communications
N.A.I.C.S.: 517112

Subsidiary (Domestic):

**Beeper Communications Israel
Ltd.** **(2)**
147 Bialik Street, Ramat Gan, 52118, Israel
Tel.: (972) 36100066
Web Site: http://www.beeper.co.il
Sales Range: $25-49.9 Million
Emp.: 900
Call Center Services
N.A.I.C.S.: 561421
Ilan Friedland *(CEO)*

MIRS Communications Limited **(2)**
Hanegv 2, Lod, 70100, Israel
Tel.: (972) 35658888
Web Site: http://www.motorolasolutions.com
Sales Range: $200-249.9 Million
Emp.: 500
Communication Service
N.A.I.C.S.: 517112
Shimon Dick *(CEO)*

Motorola Limited **(1)**
Jays Close, Viables Industrial Estate, Bas-
ingstoke, RG21 4PD, Hants, United
Kingdom **(100%)**
Tel.: (44) 1256790790
Web Site: http://www.motorolasolutions.com
Sales Range: $350-399.9 Million
Emp.: 1,000
Radio Communication Services
N.A.I.C.S.: 334220

Subsidiary (Domestic):

Airwave Solutions Limited **(2)**
Charter Court 50 Windsor Road, Slough,
SL1 2EJ, Berkshire, United Kingdom
Tel.: (44) 8000113399
Web Site:
https://www.airwavesolutions.co.uk
Secure Digital Radio Network Used by
Emergency Personnel
N.A.I.C.S.: 334220

Motorola Finance EMEA Limited **(2)**
Jays Close Viables Industrial Estate, Bas-
ingstoke, RG22 4PD, United Kingdom
Tel.: (44) 1256484000
Web Site: http://www.motorolasolutions.com
Sales Range: $650-699.9 Million
Emp.: 400
Financial Investment Services
N.A.I.C.S.: 523999

**Motorola Receivables
Corporation** **(1)**
1301 E Algonquin Rd, Schaumburg, IL
60196
Tel.: (847) 576-5000
Accounts Receivable Services
N.A.I.C.S.: 561499

Motorola S.A.S. **(1)**
Parc Des Algorithmes, 91193, Saint Aubin,
France
Tel.: (33) 160121184
Web Site: http://www.motorola.com
Sales Range: $75-99.9 Million
Emp.: 300
Communication Equipment Mfr
N.A.I.C.S.: 334220
Jaques Arames *(Mng Dir)*

**Motorola Solutions (China) Co.
Ltd.** **(1)**
No 1 Wang Jing East Road Chao Yang Dis-
trict, Beijing, 100102, China
Tel.: (86) 1084732288
Electric Device Mfr
N.A.I.C.S.: 334220
Lily Fu *(Gen Mgr-Radio Channels)*

**Motorola Solutions Argentina,
S.A.** **(1)**
Av Del Libertador 1855 Vicente Lopez
Pcia, Buenos Aires, B1638BGE, Argentina
Tel.: (54) 1148374000
Web Site: http://www.motorola.com.ar
Wireless Communications Mfr
N.A.I.C.S.: 334220

**Motorola Solutions Australia Pte.
Ltd.** **(1)**

10 Wesley Court Tally Ho Business Park,
Burwood East, 3151, VIC, Australia
Tel.: (61) 398477500
Electronic Equipment Distr
N.A.I.C.S.: 423690
Steven Crutchfield *(Mng Dir)*

Motorola Solutions CZ s.r.o. **(1)**
Strakonicka 1143/2B, 150 00, Prague,
Czech Republic **(100%)**
Tel.: (420) 527218563
Wireless Communications Products
N.A.I.C.S.: 517112

Motorola Solutions Canada Inc. **(1)**
8133 Warden Avenue, Markham, L6G 1B3,
ON, Canada
Tel.: (905) 948-5200
Electronic Equipment Distr
N.A.I.C.S.: 423690
Joe Barnett *(Project Mgr)*

Motorola Solutions Espana S.A. **(1)**
CL Martinez Villergas 52 Bloq 3, 28027,
Madrid, Spain
Tel.: (34) 91 400 2280
Web Site: http://www.motorolasolutions.com
Wireless Services
N.A.I.C.S.: 517112

Motorola Solutions France SAS **(1)**
Parc Les Algorithmes, Gif sur Yvette, Saint
Aubin, 91193, France
Tel.: (33) 169357700
Communication Equipment Mfr & Distr
N.A.I.C.S.: 334210
Christophe Poulin *(Mgr-Bus Dev)*

**Motorola Solutions Germany
GmbH** **(1)**
Serviceware-Kreisel 1, 65510, Idstein, Ger-
many
Tel.: (49) 61269576030
Electric Device Mfr
N.A.I.C.S.: 334220

Motorola Solutions India Pvt. Ltd. **(1)**
Motorola Excellence Centre 415/2 Mehrauli-
Gurgaon Road Sector 14, Gurgaon, 122
001, Haryana, India
Tel.: (91) 1244192000
Electronic Equipment Distr
N.A.I.C.S.: 423690
Subodh Vardhan *(Mng Dir)*

Motorola Solutions Israel Limited **(1)**
2 Negev St, Airport City, 70199, Israel
Tel.: (972) 35658888
Electronic Equipment Mfr & Distr
N.A.I.C.S.: 334220
Yohanan Yosef *(Mgr-Trade Compliance)*

Motorola Solutions Italia S.p.A. **(1)**
Largo Francesco Richini 6, 20122, Milan,
Italy **(100%)**
Tel.: (39) 02522071
Web Site: http://www.motorolasolutions.com
Sales Range: $125-149.9 Million
Emp.: 279
Wireless Communications Products
N.A.I.C.S.: 423690
Sirio Magliocca *(Pres)*

**Motorola Solutions Malaysia Sdn.
Bhd.** **(1)**
14th Floor Persoft Tower 6B Off Persiaran
Tropicana, 47410, Petaling Jaya, Selangor
Darul Ehsan, Malaysia
Tel.: (60) 34 065 0700
Web Site:
https://www.motorolasolutions.com
Communication Equipment Mfr
N.A.I.C.S.: 334220

**Motorola Solutions Systems Polska
Sp. z o.o.** **(1)**
Ul Czerwone Maki 82, 30-392, Krakow,
Poland
Tel.: (48) 122979000
Software Services
N.A.I.C.S.: 541511

**Motorola Solutions Venture
Capital** **(1)**
1303 E Algonquin Rd, Schaumburg, IL
60196
Tel.: (847) 576-5000
Web Site: http://www.motorolasolutions.com
Sales Range: $650-699.9 Million
Equity Investment Firm
N.A.I.C.S.: 523999

Motorola Venezuela (1)
Avenida Francisca Miranda Central Lido
Torre A Piso 15, El Rosal, Caracas, 1060,
Venezuela (100%)
Tel.: (58) 2129014600
Web Site: http://www.motorola.com.ve
Sales Range: $10-24.9 Million
Emp.: 25
Wireless Communications Distr
N.A.I.C.S.: 517112

Motorola de Costa Rica S.A. (1)
Centro de Negocios International Plaza
Roble, Edificio el Portico 1er Piso, San
Jose, Costa Rica (100%)
Tel.: (506) 2011480
Web Site: http://www.motorola.com
Sales Range: $10-24.9 Million
Emp.: 8
Wireless Communications Products
N.A.I.C.S.: 517112

Motorola de Mexico, S.A. (1)
Bosques De Alisos 125, Guadalajara,
05120, Mexico
Tel.: (52) 5552576700
Web Site: http://www.motorola.com.mx
Sales Range: $550-599.9 Million
Emp.: 2,000
Semiconductors & Related Devices
N.A.I.C.S.: 334310

Subsidiary (Non-US):

**TETRON Sicherheitsnetz Errichtungs
und BetriebsgmbH** (2)
Euro Plaza Gebaude F Technologiestrasse
5/Stiege 2/3 Stock, 1120, Vienna,
Austria (65%)
Tel.: (43) 181514130
Web Site: http://www.tetron.at
Emp.: 30
Secure Radio Network
N.A.I.C.S.: 516210
Albert Schauer (Mng Dir)
Mario Strasser (Mng Dir)

Pelco Inc. (1)
625 W Alluvial Ave, Fresno, CA 93711
Tel.: (559) 292-1981
Web Site: http://www.pelco.com
Video Security Systems Mfr
N.A.I.C.S.: 561621

Rave Mobile Safety, Inc. (1)
492 Old Connecticut Path 2nd Fl, Framing-
ham, MA 01701
Tel.: (508) 848-2484
Web Site: http://www.ravemobilesafety.com
Custom Computer Programming Services
N.A.I.C.S.: 541511
Todd Piett (CEO)
Brett Marceau (CTO)
Todd Miller (Sr VP-Strategic Programs)
Bill Price (CFO)
Matthew Serra (VP-Product Strategy)
Noah Reiter (Sr VP-Customer Success)
Jennifer Taylor (Sr VP-People Ops)
Meghan Beck (VP-Fin)
Rand Refrigeri (VP-Design Strategy)

Subsidiary (Domestic):

Swiftreach Networks, Inc. (2)
492 Old Connecticut Path, 2nd Fl, Framing-
ham, MA 01701
Tel.: (888) 605-7164
Web Site: http://www.swiftreach.com
Telecommunications Resellers
N.A.I.C.S.: 517121

Spillman Technologies, Inc. (1)
4625 Lake Park Blvd, Salt Lake City, UT
84120
Tel.: (801) 902-1200
Web Site: http://www.spillman.com
Software Publisher
N.A.I.C.S.: 513210

Twisted Pair Solutions, Inc. (1)
3131 Elliott Ave Ste 200, Seattle, WA 98121
Tel.: (206) 442-2101
Web Site: http://www.twistpair.com
Sales Range: $1-9.9 Million
Emp.: 50
Mobile Communications Services
N.A.I.C.S.: 517810

WatchGuard, Inc. (1)
415 Century Pkwy, Allen, TX 75013

Tel.: (972) 423-9777
Web Site: http://www.watchguardvideo.com
Audio & Video Equipment Mfr
N.A.I.C.S.: 334310
David Russell Walker (CFO)
Brian Kirkham (VP-Mktg)
Mark McHenry (VP-Svc & Support)
Ted Hajec (VP-Ops)
Joe VanSchuyver (VP-Professional Svcs
Grp)
Troy Montgomery (VP-Sls)
Tim Rendulic (VP-Engrg)
Rod J. McDonald (Gen Counsel & Sec)

**Wireless Technology Equipment
Company, Inc.** (1)
3382 Bartlett Blvd, Orlando, FL 32811
Tel.: (407) 843-8631
Web Site: https://www.wtecheq.com
Electrical Repair Shops
N.A.I.C.S.: 811210
David MacDonald (Founder)

MOTUS GI HOLDINGS, INC.
1301 E Broward Blvd Ste 310, Fort
Lauderdale, FL 33301
Tel.: (954) 541-8000 DE
Web Site: https://www.motusgi.com
MOTS—(NASDAQ)
Rev.: $592,000
Assets: $17,647,000
Liabilities: $14,670,000
Net Worth: $2,977,000
Earnings: ($18,597,000)
Emp.: 43
Fiscal Year-end: 12/31/22
Medical Equipment Mfr
N.A.I.C.S.: 334510
Jeff Hutchison (VP-Sls & Comml
Ops)
Scott C. Aldrich (VP-Mktg & Strategy)
Timothy P. Moran (Chm)
Mark Pomeranz (CEO)
Ravit Ram (CFO & VP-Fin)
Elad Amor (Chief Acctg Officer)
Yosi Tzabari (VP-Research & Devel-
opment)

MOUNT CARMEL PUBLIC
UTILITY CO.
316 N Market St, Mount Carmel, IL
62863
Tel.: (618) 262-5151
Web Site: https://www.mtcpu.com
MCPB—(OTCEM)
Sales Range: $10-24.9 Million
Emp.: 44
Electric & Other Services Combined
N.A.I.C.S.: 221118
Margaret Felts (Treas & Sec)
Larry Horrall (VP-Ops)
Philip Barnhard IV (Pres)

MOUNT RAINIER ACQUISI-
TION CORP.
256 W 38th St 15th Fl, New York, NY
10018
Tel.: (212) 785-4680 DE
Year Founded: 2021
RNER—(NASDAQ)
Investment Services
N.A.I.C.S.: 523999
Matthew Kearney (CEO)
Young Cho (CFO)

MOUNTAIN COMMERCE BAN-
CORP, INC.
6101 Kingston Pike, Knoxville, TN
37919
Tel.: (865) 694-5725
Web Site: https://www.mcb.com
MCBI—(OTCQX)
Rev.: $83,787,000
Assets: $1,737,770,000
Liabilities: $1,614,983,000
Net Worth: $122,787,000
Earnings: $6,914,000

Emp.: 110
Fiscal Year-end: 12/31/23
Bank Holding Company
N.A.I.C.S.: 551111
Dwight B. Ferguson (Chm)
William E. Edwards III (Vice Chm)

Subsidiaries:

Mountain Commerce Bank (1)
6101 Kingston Pike, Knoxville, TN 37919
Tel.: (865) 694-5725
Web Site: http://www.mcb.com
Sales Range: $25-49.9 Million
Emp.: 83
Commericial Banking
N.A.I.C.S.: 522110
Tim A. Topham (Pres-Knoxville & Exec VP)
Phillip Wampler (Chief Compliance Officer)
Sheila Marie Patterson (CFO & Sr VP)
William E. Edwards III (Pres & CEO)

MOUNTAIN PACIFIC BAN-
CORP, INC.
3732 Broadway, Everett, WA 98201
Tel.: (425) 263-3500 WA
Web Site: https://mp.bank
Year Founded: 2006
MPCB—(OTCIQ)
Rev.: $41,317,539
Assets: $677,132,395
Liabilities: $610,423,153
Net Worth: $66,709,242
Earnings: $8,965,000
Fiscal Year-end: 12/31/23
Bank Holding Company
N.A.I.C.S.: 551111
Mark Duffy (Pres)
Marcus Duffy (Sr VP-Officer)
Robert Fadden (Sr VP-Officer)
Tim Rawlins (Sr VP-Officer)
Laurence Coleman (VP-Officer)
Frank Jeretzky (Sr VP-Officer)
Tony Devery (VP-Officer)
Su Htet (VP-Officer)
Pete Wiseman (VP-Officer)
John Cruikshank (Sr VP-Officer)
Cory Nelson (VP-Officer)
Drew Young (VP)
Dave Gardner (Sr VP-Real Estate
Lending)
Shannon Carmody (VP & Ops Mgr)
Ayla Masterman (Asst Mgr-
Operations)
Carrie Czarnecki (VP-Acctg Mgr)
Krystal Cruz (VP)
April Hogan (Chief Banking Officer &
Exec VP)
Kirby R. Duncan (Chief Credit Officer
& Exec VP)
Nils Bajczuk (Chief Lending Officer &
Exec VP)
Racquel Folchi (CFO & Sr VP)
Rick Pedack (Chm)
Philip Yun (Sr VP & Mgr)

MOUNTAINVIEW ENERGY
LTD.
33 1st Ave SW CPM Building, Cut
Bank, MT 59427-0200
Tel.: (406) 873-2235 AB
Web Site:
http://mountainviewenergy.com
Year Founded: 2001
MNVWF—(TSXV)
Oil & Gas Exploration
N.A.I.C.S.: 213112
Joseph P. Montalban (VP-Bus Dev)
Patrick M. Montalban (Pres & CEO)
Katherine Hylland (CFO & Interim
VP-Fin)
Carla Barringer (Treas & Sec)
Justin K. Balkenbush (VP-Ops)

MOVADO GROUP, INC.
650 From Rd Ste 375, Paramus, NJ
07652-3556
Tel.: (201) 267-8000 NY

Web Site:
https://www.movadogroup.com
Year Founded: 1967
MOV—(NYSE)
Rev.: $751,898,000
Assets: $787,705,000
Liabilities: $277,161,000
Net Worth: $510,544,000
Earnings: $94,528,000
Emp.: 992
Fiscal Year-end: 01/31/23
Holding Company; Watch & Other
Personal Accessories Designer, Mfr,
Whslr, Distr & Retailer
N.A.I.C.S.: 551112
Sallie A. DeMarsilis (CFO, COO,
Principal Acctg Officer & Exec VP)
Michelle Kennedy (Sr VP-HR)
Efraim Grinberg (Chm)
Heather Cohen Sugarman (VP-PR)

Subsidiaries:

MGDL Distribution Pty Ltd (1)
Tel.: (61) 393721122
Web Site: https://mgdldistribution.com.au
Watch Distr
N.A.I.C.S.: 423940

MGI Luxury Asia Pacific Ltd. (1)
29th Floor Citicorp Centre 18 Whitfield
Road, North Point, China (Hong Kong)
Tel.: (852) 27360820
Web Site: http://www.movadogroup.com
Emp.: 100
Watch Distr
N.A.I.C.S.: 423940

MGI Luxury Group G.m.b.H. (1)
Landsberger Str 94, 80339, Munich, Ger-
many
Tel.: (49) 89820080
Web Site: http://www.movado.com
Watch Distr
N.A.I.C.S.: 423940

MGI Luxury Group, S.A. (1)
Bahnhofplatz 2B, 2502, Bienne,
Switzerland (100%)
Tel.: (41) 323293400
Web Site: http://www.movadogroupinc.com
Sales Range: $25-49.9 Million
Emp.: 140
Watch & Accessories Distr
N.A.I.C.S.: 458310
Flavio Pellegrini (Mng Dir)

Subsidiary (Domestic):

Concord Watch Company, S.A. (2)
Bahnhofplatz 2B, 2502, Biel/Bienne,
Switzerland (100%)
Tel.: (41) 323293400
Web Site: http://www.concord.ch
Sales Range: $25-49.9 Million
Emp.: 250
Watch Distr
N.A.I.C.S.: 423940

Ebel Watches S.A. (2)
Place de la Gare 2B, 2501, Biel/Bienne,
Switzerland (100%)
Tel.: (41) 329123123
Web Site: http://www.ebel.com
Sales Range: $25-49.9 Million
Watch Distr
N.A.I.C.S.: 423940

Movado Watch Company, S.A. (2)
Bettlachstrasse 8, Grenchen, 2540,
Switzerland (100%)
Tel.: (41) 326528602
Web Site: http://www.movado.ch
Sales Range: $25-49.9 Million
Watch Distr
N.A.I.C.S.: 423940

**Movado Group Deutschland
G.m.b.H.** (1)
Friedensallee 290, 22763, Hamburg, Ger-
many
Tel.: (49) 7361556160
Web Site:
https://www.movadogroupdeutschland.com
Watch Distr
N.A.I.C.S.: 423940
Christoph Albers (Mng Dir)

Movado Group, Inc.—(Continued)

Movado Group of Canada, Inc. (1)
80 Tiverton Ct Ste 602, Markham, L3R
0G4, ON, Canada (100%)
Tel.: (905) 752-6100
Web Site: http://www.movadogroup.com
Sales Range: $25-49.9 Million
Emp.: 50
Watch Distr & Repair Services
N.A.I.C.S.: 423940

Movado Retail Group, Inc. (1)
650 From Rd Ste 375, Paramus, NJ 07652
Tel.: (201) 267-8000
Watch Mfr
N.A.I.C.S.: 551112
Efraim Grinberg (Chm & CEO)

SwissAm Products Limited (1)
29th Floor Citicorp Centre 18 Whitfield
Road, Harbour City Canton Rd, North Point,
China (Hong Kong) (100%)
Tel.: (852) 27377228
Watch Repair Services
N.A.I.C.S.: 423940

MOVANO INC.
6800 Koll Ctr Pkwy, Pleasanton, CA
94566
Tel.: (415) 651-3172 DE
Web Site:
https://www.movanohealth.com
Year Founded: 2018
MOVE—(NASDAQ)
Rev.: $133,000
Assets: $13,243,000
Liabilities: $5,328,000
Net Worth: $7,915,000
Earnings: ($30,329,000)
Emp.: 34
Fiscal Year-end: 12/31/22
Medical Device Mfr
N.A.I.C.S.: 339112
Michael Leabman (Pres & CTO)
Phil Kelly (CTO & VP-Engrg)
Jeremy Cogan (CFO)
John Mastrototaro (CEO)
Emily Wang Fairbairn (Chm)
Tyla Bucher (CMO)

MOVELLA HOLDINGS INC.
3535 Executive Terminal Dr Ste 110,
Henderson, NV 89052
Tel.: (310) 481-1800 Ky
Web Site: https://www.movella.com
Year Founded: 2020
MVLA—(NASDAQ)
Rev.: $3,607,935
Assets: $328,795,516
Liabilities: $339,316,339
Net Worth: ($10,520,823)
Earnings: ($216,565)
Emp.: 221
Fiscal Year-end: 12/31/22
Information Technology & Services
N.A.I.C.S.: 513210
Eric Salzman (CEO)

**MOVEMENT INDUSTRIES
CORP.**
6829 Flinlock Rd, Houston, TX
77040
Tel.: (713) 849-1300 NV
Web Site: https://www.mvmnt.in
MVNT—(OTCIQ)
Computer System Design Services
N.A.I.C.S.: 541512
Linh Nguyen (CEO)

Subsidiaries:

Hi-Alloy Valve LLC (1)
6829 Flintlock Rd Ste A, Houston, TX
77040
Tel.: (713) 856-9777
Web Site: http://www.hialloyvalve.com
Valve Mfr
N.A.I.C.S.: 332911

**MOVING IMAGE TECHNOLO-
GIES, INC.**
17760 Newhope St Ste B, Fountain
Valley, CA 92708
Tel.: (714) 751-7998 DE
Web Site:
https://www.movingimagetech.com
Year Founded: 2003
MITQ—(NYSEAMEX)
Rev.: $20,139,000
Assets: $10,523,000
Liabilities: $4,813,000
Net Worth: $5,710,000
Earnings: ($1,372,000)
Emp.: 32
Fiscal Year-end: 06/30/24
Photographic & Photocopying Equip-
ment Mfr
N.A.I.C.S.: 333310
Bevan Wright (Co-Founder, Partner &
Exec VP-Ops)
Frank Tees (VP-Technical Sls & Sup-
port)
Phil Rafnson (Co-Founder, Chm,
Pres & CEO)
Jerry Van de Rydt (Sr VP-FF& E Sls)
Debra Anita Walker (Dir-Pur)
Ernie Estrada (Dir-Sls & Project Sup-
port)
William F. Greene (CFO)

**MPHASE TECHNOLOGIES,
INC.**
53 State St Ste 500, Boston, MA
02109
Tel.: (941) 538-6257 NJ
Web Site:
http://www.mphasetech.com
Year Founded: 1996
XDSL—(OTCIQ)
Rev.: $30,672,314
Assets: $21,021,527
Liabilities: $9,309,631
Net Worth: $11,711,896
Earnings: $1,666,011
Emp.: 20
Fiscal Year-end: 06/30/21
Broadcast Digital Television & High-
Speed Data Services
N.A.I.C.S.: 334220
Blair Agnew (Chief Admin Officer)
Thomas Butler Fore (COO)

MPM TECHNOLOGIES, INC.
1727 E Springfield Ave Ste C, Spo-
kane, WA 99202
Tel.: (509) 242-3036 WA
Year Founded: 1983
MPML—(OTCIQ)
Gold Ore Mining Services
N.A.I.C.S.: 212220
Peter Chase (Pres)

MR. COOPER GROUP INC.
Tel.: (469) 549-2000 DE
Web Site:
https://www.mrcoopergroup.com
Year Founded: 1889
COOP—(NASDAQ)
Rev.: $1,794,000,000
Assets: $14,296,000,000
Liabilities: $10,014,000,000
Net Worth: $4,282,000,000
Earnings: $500,000,000
Emp.: 6,800
Fiscal Year-end: 12/31/23
Insurance Holding Company
N.A.I.C.S.: 551112
Jay Bray (Chm & CEO)
Christopher G. Marshall (Vice Chm)
Kelly Ann Doherty (Chief People &
Comm Officer & Exec VP)
Sridhar Sharma (CIO & Exec VP)
Michael S. Weinbach (Pres)
Kenneth Posner (Sr VP-Strategic
Plng & IR)

Christen Reyenga (VP-Corp Comm)
Ethan Elzen (Exec VP-Bus Dev &
Operational Fin)
Carlos M. Pelayo (Chief Legal Officer
& Exec VP)
Christine Poland Paxton (Chief Risk
& Compliance Officer & Exec VP)
Kurt Johnson (CFO & Exec VP)
Angela Greenfeather (Chief HR Offi-
cer)
Jay Jones (Exec VP)
Snezhina Panova Bakri (Chief Audit
Officer)
Michael Rawls (Exec VP)

Subsidiaries:

Home Point Capital Inc. (1)
2211 Old Earhart Rd Ste 250, Ann Arbor,
MI 48105
Rev.: $255,647,000
Assets: $2,438,192,000
Liabilities: $1,834,656,000
Net Worth: $603,536,000
Earnings: ($163,454,000)
Emp.: 830
Fiscal Year-end: 12/31/2022
Consumer Lending Services
N.A.I.C.S.: 522291
Jean Weng (Gen Counsel)
Mark E. Elbaum (CFO)

Subsidiary (Domestic):

**Home Point Financial
Corporation** (2)
11511 Luna Rd Ste 200, Farmers Branch,
TX 75234
Tel.: (800) 686-2404
Web Site:
http://www.homepointfinancial.com
Mortgage Banking
N.A.I.C.S.: 522292
William Newman (Pres & CEO)
Kristin Supancich (Chief People Officer)

**Nationstar Mortgage Holdings
Inc.** (1)
8950 Cypress Waters Blvd, Coppell, TX
75019-4620
Tel.: (469) 549-2000
Web Site: https://www.mrcooper.com
Sales Range: $1-4.9 Billion
Mortgage Services
N.A.I.C.S.: 522310
Ramesh Lakshminarayanan (Chief Bus Offi-
cer, Chief Analytics Officer & Exec VP)
Kevin Dahlstrom (Chief Mktg Officer & Chief
Mktg Officer)
Michael Rawls (Exec VP)
Steve Covington (Chief Risk & Compliance
Officer & Chief Risk & Compliance Officer)
Transient C. Taylor (Chief HR Officer &
Exec VP)
Sridhar Sharma (CIO & Exec VP)

Subsidiary (Domestic):

Nationstar Mortgage LLC (2)
8950 Cypress Waters Blvd, Coppell, TX
75019
Tel.: (469) 549-2000
Mortgage Lending Services
N.A.I.C.S.: 522310

Subsidiary (Domestic):

Champion Mortgage Co., Inc. (3)
11 Eves Dr, Marlton, NJ 08063
Tel.: (855) 683-3095
Web Site:
http://www.championmortgage.com
Mortgage Banking
N.A.I.C.S.: 522292

Solutionstar Realty Services LLC (3)
700 E Hwy 121 Ste 100, Lewisville, TX
75067
Tel.: (469) 549-2000
Web Site: http://www.solutionstar.com
Residential Mortgage Loan Origination, De-
fault Processing, Title & Valuation Services
N.A.I.C.S.: 561499
Mark R. Johnson (Exec VP-Valuations)
Matt Slonaker (Sr VP-Bus Dev)
Kal Raman (CEO)

Subsidiary (Domestic):

**Solutionstar Settlement Services
LLC** (4)

420 Rouser Rd, Coraopolis, PA 15108
Tel.: (412) 893-1217
Web Site: http://www.solutionstar.com
Sales Range: $50-74.9 Million
Emp.: 130
Title, Closing & Appraisal Services
N.A.I.C.S.: 541191

**Roosevelt Management Company,
LLC** (1)
1540 Broadway Ste 1500, New York, NY
10036
Tel.: (212) 938-4800
Web Site: http://www.rooseveltmc.com
Intermediation
N.A.I.C.S.: 523910
Steve Barone (VP)

Title365 Company (1)
4695 MacArthur Ct Ste 550, Newport
Beach, CA 92660
Web Site: https://www.title365.com
Title Insurance & Escrow Services
N.A.I.C.S.: 524127
Bill Moody (Pres)

MRC GLOBAL INC.
1301 McKinney St Ste 2300, Hous-
ton, TX 77010-3035
Tel.: (713) 655-1005 DE
Web Site: https://www.mrcglobal.com
Year Founded: 2006
MRC—(NYSE)
Rev.: $3,363,000,000
Assets: $1,895,000,000
Liabilities: $1,509,000,000
Net Worth: $386,000,000
Earnings: $51,000,000
Emp.: 2,800
Fiscal Year-end: 12/31/22
Holding Company; Oilfield & Indus-
trial Pipes, Valves & Fittings Distr
N.A.I.C.S.: 551112
Kelly Youngblood (CFO & Exec VP)
Robert J. Saltiel Jr. (Pres & CEO)
Gillian Anderson (Chief Acctg Officer
& VP)
Shweta Kurvey-Mishra (Chief HR Of-
ficer)
Emily Shields (Sr VP)
Steve Smith (Sr VP)

Subsidiaries:

MRC Energy Piping AS (1)
Gamle Forusvei 53, 4033, Stavanger, Nor-
way
Tel.: (47) 51573900
Web Site: http://www.mrcglobal.no
Valve & Pipe Fitting Product Whslr
N.A.I.C.S.: 423830
Steinar Lea (Mng Dir)

MRC Flangefitt Limited (1)
Suite 19 St James Business Centre Wilder-
spool Causeway, Warrington, WA4 6PS,
Cheshire, United Kingdom
Tel.: (44) 1925444807
Web Site: http://www.carnegiehotel.com
Valve & Pipe Fitting Product Whslr
N.A.I.C.S.: 423830

MRC Global (Belgium) NV (1)
Vaartkaai 50, 2170, Antwerp, Belgium
Tel.: (32) 24820150
Steel Pipe & Fitting Distr
N.A.I.C.S.: 423510

MRC Global (Canada) ULC (1)
105 Oak Court, Anzac, T0P 1J0, AB,
Canada
Tel.: (780) 334-0526
Valve & Pipe Fitting Product Whslr
N.A.I.C.S.: 423830

MRC Global (Finland) Oy (1)
Viirikankaari 7, Helsinki, 1530, Vantaa, Fin-
land
Tel.: (358) 108307500
Plumbing & Heating Equipment Whslr
N.A.I.C.S.: 423620
Marcus Wickstrom (Dir-Sls)

MRC Global (Germany) GmbH (1)
Am Gewerbepark 1, 63594, Hasselroth,
Germany
Tel.: (49) 6055905920

Steel Pipe & Fitting Distr
N.A.I.C.S.: 423510

MRC Global (Italy) Srl (1)
Via Antonio Gramsci 59, 20019, Settimo
Milanese, Italy
Tel.: (39) 0293580581
Steel Pipe & Fitting Distr
N.A.I.C.S.: 423510

MRC Global (Korea) Limited (1)
38 Namyeong ro 527 beon gil, Jinhae gu,
Changwon, Gyeongsangnam-do, Korea
(South)
Tel.: (82) 557169844
Valve & Pipe Fitting Product Whslr
N.A.I.C.S.: 423830
Siron Jang (Mgr-Sls)

MRC Global (Netherlands) B.V. (1)
Spectrumlaan 7-9, 2665 NM, Bleiswijk,
Netherlands
Tel.: (31) 881414222
Steel Pipe & Fitting Distr
N.A.I.C.S.: 423510
Lodewijk Meijer (Dir-Fin)

MRC Global (New Zealand)
Limited (1)
Unit 4A 4B George Bourke Drive Mt Wel-
lington, 1060, Auckland, 1060, New Zea-
land
Tel.: (64) 92764149
Steel Pipe & Fitting Distr
N.A.I.C.S.: 423510

MRC Global (Singapore) Pte.
Ltd. (1)
16 Sungei Kadut Avenue, Singapore,
729652, Singapore
Tel.: (65) 68651020
Steel Pipe & Fitting Distr
N.A.I.C.S.: 423510

MRC Global (Sweden) AB (1)
Bultvagen 1, 451 75, Uddevalla, Sweden
Tel.: (46) 701456460
Valve & Pipe Fitting Product Whslr
N.A.I.C.S.: 423830

MRC Global (Thailand) Company
Limited (1)
349 SJ Infinite One Business Complex
Building 12th Floor Unit 1201, Vibhavadi
Rangsit Road Chomphol Chatuchak, Bang-
kok, 10900, Thailand
Tel.: (66) 20166555
Valve & Pipe Fitting Product Whslr
N.A.I.C.S.: 423830

MRC Global (US) Inc. (1)
835 Hillcrest Dr, Charleston, WV 25311-
1627
Tel.: (304) 348-5211
Web Site: http://www.mrcglobal.com
Sales Range: $125-149.9 Million
Oilfield & Industrial Supplies Distr
N.A.I.C.S.: 423840

Subsidiary (Domestic):

Greenbrier Petroleum
Corporation (2)
835 Hillcrest Dr, Charleston, WV 25311-
1627
Tel.: (304) 348-5211
Pipe, Valve & Related Product Distr
N.A.I.C.S.: 423720

Subsidiary (Non-US):

MRC Canada ULC (2)
1140 2nd St W, Brooks, T1R 1B8, AB,
Canada
Tel.: (403) 362-3800
Web Site: http://www.mrcglobal.com
Sales Range: $25-49.9 Million
Emp.: 8
Pipe, Valve & Fitting Product Distr
N.A.I.C.S.: 423720

MRC Global (France) SAS (2)
21-23 rue du Petit Albi Immeuble Cerithe
Hall 201 C2, Saint Christophe, 95800,
Cergy, France
Tel.: (33) 130736066
Pipe, Valve & Fitting Product Distr
N.A.I.C.S.: 423720

MRC Global Australia Pty Ltd (2)

5 Frederick Road, Royal Park, 5014, SA,
Australia
Tel.: (61) 883047510
Web Site: http://www.mrcglobal.com
Sales Range: $25-49.9 Million
Pipe, Valve & Fitting Product Distr
N.A.I.C.S.: 423720
Damien Wilson (Mng Dir)

Subsidiary (Domestic):

MRC Management Company (2)
2 Houston Center 909 Fannin Ste 3100,
Houston, TX 77010
Tel.: (713) 655-1005
Administrative Services
N.A.I.C.S.: 561110

Subsidiary (Non-US):

MRC Transmark (2)
Heaton House Riverside Drive Hunsworth
Lane, Bradford, BD19 4DH, United King-
dom
Tel.: (44) 1274700000
Web Site: http://www.mrcglobal.com
Emp.: 40
Valve Mfr
N.A.I.C.S.: 332919

MRC Transmark B.V. (2)
Coenecoop 19, 2741 PG, Waddinxveen,
Netherlands
Tel.: (31) 182642222
Emp.: 50
Pipe, Valve & Fitting Product Distr
N.A.I.C.S.: 423720
Marcel Bras (Mng Dir)

MRC Transmark Group B.V. (2)
Vlotbrugweg 8, Almere, 1332 AH, Flevol-
and, Netherlands
Tel.: (31) 365387387
Web Site: http://www.mrcglobal.com
Pipe, Valve & Fitting Product Distr
N.A.I.C.S.: 423720

MRC Transmark Holdings UK
Ltd. (2)
Heaton House Riverside Drive, Hunsworth
Lane, Bradford, BD19 4DH, West Yorkshire,
United Kingdom
Tel.: (44) 1274700000
Web Site: http://www.transmark.com
Emp.: 60
Investment Management Service
N.A.I.C.S.: 551112

MRC Transmark Italy srl (2)
Via Gramsci 59, 20019, Settimo Milanese,
Italy
Tel.: (39) 0293580581
Web Site: http://www.mrcglobal.com
Emp.: 2
Pipe, Valve & Fitting Product Distr
N.A.I.C.S.: 423720

MRC Transmark Limited (2)
Heaton House Riverside Drive, Bradford,
BD19 4DH, United Kingdom
Tel.: (44) 1274700000
Emp.: 40
Pipe, Valve & Fitting Product Distr
N.A.I.C.S.: 423720

MRC Transmark NV (2)
Vaartkaai 50, 2170, Antwerp, Belgium
Tel.: (32) 51320
Web Site: http://www.mrcglobal.com
Emp.: 65
Pipe, Valve & Fitting Product Distr
N.A.I.C.S.: 423720

Unit (Domestic):

MRC Valve Automation Center (2)
2501 E Interstate 20, Odessa, TX 79766
Tel.: (432) 333-6304
Web Site: http://www.mrcglobal.com
Sales Range: $25-49.9 Million
Emp.: 25
Industrial Machinery & Equipment Merchant
Whslr
N.A.I.C.S.: 423830

MRC MSD Engineering Pte. Ltd. (1)
16 Sungei Kadut Avenue, Singapore,
729652, Singapore
Tel.: (65) 64629119
Valve & Pipe Fitting Product Whslr
N.A.I.C.S.: 423830

Dan Lin (Engr-Sls & Svc)

MRC Solberg & Andersen AS (1)
Langarinden 16, Nyborg, 5132, Bergen,
Norway
Tel.: (47) 81552894
Web Site: http://www.saas.no
Emp.: 180
Valve & Pipe Fitting Product Whslr
N.A.I.C.S.: 423830

MRC Teamtrade AS (1)
Kanalarmen 12, 4033, Stavanger, Norway
Tel.: (47) 51959400
Web Site: http://www.teamtrade.no
Emp.: 170
Fluid Control Equipment Whslr
N.A.I.C.S.: 423830

MRC Transmark Kazakhstan
LLP (1)
Satpayev Street 23 A 3rd Floor, 060011,
Atyrau, Kazakhstan
Tel.: (7) 122502510
Valve & Pipe Fitting Product Whslr
N.A.I.C.S.: 423830
Arman Mukanov (Gen Dir)

PT MRC Global Indonesia (1)
Talavera Office Park 28th Floor Ji Tb Si-
matupang Kav 22-26, Jakarta, 12550, Indo-
nesia
Tel.: (62) 2175999801
Steel Pipe & Fitting Distr
N.A.I.C.S.: 423510

MSA SAFETY INCORPORATED
1000 Cranberry Woods Dr, Cranberry
Township, PA 16066-5207
Tel.: (724) 776-8600   PA
Web Site: https://www.msasafety.com
Year Founded: 1914
MSA—(NYSE)
Rev.: $1,787,647,000
Assets: $2,170,150,000
Liabilities: $1,203,348,000
Net Worth: $966,802,000
Earnings: $58,583,000
Emp.: 5,100
Fiscal Year-end: 12/31/23
Safety & Health Equipment Mfr
N.A.I.C.S.: 339999
John T. Ryan III (Executives, Bd of
Dirs)
Markus Weber (CIO & VP)
Steven C. Blanco (Pres, CEO &
COO)
Lee B. McChesney (CFO & Sr VP)
Jonathan D. Buck (Chief Acctg Offi-
cer & Controller)
David B. Mcarthur (Chief Customer
Officer & VP-Mktg-Global)
Gregory L. Martin (VP-Product Strat-
egy & Dev)
Glennis A. Williams (Chief HR Officer
& VP)
Stephanie L. Sciullo (Chief Legal Offi-
cer)
Chris Hepler (Exec Dir)

Subsidiaries:

Compania MSA de Argentina
S.A. (1)
Av Belgrano 2470, Don Torcuato,
B1611DVQ, Buenos Aires, Argentina
Tel.: (54) 114 834 4800
Web Site: http://ar.msasafety.com
Safety & Health Equipment Mfr
N.A.I.C.S.: 333131

General Monitors Inc. (1)
26806 Vista Ter, Lake Forest, CA 92630
Tel.: (949) 581-4464
Web Site:
   https://www.gmsystemsgroup.com
Sales Range: $75-99.9 Million
Mfr of Safety Monitors & Flame Detection
Instrumentation
N.A.I.C.S.: 334513

General Monitors Ireland Limited (1)
Ballybrit Business Park, Galway, H91 H6P2,
Ireland
Tel.: (353) 91751175

Web Site: http://www.generalmonitors.com
Sales Range: $25-49.9 Million
Gas Monitoring & Flame Detection Instru-
ment Mfr
N.A.I.C.S.: 334512

Globe Manufacturing Company,
Inc. (1)
37 Loudon Rd, Pittsfield, NH 03263
Web Site: http://www.globeturnoutgear.com
Emp.: 425
Protective Clothing Mfr
N.A.I.C.S.: 315250
Don Welch (Pres)

Latchways plc (1)
Hopton Park, Devizes, SN10 2JP, Wiltshire,
United Kingdom
Tel.: (44) 1380732700
Web Site: http://www.latchways.com
Sales Range: $25-49.9 Million
Industrial Safety Products Mfr, Distr & In-
staller
N.A.I.C.S.: 333120

Subsidiary (Domestic):

HCL Safety Limited (2)
Hopton Park, Devizes, SN10 2JP, Wiltshire,
United Kingdom
Tel.: (44) 8456000086
Web Site: https://www.hclsafety.com
Safety Solutions Installation Services
N.A.I.C.S.: 541690
Stuart Pierpoint (Mgr-Sls)
Roger Boulter (Mgr-Trng)

MSA Africa (Pty.) Ltd. (1)
City Deep Production Park 83 Heidelberg
Road, City Deep, South Hills, 2001, Gau-
teng, South Africa   (100%)
Tel.: (27) 116232213
Web Site: http://www.msaafrica.co.za
Sales Range: $100-124.9 Million
Emp.: 256
Mine Safety Appliances
N.A.I.C.S.: 333131

MSA Australia Pty. Limited (1)
11 Columbia Way, Baulkham Hills, 2153,
NSW, Australia
Tel.: (61) 296880333
Web Site: http://www.au.msasafety.com
Sales Range: $50-74.9 Million
Emp.: 80
Safety Equipment Mfr
N.A.I.C.S.: 333131

MSA Canada (1)
100 Westmore Drive Unit 23, Toronto, M9V
5C3, ON, Canada   (100%)
Tel.: (416) 620-4225
Web Site: http://ca.msasafety.com
Sales Range: $10-24.9 Million
Safety & Industrial Appliances Repair
N.A.I.C.S.: 561621

MSA Egypt LLC (1)
7C/4 El-Sheikh El Shaarawi St Ground Fl
Office Ste 2, Takseem El Laselky New
Maadi, Cairo, Egypt
Tel.: (20) 227538442
Web Site: http://www.msanet.com
Sales Range: $25-49.9 Million
Emp.: 4
Safety & Health Equipment Sales & Servic-
ing
N.A.I.C.S.: 423810

MSA Europe Holdings GmbH (1)
Thiemannstrasse 1, 12059, Berlin, Germany
Tel.: (49) 3068860
Web Site: http://www.msa-europe.com
Sales Range: $200-249.9 Million
Emp.: 550
Holding Company
N.A.I.C.S.: 551112

Subsidiary (Non-US):

MSA (Britain) Limited (2)
East Shawhead, Coatbridge, ML5 4TD,
Scotland, United Kingdom
Tel.: (44) 1236642066
Sales Range: $25-49.9 Million
Emp.: 38
Safety Equipment & Batteries Mfr

MSA Safety Incorporated—(Continued)

N.A.I.C.S.: 333131

MSA Belgium NV (2)
Duwijckstraat 17, 2500, Lier,
Belgium (100%)
Tel.: (32) 34919150
Web Site: http://nl.msasafety.com
Sales Range: $10-24.9 Million
Mine Safety Appliances
N.A.I.C.S.: 333131

MSA Italiana S.p.A. (2)
Via Po 13/17, 20089, Rozzano, MI, Italy
Tel.: (39) 02892171
Web Site: http://it.msasafety.com
Sales Range: $25-49.9 Million
Safety Equipment Mfr
N.A.I.C.S.: 333131

MSA Nederland, B.V. (2)
De Factorij 33, Zwaag, 1689 AK, Hoorn,
Netherlands
Tel.: (31) 229250303
Web Site: http://nl.msasafety.com
Sales Range: $25-49.9 Million
Mine Safety Equipment Whslr
N.A.I.C.S.: 333131

MSA Nordic AB (2)
Rorlaggarvagen 8, 33153, Varnamo, Swe-
den
Tel.: (46) 370780409
Web Site: http://www.msasafety.com
Sales Range: $10-24.9 Million
Emp.: 7
Safety Equipment Mfr
N.A.I.C.S.: 333131

MSA Safety Romania S.R.L. (2)
Strada Virgil Madgearu Nr 5 Sector 1,
14135, Bucharest, Romania
Tel.: (40) 212326245
Web Site: http://www.msa-auer.ro
Sales Range: $25-49.9 Million
Emp.: 3
Mining & Industrial Safety Equipment Whslr
N.A.I.C.S.: 423810

MSA Schweiz GmbH (2)
Schlusselstr 12, 8645, Rapperswil, Switzer-
land
Tel.: (41) 432558900
Web Site: http://www.msasafety.com
Emp.: 10
Mining & Industrial Safety Equipment Mfr &
Distr
N.A.I.C.S.: 333131

MSA Sordin AB (2)
Rorlaggarvagen 8, 331 53, Varnamo, 331
53, Sweden
Tel.: (46) 370693550
Web Site: https://www.sordin.com
Rev.: $10,024,400
Emp.: 30
Hearing Equipment Designer
N.A.I.C.S.: 334290

MSA Spain, S.L. (2)
Pol Ind del Sudoest Narcis Monturiol 7,
08960, Sant Just Desvern, Spain
Tel.: (34) 933725162
Web Site: http://es.msasafety.com
Safety Equipment Whslr
N.A.I.C.S.: 423810

Subsidiary (Domestic):

**MSA Technologies and Enterprise
Services GmbH** (2)
Thiemannstrasse 1, 12059, Berlin, Germany
(100%)
Tel.: (49) 3068860
Web Site: http://www.msasafety.com
Sales Range: $150-199.9 Million
Emp.: 500
Mining & Industrial Safety Equipment Mfr
N.A.I.C.S.: 333131

Subsidiary (Non-US):

MSA Safety Hungary Ltd. (3)
Francia utca 10, 1143, Budapest,
Hungary (100%)
Tel.: (36) 12513488
Web Site: http://hu.msasafety.com
Sales Range: $10-24.9 Million
Emp.: 14
Mine Safety Appliances

N.A.I.C.S.: 333131
Joakim Birgersson (Mng Dir)

MSA Safety Poland Sp.z.o.o. (3)
Ul Wschodnia 5A, 05-090, Raszyn,
Poland (100%)
Tel.: (48) 22 71150 00
Web Site: http://pl.msasafety.com
Sales Range: $25-49.9 Million
Emp.: 60
Mine Safety Products Mfr
N.A.I.C.S.: 333131

MSA-Auer Vertriebs GmbH (3)
Modecenterstrasse 22 MGC Office 4A Top
601, 1030, Vienna, Austria
Tel.: (43) 17960496
Web Site: http://at.msasafety.com
Sales Range: $125-149.9 Million
Emp.: 16
Safety & Health Equipment Mfr
N.A.I.C.S.: 333131

MSA Hong Kong Ltd. (1)
25th Floor JupiterTower No 9 Jupiter Street,
Hong Kong, China (Hong Kong)
Tel.: (852) 22587588
Web Site: http://www.msaftey.com
Safety & Health Equipment Sales & Servic-
ing
N.A.I.C.S.: 423810
Mr Chui (Gen Mgr)

MSA India Limited (1)
Ecostation Level-16 Plot No 7 Block BP
Salt Lake Sector-V, New Town Rajarhat,
Kolkata, 700091, West Bengal, India
Tel.: (91) 3323672260
Web Site: http://www.msa-india.com
Sales Range: $25-49.9 Million
Emp.: 32
Safety & Health Equipment Sales & Servic-
ing
N.A.I.C.S.: 423810

MSA International, Inc. (1)
1000 Cranberry Woods Dr, Cranberry
Township, PA 16066
Tel.: (412) 967-3000
Web Site: http://www.msasafety.com
Sales Range: $100-124.9 Million
Emp.: 900
Safety & Health Equipment Mfr
N.A.I.C.S.: 333131

MSA Italia S.R.L. (1)
Via Po 13/17 Rozzano, 20089, Milan, Italy
Tel.: (39) 02892171
Web Site: https://it.msasafety.com
Safety Products Mfr & Distr
N.A.I.C.S.: 333310

MSA Japan Ltd. (1)
Horizon 1 Bldg 2nd Fl 30-16 3-chome Nishi
Waseda, Shinjuku-ku, Tokyo, 169-0051,
Japan (100%)
Tel.: (81) 332092171
Web Site: http://www.msajapan.com
Sales Range: $25-49.9 Million
Emp.: 30
Safety Equipment Whslr
N.A.I.C.S.: 425120

MSA Middle East FZE (1)
Building 4W Block-A Office 525 Dubai Air-
port Free Zone, PO Box 54910, Dubai,
United Arab Emirates
Tel.: (971) 42996741
Web Site: http://www.msamiddleeast.com
Sales Range: $25-49.9 Million
Emp.: 30
Safety & Health Equipment Sales & Servic-
ing
N.A.I.C.S.: 423810

MSA Osterreich GmbH (1)
Modecenterstrasse 22 MGC Office 2 Top
C58, 1030, Vienna, Austria
Tel.: (43) 179604960
Mining Machinery & Equipment Mfr
N.A.I.C.S.: 333131

**MSA Produktion Deutschland
GmbH** (1)
Thiemannstr 1, 12059, Berlin, Germany
Tel.: (49) 306886112
Web Site: http://de.msasafety.com
Mining Machinery & Equipment Mfr
N.A.I.C.S.: 333131

MSA S.E. Asia Pte. Ltd. (1)

35 Marsiling Industrial Estate Road 3 04-01,
Singapore, 739257, Singapore (100%)
Tel.: (65) 63504500
Web Site: https://sg.msasafety.com
Sales Range: $10-24.9 Million
Safety Equipment Sales
N.A.I.C.S.: 423810

MSA Safety Malaysia Sdn Bhd (1)
No 22 Jalan PPU 2A Taman Perindustrian
Puchong Utama, 47100, Puchong, Selan-
gor, Malaysia
Tel.: (60) 39 767 8800
Web Site: https://my.msasafety.com
Sales Range: $125-149.9 Million
Safety & Health Equipment Mfr
N.A.I.C.S.: 333131

MSA Safety Services GmbH (1)
Thiemannstr 1, 12059, Berlin, Germany
Tel.: (49) 3068861543
Safety Equipment Consulting Services
N.A.I.C.S.: 541690

**MSA Suzhou Safety Equipment R&D
Co., Ltd.** (1)
No 8 Rui En Lane Xingpu Road, Suzhou
Industrial Park, Suzhou, 215126, China
Tel.: (86) 512628988808
Web Site: http://cn.msasafety.com
Sales Range: $75-99.9 Million
Emp.: 450
Safety & Health Equipment Mfr
N.A.I.C.S.: 333131

**MSA Technologies and Enterprise
Services SAS** (1)
Zone Industrielle Sud, 01400, Chatillon-sur-
Chalaronne, France
Tel.: (33) 474550155
Mining Machinery & Equipment Mfr
N.A.I.C.S.: 333131

MSA Thailand Limited (1)
28th Floor Suntowers Bldg B No 2801 123
Vibhavadi-Rangsit Rd, Chompon
Chatuchak, Bangkok, 10900, Thailand
Tel.: (66) 26178211
Web Site: http://www.msa-thailand.com
Sales Range: $25-49.9 Million
Emp.: 12
Safety & Health Equipment Sales & Servic-
ing
N.A.I.C.S.: 423810

**MSA de Chile, Equipos de Seguridad
Ltda.** (1)
Domingo Arteaga 600, Santiago, 7810553,
Chile
Tel.: (56) 22 947 5799
Web Site: https://cl.msasafety.com
Sales Range: $25-49.9 Million
Safety Equipment Retailer
N.A.I.C.S.: 423810

MSA de Mexico, S.A. de C.V. (1)
Avenida del Conde 6, Parque Industrial El
Marques El Marques, 76246, Queretaro,
Mexico
Tel.: (52) 14422273970
Web Site: https://mx.msasafety.com
Safety Equipment Whslr
N.A.I.C.S.: 334513

MSA del Peru S.A.C. (1)
Los Telares 139 Urb Vulcano Ate, Casilla
1933, 139, Lima, Peru
Tel.: (51) 16180900
Web Site: https://pe.msasafety.com
Safety Equipment Whslr
N.A.I.C.S.: 423810

**MSA do Brasil Equipamentos e in-
strumentos de Seguranca Ltda.** (1)
Av Roberto Gordon 138, Diadema, 09990-
901, Sao Paulo, Brazil (100%)
Tel.: (55) 114 070 5999
Web Site: https://br.msasafety.com
Sales Range: $100-124.9 Million
Safety Equipment Mfr
N.A.I.C.S.: 333131

**Mine Safety Appliances Company,
LLC** (1)
352 White St, Jacksonville, NC 28546-6730
Tel.: (910) 355-3102
Web Site: http://www.msasafety.com
Safety Products Mfr
N.A.I.C.S.: 339999

**Mine Safety Appliances Company-
Instrument Division** (1)
1000 Cranberry Woods Dr, Cranberry
Township, PA 16066-5207
Tel.: (724) 776-8600
Web Site: http://www.msasafety.com
Sales Range: $75-99.9 Million
Emp.: 500
Gas Detection Equipment
N.A.I.C.S.: 334511

**Mine Safety Appliances Company-
Safety Products Division** (1)
1100 Cranberry Woods Dr, Cranberry Town-
ship, PA 16066-5208
Tel.: (724) 776-7700
Web Site: http://www.msasafety.com
Sales Range: $10-24.9 Million
Emp.: 70
Safety Products Mfr
N.A.I.C.S.: 339999

**Mine Safety Appliances Company-
Safety Products Division** (1)
3880 Meadowbrook Rd, Murrysville, PA
15668
Tel.: (724) 733-9100
Web Site: http://www.msa.net.com
Sales Range: $100-124.9 Million
Emp.: 400
Safety Equipment Mfr
N.A.I.C.S.: 339999

PT MSA Indonesia Ltd (1)
Kompleks Multiguna Kemayoran No 1-K Jl
Rajawali Selatan, Raya Blok C5 No 2, Ja-
karta, 14410, Utara, Indonesia
Tel.: (62)-216409000
Web Site: http://www.msasafety.com
Sales Range: $25-49.9 Million
Emp.: 25
Safety & Health Equipment Sales & Servic-
ing
N.A.I.C.S.: 423810

Senscient, Ltd. (1)
F1-2 Arena Business Centre Holyrood
Close, Poole, BH17 7FP, United Kingdom
Tel.: (44) 1202606460
Web Site: http://www.senscient.com
Sensor Product Mfr
N.A.I.C.S.: 334413
Lee Richman (CTO)

Sierra Monitor Corporation (1)
1991 Tarob Ct, Milpitas, CA 95035
Tel.: (408) 262-6611
Web Site: http://www.sierramonitor.com
Rev.: $22,075,409
Assets: $10,962,931
Liabilities: $1,996,323
Net Worth: $8,966,608
Earnings: $169,760
Emp.: 82
Fiscal Year-end: 12/31/2018
Measuring & Controlling Devices
N.A.I.C.S.: 334519
Gordon R. Arnold (Chm)

**Wuxi-MSA Safety Equipment Co.
Ltd.** (1)
305 Xicheng Road, Wuxi, 214046, Jiangsu,
China (100%)
Tel.: (86) 51083121888
Web Site: http://www.msa-china.com
Sales Range: $50-74.9 Million
Emp.: 130
Mine Safety Appliances
N.A.I.C.S.: 333131

MSC INCOME FUND, INC.
1300 Post Oak Blvd 8th Fl, Houston,
TX 77056
Tel.: (713) 350-6000   MD
Web Site:
https://www.mscincomefund.com
Year Founded: 2011
MSCF—(OTC)
Investment Management Service
N.A.I.C.S.: 523999
Nicholas T. Meserve (Mng Dir)
Dwayne L. Hyzak (Chm & CEO)
David L. Magdol (Pres & CIO)
Jesse E. Morris (CFO, COO, Treas &
Exec VP)

Jason B. Beauvais *(Gen Counsel, Sec & Exec VP)*
Cory E. Gilbert *(Chief Acctg Officer, VP & Asst Treas)*

MSC INDUSTRIAL DIRECT CO., INC.

515 Broadhollow Rd Ste 1000, Melville, NY 11747
Tel.: (516) 812-2000   **NY**
Web Site: https://www.mscdirect.com
Year Founded: 1995
MSM—(NYSE)
Rev.: $3,820,951,000
Assets: $2,462,313,000
Liabilities: $1,061,031,000
Net Worth: $1,401,282,000
Earnings: $255,957,000
Emp.: 7,191
Fiscal Year-end: 08/31/24
Tools & Industrial Products Distr
N.A.I.C.S.: 423830
Erik David Gershwind *(CEO)*
Kari Heerdt *(Sr VP-New Bus Innovation & Transformation)*
Steve Baruch *(Chief Strategy & Mktg Officer & Exec VP)*
Greg Polli *(Sr VP-Supplier Enablement)*
Beth Bledsoe *(Chief People Officer & Sr VP-HR)*
Kristen Actis-Grande *(CFO & Exec VP)*
Neal Dongre *(Corp Counsel, Corp Counsel, Sr VP, VP & Head)*
Douglas Jones *(Corp Counsel, Corp Counsel, Sec, Exec VP, Sr VP, VP, VP & Head)*
Kim Shacklett *(Sr VP)*
John Chironna *(Treas)*
Martina McIsaac *(Pres, COO & Exec VP)*

Subsidiaries:

ATS Industrial Supply, S. de R.L. de C.V.   **(1)**
Boulevard Manuel J, Clouthier 21-5, Tijuana, 22550, BJ, Mexico
Tel.: (52) 6643002525
Industrial Machinery & Equipment Merchant Whslr
N.A.I.C.S.: 423830

Buckeye Industrial Supply Co. **(1)**
3989 Groves Rd, Columbus, OH 43232
Tel.: (614) 864-8400
Web Site: https://www.bisbuckeye.com
Industrial Tools
N.A.I.C.S.: 423840
Rick Meizlish *(Pres)*

Deco Tool Supply Company **(1)**
415 W 76th St, Davenport, IA 52806
Tel.: (563) 386-5970
Web Site: http://www.decotool.com
Drilling Equipment Mfr
N.A.I.C.S.: 423830
Rick Witham *(Engr-Sls)*
Kimbel Hemmingson *(Mgr-Sls)*

Engman-Taylor Company Inc. **(1)**
W 142 N 9351 Fountain Blvd, Menomonee Falls, WI 53051
Tel.: (262) 255-9300
Web Site: http://www.engman-taylor.com
Sales Range: $25-49.9 Million
Emp.: 165
Industrial Machinery & Equipment Distr
N.A.I.C.S.: 423830
Richard Star *(Pres)*

Sid Tool Co., Inc.   **(1)**
75 Maxess Rd, Melville, NY 11747-3151
Tel.: (516) 812-2000
Web Site: https://www.mscdirect.com
Cutting & Precision Tools, Abrasives, Machinery, Material Handling Equipment & Machine Shop Supplies Distr
N.A.I.C.S.: 423830
Erik David Gershwind *(Pres & CEO)*
Kari Heerdt *(Sr VP-Transformation & New Bus Innovation)*

Kim Shacklett *(Interim VP-Customer Success & Sls)*
Jim Drohan *(VP-Comml Dev & Bus)*
Neal Dongre *(VP-Legal & Asst Sec)*

Subsidiary (Domestic):

Accurate Component Sales, Inc. **(2)**
8625 Industrial Dr, Franksville, WI 53126
Tel.: (262) 770-3305
Web Site: https://www.allintegrated.com
Industrial Fasteners, Hardware & Components Distr
N.A.I.C.S.: 423710
Jerry Moehnke *(CEO)*
Mike Iannazzo *(Mgr-Sls & Mktg)*

Branch (Domestic):

Accurate Component Sales - Cedar Rapids   **(3)**
6805 4th St SW Ste 107, Cedar Rapids, IA 52404-4762
Tel.: (319) 366-7461
Web Site: https://www.allintegrated.com
Industrial Supplies & Hardware Distr
N.A.I.C.S.: 423840
Randy Rule *(Branch Mgr)*

Subsidiary (Domestic):

Barnes Distribution North America   **(2)**
1301 E 9th St Ste 700, Cleveland, OH 44114-1800
Tel.: (216) 416-7200
Web Site: http://www.barnesdistribution.com
Sales Range: $250-299.9 Million
Emp.: 1,400
Security Control Equipment & Systems
N.A.I.C.S.: 423690

Branch (Domestic):

Barnes Distribution   **(3)**
870 W Park Rd, Elizabethtown, KY 42701-3030   **(100%)**
Tel.: (270) 769-5537
Web Site: http://www.barnesdistribution.com
Sales Range: $25-49.9 Million
Emp.: 50
Hardware Distr
N.A.I.C.S.: 423840

Subsidiary (Non-US):

Barnes Distribution (Canada) Ltd.   **(3)**
2595 Skymark Ave Unit 202, Mississauga, L4K 3N7, ON, Canada **(100%)**
Tel.: (905) 219-6300
Web Site: http://www.barnesdistribution.com
Sales Range: $25-49.9 Million
Emp.: 25
Industrial Maintenance & Automotive Repair Products Mfr
N.A.I.C.S.: 441330

Subsidiary (Domestic):

Swiss Precision Instruments, Inc. **(2)**
11450 Markon Dr, Garden Grove, CA 92841
Tel.: (714) 379-6556
Web Site: http://www.swissprec.com
Industrial Machinery & Equipment Whslr
N.A.I.C.S.: 423830

Tower Fasteners Co. Inc. **(1)**
1690 N Ocean Ave, Holtsville, NY 11742-1839
Tel.: (631) 289-8800
Web Site: https://www.towerfast.com
Sales Range: $10-24.9 Million
Emp.: 110
Industrial Supplies
N.A.I.C.S.: 423840

Tru-Edge Grinding Inc.   **(1)**
752 Jim Lachey Dr., St. Henry, OH 45883
Tel.: (419) 678-4919
Web Site: http://www.tru-edge.com
Jewelry & Silverware Mfr
N.A.I.C.S.: 339910
Tim Knapke *(Mgr)*

MSCI INC.

7 World Trade Ctr 250 Greenwich St, New York, NY 10007
Tel.: (212) 804-3900   **DE**

Web Site: https://www.msci.com
MSCI—(NYSE)
Rev.: $2,528,920,000
Assets: $5,518,219,000
Liabilities: $6,257,983,000
Net Worth: ($739,764,000)
Earnings: $1,148,592,000
Emp.: 5,794
Fiscal Year-end: 12/31/23
Equity, Fixed Income & Hedge Fund Developer & Management Services
N.A.I.C.S.: 523999
Henry A. Fernandez *(Chm & CEO)*
Carroll D. Baer Pettit *(Pres & COO)*
Jorge Mina *(Head-Analytics)*
Jigar Thakkar *(CTO & Head-Engrg)*
Rob Gutowski *(Gen Counsel)*
Cristina Bondolowski *(CMO)*
Baer Pettit *(Pres)*
C. Jack Read *(Chief Acctg Officer & Controller-Global)*
Andrew C. Wiechmann *(CFO)*
Scott A. Crum *(Chief HR Officer)*

Subsidiaries:

Barra, LLC   **(1)**
2100 Milvia St, Berkeley, CA 94704
Tel.: (510) 548-5442
Emp.: 554
Risk Management Technology & Decision Support Tools Mfr
N.A.I.C.S.: 541511
Henry A. Fernandez *(CEO & Grp Chm)*

Subsidiary (Non-US):

Barra Japan K.K.   **(2)**
Hanvomon First Bldg 8 Fl, 1-4 Kogimachi Chiyoda Ku, Tokyo, 102-0083, Japan
Tel.: (81) 352268221
Web Site: http://www.msci.com
Sales Range: $25-49.9 Million
Emp.: 100
Risk Management Technology & Decision Support Tools Mfr
N.A.I.C.S.: 541511

BarraConsult, Ltda.   **(2)**
Oscar Freire 585 Rua Oscar Freire 585 6th fl Suite 114, Jardim Paulista, Sao Paulo, 01426-001, SP, Brazil
Tel.: (55) 1137061360
Web Site: http://www.msci.com
Sales Range: $75-99.9 Million
Risk Management Technology & Decision Support Tools Mfr
N.A.I.C.S.: 541511

IPD Nederland B.V.   **(1)**
Busplein 30, 1315 KV, Almere, Netherlands
Tel.: (31) 365306164
Industry Equipment Mfr
N.A.I.C.S.: 333515
Lorenzo Dorigo *(Gen Mgr)*

Investment Property Databank Limited   **(1)**
1 St Johns Lane, London, EC1M 4BL, United Kingdom
Tel.: (44) 2073369200
Application Software Development Services
N.A.I.C.S.: 541511
Oliver Gibson *(Sr Mgr-Ops)*

MSCI Barra (Suisse) Sarl **(1)**
Rue de la Confederation 8-10, 1204, Geneva, Switzerland
Tel.: (41) 228179000
Emp.: 99
Consulting Services
N.A.I.C.S.: 541611
Remy Briand *(CEO)*

MSCI Barra SA   **(1)**
8-10 Rue De La Confederation 3rd Floor, Geneva, 1204, Switzerland
Tel.: (41) 228179000
Investment Management Service
N.A.I.C.S.: 523940

MSCI Canada Inc.   **(1)**
1 First Canadian Place 100 King Street West Suite 4540, Toronto, M5B 1B1, ON, Canada
Tel.: (416) 364-9000
Application Software Development Services

N.A.I.C.S.: 541511

MSCI S. de R.L. de C.V. **(1)**
Equus Torre Norte Av Ricardo Margain 444 Piso 8, Col Valle del Campestre, 66268, Monterrey, Mexico
Tel.: (52) 47802037
Sales Range: $50-74.9 Million
Emp.: 200
Corporate Finance & Advisory Services
N.A.I.C.S.: 523940
Miguel Herrera *(Dir-Ops)*

MSCI Services Private Limited **(1)**
202 2nd floor Raheja Titanium Opp JVLR Western Express Highway, Goregaon East, Mumbai, 400 063, India
Tel.: (91) 2267849120
Investment Management Service
N.A.I.C.S.: 523999
Chandru Badrinarayanan *(Head-Sls & Exec Dir)*
Sabrina Principi *(Head-Emerging Market Sls-EMEAI & Exec Dir)*

Subsidiary (Non-US):

Carbon Delta AG   **(2)**
Freigutstrasse 16, 8002, Zurich, Switzerland
Tel.: (41) 445213780
Web Site: http://www.carbon-delta.com
Environmental & Climate Change Analysis Services
N.A.I.C.S.: 541620
Oliver Marchand *(Co-Founder & CEO)*
Elke Schaper *(Co-Founder & Head-Software Engrg)*
David Lunsford *(Co-Founder & Head-Dev)*
Andrew Black *(Mgr-Bus Dev)*
Nathan Faigle *(Mgr-Bus Dev)*

Real Capital Analytics, Inc. **(1)**
110 5th Ave 7th Fl, New York, NY 10011
Tel.: (212) 387-7103
Web Site: http://www.rcanalytics.com
Internet Publishing & Broadcasting & Web Search Portals
N.A.I.C.S.: 516210
Karen Williams *(Dir-Sls)*
Petra Blazkova *(Head-Analytics-Asia Pacific)*
Bob White *(Founder & Pres)*

RiskMetrics Group, LLC **(1)**
1 Chase Manhattan Plz 44th Fl, New York, NY 10005   **(100%)**
Tel.: (212) 981-7475
Web Site: http://www.riskmetrics.com
Sales Range: $300-349.9 Million
Emp.: 1,140
Financial Planning, Risk & Wealth Management Services
N.A.I.C.S.: 523999

Subsidiary (Non-US):

RiskMetrics (UK) Ltd.   **(2)**
92 Fleet Street, London, E1 6EG, United Kingdom
Tel.: (44) 2078420260
Web Site: http://www.msci.com
Financial Planning, Risk & Wealth Management Services
N.A.I.C.S.: 523999

Subsidiary (Domestic):

RiskMetrics Solutions, LLC **(2)**
1 Chase Manhattan Plz 44th Fl, New York, NY 10005
Tel.: (212) 981-7475
Risk Managemeng Srvices
N.A.I.C.S.: 523940

Subsidiary (Non-US):

RiskMetrics (Singapore) Pte. Ltd. **(3)**
One Raffles Quay 09-04, Singapore, 048583, Singapore
Tel.: (65) 68269339
Web Site: http://www.riskmetrics.com
Sales Range: $25-49.9 Million
Emp.: 24
Investment Management Service
N.A.I.C.S.: 523940
Raj Manghani *(Mng Dir)*

The Burgiss Group, LLC **(1)**
111 River St 10th Fl, Hoboken, NJ 07030   **(100%)**
Tel.: (201) 427-9600

MSCI Inc.—(Continued)

Web Site: https://www.burgiss.com
Software Services
N.A.I.C.S.: 541511
Will Carroll (Mng Dir-Fin)
Tom Kusner (Mng Dir)
Ken Harney (Mng Dir)
David Hsu (Mng Dir)
Susan Veksler (Mng Dir)
Luis O'Shea (Mng Dir)
Mukund Pai (Mng Dir)
Brandon Renkart (Mng Dir)
Brian Schmid (Mng Dir)

MSP RECOVERY, INC.
3150 SW 38th Ave 11th Fl, Miami, FL
33146
Tel.: (305) 614-2222 DE
Web Site:
https://www.msprecovery.com
Year Founded: 2014
LIFW—(NASDAQ)
Rev.: $23,420,000
Assets: $3,417,945,000
Liabilities: $1,232,480,000
Net Worth: $2,185,465,000
Earnings: ($7,417,000)
Emp.: 100
Fiscal Year-end: 12/31/22
Health Care Srvices
N.A.I.C.S.: 621610
John H. Ruiz (CEO)
Ricardo Rivera (CFO)

MUDRICK CAPITAL ACQUISI-TION CORPORATION II
527 Madison Ave 6th Fl, New York,
NY 10022
Tel.: (646) 747-9500
Year Founded: 2009
MUDS—(NASDAQ)
Rev.: $2,535,629
Assets: $321,261,318
Liabilities: $360,204,311
Net Worth: ($38,942,993)
Earnings: ($4,505,597)
Fiscal Year-end: 12/31/21
Financial Investment Services
N.A.I.C.S.: 523999
Jason B. Mudrick (Chm & CEO)
Victor Danh (VP)
David Kirsch (VP)
Glenn Springer (CFO)

MUELLER INDUSTRIES, INC.
150 Schilling Blvd Ste 100, Collier-ville, TN 38017
Tel.: (901) 753-3200 DE
Web Site:
https://www.muellerindustries.com
Year Founded: 1917
MLI—(NYSE)
Rev.: $3,769,345,000
Assets: $1,728,936,000
Liabilities: $471,973,000
Net Worth: $1,256,963,000
Earnings: $468,520,000
Emp.: 5,337
Fiscal Year-end: 12/25/21
Holding Company; Non-Ferrous Metal Tube, Valve & Fitting Mfr & Whslr
N.A.I.C.S.: 551112
Gregory L. Christopher (Chm & CEO)
Anthony J. Steinriede (VP & Control-ler)

Subsidiaries:

ATCO Rubber Products Inc. (1)
7101 Atco Dr, Fort Worth, TX 76118
Tel.: (817) 595-2894
Web Site: https://www.atcoflex.com
Plastics Pipe
N.A.I.C.S.: 326122

Die-Mold Tool Ltd. (1)
82 Todd Road, Georgetown, L7G 4R7, ON, Canada
Tel.: (905) 877-3071
Web Site: https://www.die-moldtool.com

Plastic Injection Mold Making Services
N.A.I.C.S.: 326199
Jim Hall (Plant Mgr)
Lynn McKenzie (Pres)

Elkhart Products Corporation (1)
1255 Oak St, Elkhart, IN 46514
Tel.: (574) 264-3181
Web Site: http://www.elkhartproducts.com
Sales Range: $125-149.9 Million
Emp.: 275
Pipe Fitting Mfr & Distr
N.A.I.C.S.: 332919

Plant (Domestic):

Elkhart Products Corp.-Elkhart
Plant (2)
1255 Oak St, Elkhart, IN 46514
Tel.: (574) 264-3181
Web Site: http://www.elkhartproducts.com
Sales Range: $100-124.9 Million
Emp.: 275
Wrot Copper Plumbing Fittings
N.A.I.C.S.: 332919
Scott Robinett (Mgr-Engrg & Sr Engr-Automation)

Elkhart Products Corporation-Industrial Division (2)
700 Rainbow Rd, Geneva, IN 46740-9700
Tel.: (260) 368-7246
Sales Range: $25-49.9 Million
Emp.: 80
Produces Copper & Aluminum Machine Tubing Products
N.A.I.C.S.: 332919

Great Lakes Copper Ltd. (1)
1010 Clarke Rd, London, N5V 5S6, ON, Canada
Tel.: (519) 455-0770
Web Site: https://www.glcopper.com
Copper Product Mfr
N.A.I.C.S.: 331420

Heatlink Group, Inc. (1)
4603E - 13th Street NE, Calgary, T2E 6M3, AB, Canada
Tel.: (800) 661-5332
Web Site: http://www.heatlink.com
Plumbing & Heating Equipment Distr
N.A.I.C.S.: 423720
Wade Peterson (VP-Sales-Marketing)
Manfred Schmidt (Pres)
Jeff Grassy (Sls Mgr-Midwest-Southwest USA)
Andrew Morrow (Product Mgr)

Kessler Sales & Distribution LLC (1)
500 Green St, Woodbridge, NJ 07095
Web Site: https://www.ksdusa.com
Plumbing Product Distr
N.A.I.C.S.: 423720

Linesets, Inc. (1)
4450 W Gibson Ln, Phoenix, AZ 85043
Tel.: (623) 215-9000
Web Site: http://www.linesetsinc.com
Sales Range: $25-49.9 Million
Emp.: 25
Copper Rolling And Drawing
N.A.I.C.S.: 331420
Daniel Berlyn (Co-Founder & Pres)
Billy Belt (Plant Mgr)
Sam Roti (Natl Sls Mgr)

Mining Remedial Recovery
Company (1)
4780 Caterpillar Rd Ste C, Redding, CA 96003
Tel.: (530) 242-8757
Nonmetallic Mineral Mineral Services
N.A.I.C.S.: 212390

Mueller Brass Co. (1)
2199 Lapeer Ave, Port Huron, MI 48060
Tel.: (810) 987-7770
Web Site: http://muellerbrass.com
Sales Range: $150-199.9 Million
Mfr of Copper Tube & Wrought Copper Fit-tings; Brass Alloy Rod; Commercial Tube; Forgings; Impact Extrusions; Refrigeration & Air Conditioning Products
N.A.I.C.S.: 331410

Subsidiary (Domestic):

Extruded Metals, Inc. (2)
302 Ashfield St, Belding, MI 48809

Tel.: (616) 794-1200
Sales Range: $350-399.9 Million
Emp.: 50
Mfr of Brass Rod, Bar & Shape Extrusions
N.A.I.C.S.: 331420
Tammy Foltz (Controller)

Micro Gauge Inc. (2)
7350 Kensington Rd, Brighton, MI 48116
Tel.: (248) 446-3720
Web Site: https://microgaugeinc.com
Sales Range: $150-199.9 Million
Emp.: 90
Mfr of Copper Tube & Wrought Copper Fit-tings; Brass Alloy Rod; Commercial Tube; Forgings; Impact Extrusions; Refrigeration & Air Conditioning Products
N.A.I.C.S.: 331410

Mueller Brass Forging Company,
Inc. (2)
2199 Lapeer Ave, Port Huron, MI 48060
Tel.: (810) 987-7770
Web Site: https://www.muellerindustries.com
Sales Range: $150-199.9 Million
Emp.: 300
Mfr of Copper Tube & Wrought Copper Fit-tings; Brass Alloy Rod; Commercial Tube; Forgings; Impact Extrusions; Refrigeration & Air Conditioning Products
N.A.I.C.S.: 331410

Mueller Copper Tube Company,
Inc. (2)
400 Mueller Rd, Fulton, MS 38843
Tel.: (662) 862-1700
Web Site: http://www.muellerindustries.com
Sales Range: $150-199.9 Million
Emp.: 400
Mfr of Copper Tube & Wrought Copper Fit-tings; Brass Alloy Rod; Commercial Tube; Forgings; Impact Extrusions; Refrigeration & Air Conditioning Products
N.A.I.C.S.: 331410

Subsidiary (Domestic):

Mueller Fittings Company (3)
3400 Mueller Brass Rd, Covington, TN 38019
Tel.: (901) 476-5858
Web Site: http://www.muellerindustries.com
Sales Range: $150-199.9 Million
Emp.: 150
Mfr of Copper Tube & Wrought Copper Fit-tings; Brass Alloy Rod; Commercial Tube; Forgings; Impact Extrusions; Refrigeration & Air Conditioning Products
N.A.I.C.S.: 331410

Subsidiary (Domestic):

Mueller Formed Tube Company,
Inc. (2)
2199 Lapeer Ave, Port Huron, MI 48060
Tel.: (800) 348-8464
Sales Range: $50-74.9 Million
Emp.: 190
Mfr of Copper Tube & Wrought Copper Fit-tings; Brass Alloy Rod; Commercial Tube; Forgings; Impact Extrusions; Refrigeration & Air Conditioning Products
N.A.I.C.S.: 331410
Jim Rourke (Pres)

Mueller Impacts Company, Inc. (2)
2409 Wills St, Marysville, MI 48040
Tel.: (810) 364-3700
Web Site:
https://www.muellerimpactsco.com
Sales Range: $150-199.9 Million
Mfr of Copper Tube & Wrought Copper Fit-tings; Brass Alloy Rod; Commercial Tube; Forgings; Impact Extrusions; Refrigeration & Air Conditioning Products
N.A.I.C.S.: 331410

Mueller Packaging, LLC (2)
409 Mueller Rd, Fulton, MS 38843
Tel.: (662) 862-7425
Metal Packaging Material Mfr
N.A.I.C.S.: 332439

Mueller Plastics Corporation, Inc. (2)
370 E Cedar, Ontario, CA 91716
Tel.: (909) 930-2060
Sales Range: $150-199.9 Million
Mfr of Copper Tube & Wrought Copper Fit-tings; Brass Alloy Rod; Commercial Tube; Forgings; Impact Extrusions; Refrigeration & Air Conditioning Products

N.A.I.C.S.: 331410

Mueller Plastics Corporation, Inc. (2)
4000 Metzger Rd, Fort Pierce, FL 34947
Tel.: (772) 460-6745
Web Site: http://www.muellerindustries.com
Sales Range: $25-49.9 Million
Emp.: 50
Mfr of Copper Tube & Wrought Copper Fit-tings; Brass Alloy Rod; Commercial Tube; Forgings; Impact Extrusions; Refrigeration & Air Conditioning Products
N.A.I.C.S.: 331410

Mueller Plastics Corporation, Inc. (2)
6700 S Sprinkle Rd, Portage, MI 49002
Tel.: (269) 323-8858
Web Site: http://www.muellerindustries.com
Sales Range: $150-199.9 Million
Mfr of Copper Tubes & Wrought Copper Fittings; Brass Alloy Rods; Commercial Tubes; Forgings; Impact Extrusions; Refrig-eration & Air Conditioning Products
N.A.I.C.S.: 331410

Mueller Refrigeration Products Com-pany, Inc. (2)
121 Rodgers St, Hartsville, TN 37074
Tel.: (615) 374-2124
Sales Range: $150-199.9 Million
Mfr of Copper Tube & Wrought Copper Fit-tings; Brass Alloy Rod; Commercial Tube; Forgings; Impact Extrusions; Refrigeration & Air Conditioning Products
N.A.I.C.S.: 331410

Subsidiary (Domestic):

Lincoln Brass Works, Inc. (3)
309 Hurricane Meadows Dr, Waynesboro, TN 38485
Tel.: (931) 722-5422
Web Site: http://www.muellerindustries.com
Sales Range: $10-24.9 Million
Emp.: 7
Mfr of Copper Tube & Wrought Copper Fit-tings; Brass Alloy Rod; Commercial Tube; Forgings; Impact Extrusions; Refrigeration & Air Conditioning Products
N.A.I.C.S.: 331410

Mueller Refrigeration LLC (3)
121 Rogers St, Hartsville, TN 37074
Tel.: (615) 374-2124
Web Site:
https://www.muellerrefrigeration.com
Sales Range: $25-49.9 Million
Emp.: 200
Industrial Refrigeration & Air Conditioning Product Mfr
N.A.I.C.S.: 333415

Subsidiary (Domestic):

Mueller Streamline Co. (2)
4190 E Santa Ana St, Ontario, CA 91761
Tel.: (909) 930-2060
Web Site: https://www.muellerstreamline.com
Copper Tube Fittings Mfr & Distr
N.A.I.C.S.: 423510

Subsidiary (Domestic):

B&K, LLC (3)
150 Schilling Blvd Ste 102, Collierville, TN 38017
Tel.: (901) 753-3200
Web Site: https://www.bkproducts.com
Industrial Valve Mfr
N.A.I.C.S.: 332911

Heatlink Group USA, LLC (3)
150 Schilling Blvd Ste 201, Collierville, TN 38017
Radiant Hydronic Heating & Cooling Sys-tem Distr
N.A.I.C.S.: 423720

Mueller Southeast, Inc. (3)
287 Wissahickon Ave, North Wales, PA 19454
Tel.: (215) 699-5801
Web Site: http://www.precisiontube.com
Industrial Valve Mfr
N.A.I.C.S.: 332911

Precision Tube Company (3)
287 Wissahickon Ave, North Wales, PA 19454
Tel.: (215) 699-5801
Web Site: http://www.precisiontube.com
Sales Range: $25-49.9 Million
Emp.: 100
Mfr of Copper Tube & Wrought Copper Fittings; Brass Alloy Rod; Commercial Tube; Forgings; Impact Extrusions; Refrigeration & Air Conditioning Products
N.A.I.C.S.: 331410

Subsidiary (Domestic):

Propipe Technologies, Inc. (2)
1800 Clayton Ave, Middletown, OH 45042
Tel.: (513) 424-5311
Web Site: https://www.muellerindustries.com
Sales Range: $150-199.9 Million
Emp.: 75
Mfr of Copper Tube & Wrought Copper Fittings; Brass Alloy Rod; Commercial Tube; Forgings; Impact Extrusions; Refrigeration & Air Conditioning Products
N.A.I.C.S.: 331410

Subsidiary (Non-US):

Streamline Copper & Brass Ltd. (2)
123 Claireville Drive, Etobicoke, M9W 6K9, ON, Canada
Tel.: (905) 673-9522
Fabricated Metal Products Mfr
N.A.I.C.S.: 332999

Mueller Comercial de Mexico S. de R.L. de C.V. (1)
Av De los Parques No 304 Edificio 2 Parque Ind Kalos Fracc Los Parques, de los Garza, 66448, San Nicolas, Nuevo Leon, Mexico
Tel.: (52) 8188655406
Sales Range: $50-74.9 Million
Emp.: 300
Steel Pipe Nipples & Copper Valves Mfr & Distr
N.A.I.C.S.: 332996

Mueller Copper Fittings Company, Inc. (1)
1033 Spring St Ext, Fulton, MS 38843
Tel.: (662) 862-2181
Web Site: http://www.muellerindustries.com
Sales Range: $150-199.9 Million
Emp.: 38
Mfr of Copper Tube & Wrought Copper Fittings; Brass Alloy Rod; Commercial Tube; Forgings; Impact Extrusions; Refrigeration & Air Conditioning Products
N.A.I.C.S.: 331410

Mueller Copper Tube Products, Inc. (1)
1525 N Falls Blvd, Wynne, AR 72396
Tel.: (870) 238-3201
Sales Range: $150-199.9 Million
Copper Tube & Wrought Copper Fittings Mfr; Brass Alloy Rod; Commercial Tube; Forgings; Impact Extrusions; Refrigeration & Air Conditioning Products
N.A.I.C.S.: 331420

Subsidiary (Domestic):

Howell Metal Company (2)
574 New Market Depot Rd, New Market, VA 22844 (100%)
Tel.: (540) 740-4700
Web Site: http://www.howellmetal.com
Emp.: 150
Copper Tubing Mfr
N.A.I.C.S.: 331420

Mueller Europe Investment Company Ltd. (1)
136 Oxford St, Bilston, WV14 7DS, West Midlands, United Kingdom
Tel.: (44) 1902499700
Web Site: http://www.muellereurope.com
Industrial Valve Mfr
N.A.I.C.S.: 332911

Mueller Europe Ltd. (1)
Oxford Street Bliston, Bilston, WV14 7DS, West Midlands, United Kingdom
Tel.: (44) 1902499700
Web Site: http://www.muellereurope.com
Sales Range: $50-74.9 Million
Emp.: 160

Mfr of Copper Tube & Wrought Copper Fittings; Brass Alloy Rod; Commercial Tube; Forgings; Impact Extrusions; Refrigeration & Air Conditioning Products
N.A.I.C.S.: 331410

Mueller Middle East B.S.C. (1)
Arcapita Building 4th Floor Building No 551 Road 4612, PO Box 820, Sea Front 346 Bahrain Bay, Manama, Bahrain
Tel.: (973) 1 756 1111
Web Site: https://www.mumtalakat.bh
Investment Management Service
N.A.I.C.S.: 523940

Mueller Streamline Copper and Brass Ltd. (1)
6325 Northam Dr, Mississauga, L4V 1H8, ON, Canada
Tel.: (519) 870-1131
Sales Range: $150-199.9 Million
Emp.: 2
Mfr of Copper Tube & Wrought Copper Fittings; Brass Alloy Rod; Commercial Tube; Forgings; Impact Extrusions; Refrigeration & Air Conditioning Products
N.A.I.C.S.: 331410

Pexcor Manufacturing Co., Inc. (1)
3615 32 Street NE, Calgary, T1Y 5Y9, AB, Canada
Tel.: (403) 717-3820
Web Site: http://www.pexcor.com
Pipe Product Mfr
N.A.I.C.S.: 332996

Tecumseh Products Company LLC (1)
5683 Hines Dr, Ann Arbor, MI 48108
Tel.: (734) 585-9500
Web Site: http://www.tecumseh.com
Sales Range: $700-749.9 Million
Compressors, Small Engines, Power-Train Products & Pump Mfr
N.A.I.C.S.: 333912
Jay Pittas (Chm)
Ricardo Maciel (CEO)
Phyllis Knight (CFO)
Chris Wiseman (Pres)
Stan Gilhool (Gen Counsel)
Regis Marques (VP)
Greg Dwyer (VP)
Hiroshi Saito (VP-Mktg)
Ricardo Ferreira (Mng Dir)
Hin Choy Chong (Mng Dir)
Sandeep Chaudhry (Mng Dir)

Subsidiary (Non-US):

Tecumseh Euro-Malaysia SDN. BHD (2)
No 18 Jalan Sultan Mohamed 4 Selat Klang Utara, 42200, Port Klang, Selangor Darul Ehsan, Malaysia
Tel.: (60) 331763886
Web Site: http://www.tecumseh.com
Hermetic Compressors Mfr
N.A.I.C.S.: 333415
HinChoy Chong (Mng Dir)

Tecumseh Europe SA (2)
2 Avenue Blaise Pascal, 38090, Vaulx-Milieu, France
Tel.: (33) 474822400
Web Site: http://www.tecumseh.com
Hermetic Compressors Mfr
N.A.I.C.S.: 333415

Division (Domestic):

Tecumseh Products Company-Paris Division (2)
2700 W Wood St, Paris, TN 38242
Tel.: (731) 642-6394
Web Site: http://www.tecumotor.com
Emp.: 80
Generator Design Services; Hermetic Motors Mfr
N.A.I.C.S.: 335312
Jeff Fowlkes (Supvr-Product Engrg)
Joseph Holland (Mgr-Product Engrg)

Subsidiary (Non-US):

Tecumseh Products India Pvt. Ltd. (2)
667P 784P Shed B and C, Kistapur Village Medchal Nagar Panchayat Medchal - Malkajgiri, Hyderabad, 501401, Andhra Pradesh, India

Tel.: (91) 4023078103
Web Site: http://www.tecumseh.com
Air & Gas Compressor Mfr
N.A.I.C.S.: 333912

Tecumseh do Brasil, Ltda. (2)
Rua Ray Wesley Herrick 700 Jardim Jockey Club, 700 Jardim Jockey Club, Sao Carlos, 13565-900, SP, Brazil
Tel.: (55) 1633637000
Web Site: http://www.tecumseh.com.br
Refrigeration & Air Conditioning Compressors Mfr
N.A.I.C.S.: 333415

Yorkshire Copper Tube (1)
East Lancashire Road, Kirkby, Liverpool, L33 7TU, Merseyside, United Kingdom
Tel.: (44) 1515455107
Web Site: http://www.yorkshirecopper.com
Copper Tube Mfr
N.A.I.C.S.: 331420

MUELLER WATER PRODUCTS, INC.
1200 Abernathy Rd NE Ste 1200, Atlanta, GA 30328
Tel.: (770) 206-4200   DE
Web Site:
  https://www.muellerwaterproducts.com
MWA—(NYSE)
Rev.: $1,275,700,000
Assets: $1,505,000,000
Liabilities: $793,500,000
Net Worth: $711,500,000
Earnings: $85,500,000
Emp.: 3,200
Fiscal Year-end: 09/30/23
Water Infrastructure & Flow Control Mfr
N.A.I.C.S.: 332911
Steven S. Heinrichs (CFO, Chief Legal Officer & Chief Compliance Officer)
Suzanne G. Smith (Chief Acctg Officer & VP)
Marietta Edmunds Zakas (CEO)
Whit Kincaid (Sr Dir-IR & Corp Dev)
Steven S. Heinrichs (CFO & Chief Legal & Compliance Officer)
William A. Cofield (Sr VP-Ops & Supply Chain)
Todd P. Helms (Chief HR Officer & Sr VP)
Chad D. Mize (Sr VP-Sls & Mktg)
Richelle R. Feyerherm (VP-Ops & Controller)
Scott P. Floyd (Sr VP-Water Flow Solutions)
Paul McAndrew (Pres, COO & Exec VP)

Subsidiaries:

Henry Pratt Company, LLC (1)
401 S Highland Ave, Aurora, IL 60506-5580
Tel.: (630) 844-4000
Web Site: http://www.henrypratt.com
Sales Range: $75-99.9 Million
Emp.: 300
Butterfly & Ball Valves & Various Valve Operators & Control Systems Mfr
N.A.I.C.S.: 332911

Subsidiary (Domestic):

Hydro Gate, LLC (2)
7010 Broadway Ste 400, Denver, CO 80221
Tel.: (303) 288-7873
Web Site: http://www.hydrogate.com
Sales Range: $10-24.9 Million
Emp.: 25
Mfr of Fabricated Structural Metal
N.A.I.C.S.: 423390

Subsidiary (Non-US):

Jingmen Pratt Valve Co. Ltd. (2)
No 159 Peigong Avenue, Duodao District, Jingmen, 448000, Hubei, China
Tel.: (86) 7242448700
Web Site: https://www.prattjingmen.com

Emp.: 142
Water Transmission Valve Mfr
N.A.I.C.S.: 332911

Subsidiary (Domestic):

Millikin Valve, LLC (2)
190 Brodhead Rd Ste 100, Bethlehem, PA 18017
Tel.: (610) 861-8803
Web Site: http://www.millikenvalve.com
Sales Range: $10-24.9 Million
Emp.: 8
Industrial Valve Mfr
N.A.I.C.S.: 332911

J.B. Smith Mfg Co., LLC (1)
6618 Navigation Blvd, Houston, TX 77011
Tel.: (713) 928-5711
Web Site: http://www.jbsmith.com
Oil Country Tubular Fittings & Bull Plugs Mfr
N.A.I.C.S.: 332996
Eddie Gomez (Plant Mgr)

James Jones Company, LLC (1)
1470 S Vintage Ave, Ontario, CA 91761
Web Site:
  http://www.joneswaterproducts.com
Sales Range: $75-99.9 Million
Emp.: 25
Mfr of Bronze Valves & Fittings
N.A.I.C.S.: 332919

Krausz Industries Ltd. (1)
6 Hapatish St, Tel Aviv, 66559, Israel
Tel.: (972) 35154000
Valve & Pipe Fitting Mfr
N.A.I.C.S.: 332919

Krausz USA Inc. (1)
331 SW 57th Ave, Ocala, FL 34474
Web Site: http://www.krauszusa.com
Valve & Pipe Fitting Mfr
N.A.I.C.S.: 332919
Alistair Edwards (VP-Ops)

Mueller Canada Holdings Corp. (1)
82 Hooper Road, Barrie, L4N 8Z9, ON, Canada
Tel.: (705) 719-9965
Web Site: https://www.muellercompany.com
Water Infrastructure & Flow Control Products Mfr
N.A.I.C.S.: 332911

Subsidiary (Domestic):

Mueller Canada Ltd. (2)
82 Hooper Road, Barrie, L4N 8Z9, ON, Canada
Tel.: (705) 719-9965
Web Site: http://www.muellercompany.com
Emp.: 30
Transmission Valve Mfr
N.A.I.C.S.: 332911

Division (Domestic):

Mueller Canada Ltd. - Echologics Division (3)
6295 Northam Drive Unit 1, Mississauga, L4V 1W8, ON, Canada
Tel.: (905) 672-3246
Web Site: https://www.echologics.com
Acoustic Leak Detectors Mfr
N.A.I.C.S.: 334519

Subsidiary (Non-US):

PCA-Echologics Pty Ltd. (4)
Unit 8/1B Kleins Rd, Northmead, 2152, Australia
Tel.: (61) 296303182
Web Site: http://www.pcaechologics.com
Geological Engineering Services
N.A.I.C.S.: 541330
Phil Ferguson (Gen Mgr)

Subsidiary (Domestic):

Mueller SV, Ltd. (2)
12850 87th Avenue, Surrey, V3W 3H9, BC, Canada
Tel.: (604) 594-5404
Web Site: http://www.singervalve.com
Automatic Water Control System Mfr
N.A.I.C.S.: 334512

Subsidiary (Non-US):

Singer Valve (Taicang) Co., Ltd. (3)

Mueller Water Products, Inc.—(Continued)

No 88 East Dalian Road, Taicang, Jiangsu, China
Tel.: (86) 51253206188
Web Site: http://www.singervalve.com
Automatic Water Control System Mfr
N.A.I.C.S.: 334514

Subsidiary (US):

Singer Valve, LLC   (3)
1873 Scott Futrell Dr, Charlotte, NC 28208
Tel.: (704) 391-5785
Web Site: http://www.singervalve.com
Hardware Mfr
N.A.I.C.S.: 332510

Mueller Co. Ltd.   (1)
500 W Eldorado St, Decatur, IL 62522-2165
Tel.: (217) 423-4471
Web Site: http://www.muellercompany.com
Sales Range: $125-149.9 Million
Emp.: 600
Mfr of Fire Hydrants, Valves, Fittings & Related Products
N.A.I.C.S.: 334513

Mueller Denmark ApS   (1)
Blegdamsvej 6, 2200, Copenhagen, Denmark
Tel.: (45) 91604060
Web Site: http://www.metricx.dk
Analysis Research Services
N.A.I.C.S.: 541910

Mueller International, LLC   (1)
1200 Abernathy Rd, Atlanta, GA 30328
Tel.: (770) 206-4200
Water Transmission Valve Mfr
N.A.I.C.S.: 332911

Mueller Middle East (FZE)   (1)
Q4-031 Sharjha Airport International Free Zone, PO Box 122416, Sharjah, United Arab Emirates
Tel.: (971) 65260270
Web Site: http://www.singervalve.com
Automatic Water Control System Mfr
N.A.I.C.S.: 334514

Mueller Property Holdings, LLC   (1)
1200 Abernathy Rd Ste 1200, Atlanta, GA 30328
Tel.: (770) 206-4246
Holding Company
N.A.I.C.S.: 551112
Gregory Highland (Pres)

Mueller Service Co., LLC   (1)
2004 Wood Ct Ste C, Plant City, FL 33563
Tel.: (813) 764-8183
Web Site: http://www.muellerservice.co
Sales Range: $25-49.9 Million
Emp.: 45
Asset Management Services
N.A.I.C.S.: 523940

Mueller Systems, LLC   (1)
10210 Statesville Blvd, Cleveland, NC 27013
Tel.: (704) 278-2221
Web Site: https://muellersystems.com
Water Transmission Valve Mfr
N.A.I.C.S.: 332911
Hassan Ali (VP & Gen Mgr)

U.S. Pipe Valve & Hydrant, LLC   (1)
500 W Eldorado St, Decatur, IL 62522
Tel.: (217) 425-2194
Web Site: https://www.uspvh.com
Pipe Valve & Hydrant Mfr
N.A.I.C.S.: 332911

i2O Water Ltd.   (1)
2 Vancouver Wharf Hazel Road, Woolston, Southampton, SO19 7BN, United Kingdom
Tel.: (44) 2380111420
Web Site: https://en.i2owater.com
Water Utility Services
N.A.I.C.S.: 221310

MULLEN AUTOMOTIVE, INC.
1405 Pioneer St, Brea, CA 92821
Tel.: (714) 613-1900   DE
Web Site:
   https://www.mullenusa.com
Year Founded: 2010
MULN—(NASDAQ)
Rev.: $366,000

Assets: $421,705,730
Liabilities: $148,897,620
Net Worth: $272,808,110
Earnings: ($972,254,582)
Emp.: 326
Fiscal Year-end: 09/30/23
Offices of Other Holding Companies
N.A.I.C.S.: 551112
Jonathan New (CFO)
David Michery (Chm, Pres & CEO)
Kerri Sadler (Chief Acctg Officer)
Mary Winter (Sec)
Marianne McInerney (Chief Strategy Officer)

Subsidiaries:

Aptito, LLC   (1)
3363 NE 163rd St Ste 606, North Miami Beach, FL 33160
Tel.: (786) 923-0533
Web Site: http://www.aptito.com
Electrical Engineering Services
N.A.I.C.S.: 541330

Electric Last Mile Solutions, Inc.   (1)
1055 W Square Lk Rd, Troy, MI 48098
Web Site: http://www.electriclastmile.com
Rev.: $66,590
Assets: $251,779,573
Liabilities: $246,779,567
Net Worth: $5,000,006
Earnings: ($29,361,225)
Emp.: 89
Fiscal Year-end: 12/31/2020
Electric Vehicle Mfr
N.A.I.C.S.: 336320
Shauna F. McIntyre (Interim Pres & Interim CEO)
Robert Song (CFO & Treas)
Jonathan Ballon (Chief Strategy & Digital Officer)
Hailiang Hu (COO)
Kev Adjemian (Chief Technical Officer)
Benjamin Wu (Gen Counse & Sec)
Jason Luo (Co-Founder)
James Taylor (Co-Founder)
Thomas M. Dono Jr. (Chief Legal Officer & Sec)

Net Element Services, LLC   (1)
3363 NE 163rd St Ste 606, North Miami Beach, FL 33160-4423
Tel.: (305) 507-8808
Web Site: http://www.netelement.com
Electrical Engineering Services
N.A.I.C.S.: 541330
Oleg Firer (CEO)

OOO Net Element Russia   (1)
Presnenskaya Emb bld 12 office a31, 123317, Moscow, Russia
Tel.: (7) 499 277 1110
Web Site: http://www.netelement.com
Holding Company; Website Publisher & Payment Processing Services
N.A.I.C.S.: 551112

TOT Group Cyprus   (1)
89 Omonia Ave, Limassol, 3048, Cyprus
Tel.: (357) 25569155
Web Site: http://www.tototheo.com
Electrical Engineering Services
N.A.I.C.S.: 541330

TOT Group Kazakhstan LLC   (1)
ul Bayzakova 280, 050040, Almaty, Kazakhstan
Tel.: (7) 7018880209
Web Site: http://www.totgroup.com
Electrical Engineering Services
N.A.I.C.S.: 541330

TOT Group, Inc.   (1)
3363 NE 163rd St Ste 705, North Miami Beach, FL 33160
Tel.: (305) 507-8808
Web Site: http://www.netelement.com
Emp.: 30
Holding Company; Payment Processing Services
N.A.I.C.S.: 551112

Subsidiary (Domestic):

Process Pink, LLC   (2)
3363 NE 163rd St Ste 705, North Miami Beach, FL 33160
Web Site: http://www.processpink.com

Credit & Debit Card Payment Processing Services
N.A.I.C.S.: 522320

Unified Payments, LLC   (2)
3363 NE 163rd St Ste 705, North Miami Beach, FL 33160
Tel.: (305) 507-8808
Web Site: http://www.unifiedpayments.com
Sales Range: $1-9.9 Million
Emp.: 26
Credit & Debit Card Payment Processing Services
N.A.I.C.S.: 522320
Vladimir Sadovskiy (Pres)
Shawn Brown (Dir-Underwriting & Risk)

Subsidiary (Domestic):

TOT New Edge, LLC   (3)
3363 NE 163rd St Ste 705, North Miami Beach, FL 33160
Tel.: (305) 507-8808
Web Site: http://www.unifiedpayments.com
Emp.: 30
Payment Processing Services
N.A.I.C.S.: 522320
Vlad Sadovskiy (Pres-Merchant Svcs)

MULTI SOLUTIONS II, INC.
4400 Biscayne Blvd 10th Fl, Miami, FL 33137
Tel.: (305) 579-8000   FL
Year Founded: 1982
MUSS—(OTCIQ)
Assets: $3,704
Liabilities: $1,157,306
Net Worth: ($1,153,602)
Earnings: ($118,473)
Fiscal Year-end: 01/31/24
Investment Services
N.A.I.C.S.: 523999
Deborah A. Fasanelli (CFO, Treas & Sec)
J. Bryant Kirkland III (Chm, Pres & CEO)

MULTICORP INTERNATIONAL, INC.
5308 Derry Ave Ste R, Agoura Hills, CA 91301
Tel.: (818) 262-6222   DE
Year Founded: 2005
MCIC—(OTCIQ)
Pharmaceuticals Product Mfr
N.A.I.C.S.: 325412
Ben Friedman (Pres)

MULTIPLAN CORP.
115 5th Ave, New York, NY 10003
Tel.: (212) 780-2000   DE
Web Site: https://www.multiplan.us
MPLN—(NYSE)
Rev.: $1,079,716,000
Assets: $7,371,104,000
Liabilities: $5,580,562,000
Net Worth: $1,790,542,000
Earnings: ($572,912,000)
Emp.: 2,500
Fiscal Year-end: 12/31/22
Miscellaneous Financial Investment Activities
N.A.I.O.O.: 520000
Jerry Hogge (COO & Exec VP)
James M. Head (CFO & Exec VP)
Dale A. White (Chm)
Travis S. Dalton (Pres & CEO)
Michael Kim (CIO & Sr VP)
Andrew Cone (Chief Revenue Officer & Sr VP)
Liz Longo (VP-Subrogation & Arbitration Solutions)
Benjamin Perryman (VP-Data Science Ops)
Luke Montgomery (Sr VP-Fin & IR)
Shawna Gasik (Assoc VP-IR)
Pamela Walker (Sr Dir-Mktg & Comm)

Subsidiaries:

MultiPlan Inc.   (1)
115 5th Ave Fl 7, New York, NY 10003
Tel.: (800) 950-7040
Web Site: http://www.multiplan.com
Emp.: 800
Medical Cost Management Services
N.A.I.C.S.: 524292
Dale A. White (Exec VP-Acct Mgmt & Sls)
Michael Ferrante (Exec VP)
David Redmond (CFO & Exec VP)
Jeff Doctoroff (Gen Counsel & Sr VP)
Laura Moore (VP-Sls & Acct Mgmt)
Brendan Miller (Sr VP-Sls & Acct Mgmt)

Branch (Domestic):

MultiPlan, Inc.   (2)
16 Crosby St, Bedford, MA 01730
Tel.: (781) 895-7500
Web Site: http://www.multiplan.com
Sales Range: $125-149.9 Million
Emp.: 800
Health Care Management Services
N.A.I.C.S.: 524114
Jeff Doctoroff (Gen Counsel & Sr VP)
Michael Kim (CIO & Sr VP)
David Redmond (CFO & Exec VP)
Derek Reis-Larson (Sr VP-Claims Pricing Svcs)
Paul Galant (Pres-New Markets)
Monica Armstrong (Sr VP-Sls & Acct Mgmt)
Andrew Cone (Chief Revenue Officer & Sr VP)
Christopher Dorn (Sr VP-Payment Integrity Svcs)
Jacqueline Kienzle (Sr VP-Sls & Acct Mgmt)
Gerald Kozel (Chief Acctg Officer & Sr VP)
Susan Mohler (Sr VP-Mktg & Product Mgmt)
Bruce Singleton (Sr VP-Network Dev Strategy)
Karen Eaton (VP-Sls & Acct Mgmt)
Kurt Fullmer (VP-Sls & Acct Mgmt)
Melbalynn Madarang (VP-Sls & Acct Mgmt)
Lucas Montgomery (Sr VP-Fin & IR)
Laura Moore (VP-Sls & Acct Mgmt)
Jim Sherry (VP-Natl Sls & Acct Mgmt)

Subsidiary (Domestic):

Viant, Inc.   (2)
535 E Diehl Rd Ste 100, Naperville, IL 60563
Tel.: (630) 649-5000
Web Site: http://www.viant.com
Emp.: 1,400
Health Care Industry Network Management & Payment Services
N.A.I.C.S.: 561499

MUNCY COLUMBIA FINANCIAL CORPORATION
232 E St, Bloomsburg, PA 17815
Tel.: (570) 784-4400   PA
Web Site:
   http://www.firstcolumbiabank.com
Year Founded: 1983
CCFN—(OTCIQ)
Rev.: $32,730,000
Assets: $855,088,000
Liabilities: $749,401,000
Net Worth: $105,687,000
Earnings: $9,332,000
Emp.: 90
Fiscal Year-end: 12/31/20
Bank Holding Company
N.A.I.C.S.: 551111
Lance O. Diehl (Pres & CEO)
Robert J. Glunk (Chm, COO & Sr Exec VP)
Jeffrey T. Arnold (Treas & Exec VP)
Nancy R. Diehl (Sec & VP)
Joseph K. O'Neill Jr. (CFO & Exec VP)

Subsidiaries:

Journey Bank   (1)
232 E St, Bloomsburg, PA 17815
Tel.: (570) 784-1660
Web Site: http://www.firstcolumbiabank.com

Sales Range: $10-24.9 Million
Emp.: 202
Banking Services
N.A.I.C.S.: 522110
Lance O. Diehl (Pres & CEO)
Robert J. Glunk (Chm)
Jeffrey T. Arnold (CFO & Sr VP)
Susan S. Hackett (Sec)
Paul K. Page (Chief Lending Officer & Sr VP)
Patrick J. Millham (VP)
Pamela A. Young (VP)
Matthew E. Beagle (Chief Wealth Mgmt Officer & Sr VP)

Muncy Bank Financial, Inc.   (1)
2 N Main St, Muncy, PA 17756
Tel.: (570) 546-2211
Web Site: http://www.muncybank.com
Rev.: $21,730,000
Assets: $489,427,000
Liabilities: $439,522,000
Net Worth: $49,905,000
Earnings: $5,242,000
Fiscal Year-end: 12/31/2019
Bank Holding Company
N.A.I.C.S.: 551111
Lance O. Diehl (Pres & CEO)
Misty D. Mark (Sr VP)
Rhonda L. Gingery (Treas)
Beth A. Benson (Sec)

MUNDUS GROUP, INC.
370 Amapola Ave Ste 200-A, Torrance, CA 90501
Tel.: (424) 358-1046   NV
Year Founded: 1992
MNDP—(OTCIQ)
Investment Management Service
N.A.I.C.S.: 525990
Frank Lkechukwu Igwealor (Chm, Pres & CEO)

MURPHY OIL CORPORATION
9805 Katy Fwy Ste G-200, Houston, TX 77024
Tel.: (281) 675-9000   DE
Web Site:
   https://www.murphyoilcorp.com
Year Founded: 1950
MUR—(NYSE)
Rev.: $3,460,147,000
Assets: $9,766,697,000
Liabilities: $4,217,044,000
Net Worth: $5,549,653,000
Earnings: $661,559,000
Emp.: 725
Fiscal Year-end: 12/31/23
Explorer & Producer of Crude Oil & Natural Gas; Refining Crude Oil & Sales of Petroleum Products
N.A.I.C.S.: 324110
Roger W. Jenkins (CEO)
Thomas J. Mireles (CFO & Exec VP)
John B. Gardner (VP-Mktg & Supply Chain)
Maria A. Martinez (VP-HR & Admin)
Paul D. Vaughan (Controller, VP & Principal Acctg Officer)
E. Ted Botner (Gen Counsel, Sec & Exec VP)
Kelly L. Whitley (VP-IR & Comm)
Louis W. Utsch (VP-Tax)
Eric M. Hambly (Pres & COO)
Leyster L. Jumawan (Treas & VP-Corp Plng)
Daniel R. Hanchera (Sr VP)
Meenambigai Palanivelu (VP)

Subsidiaries:

Murphy Exploration & Production Company   (1)
9805 Katy Fwy Ste G-200, Houston, TX 77024   **(100%)**
Tel.: (281) 675-9000
Web Site: http://www.murphyoilcorp.com
Sales Range: $1-4.9 Billion
Emp.: 270
Crude Oil & Natural Gas Exploration & Production
N.A.I.C.S.: 213112

Roger W. Jenkins (Pres)
Paul D. Vaughan (VP & Controller-US, Central & South America)

Subsidiary (Domestic):

Murphy Building Corporation   (2)
200 Peach St, El Dorado, AR 71730
Tel.: (870) 862-6411
Web Site: http://www.murphyoilcorp.com
Sales Range: $125-149.9 Million
Oil & Gas Pipeline, Offshore Platform & Related Structures Construction
N.A.I.C.S.: 237120

Murphy Oil Co., Ltd.   (1)
East Tower 4000 520 - 3 Avenue SW, Calgary, T2P 0R3, AB, Canada   **(100%)**
Tel.: (403) 294-8000
Web Site: http://www.murphyoilcorp.com
Sales Range: $750-799.9 Million
Emp.: 120
Exploration & Production of Crude Oil & Natural Gas; Extraction & Sale of Synthetic Crude; Purchasing, Transporting & Reselling of Crude Oil; Selling Petroleum Products In Canada
N.A.I.C.S.: 211120

Murphy Petroleum Ltd.   (1)
4 Beaconsfield Rd, Saint Albans, AL1 3RH, Herts, United Kingdom   **(100%)**
Tel.: (44) 1727892400
Sales Range: $50-74.9 Million
Emp.: 70
Exploration & Production of Crude Oil & Natural Gas
N.A.I.C.S.: 211120

Subsidiary (Domestic):

Murco Petroleum Ltd.   (2)
4 Beaconsfield Rd, Saint Albans, AL1 3RH, Hertfordshire, United Kingdom   **(100%)**
Tel.: (44) 1727892400
Web Site: http://www.murco.co.uk
Petroleum Refineries Operator, Petroleum Products Distr & Gasoline Stations Franchisor
N.A.I.C.S.: 324110

MURPHY USA INC.
200 E Peach St, El Dorado, AR 71730-5836
Tel.: (870) 875-7600   DE
Web Site:
   https://www.murphyusa.com
Year Founded: 1996
MUSA—(NYSE)
Rev.: $21,529,400,000
Assets: $4,340,100,000
Liabilities: $3,511,200,000
Net Worth: $828,900,000
Earnings: $556,800,000
Emp.: 5,900
Fiscal Year-end: 12/31/23
Gasoline Station Management Services
N.A.I.C.S.: 424710
Malynda K. West (COO, CFO, Treas, Exec VP & Exec VP-Fuels)
R. Andrew Clyde (Pres & CEO)
Donald R. Smith Jr. (VP & Controller)
Christian Pikul (VP-IR & FP&A)
Christopher A. Click (Exec VP-Strategy, Growth, and Innovation)

Subsidiaries:

Murphy Oil USA, Inc.   (1)
300 Peach St, El Dorado, AR 71730   **(100%)**
Tel.: (870) 862-6411
Petroleum Products Marketer
N.A.I.C.S.: 424720
R. Andrew Clyde (Pres & CEO)

Subsidiary (Domestic):

Murphy Oil Trading Company (Eastern)   (2)
200 Peach St, El Dorado, AR 71730   **(100%)**
Tel.: (870) 862-6411
Sales Range: $150-199.9 Million
Emp.: 400

Crude & Refined Petroleum Products Wholesale Trade Agency
N.A.I.C.S.: 425120
Connie Singleton (Mgr-HR)

Quick Chek Corporation   (1)
3 Old Hwy 28, Whitehouse, NJ 08889
Tel.: (908) 534-2200
Web Site: https://www.quickchek.com
Dairy Product Whslr
N.A.I.C.S.: 424430
Dean Durling (Pres)

MUSTANG BIO, INC.
377 Plantation St, Worcester, MA 01605
Tel.: (781) 652-4500   DE
Web Site:
   https://www.mustangbio.com
Year Founded: 2015
MBIO—(NASDAQ)
Rev.: $689,000
Assets: $92,422,000
Liabilities: $46,149,000
Net Worth: $46,273,000
Earnings: ($77,525,000)
Emp.: 113
Fiscal Year-end: 12/31/22
Pharmaceutical Product Mfr & Distr
N.A.I.C.S.: 325412
Eliot M. Lurier (Interim CFO)
Michael S. Weiss (Chm)
James Murphy (Interim CFO & Principal Acctg Officer)
Manuel Litchman (Pres & CEO)
Knut Niss (CTO)
Debra Manning (VP-HR)
Lynn E. Bayless (Head-Regulatory Affairs)
Greg Furrow (VP-Quality)
James Edinger (VP-Preclinical Sciences)
Scott Smith (Exec Dir & Head-Alliance & Program Mgmt)
Susan Ward (VP-Clinical Ops)
Bruce Dezube (Sr VP & Head-Clinical Dev)

MUTUAL FEDERAL BANK
2212 W Cermak Rd, Chicago, IL 60608
Tel.: (312) 447-5200   IL
Web Site:
   https://www.mutualfederalbank.com
Year Founded: 1905
MFDB—(OTCIQ)
Commercial Banking Services
N.A.I.C.S.: 522110
Stephen M. Oksas (Pres & CEO)
Rodney D. Stickle (CFO & Exec VP)

MV OIL TRUST
601 Travis St 16th Fl, Houston, TX 77002
Tel.: (713) 483-6020   DE
Web Site: https://mvo.q4web.com
Year Founded: 2006
MVO—(NYSE)
Rev.: $27,204,590
Assets: $6,883,554
Net Worth: $6,883,554
Earnings: $25,530,000
Emp.: 1,258
Fiscal Year-end: 12/31/22
Oil & Natural Gas Trust
N.A.I.C.S.: 525920
Elaina C. Rodgers (VP)

MVB FINANCIAL CORP.
301 Virginia Ave, Fairmont, WV 26554
Tel.: (304) 363-4800   WV
Web Site:
   https://www.mvbbanking.com
Year Founded: 2004
MVBF—(NASDAQ)
Rev.: $209,533,000
Assets: $3,313,882,000

Liabilities: $3,024,540,000
Net Worth: $289,342,000
Earnings: $31,232,000
Emp.: 445
Fiscal Year-end: 12/31/23
Bank Holding Company
N.A.I.C.S.: 551111
Larry F. Mazza (CEO)
J. Christopher Pallotta (Founder)
C. Brad Greathouse (Chief People & Culture Officer & Exec VP)
Lisa McCormick (Sec)
Matt A. West (Chief Strategy Officer & Exec VP)
Kelly Kroskie (Chief Ops Officer)
Angela Lucas (Chief Risk Officer)

Subsidiaries:

MVB Bank, Inc.   (1)
301 Virginia Ave, Fairmont, WV 26554
Tel.: (304) 363-4800
Web Site: https://www.mvbbanking.com
Emp.: 400
Commercial Banking
N.A.I.C.S.: 522110
William Marston Becker (Chm)

MVP HOLDINGS, INC.
3437 W Shaw Ave Ste 101, Fresno, CA 93711
Tel.: (559) 999-7571   NV
Year Founded: 2003
MVPT—(OTCIQ)
Online Shopping Retailer
N.A.I.C.S.: 561510
Casey M. Musick (CEO)
Jessica A. Musick (COO & VP)

MY CITY BUILDERS, INC.
100 Biscayne Blvd Ste 1611, Miami, FL 33132
Tel.: (214) 680-5000   NV
Web Site:
   https://www.mycitybuilders.com
Year Founded: 2010
MYCB—(OTCIQ)
Rev.: $59,300
Assets: $3,469,049
Liabilities: $2,307,369
Net Worth: $1,161,680
Earnings: $25,752
Emp.: 2
Fiscal Year-end: 07/31/24
Other Nonmetallic Mineral Mining & Quarrying
N.A.I.C.S.: 212390
Jose Maria Eduardo Gonzalez Romero (Pres, CEO, CFO & Sec)

MY FREIGHTWORLD TECHNOLOGIES, INC.
7007 College Blvd Ste 150, Overland Park, KS 66211
Web Site:
   https://www.myfreightworld.com
MYFT—(OTCIQ)
Logistic & Supply Chain Services
N.A.I.C.S.: 488510
Kevin C. Childress (Pres & CEO)

MYCELX TECHNOLOGIES CORPORATION
2420 Meadowbrook Pkwy, Duluth, GA 30096
Tel.: (770) 534-3118   GA
Web Site: http://www.mycelx.com
MYX—(AIM)
Rev.: $10,026,000
Assets: $13,619,000
Liabilities: $2,787,000
Net Worth: $10,832,000
Earnings: ($3,991,000)
Emp.: 18
Fiscal Year-end: 12/31/22

MyCelx Technologies Corporation—(Continued)

Chemical Product & Preparation Mfr
N.A.I.C.S.: 325998
Connie Mixon (CEO)
Hal Alper (Founder, Pres & Chief Scientific Officer)
Kimberly Slayton (CFO)
Jeff Hammerstrom (Sr VP & Gen Mgr)

MYERS INDUSTRIES, INC.
1293 S Main St, Akron, OH 44301
Tel.: (330) 253-5592   OH
Web Site:
https://www.myersindustries.com
Year Founded: 1933
MYE—(NYSE)
Rev.: $899,547,000
Assets: $542,634,000
Liabilities: $286,207,000
Net Worth: $256,427,000
Earnings: $60,267,000
Emp.: 2,500
Fiscal Year-end: 12/31/22
Unlaminated Plastics Profile Shape Manufacturing
N.A.I.C.S.: 326121
Lorelei Evans (VP-HR)
Grant E. Fitz (CFO & Exec VP)
Monica P. Vinay (Interim CFO)
Matthew Marchel (VP)
Kevin McElgunn (Sr Dir)
Mike Miller (VP)
Jeff Baker (Pres-Distribution Segment)
Dave Basque (VP-Special Projects)

Subsidiaries:

Akro-Mils   (1)
1293 S Main St, Akron, OH 44301
Web Site: http://www.akro-mils.com
Plastic & Steel Storage Products Mfr
N.A.I.C.S.: 326199

Ameri-Kart Corp.   (1)
19300 Grange St, Cassopolis, MI 49031
Tel.: (330) 253-5592
Web Site: http://www.amerikart.com
Sales Range: $700-749.9 Million
Emp.: 3,000
Plastics Product Mfr
N.A.I.C.S.: 326199
Eric Gottuso (Pres)

Buckhorn Inc.   (1)
400 TechneCenter Dr Ste 215, Milford, OH 45150
Tel.: (513) 831-4402
Web Site: https://www.buckhorninc.com
Sales Range: $25-49.9 Million
Emp.: 55
Holding Company
N.A.I.C.S.: 326199

Subsidiary (Domestic):

Buckhorn Services, Inc.   (2)
1258 S Lapeer Rd, Lake Orion, MI 48360
Tel.: (248) 693-9375
Web Site: https://www.buckhorntowing.com
Automotive Services
N.A.I.C.S.: 488410

Direct Source Supply, Inc.   (1)
529 Waverly Ave, Mamaroneck, NY 10543
Tel.: (014) 921 8100
Web Site: http://www.direct-source-supply.com
Construction Materials Whslr
N.A.I.C.S.: 423320
Nick Desanto (Pres)

Jamco Products, Inc.   (1)
1 Jamco Ct, South Beloit, IL 61080
Tel.: (815) 624-0400
Web Site: https://www.jamcoproducts.com
Metal Products Mfr
N.A.I.C.S.: 331221

Lone Star Plastics, Inc.   (1)
2875 Market St, Garland, TX 75041
Tel.: (800) 373-9410
Web Site: http://www.lonestarplastics.com
Polyethylene Film Products Mfr

N.A.I.C.S.: 326113

Subsidiary (Domestic):

Amerikan LLC   (2)
2006 Fortune Blvd, Sebring, FL 33870
Tel.: (863) 314-9417
Blow Molded Plastic Container Mfr
N.A.I.C.S.: 325211
Ron Buckley (Gen Mgr)

WhiteRidge Plastics, LLC   (2)
109 Sands Rd, Reidsville, NC 27320
Tel.: (336) 342-1200
Web Site: http://www.myersindustries.com
Emp.: 90
Plastic & Rubber Products Mfr
N.A.I.C.S.: 326121

MYE Canada Operations Inc.   (1)
75 Plant Farm Blvd, Brantford, N3S 7W2, ON, Canada
Tel.: (519) 753-2666
Sales Range: $75-99.9 Million
Emp.: 300
Plastic & Rubber Products Mfr
N.A.I.C.S.: 326121

Subsidiary (Domestic):

Scepter Canada Inc.   (2)
170 Midwest Road, Scarborough, M1P 3A9, ON, Canada
Tel.: (416) 751-9445
Web Site: https://www.scepter.com
Sales Range: $100-124.9 Million
Emp.: 200
Plastic Container Mfr
N.A.I.C.S.: 326199

Myers Tire Supply   (1)
1293 S Main St, Akron, OH 44301-1302
Tel.: (330) 253-5592
Web Site: http://www.myerstiresupply.com
Sales Range: $150-199.9 Million
Emp.: 100
Tire, Wheel & Automotive Repair Tools, Equipment & Supplies Retailer
N.A.I.C.S.: 441340

Subsidiary (Domestic):

MyersTireSupply.com, Inc.   (2)
1293 S Main St, Akron, OH 44301
Tel.: (330) 253-5592
Web Site: https://www.myerstiresupply.com
Online Tire, Wheel & Automotive Repair Tools, Equipment & Supplies Retailer
N.A.I.C.S.: 441330

Myers Tire Supply International, Inc.   (1)
1293 S Main St, Akron, OH 44301-1302
Tel.: (888) 333-5595
Web Site: http://www.myersindustries.com
Tire Distr
N.A.I.C.S.: 441340
John C. Orr (Pres & CEO)

Subsidiary (Non-US):

Myers de El Salvador S.A. De C.V.   (2)
Colonia Flor Blanca 4 CI Pte No 2212, San Salvador, El Salvador   (75%)
Tel.: (503) 22607636
Plastic & Rubber Products Mfr
N.A.I.C.S.: 326121

Subsidiary (Non-US):

Myers de Panama S.A.   (3)
Via Dqo Diaz, Panama, Panama
Tel.: (507) 2290926
Sales Range: $25-49.9 Million
Emp.: 50
Plastic & Rubber Products Mfr
N.A.I.C.S.: 326121

Patch Rubber Company   (1)
100 Patch Rubber Rd, Weldon, NC 27890
Tel.: (252) 536-2574
Web Site: https://www.patchrubber.com
Sales Range: $75-99.9 Million
Emp.: 200
Mfr of Tire Repair Materials
N.A.I.C.S.: 326299

Plasticos Novel do Nordeste S.A.   (1)
Estrada Aeroporto/Arembepe Km 06 BA

099, Lauro de Freitas, 42700-000, BA, Brazil
Tel.: (55) 7133698105
Web Site: http://www.novel.com.br
Beverages Mfr
N.A.I.C.S.: 312111

Subsidiary (Domestic):

Plasticos Novel do Parana S.A.   (2)
Calle Luis Carlos Zani, Santa Paula, 2949, Brazil
Tel.: (55) 4332588004
Plastics Product Mfr
N.A.I.C.S.: 326199

Signature Systems Group, LLC   (1)
1201 Lakeside Pkwy Ste 150, Flower Mound, TX 75028
Tel.: (972) 684-5736
Web Site: http://www.signaturecorp.com
Sales Range: $100-124.9 Million
Emp.: 125
Mfr of Specialty Flooring & Matting Systems
N.A.I.C.S.: 238330
David Egbert (CFO)
Jeff Condino (Pres)
Ron Bethmann (VP-Ops & Engrg)
Jim McAndrews (Acct Mgr-Strategic-Northeast Territory)
Michael Shivers (VP-Sls & Mktg)

Subsidiary (Domestic):

EventDeck   (2)
1201 Lake side Pkwy, Flower Mound, TX 75028   (100%)
Tel.: (212) 953-1116
Web Site:
http://www.signaturesystemgroup.com
Mfr of Modular Temporary Flooring & Pathway Systems
N.A.I.C.S.: 238330
Seth Gordon (Pres & COO)

Subsidiary (Non-US):

Signature (Fencing and Flooring) Systems Europe, Ltd.   (2)
Unit 1 Blackett Rd, Blackett Rd Industrial Estate, Darlington, DL1 2BJ, United Kingdom
Tel.: (44) 1642 744 990
Web Site: http://www.eventdeck.com
Emp.: 4
Modular Flooring & Fencing Systems Mfr & Distr
N.A.I.C.S.: 238330
Tony Booth (Dir)

Texon Polymer Group, Inc.   (1)
501 Precision Dr, Waco, TX 76703
Tel.: (254) 751-1300
Plastics Product Mfr
N.A.I.C.S.: 326199

Tuffy Manufacturing Industries, Inc.   (1)
140 E Ascot Ln, 44223, Cuyahoga Falls, OH
Tel.: (330) 630-1111
Web Site: http://www.tuffymfg.com
Whol Tire Retread Equipment & Supplies
N.A.I.C.S.: 423830

MYOMO, INC.
137 Portland St 4th Fl, Boston, MA 02114
Tel.: (617) 996-9058   DE
Web Site: https://www.myomo.com
Year Founded: 2004
MYO—(NYSEAMEX)
Rev.: $15,555,229
Assets: $10,162,006
Liabilities: $3,802,641
Net Worth: $6,359,365
Earnings: ($10,721,022)
Emp.: 100
Fiscal Year-end: 12/31/22
Surgical & Medical Instrument Mfr
N.A.I.C.S.: 339112
Paul R. Gudonis (Chm & CEO)
Micah Mitchell (Chief Comml Officer)
Andrew Harlan (Dir-Engrg)
Harry Kovelman (Chief Medical Officer)

Courtney Maulen (Dir-Patient Advocacy)
Kathy Sawyers (Sr Dir-Clinical Outcomes)
Barry Camrell (VP)
Joseph Chicoskie (Dir)
Galina Shtivelman (Dir)
David A. Henry (CFO)

MYPHOTOALBUM, INC.
500 7th Avenue 15th Floor, New York, NY 10018
Tel.: (212) 704-3000
Year Founded: 2005
FCT—(DEU)
Photosharing Services
N.A.I.C.S.: 541921
Peter Macnee (Founder, Pres & CEO)

MYR GROUP INC.
12150 E 112th Ave, Henderson, CO 80640
Tel.: (303) 286-8000   DE
Web Site: https://www.myrgroup.com
Year Founded: 1891
MYRG—(NASDAQ)
Rev.: $3,008,542,000
Assets: $1,398,858,000
Liabilities: $838,658,000
Net Worth: $560,200,000
Earnings: $83,381,000
Emp.: 8,500
Fiscal Year-end: 12/31/22
Electrical & Mechanical Construction Services
N.A.I.C.S.: 238210
Richard S. Swartz Jr. (Pres & CEO)
Kelly M. Huntington (CFO, Principal Acctg Officer & Sr VP)
William F. Fry (Chief Legal Officer, Sec & VP)
Don A. Egan (COO-Comml & Industrial & Sr VP)
James A. Barrett (VP)
Jean A. Luber (VP)
Wendy L. Davidson (VP)
Mindie W. McIff (VP)
Russell A. Hinnen (VP)
Marisa A. Owens (VP)
Michael L. Orndahl (VP)
Mark A. Enos (VP)
Jennifer Harper (Treas)

Subsidiaries:

CSI Electrical Contractors, Inc.   (1)
10623 Fulton Wells Ave, Santa Fe Springs, CA 90670
Tel.: (562) 946-0700
Web Site: http://www.csielectric.com
Rev.: $25,300,000
Emp.: 185
Electrical Contractor
N.A.I.C.S.: 238210
Danny Zuccaro (VP-Procurement-Logistics)
David Pelayo (Dir-Technology-Human Resources)
Louie Trujillo (Dir-Project Controls)
Jason Watts (Dir-Trng & Dev)
Paul Pica (Pres & COO)
Rick Yauney (CFO)
Patrick Draper (VP-Project Dev)
Joe Grant (VP-Bus Dev)
David Weir (VP-Bus Dev)
George Bone (VP-Safety & Risk Mgmt)
Chris Corder (Exec VP & Head)
Jeff Davis (VP)
Gene Acosta (Exec VP)
Oscar Garcia (Dir-Tech Solutions)
Roland Tamayo (VP)
Rick Salerno (Exec VP)
Andrew Soffa (Exec VP)
Amanda Hernandez (Dir-Acctg & Fin)
Matthew Johnson (VP)
Steve Watts (CEO & Founder)
Reza Zarif (Sr VP)
David Kang (VP-Engineering)
Arthur Draper (Gen Counsel)

Steve Watts *(CEO & Founder)*
Reza Zarif *(Sr VP)*
David Kang *(VP-Engineering)*
Arthur Draper *(Gen Counsel)*
Steve Watts *(CEO & Founder)*
Reza Zarif *(Sr VP)*
David Kang *(VP-Engineering)*
Arthur Draper *(Gen Counsel)*

E.S. Boulos Company (1)
45 Bradley Dr, Westbrook, ME 04092
Tel.: (207) 464-3706
Web Site: https://esboulos.com
Electrical Contractor
N.A.I.C.S.: 238210
Alan M. Ray *(Dir-Fin)*
Michael McCarron *(Mgr-Safety)*
Joe Bradley *(Ops Mgr-Commercial)*
Scott Marquis *(VP-Comml & Industrial)*
Ben Sirois *(Mgr-Commercial)*
Dan Broy *(Mgr-Telecom)*
Bob Goulet *(Reg Mgr)*
Lescar Beane *(Ops Mgr-Oakland)*
Garrett Gustafson *(Mgr-Comml,Industrial Div)*

Division (Domestic):

E.S. Boulos Company - Utilities Division (2)
127 First Flight Dr, Auburn, ME 04210
Tel.: (207) 784-0906
Web Site: http://www.esboulos.com
Electrical Contractor
N.A.I.C.S.: 238210

GSW Integrated Services, LLC (1)
1100 Topeka Way, Castle Rock, CO 80109
Tel.: (303) 688-5816
Web Site: http://www.gswis.com
Electrical Construction Services
N.A.I.C.S.: 237130

Great Southwestern Construction, Inc. (1)
1100 Topeka Way, Castle Rock, CO 80109
Tel.: (303) 688-5816
Web Site: https://www.gswc.us
Transmission & Distribution Line Construction Services
N.A.I.C.S.: 237130

Harlan Electric Company (1)
2695 Crooks Rd, Rochester Hills, MI 48309
Tel.: (248) 853-3601
Web Site: https://www.harlanelectric.com
Sales Range: $50-74.9 Million
Emp.: 110
Power Line Construction Services
N.A.I.C.S.: 237130

High Country Line Construction, Inc. (1)
2452 E 6700 S Unit A, Uintah, UT 84405
Tel.: (801) 829-4556
Web Site: https://www.highcountryline.com
Electrical Construction Services
N.A.I.C.S.: 237130
Clay Thomson *(Pres)*
Wendy Davidson *(VP)*

Huen Electric Inc. (1)
1801 W 16th St, Broadview, IL 60155
Tel.: (708) 343-5511
Web Site: https://www.huenelectric.com
General Electrical Contractor
N.A.I.C.S.: 238210
Steven C. Mayton *(Pres)*
Dan Pesavento *(COO)*
John Kovach *(VP)*
Jim Perreault *(VP)*

MYR Group Construction Canada, Ltd. (1)
3115 12th Street NE Unit 145, Calgary, T2E 7J2, AB, Canada
Tel.: (403) 455-0855
Civil Engineering Services
N.A.I.C.S.: 541330

MYR Transmission Services Canada, Ltd. (1)
882 Bradford Street, Winnipeg, R3H 0N5, MB, Canada
Tel.: (403) 455-0855
Electric Power Distribution Services
N.A.I.C.S.: 221122

MYR Transmission Services, Inc. (1)

12121 Grant St Ste 610, Thornton, CO 80241
Tel.: (303) 286-8000
Web Site: https://myrenergyservices.com
Power Transmission Line Construction Services
N.A.I.C.S.: 237130

Northern Transmission Services, Ltd. (1)
3115 12th Street NE Unit 145, Calgary, T2E 7J2, AB, Canada
Tel.: (403) 455-0855
Electric Power Distribution Services
N.A.I.C.S.: 221122

Sturgeon Electric California, LLC (1)
13501 Benson Ave, Chino, CA 91710
Tel.: (909) 591-0000
Web Site: https://myrgroup.com
Electrical Construction Services
N.A.I.C.S.: 237130

Sturgeon Electric Company (1)
12150 E 112th Ave, Henderson, CO 80640
Tel.: (303) 286-8000
Web Site: https://sturgeonelectric.com
Sales Range: $75-99.9 Million
Emp.: 500
Electrical Construction Services
N.A.I.C.S.: 238210
William A. Koertner *(CEO)*
William A. Koertner *(CEO)*
Larry Baker *(VP)*
Bryce Perkins *(VP)*
Jim Bushnell *(VP)*
Wayne Dorris *(VP)*
Mindie McIff *(VP)*
Wendy Davidson *(VP)*

Sturgeon Electric Company Inc. - Oregon (1)
1500 NE Graham Rd, Troutdale, OR 97060
Tel.: (503) 661-1568
Power Line Construction Services
N.A.I.C.S.: 237130

The L.E. Myers Co. (1)
445 Forum Pkwy, Rural Hall, NC 27045
Tel.: (336) 969-9400
Web Site: https://www.lemyers.com
Emp.: 15
Power & Communication Line Construction Services
N.A.I.C.S.: 237130

Western Pacific Enterprises Ltd. (1)
1321 Ketch Court, Coquitlam, V3K 6X7, BC, Canada
Tel.: (604) 540-1321
Web Site: https://www.wpe.ca
Electrical Contractor Services
N.A.I.C.S.: 238210
David Fettback *(Pres)*
Thomas Butterfield *(VP-Ops)*
Wayne Fettback *(Dir-Safety & Procurement)*
Derek Fettback *(District Mgr)*
Gary Bowsher *(District Mgr)*

MYREXIS, INC.
600 5th Ave 2nd Fl, New York, NY 10020
Tel.: (801) 214-7800   DE
Web Site: https://www.myrexis.com
MYRX—(OTCIQ)
Sales Range: Less than $1 Million
Emp.: 1
Pharmaceuticals Mfr
N.A.I.C.S.: 325412
Jonathan M. Couchman *(CEO & CFO)*

MYRIAD GENETICS, INC.
322 N 2200 W, Salt Lake City, UT 84116
Tel.: (801) 584-3600   DE
Web Site: https://www.myriad.com
Year Founded: 1991
MYGN—(NASDAQ)
Rev.: $690,600,000
Assets: $1,320,700,000
Liabilities: $352,900,000
Net Worth: $967,800,000
Earnings: ($27,200,000)
Emp.: 2,400

Fiscal Year-end: 12/31/21
Biopharmaceutical Developer & Mfr
N.A.I.C.S.: 325413
Paul J. Diaz *(Pres & CEO)*
Scott J. Leffler *(CFO)*
Samraat S. Raha *(COO)*
Pamela Wong *(Chief Legal Officer)*
Maggie Ancona *(Sr VP)*
Kevin R. Haas *(CTO)*
Dale Muzzey *(Chief Scientific Officer)*
Shereen Solaiman *(Chief People Officer)*
Alexander Gutin *(Sr VP)*
Elisha Hughes *(Dir)*
Helen Wan *(VP)*
Kirsten Timms *(Sr VP)*
Summer Pierson *(Dir)*
Thad Judkins *(Dir)*

Subsidiaries:

Assurex Health, Inc. (1)
6030 S Mason-Montgomery Rd, Mason, OH 45040
Tel.: (513) 234-0510
Web Site: http://www.assurexhealth.com
Sales Range: $50-74.9 Million
Emp.: 300
Medical Research
N.A.I.C.S.: 541715
Mark S. Verratti *(Pres)*
Mark H. Pollack *(Chief Medical Officer)*

Crescendo Bioscience, Inc. (1)
341 Oyster Point Blvd, South San Francisco, CA 94080   (100%)
Tel.: (650) 351-1354
Web Site: http://www.crescendobio.com
Emp.: 100
Biotechnology Research & Development Services
N.A.I.C.S.: 541714
Bernard F. Tobin *(Pres)*

Myriad Genetic Laboratories, Inc. (1)
320 S Wakara Way, Salt Lake City, UT 84108-1214
Tel.: (650) 351-1354
Web Site: http://www.myriad.com
Sales Range: $150-199.9 Million
Emp.: 850
Commercial Physical Research Services
N.A.I.C.S.: 541720
Nicole Lambert *(Pres)*

Myriad Genetics LTD (1)
The Stanley Building 7 Pancras Square, London, N1C 4AG, United Kingdom
Tel.: (44) 203 897 6620
Web Site: http://www.myriad.com
Genetics Research & Development Services
N.A.I.C.S.: 541715

Myriad RBM, Inc. (1)
3300 Duval Rd, Austin, TX 78759
Tel.: (512) 835-8026
Web Site: http://www.myriadrbm.com
Sales Range: $10-24.9 Million
Emp.: 124
Multiplexed Biomarker Testing Services
N.A.I.C.S.: 541380
James P. Mapes *(Chief Scientific Officer & Sr VP)*
Jeff Freiser *(Dir-Sls-Western Reg & Asia Pacific)*

N-ABLE, INC.
30 Corporate Dr Ste 400, Burlington, MA 01803
Tel.: (781) 328-6490   DE
Web Site: https://www.n-able.com
NABL—(NYSE)
Rev.: $371,769,000
Assets: $1,078,857,000
Liabilities: $436,786,000
Net Worth: $642,071,000
Earnings: $16,707,000
Emp.: 1,454
Fiscal Year-end: 12/31/22
Cloud Based Software Solutions
N.A.I.C.S.: 513210
Timothy O'Brien *(CFO)*
Stefan Voss *(VP-Product Mgmt)*

John Pagliuca *(Pres & CEO)*
Mike Adler *(CTO & Chief Product Officer)*
Frank Colletti *(Chief Revenue Officer)*
Kathleen Pai *(Chief People Officer)*
Peter C. Anastos *(Gen Counsel & Sec)*
Jeff Nulsen *(CMO)*
Joel Kemmerer *(CIO)*
Dave Mackinnon *(Chief Security Officer)*
Laura Dubois *(VP-Group Product)*
Manish Kamra *(VP-Group Engrg)*

NABORS ENERGY TRANSITION CORP.
515 W Greens Rd Ste 1200, Houston, TX 77067
Tel.: (281) 874-0035   DE
Web Site: https://www.nabors-etcorp.com
Year Founded: 2021
NETC—(NYSE)
Rev.: $4,073,078
Assets: $285,684,168
Liabilities: $295,941,603
Net Worth: ($10,257,435)
Earnings: $1,297,593
Emp.: 4
Fiscal Year-end: 12/31/22
Energy Generation Services
N.A.I.C.S.: 237130
Anthony G. Petrello *(Chm, Pres, CEO & Sec)*
William J. Restrepo *(CFO)*
Guillermo Sierra *(VP-Strategic Initiatives Energy Transition)*
Siggi Meissner *(Pres-Engrg & Tech)*

NACCO INDUSTRIES, INC.
5875 Landerbrook Dr Ste 220, Cleveland, OH 44124
Tel.: (440) 229-5151   DE
Web Site: https://www.nacco.com
Year Founded: 1913
NC—(NYSE)
Rev.: $241,719,000
Assets: $568,072,000
Liabilities: $141,106,000
Net Worth: $426,966,000
Earnings: $74,158,000
Emp.: 1,600
Fiscal Year-end: 12/31/22
Holding Company; Coal Mining, Materials Handling Equipment, Portable Electric Appliances, Retail Kitchenware
N.A.I.C.S.: 423830
John C. Butler Jr. *(Pres & CEO)*
Thomas A. Maxwell *(Treas & VP-Fin Plng & Analysis)*
Sarah E. Fry *(Asst Sec & Assoc Gen Counsel)*

Subsidiaries:

Demery Resources Company, LLC (1)
416 E Carrol St, Coushatta, LA 71019
Tel.: (318) 932-5386
Web Site: http://www.nacoal.com
Coal & Related Product Mfr
N.A.I.C.S.: 212114

North American Coal Royalty Company (1)
2000 Schafer St Ste D, Bismarck, ND 58501
Tel.: (701) 258-2200
Web Site: http://www.nacoal.com
Sales Range: $300-349.9 Million
Emp.: 15
Coal & Related Product Mfr
N.A.I.C.S.: 212114
Chris Friez *(Mgr-Line)*

Reed Management LLC (1)
12142 Hume Rd, Hume, VA 22639

NACCO Industries, Inc.—(Continued)

Tel.: (703) 474-2729
Investment Management Service
N.A.I.C.S.: 523940

Reed Minerals, Inc. (1)
3699 Industrial Pkwy, Jasper, AL 35501
Tel.: (205) 295-2224
Emp.: 5
Coal Mining Services
N.A.I.C.S.: 213113

TRU Energy Services, LLC (1)
PO Box 2570, Ada, OK 74821
Tel.: (580) 421-9808
Web Site:
https://www.trueenergyservices.com
Sales Range: $50-74.9 Million
Emp.: 11
Oil & Gas Exploration Services
N.A.I.C.S.: 213112
Bob Cantrell (Chm)
Kevin Cantrell (Pres)
Mike Feezel (COO)

**The North American Coal
Corporation** (1)
5340 Legacy Dr Ste 300, Plano, TX
75024 (100%)
Tel.: (972) 448-5400
Web Site: https://www.nacoal.com
Sales Range: $250-299.9 Million
Emp.: 53
Coal Mining
N.A.I.C.S.: 212114
John C. Butler Jr. (Pres & CEO)

Subsidiary (Domestic):

**Caddo Creek Resources Co.,
LLC** (2)
5340 Legacy Dr Bldg I Ste 300, Plano, TX
75024
Tel.: (972) 448-5400
Web Site: http://www.nacoal.com
Sales Range: $75-99.9 Million
Coal & Related Product Mfr
N.A.I.C.S.: 212114

Camino Real Fuels, LLC (2)
607 County Rd 305, Eagle Pass, TX 78852
Tel.: (830) 421-5017
Web Site: http://www.nacoal.com
Coal & Related Product Mfr
N.A.I.C.S.: 212114

Liberty Fuels Company, LLC (2)
4707 Hwy 493, De Kalb, MS 39328
Tel.: (601) 737-7000
Web Site: http://www.nacoal.com
Coal Mining Services
N.A.I.C.S.: 213113
Ken Kary (Project Mgr)

**Mississippi Lignite Mining
Company** (2)
1000 McIntire Rd, Ackerman, MS 39735
Tel.: (662) 387-5200
Web Site: http://www.nacoal.com
Coal & Related Product Mfr
N.A.I.C.S.: 212114
Matt Jones (Mgr-Mine)

The Coteau Properties Co. (2)
204 County Rd 15, Beulah, ND
58523 (100%)
Tel.: (701) 873-2281
Web Site: http://www.nacoal.com
Sales Range: $150-199.9 Million
Mining of Lignite
N.A.I.C.S.: 212114
Bryan Walther (Mgr-Mine)

The Falkirk Mining Co. (2)
2801 1st St SW, Underwood, ND
58576-1087 (100%)
Tel.: (701) 442-5751
Sales Range: $150-199.9 Million
Emp.: 200
Mining Machinery & Equipment Whslr
N.A.I.C.S.: 423830
Jay Kost (Mgr-Mine)

The Sabine Mining Company (2)
6501 Farm Rd 968 W, Hallsville, TX 75650-7413
Tel.: (903) 660-4200
Lignite Mining Services
N.A.I.C.S.: 213113

NAERODYNAMICS, INC.
2030 Powers Ferry Rd SE Ste 212,
Atlanta, GA 30339
Tel.: (404) 816-9220
Year Founded: 1996
NDYN—(OTCIQ)
Holding Company
N.A.I.C.S.: 551112
Erik Nelson (CEO)

NALU MEDICAL, INC.
2320 Faraday Ave Ste 100, Carlsbad,
CA 92008
Tel.: (760) 448-2360   DE
Web Site: http://www.nalumed.com
Year Founded: 2014
NALU—(NASDAQ)
Rev.: $3,795,000
Assets: $68,697,000
Liabilities: $133,441,000
Net Worth: ($64,744,000)
Earnings: ($27,820,000)
Emp.: 120
Fiscal Year-end: 12/31/20
Medical Equipment Mfr
N.A.I.C.S.: 339112
Jeff Swiecki (CFO)
Jonathan Ruais (Chief Comml Officer
& Chief Strategy Officer)
Lee Hartley (Chief Technical Officer)
Allen Meacham (Chief Bus Dev Officer)
Lakshmi Narayan Mishra (VP-R&D)
Bick Sellers (VP-HR)
Patrick Martin (VP-Clinical Affairs)
Geoff Pardo (Chm)
Thomas A. West (Pres & CEO)

NAMASTE WORLD ACQUISITION CORPORATION
3524 Silverside Rd Ste 35B, Wilmington, DE 19810-4929
Tel.: (858) 922-3770   DE
Year Founded: 2021
NWACU—(NASDAQ)
Investment Services
N.A.I.C.S.: 523999
Suresh Guduru (Chm & CEO)
Suresh Singamsetty (CFO)
Kishore Kondragunta (Chief Investment Officer & Sec)

NANO MAGIC INC.
31601 Research Park Dr, Madison
Heights, MI 48071   DE
Web Site: https://nanomagic.com
Year Founded: 1987
NMGX—(OTCQB)
Rev.: $2,577,332
Assets: $4,090,545
Liabilities: $2,473,083
Net Worth: $1,617,462
Earnings: ($2,101,589)
Emp.: 19
Fiscal Year-end: 12/31/22
Nanotechnology Based Cleaners &
Coatings Developer & Marketer
N.A.I.C.S.: 551112
Jeanne M. Rickert (Gen Counsel)
Scott E. Rickert (Chm)
Tom J. Berman (Pres & CEO)

NANO MOBILE HEALTHCARE, INC.
370 Amapola Ave Ste 200-A, Torrance, CA 90501
Tel.: (310) 895-1839   NV
Year Founded: 2010
VNTH—(OTCIQ)
Emp.: 18
Pharmaceuticals Mfr
N.A.I.C.S.: 325412
Robert Chicoski (CFO)
Frank Lkechukwu Igwealor (Pres &
CEO)

NANOFLEX POWER CORPORATION
8950 E Raintree Dr Ste 400, Scottsdale, AZ 85260
Tel.: (480) 585-4200   FL
Web Site:
https://www.nanoflexpower.com
Year Founded: 2013
OPVS—(OTCIQ)
Rev.: $293,278
Assets: $667,353
Liabilities: $19,005,559
Net Worth: ($18,338,206)
Earnings: ($13,522,196)
Emp.: 8
Fiscal Year-end: 12/31/19
Solar Cell Mfr
N.A.I.C.S.: 334419
Dean L. Ledger (CEO)
J. Norman Allen (CTO)

Subsidiaries:

**Global Photonic Energy
Corporation** (1)
20 Trading Post Way, Medford Lakes, NJ
08055 (100%)
Tel.: (609) 654-8839
Patent Holding & Technology Licensing;
Photovoltaics Research & Development
N.A.I.C.S.: 541715

NANOLOGIX, INC.
843 N Main St, Hubbard, OH 44425
Tel.: (330) 534-0800
Web Site: https://www.nanologix.com
NNLX—(OTCIQ)
Sales Range: Less than $1 Million
Emp.: 5
Research & Development in Nanotechnology
N.A.I.C.S.: 541713
Bret T. Barnhizer (Chm, Pres & CEO)

NANOMIX CORPORATION
2121 Williams St, San Leandro, CA
94577
Tel.: (510) 428-5300   DE
Web Site:
https://www.nanomixdx.com
Year Founded: 2009
NNMX—(OTCQB)
Rev.: $15,450
Assets: $982,055
Liabilities: $14,814,747
Net Worth: ($13,832,692)
Earnings: ($12,532,148)
Emp.: 30
Fiscal Year-end: 12/31/22
Pharmaceutical Preparation Manufacturing
N.A.I.C.S.: 325412
Stephen Spanos (CFO-Acting)

Subsidiaries:

Nanomix, Inc. (1)
2121 Williams St, San Leandro, CA 94577
Tel.: (510) 428-5300
Web Site: https://nanomixdx.com
Rev.: $3,520,000
Emp.: 20
Research & Development in Biotechnology
N.A.I.C.S.: 541714
Garrett Gruener (Chm)
Thomas Schlumpberger (CEO)
David Ludvigson (Sec)
Christopher R. Hetterly (CFO)
David A. Gyorke (VP-Ops)

NANOPHASE TECHNOLOGIES CORPORATION
1319 Marquette Dr, Romeoville, IL
60446
Tel.: (630) 771-6700   IL
Web Site:
https://www.nanophase.com
Year Founded: 1980
NANX—(OTCQB)
Rev.: $37,317,000

Assets: $33,558,000
Liabilities: $27,909,000
Net Worth: $5,649,000
Earnings: ($2,623,000)
Emp.: 82
Fiscal Year-end: 12/31/22
Nanocrystalline Materials Developer
for Advanced Materials Technology
N.A.I.C.S.: 331410
Jess A. Jankowski (Pres, CEO, CFO
& Principal Acctg Officer)
Richard W. Siegel (Founder)
Rebecca Janet Whitmore (Chm)
H. Glenn Judd (VP-Ops)
Kevin Cureton (COO)

NANOTECH ENTERTAINMENT, INC.
2450 Kruse Dr, San Jose, CA 95131
Tel.: (408) 414-7355
Web Site: https://www.ntek.com
Year Founded: 2007
NTEK—(OTCEM)
Sales Range: $1-9.9 Million
3D, Gaming, Media, IPTV & Mobile
Apps
N.A.I.C.S.: 513210
Karen Davis (Chm & CEO)

NANOTECH GAMING, INC.
7180 Dean Martin Dr, Las Vegas, NV
89118
Tel.: (702) 577-2895   NV
Web Site:
https://www.nanotechgaming.com
Year Founded: 2013
NTGL—(OTCIQ)
Other Gambling Industries
N.A.I.C.S.: 713290
Alan Stone (Chm & CEO)

NANOVIBRONIX, INC.
969 Pruitt Pl, Tyler, TX 75703
Tel.: (914) 233-3004   DE
Web Site:
https://www.nanovibronix.com
Year Founded: 2003
NAOV—(NASDAQ)
Rev.: $752,000
Assets: $5,879,000
Liabilities: $2,646,000
Net Worth: $3,233,000
Earnings: ($5,448,000)
Emp.: 10
Fiscal Year-end: 12/31/22
Medical Device Mfr
N.A.I.C.S.: 334510
Brian M. Murphy (CEO)
Harold Jacob (Chief Medical Officer &
Chm)
Itai Levinson (VP-Intl Sls & Mktg-
Global & Gen Mgr)
Christine Shettel (VP-Americas)
Lindsey Harrison (VP-Sales)
Christopher M. Fashek (Chm)

NANOVIRICIDES, INC.
1 Controls Dr, Shelton, CT 06484
Tel.: (203) 937-6137   NV
Web Site:
https://www.nanoviricides.com
NNVC—(NYSEAMEX)
Rev.: $271,773
Assets: $12,822,853
Liabilities: $1,358,776
Net Worth: $11,464,077
Earnings: ($8,294,146)
Emp.: 7
Fiscal Year-end: 06/30/24

Nano-Biopharmaceutical Mfr
N.A.I.C.S.: 325412
Anil R. Diwan *(Pres, CEO & Chm)*
Randall W. Barton *(Chief Scientific Officer & Chief Regulatory Officer)*
Jayant Tatake *(VP-R&D)*

NAPC DEFENSE, INC.
1501 Lake Ave SE, Largo, FL 33771
Tel.: (754) 242-6272   NV
Web Site:
https://www.napcdefense.com
Year Founded: 2016
BLIS—(OTCIQ)
Assets: $1,759,732
Liabilities: $1,045,060
Net Worth: $714,672
Earnings: ($711,986)
Fiscal Year-end: 04/30/24
Marine Salvage & Military Procurement Services
N.A.I.C.S.: 561990
Stephen L. Gurba *(Pres)*
Craig A. Huffman *(Chief Legal Officer & Sec)*
Kane Fisher *(Ops Mgr)*
Edward K. West *(Chm & CEO)*
John Spence *(CFO)*

NAPCO SECURITY TECHNOLOGIES, INC.
333 Bayview Ave, Amityville, NY 11701
Tel.: (631) 842-9400   DE
Web Site:
https://www.napcosecurity.com
Year Founded: 1969
NSSC—(NASDAQ)
Rev.: $188,820,000
Assets: $207,752,000
Liabilities: $28,863,000
Net Worth: $178,889,000
Earnings: $49,818,000
Emp.: 1,070
Fiscal Year-end: 06/30/24
Security Devices & Systems
N.A.I.C.S.: 561621
Richard L. Soloway *(Founder, Chm, CEO & Sec)*
Kevin S. Buchel *(Pres, CFO & COO)*
Michael Carrieri *(CTO & Exec VP-Engrg)*
Stephen Spinelli *(Sr VP-Sls)*

Subsidiaries:

Alarm Lock Systems, Inc.   (1)
345 Bayview Ave, Amityville, NY 11701
Tel.: (631) 842-9400
Web Site: https://www.alarmlock.com
Sales Range: $100-124.9 Million
Electronic & Mechanical Access & Egress Control Products
N.A.I.C.S.: 561621
William Sporre *(VP-Sls & Mktg-Global)*

Continental Instruments, LLC   (1)
333 Bayview Ave, Amityville, NY 11701
Tel.: (631) 842-9400
Web Site: https://napcoaccesspro.com
Security System Mfr & Distr
N.A.I.C.S.: 334290
Rich Goldsobel *(VP & Gen Mgr)*
Susanne Ruse *(Mgr-Customer Svc)*

Napco DR, S.A.   (1)
Z Franca Nigua, Santo Domingo, Dominican Republic
Tel.: (809) 5423356
Web Site: http://www.napco.com
Security Products Mfr & Distr
N.A.I.C.S.: 334290

NASB FINANCIAL, INC.
12498 S 71 Hwy, Grandview, MO 64030
Tel.: (816) 765-2200   MO
Web Site: http://www.nasb.com
Year Founded: 1998

NASB—(OTCIQ)
Rev.: $302,626,000
Assets: $2,552,198,000
Liabilities: $2,201,816,000
Net Worth: $350,382,000
Earnings: $103,505,000
Emp.: 602
Fiscal Year-end: 09/30/20
Bank Holding Company
N.A.I.C.S.: 551111

Subsidiaries:

Nor-Am Service Corporation   (1)
12498 S US Hwy 71, Grandview, MO
64030-1733   (100%)
Tel.: (816) 765-2200
Management Consulting Services
N.A.I.C.S.: 541611
Keith B. Cox *(Pres)*

North American Savings Bank,
F.S.B.   (1)
12498 S US Hwy 71, Grandview, MO
64030-1733
Tel.: (816) 765-2200
Web Site: http://www.nasb.com
Federal Savings Bank
N.A.I.C.S.: 522180
Keith B. Cox *(Pres)*

NASCENT BIOTECH INC.
631 US Hwy 1 Ste 407 N, Palm Beach, FL 33408
Tel.: (612) 961-5656   NV
Web Site:
https://www.nascentbiotech.com
NBIO—(OTCQB)
Rev.: $5,265
Assets: $552,120
Liabilities: $808,794
Net Worth: ($256,674)
Earnings: ($2,087,682)
Fiscal Year-end: 03/31/24
Biopharmaceutical Mfr
N.A.I.C.S.: 325412
Sean Carrick *(Pres, CEO & Sec)*
Lowell Thomas Holden *(CFO & Chief Acctg Officer)*

NASDAQ, INC.
151 W 42nd St, New York, NY 10036
Tel.: (212) 401-8700   DE
Web Site: https://www.nasdaq.com
Year Founded: 1971
NDAQ—(NASDAQ)
Rev.: $6,064,000,000
Assets: $32,294,000,000
Liabilities: $21,467,000,000
Net Worth: $10,827,000,000
Earnings: $1,059,000,000
Emp.: 8,525
Fiscal Year-end: 12/31/23
Holding Company; Securities Exchange Operator & Related Services
N.A.I.C.S.: 551112
P. C. Nelson Griggs *(Co-Pres & Pres-Capital Access Platforms)*
Bradley J. Peterson *(Chief Info Officer & Exec VP)*
Jeremy Skule *(Chief Strategy Officer & Exec VP)*
John A. Zecca *(Chief Legal & Regulatory Officer-Global, Gen Counsel & Exec VP)*
Sarah Youngwood *(CFO & Exec VP)*
Tal Cohen *(Co-Pres & Pres-Market Platforms)*
Bryan Smith *(Chief People Officer & Exec VP)*
Nicklas Brandstrom *(Sr VP & Head-Svc Delivery & Market Tech)*
Patrik Farnlof *(Sr VP-Platform & Product Engrg)*
Nikolai Larbalestier *(Sr VP-Enterprise Architecture & Performance Engrg)*
Michelle Daly *(Principal Acctg Officer, Sr VP & Controller)*
Roland Chai *(Exec VP)*

Edward Knight *(Vice Chm)*
Catherine Addona-Pena *(Chief Risk Officer)*
Ira Auerbach *(Sr VP)*
Michael Bartels *(Sr VP)*
Brian Buckley *(CMO)*
Jim Chen *(Sr VP)*
Eun Ah Choi *(Sr VP)*
Nick Ciubotariu *(Sr VP)*
Matthew Claus *(Sr VP)*
Jeffrey S. Davis *(Deputy Gen Counsel)*
Michael Davis *(Sr VP)*
Fredrik Ekstrom *(Sr VP)*
Andreas Gustafsson *(Gen Counsel)*
Reekiran Kahlon *(Sr VP)*
Alex Kogan *(Sr VP)*
Adam Kostyal *(Sr VP)*
Dana Laidhold *(Treas)*
Raymond Mays *(Sr VP)*
Benjamin Wolf *(Sr VP)*
Adena T. Friedman *(Chm & CEO)*

Subsidiaries:

AB NASDAQ OMX Vilnius   (1)
Lvovo Street 25 Floor 10, Vilnius, 09313, Lithuania
Tel.: (370) 52723871
Web Site: http://www.nasdaqomx.com
Sales Range: $25-49.9 Million
Emp.: 16
Securities Brokerage Services
N.A.I.C.S.: 523210

AS Latvijas Centralais
depozitarijs   (1)
Valnu iela 1, Riga, 1050, Latvia
Tel.: (371) 67212431
Securities Brokerage Services
N.A.I.C.S.: 523210
Krastena Plauka *(Mgr)*

Adenza France SARL   (1)
Le Centorial 16-18 Rue du Quatre Septembre, 75002, Paris, France
Tel.: (33) 170835100
Stock Exchange Services
N.A.I.C.S.: 523210

Adenza Hong Kong Co., Ltd.   (1)
Room 1204-8 12F Man Yee Building 68 Des Voeux Road Central, Hong Kong, China (Hong Kong)
Tel.: (852) 21672500
Stock Exchange Services
N.A.I.C.S.: 523210

Adenza Ltd.   (1)
22 Bishopsgate, London, EC2N 4AJ, United Kingdom
Tel.: (44) 2037532000
Stock Exchange Services
N.A.I.C.S.: 523210

Adenza Singapore Pte. Ltd.   (1)
18 Robinson Road 14-01, Singapore, 048547, Singapore
Tel.: (65) 69557600
Investment Banking & Fund Management Services
N.A.I.C.S.: 523150

Armenia Securities Exchange   (1)
26/1 Vazgen Sargsyan Str 5th Floor Erebuni Plaza Business Centre, Yerevan, 0010, Armenia
Tel.: (374) 60695555
Web Site: https://amx.am
Securities Exchange
N.A.I.C.S.: 523210
Martin Galstyan *(Chm-Supervisory Bd)*
Vahan Babayan *(Controller)*
Michael Volter *(Deputy Chm)*

Subsidiary (Domestic):

Central Depository of Armenia Open
Joint Stock Company   (2)
5b Mher Mkrtchyan Str, 0010, Yerevan, Armenia
Tel.: (374) 10589 151
Securities Clearing Services
N.A.I.C.S.: 523210
Vahan Stepanyan *(CEO)*
Hasmik Salnazaryan *(Head-Mktg & Comm)*

Vachik Gevorgyan *(Head-Depository Sys Servicing Dev)*
Tigran Petrosyan *(Head-Pension Sys Servicing Dept)*
Henri Bergstrom *(Chm)*

AxiomSL Holdings BV   (1)
Gustav Mahlerplein 109-115 25th floor, 1082, Amsterdam, Netherlands
Tel.: (31) 203690548
Stock Exchange Services
N.A.I.C.S.: 523210

Boardvantage, Inc.   (1)
4300 Bohannon Dr Ste 110, Menlo Park, CA 94025
Tel.: (650) 614-6000
Web Site: http://www.boardvantage.com
Sales Range: $1-9.9 Million
Corporate Executive Communication & Management Platform Software Developer & Publisher
N.A.I.C.S.: 513210

Cinnober Financial Technology
AB   (1)
Kungsgatan 36, SE-111 35, Stockholm, Sweden
Tel.: (46) 8 503 047 00
Web Site: http://www.cinnober.com
Technology Solutions to Exchange Trading Clearing, Risk Management & Other Financial Services
N.A.I.C.S.: 541519

Dorsey, Wright & Associates,
LLC   (1)
1011 Boulder Springs Dr Ste 150, Richmond, VA 23225
Tel.: (804) 320-8511
Web Site: http://www.dorseywright.com
Emp.: 50
Investment Advisory Services
N.A.I.C.S.: 523940

FTen, Inc.   (1)
1 Liberty Plz 50th Fl, New York, NY 10006
Tel.: (212) 808-8440
Sales Range: $10-24.9 Million
Emp.: 60
Financial Software Developer
N.A.I.C.S.: 513210

International Securities Exchange
Holdings, Inc.   (1)
60 Broad St, New York, NY 10004
Tel.: (212) 943-2400
Web Site: http://www.ise.com
Emp.: 188
Equity Options Exchange
N.A.I.C.S.: 523210

Subsidiary (Domestic):

ISE ETF Ventures LLC   (2)
60 Broad St, New York, NY 10004
Tel.: (212) 943-2400
Web Site: http://www.ise.com
Indexes & Investment Tracking Services
N.A.I.C.S.: 523999

International Securities Exchange
LLC   (2)
60 Broad St, New York, NY 10004
Tel.: (212) 943-2400
Web Site: http://www.ise.com
Emp.: 160
Equity Options Exchange
N.A.I.C.S.: 523210

Longitude LLC   (2)
60 Broad St, New York, NY 10004
Tel.: (212) 897-0202
Web Site: http://www.longitude.com
Gaming Technology Service Provider
N.A.I.C.S.: 541512

Lithuanian Central Securities
Depositary   (1)
Lvovo G 25, Vilnius, 9320, Lithuania
Tel.: (370) 52638510
Web Site: http://www.csdl.lt
Emp.: 29
Securities Exchange Services
N.A.I.C.S.: 523210

NASDAQ Australia Holdings Pty.
Ltd.   (1)
Level 8 68 Harrington Street The Rocks, Sydney, 2000, NSW, Australia

Nasdaq, Inc.—(Continued)
Tel.: (61) 280762600
Web Site: http://business.nasdaq.com
Stock Exchange Services
N.A.I.C.S.: 551114

NASDAQ OMX (South East Asia & Pacific) Pte. Ltd. (1)
20 Collyer Quay 17-01, Singapore, 049319, Singapore
Tel.: (65) 65056550
Emp.: 20
Software Development Services
N.A.I.C.S.: 541511
Robert Frojd (Mng Dir)

NASDAQ OMX Clearing AB (1)
Tullvaktsvagen 15, Stockholm, 105 78, Sweden
Tel.: (46) 84056000
Web Site: http://www.nasdaq.com
Stock Management Services
N.A.I.C.S.: 523210

NASDAQ OMX Europe Limited (1)
Woolgate Exchange 25 Basinghall Street, London, EC2V 5HA, United Kingdom
Tel.: (44) 2037532000
Web Site: http://www.nasdaqomx.com
Sales Range: $25-49.9 Million
Emp.: 250
Stock Exchange Services
N.A.I.C.S.: 551114

Subsidiary (Non-US):

OMX Technology Ltd. (2)
Tel.: (44) 2070658000
Electronic Trading Platform Technologies Developer & Management Services
N.A.I.C.S.: 541519

Subsidiary (Non-US):

OMX Technology Italy Srl (3)
Tel.: (39) 0276025899
Web Site: http://www.nasdaq.com
Emp.: 5
Electronic Trading Platform Technologies Developer & Management Services
N.A.I.C.S.: 541519

NASDAQ OMX Nordic Oy (1)
Fabianinkatu 14, Helsinki, 00100, Finland
Tel.: (358) 9 616 671
Web Site: http://www.nasdaqomxnordic.com
Holding Company; Securities & Commodities Exchanges
N.A.I.C.S.: 551112

Subsidiary (Non-US):

NASDAQ OMX Copenhagen A/S (2)
Nikolaj Plads 6, Postbox 1040, 1007, Copenhagen, Denmark
Tel.: (45) 33933366
Web Site: http://www.nasdaqomxnordic.com
Rev.: $37,864,234
Emp.: 50
Securities & Commodities Exchange Operator
N.A.I.C.S.: 523210
Bjorn Seiddern (Pres)

Subsidiary (Domestic):

NASDAQ OMX Helsinki Oy (2)
Fabianinkatu 14, PO Box 361, 00131, Helsinki, Finland
Tel.: (358) 9616671
Web Site: http://www.nasdaqomxnordic.com
Securities & Commodities Exchange Operator
N.A.I.C.S.: 523210

Subsidiary (Non-US):

NASDAQ OMX Iceland hf. (2)
Laugavegi 182, 105, Reykjavik, Iceland
Tel.: (354) 5252800
Web Site: http://www.nasdaqomxnordic.com
Emp.: 17
Securities & Commodities Exchange Operator
N.A.I.C.S.: 523210

Subsidiary (Domestic):

Verdbrefaskraning Islands hf. (3)
Laugavegi 182, Reykjavik, 105, Iceland
Tel.: (354) 5405500

Web Site: http://www.vbsi.is
Emp.: 7
Securities Brokerage Services
N.A.I.C.S.: 523150

Subsidiary (Non-US):

NASDAQ OMX Stockholm AB (2)
Tullvaktszagen 15, 105 78, Stockholm, Sweden
Tel.: (46) 84056000
Web Site: http://www.nasdaqomxnordic.com
Sales Range: $500-549.9 Million
Emp.: 700
Securities & Commodities Exchange Operator
N.A.I.C.S.: 523210

Subsidiary (Domestic):

OMX Technology AB (3)
Tullaktsvagen 15, 105 78, Stockholm, Sweden
Tel.: (46) 84056000
Electronic Trading Platform Technologies Developer & Management Services
N.A.I.C.S.: 541519

NASDAQ OMX PHLX, Inc. (1)
1900 Market St, Philadelphia, PA 19103-3527
Tel.: (215) 496-5000
Web Site: http://www.phlx.com
Sales Range: $1-4.9 Billion
Emp.: 416
Security & Commodity Exchanges
N.A.I.C.S.: 523210

NASDAQ OMX Tallinn AS (1)
Maakri 19/1 Maakri Kvartal 16th floor, 10145, Tallinn, Estonia
Tel.: (372) 6408800
Web Site: http://www.nasdaqomxbaltic.com
Sales Range: $25-49.9 Million
Emp.: 43
Securities Brokerage Services
N.A.I.C.S.: 523210

NASDAQ Options Services, LLC (1)
1 Liberty Plz 165 Broadway 50th Fl, New York, NY 10006
Tel.: (212) 401-8780
Securities Clearing Services
N.A.I.C.S.: 523210

Nasdaq AB (1)
Tullvaktsvagen 15, 105 78, Stockholm, Sweden
Tel.: (46) 84056000
Securities Exchange Related Services
N.A.I.C.S.: 523210

Nasdaq CSD Iceland hf (1)
Laugavegur 182, 105, Reykjavik, Iceland
Tel.: (354) 5405500
Web Site: http://www.en.vbsi.is
Financial Services
N.A.I.C.S.: 523940

Nasdaq Copenhagen A/S (1)
Nikolaj Plads 6, PO Box 1040, 1007, Copenhagen, Denmark
Tel.: (45) 33933366
Financial Services
N.A.I.C.S.: 523940

Nasdaq Helsinki Ltd (1)
Fabianinkatu 14, PO Box 361, 00131, Helsinki, Finland
Tel.: (358) 9616671
Securities Exchange Related Services
N.A.I.C.S.: 523210

Nasdaq Iceland hf (1)
Laugavegi 182, 105, Reykjavik, Iceland
Tel.: (354) 5252800
Financial Services
N.A.I.C.S.: 523940

Nasdaq Oslo ASA (1)
Karenslyst Alle, 0279, Oslo, Norway
Tel.: (47) 67528000
Securities Exchange Related Services
N.A.I.C.S.: 523210

Nasdaq Riga, AS (1)
Valnu iela 1, Riga, 1050, Latvia
Tel.: (371) 67212431
Web Site: https://nasdaqbaltic.com
Financial Services
N.A.I.C.S.: 523940

OneReport, Inc. (1)
22 High St 301, Brattleboro, VT 05301
Tel.: (802) 251-0500
Web Site: https://one-report.com
Software Development Services
N.A.I.C.S.: 541511
Janice Warren (Pres)
Dan Berger (Ops Mgr)
Heather Shand (Mgr-Client Services)

Puro.earth Oy (1)
Lapinlahdenkatu 16, 0180, Helsinki, Finland
Tel.: (358) 405858848
Web Site: https://puro.earth
Marketing & Advertising Services
N.A.I.C.S.: 541890

Simplitium Ltd. (1)
5 Ireland Yard, London, EC4V 5EH, United Kingdom
Tel.: (44) 2038669700
Web Site: http://www.simplitium.com
Software Development Services
N.A.I.C.S.: 513210
John Yonker (CEO)

Solovis, Inc. (1)
100 Glenridge Point Pkwy Ste 100, Atlanta, GA 30342-1444
Web Site: https://www.evestment.com
Marketing & Advertising Services
N.A.I.C.S.: 541890

Strategic Financial Solutions, LLC (1)
222 3rd Ave SE Ste 280, Cedar Rapids, IA 52401
Tel.: (319) 363-2509
Web Site: https://www.retiresfs.com
Financial Services
N.A.I.C.S.: 523940
Larry Witzel (Pres)
Bert McClintock (VP-Retirement Svcs)
Linda Kappler (Sr Dir-Mktg & Svcs)
Jamie Meyers (Bus Mgr)

The NASDAQ Private Market, LLC (1)
505 Howard St Ste 4201, San Francisco, CA 94105   **(100%)**
Tel.: (415) 243-3156
Web Site:
   https://www.nasdaqprivatemarket.com
Equity Services for Private Companies
N.A.I.C.S.: 525990
Jonathan Yam (CTO)
Tom Callahan (CEO)
Jimmy Ronnkvist (CFO)
Amanda Gold (CMO)
Chris Setaro (Chief Compliance Officer)
Rotem David (Chief Product Officer)
Susan George (Chief People Officer)
Brett Mock (Sr VP)
Erik Pena (Sr VP)

Subsidiary (Domestic):

NPM Securities, LLC (2)
150 Spear St Ste 1650, San Francisco, CA 94105   **(100%)**
Tel.: (415) 243-2300
Securities Related Services
N.A.I.C.S.: 523150
Robert Malin (Principal)

The NASDAQ Stock Market LLC (1)
151 W 42nd St, New York, NY 10036
Tel.: (212) 401-8700
Web Site: http://www.nastaqomx.com
Emp.: 300
Securities Exchange Operator
N.A.I.C.S.: 523210
Jeffrey S Davis (Sr VP)
Gunilla Hellqvist (Sr VP)
Phil MacKintosh (Sr VP)
Michael Ptasznik (CFO & Exec VP-Corporate Strategy)
Roland Chai (Chief Risk Officer & Sr VP)
A. Michael Smith (Sr VP)
Yolanda Goettsch (VP)
Tushar Mehta (Asst Treas)

Verafin Solutions ULC (1)
18 Hebron Way, Saint John's, A1A 0L9, NL, Canada
Web Site: https://verafin.com
Software Development Services
N.A.I.C.S.: 541511

eVestment Alliance Australia Pty Ltd (1)

Level 8 68 Harrington Street, Sydney, 2000, NSW, Australia
Tel.: (61) 282110411
Securities Exchange Related Services
N.A.I.C.S.: 523210

eVestment Alliance, LLC (1)
100 Glenridge Point Pkwy Ste 100, Atlanta, GA 30342
Tel.: (678) 569-2388
Web Site: http://www.evestment.com
Investment Information & Analytic Technology Software Developer
N.A.I.C.S.: 513210
John Molespini (Head-Insights-Global)

eVestment, Inc (1)
100 Glenridge Point Pkwy Ste 100, Atlanta, GA 30342
Web Site: http://www.evestment.com
Software Development Services
N.A.I.C.S.: 513210
Jim Minnick (Founder & CEO)

NASHVILLE RECORDS, INC.
1333 N Buffalo Dr Ste 210, Las Vegas, NV 89128
Tel.: (310) 895-1839   NV
Year Founded: 2003
NRCD—(OTCIQ)
Medical Exercise Equipment Mfr
N.A.I.C.S.: 339112
Frank Lkechukwu Igwealor (Chm, Pres, CEO & Treas)

NATCORE TECHNOLOGY INC.
47 Club Way, Red Bank, NJ 07701
Tel.: (732) 530-6737   BC
Web Site:
   http://www.natcoresolar.com
Year Founded: 2007
NXT—(DEU)
Sales Range: Less than $1 Million
Emp.: 13
Investment Services
N.A.I.C.S.: 523999
Charles R. Provini (Pres & CEO)
Brien Lundin (Founder & Chm)

NATE'S FOOD CO.
15151 Springdale St, Huntington Beach, CA 92649
Tel.: (650) 222-5141   CO
Web Site:
   https://www.natesfoodco.com
Year Founded: 2014
NI IMD—(OTCIQ)
Assets: $141,027
Liabilities: $1,254,144
Net Worth: ($1,113,117)
Earnings: ($257,384)
Fiscal Year-end: 05/31/23
Food Products Mfr
N.A.I.C.S.: 311999
Nate Steck (Pres & CEO)
Timothy Denton (Sec)

NATERA, INC.
13011 McCallen Pass Bldg A Ste 100, Austin, TX 78753
Tel.: (650) 980-9190   DE
Web Site: https://www.natera.com
Year Founded: 2003
NTRA—(NASDAQ)
Rev.: $1,082,571,000
Assets: $1,441,699,000
Liabilities: $676,372,000
Net Worth: $765,327,000
Earnings: ($434,801,000)
Emp.: 3,282
Fiscal Year-end: 12/31/23
Medical Laboratories
N.A.I.C.S.: 621511
Michael Brophy (CFO)
Solomon Moshkevich (Gen Mgr-Oncology)
Robert Schueren (COO)
Rishi Kacker (CTO)

J. Dianne Keen-Kim *(Dir-CLIA Laboratory)*
Minetta Liu *(Chief Medical Officer-Oncology)*
Lesley Bogdanow *(VP-Corp Comm)*
Jerry Diffley *(Chief Compliance Officer)*
Eric Evans *(Chief Scientific Officer)*
Chitra Kotwaliwale *(Sr VP)*
Bernie Tobin *(Gen Mgr)*
Steven Leonard Chapman *(Pres & CEO)*
Matthew Rabinowitz *(Co-Founder & Exec Chm)*
Jonathan Sheena *(Co-Founder)*

Subsidiaries:

Natera International, Inc. (1)
601 Fritz Dr, Coppell, TX 75019
Tel.: (972) 616-6100
Web Site: https://naterra.com
Sales Range: $25-49.9 Million
Emp.: 20
Fiscal Year-end: 06/30/2015
Skin Care Product Mfr
N.A.I.C.S.: 325620

NATHAN'S FAMOUS INC.
1 Jericho Plz, Jericho, NY 11753
Tel.: (516) 338-8500   DE
Web Site:
   https://www.nathansfamous.com
Year Founded: 1916
NATH—(NASDAQ)
Rev.: $130,785,000
Assets: $58,610,000
Liabilities: $103,172,000
Net Worth: ($44,562,000)
Earnings: $19,623,000
Emp.: 138
Fiscal Year-end: 03/26/23
Fast Food Franchise
N.A.I.C.S.: 722513
Eric Gatoff *(CEO)*
Robert Steinberg *(CFO, Chief Acctg Officer & VP-Fin)*
Howard M. Lorber *(Chm)*

Subsidiaries:

Nathan's Famous of Yonkers, Inc. (1)
2290 Central Park Ave, Yonkers, NY 10710
Tel.: (914) 779-1800
Sales Range: $10-24.9 Million
Emp.: 40
Restaurant Operating Services
N.A.I.C.S.: 722511

NATIONAL AMERICAN UNIVERSITY HOLDINGS, INC.
5301 Mt Rushmore Rd, Rapid City, SD 57709
Tel.: (605) 721-5200   DE
Web Site: https://www.national.edu
Year Founded: 2007
NAUH—(OTCQB)
Rev.: $12,557,000
Assets: $6,097,000
Liabilities: $13,338,000
Net Worth: ($7,241,000)
Earnings: $5,302,000
Emp.: 254
Fiscal Year-end: 05/31/22
Holding Company; Professional & Technical Postsecondary Educational Facilities Operator
N.A.I.C.S.: 551112
Robert D. Buckingham *(Vice Chm)*
Ronald L. Shape *(Pres & CEO)*
Edward D. Buckingham *(Chm)*
Thomas Bickart *(CFO)*

Subsidiaries:

Dlorah, Inc. (1)
5301 S Hwy 16 Ste 200, Rapid City, SD 57701-8932
Tel.: (605) 721-5200
Web Site: http://www.national.edu

Educational Support Services
N.A.I.C.S.: 611310

NATIONAL ART EXCHANGE, INC.
200 Vesey St 24th Fl Unit 24196, New York, NY 10080
Tel.: (646) 512-5855   NV
Year Founded: 2014
NAEX—(OTCIQ)
Sales Range: Less than $1 Million
Investment Services
N.A.I.C.S.: 523999
Qingxi Meng *(Chm, Pres & CEO)*
Jun Zhang *(CTO & Sr VP)*

NATIONAL BANK HOLDINGS CORPORATION
7800 E Orchard Rd Ste 300, Greenwood Village, CO 80111
Tel.: (720) 554-6680   DE
Web Site:
   https://www.nationalbankholdings.com
Year Founded: 2009
NBHC—(NYSE)
Rev.: $352,000,000
Assets: $9,573,243,000
Liabilities: $8,481,041,000
Net Worth: $1,092,202,000
Earnings: $71,274,000
Emp.: 1,255
Fiscal Year-end: 12/31/22
Bank Holding Company
N.A.I.C.S.: 551111
G. Timothy Laney *(Chm, Pres & CEO)*
Aldis Birkans *(CFO)*
Jody Soper *(CMO)*
Angela Petrucci *(Chief Admin Officer, Gen Counsel , Chief Admin Officer, Gen Counsel & Exec VP)*
Richard U. Newfield Jr. *(Chief Risk Mgmt Officer)*

Subsidiaries:

NBH Bank (1)
7800 E Orchard Rd, Greenwood Village, CO 80111
Tel.: (720) 554-6650
Web Site: http://www.nbhbank.com
Sales Range: $100-124.9 Million
Emp.: 300
Commercial Bank
N.A.I.C.S.: 522110
G. Timothy Laney *(Chm, Pres & CEO)*
Patrick G. Sobers *(Executives, Bd of Dirs)*
Jody Soper *(CMO)*

Division (Domestic):

Bank Midwest (2)
1111 Main St, Kansas City, MO 64105
Tel.: (816) 298-2100
Web Site: http://www.bankmw.com
Commericial Banking
N.A.I.C.S.: 522110
Whitney Bartelli *(Pres)*
Mario Boschmann *(Officer)*
Dean Best *(Mgr-Comml)*
Alan Hobbs *(Mgr-Comml)*
Matt Leadbetter *(Mgr-Comml)*
Kevin Vanderweide *(Mgr-Comml)*
Steve Schrag *(Mgr-Comml Real Estate & Sr VP)*
Aaron Dawson *(VP & Portfolio Mgr)*
Charlie Koch *(Mgr-Market-Comml Banking)*
Valerie Kramer *(Chief Digital Officer & Chief Digital Officer)*
Jon Ecker *(Officer & Asst VP)*
Chris Randall *(Exec VP)*
Brendan Zahl *(Exec VP)*
Ruth Stevenson *(Head)*
Victor Hammonds *(Sr VP)*
Chris Randall *(Exec VP)*
Brendan Zahl *(Exec VP)*
Ruth Stevenson *(Head)*
Victor Hammonds *(Sr VP)*

Community Banks of Colorado (2)
7800 E Orchard Rd Ste 100, Greenwood Village, CO 80111

Tel.: (720) 554-6650
Web Site: http://www.cobnks.com
Emp.: 6
Retail & Commercial Banking
N.A.I.C.S.: 522110
Sarah Burchett *(Mgr-Market & Comml Banking)*
Brian Martorella *(Mgr-Market & Comml Banking)*
Suzanne Pitrusu *(Mgr-Comml Relationship)*
Ed Southwick *(Mgr-Comml Relationship)*
Tom Espeland *(Mgr-Comml Relationship)*

Hillcrest Bank (2)
11111 W 95th St, Overland Park, KS 66214
Tel.: (913) 492-2828
Web Site: http://www.hillcrestbank.com
Sales Range: $50-74.9 Million
Emp.: 80
Commercial Banking Services
N.A.I.C.S.: 522110
David Terry *(Pres & Sr VP)*
Tim Huey *(Dir-Bus Banking)*
Valerie Kramer *(Chief Digital Officer, Chief Digital Officer & Chief Digital Officer)*
Jesse Jurado *(VP-Treasury Mgmt)*
Nancy Hothan *(Officer-Sales-II & VP-Treasury Mgmt)*
Rob Beuttas *(Sr VP)*
Danny Lobina *(Officer-SBA Bus Dev, Sr VP & Sls Mgr-SBA)*
Jon Ecker *(Officer-SBA Bus Resource & Asst VP)*
Megan Sheehan *(Officer-Small Bus Admin Bus Resource)*
Anita Boronkay *(Mgr-Credit-Small Bus Admin Div)*
Mario Boschmann *(Officer)*
Susan Erving *(Officer-Small Bus Admin Pkg-Closing)*
Kathy Mitchley *(VP)*
Mark Abell *(Dir)*
Robert Leonard *(Sr Officer)*
Tyler Featherston *(Officer)*
Martin Snocker *(Portfolio Mgr)*
Lindsey E. Powers *(Portfolio Mgr)*
Lisa Findley *(Ops Mgr)*
Desmond J. Fourie *(Officer & VP)*
Melissa Mitchell *(Officer)*
Gary Saiz *(Officer & VP)*
Lisa Wolff *(Dir & Sr VP)*
Brad Fontenot *(VP)*
Tyler Riles *(VP)*
Kathy Mitchley *(VP)*
Mark Abell *(Dir)*
Robert Leonard *(Sr Officer)*
Tyler Featherston *(Officer)*
Martin Snocker *(Portfolio Mgr)*
Lindsey E. Powers *(Portfolio Mgr)*
Lisa Findley *(Ops Mgr)*
Desmond J. Fourie *(Officer & VP)*
Melissa Mitchell *(Officer)*
Gary Saiz *(Officer & VP)*
Lisa Wolff *(Dir & Sr VP)*
Brad Fontenot *(VP)*
Tyler Riles *(VP)*
Colette Chester *(VP)*

NATIONAL BANK OF COXSACKIE
3-7 Reed St, Coxsackie, NY 12051-0400
Tel.: (518) 731-6161   Ca
Web Site:
   https://www.nbcoxsackie.com
Year Founded: 1852
NCXS—(OTCIQ)
Commercial Banking Services
N.A.I.C.S.: 522110
Jeffrey Britton *(Mgr-Data Processing)*
Frank Trosset *(VP)*
Dawn Keeler *(Mgr-Ops)*
Nicole M. Bliss *(VP-HR)*
Angela Osier *(Officer-Bus Dev)*
John A. Balli *(Pres & CEO)*
Jennifer Vollor *(Branch Mgr-Glenmont)*
Jody Shaw *(Officer-Bus Dev-Capital Region & VP-Capital Region)*
Keven Mathes *(VP)*
Sarah Hodgens *(Chief Compliance Officer)*
Charlene Slemp *(Chief Lending Officer)*

Donald Persico *(Chm)*
Lynn Smith *(Chief Credit Officer & VP)*
John A. Balli *(Pres & CEO)*
George Cooper *(Chief Retail Banking Officer & Sr VP)*

NATIONAL BANKSHARES, INC.
101 Hubbard St, Blacksburg, VA 24062-9002
Tel.: (540) 951-6300   VA
Web Site: https://www.nationalbankshares.com
Year Founded: 1986
NKSH—(NASDAQ)
Rev.: $62,510,000
Assets: $1,677,551,000
Liabilities: $1,554,864,000
Net Worth: $122,687,000
Earnings: $25,932,000
Emp.: 231
Fiscal Year-end: 12/31/22
Bank Holding Company
N.A.I.C.S.: 551111
F. Brad Denardo *(Chm, Pres & CEO)*
Charles E. Green III *(Vice Chm)*
Lora M. Jones *(CFO)*
Lara E. Ramsey *(COO, Sec, Exec VP & Sr VP-Admin)*
Bob D. Sanders II *(Chief Credit Officer)*

Subsidiaries:

National Bankshares Financial Services, Inc. (1)
101 Hubbard St, Blacksburg, VA 24060
Tel.: (540) 951-6360
Web Site:
   http://www.nationalbankshares.com
Insurance & Financial Investment Services
N.A.I.C.S.: 523940
F. Brad Denardo *(Chm, Pres & CEO)*

The National Bank of Blacksburg (1)
101 Hubbard St, Blacksburg, VA 24060
Tel.: (540) 951-6360
Web Site: https://www.nbbank.com
Sales Range: $125-149.9 Million
Emp.: 7
Commericial Banking
N.A.I.C.S.: 522110
F. Brad Denardo *(Chm, Pres & CEO)*
Jason Pospichal *(Sr VP-Loans)*
Bobby D. Sanders II *(Chief Credit Officer & Sr VP)*
Phillip Baker *(Sr VP)*
Jeff Irby *(VP)*
Craig McMillan *(VP-Loans)*
Brad Denardo *(Pres)*
Brooke Miller *(VP)*
Gregory Frederick *(VP)*

NATIONAL BEVERAGE CORP.
8100 SW 10th St Ste 4000, Fort Lauderdale, FL 33324
Tel.: (954) 581-0922   DE
Web Site:
   https://www.nationalbeverage.com
Year Founded: 1985
FIZZ—(NASDAQ)
Rev.: $1,191,694,000
Assets: $770,153,000
Liabilities: $210,641,000
Net Worth: $559,512,000
Earnings: $176,732,000
Emp.: 1,559
Fiscal Year-end: 04/27/24
Holding Company; Beverage Products Developer, Mfr, Marketer & Distr
N.A.I.C.S.: 312111
Nick A. Caporella *(Chm & CEO)*
George R. Bracken *(Exec VP-Fin)*

Subsidiaries:

BevCo Sales, Inc. (1)
1165 Palmour Dr, Gainesville, GA 30501
Tel.: (678) 928-3406
Web Site: http://www.beverages.com

National Beverage Corp.—(Continued)

Soft Drink Product Mfr
N.A.I.C.S.: 312111

Beverage Corporation International, Inc. (1)
3505 NW 107th St, Miami, FL 33167
Tel.: (305) 714-7000
Web Site:
http://www.nationalbeverages.com
Sales Range: $75-99.9 Million
Emp.: 100
Holding Company
N.A.I.C.S.: 424490

Big Shot Beverages, Inc. (1)
3078 Gratiot Ave, Detroit, MI 48207-1829
Tel.: (313) 925-1600
Canned & Bottled Soft Drinks Mfr
N.A.I.C.S.: 312111

Everfresh Beverages Inc. (1)
6600 E 9 Mile Rd, Warren, MI,
48091-2673 **(100%)**
Tel.: (586) 755-9500
Web Site: https://www.everfreshjuice.com
Sales Range: $50-74.9 Million
Emp.: 100
Juice & Juice-Enriched Products Mfr
N.A.I.C.S.: 484121

Faygo Beverages, Inc. (1)
3579 Gratiot Ave, Detroit, MI
48207 **(100%)**
Tel.: (313) 925-1600
Web Site: https://www.faygo.com
Sales Range: $150-199.9 Million
Emp.: 400
Soft Drinks Mfr
N.A.I.C.S.: 312111
Alan Chittaro (Pres)

Home Juice Corp. (1)
1930 George St, Melrose Park, IL 60160-1501
Tel.: (708) 345-5370
Sales Range: $25-49.9 Million
Emp.: 53
Juice & Juice Products Mfr
N.A.I.C.S.: 312111
Nick Capporella (CEO)
Mike Hoeppel (CMO)

LaCroix Sparkling Water, Inc. (1)
8100 SW 10th St Ste 4000, Fort Lauderdale, FL 33324
Tel.: (954) 581-0922
Web Site: http://www.lacroixwater.com
Beverages Mfr
N.A.I.C.S.: 312120

NewBevCo, Inc. (1)
1 N University Dr, Plantation, FL 33324-2038
Tel.: (954) 581-0922
Soft Drink Mfr & Distr
N.A.I.C.S.: 312111
Nick A. Caporella (Chm)

NutraFizz Products Corp. (1)
6600 E 9 Mile Rd, Warren, MI 48091-2673
Tel.: (586) 755-9500
Bottled & Canned Soft Drinks Mfr
N.A.I.C.S.: 312111

Shasta Beverages, Inc. (1)
26901 Industrial Blvd, Hayward, CA 94545
Tel.: (510) 783-3200
Web Site: https://www.shastapop.com
Bottled & Canned Soft Drinks Mfr
N.A.I.C.S.: 312111
Joseph G. Caporella (Exec VP)

Shasta Sales, Inc. (1)
1165 Palmour Dr, Gainesville, GA 30501
Tel.: (770) 535-2214
Soft Drink Mfr & Distr
N.A.I.C.S.: 312111

Shasta, Inc. (1)
8100 SW 10th St Ste 4000, Plantation, FL 33324 **(100%)**
Tel.: (954) 581-0922
Web Site: http://www.shastapop.com
Sales Range: $25-49.9 Million
Emp.: 58
Beverages Mfr
N.A.I.C.S.: 312111

NATIONAL CINEMEDIA, INC.

6300 S Syracuse Way Ste 300, Centennial, CO 80111
Tel.: (303) 792-3600 DE
Web Site: https://www.ncm.com
Year Founded: 1985
NCMI—(NASDAQ)
Rev.: $114,600,000
Assets: $817,400,000
Liabilities: $1,200,900,000
Net Worth: ($383,500,000)
Earnings: ($48,700,000)
Emp.: 346
Fiscal Year-end: 12/30/21
In-Theater Advertising Services
N.A.I.C.S.: 541890
Thomas F. Lesinski (CEO)
Julie L. Patterson (Principal Acctg Officer-Interim, Sr VP & Controller)
Catherine Sullivan (Pres-Sls, Mktg, and Partnerships)
Sarah Kinnick-Hilty (Gen Counsel, Sec & Exec VP)
Steve Sapp (Sr VP-Digital Out-of-Home-Sls)
Eric S. Wohl (Chief HR Officer)
Manu Singh (Sr VP-Strategic Insight & Analytics)
Mike Rosen (Chief Revenue Officer & Exec VP)
Daniel Hahn (Sr VP-Sls-East Coast)
Amy Tunick (CMO & Sr VP)
Ronnie Y. Ng (CFO)

Subsidiaries:

NCM Fathom (1)
9110 E Nichols Ave Ste 200, Centennial, CO 80112-3600
Tel.: (303) 792-3600
Web Site: http://www.ncm.com
Sales Range: $75-99.9 Million
Emp.: 300
In-Theater Advertising & Pre-Movie Entertainment Services
N.A.I.C.S.: 541890

National CineMedia, LLC (1)
6300 S Syracuse Way Ste 300, Centennial, CO 80111
Tel.: (303) 792-3600
Web Site: http://www.ncm.com
Rev.: $441,399,999
Assets: $899,500,000
Liabilities: $1,040,100,000
Net Worth: ($140,600,000)
Earnings: $98,400,000
Fiscal Year-end: 12/27/2018
Online Advertising Services
N.A.I.C.S.: 541810
Thomas F. Lesinski (CEO)

NATIONAL ENERGY SERVICES REUNITED CORP.

777 Post Oak Blvd 7th Fl, Houston, TX 77056
Tel.: (832) 925-3777 VG
Web Site: https://www.nesr.com
Year Founded: 2017
NESR—(OTCIQ)
Rev.: $909,517,000
Assets: $1,828,327,000
Liabilities: $1,025,979,000
Net Worth: $802,348,000
Earnings: ($36,420,000)
Emp.: 5,968
Fiscal Year-end: 12/31/22
Investment Services
N.A.I.C.S.: 523999
Sherif Foda (CEO & Chm)
Christopher L. Boone (CFO)
Dhiraj Dudeja (Chief Comml Officer)
Cathy Konwisarz (Gen Counsel & Sec)
Haya Kablawi (Dir-Internal Audit)
Sahar Badran (Head-Legal-Middle East)
Chokri Ben Amor (VP-Quality, Health, Safety & Environment & Exec Dir)

Salih Merghani (VP-Ops)
Hawazen Nassief (VP-Environmental, Social & Governance & External Affairs)

Subsidiaries:

Gulf energy SAOC (1)
Building 21 Way 5001 Near Al Nahdha Tower, Ghala, Muscat, Oman
Tel.: (968) 24390800
Web Site: https://www.gulfenergy-int.com
Emp.: 1,025
Oil & Gas Services
N.A.I.C.S.: 213112
Sultan Al Ghafri (VP)
Rahima Khalaf (Mgr-Payroll, Compensation & Svcs)

NPS Energy India Private Limited (1)
A-19 Karni Krupa, Hanuwant Vihar Rai Ka Bagh opposite KN College, Jodhpur, 342001, Rajasthan, India
Tel.: (91) 2912510032
Oil & Gas Services
N.A.I.C.S.: 213112

National Gulf Petroleum Services WLL (1)
Warehouse Building 31 Block 5, East Ahmadi Industrial Area, Ahmadi, Kuwait
Tel.: (965) 22021040
Oil & Gas Services
N.A.I.C.S.: 213112

National Petroleum Services JSC (1)
Abdullah Ben Masoud Street, PO Box 82873, Ben Ashour Area, Tripoli, Libya
Tel.: (218) 213614747
Oil & Gas Services
N.A.I.C.S.: 213112
Wesam Abouturkia (Mng Dir)

Sahara Petroleum Services Company S.A.E. (1)
Zahraa El Maadi Industrial Area 5th Section, PO Box 703, Cairo, 11742, Egypt
Tel.: (20) 225194800
Petrol & Gas Services
N.A.I.C.S.: 424720

NATIONAL FUEL GAS COMPANY

6363 Main St, Williamsville, NY 14221
Tel.: (716) 857-7000 NJ
Web Site:
https://www.nationalfuel.com
Year Founded: 1902
NFG—(NYSE)
Rev.: $2,173,771,000
Assets: $8,280,260,000
Liabilities: $2,932,399,000
Net Worth: $5,347,861,000
Earnings: $476,866,000
Emp.: 2,240
Fiscal Year-end: 09/30/23
Integrated Energy Company
N.A.I.C.S.: 221210
David F. Smith (Chm)
Donna L. DeCarolis (Pres-Distr Corp)
David P. Bauer (Pres & CEO)
Sarah J. Mugel (Gen Counsel & Sec)
Elena G. Mendel (Principal Acctg Officer & Controller)
Ronald C. Kraemer (COO & Pres-Supply Corp)
Martin A. Krebs (CIO)
Jeffrey F. Hart (VP-Corp Responsibility)
Michael P. Kasprzak (Pres-Midstream Company & Sr VP-Supply Corp)
Brandon J. Haspett (Dir-IR)
Timothy J. Silverstein (CFO & Treas)

Subsidiaries:

Horizon Power, Inc. (1)
6363 Main St, Buffalo, NY 14221-5855
Tel.: (716) 857-7000
Web Site: http://www.nationalfuelgas.com
Emp.: 2,500

Electrical Power Generation & Distr
N.A.I.C.S.: 221122
Stephanie Unwin (CEO)
Kylie Chamberlain (Dir)
Peter Oates (Chm-Acting)
Stephanie Unwin (CEO)
Mike Houlahan (CFO & Gen Mgr-Corp Svcs)
Andrew Blaver (Gen Mgr-Customer Experience)
Tiri Sanderson (Gen Mgr-Ops)
Darren Hill (Gen Mgr-Comml & Bus Dev)
David Tovey (Gen Mgr-Employee Experience)
Brett Hovingh (Gen Mgr-Tech & Transformation)
Evette Smeathers (Gen Mgr-External Affairs & Comm)

NFG Midstream Covington, LLC (1)
6363 Main St, Williamsville, NY 14221
Tel.: (716) 857-7501
Natural Gas Pipeline Transportation
N.A.I.C.S.: 486210
Duane A. Wassum (Pres)

National Fuel Gas Distribution Corporation (1)
6363 Main St, Williamsville, NY 14221 **(100%)**
Tel.: (716) 857-7000
Web Site: http://www.nationalfuelgas.com
Sales Range: $750-799.9 Million
Emp.: 1,547
Natural Gas Public Utility
N.A.I.C.S.: 221210
Donna L. DeCarolis (Pres)
Karen M. Camiolo (VP)
Amy Shiley (VP-HR & Payroll Dept)
Craig K. Swiech (Asst VP)
John J. Polka Jr. (Asst VP)

National Fuel Gas Supply Corporation (1)
6363 Main St, Williamsville, NY 14221 **(100%)**
Tel.: (716) 857-7740
Web Site: http://www.natfuel.com
Natural Gas Bulk Storage Services
N.A.I.C.S.: 424710
Karen M. Camiolo (Treas)
Ronald C. Kraemer (Pres)
Lee E. Hartz (Asst VP)

National Fuel Resources, Inc. (1)
165 Lawrence Bell Dr Ste 120, Williamsville, NY 14221-7074 **(100%)**
Tel.: (716) 630-6778
Web Site: http://www.nfrinc.com
Sales Range: $50-74.9 Million
Emp.: 35
Markets & Brokers Natural Gas for Utilities & Retail Customers
N.A.I.C.S.: 221122
Robert Tullio (Mgr-Sls & Mktg)
Andy Ames (Coord-Mktg)
Mark Cuda (Dir-Natural Gas Svcs)

Seneca Resources Corporation (1)
1201 Louisiana St Ste 2600, Houston, TX 77002-5604 **(100%)**
Tel.: (713) 654-2600
Web Site: http://www.nationalfuel.com
Sales Range: $50-74.9 Million
Emp.: 45
Oil & Gas Exploration & Production
N.A.I.C.S.: 213112
Justin I. Loweth (Pres)
Steven Conley (Sr VP-Ops)
Cindy D. Wilkinson (VP-Mktg & Controller)
Kevin Lestage (VP-IT)
Bradley D. Elliott (VP East Div)
Ben F. Elmore (Gen Counsel & VP)
Jeffrey J. Formica (VP-Environmental Health Safety & Quality)
Douglas Kepler (VP-Environmental Engrg)

NATIONAL GRAPHITE CORP.

PO Box 26496, Scottsdale, AZ 85255
Tel.: (602) 793-8058 NV
NGRC—(OTCIQ)
Metal Mining Services
N.A.I.C.S.: 213114

NATIONAL HEALTH INVESTORS, INC.

222 Robert Rose Dr, Murfreesboro, TN 37129
Tel.: (615) 890-9100   MD
Web Site: https://www.nhireit.com
Year Founded: 1991
NHI—(NYSE)
Rev.: $319,835,000
Assets: $2,488,480,000
Liabilities: $1,224,089,000
Net Worth: $1,264,391,000
Earnings: $135,597,000
Emp.: 26
Fiscal Year-end: 12/31/23
Healthcare Real Estate Investment Trust
N.A.I.C.S.: 525990
Kevin Pascoe (*Chief Investment Officer*)
D. Eric Mendelsohn (*Pres & CEO*)
David L. Travis (*Chief Acctg Officer*)
John L. Spaid (*CFO*)
Michelle R. Kelly (*Sr VP-Investments*)

Subsidiaries:

Bickford at Mission Springs I, L.L.C.   (1)
5300 W 61st Pl, Mission, KS 66205
Tel.: (913) 831-7700
Health Care Srvices
N.A.I.C.S.: 524298

Bickford of Carmel, LLC   (1)
5829 E 116th St, Carmel, IN 46033
Tel.: (317) 813-3232
Web Site:
   https://www.bickfordseniorliving.com
Health Care Srvices
N.A.I.C.S.: 524298

Bickford of Middletown, LLC   (1)
4375 Union Rd, Middletown, OH 45005-5241
Tel.: (937) 550-4911
Web Site:
   https://www.bickfordseniorliving.com
Health Care Srvices
N.A.I.C.S.: 524298

Bickford of Overland Park, L.L.C. (1)
10665 Barkley, Overland Park, KS 66212
Tel.: (913) 642-5400
Health Care Srvices
N.A.I.C.S.: 524298

Cedar Falls Bickford Cottage, L.L.C.   (1)
5101 University Ave, Cedar Falls, IA 50613
Tel.: (319) 266-6800
Web Site:
   http://www.enrichinghappiness.com
Health Care Srvices
N.A.I.C.S.: 524298

Crawfordsville Bickford Cottage, L.L.C.   (1)
100 Bickford Ln, Crawfordsville, IN 47933
Tel.: (765) 362-2000
Health Care Srvices
N.A.I.C.S.: 524298

Texas NHI Investors, LLC   (1)
222 Robert Rose Dr, Murfreesboro, TN 37129
Tel.: (615) 890-9100
Health Care Srvices
N.A.I.C.S.: 621610

NATIONAL HEALTHCARE CORPORATION
100 E Vine St, Murfreesboro, TN 37130
Tel.: (615) 890-2020   DE
Web Site: https://www.nhccare.com
Year Founded: 1971
NHC—(NYSEAMEX)
Rev.: $1,141,544,000
Assets: $1,310,796,000
Liabilities: $400,316,000
Net Worth: $910,480,000
Earnings: $66,798,000
Emp.: 13,123
Fiscal Year-end: 12/31/23

Skilled & Intermediate Nursing & Rehabilitation Care Through Health Care Centers
N.A.I.C.S.: 623311
R. Michael Ussery (*Pres & COO*)
Stephen Fowler Flatt (*CEO*)
Brian F. Kidd (*CFO & Sr VP*)
B. Anderson Flatt (*CIO & Sr VP*)
Bubba McIntosh (*Sr VP-Ancillary Svcs & Svc Strategy*)
Josh A. McCreary (*Gen Counsel, Sec & Sr VP*)
Vicki Dodson (*Sr VP-Patient Svcs*)

Subsidiaries:

AdamsPlace, LLC   (1)
1927 Memorial Blvd, Murfreesboro, TN 37129-1545
Tel.: (615) 904-2449
Web Site: http://www.adamsplace.org
Nursing Care Facilities
N.A.I.C.S.: 623110
Carl E. Adams (*Founder*)

Buckley HealthCare Center, LLC (1)
95 Laurel St, Greenfield, MA 01301-3106
Tel.: (413) 774-3143
Web Site: http://www.buckleyhealthcare.com
Health Care Srvices
N.A.I.C.S.: 621999

Columbia HealthCare Center, LLC   (1)
1801 Towne Dr, Columbia, MO 65202
Tel.: (573) 474-6111
Web Site:
   http://www.columbiahealthcarecenter.com
Health Care Srvices
N.A.I.C.S.: 621610

Holyoke HealthCare Center, LLC (1)
282 Cabot St, Holyoke, MA 01040
Tel.: (413) 538-7470
Web Site:
   http://www.holyokehealthcare.com
Emp.: 150
Health Care Srvices
N.A.I.C.S.: 621999

John Adams HealthCare Center, LLC   (1)
211 Franklin St, Quincy, MA 02169
Tel.: (617) 479-0837
Web Site:
   http://www.johnadamscarecenter.com
Health Care Srvices
N.A.I.C.S.: 621999

Maryland Heights Center for Behavioral Health, LLC   (1)
11100 Ayrshire Dr, Maryland Heights, MO 63043
Tel.: (314) 528-2700
Web Site: https://marylandheightsbehavioral
   health.com
Psychiatric Care Services
N.A.I.C.S.: 622210

NHC Farragut Memory Care, LLC   (1)
122 Cavette Hill Ln, Knoxville, TN 37934
Tel.: (865) 777-9000
Health Care Srvices
N.A.I.C.S.: 621610

NHC HealthCare-Charleston, LLC   (1)
2230 Ashley Crossing Dr, Charleston, SC 29414
Tel.: (843) 766-5228
Web Site:
   http://www.nhccharlestonhealthcare.com
Emp.: 150
Home Care Services
N.A.I.C.S.: 621610

NHC HealthCare-Macon, LLC   (1)
29612 Kellogg Ave, Macon, MO 63552-3702
Tel.: (660) 385-5797
Web Site:
   http://www.maconhealthcarecenter.com
Emp.: 86
Nursing Care Facilities
N.A.I.C.S.: 623110

NHC HealthCare-Osage Beach, LLC   (1)

844 Passover Rd, Osage Beach, MO 65065
Tel.: (573) 348-2225
Web Site:
   http://www.osagebeachhealthcare.com
Sales Range: $10-24.9 Million
Emp.: 77
Nursing Care Facilities
N.A.I.C.S.: 623110

NHC HealthCare-Springfield Missouri, LLC   (1)
2800 S Fort Ave, Springfield, MO 65807-3480
Tel.: (417) 882-0035
Emp.: 110
Health Care Srvices
N.A.I.C.S.: 621610
Stephanie Grant (*Gen Mgr*)

NHC HealthCare-Sumner, LLC   (1)
140 Thorne Blvd, Gallatin, TN 37066
Tel.: (615) 451-0788
Web Site: http://www.nhcplacesumner.com
Health Care Srvices
N.A.I.C.S.: 621999

NHC HealthCare/Anderson, LLC (1)
1501 E Greenville St, Anderson, SC 29621
Tel.: (864) 226-8356
Web Site: http://www.nhcanderson.com
Nursing Care Facilities
N.A.I.C.S.: 623110

NHC HealthCare/Anniston, LLC   (1)
2300 Coleman Rd, Anniston, AL 36207
Tel.: (256) 831-5730
Web Site:
   http://www.nhchealthcareanniston.com
Emp.: 120
Nursing Care Facilities
N.A.I.C.S.: 623110

NHC HealthCare/Athens, LLC   (1)
1204 Frye St, Athens, TN 37303
Tel.: (423) 745-0434
Web Site: http://www.nhcathens.com
Emp.: 100
Health Care Srvices
N.A.I.C.S.: 621610

NHC HealthCare/Bluffton, LLC   (1)
3039 Okatie Hwy, Bluffton, SC 29909
Tel.: (843) 705-8220
Web Site: http://www.nhcbluffton.com
Emp.: 100
Health Care Srvices
N.A.I.C.S.: 621610

NHC HealthCare/Chattanooga, LLC   (1)
2700 Parkwood Ave, Chattanooga, TN 37404
Tel.: (423) 624-1533
Web Site: http://www.nhcchattanooga.com
Nursing Care Facilities
N.A.I.C.S.: 623110

NHC HealthCare/Clinton, LLC   (1)
304 Jacobs Hwy, Clinton, SC 29325-7279
Tel.: (864) 833-2550
Web Site: http://www.nhcclinton.com
Health Care Srvices
N.A.I.C.S.: 621610

NHC HealthCare/Columbia, LLC (1)
101 Walnut Ln, Columbia, TN 38401
Tel.: (931) 381-3112
Web Site:
   http://www.nhccolumbiahealthcare.com
Emp.: 130
Health Care Srvices
N.A.I.C.S.: 621610

NHC HealthCare/Cool Springs, LLC   (1)
211 Cool Springs Blvd, Franklin, TN 37067
Tel.: (615) 778-6800
Web Site: http://www.nhcplace.com
Nursing Care Facilities
N.A.I.C.S.: 623110

NHC HealthCare/Desloge, LLC   (1)
801 Brim St, Desloge, MO 63601-3441
Tel.: (573) 431-0223
Web Site: http://www.nhcdesloge.com
Emp.: 97
Nursing Care Facilities
N.A.I.C.S.: 623110

NHC HealthCare/Dickson, LLC   (1)

812 N Charlotte St, Dickson, TN 37055
Tel.: (615) 446-8046
Web Site: http://www.nhcdickson.com
Nursing Care Facilities
N.A.I.C.S.: 623110

NHC HealthCare/Farragut, LLC   (1)
122 Cavette Hill Ln, Knoxville, TN 37934-6674
Tel.: (865) 777-9000
Web Site: https://nhccare.com
Emp.: 200
Nursing Care Facilities
N.A.I.C.S.: 623110

NHC HealthCare/Franklin, LLC   (1)
216 Fairground St, Franklin, TN 37064-3531
Tel.: (615) 790-0154
Web Site: http://www.nhcfranklin.com
Emp.: 80
Nursing Care Facilities
N.A.I.C.S.: 623110

NHC HealthCare/Garden City, LLC   (1)
9405 Hwy 17 Bypass, Murrells Inlet, SC 29576
Tel.: (843) 650-2213
Web Site: http://www.nhcgardencity.com
Nursing Care Facilities
N.A.I.C.S.: 623110

NHC HealthCare/Glasgow, LLC   (1)
109 Homewood Blvd, Glasgow, KY 42141-3468
Tel.: (270) 651-6126
Web Site: http://www.nhchealthcare.com
Emp.: 200
Nursing Care Facilities
N.A.I.C.S.: 623110

NHC HealthCare/Greenville, LLC (1)
1305 Boiling Springs Rd, Greer, SC 29650
Tel.: (864) 458-7566
Web Site: http://www.nhcgreenville.com
Emp.: 200
Nursing Care Facilities
N.A.I.C.S.: 623110

NHC HealthCare/Greenwood, LLC   (1)
437 E Cambridge Ave, Greenwood, SC 29646
Tel.: (864) 223-1950
Web Site: http://www.nhcgreenwood.com
Emp.: 140
Nursing Care Facilities
N.A.I.C.S.: 623110

NHC HealthCare/Heartland, LLC (1)
3025 Fernbrook Ln, Nashville, TN 37214
Tel.: (615) 885-2320
Senior Living Facility Operator
N.A.I.C.S.: 623312

NHC HealthCare/Hendersonville, LLC   (1)
370 Old Shackle Island Rd, Hendersonville, TN 37075-3082
Tel.: (615) 824-0720
Web Site: http://www.nhchendersonville.com
Nursing Care Facilities
N.A.I.C.S.: 623110

NHC HealthCare/Holston Hills, LLC   (1)
3916 Boyd's Bridge Pike, Knoxville, TN 37914
Tel.: (865) 524-1500
Web Site: http://www.nhcholston.com
Nursing Care Facilities
N.A.I.C.S.: 623110

NHC HealthCare/Johnson City, LLC   (1)
3209 Bristol Hwy, Johnson City, TN 37601
Tel.: (423) 282-3311
Web Site: http://www.nhcjc.com
Emp.: 160
Nursing Care Facilities
N.A.I.C.S.: 623110

NHC HealthCare/Joplin, LLC   (1)
2700 E 34th St, Joplin, MO 64804
Tel.: (417) 781-1737
Web Site: http://www.nhcjoplin.com
Emp.: 113
Health Care Srvices
N.A.I.C.S.: 621610

National HealthCare Corporation—(Continued)

NHC HealthCare/Kennett, LLC (1)
1120 Falcon Dr, Kennett, MO 63857
Tel.: (537) 888-1150
Web Site: http://www.nhckennett.com
Sales Range: $25-49.9 Million
Emp.: 140
Nursing Care Facilities
N.A.I.C.S.: 623110

NHC HealthCare/Kingsport, LLC (1)
2300 Pavilion Dr, Kingsport, TN 37660
Tel.: (423) 765-9655
Web Site: http://www.nhckingsport.com
Emp.: 50
Health Care Srvices
N.A.I.C.S.: 621999

NHC HealthCare/Knoxville, LLC (1)
809 Emerald Ave NE, Knoxville, TN 37917
Tel.: (865) 524-7366
Web Site: http://www.nhcknoxville.com
Nursing Care Facilities
N.A.I.C.S.: 623110

NHC HealthCare/Laurens, LLC (1)
379 Pinehaven St Ext, Laurens, SC 29360
Tel.: (864) 984-6584
Web Site: http://www.nhclaurens.com
Nursing Care Facilities
N.A.I.C.S.: 623110

NHC HealthCare/Lexington, LLC (1)
2993 Sunset Blvd, West Columbia, SC 29169
Tel.: (803) 939-0026
Web Site: http://www.nhclexington.com
Health Care Srvices
N.A.I.C.S.: 621610

NHC HealthCare/Madisonville,
LLC (1)
419 N Seminary St, Madisonville, KY 42431
Tel.: (270) 821-5564
Web Site: http://www.nhcmadisonville.com
Nursing Care Facilities
N.A.I.C.S.: 623110

NHC HealthCare/Maryland Heights,
LLC (1)
2920 Fee Fee Rd, Maryland Heights, MO 63043
Tel.: (314) 291-0121
Web Site:
   http://www.nhcmarylandheights.com
Nursing Care Facilities
N.A.I.C.S.: 623110

NHC HealthCare/Mauldin, LLC (1)
850 E Butler Rd, Greenville, SC 29607
Tel.: (864) 675-6421
Web Site: http://www.nhcmauldin.com
Nursing Care Facilities
N.A.I.C.S.: 623110

NHC HealthCare/McMinnville,
LLC (1)
928 Old Smithville Rd, McMinnville, TN 37110
Tel.: (931) 473-8431
Web Site: http://www.nhcmcminnville.com
Emp.: 100
Nursing Care Facilities
N.A.I.C.S.: 623110

NHC HealthCare/Milan, LLC (1)
8017 Dogwood Ln, Milan, TN 38358-6805
Tel.: (731) 686-8373
Web Site: http://www.nhcmilan.com
Sales Range: $25-49.9 Million
Fmp.: 130
Health Care Srvices
N.A.I.C.S.: 621610

NHC HealthCare/Moulton, LLC (1)
300 Hospital St, Moulton, AL 35650
Tel.: (256) 974-1146
Web Site: http://www.nhcmoulton.com
Nursing Care Facilities
N.A.I.C.S.: 623110

NHC HealthCare/North Augusta,
LLC (1)
350 Austin Graybill Rd, North Augusta, SC 29860
Tel.: (803) 278-4272
Web Site: http://www.nhcnorthaugusta.com
Health Care Srvices
N.A.I.C.S.: 621610

NHC HealthCare/Oakwood, LLC (1)
244 Oakwood Dr, Lewisburg, TN 37091
Tel.: (931) 359-3563
Web Site: http://www.nhcoakwood.com
Nursing Care Facilities
N.A.I.C.S.: 623110

NHC HealthCare/Pensacola, Inc. (1)
8475 University Pkwy, Pensacola, FL 32514-4917
Tel.: (850) 474-1252
Nursing Care Facilities
N.A.I.C.S.: 623110

NHC HealthCare/Pulaski, LLC (1)
993 E College St, Pulaski, TN 38478
Tel.: (931) 363-3572
Web Site: http://www.nhcpulaski.com
Emp.: 100
Nursing Care Facilities
N.A.I.C.S.: 623110

NHC HealthCare/Rossville, LLC (1)
1425 McFarland Ave, Rossville, GA 30741
Tel.: (706) 861-0863
Web Site: http://www.nhcrossville.com
Health Care Srvices
N.A.I.C.S.: 621610

NHC HealthCare/Scott, LLC (1)
2380 Buffalo Rd, Lawrenceburg, TN 38464
Tel.: (931) 762-9418
Web Site: http://www.nhcscott.com
Nursing Care Facilities
N.A.I.C.S.: 623110

NHC HealthCare/Smithville, LLC (1)
825 Fisher Ave, Smithville, TN 37166
Tel.: (615) 597-4284
Web Site: http://www.nhcsmithville.com
Emp.: 120
Nursing Care Facilities
N.A.I.C.S.: 623110

NHC HealthCare/Somerville,
LLC (1)
308 Lake Dr, Somerville, TN 38068
Tel.: (901) 465-9861
Web Site: http://www.nhcsomerville.com
Health Care Srvices
N.A.I.C.S.: 621610

NHC HealthCare/Sparta, LLC (1)
34 Gracey St, Sparta, TN 38583
Tel.: (931) 836-2211
Web Site: http://www.nhcsparta.com
Emp.: 110
Nursing Care Facilities
N.A.I.C.S.: 623110

NHC HealthCare/Springfield,
LLC (1)
608 E 8th Ave, Springfield, TN 37172
Tel.: (615) 384-8453
Web Site: http://www.nhcspringfield.com
Emp.: 115
Nursing Care Facilities
N.A.I.C.S.: 623110

NHC HealthCare/St. Charles,
LLC (1)
35 Sugar Maple Ln, Saint Charles, MO 63303-5740
Tel.: (636) 946-8887
Web Site: http://www.nhcstcharles.com
Health Care Srvices
N.A.I.C.S.: 621610

NHC HealthCare/Town &
Country (1)
13995 Clayton Rd, Town and Country, MO 63017
Tel.: (636) 227-5070
Web Site:
   http://www.nhctownandcountry.com
Nursing Care Facilities
N.A.I.C.S.: 623110

NHC HealthCare/Tullahoma,
LLC (1)
1321 Cedar Ln, Tullahoma, TN 37388
Tel.: (931) 222-4207
Web Site: http://www.nhctullahoma.com
Health Care Srvices
N.A.I.C.S.: 621999

NHC Homecare - South Carolina,
LLC (1)
1674 Cranium Dr Ste 101, Piedmont, SC 29732

Tel.: (803) 325-1455
Web Site: http://www.nhchealthcare.com
Nursing Care Facilities
N.A.I.C.S.: 623110

NHC Homecare Missouri, LLC (1)
12563 Village Circle Dr, Saint Louis, MO 63127
Tel.: (314) 434-2497
Web Site: http://www.mynhchomecare.com
Health Care Srvices
N.A.I.C.S.: 621610

NHC Homecare-South Carolina,
LLC (1)
74 Physicians Dr, Aiken, SC 29802
Tel.: (803) 643-1701
Web Site:
   http://www.nhchomecareaiken.com
Women Healthcare Services
N.A.I.C.S.: 621610

NHC Place Merritt Island, LLC (1)
2395 N Courtenay Pkwy Ste 101, Merritt Island, FL 32953
Tel.: (321) 459-9111
Home Nursing Services
N.A.I.C.S.: 621610

NHC Place at the Trace, LLC (1)
8353 Hwy 100, Nashville, TN 37221
Tel.: (629) 888-5800
Health Care Srvices
N.A.I.C.S.: 621610
Debbie Huntzinger (Dir-Community Rels)

NHC Place/Anniston, LLC (1)
1335 Greenbrier Dear Rd, Anniston, AL 36207
Tel.: (256) 835-3959
Web Site: http://www.nhcplaceanniston.com
Emp.: 65
Nursing Care Facilities
N.A.I.C.S.: 623110

NHC Place/Lake St. Charles,
LLC (1)
45 Honey Locust Ln, Saint Charles, MO 63303-5711
Tel.: (636) 947-1100
Web Site:
   http://www.lakestcharlesretirement.com
Sales Range: $10-24.9 Million
Emp.: 40
Health Care Srvices
N.A.I.C.S.: 621610
Samantha Davis (Exec Dir)
Jody Rudy (Dir-Housekeeping)

NHC-Maury Regional Transitional
Care Center, LLC (1)
5010 Trotwood Ave, Columbia, TN 38401
Tel.: (931) 398-6300
Health Care Facility Services
N.A.I.C.S.: 621999

NHC/OP, L.P. (1)
452 Cambridge Ave, Greenwood, SC 29646
Tel.: (864) 229-9888
Web Site: http://www.mynhchomecare.com
Emp.: 25
Health Care Srvices
N.A.I.C.S.: 621610

Subsidiary (Domestic):

Caris HealthCare L.P. (2)
10651 Coward Mill Rd Ste B, Knoxville, TN 37931 (100%)
Tel.: (865) 694-4988
Web Site: https://www.carishealthcare.com
Sales Range: $10-24.9 Million
Emp.: 500
Nursing Care Facilities
N.A.I.C.S.: 623110
Norman McRae (Founder)
Paul Saylor (CEO)
Alan Seivers (CFO)
Cindy Jacquemin (VP-Patient Care)
Gary Fleenor (VP-HR)
Sylvia L. Singleton (Compliance Officer)
Brad Rector (COO)
Mark Murray (Chief Medical Officer)
Darrah Whittaker (VP-Sls & Mktg)

NHC/OP, L.P. (1)
2395 N Courtenay Pkwy, Merritt Island, FL 32953
Tel.: (321) 459-9111
Health Care Srvices

N.A.I.C.S.: 621610

NHC/OP, L.P. (1)
17985 US Hwy 64, Somerville, TN 38068
Tel.: (901) 465-4101
Emp.: 20
Health Care Srvices
N.A.I.C.S.: 621610

NHC/OP, L.P. (1)
111 Smith Hines Rd Ste L, Greenville, SC 29607-5780
Tel.: (864) 289-9982
Health Care Srvices
N.A.I.C.S.: 621610

NHC/OP, L.P. (1)
111 Smith Hines Rd Ste L, Greenville, SC 29607-5780
Tel.: (864) 289-9982
Health Care Srvices
N.A.I.C.S.: 621610

NHC/OP, L.P. (1)
17985 US Hwy 64, Somerville, TN 38068
Tel.: (901) 465-4101
Emp.: 20
Health Care Srvices
N.A.I.C.S.: 621610

NHC/OP, L.P. (1)
2395 N Courtenay Pkwy, Merritt Island, FL 32953
Tel.: (321) 459-9111
Health Care Srvices
N.A.I.C.S.: 621610

National HealthCare Corporation (1)
2300 Coleman Rd, Anniston, AL 36207
Tel.: (256) 831-5730
Health Care Srvices
N.A.I.C.S.: 621610
Amanda Williams (Dir-Food & Nutrition Svcs)

National HealthCare Corporation (1)
2300 Coleman Rd, Anniston, AL 36207
Tel.: (256) 831-5730
Health Care Srvices
N.A.I.C.S.: 621610
Amanda Williams (Dir-Food & Nutrition Svcs)

National Healthcare Center of Fort
Oglethorpe, L.P. (1)
2403 Battlefield Pkwy, Fort Oglethorpe, GA 30742
Tel.: (706) 866-7700
Web Site: http://www.nhcfortoglethorpe.com
Emp.: 145
Nursing Care Facilities
N.A.I.C.S.: 623110

Nutritional Support Services, L.P. (1)
9000 Executive Park Dr A301, Knoxville, TN 37923-4646
Tel.: (865) 531-0008
Sales Range: $25-49.9 Million
Emp.: 25
Medical Equipment & Supplies Whslr
N.A.I.C.S.: 423450

Pearl Street HealthCare Center,
LLC (1)
198 Pearl St, Manchester, NH 03104-4357
Tel.: (603) 669-1660
Health Care Srvices
N.A.I.C.S.: 621610

Quarters at Des Peres, LLC (1)
13230 Manchester Rd, Des Peres, MO 63131
Tel.: (314) 821-2886
Web Site:
   http://www.thequartersatdesperes.com
Emp.: 30
Health Care Srvices
N.A.I.C.S.: 621999
Marcy Howard (Mgr-Mktg)

Standifer Place Properties, LLC (1)
2626 Walker Rd, Chattanooga, TN 37421
Tel.: (423) 490-1599
Web Site: https://standiferplace.org
Nursing Care Facilities
N.A.I.C.S.: 623110

The Health Center of Hermitage,
LLC (1)
1633 Hillview Dr, Elizabethton, TN 37643
Tel.: (423) 543-2571

Web Site:
http://www.hermitagehealthcenter.com
Emp.: 80
Nursing Care Facilities
N.A.I.C.S.: 623110

The Palmettos of Parklane, LLC (1)
7811 Parklane Rd, Columbia, SC 29223
Tel.: (803) 741-7233
Web Site:
http://www.thepalmettosparklane.com
Nursing Care Facilities
N.A.I.C.S.: 623110

Tranzion, LLC (1)
100 E Vine St, Murfreesboro, TN 37130
Tel.: (615) 624-5932
Web Site: https://www.tranzion.com
Information Technology Consulting Services
N.A.I.C.S.: 541512

Villa Crest HealthCare Center, LLC (1)
1276 Hanover St, Manchester, NH 03104
Tel.: (603) 622-3262
Web Site:
http://www.villacrestcommunity.com
Emp.: 105
Health Care Srvices
N.A.I.C.S.: 621610

Villages of Jackson Creek Memory Care, LLC (1)
19400 E 40th St Ct S, Independence, MO 64057
Tel.: (816) 478-5689
Web Site: http://www.vofjcmc.com
Health Care Srvices
N.A.I.C.S.: 621999
Candyss Camarda *(Dir-Social Svcs-Admissions-Marketing)*
Melody Johnson *(Dir-Nutritional Svcs)*
Sue Demmer *(Dir-Recreation)*
Carole McKeehan *(Dir-Nursing)*
Pam Rieves *(Asst Dir-Nursing)*
Linda Duncan *(Office Mgr)*
Tommy Leftridge *(Dir-Maintenance & Supvr-Housekeeping)*

Villages of Jackson Creek, LLC (1)
3980 S Jackson Dr, Independence, MO 64057
Tel.: (816) 795-1433
Web Site: http://www.vofjc.com
Emp.: 260
Health Care Srvices
N.A.I.C.S.: 621999
Monique Moore *(Dir-Nursing)*
Diedra Morris *(Dir-Admissions & Mktg)*
Kelly Tennison *(Dir-Assisted Living)*

Villages of St. Peters, LLC (1)
5400 Executive Center Pkwy, Saint Peters, MO 63376
Tel.: (636) 922-7600
Web Site: http://www.vofsp.com
Health Care Srvices
N.A.I.C.S.: 621999

NATIONAL HEALTHCARE LOGISTICS, INC.
370 Amapola Ave Ste 200A, Torrance, CA 90501
Tel.: (310) 895-1839   NV
Year Founded: 1999
NHLG—(OTCIQ)
Healtcare Services
N.A.I.C.S.: 621610
Frank Lkechukwu Igwealor *(Chm & CEO)*
Kuldip Singh *(Pres & CEO)*

NATIONAL HEALTHCARE PROPERTIES, INC.
540 Madison Ave 27th Fl, New York, NY 10022
Tel.: (212) 415-6500   MD
Web Site: https://nhpreit.com
Year Founded: 2012
HTIA—(NASDAQ)
Rev.: $345,925,000
Assets: $2,145,159,000
Liabilities: $1,244,576,000
Net Worth: $900,583,000
Earnings: ($86,097,000)

Fiscal Year-end: 12/31/23
Real Estate Investment Trust
N.A.I.C.S.: 525990
Trent Taylor *(Sr VP-Healthcare Asset Mgmt)*
David Ruggiero *(VP-Acquisitions)*
John Rimbach *(Pres-Healthcare Facilities)*
Angie Ehlers *(VP-Sls & Mktg)*
Kimberly Holmes *(VP-Operational Analytics)*
Susan K. Rice *(VP-Clinical Ops)*
Jason Doyle *(CFO, Treas & Sec)*
Edward Michael Weil Jr. *(Pres & CEO)*
Scott M. Lappetito *(CFO, Treas & Sec)*
Lindsay Gordon *(Sr VP)*
Michelle Stepinsky *(VP-Sales & Marketing)*

NATIONAL PRESTO INDUSTRIES, INC
3925 N Hastings Way, Eau Claire, WI 54703-3703
Tel.: (715) 839-2121   WI
Web Site: https://www.gopresto.com
Year Founded: 1905
NPK—(NYSE)
Rev.: $321,623,000
Assets: $411,847,000
Liabilities: $63,795,000
Net Worth: $348,052,000
Earnings: $20,699,000
Emp.: 973
Fiscal Year-end: 12/31/22
Housewares & Related Products Mfr
N.A.I.C.S.: 333414
Maryjo J. Cohen *(Chm, Pres & CEO)*
Douglas J. Frederick *(COO, Sec & VP)*
David J. Peuse *(Treas & Dir-Fin Reporting)*
John R. MacKenzie *(VP-Sls)*
Jeffery A. Morgan *(VP)*

Subsidiaries:

AMTEC Corporation (1)
4230 Capital Circle, Janesville, WI 53546
Tel.: (608) 752-2699
Ammunition System Mfr
N.A.I.C.S.: 332994

Unit (Domestic):

Amron (2)
920 Amron Dr, Antigo, WI 54409
Tel.: (715) 623-4176
Web Site:
https://www.nationaldefensecorp.com
Medium Caliber Cartridge Case Mfr
N.A.I.C.S.: 332992

Subsidiary (Domestic):

DSE Inc. (2)
5201 S WestShore Blvd, Tampa, FL 33611
Tel.: (813) 831-0750
Web Site: http://www.dse.net
Sales Range: $50-74.9 Million
Emp.: 75
Ammunition & Machined Metal Parts Mfr
N.A.I.C.S.: 332510
Dae Y. Shin *(CEO)*

Unit (Domestic):

Spectra Technologies, LLC (2)
Bldg 20 Highland Industrial Park, East Camden, AR 71711
Tel.: (870) 574-2555
Web Site:
https://www.spectratechnologiesllc.com
Sales Range: $1-9.9 Million
Emp.: 70
Explosives Mfr
N.A.I.C.S.: 325920

Subsidiary (Domestic):

Tech Ord (2)
47600 180th St, Clear Lake, SD 57226
Tel.: (605) 874-2631

Web Site:
https://www.nationaldefensecorp.com
Engineeering Services
N.A.I.C.S.: 541330

National Defense Corp. (1)
4230 Capital Cir Dr, Janesville, WI 53546   (100%)
Tel.: (608) 752-2699
Web Site:
https://www.nationaldefensecorp.com
Sales Range: $75-99.9 Million
Emp.: 310
Facilities Support Services
N.A.I.C.S.: 561210

National Holding Investment Co. (1)
1011 Centra Rd Ste 310, Wilmington, DE 19805   (100%)
Tel.: (302) 573-3887
Sales Range: $50-74.9 Million
Management of Funds
N.A.I.C.S.: 621999

Subsidiary (Domestic):

Canton Sales & Storage Co. (2)
555 Matthews Dr, Canton, MS 39046-3251   (100%)
Tel.: (601) 859-7313
Warehousing & Distribution
N.A.I.C.S.: 493190

Jackson Sales & Storage Co. (2)
PO Box 68361, Jackson, MS 39286-8361   (100%)
Tel.: (601) 366-3481
Warehousing & Distribution of Small Household Appliances
N.A.I.C.S.: 493110

OneEvent Technologies, Inc. (1)
505 Springdale St, Mount Horeb, WI 53572
Tel.: (608) 575-2150
Web Site: https://www.oneeventtech.com
Software Development Services
N.A.I.C.S.: 541511
Kurt Wedig *(Pres & CEO)*

Woodlawn Manufacturing, Ltd. (1)
275 Bussey Rd, Marshall, TX 75670
Tel.: (903) 938-1882
Web Site:
http://www.woodlawnmanufacturing.com
Sales Range: $1-9.9 Million
Emp.: 60
Machine Tool (Metal Cutting Types) Mfr
N.A.I.C.S.: 333517
Cory R. Mayo *(Pres & CEO)*
Suzon Tropez Holmes *(CFO)*
LaNita Burchfield *(Mgr-Pur & Inventory)*
Michael Townzen *(Mgr-Quality)*
Wanda Cameron *(Dir-HR)*

NATIONAL RESEARCH CORPORATION
1245 Q St, Lincoln, NE 68508
Tel.: (402) 475-2525   WI
Web Site: https://www.nrchealth.com
Year Founded: 1981
NRC—(NASDAQ)
Rev.: $151,568,000
Assets: $130,461,000
Liabilities: $58,428,000
Net Worth: $72,033,000
Earnings: $31,800,000
Emp.: 491
Fiscal Year-end: 12/31/22
Research & Development in the Physical, Engineering & Life Sciences (except Nanotechnology & Biotechnology)
N.A.I.C.S.: 541715
Michael D. Hays *(Founder, Pres & CEO)*
Jason Hahn *(Chief Revenue Officer)*
Helen L. Hrdy *(Chief Customer Officer)*
Jon Boumstein *(Chief Delivery Officer)*
Gregory Makoul *(Chief Transformation Officer)*

Subsidiaries:

National Research Corporation Canada (1)

7100 Woodbine Avenue Suite 411, Markham, L3R 5J2, ON, Canada
Tel.: (905) 475-8231
Web Site: http://www.nrchealth.com
Healthcare Research Services
N.A.I.C.S.: 541715

NATIONAL RURAL UTILITIES COOPERATIVE FINANCE CORPORATION
20701 Cooperative Way, Dulles, VA 20166
Tel.: (703) 467-1800   DC
Web Site: https://www.nrucfc.coop
Year Founded: 1969
NRUC—(NYSE)
Rev.: $1,593,351,000
Assets: $36,177,814,000
Liabilities: $33,165,645,000
Net Worth: $3,012,169,000
Earnings: $554,316,000
Emp.: 289
Fiscal Year-end: 05/31/24
Financial Services
N.A.I.C.S.: 525990
J. Andrew Don *(CEO)*
Brad L. Captain *(Chief Corp Affairs Officer & Sr VP)*
Yu Ling Wang *(CFO & Sr VP)*
Joel Allen *(Sr VP-Member Services)*
David E. Felkel *(Treas & Sec)*
Bruce A. Vitosh *(Pres)*
Gholam M. Saleh *(Chief Risk Officer & Sr VP)*
Gary Bradbury *(COO & Sr VP-Corp Svcs)*
Heesun Choi *(Dir-Capital Markets Rels)*
Pankaj Shah *(Principal Acctg Officer, VP & Controller)*

NATIONAL STOCK YARDS CO.
PO Box 83228, Oklahoma City, OK 73148
Tel.: (405) 235-8675   DE
Web Site: http://www.onsy.com
NSYC—(OTCIQ)
Livestock Services
N.A.I.C.S.: 541690
Chris Bakwin *(Pres)*
Edward J. Henry *(Treas & Sec)*

NATIONAL STORAGE AFFILIATES TRUST
8400 E Prentice Ave 9th Fl, Greenwood Village, CO 80111
Tel.: (720) 630-2600   MD
Web Site:
https://www.nationalstorageaffiliates.com
NSA—(NYSE)
Rev.: $801,569,000
Assets: $6,070,007,000
Liabilities: $3,680,993,000
Net Worth: $2,389,014,000
Earnings: $103,737,000
Emp.: 1,155
Fiscal Year-end: 12/31/22
Real Estate Investment Trust
N.A.I.C.S.: 525990
Tamara D. Fischer *(Chm)*
Arlen Dale Nordhagen *(Vice Chm)*
Brandon S. Togashi *(CFO & Exec VP)*
George Hoglund *(VP-IR)*
David G. Cramer *(Pres & CEO)*
Will Cowan *(Chief Strategy Officer & Exec VP)*
Derek Bergeon *(COO)*

Subsidiaries:

Aberdeen Mini Storage, L.L.C. (1)
316 S Washington St, Aberdeen, WA 98520
Tel.: (360) 538-1055
Web Site: https://www.aberdeen-storage.com
General Warehousing & Storage Services
N.A.I.C.S.: 531130

National Storage Affiliates Trust—(Continued)

All Spanaway Storage LLC (1)
21303 Mountain Hwy E, Spanaway, WA 98387
Tel.: (253) 846-2232
Self Storage Services
N.A.I.C.S.: 531130

All Stor Indian Trail, LLC (1)
4919 Unionville Indian Trail Rd W, Indian Trail, NC 28079-9596
Tel.: (704) 882-4200
General Warehousing & Storage Services
N.A.I.C.S.: 531130

All Stor MH (1)
540 Highland St, Mount Holly, NC 28120
Tel.: (704) 827-8578
Truck Rental & Leasing Services
N.A.I.C.S.: 532120

American Mini Storage-San Antonio, LLC (1)
3567 Fredericksburg Rd, San Antonio, TX 78201
Tel.: (210) 732-0041
Web Site: http://www.americanministorage-converse.com
General Warehousing & Storage Services
N.A.I.C.S.: 531130

Broadway Storage Solutions, L.L.C. (1)
3945 E Broadway Rd, Mesa, AZ 85206
Tel.: (480) 985-1836
General Warehousing & Storage Services
N.A.I.C.S.: 531130

Bullhead Freedom Storage, L.L.C. (1)
1101 S Avondale Blvd, Avondale, AZ 85323
Tel.: (623) 432-0833
General Warehousing & Storage Services
N.A.I.C.S.: 531130

Canyon Road Storage, LLC (1)
9065 S Canyon Rd, Beaverton, OR 97005
Tel.: (503) 292-1434
General Warehousing & Storage Services
N.A.I.C.S.: 531130

Colton VB, L.P. (1)
18671 Van Buren, Riverside, CA 92508
Tel.: (951) 780-0787
Truck Rental & Leasing Services
N.A.I.C.S.: 532120

Damascus Mini Storage LLC (1)
14613 Southeast Old Barn Ln, Damascus, OR 97089
Tel.: (503) 558-0802
Self Storage Services
N.A.I.C.S.: 531130

Fletcher Heights Storage Solutions, L.L.C. (1)
8266 W Lk Pleasant Pkwy, Peoria, AZ 85382
Tel.: (623) 776-1127
General Warehousing & Storage Services
N.A.I.C.S.: 531130

Fontana Universal Self Storage (1)
15007 Bridlepath Dr, Fontana, CA 92336-1107
Tel.: (909) 572-0069
Emp.: 4
General Warehousing & Storage Services
N.A.I.C.S.: 531130
Ray Halverson *(Mgr)*

Forest Grove Mini Storage, LLC (1)
620 Elm St, Forest Grove, OR 97116
Tel.: (503) 357-0111
Web Site:
http://www.forestgroveselfstorage.com
General Warehousing & Storage Services
N.A.I.C.S.: 531130

Gresham Mini & RV Storage, LLC (1)
14855 Southeast 82nd Dr, Clackamas, OR 97015
Tel.: (971) 236-9508
Emp.: 3
General Warehousing & Storage Services
N.A.I.C.S.: 531130

Highway 97 Mini Storage, LLC (1)
1600 N Highway 97, Redmond, OR 97756

Tel.: (541) 548-4817
Warehousing & Storage Leasing Services

Highway 99 Mini Storage, LLC (1)
935 Simmerhorn Rd, Galt, CA 95632
Tel.: (209) 745-1698
Web Site:
https://www.hwy99selfstorage.com
Warehousing & Storage Leasing Services
N.A.I.C.S.: 531130

ICDC II, LLC (1)
550 Newport Center Dr, Newport Beach, CA 92660
Tel.: (949) 720-2000
Residential Community Development Services
N.A.I.C.S.: 623210

Loma Linda Universal Self Storage (1)
25980 Barton Rd, Loma Linda, CA 92354-3869
Tel.: (909) 570-0025
Self Storage Service Provider
N.A.I.C.S.: 531130

NSA OP, LP (1)
9226 Teddy Ln Ste 100, Lone Tree, CO 80124
Tel.: (303) 705-8025
Warehousing & Storage Leasing Services
N.A.I.C.S.: 531130
Tamara D. Fischer *(CFO)*

Prineville SPE LLC (1)
14855 SE 82nd Dr, Clackamas, OR 97015
Tel.: (541) 416-9107
Emp.: 3
General Warehousing & Storage Services
N.A.I.C.S.: 531130

SAG Arcadia, LP (1)
5630 Peck Rd, Arcadia, CA 91006
Tel.: (626) 303-3000
Water Transportation Services
N.A.I.C.S.: 488330

SS Palm City, LLC (1)
7628 Narcoossee Rd, Orlando, FL 32822
Web Site: http://www.simplyss.com
Vehicle Parking Management Services
N.A.I.C.S.: 812930

Safegard Mini Storage, LLC (1)
10585 Sw Greenburg Rd, Tigard, OR 97223
Tel.: (503) 639-0844
Web Site: https://safegardministorage.com
Real Estate Investment Trust Services
N.A.I.C.S.: 531110

Safegard Mini Storage-Tigard (1)
10585 SW Greenburg Rd, Tigard, OR 97223
Tel.: (503) 639-0844
Web Site:
https://www.safegardministorage.com
Self Storage Service Provider
N.A.I.C.S.: 531130

Seatac Storage, LLC (1)
16219 Military Rd S, Seatac, WA 98188
Tel.: (206) 243-3639
Web Site:
https://www.seatacselfstorage.com
Self Storage Service Provider
N.A.I.C.S.: 531130

SecurCare Properties II, LLC (1)
13870 Indian St, Moreno Valley, CA 92553
Tel.: (951) 324-5601
General Warehousing & Storage Services
N.A.I.C.S.: 531130

SecurCare Self Storage, Inc. (1)
5815 Arapahoe Ave, Boulder, CO 80303
Tel.: (303) 799-5850
Web Site:
http://www.securcareselfstorage.com
Sales Range: $1-9.9 Million
Emp.: 9
Lessors of Residential Buildings & Dwellings
N.A.I.C.S.: 531110

Sherwood Storage, LLC (1)
W4746 Hwy 114, Sherwood, WI 54169
Tel.: (920) 851-5736

Web Site:
https://www.storagesherwood.com
General Warehousing & Storage Services
N.A.I.C.S.: 531130

Southern Self Storage of Destin, LLC (1)
4656 Gulfstarr Dr, Destin, FL 32541
Tel.: (850) 502-5469
Self Storage Services
N.A.I.C.S.: 531130

Southern Self Storage of Edgewater, LLC (1)
3515 S Ridgewood Ave, Edgewater, FL 32141
Tel.: (386) 261-6386
Self Storage Services
N.A.I.C.S.: 531130

Southern Self Storage of Grayton, LLC (1)
230 Grayton Village Rd, Santa Rosa Beach, FL 32459
Tel.: (850) 660-7445
Real Estate Services
N.A.I.C.S.: 531390

Southern Self Storage of Pensacola, LLC (1)
9311 Pine Forest Rd, Pensacola, FL 32534
Tel.: (850) 331-7953
Real Estate Services
N.A.I.C.S.: 531390

Town Center Self Storage, LLC (1)
7701 40th St W, University Place, WA 98466
Tel.: (253) 460-7867
Real Estate Investment Trust Services
N.A.I.C.S.: 531110

Troutdale Mini Storage, LLC (1)
1027 NE Harlow Rd, Troutdale, OR 97060
Tel.: (503) 492-4700
Web Site: https://www.troutdalestorage.com
General Warehousing & Storage Services
N.A.I.C.S.: 531130

Universal Self Storage (1)
6121 Lankershim Blvd, North Hollywood, CA 91606
Tel.: (818) 761-1600
General Warehousing & Storage Services
N.A.I.C.S.: 531130

Universal Self Storage Hesperia LLC (1)
9312 I Ave, Hesperia, CA 92345-6203
Tel.: (760) 354-8660
General Warehousing & Storage Services
N.A.I.C.S.: 531130

Universal Self Storage San Bernardino LLC (1)
3086 Kendall Dr, San Bernardino, CA 92407
Tel.: (909) 361-3341
General Warehousing & Storage Services
N.A.I.C.S.: 531130
Andy Gunn *(Reg Mgr & Project Mgr-Construction)*

Upland Universal Self Storage (1)
1695 N Benson Ave, Upland, CA 91784
Tel.: (909) 303-6664
Self Storage Service Provider
N.A.I.C.S.: 531130

WCAL, LLC (1)
610 E Main St, Allen, TX 75002
Tel.: (972) 954-9764
Self Storage Service Provider
N.A.I.C.S.: 531130

Wilsonville Just Store It, LLC (1)
14855 SE 82nd Dr, Clackamas, OR 97015
Tel.: (971) 236-9507
General Warehousing & Storage Services
N.A.I.C.S.: 531130

NATIONAL VISION HOLDINGS, INC.

2435 Commerce Ave Bldg 2200, Duluth, GA 30096
Tel.: (770) 822-3600　　　　NV
Web Site:
https://www.nationalvision.com
Year Founded: 2014

EYE—(NASDAQ)
Rev.: $2,079,525,000
Assets: $2,293,091,000
Liabilities: $1,367,111,000
Net Worth: $925,980,000
Earnings: $128,244,000
Emp.: 13,735
Fiscal Year-end: 01/01/22
Optical Retailer
N.A.I.C.S.: 456130
Patrick R. Moore *(COO)*
Paul Myrick *(Sr VP-Real Estate)*
Jacqueline Grove *(Sr VP-Talent Dev, Culture Diversity, Equity, and Inclusion)*
Debra Woyce *(Sr VP-Retail Ops-Natl Vision)*
Jared Brandman *(Gen Counsel, Sec & Sr VP)*
Melissa Rasmussen *(CFO)*
Joe VanDette *(CMO-)*
Heidi Henneman *(Sr VP & Head-Stores)*
L. Reade Fahs *(CEO)*
D. Randolph Peeler *(Chm)*

Subsidiaries:

FirstSight Vision Services, Inc. (1)
1202 Monte Vista Ave Ste 17, Upland, CA 91786
Tel.: (909) 920-5008
Web Site: https://www.firstsightvision.net
Optical Product Distr
N.A.I.C.S.: 456130

NATIONAL WASTE MANAGEMENT HOLDINGS, INC.

5920 N Florida Ave, Hernando, FL 34442
Tel.: (352) 489-6912　　　　FL
Web Site:
https://nationalwastemgmt.com
Year Founded: 2010
NWMH—(OTCIQ)
Sales Range: $1-9.9 Million
Emp.: 35
Construction & Demolition Landfill Services
N.A.I.C.S.: 562212
Louis Paveglio *(CEO)*
Jeff Chartier *(Pres)*
Dali L. Kranzthor *(CFO)*

Subsidiaries:

Northeast Data Destruction & Recycling, LLC (1)
615 Route 28, Kingston, NY 12401
Tel.: (845) 331-5554
Web Site:
http://www.northeastdatadestruction.com
Local Document Destruction Company
N.A.I.C.S.: 561990
Mark Wachtel *(Owner)*

NATURAL ALTERNATIVES INTERNATIONAL, INC.

1535 Faraday Ave, Carlsbad, CA 92008
Tel.: (760) 736-7700　　　　DE
Web Site: https://www.nai-online.com
Year Founded: 1980
NAII—(NASDAQ)
Rev.: $113,796,000
Assets: $162,342,000
Liabilities: $79,747,000
Net Worth: $82,595,000
Earnings: ($7,217,000)
Emp.: 293
Fiscal Year-end: 06/30/24
Encapsulated & Tablet Vitamins & Related Nutrients, Including Phytochemicals Derived from Botanicals & Foods
N.A.I.C.S.: 325411
Mark A. LeDoux *(Chm & CEO)*
Michael E. Fortin *(CFO)*
Gene Quast *(VP-Sls-Global)*

Andrea Lester *(VP-Quality-Global)*
James Gause *(VP-Ops-Global)*
Kenneth E. Wolf *(Pres & COO)*

Subsidiaries:

NAI Europe   (1)
Centro Galleria 1, Manno, 6928,
Switzerland   **(100%)**
Tel.: (41) 916108460
Web Site: http://www.nai.com
Sales Range: $10-24.9 Million
Emp.: 30
Provider of Encapsulated & Tablet Vitamins
& Related Nutrients, Including Phytochemi-
cals Derived from Botanicals & Foods
N.A.I.C.S.: 325411
Fausto Petrini *(Mng Dir)*

Natural Alternatives International Eu-
rope S.A.   (1)
Centro Galleria 1 Via Cantonale, 6928,
Manno, Switzerland
Tel.: (41) 916108460
Web Site: https://www.naie.ch
Sales Range: $25-49.9 Million
Emp.: 3
Nutritional Product Mfr
N.A.I.C.S.: 456191

NATURAL GAS SERVICES GROUP, INC.

404 Veterans Airpark Ln Ste 300,
Midland, TX 79705
Tel.: (432) 262-2700
Web Site: https://www.ngsgi.com
Year Founded: 1998
NGS—(NYSE)
Rev.: $84,825,000
Assets: $328,246,000
Liabilities: $98,170,000
Net Worth: $230,076,000
Earnings: ($569,000)
Emp.: 266
Fiscal Year-end: 12/31/22
Rotary Screw Compression & Gas
Flaring Equipment Used to Enhance
the Production & Gathering of Oil &
Natural Gas
N.A.I.C.S.: 237120
Stephen C. Taylor *(Chm & Interim CEO)*
Brian L. Tucker *(Pres & COO)*
John Bittner *(Interim CFO)*

NATURAL GROCERS BY VITA-MIN COTTAGE, INC.

12612 W Alameda Pkwy, Lakewood,
CO 80228
Tel.: (303) 986-4600   **DE**
Web Site:
   https://www.naturalgrocers.com
Year Founded: 1955
NGVC—(NYSE)
Rev.: $1,241,585,000
Assets: $655,476,000
Liabilities: $481,222,000
Net Worth: $174,254,000
Earnings: $33,935,000
Emp.: 3,332
Fiscal Year-end: 09/30/24
Health Foods & Nutritional Supple-
ments Retailer
N.A.I.C.S.: 456191
Zephyr Isely *(Co-Pres)*
Kemper Isely *(Chm & Co-Pres)*
Heather Isely *(Sec & Exec VP)*
Elizabeth Isely *(Exec VP)*

NATURAL ORDER ACQUISI-TION CORP.

30 Colpitts Rd, Weston, MA 02493
Tel.: (617) 395-1644   **DE**
Year Founded: 2020
NOAC—(NASDAQ)
Rev.: $2,995,697
Assets: $230,497,912
Liabilities: $241,561,716
Net Worth: ($11,063,804)

Earnings: $1,167,625
Emp.: 2
Fiscal Year-end: 12/31/21
Investment Services
N.A.I.C.S.: 523999
Paresh Patel *(Co-Founder, Pres & CEO)*
Sebastiano Cossia Castiglioni *(Co-Founder & Chm)*
John Ritacco *(CFO & Sec)*

NATURAL RESOURCE PART-NERS L.P.

1415 Louisiana St Ste 3325, Hous-
ton, TX 77002
Tel.: (713) 751-7507   **DE**
Web Site: https://www.nrplp.com
Year Founded: 2002
NRP—(NYSE)
Rev.: $216,364,000
Assets: $953,823,000
Liabilities: $697,799,000
Net Worth: $256,024,000
Earnings: $108,902,000
Emp.: 52
Fiscal Year-end: 12/31/21
Coal Reserve Property Management
& Leasing Services
N.A.I.C.S.: 551112
Corbin J. Robertson Jr. *(Chm & CEO)*
Philip T. Warman *(Gen Counsel & Sec)*
Sarah W. Watson *(Chief Sustainabil-ity Officer & Administrative)*

Subsidiaries:

Laurel Aggregates of Delaware,
LLC   (1)
250 Lakewood Ctr, Morgantown, WV 26508
Tel.: (304) 296-7501
Web Site: http://www.laurelaggregates.com
Crushed, Broken Stone Mining & Quarrying
Services
N.A.I.C.S.: 212319

McAsphalt, LLC   (1)
114 Kraft St, Clarksville, TN 37040
Tel.: (931) 647-5000
Crushed, Broken Stone Mining & Quarrying
Services
N.A.I.C.S.: 212319

McIntosh Construction Company,
LLC   (1)
114 Kraft St, Clarksville, TN 37041-0706
Tel.: (931) 648-8250
Web Site:
   https://www.mcintoshconstruction.com
Crushed, Broken Stone Mining & Quarrying
Services
N.A.I.C.S.: 212319

NRP (Operating) LLC   (1)
1201 Louis Iana Strt 3400, Houston, TX
77002
Tel.: (713) 751-7507
Web Site: http://www.nrplp.com
Emp.: 10
Coal & Lignite Mining Services
N.A.I.C.S.: 212114

Southern Aggregates, LLC   (1)
37780 Weiss Rd, Denham Springs, LA
70706
Tel.: (225) 667-5868
Crushed, Broken Stone Mining & Quarrying
Services
N.A.I.C.S.: 212319
Karl Romig *(Mgr-Quality Control)*

Winn Materials of Kentucky, LLC   (1)
1006 Dixie Beeline Hwy, Trenton, KY 42286
Tel.: (270) 466-5002
Crushed, Broken Stone Mining & Quarrying
Services
N.A.I.C.S.: 212319

Winn Materials, LLC   (1)
800 Barge Point Rd, Clarksville, TN 37042
Tel.: (931) 572-0093
Web Site: http://www.winnmaterials.com
Crushed Broken Stone Mining & Quarrying
Services
N.A.I.C.S.: 212319

NATURALSHRIMP, INC.

13601 Preston Rd E1092, Dallas, TX
75240   **NV**
Web Site:
   https://www.naturalshrimp.com
Year Founded: 2008
SHMP—(OTCQB)
Rev.: $446,301
Assets: $27,717,338
Liabilities: $38,571,859
Net Worth: ($10,854,521)
Earnings: ($15,602,411)
Emp.: 19
Fiscal Year-end: 03/31/24
Investment Services
N.A.I.C.S.: 523999
William J. Delgado *(CFO & Treas)*
Gerald Easterling *(Co-Founder, Chm, Pres, CEO & Co-Sec)*
Thomas Untermeyer *(Co-Founder, COO, CTO & Co-Sec)*

NATURE'S MIRACLE HOLDING INC.

3281 E Guasti Rd Ste 175, Ontario,
CA 91761
Tel.: (909) 218-4601   **DE**
Web Site: https://www.nature-
   miracle.com
Year Founded: 2021
NMHI—(NASDAQ)
Rev.: $9,881,622
Assets: $14,200,421
Liabilities: $20,920,358
Net Worth: ($6,719,937)
Earnings: ($7,338,171)
Emp.: 12
Fiscal Year-end: 12/31/23
Holding Company
N.A.I.C.S.: 551112

NATURE'S SUNSHINE PROD-UCTS, INC.

2901 W Bluegrass Blvd, Lehi, UT
84043
Tel.: (801) 341-7900   **UT**
Web Site:
   https://shop.naturessunshine.com
Year Founded: 1972
NATR—(NASDAQ)
Rev.: $421,910,000
Assets: $229,778,000
Liabilities: $82,731,000
Net Worth: $147,047,000
Earnings: ($390,000)
Emp.: 800
Fiscal Year-end: 12/31/22
Herbal & Homeopathic Products, Vi-
tamin & Mineral Supplements & Per-
sonal Care Products Mfr & Marketer
N.A.I.C.S.: 325412
Nathan Brower *(Gen Counsel & Exec VP)*
Bryant Yates *(Pres-Europe & Exec VP)*
Sarah Crockett *(CMO-Global)*
Terrence O. Moorehead *(Pres & CEO)*
Dan Norman *(Pres-Asia Pacific & Exec VP)*
Tracee Comstock *(VP-HR)*
Terrence O. Moorehead *(Pres & CEO)*
Jonathon Lanoy *(Sr VP-Fin & Con-troller)*
Kevin Herbert *(Pres-North America & Exec VP)*
Vallen Blackburn *(VP)*
Martin Gonzalez *(VP)*

Subsidiaries:

Nature's Sunshine Products de
Mexico S.A. de C.V.   (1)
Periferico Sur 4826 Col Arenal De Guada-
lupe, Tlalpan, 14389, Mexico, Mexico
Tel.: (52) 55 5624 0220

Web Site: http://www.misitiosunshine.com
Nutritional & Personal Care Products Mar-
keter
N.A.I.C.S.: 456191

Nature's Sunshine Products de Ven-
ezuela, C.A.   (1)
Av Francisco Solano Con Av Principal Del
Bosque, TorreCredicard Piso 11 Chacait,
Caracas, 212, Venezuela
Tel.: (58) 2129053500
Web Site: http://www.naturessunshine.com
Marketer & Sales of Nutritional & Personal
Care Products
N.A.I.C.S.: 325411

Nature's Sunshine Products of
Canada, Ltd.   (1)
44 Peel Centre Drive Suite 402, Brampton,
L6T 4B5, ON, Canada   **(100%)**
Tel.: (905) 458-6100
Web Site: https://www.naturessunshine.ca
Sales Range: $10-24.9 Million
Emp.: 15
Marketing & Sales of Nutritional & Personal
Products
N.A.I.C.S.: 456191
Terrence Moorehead *(CEO)*
Joseph Baty *(CFO)*
Nathan Brower *(Gen Counsel)*
Tracee Comstock *(VP-Human Resources)*
Dan Norman *(Pres-Asia Pacific)*
Kevin Herbert *(Pres-North America)*
Bryant Yates *(Pres-Europe)*

Nature's Sunshine Products, Inc. -
UK Branch   (1)
Sunshine House Hortonwood 32, Telford,
TF1 7YL, Shropshire, United
Kingdom   **(100%)**
Tel.: (44) 1952 671600
Web Site: http://www.naturessunshine.co.uk
Rev.: $1,800,000
Emp.: 15
Marketer & Sales of Nutritional & Personal
Care Products
N.A.I.C.S.: 456191

P.T. Synergy WorldWide
Indonesia   (1)
FX Sudirman 7th Fl Unit C Jln Jend
Sudirman, Pintu 1 Senayan Gelora Tanah
Abang, Jakarta, 10270, Indonesia
Tel.: (62) 212527335
Web Site:
   https://www.synergyworldwide.com
Nutritional & Personal Care Products Mfr
N.A.I.C.S.: 325411
Adri Tampubolon *(Gen Mgr)*

Synergy WorldWide (S) PTE Ltd.   (1)
1 Harbourfront Avenue 14-08 Keppel Bay
Tower, Singapore, 098632, Singapore
Tel.: (65) 68870004
Web Site:
   https://www.synergyworldwide.com
Emp.: 5
Nutritional & Personal Care Products Mfr
N.A.I.C.S.: 325411

Synergy WorldWide Australia PTY
Ltd.   (1)
19 Brookhollow Avenue, Baulkham Hills,
2153, NSW, Australia
Tel.: (61) 296802055
Web Site: http://au.synergyworldwide.com
Nutritional & Personal Care Products Mfr
N.A.I.C.S.: 325411

Synergy WorldWide Inc.   (1)
2901 W Bluegrass Blvd, Lehi, UT 84043
Tel.: (801) 769-7800
Web Site:
   https://www.synergyworldwide.com
Food Supplement Products Mfr
N.A.I.C.S.: 325411

Synergy WorldWide Italy S.R.L.   (1)
Via Bernardino Telesio 2, 20145, Milan, MI,
Italy
Tel.: (39) 0800684503
Web Site:
   https://www.synergyworldwide.com
Food Supplementary Product Mfr
N.A.I.C.S.: 311999
Alexandra Ghio *(Sls Mgr)*

Synergy WorldWide Marketing Sdn
Bhd   (1)
Tel.: (60) 377108228

Nature's Sunshine Products, Inc.—(Continued)

Web Site:
https://www.synergyworldwide.com
Herbal Supplements Mfr
N.A.I.C.S.: 325411

Synergy WorldWide New Zealand,
ULC   **(1)**
10A Stonedon Dr, East Tamaki, Auckland,
New Zealand
Tel.: (64) 508410466
Web Site: http://www.synergyworldwide.com
Food Supplementary Product Mfr
N.A.I.C.S.: 311999

Synergy WorldWide Philippines Distri-
bution Inc.   **(1)**
2nd floor Unit 2VB Lee Gardens Commer-
cial Center, Wack Wack, Mandaluyong,
1555, Philippines
Tel.: (63) 26969158
Web Site: http://ph.synergyworldwide.com
Sales Range: $25-49.9 Million
Emp.: 5
Herbal Supplements Mfr
N.A.I.C.S.: 325411

NAUTICUS ROBOTICS, INC.
17146 Feathercraft Ln Ste 450, Web-
ster, TX 77598
Tel.: (281) 942-9069   DE
Web Site:
https://nauticusrobotics.com
Year Founded: 2020
KITT—(NASDAQ)
Rev.: $11,434,959
Assets: $52,575,293
Liabilities: $52,575,293
Net Worth: $27,819
Earnings: ($28,260,571)
Emp.: 93
Fiscal Year-end: 12/31/22
Maritime Transportation
N.A.I.C.S.: 713930
John W. Gibson (Pres & Interim
CEO)
J. D. Yamokoski (CTO)

Subsidiaries:

Nauticus Robotics Holdings, Inc.   **(1)**
17146 Feathercraft Ln Ste 450, Webster,
TX 77598
Tel.: (281) 942-9069
Maritime Transportation
N.A.I.C.S.: 713930

NAUTILUS BIOTECHNOLOGY,
INC.
2701 Eastlake Ave E, Seattle, WA
98102
Tel.: (206) 333-2001   DE
Web Site: https://www.nautilus.bio
Year Founded: 2016
NAUT—(NASDAQ)
Rev.: $12,477,000
Assets: $305,565,000
Liabilities: $40,212,000
Net Worth: $265,353,000
Earnings: ($63,675,000)
Emp.: 167
Fiscal Year-end: 12/31/23
Research & Development in Biotech-
nology (except Nanobiotechnology)
N.A.I.C.S.: 541714
Gwen Weld (Chief People Officer)
Mary Godwin (Sr VP-Ops)
Chris Blessington (VP-Corp Mktg &
Comm)
Nick Nelson (Chief Bus Officer)
Anna Mowry (CFO)
Subra Sankar (Sr VP-Product Dev)
Matthew Murphy (Gen Counsel)
Martin Huber (VP-Biochemistry &
Flow Cell Dev)
Sheri Wilcox (VP-Probe Dev & Bioin-
formatics)
Parag Mallick (Co-Founder & Chief
Scientist)
Sujal M. Patel (Co-Founder, Pres,
CEO & Sec)

NAVIDEA BIOPHARMACEUTI-
CALS, INC.
4100 Horizons Dr Ste 205, Colum-
bus, OH 43220
Tel.: (614) 793-7500   DE
Web Site: https://www.navidea.com
Year Founded: 1983
NAVB—(NYSEAMEX)
Rev.: $65,652
Assets: $4,371,606
Liabilities: $12,514,916
Net Worth: ($8,143,310)
Earnings: ($15,177,153)
Emp.: 11
Fiscal Year-end: 12/31/22
In-Vitro Diagnostic Substance Mfr
N.A.I.C.S.: 325413
Jeff Smith (VP-Ops)
Craig A. Dais (CFO)
Michael Blue (Chief Medical Officer)
John K. Scott Jr. (Vice Chm)

NAVIENT CORPORATION
13865 Sunrise Valley Dr, Herndon,
VA 20171
Tel.: (703) 810-3000   DE
Web Site: https://www.navient.com
Year Founded: 2014
NAVI—(NASDAQ)
Rev.: $4,419,000,000
Assets: $61,375,000,000
Liabilities: $58,615,000,000
Net Worth: $2,760,000,000
Earnings: $228,000,000
Emp.: 4,500
Fiscal Year-end: 12/31/23
Financial Investment Services
N.A.I.C.S.: 522310
Jane J. Thompson (Founder)
John M. Kane (Pres-Bus Processing
Solutions-Grp)
Jennifer Walker (Chief Audit Officer &
Sr VP)
Stephen M. Hauber (Chief Admin Of-
ficer & Exec VP)
Mark L. Heleen (Chief Legal Officer,
Sec & Exec VP)
Joe Fisher (CFO, Principal Acctg Offi-
cer & Exec VP)
Patricia Nash Christel (VP)
David Green (Exec VP)
Troy Standish (Sr VP)
Edward J. Bramson (Vice Chm)

Subsidiaries:

Duncan Solutions, Inc.   **(1)**
633 W Wisconsin Ave Ste 1600, Milwaukee,
WI 53203
Tel.: (888) 993-8622
Web Site: http://www.duncansolutions.com
Parking Management Solutions Services
N.A.I.C.S.: 541519
James Kennedy (COO)
Marc Lucey (VP-Parking & Mobility Solu-
tions)
Juanita Moore (Supvr-Ops)

Gila, LLC   **(1)**
8325 Tuscany Way Bldg 4, Austin, TX
78754
Tel.: (512) 371-9995
Web Site: https://www.msbgovserv.com
Sales Range: $25-49.9 Million
Emp.: 400
Collections & Payment Processing
N.A.I.C.S.: 561440

Navient Credit Funding, LLC   **(1)**
20 Hemingway Dr, Providence, RI 02915
Tel.: (703) 810-7677
Financial Services
N.A.I.C.S.: 522291

Navient Solutions, Inc.   **(1)**
2001 Edmund Halley Dr, Reston, VA 20191
Tel.: (703) 810-3000
Emp.: 6,000
Financial Services
N.A.I.C.S.: 522291

NAVIGATOR ACQUISITION
CORP.
1 World Financial Center 200 Liberty
St 8th Fl, New York, NY 10281
Tel.: (212) 909-5870
Web Site:
https://www.navigatoracquisi
tion.com
NAQ.P—(TSXV)
Assets: $367,347
Liabilities: $59,341
Net Worth: $308,006
Earnings: ($346,144)
Fiscal Year-end: 12/31/19
Asset Management Services
N.A.I.C.S.: 523940
Kyle Shostak (Founder)

NAVITAS PETROLEUM LIM-
ITED PARTNERSHIP
5847 San Felipe St, Houston, TX
77057
Tel.: (713) 275-3175
Web Site:
https://www.navitaspet.com
NVPT.L—(TAE)
Oil & Gas Equipment Mfr
N.A.I.C.S.: 333132
Chanan Reichman (CEO)

NAVITAS SEMICONDUCTOR
CORPORATION
3520 Challenger St, Torrance, CA
90503   DE
Web Site: https://in.navitassemi.com
Year Founded: 2013
NVTS—(NASDAQ)
Rev.: $37,943,000
Assets: $425,262,000
Liabilities: $40,502,000
Net Worth: $384,760,000
Earnings: $72,887,000
Emp.: 230
Fiscal Year-end: 12/31/22
Semiconductor & Related Device
Manufacturing
N.A.I.C.S.: 334413
Richard J. Hendrix (COO)
Gene Sheridan (Co-Founder, Chm,
Pres & CEO)
Dan Kinzer (Co-Founder, COO &
CTO)

NB BANCORP, INC.
1063 Great Plain Ave, Needham, MA
02492
Tel.: (781) 444-2100   MD
Web Site:
https://www.nbbancorp.com
Year Founded: 2023
NBBK—(NASDAQ)
Rev.: $220,501,000
Assets: $4,533,412,000
Liabilities: $3,775,453,000
Net Worth: $757,959,000
Earnings: $9,825,000
Emp.: 342
Fiscal Year-end: 12/31/23
Commercial Banking Services
N.A.I.C.S.: 522110
Joseph P. Campanelli (Chm, Pres &
CEO)
Salvatore Rinaldi (COO & Exec VP)

NBT BANCORP INC.
52 S Broad St, Norwich, NY 13815
Tel.: (607) 337-2265   DE
Web Site:
https://www.nbtbancorp.com
Year Founded: 1986
NBTB—(NASDAQ)
Rev.: $539,648,000
Assets: $11,739,296,000
Liabilities: $10,565,742,000
Net Worth: $1,173,554,000
Earnings: $151,995,000
Emp.: 1,861
Fiscal Year-end: 12/31/22

Bank Holding Company
N.A.I.C.S.: 551111
Richard J. Cantele Jr. (Exec VP-
Strategic Integration)
John H. Watt Jr. (Vice Chm)
Annette L. Burns (CFO & Chief Acctg
Officer)
Scott A. Kingsley (Pres & CEO)

Subsidiaries:

Columbia Ridge Capital Manage-
ment, Inc.   **(1)**
331 Main St Ste 1, Johnson City, NY 13790
Tel.: (607) 584-4141
Web Site: https://www.nbtcapm.com
Investment Advice Services
N.A.I.C.S.: 523940

Hathaway Agency, Inc.   **(1)**
110 W Chicago St, Bronson, MI 49028
Tel.: (517) 369-7311
Web Site: https://www.hathawayagency.com
Insurance Brokerage Services
N.A.I.C.S.: 524210

Mang Insurance Agency, LLC   **(1)**
66 S Broad St, Norwich, NY 13815
Tel.: (800) 965-6264
Web Site: http://www.nbtinsurance.com
Insurance Agency & Brokerage Services
N.A.I.C.S.: 524210
David Craine (Acct Exec)
Dan Grady (Acct Exec)
George Busch (VP-Sls)

NBT Bank, N.A.   **(1)**
52 S Broad St, Norwich, NY
13815   **(100%)**
Tel.: (607) 337-6136
Web Site: https://www.nbtbank.com
Sales Range: $150-199.9 Million
Emp.: 300
National Bank
N.A.I.C.S.: 522110
John H. Watt Jr. (Vice Chm)
Joseph A. Stagliano (Pres)
Florence Doller (Sr VP & Dir-Corp Comm)

NBT Bank, N.A.   **(1)**
52 S Broad St, Norwich, NY
13815   **(100%)**
Tel.: (607) 337-6136
Web Site: https://www.nbtbank.com
Sales Range: $150-199.9 Million
Emp.: 300
National Bank
N.A.I.C.S.: 522110
John H. Watt Jr. (Vice Chm)
Joseph A. Stagliano (Pres)
Florence Doller (Sr VP & Dir-Corp Comm)

Subsidiary (Domestic):

Downeast Pension Services, Inc.   **(2)**
41 Campus Dr Ste 302, New Gloucester,
ME 04260
Tel.: (207) 688-4219
Web Site:
https://www.downeastpension.com
Sales Range: $1-9.9 Million
Insurance Related Activities
N.A.I.C.S.: 524298
Denise Randall (VP)
Leander MacVane (Mgr)
Mark L. Charest (Mgr)

NBT Capital Corp.   **(2)**
52 S Broad St, Norwich, NY 13815
Tel.: (607) 334-2178
Web Site: http://www.nbtbank.com
Venture Capital Corporation & Investment
Management Services
N.A.I.C.S.: 523940

NBT Bank, N.A.   **(1)**
52 S Broad St, Norwich, NY
13815   **(100%)**
Tel.: (607) 337-6136
Web Site: https://www.nbtbank.com
Sales Range: $150-199.9 Million
Emp.: 300
National Bank
N.A.I.C.S.: 522110
John H. Watt Jr. (Vice Chm)
Joseph A. Stagliano (Pres)
Florence Doller (Sr VP & Dir-Corp Comm)

NBT Bank, N.A.   **(1)**

52 S Broad St, Norwich, NY
13815 **(100%)**
Tel.: (607) 337-6136
Web Site: https://www.nbtbank.com
Sales Range: $150-199.9 Million
Emp.: 300
National Bank
N.A.I.C.S.: 522110
John H. Watt Jr. *(Vice Chm)*
Joseph A. Stagliano *(Pres)*
Florence Doller *(Sr VP & Dir-Corp Comm)*

Subsidiary (Domestic):

Downeast Pension Services, Inc. **(2)**
41 Campus Dr Ste 302, New Gloucester,
ME 04260
Tel.: (207) 688-4219
Web Site:
  https://www.downeastpension.com
Sales Range: $1-9.9 Million
Insurance Related Activities
N.A.I.C.S.: 524298
Denise Randall *(VP)*
Leander MacVane *(Mgr)*
Mark L. Charest *(Mgr)*

NBT Capital Corp. **(2)**
52 S Broad St, Norwich, NY 13815
Tel.: (607) 334-2178
Web Site: http://www.nbtbank.com
Venture Capital Corporation & Investment
Management Services
N.A.I.C.S.: 523940

NBT Financial Services, Inc. **(1)**
52 S Broad St, Norwich, NY
13815 **(100%)**
Tel.: (607) 337-2265
Web Site: http://www.nbtbank.com
Sales Range: $25-49.9 Million
Emp.: 50
Investment Financing Services
N.A.I.C.S.: 525990
Martin A. Dietrich *(Executives, Bd of Dirs)*

Subsidiary (Domestic):

EPIC Advisors, Inc. **(2)**
150 State St Ste 200, Rochester, NY
14614 **(100%)**
Tel.: (585) 232-9060
Web Site: http://www.epic1st.com
Retirement & Financial Planning Services
N.A.I.C.S.: 541611
Neil Steffen *(Dir-Bus Integration)*
Manuel Marques *(Pres)*
Dave Davidson *(Pres-Reg)*
Kim Beal *(VP-Bus Integration)*
Jason Knapp *(Dir-Tech & Innovation)*
Brian Lenz *(Dir-Sls & Strategic Partnerships)*
Matt Pine *(Dir-Retirement Plan Consulting)*
Spiro Theodorakakos *(Dir-Client Svc)*

Branch (Domestic):

**EPIC Retirement Plan Services,
Portland** **(3)**
5 Widgery Wharf 2nd Fl, Portland, ME
04101
Tel.: (207) 879-9200
Web Site: http://www.adsbenefits.com
Sales Range: $1-9.9 Million
Emp.: 15
Retirement Plan Consulting, Administration
& Actuarial Services
N.A.I.C.S.: 541611

Subsidiary (Domestic):

Retirement Plan Services, LLC **(3)**
1699 S Hanley Rd Ste 300, Saint Louis,
MO 63144
Tel.: (314) 721-8050
Web Site: http://www.rpsbenefits.com
Retirement Planning Services
N.A.I.C.S.: 541611
Manuel Marques *(Pres)*
Dave Davidson *(Reg Pres)*
Kim Beal *(VP-Bus Integration)*
Jason Knapp *(Dir-Tech & Innovation)*
Brian Lenz *(Dir-Sls & Strategic Partnerships)*
Matt Pine *(Dir-Retirement Plan Consulting)*
Neil Steffen *(Dir-Bus Integration)*
Spiro Theodorakakos *(Dir-Client Svc)*

Salisbury Bancorp, Inc. **(1)**
5 Bissell St, Lakeville, CT 06039

Tel.: (860) 435-9801
Web Site: https://www.salisburybank.com
Rev.: $61,713,000
Assets: $1,541,582,000
Liabilities: $1,413,227,000
Net Worth: $128,355,000
Earnings: $15,874,000
Emp.: 23,254
Fiscal Year-end: 12/31/2022
Bank Holding Company
N.A.I.C.S.: 551111

NCINO, INC.
6770 Parker Farm Dr, Wilmington,
NC 28405 **DE**
Web Site: https://www.ncino.com
Year Founded: 2011
NCNO—(NASDAQ)
Rev.: $476,543,000
Assets: $1,340,430,000
Liabilities: $291,254,000
Net Worth: $1,049,176,000
Earnings: ($42,346,000)
Emp.: 1,653
Fiscal Year-end: 01/31/24
Software Development Services
N.A.I.C.S.: 541511
Neil L. Underwood *(Founder)*
Pierre Naude *(Chm & CEO)*
Sean Desmond *(Chief Product Officer)*
Davis Brannan *(Exec VP-Global Channels & Partners)*
Jeanette Sellers *(VP-Acctg)*
Chris Ainsworth *(Chief People Officer)*
Greg Orenstein *(CFO & Treas)*

Subsidiaries:

SimpleNexus, LLC **(1)**
2000 Ashton Blvd Ste 500, Lehi, UT 84043
Web Site: http://simplenexus.com
Sales Range: $1-9.9 Million
Emp.: 100
Real Estate Services
N.A.I.C.S.: 531210
Matt Hansen *(Co-Founder)*
Ben Miller *(Co-Founder & CEO)*

Visible Equity, LLC **(1)**
2755 E Cottonwood Pkwy Ste 560, Salt
Lake City, UT 84121
Application Programming Services
N.A.I.C.S.: 541511

nCino APAC Pty Ltd **(1)**
MLC Centre Level 37 - Suite 2 19 Martin
Place, Sydney, 2000, NSW, Australia
Tel.: (61) 240444534
Application Programming Services
N.A.I.C.S.: 541511

nCino Canada, Inc. **(1)**
Suite 408 320 Bay Street, Toronto, M5H
4A6, ON, Canada
Application Programming Services
N.A.I.C.S.: 541511

nCino Global Ltd. **(1)**
Metal Box Factory 30 Great Guildford
Street, London, SE1 0HS, United Kingdom
Tel.: (44) 2036950684
Application Programming Services
N.A.I.C.S.: 541511

nCino K.K. **(1)**
18th Floor of Midtown Tower 9-7-1 Akasaka,
Minato-ku, Tokyo, 107-6218, Japan
Tel.: (81) 366255122
Web Site: http://www.ncino.co.jp
Application Programming Services
N.A.I.C.S.: 541511

nCino OpCo, Inc. **(1)**
6770 Parker Farm Dr, Wilmington, NC
28405-3183
Web Site: https://www.investor.ncino.com
Banking Services
N.A.I.C.S.: 522110

NCR ATLEOS CORPORATION
864 Spring St NW, Atlanta, GA 30308
Tel.: (937) 445-1936 **MD**
Web Site: https://www.ncratleos.com
Year Founded: 1884

NATL—(NYSE)
Rev.: $4,191,000,000
Assets: $5,741,000,000
Liabilities: $5,454,000,000
Net Worth: $287,000,000
Earnings: ($134,000,000)
Emp.: 20,000
Fiscal Year-end: 12/31/23
Commercial Banking Services
N.A.I.C.S.: 522110
Timothy C. Oliver *(Pres & CEO)*
Paul J. Campbell *(CFO & Exec VP)*
Stuart Mackinnon *(COO & Exec VP)*
Ricardo J. Nunez *(Chief Compliance
Officer, Gen Counsel, Sec & Exec
VP)*

NCR VOYIX CORPORATION.
864 Spring St NW, Atlanta, GA 30308
Tel.: (937) 445-1936 **MD**
Web Site: https://www.ncr.com .
Year Founded: 1884
VYX—(NYSE)
Rev.: $7,844,000,000
Assets: $11,507,000,000
Liabilities: $10,028,000,000
Net Worth: $1,479,000,000
Earnings: $60,000,000
Emp.: 35,000
Fiscal Year-end: 12/31/22
Automated Teller Machines, Point-of-
Sale Terminals & Bar Code Scanners
Mfr; Data Warehousing Services
N.A.I.C.S.: 334112
Owen J. Sullivan *(COO)*
David Wilkinson *(CEO)*
Anthony J. Radesca *(Chief Acctg Officer & Sr VP)*
Michael D. Hayford *(CIO)*
James G. Kelly *(Chm)*
James M. Bedore *(Gen Counsel, Sec & Exec VP)*
Timothy C. Oliver *(CFO & Sr Exec VP)*
Anthony Radesca *(Chief Acctg Officer & Sr VP)*
Ismail Amla *(Exec VP)*
Dan Antilley *(Chief Security Officer)*
Stuart MacKinnon *(Exec VP)*
Donald W. Layden Jr. *(Pres)*
Kate Mandrell *(Exec VP)*
Jennifer Personette *(CMO)*

Subsidiaries:

4Front Services Limited **(1)**
Wrightsure House 799 London Rd, Grays,
RM20 3LH, United Kingdom
Tel.: (44) 1708865511
Computer Terminal Mfr
N.A.I.C.S.: 334118

Cardtronics plc **(1)**
2050 W Sam Houston Pkwy S Ste 1300,
Houston, TX 77042
Tel.: (832) 308-4000
Web Site: http://www.cardtronics.com
Rev.: $1,093,999,000
Assets: $1,831,445,000
Liabilities: $1,452,029,000
Net Worth: $379,416,000
Earnings: $19,137,000
Emp.: 2,027
Fiscal Year-end: 12/31/2020
Holding Company; Automatic Teller Ma-
chines Network Operator
N.A.I.C.S.: 551112
Geri House *(Chief HR Officer)*
Dan Antilley *(Chief Information Security Officer & Exec VP-Ops)*
Aimie Killeen *(Gen Counsel & Sec)*
Stuart MacKinnon *(CIO & Exec VP-Tech)*
Marc Terry *(Exec VP & Mng Dir-Intl)*
Paul A. Gullo *(Chief Acctg Officer)*
Carter Hunt *(Exec VP & Mng Dir-North
America)*

Subsidiary (Non-US):

**Cardtronics Canada ATM Processing
Partnership** **(2)**
Bay 6 1420 28 Street NE, Calgary, T2A

7W6, AB, Canada
Cash & Financial Services
N.A.I.C.S.: 522320

Subsidiary (Domestic):

Cardtronics, Inc. **(2)**
3250 Briarpark Dr Ste 400, Houston, TX
77042
Tel.: (832) 308-4000
Web Site: http://www.cardtronics.com
Sales Range: $1-4.9 Billion
Holding Company; Automatic Teller Ma-
chines Network Operator
N.A.I.C.S.: 551112

Subsidiary (Domestic):

ATM National, LLC **(3)**
7315 Wisconsin Ave Ste 750 E, Bethesda,
MD 20814
Tel.: (301) 492-2100
Web Site: http://www.allpointnetwork.com
Sales Range: $125-149.9 Million
Emp.: 8
ATM Owner & Operator
N.A.I.C.S.: 522320

ATM Network, Inc. **(3)**
10749 Bren Rd E, Minnetonka, MN 55343
Tel.: (952) 767-2000
Web Site: http://www.atmnetwork.net
Sales Range: $1-9.9 Million
Automated Teller Machines Distribution &
Management Services
N.A.I.C.S.: 423420

Subsidiary (Non-US):

Cardtronics Canada, Ltd. **(3)**
Bay 6 1420 - 28 Street NE, Calgary, T2A
7W6, AB, Canada
Web Site: https://www.cardtronics.ca
Automatic Teller Machines Maintenance &
Management Services
N.A.I.C.S.: 238290

Subsidiary (Domestic):

Cardtronics Holdings, LLC **(3)**
3250 Briarpark Dr Ste 400, Houston, TX
77042
Tel.: (832) 308-4000
Investment Management Service
N.A.I.C.S.: 551111

Subsidiary (Non-US):

Cardtronics Pty. Ltd. **(3)**
87 Corporate Drive, Heatherton, 3202, VIC,
Australia
Tel.: (61) 130 030 5600
Web Site: https://www.cardtronics.com.au
Electronic Payment System Services & So-
lutions
N.A.I.C.S.: 522320

Cardtronics UK Limited **(3)**
Building 4 1st Floor Trident Place Mosquito
Way, Hatfield, AL10 9UL, Hertfordshire,
United Kingdom
Tel.: (44) 1707632800
Web Site: http://www.cardtronics-uk.com
Automated Teller Machine Network Opera-
tor
N.A.I.C.S.: 522320

Subsidiary (Domestic):

Cardpoint Limited **(4)**
Davidson House, Northwich, CW9 7TW,
United Kingdom
Tel.: (44) 8442090555
Emp.: 14
Athlete Club Operator
N.A.I.C.S.: 713940

**New Wave ATM Installations
Limited** **(4)**
Building 4 1st Floor Trident Place Mosquito
Way, Hatfield, AL10 9UL, Herts, United
Kingdom
Tel.: (44) 1707 632800
Automatic Teller Machine Installation Ser-
vices
N.A.I.C.S.: 238290

Sunwin Services Group, Limited **(4)**
Media House 5 Staithgate Lane, Bradford,
BD6 1YA, United Kingdom

NCR Voyix Corporation.—(Continued)

Tel.: (44) 8009809911
Web Site: http://www.sunwin.co.uk
Financial Management Services
N.A.I.C.S.: 541611

i-design group ltd (4)
30 City Quay Camperdown Street, Dundee,
DD1 3JA, United Kingdom
Tel.: (44) 1382 323 000
Web Site: http://www.i-designltd.com
Sales Range: $1-9.9 Million
Emp.: 33
ATM Advertising & Interface Design Solutions
N.A.I.C.S.: 513210
Jack Vincent *(Head-Bus Dev)*
Paul Gardiner *(Head-Ops & Tech)*

Subsidiary (Domestic):

i-design multimedia ltd. (5)
30 City Quay Camperdown Street, Dundee,
DD1 3JA, United Kingdom
Tel.: (44) 1382 323 000
Web Site: http://www.i-designplc.com
Emp.: 39
Software Development & Interface Design
Services
N.A.I.C.S.: 513210
Jack Vincent *(Head-Bus Dev)*
Paul Gardiner *(Head-Ops & Tech)*

Subsidiary (Domestic):

Cardtronics USA, Inc. (3)
3250 Briarpark Dr Ste 400, Houston, TX
77042
Tel.: (832) 308-4975
Autromatic Teller Machine & Financial Kiosk
Products & Services
N.A.I.C.S.: 522320

Subsidiary (Non-US):

**Cardtronics de Mexico S.A. de
C.V.**
Barranca del Muerto 329 3er Piso, Col San
Jose Insurgentes, Mexico, 03900, DF,
Mexico
Tel.: (52) 55 1102 3410
Web Site: http://www.cardtronics.com
Automatic Teller Machine Network Operator
N.A.I.C.S.: 522320

Subsidiary (Domestic):

Columbus Data Services LLC (3)
5220 Spring Valley Rd Ste 300, Dallas, TX
75254
Tel.: (214) 242-0650
Web Site: http://www.columbusdata.net
Payment Processing Services
N.A.I.C.S.: 522320

Subsidiary (Non-US):

**Spark ATM Systems Proprietary
Limited** (2)
Spark House 31 Transvaal Street Paarden
Eiland, Cape Town, 7405, South Africa
Tel.: (27) 877501000
Web Site: http://www.sparkatm.co.za
Automated Teller Machine Deployed Services
N.A.I.C.S.: 522320
Russel Berman *(Sls Dir)*
Buks Hanekom *(Mgr-Tech)*

Cimplebox Inc. (1)
6345 Balboa Blvd Ste 165, Encino, CA
91316
Tel.: (818) 342-7722
Web Site: http://www.cimplebox.com
Electronics Stores
N.A.I.C.S.: 449210

Digital Insight Corporation (1)
180 Jefferson Dr, Menlo Park, CA
94025 (100%)
Tel.: (818) 871-0000
Web Site: http://www.digitalinsight.com
Sales Range: $300-349.9 Million
Emp.: 750
Online Banking Services for Mid-Market
Banks & Credit Unions
N.A.I.C.S.: 513210

Branch (Domestic):

**Digital Insight Corporation-Product
Development** (2)

5720 Peachtree Pkwy, Norcross, GA
30092 (100%)
Tel.: (770) 349-1200
Web Site: http://www.digitalinsight.com
Sales Range: $50-74.9 Million
Emp.: 200
Online Banking Services for Mid-Market
Banks & Credit Unions
N.A.I.C.S.: 513210

First Level Technology LLC (1)
2651 Satellite Blvd, Duluth, GA 30096
Tel.: (512) 372-0222
Web Site: http://www.ncr.com
Provider of IT Services
N.A.I.C.S.: 541512

**Foremost Business Systems,
Inc.** (1)
4834 Park Glen Rd, Minneapolis, MN
55416
Tel.: (952) 920-8449
Web Site:
http://www.pointofsalesoftwaremn.com
Sales Range: $1-9.9 Million
Emp.: 12
Office Equipment Merchant Whslr
N.A.I.C.S.: 423420
Richard Polsfuss *(CEO)*

JetPay Corporation (1)
7450 Tilghman St Ste 170, Allentown, PA
18106
Tel.: (610) 797-9500
Web Site: http://www.jetpay.com
Rev.: $56,330,000
Assets: $187,210,000
Liabilities: $177,001,000
Net Worth: $10,209,000
Earnings: ($8,215,000)
Emp.: 235
Fiscal Year-end: 12/31/2016
Credit Card Sales, Transaction Processing
& Corporate Payroll Services
N.A.I.C.S.: 522320

Subsidiary (Domestic):

A.D. Computer Corporation (2)
3939 West Dr, Center Valley, PA 18034
Tel.: (610) 797-9500
Web Site: http://www.adcomputer.com
Sales Range: $10-24.9 Million
Emp.: 90
Payroll, Tax Filing & Human Resource Data
Processing Services
N.A.I.C.S.: 518210
C. Nicholas Antich *(Founder & Pres)*
Valerie Maugle *(Bus Mgr)*

ACI Merchant Systems, LLC (2)
136 E Watson Ave, Langhorne, PA 19047
Tel.: (215) 741-6970
Credit Card Processing Services
N.A.I.C.S.: 522320

Jet Pay, LLC (2)
3361 Boyington Dr Ste, 180, Carrollton, TX
75006
Tel.: (972) 503-8900
Web Site: http://www.jetpay.com
Sales Range: $10-24.9 Million
Emp.: 50
Credit Card Processing Services
N.A.I.C.S.: 522320

JetPay ISO Services, LLC (2)
3361 Boyington Dr Ste 180, Carrollton, TX
75006
Tel.: (972) 503-8900
Web Site: http://www.jetpayiso.com
Payment Processing Services
N.A.I.C.S.: 541214

JetPay Merchant Services, LLC (2)
30800 Telegraph Rd Ste 1924, Bingham
Farms, MI 48025
Tel.: (248) 540-1100
Web Site: http://www.jetpayms.com
Payment Transaction & Processing Services
N.A.I.C.S.: 541214

Payroll Tax Filing Services, Inc. (2)
3939 W Dr, Center Valley, PA 18034
Tel.: (610) 797-9595
Web Site: http://www.payroll.com
Emp.: 100
Accounting & Tax Filing Services
N.A.I.C.S.: 541213

NCR (Cyprus) Limited (1)
80 Limassol Ave, Nicosia, 2014,
Cyprus (100%)
Tel.: (357) 22423388
Web Site: http://www.ncr.cy
Sales Range: $25-49.9 Million
Emp.: 100
Provider of Computer Related Products &
Services
N.A.I.C.S.: 541512

NCR (Hong Kong) Limited (1)
22 F RPF Tower Times Sq 1 Matheson St,
Causeway Bay, China (Hong
Kong) (100%)
Tel.: (852) 29756888
Sales Range: $50-74.9 Million
Emp.: 200
Provider of Computer Related Products &
Services
N.A.I.C.S.: 541512

NCR (IRI) Ltd. (1)
80 Limassol Ave, Nicosia, 2014,
Cyprus (100%)
Tel.: (357) 22423388
Web Site: http://www.ncr.com.cy
Sales Range: $25-49.9 Million
Emp.: 150
Provider of Computer Related Products &
Services
N.A.I.C.S.: 541512

NCR (Malaysia) Sdn. Bhd. (1)
Avenue 10 The Vertical Bangsar South City
Suite 5-1 & 6 1 Level 5 & 6, Vertical Corpo-
rate Tower B No 8 Jalan Karinchi, Kuala
Lumpur, 59200, Malaysia
Tel.: (60) 321175700
Web Site: http://www.ncr.com
Provider of Computer Related Products &
Services
N.A.I.C.S.: 541512

NCR (Middle East) Limited (1)
80 Limassol Ave, Nicosia, 2014,
Cyprus (100%)
Tel.: (357) 22423388
Web Site: http://www.ncr.com
Provider of Computer Related Products &
Services
N.A.I.C.S.: 541512

Subsidiary (Non-US):

NCR (Bahrain) W.L.L. (2)
304 Government Road Ste 605 607-608,
PO Box 265, Manama, Bahrain (100%)
Tel.: (973) 17224233
Sales Range: $1-9.9 Million
Emp.: 25
Provider of Computer Related Products &
Services
N.A.I.C.S.: 541512
Panayiotis Hailis *(Mgr-Fin)*

NCR Corp. - UAE Branch (2)
Building 1 Side A Level 6 Financial Ctr Rd,
PO Box 1185, Dubai Design District, Dubai,
333300, United Arab Emirates
Tel.: (971) 43592200
Sales Range: $10-24.9 Million
Emp.: 75
Provider of Computer Related Products &
Services
N.A.I.C.S.: 541512

Retalix Ltd. (2)
9 Dafna Street, Ra'anana, 4366223, Israel
Tel.: (972) 97766677
Web Site: http://www.retalix.co.il
Integrated Software Solutions for the Food,
Fuel, Distr & Retail Industries
N.A.I.C.S.: 334610

Subsidiary (Domestic):

StoreNext Ltd. (3)
20 HaMagshimim Street, PO Box 3935, Pe-
tah Tiqwa, 49130, Israel
Tel.: (972) 3 925 1777
Web Site: http://www.storenext.co.il
Retail Software Publisher
N.A.I.C.S.: 423430
Gai Malishkevitz *(CEO)*
Felix Shendelzon *(CFO & VP-Fin Innova-
tion)*
Gal Pachter *(VP-Ops)*
Ifat Navon *(VP-HR)*

Gad Shaked *(CTO)*
Gennady Sorochan *(VP-Infrastructure &
Info Security)*

NCR (NZ) Corporation (1)
Level 13 1 Queen Street, Auckland, New
Zealand
Tel.: (64) 93566777
Electric Equipment Mfr
N.A.I.C.S.: 334419

NCR (Nigeria) PLC (1)
6 Broad Street, PO Box 509, Lagos,
102273, Nigeria
Tel.: (234) 12793970
Web Site: https://www.ncr.com.ng
Rev.: $16,625,429
Assets: $23,086,256
Liabilities: $24,558,634
Net Worth: ($1,472,377)
Earnings: ($2,602,074)
Fiscal Year-end: 12/31/2019
ATMs & Other Financial Products, Market-
ing Automation System, Financial & Retail
Software Developer & Cheque & Document
Imaging Offerings
N.A.I.C.S.: 522320
Otunba Adekunle Ojora *(Chm)*
Christiana N. Yisa *(Mng Dir)*
Chukwueke Onyekachi Caleb *(Controller-
Fin)*
Okeyanju Adeyinka *(Mgr-Svcs)*
Julius U. Amakor *(Mgr-Professional Svcs)*

NCR (North Africa) Limited (1)
80 Limassol Ave, Nicosia, 2014,
Cyprus (100%)
Tel.: (357) 22423388
Web Site: http://www.ncr.com
Sales Range: $25-49.9 Million
Emp.: 110
Provider of Computer Related Products &
Services
N.A.I.C.S.: 541512

NCR (Thailand) Limited (1)
130- 132 Wireless Road Kwaeng Lumpini
5th floor, 103 132 Wireless Rd, Bangkok,
10330, Thailand
Tel.: (66) 26894000
Sales Range: $50-74.9 Million
Emp.: 200
Provider of Computer Related Products &
Services
N.A.I.C.S.: 541512
Paul Edward *(Mng Dir)*

NCR A/O (1)
Unit 5 Kosmogamiamskaya Nab 52 Bldg,
115054, Moscow, Russia
Tel.: (7) 4959613030
Provider of Computer Related Products &
Services
N.A.I.C.S.: 541512
William R. Nuti *(Chm, Pres & CEO)*

NCR Australia Pty. Limited (1)
(100%)
Tel.: (61) 299648111
Sales Range: $75-99.9 Million
Emp.: 350
Provider of Computer Related Products &
Services
N.A.I.C.S.: 541512

NCR Belgium & Co. SNC (1)
Ave Marcel Thirylaan 79, 1200, Brussels,
Belgium
Tel.: (32) 27611311
Sales Range: $10-24.9 Million
Emp.: 20
Provider of Computer Related Products &
Services
N.A.I.C.S.: 541512
Luc Brusselaers *(Mng Dir)*

NCR Bilisim Sistemleri LS (1)
Kisikli St 35-2 Antune 0Ade, Istanbul,
34662, Turkiye
Tel.: (90) 2165542000
Web Site: http://www.ncr.com
Sales Range: $25-49.9 Million
Emp.: 100
Provider of Computer Related Products &
Services
N.A.I.C.S.: 541512

NCR Brasil Ltda. (1)
Rua Doutor Rafael De Barros 209 Bairro
Paraiso, Sao Paulo, Sao Paulo, 04003-041,
Brazil

Tel.: (55) 11 3347 1100
Web Site: http://www.ncr.com
Provider of Computer Related Products &
Services
N.A.I.C.S.: 541512

NCR Canada Ltd. (1)
6865 Century Ave, Mississauga, L5N 2E2,
ON, Canada **(100%)**
Tel.: (800) 268-2034
Provider of Computer Related Products &
Services
N.A.I.C.S.: 541512

**NCR Chile Industrial y Comercial
Limitada** (1)
Calle Miraflores 383 Piso 17, Santiago,
8320000, Chile
Tel.: (56) 2268871000
Computer Terminal Mfr
N.A.I.C.S.: 334118
Kochav Orios *(Gen Mgr)*

NCR Colombia Ltda (1)
Transversal 23 No 97-73 Offices 403404-
Parking 14 spaces, Distrito Capital, Bogota,
11001, Colombia
Tel.: (57) 12757805
Financial Management Services
N.A.I.C.S.: 541611

NCR Commerce Japan Ltd. (1)
1-21-2 Shinkawa Kayabacho Tower, Chuo-
ku, Tokyo, 104-0033, Japan
Tel.: (81) 367596000
Web Site: https://www.ncr.co.jp
Information Technology Services
N.A.I.C.S.: 541519

NCR Corporation (Philippines) (1)
6788 Ayala Avenue Oledan Square 17th
floor, Ayala Ave, Makati, 1226, Manila,
Philippines **(100%)**
Tel.: (63) 28104551
Sales Range: $10-24.9 Million
Emp.: 40
Provider of Computer Related Products &
Services
N.A.I.C.S.: 541512

**NCR Czeska Republika spol.
s.r.o.** (1)
Narodni 32, Prague, 11000, Czech
Republic **(100%)**
Tel.: (420) 222109111
Web Site: http://www.NCR.Com
Sales Range: $10-24.9 Million
Emp.: 40
Provider of Computer Related Products &
Services
N.A.I.C.S.: 541512

NCR Danmark A/S (1)
20 Rue De Langgaartz Vej 6-8, 2300, Co-
penhagen, Denmark **(100%)**
Tel.: (45) 70239100
Sales Range: $10-24.9 Million
Emp.: 50
Provider of Computer Related Products &
Services
N.A.I.C.S.: 541512

NCR Dominicana C. por A. (1)
Jose Amado Soner 44, Santo Domingo,
Dominican Republic
Tel.: (809) 565 7766
Sales Range: $100-124.9 Million
Computer Related Products & Services
N.A.I.C.S.: 541512
Deasy Periez *(Gen Mgr)*

NCR Espana, S.A. (1)
Tel.: (34) 913755000
Web Site: http://www.ncrnet.ncr.com
Sales Range: $50-74.9 Million
Emp.: 200
Provider of Computer Related Products &
Services
N.A.I.C.S.: 541512

**NCR Financial Solutions Group
Ltd.** (1)
Discovery Centre, Dundee, DD2 4SW, Scot-
land, United Kingdom
Tel.: (44) 1382611511
Web Site: http://www.ncr.com
Semiconductor Devices Mfr
N.A.I.C.S.: 334413

NCR Finland Oy (1)

Kilonpuisto 2 B 43, 2130, Espoo,
Finland **(100%)**
Tel.: (358) 010421830
Omni-Channel Solutions Mfr
N.A.I.C.S.: 541512

NCR Ghana Limited (1)
PO Box 1010, Accra, Ghana
Tel.: (233) 21220554
Web Site: http://www.ncrgh.com
Sales Range: $100-124.9 Million
Emp.: 18
Provider of Computer Related Products &
Services
N.A.I.C.S.: 541512

NCR Global Solutions Limited (1)
Unit 180 Lake View Dr, Airside Business
Park, Dublin, Ireland **(100%)**
Tel.: (353) 18909300
Web Site: http://www.ncr.co.uk
Sales Range: $10-24.9 Million
Emp.: 45
Provider of Computer Related Products &
Services
N.A.I.C.S.: 541512

NCR Government Systems LLC (1)
20370 Seneca Meadows Pkwy, German-
town, MD 20876-7004
Tel.: (301) 820-6500
Web Site: http://www.ncr.com
Sales Range: $25-49.9 Million
Emp.: 150
Computer Terminal Mfr
N.A.I.C.S.: 334118

NCR International of Puerto Rico (1)
PO Box 190939, San Juan, PR 00919-0939
Tel.: (787) 622-0404
Web Site: http://www.ncr.com
Rev.: $10,000,000
Emp.: 32
Provider of Computer Related Products &
Services
N.A.I.C.S.: 424120

NCR Italia S.r.l. (1)
150/4 Via Cusago, 20100, Milan,
Italy **(100%)**
Tel.: (39) 0247901
Provider of Computer Related Products &
Services
N.A.I.C.S.: 334112

NCR Japan, Ltd. (1)
1-21-2 Shinkawa Kayabacho Tower, Chuo-
ku, Tokyo, 104-0033, Japan **(100%)**
Tel.: (81) 36 759 6000
Web Site: https://www.ncr.co.jp
Sales Range: $500-549.9 Million
Emp.: 1,900
Data Warehousing, CRM & E-Business
Solutions
N.A.I.C.S.: 518210

NCR Kenya Ltd. (1)
Agip House Haile Selasie Avenue Ground
Floor Entrance A B, PO Box 30217 00100,
Haile Selassie Ave, Nairobi, 00200,
Kenya **(100%)**
Tel.: (254) 20310651
Sales Range: $10-24.9 Million
Emp.: 40
Provider of Computer Related Products &
Services
N.A.I.C.S.: 541512

NCR Magyarorszag Kft. (1)
Fehervari St 79 1st Fl, 1119, Budapest,
Hungary **(100%)**
Tel.: (36) 14814300
Web Site: http://www.ncr.com
Provider of Computer Related Products &
Services
N.A.I.C.S.: 541512
Agnes Diei *(Mng Dir)*

NCR Nederland N.V. (1)
(100%)
Tel.: (31) 206512345
Sales Range: $25-49.9 Million
Emp.: 150
Provider of Computer Related Products &
Services
N.A.I.C.S.: 541512

NCR Osterreich Ges.m.b.H. (1)
Storchengasse 1, 1150, Vienna,
Austria **(100%)**
Tel.: (43) 1891110

Web Site: http://www.ncr.com
Sales Range: $10-24.9 Million
Emp.: 10
Provider of Computer Related Products &
Services
N.A.I.C.S.: 541512
Hubert Schauerhoser *(Mng Dir)*

NCR Polska Sp.z.o.o. (1)
Orzechowa and Krakowiakow ul Krakowi-
akow 32 3rd Floor, PO Box 2672, Grzy-
bowska Park, 02-255, Warsaw,
Poland **(100%)**
Tel.: (48) 226061252
Sales Range: $25-49.9 Million
Emp.: 150
Provider of Computer Related Products &
Services
N.A.I.C.S.: 541512

NCR Singapore Pte Ltd. (1)
7 &9 Tampines Grande 08-11 22, Singa-
pore, 528735, Singapore
Tel.: (65) 6521 2300
Web Site: http://www.ncr.com
Provider of Computer Related Products &
Services
N.A.I.C.S.: 541512

**NCR Solutions de Mexico S. de R.L.
de C.V.** (1)
Paseo de Las Palmas 239 Pisos 6 y 7, Lo-
mas de Chapultepec, Mexico, 11000,
Mexico
Tel.: (52) 5557287177
Computer Peripherals Mfr
N.A.I.C.S.: 334118

NCR Systems Taiwan Limited (1)
No 156 Sec 3 Minsheng, Taipei, 10596,
Taiwan
Tel.: (886) 227181415
Web Site: http://www.ncr.com
Mfr of Computer Related Products & Ser-
vices
N.A.I.C.S.: 541512

NCR Taiwan Software Ltd (1)
15th Fl 156 Min Sheng E Rd Sec 3, Taipei,
105, Taiwan **(100%)**
Tel.: (886) 227191415
Web Site: http://www.ncr.com
Sales Range: $10-24.9 Million
Emp.: 70
Computer Related Products & Services
N.A.I.C.S.: 541512

NCR UK Group Limited (1)
9th Fl 5 Merchant Square, London, W2
1BQ, United Kingdom
Tel.: (44) 2077237070
Web Site: http://www.ncr.com
Sales Range: $100-124.9 Million
Provider of Computer Related Products &
Services
N.A.I.C.S.: 541512

NCR de Chile, S.A. (1)
Miraflores 383 17th Fl, Santiago, 8320149,
Chile **(100%)**
Tel.: (56) 26871000
Sales Range: $25-49.9 Million
Emp.: 200
Provider of Computer Related Products &
Services
N.A.I.C.S.: 541512

NCR del Peru S.A. (1)
Av Paseo De La Republica, San Isidro,
Lima, 3245, Peru
Tel.: (51) 14111900
Computer Terminal Mfr
N.A.I.C.S.: 334118

Orderman GmbH (1)
Bachstrasse 59, 5023, Salzburg, Austria
Tel.: (43) 6626505610
Web Site: https://www.orderman.com
Commercial & Service Industry Machinery
Mfr
N.A.I.C.S.: 333310
Wolfgang Danninger *(Head-Ops)*
Martin Aster *(Head-R&D)*
Christian Korneli *(Head-Product Mgmt &
Sls)*
Anton Haller *(Officer-Press)*

Radiant Systems, Inc. (1)
3925 Brookside Pkwy, Alpharetta, GA
30022-4429

Tel.: (770) 576-6000
Web Site: http://www.radiantsystems.com
Sales Range: $300-349.9 Million
Emp.: 1,377
Hardware & Software Solutions to Hospital-
ity, Retail & Entertainment Industries
N.A.I.C.S.: 541512

StopLift, Inc. (1)
186 Alewife Brook Pkwy Ste 300, Cam-
bridge, MA 02138
Web Site: http://www.stoplift.com
Software Services
N.A.I.C.S.: 541511

TCR Business Systems, Inc. (1)
1801 Royal Ln Ste 600, Dallas, TX 75220
Tel.: (972) 807-8000
Commercial & Service Industry Machinery
Mfr
N.A.I.C.S.: 333310
Jennifer Trichel *(Gen Mgr)*

Texas Digital Systems, Inc. (1)
400 Technology Pkwy, College Station, TX
77845
Tel.: (979) 693-9378
Commercial & Service Industry Machinery
Mfr
N.A.I.C.S.: 333310
Andrew Bettis *(Mgr-Strategic Partnerships)*

Texas Pos, Inc. (1)
16555 Village Dr, Houston, TX 77040
Tel.: (713) 896-0187
Web Site: http://www.texaspos.com
Repair Services, Nec, Nsk
N.A.I.C.S.: 811210
Brian Choate *(Founder & Pres)*

NCS MULTISTAGE HOLDINGS, INC.

19350 State Hwy 249 Ste 600, Hous-
ton, TX 77070
Tel.: (281) 453-2222   DE
Web Site:
https://www.ncsmultistage.com
Year Founded: 2012
NCSM—(NASDAQ)
Rev.: $155,632,000
Assets: $138,599,000
Liabilities: $29,337,000
Net Worth: $109,262,000
Earnings: ($1,102,000)
Emp.: 228
Fiscal Year-end: 12/31/22
Oil & Gas Field Machinery & Equip-
ment Manufacturing
N.A.I.C.S.: 333132
Michael L. Morrison *(CFO & Treas)*
Dewayne Williams *(Principal Acctg
Officer, VP & Controller)*
Robert Nipper *(Founder)*
Marty Stromquist *(COO)*
Tim Willems *(CIO)*
Ryan Hummer *(CEO)*
Lori Cole *(VP-Fin & Treas)*

Subsidiaries:

Pioneer Investment, Inc. (1)
60 State St Fl 18, Boston, MA 02109
Tel.: (617) 742-7825
Emp.: 200
Industrial Products Mfr
N.A.I.C.S.: 316990

Subsidiary (Non-US):

NCS Multistage Inc. (2)
333 7th Avenue SW 7th Floor, Calgary, T2P
2Z1, AB, Canada
Tel.: (403) 984-7674
Oil & Gas Industrial Services
N.A.I.C.S.: 213112

Subsidiary (Domestic):

Spectrum Tracer Services, LLC (2)
9111 E Pine St, Tulsa, OK 74115
Tel.: (918) 933-5653
Web Site: http://www.spectrumtracer.com
Chemical Tracer Services
N.A.I.C.S.: 333515
Jon Larue *(Exec VP-Engrg & Tech)*

STS Tracer Services, Ltd. (1)

NCS Multistage Holdings, Inc.—(Continued)

7924 10 St NE, Calgary, T2E 8W1, AB, Canada
Tel.: (403) 262-3844
Oil & Gas Industrial Services
N.A.I.C.S.: 213112

NDIVISION, INC.

7301 N State Hwy 161 Ste 100, Irving, TX 75039
Tel.: (214) 785-6355 NV
Web Site: https://ndivision.us
NDVN—(OTCIQ)
Rev.: $5,927,173
Assets: $3,897,367
Liabilities: $3,807,775
Net Worth: $89,592
Earnings: ($1,498,926)
Emp.: 45
Fiscal Year-end: 12/31/20
Information Technology Consulting Services
N.A.I.C.S.: 541512
Alan Hixon (Founder, Chm, Pres, CEO & Dir)
Brad Wiggins (Chief Admin Officer)
Justin Roby (CTO)
Andy Norstrund (CFO & Dir)

NEBULA CARAVEL ACQUISITION CORP.

4 Embarcadero Center Ste 2100, San Francisco, CA 94111
Tel.: (415) 780-9975 DE
Year Founded: 2020
NEBCU—(NASDAQ)
Investment Services
N.A.I.C.S.: 523999
Adam H. Clammer (Pres & CEO)
Rufina A. Adams (CFO & Sec)
James H. Greene Jr. (Chm)

NEFFS BANCORP, INC.

5629 Rte 873, Neffs, PA 18065
Tel.: (610) 767-3875 PA
Web Site: https://www.neffsnatl.com
Year Founded: 1986
NEFB—(OTCIQ)
Rev.: $13,400,000
Assets: $409,134,000
Liabilities: $335,261,000
Net Worth: $73,873,000
Earnings: $3,500,000
Emp.: 48
Fiscal Year-end: 12/31/20
Bank Holding Company
N.A.I.C.S.: 551111
David C. Matulevich (Treas & Sec)
Kevin A. Schmidt (VP)
Robert B. Heintzelman (Pres & CEO)
Marianne C. Eisenhauer (VP-Comml Lending & Credit Admin-Neff National Bank)
Greta D. Mast (VP-Comml Lending-Neff National Bank)
Colleen A. Worysz (VP-Customer Svc Rels-Neff National Bank)
Ronald K. Miller (VP-Retail Lending-Neff National Bank)

Subsidiaries:

The Neffs National Bank (1)
5629 PA Rte 873 PO Box 10, Neffs, PA 18065-0010
Tel.: (610) 767-3875
Web Site: http://www.neffsnatl.com
Emp.: 38
Commercial Banking
N.A.I.C.S.: 522110
John J. Remaley (Chm)
Kevin A. Schmidt (Pres & CEO)
Michael J. Bailey (COO & Exec VP)
Ronald B. Gilder (VP-Retail Lending)
David C. Matulevich (VP-Admin)
Ronald K. Miller (VP-Retail Lending)
Colleen A. Worysz (VP-Customer Svc Rels)

NEKTAR THERAPEUTICS

455 Mission Bay Blvd S, San Francisco, CA 94158
Tel.: (415) 482-5300 DE
Web Site: https://www.nektar.com
Year Founded: 1990
NKTR—(NASDAQ)
Rev.: $92,055,000
Assets: $710,600,000
Liabilities: $343,962,000
Net Worth: $366,638,000
Earnings: ($368,198,000)
Emp.: 216
Fiscal Year-end: 12/31/22
Mfr of Inhalers & Nebulizers & Developer of Pharmaceuticals for the Treatment of Diabetes & Respiratory Infections
N.A.I.C.S.: 325412
Dimitry S.A. Nuyten (Chief Medical Officer & Sr VP)
Robert Bacci (Sr VP-Human Resources & Facilities Ops)
Sandra Gardiner (CFO)
Jonathan Zalevsky (Chief R&D Officer)
Mary A. Tagliaferri (Chief Medical Officer & Sr VP)
Howard W. Robin (Pres & CEO)
Robert B. Chess (Chm)
Brian L. Kotzin (Sr VP-Clinical Dev & Head-Immunology)

Subsidiaries:

Nektar Therapeutics (India) Pvt. Ltd. (1)
Sy Nos 101/2 Genome Valley Lalgadi Malakpet, Shameerpet Mandal Rangareddy District, Hyderabad, 500 078, Telangana, India
Tel.: (91) 4067204100
Sales Range: $50-74.9 Million
Research & Development of Pharmaceuticals for the Treatment of Diabetes & Respiratory Infections
N.A.I.C.S.: 541715

NELNET, INC.

121 S 13th St Ste 201, Lincoln, NE 68508
Tel.: (402) 458-2370 NE
Web Site: https://www.nelnet.com
Year Founded: 1977
NNI—(NYSE)
Rev.: $742,806,000
Assets: $19,374,044,000
Liabilities: $16,174,142,000
Net Worth: $3,199,902,000
Earnings: $407,347,000
Emp.: 8,237
Fiscal Year-end: 12/31/22
Student Loan Products & Services
N.A.I.C.S.: 522291
Matthew W. Dunlap (Chief Bus Dev Officer & Pres-Fin Svcs)
Michael S. Dunlap (Founder & Exec Chm)
William J. Munn (Gen Counsel & Sec)
Timothy A. Tewes (Pres)
James D. Kruger (CFO)
Jeffrey R. Noordhoek (CEO)

Subsidiaries:

Allo Communications, LLC (1)
610 Broadway St, Imperial, NE 69033
Tel.: (970) 427-8750
Web Site:
  https://www.allocommunications.com
Educational Financial Services
N.A.I.C.S.: 522291
Bradley A. Moline (Pres & CEO)

Subsidiary (Domestic):

Avid Communications LLC (2)
1800 Baltimore Ave Ste 200, Kansas City, MO 64108-1919
Tel.: (816) 994-7070

Web Site: http://www.avidphone.com
Wired Telecommunications Carriers
N.A.I.C.S.: 517111
David Hollingsworth (Owner)
Taylor Cates (Dir-Sls)

BenefitEd, LLC (1)
121 S 13th St 201, Lincoln, NE 68508
Web Site: https://www.youbenefited.com
Programming Services
N.A.I.C.S.: 522291

Duluth Storage, LLC (1)
250 Garfield Ave, Duluth, MN 55802-2627
Tel.: (218) 727-7219
Logistic Services
N.A.I.C.S.: 484110

FACTS Education Solutions, LLC (1)
121 S 13th St, Lincoln, NE 68508
Tel.: (866) 213-4249
Web Site: http://www.factsed.com
Professional Development Services
N.A.I.C.S.: 611430
Patrick Haggarty (Pres)
Donna Moss (VP-Southeast)
Elizabeth Shelton (Dir-Accounts & Contracts)
Marc Hoban (VP-Northeast)
Jeremy Beck (VP-Midwest)
Carlos Hernandez (VP-Southwest)
Jackie Degel (VP-West)
Julie Greer (Mgr-Instructional Svcs)
Tiffany Wilbur (Mgr-Professional Learning & Dev)
Amy Lehnert (Acct Mgr-School)
Brian Votava (Acct Mgr-School)
Sarah Noble (Acct Mgr-School)
Hilary Farber (Coord-Event)

FACTS Management AUS Pty. Ltd. (1)
Suite 13-15 2 Brandon Park Drive Wheelers Hill, Melbourne, 3150, VIC, Australia
Tel.: (61) 1300322871
Web Site: https://factsmgt.com.au
Investment Management Service
N.A.I.C.S.: 525910

First National Life Insurance Company of the USA, Inc. (1)
PO Box 6278, Lincoln, NE 68506
Tel.: (402) 483-1776
Web Site: http://www.fnlusa.com
Fire Insurance Services
N.A.I.C.S.: 524113
Tom Massey (Pres)

Great Lakes Educational Loan Services Inc (1)
2401 International Ln, Madison, WI 53704
Tel.: (608) 246-1700
Web Site: https://www.mygreatlakes.org
Educational Loan Services
N.A.I.C.S.: 327910
Brett Lindquist (CMO & Chief Sls Officer)

Health Education Solutions, Inc. (1)
3800 S 48th St, Lincoln, NE 68506
Tel.: (402) 486-2600
Web Site: http://www.healthedsolutions.com
Emp.: 5
Online Certification & Recertification Services
N.A.I.C.S.: 923110

National Education Loan Network, Inc. (1)
121 S 13th St Ste 201, Lincoln, NE 68508
Tel.: (402) 458-2303
Web Site: http://www.nelnet.net
Education Loan Provider
N.A.I.C.S.: 522310

Nelnet Business Solutions, Inc. (1)
122 Ste 201, Lincoln, NE 68508 (100%)
Tel.: (402) 466-1063
Web Site: http://www.factsmgt.com
Sales Range: $75-99.9 Million
Emp.: 450
College Enrollment & Tuition Management Services
N.A.I.C.S.: 541618
Jim Owens (Mng Dir & Natl Sls Mgr)
DeeAnn Wenger (Co-Pres)
Scott Spethman (Co-Pres)
Michael Walters (CIO)
Danielle Egr (CTO)
Dan Hughes (Sr VP-Eastern US)
Mark Schilmoeller (COO)
Mike Spanier (Sr VP-Western US)

Subsidiary (Domestic):

Tuition Management Systems, LLC (2)
171 Service Ave Ste 200, Warwick, RI 02886
Tel.: (401) 921-3999
Web Site: http://www.afford.com
Personal Credit Services
N.A.I.C.S.: 522291

Nelnet Diversified Solutions, LLC (1)
8740 Lucent Blvd Ste 400, Highlands Ranch, CO 80129
Tel.: (303) 696-5637
Web Site: http://www.n-d-s.com
Premier Technology & Processing Solutions Provider
N.A.I.C.S.: 611710

Nelnet Finance Corp. (1)
121 S 13th St Ste 201, Lincoln, NE 68508
Tel.: (402) 458-2370
Financial Management Services
N.A.I.C.S.: 541611

Nelnet Technology Services LLC (1)
8740 Lucent Blvd Ste 400, Highlands Ranch, CO 80129
Tel.: (303) 696-5280
Web Site: http://www.5280solutions.com
Sales Range: $100-124.9 Million
Emp.: 250
Educational Loan Software
N.A.I.C.S.: 513210

Nelnet Transaction Services, LLC (1)
PO Box 82561, Lincoln, NE 68501-2561
Tel.: (303) 696-3625
Financial Management Services
N.A.I.C.S.: 541611

PaymentSpring, LLC (1)
12165 W Ctr, Omaha, NE 68144
Web Site: http://www.paymentspring.com
Information Technology Services
N.A.I.C.S.: 541511

Peterson's Nelnet, LLC (1)
Princeton Pike Corp Ctr 2000 Lenox Dr, Lawrenceville, NJ 08648-2314
Tel.: (609) 896-1800
Web Site: http://www.petersons.com
Sales Range: $75-99.9 Million
Emp.: 200
College & Career Data Information Services
N.A.I.C.S.: 513130

Sparkroom, LLC (1)
115 W Century Rd Ste 280, Paramus, NJ 07652
Tel.: (201) 477-7770
Financial Management Services
N.A.I.C.S.: 541611

Student Marketing Group, Inc. (1)
777 Sunrise Hwy Ste 300, Lynbrook, NY 11563
Tel.: (516) 593-8877
Web Site: http://www.studentmarketing.net
Sales Range: $75-99.9 Million
Educational Marketing Services
N.A.I.C.S.: 541613

Unilink Data Systems Pty Ltd (1)
Suites 13-15 Level 1, 2 Brandon Park Drive, Melbourne, 3150, VIC, Australia
Tel.: (61) 385451800
Web Site: http://www.unilink.com.au
Financial Management Services
N.A.I.C.S.: 541611

Whitetail Rock Capital Management, LLC (1)
121 S 13th St Ste 201, Lincoln, NE 68508
Tel.: (402) 458-2243
Sales Range: $25-49.9 Million
Emp.: 3
Financial Advisory Services
N.A.I.C.S.: 523940
Greer McCurley (Pres)

Whitetail Rock Quantitative Strategies I, LP (1)
121 S 13th St, Lincoln, NE 68508
Tel.: (402) 458-2243
Financial Management Services
N.A.I.C.S.: 541611

Wilcomp Software, LLC (1)

3401 Oak Trail Dr, Burleson, TX 76028
Tel.: (817) 426-6008
Software Publishing Services
N.A.I.C.S.: 513210

NEMAURA MEDICAL INC.
57 W 57th St, New York, NY 10019
Tel.: (646) 416-8000   NV
Web Site:
   https://www.nemauramedical.com
Year Founded: 2013
NMRD—(NASDAQ)
Rev.: $77,044
Assets: $14,563,233
Liabilities: $26,377,431
Net Worth: ($11,814,198)
Earnings: ($14,143,735)
Emp.: 36
Fiscal Year-end: 03/31/23
Diagnostic Medical Device Mfr
N.A.I.C.S.: 339112
Dewan Fazlul Hoque Chowdhury
*(Chm, Pres, CEO, Principal Acctg
Officer & Principal Fin Officer)*
Arash Ghadar *(COO)*

NEO TECHNOLOGY ACQUISI-
TION CORP.
800 3rd Ave Ste 2800, New York, NY
10022
Tel.: (212) 220-3967   DE
Year Founded: 2021
NFTTU—(NASDAQ)
Investment Services
N.A.I.C.S.: 523999
Yajing Li *(Chm, Pres & Exec Dir)*
Leslie Chow *(CEO)*
Yanyi Tang *(CFO)*

NEOGEN CORPORATION
620 Lesher Pl, Lansing, MI 48912
Tel.: (517) 372-9200   MI
Web Site: https://www.neogen.com
Year Founded: 1981
NEOG—(NASDAQ)
Rev.: $924,222,000
Assets: $4,548,833,000
Liabilities: $1,404,691,000
Net Worth: $3,144,142,000
Earnings: ($9,421,000)
Emp.: 2,917
Fiscal Year-end: 05/31/24
Pharmaceutical Preparation Manufac-
turing
N.A.I.C.S.: 325412
Jason W. Lilly *(VP-Intl Bus)*
Robert S. Donofrio *(Chief Scientific
Officer)*
James C. Borel *(Chm)*
John Edward Adent *(Pres & CEO)*
David H. Naemura *(CFO)*
Jerome L. Hagedorn *(VP-Food Safety
Ops)*
Julie L. Mann *(Chief HR Officer &
VP)*
Douglas E. Jones *(COO)*
Amy M. Rocklin *(Chief Legal Officer,
Chief Compliance Officer & Sec)*
David Naemura *(CFO)*

Subsidiaries:

Abbott Analytical Limited   (1)
Kemp House 160 City Rd, London, EC1V
2NX, United Kingdom
Tel.: (44) 1513456753
Web Site: https://www.abbottanalytical.co.uk
Testing Laboratory Services
N.A.I.C.S.: 541380
Tony Watson *(Bus Mgr-Development)*

Abtek (Biologicals) Ltd.   (1)
Unit 7 Brookfield Business Park Muir Road,
Liverpool, L9 7AR, United Kingdom
Tel.: (44) 1292525666
Web Site: http://www.abtekbio.com
Antibiotic Product Mfr & Distr
N.A.I.C.S.: 325412
Joanne Emerson *(Mgr)*

Acumedia Manufacturers, Inc.   (1)
620 Lesher Pl, Lansing, MI 48912 **(100%)**
Tel.: (517) 372-9200
Web Site: http://www.neogen.com
Dehydrated Culture Media Mfr
N.A.I.C.S.: 325412

BioLumix, Inc.   (1)
620 Lesher Pl, Lansing, MI 48912
Tel.: (517) 372-9200
Web Site: http://www.mybiolumix.com
Pharmaceuticals Product Mfr
N.A.I.C.S.: 334419

Centrus International, Inc.   (1)
PO Box 2003, Kingsport, TN
37662   **(100%)**
Tel.: (423) 229-5986
Microbial Contamination Diagnostic Sys-
tems Mfr
N.A.I.C.S.: 325413

Chem-Tech, Ltd.   (1)
4515 Fleur Dr Ste 303, Des Moines, IA
50321-2369
Tel.: (515) 287-6778
Web Site: http://www.chemtechlimited.com
Sales Range: $10-24.9 Million
Emp.: 40
Pesticide & Other Agricultural Chemical Mfr
N.A.I.C.S.: 325320

Delf (UK) Limited   (1)
Unit 2 Hickmans Road, Birkenhead, CH41
1JH, Wirral, United Kingdom
Tel.: (44) 1516300405
Web Site: https://www.delf-uk.com
Glycerine Mfr
N.A.I.C.S.: 622110

GeneSeek, Inc.   (1)
4131 N 48th St, Lincoln, NE
68504   **(100%)**
Tel.: (402) 435-0665
Web Site: http://www.geneseek.com
Sales Range: $25-49.9 Million
Emp.: 150
Agricultural Genetics Service Laboratory
N.A.I.C.S.: 541715

Hacco, Inc.   (1)
110 Hopkins Dr, Randolph, WI
53956-1316   **(100%)**
Tel.: (920) 326-5141
Web Site: http://www.hacco.com
Sales Range: $25-49.9 Million
Emp.: 40
Pesticide Mfr
N.A.I.C.S.: 325320

International Diagnostic Systems
Inc.   (1)
2620 S Cleveland Ave Ste 100, Saint Jo-
seph, MI 49085
Tel.: (269) 428-8400
Web Site: http://www.neogen.com
Sales Range: $1-9.9 Million
Emp.: 5
Developer, Mfr & Marketer of Test Kits to
Detect Drug Residues in Food & Animal
Feed
N.A.I.C.S.: 334516

Lab M Holdings   (1)
1 Quest Park Moss Hall Road, Heywood,
BL9 7JJ, Lancashire, United Kingdom
Tel.: (44) 1618203833
Web Site: http://www.labm.com
Holding Company
N.A.I.C.S.: 551112

Lab M Limited   (1)
1 Quest Park Moss Hall Road, Heywood,
BL9 7JJ, Lancashire, United Kingdom
Tel.: (44) 1618203833
Web Site: https://www.labm.com
Testing Laboratory Services
N.A.I.C.S.: 541380

Megazyme, Ltd.   (1)
Bray Business Park, Bray, Wicklow, A98
YV29, Ireland
Tel.: (353) 12861220
Web Site: http://www.megazyme.com
Food & Animal Safety Product Mfr
N.A.I.C.S.: 325414

Neogen Argentina S.A.   (1)
Thames 181, 1414, Buenos Aires, Argen-
tina
Tel.: (54) 1145877444

Food & Animal Safety Product Mfr
N.A.I.C.S.: 325414

Neogen Australasia Pty Limited   (1)
Building 8126 Hall Rd UQ Gatton Campus,
Gatton, 4343, QLD, Australia
Tel.: (61) 737362134
Food Safety Product Distr
N.A.I.C.S.: 424210
Russell Lyons *(Gen Mgr)*

Neogen Bio-Scientific Technology
(Shanghai) Co., Ltd.   (1)
Room 101-104 Building 13 Health Work
Park 697 Lingshi Road, Jingan District,
Shanghai, 200072, China
Tel.: (86) 2162717013
Pharmaceutical Preparation Mfr
N.A.I.C.S.: 325412

Neogen Canada   (1)
21 College Ave W, Guelph, N1G 1R7, ON,
Canada
Tel.: (226) 780-0267
Food Safety Product Distr
N.A.I.C.S.: 424210

Neogen Chile SpA   (1)
Calle Canal la Punta 8770 Bodega 44,
Renca, 8640000, Santiago, Chile
Tel.: (56) 227593117
Food & Animal Safety Product Mfr
N.A.I.C.S.: 311119

Neogen Europe Limited   (1)
The Dairy School, Auchincruive, Ayr, KA6
5HU, United Kingdom   **(100%)**
Tel.: (44) 1292439548
Web Site: http://www.neogeneurope.com
Sales Range: $150-199.9 Million
Emp.: 120
Food & Animal Safety Products Developer,
Mfr & Marketer
N.A.I.C.S.: 325412
Stephen Holmes *(Mng Dir)*

Neogen Food & Animal Security (In-
dia) Pvt, Ltd.   (1)
Uchikkal Lane Poonithura PO, Cochin,
682038, Kerala, India
Tel.: (91) 4842306598
Food Safety Product Distr
N.A.I.C.S.: 424210
Unnikrishnan V. M. *(Dir-Laboratory Svcs)*

Neogen Guatemala S.A.   (1)
7 Calle 3-24 Zona 18 Edificio Ofibodega
109 Complejo Interbodegas, Guatemala,
01018, Guatemala
Tel.: (502) 23166704
Food & Animal Safety Product Distr
N.A.I.C.S.: 424430

Neogen Latinoamerica S.A.P.I. de
C.V.   (1)
Prolongacion 5 de Mayo 27 Col Parque In-
dustrial, Col Anzures, Naucalpan,
Mexico   **(60%)**
Tel.: (52) 55 52 54 82 35
Emp.: 48
Food & Animal Safety Products Developer,
Mfr & Marketer
N.A.I.C.S.: 325412
Monica Guzman *(Mgr-Sls)*

Neogen Uruguay   (1)
Amelia Ramirez Manzana 324 Solar 21,
Lomas de Solymar, Canelones, Uruguay
Tel.: (598) 26983135
Food & Animal Safety Product Mfr
N.A.I.C.S.: 311119

Neogen do Brasil Produtos Para
Labratorios Ltda.   (1)
Rua Alberto Guizo 760, Distrito Industrial
Joao Narezzi, Indaiatuba, 13347 402, SP,
Brazil   **(94%)**
Tel.: (55) 19 3935 3727
Web Site: http://www.neogendobrasil.com.br
Food & Animal Safety Products Developer,
Mfr & Marketer
N.A.I.C.S.: 325412

Preserve International   (1)
944 Nandino Blvd, Lexington, KY 40511
Tel.: (859) 254-1221
Web Site:
   http://www.preserveinternational.com
Sanitation Product Mfr & Distr
N.A.I.C.S.: 325998

Preserve, Inc.   (1)
5605 Riggins Ct Ste 101A, Reno, NV 89502
Tel.: (775) 853-9776
Web Site:
   http://www.preserveinternational.com
Sales Range: $1-9.9 Million
Emp.: 28
Polish & Other Sanitation Good Mfr
N.A.I.C.S.: 325612
Gary Gaumer *(Pres, CEO & Treas)*

Productos Quimicos Magiar S.A.   (1)
Jose Antonio Cabrera 3288, Buenos Aires,
C1186AAJ, Argentina
Tel.: (54) 1149631525
Web Site: http://www.magiar.com.ar
Food & Animal Safety Product Mfr
N.A.I.C.S.: 311119
Martin Berger *(Owner)*

Quat-Chem Ltd.   (1)
1-4 Sandfield Industrial Park Dodgson
Street, Rochdale, OL16 5SJ, United King-
dom
Tel.: (44) 1706344797
Web Site: http://www.quatchem.com
Food Safety Product Mfr & Distr
N.A.I.C.S.: 325414

Rogama Industria Comercio
Ltda.   (1)
Av Alexandrina Das Chagas Moreira 964
Distrito Industrial, Pindamonhangaba,
12412-800, Brazil
Tel.: (55) 1236443030
Web Site: http://www.rogama.com.br
Pest Control Product Mfr & Distr
N.A.I.C.S.: 325320

Tetradyne, LLC   (1)
944 Nandino Blvd, Lexington, KY 40511
Tel.: (859) 254-1221
Web Site: http://www.tetradyne.net
Sanitation Product Mfr & Distr
N.A.I.C.S.: 325998

NEOGENOMICS, INC.
9490 Neogenomics Wy, Fort Myers,
FL 33912
Tel.: (239) 768-0600   NV
Web Site:
   https://www.neogenomics.com
Year Founded: 1998
NEO—(NASDAQ)
Rev.: $591,643,000
Assets: $1,681,229,000
Liabilities: $739,692,000
Net Worth: $941,537,000
Earnings: ($87,968,000)
Emp.: 2,100
Fiscal Year-end: 12/31/23
Cancer-Focused Genetic Testing
Laboratories
N.A.I.C.S.: 621511
Christopher M. Smith *(CEO)*
Melody Harris *(COO & Pres-
Informatics)*
Warren Stone *(Chief Comml Officer)*
Hutan Hashemi *(Chief Compliance
Officer)*
Gary Passman *(Chief Culture Officer)*
Ali Olivo *(Gen Counsel-Business De-
velopment & Exec VP)*
Jeffrey S. Sherman *(CFO)*

Subsidiaries:

Genoptix, Inc.   (1)
2131 Faraday Ave, Carlsbad, CA 92008
Tel.: (760) 268-6200
Web Site: http://www.genoptix.com
Medical Laboratory Services
N.A.I.C.S.: 541715

Subsidiary (Non-US):

Rosetta Genomics Ltd.   (2)
10 Plaut Street Science Park, PO Box
4059, Rehovot, 76706, Israel
Tel.: (972) 732220700
Web Site: http://www.rosettagenomics.com
Medical Research & Product Development
N.A.I.C.S.: 541715

NeoGenomics, Inc.—(Continued)

Subsidiary (US):

Rosetta Genomics Inc.   **(3)**
3711 Market St Ste 740, Philadelphia, PA
19104
Tel.: (215) 382-9000
Web Site: http://www.rosettagenomics.com
Medical Research & Product Development
N.A.I.C.S.: 541715

NEOLEUKIN THERAPEUTICS, INC.

188 E Blaine St Ste 450, Seattle, WA
98102
Tel.: (206) 732-2133   **DE**
Web Site: https://www.neoleukin.com
Year Founded: 2003
NLTX—(NASDAQ)
Rev.: $1,582,000
Assets: $115,948,000
Liabilities: $21,617,000
Net Worth: $94,331,000
Earnings: ($57,557,000)
Emp.: 56
Fiscal Year-end: 12/31/22
Pharmaceuticals Mfr
N.A.I.C.S.: 325412
Todd E. Simpson *(Chm)*
Daniel-Adriano Silva *(Co-Founder)*
Donna M. Cochener *(Gen Counsel & Sr VP)*
Sean Smith *(Interim CFO)*

NEOMAGIC CORPORATION

1503 N Milpitas Blvd, Milpitas, CA
95035
Tel.: (408) 428-9725   **DE**
Web Site: https://www.neomagic.com
Year Founded: 1993
NMGC—(OTCIQ)
Sales Range: $1-9.9 Million
Emp.: 4
Semiconductor & Related Device
Manufacturing
N.A.I.C.S.: 334413
Syed Zaidi *(Pres)*
David Tomasello *(Chm)*
Benjamin Bolinguit *(Dir-Ops)*
Roderick Peterson *(VP-Admin & Info)*

Subsidiaries:

Advanced Microwave, Inc.   **(1)**
33 Moffett Park Dr, Sunnyvale, CA 94089
Tel.: (408) 739-4214
Web Site: http://www.advmic.com
Rev.: $1,300,000
Emp.: 12
Radio & Television Broadcasting & Wireless
Communications Equipment Mfr
N.A.I.C.S.: 334220
Mike Ghandehari *(Pres)*

NeoMagic Israel Ltd.   **(1)**
7 Giborai Israel St Beit Adar, PO Box 8506,
Netanya, 42504, Israel   **(100%)**
Tel.: (972) 98632020
R&D Next-Generation Associative Processor Array (APA) Technology for Video & 3D
Graphics
N.A.I.C.S.: 541715

NeoMagic Semiconductor India Private Limited   **(1)**
1st Fl Polyplex Bldg B 37 Sector 1, Noida,
201301, India   **(100%)**
Tel.: (91) 1202471100
Quality Assurance & Software & Middleware
Development
N.A.I.C.S.: 423430

NEOMEDIA TECHNOLOGIES, INC.

2265 Knollwood Drive, Boulder, CO
80302
Tel.: (303) 546-7946   **DE**
Web Site: https://www.neom.com
Year Founded: 1996
NEOM—(OTCIQ)
Sales Range: $1-9.9 Million

Emp.: 27
2D Mobile Barcode Technology & Infrastructure Solutions
N.A.I.C.S.: 517810
Laura A. Marriott *(Chm & CEO)*

Subsidiaries:

NeoMedia Europe AG   **(1)**
Jens Otto Krag Str 11, Wurselen, 52146,
Germany
Tel.: (49) 2405299220
Web Site: http://www.gavitec.de
Sales Range: $100-124.9 Million
Mobile Marketing & Information Technology
Products & Solutions Mfr
N.A.I.C.S.: 513210

Triton Global Services Inc.   **(1)**
5824 Second St SW Ste 300, Calgary, T2H
0H2, AB, Canada
Tel.: (403) 257-7090
Web Site: http://www.tritonglobal.ca
Sales Range: $125-149.9 Million
Billing & Clearinghouse Functions & Information Management Services to Telecommunications Industry
N.A.I.C.S.: 522320

NEON BLOOM, INC.

23 Corporate Plaza Dr Ste 150, Newport Beach, CA 92660
Tel.: (949) 929-6226   **NV**
Year Founded: 2006
NBCO—(OTCIQ)
Sales Range: $1-9.9 Million
Emp.: 8
Aerospace & Defense
N.A.I.C.S.: 333994
Zahir Teja *(Pres & CEO)*
Teja N. Shariff *(Interim CFO)*
Fred G. Luke *(Sec)*

NEOVOLTA, INC.

13651 Danielson St Ste A, Poway,
CA 92064   **NV**
Web Site: https://www.neovolta.com
NEOV—(NASDAQ)
Rev.: $3,455,813
Assets: $6,505,864
Liabilities: $39,491
Net Worth: $6,466,373
Earnings: ($2,639,833)
Emp.: 7
Fiscal Year-end: 06/30/23
Battery Mfr
N.A.I.C.S.: 335910
Brent Willson *(Founder, Chm & CTO)*
Steve Bond *(CFO)*

NEPHROS, INC.

380 Lackawanna Pl, South Orange,
NJ 07079
Tel.: (201) 343-5202   **DE**
Web Site: https://www.nephros.com
Year Founded: 1997
NEPH—(NASDAQ)
Rev.: $9,975,000
Assets: $10,999,000
Liabilities: $2,118,000
Net Worth: $8,881,000
Earnings: ($7,382,000)
Emp.: 27
Fiscal Year-end: 12/31/22
Treatment Products for End Stage
Kidney Diseases & Other Medical
Conditions
N.A.I.C.S.: 339112
Judy F. Krandel *(CFO)*
Greg Lucas *(Founder & Pres-Aether Water Systems)*
Michael Milman *(VP-R&D)*
Robert Banks *(Pres & CEO)*
Judy Mazzini *(Controller)*
Brianne McGuire *(Dir)*
Alfred Vargas *(Dir)*
Devorah Serkin *(Dir)*

Subsidiaries:

Aether Water Systems, LLC   **(1)**

3321 Polaris Ave, Las Vegas, NV 89102
Web Site: http://www.aetherfilters.com
Water Equipment Mfr
N.A.I.C.S.: 333310
Greg Lucas *(Pres)*

Biocon 1, LLC   **(1)**
PO Box 530128, Henderson, NV 89053
Web Site: http://www.biocon1.com
Water Equipment Mfr
N.A.I.C.S.: 333310

Genarraytion Inc.   **(1)**
9700 Great Seneca Hwy Ste 325, Rockville,
MD 20850-3307
Tel.: (240) 453-6303
Web Site: http://www.genarraytion.com
Research & Development in Biotechnology
N.A.I.C.S.: 541714
Doreen Robinson *(Owner & COO)*

Specialty Renal Products, Inc.   **(1)**
211 Donelson Pike, Nashville, TN 37214
Tel.: (615) 682-8484
Web Site: http://www.specialtyrenal.com
Medical Equipment Mfr
N.A.I.C.S.: 339112
Daron Evans *(CEO)*

NEPRA FOODS INC.

7025 S Revere Pkwy Ste 100, Centennial, CO 80012
Tel.: (720) 729-8500   **CO**
Web Site:
  https://www.neprafoods.com
Year Founded: 2017
2P6—(DEU)
Other Animal Food Manufacturing
N.A.I.C.S.: 311119
David Wood *(Pres)*

NERDWALLET INC

55 Hawthorne St 10th Fl, San Francisco, CA 94105
Tel.: (415) 549-8913   **DE**
Web Site:
  https://www.nerdwallet.com
Year Founded: 2009
NRDS—(NASDAQ)
Rev.: $599,400,000
Assets: $418,600,000
Liabilities: $51,700,000
Net Worth: $366,900,000
Earnings: ($11,800,000)
Emp.: 730
Fiscal Year-end: 12/31/23
Asset Management Services
N.A.I.C.S.: 523999

NERDY INC.

Tel.: (314) 412-1227   **DE**
Year Founded: 2007
NRDY—(NYSE)
Rev.: $140,664,000
Assets: $177,145,000
Liabilities: $81,340,000
Net Worth: $95,805,000
Earnings: ($30,679,000)
Emp.: 1,000
Fiscal Year-end: 12/31/21
Investment Services
N.A.I.C.S.: 523999
Charles Cohn *(Founder, Chm & CEO)*
Jason Pello *(CFO)*
Julian Merschen *(CTO)*
Rian Schilligo *(Chief People Officer)*
Anthony Salcito *(Chief Institution Officer)*
Dan Lee *(Chief Analytics Officer)*
Chris Swenson *(Chief Legal Officer)*
Jared Wolf *(Chief Market Ops Officer)*
Jaimin Gandhi *(VP-Product)*
Jason Botel *(Head-Government Relations)*
Al Castle *(VP-Engineering)*
Andy Ketter *(VP-Performance & Growth Mktg)*
Zach Rachins *(VP-Product)*

Courtney Menges *(VP & Assoc Gen Counsel)*
Kyle Callaway *(VP & Controller)*
T. J. Lynn *(VP & Assoc Gen Counsel)*

NESTBUILDER.COM CORP.

201 W Passaic St Ste 301, Rochelle
Park, NJ 07662
Tel.: (201) 845-7001   **NV**
Year Founded: 2017
NBLD—(OTCIQ)
Rev.: $61,050
Assets: $19,622
Liabilities: $167,648
Net Worth: ($148,026)
Earnings: ($27,070)
Emp.: 2
Fiscal Year-end: 11/30/21
Digital Advertising Services
N.A.I.C.S.: 541810
Alex Aliksanyan *(CEO)*
Thomas M. Grbelja *(CFO)*
William McLeod *(Sec)*

NET LEASE OFFICE PROPERTIES

1 Manhattan W 395 9th Ave 58th Fl,
New York, NY 10001
Tel.: (212) 492-1140   **MD**
Web Site:
  https://www.nloproperties.com
Year Founded: 2022
NLOP—(NYSE)
Rev.: $174,965,000
Assets: $1,305,089,000
Liabilities: $623,659,000
Net Worth: $681,430,000
Earnings: ($131,746,000)
Emp.: 197
Fiscal Year-end: 12/31/23
Real Estate Investment Services
N.A.I.C.S.: 531190
Jason E. Fox *(Chm & CEO)*

NET MEDICAL XPRESS SOLUTIONS, INC.

8206 Louisiana Blvd NE Ste A, Albuquerque, NM 87113
Tel.: (505) 255-1999   **NV**
Web Site: https://netmedical.com
Year Founded: 1995
NMXS—(OTCIQ)
Sales Range: $1-9.9 Million
Emp.: 18
Software & Hardware Development
Services
N.A.I.C.S.: 513210
Yadira Ortiz *(CFO)*
Miguel Williams *(Dir-Ops & Technical Support)*
Trish Condon *(Mgr-Credentialing)*
Stephenie Wilson *(Dir-Project Mgmt)*
Rafael M. Rubio *(Pres)*
Ron Kubit *(Head-Sls)*
Jennifer Asbury *(Head-Mktg)*
Richard F. Govatski *(Founder, Chm, CEO & CBO)*

NET POWER INC.

320 Roney St Ste 200, Durham, NC
27701
Tel.: (919) 287-4750   **DE**
Web Site: https://netpower.com
Year Founded: 2010
NPWR—(NYSE)
Rev.: $4,898,432
Assets: $351,851,156
Liabilities: $312,312,967
Net Worth: ($39,538,189)
Earnings: $4,065,122
Emp.: 24
Fiscal Year-end: 12/31/22
Natural Gas Distribution
N.A.I.C.S.: 221210
Daniel Joseph Rice IV *(CEO)*

NETAPP, INC.
3060 Olsen Dr, San Jose, CA 95128
Tel.: (408) 822-6000 DE
Web Site: https://www.netapp.com
Year Founded: 1992
NTAP—(NASDAQ)
Rev.: $6,268,000,000
Assets: $9,887,000,000
Liabilities: $8,741,000,000
Net Worth: $1,146,000,000
Earnings: $986,000,000
Emp.: 11,800
Fiscal Year-end: 04/26/24
Computer Integrated Systems Design
Services
N.A.I.C.S.: 334112
Cesar Cernuda *(Pres)*
Kimberly S. Stevenson *(Sr VP/Gen Mgr-Foundational Data Services Business Unit)*
Kris Newton *(VP-IR)*
Haiyan Song *(Exec VP/Gen Mgr-CloudOps)*
Debra McCowan *(Chief HR Officer & Sr VP)*
Harv Bhela *(Chief Product Officer)*
Elizabeth O'Callahan *(Chief Legal Officer & Gen Counsel)*
Riccardo Di Blasio *(Sr VP-North America Sls)*
Michael J. Berry *(CFO & Exec VP)*
George Kurian *(CEO)*

Subsidiaries:

Cloud Jumper LLC (1)
381 Cleveland Crossing Dr Ste 133, Garner, NC 27529
Web Site: http://www.cloudjumper.com
Hybrid Cloud Data Services
N.A.I.C.S.: 518210
John David *(Pres)*
Drew Walz *(VP-Dev)*
Frank Picarello *(COO)*
Mark Foust *(VP-Mktg)*
Mike Walsh *(VP-Product Strategy)*

CloudCheckr LLC (1)
342 N Goodman St, Rochester, NY 14607
Tel.: (585) 413-0869
Web Site: https://cloudcheckr.com
Emp.: 200
Cloud Management Services
N.A.I.C.S.: 541618

Credativ GmbH (1)
Trompeterallee 108, 41189, Monchengladbach, Germany
Tel.: (49) 216699010
Web Site: https://www.credativ.de
Computer Software Consulting Services
N.A.I.C.S.: 541512

Instaclustr Pty. Ltd. (1)
Level A Building 23 University Drive South, Bruce, 2617, ACT, Australia
Tel.: (61) 297795600
Web Site: https://www.instaclustr.com
Laboratory Services
N.A.I.C.S.: 621511

NetApp (China) Ltd. (1)
Room 1543 Regus Beijing Parkview Green Centre, 15F Office Building A Parkview Green No 9 Dongdaqiao Rd, Beijing, 100020, Chaoyang, China
Tel.: (86) 1057306003
Web Site: http://www.netapp.com
Computer Integrated Systems Design Services
N.A.I.C.S.: 334112

NetApp (Hong Kong) Limited (1)
26/F Cambridge House Taikoo Place 979 Kings Road, Quarry Bay, Hong Kong, 411001, China (Hong Kong)
Tel.: (852) 36057700
Computer Design Services
N.A.I.C.S.: 541512

NetApp (Shanghai) Commercial Co., Ltd. (1)
338 Nan Jing Road West Tian An Center 25 Floor Units 3-6, Shanghai, 200003, China
Tel.: (86) 2161328000

Web Site: http://www.netapp.com
Emp.: 50
Computer Integrated Systems Design Services
N.A.I.C.S.: 334112

NetApp (Thailand) Limited (1)
Athenee Tower Unit 1805-1806 18th Floor 63 Wireless Road, Lumpini Pathumwan, Bangkok, 10330, Thailand
Tel.: (66) 21688400
Data Storage System Design Services
N.A.I.C.S.: 541512

NetApp Asia Pacific Holdings B.V. (1)
Boeingavenue 300, Schiphol-Rijk, 1119 PZ, Noord-Holland, Netherlands
Tel.: (31) 205039600
Holding Company
N.A.I.C.S.: 551112

NetApp Australia Pty. Ltd. (1)
Level 7 100 Pacific Highway, North Sydney, 2060, NSW, Australia
Tel.: (61) 297795600
Web Site: http://www.netapp.com
Emp.: 80
Computer Integrated Systems Design Services
N.A.I.C.S.: 541512

NetApp B.V. (1)
Boeing Avenue 300, Schiphol-Rijk, 1119, Netherlands
Tel.: (31) 205039600
Computer Integrated Systems Design Services
N.A.I.C.S.: 541512

NetApp Belgium BVBA (1)
Culliganlaan 2 Park Lane Building D, 1831, Diegem, Belgium
Tel.: (32) 24163111
Web Site: http://www.netapp.com
Emp.: 30
Computer Integrated Systems Design Services
N.A.I.C.S.: 334112

NetApp Brasil SGAD Ltda (1)
Rua Dr Fernandes Coelho 64 4th floor 42 conj, Sao Paulo, 05423-040, Brazil
Tel.: (55) 1138116644
Web Site: http://www.netapp.com
Sales Range: $25-49.9 Million
Emp.: 33
Computer Integrated Systems Design Services
N.A.I.C.S.: 541512

NetApp Chile Limitada (1)
Los Militares No 5885 Office 1404, Las Condes, Saintiago, Chile
Tel.: (56) 228408200
Computer Integrated Systems Design Services
N.A.I.C.S.: 541512

NetApp Denmark ApS (1)
Vandtarnsvej 83A, 2860, Soborg, Denmark
Tel.: (45) 70230074
Web Site: http://www.netapp.com
Emp.: 20
Computer Integrated Systems Design Services
N.A.I.C.S.: 541512

NetApp France SAS (1)
Tour Ariane 5 Place De La Pyramide, La Defense, 92088, Paris, France
Tel.: (33) 149011800
Web Site: https://www.netapp.com
Computer Integrated Systems Design Services
N.A.I.C.S.: 541512

NetApp G.K. (1)
Kyobashi Trust Tower 9 & 10 F 2-1-3 Kyobashi, Chuo-ku, Tokyo, 104-0031, Japan
Tel.: (81) 368707400
Information Technology Services
N.A.I.C.S.: 541512

NetApp India Private Ltd. (1)
Prestige Khoday Tower 4th Floor Muncipal No 5 Old No 3 and 5, Raj Bhavan Road, Bengaluru, 560001, Karnataka, India
Tel.: (91) 8061226100
Web Site: http://www.netapp.com

Computer Integrated Systems Design Services
N.A.I.C.S.: 334112
Deepak Visweswaraiah *(Mng Dir & Sr VP)*
Puneet Gupta *(VP-Sls-India & SAARC)*
Sanjay Rohatgi *(Sr VP & Gen Mgr-Asia Pacific)*

NetApp Israel Sales Ltd. (1)
18th Aharon Bart St, PO Box 10158, Petah Tiqwa, 4951038, Kiryat-Arie, Israel
Tel.: (972) 39205555
Web Site: http://www.netapp.com
Computer Integrated System Design Sales & Services
N.A.I.C.S.: 334112

NetApp Japan K.K. (1)
Kyobashi Trust Tower 9 10 Floor 2-1-3 Kyobashi, Chuo-ku Minato-ku, Tokyo, 104-0031, Japan
Tel.: (81) 368707400
Web Site: http://www.netapp.com
Sales Range: $125-149.9 Million
Computer Integrated Systems Design Services
N.A.I.C.S.: 334112

NetApp Mexico (1)
Miguel de Cervantes Saavedra 301 piso 14 Torre Sur Col Granada, Delegacion Miguel Hidalgo, 11520, Mexico, DF, Mexico
Tel.: (52) 5547745090
Web Site: https://www.netapp.com
Sales Range: $10-24.9 Million
Emp.: 4
Computer Integrated Systems Design Services
N.A.I.C.S.: 334112

NetApp RTP (1)
7301 Kit Creek Rd, Research Triangle Park, NC 27709
Tel.: (919) 476-5600
Web Site: http://www.netapp.com
Sales Range: $125-149.9 Million
Computer Integrated Systems Design Services
N.A.I.C.S.: 541512

NetApp Singapore Pte. Ltd. (1)
Millenia Tower 1 Temasek Avenue 08-01, Singapore, 039192, Singapore
Tel.: (65) 64963500
Computer Integrated Systems Design Services
N.A.I.C.S.: 541512

NetApp South Africa (Pty) Limited (1)
The Design Quarter District Building Number 11, 1st Floor Leslie Avenue East, 2055, Johannesburg, South Africa
Tel.: (27) 116911000
Web Site: http://www.netapp.com
Emp.: 25
Computer Integrated Systems Design Services
N.A.I.C.S.: 541512
Mike Styer *(District Mgr)*
Matthew Barker *(Mgr-Channel)*

NetApp Sweden AB (1)
Arena Sergel Malmskillnadsgatan 36, Kista, SE-111 57, Stockholm, Sweden
Tel.: (46) 859469580
Information Technology Services
N.A.I.C.S.: 541512

NetApp Teknoloji Limited Sirketi (1)
Armada Is Merkezi Eskisehir Yolu No 6 K 11 12 14, Sogutozu, Ankara, 06520, Turkiye
Tel.: (90) 3122956429
Computer System Design Services
N.A.I.C.S.: 541512
Efgan Efe *(Engr-Sys)*

NetApp UK Ltd. (1)
Rivermead Oxford Road, Uxbridge, UB9 4BF, Middlesex, United Kingdom
Tel.: (44) 1895516700
Web Site: http://www.netapp.com
Emp.: 275
Computer Integrated Systems Design Services
N.A.I.C.S.: 334112

Network Appliance BV The Netherlands (1)
Boeing Ave 300, 1119 PZ, Schiphol, Netherlands

Tel.: (31) 205039600
Sales Range: $125-149.9 Million
Computer Integrated Systems Design Services
N.A.I.C.S.: 334112

Network Appliance India (1)
The Estate 6th Floor, 121 Dickinson Road, Bengaluru, 560042, India
Tel.: (91) 8041843555
Sales Range: $125-149.9 Million
Computer Integrated Systems Design Services
N.A.I.C.S.: 334112

Network Appliance Saudi Arabia Ltd (1)
An Nakhil Building IT01 Unit 31 and 32 ITCC - Floor 2, Riyadh, 12382, Saudi Arabia
Tel.: (966) 118361400
Web Site: http://www.now.netapp.com
Sales Range: $25-49.9 Million
Emp.: 20
Computer Integrated Systems Design Services
N.A.I.C.S.: 541512

SolidFire, Inc. (1)
1048 Pearl St Ste 250, Boulder, CO 80302
Tel.: (720) 728-4000
Web Site: http://www.solidfire.com
Emp.: 450
Data Center Operations & All-Flash Storage Solutions
N.A.I.C.S.: 334112

Spotinist LLC (1)
3060 Olsen Dr, San Jose, CA 95128
Tel.: (408) 822-6000
Web Site: https://spot.io
Information Technology Services
N.A.I.C.S.: 541511

Spotinst LLC (1)
3060 Olsen Dr, San Jose, CA 95128
Tel.: (408) 822-6000
Web Site: https://www.spot.io
Software Development Services
N.A.I.C.S.: 541511
Jon Bock *(VP-Mktg)*

NETBRANDS CORP.
4042 Austin Blvd Ste B, Island Park, NY 11558 DE
Web Site: https://www.gdmginc.com
Year Founded: 2017
NBND—(OTCIQ)
Rev.: $1,643,138
Assets: $980,434
Liabilities: $1,691,387
Net Worth: ($710,953)
Earnings: $1,086,662
Emp.: 4
Fiscal Year-end: 12/31/22
Snack Product Mfr & Distr
N.A.I.C.S.: 311919

NETCAPITAL INC.
1 Lincoln St, Boston, MA 02111
Tel.: (781) 925-1700 UT
Web Site: https://www.netcapital.com
Year Founded: 1984
NCPL—(NASDAQ)
Rev.: $4,951,435
Assets: $41,557,306
Liabilities: $3,616,698
Net Worth: $37,940,608
Earnings: ($4,986,317)
Emp.: 21
Fiscal Year-end: 04/30/24
Online Gaming Company
N.A.I.C.S.: 541511
Coreen Kraysler *(CFO)*
Cecilia Lenk *(CEO-Netcapital Advisors Inc)*
Avi Liss *(Sec)*
Martin Kay *(Pres & CEO)*

NETFIN ACQUISITION CORP.

Netfin Acquisition Corp.—(Continued)

445 Park Ave 9th Fl, New York, NY
10022
Tel.: (972) 979-5995   Ky
Year Founded: 2019
NFINU—(NASDAQ)
Emp.: 3
Investment Services
N.A.I.C.S.: 523999
Marat Rosenberg (Pres)
Rick Maurer (CEO)
Gerry Pascale (CFO)
Martin Jaskel (Chm)

NETFLIX, INC.
121 Albright Way, Los Gatos, CA
95032
Tel.: (408) 540-3700   DE
Web Site: http://www.netflix.com
Year Founded: 1997
NFLX—(NASDAQ)
Rev.: $33,723,297,000
Assets: $48,731,992,000
Liabilities: $28,143,679,000
Net Worth: $20,588,313,000
Earnings: $5,407,990,000
Emp.: 13,000
Fiscal Year-end: 12/31/23
Online Motion Picture Streaming,
DVD & Blu-Ray Rental Services
N.A.I.C.S.: 532282
Reed Hastings (Chm)
Spencer Adam Neumann (CFO)
Jeffrey W. Karbowski (Chief Acctg
Officer & VP)
David Hyman (Chief Legal Officer)
Ted Sarandos (Pres & Co-CEO)
Bill Holmes (Head-Business
Development-Global)
Gregory K. Peters (Co-CEO, COO &
Chief Product Officer)
Dean C. Garfield (VP)
Rachel Whetstone (Chief Comm Offi-
cer)
Verna Myers (VP-Inclusion Strategy)
Anna Nagler (Dir-CEE)
Alexandra Patsavas (Dir)
Ty Warren (VP)
Bruce Daitch (VP-Production)
Daisy Lilley (Mgr)
Sean Hancock (Dir)
Michelle Slavich (VP)
Bozoma Saint John (CMO)
Scott Stuber (Head)
Fiona Lamptey (Dir-UK)
Nne Ebong (VP-Original Series)
Brian Wright (Head-Original Series)
Anna Mallett (VP-EMEA,Latin Ameri-
ca,APAC)
Bryony Gagan (VP-Bus & Legal Af-
fairs)
Dean Garfield (VP-Pub Policy)
Amy Reinhard (VP-Studio Ops)
Caitlin Smallwood (VP-Engineering)
Mark White (VP)
Allison Wright (VP)
Todd Yellin (VP-Product)
Mark Yurechko (VP-Strategy-
Planning)
Mike Verdu (VP)
Paul Debevec (Dir)
Deborah Black (VP-Engrg)
Sergio Ezama (Chief Talent Officer)
Pablo Perez De Rosso (VP-Strategy-
Planning)
Francisco Ramos (VP)
Elizabeth Stone (VP)
Larry Tanz (VP)
Peter Naylor (VP-Ad Sls)
Kenneth A. Barker (Principal Acctg
Officer)
James Foster (VP-Mktg-Europe,
Middle East & Africa)
Eunice Kim (VP)
Minyoung Kim (VP)

Marian Lee (CIO)
Spencer Wang (VP)
Maria Ferreras (Head-Partnerships-
Global)

Subsidiaries:

Netflix Pte. Ltd.   (1)
8 Marina Boulevard 01 Singapore - Marina,
Singapore, 18981, Singapore
Tel.: (65) 62289100
Entertainment Services
N.A.I.C.S.: 516210

NETGEAR, INC.
350 E Plumeria Dr, San Jose, CA
95134
Tel.: (408) 907-8000   DE
Web Site: https://www.netgear.com
NTGR—(NASDAQ)
Rev.: $740,840,000
Assets: $847,142,000
Liabilities: $311,647,000
Net Worth: $535,495,000
Earnings: ($104,767,000)
Emp.: 635
Fiscal Year-end: 12/31/23
Network Solutions Products Mfr
N.A.I.C.S.: 334118
Charles J. Prober (CEO)
Patrick C. S. Lo (Co-Founder)
Andrew Kim (Gen Counsel, Sec & Sr
VP-Corp Dev)
Mark G. Merrill (Co-Founder & CTO)
Bryan D. Murray (CFO)
Vikram Mehta (Sr VP-SMB Products
& Svcs)
Martin D. Westhead (CTO-Software)
David John Henry (Pres & Gen Mgr-
Connected Home Products & Svcs)

Subsidiaries:

Avaak, Inc   (1)
3611 Valley Ctr Dr Ste 200, San Diego, CA
92130
Tel.: (858) 453-9866
Web Site: http://www.vuecomcast.com
Electric Equipment Mfr
N.A.I.C.S.: 334416
Greg Drew (Pres & CEO)
Dan Gilbert (VP-Marketing)
George Stewart (VP-Operations)
David Buckley (VP)

Meural, Inc.   (1)
625 Broadway 11th Fl, New York, NY 10012
Web Site: http://www.meural.com
Art Frame Mfr
N.A.I.C.S.: 339940

NETGEAR (Beijing) Network Technol-
ogy Co., Ltd.   (1)
Floor 6 Tower D Torch Building Tsinghua
Science Park No 1, Zhongguancun E Rd
Haidian District, Beijing, 100084,
China   (100%)
Tel.: (86) 1082158080
Web Site: http://www.netgear.com
Sales Range: $100-124.9 Million
Distr of Branded Networking Products
N.A.I.C.S.: 541512

NETGEAR Australia Pty. Ltd.   (1)
Level 18 Tower A Zenith Centre, 821 Pacific
Hwy, Chatswood, 2067, NSW, Australia
Tel.: (61) 2 8117 6800
Web Site: http://www.netgear.com.au
Branded Networking Products Designer &
Distr
N.A.I.C.S.: 541512
Michael A. Werdann (Sr VP)
John P. McHugh (Sr VP-SMB Products &
Svcs)

NETGEAR Deutschland GmbH   (1)
Konrad-Zuse-Platz 1, 81829, Munich,
Germany   (100%)
Tel.: (49) 89452429000
Web Site: http://www.netgear.de
Sales Range: $100-124.9 Million
Designer & Distr of Branded Networking
Products
N.A.I.C.S.: 541512

Patrick C. S. Lo (Mng Dir)
Andrew Kim (Mng Dir)
Jorg Losche (Mng Dir)

NETGEAR Filial Sweden   (1)
Torshamnsgatan 30A, 164 40, Kista, Swe-
den
Tel.: (46) 854647500
Web Site: https://www.netgear.com
Branded Networking Products Distr
N.A.I.C.S.: 541512

NETGEAR France SAS   (1)
2 rue de Marly, 78150, Le Chesnay,
France   (100%)
Tel.: (33) 139239850
Web Site: http://www.netgear.fr
Sales Range: $150-199.9 Million
Designer & Distr of Branded Networking
Products
N.A.I.C.S.: 541512

NETGEAR HONG KONG
LIMITED   (1)
Unit 2201 Level 22 Tower 1 Metroplaza 223
Hing Fong Road Kwai Fong, Hong Kong,
China (Hong Kong)
Tel.: (852) 26453738
Web Site: http://www.netgear.com
Communication Equipment Mfr
N.A.I.C.S.: 334210

NETGEAR International, Inc. -
Italy   (1)
Viale Cassala 57, 20121, Milan, Italy
Tel.: (39) 0291198001
Web Site: http://www.netgear.com
Sales Range: $100-124.9 Million
Distr & Designer of Branded Networking
Products
N.A.I.C.S.: 541512

NETGEAR International, Inc. -
Korea   (1)
9F Jinil Bldg 52-7 Banpo-dong, Seoul, 137-
803, Seocho-gu, Korea (South)
Tel.: (82) 25550764
Web Site: http://www.netgear.co.kr
Sales Range: $75-99.9 Million
Emp.: 7
Distr of Branded Networking Products
N.A.I.C.S.: 541512
J. G. Kim (Mng Dir)

NETGEAR International, Inc. - Middle
East   (1)
Dubai Airport Free Zone Office #215, East
Wing 6A, Dubai, United Arab Emirates
Tel.: (971) 46091860
Web Site: http://www.netgear.com
Sales Range: $100-124.9 Million
Emp.: 3
Distr of Branded Networking Products
N.A.I.C.S.: 541512

NETGEAR International, Inc. -
Russia   (1)
Office 17 Omega Plaza Biz Center, Lenins-
kaya Sloboda St 19, Moscow, Russia
Tel.: (7) 4952690260
Web Site: http://www.netgear.com
Designer & Distr of Branded Networking
Products
N.A.I.C.S.: 541512

NETGEAR International, Inc. -
Spain   (1)
CENTRO MELIOR C/ Diego de Leon,
28006, Madrid, Spain
Tel.: (34) 933443204
Web Site: http://www.netgear.es
Branded Networking Products Distr
N.A.I.C.S.: 423430

NETGEAR Japan GK   (1)
3-7-5 Kyobashi Kintetsu Kyobashi Square
8F, Chuo-Ku, Tokyo, 104-0031,
Japan   (100%)
Tel.: (81) 33 538 2600
Web Site: https://www.netgear.com
Branded Networking Services
N.A.I.C.S.: 541512

NETGEAR Netherlands B.V.   (1)
Louis Braillelaan 80, 2719 EK, Zoetermeer,
Netherlands   (100%)
Tel.: (31) 182587000
Web Site: https://www.netgear.com
Sales Range: $100-124.9 Million
Distr of Branded Networking Products
N.A.I.C.S.: 541512

NETGEAR Poland Sp. z o.o.   (1)
Al Jerozolimskie 65/79, 00-697, Warsaw,
Poland   (100%)
Tel.: (48) 226306640
Web Site: https://www.netgear.com
Sales Range: $100-124.9 Million
Designer & Distr of Branded Networking
Products
N.A.I.C.S.: 541512

NETGEAR RUSSIA LLC   (1)
Office 17 OMEGA Plaza biz center Lenins-
kaya Sloboda St 19, Moscow, Russia
Tel.: (7) 4952690260
Communication Equipment Mfr
N.A.I.C.S.: 334210
Tatiana Andreeva (Dir-Russia)

NETGEAR Technologies India Pte.
Ltd.   (1)
No B-415 Ansal Chambers - I Bhikaji Cama
Place, New Delhi, 110066, India   (100%)
Tel.: (91) 8004194543
Web Site: https://www.netgear.com
Sales Range: $25-49.9 Million
Designer & Distr of Branded Networking
Products
N.A.I.C.S.: 541512

NETGEAR UK Limited   (1)
Reflex Cain Road, Bracknell, RG12 1HL,
Berkshire, United Kingdom   (100%)
Tel.: (44) 1344458200
Web Site: http://www.netgear.co.uk
Sales Range: $10-24.9 Million
Designer & Distr of Branded Networking
Products
N.A.I.C.S.: 541512

NETGEAR do Brasil Produtos Elec-
tronicos Ltda.   (1)
Av Dr Chucri Zaidan 920 9 Andar Edificio
Market Tower Torre 1, Morumbi, 04583 904,
Sao Paulo, SP, Brazil   (100%)
Tel.: (55) 1130484157
Web Site: http://www.netgear.com
Sales Range: $1-9.9 Million
Emp.: 3
Distr of Branded Networking Products
N.A.I.C.S.: 541512

Netgear Denmark ApS   (1)
Gydevang 39, 3450, Allerod, Denmark
Tel.: (45) 44209839
Communication Equipment Mfr
N.A.I.C.S.: 334210

Netgear Research India Pvt. Ltd.   (1)
5th Floor Embassy Star No 8 Palace Road
Vasanth Nagar, Bengaluru, 560052, India
Tel.: (91) 8045464665
Communication Equipment Mfr
N.A.I.C.S.: 334210

NETIMPACT HOLDINGS, INC.
1506 W Pioneer Pkwy Ste 107, Ar-
lington, TX 76013
Tel.: (909) 699-4295
NTHD—(OTCIQ)
Health Care Srvices
N.A.I.C.S.: 621999
John A. Paolicelli (Chm)

NETLIST, INC.
111 Academy Way Ste 100, Irvine,
CA 92617
Tel.: (949) 435-0025   DE
Web Site: https://www.netlist.com
Year Founded: 2000
NLST—(OTCIQ)
Rev.: $142,355,000
Assets: $91,176,000
Liabilities: $37,134,000
Net Worth: $54,042,000
Earnings: $4,831,000
Emp.: 120
Fiscal Year-end: 01/01/22
Semiconductor & Related Device
Manufacturing
N.A.I.C.S.: 334413
Chun K. Hong (Founder, Pres &
CEO)
Gail Sasaki (CFO, Sec & VP)

Scott Milton *(VP-Engrg)*
Raj Gandhi *(VP-ASIC Engrg)*
Jibum Kim *(Exec VP)*
Jayson Sohi *(Dir)*

Subsidiaries:

Netlist Electronics (Suzhou) Co.,
Ltd　　　　　　　　　　　　　　　　**(1)**
A1 EPZ B Zone No 288 Sheng Pu Road
SIP, Suzhou, 215121, China
Tel.: (86) 51262601068
Semiconductor Mfr
N.A.I.C.S.: 334419
June Xu *(Mgr-IT)*

NETMED, INC.

1463 Briarmeadow Dr, Worthington,
OH 43235
Tel.: (614) 537-7246　　　　　　**OH**
NTME—(OTCIQ)
Hospital Equipment Distr
N.A.I.C.S.: 423450
Trevor S. Ferger *(Pres)*
Kenneth B. Leachman *(VP-Finance)*

NETSCOUT SYSTEMS, INC.

310 Littleton Rd, Westford, MA
01886-4105
Tel.: (978) 614-4000　　　　　　**DE**
Web Site: https://www.netscout.com
Year Founded: 1984
NTCT—(NASDAQ)
Rev.: $829,455,000
Assets: $2,595,302,000
Liabilities: $703,237,000
Net Worth: $1,892,065,000
Earnings: ($147,734,000)
Emp.: 2,296
Fiscal Year-end: 03/31/24
Integrated Network Performance
Management Solutions
N.A.I.C.S.: 541512
Anil K. Singhal *(Chm, Pres & CEO)*
Michael Szabados *(COO & Vice
Chm)*
John W. Downing *(Exec VP-Sls Ops-
Worldwide)*
Ashwani Singhal *(Sr VP-Research &
Development)*
Jeff Levinson *(Sec, VP & Gen Coun-
sel)*
Daryle DeBalski *(Gen Mgr-New Mar-
kets Bus Unit)*
Kevin Keough *(Sr VP-Corporate De-
velopment)*
Thor Wallace *(CIO & Sr VP)*
Tony King *(Sr VP-Sales-Intl)*
Bruce A. Kelley Jr. *(CTO & Sr VP)*
Tom Raimondi Jr. *(CMO & Sr VP)*
Jean A. Bua *(CFO, Chief Acctg Offi-
cer, Treas & Exec VP)*

Subsidiaries:

AirMagnet, Inc.　　　　　　　　　**(1)**
2575 Augustine Dr, Santa Clara, CA 95054
Tel.: (408) 753-1500
Software Development Services
N.A.I.C.S.: 541511

NetScout Berlin GmbH & Co. KG **(1)**
Wohlrabedamm 32, 13629, Berlin, Germany
Tel.: (49) 69153253071
Web Site: http://www.netscout.com
Computer System Design Services
N.A.I.C.S.: 541512

NetScout Systems (HK) Limited **(1)**
35/F Central Plaza, 18 Harbour Road, Hong
Kong, 999077, China (Hong Kong)
Web Site: http://www.netscout.com
Integrated Network Performance Manage-
ment Services
N.A.I.C.S.: 518210

NetScout Systems (UK) Limited **(1)**
Kastor & Pollux Platz der Einheit 1, 60327,
Frankfurt, Germany
Tel.: (49) 6997503429

Sales Range: $100-124.9 Million
Integrated Network Performance Manage-
ment Services
N.A.I.C.S.: 518210

NetScout Systems Canada, Inc.　**(1)**
20 Bay St 11th Fl, Toronto, M5J 2N8, ON,
Canada
Tel.: (416) 840-5582
Sales Range: $25-49.9 Million
Emp.: 10
Computer System Design Services
N.A.I.C.S.: 541512

NetScout Systems India Pte Ltd　**(1)**
7th Floor Bajaj Brandview Old Pune-
Mumbai Road Wakdewadi, Shivajinagar Vil-
lage Bhamburda, Pune, 411 003, India
Tel.: (91) 8004401103
Web Site: http://www.netscout.com
Integrated Network Performance Manage-
ment Services
N.A.I.C.S.: 518210

NetScout Systems Japan K.K.　　**(1)**
Shiroyama Trust Tower Level 27 4-3-1 Tora-
nomon, Minato-ku, Tokyo, 105-6027, Japan
Tel.: (81) 354034749
Integrated Network Performance Manage-
ment Services
N.A.I.C.S.: 541512

NetScout Systems Mexico, S.A. de
C.V.　　　　　　　　　　　　　　　**(1)**
Leibnitz 117 Piso 3 Col Nueva Anzures Re-
gus Plaza Leibnitz, 11590, Mexico, Mexico
Tel.: (52) 8001230134
Integrated Network Performance Manage-
ment Services
N.A.I.C.S.: 541512

NetScout Systems Singapore Pte
Ltd.　　　　　　　　　　　　　　　**(1)**
238A Thomson Road 25-04/05 Novena
Square, Singapore, 307684, Singapore
Tel.: (65) 64155481
Web Site: http://www.netscout.com
Sales Range: $1-9.9 Million
Emp.: 6
Integrated Network Performance Manage-
ment Services
N.A.I.C.S.: 518210

NetScout Systems Texas, LLC　　**(1)**
3033 W President George Bush Hwy,
Plano, TX 75075
Tel.: (469) 330-4000
Software Development Services
N.A.I.C.S.: 541511

NETSOL TECHNOLOGIES, INC.

16000 Ventura Blvd Ste 770, Encino,
CA 91436
Tel.: (818) 222-9195　　　　　　**NV**
Web Site:
　https://www.netsoltech.com
NTWK—(NASDAQ)
Rev.: $52,393,215
Assets: $58,379,410
Liabilities: $21,597,657
Net Worth: $36,781,753
Earnings: ($5,243,748)
Emp.: 1,770
Fiscal Year-end: 06/30/23
Software Publisher
N.A.I.C.S.: 513210
Salim Ullah Ghauri *(Co-Founder)*
Naeem Ghauri *(Co-Founder & Pres)*
Roger K. Almond *(CFO & Principal
Acctg Officer)*
Chris Tobey *(Dir-Sls-Global Whole-
sale Fin)*
Wajih ur-Rehman *(Program Dir-
Global)*
Hui Liang *(Pres-China)*
Doug Jones *(VP-Ops-North America)*
Asad Shahab *(Pres-Asia Pacific &
Mng Dir-Europe)*
Richard Regan *(Dir-Svc Delivery-
Europe)*
Murad Baig *(Chief Innovation Officer-
Global)*
Naheed K. Haq *(Head-Svcs, Plng &
Facilitations)*

Chris Mobley *(Head-NFS Ascent
Wholesale Ops-Europe)*
Peter Minshall *(Exec VP-North
America)*
Farooq Fasih *(Mng Dir-Australia)*
Johannes Riedl *(Partner-Global
Client-Europe)*
Darryll Lewis *(Mng Dir-Europe)*
Amanda Li Linjie *(Pres)*
Eva Kellerhoff *(Partner)*
Withoon Hardat *(Head)*
Rajnish Harjika *(VP)*
Malea Farsai *(Corp Counsel)*

Subsidiaries:

NetSol Connect (Private), Ltd.　　**(1)**
43/1-Q Amna Villa-1 PECHS Block 6, Kara-
chi, 75400, Pakistan
Tel.: (92) 21111638765
Web Site: https://www.netsolir.com
Emp.: 48
Network Integration & Consulting Services
N.A.I.C.S.: 541512
Farooq Fasih Ghauri *(Mng Dir)*

NetSol Omni (Private) Ltd.　　　　**(1)**
NetSol Avenue Main Ghazi Road, Lahore,
54792, Pakistan
Tel.: (92) 42111448800
Software Designing Services
N.A.I.C.S.: 541511

NetSol Technologies Australia Pty
Limited　　　　　　　　　　　　　**(1)**
Level 2 61 York Street, Sydney, 2000,
NSW, Australia
Tel.: (61) 292212081
Software Designing Services
N.A.I.C.S.: 541511

NetSol Technologies Europe Ltd. **(1)**
25 Wilton Road, Pimlico, London, SW1V
1LW, United Kingdom　　　　**(100%)**
Tel.: (44) 1403282300
Web Site: http://www.netsoltek.co.uk
Sales Range: $10-24.9 Million
Emp.: 30
Prepackaged Software
N.A.I.C.S.: 334610

Subsidiary (Domestic):

Virtual Lease Services Limited　　**(2)**
1st Floor Vista St Davids Park, Ewloe, CH5
3DT, Flintshire, United Kingdom **(100%)**
Tel.: (44) 1244957236
Web Site: https://www.vls.uk.com
Sales Range: $25-49.9 Million
Emp.: 12
Portfolio Management Services
N.A.I.C.S.: 523940
Louise Ikonomides *(Mng Dir)*
Linda O'Neil *(Dir-Ops)*
Diane Roberts *(Fin Dir)*
Dom Rodwell *(Product Dir)*
Carly Moon *(Mktg Dir)*
Harvey Gill *(Dir-IT)*

NetSol Technologies Ltd.　　　　　**(1)**
NETSOL Avenue Main Ghazi Road, Ghazi
Road Interchange, Lahore, 54792,
Pakistan　　　　　　　　　　**(100%)**
Tel.: (92) 42111448800
Web Site: http://www.netsoltech.com
Rev.: $355,510
Assets: $450,900
Liabilities: $135,095
Net Worth: $315,805
Earnings: ($5,286)
Emp.: 1,781
Fiscal Year-end: 06/30/2022
Prepackaged Software
N.A.I.C.S.: 334610
Najeeb Ullah Ghauri *(Founder, Chm &
CEO)*
Patti L. W. McGlasson *(Gen Counsel, Sec
& Sr VP-Legal & Corp Matters)*

NetSol Technologies Ltd.　　　　　**(1)**
Abdul Rahim Place 19th Fl Rama IV Road,
Silom, Bang Rak, Bangkok, 10500, Thai-
land
Tel.: (66) 26361322
Web Site: http://www.netsoltech.com
Sales Range: $100-124.9 Million
Emp.: 500
Prepackaged Software

N.A.I.C.S.: 334610
Najeeb Ullah Ghauri *(Pres)*

NetSol Technologies Ltd. (China)　**(1)**
1905 East Tower Twin Towers 12B Jian-
guomenwai Ave Chaoyang, Beijing, 100022,
China
Tel.: (86) 1065682256
Web Site: http://www.netsoltek.com
Sales Range: $100-124.9 Million
Emp.: 20
Prepackaged Software
N.A.I.C.S.: 334610

NetSol Technologies Thailand
Limited　　　　　　　　　　　　　**(1)**
87 M Thai Tower All Seasons Place 12 FL
Witthayu Rd, Lumpini Pathumwan, Bang-
kok, 10330, Thailand
Tel.: (66) 268535523
Web Site: https://th.netsoltech.com
Software Designing Services
N.A.I.C.S.: 541511

NetSol-Abraxas Australia Pty
Ltd.　　　　　　　　　　　　　　　**(1)**
Innovation House Technology Park, Maw-
son Lakes, Salisbury, 5095, SA, Australia
Tel.: (61) 882608268
Sales Range: $10-24.9 Million
Emp.: 3
Finance & Insurance Management Software
Publisher
N.A.I.C.S.: 513210

NETSTREIT CORP.

2021 McKinney Ave Ste 1150, Dallas,
TX 75201
Tel.: (972) 200-7100　　　　　　**MD**
Web Site: https://www.netstreit.com
Year Founded: 2019
NTST—(NYSE)
Rev.: $131,905,000
Assets: $1,946,236,000
Liabilities: $672,804,000
Net Worth: $1,273,432,000
Earnings: $6,837,000
Emp.: 28
Fiscal Year-end: 12/31/23
Real Estate Investment Services
N.A.I.C.S.: 531210
Mark L. Manheimer *(Pres, CEO &
Sec)*
Daniel P. Donlan *(CFO & Treas)*
Mark Manheimer *(Pres & CEO)*
Patricia McBratney *(Chief Acctg Offi-
cer & Sr VP)*
Jeff Fuge *(Sr VP-Acquisitions)*
Randy Haugh *(Sr VP-Fin)*
Kirk Klatt *(Sr VP-Real Estate)*
Chad Shafer *(Sr VP-Credit & Under-
writing)*

NETWORK-1 TECHNOLOGIES, INC.

65 Locust Ave Ste 300, New Canaan,
CT 06840
Tel.: (203) 920-1055
Web Site: https://www.network-1.com
NTIP—(NYSEAMEX)
Rev.: $2,601,000
Assets: $52,277,000
Liabilities: $1,585,000
Net Worth: $50,692,000
Earnings: ($1,457,000)
Emp.: 2
Fiscal Year-end: 12/31/23
Security Software Product Develop-
ment
N.A.I.C.S.: 541511
Corey M. Horowitz *(Chm & CEO)*
Robert M. Mahan *(CFO)*

NEUBASE THERAPEUTICS, INC.

350 Technology Dr, Pittsburgh, PA
15219
Tel.: (646) 450-1790　　　　　　**DE**

NeuBase Therapeutics, Inc.—(Continued)

Web Site:
https://ir.neubasetherapeutics.com
Year Founded: 2018
NBSE—(NASDAQ)
Rev.: $148,556
Assets: $32,693,429
Liabilities: $9,501,549
Net Worth: $23,191,880
Earnings: ($33,776,450)
Emp.: 37
Fiscal Year-end: 09/30/22
Biotechnology Platform Company
N.A.I.C.S.: 325412
Todd P. Branning *(Interim CEO & CFO)*
Shannon McCarthy *(Chief People Officer)*
Anthony Rossomando *(CTO)*
Alan Scrivner *(Corp Counsel)*
Ron Sarkar *(Sr VP)*
Dietrich A. Stephan *(Founder)*

NEUEHEALTH, INC.
8000 Norman Ctr Dr Ste 900, Minneapolis, MN 55437
Tel.: (612) 238-1321 DE
Web Site:
https://www.neuehealth.com
Year Founded: 2015
NEUE—(NYSE)
Rev.: $2,412,030,000
Assets: $4,665,052,000
Liabilities: $4,865,542,000
Net Worth: ($200,490,000)
Earnings: ($1,495,231,000)
Emp.: 2,840
Fiscal Year-end: 12/31/22
Direct Health & Medical Insurance Carriers
N.A.I.C.S.: 524114
G. Mike Mikan *(Vice Chm, Pres & CEO)*
Robert J. Sheehy *(Co-Founder & Chm)*
Tomas Valdivia *(Co-Founder, Chief Health Officer & Chief Equity Officer)*
Brian Gambs *(CTO)*
Jon Porter *(Chief Product Officer & CEO-DocSquad)*
Jay Matushak *(CFO)*
Jeff Craig *(Gen Counsel & Sec)*

Subsidiaries:

Bright Health Management, Inc. **(1)**
219 North 2nd St, Minneapolis, MN 55401
Tel.: (888) 974-0199
Web Site: http://brighthealthplan.com
Hospital & Health Care Services
N.A.I.C.S.: 622110

Subsidiary (Domestic):

True Health New Mexico, Inc. **(2)**
2440 Louisiana Blvd NE Ste 601, Albuquerque, NM 87110
Tel.: (505) 633-8020
Web Site:
https://www.truehealthnewmexico.com
Health Plan Services
N.A.I.C.S.: 524114

NEUMORA THERAPEUTICS, INC.
490 Arsenal Way Ste 200, Watertown, MA 02472
Tel.: (857) 760-0900 DE
Web Site:
https://www.neumoratx.com
Year Founded: 2019
NMRA—(NASDAQ)
Rev.: $4,966,000
Assets: $426,234,000
Liabilities: $873,084,000
Net Worth: ($446,850,000)
Earnings: ($130,904,000)
Emp.: 110
Fiscal Year-end: 12/31/22

Pharmaceutical Preparation Manufacturing
N.A.I.C.S.: 325412
Jason Duncan *(Chief Legal Officer)*
Henry O. Gosebruch *(Pres & CEO)*
Carol Suh *(COO)*
Joshua Pinto *(CFO)*
Michael Gold *(Chief Medical Officer)*
Paul L. Berns *(Founder & Chm)*

NEURAXIS, INC.
11611 N Meridian St Ste 330, Carmel, IN 46032
Tel.: (812) 689-0791 DE
Web Site: https://www.neuraxis.com
Year Founded: 2011
NRXS—(NYSEAMEX)
Emp.: 16
Biotechnology Research & Development Services
N.A.I.C.S.: 541714
Adrian Miranda *(Chief Medical Officer)*
Brian Carrico *(Pres)*
John G. Seale *(CFO)*
Tom Carrico *(Chief Regulatory Officer)*

NEUROBO PHARMACEUTICALS, INC.
545 Concord Ave Ste 210, Cambridge, MA 02138
Tel.: (857) 702-9600 DE
Web Site:
https://www.neurobopharma.com
Year Founded: 2008
NRBO—(NASDAQ)
Rev.: $5,661,000
Assets: $33,534,000
Liabilities: $11,784,000
Net Worth: $21,750,000
Earnings: ($13,967,000)
Emp.: 2
Fiscal Year-end: 12/31/22
Pharmaceuticals Product Mfr
N.A.I.C.S.: 325412
Andrew I. Koven *(Chm)*
Marshall H. Woodworth *(CFO & Principal Acctg Officer)*
Gil Price *(Chief Medical Officer)*
Hyung Heon Kim *(Pres & CEO)*

NEUROCRINE BIOSCIENCES INC.
12780 El Camino Real, San Diego, CA 92130
Tel.: (858) 617-7600 CA
Web Site:
https://www.neurocrine.com
Year Founded: 1992
NBIX—(NASDAQ)
Rev.: $1,887,100,000
Assets: $3,251,400,000
Liabilities: $1,019,400,000
Net Worth: $2,232,000,000
Earnings: $249,700,000
Emp.: 1,400
Fiscal Year-end: 12/31/23
Treatments for Central Nervous System & Immune System Diseases
N.A.I.C.S.: 325414
Gary A. Lyons *(Co-Founder)*
Kevin C. Gorman *(Co-Founder)*
Dimitri E. Grigoriadis *(Chief Res Officer)*
Kyle W. Gano *(Pres & CEO)*
Julie Cooke *(Chief HR Officer)*
Matthew C. Abernethy *(CFO)*
Eiry W. Roberts *(Chief Medical Officer)*
Lawrence Steinman *(Co-Founder)*
David W. Boyer *(Chief Corp Affairs Officer)*
Darin M. Lippoldt *(Chief Legal Officer)*

Ingrid Delaet *(Chief Regulatory Officer)*
Jude Onyia *(Chief Scientific Officer)*
Eric S. Benevich *(Chief Comml Officer)*

Subsidiaries:

Diurnal Europe B.V. **(1)**
Van Heuven Goedhartlaan 935 A, 1181 LD, Amstelveen, Netherlands
Tel.: (31) 206615072
Web Site: https://www.diurnal.com
Pharmaceutical Mfr & Distr
N.A.I.C.S.: 325412

Diurnal Group PLC **(1)**
Cardiff Medicentre Heath Park, Cardiff, CF14 4UJ, United Kingdom
Tel.: (44) 2920682069
Rev.: $5,933,236
Assets: $56,739,119
Liabilities: $5,743,156
Net Worth: $50,995,963
Earnings: ($13,645,086)
Fiscal Year-end: 06/30/2021
Pharmaceutical Product Mfr & Distr
N.A.I.C.S.: 325412
Richard Ross *(Chief Scientific Officer)*

NEUROGENESIS, INC.
1241 Butler Rd, League City, TX 77573
Tel.: (281) 557-7877 DE
Web Site:
https://www.neurogenesis.com
Year Founded: 1984
NEUN—(OTCIQ)
Pharmaceutical Product Services
N.A.I.C.S.: 325412
Karen Coady *(VP)*

NEUROMETRIX, INC.
4b Gill St, Woburn, MA 01801
Tel.: (781) 890-9989 DE
Web Site:
https://www.neurometrix.com
Year Founded: 1996
NURO—(NASDAQ)
Rev.: $8,256,073
Assets: $24,669,615
Liabilities: $1,313,928
Net Worth: $23,355,687
Earnings: ($4,416,609)
Emp.: 27
Fiscal Year-end: 12/31/22
Neurological Diagnostic Testing Device Mfr
N.A.I.C.S.: 339112
Shai N. Gozani *(Founder, Chm, Pres, CEO & Sec)*
Thomas T. Higgins *(CFO, Treas & Sr VP)*
Susan M. Bell *(Sr VP-Population Health & Value Based Care)*
Brandi Damkier *(VP)*
J. Breck Harmel *(Dir)*

NEURONETICS, INC.
3222 Phoenixville Pike, Malvern, PA 19355
Tel.: (610) 640-4202 DE
Web Site: https://www.neurostar.com
Year Founded: 2003
STIM—(NASDAQ)
Rev.: $65,206,000
Assets: $116,884,000
Liabilities: $59,824,000
Net Worth: $57,060,000
Earnings: ($37,159,000)
Emp.: 194
Fiscal Year-end: 12/31/22
Surgical & Medical Instrument Manufacturing
N.A.I.C.S.: 339112
Keith J. Sullivan *(Pres & CEO)*
Cory Anderson *(Sr VP)*
Todd Cushman *(Sr VP)*

Rick Grubbs *(Sr VP)*
Sara Grubbs *(Chief Revenue Officer)*
Lisa Metzner-Rosas *(CMO)*

NEUROONE MEDICAL TECHNOLOGIES CORPORATION
7599 Anagram Dr, Eden Prairie, MN 55344
Tel.: (952) 426-1383 NV
Web Site: https://www.nmtc1.com
Year Founded: 2009
NMTC—(NASDAQ)
Rev.: $1,952,441
Assets: $8,097,314
Liabilities: $1,847,910
Net Worth: $6,249,404
Earnings: ($11,859,491)
Emp.: 16
Fiscal Year-end: 09/30/23
Medical, Dental & Hospital Equipment & Supplies Merchant Wholesalers
N.A.I.C.S.: 423450
Ronald McClurg *(CFO)*
David A. Rosa *(Pres & CEO)*
Steve Mertens *(CTO)*
Mark Christianson *(VP-Market Dev)*
Camilo Andres Diaz-Botia *(Dir-Electrode Dev)*
Christopher R. Volker *(COO)*
Hijaz Haris *(VP)*
Chad Wilhelmy *(VP)*

NEUROPATHIX, INC.
3805 Old Easton Rd, Doylestown, PA 18902-8400
Tel.: (858) 883-2642 DE
Web Site:
http://www.neuropathix.com
Year Founded: 2013
NPTX—(OTCIQ)
Rev.: $183,477
Assets: $224,703
Liabilities: $4,211,458
Net Worth: ($3,986,755)
Earnings: ($3,557,786)
Emp.: 6
Fiscal Year-end: 12/31/21
Mobile Phone Application Software
N.A.I.C.S.: 513210
Dean Petkanas *(CEO & Chm)*
Mark Corrao *(CFO)*
Thomas Kikis *(Founder & Chief Comm Officer)*
William A. Kinney *(Chief Scientific Officer)*

NEUTRA CORP.
2500 CityW Blvd Ste 150 161, Houston, TX 77042
Tel.: (702) 793-4121 FL
Web Site: https://neutrainc.com
Year Founded: 2011
NTRR—(OTCIQ)
Rev.: $67,996
Assets: $75,175
Liabilities: $848,995
Net Worth: ($773,820)
Earnings: ($576,862)
Emp.: 15
Fiscal Year-end: 01/31/23
Drugs & Druggists' Sundries Merchant Wholesalers
N.A.I.C.S.: 424210
Sydney Jim *(Pres, CEO, CFO, Chief Acctg Officer, Treas & Sec)*

NEVADA CANYON GOLD CORP. NV
Web Site:
https://www.nevadacanyongold.com
Year Founded: 2014
NGLD—(OTCIQ)
Rev.: $121,168
Assets: $11,121,926
Liabilities: $1,306,307
Net Worth: $9,815,619

Earnings: ($2,654,950)
Fiscal Year-end: 12/31/23
Other Nonmetallic Mineral Mining & Quarrying
N.A.I.C.S.: 212390
Jeffrey A. Cocks *(Chm, CFO, Chief Acctg Officer & Sec)*
Alan Day *(Pres & CEO)*

NEVRO CORP.

1800 Bridge Pkwy, Redwood City, CA 94065
Tel.: (650) 251-0005   DE
Web Site: https://www.nevro.com
Year Founded: 2006
NVRO—(NYSE)
Rev.: $406,365,000
Assets: $602,408,000
Liabilities: $278,532,000
Net Worth: $323,876,000
Earnings: $3,001,000
Emp.: 1,087
Fiscal Year-end: 12/31/22
Medical Device Mfr
N.A.I.C.S.: 339112
Christofer Christoforou *(COO)*
Kevin R. Thornal *(Pres & CEO)*
Greg Siller *(Chief Comml Officer & Sr VP)*
Viswanathan J. Ayer *(VP-Regulatory Affairs & Global Quality)*
Daniel Balkcom *(VP)*
Kerry Bradley *(VP-Scientific Affairs)*
Becky Chaitesipaseut *(VP)*
Yougandh Chitre *(VP-Manufacturing)*
Bryan Hix *(VP-Comml Ops)*
Jon Parker *(VP-Product Development)*
Rebecca Palbicki *(VP-Information Technology)*
Sat Pannu *(VP-Product Res & Emerging Clinical Indications)*
Meredith Vornholt *(VP-Global Mktg)*
Mark Wojtowicz *(VP-US Sls)*
Sophie Halliwell *(VP & Gen Mgr-Intl Comml)*
Carla Monacelli *(VP & Gen Mgr-International)*
Peter Socarras *(Gen Counsel, Sec & VP)*
Shana Ross *(Chief HR Officer & Sr VP)*
Angie McCabe *(VP-Investor Relations & Corporate Communications)*
Rod MacLeod *(CFO & Sr VP)*

NEVTAH CAPITAL MANAGEMENT CORP.

4400 PGA Blvd, Palm Beach Gardens, FL 33410
Tel.: (561) 626-9901
NTAH—(OTCIQ)
Asset Management Services
N.A.I.C.S.: 523940
Daniel P. Kesonen *(Chm & CEO)*

NEW AMERICA ENERGY CORP.

3651 Lindell Rd Ste D 138, Las Vegas, NV 89103
Tel.: (800) 508-6149   NV
Year Founded: 2006
NECA—(OTCIQ)
Ethanol-Methanol Gasoline Mfr
N.A.I.C.S.: 324199

Subsidiaries:

M & K Industries Limited, Co.   (1)
2200 Eubank Blvd NE, Albuquerque, NM 87112
Tel.: (505) 292-4800
Web Site: http://www.daviskitchens.com
Sales Range: $1-9.9 Million
Emp.: 75
Lumber, Plywood, And Millwork, Nsk
N.A.I.C.S.: 423310

NEW AMERICA HIGH INCOME FUND, INC.

33 Broad St, Boston, MA 02109
Tel.: (617) 263-6400   MD
Web Site: https://www.newamerica-hyb.com
HYB—(NYSE)
Rev.: $20,088,000
Assets: $328,875,000
Liabilities: $94,790,000
Net Worth: $234,085,000
Earnings: $14,548,000
Fiscal Year-end: 12/31/19
Investment Management Service
N.A.I.C.S.: 525990
Ellen E. Terry *(Pres, Chief Compliance Officer, Treas & Sec)*

NEW CONCEPT ENERGY, INC.

1603 Lyndon B Johnson Fwy Ste 800, Dallas, TX 75234
Tel.: (972) 407-8400   NV
Web Site: https://www.newconceptenergy.com
GBR—(NYSEAMEX)
Rev.: $212,000
Assets: $4,639,000
Liabilities: $63,000
Net Worth: $4,576,000
Earnings: $181,000
Emp.: 3
Fiscal Year-end: 12/31/22
Oil & Natural Gas Services; Commercial Property Management
N.A.I.C.S.: 211120
Gene S. Bertcher *(Chm, Pres, CEO, CFO, Principal Executive Officer & Dir)*
Cecilia Maynard *(Dir)*

NEW ENGLAND REALTY ASSOCIATES LIMITED PARTNERSHIP

Tel.: (617) 783-0039   MA
Web Site: https://www.thehamiltoncompany.com
Year Founded: 1977
NEN—(NYSE)
Rev.: $68,293,726
Assets: $391,820,280
Liabilities: $451,689,637
Net Worth: ($59,869,357)
Earnings: $3,723,273
Emp.: 2
Fiscal Year-end: 12/31/22
Residential & Commercial Real Estate Acquirer, Developer, Investor, Operator & Sales
N.A.I.C.S.: 531110
Ronald Brown *(Pres)*

NEW ENGLAND SERVICES COMPANY

37 NW Dr, Plainville, CT 06062
Tel.: (860) 747-1665   CT
Web Site: http://www.newenglandservicecompany.com
Year Founded: 1997
NESW—(OTCIQ)
Rev.: $7,642,073
Assets: $44,892,590
Liabilities: $28,427,841
Net Worth: $16,464,749
Earnings: $786,349
Fiscal Year-end: 12/31/19
Water Supply Services
N.A.I.C.S.: 221310
Donald J. E. Vaughan *(Pres)*

Subsidiaries:

Abenaki Water Company   (1)
32 Artisan Ct, Gilford, NH 03249
Tel.: (603) 293-8580
Web Site:
http://www.abenakiwatercompany.com
Water Utility Services
N.A.I.C.S.: 221310
Donald Vaughan *(Chm)*
Taylor De Ogburn *(Ops Mgr)*

Colonial Water Company   (1)
14 Dedham St, Dover, MA 02030
Tel.: (508) 785-0052
Web Site:
http://www.colonialwatercompany.com
Fiscal Year-end: 12/31/2013
Water Utility Services
N.A.I.C.S.: 221310
Nicholas LaChance *(Pres)*

Mountain Water Systems, Inc.   (1)
37 Northwest Dr, Plainville, CT 06062
Web Site:
http://www.mountainwatersystemsinc.com
Water Utility Services
N.A.I.C.S.: 221310
Sheryl Fairchild *(Pres)*

Valley Water Systems, Inc.   (1)
37 Northwest Dr, Plainville, CT 06062-1234
Tel.: (860) 747-8000
Web Site:
http://www.valleywatersystems.com
Emp.: 7
Water Utility Services
N.A.I.C.S.: 221310

NEW FORTRESS ENERGY INC.

111 W 19th St 8th Fl, New York, NY 10011
Tel.: (516) 268-7400   DE
Web Site:
https://www.newfortressenergy.com
Year Founded: 2015
NFE—(NASDAQ)
Rev.: $2,413,296,000
Assets: $10,501,245,000
Liabilities: $8,723,376,000
Net Worth: $1,777,869,000
Earnings: $547,882,000
Emp.: 1,390
Fiscal Year-end: 12/31/23
Oil & Natural Gas Energy Exploration Services
N.A.I.C.S.: 213112
Wesley Robert Edens *(Founder, Chm & CEO)*
Christopher S. Guinta *(CFO)*
Yunyoung Shin *(Chief Acctg Officer)*

Subsidiaries:

Golar LNG Partners LP   (1)
2nd Floor SE Pearman Building 9 Par-la-Ville Road, Hamilton, HM 11, Bermuda
Tel.: (441) 2954705
Web Site: http://www.golarlngpartners.com
Rev.: $284,734,000
Assets: $2,027,661,000
Liabilities: $1,402,340,000
Net Worth: $625,321,000
Earnings: $18,077,000
Fiscal Year-end: 12/31/2020
Natural Gas Transportation Services
N.A.I.C.S.: 213112
Tor Olav Troim *(Chm)*
Oistein Dahl *(COO)*
Karl Fredrik Staubo *(CEO)*

NEW FRONTIER ENERGY, INC.

1801 Broadway Ste 1710, Denver, CO 80202
Tel.: (303) 515-5680   CO
Year Founded: 2000
NFEI—(OTCQB)
Oil & Gas Exploration Services
N.A.I.C.S.: 211120

NEW GENERATION CONSUMER GROUP, INC.

300 Delaware Ave Ste 210, Wilmington, DE 19801
Tel.: (302) 587-8719   DE
Web Site: https://ngcg.myshopify.com
Year Founded: 1989
NGCG—(OTCIQ)
Sales Range: Less than $1 Million
Emp.: 1
Food, Beverages, Spirits & Health Supplements Distr & Sales
N.A.I.C.S.: 424490
Lucia de Fatima Oliveira *(Chm & CEO)*

NEW JERSEY RESOURCES CORPORATION

1415 Wyckoff Rd, Wall, NJ 07719
Tel.: (732) 938-1000   NJ
Web Site:
https://www.njresources.com
Year Founded: 1982
NJR—(NYSE)
Rev.: $1,962,994,000
Assets: $6,537,496,000
Liabilities: $1,778,744,000
Net Worth: $4,758,752,000
Earnings: $264,724,000
Emp.: 1,350
Fiscal Year-end: 09/30/23
Holding Company; Natural Gas for Residential, Commercial & Industrial Consumption; Real Estate Development & Management
N.A.I.C.S.: 551112
Stephen D. Westhoven *(Pres & CEO)*
Amy Cradic *(COO-Non-Utility Businesses, Strategy & External Affairs & Sr VP)*
Richard Reich *(Gen Counsel, Sec & Sr VP)*
Jacqueline K. Shea *(CIO & Sr VP)*
Roberto Bel *(Principal Fin Officer)*
David Johnson *(VP-Corp Bus Dev)*
Dennis Puma *(Dir-IR)*
Mark Aydin *(Mgr-IR)*
Keith Hartman *(VP-Retail)*
Robert Pohlman *(VP-Clean Energy Ventures & Corp Strategy)*
Stephen Skrocki *(Principal Acctg Officer)*
Kathy Wholley *(VP-Comm & Pub Affairs)*
Sean Annitto *(VP)*
Mark G. Kahrer *(Sr VP)*
Tejal K. Mehta *(Corp Counsel)*
Kraig Sanders *(VP)*
Daniel Sergott *(Treas)*
Mark F. Valori *(VP)*
John B. Wyckoff *(VP)*

Subsidiaries:

Carroll Area Wind Farm, LLC   (1)
20647 Olympic Ave, Carroll, IA 51401
Tel.: (712) 792-6372
Wind Electric Power Generation Services
N.A.I.C.S.: 221115

CleanLight Energy, LLC   (1)
11344 Coloma Rd Ste 570, Rancho Cordova, CA 95670
Electric Energy Services
N.A.I.C.S.: 221118

Leaf River Energy Center LLC   (1)
2500 City W Blvd Ste 1050, Houston, TX 77042
Web Site:
http://www.leafriverenergycenter.com
Physical Distribution & Logistic Consulting Services
N.A.I.C.S.: 541614
Gary Jones *(Sr VP-Engrg & Ops)*
Mike Martin *(VP-Ops)*
James R. Eckert *(VP)*
Kevin Dixon *(Mng Dir)*

NJR Capital Services Corporation   (1)
1415 Wyckoff Rd, Wall, NJ 07719
Tel.: (732) 938-1480
Web Site: http://www.njliving.com
Sales Range: $600-649.9 Million
Emp.: 400
Holding Company
N.A.I.C.S.: 221210

New Jersey Resources Corporation—(Continued)

Subsidiary (Domestic):

NJR Energy Holdings Corporation (2)
1415 Wykoff Rd, Wall, NJ 07719 (100%)
Tel.: (732) 938-1480
Web Site: http://www.njliving.com
Wholesale & Retail Sale of Natural Gas
N.A.I.C.S.: 238220

Subsidiary (Domestic):

Commercial Realty & Resources Corp. (3)
1415 Wyckoff Rd, Wall, NJ 07719 (100%)
Tel.: (732) 938-1111
Sales Range: $25-49.9 Million
Real Estate Development & Management Services
N.A.I.C.S.: 531390
Glenn C. Lockwood (CFO & Sr VP)
Laurence M. Downes (Chm)
Mariellen Dugan (Gen Counsel & Sr VP)
Rhonda M. Figueroa (Sec)
John Lishak Jr. (Pres)

NJR Energy Corp (3)
1415 Wyckoff Rd, Wall, NJ 07719
Tel.: (732) 938-1480
Web Site: http://www.njliving.com
Sales Range: $50-74.9 Million
Emp.: 300
Provider of Energy Services
N.A.I.C.S.: 221210

Subsidiary (Domestic):

New Jersey Natural Resources Company (4)
1415 Wyckoff Rd, Wall, NJ 07719
Tel.: (732) 938-1480
Web Site: http://www.njng.com
Gas Distr
N.A.I.C.S.: 221210

NJR Clean Energy Ventures (1)
1415 Wyckoff Rd, Wall, NJ 07719
Web Site:
http://www.njrcleanenergyventures.com
Emp.: 25
Environmentally-Friendly Energy Services
N.A.I.C.S.: 221210
Christopher Savastano (Mng Dir-Bus Dev)
Mark Valori (VP)

NJR Energy Services Company (1)
1415 Wyckoff Rd, Wall, NJ 07719
Sales Range: $25-49.9 Million
Emp.: 370
Energy Services
N.A.I.C.S.: 221210

NJR Retail Holdings Corporation (1)
1415 Wyckoff Rd, Wall, NJ 07719
Tel.: (732) 938-1000
Web Site: http://www.njliving.com
Sales Range: $200-249.9 Million
Emp.: 850
Holding Company for Retail Operations
N.A.I.C.S.: 221210

Subsidiary (Domestic):

NJR Home Services Company (2)
1415 Wyckoff Rd, Wall, NJ 07719
Tel.: (732) 938-1480
Sales Range: $100-124.9 Million
Emp.: 325
Energy Services
N.A.I.C.S.: 238210

NJR Service Corporation (1)
1415 Wyckoff Rd, Wall, NJ 07719
Tel.: (732) 938-1480
Web Site: http://www.njliving.com
Sales Range: $25-49.9 Million
Emp.: 450
Provider of Gas Distribution Services
N.A.I.C.S.: 221210

New Jersey Natural Gas Company (1)
1415 Wyckoff Rd, Wall, NJ 07719 (100%)
Tel.: (732) 938-1000
Web Site: http://www.njng.com
Sales Range: $550-599.9 Million
Emp.: 755
Distribution of Natural Gas

N.A.I.C.S.: 221210
Kraig Sanders (VP-Ops)

Two Dot Wind Farm, LLC (1)
45 Main St Ste 538, Brooklyn, NY 11201-0027
Tel.: (646) 898-3690
Eletric Power Generation Services
N.A.I.C.S.: 221118

NEW MILLENNIUM BANK
222 Bridge Plz S Ste 400, Fort Lee, NJ 07024
Tel.: (201) 585-6090 NJ
Web Site: https://nmbonline.com
Year Founded: 1998
NMBF—(OTCIQ)
Commercial Banking Services
N.A.I.C.S.: 522110
Hong S. Hur (Pres & CEO)
Anthony Suh (Sr VP)
James S. Ryu (COO & Chief Corp Officer)
Frank J. Gleeson (CFO & Sr VP)
Justin Kim (Chief Credit Officer & Sr VP)
Chan Park (CMO & Sr VP)

NEW PEOPLES BANK-SHARES, INC.
Tel.: (276) 873-7000 VA
Web Site:
https://www.newpeoples.bank
NWPP—(OTCIQ)
Rev.: $47,084,000
Assets: $826,313,000
Liabilities: $761,502,000
Net Worth: $64,811,000
Earnings: $7,184,000
Emp.: 183
Fiscal Year-end: 12/31/23
Bank Holding Company
N.A.I.C.S.: 551111
Blaine Scott White (Vice Chm)
James W. Kiser (Pres & CEO)
Christopher G. Speaks (CFO, Treas & Exec VP)
John J. Boczar (Chief Acctg Officer & Sec)
Bryan T. Booher (Chief Risk Officer & Exec VP)
Mike Ratliff (Chief Banking Officer & Exec VP)
Debbie Arrington (Sr VP-Banking Ops)
Lori Counts (Sr VP & Dir-Human Resources)
Kathy Jackson (Sr VP)
Freddy Sullivan (Sr VP-Comml Lender III)

Subsidiaries:

New Peoples Bank (1)
53 Commerce Dr, Honaker, VA 24260
Tel.: (276) 873-6288
Commericial Banking
N.A.I.C.S.: 522110
James W. Kiser (Pres & CEO)
Christopher G. Speaks (CFO, Treas & Exec VP)
Sharon Borich (Sr VP)
Debbie Arrington (Sr VP-Banking Ops)
John W. Deard Jr. (Chief Credit Officer & Exec VP)

NEW PRIDE CORPORATION
2757 E Del Amo Blvd, Rancho Dominguez, CA 90221
Tel.: (310) 631-7000
Web Site:
https://www.newpridetire.com
Year Founded: 1978
900100—(KRS)
Rev.: $51,095,676
Assets: $60,966,809
Liabilities: $7,018,161
Net Worth: $53,948,648
Earnings: $1,070,292

Fiscal Year-end: 12/31/22
Automobile Parts Mfr
N.A.I.C.S.: 336110
Edward E. Kim (CEO)

NEW RESOURCE BANK
255 California St Ste 600, San Francisco, CA 94111
Tel.: (415) 995-8100
Web Site:
http://www.newresourcebank.com
NWBN—(OTCIQ)
Commericial Banking
N.A.I.C.S.: 522110
Steve Rossi (CFO & Exec VP)
Vincent Siciliano (Pres & CEO)
Bill Peterson (Sr VP & Sr Lending Officer)
Robert S. Holden (Sr VP)
Gary Groff (Sr VP-Comml Banking)
Gabriela Selli (Sr VP-Ops & Banking Svcs Mgr)
Daniel W. Yohannes (Co-Founder)

NEW TRIPOLI BANCORP, INC.
6748 Madison St, New Tripoli, PA 18066
Tel.: (610) 298-8811
Web Site:
https://www.newtripolibank.net
Year Founded: 1910
NTBP—(OTCIQ)
Offices of Bank Holding Companies
N.A.I.C.S.: 551111
David R. Hunsicker (Chm & CEO)

Subsidiaries:

New Tripoli Bank (1)
6748 Madison St, New Tripoli, PA 18066
Tel.: (610) 298-8811
Web Site: http://www.newtripolibank.net
Sales Range: $25-49.9 Million
Emp.: 50
State Commercial Banks
N.A.I.C.S.: 522110
David R. Hunsicker (Pres & CEO)
Michele Hunsicker (CFO)
David J. Sherwin (Chief Lending Officer & Sr VP)
Hope Pearson (COO & Sr VP)
Sundra Bachman (VP)

NEW VISTA ACQUISITION CORP.
125 S Wacker Dr Ste 300, Chicago, IL 60606
Tel.: (312) 855-2083 Ky
Web Site:
http://www.newvistacap.com
Year Founded: 2020
NVSA—(NASDAQ)
Rev.: $7,679,330
Assets: $277,561,984
Liabilities: $299,257,517
Net Worth: ($21,695,533)
Earnings: $3,976,780
Emp.: 3
Fiscal Year-end: 12/31/21
Investment Services
N.A.I.C.S.: 523999
Dennis A. Muilenburg (Chm & CEO)
Kirsten Bartok Touw (Co-Pres & COO)
Travis S. Nelson (Co-Pres & CFO)

NEW WORLD GOLD CORP.
1200 N Federal Hwy Ste 200, Boca Raton, FL 33432
Tel.: (561) 210-8496 FL
Web Site:
https://www.newworldgoldcorporation.com
Year Founded: 1998
NWGC—(OTCIQ)
Gold Mining Services
N.A.I.C.S.: 212220
Robert Honigford (CEO)

NEW YORK COMMUNITY BAN-CORP, INC.
102 Duffy Ave, Hicksville, NY 11801
Tel.: (516) 683-4100 DE
Web Site: https://www.mynycb.com
NYCB—(NYSE)
Rev.: $8,178,000,000
Assets: $114,057,000,000
Liabilities: $105,690,000,000
Net Worth: $8,367,000,000
Earnings: ($79,000,000)
Emp.: 8,766
Fiscal Year-end: 12/31/23
Bank Holding Company
N.A.I.C.S.: 551112
James K. Simons (Exec VP)
Craig E. Gifford (CFO & Sr Exec VP)
Joseph M. Otting (Exec Chm, Pres & CEO)
Bryan L. Marx (Chief Acctg Officer & Exec VP)
Reginald E. Davis (Pres-Banking & Sr Exec VP)
Lee M. Smith (Pres-Mortgage & Sr Exec VP)
Meagan Belfinger (Chief Audit Officer)
Jennifer Charters (CIO)
Elizabeth Correa (Exec VP)
Salvatore J. DiMartino (Exec VP)
David W. Hollis (Chief HR Officer)
Andrew Kaplan (Exec VP)
Ross Marrazzo (Chief Compliance Officer)
Nicholas C. Munson (Chief Risk Officer)

Subsidiaries:

Flagstar Bancorp, Inc. (1)
5151 Corporate Dr, Troy, MI 48098-2639
Tel.: (248) 312-2000
Web Site: http://www.flagstar.com
Rev.: $1,854,000,000
Assets: $25,483,000,000
Liabilities: $22,765,000,000
Net Worth: $2,718,000,000
Earnings: $533,000,000
Emp.: 5,395
Fiscal Year-end: 12/31/2021
Bank Holding Company
N.A.I.C.S.: 551111
Stephen V. Figliuolo (Chief Risk Officer & Exec VP)

Subsidiary (Domestic):

Douglas Insurance Agency, Inc. (2)
11 W Main St, Dalton, OH 44618
Tel.: (330) 828-2705
Web Site: http://www.douglasagency.com
Insurance Brokerage Services
N.A.I.C.S.: 524210

Flagstar Bank, FSB (2)
5151 Corporate Dr, Troy, MI 48098-2639 (100%)
Tel.: (248) 312-2000
Web Site: http://www.flagstar.com
Federal Savings & Loan
N.A.I.C.S.: 522180
James K. Simons (Exec VP)
Craig E. Gifford (CFO & Sr Exec VP)
Joseph M. Otting (Exec Chm, Pres & CEO)
Lee Smith (COO & Exec VP)
Jenifer Robinson (Mgr-Central Reg)
Kristy Fercho (Pres-Mortgage)
Jennifer Charters (CIO)
Reginald E. Davis (Pres-Banking & Exec VP)
David W. Hollis (Chief HR Officer & Exec VP)
Michael E. Adler (Exec VP & Head-Wholesale Banking)
Mark Herron (Chief Brand Officer)

Division (Domestic):

Desert Community Bank (3)
12530 Hesperia Rd, Victorville, CA 92395
Tel.: (760) 245-8554
Web Site: http://www.dcbk.org
Commericial Banking
N.A.I.C.S.: 522110

Opes Advisors, Inc. (3)
19330 Stevens Creek Blvd, Cupertino, CA 95014
Tel.: (408) 831-5000
Web Site: http://www.flagstar-opes.com
Financial Advice & Services
N.A.I.C.S.: 523999
Susan McHan (Co-Founder & Pres-Retail Mortgage Div)
Curtis Dair (CFO)
Brian Minnie (VP-IT)
Mayank Vadodaria (VP-Software Dev)
Laura Roedel (VP-Mktg)
Steve Mageras (VP-Capital Markets)
Tom Kraft (Sr VP-Mortgage Ops)
Denise Daquino (Sr Dir-HR)
Lisa Latos (Dir-Reg Sls Support)
John Leach (Branch Mgr)

Subsidiary (Domestic):

Flagstar Commercial Corporation (2)
5151 Corporate Dr, Troy, MI 48098-2639
Tel.: (248) 312-2000
Web Site: http://www.flagstar.com
Commercial Banking Services
N.A.I.C.S.: 522110

Flagstar Investment Group, Inc. (2)
704 S Brown St, Jackson, MI 49203
Tel.: (517) 789-5791
Investment Management Service
N.A.I.C.S.: 523940

Paperless Office Solutions, Inc. (2)
99 King St 1508, Saint Augustine, FL 32085
Tel.: (904) 910-1614
Web Site: http://www.paperlessplus.com
Emp.: 32
Business Data Automation Services
N.A.I.C.S.: 518210
Anthony Deakins (CTO)

New York Commercial Bank (1)
615 Merrick Ave, Westbury, NY 11590
Tel.: (516) 683-4100
Web Site:
   http://www.newyorkcommercialbank.com
Sales Range: $25-49.9 Million
Emp.: 101
Commercial Banking Services
N.A.I.C.S.: 522110

New York Community Bank (1)
615 Merrick Ave, Westbury, NY 11590 (100%)
Tel.: (516) 683-4100
Web Site: http://www.mynycb.com
Sales Range: $125-149.9 Million
Savings Bank
N.A.I.C.S.: 522180
Thomas R. Cangemi (Chm, Pres & CEO)
Robert Wann (COO & Sr Exec VP)

NEW YORK MORTGAGE TRUST, INC.
90 Park Ave Fl 23, New York, NY 10016
Tel.: (212) 792-0107 MD
Web Site: https://www.nymtrust.com
Year Founded: 2003
NYMT—(NASDAQ)
Rev.: $258,660,000
Assets: $7,401,328,000
Liabilities: $5,801,263,000
Net Worth: $1,600,065,000
Earnings: ($90,035,000)
Emp.: 79
Fiscal Year-end: 12/31/23
Real Estate Investment Trust
N.A.I.C.S.: 525990
Jason T. Serrano (CEO)
Kristine R. Nario-Eng (CFO)
Nicholas Mah (Pres)
Steve B. Brannan (Mng Dir)
Steve L. Hogue (Mng Dir)

NEWAGE, INC.
2420 17th St Ste 220, Denver, CO 80202
Tel.: (303) 566-3030 WA
Web Site:
   http://www.newagebev.com
Year Founded: 2010

NBEV—(NASDAQ)
Rev.: $279,471,000
Assets: $443,182,000
Liabilities: $298,928,000
Net Worth: $144,254,000
Earnings: ($39,344,000)
Emp.: 1,127
Fiscal Year-end: 12/31/20
Breweries
N.A.I.C.S.: 312120
Edward J. Brennan (Chm & Interim CEO)
Lisa Mueller (VP-IR)

Subsidiaries:

ARIIX, LLC (1)
737 E 1180 S, American Fork, UT 84003
Tel.: (801) 813-3000
Web Site: http://ariix.newage.com
Sales Range: $100-124.9 Million
E-Commerce & Direct-to-Consumer Services
N.A.I.C.S.: 541860
Frederick W. Cooper (Founder)
Mark Wilson (Co-Founder & Pres)
Jeff Yates (Co-Founder)
Riley Timmer (Co-Founder & COO)
Deanna Latson (Co-Founder & Chief Product Officer)
Wenhan Harry Zhang (Co-Founder & CIO)
Ian Chandler (Co-Founder & Chief Sls Officer)

Subsidiary (Domestic):

The Limu Company LLC (2)
610 Crescent Executive Ct Ste 110, Lake Mary, FL 32746
Tel.: (407) 548-3800
Web Site: http://www.thelimucompany.com
Sales Range: $1-9.9 Million
Emp.: 22
Dry, Condensed & Evaporated Dairy Product Mfr
N.A.I.C.S.: 311514
Gary J. Raser (Founder)

Morinda Holdings Inc. (1)
737 E 1180 S, American Fork, UT 84003
Tel.: (801) 234-1000
Web Site: http://www.morinda.com
Sales Range: $1-4.9 Billion
Emp.: 444
Holding Company; Health Supplements, Beverages, Beauty & Spa Products Mfrs & Distr
N.A.I.C.S.: 551112
Kelly Olsen (Co-Founder)
Kerry Asay (Co-Founder)
Stephen Story (Co-Founder)

Subsidiary (Domestic):

Morinda Inc. (2)
737 E 1180 S, American Fork, UT 84002
Tel.: (801) 234-1000
Web Site: http://www.morinda.com
Emp.: 100
Beauty Supplies Whslr
N.A.I.C.S.: 424210
Randy Smith (Pres)

Tahitian Noni International (2)
737 E 1180 S, American Fork, UT 84003
Tel.: (801) 234-1000
Web Site: http://www.tahitiannoni.com
Sales Range: $25-49.9 Million
Emp.: 100
Natural Juice & Beverage Mfr & Distr
N.A.I.C.S.: 456191
Kelly Olsen (Founder)
John Wadsworth (Pres)
Andre Peterson (Dir-PR)
Charlie Smith (VP-Ops)

NABC, Inc. (1)
2420 17th St Ste 220, Denver, CO 80202-2507
Beverage Soft Drink Whslr
N.A.I.C.S.: 424490

NEWBERRY SPECIALTY BAKERS, INC.
14212 Inter Dr W, Houston, TX 77032
Tel.: (281) 987-8985 TX

Year Founded: 1997
NBRY—(OTCIQ)
Bakery Products Mfr
N.A.I.C.S.: 311812
William Evans (CEO)

NEWBRIDGE GLOBAL VENTURES, INC.
2545 Santa Clara Ave, Alameda, CA 94501
Tel.: (801) 362-2115 DE
Web Site:
   http://www.newbridgegv.com
Year Founded: 1983
NBGV—(OTCIQ)
Sales Range: Less than $1 Million
Emp.: 9
Healthcare Management Consulting Services
N.A.I.C.S.: 524114
Chris Bourdon (Chm & CEO)

NEWBURY STREET ACQUISITION CORP
121 High ST Fl 3, Boston, MA 02110
Tel.: (617) 894-3057 DE
Year Founded: 2020
NBST—(NASDAQ)
Rev.: $2,660,764
Assets: $22,542,028
Liabilities: $28,123,396
Net Worth: ($5,581,368)
Earnings: $97,368
Emp.: 2
Fiscal Year-end: 12/31/23
Investment Services
N.A.I.C.S.: 523999
Thomas V. Bushey (CEO)
Matthew Hong (Chm)
Thomas Bushey (CEO)
Kenneth King (CFO)

NEWCOURT ACQUISITION CORP.
2201 Broadway Ste 705, Oakland, CA 94612
Tel.: (510) 214-3750 Ky
Year Founded: 2021
NCAC—(NASDAQ)
Rev.: $9,308,291
Assets: $258,931,117
Liabilities: $272,825,427
Net Worth: ($13,894,310)
Earnings: $8,014,314
Emp.: 3
Fiscal Year-end: 12/31/22
Investment Services
N.A.I.C.S.: 523999
Michael Jordaan (Chm)
Marc Balkin (CEO)
Jurgen van de Vyver (CFO)

NEWELL BRANDS INC.
6655 Peachtree Dunwoody Rd, Atlanta, GA 30328
Tel.: (770) 418-7000 DE
Web Site:
   https://www.newellbrands.com
Year Founded: 1903
NWL—(NASDAQ)
Rev.: $8,133,000,000
Assets: $12,163,000,000
Liabilities: $9,051,000,000
Net Worth: $3,112,000,000
Earnings: ($388,000,000)
Emp.: 24,600
Fiscal Year-end: 12/31/23
Holding Company; Housewares, Tools, Writing Instruments, Commercial Products & Family Products Mfr
N.A.I.C.S.: 551112
Christopher H. Peterson (Pres & CEO)
Steve Nikolopoulos (Chief Procurement Officer)

Dennis Senovich (Chief Supply Chain Officer)
Mike Hayes (Chief Customer Officer)
Mark J. Erceg (CFO)
Dan Gustafson (CIO)
Robert A. Schmidt (Chief Acctg Officer)
Beth Stellato (VP-IR)
Sofya Tsinis (VP-IR)
Melanie A. Huet (Pres-Brand Mgmt & Innovation)

Subsidiaries:

Allegre Puericulture S.A.S. (1)
41 Rue Edouard Martel, 42000, Saint Etienne, France
Tel.: (33) 477818181
Web Site: https://www.nuk.fr
Nursery Products Mfr
N.A.I.C.S.: 424930

American Tool Companies Holding B.V. (1)
Edisonstraat 8, 5051 DS, Goirle, Netherlands
Tel.: (31) 135311607
Holding Company
N.A.I.C.S.: 551112

Apollo Holding B.V. (1)
Bordego 1, Aldeboarn, 8495 NS, Heerenveen, Netherlands
Tel.: (31) 566631919
Web Site: http://www.apollo-engineering.nl
Engineeering Services
N.A.I.C.S.: 541330

Aprica (Shanghai) Trading Co., Ltd. (1)
3/F Building D Red Town 570 Huaihai Road West, Shanghai, 200052, China
Tel.: (86) 2163901385
Baby Products Retailer
N.A.I.C.S.: 458110

Aprica Childcare Institute-Aprica Ikuji Kenkyush Kabushiki Kaisha (1)
Higashishinsaibashi 1-chome 14 Ban 9, Chuo-ku, Osaka, 542-0083, Japan
Tel.: (81) 120133778
Web Site: https://aprica-childcare-institute.com
Toy Mfr
N.A.I.C.S.: 339930

Aprica Children's Products KK (1)
Shibaura Square Building 4-9-25, Shibaura Minato-ku, Tokyo, 108-0023, Japan
Tel.: (81) 570004155
Web Site: https://www.aprica.jp
Emp.: 216
Childrens Products Mfr
N.A.I.C.S.: 339930

Aprica Korea Co., Ltd. (1)
2/F KuKu Bldg 145-18 Samsung-dong, Gangnam-gu, Seoul, 135-878, Korea (South)
Tel.: (82) 807014430
Baby Car Seat Distr
N.A.I.C.S.: 424350

Bernardin Ltd. (1)
845 Intermodal Drive Unit 1, Brampton, L6T 0C6, ON, Canada (100%)
Tel.: (800) 265-5674
Web Site: http://www.bernardin.ca
Canning Products Services
N.A.I.C.S.: 311422

Camping Gaz CS s.r.o. (1)
Ceskomoravska 2408/1a, 190 00, Prague, 9, Czech Republic
Tel.: (420) 284686711
Web Site: https://www.campingaz.cz
Propane-Fueled Barbecue & Camping Equipment & Propane Cannisters Mfr & Whslr
N.A.I.C.S.: 335220

Coleman Korea Co., Ltd. (1)
6th Daeryung Techno Town 648 Seobu Saet-gil, Geumcheon-gu 909-1 Callman Service Center, Seoul, Korea (South)
Tel.: (82) 15775932
Web Site: http://www.coleman.co.kr
Consumer Goods Product Distr
N.A.I.C.S.: 424310

Newell Brands Inc.—(Continued)

Detector Technology Limited (1)
Unit 607B-608A 6/F Tower B Manulife Financial Centre, Wai Yip Street Kwun Tong, 223-231, Kowloon, China (Hong Kong)
Tel.: (852) 27278832
Web Site: http://www.dtechnology.com.hk
Electronic Equipment Whslr
N.A.I.C.S.: 423690
Aliana Wu (Asst Mgr-Comml)

Elmer's Products Canada, Corporation (1)
1399 Kenedy Rd Unit 25, Toronto, M1P 2L6, ON, Canada
Web Site: https://www.elmers.ca
Chemical Products Mfr
N.A.I.C.S.: 325199

Elmer's Products, Inc. (1)
460 Polaris Pkwy, Westerville, OH 43082
Tel.: (614) 985-2600
Web Site: http://www.elmers.com
Adhesives, Caulks & Sealants Mfr
N.A.I.C.S.: 325520
Roger Posacki (Pres & CEO)

Ex Officio, LLC (1)
17801 Pacific Hwy S Unit CT-16 Central Terminal Sea-Tac Airport, Seattle, WA 98158
Web Site: http://www.exofficio.com
Clothing Mfr
N.A.I.C.S.: 424350

First Alert (Canada) Inc. (1)
20 Hereford St, Brampton, L6Y 0M1, ON, Canada
Tel.: (905) 488-7283
Web Site: https://www.firstalert.ca
Fire Safety Product Mfr
N.A.I.C.S.: 334290

Graco Children's Products, Inc. (1)
4110 Premier Dr, High Point, NC 27265
Web Site: https://www.gracobaby.com
Baby & Children Products & Toys Mfr
N.A.I.C.S.: 326199
Derial Sanders (Co-Pres)
Cathy Williams (Co-Pres)

Subsidiary (Non-US):

Graco UK & Ireland (2)
Halifax Avenue Fradley Park, Lichfield, WS13 8SS, Staffordshire, United Kingdom
Tel.: (44) 344 412 1212
Web Site: http://www.graco.co.uk
Mfr of Children's Automobile Safety Seats
N.A.I.C.S.: 336360

Hearthmark, LLC (1)
9999 E 121St St, Fishers, IN 46037 **(100%)**
Tel.: (800) 392-2575
Web Site: http://www.diamondbrands.co
Consumer Products Mfr & Whslr
N.A.I.C.S.: 326199
Eduardo Campos (Mgr-Tech, Architecture & Delivery)

Home Fragrance Italia S.r.l. (1)
Via del Commercio 28, 20881, Bernareggio, MB, Italy
Tel.: (39) 0399220979
Web Site: http://www.millefiorimilano.com
Glasswork Services
N.A.I.C.S.: 238150

Ignite USA, LLC (1)
180 N LaSalle St Ste 700, Chicago, IL 60601
Tel.: (312) 432-6223
Web Site: http://www.gocontigo.com
Sales Range: $25-49.9 Million
Emp.: 25
Reusable Water Bottle Containers Mfr & Distr
N.A.I.C.S.: 322219

Irwin Industrial Tool Company (1)
8935 Northpoint Executive Dr, Huntersville, NC 28078
Tel.: (704) 987-4555
Web Site: http://www.irwin.com
Sales Range: $75-99.9 Million
Emp.: 200
Power Tool Accessories Mfr & Distr
N.A.I.C.S.: 333991

Jarden Zinc Products, LLC (1)
2500 Old Stage Rd, Greeneville, TN 37744 **(100%)**
Tel.: (423) 639-8111
Web Site: https://artazn.com
Zinc Products Mfr
N.A.I.C.S.: 331491
Carl DelSorbo (Sr VP-Ops)

Lifoam Industries, LLC (1)
1303 S Batesville Rd, Greer, SC 29650
Web Site: http://www.lifoam.com
Polystyrene & Polyurathane Products Mfr
N.A.I.C.S.: 326140

Mapa Spontex S.A. (1)
B2B and Industrial 420 rue d Estienne d Orves, 92705, Colombes, Cedex, France
Tel.: (33) 1 49 64 22 82
Web Site: http://www.mapa-spontex.com
Cellulose Sponges & Latex Gloves Mfr
N.A.I.C.S.: 325211

Subsidiary (Non-US):

Mapa GmbH (2)
Industriestrasse 21-25, 27404, Zeven, Germany
Tel.: (49) 4281730
Web Site: https://www.mapa.de
Emp.: 620
Industrial Gloves & Sponges Mfr
N.A.I.C.S.: 326199

Mapa Spontex CE s.r.o. (2)
Prodasice 4, Dolni Bousov, 294 04, Mlada Boleslav, 29404, Czech Republic
Tel.: (420) 326375768
Web Site: https://www.spontex.cz
Non-Durable Goods Whslr
N.A.I.C.S.: 424990

Mapa Spontex Italia S.p.A. (2)
Via S Giovanni Bosco 24, Pogliano Milanese, 20005, Milan, Italy
Tel.: (39) 0293474111
Web Site: https://www.spontex.it
Sales Range: $10-24.9 Million
Industrial Gloves & Sponges Mfr
N.A.I.C.S.: 332999

Mapa Spontex Polska SP. z o.o. (2)
ul Jozefinska 2, 30-529, Krakow, Poland
Tel.: (48) 122900400
Web Site: https://www.spontex.pl
Emp.: 4,000
Household Goods Mfr
N.A.I.C.S.: 424990
Tomasz Budzinski (Mng Dir)

Mapa Spontex UK Limited (2)
Berkeley Business Park Wainright Road, Worcester, WR4 9ZS, Worcestershire, United Kingdom
Tel.: (44) 1905450300
Web Site: https://www.spontex.co.uk
Non-Durable Goods Whslr
N.A.I.C.S.: 424990

Marmot Mountain Europe GmbH (1)
Am Eisernen Steg 20, 65795, Hattersheim, Germany
Tel.: (49) 61909180200
Web Site: https://www.marmot.eu
Sportswear Distr
N.A.I.C.S.: 424350

NRH Limited (1)
3/F Tai Po Indl Est, 2 Dai Wang St, Tai Po, New Territories, China (Hong Kong)
Tel.: (852) 26866561
Web Site: http://www.newellrubbermaid.com
All Other Plastics Prod Mfr
N.A.I.C.S.: 326199

NWL Denmark Services Aps (1)
Stamholmen 155 2nd Floor, 2650, Hvidovre, Denmark
Tel.: (45) 43682212
Web Site: http://www.newellbrands.com
Emp.: 10
Power Tool Mfr.
N.A.I.C.S.: 333991

Newell Australia Pty. Limited (1)
500 Princes Highway Level 1, Noble Park, 3174, VIC, Australia **(100%)**
Tel.: (61) 1800727537
Sales Range: $50-74.9 Million
Emp.: 50
Writing Instruments & Accessories

N.A.I.C.S.: 424120

Newell Brands de Colombia S.A.S. (1)
Av Calle 26 69B-45 Office 503-505, Bogota, Colombia
Tel.: (57) 7462626
Web Site: https://www.ostercolombia.com
Household Appliances Mfr
N.A.I.C.S.: 335220

Newell Brands de Peru, S.A.C. (1)
Av Miguel Dasso Nro 104 Int 702 Urb Santa Isabel, San Isidro, 15073, Lima, Peru
Tel.: (51) 13191860
Web Site: https://www.oster.com.pe
Household Appliances Mfr
N.A.I.C.S.: 335220

Newell Europe Sarl (1)
Chemin de Blandonnet 10, Vernier, 1214, Geneva, Switzerland
Tel.: (41) 224190000
Commercial Product Mfr
N.A.I.C.S.: 333310
Daniele Grenacher (Sr Mgr-Global Sourcing & Fine Writing)

Newell Operating Company (1)
29 E Stephenson St, Freeport, IL 61032-4235
Tel.: (770) 407-3800
Sales Range: $250-299.9 Million
Emp.: 350
Global Consumer Goods
N.A.I.C.S.: 423620

Newell Rubbermaid (Thailand) Co., Ltd. (1)
135 Ladkrabang Industrial Estate Soi Chalongkrung 31, Chalong-Krung Road Kwaeng Lamplatew Khet Ladkrabang, Bangkok, 10520, Thailand
Tel.: (66) 23279200
Emp.: 300
All Other Plastics Materials Mfr
N.A.I.C.S.: 326199

Newell Rubbermaid Argentina S.A. (1)
Av Cabildo 2677 Piso 11, Buenos Aires, C1428AAI, Argentina
Tel.: (54) 1159182000
Commercial Product Mfr & Distr
N.A.I.C.S.: 333310

Newell Rubbermaid Asia Pacific Limited (1)
40/F Manhattan Place23 Wang Tai Road, Kowloon Bay, Hong Kong, China (Hong Kong)
Tel.: (852) 39269600
Plastic Materials Mfr
N.A.I.C.S.: 326199

Newell Rubbermaid Distribution LLC (1)
4475 S Fulton Pkwy, Atlanta, GA 30349
Tel.: (404) 684-3500
Durable Good Distr
N.A.I.C.S.: 423990

Newell Rubbermaid German Holding GmbH (1)
Schnackenburgallee 45, 22525, Hamburg, Germany
Tel.: (49) 4085550
Consumer & Commercial Products Mfr
N.A.I.C.S.: 333415

Newell Rubbermaid Inc. (1)
Halifax Ave Fradley Park, Lichfield, WS13 8SS, Staffordshire, United Kingdom **(100%)**
Tel.: (44) 1543447002
Web Site: http://www.newellrubbermaid.com
Sales Range: $200-249.9 Million
Emp.: 300
Mfr of Household & Commercial Plastics Products
N.A.I.C.S.: 326199

Newell Rubbermaid Japan Ltd. (1)
4-28-11 Taito Okachimachichuo Bldg 6f, Taito-Ku, Tokyo, 110-0016, Japan
Tel.: (81) 358181655
Kitchen Cabinet Mfr
N.A.I.C.S.: 337110

Newell Rubbermaid Middle East FZE (1)

PO Box 54554, Ajman, United Arab Emirates
Tel.: (971) 42923444
Plastics Product Mfr
N.A.I.C.S.: 326199

Newell Rubbermaid UK Services Limited (1)
Halifax Avenue, Fradley Park, Lichfield, WS13 8SS, Staffordshire, United Kingdom
Tel.: (44) 1543447001
Web Site: https://www.newbrands.com
Emp.: 300
Commercial Product Mfr & Distr
N.A.I.C.S.: 333310

Newell Rubbermaid de Mexico S. de R.L. de C.V. (1)
Av Vasco De Quiroga No 3000 Plaza 1 Floor, Federal, Mexico, 01210, Mexico
Tel.: (52) 5557293400
Emp.: 582
Plastics Product Mfr
N.A.I.C.S.: 326199

Oster GmbH (1)
Industriering 9A, 56812, Cochem, Germany
Tel.: (49) 26716051780
Web Site: https://www.oster.de
Non-Durable Goods Whslr
N.A.I.C.S.: 424990

Quickie De Mexico, S. de R.L. de C.V. (1)
Alfonso Martinez Dominguez No Km 0 800, Cadereyta Jimenez, 67480, Mexico
Tel.: (52) 8282845233
Miscellaneous Nondurable Goods Whslr
N.A.I.C.S.: 424990

Quickie Manufacturing Corporation (1)
4110 Premier Dr, High Point, NC 27265
Tel.: (800) 257-5751
Web Site: http://www.quickie.com
Cleaning Tools Mfr
N.A.I.C.S.: 339994

Rubbermaid Home Products (1)
3320 W Market St, Fairlawn, OH 44333-3306
Tel.: (330) 869-7100
Web Site: http://www.rubbermaid.com
Sales Range: $550-599.9 Million
Emp.: 6,000
Mfr & Distr of Rubber & Plastic Products for the Consumer & Institutional Markets
N.A.I.C.S.: 326199

Subsidiary (Domestic):

Rubbermaid Commercial Products LLC (2)
8900 Northpointe Executive Dr, Huntersville, NC 28078
Web Site: https://www.rubbermaidcommercial.com
Emp.: 1,700
Rubber & Plastic Commercial Products Mfr
N.A.I.C.S.: 326199

Subsidiary (Non-US):

Newell Rubbermaid Commercial Products (3)
586 Argus Road, Oakville, L6J 3J3, ON, Canada **(100%)**
Tel.: (800) 387-7845
Web Site: http://www.rubbermaidcommercial.com
Mfr & Marketer of Plastic Products
N.A.I.C.S.: 326199

Sanford L.P. (1)
2707 Butterfield Rd, Oak Brook, IL 60523
Tel.: (630) 481-2000
Web Site: https://www.sanfordcorp.com
Sales Range: $900-999.9 Million
Emp.: 2,500
Felt-Tip Markers, Specialty Marking Instruments, Paper Adhesives, Stamp Pads & Inks, Custom & Pre-Inked Stamps, Marking Inks, Porous Tip Pens, Woodcase Pencils, Colored Pencils & Art Products Mfr
N.A.I.C.S.: 339940

Sistema Plastics Limited (1)
15 Te Tiki Road, Mangere, Auckland, 2022, New Zealand
Tel.: (64) 95797903

Web Site: https://www.sistemaplastics.com
Food Packaging & Container Services
N.A.I.C.S.: 561910

Sistema Plastics UK Limited (1)
Church Walk 1 London Street, Chertsey,
KT16 8AP, Surrey, United Kingdom
Tel.: (44) 188330075
Food Packaging & Container Services
N.A.I.C.S.: 561910
Michelle Pitt (Coord-Sls & Mktg)

Soke-Hungaria Kft (1)
Gyori ut 1, 9228, Halaszi, Hungary
Tel.: (36) 96573210
Consumer Products Distr
N.A.I.C.S.: 423620

Spontex S.A.S. (1)
420 Rue D Estienne D Orves, 92705, Co-
lombes, France
Tel.: (33) 149642200
Web Site: https://www.spontex.fr
Floor Cleaning Sponge Mfr
N.A.I.C.S.: 326199

Sunbeam Corporation Pty Ltd (1)
Unit 5-6 13 Lord Street, Botany, 2019,
NSW, Australia
Tel.: (61) 296959999
Web Site: http://www.sunbeam.com.au
Household Electrical Appliance Mfr
N.A.I.C.S.: 335220
David Joyce (CFO)

Sunbeam Products, Inc. (1)
2381 NW Executive Center Dr, Boca Raton,
FL 33431
Web Site: https://www.sunbeam.com
Small Appliances Mfr
N.A.I.C.S.: 335220
Rocki Rockingham (VP-Community Rels &
Comm)

Subsidiary (Domestic):

Jarden Corp. (2)
2381 Executive Ctr Dr, Boca Raton, FL
33431-7321
Tel.: (561) 912-4100
Web Site: http://www.jarden.com
Rev.: $2,397,979,000
Emp.: 14,196
Fiscal Year-end: 12/28/2002
Appliances, Outdoor Cooking, Health at
Home, Personal Care & Professional Prod-
ucts
N.A.I.C.S.: 337126

**Sunbeam Americas Holdings,
LLC** (2)
2381 NW Executive Ctr Dr, Boca Raton, FL
33431
Tel.: (561) 912-4100
Web Site: https://www.jardencs.com
Holding Company; Household Consumer
Products Mfr
N.A.I.C.S.: 335220

**Teutonia Kinderwagenfabrik
GmbH** (1)
Siemensstrasse 35, 32120, Hiddenhausen,
Germany
Tel.: (49) 522387980
Web Site: http://www.teutonia.de
Sales Range: $25-49.9 Million
Emp.: 150
Baby Carriages, Buggies & Joggers Mfr &
Whslr
N.A.I.C.S.: 339930

The Baby Jogger Company (1)
4110 Premier Dr, High Point, NC 27265
Tel.: (800) 241-1848
Web Site: http://www.babyjogger.com
Stroller Mfr
N.A.I.C.S.: 336991

The Coleman Company, Inc. (1)
3600 N Hydraulic, Wichita, KS 67219-3812
Web Site: https://www.coleman.com
Sporting Goods & Equipment Mfr
N.A.I.C.S.: 339920

Subsidiary (Non-US):

**Camping Gaz (Deutschland)
GmbH** (2)
EZetilstrasse 5, Inheiden, 35410, Hungen,
Germany
Tel.: (49) 6402890

Web Site: https://www.campingaz.com
Propane-Fueled Barbecue & Camping
Equipment & Propane Cannisters Mfr &
Whslr
N.A.I.C.S.: 335220
Brian Decker (Mng Dir)
Andreas Streitenfeld (Mng Dir)

Camping Gaz (Schweiz) AG (2)
Route du Tir-Federal 10, 1762, Givisiez,
Switzerland
Tel.: (41) 264604040
Web Site: https://www.campingaz.ch
Propane-Fueled Barbecue & Camping
Equipment & Propane Cannisters Whslr
N.A.I.C.S.: 423620

**Coleman Guangzhou Outdoor Lei-
sure Products Company Ltd.** (2)
Rm 102-103 TianAn Technology Innovation
Mansion Panyu Energy, Guangzhou,
511400, Guangdong, China
Tel.: (86) 2039378500
Miscellaneous Nondurable Goods Whslr
N.A.I.C.S.: 424990

Coleman Japan Co., Ltd. (2)
Shibaura Square Building 4-9-25 Shibaura,
Tokyo, 108-0023, Minato-ku, Japan
Tel.: (81) 368587400
Web Site: http://www.coleman.co.jp
Camping Equipment Distr
N.A.I.C.S.: 335999
Yutaka Nakazato (Pres)

Coleman UK Limited (2)
The Courtyard Wraxhall Hill, Wraxhall, Bris-
tol, BS48 1NA, United Kingdom
Tel.: (44) 1275288255
Web Site: https://www.colemanuk.co.uk
Sporting Goods Distr
N.A.I.C.S.: 423740

Productos Coleman S.A. (2)
Canada Real De Merinas Centro Negocios
13, 28052, Madrid, Spain
Tel.: (34) 912754396
Camping Gear & Outdoor Equipment Mfr
N.A.I.C.S.: 424990

**The Yankee Candle Company,
Inc.** (1)
Yankee Candle 4110 Premier Dr, High
Point, NC 27265
Web Site: https://www.yankeecandle.com
Scented Candles Mfr
N.A.I.C.S.: 339999

USPC Holding, Inc. (1)
300 Gap Way, Erlanger, KY 41018
Tel.: (800) 543-2273
Playing Cards, Games & Playing Cards Ac-
cessories Mfr
N.A.I.C.S.: 339930

Waterman S.A.S. (1)
Saint Herblain, Cedex, Saint Herblain,
France
Tel.: (33) 240384848
Web Site: http://www.newellco.com
Sales Range: $125-149.9 Million
Emp.: 400
Writing Instruments Mfr
N.A.I.C.S.: 339940

**Yankee Candle Company (Europe)
Limited** (1)
Suite 44 42 Triangle West, Bristol, BS8
1ES, United Kingdom
Tel.: (44) 1173161200
Web Site: https://www.yankeecandle.co.uk
Candle Care Accessory Mfr
N.A.I.C.S.: 339999
Andrew Sly (Head-Information Technology)

NEWHYDROGEN, INC.
27936 Lost Canyon Rd Ste 202,
Santa Clarita, CA 91387
Tel.: (661) 251-0001   NV
Web Site:
    https://www.newhydrogen.com
Year Founded: 2006
NEWH—(OTCIQ)
Rev.: $3,054
Assets: $4,872,853
Liabilities: $3,485,362
Net Worth: $1,387,491
Earnings: ($12,085,528)

Emp.: 1
Fiscal Year-end: 12/31/22
Bio-based Material Development Ser-
vices
N.A.I.C.S.: 339999
David D. Lee (Chm, Pres & Acting
CFO)
Steven Hill (CEO)

**NEWLAKE CAPITAL PART-
NERS, INC.**
50 Locust Ave 1st Fl, New Canaan,
CT 06840
Tel.: (203) 594-1402   MD
Web Site: https://newlake.com
Year Founded: 2019
NLCP—(OTCQX)
Rev.: $44,794,000
Assets: $454,249,000
Liabilities: $23,311,000
Net Worth: $430,938,000
Earnings: $21,976,000
Emp.: 8
Fiscal Year-end: 12/31/22
Real Estate Investment Services
N.A.I.C.S.: 531190
Jarrett Annenberg (Founder, Sr VP &
Head-Investments)
Lisa Meyer (CFO, Treas & Sec)
Anthony Coniglio (Pres & CEO)

NEWMARK GROUP, INC.
125 Park Ave 1 E Pratt St, New York,
NY 10017
Tel.: (212) 372-2000   DE
Web Site: https://www.nmrk.com
Year Founded: 1929
NMRK—(NASDAQ)
Rev.: $2,470,368,000
Assets: $4,471,575,000
Liabilities: $2,892,893,000
Net Worth: $1,578,682,000
Earnings: $62,375,000
Emp.: 7,000
Fiscal Year-end: 12/31/23
Real Estate Management Services
N.A.I.C.S.: 531210
Brian S. Waterman (Vice Chm)
Stephen Merkel (Chief Legal Officer
& Exec VP)
Neil J. Goldmacher (Chm-Natl Tenant
Representation)
Jason McGruder (Head-IR)
Roger Anscher (Chief Admin Officer)
Joshua Davis (Gen Counsel)
Angie Leccese (CMO)
Sridhar Potineni (CIO)
Doug Harmon (Co-Head)
Adam Spies (Co-Head-US Capital
Markets)
Howard W. Lutnick (Chm)
James D. Kuhn Frics (Pres & Head-
Investor Svcs)
Elizabeth Hart (Pres & Pres-Leasing-
North America)
Chad Lavender (Pres & Pres-Capital
Markets for North America)
Jack Fraker (Pres & Head-Industrial,
Logistics, and Capital Markets-
Global)
Richard Holden (Pres & Pres-
Property Mgmt)
Barry M. Gosin (CEO)
Caroline A. Koster (Mng Dir, Gen
Counsel & Sec)
Michael J. Rispoli (CFO)
David A. Falk (Pres-New York Tri-
State Reg)
Kevin McCabe (Pres-West)
John D. Busi Mai (Pres-Valuation &
Advisory)
Anthony Orso (Pres-Capital Markets
Strategies)
Robert E. Griffin Jr. (Co-Head-Capital
Markets-US)

Subsidiaries:

**BERKELEY POINT CAPITAL,
LLC** (1)
One Beacon St 14th Fl, Boston, MA 02108
Tel.: (617) 523-0066
Real Estate Management Services
N.A.I.C.S.: 531210

CONTINENTAL REALTY, LTD. (1)
150 E BRd St, Columbus, OH 43215
Tel.: (614) 221-1800
Real Estate Management Services
N.A.I.C.S.: 531210

**FULCRUM COMMERCIAL REAL ES-
TATE SERVICES LLC** (1)
11500 Olympic Blvd Ste 400, Los Angeles,
CA 90064
Tel.: (310) 421-1095
Web Site: https://www.fulcrumcres.com
Real Estate Services
N.A.I.C.S.: 531210
Gabe Stuart (Principal)
Alex Skorniakoff (Principal)

Harper Dennis Hobbs Limited (1)
Langham House 302/308 Regent St, Lon-
don, W1B 3AT, United Kingdom
Tel.: (44) 2074629100
Web Site: http://www.hdh.co.uk
Real Estate Services
N.A.I.C.S.: 531190
Andrew Bathurst (Exec Dir)
Andrew Peters (Exec Dir)
Bhavini Dhutia (Head-Mktg & Branding)
Chris Dennis (COO)
Dan Hildyard (Exec Dir)
Nadine Heubel (Sr Mng Dir-Travel Retail-
North America)
Simon Black (Exec Mng Dir)

Knotel Ahoy! Berlin GMBH (1)
Wattstr 11, 13355, Berlin, Germany
Tel.: (49) 3020849740
Web Site: https://www.ahoyberlin.com
Exhibition & Event Hall Rental Services
N.A.I.C.S.: 531120

MIT National Land Services LLC (1)
1 Penn Plz Fl 34, New York, NY 10119
Tel.: (212) 239-1000
Web Site: http://www.mitnational.com
Insurance Services
N.A.I.C.S.: 524127
Marc Israel (Pres)
Gary Thorsen (Chief Title Officer)
Roy Fenichel (Dir-Bus Dev)
Alec Dadisman (Mgr-Bus Ops)
Drew Cox (Officer-Clearance)
Damion Noel (Officer-Clearance)
Maria D'Alessandro (Supvr-Recording Dept)
Lily Tam (Supvr-Applications)
Gina Fidacaro (Supvr-Escrow & Post)
Stephanie Lenti (Dir-Bus Dev)
Alon Steiner (Dir-Bus Dev)
Luis Antunano (Dir-Bus Dev)
Alan Secter (Dir-Bus Dev)
Daniel Czech (Dir-Bus Dev)
Doug Maier (VP-Natl Comml Bus Dev)

MLG Commercial, LLC (1)
757 N Broadway Ste 700, Milwaukee, WI
53202
Tel.: (414) 347-9400
Real Estate Services
N.A.I.C.S.: 531210

McCall & Almy, Inc. (1)
1 Post Ofc Sq, Boston, MA 02109
Tel.: (617) 542-4141
Web Site: http://www.mccallalmy.com
Activities Related to Real Estate
N.A.I.C.S.: 531390

**NEWMARK KNIGHT FRANK
CANADA LIMITED** (1)
100 King Street West Suite 5600, Toronto,
M5X 1C9, ON, Canada
Tel.: (416) 847-1865
Real Estate Services
N.A.I.C.S.: 531210
Pat Langdon (Mng Dir)

**NEWMARK KNIGHT FRANK VALUA-
TION & ADVISORY, LLC** (1)
125 Park Ave, New York, NY 10017
Tel.: (213) 372-2260
Real Estate Services
N.A.I.C.S.: 531210

Newmark Group, Inc.—(Continued)

Georgia Nichols *(Sr VP)*

NGA, LLC **(1)**
847 Quince Orchard Blvd F, Gaithersburg,
MD 20878
Tel.: (301) 977-9444
Real Estate Manangement Services
N.A.I.C.S.: 531210

Newmark Bh2 Llp **(1)**
6 7 & 8 Tokenhouse Yard, London, EC2R
7AS, United Kingdom
Tel.: (44) 2076005000
Web Site: https://bh2.co.uk
Real Estate Development Services
N.A.I.C.S.: 531210

Newmark Real Estate Panama,
S.A. **(1)**
Plaza 2000 Calle 53 Este Corregiduria de
Bella Vista, Obarrio, Panama, 0833-0293,
Panama
Tel.: (507) 3217761
Real Estate Services
N.A.I.C.S.: 531210

RKF Group Canada Realty **(1)**
624 King Street West Floor 3, Toronto, M5V
1M7, ON, Canada
Tel.: (416) 599-3700
Real Estate Services
N.A.I.C.S.: 531210

RKF Group Illinois LLC **(1)**
555 Skokie Blvd Ste 450, Northbrook, IL
60062
Tel.: (312) 888-2000
Real Estate Services
N.A.I.C.S.: 531210

RKF Group New Jersey LLC **(1)**
301 Route 17 N Ste 707, Rutherford, NJ
07070
Tel.: (201) 842-7700
Real Estate Services
N.A.I.C.S.: 531210

SPRING 11 LLC **(1)**
125 Park Ave 9th Fl, New York, NY 10017
Tel.: (212) 359-0011
Web Site: https://www.spring11.com
Real Estate Services
N.A.I.C.S.: 531210
Benek Oster *(Principal)*
Jack Fuchs *(Principal)*

SPRING11 ADVISORY SERVICES
LIMITED **(1)**
12 Bridewell Place Third Floor, London,
EC4V 6AP, United Kingdom
Tel.: (44) 2033189980
Web Site: http://www.spring11advisory.co.uk
Real Estate Services
N.A.I.C.S.: 531210

NEWMARKET CORPORATION
330 S 4th St, Richmond, VA 23219-
4350
Tel.: (804) 788-5000 **VA**
Web Site:
https://www.newmarket.com
Year Founded: 1921
NEU—(NYSE)
Rev.: $2,698,419,000
Assets: $2,308,871,000
Liabilities: $1,231,810,000
Net Worth: $1,077,061,000
Earnings: $388,864,000
Emp.: 2,000
Fiscal Year-end: 12/31/23
Petroleum Additives for Fuels, Lubri-
cants & Tetraethyl Lead Antiknock
Compounds Mfr & Retailer
N.A.I.C.S.: 324199
Thomas E. Gottwald *(Chm, Pres &*
CEO)
Anne-Marie Anderson *(Sec & Asst*
Counsel)
Anne-Marie M. Anderson *(Sec)*
Bruce R. Hazelgrove III *(Chief Admin*
Officer & Exec VP)
Cameron D. Warner Jr. *(Treas)*
Bryce D. Jewett III *(Gen Counsel &*
VP)

Subsidiaries:

Afton Chemical Additives
Corporation **(1)**
4245 Savannah Ave, Port Arthur, TX 77640
Tel.: (409) 989-0699
Web Site: http://www.aftonchemical.com
Emp.: 20
Petroleum Product Whslr
N.A.I.C.S.: 424720

Afton Chemical Corporation **(1)**
500 Spring St, Richmond, VA 23219
Tel.: (804) 788-5800
Web Site: https://www.aftonchemical.com
Automotive & Industrial Additives Mfr
N.A.I.C.S.: 325998

Subsidiary (Non-US):

Afton Chemical Asia Pte. Ltd. **(2)**
103 Penang Road 09-01 Visioncrest Com-
mercial, Singapore, 238467, Singapore
Tel.: (65) 67320822
Web Site: http://www.aftonchemical.com
Automotive & Industrial Additives Mfr
N.A.I.C.S.: 325998

Afton Chemical Canada
Corporation **(2)**
5045 South Service Road Suite 101, Burl-
ington, L7L 5Y7, ON, Canada
Tel.: (905) 631-5470
Automotive & Industrial Additives Mfr
N.A.I.C.S.: 325998

Afton Chemical GmbH **(2)**
Am Kaiserkai 1, 20457, Hamburg, Germany
Tel.: (49) 404292900
Sales Range: $25-49.9 Million
Emp.: 25
Automotive & Industrial Additives Mfr
N.A.I.C.S.: 325998

Afton Chemical India Private
Limited **(2)**
Lotus Corporate Park 7th Floor A Wing
Ram Mandir Lane, Western Express High-
way Goregaon East, Mumbai, 400063, India
Tel.: (91) 2262780200
Automotive & Industrial Additives Mfr
N.A.I.C.S.: 325998
Harshad Jambaulikar *(Gen Mgr)*

Afton Chemical Limited **(2)**
London Road, Bracknell, RG12 2UW, Berk-
shire, United Kingdom
Tel.: (44) 1344304141
Web Site: http://www.aftonchemical.com
Automotive & Industrial Additives Mfr
N.A.I.C.S.: 325998

Afton Chemical S.P.R.L. **(2)**
Alma Court Lenneke Marelaan 8, 1932,
Saint-Stevens-Woluwe, Belgium **(100%)**
Tel.: (32) 27152211
Web Site: http://www.aftonchemical.com
Sales Range: $10-24.9 Million
Automotive & Industrial Additives Mfr
N.A.I.C.S.: 325998

Afton Chemical de Mexico S.A. de
C.V. **(2)**
Insurgentes Sur 863 Oficina 1203, 3810,
Colonia, Mexico
Tel.: (52) 5556878999
Petroleum & Petroleum Products Whslr
N.A.I.C.S.: 424720

Afton Chemical Intangibles LLC **(1)**
330 S 4th St, Richmond, VA 23219
Tel.: (804) 788-5000
Sales Range: $150-199.9 Million
Emp.: 600
Automotive & Industrial Additives Mfr
N.A.I.C.S.: 325998

NEWMONT CORPORATION
6900 E Layton Ave, Denver, CO
80237
Tel.: (303) 863-7414 **DE**
Web Site: https://www.newmont.com
Year Founded: 1921
NEM—(NYSE)
Rev.: $11,812,000,000
Assets: $55,506,000,000
Liabilities: $26,301,000,000
Net Worth: $29,205,000,000

Earnings: ($2,494,000,000)
Emp.: 21,700
Fiscal Year-end: 12/31/23
Mineral Mining Services
N.A.I.C.S.: 212220
Logan Hennessey *(Sec, VP & Assoc*
Gen Counsel)
Nick Cotts *(Sr VP-External Rels)*
Alex Bates *(Sr VP-Australia)*
Shelly Huff *(VP-Tax)*
Bryan Teets *(VP-Internal Audit)*
Mike Wundenberg *(VP-Operational*
Tech & Innovation)
Karyn F. Ovelmen *(CFO & Exec VP)*
Natascha Viljoen *(COO & Exec VP)*
Mark Ebel *(VP & Assoc Gen Coun-*
sel)
Melissa Gustafson *(VP-Talent Mgmt)*
Suzy Retallack *(Chief Safety & Sus-*
tainability Officer)
Sebastian Soria *(VP-Total Rewards)*
Scott Sullivan *(Chief Integrity & Com-*
pliance Officer)
Peter Toth *(Chief Dev Officer)*
Joshua Cage *(Principal Acctg Officer*
& Grp Head-Acctg)
Joshua L. Cage *(Chief Acctg Officer)*
Daniel Horton *(Treas)*
David Fry *(Sr VP)*
Bernard Wessels *(Sr VP)*
Mark Rodgers *(Sr VP)*
Dave Thornton *(Sr VP)*
Lara Bruhns *(Acting VP)*
Josh Cage *(Chief Acctg Officer)*
Mia Gous *(Sr VP)*
Thomas Ronald Palmer *(Pres &*
CEO)

Subsidiaries:

Cripple Creek & Victor Gold Mining
Company LLC **(1)**
1632 County Rd 82, Cripple Creek, CO
80813
Tel.: (719) 689-4132
Metal Mining Services
N.A.I.C.S.: 212220

European Gold Refineries Holding
SA **(1)**
Via Passeggiata 3, 6828, Balerna,
Switzerland **(60.64%)**
Tel.: (41) 912600569
Web Site: http://www.valcambi.com
Holding Company; Gold Refinery
N.A.I.C.S.: 551112

Subsidiary (Domestic):

Valcambi S.A. **(2)**
Via Passeggiata 3, PO Box 359, 6828,
Balerna, Switzerland **(100%)**
Tel.: (41) 916955311
Web Site: https://www.valcambi.com
Sales Range: $25-49.9 Million
Emp.: 168
Precious Metals Refinery; Recovery of Pre-
cious Metals, Production of Precious Metals
Bars & Ingots, Minting of Coins & Medals,
Manufacturer of Watchcases & Bracelets
N.A.I.C.S.: 331491
Michael Mesaric *(CEO)*
Oris Corti *(Mgr-Security)*
Norberto Molteni *(Mgr-Production)*
Simone Knobloch *(COO)*
Fernanda Caratsch *(CFO)*
Ursula Glofre *(Head-Sis)*

GT Gold Corp. **(1)**
1100 Melville Street Suite 610, Vancouver,
V6E 4A6, BC, Canada **(100%)**
Tel.: (236) 427-5744
Web Site: http://gtgoldcorp.ca
Rev.: $142,797
Assets: $11,819,248
Liabilities: $2,037,713
Net Worth: $9,781,534
Earnings: ($8,323,601)
Fiscal Year-end: 12/31/2020
Gold Exploration
N.A.I.C.S.: 212220
Paul Harbidge *(CEO)*
Michael Skead *(VP-Project Dev)*

Galore Creek Mining Corporation **(1)**

Suite 3300 - 550 Burrard Street, Vancouver,
V6C 0B3, BC, Canada
Web Site: http://www.gcmc.ca
Mining Services
N.A.I.C.S.: 212290

Goldcorp Inc. **(1)**
Park Place Suite 3400-666 Burrard Street,
Vancouver, V6C 2X8, BC, Canada
Tel.: (604) 696-3000
Web Site: http://www.goldcorp.com
Rev.: $3,032,000,000
Assets: $16,967,000,000
Liabilities: $7,092,000,000
Net Worth: $9,875,000,000
Earnings: ($4,149,000,000)
Fiscal Year-end: 12/31/2018
Gold, Silver & Copper Mining
N.A.I.C.S.: 212220
Simon Hille *(VP-Technical Svcs, Innovation,*
Metallurgy & Processing-Global)
Wade William Bristol *(Sr VP-Ops-Canada)*
Peter Calnan *(VP-Safety & Health)*
Kim Lionel Hackney *(VP-Project Execution)*
Bill Patterson *(VP-Project Studies)*
Lisa Wade *(VP-Environment, Reclamation*
& Closure)
Ian William Telfer *(Chm)*
Anna M. Tudela *(Sec & VP-Diversity &*
Regulatory Affairs)
Brent Bergeron *(Exec VP-Corp Affairs &*
Sustainability)
David Stephens *(VP-Corp Dev & Mktg)*
Rohan Athaide *(VP-Risk Mgmt & Assur-*
ance)
Todd White *(COO & Exec VP)*
Joseph Dick *(Sr VP-Mine Optimization)*
Paul D. Harbidge *(Sr VP-Exploration)*
Luis Canepari *(VP-Tech)*
Randall Chatwin *(VP & Asst Gen Counsel)*
Rishi Ghuldu *(VP-Operational Excellence,*
Supply Chain & Asset Mgmt)
Joanne Klein *(VP-People)*
Patrick James Merrin *(Sr VP-Ops-Canada)*
John Mullally *(VP-Corp Affairs & Energy*
Regulation)
Ivan J. Mullany *(Sr VP-Technical Svcs)*
Lincoln Schreiner *(VP-Tax)*
Sean McCarthy *(VP-Bus Plng)*

Branch (Domestic):

Goldcorp Inc. - Toronto Office **(2)**
130 Adelaide St W Ste 3201, Toronto, M5H
3P5, ON, Canada
Tel.: (416) 865-0326
Web Site: http://www.goldcorp.com
Sales Range: $50-74.9 Million
Emp.: 35
Gold Mining Services
N.A.I.C.S.: 212220

Subsidiary (Non-US):

Goldcorp S.A. de C.V. **(2)**
Paseo De Las Palmas No 425 Int 15 Lo-
mas De Chapultepec, Miguel Hidalgo,
Mexico, Mexico
Tel.: (52) 5552019600
Gold Ore Mining Services
N.A.I.C.S.: 212220

Subsidiary (Domestic):

Camino Rojo S.A. de C.V. **(3)**
Paseo de las Palmas 425-15 Lomas de
Chapultepec, 11000, Mexico, Mexico
Tel.: (52) 55 5201 9600
Web Site: http://www.goldcorp.com
Mineral Mining & Exploration Services
N.A.I.C.S.: 212390

Minera Penasquito S.A. de C.V. **(3)**
Av Universidad No 103, Zacatecas, 98060,
Mexico
Tel.: (52) 4929256830
Gold Ore Mining Services
N.A.I.C.S.: 212220

Subsidiary (Non-US):

Oroplata S.A. **(2)**
Maipu 255 Piso 12, Buenos Aires, Argen-
tina
Tel.: (54) 1143237000
Mineral Ore Mining Services
N.A.I.C.S.: 212390

Hope Bay Mining Ltd. **(1)**
Suite 300 889 Harbourside Drive, North

Vancouver, V7P 3S1, BC, Canada
Tel.: (604) 985-2572
Web Site: http://www.newmontmining.com
Sales Range: $1-9.9 Million
Emp.: 400
Gold Mining
N.A.I.C.S.: 212220
Brad Skeeles *(Gen Mgr)*

Newcrest Mining Limited **(1)**
Level 8 600 St Kilda Road, Melbourne, 3004, VIC, Australia
Tel.: (61) 395225333
Web Site: https://www.newcrest.com
Rev.: $4,508,000,000
Assets: $17,521,000,000
Liabilities: $5,809,000,000
Net Worth: $11,712,000,000
Earnings: $778,000,000
Emp.: 6,576
Fiscal Year-end: 06/30/2023
Gold Exploration & Mining Services
N.A.I.C.S.: 212220
Gerard Michael Bond *(Fin Dir & Fin Dir)*
Craig Jones *(COO)*
Francesca Lee *(Chief Legal & Compliance Officer)*
Phil Stephenson *(COO-Americas)*
Lisa Ali *(Chief People & Sustainability Officer)*
Suresh Vadnagra *(Chief Tech & Projects Officer)*
Seil Song *(Chief Dev Officer)*
Sherry Duhe *(Interim CEO & CFO)*
Peter. Tomsett *(Chm)*

Subsidiary (Domestic):

Cadia Holdings Pty Ltd **(2)**
L 9 600 St Kilda Rd, Melbourne, 3004, VIC, Australia
Tel.: (61) 395225333
Sales Range: $200-249.9 Million
Emp.: 400
Gold Mining Services
N.A.I.C.S.: 212220
Greg Robinson *(CEO & Mng Dir)*

Cadia Mines Pty Ltd **(2)**
1460 Cadia Rd, Orange, 2800, New South Wales, Australia
Tel.: (61) 263922300
Sales Range: $350-399.9 Million
Emp.: 800
Gold Mining Services
N.A.I.C.S.: 212220

Cracow Holdings Pty Ltd **(2)**
L 9 600 St Kilda Rd, Melbourne, 3004, Victoria, Australia
Tel.: (61) 3 9522 5333
Financial Holding Services
N.A.I.C.S.: 551112

Subsidiary (Non-US):

LGL Resources CI SA **(2)**
Dany Center 2 Plateaux, BP 2212, Abidjan, Cote d'Ivoire
Tel.: (225) 22419161
Emp.: 500
Gold Mining Services
N.A.I.C.S.: 212220

Subsidiary (Domestic):

Newcrest Exploration Holdings Pty Ltd **(2)**
L 8 600 St Kilda Rd, Melbourne, 3004, VIC, Australia
Tel.: (61) 395225333
Web Site: http://www.newcrest.com.au
Gold Mining Services
N.A.I.C.S.: 212220
Sanjaat Biswas *(CEO)*

Newcrest Finance Pty Ltd **(2)**
L 8 600 St Kilda Rd, Melbourne, 3004, VIC, Australia
Tel.: (61) 395225333
Web Site: http://www.newcrest.com.au
Sales Range: $1-4.9 Billion
Emp.: 13,000
Financial Services
N.A.I.C.S.: 523999

Subsidiary (Non-US):

Newcrest Insurance Pte Ltd **(2)**
2 Havelock Road 03-01/02, Singapore, 059763, Singapore

Tel.: (65) 65918000
General Insurance Services
N.A.I.C.S.: 524210

Subsidiary (Domestic):

Newcrest International Pty Ltd **(2)**
Level 9 600 St Kilda Rd, Melbourne, 3004, VIC, Australia
Tel.: (61) 395225333
Web Site: http://www.newcrest.com.au
Sales Range: $100-124.9 Million
Emp.: 200
Gold Mining Services
N.A.I.C.S.: 212220

Newcrest Operations Limited **(2)**
L 8 600 St Kilda Rd, Melbourne, 3004, VIC, Australia
Tel.: (61) 395225333
Web Site: http://www.newcrest.com.au
Sales Range: $1-4.9 Billion
Emp.: 13,000
Gold Mining Services
N.A.I.C.S.: 212220

Newcrest Services Pty Ltd **(2)**
Level 9 600 St Kilda Rd, Melbourne, 3000, VIC, Australia
Tel.: (61) 395225333
Web Site: http://www.newcrest.com.au
Sales Range: $200-249.9 Million
Emp.: 280
Gold Mining Services
N.A.I.C.S.: 212220

Subsidiary (Non-US):

PT Nusa Halmahera Minerals **(2)**
Wenang Permai II No 27 Kel Kairagi I Lingkungan VI, Kec Mapanget, Manado, 95233, Sulawesi, Indonesia
Tel.: (62) 431872007
Web Site: http://www.nhm.co.id
Gold Ore Mining Services
N.A.I.C.S.: 212220

Pretium Resources Inc. **(2)**
1055 Dunsmuir Street Suite 2300, Vancouver, V7X 1L4, BC, Canada
Tel.: (604) 558-1784
Web Site: http://www.pretivm.com
Rev.: $617,585,000
Assets: $1,430,814,000
Liabilities: $501,113,000
Net Worth: $929,701,000
Earnings: ($38,438,000)
Emp.: 816
Fiscal Year-end: 12/31/2020
Gold, Silver, Copper & Other Metal Mining Services
N.A.I.C.S.: 212220
Richard T. O'Brien *(Chm)*
Vladimir Cvijetinovic *(Sec & VP-Legal)*
Greg Norton *(VP-Environment & Regulatory Affairs)*
Jacques Perron *(Pres & CEO)*
Patrick Godin *(COO & VP)*
Matthew Quinlan *(CFO & VP)*

Joint Venture (Non-US):

Red Chris Development Company Ltd. **(2)**
200 - 580 Hornby St, Vancouver, V6C 3B6, BC, Canada **(70%)**
Tel.: (604) 669-8959
Web Site: http://www.imperialmetals.com
Sales Range: $50-74.9 Million
Emp.: 30
Metal Exploration Services
N.A.I.C.S.: 213114

Newmont Australia Pty Limited **(1)**
Level 2 388 Hay Street, Subiaco, 6008, WA, Australia **(100%)**
Tel.: (61) 89 423 6100
Web Site: http://www.newmont.com
Sales Range: $25-49.9 Million
Emp.: 200
Gold Ore Mining
N.A.I.C.S.: 212220
Andrey Stialein *(Pres)*

Newmont Australia Superannuation Plan Pty Ltd **(1)**
L 1 388 Hay St, Subiaco, 6008, WA, Australia
Tel.: (61) 894236100
Web Site: http://www.newmont.com

Emp.: 25
Accounting & Bookkeeping Services
N.A.I.C.S.: 541219
Alex Bites *(VP)*

Newmont Gold Company **(1)**
6363 S Fiddlers Green Cir, Greenwood Village, CO 80111 **(100%)**
Tel.: (303) 863-7414
Web Site: http://www.newmont.com
Sales Range: $25-49.9 Million
Emp.: 800
Gold Mining
N.A.I.C.S.: 212220
William M. Zisch *(Executives)*

Newmont Mining Corporation of Canada Limited **(1)**
Fiddler's Green Cir, Greenwood Village, CO 80203 **(100%)**
Tel.: (303) 837-6005
Web Site: http://www.newmont.com
Sales Range: $1-9.9 Million
Gold Mining
N.A.I.C.S.: 212220

Newmont North America Exploration Limited **(1)**
6363 S Fiddler's Green Cir, Greenwood Village, CO 80111 **(100%)**
Tel.: (303) 863-7414
Web Site: http://www.newmont.com
Sales Range: $25-49.9 Million
Emp.: 800
Metallurgical Exploration
N.A.I.C.S.: 213114

Newmont Nusa Tenggara Holdings B.V. **(1)**
Paasheuvelweg 16, 1105 BH, Amsterdam, Netherlands
Tel.: (31) 205646160
Gold Ore Mining
N.A.I.C.S.: 212220

Suriname Gold Company, LLC **(1)**
Van t Hogerhuysstraat 15 4th floor, Paramaribo, Suriname
Tel.: (597) 427707
Web Site: http://www.surgold.com
Gold Ore Mining Services
N.A.I.C.S.: 212220

NEWPARK RESOURCES, INC.
9320 Lakeside Blvd Ste 100, The Woodlands, TX 77381
Tel.: (281) 362-6800   DE
Web Site: https://www.newpark.com
Year Founded: 1932
NR—(NYSE)
Rev.: $815,594,000
Assets: $714,875,000
Liabilities: $291,847,000
Net Worth: $423,028,000
Earnings: ($20,834,000)
Emp.: 1,540
Fiscal Year-end: 12/31/22
Oilfield & Environmental Services for Oil & Gas Exploration; Industrial Waste Removal Services
N.A.I.C.S.: 213112
Matthew S. Lanigan *(Pres & CEO)*
Gregg S. Piontek *(CFO & Sr VP)*
Douglas L. White *(Chief Acctg Officer, Treas & VP)*
David A. Paterson *(Pres-Fluids Sys & VP)*
Tasha M. Murphy *(VP-HR)*
M. Celeste Fruge *(Chief Compliance Officer, Corp Counsel, Sec & VP)*

Subsidiaries:

AVA AFRICA S.A.R.L. **(1)**
Port of Zarzis, PO Box 26, 4170, Zarzis, Tunisia
Tel.: (216) 75690465
Drilling Fluid Systems & Waste Recovery Services
N.A.I.C.S.: 213112

AVA EASTERN EUROPE D.F.& S., S.R.L. **(1)**
Calea Floreasca Nr 60 Et 9 Ap Cam 12 1, Bucharest, 14462, Romania
Tel.: (40) 213122872

Web Site: http://www.avaspa.it
Sales Range: $75-99.9 Million
Emp.: 80
Drilling Fluid Systems & Waste Recovery Services
N.A.I.C.S.: 213112

AVA, S.P.A. **(1)**
Via Salaria 1313/C, 00138, Rome, Italy
Tel.: (39) 068856111
Web Site: http://www.avaspa.it
Sales Range: $50-74.9 Million
Emp.: 35
Drilling Fluid Systems & Waste Recovery Services
N.A.I.C.S.: 213112

Batson Mill L.L.C. **(1)**
25860 FM 770 Rd, Batson, TX 77519 **(100%)**
Tel.: (936) 262-8000
Web Site: http://batsonlumber.com
Sales Range: $50-74.9 Million
Emp.: 50
Lumber Mill
N.A.I.C.S.: 321912

Cleansorb Limited **(1)**
Unit 1J Merrow Business Centre Merrow Lane, Guildford, GU4 7WA, United Kingdom
Tel.: (44) 1483300107
Web Site: https://www.cleansorb.com
Oilfield Chemical Mfr
N.A.I.C.S.: 325110

NEWPARK CANADA, INC. **(1)**
Suite 300 635 6th Ave SW, Calgary, T2P 0T5, AB, Canada
Tel.: (403) 266-7383
Web Site: http://www.newpark.ca
Emp.: 35
Drilling Fluid Systems & Technical Services
N.A.I.C.S.: 213112

NEWPARK CHILE LIMITADA **(1)**
Camino Mina Bitsch 17, Punta Arenas, Chile
Tel.: (56) 612237420
Oil & Gas Exploration Services
N.A.I.C.S.: 213112

NEWPARK DRILLING FLUIDS (AUSTRALIA) LIMITED **(1)**
11 Alacrity Place, Henderson, 6166, WA, Australia
Tel.: (61) 894108200
Emp.: 10
Oil & Gas Exploration Services
N.A.I.C.S.: 213112

NEWPARK DRILLING FLUIDS ASIA PACIFIC LLC **(1)**
11 Alacrity Place, Henderson, 6166, WA, Australia
Tel.: (61) 894108200
Drilling Oil & Gas Well Services
N.A.I.C.S.: 213111

NEWPARK DRILLING FLUIDS GERMANY GMBH **(1)**
Hannoversche Str 30a, 29221, Celle, Germany
Tel.: (49) 5141593470
Oil & Gas Field Services
N.A.I.C.S.: 213112

NEWPARK DRILLING FLUIDS INDIA PRIVATE LIMITED **(1)**
8th Floor Opposite Grand Hayatt Hotel, Santacruz East, Mumbai, 400055, Maharashtra, India
Tel.: (91) 22300515218
Civil Construction Services
N.A.I.C.S.: 541330

NEWPARK DRILLING FLUIDS do BRASIL TRATAMENTO de FLUIDOS LTDA. **(1)**
Av das Americas n 3301 - Block 03 Suite 201 - Barra Business Center, Barra da Tijuca, Rio de Janeiro, 22631-003, RJ, Brazil
Tel.: (55) 2131397000
Drilling Fluid Systems & Engineering Services
N.A.I.C.S.: 213112

Newpark Australia Pty Ltd. **(1)**
11 Alacrity Place, Perth, Henderson, 6166, WA, Australia
Tel.: (61) 8 9410 8200

Newpark Resources, Inc.—(Continued)

Web Site: http://www.newpark.com.au
Emp.: 15
Oil Field Drilling Services
N.A.I.C.S.: 213111
Juergen Trautner (Mng Dir)

Subsidiary (Non-US):

Rheochem India Pvt. **(2)**
Sneh Snedan 35-D Main Avenue, Santa-
cruz West, Mumbai, 400-054, India
Tel.: (91) 22 6703 2176
Oil Field Drilling Services
N.A.I.C.S.: 213111

Newpark Mats & Integrated Services
LLC **(1)**
2900 Hwy 93, Carencro, LA 70520 **(100%)**
Tel.: (337) 896-8976
Sales Range: $25-49.9 Million
Emp.: 300
Engineers & Manufactures Solutions for
Portable Roads & Jobsite Staging for the
Oil, Gas & Utility Industries
N.A.I.C.S.: 213112

PRAGMATIC DRILLING FLUIDS AD-
DITIVES LTD **(1)**
400 703 6th Ave SW, Calgary, T2P 0T9,
AB, Canada
Tel.: (403) 836-5152
Web Site: http://pragmaticdf.com
Oil & Gas Extraction Services
N.A.I.C.S.: 213112

Terrafirma Roadways Limited **(1)**
Thrupp Lane Radley, Abingdon, OX14 3NG,
Oxon, United Kingdom
Tel.: (44) 1235868835
Web Site: https://terrafirma-roadways.com
Emp.: 25
Construction Materials Distr
N.A.I.C.S.: 423320

NEWPOINT FINANCIAL CORP.
97101 Wilshire Blvd Ste 1000, Bev-
erly Hills, CA 90212
Tel.: (310) 494-5954　　　**DE**
Web Site:
https://www.newpointfinancial
corp.com
Year Founded: 2005
NPFC—(OTCIQ)
Assets: $50,169,343
Liabilities: $50,263,251
Net Worth: ($93,908)
Earnings: ($87,178)
Fiscal Year-end: 12/31/21
Offices of Real Estate Agents & Bro-
kers
N.A.I.C.S.: 531210
Keith David Beekmeyer (Chm &
CEO)
Andrew Bye (Chief Risk Officer)

NEWREGEN, INC.
2400 Boston Str, Baltimore, MD
21224
Tel.: (410) 522-8709　　　**NV**
Web Site: https://www.newregen.com
Year Founded: 2010
NREG—(OTCIQ)
Liabilities: $755,931
Net Worth: ($755,931)
Earnings: ($109,423)
Fiscal Year-end: 01/31/19
Investment Holding Company; Anti-
Aging & regenerative Medical Treat-
ment Services
N.A.I.C.S.: 551112

NEWRON SPORT
1333 N Buffalo Dr Ste 210, Las Ve-
gas, NV 89128
Tel.: (424) 358-1046　　　**NV**
Year Founded: 2003
NSPT—(OTCIQ)
Sports Product Mfr & Distr
N.A.I.C.S.: 339920

Frank Lkechukwu Igwealor (Pres,
CEO, Treas & Sec)

NEWS CORPORATION
1211 Ave of the Americas, New York,
NY 10036
Tel.: (212) 416-3400　　　**DE**
Web Site: https://www.newscorp.com
Year Founded: 2013
NWS—(NASDAQ)
Rev.: $10,085,000,000
Assets: $16,684,000,000
Liabilities: $7,673,000,000
Net Worth: $9,011,000,000
Earnings: $354,000,000
Emp.: 23,900
Fiscal Year-end: 06/30/24
Holding Company; Newspaper,
Magazine & Book Publishing & News
Syndication Services
N.A.I.C.S.: 551112
Lachlan Keith Murdoch (Co-Chm)
Keith Rupert Murdoch (Co-Exec
Chm)
James E. Kennedy (Chief Comm Offi-
cer & Exec VP)
Anoushka Healy (Chief Strategy Offi-
cer & Exec VP)
David B. Pitofsky (Chief Compliance
Officer, Gen Counsel & Exec VP)
Michael Miller (Chm-Australasia)
Susan Panuccio (CFO)
David Kline (CTO & Exec VP)
Michael Florin (Sr VP & Head-IR)
Marygrace DeGrazio (Chief Acctg
Officer)
Lachlan Keith Murdoch (Chm)

Subsidiaries:

1Form Online Pty Ltd **(1)**
Po Box 269, Prahran, 3181, VIC, Australia
Tel.: (61) 395211118
Newspaper Publishing Services
N.A.I.C.S.: 513110

Amplify Education, Inc. **(1)**
55 Washington St Ste 800, Brooklyn, NY
11201-1071
Tel.: (212) 213-8177
Web Site: http://amplify.com
Software Publishing Services
N.A.I.C.S.: 513210
Larry Berger (Founder & CEO)
Richard Morris (Sr VP-Fin)
Krista Curran (Sr VP & Gen Mgr-
Assessment & Intervention)
Aaron Harnly (CTO)
Pam Kirby (Sr VP-Partner Success)
Catherine Mackay (Pres & COO)
Nathan Potter (Sr VP-Engrg)
Rita Schaefer (Sr VP-Sls)
John Stewart (Sr VP-Res & Measurement)
Melissa Ulan (Sr VP & Gen Mgr-
Supplementals)
Adam Zalisk (Sr VP-Corp Strategy)
Steven Zavari (Sr VP & Gen Mgr-STEM
Curriculum)

Barrington Stoke Limited **(1)**
18 Walker Street, Edinburgh, EH3 7LP,
United Kingdom
Tel.: (44) 1312254113
Web Site: https://www.barringtonstoke.co.uk
Children Book Publisher
N.A.I.C.S.: 513130

Business Spectator Pty Ltd **(1)**
22 William Street, Melbourne, 3000, VIC,
Australia
Tel.: (61) 386243000
Internet Publishing Services
N.A.I.C.S.: 513199

Cider Mill Press Book Publishers
LLC **(1)**
501 Nelson Pl, Nashville, TN 37214
Web Site: https://www.cidermillpress.com
Cookbook & Classic Children Book Pub-
lisher
N.A.I.C.S.: 513130

Consolidated Media Holdings Pty
Limited **(1)**

Level 2 54 Park Street, Sydney, 2010,
NSW, Australia
Tel.: (61) 292828000
Holding Company
N.A.I.C.S.: 551112

Dow Jones & Company, Inc. **(1)**
1211 Avenue of the Americas, New York,
NY 10036
Tel.: (212) 416-2000
Web Site: https://www.dowjones.com
Sales Range: $1-4.9 Billion
Emp.: 7,400
Business Information Services & News Pub-
lisher
N.A.I.C.S.: 513110
Almar Latour (CEO)
Christina Van Tassell (CFO)
Ramin Beheshti (Chief Product & Tech Offi-
cer)
Jason Conti (Chief Compliance Officer, Gen
Counsel & Exec VP)
Daniel Bernard (Chief Experience Officer)
Dianne Desevo (Chief People Officer)

Subsidiary (Domestic):

Barron's **(2)**
4300 US Rte 1 N, Monmouth Junction, NJ
08852
Tel.: (212) 597-5975
Web Site: http://www.barronsmag.com
Business & Financial Publication Services
N.A.I.C.S.: 513120

Subsidiary (Non-US):

Dow Jones Canada, Inc. **(2)**
22 Adelaide St West Suite 4210, Toronto,
M5H 4E3, ON, Canada
Tel.: (416) 306-2100
Information Services
N.A.I.C.S.: 519290

Group (Domestic):

Dow Jones Enterprise Media **(2)**
1211 Ave of the Americas, New York, NY
10036
Tel.: (212) 416-2000
Web Site:
http://www.solutions.dowjones.com
Sales Range: $50-74.9 Million
Business Information Services
N.A.I.C.S.: 519290

Unit (Domestic):

Dow Jones Business & Relationship
Intelligence **(3)**
1100 Winter St Ste 4800, Waltham, MA
02451-1461
Tel.: (978) 823-5260
Web Site: http://www.gonoratoino.com
Sales Range: $50-74.9 Million
Emp.: 55
Relationship-Mapping Technology & Busi-
ness Intelligence Solutions
N.A.I.C.S.: 541511

Co-Headquarters (Non-US):

Dow Jones Business & Relationship
Intelligence Canada **(4)**
33 Prince St Ste 307, Montreal, H3C 2M7,
QC, Canada
Tel.: (514) 877-6197
Web Site: http://www.generateinc.com
Sales Range: $25-49.9 Million
Emp.: 14
Relationship-Mapping Technology & Busi-
ness Intelligence Solutions
N.A.I.O.S.: 541511

Unit (Domestic):

Dow Jones Newswires **(3)**
Harborside Financial Ctr 800 Plz 2, Jersey
City, NJ 07311
Tel.: (201) 938-5400
Web Site: http://www.djnewswires.com
Sales Range: $50-74.9 Million
Emp.: 200
Business, Financial & Political News Ser-
vices
N.A.I.C.S.: 519290
Matt Murray (Editor-in-Chief)

Subsidiary (Non-US):

Dow Jones International Ltd. **(2)**

Avmiral House 66-68 E, Smithfield, London,
E1N 1AW, United Kingdom
Tel.: (44) 2078429600
Web Site: http://www.dowjones.com
Sales Range: $10-24.9 Million
Emp.: 70
Business Information Services
N.A.I.C.S.: 519290

Dow Jones Nederland BV **(2)**
Emerald House Josef Israelskade 48-H,
1072 SB, Amsterdam, Netherlands
Tel.: (31) 8000224414
Emp.: 12
Information Services
N.A.I.C.S.: 519290

Dow Jones News GmbH **(2)**
Tower 185 33/F Friedrich-Ebert-Anlage 35-
37, 60327, Frankfurt, Germany
Tel.: (49) 80003228482
Sales Range: $100-124.9 Million
Emp.: 60
Business Information Services
N.A.I.C.S.: 519290
Guido Schenk (Mng Dir)

Dow Jones Publishing Company
(Asia), Inc. **(2)**
Suite 2501-05 & 08 Central Plaza 18 Har-
bour Road, Wanchai, China (Hong Kong)
Tel.: (852) 800901216
Sales Range: $50-74.9 Million
Emp.: 300
Business & Financial Information Publisher
N.A.I.C.S.: 513110

Subsidiary (Domestic):

The Wall Street Journal Asia **(3)**
25F Central Plz 18 Harbour Rd, Hong
Kong, China (Hong Kong)
Tel.: (852) 25737121
Web Site: http://www.wsj-asia.com
Sales Range: $10-24.9 Million
Emp.: 100
Newspaper Publishers
N.A.I.C.S.: 513110
Andrew Dowell (Editor)

Subsidiary (Domestic):

Generate, Inc. **(2)**
Six Clock Tower Pl Ste 120, Maynard, MA
01754
Tel.: (978) 823-5260
Web Site: http://www.generateinc.com
Marketing Management Services
N.A.I.C.S.: 541613
Tom Aley (Pres & CEO)
Darr Aley (CMO & Exec VP)
Howard Schneider (Sr VP-Tech)
Jeff Bruce (Exec VP-Bus Dev & Strategy)
Jack Crozier (Sr VP-Sls)
Michael J. Lukaszevicz (VP-Data Ops)
Mimi Macksoud (VP-Bus Dev & Strategy)
Rob White (VP-Product Mgmt)
Daniel Lynch (VP-Creative)
Michael Nohaile (Chief Scientific Officer)

MarketWatch, Inc. **(2)**
1211 Avenue of the Americas, New York,
NY 10036
Tel.: (415) 439-6400
Web Site: https://www.marketwatch.com
Sales Range: $25-49.9 Million
Emp.: 206
Online Financial News & Information Ser-
vices
N.A.I.C.S.: 513199
Maddy Perkins (Deputy Editor-Commerce)

Subsidiary (Non-US):

Review Publishing Company
Limited **(2)**
25/F Citicorp Centre 18 Whitfield Rd, GPO
Box 160, Hong Kong, China (Hong Kong)
Tel.: (852) 28322387
Web Site: http://www.feer.com
Sales Range: $50-74.9 Million
Emp.: 150
Business Magazine Publisher
N.A.I.C.S.: 513120

Subsidiary (Domestic):

The Wall Street Journal **(2)**
1211 Ave Americas, New York, NY 10036
Tel.: (212) 416-2000
Web Site: http://www.dowjones.com
Sales Range: $100-124.9 Million
Business Newspaper
N.A.I.C.S.: 513110

Keith Rupert Murdoch *(Chm)*
Almar Latour *(Publr)*
Christopher Matthews *(Deputy Editor-Energy)*
Emma Tucker *(Editor-in-Chief)*
Kimberly Johnson *(Editor-Election Coverage)*

Subsidiary (Non-US):

The Wall Street Journal Europe S.P.R.L. **(3)**
Commodity Quay E Smithfield, E1W 1AZ, London, United Kingdom - England
Tel.: (44) 27411414
Sales Range: $25-49.9 Million
Emp.: 80
Business Newspaper Publisher
N.A.I.C.S.: 513110

FOXTEL Cable Television Pty. Limited **(1)**
5 Thomas Holt Dr, North Ryde, 2113, NSW, Australia **(50%)**
Tel.: (61) 298136000
Web Site: http://www.foxtel.com.au
Cable Television Programming & Distribution
N.A.I.C.S.: 516210

Subsidiary (Domestic):

FOXTEL Management Pty. Ltd. **(2)**
5 Thomas Holt Drive, North Ryde, 2113, NSW, Australia **(65%)**
Tel.: (61) 298136000
Web Site: https://www.foxtel.com.au
Media & Broadcasting Services
N.A.I.C.S.: 516120
Keiren Cooney *(Chief Mktg & Sls Officer)*
Patrick Delany *(CEO)*
Lisa Cronin *(Dir-Customer Mktg & Loyalty)*

Fox Sports Australia Pty Limited **(1)**
4 Broadcast Waya, Artarmon, 2064, NSW, Australia
Tel.: (61) 297762600
Web Site: https://www.foxsports.com.au
Emp.: 400
Television Broadcasting Services
N.A.I.C.S.: 516120

Harlequin Enterprises (Australia) Pty Ltd **(1)**
Tel.: (61) 1300659500
Emp.: 29
Book Publishers
N.A.I.C.S.: 513130

Harlequin Kft. (aka Harlequin Magyarorszag Korlatolt Felelossegu Tarsasag) **(1)**
Fortuna u 21, 1014, Budapest, Hungary
Tel.: (36) 640202112
Web Site: http://www.harlequin.hu
Book Publishers
N.A.I.C.S.: 513130

Harlequin Retail Inc. **(1)**
3010 Walden Ave, Depew, NY 14043
Tel.: (716) 684-1800
Emp.: 190
Book & Newspaper Whslr
N.A.I.C.S.: 424920
Craig Swinwood *(Pres)*

Harlequin S.A. **(1)**
83-85 boulevard Vincent-Auriol, 75646, Paris, Cedex 13, France **(100%)**
Tel.: (33) 142166363
Web Site: http://www.harlequin.fr
Sales Range: $10-24.9 Million
Emp.: 60
Book Publishers
N.A.I.C.S.: 513130
Emmanuelle Bucco-Cances *(Mng Dir)*

HarperCollins (UK) **(1)**
The News Building 1 London Bridge Street, London, SE1 9GF, United Kingdom
Tel.: (44) 2087417070
Web Site: http://www.harpercollins.co.uk
Emp.: 500
Holding Company; Book Publisher
N.A.I.C.S.: 551112
Charlie Redmayne *(CEO)*
Simon Dowson-Collins *(Gen Counsel & Sec)*
John Athanasiou *(Dir-People)*

Anna Derkacz *(Grp Dir-Sls)*
David Alford *(CFO)*
Fiona Allen *(Dir-Comm)*

Subsidiary (Non-US):

HarperCollins Canada Limited **(2)**
22 Adelaide Street W 41st Floor, Toronto, M5H 4E3, ON, Canada
Tel.: (416) 975-9334
Web Site: http://www.harpercollins.ca
Television Broadcasting Services
N.A.I.C.S.: 516120

Subsidiary (Domestic):

HarperCollins Publishers Ltd **(3)**
1995 Markham Rd, Scarborough, M1B 5M8, ON, Canada
Tel.: (416) 321-2241
Web Site: http://www.harpercollins.com
Books Publishing Services
N.A.I.C.S.: 513130

Subsidiary (Non-US):

HarperCollins Publishers (Holdings) Pty. Limited **(3)**
L 13 201 Elizabeth St, Sydney, 2000, NSW, Australia
Tel.: (61) 299525000
Books Publishing Services
N.A.I.C.S.: 513130

HarperCollins Publishers Australia Pty. Limited **(2)**
Lvl 13 201 Elizabeth Street, Sydney, 2000, NSW, Australia
Tel.: (61) 299525000
Web Site: http://www.harpercollins.com.au
Books Publishing Services
N.A.I.C.S.: 513130

Subsidiary (Domestic):

HarperCollins Publishers Limited **(2)**
103 Westerhill Road, Bishopbriggs, Glasgow, G64 2QT, United Kingdom
Tel.: (44) 1413063100
Web Site: https://www.harpercollins.co.uk
Book Publishers
N.A.I.C.S.: 513130
Charlie Redmayne *(CEO)*
John Athanasiou *(Dir-People)*
Kate Elton *(Mng Dir-Fiction, Non-Fiction & Avon)*
Alvar Jover *(Dir-Growth & Analytics)*
Anna Derkacz *(Grp Dir-Sls)*
Fiona Allen *(Dir-Comm)*
David Alford *(CFO)*
Gordon Scott *(Mng Dir)*
Alex Beecroft *(Mng Dir)*

Division (Domestic):

Collins Learning **(3)**
Westerhill Road Bishopbriggs, Glasgow, G64 2QT, United Kingdom
Tel.: (44) 1539565921
Web Site: http://www.collins.co.uk
Emp.: 100
Educational Book Publisher
N.A.I.C.S.: 513130
Sheena Barclay *(Deputy Mng Dir)*

HarperCollins Christian Publishing, Inc. **(1)**
PO Box 141000, Nashville, TN 37214
Tel.: (615) 902-1855
Web Site:
	https://www.harpercollinschristian.com
Book Publishers
N.A.I.C.S.: 513130
Mark Schoenwald *(Pres & CEO)*
Michael Aulisio *(VP-Mktg-Children's & Gift Grp)*

HarperCollins Publishers India Limited **(1)**
4th Cyber City Building No 10 Tower A, Gurgaon, 122002, Haryana, India
Tel.: (91) 1244894800
Web Site: https://www.harpercollins.co.in
Book Publishers
N.A.I.C.S.: 513130
Ananth Padmanabhan *(CEO)*
Amit Abrol *(CFO)*

Intel-Assess, Inc. **(1)**

1032 Irving St Ste 445, San Francisco, CA 94122-2200
Tel.: (415) 279-2822
Educational Support Services
N.A.I.C.S.: 611710

Kidspot.com.au Pty Limited **(1)**
Level 5 HWT Tower 40 City Rd, Southbank, 3006, VIC, Australia
Tel.: (61) 1300724575
Internet Publishing Services
N.A.I.C.S.: 513199

Leckie & Leckie Limited **(1)**
Dipford House Queens Square Business Park Huddersfield Road Honley, Holmfirth, HD9 6QZ, United Kingdom
Tel.: (44) 8445768126
Web Site: http://www.leckieandleckie.co.uk
Book Publishers
N.A.I.C.S.: 513130

Makaan.com Private Limited **(1)**
Plot No 25, Institutional Area Sector-32, Gurgaon, 122001, India
Tel.: (91) 8899939993
Web Site: http://www.makaan.com
Real Estate Rental Services
N.A.I.C.S.: 531110
Dhruv Agarwala *(CEO)*
Anand Thakur *(CTO)*
Mani Rangarajan *(COO)*
Rohit Hasteer *(Chief HR Officer)*
Vikas Wadhawan *(CFO)*

Move, Inc. **(1)**
3315 Scott Blvd Ste 250, Santa Clara, CA 95054
Web Site: https://www.move.com
Holding Company; Internet Real Estate Trading Platform Developer, Operator & Services
N.A.I.C.S.: 551112
Bryan Charap *(CEO)*
Janice McDill *(VP-Corp Comm)*
Tricia Smith *(Sr VP-Sls & Ops)*
Andrew von Rosenbach-Torbeke *(Head-Delivery)*
Anne Hunt *(VP-Product Mgmt)*
Sheewon Bak *(VP-Fin)*
Michael Lam *(COO)*
Bob Evans *(VP-Industry Rels, Corp Dev & Strategy)*
Brandon Seiter *(VP-Corp Dev)*
Brett Collinson *(VP-Product Mgmt)*
Chris Patalano *(CTO)*
Debbie Neuberger *(Sr VP-Customer Care & Product Mgmt)*
Enoch Chen *(Sr VP-Product Mgmt & Emerging Markets)*
Erin Mesick *(VP-Strategy & Ops)*
Greg Taylor *(Sr VP-Performance Mktg & Media Buying)*
Hani Durzy *(VP-Comm, Economics, News & Insights)*
Ivi Ahuja *(VP-Strategic Partnerships)*
James Martin *(Sr Dir-Engrg & Property Content)*
Jamie Sampson *(Sr VP-Sls & Customer Success)*
Jason Goldberg *(VP-Engrg)*
Kat Koutsantonis *(Chief People Officer)*
Jenna Klebanoff *(VP-Mktg, CRM & Consumer Engagement)*
Joe Teitelman *(VP-Strategic Performance)*
Jonathan Carroll *(VP-Design)*
Kate Teich *(VP-Product Mgmt)*
Mausam Bhatt *(Chief Product Officer)*
Damian Eales *(CEO)*

Subsidiary (Domestic):

Moving.com, Inc. **(2)**
5401 N Pima Rd Ste 100, Scottsdale, AZ 85250
Web Site: http://www.moving.com
Household & Office Goods Moving Services
N.A.I.C.S.: 484210

Rentalutions, Inc. **(2)**
900 N Franklin St Ste 404, Chicago, IL 60610
Tel.: (312) 292-9347
Web Site: http://www.avail.co
Custom Computer Programming Services
N.A.I.C.S.: 541511
Laurence Jankelow *(Co-Founder)*

Subsidiary (Non-US):

The Hessel Group Limited **(2)**

Croham House Croham Road, Crowborough, TN6 2RW, E Sussex, United Kingdom
Tel.: (44) 1892669901
Web Site: http://www.hessel.co.uk
Management Consulting Services
N.A.I.C.S.: 541611
Geoff Davidson *(Dir-Technical)*
David Rowson *(Dir-Client Svcs)*
James Bodkin *(Mgr)*

Subsidiary (Domestic):

UpNest, Inc. **(2)**
5401 N Pima Rd Ste 100, Scottsdale, AZ 85250
Web Site: https://www.upnest.com
Sales Range: $10-24.9 Million
Emp.: 31
Real Estate Agency Services
N.A.I.C.S.: 531210
Simon Ru *(Founder & CEO)*
Rachel Newlin *(Mgr-Ops & Acctg)*
Rickey Griffey *(Dir-Client Svcs)*
Desmond Choi *(Product Mgr)*

NC Transaction, Inc. **(1)**
1211 Ave of the Americas, New York, NY 10036
Tel.: (212) 416-3400
Internet Publishing Services
N.A.I.C.S.: 513199
Robert Thompson *(CEO)*

NEWS LIMITED **(1)**
61-81 Kippax St, Surry Hills, 2010, NSW, Australia
Tel.: (61) 292883000
Web Site: http://www.news.com.au
Information Services
N.A.I.C.S.: 519290
Matt Deighton *(Editor-The Mercury)*
Michael Miller *(Chm)*

Subsidiary (Domestic):

Australian News Channel Pty. Ltd. **(2)**
Locked Bag 918, North Sydney, 2059, NSW, Australia
Tel.: (61) 298868000
Web Site: https://www.skynews.com.au
Internet Publishing & Broadcasting Services
N.A.I.C.S.: 516210

Foxtel Australia Pty Limited **(2)**
5 Thomas Holt Drive, North Ryde, 2113, NSW, Australia
Tel.: (61) 298136000
Web Site: http://www.foxtel.com.au
Internet Publishing & Broadcasting Services
N.A.I.C.S.: 516210

Subsidiary (Non-US):

GoHome H.K. Co. Ltd. **(2)**
15/F MassMutual Tower No 33 Lockhart Road, Wanchai, China (Hong Kong)
Tel.: (852) 31981818
Real Estate Services
N.A.I.C.S.: 531390

Subsidiary (Domestic):

NOVII Pty. Ltd. **(2)**
Suite 406 2 Grosvenor St, Bondi Junction, 2022, NSW, Australia
Tel.: (61) 293311333
Web Site: http://www.novii.com.au
Software Development Services
N.A.I.C.S.: 513210

News Corp Australia Pty. Limited **(2)**
2 Holt St, Surry Hills, 2010, NSW, Australia
Tel.: (61) 292883000
Web Site:
	https://www.newscorpaustralia.com
Newspaper Publishing Services
N.A.I.C.S.: 513110
Damian Eales *(COO-Publ)*

Subsidiary (Domestic):

Courier Newspaper Holdings Pty Limited **(3)**
142-154 Macquarie St, Parramatta, 2150, NSW, Australia
Tel.: (61) 296895500
Newspaper Publishing Services
N.A.I.C.S.: 513110
John Webstar *(Gen Mgr)*

News Corporation—(Continued)

Geelong Advertiser (3)
191 Ryrie St, PO Box 91, Geelong, 3220,
VIC, Australia
Tel.: (61) 352274300
Web Site:
http://www.geelongadvertiser.com.au
Sales Range: $25-49.9 Million
Emp.: 90
Newspaper Publishers
N.A.I.C.S.: 513110
Peter Farago *(Editor-Real Estate)*
Alex Oates *(Editor-Sports)*
Sarah Bieske *(Editor-Magazines & Lifestyle)*

**Gold Coast Publications Pty.
Limited** (3)
12-14 Marine Parade, Southport, 4214,
QLD, Australia
Tel.: (61) 755842000
Web Site:
http://www.goldcoastbulletin.com.au
Periodical Publishing Services
N.A.I.C.S.: 513120

HomeGuru Pty Ltd. (3)
Level 17 309 Kent St, Sydney, 2000, NSW,
Australia
Tel.: (61) 293311333
Web Site: http://www.homeguru.com.au
Emp.: 50
Information Services
N.A.I.C.S.: 519290

Hub Online Global Pty. Ltd (3)
29 Kent Street, Deakin, Canberra, 2600,
ACT, Australia
Tel.: (61) 1300793341
Television Broadcasting Services
N.A.I.C.S.: 516120

**Leader Associated Newspapers Pty.
Limited** (3)
1 Chapel St, Blackburn, 3130, VIC, Austra-
lia
Tel.: (61) 398758333
Television Broadcasting Services
N.A.I.C.S.: 516120
Fiona Mellor *(Gen Mgr)*

Nationwide News Pty. Limited (3)
61-81 Kippax St, Surry Hills, 2010, NSW,
Australia
Tel.: (61) 292883000
Web Site: http://www.news.com.au
Emp.: 1,500
Newspaper & Electronic Newsletter Publish-
ing Services
N.A.I.C.S.: 513110

Subsidiary (Domestic):

Brisbane Broncos Limited (4)
Clive Berghofer Centre 81 Fulcher Road,
Brisbane, 4059, QLD, Australia (68.87%)
Tel.: (61) 738589111
Web Site: https://www.broncos.com.au
Rev.: $51,226,561
Assets: $39,675,061
Liabilities: $10,019,867
Net Worth: $29,655,194
Earnings: $3,836,110
Fiscal Year-end: 12/31/2023
Holding Company; Professional Rugby
Team Owner & Operator
N.A.I.C.S.: 551112
Louise Anna Lanigan *(Sec & Mgr-Salary
Cap)*
Paul M. White *(CEO)*
Shirley A. Moro *(CFO)*
Belinda Findlay *(Mgr-Membership-
Merchandise)*
Karl D. Morris *(Chm)*
Christine Halliwell *(Gen Mgr-Community &
Govt Programs)*
Tain Drinkwater *(Gen Mgr-Human
Resources-Risk)*
Steele Tallon *(Gen Mgr-Communications-
Media)*
Dan Glass *(Exec Mgr-Sales)*
Peter Nolan *(Gen Mgr)*
Dave Donaghy *(CEO)*
Matt Friend *(CFO)*
Ben Ikin *(Dir)*
Kate Cullen *(Gen Mgr-People)*
Dave Donaghy *(CEO)*
Matt Friend *(CFO)*
Ben Ikin *(Dir)*
Kate Cullen *(Gen Mgr-People)*

Dave Donaghy *(CEO)*
Matt Friend *(CFO)*
Ben Ikin *(Dir)*
Kate Cullen *(Gen Mgr-People)*

Subsidiary (Domestic):

**Brisbane Broncos Management Cor-
poration Pty. Ltd.** (5)
Level 1 92 Fulcher Road, Red Hill, Bris-
bane, 4059, QLD, Australia
Tel.: (61) 738589111
Web Site: http://www.broncos.com.au
Emp.: 150
Office Administrative Services
N.A.I.C.S.: 561110

**Brisbane Broncos Rugby League
Club Pty. Ltd.** (5)
Level 1 92 Fulcher Road, Red Hill, Bris-
bane, 4059, QLD, Australia
Tel.: (61) 738589111
Web Site: http://www.broncos.com.au
Emp.: 150
Professional Rugby Sports Team
N.A.I.C.S.: 711211

Subsidiary (Domestic):

The Herald & Weekly Times Ltd. (3)
HWT Tower 40 City Rd, Southbank, 3006,
Australia (100%)
Tel.: (61) 392922000
Web Site: http://www.heraldfun.com.au
Sales Range: $50-74.9 Million
Emp.: 250
Newspapers
N.A.I.C.S.: 513110
Tamara Oppen *(Mng Dir-GoDaddy)*

**The Herald and Weekly Times Pty.
Limited** (3)
40 City Rd, Southbank, 3006, VIC, Australia
Tel.: (61) 392922000
Web Site: http://www.heraldson.com.au
Sales Range: $200-249.9 Million
Emp.: 1,200
Television Broadcasting Services
N.A.I.C.S.: 516120
Shannon Deery *(Editor-State Politics)*
John Masanauskas *(Editor-City)*
Tom Minear *(Editor-Natl Political-Canberra
Bureau)*
Nathaniel Bane *(Head-Digital News)*
Joel Cresswell *(Editor-Digital)*
Dimity Barber *(Head-Content)*
Shaun Campbell *(Editor-Digital)*
Blair Corless *(Editor)*
Paul Amy *(Editor-Sports)*
Ashley Argoon *(Editor-Education)*
Alice Coster *(Editor-Page 13)*
Matthew Johnston *(Editor-State Political)*
Nui Te Koha *(Head-Lifestyle)*
Samantha Landy *(Editor-Real Estate News)*
Grant McArthur *(Editor-Health)*
Michelle Rose *(Editor-Digital & Partner-
ships)*
Sam Weir *(Editor)*
Fiona Welsh *(Editor-Magazines & Partner-
ships)*

Subsidiary (Domestic):

Punters Paradise Pty Limited (2)
Level 6 259 Collins Street, Melbourne,
3000, VIC, Australia
Tel.: (61) 1300696397
Web Site: https://www.punters.com.au
Internet Publishing Services
N.A.I.C.S.: 513199
David Hocking *(Editor-Content)*

Subsidiary (Non-US):

Smart Expo Limited (2)
15/F MassMutual Tower No 33 Lockhart
Road, Wanchai, China (Hong Kong)
Tel.: (852) 31981818
Web Site: http://www.smartexpos.com
Investment Management Service
N.A.I.C.S.: 523940

Subsidiary (Domestic):

Smartline Home Loans Pty. Ltd. (2)
Level 2 2 Lyonpark Road, North Ryde,
2113, NSW, Australia
Tel.: (61) 298554200
Web Site: http://www.smartline.com.au
Investment Services

**The South China Morning Post Pub-
lishers Ltd.** (2)
Morning Post Ctr 22 Baisat St, Taipo Indus-
traial Estate New T, Tai Po, China (Hong
Kong) (100%)
Tel.: (852) 25652222
Web Site: http://www.scmpgroup.com
Sales Range: $300-349.9 Million
Emp.: 1,000
Newspapers
N.A.I.C.S.: 513110
Gary Liu *(CEO)*
Elsie Hoi Sze Cheung *(COO)*
Romanus Ng *(Sr VP-Adv & Mktg Solutions)*
Brian Rhoads *(Mng Editor)*
Chung-yan Chow *(Exec Editor)*
Tammy Wai Yi Tam *(Editor-in-Chief)*

Subsidiary (Domestic):

iProperty.com Pty. Ltd. (2)
138 Hall Street, PO Box 2020, Spotswood,
3015, Australia
Tel.: (61) 800432742
Web Site: http://www.iproperty.com.au
Real Estate Services
N.A.I.C.S.: 531390

Subsidiary (Non-US):

iProperty.com Singapore Pte. Ltd (2)
360 Orchard Road 03-05/10 International
Building, Singapore, 238869, Singapore
Tel.: (65) 62554411
Web Site: http://www.iproperty.com.sg
Real Estate Services
N.A.I.C.S.: 531390

**NTS Technology Services Private
Limited** (1)
7 Service Rd Pragathi Nagar Electronic
City, Bengaluru, 560100, Karnataka, India
Tel.: (91) 8046477999
Web Site:
http://www.newstechnologyservices.com
Software Development Services
N.A.I.C.S.: 541511
Nehal Khadeer *(Dir-HR)*
Mutturaj Chinnappa *(Fin Dir & Gen Mgr-
Ops-Interim)*
S. Ramachandran *(Gen Mgr-Interim & Dir-
Infrastructure)*

**News Corp Investments UK &
Ireland** (1)
1 Virginia Street, London, E1 9XY, United
Kingdom
Tel.: (44) 2077826000
Newspaper & Magazines Whslr
N.A.I.C.S.: 424920

Subsidiary (Domestic):

102.4 Wish FM Limited (2)
Orrell Lodge Orrell Road Orrell, Wigan,
WN5 8HJ, United Kingdom
Tel.: (44) 1942761024
Internet Publishing & Broadcasting Services
N.A.I.C.S.: 516210

Radiowave (Blackpool) Limited (2)
965 Mowbray Drive, Blackpool, FY3 7JR,
Lancashire, United Kingdom
Tel.: (44) 1253650300
Internet Publishing & Broadcasting Services
N.A.I.C.S.: 516210

Signal Radio Limited (2)
Stoke Road, Stoke-on-Trent, ST4 2SR,
United Kingdom
Tel.: (44) 1782441300
Internet Publishing & Broadcasting Services
N.A.I.C.S.: 516210

Subsidiary (Non-US):

Simply Zesty Limited (2)
Macken House 40 Mayor Street Upper,
Dublin, D01 C9W8, Ireland
Tel.: (353) 14792479
Web Site: http://www.simplyzesty.com
Advertising Services
N.A.I.C.S.: 541810

Subsidiary (Domestic):

Switchdigital (London) Limited (2)

1 London Bridge Street, London, SE1 9GF,
United Kingdom
Tel.: (44) 2077823177
Web Site: https://www.switchdigital.com
Internet Publishing & Broadcasting Services
N.A.I.C.S.: 516210

U105 Limited (2)
Level 7 City Quays 2 2 Clarendon Rd, Bel-
fast, BT1 3FD, United Kingdom
Tel.: (44) 2890333105
Web Site: https://www.u105.com
Internet Publishing & Broadcasting Services
N.A.I.C.S.: 516210

News Corp UK & Ireland Limited (1)
The News Building 1 London Bridge Street,
London, SE1 9GF, United Kingdom
Tel.: (44) 2077821010
Web Site: https://www.news.co.uk
Emp.: 10
News Syndication Services
N.A.I.C.S.: 516210
Angus McBride *(Gen Counsel)*
Rebekah Brooks *(CEO)*
David Dinsmore *(COO)*
Shelley Bishton *(Head-Creative Diversity)*

Subsidiary (Domestic):

Wireless Group Limited (2)
Ormeau Road, Belfast, BT7 1EB, United
Kingdom
Tel.: (44) 2077823000
Web Site: http://www.wirelessgroup.co.uk
Holding Company; Radio & Internet Broad-
casting Services
N.A.I.C.S.: 551112
Scott W. Taunton *(CEO)*
Calum Macaulay *(Gen Mgr)*
Jimmy Buckland *(Mng Dir-Wireless Studios
& Dir-Strategy)*
Liam Fisher *(Controller-Speech Radio)*
Mike Cass *(Dir-Content)*
Andrew Maybin *(Mng Dir-Digital Svcs)*
Briony Hughes *(Dir-Grp HR)*
Emma Humphreys *(CFO)*

Subsidiary (Non-US):

Capital Radio Productions Ltd (3)
Macken House Mayor Street Upper North
Wall, Dublin, 1, Ireland
Tel.: (353) 16797104
Web Site: https://www.fm104.ie
Radio Broadcasting Network Services
N.A.I.C.S.: 516210
Margaret Nelson *(Dir-Station)*
Sasha Hamrogue *(Head-Digital)*
Mark Noble *(Dir Local Content)*
Owen Harney *(Sls Mgr)*
Alice Higgins *(Mgr-S.P.D.)*

Cork Media Enterprises Limited (3)
Broadcasting House Patricks Place, Cork,
T23 E183, Ireland
Tel.: (353) 214551596
Web Site: http://www.96fm.ie
Radio Broadcasting Services
N.A.I.C.S.: 516110

Radio County Sound Limited (3)
Majestic Business Park Goolds Hill, Mallow,
Cork, Ireland
Tel.: (353) 2242103
Web Site: https://www.c103.ie
Radio Broadcasting Services
N.A.I.C.S.: 516210
Kieran McGeary *(Dir-Station)*

Subsidiary (Domestic):

The Internet Business Limited (3)
Level 7 City Quays Plaza II Clarendon
Dock, Belfast, BT1 3FD, United Kingdom
Tel.: (44) 2890331122
Web Site: https://www.tibus.com
Web Development Services
N.A.I.C.S.: 541511
Andrew Maybin *(Mng Dir)*

Subsidiary (Non-US):

Treaty Radio Limited (3)
Radio House Richmond Court Dock Road,
Limerick, V94 HF51, Ireland
Tel.: (353) 61461900
Web Site: https://www.live95fm.ie
Radio Broadcasting Services
N.A.I.C.S.: 516110

Joe Nash *(Dir-Station)*
Gary Connor *(Controller-Program)*
Julie White *(Mgr-Sls & Mktg)*
Gillian Devlin *(Head-News)*

Subsidiary (Domestic):

talkSPORT Limited (3)
1 London Bridge Street, London, SE1 9GF,
United Kingdom
Tel.: (44) 2077823000
Web Site: https://www.talksport.com
Radio Broadcasting Services
N.A.I.C.S.: 516210
Neil Leather *(Head-Bus Dev)*

News Marketing Canada (1)
3333 Cotezert 2 Suite 405, Saint Laurent,
H4R2N1, QC, Canada   **(100%)**
Tel.: (514) 956-5400
Web Site: http://www.newsamerica.com
Sales Range: $10-24.9 Million
Emp.: 10
Home-Delivery & In-Store Advertising &
Promotion Programs
N.A.I.C.S.: 541613
Charles Custeau *(Mng Dir)*

News UK & Ireland Limited (1)
1 London Bridge Street, London, SE1 9GF,
United Kingdom
Tel.: (44) 2077826000
Web Site: http://www.news.co.uk
Newspaper Publishing Services
N.A.I.C.S.: 513110
Rebekah Brooks *(CEO)*
Emma Humphreys *(CFO)*
Simon Farnsworth *(Chief Tech Officer)*
Sarah Gallo *(Chief People Officer)*

Subsidiary (Domestic):

**News International Newspapers
Limited** (2)
Kitling Road, Prescot, L34 9HN, Mersey-
side, United Kingdom
Tel.: (44) 1515462000
Sales Range: $75-99.9 Million
Emp.: 400
Television Broadcasting Services
N.A.I.C.S.: 516120

Subsidiary (Domestic):

The Sun (3)
The News Bldg 1 Ind Bridge, London,
SE19GF, United Kingdom   **(100%)**
Tel.: (44) 2077824000
Web Site: http://www.news.co.uk
Sales Range: $100-124.9 Million
Newspaper Publishing
N.A.I.C.S.: 513110
Jo Bucci *(Gen Mgr)*

The Sunday Times Limited (3)
The News Building 1 London Bridge Street,
London, SE1 9GF, United Kingdom
Tel.: (44) 2077117888
Television Broadcasting Services
N.A.I.C.S.: 516120
Alan Hunter *(Head-Digital)*
Camilla Cavendish *(Assoc Editor)*
Catherine Newman *(Dir-Mktg & Sls)*
Bongani Siqoko *(Editor)*
Lorraine Candy *(Editor-In-Chief-Style Maga-
zine & Dir-Luxury Content)*
Jon Yeomans *(Deputy Editor-Bus)*

Times Newspapers Ltd. (3)
1 London Bridge Street, London, SE1 9GF,
United Kingdom
Tel.: (44) 2077111527
Web Site: http://www.thetimes.co.uk
Sales Range: $100-124.9 Million
Publisher of Newspapers
N.A.I.C.S.: 513110

**Oil Price Information Service
LLC** (1)
9841 Washingtonian Blvd 5th Fl, Gaithers-
burg, MD 20878
Tel.: (301) 284-2000
Web Site: https://www.opisnet.com
Petroleum Information, Products & Prices
N.A.I.C.S.: 513140
Fred Rozell *(Pres)*
Tom Kloza *(Head-Energy Analysis-Global)*
Linda Herbert *(COO)*
Michael Sinsky *(CIO)*
Steve Tan *(VP-Strategic Content)*
Lindsey Bernard *(Exec Dir-Sls)*

PBL Management Pty Limited (1)
1st Flr 24 Artarmon Rd, Willoughby, 2068,
NSW, Australia
Tel.: (61) 299069999
Management Consulting Services
N.A.I.C.S.: 541611

Pavilion Books Company Limited (1)
The News Building 1 London Bridge St,
London, SE1 9GF, United Kingdom
Tel.: (44) 2087417070
Web Site: https://www.pavilionbooks.com
Books Publishing Services
N.A.I.C.S.: 513130

REA Austin Pty Ltd. (1)
Ground Floor 678 Victoria Street, Rich-
mond, 3121, VIC, Australia
Tel.: (61) 398971121
Newspaper Publishing Services
N.A.I.C.S.: 513110

REA Group Limited (1)
511 Church Street, Richmond, 3121, VIC,
Australia   **(61.6%)**
Tel.: (61) 1300853440
Web Site: https://www.rea-group.com
Rev.: $888,933,638
Assets: $1,968,188,872
Liabilities: $923,642,045
Net Worth: $1,044,546,827
Earnings: $284,792,823
Emp.: 3,100
Fiscal Year-end: 06/30/2022
Real Estate Mktg
N.A.I.C.S.: 237210
Hamish McLennan *(Chm)*
Henry Ruiz *(Chief Strategy & Customer
Product Officer)*
Janelle Hopkins *(CFO & CEO-Financial
Services)*
Owen Wilson *(CEO)*
Kul Singh *(Chief Customer Officer)*
Tamara Kayser *(Chief Legal Officer, Gen
Counsel & Sec)*
Anthony Waldron *(CFO-Financial Services)*
Steve Maidment *(CTO)*
Elisa Nerone *(Chief People Officer & Chief
Sustainability Officer)*

Subsidiary (Domestic):

Mortgage Choice Limited (2)
Level 10 100 Pacific Highway, North Syd-
ney, 2060, NSW, Australia
Tel.: (61) 137762
Web Site:
    https://www.mortgagechoice.com.au
Rev.: $124,719,583
Assets: $286,361,029
Liabilities: $225,543,751
Net Worth: $60,817,278
Earnings: $9,650,991
Emp.: 90
Fiscal Year-end: 06/30/2019
Mortgage Services
N.A.I.C.S.: 522310
Neill C. Rose-Innes *(Gen Mgr-Distr)*
Susan R. Mitchell *(CEO)*
Melissa J. McCarney *(Gen Mgr-Mktg)*
Emma A. Dupont-Brown *(Gen Mgr-Product
& Corp Comm)*
Tania J. Milnes *(Gen Mgr-Fin Plng)*
Ian Parkes *(CFO & Sec)*
Marie J. Pitton *(Gen Mgr-HR)*
Vincent C. Ten Krooden *(Gen Mgr-Tech)*
Dean Thomas *(Chief Advice Officer)*

Subsidiary (Domestic):

FinChoice Pty Limited (3)
Level 10 100 Pacific Highway, North Syd-
ney, 2060, NSW, Australia
Tel.: (61) 136674
Web Site: http://www.finchoice.com.au
Financial Investment Services
N.A.I.C.S.: 523940

Subsidiary (Non-US):

iProperty Group Limited (2)
Suite 11.01 Level 11 Menara IGB Mid Valley
City, Lingkaran Syed Putra, 59200, Kuala
Lumpur, Malaysia
Tel.: (60) 322646888
Web Site: http://www.iproperty-group.com
Online Real Estate Services
N.A.I.C.S.: 513140

Subsidiary (Domestic):

realestate.com.au Pty Ltd (2)

511 Church Street, Richmond, 3121, VIC,
Australia   **(100%)**
Tel.: (61) 1300853440
Web Site: https://www.realestate.com.au
Real Estate Services
N.A.I.C.S.: 531210

Subsidiary (Domestic):

Hometrack Australia Pty Limited (3)
Level 17 309 Kent Street, Sydney, 2000,
NSW, Australia
Tel.: (61) 282571100
Web Site: http://www.hometrack.com.au
Real Estate Development Services
N.A.I.C.S.: 531390

REA India Pte. Ltd. (1)
419 Nota One Tower-C 4Th Floor Block-B
Plot No-8 Sector-62, Noida, 201301, Uttar
Pradesh, India
Tel.: (91) 9953039482
Web Site: https://reaindia.net
Conveyor Belts Mfr
N.A.I.C.S.: 333922

ReadyConnect Concierge (1)
6800 Burleson Rd Bldg 312 Ste 125, Aus-
tin, TX 78744
Web Site: http://www.opcity.com
Real Estate Brokerage Services
N.A.I.C.S.: 531210
Ben Rubenstein *(Co-Founder)*
Michael Lam *(Co-Founder)*

Story(ation) Pty Limited (1)
Level 1 83 Bowman St, Pyrmont, 2009,
NSW, Australia
Tel.: (61) 286078502
Web Site: https://www.storyation.com
Media Marketing Services
N.A.I.C.S.: 541613
Arizona Atkinson *(Sr Mgr-Content)*
Blaise Curran *(Art Dir)*

**The Geelong Advertiser Pty.
Limited** (1)
126 Little Malop Street, Geelong, 3220,
VIC, Australia
Tel.: (61) 352274300
Web Site:
    http://www.geelongadvertiser.com.au
Internet Publishing Services
N.A.I.C.S.: 513199

The Sun US, Inc. (1)
1211 Avenue of the Americas, New York,
NY 10036
Tel.: (212) 416-4552
Web Site: http://www.the-sun.com
Media Marketing Services
N.A.I.C.S.: 541613

**Verlagsgruppe HarperCollins
Deutschland GmbH** (1)
Valentinskamp 24, 20354, Hamburg, Ger-
many
Tel.: (49) 4063664200
Web Site: https://www.harpercollins.de
Emp.: 60
Books Publishing Services
N.A.I.C.S.: 513130

**Visual Domain Australia Pty
Limited** (1)
Wurundjeri Country Level 11 40 City Road,
Southbank, 3006, VIC, Australia
Tel.: (61) 1300040718
Web Site: https://www.visualdomain.com.au
Video Production Services
N.A.I.C.S.: 512110

iProperty.com Malaysia Sdn Bhd (1)
Suite 35 01 Level 35 The Gardens South
Tower, Mid Valley City Lingkaran Syed Pu-
tra, 59200, Kuala Lumpur, Malaysia
Tel.: (60) 364195188
Web Site: https://www.iproperty.com.my
Property Management & Rental Services
N.A.I.C.S.: 531190

NEWTEKONE, INC.
4800 T Rex Ave Ste 120, Boca Ra-
ton, FL 33431
Tel.: (212) 356-9500   MD
Web Site:
    https://www.newtekone.com
Year Founded: 1999

NEWT—(NASDAQ)
Rev.: $86,244,000
Assets: $998,902,000
Liabilities: $623,544,000
Net Worth: $375,358,000
Earnings: ($6,476,000)
Emp.: 104
Fiscal Year-end: 12/31/22
All Other Business Support Services
N.A.I.C.S.: 561499
Frank M. DeMaria *(Chief Acctg Offi-
cer & Exec VP)*
Barry Sloane *(Chm, Pres & CEO)*
Nicholas J. Leger *(Treas & Sr VP)*
Halli Razon-Feingold *(Chief Admin
Officer & Sr VP-HR)*
M. Scott Price *(CFO)*

Subsidiaries:

**Advanced Cyber Security Systems,
LLC** (1)
3880 Veterans Memorial Hwy, Bohemia, NY
11716
Tel.: (631) 589-6299
Data Processing & Management Services
N.A.I.C.S.: 518210

National Bank of New York City (1)
13629 38th Ave, Flushing, NY 11354
Tel.: (718) 358-4400
Web Site: http://www.nbnyc.com
Rev.: $8,000,000
Emp.: 30
Commercial Banking Services
N.A.I.C.S.: 522110
Ellen Alderdice *(Sr VP)*

**Newtek Small Business Finance,
Inc.** (1)
212 W 35th St 2nd Fl, New York, NY 10001
Tel.: (212) 356-9510
Mortgage & Nonmortgage Loan Brokers
N.A.I.C.S.: 522310

**Summit Systems and Design,
LLC** (1)
301 Mexico Blvd Ste H4A, Brownsville, TX
78520
Tel.: (956) 982-7000
Web Site: http://www.thesba.com
Sales Range: $25-49.9 Million
Emp.: 60
Financial Planning Services
N.A.I.C.S.: 523940

Wilshire Holdings I, Inc. (1)
1440 Broadway 17th Fl, New York, NY
10018-2317
Tel.: (212) 356-9500
Investment Management Service
N.A.I.C.S.: 523940

NEWYOU, INC.
6351 Yarrow Dr Ste E, Carlsbad, CA
92011
Tel.: (561) 420-0380   NV
Year Founded: 2005
NWYU—(OTCIQ)
Rev.: $2,008,493
Assets: $197,088
Liabilities: $2,724,299
Net Worth: ($2,527,211)
Earnings: ($5,046,711)
Emp.: 5
Fiscal Year-end: 12/31/20
Cosmetic & Healthcare Products Mfr
N.A.I.C.S.: 325412
Greg Montoya *(Pres)*
James Sinkes *(Chief Acctg Officer)*
John Driscoll *(CFO)*
Ray Grimm Jr. *(CEO)*

NEXALIN TECHNOLOGY, INC.
1776 Yorktown St Ste 550, Houston,
TX 77056
Tel.: (832) 260-0222   DE
Web Site: https://nexalin.com
Year Founded: 2010
NXL—(NASDAQ)
Rev.: $1,321,357
Assets: $7,432,136
Liabilities: $1,953,449

Nexalin Technology, Inc.—(Continued)

Net Worth: $5,478,687
Earnings: ($1,697,816)
Emp.: 6
Fiscal Year-end: 12/31/22
Medicinal Product Mfr
N.A.I.C.S.: 339112
Mark White *(Pres & CEO)*
David Owens *(Chief Medical Officer)*
John Patrick Claude *(Founder)*
Joel Bradus *(Dir-Sales-Marketing)*
Marilyn Elson *(Controller)*
Leslie Bernhard *(Chm)*
Sam Namiri *(CFO)*

NEXCORE HEALTHCARE CAPITAL CORP.
1621 18th St Ste 250, Denver, CO 80202
Tel.: (303) 244-0700   CO
Web Site:
  http://www.nexcoregroup.com
Year Founded: 2003
NXCR—(OTCIQ)
Sales Range: $1-9.9 Million
Emp.: 45
Healthcare Real Estate Investment, Consulting, Property Management & Leasing Services
N.A.I.C.S.: 523999
Gregory C. Venn *(Pres & CEO)*
Robert Lawless *(CFO)*
Jarrod Daddis *(Mng Principal)*
Todd Varney *(Mng Principal)*
Tim Oliver *(Dir-Strategic Plng & Dev)*
Justin Pawlak *(VP-Dev)*
Kim Prentice *(Sr VP-Design & Construction)*
Aaron Brewster *(VP-Design & Construction)*
Ed Christen *(Exec VP-Fin & Acquisitions)*
Debbie Wedderburn *(Dir-Asset Mgmt)*
Amy Andresen *(VP-Leasing)*
Kristen Kelley *(VP-Leasing)*
Greg Hundley *(Gen Counsel & Exec VP)*
Tim Heronimus *(Exec Mng Dir-Transitional Care)*
Steve Christoff *(Sr VP-Bus Dev)*
John Duncan *(Sr VP-Design & Construction)*
Cindy Born-Mylo *(Coord-Project)*
Gaye Bass *(Mgr-Due Diligence)*
Jake Dinnen *(Dir-Leasing)*
Stacey Hall *(VP-Leasing)*
Tracy Hindman *(Dir-Mktg)*
Diana Walker *(Coord-Mktg)*
Nancy Pierzchala *(VP-Asset Mgmt & Leasing)*
Rob Boydston *(VP-Asset Mgmt & Leasing)*
Matt Hittson *(Assoc Mgr-Asset)*
Bryce Durke *(Project Mgr)*
Tony Maestas *(Mgr-Property Ops)*
Louis Martinez *(Asst Mgr-Property)*
Katie McReynolds *(Mgr-Property-Midwest)*
Lisa Perkins *(Mgr-Property-Northeast)*
Rich Klinger *(Mgr-Property-Pacific)*
Cheryl-Ann Weir *(Asst Mgr-Property-Pacific)*
Carol Kenny *(Mgr-Property-West)*
Sandy Johnson *(Asst Mgr-Property-West)*
Rob Beaudo *(Mgr-Mechanical Ops)*
Jake Knutson *(Coord-Mechanical Ops)*
Anne Cassady *(Dir-Acctg & Tax)*
Leslie Baker *(Mgr-Acctg)*
Shirl Gale *(Mgr-Corp Acctg)*
Nathan Kossoff *(Dir-IT)*
Gretchen Oswald *(Mgr-IT & Office Sys)*
Jessica Wooton *(Mgr-Office Coordination)*

Eric Roark *(Exec VP-Design & Construction)*
Vince Cozzi *(COO & Chief Investment Officer)*

NEXGEL, INC.
2150 Cabot Blvd W Ste B, Langhorne, PA 19047
Tel.: (215) 702-8550
Web Site: https://www.nexgel.com
Year Founded: 2010
NXGLW—(NASDAQ)
Rev.: $4,089,000
Assets: $9,955,000
Liabilities: $4,789,000
Net Worth: $5,166,000
Earnings: ($3,188,000)
Emp.: 19
Fiscal Year-end: 12/31/23
Surgical & Medical Instrument Mfr
N.A.I.C.S.: 339112
Adam Levy *(Pres, CEO & Dir)*
Adam E. Drapczuk III *(CFO)*

NEXGEN MINING, INC.
3983 S McCarran Blvd Ste 458, Reno, NV 89502
Tel.: (775) 250-0577   MT
Web Site: https://nxgminc.com
Year Founded: 1888
NXGM—(OTCIQ)
Mineral Exploration Services
N.A.I.C.S.: 213114
Kim Neal *(VP-Finance)*
Marc J. Andrews *(Pres & CEO)*

NEXPOINT DIVERSIFIED REAL ESTATE TRUST
300 Crescent Ct Ste 700, Dallas, TX 75201
Tel.: (214) 276-6300   DE
Web Site: https://nxdt.nexpoint.com
NXDT—(NYSE)
Rev.: $55,130,000
Assets: $1,222,902,000
Liabilities: $205,070,000
Net Worth: $1,017,832,000
Earnings: ($83,883,000)
Fiscal Year-end: 12/31/22
Real Estate Investment Management Services
N.A.I.C.S.: 531390
James David Dondero *(Chm & Pres)*
Brian Dale Mitts *(CFO, Treas, Exec VP-Fin & Asst Sec)*
James Dondero *(Chm & Pres)*
Brian Mitts *(CFO, Treas, Exec VP & Asst Sec)*
Matt McGraner *(Chief Investment Officer, Sec & Exec VP)*
Dennis Sauter Jr. *(Gen Counsel)*
Dustin Norris *(Exec VP)*

NEXPOINT REAL ESTATE FINANCE, INC.
300 Crescent Ct Ste 700, Dallas, TX 75201
Tel.: (214) 276-6300   MD
Web Site:
  https://www.nexpointfinance.com
Year Founded: 2019
NREF—(NYSE)
Rev.: $77,988,000
Assets: $8,154,136,000
Liabilities: $7,705,623,000
Net Worth: $448,513,000
Earnings: $3,234,000
Emp.: 1
Fiscal Year-end: 12/31/22
Real Estate Investment Services
N.A.I.C.S.: 531210
James David Dondero *(Chm & Pres)*
Brian Dale Mitts *(CFO, Treas, Sec & Exec VP-Fin)*
Brian Mitts *(CFO, Treas, Sec & Exec VP-Fin)*

Paul Richards *(VP-Originations & Investments)*
David Willmore *(VP-Finance)*
Matt McGraner *(Chief Investment Officer & Exec VP)*

NEXSCIENT, INC.
2029 Century Park E Ste 400, Los Angeles, CA 90067
Tel.: (310) 494-6620   DE
Web Site: https://nexscient.ai
Year Founded: 2023
NXNT—(OTCQB)
Assets: $124,383
Liabilities: $42,579
Net Worth: $81,804
Earnings: ($937,592)
Emp.: 3
Fiscal Year-end: 06/30/24
Software Development Services
N.A.I.C.S.: 541511

NEXSTAR MEDIA GROUP, INC.
545 E John Carpenter Fwy Ste 700, Irving, TX 75062
Tel.: (972) 373-8800   DE
Web Site: https://www.nexstar.tv
Year Founded: 1996
NXST—(NASDAQ)
Rev.: $4,933,000,000
Assets: $12,078,000,000
Liabilities: $9,765,000,000
Net Worth: $2,313,000,000
Earnings: $346,000,000
Emp.: 11,877
Fiscal Year-end: 12/31/23
Media Streaming Distribution Services
N.A.I.C.S.: 551112
Blake Russell *(Exec VP-Station Ops)*
Perry A. Sook *(Chm & CEO)*
Michael Biard *(Pres & COO)*
Brett E. Jenkins *(CTO & Exec VP)*
Patrick Cusick *(Sr VP & Controller)*
Mike Vaughn *(Sr VP/Reg Mgr-Brdcst Div-Nexstar Media Inc)*
Dana Zimmer *(Pres-Distr & Strategy)*
Gary Weitman *(Chief Comm Officer & Exec VP)*
Susan Tully *(Sr VP-Local Content Dev)*
Charles W. Pautsch *(VP-Labor & Employment Rels)*
Jamie Calandruccio *(Exec VP-Platform Monetization & Strategy)*
Sean Compton *(Pres-Networks)*
Ann Lee Gliha *(CFO & Exec VP)*
Chris Cook *(VP/Gen Mgr-Brdcst & Digital Ops-Nexstar Media Inc)*
Rachel Morgan *(Gen Counsel & Exec VP)*
Michael Strober *(Chief Revenue Officer & Exec VP)*
Kris Kettler *(VP)*
Tammy Phillips *(VP)*
Steven Blanchard *(VP/Gen Mgr-Brdcst & Digital Ops-Virginia)*
Brandin Stewart *(Sr VP/Reg Mgr-Brdcst)*

Subsidiaries:

Nexstar Broadcasting, Inc.   **(1)**
545 E John Carpenter Freeway Ste 700, Irving, TX 75062
Tel.: (972) 373-8800
Web Site: http://www.nexstar.tv
Television Broadcasting Stations Operator
N.A.I.C.S.: 516120
Timothy C. Busch *(Pres)*
Gary Weitman *(Chief Comm Officer & Exec VP)*

Unit (Domestic):

Inergize Digital Media   **(2)**
1600 Utica Ave S Ste 400, Minneapolis, MN 55416
Tel.: (952) 417-3083

Web Site:
  http://www.inergizedigitalmedia.com
Sales Range: $10-24.9 Million
Emp.: 25
Digital Media Services & Television-station
Web Site Development
N.A.I.C.S.: 541511

Internet Broadcasting Systems   **(2)**
355 Randolph Ave Ste 100, Saint Paul, MN 55102
Tel.: (651) 365-4000
Web Site: http://www.ibsys.com
Sales Range: $25-49.9 Million
Emp.: 150
Digital Media Services
N.A.I.C.S.: 541519

KAMR-TV   **(2)**
1015 S Filmore St, Amarillo, TX 79101
Tel.: (806) 383-3321
Web Site: http://www.myhighplains.com
Sales Range: $10-24.9 Million
Emp.: 70
Television Broadcasting Station
N.A.I.C.S.: 516120
Clint Brakebill *(Dir-Sports)*

KCAU-TV   **(2)**
5993 Gordon Dr, Sioux City, IA 51106
Tel.: (712) 277-2345
Web Site: http://www.siouxlandproud.com
Television Broadcasting Station
N.A.I.C.S.: 516120
John Curry *(Gen Mgr)*

KELO-TV   **(2)**
501 S Phillips Ave, Sioux Falls, SD 57105
Tel.: (605) 336-1100
Web Site: http://www.keloland.com
Television Broadcasting Station
N.A.I.C.S.: 516120

KFDX-TV   **(2)**
4500 Seymour Hwy, Wichita Falls, TX 76309
Tel.: (940) 691-0003
Web Site:
  http://www.texomashomepage.com
Sales Range: $10-24.9 Million
Emp.: 80
Television Broadcasting
N.A.I.C.S.: 516120
Wayne Reed *(VP & Gen Mgr)*

KGET-TV   **(2)**
2120 L St, Bakersfield, CA 93301
Tel.: (661) 283-1700
Web Site: https://www.kget.com
Sales Range: $10-24.9 Million
Emp.: 100
Television Broadcasting Station
N.A.I.C.S.: 516120
Michael Tilley *(Dir-News)*
James Galindo *(Gen Mgr-Sls)*
Scott Herrick *(Mgr-Digital Media)*
David Baker *(Chief Engr)*
Taylor Schaub *(Dir-Sports)*
Robert Price *(Mng Editor-Digital)*
Erica Torres *(Asst Dir-News)*

KLAS - TV   **(2)**
3228 Channel 8 Dr, Las Vegas, NV 89109
Tel.: (702) 792-8888
Web Site: https://www.8newsnow.com
Emp.: 80
Television Broadcasting Station
N.A.I.C.S.: 516120

Subsidiary (Domestic):

KLFY, LP   **(2)**
1808 Eraste Landry Rd, Lafayette, LA 70506
Tel.: (337) 262-0800
Web Site: https://www.klfy.com
Television Station
N.A.I.C.S.: 516120

Unit (Domestic):

KREX-TV   **(2)**
345 Hillcrest Dr, Grand Junction, CO 81501
Tel.: (970) 242-5000
Web Site: http://www.krextv.com
Sales Range: $25-49.9 Million
Emp.: 50
Television Broadcasting Station
N.A.I.C.S.: 516120
Kevin McChesney *(Mgr-Sls)*
David Ware *(Mgr-Digital Media)*

KRON-TV (2)
900 Front St 3rd Fl, San Francisco, CA 94111
Tel.: (415) 441-4444
Web Site: https://www.kron4.com
Television Broadcasting Station
N.A.I.C.S.: 516120

Subsidiary (Domestic):

KSEE Television, Inc. (2)
5035 E McKinley Ave, Fresno, CA 93727
Tel.: (559) 222-2411
Web Site: http://www.yourcentralvalley.com
Sales Range: $25-49.9 Million
Emp.: 130
Television Broadcasting Station
N.A.I.C.S.: 516120

Unit (Domestic):

KGPE-TV (3)
5035 E McKinneley Ave, Fresno, CA 93727
Tel.: (559) 222-2411
Web Site: http://www.yourcentralvalley.com
Television Broadcasting Station
N.A.I.C.S.: 516120
Hector G. Bordens (Chief Engr)

Unit (Domestic):

KSNF-TV (2)
1502 S Cleveland Ave, Joplin, MO 64801
Tel.: (417) 781-2345
Web Site:
    http://www.fourstateshomepage.com
Sales Range: $1-9.9 Million
Emp.: 70
Television Broadcasting Station
N.A.I.C.S.: 516120
John Hoffmann (Gen Mgr)
Jerry Martin (Chief Engr)
Bill May (Gen Mgr-Sls)

KSVI-TV (2)
445 S 24th St W, Billings, MT 59102
Tel.: (406) 652-4743
Web Site: http://www.yourbigsky.com
Sales Range: $10-24.9 Million
Emp.: 25
Television Broadcasting Station
N.A.I.C.S.: 516120

KTAB-TV (2)
4510 S 14th, Abilene, TX 79605
Tel.: (325) 692-4242
Web Site:
    http://www.bigcountryhomepage.com
Sales Range: $10-24.9 Million
Emp.: 100
Television Broadcasting Station
N.A.I.C.S.: 516120
David Robinett (Dir-Sports)
Victor Sotelo (Asst Dir-News)
Sari David (Sls Dir)
Albert Gutierrez (VP & Gen Mgr)
Erica Garner (Mgr-Digital Content)

KTAL-TV (2)
3150 N Market St, Shreveport, LA 71107
Tel.: (318) 629-6000
Web Site: https://www.ktalnews.com
Sales Range: $10-24.9 Million
Emp.: 60
Television Broadcasting Station
N.A.I.C.S.: 516120

KTVX-TV (2)
2175 W 1700 S, Salt Lake City, UT 84104-4200
Tel.: (801) 975-4444
Web Site: http://www.good4utah.com
Sales Range: $25-49.9 Million
Emp.: 120
Television Broadcasting Station
N.A.I.C.S.: 516120
Mark Danielson (VP)

KXRM-TV (2)
560 Wooten Rd, Colorado Springs, CO 80915-3524
Tel.: (719) 596-2100
Web Site: https://www.fox21news.com
Television Broadcasting Station
N.A.I.C.S.: 516120
Joe Cole (Dir-News)
Douglas Ducote (Chief Engr)

Subsidiary (Domestic):

LIN Television of Texas, Inc. (2)

908 W Martin Luther King Jr Blvd, Austin, TX 78701-1018
Tel.: (512) 476-3636
Television Broadcasting Stations Operator
N.A.I.C.S.: 516120

Subsidiary (Domestic):

KXAN LLC (3)
908 W Martin Luther King Jr Blvd, Austin, TX 78701
Tel.: (512) 476-3636
Web Site: https://www.kxan.com
Television Station
N.A.I.C.S.: 516120
Eric Lassberg (VP & Gen Mgr)
Chad Cross (Dir-News)
Korey Wisland (Mgr-Production)
Amy Anderson (Sls Dir)
David Cantu (Chief Engr)

Unit (Domestic):

WBRE-TV (2)
62 S Franklin St, Wilkes Barre, PA 18701
Tel.: (570) 823-2828
Web Site: http://www.pahomepage.com
Sales Range: $10-24.9 Million
Emp.: 80
Television Broadcasting Station
N.A.I.C.S.: 516120
Stephanie Cielski (Dir-Sls)
Mark Prutisto (Mgr-Digital Media)
Don Francis (Chief Engr)
Rebecca Stitzer (Dir-Creative Svcs)
Andrew Wyatt (VP & Gen Mgr)
Bill Roesch (Mgr-Local Sls)
Paul Roda (Natl Sls Mgr)

WBTW-TV (2)
101 McDonald Ct, Myrtle Beach, SC 29588
Tel.: (843) 293-1301
Web Site: https://www.wbtw.com
Television Station
N.A.I.C.S.: 516120
Dan Klintworth (Mktg Dir)
Jennifer Wolfe (Chief Engr)
Karen Hutchinson (Supvr-Inventory Control)
Robert Raff (VP)

WCBD-TV (2)
210 W Coleman Blvd, Mount Pleasant, SC 29464
Tel.: (843) 884-2222
Web Site: https://www.counton2.com
Television Broadcasting
N.A.I.C.S.: 516120

WETM-TV (2)
101 E Water St, Elmira, NY 14901
Tel.: (607) 733-5518
Web Site: https://www.mytwintiers.com
Sales Range: $10-24.9 Million
Emp.: 50
Television Broadcasting Station
N.A.I.C.S.: 516120
Steve Lucarelli (Gen Mgr-Sls)
James Carl (Mgr-Digital Media)
Andy Malnoske (Dir-Sports)
Tina Castano (VP)

WFLA-TV (2)
200 S Parker St, Tampa, FL 33606
Tel.: (813) 228-8888
Web Site: https://www.wfla.com
Television Station
N.A.I.C.S.: 516120

Subsidiary (Domestic):

WTTA-TV (3)
200 S Parker St, Tampa, FL 33606
Tel.: (813) 314-5422
Web Site: http://wfla.com
Television Broadcasting Station
N.A.I.C.S.: 516120

Unit (Domestic):

WFRV-TV (2)
1181 E Mason St, Green Bay, WI 54301
Tel.: (920) 437-5411
Web Site: https://www.wearegreenbay.com
Sales Range: $25-49.9 Million
Emp.: 100
Television Broadcasting Services
N.A.I.C.S.: 516120
Jaci Haakonson (Mgr-Programming)
Carolyn Williamsen (Mgr-Local Sls)
Julie Higgins (Sls Mgr-Digital)
Jim Arneson (Gen Sls Mgr)
Judson Beck (VP)

WHAG-TV (2)
13 E Washington St, Hagerstown, MD 21740
Tel.: (301) 797-4400
Web Site: http://www.your4state.com
Emp.: 80
Television Broadcasting Station
N.A.I.C.S.: 516120

WHBF-TV (2)
231 18th St, Rock Island, IL 61201
Tel.: (309) 786-5441
Web Site: http://www.whbf.com
Television Broadcasting Station
N.A.I.C.S.: 516120
Bob Berger (Chief Engr)
Pat Baldwin (Gen Mgr)

WHLT-TV (2)
5912 Hwy 49 Ste A, Hattiesburg, MS 39401
Tel.: (662) 545-2077
Web Site: http://www.wjtv.com
Television Broadcasting
N.A.I.C.S.: 516120

WJBF-TV (2)
1336 Augusta W Pkwy, Augusta, GA 30909
Tel.: (706) 722-6664
Web Site: https://www.wjbf.com
Television Station
N.A.I.C.S.: 516120
Brendan Robertson (Dir-Sports)

WJHL-TV (2)
338 E Main St, Johnson City, TN 37601-5730
Tel.: (423) 926-2151
Web Site: https://www.wjhl.com
Television Station
N.A.I.C.S.: 516120
Paula Jackson (VP & Gen Mgr)
Jay Quaintance (Dir-News)
Michael Creamer (Supvr-Production)

WJTV-TV (2)
1820 TV Rd, Jackson, MS 39204
Tel.: (601) 969-4590
Web Site: https://www.wjtv.com
Television Broadcasting
N.A.I.C.S.: 516120
Steve Schrader (Chief Engr)
Bruce Leach (Dir-Sls)
Jeff Guy (Gen Mgr)
Tai Takahashi (Dir-News)
Opie Cooper (Dir-Creative Svcs)

WKRG-TV (2)
555 Broadcast Dr, Mobile, AL 36606
Tel.: (251) 479-5555
Web Site: https://www.wkrg.com
Television Station
N.A.I.C.S.: 516120

WLWC-TV (2)
275 Westminster St Ste 100, Providence, RI 02903-3434
Tel.: (401) 351-8828
Web Site: http://www.thecwprov.com
Television Broadcasting Station
N.A.I.C.S.: 516120

WMBB-TV (2)
613 Harrison Ave, Panama City, FL 32401
Tel.: (850) 769-2313
Web Site: https://www.mypanhandle.com
Sales Range: $25-49.9 Million
Emp.: 60
Television Broadcasting Station
N.A.I.C.S.: 516120
Tom Lewis (Dir-News)
Lisa Quirk (Natl Sls Mgr)

WMBD-TV (2)
3131 N University St, Peoria, IL 61604
Tel.: (309) 686-9401
Web Site: http://www.ciproud.com
Sales Range: $10-24.9 Million
Emp.: 80
Television Broadcasting Station
N.A.I.C.S.: 516120

WNCT-TV (2)
3221 S Evans St, Greenville, NC 27834
Tel.: (252) 355-8500
Web Site: https://www.wnct.com
Television Station
N.A.I.C.S.: 516120

Subsidiary (Domestic):

WOWK-TV, LLC (2)

PO Box 75119, Charleston, WV 25375
Tel.: (304) 720-6550
Web Site: https://www.wowktv.com
Television Broadcasting Station
N.A.I.C.S.: 516120

Unit (Domestic):

WQRF-TV (2)
1917 N Meridian Rd, Rockford, IL 61101
Tel.: (815) 963-5413
Web Site: http://www.mystateline.com
Television Broadcasting Station
N.A.I.C.S.: 516120

WRBL-TV (2)
1350 13th Ave, Columbus, GA 31901
Tel.: (706) 323-3333
Web Site: https://www.wrbl.com
Television Station
N.A.I.C.S.: 516120
Gentry Creamer (Chief Engr)
Joe McGuire (VP)

WRIC-TV (2)
301 Arboretum Pl, Richmond, VA 23236-3464
Tel.: (804) 330-9780
Web Site: https://www.wric.com
Television Broadcasting Station
N.A.I.C.S.: 516120
Dixon Johnston (Dir-Creative Svcs)
Mike Laffey (Production Mgr)
Steve Bays (Mgr-Promo)
Darrell Cheney (Chief Engr)
Larry Cottrill (VP & Gen Mgr)
Shane Moreland (Dir-News)
Andrew Eckard (Sls Mgr-Local)

WROC-TV (2)
201 Humboldt St, Rochester, NY 14610
Tel.: (585) 288-8400
Web Site: https://www.rochesterfirst.com
Sales Range: $10-24.9 Million
Emp.: 105
Television Broadcasting Station
N.A.I.C.S.: 516120
Wendy A. Bello (VP & Gen Mgr)

WSAV-TV (2)
1430 E Victory Dr, Savannah, GA 31404-4108
Tel.: (912) 651-0300
Web Site: https://www.wsav.com
Television Station
N.A.I.C.S.: 516120

WSPA-TV (2)
250 International Dr, Spartanburg, SC 29303
Tel.: (864) 576-7777
Web Site: https://www.wspa.com
Television Broadcasting Station
N.A.I.C.S.: 516120

Affiliate (Domestic):

WYCW-TV (3)
250 International Dr, Spartanburg, SC 29303
Tel.: (864) 576-7777
Web Site: http://www.wspa.com
Television Broadcasting Station
N.A.I.C.S.: 516120
Charlie Wofford (Chief Engr)

Unit (Domestic):

WSYR-TV (2)
5904 Bridge St, East Syracuse, NY 13057
Tel.: (315) 446-9999
Web Site: https://www.localsyr.com
Sales Range: $10-24.9 Million
Emp.: 75
Television Broadcast Station
N.A.I.C.S.: 516120
Bill Evans (VP & Gen Mgr)
Jim Campagna (Dir-News)
Greg Hassett (Mgr-Digital Media)
Craig Riker (Chief Engr)
Don Richman (Sls Mgr-Local)

WTEN-TV (2)
341 Northern Blvd, Albany, NY 12204
Tel.: (518) 436-4822
Web Site: https://www.news10.com
Television Broadcasting
N.A.I.C.S.: 516120

Subsidiary (Domestic):

WTRF-TV, LLC (2)

Nexstar Media Group, Inc.—(Continued)

96 16th St, Wheeling, WV 26003
Tel.: (304) 232-7777
Web Site: https://www.wtrf.com
Television Broadcasting Station
N.A.I.C.S.: 516120
Brenda Danehart *(Dir-News)*
Lauren Hersey *(Gen Sls Mgr)*
Roger Lyons *(Gen Mgr)*
John Lynch *(Mgr-Digital)*
Katie Richardson *(Dir-Creative Svcs)*

WVNS-TV, LLC **(2)**
141 Old Cline Rd, Ghent, WV 25843
Tel.: (304) 787-5959
Web Site: https://www.wvnstv.com
Television Broadcasting Station
N.A.I.C.S.: 516120

Nexstar Finance Holdings, Inc. **(1)**
545 E John Carpenter Fwy Ste 700, Irving,
TX 75062
Tel.: (972) 373-8800
Web Site: http://www.nexstar.tv
Holding Company
N.A.I.C.S.: 551112

Sharerocket, Inc. **(1)**
5080 Spectrum Dr E Tower 10th Fl Ste
1000E, Addison, TX 75001
Web Site: http://www.sharerocket.com
Digital Media Publisher Services
N.A.I.C.S.: 541840
Chris Kraft *(Founder & CEO)*
Tim Capper *(Pres)*
Marc Montoya *(Chief Revenue Officer)*

Sutro Tower, Inc. **(1)**
1 La Avanzada St, San Francisco, CA
94131
Tel.: (415) 213-7800
Web Site: https://www.sutrotower.com
Antenna Mfr
N.A.I.C.S.: 334220

Taboola.com Ltd. **(1)**
Atrium Tower 2 Jabotinsky St 32nd Fl
5250501, Ramat Gan, Israel
Tel.: (972) 36966966
Advertising Publisher Services
N.A.I.C.S.: 541890

The CW Television Network **(1)**
3300 W Olive, Burbank, CA 91505 **(75%)**
Tel.: (818) 977-2500
Web Site: http://www.cwtv.com
Sales Range: $25-49.9 Million
Emp.: 50
Television Network
N.A.I.C.S.: 516120
Mark Pedowitz *(Chm & CEO)*
Dana Theodoratos *(Head-Casting)*
Dennis Miller *(Pres)*
Beth Feldman *(Sr VP-Comm)*
Brad Schwartz *(Pres-Entertainment)*

Unit (Domestic):

WPSG-TV **(2)**
1555 Hamilton St, Philadelphia, PA 19130
Tel.: (215) 977-5710
Web Site: http://www.cwphilly.cbslocal.com.
Sales Range: $75-99.9 Million
Emp.: 300
Television Broadcasting Services
N.A.I.C.S.: 516120
Brien Kennedy *(Pres & Gen Mgr)*

Tribune Media Company **(1)**
515 N State St, Chicago, IL 60654
Tel.: (312) 222-3394
Web Site: http://www.tribunemedia.com
Rev.: $2,009,734,000
Assets: $8,251,391,000
Liabilities: $4,728,294,000
Net Worth: $3,523,097,000
Earnings: $412,571,000
Emp.: 5,800
Fiscal Year-end: 12/31/2018
Holding Company; Television & Radio
Broadcasting, Cable Television Program-
ming, Motion Picture Production & Online
Information Publishing Services
N.A.I.C.S.: 551112
Perry A. Sook *(Chm, Pres & CEO)*
Thomas E. Carter *(Treas)*
Elizabeth Hammond Ryder *(Gen Counsel &
Sec)*

Subsidiary (Domestic):

Bottom Line Aviation, LLC **(2)**

14686 Hwy 12, Bowman, ND 58623
Tel.: (701) 523-7484
Oil Transportation Services
N.A.I.C.S.: 488190

CastTV Inc. **(2)**
374 Brannan St, San Francisco, CA 94107
Tel.: (415) 738-8854
Internet Broadcasting Services
N.A.I.C.S.: 516210

Subsidiary (Non-US):

Infostrada Concepts B.V. **(2)**
Binnenwal 2, 3432 GH, Nieuwegein, Neth-
erlands
Tel.: (31) 306007171
Television Broadcasting Services
N.A.I.C.S.: 516120
Guido Bouw *(Mng Dir)*

Subsidiary (Domestic):

PA-Morning Call, LLC **(2)**
101 N 6th St, Allentown, PA 18105
Tel.: (610) 820-6500
Web Site: https://www.mcall.com
Newspaper Publishers
N.A.I.C.S.: 513110
Jim Feher *(VP)*

Tribune Broadcasting Company **(2)**
435 N Michigan Ave TT 600, Chicago, IL
60611
Tel.: (312) 222-3333
Web Site: http://www.tribune.com
Sales Range: $1-4.9 Billion
Emp.: 3,000
Holding Company; Television & Radio
Broadcasting Stations Owner & Operator
N.A.I.C.S.: 551112

Subsidiary (Domestic):

Channel 40, Inc. **(3)**
4655 Fruitridge Rd, Sacramento, CA 95820
Tel.: (916) 733-3130
Web Site: http://fox40.com
Sales Range: $10-24.9 Million
Emp.: 128
Television Broadcasting Station
N.A.I.C.S.: 516120

KAUT-TV **(3)**
444 E Britton Rd, Oklahoma City, OK 73114
Tel.: (405) 424-4444
Web Site: http://www.freedom43tv.com
Sales Range: $10-24.9 Million
Emp.: 50
Television Broadcasting Station
N.A.I.C.S.: 516120

Unit (Domestic):

KDAF, LLC **(3)**
8001 John W Carpenter Fwy, Dallas, TX
75247
Tel.: (214) 252-3300
Web Site: https://www.cw33.com
Sales Range: $10-24.9 Million
Emp.: 100
Television Broadcasting Station
N.A.I.C.S.: 516120
John Trevino *(VP & Gen Mgr)*

KDVR-TV **(3)**
100 E Speer Blvd, Denver, CO 80203
Tel.: (303) 595-3131
Web Site: https://www.kdvr.com
Sales Range: $25-49.9 Million
Emp.: 230
Television Station
N.A.I.C.S.: 516120
Nick Griffith *(Dir-Sports)*

KFOR-TV **(3)**
444 E Britton Rd, Oklahoma City, OK 73114
Tel.: (405) 424-4444
Web Site: https://www.kfor.com
Sales Range: $25-49.9 Million
Television Broadcasting Station
N.A.I.C.S.: 516120

KFSM-TV **(3)**
318 N 13th St, Fort Smith, AR 72901-2835
Tel.: (479) 783-3131
Web Site: https://www.5newsonline.com
Sales Range: $10-24.9 Million
Emp.: 60
Television Broadcasting Station
N.A.I.C.S.: 516120

Van Comer *(Gen Mgr)*
Mark LaCrue *(Dir-Sls)*
Dave Shelly *(Dir-Creative Svcs)*
Jacob Seus *(Dir-Sports)*

Subsidiary (Domestic):

KIAH Inc. **(3)**
7700 Westpark Dr, Houston, TX 77063
Tel.: (713) 781-3939
Web Site: https://cw39.com
Sales Range: $10-24.9 Million
Emp.: 75
Television Broadcasting Station
N.A.I.C.S.: 516120

KPLR, Inc. **(3)**
2250 Ball Dr, Saint Louis, MO 63146
Tel.: (314) 213-2222
Web Site: http://www.kplr11.com
Television Broadcasting Station
N.A.I.C.S.: 516120
Kurt Krueger *(VP & Gen Mgr)*

KSTU-TV **(3)**
5020 W Amelia Earhart Dr, Salt Lake City,
UT 84116
Tel.: (801) 532-1300
Web Site: https://www.fox13now.com
Television Broadcasting Station
N.A.I.C.S.: 516120
Tim Ermish *(Gen Mgr)*

Subsidiary (Domestic):

KSTU License, LLC **(4)**
5020 Amelia Earhart Dr, Salt Lake City, UT
84116
Tel.: (859) 448-2700
Television Broadcasting Services
N.A.I.C.S.: 516120

Subsidiary (Domestic):

KSWB Inc. **(3)**
7191 Engineer Rd, San Diego, CA 92111
Tel.: (858) 492-9269
Web Site: https://www.fox5sandiego.com
Sales Range: $10-24.9 Million
Emp.: 75
Television Broadcasting Station
N.A.I.C.S.: 516120

KTLA Inc. **(3)**
5800 Sunset Blvd, Los Angeles, CA 90028
Tel.: (323) 460-5500
Web Site: https://www.ktla.com
Sales Range: $50-74.9 Million
Emp.: 350
Television Broadcasting Station
N.A.I.C.S.: 516120

Unit (Domestic):

KTVI-TV **(3)**
2250 Ball Dr, Saint Louis, MO 63146
Tel.: (314) 213-2222
Web Site: http://www.fox2now.com
Television Broadcasting Station
N.A.I.C.S.: 516120

Subsidiary (Domestic):

KWGN Inc. **(3)**
100 E Speer Blvd, Denver, CO 80401
Tel.: (303) 595-3131
Web Site: http://www.cellreception.com
Sales Range: $25-49.9 Million
Emp.: 235
Television Broadcasting Station
N.A.I.C.S.: 516120

Division (Domestic):

Tribune Entertainment Company **(3)**
5800 Sunset Blvd TEC Bldg, Los Angeles,
CA 90028
Tel.: (323) 460-5800
Web Site: http://www.tribune.com
Sales Range: $50-74.9 Million
Emp.: 400
Television Show Production & Syndication
N.A.I.C.S.: 512191

Subsidiary (Domestic):

**Tribune Television New Orleans,
Inc.** **(3)**
1 Galleria Blvd Ste 850, Metairie, LA 70001
Tel.: (504) 525-3838
Web Site: http://www.abc26.com

Sales Range: $10-24.9 Million
Emp.: 105
Television Broadcasting Station
N.A.I.C.S.: 516120
Linda C. Anderson *(Mgr-Interactive Sls)*

Subsidiary (Domestic):

WGNO-TV **(4)**
1 Galleria Blvd Ste 850, Metairie, LA 70001
Tel.: (504) 525-3838
Web Site: https://www.wgno.com
Television Broadcasting Station
N.A.I.C.S.: 516120
Gary English *(Mgr-New Bus Dev)*
Rick Erbach *(Dir-News)*
Jeff Funk *(Creative Dir-Svcs)*

WNOL-TV **(4)**
1 Galleria Blvd Ste 850, Metairie, LA 70001
Tel.: (504) 525-3838
Web Site: http://www.abc26.com
Television Broadcasting Station
N.A.I.C.S.: 516120

Subsidiary (Domestic):

**Tribune Television Northwest,
Inc.** **(3)**
1813 Westlake Ave N, Seattle, WA 98109
Tel.: (206) 674-1313
Web Site: http://www.q13fox.com
Sales Range: $10-24.9 Million
Emp.: 100
Television Broadcasting Station
N.A.I.C.S.: 516120

Subsidiary (Domestic):

JOEtv/KZJO-TV **(4)**
1813 Westlake Ave N, Seattle, WA 98109
Tel.: (206) 674-1313
Web Site: http://q13fox.com
Emp.: 100
Television Broadcasting Station
N.A.I.C.S.: 516120

KCPQ-TV **(4)**
1813 Westlake Ave N, Seattle, WA 98109
Tel.: (206) 674-1313
Web Site: http://www.q13fox.com
Emp.: 100
Television Broadcasting Station
N.A.I.C.S.: 516120

KRCW-TV **(4)**
222 SW Columbia St Ste 102, Portland, OR
97201
Tel.: (503) 464-0600
Web Site: https://www.koin.com
Television Broadcasting Station
N.A.I.C.S.: 516120

Subsidiary (Non-US):

WCCT, INC. **(3)**
Tel.: (860) 723-2166
Web Site: http://www.yourcwtv.com
Sales Range: $10-24.9 Million
Television Broadcasting Station
N.A.I.C.S.: 516120

Affiliate (Non-US):

WTIC-TV **(4)**
Tel.: (860) 723-2111
Web Site: https://fox61.com
Television Broadcasting Station
N.A.I.C.S.: 516120

Subsidiary (Domestic):

WDCW , LLC **(3)**
2121 Wisconsin Ave NW Ste 350, Washing-
ton, DC 20007 **(100%)**
Tel.: (202) 965-5050
Web Site: http://www.dc50.com
Sales Range: $10-24.9 Million
Emp.: 30
Television Broadcasting Station
N.A.I.C.S.: 516120
Ashley Messina *(VP)*

**WGN Continental Broadcasting
Company** **(3)**
2501 W Bradley Pl, Chicago, IL 60618
Tel.: (773) 528-2311
Web Site: http://www.wgntv.com
Sales Range: $25-49.9 Million
Emp.: 300

Television Broadcasting Station, Cable Television Network & Radio Station
N.A.I.C.S.: 516120

Division (Domestic):

WGN America (4)
2501 W Bradley Pl, Chicago, IL 60618-4718
Tel.: (773) 528-2311
Web Site: http://wgntv.com
Sales Range: $50-74.9 Million
Emp.: 40
Cable Television Network
N.A.I.C.S.: 516210

Unit (Domestic):

WGN Radio (4)
435 N Michigan Ave 6th Fl, Chicago, IL 60611
Tel.: (312) 222-4653
Web Site: https://www.wgnradio.com
Sales Range: $25-49.9 Million
Emp.: 90
Radio Stations
N.A.I.C.S.: 516110

Subsidiary (Domestic):

WPIX, LLC (3)
80 State St, New York, NY 10017 **(100%)**
Tel.: (212) 949-1100
Web Site: http://www.vault.com
Sales Range: $25-49.9 Million
Emp.: 300
Television Broadcasting Station
N.A.I.C.S.: 516120

WSFL, LLC (3)
500 E Broward Blvd Ste 800, Fort Lauderdale, FL 33394 **(100%)**
Tel.: (954) 627-7308
Web Site: https://www.wsfltv.com
Sales Range: $10-24.9 Million
Emp.: 55
Television Broadcasting Station
N.A.I.C.S.: 516120

Subsidiary (Domestic):

Tribune Broadcasting Denver, LLC (2)
100 E Speer Blvd, Denver, CO 80203
Tel.: (303) 595-3131
Web Site: http://www.kdvr.com
Emp.: 200
Television Broadcasting Services
N.A.I.C.S.: 516120

Tribune Broadcasting Hartford, LLC (2)
545 E John Carpenter Fwy Ste 700, Irving, TX 75062
Tel.: (860) 527-6161
Television Broadcasting Services
N.A.I.C.S.: 516120

Tribune Broadcasting Indianapolis, LLC (2)
6910 Network Pl, Indianapolis, IN 46278-1929
Tel.: (317) 632-5900
Web Site: http://www.fox59.com
Television Broadcasting Services
N.A.I.C.S.: 516120

Tribune Broadcasting Oklahoma City License, LLC (2)
444 E Britton Rd, Oklahoma City, OK 73114
Tel.: (312) 222-3894
Television Broadcasting Services
N.A.I.C.S.: 516120

Tribune CNLBC, LLC (2)
1060 W Addison St, Chicago, IL 60613-4397
Tel.: (773) 404-2827
Web Site: http://www.chicago.cubs.mlb.com
Television Broadcasting Services
N.A.I.C.S.: 516120

Tribune Interactive, Inc. (2)
435 N Michigan Ave, Chicago, IL 60611
Tel.: (312) 222-9100
Web Site: http://www.tribuneinteractive.com
Sales Range: $25-49.9 Million
Emp.: 300
Online News & Information Publisher
N.A.I.C.S.: 516210

Tribune Properties, Inc. (2)

435 N Michigan Ave Fl 2, Chicago, IL 60611
Tel.: (312) 222-3994
Property Management Services
N.A.I.C.S.: 531190

WDAF Television, Inc. (2)
3030 Summit St, Kansas City, MO 64108
Tel.: (312) 222-3333
Web Site: http://www.fox4kc.com
Television Broadcasting Services
N.A.I.C.S.: 516120

WGHP, LLC (2)
2005 Francis St, Hertford, NC 27263
Tel.: (336) 841-8888
Web Site: http://www.myfox8.com
Television Broadcasting Services
N.A.I.C.S.: 516120

WHNT, LLC (2)
200 Holmes Ave, Huntsville, AL 35801
Tel.: (256) 535-9260
Web Site: https://www.whnt.com
Sales Range: $10-24.9 Million
Emp.: 75
Television Broadcasting Station
N.A.I.C.S.: 516120

WHO Television, LLC (2)
1801 Grand Ave, Des Moines, IA 50309
Tel.: (515) 242-3500
Web Site: http://www.whotv.com
Emp.: 75
Television Broadcasting Services
N.A.I.C.S.: 516120
Angela Skinner *(Gen Mgr-Sls)*
Rod Peterson *(Dir-News)*
Bill Pierson *(Mgr-Production)*
Brad Olk *(Chief Engr)*
Bobby Totsch *(Gen Mgr)*
Nick Allard *(Dir-Creative Svcs)*
Doug Sawyer *(Dir-Digital & New Promotions)*

WHO-TV (2)
1801 Grand Ave, Des Moines, IA 50309
Tel.: (515) 242-3500
Web Site: http://www.whotv.com
Television Broadcasting Station
N.A.I.C.S.: 516120
Angela Skinner *(Gen Mgr-Sls)*
Rod Peterson *(Dir-News)*
Stuart Rauh *(Dir-Ops-Intl)*
Robert Totsch *(VP & Gen Mgr)*

WITI Television, LLC (2)
9001 N Green Bay Rd, Milwaukee, WI 53209
Tel.: (414) 355-6666
Web Site: http://www.fox6now.com
Television Broadcasting Services
N.A.I.C.S.: 516120
Mike Neale *(Gen Mgr-Sls)*
Stu Swaziek *(Mgr-Sls-Natl)*
Eric Steele *(Dir-Res)*
Lisa Leinfelder *(Mgr-Sls-Digital)*
Jenny Trick *(Coord-Sls-Local)*

WITI-TV (2)
9001 N Green Bay Rd, Milwaukee, WI 53209
Tel.: (414) 355-6666
Web Site: http://www.fox6now.com
Sales Range: $25-49.9 Million
Television Broadcasting Station
N.A.I.C.S.: 516120

WJW Television, LLC (2)
5800 S Marginal Rd, Cleveland, OH 44103
Tel.: (216) 432-4240
Web Site: http://www.fox8.com
Television Broadcasting Services
N.A.I.C.S.: 516120

WJW-TV (2)
5800 S Marginal Rd, Cleveland, OH 44103
Tel.: (216) 431-8888
Web Site: http://www.fox8.com
Sales Range: $10-24.9 Million
Emp.: 210
Television Broadcasting Station
N.A.I.C.S.: 516120

WNEP, LLC (2)
16 Montage Mountain Rd, Moosic, PA 18507
Tel.: (570) 346-7474
Web Site: http://www.wnep.com
Sales Range: $10-24.9 Million
Emp.: 115
Television Broadcasting Station

N.A.I.C.S.: 516120
Chuck Morgan *(Gen Mgr)*
Debbie Cholko *(Coord-Program)*

WPHL, LLC (2)
5001 Wynnefield Ave, Philadelphia, PA 19131
Tel.: (215) 878-1700
Web Site: http://www.phl17.com
Sales Range: $10-24.9 Million
Emp.: 50
Television Broadcasting Station
N.A.I.C.S.: 516120

WPMT, LLC (2)
2005 S Queen St, York, PA 17403 **(100%)**
Tel.: (717) 814-5536
Web Site: https://www.fox43.com
Sales Range: $10-24.9 Million
Emp.: 100
Television Broadcasting Station
N.A.I.C.S.: 516120

WQAD, LLC (2)
3003 Park 16th St, Moline, IL 61265
Tel.: (309) 764-8888
Web Site: http://www.wqad.com
Television Broadcasting Station
N.A.I.C.S.: 516120

WREG, LLC (2)
803 Channel 3 Dr, Memphis, TN 38103
Tel.: (901) 543-2333
Web Site: http://www.wreg.com
Television Broadcasting Station
N.A.I.C.S.: 516120
Mike Ceide *(Dir-Sports)*

WTKR-TV (2)
720 Boush St, Norfolk, VA 23510
Tel.: (757) 227-6406
Web Site: https://www.wtkr.com
Sales Range: $10-24.9 Million
Emp.: 120
Television Broadcasting Station
N.A.I.C.S.: 516120
Kristie Flynn *(Dir-Mktg & Res)*
Cindi Dove *(Dir-Digital)*
John Daman *(Mgr-Sls-Local)*
Kristin Mascitti *(Mgr-Natl Acct)*
John Witte *(Mgr-Local Sls)*
Lakeisha Goodman *(Coord-Digital)*
Kathy Rice *(Mgr-Local Sls)*

WTTV-TV (2)
6910 Network Pl, Indianapolis, IN 46278
Tel.: (317) 632-5900
Web Site: https://cbs4indy.com
Sales Range: $25-49.9 Million
Emp.: 180
Television Broadcasting Station
N.A.I.C.S.: 516120

WTVR, LLC (2)
3301 W Broad St, Richmond, VA 23230 **(100%)**
Tel.: (804) 254-3600
Web Site: http://www.wtvr.com
Sales Range: $25-49.9 Million
Emp.: 150
Television Broadcasting Station
N.A.I.C.S.: 516120
Stephen Hayes *(Gen Mgr)*
Steve Young *(Mgr-Sls-Local)*
James Taguchi *(Mgr-Sls-Natl)*
Matt McClain *(Dir-Creative Svcs)*
Sheryl Barnhouse *(Dir-News)*
Chris Barker *(Dir-Sls-Interactive)*
Dee Davies *(Gen Mgr-Sls)*
Scott Wise *(Dir-Digital)*
David Stotts *(Dir-Mktg)*
Misti Davidson *(Asst Dir-News)*
Misty Wiggins *(Dir-Res)*
Nick Dutton *(Mgr)*
Shannon Hopkins *(Dir-Promotions)*
Lane Casadonte *(Dir-Sports)*
Sean Robertson *(Dir-Sports)*
Brock Taylor *(Mgr-Production)*
Charlie Wood *(Chief Engr)*
Robert Hughes *(Editor-Assignment)*

WXIN-TV (2)
6910 Network Pl, Indianapolis, IN 46278
Tel.: (317) 632-5900
Web Site: http://www.fox59.com
Sales Range: $10-24.9 Million
Emp.: 100
Television Broadcasting Station
N.A.I.C.S.: 516120

WXMI, LLC (2)

3117 Plz Dr NE, Grand Rapids, MI 49525 **(100%)**
Tel.: (616) 364-8722
Web Site: http://www.fox17online.com
Sales Range: $10-24.9 Million
Emp.: 125
Television Broadcasting Station
N.A.I.C.S.: 516120
Brooks Blanton *(Sr Dir-News)*

Subsidiary (Non-US):

What's On India Media Private Limited (2)
3rd Floor A Wing Todi Estate Lower Parel W, Mumbai, 400 013, Maharashtra, India
Tel.: (91) 2261436400
Web Site: http://www.careers.whatsonindia.net
Emp.: 300
Television Broadcasting Services
N.A.I.C.S.: 516120
Indhra Prakash Hoora *(Gen Mgr)*

Yashi, Inc. (1)
1433 Hooper Ave Ste 131, Toms River, NJ 08753
Web Site: http://www.yashi.com
Advetising Agency
N.A.I.C.S.: 541810
Scott Hoffman *(Pres)*

NEXT DYNAMICS INC.
6666 Harwin Ste 664, Houston, TX 77036
Tel.: (713) 268-1610 TX
Web Site:
http://www.everybodysphonecompany.com
Year Founded: 2003
SWHID—(OTCIQ)
Sales Range: Less than $1 Million
Prepaid Local Telephone Services
N.A.I.C.S.: 517111
Norman George *(Chm, Pres & CEO)*
Stephen Michaels *(VP)*

NEXT GRAPHITE, INC.
318 N Carson St Ste 208, Carson City, NV 89701
Tel.: (949) 397-2522 NV
Web Site:
http://www.nextgraphite.com
Year Founded: 2012
GPNE—(OTCIQ)
Sales Range: Less than $1 Million
Graphite Mining
N.A.I.C.S.: 212290
Michael J. Doron *(Chm)*
Charles Cliff Bream *(Pres, CEO, CFO & Treas)*

NEXT-CHEMX CORPORATION
901 Mopac Expy S Bldg 1 Ste 300, Austin, TX 78746
Tel.: (512) 663-2690 NV
Web Site: https://www.next-chemx.com
Year Founded: 2014
CHMX—(OTCIQ)
Assets: $3,218,595
Liabilities: $2,486,727
Net Worth: $731,868
Earnings: ($1,743,799)
Emp.: 6
Fiscal Year-end: 12/31/22
Business Consulting Services
N.A.I.C.S.: 541611
Benton Wilcoxon *(Co-Founder, CEO & Dir)*
Nikolai M. Kocherginsky *(Co-Founder & Chief Scientist)*
John Michael Johnson *(Co-Founder, Pres, Officer-Finance & Dir)*
Dmitry Sindalovsky *(Co-Founder)*

NEXT10, INC.
4663 S Enterprise St, Boise, ID 83705-3527
Tel.: (612) 386-0606

Next10, Inc.—(Continued)

Web Site:
http://www.ultimateholdingscorp.com
NXTN—(OTCIQ)
Assets: $2,000
Liabilities: $26,000
Net Worth: ($24,000)
Earnings: ($11,000)
Emp.: 1
Fiscal Year-end: 12/31/19
Electric Equipment Mfr
N.A.I.C.S.: 335313
Brett S. Millar (Pres)

NEXTCURE, INC.
9000 Virginia Manor Rd Ste 200,
Beltsville, MD 20705
Tel.: (240) 399-4900   DE
Web Site: https://www.nextcure.com
Year Founded: 2015
NXTC—(NASDAQ)
Rev.: $1,176,000
Assets: $184,161,000
Liabilities: $16,631,000
Net Worth: $167,530,000
Earnings: ($74,733,000)
Emp.: 99
Fiscal Year-end: 12/31/22
Research & Development in Biotech-
nology (except Nanobiotechnology)
N.A.I.C.S.: 541714
Michael S. Richman (Pres & CEO)
Timothy Mayer (COO)
David S. Kabakoff (Chm)
Steven P. Cobourn (CFO)
Sol Langermann (Chief Scientific Offi-
cer)
Linda Liu (Sr VP-Res)
Sebastien Maloveste (VP-Bus Dev)
Dallas Flies (VP-Discovery Res)
Lieping Chen (Founder)
Zachary Cusumano (VP-Project
Mgmt & Strategy)

NEXTDECADE CORPORATION
1000 Louisiana St Ste 3300, Hous-
ton, TX 77002
Tel.: (713) 574-1880
Web Site: https://www.next-
decade.com
Year Founded: 2014
NEXT—(NASDAQ)
Assets: $312,430,000
Liabilities: $258,059,000
Net Worth: $54,371,000
Earnings: ($60,071,000)
Emp.: 102
Fiscal Year-end: 12/31/22
LNG Development Services
N.A.I.C.S.: 221210
Raquel Couri (Sr VP-HR & Admin)
Brent Wahl (CFO)
James MacTaggart (CMO)
Vera De Brito de Gyarfas (Gen Coun-
sel & Sec)
David Keane (Sr VP)
Graham McArthur (Treas)
Matthew K. Schatzman (Chm & CEO)

Subsidiaries:

Harmony Merger Corp.   (1)
1000 Louisiana St Ste 3900, Houston, TX
77002
Tel.: (713) 574-1880
Web Site: https://www.next-decade.com
Rev.: $254,870
Assets: $117,551,889
Liabilities: $112,551,887
Net Worth: $5,000,002
Earnings: ($434,698)
Emp.: 3
Fiscal Year-end: 12/31/2016
Investment Services
N.A.I.C.S.: 523999

NEXTDOOR HOLDINGS, INC.

420 Taylor St, San Francisco, CA
94102
Tel.: (415) 344-0333   DE
Web Site: https://www.nextdoor.com
KIND—(NYSE)
Rev.: $212,765,000
Assets: $699,562,000
Liabilities: $88,494,000
Net Worth: $611,068,000
Earnings: ($137,916,000)
Emp.: 704
Fiscal Year-end: 12/31/22
Financial Investment Services
N.A.I.C.S.: 523999
Matt Anderson (CFO)
James Kelm (Head-Product)
Craig Lisowski (Head-Engineering,
Data, Information Sys, and Trust)
Bryan Power (Head-People)
Sophia Contreras Schwartz (Gen
Counsel)
Kelsey Grady (Head-Global Comm)
Sarah Leary (Head-Marketing, Com-
munity, and Bus Ops)
Nirav Tolia (Co-Founder, Exec Chm,
Pres & CEO)

NEXTECH SOLUTIONS, INC.
990 Stewart Ave Ste 201, Garden
City, NY 11530
Tel.: (516) 468-4839   LA
Year Founded: 1983
NXSL—(OTCIQ)
Staffing Recruitment Services
N.A.I.C.S.: 561311
Tony Dinapoli (Pres & CEO)

NEXTERA ENERGY, INC.
700 Universe Blvd, Juno Beach, FL
33408
Tel.: (561) 694-4000   FL
Web Site:
https://www.nexteraenergy.com
Year Founded: 1925
NEE—(NYSE)
Rev.: $28,114,000,000
Assets: $177,489,000,000
Liabilities: $119,721,000,000
Net Worth: $57,768,000,000
Earnings: $7,310,000,000
Emp.: 16,800
Fiscal Year-end: 12/31/23
Holding Company; Electricity & Fiber-
Optic Services
N.A.I.C.S.: 551112
Terrell Kirk Crews II (Chief Risk Offi-
cer & Exec VP)
John W. Ketchum (Chm, Pres &
CEO)
Mark E. Hickson (Exec VP-Corp Dev
& Strategy)
Charles E. Sieving (Gen Counsel &
Exec VP)
Ronald R. Reagan (Exec VP-Engrg,
Contruction & Integrated Supply
Chain)
Kirk Crews (CFO)
Mark Lemasney (Exec VP)
Michael Dunne (Treas)

Subsidiaries:

Florida Power & Light Company   (1)
1 Energy Pl, Pensacola, FL 32520
Tel.: (800) 225-5797
Web Site: https://www.fpl.com
Rev.: $1,516,000,000
Assets: $4,797,000,000
Liabilities: $3,266,000,000
Net Worth: $1,531,000,000
Earnings: $139,000,000
Emp.: 1,288
Fiscal Year-end: 12/31/2017
Electric Power Utility Company
N.A.I.C.S.: 221111

Florida Power & Light Company   (1)
700 Universe Blvd, Juno Beach, FL
33408   (100%)

Tel.: (561) 694-4000
Web Site: https://www.nexteraenergy.com
Rev.: $17,282,000,000
Assets: $86,559,000,000
Liabilities: $47,639,000,000
Net Worth: $38,920,000,000
Earnings: $3,701,000,000
Emp.: 9,300
Fiscal Year-end: 12/31/2022
Electric Utility
N.A.I.C.S.: 221122
Deborah H. Caplan (Exec VP-HR & Corp
Svcs)
Armando Pimentel Jr. (Pres & CEO)
John W. Ketchum (Chm)
Paul I. Cutler (Treas)
Rebecca J. Kujawa (CFO & Exec VP-Fin)
Terrell Kirk Crews II (CFO)
Keith Ferguson (Controller)

NextEra Energy Capital Holdings,
Inc.   (1)
700 Universe Blvd, Juno Beach, FL
33408   (100%)
Tel.: (561) 694-4853
Investment Services
N.A.I.C.S.: 523999
Lewis Hay III (Chm & CEO)

Subsidiary (Domestic):

NextEra Energy Resources, LLC   (2)
700 Universe Blvd, Juno Beach, FL
33408   (100%)
Tel.: (561) 691-7171
Web Site:
http://www.nexteraenergyresources.com
Sales Range: $100-124.9 Million
Acquires, Manages & Syndicates Invest-
ments in Non-Utility Energy Projects
N.A.I.C.S.: 541715
Rebecca J. Kujawa (Pres & CEO)

Subsidiary (Domestic):

Gexa Energy, L.P.   (3)
601 Travis St Ste 1400, Houston, TX 77002
Tel.: (713) 470-0400
Web Site: https://www.gexaenergy.com
Retail Energy Services
N.A.I.C.S.: 221210

Northeast Energy Associates, a Lim-
ited Partnership   (3)
155 Maple St, Bellingham, MA 02019
Tel.: (508) 966-4872
Emp.: 80
Electric Power Generation
N.A.I.C.S.: 221118
Kirk Toth (Mgr)

NextEra Energy Partners, LP   (1)
700 Universe Blvd, Juno Beach, FL 33408
Tel.: (561) 694-4700
Web Site:
https://www.nexteraenergypartners.com
Rev.: $1,078,000,000
Assets: $22,511,000,000
Liabilities: $8,454,000,000
Net Worth: $14,057,000,000
Earnings: $200,000,000
Fiscal Year-end: 12/31/2023
Electronic Services
N.A.I.C.S.: 221122
John W. Ketchum (CEO)
Rebecca J. Kujawa (Pres)
James M. May (Chief Acctg Officer & Con-
troller)
Paul I. Cutler (Treas & Asst Sec)
Mark E. Hickson (Exec VP-Corp Dev &
Strategy)
Charles E. Sieving (Gen Counsel)
Michael Dunne (Treas)

Palms SC Insurance Company,
LLC   (1)
111 Preston Ave, North Charleston, SC
29420
Tel.: (843) 494-9070
Web Site: http://palms-insurance-
agency.business.site
Insurance Agency Services
N.A.I.C.S.: 524210

Palms Specialty Insurance Company,
Inc.   (1)
700 Universe Blvd, Juno Beach, FL 33408
Tel.: (561) 304-5532
Web Site: https://www.palms-insurance.com
General Insurance Services

N.A.I.C.S.: 524210

NEXTMART, INC.
335 Constance Dr, Warminster, PA
18974
Tel.: (267) 365-7949   DE
Web Site:
http://www.nextmartcorporation.com
Year Founded: 1972
NXMR—(OTCIQ)
Financial Advisory & Investment Ser-
vices
N.A.I.C.S.: 523940
Kathryn Gavin (Interim CFO, Interim
CEO, Interim Pres, Interim Treas, In-
terim Sec & Interim VP-Ops)

NEXTNAV INC.
11911 Freedom Dr Ste 200, Reston,
VA 20190   DE
Web Site: https://nextnav.com
Year Founded: 2020
NN—(NASDAQ)
Rev.: $3,926,000
Assets: $123,788,000
Liabilities: $19,924,000
Net Worth: $103,864,000
Earnings: ($40,116,000)
Emp.: 106
Fiscal Year-end: 12/31/22
Investment Services
N.A.I.C.S.: 523999

NEXTPLAT CORP.
3250 Mary St Ste 410, Coconut
Grove, FL 33133
Tel.: (305) 686-3250   NV
Web Site: https://www.nextplat.com
Year Founded: 1997
NXPL—(NASDAQ)
Rev.: $11,710,142
Assets: $28,642,048
Liabilities: $2,864,929
Net Worth: $25,777,119
Earnings: ($9,160,589)
Emp.: 18
Fiscal Year-end: 12/31/22
Satellite Telecommunications, Map-
ping & Tracking Services
N.A.I.C.S.: 517410
David Phipps (Pres & CEO-Global
Ops)
Charles M. Fernandez (Chm & CEO)
Douglas S. Ellenoff (Vice Chm)
Robert Bedwell (Chief Compliance
Officer)

Subsidiaries:

Global Telesat Communications
Limited   (1)
19-25 Nuffield Road, Poole, Dorset, BH17
ORU, United Kingdom
Tel.: (44) 1202801290
Web Site: https://www.gtc.co.uk
Telecommunication Servicesb
N.A.I.C.S.: 517112

Orbital Satcom Corp.   (1)
3250 Mary St Ste 410, Coconut Grove, FL
33133
Tel.: (305) 560-5355
Web Site: https://www.osat.com
Satellite Phone & Accessory Mfr
N.A.I.C.S.: 334220

Progressive Care, Inc.   (1)
400 Ansin Blvd Ste A, Hallandale Beach, FL
33009   (100%)
Tel.: (786) 657-2060
Web Site:
https://www.progressivecareus.com
Rev.: $40,601,859
Assets: $18,014,674
Liabilities: $10,396,623
Net Worth: $7,618,051
Earnings: ($6,445,176)
Emp.: 98
Fiscal Year-end: 12/31/2022
Pharmaceutical Retailer
N.A.I.C.S.: 456110

Pamela Roberts *(COO & Pharmacist-In-Charge)*

NEXTPLAY TECHNOLOGIES, INC.

1560 Sawgrass Corporate Pkwy 4th Fl, Sunrise, FL 33323
Tel.: (954) 888-9779   NV
Web Site:
https://www.nextplaytechnolo gies.com
Year Founded: 2015
NXTP—(NASDAQ)
Rev.: $8,203,326
Assets: $99,753,493
Liabilities: $31,892,295
Net Worth: $67,861,198
Earnings: ($37,972,770)
Emp.: 250
Fiscal Year-end: 02/28/22
Alternative Lodging Rental Industry
N.A.I.C.S.: 721199

NEXTPOINT ACQUISITION CORP.

44 S Bwdy 11th Fl, White Plains, NY 10601
Tel.: (914) 614-5626
NAC—(TSX)
Investment Services
N.A.I.C.S.: 523999
Andrew Neuberger *(Chm & CEO)*

NEXTRACKER INC.

6200 Paseo Padre Pkwy, Fremont, CA 94555
Tel.: (510) 270-2500
Web Site:
https://www.nextracker.com
Year Founded: 2013
NXT—(NASDAQ)
Rev.: $1,902,137,000
Assets: $1,419,680,000
Liabilities: $4,495,447,000
Net Worth: ($3,075,767,000)
Earnings: $121,333,000
Emp.: 606
Fiscal Year-end: 03/31/23
Solar Panel Mfr & Distr
N.A.I.C.S.: 333414

NEXUS ENERGY SERVICES, INC.

701 Anacapa St Ste C, Santa Barbara, CA 93101
Tel.: (250) 900-2031   CO
Web Site:
http://www.illegalburgerco.com
IBGR—(OTCIQ)
Restaurant Owner & Operator
N.A.I.C.S.: 722511
Brian J. Mckenzie *(Co-CEO)*
Matt Weingart *(Co-CEO)*
Barrett Evans *(Chm & CFO)*

NEXUS ENTERPRISE SOLUTIONS, INC.

5340 N Federal Hwy Ste 206, Lighthouse Point, FL 33064
Tel.: (561) 767-4346   WY
Web Site:
http://www.nexusenterprisesolu tions.com
NXES—(OTCIQ)
Sales Range: $1-9.9 Million
Emp.: 3
Insurance Lead Generation Services
N.A.I.C.S.: 513140
Scott Schluer *(CTO)*

NFINITI INC.

2100 West Loop S Ste 700, Houston, TX 77027
Tel.: (832) 510-8950   NV
Year Founded: 2012
NFTN—(OTCIQ)

Liabilities: $134,026
Net Worth: ($134,026)
Earnings: ($17,663)
Emp.: 1
Fiscal Year-end: 10/31/23
Oil & Gas Exploration
N.A.I.C.S.: 211120
Michael Noble *(Pres, CEO, CFO, Chief Acctg Officer, Treas & Sec)*

NGEN TECHNOLOGIES HOLDINGS CORP.

5430 Lyndon B. Johnson Fwy Ste 1200, Dallas, TX 75240
Tel.: (972) 663-9463   NV
Year Founded: 2011
NGRP—(OTCIQ)
Holding Company; Energy Services
N.A.I.C.S.: 551112
Scott Lucas *(CEO)*

NGL ENERGY PARTNERS LP

6120 S Yale Ave Ste 1300, Tulsa, OK 74136
Tel.: (918) 481-1119   DE
Web Site:
https://www.nglenergypartners.com
NGL—(NYSE)
Rev.: $6,956,571,000
Assets: $5,020,094,000
Liabilities: $4,572,024,000
Net Worth: $448,070,000
Earnings: ($143,124,000)
Emp.: 607
Fiscal Year-end: 03/31/24
Propane Mfr & Distr
N.A.I.C.S.: 325120
H. Michael Krimbill *(CEO)*
Jennifer Kingham *(CIO & Sr VP)*
Doug White *(Exec VP-Water Solutions)*
Lawrence J. Thuillier *(Chief Acctg Officer)*
Brad Cooper *(CFO & Exec VP)*

Subsidiaries:

Andrews Oil Buyers, Inc.   (1)
201 SE Mustang Dr, Andrews, TX 79714
Tel.: (432) 524-4405
Oil & Gas Related Services
N.A.I.C.S.: 213112

AntiCline Disposal, LLC   (1)
93 N Jonah Rd, Boulder, WY 82923
Tel.: (307) 360-3390
Emp.: 15
Engineering Services
N.A.I.C.S.: 541330

Centennial Gas Liquids, ULC   (1)
350 7 Ave Sw Ste 2700, Calgary, T2P 3N9, AB, Canada
Tel.: (403) 233-0950
Oil & Gas Related Services
N.A.I.C.S.: 213112

Choya Operating, LLC   (1)
4005 FM 2200 W, Moore, TX 78057
Tel.: (956) 763-4402
Emp.: 5
Oil & Gas Related Services
N.A.I.C.S.: 213112

Downeast Energy   (1)
18 Spring St, Brunswick, ME 04011
Tel.: (207) 729-9921
Web Site: https://www.downeastenergy.com
Coal, Firewood, Lumber & Petroleum Products Mfr
N.A.I.C.S.: 423720

E Energy Adams, LLC   (1)
13238 E Aspen Rd, Adams, NE 68301
Tel.: (402) 988-4655
Web Site: https://www.eenergyadams.com
Oil & Gas Related Services
N.A.I.C.S.: 213112
Duane Wollenburg *(Chm)*
Tom Roode *(Vice Chm)*
Dennis Boesiger *(Sec)*
Steve Dean *(Asst Sec)*

Gas Supply Resources LLC   (1)

---

370 17th Street Ste 2775, Denver, CO 80202
Tel.: (513) 528-4242
Natural Gas Extraction Services
N.A.I.C.S.: 211130

Gavilon, LLC   (1)
1331 Capitol Ave, Omaha, NE 68102-1106
Tel.: (402) 889-4000
Web Site: https://www.viterra.us
Sales Range: $350-399.9 Million
Emp.: 2,000
Energy Commodities Physical Distribution, Merchandising & Wholesale Trading Services
N.A.I.C.S.: 425120

Grassland Water Solutions, LLC   (1)
201 S College Ave Ste 205, Fort Collins, CO 80524
Tel.: (970) 672-1040
Web Site:
https://www.grasslandwatersolutions.com
Oil & Gas Related Services
N.A.I.C.S.: 213112

High Sierra Crude Oil & Marketing, LLC   (1)
3773 Cherry Creek 1000, Denver, CO 80209
Tel.: (303) 815-1010
Emp.: 17
Oil & Gas Related Services
N.A.I.C.S.: 213112

NGL Crude Logistics, LLC   (1)
1331 Capitol Ave, Omaha, NE 68102-1106
Tel.: (402) 889-4000
Web Site: http://www.gavilon.com
Scheduled Freight Air Transportation Services
N.A.I.C.S.: 481112

NGL Crude Terminals, LLC   (1)
620 N Channel Rd, Catoosa, OK 74015
Tel.: (918) 266-1584
Emp.: 27
Oil & Gas Related Services
N.A.I.C.S.: 213112
Jeorge Beiriger *(Mgr-Terminal)*

NGL Crude Transportation, LLC   (1)
6120 S Yale Ave Ste 805, Tulsa, OK 74136
Tel.: (918) 481-1119
Oil & Gas Related Services
N.A.I.C.S.: 213112

NGL Milan Investments, LLC   (1)
6120 S Yale Ave, Tulsa, OK 74136
Tel.: (918) 477-0521
Oil & Gas Related Services
N.A.I.C.S.: 213112

NGL Solids Solutions, LLC   (1)
8207 W 20th St Ste B, Greeley, CO 80634
Tel.: (970) 356-5560
Oil & Gas Related Services
N.A.I.C.S.: 213112

Osterman Propane, LLC   (1)
1 Memorial Sq, Whitinsville, MA 01588
Tel.: (508) 234-9902
Web Site: https://www.ostermangas.com
Emp.: 30
Residential Propane Delivery Services
N.A.I.C.S.: 211130

Subsidiary (Domestic):

Perry's Oil Service Inc.   (2)
240 Brushwood Rd, North Haverhill, NH 03774
Web Site: http://www.perryoil.com
Propane & Bottled Gas Distr
N.A.I.C.S.: 457210

Pacer Propane LLC   (1)
18459 NE 76th St, Redmond, WA 98052
Tel.: (425) 883-4242
Web Site:
https://pacerpropanewashington.com
Sales Range: $1-9.9 Million
Emp.: 9
Liquefied Petroleum Gas (Bottled Gas) Dealers
N.A.I.C.S.: 457210

TransMontaigne, Inc.   (1)
1670 Broadway Ste 3100, Denver, CO 80202
Tel.: (303) 626-8200

Web Site:
https://www.transmontaignepartners.com
Sales Range: $5-14.9 Billion
Emp.: 750
Crude Oil, Petroleum Products & Natural Gas
N.A.I.C.S.: 237120

Subsidiary (Domestic):

TransMontaigne Transport Inc.   (2)
200 Mansell Ct E, Roswell, GA 30076
Tel.: (770) 518-3500
Web Site:
http://www.transmontaignepartners.com
Sales Range: $10-24.9 Million
Emp.: 66
Crude Petroleum Pipelines
N.A.I.C.S.: 486110

NGM BIOPHARMACEUTICALS, INC.

333 Oyster Point Blvd, South San Francisco, CA 94080-7014
Tel.: (650) 243-5555   DE
Web Site: https://www.ngmbio.com
Year Founded: 2007
NGM—(NASDAQ)
Rev.: $55,333,000
Assets: $307,402,000
Liabilities: $47,842,000
Net Worth: $259,560,000
Earnings: ($162,667,000)
Emp.: 239
Fiscal Year-end: 12/31/22
Biopharmaceutical Product Research & Development Services
N.A.I.C.S.: 541714
William J. Rieflin *(Chm)*
Irene Perlich *(Principal Acctg Officer, VP & Controller)*
Valerie Pierce *(Chief Compliance Officer, Gen Counsel & Sr VP)*
Dan Kaplan *(Chief Scientific Officer)*
Kara Calhoun *(VP)*
Jin-Long Chen *(Founder)*
David J. Woodhouse *(CEO)*

NI HOLDINGS, INC.

1101 1st Ave N, Fargo, ND 58102
Tel.: (701) 298-4200   ND
Web Site:
https://www.niholdingsinc.com
Year Founded: 1946
NODK—(NASDAQ)
Rev.: $324,437,000
Assets: $614,232,000
Liabilities: $361,025,000
Net Worth: $253,207,000
Earnings: ($53,096,000)
Emp.: 230
Fiscal Year-end: 12/31/22
Insurance Holding Company
N.A.I.C.S.: 551112
Cindy L. Launer *(Interim CEO)*
William R. Devlin *(Vice Chm)*
Seth Daggett *(CFO, Principal Acctg Officer, Treas & Exec VP-Strategy)*

Subsidiaries:

Westminster American Insurance Company   (1)
8890 McDonogh Rd Ste 310, Owings Mills, MD 21117
Tel.: (443) 291-4040
Web Site:
http://www.westminsteramerican.com
Sales Range: $10-24.9 Million
Property Insurance Services
N.A.I.C.S.: 524126
John Scott Jr. *(Pres & CEO)*

NICHOLAS FINANCIAL, INC.

26133 Hwy 19 N Ste 300, Clearwater, FL 33763
Tel.: (727) 726-0763   FL
Web Site:
https://www.nicholasfinancial.com
Year Founded: 1981
NICK—(NASDAQ)
Rev.: $22,237,000

Nicholas Financial, Inc.—(Continued)

Assets: $59,838,000
Liabilities: $996,000
Net Worth: $58,842,000
Earnings: ($20,801,000)
Emp.: 7
Fiscal Year-end: 03/31/24
Consumer Lending Services
N.A.I.C.S.: 522291
Jeffrey C. Royal (Chm)
Mike Rost (VP-Branch Ops)

Subsidiaries:

Nicholas Data Services, Inc.   (1)
2454 McMullen Booth Rd Bldg C, Clearwater, FL 33759   (100%)
Tel.: (727) 726-0763
Web Site: https://www.nicholasfinancial.com
Sales Range: $150-199.9 Million
Emp.: 60
Software & Technical Support & Solutions
N.A.I.C.S.: 423430

NICOLET BANKSHARES, INC.

111 N Washington St, Green Bay, WI 54301
Tel.: (920) 430-1400   WI
Web Site:
https://www.nicoletbank.com
NIC—(NYSE)
Rev.: $331,838,000
Assets: $8,763,969,000
Liabilities: $7,791,440,000
Net Worth: $972,529,000
Earnings: $94,260,000
Emp.: 942
Fiscal Year-end: 12/31/22
Bank Holding Company
N.A.I.C.S.: 551111
Robert B. Atwell (Co-Founder)
Michael E. Daniels (Co-Founder, Chm, Pres & CEO)
Donald J. Long Jr. (Co-Founder)
Phil Moore (CFO)

Subsidiaries:

Brookfield Investment Partners, LLC   (1)
330 S Executive Dr Ste 307, Brookfield, WI 53005-4275
Tel.: (262) 785-6751
Web Site:
http://www.brookfieldinvestmentpartners.com
Investment Management Service
N.A.I.C.S.: 523940

Charter Bankshares, Inc.   (1)
1010 W Clairemont Ave, Eau Claire, WI 54701
Tel.: (715) 832-4254
Web Site: http://www.charterbankec.com
Rev.: $8,681,200
Emp.: 49
Bank Holding Company
N.A.I.C.S.: 551111
Dean Olson (Pres)
Susan Diel (CFO)

County Bancorp, Inc.   (1)
2400 S 44th St, Manitowoc, WI 54221
Tel.: (920) 686-9998
Web Site:
http://www.investorscommunitybank.com
Rev.: $69,725,000
Assets: $1,472,358,000
Liabilities: $1,300,582,000
Net Worth: $171,776,000
Earnings: $5,479,000
Emp.: 164
Fiscal Year-end: 12/31/2020
Bank Holding Company
N.A.I.C.S.: 551111
Glen L. Stiteley (CFO & Treas)
Mark A. Miller (Chief Risk Officer & Exec VP-Counsel-Investors Community Bank)

Subsidiary (Domestic):

Investors Community Bank   (2)
860 N Rapids Rd, Manitowoc, WI 54220
Tel.: (920) 645-6100

Web Site:
http://www.investorscommunitybank.com
Commericial Banking
N.A.I.C.S.: 522110
Timothy J. Schneider (CEO)
Mark Robert Binversie (Co-Founder & Pres)
Glen L. Stiteley (CFO & Exec VP)
Dave Coggins (Chief Banking Officer & Exec VP)
Bill Hodgkiss (Sr VP-Bus Banking)
Tim McTigue (Sr VP-Ag Banking)
Mark Miller (Chief Risk Officer & Exec VP-Counsel)
Laura Wiegert (Sr VP-Mktg)
Cyrene Wilke (Sr VP-Ops)
John Fillingim (Chief Credit Officer & Exec VP)
Matt Lemke (Chief Retail & Deposit Officer & Exec VP)
Matthew Fehrmann (VP-Tech Solutions)
Brooke Sprang (Sr VP-HR)

Nicolet Advisory Services, LLC   (1)
111 N Washington St, Green Bay, WI 54301
Tel.: (920) 617-5311
Commercial Banking Services
N.A.I.C.S.: 522110

Nicolet National Bank   (1)
111 N Washington St, Green Bay, WI 54301
Tel.: (920) 430-1400
Web Site: https://www.nicoletbank.com
Savings Bank
N.A.I.C.S.: 522180
Robert B. Atwell (Co-Founder & Chm)
Michael E. Daniels (Co-Founder, Pres & CEO)
Eric Witczak (Exec VP)
Patrick Madson (Sr VP-Wealth Mgmt)
Melissa DeVantier (VP)
Chris Dimmer (Sr VP)
Barry Martzahl (Mng Dir)
Adam Longlais (Co-Chief Investment Officer)
Mike Steppe (Co-Chief Investment Officer)
Philip Gatien (VP-Retirement Plan Svcs)
Steven Cross (VP)

Subsidiary (Domestic):

United Financial Services, Inc.   (2)
2405 York Rd Ste 201, Lutherville Timonium, MD 21093-2264   (99.2%)
Tel.: (262) 376-3000
Sales Range: $1-9.9 Million
Emp.: 25
Data Processing Services
N.A.I.C.S.: 518210

NIGHTDRAGON ACQUISITION CORP.

101 Second St Ste 1275, San Francisco, CA 94105
Tel.: (510) 306-7780   DE
Web Site: http://www.ndac.com
Year Founded: 2020
NDACU—(NASDAQ)
Rev.: $3,766,546
Assets: $346,874,077
Liabilities: $363,761,207
Net Worth: ($16,887,130)
Earnings: $2,275,306
Fiscal Year-end: 12/31/21
Investment Services
N.A.I.C.S.: 523999
David G. DeWalt (Chm)
Mark Garrett (Vice Chm)
Morgan Kyauk (CEO & Sec)
Steve Simonian (CFO)

NIGHTFOOD HOLDINGS, INC.

520 White Plains Rd Ste 500, Tarrytown, NY 10591
Tel.: (212) 828-8275   NV
Year Founded: 2013
NGTF—(OTCQB)
Rev.: $133,456
Assets: $446,511
Liabilities: $2,198,111
Net Worth: ($1,751,600)
Earnings: ($6,886,668)
Emp.: 2
Fiscal Year-end: 06/30/23
Snack Food Mfr

N.A.I.C.S.: 311919
Sean Folkson (Chm, Pres & CEO)
Jim Christensen (VP-Ice Cream)
Lei Sonny Wang (CFO)

Subsidiaries:

Nightfood, Inc.   (1)
520 White Plains Rd Ste 500, Tarrytown, NY 10591-5118
Web Site: https://www.nightfood.com
Food & Beverage Mfr
N.A.I.C.S.: 333241

NIGHTINGALE INTELLIGENT SYSTEMS INC.

8450 Central Ave, Newark, CA 94560
Tel.: (415) 363-6168   DE
Web Site:
https://www.nightingalesecurity.com
Year Founded: 2014
NGL—(ASX)
Rev.: $2,144,054
Assets: $2,656,927
Liabilities: $2,095,606
Net Worth: $561,321
Earnings: ($5,973,794)
Fiscal Year-end: 12/31/22
Software Development Services
N.A.I.C.S.: 541511
Jack Wu (Co-Founder & CEO)
John Hsu (Co-Founder & CTO)
Alan Braverman (Chm)

NIKA PHARMACEUTICALS, INC.

2269 Merrimack Valley Ave, Henderson, NV 89044
Tel.: (702) 326-3615   CO
Web Site:
https://www.nikapharmaceuticals.com
Year Founded: 2000
NIKA—(OTCIQ)
Assets: $864
Liabilities: $18,180
Net Worth: ($17,316)
Earnings: ($3,183,715)
Fiscal Year-end: 12/31/22
Pharmaceutical Developer & Mfr
N.A.I.C.S.: 325412
Dimitar Slavchev Savov (Pres, CEO & CFO)
Clifford Redekop (Sec)

Subsidiaries:

Nika BioTechnology, Inc.   (1)
2269 Merrimack Valley Ave, Henderson, NV 89044
Tel.: (702) 326-3615
Sales Range: Less than $1 Million
Biopharmaceutical Developer
N.A.I.C.S.: 325414

NIKE, INC.

1 Bowerman Dr, Beaverton, OR 97005-6453
Tel.: (503) 671-6453   OR
Web Site: https://www.nike.com
Year Founded: 1964
NKE—(NYSE)
Rev.: $51,362,000,000
Assets: $38,110,000,000
Liabilities: $23,680,000,000
Net Worth: $14,430,000,000
Earnings: $5,700,000,000
Emp.: 79,400
Fiscal Year-end: 05/31/24
Athletic Footwear, Apparel, Equipment & Accessories Designer, Marketer & Distr
N.A.I.C.S.: 339920
Heidi O'Neill (Pres-Consumer & Marketplace)
Kelly T. Killingsworth (VP-Logistics-Global)
Mary Beth Laughton (Head-Global Direct to Consumer)

Craig Anthony Williams (Pres-Geographies & Marketplace)
Michael Spillane (Pres-Consumer Creation)
G. Scott Uzzell (VP/Gen Mgr-North America)
Chris L. Abston (Principal Acctg Officer, VP & Controller)
Monique S. Matheson (Chief HR Officer & Exec VP)
Maureen Mullen Murphy (Executives)
Ann M. Miller (Chief Legal Officer & Exec VP)
Andrew Campion (Mng Dir-Strategic Bus Ventures)
Matthew Friend (CFO & Exec VP)
Jameeka Aaron (Dir-North American Tech)
Elliott Hill (Executives)
KeJuan Wilkins (Chief Comm Officer & Exec VP)
Sarah Mensah (Pres-Jordan Brand)
Mark G. Parker (Exec Chm)
Angela Wei Dong (VP-Global & Gen Mgr-China)
Philip H. Knight (Founder)
Elliott J. Hill (Pres & CEO)

Subsidiaries:

American NIKE S.L.U.   (1)
Aubiannobregat 57, Park Dasnacocis Msblau II, Barcelona, 8820, Spain   (100%)
Tel.: (34) 934804100
Web Site: http://www.nike.com
Sales Range: $125-149.9 Million
Emp.: 250
Sales & Marketing
N.A.I.C.S.: 458210
Carlos Homevas (Mng Dir)

Converse Inc.   (1)
160 North Washington Street, Boston, MA 02114
Tel.: (978) 983-3300
Web Site: http://www.converse.com
Sales Range: $550-599.9 Million
Emp.: 150
Mfr & Distr of Professional Sports & Leisure Footwear & Athletic Apparel
N.A.I.C.S.: 424340

Subsidiary (Non-US):

Converse Korea LLC   (2)
Chungbuk heungdeokgu bihadong Lotte Outlet 332-1 3rd Floor, Chongju, Korea (South)
Tel.: (82) 437172948
Web Site: http://www.conversekorea.kr
Sporting Goods Mfr
N.A.I.C.S.: 339920

Futbol Club Barcelona Merchandising, S.L.   (1)
Aristides Maillol s/n, 08028, Barcelona, Spain
Tel.: (34) 902189900
Web Site: https://www.fcbarcelona.com
Sporting Goods Mfr
N.A.I.C.S.: 339920

Manchester United Merchandising Limited   (1)
Sir Matt Busby Way Old Trafford, PO Box 263, Manchester, M16 0WD, United Kingdom
Tel.: (44) 1618688546
Footwear Merchant Whslr
N.A.I.C.S.: 424340

NIKE (Switzerland) GmbH   (1)
Grindelstrasse 5, 8303, Bassersdorf, Switzerland
Tel.: (41) 448385555
Footwear Mfr
N.A.I.C.S.: 316210

NIKE (Thailand) Limited   (1)
183 South Sathorn Road, Yan Nawa, Bangkok, 10120, Thailand
Tel.: (66) 26466100
Emp.: 30
Clothing Store Operating Services
N.A.I.C.S.: 458110

NIKE (U.K.) Limited (1)
1 Victory Way, Sunderland, SR3 3XF,
United Kingdom **(100%)**
Tel.: (44) 1914016453
Web Site: http://www.nike.com
Sales Range: $150-199.9 Million
Emp.: 150
Sales of Footwear
N.A.I.C.S.: 458210

NIKE 360 Holding B.V. (1)
Colosseum 1, 1213 NL, Hilversum, Nether-
lands
Tel.: (31) 356266453
Web Site: http://www.nike.com
Emp.: 2,100
Footwear Whslr
N.A.I.C.S.: 424340

NIKE Argentina S.R.L. (1)
Av del Libertador 2442 - 9no piso, B1636,
Lomas de Zamora, Argentina
Tel.: (54) 1148516664
Apparel & Shoe Mfr & Distr
N.A.I.C.S.: 315990

NIKE Australia Pty. Ltd. (1)
PO Box 443, Abbotsford, 3067, VIC, Austra-
lia
Tel.: (61) 1300656453
Sales Range: $50-74.9 Million
Emp.: 220
Footwear Whslr
N.A.I.C.S.: 424340

NIKE Canada Ltd. (1)
200 Willington St W 5th Fl, Toronto, M5V
3C7, Canada **(100%)**
Tel.: (905) 764-0400
Web Site: http://www.nike.ca
Sales Range: $150-199.9 Million
Emp.: 150
Sales & Marketing
N.A.I.C.S.: 458210

NIKE Denmark ApS (1)
Kokkedal Industripark 101, 2982, Kokkedal,
Denmark **(100%)**
Tel.: (45) 49185050
Web Site: http://www.nike.com
Sales Range: $100-124.9 Million
Emp.: 30
Sales & Marketing
N.A.I.C.S.: 458210

NIKE Deutschland GmbH (1)
Otto-Fleck-Schneise 7, 60528, Frankfurt am
Main, Germany
Tel.: (49) 696897890
Web Site: http://www.nike.com
Footwear Whslr
N.A.I.C.S.: 424340

**NIKE European Operations Nether-
lands B.V.** (1)
Colosseum 1, 1213 NL, Hilversum, Nether-
lands
Tel.: (31) 356266453
Web Site: http://www.nike.com
Emp.: 2,100
Sports Equipment Whslr
N.A.I.C.S.: 423910

NIKE Finland OY (1)
Pakkalankuja 6 PL 5, 01511, Vantaa, Fin-
land
Tel.: (358) 941356600
Web Site: http://www.nike.com
Sporting Goods Mfr
N.A.I.C.S.: 339920

NIKE France S.A.R.L. (1)
Rue de I Equerre ZI des Bethunes, Saint-
Ouen-l'Aumone, 95310, France **(100%)**
Tel.: (33) 134301000
Web Site: http://www.nike.com
Sales Range: $150-199.9 Million
Emp.: 200
Sales & Marketing
N.A.I.C.S.: 458210
Eric Cuenot *(Gen Dir)*

NIKE Gesellschaft m.b.H. (1)
Donau Business Center 388
Handelskai/C42, 1020, Vienna,
Austria **(100%)**
Tel.: (43) 172706
Web Site: http://www.nike.com
Sales Range: $100-124.9 Million
Emp.: 20
N.A.I.C.S.: 458210

Daniel Appiar *(Mng Dir & Gen Mgr)*

NIKE Group Holding B.V. (1)
Colosseum 1, Hilversum, 1213 NL, Noord-
Holland, Netherlands
Tel.: (31) 356266453
Footwear Distr
N.A.I.C.S.: 424340

NIKE Hong Kong Limited (1)
Hong Zhao Road 33 International Exchange
Center 29 floor, Kowloon Bay, China (Hong
Kong)
Tel.: (852) 82122122
Web Site: https://www.nike.com.hk
Footwear Mfr
N.A.I.C.S.: 316210

NIKE IHM, Inc. (1)
8 Missouri Research Park Dr, Saint
Charles, MO 63304
Tel.: (636) 939-5300
Web Site: http://www.nike.com
Sales Range: $75-99.9 Million
Mfr of Custom Extruded Plastic Sheet &
Silk Screening Facilities
N.A.I.C.S.: 326113

NIKE India Private Limited (1)
701 Tower B Millenia Towers Murphy Road
Ulsoor, Bengaluru, 560 008, India
Tel.: (91) 8041343195
Footwear Distr
N.A.I.C.S.: 424340
Avinash Pant *(Head-Mktg)*

NIKE Israel Ltd. (1)
9 Arie Shenkar Street, Herzliya Pituach,
4672509, Hertzliya, Israel
Tel.: (972) 99578777
Web Site: http://www.nike-israel.co.il
Footwear Whslr
N.A.I.C.S.: 424340

NIKE Italy S.R.L. (1)
Via Isonzo 55, 40033, Casalecchio di Reno,
Bologna, Italy
Tel.: (39) 0516115511
Web Site: http://www.nike.com
Sales & Marketing
N.A.I.C.S.: 458210

NIKE Japan Corp. (1)
Sea Fort Square Center Building 21/F
2-3-12 Higashi-Shinagawa, Tokyo, 140-
8631, Japan
Tel.: (81) 3 5463 3300
Web Site: http://www.nike.com
Footwear Whslr
N.A.I.C.S.: 424340

NIKE Poland Sp.zo.o (1)
Crown Square Ul Przyokopowa 31, 01-208,
Warsaw, Poland
Tel.: (48) 225352040
Web Site: http://www.nike.com
Sporting Goods Mfr
N.A.I.C.S.: 339920

NIKE Retail Israel Ltd. (1)
9 Senkar Street Gav Yam Building 3, Her-
zliya Pithuac, Herzliyya, Israel
Tel.: (972) 99578777
Web Site: http://www.nike.com
Sporting Goods Mfr
N.A.I.C.S.: 339920

NIKE Retail Services Inc. (1)
1 Bowerman Dr, Beaverton, OR
97005-0979 **(100%)**
Tel.: (503) 671-6453
Web Site: http://www.nike.com
Sales Range: $1-4.9 Billion
Emp.: 8,000
Footwear Athletic
N.A.I.C.S.: 458210

NIKE Sports Korea Co., Ltd. (1)
Yeoksam-Dong Gangnam-GU 737 GFC
13th Floor, Seoul, 135-081, Korea (South)
Tel.: (82) 2 2006 5700
Web Site: http://www.nike.com
Emp.: 200
Footwear Distr
N.A.I.C.S.: 424340

NIKE Sweden AB (1)
Dalvagen 16, PO Box 731, 169 27, Solna,
Sweden **(100%)**
Tel.: (46) 84447000
Web Site: http://www.nike.se

Sales Range: $100-124.9 Million
Emp.: 60
Sales & Marketing
N.A.I.C.S.: 458210
Aristoteles Barutses *(Mng Dir)*

NIKE de Chile Ltda. (1)
Av Isidora Goyenechea 3365-1st Floor, Las
Condes, 7550120, Chile
Tel.: (56) 223662700
Sporting Goods Mfr
N.A.I.C.S.: 339920

**NIKE de Mexico S de R.L. de
C.V.** (1)
Ontario 1107 Col Providencia, Guadalajara,
44620, Jalisco, Mexico
Tel.: (52) 3330032400
Footwear Distr
N.A.I.C.S.: 424340

**NIKE do Brasil Comercio e Participa-
coes Ltda.** (1)
Alameda Araguaia 1142 3 andar Alphaville
Barueri, Sao Paulo, 06455, Brazil
Tel.: (55) 1121666453
Sporting Goods Mfr
N.A.I.C.S.: 339920

SP Apparel, Inc. (1)
1237 boul Industriel, Granby, J2J 2B8, QC,
Canada **(100%)**
Tel.: (450) 776-6111
Web Site: http://www.spapparel.com
Emp.: 260
Team Sports Uniform Mfr
N.A.I.C.S.: 315250
Serge Berard *(Pres)*

NIKOLA CORP.
4141 E Broadway Rd, Phoenix, AZ
85040
Tel.: (480) 666-1038   DE
Web Site:
  https://www.nikolamotor.com
Year Founded: 2018
NKLA—(NASDAQ)
Rev.: $50,825,000
Assets: $1,236,658,000
Liabilities: $710,179,000
Net Worth: $526,479,000
Earnings: ($784,238,000)
Emp.: 1,500
Fiscal Year-end: 12/31/22
Automobile & Light Duty Motor Ve-
hicle Manufacturing
N.A.I.C.S.: 336110
Thomas B. Okray *(CFO & Principal
Acctg Officer)*
Stephen J. Girsky *(Chm)*
Britton Worthen *(Chief Legal Officer)*
Mary S. Chan *(COO)*
Michael Lohscheller *(Pres-Nikola Mo-
tor)*
Joseph Pike *(Chief HR Officer)*
Pablo Koziner *(Pres-Energy &
Comml)*
Stasy Pasterick *(CFO)*
Stephen J. Girsky *(Pres & CEO)*

Subsidiaries:

Romeo Power, Inc. (1)
4380 Ayers Ave, Vernon, CA 90058
Web Site: http://www.romeopower.com
Rev.: $16,804,000
Assets: $335,446,000
Liabilities: $56,295,000
Net Worth: $279,151,000
Earnings: $10,031,000
Emp.: 293
Fiscal Year-end: 12/31/2021
Motor Vehicle Parts Mfr
N.A.I.C.S.: 336390
Kim J. Brady *(CFO)*
Britton Worthen *(Gen Counsel, Sec & VP)*
Mark A. Russell *(Pres & CEO)*

NINE ENERGY SERVICE, INC.
2001 Kirby Dr Ste 200, Houston, TX
77019
Tel.: (281) 730-5100   DE
Web Site:
  https://www.nineenergyservice.com

Year Founded: 2013
NINE—(NYSE)
Rev.: $593,382,000
Assets: $426,834,000
Liabilities: $450,341,000
Net Worth: ($23,507,000)
Earnings: $14,393,000
Emp.: 1,212
Fiscal Year-end: 12/31/22
Oil & Gas Field Exploration Services
N.A.I.C.S.: 213112
David Crombie *(COO & Exec VP)*
Nick Pottmeyer *(Pres-Completion
Tools)*
Heather Schmidt *(VP-Strategic Dev,
Strategic Dev, and Strategic Dev)*
Joe Huwel *(Pres-Cementing & Coiled
Tubing)*
S. Brett Luz *(Chief Acctg Officer)*
Guy Sirkes *(CFO & Sr VP)*
Clair Holley *(CTO)*
Ernie L. Danner *(Chm)*
Jeff Hyre *(Pres-Wireline)*
Jasmine Huff *(Specialist-Compliance)*
Ann G. Fox *(Pres, CEO & Sec)*

Subsidiaries:

CDK Perforating Holdings, Inc. (1)
8101 Boat Club Rd Ste 330, Fort Worth, TX
76179
Tel.: (817) 945-1051
Oil & Gas Field Exploration Services
N.A.I.C.S.: 213112

**Crest Pumping Technologies,
LLC** (1)
6500 W Freeway Ste 601, Fort Worth, TX
76102
Tel.: (817) 484-5100
Oil & Gas Field Exploration Services
N.A.I.C.S.: 213112

Dak-Tana Wireline, LLC (1)
125 1/2 S Main St, Baker, MT 59313
Tel.: (406) 778-3254
Oil & Gas Field Exploration Services
N.A.I.C.S.: 213112

Frac Technology AS (1)
Kvamsvegen 9, Ytre Arna, 5265, Bergen,
Norway
Tel.: (47) 94867558
Web Site: https://www.fractechnology.com
Oil & Gas Field Machinery & Equipment Mfr
N.A.I.C.S.: 333132

Nine Energy Canada Inc. (1)
840 - 7th Avenue SW Suite 1840, Calgary,
T2P 3G2, AB, Canada
Tel.: (403) 266-0908
Oil & Gas Field Services
N.A.I.C.S.: 213112
Riley Taggart *(VP & Country Mgr)*

**Northern Production Company,
LLC** (1)
701 Sinclair St, Gillette, WY 82718
Tel.: (307) 682-5708
Web Site: http://www.npcrigs.com
Well Services
N.A.I.C.S.: 213112

**Northern States Completions,
Inc.** (1)
14069 49th St N W, Williston, ND 58801
Tel.: (701) 572-5720
Oil & Gas Field Exploration Services
N.A.I.C.S.: 213112
Rickey Green *(Owner)*

RedZone Coil Tubing, LLC (1)
1101 S Loop Rd 464, Monahans, TX 79756
Tel.: (432) 943-4501
Web Site: http://www.redzonecoil.com
Coil Tubing Services
N.A.I.C.S.: 213112

SJL Well Service, LLC (1)
7553 Hwy 81 S, Hennessey, OK 73742
Tel.: (405) 853-2044
Web Site: http://www.sjlwellservice.com
Well Services
N.A.I.C.S.: 213112

NIOCORP DEVELOPMENTS
LTD.

NioCorp Developments Ltd.—(Continued)

7000 S Yosemite St Ste 115, Centennial, CO 80112
Tel.: (720) 334-7066   BC
Web Site: https://www.niocorp.com
Year Founded: 1987
NB—(NASDAQ)
Assets: $20,070,000
Liabilities: $19,070,000
Net Worth: $1,000,000
Earnings: $11,435,000
Emp.: 7
Fiscal Year-end: 06/30/24
Metal Mining Services
N.A.I.C.S.: 212290
Jim Sims (Chief Comm Officer)
Mark Alan Smith (Exec Chm, Pres & CEO)
Scott Honan (COO)
Neal S. Shah (CFO & Sec)

Subsidiaries:

Elk Creek Resources Corp.   (1)
7000 South Yosemite St, Centennial, CO 80112
Tel.: (720) 639-4647
Metal Mining Services
N.A.I.C.S.: 212290

NISOURCE INC.
801 E 86th Ave, Merrillville, IN 46410
Tel.: (219) 647-5990   DE
Web Site: https://www.nisource.com
Year Founded: 1987
NI—(NYSE)
Rev.: $5,505,400,000
Assets: $31,077,200,000
Liabilities: $9,885,400,000
Net Worth: $21,191,800,000
Earnings: $714,300,000
Emp.: 7,364
Fiscal Year-end: 12/31/23
Holding Company: Natural Gas, Electricity & Water for Residential & Commercial Markets
N.A.I.C.S.: 221210
Lloyd M. Yates (Pres & CEO)
Shawn Anderson (CFO & Exec VP)
Gunnar J. Gode (Chief Acctg Officer, VP & Controller)
Kim Cuccia (Gen Counsel, Sec & Sr VP)
Melody Birmingham-Byrd (Grp Pres-Utilities & Exec VP)
William Jefferson (Chief Safety Officer & Exec VP-Ops)
Melanie Berman (Chief HR Officer & Sr VP)
Michael Luhrs (Chief Comml Officer & Exec VP-Strategy & Risk)
Brent Archer (Pres)
Kimra Cole (Pres)

Subsidiaries:

Columbia Gas of Kentucky, Inc. (1)
2001 Mercer Rd, Lexington, KY 40511-1018   (100%)
Tel.: (859) 288-6343
Web Site: http://www.columbiagasky.com
Rev.: $120,000,000
Emp.: 321
Gas Utility
N.A.I.C.S.: 221210

Columbia Gas of Maryland, Inc. (1)
121 Champion Way, Canonsburg, PA 15317-9585   (100%)
Tel.: (724) 416-6300
Web Site: http://www.columbiagasmd.com
Sales Range: $25-49.9 Million
Emp.: 80
Gas Utility
N.A.I.C.S.: 221210

Columbia Gas of Ohio, Inc. (1)
200 Civic Ctr Dr, Columbus, OH 43215   (100%)
Tel.: (614) 460-6000
Web Site: https://www.columbiagasohio.com

Sales Range: $1-4.9 Billion
Emp.: 1,000
Gas Utility Services
N.A.I.C.S.: 221210
Jack Laverty (Mgr)
Daniel A. Creekmur (Pres & Sr VP)
Melissa Thompson (Dir-Regulatory Policy)
Thomas Young (Mgr-Economic Dev)
Doug Nusbaum (VP)
Lisa Carmean (VP & Gen Mgr-Operations)
Frank Davis (VP)
David Musser (Dir)
David Nelson (Dir)
C. J. Anstead (Dir-Risk Management)
Staci Perkins (Dir-Communications-Community Affairs)
Don Ayers (Dir)
Sarah Poe (Mgr-Energy Efficiency Programs)

Columbia Gas of Pennsylvania, Inc. (1)
121 Champion Way, Canonsburg, PA 15317-9585   (100%)
Tel.: (724) 416-6300
Web Site: http://www.columbiagaspa.com
Sales Range: $350-399.9 Million
Emp.: 130
Gas Utility
N.A.I.C.S.: 221210

Columbia Gas of Virginia, Inc. (1)
1809 Coyote Dr, Chester, VA 23836
Tel.: (804) 323-5300
Web Site: https://www.columbiagasva.com
Sales Range: $10-24.9 Million
Emp.: 125
Gas Utility
N.A.I.C.S.: 221210

Columbia Retail Services (1)
100 International Ave, Portsmouth, NH 03801   (100%)
Tel.: (603) 422-8500
Web Site: http://www.esp-columbia.com
Sales Range: $150-199.9 Million
Emp.: 50
Gas Retail Products
N.A.I.C.S.: 213112

NiSource Energy Technologies, Inc. (1)
801 E 86th Ave, Merrillville, IN 46410-6271
Tel.: (219) 647-5590
Web Site: https://www.nisource.com
Electronic Services
N.A.I.C.S.: 221118

Northern Indiana Public Service Company LLC (1)
801 E 86th Ave, Merrillville, IN 46410   (80.1%)
Web Site: http://www.nipsco.com
Natural Gas Distr & Electric Company
N.A.I.C.S.: 221111
Dan Douglas (Sr VP)
Jim Zucal (Sr VP)
Jennifer Montague (VP-Communications)

NKARTA, INC.
1150 Veterans Blvd, South San Francisco, CA 94080
Tel.: (925) 407-1049   DE
Web Site: https://www.nkartatx.com
Year Founded: 2015
NKTX—(NASDAQ)
Rev.: $5,118,000
Assets: $472,938,000
Liabilities: $100,731,000
Net Worth: $372,207,000
Earnings: ($113,837,000)
Emp.: 163
Fiscal Year-end: 12/31/22
Biotechnology Research & Development Services
N.A.I.C.S.: 541714
Paul J. Hastings (Pres & CEO)
Kanya Rajangam (Chief Medical Officer)
James Trager (Chief Scientific Officer)
Ralph Brandenberger (Chief Technical Officer)
Alicia J. Hager (Chief Legal Officer)
Yvonne Li (Chief Admin Officer)

Alyssa Levin (Chief Fin & Bus Officer & Principal Acctg Officer)
Nadir Mahmood (Pres)
Paul J. Hastings (CEO)

NLIGHT, INC.
4637 NW 18th Ave, Camas, WA 98607
Tel.: (360) 566-4460   DE
Web Site: https://www.nlight.net
Year Founded: 2000
LASR—(NASDAQ)
Rev.: $209,921,000
Assets: $306,803,000
Liabilities: $52,384,000
Net Worth: $254,419,000
Earnings: ($41,670,000)
Emp.: 930
Fiscal Year-end: 12/31/23
Laser Mfr
N.A.I.C.S.: 334419
Robert Martinsen (CTO)
Matthew Randall (VP & Gen Mgr-Semiconductor Lasers)
Michael O'Connor (VP & Gen Mgr-Defense Lasers)
Kerry Hill (VP-HR & Treasury)
Joseph Corso (CFO)
James Nias (Chief Acctg Officer)
Chris Schechter (COO)
Julie Dimmick (Gen Counsel)
Scott Keeney (Co-Founder, Chm, Pres & CEO)

Subsidiaries:

Nutronics, Inc. (1)
1851 Lefthand Cir Ste G, Longmont, CO 80501
Tel.: (303) 530-2002
Engineeering Services
N.A.I.C.S.: 541330

NMI HOLDINGS, INC.
2100 Powell St 12th Fl, Emeryville, CA 94608
Web Site:
  https://www.nationalmi.com   DE
Year Founded: 2011
NMIH—(NASDAQ)
Rev.: $523,345,000
Assets: $2,516,030,000
Liabilities: $902,303,000
Net Worth: $1,613,727,000
Earnings: $292,902,000
Emp.: 242
Fiscal Year-end: 12/31/22
Holding Company; Mortgage Services
N.A.I.C.S.: 551112
Bradley Mize Shuster (Founder & Exec Chm)
Mohammad Yousaf (Exec VP-IT & Ops)
Norm Fitzgerald (Chief Sls Officer & Exec VP)
William J. Leatherberry (Gen Counsel & Exec VP)
Adam S. Pollitzer (Pres & CEO)
John M. Swenson (VP-IR & Treasury)
Robert Owen Smith (Chief Risk Officer & Exec VP)

NN, INC.
6210 Ardrey Kell Rd Ste 120, Charlotte, NC 28277
Tel.: (980) 264-4300   DE
Web Site: https://www.nninc.com
Year Founded: 1980
NNBR—(NASDAQ)
Rev.: $498,738,000
Assets: $546,127,000
Liabilities: $359,863,000
Net Worth: $186,264,000
Earnings: $26,098,000
Emp.: 3,363
Fiscal Year-end: 12/31/22
Precision Steel Balls & Rollers Mfr
N.A.I.C.S.: 332991

Verlin Bush (Chief Comml Officer & VP)
D. Gail Nixon (Chief HR Officer & Sr VP)
Harold C. Bevis (Pres & CEO)
David Harrison (Chief Procurement Officer)
Tim French (COO & Sr VP)
Christopher H. Bohnert (CFO & Sr VP)

Subsidiaries:

Autocam Corporation, Inc. (1)
4180 40th St SE, Kentwood, MI 49512
Tel.: (616) 698-0707
Web Site: http://www.autocam.com
Precision Machine Shop
N.A.I.C.S.: 336211

Subsidiary (Non-US):

Autocam (China) Automotive Components Co., Ltd (2)
Tel.: (86) 51081973535
Web Site: http://www.autocam.com
Precision Machined Metal Alloy Component Mfr
N.A.I.C.S.: 332721

Subsidiary (Domestic):

Autocam Corporation (2)
201 Percy St, Dowagiac, MI 49047
Tel.: (269) 782-5186
Web Site: http://www.autocam.com
Precision Metal Machining Mfr
N.A.I.C.S.: 332721

Branch (Domestic):

Autocam Corporation (2)
1511 George Brown Dr, Marshall, MI 49068
Tel.: (269) 789-4000
Web Site: http://www.autocam.com
Machined Metal Part Mfr
N.A.I.C.S.: 336390

Subsidiary (Non-US):

Autocam Corporation Bouverat Industries (2)
99 Rue des Charmilles Zl des Lecheres, 74460, Marnaz, France
Tel.: (33) 450899999
Web Site: http://www.autocam.com
Emp.: 150
Industrial Machinery Mfr
N.A.I.C.S.: 333248

Autocam Poland Sp. z.o.o. (2)
ul Jedwabna 3, 58-400, Kamienna Gora, Poland
Tel.: (48) 756451050
Precision Metal Components Mfr
N.A.I.C.S.: 332721

Autocam de Brasil Usinagem LTDA (2)
Rod De Acesso Boituva Porto Feliz 1230 km 12, Boituva, 18550-000, Sao Paulo, Brazil
Tel.: (55) 15 3363 8822
Web Site: http://www.autocam.com
Precision Metal Machining
N.A.I.C.S.: 423830

Subsidiary (Domestic):

Southeastern Technology, Inc. (2)
905 Industrial Dr, Murfreesboro, TN 37129
Tel.: (615) 890-1700
Aircraft Engine & Engine Parts Mfr
N.A.I.C.S.: 336412

Autocam International, Ltd (1)
4180 40th St SE, Kentwood, MI 49512
Tel.: (616) 698-0707
Ball & Roller Bearing Mfr
N.A.I.C.S.: 332991

Bouverat Industries, S.A.S. (1)
99 Rue des Charmilles Zl des Lecheres, 74460, Marnaz, France
Tel.: (33) 450899999
Web Site: https://www.trav.bouverat-industries.com

Ball & Roller Bearing Mfr
N.A.I.C.S.: 332991

Caprock Enclosures, LLC (1)
616 E Slaton Rd, Lubbock, TX 79404
Tel.: (806) 474-1000
Web Site:
http://www.caprockenclosures.com
Enclosure Product Mfr
N.A.I.C.S.: 335932

Caprock Manufacturing, Inc. (1)
616 E Slaton Rd, Lubbock, TX 79404
Tel.: (806) 474-1000
Web Site: http://www.caprock-mfg.com
Sales Range: $1-9.9 Million
Emp.: 80
Injection Molded Plastic Products Mfr
N.A.I.C.S.: 326199

Chelsea Grinding Co. (1)
543 N Mechanic St, Jackson, MI 49201
Tel.: (517) 796-0343
Sales Range: $1-9.9 Million
Emp.: 16
Metal Bearing Components & Precision
Metal Components Mfr
N.A.I.C.S.: 332991

Connecticut Plastics LLC (1)
1264 Old Colony Rd, Wallingford, CT 06492
Tel.: (203) 265-3299
Web Site: http://www.pepctplastics.com
Precision Machined Plastic Component Mfr
N.A.I.C.S.: 326199

General Metal Finishing LLC (1)
42 Frank Mossberg Dr, Attleboro, MA 02703
Tel.: (508) 226-5606
Web Site:
http://www.pepgenmetal.wpengine.com
Barrel Gold Electroplating Mfr
N.A.I.C.S.: 332813

Holmed, LLC (1)
48 Frank Mossberg Dr, Attleboro, MA 02703
Tel.: (774) 504-6900
Precision Steel Ball & Roller Mfr
N.A.I.C.S.: 332991

HowesTemco, LLC (1)
48 Frank Mossberg Dr, Attleboro, MA 02703
Tel.: (774) 504-6900
Web Site: http://www.howestemco.com
Precision Plastic & Metal Component Mfr
N.A.I.C.S.: 332216

**NN Life Sciences - Vandalia,
LLC** (1)
4201 Little York Rd, Dayton, OH 45414
Tel.: (937) 387-0880
Precision Steel Ball & Roller Mfr
N.A.I.C.S.: 332991
Tim Nelson *(Mgr-Quality)*

**NN Life Sciences Design & Develop-
ment, LLC** (1)
111 Forbes Blvd Ste 101, Mansfield, MA 02048
Tel.: (508) 406-2100
Precision Steel Ball & Roller Mfr
N.A.I.C.S.: 332991

NN Netherlands B.V. (1)
De Smalle Zijde 1b, 3903 LL, Veenendaal,
Netherlands
Tel.: (31) 318532111
Web Site: http://www.sheet-metal-
products.com
Emp.: 300
Roller Bearing Mfr
N.A.I.C.S.: 332991

PMC Acquisition Company, Inc. (1)
11355 Rojas Dr Ste 13-14, El Paso, TX 79936-6465
Tel.: (915) 225-8758
Emp.: 250
Ball & Roller Bearing Mfr
N.A.I.C.S.: 332991

**Precision Engineered Products,
LLC** (1)
110 Frank Mossberg Dr, Attleboro, MA 02703
Tel.: (508) 226-5600
Web Site: http://www.pep-corp.com
Medical Device & Electrical Component Mfr
N.A.I.C.S.: 339112

Subsidiary (Domestic):

**Boston Endo-Surgical Technologies
LLC** (2)

1146 Barnum Ave, Bridgeport, CT 06610
Tel.: (203) 334-9991
Web Site: http://www.pepbe-st.com
Surgical Equipment Mfr
N.A.I.C.S.: 339113

Unit (Non-US):

Brainin de Mexico S.A. de C.V. (2)
Av San Luis Tlatilco 42, Parque Industrial
Naucalpan, 53489, Mexico, Mexico
Tel.: (52) 555 301 1788
Web Site: http://www.pepbrainin.com
Precision Metal Components Mfr
N.A.I.C.S.: 332721

Subsidiary (Domestic):

Brainin-Advance Industries, LLC (2)
48 Frank Mossberg Dr, Attleboro, MA 02703
Tel.: (508) 226-1200
Web Site: https://brainin.wpengine.com
Precision Metal Components Mfr
N.A.I.C.S.: 332721

Subsidiary (Non-US):

**Brainin (Foshan) Precision Engi-
neered Products, Co. Ltd** (3)
7 Xinyue Road, Shunde Industrial Park Wusha Daliang Shunde District, Foshan,
528300, China
Tel.: (86) 75727880188
Web Site: http://pepcorp.wpengine.com
Precision Turned Product Mfr
N.A.I.C.S.: 332721

Subsidiary (Domestic):

**Lacey Manufacturing Company
LLC** (2)
1146 Barnum Ave, Bridgeport, CT 06610
Tel.: (203) 336-0121
Web Site: http://www.peplacey.com
Precision Stampings & Injection Molding
Equipment Mfr
N.A.I.C.S.: 332119

Unit (Domestic):

Polymetallurgical LLC (2)
262 Broad St, North Attleboro, MA 02760
Tel.: (508) 695-7700
Web Site: https://www.polymet.com
Precision Clad Metal Mfr
N.A.I.C.S.: 332312

**Precision Engineered Products LLC -
General Metal Finishing** (2)
42 Frank Mossberg Dr, Attleboro, MA 02703
Tel.: (508) 226-5606
Web Site: http://www.pepgenmetal.com
Metal Plating & Finishing Services
N.A.I.C.S.: 332813

**Precision Engineered Products LLC -
Wauconda** (2)
821 W Algonquin Rd, Algonquin, IL 60102
Tel.: (847) 658-4588
Web Site: http://www.pepwauconda.com
Metal Stamping Mfr & Supplier
N.A.I.C.S.: 332119

**Precision Engineered Products LLC -
microPEP** (2)
1 Catamore Blvd, East Providence, RI
02914
Tel.: (401) 434-3040
Web Site: http://www.pepmicropep.com
Plastic & Micro Molding Component Mfr
N.A.I.C.S.: 332312

Premco, Inc. (1)
55 Research Rd S Shore Park, Hingham,
MA 02043
Tel.: (781) 749-0333
Web Site: http://www.premco.net
Precision Plastic & Metal Component Mfr
N.A.I.C.S.: 332216

RFK Valjcici (1)
Hadzica Polje b b, 88400, Konjic, Bosnia &
Herzegovina
Tel.: (387) 36728084
Ball & Roller Bearing Mfr
N.A.I.C.S.: 332991

Trigon International LLC (1)
4000 Sussex Ave, Aurora, IL 60504
Tel.: (630) 978-9990
Precision Steel Ball & Roller Mfr

N.A.I.C.S.: 332991

**Wauconda Tool & Engineering
LLC** (1)
821 W Algonquin Rd, Algonquin, IL 60102
Tel.: (847) 658-4588
Precision Steel Ball & Roller Mfr
N.A.I.C.S.: 332991

Whirlaway Corporation (1)
125 Bennett St, Wellington, OH 44090
Tel.: (440) 647-4711
Web Site:
http://www.whirlawaycorporation.com
Motor Vehicle Parts & Accessories Mfr
N.A.I.C.S.: 336390

NNN REIT, INC.
450 S Orange Ave Ste 900, Orlando,
FL 32801
Tel.: (407) 265-7348   MD
Web Site: https://www.nnnreit.com
Year Founded: 1984
NNN—(NYSE)
Rev.: $828,111,000
Assets: $8,661,968,000
Liabilities: $4,504,511,000
Net Worth: $4,157,457,000
Earnings: $392,340,000
Emp.: 82
Fiscal Year-end: 12/31/23
Real Estate Investment Trust
N.A.I.C.S.: 525990
Christopher P. Tessitore *(Gen Coun-
sel, Sec & Exec VP)*
Stephen A. Horn Jr. *(Pres & CEO)*
Michelle L. Miller *(Chief Acctg Officer
& Exec VP)*
Steven D. Cosler *(Chm)*
Stephen A. Horn Jr. *(Pres & Sr VP)*

NOBILITY HOMES, INC.
3741 SW 7th St, Ocala, FL 34474
Tel.: (352) 732-5157   FL
Web Site:
https://www.nobilityhomes.com
Year Founded: 1967
NOBH—(OTCQX)
Rev.: $51,522,054
Assets: $62,361,118
Liabilities: $14,437,585
Net Worth: $47,923,533
Earnings: $7,232,029
Emp.: 145
Fiscal Year-end: 11/05/22
Mobile Homes Designer, Mfr & Re-
tailer
N.A.I.C.S.: 459930
Terry E. Trexler *(Chm, Pres & CEO)*
Thomas W. Trexler *(CFO & Exec VP)*
Jean Etheredge *(Sec)*
Lynn J. Cramer Jr. *(Principal Acctg
Officer & Treas)*

Subsidiaries:

Prestige Home Centers, Inc. (1)
3741 SW 7th St, Ocala, FL 34474 **(100%)**
Tel.: (352) 622-2955
Web Site:
https://www.prestigehomecenters.com
Sales Range: $25-49.9 Million
Emp.: 8
Mobile Home Mfr
N.A.I.C.S.: 459930

Subsidiary (Domestic):

Mountain Financial, Inc. (2)
3741 SW 7th St, Ocala, FL 34474 **(100%)**
Tel.: (352) 732-5157
Web Site: http://www.homesofnobility.com
Sales Range: $10-24.9 Million
Emp.: 2
Financial & Insurance Services
N.A.I.C.S.: 524126

**NOBLE EDUCATION ACQUISI-
TION CORP.**
1000 Brickell Plz Unit 3005, Miami,
FL 33131
Tel.: (305) 849-6729   DE

Year Founded: 2021
NEATU—(NASDAQ)
Emp.: 4
Investment Services
N.A.I.C.S.: 523999
David Noble *(Co-Chm & CEO)*
Peter Barkman *(Co-Chm & Pres)*
Angelo Biasi *(VP)*
Andrew Bilbao *(CFO)*

NOBLE ROMAN'S, INC.
6612 E 75th St Ste 450, Indianapolis,
IN 46250
Tel.: (317) 634-3377   IN
Web Site: https://www.nrom.info
Year Founded: 1972
NROM—(OTCQB)
Rev.: $14,373,574
Assets: $18,479,825
Liabilities: $16,288,942
Net Worth: $2,190,883
Earnings: $1,460,284
Emp.: 36
Fiscal Year-end: 12/31/23
Pizza Restaurants Operator
N.A.I.C.S.: 722513
Paul W. Mobley *(Chm, Exec Chm,
CFO & Principal Acctg Officer)*
A. Scott Mobley *(Pres, CEO & Sec)*
Noelle Brucki *(Controller)*
Kimberley Anderson *(Dir-Ops Area)*

**NOCOPI TECHNOLOGIES,
INC.**
480 Shoemaker Rd Ste 104, King of
Prussia, PA 19406
Tel.: (610) 834-9600   MD
Web Site: https://www.nocopi.com
Year Founded: 1983
NNUP—(OTCIQ)
Rev.: $4,627,200
Assets: $9,617,400
Liabilities: $799,000
Net Worth: $8,818,400
Earnings: $1,813,100
Emp.: 8
Fiscal Year-end: 12/31/22
Document Security & Other Printing
Products & Services
N.A.I.C.S.: 325910
Michael S. Liebowitz *(Chm & CEO)*
Matthew C. Winger *(Exec VP-Corp
Dev)*
Debra Glickman *(CFO)*

**NOCTURNE ACQUISITION
CORPORATION**
3 Germay Dr Unit 4 Ste 1066, Wilm-
ington, DE 19804
Tel.: (858) 228-7142   Ky
Year Founded: 2020
MBTC—(NASDAQ)
Rev.: $7,607
Assets: $116,649,312
Liabilities: $120,444,791
Net Worth: ($3,795,479)
Earnings: ($710,157)
Emp.: 2
Fiscal Year-end: 12/31/21
Investment Services
N.A.I.C.S.: 523999
Henry Monzon *(Chm & CEO)*
Ka Seng Ao *(CFO)*

NODECHAIN, INC.
5445 Oceanus Dr Ste 102, Hunting-
ton Beach, CA 92649
Tel.: (714) 916-9321   DE
Web Site: http://www.nodecha.in
NODC—(OTCIQ)
Sales Range: Less than $1 Million
Emp.: 2
Digital Cryptocurrency Mining &
Transaction Services
N.A.I.C.S.: 541611

Nodechain, Inc.—(Continued)

Andy Michael Ibrahim (Co-Pres, CEO, CFO, Treas & Sec)
Phillip M. Nuciola (Mng Dir-Finance & Administration)
Changzhi Shen (Co-Pres)

NOFIRE TECHNOLOGIES, INC.
5 James St S, Hackensack, NJ 07606
Tel.: (201) 818-1616   DE
Web Site: https://www.nofire.net
Year Founded: 1987
NFTI—(OTCIQ)
All Other Miscellaneous Chemical Product & Preparation Manufacturing
N.A.I.C.S.: 325998
Rob Conzett (Mgr-Intl Bus Dev)

NOGIN, INC.
1775 Flight Way Ste 400, Tustin, CA 92782
Tel.: (949) 222-0209   DE
Web Site: https://ir.nogin.com
NOGN—(NASDAQ)
Rev.: $94,471,000
Assets: $74,933,000
Liabilities: $147,957,000
Net Worth: ($73,024,000)
Earnings: ($52,726,000)
Emp.: 213
Fiscal Year-end: 12/31/22
Investment Services
N.A.I.C.S.: 523999
Jan-Christopher Nugent (Co-CEO)
Jonathan Huberman (Co-CEO)
Shahriyar Rahmati (CFO)
Subsidiaries:

Branded Online Inc.   (1)
946 W 17th St, Costa Mesa, CA 92627
Tel.: (949) 864-8136
Web Site: http://www.brandedonline.com
Sales Range: $25-49.9 Million
Emp.: 130
Online Shopping Services
N.A.I.C.S.: 541850

NON-INVASIVE MONITORING SYSTEMS, INC.
4400 Biscayne Blvd, Miami, FL 33137
Tel.: (305) 575-4200   FL
Web Site: https://www.nims-inc.com
Year Founded: 1985
NIMU—(OTCIQ)
Assets: $34,000
Liabilities: $759,000
Net Worth: ($725,000)
Earnings: ($113,000)
Fiscal Year-end: 07/31/24
Medical Equipment Mfr
N.A.I.C.S.: 334510
Jane H. Hsiao (Chm & Interim CEO)
James J. Martin (CFO & Treas)
Josh Weingard (Chief Legal Officer & Counsel-Securities)

NORDSON CORPORATION
28601 Clemens Rd, Westlake, OH 44145-4551
Tel.: (440) 892-1580   OH
Web Site: https://www.nordson.com
Year Founded: 1954
NDSN—(NASDAQ)
Rev.: $2,689,921,000
Assets: $6,000,966,000
Liabilities: $3,068,774,000
Net Worth: $2,932,192,000
Earnings: $467,284,000
Emp.: 8,000
Fiscal Year-end: 10/31/24
Liquid & Powder Coatings, Sealants & Adhesives Application Systems Mfr
N.A.I.C.S.: 333310

Stephen F. Shamrock (Chief Acctg Officer, VP & Controller)
Joseph P. Kelley (Exec VP)
Jennifer L. McDonough (Gen Counsel, Sec & Exec VP)
James E. DeVries (Exec VP-Continuous Improvement)
Daniel R. Hopgood (CFO & Exec VP)
Michael J. Merriman Jr. (Chm)
Sundaram Nagarajan (Pres & CEO)
Stephen P. Lovass (Exec VP)
Lara L. Mahoney (VP-Corp Comm & IR)
Sarah Siddiqui (Chief HR Officer & Exec VP)
Srini Subramanian (Exec VP)
Subsidiaries:

ARAG S.a. r.l.   (1)
Via A Palladio 5/A, 42048, Rubiera, Italy
Tel.: (39) 0522622011
Agriculture Machinery Mfr & Distr
N.A.I.C.S.: 333111

Ace Production Technologies, Inc.   (1)
6313 E Rutter Ave, Spokane, WA 99212
Tel.: (509) 924-4898
Web Site: http://www.ace-protech.com
Sales Range: $1-9.9 Million
Emp.: 12
Welding & Soldering Equipment Mfr
N.A.I.C.S.: 333992
Alan Cable (Pres)
Ryan Tiemann (Mgr-Customer Svc)
Kevin Valentine (Mgr-Natl Sls)

Arag Argentina S.A.U.   (1)
Juan Pablo II 5559, Santa Fe, 2000, Rosario, Argentina
Tel.: (54) 3415300840
Web Site: https://www.aragnet.com.ar
Agriculture Machinery Mfr & Distr
N.A.I.C.S.: 333111

Arag Australia Pty Ltd.   (1)
1/10 Stock Road, Cavan, 5094, SA, Australia
Tel.: (61) 883596277
Information Technology Services
N.A.I.C.S.: 541519

Arag do Brasil S.A.   (1)
Rua Tomazina 125 Bloco 10, Pinhais, Pr, Brazil
Tel.: (55) 4136687020
Information Technology Services
N.A.I.C.S.: 541519

Atrion Corporation   (1)
1 Allentown Pkwy, Allen, TX 75002
Tel.: (972) 390-9800
Web Site: https://www.atrioncorp.com
Rev.: $183,506,000
Assets: $264,712,000
Liabilities: $25,171,000
Net Worth: $239,541,000
Earnings: $35,008,000
Emp.: 722
Fiscal Year-end: 12/31/2022
Ophthalmic, Diagnostic & Cardiovascular Equipment Mfr
N.A.I.C.S.: 334510
David A. Battat (Pres & CEO)
Cindy Ferguson (CFO, Treas, Sec & VP)
Subsidiary (Domestic):

Atrion Leasing Company LLC   (2)
1 Allentown Pkwy, Allen, TX 75002-4206
Tel.: (972) 390-9800
Sales Range: $25-49.9 Million
Emp.: 98
Ophthalmic Goods Mfr
N.A.I.C.S.: 339115

Atrion Medical Products, Inc.   (2)
1426 Curt Francis Rd, Arab, AL 35016-0564   (100%)
Tel.: (256) 317-2123
Web Site: https://www.atrionmedical.com
Sales Range: $50-74.9 Million
Emp.: 250
Mfr of Medical Equipment, Injecting Molding Specialist
N.A.I.C.S.: 326199

Halkey-Roberts Corporation   (2)
2700 Halkey-Roberts Pl N, Saint Petersburg, FL 33716   (100%)
Tel.: (727) 471-4200
Web Site: https://www.halkeyroberts.com
Sales Range: $50-74.9 Million
Emp.: 200
Medical & Safety Equipment Mfr
N.A.I.C.S.: 339113
David Battat (CEO)
Steve Bello (VP-Business Development)

Quest Medical, Inc.   (2)
1 Allentown Pkwy, Allen, TX 75002-4206   (100%)
Tel.: (972) 390-9800
Web Site: https://www.questmedical.com
Sales Range: $25-49.9 Million
Emp.: 180
Cardiovascular & Intravenous Fluid Delivery Products Mfr
N.A.I.C.S.: 339112

Avalon Laboratories LLC   (1)
2610 E Homestead Pl, Rancho Dominguez, CA 90220-5610
Tel.: (310) 761-8660
Web Site: http://www.avalonlabs.com
Heart Cannulae Developer & Mfr
N.A.I.C.S.: 339112
Robert Foster (Founder, Chm & CEO)

Constructiewerkhuizen G. Verbruggen NV   (1)
Jan de Malschelaan 2, Temse, 9140, Belgium
Tel.: (32) 37111997
Flat Dies & Coextrusion Equipment Mfr
N.A.I.C.S.: 325510

CyberOptics Corporation   (1)
5900 Golden Hills Dr, Minneapolis, MN 55416
Tel.: (763) 542-5000
Web Site: http://www.cyberoptics.com
Rev.: $92,774,000
Assets: $98,022,000
Liabilities: $18,916,000
Net Worth: $79,106,000
Earnings: $12,751,000
Emp.: 189
Fiscal Year-end: 12/31/2021
Sensors & Sensor Systems Mfr
N.A.I.C.S.: 334519
Jennifer L. McDonough (Sec)
Subodh K. Kulkarni (Pres & CEO)
Subsidiary (Non-US):

CyberOptics (Singapore) Pte. Ltd.   (2)
No 21 Ubi Road 1 02-01, Singapore, 408724, Singapore
Tel.: (65) 6 744 3021
Web Site: http://www.cyberoptics.com
Sales Range: $1-9.9 Million
Emp.: 36
Developer of Process Control Sensors & Inspection Systems
N.A.I.C.S.: 334513

CyberOptics China Company Ltd.   (2)
No 1395 Hengshan Road, Kunshan, diangsu, 215300, China
Tel.: (86) 51250156306
Web Site: http://www.cyberoptics.com
Sales Range: $100-124.9 Million
Emp.: 10
Semiconductor Mfr
N.A.I.C.S.: 334413

CyberOptics Ltd.   (2)
15a Hornbeam Park Oval Hornbeam Park, Harrogate, HG2 8RB, North Yorkshire, United Kingdom   (100%)
Tel.: (44) 142 387 1411
Web Site: http://www.cyberoptics.com
Sales Range: $1-9.9 Million
Emp.: 5
Developer of Process Control Sensors & Inspection Systems
N.A.I.C.S.: 334513
Subsidiary (Domestic):

CyberOptics Semiconductor, Inc.   (2)
9130 SW Pioneer Ct Ste D, Wilsonville, OR 97070
Tel.: (503) 495-2200

Web Site: http://www.cyberopticssemi.com
Sales Range: $100-124.9 Million
Emp.: 10
Semiconductor Product Mfr
N.A.I.C.S.: 334413

Laser Design, Inc.   (2)
5900 Golden Hills Dr, Minneapolis, MN 55416
Tel.: (952) 884-9648
Web Site: http://www.laserdesign.com
Sales Range: $1-9.9 Million
Emp.: 30
3D Laser Scanning Systems Sales & Servicing
N.A.I.C.S.: 423830

Dage (SEASIA) Pte. Ltd.   (1)
2 Corporation Road Lobby A 03-11/12 Corporation Place, Singapore, 618494, Singapore
Tel.: (65) 65527533
Liquid & Powder Coating System Mfr
N.A.I.C.S.: 325510

Dage Deutschland GmbH   (1)
Kapellenstrasse 12, 85622, Feldkirchen, Germany
Tel.: (49) 892000338270
Liquid & Powder Coating System Mfr
N.A.I.C.S.: 325510
Philip Vere (Mng Dir)

Dage Holdings Limited   (1)
25 Faraday Road, Rabans Lane Industrial Area, Aylesbury, HP19 8RY, Buckinghamshire, United Kingdom
Tel.: (44) 1296317800
Web Site: http://www.nordsondage.com
Destructive & Non Destructive Mechanical Testing Component Mfr
N.A.I.C.S.: 334519
Phil Vere (Pres)

Dage Japan Co., Ltd.   (1)
D-4F Makuhari Techno Garden Bldg 1-3 Nakase , Mihama-ku, Chiba, 261-0023, Chiba, Japan
Tel.: (81) 432995851
Web Site: http://www.nordsondage.com
Sales Range: $10-24.9 Million
Emp.: 13
X Ray Inspection & Testing Equipment Mfr
N.A.I.C.S.: 334515
Toshiaki Ono (Dir-Sls-Test & Inspection)

Dage Precision Industries Limited   (1)
25 Faraday Road, Rabans Lane Industrial Estate, Aylesbury, HP19 8RY, Buckinghamshire, United Kingdom
Tel.: (44) 1296317800
Electronic Components Mfr
N.A.I.C.S.: 334419

Dage Precision Industries, Inc.   (1)
2747 Loker Ave, Carlsbad, CA 92010
Tel.: (510) 683-3930
Web Site: http://www.nordsondage.com
Sales Range: $10-24.9 Million
Emp.: 20
Xray System & Bond Testing Equipment Mfr
N.A.I.C.S.: 334516
Aram Kardjian (Mgr-Natl Sls-Bond Test)

Dage Test Systems (Suzhou) Co. Ltd.   (1)
Building 7 No 666 Jianlin Road Sub Industry Park Export Processing, Zone SND, Suzhou, 215151, Jiangsu, China
Tel.: (86) 51266652008
Liquid & Powder Coating System Mfr
N.A.I.C.S.: 333310

Dosage 2000 S.A.R.L.   (1)
40 rue des Vignobles, Chatou, 78400, Paris, France
Tel.: (33) 130826869
Precision Fluid Dispensing Equipment Mfr
N.A.I.C.S.: 333914

EDI GmbH   (1)
Bunsenstrasse 5, 51647, Gummersbach, Germany
Tel.: (49) 2261814245
Emp.: 2
Industrial Machinery Mfr
N.A.I.C.S.: 333998
Ina Schmidt (Mgr)

Extrusion Dies Industries, LLC   (1)

911 Kurth Rd, Chippewa Falls, WI 54729
Tel.: (715) 726-1201
Web Site: http://www.extrusiondies.com
Sales Range: $10-24.9 Million
Emp.: 225
Special Die & Tool Die Set Jig & Fixture Mfr
N.A.I.C.S.: 333514

Fluortek, Inc. (1)
12 McFadden Rd, Easton, PA 18045
Tel.: (610) 559-9000
Web Site: http://www.fluortek.com
Sales Range: $1-9.9 Million
All Other Plastics Product Mfr
N.A.I.C.S.: 326199
Jack P. Botti II (Founder)

Induquip, C.A. (1)
Av.Ppl Fundo La Union C.C. Centro Mayor
Local LA-5, San Diego Edo, Valencia, 2005,
Venezuela
Tel.: (58) 241 871 7195
Web Site: http://www.nordson.com
Sales Range: $10-24.9 Million
Emp.: 8
Hot Melt Adhesive System Distr
N.A.I.C.S.: 423830

Liquidyn GmbH (1)
Daimlerstrasse 5, 82054, Sauerlach, Ger-
many
Tel.: (49) 8104909440
Web Site: http://www.liquidyn.com
Electronic Components Mfr
N.A.I.C.S.: 334419

March Plasma Systems, Inc. (1)
2470 A Bates Ave, Concord, CA
94520-1122   (100%)
Tel.: (925) 827-1240
Web Site: http://www.marchplasma.com
Plasma Cleaning System Mfr
N.A.I.C.S.: 339112
James Getty (Pres)

Unit (Domestic):

**March Plasma Systems, Inc. - Florida
PCB Lab & Contract Services** (2)
1000 112th Cir N Ste 1200, Saint Peters-
burg, FL 33716
Tel.: (727) 573-4567
Web Site: http://www.nordson.com
Sales Range: $10-24.9 Million
Emp.: 22
Plasma Cleaning System Mfr
N.A.I.C.S.: 339112

**Matrix (Suzhou) Trading Co.,
Ltd.** (1)
Block D-01/03-04 Ascendas Xinsu, No 5
Xinghan Street, Suzhou, 215021, China
Tel.: (86) 13656203952
Electronic Components Mfr
N.A.I.C.S.: 334419

**Matrix Inspection Systems, Pte.
Ltd.** (1)
39 Joo Koon Circle, Singapore, 629105,
Singapore
Tel.: (65) 68982062
Web Site: http://m-xt.com
Electronic Components Mfr
N.A.I.C.S.: 334419

Matrix Technologies GmbH (1)
Kapellenstrasse 12, 85622, Feldkirchen,
Germany
Tel.: (49) 89200 033 8200
Web Site: https://www.nordsonmatrix.com
Electronic Components Mfr
N.A.I.C.S.: 334419
Eckhard Sperschneider (Mng Dir)

Matrix-FocalSpot, Inc. (1)
9915 Businesspark Ave Ste A, San Diego,
CA 92131
Tel.: (858) 536-5050
Web Site: http://www.focalspot.com
Electronic Components Mfr
N.A.I.C.S.: 334419
Frank Silva (Pres & CEO)

NDC Technologies Limited (1)
Bates Road, Essex, Maldon, CM9 5FA,
United Kingdom
Tel.: (44) 1621852244
Measurement Instrument Mfr & Distr
N.A.I.C.S.: 334513

NDC Technologies SRL (1)

Corso Cristoforo Colombo 33, Varese,
21013, Gallarate, Italy
Tel.: (39) 0331454207
Measurement Instrument Mfr & Distr
N.A.I.C.S.: 334513

NDC Technologies, Inc. (1)
8001 Technology Blvd, Dayton, OH 45424
Tel.: (937) 233-9935
Web Site: https://www.ndc.com
Measurement Instrument Mfr & Distr
N.A.I.C.S.: 334513

New Castle Rolls, Inc. (1)
1399 County Line Rd, New Castle, PA
16101
Tel.: (724) 656-5600
Emp.: 125
Industrial Machinery Mfr
N.A.I.C.S.: 333998

Nordson (Malaysia) Sdn. Bhd. (1)
11 Jalan Astaka U8/83 Seksyen U8, Bukit
Jelutong, 40150, Shah Alam, Selangor,
Malaysia   (100%)
Tel.: (60) 37 839 2200
Web Site: http://www.nordson.com
Sales Range: $10-24.9 Million
Emp.: 22
Technology Solutions Mfr & Distr
N.A.I.C.S.: 334513

**Nordson (Shanghai) Business Con-
sulting Co., Ltd.** (1)
137 Guoshoujing Road Zhangjiang Hi-Tech
Park, Pudong, Shanghai, 201203, China
Tel.: (86) 2138669166
Industrial Machinery & Equipment Distr
N.A.I.C.S.: 423830

Nordson (U.K.) Limited (1)
Unit 14 Apex Business Centre Boscombe
Road, Dunstable, LU5 4SB, Bedfordshire,
United Kingdom   (100%)
Tel.: (44) 1582691900
Adhesive Dispensing Product Mfr
N.A.I.C.S.: 325520

Nordson AB (1)
Hojdrodergatan 25, 212 39, Malmo, Scania,
Sweden
Tel.: (46) 406801700
Web Site: http://www.nordson.se
Liquid & Powder Coating System Mfr
N.A.I.C.S.: 325510

Nordson ASYMTEK, Inc. (1)
2747 Loker Ave W, Carlsbad, CA 92010-
6603
Tel.: (760) 431-1919
Web Site: http://www.nordson.com
Electronic Components Mfr
N.A.I.C.S.: 334419

**Nordson Advanced Technology (Ja-
pan) K.K.** (1)
Yamatane Fukagawa No1 Bldg 1-1-1 Etchu-
jima, Koto-ku, Tokyo, 135-0044, Japan
Tel.: (81) 35 639 7020
Web Site: https://www.nordson.com
Electronic Components Mfr
N.A.I.C.S.: 334419

**Nordson Advanced Technology (Sin-
gapore) Pte. Ltd.** (1)
2 Corporation Road 03-10/11/12 Corporation Place, Singapore, 618494, Singapore
Tel.: (65) 65527533
Electronic Components Mfr
N.A.I.C.S.: 334419

Nordson Andina Limitada (1)
Cra 49 A No 48 Sur - 100 local 109, Unidad
Industrial Las Vegas, Envigado,
Colombia   (100%)
Tel.: (57) 4 339 2500
Web Site: http://www.nordson.com.co
Sales Range: $10-24.9 Million
Emp.: 20
Industrial Machinery Mfr
N.A.I.C.S.: 333248
Alfredo Villa (Gen Mgr)

Nordson Asia Pacific, Ltd. (1)
Room 710 Topsail Plaza No 11 On Sum
Street Siu Lek Yuen, Shatin, Hong Kong,
New Territories, China (Hong Kong)
Tel.: (852) 26872828
Sales Range: $25-49.9 Million
Emp.: 50
Liquid & Powder Coating System Mfr

N.A.I.C.S.: 333310
Louisa Ko (Mng Dir)

Nordson Asymtek K.K. (1)
1-5-21 Tohshin Building 2F Katsushima,
Shinagawa-ku, Tokyo, 104-0012, Japan
Tel.: (81) 3 5762 2801
Web Site: http://www.nordson.com
Sales Range: $10-24.9 Million
Emp.: 12
Liquid & Powder Coating System Mfr
N.A.I.C.S.: 333310

Nordson Asymtek, Inc. (1)
2762 Loker Ave W, Carlsbad, CA
92010   (100%)
Tel.: (760) 431-1919
Web Site: http://www.asymtek.com
Sales Range: $50-74.9 Million
Emp.: 500
Automated Fluid Dispensing Equipment Mfr
N.A.I.C.S.: 334513
Rob Guthrie (Engr-Sls-Southern California)

Nordson Australia Pty. Limited. (1)
Unit 1 7 Anzed Court, Mulgrave, Melbourne,
3170, VIC, Australia   (100%)
Tel.: (61) 28 814 4695
Web Site: http://www.nordson.com.au
Sales Range: $25-49.9 Million
Emp.: 50
Industrial Machinery Mfr
N.A.I.C.S.: 333248

Nordson Australia Pty., Ltd. (1)
Ste 4 5-7 Meridian Pl NW Business Park,
Sydney, 2153, NSW, Australia   (100%)
Tel.: (61) 288144695
Web Site: http://www.nordson.com.au
Sales Range: $25-49.9 Million
Emp.: 30
Industrial Machinery Mfr
N.A.I.C.S.: 333248
Peter Den Brinker (Mng Dir)

Nordson B.V. (1)
Beukelsdijk 2, 5753 PA, Deurne, Nether-
lands
Tel.: (31) 49 335 2752
Web Site: https://www.nordson.com
Emp.: 70
Assembly Tool Mfr
N.A.I.C.S.: 333517
Michel Gijgerm (CEO)

Nordson BKG LLC (1)
1291 19th St Ln NW, Hickory, NC 28601
Tel.: (828) 326-9888
Electronic Components Mfr
N.A.I.C.S.: 334419

Nordson Benelux B.V. (1)
Bergerstraat 10, 6226 BD, Maastricht,
Netherlands   (100%)
Tel.: (31) 43 352 6000
Web Site: http://www.nordson.com
Sales Range: $25-49.9 Million
Emp.: 100
Industrial Machinery Mfr
N.A.I.C.S.: 333248

Subsidiary (Non-US):

Nordson Schweiz AG (2)
Barmenstrasse 13, 7324, Vilters,
Switzerland   (100%)
Tel.: (61) 614113838
Web Site: http://www.nordson.ch
Sales Range: $50-74.9 Million
Emp.: 1
Hot-Melt Applicators & Finishing Systems
Sales & Service
N.A.I.C.S.: 424950

Nordson CS, spol.s.r.o. (1)
Masarykova 413/34, 602 00, Brno, Czech
Republic   (100%)
Tel.: (420) 541240925
Web Site: http://www.nordson.cz
Sales Range: $10-24.9 Million
Emp.: 8
Industrial Machinery Mfr
N.A.I.C.S.: 333248

Nordson Canada Ltd. (1)
1211 Denison Street Unit 23, Markham,
L3R 4B3, ON, Canada   (100%)
Tel.: (905) 475-6730
Web Site: http://www.nordson.ca
Sales Range: $10-24.9 Million
Emp.: 30
Adhesive Dispensing System Mfr

N.A.I.C.S.: 325520

Nordson China Co., Ltd. (1)
137 Guoshoujing Road, Zhangjiang Hi-Tech
Park Pudong, Shanghai, 201203,
China   (100%)
Tel.: (86) 213 866 9166
Web Site: http://www.nordson.com.cn
Sales Range: $25-49.9 Million
Emp.: 60
Industrial Machinery Mfr
N.A.I.C.S.: 333248

**Nordson Corp. - Adhesive Dispensing
Systems Division** (1)
11475 Lakefield Dr, Duluth, GA 30097
Tel.: (770) 497-3400
Web Site: http://www.nordson.com
Sales Range: $75-99.9 Million
Emp.: 200
Adhesive Dispensing Equipment Mfr
N.A.I.C.S.: 333248

**Nordson Corp. - Industrial Coating
Systems Division** (1)
300 Nordson Dr, Amherst, OH 44001-2408
Tel.: (440) 985-4000
Web Site: http://www.nordson.com
Sales Range: $125-149.9 Million
Emp.: 500
Powder Spray Systems & Components, Liq-
uid Finishing Equipment & Industrial Coat-
ing Application Equipment Mfr
N.A.I.C.S.: 333248

Subsidiary (Domestic):

Nordson Sealant Equipment, Inc. (2)
28775 Beck Rd, Wixom, MI 48393
Tel.: (248) 412-7920
Web Site: http://www.nordson.com
Dispensing Systems Mfr
N.A.I.C.S.: 333914

**Nordson Corp. - UV Curing
Division** (1)
300 Nordson Dr, Amherst, OH 44001
Tel.: (440) 985-4573
Sales Range: $100-124.9 Million
UV Curing Systems & Associated Equip-
ment Mfr
N.A.I.C.S.: 334516

Nordson DAGE, Inc. (1)
25 Faraday Road, Rabans Lane Industrial
Area, Aylesbury, HP19 8RY, Buckingham-
shire, United Kingdom
Tel.: (44) 1296317800
Web Site: http://www.nordson.com
Electronic Components Mfr
N.A.I.C.S.: 334419

Nordson Danmark A/S (1)
Ostergade 1 2nd floor, 1150, Copenhagen,
Denmark   (100%)
Tel.: (45) 43660123
Web Site: http://www.nordson.dk
Sales Range: $125-149.9 Million
Emp.: 5
Industrial Machinery Whslr
N.A.I.C.S.: 423830

Nordson Deutschland GmbH (1)
Heinrich-Hertz-Strasse 42, 40699, Erkrath,
Germany   (100%)
Tel.: (49) 2 119 2050
Web Site: https://www.nordson.com
Sales Range: $50-74.9 Million
Emp.: 120
Industrial Machinery & Equipment Mfr
N.A.I.C.S.: 333248

Nordson Dima B.V. (1)
Beukelsdijk 2, 5753 PA, Deurne, Nether-
lands
Tel.: (31) 493352752
Industrial Machinery & Equipment Distr
N.A.I.C.S.: 423830

Nordson EFD LLC (1)
40 Catamore Blvd, East Providence, RI
02914
Tel.: (401) 431-7000
Web Site: https://www.nordson.com
Sales Range: $25-49.9 Million
Emp.: 100
Industrial Machinery & Equipment Mfr
N.A.I.C.S.: 334419

Nordson Engineering GmbH (1)

Nordson Corporation—(Continued)

Lilienthalstrasse 6, 21337, Luneburg, Germany **(100%)**
Tel.: (49) 4 131 8940
Web Site: https://www.nordson.com
Sales Range: $50-74.9 Million
Emp.: 330
Adhesive Application & Coating Systems Mfr
N.A.I.C.S.: 325520

Nordson Extrusion Dies Industries. LLC **(1)**
911 Kurth Rd, Chippewa Falls, WI 54729
Tel.: (715) 726-1201
Web Site: http://www.extrusiondies.com
Extrusion Die Mfr
N.A.I.C.S.: 333514

Nordson Finland Oy **(1)**
Hyttimestarinkuja 7, 02780, Espoo, Finland **(100%)**
Tel.: (358) 445022971
Web Site: http://www.nordson.fi
Sales Range: $25-49.9 Million
Emp.: 5
Industrial Machinery Mfr
N.A.I.C.S.: 333248

Nordson France, S.A. **(1)**
Parc de l Esplanade - 2 rue Charles Friedel, PO Box 90091, Saint Thibault-des-Vignes, 77462, Lagny-sur-Marne, Cedex, France **(100%)**
Tel.: (33) 16 412 1400
Web Site: http://www.nordson.fr
Sales Range: $10-24.9 Million
Emp.: 50
Industrial Machinery Mfr
N.A.I.C.S.: 333248

Nordson GmbH (Austria) **(1)**
C O Vienna City Tax, Wagramer Strasse 19, 1220, Vienna, Austria **(100%)**
Tel.: (43) 17075521
Web Site: http://www.nordson.com
Sales Range: $10-24.9 Million
Emp.: 4
Industrial Machinery Mfr
N.A.I.C.S.: 333248
Ulrich Bender *(CEO)*

Nordson Iberica S.A. **(1)**
　　　　　　　　　　　　　(100%)
Tel.: (34) 963132090
Web Site: http://www.nordson.es
Sales Range: $25-49.9 Million
Emp.: 40
Industrial Machinery Mfr
N.A.I.C.S.: 333248

Nordson India Private Limited **(1)**
143A Bommasandra Industrial Area, Chembur, Bengaluru, 560 099, India **(100%)**
Tel.: (91) 804 021 3600
Web Site: https://www.nordson.com
Sales Range: $10-24.9 Million
Emp.: 100
Industrial Machinery Whslr
N.A.I.C.S.: 423830
Supratik Das *(Mng Dir)*
H. N. Jayasimha *(Sr Mgr-Sls)*
Rahul Chowdhury *(Project Mgr-Bus Dev)*
Shivakumar Math *(Sr Engr-Quality Assurance)*

Nordson Italia S.p.A **(1)**
Centro Direzionale Milano Oltre Via Cassanese 21, Palazzo Tintoretto Segrate, 20090, Milan, Italy
Tel.: (39) 02 216 6841
Web Site: http://www.nordson.it
Industrial Machinery Mfr; Adhesives & Sealants Mfr
N.A.I.C.S.: 333248

Nordson K.K. **(1)**
8th Floor Toshin Building 5-21 Katsushima 1-chome, Shinagawa-ku, Tokyo, 140-0012, Japan **(100%)**
Web Site: http://www.nordson.co.jp
Sales Range: $50-74.9 Million
Emp.: 150
Industrial Machinery Mfr
N.A.I.C.S.: 333248
Masaru Uchida *(Pres)*

Nordson Korea **(1)**
90 Sagimakgol-ro, Jungwon-gu, Seongnam,

13211, Gyeonggi-do, Korea (South)
Tel.: (82) 31 736 8321
Web Site: http://www.nordson.com
Sales Range: $25-49.9 Million
Emp.: 53
Liquid & Powder Coating System Mfr
N.A.I.C.S.: 333310
Steve Shin *(CEO)*

Nordson MARCH, Inc **(1)**
2470-A Bates Ave, Concord, CA 94520-1294
Tel.: (925) 827-1240
Web Site: http://www.nordson.com
Electronic Components Mfr
N.A.I.C.S.: 334419
James D. Getty *(Pres)*
John Guinn *(Mgr-Product Engrg)*
Gary Monahan *(Dir-Ops)*

Nordson MEDICAL **(1)**
1270 Eagan Industrial Rd, Saint Paul, MN 55121
Tel.: (651) 452-1977
Web Site: http://www.nordsonmedical.com
Medical Applicators Mfr
N.A.I.C.S.: 339112

Subsidiary (Domestic):

Nordson Medical (NH), Inc. **(2)**
29 Northwestern Dr, Salem, NH 03079
Tel.: (603) 327-0600
Web Site: http://www.nordsonmedical.com
Plastic Profile Mfr
N.A.I.C.S.: 326121

Nordson Norge A/S **(1)**
Hojdrodergatan 25, S 212 39, Malmo, Sweden **(100%)**
Web Site: http://www.nordson.se
Sales Range: $25-49.9 Million
Emp.: 45
Industrial Machinery Mfr
N.A.I.C.S.: 333248

Nordson Osterreich GmbH **(1)**
Parkring 2, 1010, Vienna, Austria
Tel.: (43) 17075521
Web Site: http://www.nordson.at
Liquid & Powder Coating System Mfr
N.A.I.C.S.: 325510

Nordson PPS (Shanghai) Co. Ltd. **(1)**
Building 11 No 212 Jiangtian Road E, Songjiang, Shanghai, 201613, China
Tel.: (86) 215 785 0918
Web Site: https://www.nordson.com
Emp.: 215
Extrusion Die Mfr
N.A.I.C.S.: 333514

Nordson PPS GmbH **(1)**
Coermuhle 1, 48157, Munster, Germany
Tel.: (49) 251214050
Industrial Machinery Mfr
N.A.I.C.S.: 333998

Nordson Pacific, Inc. **(1)**
555 Jackson St, Amherst, OH 44001
Tel.: (440) 985-4000
Industrial Machinery Mfr
N.A.I.C.S.: 333998

Nordson Polska Sp.z.o.o. **(1)**
ul Nakielska 3, 01-106, Warsaw, Poland **(100%)**
Tel.: (48) 22 836 4495
Web Site: http://www.nordson.com
Industrial Manufacturing Parts, Products & Equipment Distr
N.A.I.C.S.: 333248

Nordson Portugal Equipamento Industrial, Ltda. **(1)**
Apartado 2038, Aguas Santas, 4429-909, Maia, Portugal **(100%)**
Tel.: (351) 229619400
Sales Range: $10-24.9 Million
Emp.: 7
Industrial Machinery Mfr
N.A.I.C.S.: 333248

Nordson Russia Limited Liability Company **(1)**
Russian Federation Dorozhnaya Street h 8 bld 1, Moscow, 117545, Russia
Tel.: (7) 4995193195
Web Site: http://www.nordson.ru

Sales Range: $10-24.9 Million
Emp.: 20
Screw Components Mfr
N.A.I.C.S.: 333515

Nordson S.E. Asia (Pte.) Limited, **(1)**
3rd Floor New City Group Building, No 216-218 Highway 13 Hiep Binh Chanh Ward Thu Duc District, Ho Chi Minh City, Vietnam
Tel.: (84) 837261684
Electronic Components Mfr
N.A.I.C.S.: 334419

Nordson S.E. Asia (Pte.), Ltd. **(1)**
2 Corporation Road 03-10/11/12 Corporation Place, Singapore, 618494, Singapore **(100%)**
Tel.: (65) 6 796 9500
Web Site: https://www.nordson.com
Sales Range: $10-24.9 Million
Emp.: 17
Industrial Machinery Mfr
N.A.I.C.S.: 333248
Chris Lui *(Mng Dir)*
Anthony Lim *(Mgr-Market-Nonwoven)*
Kenny Kok *(Controller-Fin)*
Seet Choon Chuen *(Mgr-Market-Industrial Coatings)*
Simon Varghese *(Mgr-Bus Dev-ICS)*
Spencer Tan *(Mgr-Indonesia)*
Vincent Kuan *(Mgr-PA, PPC & SEE)*
Mike Low *(Mgr-Bus & EFD)*
Choo Chiang Ngai *(Mgr-Penang)*

Nordson SA (Pty) Ltd. **(1)**
Unit 40 Northgate Business Park Block A, Gold Street Northgate Estate Brooklyn, Cape Town, 7405, South Africa
Tel.: (27) 215101888
Industrial Machinery & Equipment Distr
N.A.I.C.S.: 423830

Nordson SELECT GmbH **(1)**
Perlackerstrasse 11, Hagenbach, Germersheim, 76767, Germany
Tel.: (49) 72739494660
Industrial Machinery & Equipment Distr
N.A.I.C.S.: 423830

Nordson Sverige AB **(1)**
Hydrotherm 25, S 212 39, Malmo, Sweden **(100%)**
Tel.: (46) 406801700
Web Site: http://www.nordson.se
Sales Range: $25-49.9 Million
Emp.: 20
Industrial Machinery Mfr
N.A.I.C.S.: 333310
Jerry Ueek *(Mng Dir)*

Nordson Technology B.V. **(1)**
Bergerstraat 10, 6226 BD, Maastricht, Netherlands **(100%)**
Tel.: (31) 433526000
Web Site: http://www.nordson.com
Sales Range: $25-49.9 Million
Emp.: 100
Industrial Machinery Mfr
N.A.I.C.S.: 333248
George Gilliffen *(Mng Dir)*

Nordson Test and Inspection Americas, Inc. **(1)**
2747 Loker Ave W, Carlsbad, CA 92010
Tel.: (760) 918-8471
Adhesive Product Mfr & Distr
N.A.I.C.S.: 325520

Nordson Xaloy Incorporated **(1)**
1399 County Line Rd, New Castle, PA 16107
Tel.: (724) 656-5600
Web Site: http://www.nordson.com
Plastics Machinery Components & Equipment
N.A.I.C.S.: 333248

Subsidiary (Non-US):

Nordson Xaloy Asia (Thailand) Ltd. **(2)**
700/446 Moo 7 Donhuaroh, Muang Chonburi, Chon Buri, 20000, Thailand
Tel.: (66) 38 717 084
Web Site: http://www.xaloy.com
Mfr of Components & Melt Delivery Systems for Injection & Extrusion Machinery
N.A.I.C.S.: 333248

Nordson Xaloy Europe GmbH **(2)**

Richard-Wagner-Strasse 21, 74172, Neckarsulm, Germany
Tel.: (49) 7132 99935 0
Web Site: http://www.nordsonpolymerprocessing.com
Emp.: 15
Sales of Components & Melt Delivery Systems for Injection & Extrusion Machinery
N.A.I.C.S.: 423830

Nordson Xaloy Italia S.r.l. **(2)**
Corso Milano 26, 20052, Monza, Monza and Brianza, Italy
Tel.: (39) 039328217
Plastics Product Mfr
N.A.I.C.S.: 326199

Nordson Xaloy K.K. **(2)**
Toshin Building 2F 1-5-21, Katsushima, nagawa, 140-0012, Tokyo, Japan
Tel.: (81) 357622776
Web Site: http://www.nordsonxaloy.com
Emp.: 5
Industrial Machinery Mfr
N.A.I.C.S.: 333998
Tetsuro Kamiya *(Gen Mgr)*

Subsidiary (Domestic):

Xaloy Extrusion LLC **(2)**
1291 19th St Ln, Hickory, NC 28601
Tel.: (828) 326-9888
Web Site: http://www.nordson.com
Gear Pump Systems for Plastic Extrusion Lines
N.A.I.C.S.: 423830

Nordson YESTECH, Inc. **(1)**
2747 Loker Ave W, Carlsbad, CA 92010
Tel.: (760) 918-8471
Web Site: https://www.nordson.com
Electronic Components Mfr
N.A.I.C.S.: 334419

Nordson de Mexico, S.A. de C.V. **(1)**
Retorno El Marques No 4-A Parque Industrial El Marques, Elmarques, 76246, Queretaro, Mexico **(100%)**
Tel.: (52) 442 256 1800
Web Site: http://www.nordson.com
Sales Range: $25-49.9 Million
Emp.: 55
Industrial Machinery Mfr
N.A.I.C.S.: 333248

Nordson do Brasil Industria e Comercio Ltda. **(1)**
Avenida Aruana 50 Tambore, Barueri, 06460-010, Sao Paulo, Brazil **(100%)**
Tel.: (55) 114 195 2004
Web Site: https://www.nordson.com.br
Sales Range: $25-49.9 Million
Emp.: 40
Industrial Machinery Mfr
N.A.I.C.S.: 333248

Plas-Pak Industries, Inc. **(1)**
10 Connecticut Ave Norwich Industrial Park, Norwich, CT 06360
Tel.: (860) 889-3383
Web Site: http://www.plaspakinc.com
Emp.: 150
Plastics Product Mfr
N.A.I.C.S.: 326199
Charles M. Frey *(CEO)*

Sonoscan (Europe) Ltd. **(1)**
25 Faraday Road Rabans Lane Industrial Area, Aylesbury, HP19 8RY, Buckinghamshire, United Kingdom
Tel.: (44) 1296317800
Analytical Laboratory Instrument Mfr
N.A.I.C.S.: 334516

Sonoscan Inc. **(1)**
2149 E Pratt Blvd, Elk Grove Village, IL 60007
Tel.: (847) 437-6400
Web Site: http://www.sonoscan.com
Ultrasonic Testing Equipment
N.A.I.C.S.: 334519
Lawrence Kessler *(Founder & Pres)*

Spirex Corporation **(1)**
8469 Southern Blvd, Youngstown, OH 44512
Tel.: (330) 726-4000
Plastics Product Mfr
N.A.I.C.S.: 326199

Value Plastics, Inc. **(1)**

805 W 71st St, Loveland, CO 80538
Tel.: (970) 267-5200
Web Site: https://www.nordsonmedical.com
Sales Range: $25-49.9 Million
Emp.: 75
Plastic Tubing Fittings & Connectors Designer & Mfr
N.A.I.C.S.: 326122
Ken Davis *(Product Mgr-Global)*

WAFO Schnecken und Zylinder GmbH (1)
Moselstrasse 9, 66955, Pirmasens, Germany
Tel.: (49) 633127360
Web Site: http://en.wafo.de
Electronic Components Mfr
N.A.I.C.S.: 334419

YESTech, Inc. (1)
2747 Loker Ave W, Carlsbad, CA 92010-6603
Tel.: (760) 431-1919
Web Site: http://www.asymtek.com
Sales Range: $125-149.9 Million
Emp.: 600
Automated Optical & X Ray Inspection Equipment Mfr
N.A.I.C.S.: 334519

NORDSTROM, INC.
1617 6th Ave, Seattle, WA 98101
Tel.: (206) 628-2111   **WA**
Web Site: https://www.nordstrom.com
Year Founded: 1901
JWN—(NYSE)
Rev.: $14,693,000,000
Assets: $8,444,000,000
Liabilities: $7,596,000,000
Net Worth: $848,000,000
Earnings: $134,000,000
Emp.: 54,000
Fiscal Year-end: 02/03/24
Apparel, Shoes & Accessories Retailer
N.A.I.C.S.: 458110
Catherine R. Smith *(CFO & Treas)*
Erik B. Nordstrom *(CEO)*
Peter E. Nordstrom *(Pres & Chief Brand Officer)*
James F. Nordstrom Jr. *(Chief Stores Officer)*
Kenneth J. Worzel *(Chief Customer Officer)*
Gemma Lionello *(Pres-Rack)*
Alexis DePree *(Chief Supply Chain Officer)*
Farrell Redwine *(Chief HR Officer)*
Jamie Nordstrom *(Chief Mdsg Officer)*
Fanya Chandler *(Pres-Stores)*
Lisa Price *(Chief HR Officer)*

Subsidiaries:

HauteLook, Inc. (1)
1212 S Flower St Fl Ste 300, Los Angeles, CA 90015-2123
Tel.: (888) 547-8438
Web Site: http://www.hautelook.com
Online Retail Services
N.A.I.C.S.: 425120

Nordstrom Credit, Inc. (1)
13531 E Caley Ave, Englewood, CO 80111   (100%)
Tel.: (303) 397-4700
Web Site: http://www.nordstrom.com
Sales Range: $150-199.9 Million
Emp.: 600
Finance Retail Charge Card Receivables Generated Under Revolving Charge Accounts Through Sales of Merchandise in Nordstrom Stores
N.A.I.C.S.: 522299

Nordstrom Direct (1)
1700 7th Ave, Seattle, WA 98101-1707   (85%)
Tel.: (206) 628-2111
Web Site: http://www.nordstrom.com
Sales Range: $100-124.9 Million
Catalog & Web Sales of Department Store Goods
N.A.I.C.S.: 458110

Peter E. Nordstrom *(Pres-Mdsg & Exec VP)*

Nordstrom Distribution #89 (1)
5703 N Marine Dr, Portland, OR 97203
Tel.: (503) 240-6071
Web Site: http://www.nordstrom.com
Sales Range: $150-199.9 Million
Warehousing & Distribution
N.A.I.C.S.: 493110

Nordstrom fsb (1)
13531 E Caley Ave, Englewood, CO 80111-6505
Tel.: (303) 397-4700
Cloth Retailer
N.A.I.C.S.: 315250
Marie Aronce Cocian *(Mgr)*
Eric Liggett *(Principal-Internal Audit-I)*
Bryan Penny *(VP-Enterprise Risk Mgmt & Strategic Sourcing)*
Brandon Rhoades *(Mgr-Credit Risk)*
Ryan Gary *(VP)*

Trunk Club, Inc. (1)
325 W Ohio St, Chicago, IL 60654
Web Site: http://www.trunkclub.com
Apparel Distr
N.A.I.C.S.: 458110
Brian A. Spaly *(Founder)*

NORFOLK SOUTHERN CORPORATION
650 W Peachtree St NW, Atlanta, GA 30308
Tel.: (757) 629-2680   **VA**
Web Site:
   https://www.norfolksouthern.com
Year Founded: 1827
NSC—(NYSE)
Rev.: $12,156,000,000
Assets: $41,652,000,000
Liabilities: $28,871,000,000
Net Worth: $12,781,000,000
Earnings: $1,827,000,000
Emp.: 20,700
Fiscal Year-end: 12/31/23
Holding Company; Railroad Operator
N.A.I.C.S.: 551112
Amy E. Miles *(Chm)*
Jason A. Zampi *(CFO, Treas & Exec VP)*
Robert E. Martinez *(VP-Business Development-Real Estate)*
Claude E. Elkins *(CMO & Exec VP)*
Jeffrey M. Heller *(VP)*
Fredric M. Ehlers *(CIO & VP-IT)*
John H. Friedmann *(VP)*
Scott R. Weaver *(VP-Labor Relations)*
Frank Voyack *(VP-Govt Rels)*
John F. Orr *(COO & Exec VP)*
Denise W. Hutson *(Sec)*
Stefan Loeb *(VP-First & Final Mile Markets)*
Susan S. Stuart *(VP-Audit & Compliance)*
Karol R. Lawrence *(VP)*
Jason Morris *(VP-Law)*
Michael F. Cox *(VP-Taxation)*
Gregory R. Comstock *(VP)*
Lorri J. Kleine *(Chief Legal Officer & Sr VP)*
Josh Raglin *(Chief Sustainability Officer)*
Barbara N. Paul *(VP-HR)*
Christopher R. Neikirk *(VP-Treasury & IR)*
John S. Hatfield *(VP-Corp Comm)*
Kathleen C. Smith *(VP-Bus Dev-Real Estate)*
James Kitchin *(VP-Indus Products)*
Wai Wong *(VP-Labor Rels)*
Claiborne L. Moore *(VP & Controller)*
Shawn I. Tureman *(VP-Intermodal & Automotive Mktg)*
Edward F. Boyle Jr. *(VP-Engrg)*
Mark R. George *(Pres & CEO)*

Subsidiaries:

Atlantic Investment Company (1)

3 Commercial Pl, Norfolk, VA
23510-2108   (100%)
Tel.: (757) 629-2600
Web Site: http://www.nscorp.com
Sales Range: $125-149.9 Million
Investment Company
N.A.I.C.S.: 522310

Conrail Inc. (1)
1717 Arch St 13th Fl, Philadelphia, PA
19103   (50%)
Tel.: (215) 209-2000
Web Site: http://www.conrail.com
Sales Range: $1-4.9 Billion
Emp.: 22,000
Holding Company; Line Haul Railroad Operator
N.A.I.C.S.: 551112
Joseph D. Soto *(Gen Mgr-Field Ops)*
Rodney Gordon *(Gen Mgr-Svc Delivery)*
Anthony D. Carlini *(Treas & VP-Fin & IT)*
Jocelyn Gabrynowicz Hill *(Gen Counsel & Sec)*
Eric B. Levin *(VP-Engrg, Mechanical & Real Estate)*
Brian Gorton *(Pres & COO)*

Affiliate (Domestic):

Albany Port Railroad Co. (2)
101 Raft St, Albany, NY 12202   (50%)
Tel.: (518) 463-8679
Rev.: $1,029,000
Emp.: 11
Railroad: Switching & Terminal Company
N.A.I.C.S.: 488210

Subsidiary (Domestic):

CRC Properties Inc. (2)
1717 Arch St 13th Fl, Philadelphia, PA
19103
Tel.: (215) 209-2000
Web Site: http://www.conrail.com
Rev.: $6,049,000
Own & Lease Real Estate
N.A.I.C.S.: 482111

CRR Industries, Inc. (2)
2001 Market St 16th Fl, Philadelphia, PA
19103
Tel.: (215) 209-5000
Sales Range: $75-99.9 Million
Investment Holding Company
N.A.I.C.S.: 488510

CRR Investments, Inc. (2)
1000 Howard Blvd 4th Fl, Mount Laurel, NJ
08054   (100%)
Tel.: (856) 231-7224
Web Site: http://www.conrail.com
Rev.: $65,019,000
Cash Management Company
N.A.I.C.S.: 238220

Consolidated Rail Corporation (2)
330 Fellowship Rd Ste 300, Mount Laurel,
NJ 08054   (100%)
Tel.: (856) 231-6401
Web Site: http://www.conrail.com
Sales Range: $100-124.9 Million
Line Haul Railroad Operator
N.A.I.C.S.: 482111

Indiana Harbor Belt Railroad Co. (2)
2721 161st St, Hammond, IN 46323
Tel.: (219) 989-4703
Web Site: http://www.ihbrr.com
Rev.: $72,417,000
Emp.: 728
Railroads; Switching & Terminal Company
N.A.I.C.S.: 488210
Steve Denby *(Mgr-Accounting & Treas)*
Leo Pauwels *(Dir-Sls & Industrial Dev)*
Paula Wratten *(Mgr)*
James Gidney *(Superintendent)*
Michael Kapitan *(Mgr-Risk Management)*
Patrick McShane *(Asst Dir-Business Development)*
Michael Schroeter *(Mgr-Customer Service)*
Dawn Geeve *(Mgr-Car Mgmt-Demurrage)*
John Wright *(Gen Mgr)*
Darrell Snyder *(Gen Dir-Mechanical & Engrg)*
Joel Cornfeld *(Gen Counsel)*
Donald Bolster *(Dir-Safety)*
Dan Kelley *(Dir-Human Resources)*
Nicole Moore Parchem *(Dir-HR & Labor Rels)*
Tammy Winterfeldt *(Dir-Customer Service)*
Jim Wilson *(Comptroller)*

Tony Kazakevicius *(Asst Dir-Business Development)*
Richard Katterman *(Asst Mgr)*
Matthew Peagler *(Dir-Customer Service)*
Michael Pavlopoulos *(Mgr-Customer Service)*
Eric Ritter *(Dir-Safety)*
Cindy Morley *(Mgr-Accounting & Treas)*
Joshua Sanchez *(Dir-Risk Management)*
James Pecyna *(Sr Mgr-Labor Relations)*

Penn Central Communications Corp. (2)
2001 Market St, Philadelphia, PA
19103-7044   (100%)
Tel.: (215) 209-5000
Sales Range: $400-449.9 Million
Repository for Radio & Communication Licensing
N.A.I.C.S.: 482111

Affiliate (Domestic):

Peoria & Pekin Union Railway Co. (2)
301 Wesley Rd, Creve Coeur, IL 61610
Tel.: (802) 527-3499
Rev.: $13,030,000
Emp.: 99
Railroad; Switching & Terminal Company
N.A.I.C.S.: 488210

Norfolk Southern Properties, Inc. (1)
3 Commercial Pl, Norfolk, VA
23510   (100%)
Tel.: (757) 629-2600
Sales Range: $250-299.9 Million
Transportation Services
N.A.I.C.S.: 551112

Subsidiary (Domestic):

Arrowood-Southern Company (2)
3 Commercial Pl, Norfolk, VA
23510-2108   (100%)
Tel.: (757) 629-2600
Sales Range: $400-449.9 Million
Freight Rail Transportation
N.A.I.C.S.: 482111
David R. Goode *(Chm & CEO)*

Lambert's Point Docks, Inc. (2)
3 Commercial Pl, Norfolk, VA
23510-2108   (100%)
Tel.: (757) 446-1212
Web Site: http://www.norfolk.com
Emp.: 50
Largest Breakbulk Marine Terminals for Freight Transportation
N.A.I.C.S.: 488510
John Schools *(Mgr)*

Norfolk Southern Intermodal (2)
3 Commercial Pl, Norfolk, VA
23510-2108   (100%)
Tel.: (757) 629-2600
Web Site: http://www.nscorp.com
Sales Range: $1-9.9 Million
Emp.: 18
Freight Rail Transportation
N.A.I.C.S.: 482111

Sandusky Dock Corporation (2)
2705 W Monroe St, Sandusky, OH 44870
Tel.: (419) 626-1214
Web Site: http://www.nscorp.com
Sales Range: $25-49.9 Million
Emp.: 11
Airfreight & Logistics Services
N.A.I.C.S.: 488510

Norfolk Southern Railway Company (1)
3 Commercial Pl, Norfolk, VA
23510-2191   (93.9%)
Tel.: (757) 629-2600
Web Site: http://www.nscorp.com
Freight Transportation Services
N.A.I.C.S.: 482111

Subsidiary (Domestic):

Camp Lejeune Railroad Company (2)
3 Commercial Pl, Norfolk, VA
23510-2108   (100%)
Tel.: (757) 629-2600
Web Site: http://www.nscorp.com
Sales Range: $400-449.9 Million
Freight Rail Transportation, Railroad Line
N.A.I.C.S.: 482111

Norfolk Southern Corporation—(Continued)

Carolina and Northwestern Railway Company (2)
1500 Carson St, Raleigh, NC 27608-2604
Tel.: (919) 831-3056
Emp.: 5
Rail Freight Transport Services
N.A.I.C.S.: 482111

Central of Georgia Railroad Company (2)
3 Comml Pl, Norfolk, VA
23510-2108 **(100%)**
Tel.: (757) 629-2600
Web Site: http://www.nscorp.com
Sales Range: $50-74.9 Million
Emp.: 150
Freight Rail Transportation
N.A.I.C.S.: 482111

High Point, Randleman, Asheboro and Southern Railroad Co. (2)
3 Commercial Pl, Norfolk, VA
23510-2108 **(86%)**
Tel.: (757) 629-2600
Web Site: http://www.nscorp.com
Sales Range: $400-449.9 Million
Freight Rail Transportation
N.A.I.C.S.: 482111

Lambert's Point Barge Company, Inc. (2)
3 Commercial Pl, Norfolk, VA
23510-2108 **(100%)**
Tel.: (757) 629-2600
Web Site: http://www.nscorp.com
Freight Transportation
N.A.I.C.S.: 483211

Mobile & Birmingham Railroad Co. (2)
3 Commercial Pl, Norfolk, VA
23510-2108 **(78%)**
Tel.: (757) 629-2600
Web Site: http://www.nscorp.com
Sales Range: $400-449.9 Million
Freight Rail Transportation
N.A.I.C.S.: 482111

Norfolk and Portsmouth Belt Line Railroad Company (2)
1340 Truxton St, Chesapeake, VA 23324
Tel.: (757) 271-1800
Web Site: http://www.npblrr.com
Railway Transportation Services
N.A.I.C.S.: 482111
Cannon Moss (Pres & Gen Mgr)

Southern Rail Terminals of North Carolina, Inc. (2)
3 Commercial Pl, Norfolk, VA
23510-2108 **(100%)**
Tel.: (757) 629-2600
Railroad Terminal Stations
N.A.I.C.S.: 482111

Southern Rail Terminals, Inc. (2)
3 Commercial Pl, Norfolk, VA
23510 **(100%)**
Tel.: (757) 629-2600
Web Site: http://www.nscorp.com
Sales Range: $75-99.9 Million
Emp.: 400
Railroad Terminal Stations
N.A.I.C.S.: 488210

Southern Region Coal Transport, Inc. (2)
3 Commercial Pl, Norfolk, VA
23510 **(100%)**
Tel.: (757) 629-2600
Web Site: http://www.nscorp.com
Sales Range: $400-449.9 Million
Emp.: 656
Freight Transportation
N.A.I.C.S.: 482111

State University Railroad Co. (2)
3 Commercial Pl, Norfolk, VA
23510-2108 **(54%)**
Tel.: (757) 629-2600
Web Site: http://www.nscorp.com
Sales Range: $400-449.9 Million
Freight Rail Transportation
N.A.I.C.S.: 482111

Tennessee Railway Co. (2)
3 Commercial Pl, Norfolk, VA
23510-2108 **(100%)**

Tel.: (757) 629-2600
Web Site: http://www.nscorp.com
Sales Range: $400-449.9 Million
Emp.: 300
Freight Rail Transportation

Tennessee, Alabama & Georgia Railway Co. (2)
3 Commercial Pl, Norfolk, VA
23510-2108 **(100%)**
Tel.: (757) 629-2600
Web Site: http://www.nscorp.com
Sales Range: $400-449.9 Million
Freight Rail Transportation
N.A.I.C.S.: 482111

The Cincinnati, New Orleans & Texas Pacific Railway Co. (2)
3 Commercial Pl, Norfolk, VA
23510-2108 **(100%)**
Tel.: (757) 629-2600
Sales Range: $400-449.9 Million
Freight Rail Transportation
N.A.I.C.S.: 482111

The South Western Railroad Co. (2)
3 Comml Pl, Norfolk, VA
23510-2191 **(99.8%)**
Tel.: (757) 629-2600
Web Site: http://www.norfolksouthern.com
Sales Range: $400-449.9 Million
Freight Rail Transportation
N.A.I.C.S.: 482111

Subsidiary (Non-US):

Thoroughbred Direct Intermodal Services, Inc. (2)
Tel.: (610) 567-3360
Web Site: http://www.ns-direct.com
Airfreight & Logistics Services
N.A.I.C.S.: 488510

Subsidiary (Domestic):

Transworks Company (2)
2720 Dupont Commerce Ct Ste 230, Fort Wayne, IN 46825
Tel.: (260) 487-4400
Web Site: http://www.trnswrks.com
Software Development Services
N.A.I.C.S.: 541511

Virginia & Southwestern Railway Co. (2)
3 Commercial Pl, Norfolk, VA
23510-2108 **(100%)**
Tel.: (757) 629-2600
Web Site: http://www.nscorp.com
Sales Range: $400-449.9 Million
Freight Rail Transportation
N.A.I.C.S.: 482111

Wheelersburg Terminal LLC (2)
914 Hayport Rd, Wheelersburg, OH 45694
Tel.: (740) 574-8491
Railroad Terminal Switching Services
N.A.I.C.S.: 488210

Yadkin Railroad Co. (2)
3 Commercial Pl, Norfolk, VA
23510-2191 **(74%)**
Tel.: (757) 629-2600
Web Site: http://www.nscorp.com
Sales Range: $400-449.9 Million
Freight Rail Transportation
N.A.I.C.S.: 482111

Pocahontas Development Corporation (1)
3 Commercial Pl, Norfolk, VA 23510-2108
Tel.: (757) 629-2600
Web Site: http://www.nscorp.com
Sales Range: $300-349.9 Million
Coal Reserves Purchasing; Holdings of Timber & Natural Gas
N.A.I.C.S.: 237210

Pocahontas Land Corporation (1)
435 Kimball Ave, Roanoke, VA
24016 **(100%)**
Tel.: (540) 524-4771
Web Site: http://www.nscorp.com
Sales Range: $10-24.9 Million
Emp.: 38
Real Estate
N.A.I.C.S.: 531190

Thoroughbred Technology and Telecommunications (1)

---

3 Comml Pl, Norfolk, VA
23510-2108 **(100%)**
Tel.: (757) 629-2600
Web Site: http://www.t3inc.com
Sales Range: $150-199.9 Million
Silo Mfr
N.A.I.C.S.: 238210

Triple Crown Services, Co. (1)
2720 Dupont Commerce Ct, Fort Wayne, IN 46825
Tel.: (260) 416-3600
Web Site: http://www.triplecrownsvc.com
Sales Range: $75-99.9 Million
Freight Transportation
N.A.I.C.S.: 482111
Sam Nenis (Pres)

NORRIS INDUSTRIES, INC.
5525 N MacArthur Blvd Ste 280, Irving, TX 75038
Tel.: (214) 492-5850   NV
Web Site: https://iwpetroleum.com
Year Founded: 2014
NRIS—(OTCQB)
Rev.: $452,291
Assets: $387,068
Liabilities: $4,172,728
Net Worth: ($3,785,660)
Earnings: ($498,947)
Fiscal Year-end: 02/28/22
Crude Petroleum Extraction Services
N.A.I.C.S.: 211120
Ross Henry Ramsey (Founder & Pres-Oil & Gas Div)
Patrick L. Norris (Pres, CEO, CFO, Chief Acctg Officer & Chm)
Allen Horn (VP-Production)

NORTECH SYSTEMS INCORPORATED
7550 Meridian Cir N Ste 150, Maple Grove, MN 55369
Tel.: (952) 345-2244   MN
Web Site:
    https://www.nortechsys.com
Year Founded: 1990
NSYS—(NASDAQ)
Rev.: $134,123,000
Assets: $69,540,000
Liabilities: $41,460,000
Net Worth: $28,080,000
Earnings: $2,010,000
Emp.: 782
Fiscal Year-end: 12/31/22
Commercial & Defense Wire Harnesses, Cables, Electromechanical Assemblies, Printed Circuit Boards & Higher-Level Assemblies Mfr
N.A.I.C.S.: 334220
Curtis J. Steichen (Sr VP-Sls)
Andrew D. C. LaFrence (CFO & Sr VP-Fin)
Jay Dean Miller (Pres & CEO)
John Lindeen (Sr VP-Ops-Global)
Cathy Vold (VP-Mktg & Engrg Svcs)
Alan Nordstrom (Interim CFO & Controller)
Chris Jones (CFO)
Monica Hamling (VP)

Subsidiaries:

Devicix LLC (1)
7680 Executive Dr, Eden Prairie, MN 55344
Tel.: (952) 368-0073
Web Site: http://www.devicix.com
Sales Range: $1-9.9 Million
Emp.: 30
Medical Devices Research & Development
N.A.I.C.S.: 541715

Manufacturing Assembly Solutions of Monterrey, Inc. (1)
Av Milimex 303 Parque Industrial Milimex, Apodaca, Nuevo Leon, Mexico **(100%)**
Tel.: (52) 10900109
Web Site: https://massolutions.com.mx
Electronics Product Distr
N.A.I.C.S.: 423690

Nortech Systems -Augusta (1)

---

750 Industrial Dr, Augusta, WI 54722
Tel.: (715) 286-5549
Sales Range: $50-74.9 Million
Emp.: 100
N.A.I.C.S.: 334220

Nortech Systems -Bemidji (1)
4050 Norris Ct Nw, Bemidji, MN 56601
Tel.: (218) 444-0110
Sales Range: $1-4.9 Billion
N.A.I.C.S.: 334220

Nortech Systems -Intercon 1 (1)
12136 Crystal Lake Rd, Merrifield, MN 56465 **(100%)**
Tel.: (218) 828-3157
Web Site: http://www.nortechsys.com
Sales Range: $25-49.9 Million
Emp.: 4
N.A.I.C.S.: 334220

Nortech Systems -Merrifield (1)
12136 Crystal Lk Rd, Merrifield, MN 56465 **(100%)**
Tel.: (218) 765-3151
Sales Range: $75-99.9 Million
Emp.: 160
N.A.I.C.S.: 334220

NORTH AMERICA FRAC SAND, INC.
80 SW 8th St, Miami, FL 33130
Tel.: (260) 490-9990   FL
Web Site: https://havanaroasters.com
Year Founded: 2007
NAFS—(OTCIQ)
Development-stage Company; Investment Services
N.A.I.C.S.: 523999

NORTH AMERICAN CANNABIS HOLDINGS, INC.
701 Commerce St Ste 500, Dallas, TX 75202
Tel.: (972) 528-0162   WY
Year Founded: 2015
USMJ—(OTCIQ)
Rev.: $1,059,000
Assets: $1,014,000
Liabilities: $2,167,000
Net Worth: ($1,153,000)
Earnings: $96,000
Fiscal Year-end: 06/30/19
Beverage Product Mfr
N.A.I.C.S.: 312111
Steven B. Rash (Founder & CEO)

NORTH AMERICAN EXPLORATION CORP.
895 N Marshall Way Ste A, Layton, UT 84041
Tel.: (801) 546-6453
Web Site: https://www.nae-xploration.com
Year Founded: 1964
NAMX—(OTCIQ)
Support Activities for Metal Mining
N.A.I.C.S.: 213114
David Morris (Pres)

NORTH DALLAS BANK & TRUST CO.
12900 Preston Rd, Dallas, TX 75230
Tel.: (972) 716-7100   TX
Web Site: https://www.ndbt.com
Year Founded: 1961
NODB—(OTCIQ)
Commercial Banking Services
N.A.I.C.S.: 522110
Larry Miller (Pres)
Mike Shipman (Chm & CEO)
Pam Burdine (Chief Credit Officer & Exec VP)
Glenn henry (CFO & Exec VP)
Ron Williams (CIO & Exec VP)

NORTH EUROPEAN OIL ROYALTY TRUST
5 N Lincoln St, Keene, NH 03431

Tel.: (732) 741-4008   DE
Web Site: https://www.neort.com
NRT—(NYSE)
Rev.: $5,855,685
Assets: $1,625,344
Liabilities: $183,812
Net Worth: $1,441,532
Earnings: $5,057,813
Emp.: 2
Fiscal Year-end: 10/31/24
Oil & Gas Investment Services
N.A.I.C.S.: 523999
Lawrence A. Kobrin *(Trustee)*
Willard B. Taylor *(Trustee)*

NORTH MOUNTAIN MERGER CORP.

767 5th Ave 9th Fl, New York, NY 10153
Tel.: (646) 446-2700   DE
Year Founded: 2020
NMMC—(NASDAQ)
Rev.: $6,162,758
Assets: $132,692,941
Liabilities: $145,753,164
Net Worth: ($13,060,223)
Earnings: $4,990,116
Emp.: 2
Fiscal Year-end: 12/31/21
Investment Services
N.A.I.C.S.: 523999

NORTHAMERICAN ENERGY GROUP CORP.

1808 Snake River Rd Ste D, Katy, TX 77449
Tel.: (281) 895-8351   NV
Year Founded: 1997
NNYR—(OTCIQ)
Oil & Gas Exploration Services
N.A.I.C.S.: 213112
Jon Ginder *(Chm & CEO)*
Gene Chew *(Pres & COO)*

NORTHANN CORP.

9820 Dino Dr, Elk Grove, CA 95624
Tel.: (212) 380-7500   NV
Web Site: https://www.northann.com
Year Founded: 2022
NCL—(NYSE)
Rev.: $20,957,972
Assets: $14,409,462
Liabilities: $12,435,723
Net Worth: $1,973,739
Earnings: $929,059
Emp.: 71
Fiscal Year-end: 12/31/22
Other Millwork (including Flooring)
N.A.I.C.S.: 321918

NORTHEAST BANK

35 Canal St, Lewiston, ME 04240
Tel.: (207) 786-3245   ME
Web Site:
   https://www.northeastbank.com
Year Founded: 1872
NBN—(NASDAQ)
Rev.: $87,946,000
Assets: $1,153,858,000
Liabilities: $1,000,278,000
Net Worth: $153,580,000
Earnings: $13,884,000
Emp.: 167
Fiscal Year-end: 06/30/19
Commericial Banking
N.A.I.C.S.: 522180
Chris Delamater *(Dir-Mktg)*
Heidi Jacques *(VP-HR)*
Eric Bancroft *(VP-Small Bus Admin Lending)*
David Coletti *(VP-Small Bus Admin Lending)*
Javier Placencia *(VP-Small Bus Admin Lending)*
Thomas Blackburne *(VP-Small Bus Admin Lending)*

Daniel O'Meara *(VP-Small Bus Admin Lending)*
David Sportelli *(VP-Small Bus Admin Lending)*
Carrie Stanley *(VP-Small Bus Admin Lending)*
Claire S. Bean *(COO)*
Jeanne A. Hulit *(Pres-Community Banking)*
Jonathan W. Smith *(Sr VP & Dir-Small Bus Admin Lending)*
Daryl Wentworth *(Chief Comml Officer-Community Banking)*
Kristy Moyer *(Asst VP-Retail Banking)*
Michael Scholl *(Sr VP-Comml Loans)*
Heather Delamater *(Branch Mgr-Poland)*
Jeff Wright *(Sr VP-Retail Sls & Mgr-Ops)*
Allison Jackson *(Mgr-Bethel)*
Matthew B. Botein *(Chm)*
Richard Wayne *(Pres & CEO)*
Patrick Dignan *(Exec VP)*
Robert Banaski *(Sr VP & Dir-Community Banking)*
Brian Pinheiro *(Chief Risk Officer)*
Jean-Pierre Lapointe *(CFO)*

NORTHEAST COMMUNITY BANCORP, INC.

325 Hamilton Ave, White Plains, NY 10601
Tel.: (914) 684-2500
Web Site: https://www.necb.com
Year Founded: 2006
NECB—(NASDAQ)
Rev.: $73,685,000
Assets: $1,424,963,000
Liabilities: $1,162,974,000
Net Worth: $261,989,000
Earnings: $24,843,000
Emp.: 134
Fiscal Year-end: 12/31/22
Bank Holding Company
N.A.I.C.S.: 551111
Kenneth A. Martinek *(Chm & CEO)*
Jose M. Collazo *(Pres & COO)*

Subsidiaries:

Northeast Community Bank   (1)
325 Hamilton Ave, White Plains, NY 10601
Tel.: (914) 684-2500
Web Site: https://www.necb.com
Sales Range: $25-49.9 Million
Emp.: 30
Federal Savings Bank
N.A.I.C.S.: 522180
Kenneth A. Martinek *(Chm & CEO)*
Charles A. Martinek *(Chief Compliance Officer & Sr VP)*
Jose M. Collazo *(Pres)*

Subsidiary (Domestic):

New England Commercial Properties LLC   (2)
46 Plains Rd Unit 6, Essex, CT 06426
Tel.: (860) 767-2654
Web Site: https://www.necp.biz
Commercial Banking Services
N.A.I.C.S.: 522110

NORTHEAST INDIANA BANCORP, INC.

648 N Jefferson St, Huntington, IN 46750
Tel.: (260) 356-3311   DE
Web Site:
   https://www.firstfedindiana.bank
Year Founded: 1995
NIDB—(OTCQB)
Rev.: $20,076,951
Assets: $391,277,150
Liabilities: $345,725,439
Net Worth: $45,551,711
Earnings: $5,599,622
Emp.: 85

Fiscal Year-end: 12/31/20
Bank Holding Company
N.A.I.C.S.: 551111
Stephen E. Zahn *(Chm)*
Michael S. Zahn *(Pres & CEO)*
Randy J. Sizemore *(CFO & Sr VP)*

Subsidiaries:

First Federal Savings Bank   (1)
648 N Jefferson St, Huntington, IN 46750-0070
Tel.: (260) 356-3311
Web Site: http://www.firstfedhuntington.com
Sales Range: $1-9.9 Million
Emp.: 25
Savings Bank
N.A.I.C.S.: 522180
Thomas N. Mills *(Comml Lending Officer & Sr VP)*
Julie Crain *(Sec)*
Randy Sizemore *(CFO & Sr VP)*
Ian Hope *(VP-Comml Portfolio & Mgr-SBA)*
Donnie Haire *(Asst VP-Retail & Mortgage Lending)*
Amanda Stroup *(Asst VP & Dir-Mktg & Mortgage Lending)*
Joe Cassidy *(Asst VP-Wealth Advisor)*

NORTHERN CALIFORNIA NATIONAL BANK

1717 Mangrove Ave Ste 100, Chico, CA 95926
Tel.: (530) 879-5900
Web Site: http://www.norcalbank.com
NCNB—(OTCIQ)
Sales Range: Less than $1 Million
Emp.: 15
Banking Services
N.A.I.C.S.: 522110
John A. Lucchesi *(Chm, Pres & CEO)*
Sheila Christensen *(Sec)*
Todd Lewis *(CFO & Exec VP)*
Adrienne Veltman *(Asst Mgr-Ops)*
Nancy Mendonca *(Asst VP & Mgr-Customer Svc)*
Angela Casler *(Chief Credit Officer & Sr VP)*
Steve Jungen *(VP & Mktg Officer)*
David McAlister *(VP-Lending)*
Larry Spencer *(VP & Bus Dev Officer)*

NORTHERN GROWERS LLC

PO Box 356, Big Stone City, SD 57216
Tel.: (605) 862-7902
NGOWL—(OTCIQ)
Ethanol Product Mfr
N.A.I.C.S.: 325193
Robert Narem *(CEO & CFO)*

NORTHERN MINERALS & EXPLORATION LTD.

1267 N 680 W, Pleasant Grove, UT 84062
Tel.: (801) 885-9260   NV
Web Site:
   https://www.northernmineralsandexploration.com
Year Founded: 2006
NMEX—(OTCIQ)
Assets: $53,139
Liabilities: $270,970
Net Worth: ($217,831)
Earnings: ($170,340)
Fiscal Year-end: 07/31/24
Mining & Exploration Services
N.A.I.C.S.: 213114
Ivan Webb *(Pres & CEO)*
Noel Schaefer *(COO & Sec)*
Howard B. Siegel *(Chm)*

NORTHERN OIL & GAS, INC.

4350 Baker Rd Ste 400, Minnetonka, MN 55343
Tel.: (952) 476-9800   MN
Web Site:
   https://www.northernoil.com

Year Founded: 2006
NOG—(NYSE)
Rev.: $2,166,259,000
Assets: $4,484,256,000
Liabilities: $2,436,580,000
Net Worth: $2,047,676,000
Earnings: $922,969,000
Emp.: 38
Fiscal Year-end: 12/31/23
Oil & Gas Exploration Services
N.A.I.C.S.: 211120
Michael Lewis Reger *(Founder)*
Erik J. Romslo *(Chief Legal Officer)*
Nicholas L. O'Grady *(CEO)*
Adam A. Dirlam *(Pres & COO)*
James Evans *(Chief Technical Officer)*
Evelyn Leon Infurna *(VP-IR)*
Chad Allen *(CFO)*

NORTHERN TECHNOLOGIES INTERNATIONAL CORPORATION

4201 Woodland Rd, Circle Pines, MN 55014
Tel.: (763) 225-6600   DE
Web Site: https://www.ntic.com
Year Founded: 1993
NTIC—(NASDAQ)
Rev.: $85,059,517
Assets: $94,676,502
Liabilities: $19,501,181
Net Worth: $75,175,321
Earnings: $6,321,384
Emp.: 93
Fiscal Year-end: 08/31/24
Industrial Packaging Products, Systems & Sensing Instruments Mfr & Sales
N.A.I.C.S.: 322299
G. Patrick Lynch *(Pres & CEO)*
Matthew C. Wolsfeld *(CFO & Sec)*
Vineet R. Dalal *(VP & Dir-Global Market Dev-Natur-Tec)*

Subsidiaries:

Acobal S.A.S.   (1)
Zi Du Clos Marquet, PO Box 177, Cedex, Saint-Chamond, France
Tel.: (33) 477294740
Web Site: http://www.acobal.com
Sales Range: $10-24.9 Million
Emp.: 15
Mfr of Anti-Rust Products
N.A.I.C.S.: 325998
Jacques Manenc *(Mng Dir)*

Chong-Wah NTIA Sdn. Bhd.   (1)
Lot No 1503 Batu 8 1/2 Jalan Klang Lama, Petaling Jaya, 46000, Selangor Darul Ehsan, Malaysia
Tel.: (60) 378767066
Web Site: http://www.chongwahgroup.com
Sales Range: $75-99.9 Million
Mfr & Distributor of Anti-Rust Products
N.A.I.C.S.: 325998

Excor GmbH   (1)
Industriegelande Volkmarshausen Tonlandstrasse 2, 34346, Munich, Germany   (50%)
Tel.: (49) 5541706200
Web Site: http://www.excor.com
Sales Range: $10-24.9 Million
Emp.: 20
Mfr of Rust-Inhibiting Products
N.A.I.C.S.: 325998

Excor Iberica   (1)
Camino Portuetexe 51 Officina 213, 20018, San Sebastian, Spain
Tel.: (34) 943223828
Web Site: http://www.excor.com
Sales Range: $150-199.9 Million
Emp.: 1
Mfr of Anti-Rust Products
N.A.I.C.S.: 325998

Excor Sp. z.o.o.   (1)
Ul Jarzynowa 50, 94 204, Lodz, Poland   (50%)
Tel.: (48) 426335373

Northern Technologies International
Corporation—(Continued)

Web Site: http://www.excore.pl
Sales Range: $10-24.9 Million
Emp.: 5
Mfr of Rust Proofing Products
N.A.I.C.S.: 325998

HNTI Limited (1)
Zerust & Axxanol Division A3 Ambattur Industrial Estate, Ambattur, Chennai, 600058, India
Tel.: (91) 4426357087
Web Site: https://www.hnti.co.in
Automobile Parts Distr
N.A.I.C.S.: 423120

Harita-NTI Limited (1)
A3 1st Main Road Ambattur Industrial Estate, Ambattur, Chennai, 600, 058, India
Tel.: (91) 4426250886
Web Site: http://www.haritanti.com
Sales Range: $10-24.9 Million
Emp.: 60
Mfr of Computer Related Products
N.A.I.C.S.: 541512

Industrial de Plasticos de Chihuahua, S.A. de C.V. (1)
Carr. Aeropuerto y Calle 69a s/n Col Aeropuerto, Chihuahua, C.P. 31390, Chih, Mexico
Tel.: (52) 614 435 1022
Web Site: https://www.ipdc.mx
Sales Range: $125-149.9 Million
Mfr & Distr of Plastic Products
N.A.I.C.S.: 326199

Korea Zerust Co., Ltd. (1)
A 203 984 Shihung 3 Dong, Kimchun Gu, 153 755, Seoul, Korea (South) (50%)
Tel.: (82) 28958891
Web Site: http://www.zerust.co.kr
Sales Range: $10-24.9 Million
Emp.: 9
Mfr & Distributor of Rust & Corrosion Products
N.A.I.C.S.: 325998

NTI Facilities, Inc. (1)
23900 Mercantile Rd, Beachwood, OH 44122
Tel.: (216) 595-1740
Web Site: http://www.ntic.com
Sales Range: $25-49.9 Million
Emp.: 10
Corrosion Inhibitor Mfr
N.A.I.C.S.: 325998

NTIA Zerust Philippines, Inc. (1)
38 South West Ipil Street Marikina Heights, Marikina, Philippines
Tel.: (63) 2 9973723
Sales Range: $150-199.9 Million
Anti-Rust Products Mfr
N.A.I.C.S.: 325998

NTIC (Shanghai) Co., Ltd. (1)
No 29 Lane 6066 Songze Avenue, Qingpu District, Shanghai, 201706, China
Tel.: (86) 4006256600
Web Site: http://www.zerust-china.com
Wrapping Insulation Material Distr
N.A.I.C.S.: 423330

NTIC Europe GmbH (1)
Konigstrasse 16, 47198, Duisburg, Germany
Tel.: (49) 1788866913
Insulation Material Distr
N.A.I.C.S.: 423330

Taiyonic Ltd-(Taiyo) (1)
Sanyo-Do Nihonbashi Bldg 6F, 3-21 Nihonbashi-Horidomecho 1, Tokyo, 103 0012, Japan
Tel.: (81) 336675201
Web Site: http://www.taiyo.lpg.com
Sales Range: $25-49.9 Million
Emp.: 37
Mfr of Computer Related Products
N.A.I.C.S.: 334112
Freddy Yu (Asst Mgr)
Haruhiko Rikuta (Pres)

Zerust (U.K.) Limited (1)
Meadowfield Avenue Green Lane Industrial Estate, Spennymoor, DL16 6YJ, County Durham, United Kingdom
Tel.: (44) 388420333
Web Site: http://www.zerust.co.uk

Vapor Corrosion Inhibitors Liquids & Diffuser & Rust Removers Products Mfr
N.A.I.C.S.: 325998

Zerust AB (1)
Box 77, PO Box 77, Molndal, 43121, Sweden
Tel.: (46) 317212240
Web Site: http://www.zerust.se
Sales Range: $10-24.9 Million
Emp.: 6
Mfr of Anti-Rust Products
N.A.I.C.S.: 325998

Zerust OY (1)
Kivikonkierto 14, 5460, Hyvinkaa, Finland
Tel.: (358) 194262600
Web Site: http://www.zerust.fi
Sales Range: $10-24.9 Million
Emp.: 7
Mfr & Distributor of Rust Proofing Products
N.A.I.C.S.: 325998
Tiuja Hjerte (Mng Dir)

Zerust Prevencao de Corrosao S.A. (1)
255 Sao Bernardo do Campo Avenue, Sorocaba, Sao Paulo, 18085-310, Brazil
Tel.: (55) 1533884700
Web Site: http://www.zerust.com.br
Paint & Coating Mfr
N.A.I.C.S.: 325510

Zerust Prevencoa de Corrosao S.A. (1)
Av Sao Bernardo do Campo 255, Sorocaba, CEP 18085-310, SP, Brazil (100%)
Tel.: (55) 15 3388 4700
Web Site: http://www.zerust.com.br
Sales Range: $150-199.9 Million
Rust Protection Products Mfr
N.A.I.C.S.: 325998

Zerust Singapore Pte. Ltd. (1)
18 Boon Lay Way 09-126 TradeHub 21, Singapore, 609966, Singapore
Tel.: (65) 67952039
Web Site: http://www.zerust.com
Sales Range: $10-24.9 Million
Emp.: 3
Mfr of Anti-Rust Products
N.A.I.C.S.: 325998

Zerust Specialty Tech Co., Ltd. (1)
1/8 Moo 1 T Klong Nueng A Klong Luang, Pathumthani, Bangkok, 12120, Thailand
Tel.: (66) 28333999
Web Site: http://www.specialty.co.th
Sales Range: $10-24.9 Million
Emp.: 10
Mfr of Technology Equipment
N.A.I.C.S.: 541715

Zerust Exoor Moxioo, S, Do R.L, Do C.V
Calle Padre Mier No 961C Col Centro, 64000, Monterrey, Nuevo Leon, Mexico
Tel.: (52) 54515071
Web Site: https://www.zerust.com
Chemical Product & Preparation Mfr
N.A.I.C.S.: 325998

Zerust-NIC (Taiwan) Corp. (1)
No 243 Sec 1 Fu-Hsing South Rd King Tower Bldg B bridge, 106, Taipei, Taiwan
Tel.: (886) 227003962
Web Site: http://www.zerust.com.tw
Sales Range: $10-24.9 Million
Emp.: 5
Mfr of Corrosive Inhibitors
N.A.I.C.S.: 325998
Uemura Keiji (Chm)

NORTHERN TRUST CORPORATION

50 S LaSalle St, Chicago, IL 60603
Tel.: (312) 630-6000 DE
Web Site:
https://www.northerntrust.com
Year Founded: 1889
NTRS—(NASDAQ)
Rev.: $12,116,500,000
Assets: $150,783,100,000
Liabilities: $138,885,200,000
Net Worth: $11,897,900,000
Earnings: $1,065,500,000
Emp.: 23,100

Fiscal Year-end: 12/31/23
Financial Investment Services
N.A.I.C.S.: 551111
Joyce Mulholland St. Clair (Chief HR Officer & Exec VP)
Teresa A. Parker (Pres-Europe, Middle East & Africa & Exec VP)
Peter B. Cherecwich (Pres-Corp & Institutional Svcs & Exec VP)
Michael G. O'Grady (Chm & CEO)
Susan C. Levy (Gen Counsel, Sec & Exec VP)
Robert P. Browne (Chief Investment Officer & & Exec VP)
Jason J. Tyler (CFO)
Angelo Calvitto (Head-Asia Pacific)
Kimberly Evans (Head-Private Capital Fund Svcs)
Thomas A. South (CIO & Exec VP)
Jennifer Gravenor (Pres-Austin)
Mark C. Gossett (Chief Risk Officer & Exec VP)
Mark Bette (Sr VP & Dir-IR)
Kelly Moen Lernihan (VP-IR)
JP Ramirez (Dir-Mktg)
Paul Theiss (Sr Mng Dir-Wealth Mgmt Comml Banking Grp)
John Fumagalli (Pres-Wealth Mgmt-Central Reg)
Adam Kerbis (Sr VP)
Alexandra Kovalenko (Head-Asset Mgmt-Sweden)
Patrick Dominick (Sr Mng Dir-Barrington)
Michele Havens (Pres-Wealth Mgmt-West)
Curtiss Smith (Pres-Phoenix)
Michael Cklamovski (Sr Mng Dir & Pres-Northern California)
Michael Buzza (Head-Network Mgmt & Market Strategy-Global)
Justin Chapman (Head-Digital Assets & Fin Markets-Global)
Alvin Chia (Head-Digital Assets Innovation-Asia Pacific)
Patrick Cowan (Chief Banking Officer-West)
Aisling Keane (Head-Asset Servicing-Hong Kong)

Subsidiaries:

50 South Capital Advisors, LLC (1)
181 W Madison St 12th Fl, Chicago, IL 60603
Tel.: (312) 557-1998
Web Site: https://www.50southcapital.com
Investment Advisory Services
N.A.I.C.S.: 523940
Kevin T. Butts (Sr VP-Private Equity Grp)
Julie Canna (Sr VP)
Greg Jones (Dir)
Adam J. Magyar (Sr VP & Dir-Risk Mgmt)
Patricia Nolan (VP)
Bruce Tang (Dir)
Tristan Thomas (Mng Dir-Portfolio Strategy)
David R. Williams (Dir)
Molly B. Brister (Dir-Private Equity Grp)
Chip Davis (Dir-Private Equity Grp)
Bradley M. Dorchinecz (Mng Dir)
Adam R. Freda (Mng Dir)
Aaron Gillum (Sr VP)
Mike Marderosian (Sr VP)
John Frede (Mng Dir-Res)
Josh Abrego (Controller)
Thalia R. Lloyd (VP)
Kathleen Switala (VP)
Megan Brooks (VP)
Patrick Clavio (VP)
Reed Hunter Garetto (VP)
Thomas Needle (VP)
Phillip Schwartzman (Second VP)
Tony Sorrentino (VP)
Eli W. Tullis III (VP)
James R. Hart III (Mng Dir)

Northern Trust (Guernsey) Limited (1)
Les Banques Trafalgar Court, PO Box 71, Saint Peter Port, GY1 3DA, Guernsey
Tel.: (44) 1481745000

Sales Range: $50-74.9 Million
Emp.: 100
Asset Management Services
N.A.I.C.S.: 523940
Paul Cutts (Mng Dir)

Northern Trust Cayman International, Ltd. (1)
190 Elgin Avenue, PO Box 112, Georgetown, KY1-9005, Grand Cayman, Cayman Islands
Tel.: (345) 9433100
Sales Range: $125-149.9 Million
State Commercial Banks & Trust Companies
N.A.I.C.S.: 522110

Northern Trust Fiduciary Services (Guernsey) Limited (1)
Trafalgar Court Les Banques, PO Box 71, Saint Peter Port, GY1 3DA, Guernsey (100%)
Tel.: (44) 148 174 5000
Web Site: http://www.northerntrust.com
Banking & Fiduciary Services
N.A.I.C.S.: 523991

Northern Trust International Fund Administration Services (Guernsey) Limited (1)
Trafalgar Court Les Banques, PO Box 225, Saint Peter Port, GY1 3QL, Channel Islands, Guernsey
Tel.: (44) 1481745001
Sales Range: $50-74.9 Million
Emp.: 100
Commercial Banking Services
N.A.I.C.S.: 522110

Northern Trust International Fund Administration Services (Ireland) Limited (1)
Georges Court 54 - 62 Townsend Street, Dublin, D02 R156, Ireland
Tel.: (353) 1 542 2000
Web Site: http://www.northerntrust.com
Investment Management Service
N.A.I.C.S.: 523940

Northern Trust Luxembourg Management Company S.A. (1)
6 Rue Lou Hemmer, L-1748, Senningerberg, Luxembourg
Tel.: (352) 28294000
Web Site: http://www.northerntrust.com
Asset Management Services
N.A.I.C.S.: 523999

Northern Trust Management Services (Deutschland) GmbH (1)
Neue Mainzer Street 46-50, Frankfurt, 60311, Germany
Tel.: (49) 69365062100
Trust Management Services
N.A.I.C.S.: 813211

Northern Trust Securities Services (Ireland) Limited (1)
New Century House IFSC Mayor St Lower, Dublin, 1, Ireland (100%)
Tel.: (353) 16700300
Securities Services
N.A.I.C.S.: 523999

Northern Trust Switzerland AG (1)
Aeschenplatz 6, Basel, 4052, Switzerland
Tel.: (41) 615653000
Bank Trust Office Services
N.A.I.C.S.: 523991
Karsten Illy (COO)

The Northern Trust Company (1)
50 Bank Street, Canary Wharf, London, E14 5NT, United Kingdom (100%)
Tel.: (44) 2079822000
Web Site: http://www.northerntrust.com
Investment Management & Advice, Global Custody & Fund Administration
N.A.I.C.S.: 523940
Jean-Paul Hobeika (Head-Middle East)
Katharine Morris (Head-Global Fund Svcs Bus Dev)
Laurence Everitt (Mng Dir & Head-Global Fund Svcs)

Subsidiary (Domestic):

Northern Trust Corporation - United Kingdom (2)

50 Bank Street Canary Wharf, Canary, London, E14 5NT, United Kingdom
Tel.: (44) 207 982 2000
Web Site: http://locations.northerntrust.com
Agricultural Credit Lending Services
N.A.I.C.S.: 522299
Alison Pain (CTO-Europe, Middle East & Africa)
Teresa Parker (Pres-Europe, Middle East & Africa)

The Northern Trust Company **(1)**
50 S LaSalle St, Chicago, IL 60603 **(100%)**
Tel.: (312) 630-6000
Web Site: http://www.northerntrust.com
Federal Savings Bank
N.A.I.C.S.: 522180

Subsidiary (Domestic):

NorLease, Inc. **(2)**
50 S La Salle St, Chicago, IL 60603 **(100%)**
Tel.: (312) 630-6000
Web Site: http://www.ntrs.com
Retail & Commercial Banking
N.A.I.C.S.: 522110

Northern Trust Company of California **(2)**
580 California St Ste 1800, San Francisco, CA 94104-1096
Tel.: (415) 765-4400
Web Site: http://www.northerntrust.com
Commercial Banking Services
N.A.I.C.S.: 522110

The Northern Trust International Banking Corporation **(2)**
3 2nd St, Jersey City, NJ 07311-3988
Tel.: (201) 793-4900
Web Site: http://www.northerntrust.com
Emp.: 70
International Banking Services
N.A.I.C.S.: 522299
Francis Murgolo (Mng Dir)

Subsidiary (Non-US):

Northern Operating Services Private Limited **(3)**
RMZ Ecospace Sarjapur Outer Ring Road Campus 1C 2nd Floor, Bengaluru, 560037, India
Tel.: (91) 8040178500
Web Site: http://www.northerntrust.com
Sales Range: $450-499.9 Million
Emp.: 1,500
Commercial Banking Services
N.A.I.C.S.: 522110

Northern Trust Fund Managers (Ireland) Limited **(3)**
Georges Court 54-62 Townsend Street, Dublin, D02 R156, Ireland
Tel.: (353) 15422000
Commercial Banking Services
N.A.I.C.S.: 522110

Northern Trust Global Fund Services Cayman Limited **(3)**
94 Solaris Avenue, PO Box 1348, Camana Bay, KY1-1108, Grand Cayman, Cayman Islands
Tel.: (345) 9435499
Web Site: http://www.criterionmgt.com
Investment Management Service
N.A.I.C.S.: 523940

Northern Trust Management Services Limited **(3)**
50 Bank Street, Canary Wharf, London, E14 5NT, United Kingdom
Tel.: (44) 207 982 2000
Web Site: http://www.northerntrust.com
Emp.: 1,600
Investment Management Service
N.A.I.C.S.: 523940

Northern Trust Securities LLP **(3)**
1st Floor ganton House 22 Ganton Street, London, W1F 7FD, United Kingdom
Tel.: (44) 2072333210
Financial Investment Services
N.A.I.C.S.: 523991

The Northern Trust Company Canada **(1)**
145 King Street West Suite 1910, Olaya

District, Toronto, M5H 1J8, ON, Canada **(100%)**
Tel.: (416) 775-2223
Web Site: http://www.ntrs.com
Sales Range: $25-49.9 Million
Emp.: 50
Securities Management & Services
N.A.I.C.S.: 522299

The Northern Trust Company of Delaware **(1)**
1313 N Market St Ste 5300, Wilmington, DE 19801
Tel.: (302) 428-8700
Emp.: 19
Financial Management Services
N.A.I.C.S.: 541611
David Diamond (Pres)

The Northern Trust Company of New York **(1)**
40 W 57th St 21st Fl, New York, NY 10019
Tel.: (212) 339-7474
Web Site: http://www.ntrs.com
Sales Range: $100-124.9 Million
Emp.: 50
State Bank
N.A.I.C.S.: 523999

The Northern Trust Company of Saudi Arabia **(1)**
Al Urubah Road Level 20 Kingdom Tower, Olaya District, 12214, Riyadh, Saudi Arabia
Tel.: (966) 11 416 7922
Web Site: http://www.northerntrust.com
Emp.: 10
Financial Management Services
N.A.I.C.S.: 541611

UBS Fund Management (Switzerland) AG **(1)**
Aeschenplatz 6, PO Box 4473, 4052, Basel, Switzerland
Tel.: (41) 61 288 49 10
Asset Management Services
N.A.I.C.S.: 531390

UBS Fund Services (Luxembourg) S.A. **(1)**
33A Avenue J F Kennedy, 1855, Luxembourg, Luxembourg
Tel.: (352) 4410101
Asset Management Services
N.A.I.C.S.: 531390

NORTHFIELD BANCORP, INC.
581 Main St Ste 810, Woodbridge, NJ 07095
Tel.: (732) 499-7200 **DE**
Web Site:
https://www.enorthfield.com
NFBK—(NASDAQ)
Rev.: $187,671,000
Assets: $5,601,293,000
Liabilities: $4,899,903,000
Net Worth: $701,390,000
Earnings: $61,119,000
Emp.: 395
Fiscal Year-end: 12/31/22
Bank Holding Company
N.A.I.C.S.: 551111
Steven M. Klein (Chm, Pres & CEO)
William R. Jacobs (CFO & Exec VP)
Robin Lefkowitz (Exec VP & Dir-Branch Admin & Bus Dev-Northfield Bank)
David V. Fasanella (Chief Lending Officer & Exec VP)

Subsidiaries:

Northfield Bank **(1)**
1731 Victory Blvd, Staten Island, NY 10314-3511
Tel.: (718) 448-1000
Web Site: https://www.enorthfield.com
Sales Range: $100-124.9 Million
Federal Savings Bank
N.A.I.C.S.: 522180
Steven M. Klein (Chm, Pres & CEO)
Vickie Tomasello (Chief Risk Officer & Exec VP)

VSB Bancorp, Inc. **(1)**
4142 Hylan Blvd, Staten Island, NY 10308
Tel.: (718) 979-1100

Web Site: http://www.victorystatebank.com
Commercial Banking Services
N.A.I.C.S.: 522110
Richard Boyle (Chief Lending Officer & Sr VP)
Elizabeth Scarano (COO & Sr VP)
Joseph J. Li Bassi (Chm)
Joan Nerlino-Caddell (Sec)
Johnny Reyes (VP-Bus Dev)
David Onderko (CFO & Sr VP)
Isaac Zahavi (First VP)
Toni Scarito (VP-HR)

Subsidiary (Domestic):

Victory State Bank **(2)**
4142 Hylan Blvd, Staten Island, NY 10308
Tel.: (718) 979-1100
Web Site: http://www.victorystatebank.com
Emp.: 20
Commercial Banking Services
N.A.I.C.S.: 522110
Jonathan B. Lipschitz (VP & Controller)
Elizabeth Scarano (COO & Sr VP)
Richard Boyle (Sr VP)
Rosmerys Perez (VP-HR)

NORTHFIELD PRECISION INSTRUMENT CORP.
4400 Austin Blvd, Island Park, NY 11558
Tel.: (516) 431-1112 **NY**
Web Site: https://www.northfield.com
NFPC—(OTCIQ)
Air & Gas Compressor Manufacturing
N.A.I.C.S.: 333912
Paul DeFeo (Pres & CEO)

NORTHRIM BANCORP, INC.
3111 C St, Anchorage, AK 99524
Tel.: (907) 562-0062 **AK**
Web Site: https://www.northrim.com
Year Founded: 2001
NRIM—(NASDAQ)
Rev.: $100,328,000
Assets: $2,674,318,000
Liabilities: $2,455,689,000
Net Worth: $218,629,000
Earnings: $30,741,000
Emp.: 469
Fiscal Year-end: 12/31/22
Bank Holding Company
N.A.I.C.S.: 551111
Michael G. Huston (Co-Pres, CEO & COO)
Jed W. Ballard (CFO & Exec VP)
Michael G. Huston (Co-Pres)
Jason Criqui (Chief Lending Officer)

Subsidiaries:

Northrim Bank **(1)**
3111 C St, Anchorage, AK 99503
Tel.: (907) 562-0062
Web Site: https://www.northrim.com
Sales Range: $125-149.9 Million
Emp.: 400
Commericial Banking
N.A.I.C.S.: 522110
Joseph M. Schierhorn (Officer-Charter)
Michael G. Huston (Pres & CEO)
Latosha M. Frye (Mgr-Corp Acctg)
Katie Bates (Sr VP & Dir-Electronic Channels)
Catherine Claxton (Sr VP & Mgr-Real Estate Lending)
Amber Zins (COO, COO, Chief Admin Officer, Exec VP & Exec VP)
Mark Edwards (Chief Credit Officer & Exec VP)
Jason Criqui (Chief Banking Officer, Exec VP, Sr VP & Mgr-Comml Loan)
Michael G. Huston (Pres & Chief Lending Officer)
Kari Skinner (Sr VP & Dir-Mktg & Comm)
Cindy Fields (Sr VP & Dir-Internal Audit)
Joe Gelione (Sr VP, Sr VP, Sr VP-Comml Lending & Mgr-Comml Loan Unit)
T. J. Alinen (Sr VP & Dir-HR)
Ryan Caldwell (Sr VP-Sys & Network Infrastructure & Mgr-DevOps)
Nate Olmstead (Sr VP & Mgr-Data Analytics)

Erick Stoeckle (Sr VP & Mgr-Enterprise Architecture)
Amber R. Zins (COO & Exec VP)
Jed Ballard (Exec VP)
Nathan Reed (CIO)
Melody Charlton (Sr VP)
Sean Christian (Sr VP)
Greg Deal (Sr VP)
Josh King (Sr VP)
Doug Ladenburger (Sr VP)
Stefan Saldanha (Sr VP)
Kevin Tillotson (Sr VP)

NORTHROP GRUMMAN CORPORATION
2980 Fairview Park Dr, Falls Church, VA 22042
Tel.: (703) 280-2900 **DE**
Web Site:
https://www.northropgrumman.com
Year Founded: 1939
NOC—(NYSE)
Rev.: $39,290,000,000
Assets: $46,544,000,000
Liabilities: $31,749,000,000
Net Worth: $14,795,000,000
Earnings: $2,056,000,000
Emp.; 101,000
Fiscal Year-end: 12/31/23
Holding Company; Defense & Commercial Electronics, Ship Building & Repairing, Information Technology, Mission Systems, Systems Integration & Space Technology Products & Services
N.A.I.C.S.: 551112
Shawn N. Purvis (Pres & VP)
Kathy J. Warden (Chm, Pres & CEO)
Blake E. Larson (Pres & VP)
Sheila C. Cheston (Gen Counsel & VP)
Lesley A. Kalan (Chief Strategy & Dev Officer & VP)
Jennifer C. McGarey (Sec & VP)
Michael A. Hardesty (Chief Acctg Officer, VP & Controller)
Lucy C. Ryan (VP-Comm)
Ann M. Addison (Chief HR Officer & VP)
Todd B. Ernst (Treas & VP-IR)
Thomas H. Jones (Pres-Aeronautics Sys & VP)
Adam Barr (Dir-IR)
Tom Wilson (Pres-Space Sys & VP)
Richard Breckenridge (VP-Bus Dev & Strategy-Aeronautics Sys)
Scott Vander Hamm (VP-Strategic Command & Air Force Global Strike Command Accounts)
Ed Griebel (VP-Airborne Surveillance)
Roshan S. Roeder (Pres-Mission Sys Sector & VP)
Stephen O'Bryan (Officer-Bus Dev-Global & VP)
Vic Beck (Sr Dir-Media Ops)
Robert Fleming (Pres-Space Sys & VP)
Sheila C. Cheston (Gen Counsel & VP)

Subsidiaries:

Northrop Grumman - Corporate Government Relations **(1)**
1000 Wilson Blvd, Arlington, VA 22209-2278
Tel.: (703) 875-8400
Web Site: http://www.northropgrumman.com
Sales Range: $50-74.9 Million
Emp.: 250
Government Relations
N.A.I.C.S.: 541990

Northrop Grumman Aerospace Systems **(1)**
1 Space Park, Redondo Beach, CA 90278
Tel.: (310) 812-4321
Sales Range: $5-14.9 Billion
Emp.: 23,000
Aircraft, Spacecraft, Laser Systems, Microelectronics & Other Technology Developer, Mfr & Services

Northrop Grumman Corporation—(Continued)

N.A.I.C.S.: 927110

Unit (Domestic):

Northrop Grumman Aerospace Systems-Bethpage (2)
600 Grumman Rd W, Bethpage, NY 11714
Tel.: (516) 575-0574
Sales Range: $100-124.9 Million
Battle Management, Surveillance & Engagement Technology Developer & Mfr
N.A.I.C.S.: 334511

Northrop Grumman Aerospace Systems-El Segundo (2)
1 Northrop Grumman Ave, El Segundo, CA 90245
Tel.: (310) 332-1000
Network-Enabled Integrated Systems & Microelectronics Mfr
N.A.I.C.S.: 541512

Northrop Grumman Aerospace Systems-Saint Augustine (2)
5000 US 1 N, Saint Augustine, FL 32095
Tel.: (904) 825-3400
Sales Range: $400-449.9 Million
Emp.: 1,150
Network-Enabled Integrated Systems & Components Mfr
N.A.I.C.S.: 541512

Northrop Grumman Aerospace Systems-San Diego (2)
1 Space Park, Redondo Beach, CA 90278
Tel.: (310) 812-4321
Sales Range: $450-499.9 Million
Emp.: 1,400
Unmanned Aircraft Vehicles & Systems Mfr
N.A.I.C.S.: 336411

Northrop Grumman Synoptics
1201 Continental Blvd, Charlotte, NC 28273
Tel.: (704) 588-2340
Sales Range: $50-74.9 Million
Emp.: 240
Solid-State Laser Industry Synthetic Crystals & Optical Components Mfr
N.A.I.C.S.: 333310
Scott E. Griffin (Dir-Bus Dev)

Subsidiary (Domestic):

Scaled Composites, LLC (2)
Hangar 78 1624 Flight Line, Mojave, CA 93501-1663
Tel.: (661) 824-4541
Web Site: http://www.scaled.com
Sales Range: $75-99.9 Million
Emp.: 130
Air Vehicle & Specialty Composite Structure Designer, Mfr & Developmental Flight Testing Services
N.A.I.C.S.: 541715
Ben Diachun (Pres)

Northrop Grumman Electronic Systems (1)
1580 A W Nursery Rd, Linthicum Heights, MD 21290
Tel.: (410) 765-1000
Web Site:
   http://www.es.northropgrumman.com
Sales Range: $5-14.9 Billion
Emp.: 24,006
Electronic & Maritime Systems Developer, Mfr & Support Services
N.A.I.C.S.: 335999

Division (Domestic):

Northrop Grumman Defensive Systems (2)
600 Hicks Rd, Rolling Meadows, IL 60008-1014 (100%)
Tel.: (847) 259-9600
Web Site:
   http://www.dsd.es.northropgrumman.com
Sales Range: $550-599.9 Million
Emp.: 2,100
Defense Electronics & Systems
N.A.I.C.S.: 541512

Subsidiary (Domestic):

Amherst Systems, Inc. (3)
1740 Wehrle Dr, Buffalo, NY 14221 (100%)

Tel.: (716) 631-0610
Web Site: http://www.northropgrumman.com
Sales Range: $150-199.9 Million
Emp.: 600
Defense Electronics & Systems
N.A.I.C.S.: 541512

Unit (Domestic):

Northrop Grumman Electronic Systems (2)
101 Ind Pk Blvd, Warner Robins, GA 31088-7409
Tel.: (478) 923-3866
Sales Range: $50-74.9 Million
Emp.: 150
Radio & T.V. Communications Equipment
N.A.I.C.S.: 334220

Northrop Grumman Electronic Systems (2)
7301 Sykesville Rd, Sykesville, MD 21784-7404 (100%)
Tel.: (410) 552-2800
Web Site:
   http://www.northdopgrumman.com
Sales Range: $75-99.9 Million
Emp.: 400
Electronic Systems
N.A.I.C.S.: 334511

Plant (Domestic):

Northrop Grumman Electronic Systems (2)
601 Main St, New Town, ND 58763 (100%)
Tel.: (701) 627-4714
Web Site: http://www.northropgrumman.com
Sales Range: $25-49.9 Million
Emp.: 100
Aircraft Parts & Equipment
N.A.I.C.S.: 336412

Division (Domestic):

Northrop Grumman Navigation Systems (2)
21240 Burbank Blvd M/S W8, Woodland Hills, CA 91367-6675
Tel.: (818) 715-2000
Web Site: http://www.northropgrumman.com
Sales Range: $350-399.9 Million
Emp.: 1,800
Navigation & Guidance Systems
N.A.I.C.S.: 928110

Plant (Domestic):

Northrop Grumman - Navigation Systems (3)
2211 WN Temple, Salt Lake City, UT 84116
Tel.: (801) 539-1200
Web Site: http://www.northropgrumman.com
Sales Range: $250-299.9 Million
Emp.: 600
Electronic Components
N.A.I.C.S.: 334220

Subsidiary (Non-US):

Northrop Grumman Italia S.p.A. (3)
Via Pontina Km 27 800, 40, Pomezia, Italy
Tel.: (39) 06911921
Web Site: http://www.northropgrumman.it
Sales Range: $100-124.9 Million
Emp.: 200
Integrated Navigation Systems Mfr
N.A.I.C.S.: 334511

Northrop Grumman LITEF GmbH (3)
Loerracher Strasse 18, Freiburg, 79115, Germany
Tel.: (49) 76149010
Web Site:
   http://www.northropgrumman.litef.de
Sales Range: $125-149.9 Million
Emp.: 640
Inertial & Marine Navigation Systems
N.A.I.C.S.: 334511
Lutz Kampmann (Mng Dir)

Unit (Domestic):

Northrop Grumman-Norden Systems (2)
10 Norden Pl, Norwalk, CT 06855-1436
Tel.: (203) 852-5000
Web Site: http://www.northgrum.com

Sales Range: $150-199.9 Million
Emp.: 700
Radar Systems & Equipment
N.A.I.C.S.: 334511
John Berg (Mgr-HR)

Northrop Grumman-Xetron (2)
460 W Crescentville Rd, Cincinnati, OH 45246-1221
Tel.: (513) 881-3100
Web Site: http://www.xetron.com
Sales Range: $50-74.9 Million
Emp.: 350
Tactical Communication Equipment
N.A.I.C.S.: 334511

Subsidiary (Domestic):

Sperry Marine Inc.
1070 Seminole Trl, Charlottesville, VA 22901-2891
Tel.: (434) 974-2000
Web Site:
   http://www.sperrymarine.northropgrum man.com
Sales Range: $450-499.9 Million
Emp.: 1,300
Marine Electronics
N.A.I.C.S.: 334511

Subsidiary (Non-US):

Northrop Grumman Sperry Marine GmbH & Co. KG (3)
Woltmanstrasse 19, 20097, Hamburg, Germany
Tel.: (49) 40299000146
Web Site:
   http://www.sperrymarine.northropgrum man.com
Sales Range: $10-24.9 Million
Emp.: 55
Advanced & Conventional Marine Navigational Equipment
N.A.I.C.S.: 334511

Northrop Grumman Sperry Marine Limited (3)
Burlington House 118 Burlington Road, London, KT3 4NR, United Kingdom (100%)
Tel.: (44) 2083292000
Web Site:
   http://www.sperrymarine.northropgrum man.com
Sales Range: $25-49.9 Million
Emp.: 170
Marine Electronics
N.A.I.C.S.: 334511
Paul Stevens (CFO)

Sperry Marine Canada Limited (3)
120 4320 Viking Way, Richmond, V6V 2L4, BC, Canada
Tel.: (604) 821-2090
Web Site:
   http://www.sperrymarine.northropgrum man.com
Sales Range: $10-24.9 Million
Emp.: 10
Distr of Communications & Navigation Equipment
N.A.I.C.S.: 334290

Northrop Grumman Information Technology, Inc. (1)
7575 Colshire Dr, McLean, VA 22102 (100%)
Tel.: (703) 556-1000
Web Site:
   http://www.is.northropgrumman.com
Sales Range: $5-14.9 Billion
Emp.: 18,500
Communications & Engineering Systems
N.A.I.C.S.: 541512

Subsidiary (Domestic):

3001, Inc. (2)
10300 Eaton Pl Ste 340, Fairfax, VA 22030 (100%)
Tel.: (703) 385-3001
Sales Range: $50-74.9 Million
Geospatial Data Production & Analysis Services
N.A.I.C.S.: 541360

Essex Windermere Corporation (2)
8666 Veterans Hwy, Millersville, MD 21108
Tel.: (410) 923-2081

Web Site:
   http://www.is.northropgrumman.com
Sales Range: $25-49.9 Million
Emp.: 100
Computer Storage Device Mfr
N.A.I.C.S.: 541330

Division (Domestic):

Northrop Grumman Intelligence, Surveillance & Reconnaissance Systems (2)
12900 Federal Systems Park Dr, Fairfax, VA 22033-4411
Tel.: (703) 968-1000
Web Site:
   http://www.ms.northropgrumman.com
Sales Range: $100-124.9 Million
Intelligence, Surveillance & Reconnaissance Systems Developer & Mfr
N.A.I.C.S.: 334511

Remotec, Inc. (2)
353 JD Yarnell Pkwy, Clinton, TN 37716
Tel.: (865) 457-0689
Web Site:
   http://www.ms.northropgrumman.com
Sales Range: $100-124.9 Million
Emp.: 160
Mobile Robot Systems Developer & Mfr
N.A.I.C.S.: 335999

Northrop Grumman Innovation Systems, Inc. (1)
45101 Warp Dr, Sterling, VA 20166
Tel.: (703) 406-5000
Web Site:
   https://www.northropgrumman.com
Sales Range: $1-4.9 Billion
Holding Company; Aerospace & Defense Products Mfr
N.A.I.C.S.: 551112

Group (Domestic):

ATK Aerospace Group (2)
7900 W 4100 S Bldg 55, West Valley City, UT 84120
Tel.: (801) 251-5911
Sales Range: $200-249.9 Million
Emp.: 6,400
Rocket & Satellite Componenet Mfr
N.A.I.C.S.: 336415

Unit (Domestic):

ATK Aerospace Systems (3)
600 Pine Ave, Goleta, CA 93117-3831
Tel.: (805) 685-2262
Web Site: http://www.atk.com
Rev.: $22,066,912
Emp.: 170
Fabricated Structural Metal
N.A.I.C.S.: 541512

ATK Aerospace Systems (3)
5050 Powder Mill Rd, Beltsville, MD 20705
Tel.: (301) 595-5500
Web Site: http://www.atk.com
Sales Range: $125-149.9 Million
Emp.: 626
Satellite Component & Subsystems Mfr
N.A.I.C.S.: 334511

ATK Missle Systems (3)
Allegany Ballistics Laboratory 210 State Route 956, Keyser, WV 26726
Tel.: (304) 726-5000
Web Site: http://www.atk.com
Sales Range: $350-399.9 Million
Emp.: 800
Rocket Research Center
N.A.I.C.S.: 336415

Subsidiary (Domestic):

ATK Space Systems Inc. (3)
6033 E Bandini Blvd, Commerce, CA 90040
Tel.: (323) 722-0222
Web Site: http://www.atk.com
Popellant & Pressurant Tanks Mfr
N.A.I.C.S.: 336992

Subsidiary (Domestic):

ATK Launch Systems Inc. (2)
21839 Atlantic Blvd 45101 Warp Dr, Dulles, VA 20166
Tel.: (703) 406-5000
Web Site: http://www.orbitaatk.com

Sales Range: $350-399.9 Million
Emp.: 1,000
Missile Defense Launch Systems Mfr
N.A.I.C.S.: 336414

COI Ceramics, Inc. (2)
7130 Miramar Rd Ste 100B, San Diego, CA
92121
Tel.: (858) 621-5700
Web Site: http://www.coiceramics.com
Advanced Ceramic Product Mfr
N.A.I.C.S.: 336419
Scott Richardson (Gen Mgr)
Steve Atmur (Dir-New Bus)
Andy Szweda (Dir-Tech)
Hugh Spilker (Mgr-Ceramic Fiber Products)

Orbital Sciences Corporation (2)
45101 Warp Dr, Dulles, VA 20166
Tel.: (703) 406-5000
Web Site: http://www.orbital.com
Sales Range: $1-4.9 Billion
Emp.: 7,000
Space Vehicles & Equipment Mfr
N.A.I.C.S.: 334220

Northrop Grumman International,
Inc. (1)
1840 Century Park E, Los Angeles, CA
90067 (100%)
Tel.: (310) 553-6262
Web Site: http://www.northropgrumman.com
Sales Range: $1-4.9 Billion
Holding Company; Defense & Commercial
Electronics, Ship Building & Repairing, In-
formation Technology, Mission Systems,
Systems Integration & Space Technology
Products & Services
N.A.I.C.S.: 334511

Subsidiary (Non-US):

Northrop Grumman Integrated De-
fence Services Pty. Ltd. (2)
Airport Central Level 10 Cnr O Riordan and
Robey Streets, Mascot, 2020, NSW,
Australia (100%)
Tel.: (61) 2 9691 5006
Sales Range: $125-149.9 Million
Emp.: 500
Logistic Support of Government & Military
Aviation
N.A.I.C.S.: 541690
Gerry Roberts (Mgr-KC-30A Ops)

Northrop Grumman UK Limited (2)
Clareville House Oxendon Street, 26-27
Oxendon St, London, SW1Y 4EL, United
Kingdom (100%)
Tel.: (44) 2079304173
Web Site:
http://www.northropgrumman.co.uk
Sales Range: $250-299.9 Million
Emp.: 30
Holding Company
N.A.I.C.S.: 551112

Division (Domestic):

Northrop Grumman Mission Systems
Europe Limited (3)
Leander House 4600 Parkway, Solent Busi-
ness Park, Fareham, PO15 7AZ, Hants,
United Kingdom (100%)
Tel.: (44) 8456710267
Web Site: http://www.northropgrumman.com
Sales Range: $750-799.9 Million
Advanced Mission Systems & Services
N.A.I.C.S.: 334511

Northrop Grumman Ohio
Corporation (1)
4449 Easton Way 350, Columbus, OH
43219 (100%)
Tel.: (614) 472-2274
Sales Range: $1-9.9 Million
Emp.: 4
Business Services
N.A.I.C.S.: 561110
Jan Wilhelm (VP)

Northrop Grumman Technical Ser-
vices, Inc. (1)
2340 Dulles Corner Blvd, Herndon, VA
20171
Tel.: (703) 713-4000
Web Site:
http://www.ts.northropgrumman.com
Sales Range: $1-4.9 Billion
Emp.: 18,000

Logistics, Maintenance & Technical Ser-
vices
N.A.I.C.S.: 541990
Christopher T. Jones (Pres)

Unit (Domestic):

Northrop Grumman Technical
Services-Kansas City (2)
1286 Eisenhower Rd, Fort Leavenworth, KS
66048
Tel.: (913) 250-0130
Web Site:
http://www.ts.northropgrumman.com
Sales Range: $75-99.9 Million
Emp.: 320
Computer Systems
N.A.I.C.S.: 541512

Northrop Grumman Technical
Services-Norfolk (2)
1410 Washington Ave, Fort Eustis, VA
23604
Tel.: (757) 878-4169
Web Site:
http://www.ts.northropgrumman.com
Aircraft Maintenance & Repair Services
N.A.I.C.S.: 488190

NORTHSIGHT CAPITAL, INC.
7850 E Gray Rd Ste 103, Scottsdale,
AZ 85260
Tel.: (480) 385-3893　　　　NV
Web Site:
http://www.northsightcapital.com
Year Founded: 2008
NCAP—(OTCIQ)
Sales Range: Less than $1 Million
Emp.: 3
Investment Services
N.A.I.C.S.: 523999
John P. Venners (CFO, Chief Acctg
Officer & Exec VP-Ops)
James Janis (Exec VP & Dir-Corp
Dev)
Chris J. Kohler (Controller)

NORTHSTAR ELECTRONICS, INC.
2020 General Booth Blvd Unit 230,
Virginia Beach, VA 23451
Tel.: (647) 286-4594　　　　DE
Web Site:
http://www.northstarelectronics.com
NEIK—(OTCIQ)
Assets: $40,261
Liabilities: $5,380,088
Net Worth: ($5,339,827)
Earnings: ($580,344)
Fiscal Year-end: 12/31/19
Defense, Aerospace & Security Com-
munications Equipment Mfr
N.A.I.C.S.: 334220
Piers VanZiffle (Interim Chm, Sec &
Controller)
Howard D. Nash (Pres & CEO)

NORTHUMBERLAND BAN-CORP
245 Front St, Northumberland, PA
17857
Tel.: (570) 473-3531
Web Site: https://www.norrybank.com
Year Founded: 1903
NUBC—(OTCIQ)
Rev.: $29,409,000
Assets: $674,731,000
Liabilities: $625,616,000
Net Worth: $49,115,000
Earnings: $1,892,000
Emp.: 111
Fiscal Year-end: 12/31/23
Bank Holding Company
N.A.I.C.S.: 551111
Rodney Zechman (Branch Mgr)

Subsidiaries:

The Northumberland National
Bank (1)
245 Front St, Northumberland, PA 17857

Tel.: (570) 473-3531
Web Site: http://www.norrybank.com
Commercial Banking
N.A.I.C.S.: 522110
Jerry L. Bolig (VP-Fin)
Rodney F. Zechman (Branch Mgr-
Northumberland)
Sheri N. Zeiders (VP-IT)
J. Donald Steele Sr. (Chm & CEO)
J. Todd Troxell (Pres & COO)
Mark A. Ritter (Chief Admin Officer & Exec
VP)
Lisa M. Hassinger (Chief Risk Officer & Sr
VP)
Robert Crane (CFO & Sr VP)
Diane L. Elliott (Sr VP-Branch Admin)
Joyce A. Ruhl (VP-Deposit Svcs)

NORTHVIEW ACQUISITION CORPORATION
207 W 25th St 9th Fl, New York, NY
10001
Tel.: (212) 494-9022　　　　DE
Web Site:
https://www.northviewac.com
Year Founded: 2021
NVAC—(NASDAQ)
Rev.: $8,937,503
Assets: $194,736,486
Liabilities: $195,355,962
Net Worth: ($619,476)
Earnings: $7,167,738
Emp.: 2
Fiscal Year-end: 12/31/22
Investment Services
N.A.I.C.S.: 523999
Jack Stover (Co-Founder & CEO)
Fred Knechtel (Co-Founder & CFO)

NORTHWAY FINANCIAL, INC.
9 Main St, Berlin, NH 03570
Tel.: (603) 752-1171　　　　NH
Web Site:
https://www.northwaybank.com
Year Founded: 1997
NWYF—(OTCQB)
Rev.: $41,924,000
Assets: $1,120,692,000
Liabilities: $1,024,577,000
Net Worth: $96,115,000
Earnings: $5,244,000
Emp.: 201
Fiscal Year-end: 12/31/20
Offices of Bank Holding Companies
N.A.I.C.S.: 551111
William J. Woodward (Chm, Pres &
CEO)
Fletcher W. Adams (Vice Chm)
Paula F. Caughey (Officer-Risk Mgmt
& Sr VP)
Jo-Ann Church (Officer-Credit & Sr
VP)
Thomas D. Kaseta (Chief Credit Offi-
cer & Sr VP)
Gregory F. Nolin (Sr VP & Mgr-HR)
Gary J. Laurash (CFO & Sr VP)
Tyler S. White (CIO & Sr VP)
Arthur Scott Thimann (Chief Banking
Officer & Sr VP)
Debra A. Blair (Sec)
Michael J. Cataldo (Chief Admin Offi-
cer & Sr VP)
Albert Romero (Chief Comml Banking
Officer & Sr VP)

Subsidiaries:

Northway Bank (1)
9 Main St, Berlin, NH 03570 (100%)
Tel.: (603) 752-1171
Sales Range: $10-24.9 Million
Emp.: 225
Retail & Commercial Banking
N.A.I.C.S.: 522110
William J. Woodward (Chm, Pres & CEO)
Kelli Olsen (Mgr-Manchester)
Joe Dudek (VP & Mgr-Investment)
Vickie Routhier (Sr VP)

NORTHWEST BANCSHARES, INC.

3 Eon Oval Ste 500, Columbus, OH
43219
Tel.: (814) 726-2140　　　　WA
Web Site:
https://www.northwest.bank
Year Founded: 2001
NWBI—(NASDAQ)
Rev.: $559,647,000
Assets: $14,113,324,000
Liabilities: $12,621,838,000
Net Worth: $1,491,486,000
Earnings: $133,666,000
Emp.: 2,088
Fiscal Year-end: 12/31/22
Bank Holding Company
N.A.I.C.S.: 551111
Louis J. Torchio (Pres & CEO)
Joseph D. Canfield Jr. (Chief Acctg
Officer)
Douglas M. Schosser (CFO & Sr
Exec VP)
Timothy M. Hunter (Vice Chm)
Kyle P. Kane (Chief HR Officer &
Exec VP)
Scott J. Watson (CIO & Exec VP)
Devin Cygnar (Co-CMO & Exec VP)
Gregory J. Betchkal (Chief Risk Offi-
cer)
James M. Colestro (Exec VP)
David W. Heeter (Exec VP)
Jeffrey R. White (Head-Enterprise
Risk Mgmt)
Thomas K. Creal IV (Chief Credit Of-
ficer & Exec VP)

Subsidiaries:

Donegal Financial Services
Corporation (1)
1195 River Rd, Marietta, PA 17547 (48.2%)
Tel.: (717) 426-1931
Banking & Financial Services
N.A.I.C.S.: 522110
Donald Herbert Nikolaus (Chm)

Subsidiary (Domestic):

Union Community Bank FSB (2)
301 Centerville Rd, Lancaster, PA 17601
Tel.: (717) 735-3871
Web Site:
http://www.unioncommunitybank.com
Commercial Banking
N.A.I.C.S.: 522110
Peter J. Miklos (Chief Lending Officer)

Subsidiary (Domestic):

Union Community Bank FSB (3)
1205 River Rd, Marietta, PA 17547
Tel.: (717) 426-2602
Web Site:
http://www.unioncommunitybank.com
Sales Range: $25-49.9 Million
Emp.: 28
Commercial Banking
N.A.I.C.S.: 522110

MutualFirst Financial, Inc. (1)
110 E Charles St, Muncie, IN 47305-2400
Tel.: (765) 747-2800
Web Site: http://www.bankwithmutual.com
Rev.: $85,329,000
Assets: $2,063,776,000
Liabilities: $1,836,964,000
Net Worth: $226,812,000
Earnings: $23,751,000
Emp.: 461
Fiscal Year-end: 12/31/2019
Bank Holding Company
N.A.I.C.S.: 551111
Christopher D. Cook (CFO, Treas & Sr VP)

Subsidiary (Domestic):

Mutual Federal Investment
Company (2)
3993 Howard Hughes Pkwy, Las Vegas, NV
89169
Tel.: (702) 369-0678
Investment Management Service
N.A.I.C.S.: 523940

Summit Mortgage, Inc. (2)
8614 Saint Joe Rd, Fort Wayne, IN 46835

Northwest Bancshares, Inc.—(Continued)

Tel.: (260) 338-1888
Web Site:
  http://www.gotosummitmortgage.com
Mortgage Financial Service Provider
N.A.I.C.S.: 522390
Robert Gregory (Officer-Loan)

Northwest Bank (1)
100 Liberty St, Warren, PA
16365-2353 (100%)
Web Site: http://www.northwest.bank
Commericial Banking
N.A.I.C.S.: 522110
Louis J. Torchio (Pres & CEO)
Mark T. Reitzes (Exec VP & Head-Comml Banking)
Joseph D. Canfield Jr. (Chief Acctg Officer)
Jay DesMarteau (Chief Comml Banking Officer & Sr Exec VP)
T. K. Creal (Chief Credit officer & Sr VP)
Devin Schultis (Area Mgr-Kosciusko & Grant)
Reed Levitz (Sr VP & District Mgr-Indiana)

Subsidiary (Domestic):

B.J. Petruso Agency & Associates, Inc. (2)
568 Washington St, Meadville, PA 16335
Tel.: (814) 724-4000
Insurance Agents
N.A.I.C.S.: 524210
Daniel Petruso (VP)

Boetger Acquisition Corp. (2)
3 Holland St, Erie, PA 16507
Tel.: (814) 455-4550
Web Site: http://www.boetger.com
Actuarial & Employee Benefits Consulting Services
N.A.I.C.S.: 524298

Northwest Advisors, Inc. (2)
100 Liberty St, Warren, PA 16365
Tel.: (814) 728-7080
Web Site: http://www.northwest.bank
Investment Advisory Services
N.A.I.C.S.: 523940

Northwest Capital Group, Inc. (2)
301 2nd Ave, Warren, PA 16365 (100%)
Tel.: (814) 728-1818
Foreclosed Property Management Services
N.A.I.C.S.: 531311

Northwest Consumer Discount Company (2)
PO Box 128, Warren, PA 16365 (100%)
Tel.: (814) 728-1818
Consumer Financial Services
N.A.I.C.S.: 523940

Northwest Financial Services, Inc. (2)
9333 N Meridian St Ste 300, Indianapolis, IN 46260 (100%)
Tel.: (317) 844-0448
Web Site: https://www.northwestfinancial.net
Retail Securities Brokerage Services
N.A.I.C.S.: 523150

NORTHWEST BIOTHERAPEUTICS, INC.
4800 Montgomery Ln Ste 800, Bethesda, MD 20814
Tel.: (240) 497-9024   DE
Web Site: https://www.nwbio.com
Year Founded: 1996
NWBO—(OTCQB)
Rev.: $1,683,000
Assets: $31,323,000
Liabilities: $136,366,000
Net Worth: ($105,043,000)
Earnings: ($105,032,000)
Emp.: 22
Fiscal Year-end: 12/31/22
Pharmaceuticals Mfr
N.A.I.C.S.: 325412
Linda F. Powers (Chm, Pres, CEO, CFO & Chief Acctg Officer)
Alton L. Boynton (Co-Founder & Chief Scientific Officer)

NORTHWEST INDIANA BANCORP
9204 Columbia Ave, Munster, IN 46321
Tel.: (219) 836-4400   IN
Web Site:
  http://www.ibankpeoples.com
Year Founded: 1994
FNWD—(NASDAQ)
Rev.: $69,769,000
Assets: $1,497,525,000
Liabilities: $1,344,603,000
Net Worth: $152,922,000
Earnings: $16,604,000
Emp.: 250
Fiscal Year-end: 12/31/20
Bank Holding Company
N.A.I.C.S.: 551111
David A. Bochnowski (Chm)
Edward J. Furticella (Executives)
Robert T. Lowry (COO & Exec VP)
Benjamin J. Bochnowski (Pres & CEO)
Peymon S. Torabi (CFO, Treas & Exec VP)
Tanya A. Leetz (CIO, CTO & Exec VP)

Subsidiaries:

Peoples Bank (1)
9204 Columbia Ave, Munster, IN 46321
Tel.: (219) 836-9690
Web Site: http://www.ibankpeoples.com
Sales Range: $25-49.9 Million
State Savings Bank
N.A.I.C.S.: 522180
David A. Bochnowski (Chm)
Robert T. Lowry (COO & Exec VP)
Benjamin J. Bochnowski (CEO)
Todd M. Scheub (Pres)
Tanya A. Leetz (CIO, CTO & Exec VP)
Benjamin J. Bochnowski (CEO)

NORTHWEST NATURAL HOLDING COMPANY
250 SW Taylor St, Portland, OR 97204
Tel.: (503) 226-4211   OR
Web Site: https://www.nwnatural.com
Year Founded: 1859
NWN—(NYSE)
Rev.: $1,037,353,000
Assets: $4,748,326,000
Liabilities: $3,572,885,000
Net Worth: $1,175,441,000
Earnings: $86,303,000
Emp.: 1,258
Fiscal Year-end: 12/31/22
Holding Company; Natural Gas Distr
N.A.I.C.S.: 551112
David Hugo Anderson (Pres & CEO)
Brody J. Wilson (Chief Acctg Officer, Treas, VP & Controller)
Raymond J. Kaszuba III (CFO & Sr VP)
Brody J. Wilson (Chief Acctg Officer, Treas, VP & Controller)
Mardilyn Saathoff (Gen Counsel & Sr VP-Regulation)
Shawn M. Filippi (Chief Compliance Officer, Sec & VP)
Zach Kravitz (VP-Rate & Regulatory Affairs)

Subsidiaries:

Cascadia Water, LLC (1)
18181 State Route 525, Freeland, WA 98249
Tel.: (360) 331-7388
Web Site: https://www.cascadiawater.com
Water Utility Services
N.A.I.C.S.: 221310
Culley Lehman (Mgr)
Amy Lehman (Office Mgr)

Falls Water Co., Inc. (1)
2180 N Deborah Dr, Idaho Falls, ID 83401
Tel.: (208) 522-1300
Web Site: https://www.fallswater.com
Water Supply & Irrigation Systems
N.A.I.C.S.: 221310

Scott Bruce (Gen Mgr)

Gem State Water Company, LLC (1)
250 NW Blvd Ste 203, Coeur D'Alene, ID 83814
Web Site: https://www.gemstate-water.com
Wastewater Utility Services
N.A.I.C.S.: 221320
Leslie Abrams-Rayner (Gen Mgr)

KB Pipeline Company (1)
220 NW 2nd Ave, Portland, OR 97209
Tel.: (503) 226-4211
Natural Gas Pipeline Transportation Services
N.A.I.C.S.: 486210

NNG Financial Corporation (1)
220 NW 2nd Ave, Portland, OR 97209-3943 (100%)
Tel.: (503) 226-4211
Sales Range: $75-99.9 Million
Financial Services
N.A.I.C.S.: 523999
Greg Kantor (Pres)

NW Natural Water Company, LLC (1)
250 SW Taylor Street, Portland, OR 97204
Tel.: (800) 422-4012
Web Site: https://www.nwnaturalwater.com
Wastewater Utility Services
N.A.I.C.S.: 562998

Northwest Natural Gas Company (1)
250 SW Taylor St, Portland, OR 97204
Tel.: (503) 226-4211
Web Site: https://www.nwnatural.com
Rev.: $1,158,623,000
Assets: $4,511,377,000
Liabilities: $3,278,757,000
Net Worth: $1,232,620,000
Earnings: $104,737,000
Emp.: 1,379
Fiscal Year-end: 12/31/2023
Natural Gas Distr
N.A.I.C.S.: 221210
David Hugo Anderson (CEO)
Brody J. Wilson (Chief Acctg Officer, Treas, VP & Controller)
Malia H. Wasson (Chm)
Raymond J. Kaszuba III (CFO & Sr VP)
Joseph S. Karney (VP)
Zachary D. Kravitz (VP)
Kim Rush (CMO)

Rose Valley Water Company, Inc. (1)
PO Box 1444, Green Valley, AZ 85622-1444
Tel.: (623) 889-2275
Web Site: https://rosevalleywaterco.com
Water Utility Services
N.A.I.C.S.: 221310

Salmon Valley Water Company (1)
24525 E Welches Rd, Welches, OR 97067
Tel.: (503) 622-4083
Web Site: http://www.thesvwc.com
Wastewater Utility Services
N.A.I.C.S.: 221320
Michael Bowman (Gen Mgr)

Suncadia Water Company, LLC (1)
4244 Bullfrog Rd, Cle Elum, WA 98922
Tel.: (509) 649-6370
Web Site:
  http://www.suncadiawatercompany.com
Water Utility Services
N.A.I.C.S.: 221310
Darian Osiadacz (Supvr-Ops)

Sunriver Environmental LLC (1)
18305 Cottonwood Rd, Sunriver, OR 97707
Tel.: (541) 593-4197
Water Utility Services
N.A.I.C.S.: 221310

Sunriver Water LLC (1)
57850 W Cascade Rd, Sunriver, OR 97707
Tel.: (541) 419-6469
Web Site: http://www.sunriverwater.com
Water Utility Services
N.A.I.C.S.: 221320

T & W Water Service Company (1)
12284 FM 3083, Conroe, TX 77301
Tel.: (936) 756-7400
Web Site: http://www.twwaterservice.com
Water Supply Services
N.A.I.C.S.: 221310

NORTHWEST PIPE COMPANY
201 NE Park Plz Dr Ste 100, Vancouver, WA 98684
Tel.: (360) 397-6250   OR
Web Site: https://www.nwpipe.com
Year Founded: 1966
NWPX—(NASDAQ)
Rev.: $457,665,000
Assets: $601,340,000
Liabilities: $283,066,000
Net Worth: $318,274,000
Earnings: $31,149,000
Emp.: 1,312
Fiscal Year-end: 12/31/22
Steel Pole Mfr
N.A.I.C.S.: 331210
Aaron Wilkins (CFO, Sec & Sr VP)
Miles Brittain (Exec VP)
Megan Kendrick (VP-HR)
Michael Wray (Sr VP)
Goff Henry (VP)
William Ast (VP)
Neal Kelemen (Sls Mgr)
Gary Lewis (Sls Mgr)
Kevin Martin (Sls Mgr)
Alena Mikhaylova (Mgr)
Trevor Gonterman (Sls Dir)
Brent Keil (Dir)
Scott J. Montross (Pres & CEO)
William Smith (Exec VP-Water Transmission Engineered Sys)

Subsidiaries:

Geneva Pipe Company (1)
1465 W 400 N, Orem, UT 84057
Tel.: (801) 225-2416
Web Site: http://www.genevapipe.com
Rev.: $13,000,000
Emp.: 150
Pipe Mfr & Whslr
N.A.I.C.S.: 327332

NWPC de SLRC, S de RL de CV (1)
Via Ameron No 100 Interior B Col Las Adelitas, San Luis Rio Colorado, 83520, Sonora, Mexico
Tel.: (52) 16535772200
Plastic Tank Mfr
N.A.I.C.S.: 326122

Permalok Corporation (1)
472 Paul Ave, Saint Louis, MO 63135
Tel.: (314) 524-1900
Web Site: http://www.permalok.com
Emp.: 40
Steel Pole Mfr
N.A.I.C.S.: 331210

NORTHWESTERN CORPORATION
3010 W 69th St, Sioux Falls, SD 57108
Tel.: (605) 978-2900   DE
Web Site:
  https://www.northwesternenergy.com
Year Founded: 1923
NWE—(NASDAQ)
Rev.: $1,477,837,000
Assets: $7,317,783,000
Liabilities: $4,652,600,000
Net Worth: $2,665,183,000
Earnings: $183,008,000
Emp.: 1,530
Fiscal Year-end: 12/31/22
Electricity & Natural Gas Services
N.A.I.C.S.: 221111
Jeffrey B. Berzina (Principal Acctg Officer & Controller)
Brian B. Bird (Pres & CEO)
Michael L. Nieman (Chief Compliance Officer & Chief Audit Officer)
Dana J. Dykhouse (Chm)
Daniel L. Rausch (Treas)
Crystal D. Lail (CFO & VP)
Michael R. Cashell (VP-Transmission)
John D. Hines (VP-Supply & Montana Govt Affairs)

Timothy P. Olson *(Sec)*
Travis E. Meyer *(Dir-Corporate Finance & Officer-Investor Relations)*
Jeanne M. Vold *(VP-Tech)*
Jason Merkel *(VP-Distr)*
Cyndee Fang *(VP-Regulatory)*
Shannon M. Heim *(Gen Counsel & VP)*
Bleau LaFave *(VP-Bus Dev & Asset Mgmt)*

Subsidiaries:

Clark Fork and Blackfoot, L.L.C. **(1)**
40 E Broadway, Butte, MT 59701-9331
Tel.: (406) 497-2130
Electric & Natural Gas Transmission & Distribution Services
N.A.I.C.S.: 221210

Havre Pipeline Company, LLC **(1)**
14815 Clear Creek Rd, Havre, MT 59501
Tel.: (406) 357-2233
Natural Gas Transportation Services
N.A.I.C.S.: 486910

NorthWestern Networks, Inc. **(1)**
600 Market St, Huron, SD 57350 **(100%)**
Tel.: (605) 352-8411
Web Site: http://www.westernenergy.com
Sales Range: $50-74.9 Million
Emp.: 100
Energy Utilities
N.A.I.C.S.: 221118

NORWEGIAN CRUISE LINE HOLDINGS LTD.

7665 Corporate Ctr Dr, Miami, FL 33126
Tel.: (305) 436-4000 BM
Web Site: https://www.nclhltd.com
Year Founded: 2011
NCLH—(NYSE)
Rev.: $8,549,924,000
Assets: $19,492,990,000
Liabilities: $19,192,183,000
Net Worth: $300,807,000
Earnings: $166,178,000
Emp.: 5,100
Fiscal Year-end: 12/31/23
Holding Company; Cruise Line Operator
N.A.I.C.S.: 551112
David J. Herrera *(Pres-Norwegian Cruise Line)*
Harry J. Sommer *(Pres & CEO)*
Faye L. Ashby *(Chief Acctg Officer & Sr VP)*
Daniel S. Farkas *(Gen Counsel, Exec VP & Asst Sec)*
Mark A. Kempa *(CFO & Exec VP)*
Jason M. Montague *(Pres & CEO-Regent Seven Seas Cruises)*
Lynn White *(Chief Talent Officer)*

Subsidiaries:

NCL Corporation Ltd. **(1)**
7665 Corporate Ctr Dr, Miami, FL 33126
Tel.: (305) 436-4000
Web Site: https://www.nclhltd.com
Rev.: $4,843,759,999
Assets: $18,546,861,000
Liabilities: $18,328,060,000
Net Worth: $218,801,000
Earnings: ($1,970,431,000)
Emp.: 5,100
Fiscal Year-end: 12/31/2022
Holding Company; Passenger Cruise Operator
N.A.I.C.S.: 551112
Frank J. Del Rio *(Pres & CEO)*
Faye L. Ashby *(Chief Acctg Officer & Sr VP)*
Mark A. Kempa *(CFO & Exec VP)*
Robin Lindsay *(Exec VP)*
Lynn White *(Chief Talent Officer)*

Subsidiary (Domestic):

NCL (Bahamas) Ltd. **(2)**
7665 NW 19th St, Miami, FL 33126-1201
Tel.: (305) 436-4000
Web Site: http://www.ncl.com

Sales Range: $1-4.9 Billion
Travel Cruise Services
N.A.I.C.S.: 483112
Andrew Stuart *(Pres & CEO)*
Alex Pinelo *(VP-Key Accts)*
Nathan Hickman *(VP-Field Sls)*

Polynesian Adventure Tours Inc. **(2)**
2880 Kilihau St, Honolulu, HI 96819
Tel.: (808) 833-3000
Web Site: http://www.polyad.com
Rev.: $17,000,000
Emp.: 170
Sightseeing Tours of Hawaii
N.A.I.C.S.: 485999
Marc Rubenstein *(COO & Sr VP)*
Kelly Camps *(VP-Sls & Mktg)*
Terry Fischer *(Pres)*
Mugs Hunt *(Dir-Charter Sls)*
Lynley Minamoto *(Dir-Sls & Mktg)*

Prestige Cruises International, Inc. **(1)**
8300 NW 33rd St Ste 100, Miami, FL 33122
Tel.: (844) 473-4368
Web Site: http://www.rssc.com
Sales Range: $1-4.9 Billion
Emp.: 1,615
Cruise Ship Operator
N.A.I.C.S.: 483112

Subsidiary (Domestic):

Prestige Cruise Holdings, Inc **(2)**
8300 NW 33rd St Ste 100, Miami, FL 33122
Tel.: (844) 473-4368
Web Site: http://www.rssc.com
Sales Range: $25-49.9 Million
Emp.: 100
Holding Company; Cruise Ship Operator
N.A.I.C.S.: 551112
Robert J. Binder *(Vice Chm)*
Randall Soy *(Exec VP-Sls & Mktg)*

Holding (Non-US):

Regent Seven Seas Cruises UK Ltd **(3)**
Beresford House Town Quay, SO14 2AQ, Southampton, Hampshire, United Kingdom - England
Tel.: (44) 2380682280
Sales Range: $10-24.9 Million
Emp.: 25
Cruise Ship Owner & Operator
N.A.I.C.S.: 487210
Paul Beale *(Head-Sls)*
Kelly-Marie Gregg *(Mgr-Trng & Events)*
Steph Armengol *(VP-Hotel Ops)*
Franco Semeraro *(Sr VP-Hotel Ops)*
Carol Herron *(VP-Field Sls)*
Randall Soy *(Exec VP-Sls & Mktg-Line)*
Megan Hernandez *(CMO/Sr VP-Cruise Line)*

NORWIX INC.

31 Clinton Ave, Norwich, CT 06360
Tel.: (860) 598-8615 DE
Web Site: https://www.norwix.com
Year Founded: 1998
SORT—(OTCIQ)
Rev.: $15,004,000
Assets: $9,670,000
Liabilities: $4,635,000
Net Worth: $5,035,000
Earnings: $1,751,000
Fiscal Year-end: 12/31/20
Holding Company; Ink Jet Image Machinery Designer, Developer & Marketer
N.A.I.C.S.: 551112
Fred Lucci *(Mgr-Customer Svc)*
Carol Pace *(Coord-Inside Sls)*

Subsidiaries:

inc.jet, Inc. **(1)**
1 Winnenden Rd, Norwich, CT 06360
Tel.: (860) 823-3090
Web Site: http://www.incjet.com
Printing Products Mfr & Whslr
N.A.I.C.S.: 325910

NORWOOD FINANCIAL CORP.

717 Main St, Honesdale, PA 18431
Tel.: (570) 253-1455 PA

Web Site:
https://www.waynebank.com
Year Founded: 1995
NWFL—(NASDAQ)
Rev.: $75,666,000
Assets: $2,047,070,000
Liabilities: $1,879,985,000
Net Worth: $167,085,000
Earnings: $29,233,000
Emp.: 274
Fiscal Year-end: 12/31/22
Bank Holding Company
N.A.I.C.S.: 551111
Andrew A. Forte *(Vice Chm)*
James O. Donnelly *(Pres & CEO)*
John Martin McCaffery Jr. *(CFO & Exec VP)*

Subsidiaries:

Wayne Bank **(1)**
717 Main St, Honesdale, PA 18431
Tel.: (570) 253-1455
Web Site: http://www.waynebank.com
Sales Range: $25-49.9 Million
Emp.: 125
Community Bank
N.A.I.C.S.: 522110
Lewis J. Critelli Jr. *(Chm)*
Andrew A. Forte *(Vice Chm)*
Joseph W. Adams *(Sr VP & Dir-Wealth Mgmt & Investment Svcs)*
James O. Donnelly *(Pres & CEO)*
John Martin McCaffery Jr. *(CFO & Exec VP)*

NOTIS GLOBAL, INC.

65 Mechanic St, Red Bank, NJ 07701
Tel.: (732) 242-3264 NV
Year Founded: 1977
NGBL—(OTCIQ)
Sales Range: Less than $1 Million
Alternative Medicine Extraction & Cultivation
N.A.I.C.S.: 325411

NOUVEAU LIFE PHARMACEUTICALS, INC.

3580 Wilshire Blvd Ste 100, Los Angeles, CA 90010
Tel.: (213) 235-8554 NV
Year Founded: 1998
NOUV—(OTCIQ)
Pharmaceuticals Product Mfr
N.A.I.C.S.: 325412
Young Ju Kim *(Chm)*
Sang Tae Choi *(Pres & CEO)*

NOV, INC.

10353 Richmond Ave, Houston, TX 77042-4103
Tel.: (346) 223-3000 DE
Web Site: https://www.nov.com
Year Founded: 1995
NOV—(NYSE)
Rev.: $8,583,000,000
Assets: $11,294,000,000
Liabilities: $5,052,000,000
Net Worth: $6,242,000,000
Earnings: $993,000,000
Emp.: 33,676
Fiscal Year-end: 12/31/23
Oilwell Drilling Equipment, Pump & Machinery Mfr
N.A.I.C.S.: 333132
Jose A. Bayardo *(CFO & Sr VP)*
Clay C. Williams *(Chm, Pres & CEO)*
Joseph W. Rovig *(Pres-Energy Equipment Segment)*
Craig L. Weinstock *(Gen Counsel & Sr VP)*
David Reid *(CMO & CTO)*
Bonnie Houston *(Chief Admin Officer)*
Alex Philips *(CIO)*
Rium Johnson *(Chief Health, Safety, Security & Environmental Officer)*
Christy H. Novak *(Chief Acctg Officer, VP & Controller)*

Subsidiaries:

APL Management Pte Ltd **(1)**
8 Shenton Way 49-03 AXA Towers, Singapore, 68811, Singapore
Tel.: (65) 62221361
Web Site: http://www.nov.com
Sales Range: $25-49.9 Million
Emp.: 52
Oil Field Equipment Mfr
N.A.I.C.S.: 333132

APL Norway AS **(1)**
Vikaveien 85, Kolbjornsvik, 4816, Arendal, Norway
Tel.: (47) 45297000
Oil & Gas Drilling Equipment Mfr & Distr
N.A.I.C.S.: 333132
Jan Borre Sannaes *(Mng Dir)*

APL do Brasil Ltda **(1)**
Avenida Republica do Chile 500 24th Floor, Downtown, Rio de Janeiro, 2003-1170, Brazil
Tel.: (55) 2135750661
Web Site: http://www.nov.com
Oil & Gas Drilling Equipment Mfr & Distr
N.A.I.C.S.: 333132

Advanced Production & Loading Inc. **(1)**
2000 Dairy Ashford Ste 600, Houston, TX 77077
Tel.: (281) 293-7711
Web Site: http://www.nov.com
Emp.: 18
Oil Field Services
N.A.I.C.S.: 213112

Aggregate Plant Products Co. **(1)**
442 N WW White Rd, San Antonio, TX 78219
Tel.: (210) 333-1111
Oil & Gas Drilling Equipment Mfr & Distr
N.A.I.C.S.: 333132

Ameron Brasil Industria E Comercio de Tubos Ltda **(1)**
Aurora Maria Da Conceicao 958 - Ptb, Betim, 32530-050, Minas Gerais, Brazil
Tel.: (55) 3135920033
Oil & Gas Drilling Equipment Mfr & Distr
N.A.I.C.S.: 333132

Ameron Holdings II Pte Ltd **(1)**
7A Tuas Avenue 3, Singapore, 639407, Singapore
Tel.: (65) 68616118
Holding Company
N.A.I.C.S.: 551112

Ameron International Corporation **(1)**
245 S Los Robles Ave, Pasadena, CA 91101-3638
Tel.: (626) 683-4000
Web Site: http://www.nov.com
Mfr of Engineering Products & Materials for Industrial, Energy, Transportation & Infrastructure
N.A.I.C.S.: 327390
Clay C. Williams *(Pres)*

Subsidiary (Non-US):

American Pipe & Construction International **(2)**
Calle 193 No 31-02, Carretera Central De Norte, 90087, Bogota, D E, Colombia **(100%)**
Tel.: (57) 16684800
Web Site: http://www.apci.com.co
Sales Range: $75-99.9 Million
Emp.: 200
Mfr of Concrete & Steel Pipe
N.A.I.C.S.: 327332

Division (Domestic):

Ameron Hawaii **(2)**
2344 Pahounui Dr, Honolulu, HI 96819-2220
Tel.: (808) 832-9200
Web Site: https://www.hcdhawaii.com
Sales Range: $125-149.9 Million
Emp.: 280
Construction Product Mfr
N.A.I.C.S.: 327390
Wade H. Wakayama *(Pres)*
Eric Y. Shimabukuro *(VP-Ops-Sand Island)*
Lloyd M. Tsue *(VP-Ops)*

NOV, Inc.—(Continued)

Eileen L. Mori-Mishina *(VP-HR & Safety)*
Glenn H. Okuno *(VP-Fin)*
Rick W. Volner Jr. *(Gen Mgr-Maui Ops)*

Ameron International Water Transmission Group **(2)**
10100 W Linne Rd, Tracy, CA 95377 **(100%)**
Tel.: (209) 836-5050
Web Site: http://www.nov.com
Sales Range: $75-99.9 Million
Emp.: 160
Concrete & Steel Pipe Mfr
N.A.I.C.S.: 332919

Ameron Protective Linings Co **(2)**
201 N Berry St, Brea, CA 92821-3904 **(100%)**
Tel.: (714) 256-7755
Mfr of Protective Linings
N.A.I.C.S.: 339113

Joint Venture (Non-US):

Bondstrand Ltd. **(2)**
PO Box 589, Dammam, 31421, Saudi Arabia
Web Site: http://www.amiantit.com
Sales Range: $25-49.9 Million
Emp.: 250
Fiberglass Pipe & Fittings Mfr
N.A.I.C.S.: 326199

Subsidiary (Domestic):

Island Ready-Mix Concrete, Inc. **(2)**
91-047 Hanua St, Kapolei, HI 96707
Tel.: (808) 682-1305
Web Site: http://www.islandreadymix.com
Sales Range: $1-9.9 Million
Emp.: 32
Ready-Mix Concrete Mfr & Marketer
N.A.I.C.S.: 327320

Division (Domestic):

NOV Fiber Glass Systems **(2)**
17115 San Pedro Ave Ste 200, San Antonio, TX 78232 **(100%)**
Tel.: (210) 477-7500
Web Site: http://www.nov.com
Sales Range: $10-24.9 Million
Emp.: 9
Fiberglass Pipe & Fittings Mfr
N.A.I.C.S.: 326122

Subsidiary (Non-US):

Saudi Arabia Concrete Products Ltd. **(2)**
PO Box 7727, PO Box 7727, Jeddah, 21472, Saudi Arabia **(40%)**
Tel.: (966) 26374406
Web Site: http://www.sacop.com
Sales Range: $50-74.9 Million
Emp.: 100
Concrete Pipe Products Mfr
N.A.I.C.S.: 327332

Division (Domestic):

Steel Fabrication Division **(2)**
13032 Slover Ave, Fontana, CA 92337-6969 **(100%)**
Tel.: (909) 822-1280
Web Site: http://www.ameronpipe.com
Sales Range: $50-74.9 Million
Emp.: 250
Mfr of Steel & Steel Pipe
N.A.I.C.S.: 331210

Brandt Oilfield Services **(1)**
39 Gul Ave, Singapore, 629679, Singapore
Tel.: (65) 68621169
Oil & Gas Related Services
N.A.I.C.S.: 213112

Capital Valves Limited **(1)**
Unit 8B St Leger Drive, Newmarket, Wembley Middlesex, Suffolk, CB8 7DT, United Kingdom
Tel.: (44) 2089000471
Web Site: http://www.capitalvalves.com
Emp.: 15
Industrial Valve Mfr
N.A.I.C.S.: 332911
Anka Browne *(Mgr-Accts)*
Richard Schmieg *(Engr-Sls)*

Chemineer, Inc. **(1)**
5870 Poe Ave, Dayton, OH 45414
Tel.: (937) 454-3300
Web Site: http://www.chemineer.com
Oil & Gas Field Supporting Services
N.A.I.C.S.: 213112
Patty Breig *(Mng Dir)*

Coil Services (North Sea) Limited **(1)**
Badentoy Crescent Badentoy Park Portlethen, Aberdeen, AB12 4YD, United Kingdom
Tel.: (44) 97124989700
Web Site: http://www.nov.com
Sales Range: $10-24.9 Million
Emp.: 6
Oil Field Equipment Mfr
N.A.I.C.S.: 333132

Contubos S.A. **(1)**
Cl 193 31 02 In 2, Bogota, Colombia
Tel.: (57) 16684800
Oil & Gas Drilling Equipment Mfr & Distr
N.A.I.C.S.: 333132

Denali Incorporated **(1)**
2400 Augusta Dr Ste 340, Houston, TX 77057
Tel.: (713) 627-0933
Web Site: http://www.denaliincorporated.com
Sales Range: $50-74.9 Million
Mfr of Specialty Engineered Corrosion Resistant FRP Products Chemical, Petroleum, Water Waste Sewer Generation, Pulp & Paper Industries
N.A.I.C.S.: 339999
Tim Maynard *(COO)*
Robert B. Bennett *(CEO)*
Daimon Jacobs *(CFO)*
Chaun Trenary *(VP-Mktg & Sls)*
Carolyn Pampe *(Dir-HR)*

Subsidiary (Domestic):

Belco, Inc. **(2)**
2303 Taylors Valley Rd, Belton, TX 76513-0210 **(100%)**
Tel.: (254) 933-9000
Web Site: https://www.belco-mfg.com
Sales Range: $25-49.9 Million
Manufacture Fiberglass Tanks And Ducts
N.A.I.C.S.: 326199

Containment Solutions, Inc. **(2)**
333 N Rivershire Dr Ste 190, Conroe, TX 77304
Tel.: (936) 756-7731
Web Site: https://www.containmentsolutions.com
Emp.: 27
Fiberglass Composite & Steel Storage Tanks Mfr
N.A.I.C.S.: 339999

Ershigs, Inc. **(2)**
742 Marine Dr, Bellingham, WA 98225-1530
Tel.: (360) 733-2620
Web Site: https://www.ershigs.com
Sales Range: $50-74.9 Million
Corrosion Equipment Mfr
N.A.I.C.S.: 325998
Shawn Burns *(Gen Mgr-Field Ops)*

Dreco Energy Services ULC **(1)**
Edmonton 3620 93rd 3620 - 93 Street, Edmonton, T6E 5N3, AB, Canada
Tel.: (780) 465-9500
Web Site: http://www.nov.com
Sales Range: $25-49.9 Million
Oil Field Equipment Mfr
N.A.I.C.S.: 333132

Elmar Engineering Limited **(1)**
Unit 9-11 Westhill Industrial Estate West Hill, Aberdeen, AB32 6TQ, Aberdeenshire, United Kingdom
Tel.: (44) 1224740261
Web Site: http://www.nov.com
Emp.: 200
Oil Field Equipment Mfr
N.A.I.C.S.: 333132

Elmar Far East Pty Ltd **(1)**
Unit 2 48 Canvale Road, Perth, 6155, WA, Australia
Tel.: (61) 882795799
Web Site: http://www.elmar.co.uk
Emp.: 6

Business Support Services
N.A.I.C.S.: 561499

Elmar Services Limited **(1)**
Westhill Industrial Estate, Westhill, Aberdeen, AB32 6TQ, United Kingdom
Tel.: (44) 1224740261
Web Site: http://www.nov.com
Sales Range: $50-74.9 Million
Emp.: 25
Oil Field Equipment Mfr
N.A.I.C.S.: 333132

Elmar Services Pty Ltd **(1)**
48 Canvale Rd Unit 2, Canning Vale, 6155, WA, Australia
Tel.: (61) 894560999
Web Site: http://www.elmar.co.uk
Sales Range: $10-24.9 Million
Emp.: 6
Oil Field Equipment Mfr
N.A.I.C.S.: 333132

Enerflow Industries Inc. **(1)**
4910 80th Avenue SE, Calgary, T2C 2X3, AB, Canada
Tel.: (403) 279-9696
Web Site: http://www.enerflow.com
Rev.: $51,007,704
Emp.: 300
Oil Field Equipment Mfr
N.A.I.C.S.: 333132

Enerpro de Mexico, S.A. de C.V. **(1)**
Av Tlalnepantla - Tenayuca No 23 Tenayuca, Tlalnepantla, 54150, Mexico
Tel.: (52) 5553926566
Industrial Machinery Mfr
N.A.I.C.S.: 332216

Expo Partes S.A. de C.V. **(1)**
Avenida 5 de Mayo Este 138, Mexicali, 21210, BC, Mexico
Tel.: (52) 6865666500
Web Site: http://www.nov.com
Sales Range: $100-124.9 Million
Emp.: 250
Petroleum Production Equipment
N.A.I.C.S.: 333132

FIBERSPAR LINEPIPE CANADA LTD. **(1)**
1100 444 - 5th Ave SW, Calgary, T2P 2T8, AB, Canada
Tel.: (403) 265-9900
Web Site: http://www.nov.com
Emp.: 40
Oil & Gas Field Equipment Distr
N.A.I.C.S.: 423830

Fiber Glass Systems Holdings, LLC **(1)**
2835 Holmes Rd, Houston, TX 77051
Tel.: (713) 799-5100
Holding Company
N.A.I.C.S.: 551112

Fiberglass Systems **(1)**
17115 San Pedro Ave Ste 200, San Antonio, TX 78232
Tel.: (210) 477-7500
Web Site: http://www.onr.com
Sales Range: $10-24.9 Million
Emp.: 35
Fiberglass Piping Products
N.A.I.C.S.: 326122

Subsidiary (Domestic):

Fiber Glass Systems L.P. **(2)**
2700 W 65th St, Little Rock, AR 72209
Tel.: (501) 568-4010
Fiberglass Piping Products Mfr
N.A.I.C.S.: 332996

Subsidiary (Domestic):

Smith Fibercast **(3)**
25 S Main St, Sand Springs, OK 74063
Tel.: (918) 245-6651
Web Site: http://www.smithfibercast.com
Sales Range: $50-74.9 Million
Emp.: 80
Fiberglass Piping Products
N.A.I.C.S.: 326122

Subsidiary (Non-US):

Harbin Fiber Glass **(2)**
6 Ningbo Road Haping Road Centralized Industrial Park, Harbin, 150060, Heilongji-

ang, China
Tel.: (86) 451 8709 1722
Web Site: http://www.fgspipe.com
Fiberglass Piping Products
N.A.I.C.S.: 326191

NOV Fiber Glass Systems **(2)**
De Panoven 20, PO Box 6, 4191 GW, Geldermalsen, Netherlands **(100%)**
Tel.: (31) 345587587
Web Site: http://www.nov.com
Fiberglass Pipe & Fittings Mfr
N.A.I.C.S.: 326199

Fiberspar Australia Pty. Ltd. **(1)**
300 Adelaide Street, Brisbane, 4000, QLD, Australia
Tel.: (61) 407037092
Oil & Gas Field Equipment Distr
N.A.I.C.S.: 423830

Fiberspar Corporation **(1)**
Northwoods Industrial Park W 12239 FM 529, Houston, TX 77041
Tel.: (713) 849-2609
Web Site: http://www.fiberspar.com
Oil & Gas Field Equipment Mfr
N.A.I.C.S.: 333132

Fibra Ingenieria y Construccion S.A. **(1)**
Sta Margarita 750, San Bernardo, Santiago, Chile
Tel.: (56) 224112500
Web Site: https://www.fibra.cl
Construction Equipment Mfr
N.A.I.C.S.: 333120

Fidmash **(1)**
26 Rybalko str, 220033, Minsk, Belarus
Tel.: (375) 172021601
Web Site: https://en.fidmashnov.by
Oil & Gas Field Equipment Mfr
N.A.I.C.S.: 333132

Fjords Processing Australia Pty Ltd **(1)**
137 Kewdale Road Kewdale, Perth, 6105, WA, Australia
Tel.: (61) 863637200
Industrial Equipment Rental Services
N.A.I.C.S.: 532490

Fjords Processing Limited **(1)**
Suite 5 Building 4 3 Frimley 4 Business Park, Frimley, GU3 7SG, United Kingdom
Tel.: (44) 1276697050
Oil & Gas Field Supporting Services
N.A.I.C.S.: 213112
Andy Manning *(Ops Mgr)*
Phil Brownjohn *(Mgr-Sls)*
Glen McLellan *(Gen Mgr)*

Forth Valley Engineering Limited **(1)**
Cawburn Works Drumshoreland Rd, Broxburn, EH52 5PQ, West Lothian, United Kingdom
Tel.: (44) 1506855643
Oil & Gas Drilling Equipment Mfr & Distr
N.A.I.C.S.: 333132

GOT German Oil Tools GmbH **(1)**
Vechtaer Marsch 3-5, PO Box 1222, 49377, Vechta, Germany
Tel.: (49) 44419322300
Oil & Gas Field Supporting Services
N.A.I.C.S.: 213112

Grant Prideco (Singapore) Pte Ltd **(1)**
11 Tuas Avenue 7, Singapore, 639266, Singapore
Tel.: (65) 68614266
Web Site: http://www.nov.com
Sales Range: $25-49.9 Million
Oil Field Equipment Mfr
N.A.I.C.S.: 333132

Grant Prideco Netherlands B.V. **(1)**
Stevinstraat 2, 1704RN, Heerhugowaard, Netherlands
Tel.: (31) 725718270
Web Site: http://www.nov.com
Sales Range: $25-49.9 Million
Emp.: 12
Investment Management Service
N.A.I.C.S.: 551112

Grant Prideco, L.P. **(1)**
7909 Parkwood Cir Dr, Houston, TX 77036
Tel.: (713) 375-3700

Oil & Gas Drilling Equipment Mfr & Distr
N.A.I.C.S.: 333132

GustoMSC B.V. (1)
Karel Doormanweg 35, 3115 JD, Schiedam,
Netherlands
Tel.: (31) 10 2883 000
Web Site: http://www.gustomsc.com
Offshore Oil & Construction Industries De-
signing, Engineering & Consulting Services
N.A.I.C.S.: 541330

Hydralift AS (1)
Box 401, Kristiansand, 4604, Norway
Tel.: (47) 38192000
Web Site: http://www.nov.com
Sales Range: $600-649.9 Million
Emp.: 3,000
Oil Field Equipment Mfr
N.A.I.C.S.: 333132

Hydralift France SAS (1)
15 rue de la Metallurgie, Pays de la Loire,
Carquefou, 44482, France
Tel.: (33) 240683600
Sales Range: $50-74.9 Million
Emp.: 250
Oil Field Equipment Mfr
N.A.I.C.S.: 333132
Philippe Gadreau (Mgr)

IntelliServ Norway AS (1)
Risavika Havnering 247, PO Box 157,
4056, Tananger, Norway
Tel.: (47) 91577680
Emp.: 2
Engineering Consulting Services
N.A.I.C.S.: 541330

Intelliserv, Inc. (1)
2241 Tracy Hall Pkwy, Provo, UT 84606-
6219
Tel.: (801) 418-6700
Web Site: http://www.nov.com
Emp.: 90
Oil & Gas Drilling Equipment Mfr
N.A.I.C.S.: 333132

**Jiangyin Tuboscope Tubular Develop-
ment Co., Ltd**
Tongdu North Road 299 Room 1908, Ch-
uangxin Village, Jiangyin, 214443, Jiangsu,
China
Tel.: (86) 51086688938
Emp.: 15
Oil Field Equipment Mfr
N.A.I.C.S.: 333132

Keystone Tower Systems, Inc. (1)
5390 Pecos St, Denver, CO 80221
Tel.: (720) 295-8020
Web Site:
    https://keystonetowersystems.com
Wind Turbine Tower Mfr
N.A.I.C.S.: 333611
Eric Smith (CEO & Co-Founded)
Rosalind Takata (Co-Founder & Chief Tech-
nical Officer)
Pete Bierden (Chief Growth Officer)
Steve Lockard (Chm)
Steven C. Lockard (Chm)

M/D Totco (1)
1200 Cypress Creek Rd, Cedar Park, TX
78613
Tel.: (512) 340-5000
Sales Range: $150-199.9 Million
Emp.: 350
Sensors & Transducers
N.A.I.C.S.: 334511
Greg Hendrix (Mgr-EHS)

Merpro Americas, Inc. (1)
14811 Saint Marys Ln Ste 133, Houston,
TX 77079-2984
Tel.: (281) 493-2272
Oil & Gas Field Equipment Mfr
N.A.I.C.S.: 333132

Merpro Limited (1)
Brent Avenue, Montrose, DD10 9PB, Scot-
land, United Kingdom
Tel.: (44) 1674662200
Oil & Gas Field Equipment Mfr
N.A.I.C.S.: 333132

Mono Pumps Limited (1)
Greengate Middleton, Manchester, M24
1SA, United Kingdom
Tel.: (44) 613399000
Web Site: https://www.mono-pumps.com

Sales Range: $50-74.9 Million
Emp.: 390
Mining Pumps Mfr
N.A.I.C.S.: 333914

Subsidiary (Non-US):

**Mono Pumps (Australia) Proprietary
Limited** (2)
75 Frankston Gardens Drive, Carrum
Downs, Melbourne, 3201, VIC, Australia
Tel.: (61) 397737777
Web Site: http://www.mono-pumps.com
Oil Field Equipment Mfr
N.A.I.C.S.: 333132

Subsidiary (Domestic):

**Mono Pumps (Manufacturing)
Limited** (2)
Greengate Middletown, Manchester, M24
1SA, United Kingdom
Tel.: (44) 1613399000
Web Site: http://www.mono-pumps.com
Sales Range: $75-99.9 Million
Emp.: 40
Oil Field Construction Machinery & Pumps
Mfr
N.A.I.C.S.: 333914

Subsidiary (Non-US):

**Mono Pumps New Zealand
Company** (2)
35-41 Fremlin Place, PO Box 71-021, Avon-
dale, Auckland, 1026, New Zealand
Tel.: (64) 98290333
Web Site: https://www.monopumps.com.au
Sales Range: $25-49.9 Million
Pumps Mfr
N.A.I.C.S.: 327910

Moyno, Inc. (1)
5870 Poe Ave, Dayton, OH 45414
Tel.: (937) 454-3300
Web Site: https://www.moyno.com
Pumps Mfr
N.A.I.C.S.: 333914

**NOV ASEP Elmar (Middle East)
Limited** (1)
Enterprise Drive Westhill, Aberdeen, AB32
6TQ, United Kingdom
Tel.: (44) 1224740261
Web Site: http://www.nov.com
Emp.: 300
Oil Field Equipment Mfr
N.A.I.C.S.: 333132
Robert Bruce (Mng Dir)

NOV Australia Pty Ltd (1)
75 Frankston Gardens Drive, Carrum
Downs, 3201, VIC, Australia
Tel.: (61) 397737777
Web Site: http://www.monopumps.com.au
Pumps Mfr
N.A.I.C.S.: 333914

NOV Brandt Europe France (1)
Ancienne Gare, Provins, 77151, Montceaux
les, France
Tel.: (33) 164602890
Web Site: http://www.nov.com
Sales Range: $10-24.9 Million
Emp.: 3
Oil Field Equipment Mfr
N.A.I.C.S.: 333132

**NOV Brandt Oilfield Services Middle
East LLC**
Al Quoz Ground Floor Nov Brandt Building,
PO Box 22148, Mear Trinity Mechanical Al
Barsha, 22148, Dubai, United Arab Emir-
ates
Tel.: (971) 43472468
Oil Field Equipment Mfr
N.A.I.C.S.: 333132

NOV Canada ULC (1)
4910 - 80 Avenue SE, Calgary, T2C 2X3,
AB, Canada
Tel.: (403) 569-2222
Logistics Consulting Servies
N.A.I.C.S.: 541614

**NOV DH de Mexico, S. de R.L. de
C.V.** (1)
Calle Laurel Lote 37 Manzana 19 Ciudad
Industrial Bruno Pagliai, Tejeria, Veracruz,
91697, Mexico

Tel.: (52) 2299209532
Web Site: http://www.nov.com
Oil Field Equipments Services
N.A.I.C.S.: 333132

NOV Downhole (1)
7909 Parkwood Circle Dr, Houston, TX
77036
Tel.: (713) 375-3700
Web Site: http://www.nov.com
Sales Range: $100-124.9 Million
Oilwell Drilling Bit & Cutting Tool Mfr
N.A.I.C.S.: 333120

NOV Downhole Azerbaijan, LLC (1)
69 Nizami Street ISR Plaza Business 16th
Floor, Baku, Absheron, Azerbaijan
Tel.: (994) 125058218
Oil & Gas Drilling Equipment Mfr & Distr
N.A.I.C.S.: 333132

NOV Downhole Bolivia S.R.L. (1)
Av San Martin de Porres No 150, Santa
Cruz, Bolivia
Tel.: (591) 33558550
Web Site: http://www.nov.com
Emp.: 85
Oil & Gas Drilling Equipment Mfr & Distr
N.A.I.C.S.: 333132

**NOV Downhole Del Ecuador Cia.
Ltda.** (1)
Av Gaspar de Villaroel E10-121 y 6 de Dici-
embre Edf Oficinas Plaza, El Batan, Quito,
Pichincha, Ecuador
Tel.: (593) 23360265
Oil & Gas Drilling Equipment Mfr & Distr
N.A.I.C.S.: 333132

NOV Downhole Eurasia Limited (1)
Shuttleworth Close Gapton Hall Ind Estate,
Great Yarmouth, Norfolk, NR31 0NQ,
United Kingdom
Tel.: (44) 1224877700
Web Site: http://www.nov.com
Sales Range: $10-24.9 Million
Oil Field Equipment Mfr
N.A.I.C.S.: 333132

NOV Downhole Germany GmbH (1)
Im Bulloh 29, Lachendorf, Celle, 29331,
Niedersachsen, Germany
Tel.: (49) 5145939520
Oil & Gas Drilling Equipment Mfr & Distr
N.A.I.C.S.: 333132

NOV Downhole Italia S.R.L. (1)
Lungomare Cristoforo Colombo 52, 65126,
Pescara, Italy
Tel.: (39) 0854314046
Web Site: http://www.nov.com
Sales Range: $50-74.9 Million
Oil Field Drilling Equipment Mfr
N.A.I.C.S.: 213111

NOV Downhole Pty Ltd (1)
Lvl12/ 28 The Esplanade, Perth, 6000, WA,
Australia
Tel.: (61) 893205800
Web Site: http://www.nov.com
Sales Range: $25-49.9 Million
Emp.: 40
Oil Field Equipment Mfr
N.A.I.C.S.: 333132

NOV Enerflow ULC (1)
4910 - 80 Avenue SE, Calgary, T2C 2X3,
AB, Canada
Tel.: (403) 279-9696
Web Site: http://www.nov.com
Oil & Gas Field Equipment Mfr
N.A.I.C.S.: 333132

**NOV Holding Germany GmbH & Co
KG** (1)
Maschweg 5, 29227, Celle, Germany
Tel.: (49) 51418020
Web Site: http://www.nov.com
Emp.: 150
Oil Field Equipment Mfr
N.A.I.C.S.: 333132

NOV Kostroma LLC (1)
ulitza Novaya Dom 1, Volgorechensk, Ko-
stroma, 156901, Russia
Tel.: (7) 4952872600
Emp.: 220
Oil & Gas Drilling Equipment Mfr
N.A.I.C.S.: 333132

**NOV Mission Products UK
Limited** (1)

Seventh Avenue Team Valley Trading Es-
tate, Gateshead, NE11 0JW, United King-
dom
Tel.: (44) 1914820022
Web Site: http://www.nov.com
Sales Range: $75-99.9 Million
Emp.: 50
Oil & Gas Exploration Products Mfr
N.A.I.C.S.: 324199

**NOV Oil & Gas Services South
Africa** (1)
10 Dipka Street, Bellville, 7530, Western
Cape, South Africa
Tel.: (27) 219412900
Emp.: 14
Industrial Supplies Whslr
N.A.I.C.S.: 423840
Charles Scott (Gen Mgr)

NOV Rig Solutions Pte. Ltd. (1)
22 Jalan Terusan, Singapore, 619299, Sin-
gapore
Tel.: (65) 62651900
Emp.: 80
Oil & Gas Field Equipment Mfr
N.A.I.C.S.: 333132
John Dwyer (Dir-Ops)

NOV Rolligon (1)
6740 Hwy 30, Anderson, TX 77830
Tel.: (936) 873-2600
Web Site: http://www.nov.com
Sales Range: $1-9.9 Million
Emp.: 160
Oil & Gas Equipment Mfr
N.A.I.C.S.: 333132

NOV Sara India Private Limited (1)
Mohohewala Industrial Area, Dehradun,
248002, Uttarakhand, India
Tel.: (91) 1352640257
Web Site: http://www.sarasae.com
Sales Range: $50-74.9 Million
Emp.: 30
Oil Field Equipment Mfr
N.A.I.C.S.: 333132

NOV Tuboscope NL B.V. (1)
De Hulteweg 3B, 7741 LE, Coevorden,
Netherlands
Tel.: (31) 524525977
Pipeline Inspection Services
N.A.I.C.S.: 541990

NOV West BV (1)
Nijverheidsweg 45, 4879 AP, Etten-Leur,
Netherlands
Tel.: (31) 765083000
Web Site: http://www.nov.com
Sales Range: $50-74.9 Million
Emp.: 250
Oil Field Equipment Mfr
N.A.I.C.S.: 333132

NOV-BLM SAS (1)
15 Rue de la Metallurgie, 44482, Carque-
fou, France
Tel.: (33) 240683626
Web Site: https://www.nov.equip4ship.com
Oil Field Equipment Mfr
N.A.I.C.S.: 333132

NOV-Fabtech FZCO (1)
Plot No S10312, Dubai, United Arab Emir-
ates
Tel.: (971) 48708400
Oil & Gas Field Equipment Mfr
N.A.I.C.S.: 333132
Elie Chehade (Gen Mgr)

NOVM Holding LLC (1)
4000 Meridian Blvd, Franklin, TN 37067
Tel.: (615) 465-7000
Holding Company
N.A.I.C.S.: 551112

NQL Energy Services US, Inc. (1)
10404 Mula Rd, Stafford, TX 77477-3111
Tel.: (281) 568-1336
Oil & Gas Drilling Equipment Mfr & Distr
N.A.I.C.S.: 333132

National Oilwell Canada ULC (1)
1100 540 5th Ave, Calgary, T2P 0M2, AB,
Canada (100%)
Tel.: (403) 294-4554
Web Site: http://www.nov.com
Sales Range: $25-49.9 Million
Emp.: 100
Drilling Equipment Sales & Distr

NOV, Inc.—(Continued)
N.A.I.C.S.: 333132

Unit (Domestic):

National Oilwell Varco (2)
1507-4th Street, Nisku, T9E 7M9, AB,
Canada
Tel.: (780) 955-8828
Web Site: https://www.nov.com
Sales Range: $50-74.9 Million
Drilling Equipment
N.A.I.C.S.: 333132

National Oilwell Varco - Service
Center (2)
1507 4th St, Nisku, T9E 7M9, AB, Canada
Tel.: (780) 955-8828
Web Site: http://www.nov.com
Sales Range: $10-24.9 Million
Emp.: 100
N.A.I.C.S.: 333132

National Oilwell Varco-Estevan Ser-
vice Center (2)
Kensington Ave N, PO Box 671, Estevan,
S4A 2A6, SK, Canada
Tel.: (306) 634-8828
Web Site: http://www.nov.com
Sales Range: $10-24.9 Million
Emp.: 6
Oil & Gas Field Services
N.A.I.C.S.: 333132

National Oilwell Poland
S.p.z.o.o. (1)
Grunwaldzka 411, Gdansk, 80-309, Poland
Tel.: (48) 585220140
Web Site: http://www.nov.com
Sales Range: $25-49.9 Million
Emp.: 30
Oil Field Equipment Mfr
N.A.I.C.S.: 333132
Slawomir Konaszewski (Mng Dir)

National Oilwell Services de Mexico,
S.A. de C.V. (1)
Avenida Lopez Mateos SN Puerto Pes-
quero, 24129, Ciudad del Carmen, CAM,
Mexico
Tel.: (52) 9383820851
Web Site: http://www.nov.com
Sales Range: $25-49.9 Million
Emp.: 4
Oil Field Equipment Mfr
N.A.I.C.S.: 333132

National Oilwell Varco (1)
743 N Eckhoff St Complex at N Eckhoff N,
Poplar, Orange, CA 92868-1005
Tel.: (714) 978-1900
Web Site: http://www.nov.com
Sales Range: $150-199.9 Million
Emp.: 300
Oil & Gas
N.A.I.C.S.: 333132
Joe Rovig (CEO)

National Oilwell Varco (1)
400 N Sam Houston Pkwy E Ste 900,
Houston, TX 77060
Tel.: (281) 878-5811
Web Site: http://www.nov.com
Design, Mfr & Sale of Comprehensive Sys-
tems & Components for Oil & Gas Drilling &
Production
N.A.I.C.S.: 333132

National Oilwell Varco (1)
1530 W Sam Houston Pkwy N, Houston,
TX 77043-3113
Tel.: (713) 935-8000
Web Site: http://www.natoil.com
Sales Range: $75-99.9 Million
Emp.: 230
Oilfield Products Mfr, Service & Sales
N.A.I.C.S.: 423830

National Oilwell Varco Almansoori
Services (1)
Mussafah Industrial Area Sector 10 13
Street, PO Box 27011, Abu Dhabi, United
Arab Emirates
Tel.: (971) 25552668
Oil & Gas Field Machinery & Equipment
Distr
N.A.I.C.S.: 423830
Dave Mclean (Gen Mgr)

National Oilwell Varco Denmark
I/S (1)
Priorparken 480, Brondby, 2605, Hovedsta-
den, Denmark
Tel.: (45) 43483000
Web Site: http://www.nov.com
Emp.: 400
Oil & Gas Field Equipment Mfr
N.A.I.C.S.: 333132

National Oilwell Varco Korea Co.,
Ltd. (1)
63 ijin-Ro Onsan-Eup Ulju-Gun Formerly
745 Hwasan-ri, Ulsan, 044-998, Korea
(South)
Tel.: (82) 2502407070
Web Site: http://www.nov.com
Sales Range: $125-149.9 Million
Emp.: 650
Oil Field Equipment Mfr
N.A.I.C.S.: 333132
U. K. Kim (Mng Dir)

National Oilwell Varco MSW S.A. (1)
Avenida Bernardo Ader 3707, Buenos Aires,
B1606DVG, Argentina
Tel.: (54) 1147354301
Web Site:
http://www.nationaloilwellvarco.com
Emp.: 17
Pumps Mfr
N.A.I.C.S.: 333914

National Oilwell Varco Norway
AS (1)
Dvergsnesbakken 25, 4639, Kristiansand,
Norway
Tel.: (47) 38192000
Drilling Equipment Mfr
N.A.I.C.S.: 333132

Subsidiary (Domestic):

National Oilwell Norway Manufactur-
ing AS (2)
Birkedalsveien 100, PO Box 1073, 4682,
Sogne, Norway
Tel.: (47) 38053700
Web Site: http://www.nov.com
Sales Range: $600-649.9 Million
Emp.: 300
Oil Field Equipment Mfr
N.A.I.C.S.: 333132

National Oilwell Varco Pte. Ltd. (1)
8 6th Lok Yang Road, Singapore, 628106,
Singapore
Tel.: (65) 64102000
Oil Field Machinery Mfr
N.A.I.C.S.: 333132

National Oilwell Varco Rig Equipment
Trading (Shanghai) Co., Ltd. (1)
Floor 10 Building 10 Lvzhou Center Lane
1628 Jin Sha Jiang Road, Putuo District,
Shanghai, 200333, China
Tel.: (86) 2122168800
Web Site: http://www.nov.com
Oil Field Equipment Mfr
N.A.I.C.S.: 333132

National Oilwell Varco UK
Limited (1)
Martin Street Badentoy Pk, M34 5JA, Man-
chester, United Kingdom - England
Tel.: (44) 1224343610
Naval & Offshore Construction Services
N.A.I.C.S.: 237990

National Oilwell Varco, L.P. (1)
1202 Jane St, New Iberia, LA 70563
Tel.: (337) 365-7700
Web Site: http://www.varco.com
Oil & Gas Drilling Equipment & Compo-
nents Designer & Mfr
N.A.I.C.S.: 423440

National Oilwell Varco, L.P. (1)
7909 Parkwood Cir Dr, Houston, TX 77036
Tel.: (713) 346-7500
Oil & Gas Drilling Equipment Mfr & Distr
N.A.I.C.S.: 333132

National Oilwell Varco-P&T Servicios
Petroleros (1)
Av Intercommunal Galpon B Centro Comercial Industrial Standard II, Galpon A Calle
01 Conumen, El Tigre, Anzoategui, Venezuela
Tel.: (58) 283241775

Drilling Machine Service Facility
N.A.I.C.S.: 333132

National Oilwell de Mexico S.A. de
C.V. (1)
Av Lopez Mateos S/N, Campeche, 24129,
CAM, Mexico
Tel.: (52) 9383820851
Oil Field Equipment Mfr
N.A.I.C.S.: 333132

National-Oilwell Pte. Ltd. (1)
8 Sixth Lok Yang Rd Jurong Town, Singa-
pore, 628106, Singapore
Tel.: (65) 64102000
Oil & Gas Field Equipment Distr
N.A.I.C.S.: 423830

PT H-Tech Oilfield Equipment (1)
Jln Hang Kesturi 6 No 11, Batam, 29467,
Riau, Indonesia
Tel.: (62) 778711974
Web Site: http://www.h-tech.co.id
Conductor Pipe Mfr
N.A.I.C.S.: 333132

Pesaka Inspection Services
SDN.BHD. (1)
Asian Supply Base Jln Patau Patau, 87000,
Labuan, Sabah, Malaysia
Tel.: (60) 87411611
Web Site: http://www.nov.com
Oil Field Inspection Devices Mfr
N.A.I.C.S.: 333132

Pipex Limited (1)
Devon Enterprise Facility 1 Belliver Way,
Roborough, Plymouth, PL6 7BP, United
Kingdom
Tel.: (44) 1752581200
Oil & Gas Field Supporting Services
N.A.I.C.S.: 213112

Pipex PX (Scotland) Limited (1)
1 Ashley Drive Bothwell, Glasgow, G71
8BS, United Kingdom
Tel.: (44) 1698818022
Oil & Gas Field Supporting Services
N.A.I.C.S.: 213112

Procon Engineering Ltd. (1)
Vestry Estate, Sevenoaks, TN14 5EL, Kent,
United Kingdom
Tel.: (44) 1732781300
Web Site: https://www.proconeng.com
Emp.: 20
Industrial Equipment Mfr
N.A.I.C.S.: 334513

RE.MAC.UT. S.r.l. (1)
Via Albenga 38 Rivoli, 10090, Turin, Italy
Tel.: (39) 0119576317
Web Site: http://www.remacut.com
Industrial Equipment Mfr & Distr
N.A.I.C.S.: 333923

RHI Holding LLC (1)
45025 Aviation Dr Ste 400, Dulles, VA
20166
Tel.: (703) 478-5800
Holding Company
N.A.I.C.S.: 551112

Reed-Hycalog de Mexico, S de R.L.
de C.V. (1)
Paseo De Las Flores No 277 Jardines De,
Villahermosa, 86027, Tabasco, Mexico
Tel.: (52) 9933573439
Oil & Gas Drilling Equipment Mfr & Distr
N.A.I.C.S.: 333132

ReedHycalog UK Ltd (1)
Stonedale Road Unit 10 Oldends Lane In-
dustrial Estate, Stonehouse, GL10 3RQ,
Gloucestershire, United Kingdom
Tel.: (44) 1453853000
Web Site: http://www.novreedhycalog.com
Emp.: 250
Roller Cone Drill Mfr & Design Services
N.A.I.C.S.: 333991
Richard Jordan (Gen Mgr)

ReedHycalog, L.P. (1)
500 Conroe Park W Dr, Conroe, TX 77303
Tel.: (936) 444-4000
Oil & Gas Related Services
N.A.I.C.S.: 213112

Subsidiary (Domestic):

ReedHycalog CIS, LLC (2)

400 N Sam Houston Pkwy E Ste 900,
Houston, TX 77060-3531
Tel.: (281) 878-5607
Oil & Gas Drilling Equipment Mfr & Distr
N.A.I.C.S.: 333132

Russell Sub-Surface Systems,
Ltd. (1)
2 Isbourne Way Winchcombe, Cheltenham,
GL54 5NS, United Kingdom
Tel.: (44) 1242603975
Web Site: http://www.nov.com
Sales Range: $25-49.9 Million
Emp.: 3
Oil Field Equipment Mfr
N.A.I.C.S.: 333132

Smart Drilling GmbH (1)
Middelicher Strasse 305, 45892, Gelsen-
kirchen, Germany
Tel.: (49) 2093863420
Oil & Gas Field Drilling Services
N.A.I.C.S.: 213112

Soil Recovery A/S (1)
Nederbyvej 12, 5800, Nyborg, Denmark
Tel.: (45) 62251358
Web Site: http://www.soil-recovery.dk
Sales Range: $25-49.9 Million
Oil Field Cuttings Treatment Plant Mfr
N.A.I.C.S.: 333132

South Seas Inspection (S) PTE
LTD (1)
161 Pioneer Road, Singapore, 639604,
Singapore
Tel.: (65) 62643400
Web Site: http://www.nov.com
Sales Range: $25-49.9 Million
Emp.: 15
Industrial Construction Inspection & Opera-
tional Services
N.A.I.C.S.: 236220
John Walling (Mng Dir)

Star Fiberglass Harbin Co., Ltd. (1)
6 Ning Bo Road Haping Road Centralized
Industrial Park, Harbin Development Zone,
Harbin, 150060, Heilongjiang, China
Tel.: (86) 45187091723
Oil Field Equipment Mfr
N.A.I.C.S.: 333132
Maggie Jin (Mgr-Quality Assurance)

Stonehouse NOV Downhole Eurasia
Limited (1)
Oldends Lane Industrial Estate, Stone-
house, GL10 3RQ, GLOS, United Kingdom
Tel.: (44) 1453853000
Web Site: http://www.nov.com
Oil Extraction Services
N.A.I.C.S.: 211120

TS&M Supply (1)
314 Kensington Ave, PO Box 28, Estevan,
S4A 2A2, SK, Canada
Tel.: (306) 634-6494
Web Site: http://www.tsmsupply.com
Emp.: 190
Oil Field Equipment Mfr
N.A.I.C.S.: 333132
Ellen Phillips (Controller)
Karry Biette (VP)

Tolteq Group, LLC (1)
1200 Cypress Creek Rd, Cedar Park, TX
78613 (100%)
Tel.: (512) 340-5000
Web Site: http://www.tolteq.com
Sales Range: $10-24.9 Million
Emp.: 95
Mfr & Sales of Measurement Tools for Oil &
Gas Industries
N.A.I.C.S.: 334519
Paul Deere (Founder & Pres)

Tubos Y Activos, S. De R.L. De
C.V. (1)
Av Circulo de la Amistad No 138 Parque
Industrial IV, Sanchez Taboada, Mexicali,
21210, Baja California, Mexico
Tel.: (52) 17144561336
Building Materials Whslr
N.A.I.C.S.: 423390

Tuboscope Pipeline Services
Inc. (1)
10222 Sheldon Rd, Houston, TX 77049
Tel.: (281) 456-8881
Oil & Gas Field Equipment Mfr & Distr

N.A.I.C.S.: 333132

Subsidiary (Domestic):

Tubo-FGS, L.L.C. (2)
2835 Holmes Rd, Houston, TX 77051
Tel.: (713) 799-5100
Web Site: http://www.tuboscopenov.com
Emp.: 900
Oil Field Equipment Mfr
N.A.I.C.S.: 333132
Issac Joseph *(Pres)*

Subsidiary (Non-US):

Tuboscope Brandt de Venezuela S.A. (2)
Av 58 No 140-315 Zona Industrial, Maracaibo, Zulia, Venezuela
Tel.: (58) 2617359941
Oil Field Equipments Services
N.A.I.C.S.: 333132
Adolfo Calen *(Gen Mgr)*

Tuboscope Norge AS (2)
Ccb-Bygg K- 2 5347 Kystbasen, PO Box 59, Agotnes, Hordaland, 5347, Norway
Tel.: (47) 56312100
Emp.: 100
Oil & Gas Field Equipment Mfr & Distr
N.A.I.C.S.: 333132
Daggjet Thomassen *(Gen Mgr)*

Tuboscope Vetco (Osterreich) GmbH (2)
Bahnstrasse 49A Prottes, 2242, Ganserndorf, Lower Austria, Austria
Tel.: (43) 22823407
Emp.: 25
Oil & Gas Field Equipment Mfr & Distr
N.A.I.C.S.: 333132

Tuboscope Vetco Canada ULC (2)
2201 - 9th Street, Nisku, T9E 7Z7, AB, Canada
Tel.: (780) 955-7675
Web Site: http://www.nov.com
Emp.: 250
Oil & Gas Field Machinery Mfr
N.A.I.C.S.: 333132

Tuboscope Vetco Mexico, S.A. de C.V. (2)
Calle Laurel, 91698, Veracruz, Mexico
Tel.: (52) 2299209415
Oil & Gas Field Equipment Mfr & Distr
N.A.I.C.S.: 333132

Tuboscope Vetco Moscow CJSC (2)
Paveletskaya square 2/3 floor 6 office 7, 115054, Moscow, Russia
Tel.: (7) 4952872600
Web Site: http://www.nov.com
Emp.: 125
Oil & Gas Field Equipment Mfr & Distr
N.A.I.C.S.: 333132

Tuboscope Vetco de Argentina S.A. (2)
Av Corrientes 316 Piso 5o Of 552 Caba, Buenos Aires, C1043AAQ, Argentina
Tel.: (54) 1141301666
Oil & Gas Extraction Services
N.A.I.C.S.: 211120

Vetco Enterprise GmbH (2)
Alpenstrasse 12, 6304, Zug, Switzerland
Tel.: (41) 417090000
Investment Management Service
N.A.I.C.S.: 523940

Vallourec Drilling Oil Equipment Manufacturing LLC (1)
Mussafah Industrial Area Plant, PO BOX 9709, Abu Dhabi, United Arab Emirates
Tel.: (971) 2 551 0 553
Oil Field Equipment Mfr
N.A.I.C.S.: 333132

Vallourec Drilling Products USA, Inc. (1)
4424 W Sam Houston Pkwy N Ste 150, Houston, TX 77041
Tel.: (713) 479-3200
Drill Pipe & Other Accessories for Drilling
N.A.I.C.S.: 332812

Varco, L.P. (1)
12950 W Little York Rd, Houston, TX 77041-4212
Tel.: (713) 937-5500

Sales Range: $250-299.9 Million
Emp.: 1,200
Oil & Gas
N.A.I.C.S.: 333132

Unit (Domestic):

NOV Fluid Control (2)
221 Rue De Jean Ste 301, Lafayette, LA 70508-3283 **(100%)**
Tel.: (337) 237-5300
Web Site: http://www.nov.com
Sales Range: $300-349.9 Million
Emp.: 40
Oil & Gas Services
N.A.I.C.S.: 213112

Subsidiary (Non-US):

Varco BJ BV (2)
Nijverheidsweg 45, 4879 AP, Etten-Leur, Netherlands
Tel.: (31) 765083000
Web Site: http://www.nov.com
Sales Range: $25-49.9 Million
Oil Drilling Equipment
N.A.I.C.S.: 333132
Ruud Kerkhof *(Mng Dir)*

Varco Canada ULC (2)
1507 4th St, Nisku, T9E 7M9, AB, Canada
Tel.: (780) 955-8828
Web Site: http://www.nov.com
Sales Range: $75-99.9 Million
Emp.: 200
Designs, Manufactures & Supplies Downhole Tools, Technology & Services for Drilling Applications in the Oil & Gas, Environmental & Utility Industries
N.A.I.C.S.: 333132

Varco Sara (India) Private Limited (2)
7/1 Pritam Road Hand Allied Tools, Dehradun, 248001, Uttarakhand, India
Tel.: (91) 1352672395
Web Site: http://www.sarasae.com
Emp.: 5,000
Oil Field Equipment Mfr
N.A.I.C.S.: 333132

Visible Assets, Inc. (1)
195 Bunker Hill Ave, Stratham, NH 03885
Tel.: (603) 418-8800
Web Site: https://ru-bee.com
Oil & Gas Field Supporting Services
N.A.I.C.S.: 213112
John K. Stevens *(Chm & CEO)*
Jason August *(VP-Tech)*
Tim Pierce *(VP-Bus Dev)*

Voest Alpine Tubulars GmbH & Co KG (1)
Alpinestrasse 17, 8652, Kindberg, Aumuehl, Austria
Tel.: (43) 5030423
Web Site: https://www.voestalpine.com
Sales Range: $300-349.9 Million
Oil Field Tubular Products Supplies & Whslr
N.A.I.C.S.: 213112
Gerald Gfrerer *(Mng Dir-Technical)*
Gernot Graller-Kettler *(Mng Dir-Comml)*

Subsidiary (Domestic):

Voest Alpine Tubulars Gmbh (2)
voestalpine-Strasse 1, 4020, Linz, Austria
Tel.: (43) 5030423
Web Site: http://www.vatubulars.com
Emp.: 100
Oil Field Tubular Products Whslr
N.A.I.C.S.: 213112

XL Systems Europe B.V. (1)
Engelandweg 51/Haven-1198, Ritthem, 4389 PC, Netherlands
Tel.: (31) 118645020
Oil & Gas Field Equipment Mfr & Distr
N.A.I.C.S.: 333132

XL Systems, L.P. (1)
5780 Hagner Rd, Beaumont, TX 77705
Tel.: (409) 842-2114
Oil Field Services
N.A.I.C.S.: 213112

NOVA LIFESTYLE, INC.
6565 E Washington Blvd, Commerce, CA 90040
Tel.: (323) 888-9999 NV

Web Site: https://www.novalifestyle.com
Year Founded: 2009
NVFY—(NASDAQ)
Rev.: $12,744,871
Assets: $11,533,496
Liabilities: $4,921,666
Net Worth: $6,611,830
Earnings: ($17,101,671)
Emp.: 28
Fiscal Year-end: 12/31/22
Residential Furniture Mfr & Marketer
N.A.I.C.S.: 337122
Mindy Su *(Bd of Dirs, Executives)*
Mark Chapman *(VP-Mktg)*
Chris Steadman *(Dir-Internet Sls)*
Jeffery Chuang *(CFO)*
Thanh H. Lam *(Chm & Pres)*

Subsidiaries:

Diamond Bar Outdoors, Inc. (1)
6565 E Washington Blvd, Commerce, CA 90040
Tel.: (323) 888-1679
Web Site: https://www.diamondsofa.com
Furniture Merchant Whslr
N.A.I.C.S.: 423210

NOVA TECH ENTERPRISES, INC.
3650 S Eastern Ave Ste 100N, Las Vegas, NV 89169
Tel.: (818) 284-8662 NV
Year Founded: 2004
NTEI—(OTCIQ)
Financial Investment Services
N.A.I.C.S.: 523999
Alexander Hazan *(Pres & CEO)*

NOVABAY PHARMACEUTICALS, INC.
2000 Powell St Ste 1150, Emeryville, CA 94608
Tel.: (510) 899-8800 CA
Web Site: https://www.novabay.com
NBY—(NYSEAMEX)
Rev.: $14,404,000
Assets: $16,399,000
Liabilities: $5,845,000
Net Worth: $10,554,000
Earnings: ($16,265,000)
Emp.: 29
Fiscal Year-end: 12/31/22
Biopharmaceutical Products
N.A.I.C.S.: 325412
Tommy Law *(Interim CFO)*
Justin M. Hall *(CEO)*

NOVACCESS GLOBAL INC.
8584 E Washington St Ste 127, Chagrin Falls, OH 44023
Tel.: (469) 633-0101 CO
Web Site: https://www.novaccessglobal.com
Year Founded: 1997
XSNX—(OTCQB)
Rev.: $56,082
Assets: $62,248
Liabilities: $7,860,732
Net Worth: ($7,798,484)
Earnings: ($4,724,946)
Emp.: 1
Fiscal Year-end: 09/30/23
Magnetic Media Thin-Film Photovoltaic Products Developer & Mfr
N.A.I.C.S.: 334610
Daniel G. Martin *(Chm)*
Dwain K. Morris-Irvin *(CEO & Interim Principal Financial Officer)*

NOVAGOLD RESOURCES INC.
201 S Main St Ste 400, Salt Lake City, UT 84111
Tel.: (801) 639-0511 NS
Web Site: https://www.novagold.com
Year Founded: 1984

NG—(NYSEAMEX)
Rev.: $2,009,000
Assets: $159,189,000
Liabilities: $129,286,000
Net Worth: $29,903,000
Earnings: ($53,343,000)
Emp.: 13
Fiscal Year-end: 12/30/22
Gold Ore & Silver Ore Mining
N.A.I.C.S.: 212220
Melanie Hennessey *(VP-Corp Comm)*
Gregory A. Lang *(Pres & CEO)*
Ron Rimelman *(VP-Environment, Health, Safety & Sustainability)*
Richard Williams *(VP-Engrg & Dev)*
Tricia Pannier *(Sec)*
Jason Mercier *(Mgr-Investor Relations)*
Peter Adamek *(CFO & VP)*

Subsidiaries:

NOVAGOLD USA, Inc. (1)
201 S Main St Ste 400, Salt Lake City, UT 84111
Tel.: (801) 639-0511
Emp.: 10
Management Consulting Services
N.A.I.C.S.: 541611
Gregory A. Lang *(Pres & CEO)*

NovaGold Resources USA (1)
789 West Pender St Ste 720, Vancouver, V6C 1H2, BC, Canada **(100%)**
Tel.: (604) 669-6227
Web Site: http://www.novagold.com
Sales Range: $25-49.9 Million
Emp.: 3
N.A.I.C.S.: 541360

NOVAN, INC.
4020 Stirrup Crk Dr Ste 110, Durham, NC 27703
Tel.: (919) 485-8080 DE
Web Site: https://www.novan.com
Year Founded: 2006
NOVN—(NASDAQ)
Rev.: $23,682,000
Assets: $90,330,000
Liabilities: $85,725,000
Net Worth: $4,605,000
Earnings: ($31,311,000)
Emp.: 89
Fiscal Year-end: 12/31/22
Research & Development in Biotechnology
N.A.I.C.S.: 541714
Carri Geer *(CTO & Sr VP)*
Paula Brown Stafford *(Chm, Pres & CEO)*
Tomoko Maeda-Chubachi *(Sr VP-Medical Dermatology)*
Andrew J. Novak *(VP-Accounting-Bus Ops)*
John M. Gay *(CFO, Principal Acctg Officer & Sec)*

NOVANTA INC.
125 Middlesex Tpke, Bedford, MA 01730
Tel.: (781) 266-5700 NB
Web Site: https://www.novanta.com
Year Founded: 1970
NOVT—(NASDAQ)
Rev.: $860,903,000
Assets: $1,241,212,000
Liabilities: $663,626,000
Net Worth: $577,586,000
Earnings: $74,051,000
Emp.: 3,000
Fiscal Year-end: 12/31/22
Holding Company; Laser-Based Systems, Laser Scanning Devices & Precision Motion & Optical Control Technologies Developer & Mfr
N.A.I.C.S.: 551112
Robert J. Buckley *(CFO)*
Matthijs Glastra *(Chm & CEO)*

Novanta Inc.—(Continued)

Heinrich Dreyer *(Pres-Minimally Invasive Surgery-Grp)*
Chuck Ravetto *(Pres & VP-Group Automation Enabling Technologies)*
Michele Welsh *(Gen Counsel & Sec)*
Anna Fain *(Sr VP-Leadership Dev, Diversity, Equity, and Inclusion & VP)*
John Burke *(Chief Acctg Officer)*

Subsidiaries:

ARGES GmbH **(1)**
Werk 4, 92442, Wackersdorf, Germany
Tel.: (49) 943179840
Web Site: http://www.arges.de
Medical Laser Equipment Mfr
N.A.I.C.S.: 334510
Martin Hartmann *(CTO & Gen Mgr)*
Thomas Grebert *(Gen Mgr)*
Robert Buckley *(Gen Mgr)*
Hubert Suss *(COO)*

ATI Industrial Automation, Inc. **(1)**
1031 Goodworth Dr, Apex, NC 27539
Tel.: (919) 772-0115
Web Site: https://www.ati-ia.com
Rev.: $4,400,000
Emp.: 50
Instruments & Related Products Manufacturing for Measuring, Displaying & Controlling Industrial Process Variables
N.A.I.C.S.: 334513
Baron Kendrick *(Engr-Mechanical)*

Excel Technology, Inc. **(1)**
41 Research Way, East Setauket, NY 11733-3454
Tel.: (631) 784-6175
Web Site: http://www.exceltechinc.com
Sales Range: $150-199.9 Million
Emp.: 719
Laser Systems & Electro-Optical Components Designer, Developer & Mfr
N.A.I.C.S.: 333248

Affiliate (Non-US):

Excel Laser Technology Pvt. Ltd. **(2)**
D 6 2nd Flr Atv House D 8 Morol MIDC Road 20 Andheri East, Mumbai, 400 093, India **(50%)**
Tel.: (91) 2228222323
Web Site: http://www.exceltech-southasia.com
Sales Range: $25-49.9 Million
Emp.: 45
Laser Product Mfr
N.A.I.C.S.: 333248

GSI Group Europe GmbH **(1)**
Munchnerstr 2a, 82152, Planegg, Germany
Tel.: (49) 89317070
Web Site: http://www.synrad.com
Measuring Device Mfr
N.A.I.C.S.: 334513

GSI Group Precision Technologies (Suzhou) Co., Ltd. **(1)**
Building 8 GangTian Industrial Square GangTian Road, South Industrial Park, Suzhou, 215024, Jiangsu, China
Tel.: (86) 51262837080
Precision Motion Control Components Supplier
N.A.I.C.S.: 423690

Ingenia-CAT S.L. **(1)**
C/ Avila 124 2 B, 08018, Barcelona, Spain
Tel.: (34) 932917682
Web Site: http://www.ingeniamc.com
Robotic & Automatic Machine Tool Component Mfr
N.A.I.C.S.: 336411
Marc Vila *(Gen Mgr & Mgr-Technology)*

JADAK, LLC **(1)**
7279 William Barry Blvd, North Syracuse, NY 13212
Tel.: (315) 701-0678
Web Site: http://www.jadaktech.com
Sales Range: $1-9.9 Million
Emp.: 50
Scanning, Inspection & Tracking Devices Mfr
N.A.I.C.S.: 334118

Subsidiary (Non-US):

JADAK Europe BV **(2)**

Emmastraat 16, 4811 AG, Breda, Netherlands
Tel.: (31) 76 522 5588
Web Site: http://www.jadak.eu
Scanning, Inspection & Tracking Devices Sales
N.A.I.C.S.: 423430

Subsidiary (Domestic):

Thingmagic Inc. **(2)**
1 Cambridge Ctr, Cambridge, MA 02142
Tel.: (617) 299-2461
Web Site: http://www.thingmagic.com
Sound Recording Studios
N.A.I.C.S.: 512240

Laser Quantum GmbH **(1)**
Max-Stromeyer-Str 116, 78467, Konstanz, Germany
Tel.: (49) 7531368371
Medical Equipment Mfr
N.A.I.C.S.: 334510
Gregor Klatt *(Head-Sls)*

Laser Quantum Limited **(1)**
Emery Court Vale Road, Stockport, SK4 3GL, Cheshire, United Kingdom **(100%)**
Tel.: (44) 1619755300
Medical Equipment Mfr & Distr; DPSS Lasers, Ultrafast Lasers & Ultrafast Amplifiers
N.A.I.C.S.: 334510

Med X Change Inc. **(1)**
525 8th St W, Bradenton, FL 34205
Tel.: (941) 794-9977
Web Site: http://www.medxchange.com
Surgical Product Mfr
N.A.I.C.S.: 339113
Craig A. Scherer *(CEO)*

NDS Surgical Imaging BV **(1)**
Nijverheidscentrum 28, 2761 JP, Zuidplas, Netherlands
Tel.: (31) 180634356
Measuring Device Mfr
N.A.I.C.S.: 334513
Efe Idahosa *(Mgr-Interim General Ledger)*

NDS Surgical Imaging, LLC **(1)**
100 Paramount Dr Ste 101, Sarasota, FL 34232
Tel.: (408) 776-0085
Web Site: https://www.ndssi.com
Measuring Device Mfr
N.A.I.C.S.: 334513

Novanta Europe GmbH **(1)**
Parkring 57-59, 85748, Garching, Germany
Tel.: (49) 89317070
Medical Equipment Mfr & Distr
N.A.I.C.S.: 334510

Novanta Holdings BV **(1)**
Emmastraat 16, 4811 AG, Breda, Netherlands
Tel.: (31) 765225588
Core Technology & Medical Equipment Mfr
N.A.I.C.S.: 335999

Novanta Italy SRL **(1)**
Via Mazzini 5, Muggio, 20053, Milan, Italy
Tel.: (39) 039793710
Medical Equipment Mfr & Distr
N.A.I.C.S.: 334510

Novanta Japan Corporation **(1)**
1F East Square Omori 6-20-14 Minamioi, Shinagawa-ku, Tokyo, 140-0013, Japan
Tel.: (81) 357532460
Core Technology & Medical Equipment Mfr
N.A.I.C.S.: 335999

Reach Technology, Inc. **(1)**
5750 Hellyer Ave, San Jose, CA 95138
Tel.: (408) 754-4176
Web Site: http://www.reachtech.com
Electric Device Mfr
N.A.I.C.S.: 334419

Schneider Electric Motion USA, Inc. **(1)**
370 N Main St, Marlborough, CT 06447
Tel.: (860) 295-6102
Web Site: http://www.motion.schneider-electric.com
Sales Range: $25-49.9 Million
Emp.: 70
Industrial Electric Motor Mfr & Distr
N.A.I.C.S.: 335312

Eric Klein *(Gen Mgr)*
Tom Horan *(VP-Fin)*
Steve Henry *(Dir-Mfg)*
Clark Hummel *(Mgr-Flex Center)*
Susanna DalPonte *(Mgr-Offer)*
Russ Gibas *(Mgr-Product R&D Engrg)*
Nancy Paradie *(Partner-HR Bus)*

Synrad, Inc. **(1)**
4600 Campus Pl, Mukilteo, WA 98275
Tel.: (425) 349-3500
Web Site: http://www.synrad.com
Sales Range: $25-49.9 Million
Emp.: 150
Carbon Dioxide Laser Mfr
N.A.I.C.S.: 333517
Sandra Love *(Mgr-Cost Acctg)*

W.O.M. World of Medicine GmbH **(1)**
Salzufer 8, 10587, Berlin, Germany **(100%)**
Tel.: (49) 3039981550
Web Site: https://www.wom.group
Emp.: 500
Medical Devices Mfr & Distr
N.A.I.C.S.: 334510
Jorg R. Baffy-Schattler *(VP-Human Resources)*

Subsidiary (Non-US):

W.O.M. World of Medicine Asia Ltd. **(2)**
Workshop B1 & B2 35/F TML Tower No 3 Hoi Shing Road, Tsuen Wan, China (Hong Kong)
Tel.: (852) 21873557
Web Site: http://www.wom.group
Medical Equipment Distr
N.A.I.C.S.: 423450

Subsidiary (Domestic):

W.O.M. World of Medicine Produktions- GmbH **(2)**
Kornergasse 21, 96358, Reichenbach, Germany
Tel.: (49) 9268 973 0
Web Site: http://www.wom.group
Medical Equipment Mfr
N.A.I.C.S.: 334510

Subsidiary (US):

W.O.M. World of Medicine USA, Inc. **(2)**
4531 36th St, Orlando, FL 32811-6527
Tel.: (407) 438-8810
Medical Equipment Distr
N.A.I.C.S.: 423450

Zettlex (UK) Limited **(1)**
Faraday House 40 Darrington Road Foxton, Cambridge, CB22 6SL, United Kingdom
Tel.: (44) 1223874444
Position Sensor Mfr
N.A.I.C.S.: 334511

NOVATION COMPANIES, INC.
9229 Ward Pkwy Ste 340, Kansas City, MO 64114
Tel.: (816) 237-7000 MD
Web Site:
    http://novationcompanies.com
Year Founded: 1996
NOVC—(OTCIQ)
Rev.: $51,354,000
Assets: $12,176,000
Liabilities: $93,266,000
Net Worth: ($81,090,000)
Earnings: ($9,169,000)
Emp.: 1,025
Fiscal Year-end: 12/31/20
Holding Company; Cloud-Based Software & Data Services
N.A.I.C.S.: 551112
Barry A. Igdaloff *(Chm)*
Michael Wyse *(Chief Restructuring Officer)*

Subsidiaries:

Advent Financial Services **(1)**
2114 Central Ste 600, Kansas City, MO 64108 **(100%)**
Tel.: (816) 569-9003

Web Site: http://www.adventtax.com
Financial Settlement Services for Income Tax Preparation Businesses & Intermediary Banking Services
N.A.I.C.S.: 541213
Tanya Andrews *(Office Mgr)*

Healthcare Staffing, Inc. **(1)**
1724 Phoenix Pkwy Bldg 600, College Park, GA 30349
Tel.: (770) 991-2515
Web Site: http://www.healthcare-staffing.com
Healthcare Staff Training Services
N.A.I.C.S.: 611519

StreetLinks LLC **(1)**
7551 S Shelby St, Indianapolis, IN 46227 **(100%)**
Tel.: (317) 215-8800
Web Site: http://www.streetlinks.com
Appraisal/Valuation Solutions to Mortgage Industries
N.A.I.C.S.: 531320

Subsidiary (Domestic):

Corvisa Services LLC **(2)**
1610 N Second St Ste 101, Milwaukee, WI 53212 **(100%)**
Tel.: (414) 847-6900
Web Site: http://www.corvisa.com
Software Development, Technology, Marketing & Training Services to Novation Group of Companies
N.A.I.C.S.: 513210
Matthew Lautz *(CEO)*

NOVAVAX, INC.
21 Firstfield Rd, Gaithersburg, MD 20878
Tel.: (240) 268-2000 DE
Web Site: https://www.novavax.com
NVAX—(NASDAQ)
Rev.: $1,981,872,000
Assets: $2,258,679,000
Liabilities: $2,892,757,000
Net Worth: ($634,078,000)
Earnings: ($657,939,000)
Emp.: 1,992
Fiscal Year-end: 12/31/22
Biopharmaceutical Research & Development Services
N.A.I.C.S.: 325414
John J. Trizzino *(Pres & COO)*
James F. Young *(Chm)*
Russell P. Wilson *(Exec VP & Gen Mgr-NanoFlu)*
Sven Andreasson *(Sr VP-Corp Dev)*
Jill Hoyt *(Chief HR Officer & Exec VP)*
Brian Rosen *(Sr VP-Comml Strategy)*
Biegie Lee *(CIO & Sr VP)*
John C. Jacobs *(CEO)*
James Patrick Kelly *(CFO, Treas & Exec VP)*
Henrietta Ukwu *(Chief Regulatory & Quality Officer & Sr VP)*
Gale E. Smith *(Sr VP-Discovery & Pre-Clinical Res)*
Troy Troy *(Chief Compliance Officer)*
Elaine O'Hara *(Chief Strategy Officer)*
Marco Cacciuttolo *(Sr VP)*
Michael Kahsai *(Sr VP)*
Denny Kim *(Chief Safety Officer)*
Raburn Mallory *(Sr VP)*
Seth Toback *(Sr VP)*
Robert Walker *(Deputy Chief Medical Officer)*
Mark Casey *(Chief Legal Officer & Sec)*

Subsidiaries:

Novavax AB **(1)**
Kungsgatan 109, 753 18, Uppsala, Sweden
Tel.: (46) 18161700
Emp.: 500
Pharmaceuticals Product Mfr
N.A.I.C.S.: 325412

Novavax CZ **(1)**

Bohumil 138, Jevany, 281 63, Prague, Czech Republic
Tel.: (420) 228880267
Web Site: https://www.novavax.cz
Vaccines Mfr
N.A.I.C.S.: 325414

NOVELSTEM INTERNATIONAL CORP.
2255 Glades Rd Ste 221A, Boca Raton, FL 33431
Tel.: (561) 998-8000   FL
Web Site:
  https://www.novelstem.com
Year Founded: 1994
NSTM—(OTCIQ)
Rev.: $12,000
Assets: $2,286,204
Liabilities: $353,326
Net Worth: $1,932,878
Earnings: ($765,730)
Emp.: 15
Fiscal Year-end: 12/31/22
Online Ticketing of Entertainment News, Information & Services
N.A.I.C.S.: 519290
Jan H. Loeb *(Exec Chm, Pres & CEO)*
Christine Jenkins *(CFO, Sec & VP)*

Subsidiaries:

Tekno Books   (1)
1524 University Ave Ste 305, Green Bay, WI 54302-1878   **(51%)**
Tel.: (920) 437-6711
Books & Periodicals Publishing
N.A.I.C.S.: 513130
Larry Segriff *(VP)*

NOVO INTEGRATED SCIENCES, INC.
11120 NE 2nd St Ste 100, Bellevue, WA 98004
Tel.: (206) 617-9797   NV
Web Site:
  https://www.novointegrated.com
Year Founded: 2000
NVOS—(OTCIQ)
Rev.: $13,294,357
Assets: $32,141,276
Liabilities: $17,527,351
Net Worth: $14,613,925
Earnings: ($16,128,570)
Emp.: 115
Fiscal Year-end: 08/31/24
Health Care Srvices
N.A.I.C.S.: 621999
Christopher M. David *(COO)*
Michael Gaynor *(Sec)*
Robert Mattacchione *(Chm & CEO)*
Robert Oliva *(Pres)*
Vivek Sethi *(Principal Fin Officer & Principal Acctg Officer)*

Subsidiaries:

Acenzia, Inc.   (1)
1580 Rossi Drive, Oldcastle, Tecumseh, N9G 0B8, ON, Canada
Tel.: (519) 737-0470
Pharmaceuticals Product Mfr
N.A.I.C.S.: 325412

Clinical Consultants International LLC   (1)
11120 NE 2nd St Ste 100, Bellevue, WA 98004
Web Site: https://ccimia.com
Pharmaceutical & Biotech Services
N.A.I.C.S.: 541714

Novo Healthnet Limited   (1)
3905 Major Mackenzie Dr 115, Vaughan, L4H 4J9, ON, Canada
Tel.: (905) 660-3777
Web Site: https://www.novohealthnet.com
Emp.: 200
Healtcare Services
N.A.I.C.S.: 622110

James Asher *(Pres)*
Amanda Dalcourt *(VP)*
David Brien *(VP)*

NOVOHEART HOLDINGS, INC.
5270 California Ave Ste 300, Irvine, CA 92617
Tel.: (949) 238-8047
Web Site: http://www.novoheart.com
3NH—(STU)
Pharmaceuticals Product Mfr
N.A.I.C.S.: 325412
Ronald Li *(Founder & CEO)*

NOVUS ACQUISITION & DEVELOPMENT CORPORATION
2665 S Bayshore Dr 2nd Fl, Miami, FL 33131   NV
Web Site:
  https://www.getnovusnow.com
NDEV—(OTCIQ)
Direct Health & Medical Insurance Carriers
N.A.I.C.S.: 524114
Gary F. Labrozzi *(CEO)*

NP LIFE SCIENCES HEALTH INDUSTRY GROUP INC.
4125 Blackhawk Plz Cir Ste 166, Danville, CA 94506
Tel.: (925) 362-3169   NV
Web Site: https://www.gjcc.us
Year Founded: 2018
NPLS—(OTCQB)
Rev.: $102,002
Assets: $127,784
Liabilities: $108,468
Net Worth: $19,316
Earnings: ($18,856)
Fiscal Year-end: 12/31/22
Educational Support Services
N.A.I.C.S.: 611710
Guidong Wang *(Chm, Pres, CEO, CFO & Treas)*
Huaying Zhu *(Sec)*

NRG ENERGY, INC.
910 Louisiana St, Houston, TX 77002
Tel.: (713) 537-3000   DE
Web Site: https://www.nrg.com
Year Founded: 1989
NRG—(NYSE)
Rev.: $28,823,000,000
Assets: $26,038,000,000
Liabilities: $23,132,000,000
Net Worth: $2,906,000,000
Earnings: ($256,000,000)
Emp.: 18,131
Fiscal Year-end: 12/31/23
Electricity Distribution Services
N.A.I.C.S.: 221122
Bruce Chung *(CFO & Exec VP)*
Rasesh Patel *(Pres-NRG Consumer)*
Lawrence Stephen Coben *(Chm, Pres & CEO)*

Subsidiaries:

Allied Home Warranty GP LLC   (1)
211 Carnegie Ctr, Princeton, NJ 08540
Tel.: (609) 524-4500
Electricity Generation & Transmitting Services
N.A.I.C.S.: 221113

Allied Warranty LLC   (1)
177 S Watson Rd Ste 511, Arlington, TX 76010
Web Site:
  http://www.alliedhomewarranty.com
Home Insurance Services
N.A.I.C.S.: 524127

Alta Interconnection Management, LLC   (1)
1095 Avenue Amrcs 25th Ste A, New York, NY 10036
Tel.: (646) 829-3900
Emp.: 25
Solar Energy Equipment Distr

N.A.I.C.S.: 238220

Broken Bow Wind, LLC   (1)
80347 Rd 444, Broken Bow, NE 68822
Tel.: (308) 767-2000
Emp.: 20
Electric Energy Services
N.A.I.C.S.: 221118

Cheng Power Systems, Inc.   (1)
480 San Antonio Rd Ste 120, Mountain View, CA 94040
Tel.: (650) 941-9292
Web Site: http://www.chengpower.com
Emp.: 6
Power Generating Equipment Mfr
N.A.I.C.S.: 333611

Crosswind Transmission, LLC   (1)
3950 360th Ave, Ruthven, IA 51358
Tel.: (712) 837-5582
Automotive Repair Services
N.A.I.C.S.: 811114

Direct Energy, LP   (1)
12 Greenway Plz Ste 250, Houston, TX 77046-0813
Tel.: (713) 877-3500
Web Site: http://www.directenergy.com
Holding Company; Natural Gas & Electrical Power Products & Services
N.A.I.C.S.: 551112
Thomas Smith *(Gen Counsel & Exec VP)*

Subsidiary (Domestic):

Bounce Energy, Inc.   (2)
2802 Albany St, Houston, TX 77006
Tel.: (281) 745-9020
Web Site: http://www.bounceenergy.com
Electric Power Distr
N.A.I.C.S.: 221122

Direct Energy Business, LLC   (2)
1001 Liberty Ave Ste 1200, Pittsburgh, PA 15222
Tel.: (412) 667-5100
Web Site:
  https://www.business.directenergy.com
Sales Range: $150-199.9 Million
Emp.: 230
Commercial Electric & Natural Gas Distr
N.A.I.C.S.: 221122

Subsidiary (Domestic):

Direct Energy Business Marketing, LLC   (3)
1 Hess Plz, Woodbridge, NJ 07095-1229
Tel.: (732) 750-6000
Web Site: http://www.hessenergy.com
Sales Range: $5-14.9 Billion
Natural Gas & Electric Power Marketer & Distr
N.A.I.C.S.: 221210
Steven D. Sooby *(Sr Mgr)*

Branch (Domestic):

Direct Energy Business Marketing, LLC - Southeast Region   (4)
13850 Ballantyne Corporate Pl Ste 425, Charlotte, NC 28277
Tel.: (704) 544-6655
Web Site: http://www.hessenergy.com
Emp.: 4
Natural Gas & Electric Power Marketer & Distr
N.A.I.C.S.: 221210

Subsidiary (Domestic):

Direct Energy New York Corporation   (4)
115 Solar St Ste 102, Syracuse, NY 13204
Tel.: (315) 234-5300
Web Site: http://www.hessenergy.com
Natural Gas & Electric Power Marketer & Distr
N.A.I.C.S.: 221210

Subsidiary (Non-US):

Direct Energy Marketing Limited   (2)
2225 Sheppard Avenue East Ste 1500, Toronto, M2J 5C2, ON, Canada   **(100%)**
Tel.: (416) 221-4441
Web Site: http://www.directenergy.com
Sales Range: $5-14.9 Billion
Emp.: 4,800

Holding Company; Electric Power & Natural Gas Products Distr & Support Services
N.A.I.C.S.: 551112

Division (Domestic):

Direct Energy Marketing Ltd. - Canada Home Services   (3)
80 Allstate Parkway 3rd Floor, Markham, L3R 6H3, ON, Canada
Tel.: (905) 944-9944
Web Site: http://www.directenergy.com
Residential Heating, Ventilation, Air Conditioning & Plumbing Contractor Services
N.A.I.C.S.: 238220

Subsidiary (Non-US):

Direct Energy Resources Partnership   (2)
111 5th Avenue South West Suite 1000, Calgary, T2P 3T6, AB, Canada
Tel.: (403) 538-5000
Web Site: http://www.directenergy.com
Natural Gas Extraction & Distr
N.A.I.C.S.: 211130

Subsidiary (Domestic):

Direct Energy Services, LLC   (2)
12 Greenway Plz Ste 600, Houston, TX 77046
Tel.: (412) 667-5100
Web Site: http://www.directenergy.com
Holding Company; Heating, Ventilation, Air Conditioning & Plumbing Contractor & Energy Management Consulting Services
N.A.I.C.S.: 551112
John Schultz *(Pres)*
Bruce Stewart *(Pres-North America)*
Jim Steffes *(Exec VP-External Affairs)*
Thomas Smith *(Gen Counsel & Exec VP)*

Unit (Domestic):

Airtron Houston   (3)
3300 Bingle Rd, Houston, TX 77055
Tel.: (281) 996-5857
Web Site: http://www.airtronhouston.com
Emp.: 35
Heating & Air-Conditioning Services
N.A.I.C.S.: 238220

Subsidiary (Domestic):

Home Warranty of America, Inc.   (3)
1371 Abbott Ct Ste A, Buffalo Grove, IL 60089
Tel.: (847) 325-5143
Web Site:
  http://www.hwahomewarranty.com
Home Warranty Coverage
N.A.I.C.S.: 524128

Masters, Inc.   (3)
5123 Pegasus Ct Ste K-N, Frederick, MD 21704
Tel.: (301) 637-8279
Web Site: http://www.airtronmidatlantic.com
Heating & Air-Conditioning Services
N.A.I.C.S.: 238220

T.A. Kaiser Heating & Air, Inc.   (3)
4040 Industrial Blvd, Indianapolis, IN 46254
Tel.: (317) 608-0909
Web Site: http://www.takaiser.com
Electronic Services
N.A.I.C.S.: 238210

Subsidiary (Domestic):

First Choice Power, L.P.   (2)
225 E John Carpenter Fwy Ste 1500, Fort Worth, TX 76109
Tel.: (817) 731-0099
Sales Range: $200-249.9 Million
Electric Utility Services
N.A.I.C.S.: 221118
Brian Hayduk *(Pres)*

Frontera Generation LP   (2)
320 S Goodwin Rd, Mission, TX 78572
Tel.: (956) 519-7728
Eletric Power Generation Services
N.A.I.C.S.: 221118

Gateway Energy Services Corporation   (2)
1423 Red Ventures Dr, Fort Mill, SC 29707
Tel.: (972) 543-1040
Web Site: http://www.saveonenergy.com

NRG Energy, Inc.—(Continued)

Natural Gas & Electricity Distr
N.A.I.C.S.: 221210

Io-Tahoe LLC (2)
111 Broadway Ste 601, New York, NY
10006
Tel.: (551) 225-3800
Web Site: http://www.io-tahoe.com
Computer Software Services
N.A.I.C.S.: 541511
Rohit Mahajan (CTO)

New Millennium Academy LLC (2)
5105 Brooklyn Blvd, Brooklyn Center, MN
55429
Tel.: (763) 235-7900
Web Site:
http://www.newmillenniumacademy.org
Emp.: 750
Academy Management Services
N.A.I.C.S.: 611310
Kevin Xiong (Pres)
Thomas Thao (Principal)

WTU Retail Energy LP (2)
12 Greenway Plz Ste 600, Houston, TX
77046
Tel.: (866) 322-5563
Web Site: http://www.wturetailenergy.com
Electric Power Distribution Services
N.A.I.C.S.: 221122

Dunkirk Power LLC (1)
106 Point Dr N, Dunkirk, NY 14048
Tel.: (716) 673-6315
Electricity Generation Services
N.A.I.C.S.: 221118

El Segundo Power II LLC (1)
301 Vista del Mar, El Segundo, CA 90245
Tel.: (310) 615-6027
Electricity Generation Services
N.A.I.C.S.: 221118

Energy Plus Holdings LLC (1)
PO Box 38815, Philadelphia, PA 19104-
9728
Tel.: (703) 750-1000
Web Site:
http://www.energypluscompany.com
Holding Company
N.A.I.C.S.: 551112

Everything Energy LLC (1)
910 Louisiana St, Houston, TX 77002
Tel.: (713) 488-8766
Web Site: https://everythingenergy.com
Electric Power Distribution Services
N.A.I.C.S.: 221122

GenOn Energy, Inc. (1)
804 Carnegie Ctr, Princeton, NJ 08540
Tel.: (609) 524-4500
Rev.: $1,589,000,000
Assets: $4,404,000,000
Liabilities: $4,329,000,000
Net Worth: $75,000,000
Earnings: ($295,000,000)
Emp.: 1,339
Fiscal Year-end: 12/31/2017
Electricity & Energy Services
N.A.I.C.S.: 221111
Kirkland B. Andrews (Exec VP)
David Callen (Chief Acctg Officer & VP)

Subsidiary (Domestic):

**GenOn Americas Generation,
LLC** (2)
804 Carnegie Ctr, Princeton, NJ 08540
Tel.: (609) 524-4500
Rev.: $1,415,000,000
Assets: $2,322,000,000
Liabilities: $1,456,000,000
Net Worth: $866,000,000
Earnings: ($187,000,000)
Emp.: 506
Fiscal Year-end: 12/31/2017
Electricity & Energy Services
N.A.I.C.S.: 221111
Kirkland B. Andrews (CFO & Exec VP)
Mark Allen McFarland (Pres & CEO)
David Callen (Chief Acctg Officer & VP)

GenOn Mid-Atlantic, LLC (2)
804 Carnegie Ctr, Princeton, NJ 08540
Tel.: (609) 524-4500
Rev.: $459,000,000
Assets: $1,475,000,000

Liabilities: $594,000,000
Net Worth: $881,000,000
Earnings: ($269,000,000)
Emp.: 401
Fiscal Year-end: 12/31/2017
Electricity & Energy Services
N.A.I.C.S.: 221111
Kirkland B. Andrews (CFO & Exec VP)
Mark Allen McFarland (Pres & CEO)
David Callen (Chief Acctg Officer & VP)

Geostellar, Inc. (1)
3483 Edison Way, Menlo Park, CA 94025
Tel.: (304) 596-0229
Web Site: http://www.geostellar.com
Solar Energy Solution Services
N.A.I.C.S.: 238220

Goal Zero LLC (1)
675 W 14600 S, Bluffdale, UT 84065
Tel.: (801) 553-3654
Web Site: https://www.goalzero.com
Sales Range: $25-49.9 Million
Emp.: 130
Portable Solar Power Recharging Kits Mfr
N.A.I.C.S.: 221114
Robert Workman (Founder)
Norm Krantz (VP-Product Innovations)
Keyvan Vasefi (Head-Product Dev)
Bill Harmon (Gen Mgr)
Patrick Keller (Head-Mktg & Ecommerce)
Scott Crowther (Head-Fin)
Adam Runquist (Head-Supply Chain)
Marc Cooper (Head-Warehouse Ops)
David Grayson (Head-Sls)
Hadley Moss (Gen Counsel)

**Green Mountain Energy
Company** (1)
910 Louisiana St, Houston, TX
77002 **(100%)**
Web Site:
http://www.greenmountainenergy.com
Energy Services
N.A.I.C.S.: 221122
Cyndy Reynolds (Dir-Comml Sls)
Andrea Ortega-Toledano (Dir-Product Inno-
vation)
Rebecca Emrick (Mktg Dir)
Mark Parsons (Gen Mgr)

Huntley Power LLC (1)
3500 River Rd, Tonawanda, NY 14150
Tel.: (716) 879-3800
Eletric Power Generation Services
N.A.I.C.S.: 221118

**Independence Energy Group
LLC** (1)
1501 N Plano Rd, Richardson, TX 75081
Web Site: https://www.cirroenergy.com
Electric Power Distribution Services
N.A.I.C.S.: 221122

**Lone Star A/C & Appliance Repair,
LLC** (1)
500 E Arapaho Rd Ste 230, Richardson, TX
75081
Tel.: (713) 457-5700
Household Appliance Repair Services
N.A.I.C.S.: 811412

Midwest Generation, LLC (1)
440 S La Salle St Ste 3500, Chicago, IL
60605-5024 **(100%)**
Tel.: (312) 572-9217
Web Site: http://www.midwest-
generation.com.yeslab.org
Fiscal Year-end: 12/31/2013
Power Plant Operator
N.A.I.C.S.: 221118

Subsidiary (Domestic):

Midwest Generation EME, LLC (2)
440 South La Salle St Ste 3500, Chicago,
IL 60605-1028 **(100%)**
Tel.: (312) 583-6000
Web Site: http://www.edisonjobs.com
Rev.: $1,083,550,000
Emp.: 150
Electric Power Generation
N.A.I.C.S.: 221118
Georgia Ricci Nelson (Founder)
Guy Gorney (Pres)
Doug McFarlan (VP-Pub Affairs)
Dan McDevitt (VP-Legal Affairs)

NEO Corporation (1)
289 Silkwood Dr, Canton, NC 28716

Tel.: (828) 456-4332
Web Site: https://www.neocorporation.com
Emp.: 51
Asbestos Abatement & Building Demolition
Services
N.A.I.C.S.: 562910
Sara Tyburski (Controller)
Todd J. Escaravage (Pres)
John A. Hepler (VP)
Greg Pressley (Mgr-Western North Carolina
Div)
John Mangel (Mgr-Eastern North Carolina
Div)
Caroline Childers (Mgr-HR)
Nathan Whitson (Mgr-Bus)
Jennifer Bradish (Mgr-Compliance)
Charlotte Holmes (Mgr-Compliance)

NRG Canal 3 Development LLC (1)
211 Carnegie Ctr, Princeton, NJ 08540
Tel.: (609) 524-4500
Power Generation Services
N.A.I.C.S.: 221122

NRG Curtailment Solutions, Inc. (1)
4433 Genesee St Ste 401, Buffalo, NY
14225
Tel.: (877) 711-5453
Web Site: http://demandresponse.nrg.com
Demand Response Planning & Execution
Services for Utilities & Grid Operators
N.A.I.C.S.: 541990
Marie Pieniazek (Sr VP-Mktg & Ops)

NRG Devon Operations Inc. (1)
Naugatuck Ave, Milford, CT 06460
Tel.: (860) 346-9639
Electricity Generation Services
N.A.I.C.S.: 221118

NRG Dunkirk Operations Inc. (1)
106 Point Dr N, Dunkirk, NY 14048
Tel.: (716) 673-6322
Electric Power Distribution Services
N.A.I.C.S.: 221122

**NRG El Segundo Operations
Inc.** (1)
350 Main St, El Segundo, CA 90245
Tel.: (310) 524-2300
Web Site: https://www.elsegundo.org
Electric Power Distribution Services
N.A.I.C.S.: 221122

NRG Energy Services LLC (1)
990 Peiffers Ln, Harrisburg, PA 17109
Tel.: (717) 920-8530
Sales Range: $25-49.9 Million
Emp.: 30
Industrial Gas Distr
N.A.I.C.S.: 325120

NRG Florida, LP (1)
5200 Holopaw Rd, Saint Cloud, FL 34773
Tel.: (407) 891-2186
Electricity Generation Services
N.A.I.C.S.: 221118

**NRG Gladstone Operating Services
Pty Ltd** (1)
Gladstone Power Station 353 Hanson
Road, Gladstone, 4680, QLD, Australia
Tel.: (61) 74 976 5211
Web Site: https://www.nrggos.com.au
Emp.: 240
Electronic Services
N.A.I.C.S.: 221118

NRG Home Services LLC (1)
1050 N Post oak Rd Ste 230, Houston, TX
77055
Tel.: (713) 457-5700
Web Site: http://www.nrghomeservices.com
Housing Support Services
N.A.I.C.S.: 624229

NRG Homer City Services LLC (1)
1750 Power Plant Rd, Homer City, PA
15748
Tel.: (724) 479-9011
Web Site: http://www.nrg.com
Emp.: 200
Electricity Generation Services
N.A.I.C.S.: 221118

NRG Huntley Operations Inc. (1)
3500 River Rd, Tonawanda, NY 14150
Tel.: (716) 879-3800
Electricity Generation Services
N.A.I.C.S.: 221118

NRG Kendall, LLC (1)
211 Carnegie Ctr, Princeton, NJ 08540-
6213
Tel.: (609) 524-5363
Emp.: 5
Electrical Equipment Whslr
N.A.I.C.S.: 423610

NRG Middletown Operations Inc. (1)
1866 River Rd, Middletown, CT 06457
Tel.: (860) 638-3031
Eletric Power Generation Services
N.A.I.C.S.: 221118

NRG Montville Operations Inc. (1)
74 Lathrop Rd, Montville, CT 06353
Tel.: (860) 848-9248
Electric & Gas Services Distr
N.A.I.C.S.: 221118
Nick Ivotlurno (Plant Mgr)

NRG Renew LLC (1)
4900 N Scottsdale Rd, Scottsdale, AZ
85251
Tel.: (480) 424-1253
Emp.: 50
Electric Energy Services
N.A.I.C.S.: 221118
Craig Cornelius (Sr VP-Bus Dev)
Thomas P. Doyle (Pres & CEO)
James Brown (Sr VP-Microgrids)
Craig Cornelius (Sr VP-Bus Dev)
W. Richard Grosdidier (Sr VP-Comml Ex-
ecution)
Jennifer A. Hein (Gen Counsel)
Randall Hickok (Sr VP-Asset, Mgmt & En-
grg)
Jim Ingoldsby (Sr VP-Bus Ops)

**NRG Residential Solar Solutions
LLC** (1)
1000 N Post Oak Rd Ste 240, Houston, TX
77055
Tel.: (713) 655-1180
Web Site: https://www.picknrg.com
Emp.: 100
Solar Heating Contracting Services
N.A.I.C.S.: 238220

NRG Texas, LLC (1)
1301 McKinney Ste 2300, Houston, TX
77010
Tel.: (713) 795-6000
Web Site: http://www.nrg.com
Independent Electricity Generator
N.A.I.C.S.: 221122

ONSITE Energy, Inc. (1)
619 N Church Ave Ste 4, Bozeman, MT
59715
Tel.: (406) 551-6135
Web Site: http://www.onsiteenergyinc.com
Solar Heating Contracting Services
N.A.I.C.S.: 238220

Oswego Harbor Power LLC (1)
261 Washington Blvd, Oswego, NY 13126
Tel.: (315) 349-2341
Electric & Gas Services
N.A.I.C.S.: 221118

Pure Energies Group Inc. (1)
30 Duncan St Ste 701, Toronto, M5V 2C3,
ON, Canada
Tel.: (416) 340-7873
Web Site: http://www.pureenergies.com
Electric Energy Services
N.A.I.C.S.: 221118
Sen Kanthaswamy (Mng Dir)

**Reliant Energy Retail Holdings,
LLC** (1)
1201 Fannin St, Houston, TX 77002
Tel.: (713) 207-7777
Web Site: http://www.reliant.com
Holding Company
N.A.I.C.S.: 551112
Elizabeth Killinger (Pres)

Subsidiary (Domestic):

RRI Energy Services, Inc. (2)
1201 Fannin St, Houston, TX
77002 **(100%)**
Tel.: (832) 357-3000
Web Site: http://www.reliant.com
Sales Range: $75-99.9 Million
Emp.: 200
Electric Power Marketers

Reliant Energy Retail Holdings, LLC (1)
100 Summer St Ste 800, Boston, MA 02110
Web Site: https://www.reliant.com
Electric Power Distribution Services
N.A.I.C.S.: 221122

Reliant Energy Retail Services, LLC (1)
1111 Louisiana St, Houston, TX 77002
Tel.: (713) 208-3000
Eletric Power Generation Services
N.A.I.C.S.: 221118

Restoration Design LLC (1)
4940 Corrales Rd Ste 100, Corrales, NM 87048
Tel.: (505) 847-6376
Housing Support Services
N.A.I.C.S.: 624229

Roadrunner SunTower, LLC (1)
211 Carnegie Ctr, Princeton, NJ 08540
Tel.: (760) 710-2189
Solar Heating Contracting Services
N.A.I.C.S.: 238220

Roof Diagnostics Solar of Mass., LLC (1)
89 Washington Ave, Natick, MA 01760-3441
Tel.: (508) 545-0989
Emp.: 25
Roofing Material Whslr & Mfr
N.A.I.C.S.: 238160

SPP DG DevCo 4a, LLC (1)
80 E Sir Frnc Drake Blvd, Larkspur, CA 94939
Tel.: (415) 299-6040
Electricity Line Construction Services
N.A.I.C.S.: 237130

Saguaro Power Company, a Limited Partnership (1)
8000 Lk Mead Dr, Henderson, NV 89015
Tel.: (702) 558-1100
Sales Range: $25-49.9 Million
Emp.: 22
Electric Power Generation
N.A.I.C.S.: 221118
Larry Flashberg (Gen Mgr)

San Joaquin Energy, LLC (1)
18101 Von Karman Ave Ste 1700, Irvine, CA 92612-1046
Tel.: (661) 395-3029
Electric Energy Services
N.A.I.C.S.: 221118

Seawall Solar 9 LLC (1)
211 Carnegie Ctr, Princeton, NJ 08540
Tel.: (609) 557-3441
Emp.: 10
Solar Heating Contracting Services
N.A.I.C.S.: 238220

Spanish Town Estate Solar 1 LLC (1)
211 Carnegie Ctr, Princeton, NJ 08540
Tel.: (760) 710-2131
Solar Energy Equipment Distr
N.A.I.C.S.: 238220

Station A LLC (1)
2912 Diamond St Ste 359, San Francisco, CA 94131
Tel.: (415) 214-8700
Web Site: https://stationa.com
Electric Power Distribution Services
N.A.I.C.S.: 221122

Stream Energy Illinois, LLC (1)
804 Carnegie Ctr, Princeton, NJ 08540
Web Site: https://www.mystream.com
Electric Power Distribution Services
N.A.I.C.S.: 221122

Stream Energy Maryland, LLC (1)
PO Box 1376, Baltimore, MD 21203-1376
Eletric Power Generation Services
N.A.I.C.S.: 221118

Stream Energy New Jersey, LLC (1)
PO Box 32070, Newark, NJ 07102-0470
Eletric Power Generation Services
N.A.I.C.S.: 221118

Stream Energy New York, LLC (1)
PO Box 4873, New York, NY 10185

Eletric Power Generation Services
N.A.I.C.S.: 221118

Sunora Energy Solutions Limited Partnership (1)
2342 E University Dr, Phoenix, AZ 85034
Tel.: (602) 772-5220
Business Consulting Services
N.A.I.C.S.: 541611

US Retailers LLC (1)
1201 Fannin St, Houston, TX 77002
Tel.: (713) 537-3000
Web Site: http://www.cirroenergy.com
Electric Power Distribution Services
N.A.I.C.S.: 221122

Vivint Smart Home, Inc. (1)
4931 N 300 W, Provo, UT 84604
Tel.: (801) 377-9111
Web Site: https://www.vivint.com
Rev.: $1,682,490,000
Assets: $2,878,542,000
Liabilities: $4,580,886,000
Net Worth: ($1,702,344,000)
Earnings: ($51,734,000)
Emp.: 11,800
Fiscal Year-end: 12/31/2022
Investment Services
N.A.I.C.S.: 523999
Rasesh Patel (Pres)
Dale R. Gerard (CFO)
Joy Driscoll Durling (CIO)
Dana Russell (Treas)
Donna Benefield (Sr VP)
Michael Bramnick (Chief Compliance Officer)
Bruce Chung (CFO)
Kevin L. Cole (Treas)
Brian Curci (Gen Counsel)
Robert J. Gaudette (Exec VP)
Elizabeth Killinger (Exec VP)
Gin Kirkland Kinney (Sr VP)
Dak Liyanearachchi (Sr VP)
Chris Moser (Sr VP)
Matthew Pistner (Sr VP)
Jeanne-Mey Sun (VP)

Subsidiary (Domestic):

Legacy Vivint Smart Home, Inc. (2)
4931 N 300 W, Provo, UT 84604
Tel.: (801) 705-8011
Holding Company
N.A.I.C.S.: 551112

Subsidiary (Domestic):

APX Group Holdings, Inc. (3)
4931 N 300 W, Provo, UT 84604
Tel.: (801) 377-9111
Rev.: $1,155,981,000
Assets: $2,598,238,000
Liabilities: $4,387,560,000
Net Worth: ($1,789,322,000)
Earnings: ($395,756,000)
Fiscal Year-end: 12/31/2019
Electronic Security Product Mfr & Whslr
N.A.I.C.S.: 334290
Dale R. Gerard (CFO)
Todd R. Pedersen (Founder & CEO)
J. T. Hwang (CTO)
Patrick E. Kelliher (Chief Acctg Officer)
Todd M. Santiago (Chief Revenue Officer)
Scott R. Hardy (COO)
Shawn J. Lindquist (Chief Legal Officer & Sec)
Joy Driscoll Durling (CIO)

Subsidiary (Domestic):

Vivint, Inc. (4)
4931 N 300 W, Provo, UT 84604
Tel.: (801) 377-9111
Web Site: http://www.vivint.com
Sales Range: $350-399.9 Million
Emp.: 3,000
Home Security, Automation & Energy Management Systems Sales & Installation Services
N.A.I.C.S.: 238210
Joy Driscoll Durling (CIO & Chief Digital Enablement Officer)
Nate Randle (Chief Mktg Officer)

Western Sierra Energy, LLC (1)
18101 Von Karman Ave, Irvine, CA 92612
Tel.: (714) 730-6490
Emp.: 24
Electric Energy Services

N.A.I.C.S.: 221118

XOOM Energy Canada, ULC (1)
PO Box 2404, Calgary, T2P 5B1, AB, Canada
Portfolio Management Services
N.A.I.C.S.: 523940

XOOM Energy Georgia, LLC (1)
PO Box 650411, Dallas, TX 75265-0411
Electric Power Distribution Services
N.A.I.C.S.: 221330

XOOM Energy Michigan, LLC (1)
755 W Big Beaver Rd Ste 2020, Troy, MI 48084
Tel.: (248) 480-7264
Electric Power Distribution Services
N.A.I.C.S.: 221330

XOOM Energy New Jersey, LLC (1)
804 Carnegie Ctr, Princeton, NJ 08540
Tel.: (248) 480-7264
Portfolio Management Services
N.A.I.C.S.: 523940

XOOM Energy ONT, ULC (1)
777 Bay Street Suite C208-B, Toronto, M5G 2C8, ON, Canada
Web Site: https://xoomenergy.ca
Natural Gas Distribution Services
N.A.I.C.S.: 221210

XOOM Energy Texas, LLC (1)
1 Shell Plz 910 Louisiana St, Houston, TX 77002
Portfolio Management Services
N.A.I.C.S.: 523940

XOOM Energy, LLC (1)
804 Carnegie Ctr, Princeton, NJ 08540
Web Site: https://xoomenergy.com
Natural Gas Distribution Services
N.A.I.C.S.: 221210

XOOM Energy, LLC. (1)
11208 Statesville Rd Ste 200, Huntersville, NC 28078
Web Site: http://www.xoomenergy.com
Natural Gas Distr
N.A.I.C.S.: 221210
Thomas Ulry (CEO)

NRP STONE, INC.

1090 Center Dr, Park City, UT 84098
Tel.: (801) 214-8132   NV
Year Founded: 1998
NRPI—(OTCIQ)
Liabilities: $448
Net Worth: ($448)
Earnings: ($205,000)
Fiscal Year-end: 12/31/19
Urn Product Mfr
N.A.I.C.S.: 327420
Josh Todd Hanes (Pres)
Eric Willeitner (Sec)
Jeffrey Johnson (Treas)

NRX PHARMACEUTICALS, INC.

2645 N Federal Hwy Ste 230, Delray Beach, FL 33483
Tel.: (310) 734-2300   DE
Web Site:
   https://www.nrxpharma.com
Year Founded: 2017
NRXP—(NASDAQ)
Rev.: $4,581,000
Assets: $25,816,000
Liabilities: $18,407,000
Net Worth: $7,409,000
Earnings: ($39,754,000)
Fiscal Year-end: 12/31/22
Investment Services
N.A.I.C.S.: 523999
Richard S. Ackerman (Chm & Pres)
Seth L. Van Voorhees (CFO & Treas)
Molly Cogan (Sr Dir-Global Comm)
Carrie M. Carretta (Sr VP-Clinical Dev & Medical Affairs)
Stephen Willard (CEO)

NSTS BANCORP, INC.

700 S Lewis Ave, Waukegan, IL 60085
Tel.: (847) 336-4430   DE
Web Site:
   https://www.northshoretrust.com
Year Founded: 2021
NSTS—(NASDAQ)
Rev.: $7,728,000
Assets: $256,776,000
Liabilities: $179,231,000
Net Worth: $77,545,000
Earnings: ($3,957,000)
Emp.: 46
Fiscal Year-end: 12/31/23
Bank Holding Company
N.A.I.C.S.: 551111
Stephen G. Lear (Chm, Pres & CEO)
Carissa H. Schoolcraft (CFO)
Nathan E. Walker (Exec VP)

NU SKIN ENTERPRISES, INC.

75 W Center St, Provo, UT 84601
Tel.: (801) 345-1000   DE
Web Site: https://www.nuskin.com
Year Founded: 1984
NUS—(NYSE)
Rev.: $2,225,659,000
Assets: $1,820,970,000
Liabilities: $923,674,000
Net Worth: $897,296,000
Earnings: $104,778,000
Emp.: 13,400
Fiscal Year-end: 12/31/22
Cosmetics, Vitamins, Hair Care Products, Personal Care Products & Over-the-Counter Products Mfr & Distr
N.A.I.C.S.: 424210
Steven J. Lund (Founder & Exec Chm)
Ryan S. Napierski (Pres & CEO)
Chayce D. Clark (Gen Counsel & Exec VP)
James D. Thomas (CFO & Chief Acctg Officer)
Marion Shumway (Sr VP-Human Resources)
James D. Thomas (Interim CFO, Chief Acctg Officer & Exec VP)

Subsidiaries:

Beauty Biosciences LLC (1)
3811 Turtle Creek Blvd Ste 1300, Dallas, TX 75219
Web Site: https://beautybio.com
Personal Care Product Mfr & Distr
N.A.I.C.S.: 325620

Big Planet, Inc. (1)
75 West Ctr St, Provo, UT 84601
Tel.: (801) 345-1000
Web Site: http://www.bigplanet.com
Sales Range: $550-599.9 Million
Emp.: 1,500
Provider of Computer Services
N.A.I.C.S.: 517810

Growgenix Solutions LLC (1)
487 E 1750 N Vineyard, Lindon, UT 84042
Tel.: (801) 345-7051
Web Site: http://www.groviv.com
Farming Services
N.A.I.C.S.: 111998
Steve Lindsley (Pres)

LifeDNA, Inc. (1)
1050 Queen St 100, Honolulu, HI 96814
Web Site: https://lifedna.com
DNA Research & Testing Services
N.A.I.C.S.: 621511

My Favorite Things, Inc. (1)
1500 Carroll Ave, Chicago, IL 60607
Tel.: (740) 373-8950
Web Site: http://www.joinmavely.com
Gift, Novelty, And Souvenir Shop, Nsk
N.A.I.C.S.: 459420
Asunta Damron (Pres)
Evan Wray (Co-Founder & CEO)

NSE Korea Ltd. (1)
10F Rodamco Bldg, Yeoksam-dong,

Nu Skin Enterprises, Inc.—(Continued)

Gangnam-ku, Seoul, 135-977, Korea
(South)
Tel.: (82) 8225287245
Web Site: http://nskorea.en.ec21.com
Sales Range: $200-249.9 Million
Provider of Cosmetics, Vitamins, Hair Care
Products, Personal Care Products & Over-
the-Counter Products
N.A.I.C.S.: 456191
S.T. Han *(Pres & Gen Mgr)*

Nox Technologies, Inc.　　　　(1)
PO Box 20280, San Jose, CA 95160
Tel.: (408) 997-8094
Web Site: https://noxtechnology.com
Dietary Product Mfr & Distr
N.A.I.C.S.: 311514

**Nu Skin (China) Daily-Use and
Health Products Co., Ltd.**　　(1)
29 Longyang Industrial Park Zone, Fengx-
ian District, Shanghai, 201401, China
Tel.: (86) 2153574588
Web Site: http://www.nuskin.com
Sales Range: $1-4.9 Billion
Emp.: 1,500
Provider of Cosmetics, Vitamins, Hair Care
Products, Personal Care Products & Over-
the-Counter Products
N.A.I.C.S.: 456191

Nu Skin Asia Investment, Inc.　(1)
75 W Center St, Provo, UT 84601
Tel.: (801) 345-1000
Web Site: http://www.nuskin.com
Emp.: 3,000
Investment Services
N.A.I.C.S.: 541611
M. Truman Hunt *(Pres & CEO)*

Nu Skin Belgium, NV　　　　(1)
Da Vincilaan 9, The Corporate Village Build-
ing Elsinore, 1930, Zaventem, Belgium
Tel.: (32) 23420475
Web Site: http://www.nuskin.com
Sales Range: $10-24.9 Million
Provider of Cosmetics, Vitamins, Hair Care
Products, Personal Care Products & Over-
the-Counter Products
N.A.I.C.S.: 456191
Mikael Linder *(Pres-Europe-Middle East-
Africa)*

Nu Skin Canada, Inc.　　　　(1)
3350 Ridgeway Dr Unit 1, Mississauga, L5L
5Z9, ON, Canada
Tel.: (905) 569-5150
Web Site: https://nuskin.knowledgeowl.com
Sales Range: $200-249.9 Million
Emp.: 42
Provider of Cosmetics, Vitamins, Hair Care
Products, Personal Care Products & Over-
the-Counter Products
N.A.I.C.S.: 456191
Paul Hanson *(Gen Mgr)*

Nu Skin Eastern Europe Kft　(1)
Kft Alkotas utca 48-50, 1123, Budapest,
Hungary
Tel.: (36) 212007827
Beauty Care Product Mfr & Distr
N.A.I.C.S.: 335210

**Nu Skin Enterprises (Thailand)
Limited**　　　　　　　　　　(1)
319 Chamchuri Square Building 15th Floor
Phayathai Road, Patumwan, Bangkok,
10330, Thailand
Tel.: (66) 25061888
Personal Care Product Distr
N.A.I.C.S.: 424210

**Nu Skin Enterprises (Thailand),
Ltd.**　　　　　　　　　　　(1)
319 Chamchuri Square Building 15th Floor
Phayathai Road Pathumwan, Bangkok,
10330, Thailand
Tel.: (66) 27918500
Web Site: http://www.nuskin.com
Personal Care Product Mfr & Distr
N.A.I.C.S.: 325620

**Nu Skin Enterprises Australia,
Inc.**　　　　　　　　　　　(1)
2/2 Eden Park Dr, Macquarie Park, North
Ryde, 2113, NSW, Australia
Tel.: (61) 294910900
Web Site: http://www.nuskin.com

Sales Range: $200-249.9 Million
Provider of Cosmetics, Vitamins, Hair Care
Products, Personal Care Products & Over-
the-Counter Products
N.A.I.C.S.: 456191

**Nu Skin Enterprises Hong Kong,
Inc.**　　　　　　　　　　　(1)
10/F Lee Garden II 28 Yun Ping Road,
Causeway Bay, China (Hong Kong)
Tel.: (852) 28377700
Web Site: http://www.nuskin.com
Sales Range: $200-249.9 Million
Provider of Cosmetics, Vitamins, Hair Care
Products, Personal Care Products & Over-
the-Counter Products
N.A.I.C.S.: 456191
Angela Lau *(Pres)*

**Nu Skin Enterprises New Zealand,
Inc.**　　　　　　　　　　　(1)
Unit 16/180 Montgomerie Road, Airport
Oaks, Auckland, 2022, New
Zealand　　　　　　　　　(100%)
Tel.: (64) 294910900
Web Site: http://www.nuskin.co.nz
Sales Range: $10-24.9 Million
Emp.: 7
Provider of Cosmetics, Vitamins, Hair Care
Products, Personal Care Products & Over-
the-Counter Products
N.A.I.C.S.: 456191

**Nu Skin Enterprises Philippines
LLC**　　　　　　　　　　　(1)
23F Exquadra Tower 1 Jade Drive Cor Ex-
change Road, Ortigas Business Center,
Pasig, 1605, Philippines
Tel.: (63) 288667277
Web Site: http://www.nuskin.com
Personal Care Products Mfr & Dist
N.A.I.C.S.: 812199
Kany Virgo Soemantoro *(Pres-Nu Skin
Philippines-Indonesia)*

**Nu Skin Enterprises Philippines,
Inc.**　　　　　　　　　　　(1)
15th Floor Octagon Center 41 San Miguel
Ave, Ortigas Center, Pasig, 1605, Philip-
pines
Tel.: (63) 28687546
Web Site: http://www.nuskin.com.ph
Ant-Aging Product & Nutritional Supple-
ments Distr
N.A.I.C.S.: 325620
Kany Virgo Soemantoro *(Pres)*

**Nu Skin Enterprises Singapore Pte.
Ltd.**　　　　　　　　　　　(1)
331 North Bridge Road 18-01 Odeon Tow-
ers, Singapore, 188720, Singapore
Tel.: (65) 6 837 3363
Web Site: https://www.nuskin.com
Sales Range: $50-74.9 Million
Provider of Cosmetics, Vitamins, Hair Care
Products, Personal Care Products & Over-
the-Counter Products
N.A.I.C.S.: 456191

**Nu Skin Enterprises United States,
Inc.**　　　　　　　　　　　(1)
75 W Ctr St, Provo, UT 84601
Tel.: (801) 345-1000
Web Site: http://www.nuskin.com
Personal Care Product Mfr & Distr
N.A.I.C.S.: 325620

**Nu Skin Enterprises Vietnam,
LLC**　　　　　　　　　　　(1)
7th Floor Hanoi Centerpoint Building - 27
Le Van Luong street, Nhan Chinh ward
Thanh Xuan district, Hanoi, Vietnam
Tel.: (84) 2435643352
Personal Care Product Distr
N.A.I.C.S.: 424210
Blake M. Roney *(CEO)*

Nu Skin France, SARL　　　(1)
155 Rue Du Faubourg Saint Denis, 75010,
Paris, France
Tel.: (33) 980091440
Web Site: http://www.nuskin.com
Sales Range: $10-24.9 Million
Cosmetics, Vitamins, Hair Care Products,
Personal Care Products & Over-the-Counter
Products
N.A.I.C.S.: 456191
Mikael Linder *(Pres-EMEA)*

Nu Skin Germany GmbH　　(1)

Taunusstrasse 57, 55118, Mainz, Germany
Tel.: (49) 61314909108
Web Site: http://www.nuskin.com
Sales Range: $10-24.9 Million
Provider of Cosmetics, Vitamins, Hair Care
Products, Personal Care Products & Over-
the-Counter Products
N.A.I.C.S.: 456191

Nu Skin Italia, S.R.L.　　　(1)
Piazza F Meda 5, 20121, Milan, Italy
Tel.: (39) 0282952651
Web Site: http://www.nuskin.com
Sales Range: $200-249.9 Million
Cosmetics, Vitamins, Hair Care Products,
Personal Care Products & Over-the-Counter
Products
N.A.I.C.S.: 456191
Chris Hodges *(Gen Mgr)*

Nu Skin Japan Co., Ltd.　　(1)
Tokyo Toranomon Global Square 14F 1-3-1
Toranomon, Minato-ku, Tokyo, 105-0001,
Japan
Tel.: (81) 366261234
Web Site: http://www.nuskin.co.jp
Cosmetics, Vitamins, Hair Care Products,
Personal Care Products & Over-the-Counter
Products Mfr & Sales
N.A.I.C.S.: 456120
Kazunori Kobayashi *(Pres & CEO)*

**Nu Skin Malaysia Holdings Sdn.
Bhd.**　　　　　　　　　　　(1)
Lot 2 5 1 Level 2 PNB Perdana Commercial
Centre No 10 Jalan Binjai, 50450, Kuala
Lumpur, Malaysia
Tel.: (60) 321707700
Web Site: http://www.nuskin.com.my
Sales Range: $50-74.9 Million
Emp.: 100
Holding Company
N.A.I.C.S.: 551112

Subsidiary (Domestic):

Nu Skin (Malaysia) Sdn. Bhd.　(2)
Lot 2 5 1 Level 2 PNB Perdana Commercial
Centre No 10 Jalan Binjai, 50450, Kuala
Lumpur, Malaysia
Tel.: (60) 390784788
Web Site: http://www.nuskin.com
Sales Range: $25-49.9 Million
Provider of Cosmetics, Vitamins, Hair Care
Products, Personal Care Products & Over-
the-Counter Products
N.A.I.C.S.: 456191

Nu Skin Mexico, S.A. de C.V.　(1)
Av Presidente Masaryk 275 Colonia Po-
lanco Secc IV Delegacion, Miguel Hidalgo,
11550, Mexico, Mexico
Tel.: (52) 5546319863
Web Site: http://www.nuskin.com
Sales Range: $10-24.9 Million
Cosmetics, Vitamins, Hair Care Products,
Personal Care Products & Over-the-Counter
Products
N.A.I.C.S.: 456191

Nu Skin Netherlands, B.V.　　(1)
Amundsenweg 2, 5928 LT, Venlo, Nether-
lands
Tel.: (31) 850021853
Web Site: http://www.nuskin.com
Sales Range: $1-9.9 Million
Provider of Cosmetics, Vitamins, Hair Care
Products, Personal Care Products & Over-
the-Counter Products
N.A.I.C.S.: 456191
Bgorn Vanzayal *(Mng Dir)*

Nu Skin Norway AS　　　　(1)
Dronning Mauds Gate 11, 0250, Oslo, Nor-
way
Tel.: (47) 85295048
Emp.: 50
Anti-Aging Product & Nutritional Supple-
ments Distr
N.A.I.C.S.: 325620
Mikael Frans Georg Linder *(Pres & Gen
Mgr-Europe Middle East & Africa)*

**Nu Skin Personal Care (Thailand),
Ltd.**　　　　　　　　　　　(1)
15th Fl Unit 1-2 9-16 319 Chamchuri
Square Bldg, Phyathai Road Pathum Wan,
Bangkok, Thailand
Tel.: (66) 227918500
Web Site: http://www.nuskin.com

Sales Range: $200-249.9 Million
Provider of Cosmetics, Vitamins, Hair Care
Products, Personal Care Products & Over-
the-Counter Products
N.A.I.C.S.: 456191

Nu Skin Peru S.A.C.　　　　(1)
Av Los conquistadores 1118 Interior 6, Ur-
banizacion Santa Cruz, San Isidro, Peru
Tel.: (51) 17019148
Skin Care Products Distr
N.A.I.C.S.: 456120

Nu Skin Scandinavia A.S.　　(1)
Augusthus Amager Faelledvej 106 300,
1561, Copenhagen, Denmark
Tel.: (45) 78730602
Web Site: http://www.nuskin.com
Sales Range: $10-24.9 Million
Provider of Cosmetics, Vitamins, Hair Care
Products, Personal Care Products & Over-
the-Counter Products
N.A.I.C.S.: 456191
Michael Lund *(Mng Dir)*

Nu Skin Slovakia s.r.o.　　　(1)
Pribinova 6, 811 09, Bratislava, Slovakia
Tel.: (421) 482304532
Dietary Product Distr
N.A.I.C.S.: 424430

Nu Skin Taiwan, LLC　　　(1)
7F-1 No 189 Section 2 Jiuzong Road,
Neihu District, Taipei, 114, Taiwan
Tel.: (886) 287528555
Web Site: http://www.nuskin.com
Cosmetics, Vitamins, Hair Care Products,
Personal Care Products & Over-the-Counter
Products Mfr
N.A.I.C.S.: 456191
Charlene Chiang *(Pres)*

Nu Skin, Inc.　　　　　　　(1)
75 W Center St, Provo, UT 84601
Tel.: (801) 345-1000
Web Site: http://www.nuskin.com
Sales Range: $150-199.9 Million
Mfr & Distr of Cosmetics, Vitamins, Hair
Care Products, Personal Care Products &
Over-the-Counter Products
N.A.I.C.S.: 424210
M. Truman Hunt *(Pres & CEO)*

Pharmanex, LLC　　　　　(1)
75 W Center St, Provo, UT 84601
Tel.: (801) 345-6100
Web Site: http://www.pharmanex.com
Sales Range: $200-249.9 Million
Emp.: 1,500
Provider of Cosmetics, Vitamins, Hair Care
Products, Personal Care Products & Over-
the-Counter Products
N.A.I.C.S.: 541611

**Wasatch Product Development,
LLC**　　　　　　　　　　　(1)
427 W 11950 S, Draper, UT 84020
Tel.: (801) 566-4449
Web Site: https://wasatchlabs.com
Emp.: 200
Dental Care Product Mfr
N.A.I.C.S.: 339114

NU-MED PLUS, INC.
640 Belle Terre Rd Bldg 2 E Port,
Jefferson, NY 11777
Tel.: (631) 403-4337　　　UT
Web Site: http://www.nu-
medplus.com
Year Founded: 2011
NUMD—(OTCQB)
Assets: $13,456
Liabilities: $160,207
Net Worth: ($146,751)
Earnings: ($125,526)
Emp.: 2
Fiscal Year-end: 12/31/23
Medical Device Mfr
N.A.I.C.S.: 334510
Thomas Tait *(VP-Scientific Advance-
ment & Dev)*
Brett J. Earl *(VP-Medical Mktg)*
Keith L. Merrell *(CFO, Principal Acctg
Officer, Treas & Sec)*
William Hayde *(Chm, Pres & CEO)*

NUBEVA TECHNOLOGIES LTD.

333 W San Carlos St Ste 600, San Jose, CA 95110
Web Site: https://www.nubeva.com
NBVAF—(OTCIQ)
Rev.: $846,378
Assets: $5,498,011
Liabilities: $536,759
Net Worth: $4,961,252
Earnings: ($3,532,779)
Fiscal Year-end: 04/30/19
Custom Computer Programming Services
N.A.I.C.S.: 541511
Randy Chou *(Founder & CEO)*

NUBURU, INC.

7442 Tucson Way Ste 130, Centennial, CO 80112
Tel.: (720) 767-1400   DE
Web Site: https://www.nuburu.net
Year Founded: 2020
BURU—(NYSE)
Rev.: $13,458,254
Assets: $33,119,686
Liabilities: $51,985,247
Net Worth: ($18,865,561)
Earnings: $11,141,409
Emp.: 39
Fiscal Year-end: 12/31/22
Miscellaneous Financial Investment Activities
N.A.I.C.S.: 523999
Ron Nicol *(Exec Chm)*
R. Brian Knaley *(CEO & CFO)*
Philip Krim *(Chm)*
Mark Zediker *(Founder)*
Ron Nicol *(Exec Chm)*

NUCOR CORPORATION

1915 Rexford Rd, Charlotte, NC 28211
Tel.: (704) 366-7000   DE
Web Site: https://www.nucor.com
Year Founded: 1905
NUE—(NYSE)
Rev.: $34,713,501,000
Assets: $35,340,499,000
Liabilities: $13,216,745,000
Net Worth: $22,123,754,000
Earnings: $4,524,801,000
Emp.: 32,000
Fiscal Year-end: 12/31/23
Iron & Steel Product Mfr
N.A.I.C.S.: 331110
Michael D. Keller *(VP & Controller)*
David A. Sumoski *(COO)*
Leon J. Topalian *(Chm, Pres & CEO)*
Gregory J. Murphy *(Gen Counsel & Exec VP-Bus Svcs)*

Subsidiaries:

C.H.I. Overhead Doors, Inc.   **(1)**
1485 Sunrise Dr, Arthur, IL 61911
Tel.: (217) 543-2135
Web Site: http://www.chiohd.com
Residential Garage, Commercial Sectional & Rolling Steel Doors Mfr
N.A.I.C.S.: 332321
David Bangert *(CEO)*

California Steel Industries, Inc.   **(1)**
1 California Steel Way, Fontana, CA 92335   **(50%)**
Tel.: (909) 350-6300
Web Site: https://www.californiasteel.com
Emp.: 1,000
Flat Rolled Steel & Steel Pipe Products Mfr; Owned 50% by Companhia Vale do Rio Doce & 50% by JFE Steel Corporation
N.A.I.C.S.: 331221
Ricardo Bernardes *(CFO & Exec VP-Comml)*

Elite Storage Solutions Inc.   **(1)**
1118 W Spring St, Monroe, GA 30655
Tel.: (770) 207-0002
Web Site:
  http://www.elitestoragesolutions.com

Sales Range: $10-24.9 Million
Emp.: 125
Shelving, Office & Store, Except Wood
N.A.I.C.S.: 337126
Steve South *(Pres & CEO)*

Subsidiary (Domestic):

Elite Storage Solutions   **(2)**
1118 W Spring St, Monroe, GA 30655
Tel.: (770) 207-0002
Web Site:
  http://www.elitestoragesolutions.com
Rev.: $23,614,169
Emp.: 100
Structural & Roll Formed Racks & Storage Solutions
N.A.I.C.S.: 332312
Rod Brancher *(Asst Mgr-Maintenance)*
Gail Sliger *(Mgr-AP)*
Richard Pace *(Mgr-IT)*

Nationwide Archive Systems   **(2)**
16808 Armstrong Ave Ste 200, Irvine, CA 92606
Tel.: (949) 757-1377
Archive Management Services
N.A.I.C.S.: 519210

Harris Steel ULC   **(1)**
318 Arvin Avenue, Stoney Creek, L8E 2M2, ON, Canada
Tel.: (905) 662-0611
Web Site: http://www.harrisrebar.com
Steel & Aluminum Products Mfr; Steel Fabrication & Processing Services
N.A.I.C.S.: 332312

Subsidiary (US):

Ambassador Steel Corporation   **(2)**
1342 S Grandstaff Dr, Auburn, IN 46706-2620
Tel.: (260) 925-5440
Web Site: http://www.harrisrebar.com
Sales Range: $100-124.9 Million
Emp.: 60
Fabricated Structural Steel Products Mfr
N.A.I.C.S.: 332312

Subsidiary (Domestic):

Fisher & Ludlow   **(2)**
750 Appleby Line, Burlington, L7R 3Y8, ON, Canada
Tel.: (905) 632-2121
Web Site: http://www.fisherludlow.com
Sales Range: $75-99.9 Million
Emp.: 150
Mfr of Steel & Aluminum Grating
N.A.I.C.S.: 332312

Subsidiary (US):

Fisher & Ludlow   **(3)**
2000 Corporate Dr, Wexford, PA 15090-7611
Tel.: (724) 934-5320
Web Site: http://www.fisherludlow.com
Sales Range: $50-74.9 Million
Emp.: 125
Mfr of Steel Grating
N.A.I.C.S.: 332312
Don Nelson *(Pres)*

Subsidiary (Domestic):

Fisher & Ludlow   **(3)**
4609 64 Ave, Wetaskiwin, T9A 2G4, AB, Canada
Tel.: (780) 352-9171
Web Site: http://www.fisherludlow.com
Sales Range: $25-49.9 Million
Emp.: 40
Mfr of Steel Grating
N.A.I.C.S.: 332312

Subsidiary (Domestic):

Harris Rebar   **(2)**
318 Arvin Avenue, Stoney Creek, L8E 2M2, ON, Canada
Tel.: (905) 662-0611
Web Site: https://www.harrisrebar.com
Sales Range: $75-99.9 Million
Emp.: 115
Concrete Reinforced Steel Mfr
N.A.I.C.S.: 238120

Subsidiary (US):

Harris Rebar   **(3)**

55 Sumner St, Milford, MA 01757-3585
Tel.: (508) 473-8484
Web Site: http://www.harrisrebar.com
Sales Range: $75-99.9 Million
Concrete Reinforcing Steel & Related Products Mfr & Distr
N.A.I.C.S.: 332312

Subsidiary (Domestic):

Barker Steel Mid-Atlantic LLC   **(4)**
1601 S Haven St, Baltimore, MD 21224
Tel.: (410) 675-7600
Rev.: $14,700,000
Emp.: 70
Metal Rebar Mfr & Distr
N.A.I.C.S.: 332312

Subsidiary (US):

Harris Rebar - Atlantic   **(3)**
1700 Riverside Dr, Bethlehem, PA 18015
Tel.: (610) 882-1401
Web Site: http://www.harrisrebar.com
Concrete Reinforcing Steel & Related Products Mfr & Distr
N.A.I.C.S.: 332312

Harris Rebar Boise, Inc   **(3)**
2161 E Lanark St, Meridian, ID 83642
Tel.: (208) 888-0039
Web Site: http://www.harrisbar.com
Steel Reinforced Concrete Mfr
N.A.I.C.S.: 327390

Harris Rebar Carson City, Inc   **(3)**
70 Linehan Rd, Carson City, NV 89706
Tel.: (775) 246-8622
Web Site: http://www.harrisrebar.com
Sales Range: $25-49.9 Million
Emp.: 75
Mfr of Concrete Reinforced Steel
N.A.I.C.S.: 331221

Harris Rebar Seattle, Inc.   **(3)**
4421 192nd St, Tacoma, WA 98466
Tel.: (253) 847-5001
Web Site: http://www.harrisrebar.com
Sales Range: $100-124.9 Million
Emp.: 100
Mfr of Concrete Reinforced Steel
N.A.I.C.S.: 332919

Harris Salinas Rebar , Inc.   **(3)**
355 S Vasco Rd, Livermore, CA 94550
Tel.: (925) 373-0733
Web Site: http://www.harrisrebar.com
Sales Range: $125-149.9 Million
Mfr of Concrete Reinforced Steel
N.A.I.C.S.: 332919

Harris/Arizona Rebar, Inc.   **(3)**
2101 W Jackson St, Phoenix, AZ 85009
Tel.: (602) 254-0091
Web Site: http://www.harrisrebar.com
Sales Range: $100-124.9 Million
Emp.: 75
Mfr of Concrete Reinforced Steel
N.A.I.C.S.: 332919
Bill Dicker *(Pres)*

Subsidiary (Domestic):

Laurel Steel Limited   **(2)**
5400 Harvester Road, Burlington, L7L 5N5, ON, Canada
Tel.: (905) 681-6811
Web Site: http://www.laurelsteel.com
Sales Range: $100-124.9 Million
Emp.: 210
Mfr of Free-machining Steel
N.A.I.C.S.: 337215

Harris Steel ULC   **(1)**
4120 Yonge Street Suite 404 North York, Toronto, M2P 2B8, ON, Canada
Tel.: (416) 590-9549
Emp.: 2,284
Steel Fabrication Services
N.A.I.C.S.: 332312

Independence Tube Corporation   **(1)**
6226 W 74th St, Chicago, IL 60638
Tel.: (708) 496-0380
Web Site:
  http://www.independencetube.com
Steel Pipe & Tubes Mfr
N.A.I.C.S.: 331210

Nucor Building Systems   **(1)**

305 Industrial Pkwy, Waterloo, IN 46793-9498
Tel.: (260) 837-7891
Web Site:
  http://www.nucorbuildingsystems.com
Sales Range: $75-99.9 Million
Emp.: 280
Pre-Engineered Metal Building Systems Mfr
N.A.I.C.S.: 236220
Scott Cassel *(Controller)*
Jason Liegl *(Mgr-Engrg)*
Sean Dunwoody *(Production Mgr)*
Clint Bell *(Reg Sls Mgr-Northeast)*
Jeff Brasseur *(Reg Sls Mgr-Western Great Lakes)*
Mark VanDyken *(Gen Mgr)*
Sal Perrera *(Sls Mgr)*
A. J. Byerley *(Mgr-Sls Svc)*

Subsidiary (Domestic):

American Buildings Company   **(2)**
1150 State Docks Rd, Eufaula, AL 36027
Tel.: (334) 687-2032
Web Site:
  https://www.americanbuildings.com
Sales Range: $100-124.9 Million
Metal Building Systems
N.A.I.C.S.: 332311
Greg Kuebrich *(Mgr-Builder Svcs)*
Brad Yocum *(Sls Mgr)*

CBC Steel Buildings   **(2)**
1700 E Louise Ave, Lathrop, CA 95330
Tel.: (209) 983-0910
Web Site:
  https://www.cbcsteelbuildings.com
Sales Range: $100-124.9 Million
Steel Building Mfr
N.A.I.C.S.: 332311
Darin Gardner *(Gen Mgr)*

Kirby Building Systems, Inc.   **(2)**
124 Kirby Dr, Portland, TN 37148
Tel.: (615) 325-4165
Web Site:
  http://www.kirbybuildingsystems.com
Sales Range: $75-99.9 Million
Emp.: 200
Pre-Engineered Metal Buildings Mfr
N.A.I.C.S.: 332311
Mark Specht *(Gen Mgr)*
Chris Fuselier *(Mgr-Engrg)*
Tyler Embrey *(Controller)*

Nucor Building Systems Utah LLC   **(1)**
1050 N Watery Ln, Brigham City, UT 84302
Steel Building Mfr
N.A.I.C.S.: 332311
Alan Johnson *(Gen Mgr)*
Jacob Weaver *(Reg Sls Mgr)*
Dustin Palmer *(Sls Mgr-Svc)*
Yakov Filipets *(Mgr-Engrg)*
Travis Skeen *(Production Mgr)*

Nucor Castrip Arkansas LLC   **(1)**
5929 E State Hwy 18, Blytheville, AR 72315
Tel.: (870) 762-5500
Steel Products Mfr
N.A.I.C.S.: 331110
Gary McQuillis *(Mgr)*

Nucor Cold Finish Wisconsin, Inc.   **(1)**
7200 S 6th St, Oak Creek, WI 53154
Steel Products Mfr
N.A.I.C.S.: 332999

Nucor Cold Finish-Nebraska   **(1)**
2301 W Omaha Ave, Norfolk, NE 68702-0059
Tel.: (402) 644-8600
Web Site: http://www.nucorcoldfinish.com
Sales Range: $25-49.9 Million
Emp.: 103
Carbon, Leaded & Alloy Cold Drawn Steel Bar Mfr
N.A.I.C.S.: 331221

Nucor Cold Finish-South Carolina   **(1)**
2800 N Governors William Hwy, Darlington, SC 29540
Tel.: (843) 395-8689
Web Site: http://www.nucorcoldfinish.com
Sales Range: $25-49.9 Million
Emp.: 47
Carbon, Leaded & Alloy Cold Drawn Steel Bar Mfr

Nucor Corporation—(Continued)
N.A.I.C.S.: 331221

Nucor Energy Holdings Inc (1)
1915 Rexford Rd, Charlotte, NC 28211
Tel.: (704) 366-7000
Emp.: 5
Iron & Steel Mill Operator
N.A.I.C.S.: 331110

Nucor Fasteners (1)
6730 CR 60, Saint Joe, IN
46785-9741 **(100%)**
Tel.: (260) 337-1600
Web Site: http://www.nucor-fastener.com
Sales Range: $100-124.9 Million
Emp.: 217
Alloy & Carbon Steel Screws, Nuts & Bolts Mfr
N.A.I.C.S.: 332722
Aaron Palkovic (Sls Mgr)
Amy Upp (Supvr-Inside Sls)

Nucor Steel - Arkansas (1)
7301 E County Rd 142, Blytheville, AR
72315-6917
Tel.: (870) 762-2100
Web Site: http://www.nucorar.com
Flat Rolled Steel Plate & Coil Mfr
N.A.I.C.S.: 331221

Nucor Steel Auburn, Inc. (1)
25 Quarry Rd, Auburn, NY 13021-2008
Tel.: (315) 253-4561
Web Site: http://www.nucorauburn.com
Sales Range: $50-74.9 Million
Emp.: 200
Steel Rebar & Flat Rolled Steel Products Mfr
N.A.I.C.S.: 331110
Maryemily Slate (Gen Mgr)

Nucor Steel Birmingham, Inc. (1)
2301 F L Shuttlesworth Dr, Birmingham, AL
35234-1335
Tel.: (205) 250-7400
Web Site: http://www.nucorbar.com
Sales Range: $50-74.9 Million
Emp.: 187
Steel Rebar & Other Steel Products Mfr
N.A.I.C.S.: 331110

Nucor Steel Connecticut Inc. (1)
35 Toelles Rd, Wallingford, CT 06492
Tel.: (203) 265-0615
Steel Wire Rod Mfr & Distr
N.A.I.C.S.: 331222

Nucor Steel Decatur, LLC (1)
4301 Iverson Blvd, Trinity, AL 35673
Tel.: (256) 301-3500
Web Site: http://www.nucor-sheetmills.com
Sales Range: $150-199.9 Million
Emp.: 700
Hot & Cold Flat Rolled Steel Mfr
N.A.I.C.S.: 331221
John Sacco (Mgr-Sls & Mktg)

Nucor Steel Gallatin, LLC (1)
4831 US Hwy 42 W, Ghent, KY 41045-9704
Tel.: (859) 567-3100
Web Site: http://www.nucor.com
Emp.: 500
Flat-Rolled Carbon Steel Mfr
N.A.I.C.S.: 331221

Nucor Steel Jackson, Inc. (1)
3630 4th St, Flowood, MS 39232
Tel.: (601) 939-1623
Web Site: http://www.nucor.com
Steel Rebar & Other Steel Products Mfr
N.A.I.C.S.: 324199

Nucor Steel Kankakee, Inc. (1)
1 Nucor Way, Bourbonnais, IL
60914 **(100%)**
Web Site: http://www.nucorbar.com
Sales Range: $75-99.9 Million
Emp.: 300
Steel Rebar & Other Steel Products Mfr
N.A.I.C.S.: 331110

Nucor Steel Kingman, LLC (1)
3000 W Historic Rte 66, Kingman, AZ
86413
Tel.: (928) 718-7035
Iron & Steel Mill Operator
N.A.I.C.S.: 331110
Coreena Frashefski (Product Mgr-Rod)

Nucor Steel Longview LLC (1)
5400 W Loop 281, Longview, TX 75603
Steel Products Mfr
N.A.I.C.S.: 332999

Nucor Steel Louisiana LLC (1)
9101 Hwy 3125, Convent, LA 70723
Tel.: (225) 331-4000
Web Site: http://www.nucor.com
Metal Mining Services
N.A.I.C.S.: 332312

Nucor Steel Marion, Inc. (1)
912 Cheney Ave, Marion, OH 43302-6208
Tel.: (740) 383-4011
Web Site: http://www.nucor.com
Steel Rebar & Other Steel Products Mfr
N.A.I.C.S.: 331110
Brenda Schulz (Controller)

Nucor Steel Memphis, Inc. (1)
3601 Paul R Lowry Rd, Memphis, TN
38109
Tel.: (901) 786-5900
Web Site: http://www.nucor.com
Sales Range: $50-74.9 Million
Emp.: 4
Special Steel Bar & Other Steel Products Mfr
N.A.I.C.S.: 331110

Nucor Steel Seattle, Inc. (1)
2424 SW Andover St, Seattle, WA
98106-1100 **(100%)**
Tel.: (206) 933-2222
Web Site: http://www.nucorbar.com
Steel Rebar & Other Steel Products Mfr
N.A.I.C.S.: 331110

Nucor Steel Tuscaloosa, Inc. (1)
1700 Holt Rd, Tuscaloosa, AL 35404
Tel.: (205) 556-1310
Web Site: http://www.nucortusk.com
Sales Range: $250-299.9 Million
Emp.: 400
Carbon, High Strength Low Alloy & Pressure Vessel Steel Products Mfr
N.A.I.C.S.: 331110
Randy Charles (Mgr-Sls)
Chris Brubeck (Mgr-Maintenance & Engrg)
Jerrell Vinson (Mgr-District Sls-TX & LA)
Lisa McCollum (Product Mgr)
Al Smith (Mgr-Material Handling)
Mark Atkins (Mgr-Product)
Adam Tiller (Mgr-District Sls-GA, FL, NC, SC & Eastern TN)
Bill Dehaven (Mgr-District Sls-NE, IA, KS & MO)
Sukhi Kohli (Mgr-District Sls-TX & LA)
Nicole Montalto (Coord-E-Commerce)
Reed Norris (Controller)
Reed Raggio (Mgr-Environmental)
Michael Mayhall (Mgr-Melting & Casting)
Donnie Spencer (Supvr-Customer Svc)
Matthew Brooks (Gen Mgr)

Nucor Steel-Berkeley (1)
1455 Hagan Ave, Huger, SC 29450
Tel.: (843) 336-6000
Web Site: http://www.nucorsteel.com
Sales Range: $150-199.9 Million
Carbon Steel Sheet & Beam Mfr
N.A.I.C.S.: 331110

Nucor Steel-Indiana (1)
4537 S Nucor Rd, Crawfordsville, IN 47933
Tel.: (765) 364-1323
Web Site: http://www.nucor.com
Sales Range: $350-399.9 Million
Emp.: 800
Carbon & Stainless Flat Rolled Steel Plate & Coil Mfr
N.A.I.C.S.: 331110

Nucor Steel-Nebraska (1)
2911 E Nucor Rd, Norfolk, NE 68701-9634
Tel.: (402) 644-0200
Web Site: http://www.nucor.com
Steel Rebar & Other Steel Products Mfr
N.A.I.C.S.: 331110

Nucor Steel-South Carolina (1)
300 Steel Mill Rd, Darlington, SC 29540
Tel.: (843) 393-5841
Web Site: http://www.nucor.com
Steel Rebar, Merchant Bar & Specialty Bar Mfr
N.A.I.C.S.: 324199

Nucor Steel-Texas (1)

8812 Hwy 79 W, Jewett, TX 75846
Tel.: (903) 626-4461
Web Site: http://www.nucor.com
Steel Rebar & Other Steel Products Mfr
N.A.I.C.S.: 331110

Nucor Steel-Utah (1)
7285 W21200N W Cemetery Rd, Plymouth,
UT 84330
Tel.: (435) 458-2326
Web Site: http://www.nucor.com
Steel Rebar & Other Steel Products Mfr
N.A.I.C.S.: 331110

**Nucor Tubular Products Madison
LLC** (1)
4004 N US 421, Madison, IN 47250
Tel.: (812) 265-9255
Steel Products Mfr
N.A.I.C.S.: 332999

Nucor Tubular Products, Inc. (1)
6226 W 74th St, Chicago, IL 60638
Tel.: (708) 496-0380
Web Site: https://www.nucortubular.com
Steel Products Mfr
N.A.I.C.S.: 331110

Nucor-LMP Inc. (1)
2000 E 1st St, Maryville, MO 64468
Tel.: (660) 582-3127
Steel Products Mfr
N.A.I.C.S.: 332999

Nucor-Yamato Steel Company (1)
PO Box 1228, Blytheville, AR 72316
Tel.: (870) 762-5500
Web Site: https://www.nucoryamato.com
Sales Range: $350-399.9 Million
Emp.: 800
Structural Steel Products Mfr; Owned by
Nucor Corporation & Yamato Kogyo Co.
Ltd.
N.A.I.C.S.: 331110
Keith Prevost (Controller)
Les Jackson (Mgr-Environmental)
Rick Ramsdell (Mgr-Maintenance)
Jon McCauley (Mgr-Melt Shop)
Mike Dugan (Mgr-Rolling Ops)
Gary Crouch (Mgr-Sls)

Republic Conduit Inc. (1)
7301 Logistics Dr, Louisville, KY 40258
Tel.: (502) 995-5900
Web Site: http://www.nucortubular.com
Iron, Steel Pipe & Tube Mfr
N.A.I.C.S.: 331210

Skyline Steel, LLC (1)
1715 Hwy 35 Ste 209, Middletown, NJ
07748 **(100%)**
Tel.: (732) 671-5900
Web Site: http://www.nucorskyline.com
Emp.: 9
Structural Steel Products Mfr & Distr
N.A.I.C.S.: 332312

Southland Tube, Inc. (1)
3525 Richard Arrington Jr Blvd N, Birmingham, AL 35234-2307
Tel.: (205) 251-1884
Iron & Steel Pipe Mfr
N.A.I.C.S.: 331110

St. Louis Cold Drawn LLC (1)
1060 Pershall Rd, Saint Louis, MO 63137
Tel.: (314) 867-4301
Silo Mfr
N.A.I.C.S.: 331222
Annie You (VP)

Summit Utility Structures, LLC (1)
2027 S 12th St Bldg 5, Allentown, PA
18103-4719
Tel.: (610) 797-2225
Web Site:
http://www.summitutilitystructures.com
Fabricated Structural Metal Mfr
N.A.I.C.S.: 332312
Lew Grant (Partner & VP)

The David J. Joseph Company (1)
300 Pike St, Cincinnati, OH 45202
Tel.: (513) 419-6200
Web Site: http://www.djj.com
Emp.: 55
Metal Scrap Recycling & Brokerage Services; Railcar Rental & Leasing
N.A.I.C.S.: 423930
Craig A. Feldman (Pres)
Christopher J. Bedell (Gen Counsel & Sr VP)

Mark Schaefer (Exec VP-Brokerage & Svcs)
David Steigerwald (Exec VP-Recycling Grp)
Karen Luther (Sr VP-Employee Svcs)
Kelly Poellein (Sr VP-Fin)

Subsidiary (Domestic):

**Advantage Metals Recycling,
LLC** (2)
3005 Manchester Trafficway, Kansas City,
MO 64129 **(100%)**
Tel.: (816) 922-5100
Web Site:
http://www.advantagerecycling.com
Sales Range: $400-449.9 Million
Scrap Metal Recycling Services
N.A.I.C.S.: 562920
Jeff Davis (Pres)
John Rakos (VP-Comml)
Jeremy McRoberts (VP-Fin)
Dale Shaw (VP-Ops)

River Metals Recycling LLC (2)
334 Beechwood Rd Ste 401, Fort Mitchell,
KY 41017
Tel.: (859) 292-8400
Web Site: http://www.rmrecycling.com
Scrap Metal Recycling Services
N.A.I.C.S.: 541614
Bob Eviston (Pres)
Brian Lappin (VP-Fin)
Steve Winters (VP-Ops)
Phil Thompson (VP-Comml)
Kathy Kirn (Dir-HR)

Subsidiary (Domestic):

Recycling Asset Holdings, Inc. (3)
7100 Grade Ln, Louisville, KY 40213
Tel.: (502) 366-3452
Rev.: $61,023,000
Assets: $22,480,000
Liabilities: $11,466,000
Net Worth: $11,014,000
Earnings: ($349,000)
Emp.: 83
Fiscal Year-end: 12/31/2018
Recycling, Scrap, Waste Management &
Recycling Services
N.A.I.C.S.: 541614
Vincent J. Tyra (Chm)
Todd L. Phillips (Pres, CEO & CFO)
Jason McCorkle (Mgr-Ops-Ferrous & Non-Ferrous Grade Lane & Logistics)
Keith McDonough (Mgr-Ops-Outlying Facilities)
Mark Mullen (Mgr-Mktg-Comml Sls & Scrap Procurement)
Tom Ashby (Mgr-IT, QEHS, Pick Pull Save & Electronics Scrap)
Todd Clark (Mgr-Maintenance)

Subsidiary (Domestic):

WESSCO, LLC (4)
7100 Grade Ln, Louisville, KY
40213-3424 **(100%)**
Tel.: (502) 214-7218
Web Site: http://www.isa-inc.com
Sales Range: $25-49.9 Million
Emp.: 12
Solid Waste Equipment Sales-wholesale &
Retail
N.A.I.C.S.: 423930

Subsidiary (Domestic):

**Trademark Metals Recycling
LLC** (2)
The Lincoln Ctr 5401 W Kennedy Blvd Ste
400, Tampa, FL 33609
Tel.: (813) 247-3619
Web Site: http://www.tmrecycling.com
Scrap Metal Processing & Recycling
N.A.I.C.S.: 423930
Brian Phillippi (Pres)
Karen Alsept (Dir-HR)
John Bianculli (Mgr-Govt Rels)
Chester Jones (VP-Ops)
Clint Rice (VP)
Patrick Fuller (VP)

TrueCore, LLC (1)
801 Hunter Industrial Park Rd, Laurens, SC
29360
Tel.: (864) 300-4131
Web Site: https://www.truecorepanels.com
Insulated Metal Panel Mfr
N.A.I.C.S.: 332311

Universal Industrial Gases, LLC (1)
3001 Emrick Blvd Ste 320, Bethlehem, PA 18020
Tel.: (610) 559-7967
Web Site: https://www.uigi.com
Industrial Gas System Mfr & Distr
N.A.I.C.S.: 333132

Vulcraft of New York, Inc. (1)
621 Main St, Waverly, NY 14892
Tel.: (607) 529-9000
Steel Products Mfr
N.A.I.C.S.: 332999

Vulcraft-Alabama (1)
7205 Gault Ave N, Fort Payne, AL 35967 (100%)
Tel.: (256) 845-2460
Web Site: http://www.vulcraft.com
Sales Range: $150-199.9 Million
Emp.: 300
Structural Steel Building Components Mfr
N.A.I.C.S.: 332312
Christina Wenzel (Project Mgr)

Vulcraft-Indiana (1)
6610 County Rd 60, Saint Joe, IN 46785
Tel.: (260) 337-1800
Web Site: http://www.vulcraft.com
Sales Range: $100-124.9 Million
Emp.: 300
Structural Steel Building Components Mfr
N.A.I.C.S.: 332312
Kyle Tom (Project Mgr)

Vulcraft-Nebraska (1)
1601 W Omaha Ave, Norfolk, NE 68701 (100%)
Tel.: (402) 644-8500
Web Site: http://www.vulcraft.com
Sales Range: $150-199.9 Million
Emp.: 450
Structural Steel Building Components Mfr
N.A.I.C.S.: 332312

Vulcraft-South Carolina (1)
1501 W Darlington St, Florence, SC 29501-2100
Tel.: (843) 662-0381
Web Site: http://www.vulcraft.com
Sales Range: $100-124.9 Million
Emp.: 350
Structural Steel Building Components Mfr
N.A.I.C.S.: 332312

Vulcraft-Texas (1)
175 County Rd 2345, Grapeland, TX 75844
Tel.: (936) 687-4665
Web Site: http://www.vulcraft.com
Sales Range: $150-199.9 Million
Emp.: 300
Structural Steel Building Components Mfr
N.A.I.C.S.: 332312
Kris Lee (Mgr-Sls)
Sam Box (District Sls Mgr)
Justin Cunningham (Project Mgr)

Vulcraft-Utah (1)
I 15 Corrine 1875 W Hwy 13, Brigham City, UT 84302
Tel.: (435) 734-9433
Web Site: http://www.vulcraft.com
Sales Range: $100-124.9 Million
Emp.: 320
Structural Steel Building Components Mfr
N.A.I.C.S.: 332312
Skip Rice (Project Mgr)

NUGL, INC.
13771 Roswell Ave Ste F, Chino, CA 91710
Tel.: (714) 383-9982   OK
Web Site: https://nugl.com
Year Founded: 2017
NUGL—(OTCIQ)
Other Farm Product Raw Material Merchant Wholesalers
N.A.I.C.S.: 424590

NUKKLEUS INC.
525 Washington Blvd 14th Fl, Jersey City, NJ 07310
Tel.: (212) 791-4663   DE
Web Site: https://www.nukk.com
Year Founded: 2013
NUKK—(NASDAQ)
Rev.: $21,297,642

Assets: $3,352,625
Liabilities: $9,545,855
Net Worth: ($6,193,230)
Earnings: ($17,428,428)
Emp.: 12
Fiscal Year-end: 09/30/23
Investment Services
N.A.I.C.S.: 523999
Jamal Khurshid (CEO)
Emil Assentato (Interim CFO)

Subsidiaries:

Brilliant Acquisition Corporation (1)
99 Dan Ba Road C-9, Putuo District, Shanghai, 200062, China
Tel.: (86) 2180125497
Rev.: $234,785
Assets: $6,111,545
Liabilities: $10,031,509
Net Worth: ($3,919,964)
Earnings: ($967,614)
Emp.: 1
Fiscal Year-end: 12/31/2022
Investment Services
N.A.I.C.S.: 523999

Digital RFQ Ltd. (1)
Dawson House 5 Jewry Street, London, EC3N 2EX, United Kingdom
Tel.: (44) 2033181818
Web Site: https://digitalrfq.com
Escrow & Custody Services
N.A.I.C.S.: 523991
Jamal Khurshid (Co-Founder)
Craig Vallis (Co-Founder)
Mike Greenacre (Co-Founder)

NUNZIA PHARMACEUTICAL CORPORATION
1627 W 14th St, Long Beach, CA 90813
Tel.: (714) 609-9117   UT
Web Site:
  http://www.nunziapharma.com
Year Founded: 1986
NUNZ—(OTCIQ)
Assets: $5,131
Liabilities: $99,305
Net Worth: ($94,174)
Earnings: ($78,062,770)
Fiscal Year-end: 12/31/21
Gold Exploration & Mining Services
N.A.I.C.S.: 212220

NUO THERAPEUTICS, INC.
8285 El Rio St Ste 190, Houston, TX 77054
Tel.: (346) 396-4770   DE
Web Site: https://www.nuot.com
AURX—(OTCQB)
Rev.: $112,250
Assets: $3,047,360
Liabilities: $856,022
Net Worth: $2,191,338
Earnings: ($3,171,736)
Emp.: 10
Fiscal Year-end: 12/31/22
Biotechnology Research Services & Biological Product Mfr
N.A.I.C.S.: 325414

Subsidiaries:

Aldagen, Inc. (1)
2810 Meridian Pkwy Ste 148, Durham, NC 27713 (100%)
Tel.: (919) 484-2571
Web Site: http://www.aldagen.com
Biopharmaceutical Researcher, Developer & Mfr
N.A.I.C.S.: 325412

NURISH.ME, INC.
888 Prospect St Ste 200, La Jolla, CA 92037
Web Site: http://www.nurish.me
AVOZ—(OTCIQ)
Food Beverage Mfr & Distr
N.A.I.C.S.: 333241
David Perez (CEO)

NURIX THERAPEUTICS, INC.
1700 Owens St Ste 205, San Francisco, CA 94158
Tel.: (415) 660-5320   DE
Web Site: https://www.nurixtx.com
Year Founded: 2009
NRIX—(NASDAQ)
Rev.: $38,627,000
Assets: $416,759,000
Liabilities: $113,063,000
Net Worth: $303,696,000
Earnings: ($180,360,000)
Emp.: 297
Fiscal Year-end: 11/30/22
Biotechnology Research & Development Services
N.A.I.C.S.: 541714
Arthur T. Sands (Pres & CEO)
Eric Schlezinger (Chief People Officer)
Christine Ring (Gen Counsel & Gen Counsel)
Pierre Beaurang (Chief Bus Officer)
Gwenn Hansen (Chief Scientific Officer)
Hans van Houte (CFO)
Michael T. Lotze (Chief Cellular Therapy Officer)
Jason Kantor (Sr VP-Fin & Investment Strategy)
Robert J. Brown (Sr Vp-Clinical Dev)
Cristiana Guiducci (Sr VP-Immunology & Oncology Research)
Dane Karr (VP)
Daisy Chhokar (VP-Human Resources)
John Kuriyan (Co-Founder)
Michael Rape (Co-Founder)
Arthur Weiss (Co-Founder)
Michael Blackton (Sr VP)
Buckley Kohlhauff (Sr VP-Information Technology)
Michael Mischke-Reeds (Sr VP-Strategy)
Frederick Cohen (VP)
Su Young Kim (VP)
Raf Lambrecht (VP & Head-Regulatory Affairs)
James Nelson (VP-Quality Assurance)
Christopher B. Phelps (VP & Head)
Janine Powers (VP & Head)
Seema P. Rogers (VP & Head)
Kim Trahan (VP & Head)
Ena Wang (VP-Product Development)
Pasit Phiasivongsa (Sr VP)
Paula G. O'Connor (Sr VP)
Bev Benson (VP)
Eren Demirhan (VP)
Jen Dolan (VP)
Marine Champsaur (VP)

NUTANIX, INC.
1740 Technology Dr Ste 150, San Jose, CA 95110
Tel.: (408) 216-8360   DE
Web Site: https://www.nutanix.com
Year Founded: 2009
NTNX—(NASDAQ)
Rev.: $2,148,816,000
Assets: $2,143,918,000
Liabilities: $2,872,066,000
Net Worth: ($728,148,000)
Earnings: ($124,775,000)
Emp.: 7,150
Fiscal Year-end: 07/31/24
Cloud-Based Data Storage Services
N.A.I.C.S.: 518210
Rajiv Ramaswami (Pres & CEO)
Shyam Desirazu (Head-Engineering)
Tonya Chin (VP-IR & Corp Comm)
Benjamin Gibson (CMO)
Sankalp Saxena (Sr VP & Mng Dir-Operations)
Rukmini Sivaraman (CFO)

Mandy Dhaliwal (CMO)
Dheeraj Pandey (Founder)
Tarkan Maner (Chief Comml Officer)
Matt Maw (Dir-Channels-Australia & New Zealand)
Andrew Brinded (Chief Revenue Officer)
Monique Hyndman (Sr Mgr-Channel & Alliances-Australia & New Zealand)
Aaron Kelly (Sls Mgr-Distr-Australia & New Zealand)

Subsidiaries:

Nutanix Netherlands B. V. (1)
Mercuriusplein 1, 2132 HA, Hoofddorp, Netherlands
Tel.: (31) 238080243
Web Site: http://www.nutanix.nl
Cloud-Based Data Storage Services
N.A.I.C.S.: 518210

NUTECH ENERGY RESOURCES, INC.
3250 Oakland Hills, Fairfield, CA 94534
Tel.: (307) 920-3410
NERG—(OTCIQ)
Natural Gas Distribution Services
N.A.I.C.S.: 221210
Kevin Trizna (CEO)

NUTEX HEALTH INC.
6030 S Rice Ste C, Houston, TX 77081
Tel.: (713) 660-0557   DE
Web Site:
  https://www.nutexhealth.com
Year Founded: 2000
NUTX—(NASDAQ)
Rev.: $219,294,306
Assets: $431,751,985
Liabilities: $311,424,585
Net Worth: $120,327,400
Earnings: ($424,780,446)
Emp.: 1,150
Fiscal Year-end: 12/31/22
Holding Company; Health Care Data Analysis Software Developer
N.A.I.C.S.: 551112
Elisa Luqman (Gen Counsel & Exec VP-Fin)
Joshua DeTillio (COO)
Warren Hosseinion (Chm & CEO)
Charles Kandzierski (COO-Clinigence Health Inc)
Fred Sternberg (Pres)
Michael Bowen (CFO)
Andrew Barnett (Exec VP-Corp Dev)

Subsidiaries:

Clinigence, LLC (1)
55 Ivan Allen Jr Blvd NW Ste 875, Atlanta, GA 30308
Tel.: (678) 466-6650
Web Site: http://www.clinigence.com
Software Publisher
N.A.I.C.S.: 513210
Jacob Margolin (Co-Founder & CEO)

HealthDatix, Inc. (1)
501 1st Ave N Ste 901, Saint Petersburg, FL 33701
Tel.: (727) 828-0404
Web Site: https://www.healthdatix.com
Health Care Data Analysis Software Developer & Publisher
N.A.I.C.S.: 513210
Jerry Robinson (Pres)

NUTRA PHARMA CORP.
6400 Park of Commerce Blvd Ste 1B, Boca Raton, FL 33487
Tel.: (954) 509-0911   CA
Web Site:
  https://www.nutrapharma.com
Year Founded: 2000

Nutra Pharma Corp.—(Continued)

NPHC—(OTCEM)
Rev.: $97,735
Assets: $780,022
Liabilities: $21,657,672
Net Worth: ($20,877,650)
Earnings: ($13,095,521)
Emp.: 4
Fiscal Year-end: 12/31/21
Pharmaceuticals Mfr
N.A.I.C.S.: 325412
Dale Vanderputten *(Chief Scientific Officer)*
Michael Flax *(Chm, CEO & CFO)*
Rik J. Deitsch *(Ops Mgr)*

NUTRALIFE BIOSCIENCES, INC.

6601 Lyons Rd, Coconut Creek, FL 33073 **FL**
Web Site:
https://www.nutralifebioscien
ces.com
Year Founded: 2010
NLBS—(OTCIQ)
Rev.: $1,255,784
Assets: $4,706,708
Liabilities: $4,405,598
Net Worth: $301,110
Earnings: ($2,889,940)
Emp.: 14
Fiscal Year-end: 12/31/20
Oral Nutritional Spray & Dietary Products Mfr & Distr
N.A.I.C.S.: 325412
Edgar Ward *(Pres, CEO & Founder)*
Neil M. Catania *(VP)*

Subsidiaries:

PhytoChem Technologies, Inc. **(1)**
6601 Lyons Rd Unit L-6, Coconut Creek, FL 33073
Web Site: http://www.phytochemtech.com
Farm Management Services
N.A.I.C.S.: 115116
Zachary Trimble *(Ops Mgr)*
Edgar Ward *(Pres & CEO)*
Owen J. Morgan *(Engr-Tech)*

NUTRANOMICS INC.

605 Portland Ave Unit 154, Gladstone, OR 97027
Tel.: (408) 495-3142 **NV**
Web Site:
http://www.nutranomics.com
Year Founded: 2007
NNRX—(OTCIQ)
Rev.: $59,000
Assets: $29,000
Liabilities: $6,389,000
Net Worth: ($6,360,000)
Earnings: ($2,238,000)
Fiscal Year-end: 07/31/19
Nutritional Supplements
N.A.I.C.S.: 325412
Jonathan Bishop *(Chm & CEO)*

NUTRI PHARMACEUTICALS RESEARCH, INC.

6780 Caballo St, Las Vegas, NV 89119
Tel.: (702) 479-1028 **NV**
Web Site: http://www.o2pus.com
Year Founded: 1994
NRPR—(OTCIQ)
Food Ingredient Mfr
N.A.I.C.S.: 311999
Godfrey Yew *(Pres & CEO)*

NUTRIBAND INC.

121 S Orange Ave Ste 1500, Orlando, FL 32801
Tel.: (407) 377-6695 **NV**
Web Site: https://www.nutriband.com
Year Founded: 2016

NTRB—(NASDAQ)
Rev.: $2,079,609
Assets: $9,456,377
Liabilities: $883,387
Net Worth: $8,572,990
Earnings: ($4,483,474)
Emp.: 13
Fiscal Year-end: 01/31/23
Healthcare Products Mfr & Distr
N.A.I.C.S.: 325412
Gerald Goodman *(CFO & Chief Acctg Officer)*
Serguei Melnik *(Co-Founder, Chm & Pres)*
Gareth Sheridan *(Co-Founder & CEO)*
Alan Smith *(COO & Pres-4P Therapeutics)*
Jeff Patrick *(Chief Scientific Officer)*
Tyler Overk *(Head-Active Intelligence)*

Subsidiaries:

Pocono Pharmaceuticals Inc. **(1)**
100 Sweetree St, Cherryville, NC 28021
Tel.: (803) 560-0433
Web Site: https://poconopharma.com
Transdermal Patch Mfr
N.A.I.C.S.: 325412

NUTRITION MANAGEMENT SERVICES COMPANY

2071 Kimberton Rd, Kimberton, PA 19442
Tel.: (610) 935-2050 **PA**
Web Site: https://www.nmsc.com
Year Founded: 1979
NMSCA—(OTCIQ)
Food Service Contractors
N.A.I.C.S.: 722310
Joseph V. Roberts *(CEO)*
Kathleen A. Hill *(Pres & COO)*

NUTROGANICS, INC.

6701 Democracy Blvd Ste 300, Bethesda, MD 20817
Tel.: (301) 571-9392 **DE**
Year Founded: 1989
NUTTQ—(OTCIQ)
Packaged Food Mfr & Distr
N.A.I.C.S.: 311999
David Sackler *(CEO)*
Douglas A. Scott Jr. *(CFO)*
Jay Wright *(Chm)*

NUVALENT, INC.

1 Broadway 14th Fl, Cambridge, MA 02142
Tel.: (857) 357-7000 **DE**
Web Site: https://www.nuvalent.com
Year Founded: 2017
NUVL—(NASDAQ)
Rev.: $4,254,000
Assets: $482,459,000
Liabilities: $19,481,000
Net Worth: $462,978,000
Earnings: ($81,854,000)
Emp.: 62
Fiscal Year-end: 12/31/22
Biotechnology Research & Development Services
N.A.I.C.S.: 541714
Anna Protopapas *(Chm)*
James Porter *(CEO)*
Ruth Adams *(VP-Clinical Ops)*
Alex Balcom *(CFO)*
Joshua Horan *(VP-Chemistry)*
Benjamin Lane *(Sr VP-Technical Ops)*
Deb Miller *(Chief Legal Officer)*
Darlene Noci *(Chief Dev Officer)*
Henry Pelish *(VP-Biology)*
John Soglia *(VP-Translational Dev)*
Christopher Turner *(Chief Medical Officer)*

NUVATION BIO INC.

1500 Broadway Ste 1401, New York, NY 10036
Tel.: (332) 208-6102 **DE**
Web Site:
https://www.nuvationbio.com
Year Founded: 2018
NUVB—(NYSE)
Rev.: $15,535,000
Assets: $672,141,000
Liabilities: $17,065,000
Net Worth: $655,076,000
Earnings: ($104,199,000)
Emp.: 53
Fiscal Year-end: 12/31/22
Pharmaceutical Preparation Manufacturing
N.A.I.C.S.: 325412
Kerry A. Wentworth *(Chief Regulatory Officer)*
David Hung *(Founder, Pres & CEO)*
David Hanley *(CTO)*
Daniel G. Welch *(Chm)*
David Liu *(Chief Medical Officer)*

NUVECTIS PHARMA, INC.

1 Bridge Plz Ste 275, Fort Lee, NJ 07024
Tel.: (201) 614-3150 **DE**
Web Site: https://nuvectis.com
Year Founded: 2020
NVCT—(NASDAQ)
Rev.: $149,000
Assets: $20,405,000
Liabilities: $6,186,000
Net Worth: $14,219,000
Earnings: ($19,085,000)
Emp.: 11
Fiscal Year-end: 12/31/22
Pharmaceuticals Product Mfr
N.A.I.C.S.: 325412
Ron Bentsur *(Co-Founder, Chm, Pres & CEO)*
Enrique Poradosu *(Co-Founder, Chief Scientific Officer, Chief Bus Officer & Exec VP)*
Shay Shemesh *(Co-Founder, Chief Dev Officer & Exec VP)*
Uri Ben-Or *(CFO)*

NUVERA COMMUNICATIONS, INC.

27 N Minnesota St, New Ulm, MN 56073
Tel.: (507) 354-4111 **MN**
Web Site: https://www.nuvera.net
Year Founded: 1905
NUVR—(OTCQB)
Rev.: $65,714,469
Assets: $217,314,890
Liabilities: $114,733,038
Net Worth: $102,581,852
Earnings: $7,196,702
Emp.: 213
Fiscal Year-end: 12/31/22
Telecommunication Services
N.A.I.C.S.: 517111
Barbara A. J. Bornhoft *(COO, Sec & VP)*
Curtis Owen Kawlewski *(CFO & Treas)*
Glenn H. Zerbe *(Pres & CEO)*

Subsidiaries:

Hector Communications
Corporation **(1)**
Tel.: (507) 354-2500
Holding Company; Local Telecommunication Services
N.A.I.C.S.: 551112

Subsidiary (Non-US):

Eagle Valley Telephone
Company **(2)**
Tel.: (218) 756-2312
Web Site: http://www.eaglevalleytel.net

Sales Range: $10-24.9 Million
Emp.: 1
Telecommunications & Internet Services
N.A.I.C.S.: 517121

Pine Island Telephone Company **(2)**
Tel.: (507) 356-8302
Web Site: http://www.pitel.net
Sales Range: $10-24.9 Million
Emp.: 12
Telephone Services
N.A.I.C.S.: 517111

Sleepy Eye Telephone Company **(2)**
Tel.: (507) 794-3361
Sales Range: $10-24.9 Million
Emp.: 20
Telephone Services
N.A.I.C.S.: 517121

Hutchinson Telephone Company **(1)**
235 Franklin St SW, Hutchinson, MN 55350 **(100%)**
Tel.: (320) 587-2323
Sales Range: $10-24.9 Million
Emp.: 55
Telecommunications & Network Services
N.A.I.C.S.: 517121
Bill D. Otis *(Pres & CEO)*

TechTrends, Inc. **(1)**
15 Berens Blvd, New Ulm, MN 56073
Tel.: (507) 233-3000
Web Site: https://nuveratechtrends.com
Computer Peripheral Equipment Maintenance Services
N.A.I.C.S.: 811210

NUVIM, INC.

18327 Port Cir, Lewes, DE 19958
Tel.: (302) 827-4052 **DE**
Web Site: https://www.nuvim.com
Year Founded: 1999
NUVM—(OTCIQ)
Assets: $4,000
Liabilities: $32,000
Net Worth: ($28,000)
Earnings: ($18,000)
Fiscal Year-end: 12/31/23
Dietary Supplement Beverages Producer, Marketer & Distr
N.A.I.C.S.: 311411
Richard P. Kundrat *(Chm & CEO)*
Michael Maizes *(Sec)*

NUVVE HOLDING CORP.

2488 Historic Decatur Rd Ste 200, San Diego, CA 92106
Tel.: (619) 483-3448 **Ky**
Web Site: https://www.nuvve.com
Year Founded: 2019
NVVE—(NASDAQ)
Rev.: $5,373,383
Assets: $41,199,590
Liabilities: $13,960,946
Net Worth: $27,238,644
Earnings: ($24,018,665)
Emp.: 56
Fiscal Year-end: 12/31/22
Automatic Environmental Control Manufacturing for Residential, Commercial & Appliance Use
N.A.I.C.S.: 334512
David G. Robson *(CFO)*
Gregory Poilasne *(Founder & CEO)*
Tod Smith *(Pres & COO)*

NUWELLIS, INC.

12988 Valley View Rd, Eden Prairie, MN 55344
Tel.: (952) 345-4200 **DE**
Web Site: https://www.nuwellis.com
Year Founded: 2002
NUWE—(NASDAQ)
Rev.: $8,543,000
Assets: $24,673,000
Liabilities: $12,316,000
Net Worth: $12,357,000
Earnings: ($14,525,000)
Emp.: 70
Fiscal Year-end: 12/31/22

Medical Device Mfr
N.A.I.C.S.: 339112
Paul R. Buckman (Co-Founder)
John L. Erb (Chm)
Laurent Duhoux (VP-Bus Dev-Intl)
Nestor Jaramillo Jr. (Pres & CEO)
John Kowalczyk (Sr VP-Sales & Marketing)
Megan Cease (VP-Clinical Res & Reimbursement)
John Jefferies (Chief Medical Officer)
Rob Scott (CFO)

NUZEE, INC.
2865 Scott St Ste 107, Vista, CA 92081
Tel.: (760) 295-2408   NV
Web Site: https://www.mynuzee.com
Year Founded: 2011
NUZE—(NASDAQ)
Rev.: $3,109,162
Assets: $11,711,374
Liabilities: $1,968,575
Net Worth: $9,742,799
Earnings: ($11,797,712)
Emp.: 35
Fiscal Year-end: 09/30/22
Energy Drinks & Skin Care Products
N.A.I.C.S.: 424490
Randell Weaver (Co-Pres, CFO & COO)
Travis Gorney (Chief Innovation Officer & VP-Sls)
Masateru Higashida (Chm, Co-Pres, CEO, Treas & Sec)

NV5 GLOBAL, INC.
200 S Park Rd Ste 350, Hollywood, FL 33021
Tel.: (954) 495-2112   DE
Web Site: https://www.nv5.com
Year Founded: 1947
NVEE—(NASDAQ)
Rev.: $861,739,000
Assets: $1,170,592,000
Liabilities: $394,797,000
Net Worth: $775,795,000
Earnings: $44,613,000
Emp.: 3,813
Fiscal Year-end: 12/30/23
Engineering & Consulting Services; Project Management, Geotechnical, Environmental, Infrastructure & Building Program Management
N.A.I.C.S.: 541330
Dickerson Wright (Chm & CEO)
Alexander A. Hockman (Pres, COO & Dir)
Edward H. Codispoti (CFO)
MaryJo E. O'Brien (Exec VP)

Subsidiaries:

Allwyn Priorities, LLC   (1)
5723 W Larkspur Dr, Glendale, AZ 85304
Tel.: (623) 374-6637
Environmental Consulting Services
N.A.I.C.S.: 541620

Axim Geospatial, LLC   (1)
100 Qbe Way Ste 1225, Sun Prairie, WI 53590
Web Site: https://www.aximgeo.com
Emp.: 360
Geospatial Mapping Services
N.A.I.C.S.: 541370

Bock & Clark Corporation   (1)
3550 W Market St Ste 200, Akron, OH 44333
Tel.: (330) 665-4821
Web Site: http://www.bockandclark.com
Interactive Survey & Project Tracking
N.A.I.C.S.: 541370
Cathleen Straffen (Dir-Project Mgmt-ALTA Svcs)
Jeffrey Echko (Pres)
Scott Scibetta (COO-Survey Branches & Controller)
Julie Whitman (Mgr-Zoning)

Jamie Ziemba (Mgr-Environmental & Assessment Svcs)
Mitch Edwards (Mgr-IT)
Laura Hengle (Dir-Mktg)
James Brown (Natl Dir-Bus Dev)

Chi Engineering Services, Inc.   (1)
430 West Rd, Portsmouth, NH 03801
Tel.: (603) 433-5654
Web Site: https://www.nv5.com
Engineering Services, Nsk
N.A.I.C.S.: 541330

CivilSource, Inc.   (1)
9890 Irvine Center Dr, Irvine, CA 92618
Tel.: (949) 585-0477
Civil Engineering Consulting Services
N.A.I.C.S.: 237990

Dade Moeller and Associates, Inc.   (1)
1835 Terminal Dr Ste 200, Richland, WA 99354
Tel.: (509) 946-0410
Emp.: 260
Environmental Protection & Scientific Services
N.A.I.C.S.: 541990

Energenze Consulting Ltd.   (1)
Unit B 5/F 133 Wai Yip Street Ngau Tau Kok, Kowloon, China (Hong Kong)
Tel.: (852) 21611328
Emp.: 50
Engineering Consulting Services
N.A.I.C.S.: 541330

Energenze Consulting, LLC   (1)
200 S Park Rd Ste 350, Hollywood, FL 33021
Tel.: (954) 495-2112
Web Site: http://www.energenz.com
Engineering Consulting Services
N.A.I.C.S.: 541330
Ben Heraud (CEO)
Gary Hui (COO)

Gaudet Associates, Inc.   (1)
3021 Jupiter Park Circle, Ste 101, Jupiter, FL 33458
Tel.: (561) 748-3040
Web Site: http://www.gaudetassociates.com
Sales Range: $1-9.9 Million
Emp.: 50
Engineering Services, Nsk
N.A.I.C.S.: 541330
Joseph Gaudet (Pres)

GeoDesign, Inc.   (1)
9450 SW Commerce Cir Ste 300, Wilsonville, OR 97070
Tel.: (503) 968-8787
Engineering Consulting Services
N.A.I.C.S.: 541330

JBA Consulting Engineers   (1)
5155 W Patrick Ln, Las Vegas, NV 89118   (100%)
Tel.: (702) 362-9200
Web Site: https://www.nv5.com
Rev.: $7,900,000
Emp.: 200
International Building Consulting & Engineering Services
N.A.I.C.S.: 541330
Ralph Joeckel (Founder)

Subsidiary (Non-US):

JBA Consulting Engineers Shanghai Limited   (2)
Unit 1740 17 F Shanghai CCIG International Plaza, No 331 North Caoxi Road Xuhui, Shanghai, 200030, China
Tel.: (86) 862124225340
Real Estate Manangement Services
N.A.I.C.S.: 531390

JBA Consulting Engineers (Asia) Limited   (1)
Tel.: (853) 28757330
Real Estate Manangement Services
N.A.I.C.S.: 531390

Subsidiary (Non-US):

JBA Consulting Engineers Vietnam Limited Company   (2)
Centec Tower Level 4 Unit 017B 72-74 Nguyen Thi Minh Khai Street, Ward 6 District 3, Ho Chi Minh City, Vietnam

Tel.: (84) 862999425
Real Estate Manangement Services
N.A.I.C.S.: 531390

JBA Consulting Engineers (Asia) Limited   (1)
Unit 2905-08 Pacific Plaza 410 Des Voeux Road West, Hong Kong, China (Hong Kong)
Tel.: (852) 21611328
Engineering Consulting Services
N.A.I.C.S.: 541330
Scott Bailey (Assoc Dir)

Joslin Lesser & Associates, Inc.   (1)
44 Pleasant St, Watertown, MA 02472
Tel.: (617) 744-3110
Web Site: http://www.joslinlesser.com
Engineeering Services
N.A.I.C.S.: 541330

Lochrane Engineering, Inc.   (1)
201 S Bumby Ave, Orlando, FL 32803
Tel.: (407) 896-3317
Web Site: https://www.nv5.com
Engineeering Services
N.A.I.C.S.: 541330
Robert J. Lochrane (Sr Principal)

Marron & Associates, Inc.   (1)
4374 Alexander Blvd NE Ste K, Albuquerque, NM 87107
Tel.: (505) 898-8848
Web Site: http://www.marroninc.com
Business Consulting; Environmental Science & Planning, Natural Resources, Cultural Resources, GIS & MS4 Permitting Programs
N.A.I.C.S.: 541620
Eric Johnson (Sr Project Mgr-Environmental)

NV5 Geospatial Solutions B.V.   (1)
Nassauplein 30, 2585 EC, Hague, Netherlands
Tel.: (31) 703114171
Geospatial Software & Technology Services
N.A.I.C.S.: 541370

NV5 Geospatial Solutions France SARL   (1)
Tour de l Horloge 4 Place Louis Armand, 75603, Paris, Cedex, France
Tel.: (33) 173024620
Geospatial Software & Technology Services
N.A.I.C.S.: 541370

NV5 Geospatial Solutions GmbH   (1)
Talhofstrasse 32A, 82205, Gilching, Germany
Tel.: (49) 81053780
Geospatial Software & Technology Services
N.A.I.C.S.: 541370

NV5 Geospatial Solutions Italia s.r.l.   (1)
Via Salvo D Acquisto 31, 20863, Concorezzo, Italy
Tel.: (39) 0396058605
Geospatial Software & Technology Services
N.A.I.C.S.: 541370

NV5 Geospatial Solutions KK   (1)
Hongo 1-20-3 Nakayama Building 3F, Bunkyo-ku, Tokyo, 113-0033, Japan
Tel.: (81) 368016147
Web Site:
  https://nv5geospatialsoftware.co.jp
Geospatial Software & Technology Services
N.A.I.C.S.: 541370

NV5 Geospatial Solutions UK Limited   (1)
Venture House 2 Arlington Square Downshire Way, Bracknell, RG12 1WA, Berkshire, United Kingdom
Tel.: (44) 1189641500
Geospatial Software & Technology Services
N.A.I.C.S.: 541370

NV5 Geospatial Solutions, Inc.   (1)
385 Interlocken Crescent Ste 300, Broomfield, CO 80021
Tel.: (303) 786-9900
Web Site:
  https://www.nv5geospatialsoftware.com
Geospatial Software & Technology Services
N.A.I.C.S.: 541370

NV5 Ltd.   (1)
133 Wai Yip Street Unit B 5/F Ngau Tau

Kok Kowloon, Hong Kong, China (Hong Kong)
Tel.: (852) 21611328
Engineeering Services
N.A.I.C.S.: 541330

NV5 Malaysia, SDN, BHD   (1)
BO1-B-13A Boutique Offices 1 Menara 2 Kl Eco City No 3 Jalan Bangsar, 59200, Kuala Lumpur, Malaysia
Tel.: (60) 321816268
Building Design Engineering & Consulting Services
N.A.I.C.S.: 541330

NV5 Northeast, Inc.   (1)
308 NW 170th St, Miami, FL 33169
Tel.: (786) 248-3180
Engineeering Services
N.A.I.C.S.: 541330

NV5 West, Inc.   (1)
15092 Ave of Science Ste 200, San Diego, CA 92128
Tel.: (858) 385-0500
Emp.: 200
Engineeering Services
N.A.I.C.S.: 541330

NV5, Inc.   (1)
2015 Westwind Dr Ste 9 10, Bakersfield, CA 93301
Tel.: (661) 325-2699
Emp.: 6
Engineeering Services
N.A.I.C.S.: 541330

NV5, LLC   (1)
800 Lanidex Plz 3rd Fl, Parsippany, NJ 07054
Tel.: (973) 946-5600
Web Site: https://www.nv5.com
Sales Range: $10-24.9 Million
Emp.: 100
Environmental & Engineering Consulting Services
N.A.I.C.S.: 541620

PES Environmental, Inc.   (1)
7665 Redwood Blvd Ste 200, Novato, CA 94945
Tel.: (415) 899-1600
Web Site: http://www.pesenv.com
Sales Range: $1-9.9 Million
Emp.: 40
Engineering Services, Nsk
N.A.I.C.S.: 541330
James Dunn (Publr)
Keith O'Brien (VP-Consulting)

Page One Consultants, Inc.   (1)
5780 Hoffner Ave Ste 401, Orlando, FL 32822
Tel.: (407) 275-5120
Web Site: https://www.nv5.com
Construction & Engineering Services
N.A.I.C.S.: 541330

Red Group (M) Sdn. Bhd.   (1)
1-5-26 No 1 E-Gate Lebuh Tunku Kudin 2, 11700, Gelugor, Penang, Malaysia
Tel.: (60) 46576629
Information Technology Design & Maintenance Services
N.A.I.C.S.: 541512

Red Technologies (S) Pte, Ltd.   (1)
100 Lor 23 Geylang 09-01 D Centennial, Singapore, 388398, Singapore
Tel.: (65) 68461784
Web Site: https://www.redtechgroup.com
Information Technology Design & Maintenance Services
N.A.I.C.S.: 541512

Sage Renewable Energy Consulting, Inc.   (1)
101 Lucas Valley Rd Ste 302, San Rafael, CA 94903
Tel.: (415) 663-9914
Energy Consulting & Management Services
N.A.I.C.S.: 541690

Sebesta, Inc.   (1)
1450 Energy Park Dr Ste 300 E, Saint Paul, MN 55108
Tel.: (651) 634-0775
Web Site: http://www.sebesta.com
Engineering & Design Services
N.A.I.C.S.: 541330

NV5 Global, Inc.—(Continued)

Technical Design Services, Inc (1)
1075 Shore Rd Ste A, Naperville, IL 60563
Tel.: (630) 983-9906
Web Site: https://gotdsi.com
Rev.: $1,000,000
Emp.: 9
Computer System Design Services
N.A.I.C.S.: 541512
Frank Cerchio (Pres)

TerraTech Engineers, Inc. (1)
4905 Professional Ct, Raleigh, NC 27609
Tel.: (919) 876-9799
Web Site:
    http://www.terratechengineers.com
Rev.: $1,300,000
Emp.: 50
Engineeering Services
N.A.I.C.S.: 541330
Erwin Williams (Pres)

The Sextant Group, Inc. (1)
700 Waterfront Dr Ste 200, Pittsburgh, PA
15222
Tel.: (412) 323-8580
Web Site: http://www.thesextantgroup.com
Sales Range: $1-9.9 Million
Emp.: 24
Administrative Management & General
Management Consulting Service
N.A.I.C.S.: 541611
Archibald Cox Jr. (Executives)

Weir Environmental LLC (1)
730 Camp St Unit 1, New Orleans, LA
70130
Tel.: (855) 934-7368
Web Site: http://www.weirenv.com
Environmental Consulting, Industrial Hy-
giene & Flood Services
N.A.I.C.S.: 541620

NVE CORPORATION

11409 Valley View Rd, Eden Prairie,
MN 55344
Tel.: (952) 829-9217   MN
Web Site: https://www.nve.com
Year Founded: 1989
NVEC—(NASDAQ)
Rev.: $38,253,592
Assets: $69,255,170
Liabilities: $2,175,668
Net Worth: $67,079,502
Earnings: $22,694,458
Emp.: 51
Fiscal Year-end: 03/31/23
Spintronic Devices Developer, Mfr &
Sales
N.A.I.C.S.: 334413
Daniel A. Baker (Pres & CEO)
Daniel Nelson (Principal Fin Officer &
Mgr-Acctg)

NVIDIA CORPORATION

2788 San Tomas Expy, Santa Clara,
CA 95051
Tel.: (408) 486-2000   DE
Web Site: https://www.nvidia.com
Year Founded: 1993
NVDA—(NASDAQ)
Rev.: $60,922,000,000
Assets: $65,728,000,000
Liabilities: $22,750,000,000
Net Worth: $42,978,000,000
Earnings: $29,760,000,000
Emp.: 29,600
Fiscal Year-end: 01/28/24
Programmable Graphics Processors
& Related Software Mfr
N.A.I.C.S.: 334413
Colette M. Kress (CFO & Exec VP)
Jensen Huang (Founder, Pres &
CEO)
Chris A. Malachowsky (Co-Founder)
Ajay K. Puri (Exec VP-Worldwide
Field Ops)
Debora Shoquist (Exec VP-Ops)
Timothy S. Teter (Gen Counsel, Sec
& Exec VP)
Donald F. Robertson Jr. (Chief Acctg
Officer & VP)

Subsidiaries:

Cumulus Networks, Inc. (1)
185 E Dana St, Mountain View, CA 94041
Tel.: (650) 383-6700
Web Site: http://www.cumulusnetworks.com
Computer Software Services
N.A.I.C.S.: 541511

Icera Inc. (1)
2520 The Quadrant, Aztec West, Bristol,
BS32 4AQ, United Kingdom
Tel.: (44) 1454284800
Web Site: https://www.icerasemi.com
Sales Range: $25-49.9 Million
Emp.: 120
Fabless Semiconductor Products Mfr
N.A.I.C.S.: 334413
Stan Boland (Co-Founder, Pres & CEO)
Simon Knowles (Co-Founder & VP-Strategy
& DXP Tech)
Steve Allpress (Co-Founder, CTO & VP-
Modem Software)
Peter Hughes (VP-Silicon Engrg & Ops)
Rick Dingle (VP-Customer Product Engrg)
Steve Chandler (VP-Legal & Intellectual
Property)
Fabrice Moizan (VP-Sls-Global)
Pete Cumming (VP-Sys Engrg)
Sonia Talamelli (VP-HR)

Subsidiary (US):

Icera Inc. (2)
740 E Campbell Rd Ste 300, Richardson,
TX 75081
Tel.: (214) 269-2770
Web Site: http://www.icerasemi.com
Sales Range: $25-49.9 Million
Emp.: 41
Fabless Semiconductor Mfr
N.A.I.C.S.: 334413

Icera LLC (1)
PO Box 27777, Santa Ana, CA 92799
Web Site: http://www.icerausa.com
Sanitary Toilet Vanity Mfr & Distr
N.A.I.C.S.: 325620

Mellanox Technologies, Ltd. (1)
Beit Mellanox, Yokneam, 20692, Israel
Tel.: (972) 49097200
Web Site: http://www.mellanox.com
Rev.: $1,330,576,000
Assets: $2,119,789,000
Liabilities: $463,944,000
Net Worth: $1,655,845,000
Earnings: $205,095,000
Emp.: 2,660
Fiscal Year-end: 12/31/2019
Semiconductor Mfr
N.A.I.C.S.: 334413
Michael Kagan (Co-Founder & CTO)
Eyal Bablsh (Sr VP-Ops & Hardware Engrg)
Dror Goldenberg (Sr VP-Software Architec-
ture)
Einat Zuk (Sr VP-HR)
Amit Krig (Sr VP-Software)
Gilad Shainer (Sr VP-Mktg)
Amir Prescher (Sr VP-End-User Sls & Bus
Dev)
Kevin Deierling (Sr VP-Mktg)
Nimrod Gindi (Sr VP-Merger & Acquisition
& Head-Investments)
Udi Weinstein (CIO)
Chuck Tybur (Sr VP-Worldwide OEM &
Channel Sls)

Subsidiary (Non-US):

**Mellanox Technologies Denmark
A/S** (2)
Ledreborg Alle 130B, 4000, Roskilde, Den-
mark
Tel.: (45) 46304800
Integrated Circuits Mfr
N.A.I.C.S.: 334417

**Mellanox Technologies Japan
K.K.** (2)
Suite 102 KDX Nishi Shinjuku Building
7-22-45, Nishi Shinjuku Shinjuku-ku, Tokyo,
160-0023, Japan
Tel.: (81) 359363117
Web Site: http://www.mellanox.co.jp
Internet Communication Services
N.A.I.C.S.: 517112

Subsidiary (US):

Mellanox Technologies, Inc. (2)

350 Oakmead Pkwy Ste 100, Sunnyvale,
CA 94085
Tel.: (408) 970-3400
Web Site: http://www.mellanox.com
Sales Range: $25-49.9 Million
Emp.: 60
Semiconductor Components Mfr
N.A.I.C.S.: 334413

Subsidiary (Domestic):

Mellanox Federal Systems, LLC (3)
575 Herndon Pkwy Ste 130, Herndon, VA
20170
Tel.: (703) 969-5735
Web Site: http://www.mellanoxfederal.com
Information Technology Consulting Services
N.A.I.C.S.: 541512

NVIDIA ARC GmbH (1)
Fasanenstr 81, 10623, Berlin, Germany
Tel.: (49) 303159970
Web Site: http://www.nvidia-arc.com
Computer Graphics Processing Unit Mfr
N.A.I.C.S.: 334413

NVIDIA Development UK Limited (1)
3rd Floor 100 Brook Drive, Green Park,
Reading, RG2 6UJ, Berkshire, United King-
dom
Computer Graphics Processing Unit Mfr
N.A.I.C.S.: 334413

NVIDIA FZ-LLC (1)
Dubai Internet City Executive Office No 5
Floor 1 Building 12, Dubai, United Arab
Emirates
Tel.: (971) 43751177
Electronic Components Mfr
N.A.I.C.S.: 334419

NVIDIA GK (1)
ATT New Tower 13th Floor 2-11-7 Akasaka,
Minato-ku, Tokyo, 107-0052, Japan
Tel.: (81) 367438699
Web Site: http://www.ndivia.com
Computer Graphics Processing Unit Mfr
N.A.I.C.S.: 334413

NVIDIA Ltd. (1)
8th Floor 20 Farringdon Street, London,   (100%)
EC4A 4AB, United Kingdom
Tel.: (44) 1189184340
Mfr of 3D Graphics
N.A.I.C.S.: 334610

**NVIDIA Semiconductor (Shenzhen)
Co., Ltd.** (1)
Productivity Building 5 Hi-tech Middle 2nd
Road, Shenzhen Hi-Tech Industrial Park
Nanshan District, Shenzhen, 518057, China
Tel.: (86) 75586029500
Computer Graphics Processing Unit Mfr
N.A.I.C.S.: 334413

NVIDIA Technology UK Limited (1)
8th Floor 20 Farringdon Street, Aztec West,
London, EC4A 4AB, North Somerset,
United Kingdom
Tel.: (44) 1454284800
Sales Range: $25-49.9 Million
Emp.: 130
Computer Graphics Processing Unit Mfr
N.A.I.C.S.: 334413
Anna Stewart (Office Mgr)

SwiftStack, Inc. (1)
660 Market St Ste 500, San Francisco, CA
94104
Tel.: (415) 625-0293
Web Site: http://www.swiftstack.com
Data Processing Services
N.A.I.C.S.: 518210
Don Jaworski (CEO)
Joe Arnold (Co-Founder, Pres & Chief Prod-
uct Officer)
Anders Tjernlund (Co-Founder & COO)
Bert Condensa (VP-Sls)
Erik Pounds (VP-Mktg)

The Portland Group, Inc. (1)
2 Centerpointe Dr Ste 320, Lake Oswego,
OR 97035
Tel.: (503) 682-2806
Web Site: http://www.pgroup.com
Emp.: 534
Compilers & Software Development Tools
Developer & Mfr
N.A.I.C.S.: 334118

NVR INCORPORATED

11700 Plz America Dr Ste 500, Res-
ton, VA 20190
Tel.: (703) 956-4000   VA
Web Site: https://www.nvrinc.com
Year Founded: 1987
NVR—(NYSE)
Rev.: $9,314,605,000
Assets: $6,601,757,000
Liabilities: $2,237,032,000
Net Worth: $4,364,725,000
Earnings: $1,591,611,000
Emp.: 6,300
Fiscal Year-end: 12/31/23
Builder of Houses; Financial Services
Company
N.A.I.C.S.: 236118
Paul C. Saville (Exec Chm)
Daniel D. Malzahn (CFO, Treas & Sr
VP)
Matthew B. Kelpy (Chief Acctg Offi-
cer, VP & Controller)

Subsidiaries:

Fox Ridge Homes (1)
93 Seaboard Ln Ste 201, Brentwood, TN
37027
Tel.: (615) 377-6840
Web Site: http://www.foxridgehomes.com
Sales Range: $50-74.9 Million
Emp.: 50
Builder of Houses
N.A.I.C.S.: 236115

NVR Funding II, Inc. (1)
1105 N Market St, Wilmington, DE 19801
Tel.: (302) 427-0974
Emp.: 2
Mortgage Banking Services
N.A.I.C.S.: 522292

NVR Mortgage Finance, Inc. (1)
3926 Pender Dr Ste 200, Fairfax, VA
22030   (100%)
Tel.: (703) 286-5686
Web Site: http://www.nvrmortgage.com
Sales Range: $50-74.9 Million
Residential Construction
N.A.I.C.S.: 522292
Eugene James Bredow (Pres)

NVR Services, Inc. (1)
9720 Patuxent Woods Dr City, Columbia,
MD 21046
Tel.: (410) 750-9050
Web Site: http://www.nvrinc.com
Emp.: 150
Mortgage & Nonmortgage Loan Broker
N.A.I.C.S.: 522310

NW TECH CAPITAL, INC.

9663 Santa Monica Blvd Ste 1171,
Beverly Hills, CA 90210
Tel.: (209) 493-6427   NV
Year Founded: 1996
NWTT—(OTCIQ)
Telecommunication Servicesb
N.A.I.C.S.: 517112
Cedric Yengo (Chm, Pres, CEO,
Treas & Sec)

NXGEN BRANDS LLC

8466 Violet Ct, Arvada, CO 80007
Tel.: (720) 844-6076   NV
Web Site: http://www.leafywell.com
NXGB—(OTCIQ)
Drug Product Distr
N.A.I.C.S.: 424210
Joseph Lawanson (CEO)

NXU INC.

1828 N Higley Rd, Mesa, AZ 85205
Tel.: (602) 309-5425   DE
Web Site:
    https://www.nxuenergy.com
Year Founded: 2016
NXU—(NASDAQ)
Rev.: $166,000
Assets: $7,038,000
Liabilities: $16,086,000
Net Worth: ($9,048,000)
Earnings: ($70,681,000)

Emp.: 93
Fiscal Year-end: 12/31/22
Battery Mfr
N.A.I.C.S.: 335910
Jordan Christensen (Chief Legal Officer)
Apoorv Dwivedi (CFO)
Mark Hanchett (Founder)
Srinivas Jasthi (VP)

NYIAX, INC.
180 Maiden Ln 11th Fl, New York, NY 10005
Tel.: (917) 444-9259   DE
Web Site: https://www.nyiax.com
Year Founded: 2012
NYX—(NASDAQ)
Rev.: $656,100
Assets: $4,244,847
Liabilities: $7,976,246
Net Worth: ($3,731,399)
Earnings: ($8,724,863)
Emp.: 6
Fiscal Year-end: 12/31/23
Advertising Agency Services
N.A.I.C.S.: 541810
Carolina Abenante (Vice Chm)
William Feldman (CFO)

NZJ HOLDINGS, INC.
1712 Pioneer Ave Ste 135, Cheyenne, WY 82001
Tel.: (307) 999-7422   NV
Year Founded: 2000
NZIH—(OTCIQ)
Holding Company
N.A.I.C.S.: 551112
Danny Tsang (Pres & CEO)

O'REILLY AUTOMOTIVE, INC.
233 S Patterson Ave, Springfield, MO 65802
Tel.: (417) 862-6708   MO
Web Site:
  https://www.oreillyauto.com
Year Founded: 2010
ORLY—(NASDAQ)
Rev.: $15,812,250,000
Assets: $13,872,995,000
Liabilities: $15,612,273,000
Net Worth: ($1,739,278,000)
Earnings: $2,346,581,000
Emp.: 75,614
Fiscal Year-end: 12/31/23
Holding Company; Automotive Parts & Accessories Retailer & Distr
N.A.I.C.S.: 551112
Gregory L. Henslee (Chm)
Lawrence P. O'Reilly (Vice Chm)
Brad Beckham (CEO)

Subsidiaries:

O'Reilly Automotive Stores, Inc.   (1)
233 S Patterson Ave, Springfield, MO 65802
Tel.: (417) 862-6708
Web Site: https://www.oreillyauto.com
Automotive Parts & Accessories Retailer & Distr
N.A.I.C.S.: 441330
Brent G. Kirby (Pres)
Brad Beckham (CEO)
Jeremy Fletcher (CFO & Exec VP)
Robert Allen Dumas (Sr VP-Eastern Store Ops & Sls)
Larry L. Ellis (Sr VP-Distr)
Jeffrey L. Groves (Gen Counsel & Sr VP-Legal)
Jeffrey Alan Lauro (Sr VP-IT)
Jason Tarrant (Sr VP-Western Store Ops & Sls)
Darin Venosdel (Sr VP-Inventory Mgmt)
C. David Wilbanks (Sr VP-Mdse)
Jonathan Andrews (Sr VP-HR & Trng)
Tom McFall (Exec VP)
Phil Hopper (Sr VP)
Chris Mancini (Sr VP)
Mark Merz (Sr VP)

Ozark Automotive Distributors, Inc.   (1)
233 S Patterson Ave, Springfield, MO 65802-2298
Tel.: (417) 829-5727
Web Site: http://www.oreillyauto.com
Sales Range: $200-249.9 Million
Emp.: 500
Distr & Retailer of Auto Parts & Supplies
N.A.I.C.S.: 423120
Gregory L. Henslee (CEO)

O-I GLASS, INC.
1 Michael Owens Way, Perrysburg, OH 43551
Tel.: (567) 336-5000   DE
Web Site: https://www.o-i.com
Year Founded: 1907
OI—(NYSE)
Rev.: $6,856,000,000
Assets: $9,061,000,000
Liabilities: $7,533,000,000
Net Worth: $1,528,000,000
Earnings: $584,000,000
Emp.: 24,000
Fiscal Year-end: 12/31/22
Glass Container Mfr
N.A.I.C.S.: 327213
Gordon J. Hardie (Pres & CEO)
Vitaliano Torno (Pres-Bus Ops-Europe)
Arnaud Aujouannet (CMO, Chief Sls Officer & Sr VP)
Darrow A. Abrahams (Gen Counsel, Sec & Sr VP)
Randolph Burns (Chief Sustainability & Corporate Affairs Officer & VP)
Giancarlo Currarino (Sr VP-Bus Ops Americas)
John A. Haudrich (CFO & Sr VP)

Subsidiaries:

Cristaleria del Ecuador, S.A.   (1)
Km 22 5 via Perimental, Guayaquil, Ecuador
Tel.: (593) 43704800
Web Site: http://www.o-i.com
Glass Containers & Glass Products
N.A.I.C.S.: 327211

O-I (Shanghai) Glass Container Co., Ltd.   (1)
Suite 308 Block E Gold Hongqiao Business Plaza, No 2 Lane 686 Wuzhong Road, Shanghai, 201103, China
Tel.: (86) 2164766055
Glass Packaging Container Distr
N.A.I.C.S.: 423840

O-I Asia Pacific   (1)
36-38 Burwood Rd, Hawthorn, 3122, VIC, Australia
Tel.: (61) 392362311
Web Site: http://www.o-i.com
Sales Range: $150-199.9 Million
Emp.: 200
Glass Containers & Glass Products Mfr
N.A.I.C.S.: 327213

Subsidiary (Non-US):

ACI Guangdong Glass Company Ltd.   (2)
4th Side Road, Tianhe District, Guangzhou, 510655, China   (100%)
Tel.: (86) 85525021
Sales Range: $150-199.9 Million
Glass Container Mfr
N.A.I.C.S.: 327213

ACI Operations NZ Limited   (2)
752 Great South Road, Penrose, Auckland, 1061, New Zealand   (100%)
Tel.: (64) 9 976 7100
Sales Range: $50-74.9 Million
Emp.: 200
Glass Bottle & Jar Mfr
N.A.I.C.S.: 327213

ACI Tianjin Mould Company Limited   (2)
30 Hua Sheng Road Bei Chen Technology Zone, Tianjin, 300409, China
Tel.: (86) 22 8698 6716

Glass Packaging Supplier
N.A.I.C.S.: 327213

O-I China   (2)
Suite 308 Block E Gold Hongqiao Business Plaza, No 2 Lane 686 Wuzhong Road, Shanghai, 201103, China   (100%)
Tel.: (86) 2164766055
Web Site: http://www.o-i.com
Sales Range: $150-199.9 Million
Glass Container Mfr
N.A.I.C.S.: 327213

Plastics New Zealand   (2)
First Floor 2 - 8 Freight Place Airport Oaks, Auckland, 2022, New Zealand   (100%)
Tel.: (64) 92555662
Web Site: http://www.plastics.org.nz
Sales Range: $150-199.9 Million
Emp.: 3
Glass Containers & Glass Products
N.A.I.C.S.: 327213
Mark Field (Pres)

Wuhan Owens Glass Container Company Limited   (2)
32-1 Gu Tian Road, Wuhan, 430035, China
Tel.: (86) 27 8341 1253
Glass Containers
N.A.I.C.S.: 327213

O-I Czech Republic A.S.   (1)
Ruska 113/80, 417 03, Dubi, Czech Republic
Tel.: (420) 417517111
Glass Bottle Mfr
N.A.I.C.S.: 327213
Klara Sokolova (Mgr-Quality)

O-I Estonia AS   (1)
Tehaste 7, 79101, Jarvakandi, Estonia
Tel.: (372) 4892202
Glass Packaging Container Distr
N.A.I.C.S.: 423840

O-I France SAS   (1)
2 Rue Maurice Moissonnier, 69120, Vaulx-en-Velin, France
Tel.: (33) 426686500
Glass Bottle Mfr
N.A.I.C.S.: 327213

O-I Germany GmbH & Co. KG   (1)
Goethestrasse 75, 40237, Dusseldorf, Germany
Tel.: (49) 2119320
Glass Container Mfr
N.A.I.C.S.: 327213

O-I Glass Limited   (1)
Edinburgh Way, Harlow, CM20 2UG, Essex, United Kingdom
Tel.: (44) 1279422222
Glass Bottle Mfr
N.A.I.C.S.: 327213

O-I Netherlands B.V.   (1)
Spoorstraat 7, 3112 HD, Schiedam, Netherlands
Tel.: (31) 104094444
Glass Bottle Mfr
N.A.I.C.S.: 327213
Joost Laven (Mgr-EHS)

O-I Packaging Solutions, LLC   (1)
5200 Tennyson Pkwy Ste 100, Plano, TX 75024
Tel.: (469) 708-5763
Web Site: http://www.o-ipackagingsolutions.com
Glass Container Mfr
N.A.I.C.S.: 327213

Owens-Illinois General Inc.   (1)
1700 State St, Zanesville, OH 43701
Tel.: (567) 336-5700
Web Site: http://www.o-i.com
Glass Bottle Mfr
N.A.I.C.S.: 339999

Owens-Illinois Group, Inc.   (1)
One Michael Owens Way, Perrysburg, OH 43551-2999
Tel.: (567) 336-5000
Web Site: http://www.o-i.com
Sales Range: $5-14.9 Billion
Glass Container Mfr
N.A.I.C.S.: 327213

Owens-Illinois International B.V.   (1)

Buitenhavenweg 146, Schiedam, 3113 BE, Netherlands
Tel.: (31) 104094444
Sales Range: $250-299.9 Million
Holding Company
N.A.I.C.S.: 551112
Vitaliano Torno (Mng Dir-Europe)
Ernst P. Knupfer (Mng Dir)

Subsidiary (Non-US):

O-I Glasspack Beteiligungs & Verwaltungsgesellschaft GmbH   (2)
Goethestrasse 75, 40237, Dusseldorf, Germany
Tel.: (49) 2119320
Web Site: http://www.o-i.com
Emp.: 50
Glass Container Mfr
N.A.I.C.S.: 327213

Subsidiary (Domestic):

OI Glasspack GmbH & Co. KG   (3)
Alter Postweg 3, 37603, Holzminden, Germany
Tel.: (49) 55311210
Glass Container Distr
N.A.I.C.S.: 423220

Subsidiary (Non-US):

O-I Manufacturing Czech Republic A.S.   (2)
Ruska 113/80, 417 03, Dubi, Czech Republic   (100%)
Tel.: (420) 417517111
Web Site: http://www.o-i.com
Sales Range: $150-199.9 Million
Glass Containers & Glass Products Mfr
N.A.I.C.S.: 327213

O-I Manufacturing France SAS   (2)
2 Rue Maurice Moissonnier, 69120, Vaulx-en-Velin, France   (100%)
Tel.: (33) 426686500
Glass Bottle Mfr
N.A.I.C.S.: 327215

Subsidiary (Domestic):

BSN Gasspack France   (3)
64 Blvd Du 11 Novembre 1918, BP 1228, Villeurbanne, 69100, Cedex, France   (100%)
Tel.: (33) 426686500
Web Site: http://www.oi.com
Sales Range: $50-74.9 Million
Glass Bottle Mfr
N.A.I.C.S.: 327213

Subsidiary (Non-US):

BSN Glasspack Spain   (3)
Sector C Calle D 1-9, 08040, Barcelona, Spain
Tel.: (34) 93 264 94 01
Web Site: http://www.bsnglasspack.com
Sales Range: $100-124.9 Million
Glass Bottle Mfr
N.A.I.C.S.: 327213

Subsidiary (Domestic):

Verdome Exploitation SA   (3)
21 Avenue Edouard Vaillant, Puy-Guillaume, 63290, France
Tel.: (33) 4 73 94 78 08
Glass Bottle Mfr
N.A.I.C.S.: 327213

Subsidiary (Non-US):

O-I Manufacturing Italy S.p.A.   (2)
Via I Maggio 18 Orrigio, 21040, Varese, Italy   (100%)
Tel.: (39) 02434531
Web Site: http://www.bsnglasspack.com
Sales Range: $25-49.9 Million
Emp.: 3,689
Glass Containers & Glass Products Mfr
N.A.I.C.S.: 327213

Subsidiary (Domestic):

O-I Sales and Distribution Italy S.r.l.   (3)
Via Washington 70, Milan, 21040, Italy
Tel.: (39) 02434531
Carbonated Beverages Mfr

O-I Glass, Inc.—(Continued)

N.A.I.C.S.: 312111

San Domenico Vetraria S.r.l.   **(3)**
Viale San Domenico ZI, Ottaviano, Naples, 80044, Italy   **(100%)**
Tel.: (39) 0818270963
Glass Containers & Glass Products Mfr
N.A.I.C.S.: 327213

Vetrerie Meridionali S.p.A.   **(3)**
Via Conversano 144, 70013, Castellana Grotte, BA, Italy   **(100%)**
Tel.: (39) 08955003042
Web Site: http://www.o-i.com
Glass Containers & Glass Products Mfr
N.A.I.C.S.: 327213

Subsidiary (Non-US):

O-I Manufacturing Ltd.   **(2)**
Csorvasi ut 5, 5900, Oroshaza, Hungary   **(100%)**
Tel.: (36) 68814700
Web Site: http://www.o-i.com
Sales Range: $150-199.9 Million
Glass Containers & Glass Products Mfr
N.A.I.C.S.: 327213

Subsidiary (Domestic):

O-I Netherlands B.V.   **(2)**
Spoorstraat 7, PB 46, 3112 HD, Schiedam, Netherlands
Tel.: (31) 104094444
Sales Range: $50-74.9 Million
Emp.: 20
Glass Mfr
N.A.I.C.S.: 327213

Subsidiary (Non-US):

OI Finnish Holdings Oy   **(2)**
Tehaste 7 Rapla, Jarvakandi, 79101, Estonia   **(100%)**
Tel.: (372) 4892200
Sales Range: $150-199.9 Million
Emp.: 150
Glass Containers & Glass Products
N.A.I.C.S.: 327213
Ethael Moor *(Mgr-HR)*

Subsidiary (Domestic):

A/S Jarvakandi Klaas   **(3)**
Tehaste 7, 79101, Jarvakandi, Estonia   **(100%)**
Tel.: (372) 4892202
Sales Range: $150-199.9 Million
Glass Containers & Glass Products
N.A.I.C.S.: 327213

Affiliate (Non-US):

Karhulan Lasi Oy   **(3)**
Lasimestarintie 9, 48600, Karhula, Finland   **(100%)**
Tel.: (358) 102342711
Sales Range: $150-199.9 Million
Glass Containers & Glass Products Mfr
N.A.I.C.S.: 327213

Subsidiary (Non-US):

O-I Sales and Distribution LT   **(3)**
Sv Mykol 14-2, 01124, Vilnius, Lithuania
Tel.: (370) 5 2313691
Web Site: http://www.o-i.com
Emp.: 3
Glass Container Mfr
N.A.I.C.S.: 327213

Subsidiary (Non-US):

Owens-Illinois Polska S.A.   **(2)**
ul Morawska 1, 37-500, Jaroslaw, Poland   **(100%)**
Tel.: (48) 166249200
Web Site: http://www.oi.com
Sales Range: $150-199.9 Million
Glass Containers & Glass Products Mfr & Distr
N.A.I.C.S.: 327213

Subsidiary (Non-US):

O-I Glass Limited   **(3)**
Edinburgh Way, PO Box 6068, Harlow, CM20 2UG, Essex, United Kingdom
Tel.: (44) 1279422218
Web Site: http://www.o-i.europe.com

Glass Containers & Glass Products Mfr
N.A.I.C.S.: 327213

United Glass Group Ltd.   **(3)**
Edinburgh Way, Harlow, CM20 2DB, Essex, United Kingdom
Tel.: (44) 1279422222
Web Site: http://www.o-i.com
Plastics Bottle Mfr
N.A.I.C.S.: 326160

Owens-Illinois Peru S.A.   **(1)**
Jiron Pedro Conde 157, 15001, Lince, Peru   **(100%)**
Tel.: (51) 919441777
Web Site: https://www.oiperu.com
Sales Range: $75-99.9 Million
Emp.: 150
Glass Containers & Glass Products Mfr
N.A.I.C.S.: 327213

PT Kangar Consolidated Industries   **(1)**
JL Raya Bekasi Km 24 5, Cakung, Jakarta, 13960, Timur, Indonesia
Tel.: (62) 2146951000
Web Site: http://www.oi.com
Sales Range: $25-49.9 Million
Glass Containers & Glass Products
N.A.I.C.S.: 327213

Vidrieria Rovira, S.A.   **(1)**
Pol Ind Zona Franca Sector C Calle D 1-15, 08040, Barcelona, Spain
Tel.: (34) 932649401
Sales Range: $100-124.9 Million
Emp.: 215
Glass Containers & Glass Products Mfr
N.A.I.C.S.: 327213

OAK RIDGE FINANCIAL SERVICES, INC.
2211 Oak Ridge Rd, Oak Ridge, NC 27310
Tel.: (336) 644-9944   **NC**
Web Site:
   http://www.bankofoakridge.com
BKOR—(OTCIQ)
Sales Range: $1-9.9 Million
Emp.: 89
Bank Holding Company
N.A.I.C.S.: 551111
Douglas G. Boike *(Chm)*
Thomas W. Wayne *(CEO & CFO)*

Subsidiaries:

Bank of Oak Ridge   **(1)**
2211 Oak Rdg Rd Hwy 150, Oak Ridge, NC 27310   **(100%)**
Tol.: (336) 644 0044
Web Site: http://www.bankofoakridge.com
Sales Range: $125-149.9 Million
Emp.: 90
Commericial Banking
N.A.I.C.S.: 522110
Jason Woods *(VP & Mgr-Retail Projects)*
Beth Buczkowski *(Controller)*
Sean Parshley *(Mgr-Lake Jeanette & New Garden Crossing)*
Thomas W. Wayne *(CEO & CFO)*
Skylar Mearing *(Mgr-Mktg & Comm)*
Fred Smith *(VP & Mgr-Bus Relationship)*
Douglas G. Boike *(Chm)*

OAK VALLEY BANCORP
125 N 3rd Ave, Oakdale, CA 95361
Tel.: (209) 848-2265   **CA**
Web Site: https://www.ovcb.com
Year Founded: 2008
OVLY—(NASDAQ)
Rev.: $66,766,000
Assets: $1,968,346,000
Liabilities: $1,841,720,000
Net Worth: $126,626,000
Earnings: $22,902,000
Emp.: 174
Fiscal Year-end: 12/31/22
Bank Holding Company
N.A.I.C.S.: 551111
Michael J. Rodrigues *(Chief Credit Officer & Exec VP)*
Jeffrey A. Gall *(CFO & Principal Acctg Officer)*

Richard A. McCarty *(Pres & COO)*
Daniel J. Leonard *(Vice Chm)*
Christopher M. Courtney *(CEO)*

Subsidiaries:

Oak Valley Community Bank   **(1)**
125 N 3rd Ave, Oakdale, CA 95361
Tel.: (209) 848-2265
Web Site: http://www.ovcb.com
Commericial Banking
N.A.I.C.S.: 522110
Michael J. Rodrigues *(Chief Credit Officer & Exec VP)*
Jeffrey A. Gall *(CFO & Sr VP)*
Richard A. McCarty *(Pres & COO)*
Danny L. Titus *(Executives, Bd of Dirs)*
Terrance P. Withrow *(Chm)*
Christopher M. Courtney *(CEO)*
Bill Nunes *(Sr VP-Mktg)*
Gary W. Stephens *(Exec VP-Comml Banking Grp)*
Janis L. Powers *(Exec VP-Risk Mgmt)*
Russell E. Stahl *(CIO & Exec VP)*
Kim Booke *(Sr VP-Credit Admin)*
Michael Stevens *(Officer-Comml Loan & VP-Stockton)*
Victoria Gaffney *(Officer-Comml Loan & VP-Modesto & Turlock)*
Hamit Utush *(VP-Comml Real Estate Grp-Sacramento)*
Linda Spinelli *(Sr VP & Mgr-Central Ops)*
Melissa Fuller *(Sr VP-HR)*
Rafael Martinez *(Asst VP-Turlock)*
Damon K. Munoz *(VP-Comml Banking)*

OAKRIDGE GLOBAL ENERGY SOLUTIONS, INC.
3520 Dixie Hwy NE, Palm Bay, FL 32905
Tel.: (321) 610-7959   **CO**
Year Founded: 1986
OGES—(OTCIQ)
Thin-Film lithium & Lithium-Ion Battery Mfr
N.A.I.C.S.: 335910
Stephen J. Barber *(Chm)*
Suzanna Barber *(VP-Corp & Legal Affairs)*
Brendan Melling *(Dir-Strategic Product Dev & Mktg)*

Subsidiaries:

Leclanche SA   **(1)**
Avenue des Decouvertes 14C, 1400, Yverdon-les-Bains, Switzerland
Tel.: (41) 244246500
Web Site: https://www.leclanche.com
Rev.: $22,243,879
Assets: $126,044,688
Liabilities: $191,115,998
Net Worth: ($65,071,310)
Earnings: ($83,826,955)
Emp.: 362
Fiscal Year-end: 12/31/2023
Battery Manufacturing
N.A.I.C.S.: 335910
Fabrizio Marzolini *(Exec VP-Speciality Battery Sys BU)*
Pierre Blanc *(Chief Tech Industrial Officer)*
Stefan A. Muller *(Chm)*
Anil Srivastava *(CEO)*
Philip Broad *(Exec VP-e-Transport Solutions)*
Pasquale Foglia *(Acting CFO & Sr VP-Fin)*

Subsidiary (Non-US):

Leclanche GmbH   **(2)**
Industriestrasse 1, Willstatt, 77731, Baden-Wurttemberg, Germany   **(100%)**
Tel.: (49) 785281800
Web Site: http://www.leclanche.com
Emp.: 60
Lithium Battery Mfr
N.A.I.C.S.: 335910
Pierre Blanc *(CTO)*
Anil Srivastava *(Mng Dir)*

OBLONG, INC.
110 16th St Ste 1400 Ste 1024, Denver, CO 80202
Tel.: (303) 640-3838   **DE**
Web Site: https://www.oblong.com

Year Founded: 2000
OBLG—(NASDAQ)
Rev.: $5,476,000
Assets: $5,661,000
Liabilities: $2,044,000
Net Worth: $3,617,000
Earnings: ($21,941,000)
Emp.: 20
Fiscal Year-end: 12/31/22
All Other Telecommunications
N.A.I.C.S.: 517810
Peter J. Holst *(Pres & CEO)*
Sam Moore *(Sr VP-IT & Ops)*
Matthew Blumberg *(Chm)*
Amanda Messbauer *(VP-Sls)*
David C. Clark *(CFO & Sec)*

Subsidiaries:

ALLCOM Products LLC   **(1)**
695 Sundown Rd, South Elgin, IL 60177   **(100%)**
Tel.: (847) 468-8830
Web Site: https://www.allcompc.com
Sales Range: $100-124.9 Million
Cable Assemblies, Coaxial Lighting Protection & Specialized Data & Lan Products Mfr
N.A.I.C.S.: 334418
Bill Kohl *(Mng Partner-Sls & Mktg)*
Cathy Parsons *(Office Mgr)*
David Dunlap *(Mng Partner-Ops)*

GP Communications, LLC   **(1)**
430 Mountain Ave Ste 301, New Providence, NJ 07974
Tel.: (973) 855-3411
Communication Service
N.A.I.C.S.: 561421

Oblong Industries, Inc.   **(1)**
923 E 3rd St Ste 111, Los Angeles, CA 90013
Tel.: (213) 683-8863
Web Site: https://www.oblong.com
Software Development Services
N.A.I.C.S.: 541511

OC BEVERAGES, INC.
8101 Scholarship Rd, Irvine, CA 92612
Tel.: (949) 481-2776
OCBG—(OTCIQ)
Bottle Beverage Mfr
N.A.I.C.S.: 312111
Lee Danna *(Pres & CEO)*

OCA ACQUISITION CORP.
1345 Avenue of the Americas 33rd Fl, New York, NY 10105
Tel.: (212) 201-8533   **DE**
Web Site:
   https://www.ocaacquisition.com
Year Founded: 2020
OCAX—(NASDAQ)
Rev.: $9,031,029
Assets: $153,981,976
Liabilities: $162,205,445
Net Worth: ($8,223,469)
Earnings: $7,396,606
Emp.: 2
Fiscal Year-end: 12/31/22
Investment Services
N.A.I.C.S.: 523999
David Shen *(Pres & CEO)*
Jeffrey Glat *(CFO, Treas & Sec)*
Humberto Galleno *(VP-Corp & Business Development)*

OCCIDENTAL PETROLEUM CORPORATION
5 Greenway Plz Ste 110, Houston, TX 77046-0521
Tel.: (713) 215-7000   **DE**
Web Site: https://www.oxy.com
Year Founded: 1920
OXY—(NYSE)
Rev.: $28,918,000,000
Assets: $74,008,000,000
Liabilities: $43,659,000,000
Net Worth: $30,349,000,000

Earnings: $3,773,000,000
Emp.: 12,570
Fiscal Year-end: 12/31/23
Crude Oil & Natural Gas Explorer, Developer, Producer & Marketer; Basic Chemicals Marketer & Mfr
N.A.I.C.S.: 211120
Vicki A. Hollub (Pres & CEO)
Edward A. Lowe (Chm-Middle East & Exec VP)
Robert L. Peterson (Exec VP-Essential Chemistry & Sr VP)
Sunil Mathew (CFO & Sr VP)
Christopher O. Champion (Chief Acctg Officer, VP & Controller)
Neil Backhouse (Dir-IR)
Peter J. Bennett (VP)
Sylvia Kerrigan (Chief Legal Officer)
Yanni Charalambous (CIO)
Nicole Clark (Sec)
Thomas Janiszewski (VP)
Angela Johnson (VP)
Darin Moss (VP)
Karen Sinard (VP)

Subsidiaries:

Anadarko Petroleum Corporation (1)
1201 Lake Robbins Dr, The Woodlands, TX 77380-1046
Tel.: (832) 636-1000
Web Site: http://www.anadarko.com
Rev.: $13,382,000,000
Assets: $40,376,000,000
Liabilities: $29,433,000,000
Net Worth: $10,943,000,000
Earnings: $615,000,000
Emp.: 4,700
Fiscal Year-end: 12/31/2018
Exploration, Production & Pipeline Transportation of Natural Gas & Petroleum; Operator of Mineral Mines
N.A.I.C.S.: 211120

Subsidiary (Non-US):

Anadarko Algeria Company, LLC (2)
4 Chemin des Glycines, 16000, Algiers, Algeria
Tel.: (213) 21230589
Web Site: http://www.anadarko.com
Oil & Gas Exploration & Production
N.A.I.C.S.: 211120

Subsidiary (Domestic):

Anadarko Oil & Gas Company (2)
1201 Lake Robbins Dr, The Woodlands, TX 77380
Tel.: (832) 636-1000
Web Site: http://www.anadarko.com
Sales Range: $1-4.9 Billion
Emp.: 1,000
Oil & Gas Exploration & Production
N.A.I.C.S.: 424710

Anadarko US Offshore Corporation (2)
1201 Lake Robbins Dr, The Woodlands, TX 77380
Tel.: (832) 636-1000
Web Site: http://www.anadarko.com
Emp.: 4,000
Petroleum Extraction Services
N.A.I.C.S.: 211120
R. A. Walker (Pres)

Anadarko Uintah Midstream, LLC (2)
1099 18th St, Denver, CO 80202-1908
Tel.: (720) 929-6000
Natural Gas Distr
N.A.I.C.S.: 221210

Delaware Basin Midstream, LLC (2)
1221 Lamar Ste 1100, Houston, TX 77010
Tel.: (713) 337-6550
Web Site: http://www.nuevomidstream.com
Oil & Gas Field Engineering Services
N.A.I.C.S.: 333132

Kerr-McGee Oil and Gas Corporation (2)
1201 Lake Robbins Dr, The Woodlands, TX 77380-1176
Tel.: (832) 636-1000
Web Site: http://www.anadarko.com

Oil & Gas Exploration Services
N.A.I.C.S.: 213112

WGR Asset Holding Company LLC (2)
1201 Lake Robins Dr Ste 1800, The Woodlands, TX 77380
Tel.: (832) 636-3431
Petroleum Extraction Services
N.A.I.C.S.: 211120

California Heavy Oil, Inc. (1)
270 Quail Ct Ste 201, Santa Paula, CA 93060
Tel.: (805) 525-8008
Petroleum Product Mfr
N.A.I.C.S.: 324199
Todd Stevens (Pres)

Centurion Pipeline L.P. (1)
3600 W Sam Houston Pkwy Ste 500, Houston, TX 77042
Tel.: (346) 803-2800
Web Site: https://www.centurionpipeline.com
Crude Petroleum & Natural Gas Distribution Services
N.A.I.C.S.: 213111

Centurion Pipeline LP, Inc. (1)
3600 W Sam Houston Pkwy Ste 500, Houston, TX 77042
Tel.: (346) 803-2800
Web Site: http://www.centurionpipeline.com
Sales Range: $1-4.9 Billion
Emp.: 3,000
Petroleum Refinery Services
N.A.I.C.S.: 324110

Glenn Springs Holdings, Inc. (1)
127 Main St, Ducktown, TN 37326
Tel.: (423) 496-7900
Web Site: http://www.glennsprings-copperbasinproject.com
Sales Range: $25-49.9 Million
Emp.: 99
Land Subdivision Services
N.A.I.C.S.: 237210

Grupo OxyChem de Mexico, S.A. de C.V. (1)
Calle Periferico Sur 3345 Piso 5 Distrito Federal, La Magdalena Contreras, 10200, Mexico, Mexico
Tel.: (52) 5555459372
Web Site: http://www.oxy.com
Emp.: 3
Fabricated Metal Products Mfr
N.A.I.C.S.: 332312

INDSPEC Chemical Export Sales, LLC (1)
1010 William Pitt Way, Pittsburgh, PA 15238-1336
Tel.: (412) 826-3666
Emp.: 20
Chemical Products Mfr
N.A.I.C.S.: 325199

Ingleside Cogeneration Limited Partnership (1)
5 Greenway Plz Ste 1500, Houston, TX 77046
Tel.: (713) 215-7962
Petroleum Refineries
N.A.I.C.S.: 324110

Interseqt, LLC (1)
311 Ray St, Pleasanton, CA 94566
Tel.: (408) 451-1000
Web Site: http://www.intersectgroup.com
Technology Consulting & Research Services
N.A.I.C.S.: 541690

Monument Production, Inc. (1)
3585 Maple St, Ventura, CA 93003
Tel.: (805) 644-8555
Oil & Gas Well Drilling Services
N.A.I.C.S.: 213111

OXY USA Inc. (1)
PO Box 27570, Houston, TX 77227-7757
Tel.: (713) 215-7231
Crude Petroleum & Natural Gas Distribution Services
N.A.I.C.S.: 213111

Occidental Chemical Asia, Limited (1)
7F Urban Toranomon Building 1-16-4 Tora-

nomon, Minato-ku, Tokyo, 105-0001, Japan
Tel.: (81) 362054220
Web Site: https://www.oxychem-japan.com
Emp.: 4
Chemical Products Mfr
N.A.I.C.S.: 325199

Occidental Chemical Belgium B.V.B.A. (1)
Nieuwlandlaan 111/202, 3200, Aarschot, Belgium
Tel.: (32) 16479890
Web Site: http://www.oxychem.com
Chemical Products Mfr
N.A.I.C.S.: 325199

Occidental Chemical Chile Limitada (1)
Bucarest 150 Oficina, Providencia, 1601, Santiago, Chile
Tel.: (56) 227185000
Web Site: https://www.oxychile.cl
Emp.: 120
Petroleum Refinery Services
N.A.I.C.S.: 324110

Occidental Chemical Corporation (1)
1000 Tidal Rd, Deer Park, TX 77536 (100%)
Tel.: (972) 404-3800
Web Site: http://www.oxychem.com
Sales Range: $1-4.9 Billion
Emp.: 100
Chemicals, Chlorine & Caustic Soda, PVC & Specialty Chemicals Mfr
N.A.I.C.S.: 325180

Joint Venture (Domestic):

Armand Products Company (2)
469 N Harrison St, Princeton, NJ 08543-5297
Tel.: (609) 683-7090
Web Site: https://www.armandproducts.com
Sales Range: $150-199.9 Million
Emp.: 350
Potassium Carbonate & Bicarbonate Products Mfr; Owned by Church & Dwight Co., Inc. & Occidental Chemical Corporation
N.A.I.C.S.: 325180

Subsidiary (Domestic):

INDSPEC Chemical Corporation (2)
133 Main St, Petrolia, PA 16050
Tel.: (724) 756-2370
Resorcinol Producer
N.A.I.C.S.: 325998

Unit (Domestic):

OxyChem - Ludington (2)
1600 S Madison St, Ludington, MI 49431-2568
Tel.: (231) 845-4411
Web Site: http://www.oxy.com
Sales Range: $10-24.9 Million
Emp.: 132
Calcium Chloride Mfr
N.A.I.C.S.: 325199

Occidental Chemical Far East Limited (1)
Room 1402 14/F 18 Hysan Avenue, Causeway Bay, China (Hong Kong)
Tel.: (852) 25072033
Crude Petroleum & Natural Gas Distribution Services
N.A.I.C.S.: 213111

Occidental Chemical Holding Corporation (1)
14555 Dallas Pkwy Ste 400, Dallas, TX 75254
Tel.: (972) 404-3800
Web Site: http://www.oxy.com
Holding Company; Organic Chemical Mfr
N.A.I.C.S.: 551112

Occidental Chemical de Mexico, S.A. de C.V. (1)
Periferico Sur 3343 Piso 5 Col San Jeronimo Lidice, 10200, Mexico, Mexico
Tel.: (52) 5556680554
Web Site: http://www.oxy.com
Emp.: 3
Petroleum Product Distr
N.A.I.C.S.: 424710

Occidental Energy Marketing, Inc. (1)

5 Greenway Plz Ste 110, Houston, TX 77046-0521 (100%)
Tel.: (713) 215-7000
Web Site: http://www.oxy.com
Sales Range: $150-199.9 Million
Oil & Gas Marketing Services
N.A.I.C.S.: 213112

Subsidiary (Domestic):

Occidental Energy Transportation LLC (2)
5 Greenway Plz Ste 110, Houston, TX 77046
Tel.: (713) 215-7637
Petroleum Product Trucking Services
N.A.I.C.S.: 484230
Bill Boyer (Pres)

Occidental Energy Ventures Corp. (1)
5 Greenway Plz Ste 110, Houston, TX 77046
Tel.: (713) 215-7000
Petroleum Product Mfr
N.A.I.C.S.: 324199

Occidental International Corporation (1)
1230 Ave of the Americas Ste 1600, New York, NY 10020
Tel.: (212) 603-8111
Emp.: 20
Oil & Gas Exploration Services
N.A.I.C.S.: 213112

Occidental Oil & Gas Corporation (1)
5 Greeway Plz Ste 110, Houston, TX 77046-0521 (100%)
Tel.: (713) 215-7000
Web Site: http://www.oxy.com
Sales Range: $250-299.9 Million
Emp.: 1,700
Explorer & Producer of Worldwide Oil & Gas
N.A.I.C.S.: 211120

Subsidiary (Domestic):

Centurion Pipeline (2)
3600 W Sam Houston Pkwy Ste 500, Houston, TX 77046
Tel.: (346) 803-2800
Web Site: http://www.centurionpipeline.com
Sales Range: $10-24.9 Million
Emp.: 8
Crude Petroleum Oil
N.A.I.C.S.: 486110

Centurion Pipeline (2)
5 Greenway Plz Ste 1600, Houston, TX 77046
Tel.: (713) 497-2470
Web Site: http://www.centurionpipeline.com
Sales Range: $10-24.9 Million
Emp.: 20
Administrative Management
N.A.I.C.S.: 561110

Occidental Permian Ltd. (1)
PO Box 4294, Houston, TX 77210-4294
Tel.: (713) 350-4682
Petroleum Product Distr
N.A.I.C.S.: 424710

Occidental Petroleum Investment Co. (1)
10889 Wilshire Blvd Fl 10, Los Angeles, CA 90024
Tel.: (310) 208-8800
Oil & Gas Exploration Services
N.A.I.C.S.: 213112

Occidental Power Marketing, L.P. (1)
5 Greenway Plz Ste 110, Houston, TX 77046
Tel.: (713) 215-7844
Natural Gas Distr
N.A.I.C.S.: 221210

Occidental Research Corporation (1)
2100 SE Main St, Irvine, CA 92614
Tel.: (714) 957-7167
Chemical Products Mfr
N.A.I.C.S.: 325199

Occidental Tower Corporation (1)
5 Greenway Plz Ste 110, Houston, TX 77046-0521

Occidental Petroleum Corporation—(Continued)

Tel.: (713) 215-7000
Financial Services
N.A.I.C.S.: 522320

Occidental de Colombia, Inc. (1)
Calle 77A 11, Bogota, Colombia (100%)
Tel.: (57) 13454155
Sales Range: $250-299.9 Million
Emp.: 300
Explores & Produces Petroleum & Petroleum Products
N.A.I.C.S.: 211120

Occidental of Elk Hills, Inc. (1)
1117 River Run Blvd, Bakersfield, CA 93311
Tel.: (661) 763-6000
Web Site: http://www.oxy.com
Oil & Natural Gas Distr
N.A.I.C.S.: 221210

Oxy Vinyls Canada Co. (1)
8800 Thorold Town Line, Niagara Falls, L2E 6V9, ON, Canada
Tel.: (905) 357-3131
Emp.: 163
Plastics Material Mfr
N.A.I.C.S.: 325211
Jim Segata (Gen Mgr)

Oxy Vinyls Export Sales, LLC (1)
5005 LBJ Fwy Fl 22, Dallas, TX 75244-6119
Tel.: (972) 404-2337
Chemical Products Distr
N.A.I.C.S.: 424690

Oxy Vinyls, LP (1)
14555 Dallas Pkwy Ste 400, Dallas, TX 75254
Tel.: (972) 720-7408
Web Site: https://www.oxy.com
Polyvinyl Chloride Resins Mfr
N.A.I.C.S.: 324110

OxyChem do Brasil Ltda. (1)
Caixa Postal 541, Sao Paulo, 01031-970, Brazil
Tel.: (55) 11967970010
Crude Petroleum & Natural Gas Distribution Services
N.A.I.C.S.: 213111

San Patricio Pipeline LLC (1)
5 Greenway Plz Ste 110, Houston, TX 77227
Tel.: (713) 366-5528
Pipeline Construction Services
N.A.I.C.S.: 237120

Vintage Production California LLC (1)
9600 Ming Ave Ste 300, Bakersfield, CA 93311
Tel.: (661) 869-8000
Web Site: http://www.oxy.com
Emp.: 12
Oil & Gas Exploration Services
N.A.I.C.S.: 213112

OCEAN BIOMEDICAL, INC.
Tel.: (401) 444-7375 DE
Web Site:
https://www.oceanbiomedical.com
Year Founded: 2021
OCEA—(NASDAQ)
Assets: $5,501,000
Liabilities: $96,264,000
Net Worth: ($90,763,000)
Earnings: ($114,466,000)
Emp.: 7
Fiscal Year-end: 12/31/23
Biotechnology Research & Development
N.A.I.C.S.: 541714
Daniel Behr (Exec VP & Head-External Innovation and Academic Partnerships)
Elizabeth Ng (CEO)
Inderjote Kathuria (Chief Strategy Officer)
Suren Ajjarapu (Chm & CEO)
Howard A. Doss (CFO & Sec)
Chirinjeev Kathuria (Founder & Chm)
Surendra Ajjarapu (Chm & CEO)

Subsidiaries:

Ocean Biomedical Holdings, Inc. (1)
55 Claverick St Room 325, Providence, RI 02903
Tel.: (401) 444-7375
Assets: $386,000
Liabilities: $2,271,000
Net Worth: ($1,885,000)
Earnings: ($1,653,000)
Emp.: 9
Fiscal Year-end: 12/31/2020
Holding Company; Biotechnology Research & Development Services
N.A.I.C.S.: 551112
Chirinjeev Kathuria (Co-Founder & Chm)
Jack A. Elias (Co-Founder)
Sharon Talcott (VP-Strategic Partnerships)
Kevin Kertscher (Dir-Comm)

OCEAN POWER TECHNOLOGIES, INC.
28 Engelhard Dr Ste B, Monroe Township, NJ 08831
Tel.: (609) 730-0400 DE
Web Site:
https://www.oceanpowertechnologies.com
OPTT—(NYSEAMEX)
Rev.: $5,525,000
Assets: $28,704,000
Liabilities: $9,360,000
Net Worth: $19,344,000
Earnings: ($27,483,000)
Emp.: 43
Fiscal Year-end: 04/30/24
Wave Energy Electricity Generating Systems
N.A.I.C.S.: 423610
Terence James Cryan (Chm)
Jose H. Vazquez (VP-Strategic Consulting Svcs)
Jeffrey R. Wiener (VP-Sls-Global)
Robert P. Powers (CFO, Principal Acctg Officer & Sr VP)
Ethan Butler (VP-Engrg & Ops)
Joseph DiPietro (Principal Acctg Officer, Treas & Controller)
J. Philipp Stratmann (Pres & CEO)
Matthew Burdyny (VP-Global Sls & Marketing)

Subsidiaries:

3Dent Technology, LLC (1)
2444 Times Blvd Ste 200, Houston, TX 77005-3253
Tel.: (832) 519-0604
Web Site: https://www.3denttech.com
Engineeering Services
N.A.I.C.S.: 541330

Marine Advanced Robotics, Inc. (1)
1401 Marina Way S Ste 310 and 320, Richmond, CA 94804
Tel.: (510) 232-1685
Autonomous Surface Vehicle Mfr
N.A.I.C.S.: 336612

Ocean Power Technologies, Ltd. (1)
Warwick Innovation Centre Gallows Hill, Warwick, CV34 6UW, United Kingdom (100%)
Tel.: (44) 1926623370
Web Site: http://www.oceanpowertech.com
Sales Range: $50-74.9 Million
Emp.: 0
Utilizing Ocean Power for Electrical Generation
N.A.I.C.S.: 221111

OCEAN THERMAL ENERGY CORPORATION
800 S Queen St, Lancaster, PA 17603
Tel.: (717) 299-1344 NV
Web Site:
http://www.otecorporation.com
Year Founded: 2006
CPWR—(OTCEM)
Assets: $6,404
Liabilities: $36,205,430

Net Worth: ($36,199,026)
Earnings: ($6,912,102)
Emp.: 2
Fiscal Year-end: 12/31/22
Renewable Energy Systems Mfr
N.A.I.C.S.: 237130
Jeremy P. Feakins (Chm, CEO, CFO, Treas & Sec)
Gerald S. Koenig (Gen Counsel & Head-Govt Affairs)
Andy C. Welch (VP-Project Mgmt)
Melanie Roach (VP-Ops-Bahamas)
Paula Vitz (Dir-Bus Dev)
Cinthia M. Kettering (Comml Dir)

OCEANEERING INTERNATIONAL, INC.
5875 N Sam Houston Pkwy W Ste 400, Houston, TX 77086
Tel.: (713) 329-4500 DE
Web Site:
https://www.oceaneering.com
Year Founded: 1964
OII—(NYSE)
Rev.: $2,066,084,000
Assets: $2,031,683,000
Liabilities: $1,505,879,000
Net Worth: $525,804,000
Earnings: $25,941,000
Emp.: 9,200
Fiscal Year-end: 12/31/22
Technical Services & Hardware for Operation in Marine, Space & other Harsh Environments
N.A.I.C.S.: 213112
Roderick A. Larson (Pres & CEO)
Philip G. Beierl (Sr VP-Aerospace & Defense Technologies)
Alan R. Curtis (CFO & Sr VP)
David K. Lawrence (Gen Counsel, Sec & Sr VP)
Eric A. Silva (Sr VP-Strategic Plng)
Christopher J. Dyer (Sr VP-Offshore Projects Grp)
Leonardo P. Granato (Sr VP-Integrity Mgmt & Digital Solutions)
Hilary Frisbie (Sr Dir-IR)
Jennifer F. Simons (Chief Legal Officer, Sec & Sr VP)
Earl F. Childress (Chief Comml Officer & Sr VP)
Holly D. Kriendler (Chief HR Officer & Sr VP)
Benjamin M. Laura (Chief Innovation Officer & Sr VP)
Martin J. McDonald (Sr VP-Subsea Robotics)
Shaun R. Roedel (Sr VP-Manufactured Products)

Subsidiaries:

Airsis, Inc. (1)
9085 Aero Dr Ste A, San Diego, CA 92123
Tel.: (858) 586-0933
Web Site: http://www.airsis.com
Sales Range: $1-9.9 Million
Emp.: 28
Internet Software Development Services
N.A.I.C.S.: 541511

Blue Ocean Technologies LLC (1)
3321 E Davis St, Conroe, TX 77301
Tel.: (281) 419-4777
Web Site: http://www.blueoceansubsea.com
Industrial Machinery & Equipment Merchant Whslr
N.A.I.C.S.: 423830
Neil Crawford (Pres)

Consolidated Launcher Technology, Inc. (1)
804-D Industrial Ave, Chesapeake, VA 23324
Tel.: (757) 545-2200
Shipboard Repair & Maintenance Services
N.A.I.C.S.: 336611

Frog AGV Systems B.V. (1)
Tractieweg 190, Utrecht, 3534 AP, Netherlands

Tel.: (31) 302440550
Web Site: http://www.frog.nl
Oil & Gas Field Engineering Services
N.A.I.C.S.: 333132

Grayloc Products Canada Ltd. (1)
1129 Northside Road Unit 1, Burlington, L7M 1H5, ON, Canada
Tel.: (905) 842-3150
Web Site: http://www.Grayloc.com
Sales Range: $50-74.9 Million
Emp.: 20
Oil & Gas Clamp Connectors Mfr & Distr
N.A.I.C.S.: 213112

Grayloc Products Ltd. (1)
Site 39 Silverburn Place, Bridge of Don Industrial Estate, Aberdeen, AB23 8EG, United Kingdom
Tel.: (44) 1224222790
Sales Range: $50-74.9 Million
Emp.: 40
Connector & Related Product Distr
N.A.I.C.S.: 423690

Grayloc Products, L.L.C. (1)
9342 Telge Rd, Houston, TX 77095
Tel.: (713) 466-8853
Connector & Related Product Distr
N.A.I.C.S.: 423690
Mike Robbins (Office Mgr)

Oceaneering AS (1)
Vestre Svanholmen 24, 4313, Sandnes, Norway
Tel.: (47) 52913000
Web Site: http://www.oceaneering.com
Emp.: 1,000
Offshore Engineering Services
N.A.I.C.S.: 541330

Subsidiary (Domestic):

Oceaneering Rotator AS (2)
Hagen 20, 4645, Nodeland, Norway (100%)
Tel.: (47) 5 291 3000
Web Site: http://www.rotator.no
Sales Range: $50-74.9 Million
Emp.: 120
Shipbuilding & Repairing Services & Machines
N.A.I.C.S.: 336611
Paul A. Frikstad (Mng Dir)

Oceaneering Angola, S.A. (1)
Avenida Deolinda Rodrigues No 495 Terra Nova, Luanda, Angola
Tel.: (244) 222635400
Vessel Management Services
N.A.I.C.S.: 541618

Oceaneering Asset Integrity AS (1)
Sandslimarka 61, Stavanger, 5254, Sandsli, Norway
Tel.: (47) 52913000
Oil & Gas Field Engineering Services
N.A.I.C.S.: 333132

Oceaneering Australia Pty, Limited (1)
634 Karel Ave, Jandakot, West Perth, 6164, WA, Australia
Tel.: (61) 864990000
Offshore Engineering Services
N.A.I.C.S.: 541330

Oceaneering Canada Limited (1)
214 McNamara Drive, Paradise, A1L 0A6, NL, Canada
Tel.: (709) 570-7072
Web Site: http://www.oceaneering.com
Engineeering Services
N.A.I.C.S.: 541330

Oceaneering International GmbH (1)
Industriestrasse 24, 6300, Zug, Switzerland (100%)
Tel.: (41) 417672500
Web Site: http://www.oceaneering.com
Offshore Engineering Services
N.A.I.C.S.: 541330

Oceaneering International Pte. Ltd. (1)
1 Kwong Min Road, Singapore, 628704, Singapore (100%)
Tel.: (65) 62613211
Web Site: http://www.oceaneering.com
Sales Range: $25-49.9 Million
Emp.: 40
Underwater Service Company

N.A.I.C.S.: 213112

Oceaneering International Services, Ltd. (1)
Building 3 Levels 2&3 Aberdeen International Business Park Dyce Drive, Aberdeen, AB21 0BR, United Kingdom **(100%)**
Tel.: (44) 122 475 8500
Web Site: http://www.oceaneering.com
Underwater Service Company
N.A.I.C.S.: 213112

Oceaneering Intervention Engineering (1)
11915 FM 529, Houston, TX 77041-3000
Tel.: (832) 467-7600
Web Site: http://www.oceaneering.com
Sales Range: $125-149.9 Million
Emp.: 600
Subsea Oil & Gas Production & Pipeline Connection Operations Engineer & Mfr
N.A.I.C.S.: 541330
F. Richard Frisbie (Sr VP-Deepwater Tech)

Oceaneering Pipetech AS (1)
Lonavegen, PO Box 163, 5342, Straume, Norway
Tel.: (47) 56316000
Oil & Gas Field Engineering Services
N.A.I.C.S.: 333132

Oceaneering Services Australia Pty Ltd. (1)
Level 7 342 Flinders Street, Melbourne, 3000, VIC, Australia
Tel.: (61) 386258400
Project Management Services
N.A.I.C.S.: 561110

Oceaneering Space Systems (1)
16665 Spc Ctr Blvd, Houston, TX 77058-2253 **(100%)**
Tel.: (281) 228-5300
Web Site: http://www.oceaneering.com
Sales Range: $100-124.9 Million
Emp.: 200
Engineering, Research & Technology
N.A.I.C.S.: 332510

Oceaneering Technologies (1)
7001 Dorsey Rd Hillside Business Pk, Hanover, MD 21076
Tel.: (301) 249-3300
Web Site: http://www.oceaneering.com
Sales Range: $150-199.9 Million
Emp.: 400
Designer, Developer & Operator of Advanced Robotic Systems & Remotely Operated Vehicles (ROVs)
N.A.I.C.S.: 561499

Oceaneering Umbilical Solutions (1)
11911 FM 529, Houston, TX 77041-3000
Tel.: (713) 329-4500
Web Site: http://www.oceaneering.com
Sales Range: $25-49.9 Million
Emp.: 120
Crude Petroleum & Natural Gas
N.A.I.C.S.: 326220

Technology Design Limited. (1)
Wharton Park House Nat Lane, Winsford, CW7 3BS, United Kingdom
Tel.: (44) 1606590123
Web Site:
    http://www.technologydesign.co.uk
Sales Range: $10-24.9 Million
Emp.: 16
Ultrasonic Data Acquisition Systems Mfr
N.A.I.C.S.: 335999

OCEANFIRST FINANCIAL CORP.
975 Hooper Ave, Toms River, NJ 08753
Tel.: (732) 240-4500 DE
Web Site: https://www.oceanfirst.com
Year Founded: 1996
OCFC—(NASDAQ)
Rev.: $607,974,000
Assets: $13,538,253,000
Liabilities: $11,876,308,000
Net Worth: $1,661,945,000
Earnings: $100,013,000
Emp.: 857
Fiscal Year-end: 12/31/23
Offices of Bank Holding Companies

N.A.I.C.S.: 551111
Steven J. Tsimbinos (Gen Counsel, Sec & Exec VP)
Christopher D. Maher (Chm & CEO)
Patrick S. Barrett (CFO & Exec VP)
Patrick Chong (Principal Acctg Officer)
Michele B. Estep (Chief Admin Officer)
Karthik Sridharan (CIO)
Anthony Giordano III (Exec VP)

Subsidiaries:

Country Bank Holding Company, Inc. (1)
655 3rd Ave, New York, NY 10017
Tel.: (212) 818-9090
Web Site: http://www.countrybnk.com
Bank Holding Company
N.A.I.C.S.: 551111
Joseph M. Murphy Jr. (Pres)
Joseph M. Murphy Sr. (CEO)

Subsidiary (Domestic):

Country Bank (2)
655 3rd Ave 9th Fl, New York, NY 10017
Tel.: (212) 818-9090
Web Site: http://www.countrybnk.com
Sales Range: $25-49.9 Million
Emp.: 60
Commericial Banking
N.A.I.C.S.: 522110
Timothy Moffett (Sr VP)
AnnMarie Sorena (Sr VP)

OceanFirst Bank, National Association (1)
975 Hooper Ave, Toms River, NJ 08753
Web Site: http://oceanfirst.com
Federal Savings Bank
N.A.I.C.S.: 522180
Angela K. Ho (Chief Compliance Officer & Sr VP)
Christopher D. Maher (Chm & CEO)
Patrick S. Barrett (CFO & Exec VP)
Joseph J. Lebel III (Pres & COO)
Karthik Sridharan (CIO & Exec VP)

Trident Abstract Title Agency, LLC (1)
1340 A Campus Pkwy, Wall Township, NJ 07753
Tel.: (732) 431-3134
Web Site: https://tridentabstract.com
Real Estate Management Services
N.A.I.C.S.: 531210

Two River Bancorp (1)
766 Shrewsbury Ave, Tinton Falls, NJ 07724
Tel.: (732) 389-8722
Web Site: http://www.tworiverbank.com
Sales Range: $50-74.9 Million
Bank Holding Company
N.A.I.C.S.: 551111
James M. Bollerman (Vice Chm)
Robin Zager (Sec)

Subsidiary (Domestic):

Two River Community Bank (2)
766 Shrewsbury Ave, Tinton Falls, NJ 07724
Tel.: (732) 389-8722
Web Site: http://www.tworiverbank.com
Sales Range: $25-49.9 Million
Emp.: 100
Commercial Banking Services
N.A.I.C.S.: 522110
James M. Bollerman (Vice Chm)
William D. Moss (Pres & CEO)
A. Richard Abrahamian (CFO & Exec VP)

OCEANTECH ACQUISITIONS I CORP.
515 Madison Ave 8th Fl Ste 8133, New York, NY 10022
Tel.: (929) 412-1272 DE
Web Site: https://oceantechspac.com
Year Founded: 2021
OTEC—(NASDAQ)
Rev.: $4,320,843
Assets: $19,465,424
Liabilities: $27,940,468

Net Worth: ($8,475,044)
Earnings: $1,964,948
Emp.: 2
Fiscal Year-end: 12/31/22
Blank Check Company
N.A.I.C.S.: 523999
Surendra Ajjarapu (Chm & CEO)

OCONEE FEDERAL FINANCIAL CORP.
115 E N 2nd St, Seneca, SC 29678
Tel.: (864) 882-2765
Web Site:
    https://www.oconeefederal.com
Year Founded: 2010
OFED—(NASDAQ)
Rev.: $18,050,000
Assets: $544,792,000
Liabilities: $469,535,000
Net Worth: $75,257,000
Earnings: $4,099,000
Emp.: 79
Fiscal Year-end: 06/30/22
Bank Holding Company
N.A.I.C.S.: 551111
Curtis T. Evatt (Pres & CEO)
John W. Hobbs (CFO)
Robert N. McLellan Jr. (Chm)

Subsidiaries:

Oconee Federal Savings & Loan Associaton, Inc. (1)
201 E N 2nd St, Seneca, SC 29678
Tel.: (864) 882-2765
Web Site: http://www.oconeefederal.com
Federal Savings & Loan Services
N.A.I.C.S.: 522180
T. Rhett Evatt (Chm)
Curtis T. Evatt (Pres & CEO)

Subsidiary (Domestic):

Mutual Savings Bank (2)
330 W Carolina Ave, Hartsville, SC 29550
Tel.: (843) 383-3050
Web Site: http://www.mutualsavings.net
Rev.: $9,000,000
Emp.: 24
Fiscal Year-end: 12/31/2006
Federal Savings Institutions
N.A.I.C.S.: 522180

OCONEE FINANCIAL CORP.
41 N Main St, Watkinsville, GA 30677
Tel.: (706) 769-6611 GA
Year Founded: 1998
OSBK—(OTCIQ)
Rev.: $14,464,253
Assets: $399,521,439
Liabilities: $363,854,343
Net Worth: $35,667,096
Earnings: $3,759,366
Fiscal Year-end: 12/31/19
Financial Investment Services
N.A.I.C.S.: 523999
James R. McLemore (CFO)
Pamela J. Lewallen (Controller)
Virginia Wells McGeary (Chm)
T. Neil Stevens (Pres & CEO)

OCONOMOWOC BANCSHARES, INC.
Tel.: (262) 569-9900
Web Site: https://www.fbfcwi.com
OCNB—(OTCIQ)
Bank Holding Company
N.A.I.C.S.: 551111
Robert W. Snyder (Chm)
Nate Zastrow (CFO & Exec VP)
Mark T. McCune (Exec VP & Chief Lending Officer)

Subsidiaries:

First Bank Financial Centre (1)
155 W Wisconsin Ave, Oconomowoc, WI 53066
Tel.: (262) 569-9900
Web Site: http://www.fbfcwi.com

Sales Range: $75-99.9 Million
Emp.: 211
Banking Services
N.A.I.C.S.: 522110
Charles J. Folkman (Vice Chm)
Mark McCune (Chief Lending Officer & Sr VP)
Mark W. Mohr (Pres & CEO)
Robert Snyder (Chm)
Nate Zastrow (CFO & Exec VP)
Tyson Goecks (Coord-Cash Mgmt-Oconomowoc)
Nick Collins (VP)
Dave Sutton (Sr VP & Dir-Retail & Wealth Mgmt)
Lee McLean (VP)
Craig Kouba (Sr VP)
Aaron Pearson (VP & Deputy Dir-SBA BDO Sls)
Laura Edwards (Asst VP)
Scott Wisniewski (VP)

OCUGEN, INC.
11 Great Valley Pkwy, Malvern, PA 19355
Tel.: (484) 328-4701 DE
Web Site: https://www.ocugen.com
Year Founded: 2000
OCGN—(NASDAQ)
Rev.: $6,036,000
Assets: $64,647,000
Liabilities: $23,983,000
Net Worth: $40,664,000
Earnings: ($63,078,000)
Emp.: 65
Fiscal Year-end: 12/31/23
Orthopedic Medical Device Mfr
N.A.I.C.S.: 339112
Shankar Musunuri (Co-Founder, Chm & CEO)
Uday B. Kompella (Co-Founder)
Bruce D. Forrest (Chief Medical Officer-Acting)
Mike Shine (Sr VP-Comml)
Zara Gaudioso (Head-HR)
Ranjit R. Deshmukh (VP)
Tiffany J. Hamilton (Head)
Jyothy Pillai (Head)
Huma Qamar (Head)
Jesse Simmers (Head)

Subsidiaries:

Prochon BioTech, Ltd. (1)
7 Golda Meir St, PO Box 1482, Nes Ziyyona, Israel
Tel.: (972) 89303000
Biotechnology Research & Development Services
N.A.I.C.S.: 541714

OCULAR THERAPEUTIX, INC.
15 Crosby Dr, Bedford, MA 01730
Tel.: (781) 357-4000 DE
Web Site: https://www.ocutx.com
Year Founded: 2006
OCUL—(NASDAQ)
Rev.: $58,443,000
Assets: $252,060,000
Liabilities: $160,929,000
Net Worth: $91,131,000
Earnings: ($80,736,000)
Emp.: 267
Fiscal Year-end: 12/31/23
Biopharmaceutical Mfr
N.A.I.C.S.: 325412
Charles Warden (Chm)
Peter Jarrett (Chief Scientific Officer)
Pravin U. Dugel (Exec Chm, Pres & CEO)
Nadia K. Waheed (Chief Medical Officer)
Gurses Ozden (Sr VP-Clinical Dev)
Tracy Smith (VP-HR)
Philip Strassburger (Gen Counsel)
Nadia K. Waheed (Chief Medical Officer)
Karen-Leigh Edwards (Sr VP-Technical Ops)

Ocular Therapeutix, Inc.—(Continued)

Steve Meyers (*Sr VP*)
Donald Notman (*CFO, COO & Principal Acctg Officer*)

OCUPHIRE PHARMA, INC.

37000 Grand River Ave Ste 120,
Farmington Hills, MI 48335
Tel.: (248) 957-9024   DE
Web Site: https://www.ocuphire.com
Year Founded: 2001
OCUP—(NASDAQ)
Rev.: $39,850,000
Assets: $48,992,000
Liabilities: $2,753,000
Net Worth: $46,239,000
Earnings: $17,888,000
Emp.: 10
Fiscal Year-end: 12/31/22
Biopharmaceutical Developer & Mfr
N.A.I.C.S.: 325412
Joseph K. Schachle (*COO*)
Amy Zaremba Rabourn (*Sr VP-Fin*)
Ronil Patel (*Chief Bus Officer*)
George Magrath (*CEO*)

ODONATE THERAPEUTICS, INC.

3 E 28th St 10th Fl, New York, NY
10016
Tel.: (332) 206-0935   DE
Web Site: http://www.odonate.com
Year Founded: 2013
ODT—(NASDAQ)
Rev.: $1,083,000
Assets: $167,886,000
Liabilities: $31,741,000
Net Worth: $136,145,000
Earnings: ($126,350,000)
Emp.: 137
Fiscal Year-end: 12/31/20
Biotechnology Research & Development Services
N.A.I.C.S.: 541714
Stewart M. Kroll (*Chief Dev Officer*)
Kevin C. Tang (*Chm & CEO*)
Joseph P. O'Connell (*Chief Medical Officer*)
Thomas Wei (*Chief Scientific Officer*)
Steven S. Pfeiffer (*Sr VP-Technical Ops*)
Michael S. Hearne (*CFO*)
Ryan Cole (*Sr VP-Ops*)
Jennifer Schroeder (*Sr VP-Program Mgmt & Tech*)
Tracey McKennon (*Sr VP-Quality Assurance*)
Jill Krause (*VP-Clinical Quality & Trng*)
Kim Ma (*Sr VP-Clinical Ops*)
Christian Gagel (*VP-Fin & Acctg*)
Jeffrey L. Vacirca (*Co-Founder*)

ODYSSEY HEALTH, INC.

2300 W Sahara Ave Ste 800 Ste
4012, Las Vegas, NV 89102
Tel.: (702) 780-6559   NV
Web Site:
https://www.odysseyhealthinc.com
Year Founded: 2014
ODYY—(OTCIQ)
Assets: $610,533
Liabilities: $3,377,887
Net Worth: ($2,767,354)
Earnings: ($16,883,095)
Emp.: 4
Fiscal Year-end: 07/31/21
Pharmaceutical Preparation Manufacturing
N.A.I.C.S.: 325412
Joseph Michael Redmond (*Chm, Pres & CEO*)

ODYSSEY MARINE EXPLORATION, INC.

205 S Hoover Blvd Ste 210, Tampa,
FL 33609
Tel.: (813) 876-1776   NV
Web Site:
https://www.odysseymarine.com
Year Founded: 1994
OMEX—(NASDAQ)
Rev.: $803,799
Assets: $22,752,297
Liabilities: $108,658,831
Net Worth: ($85,906,534)
Earnings: ($3,884,602)
Emp.: 11
Fiscal Year-end: 12/31/23
Deep-Water Shipwrecks Exploration
& Recovery Services Throughout the
World; Traveling Exhibits & Attractions Operator
N.A.I.C.S.: 483112
Laura Lionetti Barton (*Chief Bus Officer & Sec*)
Gregory P. Stemm (*Founder*)
Mark D. Gordon (*Chm & CEO*)
John M. Oppermann (*VP & Dir-Res & Scientific Svcs*)
John D. Longley Jr. (*Pres & COO*)

Subsidiaries:

Odyssey Marine Entertainment,
Inc.   (1)
5215 W Laurel St Ste 210, Tampa, FL
33607   (100%)
Tel.: (813) 876-1776
Web Site: http://www.shipwreck.net
Sales Range: $25-49.9 Million
Development, Design & Merchandising of
Shipwreck Attractions
N.A.I.C.S.: 487210

Shipwreck Heritage Press LLC   (1)
5215 W Laurel St Ste 210, Tampa, FL
33607   (100%)
Tel.: (813) 876-1776
Web Site: http://www.shipwreck.net
Sales Range: $100-124.9 Million
Development & Distribution of Books Related to Marine Enterprises
N.A.I.C.S.: 323117

OFFERPAD SOLUTIONS INC.

2150 E Germann Rd Ste 1, Chandler,
AZ 85286   DE
Web Site: https://www.offerpad.com
Year Founded: 2015
OPAD—(NYSE)
Rev.: $3,952,314,000
Assets: $825,069,000
Liabilities: $703,192,000
Net Worth: $121,877,000
Earnings: ($148,613,000)
Emp.: 900
Fiscal Year-end: 12/31/22
Home Buying & Real Estate Services
N.A.I.C.S.: 531390
Peter Knag (*CFO & Principal Acctg Officer*)
Benjamin Aronovitch (*Chief Legal Officer*)
Dan Mayes (*CIO*)
Jaidip Singh (*Chief Risk Officer*)
Vaughn Bair (*Chief Real Estate Officer*)
David Connelly (*Chief Growth Officer*)
Lisa Hickle (*Sr VP-People Ops, Facilities, and Procurement*)
Brian Bair (*Founder, Chm & CEO*)

OFG BANCORP

254 Munoz Rivera Ave, San Juan,
PR 00918
Tel.: (787) 771-6800   PR
Web Site:
https://www.ofgbancorp.com
Year Founded: 1964
OFG—(NYSE)
Rev.: $647,263,000
Assets: $9,818,780,000
Liabilities: $8,776,374,000
Net Worth: $1,042,406,000

Earnings: $166,239,000
Emp.: 2,253
Fiscal Year-end: 12/31/22
Diversified Financial Holding Company
N.A.I.C.S.: 551111
Mari Evelyn Rodriguez Mimoso (*Chief Banking Officer*)
Ganesh Kumar (*Chief Strategy Officer-US Bus-US*)
Jose Rafael Fernandez (*Co-Chm, Pres & CEO*)
Jorge Colon-Gerena (*Vice Chm*)
Cesar A. Ortiz (*Chief Risk Officer*)
Ada Garcia Castello (*Mng Dir-Customer Intelligence & Operations*)
Patrick J. Haggarty (*Mng Dir-Commercial Banking*)
Hugh Gonzalez (*Gen Counsel & Sec*)

Subsidiaries:

Oriental Bank   (1)
Marginal San Roberto 997 Professional Ofc
Park, Rio Piedras, PR 00927
Tel.: (787) 620-0000
Web Site: https://orientalbank.com
Commericial Banking
N.A.I.C.S.: 522110
Jose Rafael Fernández (*Chm, Pres & CEO*)
Ganesh Kumar (*COO*)
Ada Garcia (*Mng Dir*)
Cesar A. Ortiz (*Mng Dir*)
Hugh Gonzalez (*Gen Counsel*)
Jennifer Zapata (*Mng Dir*)
Jose E. Cabrera (*Chief Risk Officer*)
Maritza Arizmendi (*CFO*)
Patrick Haggarty (*Mng Dir*)

Representative Office (Domestic):

Oriental Bank - US Virgin Islands (2)
214 C Altone, Saint Thomas, VI 00802
Tel.: (340) 774-0037
Web Site: https://orientalbank.com
Commericial Banking
N.A.I.C.S.: 522110

Oriental Financial Services LLC (1)
996 San Roberto St Oriental Ctr 9th Fl Professional Offices Park, San Juan, PR 00926
Tel.: (787) 771-6800
Security Brokers
N.A.I.C.S.: 523150

Oriental Pension Consultants,
Inc.   (1)
1900 NW Corporate Blvd Ste 400 W, Boca
Raton, FL 33431
Tel.: (561) 392-5149
Web Site: http://www.orientalpc.com
Pension Plan Consulting Services
N.A.I.C.S.: 525110
Jose Rafael Fernandez (*Pres & CEO*)
Ed Moss (*Dir-Daily Svcs*)

OFS CAPITAL CORPORATION

10 S Wacker Dr Ste 2500, Chicago,
IL 60606
Tel.: (847) 734-2084   DE
Web Site: https://www.ofscapital.com
Year Founded: 2010
OFS—(NASDAQ)
Rev.: $48,744,000
Assets: $520,717,000
Liabilities: $340,294,000
Net Worth: $180,423,000
Earnings: $10,052,000
Emp.: 50
Fiscal Year-end: 12/31/22
Management Investment Services
N.A.I.C.S.: 523999
Ross A. Teune (*Chief Acctg Officer*)
Bilal Rashid (*Chm & CEO*)
Mukya S. Porter (*Chief Compliance Officer*)
Kyle Spina (*Chief Acctg Officer*)
Tod Reichert (*Sec*)

OFS CREDIT COMPANY, INC

10 S Wacker Dr Ste 2500, Chicago,
IL 60606
Tel.: (847) 734-2085   DE

Web Site:
https://www.ofscreditcompany.com
Year Founded: 2017
OCCIO—(NASDAQ)
Investment Services
N.A.I.C.S.: 523999
Bilal Rashid (*Chm, Pres & CEO*)
Mukya S. Porter (*Chief Compliance Officer*)
Tod K. Reichert (*Sec*)
Kyle Spina (*Chief Acctg Officer*)

OGE ENERGY CORP.

321 N Harvey, Oklahoma City, OK
73101-0321
Tel.: (405) 553-3000   OK
Web Site: https://www.oge.com
Year Founded: 1902
OGE—(NYSE)
Rev.: $2,674,300,000
Assets: $12,790,700,000
Liabilities: $8,279,100,000
Net Worth: $4,511,600,000
Earnings: $416,800,000
Emp.: 2,329
Fiscal Year-end: 12/31/23
Public Utility Holding Company
N.A.I.C.S.: 551112
Cristina Fernandez McQuistion (*VP-Corp Responsibility & Stewardship*)
Sean Trauschke (*Chm, Pres & CEO*)
Charles B. Walworth (*Treas*)
W. Bryan Buckler (*CFO & VP*)
Sarah R. Stafford (*Chief Acctg Officer & Controller*)
Kenneth A. Miller (*VP-Regulatory & Legislative Affairs-OG&E*)

Subsidiaries:

Oklahoma Gas & Electric
Company   (1)
321 N Harvey, Oklahoma City, OK
73101-0321   (100%)
Tel.: (405) 553-3000
Web Site: https://www.oge.com
Rev.: $2,607,299,999
Assets: $12,642,600,000
Liabilities: $7,667,900,000
Net Worth: $4,974,700,000
Earnings: $426,400,000
Emp.: 1,936
Fiscal Year-end: 12/31/2023
Gas & Electricity Distr
N.A.I.C.S.: 221121
Cristina Fernandez McQuistion (*VP-Corp Responsibility & Stewardship*)
Sean Trauschke (*Pres & CEO*)
Charles B. Walworth (*Treas*)
W. Bryan Buckler (*CFO*)
Donnie Jones (*VP-Utility Ops*)
Sarah R. Stafford (*Chief Acctg Officer & Controller*)
Andrea Dennis (*VP-Transmission & Distr Ops*)
Scott A. Briggs (*VP-Human Resources*)
Robert J. Burch (*VP*)
David A. Parker (*VP*)
Matthew J. Schuermann (*VP*)
Keith Erickson (*VP*)
Johnny Whitfield (*VP*)
Christine O. Woodworth (*VP*)

Subsidiary (Domestic):

AES Shady Point LLC   (2)
3 Mile E Of Jct 31, Panama, OK 74561
Tel.: (918) 962-9451
Power Generation Plant
N.A.I.C.S.: 221118

OHANA PACIFIC BANK

1357 Kapiolani Blvd Ste 102, Honolulu, HI 96814
Tel.: (808) 237-6551   DE
Web Site:
http://www.ohanapacificbank.com
OHPB—(OTCIQ)
Commercial Banking Services
N.A.I.C.S.: 522110
James C. Hong (*Pres & CEO*)
Nicole Byun (*Chief Credit Officer & Exec VP*)

Paul Lee *(CMO & Exec VP)*
Donald B. S. Kang *(Chm)*
Wayne T. Miyao *(Vice Chm)*

OHIO VALLEY BANC CORP.
420 3rd Ave, Gallipolis, OH 45631
Tel.: (740) 446-2631   OH
Web Site: https://www.ovbc.com
Year Founded: 1992
OVBC—(NASDAQ)
Rev.: $57,778,000
Assets: $1,210,787,000
Liabilities: $1,075,759,000
Net Worth: $135,028,000
Earnings: $13,338,000
Emp.: 275
Fiscal Year-end: 12/31/22
Bank Holding Company
N.A.I.C.S.: 551111
Larry E. Miller II *(Pres & CEO)*
Ryan J. Jones *(COO)*
Scott W. Shockey *(Sr VP)*
Brandon O. Huff *(VP)*

Subsidiaries:

Loan Central, Inc.   (1)
1828 Eastern Ave, Gallipolis, OH
45631   (100%)
Tel.: (740) 446-0965
Web Site: https://www.myloancentral.com
Sales Range: $125-149.9 Million
Mortgage Lending Services
N.A.I.C.S.: 522292

The Ohio Valley Bank Company   (1)
420 3rd Ave, Gallipolis, OH 45631 (100%)
Tel.: (740) 446-2631
Web Site: https://www.ovbc.com
Emp.: 300
Commericial Banking
N.A.I.C.S.: 522110
Larry E. Miller II *(Pres & CEO)*
Thomas E. Wiseman *(Chm & CEO)*
Ryan J. Jones *(COO)*
Shawn R. Siders *(Officer-Credit & VP)*
Brandon O. Huff *(Asst VP & Dir-Information Technology)*
Cherie A. Elliott *(VP)*

OIDON CO., LTD.
75 Rockerfeller Plz Ste 1926, New
York, NY 10019
Tel.: (212) 710-0330
OIDN—(OTCIQ)
Software Development Services
N.A.I.C.S.: 541511
Keisuke Hayashi *(CMO)*

OIL STATES INTERNATIONAL, INC.
333 Clay St Ste 4620, Houston, TX
77002
Tel.: (713) 652-0582   DE
Web Site:
   https://www.oilstatesintl.com
OIS—(NYSE)
Rev.: $782,283,000
Assets: $1,046,486,000
Liabilities: $336,941,000
Net Worth: $709,545,000
Earnings: $12,891,000
Emp.: 2,752
Fiscal Year-end: 12/31/23
Oil & Gas Drilling & Production Services
N.A.I.C.S.: 211130
Cynthia B. Taylor *(Pres & CEO)*
Lloyd A. Hajdik *(CFO, Treas & Exec VP)*
Philip Scott Moses *(COO & Exec VP)*
Brian E. Taylor *(Chief Acctg Officer, Sr VP & Controller)*

Subsidiaries:

Acute Technological Services,
Inc.   (1)
11925 Brittmoore Park Dr, Houston,
TX 77041-7226
Tel.: (713) 983-9353

Web Site: http://www.acutetechserv.com
Sales Range: $10-24.9 Million
Emp.: 85
Engineeering Services
N.A.I.C.S.: 541330

Civeo Canada Inc.   (1)
3790 98th Street NW, Edmonton, T6E 6B4,
AB, Canada
Tel.: (780) 463-8872
Web Site: http://www.civeo.com
Workforce Accommodation Services
N.A.I.C.S.: 541618

GEODynamics (U.K.) Limited   (1)
Gateway Business Park Moss Road, Nigg,
Aberdeen, AB12 3GQ, United Kingdom
Tel.: (44) 1224961161
Oil & Gas Well Completion Services
N.A.I.C.S.: 213111
Ian Tomlinson *(Ops Mgr-North Sea)*

GEODynamics, Inc.   (1)
10400 W Interstate 20, Millsap, TX 76066
Tel.: (817) 341-5300
Web Site: https://www.perf.com
Oil Field Equipment Mfr & Distr
N.A.I.C.S.: 333132
Benjamin Smith *(Pres & CEO)*
John Hardesty *(VP-Engineering-Product Development)*
Chris Chalker *(VP)*
Raymond Shaffer *(VP-Technology)*
Joel Barlow *(VP)*
Kevin George *(Dir)*
Robert Davis *(Mgr, Founder & , Officer-Corporate Development)*
Josh Spraker *(VP-Sales)*
Tracy Smith *(Dir-Administration-Human Resources)*
John Berner *(VP-Manufacturing-Supply Chain)*
Wenbo Yang *(Dir)*
Chris Green *(Dir)*
Brett Wilson *(Mgr)*
Michael Wroblicky *(Mgr)*
Jason Ansley *(Mgr)*
Poncho Wilson *(Dir)*
Rayn McNeely *(Sr Mgr-Business Development)*
Santo Petitto *(Sr Mgr-Business Development)*
Wes Goff *(Sr Mgr-Business Development)*
Lindsey Buck *(Sr Mgr-Business Development)*
Eric Michaels *(Sr Mgr-Business Development)*
Shaun Garcia *(Sr Mgr-Business Development)*
Josh Audet *(Sr Mgr-Business Development)*
Keith Slone *(Dir)*

OSES International, LLC   (1)
365 Lafayette Dr, Miami Springs, FL 33166
Tel.: (305) 871-8115
Business Services
N.A.I.C.S.: 561990

Oil States   (1)
6120 E Orem Dr, Houston, TX
77048   (100%)
Tel.: (713) 445-2210
Web Site: http://www.oilstates.com
Sales Range: $75-99.9 Million
Emp.: 250
Vendor for Marine Equipment, Subsea Systems, Oil Field & Industrial Structures
N.A.I.C.S.: 541330

Oil States Energy Services (Canada)
Inc.   (1)
334 Burnt Park Way, Red Deer, T4S 2L4,
AB, Canada
Tel.: (403) 340-0716
Oil & Gas Exploration Services
N.A.I.C.S.: 213112

Oil States Energy Services Holding,
Inc.   (1)
333 Clay St Ste 4620, Houston, TX 77002-
4004
Tel.: (713) 652-0582
Holding Company
N.A.I.C.S.: 551114

Oil States Energy Services
L.L.C.   (1)
3 Allen Ctr 333 Clay St Ste 4620, Houston,
TX 77002
Tel.: (713) 425-2400

Web Site: https://www.oses.com
Oil & Gas Drilling Services
N.A.I.C.S.: 213112

Oil States Energy Services, Inc. (1)
333 Clay St Ste 4620, Houston, TX 77002-
4004
Tel.: (713) 652-0582
Oil & Gas Field Equipment Sales & Maintenance Services
N.A.I.C.S.: 213112

Division (Domestic):

Oil States Energy Services, Inc. (2)
5300 SW 33rd St, Oklahoma City, OK
73179
Tel.: (405) 702-6500
Web Site: http://www.oilstates.com
Sales Range: $75-99.9 Million
Emp.: 110
Oil Field Services
N.A.I.C.S.: 213112

Oil States HydroTech   (1)
1155 Dairy Ashford St Ste 700, Houston,
TX 77079-3016   (100%)
Tel.: (713) 510-2200
Web Site: http://www.oilstates.com
Sales Range: $75-99.9 Million
Emp.: 200
Contractor Specializing in Design, Engineering, Manufacturing, Sales & Service of Subsea Pipeline Connection & Repair Products
N.A.I.C.S.: 332996

Subsidiary (Domestic):

Oil States Hydrotech Systems   (2)
13111 NW Fwy, Houston, TX
77040-6311   (100%)
Tel.: (713) 510-2200
Web Site: http://www.oilstates.com
Sales Range: $75-99.9 Million
Water, Sewer & Utility Lines
N.A.I.C.S.: 332996

Oil States Industries (Asia) Pte
Ltd.   (1)
42-H Penjuru Road, Singapore, 609158,
Singapore   (100%)
Tel.: (65) 6 773 7555
Web Site: https://www.oilstates.com
Sales for the Asia-Pacific Region
N.A.I.C.S.: 333132

Oil States Industries (UK) Ltd. (1)
Moss Road Gateway Business Park, Nigg,
Aberdeen, AB12 3GQ, United Kingdom
Tel.: (44) 1224290000
Web Site: https://www.oilstates.com
Sales Range: $25-49.9 Million
Emp.: 140
Connector Products, Engineering, Fabrication, Test Laboratory & Recruitment Services
N.A.I.C.S.: 541380

Oil States Industries, Inc.   (1)
7701 S Cooper St, Arlington, TX 76001
Tel.: (817) 548-4200
Web Site: https://www.oilstates.com
Deepwater Drilling Rig Mfr
N.A.I.C.S.: 213112
Christopher E. Cragg *(Sr VP-Ops)*
Cynthia B. Taylor *(Pres & CEO)*

Subsidiary (Domestic):

Montgomery Machine Co., Inc.   (2)
1005 Mae Dr, Houston, TX 77015
Tel.: (713) 453-6381
Web Site: http://montgomerymachine.com
Sales Range: $1-9.9 Million
Emp.: 50
Industrial Machinery
N.A.I.C.S.: 332710

Oil States QCS   (2)
7250 W 43rd St Ste 100, Houston, TX
77092
Tel.: (713) 920-9800
Web Site: http://oilstates.com
Pipeline Connector Mfr
N.A.I.C.S.: 333248

Oil States Skagit SMATCO
L.L.C.   (1)
1180 Mulberry Rd, Houma, LA 70363
Tel.: (985) 868-0630
Oil & Gas Field Machinery Mfr

N.A.I.C.S.: 213112

PTI USA Manufacturing L.L.C.   (1)
390 Mountain View Rd, Berthoud, CO
80513
Tel.: (970) 670-6200
Workforce Accommodation Services
N.A.I.C.S.: 561990
Matt Henkener *(Mgr-Production)*

Stinger Wellhead Protection (Canada)
Incorporated   (1)
1422 510 5 Street SW, Calgary, T2P 3S2,
AB, Canada
Tel.: (403) 296-6400
Web Site:
   http://www.schoonerpetroleum.com
Oil & Gas Drilling Services
N.A.I.C.S.: 213112

Tempress Technologies Inc.   (1)
2200 Lind Ave SW Bldg A Ste 108, Renton,
WA 98057
Tel.: (425) 251-8120
Web Site: https://www.tempresstech.com
Industrial Machinery Mfr
N.A.I.C.S.: 333993

OIL-DRI CORPORATION OF AMERICA
410 N Michigan Ave Ste 400, Chicago, IL 60611
Tel.: (312) 321-1515   DE
Web Site: https://www.oildri.com
Year Founded: 1941
ODC—(NYSE)
Rev.: $437,587,000
Assets: $354,605,000
Liabilities: $144,017,000
Net Worth: $210,588,000
Earnings: $39,426,000
Emp.: 949
Fiscal Year-end: 07/31/24
Sorbent Products Mfr for Consumer,
Industrial, Environmental, Agricultural
& Fluids Purification Markets
N.A.I.C.S.: 325998
Lawrence E. Washow *(Vice Chm)*
Daniel S. Jaffee *(Chm, Pres & CEO)*
Wade Robey *(VP-Agriculture & Amlan Mktg)*
Laura G. Scheland *(Gen Counsel, Sec & VP)*
Susan M. Kreh *(CFO & CIO)*
Jessica D. Moskowitz *(VP & Gen Mgr-Consumer Products Div)*
David M. Atkinson *(VP & Controller)*
Christopher B. Lamson *(Grp VP-Retail & Wholesale)*
Patrick J. Walsh *(VP-HR)*
Aaron V. Christiansen *(VP-Ops)*
Yasmith Bernal *(VP-Crop & Horticulture)*
Leslie A. Garber *(Mgr-IR)*

Subsidiaries:

Amlan International   (1)
410 N Michigan Ave Ste 400, Chicago, IL
60611
Tel.: (312) 321-1515
Web Site: http://www.amlan.com
Livestock Health Managememt Services
N.A.I.C.S.: 541940
Fang Chi *(Sr Dir-Technical Svc)*
Leann Johnston *(Mgr-Technical Svc)*
Chris Ching *(Mgr-Technical Res)*
Hongyu Xue *(Dir-Life Sciences)*
Kreangkrai Sangthongdang *(Mgr-Thailand)*
Fred H. Kao *(VP-Sls-Global)*
Heath Wessels *(Sls Dir-North America)*
Harold Zhou *(Dir-Ops-China)*
Daniel S. Jaffee *(Pres & Gen Mgr)*
Saksake Pacharadit *(Sls Mgr-Asia Pacific)*
Nguyen Hai *(Mgr-Comml-Vietnam)*
Chuck Snipes *(Acct Mgr-Key-Coastal Reg)*
Betty Yuriko *(Country Mgr-Indonesia)*
Xin WU *(Sls Mgr-Technical)*

Blue Mountain Production Co.   (1)
31 County Rd 827, Blue Mountain, MS
38610-9081   (100%)
Tel.: (662) 685-4386

Oil-Dri Corporation of America—(Continued)

Sales Range: $100-124.9 Million
Emp.: 85
Mfr Marketer & Developer of Sorbent Products For Consumer, Industrial, Agricultural & Fluids Purif
N.A.I.C.S.: 327992

Favorite Products Company Ltd. (1)
730 Rue Salaberry, Laval, H7S 1H3, QC, Canada (100%)
Tel.: (450) 663-5750
Web Site: http://www.catstreedsarular.com
Sales Range: $10-24.9 Million
Emp.: 42
Synthetic Absorbents Mfr
N.A.I.C.S.: 325998
Gim Aruda (Controller)

Oil-Dri (U.K.) Ltd. (1)
Bannisters Row, Wisbech, PE13 3HZ, Cambridgeshire, United Kingdom (100%)
Tel.: (44) 1945581244
Web Site: http://www.oil-dri.co.uk
Sales Range: $25-49.9 Million
Emp.: 20
Mineral Absorbents Mfr & Sales
N.A.I.C.S.: 325998

Oil-Dri Canada ULC (1)
730 Rue Salaberry, Laval, H7S 1H3, QC, Canada
Tel.: (450) 663-5750
Web Site: https://www.oildri.com
Sales Range: $25-49.9 Million
Emp.: 20
Filtration & Separation Equipment Mfr & Distr
N.A.I.C.S.: 325998

Oil-Dri Corporation of America - Industrial & Automotive Division (1)
914 Curie Dr, Alpharetta, GA 30005-8369 (100%)
Tel.: (770) 475-3993
Sales Range: $50-74.9 Million
Emp.: 30
Oil Spill Clean-Up Products Mfr & Distr
N.A.I.C.S.: 424690

Oil-Dri Corporation of Georgia (1)
28990 Georgia Hwy 3 N, Ochlocknee, GA 31773-0662 (100%)
Tel.: (229) 574-5131
Web Site: http://www.oildri.net
Sales Range: $125-149.9 Million
Emp.: 400
Mfr of Absorbant Clay Products
N.A.I.C.S.: 327992
Daniel S. Jaffee (Pres & CEO)

Oil-Dri Production Company (1)
1800 City Ave N, Ripley, MS 38663-0476 (100%)
Tel.: (662) 837-9263
Sales Range: $50-74.9 Million
Emp.: 65
Mfr of Absorbent Clay Products
N.A.I.C.S.: 327992

Oil-Dri S.A. (1)
Pl du Four 1, 1296, Coppet, Switzerland (100%)
Tel.: (41) 229607282
Sales Range: $25-49.9 Million
Emp.: 3
Sales of Mineral Absorbents
N.A.I.C.S.: 424690

Oil-Dri SARL (1)
Pl du Four 1, 1296, Coppet, Switzerland
Tel.: (41) 229607282
Floor Absorbent Mfr
N.A.I.C.S.: 325612

Taft Production Company (1)
950 Petroleum Club Rd, Taft, CA 93268
Tel.: (661) 765-7194
Sales Range: $25-49.9 Million
Emp.: 76
Kitty Litter, Oil Absorbant & Agricultural Additive Mfr
N.A.I.C.S.: 325320

Ultra Pet Company, Inc. (1)
4325 Old Mill Rd Ste 2C, Anderson, SC 29621
Tel.: (864) 261-3546
Web Site: http://www.ultrapet.com

Sales Range: $1-9.9 Million
Emp.: 13
Pet & Pet Supplies Stores
N.A.I.C.S.: 459910
David Dyke (Controller)

OJAI OIL COMPANY
4081 Mission Oaks Blvd Ste A, Camarillo, CA 93012
Tel.: (805) 388-5858   CA
Web Site: https://www.ojaioil.com
OJOC—(OTCIQ)
Rev.: $10,725,780
Assets: $52,411,248
Liabilities: $30,976,704
Net Worth: $21,434,544
Earnings: $1,032,118
Fiscal Year-end: 12/31/19
Other Activities Related to Real Estate
N.A.I.C.S.: 531390
Tracy Off (VP-Corp)
Roger Cook (Auditor-Acctg)
Shelly Walters (Mgr-Acctg)
Douglas Off (Pres-Corp)
David Edward (VP-Corp)

Subsidiaries:

Golden State Storage One, LLC (1)
300 W Ventura Blvd, Camarillo, CA 93010
Tel.: (805) 521-4432
Web Site:
  http://www.goldenstatestorage.com
Self Storage Services
N.A.I.C.S.: 531130

OJSYS, INC.
363 Mira Vista Ter, Pasadena, CA 91105
Tel.: (818) 307-6117   FL
OJSY—(OTCIQ)
Dental Laboratory Services
N.A.I.C.S.: 339116
Ralph Boyd (Pres, CEO & Sec)
Adam S. Tracy (Gen Counsel)

OKMIN RESOURCES, INC.
16501 Ventura Blvd Ste 400, Encino, CA 91436
Tel.: (818) 201-3727   NV
Web Site:
  https://www.okminresources.com
Year Founded: 2020
OKMN—(OTCQB)
Rev.: $42,543
Assets: $366,621
Liabilities: $533,159
Net Worth: ($166,538)
Earnings: ($873,214)
Fiscal Year-end: 06/30/24
Natural Gas Extraction
N.A.I.C.S.: 211130
Jonathan Herzog (Pres, CEO & CFO)

OKTA, INC.
100 1st St Ste 600, San Francisco, CA 94105   DE
Web Site: https://www.okta.com
Year Founded: 2009
OKTA—(NASDAQ)
Rev.: $2,263,000,000
Assets: $8,989,000,000
Liabilities: $3,101,000,000
Net Worth: $5,888,000,000
Earnings: ($355,000,000)
Emp.: 5,908
Fiscal Year-end: 01/31/24
Software Development Services
N.A.I.C.S.: 541511
J. Frederic Kerrest (Co-Founder & Vice Chm)
Jesper Frederiksen (Gen Mgr-EMEA)
David Bradbury (Chief Security Officer)
Steve Rowland (Chief Revenue Officer)

Cole Breidenbach (VP)
Brett Tighe (CFO)
Todd McKinnon (Co-Founder, Chm & CEO)

Subsidiaries:

Okta Australia PTY Limited (1)
80 Pacific Hwy Level 14, North Sydney, 2060, NSW, Australia
Tel.: (61) 283104484
Web Site: https://www.okta.com
Software Development Services
N.A.I.C.S.: 541511

OLAPLEX HOLDINGS, INC.
1187 Coast Village Rd Ste 1-520, Santa Barbara, CA 93108
Tel.: (310) 691-0776   DE
Web Site: https://www.olaplex.com
Year Founded: 2021
OLPX—(NASDAQ)
Rev.: $458,300,000
Assets: $1,740,338,000
Liabilities: $895,370,000
Net Worth: $844,968,000
Earnings: $61,587,000
Emp.: 233
Fiscal Year-end: 12/31/23
Holding Company
N.A.I.C.S.: 551112
John P. Bilbrey (Exec Chm)
Catherine Dunleavy (CFO & COO)
Kristi Belhumeur (Chief Acctg Officer)
Amanda Baldwin (CEO)

OLD DOMINION FREIGHT LINE, INC.
500 Old Dominion Way, Thomasville, NC 27360
Tel.: (336) 889-5000   VA
Web Site: https://www.odfl.com
Year Founded: 1934
ODFL—(NASDAQ)
Rev.: $5,866,152,000
Assets: $5,512,393,000
Liabilities: $1,254,582,000
Net Worth: $4,257,811,000
Earnings: $1,239,502,000
Emp.: 22,902
Fiscal Year-end: 12/31/23
Freight Shipping Services
N.A.I.C.S.: 483113
David S. Congdon (Exec Chm)
Gregory B. Plemmons (COO & Exec VP)
Ross H. Parr (Gen Counsel, Sec & Sr VP-Legal Affairs)
Adam N. Satterfield (CFO, Exec VP-Fin & Asst Sec)
David J. Bates (Sr VP-Ops)
Christopher T. Brooks (Sr VP-HR & Safety)
Christopher J. Kelley (Sr VP-Operations)
Steven W. Hartsell (Sr VP-Sls)
Kevin Marty Freeman (Pres & CEO)
Cecil E. Overbey Jr. (Sr VP-Strategic Dev)

OLD NATIONAL BANCORP
1 Main St, Evansville, IN 47708
Tel.: (812) 464-1425   IN
Web Site:
  https://www.oldnational.com
Year Founded: 1982
ONB—(NASDAQ)
Rev.: $2,206,821,000
Assets: $49,089,836,000
Liabilities: $43,526,936,000
Net Worth: $5,562,900,000
Earnings: $581,992,000
Emp.: 3,940
Fiscal Year-end: 12/31/23
Bank Holding Company
N.A.I.C.S.: 551111
John V. Moran IV (CFO, Chief Strategy Officer & Sr Exec VP)

Nicholas J. Chulos (Chief Legal Officer & Sec)
Jeff C. Newcom (COO)
Angela L. Putnam (Chief Acctg Officer)
Joan M. Kissel (Chief Auditing & Ethics Officer)
Caroline J. Ellspermann (Chief People Officer)
Kendra L. Vanzo (Chief Admin Officer)
James A. Sandgren (CEO-Comml Banking)
Scott J. Evernham (Chief Risk Officer)
Chady M. AlAhmar (CEO-Wealth Mgmt)
Paul S. Kilroy (CIO)
Roland B. Shelton (Chief Strategic Bus Partnership Officer)
John V. Moran (Chief Strategy Officer)
Nicholas J. Chulos (Chief Legal Officer & Sec)
Corliss V. Garner (Chief Diversity , Equity & Inclusion Officer)
Mark G. Sander (Pres)
James V. Stadler (CMO)
Rafael A. Sanchez (Chief Impact Officer)
Brent R. Tischler (CEO-Community Banking)
James C. Ryan III (Chm & CEO)

Subsidiaries:

1834 Investment Advisors Co. (1)
511 N Broadway St Ste 801, Milwaukee, WI 53202
Tel.: (414) 615-1012
Web Site:
  https://www.1834investmentadvisors.com
Finance Investment Services
N.A.I.C.S.: 523999

CapStar Financial Holdings, Inc. (1)
1201 Demonbreun St Ste 700, Nashville, TN 37203
Tel.: (615) 732-6400
Web Site: https://ir.capstarbank.com
Rev.: $138,055,000
Assets: $3,117,169,000
Liabilities: $2,762,987,000
Net Worth: $354,182,000
Earnings: $39,017,000
Emp.: 397
Fiscal Year-end: 12/31/2022
Bank Holding Company
N.A.I.C.S.: 551111
Kenneth E. Webb (Interim Exec VP-Bank Ops)
Christopher A. Higgins (Pres-Middle Tennessee Market)
Christopher G. Tietz (Chief Banking Officer)
Timothy K. Schools (Pres & CEO)
Michael J. Fowler (CFO & Exec VP)
Ali Jefferson (Interim Principal Acctg Officer & Interim Controller)
Christopher A. Higgins (Pres-Middle Tennessee)
Amy C. Goodin (Chief Risk Officer)
Kevin L. Lambert (Chief Credit Officer)

First Midwest Bancorp, Inc. (1)
8750 W Bryn Mawr Ave Ste 1300, Chicago, IL 60631-3655
Tel.: (708) 831-7483
Rev.: $791,971,000
Assets: $20,838,678,000
Liabilities: $18,148,672,000
Net Worth: $2,690,006,000
Earnings: $107,898,000
Emp.: 2,074
Fiscal Year-end: 12/31/2020
Bank Holding Company
N.A.I.C.S.: 551111
Angela L. Putnam (Chief Acctg Officer & Sr VP)
Jo Ann Boylan (Chief Information & Ops Officer & Exec VP)

Subsidiary (Domestic):

Bankmanagers Corp. (2)

7540 W Capitol Dr, Milwaukee, WI 53216-1918
Tel.: (414) 466-8000
Web Site: http://www.parkbankonline.com
Sales Range: $100-124.9 Million
Bank Holding Company
N.A.I.C.S.: 551111

Bridgeview Bancorp, Inc. **(2)**
7940 S Harlem Ave, Bridgeview, IL 60455
Tel.: (708) 594-7400
Web Site: http://www.bridgeviewbank.com
Bank Holding Company
N.A.I.C.S.: 551111
Bill Conaghan *(Vice Chm & CEO)*
Peter J. Haleas *(Chm)*
Nicolas Mando *(COO)*
Tom Haleas *(Exec VP)*
Chris Esposito *(Pres-Sls)*

Bridgeview Bank Group **(2)**
7940 S Harlem Ave, Bridgeview, IL 60455
Tel.: (708) 594-7400
Commericial Banking
N.A.I.C.S.: 522110

Bridgeview Capital Solutions, LLC **(2)**
2847 Veterans Memorial Hwy 1685, Austell, GA 30168
Tel.: (404) 267-1177
Web Site: http://www.bridgeviewcs.com
Rev.: $2,300,000
Emp.: 2
Commercial Lender
N.A.I.C.S.: 522291
Gail Johnson *(VP)*

First Midwest Bank **(2)**
1 Pierce Pl, Itasca, IL 60143 **(100%)**
Tel.: (800) 322-3623
Web Site: http://www.firstmidwest.com
Commercial Banking Services
N.A.I.C.S.: 522110
Jo Ann Boylan *(COO, CIO & Exec VP)*
Paul W. Hoefert *(Dir-Private Banking)*
Heidi Smithson *(Exec VP & Dir-Comml Real Estate)*
David Hall *(Exec VP & Dir-Comml Real Estate)*
James V. Stadler *(CMO, Chief Comm Officer & Exec VP)*
Kevin P. Geoghegan *(Chief Credit Officer & Exec VP)*

First Midwest Equipment Finance Co. **(2)**
80 N Gordon St, Elk Grove Village, IL 60007-1119
Tel.: (847) 228-7779
Web Site: http://netlease.com
Sales Financing & Leasing Services
N.A.I.C.S.: 522220
Chris Chiappetta *(Pres & CEO)*
Rick Lang *(Sr VP & Sls Dir)*
Chip Lupacchino *(VP & Mgr-Indirect Leasing Sls)*
Ralph Fuchs *(VP & Sls Mgr)*
Matt Brennan *(Sr VP)*
Steven Post *(VP)*
Dave Mistic *(Sr VP)*

First Midwest Trust Co. **(2)**
506 15th St, Moline, IL 61265
Tel.: (309) 797-7500
Investment Management Service
N.A.I.C.S.: 523999

Northern Oak Wealth Management Inc. **(2)**
207 E Michigan St, Suite 200, Milwaukee, WI 53202
Tel.: (414) 278-0590
Web Site: http://www.northern-oak.com
Investment Advisor
N.A.I.C.S.: 523910
David P. Becker *(Pres)*
Kerri Schanowski *(Mgr-Client Rels)*
Matthew Bappert *(Portfolio Mgr)*

Park Bank **(2)**
330 E Kilbourn Ave, Milwaukee, WI 53202
Tel.: (414) 466-8000
Web Site: http://www.parkbankonline.com
Sales Range: $25-49.9 Million
Emp.: 109
Commercial Banking
N.A.I.C.S.: 522110
P. Michael Mahoney *(Pres & CEO)*
Michael Bradburn *(VP-Comml Banking)*

Bryan Swanson *(First VP-Comml Sls & Strategy)*
C. J. Dykstra *(VP-HR)*
Mechelle King *(Asst VP-Digital Mktg)*
Karen Lanser *(Asst VP-Bus Info Sys)*
Tahir Hassan *(CIO)*
Robert J. Makowski Jr. *(CFO & Exec VP)*

Old National Bank **(1)**
1 Main St, Evansville, IN 47708-1503 **(100%)**
Tel.: (812) 464-1425
Web Site: https://www.oldnational.com
Sales Range: $500-549.9 Million
Federal Savings Bank
N.A.I.C.S.: 522180
John V. Moran IV *(CFO & Chief Strategy Officer)*
Nicholas J. Chulos *(Chief Legal Officer & Sec)*
Angela L. Putnam *(Chief Acctg Officer)*
Kendra L. Vanzo *(Chief Admin Officer)*
James A. Sandgren *(CEO-Comml Banking)*
Scott J. Evernham *(Chief Risk Officer)*
Chady M. AlAhmar *(CEO-Wealth Mgmt)*
Mark G. Sander *(Pres & COO)*
Brent R. Tischler *(CEO-Community Banking)*
James C. Ryan III *(Chm & CEO)*
Joe Kiser *(Pres-Old National Bank Foundation)*
Mark Sander *(Pres & COO)*
Carrie Goldfeder *(Chief Credit Officer)*

Subsidiary (Domestic):

American National Trust & Investment Management Corp. **(2)**
1 Main St, Evansville, IN 47708
Tel.: (812) 464-1294
Web Site: http://www.oldnational.com
Wealth Management & Trust Services
N.A.I.C.S.: 523940
Caroline J. Ellspermann *(CEO)*

Division (Domestic):

CapStar Bank **(2)**
1201 Demonbreun St Ste 700, Nashville, TN 37230
Tel.: (615) 732-6400
Web Site: http://www.capstarbank.com
Emp.: 100
Retail & Commercial Banking
N.A.I.C.S.: 522110
Toby S. Wilt *(Founder)*
Claire W. Tucker *(Co-Founder)*
Christopher A. Higgins *(Pres-Middle Tennessee Market)*
Dennis C. Bottorff *(Chm)*
L. Earl Bentz *(Founder)*
Christopher G. Tietz *(Chief Banking Officer)*
Robert B. Anderson *(CFO & Chief Admin Officer)*
Timothy K. Schools *(Pres & CEO)*
Christopher A. Higgins *(Pres-Middle Tennessee)*
Mark D. Mattson *(Exec VP & Mgr-Healthcare Grp)*
Lee Hunter *(Exec VP-Comml Real Estate)*
Julie D. Frist *(Co-Founder)*
Jennie O'Bryan *(Chief Culture Officer & Exec VP)*
Shane Sewell *(Sr VP & Mgr-Lending)*
Nicole Gibbs *(Dir-Mktg)*
Chris Adams *(Officer-Bus Dev & Sr VP)*
Greg Lindsay *(Sr VP & Mgr-Comml Relationship)*
Mike Hill *(Pres-East Tennessee)*
Steve Groom *(Chief Risk Officer & Gen Counsel)*
Hart Weatherford *(Exec VP-Mortgage)*

Subsidiary (Domestic):

Southland Finance, Inc. **(3)**
516 S Congress Pkwy, Athens, TN 37303-2258
Tel.: (423) 744-9554
Web Site: https://www.southlandfinance.net
Mortgage & Nonmortgage Loan Brokers
N.A.I.C.S.: 522310

Subsidiary (Domestic):

Employee Plans, LLC **(2)**
1111 Chestnut Hills Pkwy, Fort Wayne, IN 46814
Tel.: (260) 625-7470

Web Site: https://www.employeeplansllc.com
Rev.: $12,000,000
Emp.: 110
Insurance Services
N.A.I.C.S.: 524210

Division (Domestic):

ONB Investment Services **(2)**
123 Main St, Evansville, IN 47708
Tel.: (812) 464-1406
Web Site: http://www.oldnational.com
Investment Banking Services
N.A.I.C.S.: 523150

OLD POINT FINANCIAL CORPORATION
101 E Queen St Ste 250, Hampton, VA 23669
Tel.: (757) 728-1200 VA
Web Site: https://www.oldpoint.com
Year Founded: 1984
OPOF—(NASDAQ)
Rev.: $61,548,000
Assets: $1,355,335,000
Liabilities: $1,256,601,000
Net Worth: $98,734,000
Earnings: $9,108,000
Emp.: 294
Fiscal Year-end: 12/31/22
Bank Holding Company
N.A.I.C.S.: 551111
Donald S. Buckless *(Chief Lending Officer & Exec VP-Old Point National Bank)*
Cathy W. Liles *(CFO & Sr VP)*
Laura Wright *(VP & Mktg Dir)*

Subsidiaries:

Old Point Trust & Financial Services, N.A. **(1)**
11780 Jefferson Ave Ste D, Newport News, VA 23606 **(100%)**
Tel.: (757) 599-2200
Web Site: http://www.oldpointtrust.com
Sales Range: $125-149.9 Million
Emp.: 250
Wealth Management Services
N.A.I.C.S.: 523940
Eugene M. Jordan II *(Chm, Pres & CEO)*

The Old Point National Bank of Phoebus **(1)**
1 W Mellen St, Hampton, VA 23663 **(100%)**
Tel.: (757) 728-1205
Sales Range: $25-49.9 Million
Commericial Banking
N.A.I.C.S.: 522110
Cathy W. Liles *(CFO & Exec VP)*

OLD REPUBLIC INTERNATIONAL CORPORATION
307 N Michigan Ave, Chicago, IL 60601
Tel.: (312) 346-8100 DE
Web Site:
 https://www.oldrepublic.com
Year Founded: 1923
ORI—(NYSE)
Rev.: $7,258,300,000
Assets: $26,501,400,000
Liabilities: $20,090,700,000
Net Worth: $6,410,700,000
Earnings: $598,600,000
Emp.: 9,200
Fiscal Year-end: 12/31/23
Financial Investment Services
N.A.I.C.S.: 551112
Craig R. Smiddy *(Pres & CEO)*
Frank J. Sodaro *(CFO, Chief Acctg Officer & Sr VP)*
W. Todd Gray *(Treas & Sr VP)*
Stephen J. Oberst *(Exec VP)*
Kivin Jones *(Chief HR Officer & Sr VP)*

Subsidiaries:

Genesis Abstract, LLC **(1)**

25 W Moreland Ave, Hatboro, PA 19040
Tel.: (215) 441-5500
Web Site: https://genesisabstract.com
Real Estate Business Insurance Services
N.A.I.C.S.: 524210

Inter Capital Realty Corporation **(1)**
1700 Broadway Lbby 1, New York, NY 10019-5905
Tel.: (212) 664-1806
Investment Management Service
N.A.I.C.S.: 523940

Old Republic Contractors Insurance Group, Inc. **(1)**
225 S Lake Ave Ste 1050, Pasadena, CA 91101 **(99%)**
Tel.: (626) 683-5200
Web Site: https://www.orcig.com
Insurance Brokerage Services
N.A.I.C.S.: 524210
Andrew Ovadya *(Asst VP & Mgr-Western Reg)*
Dianna Kaplan *(VP-Premium Audit)*
Oscar Pereyra *(VP-Client Svcs)*
Lorraine Wong *(Sr VP & Dir-Ops)*
Vicente Barajas *(Asst VP)*
Jason Jurado *(VP)*

Old Republic Dealer Service Corporation **(1)**
307 N Michigan Ave Fl 19, Chicago, IL 60601 **(100%)**
Tel.: (312) 346-8100
Sales Range: $125-149.9 Million
Emp.: 3
Automobile Dealership Credit Life & Disability Insurance Products & Services
N.A.I.C.S.: 524126

Old Republic General Insurance Group, Inc. **(1)**
307 N Michigan Ave, Chicago, IL 60601 **(100%)**
Tel.: (312) 750-8800
Sales Range: $1-4.9 Billion
Emp.: 6,700
Holding Company; Property & Casualty Insurance Products & Services
N.A.I.C.S.: 551112

Subsidiary (Domestic):

Bitco Corporation **(2)**
3700 Market Square Cir, Davenport, IA 52807 **(100%)**
Web Site: https://www.bitco.com
Holding Company
N.A.I.C.S.: 524126

Subsidiary (Domestic):

Bituminous Casualty Corporation **(3)**
3700 Market Square Circle, Davenport, IA 52807 **(100%)**
Tel.: (309) 786-5401
Web Site: http://www.bitco.com
Sales Range: $350-399.9 Million
Emp.: 600
Property & Liability Insurance Services
N.A.I.C.S.: 524126

Bituminous Fire and Marine Insurance Company **(3)**
320 18th St, Rock Island, IL 61201 **(100%)**
Tel.: (309) 786-5401
Web Site:
 http://www.bituminousinsurance.com
Sales Range: $100-124.9 Million
Emp.: 200
Fire & Marine Insurance
N.A.I.C.S.: 524126

Subsidiary (Domestic):

ORHP Management Company **(2)**
PO Box 5017, San Ramon, CA 94583-0917
Tel.: (800) 445-6999
Real Estate Professional Services
N.A.I.C.S.: 531210

ORI Great West Holding, Inc. **(2)**
307 N Michigan Ave, Chicago, IL 60601 **(100%)**
Tel.: (402) 494-2411
Sales Range: $250-299.9 Million
Holding Company
N.A.I.C.S.: 551112

Subsidiary (Domestic):

Great West Casualty Company **(3)**

Old Republic International Corporation—(Continued)

1100 W 29th St, South Sioux City, NE 68776-0277 **(100%)**
Tel.: (402) 494-2411
Web Site: https://www.gwccnet.com
Sales Range: $250-299.9 Million
Emp.: 450
Underwriter of Commercial Truck Insurance
N.A.I.C.S.: 524126
James Jensen (CEO)
Jeff Allen (Exec VP)
Mary Anderson (CFO, Treas & Sr VP)
Mandy Graham (COO & Exec VP)
Terry Keime (Exec VP-Admin Underwriting & Safety Svcs)
Dick Lehr (Exec VP)
Steve Olson (Pres & Chief Underwriting Officer)
Steve Ponder (Exec VP)
Craig Posson (Gen Counsel & Sec)
Sarah Hansen (Exec VP)
Jesse Wendlandt (Exec VP)

Subsidiary (Domestic):

Old Republic Aerospace, Inc. **(2)**
1990 Vaughn Rd, Kennesaw, GA 30144
Tel.: (770) 590-4950
Web Site:
    https://www.oldrepublicaerospace.com
Insurance Underwriting Services
N.A.I.C.S.: 524298
Ralph H. Sohl (Pres, CEO & Chief Underwriting Officer)
Michael E. Warren (Gen Counsel, Exec VP & Dir-Claims)
Craig Benn (Exec VP)
Gary Churchill (COO-Gen Aviation Underwriting & Exec VP)
Gordon Murray (Sr VP-Admin & Compliance)
Daniel Bullard (Branch Mgr-Dallas)
Paul Howard (Branch Mgr-New York)
Brian Donnelly (Sr VP-Major Risks Underwriting)
Matthew Maddox (CIO & Sr VP)
Jeff Moitozo (Sr VP-Corp, Airport & NCP Underwriting)
Wes Collier (VP-Pleasure & Bus Underwriting)
John Helms (VP-Agricultural Aviation Underwriting)
Gary Fey (Branch Mgr-Atlanta)
Michael Prahl (Branch Mgr-Chicago)
John Pristas (Branch Mgr-Seattle)

Old Republic Agribusiness Underwriters, Inc. **(2)**
4685 Merle Hay Rd Ste 202, Des Moines, IA 50322
Tel.: (515) 251-5190
Web Site:
    http://www.oldrepublicagribusiness.com
Emp.: 12
Insurance Brokerage Services
N.A.I.C.S.: 524210

Old Republic General Insurance Corporation **(2)**
307 N Michigan Ave, Chicago, IL 60601 **(100%)**
Tel.: (312) 346-8100
Web Site: http://www.oldrepublic.com
Sales Range: $50-74.9 Million
Emp.: 300
Property & Casualty Insurance Underwriting Services
N.A.I.C.S.: 524298
Aldo Charles Zucaro (Chm & CEO)

Old Republic Home Protection Company, Inc. **(2)**
Two Annabel Ln Ste 112, San Ramon, CA 94583-0917
Web Site: https://www.orhp.com
Sales Range: $75-99.9 Million
Emp.: 200
Warranty Insurance Services
N.A.I.C.S.: 524128
Gwen Gallagher (Pres)

Old Republic Insurance Company **(2)**
133 Oakland Ave, Greensburg, PA 15601-0789 **(100%)**
Tel.: (724) 834-5000
Web Site: http://www.orinsco.com
Sales Range: $50-74.9 Million
Emp.: 100

Property & Casualty Insurance & Workmens Compensation
N.A.I.C.S.: 524114

Old Republic Professional Liability, Inc. **(2)**
191 N Wacker Dr Ste 1000, Chicago, IL 60606-1905
Tel.: (312) 750-8800
Web Site: https://www.oldrepublicpro.com
Insurance Brokerage Services
N.A.I.C.S.: 524210
Clancy P. Foley (VP-Underwriting)
Frank J. Kastelic (Pres-Underwriting)
Joseph V. Rizzo (Chief Acctg Officer & VP-Acctg)
Vivian Y. Cohn (Gen Counsel & Sr VP)
Tracy L. Burns (VP-Underwriting)
Timothy J. Kerber (Sr VP & Office Mgr-Denver)
Devin Bilgi (VP-Underwriting)
Frederick W. Brown (VP-Underwriting)
Vu N. Le (VP-Underwriting)
Mike Silver (Exec VP-Underwriting & Bus Dev)
Bronson Smith (VP-Underwriting)
David H. White (Sr VP-Underwriting & Dir-Res)
Michael W. Early (VP & Deputy Gen Counsel)
Marc London (Sr VP-Underwriting-New York)
Brian Stokley (Mgr-Admin-Denver)
Luke Knowles (Asst VP-Underwriting-Denver)
Mary Carrow (Sr VP-Underwriting)
Reed Henderson (VP-Underwriting-Los Angeles)
Sarah Morris (Asst VP)
Linda Fisher (VP-Underwriting)
Jackie Foresta (Coord-Compliance)
Richard F. Mealle Jr. (VP-Underwriting)

Old Republic Risk Management, Inc. **(2)**
445 S Moorland Rd Ste 300, Brookfield, WI 53005
Tel.: (262) 797-3400
Web Site: https://www.orrm.com
Insurance Management Services
N.A.I.C.S.: 524298
Steve Oberst (CEO)
Larry Francione (CFO & Sr VP)
Barry Martin (Exec VP)
Linda Johnson (Chief Underwriting Officer)
Terri Minik (Co-Pres & COO)
Scott Schaefer (Sr VP-Claims)
Jeff Woodcock (Sr VP-Ops)
Paul Carleton (Sr VP)
Helen Kim (Sr VP)
Kevin Truhlar (Sr VP)
Jim Duffy (Asst VP)
Alison Luebbers (Asst VP)

Old Republic Specialty Insurance Underwriters, Inc. **(2)**
790 Township Line Rd Ste 230, Yardley, PA 19067
Tel.: (215) 860-4960
Web Site: https://www.orsiu.com
Business Insurance Services
N.A.I.C.S.: 524210
William Franchi (Pres)
Trish Egan (COO)
Judith Johnson (Sr VP)
Robert Gambell (Sr VP)
Barb Kenyon (Sr VP)
Russ Buckley (Sr VP)
Steven Assennata (Sr VP)

Old Republic Surety Group, Inc. **(2)**
310 E 4500 S Ste 350, Murray, UT 84107-4262
Tel.: (801) 262-9801
Web Site: http://www.orsurety.com
Emp.: 3
Insurance Brokerage Services
N.A.I.C.S.: 524210

Subsidiary (Domestic):

Old Republic Surety Company **(3)**
445 S Moorland Rd Ste 200, Brookfield, WI 53005
Tel.: (262) 797-2640
Web Site: https://www.orsurety.com
Investment Management Service
N.A.I.C.S.: 523940

Alan Pavlic (Pres & COO)
Joel Vandendriessche (VP-Underwriting & Dir-Underwriter Dev)
Traci Catalano (Sr VP-Mktg)
Karen Haffner (Sr VP-Admin & Fin)
Michael Kahler (VP-Information Sys)
Rich Marshall (Sr VP)
Dennis McDonnell (VP-Claims)
Brady Mayer (Asst VP-Underwriting)
Eric Kirchner (VP-Comml Surety)
Aron Albrecht (Reg VP)
Darrel Lamb (Reg VP)
Jeff Norris (Reg VP)
Dan Pope (Reg VP)
Rich Sghiatti (Reg VP)

Subsidiary (Domestic):

PMA Companies, Inc. **(2)**
380 Sentry Pkwy, Blue Bell, PA 19422
Tel.: (610) 941-6861
Web Site: https://www.pmacompanies.com
Sales Range: $500-549.9 Million
Emp.: 1,362
Insurance Holding Company
N.A.I.C.S.: 551112
Vincent T. Donnelly (Chm)
Ken Stanley (Sr VP-Distr & Field Ops)
John Santulli (Pres & COO)
Kevin M. Brady (Chief Actuary & Sr VP)
Drew Jones (Exec VP-Insurance Segments Ops)
Ray J. DiCello (Chief Insurance Claims Officer & Sr VP)
Robert Bell (CFO & Sr VP)
Derek Hopper (Sr VP-Shared Svcs)

Subsidiary (Domestic):

Mid Atlantic States Investment Company **(3)**
103 Foulk Rd, Wilmington, DE 19803-3742
Tel.: (302) 421-7361
Investment Management Service
N.A.I.C.S.: 523940

PMA Management Corp. **(3)**
380 Sentry Pkwy, Blue Bell, PA 19422-0754 **(100%)**
Tel.: (610) 397-5000
Web Site: http://www.pmamc.com
Sales Range: $150-199.9 Million
Third Party Insurance Administration Services
N.A.I.C.S.: 524292

PMA Management Corporation of New England **(3)**
530 Preston Ave, Meriden, CT 06450-4893
Tel.: (203) 379-3439
Web Site: http://www.pmamcne.com
Third Party Administration Insurance Services
N.A.I.C.S.: 524292

Group (Domestic):

Pennsylvania Manufacturers' Association Insurance Company **(3)**
380 Sentry Pkwy, Blue Bell, PA 19422-0754 **(100%)**
Tel.: (610) 941-6861
Web Site: http://www.pmagroup.com
Sales Range: $150-199.9 Million
Workers' Compensation Risk Solutions & Commercial Insurance Products
N.A.I.C.S.: 524126

Subsidiary (Domestic):

Manufacturers Alliance Insurance Company **(4)**
380 Sentry Pkwy, Blue Bell, PA 19422-0754 **(100%)**
Tel.: (610) 397-5136
Web Site: http://www.pmagroup.com
Workers' Compensation Risk Solutions & Commercial Insurance Products
N.A.I.C.S.: 524126

Pennsylvania Manufacturers Indemnity Company **(4)**
380 Sentry Pkwy, Blue Bell, PA 19422-2357 **(100%)**
Tel.: (610) 397-5000
Web Site: http://www.pmagroup.com
Workers' Compensation Risk Solutions & Commercial Insurance Products
N.A.I.C.S.: 524126

Old Republic Insurance Company of Canada **(1)**
100 King Street West, Box 557, Hamilton, L8N 3K9, ON, Canada
Tel.: (905) 523-5936
Web Site: https://www.orican.com
Sales Range: $25-49.9 Million
Emp.: 100
Insurance Management Services
N.A.I.C.S.: 524298
Paul M. Field (CEO)

Old Republic Insured Automotive Services, Inc. **(1)**
8282 S Memorial Dr Ste 202, Tulsa, OK 74133-4352
Tel.: (918) 307-1000
Web Site: https://www.orias.com
Sales Range: $25-49.9 Million
Emp.: 36
Automobile Insurance Services
N.A.I.C.S.: 524298
Mike Cescon (Pres)
Mary A. Gant (Sr VP & Controller)
Rob Davis (VP-Claims)
Brad Hill (Dir-Ops)

Old Republic Life Insurance Group, Inc. **(1)**
307 N Michigan Ave, Chicago, IL 60601 **(100%)**
Tel.: (312) 346-8100
Web Site:
    http://www.oldrepublicinsurancegroup.com
Sales Range: $650-699.9 Million
Holding Company; Life Insurance Products & Services
N.A.I.C.S.: 551112
Aldo Charles Zucaro (Chm & CEO)

Subsidiary (Domestic):

Old Republic Life Insurance Company **(2)**
307 N Michigan Ave, Chicago, IL 60601 **(100%)**
Tel.: (312) 346-8100
Web Site: http://www.oldrepublic.com
Life Insurance Products & Services
N.A.I.C.S.: 524126

Old Republic Mortgage Guaranty Group, Inc. **(1)**
307 N Michigan Ave, Chicago, IL 60601 **(100%)**
Tel.: (312) 346-8100
Web Site: http://www.oldrepublic.com
Sales Range: $75-99.9 Million
Holding Company; Mortgage Protection Insurance Products & Services
N.A.I.C.S.: 551112

Old Republic Title Insurance Group, Inc. **(1)**
400 Second Ave S, Minneapolis, MN 55401-2499 **(100%)**
Tel.: (612) 371-1132
Web Site: http://www.oldrepublictitle.com
Sales Range: $900-999.9 Million
Holding Company; Title Insurance Products & Services
N.A.I.C.S.: 551112
Charles J. Kovaleski (Exec VP)

Subsidiary (Domestic):

Old Republic National Title Holding Company **(2)**
400 2nd Ave S, Minneapolis, MN 55401-2499 **(100%)**
Tel.: (612) 371-1111
Emp.: 13
Holding Company
N.A.I.C.S.: 551112
Mark A. Bilbrey (Pres)

Subsidiary (Domestic):

American Guaranty Title Insurance Company **(3)**
4040 N Tulsa, Oklahoma City, OK 73112 **(100%)**
Tel.: (405) 942-4848
Web Site: http://www.oldrepublictitle.com
Emp.: 81
Title Insurance Products & Services
N.A.I.C.S.: 524127

Compass Abstract, Inc. **(3)**

25 W Moreland Ave, Hatboro, PA 19040
Tel.: (215) 441-5500
Web Site: https://compassabstract.com
Insurance Management Services
N.A.I.C.S.: 524298

L.T. Service Corporation (3)
521 5th Ave 23rd Fl, New York, NY 10175
Tel.: (212) 599-1300
Property Insurance Services
N.A.I.C.S.: 524126

Lenders Inspection Company (3)
4040 N Tulsa Ave, Oklahoma City, OK 73112
Tel.: (405) 947-6804
Building Inspection Services
N.A.I.C.S.: 541350

Lex Terrae National Title Services, Inc. (3)
2 Hudson Pl 5th Fl, Hoboken, NJ 07030 (100%)
Tel.: (201) 610-9455
Web Site: http://www.oldrepublictitle.com
Insurance Brokerage Services
N.A.I.C.S.: 524210

Lex Terrae, Ltd. (3)
331 Madison Ave 9th Fl, New York, NY 10017
Tel.: (212) 599-1300
Web Site: http://www.oldrepublictitle.com
Title Insurance Services
N.A.I.C.S.: 524127
Richard M. Icklan (Pres)
Susan S. Icklan (COO)

Old Republic National Title Insurance Company (3)
400 2nd Ave S, Minneapolis, MN 55401-2499
Tel.: (612) 371-1111
Web Site: http://www.oldrepublictitle.com
Title Insurance Carrier Services
N.A.I.C.S.: 524127
Michael Hendry (Senior Escrow Officer, VP & Mgr)

Subsidiary (Domestic):

Mississippi Valley Title Insurance Company (4)
1022 Highland Colony Pkwy Ste 200, Ridgeland, MS 39157 (100%)
Tel.: (601) 969-0222
Web Site: http://www.mvt.com
Title Insurance Products & Services
N.A.I.C.S.: 524127
Mark B. Higdon (Chm & Pres)
J. Morton Matrick (Exec VP)
W. Parrish Fortenberry (Exec VP)
Scott Magee (VP & Mgr-Title Svcs Dept)
Terry P. Weill (VP & Mgr-Agency)
Claire Ewing (Mgr-Mktg)

Mountain View Title & Escrow Co. (4)
5732 S 1475 E Ste 100, Ogden, UT 84403
Tel.: (801) 479-1191
Web Site: https://www.mvte.com
Rev.: $7,000,000
Emp.: 20
Direct Title Insurance Carriers
N.A.I.C.S.: 524127
Michael L. Hendry (Pres)
Sandi Hendry (CEO)
Carolyn Robinson (Mgr)

Subsidiary (Domestic):

Old Republic Specialized Agency Solutions (3)
530 S Main St Ste 1031, Akron, OH 44311-4423
Tel.: (330) 436-6000
Web Site: http://www.oldrepublictitle.com
Title Insurance Product & Services
N.A.I.C.S.: 524127

Old Republic Title Company of Conroe (3)
150 N Main, Conroe, TX 77301 (100%)
Tel.: (936) 539-3121
Web Site: http://www.oldrepublictitle.com
Insurance Brokerage Services
N.A.I.C.S.: 524210

Old Republic Title Company of Houston (3)

777 Post Oak Blvd Ste 240, Houston, TX 77056
Tel.: (713) 877-1780
Web Site: http://www.oldrepublictitle.com
Sales Range: $1-9.9 Million
Title Insurance Agency
N.A.I.C.S.: 524210
Dan Hassen (Pres)

Old Republic Title Company of Oklahoma (3)
4040 N Tulsa, Oklahoma City, OK 73112
Tel.: (405) 942-4848
Web Site: http://www.oldrepublictitle.com
Insurance Brokerage Services
N.A.I.C.S.: 524210
Chaney Haynes (Officer-Ops)
Jeff Noble (Sr VP-ORTCOK)
Carla Hawkins (Controller & Supvr-Acctg)
Liz Potts (Mgr-Residential Escrow)
Lisa Yates (Pres-Ortcok)
Jan Foreman (Dir-Residential Sls)
Kayla Reed (Coord-Mktg)
Terri Mercado (Mgr-Residential Escrow)
Alison Nobs (Mgr-Comml Escrow)

Old Republic Title Company of St. Louis, Inc. (3)
9645 Clayton Rd 2nd Fl, Ladue, MO 63124
Tel.: (314) 692-8565
Web Site: http://www.oldrepublictitle.com
Emp.: 6
Insurance Brokerage Services
N.A.I.C.S.: 524210
Stephen A. Bolla (VP & Gen Counsel)
Lisa McCarthy (Supvr-Escrow)

Sentry Abstract Company (3)
12 Commerce Dr, Wyomissing, PA 19610
Tel.: (610) 376-4500
Web Site: https://sentryabstract.com
Emp.: 10
Insurance Brokerage Services
N.A.I.C.S.: 524210
Chip Lutz (Pres)
Diana Edwards (Sr VP)
Larry Jones (Chief Title Officer)
Sharon Johnson (Officer-Settlement)
Tina Miller (Officer-Settlement)

The Title Company of North Carolina (3)
414 Chestnut St Ste 302, Wilmington, NC 28401
Tel.: (910) 343-8374
Web Site: http://www.oldrepublictitle.com
Emp.: 5
Title Insurance Services
N.A.I.C.S.: 524127
Gary W. Chadwick (Sr VP)

Troon Management Corporation (3)
25 W Moreland Ave, Hatboro, PA 19040
Tel.: (215) 441-5500
Web Site: https://troonmanagement.com
Investment Management Service
N.A.I.C.S.: 523940
Anne L. Anastasi (Pres)
John F. Lutz (VP)

eRecording Partners Network, LLC (3)
400 2nd Ave S, Minneapolis, MN 55401
Web Site: https://www.goepn.com
Emp.: 15
Software Publisher
N.A.I.C.S.: 513210
Pam Trombo (VP-eRecording)
Jerry Lewallen (Pres)
Chris Stephan (Sr VP-Client Svcs)
Ryan Clegg (VP-Client Svcs Ops)

Subsidiary (Domestic):

Old Republic Title Holding Company, Inc. (2)
265 Montgomery St, San Francisco, CA 94104 (100%)
Tel.: (415) 421-9770
Web Site: http://www.orgc.com
Sales Range: $25-49.9 Million
Emp.: 30
Holding Company; Regional Managing Office
N.A.I.C.S.: 551112
Ivy Anderson (Pres)
Sam Carlisi (COO & Exec VP)
Rick Dosa (Corp Counsel & Exec VP)
Kathy Brolin (Exec VP & Reg Mgr)

Ernie Collins (Exec VP & Reg Mgr)
John Hall (Sr VP & Mgr-Agency-Western Title Div)
Michelle Lenahan (Sr VP & Mgr-Mktg-Western Title Div)

Subsidiary (Domestic):

Mara Escrow Company (3)
15760 Ventura Blvd Ste 100, Encino, CA 91436
Tel.: (818) 386-2244
Web Site: http://www.maraescrow.com
Real Estate Escrow Services
N.A.I.C.S.: 531390

Old Republic Title Company of Nevada (3)
4730 S Fort Apache Rd Ste 100, Las Vegas, NV 89147 (100%)
Tel.: (702) 313-2088
Web Site: http://www.oldrepublictitle.com
Insurance Brokerage Services
N.A.I.C.S.: 524210

Old Republic Title Information Concepts (3)
524 Gibson Dr, Roseville, CA 95678-5799
Tel.: (916) 781-4100
Web Site: http://www.oldrepublictitle.com
Insurance Brokerage Services
N.A.I.C.S.: 524210

Old Republic Title Insurance Agency, Inc. (3)
2375 E Camelback Rd Ste 180, Phoenix, AZ 85016-3424
Tel.: (602) 631-3700
Insurance Management Services
N.A.I.C.S.: 524298

Old Republic Title and Escrow of Hawaii, Ltd. (3)
737 Bishop St Ste 2200, Honolulu, HI 96813
Tel.: (808) 566-0100
Web Site: http://www.ortc.com
Title & Escrow Services
N.A.I.C.S.: 531390
Jackye Chai (Mgr-State)

Veritas Title Partners LLC (3)
2415 W Alabama St Ste 203, Houston, TX 77098-2263
Tel.: (713) 482-2800
Web Site: http://www.veritastitlepartners.com
Intermediation Services
N.A.I.C.S.: 523910
Laura Underwood (Mgr-Comml Bus Dev)
Summer Bell (Mgr-Bus Dev-Austin)

RMIC Corporation (1)
101 N Cherry St Ste 101, Winston Salem, NC 27101
Tel.: (336) 661-0015
Web Site: http://www.rmic.com
Mortgage Insurance Services
N.A.I.C.S.: 524126
David Delcamp (CTO)

RamQuest Software, Inc. (1)
6111 W Plano Pkwy Ste 3800, Plano, TX 75093
Tel.: (214) 291-1616
Web Site: https://www.ramquest.com
Emp.: 80
Software Development Services
N.A.I.C.S.: 541511
Ben Cork (Chief Strategy Officer)
Mary Schuster (Sr VP-Industry Rels)
Brooks Yeager (Pres)

Reliable Life Insurance Company (1)
100 King Street West, Hamilton, L8N 3K9, ON, Canada
Tel.: (905) 523-5587
Web Site: http://www.reliablelifeinsurance.com
Emp.: 150
Insurance Brokerage Services
N.A.I.C.S.: 524210

Republic Financial Indemnity Group, Inc. (1)
307 N Michigan Ave, Chicago, IL 60601
Tel.: (312) 346-8100
Mortgage Insurance Services
N.A.I.C.S.: 524126

Republic Mortgage Insurance Company of North Carolina (1)
101 N Cherry St Ste 101, Winston Salem, NC 27101
Tel.: (336) 661-0015
Web Site: https://www.rmic.com
Emp.: 100
Insurance Brokerage Services
N.A.I.C.S.: 524210

OLD SECOND BANCORP, INC.
1st Fl NOE 37 S River St, Aurora, IL 60506-4172
Tel.: (630) 892-0202 DE
Web Site:
https://www.oldsecond.com
OSBC—(NASDAQ)
Rev.: $259,589,000
Assets: $5,888,317,000
Liabilities: $5,427,176,000
Net Worth: $461,141,000
Earnings: $67,405,000
Emp.: 819
Fiscal Year-end: 12/31/22
Holding Company
N.A.I.C.S.: 522110
Bradley S. Adams (CFO, COO & Exec VP)
James L. Eccher (Chm, Pres & CEO)
Gary S. Collins (Vice Chm)

Subsidiaries:

Old Second National Bank (1)
37 S River St, Aurora, IL 60506-4173
Tel.: (630) 892-0202
Web Site: https://www.oldsecond.com
Sales Range: $125-149.9 Million
Emp.: 100
Commercial Banking Services
N.A.I.C.S.: 522110
Bradley S. Adams (CFO)
James L. Eccher (Chm, Pres & CEO)
Derek Sammons (Sr VP-Comml Lending)
Mike Cava (VP & Sr Portfolio Mgr)
Andrew Crouch (Sr VP & Head-Trust & Fiduciary Svcs)
Edward Gorenz (Officer-Trust & VP)
Brad Johnson (Officer-Trust & VP)
Steve Meves (Chief Investment Officer)
Michele Morgan (Officer-Trust & VP)
Sandra Nies (Officer-Bus Dev Trust & VP)
Sean O'Connor (Officer-Retirement Benefits & First VP)
Mary Randel (Officer-Retirement Benefits)
Andy Roche (Officer-Trust, Sr VP & Head-Tax & Ops)
Jacqueline A. Runnberg (Sr VP)
Yamilet Suarez (Asst VP)
Carolyn S. Swafford (Officer-Trust & VP)
Jacquelyn Volkert (Sr VP-Wealth Mgmt)
Richard A. Gartelmann Jr. (Exec VP & Head-Wealth Mgmt)

West Suburban Bancorp, Inc. (1)
711 S Meyers Rd, Lombard, IL 60148
Tel.: (630) 652-2000
Web Site:
http://www.westsuburbanbank.com
Rev.: $85,920,000
Assets: $2,753,459,000
Liabilities: $2,518,722,000
Net Worth: $234,737,000
Earnings: $10,691,000
Emp.: 384
Fiscal Year-end: 12/31/2020
Bank Holding Company
N.A.I.C.S.: 551111
Kevin J. Acker (Chm)

Subsidiary (Domestic):

West Suburban Bank (2)
711 S Meyers Rd, Lombard, IL 60148-3712 (100%)
Tel.: (630) 652-2000
Web Site:
http://www.westsuburbanbank.com
Emp.: 200
Retail & Commercial Banking
N.A.I.C.S.: 522110
Duane G. Debs (Sr VP & Comptroller)
Kevin J. Acker (Sr VP-Mktg)
Keith W. Acker (Pres)

Old Second Bancorp, Inc.—(Continued)

Michael P. Brosnahan *(Sr VP-Lending)*
Glenn Mazade *(Chief Lending Officer & Sr VP)*

OLEMA PHARMACEUTICALS, INC.
512 2nd St 4th Fl, San Francisco, CA 94197
Tel.: (415) 651-3316   **DE**
Web Site: https://www.olema.com
Year Founded: 2006
OLMA—(NASDAQ)
Rev.: $2,228,000
Assets: $215,645,000
Liabilities: $18,099,000
Net Worth: $197,546,000
Earnings: ($104,787,000)
Emp.: 83
Fiscal Year-end: 12/31/22
Biotechnology Research & Development Services
N.A.I.C.S.: 541714
Ian T. Clark *(Chm)*
Cyrus L. Harmon *(CTO)*
Pamela M. Klein *(Chief Medical Officer)*
Sean P. Bohen *(Pres & CEO)*
Peter J. Kushner *(Co-Founder)*
Shane Kovacs *(CFO & COO)*
David C. Myles *(Chief Dev Officer)*
Ian Clark *(Chm)*
Demiana Faltaos *(VP & Head-Clinical Pharmacology)*
Kristin Lanzi *(VP-IT)*
Naseem Zojwalla *(Chief Medical Officer)*
Sasha Austin *(VP)*
Richard Hernandez *(VP)*
Kamesh Kuchimanchi *(VP)*
Gopinath Palanisamy *(VP)*
Mark Shilkrut *(VP)*
Jim Zhang *(VP)*
Geoffrey Mogilner *(VP-IR & Comm)*

OLFACTORY BIOSCIENCES CORP.
333 E Lancaster Ave Ste 317, Wynnewood, PA 19096
Tel.: (484) 278-1626
Year Founded: 1999
OLFC—(OTCIQ)
Health Care Services
N.A.I.C.S.: 621999
Richard Stevenson *(Pres & CEO)*

OLIN CORPORATION
190 Carondelet Plz Ste 1530, Clayton, MO 63105
Tel.: (314) 480-1400   **VA**
Web Site: https://www.olin.com
Year Founded: 1892
OLN—(NYSE)
Rev.: $6,833,000,000
Assets: $7,713,200,000
Liabilities: $5,444,900,000
Net Worth: $2,268,300,000
Earnings: $460,200,000
Emp.: 7,326
Fiscal Year-end: 12/31/23
Mfr & Distr of Chemicals & Sporting & Small Caliber Military Ammunition & Components
N.A.I.C.S.: 325180
Randee N. Sumner *(VP & Controller)*
Dana C. O'Brien *(Gen Counsel, Sec & Sr VP)*
Kenneth T. Lane *(Pres & CEO)*
Dana C. O'Brien *(Gen Counsel, Sec & Sr VP)*

Subsidiaries:

Blue Cube Belgium BVBA   **(1)**
Avenue Du Port 86c Internal, Postal Box 204, Brussels, 1000, Belgium
Tel.: (32) 34502011

Chemical & Allied Product Merchant Whslr
N.A.I.C.S.: 424690

Blue Cube Chemicals FZE   **(1)**
Jafza View 19, Dubai, United Arab Emirates
Tel.: (971) 48137864
Chemical & Allied Product Merchant Whslr
N.A.I.C.S.: 424690
Arshad Jamil *(Gen Mgr)*

Blue Cube Colombia Ltda.   **(1)**
Calle 72 10 07 of 401, Bogota, 208, Colombia
Tel.: (57) 17461000
Industrial Organic Chemicals Mfr
N.A.I.C.S.: 325199

CANSO Chemicals Limited   **(1)**
189 Abercombie Branch Granton Rd, New Glasgow, B2H 5C9, NS, Canada
Tel.: (902) 755-1785
Emp.: 3
Warehousing & Storage Services
N.A.I.C.S.: 493190

K. A. Steel Chemicals   **(1)**
15185 Main St, Lemont, IL 60439
Tel.: (630) 257-3900
Web Site: http://www.kasteelchemicals.com
Inorganic Chemical Mfr
N.A.I.C.S.: 325998

K.A. Steel Chemicals Inc.   **(1)**
15185 Main St, Lemont, IL 60439
Tel.: (630) 257-3900
Web Site: http://www.kasteelchemicals.com
Sales Range: $400-449.9 Million
Emp.: 87
Chemicals & Allied Products Mfr & Distr
N.A.I.C.S.: 325998

Olin Corporation - Chlor Alkali Products Division   **(1)**
490 Stuart Rd NE, Cleveland, TN 37312   **(100%)**
Tel.: (423) 336-4850
Web Site: http://www.olinchloralkali.com
Sales Range: $25-49.9 Million
Emp.: 75
Chlorine & Caustic Soda Mfr
N.A.I.C.S.: 325180

Subsidiary (Domestic):

Olin Chlor Alkali Products   **(2)**
2400 Buffalo Ave, Niagara Falls, NY 14302   **(100%)**
Tel.: (716) 278-6411
Web Site: http://www.olinchloralkali.com
Sales Range: $50-74.9 Million
Emp.: 180
Chlorine, Sodium Hypochlorite, Hydrochloric & Sulfuric Acid Mfr
N.A.I.C.S.: 325180

Olin Corporation - Winchester Division   **(1)**
600 Powder Mill Rd, East Alton, IL 62024   **(100%)**
Tel.: (618) 258-2000
Web Site: http://www.winchester.com
Firearm Ammunition Mfr
N.A.I.C.S.: 332992
Richard M. Hammett *(Pres)*

Subsidiary (Non-US):

Olin Australia Limited   **(2)**
65 Hays Rd Point Henry Geelong, PO Box 776, Geelong, 3220, VIC, Australia **(100%)**
Tel.: (61) 352452400
Web Site:
http://www.winchesteraustralia.com.au
Sales Range: $50-74.9 Million
Emp.: 65
Sporting Ammunition Retailer & Mfr
N.A.I.C.S.: 332992

Pioneer Americas LLC   **(1)**
490 Stuart Rd, Cleveland, TN 37312
Tel.: (423) 336-4850
Web Site: https://www.olinchloralkali.com
Chemicals Mfr
N.A.I.C.S.: 325199

Winchester Australia Limited   **(1)**
65 Hays Road, Moolap, Geelong, 3224, VIC, Australia   **(100%)**
Tel.: (61) 352452400
Web Site:
https://www.winchesteraustralia.com.au

Shotshell & Centrefire Products Mfr
N.A.I.C.S.: 332992

OLIVEDA INTERNATIONAL, INC.
401 Wilshire Blvd 12th Fl, Santa Monica, CA 90401
Tel.: (424) 252-4251
Web Site:
https://us.olivetreepeople.com
OLVI—(OTCIQ)
Toilet Preparation Manufacturing
N.A.I.C.S.: 325620
Thomas Lommel *(CEO)*

OLO INC.
99 Hudson St 10th Fl, New York, NY 10013
Tel.: (212) 260-0895   **DE**
Web Site: https://www.olo.com
Year Founded: 2005
OLO—(NYSE)
Rev.: $228,289,000
Assets: $742,819,000
Liabilities: $91,348,000
Net Worth: $651,471,000
Earnings: ($58,287,000)
Emp.: 683
Fiscal Year-end: 12/31/23
Mobile Software Development Services
N.A.I.C.S.: 541511
Joanna Lambert *(COO)*
Peter Benevides *(CFO)*
Marty Hahnfeld *(Chief Customer Officer)*
Andrew Murray *(CTO)*
Deanne Rhynard *(Chief People Officer)*
Brandon Gardner *(Chm)*
Robert Morvillo *(Gen Counsel & Sec)*
Noah H. Glass *(Founder & CEO)*

OLYMPIC STEEL INC.
22901 Millcreek Blvd Ste 650, Highland Hills, OH 44122
Tel.: (216) 292-3800   **OH**
Web Site: https://www.olysteel.com
Year Founded: 1954
ZEUS—(NASDAQ)
Rev.: $2,559,990,000
Assets: $891,627,000
Liabilities: $375,659,000
Net Worth: $515,968,000
Earnings: $90,931,000
Emp.: 1,668
Fiscal Year-end: 12/31/22
Metals Service Center
N.A.I.C.S.: 423510
Richard T. Marabito *(CEO)*
Francis M. Ruane *(Exec VP-Supply Chain)*
Richard A. Manson *(CFO)*
Andrew S. Greiff *(Pres & COO)*
Terry J. Rohde *(VP-Ops)*
Andy Markowitz *(Pres-Specialty Metals)*
John J. Mooney *(Mng Dir-Comml)*
Michelle Pearson-Casey *(VP-Corp Comm & Mktg)*
James D. Post *(Reg VP & Gen Mgr)*
Christopher J. Garrett *(VP-Information Svcs-Flat Rolled)*
Zachary J. Siegal *(VP-Strategic Dev)*
Andrew F. Wolfort *(VP-Specialty Metals)*
David J. Gea *(Pres-Carbon Flat Rolled)*
Thomas J. Sacco *(Reg VP & Gen Mgr)*
Cassandra Powers *(VP-HR)*
Brian C. Harkins *(VP-Aluminum)*
Michael Heenan *(Gen Mgr)*
Jerry Gideon *(Comml Dir-Specialty Metals)*
Richard Ranells *(Gen Mgr)*

Scott Silverman *(Gen Mgr)*
Edward Fitzgerald *(VP-Fabrication)*
Matthew Grussing *(Dir-Sls-Fabrication)*

Subsidiaries:

Action Stainless & Alloys Inc.   **(1)**
1505 Halsey Way, Carrollton, TX 75007
Tel.: (972) 466-1500
Web Site: http://www.actionstainless.com
Rev.: $30,000,000
Emp.: 175
Metals Service Centers & Offices
N.A.I.C.S.: 423510
Lisa Kelly *(Mgr-Credit)*
Jessica L. Burroughs *(VP)*

Berlin Metals LLC   **(1)**
3200 Sheffield Ave, Hammond, IN 46327
Tel.: (219) 933-0111
Web Site: https://www.berlinmetals.com
Metals Service Center
N.A.I.C.S.: 423510
Bob Thompson *(Ops Mgr)*
Jim Cillo *(Dir-Sls)*
Dan Harnois *(Gen Mgr)*
Michele Hartigan *(Mgr-Acctg)*
Deanna Pizer *(Mgr-Inside Sls)*

Central Tube & Bar, Inc.   **(1)**
25 Middle Rd, Conway, AR 72032
Tel.: (918) 995-4968
Web Site: http://centraltubeandbar.com
Industrial Machinery & Equipment Merchant Whslr
N.A.I.C.S.: 423830

Chicago Tube & Iron Co.   **(1)**
1 Chicago Tube Dr, Romeoville, IL 60446
Tel.: (815) 834-2500
Web Site: https://www.chicagotube.com
Sales Range: $125-149.9 Million
Emp.: 400
Steel Products Mfr & Distr
N.A.I.C.S.: 423510
Donald R. McNeeley *(Chm)*
Melissa Conner *(Mgr-Corp Credit)*
Janeth Villalobos-Quiroz *(VP-Admin)*
Elidia Vazquez *(Mgr-Process Engrg)*
Joe Canelo *(Plant Mgr)*

Goss Steel Co.   **(1)**
3600 Military St, Detroit, MI 48210-2964   **(49%)**
Tel.: (734) 847-7706
Sales Range: $10-24.9 Million
Emp.: 15
Flat Rolled Steel Warehousing & Value-Added Processing for the Automotive Industry
N.A.I.C.S.: 331221

Mccullough Industries, Inc.   **(1)**
13047 County Road 175, Kenton, OH 43326
Tel.: (800) 245-9490
Web Site: http://www.mcculloughind.com
Mfg Industrial Trucks/Tractors
N.A.I.C.S.: 333924

Olympic Laser Processing, LLC   **(1)**
5096 Richmond Rd, Bedford Heights, OH 44146
Tel.: (734) 482-1750
Web Site: http://www.olysteel.com
Sales Range: $50-74.9 Million
Emp.: 125
Process Laser Welded Sheet Steel Blanks;
Joint Venture Between Olympic Steel Inc. & U.S. Steel
N.A.I.C.S.: 332111
David A. Wolfort *(Pres)*

Olympic Steel Inc. - Siler City   **(1)**
3031 Hamp Stone Rd, Siler City, NC 27344
Tel.: (919) 742-5832
Web Site: http://www.olysteel.com
Fabricated Metal Assembly & Mfr
N.A.I.C.S.: 332999

Olympic Steel Iowa, Inc.   **(1)**
6425 State St, Bettendorf, IA 52722
Tel.: (563) 332-7785
Sales Range: $75-99.9 Million
Emp.: 145
Processes Hot Rolled & Oiled Carbon Coil, Sheet, Strip, Hot Rolled Plate, Cold Rolled Sheet & Stainless Steel
N.A.I.C.S.: 423510

Michael Siegel *(CEO)*

Olympic Steel Lafayette, Inc. (1)
3600 N Military, Detroit, MI 48210
Tel.: (313) 894-4552
Web Site: http://www.olympicsteel.com
Sales Range: $50-74.9 Million
Emp.: 100
Metal Product Distr
N.A.I.C.S.: 423510
Michael D. Siegal *(Chm & CEO)*
David A. Wolfort *(Pres)*

Olympic Steel Trading, Inc. (1)
2665 S Byshore Dr Ste 304, Miami, FL 33133
Tel.: (786) 477-5944
Emp.: 6
Metal Product Whslr
N.A.I.C.S.: 423510

Subsidiary (Non-US):

Metales De Olympic, S. de R. L. de C.V. (2)
Calz San Pedro 217, Col Del Valle San Pedro, 66220, Garza Garcia, NL, Mexico
Tel.: (52) 8183356060
Emp.: 10
Steel Product Distr
N.A.I.C.S.: 423390

Olympic Steel-Chambersburg Division (1)
1530 1599 Nitterhouse Dr, Chambersburg, PA 17201 (100%)
Tel.: (717) 709-1515
Web Site: http://www.olysteel.com
Sales Range: $25-49.9 Million
Emp.: 46
Plate Processing & Machining
N.A.I.C.S.: 423510

Olympic Steel-Chicago Division (1)
1901 Mitchell Blvd, Schaumburg, IL 60193 (100%)
Tel.: (847) 584-4000
Web Site: http://www.olysteel.com
Sales Range: $25-49.9 Million
Emp.: 65
Stainless Steel & Heavy Gauge Hot Rolled Plate, Cold Rolled Coil & Sheet, Warehouse, Distribution & Processor
N.A.I.C.S.: 423510

Olympic Steel-Cleveland Division (1)
5060 5080 5096 Richmond Rd, Bedford Heights, OH 44146 (100%)
Tel.: (216) 292-3800
Web Site: http://www.olysteel.com
Sales Range: $50-74.9 Million
Emp.: 121
Carbon Hot Rolled Sheet & Plate, Carbon Cold Rolled Sheet, Stainless Steel Sheet & Alloy Plate Warehousing, Distribution & Processing
N.A.I.C.S.: 423510

Olympic Steel-Connecticut Division (1)
1 Eastern Steel Rd, Milford, CT 06460 (100%)
Tel.: (203) 878-9381
Web Site: http://www.olysteel.com
Sales Range: $25-49.9 Million
Emp.: 74
Cold & Hot Rolled Sheet & Strip, Galvanized & Electro Zinc Coated & In Coils, Sheets, Blanks, Warehouse Distribution & Processor, Stainless Sheet, Plate & Coil
N.A.I.C.S.: 423510

Olympic Steel-Detroit (1)
3600 N Military, Detroit, MI 48210 (100%)
Tel.: (313) 894-4552
Web Site: http://www.olysteel.com
Sales Range: $50-74.9 Million
Emp.: 100
Flatroll Steel Warehouse & Processor
N.A.I.C.S.: 423510

Olympic Steel-Minneapolis Division (1)
625 Xenium Ln N, Minneapolis, MN 55441 (100%)
Tel.: (763) 544-7100
Web Site: http://www.olysteel.com
Sales Range: $75-99.9 Million
Emp.: 179

Hot & Cold Rolled Coil, Sheet, Plate & Stainless Steel Warehouse, Distribution & Processig
N.A.I.C.S.: 423510

Olympic Steel-Southern Division (1)
509 Bankhead Hwy, Winder, GA 30680 (100%)
Tel.: (770) 867-0166
Web Site: https://www.olysteel.com
Sales Range: $25-49.9 Million
Emp.: 52
Heavy Gauge Hot Rolled & Cold Rolled Steel Warehouse Distribution & Processing
N.A.I.C.S.: 331318

Tinsley Group - PS&W, Inc. (1)
3031 Hamp Stone Rd, Siler City, NC 27344-1426
Tel.: (919) 742-5832
Fabricated Metal Merchant Whslr
N.A.I.C.S.: 423390

OMAGINE, INC.
136 Madison Ave 5th Fl, New York, NY 10016
Tel.: (212) 563-4141 DE
Web Site: http://www.omagine.com
Year Founded: 1978
OMAG—(OTCIQ)
Emp.: 5
Real Estate Developers
N.A.I.C.S.: 236220
Frank J. Drohan *(Chm, Pres, CEO & CFO)*
William Hanley *(Chief Acctg Officer & Controller)*

OMEGA ALPHA SPAC
888 Boylston St Ste 1111, Boston, MA 02199
Tel.: (617) 502-6530 Ky
Year Founded: 2020
OMEG—(NASDAQ)
Rev.: $13,386
Assets: $138,926,625
Liabilities: $142,885,135
Net Worth: ($3,958,510)
Earnings: ($831,730)
Emp.: 4
Fiscal Year-end: 12/31/21
Investment Services
N.A.I.C.S.: 523999
Otello Stampacchia *(Chm & CEO)*
Michelle Doig *(Pres)*
Francesco Draetta *(CFO)*
Vincent Ossipow *(Chief Scientific Officer)*

OMEGA COMMERCIAL FINANCE CORPORATION
1000 5th St Ste 200, Miami, FL 33139
Tel.: (305) 704-3294 WY
Web Site: http://www.ocfn.co
Year Founded: 1973
OCFN—(OTCIQ)
Real Estate Financial Services
N.A.I.C.S.: 522310
Todd C. Buxton *(CEO)*
Timothy L. Fussell *(Exec VP-Bus Affairs)*

OMEGA FLEX, INC.
451 Creamery Way, Exton, PA 19341
Tel.: (610) 524-7272 PA
Web Site:
https://www.omegaflex.com
OFLX—(NASDAQ)
Rev.: $125,487,000
Assets: $97,684,000
Liabilities: $26,511,000
Net Worth: $71,173,000
Earnings: $23,652,000
Emp.: 177
Fiscal Year-end: 12/31/22
Flexible Gas Piping Systems Mfr
N.A.I.C.S.: 236220

Stewart B. Reed *(Vice Chm)*
Matthew F. Unger *(CFO & VP-Fin)*
Luke S. Hawk *(Controller)*
Kevin R. Hoben *(Exec Chm)*
Edwin B. Moran *(Pres)*
Dean W. Rivest *(CEO)*

Subsidiaries:

Exton Ranch, LLC (1)
451 Creamery Way, Exton, PA 19341-2508
Tel.: (610) 524-7272
Real Estate Services
N.A.I.C.S.: 531210

OMEGA HEALTHCARE INVESTORS, INC.
303 International Cir Ste 200, Hunt Valley, MD 21030
Tel.: (410) 427-1700 MD
Web Site:
https://www.omegahealthcare.com
Year Founded: 1992
OHI—(NYSE)
Rev.: $949,740,000
Assets: $9,117,402,000
Liabilities: $5,355,111,000
Net Worth: $3,762,291,000
Earnings: $242,180,000
Emp.: 57
Fiscal Year-end: 12/31/23
Healthcare Real Estate Investment Trust
N.A.I.C.S.: 525990
C. Taylor Pickett *(CEO)*
Robert O. Stephenson *(CFO)*
Daniel J. Booth *(COO)*
Gail D. Makode *(Chief Legal Officer & Gen Counsel)*
Matthew P. Gourmand *(Sr VP-Corp Strategy & IR)*
Vikas Gupta *(Sr VP-Acquisitions & Dev)*
Megan M. Krull *(Sr VP-Ops)*
Neal A. Ballew *(Chief Acctg Officer & Sr VP)*

Subsidiaries:

Bayside Street Incorporated (1)
200 International Cir Ste 3500, Hunt Valley, MD 21030
Tel.: (410) 427-1726
Web Site: http://www.omegahealthcare.com
Sales Range: $1-9.9 Million
Real Estate Lessor
N.A.I.C.S.: 531190

Conifer Inc (1)
PO box 177, Medina, WA 98039
Tel.: (425) 486-3334
Web Site: http://www.conifer-inc.com
Sales Range: $300-349.9 Million
Lessor of Real Estate Property
N.A.I.C.S.: 531190

Delta Investors (1)
200 International Cir Ste 3500, Hunt Valley, MD 21030
Tel.: (410) 427-1700
Web Site: http://www.omegahealthcare.com
Sales Range: $1-9.9 Million
Emp.: 20
Lessors of Other Real Estate Property
N.A.I.C.S.: 531190

Dixie White House Nursing Home, LLC (1)
538 Menge Ave, Pass Christian, MS 39571
Tel.: (228) 452-4344
Web Site:
http://www.passchristianhealthrehab.com
Nursing Care Facilities Services
N.A.I.C.S.: 623110

Dixon Health Care Center (1)
135 Reichart Ave, Wintersville, OH 43953
Tel.: (740) 264-1155
Sales Range: $50-74.9 Million
Lessor of Real Estate
N.A.I.C.S.: 531190
Jim Burke *(Mgr-Admin)*

OHI Asset (CO) Mesa, LLC (1)
2121 Mesa Dr, Boulder, CO 80304

Tel.: (303) 442-4037
Healthcare Financial Services
N.A.I.C.S.: 531120

OHI Asset (IN) Greensburg, LLC (1)
200 International Cir Ste 3500, Hunt Valley, MD 21030
Tel.: (410) 427-1700
Real Estate Investment Services
N.A.I.C.S.: 531210

OHI Connecticut Inc (1)
915 Ellen T Grasso Blvd, New Haven, CT 06519
Tel.: (410) 427-1700
Sales Range: $300-349.9 Million
Lessors of Other Real Estate Property
N.A.I.C.S.: 531190

OHI Healthcare Properties Limited Partnership (1)
303 International Cir Ste 200, Hunt Valley, MD 21030
Tel.: (410) 427-1700
Rev.: $928,829,999
Assets: $9,796,123,999
Liabilities: $5,459,529,999
Net Worth: $4,336,593,999
Earnings: $351,959,000
Emp.: 48
Fiscal Year-end: 12/31/2019
Real Estate Asset Management Services
N.A.I.C.S.: 531390
C. Taylor Pickett *(CEO)*

OHI Heath Lodge and Autumn Vale Ltd (1)
Tower 42 25 Old Broad Street, London, EC2N 1HQ, United Kingdom
Tel.: (44) 1895257010
Healthcare Financial Services
N.A.I.C.S.: 531120

OHI Hillings Ltd (1)
Grenville Way, Saint Neots, PE19 8HZ, Cambridgeshire, United Kingdom
Tel.: (44) 1480214020
Healthcare Financial Services
N.A.I.C.S.: 531120

Omega Healthcare Investors Inc.-Maryland (1)
303 International Cir Ste 200, Cockeysville, MD 21030
Tel.: (410) 427-1700
Lessors of Other Real Estate Property
N.A.I.C.S.: 531190

Panama City Nursing Center LLC (1)
924 W 13th St, Panama City, FL 32401
Tel.: (850) 763-8463
Web Site: http://www.gchc.com
Sales Range: $25-49.9 Million
Nursing Care Facilities Services
N.A.I.C.S.: 623110

Parkview - Skilled Nursing, Inc. (1)
2200 W White River Blvd, Muncie, IN 47303
Tel.: (765) 289-3341
Nursing Care Facilities Services
N.A.I.C.S.: 623110

Pavillion Nursing Center North, Inc. (1)
9800 Old Perry Hwy, Wexford, PA 15090
Tel.: (412) 366-7453
Nursing Care Facilities Services
N.A.I.C.S.: 623110

Skyler Boyington, Inc. (1)
2 N Palafox St, Pensacola, FL 32502
Tel.: (850) 432-0650
Emp.: 5
Health Care Srvices
N.A.I.C.S.: 623311

Southern Indiana Rehabilitation Hospital (1)
3104 Blackiston Blvd, New Albany, IN 47150
Tel.: (812) 941-8300
Disability Assistance Services
N.A.I.C.S.: 624120

St. Mary's Properties, Inc. (1)
12811 Three Sisters Rd, Rockville, MD 20854
Tel.: (410) 427-1700

Omega Healthcare Investors, Inc.—(Continued)

Sales Range: $300-349.9 Million
Real Estate Services
N.A.I.C.S.: 531390

Sterling Acquistion Corp (1)
300 International Cir Ste 3500, Hunt Valley, MD 21030
Tel.: (410) 427-1700
Sales Range: $300-349.9 Million
Emp.: 21
Lessors of Other Real Estate Property
N.A.I.C.S.: 531190
Taylor Pickett (CEO)

Suburban Pavillion Inc. (1)
20265 Emery Rd, North Randall, OH 44128
Tel.: (216) 475-8880
Sales Range: $10-24.9 Million
Lessors of Other Real Estate Property
N.A.I.C.S.: 531190
Douglas Pearson (Pres)

The Suburban Pavilion, LLC (1)
20265 Emery Rd, North Randall, OH 44128
Tel.: (216) 475-8880
Healthcare Financial Services
N.A.I.C.S.: 531120

OMEGA THERAPEUTICS, INC.
140 First St Ste 501, Cambridge, MA 02141
Tel.: (617) 949-4360   DE
Web Site:
   https://www.omegatherapeutics.com
Year Founded: 2016
OMGA—(NASDAQ)
Rev.: $2,073,000
Assets: $145,998,000
Liabilities: $40,027,000
Net Worth: $105,971,000
Earnings: ($102,701,000)
Emp.: 116
Fiscal Year-end: 12/31/22
Research & Development in Biotechnology (except Nanobiotechnology)
N.A.I.C.S.: 541714
Barbara Y. Chan (Principal Fin Officer, Principal Acctg Officer, Treas & Sr VP-Fin)
Noubar B. Afeyan (Co-Founder)
Noubar B. Afeyan (Co-Founder & Chm)
David A. Berry (Co-Founder)
Mahesh Karande (Pres & CEO)
Roger Sawhney (Chief Bus Officer)
Thomas McCauley (Chief Scientific Officer)
Barbara Chan (Sr VP-Fin)
Ramola Bhandarkar (VP-Regulatory Affairs)
Ann Darda (VP & Head-HR)
Jeffrey Kopacz (VP-Intellectual Property)
Joe Newman (VP-Biology)
Charles O'Donnell (VP & Head-Computational Genomics & Data Sciences)
Samir Padalkar (VP-Data & IT)
Chinmaya Rath (VP-Strategic Alliance & Innovation)
Sivakesava Sakhamuri (VP & Head-Technical Ops)
Chris Schade (Chm)

OMEROS CORPORATION
201 Elliott Ave W, Seattle, WA 98119
Tel.: (206) 676-5000   WA
Web Site: https://www.omeros.com
Year Founded: 1994
OMER—(NASDAQ)
Rev.: $4,062,000
Assets: $590,969,000
Liabilities: $505,285,000
Net Worth: $85,684,000
Earnings: $47,417,000
Emp.: 196
Fiscal Year-end: 12/31/22
Biopharmaceutical Researcher & Mfr

N.A.I.C.S.: 325412
Gregory A. Demopulos (Founder, Chm, Pres & CEO)
George A. Gaitanaris (Chief Scientific Officer & VP-Science)
Catherine A. Melfi (Chief Regulatory Officer & VP-Regulatory Affairs & Quality Sys)
J. Steven Whitaker (Chief Medical Officer & VP)
Timothy M. Duffy (VP-Bus Dev)
Christopher S. Bral (VP-Nonclinical Dev)
Peter B. Cancelmo (Gen Counsel, Sec & VP)
Bruce Meiklejohn (VP-Chemistry, Mfg, and Controls)
Tina Quinton (VP-Patents)
Nadia Dac (Chief Comml Officer & VP)
Peter W. Williams (VP-HR)
Mariana N. Dimitrova (VP)
Debra K. Bowes (Chief Bus Dev Officer)

OMID HOLDINGS, INC.
Tel.: (908) 386-2880   FL
Web Site:
   https://www.omidholdingsinc.com
Year Founded: 1998
OMID—(OTCIQ)
Offices of Other Holding Companies
N.A.I.C.S.: 551112
Adam Frank (Chm & CEO)
Kevin Anderson (Pres & COO)
Jesse Frank (Supervisor-Production)

OMINTO, INC.
1515 S Federal Hwy Ste 307, Boca Raton, FL 33432
Tel.: (561) 362-2393   NV
Web Site: http://inc.ominto.com
OMNT—(OTCIQ)
Sales Range: $10-24.9 Million
Emp.: 30
Holding Company; Cash Back Shopping Services
N.A.I.C.S.: 551112
Sarwar Uddin (CFO)
Nickolas Sharp (CTO)
Michael B. Hansen (Chm & CEO)
Betina Dupont Sorenson (COO)
Ari Hunsaker (Product Mgr)
Bicky Carlra (Exec VP-Bus Strategy)
Alex Petrllak (Exec VP-Partner Program)
Jerry Yerke (Chief Network Officer-North America & Asia Pacific)
Fiona Lewandowski (Gen Counsel & Sec)

OMNI SHRIMP, INC.
13613 Gulf Blvd, Madeira Beach, FL 33738
Tel.: (727) 398-2692   NV
OMSH—(OTCIQ)
Sales Range: $1-9.9 Million
Emp.: 3
Seafood Marketing Services
N.A.I.C.S.: 424460
Colm Wrynn (Chm & CEO)
Daniel Stelcer (COO & Sec)
Linda Giampietro (VP)

OMNI-LITE INDUSTRIES CANADA INC.
17210 Edwards Rd, Cerritos, CA 90703
Tel.: (562) 404-8510   AB
Web Site: https://www.omni-lite.com
Year Founded: 1992
OLNCF—(OTCIQ)
Rev.: $6,683,776
Assets: $14,850,274
Liabilities: $2,402,171
Net Worth: $12,448,103

Earnings: ($618,092)
Emp.: 28
Fiscal Year-end: 12/31/20
Iron & Steel Forging
N.A.I.C.S.: 332111
Michael K. Walker (VP-R&D)
David Robbins (CEO)
Vern Brown (Pres)

Subsidiaries:

Monzite Corporation (1)
165 Ledge St Ste 3, Nashua, NH 03060-3026
Tel.: (603) 689-1414
Web Site: http://www.monzite.com
Electronic Components Mfr
N.A.I.C.S.: 334419

OMNIA WELLNESS, INC.
999 18th Street Suite 3000, Denver, CO 80202
Tel.: (888) 320-5711   NV
Web Site: http://www.glolex-inc.net
Year Founded: 2016
OMWS—(OTCIQ)
Rev.: $218,874
Assets: $2,161,654
Liabilities: $5,570,294
Net Worth: ($3,408,640)
Earnings: ($2,235,075)
Emp.: 16
Fiscal Year-end: 03/31/21
Business Consulting Services
N.A.I.C.S.: 561499
Andrew E. Trumbach (CFO)
Steve R. Howe (Chm)
Jainal Bhuiyan (Pres)

OMNIAB, INC.
5980 Horton St Ste 600, Emeryville, CA 94608
Tel.: (510) 250-7800   Ky
Web Site: https://www.omniab.com
Year Founded: 2021
OABI—(NASDAQ)
Miscellaneous Financial Investment Activities
N.A.I.C.S.: 523999
Matthew W. Foehr (CEO)

Subsidiaries:

OmniAb Operations, Inc. (1)
2747 Ross Rd Ste A, Palo Alto, CA 94303
Tel.: (650) 224-6835
Web Site: http://www.omniab.com
Biotechnology Research & Development Services
N.A.I.C.S.: 541714

OMNICANNA HEALTH SOLUTIONS, INC.
2910 N Powers Blvd Ste 125, Colorado Springs, CO 80922   NV
Year Founded: 1969
ENDO—(OTCEM)
Biological Products
N.A.I.C.S.: 325414

OMNICELL, INC.
4220 N Freeway, Fort Worth, TX 76137
Tel.: (650) 251-6100   DE
Web Site: https://www.omnicell.com
Year Founded: 1992
OMCL—(NASDAQ)
Rev.: $1,295,947,000
Assets: $2,210,758,000
Liabilities: $1,080,621,000
Net Worth: $1,130,137,000
Earnings: $5,648,000
Emp.: 4,230
Fiscal Year-end: 12/31/22
Pharmacy & Supply Systems to the Health Care Industry
N.A.I.C.S.: 621511

Randall A. Lipps (Chm, Pres & CEO)
Dan S. Johnston (Chief Legal & Admin Officer & Exec VP)
Robin Gene Seim (Executives)
Brian H. Nutt (Chief Acctg Officer, VP & Controller)
Giri Chodavarapu (CIO & Sr VP)
Diane Kaye (Chief Product Officer & Sr VP)
Minoo Mortazavi (Chief Global Supply Chain & Mfg Officer & Sr VP)
Lisa Ritsky-Lamb (Sr VP-Fin-North America)
Kathleen Nemeth (Sr VP-Investor Relations)
Nchacha E. Etta (CFO & Exec VP)
Christine Mellon (Chief Admin Officer)
Corey Manley (Chief Legal Officer)
Pat Carroll (VP)

Subsidiaries:

Aesynt Holdings, Inc. (1)
725 Sycamore Dr, Milpitas, CA 95035
Tel.: (650) 251-6100
Pharmaceutical Products Distr
N.A.I.C.S.: 424210

Aesynt, Inc. (1)
3661 Burwood Dr, Waukegan, IL 60085-9100
Tel.: (800) 910-2220
Pharmaceutical Products Distr
N.A.I.C.S.: 424210

Ateb Canada Ltd. (1)
3760 14th Avenue Suite 300, Markham, L3R 3T7, ON, Canada
Tel.: (866) 388-5629
Health Care Medical Laboratory Services
N.A.I.C.S.: 621511

Ateb, Inc. (1)
4220 N Fwy, Fort Worth, TX 76137
Tel.: (919) 872-1275
Web Site: https://enlivenhealth.co
Sales Range: $1-9.9 Million
Emp.: 165
Computer System Design Services
N.A.I.C.S.: 541512

Avantec Healthcare Ltd. (1)
Marlborough Road Lancing Business Park, Lancing, BN15 8TG, West Sussex, United Kingdom
Tel.: (44) 8704328250
Web Site: http://www.avantec.uk.com
Medical Store Operator
N.A.I.C.S.: 456199

Mach 4 Automatisierungs technik, GmbH. (1)
Limbeckstr 63-65, 44894, Bochum, Germany
Tel.: (49) 234588340
Web Site: http://www.mach4.de
Automation System Design Services
N.A.I.C.S.: 541512

Omnicell B.V. (1)
Hoogoorddreef 15, 1101 BA, Amsterdam, Netherlands
Tel.: (31) 202600183
Medical Laboratory Services
N.A.I.C.S.: 621511

Omnicell GmbH (1)
Robert-Bosch-Str 7, 64293, Darmstadt, Germany
Tel.: (49) 61518001651
Web Site: https://www.omnicell.de
Medical Store Operator
N.A.I.C.S.: 456199
Arthur van Dongen (CEO)

Omnicell Ltd. (1)
Two Omega Drive River Bend Technology Center Irlam, Manchester, M44 5GR, United Kingdom
Tel.: (44) 1614135333
Web Site: https://www.omnicell.co.uk
Health Care Medical Laboratory Services
N.A.I.C.S.: 621511

Omnicell Pty Ltd (1)
15 Corporate Drive, Heatherton, 3202, VIC, Australia
Tel.: (61) 1300846625

Web Site: https://www.omnicell.com.au
Medical Laboratory Services
N.A.I.C.S.: 621511

Omnicell S.r.l. (1)
Piazzale Legnami 1/b Building n 9 - Gaslini,
34145, Trieste, Italy
Tel.: (39) 0403494211
Medical Laboratory Services
N.A.I.C.S.: 621511

OMNICHANNEL ACQUISITION CORP.
485 Springfield Ave Ste 8, Summit,
NJ 07901
Tel.: (908) 271-6641 DE
Year Founded: 2020
OCAU—(NYSE)
Investment Services
N.A.I.C.S.: 523999
Matt Higgins (Chm & CEO)
Chris Pantoya (CFO)
Austin Simon (COO)

OMNICOM GROUP INC.
280 Park Ave, New York, NY 10017
Tel.: (212) 415-3672 NY
Web Site:
https://www.omnicomgroup.com
Year Founded: 1986
OMC—(NYSE)
Rev.: $14,692,200,000
Assets: $28,044,600,000
Liabilities: $23,819,500,000
Net Worth: $4,225,100,000
Earnings: $1,391,400,000
Emp.: 75,900
Fiscal Year-end: 12/31/23
Holding Company; Advertising Services
N.A.I.C.S.: 551112
Daryl D. Simm (Pres & COO)
John D. Wren (Founder, Chm & CEO)
Philip J. Angelastro (CFO & Exec VP)
Jonathan Nelson (CEO-Omnicom Digital)
Shub Mukherjee (VP-Investor Relations)
Rochelle Tarlowe (Treas & Sr VP)
Louis F. Januzzi (Gen Counsel, Sec & Sr VP)
Joanne Trout (Chief Comm Officer)
Andrew L. Castellaneta (Chief Acctg Officer & Sr VP)

Subsidiaries:

AMCI (1)
4755 Alla Rd, Marina Del Rey, CA 90292
Tel.: (310) 765-4100
Web Site: http://www.amciglobal.com
Sales Range: $25-49.9 Million
Emp.: 60
N.A.I.C.S.: 541810

Abbott Mead Vickers Group Limited (1)
151 Marylebone Road, London, NW1 5QE,
United Kingdom
Tel.: (44) 2076163500
Web Site: http://www.amvbbdo.com
Emp.: 1,250
Advertising Agency Services
N.A.I.C.S.: 541810

Adelphi Eden Health Communications (1)
30 Irving Pl 10th Fl, New York, NY 10003
Tel.: (646) 602-7060
N.A.I.C.S.: 541810

Adelphi Group Limited (1)
Adelphi Mill Grimshaw Lane Bollington,
Macclesfield, SK10 5JB, Cheshire, United
Kingdom
Tel.: (44) 1 625 577233
Web Site: http://www.adelphi-group.com
Sales Range: $50-74.9 Million
Emp.: 240
N.A.I.C.S.: 541810

Agency Republic (1)

1 Battersea Bridge Rd, London, SW11 3BZ,
United Kingdom
Tel.: (44) 207 942 0000
Web Site: http://www.agencyrepublic.com
Sales Range: $10-24.9 Million
Emp.: 75
N.A.I.C.S.: 541810

Alcone Marketing Group (1)
4 Studebaker, Irvine, CA 92618-2012
Tel.: (949) 770-4400
Web Site: http://www.alcone.com
Sales Range: $50-74.9 Million
Emp.: 200
Advetising Agency
N.A.I.C.S.: 541810
Matt Alcone (Founder)
Teal Williams (Mng Dir & Sr VP)

Branch (Domestic):

Alcone Marketing Group (2)
320 Post Rd, Darien, CT 06820
Tel.: (949) 770-4400
Web Site: http://www.alcone.com
Sales Range: $25-49.9 Million
Emp.: 100
Advertising Specialties, Consumer Marketing, Sales Promotion
N.A.I.C.S.: 541810

Arnell (1)
7th World Trade Ctr Fl 36, New York, NY
10007
Tel.: (212) 285-2593
Web Site: http://www.arnellgroup.com
Sales Range: $10-24.9 Million
Emp.: 1,175
Advertising Services
N.A.I.C.S.: 541810

AvreaFoster Inc. (1)
500 N Akard St Ste 2000, Dallas, TX 75201
Tel.: (214) 855-1400
Web Site: http://www.avreafoster.com
Sales Range: $1-9.9 Million
Emp.: 30
Brand Development, Collateral, Communications, Direct Marketing, Event Marketing,
Full Service, Interactive Agencies,
Internet/Web Design, Out-of-Home Media,
Publicity/Promotions, Recruitment
N.A.I.C.S.: 541810
Dave Foster (CEO)
Darren Avrea (Chm)
Suzanne Miller (Sr VP-Client Relationships)
Andrew Skola (Sr VP-Strategy)
Lisa Goin (Sr VP-Creative)
Kenny Osborne (Creative Dir)
Christine Guiang (VP-Acct Svc)
Linda Mojica (Dir-HR Ops)

BBDO Canada Corp. (1)
2 Bloor Street West Suite 3200, Toronto,
M4W 3E2, ON, Canada
Tel.: (416) 972-1505
Web Site: http://www.bbdo.ca
Advertising Agency Services
N.A.I.C.S.: 541810

BBDO Worldwide Inc. (1)
1285 Avenue of the Americas, New York,
NY 10019
Tel.: (212) 459-5000
Web Site: https://www.bbdo.com
Sales Range: $100-124.9 Million
Emp.: 16,000
Advertising Services
N.A.I.C.S.: 541810
Andrew Robertson (Pres & CEO)
Jim Moser (Chm-Europe)
Jason Rosario (Chief Diversity, Equity & Inclusion Officer)

Branch (Non-US):

140 BBDO (2)
Unknown Union 2nd Floor 44 Bloem ST,
Cape Town City Centre, Cape Town, 8000,
South Africa
Tel.: (27) 119120000
Web Site: http://www.140bbdo.com
Advertising Services
N.A.I.C.S.: 541810
Mike Schalit (Chief Creative Officer)
Ivan Johnson (Exec Dir-Creative)
Keith Shipley (CEO)

ANR BBDO (2)
David Bagares gata 5, PO Box 5438,

Stockholm, 111 38, Sweden
Tel.: (46) 8 555 77600
Web Site: http://www.anrbbdo.se
Sales Range: $25-49.9 Million
Emp.: 30
Advertising Services
N.A.I.C.S.: 541810
Pontus Karlsson (CEO)
Katja Janford (Copywriter)
Rikard Linder (Art Dir)
Hilda Carlsson (Mgr-Acct)
Jacob Nathanson (Designer-Graphic)
Viktor Bergabo (Art Dir)

ANR BBDO (2)
Grev Turegatan 18, 114 46, Stockholm,
Sweden
Tel.: (46) 855577600
Web Site: https://www.anrplus1.se
Sales Range: $25-49.9 Million
Emp.: 24
Advertising Services
N.A.I.C.S.: 541810

Abbott Mead Vickers BBDO (2)
Bankside 3 Southwark Street, London, SE1
0SW, United Kingdom
Tel.: (44) 2037870100
Web Site: http://www.amvbbdo.com
Sales Range: $75-99.9 Million
Emp.: 400
Advertising Services
N.A.I.C.S.: 541810
Bridget Angear (Co-Chief Strategy Officer)
Craig Mawdsley (Co-Chief Strategy Officer)
Tim Riley (Partner-Creative)
Tom White (Partner-Strategy)
John McDonald (Partner-Strategy)
David Murray (Partner-Strategy)
Brenda Frixa (Mng Partner)
David Edwards (Head-Strategy)
Chris Chapman (Head-Design)
Paul Goodwin (Head-Creative Production)
Katy Talikowska (Head-Client Svcs)
Maxine Thompson (Head-Bus Affairs)
Abdul Owdud (Head-Analytics)
Steve Stretton (Head-AMV Red)
Raj Nathwani (Dir-Insight)
Kelly Knight (Dir-HR)
Ingi Settecasi (Dir-Guest Svcs)
Marion Mitchell (Dir-Admin Svcs)
Michael Pring (Deputy Chm & CMO)
Claire Hollands (Chief Client Officer)
Suzanne Gilson (CFO)

Alice BBDO (2)
Dereboyu Caddesi Science Street No 5 Sun
Plaza BBDO Blok Maslak, 34398, Istanbul,
Turkiye
Tel.: (90) 2122769010
Web Site: http://www.bbdo.com.tr
Sales Range: $25-49.9 Million
Emp.: 60
Advertising Services
N.A.I.C.S.: 541810

Almap BBDO (2)
Avenida Roque Petroni Jr 999 3rd 5th 6th E
7th Fl, Sao Paulo, 04707-000, Brazil
Tel.: (55) 1123954000
Web Site: http://www.almapbbdo.com.br
Advertising Services
N.A.I.C.S.: 541810
Luiz Sanches (Partner & Gen Dir-Creative)

Apex BBDO Publicidad (2)
85 Ave Norte Edificio 619, Colonia Escalon,
San Salvador, El Salvador
Tel.: (503) 25601000
Web Site: https://www.apexbbdo.com
Sales Range: $25-49.9 Million
Emp.: 40
Advertising Services
N.A.I.C.S.: 541810
Sherman Calvo (CEO)
Salvador Martinez (Chief Creative Officer)
Jose Antonio Flores (Assoc Dir-Creative)

BBDO (2)
Ul Burakowska 5/7, Warsaw, 1066, Poland
Tel.: (48) 22 532 9500
Web Site: http://www.bbdo.pl
Sales Range: $25-49.9 Million
Emp.: 60
Advertising Services
N.A.I.C.S.: 541810
Kamil Redestowicz (Dir-Creative)

BBDO Argentina (2)
Arenales 495 Vicente Lopez, Vincente Lo-

pez, Buenos Aires, B1638BRC, Argentina
Tel.: (54) 1160912700
Web Site: http://www.bbdoargentina.com
Sales Range: $25-49.9 Million
Emp.: 50
Advertising Services
N.A.I.C.S.: 541810

BBDO Asia/Pacific (2)
Suite 1501 15/F Cityplaza 4 12 Taikoo Wan
Road, 12 Taikoo Wan Rd, Taikoo Shing,
China (Hong Kong)
Tel.: (852) 28201888
Web Site: http://www.bbdo.com.hk
Advertising Services
N.A.I.C.S.: 541810
Florence Shui (Dir-Fin)
Soo Siong Keoy (CFO)
Samantha Weir (Mgr-Reg Comm)

BBDO Athens (2)
41-45 Marinou Antypa Street, 14121, Athens, Greece
Tel.: (30) 2106784000
Web Site: http://www.bbdoathens.gr
Sales Range: $25-49.9 Million
Emp.: 50
Advertising Services
N.A.I.C.S.: 541810
Tassos Prassinos (Pres & CEO)
Fay Apostolidou (COO)
Theodosis Papanikolaou (Exec Dir-Creative)
Yiannis Fragoulis (CFO)

Branch (Domestic):

Arrow S.A. (3)
Kifissias Ave & 2 Kapodistriou Ave, 151 23,
Maroussi, Greece
Tel.: (30) 210 687 3600
Sales Range: $25-49.9 Million
Emp.: 18
Advertising Services
N.A.I.C.S.: 541810
Niki Boutari (CEO)
Nikos Roulias (Dir-Fin)
Daphne Zannia (Dir-Creative)

Team/Athens (3)
Narino Antista 41/45, Halandri, 15231, Athens, Greece
Tel.: (30) 210 6784 040
Web Site: http://www.teamathens.gr
Sales Range: $25-49.9 Million
Emp.: 37
Advertising Services
N.A.I.C.S.: 541810

Branch (Domestic):

BBDO Atlanta (2)
3500 Lenox Rd NE Ste 1900, Atlanta, GA
30326
Tel.: (404) 231-1700
Web Site: http://www.bbdoatl.com
Sales Range: $50-74.9 Million
Emp.: 220
Advertising Services
N.A.I.C.S.: 541810
Robin Fitzgerald (Chief Creative Officer)
Peter Bunarek (Mng Dir)
Sara Jones (CFO)
Marla Ulrich (Sr VP & Head-Production)
Jessica Welch (VP & Head-People)
Tami Oliva (Exec VP-Acct Mgmt)
Emmet Breen (Exec VP-Acct Mgmt)

Branch (Non-US):

BBDO Bangkok (2)
18/F U Chu Liang Building 968 Rama IV
Road Silom, 968 Rama IV Rd Silom, Bangkok, 10500, Thailand
Tel.: (66) 26375999
Sales Range: $25-49.9 Million
Emp.: 60
Advertising Services
N.A.I.C.S.: 541810
Thipayachand Hasdin (Mng Dir)
Anuwat Nitipanont (Chief Creative Officer)
Somkiat Larptanunchaiwong (CEO)
Thasorn Boonyanate (Chief Creative Officer)

BBDO Bangladesh (2)
Flat C1 Kohen Villa House 26 Road 1/A
Block J Dhaka Gulshan 1, Gulshan-1,
Dhaka, 1212, Bangladesh

Omnicom Group Inc.—(Continued)
Tel.: (880) 1619267171
Web Site: http://www.bbdo.com.bd
Advertising Services
N.A.I.C.S.: 541810

BBDO Budapest (2)
Szep u 2, Budapest, 1053, Hungary
Tel.: (36) 14292400
Web Site: http://www.bbdo.hu
Advertising Services
N.A.I.C.S.: 541810

BBDO CentroAmerica (2)
Edificio Via Lindora Santa Ana, 3er Piso,
San Jose, Costa Rica
Tel.: (506) 205 4000
Advertising Services
N.A.I.C.S.: 541810

BBDO Chile (2)
Avenida del Valle 787 piso 3, Santiago,
Chile
Tel.: (56) 27514100
Web Site: http://www.bbdo.cl
Sales Range: $25-49.9 Million
Emp.: 90
Advertising Services
N.A.I.C.S.: 541810

BBDO China (2)
42/F 1 Grand Gateway No 1 Hong Qiao
Road, NO 1 Hong Qiao Road, Shanghai,
200030, China
Tel.: (86) 2124018000
Web Site: http://www.bbdoasia.com
Advertising Services
N.A.I.C.S.: 541810
Wai Foong Leong (Chm & Co-Chief Creative Officer)
Tze Kiat Tan (CEO-Asia)
Aricio Fortes (Co-Chief Creative Officer)

BBDO China (2)
Room 7E08 Lei Shin Hong Center Build 1
No 8 Guangshun Avenue South, Chao
Yang District, Beijing, 100102, China
Tel.: (86) 1056116500
Web Site: http://www.bbdoasia.com
Advertising Services
N.A.I.C.S.: 541810

BBDO Dublin (2)
17 Gilford Road Sandymount, Sandymount,
Dublin, D04 RK29, Ireland
Tel.: (353) 12060600
Web Site: http://www.bbdo.ie
Advertising Services
N.A.I.C.S.: 541810
Neal Davies (CEO)
Caitriona Ni Laoire (Head-Acct Mgmt)
Robert Boyle (Creative Dir)
Elana Murphy (Acct Mgr)
Neil O'Reilly (Mgr-IR)
Emma Corcoran (Project Dir)
Noel Byrne (Head-Production)
Rosanne Clarke (Acct Dir)
Sinead Lee (Dir-Client Svcs)
Agnieszka Krauze (Acct Mgr)
David Power (Acct Dir)
Emma Blaney (Acct Mgr)
Kate O'Callaghan (Acct Mgr)
Laura Webster (Grp Dir-Acct)
Sarah Hughes (Head-Plng)
Alex Bouches (Mgr-Digital & Social)
Derek Ledwidge (Controller-Fin)
Enda Conway (Head-Innovation)
Jackie Smith (Creative Dir)
Rob Murray (Creative Dir)
Shane O'Brien (Exec Creative Dir)
Alyson Rice (Acct Dir)
Daniel Harnett (Acct Mgr)
Des Kavanagh (Creative Dir)
Bairbre McGlade (Dir-Creative)
Eoin Conlon (Dir-Creative)
Jess Derby (Head-Content & Production)
Karen Austin (Dir-Bus & Ops)
Katie Cunningham (Head-Acct Mgmt)

BBDO Dusseldorf (2)
Koenigsallee 92, 40212, Dusseldorf, Germany
Tel.: (49) 211 1379 0
Web Site: http://www.bbdo.de
Emp.: 400
Advertising Services
N.A.I.C.S.: 541810
Annett Hausmann (Officer-HR People)
Kristoffer Heilemann (Mng Dir-Creative)

Cornelius Kolblin (Mng Dir)
Patrick Hammer (Mng Dir)
Gordon Euchler (Head-Plng)

BBDO EMEA (2)
3 Bankside 90 Southwark Street, London,
SE1 0SW, United Kingdom
Tel.: (44) 2037870100
Web Site: http://www.bbdo.com
Sales Range: $25-49.9 Million
Emp.: 20
Advertising Services
N.A.I.C.S.: 541810

BBDO Guatemala (2)
5 av 5-55 z14 Europlaza Building Tower IV
N 17, Nivel 17, Guatemala, 01014, Guatemala
Tel.: (502) 23822236
Web Site: http://www.bbdo.com.gt
Sales Range: $25-49.9 Million
Emp.: 112
Advertising Services
N.A.I.C.S.: 541810

BBDO Guerrero (2)
17/F Frabelle Business Center 111 Rada
Street, Legazpi Village, Makati, 1229, Philippines
Tel.: (63) 288920701
Web Site: https://bbdoguerrero.com
Sales Range: $25-49.9 Million
Emp.: 97
Advertising Services
N.A.I.C.S.: 541810
David Guerrero (Chm-Creative)

BBDO Honduras (2)
Condominio Metropolis Torre 2 piso 23, Tegucigalpa, Honduras
Tel.: (504) 22802236
Web Site: http://bbdohonduras.com
Advertising Services
N.A.I.C.S.: 541810

BBDO India (2)
Omnicom House 7th Floor Survey No-368
Hissa 41 Kole Kalyan, Vakola Opp - Grand
Hyatt Santacruz, Mumbai, 400055, Haryana, India
Tel.: (91) 2261544444
Web Site: http://www.bbdoindia.com
Sales Range: $25-49.9 Million
Emp.: 55
Advertising Services
N.A.I.C.S.: 541810
Josy Paul (Chm & Chief Credit Officer)
Rajesh Sikroria (Pres)
Jean-Paul Burge (Chm/CEO-Asia)
Agam Gulati (Dir-Fin)
Nikhil Mahajan (Chief Growth Officer & Gen Mgr-Delhi)
Akashneel Dasgupta (Chief Creative Officer-Gurugram)
Suraja Kishore (CEO)
Kaizad Pardiwalla (Chief Digital Officer & Gen Mgr)

BBDO Komunika (2)
Hero Bldg II 7th Fl JL Gatot Subroto, 177 A
Kav 64, Jakarta, 12870, Indonesia
Tel.: (62) 21 831 7780
Web Site: http://www.bbdoasia.com
Advertising Services
N.A.I.C.S.: 541810
Syeda Ayesha Ikram (Exec Creative Dir)
Talha Hisaam (Mng Dir)

BBDO Korea (2)
Amorepacific BLDG 1Core 14F 100
Hangang-Daero, Jung-Gu, Seoul, 100-230,
Korea (South)
Tel.: (82) 234499000
Web Site: http://www.bbdo.co.kr
Sales Range: $25-49.9 Million
Emp.: 90
Advertising Services
N.A.I.C.S.: 541810

BBDO Malaysia (2)
Suite 50-01-01 Wisma UOA Damansara 50
Jalan Dungun, Damansara Heights, 50490,
Kuala Lumpur, Malaysia
Tel.: (60) 20946300
Web Site: http://www.bbdo.com.my
Sales Range: $25-49.9 Million
Emp.: 80
Advertising Services
N.A.I.C.S.: 541810
Farrah Harith McPherson (Gen Mgr)
Donevan Chew (Exec Creative Dir)
Krishna Kumar (Head-Strategy)

BBDO Mexico (2)
Guillermo Gonzalez Camarena 800 3rd Fl,
Col Santa Fe Del Alvaro Obregon, 01210,
Mexico, Mexico
Tel.: (52) 5552671500
Web Site: http://www.bbdomexico.com
Emp.: 201
Advertising Services
N.A.I.C.S.: 541810
Carlos Vaca (CEO)
Jimena Lopez (Mgr-Project)
Mercedes Meneses (Mgr-Community)
Ana Paramo (Mgr-Community)
Ana Gabriela Rios (Mgr-Bus)
Elizabeth Maya (Mgr-Bus)
Ariel Soto (Chief Creative Officer)

Branch (Domestic):

BBDO Minneapolis (2)
150 S 5th St Ste 1000, Minneapolis, MN
55402
Tel.: (612) 338-8401
Web Site: http://bbdompls.com
Sales Range: $25-49.9 Million
Emp.: 50
Marketing & Advertising
N.A.I.C.S.: 541810
Neil White (Pres & CEO)
Alison Siviter (Sr VP & Acct Dir-Grp)
Angela Johnson Lund (Acct Dir-Grp)
Monica Hazelwood (Mgr-Creative Svcs)
Ryan Renneke (Dir-Fin)
Theo Schweitz (Dir-Plng)
Jess Teigen (Dir-Project Mgmt & Production)
Leslie Crayne (Dir-HR & Culture)

Branch (Non-US):

BBDO Moscow (2)
7 Derbenevskaya emb bldg 13, 115114,
Moscow, Russia
Tel.: (7) 4957875778
Web Site: http://bbdo-moscow.ru
Sales Range: $75-99.9 Million
Emp.: 300
Advertising Services
N.A.I.C.S.: 541810
Alexey Fedorov (Exec Creative Dir)
Olga Gramolina (Mng Dir)
Vladlena Obukhova (Mng Dir)
Nikolay Megvelidze (Chief Creative Officer)
Natalia Tsyganova (Mng Dir)
Sergey Kozhevnikov (Dir-Creative)
Daria Bulakhtina (Creative Dir)

Branch (Domestic):

BBDO New York (2)
1285 Avenue of the Americas, New York,
NY 10019
Tel.: (212) 460 5000
Web Site: http://www.bbdo.com
Emp.: 600
Marketing & Advertising
N.A.I.C.S.: 541810
Kirsten Flanik (Pres & CEO)

Branch (Non-US):

BBDO Nicaragua (2)
Ofiplaza El Retirode La Rotonda El Periodista 300 M Sur Edificio 8, PO Box 6007,
Suite 813, Managua, 6007, Nicaragua
Tel.: (505) 22547514
Sales Range: $25-49.9 Million
Emp.: 17
Advertising Services
N.A.I.C.S.: 541810

Branch (Domestic):

BBDO North America (2)
1285 Avenue of the Americas, New York,
NY 10019
Tel.: (212) 459-5000
Web Site: http://www.bbdo.com
Advertising Agencies
N.A.I.C.S.: 541810
John Osborn (Pres & CEO)

Branch (Non-US):

BBDO Panama (2)
Calle 74 Ph Midtown 17Th Floor Office
1703, Ste 3802 15th Fl, Panama, 507,
Panama
Tel.: (507) 3407800
Web Site: https://bbdopa.com

Emp.: 35
Advertising Services
N.A.I.C.S.: 541810
Ricardo Rios (Gen Mgr)
Ricardo Rion (Dir Gen)

BBDO Portugal (2)
Av Eng Duarte Pacheco 26, No 26 12th
Andar, 1070-110, Lisbon, Portugal
Tel.: (351) 21 891 0500
Web Site: http://www.bbdoathens.gr
Sales Range: $10-24.9 Million
Emp.: 60
Advertising Services
N.A.I.C.S.: 541810
Tassos Prassinos (Pres & CEO)
Fay Apostolidou (COO)
Yiannis Fragoulis (CFO)
Theodosis Papanikolaou (Exec Creative
Dir)

Branch (Domestic):

BBDO Puerto Rico (2)
Metro Office Park 14 Calle 2 Ste 400,
Guaynabo, PR 00968-1706
Tel.: (787) 620-2000
Web Site: http://www.bbdopr.com
Sales Range: $25-49.9 Million
Emp.: 43
Marketing & Advertising
N.A.I.C.S.: 541810
Ramiro Millan (Pres & CEO)

BBDO San Francisco (2)
600 California St, San Francisco, CA 94108
Tel.: (415) 808-6200
Web Site: http://www.bbdosf.com
Emp.: 100
Advertising Services
N.A.I.C.S.: 541810
Linda Domercq (CFO)
Melissa Miller (Sr VP & Dir-Plng)
Matt Miller (Chief Creative Officer)
Djanikian Falcon (Sr VP & Head-HR)
Anna Lee (Mgr-HR & Ops)
Courtney Abel (Dir-Project Mgmt)
Elana Shea (Sr VP & Grp Acct Dir)
Evyn Zell-Groner (Exec VP & Acct Dir-Grp)
Jacqueline Djanikian (Dir-Bus Affairs)
Kimberly Fredkin (Sr VP & Acct Dir-Grp)
Louise Doherty (Head-Integrated Production)
Nicole Dongara (Acct Dir)
Rachael Kelly (Sr Dir-Art)
Rich Garbarino (Mgr-Studio)
Jason Moussalli (Mgr-Studio)
Elizabeth Clarity (Supvr-Mgmt)
Curtis Mackenzie (Acct Exec)
Jared Johnsen (Copywriter)
James Campbell (VP & Sr Dir-Acct)
Dalan McNabola (Head-Content & Sr Editor)
Kyle Rodriguez (Supvr-Mgmt)
Ashleigh Serrao (VP & Sr Dir-Acct)
Adam Balogh (Dir-Creative)
Gerardo Juan (Supvr-Fin)
Alex Hamill (Supvr-Acct)
Craig Nelson (Sr Dir-Art)
Kate Davis (Project Mgr)
Carter Nance (Exec VP & Dir-Bus-Worldwide)
Amani Brown (Copywriter)
Andrew Shaffer (Assoc Dir-Creative)
Alee Bono (Art Dir)
Eric Liebhauser (Creative Dir)
Jacquelyn Lopez (Supvr-Acct)
Kimberly Bodker (Supvr-Acct)
Kristie Lee (Dir-Comm Plng)
Laura Paulino (Dir-Project Mgmt)
Maddy Thompson (Art Dir)
Mary Cao (Supvr-Acct)
Minjia Qiu (Sr Acct Dir)
Nadir Nelson (Mgr-Traffic)
Natasha Hoban (Acct Dir)
Neil Slotterback (Dir-Plng)
Virginia Cardozo (Supvr-Acct)

Branch (Non-US):

BBDO Singapore (2)
30 Merchant Road Suite 03-12 Riverside
Point, Riverside Point, Singapore, 058282,
Singapore
Tel.: (65) 65332200
Web Site: http://www.bbdoasia.com
Sales Range: Less than $1 Million
Emp.: 150
Advertising Services

N.A.I.C.S.: 541810
Monica Hynds (Dir-Client Svcs)
Tay Guan Hin (Chm-Creative)
Melvin Kuek (CEO)

BBDO Stuttgart (2)
Breitscheidstrasse 8, 70174, Stuttgart, Germany
Tel.: (49) 7112109910
Web Site: http://www.bbdo.de
Advertising Services
N.A.I.C.S.: 541810

BBDO Taiwan (2)
16F No 97 Song-Ren Rd, Taipei, 110, Taiwan
Tel.: (886) 287866788
Web Site: http://www.bbdoasia.com
Sales Range: $25-49.9 Million
Emp.: 80
Advertising Services
N.A.I.C.S.: 541810
Alan Hung (Mng Dir)
Shih-Yen Lee (Chief Creative Officer)

BBDO Toronto (2)
2 Bloor Street West, Toronto, M4W 3E2, ON, Canada
Tel.: (416) 972-1505
Web Site: http://www.bbdo.ca
Sales Range: $50-74.9 Million
Emp.: 200
Advertising Services
N.A.I.C.S.: 541810
Paul J. Reilly (COO)

Branch (Domestic):

BBDO West (2)
10960 Wilshire Blvd, Los Angeles, CA 90024
Tel.: (310) 444-4500
Sales Range: $10-24.9 Million
Emp.: 10
N.A.I.C.S.: 541810

Branch (Non-US):

BBDO Zagreb (2)
Sostariceva 10/3, 10000, Zagreb, Croatia
Tel.: (385) 14813300
Web Site: http://www.bbdo.hr
Sales Range: $25-49.9 Million
Emp.: 35
Advertising Services
N.A.I.C.S.: 541810
Luka Dubokovic (Mng Dir)

BBDO/Proximity Singapore (2)
30 Merchant Road 03-12 Riverside Point, Singapore, 58282, Singapore
Tel.: (65) 6533 2200
Web Site: http://www.bbdo.com
Advertising Services
N.A.I.C.S.: 541810

CLM BBDO (2)
52 Avenue Emile Zola 90072, Paris, 92772, France
Tel.: (33) 1 4123 4123
Web Site: http://www.clmbbdo.fr
Sales Range: $75-99.9 Million
Emp.: 300
Advertising Services
N.A.I.C.S.: 541810
Gilles Fichtenberg (Chief Creative Officer & VP)

Unit (Domestic):

Proximity BBDO (3)
52 Avenue Emile Zola, 92100, Boulogne, France
Tel.: (33) 1 4123 4123
Web Site: http://www.proximity.bbdo.fr
Sales Range: $50-74.9 Million
Emp.: 130
Advertising Services
N.A.I.C.S.: 541810
Oliver Rippe (CEO)
Nicolas Simonnet (Pres-BUY)
Emmanuel Devezeaux (Sr VP)
Audrey Tamic (Exec Dir-Creative)
Loic Mercier (Dir-Strategy)
Hugues Bolloch (Dir-Fin & Admin)
Jonathan Bobo (Dir-Tech)
Nicolas Demeersman (Dir-Creative)
Pierre Engelibert (Head-Social Media)

Branch (Non-US):

CP Communication (2)

Posadas 1436 1 piso, Buenos Aires, C1011ABJ, Argentina
Tel.: (54) 11 4312 1560
Sales Range: $25-49.9 Million
Emp.: 30
Advertising Services
N.A.I.C.S.: 541810

Campagnani BBDO (2)
Av Manuel Espinosa Batista Y V, Panama, Panama
Tel.: (507) 269 4414
Web Site: http://www.bbdo.com
Sales Range: $25-49.9 Million
Emp.: 38
Advertising Services
N.A.I.C.S.: 541810

Colenso BBDO (2)
100 College Hill, PO Box 47491, Ponsonby, Auckland, 1011, New Zealand
Tel.: (64) 93603777
Web Site: http://www.colensobbdo.co.nz
Sales Range: $25-49.9 Million
Emp.: 60
Advertising Services
N.A.I.C.S.: 541810
Nick Worthington (Chm-Creative)
Scott Coldham (Mng Dir)
Henry Kozak (Dir-Strategy)
Duncan Bone (Grp Dir-Creative)
Si Vicars (Chief Creative Officer)

Branch (Domestic):

Media Direction (3)
33 College Hill Rd, Ponsonby, Auckland, New Zealand
Tel.: (64) 9 353 7440
Advertising Services
N.A.I.C.S.: 541830

Branch (Non-US):

Contrapunto (2)
Cardenal Marcelo Spinola 4, 28016, Madrid, Spain
Tel.: (34) 917872000
Web Site: https://www.contrapuntobbdo.es
Sales Range: $25-49.9 Million
Emp.: 100
Advertising Services
N.A.I.C.S.: 541810

D'Adda, Lorenzini, Vigorelli, BBDO (2)
Via Lanzone 4, 20123, Milan, Italy
Tel.: (39) 02880071
Web Site: http://www.dlvbbdo.com
Sales Range: $25-49.9 Million
Emp.: 50
Advertising Services
N.A.I.C.S.: 541810

Darwin BBDO (2)
Scheldestraat 122, 1080, Sint-Jans-Molenbeek, Belgium
Tel.: (32) 27259710
Web Site: http://www.darwin.be
Sales Range: $25-49.9 Million
Emp.: 25
Advertising Services
N.A.I.C.S.: 541810
Guy Geerts (Mng Dir)
Hannelore van Cauwenberghe (Acct Dir)
Jan Seurinck (Dir-Digital)
Kendy Smits (Dir-Digital)
Klaartje Galle (Creative Dir)
Eva Maes (Acct Dir)

Data Pro Proximity (2)
Weissburg St 19, Zahala, Tel Aviv, 69358, Israel
Tel.: (972) 37654000
Web Site: https://www.datapro.co.il
Sales Range: $25-49.9 Million
Emp.: 40
Advertising Services
N.A.I.C.S.: 541810

Domino (2)
30 Terbatas Street, Riga, LV 1011, Latvia
Tel.: (371) 67114868
Sales Range: $25-49.9 Million
Emp.: 25
Advertising Services
N.A.I.C.S.: 541810

Dynamic Media Tirana (2)
Bluevard Gjergj fishta 10 10 6, 1001, Tirana, Albania
Tel.: (355) 4241969
Web Site: http://www.dynamicmediatirana.com
Sales Range: $25-49.9 Million
Emp.: 5
Advertising Services
N.A.I.C.S.: 541810

Branch (Domestic):

Energy BBDO (2)
225 N Michigan Ave, Chicago, IL 60601
Tel.: (312) 337-7860
Web Site: http://www.energybbdo.com
Sales Range: $50-74.9 Million
Emp.: 200
Marketing & Advertising
N.A.I.C.S.: 541810
Tonise Paul (Chm)
Jeff Adkins (Pres & CEO)
Larry Gies (Chief Strategy Officer)
Josh Gross (Co-Chief Creative Officer)
Pedro Perez (Co-Chief Creative Officer)
Emily Doskow (Exec VP & Dir-Bus Dev)
Alan Parker (Chief Innovation Officer)
Josh Ehart (Chief Data Officer)
Kathy Alvarez (CFO)
Lianne Sinclair (Mng Dir)
Miriam Kaggwa (Co-CFO)
Katie Clow (Exec VP & Dir-Worldwide Client Svc)
Carla Eboli (Exec VP-Multicultural Market)

Branch (Non-US):

FHV BBDO (2)
Amsterdamseweg 204, Amstelveen, 1182 HL, Netherlands
Tel.: (31) 205437777
Web Site: http://www.fhv.bbdo.nl
Sales Range: $25-49.9 Million
Emp.: 40
Advertising Services
N.A.I.C.S.: 541810

First City Advertising (2)
22 Goodge Pl, London, W1T 4SL, United Kingdom
Tel.: (44) 2074367020
Web Site: http://www.firstcityadvertising.co.uk
Advertising Services
N.A.I.C.S.: 541810

Formitas (2)
Dunajska cesta 5, 1000, Ljubljana, Slovenia
Tel.: (386) 14301700
Web Site: http://www.formitas.si
Sales Range: $10-24.9 Million
Emp.: 34
Advertising Services
N.A.I.C.S.: 541810
Mojca Randl (CEO & Partner-Formitas BBDO)

Garnier BBDO (2)
Centro Comercial Via Lindora Edificio BLP Piso 2 pozos, 1000, San Jose, Costa Rica
Tel.: (506) 41105000
Web Site: http://www.garnierbbdo.com
Sales Range: $25-49.9 Million
Emp.: 90
Advertising Services
N.A.I.C.S.: 541820

Garwich BBDO (2)
Av Salaverry 2991-San Isidro 27, San Isidro, Lima, 18, Peru
Tel.: (51) 1 611 7200
Web Site: http://www.bbdo.com
Advertising Services
N.A.I.C.S.: 541810

Garwich BBDO (Quito) (2)
Edificio Milenium Plaza Av Eloy Alfaro N35-09 y Portugal, Piso 4 - Of 404, Quito, Ecuador
Tel.: (593) 43709890
Web Site: http://www.bbdo.com
Advertising Services
N.A.I.C.S.: 541810

Germaine (2)
Ballaarstraat 99, 2018, Antwerp, Belgium
Tel.: (32) 32163003
Web Site: http://www.germaine.be
Sales Range: $25-49.9 Million
Emp.: 20
Advertising Services

N.A.I.C.S.: 541810
Bart Klerckx (Dir-Creative)

GitamBBDO (2)
8 Raul Wallenberg Street, Tel Aviv, 39719, Israel
Tel.: (972) 35765757
Web Site: http://www.gitam.co.il
Advertising Services
N.A.I.C.S.: 541810

Graffiti BBDO (2)
Strada Iordache Golescu 17, Bucharest, 11302, Romania
Tel.: (40) 213160200
Web Site: http://www.graffiti.bbdo.ro
Sales Range: $25-49.9 Million
Emp.: 70
Advertising Services
N.A.I.C.S.: 541810
Dan Moraru (CEO)
Ioana Avram (Dir-Creative & Dir-Art)
Mihai Gongu (Dir-Creative)
Radu Olteanu (Grp Dir-Creative)
Alex Strimbeanu (Copywriter)
Vlad Lazar (Creative Dir)
Titus Domitrescu (Dir-Creative)

Graffiti BBDO Sofia (2)
3A Nikolay Haytov Str Fl 3, 1113, Sofia, Bulgaria
Tel.: (359) 28651138
Web Site: http://www.graffiti-bbdo.bg
Sales Range: $25-49.9 Million
Emp.: 50
Advertising Services
N.A.I.C.S.: 541810
Greta Koleva-Hikova (Mng Dir)
Kiril Stoyanov (Dir-Creative)

I&S BBDO Inc. (2)
Harumi Triton Square X 1-8-10 Harumi, Chuo-ku, Tokyo, 104-6038, Japan
Tel.: (81) 362218585
Web Site: http://www.isbbdo.co.jp
Sales Range: Less than $1 Million
Emp.: 400
Advertising Services
N.A.I.C.S.: 541810
Yoshihiro Nagai (Pres)
Keoy Soo Siong (Vice Chm)
Kazuo Kano (Dir-Fin)

Branch (Domestic):

BBDO Japan Inc. (3)
Harumi Triton Square X 1-8-10, Chuo-ku, Tokyo, 104-6038, Japan
Tel.: (81) 362218040
Web Site: https://www.bbdojapan.com
Direct & Relationship Marketing Agency Integrating Communications, Digital Marketing & Sales Promotions
N.A.I.C.S.: 541810

BBDO/J West Inc. Headquarters (3)
4-1-32 Tenjin, Chou-ku, Fukuoka, 810-0001, Japan
Tel.: (81) 927512466
Web Site: https://www.bbdojw.co.jp
Advertising Services
N.A.I.C.S.: 541810

BBDO/J West Inc. Hiroshima Branch (3)
6F Churisu Hatchobori 6-7 Hatchobori, Naka-ku, Hiroshima, 730-0013, Japan
Tel.: (81) 82 221 2526
Web Site: http://www.isbbdo.co.jp
Rev.: $38,000,000
Emp.: 10
Advertising Services
N.A.I.C.S.: 541810

BBDO/J West Inc. Kita-Kyushu Branch (3)
2F Sunshine Nangoku Bldg 1-1-204 Konya, Kokurakita-ku, Kitakyushu, 802-0081, Japan
Tel.: (81) 935513881
Web Site: http://www.bbdojw.co.jp
Advertising Services
N.A.I.C.S.: 541810

BBDO/J West Inc. Okinawa Branch (3)
8F Ryukyu Lease Sogo Bldg 1-7-1 Kumoji, Naha, 900-0015, Japan
Tel.: (81) 988695234
Web Site: http://www.bbdojw.co.jp
Rev.: $2,100,000

Omnicom Group Inc.—(Continued)

Advertising Services
N.A.I.C.S.: 541810

I&S/BBDO Kansai Regional Head Office (3)
23F Nakanoshima Mitsui Bldg 3-3-3 Na-kanoshima, Kita-ku, Osaka, 530-0005, Japan
Tel.: (81) 664481501
Web Site: http://www.isbbdo.co.jp
Advertising Services
N.A.I.C.S.: 541810

I&S/BBDO Kyoto Regional Head Office (3)
3F Nittochi Kyoto Bldg 535 Akinono-cho Oshikoji Agaru Karasuma-dor, Nakagyo-ku, Kyoto, 604-0847, Japan
Tel.: (81) 75 213 1091
Web Site: http://www.isbbdo.co.jp
Rev.: $21,300,000
Advertising Services
N.A.I.C.S.: 541810

I&S/BBDO Nagoya Regional Head Office (3)
Lion Building 3-19-1 Marunouchi, Naka-ku, Nagoya, 460-0002, Japan
Tel.: (81) 52 962 6791
Web Site: http://www.isbbdo.co.jp
Advertising Services
N.A.I.C.S.: 541810

I&S/BBDO Sapporo Branch (3)
Sakura-N3 7-1-1Kita-Sanjo-Nishi 3-1 Kita-nijo-nishi, Chou-ku, Sapporo, 060-0003, Japan
Tel.: (81) 8098903345
Web Site: http://www.isbbdo.co.jp
Advertising Services
N.A.I.C.S.: 541810

Branch (Non-US):

Impact BBDO (2)
Ali Reza Twr 1 Fl Medina Rd, PO Box 7242, Jeddah, 21462, Saudi Arabia
Tel.: (966) 26515566
Web Site: http://www.impactbbdo.com
Sales Range: $25-49.9 Million
Emp.: 45
Advertising Services
N.A.I.C.S.: 541810

Branch (Domestic):

Impact BBDO (3)
Cercon Building 6 2nd Floor, PO Box 615, Olaya, Riyadh, 11372, Saudi Arabia
Tel.: (966) 14653550
Web Site: http://www.impactbbdo.com
Sales Range: $25-49.9 Million
Emp.: 40
Advertising Services
N.A.I.C.S.: 541810

Branch (Non-US):

Impact BBDO (2)
Sharq Mutanabi Street Building No 42, Safat 13071, Kuwait, 13071, Kuwait
Tel.: (965) 24964440
Web Site: http://www.impactbbdo.com
Sales Range: $25-49.9 Million
Emp.: 37
Advertising Services
N.A.I.C.S.: 541810
Colin Farmer *(Mng Dir)*

Impact BBDO (2)
15 Hassan Sabry, Zamalek, Cairo, 11311, Egypt
Tel.: (20) 227283400
Web Site: http://www.impactbbdo.com
Sales Range: $25-49.9 Million
Emp.: 63
Advertising Services
N.A.I.C.S.: 541810
Dani Richa *(Chm & CEO-Middle East, Africa & Pakistan)*

Impact BBDO (2)
Emirates Towers 17th Floor Sheikh Zayed Road, PO Box 19791, Dubai, United Arab Emirates
Tel.: (971) 43304010
Web Site: http://www.impactbbdo.com
Rev.: $294,000,000
Emp.: 350

Advertising Services
N.A.I.C.S.: 541810
Alain Khouri *(Founder)*
Colin Farmer *(VP-Talent Dev)*
Samantha Stuart-Palmer *(Mng Dir)*
Paul Shearer *(Chief Creative Officer)*
Jackie Hughes *(Chief Strategy Officer)*

Impact BBDO (2)
Cercon Bldg 6 2nd Fl, Olaya, Riyadh, 11372, Saudi Arabia
Tel.: (966) 14653550
Web Site: http://www.impactbbdo.com
Sales Range: $25-49.9 Million
Emp.: 55
Public Relations Services
N.A.I.C.S.: 541820

Impact BBDO (2)
Bldg 635 Omar Daouk Street, PO Box 11-8483, Ain-Mreyseeh, Beirut, 30621, Lebanon
Tel.: (961) 1367890
Web Site: http://www.impactbbdo.com
Sales Range: $25-49.9 Million
Emp.: 80
Advertising Services
N.A.I.C.S.: 541810

Interone Worldwide
Blumenstrasse 28, 80331, Munich, Germany
Tel.: (49) 89551860
Web Site: https://www.interone.de
Sales Range: $50-74.9 Million
Emp.: 150
Advertising Services
N.A.I.C.S.: 541810
Michael Wong *(Exec Creative Dir-China)*
Catherine Zhu *(Mng Dir-China)*

Branch (Domestic):

Interone Cologne (3)
Thebaerstrasse 17, 50825, Cologne, Germany
Tel.: (49) 221 549 60 0
Advertising Agencies
N.A.I.C.S.: 541810

Interone Hamburg (3)
Zirkusweg 1, 20359, Hamburg, Germany
Tel.: (49) 40 432 969 0
Web Site: http://www.interone.de
Emp.: 200
Advertising Services
N.A.I.C.S.: 541810
Christo Zonnev *(CTO)*

Branch (Non-US):

KNSK Werbeagentur GmbH (2)
An der Alster 1, 20099, Hamburg, Germany
Tel.: (49) 404418901
Web Site: http://www.knsk.de
Sales Range: $25-49.9 Million
Emp.: 100
Advertising Services
N.A.I.C.S.: 541810
Werner Knopf *(Mng Partner & Mng Dir)*
Detmar Karpinski *(Mng Partner & Mng Dir)*
Tim Krink *(Partner & Dir-Creative)*
Ulrike Wegert *(Dir-Creative)*

Lukrecija BBDO (2)
K Kalinausko G 2B, LT-03107, Vilnius, Lithuania
Tel.: (370) 5 2338 383
Web Site: http://www.lukrecija.lt
Sales Range: $25-49.9 Million
Emp.: 30
Advertising Services
N.A.I.C.S.: 541810
Marius Vaupsas *(Partner)*
Gintas Lapenas *(Partner & Sr Dir-Creative)*

Lunar BBDO (2)
35-41 Folgate Street, London, E1 6BX, United Kingdom
Tel.: (44) 20 7611 3711
Web Site: http://www.lunarbbdo.com
Advertising Services
N.A.I.C.S.: 541810

Mark BBDO (2)
Krizikova 71, 186 00, Prague, Czech Republic
Tel.: (420) 251001511
Web Site: http://www.markbbdo.cz
Advertising Services
N.A.I.C.S.: 541810

Katka Netolicka *(Sr Mgr-Acct)*
Marie Kalinova *(Mgr-Social Media)*
Tereza Kohlerova *(Mgr-Fin)*
Klara Hatle *(Mgr-Acct)*
Anna Nedvedova *(Mgr-Acct)*
Barbora Pelcova *(Mgr-Acct)*
Aneta Pospisilova *(Mgr-Acct)*
Tereza Skacelova *(Dir-Art)*
Katka Tumova *(Mgr-Acct)*
Jiri Huska *(Dir-Creative)*
Jakub Mach *(Dir-Art)*
Bernard Netopil *(Dir-Art)*
Dana Felgrova *(Dir-Acct)*

Mark BBDO (2)
Zamocka 5, PO Box 301, Bratislava, 811 01, Slovakia
Tel.: (421) 254411331
Web Site: http://www.bbdo.sk
Sales Range: $25-49.9 Million
Emp.: 20
Marketing & Advertising
N.A.I.C.S.: 541810

Net#work BBDO (2)
3 Sandown Valley Crescent, Sandown, Sandton, 2031, Gauteng, South Africa
Tel.: (27) 119120000
Web Site: http://www.networkbbdo.co.za
Sales Range: $25-49.9 Million
Emp.: 65
Advertising Services
N.A.I.C.S.: 541810
Clinton Mitri *(COO)*
Boniswa Pezisa *(Grp CEO)*
Leo Manne *(Mng Dir)*
Roanna Williams *(Partner & Chief Creative Officer)*

Ovation Advertising (2)
Guro Gakovik 56, Skopje, 1000, North Macedonia
Tel.: (389) 2 3212 983
Web Site: http://www.ovation.com.mk
Sales Range: $25-49.9 Million
Emp.: 11
Advertising Services
N.A.I.C.S.: 541810
Elena Stefanova *(Gen Mgr)*
Biljana Trajkovska *(Mgr-Media)*
Nikola Anchevski *(Dir-Creative)*
Aleksandra Lukic Kamilovska *(Dir-Acct)*

P&V BBDO (2)
Av Peru 202 Esq Rio de Janeiro, PO Box 1951, Asuncion, Paraguay
Tel.: (595) 21 200 773
Web Site: http://www.pyvbbdo.com.py
Sales Range: $25-49.9 Million
Emp.: 15
Advertising Services
N.A.I.C.S.: 541810

PKP BBDO (2)
Guglgasse 7-9, 1030, Vienna, Austria
Tel.: (43) 1955000
Web Site: http://www.bbdo.at
Sales Range: $25-49.9 Million
Emp.: 13
Advertising Services
N.A.I.C.S.: 541810
Roman Sindelar *(Mng Dir)*
Erich Enzenberger *(Dir-Creative)*
Sabine Luke *(Dir-Fin)*

Pages BBDO (2)
Abraham Lincoln 1019 Edificio Federico Pages More, Santo Domingo, Dominican Republic
Tel.: (809) 5415331
Web Site: http://www.pagesbbdo.com
Advertising Services
N.A.I.C.S.: 541810

Perez y Villa BBDO (2)
Calle 19 No 43G-130 Loc 9 Plaza Del Rio Building, Sector Ciudad Del Rio Antioquia, Medellin, Colombia
Tel.: (57) 43208080
Web Site: http://www.perezyvilla.com
Rev.: $7,530,000
Emp.: 36
Advertising Services
N.A.I.C.S.: 541810

Pleon Impact (2)
Pernerova 652/55, Karlin, 186 00, Prague, Czech Republic
Tel.: (420) 724767532
Web Site: http://www.pleon-impact.cz
Rev.: $2,404,767

Emp.: 20
Public Relations Services
N.A.I.C.S.: 541820
Zdenka Svoboda Kuhnova *(Mng Partner)*

R.K. Swamy BBDO (2)
605-606 Anna Salai, Chennai, 600 006, India
Tel.: (91) 44 3988 3500
Web Site: http://www.rkswamybbdo.com
Emp.: 150
Advertising Services
N.A.I.C.S.: 541810
Shekar Swamy *(CEO)*
V. V. Vijay Gopal *(Pres-South & East)*
G. Suresh *(VP-IT)*
Sangeetha Narasimhan *(Chief Digital Officer & Sr VP)*
Srinivasan K. Swamy *(Chm & Mng Dir)*
Navneet Virk *(Sr Partner)*
Sankar Nagarajan *(VP-Fin)*
K. Paarthasarathy *(Sr VP-Fin)*
Sunil Kukreti *(Sr VP & Gen Mgr)*
Gautam Pandit *(Sr Partner & Exec Dir-Creative)*
Chandrashekhar Vaidya *(Sr Partner & Exec Dir-Creative)*
Ambareesh Chakraborty *(Sr Partner & Exec Dir-Creative)*
K. V. Sasidharan *(Sr Partner & Dir-Natl-Special Projects)*
Rajesh Nambiar *(Sr Partner)*
Atul Dube *(Sr Partner)*
Nirvic Guha *(Sr Partner)*
V. Seshagiri Rao *(Sr Partner)*
Sandeep Sharma *(Pres-Media)*
Veena Kotian *(Partner & Sr Gen Mgr-HR)*
Ankur Suman *(Partner & Exec Creative Dir)*
Lata Ramaseshan *(Gen Mgr-IRC)*
Vivek Shenoy *(Gen Mgr)*
P. Vishwamohan *(COO-Pharma Direction)*
Kaushik Tiwari *(Chief Bus Officer & Sr Partner)*

Branch (Domestic):

R.K. Swamy/BBDO (3)
Film Chamber Building 605/606 2nd Floor Anna Salai, Chennai, 600 006, India
Tel.: (91) 44 3988 3500
Web Site: http://www.rkswamybbdo.com
Sales Range: $25-49.9 Million
Emp.: 110
Advertising Services
N.A.I.C.S.: 541810
V. V. Vijay Gopal *(Pres-South & East)*

R.K. Swamy/BBDO (3)
E/1 Jhandewalan Extn, New Delhi, 110 055, India
Tel.: (91) 1130583403
Web Site: http://www.rkswamybbdo.com
Sales Range: $25-49.9 Million
Emp.: 45
Advertising Services
N.A.I.C.S.: 541810
Sunil Kukreti *(Sr VP & Gen Mgr)*
G. Suresh *(VP-IT)*
Sankar Nagarajan *(VP-Fin)*
K. Satyanarayana *(Sr VP-Media)*
K. Paarthasarathy *(Sr VP-Fin)*
K. V. Sasidharan *(Sr Partner & Dir-Special Projects-Natl)*
Kaushik Tiwari *(Sr Partner & Chief Bus Officer)*
Gautam Pandit *(Sr Partner)*
Chandrashekhar Vaidya *(Sr Partner)*
Ambareesh Chakraborty *(Sr Partner)*
Navneet Virk *(Sr Partner)*
Rajesh Nambiar *(Sr Partner)*
Atul Dube *(Sr Partner)*
Nirvic Guha *(Sr Partner)*
V. Seshagiri Rao *(Sr Partner)*
Sangeetha N. *(Pres-West & NCD)*
V. V. Vijaygopal *(Pres-South & East)*
Veena Kotian *(Partner & Sr Gen Mgr-HR)*
Ankur Suman *(Partner & Exec Creative Dir)*
Lata Ramaseshan *(Gen Mgr-IRC)*
R. Vishwamohan *(COO-Pharma Direction)*
Srinivasan Swamy *(Chm & Mng Dir)*
S. Narasimhan *(Chief Digital Officer & Sr VP)*
Shekar Swamy *(CEO)*

R.K. Swamy/BBDO (3)
Plot No 38 L & T Building 1st Floor Cubbon Road, No 2 Residency Road, Bengaluru, 560 001, India
Tel.: (91) 8041840700

Web Site: http://www.rkswamybbdo.com
Emp.: 50
Advertising Services
N.A.I.C.S.: 541810
Shekar Swamy (CEO-Grp)

R.K. Swamy/BBDO (3)
6-3-1089 /B Gulmohar Avenue Somajiguda,
Hyderabad, 500 082, India
Tel.: (91) 4023372028
Web Site: http://www.rkswamybbdo.com
Sales Range: $25-49.9 Million
Emp.: 32
Advertising Services
N.A.I.C.S.: 541810
V. Seshagiri Rao (Sr Partner)
R. Vishwa Mohan (COO-Pharma Direction)
Srinivasan Swamy (Chm & Mng Dir)
N. Sangeetha (Pres-West & NCD)
Sandeep Sharma (Pres-Media)
S. Narasimhan (Chief Digital Officer & Sr VP)
K. Satyanarayana (Sr VP-Media)
Kaushik Tiwari (Sr Partner & Chief Bus Officer)
Sankar Nagarajan (VP-Fin)
G. Suresh (VP-IT)
Anukar Suman (Partner & Exec Creative Dir)
Vivek Shenoy (Gen Mgr)
Lata Ramaseshan (Gen Mgr-IRC)

R.K. Swamy/BBDO (3)
Esplanade House 29 Hazarimal Somani
Marg, Fort, Mumbai, 400 001, India
Tel.: (91) 2222077476
Web Site: http://www.rkswamybbdo.com
Sales Range: $25-49.9 Million
Emp.: 83
Advertising Services
N.A.I.C.S.: 541810
S. Narasimhan (Chief Digital Officer & Sr VP)
G. Suresh (VP-IT)
Sankar Nagarajan (VP-Fin)
K. Satyanarayan (Sr VP-Media)
K. Paarthasarathy (Sr VP-Fin)
Sunil Kukreti (Sr VP & Gen Mgr)
K. V. Sasidharan (Sr Partner & Dir-Special Projects-Natl)
Gautam Pandit (Sr Partner)
Chandrashekhar Vaidya (Sr Partner)
Ambareesh Chakraborty (Sr Partner)
Navneet Virk (Sr Partner)
Rajesh Nambiar (Sr Partner)
Atul Dube (Sr Partner)
Nirvic Guha (Sr Partner)
V. Seshagiri Rao (Sr Partner)
N. Sangeetha (Pres-West & NCD)
V. V. Vijaygopal (Pres-South & East)
Sandeep Sharma (Pres-Media)
Veena Kotian (Partner & Sr Gen Mgr-HR)
Ankur Suman (Partner & Exec Dir-Creative)
Lata Ramaseshan (Gen Mgr)
Vivek Shenoy (Gen Mgr)
R. Vishwamohan (COO-Pharma Direction)
Srinivasan Swamy (Chm & Mng Dir)
Kaushik Tiwari (Chief Bus Officer & Sr Partner)

Branch (Non-US):

Sancho BBDO (2)
Calle 98 Ste 9-03 Piso 2, Bogota, Colombia
Tel.: (57) 16510651
Web Site: http://www.sanchobbdo.com.co
Sales Range: $75-99.9 Million
Emp.: 350
Advertising Services
N.A.I.C.S.: 541810
Alvaro Arango Correa (Pres)

TBWA & BBDO A/S (2)
St Kongensgade 59 E, 1264, Copenhagen, Denmark
Tel.: (45) 39278899
Web Site: https://www.tbwa.dk
Sales Range: $25-49.9 Million
Emp.: 43
Advertising Services
N.A.I.C.S.: 541810
Erich Karsholt (Mng Dir)
Merete Ausig Weiss (Acct Dir)
Jens Finnur Eliasson (Head-Digital)
Merete Hubertz (Acct Dir)
Louise Sonne Thaning (Dir-Strategic)
Peder Stryhn (Sr Dir-Art)
Malene Zarp (Head-Administration)

Telia & Pavla BBDO (2)

62 Pericleous Street 2021 Strovolos, PO
Box 23930, 1687, Nicosia, Cyprus
Tel.: (357) 22377745
Web Site: http://www.tpbbdo.com.cy
Sales Range: $25-49.9 Million
Emp.: 39
Advertising Services
N.A.I.C.S.: 541810
Stelios Anastassiades (Mng Dir)
Athos Kyriakou (Deputy Mng Dir & Head-Client Svc)
Chris Piperaris (Controller-Fin)
Anastasia Tsami (Exec Creative Dir)
Areti Anastassiades (Mng Dir)
Eleni Avraamidou (Dir-Media)
Ioanna Savvidou (Asst Dir-Creative)
Andreas Spyropoulos (Dir-Art)
Popi Savva (Coord-Production)
Evanthia Diakou (Accountant)
Andreas Anastasiades (Dir-Strategy)
Konstantinos Kosmas (Dir-Client Svcs)
Valentinos Christodoulou (Acct Mgr)
Marianna Kourti (Copywriter)
Constantinos Karayiannis (Mgr-Digital Community)

Subsidiary (Non-US):

The Clemenger Group Ltd. (2)
120 Pacific Highway, Saint Leonards, 2065,
NSW, Australia (74%)
Tel.: (61) 2 9925 5333
Web Site: http://www.clemenger.com.au
Sales Range: $125-149.9 Million
Emp.: 1,700
Advertising Services
N.A.I.C.S.: 541810
Robert Morgan (Chm)
Jonathan Isaacs (CFO)
Melissa Anderson (Chief HR Officer-New Zealand)
Strahan Wallis (CEO-New Zealand)

Branch (Domestic):

Clemenger BBDO Adelaide (3)
Level 1 8 Leigh St, Adelaide, 5000, SA, Australia
Tel.: (61) 8 8301 2444
Web Site:
http://www.clemengerbbdo.com.au
Advetising Agency
N.A.I.C.S.: 541810

Clemenger BBDO Brisbane (3)
LEVEL 3 200 ADELAIDE STREET, Brisbane, 4000, QLD, Australia
Tel.: (61) 7 3833 3666
Web Site: http://www.clemenger.com.au
Sales Range: $25-49.9 Million
Emp.: 34
Full Service
N.A.I.C.S.: 541810
Christine Gannon (Mng Partner-Client Svc)

Clemenger BBDO Melbourne (3)
Level 3 474 St Kilda Road, Melbourne, 3004, VIC, Australia
Tel.: (61) 398694444
Web Site:
http://www.clemengerbbdo.com.au
Emp.: 200
Full Service
N.A.I.C.S.: 541810
James McGrath (Chm)
Jonny Berger (Gen Mgr)
Simon Lamplough (Mng Dir)
Nick Zonnios (Head-PR)
Adrian Ciabotti (CFO)
Pippa O'Regan (Exec Dir-Retail)
Lea Egan (Creative Dir)
Lauren Hunt (Dir-Bus)
Daniel Pizzato (Creative Dir)
Jim Gall (CEO)
Ryan Fitzgerald (Exec Creative Dir)
Dave Keating (COO)
Jacqueline Witts (Head-Plng)
Leigh Arbon (Dir-Plng)
Paul Rees Jones (Exec Dir-Plng)
Rich Williams (Exec Creative Dir)
Darren Wright (Exec Creative Dir)

Clemenger BBDO Sydney (3)
Pier 9 23 Hickson Road, Walsh Bay, 2000,
NSW, Australia
Tel.: (61) 299255333
Web Site:
http://www.clemengerbbdo.com.au
Rev.: $118,827,800
Emp.: 150

N.A.I.C.S.: 541810
Tristan Graham (Exec Creative Dir)
Peter Bosilkovski (CEO)
Lilian Sor (Chief Strategy Officer)
Brad Morris (Mng Partner)
Adrian Ciabotti (CFO)
Jim Curtis (Chief Creative Officer)
Brendan Willenberg (Exec Creative Dir)
Lewis Steele (Head-Social)

Branch (Non-US):

Clemenger BBDO Wellington (3)
Level 2 1 Post Office Square, Wellington,
6011, New Zealand
Tel.: (64) 48023333
Web Site: https://www.clemengerbbdo.co.nz
Sales Range: $25-49.9 Million
Emp.: 100
N.A.I.C.S.: 541810

Branch (Non-US):

The Icelandic Ad Agency (2)
Laufasvefur 49-51 101, Reykjavik, Iceland
Tel.: (354) 5914300
Web Site: http://www.islenska.is
Sales Range: $25-49.9 Million
Emp.: 40
Advertising Services
N.A.I.C.S.: 541810
Olafur Ingi Olafsson (Mng Dir)

Tiempo BBDO (2)
Tuset 5 6a Planta, 08006, Barcelona, Spain
Tel.: (34) 933069000
Web Site: http://www.tiempobbdo.com
Sales Range: $25-49.9 Million
Emp.: 100
Advertising Services
N.A.I.C.S.: 541810

Tiempo BBDO (2)
Marcelo Spinola 4, 28016, Madrid, Spain
Tel.: (34) 917870885
Web Site: http://www.tiempobbdo.com
Advertising Services
N.A.I.C.S.: 541810

VVL BBDO (2)
Rue De I Escaut 122, Molenbeek-Saint-Jean, 1080, Brussels, Belgium
Tel.: (32) 24212200
Web Site: http://www.bbdo.be
Sales Range: $50-74.9 Million
Emp.: 200
Advertising Services
N.A.I.C.S.: 541810

Zavod BBDO (2)
Poska 51a, Tallinn, 10150, Estonia
Tel.: (372) 6 8 11 800
Web Site: http://www.zavod.ee
Sales Range: Less than $1 Million
Emp.: 11
N.A.I.C.S.: 541810

Zea BBDO (2)
Prolongacion Calle Vargas Con Segunda
Transversal Edificio Sanofi, Torre Sur Piso 5
PB Boleita Norte, Caracas, 1017, Miranda,
Venezuela
Tel.: (58) 2127189441
Web Site: http://www.zeabbdo.com
Sales Range: $25-49.9 Million
Emp.: 40
Marketing & Advertising
N.A.I.C.S.: 541810

Beanstalk (1)
1285 Avenue of the Americas 5th Fl, New
York, NY 10019
Tel.: (212) 421-6060
Web Site: http://www.beanstalk.com
Sales Range: $10-24.9 Million
Emp.: 25
Marketing Consulting Services
N.A.I.C.S.: 541613
Michael S. Stone (Founder & Chm)
Allison Ames (Pres & CEO)
Oliver Herzfeld (Chief Legal Officer & Sr VP)
Celia Asprea (VP-HR)
Debra Restler (Sr VP-Bus Dev & Mktg)
Caren Chacko (VP-Brand Mgmt)
Linda Morgenstern (VP-Brand Mgmt)
Marc Schneider (CFO & COO)
Martin Cribbs (VP-Brand Mgmt)
Serena Sibbald (VP-Brand Dev, Licensing &
New Bus)
Bryan Graham (Head-Audit Svcs Div)
Emmanuel Fordjour (VP-Fin)

BioPharm Communications, LLC (1)
580 Union Sq Dr, New Hope, PA 18938
Tel.: (215) 862-4902
Web Site:
http://www.biopharmcommunications.com
Sales Range: $10-24.9 Million
Emp.: 35
Pharmaceutical Industry-Focused Advertising Agency
N.A.I.C.S.: 541810
Norm Phillips (CMO & Exec VP)
Jeff Persinger (Chm & CEO)
Steve Carickhoff (Pres)
Lars Nordmann (Exec VP-Analytics)
Vanessa Trainor (Sr VP-Client Solutions)
Brian Puckett (VP-Medical Strategy)
Melissa Hefner (VP-Client Solutions)
Michael Chiefa (VP-Client Solutions)
Michael J. Meloney (VP-Fin)
Rich Patterson (Exec VP-Omnichannel Strategy)
Glenn Kapuscienski (VP-Targeted Media)
Marie Woods (VP-Client Solutions)
Jaclene Johnson (Asst VP-CRM)
Kortney Felice (Asst VP-Creative)
Matt Schneider (VP-Account Svcs)
Calvin Butts Jr. (VP-Agency Partnerships)
Clay Romweber III (Chief Growth Officer & Exec VP)

BrandWizard (1)
2070 N Broadway Ste 5286, Walnut Creek,
CA 94596
Tel.: (508) 532-0700
Web Site: http://www.brandwizard.com
Sales Range: $100-124.9 Million
Emp.: 15
Advertising Services
N.A.I.C.S.: 541810

Brodeur Partners (1)
535 Boylston St, Boston, MA 02116
Tel.: (617) 587-2800
Web Site: http://www.brodeur.com
Sales Range: $75-99.9 Million
Public Relations Services
N.A.I.C.S.: 541820
Andrea Coville (CEO)
Michael Brewer (Partner)
Jerry Johnson (Partner)
Steve Marchant (Partner)
Renzo Bardetti (CFO & COO)
John Brodeur (Chm)
Steve McGrath (VP)
Angela Hayes (Sr VP-Diversity & Inclusion)
Linda Capcara (Sr VP)
Christine Dotts (Sr VP)
Lauren Levinson (Sr VP)
James Ernst (Sr VP)
Jeff Aubin (Sr VP)
Keith Lindenburg (Partner)
Scott Beaudoin (Exec VP-Social Purpose & Sustainability)
Christine Lecompte (Exec VP)
Steve Hodgdon (Exec VP)
Cleve Langton (Chief Partnership Officer)
Teena Maddox (VP)

Branch (Domestic):

Beaupre & Co. Public Relations Inc. (2)
1 Harbour Pl Ste 230, Portsmouth, NH
03801-3837
Tel.: (603) 436-6690
Web Site: http://www.beaupre.com
Sales Range: $25-49.9 Million
Emp.: 20
Public Relations Services
N.A.I.C.S.: 541820
Jeff Aubin (VP)

Branch (Non-US):

Brodeur Brazil (2)
Av Juscelino Kubitschek No 1726 14 andar,
Sao Paulo, 04543-000, Brazil
Tel.: (55) 11 3323 1607
Web Site:
http://www.impressborternovelli.com.br
Sales Range: $25-49.9 Million
Emp.: 20
Public Relations Services
N.A.I.C.S.: 541820
Cristina Moretti (CEO)

Brodeur Martec (2)
La Fontaine 36, Chapultepec Polanco,
Mexico, 11560, Mexico

Omicom Group Inc.—(Continued)

Tel.: (52) 55 5010 3200
Web Site: http://www.porternovelli.com
Sales Range: $25-49.9 Million
Emp.: 110
Public Relations Services
N.A.I.C.S.: 541820
Sandra Kleinburg (Mng Dir)

Branch (Domestic):

Brodeur Partners (2)
300 Park Ave 14th Fl, New York, NY 10022
Tel.: (646) 746-5600
Web Site: http://www.brodeur.com
Sales Range: $25-49.9 Million
Emp.: 10
Public Relations Services
N.A.I.C.S.: 541820
Keith Lindenburg (Partner)
Steve McGrath (VP)
Angela Hayes (Sr VP-Diversity & Inclusion)
Jeff Aubin (Sr VP)
Jamie Ernst (Sr VP)
Lauren Levinson (Sr VP)
Christine Dotts (Sr VP)
Linda Capcara (Sr VP)
Jerry Johnson (Partner)
Steve Marchant (Partner)
Michael Brewer (Partner)
Scott Beaudoin (Exec VP-Social Purpose &
Sustainability)
Steve Hodgdon (Exec VP)
Christine LeCompte (Exec VP)
John Brodeur (Chm)
Cleve Langton (Chief Partnership Officer)
Renzo Bardetti (CFO & COO)

Brodeur Partners (2)
2355 E Camelback Rd Ste 515, Phoenix,
AZ 85016
Tel.: (480) 308-0300
Web Site: http://www.brodeur.com
Sales Range: Less than $1 Million
Emp.: 4
Public Relations Services
N.A.I.C.S.: 541820

Brodeur Partners (2)
1875 K St NW, Washington, DC 20006
Tel.: (202) 350-3220
Web Site: http://www.brodeur.com
Sales Range: $25-49.9 Million
Emp.: 15
Public Relations Services
N.A.I.C.S.: 541820
Jerry Johnson (Partner)
Steve McGrath (VP)
Angela Hayes (Sr VP-Diversity & Inclusion)
Jeff Aubin (Sr VP)
Jamie Ernst (Sr VP)
Lauren Levinson (Sr VP)
Christine Dotts (Sr VP)
Linda Capcara (Sr VP)
Keith Lindenburg (Partner)
Steve Marchant (Partner)
Michael Brewer (Partner)
Scott Beaudoin (Exec VP-Social Purpose &
Sustainability)
Steve Hodgdon (Exec VP)
Christine LeCompte (Exec VP)
John Brodeur (Chm)
Cleve Langton (Chief Partnership Officer)
Renzo Bardetti (CFO & COO)
Andrea Coville (CEO)

Affiliate (Non-US):

Communication by Design (2)
26 Willcott Street Mt Albert, PO Box 90 349,
Auckland, 1142, New Zealand
Tel.: (64) 98155441
Web Site: http://www.communication-by-
design.net
Sales Range: Less than $1 Million
Emp.: 4
Public Relations Services
N.A.I.C.S.: 541820

Branch (Non-US):

EASTWEST Public Relations (2)
7 Temasek Boulevard 12-07 Suntec Tower
One, Singapore, 038987, Singapore
Tel.: (65) 62220306
Web Site: https://www.eastwestpr.com
Sales Range: $10-24.9 Million
Emp.: 4
Public Relations Services

N.A.I.C.S.: 541820
Jim James (Founder)

EBA Communications Ltd (2)
Unite B 19/F On Hing Building 1 On Hing
Terrace, Central, China (Hong Kong)
Tel.: (852) 2537 8022
Web Site: http://www.ebacomms.com
Sales Range: $25-49.9 Million
Emp.: 65
Public Relations
N.A.I.C.S.: 541820
Fanny Feng (Mng Dir-China)

Branch (Non-US):

EBA Communications - Beijing (3)
Jian Guo Men Wai Avenue 22, Wai Da Jie,
Beijing, 100004, China
Tel.: (86) 10 6522 8081
Web Site: http://www.eba.com.hk
Sales Range: $25-49.9 Million
Emp.: 20
Public Relations
N.A.I.C.S.: 541820
Fanny Feng (Mgr)
Andy Wong (Gen Mgr)
Brian Paterson (Dir)

**EBA Communications -
Shanghai** (3)
Rm 1608 Shanghai CITS Bldg 1277 Beijing
Rd W, Shanghai, 200040, China
Tel.: (86) 21 6289 3488
Web Site: http://www.eba.com.hk
Public Relations
N.A.I.C.S.: 541820
Claudia Choi (Mng Dir)
Urs Rellstab (CEO-Switzerland)

Branch (Non-US):

InComm Brodeur (2)
24th Floor City Air Tower 159-9 Samsung-
Dong, Kannam-Ku, Seoul, Korea (South)
Tel.: (82) 2 516 4936
Sales Range: $25-49.9 Million
Emp.: 70
Public Relations Services
N.A.I.C.S.: 541820

Prisma Public Relations (2)
Jl Padang No 18, Jakarta, 12970, Indonesia
Tel.: (62) 21 829 5454
Web Site: http://www.prismapr.co.id
Sales Range: $25-49.9 Million
Emp.: 30
Public Relations Services
N.A.I.C.S.: 541820
Rulita Anggraini (Chm)

Affiliate (Non-US):

Recognition Public Relations (2)
Level 2 51 Pitt Street, Sydney, 2000, NSW,
Australia
Tel.: (61) 2 9252 2266
Web Site: http://www.recognition.com.au
Sales Range: $25-49.9 Million
Emp.: 30
Public Relations Services
N.A.I.C.S.: 541820

Branch (Non-US):

Sefin Marketing (2)
Lobedu House 3 Simba Road, Sunninghill,
Johannesburg, South Africa
Tel.: (27) 82 442 6995
Web Site: http://www.sefin.co.za
Sales Range: $25-49.9 Million
Emp.: 7
Public Relations Services
N.A.I.C.S.: 541820
Vivienne Segal (CEO)

Spark Communications (2)
11/F One Pacific Place, 140 Sukhumvit
Road Klong Toey, Bangkok, 10110, Thai-
land
Tel.: (66) 26532717
Web Site: http://www.spark.co.th
Emp.: 17
Public Relations Services
N.A.I.C.S.: 541820
Tom Athey (Founder & Mng Dir)

Spot On Public Relations (2)
Office 311 Rose House Street 25 Al Satwa,
PO Box 71578, Dubai, United Arab Emir-
ates

Tel.: (971) 4 3491 686
Web Site: http://www.spotonpr.com
Sales Range: Less than $1 Million
Emp.: 12
Public Relations Services
N.A.I.C.S.: 541820

The Koteret Group (2)
4 Gershon Street, Tel Aviv, 67017, Israel
Tel.: (972) 35611424
Web Site: http://www.koteret.com
Sales Range: $25-49.9 Million
Emp.: 20
Public Relations Services
N.A.I.C.S.: 541820
Yoram Brosh (Owner & Chm)
Nisso Cohen (Founder)

Turbolin PR (2)
Tegnergatan 35, 111 61, Stockholm, Swe-
den
Tel.: (46) 8 660 25 25
Sales Range: $25-49.9 Million
Emp.: 6
Public Relations Services
N.A.I.C.S.: 541820

C2 Creative (1)
130 5th Ave 2nd Fl, New York, NY 10011
Tel.: (212) 594-7464
Sales Range: $25-49.9 Million
Emp.: 47
N.A.I.C.S.: 541810

COLANGELO (1)
320 Post Rd, Darien, CT 06820
Tel.: (203) 662-6600
Web Site: http://www.colangelo-sm.com
Sales Range: $75-99.9 Million
Emp.: 50
Advetising Agency
N.A.I.C.S.: 541810
Susan D. Cocco (Exec Dir-Strategy & Con-
sumer Insights)
Don Growhoski (Owner & Mng Partner)
Joann Abbate (Exec Dir-Digital Strategy)

CPM (1)
47 Aylesbury Road, Oxon, Thame, OX9
3PG, Oxfordshire, United Kingdom
Tel.: (44) 1844261777
Web Site: http://www.uk.cpm-int.com
Sales Range: $100-124.9 Million
Emp.: 500
N.A.I.C.S.: 541810
Marie Clarke (Sr Mgr-Sls)
Kevin Ingham (Mgr-Natl Sls)
Lee Clarke (Mgr-Client Svc)
Jo Farnham (Dir-Client Svc)

Branch (Non-US):

CPM Australia (2)
Level 1 7 Electric Street Cremorne, Rich-
mond, 3121, VIC, Australia
Tel.: (61) 392266400
Web Site: http://www.cpm-aus.com.au
Emp.: 200
N.A.I.C.S.: 541810
Andrew Potter (Mng Dir-Grp)
Paul Crummy (Mng Dir-Direct Sls)
Nabih Awad (Mng Dir-Retail Safari)
Cath Upham (Dir-Comml, Capability & Tal-
ent)
Sarah Strachan (Grp Dir-Acct)
Scott James (Gen Mgr-Sls)
Cara Berthot-Craig (Grp Dir-Acct)
Mariluz Restrepo (Mgr-Insights & Mktg)
Stephen Shipperlee (CFO)
Sudhakar Gollapalli (Grp Dir-IT & Analytics)

CPM Australia (2)
Ground Floor 1-7 Wellington Street, Chip-
pendale, Sydney, 2008, NSW, Australia
Tel.: (61) 281975101
Web Site: http://www.cpm-aus.com.au
N.A.I.C.S.: 541810

CPM Austria (2)
Brauhausgasse 37, 1050, Vienna, Austria
Tel.: (43) 1 503 68 66
Web Site: http://www.at.cpm-int.com
N.A.I.C.S.: 541810

CPM Belgium (2)
Rue de L Artisanat 2b, 1420, Braine-
l'Alleud, Belgium
Tel.: (32) 23873383
Web Site: http://www.kreasalescpm.com
Sales Range: $10-24.9 Million
Emp.: 25
N.A.I.C.S.: 541810

Youri Perneel (Mng Dir)

CPM France (2)
14 Boulevard des Freres Voisin, Issy les
Moulineaux, 92130, Paris, France
Tel.: (33) 1 40 95 25 00
Web Site: http://www.fr.cpm-int.com
Emp.: 5,000
Advertising Services
N.A.I.C.S.: 541810
Zeria Perez (Head-Sls)
Benjamin Courtois-Hervot (Mgr-Customer)

CPM Germany GmbH (2)
Im Atzelnest 5, 61352, Bad Homburg, Ger-
many
Tel.: (49) 61728050
Web Site: http://www.de.cpm-int.com
N.A.I.C.S.: 541810

CPM Ireland (2)
Penthouse Suite Block C Cookstown Court
Belgard Road, Dublin, Ireland
Tel.: (353) 17080300
Web Site: http://www.ie.cpm-int.com
Sales Range: $75-99.9 Million
Emp.: 40
N.A.I.C.S.: 541810
Lorraine Butler (Mng Dir)
Heather Carson (Mgr-Recruitment)
Kevin Thomas (Mgr-Natl Sls)
Gerry Lawlor (Mgr-Natl Sls)
Killian Doherty (Mgr-HR)
Ger Lynch (Mgr-Field Svc)

CPM Netherlands (2)
Prof W H Keesomlaan 4, Wildenborch 4,
1183 DJ, Amstelveen, Netherlands
Tel.: (31) 207122000
Web Site: http://www.nl.cpm-int.com
Sales Range: $10-24.9 Million
Emp.: 70
N.A.I.C.S.: 541810
Bastiaan van Houten (Mng Dir)

CPM Netherlands (2)
Delflandlaan 4, 1062 EB, Amsterdam, Neth-
erlands
Tel.: (31) 07122000
Web Site: http://www.nl.cpm-int.com
Advetising Agency
N.A.I.C.S.: 541810

CPM Spain (2)
Can Fatjo Dels Aurons 3 Planta 1 Edificio
Mapfre CUB 1, Saint Cugat del Valles,
08173, Barcelona, Spain
Tel.: (34) 93 206 4080
Web Site: http://www.cpm-int.com
N.A.I.C.S.: 541810
Alberto Almar (CEO)

CPM Switzerland (2)
Seestrasse 07, 8800, Thalwil, Switzerland
Tel.: (41) 433222050
Web Site: http://www.cpmswitzerland.ch
N.A.I.C.S.: 541810
Liliana Varzi (Sr Mgr-Client Svc)
Manon Westrick (Sr Mgr-Client Svc)
Peter Schmid (Mng Dir)
Laura Jacoma (Mgr-Recruiting)
Claudia Balleys (Mgr-HR)
Helen Mantel (Mgr-Fin)
Baran Yasar (Mgr-Client Svc)
Anel Kulic (Mgr-Client Svc)
Lorenzo Gargiulo (Mgr-Client Svc)
Paola Cipolli (Head-Recruitment)
Beat Staege (Dir-Ops)
Shelly Attas (Dir-Client Svc & Bus Dev)
Nicola Tomasi (Acct Mgr)

Branch (US):

CPM USA (2)
7425 16th St E Ste 101, Sarasota, FL
34243
Tel.: (214) 334-9807
Web Site: http://www.us.cpm-int.com
Sales Range: $10-24.9 Million
Emp.: 50
N.A.I.C.S.: 541870

Branch (Non-US):

Inventa CPM s.r.l. (2)
Corso Vercelli 40, 20145, Milan, Italy
Tel.: (39) 028310111
Web Site: http://www.inventacpm.it
Marketing Services
N.A.I.C.S.: 541613
Pierpaolo Bertocco (Mng Dir)

Cedar (1)
Bankside 3 90-100 Southwark Street, London, SE1 0SW, United Kingdom
Tel.: (44) 2075508000
Web Site: http://www.cedarcom.co.uk
Emp.: 150
N.A.I.C.S.: 541810
Clare Broadbent (CEO-Global)
Christina Da Silva (Dir-Global Transformation & Growth)
Stuart Purcell (Chief Creative Officer-Global)
Justine Daly (Dir-Comml-Global)
Chris Rayment (Dir-Insight)
Karen Huxley (Dir-Compliance)
Joseph Costello (Dir-Bus)
Ann Hartland (Dir-Bus & Strategy-Grp)
Gina Roughan (Dir-Global Content)
Rebekah Billingsley (Dir-Global Innovation)
Kat McLeod (Dir-Bus)

Changing Our World (1)
220 E 42nd St 11th Fl, New York, NY 10017
Tel.: (212) 499-0866
Web Site: http://www.changingourworld.com
Sales Range: $25-49.9 Million
Emp.: 4
N.A.I.C.S.: 541613
Michael P. Hoffman (Founder & Chm)
Brian Crimmins (CEO)
Thomas Farrell (Sr Mng Dir)
Maureen Flynn (Sr Mng Dir)
Kate Golden (Mng Dir)
Yelena Ilyazarov (CFO & Controller-Fin)
Mary Beth Martin (Sr Mng Dir)
Marie Molese (Sr Mng Dir)
Gavan Mooney (Pres & Chief Client Officer)
Rich Rau (Mng Dir)
Lyndsay Reville (Sr Mng Dir)
Mandy Ryan (Mng Dir)
Shawn M. Trahan (Sr Mng Dir)
Colleen M. Burdick (Sr Mng Dir)
Jed Dorney (Mng Dir)
Lauren Kane (Mng Dir)
Kaitlin McTighe (Mng Dir)
Nick Walsh (Mng Dir)
Katherine Austin-Evelyn (Mng Dir)
Mary Doorley Simboski (Mng Dir)

Cline, Davis & Mann, Inc. (1)
220 E 42nd St, New York, NY 10017
Tel.: (212) 907-4300
Web Site: http://www.clinedavis.com
Sales Range: $250-299.9 Million
Emp.: 950
Advetising Agency
N.A.I.C.S.: 541810
Debra Polkes (Chief Creative Officer)
Chris Palmer (CEO)
Lila Shah-Wright (COO)
Denise Henry (Chief Strategy Officer)

Branch (Non-US):

Cline, Davis & Mann, Inc. - Europe (2)
1 Riverside Manbre Road, London, W69 WA, United Kingdom
Tel.: (44) 2087358180
Web Site: http://www.clinedavis.com
Sales Range: $25-49.9 Million
Emp.: 30
Advertising Agency
N.A.I.C.S.: 541810
Josh Prince (Chief Creative Officer)

Branch (Domestic):

Cline, Davis & Mann, Inc. - Los Angeles (2)
10960 Wilshire Blvd Ste 1750, Los Angeles, CA 90024
Tel.: (212) 907-6919
Sales Range: $25-49.9 Million
Emp.: 20
Advetising Agency
N.A.I.C.S.: 541810

Cline, Davis & Mann, Inc. - Princeton (2)
210 Carnegie Ctr Ste 200, Princeton, NJ 08540-6226
Tel.: (609) 936-5600
Web Site: http://www.clinedavis.com
Sales Range: $100-124.9 Million
Emp.: 100
Advetising Agency
N.A.I.C.S.: 541810

Kyle Barich (CEO)

Unit (Domestic):

Patients & Purpose, LLC (2)
200 Varick St 4th Fl, New York, NY 10014
Tel.: (212) 798-4400
Web Site:
    http://www.patientsandpurpose.com
Advetising Agency
N.A.I.C.S.: 541810
Dina Peck (Mng Partner & Chief Creative Officer)
Deb Deaver (CEO)
Eliot Tyler (Pres)
Tom Galati (Assoc Partner & Creative Dir)
John Deely (Exec VP & Dir-Digital Experience)

Cone (1)
225 Franklin St 10th Fl, Boston, MA 02210
Tel.: (617) 227-2111
Web Site: http://www.conecomm.com
Sales Range: $10-24.9 Million
Emp.: 75
Public Relations Services
N.A.I.C.S.: 541613
Mike Lawrence (Chief Reputation Officer & Exec VP)
Marc Berliner (Sr VP)
Heather Breslau (Sr VP)
Ryan Raulie (Dir-Creative & Art)
Whitney Dailey (VP-Mktg)
Jenna Walsh (VP)
Chrissy Redmond (VP)
Sarah Faith (VP)
Molly Finnegan (VP)
Katie Goudey (Mgr-Acct)
Andrea List (Mgr-Insights)
Emilee Ragan (Mgr-Acct)
Molly Owen (Mgr-Acct)
Katy Cirrone (Mgr-Acct)

Consultech (1)
16/F Huapu International Plaza No 19 Chaowai Street, Chaoyang District, Beijing, 100020, China
Tel.: (86) 1065801090
Web Site: http://www.consultech.com.cn
Sales Range: $100-124.9 Million
Advetising Agency
N.A.I.C.S.: 541810

DAS Holdings Inc. (1)
437 Madison Ave, New York, NY 10022 (100%)
Tel.: (212) 415-3700
Customer Relationship Management, Public Relations & Communications Services
N.A.I.C.S.: 541810
Emma Sergeant (Pres-EMEA)
Michael Larson (Pres)

DDB Group Korea (1)
5th floor Trees Building 727 Eonju-ro, Seoul, 6050, Korea (South)
Tel.: (82) 234153800
Web Site: http://www.ddbkorea.com
Sales Range: $25-49.9 Million
Emp.: 42
Advertising Agency
N.A.I.C.S.: 541810
Kevin Koh (CEO)
Euiki Song (Chief Bus Officer)
Jinho Jeon (Dir-Client Svc)
Hanchul Cho (CFO)
Justin Cho (Dir-Client Svc)
Hansu Kyung (Dir-Client Svc)
Changhyun Kim (Dir-Client Svc)
Donghoon Kim (Dir-Client Svc)
Seman Oh (Gen Mgr & Dir-Client Svc)

DDB Worldwide Communications Group Inc. (1)
195 Broadway, New York, NY 10007
Tel.: (212) 415-2000
Web Site: http://www.ddb.com
Sales Range: $1-4.9 Billion
Advertising Services
N.A.I.C.S.: 541810
Marty O'Halloran (CEO)
Donna Tobin (Chief Mktg & Creative Officer-Global)
Mat Bisher (Chief Creative Officer)

Branch (Non-US):

ARS Publicidad (2)
ARS Building Av Diego Cisneros, Los Ruices, Caracas, 1071, Venezuela

Tel.: (58) 2122391946
Web Site: http://www.ddb.com
Emp.: 150
Advertising Services
N.A.I.C.S.: 541810

Adam & Eve/DDB (2)
12 Bishops Bridge Road, London, W2 6AA, United Kingdom
Tel.: (44) 2072583979
Web Site: http://www.adamandeveddb.com
Advertising Services
N.A.I.C.S.: 541810
Alex Hesz (Chief Strategy Officer)
Tammy Einav (Co-CEO)
Mat Goff (Co-CEO)
Anthony Falco (Chief Production Officer)
Richard Brim (Chief Creative Officer)

Anderson DDB Health & Lifestyle (2)
1700 - 33 Bloor Street East, Toronto, M4W 3T4, ON, Canada
Tel.: (416) 934-7498
Web Site: http://www.andersonddb.com
Sales Range: $10-24.9 Million
Emp.: 100
Advertising Services
N.A.I.C.S.: 541810
Gordon Desveaux (Exec VP & Dir-Strategy)

Branch (US):

Anderson DDB Health & Lifestyle (3)
437 Madison Ave, New York, NY 10022
Tel.: (201) 341-4085
Web Site: http://www.andersonddb.com
Advertising Services
N.A.I.C.S.: 541810

Branch (Domestic):

Anderson DDB Sante.Vie.Esprit. (3)
3500 De Maisonneuve Blvd West Tower 2 Suite 610, Westmount, H3Z 3C1, QC, Canada
Tel.: (514) 844-9505
Web Site: http://www.andersonddb.com
Advertising Services
N.A.I.C.S.: 541810

Branch (US):

DDB Remedy (3)
555 Market St 8th Fl, San Francisco, CA 94105-5804
Tel.: (415) 692-2800
Web Site: http://www.andersonddb.com
Advertising Services
N.A.I.C.S.: 541810
Nancy Kramarich (VP-Strategy & Res)
Tony Miller (VP & Exec Creative Dir)
Randy Vogel (Sr Acct Dir)
Kevin Brady (Pres & CEO)
Steve Benson (Mng Dir-Flexx Studio)
Gord Desveaux (Exec VP & Dir-Strategy)
Arujun Brahmendra (Editor-Medical)
Fady Nakhla (Dir-Fin)
Mark Boutte (Dir-Digital Strategy & Svcs)
Tyler Campbell (Dir-Digital Acct)
Enza Pitrolo (Assoc Dir-Creative)
Anthony Duguay (Assoc Dir-Creative)
Pat Browne (Acct Dir)
Linda Hawthorne (Acct Dir)

Branch (Non-US):

Blitz DDB (2)
10th Floor Clifton Diamond BC 10 Block 4 Clifton, Karachi, 75530, Pakistan
Tel.: (92) 2135291237
Web Site: http://www.blitz.pk
Advertising Services
N.A.I.C.S.: 541810
Ahsen Idris (CEO)
Daniyal Zuberi (Dir-Bus)
Asif Ali (Head-Buying)
Yasser Hameed (Head-Ops)
Muhammad Moiez Jaweed (Head-Media Accounts)
Bilal Chughtai (Head-Digital)
Ammar Anwer (Deputy Gen Mgr-Client Svcs)
Muhammad Munawar Jamal (Assoc Dir-Strategy & Plng)
Usaid Farooqui (Sr Mgr-Strategy & Plng)
Ali Raza (CFO)
Kashif Amin (Chief Bus Dev Officer)
Sahar Kayani (Acct Dir)

Aamir A. Mallick (Dir-Creative)
Saeed Iqbal Paracha (Dir-Art)
Yaqub Mirza (Exec Dir-Creative)
Faizan Ul Haq (Mgr-Plng & Res)
Afzal Baig (Mgr-Buying)
Omar Waqar (Mgr-Buying)
Ammara Rasheed (Mgr-Plng)
Sadia Faheem (Mgr-Comm Design)
Umair Saeed (COO)
Muzammil Ibrahim (Head-Visual Arts)
Sehrish Roshan Ali (Sr Mgr-Acct)
Shahbaz Patel (Sr Mgr-Acct)
Faheem Akhter (Mgr-Creative)
Mohammad Amir (Sr Mgr-Corp Fin)
Farhan Wasay Zafar (Assoc Dir-Creative)
Hassan Raza (Acct Dir)
Faisal Zahid (Mgr-Media Ops)
Aamir Masood (Mgr-Media Insights & Res)
Muhammad Mohib Ali Naqvi (Asst Mgr-Talent)
Shakeeb Faruqui (Creative Dir)
Mehvish Mumtaz (Acct Mgr-Grp)
Aqueel Abbas (Fin Mgr)
Muhammad Hassaan Hashmi (Mgr-Client Svcs)
Shakeb Sultan (Mgr-Creative)
Ziad Ahmad Khan (Asst Mgr-Digital Media)
Ayusha Niaz (Mgr-Content)
Shazin Javed (Mgr-Client Rels)
Ali Ahmed (Assoc Dir-Art)
Muhammad Kamran Khan (Assoc Dir-Art)
Hamza Askary (Asst Mgr-Res)
Ghulam Naseeruddin Ahmad (Asst Mgr-Admin & IT)
Rao Abdul Rab (Asst Mgr-Recovery)
Wardah Pervaiz Hussain (Asst Mgr-Client Svcs)
Taha Shaikh (Asst Mgr-Digital Media)
Jaiser Abbas (Asst Mgr-Digital Media)
Benish Rafique (Asst Mgr-Print)

Bovil DDB (2)
Klokgebouw 111, 5617 AB, Eindhoven, Netherlands
Tel.: (31) 402526499
Web Site: http://www.bovil.nl
Emp.: 25
Advertising Agencies
N.A.I.C.S.: 541810
Michiel Scheerin (Mng Dir)

Corporate Profiles DDB (2)
DDB Warszawa Sp Z o o Ul Wybrzeze Gdynskie 6c, Wybreze Gdyrishie St, 01-531, Warsaw, Poland
Tel.: (48) 22 560 3400
Web Site: http://ddbtribal.pl
Emp.: 100
Advertising Services
N.A.I.C.S.: 541810
Marcin Mroszczak (Chm-Creative)
Pawel Kastory (CEO)

DDB (2)
226 Outram Rd Tiong Bahru, Singapore, 169039, Singapore
Tel.: (65) 6323 4811
Emp.: 180
Advertising Agencies, Advertising Specialties
N.A.I.C.S.: 541810
Josiah Ng (Head-Film & Social Content)
Benjamin Lee (Head-Digital & Social Content Strategy)
Jeff Cheong (Pres-Tribal Worldwide Asia)
Joshua Lee (Chief Bus Officer)
Leslie Goh (COO)
Yak Yih Cheng (Head-Bus Tech)
Michael Lung (Head-Bus Transformation)
Pierre Croft (Dir-Experience)
Benson Toh (Dir-Creative)

DDB Advis (2)
Jl Proklamasi No49, Jakarta, 10320, Indonesia
Tel.: (62) 21 391 9549
Web Site: http://www.ddb.com
Emp.: 20
Advertising Services
N.A.I.C.S.: 541810

DDB Amsterdam (2)
Prof WH Keesomlaan 4, 1183 DJ, Amstelveen, Netherlands
Tel.: (31) 20 406 5406
Web Site: http://www.ddbamsterdam.nl
Emp.: 200
Advertising Services
N.A.I.C.S.: 541810

Omnicom Group Inc.—(Continued)

Folkert Van Dijk *(CFO)*

Affiliate (Domestic):

Eigen Fabrikaat bu (3)
Prof WH Keesomlaan 4, 1183 DJ, Amstelveen, Netherlands
Tel.: (31) 204065206
Web Site: https://www.eigenfabrikaat.nl
Emp.: 40
Advertising Services
N.A.I.C.S.: 541810
Karina Buitenhuis *(Mng Partner)*
Peter Scholtens *(Dir-Creative)*
Gerrit Winkel *(Mng Partner)*
Robin Verhoek *(Acct Dir)*
Paulien Hendriksen *(Sr Project Mgr)*
Esper Buursen *(Project Mgr)*
Kelly van der Beek *(Sr Project Mgr)*
Joshua Hartman *(Acct Dir)*
Dick Tichelaar *(Mgr-Traffic & Production)*
Joanna van Unen *(Project Mgr)*
Linde van der Meulen *(Project Mgr)*
Mandy Coppee *(Project Mgr)*
Wendy Vonk *(Project Mgr)*

Branch (Non-US):

DDB Argentina (2)
Alem 855 Piso 21, C1062ABM, Buenos Aires, Argentina
Tel.: (54) 1157775000
Web Site: http://www.ddbargentina.com
Sales Range: $10-24.9 Million
Emp.: 100
Advertising Services
N.A.I.C.S.: 541810

DDB Barcelona S.A. (2)
Torre Mapfre Marina 16-18 Planta 36, 08005, Barcelona, Spain
Tel.: (34) 932283400
Web Site: http://www.es.ddb.com
Advertising Services
N.A.I.C.S.: 541810
Jose Maria Roca de Vinals *(Chief Creative Officer & VP)*
Jose Maria Rull *(Pres & CEO)*
Samanta Judez *(Gen Dir)*
Oscar Coto *(Gen Mgr-DDB Experience)*

DDB Berlin (2)
Friedrich Strasse 200, 10117, Berlin, Germany
Tel.: (49) 302 40840
Web Site: http://www.de.ddb.com
Emp.: 175
Advertising Services
N.A.I.C.S.: 541810

DDB Brainstorm (2)
Jalan Kemang Utara 34 Mampang Prapatan-Bangka, 12730, Jakarta, Indonesia
Tel.: (62) 217190323
Emp.: 45
Advertising Services
N.A.I.C.S.: 541810

DDB Bratislava (2)
Zaborskeho 10303/19 Nove Mesto, 831 03, Bratislava, Slovakia
Tel.: (421) 2 44 64 1141
Web Site: http://www.ddb.com
Advertising Services
N.A.I.C.S.: 541810

DDB Brazil (2)
Av Brigadeiro Luis Antonio 5013, 01452-000, Sao Paulo, SP, Brazil
Tel.: (55) 11 3054 0000
Web Site: http://www.ddb.com
Emp.: 350
Advertising Services
N.A.I.C.S.: 541810

DDB Bucharest (2)
3 Praga Street, Sector 5, 011801, Bucharest, Romania
Tel.: (40) 212062200
Web Site: http://www.ddb.com
Emp.: 34
Advertising Services
N.A.I.C.S.: 541810

DDB Budapest (2)
Liget Center Dozsa Gyorgy Ut 84/a, 1068, Budapest, Hungary
Tel.: (36) 14612800

Web Site: http://www.ddb.hu
Rev.: $120,000,000
Emp.: 70
Advertising Services
N.A.I.C.S.: 541810
Hannes Wirnsberger *(Mng Dir)*

DDB Canada - Vancouver (2)
1600-777 Hornby St, Vancouver, V6Z 2T3, BC, Canada
Tel.: (604) 687-7911
Web Site: http://www.ddbcanada.com
Rev.: $200,000,000
Emp.: 125
Advertising Services
N.A.I.C.S.: 541810
Brent Choi *(CEO & Chief Creative Officer)*

Branch (Domestic):

DDB Canada - Edmonton (3)
1900 - 10025 102A Avenue, Edmonton, T5J 2Z2, AB, Canada
Tel.: (780) 424-7000
Web Site: https://www.ddb.ca
Emp.: 30
Advertising Services
N.A.I.C.S.: 541810
Helene Leggatt *(Pres-Edmonton)*

DDB Canada - Toronto (3)
33 Bloor Street East Suite 1700, Toronto, M4W 3T4, ON, Canada
Tel.: (416) 925-9819
Web Site: http://www.ddb.com
Emp.: 100
Advertising Services
N.A.I.C.S.: 541810
Martine Levy *(Mng Dir-PR)*

Branch (Non-US):

DDB Casers (2)
6 Adeola Hopewell St, Victoria Island, Lagos, Nigeria
Tel.: (234) 1 493 6587
Web Site: http://www.ddblagos.com
Advertising Services
N.A.I.C.S.: 541810

Branch (Domestic):

DDB Chicago (2)
225 N Michigan Ave 10th Fl, Chicago, IL 60601
Tel.: (312) 552-6000
Advertising Services
N.A.I.C.S.: 541810
Diane Jackson *(Chief Production Officer)*
Tony Malcom *(Exec Dir-Creative-McDonald's)*
Jamie McGarry *(VP & Dir-Bus Dev)*
David Banta *(Sr VP & Grp Dir-Creative)*
Richard Casky *(Dir-Programs)*
Myra Nussbaum *(Sr VP & Grp Dir-Creative)*
Britt Hayes *(Chief HR Officer-North America)*
Eric Zuncic *(Chief Strategy Officer-North America)*
Britt Nolan *(Chief Creative Officer-North America)*
Andrea Diquez *(CEO)*
Milo Chao *(Chief Strategy Officer)*

Branch (Non-US):

DDB Chile (2)
Av Del Vallee 945 4 Piso of 4615, Ciudad Empresarial, Santiago, Chile
Tel.: (56) 2 677 8888
Web Site: http://www.ddbchile.com
Advertising Services
N.A.I.C.S.: 541810

DDB China - Shanghai (2)
4/F Block 2 Park2Space No 169 Mengzi Rd, Luwan District, Shanghai, 200023, China
Tel.: (86) 21 6151 3300
Web Site: http://www.ddb.com
Emp.: 89
Advertising Services
N.A.I.C.S.: 541810
Danny Mok *(Pres & CEO)*

Branch (Domestic):

DDB Guoan - Guangzhou (3)
Room 3707 Tower B Center Plz, 161 Linhe Road West, Tianhe District, Guangzhou, China

Tel.: (86) 20 3825 1088
Emp.: 1
Advertising Services
N.A.I.C.S.: 541810

Branch (Non-US):

DDB Communication France (2)
73-75 Rue La Condamine, Paris, 75017, France
Tel.: (33) 1 5332 6000
Web Site: http://www.ddb.fr
Emp.: 800
Advertising Services
N.A.I.C.S.: 541810
Valerie de la Rochebrochard *(Mng Dir)*
Vincent Leorat *(VP)*
Christian Vince *(VP)*
Jean-Luc Bravi *(Pres & Dir-Publication)*
Marine Hakim *(Mng Dir)*
Sebastien Genty *(Mng Dir)*
Paul Ducre *(Mng Dir)*
Alban Callet *(Mng Dir)*
Xavier Mendiola *(Mng Dir)*
Alexander Kalchev *(Exec Dir-Creative)*
Safia Garel *(Dir-Bus-Intl)*
Michel Huppert *(CFO)*

DDB Costa Rica (2)
Edificio Via Lindora Piso 2 N Centro Commercial Via Lindora, Ed Garnier 2 Piso, San Jose, Costa Rica
Tel.: (506) 2205 4200
Web Site: http://www.ddb.com
Advertising Services
N.A.I.C.S.: 541810

DDB Denmark (2)
Montergade 1 2nd floor, PO Box 2074, 1116, Copenhagen, Denmark
Tel.: (45) 33463000
Web Site: http://ddbcopenhagen.dk
Emp.: 48
Advertising Services
N.A.I.C.S.: 541810
Thomas Erichsen *(CEO)*

DDB Dusseldorf (2)
Breite Strasse 67-69, D-40213, Dusseldorf, Germany
Tel.: (49) 211 6013 3000
Web Site: http://www.de.ddb.com
Emp.: 80
Advertising Services
N.A.I.C.S.: 541810

DDB Egypt (2)
18 Nawal Street, Agouza Giza, Cairo, Egypt
Tel.: (20) 23360125
Web Site: http://www.ddb.com
Emp.: 25
Advertising Services
N.A.I.C.S.: 541810

DDB Estonia Ltd. (2)
Sakala 10/Kentmanni 4, 10116, Tallinn, Estonia
Tel.: (372) 6998600
Web Site: http://ddb.ee
Emp.: 18
Advertising Services
N.A.I.C.S.: 541810

DDB Europe (2)
12 Bishop's Bridge Road, London, W2 6AA, United Kingdom
Tel.: (44) 207262001
Web Site: http://www.ddb.com
Advertising Services
N.A.I.C.S.: 541810

DDB Group Belgium (2)
17 Saint Hubert street, 1150, Brussels, Belgium
Tel.: (32) 2 761 19 00
Web Site: http://www.ddb.be
Emp.: 64
Advertising Services
N.A.I.C.S.: 541810
Dieter Riemaeker *(Head-Strategy)*
Wim Vangramberen *(CFO)*
Maarten Vanthemsche *(Mng Dir)*
Kwint de Meyer *(Creative Dir)*

DDB Group Germany (2)
Friedrichstrasse 200, Berlin, 10117, Germany
Tel.: (49) 302 4084 0
Web Site: http://www.de.ddb.com
Emp.: 630

Advertising Services
N.A.I.C.S.: 541810

DDB Guoan Communications Beijing Co., Ltd. (2)
7/F Ocean Center Building D 62 East 4th, Ring Road, Chaoyang District, Beijing, 100025, China
Tel.: (86) 10 5929 3300
Emp.: 2
Advertising Services
N.A.I.C.S.: 541810

DDB Hamburg GmbH (2)
Willy Brandt Strasse 55, Hamburg, 20457, Germany
Tel.: (49) 40 32808 0
Web Site: http://www.de.ddb.com
Advertising Services
N.A.I.C.S.: 541810

DDB Hash Three (2)
78 Churchill Avenue Alexandra Park, Harare, Zimbabwe
Tel.: (263) 4 744 386
Web Site: http://www.ddb.com
Advertising Services
N.A.I.C.S.: 541810

DDB Helsinki (2)
Lapinlahdenkatu 1 C 1Krs, Helsinki, 00180, Finland
Tel.: (358) 424 7471
Web Site: http://www.nordddb.com
Emp.: 20
Advertising Services
N.A.I.C.S.: 541810
Andreas Dahlqvist *(Chief Creative Officer)*
Nichlas Melin *(CEO-Nordic)*
Kalle Wallin *(Creative Dir)*

DDB Honduras (2)
Bo Rio de Piedras 19 Ave 8 y 9 Calles S O, San Pedro Sula, Cortes, Honduras
Tel.: (504) 25525138
Web Site: http://www.ddb.com
Advertising Services
N.A.I.C.S.: 541810

DDB Indonesia (2)
88 Kasablanka Office Tower A 32 Floor Unit E Jalan Casablanka Kav 88, 12870, Jakarta, Indonesia
Tel.: (62) 2129820210
Web Site: http://www.ddb.com
Advertising Services
N.A.I.C.S.: 541810

DDB Japan (2)
40th Floor Harumi Triton Square X 1-8-10 Harumi, Chuo-ku, Tokyo, 104-6038, Japan
Tel.: (81) 357911020
Web Site: http://www.ddb.com
Emp.: 80
Advertising Services
N.A.I.C.S.: 541810

Branch (Domestic):

DDB Latin America (2)
770 S Dixie Hwy Ste 109, Miami, FL 33146
Tel.: (305) 341-2555
Web Site: http://www.ddb.com
Emp.: 10
Advertising Services
N.A.I.C.S.: 541810

Branch (Non-US):

DDB Lisboa (2)
Avenida Engenheiro Duarte Pacheco 26, Lisbon, 1070-110, Portugal
Tel.: (351) 218910500
Web Site: http://ddb.pt
Emp.: 20
Advertising Services
N.A.I.C.S.: 541810
Maria Manuela Gomes *(CFO)*
Alexandra Pereira *(Mng Dir)*

Branch (Domestic):

DDB Los Angeles (2)
10960 Wilshire Blvd, Los Angeles, CA 90024
Tel.: (310) 907-1500
Web Site: http://www.ddb.com
Emp.: 45
Advertising Services
N.A.I.C.S.: 541810

Branch (Non-US):

DDB Madrid, S.A. **(2)**
C/ Cardenal Marcelo Spinola 4 Planta 3,
28016, Madrid, Spain
Tel.: (34) 914564400
Web Site: http://www.es.ddb.com
Emp.: 100
Advertising Services
N.A.I.C.S.: 541810
Jose Maria Rull *(Pres & CEO)*
Jose Maria Roca de Vinals *(Chief Creative Officer & VP)*
Daniel Rodriguez *(Exec Creative Dir)*
Nerea Cierco *(Exec Creative Dir)*
Alfredo Vaz *(Head-Art)*

DDB Melbourne Pty. Ltd. **(2)**
7 Electric Street, Cremorne, Richmond,
3121, VIC, Australia
Tel.: (61) 3 9254 3600
Web Site: http://www.ddb.com.au
Emp.: 115
Communications
N.A.I.C.S.: 541810
Anthony Moss *(Exec Creative Dir)*

DDB Mexico **(2)**
Av Santa Fe 505 Piso 16 Col Cruz Manca
Del Cuajimalpa, Col Lomas de Chapulte-
pec, 05349, Mexico, Mexico
Tel.: (52) 5 5 91598800
Web Site: http://ddbmexico.com
Marketing & Advertising
N.A.I.C.S.: 541810

Branch (Domestic):

DDB Miami **(2)**
2601 S Bayshore Dr 4th Fl, Coconut Grove,
FL 33133
Tel.: (305) 662-3175
Web Site: http://www.ddb.com
Sales Range: $10-24.9 Million
Emp.: 18
Advertising Services
N.A.I.C.S.: 541810

Branch (Non-US):

DDB Mozambique **(2)**
Avenida Fernao de Magalhaes 34 3 Andar,
3050, Maputo, Mozambique
Tel.: (258) 21302267
Web Site: http://www.ddb.co.mz
Advertising Agencies
N.A.I.C.S.: 541810

Branch (Domestic):

DDB New York **(2)**
195 Broadway, New York, NY 10007
Tel.: (212) 415-2000
Web Site: http://www.ddb.com
Advertising Services
N.A.I.C.S.: 541810

Branch (Non-US):

DDB New Zealand Ltd. **(2)**
Level 4/119 Great North RoadGrey Lynn,
Auckland, 1021, New Zealand
Tel.: (64) 93034299
Web Site: http://www.ddb.co.nz
Emp.: 200
Marketing & Advertising
N.A.I.C.S.: 541810

DDB Oslo A.S. **(2)**
Froyas Gate 15, 0273, Oslo, Norway
Tel.: (47) 22 59 32 00
Web Site: http://www.ddb.no
Emp.: 50
Full Service
N.A.I.C.S.: 541810

DDB Paris **(2)**
73-75 rue La Condamine, 75017, Paris,
France
Tel.: (33) 153326000
Web Site: https://www.ddb.fr
Emp.: 100
N.A.I.C.S.: 541810
Jean-Luc Bravi *(CEO)*
Vincent Leorat *(VP)*
Sebastien Genty *(Mng Dir)*
Alexander Kalchev *(Exec Creative Dir)*
Alban Callet *(Mng Dir)*
Paul Ducre *(Mng Dir)*
Marine Hakim *(Mng Dir)*
Michel Huppert *(CFO)*

Xavier Mendiola *(Mng Dir)*
Christian Vince *(VP)*
Safia Garel *(Dir-Intl Bus)*

DDB Philippines Inc. **(2)**
16th Fl Two World Square 22 Upper Mckin-
ley Road McKinley Hill, Fort Bonifacio,
Taguig, 1634, Philippines
Tel.: (63) 28567888
Web Site: http://www.ddb.com
N.A.I.C.S.: 541810
Gil G. Chua *(Chm & CEO)*

DDB Prague **(2)**
Lomnickeho 1705/9 Heroes House, 140 00,
Prague, Czech Republic
Tel.: (420) 221013111
Web Site: http://www.ddb.cz
Emp.: 30
Marketing & Advertising
N.A.I.C.S.: 541810

DDB Russia **(2)**
Bldg 3 40/2 Prechistenka Str, 119034, Mos-
cow, Russia
Tel.: (7) 4957855765
Web Site: http://www.ddb.ru
Emp.: 150
Advetising Agency
N.A.I.C.S.: 541810

DDB S.r.L. Advertising **(2)**
Via Savona 97, 20144, Milan, Italy
Tel.: (39) 02581931
Web Site: http://www.stvddb.it
Emp.: 60
Full Service
N.A.I.C.S.: 541810
Sonia Magri *(Gen Mgr)*
Luca Cortesini *(Exec Creative Dir)*
Gabriele Caeti *(Exec Creative Dir)*
Alessandro Gesmundo *(CFO)*
Niccolo Arletti *(CEO)*

Branch (Domestic):

DDB San Francisco **(2)**
600 Ca 7, San Francisco, CA 94108
Tel.: (415) 732-3600
Web Site: http://www.ddb.com
Emp.: 50
Advertising Services
N.A.I.C.S.: 541810
Todd Grantham *(Pres & CEO)*

Branch (Non-US):

DDB Sofia **(2)**
95 Hristo Botev Blvd, Bldg 1A, 1303, Sofia,
Bulgaria
Tel.: (359) 877782984
Web Site: https://gutsandbrainsddb.bg
Emp.: 12
N.A.I.C.S.: 541810

DDB South Africa **(2)**
3 Sandown Valley Crescent, Sandown,
Sandton, 2031, South Africa
Tel.: (27) 112672800
Web Site: http://www.ddb.co.za
Emp.: 90
N.A.I.C.S.: 541810
Louise Johnston *(Mng Dir)*
Melissa Daniels *(CEO)*

DDB Stockholm **(2)**
Torsgatan 19, PO Box 6016, Stockholm,
102 31, Sweden
Tel.: (46) 8588 980 00
Web Site: http://www.ddb.se
Emp.: 100
Advertising Services
N.A.I.C.S.: 541810

Subsidiary (Domestic):

**Ehrenstrahle & Co. i Stockholm
AB** **(3)**
Sveavagen 75, PO Box 70352, 113 50,
Stockholm, Sweden
Tel.: (46) 87871000
Web Site: http://www.ehrenstrahle.se
Emp.: 27
Advertising & Public Relations Agency
N.A.I.C.S.: 541810

Branch (Non-US):

DDB Sydney Pty. Ltd. **(2)**
3/46-52 Mtn St Ultimo, Sydney, 2007, NSW,
Australia

Tel.: (61) 2 8260 2222
Web Site: http://www.ddb.com.au
Marketing & Advertising
N.A.I.C.S.: 541810
Priya Patel *(CEO-New Zealand)*
Carl Ratcliff *(Chief Strategy Officer)*
Matt Chandler *(Exec Creative Dir)*
Alex Watts *(Head-Social-McDonald's)*
Nikki McKelvie *(Mng Dir)*
Michael Sinclair *(Head-Brand Performance)*
Sheryl Marjoram *(CEO)*
Fran Clayton *(Chief Strategy Officer)*

DDB Tribal Vienna **(2)**
Guglgasse 729, Vienna, 1030, Austria
Tel.: (43) 1 491 91 0
Sales Range: $10-24.9 Million
Emp.: 50
N.A.I.C.S.: 541810

DDB Vietnam Advertising **(2)**
6/F 21 Phung Khac Khoan District 1, Ho
Chi Minh City, Vietnam
Tel.: (84) 931861913
Web Site: http://www.ddb.com
N.A.I.C.S.: 541810

DDB Worldwide **(2)**
85 Avenida Norte #629, Colonia Escalon,
San Salvador, El Salvador
Tel.: (503) 2528 7300
Emp.: 40
N.A.I.C.S.: 541810

DDB Worldwide Colombia S.A. **(2)**
Diagonal 97 17-60 Piso 10, Bogota, 1001,
Colombia
Tel.: (57) 1 257 0188
Web Site: http://www.ddbcol.com.co
Sales Range: $75-99.9 Million
Emp.: 2
N.A.I.C.S.: 541810

DDB Worldwide Colombia S.A. **(2)**
Calle 23 S 42 B 66 Envigado Antioquia,
Medellin, Colombia
Tel.: (57) 4 444 8444
Web Site: http://www.ddbcol.com.co
Sales Range: $10-24.9 Million
Emp.: 25
N.A.I.C.S.: 541810

DDB Worldwide Colombia, S.A. **(2)**
Cl 6 Oe 1 B-72Cali - Valle Del Cauca, Cali,
Colombia
Tel.: (57) 2 892 6450
Web Site: http://www.ddbcol.com.co
Emp.: 15
N.A.I.C.S.: 541810

DDB Worldwide Inc. **(2)**
14F No 132 Sec 3 Minsheng E Rd Song-
shan Dist, Sec 3, Taipei, 10596, Taiwan
Tel.: (886) 2 2719 6696
Emp.: 50
Full Service
N.A.I.C.S.: 541810

DDB Worldwide Ltd. **(2)**
Unit 1201 Core E Cyberport 3, 100 Cyber-
port Road, Hong Kong, China (Hong Kong)
Tel.: (852) 28280328
Web Site: http://www.ddb.com
Emp.: 154
Advertising Agencies, Direct Marketing,
Internet/Web Design, Sales Promotion,
Strategic Planning/Research
N.A.I.C.S.: 541810
Peter Rodenbeck *(VP & Reg Dir)*
Irene Tsui *(Mng Dir)*
Jamal Hamidi *(Exec Creative Dir-Global
Bus)*
Doris Yim *(CFO)*
Andreas Krasser *(CEO)*

DDB srl Advertising **(2)**
Via G Oberdan 7, 37121, Verona, Italy
Tel.: (39) 045 590 744
Web Site: http://www.ddb.com
Emp.: 13
N.A.I.C.S.: 541810

Far East DDB **(2)**
465/1-467 Si Ayutthaya Road, Thun-
gphayathai Ratchathewi, Bangkok, 10400,
Thailand
Tel.: (66) 23543333
Web Site:
https://www.fareastfamelineddb.com
Emp.: 100
N.A.I.C.S.: 541810

Malee Leelasiriwongse *(Mgr-HR)*
Boonchai Chokwatana *(Chm)*

Fire Advertainment **(2)**
Ciudad de la Paz 66, Acassuso, Buenos
Aires, 1641, Argentina
Tel.: (54) 1152355000
Emp.: 10
N.A.I.C.S.: 541810

Futura DDB **(2)**
Poljanski Nasip 6, 1000, Ljubljana, Slovenia
Tel.: (386) 13004000
Web Site: http://www.futura.si
Emp.: 45
N.A.I.C.S.: 541810
Marko Vicic *(Partner)*
Mija Gacnik Krpic *(Mng Dir)*
Marjana Robavs *(Partner & Dir-Media)*
Gregor Firbas *(Dir-Digital)*
Masa Crnkovic *(Head-Analytics & User Ex-
perience)*
Dragana Josipovic *(Dir-Project)*
Urska Nucic *(Project Mgr)*
Alenka Pulec Jurjevcic *(Dir-Project)*
Anusa Zagar *(Mgr-Project)*
Zare Kerin *(Dir-Creative)*
Zoran Gabrijan *(Partner & Dir-Creative)*
Robert Krizmancic *(Head-Design & Dir-Art)*
Bostjan Napotnik *(Dir-Creative)*
Marusa Kozelj *(Dir-Art)*
Uros Strazisar *(Dir-Art)*
Ziga Pavlin *(Head-Dev)*
Goran Lang *(Mgr-Project)*
Eva Stopar *(Copywriter)*
Marjan Bozic *(Head-IT)*
Joze Gerecnik *(Dir-Creative)*
Robert Bohinec *(Dir-Creative)*
Nino Bavcar *(Copywriter)*
Peter Dobovicnik *(Project Mgr)*
Jure Novak *(Project Mgr)*

GHA/DDB **(2)**
No 22 George Street Belleville, PO Box
1044, Saint Michael, Barbados
Tel.: (246) 431 0411
Web Site: http://www.greghoyos.com
Emp.: 20
Full Service
N.A.I.C.S.: 541810
Greg Hoyos *(Chm)*
Pamela Cave-Small *(Mgr-Ops)*
Robert Marshall *(Dir-Art)*
Lana Alleyne *(Mng Dir)*

Ghirotti & Companhia **(2)**
Av Engenheiro Luiz Carlos Berrini 550 an 6
Cidade Moncoes, Sao Paulo, 04571-925,
Brazil
Tel.: (55) 11 5505 6711
N.A.I.C.S.: 541810
Paulo Ghirotti *(Pres & Dir-Creative)*
Francisco Costa *(Partner & Dir-Fin)*

Heye GmbH **(2)**
Blumenstrasse 28, 80331, Munich, Ger-
many
Tel.: (49) 89 66532 00
Emp.: 50
Advertising Services
N.A.I.C.S.: 541810
Thomas Diekmann *(Mng Dir & Member-
Mgmt Bd)*
Mark Niedzballa *(CEO, Mng Dir & Member-
Mgmt Bd)*

Branch (Non-US):

DDB Wien GmbH **(3)**
Thaliastrasse 125B, Vienna, A-1160, Austria
Tel.: (43) 1 491 91 11
Web Site: http://www.ddb.at
Emp.: 100
Advertising Services
N.A.I.C.S.: 541810
Thomas Tatzl *(Exec Creative Dir)*
Susanna Dusing *(Dir-Client Svc)*
Andreas Spielvogel *(Exec Creative Dir)*

Branch (Domestic):

**GBK, Heye Werbeagentur
GMBH** **(3)**
Linprunstr 16, 80335, Munich, Germany
Tel.: (49) 895424430
Emp.: 18
Advertising Services
N.A.I.C.S.: 541810

**Heye & Partner GmbH -
Hamburg** **(3)**

Omnicom Group Inc.—(Continued)

Gansemarkt 35, 20354, Hamburg, Germany
Tel.: (49) 40 229 33 01
Sales Range: $50-74.9 Million
Emp.: 80
Advertising Services
N.A.I.C.S.: 541810

Heye Media OMD GmbH (3)
Grunstrasse 15, 40212, Dusseldorf, Germany
Tel.: (49) 89 665 3205
Web Site: http://www.omdgermany.de
Emp.: 27
Advertising Services
N.A.I.C.S.: 541810

Branch (Non-US):

Medina/Turgul DDB (2)
Esentepe mah Ali Kaya Sok No 3 Kat 4,
Apa Nef Plaza Sisli, 34394, Istanbul, Turkiye
Tel.: (90) 2123114940
Web Site: http://www.istanbul.ddb.com
Emp.: 100
Advertising Services
N.A.I.C.S.: 541810
Bill Bernbach (Partner)
Yavuz Turgul (Partner)
Jeffi Medina (Partner)

Milk+Co (2)
Level 3 02 Block A PJ Trade Centre No 8
Jalan PJU 8/8A, Damansara Heights,
47820, Petaling Jaya, Malaysia
Tel.: (60) 377223440
Web Site: http://www.milknco.com
Emp.: 45
Advertising Services
N.A.I.C.S.: 541810

Mudra Communications Pvt. Ltd. (2)
Ganpat Rao Kadam Marg Shree Ram Mills
Premises, Worli, Mumbai, 400 013, India
Tel.: (91) 2230408001
Web Site: http://www.mudra.com
Emp.: 1,000
Advertising Services
N.A.I.C.S.: 541810

Naga DDB Sdn. Bhd. (2)
D-708 7th Floor Block D Kelana Square, No
17 Jalan SS7/26 Kelana Jaya, 47301, Petaling Jaya, Selangor Darul Ehsan, Malaysia
Tel.: (60) 378037144
Web Site: http://www.nagaddb.com.my
Emp.: 110
Advertising Services
N.A.I.C.S.: 541810
Kristian Lee (CEO)
Clarence Koh (COO)

Owens DDB (2)
Floor 1 23-25 Grantham Street, Dublin,
Ireland
Tel.: (353) 14054900
Web Site: http://www.owensddb.com
Emp.: 40
Advertising Services
N.A.I.C.S.: 541810

Unit (Domestic):

Roberts + Langer DDB (2)
437 Madison Ave 12th Fl, New York, NY
10022
Tel.: (646) 289-7300
Web Site: http://www.robertsandlanger.com
Rev.: $175,000,000
Emp.: 50
Advertising Services
N.A.I.C.S.: 541810

Spike/DDB (2)
55 Washington St Ste 650, Brooklyn, NY
11201
Tel.: (718) 596-5400
Web Site: http://www.spikeddb.com
Sales Range: $10-24.9 Million
Emp.: 30
Advertising Services
N.A.I.C.S.: 541810
Spike Lee (CEO & COO)
Natasha Williamson (Grp Acct Dir)
Julie Shell (Fin Dir)
Alex Tyree (Dir-Client & Content)
Lolita Josephs (Coord-Budget)
Briana Bednarski (Art Dir)

Tribal DDB Worldwide (2)
437 Madison Ave 8th Fl, New York, NY
10022
Tel.: (212) 515-8600
Sales Range: $75-99.9 Million
Emp.: 1,200
Advertising Services
N.A.I.C.S.: 541810

Branch (Non-US):

Rapp/Tribal (3)
Level 6 80 Greys Ave, Auckland, 1040, New
Zealand
Tel.: (64) 93034299
Web Site: http://www.ddb.co.nz
Advertising Services
N.A.I.C.S.: 541810

Tribal DDB (3)
Prof WH Keesomlaan 4, 1183 DJ, Amstelveen, Netherlands
Tel.: (31) 204065106
Web Site: http://www.tribalddb.nl
Emp.: 125
Advertising Services
N.A.I.C.S.: 541810

Tribal DDB Athens (3)
4 Kastorias Str, Gerakas, 15344, Athens,
Greece
Tel.: (30) 2106175500
Web Site: http://tribalworldwide.gr
Advertising Services
N.A.I.C.S.: 541810
Agathi Plota (Mng Dir)

Tribal DDB Barcelona (3)
Enrique Granados No 86-88, 08008, Barcelona, Spain
Tel.: (34) 93 238 9010
Advertising Services
N.A.I.C.S.: 541810

Tribal DDB Budapest (3)
Dozsa Gyorgy ut 84/A, Budapest, H-1068,
Hungary
Tel.: (36) 14612800
Web Site: http://www.ddb.com
Emp.: 100
Advertising Services
N.A.I.C.S.: 541810

Branch (Domestic):

Tribal DDB Chicago (3)
225 N Michigan Ave 10th Fl, Chicago, IL
60601
Tel.: (312) 552-6000
Emp.: 55
Advertising Services
N.A.I.C.S.: 541810

Branch (Non-US):

Tribal DDB Colombia (3)
Sede Medellin Calle 16 AA Sur No 42-95,
El Poblado, Antioquia, Colombia
Tel.: (57) 1 635 61 01
Advertising Services
N.A.I.C.S.: 541810

Tribal DDB Copenhagen (3)
Bredgade 6, PO Box 2074, DK-1260, Copenhagen, Denmark
Tel.: (45) 33 46 47 48
Emp.: 3
Advertising Services
N.A.I.C.S.: 541810

Tribal DDB Hong Kong (3)
Suite 1201 Core E Cyberport 3, 100 Cyberport Rd, Hong Kong, China (Hong Kong)
Tel.: (852) 2828 0542
Advertising Services
N.A.I.C.S.: 541810

Tribal DDB India (3)
410/411 Khatau House Mogul Lane Mahim
West, Off Senapati Bapat Marg Mahim W,
Mumbai, 400016, Maharashtra, India
Tel.: (91) 22 3047 0200
Web Site: http://www.esuppliersindia.com
Advertising Services
N.A.I.C.S.: 541810

Tribal DDB Madrid (3)
Torre Picasso planta 36 plaza Ruiz Picasso,
28020, Madrid, Spain
Tel.: (34) 932283400
Emp.: 45

Tribal DDB Malaysia (3)
D601-605 6th Floor Block D Kelana Square
17 Jalan SS7/26 Selangor, 47301, Petaling
Jaya, Malaysia
Tel.: (60) 3 7844 7898
Advertising Services
N.A.I.C.S.: 541810

Tribal DDB Melbourne (3)
7 Electric St, Cremorne, 3121, VIC, Australia
Tel.: (61) 392543600
Web Site:
    http://www.tribalddbmelbourne.com.au
Advertising Services
N.A.I.C.S.: 541810

Tribal DDB Milan (3)
via Sabano 97, 20144, Milan, Italy
Tel.: (39) 02581931
Emp.: 20
Advertising Services
N.A.I.C.S.: 541810

Branch (Domestic):

**Tribal DDB North America/New
York** (3)
437 Madison Ave 8th Fl, New York, NY
10022
Tel.: (212) 515-8600
Web Site: http://tribalworldwide.com
Advertising Services
N.A.I.C.S.: 541810
Richard Guest (Mng Dir)

Branch (Non-US):

Tribal DDB Oslo (3)
Wergelandsvein 21, PO Box 7084, Majorstua, Oslo, 0305, Norway
Tel.: (47) 22 59 32 94
Advertising Services
N.A.I.C.S.: 541810

Tribal DDB Paris (3)
55 rue d Amsterdam, Paris, 75008, France
Tel.: (33) 892977099
Web Site: http://www.tribalddb.fr
Advertising Services
N.A.I.C.S.: 541810
Jerome Duchamps (Mng Dir)

Branch (Domestic):

Tribal DDB San Francisco (3)
555 Market St Ste 500, San Francisco, CA
94105-5810
Tel.: (415) 732-2200
Advertising Services
N.A.I.C.S.: 541810

Branch (Non-US):

Tribal DDB Sao Paulo (3)
SP - Avenida Brigadiéro Luis Antonio, Sao
Paulo, 01401002, Brazil
Tel.: (55) 1130549937
Advertising Services
N.A.I.C.S.: 541810

Tribal DDB Singapore (3)
226 Outram Road, 169039, Singapore, Singapore
Tel.: (65) 6323 4811
Advertising Services
N.A.I.C.S.: 541810

Tribal DDB Sydney (3)
Wilcox Mofflin Bldg 46-52 Mountain St, Ultimo, Sydney, 2007, Australia
Tel.: (61) 2 8260 2828
Web Site:
    http://www.tribalworldwideaustralia.com
Emp.: 30
Advertising Services
N.A.I.C.S.: 541810
Phil Dowgierd (Mng Dir)

Tribal DDB Tel Aviv (3)
10 Haomanim, Tel Aviv, 67897, Israel
Tel.: (972) 3 5611558
Emp.: 4
Advertising Services
N.A.I.C.S.: 541810

Tribal DDB Tokyo (3)
9th Floor Hiroo Plaza 5-6-6 Hiroo, Shibuya-Ku, Tokyo, 150-0012, Japan

Xavier Mendiola (Mng)
Cristian Vince (VP)

Advertising Services
N.A.I.C.S.: 541810
Issei Matsui (Mng Dir)

Tribal DDB Toronto (3)
33 Bloor Street East 17th Floor, Toronto,
M4W 3T4, ON, Canada
Tel.: (416) 925-9819
Emp.: 30
Advertising Services
N.A.I.C.S.: 541810
Andrew McCartney (Pres-Tribal Worldwide
Canada)
Louis-Philippe Tremblay (Dir-Creative)
Ciaran Cunningham (CEO)
David Winterlich (Mng Dir)
Duri Alajrami (VP-Brand Experience)
Erin Kawalecki (Dir-Creative)
Marketa Krivy (Exec Dir-Creative)
Diego Bertagni (Dir-Creative)

Tribal DDB Vancouver (3)
1600-777 Hornby St, Vancouver, V6Z 2T3,
BC, Canada
Tel.: (604) 608-4451
Web Site: http://www.tribalddb.ca
Emp.: 20
Advertising Services
N.A.I.C.S.: 541810

Tribal Worldwide London (3)
12 Bishop's Bridge Road, Paddington, London, W2 6AA, United Kingdom
Tel.: (44) 2072620011
Web Site: http://www.tribalworldwide.co.uk
Advertising Services
N.A.I.C.S.: 541810
Victoria Buchanan (Exec Dir-Creative)
Andrew Liles (CTO)
Yasmin Borain (Chief Experience Officer)
Jamie Willey (Dir-Bus Dev)
Jason Galla-Barth (Mng Partner)

Branch (Non-US):

Verba S.r.l. Advertising (2)
Via Savona 97, 20144, Milan, Italy
Tel.: (39) 02 89 42 08 07
Web Site: http://www.spgddb.it
Emp.: 20
Advertising Services
N.A.I.C.S.: 541810
Francesco Vigorito (CEO)

dos: Puntos DDB (2)
Km 86 antigua carretera a El Salvador Centro Corporativo Muxbal, Torre Este Nivel 9,
Guatemala, 1008, Guatemala
Tel.: (502) 2326 3800
Web Site: http://www.ddb.com
Emp.: 53
N.A.I.C.S.: 541810

DDB Worldwide Pty. Ltd. (1)
Level 3 46-52 Mountain Street, Ultimo, Sydney, 2007, NSW, Australia
Tel.: (61) 282602222
Web Site: http://www.ddb.com.au
Emp.: 450
Advertising Agency Services
N.A.I.C.S.: 541810

Dieste (1)
1999 Bryan St Ste 2500, Dallas, TX 75201
Tel.: (214) 259-8000
Web Site: http://www.dieste.com
Sales Range: $25-49.9 Million
Emp.: 130
Advetising Agency
N.A.I.C.S.: 541810

Branch (Domestic):

Dieste (2)
1285 Avenue of the Americas, New York,
NY 10019
Tel.: (214) 259-8000
Web Site: http://dieste.com
Sales Range: $25-49.9 Million
Emp.: 5
Advetising Agency
N.A.I.C.S.: 541810

Direct Partners (1)
12777 West Jefferson Blvd Bldg C, Los Angeles, CA 90066
Tel.: (310) 482-4200
Web Site: http://www.directpartners.com
Sales Range: $25-49.9 Million
Emp.: 100
Advertising Services

N.A.I.C.S.: 541810

Branch (Domestic):

Direct Partners (2)
55 Union St 2nd Fl, San Francisco, CA
94111
Tel.: (415) 262-3000
Web Site: http://www.directpartners.com
Sales Range: $25-49.9 Million
Emp.: 30
N.A.I.C.S.: 541810

Doremus (1)
1285 Avenue of the Americas 4th Fl, New
York, NY 10019
Tel.: (212) 366-3076
Web Site: http://www.doremus.com
Sales Range: $25-49.9 Million
Emp.: 100
Advertising Services
N.A.I.C.S.: 541810
Stu Garrett (Dir-Creative)
Patricia Byrnes (VP & Assoc Dir-Creative)
Alice Wang (Supvr-Mgmt)
Chloe Blacker (Supvr-Acct)
Ernest Kuo (Sr Mgr-Integrated Project)
Clarissa Chan (Reg Mgr-Fin)
Garrett Lawrence (Pres)
Joanna Chen (Mgr-HR & Admin)
Amanda Levy (Mgr-Creative Svcs)
Mike Essex (Mgr-Analytics)
Qian Zheng (Acct Mgr)
Cynthia Cormier (Dir-HR)
Bob Waldner (Dir-Creative)
Mark Butorac (Dir-Creative)
Hoffman Chu (Dir-Bus)
Raymond Ho (Dir-Art)
Courtney Cochrane (Dir-ACD & Art)
Kimberly Brandt (Dir-Acct)
Jerone Abueva (Dir-Acct)
James Engel (Dir-Acct)
Stephanie Kowalski (Dir-Acct)
Chris Masuret (Dir-Acct)
Michael Winter (Dir-Acct)
Christopher Cappello (Controller)

Branch (Non-US):

**Advantage Corporate Communica-
tions GmbH** (2)
Salient Doremus Lindleystrasse 12, 60314,
Frankfurt am Main, Germany
Tel.: (49) 696500960
Web Site: http://www.advantage.de
Sales Range: $25-49.9 Million
Emp.: 10
Financial, Full Service
N.A.I.C.S.: 541810
Can Vardar (Mng Dir)
Arman Vardar (Mng Dir)
Britta Vardar (Mng Dir)

Doremus (Hong Kong) (2)
Suite 1501 Cityplaza 4 12 Taikoo Wan
Road, Taikoo Shing, China (Hong Kong)
Tel.: (852) 228612721
Web Site: https://www.doremus.com.hk
Sales Range: $25-49.9 Million
Emp.: 25
Advertising Services
N.A.I.C.S.: 541810

Branch (Domestic):

Doremus (San Francisco) (2)
550 3rd St, San Francisco, CA 94107
Tel.: (415) 273-7800
Web Site: http://www.doremussf.com
Sales Range: $25-49.9 Million
Emp.: 50
Advertising Services
N.A.I.C.S.: 541810
Garrett Lawrence (Pres)

Branch (Non-US):

Doremus London (2)
Bankside 3 100 Southwark Street, London,
SE1 0SW, United Kingdom
Tel.: (44) 2086181900
Web Site: http://www.doremus.com
Advertising Services
N.A.I.C.S.: 541810
Alasdair Morrison (Pres)
Ronnie Brown (Chief Creative Officer)

Downtown Partners Chicago (1)
200 E Randolph St Ste 3400, Chicago, IL
60601

Tel.: (312) 552-5800
Web Site:
http://www.downtownpartners.com
Sales Range: $10-24.9 Million
Emp.: 22
N.A.I.C.S.: 541810

EVB-Evolution Bureau (1)
55 Union, San Francisco, CA 94111
Tel.: (415) 281-3950
Web Site: http://www.evb.com
Sales Range: $100-124.9 Million
Emp.: 25
Children's Market, Information Technology,
Interactive Agencies
N.A.I.C.S.: 541810
Daniel Stein (Founder & CEO)
James Gassel (COO)
Shane Ginsberg (Pres)
Caitlin Russell (Dir-Strategy)
Renata Di Iulio (Dir-Client Svcs)
Diana Chen (Creative Dir)
Kirsten Merit (Acct Supvr)

**Excerpta Medica Medical Communi-
cations BV** (1)
Herikerbergweg 17, 1101 CN, Amsterdam,
Netherlands
Tel.: (31) 207971400
Web Site: http://www.excerptamedica.com
Sales Range: $25-49.9 Million
Emp.: 100
Medical Information Publishing & Communi-
cations Services
N.A.I.C.S.: 513120

Fathom Communications (1)
300 Park Ave Fl 12, New York, NY 10022
Tel.: (212) 817-6600
Web Site: https://www.docu-branding.com
Rev.: $75,000,000
Emp.: 15
Advertising Services
N.A.I.C.S.: 541810

Branch (Domestic):

Fathom Communications (2)
200 E Randolph St Ste 3800, Chicago, IL
60601
Tel.: (312) 552-6900
N.A.I.C.S.: 541810

Flamingo (1)
1st Floor 1 Riverside Manbre Road, Lon-
don, W6 9WA, United Kingdom
Tel.: (44) 2037900400
Web Site: http://flamingogroup.com
Emp.: 120
N.A.I.C.S.: 541810

FleishmanHillard (1)
200 N Broadway, Saint Louis, MO 63102-
2796
Tel.: (314) 982-1700
Web Site: https://fleishmanhillard.com
Public Relations Agency
N.A.I.C.S.: 541810
John Saunders (Pres & CEO)
J.J. Carter (COO & Pres-Americas)
Patti Portnoy (Partner, CFO & Sr VP)
Marjorie Benzkofer (Sr Partner, Chief Strat-
egy Officer & Sr VP)
Della Sweetman (Co-Pres, Chief Strategy
Officer & Chief Bus Dev Officer)
Lisa Moehlenkamp (COO & Chief Talent
Officer)
Mark Mortell (Chief Global Client Leader-
ship Officer & Head-Practices & Sectors)
Terri Owen (Gen Mgr)
Emily Frager (Chief Client Officer & Gen
Mgr-Southern California)
Fred Rohlfing (Board of Directors & CFO)

Subsidiary (Non-US):

BlueCurrent Japan (2)
38F Harumi Triton Square X, 6-19-20 Tsukiji
Chuo-Ku, Tokyo, 104-6038, Japan
Tel.: (81) 362044141
Web Site:
http://www.bluecurrentprjapan.com
N.A.I.C.S.: 541810

Bluecurrent Hong Kong (2)
Suite 1501 Cityplaza 4, 12 Taikoo Wan
Road, Taikoo Shing, China (Hong Kong)
Tel.: (852) 229676770
Advetising Agency
N.A.I.C.S.: 541810

**Fleishman-Hillard Australia Pty.
Ltd.** (2)
137 Pyrmont Street Level 3, Pyrmont, 2009,
NSW, Australia
Tel.: (61) 285845500
Web Site:
https://www.fleishmanhillard.com.au
Sales Range: $25-49.9 Million
Emp.: 15
Communications, Public Relations
N.A.I.C.S.: 541820

Fleishman-Hillard B.V. (2)
Prof Wh Keesomlann 4, 1183 DJ, Am-
stelveen, Netherlands
Tel.: (31) 204065930
Web Site: http://www.fleishman.nl
Sales Range: $25-49.9 Million
Emp.: 45
N.A.I.C.S.: 541820
Rosalinde Van Dewall (Mng Dir)
John Saunders (Pres & CEO)
Olivier Beheydt (COO)

Fleishman-Hillard Beijing (2)
7F Building A LSH Center 8th Yard Guangs-
hun Avenue South, Chaoyang District, Bei-
jing, 100102, China
Tel.: (86) 1057755888
Web Site: https://fleishmanhillard.cn
Sales Range: $25-49.9 Million
Communications & Public Relations Agency
N.A.I.C.S.: 541820
Jerry Zou (Partner, Sr VP & Gen Mgr)

**Fleishman-Hillard Czech
Republic** (2)
Lomnickeho 1705/9, 140 00, Prague, 4,
Czech Republic
Tel.: (420) 224232650
Web Site: http://fleishmanhillard.cz
Sales Range: $25-49.9 Million
Emp.: 16
Communications, Public Relations
N.A.I.C.S.: 541820

Fleishman-Hillard France (2)
50/54 Rue de Silly, Boulogne-Billancourt,
92100, Paris, France
Tel.: (33) 153325500
Web Site: http://www.fleishmanhillard.fr
Sales Range: $25-49.9 Million
Emp.: 40
Communications, Public Relations
N.A.I.C.S.: 541820
Olivier Beheydt (COO-EMEA)

**Fleishman-Hillard Germany
GmbH** (2)
Hanauer Landstrasse 182a, 60314, Frank-
furt am Main, Germany
Tel.: (49) 694057020
Web Site: https://fleishmanhillard.de
Sales Range: $25-49.9 Million
Emp.: 40
Communications, Public Relations
N.A.I.C.S.: 541820
Hanning Kempe (CEO)
Olivier Beheydt (COO-EMEA)
Volker Pulskamp (Head-Corp Comm)
Nadine Dusberger (Head-Healthcare)
Matthias Lass (Dir-Creative)
Sybille Goepel (CFO)
Thies Clausen (Head-Corp & Pub Affairs)
Enno Hennrichs (Head-Tech)
Judith Christina Pierau (Head-Brand Affairs)
John Saunders (Pres & CEO)

Branch (Domestic):

**Fleishman-Hillard Germany GmbH -
Berlin** (3)
Friedrichstrasse 200, 10117, Berlin, Ger-
many
Tel.: (49) 3059004330
Web Site: http://www.fleishmanhillard.de
Sales Range: $25-49.9 Million
Emp.: 15
N.A.I.C.S.: 541820
Hanning Kempe (CEO)
Olivier Beheydt (COO)
Volker Pulskamp (Head-Corp Comm)
Nadine Dusberger (Head-Healthcare)
Matthias Lass (Dir-Creative)

**Fleishman-Hillard Germany GmbH -
Munich** (3)
Blumenstrasse 28, 80331, Munich, Ger-
many

Tel.: (49) 892303160
Web Site: http://www.fleishmanhillard.de
Sales Range: $25-49.9 Million
Emp.: 20
Communications, Public Relations
N.A.I.C.S.: 541820

Subsidiary (Non-US):

Fleishman-Hillard Group Ltd. (2)
Bankside 2 100 Southwark Street, Covent
Garden, London, SE1 0SW, United King-
dom
Tel.: (44) 2086182800
Web Site: http://www.fleishman.com
Sales Range: $50-74.9 Million
Emp.: 175
Communications, Public Relations
N.A.I.C.S.: 541820

Branch (Domestic):

**Fleishman-Hillard Group Ltd. -
Edinburgh** (3)
22 Calton Rd, Edinburgh, EH8 8DP, United
Kingdom
Tel.: (44) 131 558 4900
Sales Range: $25-49.9 Million
Emp.: 25
Communications,
Government/Political/Public Affairs, Public
Relations
N.A.I.C.S.: 541820

Subsidiary (Non-US):

Fleishman-Hillard Guangzhou (2)
3707 F Center Plz No 161 Linhe Road W,
Tianhe District, Guangzhou, China
Tel.: (86) 20 3825 1368
N.A.I.C.S.: 541820

**Fleishman-Hillard Hong Kong
Ltd.** (2)
12 Taikoo Wan Road Suite 1501, Taikoo
Shing, China (Hong Kong)
Tel.: (852) 25300228
Web Site: http://www.fleishman.com
Emp.: 70
Communications, Public Relations
N.A.I.C.S.: 541820
Lynne Anne Davis (Reg Pres-Asia Pacific)
Rachel Catanach (Pres & Partner)
Patrick Yu (Sr VP & Gen Mgr)
Kitty Lee (Sr VP & Deputy Gen Mgr)

Branch (Domestic):

Fleishman-Hillard Inc. (2)
200 N Broadway, Saint Louis, MO 63102-
2796
Tel.: (314) 982-1700
Web Site: http://www.fleishmanhillard.com
Sales Range: $25-49.9 Million
Emp.: 25
Public Relations Agency
N.A.I.C.S.: 541810

Fleishman-Hillard Inc. (2)
1999 Bryan St Ste 3400, Dallas, TX 75201-
6848
Tel.: (214) 665-1300
Web Site: http://www.fleishman.com
Public Relations Agency
N.A.I.C.S.: 541820
Dick Mullinax (Sr Partner, Sr VP & Gen
Mgr-Dallas)

Fleishman-Hillard Inc. (2)
828 W 6th St, Austin, TX 78703
Tel.: (512) 474-9848
Web Site: http://www.fleishman.com
Sales Range: $25-49.9 Million
Emp.: 25
Public Relations Agency
N.A.I.C.S.: 541820

Fleishman-Hillard Inc. (2)
2 Alhambra Plz Ste 600, Coral Gables, FL
33134
Tel.: (305) 520-2000
Web Site: http://www.fleishman.com
Sales Range: $10-24.9 Million
Emp.: 20
Public Relations Agency
N.A.I.C.S.: 541820

Fleishman-Hillard Inc. (2)
150 S 5th St Ste 1030, Minneapolis, MN
55402
Tel.: (612) 573-3100

Omnicom Group Inc.—(Continued)

Web Site: http://www.fleishman.com
Sales Range: $25-49.9 Million
Emp.: 37
Public Relations Agency
N.A.I.C.S.: 541820

Fleishman-Hillard Inc. (2)
8910 University Center Ln Ste 1100, San
Diego, CA 92122
Tel.: (858) 203-1123
Web Site: http://www.fleishman.com
Sales Range: $25-49.9 Million
Emp.: 20
Public Relations Agency
N.A.I.C.S.: 541820

Fleishman-Hillard Inc. (2)
720 California St 6th Fl, San Francisco, CA
94108
Tel.: (415) 318-4000
Web Site: http://www.fleishman.com
Sales Range: $25-49.9 Million
Emp.: 50
Public Relations Agency
N.A.I.C.S.: 541820
John Saunders (Pres & CEO)

Fleishman-Hillard Inc. (2)
1285 Avenue of the Americas Fl 5, New
York, NY 10019
Tel.: (212) 453-2000
Web Site: http://www.fleishman.com
Sales Range: $25-49.9 Million
Emp.: 140
Public Relations Agency
N.A.I.C.S.: 541820
Anne de Schweinitz (Mng Dir-Healthcare-
Global)
Ephraim Cohen (Gen Mgr)

Fleishman-Hillard Inc. (2)
2405 Grand Blvd Ste 1000, Kansas City,
MO 64108-2522
Tel.: (816) 474-9407
Web Site: http://www.fleishman.com
Sales Range: $25-49.9 Million
Emp.: 45
Public Relations Agency
N.A.I.C.S.: 541820

Fleishman-Hillard Inc. (2)
4745 Alla Rd, Marina Del Rey, CA 90292
Tel.: (310) 482-4279
Web Site: http://www.fleishman.com
Sales Range: $25-49.9 Million
Emp.: 25
Public Relations Agency
N.A.I.C.S.: 541820
Della Sweetman (Chief Bus Dev Officer)
Emily Frager (Gen Mgr-Southern California)

Fleishman-Hillard Inc. (2)
One Alliance Ctr Ste 2000 3500 Lenox Rd,
Atlanta, GA 30326
Tel.: (404) 659-4446
Web Site: http://www.fleishman.com
Sales Range: $10-24.9 Million
Emp.: 20
Public Relations Agency
N.A.I.C.S.: 541820

Fleishman-Hillard Inc. (2)
1121 L St Ste 1123, Sacramento, CA
95814-4348
Tel.: (916) 441-7606
Web Site: http://www.fleishman.com
Sales Range: $25-49.9 Million
Emp.: 18
Public Relations Agency
N.A.I.C.S.: 541820
Dan Barber (Gen Mgr)

Fleishman-Hillard Inc. (2)
225 N Michigan Ave Fl 21, Chicago, IL
60601-6513
Tel.: (312) 729-3700
Web Site: http://www.fleishman.com
Sales Range: $25-49.9 Million
Emp.: 76
Public Relations Agency
N.A.I.C.S.: 541820

Fleishman-Hillard Inc. (2)
1300 Post Oak Blvd Ste 1350, Houston, TX
77056-3043
Tel.: (713) 513-9500
Web Site: http://www.fleishman.com
Sales Range: $10-24.9 Million
Emp.: 20
Public Relations Agency

N.A.I.C.S.: 541820
Fleishman-Hillard Inc. (2)
3050 K St NW Ste 100, Washington, DC
20007
Tel.: (202) 659-0330
Web Site: http://www.fleishman.com
Sales Range: $25-49.9 Million
Emp.: 10
Public Relations Agency
N.A.I.C.S.: 541820

Fleishman-Hillard Inc. (2)
1930 Camden Rd Ste 225, Charlotte, NC
28203
Tel.: (704) 421-9600
Web Site: http://www.fleishman.com
Sales Range: $25-49.9 Million
Emp.: 57
Public Relations Agency
N.A.I.C.S.: 541820

Fleishman-Hillard Inc. (2)
1201 Edwards Mill Rd Ste 400, Raleigh, NC
27607
Tel.: (919) 457-0744
Web Site: http://www.fleishman.com
Sales Range: $25-49.9 Million
Emp.: 25
Public Relations Agency
N.A.I.C.S.: 541820

Fleishman-Hillard Inc. - Boston (2)
290 Congress St 6th Fl, Boston, MA 02210
Tel.: (617) 986-5719
Web Site: http://www.fleishman.com
Public Relations Agency
N.A.I.C.S.: 541820

Fleishman-Hillard Inc. - Irvine (2)
4 Studebaker, Irvine, CA 92618
Tel.: (949) 855-5997
Web Site: http://www.fleishmanhillard.com
Public Relations Agency
N.A.I.C.S.: 541820
J. J. Carter (Pres-The Americas & COO-
Global)
Emily Frager (Gen Mgr-South California)

**Fleishman-Hillard Inc. - Puerto
Rico** (2)
210 Rd 165 Ste 40, Guaynabo, PR 00968
Tel.: (787) 620-1400
Web Site: http://www.fleishman.com
Sales Range: $25-49.9 Million
Emp.: 2
Public Relations Agency
N.A.I.C.S.: 541820

Subsidiary (Non-US):

Fleishman-Hillard Italia S.r.l. (2)
Via Solari 11, 20144, Milan, Italy
Tel.: (39) 02 31804 1
Web Site: http://www.fleishman.com
Sales Range: $25-49.9 Million
Emp.: 20
Communications, Public Relations
N.A.I.C.S.: 541820

Fleishman-Hillard Japan KK (2)
Harumi Triton Square X 39th floor 1-8-10,
Harumi Chuo-ku, Tokyo, 104-6038, Japan
Tel.: (81) 362044300
Web Site: http://www.fleishman.co.jp
Sales Range: $25-49.9 Million
Emp.: 45
Communications, Public Relations
N.A.I.C.S.: 541820
Shin Tanaka (Pres)

Fleishman-Hillard Korea (2)
7F J Tower Dosan Daero 139 Gangnamgu,
Seoul, 006-036, Korea (South)
Tel.: (82) 220517077
Web Site: http://fleishmanhillard.co.kr
Communications; Public Relations & Repu-
tation Management
N.A.I.C.S.: 541820
Yvonne Park (Mng Dir)

Fleishman-Hillard Limited (2)
15 Fitzwilliam Quay, Dublin, Ireland
Tel.: (353) 16188444
Web Site: http://fleishmanhillard.ie
Sales Range: $25-49.9 Million
Emp.: 35
Communications, Public Relations
N.A.I.C.S.: 541820
Rhona Blake (Gen Mgr)
Gill Madden (Head-Brand Mktg)
John Saunders (Pres & CEO)

Fleishman-Hillard Manila (2)
17th Floor Frabelle Business Center 111
Rada Street, Legaspi Village Makati City,
Manila, 1229, Philippines
Tel.: (63) 288920701
Web Site: http://fleishmanhillard.ph
Sales Range: $10-24.9 Million
Emp.: 16
Communications, Public Relations
N.A.I.C.S.: 541820

**Fleishman-Hillard Mexico, S.A. de
C.V.** (2)
Monte Pelvoux No 210 3er Piso, B Col-
Lomas de Chapultepec, 11560, Mexico, DF,
Mexico
Tel.: (52) 5555406031
Web Site: http://www.fleishman.com
Communications
N.A.I.C.S.: 541820
Flavio Diaz Tueme (Gen Mgr)

**Fleishman-Hillard Polska Sp. z
o.o.** (2)
ul Ogrodowa 58, 00-876, Warsaw, Poland
Tel.: (48) 225201301
Web Site: https://fleishmanhillard.pl
Sales Range: $10-24.9 Million
Emp.: 20
N.A.I.C.S.: 541820
John Saunders (Pres & CEO)
Olivier Beheydt (COO)

Fleishman-Hillard Pte. Ltd. (2)
20 Kallang Avenue, Pico Creative Centre
Level 8, Singapore, 339411, Singapore
Tel.: (65) 63391066
Web Site: http://www.fleishmanhillard.com
Sales Range: $25-49.9 Million
Emp.: 30
Communications, Public Relations
N.A.I.C.S.: 541820

Fleishman-Hillard SA/NV (2)
Rue Belliard 40, 1040, Brussels, Belgium
Tel.: (32) 22300545
Web Site: http://fleishmanhillard.eu
Sales Range: $25-49.9 Million
Emp.: 80
Communications,
Government/Political/Public Affairs, Public
Relations
N.A.I.C.S.: 541820

**Fleishman-Hillard South Africa (Pty)
Ltd.** (2)
3 Sandown Valley Crescent 6th floor, PO
Box 71181, Sandown, Sandton, 2031,
South Africa
Tel.: (27) 115482000
Web Site: http://www.fleishmanhillard.co.za
Sales Range: $25-49.9 Million
Emp.: 50
Communications, Public Relations
N.A.I.C.S.: 541820
Sharon Piehl (Partner & Gen Mgr)
John Saunders (Pres & CEO)
Olivier Beheydt (COO)

Fleishman-Hillard Spain, S.A. (2)
C/ Luchana 23 4th Floor, 28010, Madrid,
Spain
Tel.: (34) 917883200
Sales Range: $25-49.9 Million
Emp.: 70
N.A.I.C.S.: 541820

FleishmanHillard HighRoad (2)
3575 boul St-Laurent bureau 300, Montreal,
H2X 2T7, QC, Canada
Tel.: (514) 908-0110
Web Site: http://www.fhhighroad.com
Public Relations; Communications Services
N.A.I.C.S.: 541820
Neil Johnson (Partner & Exec Dir-Creative)
Mark Reder (Sr VP)
Cheryl Stewart-Walsh (Sr VP)
Vanessa Cohen (VP)
Jackie Asante (Sr VP)
Jen Anthony (Sr VP)
Charles Muggeridge (Partner)

Branch (Domestic):

**Fleishman-Hillard Canada Inc. -
Calgary** (3)
1410-540 5 Ave Sw, Calgary, T2P 0M2, AB,
Canada
Tel.: (403) 266-4710

Web Site: http://www.fleishman.ca
Communications,
Government/Political/Public Affairs, Public
Relations
N.A.I.C.S.: 541820

**Fleishman-Hillard Canada Inc. -
Ottawa** (3)
45 O'Connor Street Suite 1200, Ottawa,
K1P 1A4, ON, Canada
Tel.: (613) 238-2090
Communications,
Government/Political/Public Affairs, Public
Relations
N.A.I.C.S.: 541820

**Fleishman-Hillard Canada Inc. -
Toronto** (3)
33 Bloor Street E Suite 1500, Toronto, M4W
3H1, ON, Canada
Tel.: (416) 214-0701
Web Site: http://www.fleishman.ca
Sales Range: $25-49.9 Million
Emp.: 40
N.A.I.C.S.: 541810
Angela Carmichael (Sr VP & Gen Mgr)

**Fleishman-Hillard Canada Inc. -
Vancouver** (3)
777 Hornby St Suite #1600, Vancouver,
V6Z 2T3, BC, Canada
Tel.: (604) 688-2505
Communications,
Government/Political/Public Affairs, Public
Relations
N.A.I.C.S.: 541820

Subsidiary (Domestic):

GMMB Inc. (2)
3050 K St NW Ste 100, Washington, DC
20007-3606
Tel.: (202) 338-8700
Web Site: http://gmmb.com
Emp.: 200
Public Relations Agency
N.A.I.C.S.: 541820
Trudi Benford (Sr VP & Dir-Creative Svcs)
Adam Ferrari (Sr VP)
Alexandra Rodriguez (Acct Exec)
Alison Kruzel (Sr VP)
Allie McKay (VP)
Allison Thomas (Sr VP)
Ally Flaherty (Acct Supvr)
Alyson McColl (Mng Dir & Sr VP-Health &
Dev-Global)
Angela Landers (VP-Pub Health)
Anne Hilton (VP)
Annie Adair (Acct Exec-Political Campaigns)
Annie Burns (Partner)
Ashley Middleton (Sr VP-Climate Change,
Environmental Justice & Pub Health)
Ben Hawkins (Sr VP & Dir-Creative)
Bradley Perseke (Partner-Politics)
Chantal Wong (Acct Exec-Issue Comm &
Pub Health)
Kimberly Hefling (VP)
Eric Conrad (VP-Issue Comm & Corp So-
cial Impact)
Dana Cronyn (VP-Issue Comm & Con-
sumer Advocacy)
Jenny Selzer (VP-Issue Comm & Consumer
Advocacy)
Jodi Quintero (VP-Issue Comm & Con-
sumer Advocacy)
Frances Bresnahan (VP-Brand Positioning,
Issue Comm & Environment)
Joe Brener (VP & Dir)
Emily Meyer (Supvr-Acct-Issue Comm &
Corp Social Impact)
Dylan Tyne (Supvr-Acct-Issue Comm)
Harper Lawson (Sr VP-Political Campaigns)
Erica Monteith (Sr VP-Paid Media)
Garth Moore (Sr VP-Digital)
Don Corrigan (Sr VP & Dir-Creative)
Debbie Ashpes (Sr Mgr-Brdcst Production)
Jim Margolis (Partner-Political Campaigns &
Issue Comm)
Frank Greer (Partner-Political Campaigns &
Education)
Daniel Jester (Partner-Media Plng & Politi-
cal Campaigns)
Jacquie Lawing Ebert (Partner-Issue
Comm, Social Justice & Education)
Jaime Zapata (Partner-Issue Comm, Social
Justice & Corp Social Impact)
Ellen Frawley (Partner-Issue Comm & Con-
sumer Advocacy)
Janet Goss (Partner-Brand Positioning, Is-
sue Comm & Social Justice)

Anson Kaye *(Partner)*
D. J. Mash *(Mgr-Design Production)*
Alejandro Diaz Blanquez *(Mgr-Adv Ops)*
Greg Miller *(Controller)*
Bill Brocato *(CFO)*
Alaina Goff *(Sr Project Mgr)*
Alyssa Peterson *(Project Mgr)*
Augusta Burney *(VP & Sr Mgr-Contract)*
Blythe Lloyd *(Sr Project Mgr-Digital)*
Caitlin McLean *(Project Mgr)*
Gina Pham *(Bus Mgr)*
James Jahr *(Mgr-IT)*
Jesse Demastrie *(Sr VP & Media Dir-Politics)*
Jessica Selander *(Sr VP & Creative Dir)*
John Rimel *(Sr VP)*
Julia Rothenberg *(VP-Digital)*
Julie Green Bataille *(Sr VP)*
Kaia Lenhart *(Partner-Health & Dev-Global)*
Katelyn Creech *(VP)*
Katie Schofield *(VP)*
Katie Stevenson *(VP-Corp Social Impact & Pub Health)*
Keeley Smith *(VP)*
Kelly Carey *(Mng Dir & Sr VP)*
Kevin Steele *(VP & Dir-IT)*
Kristen Handley *(VP)*
Kristen Palmisano *(Sr Project Mgr)*
Larissa McCartney *(Sr Dir-Art)*
Madalene Milano *(Partner-Corp Social Impact)*
Maru Becker *(Sr VP-Politics)*
Micheline Kennedy *(Partner-Health & Dev-Global)*

Branch (Domestic):

GMMB Inc. - Seattle (3)
1200 Westlake Ave N Ste 1005, Seattle, WA 98109
Tel.: (206) 352-8598
Web Site: http://gmmb.com
Sales Range: $25-49.9 Million
Emp.: 25
Public Relations Agency
N.A.I.C.S.: 541820
Bill Brocato *(CFO)*
Anson Kaye *(Partner-Politics)*

Subsidiary (Non-US):

High Road Communications (2)
100 Queen St ste 1300, Ottawa, K1Y 4S1, ON, Canada
Tel.: (613) 236-0909
Web Site: http://www.highroad.com
Sales Range: $10-24.9 Million
Emp.: 23
Communications, Public Relations
N.A.I.C.S.: 541820

High Road Communications (2)
3575 Blvd St-Laurent Ste 200, Montreal, H2X 2T7, QC, Canada
Tel.: (514) 908-0110
Communications, Government/Political/Public Affairs, Public Relations
N.A.I.C.S.: 541820

High Road Communications (2)
360 Adelaide St W 4th Fl, Toronto, M5V 1R7, ON, Canada
Tel.: (416) 214-0701
Communications, High Technology, Public Relations
N.A.I.C.S.: 541820

Subsidiary (Domestic):

Lois Paul & Partners (2)
150 Presidential Way Ste 400, Woburn, MA 01801
Tel.: (781) 782-5000
Web Site: http://www.lpp.com
Public Relations Agency
N.A.I.C.S.: 541820

Branch (Domestic):

Lois Paul & Partners (3)
515 Congress Ave Ste 2150, Austin, TX 78701-3561
Tel.: (512) 638-5300
Web Site: http://www.loispaul.com
Sales Range: $25-49.9 Million
Emp.: 4
Public Relations Agency
N.A.I.C.S.: 541820

Subsidiary (Non-US):

PT Fleishman-Hilliard (2)
EightyEight Kasablanka 33rd floor Jl Casablanca Raya kav 88, Jakarta, 12870, Indonesia
Tel.: (62) 2129820233
Web Site: https://fleishmanhillard.co.id
N.A.I.C.S.: 541810

Subsidiary (Domestic):

Stratacomm LLC (2)
1156 15th St NW Ste 800, Washington, DC 20005
Tel.: (202) 289-2001
Web Site: http://www.stratacomm.net
Sales Range: $25-49.9 Million
Emp.: 30
Public Relations Agency
N.A.I.C.S.: 541820
Bill Buff *(Mng Partner)*
John Fitzpatrick *(Mng Partner)*
Sharon Hegarty *(Sr Partner & Sr VP)*
Kristin Tyll *(Partner & Mng Dir-Detroit)*
Charlotte Seigler *(Partner & Sr VP)*
Shannon Hartnett *(Partner & VP)*
Travis Austin *(Sr Partner)*
April Harding *(Dir-Digital)*

Branch (Domestic):

Stratacomm LLC - Detroit Office (3)
30200 Telegraph Rd Ste 137, Bingham Farms, MI 48025
Tel.: (248) 213-7337
Web Site: http://www.stratacomm.net
Sales Range: Less than $1 Million
Emp.: 10
Public Relations Agency
N.A.I.C.S.: 541820

Footsteps (1)
114 John St Ste 930, New York, NY 10272
Tel.: (917) 994-1848
Web Site: http://www.footstepsorg.org
Sales Range: $10-24.9 Million
Emp.: 20
Advertising Services
N.A.I.C.S.: 541810
Carrie Shapiro *(Treas)*
Lani Santo *(CEO)*
Chani Getter *(Sr Dir-Organizational Dev)*
Yael Reisman *(Dir-Field & Movement Building)*
Chavie Weisberger *(Dir-Community Engagement)*
Julia Jerusalmi-Henig *(Mgr-Member Engagement)*
Yomaly Suero *(Mgr-Economic Empowerment Program)*
Hoda Elmahdy *(Sr Dir-Programs)*
Jessica Markowitz *(Sr Dir-Fin, Data & Admin)*
Stephanie Oster *(Sr Dir-Dev)*
Naomi Moskowitz *(Dir-Economic Empowerment)*
Leon Setton *(Dir-Clinical Svcs)*
Katharine Dow *(Mgr-Institutional Rels)*
Emma Kraft *(Mgr-Donor Rels)*
Ayelet Parness *(Comm Mgr)*
Pesach Eisen *(Mgr-Case)*
Molly Weilbacher *(Coord-Dev Ops)*
Jamie Hooper *(Co-Chm)*

GEOMEDIA N.V. (1)
Rue de Stalle 65, 1180, Brussels, Belgium
Tel.: (32) 23330907
Sales Range: $10-24.9 Million
Emp.: 10
Advetising Agency
N.A.I.C.S.: 541810

GSD&M Idea City LLC (1)
828 W 6th St, Austin, TX 78703
Tel.: (512) 242-4736
Web Site: http://www.gsdm.com
Advertising, Brand Development & Integration
N.A.I.C.S.: 541810
Steve Gurasich *(Co-Founder)*
Judy Trabulsi *(Co-Founder)*
Duff Stewart *(CEO)*
Marianne Malina *(Pres)*
Jay Russell *(Chief Creative Officer)*
Roy Spence *(Co-Founder)*

Branch (Domestic):

GSD&M Chicago (2)

225 N Michigan Ave 8th Fl, Chicago, IL 60601
Tel.: (312) 464-8200
Web Site: http://www.gsdm.com
Sales Range: $25-49.9 Million
Emp.: 75
Media Buying Services
N.A.I.C.S.: 541810

Goodby, Silverstein & Partners, Inc. (1)
720 California St, San Francisco, CA 94108
Tel.: (415) 392-0669
Web Site: http://goodbysilverstein.com
Sales Range: $100-124.9 Million
Emp.: 525
Marketing & Advertising
N.A.I.C.S.: 541810
Richard Silverstein *(Co-Founder, Co-Chm & Partner)*
Jeffrey Goodby *(Co-Founder, Co-Chm & Partner)*
Margaret Johnson *(Partner & Chief Creative Officer)*
Derek Robson *(Pres & Mng Partner)*
Brian McPherson *(Mng Partner)*
Christine Chen *(Partner & Head-Comm Strategy)*
Leslie Barrett *(Mng Partner)*
Bonnie Wan *(Partner & Head-Brand Strategy)*
Meredith Vellines *(Dir-Comm)*
Julie Whitecotton *(Dir-New Bus)*

Branch (Domestic):

Goodby, Silverstein & Partners, Inc. - New York (2)
200 Varick 6th Fl, New York, NY 10014
Tel.: (212) 266-0155
Advertising Services
N.A.I.C.S.: 541810
Will Elliott *(Assoc Partner)*
Justin Moore *(Assoc Partner)*
Patrick Knowlton *(Dir-Creative)*
Jon Wolanske *(Dir-Creative)*
Roger Baran *(Dir-Creative)*
Sam Luchini *(Dir-Creative)*
Eric Kallman *(Exec Dir-Creative)*

Grupo ABC Ltda. (1)
Rua Alvorada 1151 3 andar, Vila Olimpia, Sao Paulo, 04550-004, Brazil
Tel.: (55) 1130949969
Web Site: http://www.grupoabc.com
Emp.: 5,000
Holding Company; Advertising Agency
N.A.I.C.S.: 541810
Guga Valente *(Founder & CEO)*

Subsidiary (Domestic):

CDN Comunicacao Corporativa Ltda. (2)
Av Brigadeiro Faria Lima 2 601 9 E 10 Andar, Jardim Paulistano, 01452-000, Sao Paulo, Brazil
Tel.: (55) 11 3643 2700
Web Site: http://cdn.com.br
Emp.: 500
Marketing & Advertising Services
N.A.I.C.S.: 541613
Joao Rodarte *(Founder & Pres)*
Alexandre Pinheiro *(Dir)*
Silvia Ruiz *(Head-Innovation)*
Fernanda Dantas *(Exec Dir)*
Jussara Leal *(Exec Dir)*
Ludmilla Le Maitre *(Exec Dir)*

Interbrand (2)
Rua Olimpiadas 242 - 8 andar, Conjunto 82 Vila Madalena, Sao Paulo, 05433-000, Brazil
Tel.: (55) 1137078500
Marketing & Advertising Services
N.A.I.C.S.: 541613
Beto Almeida *(CEO-Sao Paulo)*
Laura Garcia Miloski *(Dir-Strategy)*
Sergio Cury *(Dir-Creative)*
Andy Payne *(Chief Creative Officer-Global)*
Kelly Gall *(Chief Comml Officer)*
Gonzalo Brujo *(Chief Growth Officer-Global)*
Manfredi Ricca *(Chief Strategy Officer-Global)*
Jane Parker *(CEO-InterbrandHealth-North America)*
Paola Norambuena *(Chief Content Officer-Mexico)*

Morya Comunicacao e Propaganda Ltda (2)

Av Lafayete Coutinho 1010, Bahia Marina Comercio, 40015-160, Salvador, Brazil
Tel.: (55) 71 2105 7442
Web Site: http://grupoabc.com
Emp.: 150
Advertising Services
N.A.I.C.S.: 541810
Gustavo Queiroz *(Pres & Partner)*

NewStyle (2)
Rua Texas 686, Brooklin, 04557-000, Sao Paulo, Brazil
Tel.: (55) 11 5185 5252
Web Site: http://www.newstyle.com.br
Emp.: 150
Marketing & Advertising Services
N.A.I.C.S.: 541613

RockerHeads (2)
R Brejo Alegre 581, Brooklin, Sao Paulo, 04557-051, Brazil
Tel.: (55) 11 5103 5899
Web Site: http://www.rockerheads.com.br
Emp.: 50
Advertising Services
N.A.I.C.S.: 541810
Sergio Baldassari *(Creative Dir)*

SalveTribal Worldwide (2)
Av Brigadeiro Luis Antonio 4980, 01402-002, Sao Paulo, Brazil
Tel.: (55) 11 3027 9999
Web Site: http://salvetribal.com.br
Advertising Services
N.A.I.C.S.: 541810
Carlos Pitchu *(Co-Pres)*
Ricardo Schreiner *(Chief Experience Officer)*
Alcir Gomes Leite *(Co-Pres)*
Daniele Bornato *(CFO)*

Sunset Comunicacao (2)
Rua Alvorada 1151, Villa Olimpia, Sao Paulo, 04550-004, Brazil
Tel.: (55) 11 3371 0377
Web Site: http://www.sunsetcom.com.br
Marketing & Advertising Services
N.A.I.C.S.: 541810
Guto Cappio *(Pres)*

Tudo Eventos e Promocoes Ltda (2)
Rua Canada n 301, Jd America, Rio de Janeiro, 01436-000, Brazil
Tel.: (55) 11 3811 1999
Web Site: http://www.agenciatudo.com.br
Marketing & Advertising Services
N.A.I.C.S.: 541810
Mauricio Magalhaes *(CEO)*

Hall and Partners (1)
195 Broadway 18th Fl, New York, NY 10007
Tel.: (212) 925-7844
Web Site: http://www.hallandpartners.com
Rev.: $1,000,000
Emp.: 90
Advertising Services
N.A.I.C.S.: 541810
Josh Shames *(Mng Partner-Chicago)*
Vanella Jackson *(Chm)*
Lee Gazey *(Mng Partner-UK Health)*
Timothy Wragg *(CEO)*

Harrison & Shriftman LLC (1)
158 W 29th St 6th Fl, New York, NY 10001
Tel.: (917) 351-8600
Web Site: http://www.hs-pr.com
Sales Range: $10-24.9 Million
Emp.: 35
Advertising Services
N.A.I.C.S.: 541810
Elizabeth Harrison *(Founder & CEO)*
Veronica Rodriguez *(Chief Brand Officer)*

Branch (Domestic):

Harrison & Shriftman (2)
12777 W Jefferson Blvd Bldg C, Los Angeles, CA 90066
Tel.: (310) 437-2600
Web Site: http://www.hs-pr.com
Emp.: 12
N.A.I.C.S.: 541810

Harrison & Shriftman (2)
1111 Lincoln Rd Ste 801, Miami Beach, FL 33139
Tel.: (786) 257-4010
Web Site: http://www.hs-pr.com
Emp.: 12
N.A.I.C.S.: 541810

Omnicom Group Inc.—(Continued)

Harrison and Star (1)
75 Varick St 6th Fl, New York, NY 10013
Tel.: (212) 727-1330
Web Site: http://www.harrisonandstar.com
Sales Range: $75-99.9 Million
Emp.: 350
N.A.I.C.S.: 541810
Thomas L. Harrison (Founder)
Mario Muredda (CEO)
Terese Kung (Chief Strategy Officer & Exec VP)
Paulette Robinson (Exec VP & Dir-Ops)
Adam Hessel (Chief Creative Officer & Exec VP)
Mike Sullivan (Sr VP & Creative Dir-Copy)
Bella Wess (Art Dir)
Eva Tolk (Sr VP)
Caroline Burton (Sr VP & Creative Dir)
Erik Vervroegen (Sr VP & Creative Dir)
Will Beck (Sr VP & Creative Dir)
Rob Perota (Sr VP & Creative Dir)
Eileen Boshko (Sr VP-Fin)
Mary Sheeran (Mgr-Editorial)

Healthcare Consultancy Group (1)
488 Madison Ave 5th Fl, New York, NY 10022
Tel.: (203) 992-6703
Web Site: http://www.hcg-int.com
Emp.: 130
Healthcare Marketing Consulting Services
N.A.I.C.S.: 541613
Brian Kielty (Pres & COO)
Matt D'Auria (CEO)
Elizabeth Robinson (Exec VP & Dir-Talent Engagement & Dev)
Akarsh Sakalaspur (Exec VP & Head-Digital)
Bill Mulligan (Chief Client Officer)
Gregory Imber (Chief Engagement Officer)
Markus Vaga (Exec Creative Dir)

Subsidiary (Domestic):

Health Science Communications (2)
220 E 42nd St 11th Fl, New York, NY 10017
Tel.: (212) 849-7900
Web Site: http://www.hsci.com
Sales Range: $10-24.9 Million
Emp.: 120
Advertising Services
N.A.I.C.S.: 541810
Delphine Dubois (CEO)
Fariba Ghodrati (Exec VP & Dir-Bus Strategy)
Jan-Willem Van Doorn (Pres)
Diala Habib (Sr VP-Medical & Scientific Svcs)
Nikolay Nikolov (Sr VP & Creative Dir)
Michael Weems (CFO)

Hyphen Digital (2)
488 Madison Ave 5th Fl, New York, NY 10022
Tel.: (212) 849-7700
Web Site: http://www.hyphenhealth.com
Sales Range: $10-24.9 Million
Emp.: 15
Advetising Agency
N.A.I.C.S.: 541810
Gregory Imber (Pres)
Deborah Pagano (VP & Dir-Production)
David Ferguson (VP & Creative Dir-Scientific Visual Strategy)
Matthew Lear (Sr VP & Creative Dir)
Akarsh Sakalaspur (VP-Digital Svcs)

ICON International Inc. (1)
105 Hoberson Drive, Ajax, L1T 3Z6, ON, Canada
Tel.: (416) 275-1270
Web Site: http://www.icon-intl.com
Sales Range: $25-49.9 Million
Emp.: 10
N.A.I.C.S.: 541830

Integrated Merchandising Systems (1)
8338 Austin Ave, Morton Grove, IL 60053-3209
Tel.: (847) 966-2550
Web Site: http://www.imsretail.com
Sales Range: $50-74.9 Million
Emp.: 200
Consumer Marketing
N.A.I.C.S.: 541870

Rick Remick (Chm)

Interbrand Corporation (1)
195 Broadway 18th Fl, New York, NY 10007
Tel.: (212) 798-7500
Sales Range: $25-49.9 Million
Emp.: 110
Advertising Services
N.A.I.C.S.: 541810
Andy Payne (Chief Creative Officer-Global)
Ashish Mishra (Mng Dir-India)
Daniel Binns (CEO-New York)
Charles Trevail (CEO-Global)
Gonzalo Brujo (Pres-Global)
Rebecca Robins (Chief Learning & Culture Officer-Global)
Manfredi Ricca (Chief Strategy Officer-Global)
Georgina Collins (Chief Talent Officer-Global)
Maximo Rainuzzo (Pres-Buenos Aires)
Laura Krajecki (Chief Human Truths Officer-Global)
David Bachmann (CFO & COO-Global)
Satish Krishnamurthy (Chief Strategy Officer-India)
Ameya Kapnadak (Chief Growth Officer-India & Head-India)
Payal Shah (Head-Human Truths-India & Dir-Strategy-India)
Rahul Bansal (Head-Brand Economics-India & Dir-Strategy-India)

Branch (Non-US):

Interbrand (2)
3 Bankside 90-100 Southwark Street, London, SE1 0SW, United Kingdom
Tel.: (44) 2075541000
Emp.: 60
Advertising Services
N.A.I.C.S.: 541810
Christian Purser (CEO)
Rebecca Robins (Chief Learning & Culture Officer-Global)

Branch (Domestic):

InterbrandHealth (2)
195 Broadway 18th Fl, New York, NY 10007
Tel.: (212) 798-7500
Web Site: http://www.interbrandhealth.com
Advertising Services
N.A.I.C.S.: 541810
Jane Parker (CEO)
Jim Mackie (Exec Dir-Strategy & Analytics)
R. John Fidelino (Exec Dir-Creative)
Barry Silverstein (Exec Dir-Client Svcs)

Interbrand Design Forum (1)
7575 Paragon Rd, Dayton, OH 45459
Tel.: (937) 439-4400
Sales Range: $75-99.9 Million
Emp.: 70
Advertising Services
N.A.I.C.S.: 541810
Vicky Leavitt (CEO)

Branch (Domestic):

Interbrand San Francisco (2)
600 California, San Francisco, CA 94108
Tel.: (212) 798-7500
Emp.: 20
Advertising Services
N.A.I.C.S.: 541810
Daniel Binns (CEO-New York)

Javelin (1)
7850 N Belt Line Rd, Irving, TX 75063
Tel.: (972) 443-7000
Web Site: https://javelinagency.com
Sales Range: $75-99.9 Million
Emp.: 153
Advertising Services
N.A.I.C.S.: 541810
Mike McCartin (CEO)
David Selwood (Chief Analytics Officer)
Leigh Ober (Chief People Officer)

Kaleidoscope (1)
64 Wooster St 6th Fl, New York, NY 10012
Tel.: (212) 358-7750
Web Site: http://www.kscopecreative.com
Sales Range: $10-24.9 Million
Emp.: 11
Advertising Services
N.A.I.C.S.: 541810

Matt Kornau (CEO)
Linda L. Singh (Founder)
S. Ravi Kumar (Chm)

Ketchum, Inc. (1)
1285 Avenue of the Americas 4th Fl, New York, NY 10019
Tel.: (646) 935-3900
Web Site: http://www.ketchum.com
Sales Range: $100-124.9 Million
Emp.: 170
Advetising Agency
N.A.I.C.S.: 541810
Barri Rafferty (CEO)
James Peters (Partner & Mng Dir-Retail-North America)

Subsidiary (Domestic):

Access Emanate Communications (2)
1285 Ave of the Americas, 6th Fl, New York, NY 10019
Tel.: (212) 805-8000
Web Site:
   https://www.accesstheagency.com
Emp.: 151
Public Relations & Communications Services
N.A.I.C.S.: 541820

Subsidiary (Non-US):

C-Matrix Communications AG (2)
Backerstrasse 52, 8004, Zurich, Switzerland
Tel.: (41) 433005656
Web Site: http://www.cmatrix.ch
Emp.: 8
Public Relations Services
N.A.I.C.S.: 541820
Alfred Kocher (Mng Partner)
Mathias Ulrich Koch (Dir-Bus Dev)
Victoria Tanner (Partner)
Daniel Pasquier (Partner)
Frederic Vormus (Partner)

Subsidiary (Domestic):

Concentric Communications (2)
1285 6th Ave Fl #3, New York, NY 10019
Tel.: (212) 209-4550
Emp.: 20
Public Relations Services
N.A.I.C.S.: 541820
Karen Day (Partner & VP)
Olan Beam (Pres & Partner)

Emanate (2)
25 W 43rd St, New York, NY 10036
Tel.: (212) 805-8000
Web Site: http://www.emanatepr.com
Emp.: 50
Advertising Services
N.A.I.C.S.: 541810

Subsidiary (Non-US):

ICON International Communications Singapore Pte. Ltd. (2)
30 Merchant Road 03 12 Riverside Point, Singapore, 058282, Singapore
Tel.: (65) 62202623
Web Site: http://www.ketchum.com
Emp.: 50
Advetising Agency
N.A.I.C.S.: 541810

Branch (Domestic):

Ketchum (2)
6 Ppg Pl Fl 12, Pittsburgh, PA 15222
Tel.: (412) 456-3885
Web Site: http://www.ketchum.com
Emp.: 20
Advertising & Public Relations Agency
N.A.I.C.S.: 541810

Ketchum (2)
1050 Battery St, San Francisco, CA 94111
Tel.: (415) 984-6100
Web Site: http://www.ketchum.com
Emp.: 60
Advertising & Public Relations Agency
N.A.I.C.S.: 541810
Mike Doyle (Pres & CEO)

Ketchum (2)
225 N Michigan Ave 7th Fl, Chicago, IL 60601
Tel.: (312) 228-6800
Web Site: http://www.ketchum.com

Emp.: 50
Advertising & Public Relations Agency
N.A.I.C.S.: 541810
Brian Rafferty (CEO)

Ketchum (2)
1615 L St NW Ste 500, Washington, DC 20036
Tel.: (202) 835-8800
Web Site: http://www.ketchum.com
Advertising & Public Relations Agency
N.A.I.C.S.: 541810
Jerry Olszewski (Mng Dir)

Ketchum (2)
3500 Lenox Rd Ste 2000, Atlanta, GA 30326
Tel.: (404) 879-9220
Web Site: http://www.ketchum.com
Advertising & Public Relations Agency
N.A.I.C.S.: 541810

Ketchum (2)
340 Main St Ste 200, Venice, CA 90291
Tel.: (310) 584-8300
Emp.: 40
Advertising Services
N.A.I.C.S.: 541810

Branch (Non-US):

Ketchum (2)
Via Leto Pomponio 3/5, 20146, Milan, Italy
Tel.: (39) 0262411911
Web Site: http://www.ketchum.it
Emp.: 32
Public Relations Services
N.A.I.C.S.: 541810
Andrea Cornelli (Chm & CEO)

Ketchum (2)
54 Rue de Clichy, 75009, Paris, Cedex, France
Tel.: (33) 153325500
Emp.: 65
Public Relations Services
N.A.I.C.S.: 541820

Ketchum (2)
R Alvaro Rodrigues 182-2 andar, Brooklin, Sao Paulo, 04582-000, SP, Brazil
Tel.: (55) 11 5096 4334
Web Site: http://www.ketchum.com.br
Emp.: 100
Public Relations Services
N.A.I.C.S.: 541820
Valeria Perito (Founder)

Branch (Domestic):

Ketchum (2)
Harwood Ctr 1999 Bryan St Ste 2500, Dallas, TX 75201
Tel.: (214) 259-3414
Web Site: http://www.ketchum.com
Sales Range: $10-24.9 Million
Emp.: 20
Advertising & Public Relations Services
N.A.I.C.S.: 541810
Courtney Wohrman (VP)

Branch (Non-US):

Ketchum (2)
90 Southwark St, London, SE1 0SW, United Kingdom
Tel.: (44) 2037556400
Web Site: http://www.ketchum.com
Public Relations Services
N.A.I.C.S.: 541820
Richard Griffiths (Dir-Strategic Comm)
Barri Rafferty (CEO)
Con Franklin (Mng Dir-Healthcare)
Alicia Solanki (Mng Dir-Client Experience)
Gavin Cooper (CFO)
James Coyle (Chief Client Officer)
Janita Lakhanpal (Dir-New Bus)
Indy Selvarajah (Exec Creative Dir)
Sophie Raine (Mng Dir-Brand)
Camilla Dormer (Deputy Mng Dir-Health)

Subsidiary (Non-US):

Ketchum Canada (2)
1607-33 Bloor St E, Toronto, M4W 3H1, ON, Canada
Tel.: (416) 355-7431
Web Site: http://www.ketchum.com
Sales Range: $10-24.9 Million
Emp.: 194
Public Relations Services

N.A.I.C.S.: 541820
Erin Manning (Assoc Mng Dir)

Branch (Non-US):

Ketchum Chengdu (2)
1205A Western Tower No 19 4th Section
Ren Min Nan Road, Chengdu, 610041, Si-
chuan, China
Tel.: (86) 28 8526 8983
Advertising Services
N.A.I.C.S.: 541810
Vivien Teo (Dir-Digital Strategy-Greater
China)

Subsidiary (Domestic):

**Ketchum Directory
Advertising/Kansas City** (2)
7015 College Blvd Ste 700, Overland Park,
KS 66211
Tel.: (913) 344-1900
Web Site: http://www.kda.com
Sales Range: $10-24.9 Million
Emp.: 46
Advetising Agency
N.A.I.C.S.: 541810

Branch (Domestic):

**Ketchum Directory
Advertising/Louisville** (3)
4360 Brownsboro Rd Ste 200, Louisville,
KY 40207-1642
Tel.: (502) 894-3220
Web Site: http://www.kda.com
Sales Range: $10-24.9 Million
Advetising Agency
N.A.I.C.S.: 541810

**Ketchum Directory
Advertising/Pittsburgh** (3)
6 PPG Pl, Pittsburgh, PA 15222-5425
Tel.: (412) 316-8000
Web Site: http://www.kda.com
Emp.: 41
Advetising Agency
N.A.I.C.S.: 541810

Branch (Non-US):

Ketchum Pleon (2)
Theresienhoehe 12, Munich, 80339, Ger-
many
Tel.: (49) 89590421140
Web Site: http://www.ketchumpleon.com
Emp.: 50
Public Relations Services
N.A.I.C.S.: 541820
Sabine Huckmann (CEO)

Ketchum Pleon (2)
Generaal Vetterstraat 82, 1059 BW, Am-
sterdam, Netherlands
Tel.: (31) 204874000
Web Site: http://www.ketchumpleon.com
Emp.: 45
Public Relations Services
N.A.I.C.S.: 541820

Ketchum Pleon (2)
35-41 Folgate Street, London, E16 8X,
United Kingdom
Tel.: (44) 207 479 5656
Web Site: http://www.ketchumpleon.com
Emp.: 150
Public Relations Services
N.A.I.C.S.: 541820

Ketchum Pleon Gmbh (2)
Bahnstrasse 2, 40212, Dusseldorf, Ger-
many
Tel.: (49) 21195412124
Web Site: http://www.ketchum.com
Emp.: 50
Public Relations Services
N.A.I.C.S.: 541820
Rudiger Maessen (Mng Partner)

Ketchum Pleon Milano (2)
Via G Lorenzini 4, 20139, Milan, Italy
Tel.: (39) 02 006 620 0
Emp.: 40
Public Relations Services
N.A.I.C.S.: 541820
Gianni Catalfamo (Dir-European-Ketchum)
Myriam Koppel (Partner)
Marcello Laugelli (CEO)

Ketchum Pleon Roma (2)
Via Cassia 1081, 189, Rome, Italy

Tel.: (39) 06 3026 0341
Emp.: 3
Public Relations Services
N.A.I.C.S.: 541820

Ketchum Pleon Stuttgart (2)
Breitscheidstr 8, 70174, Stuttgart, Germany
Tel.: (49) 711 21099 0
Web Site: http://www.ketchum.de
Sales Range: $50-74.9 Million
Emp.: 20
Public Relations Services
N.A.I.C.S.: 541820
Sabine Hueckmann (CEO)

Ketchum Publico (2)
Guglgasse 7-9, 1030, Vienna, Austria
Tel.: (43) 1717860
Web Site: http://www.ketchum.com
Emp.: 40
Advertising & Public Relations Services
N.A.I.C.S.: 541820
Saskia Wallner (CEO)

Subsidiary (Non-US):

Ketchum Sampark Pvt. Ltd
Mangalam House 38 Walchand Hirachand
Marg, Mumbai, 400 001, India
Tel.: (91) 2240425550
Web Site: http://www.ketchum.com
Public Relations Services
N.A.I.C.S.: 541820
Bela Rajan (Founder)

Ketchum Spain (2)
Calle Luchana 23 4th Floor, 28010, Madrid,
Spain
Tel.: (34) 91 788 3200
Web Site: http://www.ketchum.com
Public Relations Services
N.A.I.C.S.: 541820

Ketchum Taipei (2)
3F-2 No 51 Sec 2 Keelung Rd, 110 Hsinyi
District, Taipei, 110, Taiwan
Tel.: (886) 2 27383038
Web Site: http://www.ketchum.com
Public Relations Services
N.A.I.C.S.: 541820

Branch (Non-US):

Ketchum-Public Relations (2)
Rm 2707-2710 Tower One Kerry Everbright
City, No 218 Tian Mu Rd W, Shanghai,
200070, China
Tel.: (86) 21 5289 5838
Web Site: http://www.ketchum.com
Public Relations Services
N.A.I.C.S.: 541820
Eddi Yang (Chief Client & Operating Officer-
China)
Prince Zhang (CEO-Greater China)

Ketchum-Public Relations (2)
33rd Floor Two Chinachem Exchange
Square 338 Kings Road, 3309 King's Road,
North Point, China (Hong Kong)
Tel.: (852) 2566 1311
Web Site: http://www.ketchum.com
Emp.: 50
Public Relations Services
N.A.I.C.S.: 541820
Simeon Mellalieu (Partner-Client Dev)
Louann Wong (Grp Acct Dir)
Jessica Clifton (Acct Dir-Digital)

Ketchum-Public Relations (2)
Room 2003 Peace World Plaza 362-366
Huanshi Dong Lu, Guangzhou, 510060,
China
Tel.: (86) 20 8387 0810
Web Site: http://www.ketchum.com
Public Relations Services
N.A.I.C.S.: 541820

Subsidiary (Non-US):

Ketchum-Public Relations Ltd. (2)
10/f Tower A Vantone Center No 6 Chaowai
Street, Chaoyang District, Beijing, 100020,
China
Tel.: (86) 10 5907 0055
Web Site: http://www.ketchum.com
Public Relations Services
N.A.I.C.S.: 541820

Subsidiary (Domestic):

Zocalo Group (2)

255 N Michigan Ave Ste 2050, Chicago, IL
60601
Tel.: (312) 596-6300
Web Site: http://www.zocalogroup.com
Emp.: 130
Advertising Services
N.A.I.C.S.: 541810
Josh Hammond (Sr Dir-Client Dev)

Kreab Worldwide AB (1)
Master Samuelsgatan 17, 111 44, Stock-
holm, Sweden
Tel.: (46) 850645200
Web Site: http://www.kreab.com
Emp.: 30
Holding Company; Public Relations Agen-
cies
N.A.I.C.S.: 551112
John Lagerquist (Dir-Global Fin)
Johan Hallsenius (Sr Partner)
Birgitta Stal (Partner)
Bengt Ludvigsson (Mng Partner)
Henrik Olsson Werner (Dir)
Anders Oxelstrom (Dir)
Ulf Perbo (Dir)
Kristina Scharp (Dir)
Fredrik Segerfeldt (Dir)
Peter Sellgren (Dir)
Sara Evedius Zirn (Deputy Mng Partner)
Yassir Butt (CFO-Global)
Cecilia Alpstig (Assoc Dir)
Robert Noord (Assoc Dir)

Subsidiary (US):

**Chlopak, Leonard, Schechter &
Associates**
1850 M St NW Ste 900, Washington, DC
20036
Tel.: (202) 289-5900
Web Site: http://www.clsstrategies.com
Rev.: $3,000,000
Emp.: 40
Public Relations Agency
N.A.I.C.S.: 541820

Subsidiary (Non-US):

Kreab (Hong Kong) Limited (2)
20/F Chinachem Hollywood Centre 1-3 Hol-
lywood Road, Central, China (Hong Kong)
Tel.: (852) 5806 0370
Web Site: http://www.kreab.com
Emp.: 9
Public Relations Agency
N.A.I.C.S.: 541820
Sophie Sophaon (Mng Partner)
Phyllis Tam (Fin Dir)
Priscella Kwok (Sr Mgr-Office)

Subsidiary (Domestic):

Kreab AB (2)
Master Samuelsgatan 17, 111 44, Stock-
holm, Sweden
Tel.: (46) 735225277
Web Site: http://www.kreab.com
Public Relations Agency
N.A.I.C.S.: 541820
Bengt Ludvigsson (Mng Partner)
Peje Emilsson (Chm)
Henrik Olsson Werner (Partner)
Birgitta Stal (Partner)

Branch (Non-US):

Kreab Brussels (2)
Rond Point Schuman 2-4, 1040, Brussels,
Belgium
Tel.: (32) 27376900
Web Site: http://www.kreab.com
Emp.: 40
Public Relations Agency
N.A.I.C.S.: 541820
Karl Isaksson (Mng Partner & Exec VP-
Worldwide)
David Reed (Head-Fin Policy)
Sebastian Remoy (Head-Pub Affairs)
Anna Lekston (Partner)
Winston Beck (Partner)
Alberta Laschena (Partner)
Michele Morena (Partner)
Sandrell Sultana (Partner)
Marie Gorkem (Partner)

Subsidiary (Non-US):

Kreab Espana S.L. (2)
Calle del Poeta Joan Maragall 38, 28020,
Madrid, Spain

Tel.: (34) 91 702 71 70
Web Site: http://www.kreab.com
Public Relations Agency
N.A.I.C.S.: 541820
Pablo Zamorano (Partner)
Francisco Calderon (Partner)
Alberto Muelas (Dir-Sustainability)
Eduardo Madina (Dir-Research Unit)
Maria Rubinos (Dir-Reputation & Intan-
gibles)
Manuel de la Fuente (Dir-Pub Affairs)
Iban Rabasa (Dir-Pub Affairs)
Lucas Calvo (Dir-Pub Affairs)
Elena de la Mata (Dir-Internal Comm)
Irune Casas (Dir-HR)
Jose Luis Gonzalez (Dir-Fin Comm)
Xavier Cima (Dir-Digital Policy)
Borja Bergareche (Dir-Digital)
Miguel Alba (Dir-Data & Media)
Rosario Correro (Dir-Corp Comm)
Cristina Fontgivell (Dir-Corp Comm)
Alba Malaga (Dir-Corp Comm)
Oscar Masso (Dir-Comm & Mktg)
Jaime Olmos (Deputy Mng Dir)
Gonzalo Soto (CFO)
Antonio San Jose (Partner)
Angel Garcia Merino (Dir-Corp Comm)
Javier Dorado (Dir-Pub Affairs)
Oscar Torres (Dir-Fin Comm)
Gonzalo Torres (Partner-Fin Comm)

Branch (Domestic):

Kreab Espana S.L. - Barcelona (3)
Diagonal 609-615 7th E y F, 08028, Barce-
lona, Spain
Tel.: (34) 93 418 5387
Web Site: http://www.kreab.com
Emp.: 8
Public Relations Agency
N.A.I.C.S.: 541820
Teresa Lloret (Partner & Head)
Pablo Zamorano (Partner)
Francisco Calderon (Partner)
Carmen Basagoiti (Mng Partner)
Alberto Muelas (Dir-Sustainability)
Eduardo Madina (Dir-Res Unit)
Maria Rubinos (Dir-Reputation & Intan-
gibles)
Manuel de la Fuente (Dir-Pub Affairs)
Iban Rabasa (Dir-Pub Affairs)
Lucas Calvo (Dir-Pub Affairs)
Borja Bergareche (Dir-Kreab Digital)
Elena de la Mata (Dir-Internal Comm)
Irune Casas (Dir-HR)
Gonzalo Torres (Dir-Fin Comm)
Jose Luis Gonzalez (Dir-Fin Comm)
Xavier Cima (Dir-Digital Policy)
Maria Peris (Dir-Digital Comm)
Miguel Alba (Dir-Data & Media)
Cristina Fontgivell (Dir-Corp Comm)
Alba Malaga (Dir-Corp Comm)
Rosario Correro (Dir-Corp Comm)
Manuel Garcia-Vila (Dir-Corp Comm)
Oscar Masso (Dir-Comm & Mktg)
Jaime Olmos (Deputy Mng Partner)
Gonzalo Soto (CFO)

Subsidiary (Non-US):

Kreab K.K. (2)
Atago Green Hills Mori Tower 9F 2-5-1
Atago, Minato-ku, Tokyo, 105-6209, Japan
Tel.: (81) 354040640
Web Site: http://www.kreab.com
Emp.: 36
Public Relations Agency
N.A.I.C.S.: 541820
Masami Doi (Mng Partner)
Kazumoto Eguchi (Partner & Head-Pub
Policy & Govt Rels)
Kentaro Matsuda (Fin Dir)
Jean-marc Rocher (Assoc Dir)
Anders Lenart (Assoc Dir)
Chung Hyon Suk (Assoc Dir)
Michael Lintaro Egi (Assoc Dir)
Rio Tomohiro (Assoc Dir)
Tomoko Hamabata (Assoc Dir)

Kreab Limited (2)
6th Floor 90 Long Acre, London, WC2E
9RA, United Kingdom
Tel.: (44) 2070741800
Web Site: http://www.kreab.com
Public Relations Agency
N.A.I.C.S.: 541820
Chris Philipsborn (Mng Partner)
Jeremy Walker (Dir-Fin-Global)
Sebastian Remoy (Exec VP & Head-Pub
Affairs-Global)

Omnicom Group Inc.—(Continued)

Victoria Marchant *(Mgr-Fin)*
Sondra Sheriff *(Head-Design)*
Fiona Cumberland *(Dir)*
Anna Hellstrand *(Dir)*
Jane Kerr *(Dir)*

Branch (Non-US):

Kreab Lisbon (2)
Av Joao Crisostomo 30 - 6 esq, 1050-127,
Lisbon, Portugal
Tel.: (351) 21 319 5640
Web Site: http://www.kreab.com
Public Relations Agency
N.A.I.C.S.: 541820
Sofia Gaio *(Partner)*
Joao Tocha *(Mng Partner)*
Joao Tomasio *(Head-Digital)*
Alexandra Brito *(Head-Content)*
Marisa Ferreira *(Coord-Clients)*

Subsidiary (Non-US):

Kreab Oy (2)
Mikonkatu 5, 00100, Helsinki, Finland
Tel.: (358) 50 554 1615
Web Site: http://www.kreab.com
Emp.: 28
Public Relations Agency
N.A.I.C.S.: 541820
Mikael Jungner *(Mng Partner)*
Virve Wright *(Sr Dir)*
Sari Siikasalmi *(Dir-Insight)*
Lauri Hyppola *(Dir-Fin Comm)*
Tuomas Tierala *(Partner)*
Anna-maria Laine *(Assoc Dir)*
Eva Opas *(Partner)*
Tero Lehtinen *(Assoc Dir)*
Tero Salmela *(Art Dir)*
Perttu Eskelinen *(Art Dir)*
Annika Paananen *(Fin Dir)*

Kreab Pte. Ltd. (2)
24 Raffles Place 21-05 Clifford Centre, Sin-
gapore, 048621, Singapore
Tel.: (65) 3163 7479
Web Site: http://www.kreab.com
Emp.: 10
Public Relations Agency
N.A.I.C.S.: 541820
Wei Joo Ng *(Mng Partner)*
Sharon Cheah *(Assoc Dir)*

LatinWorks Marketing, Inc. (1)
410 Baylor St, Austin, TX 78703
Tel.: (512) 479-6200
Web Site: http://www.latinworks.com
Sales Range: $125-149.9 Million
Emp.: 100
Advertising Services
N.A.I.C.S.: 541810
Manny Flores *(Co-Founder, CEO & Mng
Partner)*
Alejandro Ruelas *(Co-Founder, Mng Partner
& CMO)*
Scott Radigk *(CFO)*
Leo Olper *(Mng Dir & Sr VP)*
Michelle Aldrich *(VP-Fin Ops)*
Luis Guido *(VP-Experiential Mktg)*
Serge Flores *(Exec Creative Dir)*
Jaime Gonzalez-Mir *(VP & Grp Dir)*
Chloe King *(Dir-Media Buying Grp)*
Nicole Arena *(Dir-Media)*

M/A/R/C Research (1)
1425 Greenway Dr Ste 300, Irving, TX
75038
Tel.: (972) 506-3901
Web Site: http://www.marcresearch.com
Rev.: $1,000,000
Advetising Agency
N.A.I.C.S.: 541810
Merrill Dubrow *(CEO)*
Susan Hurry *(Exec VP)*
Randall A. Wahl *(Pres)*
Patricia Wakim *(Sr VP-Fin)*
Susan Hanks *(Sr VP-Insights & Strategies)*
Brian Barnes *(VP-Qualitative Svcs)*
Lynn Dagar *(Sr VP-Insights & Strategies)*
Sherrie Binke *(Exec)*
Brad Seipel *(Sr VP-Acct Mgmt)*
Jim O'Hara *(Sr VP-Accelerated Solutions)*
Jill Rogers *(Sr VP-Acct Mgmt)*
Dan Soulas *(Sr VP-Acct Mgmt)*
Eileen Rozic *(Sr VP-Acct Mgmt)*

MMG (1)
7529 Standish Pl Ste 100, Rockville, MD
20855

Tel.: (301) 984-7191
Web Site: http://www.mmgct.com
Sales Range: $50-74.9 Million
Emp.: 100
Communications, Health Care, Medical,
Pharmaceutical
N.A.I.C.S.: 541890
Helen West *(Pres)*
Ann Kottcamp *(COO)*
Kate Clarke *(Sr VP-Fin)*

Martin/Williams Advertising Inc. (1)
150 S 5th St Ste 900, Minneapolis, MN
55402
Tel.: (612) 340-0800
Web Site: http://www.martinwilliams.com
Sales Range: $100-124.9 Million
Emp.: 200
Advetising Agency
N.A.I.C.S.: 541810
Lori Yeager Davis *(Pres)*
Steve Casey *(Sr VP & Exec Dir-Creative)*
Swapna Desai *(Sr VP & Dir-Bus Strategy)*
Marty Enerson *(Sr VP & Dir-Ops)*
Brian McHugh *(CFO)*
Jessica Garrett *(Sr VP & Dir-New Bus)*
Brock Davis *(Chief Creative Officer)*
Jason Wynne *(Dir-Creative Tech)*
Melissa Clark *(VP & Dir-Strategy & Perfor-
mance)*

Division (Domestic):

Karwoski & Courage (2)
5th Street Towers 150 S 5th St Ste 900,
Minneapolis, MN 55402
Tel.: (612) 342-9898
Web Site: http://creativepr.com
Sales Range: $25-49.9 Million
Emp.: 17
Public Relations
N.A.I.C.S.: 541820
Glenn Karwoski *(Mng Dir & Sr VP)*

TripleInk (2)
150 S 5th St Ste 900, Minneapolis, MN
55402
Tel.: (612) 342-9800
Web Site: http://www.tripleink.com
Sales Range: $25-49.9 Million
Emp.: 11
Communications
N.A.I.C.S.: 541810
Uta Moncur *(Founder & Pres)*

Maslansky, Luntz & Partners (1)
200 Varick St Rm 601, New York, NY
10014
Tel.: (917) 606-6900
Web Site: http://www.maslansky.com
Sales Range: $10-24.9 Million
Emp.: 20
Marketing Research & Public Opinion Poll-
ing
N.A.I.C.S.: 541910
Michael Maslansky *(CEO)*
Nicole Babalas Nichols *(Sr Dir)*
Abigail Thompson *(Dir-Employee Experi-
ence)*
Hana Veseli *(Dir-Field Ops Recruiting)*
Jacqui Hardenburg *(Sr Project Mgr)*
Robert Ledniczky *(Dir)*
Keith Yazmir *(Partner)*
Maria Boos *(Sr VP)*
Clint Sievers *(Sr VP & Head-Ops)*
Katie Cronen *(Sr VP)*
Lindsay Naze *(CFO)*
Catherine Farr *(VP)*
Nile Hull *(VP-Talent)*
Leemor Nir Grunberg *(VP)*
Sachi Pettit *(VP)*
Emily Arnold *(Fin Mgr)*
Frank Goldbach *(Dir-IT)*
Sarah Hendry *(VP)*
Will Howard *(VP)*
John La Valle *(Coord-Field Ops)*
Katarina Starcevic *(Sr Dir)*

Merkley + Partners (1)
200 Varick St, New York, NY 10014
Tel.: (212) 805-7500
Web Site:
https://www.merkleyandpartners.com
Rev.: $728,000,000
Emp.: 238
Advertising Services
N.A.I.C.S.: 541810
Alex Gellert *(CEO)*
Kyle Daley *(Dir-Creative Svcs)*

Cynthia Davis *(Chief Client Officer)*
Stacey Lesser *(Chief Strategic Officer)*
Adam Arnegger *(Chief Media Officer)*
Scott Gelber *(Pres)*
Max Godsil *(Grp Dir-Creative)*
Aaron Eiseman *(Grp Dir-Creative)*
Eddie Van Bloem *(Grp Dir-Creative)*
Michael Garone *(Mgr-Traffic)*
Pam Carden *(Dir-Brdcst Bus)*
Greg Wells *(Creative Dir)*
Francesco Deluca *(Acct Dir)*
Samantha Kaufman *(Dir-Media)*
Drummond Berman *(Dir-Creative)*
James Garvey *(Mgr-Talent)*
Alex Grossman *(Exec VP & Dir-Grp Plng)*
Suzanne Glickstein *(Mgr-Presentations)*
Zoe Gepfert *(Supvr-Acct)*
Meaghan Boegel *(Supvr-Acct)*
Jackson Klein *(Supvr-Acct)*
Giancarlo Alvarez *(Supvr-Acct)*
Pat Milo *(Sr Mgr-Bus-Brdcst Production)*
Valencia Lewis *(Mgr-Project)*
Maureen Kennny *(Mgr-Production)*
Lisa Manarelli-Puleo *(Exec VP & Dir-Acct)*
Rebecca Lax *(Exec Dir-HR)*
Salen Andrews *(Dir-Plng)*
Melissa Whitcomb *(Dir-Media)*
Taryn Young *(Dir-Field Acct)*
Bev Don *(Dir-Art Production)*
Yuxin Xiong *(Dir-Art)*
Julia Endow *(Dir-Art)*
Alison Stelzer *(Dir-Acct)*
Jordan Sabourin *(Dir-Acct)*
Amy Winter *(Dir-Acct)*
Taylor Rhodes *(Dir-Acct)*
Maggi Vale *(Dir-Acct)*
Michael Williams *(Copywriter)*
Heather Hopkins *(Assoc Dir-Digital Produc-
tion)*
David Ganassi *(Assoc Dir-Creative)*
Kimberly Price *(Assoc Dir-Social Media)*
Jennifer Cimmino *(Exec VP & Dir-Digital
Integration)*
David Croll *(Editor-AVID)*
Frank Adames *(Dir-Integrated Studio)*
Lisa Nickerson *(Acct Dir)*
Greg Kucher *(Dir-Integrated Presentations)*
Carter Rose *(Grp Dir-Acct)*
Diane Hernandez *(Exec VP & Grp Dir-Acct)*
Cynthia Gracia *(Grp Dir-Acct)*
Saki Hoshiko *(Project Mgr)*
Tom McConville *(Grp Dir-Creative)*
Ryan Karell *(Creative Dir)*
Matt Hankin *(Art Dir)*
Gabi Hastings *(Sr Dir-Art)*
Kirk Mosel *(Creative Dir)*
Eric Bellino *(Project Mgr-Digital)*
Chuck Borghese *(Creative Dir)*
Beth Stirling *(Assoc Dir-Media)*
Gillian Greene *(Coord-Fin)*
Beth Liss *(Grp Dir-Acct)*
Max Benington *(Grp Dir-Digital Production)*

Branch (Domestic):

Merkley + Partners/Healthworks (2)
200 Varick St Fl 12, New York, NY 10014
Tel.: (212) 366-3500
Web Site:
http://www.merkleyandpartners.com
Sales Range: $10-24.9 Million
Emp.: 200
Advertising Services
N.A.I.C.S.: 541810

Millsport (1)
1999 Bryan St Ste 1800, Dallas, TX 75201
Tel.: (214) 259-3200
Web Site: http://www.millsport.com
Sales Range: $10-24.9 Million
Emp.: 45
Advertising Services
N.A.I.C.S.: 541810

Branch (Domestic):

Millsport (2)
7575 Westwinds Blvd NW A, Concord, NC
28027
Tel.: (704) 454-5551
Emp.: 8
Advertising Services
N.A.I.C.S.: 541810

Novus Media Inc (1)
7900 Xerxes Ave Ste310, Bloomington, MN
55431
Tel.: (612) 758-8600
Web Site: https://novusmedia.com
Rev.: $500,000,000

Emp.: 130
Media Buying Services
N.A.I.C.S.: 541830
Margy Campion *(COO)*
Rob Davis *(Pres & CMO)*
Jon Madrid *(Chief Transformation Officer)*
Michael Buck *(CFO)*
Melony Rios *(CEO)*
Candi Atteberry *(VP-Client Svcs)*
Montrew Newman *(Sr VP & Head-Strategy)*
Bridgit Wallace *(VP-Media Investment)*
Jennifer Bunner *(VP-Analytics)*
Sarah Barber *(VP-Strategic Pricing)*
Paul DeJarnatt *(VP-Digital)*
Chris Aubin *(VP-Integrated Client Strategy)*

OMD Worldwide (1)
195 Broadway, New York, NY 10007
Tel.: (212) 590-7100
Web Site: http://www.omd.com
Sales Range: $150-199.9 Million
Emp.: 700
Media Communication Services
N.A.I.C.S.: 541810
John Osborn *(CEO)*
Monica Karo *(Chief Client Officer-Global)*
Stephen Li *(CEO-Asia Pacific)*
Damian Winstanley *(CMO-Global)*
Chrissie Hanson *(Chief Strategy Officer-
Global)*
Robert Habeck *(Chief Dev Officer)*
George Manas *(Pres & Chief Media Officer)*
Shreya Kushari *(Chief Client Officer)*
Scott Downs *(COO)*

Branch (Non-US):

OMD (2)
Oranienplatz 4, 10999, Berlin, Germany
Tel.: (49) 211167050
Web Site: https://www.omd.com
Emp.: 13
Media Communication Services
N.A.I.C.S.: 541810

OMD Australia (2)
Bay 7 2 Locomotive Street, South Eveleigh,
Sydney, 2015, NSW, Australia
Tel.: (61) 296922000
Web Site: http://www.omd.com
Emp.: 350
Media Communication Services
N.A.I.C.S.: 541870
Gavin Gibson *(Chief Strategy Officer)*
Aimee Buchanan *(CEO)*

OMD Beijing (2)
7F Tower A E Zone Li Xing Hang Center No
8 Guangshun South Street, Chaoyang Dis-
trict, Beijing, 100020, China
Tel.: (86) 1057755100
Emp.: 150
Media Communication Services
N.A.I.C.S.: 541810
Deric Wong *(Mng Partner-Strategy)*

OMD Canada (2)
1300-33 Bloor St East, Toronto, M4W 3H1,
ON, Canada
Tel.: (416) 681-5600
Emp.: 250
Media Communication Services
N.A.I.C.S.: 541810
Bruce Baumann *(Mng Dir)*

OMD Finland Oy (2)
Lintulahdenkatu 3, 00530, Helsinki, Finland
Tel.: (358) 102711640
Web Site: https://omdblog.fi
Emp.: 50
Media Communication Services
N.A.I.C.S.: 541810

**OMD Germany GmbH & OMD Dus-
seldorf GmbH** (2)
Grunstr 15, 40212, Dusseldorf, Germany
Tel.: (49) 211388070
Web Site: http://www.omdg.de
Emp.: 200
Media Communication Services
N.A.I.C.S.: 541810
Thomas Hinkel *(COO)*

OMD Guangzhou (2)
Floor 66 28 Zhujiang E Rd, Yuexiu Finan-
cial Tower, Guangzhou, 510610, Guang-
dong, China
Tel.: (86) 2038251088
Emp.: 85
Media Communication Services

N.A.I.C.S.: 541870

OMD Hong Kong (2)
Unit 808 Core E Cyberport 3, 100 Cyberport Road, Hong Kong, China (Hong Kong)
Tel.: (852) 29111668
Web Site: http://www.omd.com
Emp.: 130
Media Communication Services
N.A.I.C.S.: 541810
Deric Wong (CEO)

OMD Nederland (2)
Prof Wh Keesomlaan 4, Postbus 682, 1180 AR, Amstelveen, Netherlands
Tel.: (31) 207120000
Web Site: http://www.omd.com
Emp.: 100
Media Communication Services
N.A.I.C.S.: 541810

OMD New Zealand/Auckland (2)
Level 1 Eden 3 16 Normanby Road Mount Eden, PO Box 3709, Auckland, 1010, New Zealand
Tel.: (64) 96321500
Web Site: http://www.omd.com
Emp.: 70
Media Communication Services
N.A.I.C.S.: 541830

OMD Philippines (2)
11th Floor Bankmer Building, 6756 Ayala Avenue, Makati, 1226, Philippines
Tel.: (63) 2 889 8663
Media Communication Services
N.A.I.C.S.: 541830

OMD Shanghai (2)
11F 1788 Square No 1788 West Nanjing Road, No 1 Hong Qiao Rd, Shanghai, 200040, China
Tel.: (86) 2162633000
Emp.: 200
Media Communication Services
N.A.I.C.S.: 541810

OMD Singapore (2)
29 Media Circle alice Mediapolis Unit 11-02, Singapore, 138565, Singapore
Tel.: (65) 68766880
Web Site: http://www.omd.com
Sales Range: $125-149.9 Million
Media Communication Services
N.A.I.C.S.: 541830

OMD Turkey (2)
Talatpasa Caddesi No 5 Kat 3, Levent, Istanbul, 43494, Türkiye
Tel.: (90) 2122815454
Web Site: http://www.omd.com.tr
Media Communication Services
N.A.I.C.S.: 541810
Oguz Yavuz (CEO)

OMD UK (2)
90-100 Southwark Street, London, SE1 0SW, United Kingdom
Tel.: (44) 2030234500
Web Site: http://www.omduk.com
Emp.: 450
Media Communication Services
N.A.I.C.S.: 541830
Jessica Roberts (Chief Client Officer)
Vicky Fox (Chief Plng Officer)

OMD Vancouver (2)
1210-900 West Hastings St, Vancouver, V6C 1E5, BC, Canada
Tel.: (604) 640-4336
Media Communication Services
N.A.I.C.S.: 541810

Division (Domestic):

OMD-USA (2)
195 Broadway, New York, NY 10007
Tel.: (212) 590-7100
Web Site: http://www.omd.com
Sales Range: $100-124.9 Million
Emp.: 500
Media Communication Services
N.A.I.C.S.: 541840
Rolf Olsen (Chief Analytics Officer)

Branch (Domestic):

OMD Atlanta (3)
3500 Lenox Rd Ste 1200, Atlanta, GA 30326
Tel.: (404) 443-6800

Web Site: http://www.omd.com
Media Communication Services
N.A.I.C.S.: 541810

OMD Chicago (3)
225 N Michigan Ave 19th Fl, Chicago, IL 60601
Tel.: (312) 324-7000
Web Site: http://www.omd.com
Emp.: 250
Media Communication Services
N.A.I.C.S.: 541830

OMD Dallas (3)
1999 Bryan St Ste 2425, Dallas, TX 75201
Tel.: (303) 939-3111
Media Communication Services
N.A.I.C.S.: 541830

OMD Latino (3)
6205 Blue Lagoon Dr Ste 650, Miami, FL 33126
Tel.: (305) 341-2530
Media Communication Services
N.A.I.C.S.: 541810

OMD Los Angeles (3)
5353 Grosvenor Blvd, Los Angeles, CA 90066
Tel.: (310) 301-3600
Web Site: http://www.omd.com
Emp.: 100
Media Communication Services
N.A.I.C.S.: 541830

OMD San Francisco (3)
600 California St Ste 700, San Francisco, CA 94108
Tel.: (415) 229-8500
Web Site: http://www.omd.com
Emp.: 100
Media Communication Services
N.A.I.C.S.: 541830

OMD Seattle (3)
710 2nd Ave 13th Fl, Seattle, WA 98104
Tel.: (206) 344-3364
Web Site: https://www.omd.com
Emp.: 20
Media Communication Services
N.A.I.C.S.: 541830

Prometheus (3)
225 N Michigan Ave, Chicago, IL 60601
Tel.: (312) 324-7000
Web Site: http://www.prometheus.com
Emp.: 200
Media Communication Services
N.A.I.C.S.: 541830

Omnicom Canada Corp. (1)
655 Bay St Suite 1001, Toronto, M5G 2K4, ON, Canada
Tel.: (416) 922-0217
Advertising Agency Services
N.A.I.C.S.: 541810

Omnicom Capital Inc (1)
1 E Weaver St, Greenwich, CT 06831-5172
Tel.: (203) 625-3000
Financial Services
N.A.I.C.S.: 523999

Omnicom Europe Limited (1)
6th Floor Bankside 2 90-100 Southwark Street, London, SE1 0SW, United Kingdom
Tel.: (44) 2072987082
Web Site: http://www.omnicomeurope.co.uk
Emp.: 100
Advertising Agency Services
N.A.I.C.S.: 541810

Omnicom Media Group Asia Pacific Pte Ltd (1)
3 Anson Road 09-02 Springleaf Tower, Singapore, 079909, Singapore
Tel.: (65) 68766800
Media & Communication Services
N.A.I.C.S.: 517112
Paul Shepherd (Chief Investment Officer)
Tony Harradine (CEO)
Justin Low (Chief Comm Officer)
Bharat Khatri (Chief Digital Officer)

Omnicom Media Group Holdings Inc (1)
195 Broadway 8th Fl, New York, NY 10007
Tel.: (212) 590-7020
Web Site:
http://www.omnicommediagroup.com
Holding Company

N.A.I.C.S.: 551112

Subsidiary (Domestic):

Omnicom Media Group (2)
195 Broadway 8th Fl, New York, NY 10007
Tel.: (212) 590-7020
Web Site:
http://www.omnicommediagroup.com
Media Buying Services
N.A.I.C.S.: 541830
Florian Adamski (CEO)
Mike Cooper (CEO-EMEA)
Rochelle Chhaya (CEO-Thailand)
Claudine Kwek (COO-China)
Parweez Mulbocus (Head-E-Commerce)
Kiron Kesav (Chief Strategy Officer-Malaysia)
Eileen Ooi (CEO-Malaysia)
Kartik Sharma (CEO-India)
Anand Chakravarthy (Chief Growth Officer-India)

Omnicom Public Relations Group, Inc. (1)
1285 6th Ave 5th Fl, New York, NY 10019
Tel.: (212) 415-3072
Web Site: https://teamoprg.com
Public Relations & Communications Services
N.A.I.C.S.: 541820
Chris Foster (CEO)

Subsidiary (Domestic):

FP1 Strategies LLC (2)
3001 Washington Blvd 7th Fl, Arlington, VA 22201
Tel.: (202) 677-7060
Emp.: 125
Electronics Stores
N.A.I.C.S.: 449210

One & All (1)
3500 Lenox Rd NE Ste 1900, Atlanta, GA 30303
Tel.: (404) 522-8330
Web Site: http://www.oneandall.com
Advetising Agency
N.A.I.C.S.: 541810
R. Kevin White (Pres)
DeSean Brown (VP-Client Strategy & Success)
Jennifer Houston (Sr VP-Client Strategy & Success)

One & All (1)
2 N Lake Ave Ste 600, Pasadena, CA 91101
Tel.: (626) 449-6100
Web Site: http://www.oneandall.com
Advetising Agency
N.A.I.C.S.: 541810

Organic, Inc. (1)
12777 W Jefferson Blvd Bldg C, Los Angeles, CA 90066
Tel.: (415) 581-5300
Web Site: http://www.organic.com
Sales Range: $100-124.9 Million
Emp.: 30
Advertising Services
N.A.I.C.S.: 541810
David Bryant (Chief Creative Officer)

Branch (Domestic):

Organic, Inc. (2)
220 E 42nd St 12th Fl, New York, NY 10017
Tel.: (212) 827-2200
Web Site: http://www.organic.com
Emp.: 135
Advertising Services
N.A.I.C.S.: 541810

Organic, Inc. (2)
888 W Big Beaver Rd Ste 1100, Troy, MI 48084
Tel.: (248) 454-4000
Web Site: http://www.organic.com
Emp.: 5
Advertising Services
N.A.I.C.S.: 541810

Branch (Non-US):

Organic, Inc. (2)
360 Adelaide St W Ste 100, Toronto, M5V 1R7, ON, Canada
Tel.: (416) 874-7000

Web Site: http://www.organic.com
Emp.: 50
Advertising Services
N.A.I.C.S.: 541810

PHD (1)
220 E 42nd St 9th Fl, New York, NY 10017
Tel.: (212) 894-6600
Web Site: http://www.phdmedia.com
Sales Range: $125-149.9 Million
Emp.: 530
Advertising Services
N.A.I.C.S.: 541830
Patrick Ryan (Chief Comml Officer-Worldwide)
Luca Allam (Mng Dir-Dubai)
Clement Chung (Mng Dir-Hong Kong)
Gemma Teeling (Deputy Mng Dir-Ireland)
Jason Nebanzahl (Mng Dir-Ireland)
Jyoti Kumar Bansal (CEO-India)
James Hawkins (CEO-Asia Pacific)
Geri Hsu (Gen Mgr-Taiwan)
Simon Pugh (Pres-West Coast)
Mary Carpenter (Pres-Midwest)
Robert DiGiovanni (Pres-East Coast)
Stacy Deriso (Co-COO)
Will Wiseman (Chief Strategy Officer)
Anthony Koziarski (Chief Media Officer)
Frederick Stallings (Chief Data & Analytics Officer)
Bill Neblock (CFO)
Nathan Brown (CEO)
Jen Park (Head-Content)
Jonathan Anselmo (Chief Innovation Officer)
Josh Palau (Chief Media & Activation Officer)
Katie Klein (Pres-Integrated Investment)
Mike Roca (Head-Culture)
Mike Solomon (Co-COO)
Risa Sanchez (Head-Diversity & Inclusion)
Sarah Clayton (Head-Commerce)
Shaina Boone (Chief Data & Analytics Officer)
Sonny Dicamilo (Head-HR)
Tracy Richards (Exec Dir-Bus Dev & Mktg)
Avin Narasimhan (Co-Chief Strategy Officer)
David Soo (Mng Dir-Malaysia)
Antony Yiu (CEO-Hong Kong)

Branch (Domestic):

PHD Chicago (2)
225 N Michigan Ave 20th Fl, Chicago, IL 60601
Tel.: (312) 881-1100
Web Site: http://www.phdmedia.com
Emp.: 32
Advertising Services
N.A.I.C.S.: 541810

Branch (Non-US):

PHD China (2)
12F Eco City No 1788 West Nanjing Road, Shanghai, 200040, China
Tel.: (86) 216263 3500
Emp.: 200
Advertising Services
N.A.I.C.S.: 541810
Lars Bjorge (Chief Digital Officer-Greater China)
Mark Bowling (Chief Strategy Officer)
Ge Yun (Head-Innovation & Content)
Jonah Brown (Grp Dir-Strategy)
Linda Hou (Dir-Strategy)
Renee Zhang (Dir-Strategy)
Anna Chitty (CEO)
James Zhu (Mng Dir)
Sandy Tan (Mng Dir-Ops-Data & Tech Integration)
Ian Dolan (Head-Strategy & Plng-United Arab Emirates)
Nancy Yang (Grp Dir-Strategy)
Jordan Heathfield (Dir-Strategy-Digital Solutions)
Susan Suo (Gen Mgr-Global Bus)
Jim Lerch (Mng Partner)

Branch (Domestic):

PHD Detroit (2)
900 Tower Dr, Troy, MI 48098
Tel.: (248) 925-5000
Emp.: 155
Advertising Services
N.A.I.C.S.: 541830

PHD Los Angeles (2)

Omnicom Group Inc.—(Continued)

12777 W Jefferson Blvd Bldg C, Los Angeles, CA 90066
Tel.: (310) 405-8700
Emp.: 50
Media Planning
N.A.I.C.S.: 541830

PHD New York (2)
220 E 42nd St 9th Fl, New York, NY 10017-5806
Tel.: (212) 894-6600
Web Site: http://www.phdmedia.com
Emp.: 100
Advertising Services
N.A.I.C.S.: 541810

Branch (Non-US):

PHD New Zealand (2)
Level 2 Eden Business Centre 14 Normanby Road Mt Eden, 385 Queen St, Auckland, 1024, New Zealand
Tel.: (64) 96381200
Emp.: 70
Advertising Services
N.A.I.C.S.: 541810
Nikki Grafton (CEO)
Lee-ann Morris (Mng Dir)
Christophe Spencer (CTO)
Scott Keddie (Chief Investment Officer)
Penny Harvie (Dir-Ops-Grp)
Simon Bird (Chief Product & Strategy Officer)
Rachel Bayfield (Chief Tech & Innovation Officer)

Branch (Domestic):

PHD San Francisco (2)
600 California St 7th Fl, San Francisco, CA 94109
Tel.: (415) 356-1300
Emp.: 30
Media Buying Services
N.A.I.C.S.: 541830

Branch (Non-US):

PHD Toronto (2)
96 Spadina Avenue 7 th floor, Toronto, M5V 2J6, ON, Canada
Tel.: (416) 922-0217
Web Site: http://www.phdca.com
Emp.: 135
Advertising Services
N.A.I.C.S.: 541810
Fred Auchterlonie (Exec VP-Client Ops)
Michael Bolt (VP-Client Svcs)
Angie Genovese (VP-Client Svcs)
Caroline Moul (Pres)
Matt Devlin (Mng Dir-Mktg Science)
Christina Laczka (Mng Dir-Investment & VP)

Touche PHD (2)
3575 Boul Saint Laurent Bureau, Montreal, H2X 2T7, QC, Canada
Tel.: (514) 286-9000
Web Site: http://www.touchephd.com
Sales Range: $10-24.9 Million
Emp.: 70
Advertising Services
N.A.I.C.S.: 541810

PHD Media UK (1)
Bankside 2 90-100 Southwark Street, Chenies St, London, SE1 0SW, United Kingdom
Tel.: (44) 2074460555
Web Site: http://www.phd.co.uk
Sales Range: $50-74.9 Million
Emp.: 350
Advertising Services
N.A.I.C.S.: 541810
Verica Djurdjevic (CEO)
Malcolm Devoy (Chief Strategy Officer-EMEA)
Euan Hudghton (Chief Brand & Experience Officer)
Hattie Whiting (Chief Client Officer)
Lucy Formosa Morgan (Mng Dir-Magna)
Kirsten Oates (Partner-People Bus & Head-People)
Tom Blaza (Mng Partner-Acting)
Chris Walsh (Chief Comml & Ops Officer)
Anna Hancock (Mng Partner)
Fergus Barnett (Mng Partner)
Jake Hayter (Mng Partner)
Lucy Holmes (Mng Partner)

James Appleby (Mng Partner)
Sarah Nugent (Mng Partner)
Damien Glackin (Fin Dir)
Emma Flaxman (Dir-Mktg & New Bus)
Hugh Cameron (Chm)
Mike Florence (Chief Strategy Officer)

Branch (Non-US):

PHD Canada (2)
33 Bloor St Suite 1300, Toronto, M4W 1A6, ON, Canada
Tel.: (416) 922-0217
Web Site: http://www.phdmedia.com
Sales Range: $75-99.9 Million
Emp.: 150
Advertising Services
N.A.I.C.S.: 541870
Fred Auchterlonie (Exec VP-Client Ops-Toronto)

Porter Novelli (1)
220 E 42nd St 11th Fl, New York, NY 00017
Tel.: (212) 601-8000
Web Site: http://www.porternovelli.com
Sales Range: $75-99.9 Million
Public Relations Services
N.A.I.C.S.: 541820
Karen Ovseyevitz (Pres & Partner-Latin America)
Kate Cusick (CMO)
Ravi Sunnak (Exec VP-Sustainable Dev Goals)
Patrick Resk (CFO)
Sean Smith (Exec VP-Reputation)
Jana Thomas (Exec VP-Organization Change & Effectiveness-Global)
Margaret-Ann Cole (Exec VP-Talent)
David Bentley (CEO)
Ayanna Robinson (Chief Client Officer-Global)
Stefanie Tuck (VP)

Branch (Non-US):

APRA Porter Novelli (2)
111 Georgi S Rakovski Str, 1000, Sofia, Bulgaria
Tel.: (359) 29814190
Web Site: http://www.apraagency.com
Emp.: 20
Public Relations
N.A.I.C.S.: 541820
Rumena Kazakova (CEO)

ATD Porter Novelli (2)
Bvar Artigas 1181, 11300, Montevideo, Uruguay
Tel.: (598) 2 401 44 45
Sales Range: $25-49.9 Million
Emp.: 17
Public Relations Services
N.A.I.C.S.: 541820

Argentina Porter Novelli (2)
Av del Libertador 6250 Piso 1, Buenos Aires, C1428ATB, Argentina
Tel.: (54) 52736450
Web Site: http://www.porternovelli.com
Emp.: 50
Public Relations Services
N.A.I.C.S.: 541820

Bangkok PR Porter Novelli (2)
622 Emporium Tower Floor 22/4 Sukhumvit Road, Klongton Klongtoey, Bangkok, 10110, Thailand
Tel.: (66) 26649500
Emp.: 14
Public Relations
N.A.I.C.S.: 541820
Hasan Basar (Partner & Mng Dir)
Chachadapa Vichitrananda (Partner)
Kanthicha Bunphokaew (Partner)

Bentley Porter Novelli-Shanghai (2)
International Rm 2012 Cloud Nine International Plz No1018 Changning Rd, Shanghai, 200042, China
Tel.: (86) 1058 6969 48
Web Site: http://www.porternovelli.com
Emp.: 400
Public Relations Services
N.A.I.C.S.: 541820

CM Porter Novelli-Scotland (2)
45 Hanover Str, Edinburgh, EH2 2PJ, United Kingdom
Tel.: (44) 1314703400

Sales Range: Less than $1 Million
Emp.: 5
Public Relations
N.A.I.C.S.: 541820

Centroamerica Porter Novelli-Costa Rica (2)
Centro Empresarial Via Lindora Piso 3, Detras del Centro Comercial Via Lindora, 12765-1000, San Jose, Costa Rica
Tel.: (506) 22054100
Web Site: http://www.porternovelli.com
Emp.: 30
Public Relations Services
N.A.I.C.S.: 541820

Centroamerica Porter Novelli-El Salvador (2)
85 Avenida Norte 619 Colonia Escalon, Antiguo Cuscatlan La Libertad, San Salvador, El Salvador
Tel.: (503) 25287300
Web Site: http://www.porternovelli.com
Emp.: 15
Public Relations Services
N.A.I.C.S.: 541820

Centroamerica Porter Novelli-Guatemala (2)
5 Av 5-55 Z-14 Edif Europlaza T2 Niv 10, Torre 2 Nivel 10 Oficina 1001, 1001, Guatemala, Guatemala
Tel.: (502) 3885100
Web Site: http://www.porternovelli.com
Emp.: 24
Public Relations Services
N.A.I.C.S.: 541820

Centroamerica Porter Novelli-Nicaragua (2)
Bo Julio Buitrago Delicias del Volga 2c al E 1c al N, Managua, Nicaragua
Tel.: (505) 2685017
Web Site: http://www.porternovelli.com
Emp.: 15
Public Relations Services
N.A.I.C.S.: 541820

Compass Porter Novelli (2)
Carrera 13 No 96 - 67, Bogota, Colombia
Tel.: (57) 17029686
Web Site:
http://www.compassporternovelli.com
Emp.: 12
Public Relations Services
N.A.I.C.S.: 541820

Coordinamos Porter Novelli (2)
Av Colon E4-105 & October 9 Solamar building 1st floor, Office 102, Quito, Ecuador
Tel.: (593) 2 252 6819
Web Site: http://www.coordinamos.com
Emp.: 12
Public Relations Services
N.A.I.C.S.: 541820
Rosa Alarcoa (CEO)

Dominicana Porter Novelli (2)
Filomena Gomez De Cova No 24, Ensanche Piatini, Santo Domingo, Dominican Republic
Tel.: (809) 274 6813
Emp.: 18
Public Relations Services
N.A.I.C.S.: 541820
Rosanna Camarena (Gen Mgr)

F&H Porter Novelli (2)
Brabanter Str 4, 80805, Munich, Germany
Tel.: (49) 89 121 750
Web Site: http://www.f-und-h.de
Emp.: 50
Public Relations Services
N.A.I.C.S.: 541820
Helmut Freiherr von Fircks (CEO & Mng Dir)
Christina Harvey-Duwe (Head-B2C & Dir)

FTC (2)
Chemin des Hauts - Crets 110, Vandoeuvres, 1253, Carouge, Switzerland
Tel.: (41) 223481411
Web Site: http://www.ftc.ch
Sales Range: Less than $1 Million
Emp.: 7
Public Relations Services
N.A.I.C.S.: 541820
Frederic Burnand (Partner)
Francois Huguenet (Partner)

Melina Vigliotta (Mgr-Project)
Fabien Wildi (Mgr-Project)
Nabila Bouzouina (Head-Geneva Office)

Farner Consulting AG (2)
Lowenstrasse 2, 8001, Zurich, Switzerland
Tel.: (41) 442666767
Web Site: http://www.farner.ch
Emp.: 50
Public Relations Services
N.A.I.C.S.: 541820

Farner Porter Novelli (2)
Aarbergergasse 56, Bern, 3000, Switzerland
Tel.: (41) 31 312 3311
Web Site: http://www.farner.ch
Emp.: 11
Public Relations Services
N.A.I.C.S.: 541820

Farner Teuber Communication (2)
Avenue Dapples 54, PO Box 655, 1006, Lausanne, Switzerland
Tel.: (41) 216147777
Web Site: http://www.ftc.ch
Emp.: 5
Public Relations Services
N.A.I.C.S.: 541810

Gitam Porter Novelli (2)
Gitam House 8 Raul Walenberg St, 69719, Tel Aviv, Israel
Tel.: (972) 3 576 5757
Emp.: 16
Public Relations Services
N.A.I.C.S.: 541820
Orna Gourell (Mng Dir)

Gullers Group Porter Novelli (2)
Stadsgarden 6, PO Box 7004, 103 86, Stockholm, Sweden
Tel.: (46) 86790940
Web Site: http://www.gullers.se
Emp.: 40
Public Relations
N.A.I.C.S.: 541820
Hans Gennerud (CEO)

IKON Porter Novelli (2)
41-45 Marinou Antypa Street Neo Heraklio, 141 21, Athens, Greece
Tel.: (30) 2106784350
Web Site: http://www.ikon-pr.gr
Emp.: 15
Public Relations Services
N.A.I.C.S.: 541820

Impact Porter Novelli (2)
Charles Malek Avenue Ashrafieh Tabaris 812 Bldg, PO Box 11-8483, Beirut, Lebanon
Tel.: (961) 1384622
Emp.: 75
Public Relations Services
N.A.I.C.S.: 541820

Impact Porter Novelli (2)
Ali Reza Tower 1st Fl Medina Road, PO Box 7242, Jeddah, 21462, Saudi Arabia
Tel.: (966) 126515566
Public Relations Services
N.A.I.C.S.: 541820
Tim Walmsley (Mng Dir)

Impact Porter Novelli Dubai (2)
21st Fl Emirates Towers, PO Box 19791, Dubai, United Arab Emirates
Tel.: (971) 43304030
Web Site: http://www.porternovelli.com
Emp.: 22
Public Relations Agency
N.A.I.C.S.: 541820

In Press Porter Novelli (2)
R Voluntarios da Patria 89, Botafogo, Rio de Janeiro, 22270-000, RJ, Brazil
Tel.: (55) 2137238080
Web Site: http://www.inpresspni.com.br
Emp.: 300
Public Relations Services
N.A.I.C.S.: 541820

InPress Porter Novelli-Sao Paulo (2)
Rua Henrique Schaumann 270 - 7 Andar, Jardim Paulista, Sao Paulo, 05413-010, SP, Brazil
Tel.: (55) 1133231520
Web Site: http://www.inpresspni.com.br
Emp.: 130
Public Relations Services
N.A.I.C.S.: 541820

Jop, Ove & Myrthu (2)
Kannikegade 18-1, Arhus, DK-8000, Denmark
Tel.: (45) 86 76 16 20
Web Site: http://www.jom.dk
Emp.: 28
Public Relations
N.A.I.C.S.: 541820
Kim Ruberg (CEO & Partner)
Erik Ove (Co-Founder)
Jorgen Pedersen (Co-Founder)

Jop, Ove & Myrthu (2)
Aldersrogade 5, 2100, Copenhagen, Denmark
Tel.: (45) 39 27 50 50
Web Site: http://www.jom.dk
Emp.: 30
Public Relations
N.A.I.C.S.: 541820
Jess Myrthu (Founder & Chm)
Soren Petersen (Partner)

KorCom Porter Novelli (2)
16F Daewoo Foundation Building 526
Namdaemoon-ro 5-ga, Jung-gu, 100-095,
Seoul, Korea (South)
Tel.: (82) 263661507
Web Site: http://www.korcom.com
Sales Range: $10-24.9 Million
Emp.: 32
Public Relations Services
N.A.I.C.S.: 541820

LHC Porter Novelli (2)
No 30 Patch Road 13th Floor Section 3,
Taipei, Taiwan
Tel.: (886) 6225787768
Emp.: 21
Public Relations Services
N.A.I.C.S.: 541820

Lynx Porter Novelli AS (2)
Wilses gate 6, 0178, Oslo, Norway
Tel.: (47) 23131480
Web Site: http://www.lynx.no
Sales Range: Less than $1 Million
Emp.: 8
Public Relations Services
N.A.I.C.S.: 541820

Martec Porter Novelli (2)
La Fontaine 36, Chapultepec Polanco,
11560, Mexico, Mexico
Tel.: (52) 5550103200
Web Site: http://www.porternovelli.com
Emp.: 83
Public Relations Services
N.A.I.C.S.: 541820
Karen Ovseyevitz (Partner & Pres-Latin America)
Sandra Kleinburg (Mng Dir)

Nords Porter Novelli (2)
40-24 Brivibas Street, Riga, 1050, Latvia
Tel.: (371) 67505285
Web Site: http://www.porternovelli.lv
Emp.: 10
Public Relations Services
N.A.I.C.S.: 541820

PR Pundit Porter Novelli (2)
505 Shah & Nahar Industrial Estate, Off Dr
E Moses Road Worli, Mumbai, 400018,
India
Tel.: (91) 22 40023074
Emp.: 17
Public Relations Services
N.A.I.C.S.: 541820

Branch (Domestic):

Porter Novelli (2)
3500 Lenox Rd Ste 1900, Atlanta, GA
30326
Tel.: (404) 995-4500
Web Site: http://www.porternovelli.com
Emp.: 50
Public Relations Services
N.A.I.C.S.: 541820
Conroy Boxhill (Mng Dir)

Branch (Non-US):

Porter Novelli (2)
600 999 Canada Place, Vancouver, V6Z
2T3, BC, Canada
Tel.: (604) 602-6401
Web Site: http://www.porternovelli.ca
Emp.: 4

Public Relations Services
N.A.I.C.S.: 541820

Porter Novelli (2)
Scheldestraat 122, 1080, Brussels, Belgium
Tel.: (32) 24212200
Web Site: http://www.porternovelli.com
Emp.: 25
Public Relations
N.A.I.C.S.: 541820

Porter Novelli (2)
Prof WH Keesomlaan 4, 1183 DJ, Amstelveen, Netherlands
Tel.: (31) 204065930
Web Site: http://www.porternovelli.nl
Emp.: 25
Public Relations
N.A.I.C.S.: 541820
Monique Botman (Mng Dir-Netherlands)

Porter Novelli (2)
Av Engenheiro Duarte Pacheco n 26 11 flr,
1070-110, Lisbon, Portugal
Tel.: (351) 21 313 61 00
Web Site: http://www.porternovelli.pt
Emp.: 10
Public Relations Services
N.A.I.C.S.: 541820
Mariana Victorino (Mng Dir)
Higenio Martenez (Mng Dir)

Porter Novelli (2)
Luchana 23 4th Floor, 28010, Madrid,
Spain
Tel.: (34) 91 702 7300
Web Site: http://www.porternovelli.es
Emp.: 70
Public Relations Services
N.A.I.C.S.: 541820
Higinio Martinez (Mng Dir-Madrid Office)

Porter Novelli (2)
Calle San Vicente Martir 16 3 5, 46002, Valencia, Spain
Tel.: (34) 96 394 39 42
Web Site: http://www.porternovelli.es
Emp.: 9
Public Relations Services
N.A.I.C.S.: 541820

Porter Novelli (2)
Arago 182 7 Planta, Barcelona, 08011,
Spain
Tel.: (34) 93 457 1300
Web Site: http://www.porternovelli.es
Emp.: 10
Public Relations Services
N.A.I.C.S.: 541820
Higinio Martinez (Mng Dir)

**Porter Novelli
Australia-Melbourne** (2)
3/650 Chapel St, South Yarra, 3141, VIC,
Australia
Tel.: (61) 392899555
Web Site: http://www.porternovelli.com.au
Emp.: 20
Public Relations Services
N.A.I.C.S.: 541820
Peter Kent (CEO)
Natalee Ward (Mng Partner)
Rhys Ryan (Mng Dir)

Porter Novelli Canada-Montreal (2)
3575 Boulevard Saint-Laurent Bureau 200,
Montreal, H2X 2T6, QC, Canada
Tel.: (416) 422-7200
Web Site: http://www.porternovelli.ca
Emp.: 2
Public Relations Services
N.A.I.C.S.: 541820

**Porter Novelli New
Zealand-Auckland** (2)
Zone 23 110/23 Edwin St Mt Eden, PO Box
108 188, Symonds St, Auckland, 1024,
New Zealand
Tel.: (64) 9 632 0500
Web Site: http://www.porternovelli.co.nz
Emp.: 15
Public Relations Services
N.A.I.C.S.: 541820
Louise Wright (Exec Dir)

**Porter Novelli Pte. Ltd. -
Singapore** (2)
20 Kallang Avenue Level 7A Pico Creative
Centre, Singapore, 339411, Singapore
Tel.: (65) 66714700

Web Site: http://www.porternovelli.com.sg
Emp.: 12
Public Relations Services
N.A.I.C.S.: 541820
Shafaat Hussain (Mng Dir)

Porter Novelli Sydney (2)
Level 2 Pier 8/9 23 Hickson Rd, Walsh Bay,
2000, NSW, Australia
Tel.: (61) 289872100
Web Site: http://www.porternovelli.com.au
Public Relations Services
N.A.I.C.S.: 541820

Porter Novelli Tasmania (2)
162 Macquarie St Level 3, Hobart, 7000,
TAS, Australia
Tel.: (61) 362242598
Emp.: 12
Public Relations Services
N.A.I.C.S.: 541820

Branch (Domestic):

Porter Novelli-Austin (2)
828 W 6th St 101, Austin, TX 78731
Tel.: (512) 527-9881
Web Site: http://www.porternovelli.com
Rev.: $50,000,000
Emp.: 20
Public Relations Services
N.A.I.C.S.: 541820

**Porter Novelli-Bay Area-San
Francisco** (2)
550 3rd St, San Francisco, CA 94107
Tel.: (415) 975-2200
Web Site: http://www.porternovelli.com
Sales Range: $10-24.9 Million
Emp.: 75
Public Relations Services
N.A.I.C.S.: 541820
Karen Ovseyevitz (Mng Dir)

Branch (Non-US):

Porter Novelli-Beijing (2)
Unit E01 7F Tower 1 Lei Shing Hong Center No 8 Guangshun South Street, Chaoyang District, Beijing, 100102, China
Tel.: (86) 1085658508
Web Site: http://www.porternovelli.com
Public Relations Services
N.A.I.C.S.: 541820

Branch (Domestic):

Porter Novelli-Boston (2)
225 Franklin St 10th Fl, Boston, MA 02210
Tel.: (617) 897-8200
Web Site: http://www.porternovelli.com
Emp.: 35
Public Relations Services
N.A.I.C.S.: 541820

Porter Novelli-Chicago (2)
225 N Michigan Ave 10th Fl, Chicago, IL
60601-7683
Tel.: (312) 552-6300
Web Site: http://www.porternovelli.com
Emp.: 4,000
Public Relations Services
N.A.I.C.S.: 541820
Eddie Garrett (Exec VP-Global Digital Strategies)

Porter Novelli-Ft. Lauderdale (2)
6600 N Andrews Ave, Fort Lauderdale, FL
33309
Tel.: (954) 331-6262
Web Site: http://www.porternovelli.com
Emp.: 15
Public Relations Services
N.A.I.C.S.: 541820

Porter Novelli-Irvine (2)
4 Studebaker, Irvine, CA 92618
Tel.: (949) 583-2600
Web Site: http://www.porternovelli.com
Sales Range: Less than $1 Million
Emp.: 5
Public Relations Services
N.A.I.C.S.: 541820

Branch (Non-US):

Porter Novelli-London (2)
31 St Petersburgh Pl, London, W2 4LA,
United Kingdom
Tel.: (44) 20 7853 2222
Web Site: http://www.porternovelli.co.uk

Emp.: 75
Public Relations Services
N.A.I.C.S.: 541820
Fenella Grey (Chm)
Jo Patterson (Deputy Mng Dir)
Nicole Yost (Deputy Mng Dir)

Branch (Domestic):

Porter Novelli-Los Angeles (2)
5353 Grosvenor Blvd, Los Angeles, CA
90066
Tel.: (310) 754-4133
Web Site: http://www.porternovelli.com
Emp.: 20
Public Relations Services
N.A.I.C.S.: 541820
Strahan Wallis (Mng Dir)

Branch (Non-US):

Porter Novelli-Paris (2)
39 Rue de la Bienfaisance, 75008, Paris,
France
Tel.: (33) 147429279
Emp.: 55
Public Relations Services
N.A.I.C.S.: 541820

Branch (Domestic):

Porter Novelli-San Diego (2)
3033 5th Ave 400, San Diego, CA 92103
Tel.: (619) 687-7000
Web Site: http://www.porternovelli.com
Emp.: 2
Public Relations Services
N.A.I.C.S.: 541820

Porter Novelli-Seattle (2)
925 4th Ave 21st Fl, Seattle, WA 98104
Tel.: (206) 727-2880
Web Site: http://www.porternovelli.com
Emp.: 26
Public Relations Services
N.A.I.C.S.: 541820

Branch (Non-US):

Porter Novelli-Toronto (2)
2 Bloor Street West Suite 2900, Toronto,
M4W 3E2, ON, Canada
Tel.: (416) 422-7200
Web Site: http://www.porternovelli.com
Emp.: 22
Public Relations Services
N.A.I.C.S.: 541820

Branch (Domestic):

Porter Novelli-Washington (2)
1615 L St Ste 1150, Washington, DC 20036
Tel.: (202) 973-5800
Web Site: http://www.porternovelli.com
Emp.: 120
Public Relations Services
N.A.I.C.S.: 541820
Joe Farren (Mng Dir)

Branch (Non-US):

**Quasar Comunicaciones Porter
Novelli** (2)
Av Del Parque 5339 Office 501, Huechuraba, Santiago, Chile
Tel.: (56) 2 580 8315
Web Site: http://www.qu.cl
Emp.: 24
Public Relations Services
N.A.I.C.S.: 541820

R.I.M. Porter Novelli (2)
36 bld 4 B Novodmitrovskaya st office centre Khrustalny, 127015, Moscow, Russia
Tel.: (7) 4957830826
Web Site: http://www.rim-pn.ru
Emp.: 34
Public Relations Services
N.A.I.C.S.: 541820
Igor Pisarsky (Chm & Partner)
Jacob Minevich (CEO & Partner)
Alexandra Boeva (Head-Mktg Comm Practice)
Tatyana Ruzina (Partner)
Andrey Sinitsa (Partner)
Anastasia Zaichikova (Partner)
Marina Konstantinova (Partner & CFO)
Elena Malyvanova (Acct Dir)

RU&A Porter Novelli (2)

Omnicom Group Inc.—(Continued)

Samuel Lewis Avenue Plaza Obarrio Building 2nd Floor Office 210, PO Box 8321014, Avenida Samuel Lewis, Panama, Panama
Tel.: (507) 2650560
Web Site: http://www.ruapn.com
Emp.: 60
Public Relations Services
N.A.I.C.S.: 541810
Rossana Uribe (Pres)

Report Porter Novelli (2)
Piazza Grandi Giuseppe 24, 20129, Milan, Italy
Tel.: (39) 02 701 5161
Sales Range: $75-99.9 Million
Emp.: 17
Public Relations
N.A.I.C.S.: 541820
Natale Pierluigi Arcuri (Mng Dir)

Report Porter Novelli-Rome (2)
Via Poli 29, 00187, Rome, Italy
Tel.: (39) 06 699 2 4578
Emp.: 6
Public Relations Services
N.A.I.C.S.: 541820
Natale Pierluigi Arcuri (CEO-Responsible Report Porter Novelli)

SPEM Communication Group (2)
Ulica Skofa Maksimiljana Drzecnika 6, 2000, Maribor, Slovenia
Tel.: (386) 2 228 44 30
Web Site: http://www.spem.si
Emp.: 25
Public Relations Services
N.A.I.C.S.: 541820
Tomaz Mihelin Ritlop (Gen Mgr)

SPEM Porter Novelli-Croatia (2)
Savska 41, Zagreb, 10000, Croatia
Tel.: (385) 16121726
Web Site: http://www.spem-group.com
Emp.: 40
Public Relations Services
N.A.I.C.S.: 541820

The PRactice Porter Novelli (2)
No 43 2nd Floor 80 Feet Road HAL 2nd Stage Indiranagar, Airport Rd, Bengaluru, 560 038, India
Tel.: (91) 8042504242
Web Site: http://www.the-practice.net
Emp.: 70
Public Relations Services
N.A.I.C.S.: 541820

Branch (Domestic):

Voce Communications (2)
75 E Santa Clara St 7th fl, San Jose, CA 95113
Tel.: (408) 738-7840
Web Site: http://vocecommunications.com
Emp.: 40
Public Relations Services
N.A.I.C.S.: 541820
Dave Black (Co-Founder)

RAPP (1)
437 Madison Ave 3rd Fl, New York, NY 10022
Tel.: (212) 817-6800
Web Site: http://www.rapp.com
Sales Range: $350-399.9 Million
Emp.: 2,000
Advertising Services
N.A.I.C.S.: 541810
Marco Scognamiglio (CEO)
Anne Marie Neal (CMO-Global)
Perri Grinberg (VP-HR)
Moa Netto (Chief Creative Officer)
Shari Reichenberg (Mng Dir)

Branch (Non-US):

AID-Analyse Informatique de Donnees (2)
4 Rue Henri Le Sidamer, 78000, Versailles, France
Tel.: (33) 139239301
Web Site: http://www.aid.fr
Sales Range: $10-24.9 Million
Emp.: 40
Direct Marketing Services
N.A.I.C.S.: 541810

Brummel Kanepi Pirita (2)
Raua 14-4, 10124, Tallinn, Estonia

Tel.: (372) 6278760
Web Site: http://www.bkp.ee
Emp.: 12
Direct Marketing Services
N.A.I.C.S.: 541810

Subsidiary (Non-US):

Haygarth Communications Limited (2)
28-31 High Street, Wimbledon Village, London, SW19 5BY, United Kingdom
Tel.: (44) 2089713300
Web Site: https://www.haygarth.co.uk
Emp.: 100
Marketing Services
N.A.I.C.S.: 541810
Marcus Sandwith (CEO)
Steven Gray (Co-Mng Dir)
Steve Rogers (Chief Creative Officer)
Charlotte Amos (Co-Mng Dir)
Mark Watkins (Dir-Fin)

Branch (Non-US):

Marketing Power Rapp (2)
Sint-Huibrechtsstraat 17, 1150, Brussels, Sint-Pieters-Woluwe, Belgium
Tel.: (32) 27612814
Web Site: http://www.marketingpower.be
Emp.: 20
Marketing Services
N.A.I.C.S.: 541810

Branch (Domestic):

Optima Direct, Inc. (2)
8618 Westwood Ctr Dr Ste 400, Vienna, VA 22182
Tel.: (703) 918-9000
Sales Range: $25-49.9 Million
Emp.: 40
Advertising Services
N.A.I.C.S.: 541810

Branch (Non-US):

Rapp Argentina (2)
Minones 1856, Buenos Aires, 1428, Argentina
Tel.: (54) 1155547277
Web Site: http://www.rappargentina.com.ar
Emp.: 100
Marketing Services
N.A.I.C.S.: 541810
Connie Benuru (CEO)

Rapp Barcelona (2)
Enrique Granados 86-88, 08008, Barcelona, Spain
Tel.: (34) 93 238 9010
Web Site: http://www.rappcollins.com
Emp.: 25
Marketing Services
N.A.I.C.S.: 541810

Rapp Brazil (2)
Rua Alexandre Dumas 2 200 - 6 andar Chacara Santo Antonio, 4 e 5 andares Itam Bibi, Sao Paulo, SP, Brazil
Tel.: (55) 11 3077 1300
Web Site: http://www.rappbrasil.com.br
Marketing Services
N.A.I.C.S.: 541810
Andre Pasquali (Chm)

Rapp Budapest (2)
Liget Center Dozsa Gyorgy ut 84/a, H-1068, Budapest, Hungary
Tel.: (36) 1 461 28 00
Web Site: http://www.rappcollins.hu
Emp.: 25
Marketing Services
N.A.I.C.S.: 541810
Zsuzsa Bator (Art Dir)

Rapp Centro America (2)
Barrio Tournon Del Parqueo del Centro Commercial, Publicidad Garneier Diagonal, El Pueblo 100 Meters North, San Jose, Costa Rica
Tel.: (506) 21 6222
Web Site: http://www.rapp.com
Emp.: 60
Marketing Services
N.A.I.C.S.: 541810

Branch (Domestic):

Rapp Dallas (2)

7850 N Belt Line Rd, Irving, TX 75063
Tel.: (972) 582-2000
Web Site: http://www.rapp.com
Marketing Services
N.A.I.C.S.: 541810

Rapp Healthcare (2)
437 Madison Ave 3rd Fl, New York, NY 10022
Tel.: (212) 817-6800
Marketing Services
N.A.I.C.S.: 541810

Branch (Non-US):

Rapp Hong Kong (2)
Suite 1101 Cityplaza One 1111 Kings Road, Taikoo Shing, Hong Kong, China (Hong Kong)
Tel.: (852) 2838 0400
Web Site: http://www.rappcollins.com
Emp.: 9
Marketing Services
N.A.I.C.S.: 541810

Rapp London (2)
1 Riverside Manbre Road, London, W6 9WA, United Kingdom
Tel.: (44) 2078358667
Web Site: http://www.rapp.com
Emp.: 400
Marketing Services
N.A.I.C.S.: 541810
Marco Scognamiglio (CEO-Worldwide)
Carolyne E. Stebbings (Sr VP-Data & Tech Solutions)
Chris Freeland (CEO)

Branch (Domestic):

WWAV Rapp Collins West (3)
40 Berkeley Square, Bristol, BS8 1HU, United Kingdom
Tel.: (44) 1179041243
Emp.: 22
Marketing Services
N.A.I.C.S.: 541810

Branch (Domestic):

Rapp Los Angeles (2)
12777 W Jefferson Blvd Bldg C, Los Angeles, CA 90066-5644
Tel.: (310) 563-7200
Web Site: http://www.rappcollins.com
Sales Range: $10-24.9 Million
Emp.: 100
Direct Mail Advertising Services
N.A.I.C.S.: 541860
John Wells (Pres)
Paul Blockey (Sr VP & Dir-Experience Strategy & Design)
Michael Tinaza (Sr VP-Delivery)
John Cim (Sr VP Mktg Science US)
Jason Henry (Sr VP & Dir-Fin & Ops)
Hamish McCollester (Sr VP & Dir-Creative)
Thibault Dargeou (Mng Partner & Sr VP-Tech US)

Branch (Non-US):

Rapp Malaysia (2)
15th Floor Block B Meena Zurich 12 Jalan Gelenggang, Bukit Damansara, 50490, Kuala Lumpur, Selangor Darul Ehsan, Malaysia
Tel.: (60) 378065799
Web Site: http://www.rapp.com.my
Emp.: 70
Marketing Services
N.A.I.C.S.: 541810
Lim Wai Yee (COO)
Jeff Ooi (Creative Dir)

Rapp Mexico (2)
Ave Santa Fe 505 Floor 21 Office 21-132 Col Cruz Manca, 5349, Mexico, Mexico
Tel.: (52) 5552545880
Web Site: http://www.rapp.com.mx
Emp.: 25
Marketing Services
N.A.I.C.S.: 541810
Carlos Porras (Mng Dir)
Paul Garnier (Pres)

Branch (Domestic):

Rapp New York (2)
220 E 42nd St 12 Fl, New York, NY 10017
Tel.: (212) 817-6800
Web Site: http://www.rapp.com

Direct Marketing Services
N.A.I.C.S.: 541810
Marco Scognamiglio (Exec Creative Dir)
Perri Grinberg (VP-HR)

Branch (Non-US):

Rapp Paris (2)
162 rue de Billancourt, 92100, Boulogne-Billancourt, France
Tel.: (33) 153325757
Web Site: http://www.rappcollins.com
Rev.: $20,000,000
Emp.: 100
Marketing Services
N.A.I.C.S.: 541810
Philippe Bonnet (CEO)

Rapp Tokyo (2)
Hiroo Plaza 9th Floor 5-6-6 Hiroo, Shibuya-ku, Tokyo, 150-0012, Japan
Tel.: (81) 8033597287
Web Site: http://www.rappcollins.com
Marketing Services
N.A.I.C.S.: 541810

Rapp UK (2)
Floor 4 Bankside 3 90 Southwark Street, London, SE1 0SW, United Kingdom
Tel.: (44) 2037557168
Web Site: http://www.rapp.com
Rev.: $21,000,000
Emp.: 30
Marketing Services
N.A.I.C.S.: 541810
Chris Freeland (Co-CEO)
Al Mackie (Chief Creative Officer)
Shiona McDougall (Chief Strategy Officer-Global)
Carolyn E. Stebbings (Sr VP-Data & Tech Solutions)
Andy Rowe (Chief Mktg Science Officer)
Gabby Ludzker (Co-CEO)
Paul Tomlinson (CFO-Grp)
Chris Buckley (Sr VP-Bus Dev & Mktg)
Joe Braithwaite (Mng Dir)
Ed Freed (CTO)
Laura Sherwood (Dir-People)

Rapp UK (2)
Olympic House Birches Industrial Estate, East Grinstead, RH19 1EH, West Sussex, United Kingdom
Tel.: (44) 1342 33 6300
Web Site: http://www.uk.rapp.com
Emp.: 200
N.A.I.C.S.: 541810
Carolyn E. Stebbings (Sr VP-Data & Tech Solutions)
Al Mackie (Chief Creative Officer)
Chris Freeland (CEO)

Rapp Worldwide (2)
33 Bloor Street East 17th Floor, Toronto, M4W 3H1, ON, Canada
Tel.: (416) 972-7700
Emp.: 25
Marketing Services
N.A.I.C.S.: 541810
Paul Tedesco (Mng Dir)

RappData Company (2)
Av Juscelino Kubetischek, CEP 04543-000, Sao Paulo, SP, Brazil
Tel.: (55) 11 3077 1300
Web Site: http://www.rappbrasil.com.br
Emp.: 260
Marketing Services
N.A.I.C.S.: 541810

RappDigital Brazil (2)
Rua Alexandre Dumas 2 200 - 6 andar Chacara Santo Antonio, Sao Paulo, 04717-910, SP, Brazil
Tel.: (55) 1122221300
Emp.: 35
Marketing Services
N.A.I.C.S.: 541810

Branch (Domestic):

RappMedia (2)
220 E 42nd St, New York, NY 10017
Tel.: (212) 209-1600
Web Site: http://www.rappcollins.com
Emp.: 40
Direct Marketing, Media Buying Services
N.A.I.C.S.: 541810

Branch (Non-US):

TRACK (2)

Bernhard-Nocht-Strasse 113, 20359, Hamburg, Germany
Tel.: (49) 40339590
Web Site: https://www.track.de
Emp.: 260
Marketing Services
N.A.I.C.S.: 541810

Branch (Domestic):

The Kern Organization, Inc. (2)
20955 Warner Ctr Ln, Woodland Hills, CA 91367
Tel.: (818) 703-8775
Web Site: http://www.kernagency.com
Marketing Services
N.A.I.C.S.: 541810
Russell Kern (Founder & CEO)
Desmond Burrows (Exec Creative Dir)
Camilla Grozian-Lorentzen (Exec VP)
Nick Lavacca (VP-Ops)
Lynn Farely (CFO & COO)
Van Tran (VP-Strategy & Digital Svcs)

Branch (Non-US):

WWAV (2)
Ellermanstraat 23, PO Box 2024, 1114 AK, Amsterdam, Netherlands
Tel.: (31) 205715871
Web Site: https://www.wwav.nl
Emp.: 20
Marketing Services
N.A.I.C.S.: 541810
Ard Lok (Partner)
Erik van Benten (Dir-Production)
Wieb van de Donk (Mng Dir)
Marie-Claire de Waal (Partner)

Zebra Rapp Madrid (2)
Serrano 6 Atico, Madrid, 28001, Spain
Tel.: (34) 91 781 8700
Web Site: http://www.rappcollins.com
Emp.: 25
Marketing Services
N.A.I.C.S.: 541810

Radiate Group (1)
225 N Michigan Ave Ste 2310, Chicago, IL 60601
Tel.: (312) 324-8980
Sales Range: $100-124.9 Million
Advertising Services
N.A.I.C.S.: 541810

Division (Domestic):

GMR Entertainment (2)
220 E 42nd St, New York, NY 10017
Tel.: (212) 515-1915
Web Site: http://www.gmrentertainment.com
Rev.: $8,000,000
Advertising Services
N.A.I.C.S.: 541810

Division (Non-US):

GMR London (2)
85 Strand, London, WC2R 0DW, United Kingdom
Tel.: (44) 207 554 1111
Web Site: http://www.gmrmarketing.com
Sales Range: $10-24.9 Million
Emp.: 50
Advertising Services
N.A.I.C.S.: 541810

Division (Domestic):

GMR Marketing LLC (2)
5000 S Towne Dr, New Berlin, WI 53151-7956
Tel.: (262) 780-5600
Web Site: http://www.gmrmarketing.com
Emp.: 355
Public Relations Services
N.A.I.C.S.: 541820
Tyson Webber (Pres)

Branch (Domestic):

GMR Marketing (3)
1435 W Morehead St Ste 190, Charlotte, NC 28208
Tel.: (704) 342-4450
Web Site: http://www.gmrmarketing.com
Sales Range: $10-24.9 Million
Emp.: 67
Advertising Services
N.A.I.C.S.: 541810

Tyson Webber (Pres)
Cameron Parsons (CEO)

GMR Marketing (3)
14931 72nd Pl NE Ste A, Kenmore, WA 98028
Tel.: (206) 529-4891
Web Site: http://www.gmrmarketing.com
Emp.: 850
Advertising Services
N.A.I.C.S.: 541810

Branch (Non-US):

GMR Marketing (3)
33 Bloor St E, Toronto, M4W 3H1, ON, Canada
Tel.: (416) 342-5500
Web Site: http://www.gmrmarketing.com
Advertising Services
N.A.I.C.S.: 541810

Branch (Domestic):

GMR Marketing (3)
488 Madison Ave 7th Fl, New York, NY 10022
Tel.: (212) 505-3636
Web Site: http://www.gmrlive.com
Emp.: 20
Advertising Services
N.A.I.C.S.: 541810

GMR Marketing (3)
225 N Michigan Ave 8th Fl, Chicago, IL 60601-6533
Tel.: (312) 324-8950
Web Site: http://www.gmrmarketing.com
Emp.: 40
Advertising Services
N.A.I.C.S.: 541810

GMR Marketing (3)
55 Union St 2nd Fl, San Francisco, CA 94111
Tel.: (415) 538-7500
Web Site: http://www.gmrmarketing.com
Emp.: 60
Advertising Services
N.A.I.C.S.: 541810

Branch (Non-US):

GMR Marketing Spain (3)
Aviador Lindbergh 3, 28002, Madrid, Spain
Tel.: (34) 91 570 5475
Web Site: http://www.gmrmarketing.com
Sales Range: $10-24.9 Million
Emp.: 45
Advertising Services
N.A.I.C.S.: 541810

Division (Domestic):

Pierce Promotions & Event Management (2)
178 Middle St Ste. 200, Portland, ME 04101
Tel.: (207) 523-1700
Advertising Services
N.A.I.C.S.: 541810

Branch (Domestic):

Radiate Group (2)
5000 S Towne Dr, New Berlin, WI 53151
Tel.: (262) 780-5939
Emp.: 7
Advertising Services
N.A.I.C.S.: 541810
Marc Smathers (Exec VP)
Rick Vander Heiden (CFO)

Red Urban (1)
Blumen Str 28, Munich, 80331, Germany
Tel.: (49) 896653200
Web Site: http://www.redurban.de
Sales Range: $25-49.9 Million
Emp.: 300
N.A.I.C.S.: 541810

Resolution Media (1)
225 Michigan Ave, Chicago, IL 60601
Tel.: (312) 980-1600
Advertising Services
N.A.I.C.S.: 541810

Rodgers Townsend, LLC (1)
200 N Broadway 12th Fl, Saint Louis, MO 63102
Tel.: (314) 436-9960

Web Site: http://www.rodgerstownsend.com
Sales Range: $25-49.9 Million
Emp.: 75
Advertising Agencies
N.A.I.C.S.: 541810
Crystal Merritt (Dir-Acct Plng)
Michael McCormick (Chief Creative Officer)
Andrew Dauska (CEO)
Angela Biebel (VP & Dir-Strategy)
Eric Nelson (VP & Dir-Media)

Sage Collective Inc. (1)
115 W Century Rd Ste 110, Paramus, NJ 07652
Tel.: (201) 350-1200
Web Site: http://www.sagecollective.com
Sales Range: $25-49.9 Million
Emp.: 21
N.A.I.C.S.: 541810

Serino Coyne LLC (1)
1285 Avenue of the Americas 5th Fl, New York, NY 10019
Tel.: (212) 626-2700
Web Site: http://www.serinocoyne.com
Sales Range: $10-24.9 Million
Emp.: 95
Advetising Agency
N.A.I.C.S.: 541810
Thomas Callahan (VP-Creative Strategy)
Catherine Reid (CFO)
Scott Yambor (VP-Media Svcs)
Leslie Barrett (Mng Dir)
Kimberly Hewski (VP-Res)
Gregory Corradetti (Pres)
Suzanne Tobak (Sr Dir-Events)
Matthew Upshaw (CEO)
Michael Hartman (Mng Dir)
Hailey Barton (Dir-Digital Media)
Christy Borg (Art Dir)
Simone Boyd-Decastro (Supvr-Client Acctg)
Preston Burford (Designer-Motion Graphics)
Anthony Catala (Creative Dir)
Jay Cooper (Exec Dir-Creative)
Bruce Council (Supvr-Media)
Matthew Dec (Asst Mgr-Events)
Cheri Fontanez (Mgr-Client Acctg)
Peter Gunther (Art Dir)
Kevin Hirst (Grp Dir)
Meghan Kerrigan (Dir-Digital Strategy)
Jonathan Laprade (Editor-Brdcst)
Diana Salameh (Dir-Mktg & Comm)
Heather Troy (Supvr-Visual Assets)
Jolene Malloy (Supvr-Print Production)
Rosa Monserrat (Supvr-Client Acctg)
Zhanna Kirtsman (Supvr-Accounts Payable)
Michael Luciano (Sr Editor-Brdcst)
Erin Privratsky (Project Mgr-Integrated)
Harper Yi (Mgr-Mktg)
Jenna Tatman (Mgr-Community-Interactive)
Danielle Boyle (Grp Dir)
Jon Erwin (Grp Dir)
Vanessa Javier (Grp Dir)
Marci Kaufman Meyers (Grp Dir)
Andrew Hemmings (Editor-Video-Interactive)
Erik Piepenburg (Editor-Features)
Maria Marrocchino (Dir-Integrated Production)
Calvin Walker (Dir-Content)
Grace Zoleta (Dir-Acctg)
Connie Wong (Coord-HR)
Tee Panton (Asst Mgr-Office)
Alex Diaz (Assoc Dir-Creative-Video)
Garth Wingfield (Assoc Dir-Creative)
Kat Marotta-Hertzfeld (Assoc Dir)
Kailey Smith (Supvr-Digital Media)

Sid Lee (1)
1505 5th Ave Ste 600, Seattle, WA 98101
Tel.: (206) 467-5800
Web Site: https://sidlee.com
Sales Range: $25-49.9 Million
Emp.: 125
Advertising Services
N.A.I.C.S.: 541810

Siegel+Gale (1)
195 Broadway 7th Fl, New York, NY 10007
Tel.: (212) 453-0400
Web Site: http://www.siegelgale.com
Rev.: $50,000,000
Emp.: 175
Advertising Services
N.A.I.C.S.: 541810
David B. Srere (Co-CEO & Chief Strategy Officer)
Jason Cieslak (Pres-Pacific Rim)
Rolf M. Wulfsberg (Dir-Bus Analytics-Global)

Brian Rafferty (Dir-Bus Analytics & Insights-Global)
Margaret Molloy (CMO-Global & Head-Bus Dev)
Johnson Gu (Gen Mgr & Exec Dir-Creative-Shanghai)
Molly Muldoon (Assoc Dir-PR)
Philip Davies (Pres-EMEA)
Kerry Held (Dir-Strategy-Employee Engagement)
Michael Gross (CFO)
Lori Almeida (Chief Talent Officer)
Zouheir Zoueihed (Mng Dir)
Lisa Kane (Grp Dir-Strategy)
Douglas Sellers (Exec Dir-Creative)
Matthias Mencke (Grp Dir-Creative)
Ben Osborne (Head-Insights-EMEA)
Billy Kingsland (Grp Dir-Brand Comm)
Gina Kim (Grp Dir-Brand Comm)
Lea Chu (Grp Dir-Naming)
Aaron Hall (Grp Dir-Naming)
Lauren Thebault (Dir-Activation & Brand Mgmt)
Steffanie Haase (Grp Dir-Creative Svcs)
Shana Orth (Grp Dir-Acct Mgmt)
Rana Brightman (Grp Dir-Strategy)
Matt Egan (Exec Dir-Strategy)
Amanda Bowers Wong (Dir-Design)
Amy Chen (Assoc Dir-Experience)
Brice McGowen (Assoc Dir-Creative)
Casey Seijas (Dir-Brand Comm)
Christie Ryan (Grp Dir-Acct Mgmt)
Clinton Clarke (Dir-Digital Creative)
Derrick Mead (Dir-Brand Comm)
Howard Belk (Co-CEO & Chief Creative Officer)
James Barnes (Dir-Experience)
Jared Fink (Grp Dir-Experience)
Kira Sea (Dir-Design)
Laura Marino (Sr Dir-Acct Mgmt)
Marc Desmond (Dir-Analytics & Insights)
Melanie McShane (Sr Dir-Strategy)
Mitesh Rathod (Mgr-Knowledge)
Nijel Taylor (Dir-Design)
Rafael Medina (Creative Dir)
Scott Buschkuhl (Creative Dir)
Patrick Gough (Mktg Dir)
Peter Competello (Sr VP-Bus Dev)
Regina Puno (Dir-Design)
Whitney Wortman (VP-Bus Dev)

Branch (Domestic):

Siegel+Gale - Los Angeles (2)
5353 Grosvenor Blvd, Los Angeles, CA 90066
Tel.: (310) 312-2200
Web Site: http://www.siegelgale.com
Emp.: 40
Advertising Services
N.A.I.C.S.: 541810

Signature Graphics (1)
1000 Signature Dr, Porter, IN 46304
Tel.: (219) 926-4994
Web Site: https://signaturegraphicsinc.com
Sales Range: $25-49.9 Million
Emp.: 100
N.A.I.C.S.: 541810

Singer Direct LLC (1)
800 Westchester Ave, Rye Brook, NY 10573
Tel.: (212) 209-1900
Sales Range: $25-49.9 Million
Emp.: 40
Direct Response Marketing, Media Buying Services, Media Planning
N.A.I.C.S.: 541830

Specialist UK Ltd. (1)
Embassy House Queens Avenue, Bristol, BS8 1SB, United Kingdom
Tel.: (44) 1179251696
Web Site: http://www.specialistuk.com
Sales Range: $10-24.9 Million
Emp.: 40
Advertising Services
N.A.I.C.S.: 541810
Niki Webb (CEO)
A. J. Howe (Dir-Creative)
Ross Wilkinson (Deputy CEO)
Philippe Crump (CMO)
Jill Fitzgerald (Controller-Fin)
Peter Wilson (Dir-Editorial)
Caron Parsons (Dir-Bus & Corp)
Janet Meadowcroft (Dir-Insight & Plng)
Jo Howell (Dir-Creative Svcs)
Luke Ellen (Acct Exec)

Omnicom Group Inc.—(Continued)

Charlie Michael *(Mgr-Acct)*
Cloe Roycroft *(Acct Dir)*
Sophie Thompson *(Mgr-Paid Media)*
Kate Winfield *(Sr Acct Mgr)*
Ciaran Pillay *(Sr Acct Mgr)*
Sarah Bowler *(Editor-Food Science & Mgr-Channel)*
Abi Grogan *(Mng Editor)*
Charlotte Williams *(Mgr-Acct-Corp Comm)*
Daisy Blacklock *(Editor)*
Dave Jones *(Head-Digital Strategy)*
Desmond Hinton-Beales *(Editor)*
Emily Cooter *(Mgr-Acct)*
Hannah Richards *(Head-Insight)*
Kevin Moir *(Head-Digital Design-Productions)*
Louise Fenerci *(Head-Pictures)*
Marisa Domizio *(Mgr-Digital Project)*
Matthew Colledge *(Editor)*
Matt Tuffin *(Editor)*
Nigel Morrison *(Mgr-Creative & IT)*
Paul Thornton Page *(Dir-Digital Dev)*
Pip Leyland *(Mgr-Production & Promo)*
Sharon Eves *(Mgr-Fin)*
Dan De Luca *(Mgr-Digital Dev)*
Esther Rees-Lamb *(Head-Digital Design-Front End)*
Ryan McMurtry *(Copywriter)*
Rosie Hayward *(Acct Mgr-Corp & Pub Affairs)*

Star Marketing Services   (1)
711 3rd Ave 11th Fl, New York, NY 10017
Tel.: (212) 801-8380
Web Site: http://www.starmsgroup.com
Sales Range: Less than $1 Million
Emp.: 12
Advertising Services
N.A.I.C.S.: 541810

Subsidiary (Non-US):

Critical Mass Inc.   (2)
1011 9th Ave Se Suite 300, Calgary, T2G
0H7, AB, Canada   (100%)
Tel.: (403) 262-3006
Web Site: https://www.criticalmass.com
Advertising Services
N.A.I.C.S.: 541810
Dianne Wilkins *(CEO)*

Branch (Non-US):

Critical Mass - London   (3)
100 Southwark Street Bankside 2, Holborn,
London, SE1 0SW, United Kingdom
Tel.: (44) 2086181750
Web Site: http://www.criticalmass.com
Advertising Services
N.A.I.C.S.: 541810
Andrea Lennon *(Pres)*

Branch (Domestic):

Critical Mass Inc.   (3)
2 Bloor Street West Suite 3200, Toronto,
M4W 3E2, ON, Canada
Tel.: (416) 673-5275
Web Site: http://www.criticalmass.com
Emp.: 100
Advertising Services
N.A.I.C.S.: 541810
Mark Ashbaugh *(Exec VP & Gen Mgr-Toronto)*

Branch (US):

Critical Mass Inc. - Chicago   (3)
225 N Michigan Ave Ste 700, Chicago, IL
60601
Tel.: (312) 288-2500
Web Site: http://www.criticalmass.com
Emp.: 105
Advertising Services
N.A.I.C.S.: 541870
Deb Pasquale *(Partner-Client & Exec VP)*
Lisa Penelton *(Exec VP-Strategy)*
Jocelyn Loria *(Exec VP-Fin)*

Critical Mass Inc. - New York   (3)
200 Varick St Ste 610, New York, NY 10014
Tel.: (917) 606-8000
Web Site: http://www.criticalmass.com
Advertising Services
N.A.I.C.S.: 541810
Darryl Braunmiller *(Exec VP & Gen Mgr)*

Unit (Domestic):

Innovyx   (2)

1000 2nd Ave Ste 900, Seattle, WA 98104
Tel.: (206) 674-8720
Advertising Services
N.A.I.C.S.: 541810

Branch (Domestic):

Innovyx   (3)
1660 N Westridge Cir, Irving, TX 75038
Tel.: (972) 582-2233
Advertising Services
N.A.I.C.S.: 541860

Branch (Non-US):

Innovyx   (3)
1 Riverside Manbre Rd, London, W6 9WA,
United Kingdom
Tel.: (44) 208 735 8649
Direct Marketing, Electronic Media, Interactive Agencies
N.A.I.C.S.: 541860

Branch (Domestic):

Innovyx   (3)
711 3rd Ave, New York, NY 10017-4014
Tel.: (212) 817-6812
Emp.: 1
Advertising Services
N.A.I.C.S.: 541810

Unit (Domestic):

SigmaWorks Group   (2)
54 Danbury Rd Ste 257, Ridgefield, CT
06877
Tel.: (212) 801-8360
Web Site: http://www.sigmaworksgroup.com
N.A.I.C.S.: 541810
Bernard Nneji *(Founder & Pres)*

Steiner Sports Marketing   (1)
145 Huguenot St, New Rochelle, NY 10801
Tel.: (914) 307-1000
Web Site: http://www.steinersports.com
Sales Range: $50-74.9 Million
Emp.: 100
Advertising Services
N.A.I.C.S.: 541810

Sterling Brands   (1)
195 Broadway 18th Fl, New York, NY
10007
Tel.: (212) 329-4620
Web Site: http://www.sterlingbrands.com
Emp.: 70
N.A.I.C.S.: 541810
DeeDee Gordon *(Pres-Innovation)*
Susan Cantor *(CEO)*
David Israel *(Chief Creative Officer)*
Peter Mundy *(COO)*
Kimberly Heath *(Chief Talent Officer)*
Terrica Gay *(Dir-Office Ops)*
Jessica Trief *(Chief Strategy Officer)*

TBWA Worldwide Inc.   (1)
220 E 42nd St, New York, NY 10017
Tel.: (212) 804-1300
Web Site: http://www.tbwa.com
Sales Range: $1-4.9 Billion
Emp.: 11,000
Advertising Agency Services
N.A.I.C.S.: 541810
Jean-Marie Dru *(Chm)*
Denis Streiff *(CFO)*
John Hunt *(Chm-Creative)*
Luke Eid *(Chief Innovation Officer)*
Troy Ruhanen *(Pres & Co-CEO)*
Jon Castle *(Pres-Clients-Global)*
Anaka Kobzev *(Head-Comm-Global)*
Ted Colgate *(CIO)*
Elaine Stein *(Gen Counsel)*
Philip Brett *(COO)*
Mehmet Cem Topcuoglu *(Pres-Intl)*
Jean-marie Prenaud *(Sr VP-Clients-Intl)*
Damasia Merbilhaa *(VP-Growth & Ops-Latin America)*
Paul Hosea *(Co-CEO)*
Tessa Conrad *(Dir-Ops-Global)*
Rhonda George-Denniston *(Dir-Talent Dev-Global)*
Mairead McCan *(VP-Fin)*
Nicolas Bordas *(VP-Intl)*
Chay Lee *(Exec Dir-Backslash)*
Theodor Arhio *(Dir-Creative & Content-Global)*
Juuso Myllyrinne *(Head-Performance Mktg-Global)*
Catherine Harris *(CEO-New Zealand)*

Amie Miller *(Chief Talent Officer)*
Agathe Guerrier *(Chief Strategy Officer-Global)*
Deepthi Prakash *(Product Dir & Mktg)*

Subsidiary (Non-US):

Agency.com   (2)
Kroonlaan 165 Avenue de la Couronne,
Ixelles, 1050, Brussels, Belgium
Tel.: (32) 2 789 39 39
Web Site: http://www.agency.com
Sales Range: $25-49.9 Million
Emp.: 200
N.A.I.C.S.: 541810
Gert Pauwels *(Mng Dir-Digital)*

Agency.com   (2)
Via Leto Pomponio 3/5, Lombardy, 20146,
Milan, Italy
Tel.: (39) 02 89 04 21
Web Site: http://www.agency.com
Sales Range: $25-49.9 Million
Emp.: 30
N.A.I.C.S.: 541810

Agency.com   (2)
7-9F 71 West Suzhou Road, Shanghai,
200041, China
Tel.: (86) 21 3353 1166
Web Site: http://www.agency.com
Sales Range: $25-49.9 Million
Emp.: 20
N.A.I.C.S.: 541810

CAMARA/TBWA   (2)
Somme 1612, 11500, Montevideo, Uruguay
Tel.: (598) 27073946
Web Site: http://www.camaratbwa.com
Sales Range: $25-49.9 Million
Emp.: 32
N.A.I.C.S.: 541810
Emir Camara Viera *(Pres)*

Cayenne/TBWA   (2)
Calle Federico Geraldino 60, Piantini, Santo
Domingo, Dominican Republic
Tel.: (809) 8095422635
Web Site: http://tbwa.com
Advetising Agency
N.A.I.C.S.: 541810

MAL/Tokyo   (2)
1-13-10 Shibaura, Tokyo, 105-0023, Japan
Tel.: (81) 3 5446 7400
Web Site: http://www.tbwa.co.jp
Sales Range: $75-99.9 Million
Emp.: 300
N.A.I.C.S.: 541810

Savaglio TBWA   (2)
Alicia Moreau de Justo 270 1st Floor,
C1107AAF, Buenos Aires, Argentina
Tel.: (54) 11 5252 1170
Web Site: http://www.tbwabuenosaires.com
Sales Range: $25-49.9 Million
Emp.: 50
Full Service
N.A.I.C.S.: 541810
Ernesto Savaglio *(Exec Dir-Creative)*

Group (Non-US):

**TBWA (Deutschland) Holding
GmbH**   (2)
Schanzenstrasse 56, 40549, Dusseldorf,
Germany
Tel.: (49) 211864350
Web Site: http://www.tbwa.de
Advetising Agency
N.A.I.C.S.: 541810
Alexander Milstein *(COO & Mng Dir-Worldwide)*
Madlen Grenzmann *(Exec Dir-Strategy)*
Matthias von Bechtolsheim *(Chm)*
Peter Kopecky *(CFO)*
Winfried Bockius *(Fin Dir-Austria, Germany & Switzerland)*
Benjamin Muller-Grote *(Mng Dir)*
Alexander Muhl *(Chief Digital Officer)*
Tobias Jung *(CEO)*

Subsidiary (Domestic):

DO IT!   (3)
Bahnstrasse 2, 40212, Dusseldorf, Germany
Tel.: (49) 211864120
Web Site: http://www.doit.de

Sales Range: $25-49.9 Million
Emp.: 50
Event Marketing
N.A.I.C.S.: 541810
Ercan Aslan *(Member-Mgmt Bd)*

Subsidiary (Non-US):

Design Center   (3)
Muellnergasse 31, 1090, Vienna, Austria
Tel.: (43) 1248880
Web Site: http://www.design-center.co.at
Sales Range: $25-49.9 Million
Emp.: 20
Logo & Package Design
N.A.I.C.S.: 541810

E-Graphics   (3)
Ul Rzymowskiego 34, 02-697, Warsaw,
Poland
Tel.: (48) 22 457 05 80
N.A.I.C.S.: 541810

Inverse   (3)
ul Rzymowskiego 34, 02-697, Warsaw, Poland
Tel.: (48) 22 457 0670
Sales Range: $25-49.9 Million
Emp.: 100
N.A.I.C.S.: 541810

LUNA TBWA Belgrade   (3)
Cara Dusana 10A, 11000, Belgrade, Serbia
Tel.: (381) 112624414
Web Site: http://www.lunatbwa.rs
Full-service Agency; Advertising
N.A.I.C.S.: 541810

LUNA TBWA Sarajevo   (3)
Fra Andjela Zvizdovica 1, 71000, Sarajevo,
Bosnia & Herzegovina
Tel.: (387) 33943800
Web Site: http://www.lunatbwa.ba
Marketing Advertising Agency
N.A.I.C.S.: 541810
Mair Oruc *(Mng Dir)*
Elma Karcic *(Office Mgr)*
Dejan Balaban *(Mgr- Pub Rels)*

Luna TBWA   (3)
Koprska 106a, 1000, Ljubljana, Slovenia
Tel.: (386) 12004170
Web Site: https://www.lunatbwa.si
Sales Range: $25-49.9 Million
Emp.: 33
Advertising Agencies
N.A.I.C.S.: 541810
Dali Bungic *(Mng Dir)*

TBWA Adriatic Region   (3)
Koprska 106a, 11000, Ljubljana, Slovenia
Tel.: (386) 1 200 4170
Web Site: http://www.luna.si
Emp.: 20
N.A.I.C.S.: 541810
Mitja Milavec *(VP)*
Janez Rakuscek *(Exec Creative Dir)*
Dali Bungic *(Dir)*

TBWA Athens   (3)
1 Flias & Salaminos 4 Streets, 15124, Athens, Greece
Tel.: (30) 2108125400
Sales Range: $25-49.9 Million
Emp.: 45
Full Service
N.A.I.C.S.: 541810

TBWA Belarus   (3)
Of 303 50 Lenin str, 220030, Minsk, Belarus
Tel.: (375) 297575912
Web Site: http://www.tbwa.by
Sales Range: $25-49.9 Million
Emp.: 9
N.A.I.C.S.: 541810
Oleg Romanov *(CEO & Creative Dir)*
Ivan Ponomariov *(Dir-Strategy & Integrated Comm)*
Nadya Prilutskaya *(Art Dir)*
Karina Shapovalova *(Mgr-Project)*

TBWA Budapest   (3)
Dozsa Gyorgy ut 84/a 5 em, Budapest,
1068, Hungary
Tel.: (36) 1 279 2800
Web Site: http://www.tbwa.hu
Sales Range: $25-49.9 Million
Emp.: 6
Full Service
N.A.I.C.S.: 541810

Torday Gabor *(Dir-Creative)*
Doris Danner *(Mng Dir)*
Kolipka Ilona *(Dir-Client Svc)*
Wolcsanszky Krisztian *(Art Dir)*

TBWA Copenhagen   (3)
St Kongensgade 59E, 1264, Copenhagen,
Denmark
Tel.: (45) 39278899
Web Site: https://en.tbwa.dk
Sales Range: $25-49.9 Million
Emp.: 20
Full Service
N.A.I.C.S.: 541810

TBWA EMCG   (3)
6/2 Presnenskaya embankment BC Mos-
cow City Empire Tower Floor 16, 123112,
Moscow, Russia
Tel.: (7) 4957758500
Web Site: http://www.emcg.com
Advetising Agency
N.A.I.C.S.: 541810

TBWA Estonia   (3)
Pamu mnt 139a, 11317, Tallinn, Estonia
Tel.: (372) 665 95 50
Web Site: http://www.tbwa.ee
Sales Range: $25-49.9 Million
Emp.: 18
Full Service
N.A.I.C.S.: 541810

TBWA Group Poland   (3)
ul Rzymowskiego 34, 05-077, Warsaw, Po-
land
Tel.: (48) 22 457 05 00
Emp.: 30
N.A.I.C.S.: 541810
Christian Lanier *(CEO)*

TBWA Health A.G.   (3)
Seefeldstrasse 19, 8008, Zurich, Switzer-
land
Tel.: (41) 449133131
Web Site: http://www.tbwa.ch
Sales Range: $25-49.9 Million
Emp.: 40
N.A.I.C.S.: 541810
Matthias Kiess *(CEO)*
Manuel Wenzel *(Exec Dir-Creative)*
Angelo Sciullo *(Dir-Creative)*
Danijel Sljivo *(Bus Dir)*
Stephanie Trachsel *(Dir-Strategie)*
Stephan Sliwensky *(Head-Digital)*
Tizian Walti *(Creative Dir)*

TBWA Interactive   (3)
St Kongensgade 59E, Copenhagen, 1264,
Denmark
Tel.: (45) 39278899
Web Site: http://www.tbwa.dk
Emp.: 50
Internet/Web Design
N.A.I.C.S.: 541810

TBWA Istanbul   (3)
Tanburi Ali Efendi Sok No 15, 34337, Istan-
bul, Turkiye
Tel.: (90) 2127075500
Web Site: http://www.tbwa.com.tr
Advertising, Marketing Agencies
N.A.I.C.S.: 541810
Ilkay Gurpinar *(Chief Creative Officer)*
Burcu Kayimtu *(CEO)*
Toygun Yilmazer *(Chief Strategy Officer)*

TBWA Italia   (3)
Via Leto Pomponio 3/5, 20146, Milan, Italy
Tel.: (39) 02499851
Web Site: http://www.tbwa.it
Sales Range: $25-49.9 Million
Emp.: 90
Full Service
N.A.I.C.S.: 541810
Marco Fanfani *(CEO & Country Mgr)*

TBWA Latvija   (3)
Arsenala str 3-3, Riga, 1050, Latvia
Tel.: (371) 67505310
Web Site: http://www.tbwa.lv
Sales Range: $25-49.9 Million
Emp.: 2
Full Service
N.A.I.C.S.: 541810
Sarlote Janovica *(Acct Mgr)*
Liene Birzniece *(Acct Mgr)*
Kristine Kalnina *(Dir-Client Svcs)*
Gunta Vilcane *(Dir-Acct)*
Oskars Laksevics *(CEO & Mng Dir)*

TBWA Merlin   (3)
Logofat Luca Stroici 3, Bucharest, 50908,
Romania
Tel.: (40) 722134032
Web Site: http://www.friends-tbwa.ro
Full Service
N.A.I.C.S.: 541810

TBWA Moscow   (3)
Paveletskaya square 2 p 1 floor 12,
115054, Moscow, Russia
Tel.: (7) 4955445949
Web Site: http://www.tbwa.ru
Advertising, Branding & Marketing Com-
pany
N.A.I.C.S.: 541810

TBWA PHS   (3)
Fredrikinkatu 42, 00100, Helsinki, Finland
Tel.: (358) 102704000
Web Site: http://www.tbwa.fi
Sales Range: $50-74.9 Million
Full Service
N.A.I.C.S.: 541810

TBWA PR   (3)
ul Rzymowskiego 34, 02-697, Warsaw, Po-
land
Tel.: (48) 22 457 06 80
Web Site: http://www.tbwa-pr.pl
Sales Range: $25-49.9 Million
Emp.: 13
N.A.I.C.S.: 541810

TBWA Praha   (3)
Frantiska Krizka 1/362, 170 00, Prague,
Czech Republic
Tel.: (420) 220 412 501
Web Site: http://www.tbwa.cz
Sales Range: $25-49.9 Million
Emp.: 40
Full Service
N.A.I.C.S.: 541810

TBWA Roma   (3)
Via Flaminia 495, 00191, Rome, Italy
Tel.: (39) 063322681
Web Site: http://www.tbwa.it
Emp.: 100
Full Service
N.A.I.C.S.: 541810

TBWA Sofia   (3)
4 Chervena stena Str, Sofia, 1463, Bulgaria
Tel.: (359) 29634822
Advetising Agency
N.A.I.C.S.: 541810

TBWA Switzerland A.G.   (3)
Seefeldstrasse 19, 8008, Zurich, Switzer-
land
Tel.: (41) 449133131
Web Site: http://www.tbwa.ch
Sales Range: $25-49.9 Million
Emp.: 50
Full Service
N.A.I.C.S.: 541810
Matthias Kiess *(CEO)*
Manuel Wenzel *(Exec Creative Dir)*

TBWA Ukraine   (3)
Pimonenka vul 13 Office No 6A/24, Kiev,
04050, Ukraine
Tel.: (380) 445947733
Web Site: http://www.tbwa.com.ua
Advertising Company
N.A.I.C.S.: 541810

TBWA Vilnius   (3)
Raugyklos str 3-10, Vilnius, 1101, Lithuania
Tel.: (370) 64037704
Web Site: http://www.tbwa.lt
Full Service
N.A.I.C.S.: 541810
Raimundas Daubaras *(CEO)*

TBWA Warszawa   (3)
Ul Rzymowskiego 34, 02-697, Warsaw,
Poland
Tel.: (48) 22 457 05 00
Web Site: http://www.tbwa-warszawa.pl
Sales Range: $50-74.9 Million
Full Service
N.A.I.C.S.: 541810
Christian Lainer *(CEO)*
Radek Kowalik-Miklaszewski *(Mng Dir-Bus
Dev)*

TBWA Wien   (3)
Dannebergplatz 16/2, 1030, Vienna, Austria
Tel.: (43) 1316000

Web Site: http://www.tbwa.at
Sales Range: $25-49.9 Million
Emp.: 25
Full Service
N.A.I.C.S.: 541810

TBWA Zagreb   (3)
Petrovaradinska 7, 10000, Zagreb, Croatia
Tel.: (385) 1 563 1166
Web Site: http://www.tbwa.hr
Full Service
N.A.I.C.S.: 541810

Subsidiary (Domestic):

TBWA/Group Germany   (3)
Schanzenstrasse 54, 40549, Dusseldorf,
Germany
Tel.: (49) 211864350
Web Site: http://www.tbwa.de
Communications
N.A.I.C.S.: 541810

Group (Non-US):

TBWA Asia Pacific   (2)
16 & 17/F Cambridge House Taikoo Place,
979 King's Road, Quarry Bay, China (Hong
Kong)
Tel.: (852) 2573 3180
Web Site: http://www.tbwa.com.hk
Sales Range: $25-49.9 Million
Emp.: 2,500
Regional Managing Office; Advertising
Agencies
N.A.I.C.S.: 551114

Subsidiary (Non-US):

Creative Juice G1   (3)
161/1 SG Tower 2nd Floor Soi Mahadle
Kluang 3 Rajdamri Road, Lumpini Pat,
Bangkok, 10330, Thailand
Tel.: (66) 26504546
Sales Range: $25-49.9 Million
Emp.: 129
N.A.I.C.S.: 541810
Johanan Sen *(Dir-Content Strategy-Kuala
Lumpur)*
Adlln Rosli *(Grp Head-Creative-Kuala Lum-
pur)*

TBWA Greater China   (3)
343 Jiao Zhou Road, Shanghai, 200040,
China
Tel.: (86) 2133531166
Web Site: https://www.tbwa.com.cn
Emp.: 11,300
Advetising Agency
N.A.I.C.S.: 541810
Antoine Gouin *(Mng Dir)*
Joanne Lao *(CEO)*

Subsidiary (Domestic):

TBWA Hong Kong Limited   (3)
16/F Cambridge House Taikoo Place 979
King's Road, Quarry Bay, China (Hong
Kong)
Tel.: (852) 28332033
Web Site: http://www.tbwa.com.hk
Sales Range: $25-49.9 Million
Emp.: 90
Full Service
N.A.I.C.S.: 541810
Silvia Hellbach *(Dir-Ops)*

Subsidiary (Non-US):

TBWA ISC Malaysia   (3)
15th Floor Block B Hp Towers No 12 Jalan
Gelenggang, Kuala Lumpur, 50490, Malay-
sia
Tel.: (60) 320808200
Sales Range: $25-49.9 Million
Emp.: 85
Full Service
N.A.I.C.S.: 541810
Sa'ad Hussein *(Chm)*

TBWA India   (3)
Millenium Plaza Ground Floor Tower 'B' Su-
shant Lok-I Sector-27, Gurgaon, New Delhi,
122 002, India
Tel.: (91) 12 4432 6666
Web Site: http://www.tbwaindia.com
Sales Range: $25-49.9 Million
Emp.: 50
Full Service
N.A.I.C.S.: 541810

TBWA Korea   (3)
7-12F J-Tower 538 Sinsa Dong, Kangnam
Gu, Seoul, 135-889, Korea (South)
Tel.: (82) 2 501 8888
Web Site: http://www.tbwakorea.com
Sales Range: $50-74.9 Million
Emp.: 200
Full Service
N.A.I.C.S.: 541810
Woong Hyun Park *(Chief Content Officer)*
Soowon Lee *(CEO)*
Sue Lee *(Head-DAN Seoul & Exec Dir)*
Gon Woo Yang *(Head-Plng2 Div & Exec
Acct Dir)*
Sang Ho Kim *(Exec Dir-Creative)*
Min Ky Jeon *(Head-BEING Plng Div & Exec
Acct Dir)*
Jae Woo Kim *(Exec Dir-Media)*
Won Bin Lee *(CFO)*

TBWA Santiago Mangada Puno   (3)
Unit 101 Three Salcedo Place Tordesillas
St, Salcedo Village Makati City, Manila,
1227, Philippines
Tel.: (63) 279438888
Web Site: http://www.tbwa-smp.com
Full Service
N.A.I.C.S.: 541810

TBWA Shanghai   (3)
9F 71 West Suzhou Road, Shanghai,
200041, China
Tel.: (86) 21 3353 1166
N.A.I.C.S.: 541810
Muriel Lechaczynski *(Mng Dir)*

TBWA Singapore   (3)
01-12 991C Alexandra Rd, Singapore,
119971, Singapore
Tel.: (65) 62255288
Web Site: http://www.tbwa.com.sg
Sales Range: $75-99.9 Million
Full Service
N.A.I.C.S.: 541810
Robin Nayak *(Chief Strategy Officer-
Southeast Asia)*
Alrick Dorett *(Chief Client Compensation
Officer-Asia)*
Ara Hampartsoumian *(CEO)*
Mandy Wong *(Mng Dir)*
Andy Grant *(Exec Creative Dir)*
Jolene Huang *(Dir-HR)*
Peter Etheridge *(Dir-Brand Grp)*
Mandy Goh *(Dir-New Bus & Talent Dev)*

TBWA Thailand   (3)
394 Block28 G Building Units G201-G301
Floor 2-3 Soi Chula7 Wang mai, Pathum
Wan, Bangkok, 10330, Thailand
Tel.: (66) 26877400
Web Site: http://www.tbwathailand.com
Emp.: 5
Full Service
N.A.I.C.S.: 541810
Rapeepun Sudharomna *(Exec Dir-Plng)*
Nualrat Chotikaranan *(Dir-HR)*
Narong Chokpiboonkarn *(Co-CEO & Exec
Dir)*

TBWA/ Group Vietnam   (3)
Web Site: http://www.tbwa.com.vn
Emp.: 100
Advetising Agency
N.A.I.C.S.: 541810
Tan Nguyen *(Mng Dir)*
To Lien Dinh *(Grp Dir-Creative)*
Kim Chi Nguyen *(COO)*

TBWA/Australia   (3)
137 Pyrmont Street, Pyrmont, Sydney,
2009, NSW, Australia
Tel.: (61) 285845500
Web Site: http://www.tbwa.com.au
Advetising Agency
N.A.I.C.S.: 541810
Paul Bradbury *(CEO-Australia & New Zea-
land)*
Nitsa Lotus *(Mng Dir)*
Evan Roberts *(Chief Creative Officer)*

TCP-TBWA Indonesia   (3)
Mulia Business Park T Garden, Jakarta,
12780, Indonesia
Tel.: (62) 21 797 6233
N.A.I.C.S.: 541810
Saumyajit Banerjee *(CEO)*
Chris Garbutt *(Chief Creative Officer-
Worldwide)*
Gavin Simpson *(Chief Creative Officer)*

Omnicom Group Inc.—(Continued)

Whybin TBWA (3)
288 Coventry Street, South Melbourne,
3205, VIC, Australia
Tel.: (61) 3 9690 8555
Web Site: http://www.whybintbwa.com.au
Sales Range: $25-49.9 Million
Emp.: 100
Full Service
N.A.I.C.S.: 541810

Group (Non-US):

TBWA Central Asia (2)
Tole Bi 83, Almaty, 050012, Kazakhstan
Tel.: (7) 273111017
N.A.I.C.S.: 541810

Subsidiary (Non-US):

TBWA Concept Unit (2)
TBWA 5 Harold Shodipo Crescent GRA
Ikeja, Lagos, Nigeria
Tel.: (234) 8091440559
Web Site: http://www.tbwaconcept.com
Direct Marketing
N.A.I.C.S.: 541810
Kelechi Nwosu (Mng Dir)
Omomeji Samuel (Head-HR & Ops)
Saheed Rasheed (Head-Fin)
Ranti Atunwa (Exec Dir-Creative)
Osibo Imhoitsike (Dir-Bus)

TBWA Costa Rica (2)
Diagonal to the Chamber of Commerce
Barrio TournOn, 3312-1000, San Jose,
Costa Rica
Tel.: (506) 21051700
Web Site: https://www.riot.cr
Full Service
N.A.I.C.S.: 541810

Group (Non-US):

TBWA Europe (2)
50/54 rue de Silly, PO Box 411, Boulogne-
Billancourt, 92100, France
Tel.: (33) 1 49 09 80 00
N.A.I.C.S.: 541810
Perry Valkenburg (Mng Dir)

Subsidiary (Non-US):

ARA Groep B.V. (3)
Kratonkade 3, 3024 ES, Rotterdam, Nether-
lands
Tel.: (31) 104057277
Web Site: http://www.ara.nl
Sales Range: $10-24.9 Million
Emp.: 40
Advetising Agency
N.A.I.C.S.: 541810
Alex van der Reek (Dir-Fin)
Andy Mosmans (Dir-Strategy)
Paul Kroef (Mng Dir)
Helmutt Vleugels (Dir-Creative)
Danielle Slieker (Mgr-Traffic)
Douwe Oppedijk (Dir-Acct)
Lon de Grunt (Dir-Creative)
Marion Marsman (Mgr-Acct)
Leon Bouwman (Dir-Art)
Kees Lieshout (Head-Digital)
Wietze Bosma (Mgr-Media)
Thea Slieker (Office Mgr)
Berend Blok (Acct Mgr)

Division (Domestic):

ARA Direct Communications (4)
Kratonkade 3, Rotterdam, Netherlands
Tel.: (31) 104057200
Emp.: 35
Advertising Services
N.A.I.C.S.: 541810
Alex van der Reek (Dir-Fin)
Andy Mosmans (Dir-Strategy)

ARA Interactive (4)
Kratonkade 3, 3024 ES, Rotterdam, Nether-
lands
Tel.: (31) 104057180
Emp.: 35
Internet/Web Design
N.A.I.C.S.: 541810

ARA M/V (4)
Kratonkade 3, 3024 ES, Rotterdam, Nether-
lands
Tel.: (31) 10 405 7100
Web Site: http://www.ara.nl

Emp.: 35
Corporate Identity
N.A.I.C.S.: 541810

Subsidiary (Domestic):

Auditoire (3)
44 rue Copernic, 75116, Paris, France
Tel.: (33) 156035703
Web Site: http://www.auditoire.com
Sales Range: $25-49.9 Million
Emp.: 150
N.A.I.C.S.: 541810
Cyril Giorgini (Co-Founder & CEO-
Worldwide)
Cyril de Froissard (Co-Founder & Mng Dir)
Amaury Germe (Dir-New-Bus)
Philippe Castanet (COO)
Antoine de Tavernost (Gen Mgr)

BDDP & Fils (3)
146 rue du Faubourg Poissonnière, 75010,
Paris, France
Tel.: (33) 1 53 21 28 00
Web Site: http://www.ecebardas.com
Sales Range: $25-49.9 Million
Emp.: 70
Full Service
N.A.I.C.S.: 541810
Marco De La Fuente (VP)
Guillaume-Ulrich Chifflot (Dir-Creative)
Laurence Petolat-Vivares (Mng Dir)
Celine Colin (Deputy Mng Dir)
Perrine Collin (Dir-Comm)
Christian Baujard (Dir-Strategic Plng)
Flore Maurice (Mgr-Admin & Fin)
Fabien Nunez (Dir-Art)
Arnaud Ibanez (Dir-Art)
Aurore De Sousa (Dir-Art)

Being (3)
50/54 rue du Silly, 92513, Boulogne-
Billancourt, France
Tel.: (33) 1 49 09 72 23
Web Site: http://www.being.fr
N.A.I.C.S.: 541810

Subsidiary (Non-US):

Bovaco (3)
Parkstraat 83, Hague, 2514 JG, Nether-
lands
Tel.: (31) 70 346 9705
Sales Range: $25-49.9 Million
Emp.: 25
Advertising Agencies
N.A.I.C.S.: 541810

Brain Box (3)
Mozartlaan 27c, 1217 CM, Hilversum, Neth-
erlands
Tel.: (31) 35 628 1870
Web Site: http://www.brain-box.nl
Sales Range: $25-49.9 Million
Emp.: 8
N.A.I.C.S.: 541810
Klaas Pieter Rieksen (Mng Partner)
Johan Sponselee (Mng Partner)

Downtown Action Marketing (3)
General Vetter Straat 82, 1059 BW, Amster-
dam, Netherlands
Tel.: (31) 20 589 8787
Web Site: http://www.tbwa.nl
Sales Range: $50-74.9 Million
Emp.: 200
N.A.I.C.S.: 541810
Helene Hoogeboom (Mng Dir-Downtown)

Subsidiary (Domestic):

Eq+ Worldwide (3)
52 avenue Emile Zola, 92100, Boulogne-
Billancourt, France
Tel.: (33) 149092535
Web Site: http://www.egplusww.com
Advetising Agency
N.A.I.C.S.: 541810
Pascal Mariani (CEO)

Subsidiary (Non-US):

HVR Group (3)
Lulofsstraat 55 - Unit 16, AL Den Haag,
Hague, 2521, Netherlands
Tel.: (31) 703463616
Web Site: https://www.hvrgroup.nl
Public Relations
N.A.I.C.S.: 541820
Patrick Dekkers (Partner)

Headline Publishing Agency (3)
Vorstermanstraat 14A, 2000, Antwerp, Bel-
gium
Tel.: (32) 3 260 08 30
Web Site: http://www.headlinepublishing.be
Sales Range: $25-49.9 Million
Emp.: 10
Print
N.A.I.C.S.: 541810
Anne Thys (Mng Dir)
Johan Copermans (Editor-in-Chief)
Valerie de Vooght (Mgr-Project)
Sophie Coppens (Mgr-Project)
Lies Schrevens (Dir-Art)
Ann De Beukelaer (Mgr-Project)
Marijke Aps (Mgr-Project)
Paul Thomas (Dir-Art)
Kathy De Vleminck (Copywriter)

Subsidiary (Domestic):

Jump (3)
23 rue des Grands Augustins, 75006, Paris,
France
Tel.: (33) 1 44 41 63 00
Advertising Services
N.A.I.C.S.: 541810

La Mode en Images (3)
5 rue du Cirque, 75008, Paris, France
Tel.: (33) 148049755
Web Site: http://www.lamodeenimages.com
Emp.: 25
N.A.I.C.S.: 541810
Olivier Massart (CEO)

Subsidiary (Non-US):

Maher Bird Associates (3)
The Stanley Building 7 Pancras Square,
London, N1C4AG, United Kingdom
Tel.: (44) 207 309 7200
Web Site: http://www.mba.co.uk
Sales Range: $25-49.9 Million
Emp.: 40
Full Service
N.A.I.C.S.: 541810

Subsidiary (Domestic):

Medias & Supports (3)
146 rue du Faubourg Poissonnière, 75010,
Paris, France
Tel.: (33) 1 53 21 22 40
Web Site: http://www.medias-
supports.bddpunlimited.com
Sales Range: $25-49.9 Million
Emp.: 10
N.A.I.C.S.: 541810
About Gilles (Pres)
Louis Housset (Deputy Gen Mgr)
Emma Slater (Deputy Mng Dir & Head-
Strategy)
Mark Varloy (Head Intoraoion)
Simon Price (Head-Brdcst & Dir-Client
Svcs)
Kirtsy Donkersley (Acct Mgr)

Subsidiary (Non-US):

Neboko Live (3)
Generaal Vetterstraat 82, 1059 BW, Am-
sterdam, Netherlands
Tel.: (31) 205715500
Web Site: http://www.tbwa.nl
Marketing & Advertising Services
N.A.I.C.S.: 541810

Subsidiary (Domestic):

Nouvelle Vague (3)
8 rue de Rieux building D, 44000, Nantes,
France
Tel.: (33) 251860800
Web Site: http://www.nouvellevague.fr
Emp.: 27
Full Service
N.A.I.C.S.: 541810
Manuel Cornet (Mng Dir)

Qualicontact (3)
38 Rue Mozart, 92110, Clichy, France
Tel.: (33) 141404000
Web Site: https://www.qualicontact.com
Sales Range: $25-49.9 Million
Emp.: 80
Telemarketing
N.A.I.C.S.: 541810

Subsidiary (Non-US):

Staniforth/ (3)

Parklands 825A Wilsmlow Rd, Didsbury,
Manchester, M20 2RE, United Kingdom
Tel.: (44) 161 919 8945
Sales Range: $25-49.9 Million
Emp.: 45
Public Relations
N.A.I.C.S.: 541820

TBWA Brussels (3)
Excelsiorlaan 75/77, 1930, Brussels, Bel-
gium
Tel.: (32) 26797500
Web Site: https://www.tbwagroup.be
Sales Range: $50-74.9 Million
Emp.: 150
Advertising Agencies
N.A.I.C.S.: 541810

TBWA Company Group (3)
Prof W H Keesomlaan 8, 1183 DJ, Am-
stelveen, Netherlands
Tel.: (31) 205715300
Web Site: http://www.tbwa.nl
Sales Range: $200-249.9 Million
Emp.: 240
Full Service
N.A.I.C.S.: 541810
Rik Ledder (CEO)
Patritia Pahladsingh (Mng Dir)
Geoff Coyle (Mng Partner)
Darre Van Dijk (Chief Creative Officer)
Natalie Gruis (Chief Strategy Officer)

Subsidiary (Domestic):

TBWA France (3)
50-54 Rue De Silly, BP 411, 92103,
Boulogne-Billancourt, France
Tel.: (33) 149098000
Web Site: http://wwwtbwa-france.com
N.A.I.C.S.: 541810

Subsidiary (Domestic):

TBWA Corporate (4)
52 avenue Emile Zola, 92100, Boulogne-
Billancourt, France
Tel.: (33) 149092525
Web Site: http://www.tbwa-corporate.com
Corporate Identity
N.A.I.C.S.: 541810
Jean-Charles Davin (Dir-Creative)
Emlyn Korengold (Pres)

TBWA FKGB (4)
162 Rue De Billancourt, PO Box 411,
92100, Boulogne, France
Tel.: (33) 149097010
Web Site: http://www.tbwa.fr
N.A.I.C.S.: 541810

TBWA Paris (4)
162-164 rue de Billancourt, PO Box 411,
92100, Boulogne-Billancourt, France
Tel.: (33) 149097010
Web Site: http://www.tbwa-paris.com
Emp.: 400
N.A.I.C.S.: 541810
Philippe Simonet (VP)
Benjamin Marchal (Exec Dir-Creative)
Faustin Claverie (Exec Dir-Creative)

TBWA/Compact (4)
9 Place Alfonse Jourdain the Caffarellis, PO
Box 1248, 31000, Toulouse, France
Tel.: (33) 561190202
Web Site: https://www.new-compact.com
Sales Range: $25-49.9 Million
Emp.: 50
Full Service
N.A.I.C.S.: 541810
Isabelle de Colonges (Dir)

TBWA/G1 (4)
162-164 Rue de Billancourt, Boulogne-
Billancourt, 92100, France
Tel.: (33) 1 49 09 70 10
Web Site: http://www.tbwa-france.com
Full Service
N.A.I.C.S.: 541810
Ewan Veitch (Mng Dir)

Subsidiary (Non-US):

TBWA Group (3)
Kroonlaan Ave de la Couronne 165, 1050,
Brussels, Belgium
Tel.: (32) 2 679 7500
Web Site: http://www.tbwagroup.be
Emp.: 200
Advertising Agencies

N.A.I.C.S.: 541810

TBWA Lisbon (3)
Av Engenheiro Duarte Pacheco 36 9, 1070-110, Lisbon, Portugal
Tel.: (351) 213223200
Sales Range: $25-49.9 Million
Emp.: 40
Advetising Agency
N.A.I.C.S.: 541810
Claudia Domingues (Dir-Client Svcs)
Luis Quinaz (Dir-Fin)
Ana Filipa Neves (Dir-Art)
Maria Ferreira Lima (Pres-PA)
Joana Heitor (Acct Dir)

TBWA Neboko (3)
Generaal Vetterstraat 82, 1059 BW, Amsterdam, Netherlands
Tel.: (31) 205715500
Web Site: https://www.tbwa.nl
Sales Range: $25-49.9 Million
Emp.: 250
Advetising Agency
N.A.I.C.S.: 541810
Patritia Pahladsingh (Mng Dir)
Geoff Coyle (Mng Dir)
Nishant Dogra (Chief Experience Officer)
Darre van Dijk (Chief Creative Officer)
Rik Ledder (CEO)

TBWA Paling Walters (3)
76-80 Whitfield St, London, W1T 4EZ, United Kingdom
Tel.: (44) 2075736666
Web Site: http://www.tbwapalingwalters.com
Rev.: $45,000,000
Emp.: 45
Advetising Agency
N.A.I.C.S.: 541810

TBWA UK Group Limited (3)
5Th Floor 85 Strand Strand, London, WC2R 0DW, United Kingdom
Tel.: (44) 2036669200
Web Site: http://www.tbwa.com
Sales Range: $50-74.9 Million
Emp.: 200
Holding Company; Advetising Agency
N.A.I.C.S.: 551112

TBWA United (3)
Generaal Vetterstraat 82, 1059 BW, Amsterdam, Netherlands
Tel.: (31) 205715500
Web Site: http://www.tbwa.nl
Brand Development
N.A.I.C.S.: 541810

TBWA/ALIF (3)
rue Najib Mahfoud 3rd floor, Cote D Emeraude, Casablanca, 20500, Morocco
Tel.: (212) 222798080
Web Site: https://www.tbwaalif.com
Sales Range: $125-149.9 Million
Emp.: 21
Full Service
N.A.I.C.S.: 541810
Souad Benyahia (Mng Dir)

TBWA/Dublin (3)
Kodak Building Blackberry Lane, Rathmines, Dublin, 6, Ireland
Tel.: (353) 14966920
Web Site: http://www.tbwa-dublin.com
Advetising Agency
N.A.I.C.S.: 541810

TBWA/London Limited (3)
Bankside 2 100 Southwark St, London, SE1 0SW, United Kingdom
Tel.: (44) 2036669200
Web Site: https://www.tbwa-london.com
Sales Range: $25-49.9 Million
Emp.: 142
Full Service
N.A.I.C.S.: 541810
Peter Souter (Chm)
Katie Jackson (Mng Dir)
Tim Noblett (Partner-Digital Strategy)
Poppy Manning (Head-Production)
Michelle Gilson (Head-Plng)
Alex Morris (Head-People)
Anna Vogt (Chief Strategy Officer)
Andy Jex (Chief Creative Officer)
Brian Swords (Partner-Client-Global & Head-Intl)
Marie Conley (Head-Plng)
Oliver Kunze (Dir-Intl Data)
Larissa Vince (CEO)
Melody Sylvester (Chief Production Officer)

TBWA/Manchester (3)
Canada House4th Floor 3 Chepstow St, Manchester, M1 5FW, United Kingdom
Tel.: (44) 1615215299
Web Site: https://www.tbwamcr.com
Sales Range: $25-49.9 Million
Emp.: 70
Full Service
N.A.I.C.S.: 541810
Fergus McCallum (CEO)
John Triner (Mng Partner-Client Svcs)
Gary Fawcett (Exec Creative Dir)
Lisa Nichols (Exec Creative Dir)
Paul Tinker (Dir-Fin)
Lorna Hawtin (Dir-Disruption)

Subsidiary (Domestic):

Textuel (3)
146 rue du Faubourg Poissonniere, 75010, Paris, France
Tel.: (33) 1 53 21 21 00
Web Site: http://www.textuel.fr
Sales Range: $50-74.9 Million
Emp.: 130
Business Publications
N.A.I.C.S.: 541810
About Gilles (Pres)
Laurence Vignon (VP)
Stanislaus Pajot (Dir Gen)

Textuel La Mine (3)
146 rue du Faubourg Poissonniere, 75010, Paris, France
Tel.: (33) 153212100
Web Site: http://www.icibarbes.com
Sales Range: $10-24.9 Million
Emp.: 25
Electronic Media
N.A.I.C.S.: 541810

Subsidiary (Non-US):

Thabasco (3)
Verlengde Hereweg 174, 9722 AM, Groningen, Netherlands
Tel.: (31) 50 319 9566
Emp.: 15
N.A.I.C.S.: 541810

Subsidiary (Non-US):

TBWA Frederick (2)
Avda Italia 850 2 Fl, Providencia, Santiago, Chile
Tel.: (56) 2 540 6700
Web Site: http://www.tbwachile.cl
Sales Range: $25-49.9 Million
Emp.: 50
N.A.I.C.S.: 541810

TBWA India (3)
Prestige Technostar 8th Floor B-2 Building, Doddanakundi Industrial Area 2 Phase 1 Doddanekkundi, Bengaluru, 560048, Karnataka, India
Tel.: (91) 8067999799
Web Site: http://www.tbwaindia.com
Emp.: 20
N.A.I.C.S.: 541810

TBWA India (2)
No 62 1st Fl 3rd St, Abhiramapuram, 600018, Chennai, India
Tel.: (91) 44 5211 2800
Web Site: http://www.tbwaindia.com
Emp.: 15
N.A.I.C.S.: 541810

TBWA India (2)
1st Floor, Kochi, 682020, India
Tel.: (91) 484 238 22273
Web Site: http://www.tbwaindia.com
N.A.I.C.S.: 541810

TBWA India (2)
1st Floor Survey No 368 Kole Kalayn Opp Grand Hyatt Vakola, Santacruz East, Mumbai, 400055, Maharashtra, India
Tel.: (91) 2269139999
Web Site: http://www.tbwaindia.com
Emp.: 80
Advetising Agency
N.A.I.C.S.: 541810
Govind Pandey (CEO)
Subramanian Krishnan (Chief Strategy Officer)
Pratul Gaur (CFO-Grp)

Parixit Bhattacharya (Mng Partner-Creative)
Antony Rajkumar (Dir-Strategy-Natl)
Ashwin Parthiban (Mng Partner-Creative)
Srijib Mallik (Exec Dir)
Namrata Nandan (Exec Dir)

TBWA India Corporate (2)
Unit 1 Ground Floor Tower B Millenium Plaza, Susahnt Lok Gurgaon, New Delhi, 122002, India
Tel.: (91) 124 432 6666
Web Site: http://www.tbwaindia.com
N.A.I.C.S.: 541810
Govind Pandey (CEO)

TBWA Oslo (2)
Drammensveien 130 C-22, 277, Oslo, Norway
Tel.: (47) 22 12 99 99
Web Site: http://www.tbwa.no
Sales Range: $25-49.9 Million
Emp.: 1
Full Service
N.A.I.C.S.: 541810

TBWA Peru (2)
San Ignacia de Loyola 150, Miraflores, Lima, 18, Peru
Tel.: (51) 1 243 1200
Web Site: http://www.tbwaperu.com
Sales Range: $25-49.9 Million
Emp.: 45
Full Service
N.A.I.C.S.: 541810

TBWA Raad (2)
Emaar Square - Burj Khalifa Building 1 Floor 6, PO Box 40604, Deira, Dubai, United Arab Emirates
Tel.: (971) 44258888
Web Site: http://www.tbwaraad.com
Sales Range: $25-49.9 Million
Emp.: 90
Full Service
N.A.I.C.S.: 541810
Ramzi Raad (Chm)

Group (Non-US):

TBWA South Africa Group (2)
3 Sandown Valley Crescent Sandton, PO Box 785203, Johannesburg, 2196, South Africa
Tel.: (27) 113223100
Web Site: http://www.tbwa.co.za
Sales Range: $50-74.9 Million
Emp.: 200
N.A.I.C.S.: 541810
Reg Lascaris (Owner)

Subsidiary (Domestic):

Magna Carta (3)
North Tower 4th Floor 3 Sandown Valley Crescent, Sandown, Johannesburg,*2196, Gauteng, South Africa
Tel.: (27) 117842598
Web Site: http://www.magna-carta.co.za
Sales Range: $25-49.9 Million
Emp.: 60
Public Relations
N.A.I.C.S.: 541820
Moliehi Molekoa (Mng Dir)
Mary Gearing (Deputy Mng Dir)
Hilary Macaulay (Head-Bus Unit)

TBWA AME MED (3)
3 Sandown Valley Crescent Sandown, Johannesburg, 2196, South Africa
Tel.: (27) 11 322 3280
Web Site: http://www.tbwa.co.za
Sales Range: $50-74.9 Million
Emp.: 200
Advetising Agency
N.A.I.C.S.: 541810
Reg Lascaris (Chm)

TBWA Durban (3)
Colchester Essex Gardens 1 Nelson Road, Westville Kwa Zulu Natal, Durban, 3630, South Africa
Tel.: (27) 31 267 6690
Web Site: http://www.tbwa.co.za
Emp.: 100
N.A.I.C.S.: 541810
James Porter (Chm)

TBWA Hunt Lascaris (Cape Town) Proprietary Limited (3)
74 Prestwich Street De Waterkant, Woodstock, Cape Town, 8001, South Africa
Tel.: (27) 214214804
Web Site: http://www.tbwa-africa.com
Emp.: 12
Advetising Agency
N.A.I.C.S.: 541810
Karabo Denalane (CEO)

TBWA Hunt Lascaris (Durban) Pty. Ltd. (3)
South End Nelson Road Essex Terrace, Durban, 3629, South Africa
Tel.: (27) 31 267 6600
Web Site: http://www.tbwa.co.za
Emp.: 160
Advetising Agency
N.A.I.C.S.: 541810
Sean Donovan (Mng Dir)

TBWA Hunt Lascaris (Johannesburg) Pty. Ltd. (3)
3 Sandown Valley Cres, Sandton, 2196, South Africa
Tel.: (27) 113223100
Web Site: http://www.tbwa.co.za
Sales Range: $10-24.9 Million
Emp.: 150
Advetising Agency
N.A.I.C.S.: 541810
Reg Lascaris (Founder & Partner)

Subsidiary (Non-US):

TBWA Stockholm (2)
Slupskjulsvagen 19, 111 49, Stockholm, Sweden
Tel.: (46) 841063080
Web Site: http://www.tbwa.se
Sales Range: $25-49.9 Million
Emp.: 35
Advetising Agency
N.A.I.C.S.: 541810
Kalle Widgren (CEO)

TBWA Tango/ Helsinki (2)
Fredrikinkatu 42, 00100, Helsinki, Finland
Tel.: (358) 102704000
Web Site: http://www.tbwa.fi
Advetising Agency
N.A.I.C.S.: 541810
Sami Tikkanen (Chm & CEO)
Marco Makinen (Exec VP & Strategist)
Taneli Mattelmaki (VP)
Juha-Matti Raunio (VP & Head-Innovations)
Anna Masalin (Head-Ops)
Mikko Pietila (Exec Creative Dir)
Miika Luoma (Dir-Media & Audience)
Juhana Hokkanen (Dir-Innovation)
Markus Nieminen (Dir-Creative & Content)
Erno Reinikainen (Creative Dir)
Laura Paikkari (Creative Dir)
Mikko Halonen (Creative Dir)
Ville Ohtonen (Creative Dir)
Jyrki Poutanen (Chief Creative Officer)
Kristiina Kalliokoski (CFO)

TBWA Venezuela (2)
Avenida Diego Cisneros Edificio Oficentro, Los Ruices PB Ofic F, Caracas, Venezuela
Tel.: (58) 212 235 1667
Web Site: http://www.tbwa.com.ve
N.A.I.C.S.: 541810

TBWA Whybin Limited (2)
11 Mayoral Drive, PO Box 7040, Auckland CBD, Auckland, 1010, New Zealand
Tel.: (64) 93666266
Web Site: https://tbwa.co.nz
Sales Range: $25-49.9 Million
Emp.: 100
Full Service
N.A.I.C.S.: 541810

Group (Domestic):

TBWA/Chiat/Day (2)
220 E 42nd St, New York, NY 10017
Tel.: (212) 804-1000
Web Site: http://www.tbwachiatdayny.com
Regional Managing Office
N.A.I.C.S.: 551114
Chris Rowson (Head-Design)
John Doris (Head-Integrated Production)
Amie Miller (Chief Talent Officer)
Nancy Reyes (Pres)
Walter Connelly (Exec Creative Dir)
Julia Neumann (Exec Creative Dir)
Amy Ferguson (Chief Creative Officer)
Al Merry (Exec Creative Dir)
Ricard Valero (Exec Creative Dir)

Omnicom Group Inc.—(Continued)

Sophia Barnett-Wiltshire (Dir-Ops)
Lauren Smiley (Dir-Bus-Design By Disruption)
Ulrich Proeschel (CMO-Global)
James Sowden (Chief Strategy Officer)
Chris Beresford-Hill (Chief Creative Officer)
Bradley Aplegren (CFO)
Amanda Davis (Head-Content)
Nancy Reyes (CEO)
Rori DuBoff (Chief Innovation Officer)
Shanon Wille (Assoc Dir-Creative)
Michael Boulia (Creative Dir)
Jim Nolan (Creative Dir)

Subsidiary (Domestic):

Brand Architecture International   (3)
488 Madison Ave, New York, NY 10022
Tel.: (212) 804-1000
Advetising Agency
N.A.I.C.S.: 541810

Cutwater   (3)
950 Battery St Fl 4, San Francisco, CA
94111
Tel.: (415) 341-9100
Web Site: https://www.cutwateragency.com
Sales Range: $25-49.9 Million
Emp.: 45
Advetising Agency
N.A.I.C.S.: 541810
Christian Hughes (Pres & Principal)

Unit (Domestic):

EJE TBWA   (3)
PO Box 195006, San Juan, PR 00919
Tel.: (787) 766-7140
Sales Range: $25-49.9 Million
Emp.: 82
Advetising Agency
N.A.I.C.S.: 541810
Edgardo Rivera (Pres)
Enrique Renta (Dir-Creative)

Subsidiary (Non-US):

Juniper Park LP   (3)
33 Bloor Street East 14th Floor, Toronto,
M4W 3H1, ON, Canada
Tel.: (416) 260-6600
Web Site: https://www.juniperparktbwa.com
Sales Range: $25-49.9 Million
Emp.: 160
Advertising Services
N.A.I.C.S.: 541810
Jill Nykoliation (CEO)
David Toto (Pres)
Des Jones (Chief Strategy Officer)

Branch (Domestic):

TBWA California   (3)
5353 Grosvenor Blvd, Los Angeles, CA
90066
Tel.: (310) 305-5000
Web Site: http://www.tbwachiat.com
Advetising Agency
N.A.I.C.S.: 541810

Unit (Domestic):

TBWA Chiat Day Los Angeles   (3)
5353 Grosvenor Blvd, Los Angeles, CA
90066
Tel.: (310) 305-5000
Web Site: http://www.tbwachiat.com
Sales Range: $100-124.9 Million
Advetising Agency
N.A.I.C.S.: 541810
Frin Riley (Pres)
Michael Claypool (Mng Dir)
Baker Lambert (Dir-Data-Global)
Kelly Rosen (Dir-Bus Dev)
Simon Wassef (Chief Strategy Officer)
John Minty (CFO)

TBWA Chiat Day New York   (3)
220 E 42nd St, New York, NY 10017
Tel.: (212) 804-1000
Web Site: http://www.tbwachiat.com
Sales Range: $75-99.9 Million
Advetising Agency
N.A.I.C.S.: 541810
Erin Riley (Pres)
Renato Fernandez (Chief Creative Officer)
Jen Costello (Head-Strategy)
Sheri Thorburn (Dir-HR)
John Minty (CFO)

Michael Claypool (Mng Dir)
Kelly Rosen (Dir-New Bus Dev)
Anh-Thu Le (Dir-Content Production)
Guia Iacomin (Dir-Content Production)

Branch (Non-US):

TBWA Toronto   (3)
33 Bloor Street East 14th Floor, Toronto,
M4W 3H1, ON, Canada
Tel.: (416) 260-6600
Web Site: http://www.juniperparktbwa.com
Sales Range: $25-49.9 Million
Emp.: 75
Advetising Agency
N.A.I.C.S.: 541810

TBWA Vancouver
Suite 300-455 Granville Street, Vancouver,
V6C 1T1, BC, Canada
Tel.: (604) 669-4444
Sales Range: $25-49.9 Million
Emp.: 35
Advetising Agency
N.A.I.C.S.: 541810

Branch (Domestic):

TBWA/Chiat/Day Los Angeles
Inc.   (3)
5353 Grosvenor Blvd, Los Angeles, CA
90066-6913
Tel.: (310) 305-5000
Web Site: http://www.tbwachiatdayla.com
Sales Range: $25-49.9 Million
Advetising Agency
N.A.I.C.S.: 541810
Erin Riley (CEO)
Renato Fernandez (Chief Creative Officer)
John Minty (CFO)
Kelly Rosen (Dir-Bus Dev)
Michael Claypool (Mng Dir)
Jen Costello (Chief Strategy Officer)
Sheri Thorburn (Exec Dir-HR)
Anh-Thu Le (Dir-Content Production)
Guia Iacomin (Dir-Content Production)

Unit (Domestic):

TBWA/Media Arts Lab   (3)
12539 Beatrice St, Los Angeles, CA 90066
Tel.: (310) 305-4400
Web Site: http://www.tbwamal.com
Sales Range: $50-74.9 Million
Emp.: 150
Advetising Agency
N.A.I.C.S.: 541810
Duncan Milner (Pres-Creative-Global)
Brent Anderson (Chief Creative Officer-Global)
Katrien De Bauw (Pres-Global)
Kenny Blumenschein (Exec Creative Dir-Asia Pacific)
Michaela Futcher (Mng Dir)

TBWA/WorldHealth   (3)
220 E 42nd St 14th Fl, New York, NY
10017
Tel.: (212) 771-3000
Web Site: http://tbwaworldhealth.com
Advetising Agency
N.A.I.C.S.: 541810
Robin Shapiro (Pres-Global)
Jonathan Isaacs (Chief Creative Officer-London)

Subsidiary (Non-US):

TEQUILA Austria   (3)
Heiligenstadter St 31/3/401, A-1190, Vienna, Austria
Tol.: (43) 1 316 00 0
Web Site: http://www.tbwa.at
Sales Range: $25-49.9 Million
Emp.: 6
Advetising Agency
N.A.I.C.S.: 541810

TEQUILA BR   (3)
Pres Juscelino Kubitchek 1851, 04543 011,
Sao Paulo, SP, Brazil
Tel.: (55) 11 3038 0500
Web Site: http://www.tbwa.com.br
Advetising Agency
N.A.I.C.S.: 541810
Jaques Lewkowicz (Founder)

TEQUILA Belgium   (3)
Avenue de la Couronne 165, 1050, Brussels, Belgium

Tel.: (32) 2 523 19 11
Web Site: http://www.tequila.be
Sales Range: $25-49.9 Million
Emp.: 20
Advetising Agency
N.A.I.C.S.: 541810
Luc Perdieus (Mng Dir & Dir-New Bus)

TEQUILA China   (3)
3F 1295 South Suzhou Road, Shanghai,
200021, China
Tel.: (86) 21 6327 6018
Advetising Agency
N.A.I.C.S.: 541810

TEQUILA Digital   (3)
ul Rzymowskiego 34, Warsaw, 02-697, Poland
Tel.: (48) 224570500
Web Site: http://www.tequilapolska.pl
Advertising Agency
N.A.I.C.S.: 541810

TEQUILA Durban Marketing
Services   (3)
Colchester Essex Gardens Nelson Road,
Westville, Durban, 3630, South Africa
Tel.: (27) 31 267 6690
Web Site: http://www.tequila-sa.com
Sales Range: Less than $1 Million
Emp.: 160
Advetising Agency
N.A.I.C.S.: 541810

TEQUILA Esece   (3)
Ellauri 1232, Montevideo, 11300, Uruguay
Tel.: (598) 2707 4277
Web Site: http://www.tequilaesece.com
Sales Range: $25-49.9 Million
Emp.: 25
Advetising Agency
N.A.I.C.S.: 541810

TEQUILA France   (3)
162 Rue De Billancourt, BP 20401, 92103,
Boulogne-Billancourt, Cedex, France
Tel.: (33) 1 49 09 70 10
Web Site: http://www.tequila-france.com
Sales Range: $50-74.9 Million
Advetising Agency
N.A.I.C.S.: 541810

TEQUILA Guatemala   (3)
7A Avenida 14-44 Zona 9 Edificio La Galeria Local 25 Segundo Nivel, Guatemala,
1009, Guatemala
Tel.: (502) 2385 9645
Web Site: http://www.tequila-guatemala.com
Sales Range: $25-49.9 Million
Emp.: 12
Advetising Agency
N.A.I.C.S.: 541810

TEQUILA Hong Kong   (3)
Taikoo Place Cambridge House 981 King s
Road, 979 King's Road, Quarry Bay, China
(Hong Kong)
Tel.: (852) 28332033
Web Site: http://www.tequila.com
Advetising Agency
N.A.I.C.S.: 541810

TEQUILA India   (3)
G-11/12 Paragon Centre Opposite Century
Mills Pandurang Budhkar Marg, Lower
Parel, Mumbai, 400013, Maharashtra, India
Tel.: (91) 2243546666
Web Site: http://www.tbwaindia.com
Advetising Agency
N.A.I.C.S.: 541810

TEQUILA Ireland   (3)
41A Blackberry Ln, Rathmines, Dublin, 6,
Ireland
Tel.: (353) 1 496 6920
Sales Range: $25-49.9 Million
Emp.: 12
Advetising Agency
N.A.I.C.S.: 541810

TEQUILA Italia   (3)
Via Flaminia Vecchia 495, 00191, Rome,
Italy
Tel.: (39) 06 332 2681
Web Site: http://www.tbwa.it
Sales Range: $25-49.9 Million
Advetising Agency
N.A.I.C.S.: 541810

TEQUILA Italia   (3)
Via Leto Pomponia 3/5, 20146, Milan, Italy

Tel.: (39) 02 8053 219
Sales Range: $25-49.9 Million
Emp.: 25
Advetising Agency
N.A.I.C.S.: 541810

TEQUILA Johannesburg   (3)
3 Sandown Valley Cre, Crescent, Sandton,
2196, Gauteng, South Africa
Tel.: (27) 113223100
Web Site: http://www.tequila.co.za
Sales Range: $25-49.9 Million
Emp.: 10
Advetising Agency
N.A.I.C.S.: 541810
Eunene Sucevic (COO)
Bronwen Briggeford (Dir-Creative)
Louis Vanwyngaard (Dir-Creative)

TEQUILA London   (3)
1 Riverside Manbre Road, London, W6
9WA, United Kingdom
Tel.: (44) 20 7440 1100
Web Site: http://www.tequila-uk.com
Advetising Agency
N.A.I.C.S.: 541810

TEQUILA Manila   (3)
1195 Chino Roces Avenue Corner Yakal
Street, San Antonio Village, Makati, 1203,
Philippines
Tel.: (63) 25087809
Web Site: http://www.tbwa-smp.com
Advetising Agency
N.A.I.C.S.: 541810

TEQUILA Myalo   (3)
Wisma Semantan 15th Floor Jalan Gelenggan, Bukit Damansara, 50490, Kuala Lumpur, Malaysia
Tel.: (60) 3 2092 5130
Web Site: http://www.tequilamy.com
Advetising Agency
N.A.I.C.S.: 541810
Tim Garland (COO)

TEQUILA Polska SP ZOO   (3)
Ul Wincentego Rzymowskiego 34, 02-697,
Warsaw, Mazowieckie, Poland
Tel.: (48) 224570500
Web Site: http://www.tequilapolska.pl
Advetising Agency
N.A.I.C.S.: 541810
Alena Suszycka (Mng Dir)
Przemyslaw Jedrowski (Creative Dir)

TEQUILA Portugal   (3)
Avenida de Liberdade 38-6, 1250-145, Lisbon, Portugal
Tel.: (351) 21 322 3200
Sales Range: $25-49.9 Million
Advetising Agency
N.A.I.C.S.: 541810

TEQUILA RAAD   (3)
EMMAR Square Bldg 1 6th Fl, PO Box
40604, Dubai, United Arab Emirates
Tel.: (971) 4 222 6667
Web Site: http://www.tbwaraad.com
Advetising Agency
N.A.I.C.S.: 541810

TEQUILA Singapore   (3)
991 C alexander Road, 119971, Singapore,
Singapore
Tel.: (65) 6324 3002
Web Site: http://www.tequila.com
Sales Range: $50-74.9 Million
Emp.: 100
Advetising Agency
N.A.I.C.S.: 541810

TEQUILA Switzerland AG   (3)
Holbeinstrasse 25, 8008, Zurich, Switzerland
Tel.: (41) 449133232
Web Site: http://www.tbwa.ch
Sales Range: $25-49.9 Million
Advetising Agency
N.A.I.C.S.: 541810

Branch (Non-US):

Tam-Tam/TBWA   (3)
1470 rue Peel bureau A-700, Montreal, H3A
1T1, QC, Canada
Tel.: (514) 285-1470
Web Site: http://www.tamtamtbwa.com
Sales Range: $25-49.9 Million
Emp.: 25
Advetising Agency

N.A.I.C.S.: 541810

Subsidiary (Non-US):

**TBWA/Colombia Suiza de Publicidad
Ltda** (2)
Diagonal 97 # 17/60 Edificio Centro Empresarial, 3rd Floor, 11001, Bogota, DC, Colombia
Tel.: (57) 1 635 6090
Web Site: http://www.tbwacolombia.com
Sales Range: $25-49.9 Million
Emp.: 45
Advetising Agency
N.A.I.C.S.: 541810
Rafael de Nicolas (CEO)

TBWA/El Salvador (2)
Final 105 Avenida Sur, Colonia Escalon,
5510, San Salvador, El Salvador
Tel.: (503) 264 0400
Full Service
N.A.I.C.S.: 541810

TBWA/Guatemala (2)
23 Calle 15-14 Zone 13, Guatemala, 1013,
Guatemala
Tel.: (502) 23136300
Web Site: http://www.tbwa.com
Global Advertising Agency
N.A.I.C.S.: 541810

TBWA/JAIMEURIBE (2)
Carrera 35 #5 G 107 Edificio San Angel,
Medellin, Colombia
Tel.: (57) 4 318 9100
Web Site: http://www.juas.com
Rev.: $40,000,000
Emp.: 95
Advetising Agency
N.A.I.C.S.: 541810

TBWA/Paragon (2)
40 Eros Road, Windhoek, Namibia
Tel.: (264) 61387130
Web Site: http://www.paragonnamibia.com
Sales Range: $25-49.9 Million
Emp.: 25
Full Service
N.A.I.C.S.: 541810

Teran TBWA (2)
Monte Pelvoux 210 Col, Lomas de
Chapultepec, 11000, Mexico, DF, Mexico
Tel.: (52) 5559803101
Web Site: https://terantbwa.mx
Full Service
N.A.I.C.S.: 541810
Jose Alberto Teran (Pres & CEO)
Jorge Vallejo (CFO & COO)

Viteri/TBWA (2)
Avenida Eloy Alfaro, N34-230 Y Catalina
Aldaz, Quito, Ecuador
Tel.: (593) 2 244 6639
Web Site: http://www.tbwaecuador.com
Full Service
N.A.I.C.S.: 541810

Waterswidgren/TBWA AB (2)
Wallingatan 2, Stockholm, 111 60, Sweden
Tel.: (46) 841004000
Web Site: http://www.waterswidgren.se
Emp.: 29
N.A.I.C.S.: 541810
Kalle Widgren (CEO & Dir-Creative)

Yehoshua TBWA (2)
1 Nirim Street, Tel Aviv, 67060, Israel
Tel.: (972) 36361818
Web Site: http://www.ytbwa.co.il
Sales Range: $25-49.9 Million
Emp.: 140
Full Service
N.A.I.C.S.: 541810
Rami Yehoshua (Chm & CEO)
Maya Sharan (VP-Creative)

TBWA/WorldHealth New York (1)
220 E 42nd St 15th Fl, New York, NY
10017
Tel.: (212) 771-3000
Web Site: http://www.tbwa.com
Advertising Services
N.A.I.C.S.: 541810
Sharon Callahan (CEO)

TBWA WorldHealth Chicago Inc. (1)
225 N Michigan Ave. Fl 21, Chicago, IL
60601
Tel.: (800) 306-7508

Web Site: https://tbwaworldhealth.com
Advertising Services
N.A.I.C.S.: 541810
Robin Shapiro (CEO)
Suri Harris (Exec VP)

Unit (Domestic):

**Iris Global Clinical Trials
Solutions** (2)
211 E Chicago Ave Ste 1300, Chicago, IL
60611
Tel.: (312) 475-3628
Advertising Services
N.A.I.C.S.: 541810
Robin Shapiro (Pres)

Kinect (2)
211 E Chicago Ave, Chicago, IL 60611
Tel.: (312) 475-2607
Sales Range: $25-49.9 Million
Emp.: 20
Advertising Services
N.A.I.C.S.: 541810
Chuck Russo (Mng Dir)

TPG Direct (1)
230 S Broad St 17th Fl, Philadelphia, PA
19102-4103
Tel.: (215) 592-8381
Web Site: https://www.tpgdirect.com
N.A.I.C.S.: 541810

TPN Inc. (1)
1999 Bryan St Ste 3000, Dallas, TX 75201
Tel.: (214) 692-1522
Web Site: http://www.tpnretail.com
Sales Range: $25-49.9 Million
Emp.: 200
N.A.I.C.S.: 541810
Sharon Love (CEO)
Kayla Waters (CFO)
Cheryl Policastro (Chief Strategy Officer)

Targetbase (1)
7850 N Belt Line Rd, Irving, TX
75063 (100%)
Tel.: (972) 506-3800
Web Site: http://www.targetbase.com
Marketing Services
N.A.I.C.S.: 541613
Genine Balliet (Chief Bus Solutions &
People Officer)
Mark Wright (CEO)
Kimberley Walsh (Chief Creative Officer)
Erik Lindholm (CFO)
Beth Kuykendall (Chief Strategy Officer)
Chris Sealy (Sr VP-Client Svc)
Stacey Crumbley (Pres & Chief Client Officer)
Jimmy Rhodes (Mng Dir)
Kevin Bishop (CTO)

Branch (Domestic):

Targetbase - Greensboro (2)
202 CentrePort Dr Ste 300, Greensboro,
NC 27409
Tel.: (336) 665-3800
Web Site: http://www.targetbase.com
Marketing Services
N.A.I.C.S.: 541810
Mark Wright (Chm)
Kimberley Walsh (Chief Creative Officer)

Branch (Non-US):

Targetbase Claydon Heeley (2)
Glassmill 1 Battersea Bridge Rd, London,
SW11 3BZ, United Kingdom
Tel.: (44) 2079243000
Emp.: 35
Marketing Services
N.A.I.C.S.: 541810

The Designory (1)
211 E Ocean Blvd Ste 100, Long Beach,
CA 90802
Tel.: (562) 624-0200
Web Site: http://www.designory.com
Sales Range: $25-49.9 Million
Emp.: 165
Advertising Services
N.A.I.C.S.: 541810
Lynne Grigg (Chief Creative Officer)
Janet Wood (Dir-HR)
Erica Amestoy (Acct Dir-Global)
Michael Lane (Mng Dir-Chicago)
Alex Berger (Dir-Tech)
Alain Rhone (COO-Intl)

Shawn Tamura (CFO)
Neal Grossman (COO)
Patti Thurston (VP-Efficacy)
Rick Multari (Mng Dir)

The GMR Group (1)
755 Business Ctr Dr Ste 250, Horsham, PA
19044-3444
Tel.: (215) 653-7401
Sales Range: Less than $1 Million
Emp.: 20
N.A.I.C.S.: 541810

The Integer Group, LLC (1)
7245 W Alaska Dr 3rd Fl, Denver, CO
80226
Tel.: (303) 393-3000
Web Site: http://www.integer.com
Sales Range: $150-199.9 Million
Emp.: 838
Advetising Agency
N.A.I.C.S.: 541810
Marc Ducnuigeen (COO)
Ellen Cook (CEO)
Dani Coplen (Exec VP & Exec Dir-Creative)
Craig Elston (Chief Strategy Officer-Global)
Jim McKinnis (Exec VP & Exec Creative
Dir)
Gail Obaseki (Dir-Diversity, Equality & Inclusion)

Branch (Domestic):

The Integer Group, LLC - Dallas (2)
1999 Bryan St Ste 1700, Dallas, TX 75201
Tel.: (214) 758-6800
Web Site: http://www.integer.com
Sales Range: $25-49.9 Million
Emp.: 75
Advetising Agency
N.A.I.C.S.: 541810
Ellen Cook (CEO)

**The Integer Group, LLC -
Midwest** (2)
500 Locust St Ste 115, Des Moines, IA
50309
Tel.: (515) 288-7910
Web Site: http://www.integer.com
Sales Range: $25-49.9 Million
Emp.: 125
Advetising Agency
N.A.I.C.S.: 541810
Frank Maher (COO & Pres-Grp)
Mike Sweeney (Chm)
Marc Ducnuigeen (Co-COO)

The Marketing Arm (1)
1999 Bryan St 32nd Fl, Dallas, TX 75201
Tel.: (214) 259-3200
Web Site: https://www.wearetma.agency
Sales Range: $25-49.9 Million
Emp.: 30
Advertising Services
N.A.I.C.S.: 541810
Michelle Palmer (Pres-Sports & Experiential)
Harris Wilkinson (Chief Creative Officer)

Branch (Domestic):

The Marketing Arm (2)
1285 6th Ave 6th Fl, New York, NY 10019
Tel.: (917) 305-5600
Web Site: http://www.themarketingarm.com
Advertising Services
N.A.I.C.S.: 541810

TracyLocke (1)
7850 N Belt Line Rd, Irving, TX 75063
Tel.: (214) 259-3500
Web Site: http://www.tracylocke.com
Sales Range: $125-149.9 Million
Emp.: 200
Advertising Agency
N.A.I.C.S.: 541810
Stewart Campbell (CFO-Global)
Michael Bartlett (Mng Partner)
Sandy Stein (VP & Exec Dir-Creative-
Global)
Ivan Mayes (Sr VP & Dir-Tech)
Michael Lovegrove (Pres & Chief Creative
Officer)
Stephen Miller (Mng Partner)
Nancy Shamberg (Mng Partner)
Kryslyn Burks (Gen Mgr & Dir-Client Svc)
Rob Webber (Exec Dir-Studio Svcs)
Phil Camarota (Exec Dir-Creative)
Dan Cishek (Exec Dir-Creative)
Sabrina Diez (Exec Dir-Creative)

Shawn Kraemer (Exec Dir-Creative)
Teresa Brammer (Dir-HR)
Andrea Farina (Dir-Creative)
Kyle Grummun (Dir-Creative)
Brain Hutter (Dir-Creative)
Cheal Kerski (Dir-Client Svcs)
Bill Natlo (Dir-Client Svcs)
Michelle Tisdale (Dir-Analytics)
Brooke Alexander (Dir-Acct)
Tanya Greene (Dir-Acct)
Rob Guarino (Dir-Acct)
Meg Herlihy (Dir-Acct)
Darren O'Rourk (Dir-Acct)
Carol Pernikar (Chief Strategy Officer)
Maria Zanghetti (CFO)

Branch (Domestic):

TracyLocke (2)
903 N 47th St Ste 300, Rogers, AR 72756
Tel.: (214) 259-3500
Web Site: http://www.tracylocke.com
Advertising Agency
N.A.I.C.S.: 541810

TracyLocke - Wilton Office (2)
131 Danbury Rd, Wilton, CT 06897
Tel.: (203) 762-2400
Web Site: http://www.tracylocke.com
Sales Range: $100-124.9 Million
Emp.: 220
Advertising Agency
N.A.I.C.S.: 541810
Jim Sexton (Mng Dir-Global)
Michael Lovegrove (Chm & CEO)

USMP (1)
4721 Alla Rd, Marina Del Rey, CA 90292
Tel.: (310) 754-3000
Web Site: http://www.usmpagency.com
Sales Range: $25-49.9 Million
Emp.: 75
Advertising Agency
N.A.I.C.S.: 541810

Unisono Fieldmarketing (1)
Building 5 29 Shajing Road, Shanghai,
200080, China
Tel.: (86) 21 25012888
Web Site:
http://www.unisonofieldmarketing.com
Sales Range: $75-99.9 Million
Emp.: 40
Marketing Consulting Services
N.A.I.C.S.: 541613

Branch (Domestic):

Unisono Fieldmarketing (2)
L 0323 Building A SOHO New Town, 88 Jianguo Road, Beijing, 100022, Chaoyang,
China
Tel.: (86) 10 8580 2928
Web Site: http://www.unisono.com
Marketing Consulting Services
N.A.I.C.S.: 541613

Unisono Fieldmarketing (2)
Block A G&H 25 F Zhongqiao Building, 76
Xianlie Middle Rd, Guangzhou, 510070,
China
Tel.: (86) 20 8732 1446
Web Site: http://www.unisono.com
Marketing Consulting Services
N.A.I.C.S.: 541613

Weapon 7 (1)
77 Kingsway, London, WC2B 6SR, United
Kingdom
Tel.: (44) 2070743555
Sales Range: $25-49.9 Million
Emp.: 40
N.A.I.C.S.: 541810
Jeremy Garner (Dir-Creative)

Wolff Olins (1)
Bankside 3 90-100 Southwark Street, London, SE1 0SW, United Kingdom
Tel.: (44) 2036559850
Web Site: http://www.wolffolins.com
Sales Range: $25-49.9 Million
Emp.: 80
N.A.I.C.S.: 541810
Sairah Ashman (CEO)

Branch (US):

Wolff Olins-New York (2)
195 Broadway 17th Fl, New York, NY
10007

Omnicom Group Inc.—(Continued)

Tel.: (212) 505-7337
Web Site: http://www.wolff-olins.com
Emp.: 45
N.A.I.C.S.: 541810
Sairah Ashman (CEO)
Amanda Munilla (Mng Dir-San Francisco)
Manlio Minale (Head-Strategy-London)
Emma Woodhead White (Dir-Strategy)
Ioana Boldor (Dir-Engagement-London)

Zimmerman Advertising LLC (1)
6600 N Andrews Ave, Fort Lauderdale, FL 33309
Tel.: (954) 644-4000
Web Site: http://www.zadv.com
Rev.: $2,500,000,000
Emp.: 1,000
Advetising Agency
N.A.I.C.S.: 541810
David Nathanson (Chief Creative Officer & Exec VP)
David Kissell (COO)
Adam Herman (Chief Integrated Media Officer & Exec VP)
Joel Weiner (CFO)
Jill Schneider-Sutcliffe (Exec VP-Retail Acct Svcs)
Ronnie Haligman (Pres)
Brad Higdon (CMO)
Laura Duane (VP & Dir-Strategy)
Kristin Regan (VP & Grp Acct Dir)
Klim Kavall (VP & Dir-Digital Media)
Katy Graff (Supvr-Acct)
Phil Bannister (Sr VP-Retail Technologies)
Daniel Rooney (Sr VP & Grp Acct Dir)
Dan Kissell (Mng Dir-Automotive Div & Exec VP)
Nicole Fortier (Mgr-Brdcst Bus)
Annemarie Lattke (Grp Acct Dir)
Carol Koepke (Grp Acct Dir)
Chad Garcia (Exec VP & Exec Creative Dir-StudioZ)
David Crawford (Exec Creative Dir)
Maria Rico (VP & Dir-Ops)
Jody Sadler (Dir-Integrated Media Plng-Grp)
Taj McClymont (Dir-Grp Digital Media)
Jackie Guerra (Dir-Creative & Copywriter)
Mildred Aldridge (Coord-Acct Payable)
Lisa Rossi (Chief Client Officer)
Stephen Roach (Assoc Dir-Data Strategy)
Allie Rubin (Acct Dir)
Stephanie Naranjo (Acct Dir)
Stephanie Loy (Acct Dir)
Kelly Mullinax (Acct Dir)
Katherine Perez (Acct Dir)
Brian Anderson (VP & Creative Dir-Grp)
David Bork (Dir-Grp Integrated Media Plng)
Christina Famy (Acct Dir)

Branch (Domestic):

Zimmerman Advertising LLC - Chicago (2)
2 Mid America Plz Ste 510, Oakbrook Terrace, IL 60181-1937
Tel.: (630) 574-1059
Web Site: http://www.zadv.com
Sales Range: $25-49.9 Million
Emp.: 8
Advetising Agency
N.A.I.C.S.: 541810

Zimmerman Advertising LLC - Los Angeles (2)
5353 Grosvenor Blvd, Los Angeles, CA 90066
Tel.: (310) 305-5700
Web Site: http://www.zadv.com
Sales Range: $25-49.9 Million
Emp.: 8
Advetising Agency
N.A.I.C.S.: 541810

Zimmerman Advertising LLC - New York (2)
88 Madison Ave, New York, NY 10016
Tel.: (212) 804-1345
Web Site: http://www.zadv.com
Sales Range: $25-49.9 Million
Emp.: 10
Advetising Agency
N.A.I.C.S.: 541810

ipsh! (1)
555 Market St Ste 1650, San Francisco, CA 94105
Tel.: (415) 355-9313

Sales Range: $10-24.9 Million
Emp.: 20
Advertising Services
N.A.I.C.S.: 541810

OMNIQ CORP.
1865 W 2100 S Ste 250, Salt Lake City, UT 84119
Tel.: (500) 322-1770 **DE**
Web Site: https://www.omniq.com
Year Founded: 1973
OMQS—(NASDAQ)
Rev.: $102,545,000
Assets: $64,811,000
Liabilities: $75,337,000
Net Worth: ($10,526,000)
Earnings: ($13,820,000)
Emp.: 216
Fiscal Year-end: 12/31/22
Mobile Invoicing Software Solutions
N.A.I.C.S.: 513210
Shai S. Lustgarten (Chm, CEO & Interim CFO)
Yoram Hofman (CTO)

Subsidiaries:

HTS (USA) Inc. (1)
4328 E Tradewinds Ave, Lauderdale by the Sea, FL 33308
Tel.: (561) 450-6974
Web Site: http://www.hts-usa.com
Emp.: 280
Party Tent & Accessory Mfr
N.A.I.C.S.: 314910

Quest Marketing, Inc. (1)
522 Lyndale St, Mankato, MN 56003
Tel.: (507) 388-1384
Web Site: https://www.questmarketing.net
Apparel Accessory Distr
N.A.I.C.S.: 458110

OMNITEK ENGINEERING CORP.
1345 Specialty Dr Ste E, Vista, CA 92081
Tel.: (760) 591-0089 **CA**
Web Site: https://www.omnitekcorp.com
Year Founded: 2001
OMTK—(OTCQB)
Rev.: $1,070,787
Assets: $1,113,089
Liabilities: $2,099,149
Net Worth: ($986,060)
Earnings: ($196,709)
Emp.: 6
Fiscal Year-end: 12/31/22
Engines & Other Motor Vehicle Parts Mfr
N.A.I.C.S.: 336310
Werner Funk (Founder, Pres, CEO, Principal Acctg Officer & Sec)

ON SEMICONDUCTOR CORPORATION
5701 N Pima Rd, Scottsdale, AZ 85250
Tel.: (602) 244-6600 **DE**
Web Site: http://www.onsemi.com
Year Founded: 1999
ON—(NASDAQ)
Rev.: $8,253,000,000
Assets: $13,215,200,000
Liabilities: $5,414,600,000
Net Worth: $7,800,600,000
Earnings: $2,183,700,000
Emp.: 30,000
Fiscal Year-end: 12/31/23
Analog, Logic & Discrete Semiconductor Mfr
N.A.I.C.S.: 334413
Alan Campbell (Chm)
Thad Trent (CFO, Principal Acctg Officer, Treas & Exec VP)
Parag Agarwal (VP-IR & Corp Dev)
Simon Keeton (Exec VP & Gen Mgr-Power Solutions Grp)

Hassane S. El-Khoury (Pres & CEO)
Thad Trent (CFO & Exec VP)
Catherine Cote (VP)
Bernard R. Colpitts Jr. (Chief Acctg Officer)
Christopher R. Adams (VP/Gen Mgr-Automotive Sensing Div)

Subsidiaries:

AMI Semiconductor Canada Company (1)
200-611 Kumpf Dr, Waterloo, N2V 1K8, ON, Canada
Tel.: (519) 884-9696
Sales Range: $25-49.9 Million
Emp.: 50
Semiconductor Devices Mfr
N.A.I.C.S.: 334413

Aptina (UK) Limited (1)
Century Court Millennium Way, Bracknell, RG12 2XT, Berkshire, United Kingdom
Tel.: (44) 1344383300
Semiconductor Components Mfr
N.A.I.C.S.: 334413

Aptina India Private Limited (1)
No 14 Frontier Grandur Walton Road, Bengaluru, 560001, India
Tel.: (91) 8042774100
Semiconductor Components Mfr
N.A.I.C.S.: 334413

Leshan-Phoenix Semiconductor Co., Ltd. (1)
A 27 Remmin West Rd, Leshan, 614000, China
Tel.: (86) 8332127909
Sales Range: $500-549.9 Million
Emp.: 2,000
Semiconductor Mfr
N.A.I.C.S.: 334413

ON Design Czech s.r.o. (1)
Na Perstyne 325/38, 460 01, Liberec, Czech Republic
Tel.: (420) 608873587
Web Site: http://www.on-design.cz
Sales Range: $25-49.9 Million
Integrated Circuit Design Services
N.A.I.C.S.: 541490

ON Semiconductor (1)
2300 W Buckskin Rd, Pocatello, ID 83201
Tel.: (208) 233-4690
Web Site: http://www.onsemi.com
Sales Range: $450-499.9 Million
Emp.: 1,500
Semiconductor Designer & Mfr
N.A.I.C.S.: 334413

ON Semiconductor (1)
5701 N Pima Rd, Scottsdale, AZ 85250 (100%)
Tel.: (602) 244-6600
Web Site: https://www.onsemi.com
Emp.: 975
Mfr of Integrated Circuits
N.A.I.C.S.: 334413
Simon Keeton (Exec VP & Gen Mgr-Power Solutions Grp)
Vincent C. Hopkin (Exec VP & Gen Mgr-Analog Solutions Grp)

ON Semiconductor Connectivity Solutions, Inc. (1)
1704 Automation Pkwy, San Jose, CA 95131
Tel.: (669) 209-5500
Web Site: http://www.quantenna.com
Rev.: $220,460,000
Assets: $245,656,000
Liabilities: $39,169,000
Net Worth: $206,487,000
Earnings: $3,083,000
Emp.: 415
Fiscal Year-end: 12/31/2018
Semiconductor Product Mfr
N.A.I.C.S.: 334413
Andrea J. Goldsmith (Co-Founder)

ON Semiconductor Czech Republic a.s. (1)
Vyroba kremiku vyroba cipu 1 maje 2230, 756 61, Roznov pod Radhostem, Czech Republic (100%)
Tel.: (420) 571753111
Web Site: https://kariera-onsemi.cz

Sales Range: $50-74.9 Million
Semiconductor Mfr
N.A.I.C.S.: 334413

ON Semiconductor France SAS (1)
6 Rue Dewoitine, Velizy, Paris, 78140, France
Tel.: (33) 139264100
Sales Range: $25-49.9 Million
Emp.: 25
Semiconductor Component Distr
N.A.I.C.S.: 423690
Patrice Levent (Dir-Sls)

ON Semiconductor Germany GmbH (1)
Einsteinring 28, Aschheim, 85609, Munich, Germany (100%)
Tel.: (49) 8993080080
Web Site: http://www.onsemi.com
Sales Range: $10-24.9 Million
Semiconductor Mfr
N.A.I.C.S.: 334413

ON Semiconductor Hong Kong Design Ltd. (1)
2/f No 1 Science Park East Ave Hk Science Park, Sha Tin, China (Hong Kong) (100%)
Tel.: (852) 26890088
Web Site: http://www.onsemi.com
Sales Range: $50-74.9 Million
Emp.: 180
Semiconductor Mfr
N.A.I.C.S.: 334413

ON Semiconductor Image Sensor BVBA (1)
Schalienhoevedreef 20 B, Mechelen, 2800, Belgium
Tel.: (32) 15446333
Web Site: http://www.onsemi.com
Sales Range: $25-49.9 Million
Emp.: 100
Semiconductor Based Sensor Mfr
N.A.I.C.S.: 334413
Chad Smith (Pres)

ON Semiconductor Italy S.r.l (1)
Via Gobetti 2/c, 20063, Cernusco sul Naviglio, Italy
Tel.: (39) 029239311
Web Site: http://www.onsemi.com
Power Supply Applications; Semiconductor Mfr
N.A.I.C.S.: 334413

ON Semiconductor Leasing BVBA (1)
Schalienhoevedreef 20b, Eine, 2800, Mechelen, Belgium
Tel.: (32) 488098989
Web Site: http://www.onsemi.com
Semiconductor Components Mfr
N.A.I.C.S.: 334413

ON Semiconductor Slovakia a.s. (1)
Vrbovska cesta 2617/102, 921 01, Piestany, Slovakia
Tel.: (421) 337902338
Web Site: http://www.onsemi.com
Sales Range: $75-99.9 Million
Semiconductor Mfr
N.A.I.C.S.: 334413

ON Semiconductor Switzerland S.A. (1)
Av Des Champs-montants 12a, 2074, Marin-Epagnier, Switzerland
Tel.: (41) 327557400
Sales Range: $25-49.9 Million
Emp.: 25
Semiconductor Devices Mfr
N.A.I.C.S.: 334413

ON Semiconductor Technology India Private Limited (1)
No 105 Prestige Saleh Ahmed Infantry Road, Bengaluru, 560001, Karnataka, India
Tel.: (91) 8042774188
Web Site: http://www.onsemi.com
Emp.: 60
Semiconductor Components Mfr
N.A.I.C.S.: 334413

ON Semiconductor Technology Japan Ltd. (1)
Nakamegurogsdaiichi Bldg, 2-9-1 Kamimeguro, Tokyo, 153 0051, Japan (100%)
Tel.: (81) 357733880

Sales Range: $10-24.9 Million
Emp.: 25
Semiconductor Mfr
N.A.I.C.S.: 334413

SCG Czech Design Center s.r.o. (1)
Design Center for Integrated Circuits 1 May
2594, 75661, Roznov pod Radhostem,
Czech Republic (100%)
Tel.: (420) 571754100
Sales Range: $25-49.9 Million
Emp.: 300
Semiconductor Mfr
N.A.I.C.S.: 334413

SCG Hong Kong SAR Ltd. (1)
Z F HK Science Park 1, Sha Tin, China
(Hong Kong) (100%)
Tel.: (852) 26890088
Sales Range: $1-9.9 Million
Emp.: 60
Semiconductor Mfr
N.A.I.C.S.: 334413
Cy Wong (Controller)

Sanyo Semiconductor Co., Ltd. (1)
1-1 Sakata 1-chome Oizumi-machi, Ora-
gun, Gunma, 370-0596, Japan
Tel.: (81) 276 61 8341
Web Site: http://www.sanyosemi.com
Sales Range: $1-4.9 Billion
Emp.: 1,236
Semiconductors Mfr & Distr
N.A.I.C.S.: 334413

Subsidiary (Domestic):

**Kanto SANYO Semiconductor Co.,
Ltd.** (2)
476 Hideyasu, Hanyu, 348-0032, Japan
Tel.: (81) 485610081
Semiconductor Device & Integrated Circuit
Mfr
N.A.I.C.S.: 334413

Subsidiary (Non-US):

**SANYO Semiconductor (Thailand)
Co., Ltd.** (2)
1/7 Moo 5 Rojana Industrial Park Karnham,
Uthai, Bangkok, 13210, Thailand
Tel.: (66) 3533011624
Integrated Circuits Mfr
N.A.I.C.S.: 334413

**Sanyo Semiconductor (H.K.) Co.,
Ltd.** (2)
Rm 201-205 fl 1 Science Park East First
Ave Hong Kong Science Park, Sha Tin,
China (Hong Kong) (100%)
Tel.: (852) 23111198
Sales Range: $50-74.9 Million
Emp.: 130
Semiconductors Sales
N.A.I.C.S.: 423690

Subsidiary (US):

**Sanyo Semiconductor
Corporation** (2)
Park AD W Plz 2, Saddle Brook, NJ 07663
Tel.: (201) 825-8080
Sales Range: $25-49.9 Million
Emp.: 30
Semiconductors Sales
N.A.I.C.S.: 423690

Subsidiary (Non-US):

**Sanyo Semiconductor Manufacturing
Philippines Corporation** (1)
Luisita Idustrial Park Special Export Pro-
cessing Zone, San Miguel, Tarlac, 2300,
Philippines
Tel.: (63) 459850564
Semiconductor Mfr
N.A.I.C.S.: 334413

**Semiconductor Components Indus-
tries Singapore Pte. Ltd.** (1)
34 Penjuru Lane 05-01 Penjuru Logistic
Hub, Singapore, 609201, Singapore
Tel.: (65) 65126286
Electric Device Mfr
N.A.I.C.S.: 334413
Allen Lo (Gen Mgr)

**Semiconductor Components Indus-
tries, LLC** (1)

621 NW 53rd St Ste 240, Boca Raton, FL
33487-8291
Tel.: (561) 996-1486
Sales Range: $150-199.9 Million
Electronic Parts Whslr
N.A.I.C.S.: 423690
William A. Schromm (COO & Exec VP)
Thad Trent (CFO, Treas & Exec VP)
Bernard R. Colpitts Jr. (Chief Acctg Officer
& VP-Fin & Treasury)
Hassane S. El-Khoury (Pres & CEO)

Subsidiary (Domestic):

**Semiconductor Components Indus-
tries of Rhode Island, Inc.** (2)
1900 S County Trl, East Greenwich, RI
02818
Tel.: (401) 885-3600
Semiconductor Mfr
N.A.I.C.S.: 334413
Keith D. Jackson (Pres & CEO)

Subsidiary (Non-US):

System General Corporation (2)
6F No 205-3 Sec 3 Beixin Rd, Xindian Dis-
trict, Taipei, Taiwan
Tel.: (886) 289131997
Web Site: http://www.sg.com.tw
Semiconductors & Related Devices Mfr
N.A.I.C.S.: 334413

SensL Technologies Limited (1)
Building 6800 Avenue 6000 Cork Airport
Business Park, Cork, T12 CDF7, Ireland
Tel.: (353) 212407110
Emp.: 34,000
Silicon Photomultiplier & Measurement In-
strument Mfr
N.A.I.C.S.: 334413
Bryan Campbell (CEO)
Carl Jackson (CTO & VP-Engrg)
Wade Appelman (VP-Sls & Mktg)

Sound Design Technologies Ltd. (1)
970 Fraser Drive, Burlington, L7L 5P5, ON,
Canada
Tel.: (905) 635-0800
Emp.: 140
Semiconductor Devices Mfr
N.A.I.C.S.: 334413

System Solutions Co., Ltd. (1)
1-1 Sakata 1-chome, Oizumi, Gunma, 370-
0596, Japan
Tel.: (81) 276618341
Semiconductor Components Mfr
N.A.I.C.S.: 334413

ON24, INC.
50 Beale St 8th Fl, San Francisco,
CA 94105
Tel.: (415) 369-8000   CA
Web Site: https://www.on24.com
Year Founded: 1998
ONTF—(NYSE)
Rev.: $190,872,000
Assets: $425,473,000
Liabilities: $117,512,000
Net Worth: $307,961,000
Earnings: ($58,208,000)
Emp.: 640
Fiscal Year-end: 12/31/22
Webcasting, Online Trade Shows &
Events
N.A.I.C.S.: 516210
Jayesh Sahasi (CTO & Exec VP-
Product)
Mahesh Kheny (VP-Engrg)
Steven Vattuone (CFO)
James Blackie (Chief Revenue Offi-
cer)
Mike Badgis (VP-HR-Global)
Bill Weeser (Gen Counsel)
Byron Bardy (VP-Corp Dev & Strate-
gic Alliances)
Matt French (VP-Fin Plng & Analysis)
Mary Daquioag (VP-Facilities &
Procurement-Global)
Tessa Barron (VP-Brand & Field
Mktg)
Mark Bornstein (VP-Content Mktg)
Daniel Harrison (VP-APAC & Japan)

Steven Long (CIO)
Shalini Mitha (VP-Product Mktg)
Jason Olkowski (Chief Customer
Success Officer)
Callan Young (CMO)
Cheri Hulse (VP)
Sharat Sharan (Bd of Dirs, Co-
Founder, Chm, Pres & CEO)

Subsidiaries:

Imaste-ips S.L. (1)
Calle del Conde de Penalver 22, 28006,
Madrid, Spain
Tel.: (34) 915360503
Web Site: http://www.imaste-ips.com
Marketing Consulting Services
N.A.I.C.S.: 541613
Joanna Szymanska (COO)

ON24 Pte Ltd (1)
Level 2 15 Beach Road, Singapore,
189677, Singapore
Tel.: (65) 68714859
Webcasting, Online Trade Shows & Events
N.A.I.C.S.: 516210

ON24 UK (1)
6th Floor 210 Pentonville Road, Kings
Cross, London, N1 9JY, United Kingdom
Tel.: (44) 2070627575
Web Site: http://www.on24.com
Emp.: 20
Webcasting Online Trade Show & Event
Services
N.A.I.C.S.: 516210

ON4 COMMUNICATIONS INC.
44 W 44th Str, New York, NY 11710
Tel.: (516) 637-4061   DE
Year Founded: 2001
ONCI—(OTCIQ)
Emp.: 1
Communication Devices Mfr
N.A.I.C.S.: 334290

ONASSIS HOLDINGS CORP.
39 Broadway Ste 3010, New York,
NY 10006
Tel.: (929) 229-9864   NV
Web Site: https://www.onassis-
holdings.com
Year Founded: 2004
ONSS—(OTCIQ)
Mineral Exploration Services
N.A.I.C.S.: 213115
Eliron Yaron (Chm & Pres)

ONCOCYTE CORPORATION
15 Cushing, Irvine, CA 92618
Tel.: (949) 409-7600   CA
Web Site: https://www.oncocyte.com
Year Founded: 2009
OCX—(NASDAQ)
Rev.: $958,000
Assets: $100,091,000
Liabilities: $65,799,000
Net Worth: $34,292,000
Earnings: ($72,902,000)
Emp.: 75
Fiscal Year-end: 12/31/22
Biotechnology Research & Develop-
ment Services
N.A.I.C.S.: 541714
Andrew Arno (Chm)
Padma Sundar (Chief Comml Officer)
Joshua Riggs (Pres & CEO)
Andrea James (CFO)
James Liu (Principal Acctg Officer,
Controller & Sr Dir)

Subsidiaries:

Insight Genetics, Inc. (1)
2 International Plaza Dr Ste 510, Nashville,
TN 37217
Tel.: (615) 255-8880
Web Site: http://www.insightgenetics.com
Healtcare Services
N.A.I.C.S.: 621999

Razor Genomics, Inc. (1)

150 N Hill Dr Ste 14, Brisbane, CA 94005
Web Site: https://www.razorgenomics.com
Health Care Srvices
N.A.I.C.S.: 621999

ONCOLIX INC.
14405 Walters Rd Ste 780, Houston,
TX 77014
Tel.: (281) 402-3167   FL
Year Founded: 2013
ONCX—(OTCIQ)
Vehicle Research Consulting Ser-
vices
N.A.I.C.S.: 541690
Michael T. Rodman (Pres & CEO)

ONCOLOGY PHARMA, INC.
1 Sansome St Ste 3500, San Fran-
cisco, CA 94104
Tel.: (415) 869-1038
Web Site: http://www.oncology-
pharma.com
ONPHD—(OTCIQ)
Assets: $230,000
Liabilities: $294,000
Net Worth: ($64,000)
Earnings: ($207,000)
Emp.: 4
Fiscal Year-end: 03/31/20
Rare Earth Metals & Elements Explo-
ration & Development
N.A.I.C.S.: 212290
James Smith (CFO)

ONCORUS, INC.
4 Corporate Dr, Andover, MA 01810
Tel.: (339) 240-3330   DE
Web Site: https://www.oncorus.com
Year Founded: 2015
ONCR—(NASDAQ)
Rev.: $210,000
Assets: $145,586,000
Liabilities: $85,061,000
Net Worth: $60,525,000
Earnings: ($77,422,000)
Emp.: 64
Fiscal Year-end: 12/31/22
Biotechnology Research & Develop-
ment Services
N.A.I.C.S.: 541714
Theodore T. Ashburn (Chm)
Stephen W. Harbin (COO & Head-
Staff)
Mitchell H. Finer (Founder)
John M. Goldberg (Sr VP-Clinical
Dev)
Lorena Lerner (VP-Molecular Biology)
Christophe Queva (Chief Scientific
Officer & Sr VP-Res)
Stephanie Duncanson (VP-Corp
Strategy & Bus Dev)
Brett Belongia (VP-CMC Ops)
Mitchell H. Finer (Chm)
Brian Haines (VP-Pharmacology &
Toxicology)
Alexander Nolte (Principal Fin Officer,
Principal Acctg Officer & Treas)

ONCOSEC MEDICAL INCOR-
PORATED
365 W Passaic St Ste 400, Rochelle
Park, NJ 07662
Tel.: (201) 845-1000   NV
Web Site: https://www.oncosec.com
Year Founded: 2008
ONCSQ—(NASDAQ)
Assets: $56,275,924
Liabilities: $18,200,123
Net Worth: $38,075,801
Earnings: ($45,167,731)
Emp.: 54
Fiscal Year-end: 07/31/21
Surgical & Medical Instrument Manu-
facturing
N.A.I.C.S.: 339112

OncoSec Medical Incorporated—(Continued)

Robert J. DelAversano (Principal Acctg Officer, VP-Fin & Controller)
Sandra Aung (Chief Clinical Dev Officer & Sr VP)
Robert M. Schinagl (VP-Program & Alliance Mgmt)
Jeff Silverman (VP-Product Engrg)
Bridget O'Keeffe (VP-Clinical Dev)
Joe Smith (VP-Bus Dev)
David Canton (VP)

ONCOTELIC THERAPEUTICS, INC.

29397 Agoura Rd Ste 107, Agoura Hills, CA 91301
Tel.: (650) 635-7000　　DE
Web Site: https://www.oncotelic.com
OTLC—(OTCQB)
Rev.: $14,398,256
Assets: $36,116,819
Liabilities: $16,923,407
Net Worth: $19,193,412
Earnings: $5,094,981
Emp.: 22
Fiscal Year-end: 12/31/22
Cancer Fighting Therapies
N.A.I.C.S.: 325414
Anthony E. Maida III (Chief Clinical Officer-Translational Medicine)
Amit Bhupendra Shah (CFO)
Seymour Fein (Chief Medical Officer)
Vuong Trieu (Chm, Pres & CEO)
Chulho Park (Founder)
Saran Saund (Chief Bus Officer & Gen Mgr-AI Div)

ONCTERNAL THERAPEUTICS, INC.

12230 El Camino Real Ste 230, San Diego, CA 92130
Tel.: (858) 434-1113　　DE
Web Site: https://www.oncternal.com
Year Founded: 1997
ONCT—(NASDAQ)
Rev.: $1,490,000
Assets: $68,651,000
Liabilities: $7,682,000
Net Worth: $60,969,000
Earnings: ($44,170,000)
Emp.: 30
Fiscal Year-end: 12/31/22
Hormone-Targeting Drug Developer
N.A.I.C.S.: 325412
Cam L. Garner (Co-Founder)
Kathleen Scott (CFO)
Richard G. Vincent (CTO)
Rajesh Krishnan (COO)
Pablo Urbaneja (Sr VP-Corp Dev)
Chase Leavitt (Gen Counsel)
James D. Breitmeyer (Pres & CEO)
David F. Hale (Co-Founder & Chm)
Richard G. Vincent (CIO)

ONDAS HOLDINGS, INC.

53 Brigham St Unit 4, Marlborough, MA 01752　　NV
Web Site: https://www.ondas.com
Year Founded: 2014
ONDS—(NASDAQ)
Rev.: $2,125,817
Assets: $97,945,245
Liabilities: $39,722,338
Net Worth: $58,222,907
Earnings: ($73,241,805)
Emp.: 116
Fiscal Year-end: 12/31/22
Sporting Tickets Reseller
N.A.I.C.S.: 459999
Eric A. Brock (Chm)
Menashe Shahar (Founder & CTO)
Susan Roberts (Pres, CEO, CFO & VP)
Neil J. Laird (Principal Acctg Officer, Treas & Sec)

Subsidiaries:

Airobotics Ltd.　　(1)
Modi'In Street 8, Petah Tikva, 4969107, Israel
Tel.: (972) 35374946
Web Site: http://www.airoboticsdrones.com
Rev.: $544,000
Assets: $8,036,000
Liabilities: $4,547,000
Net Worth: $3,489,000
Earnings: ($6,135,000)
Fiscal Year-end: 06/30/2022
Automation Product Mfr
N.A.I.C.S.: 333998
Yishay Curelaru (CFO)
Ron Stern (Chm)
Ran Krauss (Co-Founder & Pres)
Meir Kliner (Co-Founder & CEO)
Eitan Rotberg (Sr VP-Product & Sls)
Niv Russo (VP-Aviation & Regulation)

American Robotics, Inc.　　(1)
411 Waverly Oaks Rd, Waltham, MA 02452
Tel.: (410) 835-9890
Web Site: https://www.american-robotics.com
Automation Machinery Mfr
N.A.I.C.S.: 423830

Ondas Networks Inc.　　(1)
165 Gibraltar Ct, Sunnyvale, CA 94089
Tel.: (888) 350-9994
Web Site: http://www.ondas.com
Wireless Networking Company; Multi-patented, Software Defined Radio (SDR) Designer & Mfr
N.A.I.C.S.: 517111
Stewart G. Kantor (Co-Founder, Pres & CFO)
Eric A. Brock (Chm & CEO)
Menashe Shahar (Co-Founder & CTO)
Guy R. Simpson (COO)
Robert Burchard (Dir-Bus Dev)
Suresh Palliparambil (Chief Revenue Officer)
Jim Jim (Pres-Transportation Bus Unit)
Philip Chu (VP-Asia)
Martin Paget (VP-Indus Solutions)
Kathy Nelson (Dir-Technical Product Mktg & IR)

ONE BIO, CORP.

19950 W Country Club Dr Ste 100, Aventura, FL 33180
Tel.: (305) 328-8662　　FL
Year Founded: 2000
ONBI—(OTCEM)
Sales Range $50-74.9 Million
Emp.: 358
Chemical Intermediates, Herbal Extracts, Natural Supplements & Organic Products Mfr
N.A.I.C.S.: 325998
Cris Neely (CFO)
Marius Silvasan (CEO)

ONE GAS, INC.

15 E 5th St, Tulsa, OK 74103
Tel.: (918) 947-7000　　OK
Web Site: https://www.onegas.com
Year Founded: 1906
OGS—(NYSE)
Rev.: $2,578,005,000
Assets: $7,776,396,000
Liabilities: $2,530,227,000
Net Worth: $5,246,169,000
Earnings: $221,742,000
Emp.: 3,800
Fiscal Year-end: 12/31/22
Natural Gas Distribution Services
N.A.I.C.S.: 221210
W. Kent Shortridge (Sr VP-Ops & Customer Svc)
Curtis L. Dinan (COO & Sr VP)
Joseph L. McCormick (Gen Counsel, Sr VP & Asst Sec)
Robert S. McAnnally (Pres & CEO)
Christopher P. Sighinolfi (CFO & Sr VP)
Angela E. Kouplen (Chief HR Officer & Sr VP)

Brian F. Brumfield (Chief Acctg Officer, VP & Controller)
Mark A. Bender (CIO & Sr VP-Admin)

ONE LIBERTY PROPERTIES, INC.

60 Cutter Mill Rd Ste 303, Great Neck, NY 11021
Tel.: (516) 466-3100　　MD
Web Site: https://www.1liberty.com
Year Founded: 1982
OLP—(NYSE)
Rev.: $92,216,000
Assets: $783,255,000
Liabilities: $466,318,000
Net Worth: $316,937,000
Earnings: $42,177,000
Emp.: 10
Fiscal Year-end: 12/31/22
Other Financial Vehicles
N.A.I.C.S.: 525990
Alysa Block (Treas)
David W. Kalish (Sr VP-Fin)
Lawrence G. Ricketts Jr. (COO & Exec VP)
Mark H. Lundy (Sr VP)
Justin S. Clair (Exec VP)
Isaac Kalish (CFO)
Mili Mathew (Chief Acctg Officer & VP-Fin)
Jeffrey A. Gould (Sr VP)
Fredric H. Gould (Vice Chm)
Israel Rosenzweig (Sr VP)
Patrick J. Callan Jr. (Pres & CEO)

Subsidiaries:

OLP Selden, Inc.　　(1)
60 Cuttermill Rd Ste 303, Great Neck, NY 11021-3104
Tel.: (516) 466-3100
Real Estate Agency & Brokerage Services
N.A.I.C.S.: 531210

ONE STEP VENDING CORP.

600 Mamaroneck Ave, Harrison, NY 10528
Tel.: (619) 701-6799
Web Site: http://www.onestepvend.com
KOSK—(OTCIQ)
Financial Support Services
N.A.I.C.S.: 541611
Vasiliki Anagnostou (Sec)

ONE STOP SYSTEMS, INC.

2235 Enterprise St Ste 110, Escondido, CA 92029
Tel.: (760) 745-9883　　CA
Web Site: https://www.onestopsystems.com
Year Founded: 1998
OSS—(NASDAQ)
Rev.: $72,421,345
Assets: $56,364,571
Liabilities: $12,040,822
Net Worth: $44,323,749
Earnings: ($2,229,055)
Emp.: 104
Fiscal Year-end: 12/31/22
Computer Mfr
N.A.I.C.S.: 334111
Kenneth F. Potashner (Chm)
Jim Ison (Chief Sls & Mktg Officer)
Michael Knowles (Pres & CEO)
Katie Rivera (Mgr-Mktg Comm)
John W. Morrison Jr. (CFO)
Robert Kalebaugh (VP-Sales)
Martin Stiborski (Mng Dir-Bressner Tech)

Subsidiaries:

Bressner Technology GmbH　　(1)
Industriestrasse 51, 82194, Grobenzell, Germany
Tel.: (49) 8142472840
Web Site: https://www.bressner.de
Computer Hardware Distr

N.A.I.C.S.: 423430
Martin Stiborski (Mng Dir)
Florian Jaeger (Head-Mktg & Design)

Magma　　(1)
9918 Via Pasar, San Diego, CA 92126
Tel.: (858) 530-2511
Web Site: http://www.magma.com
Computer Systems Developer & Mfr
N.A.I.C.S.: 334118

ONE WORLD PRODUCTS, INC.

6605 Grand Montecito Pkwy ste 100, Las Vegas, NV 89149　　NV
Web Site: https://www.oneworldpharma.com
Year Founded: 2014
OWPC—(OTCQB)
Rev.: $7,589
Assets: $98,882
Liabilities: $8,446,956
Net Worth: ($8,348,074)
Earnings: ($3,953,321)
Emp.: 10
Fiscal Year-end: 12/31/23
Software Development Services
N.A.I.C.S.: 513210
Todd Peterson (CFO)
Isiah L. Thomas III (Vice Chm & CEO)
Kenneth L. Perego II (Chm)

ONE WORLD VENTURES, INC.

3370 Pinks Pl Ste F, Las Vegas, NV 89102
Tel.: (702) 331-9700
Web Site: https://www.oneworldventuresinc.com
OWVI—(OTCIQ)
Rev.: $62,340
Assets: $833,262
Liabilities: $94,970
Net Worth: $738,292
Earnings: ($1,154,336)
Emp.: 3
Fiscal Year-end: 12/31/22
Medicinal & Botanical Manufacturing
N.A.I.C.S.: 325411
Damu Lin (CEO)

ONELIFE TECHNOLOGIES CORP.

5005 Newport Dr, Rolling Meadows, IL 60008
Tel.: (708) 469-7378　　NV
Web Site: http://www.onelifetc.com
Year Founded: 2014
OLMM—(OTCEM)
Assets: $1,752,719
Liabilities: $3,359,766
Net Worth: ($1,607,047)
Earnings: ($753,449)
Emp.: 3
Fiscal Year-end: 12/31/18
Investment Services
N.A.I.C.S.: 523999
Jody M. Janson (Dir-Investor Relations)

ONEMETA, INC.

1 Hampshire Ct, Newport Beach, CA 92660
Tel.: (949) 642-7816　　NV
Web Site: https://www.onemeta.ai
Year Founded: 2006
ONEI—(OTCQB)
Sales Range: $1-9.9 Million
Software Producer
N.A.I.C.S.: 513210
Rowland W. Day II (Chm, CEO & CFO)

ONEOK, INC.

100 W 5th St, Tulsa, OK 74103
Tel.: (918) 588-7000　　OK
Web Site: https://www.oneok.com
Year Founded: 1906

OKE—(NYSE)
Rev.: $17,677,000,000
Assets: $44,266,000,000
Liabilities: $27,782,000,000
Net Worth: $16,484,000,000
Earnings: $2,658,000,000
Emp.: 4,775
Fiscal Year-end: 12/31/23
Natural Gas Extraction Services
N.A.I.C.S.: 211130
Pierce H. Norton II *(Pres & CEO)*
Julie H. Edwards *(Chm)*
Walter S. Hulse III *(CFO, Treas & Exec VP-Strategic Plng & Corp Affairs)*
Kevin L. Burdick *(Chief Comml Officer & Exec VP)*
Stephen B. Allen *(Gen Counsel, Sr VP & Asst Sec)*
Patrick Cipolla *(Sec, VP & Assoc Gen Counsel)*
Darren J. Wallis *(Sr VP-Comm & Community Rels)*

Subsidiaries:

Kansas Gas Service Company **(1)**
7421 W 129th St, Overland Park, KS 66213
Tel.: (913) 319-8600
Web Site:
   https://www.kansasgasservice.com
Sales Range: $650-699.9 Million
Emp.: 1,000
Gas Utility
N.A.I.C.S.: 221210

Magellan Midstream Partners,
L.P. **(1)**
1 Williams Ctr, Tulsa, OK 74121-2186
Tel.: (918) 574-7000
Web Site: https://www.magellanlp.com
Rev.: $3,200,400,000
Assets: $7,707,700,000
Liabilities: $6,022,800,000
Net Worth: $1,684,900,000
Earnings: $1,036,400,000
Emp.: 1,655
Fiscal Year-end: 12/31/2022
Transporter, Distributor & Warehousing of Refined Petroleum Products & Ammonia
N.A.I.C.S.: 424710

Joint Venture (Non-US):

BridgeTex Pipeline Company,
LLC **(2)**

Subsidiary (Domestic):

Magellan Pipeline Company, L.P. **(2)**
2120 S 33rd W Ave, Tulsa, OK 74107
Tel.: (918) 587-2961
Petroleum Product Pipeline Transportation Services
N.A.I.C.S.: 486910

Magellan Pipeline LP **(2)**
2503 SE 43rd St, Des Moines, IA 50327
Tel.: (918) 574-7011
Sales Range: $25-49.9 Million
Emp.: 22
Refined Petroleum Pipelines
N.A.I.C.S.: 486910

Magellan Processing, L.P. **(2)**
1 One Williams Ctr, Tulsa, OK 74172
Tel.: (918) 574-7000
Petroleum Bulk Stations & Terminal Operator
N.A.I.C.S.: 424710

ONEOK Energy Marketing & Trading
Company, II **(1)**
100 W 5th St, Tulsa, OK 74103
Tel.: (918) 588-7000
Web Site: http://www.oneok.com
Natural Gas
N.A.I.C.S.: 221210

ONEOK Energy Resources
Company **(1)**
100 W 5th St, Tulsa, OK 74103 **(100%)**
Tel.: (918) 588-7000
Sales Range: $125-149.9 Million
Emp.: 150
Oil & Gas Exploration & Production
N.A.I.C.S.: 213111

ONEOK Field Services Company,
L.L.C. **(1)**
114 W 2nd St, Hugoton, KS 67951-2004
Tel.: (620) 544-2179
Natural Gas Distribution
N.A.I.C.S.: 221210

ONEOK Foundation, Inc. **(1)**
100 W Fifth St, Tulsa, OK 74103
Tel.: (918) 588-7000
Educational Support Services
N.A.I.C.S.: 611710
Terri Pirtle *(Exec Dir)*

ONEOK Gas Processing, LLC **(1)**
100 W 5th St Ste Ll, Tulsa, OK
74103 **(100%)**
Tel.: (918) 588-7000
Web Site: http://www.ong.com
Rev.: $77,980,000
Emp.: 400
Gas Liquids Extraction
N.A.I.C.S.: 486210

ONEOK Leasing Company **(1)**
100 W 5th St Ste LL, Tulsa, OK 74103
Tel.: (918) 591-5000
Emp.: 7
Natural Gas Pipeline Transportation Services
N.A.I.C.S.: 486210

ONEOK Partners, L.P. **(1)**
100 W 5th St, Tulsa, OK 74103 **(100%)**
Tel.: (918) 588-7000
Web Site: http://www.oneokpartners.com
Rev.: $8,918,459,000
Assets: $15,469,347,000
Liabilities: $9,291,527,000
Net Worth: $6,177,820,000
Earnings: $1,066,767,000
Fiscal Year-end: 12/31/2016
Holding Company; Natural Gas Collection, Processing, Storage & Transportation
N.A.I.C.S.: 551112

Subsidiary (Domestic):

Guardian Pipeline, L.L.C. **(2)**
100 W 5th St MD 2, Tulsa, OK 74103
Tel.: (918) 588-7770
Web Site: https://www.oneok.com
Natural Gas Distribution
N.A.I.C.S.: 221210

Midwestern Gas Transmission
Company **(2)**
100 W 5th St MD 12-4, Tulsa, OK 74103
Tel.: (918) 588-7770
Web Site: https://www.oneok.com
Sales Range: $400-449.9 Million
Emp.: 43
Operator of Natural Gas Pipeline
N.A.I.C.S.: 221210

ONEOK Gas Storage, LLC **(2)**
PO Box 871, Tulsa, OK
74102-0871 **(100%)**
Tel.: (918) 588-7000
Sales Range: $500-549.9 Million
Emp.: 1,000
Operator of Natural Gas Underground Storage & Transmission System
N.A.I.C.S.: 486210

ONEOK Gas Transportation,
LLC **(2)**
100 W 5th St, Tulsa, OK
74103-4298 **(100%)**
Tel.: (918) 588-7851
Web Site: http://www.oneok.com
Sales Range: $1-9.9 Million
Operator of Natural Gas Pipeline System
N.A.I.C.S.: 486210

ONEOK Hydrocarbon, L.L.C. **(2)**
462 Hwy 56, Conway, KS 67460-6129
Tel.: (620) 834-2204
Natural Gas Distribution
N.A.I.C.S.: 221210

Viking Gas Transmission
Company **(2)**
100 W 5th St MD 2, Tulsa, OK 74103
Tel.: (918) 588-7770
Gas Transmission
N.A.I.C.S.: 486110
John W. Gibson *(Chm & CEO)*
John William Gibson *(Chm & CEO)*
Pierce H. Norton II *(Exec VP-Natural Gas)*

Oklahoma Natural Gas Company **(1)**
401 N Harvey, Oklahoma City, OK 73101-0401
Tel.: (918) 831-8240
Web Site:
   http://www.oklahomanaturalgas.com
Rev.: $1,400,000,000
Emp.: 1,100
Purchase, Transmission, Storage & Distribution of Natural Gas; Leasing Pipeline Capacity
N.A.I.C.S.: 221210

Texas Gas Service Co. **(1)**
1301 S Mopac Expwy Ste 400, Austin, TX 78746
Tel.: (512) 947-2199
Web Site: https://www.texasgasservice.com
Sales Range: $50-74.9 Million
Emp.: 860
Natural Gas Distribution Company
N.A.I.C.S.: 221210

West Texas LPG Pipeline Limited
Partnership **(1)**
4800 Fournace Pl, Bellaire, TX 77401
Tel.: (713) 432-2866
Gas Liquids Pipeline Transportation Services
N.A.I.C.S.: 486210

ONEROOF ENERGY GROUP, INC.
4445 Eastgate Mall Rd Ste 240, San Diego, CA 92121
Tel.: (858) 458-0533 ON
Web Site:
   http://www.oneroofenergy.com
Year Founded: 2010
ON—(TSXV)
Sales Range: $1-9.9 Million
Solar Energy Systems
N.A.I.C.S.: 333415
David Field *(Co-Founder, Pres & CEO)*
Dale Vander Woude *(Exec VP-Capital Markets, Strategy & Mergers & Acq)*
Valerie Iwinski *(Sr VP-Ops)*
Dalton Sprinkle *(Gen Counsel & Sr VP)*
Alan Whiting *(Co-Founder & Sr VP-Fin)*
Kirk Mulligan *(VP-Bus Strategy & Dev)*
Michael W. Allman *(Chm)*
Brian Alexson *(COO)*
John Bunnel *(Interim CFO)*

Subsidiaries:

OneRoof Energy, Inc. **(1)**
4445 Eastgate Mall Rd Ste 240, San Diego, CA 92121
Tel.: (858) 785-9554
Web Site: http://www.oneroofenergy.com
Electronic Parts & Equipment Merchant Whslr
N.A.I.C.S.: 423690
Nick Hofer *(VP-Sls & Mktg)*
Brian Alexson *(COO)*
Robert Martorano Jr. *(Exec VP-Capital Markets)*

ONESCREEN, INC.
310 Commerce Ste 200, Irvine, CA 92602
Tel.: (714) 363-5250 DE
Web Site: http://www.onescreen.com
OSCN—(OTCIQ)
Sales Range: Less than $1 Million
Emp.: 18
Video Programming & Content Distr
N.A.I.C.S.: 516210
Atul Patel *(Founder)*
David Eakles *(Dir-Education)*
Sufian Munir *(CEO)*

ONESPAN INC.
1 Marina Park Dr Unit 1410, Boston, MA 02210
Tel.: (312) 766-4001 DE

Web Site: https://www.onespan.com
OSPN—(NASDAQ)
Rev.: $219,006,000
Assets: $335,082,000
Liabilities: $131,771,000
Net Worth: $203,311,000
Earnings: ($14,434,000)
Emp.: 790
Fiscal Year-end: 12/31/22
Authentication & Digital Signature Technologies to Secure Intranets, Extranets & Local Area Networks
N.A.I.C.S.: 541512
Michael W. Lillie *(CIO)*
John Gunn *(CMO)*
Tracy McCarthy *(Chief HR Officer)*
Joe Maxa *(VP-IR)*
Jorge Garcia Martell *(CFO & Principal Acctg Officer)*
Giovanni Verhaeghe *(VP-Corp Dev & Hardware Ops)*
Ajay Keni *(CTO)*
Lara Mataac *(Chief Compliance Officer & Gen Counsel)*
Stuti Bhargava *(Chief Customer Experience Officer)*
M. Samy Ibrahim *(Chief Revenue Officer)*
Tom Aurelio *(Chief People Officer)*
Sameer Hajarnis *(Chief Product Officer)*
Eric Hanson *(CMO)*
Caroline Vignollet *(Sr VP)*
Victor T. Limongelli *(Pres & CEO)*

Subsidiaries:

Cronto Limited **(1)**
5 Churchill Place 10th Floor, London, E14 5HU, United Kingdom
Tel.: (44) 15083663400
Web Site: http://www.cronto.com
Banking Services
N.A.I.C.S.: 523150

Kabushiki Kaisha VASCO Data Security Japan **(1)**
Level 8 Kishimoto Building 2-2-1, Marunouchi Chiyoda-ku, Tokyo, 100-0005, Japan
Tel.: (81) 345806080
Data Security Software Publisher
N.A.I.C.S.: 513210

OneSpan Canada Inc. **(1)**
Windsor Station 1100 Ave des Canadiens-de-Montreal Suite 250, Montreal, H3B 2S2, QC, Canada
Tel.: (514) 337-5255
Security & Electronic Signature Services
N.A.I.C.S.: 541511

VASCO Data Security Australia Pty
Ltd **(1)**
Level 12 680 George Street, 503-505 Kent Street, Sydney, 2000, NSW, Australia
Tel.: (61) 280613700
Sales Range: $10-24.9 Million
Emp.: 5
Authentication & Digital Signature Solution Provider
N.A.I.C.S.: 513210

VASCO Data Security Austria
GmbH **(1)**
Perfektastrasse 45, 1230, Vienna, Austria
Tel.: (43) 190431320
Sales Range: $25-49.9 Million
Emp.: 17
Authentication & Digital Signature Solution Provider
N.A.I.C.S.: 541511

VASCO Data Security International,
GmbH **(1)**
Scharenmoosstrasse 77, 8052, Zurich, Switzerland
Tel.: (41) 435553500
Emp.: 30
Authentication & Digital Signature Solutions Provider
N.A.I.C.S.: 541511

VASCO Data Security Middle East
FZE **(1)**

OneSpan Inc.—(Continued)

Dubai Silicon Oasis HQ B Wing Office 303
302, PO Box 341093, Dubai, United Arab
Emirates
Tel.: (971) 43712989
Cybersecurity; Authentication & Digital Sig-
nature Services
N.A.I.C.S.: 541512

VASCO Data Security NV/SA (1)
Romeinsesteenweg 564 C, 1853,
Strombeek-Bever, Belgium
Tel.: (32) 26099700
Emp.: 300
Semiconductor Materials & Packaging Prod-
ucts Mfr
N.A.I.C.S.: 334413

VASCO Data Security, Inc. (1)
121 W Wacker Dr Ste 2050, Chicago, IL
60601
Tel.: (312) 766-4001
Web Site: https://www.onespan.com
Sales Range: $25-49.9 Million
Emp.: 850
Computer System Integration Services
N.A.I.C.S.: 541512

**Vasco Data Security Asia-Pacific Pte
Ltd** (1)
128 Neil Road, Singapore, 088858, Singa-
pore
Tel.: (65) 63230906
Sales Range: $1-9.9 Million
Emp.: 10
Computer Security Software Publisher
N.A.I.C.S.: 513210

Vasco Data Security B.V. (1)
Staringstraat 28 H, 1054 VR, Amsterdam,
Netherlands
Tel.: (31) 852016106
Sales Range: $50-74.9 Million
Emp.: 40
Computer Security Software Publisher
N.A.I.C.S.: 513210

**Vasco Data Security Europe
NV/SA** (1)
Koningin Astridlaan 164, 1780, Wemmel,
Belgium
Tel.: (32) 26099700
Web Site: http://www.vasco.com
Sales Range: $25-49.9 Million
Emp.: 200
Computer Security Software Publisher
N.A.I.C.S.: 513210

Vasco Data Security Pty Ltd (1)
Damiano House Level 12 503-505, Kent
Street, Sydney, 2000, NSW, Australia
Tel.: (61) 280613700
Web Site: http://www.vasco.com
Computer Security Software Publisher
N.A.I.C.S.: 513210

ONESPAWORLD HOLDINGS LIMITED

770 S Dixie Hwy Ste 200, Coral
Gables, FL 33146
Tel.: (305) 284-1400   BS
Web Site:
   https://www.onespaworld.com
Year Founded: 1901
OSW—(NASDAQ)
Rev.: $546,259,000
Assets: $717,435,000
Liabilities: $351,626,000
Net Worth: $365,809,000
Earnings: $53,159,000
Emp.: 4,452
Fiscal Year-end: 12/31/22
Holding Company
N.A.I.C.S.: 551112
Steven J. Heyer (Vice Chm)
Stephen B. Lazarus (CFO & COO)
Kyle Mendes (Sr VP-Fin & Bus Intelli-
gence)
Trent Munday (Sr VP-Resort Ops-
Asia)
Tim Dux (Sr VP-Maritime Ops)
Eduardo Chamia (Sr VP-Sls & Rev-
enue)
Jesus Padilla (VP-Resort Ops)

Youlanda Deveaux (VP-Resort Ops-
Caribbean & Latin America)
Darryll Leiman (VP-Resort Ops-
Pacific)
Robert Schaverien (Mng Dir-London
Wellness Academy)
Leonard Fluxman (Exec Chm, Pres &
Co-CEO)

Subsidiaries:

Mandara Spa (Bahamas) Limited (1)
PO Box N-4777, Nassau, Bahamas
Tel.: (242) 3633000
Spa Services
N.A.I.C.S.: 812199

Mandara Spa Aruba N.V. (1)
101 LG Smith Blvd, Palm Beach,
Oranjestad, Aruba
Tel.: (297) 5206750
Spa Services
N.A.I.C.S.: 812199

Mandara Spa Palau (1)
PO Box 10108, Koror, PW 96940
Tel.: (680) 488-2000
Web Site: http://www.palau-royal-resort.com
Spa Services
N.A.I.C.S.: 812199

Mandara Spa Puerto Rico, Inc. (1)
6000 Rio Mar Blvd, Rio Grande, PR 00745-
6100
Tel.: (787) 888-6285
Spa Services
N.A.I.C.S.: 812199

PT Mandara Spa Indonesia (1)
Jl Raya Nusa Dua Selatan Nusa Dua, Bali,
80363, Indonesia
Tel.: (62) 361773377
Spa Services
N.A.I.C.S.: 812199

ONEWATER MARINE INC.

6275 Lanier Islands Pkwy, Buford,
GA 30518
Tel.: (678) 541-6300   DE
Web Site:
   https://www.onewatermarine.com
Year Founded: 2019
ONEW—(NASDAQ)
Rev.: $1,772,630,000
Assets: $1,589,989,000
Liabilities: $1,199,236,000
Net Worth: $390,753,000
Earnings: ($6,176,000)
Emp.: 2,203
Fiscal Year-end: 09/30/24
Boat Retailer
N.A.I.C.S.: 441222
Philip Austin Singleton Jr. (Founder &
CEO)
Anthony M. Aisquith (Pres & COO)
Jack Ezzell (CFO)
John F. Schraudenbach (Chm)
Scott Cunningham Sr. (Exec VP)

Subsidiaries:

All Oceans Closings LLC (1)
850 NE 3rd St Ste 203, Dania Beach, FL
33004
Tel.: (954) 500-2556
Web Site:
   https://www.alloceansclosings.com
Marine Yacht Documentation Services
N.A.I.C.S.: 541990

Denison Yachting, LLC (1)
850 NE 3rd St, Dania Beach, FL 33004
Tel.: (954) 763-3971
Web Site:
   https://www.denisonyachtsales.com
Yacht Finance & Insurance Services
N.A.I.C.S.: 524210

Norfolk Marine Company (1)
5221 E Virginia Beach Blvd, Norfolk, VA
23502-3414
Tel.: (757) 461-3391
Web Site: http://www.norfolkmarine.com
Fishing
N.A.I.C.S.: 114111
Jason Murphy (Pres)

Ocean Bio-Chem, LLC (1)
4041 SW 47th Ave, Fort Lauderdale, FL
33314-4023
Tel.: (954) 587-6280
Rev.: $64,298,595
Assets: $60,277,704
Liabilities: $12,841,586
Net Worth: $47,436,118
Earnings: $8,403,968
Emp.: 195
Fiscal Year-end: 12/31/2021
Cleaning & Polishing Agents For Boats,
Cars & Aircraft Mfr
N.A.I.C.S.: 325612

Division (Domestic):

Kinpak, Inc. (2)
2780 Gunter Park Dr E, Montgomery, AL
36109-1403   (100%)
Tel.: (334) 279-6550
Web Site: http://www.starbrite.com
Sales Range: $1-9.9 Million
Emp.: 70
Chemical Formulation Filling & Packaging &
Plastic Container Manufacturing
N.A.I.C.S.: 325612

Subsidiary (Domestic):

OdorStar Technology, LLC (2)
4041 SW 47th Ave, Fort Lauderdale, FL
33314
Tel.: (954) 587-6280
Web Site: https://odorstar.com
Chemical Products Mfr
N.A.I.C.S.: 424690

Star brite Corp. (2)
4041 SW 47th Ave, Fort Lauderdale, FL
33314
Tel.: (954) 587-6280
Web Site: http://www.starbrite.com
Sales Range: $10-24.9 Million
Emp.: 45
Mfr of Marine, Automotive & RV Chemical
Appearance Products; Brushes, Straps, Tie
Downs
N.A.I.C.S.: 325612
Peter G. Dornau (Pres & CEO)
Victor Phillpotts (VP-Bus Dev)
Marc Emmi (Sr VP-Sls)
Kouri Carey (Mktg Dir)
Justin Gould (VP-Tech)
Eric Hahn (Dir-Sls & Mktg)
Natalie Fino (VP-Customer Svc)
Erik Applegate (Dir-Sls & Mktg)
Derick Cote (Dir-Sls & Mktg)

Star brite Distributing, Inc. (2)
4041 SW 47th Ave, Fort Lauderdale, FL
33314
Tel.: (954) 587-6280
Web Site: http://www.starbrite.com
Polishing & Cleaning Preparations Mfr
N.A.I.C.S.: 325612

Subsidiary (Domestic):

Snappy Marine Inc. (3)
4041 SW 47th Ave,, Fort Lauderdale, FL
33314
Tel.: (954) 486-3513
Web Site: http://www.starbrite.com
Chemicals Mfr
N.A.I.C.S.: 325998
Gerri Evans (Pres)

Star Brite Europe, LLC (1)
4041 SW 47th Ave, Fort Lauderdale, FL
33314
Tel.: (954) 587-6280
Web Site: https://www.starbrite.com
Marine Cleaning Chemical Mfr & Distr
N.A.I.C.S.: 325611

Taylor Marine Center, Inc. (1)
22699 Argos Corner Rd, Milford, DE 19963
Tel.: (302) 422-9177
Web Site:
   http://www.taylormarinecenter.com
Boat Dealers
N.A.I.C.S.: 441222

ONFOLIO HOLDINGS INC.

1007 N Orange St 4th Fl, Wilmington,
DE 19801
Tel.: (682) 990-6920   DE
Web Site: https://onfolio.com

Year Founded: 2020
ONFO—(NASDAQ)
Rev.: $2,219,815
Assets: $15,775,826
Liabilities: $3,303,391
Net Worth: $12,472,435
Earnings: ($4,429,502)
Emp.: 7
Fiscal Year-end: 12/31/22
Holding Company
N.A.I.C.S.: 551112
Dominic Wells (CEO, Chief Revenue
Officer, Chm, Treas & Sec)
Esbe van Heerden (Pres & CFO)
Adam Trainor (COO)

ONITY GROUP INC.

1661 Worthington Rd Ste 100, West
Palm Beach, FL 33409
Tel.: (561) 682-8000   FL
Web Site: https://www.ocwen.com
Year Founded: 1988
ONIT—(NYSE)
Rev.: $953,900,000
Assets: $12,399,200,000
Liabilities: $11,942,500,000
Net Worth: $456,700,000
Earnings: $25,700,000
Emp.: 4,900
Fiscal Year-end: 12/31/22
Holding Company; Mortgage Lending
Services
N.A.I.C.S.: 551112
Andy Peach (Sr VP-Correspondent
Sls)
Glen A. Messina (Pres & CEO)
Scott W. Anderson (Chief Servicing
Officer & Exec VP)
Albert Celini (Chief Risk & Compli-
ance Officer & Sr VP)
Francois Grunenwald (Chief Acctg
Officer & Sr VP)
Dennis Zeleny (Chief Admin Officer &
Exec VP)
Sean O'Neil (CFO & Exec VP)
Aaron Wade (Chief Investment Offi-
cer)

Subsidiaries:

Automotive Capital Services, Inc. (1)
16675 Addison Rd, Addison, TX 75001
Tel.: (800) 800-6494
Web Site: http://www.autocapservices.com
Used Vehicle Retailer
N.A.I.C.S.: 441110

Ocwen Loan Servicing, LLC (1)
1661 Worthington Rd Ste 100, West Palm
Beach, FL 33409
Tel.: (561) 682-8000
Web Site: http://www.ocwencustomers.com
Home Loan Mortgage Services
N.A.I.C.S.: 522299

Ocwen Mortgage Servicing, Inc. (1)
402 Strand St, Frederiksted, VI 00840-3531
Tel.: (561) 682-7671
Financial Management Services
N.A.I.C.S.: 541611

PHH Corporation (1)
3000 Leadenhall Rd, Mount Laurel, NJ
08054
Tel.: (856) 917-1744
Web Site: http://www.phh.com
Rev.: $456,000,000
Assets: $1,811,000,000
Liabilities: $1,258,000,000
Net Worth: $553,000,000
Earnings: ($217,000,000)
Emp.: 1,365
Fiscal Year-end: 12/31/2017
Direct Consumer Mortgages & Fleet Man-
agement Services
N.A.I.C.S.: 522310

Subsidiary (Domestic):

CUNA Mutual Mortgage (2)
1661 Worthington Rd Ste 100, West Palm
Beach, FL 33409

Tel.: (608) 231-2516
Web Site: https://www.ocwen.com
Sales Range: $125-149.9 Million
Mortgage Banking Services for Credit
Unions & Credit Union Services
N.A.I.C.S.: 522292

Center for Transportation Safety,
LLC (2)
10233 S Parker Rd Ste 300, Parker, CO
80134
Web Site: https://drivingcts.com
Automobile Driving School Services
N.A.I.C.S.: 611692

PHH Home Loans, LLC (2)
3000 Leadenhall Rd, Mount Laurel, NJ
08054
Tel.: (952) 844-6300
Mortgage & Nonmortgage Loan Broker
N.A.I.C.S.: 522310

PHH Mortgage Capital LLC (2)
1 Mortgage Way, Mount Laurel, NJ 08054
Tel.: (866) 946-0081
Mortgage & Nonmortgage Loan Broker
N.A.I.C.S.: 522310

PHH Mortgage Corporation (2)
2000 Midlantic Dr Ste 410-A, Mount Laurel,
NJ 08054
Tel.: (856) 917-1744
Web Site: https://www.phhmortgage.com
Sales Range: $1-4.9 Billion
Retail Residential Mortgage Services
N.A.I.C.S.: 522310

Reverse Mortgage Solutions,
Inc. (2)
14405 Walters Rd Ste 200, Houston, TX
77014
Web Site: http://www.rmsnav.com
Mortgage Loan Brokerage Services
N.A.I.C.S.: 522310
Jeffrey P. Baker (Pres)

Williamsburg Motors, Inc. (2)
701 E Rochambeau Dr, Williamsburg, VA
23188
Tel.: (888) 409-2130
Web Site: http://www.williamsburgford.com
New & Used Car Dealer Services
N.A.I.C.S.: 441110
Steve Mullen (Sls Mgr)
Paul Caswell (Mgr-Parts)
Jess Centry (Gen Mgr)
Gordan Hatcher (Sls Mgr)
Jack Bizzell (Mgr-Comml & Fleet)
Russ Beach (Fin Mgr)
Angela Hastings (Fin Mgr)
Deborah McMillian (Sls Mgr-Internet)
Mike Romano (Dir-Fixed Ops)
Brain Phipps (Mgr-Svc)
Tray Gibson (Mgr-Parts)

ONKURE THERAPEUTICS,
INC.
6707 Winchester Cir Ste 400, Boul-
der, CO 80301
Tel.: (720) 307-2892 DE
Web Site:
https://onkuretherapeutics.com
Year Founded: 2014
OKUR—(NASDAQ)
Rev.: $1,893,000
Assets: $108,182,000
Liabilities: $8,212,000
Net Worth: $99,970,000
Earnings: ($51,955,000)
Emp.: 36
Fiscal Year-end: 12/31/22
Biopharmaceutical Developer
N.A.I.C.S.: 325412
Alejandro Dorenbaum (Chief Medical
Officer)
Lynn Purkins (VP-Clinical Ops)
Niall O'Donnell (Founder)
Deborah Tower (VP-Fin & Admin)
Ashley F. Hall (Chief Dev Officer)
Gregory J. Flesher (Pres & CEO)
Michael P. Cruse (COO)
Jennifer P. Lam (Principal Fin & Acctg
Officer)
Michael G. Grey (Chm)

Subsidiaries:

OnKure, Inc. (1)
6707 Winchester Cir Ste 400, Boulder, CO
80301
Tel.: (720) 307-2892
Biopharmaceutical Developer
N.A.I.C.S.: 325412

ONLINE DISRUPTIVE TECH-
NOLOGIES, INC.
10 Stevens St, Andover, MA 01810-
3572
Tel.: (978) 886-1071 NV
Year Founded: 2009
ONDR—(OTCIQ)
Sales Range: Less than $1 Million
Emp.: 10
Social Media Network Services
N.A.I.C.S.: 516210
Giora Davidovits (Pres, CEO, CFO &
Treas)

ONLINE VACATION CENTER
HOLDINGS CORP.
2307 W Broward Blvd Ste 400, Fort
Lauderdale, FL 33312-1417
Tel.: (954) 377-6400 FL
Web Site:
https://www.onlinevacationcen
ter.com
Year Founded: 1996
ONVC—(OTCIQ)
Sales Range: $10-24.9 Million
Emp.: 80
Tour Operator
N.A.I.C.S.: 561510
Edward B. Rudner (Chm & CEO)
Stephen A. Rudner (Pres)

Subsidiaries:

Online Vacation Center, Inc. (1)
2307 W Broward Blvd Ste 400, Fort Lauder-
dale, FL 33312-4534
Tel.: (954) 377-6400
Web Site:
http://www.onlinevacationcenter.com
Travel Agencies
N.A.I.C.S.: 561510
Edward B. Rudner (Chm, Pres, CEO &
CFO)
Stephen A. Rudner (CFO, VP & Head-IT
Dept)

ONS ACQUISITION CORP.
407 N Maple Dr Ground Fl, Beverly
Hills, CA 90210
Tel.: (424) 210-9848 Ky
Year Founded: 2020
ONS'U—(NYSE)
Investment Services
N.A.I.C.S.: 523999
Alexander Crutchfield (CEO & Chm)
Joachim Gfoeller (CFO)

ONTO INNOVATION INC.
16 Jonspin Rd, Wilmington, MA
01887
Tel.: (978) 253-6200 DE
Web Site:
https://www.ontoinnovation.com
Year Founded: 1975
ONTO—(NYSE)
Rev.: $788,899,000
Assets: $1,649,813,000
Liabilities: $223,758,000
Net Worth: $1,426,055,000
Earnings: $142,349,000
Emp.: 1,411
Fiscal Year-end: 01/01/22
Holding Company; High-Performance
Process Control Metrology Systems
Designer & Mfr
N.A.I.C.S.: 551112
Michael P. Plisinski (CEO)
Christopher A. Seams (Chm)
Mark Slicer (CFO)
Ramil Yaldaei (COO)

Mark R. Slicer (CFO)
Cody Harlow (COO)
Michel Ross (CMO)
Srini Vedula (Sr VP)
Yoon Ah Oh (Gen Counsel)
Barry Hartunian (Sr VP)

Subsidiaries:

4D Technology Corporation (1)
3280 E Hemisphere Loop Ste 146, Tucson,
AZ 85706
Tel.: (520) 294-5600
Web Site: https://www.4dtechnology.com
Emp.: 35
Optical Instrument & Lens Mfr
N.A.I.C.S.: 333310

Nanometrics China Company
Ltd. (1)
4F-1 No 28 Xin Jin Qiao Road, Pudong,
Shanghai, 201206, China
Tel.: (86) 2158543030
Semiconductor Machinery Mfr
N.A.I.C.S.: 333242

Nanometrics U.K. Ltd. (1)
3-7 Rose Ave York Business Park Nether
Poppleton, York, YO26 6RU, United King-
dom
Tel.: (44) 1904529700
Web Site: http://www.nanometrics.com
Emp.: 39
Optoelectronic Device Mfr
N.A.I.C.S.: 334413

Onto Innovation Southeast Asia Pte.
Limited (1)
6 Serangoon North Avenue 5 05-12, Singa-
pore, 554910, Singapore
Tel.: (65) 65710550
Semiconductor Mfr
N.A.I.C.S.: 334413

Rudolph Technologies, Inc. (1)
16 Jonspin Rd, Wilmington, MA 01887
Tel.: (978) 253-6200
Web Site: http://www.rudolphtech.com
Rev.: $273,784,000
Assets: $418,040,000
Liabilities: $56,152,000
Net Worth: $361,888,000
Earnings: $45,096,000
Emp.: 651
Fiscal Year-end: 12/31/2018
Process Control Metrology & Defect Inspec-
tion Equipment Mfr
N.A.I.C.S.: 334513

Subsidiary (Non-US):

Onto Innovation Europe, B.V. (2)
Suite 7 Stuart House, Eskmills Business
Park, Musselburgh, EH21 7PB, United
Kingdom
Tel.: (44) 1312734321
Semiconductor & Related Device Mfr
N.A.I.C.S.: 334413

Unit (Domestic):

Rudolph Technologies, Inc. - Inspec-
tion Systems (2)
4900 W 78th St, Bloomington, MN 55435
Tel.: (952) 820-0080
Web Site: https://ontoinnovation.com
Automated Visual Inspection Equipment Mfr
N.A.I.C.S.: 335999

ONTRAK, INC.
333 S E 2nd Ave Ste 2000, Miami,
FL 33131
Tel.: (310) 444-4300 DE
Web Site:
https://www.ontrakhealth.com
OTRK—(NASDAQ)
Rev.: $14,514,000
Assets: $25,757,000
Liabilities: $20,080,000
Net Worth: $5,677,000
Earnings: ($60,527,000)
Emp.: 118
Fiscal Year-end: 12/31/22
Behavioral Health Management Ser-
vices
N.A.I.C.S.: 621420

Terren S. Peizer (Exec Chm & CEO)
Susan Etzel (Sr VP-Fin)
Patrick Traynor (Sr VP-Engrg & Ops)
Charles Polatsek (VP-Sls)
Sandy Gyenes (Sr VP-HR)
Brandon H. LaVerne (Co-Pres &
COO)
Jaime Prieto (CMO)
Jonathan Mayhew (CEO)
Judith Feld (Chief Medical Officer)
Sunmi Janicek (Chief Compliance &
Privacy Officer)
Brandy Butler (VP-Ops, Trng & Dev)
Arik Hill (CIO)
James Park (CFO)
Mary Lou Osborne (Co-Pres & Chief
Comml Officer)

Subsidiaries:

LifeDojo Inc. (1)
2200 Paseo Verde Pkwy Ste 280, Hender-
son, NV 89052
Tel.: (415) 604-1700
Web Site: https://www.lifedojo.com
Management Consulting Services
N.A.I.C.S.: 541618

OOMA, INC.
525 Almanor Ave Ste 200, Sunny-
vale, CA 94085
Tel.: (650) 566-6600 DE
Web Site: https://www.ooma.com
Year Founded: 2004
OOMA—(NYSE)
Rev.: $216,165,000
Assets: $131,005,000
Liabilities: $67,861,000
Net Worth: $63,144,000
Earnings: ($3,655,000)
Emp.: 454
Fiscal Year-end: 01/31/23
Communications Software
N.A.I.C.S.: 513210
James A. Gustke (VP-Mktg)
Tobin E. Farrand (VP-Engrg & Ops)
Dennis C. Peng (VP-Product Mgmt)
Timothy J. Sullivan (VP-Sls)
Shigeyuki Hamamatsu (CFO, Treas &
VP)
Chris Burgy (VP-Corp Dev)
Dayton Turner (VP-Enterprise Prod-
uct)
Robert Ferrer (VP-Bus Sls)
Matthew S. Robison (Dir-IR & Corp
Dev)
Ray Apple (VP-Customer Svc)
Namrata Sabharwal (Chief Acctg Offi-
cer)
Eric Bradford Stang (Chm, Pres &
CEO)
Jenny C. Yeh (Gen Counsel & Sec)

Subsidiaries:

Broadsmart Global, Inc. (1)
4910 Communication Ave Ste 110, Boca
Raton, FL 33431
Tel.: (954) 449-8000
Web Site: https://www.broadsmart.com
Broadband & Cloud-based Data & Voice
Solutions Provider
N.A.I.C.S.: 518210

Junction Networks Inc. (1)
55 Broad St 20th Fl, New York, NY 10004
Tel.: (212) 933-9190
Web Site: http://www.onsip.com
Telecommunications
N.A.I.C.S.: 517810

OP BANCORP
1000 Wilshire Blvd Ste 500, Los An-
geles, CA 90017
Tel.: (213) 892-9999 CA
Web Site:
https://www.myopenbank.com
Year Founded: 2016
OPBK—(NASDAQ)
Rev.: $105,831,000

OP Bancorp—(Continued)

Assets: $2,094,497,000
Liabilities: $1,917,581,000
Net Worth: $176,916,000
Earnings: $33,310,000
Emp.: 221
Fiscal Year-end: 12/31/22
Bank Holding Company
N.A.I.C.S.: 551111
Brian Choi (Chm)
Min Jung Kim (Pres & CEO)
Christine Yoon Oh (CFO & Exec VP)
Ihnsuk J. Bang (Chief Banking Officer & Exec VP)
Jae H. Park (Chief Risk Officer-Bank & Exec VP)
Sang Kyo Oh (Chief Credit Officer-Bank, Chief Credit Officer & Exec VP)
Ryan Shin (Chief SBA Officer & Exec VP)

OPAL FUELS INC.

1 N Lexington Ave, White Plains, NY 10601
Tel.: (914) 705-4000   DE
Web Site: https://www.opalfuels.com
Year Founded: 2021
OPAL—(NASDAQ)
Rev.: $235,531,000
Assets: $644,856,000
Liabilities: $1,419,012,000
Net Worth: ($774,156,000)
Earnings: $32,579,000
Emp.: 298
Fiscal Year-end: 12/31/22
Natural Gas Distribution
N.A.I.C.S.: 221210
Scott Contino (Interim CFO & Principal Acctg Officer)
Ann Anthony (CEO)

OPEN LENDING CORPORATION

1501 S MoPac Expy Ste 450, Austin, TX 78746
Tel.: (512) 892-0400   DE
Web Site:
    https://www.openlending.com
Year Founded: 2017
LPRO—(NASDAQ)
Rev.: $179,594,000
Assets: $379,631,000
Liabilities: $166,807,000
Net Worth: $212,824,000
Earnings: $66,620,000
Emp.: 180
Fiscal Year-end: 12/31/22
Investment Services
N.A.I.C.S.: 523999
Charles D. Jehl (CFO, Treas & Exec VP)
John J. Flynn (Founder)
Matthew R. Roe (Chief Revenue Officer)
Jessica Snyder (Chm)
Sarah Lackey (CTO)
Matt Moody (VP-IT Integrations)
Cecilia Camarillo (Chief Acctg Officer)
Matthew Stark (Exec VP)
Scott Pryal (Sr VP)
Kevin Filan (Sr VP)
Charles D. Jehl (CEO & Interim CFO)

Subsidiaries:

Open Lending, LLC   (1)
1501 S Mopac Expy Ste 450, Austin, TX 78746
Tel.: (512) 892-0400
Web Site: http://www.openlending.com
Secondary Market Financing
N.A.I.C.S.: 522299

OPENDOOR TECHNOLOGIES INC.

410 N Scottsdale Rd Ste 1600, Tempe, AZ 85288
Tel.: (480) 618-6760   DE
Web Site: https://www.opendoor.com
Year Founded: 2013
OPEN—(NASDAQ)
Rev.: $15,567,000,000
Assets: $6,608,000,000
Liabilities: $5,522,000,000
Net Worth: $1,086,000,000
Earnings: ($1,353,000,000)
Emp.: 2,570
Fiscal Year-end: 12/31/22
Offices of Other Holding Companies
N.A.I.C.S.: 551112
Eric Wu (Founder)
Carrie Wheeler (Pres, Gen Counsel & Sec)
Amelia Generalis (Chief People Officer)
Christy Schwartz (CFO)
Raji Subramanian (CTO)
Carrie A. Wheeler (CEO)

Subsidiaries:

OS National LLC   (1)
3097 Satellite Blvd Ste 600, Duluth, GA 30096
Tel.: (770) 497-9100
Web Site: https://osnational.com
Commercial Insurance Services
N.A.I.C.S.: 524210

OSN Texas LLC   (1)
5307 E Mockingbird Ln Ste 221, Dallas, TX 75206
Tel.: (972) 797-9900
Title Insurance Agency Services
N.A.I.C.S.: 524127

Opendoor Brokerage Inc.   (1)
410 N Scottsdale Rd Ste 1600, Tempe, AZ 85288
Web Site: https://www.opendoor.com
Real Estate Services
N.A.I.C.S.: 531210

OPENLANE, INC.

11299 N Illinois St Ste 500, Carmel, IN 46032
Tel.: (317) 815-1100   DE
Web Site:
    https://corporate.openlane.com
KAR—(NYSE)
Rev.: $1,645,100,000
Assets: $4,726,300,000
Liabilities: $3,399,300,000
Net Worth: $1,327,000,000
Earnings: ($154,100,000)
Emp.: 4,500
Fiscal Year-end: 12/31/23
Offices of Other Holding Companies
N.A.I.C.S.: 551112
Lisa A. Price (Chief People Officer & Exec VP)
Peter J. Kelly (Pres & CEO)
Michael T. Kestner (Chm)
Brad S. Lakhia (CFO & Exec VP)
James E. Money (Pres-Automotive Fin Corp)
Tobin Richer (Sr VP-Mktg & Comm)
Jason Ferreri (Exec VP)

Subsidiaries:

A.D.E. of Ark-La-Tex, Inc.   (1)
7666 Hwy 8880, Shreveport, LA 71149
Tel.: (318) 938-7903
Used Vehicle Auction Services
N.A.I.C.S.: 423110
Philips Willis (Mgr-HR)

ADESA, Inc.   (1)
11299 N Illinois St, Carmel, IN 46032
Tel.: (317) 815-1100
Web Site: https://www.adesa.com
Sales Range: $1-4.9 Billion
Used & Salvage Vehicle Redistribution Services
N.A.I.C.S.: 423110
Mike Caggiano (Exec VP-Ops-East Reg)
John Combs (VP-Comml Sls)

Scott Meyer (VP-Fin)
J. Marty Nowlin (VP-HR)
Doug Shore (VP-Ops-Central)
Geoff Parker (VP-Ops-Midwest)
Heather Cameron (VP-Legal)
Ben Murdock (VP-Bus Dev)
Summer Ernsberger (VP-Sls & Ops-Online Svcs)

Subsidiary (Domestic):

ADESA Arkansas, LLC   (2)
8700 Hwy 70, North Little Rock, AR 72117
Tel.: (501) 945-2444
Web Site: http://www.adesa.com
Sales Range: $25-49.9 Million
Automobile Auction
N.A.I.C.S.: 423110

ADESA Atlanta, LLC   (2)
5055 Oakley Industrial Blvd, Fairburn, GA 30213
Tel.: (770) 357-2277
Web Site: http://www.adesa.com
Sales Range: $150-199.9 Million
Salvage Auctions
N.A.I.C.S.: 423110

Branch (Domestic):

ADESA Auctions Pittsburgh   (2)
758 Franklin Rd, Mercer, PA 16137
Tel.: (724) 662-4500
Web Site: http://www.adesa.com
Auto Auctions
N.A.I.C.S.: 423110

Subsidiary (Non-US):

ADESA Belgium NV   (2)
Grijpenlaan 19A, 3300, Tienen, Belgium
Tel.: (32) 16380068
Car Distr
N.A.I.C.S.: 441120
Lars Agten (Mgr)

Subsidiary (Domestic):

ADESA Birmingham, LLC   (2)
804 Sollie Dr, Moody, AL 35004
Tel.: (205) 640-1010
Web Site: http://www.adesa.com
Automobile Auction Whslr
N.A.I.C.S.: 425120

ADESA Colorado, LLC   (2)
10680 Charter Oak Ranch Rd, Fountain, CO 80817
Tel.: (719) 391-6600
Web Site: http://www.adesa.com
Sales Range: $75-99.9 Million
Automotive Remarketing Services
N.A.I.C.S.: 423110

ADESA Des Moines, LLC   (2)
1800 SE Gateway Dr, Grimes, IA 50111
Tel.: (424) 218-9800
Web Site: http://www.adesa.com
Automobile Auction Whslr
N.A.I.C.S.: 425120

Subsidiary (Non-US):

ADESA Deutschland GmbH   (2)
Gewerbepark 2, 92289, Ursensollen, Germany
Tel.: (49) 3689900
Car Distr
N.A.I.C.S.: 441120
Jessica Suma (Officer-Sls Dev)

ADESA Europe NV   (2)
Grijpenlaan 19A, 3300, Tienen, Belgium
Tel.: (32) 16380068
Car Distr
N.A.I.C.S.: 441120
Johan Meyssen (CEO)

ADESA France SAS   (2)
104 Avenue Albert 1er, 92500, Rueil-Malmaison, France
Tel.: (33) 141440707
Car Distr
N.A.I.C.S.: 441120

ADESA Italia S.R.L.   (2)
Via dei Missaglia 97 Ed B2, 20142, Milan, Italy
Tel.: (39) 0245712673
Car Distr
N.A.I.C.S.: 441120
Daniele Manente (Mgr-Sls & Mktg)

Subsidiary (Domestic):

ADESA Lansing, LLC   (2)
6956 Lansing Rd, Dimondale, MI 48821
Tel.: (517) 322-2444
Sales Range: $25-49.9 Million
Emp.: 100
Vehicle Remarketing Services
N.A.I.C.S.: 425120
Matt Noecker (Gen Mgr)

ADESA Lexington, LLC   (2)
672 Blue Sky Pkwy, Lexington, KY 40509
Tel.: (859) 263-6200
Sales Range: $50-74.9 Million
Emp.: 150
Automobile Auction Whslr
N.A.I.C.S.: 425120
Charles Osborne (Mgr-Dealer Sls & Svcs)

ADESA Mexico, LLC   (2)
13085 Hamilton Crossing Blvd, Carmel, IN 46032
Tel.: (800) 923-3725
Sales Range: $300-349.9 Million
Emp.: 800
Automobile Auction Whslr
N.A.I.C.S.: 425120

ADESA Minnesota, LLC   (2)
18270 Territorial Rd, Dayton, MN 55369
Tel.: (763) 428-8777
Automobile Auction Whslr
N.A.I.C.S.: 425120

Subsidiary (Non-US):

ADESA Nederland B.V.   (2)
Lange Dreef 11/M, 4131 NJ, Vianen, Netherlands
Tel.: (31) 347763735
Car Distr
N.A.I.C.S.: 441120
Erik Schonberger (Mgr)

Subsidiary (Domestic):

ADESA New Jersey, LLC   (2)
200 N Main St, Manville, NJ 08835
Tel.: (908) 725-2200
Web Site: http://www.adesa.com
Sales Range: $250-299.9 Million
Auto Auctions
N.A.I.C.S.: 441120

ADESA New York, LLC   (2)
12200 Main St, Akron, NY 14001
Tel.: (716) 542-3300
Automobile Auction Services
N.A.I.C.S.: 425120

ADESA Ohio, LLC   (2)
4400 William C Good Blvd, Franklin, OH 45005
Tel.: (937) 746-4000
Automobile Auction Whslr
N.A.I.C.S.: 425120

ADESA Oregon, LLC   (2)
23585 NE Sandy Blvd, Wood Village, OR 97060
Tel.: (503) 492-9200
Web Site: http://www.adesa.com
Used Car Whslr
N.A.I.C.S.: 441120
John Hammer (Pres)
Richard Griskie (CIO)
Srisu Subrahmanyam (COO)
Jason Ferreri (Exec VP-Online Svcs)
John Combs (VP-Comml Sls)
Steve Dudash (VP-Dealer Svcs)
Mike Caggiano (Exec VP-Ops-East Reg)
Doug Shore (VP-Ops-Central Reg)
Geoff Parker (VP-Ops-Midwest Reg)
Lawrence Cubitt (VP-Auction Ops-West Reg)
Heather Cameron (VP-Legal)
Scott Meyer (VP-Fin)
Ben Murdock (VP-Bus Dev)
Summer Ernsberger (VP-Sls & Ops-Online Svcs)
Anil Nair (VP-Process Excellence)
Scott Drehs (VP-Major Dealer Accounts)

ADESA Pennsylvania, LLC   (2)
30 Industrial Rd, York, PA 17406
Tel.: (717) 266-6611

Sales Range: $50-74.9 Million
Emp.: 200
Automobile Auction Whslr
N.A.I.C.S.: 425120
Igor Skinder *(Mgr-Dealer Sls & Svcs)*

ADESA Phoenix, LLC (2)
400 N Beck Ave, Chandler, AZ 85226
Tel.: (480) 961-1161
Web Site: http://www.adesa.com
Sales Range: $200-249.9 Million
Wholesale Automobile Auctions
N.A.I.C.S.: 423110

Subsidiary (Non-US):

ADESA Quebec Corporation (2)
500 1st Avenue, Levis, G6W 5M6, QC,
Canada
Tel.: (418) 839-0070
Automobile Auction Whslr
N.A.I.C.S.: 425120

ADESA Remarketing Services
Inc. (2)
50 Burnhamthorpe Road W Suite 80, Mis-
sissauga, L5B 3C2, ON, Canada
Tel.: (905) 896-4400
Automobile Auction Whslr
N.A.I.C.S.: 425120

Subsidiary (Domestic):

ADESA San Diego, LLC (2)
2175 Cactus Rd, San Diego, CA 92154
Tel.: (619) 661-5565
Web Site: http://www.adesa.com
Sales Range: $50-74.9 Million
Automobile Auction Whslr
N.A.I.C.S.: 425120

Subsidiary (Non-US):

ADESA Subastas Espana,
S.L.U. (2)
C/ Huelva 3 Dpl, 28002, Madrid, Spain
Tel.: (34) 16380068
Car Distr
N.A.I.C.S.: 441120

Subsidiary (Domestic):

ADESA Wisconsin, LLC (2)
W 10415 State Rd 33, Portage, WI 53901
Tel.: (608) 742-8245
Web Site: http://www.adesa.com
Emp.: 100
Automobile Auction Whslr
N.A.I.C.S.: 425120

Branch (Domestic):

ADESA-Golden Gate (2)
18501 W Stanford Rd, Tracy, CA 95377
Tel.: (209) 839-8000
Web Site: http://www.adesa.com
Sales Range: $25-49.9 Million
Emp.: 75
Utility Operations Including Electric, Water,
Wastewater & Gas Operations; Utility-
Related Businese
N.A.I.C.S.: 423110

ADESA-Kansas City (2)
15511 Adesa Dr, Belton, MO 64012
Tel.: (816) 525-1100
Web Site: http://www.adesa.com
Sales Range: $100-124.9 Million
Emp.: 280
Automobile Auction
N.A.I.C.S.: 423110

ADESA-Seattle (2)
621 37th St NW, Auburn, WA 98001
Tel.: (253) 735-1600
Web Site: http://www.adesa.com
Sales Range: $125-149.9 Million
Emp.: 280
Auto Auctions
N.A.I.C.S.: 423110

ADESA-Tampa (2)
3225 N 50th St, Tampa, FL 33619-2323
Tel.: (813) 620-3600
Web Site: http://www.adesa.com
Emp.: 50
Wholesale Distribution of Automobiles &
Other Motor Vehicles
N.A.I.C.S.: 441330

Subsidiary (Domestic):

AutoVIN, Inc. (2)
50 Mansell Ct, Roswell, GA 30076 **(100%)**
Tel.: (678) 585-8000
Sales Range: $100-124.9 Million
Field Information Services for Automotive
Industry
N.A.I.C.S.: 561499

Automotive Finance Corporation (2)
11550 N Meridian St Ste 180, Carmel, IN
46032
Tel.: (317) 706-8088
Web Site: http://www.afcdealer.com
Sales Range: $75-99.9 Million
Used Car Dealer Financing
N.A.I.C.S.: 522299
Jim Money *(Pres)*

PAR, Inc. (2)
12800 N Meridian St Ste 350, Carmel, IN
46032-8100
Tel.: (317) 818-4500
Web Site: http://www.parnorthamerica.com
Sales Range: $150-199.9 Million
Emp.: 100
Vehicle Transition Services
N.A.I.C.S.: 423110
Lisa Scott *(Pres)*
Jessie Herdrich-Irwin *(VP-Compliance &*
Ops)
Stacey White *(Sr VP-Remarketing)*
Lauren Clason *(Mgr-HR)*
Jennifer Perry *(Mgr-Titles Svcs)*
Jon Armstrong *(Mgr-Recovery Svcs)*
Mike Fischer *(Sr Dir-Ops)*
Peggy Hood *(Mgr-Product)*
Shannon Berry *(Mgr-Skip Svcs)*
Kelsey Minier *(Mgr-Compliance)*
Jeremy Dunn *(Dir-Legal)*
Jason Sinicropi *(Mgr-Software Engrg)*
Kristina Haas *(Mgr-Client Ops)*

Sanford Auto Dealers Exchange,
Inc. (2)
2851 Saint Johns Pkwy, Sanford, FL 32771
Tel.: (407) 936-7233
Web Site:
http://www.sanfordautodealers.com
Motor Vehicle Auctioneer
N.A.I.C.S.: 425120

Sioux Falls Auto Auction, Inc. (2)
46893 271st St, Tea, SD 57064
Tel.: (605) 368-5364
Web Site: http://www.adesa.com
Sales Range: $10-24.9 Million
Motor Vehicle Parts & Supplies Whslr
N.A.I.C.S.: 423110

Tri-State Auction Co., Inc. (2)
1650 E Main Ave, West Fargo, ND 58078
Tel.: (701) 282-8203
Emp.: 5
Motor Vehicle Parts & Supplies Whslr
N.A.I.C.S.: 423110

Auction Frontier, LLC (1)
568 N Sunrise Ave, Roseville, CA 95661
Tel.: (916) 252-0252
Web Site: https://www.velocicast.com
Internet Software Services
N.A.I.C.S.: 541511

Auto Dealers Exchange of Concord,
LLC (1)
63 Western Ave, Framingham, MA 01702
Tel.: (508) 626-7000
Automobile Auction Services
N.A.I.C.S.: 425120

Auto Dealers Exchange of Memphis,
LLC (1)
5400 Getwell Rd, Memphis, TN 38118
Tel.: (901) 365-6300
Web Site: http://www.adesa.com
Automobile Auction Whslr
N.A.I.C.S.: 425120

Auto Portfolio Services, LLC (1)
5295 DTC Pkwy Ste 200, Greenwood Vil-
lage, CO 80155
Tel.: (877) 761-3111
Web Site:
http://www.autoportfolioservices.com
Sales Range: $25-49.9 Million
Emp.: 30
Investment Management Service
N.A.I.C.S.: 523940

AutoVIN Canada Inc. (1)
50 Burnhamthorpe Rd W, Mississauga, L5B
3C2, ON, Canada
Tel.: (905) 361-0620
Automated Vehicle Information Services
N.A.I.C.S.: 519290

BacklotCars, Inc. (1)
11299 N Illinois St, Carmel, IN 46032
Web Site: https://www.backlotcars.com
Online Vehicle Distr
N.A.I.C.S.: 441120

Car Quality Services GmbH (1)
Moritzstrasse 14, 42117, Wuppertal, Ger-
many
Tel.: (49) 21299271162
Web Site: https://www.gwliste.de
Emp.: 20
Car Distr
N.A.I.C.S.: 441120
Benjamin Skuy *(Mng Dir)*
Eric Loughmiller *(Mng Dir)*
Ingo Schlosserstrong *(CEO & Mng Dir)*
Philipp Holz *(Ops Mgr)*
Philipp Holz *(Ops Mgr)*

Clearplan, LLC (1)
1620 S Stapley Dr Ste 232, Mesa, AZ
85204
Tel.: (817) 204-0298
Web Site: https://www.clearplan.io
Software Development Services
N.A.I.C.S.: 513210

LiveBlock Auctions International
Inc (1)
No 200 2125 11th Avenue, Regina, S4P
3X3, SK, Canada
Tel.: (306) 584-1383
Web Site: http://www.liveblockauctions.com
Software Development Services
N.A.I.C.S.: 541511
Walter Dvorak *(VP-IT Ops)*
Roe Peterson *(Dir-R&D)*
Alex Wang *(Mgr-Technical Svcs)*
Rob Howie *(Mgr-Sls & Bus Dev)*
Milton Calnek *(Mgr-Ops)*
Yolanda Mabanglo *(Dir-Quality Engrg)*
Joe Song *(Mgr-Application Dev)*

MobileTrac LLC (1)
10755 Scripps Poway Pkwy St 703, San
Diego, CA 92131
Tel.: (858) 454-6782
Web Site: http://www.instavin.com
Automobile Tracking Data Providing Ser-
vices
N.A.I.C.S.: 518210
Adam Siner *(VP-Ops)*

OPENLANE Belgium N.V. (1)
Grijpenlaan 19A, 3300, Tienen, Belgium
Tel.: (32) 16380068
Automotive Mfr & Distr
N.A.I.C.S.: 336211

OPENLANE Deutschland GmbH (1)
Gewerbepark 2, 92289, Ursensollen, Ger-
many
Tel.: (49) 96283689900
Automotive Mfr & Distr
N.A.I.C.S.: 336211

OPENLANE Europe N.V. (1)
Grijpenlaan 19A, 3300, Tienen, Belgium
Tel.: (32) 16380068
Web Site: https://www.openlane.eu
Automotive Mfr & Distr
N.A.I.C.S.: 336211

OPENLANE France S.A.S. (1)
104 Avenue Albert 1er, 92500, Rueil-
Malmaison, France
Tel.: (33) 141440707
Automotive Mfr & Distr
N.A.I.C.S.: 336211

OPENLANE Italia S.R.L. (1)
Via dei Missaglia 97 Ed B2, 20142, Milan,
Italy
Tel.: (39) 045712673
Automotive Retailer
N.A.I.C.S.: 423110

OPENLANE Nederland B.V. (1)
Lange Dreef 11/M, 4131NJ, Vianen, Nether-
lands
Tel.: (31) 347763735
Automotive Mfr & Distr
N.A.I.C.S.: 336211

OPENLANE Remarketing
Limited (1)
Deva House Sandpiper Court Chester Busi-
ness Park, Chester, CH4 9QZ, United King-
dom
Tel.: (44) 3442255477
Automotive Retailer
N.A.I.C.S.: 423110

OPENLANE Subastas Espana,
S.L. (1)
C/ Huelva 3 Dpl, 28002, Madrid, Spain
Tel.: (34) 16380068
Automotive Retailer
N.A.I.C.S.: 423110

OPENLANE US, Inc. (1)
11299 N Illinois St, Carmel, IN 46032
Web Site: https://www.openlane.com
Sales Range: $25-49.9 Million
Emp.: 100
Online Automobile Auction Services
N.A.I.C.S.: 551112

Preferred Warranties, Inc. (1)
200 Pinebrook Pl, Orwigsburg, PA 17961
Tel.: (570) 366-1146
Web Site:
https://www.preferredwarranties.com
Sales Range: $10-24.9 Million
Emp.: 70
Insurance Services
N.A.I.C.S.: 524128
Deborah Herring *(Sec)*

Recovery Database Network,
Inc. (1)
1620 S Stapley Dr Ste 232, Mesa, AZ
85204
Tel.: (817) 204-0298
Web Site: https://www.recoverydatabase.net
Software Development Services
N.A.I.C.S.: 541511

Saperium, Inc. (1)
8/F NEO/TWO 3rd Avenue Corner 28th
Street, Fort Bonifacio Global City, Taguig,
1624, Philippines
Tel.: (63) 28006883
Web Site: https://www.saperium.com
Software Development Services
N.A.I.C.S.: 541511

TradeRev USA LLC (1)
11299 N Illinois St, Carmel, IN 46032
Web Site: https://www.traderev.com
Used Car Whslr
N.A.I.C.S.: 441120
Mark Endras *(Founder)*

OPGEN, INC.
9717 Key W Ave Ste 100, Rockville,
MD 20850
Tel.: (301) 869-9683 DE
Web Site: https://www.opgen.com
Year Founded: 2001
OPGN—(NASDAQ)
Rev.: $2,607,293
Assets: $25,813,149
Liabilities: $18,237,601
Net Worth: $7,575,548
Earnings: ($37,283,233)
Emp.: 85
Fiscal Year-end: 12/31/22
Medical Laboratories
N.A.I.C.S.: 621511
Albert Weber *(CFO & VP)*
Johannes Bacher *(COO)*
Faranak Atrzadeh *(Chief Mktg & Sci-*
entific Affairs Officer)
David E. Lazar *(Chm & CEO)*

Subsidiaries:

Ares Genetics GmbH (1)
Karl-Farkas-Gasse 18, 1030, Vienna, Aus-
tria
Tel.: (43) 13618880
Web Site: https://www.ares-genetics.com
Diagnostic Services
N.A.I.C.S.: 621512
Arne Materna *(CEO & Mng Dir)*
Stephan Beisken *(Dir-Bioinformatics & Ana-*
lytics)
Johannes Weinberger *(Dir-NGS Laboratory)*

Curetis USA (1)

OpGen, Inc.—(Continued)

708 Quince Orchard Rd, Gaithersburg, MD
20878
Tel.: (619) 452-3644
Web Site: http://www.curetisusa.com
Diagnostic Panel Mfr
N.A.I.C.S.: 325413

OPKO HEALTH, INC.

4400 Biscayne Blvd, Miami, FL
33137
Tel.: (305) 575-4100   DE
Web Site: https://www.opko.com
OPK—(NASDAQ)
Rev.: $1,004,196,000
Assets: $2,167,259,000
Liabilities: $605,611,000
Net Worth: $1,561,648,000
Earnings: ($328,405,000)
Emp.: 4,196
Fiscal Year-end: 12/31/22
Ophthalmic Pharmaceutical Devel-
oper & Mfr
N.A.I.C.S.: 325412
Steven D. Rubin (Exec VP-Admin)
Phillip Allan Gamma Frost (Chm &
CEO)
Adam E. Logal (CFO, Chief Acctg
Officer, Treas & Sr VP)
Jane H. Hsiao (Vice Chm & CTO)
L. Arie Gutman (Pres-API)
Charles Bishop (CEO-OPKO Renal)
Tony Cruz (Pres-Transition Therapeu-
tics)
Hans Berner (Pres-OPKO Health
Iberoamerica)
Damien Burke (CEO-EirGen Pharma)
Elias A. Zerhouni (Vice Chm)
Jane Pine Wood (Chief Legal Officer)
Gary J. Nabel (Chief Innovation Offi-
cer)
Elias Adam Zerhouni (Vice Chm &
Pres)

Subsidiaries:

Bio-Reference Laboratories, Inc.   (1)
481 Edward H Ross Dr, Elmwood Park, NJ
07407
Tel.: (201) 791-2600
Web Site: https://www.bioreference.com
Emp.: 5,000
Diagnostic Testing Services
N.A.I.C.S.: 621511
James Weisberger (Chief Medical Officer,
Exec VP & Dir-Laboratory)
Jane Pine Wood (Chief Legal Officer)
Geoff Monk (Pres)
John Mooney (CIO)
Craig Allen (COO & Sr VP)
Natalie Cummins (Chief Comml Officer & Sr
VP)
Cindy Jacke (Sr VP-Strategic Venture Svcs)
Greg Cahill (VP-HR)
Robert Rossi (Chief Compliance & Privacy
Officer & VP)
Regina Stewart (Sr VP-Clinical Laboratory
Ops)
Richard Schwabacher (Chief Digital Officer
& Sr VP-Digital Health)

EirGen Pharma Ltd.   (1)
Westside Business Park Old Kilmeaden
Road, Waterford, X91 YV67, Ireland
Tel.: (353) 5 159 1944
Web Site: https://www.eirgen.com
Sales Range: $1-9.9 Million
Emp.: 130
Pharmaceuticals Product Mfr
N.A.I.C.S.: 325412
Damien Burke (Co-CEO)
Gillian Prendergast (Head-Scientific Affairs)
Kay O'Shea (CTO)
Joanne Jacques (Head-Sterile Ops)
Dan Delaney (Head-Comml Ops)
Mike Walsh (Head-Quality)

OPKO Biologics, Ltd   (1)
16 Ashlagan St, Kiryat Gat, 8211804, Israel
Tel.: (972) 8 930 0051
Web Site: https://www.opkobiologics.com
Health Care Srvices
N.A.I.C.S.: 621512

Laura Moschcovich (Gen Mgr)
Ahuva Bar-Ilan (VP-Preclinical & Clinical
Pharmacology)
Yifat Philip (VP-Legal Affairs & HR)
Sagit Pinto-Finkel (VP-Fin)
Guy Ben-Bashat (Sr Dir-Clinical Affairs)
Miri Gerzon-Zakar (Dir-CMC)
Dana Avraham (Dir-QA)

OPKO Chile, S.A.
Av El Parque 1307 Bodega 9, Pudahuel,
Chile
Tel.: (56) 27130700
Web Site: https://www.opko.cl
Medical Equipment Whslr
N.A.I.C.S.: 423450

OPKO Diagnostics, LLC   (1)
4400 Biscayne Blvd Ste E, Miami, FL
33137
Tel.: (781) 933-8012
Medical Equipment Whslr
N.A.I.C.S.: 423450
Michael Reeve (Dir-Quality & Regulatory
Compliance)

OPKO Health Europe, S.L.
Placa Europa 13-15, L'Hospitalet de Llobre-
gat, 08908, Barcelona, Spain
Tel.: (34) 93 409 9040
Web Site: https://www.opkoeurope.com
Pharmaceuticals Product Mfr
N.A.I.C.S.: 325412

OPKO Lab, LLC   (1)
1450 Elm Hill Pike, Nashville, TN 37210
Tel.: (615) 874-0410
Web Site: http://clinical.opko.com
Health Care Srvices
N.A.I.C.S.: 621512

OPKO Renal, LLC   (1)
100 Allstate Parkway Suite 600, Markham,
L3R 6H3, ON, Canada
Tel.: (905) 479-5306
Web Site: http://www.opkorenal.com
Health Care Srvices
N.A.I.C.S.: 621512

OPKO do Brasil Comercio de Produ-
tos Farmaceuticos, Ltda   (1)
R Salvador Simoes 533 Ipiranga, Sao
Paulo, 04276-000, Brazil
Tel.: (55) 1150615121
Biotechnology Research Services
N.A.I.C.S.: 541714

Pharmacos Exakta S.A. de C.V.   (1)
Av Nino Obrero N 651 Col Chapalita, Gua-
dalajara, 45040, Mexico
Tel.: (52) 3331212761
Pharmaceutical Preparation Mfr
N.A.I.C.S.: 325412

Transition Therapeutics Inc.   (1)
101 College Street Suite 220, Toronto, M5G
1L7, ON, Canada
Tel.: (416) 260-7770
Web Site:
  http://www.transitiontherapeutics.com
Sales Range: Less than $1 Million
Biopharmaceutical Developer, Researcher &
Mfr
N.A.I.C.S.: 325412
Aleksandra Pastrak (Officer-Medical & VP-
Clinical Dev)
Bruce Connop (VP-Non-Clinical & Pharma-
ceutical Dev)
Tony Cruz (CEO)

OPORTUN FINANCIAL COR-
PORATION

2 Cir Star Way, San Carlos, CA
94070
Tel.: (650) 810-8823   DE
Web Site: https://www.oportun.com
Year Founded: 2011
OPRT—(NASDAQ)
Rev.: $952,545,000
Assets: $3,613,695,000
Liabilities: $3,066,096,000
Net Worth: $547,599,000
Earnings: ($77,744,000)
Emp.: 3,000
Fiscal Year-end: 12/31/22
Holding Company
N.A.I.C.S.: 551112

Casey Mueller (Chief Acctg Officer)
Joan Aristei (Chief Risk Officer & Gen
Counsel)
Raul Vazquez (Pres & CEO)
Jonathan Coblentz (CFO & Cheif Ad-
min Officer)

Subsidiaries:

Hello Digit, LLC   (1)
100 Pine St 20th Fl, San Francisco, CA
94111
Web Site: http://digit.co
Emp.: 100
Online Investment, Wealth Management &
Financial Advisory Data Services
N.A.I.C.S.: 522320
Ethan Bloch (Founder & CEO)

OPPENHEIMER HOLDINGS
INC.

85 Broad St, New York, NY 10004
Tel.: (212) 668-8000   DE
Web Site:
  https://www.oppenheimer.com
Year Founded: 1933
OPY—(NYSE)
Rev.: $1,110,941,000
Assets: $2,714,392,000
Liabilities: $1,919,437,000
Net Worth: $794,955,000
Earnings: $32,351,000
Emp.: 2,912
Fiscal Year-end: 12/31/22
Investment Services
N.A.I.C.S.: 523150
Albert Grinsfelder Lowenthal (Chm &
CEO)
Bryan Edward McKigney (Pres-Asset
Mgmt-Oppenheimer & Co. Inc)
Robert S. Lowenthal (Pres)
Brad M. Watkins (CFO & Exec VP)
Ed Harrington (Exec VP-Private Cli-
ent Div)
John Hellier (Sr Mng Dir-Equities)
Joan Khoury (Mng Dir & CMO)
Dennis McNamara (Gen Counsel &
Exec VP)
Leon Molokie (COO & Exec VP)
Thomas Riordan (Sr Mng Dir & CIO)
Douglas Siegel (Mng Dir & Chief
Compliance Officer)

Subsidiaries:

Freedom Investments, Inc.   (1)
375 Raritan Ctr Pkwy, Edison, NJ
08837   (100%)
Web Site:
  https://www.freedominvestments.com
Brokerage Services
N.A.I.C.S.: 523150

Oppenheimer & Co. Inc.   (1)
85 Broad St, New York, NY
10004-2400   (100%)
Tel.: (212) 668-8000
Web Site: https://www.oppenheimer.com
Sales Range: $450-499.9 Million
Emp.: 3,000
Securities Brokerage, Trading, Investment
Advisory & Other Financial Services
N.A.I.C.S.: 541910
Albert Grinsfelder Lowenthal (Chm & CEO)
Robert S. Lowenthal (Chm, Pres, Sr Mng
Dir & Head-Investment Banking)
Brad M. Watkins (CFO & Exec VP)
John Hellier (Sr Mng Dir-Equities)
Joan Khoury (Sr Mng Dir, Mng Dir, CMO &
CMO)
Douglas Siegel (Mng Dir & Chief Compli-
ance Officer)
Thomas Riordan (Sr Mng Dir & CIO)
Leon Molokie (Co-COO & Exec VP)
Peter Albano (Sr Mng Dir & Head-Fixed
Income-Global)
Dennis McNamara (Gen Counsel & Exec
VP)

Branch (Domestic):

Oppenheimer & Co. Inc. - New York,
Park Ave   (2)

200 Park Ave Fl 25, New York, NY 10166-
2599
Tel.: (212) 907-4000
Web Site: http://www.oppenheimer.com
Sales Range: $75-99.9 Million
Emp.: 300
Provider of Investment Services
N.A.I.C.S.: 561499
Albert Grinsfelder Lowenthal (Chm & CEO)

Oppenheimer & Co. Inc. - Troy   (2)
3310 W Big Beaver Rd Ste 205, Troy, MI
48084
Tel.: (248) 637-8300
Web Site: http://www.opco.com
Sales Range: $25-49.9 Million
Emp.: 50
Brokerage Services
N.A.I.C.S.: 523940

Oppenheimer Asset Management
Inc.   (1)
85 Broad St, New York, NY 10004
Tel.: (212) 667-4395
Web Site: http://www.opco.com
Investment Advisory Services
N.A.I.C.S.: 523940

Oppenheimer Europe Ltd.   (1)
125 Wood Street, London, EC2V 7AN,
United Kingdom
Tel.: (44) 2072201900
Finance & Banking Services
N.A.I.C.S.: 541611

OPPFI INC.

130 E Randolph St Ste 3400, Chi-
cago, IL 60601
Tel.: (312) 212-8079   DE
Web Site: https://www.oppfi.com
Year Founded: 2020
OPFI—(NYSE)
Rev.: $452,859,000
Assets: $579,839,000
Liabilities: $420,689,000
Net Worth: $159,150,000
Earnings: $7,098,000
Emp.: 465
Fiscal Year-end: 12/31/22
Investment Services
N.A.I.C.S.: 523999
Pamela D. Johnson (CFO)
Todd G. Schwartz (Chm & CEO)
Christopher McKay (Chief Risk &
Analytics Officer)
Shaun Smolarz (Head-IR)

OPT-SCIENCES CORPORA-
TION

1912 Bannard St, Cinnaminson, NJ
08077
Tel.: (856) 829-2800   NJ
Web Site:
  https://www.optsciences.com
Year Founded: 1959
OPST—(OTCIQ)
Optical Coatings & Instrument Glass
Mfr
N.A.I.C.S.: 333310
Anderson L. McCabe (Pres)
Arthur Kania (Sec)

OPTEC INTERNATIONAL, INC.

412 N Main street Suite 100, Buffalo,
WY 82834
Tel.: (760) 444-5566   WY
Web Site: http://www.optecintl.com
Year Founded: 2012
OPTI—(OTCIQ)
Rev.: $1,011,000
Assets: $973,000
Liabilities: $7,412,000
Net Worth: ($6,439,000)
Earnings: ($1,199,000)
Emp.: 1
Fiscal Year-end: 06/30/20
Pet Pain Relief Products Mfr; Opti-
mized Fuel Technologies
N.A.I.C.S.: 325412

Roger Pawson (Founder & CEO)
Christine Carter (Mgr-Distr)
Jose Cruz (Accountant-Corp)

OPTEX SYSTEMS HOLDINGS, INC.

1420 Presidential Dr, Richardson, TX
75081-2439
Tel.: (972) 764-5700   DE
Web Site: https://www.optexsys.com
Year Founded: 2006
OPXS—(NASDAQ)
Rev.: $33,995,000
Assets: $25,518,000
Liabilities: $6,710,000
Net Worth: $18,808,000
Earnings: $3,768,000
Emp.: 128
Fiscal Year-end: 09/29/24
Optical, Lighting & Navigational Systems Mfr
N.A.I.C.S.: 333310
Danny Robert Schoening (Chm, CEO & COO)
Karen L. Hawkins (CFO & Principal Acctg Officer)
Bill Bates (Gen Mgr-Applied Optics Center)

OPTICAL CABLE CORPORATION

5290 Concourse Dr, Roanoke, VA
24019
Tel.: (540) 265-0690   VA
Web Site: https://www.occfiber.com
Year Founded: 1983
OCC—(NASDAQ)
Rev.: $72,173,752
Assets: $43,878,901
Liabilities: $19,157,057
Net Worth: $24,721,844
Earnings: $2,066,498
Emp.: 327
Fiscal Year-end: 10/31/23
Fiber-Optic Cables For Telecommunications
N.A.I.C.S.: 335921
Tracy G. Smith (CFO & Sr VP)
Neil D. Wilkin Jr. (Chm, Pres & CEO)

Subsidiaries:

Applied Optical Systems, Inc.   (1)
1700 Capital Ave Ste 150, Plano, TX
75074-1203
Tel.: (972) 509-1500
Web Site: http://www.occfiber.com
Sales Range: $1-9.9 Million
Fiber Optic Cable Mfr
N.A.I.C.S.: 335921

Centric Solutions LLC   (1)
1700 Capital Ave Ste 150, Plano, TX 75074
Tel.: (972) 745-8010
Web Site: https://www.centricsolutions.com
Fiber Optic Cable Mfr
N.A.I.C.S.: 335921

Optical Cable Corp. - Asheville   (1)
33 Superior Way, Swannanoa, NC
28778   (100%)
Tel.: (828) 298-2260
Web Site: http://www.occfiber.com
Wiring Products Mfr
N.A.I.C.S.: 335931

OPTIMIZERX CORPORATION

260 Charles St Ste 302, Waltham,
MA 02453
Tel.: (248) 651-6568   NV
Web Site:
   https://www.optimizerx.com
Year Founded: 2006
OPRX—(NASDAQ)
Rev.: $62,450,156
Assets: $134,651,185
Liabilities: $8,540,408
Net Worth: $126,110,777
Earnings: ($11,438,440)
Emp.: 109

Fiscal Year-end: 12/31/22
Website Publisher & Marketing Services That Creates, Promotes & Fulfills Custom Marketing & Advertising Programs
N.A.I.C.S.: 541613
William J. Febbo (CEO)
Stephen L. Silvestro (Chief Comml Officer)
Todd Inman (CTO)
Marion K. Odence-Ford (Chief Compliance Officer & Gen Counsel)
Edward Stelmakh (CFO & COO)
Douglas P. Baker (Exec VP-Acctg & Fin)

OPTIMUM SOURCE INTERNATIONAL, LTD.

3325 Griffin Rd Ste 200, Fort Lauderdale, FL 33312   WI
OSIN—(OTCIQ)
Media Advertising Services
N.A.I.C.S.: 541840
Ann Marie Aless (Exec Dir)

OPTIMUMBANK HOLDINGS INC.

2929 E Commercial Blvd Ste 101,
Fort Lauderdale, FL 33308
Tel.: (954) 900-2800   FL
Web Site:
   https://www.optimumbank.com
Year Founded: 2004
OPHC—(NASDAQ)
Rev.: $22,842,000
Assets: $585,219,000
Liabilities: $522,639,000
Net Worth: $62,580,000
Earnings: $4,023,000
Emp.: 48
Fiscal Year-end: 12/31/22
Offices of Bank Holding Companies
N.A.I.C.S.: 551111
Moishe Gubin (Chm)
Joel J. Klein (Interim Chief Financial Officer)

Subsidiaries:

OptimumBank   (1)
10197 Cleary Blvd, Plantation, FL
33324   (100%)
Tel.: (954) 452-9501
Web Site: http://www.optimumbank.com
Sales Range: $125-149.9 Million
Emp.: 23
Commericial Banking
N.A.I.C.S.: 522110
Timothy Terry (CEO)

OPTIMUS HEALTHCARE SERVICES, INC.

1400 Old Country Rd Ste 306, Westbury, NY 11590
Tel.: (516) 806-4201   FL
Web Site:
   https://www.optimushealthcare.com
Year Founded: 1990
OHCS—(OTCIQ)
Rev.: $1,497,779
Assets: $1,070,098
Liabilities: $8,211,060
Net Worth: ($7,140,962)
Earnings: ($11,103,503)
Emp.: 11
Fiscal Year-end: 12/31/23
Health Care Srvices
N.A.I.C.S.: 621610
Cliff Saffron (Pres, Interim CEO, COO, Gen Counsel & Sr VP)
Marc Wiener (Treas)
Philip Scala (Chm)

OPTINOSE, INC.

777 Township Line Rd Ste 300, Yardley, PA 19067
Tel.: (267) 364-3500   DE
Web Site: https://www.optinose.com

Year Founded: 2010
OPTN—(NASDAQ)
Rev.: $76,276,000
Assets: $144,222,000
Liabilities: $200,846,000
Net Worth: ($56,624,000)
Earnings: ($74,833,000)
Emp.: 141
Fiscal Year-end: 12/31/22
Research & Development in Biotechnology (except Nanobiotechnology)
N.A.I.C.S.: 541714
Peter K. Miller (CEO)
Ramy A. Mahmoud (Pres & COO)
Michael F. Marino (Chief Legal Officer)
John Messina (Sr VP-Clinical Dev & Medical Affairs)
Karen E. Brophy (Chief HR Officer)
Michael C. Berkey (VP-Technical Ops)
Joseph C. Scodari (Chm)
Anthony Krick (Chief Acctg Officer & VP)
Paul Spence Jr. (Chief Comml Officer)

Subsidiaries:

OptiNose US, Inc.   (1)
777 Township Line Rd Ste 300, Yardley, PA
19067
Tel.: (267) 364-3500
Web Site: https://www.optinose.com
Pharmaceutical Product Mfr & Distr
N.A.I.C.S.: 325412
Mike Marino (Chief Legal Officer)
Michele Janis (VP-Fin)
Karen E Brophy (VP-HR)
Ramy A. Mahmoud (CEO)
Paul Spence (Chief Comml Officer)
Anthony Krick (Chief Acctg Officer)
John Messina (Sr VP)
Michael C. Berkey (VP)
Jonathan Neely (VP-Business Development)

Optinose AS   (1)
Gaustadalleen 21, 0349, Oslo, Norway
Tel.: (47) 21403288
Pharmaceutical Products Distr
N.A.I.C.S.: 424210
Per G. Djupesland (Founder & Chief Scientific Officer)

OPTION CARE HEALTH, INC.

3000 Lakeside Dr Ste 300N, Bannockburn, IL 60015
Tel.: (312) 940-2443   DE
Web Site:
   https://www.optioncarehealth.com
Year Founded: 2004
OPCH—(NASDAQ)
Rev.: $4,302,324,000
Assets: $3,217,035,000
Liabilities: $1,795,363,000
Net Worth: $1,421,672,000
Earnings: $267,090,000
Emp.: 5,809
Fiscal Year-end: 12/31/23
Holding Company; Community Pharmacies, Pharmacy Benefit Management, Specialty Infusion Therapy & Mail-Order Fulfillment Services
N.A.I.C.S.: 551112
John C. Rademacher (Pres & CEO)
Brett Michalak (CIO)
Mike Shapiro (CFO & Sr VP)
Luke Whitworth (COO)
Mike Bavaro (Chief HR Officer)
Collin Smyser (Gen Counsel)
Caroline Budde (Chief Compliance Officer)
Chris Grashoff (Sr VP)
Maritza DeGagne (Sr VP)
Roman Fry (Sr VP)
Kim Harvey (Sr VP)
Benson Yang (Sr VP)

Subsidiaries:

Applied Health Care, Ltd.   (1)

9360 Kirby Dr Ste 100, Houston, TX 77054
Tel.: (713) 782-4442
Sales Range: $1-9.9 Million
Emp.: 40
Women Healthcare Services
N.A.I.C.S.: 621610

BioScrip Infusion Services, LLC   (1)
102 The American Rd, Morris Plains, NJ
07950
Tel.: (973) 597-0444
Web Site: https://www.bioscrip.com
Sales Range: $25-49.9 Million
Emp.: 200
Women Healthcare Services
N.A.I.C.S.: 621610

BioScrip Medical Supply Services,
LLC   (1)
10050 Crosstown Cir Ste 300, Eden Prairie,
MN 55344-3348
Tel.: (952) 979-3680
Pharmaceutical Products Distr
N.A.I.C.S.: 424210

BioScrip Nursing Services, LLC   (1)
80 Red Schoolhouse Rd, Chestnut Ridge,
NY 10977
Tel.: (845) 425-1706
Emp.: 6
Nursing Services
N.A.I.C.S.: 623110
Casha Scott (Gen Mgr)

BioScrip PBM Services, LLC   (1)
1 Vermont Dr, Lake Success, NY 11042
Tel.: (914) 460-1600
Web Site: https://www.bioscrip.com
Pharmacy Benefit Management Services
N.A.I.C.S.: 456110

BioScrip Pharmacy, Inc.   (1)
10050 Crosstown Cir Ste 300, Eden Prairie,
MN 55344-3344
Tel.: (952) 979-3600
Web Site: http://www.bioscrip.com
Sales Range: $50-74.9 Million
Emp.: 350
Community Pharmacy Management Services
N.A.I.C.S.: 456110

Subsidiary (Domestic):

BioScrip Pharmacy Services,
Inc.   (2)
5700 Perimeter Dr Ste B, Dublin, OH 43017
Tel.: (614) 850-6700
Web Site: https://www.bioscrip.com
Sales Range: $25-49.9 Million
Emp.: 100
Pharmacy Services
N.A.I.C.S.: 621399
Russ Corvese (Sr VP)

Critical Homecare Solutions, Inc.   (1)
One Fayette St Two Tower Bridge Ste 150,
Conshohocken, PA 19428
Tel.: (610) 825-2061
Web Site: http://www.criticalhs.com
Sales Range: $150-199.9 Million
Emp.: 1,339
Women Healthcare Services
N.A.I.C.S.: 621610

HomeChoice Partners, Inc   (1)
5365 Robin Hood Rd Ste 200, Norfolk, VA
23513
Tel.: (757) 855-4255
Web Site:
   https://www.homechoicepartners.com
Sales Range: $50-74.9 Million
Emp.: 10
Pharmacy Services
N.A.I.C.S.: 621399

InfuScience, Inc.   (1)
4151 Lafayette Center Dr Ste 600, Chantilly, VA 20151
Tel.: (703) 230-4638
Web Site: http://www.infuscience.com
Pharmacy Services
N.A.I.C.S.: 621399

Option Care Health, Inc.—(Continued)

Infusion Partners, LLC (1)
560 1st St Ste 104, Lake Oswego, OR 97034
Tel.: (503) 699-3511
Web Site:
https://www.infusionpartnersllc.com
Pharmacy Services
N.A.I.C.S.: 621610

Subsidiary (Domestic):

Infusion Partners of Brunswick, LLC (2)
18 Canal Rd Plz, Brunswick, GA 31525
Tel.: (912) 267-6192
Medical Equipment Distr
N.A.I.C.S.: 423450
Daniel Clemmons *(Gen Mgr)*

Infusion Partners of Melbourne, LLC (2)
3040 Venture Ln Ste 103, Melbourne, FL 32934
Tel.: (321) 242-2996
Web Site: http://www.bioscrip.com
Medical Equipment Distr
N.A.I.C.S.: 423450

Infusioncare (1)
1220 Ward Ave Ste 250, West Chester, PA 19380
Tel.: (610) 344-0450
Web Site: http://www.bioscrip.com
Sales Range: $10-24.9 Million
Emp.: 15
Women Healthcare Services
N.A.I.C.S.: 621610

Infusions Solutions Corp. (1)
8 Technology Dr, Bedford, NH 03110
Tel.: (603) 626-6200
Emp.: 28
Women Healthcare Services
N.A.I.C.S.: 621610
Thomas Fontaine *(Mgr-Distr)*

National Health Infusion (1)
3449 Technology Dr Unit 311, North Venice, FL 34275
Tel.: (941) 484-5626
Women Healthcare Services
N.A.I.C.S.: 621610

Natural Living, Inc. (1)
2694 Pemberton Dr, Apopka, FL 32703
Tel.: (407) 682-2440
Web Site: https://www.naturallivingusa.com
Sales Range: $25-49.9 Million
Emp.: 12
Health Supplement Retailer
N.A.I.C.S.: 456191
Noe Alvarez *(Founder)*

Naven Health, Inc. (1)
1626 Barber Rd Ste B, Sarasota, FL 34240
Web Site: https://navenhealth.com
Infusion Nursing & Support Services
N.A.I.C.S.: 621498

New England Home Therapies Inc. (1)
337 Turnpike Rd, Southborough, MA 01772
Tel.: (508) 480-8409
Web Site: http://www.nehtinc.com
Sales Range: $10-24.9 Million
Emp.: 150
Women Healthcare Services
N.A.I.C.S.: 621610

Nutri USA, Inc. (1)
103 Skillman St Apt 5b, Brooklyn, NY 11205
Tel.: (718) 486-6599
Pharmaceutical Products Distr
N.A.I.C.S.: 424210

Option Care Enterprises, Inc. (1)
485 E Half Day Rd Ste 300, Buffalo Grove, IL 60089-8806
Tel.: (847) 465-2100
Women Healthcare Services
N.A.I.C.S.: 621610

Subsidiary (Domestic):

Option Care Home Health, L.L.C. (2)
477 W Horton Rd, Bellingham, WA 98226-1205
Tel.: (360) 733-7799

Women Healthcare Services
N.A.I.C.S.: 621610
Sarah Schroeder *(Gen Mgr)*

Option Care of New York, Inc. (2)
1035 Coney Island Ave, Brooklyn, NY 11230
Tel.: (718) 961-1634
Women Healthcare Services
N.A.I.C.S.: 621610

Option Care, Inc. (2)
485 Half Day Rd Ste 300, Buffalo Grove, IL 60089
Tel.: (847) 465-2100
Web Site: http://www.optioncare.com
Sales Range: $650-699.9 Million
Infusion Therapy & Other Home Health Care Services
N.A.I.C.S.: 621610

Walgreens Home Care, Inc. (2)
200 Wilmot Rd, Deerfield, IL 60015
Tel.: (847) 229-7750
Sales Range: $50-74.9 Million
Retail Health Care Maintenance Services
N.A.I.C.S.: 621610

Option Health, Ltd. (1)
985 Ave of the Cities, Silvis, IL 61282
Tel.: (309) 792-7200
Web Site: http://www.bioscrip.com
Women Healthcare Services
N.A.I.C.S.: 621610

Professional Home Care Services, Inc. (1)
106 Sebethe Dr Ste A, Cromwell, CT 06416
Tel.: (860) 632-3600
Web Site: https://optioncarehealth.com
Women Healthcare Services
N.A.I.C.S.: 621610

Wilcox Medical, Inc. (1)
3000 Lakeside Dr Ste 300N, Bannockburn, IL 60015
Tel.: (802) 775-2808
Women Healthcare Services
N.A.I.C.S.: 621610

ORACLE CORPORATION
2300 Oracle Way, Austin, TX 78741
Tel.: (737) 867-1000 DE
Web Site: https://www.oracle.com
Year Founded: 1977
ORCL—(NYSE)
Rev.: $49,954,000,000
Assets: $134,384,000,000
Liabilities: $132,828,000,000
Net Worth: $1,556,000,000
Earnings: $8,503,000,000
Emp.: 164,000
Fiscal Year-end: 05/31/23
Database Management Software Whslr
N.A.I.C.S.: 513210
Dorian E. Daley *(Gen Counsel & Exec VP)*
Brian S. Higgins *(Sec, Sr VP & Assoc Gen Counsel)*
Jeffrey O. Henley *(Vice Chm)*
Mike Sicilia *(Exec VP-Global Bus Unit)*
Raymond J. Lane *(Executives, Bd of Dirs)*
Lawrence J. Ellison *(Founder, Chm & CTO)*
Maria Smith *(Chief Acctg Officer)*

Subsidiaries:

Acme Packet, Inc. (1)
100 Crosby Dr, Bedford, MA 01730-1438
Tel.: (781) 328-4400
Web Site: http://www.acmepacket.com
Rev.: $274,437,000
Assets: $579,212,000
Liabilities: $71,488,000
Net Worth: $507,724,000
Earnings: ($5,242,000)
Emp.: 880
Fiscal Year-end: 12/31/2012
Interactive Voice, Video & Multimedia Communications
N.A.I.C.S.: 334419

AddThis, Inc. (1)
1595 Spring Hill Rd Ste 300, Vienna, VA 22182
Tel.: (703) 677-3999
Web Site: http://www.addthis.com
Software Publisher
N.A.I.C.S.: 513210

Blue Kai, Inc. (1)
20883 Stevens Creek Blvd Ste 200, Cupertino, CA 95014
Tel.: (408) 200-8300
Web Site: http://www.bluekai.com
Emp.: 51
Data Management Services
N.A.I.C.S.: 518210

Cerner Corporation (1)
2800 Rockcreek Pkwy, Kansas City, MO 64117-2551
Tel.: (816) 221-1024
Web Site: http://www.cerner.com
Rev.: $5,764,824,000
Assets: $7,434,158,000
Liabilities: $3,753,696,000
Net Worth: $3,680,462,000
Earnings: $555,596,000
Emp.: 25,150
Fiscal Year-end: 12/31/2021
Information Technology Solutions for the Healthcare Industry
N.A.I.C.S.: 541512
Clifford W. Illig *(Chm, CEO & Founder)*

Subsidiary (Domestic):

AbleVets LLC (2)
15049 Conference Center Dr Ste 500, Chantilly, VA 20151
Tel.: (703) 594-8640
Web Site: http://www.ablevets.com
Emp.: 300
IT Consulting & Engineering Services
N.A.I.C.S.: 541330
Rich Lowell *(VP)*
Jim Dolatowski *(VP-Bus Ops)*
Avinay Vaswani *(VP)*
Cathy O'Hagan *(Dir)*
Matt Pavlak *(Dir)*

Subsidiary (Non-US):

Cerner (Malaysia) SDN BHD (2)
Level 23 Nu Tower 2 Kuala Lumpur Sentral, Jalan Tun Sambanthan, 50470, Kuala Lumpur, Malaysia
Tel.: (60) 3 2727 1740
Healthcare Equipment Technology Services
N.A.I.C.S.: 541512

Cerner Canada ULC (2)
675 Cochrane Drive East Tower 6th Floor, Markham, L3R 0B8, ON, Canada
Tel.: (905) 530-2160
Web Site: https://www.cerner.com
Information Technology Consulting Services
N.A.I.C.S.: 541512

Branch (Domestic):

Cerner Corporation - Clairvia (2)
2525 Meridian Pkwy Ste 100 150, Durham, NC 27713
Tel.: (919) 382-8282
Web Site: http://www.clairvia.com
Sales Range: $1-9.9 Million
Emp.: 59
Custom Computer Programming Services
N.A.I.C.S.: 541511

Subsidiary (Non-US):

Cerner Corporation PTY Limited (2)
4 Julius Avenue, North Ryde, 2113, NSW, Australia
Tel.: (61) 294911000
Web Site: https://www.cerner.com
Healtcare Services
N.A.I.C.S.: 621610

Cerner Deutschland GmbH (2)
Cunoweg 1, 65510, Idstein, Germany
Tel.: (49) 61269520
Emp.: 100
Medical Software Publisher
N.A.I.C.S.: 513210
Arne Westphal *(Gen Mgr)*

Cerner Egypt L.L.C. (2)
Offices Suites M006 M007 Raya Office New

Cairo Land No 133, Banking Sector, Cairo, Egypt
Tel.: (20) 224802727
Healtcare Services
N.A.I.C.S.: 621610

Cerner France SAS (2)
Tour Manhattan La Defense 2, 5/6 Place de L, 92400, Courbevoie, France
Tel.: (33) 176740700
Medical Software Publisher
N.A.I.C.S.: 513210

Cerner Health Services Deutschland GmbH (2)
Siemensdamm 50, 13629, Berlin, Germany
Tel.: (49) 30383700
Web Site: http://www.cerner.com
Emp.: 120
Information Technology Consulting Services
N.A.I.C.S.: 541512

Subsidiary (Domestic):

Cerner Health Services, Inc. (2)
2750 E Cottonwood Pkwy Ste 100, Salt Lake City, UT 84121
Tel.: (801) 539-4600
Writing Software For Hospitals & Health Care
N.A.I.C.S.: 541511

Subsidiary (Non-US):

Cerner Healthcare Solutions India Private Limited (2)
Ground Floor Wing B Block H2 Mountain Ash Manyata, Embassy Business Park Nagawara, Bengaluru, 560 045, India
Tel.: (91) 8033010400
Information Technology Services
N.A.I.C.S.: 541511
Rekha M. *(Engr-Software)*

Cerner Iberia, S.L. (2)
Paseo de la Castellana 79 Planta 8, 28046, Madrid, Spain
Tel.: (34) 917916650
Healtcare Services
N.A.I.C.S.: 621610

Cerner Ireland Limited (2)
Newenham House Northern Cross Business Park Fourth Level Malahide Rd, Dublin, 17, Ireland
Tel.: (353) 12563100
Web Site: https://www.cerner.com
Healtcare Services
N.A.I.C.S.: 621610

Cerner Limited (2)
6th Floor the Point 37 North Wharf Road, London, W2 1AF, United Kingdom
Tel.: (44) 2074328100
Healtcare Services
N.A.I.C.S.: 621610

Cerner Middle East FZ-LLC (2)
3rd floor Block B Office Park Bldg Knowledge Village, PO Box 500542, Dubai, United Arab Emirates
Tel.: (971) 43754900
Healtcare Services
N.A.I.C.S.: 621610

Subsidiary (Domestic):

Cerner Multum, Inc. (2)
Colorado Ctr Tower One 2000 S Colorado Blvd Ste 11000, Denver, CO 80222
Tel.: (303) 733-4447
Web Site: http://www.multum.com
Medical Care Management Services
N.A.I.C.S.: 621999

Subsidiary (Non-US):

Cerner Nederland B.V. (2)
De Haagsche Zwaan Level 15, Schenkkade 50, Hague, 2595, Netherlands
Tel.: (31) 70 7100610
Information Technology Consulting Services
N.A.I.C.S.: 541512

Cerner Osterreich GmbH (2)
Lassallestrase 7a/Unit 4/Top 7, 1020, Vienna, Austria
Tel.: (43) 1253003200
Information Technology Consulting Services
N.A.I.C.S.: 541512
Stefan Radatz *(Gen Mgr)*

Subsidiary (Domestic):

Cerner Properties, Inc. (2)
2800 Rockcreek Pkwy, Kansas City, MO
64117-2521
Tel.: (816) 221-7800
Web Site: http://www.cerner.com
Real Estate Agency & Brokerage Services
N.A.I.C.S.: 531210

Kantar Health (2)
11 Madison Ave, New York, NY 10010
Tel.: (212) 647-7200
Web Site: http://www.kantarhealth.com
Healtcare Services
N.A.I.C.S.: 621999
Lynnette Cooke *(CEO)*
Tom Haskell *(Head-Global)*
Jeremy Brody *(Chief Strategy Officer)*

**Corente, Inc. - Engineering
Center** (1)
758 State Rte 18, East Brunswick, NJ
08816-4910
Tel.: (732) 254-2940
Web Site: http://www.corente.com
Cloud Platform Development
N.A.I.C.S.: 541511

Dynamic Network Services, Inc. (1)
150 Dow St, Manchester, NH 03101
Tel.: (603) 668-4998
Web Site: http://www.dyn.com
Software Publisher
N.A.I.C.S.: 513210
Kevin Bisson *(CFO)*
Jeremy P. Hitchcock *(Co-Founder)*

Eloqua, Inc. (1)
1921 Gallows Rd Ste 250, Vienna, VA
22182-3900
Tel.: (703) 584-2750
Web Site: http://www.eloqua.com
Sales Range: $50-74.9 Million
Emp.: 300
Marketing Automation Solutions
N.A.I.C.S.: 513210

Greenbytes, Inc. (1)
275 Promenade St Ste 225, Providence, RI
02908
Tel.: (401) 315-5580
Web Site: http://www.getgreenbytes.com
Storage Optimization Software Development Services
N.A.I.C.S.: 541511
Robert Petrocelli *(Founder)*

NetSuite Inc. (1)
2955 Campus Dr Ste 250, San Mateo, CA
94403-2511
Tel.: (650) 627-1000
Web Site: http://www.netsuite.com
Enterprise Resource Planning & Customer
Relationship Management Software & Services
N.A.I.C.S.: 513210
Evan Goldberg *(Founder & Exec VP)*
Jason Maynard *(Sr VP-Global Field Ops & Bus Unit)*
David Rodman *(Sr VP-Customer Success & Global Bus Unit)*
Gustavo Moussalli *(Head-LAD & Global Bus Unit)*

Subsidiary (Domestic):

Bronto Software, LLC (2)
Washington Bldg 324 Blackwell St Ste 410,
Durham, NC 27701
Tel.: (919) 595-2500
Web Site: http://www.bronto.com
Software Publisher
N.A.I.C.S.: 513210

Subsidiary (Non-US):

NetSuite Australia Pty. Ltd. (2)
Level 13, 100 Arthur Street, North Sydney,
2060, NSW, Australia
Tel.: (61) 294646100
Web Site: http://www.netsuite.com.au
Enterprise Resource Planning & Customer
Relationship Management Software & Services
N.A.I.C.S.: 513210

NetSuite Canada Inc. (2)
5800 Explorer Drive Suite 100, Mississauga, L4W 5K9, ON, Canada

Tel.: (905) 629-8486
Web Site: http://www.netsuite.com
Intergrated Business Management Software
Provider
N.A.I.C.S.: 541511

NetSuite Philippines Inc. (2)
RCBC Plaza 6819 Ayala Avenue corner
Sen Gil Puyat Avenue, Makati, 1200, Philippines
Tel.: (63) 28563888
Web Site: http://www.netsuite.com
Business Management Software Publisher
N.A.I.C.S.: 513210

Venda Limited (2)
7th Floor 5 New Street Square New Fetter
Lane, London, EC4A 3BF, United Kingdom
Tel.: (44) 2070707000
Web Site: http://www.venda.com
Software Designing Services
N.A.I.C.S.: 541511

Oracle America, Inc. (1)
4230 Leonard Stocking Dr, Santa Clara, CA
95054 **(100%)**
Tel.: (408) 276-0000
Sales Range: $5-14.9 Billion
Emp.: 29,000
Holding Company; Computer Workstations,
Servers, Programming & Productivity Software Mfr
N.A.I.C.S.: 551112

Subsidiary (Non-US):

MySQL AB (2)
Bangardsgatan 8, Uppsala, 753 20, Sweden
Tel.: (46) 18101890
Web Site: http://www.mysql.com
Sales Range: $100-124.9 Million
Emp.: 400
Open Source Database Software
N.A.I.C.S.: 513210

Oracle Hardware Russia (2)
Village Moskovsky 22nd Km Kievskoe
Route, Presnenskaya Nab 10, 108811,
Moscow, Russia **(100%)**
Tel.: (7) 495 641 1400
Web Site: http://www.oracle.com
Sales Range: $100-124.9 Million
Emp.: 400
Sales of Computers & Related Technology
Services
N.A.I.C.S.: 541512

**Sun Microsystems Australia Pty.
Ltd.** (2)
828 Pacific Hwy, PO Box 10, Gordon, 2072,
NSW, Australia
Tel.: (61) 298445000
Web Site: http://www.sun.com.au
Sales Range: $150-199.9 Million
Emp.: 350
Computers & Software Services
N.A.I.C.S.: 449210

Sun Microsystems France, S.A. (2)
13 Ave Morane Saulnier, PO Box 53,
78142, Velizy-Villacoublay, France **(100%)**
Tel.: (33) 134030000
Web Site: http://www.oracle.fr
Sales Range: $200-249.9 Million
Emp.: 700
Computer Software Services
N.A.I.C.S.: 449210

Sun Microsystems Korea, Ltd. (2)
15 16/F Asem Tower Bldg 159 - 1
Samseong-Dong Gangnam-Gu, Seoul, 135-
090, Korea (South)
Tel.: (82) 221935114
Web Site: http://www.oracle.com
Sales Range: $100-124.9 Million
Emp.: 1,300
Computer Software Developer
N.A.I.C.S.: 513210

**Sun Microsystems Luxembourg
SARL** (2)
77-79 Parc D Activites, L-8308, Capellen,
Luxembourg **(100%)**
Tel.: (352) 49 113329
Web Site: http://be.sun.com
Sales Range: $100-124.9 Million
Emp.: 60
Computer Related Services
N.A.I.C.S.: 541513

**Sun Microsystems Nederland,
B.V.** (2)
Saturnus 1, PO Box 1050, 3800 BB,
Amersfoort, Netherlands
Tel.: (31) 334515000
Web Site: http://www.sun.nl
Sales Range: $150-199.9 Million
Emp.: 450
Computers & Equipment Services
N.A.I.C.S.: 449210

Sun Microsystems de Chile S.A. (2)
Avenida Mariano Sanchez Fontecilla 310 5
Piso, Las Condes, Santiago, Chile **(100%)**
Tel.: (56) 23724500
Web Site: http://mx.sun.com
Sales Range: $25-49.9 Million
Emp.: 60
Computer Software Services
N.A.I.C.S.: 423430

**Sun Microsystems de Mexico, S.A.
de C.V.** (2)
Plz Reforma Prolong Paseo De La Reforma
N 600 piso 2, Edificio B Col Pena Blanca
Santa Fe, Mexico, 01210, Mexico **(100%)**
Tel.: (52) 586100
Web Site: http://www.oracle.com
Sales Range: $75-99.9 Million
Emp.: 200
Computer Software Services
N.A.I.C.S.: 423430

**Sun Microsystems do Brasil Industria
e Comercio Ltda.** (2)
Rua Alexandre Dumas 2016 Chacara Santo
Antonio, Sao Paulo, 04717-004, SP,
Brazil **(100%)**
Tel.: (55) 1130854173
Sales Range: $150-199.9 Million
Computer Software Services
N.A.I.C.S.: 423430

Oracle Argentina S.A. (1)
Calle Humberto Primo 59 Capital Federal,
C1103ACA, Buenos Aires, Argentina
Tel.: (54) 01143418100
Web Site: http://www.peoplesoft.com.ar
Sales Range: $100-124.9 Million
Business Software
N.A.I.C.S.: 334610

Oracle Canada ULC (1)
100 Milverton Drive, Mississauga, L5R 4H1,
ON, Canada
Tel.: (905) 890-8100
Web Site: http://www.oracle.com
Sales Range: $350-399.9 Million
Emp.: 1,000
Regional Managing Office; Software &
Computer Hardware Mfr & Whslr
N.A.I.C.S.: 551114

Branch (Domestic):

**Oracle Canada - Hospitality -
Richmond** (2)
Unit 135 3751 Shell Road, Richmond, V6X
2W2, BC, Canada **(100%)**
Tel.: (604) 303-9902
Sales Range: $10-24.9 Million
Emp.: 20
Restaurant, Hospitality & Specialty Retail
Equipment Software Distr & Support Services
N.A.I.C.S.: 423430
Mark Scott *(Reg VP-Hospitality Unit)*

Oracle Canada ULC - Markham (2)
7th Floor 27 Allstate Parkway, Markham,
L3R 5L7, ON, Canada **(100%)**
Tel.: (905) 477-6745
Web Site: http://www.oracle.com
Sales Range: $25-49.9 Million
Emp.: 150
Computer Sales & Services
N.A.I.C.S.: 449210

Oracle Canada ULC - Montreal (2)
600 blvd de Maisonneuve Ouest Ste 1900,
Montreal, H3A 3J2, QC, Canada
Tel.: (514) 905-8400
Web Site: http://www.oracle.com
Sales Range: $25-49.9 Million
Emp.: 100
Custom Computer Programming Services
N.A.I.C.S.: 541511

Oracle Caribbean, Inc. (1)
American International Plz 250 Munoz Ri-

vera Ave Ste 300 3rd Fl, San Juan, PR
00918-1901
Tel.: (787) 999-3100
Sales Range: $10-24.9 Million
Emp.: 70
Prepackaged Software
N.A.I.C.S.: 513210
Carlos Ruiz *(Mng Dir)*
Raul Bernal *(Sr Dir-Fin & Controller)*

Oracle Colombia Limitada (1)
Calle 127 A No 53A-45 Torre 2 Piso 9, Bogota, Colombia **(100%)**
Tel.: (57) 16119600
Web Site: http://www.oracle.com
Sales Range: $25-49.9 Million
Emp.: 100
Develops, Manufactures & Sells Computer
Software Used for Database Management,
Applications Development & Decision Support
N.A.I.C.S.: 334610

**Oracle Corporation Singapore Pte
Ltd** (1)
1 Fusionopolis Place Level 12 Galaxis, Singapore, 138522, Singapore **(100%)**
Tel.: (65) 64361000
Web Site: http://www.oracle.com
Sales Range: $200-249.9 Million
Emp.: 1,000
Develops, Manufactures & Sells Computer
Software Used for Database Management,
Applications Development & Decision Support
N.A.I.C.S.: 334610

Subsidiary (Non-US):

**Oracle (China) Software Systems
Co., Ltd.** (2)
Room 2208 China World Trade Center
Tower 2, No 1 Jian Guo Men Wai Da Jie,
Beijing, 100004, China
Tel.: (86) 65386688
Web Site: http://www.oracle.com
Sales Range: $100-124.9 Million
Develops, Manufactures & Sells Computer
Software Used for Database Management,
Applications Development & Decision Support
N.A.I.C.S.: 334610

Branch (Domestic):

**Oracle (China) Software Systems
Co., Ltd.-Shanghai** (3)
155 Tianjin Road 12th Floor Henderson
Metropolitan, Shanghai, 200021,
China **(100%)**
Tel.: (86) 2123023000
Web Site: http://www.oracle.com
Sales Range: $50-74.9 Million
Emp.: 400
Develops, Manufactures & Sells Computer
Software Used for Database Management,
Applications Development & Decision Support
N.A.I.C.S.: 334610

Subsidiary (Non-US):

**Oracle Corporation (Australia) Pty.
Ltd.** (2)
Riverside Corporate Park, 4 Julius Ave,
North Ryde, 2113, NSW, Australia **(100%)**
Tel.: (61) 2949 11000
Web Site: http://www.oracle.com
Sales Range: $100-124.9 Million
Emp.: 900
Develops, Manufactures & Sells Computer
Software Used for Database Management,
Applications Development & Decision Support
N.A.I.C.S.: 334610
Alistair Green *(Sr VP-Cloud Engrg-Japan &
Asia Pacific & Interim Mng Dir-Australia &
New Zealand)*

Unit (Domestic):

**MICROS-Fidelio Australia Pty
Ltd.** (3)
Ste 7 1st Fl 13 Narabang Way, Belrose,
2085, NSW, Australia **(100%)**
Tel.: (61) 2 9485 1200
Web Site: http://www.micros-fidelio.com.au
Emp.: 100

Oracle Corporation—(Continued)

Restaurant, Hospitality & Specialty Retail
Equipment Software Distr & Support Services
N.A.I.C.S.: 423430

Subsidiary (Non-US):

**Oracle Corporation (Philippines),
Inc.** (2)
33rd Floor Zuelling Building Makati Avenue
corner paseo de Roxas, Corner Makati Avenues, 1200, Makati, Manila,
Philippines (100%)
Tel.: (63) 29768600
Web Site: http://www.oracle.com
Sales Range: $25-49.9 Million
Emp.: 100
Computer Software Used for Database
Management, Applications Development &
Decision Support Developer Mfr & Whslr
N.A.I.C.S.: 334610

Oracle Corporation (Thailand) Company Ltd. (2)
16th Floor Ramaland Bldg Suriyawong Bangrak, 952 Rama IV Road, Bangkok, 10500,
Thailand (100%)
Tel.: (66) 26968000
Web Site: http://www.oracle.com
Sales Range: $25-49.9 Million
Emp.: 124
Develops, Manufactures & Sells Computer
Software Used for Database Management,
Applications Development & Decision Support
N.A.I.C.S.: 334610

Oracle Corporation Japan (2)
Oracle Aoyama Centre 2-5-8 Kita-Aoyama,
Minato-ku, Tokyo, 107-0061, Japan
Tel.: (81) 368346666
Web Site: http://www.oracle.com
Sales Range: $100-124.9 Million
Business Software Mfr
N.A.I.C.S.: 334610

**Oracle Corporation Malaysia Sdn.
Bhd.** (2)
Level 23 The Gardens North Tower Mid Valley City, Lingkaran Syed Putra, 59200,
Kuala Lumpur, Malaysia
Tel.: (60) 3 2299 3600
Web Site: http://www.oracle.com
Sales Range: $25-49.9 Million
Emp.: 170
Develops, Manufactures & Sells Computer
Software Used for Database Management,
Applications Development & Decision Support
N.A.I.C.S.: 334610
Fitri Abdullah (Mng Dir)

Oracle Hong Kong Limited (2)
39/F The Lee Gardens 33 Hysan Avenue,
Causeway Bay, China (Hong Kong)
Tel.: (852) 36557400
Web Site: http://www.oracle.com
Sales Range: $100-124.9 Million
Business Software
N.A.I.C.S.: 334610

Subsidiary (Domestic):

MICROS-Fidelio Hong Kong Ltd. (3)
39/F The Lee Gardens 33 Hysan Avenue,
Causeway Bay, China (Hong
Kong) (100%)
Tel.: (852) 3655 7400
Emp.: 30
Restaurant, Hospitality & Specialty Retail
Equipment Software Distr & Support Services
N.A.I.C.S.: 423430
Michael Sacks (Sr Dir-Sls-Casino)

Subsidiary (Non-US):

Oracle India Private Limited (2)
DLF Infinity Tower A 3rd Floor, DLF Cyber
City DLF Phase II, Gurgaon, 122 002, Haryana, India
Tel.: (91) 1246788000
Business Software Solutions
N.A.I.C.S.: 334610

Unit (Domestic):

Fidelio India Private Ltd. (3)

The Mira Corporate Suites Block A-1 Plot
No 1 2 Old Ishwar Nagar, New Delhi, 110
065, India (100%)
Tel.: (91) 11 6661 6000
Sales Range: $10-24.9 Million
Emp.: 30
Restaurant, Hospitality & Specialty Retail
Equipment & Software Distr & Support Services
N.A.I.C.S.: 423430
Sagun Sawhney (Head-Sls-Hospitality)

Branch (Domestic):

Oracle India Private Limited (3)
Cyber Park - Salarpuria Plot 67, Hitec City
Madhapur, Hyderabad, 500 081, India
Tel.: (91) 4067244474
Web Site: http://www.oracle.com
Sales Range: $25-49.9 Million
Emp.: 100
Integrated Data Management
N.A.I.C.S.: 541511

Subsidiary (Non-US):

Oracle Korea Ltd. (2)
Asem Tower 159-1 Samsung-Dong,
Kangnam-Gu, Seoul, Korea (South)
Tel.: (82) 221948000
Web Site: http://www.oracle.com
Sales Range: $150-199.9 Million
Emp.: 1,300
Develops, Manufactures & Sells Computer
Software Used for Database Management,
Applications Development & Decision Support
N.A.I.C.S.: 334610
Wonsik Yoo (Mng Dir)

Oracle Taiwan, LLC (2)
2765 28th Floor No 68 Zhongxiao East
Road, Taipei, 11065, Taiwan (100%)
Tel.: (886) 287267000
Web Site: http://www.oracle.com
Sales Range: $50-74.9 Million
Emp.: 300
Develops, Manufactures & Sells Computer
Software Used for Database Management,
Applications Development & Decision Support
N.A.I.C.S.: 334610

P.T. Oracle Indonesia (2)
Sentral Senayan 1 Office Tower 9/F JI Asia
Afrika No 8, Jakarta, 10270, Indonesia
Tel.: (62) 21 2555 2168
Web Site: http://www.oracle.com
Computer Software & Services
N.A.I.C.S.: 423430

Oracle EMEA Limited (1)
East Point Business Park, Fairview, Dublin,
3, Ireland (100%)
Tel.: (353) 18039000
Web Site: http://www.oracle.com
Sales Range: $350-399.9 Million
Emp.: 1,000
Develops, Manufactures & Sells Computer
Software Used for Database Management,
Applications Development & Decision Support
N.A.I.C.S.: 334610

Subsidiary (Non-US):

Oracle Austria GmbH (2)
Donau-City-Strasse 7, 1220, Vienna, Austria
Tel.: (43) 1337770
Sales Range: $50-74.9 Million
Emp.: 250
Business Software
N.A.I.C.S.: 513210
Arno Gantner (Sls Mgr)

Oracle Belgium BVBA (2)
Medialaan 50, 1800, Vilvoorde, Belgium
Tel.: (32) 27191211
Web Site: http://www.oracle.be
Sales Range: $100-124.9 Million
Emp.: 300
Business Software
N.A.I.C.S.: 334610

Oracle Corporation U.K. Ltd. (2)
Oracle Parkway Thames Valley Park, Reading, RG6 1RA, Berkshire, United
Kingdom (100%)
Tel.: (44) 1189240000
Web Site: https://www.oracle.com

Sales Range: $350-399.9 Million
Computer Software Developer, Mfr & Sales
for Computer Software Used for Database
Management, Applications Development &
Decision Support
N.A.I.C.S.: 334610
William Hardie (VP-Database Product
Mgmt)

Subsidiary (Domestic):

MICROS Systems UK Limited (3)
Houghton Hall Business Park Houghton Regis, Dunstable, LU5 5YG, Bedfordshire,
United Kingdom
Tel.: (44) 1582869600
Sales Range: $300-349.9 Million
Emp.: 2,100
Retail Information Technology Systems,
Equipment, Software & Services
N.A.I.C.S.: 561499
Greg Huntley (Dir-Ops-UK & Ireland)

Subsidiary (Domestic):

**MICROS Retail Services UK
Limited** (4)
2426 Vincent Ave Crown Hill, Milton
Keynes, MK8 0AB, United Kingdom
Tel.: (44) 1908226226
Sales Range: $25-49.9 Million
Emp.: 75
Holding Company; Retail Information Technology Products & Services
N.A.I.C.S.: 551112
Nicholas Boyce (Acct Mgr)
Des Thomas (Mgr-Ops)

Unit (Domestic):

**MICROS Systems UK Limited -
Bolton** (4)
Crompton House Barrs Fold Road Wingates
Industrial Park, Westhoughton, Bolton, BL5
3XP, Lancs, United Kingdom
Tel.: (44) 1942854300
Sales Range: $25-49.9 Million
Emp.: 60
Retail Point-of-Sale Systems, Software &
Equipment Developer & Whslr
N.A.I.C.S.: 333310

Subsidiary (Domestic):

MICROS-Fidelio U.K. Ltd. (4)
Micros Fidelio House 6 8 The Grove,
Slough, SL1 1QP, United Kingdom (100%)
Tel.: (44) 1753536969
Web Site: http://www.micro-fidelio.co.uk
Sales Range: $25-49.9 Million
Emp.: 140
Restaurant, Hospitality & Specialty Retail
Equipment & Software Distr & Support Services
N.A.I.C.S.: 423420

Branch (Domestic):

**Oracle Corporation UK
Ltd.-London** (3)
One South Place, London, EC2M 2RB,
United Kingdom
Tel.: (44) 2078167500
Web Site: http://www.oracle.com
Sales Range: $10-24.9 Million
Emp.: 150
Computer Services
N.A.I.C.S.: 541512

Subsidiary (Non-US):

**Oracle Deutschland B.V. & Co.
KG** (3)
Riesstrasse 25, 80992, Munich,
Germany (100%)
Tel.: (49) 8914300
Web Site: http://www.oracle.com
Sales Range: $50-74.9 Million
Emp.: 225
Computer Software Developer, Mfr & Sales
for Computer Software Used for Database
Management, Applications Development &
Decision Support
N.A.I.C.S.: 334610

Branch (Domestic):

**Oracle Deutschland B.V. & Co.
KG** (4)
Europadamm 2-6, 41460, Neuss, Germany

Tel.: (49) 2131137113
Web Site: http://www.oracle.com
Emp.: 160
Holding Company; Regional Managing Office
N.A.I.C.S.: 551112

Subsidiary (Domestic):

Fidelio Cruise Software GmbH (5)
Borselstrasse 16 C, Hamburg, 22765, Germany
Tel.: (49) 40398070
Web Site: http://www.fideliocruise.com
Sales Range: $10-24.9 Million
Emp.: 30
Hospitality Business Software Developer &
Publisher
N.A.I.C.S.: 513210

Subsidiary (Non-US):

Oracle Finland Oy (4)
Grasantorma 2, PO Box 47, 02201, Espoo,
Finland (100%)
Tel.: (358) 954941000
Web Site: http://www.oracle.fi
Sales Range: $50-74.9 Million
Emp.: 200
Develops, Manufactures & Sells Computer
Software Used for Database Management,
Applications Development & Decision Support
N.A.I.C.S.: 334610
Kimmo Vilen (Mng Dir)

Subsidiary (Non-US):

Oracle Denmark ApS (2)
Metalbuen 66, 2750, Ballerup,
Denmark (100%)
Tel.: (45) 44808080
Web Site: http://www.oracle.com
Sales Range: $50-74.9 Million
Emp.: 240
Computer Software Developer, Mfr & Sales
for Database Management, Applications
Development & Decision Support
N.A.I.C.S.: 334610

Oracle Egypt Ltd. (2)
2 El Hegaz Strasse Cedare Building, Heliopolis, Cairo, 11737, Egypt
Tel.: (20) 224802777
Web Site: http://www.oracle.com
Computer Software Developer, Mfr & Sales
N.A.I.C.S.: 334610

**Oracle Financial Services Software
Limited** (2)
Oracle Park Off Western Express Highway
Goregaon East, Mumbai, 400 063, Maharashtra, India (81%)
Tel.: (91) 2267183000
Web Site: http://www.oracle.com
Rev.: $706,210,899
Assets: $1,112,108,387
Liabilities: $217,808,645
Net Worth: $894,299,742
Earnings: $216,550,686
Emp.: 7,680
Fiscal Year-end: 03/31/2023
Financial Information Technology Services
N.A.I.C.S.: 513210

Subsidiary (US):

**Oracle (OFSS) BPO Services
Inc.** (3)
17682 Mitchell N Ste 201, Irvine, CA 92614-
6037
Tel.: (949) 250-1445
Financial Information Technology Services
N.A.I.C.S.: 513210

Subsidiary (Domestic):

**Oracle (OFSS) BPO Services
Limited** (3)
DLF Infinity Tower A 3rd Floor DLF Cyber
City Phase II, Gurgaon, 122 002, India
Tel.: (91) 124 433 0200
Financial Information Technology Services
N.A.I.C.S.: 513210

Subsidiary (Non-US):

**Oracle Financial Services Software
Pte. Ltd.** (3)
4/F Samhwa Building Samsung-Dong

Kangnam-Gu, Seoul, Korea (South)
Tel.: (82) 2 6241 6413
Financial Information Technology Services
N.A.I.C.S.: 513210

**Oracle Financial Services Software
b.v.**   **(3)**
Claude Debussylaan 32 14th floor Vinoly
building, Strawinskylaan 1245, 1077 MD,
Amsterdam, Netherlands
Tel.: (31) 205754200
Web Site: http://www.oracle.com
Sales Range: $100-124.9 Million
Emp.: 1,200
Financial Information Technology Services
N.A.I.C.S.: 513210

**Oracle Financial Services Software
b.v.**   **(3)**
Eastpoint Business Park Fairview, Dublin,
Ireland
Tel.: (353) 1 803 1000
Financial Information Technology Services
N.A.I.C.S.: 513210

**Oracle Financial Services Software
s.a.**   **(3)**
14 Paradeisou & 1 Patroklou Street 151 25
Marousi, Athens, Greece
Tel.: (30) 211 10 40000
Financial Information Technology Services
N.A.I.C.S.: 513210

Subsidiary (US):

**Oracle Financial Services Software,
Inc.**   **(3)**
399 Thornall St 6th Fl, Edison, NJ 08837
Tel.: (732) 623-0399
Web Site: http://www.oracle.com
Sales Range: $10-24.9 Million
Emp.: 200
Financial Services Software
N.A.I.C.S.: 513210

Branch (Domestic):

**Oracle Financial Services Software,
Inc-Minneapolis**   **(4)**
8000 Norman Center Dr Ste 900, Blooming-
ton, MN 55437
Tel.: (952) 897-4000
Web Site: http://www.oracle.com
Financial Services Software
N.A.I.C.S.: 513210

Subsidiary (Non-US):

Oracle France S.A.S.   **(2)**
15 Boulevard Charles De Gaulle, 92715,
Colombes, Cedex, France   **(100%)**
Tel.: (33) 157602020
Web Site: http://www.oracle.com
Sales Range: $200-249.9 Million
Emp.: 900
Computer Software Developer, Mfr & Sales
for Computer Software Used for Database
Management, Applications Development &
Decision Support
N.A.I.C.S.: 334610

Oracle Hellas, S.A.   **(2)**
265 Mesogion Ave, Neo Psychiko, 154 51,
Athens, Greece   **(100%)**
Tel.: (30) 2106789200
Web Site: http://www.oracle.com
Sales Range: $25-49.9 Million
Emp.: 130
Computer Software Developer, Mfr & Sales
N.A.I.C.S.: 334610

Oracle Iberica SA   **(2)**
Avda Diagonal 615 8 planta, 08028, Barce-
lona, Spain   **(100%)**
Tel.: (34) 902302302
Web Site: http://www.oracle.com
Sales Range: $25-49.9 Million
Emp.: 150
Develops, Mfr & Sells Computer Software
Used for Database Management, Applica-
tions Development & Decision Support
N.A.I.C.S.: 334610

Oracle Italia S.r.l.   **(2)**
V le Fulvio Testi 136, 20092, Cinisello Bal-
samo, MI, Italy
Tel.: (39) 02 249591
Sales Range: $100-124.9 Million
Business Software
N.A.I.C.S.: 334610

Oracle Nederland B.V.   **(2)**
Hertogswetering 163-167, 3543 AS,
Utrecht, Netherlands
Tel.: (31) 306699000
Web Site: http://education.oracle.com
Sales Range: $350-399.9 Million
Emp.: 1,000
Computer Software Developer, Mfr & Sales
for Database Management, Applications
Development & Decision Support
N.A.I.C.S.: 334610

Subsidiary (Non-US):

Oracle Svenska AB   **(3)**
Rasundavagen 4, 169 67, Solna, Sweden
Tel.: (46) 8 4773300
Web Site: http://www.oracle.se
Emp.: 411
Develops, Manufactures & Sells Computer
Software Used for Database Management,
Applications Development & Decision Sup-
port
N.A.I.C.S.: 513210

Subsidiary (Domestic):

MICROS-Fidelio Sweden AB   **(4)**
Dalvagen 2, PO Box 1429, 171 27, Solna,
Sweden   **(100%)**
Tel.: (46) 8 6291900
Web Site: http://www.fideliosswe.se
Emp.: 32
Restaurant, Hospitality & Specialty Retail
Equipment Software Distr & Support Ser-
vices
N.A.I.C.S.: 423430

Branch (Domestic):

Oracle Svenska AB   **(4)**
Soder Malarstrand 57, PO Box 17084, 118
25, Stockholm, Sweden
Tel.: (46) 84773300
Web Site: http://www.oracle.se
Sales Range: $75-99.9 Million
Emp.: 250
Develops, Manufactures & Sells Computer
Software Used for Database Management,
Applications Development & Decision Sup-
port
N.A.I.C.S.: 334610

Oracle Svenska AB   **(4)**
Grafiska Vagen 2, Solna, 412 63, Gothen-
burg, Sweden
Tel.: (46) 84773300
Web Site: http://www.oracle.se
Sales Range: $100-124.9 Million
Emp.: 250
Business Software
N.A.I.C.S.: 334610

Subsidiary (Non-US):

Oracle Norge A/S   **(2)**
Vollsveien 2A, 1366, Lysaker,
Norway   **(100%)**
Tel.: (47) 067526700
Web Site: http://www.oracle.com
Sales Range: $25-49.9 Million
Emp.: 180
Develops, Mfr & Sells Computer Software
Used for Database Management, Applica-
tions Development & Decision Support
N.A.I.C.S.: 334610

Oracle Polska Sp.z.o.o.   **(2)**
Przyokopowa 31, 01 208, Warsaw, Poland
Tel.: (48) 226908700
Web Site: http://www.oracle.com
Sales Range: $25-49.9 Million
Emp.: 250
Computer Software Developer, Mfr & Sales
N.A.I.C.S.: 334610

**Oracle Portugal-Sistemas de Informa-
cao Lda.**   **(2)**
Lagoas Park Edificio n 8, Salvo, 2740-244,
Porto, Portugal
Tel.: (351) 214235000
Web Site: http://www.oracle.com
Sales Range: $50-74.9 Million
Emp.: 150
Develops, Mfr & Sells Computer Software
Used for Database Management, Applica-
tions Development & Decision Support
N.A.I.C.S.: 334610

Oracle Software (Schweiz) AG   **(2)**

Tel.: (41) 564833111
Web Site: https://www.oracle.com
Sales Range: $25-49.9 Million
Emp.: 200
Develops, Mfr & Sells Computer Software
Used for Database Management, Applica-
tions Development & Decision Support
N.A.I.C.S.: 334610

Oracle Software d.o.o.   **(2)**
Dunajska Cesta 156, 1000, Ljubljana,
Slovenia   **(100%)**
Tel.: (386) 15888800
Web Site: http://www.oracle.com
Sales Range: $10-24.9 Million
Emp.: 45
Computer Software Developer, Mfr & Sales
N.A.I.C.S.: 334610

Oracle Hospitality   **(1)**
7031 Columbia Gateway Dr, Columbia, MD
21046-2583
Tel.: (667) 786-5017
Web Site: http://www.oracle.com
Sales Range: $1-4.9 Billion
Emp.: 6,809
Restaurant, Hospitality & Specialty Retail
Equipment Software Mfr, Distr & Support
Services
N.A.I.C.S.: 513210
Alex Alt *(Sr VP & Gen Mgr)*

Oracle New Zealand Limited   **(1)**
Level 4 Oracle House, 162 Victoria Street
West, Auckland, 1010, New
Zealand   **(100%)**
Tel.: (64) 9 977 2100
Web Site: http://www.oracle.com
Sales Range: $75-99.9 Million
Emp.: 100
Computer Software Distr & Support Ser-
vices, Related Training & Consulting Ser-
vices & Network Infrastructure Solutions
N.A.I.C.S.: 423430
Rob Willis *(Mng Dir)*

Branch (Domestic):

Oracle New Zealand Limited   **(2)**
Level 10 Todd Building, 93-97 Custom-
house Quay, Wellington, 6011, New
Zealand   **(100%)**
Tel.: (64) 49785400
Web Site: http://www.oracle.com
Emp.: 50
Computer Software Services
N.A.I.C.S.: 423430

Oracle Numetrix Co.   **(1)**
145 King Street West Suite 500, Toronto,
M5H 1J8, ON, Canada   **(100%)**
Tel.: (416) 642-9800
Web Site: http://www.oracle.com
Sales Range: $100-124.9 Million
Business Software Mfr
N.A.I.C.S.: 334610

**Oracle Software Technology
GmbH**   **(1)**
29 Route de Pre-Bois, Geneva, Switzerland
Tel.: (41) 564833111
Software Development Services
N.A.I.C.S.: 541511

Oracle South Africa (Pty) Ltd.   **(1)**
Woodmead North Office Park 54 Maxwell
Drive, Jukskeiview, Sandton, 2196, South
Africa
Tel.: (27) 11 319 4000
Web Site: http://www.oracle.com
Emp.: 55
Business Software Sales & Service
N.A.I.C.S.: 423430

Oracle Technology Company   **(1)**
Eastpoint Business Park, Fairview, Dublin,
Ireland
Tel.: (353) 18031000
Web Site: http://www.oracle.com
Software Development Services
N.A.I.C.S.: 513210

Oracle de Centro America S.A.   **(1)**
Parque Empresarial Forum 2 Edificio J 4th
Floor, Santa Ana, San Jose, Costa Rica
Tel.: (506) 22055500
Web Site: http://www.oracle.com
Develops, Manufactures & Sells Computer
Software Used for Database Management,
Applications Development & Decision Sup-
port

N.A.I.C.S.: 334610

Oracle de Mexico, S.A. de C.V.   **(1)**
Montes Urales Norte 470 Lomas de
Chapultepec Miguel Hidalgo, Mexico,
11000, DF, Mexico
Tel.: (52) 5552845200
Sales Range: $25-49.9 Million
Emp.: 100
Business Software
N.A.I.C.S.: 334610

Oracle de Venezuela, S.A.   **(1)**
Av Francisco De Miranda Entre Av El
Parque Y Av Mohedano C Empresarial, Ga-
lipan Torre B piso 13, Caracas, 1060, El
Rosal, Venezuela
Tel.: (58) 212 955 1300
Web Site: http://www.oracle.com
Sales Range: $100-124.9 Million
Develops, Manufactures & Sells Computer
Software Used for Database Management,
Applications Development & Decision Sup-
port
N.A.I.C.S.: 334610

**Oracle do Brasil Sistemas
Limitada**   **(1)**
Rua Dr Jose Aureo Bustamante 455-Vila
Cordeiro, 04710-090, Sao Paulo,
Brazil   **(100%)**
Tel.: (55) 1151891000
Web Site: http://www.oracle.com
Sales Range: $75-99.9 Million
Emp.: 1,200
Develops, Mfr & Sells Computer Software
Used for Database Management, Applica-
tions Development & Decision Support
N.A.I.C.S.: 334610

Passlogix, Inc.   **(1)**
160 Pearl St, New York, NY 10005
Tel.: (212) 825-9100
Web Site: http://www.passlogix.com
Sales Range: $25-49.9 Million
Emp.: 50
Security Software Developer
N.A.I.C.S.: 513210

Phase Forward Europe Limited   **(1)**
Voyager Place Shoppenhangers Road,
Maidenhead, SL6 2PJ, Berkshire, United
Kingdom
Tel.: (44) 1628640700
Sales Range: $25-49.9 Million
Emp.: 150
Integrated Data Management Solutions for
Clinical Trials & Drug Safety
N.A.I.C.S.: 541511

Subsidiary (Non-US):

Phase Forward Pty Limited   **(2)**
SE 7 1 Central Ave Australian Technology
Park, Eveleigh, Sydney, 1430, NSW, Aus-
tralia
Tel.: (61) 296902425
Web Site: http://www.phaseforward.com
Sales Range: $100-124.9 Million
Emp.: 10
Integrated Data Management Solutions for
Clinical Trials & Drug Safety
N.A.I.C.S.: 541511

Responsys, Inc.   **(1)**
475 Sansone St Ste 15, San Francisco, CA
94111
Tel.: (415) 402-7200
Web Site: http://www.responsys.com
Sales Range: $150-199.9 Million
Emp.: 866
Computer Programming Services for Elec-
tronic Mail Marketing
N.A.I.C.S.: 541511

SPL WorldGroup, Inc.   **(1)**
525 Market St 33rd Fl, San Francisco, CA
94105
Tel.: (415) 541-9462
Sales Range: $150-199.9 Million
Emp.: 550
Software Solutions
N.A.I.C.S.: 513210

Sistemas Oracle de Chile, S.A.   **(1)**
Avenida Vitacura 2939 Pisos 6 Las Condes,
Huechuraba, Santiago, Chile   **(100%)**
Tel.: (56) 226665000
Web Site: http://www.oracle.com
Sales Range: $25-49.9 Million
Emp.: 100

Oracle Corporation—(Continued)

Develops, Mfr & Sells Computer Software
Used for Database Management, Applica-
tions Development & Decision Support
N.A.I.C.S.: 334610

ORAGENICS, INC.
4902 Eisenhower Blvd Ste 125,
Tampa, FL 33634
Tel.: (813) 286-7900   FL
Web Site: https://www.oragenics.com
OGEN—(NYSEAMEX)
Rev.: $131,521
Assets: $14,758,025
Liabilities: $1,748,723
Net Worth: $13,009,302
Earnings: ($14,288,389)
Emp.: 6
Fiscal Year-end: 12/31/22
Biopharmaceutical Research Services
N.A.I.C.S.: 325412
Robert T. Zahradnik (Co-Founder)
Jeffrey D. Hillman (Co-Founder)
Martin Handfield (Sr VP-Discovery
Res)
Joseph Michael Redmond (Pres &
Interim Principal Exec Officer)
Charles L. Pope (Interim Exec Chm)
Janet Huffman (CFO, Treas & Sec)

ORAMED PHARMACEUTI-
CALS INC.
1185 Avenue of the Americas, New
York, NY 10036   DE
Web Site: https://www.oramed.com
Year Founded: 2006
ORMP—(NASDAQ)
Rev.: $2,703,000
Assets: $161,642,000
Liabilities: $10,486,000
Net Worth: $151,156,000
Earnings: $36,561,000
Fiscal Year-end: 12/31/22
Pharmaceutical Preparation Manufac-
turing
N.A.I.C.S.: 325412
Nadav Kidron (Co-Founder, Pres &
CEO)
Miriam Kidron (Co-Founder & Chief
Scientific Officer)
Michael Rabinowitz (Chief Comml
Officer)
Josh Hexter (COO)
Netanel Derovan (Chief Legal Officer)
Avraham Qabay (CFO, Treas & Sec)
Kevin L. Rakin (Chm)

Subsidiaries:

Oramed Ltd   (1)
20 Mamilla Ave 3rd Floor, PO Box 39098,
Jerusalem, 9414904, Israel
Tel.: (972) 25660001
Web Site: http://www.oramed.com
Sales Range: $25-49.9 Million
Emp.: 11
Pharmaceuticals Product Mfr
N.A.I.C.S.: 325412

ORANCO, INC.
1 Liberty Plz Ste 2310 PMB Ste 21,
New York, NY 10006
Tel.: (040) 759-3014   NV
ORNC—(OTCIQ)
Rev.: $15,188,650
Assets: $22,106,777
Liabilities: $15,553,768
Net Worth: $6,553,009
Earnings: $5,823,806
Emp.: 60
Fiscal Year-end: 06/30/19
Investment Services
N.A.I.C.S.: 523999
Peng Yang (Pres & Sec)
Sze Lok Wong (CFO)

ORANGE COUNTY BANCORP,
INC.

212 Dolson Ave, Middletown, NY
10940
Tel.: (845) 341-5050   DE
Web Site:
   https://www.orangebanktrust.com
Year Founded: 2007
OBT—(NASDAQ)
Rev.: $96,219,000
Assets: $2,287,334,000
Liabilities: $2,149,196,000
Net Worth: $138,138,000
Earnings: $24,363,000
Emp.: 204
Fiscal Year-end: 12/31/22
Bank Holding Company
N.A.I.C.S.: 551111
Michael J. Gilfeather (Pres & CEO)
Michael Listner (Chief Credit Officer
& Sr VP)
Michael Lesler (CFO & Exec VP)
Michael J. Coulter (Chief Lending Of-
ficer & Exec VP-Strategic Lending
Relationship Exec)
Gregory F. Sousa (Chief Lending Offi-
cer, Chief Comml Banking Officer &
Exec VP)
David Dineen (Sr VP & Dir-Wealth
Svcs)
Elizabeth Jones (COO & Sr VP)
Jacob Rahiman (Chief HR Officer &
Sr VP)
Anthony Pili (Chief Innovation Officer
& Sr VP)
Steven Rooney (Chief Credit Officer
& Sr VP)
Redwan Ahmed (CIO & Sr VP)

Subsidiaries:

Orange Bank & Trust Company   (1)
212 Dolson Ave, Middletown, NY 10940
Tel.: (845) 341-5000
Web Site: https://www.orangebanktrust.com
Sales Range: $10-24.9 Million
Emp.: 110
Commericial Banking
N.A.I.C.S.: 522110
Michael J. Gilfeather (Pres & CEO)
Timothy S. McCausland (Chief Strategy Of-
ficer & Sr VP)
Michael J. Gilfeather (Pres & CEO)
Louis Heimbach (Chm)
Christopher Hayden (COO)

ORANGEHOOK, INC.
319 Barry Ave S Ste 110, Wayzata,
MN 55391
Tel.: (442) 500-4665   MN
Web Site:
   https://www.orangehook.com
Year Founded: 2009
ORHK—(OTCIQ)
Sales Range: $1-9.9 Million
Emp.: 47
Investment Services
N.A.I.C.S.: 523999
Richard Resnick (Exec VP-Ops)
James L. Mandel (Pres & CEO)
David Batchelor (Chief Rels Officer)
Jeffrey J. Hattara (Chief Strategy Offi-
cer)
Donald M. Miller (Chm)

ORASURE TECHNOLOGIES,
INC.
220 E 1st St, Bethlehem, PA 18015
Tel.: (610) 882-1820   DE
Web Site: https://www.orasure.com
Year Founded: 1985
OSUR—(NASDAQ)
Rev.: $387,479,000
Assets: $444,708,000
Liabilities: $81,084,000
Net Worth: $363,624,000
Earnings: ($17,934,000)
Emp.: 840
Fiscal Year-end: 12/31/22

Oral Fluid Diagnostic Testing, Infec-
tious Disease Testing & Substance
Abuse Testing
N.A.I.C.S.: 541720
Kathleen G. Weber (Chief Product
Officer)
David Rappaport (Sr VP-Corp Dev,
Strategy & Integration)
Carrie Eglinton Manner (Pres & CEO)
Kenneth J. McGrath (CFO)
Michele Anthony (Chief Acctg Officer)
Zachary Wert (Sr VP)
Stefano Taucer (Gen Counsel)
Trace Custer (Sr VP)
Rafal Iwasiow (VP)

Subsidiaries:

DNA Genotek Inc.   (1)
3000 - 500 Palladium Drive, Ottawa, K2V
1C2, ON, Canada
Tel.: (613) 723-5757
Web Site: https://www.dnagenotek.com
Sales Range: $25-49.9 Million
Emp.: 80
DNA Sample Collection Kit Mfr
N.A.I.C.S.: 339113

ORBCOMM, INC.
395 W Passaic St, Rochelle Park, NJ
07662
Tel.: (703) 433-6300   DE
Web Site: http://www.orbcomm.com
ORBC—(NASDAQ)
Rev.: $248,466,000
Assets: $510,845,000
Liabilities: $301,430,000
Net Worth: $209,415,000
Earnings: ($33,940,000)
Emp.: 700
Fiscal Year-end: 12/31/20
Commercial Wireless Messaging Sys-
tems
N.A.I.C.S.: 517410
Marc J. Eisenberg (CEO)
Christian G. Le Brun (Gen Counsel &
Exec VP)
Constantine Milcos (CFO & Exec VP)
Craig E. Malone (Exec VP-Product
Dev)
David Schmoock (COO)

Subsidiaries:

Blue Tree Systems GmbH   (1)
Furstenrieder Strasse 5, 80687, Munich,
Germany
Tel.: (49) 228926380
Web Site: http://www.orbcomm.com
Satellite Track Services
N.A.I.C.S.: 517410

Blue Tree Systems Inc.   (1)
101 Centreport Dr Ste 140, Greensboro,
NC 27409
Tel.: (800) 477-7052
Commercial Wireless Messaging Services
N.A.I.C.S.: 517410

Blue Tree Systems Ltd.   (1)
Galway Business Park Dangan, Galway,
Ireland
Tel.: (353) 91520053
Satellite Track Services
N.A.I.C.S.: 517410
David Miller (VP-Software)

Blue Tree Systems SARL   (1)
Batiment Cap Arrow Avenue Satolas Green,
Pusignan, 69330, France
Tel.: (33) 427190097
Satellite Track Services
N.A.I.C.S.: 517410

InSync Information Systems, Pvt.
Ltd.   (1)
1st Floor GNR s RV Insignia Plot No 28-30
Silicon Valley Layout Image, Garden Road
Madhapur, Hyderabad, 500081, India
Tel.: (91) 4040021258
Software Development Services
N.A.I.C.S.: 513210

Insync Software, Inc.   (1)
181 Metro Dr 540, San Jose, CA 95110

Tel.: (408) 352-0604
Web Site: http://www.insyncinfo.com
Sales Range: $1-9.9 Million
Emp.: 25
Computer & Software Stores
N.A.I.C.S.: 449210

ORBCOMM Europe GmbH   (1)
Maarstrasse 84, 53227, Bonn, Germany
Tel.: (49) 228926380
Satellite Track Services
N.A.I.C.S.: 517410

ORBCOMM Europe, B.V.   (1)
Handelstraat 18, 6433 KB, Hoensbroek,
Netherlands
Tel.: (31) 455285763
Satellite Track Services
N.A.I.C.S.: 517410
Peter Kuijt (VP-Sls)

ORBCOMM Ireland Ltd.   (1)
Galway Business Park, Dangan, Galway,
H91 P2DK, Ireland
Tel.: (353) 91520053
Satellite Communication Services
N.A.I.C.S.: 517410

SkyWave Mobile Communications
(HK) Limited   (1)
Unit 30 12/F Corporation Park 11 On Lai
Street, Sha Tin, New Territories, China
(Hong Kong)
Tel.: (852) 23143181
Web Site: http://www.orbcomm.com
Software Development Services
N.A.I.C.S.: 513210

StarTrak Information Technologies,
LLC   (1)
408 American Rd, Morris Plains, NJ 07950
Tel.: (973) 993-5760
Web Site: http://www.startrak.com
Wireless Information Technology Services
N.A.I.C.S.: 517112

inthinc, Inc.   (1)
341 S Main St Ste 300, Salt Lake City, UT
84111
Tel.: (703) 433-6300
Web Site: http://www.inthinc.com
Sales Range: $1-9.9 Million
Emp.: 85
Global Telematics Solutions Provider
N.A.I.C.S.: 334412

ORBIT INTERNATIONAL
CORP.
80 Cabot Ct, Hauppauge, NY 11788
Tel.: (631) 435-0300   DE
Web Site: https://www.orbitintl.com
ORBT—(OTCIQ)
Rev.: $25,924,000
Assets: $22,970,000
Liabilities: $5,579,000
Net Worth: $17,391,000
Earnings: $641,000
Emp.: 87
Fiscal Year-end: 12/31/20
Other Electronic Component Manu-
facturing
N.A.I.C.S.: 334419
Karl Schmidt (COO)
Mitchell Binder (Pres & CEO)
David Goldman (CFO, Treas & Asst
Sec)
Marcus Bryant (Sec)

Subsidiaries:

Behlman Electronics, Inc.   (1)
80 Cabot Ct, Hauppauge, NY 11788
Tel.: (631) 435-0410
Web Site: http://www.behlman.com
Sales Range: $100-124.9 Million
Emp.: 50
Power Inverters, Power Supplies & Fre-
quency Converter Mfr
N.A.I.C.S.: 335311

Integrated Combat Systems, Inc.   (1)
130 Rochester Dr, Louisville, KY
40214   (100%)
Tel.: (502) 364-5473

Sales Range: $1-4.9 Billion
Designs & Manufactures Customized Electronic Components & Subsystems
N.A.I.C.S.: 334419

Tulip Development Laboratory, Inc. (1)
300 Commerce Blvd, Quakertown, PA 18951
Tel.: (215) 538-8820
Web Site: http://www.tuliplabs.com
Sales Range: $300-349.9 Million
Emp.: 30
Avionic Display Mfr
N.A.I.C.S.: 336413
David Gutman (Pres & COO)

ORBITAL INFRASTRUCTURE GROUP, INC.
5444 Westheimer Rd Ste 1650, Houston, TX 77056
Tel.: (832) 467-1420   CO
Web Site:
   https://www.orbitalinfrastructure group.com
OIG—(NASDAQ)
Rev.: $322,217,000
Assets: $271,571,000
Liabilities: $416,307,000
Net Worth: ($144,736,000)
Earnings: ($276,187,000)
Emp.: 1,493
Fiscal Year-end: 12/31/22
Technological Products
N.A.I.C.S.: 334111
Paul D. White (Sr VP)
William J. Clough (Chm & Chief Legal Officer)
Daniel N. Ford (COO)
James F. O'Neil III (Vice Chm & CEO)
Nick Grindstaff (CFO)

Subsidiaries:

CUI-Canada, Inc. (1)
39 Kodiak Crescent, Toronto, M3J 3E5, ON, Canada
Tel.: (416) 630-8108
Electronic Components Distr
N.A.I.C.S.: 423690

Coax Fiber Solutions, LLC (1)
1252 Nathan Blvd, Loganville, GA 30052
Tel.: (770) 609-8378
Web Site: https://cfssouth.com
Fibber Installation Services
N.A.I.C.S.: 238210

Eclipse Foundation Group, Inc. (1)
1924 Aldine Western, Houston, TX 77038
Tel.: (832) 467-1420
Web Site:
   https://www.eclipsefoundationgroup.com
Communication Tower Construction Services
N.A.I.C.S.: 237130
Michael Cutrone (Pres)

Orbital Gas Systems Ltd. (1)
Cold Meece, Stone, ST15 0QN, Staffordshire, United Kingdom
Tel.: (44) 1785857000
Web Site: https://www.orbital-uk.com
Electronic Components Distr
N.A.I.C.S.: 423690

Orbital Gas Systems, North America, Inc. (1)
1924 Aldine Western Rd, Houston, TX 77038
Tel.: (832) 467-1420
Web Site: http://orbitalgas.com
Electronic Components Distr
N.A.I.C.S.: 423690

Orbital Power, Inc. (1)
400 E Las Colinas Blvd Ste 700, Irving, TX 75039
Tel.: (214) 367-6600
Web Site:
   https://orbitalinfrastructuregroup.com
Electrical Power Maintenance Services
N.A.I.C.S.: 221122
Nicholas Clough (Dir-Ops & Mktg)
Marcos Perez (Mgr-HR)

Orbital Renewables, LLC (1)
1924 Aldine Western, Houston, TX 77038
Tel.: (832) 467-1420
Web Site: http://www.orbitalrenewables.com
Solar Farm Construction Services
N.A.I.C.S.: 221114
Evan Kirchen (CEO)
Daniel N. Ford (CFO)

Orbital Solar Services, LLC (1)
Cap Trust Tower 4208 6 Forks Rd Ste 1000, Raleigh, NC 27609
Tel.: (919) 267-9935
Web Site: https://www.orbitalsolar.com
Solar Farm Construction Services
N.A.I.C.S.: 221114
Brandon Martin Sr. (CEO)

ORCHESTRA BIOMED HOLDINGS, INC.
150 Union Sq Dr, New Hope, PA 18938
Tel.: (215) 862-5797   Ky
Web Site:
   https://www.orchestrabiomed.com
Year Founded: 2020
OBIO—(NASDAQ)
Rev.: $3,533,000
Assets: $95,572,000
Liabilities: $43,038,000
Net Worth: $52,534,000
Earnings: ($33,608,000)
Emp.: 56
Fiscal Year-end: 12/31/22
Holding Company
N.A.I.C.S.: 551112
David P. Hochman (Founder, Chm & CEO)
Darren R. Sherman (Pres & COO)
Andrew Taylor (CFO)
Yuval Mika (CTO-Bioelectronic Therapies & Gen Mgr)
George Papandreou (Sr VP-Focal Therapies & Gen Mgr)
Hans-Peter Stoll (Chief Clinical Officer)
Bill Little (Exec VP-Corporate Development & Strategy)
Avi Fischer (Sr VP-Medical Affairs & Innovation)
Kunal Faldu (VP-Pharmaceutical Dev & Focal Therapies)
Eileen Bailey (VP-Quality)
William Baumbach (VP-Scientific Affairs & Focal Therapies)
Ziv Belsky (VP-Research & Development & Bioelectronic Therapies)
Bob Laughner (Sr VP-Regulatory & Quality)
Juan Lorenzo (Sr VP-Product Development)
Steven Evans (Dir-Medical & Bioelectronic Therapies)

ORCHID ISLAND CAPITAL, INC.
3305 Flamingo Dr, Vero Beach, FL 32963
Tel.: (772) 231-1400   MD
Web Site:
   https://www.orchidislandcapital.com
Year Founded: 2010
ORC—(NYSE)
Rev.: $177,569,000
Assets: $4,264,947,000
Liabilities: $3,795,002,000
Net Worth: $469,945,000
Earnings: ($39,226,000)
Fiscal Year-end: 12/31/23
Real Estate Investment Services
N.A.I.C.S.: 523999
Jerry M. Sintes (Treas & VP)
Robert E. Cauley (Chm, Pres & CEO)
George Hunter Haas IV (CFO, Chief Investment Officer & Sec)

ORCHID VENTURES, INC.

22762 Antonio Pkwy Ste L-1-631, Ladera Ranch, CA 92694
Tel.: (949) 357-5818   BC
Web Site:
   http://www.orchidessentials.com
Year Founded: 2011
ORVRF—(OTCEM)
Rev.: $3,720,366
Assets: $2,182,197
Liabilities: $3,724,071
Net Worth: ($1,541,874)
Earnings: ($3,150,866)
Fiscal Year-end: 06/30/21
Investment Services
N.A.I.C.S.: 523999
Richard Brown (Pres)
Corey Mangold (Chm & CEO)
Yousuf Jaffar (CFO)
Katelyn Daffron (Fin Dir)
Luke Charles Hemphill (Chief Revenue Officer)

OREGON BANCORP, INC.
101 High St NE, Salem, OR 97301
Tel.: (503) 644-5321   OR
Year Founded: 2008
ORBN—(OTCIQ)
Bank Holding Company
N.A.I.C.S.: 551111
David Gonzales (CFO)
Eric Gerhart (Chief Lending Officer)
Tim Gauhier (Controller)
Joseph J. Minniti (Chm)
Ryan D. Dempster (Pres & CEO)

Subsidiaries:

Willamette Valley Bank (1)
101 High St NE, Salem, OR 97301
Tel.: (503) 485-2222
Web Site:
   http://www.willamettevalleybank.com
Rev.: $6,455,104
Emp.: 60
Commericial Banking
N.A.I.C.S.: 522110
Douglas L. Zielinski (Owner)
Edgar B. Martin (Chm)
Joseph J. Minniti (VP)
Craig Hummel (Chief Credit Officer & Exec VP)
Dan King (Sr VP-Residential Lending)
Jennifer Schaffner (Sr VP & Mgr-Bank Ops)
Lisa A. Schrunk (Chief Lending Officer & Exec VP)
Ryan Dempster (Pres & CEO)
Ryan Allbritton (Chief Banking Officer & Sr VP)

OREGON PACIFIC BANCORP
1355 Hwy 101, Florence, OR 97439
Tel.: (541) 997-7121   OR
Web Site:
   https://www.oregonpacificbank.com
Year Founded: 2002
ORPB—(OTCIQ)
Rev.: $34,286,000
Assets: $760,986,000
Liabilities: $704,605,000
Net Worth: $56,381,000
Earnings: $9,231,000
Fiscal Year-end: 12/31/23
Banking Holding Company
N.A.I.C.S.: 551111
Ronald S. Green (Pres & CEO)
James Atwood (Chief Credit Officer & Exec VP)
John Raleigh (Chief Lending Officer & Exec VP)
Amber White (CFO & Exec VP)

ORGANA TECHNOLOGIES GROUP INC.
1900 S Harbor City Blvd Ste 315, Melbourne, FL 32901
Year Founded: 2002
OGNT—(OTCIQ)
Software Installation & Training Services
N.A.I.C.S.: 611420

Gina L. Bennett (CEO-Interim)

ORGANICELL REGENERATIVE MEDICINE, INC.
3321 College Ave Ste 246, Davie, FL 33314   NV
Web Site: https://www.organicell.com
Year Founded: 2011
OCEL—(OTCQB)
Rev.: $4,558,278
Assets: $2,782,200
Liabilities: $4,023,219
Net Worth: ($1,241,019)
Earnings: ($6,986,708)
Emp.: 23
Fiscal Year-end: 10/31/23
Holding Company; Biotechnologies Research & Development
N.A.I.C.S.: 551112
Albert Mitrani (Founder)
George C. Shapiro (Chief Medical Officer)
Ian T. Bothwell (Interim CEO & CFO)
Julian Milberg (Engr-Process)
Zanub Abdullah (Specialist-Cell Processing)
David Aciego (CIO)
Bhupendra Kumar Modi (Chm)
Chuck Bretz (Vice Chm)

Subsidiaries:

Livin Again Inc. (1)
245 S Highland St Ste 5, Mount Dora, FL 32757
Tel.: (352) 729-2225
Web Site: http://www.livingagain.org
Empowering Community Development Services
N.A.I.C.S.: 813319
Missy Stephenson (Co-Founder)
Kathy Briner (Co-Founder)

ORGANOGENESIS HOLDINGS INC.
85 Dan Rd, Canton, MA 02021
Tel.: (781) 575-0775   DE
Web Site:
   https://www.organogenesis.com
Year Founded: 2015
ORGO—(NASDAQ)
Rev.: $450,893,000
Assets: $449,359,000
Liabilities: $183,690,000
Net Worth: $265,669,000
Earnings: $15,532,000
Emp.: 1,030
Fiscal Year-end: 12/31/22
Holding Company; Pharmaceutical Mfr
N.A.I.C.S.: 551112
Alan A. Ades (Chm)
Gary S. Gillheeney Sr. (Pres & CEO)
Patrick Bilbo (COO)

Subsidiaries:

Organogenesis Inc. (1)
85 Dan Rd, Canton, MA 02021
Tel.: (781) 575-0775
Web Site: https://www.organogenesis.com
Emp.: 600
Designs Living Cells & Natural Connective Tissue Medical Products Mfr
N.A.I.C.S.: 325414
Gary S. Gillheeney Sr. (Pres & CEO)
Patrick Bilbo (COO)
Brian Grow (Chief Comml Officer)
Antonio S. Montecalvo (VP-Health Policy & Contracting)
Lori Freedman (Gen Counsel & VP)
David C. Francisco (CFO)
Robert Cavorsi (VP-Strategy)

Subsidiary (Non-US):

Organogenesis Switzerland GmbH (2)
Christoph Merian-Ring 11, 4153, Reinach, Switzerland
Tel.: (41) 79651656363
Pharmaceutical Product Mfr & Distr

Organogenesis Holdings Inc.—(Continued)

N.A.I.C.S.: 424210

ORGANON & CO.
30 Hudson St, Jersey City, NJ 07302
Tel.: (551) 430-6000   **DE**
Web Site: https://www.organon.com
OGN—(NYSE)
Rev.: $6,263,000,000
Assets: $12,058,000,000
Liabilities: $12,128,000,000
Net Worth: ($70,000,000)
Earnings: $1,023,000,000
Emp.: 10,000
Fiscal Year-end: 12/31/23
Pharmaceutical Drugs & Medicines
Mfr
N.A.I.C.S.: 325412

Subsidiaries:

Dermavant Sciences Ltd.   (1)
Suite 1, 3rd Floor 11-12 St Jamess Square,
London, SW1Y 4LB, United Kingdom
Tel.: (44) 2074003347
Assets: $18,101,609
Liabilities: $124,533,772
Net Worth: ($106,432,163)
Earnings: ($255,346,194)
Fiscal Year-end: 03/31/2019
Pharmaceutical Products Distr
N.A.I.C.S.: 424210
Todd Zavodnick *(CEO)*
Michael C. Swartzburg *(CFO)*

Fulford (India) Ltd.   (1)
Platina 8th Floor C-59 G-Block Bandra-
Kurla Complex, Bandra East, Mumbai,
400098, India
Tel.: (91) 2267898888
Web Site: http://www.fulfordindia.com
Rev.: $17,027,803
Assets: $32,489,589
Liabilities: $4,086,225
Net Worth: $28,403,364
Earnings: $3,985,173
Emp.: 73
Fiscal Year-end: 03/31/2019
Health Care Products Mfr & Distr
N.A.I.C.S.: 456199
Rajesh Tendolkar *(Chm)*

Organon (Ireland) Ltd   (1)
2 Dublin Landings North Wall Quay - North
Dock, Dublin, D01 V4A3, Ireland
Tel.: (353) 15828250
Emp.: 550
Pharmaceuticals Product Mfr
N.A.I.C.S.: 325412

Organon (Philippines) Inc.   (1)
23W117 & 23W118 Menarco Tower 32nd
Street, Taguig, 1634, Metro Manila, Philip-
pines
Tel.: (63) 284244260
Pharmaceutical Drugs & Medicines Mfr
N.A.I.C.S.: 325412

Organon (Shanghai) Pharmaceutical
Technology Co., Ltd.   (1)
6th-8th Floor WeWork One ITC Tower A No
1901 Huashan Road, Xuhui District, Shang-
hai, China
Tel.: (86) 2180500100
Pharmaceutical Drugs & Medicines Mfr
N.A.I.C.S.: 325412

Organon (Thailand) Ltd.   (1)
No 00 The Parq Building 7th Floor East
Wing Unit 07-101, Ratchadaphisek Road
Klongtoey Sub-district Klongtoey District,
Bangkok, 10110, Thailand
Tel.: (66) 22572500
Pharmaceutical Drugs & Medicines Mfr
N.A.I.C.S.: 325412

Organon - Ecuador S.A.   (1)
AV Republica de El Salvador E10-44 y Na-
ciones Unidas, Edificio Citiplaza Piso 7,
Quito, Ecuador
Tel.: (593) 1800222230
Web Site: https://organonecuador.com
Pharmaceutical Drugs & Medicines Mfr
N.A.I.C.S.: 325412

Organon Argentina S.R.L.   (1)
Blas Parera 3551 Piso 4 Oficina 101, Oli-

vos, 1636, Buenos Aires, Argentina
Tel.: (54) 1122068900
Pharmaceutical Drugs & Medicines Mfr
N.A.I.C.S.: 325412

Organon Asia Pacific Services Pte.
Ltd.   (1)
150 Beach Road 36-01/08, Singapore,
189720, Singapore
Tel.: (65) 69830780
Pharmaceutical Drugs & Medicines Mfr
N.A.I.C.S.: 325412

Organon Austria GmbH   (1)
Karntner Ring 12, 1010, Vienna, Austria
Tel.: (43) 12632865
Pharmaceutical Drugs & Medicines Mfr
N.A.I.C.S.: 325412

Organon Belgium BV   (1)
Handelsstraat 31 / Rue du Commerce 31,
1000, Brussels, Belgium
Tel.: (32) 28989600
Pharmaceutical Drugs & Medicines Mfr
N.A.I.C.S.: 325412

Organon Canada Holdings LLC   (1)
30 Hudson St, Jersey City, NJ 07302
Pharmaceutical Drugs & Medicines Mfr
N.A.I.C.S.: 325412

Organon Central East GmbH   (1)
Weystrasse 20, 5006, Lucerne, Switzerland
Tel.: (41) 586183030
Pharmaceutical Drugs & Medicines Mfr
N.A.I.C.S.: 325412

Organon Colombia S.A.S.   (1)
Calle 127A No 53A - 45 Piso 8, Bogota,
Colombia
Tel.: (57) 15924400
Pharmaceutical Drugs & Medicines Mfr
N.A.I.C.S.: 325412

Organon Comercializadora, S. de
R.L. de C.V.   (1)
Av San Jeronimo 369 Piso 8 Col La Otra
Banda Alcaldia, Alvaro Obregon, 01090,
Mexico, Mexico
Tel.: (52) 88755500
Pharmaceutical Drugs & Medicines Mfr
N.A.I.C.S.: 325412

Organon Czech Republic s.r.o.   (1)
Narodni 135/14, 110 00, Prague, 1, Czech
Republic
Tel.: (420) 233010300
Pharmaceutical Drugs & Medicines Mfr
N.A.I.C.S.: 325412

Organon Denmark ApS   (1)
Bredgade 6, 1260, Copenhagen, Denmark
Tel.: (45) 44846800
Pharmaceutical Drugs & Medicines Mfr
N.A.I.C.S.: 325412

Organon Egypt Ltd   (1)
Red-Con Building Zone 1 Banking road
From 90th Street, New Cairo, Egypt
Tel.: (20) 221232437
Pharmaceutical Drugs & Medicines Mfr
N.A.I.C.S.: 325412

Organon Finland Oy   (1)
Puolikkotie 8, 02230, Espoo, Finland
Tel.: (358) 291703520
Pharmaceutical Drugs & Medicines Mfr
N.A.I.C.S.: 325412

Organon France   (1)
106 boulevard Haussmann, 75008, Paris,
France
Tel.: (33) 157773200
Pharmaceutical Drugs & Medicines Mfr
N.A.I.C.S.: 325412

Organon Global Inc.   (1)
30 Hudson St, Jersey City, NJ 07302
Pharmaceutical Drugs & Medicines Mfr
N.A.I.C.S.: 325412

Organon GmbH   (1)
Weystrasse 20, 6006, Lucerne, Switzerland
Tel.: (41) 581237373
Web Site: https://www.organon.com
Healtcare Services
N.A.I.C.S.: 621610

Organon Healthcare GmbH   (1)
Neuturmstraat 5, 80331, Munich, Ger-
many
Tel.: (49) 8003384726

Pharmaceutical Drugs & Medicines Mfr
N.A.I.C.S.: 325412

Organon Hong Kong Limited   (1)
Unit 48-136 48/F Lee Garden One 33
Hysan Avenue, Causeway Bay, China
(Hong Kong)
Tel.: (852) 34278178
Pharmaceutical Drugs & Medicines Mfr
N.A.I.C.S.: 325412

Organon International Services
GmbH   (1)
Weystrasse 20, 5006, Lucerne, Switzerland
Tel.: (41) 586183030
Pharmaceutical Drugs & Medicines Mfr
N.A.I.C.S.: 325412

Organon Italia S.r.l.   (1)
Piazza Carlo Magno 21, 00162, Rome, Italy
Tel.: (39) 063336407
Pharmaceutical Drugs & Medicines Mfr
N.A.I.C.S.: 325412

Organon Italia SpA   (1)
15 Via Ostilia, 00184, Rome, Italy
Tel.: (39) 00670 1921
Web Site: http://www.organon.it
Emp.: 160
Pharmaceutical Mfr, Marketer & Whslr
N.A.I.C.S.: 325412

Organon KSA GmbH   (1)
Weystrasse 20, 5006, Lucerne, Switzerland
Tel.: (41) 586183030
Pharmaceutical Drugs & Medicines Mfr
N.A.I.C.S.: 325412

Organon Korea Co. Ltd.   (1)
4F Jongro1Gil 50, Jongro-Gu, Seoul, 031-
42, Korea (South)
Tel.: (82) 215778582
Pharmaceutical Drugs & Medicines Mfr
N.A.I.C.S.: 325412

Organon LLC   (1)
30 Hudson St, Jersey City, NJ 07302
Pharmaceutical Drugs & Medicines Mfr
N.A.I.C.S.: 325412

Organon Malaysia Sdn. Bhd.   (1)
Mercu 2 Level 40 Office 39-W022 No 3
Jalan Bangsar, KL Eco City, 59200, Kuala
Lumpur, Wilayah Persekutuan, Malaysia
Tel.: (60) 323862008
Pharmaceutical Drugs & Medicines Mfr
N.A.I.C.S.: 325412

Organon Maroc S.A.R.L.   (1)
Tour Ouest Niv 1 Anfa Place bd de la cor-
nich, Ain diab, 20180, Casablanca, Morocco
Tel.: (212) 520241630
Pharmaceutical Drugs & Medicines Mfr
N.A.I.C.S.: 325412

Organon New Zealand Limited   (1)
Level 7 36 Brandon Street, Wellington,
6011, New Zealand
Tel.: (64) 800111700
Pharmaceutical Drugs & Medicines Mfr
N.A.I.C.S.: 325412

Organon Pharma B.V.   (1)
Fred Roeskestraat 115, 1076 EE, Amster-
dam, Netherlands
Tel.: (31) 207990500
Pharmaceutical Drugs & Medicines Mfr
N.A.I.C.S.: 325412

Organon Pharma FZ-LLC   (1)
Al Faris Building No 39 3rd floor, PO Box
505229, Dubai, United Arab Emirates
Tel.: (971) 45639700
Pharmaceutical Drugs & Medicines Mfr
N.A.I.C.S.: 325412

Organon Pharma Holdings LLC   (1)
30 Hudson St, Jersey City, NJ 07302
Pharmaceutical Drugs & Medicines Mfr
N.A.I.C.S.: 325412

Organon Pharma Pty Ltd   (1)
Building A Level 3 26 Talavera Road, Mac-
quarie Park, 2113, NSW, Australia
Tel.: (61) 279065700
Pharmaceutical Drugs & Medicines Mfr
N.A.I.C.S.: 325412

Organon Pharma S. de R.L.   (1)
Financial Park Tower 35 th Floor Boulevard
Costa del Este, Panama, Panama
Tel.: (507) 2827200

Pharmaceutical Drugs & Medicines Mfr
N.A.I.C.S.: 325412

Organon Polska Sp. z o.o.   (1)
ul Marszalkowskiej 126/134, 00-008, War-
saw, Poland
Tel.: (48) 221055001
Web Site: https://organoncare.pl
Pharmaceutical Drugs & Medicines Mfr
N.A.I.C.S.: 325412

Organon Portugal Sociedade Unipes-
soal Lda   (1)
Rua Alexandre Herculano 50 - Piso 9,
1250-048, Lisbon, Portugal
Tel.: (351) 218705500
Web Site: https://organonpro.com
Pharmaceutical Drugs & Medicines Mfr
N.A.I.C.S.: 325412

Organon Salud, S.L.   (1)
Paseo de la Castellana n 77 Piso 7 Pta 1,
28046, Madrid, Spain
Tel.: (34) 915911279
Pharmaceutical Drugs & Medicines Mfr
N.A.I.C.S.: 325412

Organon Singapore Pte. Ltd.   (1)
150 Beach Road Gateway West 36-01/08,
Singapore, 189720, Singapore
Tel.: (65) 69830780
Pharmaceutical Drugs & Medicines Mfr
N.A.I.C.S.: 325412

Organon Slovakia s.r.o.   (1)
Karadzicova 8/A, 821 08, Bratislava, Slova-
kia
Tel.: (421) 244889888
Pharmaceutical Drugs & Medicines Mfr
N.A.I.C.S.: 325412

Organon South Africa (Pty) Ltd.   (1)
1st floor 22 Magwa Crescent Gateway West
Waterfall City, Midrand, 2090, Gauteng,
South Africa
Tel.: (27) 871069655
Pharmaceutical Drugs & Medicines Mfr
N.A.I.C.S.: 325412

Organon Trade LLC   (1)
30 Hudson St, Jersey City, NJ 07302
Pharmaceutical Drugs & Medicines Mfr
N.A.I.C.S.: 325412

Organon Turkey Ilaclari Limited
Sirketi   (1)
Buyukdere Cad No 185 Kanyon Ofis Blogu
Kat 6, Levent, 34394, Istanbul, Turkiye
Tel.: (90) 2122682068
Pharmaceutical Drugs & Medicines Mfr
N.A.I.C.S.: 325412

Schering-Plough Labo NV   (1)
Industriepark 30, 2220, Heist-op-den-Berg,
Belgium
Tel.: (32) 15258711
Web Site: http://www.msd-belgium.be
Emp.: 80
Pharmaceuticals Product Mfr
N.A.I.C.S.: 325412
Francios Marivoet *(Gen Mgr)*

ORGANOVO HOLDINGS, INC.
11555 Sorrento Valley Rd Ste 100,
San Diego, CA 92121
Tel.: (858) 224-1000   **DE**
Web Site: https://www.organovo.com
ONVO—(NASDAQ)
Rev.: $370,000
Assets: $20,313,000
Liabilities: $4,984,000
Net Worth: $15,329,000
Earnings: ($17,259,000)
Emp.: 15
Fiscal Year-end: 03/31/23
3D Biological Technology Services
N.A.I.C.S.: 339112
Thomas P. Hess *(Pres & CFO)*

ORGENESIS INC.
20271 Goldenrod Ln, Germantown,
MD 20876
Tel.: (480) 659-6404   **NV**
Web Site: https://www.orgenesis.com
Year Founded: 2008
ORGS—(NASDAQ)
Rev.: $36,025,000

Assets: $90,928,000
Liabilities: $61,857,000
Net Worth: $29,071,000
Earnings: $14,889,000
Emp.: 167
Fiscal Year-end: 12/31/22
In-Vitro Diagnostic Substance Mfr
N.A.I.C.S.: 325413
Victor Miller (CFO)
Vered Caplan (CEO & Chm)
Greg Roumeliotis (VP)
Osher Partok Rheinisch (Compliance Officer)
Vincent Vandamme (Sr VP)
Heiko von der Leyen (Dir)
Efrat Assa Kunik (Chief Dev Officer)

Subsidiaries:

Atvio Biotech Ltd.   (1)
3 Hadolev Ave Bar-Lev High-Tech Park, Misgav, 2015600, Israel
Tel.: (972) 778804900
Web Site: https://www.advabio.com
Vaccine & Toxoid Mfr
N.A.I.C.S.: 325414
Dana Fuchs-Telem (Dir-Dev)
Dana Atia-Glikin (Head-Mktg & Dir-Project Mgmt)
Shandy Benn (Mgr-Pur & Logistics)

Koligo Therapeutics, Inc.   (1)
2113 State St, New Albany, IN 47150
Tel.: (502) 265-4830
Web Site: http://www.koligo.net
Medical Instrument Mfr
N.A.I.C.S.: 339112
Matthew Lehman (CEO)

Subsidiary (Domestic):

Tissue Genesis, Inc.   (2)
2113 State St, New Albany, IN 47150
Tel.: (808) 539-9331
Web Site: http://www.tissuegenesis.com
Rev.: $1,900,000
Emp.: 25
Fiscal Year-end: 12/31/2006
Tissue Engineering & Cell Therapy Services
N.A.I.C.S.: 541715

ORHUB, INC.
6865 Alton Pkwy 210, Irvine, CA 92618
Tel.: (425) 577-6266
Web Site: https://www.orhub.com
ORHB—(OTCIQ)
Financial Support Services
N.A.I.C.S.: 541611
Barney Monte (CFO)

ORIC PHARMACEUTICALS, INC.
240 E Grand Ave 2nd Fl, South San Francisco, CA 94080
Tel.: (650) 388-5600   DE
Web Site:
https://www.oricpharma.com
Year Founded: 2014
ORIC—(NASDAQ)
Rev.: $2,645,000
Assets: $247,178,000
Liabilities: $24,827,000
Net Worth: $222,351,000
Earnings: ($89,122,000)
Emp.: 86
Fiscal Year-end: 12/31/22
Pharmaceutical Product Mfr & Distr
N.A.I.C.S.: 325412
Richard A. Heyman (Co-Founder & Chm)
Charles Sawyers (Co-Founder)
Scott Lowe (Co-Founder)
Dominic Piscitelli (CFO)
Lori Friedman (Chief Scientific Officer)
Matthew Panuwat (Chief Bus Officer)
Christian V. Kuhlen (Gen Counsel)
Edna Chow Maneval (Sr VP-Clinical Dev)

Keith Lui (Sr VP-Commercial & Medical Affairs)
Dan Iazzetti (Sec)
Jacob M. Chacko (Pres & CEO)
Pratik S. Multani (Chief Medical Officer)
Richard A. Heyman (Co-Founder & Chm)

ORIENTAL MAGIC SOUP, INC.
700 N Valley St Ste B #14917, Anaheim, CA 92801
Tel.: (323) 978-0870   NV
Year Founded: 2013
CQGU—(OTCIQ)
Investment Services
N.A.I.C.S.: 523999

ORIGIN BANCORP, INC.
500 S Service Rd E, Ruston, LA 71270
Tel.: (318) 255-2222   LA
Web Site: https://www.origin.bank
Year Founded: 1912
OBK—(NYSE)
Rev.: $383,878,000
Assets: $9,686,067,000
Liabilities: $8,736,124,000
Net Worth: $949,943,000
Earnings: $87,715,000
Emp.: 1,011
Fiscal Year-end: 12/31/22
Bank Holding Company
N.A.I.C.S.: 551111
Drake D. Mills (Chm, Pres & CEO)
William Wallace (CFO & Sr Exec Officer)
M. Lance Hall (Pres, COO & CEO-Origin Bank)
Stephen H. Brolly (Chief Acctg Officer & Sr Exec Officer)
Jim Crotwell (Chief Risk Officer)
Josh Hammett (CIO)
Russ Chase (Chief Community Banking Officer)
Ryan Kilpatrick (Chief Brand & Comm Officer)
Regina McNeill (Dir-Strategic Plng & Market Analytics)
Preston Moore (Chief Credit & Banking Officer)
Lonnie Scarborough (Officer-Talent Dev)
Brandi Gregg (Chief Compliance Officer)
Ashlea Price (Chief HR Officer)
Chris Reigelman (Dir-Investor Relations & Corp Sustainability)
Warrie Birdwell (Pres & Reg Pres-North Texas)
Carmen Jordan (Pres & Reg Pres-Houston)
Larry Little (Pres & Pres-Louisiana)
Larry Ratzlaff (Pres & Pres-State & Mississippi)
Jody Proler (COO & COO-Houston)
David Helms (Chief Experience Officer)

Subsidiaries:

Davison Insurance Agency, LLC   (1)
915 N Main St, Boerne, TX 78006
Tel.: (830) 249-6112
Web Site: https://www.davison-insurance.com
General Insurance Services
N.A.I.C.S.: 524210

Origin Bank   (1)
3921 Elm St, Choudrant, LA 71227
Tel.: (318) 232-7390
Web Site: https://www.origin.bank
Commericial Banking
N.A.I.C.S.: 522110
Drake D. Mills (Pres & COO)
William Wallace (CFO & Sr Exec Officer)
Lori Sirman (Pres-East Texas Market & Exec VP)

M. Lance Hall (Pres & CEO)
Stephen H. Brolly (Chief Acctg Officer)
Larry Little (Pres-Louisiana)
Russ Chase (Chief Community Banking Officer)
Ryan Kilpatrick (Chief Brand & Comm Officer)
Regina McNeill (Dir-Strategic Plng & Market Analytics)
Preston Moore (Chief Credit Officer & Chief Banking Officer)
Debbie Williamson (COO)

ORIGIN MATERIALS, INC.
930 Riverside Pkwy Ste 10, West Sacramento, CA 95605
Tel.: (916) 231-9329   Ky
Web Site:
https://www.originmaterials.com
Year Founded: 2020
ORGN—(NASDAQ)
Assets: $493,700,000
Liabilities: $116,795,000
Net Worth: $376,905,000
Earnings: $78,569,000
Emp.: 201
Fiscal Year-end: 12/31/22
Miscellaneous Financial Investment Activities
N.A.I.C.S.: 523999
Rich Riley (Co-CEO)
Matthew T. Plavan (CFO)
Pamela Haley (Sr VP-Acctg & Fin)
Charles Drucker (Chm)
John Bissell (Co-Founder & Co-CEO)
Rich Riley (Co-CEO)
Ryan Smith (CO-Founder & CTO)

Subsidiaries:

Micromidas, Inc.   (1)
930 Riverside Pkwy Ste 10, Sacramento, CA 95864-6922
Tel.: (916) 231-9329
Web Site: http://www.micromidas.com
Sewage Treatment Facilities
N.A.I.C.S.: 221320
John Bissell (Co-Founder & CEO)

ORIGINAL SIXTEEN TO ONE MINE, INC.
PO Box 909, Alleghany, CA 95910
Tel.: (530) 287-3223   CA
Web Site: http://www.origsix.com
Year Founded: 1896
OSTO—(OTCIQ)
Rev.: $90,000
Assets: $718,000
Liabilities: $2,245,000
Net Worth: ($1,527,000)
Earnings: ($173,000)
Fiscal Year-end: 12/31/20
Gold Mining
N.A.I.C.S.: 212220
Robert Beso (Treas)

ORIGINCLEAR, INC.
13575 58th St N Ste 200, Clearwater, FL 33760-3739
Tel.: (727) 440-4603   NV
Web Site:
https://www.originclear.com
Year Founded: 2007
OCLN—(OTCIQ)
Rev.: $10,376,573
Assets: $6,349,489
Liabilities: $32,366,276
Net Worth: ($26,016,787)
Earnings: ($10,790,721)
Emp.: 35
Fiscal Year-end: 12/31/22
Crude Petroleum Extraction Services
N.A.I.C.S.: 211120
T. Riggs Eckelberry (Chm, Pres, CEO, Treas & Sec)
Marc Stevens (Pres-Progressive Water Treatment)
Tom Marchesello (COO)
Prasad Tare (CFO)

Subsidiaries:

Progressive Water Treatment, Inc.   (1)
2535 E University Dr, McKinney, TX 75069
Tel.: (972) 562-3002
Web Site: https://www.progressivewater.com
Sales Range: $1-9.9 Million
Emp.: 18
Waste Treatment Services
N.A.I.C.S.: 221310

ORION ACQUISITION CORP.
767 3rd Ave 11th Fl, New York, NY 10017
Tel.: (212) 583-8540   DE
Web Site: http://www.orionhp.com
Year Founded: 2020
OHPAU—(NASDAQ)
Investment Services
N.A.I.C.S.: 523999
Beau Garverick (Co-Founder, CEO & CFO)
Randy Simpson (Co-Founder)
Kenneth A. Burdicka (Chm)
Kevin Berena (Head-Corp Dev, Strategy & IR)
Jason Dunn (VP)

ORION BIOTECH OPPORTUNITIES CORP.
1 Vanderbilt Ave 26th Fl, New York, NY 10017
Tel.: (212) 303-1650   Ky
Web Site:
https://www.orionbiotechopportunities.com
Year Founded: 2021
ORIA—(NASDAQ)
Rev.: $2,884,887
Assets: $203,332,786
Liabilities: $211,125,225
Net Worth: ($7,792,439)
Earnings: $8,756,297
Emp.: 3
Fiscal Year-end: 12/31/22
Investment Services
N.A.I.C.S.: 523999
James Huang (CEO)
Chrystyna Bedrij Stecyk (VP)
Mark Kayal (CFO & Sec)
Robert Simonds (Gen Counsel, VP & Asst Sec)

ORION DIVERSIFIED HOLDINGS CO. INC.
1111 S Roop St Ste 100, Carson City, NV 89702
Tel.: (760) 889-3435   NV
Year Founded: 2008
OODH—(OTCIQ)
Financial Management Services
N.A.I.C.S.: 522320
Tom Lull (Pres, CEO & Sec)

ORION ENERGY SYSTEMS, INC.
2210 Woodland Dr, Manitowoc, WI 54220
Tel.: (920) 892-9340   WI
Web Site:
https://www.orionlighting.com
OESX—(NASDAQ)
Rev.: $90,581,000
Assets: $63,169,000
Liabilities: $40,627,000
Net Worth: $22,542,000
Earnings: ($11,671,000)
Emp.: 260
Fiscal Year-end: 03/31/24
Energy Management Systems Utilizing Energy Efficient Lighting Systems, Controls & Related Services
N.A.I.C.S.: 335132
Anthony L. Otten (Chm)
Scott A. Green (Pres-Orion Svcs Grp & Exec VP)

Orion Energy Systems, Inc.—(Continued)

J. Per Brodin (CFO, Chief Acctg Officer & Treas)
Michael H. Jenkins (CEO)
Steve Paulus (Dir-Mktg & Comm)

Subsidiaries:

Clean Energy Solutions, LLC (1)
210 Young St, West Babylon, NY 11704
Tel.: (631) 587-3325
Web Site:
http://www.cleanenergysolutionsllc.com
Solar Electric & Heating Equipment Mfr
N.A.I.C.S.: 221118

Great Lakes Energy Technologies, LLC (1)
2001 Mirro Dr, Manitowoc, WI 54220-6717
Tel.: (920) 892-9340
Web Site: http://www.oesx.com
Electric Lighting Fixture Mfr
N.A.I.C.S.: 335131
John Scribanpe (CEO)

Stay-Lite Lighting, Inc. (1)
W233 N2800 Roundy Cir W, Pewaukee, WI 53072
Tel.: (262) 547-6811
Web Site: http://www.stay-lite.com
Home Furnishing Merchant Whslr
N.A.I.C.S.: 423220
Melissa Engaldo (Mgr-HR)

Voltrek, LLC (1)
280 Merrimack St Ste 554, Lawrence, MA 01843
Tel.: (978) 378-0910
Web Site: https://www.voltrek.com
Electric Vehicle Charging Infrastructure Mfr
N.A.I.C.S.: 335312

ORION GROUP HOLDINGS, INC.

12000 Aerospace Ave Ste 300, Houston, TX 77034
Tel.: (713) 852-6500 DE
Web Site:
https://www.oriongroupholdings
inc.com
Year Founded: 1994
ORN—(NYSE)
Rev.: $748,322,000
Assets: $367,155,000
Liabilities: $229,355,000
Net Worth: $137,800,000
Earnings: ($12,612,000)
Emp.: 483
Fiscal Year-end: 12/31/22
Marine Construction Services
N.A.I.C.S.: 237990
Austin J. Shanfelter (Chm)
Edward Chipman Earle (Chief Compliance Officer, Chief Admin Officer, Gen Counsel, Sec & Exec VP)
Scott H. Cromack (Exec VP-Marine Grp)
Travis J. Boone (Pres & CEO)
Ardell C. Allred (Exec VP)
Shallee E. Biondo (VP)
Barry C. Loudermilk (VP)

Subsidiaries:

Orion Administrative Services, Inc. (1)
12000 Aerospace Ave Ste 300, Houston, TX 77034
Tel.: (713) 852-6500
Web Site:
http://www.oriongroupholdingsinc.com
Office Administrative Services
N.A.I.C.S.: 561110

Orion Construction LP (1)
4440 Hwy 225 Ste 180, Deer Park, TX 77536 (100%)
Tel.: (713) 852-6500
Web Site: http://www.orionconstruction.net
Sales Range: $400-449.9 Million
Emp.: 450
Marine Construction, Dredging & Pipeline Installation
N.A.I.C.S.: 236210

Mark R. Stauffer (Pres & CEO)

Subsidiary (Domestic):

Orion Marine Construction, Inc. (2)
1715 N Westshore Blvd Ste 875, Tampa, FL 33607
Tel.: (813) 839-8441
Web Site: http://www.orionmarinegroup.com
Emp.: 300
Marine Construction Services
N.A.I.C.S.: 237990

Orion Industrial Construction, LLC (1)
4440 Hwy 225 Ste 180, Houston, TX 77536 (100%)
Tel.: (713) 852-6500
Web Site: http://www.orionmarinegroup.com
Civil Engineering & Marine Construction
N.A.I.C.S.: 237990

Orion Marine Contractors, Inc. (1)
1112 E Alexander Ave, Tacoma, WA 98421
Tel.: (253) 552-1140
Web Site: http://www.orionmarinegroup.com
Sales Range: $25-49.9 Million
Emp.: 45
Marine Construction Services
N.A.I.C.S.: 237990
Tom Coultas (Mng Dir)

T.A.S. Commercial Concrete Solutions, LLC (1)
2436 County Rd 311, Jarrell, TX 76537
Tel.: (512) 746-2247
Web Site: http://www.tasconcrete.com
Emp.: 1,500
Civil Engineering Construction Services
N.A.I.C.S.: 237990

TAS Commercial Concrete Construction, L.P. (1)
19319 Oil Ctr Blvd, Houston, TX 77073
Tel.: (281) 230-7500
Web Site: http://www.tasconcrete.com
Concrete Construction Services
N.A.I.C.S.: 238110
Bob Bacon (CFO)

TAS Concrete Construction, LLC (1)
19319 Oil Ctr Blvd, Houston, TX 77073
Tel.: (281) 230-7500
Web Site: https://www.tasconcrete.com
Commercial Concrete Contract Services
N.A.I.C.S.: 238110

ORION OFFICE REIT, INC.

2398 E Camelback Rd Ste 1060, Phoenix, AZ 85016
Tel.: (602) 698-1002 MD
Web Site: https://www.onlreit.com
Year Founded: 2021
ONL—(NYSE)
Rev.: $208,118,000
Assets: $1,571,073,000
Liabilities: $595,215,000
Net Worth: $975,858,000
Earnings: ($97,474,000)
Emp.: 35
Fiscal Year-end: 12/31/22
Lessors of Other Real Estate Property
N.A.I.C.S.: 531190
Paul H. Mcdowell (Pres & CEO)
Christopher H. Day (COO)
Gavin B. Brandon (Treas)
Paul C. Hughes (Gen Counsel)

ORMAT TECHNOLOGIES, INC.

6140 Plumas St, Reno, NV 89519-6075
Tel.: (775) 356-9029 DE
Web Site: https://www.ormat.com
Year Founded: 1994
ORA—(NYSE)
Rev.: $734,159,000
Assets: $4,611,579,000
Liabilities: $2,590,604,000
Net Worth: $2,020,975,000
Earnings: $65,841,000
Emp.: 1,480
Fiscal Year-end: 12/31/22

Geothermal & Recovered Energy Power Services
N.A.I.C.S.: 221122
Shimon Hatzir (Exec VP-Electricity Segment)
Bob Sullivan (Exec VP-Bus Dev)
Doron Blachar (CEO)
Assaf Ginzburg (CFO)
Ofer Benyosef (Exec VP-Energy Storage & Bus Dev)
Liza Tavori (Exec VP)

Subsidiaries:

Mammoth Pacific LP (1)
Jct Hwy 395 & Hwy 203, Mammoth Lakes, CA 93546
Tel.: (760) 934-4893
Sales Range: $50-74.9 Million
Emp.: 21
Geothermal Electric Services
N.A.I.C.S.: 221118
Larry Nickerson (Mng Partner)

Ormat Industries Ltd. (1)
Shydlowski Road, PO Box 68, New Industrial Zone, Yavne, 81100, Israel
Tel.: (972) 89433777
Web Site: http://www.ormat.com
Sales Range: $400-449.9 Million
Mfr, Designer, Engineering, Construction, Selling & Operation of Power Plants
N.A.I.C.S.: 335311

Ormat Nevada Inc. (1)
6225 Neil Rd, Reno, NV 89511
Tel.: (775) 356-9029
Web Site: https://www.ormat.com
Sales Range: $25-49.9 Million
Emp.: 85
Geothermal Power Structure Construction Services
N.A.I.C.S.: 237130

Ortitlan Limitada (1)
Avenida Reforma 7 62 Zona 9 Aristo Oficina 310, Guatemala, 1009, Guatemala
Tel.: (502) 23624687
Web Site: http://www.ormat.com
Sales Range: $25-49.9 Million
Emp.: 54
Geothermal Power Structure Construction Services
N.A.I.C.S.: 237130

Puna Geothermal Venture L.P. (1)
14 3860 Kapoho Pahoa Rd, Pahoa, HI 96778
Tel.: (808) 965-6233
Web Site:
http://www.punageothermalventure.com
Sales Range: $50-74.9 Million
Emp.: 26
Geothermal Exploration Services
N.A.I.C.S.: 221330

Viridity Energy, Inc. (1)
1801 Market St Ste 2701, Philadelphia, PA 19103
Tel.: (484) 534-2222
Web Site: http://www.viridityenergy.com
Optimization Software & Technology
N.A.I.C.S.: 541519
Russell M. Stidolph (Bd of Dirs, Executives)
Ofer Haiat (CFO)
Ofer Benyosef (Exec VP-Energy Storage & Bus Dev)
Rahm Orenstein (Head-Bus Dev & Energy Storage)
Idan Barak (Head-Tech Storage & Energy Solution)
Troy Palermo (Partner-HR Bus)
Mike Pavo (Head-Ops)

ORMET CORP.

43840 State Rte 7, Hannibal, OH 43931
Tel.: (740) 483-2776 DE
Year Founded: 1989
ORMTQ—(OTCIQ)
Metal Products Mfr
N.A.I.C.S.: 332999
Michael A. Tanchuk (Pres & CEO)
Tommy Temple (VP-Engineering)
Lisa Riedel (VP-Human Resources)

Michael Griffin (VP-Operations)
James A. Riley (CFO, Treas & Sec)
Thomas A. Notaro (Controller, Asst Sec & Asst Treas)

ORO EAST MINING, INC.

7817 Oakport St Ste 205, Oakland, CA 94621
Tel.: (510) 638-5000 DE
Web Site: http://www.oroeast.com
Year Founded: 2008
OROE—(OTCIQ)
Gold, Copper & Other Metal Mining
N.A.I.C.S.: 212220

ORPHEUM PROPERTY, INC.

2407 Plantation Ctr Dr Ste 100, Matthews, NC 28105
Tel.: (704) 579-6771 DE
Year Founded: 1994
PLFF—(OTCIQ)
Property Development Services
N.A.I.C.S.: 531390
Jeffrey B. Montalbano (Chm)
Randolph F. Franklin (CEO)
Andrew L. Kramer (Sec)
Anthony Melikhov (Vice Chm)

ORRSTOWN FINANCIAL SERVICES, INC.

77 E King St, Shippensburg, PA 17257
Tel.: (717) 532-6114 PA
Web Site: https://www.orrstown.com
ORRF—(NASDAQ)
Rev.: $135,606,000
Assets: $2,922,408,000
Liabilities: $2,693,512,000
Net Worth: $228,896,000
Earnings: $22,037,000
Emp.: 404
Fiscal Year-end: 12/31/22
Bank Holding Company
N.A.I.C.S.: 551111
Thomas Rodney Quinn Jr. (Pres & CEO)
Robert G. Coradi (Chief Risk Officer & Exec VP)
Adam L. Metz (Chief Revenue Officer & Exec VP)
Luke M. Bernstein (Chief Ops & Fin Officer & Exec VP)
Christopher D. Holt (Pres-Market & Exec VP)
David Tod Hornberger (Pres-Market & Exec VP)
Zachary Moses Khuri (Pres-Market & Exec VP)
Neelesh Kalani (CFO, Principal Acctg Officer & Exec VP)
Sean P. Mulcahy (Chief Acctg Officer)
Adam D. Bonanno (CTO)
Matthew Dyckman (Gen Counsel)
William Ziegler (Chief Credit Officer)

Subsidiaries:

Codorus Valley Bancorp, Inc. (1)
105 Leader Heights Rd, York, PA 17403
Tel.: (717) 543-0059
Web Site: https://www.peoplesbanknet.com
Rev.: $99,507,000
Assets: $2,195,052,000
Liabilities: $2,017,752,000
Net Worth: $177,300,000
Earnings: $20,092,000
Emp.: 327
Fiscal Year-end: 12/31/2022
Offices of Bank Holding Companies
N.A.I.C.S.: 551111
Craig L. Kauffman (Pres & CEO)
John Rodney Messick (Chm)

Orrstown Bank (1)
77 E King St, Shippensburg, PA 17257
Tel.: (717) 530-2506
Web Site: https://www.orrstown.com
Commercial Banking Services
N.A.I.C.S.: 522110

Thomas Rodney Quinn Jr. *(Pres & CEO)*
Robert G. Coradi *(Chief Risk Officer & Exec VP)*
David Tod Hornberger *(Pres-Market & Exec VP)*

Division (Domestic):

PeoplesBank, A Codorus Valley Company **(2)**
Codorus Valley Corporate Ctr 105 Leader Heights Rd, York, PA 17403
Tel.: (717) 543-0059
Web Site: https://www.peoplesbanknet.com
Sales Range: $50-74.9 Million
Commericial Banking
N.A.I.C.S.: 522110
Diane E. Baker *(COO, Chief Risk Officer & Exec VP)*
Larry D. Pickett *(Treas)*
Amy L. Doll *(Chief Revenue & Lending Officer & Sr VP)*
Stephen M. Altland *(Sr VP-Wealth Mgmt Div)*
Scott R. Campagna *(CIO & Sr VP)*
Hal E. Carney *(Sr VP & Dir-Comml Banking)*
Chad M. Clabaugh *(Sr VP-Retail Sls & Svcs Div)*
Matthew A. Clemens *(Chief Admin Officer & Sr VP)*
Dennis Ginder *(Chief Credit Officer & Sr VP)*
Kristen M. Heisey *(Sr VP)*
Kent A. Ketterman *(Sr VP & Dir-Comml Real Estate Lending)*
Timothy J. Nieman *(Gen Counsel)*
Todd A. Tyson *(Officer-Gen Svcs Div & Security & Sr VP)*

Subsidiary (Domestic):

SYC Settlement Services, Inc. **(3)**
105 Leaders Heights Rd, York, PA 17403
Tel.: (717) 747-1524
Emp.: 3
Title Settlement Services
N.A.I.C.S.: 541191

Wheatland Advisors, Inc **(1)**
144 E Chestnut St, Lancaster, PA 17602
Tel.: (717) 299-6090
Web Site:
    http://www.wheatlandadvisors.com
Investment Management Service
N.A.I.C.S.: 523940
Renee Laychur *(Mng Dir & Sr VP)*
Ernie Irwin *(VP)*

ORTHOFIX MEDICAL INC.
3451 Plano Pkwy, Lewisville, TX 75056
Tel.: (214) 937-2000   DE
Web Site: https://www.orthofix.com
Year Founded: 1980
OFIX—(NASDAQ)
Rev.: $460,713,000
Assets: $458,629,000
Liabilities: $121,769,000
Net Worth: $336,860,000
Earnings: ($19,749,000)
Emp.: 1,734
Fiscal Year-end: 12/31/22
Surgical Appliance & Supplies Manufacturing
N.A.I.C.S.: 339113
Kimberley A. Elting *(Pres-Global Orthopedics)*
Catherine M. Burzik *(Chm)*
Jon C. Serbousek *(Exec Chm)*
Massimo Calafiore *(Pres & CEO)*
Suzanne Armstrong *(Chief HR Officer)*
Roberto Donadello *(Sr VP)*
Ehab Esmail *(Sr VP)*
Tyler Lipschultz *(Pres-Global Biologics)*
Beau Standish *(Pres-Global Enabling Technologies)*
Frank Vizesi *(Chief Scientific Officer)*
Julie B. Andrews *(CFO)*

Subsidiaries:

AMEI Technologies, Inc. **(1)**

1105 N Market St 1300, Wilmington, DE 19801
Tel.: (302) 655-4237
Investment Advisory Services
N.A.I.C.S.: 523940

Implantes Y Sistemas Medicos, Inc. **(1)**
Calle Diana Ste 22 Esquina calle Emma Amelia Industrial Park, Guaynabo, PR 00969
Tel.: (787) 273-8115
Web Site: http://www.orthofix.com
Medical Equipment Distr
N.A.I.C.S.: 423450

Neomedics, Inc. **(1)**
2655 S Le Jeune Rd Ste 810, Coral Gables, FL 33134-5814
Tel.: (305) 444-3589
Surgical & Medical Instrument Mfr
N.A.I.C.S.: 339112

Orthofix AG **(1)**
Bundesstrasse 3, 6302, Zug, Switzerland
Tel.: (41) 7485360
Surgical Laboratory Equipment Mfr & Distr
N.A.I.C.S.: 339113

Orthofix Australia Pty Limited **(1)**
3451 Plano Pkwy, Lewisville, TX 75056
Tel.: (214) 937-2000
Surgical & Medical Instrument Mfr
N.A.I.C.S.: 339112

Orthofix GmbH **(1)**
Siemensstrasse 5, 85521, Ottobrunn, Germany
Tel.: (49) 8935499990
Medical & Surgical Equipment Mfr
N.A.I.C.S.: 339112

Orthofix Inc. **(1)**
3451 Plano Pkwy, Lewisville, TX 75056
Tel.: (214) 937-2000
Web Site: http://ir.orthofix.com
Emp.: 900
Surgical Laboratory Equipment Mfr
N.A.I.C.S.: 339113

Unit (Domestic):

Orthofix Orthopedics North America **(2)**
3451 Plano Pkwy, Lewisville, TX 75056
Tel.: (214) 937-2000
Web Site: http://www.orthofix.com
Pharmaceutical Products Mfr & Distr
N.A.I.C.S.: 325412
Brad V. Niemann *(Sr VP)*

Subsidiary (Domestic):

Orthofix Sports Medicine Breg, Inc. **(2)**
2611 Commerce Way, Vista, CA 92081
Tel.: (760) 599-3000
Pharmaceuticals Product Mfr
N.A.I.C.S.: 325412

Plant (Non-US):

Orthofix Sports Medicine Breg, Inc. - Manufacturing Facility **(3)**
Calzada Venustiano Carranza 33 Parque Industrial Palaco, Mexicali, 21385, Baja California, Mexico
Tel.: (52) 6865821500
Medical & Surgical Equipment Mfr
N.A.I.C.S.: 339112
Casey Parker *(Mng Dir)*

Orthofix Limited **(1)**
6 Waltham Park Waltham Road, White Waltham, Maidenhead, SL6 3TN, Berkshire, United Kingdom
Tel.: (44) 1628594500
Medical & Orthopedic Equipment Distr
N.A.I.C.S.: 423450

Orthofix Orthopedics **(1)**
Alameda Santos 1978 16 Andar - Sala 162 Cerqueira Cesar, Sao Paulo, 01418-102, Brazil
Tel.: (55) 1130872260
Web Site: http://www.orthofix.br
Pharmaceutical Product Mfr
N.A.I.C.S.: 325412

Orthofix S.r.l. **(1)**
Via delle Nazioni 9, 37012, Bussolengo,

Verona, Italy
Tel.: (39) 0456719380
Medical & Surgical Equipment Mfr
N.A.I.C.S.: 339112

Orthofix SA **(1)**
21-37 Rue de Stalingrad 24/28 Villa Baudran, 94110, Arcueil, France
Tel.: (33) 14 198 3333
Web Site: http://web.orthofix.com
Emp.: 15
Medical & Surgical Equipment Distr
N.A.I.C.S.: 423450
Olivia Trapp *(Mng Dir)*

Orthofix Spine G.m.b.H. **(1)**
Tel.: (49) 73339259986
Surgical & Medical Instrument Mfr
N.A.I.C.S.: 339112
Thomas Kalin *(Acct Mgr)*

Orthofix UK Limited **(1)**
6 Waltham Park Waltham Road, White Waltham, Maidenhead, SL6 3TN, Berkshire, United Kingdom
Tel.: (44) 1628594500
Web Site: http://www.orthofix.co.uk
Emp.: 15
Medical & Surgical Equipment Whslr
N.A.I.C.S.: 423450

Orthofix do Brasil Ltda. **(1)**
Alameda Santos 1978 16 Andar - Sala 162, Cerqueira Cesar, Sao Paulo, 01418-102, Brazil
Tel.: (55) 1130872260
Surgical & Medical Instrument Mfr
N.A.I.C.S.: 339112

Orthosonics Ltd. **(1)**
Burney Court Cordwallis Park, Maidenhead, SL6 7BZ, Berkshire, United Kingdom
Tel.: (44) 1628594500
Web Site: http://www.orthosonics.com
Sales Range: $25-49.9 Million
Emp.: 20
Orthopaedic Product Mfr
N.A.I.C.S.: 339112

Spinal Kinetics, LLC **(1)**
246 Tierney Dr Ste 1, New Richmond, WI 54017
Tel.: (408) 636-2500
Web Site: https://www.thespinalkinetics.com
Artificial Discs & Other Medical Device Mfr;
N.A.I.C.S.: 339112

ORTHOPEDIATRICS CORP.
2850 Frontier Dr, Warsaw, IN 46582
Tel.: (574) 268-6379   DE
Web Site:
    https://www.orthopediatrics.com
Year Founded: 2007
KIDS—(NASDAQ)
Rev.: $122,289,000
Assets: $427,727,000
Liabilities: $49,079,000
Net Worth: $378,648,000
Earnings: $1,258,000
Emp.: 203
Fiscal Year-end: 12/31/22
Surgical Appliance & Supplies Manufacturing
N.A.I.C.S.: 339113
Mark C. Throdahl *(Chm)*
Fred L. Hite *(CFO & COO)*
David R. Bailey *(Pres & CEO)*
Mark Karshner *(Sr VP-Intl Sls)*

Subsidiaries:

ApiFix Ltd. **(1)**
1 Hacarmel Street Kochav Yokneam Bldg, Yokneam, 2069207, Israel
Tel.: (972) 8772686339
Web Site: https://www.apifix.com
Orthopaedic Healthcare Services
N.A.I.C.S.: 621111

Boston Brace International, Inc. **(1)**
20 Ledin Dr, Avon, MA 02322
Tel.: (508) 588-6060
Web Site: http://www.bostonbrace.com
Rev.: $11,900,000
Emp.: 150
Surgical Appliances & Supplies
N.A.I.C.S.: 339113

Tom Morrissey *(Pres)*

Vilex in Tennessee, Inc. **(1)**
111 Moffitt St, McMinnville, TN 37110
Tel.: (931) 474-7550
Web Site: https://www.vilex.com
Medical Device Mfr
N.A.I.C.S.: 339112

ORYX TECHNOLOGY CORP.
PO Box 1822, Morgan Hill, CA 95038
Tel.: (408) 979-2955   DE
ORYX—(OTCIQ)
Electrical Industrial Apparatus Distr
N.A.I.C.S.: 423610
Philip A. Micciche *(Pres, CEO & CFO)*

OS ACQUISITION CORP.
310 Busse Hwy Ste 490, Park Ridge, IL 60068
Tel.: (415) 944-5464   DE
Year Founded: 2021
OSAAU—(NASDAQ)
Emp.: 2
Investment Services
N.A.I.C.S.: 523999
Jeff Klunzinger *(CEO)*
Mark Ghobrial *(CFO)*
Lily Kim *(Chief Scientific Officer)*

OSCAR HEALTH, INC.
75 Varick St 5th Fl, New York, NY 10013
Tel.: (646) 403-3677   DE
Web Site: https://www.hioscar.com
Year Founded: 2012
OSCR—(NYSE)
Rev.: $3,963,638,000
Assets: $4,526,601,000
Liabilities: $3,634,201,000
Net Worth: $892,400,000
Earnings: ($606,275,000)
Emp.: 2,714
Fiscal Year-end: 12/31/22
Holding Company
N.A.I.C.S.: 551112
R. Scott Blackley *(CFO)*
Joel I. Klein *(Chief Policy & Strategy Officer)*
Ranmali Bopitiya *(Chief Legal Officer)*
R. Scott Blackley *(Chief Transformation Officer & Principal Operating Officer)*
Sean Martin *(Chief Medical Officer)*
Alessa Quane *(Chief Insurance Officer)*
JoAnna Di Tullio *(Sr Dir-Comm)*
Jeffery Boyd *(Chm)*
Cornelia Miller *(VP-IR)*
Mario Schlosser *(Founder, CTO & Pres-Tech)*
Joshua Kushner *(Vice Chm)*
Mark T. Bertolini *(CEO)*

OSCEOLA GOLD, INC.
Tel.: (740) 632-5313   DE
Web Site:
    https://www.osceolagoldinc.com
Year Founded: 2008
OSCI—(OTCIQ)
Gold Exploration & Mining Services
N.A.I.C.S.: 212220
Tracy Leigh Pizzoferrato *(Controller)*

OSHKOSH CORPORATION
1917 Four Wheel Dr, Oshkosh, WI 54902
Tel.: (920) 502-3009   WI
Web Site:
    https://www.oshkoshcorp.com
Year Founded: 1917
OSK—(NYSE)
Rev.: $9,657,900,000
Assets: $9,129,200,000

Oshkosh Corporation—(Continued)

Liabilities: $5,423,900,000
Net Worth: $3,705,300,000
Earnings: $598,000,000
Emp.: 17,300
Fiscal Year-end: 12/31/23
Mfr, Designer & Marketer of Specialty Commercial, Fire, Emergency & Military Trucks
N.A.I.C.S.: 336120
John Charles Pfeifer (CEO)
Bryan K. Brandt (CMO & Sr VP)
Anupam Khare (CIO & Sr VP)
Michael E. Pack (Pres, CFO & Exec VP)
Jayanthi Iyengar (Chief Technology & Strategic Sourcing Officer & Exec VP)
Victoria Connelly (Sr Mgr-IR)
Jason P. Baab (Sr VP-Corp Dev & Strategy)
Emma M. McTague (Chief HR Officer & Sr VP)
Jennifer Stiansen (VP-Branding & Comm-Global)
James Chris Freeders (Sr VP)
John S. Verich (Treas)
Ignacio A. Cortina (Chief Legal Officer, Sec & Exec VP)

Subsidiaries:

AK Specialty Vehicles B.V.   (1)
Buys Ballotstraat 6, 3261 LA, Oud-Beijerland, Netherlands
Tel.: (31) 186614322
Mobile Medical Vehicles Mfr
N.A.I.C.S.: 336390
Gereen Schmidt (Gen Mgr)

Audubon Manufacturing
Corporation   (1)
814 Wurlitzer Dr, North Tonawanda, NY 14120
Tel.: (716) 564-5165
Web Site:
   http://www.audubonmachinery.com
Sales Range: $10-24.9 Million
Emp.: 20
Oxygen Generating Systems & Solar Panel Mfr
N.A.I.C.S.: 336120

Hinowa S.p.A.   (1)
Via Fontana, 37054, Nogara, VR, Italy
Tel.: (39) 0442539100
Web Site: https://www.hinowa.com
Earthmoving Equipment Mfr & Distr
N.A.I.C.S.: 333131

Iowa Mold Tooling Co., Inc.   (1)
500 Hwy 18 W, Garner, IA 50438-0189
Tel.: (641) 923-3711
Web Site: https://www.imt.com
Sales Range: $50-74.9 Million
Emp.: 400
Mfr & Designer of Hydraulic Truck-Mounted Cranes, Teel Loaders & Tire Handling Equipment for Off-Road Vehicles
N.A.I.C.S.: 333120

JBT AeroTech Corporation   (1)
7300 Presidents Dr, Orlando, FL 32809
Tel.: (407) 851-3377
Web Site: http://www.jbtaerotech.com
Sales Range: $75-99.9 Million
Emp.: 200
Aircraft Equipment Mfr
N.A.I.C.S.: 336412

Unit (Domestic):

Airport Systems Utah-Ground
Equipment   (2)
1805 W 2550 S, Ogden, UT 84401
Tel.: (801) 627-6600
Web Site: http://www.jbtaerotech.com
Airline Ground Support Equipment Mfr
N.A.I.C.S.: 336413

JBT AeroTech-Ground Support
Equipment   (2)
7300 Presidents Dr, Orlando, FL 32809
Tel.: (407) 851-3377
Web Site: http://www.jbtaerotech.com

Sales Range: $125-149.9 Million
Emp.: 200
Airline Ground Support Equipment Mfr
N.A.I.C.S.: 336413
Charles Durst (Pres)
Chuck Durst (Pres)

Subsidiary (Domestic):

John Bean Technologies Automated
Guided Vehicles, Inc.   (2)
400 Highpoint Dr, Chalfont, PA 18914
Tel.: (215) 822-4600
Web Site: http://www.jbtc-agv.com
Sales Range: $75-99.9 Million
Emp.: 100
Material Movement Equipment Mfr
N.A.I.C.S.: 333922

JLG EMEA B.V.   (1)
Polaris Avenue 63, 2132 JH, Hoofddorp, Netherlands
Tel.: (31) 235655665
Web Site: http://www.jlg.com
Emp.: 47
Industrial Equipment Whsr
N.A.I.C.S.: 423830

Subsidiary (Non-US):

JLG Ground Support Europe
BVBA   (2)
Incubathor Thor Park 8300, 3600, Genk, Belgium
Tel.: (32) 89774974
Industrial Equipment Mfr
N.A.I.C.S.: 423840
Tom Erna (Mgr-Quality)

JLG Equipment Services Limited   (1)
Room No 7 Level 11 Landmark North 39 Lung Sum Ave, Sheung Shui, NT, China (Hong Kong)
Tel.: (852) 26395783
Web Site: http://www.jlg.com
Sales Range: $10-24.9 Million
Emp.: 4
Industrial Equipment Mfr
N.A.I.C.S.: 333248

Subsidiary (Non-US):

Oshkosh JLG (Tianjin) Equipment
Technology Co. Limited   (2)
No 228 Jing San Road Tianjin Airport Economic Area, Fengxian, Tianjin, 300308, China
Tel.: (86) 2258919200
Commercial Equipment Whslr
N.A.I.C.S.: 423440
Defmond Soh (CEO)

JLG Industries GmbH   (1)
Max-Planck-Str 21, 27721, Ritterhude, 27721, Germany
Tel.: (49) 4216935056
Web Site: http://www.jlg.com
Sales Range: $10-24.9 Million
Emp.: 2
Access Equipment Mfr
N.A.I.C.S.: 333248

JLG Industries India Private
Limited   (1)
1st & 2nd Floor E-20, Hauz Khas, New Delhi, 110016, India
Tel.: (91) 1166172452
Access Equipment Sale & Services
N.A.I.C.S.: 532490

JLG Industries, Inc.   (1)
1 JLG Dr, McConnellsburg, PA 17233-9533
Tel.: (717) 485-5161
Web Site: https://www.jlg.com
Sales Range: $1-4.9 Billion
Emp.: 4,088
Specialized Hydraulic Machinery Mfr
N.A.I.C.S.: 333923

Subsidiary (Non-US):

JLG Deutschland GmbH   (2)
Max-Planck-Str 21, Ihlpohl, 27721, Ritterhude, Germany
Tel.: (49) 421693500
Web Site: https://www.jlg.com
Sales Range: $10-24.9 Million
Emp.: 20
Mfr of Work Platforms
N.A.I.C.S.: 333923

Laurent Montenay (Mng Dir)

Subsidiary (Domestic):

JLG Financial Solutions   (2)
13712 Crayton Blvd, Hagerstown, MD 21742
Tel.: (240) 420-2661
Web Site: http://www.jlg.com
Sales Range: $450-499.9 Million
Emp.: 1,500
Financial & Leasing Services
N.A.I.C.S.: 525990
Kevin S. Ramsburg (Mng Dir & VP)

Subsidiary (Non-US):

JLG France Sarl   (2)
83 Impasse Guillaume Mon Amy, 47400, Fauillet, 47400, France
Tel.: (33) 553883170
Web Site: http://www.jlgeurope.com
Sales Range: $50-74.9 Million
Emp.: 150
Industrial Equipment & Supplies Sales
N.A.I.C.S.: 333248

JLG Industries (Italia) s.r.l.   (2)
Via Po 22, Pregnana Milanese, 20010, Milan, Italy
Tel.: (39) 0293595210
Web Site: https://www.jlg.com
Sales Range: $125-149.9 Million
Mfr of Work Platforms
N.A.I.C.S.: 333923

JLG Industries (United Kingdom)
Limited   (2)
Bentley House Bentley Avenue, Middleton, M24 2GP, Greater Manchester, United Kingdom
Tel.: (44) 1616541000
Access Equipment Mfr & Distr
N.A.I.C.S.: 333924
Wayne Lawson (Mng Dir & VP)

Subsidiary (Domestic):

JLG Industries, Inc.   (2)
1 JLG Dr, McConnellsburg, PA 17233-9533
Tel.: (717) 485-5161
Web Site: http://www.jlg.com
Sales Range: $100-124.9 Million
Emp.: 2,000
Mfr of Work Platforms
N.A.I.C.S.: 333248
Frank R. Nerenhausen (Pres)

Subsidiary (Domestic):

JLG Equipment Services, Inc.   (3)
253 Success Dr, McConnellsburg, PA 17233-9502
Tel.: (717) 485-5161
Web Site: http://www.jlg.com
Construction Equipment Mfr
N.A.I.C.S.: 333120

Subsidiary (Non-US):

JLG New Zealand Access Equipment
& Service   (4)
2B Fisher Crescent Mt Wellington, 1060, Auckland, New Zealand
Tel.: (64) 92761728
Lift Equipment Mfr & Distr
N.A.I.C.S.: 333924

Subsidiary (Non-US):

JLG Properties Australia Pty
Limited   (3)
358 Park Road Regents Park, Sydney, 2143, NSW, Australia
Tel.: (61) 287186300
Web Site: http://www.jlg.com
Elevated Work Platforms
N.A.I.C.S.: 336211

Subsidiary (Domestic):

JLG Industries, Inc.   (2)
221 Success Dr, McConnellsburg, PA 17233
Tel.: (717) 485-6464
Web Site: http://www.jlg.com
Sales Range: $25-49.9 Million
Emp.: 30
Specialized Hydraulic Machinery Service Center
N.A.I.C.S.: 333998

Subsidiary (Non-US):

JLG Latino Americana Ltda.   (2)
Rua Antonia Martins Luiz 580 Distrito Industrial Joao Narezzi, Indaiatuba, Sao Paulo, 13347-404, Brazil
Tel.: (55) 1939368870
Web Site: http://www.jlg.com
Access Equipment & Work Platforms Designer, Marketer & Mfr
N.A.I.C.S.: 333923

JLG Sverige AB   (2)
Garpebodavagen 6, PO Box 704, 196 37, Kungsangen, Stockholm, Sweden
Tel.: (46) 850659500
Web Site: http://www.jlgeurope.com
Sales Range: $10-24.9 Million
Emp.: 15
Mfr of Work Platforms
N.A.I.C.S.: 333923
Thomas Wolke (Mng Dir)

Platforma Elevadoras JLG Iberica
S.L.   (2)
C/ Suero de Quinones 34-36, 28002, Madrid, Spain
Tel.: (34) 937724700
Web Site: http://www.jlg.com
Sales Range: $10-24.9 Million
Emp.: 3
Mfr of Work Platforms
N.A.I.C.S.: 333923

Jerr-Dan Corporation   (1)
12835 Salem Ave, Hagerstown, MD 21742-2678
Tel.: (717) 597-7111
Web Site: https://www.jerrdan.com
Rollback Carriers & Wreckers Mfr & Distr
N.A.I.C.S.: 336211

Kewaunee Fabrications, LLC   (1)
520 N Main St, Kewaunee, WI 54216
Tel.: (920) 388-2000
Web Site:
   https://www.kewauneefabrications.com
Sales Range: $125-149.9 Million
Emp.: 250
Structural Steel Mfr
N.A.I.C.S.: 332312

London (Mtl) Inc.   (1)
2017 Rue Halpern, Saint Laurent, H4S 1S3, Canada
Tel.: (514) 368-4303
Web Site:
   http://www.oshkoshcorporation.com
Sales Range: $10-24.9 Million
Emp.: 4
Construction Machinery Mfr
N.A.I.C.S.: 333120

McNeilus Companies, Inc.   (1)
524 E Hwy St, Dodge Center, MN 55927   (100%)
Tel.: (507) 374-6321
Web Site:
   http://www.mcneiluscompanies.com
Sales Range: $150-199.9 Million
Emp.: 400
Mfr of Concrete; Construction & Oil Lease; Construction Equipment
N.A.I.C.S.: 336211

Subsidiary (Domestic):

Iowa Contract Fabricators, Inc.   (2)
12150 Addison Ave, Riceville, IA 50466-7003
Tel.: (641) 985-2900
Web Site:
   http://www.mcneiluscompanies.com
Sales Range: $25-49.9 Million
Emp.: 150
Truck Equipment & Parts Mfr
N.A.I.C.S.: 336120

Subsidiary (Non-US):

London Machinery Inc.   (2)
15790 Robin's Hill Road, Vancouver, N5V 0A4, ON, Canada
Tel.: (519) 963-2500
Web Site: https://www.lmi.ca
Heavy Duty Truck Distr
N.A.I.C.S.: 423120
Ryan Bisson (Dir-Sls-Mixer Platform, Concrete Mixers Sls & Support)

McNeilus Truck & Manufacturing, Inc. (1)
524 E Hwy St, Dodge Center, MN 55927
Tel.: (507) 374-6321
Web Site:
http://www.mcneiluscompanies.com
Truck Body Mfr
N.A.I.C.S.: 336211

Medtec Ambulance Corp. (1)
2429 Lincoln Way E, Goshen, IN 46526
Tel.: (574) 534-2631
Sales Range: $100-124.9 Million
Emp.: 250
Ambulance & Rescue Truck Mfr
N.A.I.C.S.: 336110

Oshkosh Airport Products, LLC (1)
1515 County Rd O, Neenah, WI 54954
Tel.: (920) 832-3000
Web Site: https://www.oshkoshairport.com
Heavy Duty Truck Mfr
N.A.I.C.S.: 336120

Oshkosh Commercial (Beijing) Co., Limited (1)
10-11 Level 11 Tower C1 Oriental Plaza No 1 East Chang An Ave, Dong Cheng, Beijing, 100738, China
Tel.: (86) 1085185100
Truck Body Mfr & Distr
N.A.I.C.S.: 336211

Oshkosh Defense Canada Incorporated (1)
50 O'Connor St Ste 1607, Ottawa, K1P 6L2, ON, Canada
Tel.: (613) 564-1102
Web Site: http://en.oshkoshdefense.ca
Truck Body Mfr
N.A.I.C.S.: 336211
John J. Bryant (Pres)

Oshkosh Defense, LLC (1)
2307 Oregon St, Oshkosh, WI 54902
Tel.: (920) 235-9150
Web Site: https://www.oshkoshdefense.com
Industrial Equipment Mfr
N.A.I.C.S.: 423830
John J. Blossom (VP-IT)
Don Bent (COO)
Jori Hartwig (VP-Global Strategy & Mktg)
George Mansfield (VP & Gen Mgr-Joint Programs)
Mark Meservey (VP-Govt Ops)
Chad Frees (VP)
Kyle Whitcomb (VP)

Oshkosh Europe B.V. (1)
Polarisavenue 63, 2132 JH, Hoofddorp, Netherlands
Tel.: (31) 235655665
Heavy Duty Truck Mfr
N.A.I.C.S.: 336120

Oshkosh Italy B.V. (1)
Polarisavenue 63, 2132 JH, Hoofddorp, Netherlands
Tel.: (31) 235655665
Financial Investment Services
N.A.I.C.S.: 523999

Oshkosh Logistics Corporation (1)
2307 Oregon St, Oshkosh, WI 54902
Tel.: (920) 235-9150
Freight Transportation Arrangement Services
N.A.I.C.S.: 488510

Oshkosh Specialty Vehicles (1)
12770 44th St N, Clearwater, FL 33762
Tel.: (727) 573-0400
Web Site: https://www.oshkoshsv.com
Sales Range: $250-299.9 Million
Specialty Truck, Trailer & Van Mfr & Retailer
N.A.I.C.S.: 336120
Joey Loncharich (Mgr-Svc)

Oshkosh-JLG (Shanghai) Enterprise Development Co., Ltd. (1)
465 Xiaonan Road, Fengxian, Shanghai, 201401, China
Tel.: (86) 2160311500
Crane Mfr & Distr
N.A.I.C.S.: 333923

Oshkosh-JLG (Singapore) Technology Equipment Private Limited (1)
35 Tuas Ave 2, Singapore, 639464, Singapore

Tel.: (65) 65919368
Truck Body Mfr
N.A.I.C.S.: 336211

Pierce Manufacturing, Inc. (1)
2600 American Dr, Appleton, WI 54912-2017 (100%)
Tel.: (920) 832-3000
Web Site: http://www.piercemfg.com
Sales Range: $350-399.9 Million
Emp.: 1,500
Fire Trucks & Emergency Vehicles Mfr
N.A.I.C.S.: 336120
Jim Johnson (Pres)

Division (Domestic):

Frontline Communications (2)
12770 44th St N, Clearwater, FL 33762-4713
Tel.: (727) 573-0400
Web Site: https://www.frontlinecomm.com
Custom Broadcast & Communications Vehicle Mfr
N.A.I.C.S.: 336110

Platformas Elevadoras JLG Iberica S.L
C/ Suero de Quinones 34-36, 28002, Madrid, Spain
Tel.: (34) 937724700
Web Site: http://www.glg.com
Emp.: 7
Commercial Equipment Whslr
N.A.I.C.S.: 423440

Power Towers Limited (1)
Unit 3 Leicester Distribution Park 45 Sunningdale Road, Leicester, LE3 1UX, United Kingdom
Tel.: (44) 1616541000
Web Site: https://www.powertowers.com
Industrial Equipment Mfr
N.A.I.C.S.: 423830

Subsidiary (Non-US):

Power Towers Netherlands BV (2)
Veerweg 1-a, 3281 LX, Numansdorp, Netherlands
Tel.: (31) 883434400
Heavy Duty Truck Mfr
N.A.I.C.S.: 336120

Pratt & Miller Engineering & Fabrication, Inc. (1)
29600 Wk Smith Rd, New Hudson, MI 48165
Tel.: (248) 446-9800
Web Site: http://www.prattmiller.com
Rev.: $3,950,000
Emp.: 25
Engineeering Services
N.A.I.C.S.: 541330
Gary Pratt (VP)
Kris Houghton (Dir-Engrg Svc)
Brandon Widmer (Dir-Bus Dev)
Sara Blackmer (Dir-Govt Markets)
Charlie Ping (Project Mgr-IndyCar Race Ops)
Francis Wilson (Mgr-Quality Assurance)

Viking Truck & Equipment Sales (OH), Inc. (1)
8997 Lesaint Dr, Fairfield, OH 45014
Tel.: (513) 874-2022
Commercial Equipment Whslr
N.A.I.C.S.: 423440

OSI SYSTEMS, INC.

12525 Chadron Ave, Hawthorne, CA 90250
Tel.: (310) 978-0516   CA
Web Site: https://www.osi-systems.com
OSIS—(NASDAQ)
Rev.: $1,538,758,000
Assets: $1,936,008,000
Liabilities: $1,072,525,000
Net Worth: $863,483,000
Earnings: $128,154,000
Emp.: 6,681
Fiscal Year-end: 06/30/24
Devices, Subsystems & End-Products Based on Optoelectronic Technology
N.A.I.C.S.: 334517

Ajay Mehra (Pres-Solutions Bus & Exec VP)
Victor S. Sze (Sec, Exec VP & Gen Counsel)
Manoocher Mansouri (Pres-Optoelectronics-Mfg Div)
Ajay Vashishat (VP-Business Development)
Paul Morben (Pres-Electronics)
Shalabh Chandra (Pres-Healthcare Div)
Glenn Grindstaff (Chief HR Officer)
Deepak Chopra (Chm, Pres & CEO)

Subsidiaries:

Altaflex (1)
336 Martin Ave, Santa Clara, CA 95050
Tel.: (408) 727-6614
Web Site: https://www.altaflex.com
Semiconductor Devices Mfr
N.A.I.C.S.: 334413

American Science and Engineering, Inc. (1)
829 Middlesex Tpke, Billerica, MA 01821
Tel.: (978) 262-8700
Web Site: http://www.rapiscan-ase.com
Sales Range: $100-124.9 Million
X-Ray Inspection Systems & Instrumentation Used in Scientific Applications & Industry Control Systems
N.A.I.C.S.: 334517

Subsidiary (Domestic):

Nucsafe, Inc. (2)
601 Oak Rdg Tpke, Oak Ridge, TN 37830-7040
Tel.: (724) 263-5500
Web Site: http://www.nucsafe.com
Analytical Laboratory Instrument Mfr
N.A.I.C.S.: 334516
Andy Veach (Mgr-Svc)

Briton EMS Limited (1)
4 Shuttleworth Road, Elms Industrial Estate, Bedford, MK41 0EP, United Kingdom
Tel.: (44) 1234266300
Web Site: http://www.britonems.co.uk
Communication Equipment Mfr
N.A.I.C.S.: 334290

Corrigan Canada, Ltd. (1)
55 Sinclair Ave, Georgetown, L7G 4X4, ON, Canada
Tel.: (905) 696-0664
Sales Range: $100-124.9 Million
Mfr of Security Equipment
N.A.I.C.S.: 561621

Foamhand Limited (1)
4th Floor Imperial House 15 Kingsway, London, WC2B 6UN, United Kingdom
Tel.: (44) 2072054105
Web Site: http://www.foamhand.com
Management Consulting Services
N.A.I.C.S.: 541611
Adam Down (Exec Dir)
Eoghan Gill (Dir-Strategy)
Calum Nicholson (Dir-Technical)

Gatekeeper Intelligent Security UK Ltd. (1)
Spring Close Cottage Lyburn Road, Nomansland, Salisbury, SP5 2DF, Wiltshire, United Kingdom
Tel.: (44) 7983126408
Cargo Moving Services
N.A.I.C.S.: 484210

Gatekeeper Security Middle East FTZ (1)
LIU 3 Block A6 Dubai Silicon Oasis, PO Box 341378, Dubai, United Arab Emirates
Tel.: (971) 43922033
Cargo Moving Services
N.A.I.C.S.: 484210

Metrax GmbH (1)
Rheinwaldstrasse 22, 78628, Rottweil, Germany
Tel.: (49) 7412570
Communication Equipment Mfr
N.A.I.C.S.: 334290

OSI Electronics (UK) Ltd. (1)
5 Marlborough Road, Colmworth Business Park, Saint Neots, PE19 8YP, Cam-

bridgeshire, United Kingdom
Tel.: (44) 1480222480
Electronic Assembly Mfr
N.A.I.C.S.: 334418

OSI Electronics, Inc. (1)
12533 Chadron Ave, Hawthorne, CA 90250
Tel.: (310) 978-0516
Web Site: https://www.osielectronics.com
Printed Circuit Board Mfr
N.A.I.C.S.: 334418
Paul Morben (Pres)

OSI Optoelectronics Inc. (1)
12525 Chadron Ave, Hawthorne, CA 90250-4807
Tel.: (310) 978-0516
Web Site: https://www.osioptoelectronics.com
Sales Range: $100-124.9 Million
High Performance Light Sensor Products Designer, Developer, Mfr & Marketer
N.A.I.C.S.: 334413
Alan Edrick (CFO)

Subsidiary (Domestic):

Ferson Technologies, Inc. (2)
5801 Gulf Tech Dr, Ocean Springs, MS 39564-8225
Tel.: (228) 875-8146
Web Site: http://www.ferson.com
Sales Range: $10-24.9 Million
Emp.: 30
Mfr of Standard & Custom Optical Components & Optical Subassemblies
N.A.I.C.S.: 333310

OSI Laser Diode, Inc. (2)
4 Olsen Ave, Edison, NJ 08820-2419
Tel.: (732) 549-9001
Web Site: https://www.laserdiode.com
Sales Range: $1-9.9 Million
Emp.: 50
Optoelectronic Product Mfr
N.A.I.C.S.: 334413
Rollin Ball (Pres)

Subsidiary (Non-US):

OSI Optoelectronics AS (2)
Kongeveien 79, PO Box 83, Horten, 3188, Norway (100%)
Tel.: (47) 33030300
Web Site: http://www.osioptoelectronics.no
Sales Range: $10-24.9 Million
Emp.: 2
Mfr of Advanced Micro Electronics
N.A.I.C.S.: 334419

Division (Domestic):

Statcorp Medical (2)
35301 SE Ctr St, Snoqualmie, WA 98065
Tel.: (425) 396-3304
Web Site: http://www.statcorpmedical.com
Surgical & Medical Instruments Mfr
N.A.I.C.S.: 339112

OSI Optoelectronics Limited. (1)
12525 Chadron Ave, Hawthorne, CA 90250
Tel.: (310) 978-0516
Web Site: http://www.osioptoelectronics.com
Sales Range: $25-49.9 Million
Emp.: 200
Optoelectronics Mfr
N.A.I.C.S.: 334413
Manoocher Mansouri (Pres-Mfg Div)

Opto Sensors Hong Kong Limited (1)
Unit 1811 Nan Fung Commercial Center 19 Lam Lok Street Kowloon Bay, Kowloon, China (Hong Kong)
Tel.: (852) 23671030
Imaging & Medical Device Mfr
N.A.I.C.S.: 334510

Osteometer MediTech, Inc. (1)
2747 Signal Hill Parkway, Signal Hill, CA 90755
Tel.: (310) 802-3711
Web Site: http://www.osteometer.com
Sales Range: $10-24.9 Million
Emp.: 20
Mfr of Scanners & Densitometers for Diagnosis of Osteoporosis
N.A.I.C.S.: 339112
Ajay Mehra (Pres)

OSI Systems, Inc.—(Continued)

PFC Flexible Circuits Limited (1)
11 Canadian Rd Suite 7, Scarborough, M1R
5G1, ON, Canada
Tel.: (416) 750-8433
Web Site: https://www.pfcflex.com
Semiconductor Devices Mfr
N.A.I.C.S.: 334413

Prima Electronic Services
Limited (1)
4 Harding Way, Saint Ives, PE27 3WR,
Cambs, United Kingdom
Tel.: (44) 1480498338
Web Site: https://www.primagroup.co.uk
Electronic Products Mfr
N.A.I.C.S.: 334111

Quadratica (UK) Limited (1)
Europarc Innovation Centre Innovation
Way, Grimsby, DN37 9TT, United Kingdom
Tel.: (44) 1472898751
Web Site: https://www.quadratica.co.uk
Information Technology Services
N.A.I.C.S.: 611420

Rapiscan Security Products (USA),
Inc. (1)
3232 W El Segundo Blvd, Hawthorne, CA
90250
Tel.: (310) 978-1457
Web Site: http://www.rapiscan.com
Sales Range: $100-124.9 Million
Emp.: 210
Mfr of X-ray Screening & Explosive Detec-
tion Systems
N.A.I.C.S.: 423710
Ajay Mehra (Pres)

Subsidiary (Non-US):

Rapiscan Systems Ltd. (2)
X-Ray House Bonehurst Road, Salfords,
RH1 5GG, Surrey, United Kingdom
Tel.: (44) 8707774301
Web Site: http://www.rapiscansystems.com
Sales Range: $25-49.9 Million
Emp.: 150
Mfr of X-ray Screening & Explosive Detec-
tion Systems
N.A.I.C.S.: 334517

Rapiscan Systems Australia Pty
Ltd (1)
Unit 9 & 10 11-21 Underwood Road, Home-
bush, 2140, NSW, Australia
Tel.: (61) 399294600
Web Site:
http://www.rapiscansystems.com.au
Emp.: 6
Baggage & Parcel Inspection Support Ser-
vices
N.A.I.C.S.: 561990
Rob Hamilton (Gen Mgr)

Rapiscan Systems Hong Kong
Limited (1)
Unit 2617-18 26/F Tower 1 Metro plaza 223
Hing Fong Road, Kwai Fong, NT, China
(Hong Kong)
Tel.: (852) 24222610
Security Equipment Mfr
N.A.I.C.S.: 334290

Rapiscan Systems Oy (1)
Klovinpellontie 3 Torni 2, 2180, Espoo, Fin-
land
Tel.: (358) 207871900
Web Site: http://www.rapiscansystems.com
Emp.: 20
Metal Detector Mfr
N.A.I.C.S.: 334519
Petri Ikonen (Mng Dir)

Rapiscan Systems Pte. Ltd. (1)
240 Macpherson Road 03-04 Pines Indus-
trial Building, Singapore, 348574, Singapore
Tel.: (65) 96439375
Web Site: http://www.rapiscansystems.com
Emp.: 10
Security Screening Provider
N.A.I.C.S.: 561621

Rapiscan Systems, Inc. (1)
2805 Columbia St, Torrance, CA 90503
Tel.: (310) 978-1457
Web Site: https://www.rapiscansystems.com
Imaging Products & Advanced Threat Iden-
tification Technique Services

N.A.I.C.S.: 561621

Spacelabs Healthcare (Canada),
Inc. (1)
125 Topflight Drive, Mississauga, L5S 1Y1,
ON, Canada
Tel.: (905) 564-2229
Web Site: https://spacelabshealthcare.com
Sales Range: $25-49.9 Million
Emp.: 20
Medical Equipment Whslr
N.A.I.C.S.: 423450

Spacelabs Healthcare Ltd. (1)
Unit B Foxholes Centre John Tate Road,
Hertford, SG13 7DT, Hertfordshire, United
Kingdom
Tel.: (44) 1992507700
Sales Range: $25-49.9 Million
Emp.: 30
Medical Equipment Whslr
N.A.I.C.S.: 423450
Marcus Barkham (Mng Dir)

Spacelabs Healthcare, Inc. (1)
35301 SE Center St, Snoqualmie, WA
98065
Tel.: (425) 396-3300
Web Site:
https://www.spacelabshealthcare.com
Medical Equipment Mfr & Distr
N.A.I.C.S.: 339112
Deepak Chopra (CEQ)
Alan Edrick (CFO)
Victor Sze (Gen Counsel & Sec)
Shalabh Chandra (Pres)

Subsidiary (Non-US):

Spacelabs Healthcare SAS (2)
Europarc - 20 rue Eugene DUPUIS, 94045,
Creteil, Cedex, France
Tel.: (33) 145132200
Sales Range: $25-49.9 Million
Emp.: 20
Medical & Hospital Equipment Whslr
N.A.I.C.S.: 423450
Jean-Michel Motyka (Gen Mgr)

Spacelabs Healthcare, LLC (1)
5150 220th Ave SE, Issaquah, WA 98029
Tel.: (425) 657-7200
Medical Device Distr
N.A.I.C.S.: 423450

Spacelabs Medical, Inc. (1)
5150 220th Ave SE, Issaquah, WA 98029
Tel.: (425) 657-7200
Web Site: http://www.spacelabs.com
Sales Range: $450-499.9 Million
Emp.: 1,177
Mfr of Healthcare Information Technologies
Including Information Systems, Patient
Monitoring Equipment, Diagnostic & Con-
sumer Monitoring Products & Supplies
N.A.I.C.S.: 334510

Subsidiary (Non-US):

Spacelabs Medical UK S.p.A. (2)
Esperanpo 24, San Giovanni, 37057, Milan,
Italy
Tel.: (39) 0458757000
Sales Range: $100-124.9 Million
Mfr of Healthcare Information Technologies
Including Information Systems, Patient
Monitoring Equipment, Diagnostic & Con-
sumer Monitoring Products & Supplies &
Corporate Web Sites
N.A.I.C.S.: 334510

OSIRIS ACQUISITION CORP.
95 5th Ave 6th Fl, New York, NY
10003
Tel.: (646) 993-4635 DE
Web Site:
https://www.osirisacquisition
corp.com
Year Founded: 2020
OSI—(NYSE)
Rev.: $2,885,369
Assets: $33,157,227
Liabilities: $45,089,057
Net Worth: ($11,931,830)
Earnings: $6,960,758
Emp.: 3
Fiscal Year-end: 12/31/22
N.A.I.C.S.:

Benjamin E. Black (CEO)
Michael Abt (Chm)
Brad Bisca (CFO & Sec)

OSIRIS CORP.
14707 California St Ste 5, Omaha,
NE 68154
Tel.: (402) 934-2020 DE
OSRS—(OTCIQ)
Construction Machinery Mfr
N.A.I.C.S.: 333120
Michael S. Luther (CEO & Chief Re-
structuring Officer)

OSPREY MEDICAL INC.
5600 Rowland Road Suite 250, Min-
netonka, MN 55343
Tel.: (952) 955-8230
Web Site: http://www.ospreymed.com
Year Founded: 2005
OSP—(ASX)
Rev.: $1,671,868
Assets: $7,888,101
Liabilities: $3,493,253
Net Worth: $4,394,848
Earnings: ($13,378,070)
Emp.: 19
Fiscal Year-end: 12/31/20
Medical Device Mfr
N.A.I.C.S.: 339112
Mike McCormick (Pres & CEO)
Rodney Houfburg (VP-R&D)
Nancy Ness (VP-Fin)
Doug Schoenberg (VP-Mktg, Educa-
tion & Reimbursement)
Vic Fabano (VP-Ops & IT)
Melanie Hess (VP-Regulatory, Com-
pliance & Quality)
Sarah Runde (Sr Dir-Clinical Affairs)

OSYKA CORPORATION
5440 Morehouse Dr Ste 4400, San
Diego, CA 92121
Tel.: (858) 558-1001 NV
Web Site: https://osykacorp.com
Year Founded: 1990
OSKA—(OTCIQ)
Oil & Gas Exploration Services
N.A.I.C.S.: 213112
Morgan Scudi (Pres, CEO, Treas &
Sec)

Subsidiaries:

International Energy Trading LLC (1)
934 N University Dr Ste 224, Coral Springs,
FL 33071
Tel.: (305) 438-8971
Web Site: http://www.intlenergytrading.com
Petroleum Consulting & Trading Services
N.A.I.C.S.: 213112

OTC MARKETS GROUP INC.
300 Vesey St 12th Fl, New York, NY
10282
Tel.: (212) 896-4400 DE
Web Site:
https://www.otcmarkets.com
Year Founded: 1913
OTCM—(OTCIQ)
Rev.: $71,229,000
Assets: $64,810,000
Liabilities: $45,264,000
Net Worth: $19,546,000
Earnings: $18,274,000
Emp.: 102
Fiscal Year-end: 12/31/20
Pricing & Financial Information for the
OTC Securities Market; Company
Information Publisher
N.A.I.C.S.: 523210
R. Cromwell Coulson (Pres & CEO)
Lisabeth Heese (Exec VP-Issuer &
Information Svcs)
Jason Paltrowitz (Exec VP-Corp
Svcs)
Matthew Fuchs (Exec VP-Market
Data)

Daniel Zinn (Gen Counsel)
Neal Wolkoff (Chm)
Kristie Harkins (CMO)
Bruce Ostrover (CTO)
Antonia Georgieva (CFO)

Subsidiaries:

Blue Sky Data Corp. (1)
90 E Halsey Rd Ste 100, Parsippany, NJ
07054-3709
Tel.: (973) 560-9393
Web Site: http://www.blueskydata.com
All Other Personal Services
N.A.I.C.S.: 812990
Linda Graves (Pres)

OTIS WORLDWIDE CORPORA-
TION
1 Carrier Pl, Farmington, CT 06032
Tel.: (860) 674-3000 DE
Web Site: https://www.otis.com
Year Founded: 1853
OTIS—(NYSE)
Rev.: $14,209,000,000
Assets: $10,117,000,000
Liabilities: $14,972,000,000
Net Worth: ($4,855,000,000)
Earnings: $1,406,000,000
Emp.: 71,000
Fiscal Year-end: 12/31/23
Holding Company; Elevator & Escala-
tor Mfr & Whslr
N.A.I.C.S.: 551112
Neil Green (Chief Digital Officer &
Exec VP)
Judith F. Marks (Chm, Pres & CEO)
Michael P. Ryan (Chief Acctg Officer
& VP)
Nora E. LaFreniere (Exec VP & Gen
Counsel)
Todd Glance (Exec VP-Ops)
Luis Molina (Exec VP-Growth & Strat-
egy)
Ricardo Munoz (Sr VP-Engrg)
Randi Tanguay (Chief Comm Officer
& VP)
Robin Fiala (VP-Sls & Mktg)
Rajesh Krishnamurthy (VP-Product
Mgmt)
Stacy Laszewski (VP-FP&A & IR)
Abbe Luersman (Chief HR Officer &
Exec VP)
Peiming Zheng (Chief Product, Deliv-
ery & Customer Officer & Exec VP)
Michael Rednor (Sr Dir-IR)
Sally Loh (Pres-China)
Stephane de Montlivault (Pres)
Sebi Joseph (Pres)
Sridhar Rajagopal (Head)
Alok Mahajan (Dir)
C. A. Nagaraj (Dir)
Hrishikesh Pawar (Dir)
Debraj Chowdhury (Dir)

Subsidiaries:

Otis Elevator Company (1)
1 Carrier Pl, Farmington, CT
06034 (100%)
Tel.: (860) 674-3000
Web Site: https://www.otis.com
Sales Range: $5-14.9 Billion
Elevator & Escalator Mfr & Whslr
N.A.I.C.S.: 333921
Neil Green (Chief Digital Officer & Exec VP)
Judith F. Marks (Chm, Pres & CEO)
Randi Tanguay (Chief Comm Officer)
Robin Fiala (VP-Sls & Mktg)
Rajesh Krishnamurthy (VP-Product Mgmt)
Ricardo Munoz (Sr VP-Engrg)
Todd Glance (Exec VP-Ops)
Nora LaFreniere (Gen Counsel, Sec & Exec
VP)

Subsidiary (Non-US):

9G Elevator Pte. Ltd. (2)
8 Kallang Ave 07-01 Aperia Tower 1, Singapore, 339509, Singapore
Tel.: (65) 62837530
Web Site: https://9g.sg

Lift & Escalator Maintenance Services
N.A.I.C.S.: 238290
Mervyn Yong (Mgr-EHS)

Subsidiary (Domestic):

ACM Elevator Co. (2)
54 Eisenhower Ln N, Lombard, IL 60148
Tel.: (630) 953-7357
Web Site: http://www.acmelevator.com
Sales Range: $100-124.9 Million
Emp.: 60
Installation, Inspection, Service & Repair of
Elevators
N.A.I.C.S.: 811490

Delta Elevator Service Corp. (2)
274 Hampden St Roxbury, Boston, MA
02119
Tel.: (617) 427-5525
Sales Range: $50-74.9 Million
Emp.: 150
Mfr Elevators & Dumbwaiters
N.A.I.C.S.: 238290
Daniel Too (Mng Dir)

Subsidiary (Non-US):

Elevadores Otis Ltda. (2)
Rua Elisha Otis 2 200 Bairro Cooperativa,
Sao Bernardo Do Campo, Sao Paulo,
09852-075, Brazil
Tel.: (55) 8007048783
Web Site: http://www.otis.com
Elevators & Stair Installation Services
N.A.I.C.S.: 238290

Elevadores Otis S/A (2)
R San Jose 70 13 Andar Centro, CEP
20010 020, Rio de Janeiro, RJ,
Brazil (100%)
Tel.: (55) 2125242009
Web Site: http://www.otis.com
Sales Range: $50-74.9 Million
Sales & Service of Elevators
N.A.I.C.S.: 423830

Elevadores Otis, S.A. de C.V. (2)
Av Revolucion No 507 3er Piso Col San
Pedro de los Pinos, Alvaro Obregon,
03800, Mexico, DF, Mexico
Tel.: (52) 5526363000
Web Site: https://www.otis.com
Sales Range: $200-249.9 Million
Elevator Mfr
N.A.I.C.S.: 333921

Hankook Otis Elevator Company (2)
16-2 Youido-dong Yongdungpo-ku, Seoul,
135-708, Korea (South)
Tel.: (82) 27842341
Web Site: http://www.otis.com
Sales Range: $100-124.9 Million
Emp.: 250
Manufacturing, Installation & Maintenance
of Hydraulic & Cable Type Passenger &
Cargo Elevators
N.A.I.C.S.: 333921
Pierre Dejoux (Pres-South Asia Pacific &
Gulf Area)

Nippon Otis Elevator Company (2)
23rd floor Bunkyo Green Court 2-28-8
Honkomagome, Bunkyo-Ku, Tokyo, 113-
0021, Japan
Tel.: (81) 35 981 0300
Web Site: https://www.otis.com
Heating & Air Conditioner Mfr
N.A.I.C.S.: 333415

Subsidiary (Domestic):

Mercury Ascensore Co.,Ltd. (3)
29-22 Kamoiwada Town, Kagoshima, 890-
0055, Japan
Tel.: (81) 99 257 9113
Web Site: http://www.ascensore.co.jp
Emp.: 213
Elevator & Escalator Installation Services
N.A.I.C.S.: 238290
Masayoshi Kurahashi (Pres)

Subsidiary (Non-US):

OTIS GmbH & Co. OHG (2)
Otisstrasse 33, 13507, Berlin, Germany
Tel.: (49) 3043040
Web Site: http://www.otis.com
Capital Investment Services
N.A.I.C.S.: 523999

Otis AB (2)
Dalvagen 2, PO Box 3096, Solna, 169 03,
Sweden
Tel.: (46) 856203200
Web Site: http://www.otis.com
Sales Range: $25-49.9 Million
Emp.: 200
Wholesale & Service of Elevators
N.A.I.C.S.: 423830

Otis Canada, Inc. (2)
1655 The Queensway East, Mississauga,
L4X 2Z5, ON, Canada (100%)
Tel.: (905) 276-5577
Web Site: http://www.otis.com
Sales Range: $10-24.9 Million
Sales & Service of Elevators
N.A.I.C.S.: 333921

**Otis Elevator (China) Company
Limited** (2)
No 443 South Jiefang Road He'xi District,
Tianjin, China
Tel.: (86) 2228101188
Web Site: http://www.otis.com
Elevator Mfr
N.A.I.C.S.: 333921

**Otis Elevator (China) Investment
Company Limited** (2)
No 443 Jiefang South Road, Hexi District,
Tianjin, China
Tel.: (86) 2228101188
Web Site: http://www.otis.com
Elevator Mfr
N.A.I.C.S.: 333921

Otis Elevator Co. Pty. Ltd. (2)
Lvl 23 363 George Street, Sydney, 2000,
NSW, Australia (100%)
Tel.: (61) 283382700
Web Site: http://www.otis.com
Sales Range: $125-149.9 Million
Emp.: 100
Elevators
N.A.I.C.S.: 333921
Ken Muller (Pres)

**Otis Elevator Company (India)
Limited** (2)
Magnus Towers 9th Floor Mindspace Link
Road, Malad West, Mumbai, 400 064, India
Tel.: (91) 2228449700
Web Site: http://www.otis.com
Elevator Mfr
N.A.I.C.S.: 333921

Subsidiary (Domestic):

**Otis Elevator Company -
Pittsburgh** (2)
4499 Campbells Run Rd, Pittsburgh, PA
15205
Tel.: (412) 788-5824
Web Site: http://www.otis.com
Sales Range: $25-49.9 Million
Emp.: 75
Elevator & Escalator Mfr
N.A.I.C.S.: 238290

Subsidiary (Non-US):

Otis Elevator Limited (2)
Building 5 566 Chiswick High Rd, London,
W4 5YF, United Kingdom
Tel.: (44) 2084957750
Web Site: http://www.otis.com
Sales Range: $50-74.9 Million
Emp.: 150
Elevators
N.A.I.C.S.: 333921

Otis Gesellschaft m.b.H. (2)
Modecenterstrasse 17/Objekt 1, Business
Park Marximum, 1110, Vienna, Austria
Tel.: (43) 1610050
Web Site: https://www.otis.com
Elevator & Moving Stairway Mfr
N.A.I.C.S.: 333921

Otis GmbH & Co. OHG (2)
Otis Strasse 33, Berlin, 13507, Germany
Tel.: (49) 3043040
Web Site: http://www.otis.com
Sales Range: $800-899.9 Million
Elevators & Moving Stairways Mfr
N.A.I.C.S.: 333921

Otis Holdings GmbH & Co. OHG (2)
Otisstrasse 33, 13507, Berlin, Germany

Tel.: (49) 3043040
Web Site: http://www.otis.com
Elevator Mfr
N.A.I.C.S.: 333921

Subsidiary (Domestic):

Hutter Aufzuge GmbH (3)
Siemensstrasse 11, Glinde, 21509, Ger-
many
Tel.: (49) 40 72 77 66 0
Web Site: http://www.huetter-aufzuege.de
Sales Range: $10-24.9 Million
Emp.: 35
Elevator Repair & Maintenance Services
N.A.I.C.S.: 811198

Subsidiary (Non-US):

**Otis International Holdings
GmbH** (2)
Otisstrasse 33, 13507, Berlin, Germany
Tel.: (49) 3043042965
Holding Company
N.A.I.C.S.: 551112

Otis Investments Limited (2)
Unit 24 Howley Park Business Village,
Leeds, LS27 0BZ, West Yorkshire, United
Kingdom
Tel.: (44) 1132523319
Investment Management Service
N.A.I.C.S.: 523940

Otis Limited (2)
Building 5 566 Chiswick High Road, Lon-
don, W4 5YF, United Kingdom
Tel.: (44) 2084957750
Web Site: http://www.otis.com
Elevator Product Mfr
N.A.I.C.S.: 333248

Otis Pacific Holdings B.V. (2)
Terminalweg 27, Amersfoort, 3821 AJ,
Utrecht, Netherlands
Tel.: (31) 337502100
Machinery Suppliers
N.A.I.C.S.: 333248

Otis S.C.S. (2)
3 Place de la Pyramide, Puteaux, 92800,
France
Tel.: (33) 146916000
Elevator Mfr
N.A.I.C.S.: 333921

Subsidiary (Domestic):

**Poma-Otis Transportation
Systems** (2)
Five Farm Springs Rd, Farmington, CT
06032-2573
Tel.: (860) 676-6000
Web Site: http://www.otis.com
Sales Range: $10-24.9 Million
Emp.: 23
Shuttle System Installation
N.A.I.C.S.: 238290

**Otis Elevator Company (Taiwan)
Limited** (1)
37F No 16-1, Xinzhan Road, Banqiao Dis-
trict, New Taipei City, 22041, Taiwan
Tel.: (886) 0277273888
Web Site: https://www.otis.com
Elevator & Escalator Mfr & Whslr
N.A.I.C.S.: 333921

Subsidiary (Domestic):

Jardine Schindler Lifts Ltd. (2)
9th floor 35 Kwang Fu South Road, Taipei,
00105, Taiwan
Tel.: (886) 225286626
Web Site: https://www.schindler.com
Sales Range: $25-49.9 Million
Elevators, Escalators & Passenger Convey-
ors
N.A.I.C.S.: 333921

Otis S.A. (1)
Route de Moncor 12, PO Box 464, 1701,
Fribourg, Switzerland
Tel.: (41) 264074111
Web Site: http://www.otis.com
Elevator & Moving Walkway Mfr
N.A.I.C.S.: 333921

Otis Serviz, S.r.l. (1)
Via Roma 108, 20051, Cassina de' Pecchi,
MI, Italy

Tel.: (39) 0800824024
Web Site: http://www.otis.com
Elevator & Moving Walkway Mfr
N.A.I.C.S.: 333921

Otis a.s. (1)
Plzenska 3350/18, 150 00, Prague, Czech
Republic
Tel.: (420) 800107525
Elevator Product Mfr & Distr
N.A.I.C.S.: 333921

Sigma Elevator (HK) Limited (1)
9-11/F Octa Tower 8 Lam Chak Road, Kow-
loon Bay, China (Hong Kong)
Tel.: (852) 25986822
Elevator & Moving Walkway Mfr
N.A.I.C.S.: 333921

Zardoya Otis, S.A. (1)
Golfo de Salonica 73, 28033, Madrid, Spain
Tel.: (34) 913435100
Web Site: http://www.otis.com
Rev.: $993,256,808
Assets: $892,388,826
Liabilities: $362,336,941
Net Worth: $530,051,885
Earnings: $179,025,806
Emp.: 5,552
Fiscal Year-end: 11/30/2022
Elevator & Moving Stairways
N.A.I.C.S.: 333921

OTONOMY, INC.
4796 Executive Dr, San Diego, CA
92121
Tel.: (619) 323-2200 DE
Web Site: http://www.otonomy.com
Year Founded: 2008
OTIC—(NASDAQ)
Rev.: $125,000
Assets: $95,637,000
Liabilities: $40,730,000
Net Worth: $54,907,000
Earnings: ($51,181,000)
Emp.: 51
Fiscal Year-end: 12/31/21
Pharmaceuticals Mfr
N.A.I.C.S.: 325412
David Allen Weber (CEO)
Jay B. Lichter (Chm)
Carla da Luz Boren (Chief HR Officer
& Gen Counsel)
Julie D. Burgess (VP-Fin)
Barbara M. Finn (VP-Regulatory Af-
fairs & Quality Assurance)
Alan C. Foster (VP-Res)
Fabrice Piu (VP-Res & Preclinical
Dev)
David Skarinsky (VP-Clinical)
Anna Stepanenko (VP-Technical
Ops)
David Maggio (Pres & Sec)

OTR ACQUISITION CORP.
1395 Brickell Ave Ste 800, Miami, FL
33131
Tel.: (305) 697-9600 DE
Year Founded: 2020
OTRAU—(NASDAQ)
Investment Services
N.A.I.C.S.: 523999
Nicholas Singer (Chm, CEO & CFO)

OTTAWA BANCORP, INC.
925 LaSalle St, Ottawa, IL 61350
Tel.: (815) 433-2525
Web Site:
https://www.ottawasavings.com
Year Founded: 2005
OTTW—(NASDAQ)
Rev.: $12,517,112
Assets: $300,531,696
Liabilities: $249,820,821
Net Worth: $50,710,875
Earnings: $1,937,347
Emp.: 57
Fiscal Year-end: 12/31/19
Bank Holding Company
N.A.I.C.S.: 551111

Ottawa Bancorp, Inc.—(Continued)

Jon L. Kranov *(Chm)*
Craig M. Hepner *(Pres & CEO)*

OTTER TAIL CORPORATION

215 S Cascade St, Fergus Falls, MN
56538-0496
Tel.: (218) 739-8479   MN
Web Site: https://www.ottertail.com
Year Founded: 1907
OTTR—(NASDAQ)
Rev.: $1,349,166,000
Assets: $3,242,568,000
Liabilities: $975,503,000
Net Worth: $2,267,065,000
Earnings: $294,191,000
Emp.: 2,655
Fiscal Year-end: 12/31/23
Electric Utility
N.A.I.C.S.: 221122
Todd R. Wahlund *(CFO & VP)*
John D. Erickson *(Bd of Dirs, Executives)*
Charles S. MacFarlane *(Pres & CEO)*
Jennifer O. Smestad *(Gen Counsel, Sec & VP)*
Stephanie A. Hoff *(Dir-Corp Comm)*
Timothy J. Rogelstad *(Sr VP-Electric Platform)*
John S. Abbott *(Sr.VP-Mfg Platform)*
Paul L. Knutson *(VP-HR)*

Subsidiaries:

BTD Manufacturing, Inc.   (1)
1111 13th Ave SE, Detroit Lakes, MN 56501
Tel.: (218) 847-4446
Web Site: https://www.btdmfg.com
Sales Range: $125-149.9 Million
Metal Stampings, Tool & Die Mfr
N.A.I.C.S.: 333514

DMI Canada, Inc.   (1)
2677 Winger Rd, Fort Erie, L0S 1S0, ON, Canada
Tel.: (905) 382-5793
Farm Machinery & Equipment Mfr
N.A.I.C.S.: 333111

Northern Pipe Product Inc.   (1)
1302 39th Str NW, Fargo, ND 58102-2808
Tel.: (701) 282-7655
Web Site: https://www.northernpipe.com
Sales Range: $25-49.9 Million
Manufacturer of PVC Plastic Pipes
N.A.I.C.S.: 326122

Otter Tail Power Company   (1)
215 S Cascade St, Fergus Falls, MN 56537
Tel.: (218) 739-8877
Web Site: https://www.otpco.com
Sales Range: $750-799.9 Million
Emp.: 750
Electricity & Energy Services
N.A.I.C.S.: 221122
Jennifer O. Smestad *(Gen Counsel & VP-Legal Affairs)*
Bradley E. Tollerson *(VP-Energy Supply)*
JoAnn M. Thompson *(VP-Asset Mgmt)*
Mark B. Bring *(Dir-Legislative Affairs & Assoc Gen Counsel)*
Peter E. Wasberg *(Dir-HR & Safety)*
Timothy J. Rogelstad *(Pres)*
Bruce G. Gerhardson *(VP-Regulatory Affairs)*
Don L. Redden *(VP-IT)*
Steve J. Schoeneck *(VP-Customer Svc)*

Shoreline Industries, Inc.   (1)
1025 International Dr, Fergus Falls, MN 56537
Tel.: (218) 587-8700
Web Site:
    http://www.shorelineindustries.com
Emp.: 110
Dock & Lift Accessories Mfr
N.A.I.C.S.: 333923
Don Hurley *(Pres)*

T.O. Plastics, Inc.   (1)
830 County Rd 75, Clearwater, MN 55320
Tel.: (320) 558-2407
Web Site: https://www.toplastics.com
Sales Range: $75-99.9 Million
Emp.: 160
Mfr of Plastic Products

N.A.I.C.S.: 326199
Charles Goers *(Pres, CEO & Treas)*
Don Jaeger *(VP-Sales-Marketing)*
Jessica Fleming *(Mgr-Reg Sls-Southeast)*
Jared Rusch *(Dir-Sls & Mktg-Horticulture)*
James Rowley *(Mgr-Reg Sls-Northeast)*
Paul Meschke *(Pres)*
Jason Greni *(VP-Finance)*
Julia Nguyen *(VP-Human Resources)*
Kevin Kieke *(Dir-Engineering-Quality)*
Brad Evert *(VP-Operations)*
Dyann Turner *(Dir-Human Resources)*
Tom Murphy *(Fin Dir)*
Scott Klein *(Dir-Quality)*

Varistar Corporation   (1)
4334 18th Ave SW Ste 200, Fargo, ND 58103
Tel.: (701) 232-4225
Sales Range: $25-49.9 Million
Emp.: 50
Investment Management Service
N.A.I.C.S.: 551112

Vinyltech Corporation   (1)
201 S 61st Ave, Phoenix, AZ 85043
Tel.: (602) 233-0071
Web Site: https://vtpipe.com
Sales Range: $1-9.9 Million
Large Water & Waste Water Pipes Mfr
N.A.I.C.S.: 237120

OUSTER, INC.

350 Treat Ave, San Francisco, CA 94110
Tel.: (415) 949-0108   DE
Web Site: https://ouster.com
Year Founded: 2020
OUST—(NYSE)
Rev.: $41,029,000
Assets: $256,137,000
Liabilities: $84,518,000
Net Worth: $171,619,000
Earnings: ($138,560,000)
Emp.: 270
Fiscal Year-end: 12/31/22
Electronics Mfr
N.A.I.C.S.: 334419
Cyrille Jacquemet *(Sr VP-Global Sls)*
Darien Spencer *(COO)*
Mark Weinswig *(CFO)*
Megan Chung *(Gen Counsel)*
Mark Frichtl *(Co-Founder & CTO)*
Susan Heystee *(Vice Chm)*
Angus Pacala *(Co-Founder & CEO)*

Subsidiaries:

Velodyne Lidar, Inc.   (1)
5521 Hellyer Ave, San Jose, CA 95138
Tel.: (669) 275-2251
Web Site: http://velodynelidar.com
Rev.: $61,924,000
Assets: $375,421,000
Liabilities: $76,158,000
Net Worth: $299,263,000
Earnings: ($212,236,000)
Emp.: 407
Fiscal Year-end: 12/31/2021
Lidar Sensor Technologies
N.A.I.C.S.: 334511
Theodore L. Tewksbury *(CEO)*
Mark B. Weinswig *(CFO)*
Matt Rekow *(CTO)*
Kathryn McBeath *(Chief People Officer)*
Sally Frykman *(Chief Mktg Officer)*
Dan Horwood *(Gen Counsel)*
Theodore L. Tewksbury *(CEO)*
Mark B. Weinswig *(CFO)*
Virginia Boulet *(Chm)*

OUTBACK OIL & MINERAL EXPLORATION CORP.

626 RXR Plz Ctr W Tower, Uniondale, NY 11556
Tel.: (516) 229-2346   DE
Year Founded: 1980
OUTB—(OTCIQ)
Oil & Gas Exploration Services
N.A.I.C.S.: 213112
Barry Martin Gleicher *(Pres, Treas & Sec)*

OUTBRAIN INC.

111 W 19th St 3rd Fl, New York, NY 10011
Tel.: (646) 867-0149   DE
Web Site: https://www.outbrain.com
Year Founded: 2006
OB—(NASDAQ)
Rev.: $935,818,000
Assets: $664,637,000
Liabilities: $441,573,000
Net Worth: $223,064,000
Earnings: $10,242,000
Emp.: 942
Fiscal Year-end: 12/31/23
Advertising Services
N.A.I.C.S.: 541810
Gilad De Vries *(Chief Strategy Officer)*
David Kostman *(CEO)*
Yossi Amara *(CIO)*
Asaf Porat *(COO)*
Daphna Michaeli *(Chief People Officer)*
Veronica Gonzalez *(Chief Admin Officer & Gen Counsel)*
Sarah Baird *(Gen Mgr-North America)*
Wenkai Bradshaw *(Chief Acctg Officer)*
Andraz Tori *(Chief Product Officer)*
Yonatan Maman *(CTO)*
Liesbeth Mack-de Boer *(Mng Dir)*
Yaron Galai *(Founder)*

Subsidiaries:

Outbrain Australia Pty Ltd   (1)
35 King St, Sydney, 2000, NSW, Australia
Tel.: (61) 290993923
Media Services
N.A.I.C.S.: 541840
Elise Bennett *(Head-Account Management)*
Eve Solomon *(VP-Business Development)*

Outbrain Belgium BVBA   (1)
31 Commercestraat, 1000, Brussels, Belgium
Tel.: (32) 27906171
Media Services
N.A.I.C.S.: 541840

Outbrain France SAS   (1)
10 rue Chaptal, 75009, Paris, France
Tel.: (33) 188880266
Media Services
N.A.I.C.S.: 541840
Francois-Xavier Preaut *(Gen Mgr)*
Thibaut Lozivit *(Head-Sales)*
Benjamin Rolland *(Head-Account Management)*
Agathe Rakowicz *(VP-Global Demand Enablement)*
Nicolas Ficca *(Mng Dir-Business Development)*

Outbrain Germany GmbH   (1)
Oberanger 28, 80331, Munich, Germany
Tel.: (49) 8926200478
Media Services
N.A.I.C.S.: 541840
Liesbeth Mack-de Boer *(Mng Dir)*
Daniel School *(Head-Sales)*
Katarina Eres *(Head-Account Management)*
Phillip Laudien *(Mng Dir)*

Outbrain India Private Limited   (1)
5th Floor DLF Two Horizon Centre DLF, Phase 5 Sector 43, Gurgaon, 122002, Haryana, India
Tel.: (91) 2268181920
Media Services
N.A.I.C.S.: 541840
Shouneel Charles *(Gen Mgr)*

Outbrain Israel Ltd.   (1)
Arieh Regev Street 6, Netanya, Israel
Tel.: (972) 732238900
Media Services
N.A.I.C.S.: 541840
Ori Lahav *(Co-Founder, CTO & Gen Mgr)*

Outbrain Italy SRL   (1)
Tel.: (39) 0230566627
Media Services
N.A.I.C.S.: 541840

Outbrain Japan KK   (1)

1 Chome-20-5 Ebisunishi, Shibuya-ku, Tokyo, 150-0021, Japan
Tel.: (81) 364096061
Media Services
N.A.I.C.S.: 541840
Takeshi Iryo *(Country Mgr)*
Atsushi Masuda *(Mng Dir)*

Outbrain Netherlands B.V.   (1)
Nieuwezijds Voorburgwal 162, 1012 SJ, Amsterdam, Netherlands
Tel.: (31) 203997666
Media Services
N.A.I.C.S.: 541840

Outbrain Services Monetizacao de Conteudo Ltda   (1)
R Cap Antonio Rosa 409, Jardim Paulista, Sao Paulo, 01443-010, SP, Brazil
Tel.: (55) 1147809573
Media Services
N.A.I.C.S.: 541840
Laura Assis *(Head-Sales)*

Outbrain Singapore Pte. Ltd.   (1)
5 Shenton Way UIC Building 10-01, Singapore, 068808, Singapore
Tel.: (65) 31590518
Media Services
N.A.I.C.S.: 541840
Amrita De La Pena *(Mng Dir)*

Outbrain Spain S.L.   (1)
Santa Engracia 23, 28010, Madrid, Spain
Tel.: (34) 919347436
Media Services
N.A.I.C.S.: 541840
Rafael Amieva *(Gen Mgr)*
Brigitte Linares *(Head-Account Management)*
Alejandra Molina Valiente *(Head-Sales)*

Outbrain UK Limited   (1)
121 Kingsway First Floor, London, WC2B6PA, United Kingdom
Tel.: (44) 2079539678
Media Services
N.A.I.C.S.: 541840
Alex Cheeseman *(Head-Northern Europe)*
Alexandre Simo *(Head-Account Management)*
Sam Maloney *(Head-Sales-Northern Europe)*
Stephanie Himoff *(Exec VP-Global Publishers)*
Richard Chambers *(Mng Dir-Business Development)*
Kyle Staib *(Head-Partner Mgmt)*

OUTDOOR SPECIALTY PRODUCTS, INC.

3842 Quail Hollow Dr, Salt Lake City, UT 84109
Tel.: (801) 560-5184   UT
Web Site:
    https://www.outdoorspecialtyproducts.com
ODRS—(OTCIQ)
Rev.: $163
Assets: $16,461
Liabilities: $158,427
Net Worth: ($141,966)
Earnings: ($43,565)
Fiscal Year-end: 09/30/24
Sporting Goods Distr
N.A.I.C.S.: 423910

OUTFRONT MEDIA INC.

90 Park Ave, New York, NY 10016
Tel.: (212) 297-6400   MD
Web Site: https://www.outfront.com
Year Founded: 2013
OUT—(NYSE)
Rev.: $1,772,100,000
Assets: $5,990,000,000
Liabilities: $4,640,800,000
Net Worth: $1,349,200,000
Earnings: $147,900,000
Emp.: 2,357
Fiscal Year-end: 12/31/22

Holding Company; Outdoor Advertising Services
N.A.I.C.S.: 551112
Jodi Senese (CMO & Exec VP)
Clive Punter (Chief Revenue Officer & Exec VP)
Richard Sauer (Gen Counsel & Exec VP)
Chris Steinbacher (Exec VP-Real Estate)
Lowell Simpson (CIO & Exec VP)
Art Martinez (Sr VP-Midwest Reg)
Marc Miller (Sr VP-Sls-Natl Trading)
Phil Stimpson (Exec VP-East Reg)
Ryan Brooks (Exec VP-Govt Affairs)
Mark Bonanni (Sr VP-South Region)
Michael Wells (Sr VP-West Region)
Matthew Siegel (CFO & Exec VP)
Andrew R. Sriubas (Chief Comml Officer)
Nancy Tostanoski (Chief HR Officer & Exec VP)
Steve Hillwig (Exec VP-Ops)
Jeremy J. Male (Chm & CEO)

Subsidiaries:

Millenium Billboards L.L.C.   (1)
405 Lexington Ave, New York, NY 10174
Tel.: (212) 297-6484
Outdoor Advertising Services
N.A.I.C.S.: 541850

Outfront Media Chicago LLC   (1)
405 Lexington Ave 17th Fl, New York, NY 10174
Tel.: (212) 297-6400
Outdoor Advertising Services
N.A.I.C.S.: 541850

Outfront Media LLC   (1)
405 Lexington Ave, New York, NY 10174
Tel.: (212) 297-6400
Web Site: https://www.outfrontmedia.com
Transit, Billboard & Special Display Advertising Services
N.A.I.C.S.: 541850

Branch (Domestic):

Outfront Media - Phoenix   (2)
2400 N Black Canyon Hwy, Phoenix, AZ 85009
Tel.: (602) 246-9569
Web Site: http://www.outfrontmedia.com
Transit, Billboard & Special Display Advertising Services
N.A.I.C.S.: 541850

Subsidiary (Non-US):

Outfront Media Canada LP   (2)
377 Horner Avenue, Toronto, M8W 1Z6, ON, Canada
Tel.: (416) 255-1392
Web Site: http://www.outfrontmedia.ca
Sales Range: $25-49.9 Million
Emp.: 180
Outdoor Media & Advertising Services
N.A.I.C.S.: 541850
Michele Erskine (CEO)
Esther Niven (VP-HR)
Nadine Schiratti (CFO)
George Jakji (VP-Sls)
Paul Desjardins (VP-Sls-Eastern)
Melody Warman (VP-Sls-Western)
Vincent Aloi (VP-Sls)
Lisa Roscoe (VP-Real Estate & Legal Affairs)
Joel Heard (VP-IT)
Tim Bouchard (VP-Ops)

Outfront Media VW Communications LLC   (1)
800 3rd Ave, New York, NY 10022
Tel.: (212) 699-8400
Web Site: https://www.vanwagner.com
Marketing & Advertising Services
N.A.I.C.S.: 541613

Reynolds Outdoor Media   (1)
3838 Oak Lawn Ave Ste 606, Dallas, TX 75219
Tel.: (214) 219-7400
Web Site: http://www.reynoldsoutdoor.com
Outdoor Advertising
N.A.I.C.S.: 541850

Scott Reynolds (Owner)

OUTLOOK THERAPEUTICS, INC.

111 S Wood Ave Unit 100, Iselin, NJ 08830
Tel.: (609) 619-3990   DE
Web Site:
  https://www.outlooktherapeutics.com
Year Founded: 2010
OTLK—(NASDAQ)
Assets: $32,300,601
Liabilities: $46,738,378
Net Worth: ($14,437,777)
Earnings: ($58,982,668)
Emp.: 24
Fiscal Year-end: 09/30/23
Biopharmaceutical Mfr
N.A.I.C.S.: 325414
Ralph H. Thurman (Exec Chm)
Jeffrey Evanson (Chief Comml Officer)
Lawrence A. Kenyon (CFO, Treas, Sec & Exec VP)
Jedd Comiskey (Sr VP & Head-Europe)
C. Russell Trenary III (Pres & CEO)

OUTSET MEDICAL, INC.

3052 Orchard Dr, San Jose, CA 95134
Tel.: (669) 231-8200   DE
Web Site:
  https://www.outsetmedical.com
Year Founded: 2003
OM—(NASDAQ)
Rev.: $130,376,000
Assets: $313,801,000
Liabilities: $190,915,000
Net Worth: $122,886,000
Earnings: ($172,797,000)
Emp.: 480
Fiscal Year-end: 12/31/23
Medical Equipment Mfr
N.A.I.C.S.: 334510
Michael Aragon (Chief Medical Officer)
Nicole Shannon (Dir-Mktg Comm)
Nabeel Ahmed (Principal Acctg Officer)
Stacey Porter (Chief People Officer)
Leslie L. Trigg (Chm, Pres & CEO)

OVID THERAPEUTICS INC.

441 9th Ave, New York, NY 10001
Tel.: (646) 661-7661   DE
Web Site: https://www.ovidrx.com
Year Founded: 2014
OVID—(NASDAQ)
Rev.: $1,502,748
Assets: $155,265,814
Liabilities: $22,993,250
Net Worth: $132,272,564
Earnings: ($54,169,029)
Emp.: 44
Fiscal Year-end: 12/31/22
Biotechnology Research & Development Services
N.A.I.C.S.: 541713
Claude Nicaise (Head-Rare Disease Strategy)
Jeffrey A. Rona (Chief Bus & Fin Officer)
Zhong Zhong (Chief Scientific Officer)
Manoj Malhotra (Chief Medical Officer)
Julia Tsai (Sr VP)
Simon Kelner (Chief HR Officer)
Todd Baumgartner (Sr VP)
Jeremy Max Levin (Chm & CEO)
Margaret Alexander (Pres & COO)

OVINTIV INC.

Ste 1700 370 17th St, Denver, CO 80202
Tel.: (303) 623-2300   DE
Web Site: https://www.ovintiv.com
Year Founded: 2020
OVV—(NYSE)
Rev.: $10,883,000,000
Assets: $19,987,000,000
Liabilities: $9,617,000,000
Net Worth: $10,370,000,000
Earnings: $2,085,000,000
Emp.: 1,743
Fiscal Year-end: 12/31/23
Holding Company; Natural Gas Exploration Services
N.A.I.C.S.: 551112
Corey D. Code (CFO & Exec VP)
Brendan M. McCracken (Pres & CEO)
Gregory D. Givens (COO & Exec VP)
Rachel M. Moore (Exec VP-Corp Svcs)
Meghan Eilers (Gen Counsel, Sec & Exec VP)

Subsidiaries:

Encana Corporation   (1)
Suite 4400 500 Centre Street SE, PO Box 2850, Calgary, T2P 2S5, AB, Canada
Tel.: (403) 645-2000
Oil & Gas Exploration, Production, Gas Storage & Processing
N.A.I.C.S.: 211120

Subsidiary (US):

Alenco Inc.   (2)
16201 W 110th St, Lenexa, KS 66219
Tel.: (913) 686-6166
Web Site: https://www.alenconline.com
Natural Gas Extraction Services
N.A.I.C.S.: 211130

Branch (Domestic):

Encana Corporation - Eastern Canada Office   (2)
1701 Hollis Street Suite 700, Halifax, B3J 3M8, NS, Canada
Tel.: (902) 422-4500
Oil & Gas Exploration, Production, Pipelining & Gas Storage & Processing
N.A.I.C.S.: 211120

Subsidiary (Non-US):

Encana Global Holdings S.a r.l.   (2)
8-10 Avenue De La Gare, 1610, Luxembourg, Luxembourg
Tel.: (352) 26649773
Holding Company
N.A.I.C.S.: 551112

Encana Oil & Gas (USA) Inc.   (2)
Tel.: (303) 623-2300
Web Site: http://www.encana.com
Sales Range: $750-799.9 Million
Emp.: 1,400
Oil & Gas Exploration & Production
N.A.I.C.S.: 211120

Subsidiary (Domestic):

Encana Marketing (USA) Inc.   (3)
370 - 17th St Ste 1700, Denver, CO 80202
Tel.: (303) 623-2300
Sales Range: $500-549.9 Million
Emp.: 991
Natural Gas Distribution Services
N.A.I.C.S.: 221210

OWENS & MINOR, INC.

9120 Lockwood Blvd, Mechanicsville, VA 23116
Tel.: (804) 723-7000   VA
Web Site: https://www.owens-minor.com
Year Founded: 1882
OMI—(NYSE)
Rev.: $10,333,967,000
Assets: $5,093,322,000
Liabilities: $4,169,156,000
Net Worth: $924,166,000
Earnings: ($41,301,000)
Emp.: 13,700
Fiscal Year-end: 12/31/23

Holding Company; Medical & Surgical Supplies Distr
N.A.I.C.S.: 551112
Edward A. Pesicka (Pres & CEO)
Andrew G. Long (CEO-Products & Healthcare Svcs & Exec VP)
Alex Jost (Dir-IR)
Heath H. Galloway (Corp Counsel, Sec & Exec VP)
Perry A. Bernocchi (Exec VP)
Michael W. Lowry (Chief Acctg Officer)
Jonathan A. Leon (CFO & Exec VP)

Subsidiaries:

ArcRoyal Unlimited   (1)
Virginia Road, Kells, Meath, Ireland
Tel.: (353) 46 928 0100
Web Site: https://www.arcroyal.ie
Medical Equipment Mfr
N.A.I.C.S.: 339112

Byram Healthcare Centers, Inc.   (1)
120 Bloomingdale Rd Ste 301, White Plains, NY 10605-1518
Tel.: (914) 286-2000
Web Site: https://www.byramhealthcare.com
Medical Equipment Distr
N.A.I.C.S.: 423450
Nicholas Piecora (CIO)
Richard Adams (VP)
Rick Livingston (VP-HR)
Perry Bernocchi (CEO)
Marcel Overweel (CFO)
Marianne Hines (Exec VP-Sales-Marketing)
W. Milligan (VP-Natl)
Jeffrey Mignone (Sr VP)
John W. Ras (Chief Compliance Officer)
Judy Manning (Sr VP-Marketing)
Michelle L. Knowles (Sec & Gen Counsel)
Neel Vadhan (VP-Purchasing)
Perry Bernocchi (CEO)
Marcel Overweel (CFO)
Marianne Hines (Exec VP-Sales-Marketing)
W. Milligan (VP-Natl)
Jeffrey Mignone (Sr VP)
John W. Ras (Chief Compliance Officer)
Judy Manning (Sr VP-Marketing)
Michelle L. Knowles (Sec & Gen Counsel)
Neel Vadhan (VP-Purchasing)
Perry Bernocchi (CEO)
Marcel Overweel (CFO)
Marianne Hines (Exec VP-Sales-Marketing)
W. Milligan (VP-Natl)
Jeffrey Mignone (Sr VP)
John W. Ras (Chief Compliance Officer)
Judy Manning (Sr VP-Marketing)
Michelle L. Knowles (Sec & Gen Counsel)
Neel Vadhan (VP-Purchasing)
Steve Ouellette (Sr VP)
Rebecca Quinones (VP)
Brian Worthington (Sr VP)

Byram Healthcare Centers, Inc.   (1)
500 Apgar Dr Ste 2, Somerset, NJ 08873-1156
Tel.: (732) 302-1600
Medical Device Distr
N.A.I.C.S.: 423450
Victor M. Perez (Mgr-Pur)

Lofta, Inc.   (1)
9225 Brown Deer Rd, San Diego, CA 92121
Web Site: https://www.lofta.com
Skin Care Product Mfr & Distr
N.A.I.C.S.: 325620

Medical Action Industries Inc.   (1)
500 Expy Dr S, Brentwood, NY 11717
Tel.: (631) 231-4600
Web Site:
  https://www.medicalaction.rhoadsdev.com
Disposable Medical Products Mfr
N.A.I.C.S.: 339113

Subsidiary (Domestic):

Avid Medical, Inc.   (2)
9000 Westmont Dr Stonehouse Commerce Park, Toano, VA 23168
Tel.: (757) 566-3510
Web Site: https://www.avidmedical.com
Medical Equipment Distr & Sls

Owens & Minor, Inc.—(Continued)
N.A.I.C.S.: 339112

Movianto Belgium NV (1)
Waterkeringstraat 1, 9320, Erembodegem, Belgium
Tel.: (32) 53859000
Logistics Consulting Servies
N.A.I.C.S.: 541614

Movianto Ceska republika sro (1)
Podoli 78e, Podoli, 66403, Prague, Czech Republic
Tel.: (420) 548134400
Logistics Consulting Servies
N.A.I.C.S.: 541614

Movianto Espana SL (1)
C/ Helena Rubinstein 4 Pol Ind El Lomo, Getafe, 28906, Madrid, Spain
Tel.: (34) 918753504
Web Site: https://movianto.com
Emp.: 140
Medical Equipment Distr
N.A.I.C.S.: 423450

Movianto France SAS (1)
Tel.: (33) 134077500
Logistics Consulting Servies
N.A.I.C.S.: 541614
Nicolas Richer (Pres)

Movianto Nordic Aps (1)
Ventrupvej 27, 2670, Greve, Denmark
Tel.: (45) 43300200
Web Site: https://movianto.com
Emp.: 60
Medical Equipment Distr
N.A.I.C.S.: 423450
Marina Steensen (Mng Dir)

Movianto Schweiz GmbH (1)
Laupenstrasse 45, 3176, Neuenegg, Switzerland
Tel.: (41) 317441400
Web Site: https://movianto.com
Medical Equipment Distr
N.A.I.C.S.: 423450
Thomas Creuzberger (Mng Dir)

Movianto Slovensko sro (1)
Dialnicna cesta 4431/14a, 903 01, Senec, Slovakia
Tel.: (421) 232334211
Web Site: https://movianto.com
Emp.: 30
Medical Equipment Distr
N.A.I.C.S.: 423450
Jana Krcalova (Key Acct Mgr & Mgr-Quality)
Roman Harviscak (Mng Dir)

Movianto Transport Solutions Ltd. (1)
1 Progress Park, Bedford, MK42 9XE, Bedfordshire, United Kingdom
Tel.: (44) 1234248603
Freight Forwarding Services
N.A.I.C.S.: 488510
David Evans (Dir-Grp Transport)
David Clark (Mgr-Ops)

Movianto UK Ltd. (1)
1 Progress Park, Bedford, MK42 9XE, United Kingdom
Tel.: (44) 1234248500
Web Site: https://movianto.com
Medical Equipment Distr
N.A.I.C.S.: 423450
Paul Wilkinson (Pres)

O&M Halvard France (1)
4-6 Rue des Chauffours, PO Box 40115, 95000, Cergy, Cedex, France
Tel.: (33) 805542751
Healtcare Services
N.A.I.C.S.: 621491

O&M Halyard Health India Private Limited (1)
World Trade Center Tower 1 Unit 308, Kharadi, Pune, 411014, Maharashtra, India
Tel.: (91) 2046845500
Web Site: https://www.halyardhealth.in
Hospital & Health Care Services
N.A.I.C.S.: 622110

O&M Halyard Japan GK (1)
The Front Tower Shiba Koen 2-6-3, Minato, Tokyo, 105-0011, Japan

Tel.: (81) 345654576
Healtcare Services
N.A.I.C.S.: 621491

O&M-Movianto Nederland B.V. (1)
Keltenweg 70, 5342 LP, Oss, Netherlands
Tel.: (31) 412406420
Web Site: http://www.movianto.com
Logistics Consulting Servies
N.A.I.C.S.: 541614
Patrick Verkuijlen (Mng Dir)
Eric Willems (Mgr-Commercial)
Eric Willems (Mgr-Commercial)

Owens & Minor Distribution, Inc. (1)
9120 Lockwood Blvd, Mechanicsville, VA 23116 (100%)
Tel.: (804) 723-7000
Web Site: https://www.owens-minor.com
Sales Range: $5-14.9 Billion
Medical & Surgical Supplies Distr & Logistics Services; Supply Management & Consulting Services
N.A.I.C.S.: 423450
James L. Bierman (Pres & CEO)

Owens & Minor Global Services (1)
Block 10-4 Blanchardstown Corporate Park, Ballycoolin, Dublin, D15 X98N, Ireland
Tel.: (353) 14869400
Health Care Srvices
N.A.I.C.S.: 621610

OWENS CORNING

1 Owens Corning Pkwy, Toledo, OH 43659
Tel.: (419) 248-8000 DE
Web Site:
https://www.owenscorning.com
Year Founded: 1938
OC—(NYSE)
Rev.: $9,677,000,000
Assets: $11,237,000,000
Liabilities: $6,052,000,000
Net Worth: $5,185,000,000
Earnings: $1,196,000,000
Emp.: 18,000
Fiscal Year-end: 12/31/23
Glass Composites & Building Materials Systems Mfr
N.A.I.C.S.: 324122
Todd W. Fister (CFO & Exec VP)
Gunner S. Smith (Pres-Roofing)
Paula Russell (Chief HR Officer & Exec VP)
Jose Mendez-Andlno (Chief R&D Officer & Exec VP)
Nicolas Del Monaco (Pres-Insulation)
Brian D. Chambers (Chm, Pres & CEO)

Subsidiaries:

AS Paroc (1)
Parnu mnt 158, EE-11317, Tallinn, Estonia
Tel.: (372) 6518100
Insulation Products Distr
N.A.I.C.S.: 423330

American Rockwool, Inc. (1)
820 E Nash St, Spring Hope, NC 27882
Tel.: (252) 563-2111
Glass Composites & Building Materials Mfr
N.A.I.C.S.: 324122

Amiantit Fiberglass Industrial, Ltd. (1)
PO Box 589, Dammam, 31421, Saudi Arabia (90%)
Tel.: (966) 38471500
Web Site: https://www.amiantit.com
Sales Range: $800-899.9 Million
Emp.: 3,500
Mfr of Fiberglass Products
N.A.I.C.S.: 327993

Arabian Fiberglass Insulation Co. (1)
6581 Unit No 1, PO Box 1289, Dammam, 34325 - 2799, Saudi Arabia (49%)
Tel.: (966) 133313333
Web Site: https://www.afico.com.sa
Sales Range: $50-74.9 Million
Emp.: 107
Mfr of Fiberglass Products
N.A.I.C.S.: 327993

CDC Corporation (1)
800 Gustafson Rd, Ladysmith, WI 54848
Tel.: (715) 532-5548
Web Site:
http://www.conweddesignscape.com
Sales Range: $25-49.9 Million
Emp.: 80
Custom Acoustical Walls, Ceilings & Related Products Mfr
N.A.I.C.S.: 561790

Cultured Stone Corporation (1)
Hwy 29 N Tower Rd, Napa, CA 94559
Tel.: (707) 255-1727
Web Site: http://www.culturedstone.com
Sales Range: $150-199.9 Million
Emp.: 86
Stone Mfr
N.A.I.C.S.: 325211

Deutsche Foamglas GmbH (1)
Itterpark 1, 40724, Hilden, Germany
Tel.: (49) 2103249570
Web Site: https://www.foamglas.com
Foam Glass Distr
N.A.I.C.S.: 423330

European Owens Corning Fiberglas SPRL (1)
166 Chaussee de la Hulpe, 1170, Brussels, Belgium
Tel.: (32) 26748211
Web Site:
http://www.ocvreinforcements.com
Sales of Fiberglass
N.A.I.C.S.: 423390

FiberTEK Insulation LLC (1)
925 S 4400 W, Salt Lake City, UT 84104
Web Site: https://www.fibertekinsulation.com
Sales Range: $25-49.9 Million
Emp.: 100
Mineral Wool Mfr
N.A.I.C.S.: 327993

Foamglas (Italia) SRL (1)
Via Giuseppe Parini 10, 20842, Besana in Brianza, MB, Italy
Tel.: (39) 036296419
Web Site: https://www.foamglas.com
Foam Glass Distr
N.A.I.C.S.: 423330

Foamglas (Nordic) AB (1)
Hallebergsvagen 7, 443 60, Stenkullen, Sweden
Tel.: (46) 30237856
Web Site: https://www.foamglas.com
Foam Glass Distr
N.A.I.C.S.: 423330

InterWrap Corp. Pvt. Ltd. (1)
No 602 Antariksh Thakur House Makwana Hoad Marol Andheri East, Mumbai, 400 059, Maharashtra, India
Tel.: (91) 9867557853
Roofing Material Distr
N.A.I.C.S.: 423330

International Packaging Products Pvt. Ltd. (1)
Survey No 380/2 Village Dapada Khanwel Road, Silvassa, 396 230, Dadra & Nagar Haveli, India
Tel.: (91) 8048602114
Roofing Material Distr
N.A.I.C.S.: 423330

LMP Impianti Srl (1)
Via Torino 101, Volpiano, Italy (100%)
Tel.: (39) 0119951040
Web Site: http://www.lmpimpianti.it
Sales Range: $1-9.9 Million
Emp.: 21
Mfr Industrial Machinery
N.A.I.C.S.: 333248

Masonite International Corporation (1)
2771 Rutherford Road, Concord, L4K 2N6, ON, Canada
Tel.: (813) 877-2726
Web Site: http://www.masonite.com
Rev.: $2,891,687,000
Assets: $2,248,178,000
Liabilities: $1,505,396,000
Net Worth: $742,782,000
Earnings: $214,233,000
Emp.: 10,000
Fiscal Year-end: 01/01/2023

Holding Company; Interior & Exterior Doorsr Mfr
N.A.I.C.S.: 551112
Katie Shellabarger (Chief Acctg Officer & VP)
Clare R. Doyle (Chief Sustainability Officer & Sr VP)
Robert A. Paxton (Sr VP-HR)
Christopher Ball (Pres)
Dan Shirk (CIO & Sr VP)
Cory Sorice (Chief Innovation Officer & Sr VP)
Jennifer Renaud (CMO & Sr VP)
Richard Leland (Treas & VP-Fin)
Vicky Philemon (Sr VP & Gen Mgr-Europe)
Marcus Devlin (Dir-IR)
Patrick D. Brisley (Chief Acctg Officer)
James Pelletier (Gen Counsel)

Subsidiary (Non-US):

Batimetal S.A.S. (2)
Voie des Allies, 14440, Douvres-la-Delivrande, France
Tel.: (33) 231363136
Plastic Door Mfr
N.A.I.C.S.: 326199

Subsidiary (US):

Bridgewater Wholesalers, Inc. (2)
210 Industrial Pkwy, Branchburg, NJ 08876
Web Site: https://www.bwi-distribution.com
Lumber, Plywood, Millwork & Wood Panel Merchant Whslr
N.A.I.C.S.: 423310

Subsidiary (Domestic):

Crown Door Corp. (2)
31083 Wheel Ave, Abbotsford, V2T 6H1, BC, Canada
Tel.: (604) 504-1658
Web Site: https://www.crowndoor.ca
Door Distr
N.A.I.C.S.: 423310

Subsidiary (US):

Dominance Industries, Inc. (2)
610 W State Hwy 3 Unit A, Broken Bow, OK 74728
Tel.: (580) 584-6247
Web Site:
https://www.panpacificproducts.com
Emp.: 130
Door Mfr & Distr
N.A.I.C.S.: 332510

Subsidiary (Non-US):

Door-Stop International Limited (2)
Export Drive, Huthwaite, NG17 6AF, Notts, United Kingdom
Tel.: (44) 1623446336
Web Site: https://www.door-stop.co.uk
Metal Window & Door Mfr
N.A.I.C.S.: 332321

Subsidiary (US):

Eger Properties (2)
1 N Dale Mabry Hwy Ste 950, Tampa, FL 33609
Tel.: (813) 877-2726
Door Distr
N.A.I.C.S.: 423310

Endura Products Inc. (2)
8817 W Market St, Colfax, NC 27235-7235
Web Site: https://www.enduraproducts.com
Metal Window & Door Mfr
N.A.I.C.S.: 332321
Katie Shellabarger (Interim CFO)
Charlie Headrick (Product Mgr-Dev)

Florida Made Door Co. (2)
4406 Madison Industrial Ln Ste 107, Tampa, FL 33619
Tel.: (813) 261-5550
Web Site: https://www.floridamadedoor.com
Door Mfr & Distr
N.A.I.C.S.: 321911

Subsidiary (Non-US):

Hickman Industries Limited (2)
Sutherland Sawmills Sutherland Avenue Bilston Road, Wolverhampton, WV2 2JQ, West Midlands, United Kingdom
Tel.: (44) 1902352535

Web Site:
https://www.nationalhickman.co.uk
Building Materials Distr
N.A.I.C.S.: 423310

Magna Foremost Sdn Bhd (2)
814 Jepak Industrial Estate, Tatau, 97013,
Bintulu, Sarawak, Malaysia
Tel.: (60) 86316104
Door Distr
N.A.I.C.S.: 423210
Erwin Doble (Mgr-Maintenance)

Magri S.A.S. (2)
Route De Pannecieres, PO Box 20, Thignonville, Sermaises, 45300, France
Tel.: (33) 238397999
Plastic Door Mfr
N.A.I.C.S.: 326199

Masonite CZ spol S.R.O. (2)
Hruskove Dvory 82, 586 01, Jihlava, Czech
Republic
Tel.: (420) 567121428
Web Site: https://www.doornite.cz
Door Mfr & Distr
N.A.I.C.S.: 332510

Subsidiary (Domestic):

Masonite Canada Corporation (2)
2771 Rutherford Rd, Concord, L4K 2N6,
ON, Canada (100%)
Tel.: (905) 670-6500
Web Site: https://www.masonite.com
Door, Door Component & Door Entry System Mfr
N.A.I.C.S.: 321911

Plant (Domestic):

Masonite Canada Corp. - Yarrow (3)
41916 Yarrow Central Road, PO Box 4219,
Chilliwack, V2R 5E7, BC, Canada
Tel.: (604) 823-6223
Web Site: https://www.masonite.com
Sales Range: $50-74.9 Million
Emp.: 130
Wood & Steel Doors, Wood Mouldings
N.A.I.C.S.: 321911

Subsidiary (Non-US):

Masonite Chile Holdings (2)
Ruta Q-50 KM 1 5, Cabrero, Biobio, Chile
Tel.: (56) 432404400
Emp.: 500
Holding Company
N.A.I.C.S.: 551112

Masonite Chile S.A. (2)
Ruta Q-50 KM 1 5, Region del Biobio, Cabrero, Biobio, Chile
Tel.: (56) 432404400
Emp.: 120
Door Distr
N.A.I.C.S.: 423310

Subsidiary (US):

Masonite Corporation (2)
1242 E 5th Ave, Tampa, FL 33605 (100%)
Tel.: (813) 877-2726
Web Site: https://www.masonite.com
Rev.: $60,000,000
Emp.: 140
Mfr of Steel Doors & Door Frames
N.A.I.C.S.: 321911
Glenwood E. Coulter Jr. (Exec VP-Global
Ops & Europe)

Subsidiary (Domestic):

Algoma Hardwoods, Inc. (3)
1001 Perry St, Algoma, WI 54201
Tel.: (920) 487-5221
Web Site: https://www.masonite.com
Sales Range: $25-49.9 Million
Emp.: 400
Wood Door Mfr
N.A.I.C.S.: 321911

Marshfield DoorSystems, Inc. (3)
1401 E 4th St, Marshfield, WI 54449-7780
Tel.: (715) 384-2141
Web Site: http://www.marshfielddoors.com
Sales Range: $100-124.9 Million
Wood Door Mfr
N.A.I.C.S.: 321911

Plant (Domestic):

Masonite Corp. - Corning (3)
22885 S Ave, Corning, CA 96021
Tel.: (530) 824-2121
Sales Range: $25-49.9 Million
Emp.: 71
Wood Door Mfr
N.A.I.C.S.: 321911

Masonite Corp. - Dickson (3)
1 Premdor Dr, Dickson, TN 37055
Tel.: (615) 446-6220
Web Site: https://www.masonite.com
Sales Range: $50-74.9 Million
Emp.: 120
Wood Door Mfr
N.A.I.C.S.: 321911

Masonite Corp. - Greenville (3)
6308 Industrial Dr, Greenville, TX 75402-5712
Tel.: (903) 454-9500
Web Site: https://www.masonite.com
Sales Range: $75-99.9 Million
Door Mfr
N.A.I.C.S.: 321911

Masonite Corp. - North Platte (3)
1120 Industrial Ave, North Platte, NE 69101
Tel.: (308) 534-1102
Web Site: https://www.masonite.com
Sales Range: $25-49.9 Million
Emp.: 100
Wood Door Mfr
N.A.I.C.S.: 321911

Masonite Corp. - Stanley (3)
280 Donovan Dr, Stanley, VA 22851
Tel.: (540) 778-2211
Web Site: https://www.masonite.com
Wood Door Mfr
N.A.I.C.S.: 321911

Masonite Corp. - West Chicago (3)
1955 Powis Rd, West Chicago, IL 60185
Tel.: (630) 584-6330
Web Site: https://www.masonite.com
Sales Range: $25-49.9 Million
Emp.: 100
Door Product Research & Development;
Special Die Mfr
N.A.I.C.S.: 541715

Subsidiary (Domestic):

Mohawk Flush Doors, Inc. (3)
980 Point Township Dr, Northumberland, PA
17857
Tel.: (570) 473-3557
Web Site: https://www.mohawkdoors.com
Sales Range: $75-99.9 Million
Wood Door Mfr
N.A.I.C.S.: 321911

Subsidiary (Non-US):

Masonite Doors Private Ltd. (2)
S-6A Triveni Complex Sheikh Sarai Phase-I,
New Delhi, 110017, India
Tel.: (91) 1140534851
Door Mfr & Distr
N.A.I.C.S.: 332510

Masonite Ireland (2)
Saint Ann's Church of Ireland, Carrick-on-Shannon, Leitrim, Ireland
Tel.: (353) 719659500
Door Mfr & Distr
N.A.I.C.S.: 332510
Cormac Kearns (Mng Dir)

Performance Doorset Solutions, Inc. (2)
Greenvale Business Park Todmorden Road,
Littleborough, 0L15 9AZ, Lancashire, United
Kingdom
Tel.: (44) 1706370001
Web Site: https://www.pdsdoorsets.co.uk
Window & Door Mfr & Distr
N.A.I.C.S.: 321911

Premdor Crosby Limited (2)
Birthwaite Business Park Huddersfield
Road, Darton, Barnsley, S75 5JS, South
Yorkshire, United Kingdom
Tel.: (44) 8442090008
Metal Window & Door Mfr
N.A.I.C.S.: 332321

Premdor U.K. Holdings Limited (2)

Birthwaite Business Park Huddersfield
Road, Darton, Barnsley, S75 5JS, South
Yorkshire, United Kingdom
Tel.: (44) 1226383434
Holding Company
N.A.I.C.S.: 551112

Reseau Bois S.A.R.L. (2)
Avenue De L Industrie zone Industrielle Du
Martray, 14730, Giberville, France
Tel.: (33) 231725000
Door Distr
N.A.I.C.S.: 423310

Subsidiary (Domestic):

Sacopan, Inc. (2)
642 chemin du Moulin, Sacre-Coeur, Quebec, G0T 1Y0, QC, Canada
Tel.: (418) 236-1414
Web Site: https://www.sacopan.com
Door Mfr & Distr
N.A.I.C.S.: 332510
Marie-josee Gagne (Reg Dir-HR)
Marc-andre Bouchard (Supvr)
Guy Deschenes (Pres)
Richard R. Drouin (Sec)
Eddy Gap Franken (VP)
Russell T. Tiejema (CFO)
Steve St-Gelais (Pres)

Subsidiary (US):

Sierra Lumber, Inc. (2)
288 S Railroad Ave, Willcox, AZ 85643
Tel.: (520) 384-3352
Web Site: https://sierralumberllc.com
Hardware Store Services
N.A.I.C.S.: 444140

Subsidiary (Non-US):

Solidor Limited (2)
Meir Park Whittle Rd, Stoke-on-Trent, ST3
7TU, United Kingdom
Tel.: (44) 1782847300
Web Site: https://www.solidor.co.uk
Composite Door Mfr & Distr
N.A.I.C.S.: 321911

Subsidiary (US):

USA Wood Door, Inc. (2)
1475 Imperial Way, Thorofare, NJ 08086
Tel.: (856) 384-9663
Web Site: https://www.usawooddoor.com
Sales Range: $10-24.9 Million
Emp.: 50
Wood Door Mfr
N.A.I.C.S.: 321911
John Krause (Pres)

Subsidiary (Non-US):

Window Widgets LLP (2)
Unit C Quedgeley Trading Estate, Bristol,
GL2 4PA, Gloucester, United Kingdom
Tel.: (44) 1452300912
Web Site: https://www.windowwidgets.co.uk
Wood Window & Door Distr
N.A.I.C.S.: 423310

N.V. Owens-Corning S.A. (1)
Chaussee De La Hulpe 166, 1170, Brussels, Belgium (100%)
Tel.: (32) 26748320
Sales Range: $25-49.9 Million
Emp.: 25
Mfr Plant
N.A.I.C.S.: 327993

Northern Elastomeric, Inc. (1)
61 Pine Rd, Brentwood, NH 03833
Tel.: (603) 778-8899
Web Site: http://www.nei-act.com
Glass Composites & Building Materials Mfr
N.A.I.C.S.: 324122

OC Latin American Holdings GmbH (1)
Teinfaltstrsse 8/4, Vienna, 1010, Austria
Tel.: (43) 15339630
Holding Company
N.A.I.C.S.: 551112

OCV Chambery International (1)
767 quai des Allobroges, BP 929, 73009,
Chambery, Cedex, France
Tel.: (33) 479755000
Roofing & Insulation Whslr
N.A.I.C.S.: 423330

OCV Distribution Anz Pty Ltd (1)
635 Queensberry St, Melbourne, Australia
Tel.: (61) 393290111
Glass Composites & Building Materials Systems Mfr
N.A.I.C.S.: 327993

OCV Fabrics US, Inc. (1)
43 Bibber Pkwy, Brunswick, ME 04011
Tel.: (207) 729-7792
Glass Composites & Building Materials Systems Mfr
N.A.I.C.S.: 327993

Plant (Domestic):

Owens Corning OCV Technical Fabrics (2)
211 Randy Dr Arrowhead Industrial Park,
Wichita Falls, TX 76306 (100%)
Tel.: (940) 723-5998
Web Site:
http://www.ocvtechnicalfabrics.com
Sales Range: $25-49.9 Million
Emp.: 67
Technical Fabric Mfr
N.A.I.C.S.: 313210

OCV Mexico S. de R.L. de C.V. (1)
Coaxamalucan 502 Ciudad Industrial Xicohtencatl 1, Tetla de la Solidaridad, Tlaxcala,
90431, Mexico
Tel.: (52) 2414188600
Web Site: http://www.owenscorning.com
Emp.: 200
Glass Composites & Building Materials Mfr
N.A.I.C.S.: 324122

OCV Reinforcements (Hangzhou) Co., Ltd. (1)
343 Shenban Road, Gongshu District,
Hangzhou, 310022, China
Tel.: (86) 57188130808
Glass Products Mfr
N.A.I.C.S.: 327215

OCV Reinforcements Alcala Spain, S.L. (1)
Carretera Madrid-Barcelona km 34 5 Apdo
60, 28800, Alcala de Henares, Madrid,
Spain
Tel.: (34) 918855710
Web Site:
http://www.ocvreinforcements.com
Sales Range: $25-49.9 Million
Emp.: 100
Glass Products Mfr
N.A.I.C.S.: 327215

OEM Solutions (1)
2501 Nelson Miller Pkwy Ste 103, Louisville, KY 40223 (100%)
Tel.: (502) 394-5800
Sales Range: $25-49.9 Million
Emp.: 35
Provider of OEM Solutions
N.A.I.C.S.: 327993

Holding (Non-US):

Owens Corning - OEM Solutions Group (2)
11 Spalding Dr, Brantford, N3T 5R7, ON,
Canada (100%)
Tel.: (519) 752-5436
Sales Range: $25-49.9 Million
Emp.: 35
Mfr of Motor Vehicles Parts & Accessories
N.A.I.C.S.: 336340

Owens Corning (Shanghai) Trading Co., Ltd. (1)
Pudong Kerry Parkside 1155 Fang Dian Rd
Pudong, No 710 Dongfang Ro, Shanghai,
201204, China
Tel.: (86) 2161019666
Web Site: http://www.owenscorning.com
Emp.: 150
Building Materials Mfr
N.A.I.C.S.: 444180

Owens Corning Australia Pty Ltd (1)
Suite 2 90-94 Tram Road, Doncaster, 3108,
VIC, Australia
Tel.: (61) 398513000
Web Site: http://www.owenscorning.com
Sales Range: $25-49.9 Million
Emp.: 2
Glass Composites & Building Materials Systems Mfr

Owens Corning—(Continued)

N.A.I.C.S.: 327993

Owens Corning Canada GP Inc. (1)
245 York Road, Guelph, N1E 3G4, ON, Canada
Tel.: (519) 823-7280
Building Materials Mfr
N.A.I.C.S.: 236220

Owens Corning Composites (Beijing) Co., Ltd. (1)
Doudian Mailbox 293 Fang Shan District, Beijing, 102402, China
Tel.: (86) 1080332785
Glass Composites & Building Materials Mfr
N.A.I.C.S.: 324122

Owens Corning Composites (China) Co., Ltd. (1)
118 Hongda Road Yuhang Economic & Development Zone, Hangzhou, 311100, China
Tel.: (86) 57189285271
Glass Composites & Building Materials Mfr
N.A.I.C.S.: 324122

Owens Corning Fiberglas A.S. Limitada (1)
Avenida Brasil 2567 Distrito Industrial, 13505-600, Rio Claro, 13505-600, SP, Brazil
Tel.: (55) 1935359315
Fiber Glass Product Distr
N.A.I.C.S.: 423990
Reinaldo Schlittler *(Coord-Maintenance Projects)*

Owens Corning Fiberglas France (1)
Zone Industrielle Voie N1, 30290, Laudun-l'Ardoise, France
Tel.: (33) 466903838
Flat Glass Product Distr
N.A.I.C.S.: 423390

Owens Corning Holdings Holland B.V. (1)
Laan Van Westenenk 5, Apeldoorn, 7336 AZ, Gelderland, Netherlands
Tel.: (31) 555386386
Holding Company
N.A.I.C.S.: 551112

Owens Corning Japan LLC (1)
5th floor Meikoji Building New Building 2-5-16, Kanda Nishikicho Chiyoda-ku, Tokyo, 101-0054, Japan
Tel.: (81) 363654300
Web Site: https://www.owenscorning.com
Residential & Commercial Building Materials, Glass Fiber Reinforcements & Engineered Materials Mfr
N.A.I.C.S.: 313310

Owens Corning Korea (1)
18F Ilsong Building Teheran ro 507, Seoul, 135-880, Korea (South) (70%)
Tel.: (82) 220507492
Web Site: http://www.owenscorning.co.kr
Sales Range: $125-149.9 Million
Mfr & Retailer of Glass Fiber Products
N.A.I.C.S.: 327212
H. P. Kim *(Mng Dir)*

Owens Corning Mexico S. de RL de C.V. (1)
Av Acueducto 459 Col Zacatenco, 07360, Mexico, DF, Mexico
Tel.: (52) 50896700
Web Site:
http://www.ocvreinforcements.com
Glass Reinforcement Products Mfr
N.A.I.C.S.: 327211

Owens Corning Netherland (1)
Laan Van Westenenk 5, 7336 AZ, Apeldoorn, Netherlands (100%)
Tel.: (31) 555386386
Web Site: http://www.owenscorning.com
Sales Range: $50-74.9 Million
Emp.: 140
Mfr Plant
N.A.I.C.S.: 327993

Owens-Corning (Guangzhou) Fiberglas Co. Ltd. (1)
No 1 Xiayuan Rd Dongji Industri, Guangzhou, 510730, China (90%)
Tel.: (86) 20822198
Sales Range: $150-199.9 Million
Thermal & Acoustical Insulation Mfr & Distr
N.A.I.C.S.: 423330

Owens-Corning (India) Limited (1)
7th Floor Alpha Towers Hiranandani Garden, Powai, Mumbai, 400076, India (50%)
Tel.: (91) 2266681700
Web Site:
http://www.owenscorningindia.com
Sales Range: $300-349.9 Million
Mfr, Market & Sell Advanced Composite Materials
N.A.I.C.S.: 322219

Owens-Corning Canada (1)
3450 McNicoll Ave, Scarborough, M1V 1Z5, ON, Canada (100%)
Tel.: (416) 292-4000
Web Site: http://www.owenscorning.com
Sales Range: $750-799.9 Million
Emp.: 1,000
Mfr of Glass-Fiber Materials & Polyester Resins
N.A.I.C.S.: 325211

Subsidiary (Domestic):

InterWrap, Inc. (2)
7163 Beatty Drive, Mission, V2V 6C4, BC, Canada
Tel.: (778) 945-2888
Web Site: http://www.interwrap.com
Packaging Products Mfr
N.A.I.C.S.: 322220

Subsidiary (US):

Interwrap Corp. (3)
6555 Fain Blvd, Charleston, SC 29456
Tel.: (843) 553-2996
Web Site: http://www.interwrap.com
Packaging Products Mfr
N.A.I.C.S.: 322220

Owens-Corning Fiberglass France S.A. (1)
Zone Industrielle Voie N1, 30290, Laudun-l'Ardoise, France (100%)
Tel.: (33) 46 690 3838
Web Site:
https://www.ocvreinforcements.com
Sales Range: $125-149.9 Million
Emp.: 300
Sales Office
N.A.I.C.S.: 444180

Subsidiary (Domestic):

Owens-Corning Composite Solutions (2)
767 quai des Allobroges, Chambery, 73009, France
Tel.: (33) 479755300
Web Site: http://www.ocvreinforements.com
Sales Range: $125-149.9 Million
Supplies Products for Reinforcement of High Performance Composites
N.A.I.C.S.: 541330

Owens-Corning Ontario Holdings Inc. (1)
3 Robert Speck Pkwy Ste 800, Mississauga, L4Z 2G5, ON, Canada
Sales Range: $250-299.9 Million
Holding Company
N.A.I.C.S.: 551112

Owens-Corning Veil U.K. Limited (1)
Hare Park Ln, Liversedge, WF15 8AA, W Yorkshire, United Kingdom (100%)
Tel.: (44) 1274863329
Sales Range: $25-49.9 Million
Emp.: 81
Mfr of Fiberglass Products
N.A.I.C.S.: 327993

Paroc AB (1)
Bruksgatan 2, 541 86, Skovde, Sweden
Tel.: (46) 500469000
Web Site: https://www.paroc.se
Insulation Product Mfr
N.A.I.C.S.: 327993
Elisabeth Andersson *(Mgr-Customer Svc)*

Paroc GmbH (1)
Heidenkampsweg 51, 20097, Hamburg, Germany
Tel.: (49) 40334960000
Web Site: https://www.paroc.de
Insulation Product Mfr
N.A.I.C.S.: 327993

Paroc Group Oy (1)
Energiakuja 3, PO Box 240, 00181, Helsinki, Finland
Tel.: (358) 468768000
Web Site: https://www.paroc.com
Insulation Product Mfr
N.A.I.C.S.: 327993

Paroc Limited (1)
70 Tradewind Square Liberty Place, East Village, Liverpool, L1 5BG, United Kingdom
Tel.: (44) 1706365568
Web Site: https://www.paroc.co.uk
Insulation Product Mfr
N.A.I.C.S.: 327993
Craig Treanor *(Mgr-Technical)*

Paroc Oy AB (1)
Skrabbolentie 14-16, 21600, Pargas, Finland
Tel.: (358) 468768000
Insulation Products Distr
N.A.I.C.S.: 423330

Paroc Polska Sp. z o.o. (1)
ul Gnieznienska 4, 62-240, Trzemeszno, Poland
Tel.: (48) 614682190
Web Site: https://www.paroc.pl
Insulation Product Mfr
N.A.I.C.S.: 327993

Pittsburgh Corning (United Kingdom) Limited (1)
31-35 Kirby Street, London, EC1N 8TE, United Kingdom
Tel.: (44) 3301221638
Web Site: http://uk.foamglas.com
Cellular Glass Insulation Material Distr
N.A.I.C.S.: 423330

Pittsburgh Corning CR, S.R.O. (1)
IP Verne Prumyslova 3, 431 51, Klasterec nad Ohri, Czech Republic
Tel.: (420) 474359989
Web Site: https://www.foamglas.com
Foam Glass Mfr & Distr
N.A.I.C.S.: 327993

Pittsburgh Corning France (1)
Centre d'Affaires Renaissance Batiment D 8 rue de la Renaissance, 92160, Antony, France
Tel.: (33) 158351790
Web Site: https://www.foamglas.com
Foam Glass Distr
N.A.I.C.S.: 423330

Pittsburgh Corning Gesellschaft m.b.h. (1)
Schillerstrasse 12, 4020, Linz, Austria
Tel.: (43) 732730963
Web Site: https://www.foamglas.com
Foam Glass Distr
N.A.I.C.S.: 423330

Pittsburgh Corning Nederland B.V. (1)
De Limiet 15 B, 4131 NR, Vianen, Netherlands
Tel.: (31) 306035241
Web Site: https://www.foamglas.com
Foam Glass Distr
N.A.I.C.S.: 423330

Pittsburgh Corning Suisse SA (1)
Route De Denges 28 D, 1027, Lonay, Switzerland
Tel.: (41) 218030552
Foam Glass Distr
N.A.I.C.S.: 423330

Pittsburgh Corning, LLC (1)
1 Owens Corning Pkwy, Toledo, OH 43659
Web Site: http://www.foamglas.com
Glass Insulator Mfr
N.A.I.C.S.: 327212

Subsidiary (Non-US):

Pittsburgh Corning Europe, N.V. (2)
Albertkade 1, 3980, Tessenderlo, Belgium (50%)
Tel.: (32) 13661721
Web Site: http://int.foamglas.com
Cellular Glass Insulation Mfr
N.A.I.C.S.: 327211

SIA Paroc (1)
Vienibas gatve 109, Riga, 1058, Latvia
Tel.: (371) 67375070

Web Site: https://www.paroc.lv
Insulation Product Mfr
N.A.I.C.S.: 327993

Thermafiber, Inc. (1)
3711 Mill St, Wabash, IN 46992
Tel.: (260) 563-2111
Web Site: https://www.thermafiber.com
Mineral Wool Mfr
N.A.I.C.S.: 327993
Michael J. Williams *(Exec VP)*

Thin-Wall, LLC (1)
939 Hillcrest Dr 68434, Seward, NE 68434
Tel.: (402) 641-7667
Web Site: https://www.thin-wall.com
Engineering Support Services
N.A.I.C.S.: 541330

Transandina de Comercio S.A. (1)
Valenzuela Castillo 10, Region Metropolitana, Santiago, 7500722, Chile
Tel.: (56) 24218070
Web Site: http://www.transaco.cl
Glass Composites & Building Materials Mfr
N.A.I.C.S.: 324122

UAB Paroc (1)
Savanoriu 124, 03153, Vilnius, Lithuania
Tel.: (370) 52740000
Insulation Products Distr
N.A.I.C.S.: 423330

OWLET, INC.
3300 N Ashton Blvd Ste 300, Lehi, UT 84043 DE
Web Site: https://owletcare.com
Year Founded: 2020
OWLT—(NYSE)
Rev.: $69,202,000
Assets: $58,104,000
Liabilities: $68,739,000
Net Worth: ($10,635,000)
Earnings: ($79,336,000)
Emp.: 106
Fiscal Year-end: 12/31/22
Baby Monitor Distr
N.A.I.C.S.: 423620
Jonathan Harris *(Pres & Chief Revenue Officer)*
Kurt Workman *(Founder & CEO)*
Jonathan Harris *(Pres & Chief Revenue Officer)*
Burc Sahinoglu *(CTO)*
David Kizer *(COO)*
Elizabeth Teran *(CMO)*
Amanda Twede Crawford *(CFO)*

OXFORD BANK CORPORATION
Tel.: (248) 628-2533 MI
Web Site:
https://www.oxfordbank.bank
Year Founded: 1987
OXBC—(OTCIQ)
Rev.: $25,073,000
Assets: $505,402,000
Liabilities: $458,814,000
Net Worth: $46,588,000
Earnings: $5,277,000
Emp.: 107
Fiscal Year-end: 12/31/19
Bank Holding Company
N.A.I.C.S.: 551111
David P. Lamb *(Chm, Pres & CEO)*
Matt Chapman *(VP & Mgr-IT)*

Subsidiaries:

Factors Southwest, LLC (1)
4530 E Shea Blvd Ste 142, Phoenix, AZ 85028-6067
Tel.: (602) 535-5984
Web Site: http://www.factors-southwest.com
Nondepository Credit Intermediation
N.A.I.C.S.: 522299
Robyn S. Barrett *(Mgr)*

Oxford Bank (1)
60 S Washington St, Oxford, MI 48371
Tel.: (248) 628-2533
Web Site: http://www.oxfordbank.com

Sales Range: $25-49.9 Million
Commercial Banking
N.A.I.C.S.: 522110
David P. Lamb *(Chm, Pres & CEO)*
Matthew Lowman *(Chief Risk Officer & Exec VP)*

OXFORD INDUSTRIES, INC.
999 Peachtree St NE Ste 688, Atlanta, GA 30309
Tel.: (404) 659-2424   **GA**
Web Site: https://www.oxfordinc.com
Year Founded: 1942
OXM—(NYSE)
Rev.: $1,411,528,000
Assets: $1,188,665,000
Liabilities: $632,395,000
Net Worth: $556,270,000
Earnings: $165,735,000
Emp.: 6,000
Fiscal Year-end: 01/28/23
Consumer Apparel for Men, Women & Children
N.A.I.C.S.: 313320
Thomas Caldecot Chubb III *(Chm, Pres & CEO)*
K. Scott Grassmyer *(CFO, COO & , Exec VP-Fin)*
Thomas E. Campbell *(CIO & Exec VP)*
Douglas B. Wood *(CEO-Tommy Bahama Grp)*
Michelle McQuality Kelly *(CEO-Lilly Pulitzer Grp)*
Suraj A. Palakshappa *(Gen Counsel, Sec & VP-Law)*
Tracey Hernandez *(VP-HR)*
Janice A. Tanner *(VP-Corp Acctg)*
Rob Trauber *(CEO-Johnny Was)*
Mark Kirby *(Sr VP-Operations)*
Betts Copenhaver *(VP-Strategic Planning & Business Development)*
Markey Hutchinson *(CEO-The Beaufort Bonnet Company)*

Subsidiaries:

Ben Sherman Limited   **(1)**
2100 Century Way, Thorpe Park, Leeds, LS15 8ZB, United Kingdom
Tel.: (44) 2078125300
Web Site: https://www.bensherman.co.uk
Sales Range: $200-249.9 Million
Emp.: 100
Apparel & Footwear Designer & Distr
N.A.I.C.S.: 315990

Unit (US):

Ben Sherman USA   **(2)**
1071 Ave of the Americas 10th Fl, New York, NY 10018
Tel.: (573) 615-1066
Web Site: https://www.bensherman.com
Sales Range: $50-74.9 Million
Emp.: 25
Apparel & Accessories Distr
N.A.I.C.S.: 424350

Johnny Was, LLC   **(1)**
3775 Broadway Pl, Los Angeles, CA 90007
Tel.: (323) 231-8222
Web Site: https://www.johnnywas.com
Sales Range: $1-9.9 Million
Emp.: 26
Women's & Girls' Cut & Sew Other Outerwear Mfr
N.A.I.C.S.: 315250
Adi Levite *(VP)*
Rob Trauber *(CEO)*

Oxford Caribbean, Inc.   **(1)**
1105 N Market St, Wilmington, DE 19801
Tel.: (302) 777-4736
Emp.: 2
Fashion Apparel Distr
N.A.I.C.S.: 458110

Oxford Garment, Inc.   **(1)**
1105 N Market St, Wilmington, DE 19801-1241
Tel.: (302) 654-9574
Fashion Apparel Distr
N.A.I.C.S.: 458110

Oxford Products (International) Limited   **(1)**
RM 12-18 13/Floor Tower 1 388 Kwun Tong Road, Kwun Tong, 999077, China (Hong Kong)
Tel.: (852) 24812000
Apparel Clothing Retailer
N.A.I.C.S.: 424350

Subsidiary (Non-US):

Industrias Oxford de Merida S.A. de CV   **(2)**
Carr Merida-Progreso Km 125 No Revolution Unit Cordemex, Revolution Unit Cordemex, 97110, Merida, Yucatan, Mexico
Tel.: (52) 9999410120
Sales Range: $200-249.9 Million
Emp.: 600
Fashion Apparel Distr
N.A.I.C.S.: 424350
Mario E. Mendoza Garay *(Gen Mgr)*

Subsidiary (Domestic):

Tommy Bahama Global Sourcing Limited   **(2)**
Unit 2-10 37/F Tower 1 Millenium City 1, Kwun Tong, Kowloon, China (Hong Kong)
Tel.: (852) 27511031
Web Site: http://www.tommybahama.com
Consumer Apparel for Men Women & Children Mfr
N.A.I.C.S.: 313320

Subsidiary (Non-US):

Tommy Bahama Australia Pty Ltd   **(3)**
19 Roseby Street, Drummoyne, 2047, NSW, Australia
Tel.: (61) 297192357
Web Site: https://www.tommybahama.com.au
Emp.: 9
Clothing Store Operator
N.A.I.C.S.: 458110
Petra Stroncerova *(Gen Mgr)*

Tommy Bahama Canada ULC   **(3)**
2901 Bayview Avenue Unit 29, Willowdale, M2K 1E6, ON, Canada
Tel.: (416) 223-3919
Clothing Store Operator
N.A.I.C.S.: 458110

Subsidiary (Domestic):

Tommy Bahama Limited   **(3)**
Shop No 1B J Senses 60 60-66 Johnston Road, Wanchai, China (Hong Kong)
Tel.: (852) 25430383
Web Site: http://www.tommybahama.com
Clothing Store Operator
N.A.I.C.S.: 458110

Piedmont Apparel Corporation   **(1)**
1105 N Market St, Wilmington, DE 19801
Tel.: (302) 427-0133
Fashion Apparel Distr
N.A.I.C.S.: 458110

Southern Tide, LLC   **(1)**
84 Villa Rd Ste 101, Greenville, SC 29615
Tel.: (864) 236-8015
Web Site: https://www.southerntide.com
Fashion Apparels Mfr
N.A.I.C.S.: 315250

Sugartown Worldwide LLC   **(1)**
800 3rd Ave, King of Prussia, PA 19406   **(100%)**
Tel.: (610) 878-5550
Web Site: https://www.lillypulitzer.com
Women's Apparel & Accessories Design, Mfr & Marketer
N.A.I.C.S.: 315250

The Beaufort Bonnet Company, LLC   **(1)**
400 Old Vine St, Lexington, KY 40507   **(100%)**
Tel.: (859) 317-8270
Web Site: https://www.thebeaufortbonnetcompany.com
Baby Product Whslr
N.A.I.C.S.: 458110

Tommy Bahama Group, Inc.   **(1)**

400 Fairview Ave N Ste 488, Seattle, WA 98109
Tel.: (206) 622-8688
Web Site: https://www.tommybahama.com
Sales Range: $250-299.9 Million
Emp.: 300
Men's & Women's Clothing, Accessories & Home Furnishings Mfr
N.A.I.C.S.: 458110

Subsidiary (Domestic):

Tommy Bahama Sarasota LLC   **(2)**
300 John Ringling Blvd, Sarasota, FL 34236
Tel.: (941) 388-2888
Web Site: http://www.tommybahama.com
Sales Range: $10-24.9 Million
Emp.: 80
Family Clothing Retail
N.A.I.C.S.: 458110

Tommy Bahama Texas Beverages LLC   **(2)**
9595 6 Pines Dr, Spring, TX 77380
Tel.: (954) 777-8946
Fashion Apparel Distr
N.A.I.C.S.: 458110

OXFORD LANE CAPITAL CORP.
8 Sound Shore Dr Ste 255, Greenwich, CT 06830
Tel.: (203) 983-5275
Web Site: https://www.oxfordlanecapital.com
Year Founded: 2010
OXLC—(NASDAQ)
Investment Services
N.A.I.C.S.: 523999
Bruce L. Rubin *(CFO)*
Jonathan Harris Cohen *(CEO)*
Saul Barak Rosenthal *(Pres)*
Vincent Gurrera *(Asst Controller)*
Mark Jeffrey Ashenfelter *(Chm)*
Gerald Cummins *(Chief Compliance Officer)*

OXFORD SQUARE CAPITAL CORP.
8 Sound Shore Dr Ste 255, Greenwich, CT 06830
Tel.: (203) 983-5275   **MD**
Web Site: https://www.oxfordsquarecapital.com
OXSQ—(NASDAQ)
Rev.: $43,118,112
Assets: $327,994,435
Liabilities: $189,322,473
Net Worth: $138,671,962
Earnings: $20,687,578
Fiscal Year-end: 12/31/22
Investment Services
N.A.I.C.S.: 523940
Bruce L. Rubin *(CFO, Treas & Sec)*
Jonathan Harris Cohen *(CEO)*
Saul Barak Rosenthal *(Pres & COO)*
Vincent Gurrera *(VP-Fin & Controller)*
Steven P. Novak *(Chm)*
Barry A. Osherow *(Executives)*
Gerald Cummins *(Chief Compliance Officer)*
Debdeep Maji *(Sr Mng Dir & Portfolio Mgr-Oxford Funds LLC)*

OYSTER ENTERPRISES ACQUISITION CORP.
300 Main St, Stamford, CT 06901
Tel.: (212) 888-5500   **DE**
Year Founded: 2020
OSTRU—(NASDAQ)
Rev.: $8,742,941
Assets: $230,687,845
Liabilities: $247,082,067
Net Worth: $(16,394,222)
Earnings: $7,959,366
Emp.: 3
Fiscal Year-end: 12/31/21

Investment Services
N.A.I.C.S.: 523999
Heath B. Freeman *(Vice Chm & CEO)*
Joshua P. Kleban *(CFO)*
Michael J. Monticciolo *(COO, Chief Legal Officer & Sec)*
Randall D. Smith *(Chm)*

OZOP ENERGY SOLUTIONS, INC.
55 Ronald Reagan Blvd, Warwick, NY 10990
Tel.: (845) 397-2956   **NV**
Web Site: https://www.ozopenergy.com
Year Founded: 2015
OZSC—(OTCIQ)
Rev.: $16,629,450
Assets: $9,489,342
Liabilities: $30,466,111
Net Worth: $(20,976,769)
Earnings: $6,025,812
Emp.: 9
Fiscal Year-end: 12/31/22
Motorcycle, Bicycle & Parts Manufacturing
N.A.I.C.S.: 336991
Brian P. Conway *(Chm, CEO & Interim CFO)*

P.A.M. TRANSPORTATION SERVICES, INC.
297 W Henri de Tonti Blvd, Tontitown, AR 72770
Tel.: (479) 361-9111   **DE**
Web Site: https://www.pamtransport.com
Year Founded: 1986
PTSI—(NASDAQ)
Rev.: $810,807,000
Assets: $760,457,000
Liabilities: $446,241,000
Net Worth: $314,216,000
Earnings: $18,416,000
Emp.: 2,512
Fiscal Year-end: 12/31/23
Transportation Services; Holding Company
N.A.I.C.S.: 484230
Lance K. Stewart *(CFO, Treas & VP-Finance)*
Matthew T. Moroun *(Chm)*
Joseph A. Vitiritto *(Pres & CEO)*

Subsidiaries:

East Coast Transport and Logistics, LLC   **(1)**
195 Borrelli Blvd Ste A, Paulsboro, NJ 08066
Tel.: (856) 423-6200
Web Site: https://ect3pl.squarespace.com
Truck Transportation Services
N.A.I.C.S.: 484121

Metropolitan Trucking, Inc.   **(1)**
299 Market St Ste 300, Saddle Brook, NJ 07663-5312
Tel.: (973) 742-3000
Web Site: http://www.mtrk.com
Sales Range: $50-74.9 Million
Emp.: 15
Trucking Except Local
N.A.I.C.S.: 484121
Wayne Beaudry *(VP-Maintenance)*
Michael A. Maiore *(Exec VP)*
Matthew Sullivan *(CFO)*
Joseph Mangino Jr. *(Owner & Pres)*

Branch (Domestic):

Metropolitan Trucking Inc.   **(2)**
6675 Low St, Bloomsburg, PA 17815-8613
Tel.: (570) 389-8950
Web Site: http://www.mtrk.com
Sales Range: $25-49.9 Million
Trucking Service
N.A.I.C.S.: 484121
Michael A. Maiore *(Exec VP)*
Joseph Mangino Jr. *(Owner & Pres)*

P.A.M. Transportation Services, Inc.—(Continued)

P.A.M. Dedicated Services, Inc. (1)
1450 N Bailey Rd, North Jackson, OH 44451
Tel.: (479) 361-9111
Web Site: http://www.pamt.com
Rev.: $30,000,000
Emp.: 40
Trucking Service
N.A.I.C.S.: 811111

P.A.M. Transport, Inc. (1)
297 W Henri de Tonti Blvd, Tontitown, AR 72770
Tel.: (479) 361-9111
Web Site: https://www.pamtransport.com
Sales Range: $50-74.9 Million
Emp.: 800
Trucking Service
N.A.I.C.S.: 484121

Transcend Logistics, Inc. (1)
297 W Henri DeTonti Blvd, Tontitown, AR 72770
Tel.: (479) 361-5139
Freight Trucking Services
N.A.I.C.S.: 484110

P10, INC.
4514 Cole Ave Ste 1600, Dallas, TX 75205
Tel.: (214) 865-7998   DE
Web Site: https://www.p10alts.com
Year Founded: 2021
PX—(NYSE)
Rev.: $198,360,000
Assets: $826,360,000
Liabilities: $392,477,000
Net Worth: $433,883,000
Earnings: $29,206,000
Emp.: 127
Fiscal Year-end: 12/31/22
Asset Management Investment Services
N.A.I.C.S.: 523940
Amanda N. Coussens (CFO & Chief Compliance Officer)
Robert Hudson Alpert (Co-Founder)
Robert H. Alpert (Co-Founder & Exec Chm)
C. Clark Webb (Co-Founder & Vice Chm)
Amanda Coussens (CFO & Chief Compliance Officer)
Mark Hood (Chief Admin Officer & Exec VP)
Luke A. Sarsfield III (Chm & CEO)

Subsidiaries:

Bonaccord Capital Partners LLC (1)
299 Park Ave 36th Fl, New York, NY 10171
Tel.: (332) 322-3220
Web Site: https://www.bonaccordcapital.com
Emp.: 200
Investment Services
N.A.I.C.S.: 523999
Farhad Dehesh (Partner)

P10 Holdings, Inc. (1)
4514 Cole Ave Ste 1600, Dallas, TX 75205
Tel.: (214) 865-7998
Web Site: https://www.p10alts.com
Rev.: $67,368,000
Assets: $582,426,000
Liabilities: $522,585,000
Net Worth: $59,841,000
Earnings: $23,086,000
Fiscal Year-end: 12/31/2020
Holding Company
N.A.I.C.S.: 551112
Amanda N. Coussens (CFO)
Robert Hudson Alpert (Chm & Co-CEO)
C. Clark Webb (Co-CEO)
William Souder (COO)
Amanda Coussens (CFO)
Kevin Kelly (CIO)
Andrew Corsi (Controller)
Mark Hood (Dir-IR)
Karsen Kiefer (Mgr-Fin Plng & Analysis)
Caryn Peeples (Office Mgr)
Tarra Thompson (Mgr-HR)
Michelle Yakhnis (Accountant-Staff)

P3 HEALTH PARTNERS INC.

2370 Corporate Cir Ste 300, Henderson, NV 89074
Tel.: (702) 910-3950   DE
Web Site: https://p3hp.org
Year Founded: 2020
PIII—(NASDAQ)
Rev.: $1,049,471,000
Assets: $876,571,000
Liabilities: $870,717,000
Net Worth: $5,854,000
Earnings: ($1,561,557,000)
Emp.: 600
Fiscal Year-end: 12/31/22
Investment Services
N.A.I.C.S.: 523999
Aric Coffman (Pres & CEO)
Allen Pate (Pres-Market)
Jeffrey Wagner (VP-Clinical Affairs)
Sherif Abdou (Co-Founder & CEO)
Greg Wasson (Chm)
Amir Bacchus (Co-Founder & Chief Medical Officer)

PACCAR INC.
777-106th Ave NE, Bellevue, WA 98004
Tel.: (425) 468-7400   DE
Web Site: https://www.paccar.com
Year Founded: 1905
PCAR—(NASDAQ)
Rev.: $33,315,500,000
Assets: $40,823,400,000
Liabilities: $24,944,600,000
Net Worth: $15,878,800,000
Earnings: $4,600,800,000
Emp.: 32,400
Fiscal Year-end: 12/31/23
Heavy Duty On & Off Road Trucks Mfr; Industrial Winches Mfr & Marketer; General Automotive Parts & Accessories Marketer
N.A.I.C.S.: 336120
R. Preston Feight (CEO)
Harrie C. A. M. Schippers (Pres & CFO)
Mark C. Pigott (Exec Chm)
Alma Lily Ley (CIO & VP)
Todd R. Hubbard (VP-Fin Svcs-Global)
Jason P. Skoog (VP)
Harry M. B. Wolters (VP)
Michael K. Walton (Gen Counsel & VP)
John Rich (CTO & VP)
Brico J. Poplawcki (VP & Controllor)

Subsidiaries:

DAF Caminhoes Brasil Industria Ltda. (1)
Av Senador Flavio Carvalho Guimaraes 6000, Neighborhood Boa Vista, Ponta Grossa, 84072-190, Brazil
Tel.: (55) 4231228400
Web Site: https://www.dafcaminhoes.com.br
Trucks Mfr
N.A.I.C.S.: 336120

DAF Trucks Deutschland GmbH (1)
Daf-Allee 1, 50226, Frechen, Germany
Tel.: (49) 22345060
Web Site: https://www.daftrucks.de
Sales Range: $25-49.9 Million
Trucking Service
N.A.I.C.S.: 484121

DAF Trucks France, S.A.R.L. (1)
ZI Paris Nord II Bat N 64 rue des Vanesses CS 52396, 95943, Roissy-en-France, Cedex, France
Tel.: (33) 149908000
Web Site: https://www.daf.fr
Heavy Duty Truck Mfr
N.A.I.C.S.: 336120

DAF Trucks France, S.A.R.L. (1)
ZI PARIS NORTH II Building N 64 rue des Vanesses CS 52396, 95943, Roissy-en-France, Cedex, France
Tel.: (33) 149908000
Web Site: https://www.daf.fr
Heavy Duty Truck Mfr

DAF Trucks Ltd. (1)
Eastern Bypass, Thame, OX9 3FB, Oxfordshire, United Kingdom
Tel.: (44) 1844261111
Web Site: https://tendurance.daftrucks.com
Sales Range: $25-49.9 Million
Emp.: 80
Truck Administration & Sales Services
N.A.I.C.S.: 336120

DAF Trucks N.V. (1)
Hugo van der Goeslaan 1, 5643 TW, Eindhoven, Netherlands
Tel.: (31) 402149111
Web Site: https://www.daf.com
Sales Range: $1-4.9 Billion
Emp.: 6,764
Light, Medium & Heavy Duty Trucks; Vans, Bus Components, Diesel Engines & Related Truck Parts Mfr & Distr; Financial Services
N.A.I.C.S.: 336211

Subsidiary (Non-US):

DAF Trucks Vlaanderen N.V. (2)
Van Doornelaan 1, 2260, Westerlo, Belgium
Tel.: (32) 14568000
Web Site: http://www.daftrucks.com
Sales Range: $300-349.9 Million
Trucks Mfr
N.A.I.C.S.: 336120

DAF Trucks Polska SP.Z.O.O. (1)
Ul Krakowiakow 48, 02-255, Warsaw, Poland
Tel.: (48) 224589500
Web Site: https://www.daftrucks.pl
Heavy Duty Truck Mfr
N.A.I.C.S.: 336120

DAF Vehiculos Industriales S.A. (1)
Edificio Francia 1 Escalera B, San Fernando Business Park, 28830, Madrid, Spain
Tel.: (34) 916600255
Web Site: https://www.daf.es
Trucks Mfr
N.A.I.C.S.: 336120

DAF Veicoli Industriali S.p.A. (1)
Via del Bosco Rinnovato 8, Assago Milanofiori Nord, 20090, Milan, Italy
Tel.: (39) 02484291
Web Site: https://www.daftrucks.it
Emp.: 45
Used Truck Dealers
N.A.I.C.S.: 423110

Dynacraft (1)
650 Milwaukee Ave N, Algona, WA 98001   (100%)
Tel.: (253) 333-3000
Web Site: http://www.dynacraftnet.com
Sales Range: $200-249.9 Million
Emp.: 400
Mfr of High Quality Hoses, Valves, Adapters, Fittings, V-Belts & Electrical Cables
N.A.I.C.S.: 423120

Subsidiary (Domestic):

Dynacraft (2)
10901 Greenbelt Hwy, Louisville, KY 40258
Tel.: (502) 933-4965
Web Site: http://www.dynacraft.com
Sales Range: $75-99.9 Million
Truck Parts & Components
N.A.I.C.S.: 423120

Kenworth Mexicana, S.A. de C.V. (1)
Km 10 5 Carretera a San Luis, Mexicali, 21100, Mexico   (100%)
Tel.: (52) 6865628000
Web Site: https://www.kenmex.com
Sales Range: $300-349.9 Million
Emp.: 2,500
Truck Manufacturing
N.A.I.C.S.: 336120

Kenworth Truck Co. (1)
10630 NE 38th Pl, Kirkland, WA 98033-7909
Tel.: (425) 828-5000
Web Site: http://www.kenworth.com
Sales Range: $550-599.9 Million
Emp.: 300
Heavy & Medium Duty Trucks Mfr & Distr
N.A.I.C.S.: 336120

Leyland Trucks Limited (1)
Croston Road, Leyland, PR26 6LZ, Lancashire, United Kingdom   (100%)
Tel.: (44) 1772621400
Web Site: https://www.leylandtrucksltd.co.uk
Sales Range: $450-499.9 Million
Emp.: 1,000
Truck Manufacturing
N.A.I.C.S.: 336120

PACCAR Australia Pty. Ltd. (1)
64 Canterbury Road, Bayswater North, Bayswater, 3153, VIC, Australia   (100%)
Tel.: (61) 397211500
Web Site: https://www.paccar.com.au
Sales Range: $200-249.9 Million
Trucks & Tractors Mfr
N.A.I.C.S.: 336120

PACCAR Engine Company (1)
1000 Paccar Dr, Columbus, MS 39701
Tel.: (662) 329-6700
Heavy Duty Truck Distr
N.A.I.C.S.: 423110
Lance Walters (Plant Mgr)

PACCAR Financial Belux BVBA (1)
Luxemburgstraat 17, 9140, Temse, Oost-Vlaanderen, Belgium
Tel.: (32) 37101411
Sales Range: $25-49.9 Million
Emp.: 9
Truck Financing & Leasing Services
N.A.I.C.S.: 523910

PACCAR Financial Corp. (1)
777 106th Ave NE, Bellevue, WA 98004   (100%)
Tel.: (425) 468-7100
Web Site: https://www.paccarfinancial.com
Rev.: $734,100,000
Assets: $11,997,000,000
Liabilities: $10,065,800,000
Net Worth: $1,931,200,000
Earnings: $139,500,000
Emp.: 354
Fiscal Year-end: 12/31/2023
Truck & Equipment Financing Services
N.A.I.C.S.: 532120
T. R. Hubbard (CFO)
C. R. Gryniewicz (Pres)
H. C. A. M. Schippers (CEO)
Harrie C. A. M. Schippers (Pres)
Laura J. Bloch (VP)
Paulo H. Bolgar (Chief HR Officer)
Harald P. Seidel (VP)

PACCAR Financial Deutschland GmbH (1)
Daf-Allee 1, 50226, Frechen, Germany
Tel.: (49) 2234519300
Emp.: 20
Truck Rental Services
N.A.I.C.S.: 532120
Robert Bengston (Mng Dir)

PACCAR Financial Espana S.r.l. (1)
Parque Empresarial San Fernando, San Fernando De Henares, Madrid, 28830, Spain
Tel.: (34) 916600255
Truck Financing & Leasing Services
N.A.I.C.S.: 523910

PACCAR Financial Europe B.V. (1)
PO Box 90065, 5600 PT, Eindhoven, Netherlands
Tel.: (31) 620964310
Heavy Duty Truck Mfr
N.A.I.C.S.: 336120

PACCAR Financial France C.A.S. (1)
Paris-Nord II 64-66 rue des Vanesses, 95943, Roissy-en-France, France
Tel.: (33) 149908069
Web Site: http://www.pacca.com
Truck Financing & Leasing Services
N.A.I.C.S.: 522220

PACCAR Financial Italia Srl (1)
Via Del Bosco Rinnovato 8, Milan, 20090, Assago, 20090, Italy
Tel.: (39) 024847191
Web Site: http://www.paccarfinancial.it
Sales Range: $25-49.9 Million
Emp.: 15
Truck Financing & Leasing Services
N.A.I.C.S.: 523910

PACCAR Financial Ltd. (1)

6711 Mississauga Road N Suite 500, Mississauga, L5N 4J8, ON, Canada
Tel.: (905) 858-2670
Web Site: https://www.paccarfinancial.com
Truck Financing & Leasing Services
N.A.I.C.S.: 523910

PACCAR Financial Mexico (1)
Calz Gustavo Vildosola Castro 2000 Unidad Ind PACCAR Mexico, 21385, Mexicali, Mexico
Tel.: (52) 6865628000
Heavy Duty Truck Mfr
N.A.I.C.S.: 336120

PACCAR Financial Mexico, S.A. de C.V., SOFOM, E.N.R. (1)
Calz Gustavo Vildosola Castro 2000, Unidad Ind PACCAR Mexico, 21385, Mexicali, 21385, Baja California, Mexico
Tel.: (52) 11526865628000
Consumer Lending Services
N.A.I.C.S.: 522291
Indira Cevallos De La Torre (Sec)
Donald H. Stewart II (Dir-Fin)

PACCAR Financial PLC (1)
Haddenham Business Park Pegasus Way, PO Box 82, Haddenham, HP17 8LJ, United Kingdom
Tel.: (44) 8456036175
Web Site: http://www.paccarfinancial.co.uk
Emp.: 200
Truck Financing & Leasing Services
N.A.I.C.S.: 523910
Steve Barfoot (Mng Dir)

PACCAR Financial Pty. Ltd. (1)
66 Canterbury Road, PO Box 60, Bayswater, 3153, VIC, Australia
Tel.: (61) 1800455155
Web Site: http://www.paccarfinancial.com.au
Transport Equipment Financial Services
N.A.I.C.S.: 522220

PACCAR Financial Pty. Ltd. (1)
66 Canterbury Road, Bayswater, 3153, VIC, Australia **(100%)**
Tel.: (61) 800455155
Sales Range: $75-99.9 Million
Emp.: 200
Financial Services
N.A.I.C.S.: 522320

PACCAR Financial Services Corp. (1)
777 106th Ave NE, Bellevue, WA 98004
Tel.: (425) 468-7100
Web Site: http://www.paccar.com
Truck Financing & Leasing Services
N.A.I.C.S.: 522220
Mark C. Pigott (Chm)

PACCAR Financial Services Ltd. (1)
6711 Mississauga Rd Ste 501, Mississauga, L5N 4J8, ON, Canada
Tel.: (905) 858-7050
Sales Range: $75-99.9 Million
Emp.: 42
Financial Services
N.A.I.C.S.: 523991

PACCAR Global Sales (1)
10630 NE 38th Pl, Kirkland, WA 98033
Tel.: (425) 828-5900
Web Site: http://www.paccar.com
Sales Range: $25-49.9 Million
Emp.: 30
Commercial Vehicles Export Sales
N.A.I.C.S.: 336120

PACCAR Leasing Co. (1)
777 106th Ave NE, Bellevue, WA 98004 **(100%)**
Tel.: (425) 468-7877
Web Site: http://www.paclease.com
Sales Range: $10-24.9 Million
Emp.: 55
Truck & Equipment Leasing
N.A.I.C.S.: 532120
Andy Wold (Treas)

PACCAR Leasing GmbH (1)
Industriestrasse 22-24, 64807, Dieburg, Germany
Tel.: (49) 607198890
Web Site: https://www.paclease.de
Emp.: 100
Truck & Trailer Rental Services
N.A.I.C.S.: 532120

PACCAR Mexico, S.A. de C.V. (1)
Calz Gustavo Vildosola Castro 2000, Unidad Ind Paccar Mexico, 21385, Mexicali, 21385, BC, Mexico
Tel.: (52) 6865628000
Heavy Duty Truck Mfr
N.A.I.C.S.: 336120

PACCAR Parts (1)
750 Houser Way N, Renton, WA 98057
Tel.: (425) 254-4400
Web Site: http://www.paccar.com
Sales Range: $10-24.9 Million
Emp.: 300
Truck Parts Distr
N.A.I.C.S.: 336390

PACCAR Parts Mexico, S.A. de C.V. (1)
Ave Industrias 4500 ESQ Con EJE 130, San Luis Potosi, Mexico
Tel.: (52) 4448268600
Motor Vehicle Supplies & New Parts Merchant Whslr
N.A.I.C.S.: 423120

PACCAR Parts U.K. Limited (1)
Croston Road, Leyland, PR26 6LZ, United Kingdom
Tel.: (44) 1772621400
Web Site: http://www.paccar.com
Emp.: 1,500
Trucks Mfr
N.A.I.C.S.: 336120

PACCAR Sales North America, Inc. (1)
777 106th Ave NE, Bellevue, WA 98004-5027
Tel.: (425) 468-7400
Web Site: http://www.paccar.com
Trucks Mfr
N.A.I.C.S.: 336120

PACCAR Technical Center (1)
12479 Farm To Market Rd, Mount Vernon, WA 98273
Tel.: (360) 757-8311
Web Site: http://www.paccar.com
Sales Range: $25-49.9 Million
Emp.: 340
Test Facility Craft for Semi-Large Trucks
N.A.I.C.S.: 541715

PACCAR Trucks U.K. Ltd. (1)
9400 Garsington Road Oxford Business Park, Oxford, OX4 2HN, United Kingdom
Tel.: (44) 441772621400
Trucks Mfr
N.A.I.C.S.: 336120

PACCAR Winch Division (1)
800 E Dallas St, Broken Arrow, OK 74012-4300
Tel.: (918) 251-8511
Web Site: http://www.paccarwinch.com
Sales Range: $50-74.9 Million
Mfr of Electric, Mechanical & Hydraulic Worm Gear Winches, Planetary Winches & Construction Hoists, Gear Boxes, Turning Mechanisms, Tractor & Skid-Mounted Winches
N.A.I.C.S.: 333923
Mark C. Pigott (Chm)

PACCAR of Canada Ltd. (1)
6711 Mississauga Road Ste 500, Mississauga, L5N 4J8, ON, Canada **(100%)**
Tel.: (905) 858-7000
Web Site: http://www.paccar.com
Sales Range: $25-49.9 Million
Mfr of Trucks
N.A.I.C.S.: 336120

PacLease Mexicana, S.A. de C.V. (1)
Calz Gustavo Vildosola Castro 2000 Unidad Ind Paccar Mexico, CP 21385, Mexicali, Mexico
Tel.: (52) 6865628000
Heavy Duty Truck Mfr
N.A.I.C.S.: 336120

Peterbilt Motors Co. (1)
1700 Woodbrook St, Denton, TX 76205-7864
Tel.: (940) 591-4000
Web Site: http://www.peterbilt.com
Sales Range: $550-599.9 Million
Emp.: 2,300
Mfr Heavy Duty Trucks

N.A.I.C.S.: 333924

Peterbilt of Canada (1)
501-6711 Mississauga Rd, Mississauga, L5N 4J8, ON, Canada
Tel.: (905) 858-7090
Web Site: http://www.peterbilt.com
Sales Range: $10-24.9 Million
Emp.: 5
Truck Distr
N.A.I.C.S.: 336120

PACIFIC ALLIANCE BANK
641 W Las Tunas Dr, San Gabriel, CA 91776
Tel.: (626) 773-8888   CA
Web Site:
https://www.pacificalliancebank.com
Year Founded: 2006
PFBN—(OTCIQ)
Commercial Banking Services
N.A.I.C.S.: 522110
Benjamin J. B. Lin (Pres & CEO)
Andy Lin (Exec VP)
Andy Lin (Chief Credit Officer & Exec VP)
Chris Chan (CFO & Exec VP)
Robert Lin (Chief Lending OfficerÂ & Exec VP)
Andrew Su (Chm)

PACIFIC BIOSCIENCES OF CALIFORNIA, INC.
1305 OBrien Dr, Menlo Park, CA 94025
Tel.: (650) 521-8000   DE
Web Site: https://www.pacb.com
Year Founded: 2000
PACB—(NASDAQ)
Rev.: $128,304,000
Assets: $1,767,086,000
Liabilities: $1,204,182,000
Net Worth: $562,904,000
Earnings: ($314,248)
Emp.: 769
Fiscal Year-end: 12/31/22
Analytical Instrument Mfr
N.A.I.C.S.: 334516
John F. Milligan (Chm)
Jeff Eidel (Chief Comml Officer)
Brett Atkins (Gen Counsel)
Mike Goloubef (Sr VP-Manufacturing & Quality)
Natalie Welch (Chief People Officer)
Stephen Turner (Founder & Chief Technical Officer)
Susan G. Kim (CFO)
Mark Van Oene (COO)
Jonas Korlach (Chief Scientific Officer)
Michele Farmer (Chief Acctg Officer & VP)
Neil Ward (VP & Gen Mgr-EMEA)
Christian O. Henry (Pres & CEO)

PACIFIC ENTERPRISE BANCORP
17748 Skypark Cir Ste 100, Irvine, CA 92614
Tel.: (949) 623-7600
Web Site:
http://www.pacificenterprise bank.com
PEBN—(OTCIQ)
Bank Holding Company
N.A.I.C.S.: 551111
Sue Choi (Sr VP & Mgr-Rels)

Subsidiaries:

Pacific Enterprise Bank (1)
17748 Skypark Cir Ste 100, Irvine, CA 92614
Tel.: (949) 623-7600
Web Site:
http://www.pacificenterprisebank.com
Sales Range: $25-49.9 Million
Emp.: 103
Commericial Banking

N.A.I.C.S.: 522110
Russell J. Smith (Chief Lending Officer & Exec VP)
Brian Halle (Pres & CEO)
Frank Smith (CFO, Sec & Exec VP)

PACIFIC FINANCIAL CORPORATION
1216 Skyview Dr, Aberdeen, WA 98520
Tel.: (360) 537-4059   WA
Web Site:
http://www.bankofthepacific.com
PFLC—(OTCQX)
Rev.: $59,720,000
Assets: $1,167,293,000
Liabilities: $1,053,107,000
Net Worth: $114,186,000
Earnings: $11,384,000
Emp.: 253
Fiscal Year-end: 12/31/20
Bank Holding Company
N.A.I.C.S.: 551111
Carla F. Tucker (CFO & Exec VP)
Denise J. Portmann (Pres & CEO)
Daniel E. Kuenzi (Chief Credit Officer & Exec VP)
Carla F. Tucker (CFO & Exec VP)
Randy W. Rognlin (Chm)
Douglas M. Schermer (Vice Chm)
Walker Evans (Chief Lending Officer & Exec VP)
Terri McKinnis (COO & Exec VP)
Darla Johnson (Sec)

Subsidiaries:

The Bank of the Pacific (1)
300 E Market St, Aberdeen, WA 98520
Tel.: (360) 533-8870
Web Site: http://www.thebankofpacific.com
Sales Range: $75-99.9 Million
Assets: $530,000,000
Emp.: 215
Bank
N.A.I.C.S.: 522110
Denise J. Portmann (Pres & CEO)
Carla F. Tucker (CFO & Exec VP)
Denise J. Portmann (Pres & CEO)
Lorraine Morris (Mgr-Ferndale)
Tom Mathewson (Asst VP & Mgr-Bellingham)

PACIFIC GREEN TECHNOLOGIES INC.
8 The Green Ste 10212, Dover, DE 19901
Tel.: (302) 601-4659   DE
Web Site:
https://www.pacificgreen.com
PGTK—(OTCQB)
Rev.: $7,639,165
Assets: $30,566,166
Liabilities: $15,750,586
Net Worth: $14,815,580
Earnings: ($11,317,344)
Emp.: 45
Fiscal Year-end: 03/31/23
Environmental Products
N.A.I.C.S.: 333248
Scott Poulter (Chm & CEO)
James Tindal-Robertson (CFO)
Riseley D'Souza (VP-Operations)

Subsidiaries:

Pacific Green Energy Storage Technologies Inc. (1)
8 The Grn Ste 10212, Dover, DE 19901
Tel.: (302) 601-4659
Web Site: https://www.pacificgreen-energystorage.com
Lithium Ion Battery Mfr
N.A.I.C.S.: 325180

Pacific Green Marine Technologies Inc. (1)
8 The Grn Ste 10212, Dover, DE 19901
Tel.: (302) 601-4659
Web Site: https://www.pacificgreen-marine.com
Marine Engineering Services
N.A.I.C.S.: 541715

PACIFIC HEALTH CARE ORGANIZATION, INC.
2618 San Miguel Dr Ste 477, Newport Beach, CA 92660
Tel.: (949) 721-8272
Web Site:
https://www.pacifichealthcareorganization.com
Year Founded: 1970
PFHO—(OTCQB)
Rev.: $5,744,957
Assets: $12,052,356
Liabilities: $735,065
Net Worth: $11,317,291
Earnings: $492,886
Emp.: 31
Fiscal Year-end: 12/31/22
Health Organization Management Services
N.A.I.C.S.: 541611
Lauren Kubota (Sec & VP)

Subsidiaries:

Medex Healthcare, Inc.   (1)
2618 San Miguel Dr Ste 477, Newport Beach, CA 92660
Tel.: (949) 221-1700
Web Site: https://www.medexhco.com
Health Care Srvices
N.A.I.C.S.: 622110
David Kim (COO)
Alex Lampone (Dir-Medical)

PACIFIC OAK STRATEGIC OPPORTUNITY REIT, INC.
3200 Park Center Dr Ste 800, Costa Mesa, CA 92626
Tel.: (424) 208-8100   MD
Web Site:
https://pacificoakcapital.com
PCOK—(OTCEM)
Rev.: $162,058,000
Assets: $1,559,245,000
Liabilities: $1,142,852,000
Net Worth: $416,393,000
Earnings: ($43,242,000)
Fiscal Year-end: 12/31/22
Other Financial Vehicles
N.A.I.C.S.: 525990
Keith D. Hall (CEO)
Peter B. McMillan III (Chm & Pres)
Michael A. Bender (CFO)

Subsidiaries:

DMH Realty, LLC   (1)
7909 Weeping Ash Way, Eagle Mountain, UT 84005
Tel.: (801) 836-0888
Web Site: http://dmhrealty.com
Real Estate Services
N.A.I.C.S.: 531390

Pacific Oak Residential Trust, Inc.   (1)
875 Prospect St Ste 304, La Jolla, CA 92037
Tel.: (858) 459-4000
Web Site: http://www.revenhousingreit.com
Rev.: $8,914,440
Assets: $83,101,522
Liabilities: $52,530,093
Net Worth: $30,571,429
Earnings: ($3,154,573)
Emp.: 3
Fiscal Year-end: 12/31/2018
Real Estate Investment Trust
N.A.I.C.S.: 531390
Keith D. Hall (CEO)
Peter B. McMillan III (Pres)

PACIFIC PREMIER BANCORP, INC.
17901 Von Karman Ave Ste 1200, Irvine, CA 92614
Tel.: (949) 864-8000   DE
Web Site: https://www.ppbi.com
Year Founded: 1997

PPBI—(NASDAQ)
Rev.: $857,326,000
Assets: $21,688,017,000
Liabilities: $18,889,628,000
Net Worth: $2,798,389,000
Earnings: $283,743,000
Emp.: 1,430
Fiscal Year-end: 12/31/22
Bank Holding Company
N.A.I.C.S.: 551111
Steven R. Gardner (Chm, Pres & CEO)
Lori R. Wright (Chief Acctg Officer & Exec VP)
Ronald J. Nicolas Jr. (CFO & Sr Exec VP)
Sherri V. Scott (Sr Exec VP & Dir-Environmental, Social, Governance & Corp Responsibility)

Subsidiaries:

Pacific Premier Bank   (1)
17901 Von Karman Ave Ste 1200, Irvine, CA 92614
Tel.: (949) 864-8000
Web Site: https://www.ppbi.com
Sales Range: $450-499.9 Million
Savings Bank
N.A.I.C.S.: 522180
Steven R. Gardner (Chm & CEO)
Thomas Rice (Chief Innovation Officer & Sr Exec VP)
Lori R. Wright (Deputy CFO & Sr Exec VP)
Ronald J. Nicolas Jr. (CFO & Sr Exec VP)
Thomas Galindo (Reg Pres & Exec VP)
Brooks Wise (Reg Pres & Exec VP)
Stephen Friedman (Reg Pres & Sr Exec VP)

Division (Domestic):

Commerce Escrow Company   (2)
1055 Wilshire Blvd Ste 1000, Los Angeles, CA 90017
Tel.: (213) 484-0855
Web Site: https://www.comescrow.com
Real Estate & Commercial Business Services
N.A.I.C.S.: 531390

Pacific Premier Trust   (2)
275 Battery St Ste 1220, San Francisco, CA 94111
Tel.: (415) 274-5600
Web Site:
http://www.pacificpremiertrust.com
Investment Advisory & Management Services
N.A.I.C.S.: 523940

PACIFIC SPORTS EXCHANGE, INC.
3055 NW Yeon Ave Ste 236, Portland, OR 97210
Tel.: (971) 279-2764   NV
Web Site: https://www.pacificsportsexchange.com
Year Founded: 2018
PSPX—(NASDAQ)
Rev.: $5,400
Assets: $1,264
Liabilities: $80,419
Net Worth: ($79,155)
Earnings: $9,928
Fiscal Year-end: 08/31/24
Sporting Goods Distr
N.A.I.C.S.: 423910
Timothy Conte (Pres, CEO & CFO)
Jennifer Whitesides (Treas & Sec)

PACIFIC VALLEY BANK
Pacific Valley Bank, Salinas, CA 93912-3648
Tel.: (831) 771-4330
Web Site:
https://www.pacificvalleybank.com
PVBK—(OTCIQ)
Banking Services
N.A.I.C.S.: 522110

Anker Fanoe (Pres & CEO)
Lee-Ann Cimino (Exec VP & CFO)
Carol Corsetti (Exec VP & Chief Credit Officer)

PACIFIC VENTURES GROUP, INC.
117 W 9th St Ste 316, Los Angeles, CA 90015
Tel.: (310) 392-5606   DE
Web Site:
https://www.pacvgroup.com
Year Founded: 1986
PACV—(OTCIQ)
Rev.: $41,991,172
Assets: $7,619,380
Liabilities: $22,357,138
Net Worth: ($14,737,757)
Earnings: ($5,557,679)
Emp.: 5
Fiscal Year-end: 12/31/21
Holding Company; Food & Beverage Distr
N.A.I.C.S.: 551112
Marc Shenkman (Chm)
Shannon Masjedi (Pres, CEO, Interim CFO & Sec)

Subsidiaries:

Seaport Meat Company   (1)
2533 Folex Way, Spring Valley, CA 91978
Tel.: (619) 713-2278
Web Site: http://www.seaportmeat.com
Food Distr & Whslr
N.A.I.C.S.: 424470

PACIFIC WEST BANK
2040 8th Ave, West Linn, OR 97068
Tel.: (503) 905-2222
Web Site:
http://www.bankpacificwest.com
Year Founded: 2004
PWBO—(OTCIQ)
Financial Banking Services
N.A.I.C.S.: 522110
Terry Peterson (CEO)

PACIFICHEALTH LABORATORIES, INC.
100 Lanidex Plz Ste 120, Parsippany, NJ 07054
Tel.: (732) 739-2900   DE
Web Site:
https://www.pacifichealthlabs.com
Year Founded: 1995
PHLI—(OTCIQ)
Researcher, Developer & Marketer of Nutritional & Natural Sports Nutrition, Weight Loss & Diabetes Products
N.A.I.C.S.: 325411

PACIRA BIOSCIENCES, INC.
5401 W Kennedy Blvd Lincoln Ctr Ste 890, Tampa, FL 33609
Tel.: (813) 553-6680   DE
Web Site: https://www.pacira.com
Year Founded: 2007
PCRX—(NASDAQ)
Rev.: $541,533,000
Assets: $2,075,353,000
Liabilities: $1,344,945,000
Net Worth: $730,408,000
Earnings: $41,980,000
Emp.: 697
Fiscal Year-end: 12/31/21
Pharmaceutical Preparation Manufacturing
N.A.I.C.S.: 325412
Kristen Williams (Chief Admin Officer & Sec)
Charles Laranjeira (Chief Technical Officer)
Dennis McLoughlin (Chief Customer Officer)
Max Reinhardt (Pres-Rest of World)
Daryl Gaugler (COO)

Ron Ellis (Chief Strategy Officer)
Christopher Young (Chief Mfg Officer)
Anthony Molloy III (Chief Legal Officer)
Jonathan Slonin (Chief Clinical Officer)
Frank D. Lee (CEO)

Subsidiaries:

Flexion Therapeutics, Inc.   (1)
10 Mall Rd Ste 301, Burlington, MA 01803
Tel.: (781) 305-7777
Web Site:
http://www.flexiontherapeutics.com
Rev.: $85,552,000
Assets: $251,926,000
Liabilities: $268,586,000
Net Worth: ($16,660,000)
Earnings: ($113,706,000)
Emp.: 257
Fiscal Year-end: 12/31/2020
Pharmaceuticals Mfr
N.A.I.C.S.: 325412
Neil Bodick (Co-Founder)
Christina Willwerth (Chief Strategy Officer)
Scott Young (VP-Corp Comm & IR)
Mark S. Levine (Gen Counsel & Sec)
Adam L. Muzikant (Chief Bus Officer)
Julie Downs (Assoc Dir-Corp Comm & IR)
Melissa Layman (Chief Comml Officer)

Pacira - San Diego   (1)
10410 Science Center Dr, San Diego, CA 92121
Tel.: (858) 625-2424
Web Site: http://www.pacira.com
Sales Range: $10-24.9 Million
Emp.: 300
Medical Research
N.A.I.C.S.: 541720

Pacira CryoTech, Inc.   (1)
5401 W Kennedy Blvd Lincoln Ctr Ste 890, Tampa, FL 33609
Tel.: (510) 933-1500
Web Site: http://www.iovera.com
Pharmaceuticals Equipment & Supplies Mfr
N.A.I.C.S.: 325412

Pacira Pharmaceuticals, Inc.   (1)
10410 Science Ctr Dr, San Diego, CA 92121
Tel.: (858) 625-2424
Pharmaceuticals Product Mfr
N.A.I.C.S.: 325412

PACKAGING CORPORATION OF AMERICA
1 N Field Ct, Lake Forest, IL 60045
Tel.: (847) 482-3000   DE
Web Site:
https://www.packagingcorp.com
Year Founded: 1959
PKG—(NYSE)
Rev.: $7,802,400,000
Assets: $8,681,100,000
Liabilities: $4,683,800,000
Net Worth: $3,997,300,000
Earnings: $765,200,000
Emp.: 14,900
Fiscal Year-end: 12/31/23
Packaging Products Mfr
N.A.I.C.S.: 322220
Robert P. Mundy (CFO, Principal Acctg Officer & Exec VP)
Mark W. Kowlzan (Chm & CEO)
Kent A. Pflederer (Gen Counsel, Sec & Sr VP)
Thomas A. Hassfurther (Exec VP-Corrugated Products)
Robert A. Schneider (CIO & Sr VP)
D. Ray Shirley (Sr VP-Corp Engrg & Process Tech)
Jeff S. Kaser (Sr VP-Corrugated Products)
Bruce A. Ridley (Sr VP-Environmental Health, Safety & Operational Svcs)
Darla J. Olivier (Sr VP)

Subsidiaries:

Boise Paper - Idaho   (1)

101 S Capitol Blvd Ste 800, Boise, ID
83702
Tel.: (208) 805-1200
Web Site: http://www.boisepaper.com
N.A.I.C.S.: 322299
Mark W. Kowlzan (CEO)

Subsidiary (Non-US):

Besin Amboise SA   (2)
455 Chemin Roi, 37400, Amboise, France
Tel.: (33) 247231150
Emp.: 33
Packaging Materials Mfr
N.A.I.C.S.: 322220
Eric Santos (Gen Mgr)

Subsidiary (Domestic):

Boise White Paper, LLC   (2)
1111 W Jefferson St, Boise, ID 83728
Tel.: (208) 384-6161
Paper Products Mfr
N.A.I.C.S.: 322299
W. Thomas Stephens (CEO)

Hexacomb Corporation   (2)
1296 Barclay Blvd, Buffalo Grove, IL 60089
Tel.: (847) 955-7893
Web Site: http://www.hexacomb.com
Sales Range: $100-124.9 Million
Emp.: 440
Converted Paper Products
N.A.I.C.S.: 322299

Tharco Packaging, Inc.   (2)
10810 Painter Ave, Santa Fe Springs, CA
90670
Tel.: (510) 276-8600
Web Site: http://www.boiseinc.com
Holding Company; Box & Packaging Materi-
als Mfr
N.A.I.C.S.: 551112

Subsidiary (Domestic):

Tharco Containers, Inc.   (3)
2222 Grant Ave, San Lorenzo, CA 94580-
1804
Tel.: (510) 276-8600
Web Site: http://www.tharco.com
Sales Range: $200-249.9 Million
Emp.: 1,100
Corrugated & Solid Fiber Boxes Mfr
N.A.I.C.S.: 322211

Subsidiary (Domestic):

Tharco Containers Texas, Inc.   (4)
150 Precision, Buda, TX 78610-5856
Tel.: (512) 312-1222
Web Site: http://www.tharco.com
Emp.: 150
Corrugated Box Mfr
N.A.I.C.S.: 322211

PCA Southern Indiana Corrugated,
LLC   (1)
3460 Commerce Dr, Columbus, IN 47201
Tel.: (812) 376-9301
Emp.: 4
Containerboard & Corrugated Product Mfr
N.A.I.C.S.: 322211

Packaging Corporation of America -
Chicago Full-Line Plant   (1)
5445 W 73rd St, Bedford Park, IL 60638
Tel.: (708) 821-1600
Web Site: http://www.packagingcorp.com
Corrugated & Solid Fiber Boxes
N.A.I.C.S.: 322211

Packaging Corporation of America -
Huntsville Sheet Plant   (1)
222 Celtic Dr, Madison, AL 35758
Tel.: (256) 772-9696
Web Site: https://www.packagingcorp.com
Corrugated Package Box Mfr
N.A.I.C.S.: 322211

Packaging Corporation of Illinois (1)
5445 W 73rd St, Bedford Park, IL 60638
Tel.: (708) 821-1600
Packaging Material Whslr
N.A.I.C.S.: 423840
Steve Toffler (Gen Mgr)

PACTIV EVERGREEN INC.
1900 W Field Ct, Lake Forest, IL
60045

Tel.: (847) 482-2000   NZ
Web Site:
   https://www.pactivevergreen.com
PTVE—(NASDAQ)
Rev.: $5,510,000,000
Assets: $6,395,000,000
Liabilities: $5,046,000,000
Net Worth: $1,349,000,000
Earnings: ($223,000,000)
Emp.: 15,000
Fiscal Year-end: 12/31/23
Holding Company; Beverage & Food-
service Packaging Products Mfr &
Whslr
N.A.I.C.S.: 551112
Jonathan H. Baksht (CFO & Principal
Acctg Officer)
Tim Levenda (Pres-Foodservice)
Frank Petlak (VP-Innovation & New
Product Dev)
J. D. Bowlin (Chief HR & Comm Offi-
cer)
Lynn Dyer (Chief Sustainability & Pub
Affairs Officer)
Chandra Mitchell (Chief Legal Officer)
Byron Racki (Chief Growth Officer)
Mark Dutt (Sr VP)
Charles Whittington (Sr VP)
Ricardo Alvergue (VP)
Robyn Barber (Dir)
Mike Betz (CIO)
Dave Bogan (VP)
Rich Boucher (VP)
Ron Boyer (Sr VP)
Jody Campbell (VP)
Jordan Cheifetz (CFO)
Dewitt Clark (VP)
Sandy Cobden (VP)
Joel Corder (VP)
Terry Coyne (Sr Dir)
Tommy Darby (VP)
Christi Dees (VP)
David Dinius (Dir)
Mike Finnamore (VP)
Rafael Garcia (VP)
Joel Hanik (VP)
Dan Henderlight (VP)
Beth Kelly (Sr Dir)
Steve Kipnis (Dir)
Ryan Lindenberg (Mgr)
Myron Lee (Dir)
John Maloney (VP)
Michael J. King (Pres & CEO)

Subsidiaries:

Dopaco, Inc.   (1)
100 Arrandale Blvd, Exton, PA
19341   (100%)
Tel.: (610) 269-1776
Sales Range: $450-499.9 Million
Emp.: 1,700
Cup & Folding Carton Mfr
N.A.I.C.S.: 322212

Fabri-Kal Corporation   (1)
Plastics Pl, Kalamazoo, MI 49001
Tel.: (269) 385-5050
Web Site: http://www.fabrikal.com
Sales Range: $75-99.9 Million
Emp.: 1,000
Mfr of Plastic Products
N.A.I.C.S.: 326199
R. P. Kittredge (CEO)

Graham Packaging Holdings
Company   (1)
700 Indian Springs Dr, Lancaster, PA 17601
Tel.: (717) 849-8500
Web Site: http://www.grahampackaging.com
Holding Company; Plastic Container De-
signer, Mfr & Sales
N.A.I.C.S.: 551112
Dorota Przybysz (Mgr-HR)

Subsidiary (Domestic):

Graham Packaging Company
Inc.   (2)
700 Indian Springs Dr Ste 100, Lancaster,
PA 17601
Tel.: (717) 849-8500

Web Site:
   https://www.grahampackaging.com
Sales Range: $1-4.9 Billion
Emp.: 8,300
Customized Blow-Molded Plastic Containers
Mfr
N.A.I.C.S.: 325211
Robert Pyle (Pres)
Tracee Auld (Chief Strategy Officer)
Doug Cassel (Gen Counsel)
Stephen Estok (Pres)
Kevin Gilligan (Pres)
Desen Lu (Sr VP)
Rolfe Olsen (Pres)
Lisa Santin (Exec VP)
Chad Stephens (Chief Technical Officer)
Kris Warfel (CFO)

Subsidiary (Non-US):

Graham Packaging Company Italia
S.r.l.   (3)
Via della Tecnica 1, 40023, Castel Guelfo di
Bologna, Bologna, Italy
Tel.: (39) 0542 639901
Web Site: http://www.technespa.com
Industrial Mold Mfr
N.A.I.C.S.: 333511

Graham Packaging France,
S.A.S.   (3)
4 Rue Joseph Monier, 92859, Rueil-
Malmaison, France
Tel.: (33) 41290539
Web Site:
   http://www.grahampackagingeurope.com
Sales Range: $25-49.9 Million
Emp.: 15
Plastic Containers Mfr
N.A.I.C.S.: 325211

Subsidiary (Non-US):

Graham Packaging Company BV (4)
Vossendaal 12, 4878 AE, Etten-Leur, Neth-
erlands
Tel.: (31) 76 501 40 00
Web Site: http://www.gpceurope.eu
Emp.: 65
Pet Bottle Mfr
N.A.I.C.S.: 332439
Will Huijps (Controller-Fin)

Graham Packaging Company
OY   (4)
Merimiestie, 12310, Helsinki, Finland
Tel.: (358) 10 279 5004
Pet Bottle Mfr
N.A.I.C.S.: 332439
Kari Kattainen (Plant Mgr)

Graham Packaging Plastics Ltd. (4)
Irton House Tower Estate Warpsgrove Lane
Industrial Estate, Chalgrove, OX44 7TH,
Oxfordshire, United Kingdom
Tel.: (44) 1865893000
Pet Bottle Mfr
N.A.I.C.S.: 332439
Simone Gill (Key Acct Mgr)

Graham Packaging Poland Sp.
z.o.o.   (4)
Ul Zelazna 32, 05-071, Warsaw, Poland
Tel.: (48) 22 7830910
Pet Bottle Mfr
N.A.I.C.S.: 332439

Graham Plastpak Plastik Ambalaj
Sanayi A.S.   (4)
Eski Izmit ankara Yolu Uzeri Tepeoren-
Mevkii Akfirat No 54 Tuzla, 234959, Istan-
bul, Turkiye
Tel.: (90) 216 304 06 10
Pet Bottle Mfr
N.A.I.C.S.: 332439
Ziya Etig (Mgr-Production)

Pactiv LLC   (1)
1900 W Field Ct, Lake Forest, IL 60045-
4828
Tel.: (847) 482-2000
Sales Range: $1-4.9 Billion
Emp.: 12,000
Specialty Packaging Products Mfr
N.A.I.C.S.: 322220

Subsidiary (Domestic):

International Tray Pads & Packaging,
Inc.   (2)

3299 NC 5 Hwy, Aberdeen, NC 28315
Tel.: (910) 944-1800
Sales Range: $1-9.9 Million
Emp.: 35
Urethane & Other Foam Product, except
Polystyrene, Mfr
N.A.I.C.S.: 326150
Shaen Kirkpatrick (Mgr-Sls)

PWP Industries, Inc.   (2)
5500 S Boyle Ave, Vernon, CA 90058-3933
Tel.: (323) 513-9000
Web Site: http://www.pwpindustries.com
Sales Range: $125-149.9 Million
Emp.: 600
Plastic Food Packaging Products Mfr &
Whslr
N.A.I.C.S.: 326199

Plant (Domestic):

Pactiv Corp. - Beech Island   (2)
578 Old Jackson Hwy, Beech Island, SC
29842
Tel.: (803) 827-5200
Sales Range: $125-149.9 Million
Polystyrene Products, Disposable Food &
Produce Containers
N.A.I.C.S.: 326199
Joseph Garrison (Gen Mgr)

Pactiv Corp. - Belvidere   (2)
801 5th Ave, Belvidere, IL 61008-5110
Tel.: (815) 547-1200
Web Site: http://www.pactiv.com
Sales Range: $25-49.9 Million
Emp.: 52
Microwave Food Container Mfr
N.A.I.C.S.: 326199
Kevin J. Bohan (Sr Dir-HR)
Joe Sangregorio (VP-HR)
Kevin Quinn (VP-Ops)
Mike Oliver (Chief HR Officer & VP)
Darci Lorenzo (Mgr-Carrier, Transportation
& Logistics)

Subsidiary (Domestic):

Prairie Packaging, Inc.   (2)
7200 S Mason Ave, Bedford Park, IL
60638-6226
Tel.: (708) 496-2900
Sales Range: $350-399.9 Million
Tableware & Foodservice Products
N.A.I.C.S.: 326199

Reynolds Consumer Products
Inc.   (1)
1900 W Field Ct, Lake Forest, IL 60045
Tel.: (224) 295-6800
Web Site: https://www.reynoldsconsumerpro
ducts.com
Rev.: $3,756,000,000
Assets: $4,780,000,000
Liabilities: $2,797,000,000
Net Worth: $1,983,000,000
Earnings: $298,000,000
Emp.: 6,000
Fiscal Year-end: 12/31/2023
Flexible Packaging, Aluminum Foil & Clo-
sure System Mfr
N.A.I.C.S.: 322220
Chris Mayrhofer (Principal Acctg Officer, Sr
VP & Controller)
V. Lance Mitchell (Pres & CEO)
Scott E. Huckins (CFO, Treas & VP)
Judith Buckner (Pres-Reynolds Cooking &
Baking)
Richard Noll (Chm)
Mark Swartzberg (VP-IR)
Lisa Smith (Pres-Hefty Waste & Storage)
Steve Estes (Chief Admin Officer)
Rita Fisher (CIO & Exec VP-Supply Chain)
Christopher Corey (Pres-Presto Products)
Rachel R. Bishop (Pres-Hefty Tableware)

Subsidiary (Non-US):

Baco Consumer Products Ltd. (2)
Raans Road, Amersham, HP6 6JY, Bucks,
United Kingdom
Tel.: (44) 1494656800
Web Site: http://www.baco.co.uk
Sales Range: $200-249.9 Million
Emp.: 300
Aluminum Foil Mfr
N.A.I.C.S.: 331318

Reynolds Consumer Products
Canada Inc.   (2)

Pactiv Evergreen Inc.—(Continued)

6500 Tomken Road, Mississauga, L5T 2E9,
ON, Canada
Tel.: (224) 295-6801
Sales Range: $25-49.9 Million
Emp.: 200
Household Foil Product & Packaging Mfr &
Whslr
N.A.I.C.S.: 331315

Subsidiary (Domestic):

Reynolds Presto Products Inc.   **(2)**
670 N Perkins St, Appleton, WI 54912-2399
Tel.: (920) 739-9471
Web Site: http://www.prestoproducts.com
Sales Range: $550-599.9 Million
Emp.: 600
Plastic Bag, Wrap & Food Container Mfr
N.A.I.C.S.: 326112

Reynolds Flexible Packaging   **(1)**
6641 W Broad St, Richmond, VA 23230
Tel.: (804) 281-2600
Web Site: http://www.reynoldspkg.com
Sales Range: $25-49.9 Million
Emp.: 100
Plastic & Foil Food, Pharmaceutical & Re-
tail Packaging Mfr
N.A.I.C.S.: 326112

Plant (Domestic):

**Reynolds Flexible Packaging-
Bellwood Printing Plant**   **(2)**
2001 Reymet Rd, Richmond, VA 23237
Tel.: (804) 743-6231
Web Site: http://www.reynoldspkg.com
Sales Range: $125-149.9 Million
Rotogravure Packaging Printing Plant
N.A.I.C.S.: 323111

**Reynolds Flexible Packaging-
Grottoes Plastics Plant**   **(2)**
149 Grand Taverns Dr, Grottoes, VA 24441
Tel.: (540) 249-5711
Web Site: http://www.reynoldspkg.com
Plastic Packaging Mfr
N.A.I.C.S.: 326113

Reynolds Food Packaging LLC   **(1)**
Tel.: (804) 281-2000
Disposable Food Container & Packaging
Mfr
N.A.I.C.S.: 322219

Plant (Non-US):

Reynolds Food Packaging   **(2)**
Tel.: (606) 256-5164
Sales Range: $75-99.9 Million
Emp.: 80
Plastic Food Containers Mfr
N.A.I.C.S.: 326199

Reynolds Food Packaging   **(2)**
Tel.: (724) 458-1800
Sales Range: $150-199.9 Million
Emp.: 230
Food Packaging Mfr
N.A.I.C.S.: 322220

Reynolds Food Packaging   **(2)**
Tel.: (763) 428-8340
Web Site: http://www.reynoldspkg.com
Sales Range: $300-349.9 Million
Emp.: 300
Food Packaging Mfr
N.A.I.C.S.: 322220

**Reynolds Food
Packaging-Chicago**   **(2)**
Tel.: (847) 945-9100
Web Site: http://www.reynoldspkg.com
Disposable Food Container & Packaging
Mfr
N.A.I.C.S.: 326113

PACWEST EQUITIES, INC.
8145 Signal Ct, Sacramento, CA
95824   NV
Year Founded: 2004
PWEI—(OTCIQ)
Financial Consulting Services
N.A.I.C.S.: 541611
Geoff Bagatelos (Pres)

PAGAYA TECHNOLOGIES LTD.

90 Park Ave 20th Fl, New York, NY
10016
Tel.: (646) 710-7714   II
Web Site: https://www.pagaya.com
Year Founded: 2016
PGY—(NASDAQ)
Rev.: $812,051,000
Assets: $1,208,376,000
Liabilities: $542,627,000
Net Worth: $665,749,000
Earnings: ($196,739,000)
Emp.: 142
Fiscal Year-end: 12/31/23
Software Development Services
N.A.I.C.S.: 541511

PAGERDUTY, INC.
600 Townsend St Ste 125, San Fran-
cisco, CA 94103
Tel.: (650) 989-2965   DE
Web Site: https://www.pagerduty.com
Year Founded: 2010
PD—(NYSE)
Rev.: $370,793,000
Assets: $817,873,000
Liabilities: $576,895,000
Net Worth: $240,978,000
Earnings: ($128,423,000)
Emp.: 1,166
Fiscal Year-end: 01/31/23
Information Technology Support Ser-
vices
N.A.I.C.S.: 541512
Owen Howard Wilson (CFO & Interim
Principal Acctg Officer)
Jennifer Tejada (Chm & CEO)
Jukka Alanen (Sr VP-Bus Dev & Corp
Strategy)
Tim Armandpour (CTO)
Olivia Khalili (Exec Dir-Social Impact
& Corp Responsibility)
Jonathan Rende (Sr VP & Gen Mgr-
Customer Svc)
Alex Solomon (Co-Founder & Gen
Mgr)
Baskar Puvanathasan (Co-Founder)
Andrew Gregory Miklas (Co-Founder)
Joe Militello (Chief People Officer)
Sean Scott (Chief Product Officer)
Manjula Talreja (Chief Customer Offi-
cer)
Katherine Post Calvert (CMO)
Mitra Rezvan (Principal Acctg Officer)
Shelley Webb (Gen Counsel & Sr
VP Legal)
Jeremy Kmet (Sr VP-Global Field
Ops)
Eric Johnson (CIO)

PAID, INC.
225 Cedar Hill St Ste 200, Marlbor-
ough, MA 01752
Tel.: (617) 861-6050   DE
Web Site: http://paid.com
PAYD—(OTCIQ)
Rev.: $16,585,929
Assets: $6,421,724
Liabilities: $3,049,612
Net Worth: $3,372,112
Earnings: $652,146
Emp.: 22
Fiscal Year-end: 12/31/22
Brand Management, Brand Market-
ing, Social Media Marketing, Product
Design, Product Merchandising &
Website Design to Businesses & Ce-
lebrity Clients
N.A.I.C.S.: 541890
William Austin Lewis IV (Pres, CEO,
CFO & CFO)

PALANTIR TECHNOLOGIES
INC.
1200 17th St Fl 15, Denver, CO
80202
Tel.: (720) 358-3679   DE

Web Site: https://www.palantir.com
Year Founded: 2003
PLTR—(NYSE)
Rev.: $2,225,012,000
Assets: $4,522,425,000
Liabilities: $961,460,000
Net Worth: $3,560,965,000
Earnings: $209,825,000
Emp.: 3,735
Fiscal Year-end: 12/31/23
Software Development Services
N.A.I.C.S.: 541511
Shyam Sankar (CTO & Exec VP)
Stephen Cohen (Co-Founder, Pres &
Sec)
David Glazer (CFO & Treas)
Ryan Taylor (Chief Legal Officer &
Chief Revenue Officer)
Peter Thiel (Co-Founder)
Heather Planishek (Chief Acctg Offi-
cer)
Alexander C. Karp (Co-Founder &
CEO)

PALATIN TECHNOLOGIES INC.
4 B Cedar Brook Dr Cedar Brook
Corporate Center, Cranbury, NJ
08512
Tel.: (609) 495-2200   DE
Web Site: https://www.palatin.com
Year Founded: 1996
PTN—(NYSEAMEX)
Rev.: $4,490,090
Assets: $10,742,266
Liabilities: $10,853,763
Net Worth: ($111,497)
Earnings: ($29,736,113)
Emp.: 30
Fiscal Year-end: 06/30/24
Biopharmaceutical Research & De-
velopment
N.A.I.C.S.: 325412
Nicole Pederson (Exec Dir-Quality
Assurance)
Samrat Sisodia (Exec Dir-Regulatory
Affairs)
Robert Jordan (Sr VP-Program Ops)
John Dodd (Sr VP-Preclinical Dev)
Paul Kayne (Exec Dir-Biological Sci-
ences)
James E. Hattersley (Sr VP-Bus Dev)
Stephen A. Slusher (Chief Legal Offi-
cer & Asst Sec)
Stephen T. Wills (CFO, COO, Treas
& Sec)

PALAYAN RESOURCES, INC.
850 Teague Trail Ste 580, Lady Lake,
FL 32159
Tel.: (407) 536-9422   NV
Year Founded: 2013
PLYN—(OTCIQ)
Rev.: $142,104
Assets: $3,167
Liabilities: $507,245
Net Worth: ($504,078)
Earnings: ($293,045)
Fiscal Year-end: 03/31/22
Gold Mining
N.A.I.C.S.: 212220
James E. Jenkins (Pres, CEO, CFO,
Chm, Treas & Sec)

PALEO RESOURCES, INC.
716 S Frio St Ste 201, San Antonio,
TX 78207
Tel.: (254) 699-0975   QC
Web Site:
http://www.paleoresources.com
Year Founded: 1946
PRE—(OTCIQ)
Rev.: $3,078,291
Assets: $10,528,911
Liabilities: $7,378,713
Net Worth: $3,150,198
Earnings: $1,479,561

Fiscal Year-end: 12/31/19
Oil & Gas Exploration Services
N.A.I.C.S.: 211120
Paul C. Sewell (Sec)
Casey Minshew (Chief Comml Offi-
cer)
Kim Vo (CFO)
Roger S. Braugh Jr. (Chm & CEO-
Interim)
Thomas M. Crain Jr. (Pres)

PALISADE BIO, INC.
7750 El Camino Real Ste 2A, Carls-
bad, CA 92009
Tel.: (858) 704-4900   DE
Web Site:
https://www.palisadebio.com
Year Founded: 1996
PALI—(NASDAQ)
Rev.: $1,461,000
Assets: $15,763,000
Liabilities: $3,284,000
Net Worth: $12,479,000
Earnings: ($14,260,000)
Emp.: 12
Fiscal Year-end: 12/31/22
Stem Cell Research & Development
Services
N.A.I.C.S.: 541715
Mitchell L. Jones (Chief Medical Offi-
cer)
J. D. Finley (Interim CEO & CFO)
Robert McRae (COO)
Nicholas McCoy (VP)

PALLADYNE AI CORP.
650 S 500 W Ste 150, Salt Lake City,
UT 84101
Tel.: (801) 456-9910   DE
Web Site:
https://www.palladyneai.com
Year Founded: 2020
PDYN—(NASDAQ)
Rev.: $14,569,000
Assets: $167,625,000
Liabilities: $23,175,000
Net Worth: $144,450,000
Earnings: ($157,130,000)
Emp.: 280
Fiscal Year-end: 12/31/22
Investment Services
N.A.I.C.S.: 523999
Benjamin G. Wolff (Chm)
Sam S. Potter (VP-Corp Dev)
Denis Garagic (CTO)
Laura J. Peterson (Vice Chm)
Benjamin G. Wolff (Co-Founder, Pres
& CEO)

Subsidiaries:

Re2, Inc.   **(1)**
32 39th St, Pittsburgh, PA 15201
Tel.: (412) 681-6382
Web Site: http://www.resquared.com
Sales Range: $1-9.9 Million
Emp.: 46
Robotic Technologies Developers
N.A.I.C.S.: 541519
Jorgen Pedersen (Pres & CEO)
Keith Gunnett (CTO)
Patrick Rowe (VP-R&D)
Douglas Peters (VP-Ops)
Heeg Allen (Dir-Bus Dev)
Jack Reinhart (Dir-Product & Project Mgmt)
Mike Cozza (VP-Engrg)

PALMER SQUARE CAPITAL
BDC INC.
1900 Shawnee Mission Pkwy Ste
315, Mission Woods, KS 66205
Tel.: (816) 994-3200   MD
Web Site:
https://www.palmersquarebdc.com
Year Founded: 2019
PSBD—(NYSE)
Rev.: $74,499,900
Assets: $1,057,453,028
Liabilities: $694,009,546

Net Worth: $363,443,482
Earnings: $41,080,832
Emp.: 370
Fiscal Year-end: 12/31/22
Investment Services
N.A.I.C.S.: 523940
Christopher D. Long *(Pres, CEO & Chm)*
Jeffrey D. Fox *(CFO & Treas)*

PALMETTO REAL ESTATE TRUST

45 Liberty Ln, Greenville, SC 29607-2341
Tel.: (803) 233-6007
PTTTS—(NASDAQ)
Offices of Real Estate Agents & Brokers
N.A.I.C.S.: 531210
Laney Younts *(Pres)*

PALO ALTO NETWORKS, INC.

3000 Tannery Way, Santa Clara, CA 95054
Tel.: (408) 753-4000   DE
Web Site:
  https://www.paloaltonetworks.com
Year Founded: 2005
PANW—(NASDAQ)
Rev.: $8,027,500,000
Assets: $19,990,900,000
Liabilities: $14,821,200,000
Net Worth: $5,169,700,000
Earnings: $2,577,600,000
Emp.: 15,289
Fiscal Year-end: 07/31/24
Internet Security Software
N.A.I.C.S.: 513210
Amit K. Singh *(Chief Bus Officer)*
Nir Zuk *(CTO)*
Lee Klarich *(Chief Product Officer)*
Liane Hornsey *(Exec VP)*
Eric Trexler *(Sr VP-US Pub Sector)*
Jean Compeau *(Deputy CFO)*
Liane Hornsey *(Chief People Officer)*
Patricia A. Hatter *(Chief Customer Officer)*
Mario Queiroz *(Exec VP-Special Projects)*
Dipak Golechha *(CFO & Exec VP)*
William Jenkins *(Pres)*
Zeynep Inanoglu Ozdemir *(CMO)*
Bruce Byrd *(Gen Counsel)*
Patty Hatter *(Chief Customer Officer)*
Meerah Rajavel *(CIO)*
Helmut Reisinger *(CEO-Europe, Middle East & Africa & Latin America)*
Josh Paul *(Chief Acctg Officer)*
Nikesh Arora *(Chm & CEO)*

Subsidiaries:

CloudGenix Inc.   (1)
2933 Bunker Hill Ln 205, Santa Clara, CA 95054
Tel.: (916) 960-9161
Web Site: http://www.cloudgenix.com
Computer Network Software Developer
N.A.I.C.S.: 513210
Kumar Ramachandran *(Co-Founder)*
Venkataraman Anand *(Co-Founder)*
Mani Ramasamy *(Co-Founder)*

PANW (Portugal) Unipessoal, LDA   (1)
Centro Empresarial Torres de Lisboa Rue Tomas da Fonseca Torre G, 1600-209, Lisbon, Portugal
Tel.: (351) 208084600
Cloud Network Security Services
N.A.I.C.S.: 518210

Palo Alto Networks (EU) B.V.   (1)
Beethovenstraat 539, 1083 HK, Amsterdam, Netherlands
Tel.: (31) 208881883
Software Development Services
N.A.I.C.S.: 513210

Palo Alto Networks (Israel Analytics) Ltd.   (1)

94a Yigal Alon St Alon 1 Tower 12th floor, Tel Aviv, 6789155, Israel
Tel.: (972) 39786844
Software Development Services
N.A.I.C.S.: 513210

Palo Alto Networks Denmark ApS   (1)
Lautruphoej 1-3, Ballerup, 2750, Copenhagen, Denmark
Tel.: (45) 80251668
Software Development Services
N.A.I.C.S.: 513210

Palo Alto Networks Saudi Arabian Limited Company   (1)
Building 13 Laysen Valley Ground Floor Levels 1 2 3, PO Box 99939, Riyadh, Central, Saudi Arabia
Tel.: (966) 21484656
Software Development Services
N.A.I.C.S.: 513210

RedLock, Inc.   (1)
101 Jefferson Dr Ste 225, Menlo Park, CA 94025
Tel.: (650) 665-9480
Internet Security Software Services
N.A.I.C.S.: 513210

PALOMA RESOURCES, LLC

1100 Louisiana Ste 5100, Houston, TX 77002
Tel.: (713) 650-8500
Web Site:
  http://www.palomaresources.com
Year Founded: 2004
PLO.H—(TSX)
Oil & Gas Exploration Services
N.A.I.C.S.: 213112
Christopher N. O'sullivan *(Pres)*

PALOMAR HOLDINGS, INC.

7979 Ivanhoe Ave Ste 500, La Jolla, CA 92037
Tel.: (619) 567-5290   DE
Web Site: https://plmr.com
Year Founded: 2013
PLMR—(NASDAQ)
Rev.: $327,086,000
Assets: $1,306,450,000
Liabilities: $921,696,000
Net Worth: $384,754,000
Earnings: $52,170,000
Emp.: 191
Fiscal Year-end: 12/31/22
Holding Company
N.A.I.C.S.: 523999
Mac Armstrong *(Co-Founder & CEO)*
Jon Christianson *(Pres)*
T. Christopher Uchida *(CFO)*
Angela Grant *(Chief Legal Officer)*
Jon Knutzen *(Chief Risk Officer)*
Robert Beyerle *(Chief Underwriting Officer)*
Elizabeth Seitz *(Treas, Exec VP & Financial Ops)*
Jake Armstrong *(Exec VP-Operations)*
Matthew Grunewald *(Exec VP-Reinsurance)*
Kyle Morgan *(Exec VP-Corp & Business Development)*
Jason Sears *(Exec VP & Head)*
Ethan Genteman *(Exec VP & Head)*

PALTALK, INC.

Tel.: (212) 967-5120   DE
Web Site: https://www.paltalk.com
Year Founded: 2005
PALT—(NASDAQ)
Rev.: $10,989,545
Assets: $25,431,608
Liabilities: $4,457,366
Net Worth: $20,974,242
Earnings: ($3,412,250)
Emp.: 19
Fiscal Year-end: 12/31/22
Online Dating Services & Applications
N.A.I.C.S.: 812990

Jason Katz *(Chm, Pres, CEO & COO)*
Kara Jenny *(CFO)*

PANACEA LIFE SCIENCES HOLDINGS, INC.

16194 W 45th Dr, Golden, CO 80403
Web Site: https://panacealife.com
Year Founded: 2008
PLSH—(OTCQB)
Rev.: $1,626,978
Assets: $19,489,449
Liabilities: $21,633,993
Net Worth: ($2,144,544)
Earnings: ($9,142,584)
Emp.: 19
Fiscal Year-end: 12/31/22
Offices of Other Holding Companies
N.A.I.C.S.: 551112
Lawrence J. Wert *(Chm)*
Leslie Buttorff *(CEO & CFO)*

PANAMERA HOLDINGS CORPORATION

2000 W Loop S Ste 1820, Houston, TX 77027
Tel.: (713) 878-7200   NV
Web Site:
  https://panameraholdings.com
Year Founded: 2014
PHCI—(OTCIQ)
Rev.: $100,001
Assets: $129,602
Liabilities: $79,884
Net Worth: $49,718
Earnings: ($7,124,658)
Fiscal Year-end: 07/31/23
Holding Company
N.A.I.C.S.: 551112
Curtis Summers *(Co-Founder, Chm, Pres & CEO)*
Douglas G. Baker *(Co-Founder, CFO, Treas & Sec)*

PANBELA THERAPEUTICS, INC.

712 Vista Blvd Ste 305, Waconia, MN 55387
Tel.: (952) 479-1196   UT
Web Site: https://www.panbela.com
Year Founded: 1995
PBLA—(NASDAQ)
Rev.: $14,000
Assets: $4,978,000
Liabilities: $13,027,000
Net Worth: ($8,049,000)
Earnings: ($34,933,000)
Emp.: 6
Fiscal Year-end: 12/31/22
Pharmaceutical Preparation Mfr
N.A.I.C.S.: 325412
Michael T. Cullen *(Chm)*
Suzanne Gagnon *(Chief Medical Officer)*
Susan Horvath *(CFO, Treas, Sec & VP-Fin)*
Jennifer K. Simpson *(Pres & CEO)*
Jeffrey S. Mathiesen *(Vice Chm)*
Elizabeth Bruckheimer *(Chief Scientific Officer)*
Ashok Chavan *(VP)*
Rachel Bragg *(VP)*

Subsidiaries:

Cancer Prevention Pharmaceuticals, Inc.   (1)
1760 E River Rd Ste 250, Tucson, AZ 85718
Tel.: (520) 908-7774
Web Site: http://www.canprevent.com
Biopharmaceutical Product Mfr
N.A.I.C.S.: 325412
Jeffrey Jacob *(Chm & CEO)*
Eugene W. Gerner *(Chief Scientific Officer)*
Kathryn Grenier *(VP-Clinical Ops)*
Alfred M. Cohen *(Chief Medical Officer)*
Elizabeth Bruckheimer *(VP-Drug Dev)*

Christopher R. Richied *(CFO)*
Michelle Boytim *(Program Mgr)*
Christine Brannen *(Mgr-Ops)*

PANELTECH INTERNATIONAL HOLDINGS, INC.

2999 John Stevens Way, Hoquiam, WA 98550
Tel.: (360) 538-1480   DE
Year Founded: 2006
PNLT—(OTCIQ)
Paper Products Mfr
N.A.I.C.S.: 322299
Leroy A. Nott *(Pres & CEO)*
Scott Olmstead *(CFO & Sec)*

PANGAEA LOGISTICS SOLUTIONS LTD.

109 Long Wharf, Newport, RI 02840
Tel.: (401) 846-7790   BM
Web Site:
  https://www.pangaeals.com
Year Founded: 2014
PANL—(NASDAQ)
Rev.: $699,706,906
Assets: $748,241,470
Liabilities: $379,519,940
Net Worth: $368,721,530
Earnings: $79,491,413
Emp.: 70
Fiscal Year-end: 12/31/22
Holding Company; Freight Shipping Services
N.A.I.C.S.: 551112
Carl Claus Boggild *(Co-Founder & Pres)*
Mads Boye Petersen *(COO)*
Peter Koken *(Dir-Comml)*
Neil McLaughlin *(Dir-Projects & Fin)*
Barbara Gradley *(Office Mgr)*
Steve Tremblay *(Dir-IT)*
Courtney Renault *(Dir-Global Chartering)*
Brent Mahana *(VP-Business Development)*
Mark L. Filanowski *(CEO & Dir)*
Gianni Del Signore *(CFO & CFO)*
Sam Sirrico *(VP-Ops & Dir-Ports, Projects, and Logistics)*
Eric S. Rosenfeld *(Dir)*
Richard T. du Moulin *(Chm & Dir)*

Subsidiaries:

Bulk Partners (Bermuda) Ltd.   (1)
109 Long Wharf 2nd Fl, Newport, RI 02840   **(100%)**
Tel.: (401) 846-7790
Web Site:
  http://www.bulkcommercialservices.com
Sales Range: $350-399.9 Million
Emp.: 25
Freight Shipping Services
N.A.I.C.S.: 483111
Anthony Laura *(CFO)*
Carl Claus Boggild *(Pres)*

Nordic Bulk Carriers A/S   (1)
Tuborg Havnevej 4-8 1st Floor, 2900, Hellerup, Denmark
Tel.: (45) 39100800
Web Site: http://www.nordicbulkcarriers.com
Marine Cargo Handling Services
N.A.I.C.S.: 488320

Nordic Bulk Carriers Singapore Pte. Ltd.   (1)
24C Duxton Hill, Singapore, 089607, Singapore
Tel.: (65) 31585792
Maritime Transportation Services
N.A.I.C.S.: 483111

Phoenix Bulk Carriers (US) LLC   (1)
109 Long Wharf, Newport, RI 02840
Tel.: (401) 846-7790
Web Site: http://www.pangaeals.com
Emp.: 25
Freight Transportation Services
N.A.I.C.S.: 488510

Seamar Management S.A.   (1)

Pangaea Logistics Solutions Ltd.—(Continued)

Leof Kifisias 90, 15125, Maroussi, Greece
Tel.: (30) 2109242484
Web Site: https://www.seamar.gr
Ship Management & Consultancy Services
N.A.I.C.S.: 541618

PANORAMA CAPITAL CORP.

2440 Sand Hill Rd Ste 302, Menlo Park, CA 94025
Tel.: (650) 234-1450   DE
Web Site:
   http://www.panoramacapital.com
PANO.P—(TSXV)
Assets: $420,163
Liabilities: $4,056
Net Worth: $416,107
Earnings: ($84,835)
Fiscal Year-end: 02/29/20
Asset Management Services
N.A.I.C.S.: 523940

Subsidiaries:

Presidio Pharmaceuticals, Inc.   (1)
1700 Owens St Ste 184, San Francisco, CA 94158
Tel.: (415) 655-7560
Web Site: http://www.presidiopharma.com
Pharmaceuticals Product Mfr
N.A.I.C.S.: 325412

PAPA JOHN'S INTERNA-
TIONAL, INC.

2002 Papa Johns Blvd, Louisville, KY 40299-2367
Tel.: (502) 261-7272   DE
Web Site:
   https://www.papajohns.com
Year Founded: 1985
PZZA—(NASDAQ)
Rev.: $2,102,103,000
Assets: $864,227,000
Liabilities: $1,134,891,000
Net Worth: ($270,664,000)
Earnings: $67,772,000
Emp.: 12,000
Fiscal Year-end: 12/31/22
Restaurant Operators
N.A.I.C.S.: 722513
Caroline Miller Oyler (Chief Legal & Risk Officer & Sec)
Justin Falciola (CTO & Chief Insights Officer)
Mark Shambura (CMO)
Shane Hutchins (Chief Supply Chain Officer)
Amanda Clark (Chief Dev Officer)
Joe Sieve (Chief Restaurant Officer)
Harrison Sheffield (Sr Mgr-Comm)
Elias Reyna (Chief People & Diversity Officer)
Chris Collins (VP-Tax & Treasury)
Todd Allan Penegor (Pres & CEO)
Ravi Thanawala (CFO & Principal Acctg Officer)

Subsidiaries:

Trans Papa Logistics, Inc.   (1)
2002 Papa Johns Blvd, Louisville, KY 40299
Tel.: (502) 261-7272
Emp.: 16
Restaurant Operating Services
N.A.I.C.S.: 722511

PAPERCLIP INC.

1 University Plz Ste 518, Hackensack, NJ 07601
Tel.: (201) 525-1221   DE
Web Site: https://www.paperclip.com
Year Founded: 1991
PCPJ—(OTCIQ)
Paper Product Distr
N.A.I.C.S.: 424130
William Weiss (Founder & CEO)
D. Michael Bridges (Pres)
Michael Suleski (VP-Dev)

PAPERFREE MEDICAL SOLU-
TIONS, INC.

3445 Lawrence Ave, Oceanside, NY 11572
Tel.: (646) 768-8417   NV
PFMS—(OTCIQ)
Medical Record Management Services
N.A.I.C.S.: 621999
David Lazar (CEO)

PAR PACIFIC HOLDINGS, INC.

825 Town and Country Ln Ste 1500, Houston, TX 77024
Tel.: (281) 899-4800   DE
Web Site: https://www.parpacific.com
Year Founded: 1984
PARR—(NYSE)
Rev.: $8,231,955,000
Assets: $3,863,950,000
Liabilities: $2,528,526,000
Net Worth: $1,335,424,000
Earnings: $728,642,000
Emp.: 1,814
Fiscal Year-end: 12/31/23
Holding Company; Oil Refinery & Crude Petroleum Distr
N.A.I.C.S.: 551112
Jim R. Yates (Exec VP-Retail)
William A. Monteleone (Pres & CEO)
William C. Pate (CEO)
Richard Creamer (Exec VP-Refining & Logistics)
Ashimi Patel (Dir-IR)
Shawn Flores (CFO & Sr VP)
Ryan Kelley (CIO)
Matthew Legg (Chief HR Officer)
Danielle Mattiussi (Chief Retail Officer)
Eric Wright (Sr VP-Logistics)

Subsidiaries:

Inter Island Petroleum, Inc.   (1)
1221 Mokulua Dr, Kailua, HI 96734
Tel.: (808) 263-4345
Fuel Oil Distr
N.A.I.C.S.: 424720

Island Petroleum, Inc.   (1)
10 Wharf Rd & Beach Pl, Kaunakakai, HI 96748
Tel.: (808) 553-5481
Fuel Oil Mfr
N.A.I.C.S.: 324110

Kauai Petroleum Co., Ltd.   (1)
PO Box 1128, Lihue, HI 96766
Tel.: (808) 245-4916
Fuel Oil Mfr
N.A.I.C.S.: 324110

Laramie Energy, LLC   (1)
1700 Lincoln St Ste 3950, Denver, CO 80203
Tel.: (303) 339-4400
Web Site: https://www.laramie-energy.com
Oil & Gas Well Drilling Services
N.A.I.C.S.: 213111
Robert S. Boswell (Chm & CEO)
Jim Hohenstein (VP-Land)
Ben Hamilton (CFO & Exec VP)
Chris Clark (VP-Field Ops)
Nancy Thornton (Mgr-Lease Records)

Mid Pac C3, LLC   (1)
800 Gessner Rd Ste 875, Houston, TX 77024
Tel.: (281) 899-4838
Fuel Oil Distr
N.A.I.C.S.: 424720

Par Hawaii Refining, LLC   (1)
91-325 Komohana St, Kapolei, HI 96707   (100%)
Tel.: (808) 547-3111
Web Site: http://parhawaii.com
Petroleum Refining
N.A.I.C.S.: 324110
Joseph A. Israel (Pres & CEO)

Par Hawaii, Inc.   (1)
1132 Bishop St Ste 2500, Honolulu, HI 96813

Tel.: (808) 535-5999
Web Site: http://www.parhawaii.com
Emp.: 660
Petroleum Marketer & Distr
N.A.I.C.S.: 424720
Jim R. Yates (Pres)
Eric Lee (VP-Branded Retail)
Keith Yoshida (VP-Plng & Bus Dev)
Eric Wright (Sr VP)

Par Piceance Energy Equity, LLC   (1)
800 Gessner Rd Ste 875, Houston, TX 77024
Tel.: (281) 899-4838
Petroleum Product Whslr
N.A.I.C.S.: 211120

Senter Petroleum, Inc.   (1)
3011 Aukele St, Lihue, HI 96766
Tel.: (808) 245-1911
Web Site: https://senterkauai.com
Fuel Oil Distr
N.A.I.C.S.: 424720

Texadian Energy Canada Limited   (1)
633 6th Ave SW Ste 200, Calgary, T2P 2Y5, AB, Canada
Tel.: (403) 206-3222
Gasoline Station Operator
N.A.I.C.S.: 424710

U.S. Oil Trading LLC   (1)
3001 E Marshall Ave, Tacoma, WA 98421-3116
Tel.: (253) 383-1651
Web Site: http://www.usor.com
Sales Range: $100-124.9 Million
Petroleum Refining
N.A.I.C.S.: 324110
Marcia E. Nielsen (Mgr-Admin Svcs)
Cameron G. Proudfoot (Pres)
Rupesh S. Sansgiri (Controller)
Thor A. Nielsen (CFO & VP-Fin)
Edward H. Nadler (VP-Product Supply & Mktg)
Brady Winder (VP-Mfg)

Subsidiary (Domestic):

McChord Pipeline Company   (2)
3001 Marshall Ave, Tacoma, WA 98421
Tel.: (253) 593-6085
Web Site: https://www.mcchordpipeline.com
Emp.: 200
Jet Fuel Pipeline
N.A.I.C.S.: 486910
Cameron Proudfoot (CEO)

PAR TECHNOLOGY CORPO-
RATION

8383 Seneca Turnpike Ste 3, New Hartford, NY 13413
Tel.: (315) 738-0600   DE
Web Site: https://www.partech.com
Year Founded: 1968
PAR—(NYSE)
Rev.: $355,795,000
Assets: $854,858,000
Liabilities: $479,664,000
Net Worth: $375,194,000
Earnings: ($69,319,000)
Emp.: 1,719
Fiscal Year-end: 12/31/22
Other Measuring & Controlling Device Manufacturing
N.A.I.C.S.: 334519
Candice Levy (HR)
Steven Berkovitz (CTO)
Don Wight (Chief Sls Officer)
Oliver Ostertag (Gen Mgr)
Marcus Wasdin (Gen Mgr)
Tiffany Disher (Gen Mgr)
Joseph Yetter (Gen Mgr)
Jason Riggs (Gen Mgr)
Michael A. Steenberge (Chief Acctg Officer)
Savneet Singh (Pres & CEO)

Subsidiaries:

ParTech, Inc.   (1)
8383 Seneca Tpke Ste 3, New Hartford, NY 13413   (100%)
Tel.: (315) 738-0600

Web Site: http://www.partech.com
Micro-Processor-Based Electronic Point-of-Sales Systems Mfr, Designer & Developer for the Food Industry
N.A.I.C.S.: 333310

Subsidiary (Domestic):

AccSys LLC   (2)
4010 W Boy Scout Blvd Ste 300, Tampa, FL 33607
Tel.: (813) 288-2633
Web Site: http://www.restaurantmagic.com
Back-office Restaurant Management Software Publisher
N.A.I.C.S.: 541511

PARABELLUM ACQUISITION
CORP.

3811 Turtle Creek Blvd Ste 2125, Dallas, TX 75219
Tel.: (972) 591-8349   DE
Year Founded: 2021
PRBM—(NYSE)
Investment Services
N.A.I.C.S.: 523999
Narbeh Derhacobian (Chm & CEO)
Ron Shelton (CFO)

PARADIGM MEDICAL INDUS-
TRIES, INC.

57 W 200 S Ste 310, Salt Lake City, UT 84101
Tel.: (801) 575-5000   DE
PDMI—(OTCIQ)
Medical Device Mfr & Distr
N.A.I.C.S.: 339112
Stephen A. Davis (Pres & CEO)
Heber Maughan (CFO)

PARADIGM SYSTEM SOLU-
TIONS, INC.

2173 Salk Ave Ste 250, Carlsbad, CA 92008
Tel.: (760) 579-7673   AZ
PSYS—(OTCIQ)
Computer Equipment Distr
N.A.I.C.S.: 423430
Roger E. Pawson (CEO)

PARAFIN CORP.

1111 S Roop St Ste 100, Carson City, NV 89702
Tel.: (213) 604-6504   WY
Year Founded: 1978
PFNO—(OTCIQ)
Drilling Oil & Gas Services
N.A.I.C.S.: 213111
Sidney B. Fowlds (Pres)
Darcy Fowlds (VP-Administration)
Tanya L. Wright (Treas & Sec)

PARAGON 28, INC.

14445 Grasslands Dr, Englewood, CO 80112
Tel.: (720) 399-3400   DE
Web Site:
   https://www.paragon28.com
Year Founded: 2010
FNA—(NYSE)
Rev.: $216,389,000
Assets: $340,699,000
Liabilities: $162,958,000
Net Worth: $177,741,000
Earnings: ($47,841,000)
Emp.: 574
Fiscal Year-end: 12/31/23
Medical, Dental & Hospital Equipment & Supplies Merchant Wholesalers
N.A.I.C.S.: 423450
John Shumaker (Exec VP-Sls-US)
Albert DaCosta (Co-Founder, Chm, Pres & CEO)
Kristina Wright (Interim CFO)
Chadi Chahine (CFO & Exec VP-Supply Chain Ops)

PARAGON FINANCIAL SOLUTIONS, INC.
5400 Poplar Ave Ste 350, Memphis, TN 38119
Tel.: (901) 273-2900   TN
Year Founded: 2014
PGNN—(OTCIQ)
Bank Holding Company
N.A.I.C.S.: 551111
Andrew Taylor (Exec VP)
Craig L. Weiss (Chm)
Lewis Perkins (CFO & Exec VP)
Robert S. Shaw Jr. (CEO)

PARAGON TECHNOLOGIES, INC.
101 Larry Holmes Dr Ste 500, Easton, PA 18042
Tel.: (610) 252-3205   DE
Web Site: https://www.pgntgroup.com
Year Founded: 1958
PGNT—(OTCIQ)
Rev.: $107,998,000
Assets: $42,533,000
Liabilities: $30,731,000
Net Worth: $11,802,000
Earnings: $3,601,000
Emp.: 214
Fiscal Year-end: 12/31/20
Holding Company; Automated Material Handling & Order Selection Equipment Mfr
N.A.I.C.S.: 551112
Leticia D. Cardonick (CFO)
Hesham M. Gad (Chm & CEO)

Subsidiaries:

SED International de Colombia Ltda.   (1)
Cra 1 No 7-320 Variante Chia-Cota km 1, Chia Cundinamarca, Bogota, Colombia
Tel.: (57) 18614000
Web Site: http://www.sedcolombia.com
Sales Range: $10-24.9 Million
Emp.: 83
Provider of Computers & Software
N.A.I.C.S.: 449210
Carla Giussani (VP & Gen Mgr)

SI Systems, Inc.   (1)
101 Larry Holmes Dr, Easton, PA 18042   (100%)
Tel.: (610) 252-7321
Web Site: http://www.sihs.com
Sales Range: $25-49.9 Million
Material Handling Systems & Equipment Mfr
N.A.I.C.S.: 333922
John Molloy (Pres & CEO)

Subsidiary (Domestic):

Innovative Automation, Inc.   (2)
6540 Lusk Blvd Ste C-176, San Diego, CA 92121
Tel.: (858) 452-2004
Web Site: http://www.iasoftware.com
Sales Range: $10-24.9 Million
Emp.: 5
Software Mfr
N.A.I.C.S.: 513210

PARAMOUNT GOLD NEVADA CORP.
665 Anderson St, Winnemucca, NV 89445
Tel.: (775) 625-3600   NV
Web Site:
    https://www.paramountnevada.com
PZG—(NYSEAMEX)
Rev.: $2,511,660
Assets: $56,361,612
Liabilities: $18,206,172
Net Worth: $38,155,440
Earnings: $8,056,445
Emp.: 6
Fiscal Year-end: 06/30/24
Gold Exploration & Mining
N.A.I.C.S.: 213114

Rudi P. Fronk (Chm)
Carlo Buffone (CFO)
Glen Van Treek (Pres & COO)
Rachel Goldman (CEO)
Christos Theodossiou (Dir-Corp Comm)

Subsidiaries:

New Sleeper Gold, LLC   (1)
700 Smithridge Dr, Reno, NV 89502
Tel.: (775) 813-1516
Metal Exploration Services
N.A.I.C.S.: 213114

PARAMOUNT GROUP INC.
1633 Broadway, New York, NY 10019
Tel.: (212) 237-3100   MD
Web Site: https://www.pgre.com
PGRE—(NYSE)
Rev.: $742,788,000
Assets: $8,006,215,000
Liabilities: $3,991,327,000
Net Worth: $4,014,888,000
Earnings: ($259,744,000)
Emp.: 329
Fiscal Year-end: 12/31/23
Real Estate Investment Trust
N.A.I.C.S.: 525990
Albert P. Behler (Chm, Pres & CEO)
Gage Johnson (Gen Counsel, Sec & Sr VP)
Peter R. C. Brindley (Exec VP & Head-Real Estate)
Wilbur Paes (CFO, COO & Treas)
Ermelinda Berberi (Chief Acctg Officer & Sr VP)

Subsidiaries:

1325 Avenue of the Americas, L.P.   (1)
1325 Avenue of Americas Management Office 23rd Fl, New York, NY 10019
Web Site:
    https://www.1325aveoftheamericas.info
Real Estate Manangement Services
N.A.I.C.S.: 531210

50 Beale Street LLC   (1)
1221 Ave of the Americas, New York, NY 10020
Tel.: (212) 282-2000
Asset Management Services
N.A.I.C.S.: 531390

PPF Paramount One Market Plaza Owner, L.P.   (1)
1 Market Pl, San Francisco, CA 94105
Tel.: (415) 814-6480
Emp.: 3
Commercial Building Construction Services
N.A.I.C.S.: 236220

Paramount Group Real Estate Advisor LLC   (1)
1633 Broadway Ste 1801, New York, NY 10019
Tel.: (212) 237-3100
Asset Management Services
N.A.I.C.S.: 531390

WvF-Paramount 745 Investor, L.P.   (1)
745 5th Ave, New York, NY 10151
Tel.: (212) 237-3124
Investment Advisory Services
N.A.I.C.S.: 523940

PARDEE RESOURCES COMPANY
1500 Chestnut St Ste 2 Ste 1950, Philadelphia, PA 19102
Tel.: (215) 405-1260   PA
Web Site: https://www.pardee.com
PDER—(OTCIQ)
Natural Gas Extraction
N.A.I.C.S.: 211130
Carleton P. Erdman (Pres & CEO)
William G. Foulke (Chm)
Jeffery W. Allen (VP)

Stephen D. Harp (Sr VP-Timber & Surface)
Jeffery A. Brown (Sr VP-Oil & Gas)
Steven J. Rolle (Sr VP-Fin)

PARETEUM CORPORATION
1185 Ave of the Americas, New York, NY 10036
Tel.: (646) 975-0400   DE
Web Site: http://www.pareteum.com
Year Founded: 2001
TEUM—(NASDAQ)
Rev.: $69,637,000
Assets: $61,258,000
Liabilities: $101,659,000
Net Worth: ($40,401,000)
Earnings: ($45,477,000)
Emp.: 199
Fiscal Year-end: 12/31/20
Telecommunications Software
N.A.I.C.S.: 513210
Bart Weijermars (Interim CEO & Chief Strategy Officer)
Robert Hal Turner (Founder)
Laura W. Thomas (Interim CFO)
Mary Beth Vitale (Chm)

Subsidiaries:

Artilium plc   (1)
9-13 St Andrew Street, London, EC4A 3AF, United Kingdom
Tel.: (44) 20 8133 3858
Web Site: http://www.artilium.com
Rev.: $11,180,922
Assets: $29,795,468
Liabilities: $11,177,713
Net Worth: $18,617,755
Earnings: ($1,882,742)
Emp.: 73
Fiscal Year-end: 06/30/2017
Developer of Mobile Internet Application Software
N.A.I.C.S.: 513210
Rupert Hutton (CFO)

Subsidiary (Non-US):

Artilium N.V.   (2)
Autobaan 20, Brugge, 8210, West Flanders, Belgium
Tel.: (32) 50230300
Web Site: http://www.artilium.com
Sales Range: $25-49.9 Million
Emp.: 40
Mobile Software Design Services
N.A.I.C.S.: 541511

ET Europe Holding BV   (1)
Hornweg 7, Aalsmeer, 1432 GD, Netherlands
Tel.: (31) 206535916
Software Development Services
N.A.I.C.S.: 513210

iPass, Inc.   (1)
3800 Bridge Pkwy, Redwood Shores, CA 94065
Tel.: (650) 232-4100
Web Site: http://www.ipass.com
Sales Range: $50-74.9 Million
Software-Enabled Enterprise Connectivity & Endpoint Management Services
N.A.I.C.S.: 518210
Michael J. Tedesco (Chm)

Subsidiary (Non-US):

iPass Asia Pte Ltd.   (2)
229 Mountbatten Road,, #23-02 Suntec Tower One, Singapore, 398007, Singapore
Tel.: (65) 63348783
Sales Range: $10-24.9 Million
Emp.: 7
Software-Enabled Enterprise Connectivity & Endpoint Management Services
N.A.I.C.S.: 518210

iPass Deutschland GmbH   (2)
Wiener Platz 7, D 81667, Munich, Germany
Tel.: (49) 8944142100
Web Site: http://www.ipass.de
Sales Range: $900-999.9 Million
Emp.: 6
Software-Enabled Enterprise Connectivity & Endpoint Management Services
N.A.I.C.S.: 518210

iPass India Private Limited   (2)
Level 5 Prestige Solitare, No 6 Brunton Road, Bengaluru, 560001, Karanataka, India
Tel.: (91) 8041380800
Web Site: http://www.ipass.com
Sales Range: $25-49.9 Million
Emp.: 100
Data Processing Hosting & Related Services
N.A.I.C.S.: 518210

iPass Japan K.K.   (2)
Yurakucho ITOCiA 12F 2-7-1 Yurakucho, Chiyoda-ku, Tokyo, 100 0006, Japan
Tel.: (81) 368604520
Web Site: http://www3.ipass.co.jp
Sales Range: $75-99.9 Million
Software-Enabled Enterprise Connectivity & Endpoint Management Services
N.A.I.C.S.: 518210

iPass UK Ltd   (2)
130 Jermyn St 6th Fl, London, SW1Y 4UR, United Kingdom
Tel.: (44) 2075344900
Sales Range: $25-49.9 Million
Emp.: 20
Software-Enabled Enterprise Connectivity & Endpoint Management Services
N.A.I.C.S.: 518210

PARK AEROSPACE CORPORATION
1400 Old Country Rd Ste 409N, Westbury, NY 11590
Tel.: (631) 465-3600   NY
Web Site:
    https://www.parkaerospace.com
Year Founded: 1954
PKE—(NYSE)
Rev.: $56,004,000
Assets: $132,309,000
Liabilities: $19,395,000
Net Worth: $112,914,000
Earnings: $7,473,000
Emp.: 123
Fiscal Year-end: 03/03/24
Mfr of Electronics & Printed Circuit Board Materials
N.A.I.C.S.: 334412
Brian E. Shore (Chm & CEO)
Mark A. Esquivel (Pres & COO)
Cory L. Nickel (Sr VP & Gen Mgr)
Kenneth Kim (VP-Bus Dev & Program Mgmt)

Subsidiaries:

Park Aerospace Technologies Asia Pte. Ltd.   (1)
486 N Oliver Rd Bldg Z, Newton, KS 67114
Tel.: (316) 283-6500
Web Site: http://www.parkaerospace.com
Composite Material Mfr
N.A.I.C.S.: 335991

PARK HOTELS & RESORTS INC.
1775 Tysons Blvd 7F, Tysons, VA 22102
Tel.: (571) 302-5757   DE
Web Site:
    https://www.pkhotelsandresorts.com
Year Founded: 1946
PK—(NYSE)
Rev.: $2,698,000,000
Assets: $9,419,000,000
Liabilities: $5,651,000,000
Net Worth: $3,768,000,000
Earnings: $106,000,000
Emp.: 90
Fiscal Year-end: 12/31/23
Hotel & Resort Real Estate Investment Trust
N.A.I.C.S.: 525990
Darren W. Robb (Chief Acctg Officer & Sr VP)
Ian C. Weissman (Sr VP-Corp Strategy)

Park Hotels & Resorts Inc.—(Continued)

Thomas C. Morey (*Chief Investment Officer & Exec VP*)
Jill C. Olander (*Exec VP-HR*)
Scott D. Winer (*Sr VP-Tax*)
Carl A. Mayfield (*Exec VP-Design & Construction*)
Diem T. Larsen (*Sr VP-Fin Plng & Analysis*)
Jonathan H. Fuisz (*Sr VP-Investments*)
Rebecca L. Flemming (*Sr VP*)
Joseph M. Piantedosi (*Sr VP*)
Thomas J. Baltimore Jr. (*Chm, Pres & CEO*)

Subsidiaries:

Buckingham's Chicago, LLC   **(1)**
59 E Van Buren St, Chicago, IL 60605
Tel.: (312) 471-1707
Web Site:
    https://www.thebuckinghamchicago.com
Residential Management Services
N.A.I.C.S.: 623210

Chesapeake Lodging Trust   **(1)**
4300 Wilson Blvd Ste 625, Arlington, VA 22203
Tel.: (571) 349-9450
Rev.: $597,172,000
Assets: $1,909,077,000
Liabilities: $855,099,000
Net Worth: $1,053,978,000
Earnings: $96,966,000
Emp.: 13
Fiscal Year-end: 12/31/2018
Hotel Investment Services
N.A.I.C.S.: 525990
Graham J. Wootten (*Chief Acctg Officer, Sec & Sr VP*)
D. Rick Adams (*COO & Exec VP*)
James L. Francis (*Pres & CEO*)
Douglas W. Vicari (*CFO & Exec VP*)

Subsidiary (Domestic):

W Chicago - Lakeshore Hotel   **(2)**
644 N Lk Shore Dr, Chicago, IL 60611-3017
Tel.: (312) 943-9200
Web Site: http://www.wchicago-
    lakeshore.com
Sales Range: $25-49.9 Million
Hotel Operations
N.A.I.C.S.: 721199

Chicago Hilton LLC   **(1)**
720 S Michigan Ave, Chicago, IL 60605
Tel.: (312) 922-4400
Web Site: https://www.hilton.com
Hotel & Resort Operator
N.A.I.C.S.: 721110

Doubletree Spokane City Center LLC   **(1)**
322 N Spokane Falls Ct, Spokane, WA 99201
Tel.: (509) 455-9600
Hotel & Resort Services
N.A.I.C.S.: 721110
Barry Wright (*Dir-Property Ops*)

Embassy Suites Phoenix Airport LLC   **(1)**
2333 E Thomas Rd, Phoenix, AZ 85016
Tel.: (602) 957-1910
Hotel & Resort Services
N.A.I.C.S.: 721110
Doug Ramsay (*Gen Mgr*)

PARK NATIONAL CORPORATION

50 N 3rd St, Newark, OH 43058-3500
Tel.: (740) 399-5516   **OH**
Web Site:
    https://www.parknationalcorp.com
Year Founded: 1905
PRK—(NYSEAMEX)
Rev.: $378,247,000
Assets: $9,854,993,000
Liabilities: $8,785,767,000
Net Worth: $1,069,226,000
Earnings: $148,351,000
Emp.: 1,725
Fiscal Year-end: 12/31/22

Bank Holding Company
N.A.I.C.S.: 551111
David L. Trautman (*Chm & CEO*)
Brady T. Burt (*CFO, Treas & Sec*)
Matthew R. Miller (*Pres*)
Kelly A. Herreman (*Chief Acctg Officer*)

Subsidiaries:

CAB Financial Corporation   **(1)**
200 S Church St, Spartanburg, SC 29306
Tel.: (864) 208-2265
Web Site:
    http://www.carolinaalliancebank.com
Rev.: $30,446,535
Assets: $685,261,551
Liabilities: $607,193,131
Net Worth: $78,068,420
Earnings: $4,685,708
Emp.: 119
Fiscal Year-end: 12/31/2017
Bank Holding Company
N.A.I.C.S.: 551111

Subsidiary (Domestic):

Carolina Alliance Bank   **(2)**
200 S Church St, Spartanburg, SC 29306
Tel.: (864) 208-2265
Web Site:
    http://www.carolinaalliancebank.com
Commericial Banking
N.A.I.C.S.: 522110

The Park National Bank   **(1)**
50 N 3rd St, Newark, OH 43055
Tel.: (740) 349-8451
Web Site:
    https://www.parknationalbank.com
Sales Range: $150-199.9 Million
Emp.: 500
Retail & Commercial Banking
N.A.I.C.S.: 522180
David L. Trautman (*Chm & CEO*)
Matthew R. Miller (*Pres*)
Tom Cummiskey (*Officer-Trust & Sr VP*)
Megan Warman (*Officer-Trust*)
Cindy Neely (*Mgr-Main Office*)
Ruth Sawyer (*Mgr-Granville Office*)
David Lundregan (*Officer-Trust-Bus Dev & VP*)
Jim Buskirk (*Officer-Trust & Investments*)
Brad Zellar (*Officer-Trust & Investments*)
Eric Baker (*Officer-Trust & Asst VP*)
Kathy Barclay (*Officer-Trust-Retirement Plan Svcs*)
David Hardy (*Officer-Trust*)
Adam Hoar (*Officer-Trust-Investments*)
Damon Howarth (*Officer-Trust & VP*)
Lauren Kellett (*Officer-Trust*)
Teresa Kroll (*Officer-Trust-Retirement Plan Svcs*)
Jamie Norckauer (*Officer-Trust*)
Abigail Rehbeck (*Officer-Trust*)
Mareion Royster (*Officer-Trust*)
John Uible (*Officer-Trust & VP*)
Karen Rice (*Dir-Freedom Years*)
Darcy Grossett (*Mgr-Heath 30th Street & Southgate Office*)
Micheal Nagel (*Officer-Trust*)
Mallory Wilkins (*Mgr-Freedom Years*)
Micheal Keeler (*Asst Mgr*)
Ginger Varner (*Mgr-North Office*)
Stephen Malloy (*Mgr-Southwest Office*)
Eric Runkle (*Asst Mgr-Southwest Office*)
Richard Patellos Jr. (*Officer-Trust & Mgr-Tax*)

Subsidiary (Domestic):

Century National Bank   **(2)**
14 S Fifth St, Zanesville, OH 43701
Tel.: (740) 455-7230
Web Site:
    http://www.centurynationalbank.com
Sales Range: $75-99.9 Million
Emp.: 180
Commercial Banking Services
N.A.I.C.S.: 522110
Theresa Gilligan (*Officer-Bus Dev*)
Paul Masterson (*Sr VP-Bus Dev*)
Darin Alexander (*Mgr-Main Office*)

Division (Domestic):

Fairfield National Bank   **(2)**
143 W Main St, Lancaster, OH 43130   **(100%)**

Tel.: (740) 653-7242
Web Site:
    http://www.fairfieldnationalbank.com
Sales Range: $25-49.9 Million
Emp.: 120
Commercial Bank
N.A.I.C.S.: 522110
Luann Snyder (*Officer-Trust & VP*)
Nicole Davis (*Officer-Trust*)

Farmers Bank   **(2)**
120 N Water St, Loudonville, OH 44842   **(100%)**
Tel.: (419) 994-4115
Web Site:
    http://www.farmersandsavings.com
Sales Range: $1-9.9 Million
Emp.: 30
Commercial Bank
N.A.I.C.S.: 522110

First-Knox National Bank   **(2)**
1 S Main St, Mount Vernon, OH 43050   **(100%)**
Tel.: (740) 399-5500
Web Site: http://www.firstknox.com
Sales Range: $50-74.9 Million
Emp.: 145
Commercial Bank
N.A.I.C.S.: 522110
James W. Hobson (*Sr VP*)
Vicki Sant (*Chm*)
Adam Hoar (*Officer-Trust & Investments*)

Richland Bank   **(2)**
3 N Main St, Mansfield, OH 44902 **(100%)**
Tel.: (419) 525-3319
Web Site: http://www.richlandbank.com
Sales Range: $50-74.9 Million
Emp.: 150
Commercial Banking Services
N.A.I.C.S.: 522110
Charla A. Irvin (*Officer-Trust*)
Scott Heimann (*Officer-Trust*)
Andrew Wetzel (*Portfolio Mgr*)
Brad Zellar (*Officer-Trust & Investments*)

Subsidiary (Domestic):

Scope Leasing, Inc.   **(2)**
200 Civic Ctr Dr Ste 110, Columbus, OH 43215-5114
Tel.: (614) 221-5773
Web Site: https://www.scopeair.com
Sales Range: $25-49.9 Million
Emp.: 7
Aircraft Charter Rental & Leasing Services
N.A.I.C.S.: 533110
Donna Parsley (*Mgr-Operations*)
Jessica Neptune (*Mgr-Closing*)
Mike Smith (*Pres*)

Division (Domestic):

Second National Bank   **(2)**
499 S Broadway, Greenville, OH 45331
Tel.: (937) 548-2122
Web Site: http://www.secondnational.com
Sales Range: $25-49.9 Million
Emp.: 70
Banking Services
N.A.I.C.S.: 522180

Security National Bank   **(2)**
40 S Limestone St, Springfield, OH 45502
Tel.: (937) 324-6873
Web Site:
    http://www.securitynationalbank.com
Retail & Commercial Banking
N.A.I.C.S.: 522110
John Brown (*Pres*)
Cathy Hill (*Officer-Trust & Asst VP*)
Amanda Knott (*Officer-Trust*)
James Kreckman (*Officer-Trust Investment & VP*)
Peg Foley (*Officer-Trust*)
Missy Hallmark (*Asst Portfolio Mgr*)
Andy Irick (*Sr VP*)
Connie Craig (*Sr VP*)
Rachel Brewer (*Officer-Trust & Asst VP*)

United Bank   **(2)**
401 S Sandusky Ave, Bucyrus, OH 44820-2624
Tel.: (419) 562-3040
Web Site: http://www.unitedbankohio.com
Sales Range: $1-9.9 Million
Emp.: 30
Banking Services
N.A.I.C.S.: 522180

Donald Stone (*Pres*)
Kathrine Wood (*Ops Mgr*)

Unity National Bank   **(2)**
215 N Wayne St, Piqua, OH 45356
Tel.: (937) 615-1042
Web Site: http://www.unitynationalbk.com
Commercial Banking Services
N.A.I.C.S.: 523940
Ken Magoteaux (*Officer-Trust*)

PARK-OHIO HOLDINGS CORP.

6065 Parkland Blvd, Cleveland, OH 44124
Tel.: (440) 947-2000   **OH**
Web Site: https://www.pkoh.com
Year Founded: 1998
PKOH—(NASDAQ)
Rev.: $1,492,900,000
Assets: $1,436,600,000
Liabilities: $1,168,700,000
Net Worth: $267,900,000
Earnings: ($14,200,000)
Emp.: 7,100
Fiscal Year-end: 12/31/22
Holding Company
N.A.I.C.S.: 551112
Matthew V. Crawford (*Chm & CEO*)
Patrick W. Fogarty (*CFO & VP*)

Subsidiaries:

Apollo Aerospace Components India Private Limited   **(1)**
1 Prestige Atrium Unit 405 3rd Floor Central Street, Bengaluru, 56001, Karnataka, India
Tel.: (91) 8041620101
Web Site:
    http://www.apolloaerospacecompo
    nents.com
Aircraft Component Distr
N.A.I.C.S.: 423860

Apollo Aerospace Components Limited   **(1)**
Unit 12b Two Locks, Hurst Business Park, Brierley Hill, DY5 1UU, West Midlands, United Kingdom
Tel.: (44) 1384566666
Web Site:
    http://www.apolloaerospacecompo
    nents.com
Emp.: 20
Aircraft Component Mfr & Distr
N.A.I.C.S.: 336411

Apollo Aerospace Components Sp.Z.o.o.   **(1)**
Tel.: (48) 178811300
Aircraft Component Distr
N.A.I.C.S.: 423860
Arek Pazdziora (*Gen Mgr*)

EFCO Inc.   **(1)**
1253 W 12th St, Erie, PA 16501-1518
Tel.: (814) 455-3941
Web Site: http://www.eriepress.com
Mechanical & Hydraulic Presses
N.A.I.C.S.: 333517

Elastomeros Tecnicos Moldeados, S. de R. L. de C.V.   **(1)**
Avenida Presa la Amistad Km, Ciudad Acuna, 26269, Coahuila, Mexico
Tel.: (52) 8777731894
Rubber Products Mfr
N.A.I.C.S.: 326299

Europower CH s.r.o.   **(1)**
Sumperska 1345, Unicov, 783 91, Czech Republic
Tel.: (420) 585093247
Web Site: http://www.europowerinc.com
Emp.: 4
Rubber Products Mfr
N.A.I.C.S.: 326299

Foundry Service GmbH   **(1)**
Sonnenblumenallee 12, D-58675, Hemer, Germany
Tel.: (49) 237255980
Web Site: https://www.foundry-service.de
Sales Range: $25-49.9 Million
Emp.: 40
Industrial Supply Chain Logistics Services
N.A.I.C.S.: 541614

Iraklis Papadopoulos (Mng Dir)
Peter Linke (Mng Dir)

Foundry Service GmbH (1)
Sonnenblumenallee 12, D-58675, Hemer,
Germany
Tel.: (49) 237255980
Web Site: https://www.foundry-service.de
Sales Range: $25-49.9 Million
Emp.: 40
Industrial Supply Chain Logistics Services
N.A.I.C.S.: 541614
Iraklis Papadopoulos (Mng Dir)
Peter Linke (Mng Dir)

Foundry Service GmbH (1)
Sonnenblumenallee 12, D-58675, Hemer,
Germany
Tel.: (49) 237255980
Web Site: https://www.foundry-service.de
Sales Range: $25-49.9 Million
Emp.: 40
Industrial Supply Chain Logistics Services
N.A.I.C.S.: 541614
Iraklis Papadopoulos (Mng Dir)
Peter Linke (Mng Dir)

Foundry Service GmbH (1)
Sonnenblumenallee 12, D-58675, Hemer,
Germany
Tel.: (49) 237255980
Web Site: https://www.foundry-service.de
Sales Range: $25-49.9 Million
Emp.: 40
Industrial Supply Chain Logistics Services
N.A.I.C.S.: 541614
Iraklis Papadopoulos (Mng Dir)
Peter Linke (Mng Dir)

GH Electrothermie, S.A.S. (1)
Tel.: (33) 389233866
Web Site: https://ghinduction.com
Logistics Consulting Servies
N.A.I.C.S.: 541614

GH Induction Atmospheres, LLC (1)
35 Industrial Park Cir, Rochester, NY 14624
Tel.: (585) 368-2120
Web Site: https://www.gh-ia.com
Emp.: 30
Logistics Consulting Servies
N.A.I.C.S.: 541614

GH Induction Deutschland Gmbh (1)
Hainbrunner Strasse 10, Hessen, 69434,
Hirschhorn, Germany
Tel.: (49) 6272921610
Web Site: https://www.gh-induction.de
Logistics Consulting Servies
N.A.I.C.S.: 541614

**GH Induction Equipment Shanghai
Co. Ltd.** (1)
Office 102 No 7 Building No 51Lane 1895
Hutai Road, Shanghai, 200436, China
Tel.: (86) 2136552996
Web Site: https://ghinduction.com
Logistics Consulting Servies
N.A.I.C.S.: 541614

GH Induction India Pvt. Ltd. (1)
145 12th Main Road, Sidco Industrial Estate
Thirumudivakkam, Chennai, 600 044, India
Tel.: (91) 4424781042
Logistics Consulting Servies
N.A.I.C.S.: 541614
Rishikesh Nagarajan (Deputy Mgr)

GH Mexicana, S.A. de C.V. (1)
Tel.: (52) 4616100380
Web Site: https://www.ghinduction.com
Logistics Consulting Servies
N.A.I.C.S.: 541614

**Heads & Allthreads Private
Limited** (1)
Gut No 144-1/2/3 Chimbali Phata Opposite
Pavana Sahakari Bank, Kurali, Pune,
410501, Maharashtra, India
Tel.: (91) 8048372552
Web Site: http://www.indiamart.com
Bolt & Nut Whslr
N.A.I.C.S.: 423710

Hydrapower Dynamics Limited (1)
St Mark Street, Birmingham, United King-
dom
Tel.: (44) 1214565656
Fluid Handling Equipment Mfr
N.A.I.C.S.: 332912

**ILS Supply Technologies SA de
CV** (1)
Ave Apolo 511, Centro de Negocios Kalos,
66350, Santa Catarina, NL, Mexico
Tel.: (52) 8183084140
Engineeering Services
N.A.I.C.S.: 541330

**Induction Equipment (India) Private
Limited** (1)
T-117 Bhosari Industrial Estate, Pune,
411026, India
Tel.: (91) 206 634 6100
Web Site: https://www.inductionindia.com
Emp.: 100
Induction Heat Treatment Equipment Mfr
N.A.I.C.S.: 333994

Inova Lab S.r.l. (1)
vicolo Bellini 10F, 35131, Padua, Italy
Tel.: (39) 0498088373
Web Site: https://www.inovalab.eu
Heat Treatment Equipment Mfr
N.A.I.C.S.: 333994
Marcello Zerbetto (CEO, Partner & Mgr-
Organizational)
Fabrizio Dughiero (Co-Founder)
Michele Forzan (Co-Founder & Head-
Numerical Simulations)

**Japan Ajax Magnethermic Co.,
Ltd.** (1)
2-4-14 Toyo Mitsui Woody Building 2nd
Floor, Koto-ku, Tokyo, 135-0016, Japan
Tel.: (81) 336477661
Web Site: http://www.ajaxtocco.co.jp
Sales Range: $25-49.9 Million
Emp.: 40
Induction Equipment Whslr
N.A.I.C.S.: 423830

Langstone Supplies Limited (1)
3 St Johns Court Upper Fforest Way,
Llansamlet, Swansea, SA6 8QQ, United
Kingdom
Tel.: (44) 1792535500
Web Site:
https://www.langstonesafetywear.co.uk
Logistics Consulting Servies
N.A.I.C.S.: 541614

M.P. Colinet S.P.R.L.U. (1)
Faubourg de Mignault 17, 7070, Le Roeulx,
Belgium
Tel.: (32) 64673777
Engineeering Services
N.A.I.C.S.: 541330

Park-Ohio Industries, Inc. (1)
6065 Parkland Blvd, Cleveland, OH 44124
Tel.: (440) 947-2000
Web Site: https://www.pkoh.com
Rev.: $1,492,899,999
Assets: $1,457,600,000
Liabilities: $1,176,300,000
Net Worth: $281,300,000
Earnings: ($13,500,000)
Emp.: 7,100
Fiscal Year-end: 12/31/2022
Diversified Industrial Products Mfr & Sup-
plier
N.A.I.C.S.: 423840
Matthew V. Crawford (Chm & CEO)
Patrick W. Fogarty (CFO & VP)

Subsidiary (Domestic):

**Ajax Tocco Magnethermic
Corporation** (2)
1745 Overland Ave, Warren, OH 44483-
2860
Tel.: (330) 372-8511
Web Site: https://www.ajaxtocco.com
Sales Range: $100-124.9 Million
Emp.: 600
Mfr of Induction Heating & Melting Equip-
ment for Metal Working Industry
N.A.I.C.S.: 333994

Subsidiary (Non-US):

Ajax Tocco International Ltd. (3)
2 Dorset Road, Saltley Business Park Salt-
ley, Birmingham, B8 1BG, United
Kingdom (100%)
Tel.: (44) 1213228000
Web Site: https://www.ajaxtocco.co.uk
Sales Range: $10-24.9 Million
Emp.: 40
Mfr Induction Heating & Melting Equipment

N.A.I.C.S.: 333994

**Ajax Tocco Magnethermic Canada
Limited** (3)
333 Station Street, Ajax, L1S 1S3, ON,
Canada (100%)
Tel.: (905) 683-4980
Web Site: http://www.ajaxtocco.ca
Sales Range: $25-49.9 Million
Emp.: 30
Mfr Induction Heating & Melting Equipment
N.A.I.C.S.: 333994

**Ajax Tocco Magnethermic
Corporation** (3)
2-4-14 Toyo, Koto-ku, Tokyo, 135-0016,
Japan (100%)
Tel.: (81) 336477661
Web Site: http://www.ajaxtocco.co.jp
Sales Range: $10-24.9 Million
Emp.: 22
Mfr of Induction Heating & Melting Equip-
ment
N.A.I.C.S.: 333994

Subsidiary (Domestic):

**Ajax Tocco Magnethermic
Corporation** (3)
6325 US Hwy 431, Albertville, AL
35950 (100%)
Tel.: (256) 279-1200
Web Site: http://www.ajaxtocco.com
Sales Range: $25-49.9 Million
Emp.: 60
Precision Induction Heat Treating Equip-
ment Mfr
N.A.I.C.S.: 333994

Subsidiary (Non-US):

Ajax Tocco Magnethermic GmbH (3)
Ersheimer Str 87, 69434, Hirschhorn, Ger-
many
Tel.: (49) 62729217500
Web Site: https://www.ajaxtocco.de
Sales Range: $25-49.9 Million
Emp.: 40
Induction Equipment Technology Provider
N.A.I.C.S.: 333994
Robert D. Vilsack (Mng Dir)
Thomas M. Illencik (Mng Dir)

**Ajax Tocco de Mexico, S.A. de
C.V.** (3)
Avenue Manantiales No 11 Esq Acueducto
Parque Industrial Bernardo, Quintana El
Marques, 76246, Queretaro, Mexico
Tel.: (52) 4422215415
Web Site: https://www.ajaxtocco.com.mx
Sales Range: $25-49.9 Million
Emp.: 35
Melting & Heat Treating Coils Repair Ser-
vices
N.A.I.C.S.: 332811

Subsidiary (Domestic):

Control Transformer Corp. (3)
3701 Warren Meadville Rd, Cortland, OH
44410-9464 (100%)
Tel.: (330) 637-6015
Web Site: https://www.control-
transformer.com
Sales Range: $10-24.9 Million
Emp.: 35
Mfr of Control & Specialty Transformers
N.A.I.C.S.: 335311

Subsidiary (Domestic):

**Autoform Tool & Manufacturing,
LLC** (2)
1501 Wohlert St, Angola, IN 46703
Tel.: (260) 624-2014
Web Site: https://www.autoformtool.com
Fuel Rail Mfr & Distr
N.A.I.C.S.: 336310

Canton Drop Forge, Inc. (2)
4575 Southway St SW, Canton, OH 44706
Tel.: (330) 477-4511
Web Site: https://www.cantondropforge.com
Closed Die Forgings
N.A.I.C.S.: 332111
James J. O'Sullivan Jr. (Chm)

Columbia Nut & Bolt LLC (2)
50 Graphic Pl, Moonachie, NJ 07074
Tel.: (201) 641-7600

N.A.I.C.S.: 333994

Hardware Mfr
N.A.I.C.S.: 332510
Debbie Walsh (Supvr-Govt Pur & Sls)
Bruce Rosenberg (Gen Mgr)

EP Cleveland, Inc. (2)
7621 Hub Pkwy, Valley View, OH 44125
Tel.: (216) 447-0898
Hydraulic Hose & Hose Coupling Mfr
N.A.I.C.S.: 332912
Ronald Ciocca Jr. (Mgr-Ops)

**Elastomeros Tecnicos Moldeados,
Inc.** (2)
100 Lupita Cir, Del Rio, Del Rio, TX 78840
Tel.: (231) 499-6853
Rubber Products Mfr
N.A.I.C.S.: 326299

**Engineering Design & Manufacturing
Services, Inc.** (2)
661 Millers Bluff Rd, Surgoinsville, TN
37873
Tel.: (423) 345-5086
Web Site: https://www.edmsinduction.com
Emp.: 9
Engineeering Services
N.A.I.C.S.: 541330
Frank Cole (Pres)
Sanford Hileman (VP)

Feco Ajax Inc. (2)
1745 Overland Ave, Warren, OH
44483 (100%)
Tel.: (216) 531-1010
Web Site: http://www.ajaxtocco.com
Sales Range: $25-49.9 Million
Emp.: 50
Forging Presses Mfr
N.A.I.C.S.: 333248

Fluid Routing Solutions, LLC (2)
25800 Northwestern Hwy Ste 550, South-
field, MI 48075
Tel.: (248) 228-8900
Web Site: http://www.fluidrouting.com
Emp.: 800
Industrial Hose Product Mfr
N.A.I.C.S.: 326220

**General Aluminum Manufacturing
Company** (2)
5159 S Prospect St, Ravenna, OH 44266
Tel.: (330) 297-1225
Web Site:
https://www.generalaluminum.com
Sales Range: $350-399.9 Million
Emp.: 800
Aluminum Product Whslr
N.A.I.C.S.: 423510

Plant (Domestic):

General Aluminum (3)
13663 Short Rd, Wapakoneta, OH 45895
Tel.: (419) 739-9300
Web Site: http://www.generalaluminum.com
Sales Range: $75-99.9 Million
Emp.: 160
Automotive Suspension Components Mfr
N.A.I.C.S.: 332913

Subsidiary (Domestic):

PMC Industries Inc. (2)
87 Spring Ln, Plainville, CT 06062
Tel.: (860) 351-0686
Web Site: https://pmcind.com
Sales Range: $50-74.9 Million
Emp.: 92
Gages, Instruments, Machinery, Tools &
Sub-Contract Graphic Instrumentation; High
Speed Machinery Threading & Tapping
N.A.I.C.S.: 333517

PMC-Colinet, Inc. (2)
29100 Lakeland Blvd, Wickliffe, OH 44092
Tel.: (440) 943-3300
Web Site: https://www.pmc-colinet.com
Emp.: 92
Pipe Machine Tools Mfr
N.A.I.C.S.: 333515

Subsidiary (Non-US):

**Park-Ohio Industries (Shanghai) Co.
Ltd.** (2)
Lot 20 Yuan-zhong Road Nanhui Industrial
Zone, Nanhui, Shanghai, 201300, China
Tel.: (86) 2162190774

Park-Ohio Holdings Corp.—(Continued)

Web Site: http://www.pkoh.com
Sales Range: $700-749.9 Million
Diversified Industrial Products Mfr & Supplier
N.A.I.C.S.: 326299

Division (Domestic):

Park-Ohio Industries, Inc. - Ohio
Crankshaft Division   **(2)**
3800 Harvard Ave, Cleveland, OH 44105-3208
Tel.: (216) 341-2300
Web Site: https://www.ohio-crankshaft.com
Sales Range: $50-74.9 Million
Emp.: 60
Mfr Cranksaft & Camshaft Machining
N.A.I.C.S.: 336310

Subsidiary (Domestic):

Park-Ohio Products, Inc.   **(2)**
6065 Parkland Blvd, Cleveland, OH 44124
Tel.: (440) 947-2000
Web Site: http://www.pkoh.com
Sales Range: $150-199.9 Million
Emp.: 150
Molded Rubber, Silicone & Plastic Products
Mfr
N.A.I.C.S.: 326299

RB&W-Manufacturing LLC   **(2)**
10080 Wellman Rd, Streetsboro, OH
44241   **(100%)**
Tel.: (234) 380-8540
Web Site: https://www.rbwmfg.com
Sales Range: $25-49.9 Million
Emp.: 1,800
Provider of Cold Forming Technology Services
N.A.I.C.S.: 332722

Subsidiary (Non-US):

RB&W Corporation of Canada   **(3)**
10 Sun Pac Blvd, Brampton, L6S 4R5, ON,
Canada
Tel.: (905) 595-9700
Bolts & Nuts Mfr
N.A.I.C.S.: 332722

Subsidiary (Domestic):

Snow Dragon LLC   **(2)**
29100 Lakeland Blvd, Wickliffe, OH 44092
Tel.: (440) 295-0238
Web Site:
    https://www.snowdragonmelters.com
Emp.: 3
Snowmelters Mfr & Distr
N.A.I.C.S.: 332410

Southwest Steel Processing LLC   **(2)**
4900 Lighthouse Dr, Newport, AR 72112
Tel.: (870) 523-8791
Web Site:
    https://southweststeelprocessing.com
Emp.: 100
Blast Furnaces & Steel Forging Services
N.A.I.C.S.: 332111

Supply Technologies LLC   **(2)**
6065 Parkland Blvd, Cleveland, OH 44124
Tel.: (440) 947-2100
Web Site:
    https://www.supplytechnologies.com
Sales Range: $900-999.9 Million
Emp.: 1,500
Supply Chain Management Services
N.A.I.C.S.: 423840

Plant (Domestic):

Supply Technologies   **(3)**
4837 Azelia Ave N Ste 100, Minneapolis,
MN 55429-3843   **(100%)**
Tel.: (763) 412-1044
Web Site:
    http://www.supplytechnologies.com
Sales Range: $75-99.9 Million
Emp.: 165
Small Parts Management & Logistics Services
N.A.I.C.S.: 423710

Supply Technologies   **(3)**
4905 Southridge Blvd Ste 4-10, Memphis,
TN 38141-8390
Tel.: (901) 363-1245

Web Site:
    http://www.supplytechnologies.com
Sales Range: $150-199.9 Million
Emp.: 30
Small Parts Management & Logistics Services
N.A.I.C.S.: 423840

Subsidiary (Non-US):

Supply Technologies (India) Private
Limited   **(3)**
47/4 2nd Floor Plot No B-32 1st Avenue
100ft Road, Ashok Nagar, Chennai, 600
083, Tamil Nadu, India
Tel.: (91) 4442125291
Web Site:
    https://www.supplytechnologies.co.in
Supply Chain Management & Logistics Services
N.A.I.C.S.: 541614

Supply Technologies Company of
Canada   **(3)**
6670 Excelsior Court, Mississauga, L5T
2J2, ON, Canada
Tel.: (905) 791-0606
Emp.: 12
Chain Management & Logistics Services
N.A.I.C.S.: 541614

Supply Technologies Company of
Puerto Rico   **(3)**
Tel.: (787) 945-0145
Sales Range: $25-49.9 Million
Emp.: 7
Chain Management & Logistics Services
N.A.I.C.S.: 541614
Abimael Miranda *(Mgr-Warehouse)*

Supply Technologies Kft   **(3)**
Ocsai u 1-3, 1239, Budapest, Hungary
Tel.: (36) 12873291
Supply Chain Management Services
N.A.I.C.S.: 541614

Supply Technologies Limited   **(3)**
Unit 4 Imperial Park West Avenue, Linwood,
PA1 2FB, Renfrewshire, United Kingdom
Tel.: (44) 1413437703
Web Site:
    http://www.supplytechnologies.co.uk
Emp.: 30
Supply Chain Management & Logistics Services
N.A.I.C.S.: 541614

Supply Technologies Limited   **(3)**
Unit 803A 8/F Mirror Tower 61 Mody Road,
Tsimshatsui, Kowloon, China (Hong Kong)
Tel.: (852) 36223740
Sales Range: $25-49.9 Million
Emp.: 4
Supply Chain Management & Logistics Services
N.A.I.C.S.: 541614

Supply Technologies Pte. Ltd.   **(3)**
21 UBI Road 1 04-01, Singapore, 408724,
Singapore
Tel.: (65) 67440518
Sales Range: $25-49.9 Million
Emp.: 8
Chain Management & Logistics Services
N.A.I.C.S.: 541614

Subsidiary (Domestic):

TW Manufacturing Co.   **(2)**
560 Solon Rd, Bedford Heights, OH 44146
Tel.: (440) 439-3243
Sales Range: $25-49.9 Million
Emp.: 26
Industrial Pattern Design Mfr
N.A.I.C.S.: 332999

QEF (Global) Ireland Limited   **(1)**
8th Floor Block E Iveagh Court Hardcourt
Road, Dublin, 2, Ireland
Tel.: (353) 214968480
Supply Chain Optimization Services
N.A.I.C.S.: 541614
Mike Nolan *(CEO)*

SAET S.p.A.   **(1)**
Via Torino 213, Turin, 10040, Leini, TO, Italy
Tel.: (39) 0119977999
Web Site: https://www.saetemmedi.com
Emp.: 145
Induction Heat Treatment Equipment Mfr

N.A.I.C.S.: 333994

Saet Induction Equipment (Shanghai)
Co. Ltd.   **(1)**
No 388 Sanbang Rd, Songjiang, Shanghai,
China
Tel.: (86) 2137601498
Induction Heat Treatment Equipment Mfr
N.A.I.C.S.: 333994
Michele Straniero *(Gen Mgr)*

Southern Fasteners & Supply,
Inc.   **(1)**
2421 W Clemmonsville Rd, Winston Salem,
NC 27127-8783
Tel.: (336) 765-1790
Web Site: http://www.southernfasteners.com
Hardware Merchant Whslr
N.A.I.C.S.: 423710
Michael Hunt *(Coord-Sls)*

Supply Technologies CR s.r.o.   **(1)**
Karlovarska ulice 5926, 430 01, Chomutov,
Czech Republic
Tel.: (420) 474620771
Hardware Products Distr
N.A.I.C.S.: 423710

PARKE BANCORP, INC.
601 Delsea Dr, Sewell, NJ 08080
Tel.: (856) 256-2500
Web Site:
    https://www.parkebank.com
Year Founded: 2005
PKBK—(NASDAQ)
Rev.: $95,865,000
Assets: $1,984,915,000
Liabilities: $1,718,881,000
Net Worth: $266,034,000
Earnings: $41,823,000
Emp.: 104
Fiscal Year-end: 12/31/22
Offices of Bank Holding Companies
N.A.I.C.S.: 551111
Vito S. Pantilione *(Pres & CEO)*
Arret F. Dobson *(Vice Chm)*
Ralph Gallo *(COO & Exec VP)*
Paul E. Palmieri *(Chief Credit Officer
& Sr VP)*
John S. Kaufman *(CFO & Sr VP)*
Nicholas J. Pantilione *(Chief Lending
Officer & Sr VP)*
Jonathan D. Hill *(CFO & Sr VP)*

Subsidiaries:

Parke Bank   **(1)**
601 Delsea Dr, Sewell, NJ 08080   **(100%)**
Tel.: (856) 256-2500
Web Site: https://www.parkebank.com
Emp.: 1,000
Commercial Banking Services
N.A.I.C.S.: 522110
Vito S. Pantilione *(Pres & CEO)*
Arret F. Dobson *(Vice Chm)*
Edward Infantolino *(Founder)*
Ralph Gallo *(COO & Exec VP)*
Paul Palmieri *(Chief Credit Officer & Sr VP)*
Jonathan D. Hill *(CFO)*
Nicholas J. Pantilione *(Chief Lending Officer)*

Subsidiary (Domestic):

**PARKER HANNIFIN CORPO-
RATION**
6035 Parkland Blvd, Cleveland, OH
44124-4141
Tel.: (216) 896-3000   **OH**
Web Site: https://www.parker.com
Year Founded: 1938
PH—(NYSE)
Rev.: $19,929,606,000
Assets: $29,297,842,000
Liabilities: $17,216,949,000
Net Worth: $12,080,893,000
Earnings: $2,844,936,000
Emp.: 61,120
Fiscal Year-end: 06/30/24
Areospace Mfr
N.A.I.C.S.: 334511
Thomas L. Williams *(Exec Chm)*
Aidan Gormley *(Dir-Global Comm &
Branding)*

Andrew D. Ross *(Pres & COO)*
Joseph R. Leonti *(Gen Counsel, Sec
& VP)*
Mark J. Hart *(Exec VP-HR & External
Affairs)*
Robin J. Davenport *(VP-Corp Fin &
VP-Bus Dev & Plng)*
William R. Bowman *(Pres-
Instrumentation Grp & VP)*
Thomas C. Gentile *(VP-Supply
Chain-Global)*
Joachim Guhe *(Pres-Europe, Middle
East & Africa Grp)*
Michael J. O'Hara *(VP-Mktg & Sls-
Global)*
Dinu J. Parel *(CIO, Chief Digital Officer & VP)*
Michael Wee *(Pres-Asia Pacific Grp)*
Angela R. Ives *(Principal Acctg Officer, VP & Controller)*
Berend Bracht *(Pres-Motion Sys Grp
& VP)*
Mark T. Czaja *(Chief Tech & Innovation Officer & VP)*
Steve Zimmerman *(Gen Mgr-Engine
Mobile Aftermarket)*
Steve Barnes *(VP-Ops-Engine Mobile
& Hydraulic Platform)*
Robert W. Malone *(Pres-Filtration
Grp)*
Todd M. Leombruno *(CFO & Exec
VP)*
Jennifer A. Parmentier *(Chm & CEO)*

Subsidiaries:

9183-7252 Quebec Inc.   **(1)**
730 Boul Industriel, Blainville, J7C 3V4, QC,
Canada
Tel.: (450) 979-8700
Industrial Drier Mfr
N.A.I.C.S.: 333994

Annapurna Kenmore Tube Products
Pvt. Ltd.   **(1)**
Plot No 19/B Ida Balanagar, Hyderabad,
500037, Andhra Pradesh, India
Tel.: (91) 4023075683
Web Site:
    http://www.annapurnakenmore.com
Emp.: 40
Fluid Power Pump & Motor Mfr
N.A.I.C.S.: 333996
G. Raghuram Sarma *(Mng Dir)*

Arosellos, S.A. de C.V.   **(1)**
Rio Lerma No 219, Tlalnepantla, 54030,
Mexico
Tel.: (52) 5555653622
Rubber Stamp Whslr
N.A.I.C.S.: 423990

Avifil SAS   **(1)**
520 av Blaise Pascal, BP 36, 77550,
Moissy-Cramayel, France
Tel.: (33) 160602600
Web Site: http://www.avifil.fr
Industrial Machinery & Equipment Mfr &
Distr
N.A.I.C.S.: 333998

BHA Altair, LLC   **(1)**
11501 Outlook St Ste 100, Overland Park,
KS 66211
Tel.: (816) 356-8400
Air Purification Equipment Mfr
N.A.I.C.S.: 333413

Baldwin Filters, Inc.   **(1)**
4400 E Hwy 30, Kearney, NE
68847   **(100%)**
Tel.: (308) 234-1951
Web Site: https://www.baldwinfilters.com
Mfr of Filters for Internal Combustion Engines
N.A.I.C.S.: 336390
Janet Pratt *(Dir-Matl)*

Subsidiary (Non-US):

Baldwin Filters (Aust) Pty Limited   **(2)**
196-206 Abbotts Road, Dandenong, 3175,
VIC, Australia
Tel.: (61) 387876280
Industrial Supplies Merchant Whslr

N.A.I.C.S.: 423840

Baldwin Filters (Pty) Ltd. SA (2)
53 Kiepersol Crescent Atlas Gardens Industrial Park, Contermanskloof Road, Durbanville, South Africa
Tel.: (27) 215564730
Industrial Supplies Merchant Whslr
N.A.I.C.S.: 423840

Filtros Baldwin de Mexico S.A. de C.V. (2)
Retorno El Marques 4 Parque Industrial, El Marques, 76246, Queretaro, Mexico
Tel.: (52) 4422273400
Air Conditioning Equipment Distr
N.A.I.C.S.: 423730

CLARCOR Air Filtration Products Inc. (1)
100 River Ridge Cir, Jeffersonville, IN 47130-8974
Tel.: (502) 969-2304
Mfr & Distributer of Air Filtration Products
N.A.I.C.S.: 333413

Clark Filter, Inc. (1)
3649 Hempland Rd, Lancaster, PA 17601-1323 (100%)
Tel.: (717) 285-5941
Mfr of Filters
N.A.I.C.S.: 336510

Drilling & Production Resources, Inc. (1)
9455 Baythorne Dr, Houston, TX 77041-7709
Tel.: (713) 996-7600
Web Site: http://www.dprhou.com
Emp.: 25
Industrial Machinery Whslr
N.A.I.C.S.: 423830

GSF Europe B.V. (1)
Populierenlaan 49, PO Box 30, 1911, Uitgeest, Noord-Holland, Netherlands
Tel.: (31) 251361280
Web Site: http://www.gsfe.nl
Industrial Filter Mfr
N.A.I.C.S.: 333998

Ingenieria y Servicios Metalcrom Ltda. (1)
Las Catalpas 500, Santiago, Chile
Tel.: (56) 29493585
Industrial Machinery Mfr
N.A.I.C.S.: 333998

Kittiwake Developments Limited (1)
3 - 6 Thorgate Road, Littlehampton, BN17 7LU, United Kingdom
Tel.: (44) 1903731470
Web Site: http://www.kittiwake.com
Emp.: 70
Electronic Equipment Whslr
N.A.I.C.S.: 423690

Kuroda Pneumatics Ltd. (1)
10243 Kamakazu Asahi-shi, Chiba, 289-2505, Japan
Tel.: (81) 479623211
Web Site: http://www.parkerkuroda.com
Pneumatic Component Mfr
N.A.I.C.S.: 333995

LORD Corporation (1)
111 Lord Dr, Cary, NC 27511-7923
Tel.: (919) 468-5979
Web Site: http://www.lord.com
Sales Range: $800-899.9 Million
Emp.: 2,900
Adhesive Mfr
N.A.I.C.S.: 325520
Douglas W. Lorenz (Pres-Performance Materials Bus-Global)

Subsidiary (Non-US):

LORD (Thailand) Ltd. (2)
111/14 Moo 11 Bangna - Trad K M 19 Road, T Bangchalong Bangplee, A Bangplee, Samut Prakan, 10540, Thailand
Tel.: (66) 23124956
Web Site: http://www.lord.co.th
Adhesive Mfr
N.A.I.C.S.: 325520

LORD Asia International Ltd (2)
Suites 01-04 20/F Tower 2 The Gateway, Harbour City Tsimshatsui, Hong Kong, China (Hong Kong)

Tel.: (852) 24288008
Web Site: http://www.lord.com
Customer Service, Marketing, Finance, Human Resources & General Administration Services
N.A.I.C.S.: 923130

Subsidiary (Non-US):

Lord Far East, Inc. (3)
Nonura Nishi Shinjuku Building 8F 8-4-2 Nishi-Shinguku, Shinjuku-ku, Tokyo, 160-0023, Japan (100%)
Tel.: (81) 353389011
Web Site: http://www.lord.com
Sales Range: $25-49.9 Million
Emp.: 20
Mfr of Paints, Adhesives & Sealants, Industrial Organic Chemicals, Plastic Products
N.A.I.C.S.: 325510

Lord Korea, Ltd. (3)
#422-1 Bangchuk-Li Koduk-Myun Pyungtaek, Seoul, 451-840, Kyounggi, Korea (South) (75%)
Tel.: (82) 31 664 5371
Web Site: http://www.lord.com
Sales Range: $25-49.9 Million
Emp.: 17
Adhesives & Coatings Mfr
N.A.I.C.S.: 325520

Subsidiary (Non-US):

LORD Chemical (Shanghai) Co., Ltd. (2)
No 9 Luo Gong Road Shanghai Chemical Industry Park, Shanghai, 201507, China
Tel.: (86) 2131330425
Sales Range: $10-24.9 Million
Emp.: 100
Chemical Products Mfr
N.A.I.C.S.: 325998
Mike Wang (Mgr-Factory)

LORD Chemical Products (Malaysia) Sdn. Bhd. (2)
Centrepoint South Mid Valley, Lingkaran Syed Putra, 59200, Kuala Lumpur, Malaysia
Tel.: (60) 322871689
Chemical & Allied Product Whslr
N.A.I.C.S.: 424690

LORD Corporation (Europe) Ltd (2)
The Coliseum Business Centre Ste 14 Riverside Way, Camberley, GU15 3YL, Surrey, United Kingdom (100%)
Tel.: (44) 1618668666
Web Site: http://www.lord.com
Sales Range: $10-24.9 Million
Emp.: 4
Sales & Administration of Noise Vibration & Shock Control Products
N.A.I.C.S.: 423450

LORD Corporation Products and Engineering, Ltd. (2)
Omer Industrial Park, PO Box 3028, Omer, 84965, Israel
Tel.: (972) 86900801
Chemical & Allied Product Whslr
N.A.I.C.S.: 424690

LORD Corporation Slovakia s.r.o. (2)
Tel.: (421) 259420000
Chemical & Allied Product Mfr
N.A.I.C.S.: 325998

LORD Germany GmbH (2)
Tel.: (49) 243352570
Facility Management, Quality Management, EHS Management & Materials Management Services
N.A.I.C.S.: 523940

LORD India Pvt. Ltd. (2)
A/401-404 4th Fl 215 Atrium Andheri Kurla Road Chakala, Andheri E, Mumbai, 400093, Maharashtra, India
Tel.: (91) 2261316500
Web Site: http://www.lord.com
Emp.: 12
Chemical & Allied Product Mfr
N.A.I.C.S.: 325998
Vilas Dhavale (Mng Dir)

LORD International Trading (Shanghai) Co., Ltd. (2)

No 333 Ri Ying Road North Wai Gao Qiao Free TradeZone, Pudong, Shanghai, 200131, China
Tel.: (86) 2131330800
Chemical & Allied Product Whslr
N.A.I.C.S.: 424690

LORD Korea, Ltd. (2)
Chemical Products Mfr
N.A.I.C.S.: 325998

LORD Suisse Sarl (2)
2 Chemin du Pavillon Le Grand Saconnex, 1218, Geneva, Switzerland
Tel.: (41) 227615060
Web Site: http://www.lord.com
Adhesive & Coating Mfr
N.A.I.C.S.: 325510

Unit (Domestic):

Lord Corp. - Erie (2)
2000 W Grandview Blvd, Erie, PA 16509-1029
Tel.: (814) 868-3611
Sales Range: $25-49.9 Million
Emp.: 500
Chemical & Mechanical Devices & Electromechanical Systems Mfr & Sales
N.A.I.C.S.: 336412
Criss Rotko (Coord-HR)

Lord Corp. Research & Development (2)
110 Lord Dr, Cary, NC 27511-6497
Tel.: (919) 469-2500
Web Site: http://www.lord.com
Sales Range: $25-49.9 Million
Emp.: 325
Research Facility
N.A.I.C.S.: 541720

Subsidiary (Non-US):

Lord Industrial Ltda. (2)
Rua Hughson 55 Industrial District, Jundiai, 13213 110, Sao Paulo, Brazil (100%)
Tel.: (55) 1121367755
Web Site: http://www.lordla.com.br
Sales Range: $10-24.9 Million
Emp.: 50
Mfr of Chemical Additives
N.A.I.C.S.: 325998
Sandro Leoner (Mng Dir)

LORD Italia S.r.l. (1)
Via Moscatello 64, Castellaro di Monzambano, 46040, Mantua, Italy
Tel.: (39) 03761900111
Adhesive & Coating Product Mfr
N.A.I.C.S.: 325520

LORD Solutions France (1)
400 chemin des molles - ZAC Les Vinays, Pont de l'Isere, 26600, Valence, France
Tel.: (33) 487960200
Adhesive & Coating Product Mfr
N.A.I.C.S.: 325520

LORD Technol, Inc. (1)
4535 Hummingbird Ln, Fairfax, VA 22033
Tel.: (703) 473-1400
Web Site: https://www.lordstechnologies.com
Information Technology Services
N.A.I.C.S.: 541511

Meggitt PLC (1)
Atlantic House Aviation Park West Bournemouth International Airport, Christchurch, BH23 6EW, Dorset, United Kingdom
Tel.: (44) 1202597597
Web Site: http://www.meggitt.com
Rev.: $2,286,536,252
Assets: $5,428,300,332
Liabilities: $2,668,598,660
Net Worth: $2,759,701,672
Earnings: $426,595,624
Fiscal Year-end: 12/31/2020
Aerospace & Defense Equipment, Control Systems & Electronics Mfr
N.A.I.C.S.: 336413
Marina L. Thomas (Sec-Grp & Exec VP-Ethics & Comm)
Tony Wood (CEO)
Adrian Bunn (Sr VP & Gen Mgr-Svcs & Support Div)
Louisa Burdett (CFO)
Jessica Barrett (Mgr-IR)

Paul Devaux (Pres-Energy & Equipment & Grp Dir-Ops)
Chris Allen (Pres-Airframe Sys)
Dennis Hutton (Co-Pres-Engine Sys)
Hugh Clayton (Grp Dir-Engrg & Strategy)
Geoff Lloyd (Grp Dir-HR)
Andrew Garard (Gen Counsel-Grp & Dir-Corp Affairs)
Troy Peterson (Co-Pres-Engine Sys)

Unit (Domestic):

Heatric (2)
46 Holton Road, Holton Heath, Poole, BH16 6LT, Dorset, United Kingdom (100%)
Tel.: (44) 1202627000
Web Site: http://www.heatric.com
Sales Range: $50-74.9 Million
Emp.: 400
Mfr & Designer of Compact Printed Circuit Heat Exchangers & Reactors
N.A.I.C.S.: 332410

Subsidiary (US):

Meggitt (Baltimore) Inc. (2)
3310 Carlins Park Dr, Baltimore, MD 21215
Tel.: (410) 542-1700
Web Site: http://www.meggittbaltimore.com
Aircraft Mfr
N.A.I.C.S.: 336411

Subsidiary (Non-US):

Meggitt (France) SAS (2)
10 Rue Mercoeur, Paris, France
Tel.: (33) 143700202
Aircraft Part Mfr
N.A.I.C.S.: 336413

Meggitt (Sensorex) SAS (2)
196 Rue Louis Rustin ArchParc, 74160, Archamps, France
Tel.: (33) 450954355
Web Site: https://www.meggittsensorex.fr
Accelerometers Mfr
N.A.I.C.S.: 334519

Meggitt (Xiamen) Sensors & Controls Co Limited (2)
230 South 5 Gao Qi Road, Xiamen, 361006, Fujian, China
Tel.: (86) 5925733666
Web Site: https://meggittxiamen.com
Sales Range: $50-74.9 Million
Sensor & Controlling Device Mfr
N.A.I.C.S.: 334513

Subsidiary (Domestic):

Meggitt Advanced Composites Ltd. (2)
Gelders Hall Rd, Shepshed, Loughborough, LE12 9NH, Leics, United Kingdom (100%)
Tel.: (44) 1509504541
Sales Range: $50-74.9 Million
Emp.: 170
Aerospace, Defense & Industrial Composite Components Designer & Mfr
N.A.I.C.S.: 332812
Ian Richardson (Dir-Sls & Mktg)
Russ Meddes (Mgr-Bus Dev)
Ian Brace (Dir-Fin)

Unit (Domestic):

Meggitt Polymer Solutions (3)
Ashbey Road, Shepshed, Loughborough, LE12 9EQ, Leics, United Kingdom
Tel.: (44) 1509500000
Sales Range: $200-249.9 Million
Emp.: 500
Polymers Mfr
N.A.I.C.S.: 339999
Jim Johnstone (Dir-Sls & Mktg)
Chris Hopper (Mng Dir)

Subsidiary (Non-US):

Meggitt Aerospace Asia Pacific Pte Limited (2)
1A Seletar Aerospace Link Seletar Aerospace Park, Singapore, 797552, Singapore
Tel.: (65) 65117200
Emp.: 40
Aircraft Equipment Whslr
N.A.I.C.S.: 423860
Adrian Plevin (VP & Gen Mgr)

Parker Hannifin Corporation—(Continued)

Subsidiary (Domestic):

Meggitt Aerospace Limited (2)
Holbrook Lane, Coventry, CV6 4QY, W Midlands, United Kingdom
Tel.: (44) 2476294200
Emp.: 145
Aerospace Equipment Mfr
N.A.I.C.S.: 334511
Kevin Brown (Gen Mgr)

Unit (Domestic):

Meggitt Avionics (2)
Units 2-5 Titchfield Park 20-26 Barnes Wallis Road, Fareham, PO15 5TT, HANTS, United Kingdom
Tel.: (44) 1489483300
Web Site: http://www.meggitt-avionics.co.uk
Emp.: 200
Aircraft Engine Monitoring Equipment, Flight Instrument & Test Equipment, Life Support Equipment, Marine Navigation Instrumentation Systems & Related Test Equipment Mfr
N.A.I.C.S.: 336413

Subsidiary (Domestic):

Meggitt Defence Systems Ltd. (2)
The Boulevard Orbital Park, Ashford, TN24 0GA, Kent, United Kingdom (100%)
Tel.: (44) 1233505300
Sales Range: $25-49.9 Million
Emp.: 100
Mfr, Design & Operations of Remotely Piloted Targets & Surveillance Systems
N.A.I.C.S.: 334511
Teresa Horton (Head-Sls & Mktg)

Subsidiary (Non-US):

Meggitt India Pvt Ltd (2)
Unit 901 Brigade Rubux No 20 Hmt Main Rd, HMT Township, Bengaluru, 560 022, India
Tel.: (91) 80 43446475
Web Site: http://www.meggitt.com
Brake Control System Mfr
N.A.I.C.S.: 336340

Plant (Non-US):

Meggitt PLC - Angouleme Facility (2)
8 chemin de l'Etang, PO Box 15, 16730, Fleac, France
Tel.: (33) 5 4524 0404
Web Site: http://www.meggitt.com
Sales Range: $25-49.9 Million
Emp.: 100
Sensor System Mfr
N.A.I.C.S.: 334511

Meggitt PLC - Archamps Facility (2)
Parc d'Affaires International, 74166, Archamps, France
Tel.: (33) 450954355
Web Site: http://www.meggitt.com
Sales Range: $50-74.9 Million
Emp.: 145
Sensing System Mfr
N.A.I.C.S.: 334511

Plant (Domestic):

Meggitt PLC - Basingstoke Facility (2)
The Laurels Jays Close Viables Industrial Estate, Basingstoke, RG22 4BS, Hampshire, United Kingdom
Tel.: (44) 1256 843193
Emp.: 180
Rotational Speed Sensor Mfr
N.A.I.C.S.: 334511
Mark Crompton (Dir-Site)

Plant (Non-US):

Meggitt PLC - Fribourg Facility (2)
Rte de Moncor 4, PO Box 1616, 1701, Fribourg, Switzerland
Tel.: (41) 264071111
Sales Range: $200-249.9 Million
Emp.: 600
Sensor System Mfr
N.A.I.C.S.: 334511
Helge Huerkamp (Gen Mgr)

Meggitt PLC - HCL - Meggitt ODC Factory (2)
129 Bommasandra Jigani Link Road, Bengaluru, 562 106, Karnataka, India
Tel.: (91) 80 39610000
Web Site: http://www.meggitt.com
Sensor System Mfr
N.A.I.C.S.: 334511

Meggitt PLC - Kvistgaard Facility (2)
Porthusvej 4, 3490, Kvistgaard, Denmark
Tel.: (45) 49127100
Sales Range: $25-49.9 Million
Emp.: 25
Monitoring System Mfr
N.A.I.C.S.: 334519
Coreston Eovep (Gen Mgr)
Torsten Bove (Gen Mgr)

Meggitt PLC - Meggitt Shanghai Facility (2)
A Room 1107 No 319 Xianxia Road, Changning District, Shanghai, 200051, China
Tel.: (86) 2162781096
Web Site: http://meggittxiamen.com
Sensor System Mfr
N.A.I.C.S.: 334511

Plant (Domestic):

Meggitt PLC - Rugby Facility (2)
5 Triton Park Swift Valley Industrial Estate, Rugby, CV21 1SG, United Kingdom
Tel.: (44) 1788 537199
Aerospace Component Mfr
N.A.I.C.S.: 336413

Subsidiary (Non-US):

Meggitt SA (2)
Rte De Moncor 4, PO Box 1616, 1701, Fribourg, Switzerland
Tel.: (41) 264071111
Web Site: http://meggittsensing.com
Vibration Monitoring System Mfr
N.A.I.C.S.: 334513

Subsidiary (US):

Meggitt-USA, Inc. (2)
1955 N Surveyor Ave, Simi Valley, CA 93063-3386 (100%)
Tel.: (805) 526-5700
Web Site: http://www.meggitt.com
Sales Range: $75-99.9 Million
Emp.: 100
Holding Company; Aerospace & Defense Systems & Components Mfr
N.A.I.C.S.: 336413

Subsidiary (Domestic):

K&F Industries Holdings, Inc. (3)
50 Main St, White Plains, NY 10606-1974
Tel.: (914) 448-2700
Web Site: http://www.kandfindustries.com
Sales Range: $400-449.9 Million
Holding Company; Aviation Equipment Mfr
N.A.I.C.S.: 551112

Holding (Domestic):

K&F Industries, Inc. (4)
50 Main St, White Plains, NY 10606-1974
Tel.: (914) 448-2700
Sales Range: $400-449.9 Million
Emp.: 1,431
Aircraft Brakes & Fuel Tank Components Mfr
N.A.I.C.S.: 336413

Subsidiary (Domestic):

Aircraft Braking Systems Corporation (5)
1204 Massillon Rd, Akron, OH 44306-4186
Tel.: (330) 796-4400
Web Site: http://www.aircraftbraking.com
Sales Range: $125-149.9 Million
Emp.: 770
Aircraft Wheels, Brakes & Braking Systems Mfr
N.A.I.C.S.: 336413

Engineered Fabrics Corporation (5)
669 Goodyear St, Rockmart, GA 30153 (100%)
Tel.: (770) 684-7855
Sales Range: $150-199.9 Million
Emp.: 1,000

Aircraft Fuel Tanks & Other Technologies Mfr
N.A.I.C.S.: 336413

Subsidiary (Domestic):

Meggitt (New Hampshire), Inc (3)
144 Harvey Rd, Londonderry, NH 03053-7449
Tel.: (603) 669-0940
Aircraft Parts Mfr & Whslr
N.A.I.C.S.: 336413

Meggitt (North Holywood), Inc. (3)
12838 Saticoy St, North Hollywood, CA 91605-3505
Tel.: (818) 765-8160
Web Site: http://www.wkr.com
Industrial Valve Mfr
N.A.I.C.S.: 332911
Ron Patitz (Pres)

Meggitt (Rockmart), Inc. (3)
669 Goodyear Ave, Rockmart, GA 30153-2554
Tel.: (770) 684-7855
Aircraft Fuel Tank Mfr
N.A.I.C.S.: 336413
Mark Grindstaff (Gen Mgr)

Meggitt Aircraft Braking Systems Corporation (3)
1204 Massillon Rd, Akron, OH 44306-4186
Tel.: (330) 796-4400
Web Site: https://www.meggitt-mabs.com
Aircraft Braking System Distr
N.A.I.C.S.: 423860

Plant (Domestic):

Meggitt Aircraft Braking Systems Corporation - Danville Facility (4)
190 Corporate Dr, Danville, KY 40422
Tel.: (859) 936-4600
Web Site: http://www.meggitt.com
Airport Baggage Handling Services
N.A.I.C.S.: 488119

Subsidiary (Domestic):

NASCO Aircraft Brake Inc. (4)
13300 Estrella Ave, Gardena, CA 90248 (100%)
Tel.: (310) 532-4430
Web Site: https://www.nascoaircraft.com
Aircraft Wheel & Brake System Mfr & Whslr
N.A.I.C.S.: 336413

Subsidiary (Non-US):

Queretaro S de RL de CV (4)
Avenida Del Conde No 4-B Parque Industrial El Marques, El Marques, Queretaro, 76246, Mexico
Tel.: (52) 442 153 4300
Aircraft Braking System Mfr
N.A.I.C.S.: 336413
Alberto Barrera (Plant Mgr)

Subsidiary (Domestic):

Meggitt Airdynamics, Inc. (3)
2616 Research Dr, Corona, CA 92882-6917
Tel.: (951) 734-0070
Web Site: http://www.meggair.com
Sales Range: $25-49.9 Million
Emp.: 75
Mfr of Mechanical & Electrical Fans, Compressors & Hydraulic Pumps
N.A.I.C.S.: 333413

Meggitt Avionics (3)
Municipal Airport 1 S-TEC Way, Mineral Wells, TX 76067 (100%)
Tel.: (940) 325-9406
Web Site: http://www.s-tec.com
Sales Range: $50-74.9 Million
Supplier of Retrofit Systems & Original Equipment for Autopilots
N.A.I.C.S.: 336411

Division (Domestic):

Meggitt Control Systems (3)
13035 Saticoy St, North Hollywood, CA 91605-3511
Tel.: (818) 765-8161
Web Site: http://www.meggittcontrolsystems.com
Aircraft Part & Auxiliary Equipment Mfr
N.A.I.C.S.: 336413

Branch (Domestic):

Meggitt Control Systems - San Diego (4)
11661 Sorrento Valley Rd, San Diego, CA 92121
Tel.: (858) 792-3261
Web Site: http://www.meggitt.com
Aerospace Engine Control Systems Developer & Mfr
N.A.I.C.S.: 336413

Subsidiary (Domestic):

Meggitt Defense Systems, Inc. (3)
9801 Muirlands Blvd, Irvine, CA 92618-2521 (100%)
Tel.: (949) 465-7700
Web Site: https://www.meggittdefense.com
Sales Range: $25-49.9 Million
Emp.: 100
Air & Ground Based Weaponry & Targeting Systems Designer & Mfr
N.A.I.C.S.: 336992
Rich Haddad (VP-Bus Dev)

Subsidiary (Domestic):

InVeris Training Solutions, Inc. (4)
296 Brogdon Rd, Suwanee, GA 30024
Tel.: (678) 288-1090
Web Site:
http://www.meggitttrainingsystems.com
Sales Range: $75-99.9 Million
Firearm Simulation & Training Systems & Services Designer, Mfr & Marketer
N.A.I.C.S.: 334419

Unit (Domestic):

Meggitt Defense Systems (4)
9801 Muirlands Blvd, Irvine, CA 92618-2521 (100%)
Tel.: (949) 465-7700
Web Site: http://www.meggittdefense.com
Sales Range: $25-49.9 Million
Emp.: 64
Military Aerial-Towed & Glide Target & Deployment Systems Designer & Mfr
N.A.I.C.S.: 336413

Meggitt Defense Systems (4)
9801 Muirlands Blvd, Irvine, CA 92618
Tel.: (949) 465-7700
Web Site: http://www.meggittdefense.com
Mfr & Designer of Aerial Tow Targets, IR Augmenting Devices & IR Suppressor Kits
N.A.I.C.S.: 336413

Subsidiary (Domestic):

Meggitt Safety Systems, Inc. (3)
1915 Voyager Ave, Simi Valley, CA 93063-3386
Tel.: (805) 584-4100
Web Site: http://www.meggittsafety.com
Mfr of Fire & Overheat Detection Systems For Aerospace & Commercial Applications
N.A.I.C.S.: 336413

Meggitt-USA Holdings LLC (3)
1955 N Surveyor Ave, Simi Valley, CA 93063-3369
Tel.: (805) 526-5700
Web Site: http://www.meggitt.com
Investment Management Service
N.A.I.C.S.: 523999

Plant (Domestic):

Meggitt-USA, Inc. - Germantown Facility (3)
20511 Seneca Meadows Pkwy, Germantown, MD 20876
Tel.: (301) 330-8811
Web Site: http://www.meggitt.com
Sensor System Mfr
N.A.I.C.S.: 334511

Subsidiary (Domestic):

Piher International Corporation (3)
1640 Northwind Blvd, Libertyville, IL 60048-9634 (100%)
Tel.: (847) 918-9300
Web Site: http://www.piher.net
Sales Range: $50-74.9 Million
Distr of Potentimeters, Trimmers & Switch Attenuators.
N.A.I.C.S.: 423690

Subsidiary (Non-US):

Navarra de Componentes Electronicos SA (NACESA) (2)
Poligono Industrial Vial T2 N 22, 31500, Tudela, Spain (100%)
Tel.: (34) 948820450
Web Site: http://www.piher-nacesa.com
Sales Range: $125-149.9 Million
Emp.: 350
Mfr of Carbon & Cermet Potentiometers, Trimmers, Switches, Rotary & Linear Position Sensors, Thick Film Circuits, Attenuators
N.A.I.C.S.: 325180
Rafael Fernandez Ladreda *(Mng Dir)*

Subsidiary (Domestic):

Pacific Scientific Aviation Services Company (2)
Howarth Rd, Maidenhead, SL6 1AP, Berkshire, United Kingdom (100%)
Tel.: (44) 1628682200
Web Site: http://www.pacsciuk.com
Emp.: 20
Sales of Industrial Machinery & Equipment
N.A.I.C.S.: 423830

Division (Non-US):

Artus SAS (3)
37 Chemin Du Champ Des Martyrs, BP 20009, 49241, Avrille, Cedex, France (100%)
Tel.: (33) 241336340
Web Site: https://meggittpower.com
Designs, Mfr & Markets Industrial Process & Environmental Controls & Tools & Components
N.A.I.C.S.: 334512
Alain Levy *(Dir-Sls & Mktg)*

Subsidiary (US):

OECO LLC (3)
4607 SE International Way, Milwaukie, OR 97222
Tel.: (503) 659-5999
Web Site: https://www.oeco.com
Cores, Magnetic
N.A.I.C.S.: 334419

Division (US):

Pacific Scientific HTL (3)
1800 Highland Ave, Duarte, CA 91010 (100%)
Tel.: (626) 359-9317
Nautical Instrument Mfr
N.A.I.C.S.: 334511

Subsidiary (US):

Securaplane Technologies Inc. (3)
12350 N Vistoso Park Rd, Oro Valley, AZ 85755
Tel.: (520) 297-0844
Web Site: http://www.securaplane.com
Avionic Equipment Mfr
N.A.I.C.S.: 336413
Shubhayu Chakraborty *(Pres)*

Subsidiary (Non-US):

Piher International GmbH (2)
Orchideenstrasse 6, Eckental, 90542, Germany (100%)
Tel.: (49) 91268085
Web Site: http://www.piher-international.de
Sales Range: $25-49.9 Million
Emp.: 12
Potentiometers, Trimmers, Switches, Rotary & Linear Position Sensors & Attenuators Distr
N.A.I.C.S.: 334513

Subsidiary (Domestic):

Piher International Ltd. (2)
Unit 20 Ash Kembrey Pk, Swindon, SN2 8UN, Wilcshire, United Kingdom (100%)
Tel.: (44) 793432235
Web Site: http://www.piher-nacesa.com
Sales Range: $25-49.9 Million
Emp.: 1
Distr of Potentiometers, Trimmers, Switches & Attenuators
N.A.I.C.S.: 238220

Subsidiary (US):

Precision Engine Controls Corporation (2)
11661 Sorrento Valley Rd, San Diego, CA 92121
Tel.: (858) 792-3217
Web Site: http://www.precisioneng.com
Gas Turbine Mfr
N.A.I.C.S.: 333611

Subsidiary (Domestic):

VBI Ltd (2)
Harwood St, Blackburn, BB1 3BD, United Kingdom (100%)
Tel.: (44) 254686018
Web Site: http://www.vbilimited.com
Sales Range: $25-49.9 Million
Emp.: 60
Fleet Fuel Monitoring & Outdoor Payment Systems Designer & Mfr
N.A.I.C.S.: 334513

Subsidiary (Non-US):

Zambra Legal Pty Limited (2)
Suite 2 Level 11 60 Castlereagh Street, Sydney, 2000, NSW, Australia
Tel.: (61) 280110530
Web Site: http://www.zambralegal.com.au
Law firm
N.A.I.C.S.: 541199
Erin Devery *(Gen Counsel)*
Lidia Lucic *(Office Mgr)*

Oil Air Holdings Inc. (1)
1105 N Market St, Wilmington, DE 19801
Tel.: (302) 429-8745
Holding Company
N.A.I.C.S.: 551112

Olaer AS (1)
Dynamitveien 23, PB 133, 1401, Ski, Norway
Tel.: (47) 64911180
Web Site: http://www.olaer.no
Industrial Machinery Whslr
N.A.I.C.S.: 423830

Olaer Australia Pty Ltd (1)
9 Carrington Rd Parker Filtration, Cromer, 2154, Australia
Tel.: (61) 299816888
Web Site: http://www.olaer.com.au
Fluid Component Mfr
N.A.I.C.S.: 332912
Tom Mudie *(Gen Mgr & Dir-Fin)*
Ray Butcher *(Mgr-Bus Dev)*
Rodney So *(Mgr-Ops)*
Charlie Daoud *(Project Engr)*
Solomon Pihama *(Engr-Applications)*

Olaer Austria GmbH (1)
Wachtelstrasse 25, 4053, Haid, Austria
Tel.: (43) 722980306
Industrial Machinery Whslr
N.A.I.C.S.: 423830

Olaer Hydraulics (India) Pvt. Ltd (1)
No 21/C KIADB 1st Phase Kumbalgod Industrial Estate, Bangalore-Mysore Highway, Bengaluru, 560 074, Karnataka, India
Tel.: (91) 8028437690
Web Site: http://www.olaer.in
Emp.: 26
Industrial Machinery Mfr
N.A.I.C.S.: 333998

Olaer Tianjin Hydraulic Manufacturing Co.,Ltd (1)
D3-1 XEDA International Industrial City, XIQING Economic Development Area, Tianjin, 300 385, China
Tel.: (86) 2223889096
Industrial Machinery Mfr
N.A.I.C.S.: 333998

Olaer USA, Inc. (1)
15102 Sommermeyer St Ste 125, Houston, TX 77041
Tel.: (713) 937-8900
Web Site: http://www.olaerusa.com
Industrial Machinery Whslr
N.A.I.C.S.: 423830

PGI International, Ltd. (1)
16101 Vallen Dr, Houston, TX 77041
Tel.: (713) 466-0056
Web Site: http://www.pgiint.com
Industrial Machinery Whslr

N.A.I.C.S.: 423830

PT Parker Hannifin Indonesia (1)
Industrial Machinery Whslr
N.A.I.C.S.: 423830
Yoli Yan Oktory *(Mgr-Territory Sls)*

Parker Aerospace (1)
14300 Alton Pkwy, Irvine, CA 92618-1814
Tel.: (949) 833-3000
Web Site: http://www.parker.com
Sales Range: $400-449.9 Million
Emp.: 2,500
Specialty Sealing Devices, O-Rings, Gaskets, Fastener Seals & Packing Products Mfr
N.A.I.C.S.: 339991

Division (Domestic):

Parker Chomerics (2)
77 Dragon Ct, Woburn, MA 01801-1039
Tel.: (781) 935-4850
Web Site: http://www.chomerics.com
Sales Range: $100-124.9 Million
Emp.: 300
Electromagnetic Interference Shielding & Thermal Management Materials Mfr
N.A.I.C.S.: 325520

Unit (Domestic):

Parker Chomerics (3)
135 Bryant Ave, Cranford, NJ 07016-3217
Tel.: (908) 272-5500
Web Site: http://www.parker.com
EMI Shielding & Conductive Materials Mfr
N.A.I.C.S.: 332618

Parker Chomerics Optical Products (3)
525 Orange St, Millville, NJ 08332
Tel.: (856) 825-8900
Web Site: http://www.silver-cloud.com
Sales Range: $1-9.9 Million
Emp.: 54
Custom Displays, Filters & Lenses Mfr
N.A.I.C.S.: 333310

Division (Domestic):

Parker Hannifin Composite Sealing Systems Division (2)
7664 Panasonic Way, San Diego, CA 92154-8206 (100%)
Tel.: (619) 661-7000
Web Site: http://www.parker.com
Sales Range: $50-74.9 Million
Emp.: 150
Mfrs., Designs & Engineers Seals & Sealing Systems
N.A.I.C.S.: 339991

Parker Hannifin Corp., TechSeal Div. (2)
3025 W Croft Cir, Spartanburg, SC 29302-4801
Tel.: (864) 573-7332
Sales Range: $25-49.9 Million
Emp.: 50
Mfr of Industrial Components
N.A.I.C.S.: 326299

Parker Hannifin Corporation, Engineered Seals Division, Syracuse (2)
501 S Sycamore St, Syracuse, IN 46567-1529 (100%)
Tel.: (574) 528-9400
Web Site: http://www.parker.com
Sales Range: $75-99.9 Million
Emp.: 180
Mfr of Automotive Rubber Goods
N.A.I.C.S.: 326291

Parker Hannifin Engineered Polymer Systems Div. (2)
2220 S 3600 W, Salt Lake City, UT 84119-1124 (100%)
Tel.: (801) 972-3000
Web Site: http://www.parker.com
Sales Range: $100-124.9 Million
Emp.: 300
Mfr of Packaging Products
N.A.I.C.S.: 325520

Parker Hannifin Engineered Polymer Systems Division (2)
2565 NW Pkwy, Elgin, IL 60123-7870 (100%)
Tel.: (847) 783-4300

Web Site: http://www.parker.com
Sales Range: $25-49.9 Million
Emp.: 75
Mfr of Polymer Products
N.A.I.C.S.: 423830

Unit (Non-US):

Parker Hannifin Manufacturing Germany GmbH & Co. KG Aerospace Hydraulic Division (2)
Lorenz-Schott Strasse 9, Mainz-Kastel, 55252, Mainz, Germany
Tel.: (49) 61342040
Web Site: http://www.parker.com
Mfr of Instrumentation Products
N.A.I.C.S.: 334513

Division (Domestic):

Parker Hannifin Pan American Division (2)
7400 NW 19th St Ste A, Miami, FL 33126-1217
Tel.: (305) 470-8800
Web Site: http://www.parker.com
Sales Range: $25-49.9 Million
Emp.: 20
Mfr of Valves & Pipe Fittings
N.A.I.C.S.: 333914

Unit (Non-US):

Parker Aerospace, Sao Paulo Customer Service Center (3)
Avenida Lucas Nogueira Garcez 2181, Esperanca, 12325 900, Jacarei, SP, Brazil (100%)
Tel.: (55) 1239545100
Web Site: http://www.parker.com
Sales Range: $1-9.9 Million
Emp.: 10
Customer Support Services
N.A.I.C.S.: 541613
Candido Lima *(Pres-Latin America)*

Division (Domestic):

Parker Hannifin Power Train Division (2)
3700 Mayflower Dr, Lynchburg, VA 24501-5023 (100%)
Tel.: (434) 846-6541
Web Site: http://www.parkerseals.com
Sales Range: $50-74.9 Million
Emp.: 250
Mfr of Seals & Sealing Systems for Transmissions & Engines
N.A.I.C.S.: 339991

Parker Hannifin Watts Fluid Air (2)
9 Cutts Rd, Kittery, ME 03904-5567 (100%)
Tel.: (207) 439-9511
Web Site: http://www.parker.com
Sales Range: $50-74.9 Million
Emp.: 100
Mfr of Compressed Air Line Filters, Regulators, Lubricators & Valves
N.A.I.C.S.: 336390

Parker Seal O-Ring Division (2)
2360 Palumbo Dr, Lexington, KY 40509-1048
Tel.: (859) 269-2351
Web Site: http://www.parkerorings.com
Sales Range: $75-99.9 Million
Emp.: 150
Mfr of Elastomeric O-Rings & Custom Engineered Rubber Sealing Solutions
N.A.I.C.S.: 493110

Subsidiary (Domestic):

SprayCool, Inc. (2)
2218 N Molter Rd, Liberty Lake, WA 99019
Tel.: (509) 232-2600
Web Site: http://www.parker.com
Sales Range: $10-24.9 Million
Emp.: 35
Power Management Technology Services
N.A.I.C.S.: 334118

Parker Aerospace Customer Support Inc. (1)
45 Changi N Crescent, Singapore, 499622, Singapore (100%)
Tel.: (65) 420777

Parker Hannifin Corporation—(Continued)

Sales Range: $1-9.9 Million
Emp.: 6
Provider of Customer Support Services
N.A.I.C.S.: 541613
Adelina Tan *(Office Mgr)*

Parker Canada Holding Co. **(1)**
4625 Durham Rd S, Grimsby, L0R 1B0,
ON, Canada
Tel.: (905) 309-8311
Bank Holding Company
N.A.I.C.S.: 551111

**Parker Filtration & Separation
BV** **(1)**
Oude Kerkstr 4, Etten-Leur, 4878, Nether-
lands
Tel.: (31) 765085300
Web Site: http://www.parker.com
Emp.: 80
Fluid Power & Gas Generation Products Mfr
N.A.I.C.S.: 333996

Parker Filtration B.V. **(1)**
Stieltjesweg 8, Arnhem, 6827, BV, Nether-
lands
Tel.: (31) 263760376
Sales Range: $25-49.9 Million
Emp.: 60
Fluid Power Pump & Motor Mfr
N.A.I.C.S.: 333996
Mikko Uusitalo *(Gen Mgr)*

Parker Hannifin (Espana) S.A. **(1)**
C / Stations 8 Pol Ind Nuns, Torrejon de
Ardoz, 28850, Madrid, Spain
Tel.: (34) 916757300
Emp.: 50
Motion & Control Systems Mfr
N.A.I.C.S.: 334513
Barry MacKkay *(Gen Mgr)*

Parker Hannifin (NZ) Ltd. **(1)**
5 Bowden Road Wellington, Auckland,
14906, New Zealand **(100%)**
Tel.: (64) 95741744
Web Site: http://www.parkerenzed.co.nz
Sales Range: $50-74.9 Million
Emp.: 20
Mfr of Valves & Pipe Fittings
N.A.I.C.S.: 332919

Parker Hannifin Aktiebolag **(1)**
Almenasvagen 20, 506 32, Boras, Vastra
Gotalands lan, Sweden
Tel.: (46) 337005200
Industrial Machinery Whslr
N.A.I.C.S.: 423830

**Parker Hannifin Australia Pty.
Ltd.** **(1)**
9 Carrington Rd, Castle Hill, 2154, NSW,
Australia **(100%)**
Tel.: (61) 298425150
Web Site: https://www.parker.com
Sales Range: $75-99.9 Million
Emp.: 200
Mfr of Motor Vehicle Parts & Accessories
N.A.I.C.S.: 336340

Subsidiary (Non-US):

Parker Hannifin (NZ) Ltd. **(2)**
5 Bowden Road Mount Wellington, Auck-
land, 1060, New Zealand **(100%)**
Tel.: (64) 95741744
Web Site: http://www.parkerenzed.co.nz
Sales Range: $50-74.9 Million
Emp.: 50
Mfr of Hydraulic Hoses & Fittings
N.A.I.C.S.: 332919

**Parker Hannifin Automation
Group** **(1)**
6035 Parkland Blvd, Cleveland, OH 44124-
4186
Tel.: (216) 896-3000
Web Site: http://www.parker.com
Sales Range: $25-49.9 Million
Emp.: 20
Mfr of Major Fluid Power Components
N.A.I.C.S.: 333996

Subsidiary (Non-US):

Parker Hannifin Argentina SAIC **(2)**
Stephenson 2711, B 1667 AKC, Tortuguitas,
Buenos Aires, Argentina
Tel.: (54) 3327444129

Web Site: http://www.parker.com
Control Equipment Mfr
N.A.I.C.S.: 335314

Division (Domestic):

**Parker Hannifin Compumotor
Corp.** **(2)**
5500 Business Park Dr, Rohnert Park, CA
94928-7904
Tel.: (707) 584-7558
Web Site: http://www.parkermotion.com
Sales Range: $125-149.9 Million
Mfr of Hydraulic Pumps & Motors & Meter-
ing Pumps for Chemical Processes
N.A.I.C.S.: 335314

Parker Hannifin Daedal Division **(2)**
1140 Sandy Hill Rd, Irwin, PA 15642-4742
Tel.: (724) 861-8200
Web Site: http://www.daedalpositioning.com
Sales Range: $25-49.9 Million
Mfr of Positioning Tables for Precision
Manufacturing & Assembly Applications
N.A.I.C.S.: 333310

Subsidiary (Non-US):

**Parker Hannifin GmbH & Co. KG
Electromechanical Automation** **(2)**
Robert Bosch Str 22, Offenburg, 77656,
Germany **(100%)**
Tel.: (49) 7815090
Web Site: http://www.parker.com
Sales Range: $50-74.9 Million
Mfr of Electromechanical Products
N.A.I.C.S.: 334514

**Parker Hannifin Industria e Comercio
Ltda.** **(2)**
Av Lucas Nogueira Garcez 2181, Esper-
anca, Jacarei, 12325 900, SP,
Brazil **(100%)**
Tel.: (55) 1239545100
Web Site: http://www.parker.com.br
Mfr of Industrial Components, Including Mo-
tion & Control Products, Pneumatics, Hy-
draulics, Fluid Connectors, Filters & Seals
N.A.I.C.S.: 333310

Division (Domestic):

**Parker Hannifin Pneumatic
Division** **(2)**
8676 E M 89, Richland, MI 49083-9580
Tel.: (216) 896-3000
Web Site: http://www.parker.com
Sales Range: $125-149.9 Million
Mfr of Air Control Valves, Regulators, Con-
trols & Lubricators
N.A.I.C.S.: 332919

Division (Domestic):

**Parker Hannifin Pneumatic Division
North America Watts Fluidair** **(3)**
9 Cutts Rd, Kittery, ME 03904-5567
Tel.: (207) 439-9511
Web Site: http://www.parkerhannifin.com
Sales Range: $25-49.9 Million
Emp.: 100
Mfr of Filters, Regulators & Lubricators
N.A.I.C.S.: 336390

Division (Domestic):

**Parker Hannifin Pneumatic Division-
North America** **(2)**
8676 E M89, Richland, MI 49083
Tel.: (269) 629-5000
Web Site: http://www.parker.com
Sales Range: $50-74.0 Million
Mfr of Pneumatic & Hydraulic Rotary Actua-
tors
N.A.I.C.S.: 333995

Subsidiary (Non-US):

SSD Drives Ltd. **(2)**
New Courtwick Ln, Littlehampton, BN17
7RZ, W Sussex, United Kingdom
Tel.: (44) 1903737000
Web Site: http://www.ssddrives.com
Emp.: 100
Mfr of Industrial Drives
N.A.I.C.S.: 334513

Subsidiary (US):

SSD Drives, Inc. **(3)**

9225 Forsyth Park Dr, Charlotte, NC 28273-
3884
Tel.: (704) 588-3246
Web Site: http://www.ssddrives.com
Sales Range: $25-49.9 Million
Emp.: 130
Industrial Drives Mfr
N.A.I.C.S.: 334419

Parker Hannifin Chile Limitada **(1)**
2760-E Conchali, Santiago, 8551395, Chile
Tel.: (56) 2 623 1216
Web Site: http://www.parkerchile.cl
Sales Range: $25-49.9 Million
Emp.: 7
Power Pump & Motor Mfr.
N.A.I.C.S.: 333996

**Parker Hannifin Chomerics (M) Sdn.
Bhd.** **(1)**
Lot 15 Jalan Gudang 16/9 Section 16, Shah
Alam Industrial Estate, 40200, Shah Alam,
Selangor Darul Ehsan, Malaysia
Tel.: (60) 355109188
Web Site: http://www.chomerics.com
Industrial Product Whslr
N.A.I.C.S.: 423840

**Parker Hannifin Climate & Industrial
Controls Group** **(1)**
6035 Parkland Blvd, Cleveland, OH 44124-
4186
Tel.: (216) 896-3000
Web Site: http://www.parker.com
Automotive & Refrigeration Components Mfr
& Distr
N.A.I.C.S.: 333415

Division (Domestic):

Fluid Control Division **(2)**
95 Edgewood Ave, New Britain, CT 06051-
4151
Tel.: (860) 827-2300
Web Site: http://www.parker.com
Sales Range: $100-124.9 Million
Emp.: 200
Mfr of Environmental Controls for Resi-
dences, Small Commercial & Light-
Industrial Combustion Controls & Systems;
Electronic Air Cleaners; Solenoid Valves
N.A.I.C.S.: 332911

Subsidiary (Non-US):

Parker Hannifin Africa Pty Ltd. **(2)**
Parker Pl 10 Berne Ave, Kempton Park,
1620, South Africa **(100%)**
Tel.: (27) 119610700
Web Site: http://www.parker.com
Sales Range: $1-9.9 Million
Emp.: 130
Mfr of Valves & Pipe Fittings
N.A.I.C.S.: 332919
Christian Malan *(Mng Dir)*

Division (Domestic):

**Parker Hannifin Fluid Control
Division** **(2)**
147 W Hoy Rd, Madison, MS
39110 **(100%)**
Tel.: (601) 856-4123
Web Site: http://www.parker.com
Sales Range: $75-99.9 Million
Emp.: 125
Mfr of Valves
N.A.I.C.S.: 332911

Subsidiary (Non-US):

Parker Hannifin GmbH & Co. **(2)**
Freiherr-Vom-Stein-Strasse 1-3, PO Box
1120, 35325, Mucke, Germany **(100%)**
Tel.: (49) 64009220
Web Site: http://www.parker.com
Sales Range: $75-99.9 Million
Emp.: 200
Mfr & Sales of Valves & Pipe Fittings
N.A.I.C.S.: 332919

Division (Domestic):

**Parker Hannifin Mobile Business
Unit** **(2)**
100 Dunn Rd, Lyons, NY
14489-9767 **(100%)**
Tel.: (315) 946-4891
Web Site: http://www.parkerhannifin.com

Sales Range: $150-199.9 Million
Emp.: 500
Mfr of Commercial Refrigerant Accumula-
tors, Capillary Tubing Assemblies, Check
Valves & Thermostatic Expansion Valves
N.A.I.C.S.: 333415

**Parker Hannifin Refrigerating Special-
ties Div.** **(2)**
2445 S 25th Ave, Broadview, IL 60155-
3858
Tel.: (708) 681-6300
Web Site: http://www.parker.com
Sales Range: $50-74.9 Million
Emp.: 35
Mfr of Control Valves for Ammonia & Halo-
carbon Industrial Refrigeration Products
N.A.I.C.S.: 332911

**Parker Hannifin Refrigeration & Air
Conditioning Division** **(2)**
200 Parker Dr, Booneville, MS 38829-5500
Tel.: (662) 728-3141
Sales Range: $125-149.9 Million
Mfr of Refrigeration & Air Conditioning
Equipment
N.A.I.C.S.: 333415

Subsidiary (Non-US):

**Parker Hannifin SA Climate & Indus-
trial Controls** **(2)**
142 Rue de Lasoret, Contanine, 74130,
Gennevilliers, France **(100%)**
Tel.: (33) 450258025
Web Site: http://www.parkerfrance.fr
Sales Range: $100-124.9 Million
Emp.: 200
Mfr of Valves & Pipe Fittings
N.A.I.C.S.: 332919

Parker Hannifin plc **(2)**
55 Maylands Ave, Hemel Hempstead, HP2
4SJ, Herts, United Kingdom **(100%)**
Tel.: (44) 1442458000
Web Site: http://www.parker.com
Sales Range: $125-149.9 Million
Emp.: 150
Pneumatic Equipment Mfr
N.A.I.C.S.: 333922

Division (Domestic):

Parker Sporlan Division **(2)**
10801 Rose Ave, New Haven, IN 46774-
9576
Tel.: (260) 748-6000
Web Site: http://www.parker.com
Sales Range: $50-74.9 Million
Emp.: 100
Mfr of Air Conditioning & Refrigeration Cou-
plings, Valves, Flow Control Devices & As-
semblies
N.A.I.C.S.: 332912

Division (Domestic):

**Parker Hannifin Refrigeration & Air
Conditioning Div.** **(3)**
100 Parker Rd, Greenfield, TN 38230-3957
Tel.: (731) 235-3122
Web Site: http://www.sporlan.com
Sales Range: $50-74.9 Million
Emp.: 100
Mfr of Copper Products
N.A.I.C.S.: 331529

Division (Domestic):

Sporlan Valve Company **(2)**
206 Lange Dr, Washington, MO 63090-
1040
Tel.: (636) 239-1111
Web Site: http://www.parker.com
Sales Range: $125-149.9 Million
Emp.: 600
Refrigeration & Air Conditioning Controls &
Components Mfr
N.A.I.C.S.: 332911

**Parker Hannifin Co., Ltd.-Aerospace
Customer Support** **(1)**
Ste B 9- B 11,21st Fl No 7 Gunghua, Cha-
oyang Road, 100004, Beijing,
China **(100%)**
Tel.: (86) 1065610520
Web Site: http://www.parker.com
Sales Range: $25-49.9 Million
Aeronautical Customer Support Services
N.A.I.C.S.: 541613

Parker Hannifin Connectors, Ltd. **(1)**
215 Yoosan Dong, Yangsan, 626 230, Kyo-
ungnam, Korea (South) **(100%)**
Tel.: (82) 553713300
Web Site: http://www.phconnectors.co.kr
Emp.: 250
Mfr of Connectors
N.A.I.C.S.: 334417

Parker Hannifin Corporation Chile
Ltda **(1)**
Av Panamericana Norte 6199 Oficina, Con-
chali, 1102, Santiago, Chile
Tel.: (56) 223039640
Industrial Machinery Whslr
N.A.I.C.S.: 423830

Parker Hannifin Czech Republic
Sro **(1)**
Parker 623, 250 67, Klecany, Czech Re-
public
Tel.: (420) 284083111
Web Site: http://www.parker.com
Emp.: 64
Fluid Power Pump & Motor Mfr
N.A.I.C.S.: 333996

Parker Hannifin EMEA S.a.r.l. **(1)**
La Tuiliere 6, 1163, Etoy, Switzerland
Tel.: (41) 218218700
Industrial Machinery & Equipment Whslr
N.A.I.C.S.: 423830

Parker Hannifin ESSC Sp z.o.o. **(1)**
Centrum Usug Wspolnych ul Srubowa 1,
53-611, Wroclaw, Poland
Tel.: (48) 713820100
Web Site: http://www.parkerw.com
Industrial Machinery Mfr
N.A.I.C.S.: 333998
Peter Brzuchnalski *(Dir-Ctr)*
Remigiusz Kubiaczyk *(Mgr-Accts Payable)*
Katherine Bogdanovich *(Mgr-HR)*
Marcin Brodacki *(Controller-Location)*
Katarzyna Kostka-Giczewska *(Sr
Accountant-Accts Payable)*
Malgorzata Modzelewska *(Accountant)*
Aleksandra Brzozowska *(Accountant-Accts
Payable)*

Parker Hannifin Filtration Group **(1)**
6035 Parkland Blvd, Cleveland, OH 44124-
4186
Tel.: (216) 896-3000
Web Site: http://www.parker.com
Sales Range: $1-4.9 Billion
Emp.: 700
Mfr of Hydraulic, Lubrication & Coolant Fil-
ters & Related Products
N.A.I.C.S.: 333996

Division (Domestic):

Parker Airtek **(2)**
4087 Walden Ave, Lancaster, NY 14086-
1512
Tel.: (716) 685-4040
Web Site: http://www.airtek.com
Sales Range: $75-99.9 Million
Emp.: 150
Compressed Air Treatment Equipment Mfr
N.A.I.C.S.: 333415

Parker Hannifin Corp. Filtration &
Separation Division **(2)**
500 S Glaspie St, Oxford, MI 48371-5132
Tel.: (248) 628-6400
Sales Range: $125-149.9 Million
Emp.: 100
Mfr of Pneumatic Coalescing Filters for In-
strument Air & Plant Compressed Air
N.A.I.C.S.: 333414
Bruce Weber *(Gen Mgr)*

Unit (Domestic):

Parker Hannifin Filtration & Separa-
tion Division-Balston Products **(3)**
242 Neck Rd, Haverhill, MA 01835
Tel.: (978) 858-0505
Web Site: http://www.parker.com
Sales Range: $25-49.9 Million
Emp.: 50
Mfr of Filtration Products
N.A.I.C.S.: 333998

Division (Domestic):

Parker Hannifin Hydraulic Filter
Division **(2)**

16810 Fulton County Rd Ste 2, Metamora,
OH 43540-9714
Tel.: (419) 644-4311
Web Site: http://www.parkerhfde.com
Sales Range: $125-149.9 Million
Emp.: 150
Mfr of Hydraulic & Other Fuel Filters
N.A.I.C.S.: 333517

Subsidiary (Non-US):

Parker Hannifin Oy Filter Division
Europe **(2)**
Salmentei 260, FIN 31700, Urjala,
Finland **(100%)**
Tel.: (358) 207532500
Web Site: http://www.parker.com
Sales Range: $50-74.9 Million
Emp.: 200
Mfr of Hydraulic, Diesel, Vehicle Cab-air &
Particle Filters
N.A.I.C.S.: 325998
Mikko Uusitalo *(Mng Dir)*

Division (Domestic):

Parker Hannifin Process Advanced
Filtration Division **(2)**
2002 Main St, Tell City, IN 47586 **(100%)**
Tel.: (812) 547-2371
Web Site: http://www.parker.com
Sales Range: $75-99.9 Million
Emp.: 200
Mfr of Industrial Filters
N.A.I.C.S.: 333998

Parker Hannifin Racor **(2)**
3400 Finch Rd, Modesto, CA 95354-4125
Tel.: (209) 521-7860
Web Site: http://www.racor.com
Sales Range: $200-249.9 Million
Emp.: 700
Mfr of Fuel Filters
N.A.I.C.S.: 333998

Unit (Non-US):

Parker Hannifin Racor - Filters **(3)**
Churwell Vale Shaw Cross Business Pk,
Dewsbury, WF12 7RD, W Yorkshire, United
Kingdom **(100%)**
Tel.: (44) 01924487000
Web Site: http://www.parker.com
Sales Range: $5-14.9 Billion
Emp.: 210
Mfr of Filters
N.A.I.C.S.: 333998

Subsidiary (Non-US):

domnick hunter group ltd. **(2)**
Durham Road, Birtley, DH3 2SF, United
Kingdom
Tel.: (44) 01914105121
Web Site: http://www.parker.com
Sales Range: $250-299.9 Million
Emp.: 250
Filtration, Separation & Purification Products
Designer & Mfr
N.A.I.C.S.: 333414

Parker Hannifin Filtration Products
and Systems (Shanghai) Co.,
Ltd. **(1)**
9 Jinshun Rd, Zhuqiao Town Pudong Dist,
Shanghai, 201201, China
Tel.: (86) 2120672067
Industrial Machinery Mfr
N.A.I.C.S.: 333998

Parker Hannifin Fluid Power Systems
& Components Co., Ltd. **(1)**
2280 Yun Qiao Rd, Jian Qiao Export Pro-
cessing Zo, Shanghai, 201206, Shang,
China **(100%)**
Tel.: (86) 2150312525
Mfr of Fluid Power Products
N.A.I.C.S.: 332919

Parker Hannifin Fluid System Con-
nectors Group **(1)**
300 Parker Dr, Otsego, MI 49078
Tel.: (269) 692-6555
Sales Range: $25-49.9 Million
Emp.: 50
Hydraulic & Pneumatic Industrial Systems
N.A.I.C.S.: 333996

Subsidiary (Non-US):

Legris S.A.S. **(2)**

74 rue de Paris, 35704, Rennes, Cedex,
France **(100%)**
Tel.: (33) 299255500
Web Site: http://www.legris.com
Industrial Fluid Circuit Components De-
signer, Mfr & Whslr
N.A.I.C.S.: 332912

Subsidiary (Non-US):

Legris Danmark APS **(3)**
C/o Parker Hannifin Danmark A/S, Industri-
parken 35-37, Ballerup, 2750,
Denmark **(100%)**
Tel.: (45) 43560400
Web Site: http://www.legris.com
Sales Range: $25-49.9 Million
Emp.: 82
Industrial Fluid Circuit Components De-
signer, Mfr & Whslr
N.A.I.C.S.: 332912

Legris Hungaria Kft **(3)**
100 u Egressy, HU-1149, Budapest,
Hungary **(100%)**
Tel.: (36) 13030568
Web Site: http://www.legris.com
Sales Range: $10-24.9 Million
Emp.: 5
Industrial Fluid Circuit Components De-
signer, Mfr & Whslr
N.A.I.C.S.: 332912

Legris India Pvt. Ltd. **(3)**
C-48 Site-C, Surajpur, Noida, 201 306, Ut-
tar Pradesh, India **(74%)**
Tel.: (91) 1244590600
Web Site: https://laminarindia.in
Sales Range: $25-49.9 Million
Emp.: 60
Industrial Fluid Circuit Components De-
signer, Mfr & Whslr
N.A.I.C.S.: 332912

Legris Poland Sp. z.o.o. **(3)**
ul Rownolegla 8, 02-235, Warsaw,
Poland **(100%)**
Tel.: (48) 225732400
Web Site: http://www.legris.com
Sales Range: $25-49.9 Million
Emp.: 100
Industrial Fluid Circuit Components De-
signer, Mfr & Whslr
N.A.I.C.S.: 332912

Legris do Brasil Ltda. **(3)**
Lucas Nogueira Garcez Av 2181, 12325-
900, Jacarei, SP, Brazil **(100%)**
Tel.: (55) 12 3954 5100
Web Site: http://www.legris.com
Sales Range: $350-399.9 Million
Industrial Fluid Circuit Components De-
signer, Mfr & Whslr
N.A.I.C.S.: 332912

Legris, S.r.o. **(3)**
Brnenska 668, Modrice, 664 42, Brno,
Czech Republic **(100%)**
Tel.: (420) 547 216 304
Web Site: http://www.legris.com
Industrial Fluid Circuit Components De-
signer, Mfr & Whslr
N.A.I.C.S.: 332912

Parker Hannifin Espana SA **(3)**
C/ Estaciones 8 / P L Las Monjas, PO Box
74, 08850, Torrejon de Ardoz,
Spain **(100%)**
Tel.: (34) 902330001
Web Site: http://www.legris.com
Industrial Fluid Circuit Components De-
signer, Mfr & Whslr
N.A.I.C.S.: 332912

Parker Hannifin Ges.m.b.H. **(3)**
Badener Strasse 12, A-2700, Wiener
Neustadt, Austria **(100%)**
Tel.: (43) 2622235010
Web Site: http://www.legris.com
Sales Range: $25-49.9 Million
Emp.: 100
Industrial Fluid Circuit Components De-
signer, Mfr & Whslr
N.A.I.C.S.: 332912

Subsidiary (Non-US):

Parker Canada **(3)**
4635 S Durham Rd, PO Box 158, Grimsby,
L3M 4G4, ON, Canada **(100%)**
Tel.: (905) 945-2274

Web Site: http://www.parker.com
Sales Range: $75-99.9 Million
Emp.: 250
Mfr of Valves & Pipe Fittings
N.A.I.C.S.: 332919

Parker Fluid Connectors de
Mexico **(2)**
Antiguo Camino A San Lorenzo 338, To-
luca, 50010, Estado De Mexico,
Mexico **(100%)**
Tel.: (52) 7222722222
Web Site: http://www.parker.com
Sales Range: $75-99.9 Million
Mfr of Aircraft Parts
N.A.I.C.S.: 336413

Parker Hannifin **(2)**
Fagerstagatan 51 18B, PO Box 8314,
Spanga, S 16308, Stockholm,
Sweden **(100%)**
Tel.: (46) 859795000
Web Site: http://www.parker.com
Sales Range: $25-49.9 Million
Emp.: 30
Mfr of Industrial Components
N.A.I.C.S.: 333310

Parker Hannifin A/S **(2)**
Solbraarveiem 32 B, 1383, Asker, Oslo,
Norway **(100%)**
Tel.: (47) 66753400
Web Site: http://www.parker.com
Sales Range: $50-74.9 Million
Emp.: 50
Fluid Connectors Mfr & Sales
N.A.I.C.S.: 332912

Branch (Domestic):

Parker Hannifin A/S **(3)**
Auglendsmyra 2, PO Box 491, Stavanger,
4003, AB, Norway **(100%)**
Tel.: (47) 51826300
Web Site: http://www.parker.com
Sales Range: $10-24.9 Million
Emp.: 14
Mfr of Air Conditioning & Heating Equip-
ment
N.A.I.C.S.: 333415

Parker Hannifin A/S **(3)**
Breivika Industry 11, Alesund, 6018,
Norway **(100%)**
Tel.: (47) 70177680
Web Site: http://www.parkerhannifin.com
Sales Range: $25-49.9 Million
Emp.: 20
Mfr of Valves & Pipe Fittings
N.A.I.C.S.: 332919

Subsidiary (Non-US):

Parker Hannifin Almelo **(2)**
Evison Straat 1, Oldenzaal, 7575,
Netherlands **(100%)**
Tel.: (31) 546488777
Sales Range: $25-49.9 Million
Emp.: 50
Mfr of Valves & Pipe Fittings
N.A.I.C.S.: 332919

Parker Hannifin Automotive Connec-
tors Do Brasil **(2)**
Avenida Lucas Nogueira Garcez 2181, Ja-
carei, 12325 900, SP, Brazil
Tel.: (55) 1239545100
Sales Range: $100-124.9 Million
Mfr of Connectors
N.A.I.C.S.: 334417
Eduardo Rampenelle *(Gen Mgr)*

Parker Hannifin BV, Netherlands
Sales & Service **(2)**
Edisonstraat 1, PO Box 340, 7575 AH, Old-
enzaal, Netherlands **(100%)**
Tel.: (31) 541585000
Sales Range: $75-99.9 Million
Mfr of Valves & Pipe Fittings
N.A.I.C.S.: 332919

Division (Domestic):

Parker Hannifin Brass Products
Div. **(2)**
300 Parker Dr, Otsego, MI 49078-1472
Tel.: (269) 694-9411
Mfr of Brass Fittings, Bushings, Couplings &
Valves
N.A.I.C.S.: 331529

Parker Hannifin Corporation—(Continued)

Chris Tenick *(Gen Mgr)*

Subsidiary (Non-US):

Parker Hannifin Corp., Slovenia **(2)**
Vel Bucna Vas 7, 8000, Novo Mesto,
Slovenia **(100%)**
Tel.: (386) 73376650
Web Site: http://www.parker.sl
Sales Range: $25-49.9 Million
Emp.: 2
Mfr of Valves & Pipe Fittings
N.A.I.C.S.: 332919
Busa Kaftrevc *(Mng Dir)*

Parker Hannifin Corporation-East Eu-
ropean Sales Office
Badener Strasse 12, Wiener Neustadt,
2700, Austria
Tel.: (43) 2622235010
Web Site: http://www.parker.com
Sales Range: $25-49.9 Million
Emp.: 60
Mfr of Valves & Pipe Fittings
N.A.I.C.S.: 332919

Parker Hannifin Danmark A/S **(2)**
Industrin parken 37, Ishoj, 2750 Ballerup,
Denmark **(100%)**
Tel.: (45) 43560400
Web Site: http://www.parker.com
Sales Range: $25-49.9 Million
Emp.: 100
Mfr of Conveyors
N.A.I.C.S.: 333922

Parker Hannifin GmbH **(2)**
Badener Strasse 12, PO Box 113, 2700,
Wiener Neustadt, 2700, Austria **(100%)**
Tel.: (43) 2622235010
Web Site: http://www.parker-austria.com
Sales Range: $25-49.9 Million
Emp.: 50
Mfr of Fluid Connectors
N.A.I.C.S.: 332912

Division (Domestic):

Parker Hannifin Hose Products
Division **(2)**
30240 Lakeland Blvd, Wickliffe, OH 44092-
1747
Tel.: (440) 943-5700
Web Site: http://www.parker.com
Sales Range: $125-149.9 Million
Hose & Fittings Mfr
N.A.I.C.S.: 332912

Subsidiary (Non-US):

Parker Hannifin GmbH & Co. KG
Hose Products Division Europe **(3)**
Freiherr Vom Stein Strasse 2, PO Box
1120, D 35325, Mucke, Germany **(100%)**
Tel.: (49) 64009220
Web Site: http://www.parker.com
Sales Range: $75-99.9 Million
Emp.: 150
Mfr of Fluid Connectors
N.A.I.C.S.: 332912
Susanne Becker *(Sec)*

Parker Hannifin Hoogezand B.V. **(3)**
Fultonweg 2, 9601 MK, Hoogezand,
Netherlands **(100%)**
Tel.: (31) 598343555
Web Site: http://www.parker.com
Mfr of Valves & Pipe Fittings
N.A.I.C.S.: 332919

Division (Domestic):

Parker Hannifin Industrial Hose Prod-
ucts Division **(2)**
30242 Lakeland Blvd, Wickliffe, OH 44092
Tel.: (440) 268-2120
Web Site: http://www.safehose.com
Sales Range: $25-49.9 Million
Emp.: 40
Industrial Hose Systems
N.A.I.C.S.: 332912

Subsidiary (Domestic):

Parker Hannifin Industrial Hose Prod-
ucts Division **(3)**
11121 Garfield Ave, South Gate, CA 90280
Tel.: (562) 862-1922
Web Site: http://www.parker.com

Sales Range: $25-49.9 Million
Rubber Hose Mfr
N.A.I.C.S.: 326220

Division (Domestic):

Parker Hannifin Kit Operations **(2)**
1290 Waterville Monclova Rd, Waterville,
OH 43566-1066 **(100%)**
Tel.: (419) 878-7000
Web Site: http://www.parker.com
Sales Range: $25-49.9 Million
Mfr of Valves & Pipe Fittings
N.A.I.C.S.: 493110

Subsidiary (Non-US):

Parker Hannifin Manufacturing
France S.A.S. **(2)**
Parc Alcyone - Bat D 1 rue Andre et
Yvonne Meynier, CS 46911, 35069,
Rennes, Cedex, France **(100%)**
Tel.: (33) 299255500
Sales Range: $125-149.9 Million
Valves & Automatic Controls Mfr
N.A.I.C.S.: 332911

Parker Hannifin Moscow **(2)**
8 go Marta St 6a Building 1, Moscow,
127083, Russia **(100%)**
Tel.: (7) 4956452156
Web Site: http://www.parkerhannifin.ru
Sales Range: $25-49.9 Million
Emp.: 40
Mfr of Valves & Pipe Fittings
N.A.I.C.S.: 332919

Division (Domestic):

Parker Hannifin Parflex Div., Ravenna
Plant **(2)**
1300 N Freedom St, Ravenna, OH
44266-9137 **(100%)**
Tel.: (330) 296-2871
Web Site: http://www.parker.com
Sales Range: $100-124.9 Million
Emp.: 100
Mfr of Hose, Tubing & Fittings
N.A.I.C.S.: 326130

Parker Hannifin Parflex Division -
Parker-TexLoc **(2)**
4700 Lone Star Blvd, Fort Worth, TX 76106
Tel.: (817) 625-5081
Web Site: http://www.texloc.com
Sales Range: $10-24.9 Million
Emp.: 100
Plastic Hose Mfr
N.A.I.C.S.: 326220

Parker Hannifin Polyflex **(2)**
6035 Parkland Blvd, Cleveland, OH 44124
Tel.: (216) 896-3000
Web Site: http://www.parker.com
Sales Range: $25-49.9 Million
Emp.: 600
Mfr of Thermoplastic & Ultra High Pressure
Hoses, Fittings & Assemblies
N.A.I.C.S.: 423840

Subsidiary (Non-US):

Parker Hannifin GmbH & Co. KG
Polyflex Division **(3)**
An Der Tuchbleiche 4, Lampertheim,
68623, Germany **(100%)**
Tel.: (49) 6256810
Web Site: http://www.parker.com
Sales Range: $75-99.9 Million
Emp.: 140
Mfr of Valves & Pipe Fittings
N.A.I.C.S.: 332919

Subsidiary (Non-US):

Parker Hannifin Portugal, Lda **(2)**
Travessa Da Bataria 184 R C, Dto 1 Esq,
Leca da Palmeira, 4450 625,
Portugal **(100%)**
Tel.: (351) 229997360
Web Site: http://www.parker.com
Sales Range: Less than $1 Million
Emp.: 15
Mfr of Valves & Pipe Fittings
N.A.I.C.S.: 332919

Parker Hannifin Sp. z.o.o. **(2)**
Ul Rownolegla 8, 02 235, Warsaw, Poland
Tel.: (48) 225732400

Sales Range: $25-49.9 Million
Emp.: 50
Mfr of Valves & Pipe Fittings
N.A.I.C.S.: 332919
Padeusz Krawczuk *(Gen Mgr)*

Division (Non-US):

Parker Hannifin SpA Fluid Control
Division **(3)**
Via E Fermi 5, Gessate, 20060, MI,
Italy **(100%)**
Tel.: (39) 02951251
Web Site: http://www.parker.com
Sales Range: $50-74.9 Million
Mfr of Valves & Pipe Fittings
N.A.I.C.S.: 332919

Division (Domestic):

Parker Hannifin Stratoflex **(2)**
3800 Calle Tecate, Camarillo, CA 93012-
5070
Tel.: (805) 484-8533
Web Site: http://www.parkerhannifin.com
Sales Range: $125-149.9 Million
Mfr of Couplings
N.A.I.C.S.: 333414

Parker Hannifin Stratoflex Products
Div **(2)**
220 Roberts Cut Off Rd, Fort Worth, TX
76114 **(100%)**
Tel.: (817) 738-6543
Web Site: http://www.parker.com
Sales Range: $125-149.9 Million
Mfr of Hoses, Fittings & Adaptors for Auto-
motive, Industrial & Aerospace Applications
N.A.I.C.S.: 333998

Parker Hannifin Stratoflex Products
Division-Mansfield Hose Plant **(2)**
220 S Roberts Cut Off Rd, Fort Worth, TX
76114
Tel.: (817) 473-9341
Web Site: http://www.kajimausa.com
Sales Range: $25-49.9 Million
Emp.: 27
Mfr of Metal Fittings
N.A.I.C.S.: 332912

Parker Hannifin Tube Fittings
Div. **(2)**
3885 Gateway Blvd, Columbus, OH 43228-
9747
Tel.: (614) 279-7070
Mfr of Tube Fittings, Instrumentation Valves
& Tube Working Tools
N.A.I.C.S.: 332919
Shane Terblanche *(Gen Mgr-Hybrid Drive
Sys)*

Subsidiary (Non-US):

Parker Hannifin B.V. **(3)**
Edisonstraat 1, PO Box 340, 7570 AH, Old-
enzaal, Netherlands **(100%)**
Tel.: (31) 541585300
Web Site: https://www.parker.com
Sales Range: $50-74.9 Million
Emp.: 150
Mfr of Conveyors
N.A.I.C.S.: 333922

Parker Hannifin GmbH **(3)**
Am Metalwerk 9, 33659, Bielefeld,
Germany **(100%)**
Tel.: (49) 213140160
Web Site: https://www.parker.com
Sales Range: $150-199.9 Million
Emp.: 800
Mfr of Fluid Connectors
N.A.I.C.S.: 332912

Parker Hannifin Mfg Poland Sp.
z.o.o. **(3)**
Ul Kwiatkowskiego 16, 55 011, Siechnice,
Poland
Tel.: (48) 713013800
Web Site: http://www.parker.com
Mfr of Valves & Pipe Fittings
N.A.I.C.S.: 332919

Division (Domestic):

Parker Hannifin Tube Fittings
Division-Custom Manufacturing Busi-
ness Unit **(2)**
80 Parker Ave, Brookville, OH 45309-1925
Tel.: (937) 833-2527

Web Site: http://www.parkerhannifin.com
Sales Range: $50-74.9 Million
Mfr of Tube Fittings
N.A.I.C.S.: 333996

Subsidiary (Non-US):

Parker Hannifin de Mexico **(2)**
(100%)
Sales Range: $100-124.9 Million
Mfr of Valves & Pipe Fittings
N.A.I.C.S.: 332919
Carlos A. Rodriguez *(Gen Mgr)*

Parker Hannifin plc **(2)**
Stone Bench Way Tongue Ln Industrial Est,
Buxton, SK17 7LZ, Derbyshire, United King-
dom
Tel.: (44) 129871231
Sales Range: $25-49.9 Million
Emp.: 25
Mfr of Extrudit Products
N.A.I.C.S.: 332919

Parker Hannifin s.r.o. **(2)**
Parkerova 623, 250 67, Klecany, Czech
Republic **(100%)**
Tel.: (420) 284083111
Web Site: http://www.parker.com
Sales Range: $25-49.9 Million
Emp.: 50
Mfr of Valves & Pipe Fittings
N.A.I.C.S.: 332919

Division (Domestic):

Parker Hannifin, Quick Coupling
Div. **(2)**
8145 Lewis Rd, Minneapolis, MN 55427-
4416
Tel.: (763) 544-7781
Web Site: http://www.parker.com
Sales Range: $125-149.9 Million
Hydraulics Couplers for Farm Equipment &
Industrial Quick Coupling Mfr
N.A.I.C.S.: 332919

Subsidiary (Non-US):

Parker Hannifin-Hydraulics
Division **(2)**
Tachbrook Pk Dr, Tachbrook Park, Warwick,
CV34 6TU, Berkshire, United
Kingdom **(100%)**
Tel.: (44) 1926317878
Web Site: http://www.parker.com
Hydraulic Products Mfr
N.A.I.C.S.: 325998

Rectus AG **(2)**
Tel.: (49) 70421000
Web Site: http://www.parker.com
Sales Range: $100-124.9 Million
Emp.: 150
Automotive Couplings
N.A.I.C.S.: 332111

Subsidiary (Non-US):

Nycoil Company **(3)**
Tel.: (336) 495-0004
Web Site: http://www.nycoil.com
Rev.: $10,000,000
Emp.: 45
Fluid Power Valves & Hose Fittings
N.A.I.C.S.: 332912

Parker Hannifin France SAS **(1)**
142 rue de la Foret, Contamine-Sur-Arve,
France
Tel.: (33) 450258025
Fluid Power Pump & Motor Mfr
N.A.I.C.S.: 333996

Parker Hannifin France SAS **(1)**
142 rue de la Foret, 74130, Contamine-Sur-
Arve, France
Tel.: (33) 450258025
Web Site: https://www.parker.com
Electronic Equipment Whslr
N.A.I.C.S.: 423690

Parker Hannifin GB Ltd. **(1)**
Tachbrook Park Drive, Tachbrook Park,
Warwick, CV34 6TU, United Kingdom
Tel.: (44) 1926317878
Web Site: http://www.parker.com
Fluid Power Pump & Motor Mfr
N.A.I.C.S.: 333996

Parker Hannifin Global Capital Management S.a r.l. (1)
22 Rue Goethe, Luxembourg, 1637, Luxembourg
Tel.: (352) 248378
Investment Management Service
N.A.I.C.S.: 523999

Parker Hannifin GmbH & Co. KG Vertriebs- und Servicezentrale (1)
Pat-Parker-Platz 1, 41564, Kaarst, Germany (100%)
Tel.: (49) 213140160
Web Site: http://www.parker-deutschland.de
Sales Range: $50-74.9 Million
Emp.: 120
Product Sales & Services
N.A.I.C.S.: 423830
Gunter Schrank (Mng Dir)

Parker Hannifin Gmbh (1)
Fasanenweg 5, 65451, Kelsterbach, Germany
Tel.: (49) 610790390
Web Site: http://www.parker.com
Industrial Machinery Whslr
N.A.I.C.S.: 423830

Parker Hannifin Holding, S. de R.L. de C.V. (1)
Via De Ferrocarril A Matamoros No 730, Apodaca, 66600, Nuevo Leon, Mexico
Tel.: (52) 8181566000
Holding Company
N.A.I.C.S.: 551112

Parker Hannifin Hong Kong Ltd. (1)
Suites 01-04 20/F Tower 2 The Gateway Harbour City, Tsimshatsui, Kowloon, China (Hong Kong) (100%)
Tel.: (852) 24288008
Sales Range: $75-99.9 Million
Emp.: 55
Commercial, Mobile, Industrial & Aerospace Market Motion & Control Technologies Mfr
N.A.I.C.S.: 551112
Yoon Michael Chung (Pres-Asia Pacific Grp)

Parker Hannifin Hydraulics Group (1)
6035 Parkland Blvd, Cleveland, OH 44124-4186 (100%)
Tel.: (216) 896-3000
Sales Range: $100-124.9 Million
Emp.: 800
Hydraulic Pump & Control Systems Developer & Mfr
N.A.I.C.S.: 333996

Division (Domestic):

Parker Hannifin Custom Cylinder Operations (2)
29289 Airport Rd, Eugene, OR 97402-9523
Tel.: (541) 689-9111
Sales Range: $75-99.9 Million
Emp.: 150
Mfr of Heavy-Duty Tie Rod Pneumatic & Hydraulic Cylinders, Electronic Feedback Actuators, Custom Cylinders & Welded Hydraulic Cylinders
N.A.I.C.S.: 333996
Steve Jaques (Plant Mgr)

Parker Hannifin Cylinder Division (2)
500 S Wolf Rd, Des Plaines, IL 60016-3139
Tel.: (847) 298-2400
Web Site: http://www.parker.com
Sales Range: $50-74.9 Million
Emp.: 100
Mfr of Air & Hydraulic Cylinders
N.A.I.C.S.: 423830

Division (Non-US):

Parker Hannifin (Canada) Inc., Cylinder Division (3)
160 Chisholm Dr, Milton, L9T 3G9, ON, Canada (100%)
Tel.: (905) 693-3000
Web Site: http://www.parker.com
Sales Range: $50-74.9 Million
Emp.: 100
Mfr of Valves & Pipe Fittings
N.A.I.C.S.: 332919

Parker Hannifin Cylinder Division (3)
Delmenhorster Str 10, 50735, Cologne, Germany (100%)

Tel.: (49) 22171720
Sales Range: $25-49.9 Million
Emp.: 70
Mfr of Cylinders
N.A.I.C.S.: 333995
Stefan Bus (Mgr-Bus Dev)

Parker Hannifin Cylinder Division, Sweden (3)
Fredesgatan 2, PO Box 753, 521 22, Falkoping, Sweden (100%)
Tel.: (46) 515674200
Web Site: http://www.parker.com
Sales Range: $25-49.9 Million
Emp.: 100
Mfr of Cylinders
N.A.I.C.S.: 333995

Parker Hannifin Manufacturing Ltd.- Cylinder Division (3)
Tachbrook Park Drive, Warwick, CV34 6TU, United Kingdom (100%)
Tel.: (44) 1926 833700
Web Site: http://www.parker.com
Sales Range: $25-49.9 Million
Emp.: 75
Mfr of Cylinders, Pneumatic & Industrial Hydraulic Products
N.A.I.C.S.: 333995

Parker Hannifin SpA Cylinder Division (3)
Via Carducci 11, 21010, Arsago Seprio, Italy (100%)
Tel.: (39) 0331765661
Sales Range: $25-49.9 Million
Emp.: 80
Mfr of Cylinders
N.A.I.C.S.: 333995

Subsidiary (Domestic):

Parker-Helac Division (3)
225 Battersby Ave, Enumclaw, WA 98022
Tel.: (360) 825-1601
Web Site: http://www.helac.com
Helical Rotary Actuators Mfr
N.A.I.C.S.: 333995

Division (Domestic):

Parker Hannifin Gear Pump Division (2)
2701 Intertech Dr, Youngstown, OH 44509
Tel.: (330) 270-6000
Web Site: http://www.parker.com
Sales Range: $50-74.9 Million
Emp.: 140
Mfr of Gear Pumps
N.A.I.C.S.: 333995

Subsidiary (Non-US):

Parker Hannifin GmbH & Co. KG Hydraulic Controls Division Europe (2)
Gutenbergstrasse 38, D-41564, Kaarst, Germany (100%)
Tel.: (49) 21315130
Web Site: http://www.parker.com
Sales Range: $75-99.9 Million
Emp.: 400
Mfr of Hydraulic Components
N.A.I.C.S.: 333995

Division (Domestic):

Parker Hannifin Hydraulic Accumulator Division (2)
10711 N 2nd St, Machesney Park, IL 61115-1459 (100%)
Tel.: (815) 636-4100
Web Site: http://www.parker.com
Sales Range: $50-74.9 Million
Emp.: 100
Mfr of Hydraulic Accumulators
N.A.I.C.S.: 336413

Parker Hannifin Hydraulic Pump & Motor Div. (2)
2745 Snapps Ferry Rd, Greeneville, TN 37744-1641 (100%)
Tel.: (423) 639-8151
Web Site: http://www.parker.com
Sales Range: $75-99.9 Million
Emp.: 400
Mfr of Fluid Power Pumps
N.A.I.C.S.: 332111

Parker Hannifin Hydraulic Valve Div. (2)

520 Ternes Ln, Elyria, OH 44035-6252
Tel.: (440) 366-5100
Web Site: http://www.parker.com
Sales Range: $100-124.9 Million
Emp.: 280
Mfr of Hydraulic Pumps, Pump Controls & Pump Motors
N.A.I.C.S.: 332912

Subsidiary (Non-US):

Parker Hannifin Hydraulics Division, Brazil (2)
Av Frederico Ritter 1100, Distrito Industrial, Cachoeira, 94930-000, RS, Brazil (100%)
Tel.: (55) 5134709144
Web Site: http://www.parker.com
Emp.: 200
Mfr of Motion & Control Technologies
N.A.I.C.S.: 334519

Division (Domestic):

Parker Hannifin Integrated Hydraulics Division (2)
595 Schelter Rd, Lincolnshire, IL 60069-4220 (100%)
Tel.: (847) 955-5000
Web Site: http://www.parker.com
Sales Range: $75-99.9 Million
Emp.: 200
Mfr of Hydraullics
N.A.I.C.S.: 333996

Parker Hannifin Mobile Cylinder Division (2)
1775 Logan Ave, Youngstown, OH 44505-4023 (100%)
Tel.: (330) 740-8670
Sales Range: $25-49.9 Million
Emp.: 18
Mfr of Mobile Cylinders
N.A.I.C.S.: 333995

Parker Hannifin Mobile Systems Division (2)
595 Schelter Rd, Lincolnshire, IL 60069-4220
Tel.: (847) 955-5000
Web Site: http://www.parker.com
Sales Range: $75-99.9 Million
Emp.: 200
Mfr of Mobile System Products
N.A.I.C.S.: 333996

Subsidiary (Non-US):

Parker Hannifin Motion & Control Sales Division Canada (2)
160 Chisholm Dr, Milton, L9T 3G9, ON, Canada (100%)
Tel.: (905) 693-3000
Sales Range: $75-99.9 Million
Emp.: 180
Mfr of Valves & Pipe Fittings
N.A.I.C.S.: 332919
Joe Gallant (Mgr-Sls)
Jim Fillyer (Dir-HR)
Cecilia Kwinecki (Controller)

Parker Hannifin Motion And Control (2)
Eje 1 Nte 100, Toluca, 50100, Mexico (100%)
Tel.: (52) 7222754200
Web Site: http://www.parker-automation.com
Sales Range: $25-49.9 Million
Emp.: 180
Mfr of Industrial Components
N.A.I.C.S.: 334513

Division (Domestic):

Parker Hannifin Oildyne Division (2)
5520 Hwy 169 N, Minneapolis, MN 55428-3602
Tel.: (763) 533-1600
Web Site: http://www.parkerhannifin.com
Sales Range: $75-99.9 Million
Emp.: 180
Mfr of Valves & Pipe Fittings
N.A.I.C.S.: 333996

Subsidiary (Non-US):

Parker Hannifin S.A. (2)
Parc D Activities De La Foret, PO Box 3124, 27031, Evreux, France (100%)
Tel.: (33) 232233400

Web Site: http://www.parker.com
Sales Range: $75-99.9 Million
Emp.: 138
Mfr of Pipe Fittings & Valves
N.A.I.C.S.: 332919

Parker Hannifin, SA (2)
142 Rue De La Foret, 74130, Contamine-Sur-Arve, Contamine Sur Arve, France (100%)
Tel.: (33) 0450258025
Web Site: http://www.parker.com
Sales Range: $75-99.9 Million
Emp.: 200
Mfr of Valves & Pipe Fittings
N.A.I.C.S.: 332919

Division (Non-US):

Parker Vansco Electronic Controls Division (2)
1305 Clarence Avenue, Winnipeg, R3T 1T4, MB, Canada
Tel.: (204) 452-6776
Web Site: http://www.vansco.ca
Sales Range: $150-199.9 Million
Electromechanical & Electrohydraulic Control Systems Developer & Mfr
N.A.I.C.S.: 335314

Parker Hannifin India Pvt. Ltd. (1)
Plot EL-26 MIDC TTC Industrial Area Mahape, Navi Mumbai, 400 709, India
Tel.: (91) 2241242828
Web Site: https://www.parker.com
Valves & Pipe Fittings Mfr
N.A.I.C.S.: 332919

Parker Hannifin Industrial s.r.o. (1)
Na Morani 5480, 430 01, Chomutov, Czech Republic (100%)
Tel.: (420) 474400111
Web Site: http://www.parker.com
Sales Range: $100-124.9 Million
Emp.: 200
Mfr of Fluid Connectors
N.A.I.C.S.: 332919

Parker Hannifin Instrumentation Group (1)
6035 Parkland Blvd, Cleveland, OH 44124-4186 (100%)
Tel.: (216) 896-3000
Web Site: http://www.parker.com
Sales Range: $250-299.9 Million
Emp.: 800
Mfr of Instrumentation Fittings, Valves & Components
N.A.I.C.S.: 333996
Lee C. Banks (Pres & COO)
William Bowman (Co-Pres & VP)

Division (Domestic):

Parker Hannifin - Instrumentation Products Div (2)
1005 A Cleaner Way, Huntsville, AL 35805
Tel.: (256) 881-2040
Sales Range: $100-124.9 Million
Specialty Fittings for Petroleum & Chemical Processing Industries
N.A.I.C.S.: 334513

Parker Hannifin General Valve Operation Pneutronics Division (2)
45 Route 46 E, Pine Brook, NJ 07058-3305
Tel.: (973) 575-4844
Web Site: http://www.parker.com
Sales Range: $75-99.9 Million
Emp.: 50
Mfr of Valves & Pipe Fittings
N.A.I.C.S.: 332911

Parker Hannifin Precision Fluidics Division (2)
26 Clinton Dr Unit 103, Hollis, NH 03049
Tel.: (603) 595-1500
Web Site: http://www.parker.com
Sales Range: $25-49.9 Million
Emp.: 120
Mfr of Miniature Fluidic Components & System Solutions for Medical & Analytical Instrumentation.
N.A.I.C.S.: 334513

Parker Hannifin Veriflo Division (2)
250 Canal Blvd, Richmond, CA 94804-2002
Tel.: (510) 235-9590
Web Site: http://www.veriflo.com

Parker Hannifin Corporation—(Continued)

Sales Range: $75-99.9 Million
Emp.: 240
Mfr of Precision Valves, Regulators &
Transducers
N.A.I.C.S.: 334513

Division (Non-US):

**Parker Hannifin plc - Instrumentation
Division** (2)
Riverside Road Pottington Industrial Estate,
Barnstaple, EX31 1NP, Devonshire, United
Kingdom
Tel.: (44) 1271313131
Web Site: http://www.parker.com
Sales Range: $100-124.9 Million
Emp.: 250
Mfr of Industrial Components
N.A.I.C.S.: 333310

Parker Hannifin Italy srl (1)
Tel.: (39) 02451921
Web Site: https://www.parker.com
Industrial Machinery Whslr
N.A.I.C.S.: 423830

**Parker Hannifin Italy srl Sucursal en
Espana** (1)
Tel.: (34) 916757300
Aerospace Systems & Technology Device
Mfr & Distr
N.A.I.C.S.: 334519

**Parker Hannifin Japan Holdings
GK** (1)
Tokyo Front Terrace 16F 2-3-14 Higashishi-
nagawa, Shinagawa Ku, Tokyo, 140-0002,
Japan
Tel.: (81) 363654020
Web Site: http://www.parkerstore.jp
Emp.: 80
Holding Company
N.A.I.C.S.: 551112

Parker Hannifin Japan Ltd. (1)
3-2-10 Shirokanedai, Minato-ku, Tokyo,
108-0071, Japan (100%)
Tel.: (81) 364083901
Web Site: http://www.parker.com
Sales Range: $50-74.9 Million
Emp.: 75
Mfr of Valves & Pipe Fittings
N.A.I.C.S.: 332919
Tatsunobu Takeyama (Mng Dir)

Branch (Domestic):

Parker Hannifin Japan Ltd. (2)
Tokyo Front Terrace 16F 2-3-14 Higashishi-
nagawa, Shinagawa Ku, Tokyo, 140-0002,
Japan
Tel.: (01) 363654020
Web Site: http://www.parker.com
Mfr of Pipe Fittings & Valves
N.A.I.C.S.: 332919

Parker Hannifin Korea (1)
11F Uspace 1B 660 Daewangpangyo-ro,
Bundang-gu Seongnam-si, Yongin, 13494,
Gyeonggi-do, Korea (South)
Tel.: (82) 8225590400
Web Site: http://www.parker.com
Valves & Pipe Fittings Mfr
N.A.I.C.S.: 332919

Parker Hannifin LLC (1)
8-Go Marta St 6A Building 1, Moscow, Rus-
sia
Tel.: (7) 495 645 21 56
Web Site: http://www.parker.com
Emp.: 18
Fluid Power Pump & Motor Mfr
N.A.I.C.S.: 333996

Parker Hannifin Limited (1)
Pilot Way, Ansty Business Park, Coventry,
CV34 6TU, United Kingdom (100%)
Tel.: (44) 1926317878
Sales Range: $25-49.9 Million
Emp.: 150
Industrial Fluid Circuit Components De-
signer, Mfr & Whslr
N.A.I.C.S.: 332912

**Parker Hannifin Malaysia Sdn.
Bhd** (1)
Lot 9 Jalan U1/26, Hicom-Glenmarie, Shah
Alam, 47200, Malaysia
Tel.: (60) 380243163

Emp.: 31
Motion & Control Systems Mfr
N.A.I.C.S.: 336413

**Parker Hannifin Manufacturing (UK)
Limited** (1)
Shaw Cross Business Park Churwell Vale,
Dewsbury, WF12 7RD, United Kingdom
Tel.: (44) 1924487000
Emp.: 250
Industrial Machinery Whslr
N.A.I.C.S.: 423830
Chris Mason (Mng Dir)

**Parker Hannifin Manufacturing Bel-
gium BVBA** (1)
Rupelweg 11, Boom, 2850, Belgium
Tel.: (32) 38808150
Web Site: http://www.parker.com
Emp.: 7
Fluid Power Pump & Motor Mfr
N.A.I.C.S.: 333996

**Parker Hannifin Manufacturing Fin-
land OY** (1)
Polunmaenkatu 22, Tampere, 33720, Fin-
land
Tel.: (358) 207532600
Web Site: http://www.parker.com
Sales Range: $25-49.9 Million
Emp.: 100
Fluid Power Pump & Motor Mfr
N.A.I.C.S.: 333996

**Parker Hannifin Manufacturing Ger-
many GmbH & Co. KG** (1)
Daimlerstr 7, 71735, Eberdingen, Germany
Tel.: (49) 70421000
Web Site: http://www.parker.com
Emp.: 140
Industrial Machinery Mfr
N.A.I.C.S.: 333998

**Parker Hannifin Manufacturing Neth-
erlands (Filtration and Separation)
B.V.** (1)
Oude Kerkstraat 4, 4878, Etten-Leur, Neth-
erlands
Tel.: (31) 765085300
Industrial Machinery Mfr
N.A.I.C.S.: 333998
Richard Meeuwissen (Mgr-Ops)

**Parker Hannifin Manufacturing Neth-
erlands (Filtration) B.V.** (1)
Stieltesweg 8, Arnhem, 6827, Netherlands
Tel.: (31) 263760376
Web Site: http://www.parker.com
Emp.: 40
Industrial Machinery Mfr
N.A.I.C.S.: 333998
Mikko Uusitalo (Mng Dir)

**Parker Hannifin Manufacturing Neth-
erlands (Hose) B.V.** (1)
Fultonweg 2, 9601, Hoogezand, Groningen,
Netherlands
Tel.: (31) 598343555
Industrial Machinery Mfr
N.A.I.C.S.: 333998

**Parker Hannifin Manufacturing Neth-
erlands (Pneumatic) B.V.** (1)
Industrial Machinery Mfr
N.A.I.C.S.: 333998

**Parker Hannifin Manufacturing Po-
land Sp z.o.o.** (1)
Parker Store, Gdansk, 80-041, Poland
Tel.: (48) 225732400
Web Site: http://www.parker.com
Industrial Machinery Mfr
N.A.I.C.S.: 333998

**Parker Hannifin Manufacturing
SRL** (1)
Strada Fantasia n 83, 10040, Leini, Turin,
Italy
Tel.: (39) 0119918511
Web Site: http://www.parker.com
Industrial Machinery Whslr
N.A.I.C.S.: 423830

**Parker Hannifin Manufacturing Spain
SL** (1)
C/ Anoia 5A, 08223, Terrassa, Barcelona,
Spain
Tel.: (34) 937852504

Emp.: 100
Fluid Power Pump & Motor Mfr
N.A.I.C.S.: 333996
Joaquin Furriol (Plant Mgr)

**Parker Hannifin Manufacturing
srl** (1)
Via Caboto 1, Veniano, 20094, Corsico, MI,
Italy
Tel.: (39) 031936111
Industrial Machinery Mfr
N.A.I.C.S.: 332912

**Parker Hannifin Motion & Control
(Shanghai) Co. Ltd.** (1)
280 YunQiao Road Jin Qiao Export Pro-
cessing Zone, Shanghai, 201206, China
Tel.: (86) 2128995000
Web Site: https://www.parker.com
Industrial Machinery Mfr
N.A.I.C.S.: 333998

**Parker Hannifin Netherlands Holdings
2 B.V.** (1)
Edisonstraat 1, 7575 AT, Oldenzaal, Nether-
lands
Tel.: (31) 541585000
Web Site: http://www.parker.com
Sales Range: $25-49.9 Million
Emp.: 20
Fluid Power Pump & Motor Mfr
N.A.I.C.S.: 333996

**Parker Hannifin Netherlands Holdings
B.V.** (1)
Edisonstraat 1, Oldenzaal, 7575, Overijssel,
Netherlands
Tel.: (31) 541585000
Web Site: http://www.parker.com
Emp.: 150
Holding Company
N.A.I.C.S.: 551112

Parker Hannifin Partner B LLC (1)
6035 Parkland Blvd, Cleveland, OH 44124-
4141
Tel.: (216) 896-3000
Web Site: http://www.parker.com
Industrial Machinery Whslr
N.A.I.C.S.: 423830

**Parker Hannifin Portugal Unipessoal
Lda** (1)
Travessa da Bataria 184 R/C Dto /1 Esq,
4450-625, Leca da Palmeira, Portugal
Tel.: (351) 229997360
Industrial Machinery Whslr
N.A.I.C.S.: 423830

**Parker Hannifin Refrigeration & Air
Conditioning (Wuxi) Co., Ltd.** (1)
1 Xingchuang Yi Lu Wuxi Singapore Ind
Park, Wuxi, 214028, China
Tel.: (86) 51085282071
Industrial Machinery Mfr
N.A.I.C.S.: 333998

Parker Hannifin Seal Group (1)
14300 Alton Pkwy, Irvine, CA
92618-1814 (100%)
Tel.: (949) 833-3000
Web Site: http://www.parker.com
Sales Range: $450-499.9 Million
Emp.: 1,500
Mfr of Miscellaneous Aircraft Equipment
N.A.I.C.S.: 336413

Subsidiary (Non-US):

Chomerics Division-Europe (2)
Unit 6 Century Point Halifax Road, High
Wycombe, HP12 3SL, Bucks, United King-
dom
Tel.: (44) 1494 455400
Web Site: http://www.parker.com
EMI Shielded Gaskets, Vents & Windows
Mfr
N.A.I.C.S.: 339991

**PTFE Polar Packaging Mfg./Seals
ApS** (2)
Bjerg vangen 2, Bellerup, DK 3060, Esper-
gaerde, Denmark (100%)
Tel.: (45) 49121700
Web Site: http://www.parker.com
Sales Range: $25-49.9 Million
Emp.: 65
Mfr of Polytetrafluoroethylene (PTFE) Seal-
ing Products for Industrial, Chemical, Auto-
motive, Medical & Other Markets

N.A.I.C.S.: 325211

Division (Domestic):

**Parker Aircraft Control Systems
Div.** (2)
14300 Alton Pkwy, Irvine, CA 92618-1814
Tel.: (949) 833-3000
Web Site: http://www.parker.com
Sales Range: $50-74.9 Million
Emp.: 150
Mfr of Aircraft Controls, Valves & Hydraulic
Components
N.A.I.C.S.: 336413

**Parker Controls Systems
Division** (2)
2010 Waldrep Industrial Blvd, Dublin, GA
31021-2630
Tel.: (478) 275-4030
Web Site: http://www.parker.com
Sales Range: $100-124.9 Million
Emp.: 257
Mfr of Aircraft Controls
N.A.I.C.S.: 336413

**Parker Hannifin Advanced Products
Company** (2)
33 Defco Park Rd, North Haven, CT
06473 (100%)
Tel.: (203) 239-3341
Sales Range: $25-49.9 Million
Emp.: 82
Metallic & Polymer Spring Energized Seal
Mfr
N.A.I.C.S.: 339991
Greg More (Mgr-Bus Unit)

**Parker Hannifin Corp. - Fluid Sys-
tems Division** (2)
16666 Von Karman Ave, Irvine, CA 92606
Tel.: (949) 833-3000
Web Site: http://www.parker.com
Aerospace & Aircraft Products Mfr
N.A.I.C.S.: 333996

**Parker Hannifin Corp., Aircraft Wheel
& Brake Division** (2)
1160 Center Rd, Avon, OH 44011-1208
Tel.: (440) 937-6211
Web Site: http://www.parker.com
Sales Range: $25-49.9 Million
Emp.: 130
Mfr of Aircraft Wheel Assemblies & Brakes
N.A.I.C.S.: 425120

**Parker Hannifin Corp., Gas Turbine
Fuel Systems Div.** (2)
8940 Tyler Blvd, Mentor, OH 44060-1882
Tel.: (440) 266-2300
Sales Range: $25-49.9 Million
Emp.: 150
Mfr of Fueling Systems for Aircraft
N.A.I.C.S.: 541715

**Parker Hannifin Corporation, Airborne
Division** (2)
711 Taylor St, Elyria, OH
44035-6229 (100%)
Tel.: (440) 284-6300
Web Site: http://www.parker.com
Sales Range: $75-99.9 Million
Emp.: 130
Mfr of Aircraft Components, Aircraft Acces-
sories, Parts & Supplies
N.A.I.C.S.: 336413
Erick Mitchell (CEO)

**Parker Hannifin Customer Support
Commercial Division** (2)
14300 Alton Pkwy, Irvine, CA 92618-1814
Tel.: (949) 833-3000
Sales Range: $10-24.9 Million
Emp.: 25
Provider of Customer Support Services
N.A.I.C.S.: 336413

**Parker Hannifin Electronic Systems
Div.** (2)
300 Marcus Blvd, Smithtown, NY 11787-
2044
Tel.: (631) 231-3737
Web Site: http://www.parker.com
Sales Range: $50-74.9 Million
Emp.: 260
Mfr of Fuel Gaging & Monitoring Comput-
ers, Fire-Suppression Systems &
Navigation-Monitoring Computers for Mili-
tary & Commercial Aviation

N.A.I.C.S.: 334519

Plant (Domestic):

Parker Hannifin Engineered Seals Division (2)
1525 S 10th St, Goshen, IN 46526-4505
Tel.: (574) 533-1111
Web Site: http://www.parkerhannifin.com
Rev.: $125,000,000
Emp.: 150
Mfr of Custom Molded & Automatic Machine-Cut Industrial & Mechanical Rubber Products
N.A.I.C.S.: 326291

Subsidiary (Non-US):

Parker Hannifin Fluid Connectors & Seal Group (2)
74 Rue De Paris, PO Box 524, Ville La Grand, Rennes, 74112, France (100%)
Tel.: (33) 450878080
Sales Range: $75-99.9 Million
Emp.: 180
Mfr of Fluid Connectors
N.A.I.C.S.: 335931
Isabelle Vedonne (Dir-Fin)

Parker Hannifin GmbH & Co. KG O-Ring Division Europe (2)
Stuifenstrasse 55, Pleidelsheim, 74385, Germany (100%)
Tel.: (49) 71442060
Web Site: http://www.parker.com
Sales Range: $100-124.9 Million
Emp.: 250
Mfr of Valves & Pipe Fittings
N.A.I.C.S.: 332919
Dan Wezhkeewicz (Pres)

Parker Hannifin GmbH & Co. KG Packing Division Europe (2)
Arnold Jager Strasse 1, Bietigheim-Bissingen, 74321, Germany (100%)
Tel.: (49) 71423510
Web Site: http://www.parker.com
Sales Range: $75-99.9 Million
Emp.: 430
Mfr of Valves & Pipe Fittings
N.A.I.C.S.: 332919

Division (Domestic):

Parker Hannifin Hydraulics Systems Division (2)
2220 Palmer Ave, Kalamazoo, MI 49001-4122 (100%)
Tel.: (269) 384-3400
Web Site: http://www.parker.com
Sales Range: $200-249.9 Million
Emp.: 500
Mfr of Actuators, Valves & Filters
N.A.I.C.S.: 336413

Parker Hannifin Nichols Airborne Div (2)
14 Robbins Pond Rd, Devens, MA 01434-5641 (100%)
Tel.: (978) 784-1200
Sales Range: $50-74.9 Million
Emp.: 120
Mfr of Aircraft Engine Pumps & Lubrication Pumps; Overhaul & Repair of Aircraft Lubrication Engine & Generator Pumps
N.A.I.C.S.: 333996
Melissa Hertel (Mgr-HR)

Parker Hannifin Seal Group - Engineered Polymer Systems Division (2)
403 Industrial Dr, Nacogdoches, TX 75964-1297
Tel.: (801) 972-3000
Web Site: http://www.parker.com
Sales Range: $25-49.9 Million
Emp.: 50
Sealing Products Mfr
N.A.I.C.S.: 325520

Plant (Non-US):

Parker Hannifin de Mexico-Seal de Matamoros Facility
Diagonal Lorenzo de la Garza No 13, Matamoros, 87499, Mexico (100%)
Tel.: (52) 8688129000
Sales Range: $25-49.9 Million
Emp.: 100
Mfr of Climate Control Products

N.A.I.C.S.: 334513

Subsidiary (Non-US):

Parker Hannifin s.r.o., Packing Division (2)
Podebradska 1005, Sadska, 28912, Czech Republic (100%)
Web Site: http://www.parkerhannifin.com
Sales Range: $150-199.9 Million
Emp.: 500
Mfr of Packing Products
N.A.I.C.S.: 424130

Division (Domestic):

Parker Hannifin, Control Systems Division (2)
1425 W 2675 N, Ogden, UT 84404-2665
Tel.: (801) 786-3000
Sales Range: $75-99.9 Million
Emp.: 450
Mfr of Aircraft Controls, Valves & Hydraulic Components
N.A.I.C.S.: 334511
Guy Martin (Gen Mgr)

Subsidiary (Non-US):

Parker Seal De Mexico, S.A. (2)
Rio Lerma No 221, Fraccionamiento Industrial, 54060, Tlalnepantla, Tlanepantla, Mexico (100%)
Tel.: (52) 5555653622
Sales Range: $125-149.9 Million
Emp.: 300
Mfr of Valves & Pipe Fittings
N.A.I.C.S.: 332919

Division (Domestic):

Chomerics - Mexico (3)
Carretera Base Aerea No 5850 Km 5 Modulo 17, 45100, Zapopan, Jalisco, Mexico (100%)
Tel.: (52) 8262630000
Web Site: http://www.parker.com
Mfr of Valves & Pipe Fittings
N.A.I.C.S.: 332919

Division (Domestic):

Parker Seals (2)
104 Hartman Dr, Lebanon, TN 37087-2516
Tel.: (615) 444-0191
Web Site: http://www.parker.com
Sales Range: $50-74.9 Million
Emp.: 50
Gasket & Sealing Device Mfr
N.A.I.C.S.: 339991

Parker Tech Seal Division (2)
3025 W Croft Cir, Spartanburg, SC 29302
Tel.: (864) 573-7332
Web Site: http://www.parker.com
Sales Range: $25-49.9 Million
Emp.: 110
Mfr of Reclaimed Rubber & Specialty Rubber Compounds
N.A.I.C.S.: 326299

Parker Hannifin Singapore Pte. Ltd. (1)
11 Fourth Chin Bee Road, Singapore, 619702, Singapore (100%)
Tel.: (65) 68876300
Web Site: https://www.parker.com
Sales Range: $10-24.9 Million
Emp.: 100
Mfr of Industrial Components
N.A.I.C.S.: 334513
Sean Fredericks (Mng Dir)

Parker Hannifin Sweden Sales AB (1)
Almenasvagen 20, 506 32, Boras, Sweden
Tel.: (46) 337005200
Web Site: http://www.parker.com
Sales Range: $75-99.9 Million
Emp.: 35
Fluid Power Pump & Motor Mfr
N.A.I.C.S.: 333996

Parker Hannifin Taiwan Co. Ltd. (1)
8 Fl 22 Wuquan 7th Rd Wugu Dist, New Taipei City, 248, Taiwan (100%)
Tel.: (886) 222988987
Web Site: http://www.parker.com

Sales Range: $25-49.9 Million
Emp.: 40
Mfr of Pipe Fittings
N.A.I.C.S.: 332919

Parker Hannifin Thailand Co. Ltd. (1)
1265 Rama 9 Road Suanluang, Bangkok, 10250, Thailand (100%)
Tel.: (66) 2186 7000
Web Site: http://www.parker.com
Sales Range: $100-124.9 Million
Mfr of Valves & Pipe Fittings
N.A.I.C.S.: 332919

Parker Hannifin Verwaltungs-GmbH (1)
Am Metallwerk 9, 33659, Bielefeld, Germany
Tel.: (49) 52140480
Industrial Machinery Whslr
N.A.I.C.S.: 423830

Parker Hannifin de Mexico S.A. de C.V. (1)
Antiguo Camino A San Lorenzo 338 Zona Industrial, Toluca, Edo Mex, Mexico
Tel.: (52) 7222754200
Web Site: https://www.parker.com
Fluid Power Pump & Motor Mfr
N.A.I.C.S.: 333996

Parker Hareket ve Kontrol Sistemleri Tic. A.S. (1)
Arif Month Sokak No 20th, Istanbul, 34774, Turkiye
Tel.: (90) 2164997081
Web Site: http://www.parker.com
Emp.: 40
Power Generation Equipment & Motor Mfr
N.A.I.C.S.: 333996

Parker Hose BV (1)
Fultonweg 2, PB 338, Hoogezand, 9601 MK, Netherlands
Tel.: (31) 598343555
Fluid Power Pump & Motor Mfr
N.A.I.C.S.: 333996

Parker Italy Holding S.r.l. (1)
Via Privata Archimede 1, Corsico, 20094, Italy
Tel.: (39) 02451921
Web Site: http://www.parker.com
Fluid Power Pump & Motor Mfr
N.A.I.C.S.: 333996

Subsidiary (Domestic):

Parker Hannifin Srl (2)
Via Privata Archimede 1, Corsico, 20094, Milan, Italy
Tel.: (39) 02451921
Web Site: http://www.parker.com
Emp.: 240
Fluid Power Pump & Motor Mfr
N.A.I.C.S.: 333996

Division (Domestic):

Hiross Zander Division (3)
Strada Zona Industriale 4, San Angelo di Piove, I-35020, Padua, Italy
Tel.: (39) 0499712111
Sales Range: $125-149.9 Million
Electric Equipment Mfr
N.A.I.C.S.: 444180

Parker Korea Ltd. (1)
23 1-Gil Jangan-Gongdan PHK Div/Jangan Plant, Hwaseong, 18579, Gyeonggi-Do, Korea (South)
Tel.: (82) 313590700
Fluid Power & Gas Generation Products Mfr
N.A.I.C.S.: 333996

Parker Lklim Kontrol Sistemleri Sanayi ve Tic AS (1)
Inonu Mah Balcik Yolu Innou Mah Geposb 92 Sok, Gebze, Kocaeli, 41700, Turkiye
Tel.: (90) 2627513233
Fluid Power Pump & Motor Mfr
N.A.I.C.S.: 333996

Parker Maritime AS (1)
Heiamyra 1, N-4033, Stavanger, Norway
Tel.: (47) 51708500
Web Site: http://www.parkermaritime.no
Emp.: 40
Surveying & Consulting Services

N.A.I.C.S.: 488330

Parker Middle East FZE (1)
Jafza View 19 Office 2205, PO Box 262193, Jebel Ali, Dubai, United Arab Emirates
Emp.: 30
Industrial Machinery Whslr
N.A.I.C.S.: 423830

Parker Ontario Holding Inc. (1)
Durham Rd S 4625, Grimsby, Thorold, L3M 4H8, ON, Canada
Tel.: (905) 309-8230
Holding Company
N.A.I.C.S.: 551112

Parker Polyflex BV (1)
van maasdijkweg 2, Almelo, 7602 pz, Netherlands
Tel.: (31) 546488777
Fluid Power Pump & Motor Mfr
N.A.I.C.S.: 333996

Parker Sales (Ireland) Limited (1)
Baldonnell Business Park Naas Rd, Dublin, Ireland
Tel.: (353) 14666370
Web Site: http://www.parker.com
Emp.: 20
Motion & Control Products Mfr
N.A.I.C.S.: 334519

Parker Servicio's de Mexico, S.A. de C.V. (1)
Via De Ferrocarril A Matamoros S/N, Apodaca, 66600, NL, Mexico
Tel.: (52) 8181566800
Web Site: http://www.parker.com
Emp.: 500
Fluid Power & Gas Generation Products Mfr
N.A.I.C.S.: 333996

Parker-Hannifin International Corp. (1)
6035 Parkland Blvd, Cleveland, OH 44124-4186
Tel.: (216) 896-3000
Web Site: http://www.parker.com
Emp.: 800
Fluid Power Pumps Mfr
N.A.I.C.S.: 333996

Rayco Technologies Pte. Ltd. (1)
1020 Tai Seng Ave 07-3506 Tai Seng Industrial Estate, Singapore, 534416, Singapore
Tel.: (65) 62800366
Web Site: http://www.parker.com
Emp.: 25
Precision Elastomer Components Mfr
N.A.I.C.S.: 332721

Sterling-Velcon Filters Corp. (1)
Garden of the Gods Rd, Colorado Springs, CO 80907
Tel.: (719) 531-5855
Industrial Machinery Mfr
N.A.I.C.S.: 333998

Taiyo Techno, Ltd. (1)
1-1-1 Kita Eguchi Higashi Yodogawa-ku, Osaka, 533-0002, Japan
Tel.: (81) 663401600
Industrial Machinery Whslr
N.A.I.C.S.: 423830
Ito Mitro (Mgr)

Taiyo, Ltd. (1)
2-6-8 Bingomachi, Chuo-ku, Osaka, 541-0051, Japan (56.49%)
Tel.: (81) 649671100
Web Site: http://www.taiyo-ltd.co.jp
Sales Range: $125-149.9 Million
Emp.: 533
Hydraulic, Pneumatic, Environmental, Semiconductor, Electronic Control, Conveyor, Robotic & Assembly Line Equipment Developer, Mfr, Exporter & Sales
N.A.I.C.S.: 333996
Takashi Ishikawa (Pres & Gen Mgr)
Miwa Hirai (Exec Dir)

Subsidiary (US):

Taiyo America, Inc. (2)
1702 E Spring St, Saint Marys, OH 45885
Tel.: (419) 300-8811
Web Site: http://www.taiyoamericainc.com
Sales Range: $10-24.9 Million
Emp.: 9
Electric Equipment Mfr

Parker Hannifin Corporation—(Continued)

N.A.I.C.S.: 334419

Subsidiary (Domestic):

Circuit Automation Inc (3)
5292 System Dr, Huntington Beach, CA 92649
Tel.: (714) 763-4180
Web Site:
http://www.s197420823.onlinehome.us
Rev.: $2,000,000
Emp.: 20
Radio & Television Broadcasting & Wireless Communications Equipment Mfr
N.A.I.C.S.: 334220
Thomas R. Meeker (Pres)
Yuki Kojima (Exec VP)

Subsidiary (Non-US):

Taiyo Parker Fluidpower (Shanghai) Co., Ltd. (2)
No 33 Fuhua Rd, Jiading District, Shanghai, China
Tel.: (86) 2159900701
Web Site: http://www.taipa.com.cn
Sales Range: $10-24.9 Million
Emp.: 23
Hydraulic & Pneumatic Equipment Mfr
N.A.I.C.S.: 333995
Masaru Fukumori (Sls Mgr)

Subsidiary (Domestic):

Taiyo Tech Co., Ltd. (2)
2-2-15 Ninomiya higashi, Akiruno City, Tokyo, 197-0815, Japan
Tel.: (81) 425583334
Fluid Power Pump & Motor Mfr
N.A.I.C.S.: 333996

Total Filtration Services, Inc. (1)
755 W Big Beaver Rd Ste 700, Troy, MI 48084
Tel.: (248) 377-4004
Web Site:
https://www.totalfiltrationservices.com
Industrial Supplies Whslr
N.A.I.C.S.: 423840
Mark Roesner (Pres)

Twin Filter N.A., Inc. (1)
5177 Richmond Ave Ste 1145, Houston, TX 77056
Tel.: (713) 255-7255
Industrial Machinery Mfr
N.A.I.C.S.: 333998

Twin Filter South America Ltda (1)
Av Bernardino de Campos 98 14th floor Paraiso, 04004-040, Sao Paulo, Brazil
Tel: (55) 1240093537
Filteration Equipment Mfr
N.A.I.C.S.: 334419

PARKER WELLBORE COMPANY

2103 CityWest Blvd Ste 400, Houston, TX 77042-2835
Tel.: (281) 406-2000   DE
Web Site: https://parkerwellbore.com
Year Founded: 1934
PKDC—(OTCEM)
Rev.: $480,821,000
Assets: $828,414,000
Liabilities: $701,498,000
Net Worth: $126,916,000
Earnings: ($165,697,000)
Emp.: 2,425
Fiscal Year-end: 12/31/18
Barge & Off-Shore Drilling, Work-Over Services, International Land Drilling & Specialized Oil Tool Rentals
N.A.I.C.S.: 213112
Bryan R. Collins (Sr VP-Bus Dev-Global)
Brage Johannessen (Sr VP-Global Ops)
Alexander Esslemont (Pres & CEO)
Michael W. Sumruld (CFO & Sr VP)

Subsidiaries:

2M-Tek, Inc. (1)
205 Marcon Dr, Lafayette, LA 70507

Tel.: (337) 234-0636
Web Site: http://www.2m-tek.com
Electronic Components Mfr
N.A.I.C.S.: 334220
Andrew Gherardi (Mgr-Site)

ITS Netherlands B.V. (1)
Takelaarsweg 13, 1786 PR, Den Helder, Netherlands
Tel.: (31) 881307100
Land Drilling Services
N.A.I.C.S.: 213111

International Tubular Services De Mexico, S. De R.I. De C.V. (1)
Av De Los Encinos No 1011-E, Reynosa, 88730, Tamps, Mexico
Tel.: (52) 8999518246
Oil & Gas Field Equipment Mfr
N.A.I.C.S.: 333132

International Tubulars FZE (1)
Plot No 4H 02 & 03 Phase 2 Hamriyah Free Zone, PO Box 42150, Hamriyah Free Zone, Sharjah, United Arab Emirates
Tel.: (971) 65269172
Equipment Mfr
N.A.I.C.S.: 333132
Pooja Harmalkar (Mgr-Contracts)

Parker Drilling Arctic Operating Inc. (1)
1420 E Tudor Rd, Anchorage, AK 99507
Tel.: (907) 339-4000
Web Site: http://www.parkerdrilling.com
Sales Range: $100-124.9 Million
Emp.: 250
Drilling Oil & Gas Well Services
N.A.I.C.S.: 213111

Subsidiary (Domestic):

Parker Drilling Alaska Services, Ltd (2)
1420 E Tudor Rd, Anchorage, AK 99507
Tel.: (907) 339-4000
Oil & Gas Well Drilling Services
N.A.I.C.S.: 237110

Parker Drilling Canada Company (1)
Atlantic Place Suite 802/215 Water Street, PO Box 74, Saint John's, A1C 6C9, NL, Canada
Tel.: (709) 753-3961
Land Drilling Services
N.A.I.C.S.: 213111

Parker Drilling Company (1)
1110 Unifab Rd, New Iberia, LA 70560 (100%)
Tel.: (337) 364-3122
Web Site: http://www.parkerdrilling.com
Sales Range: $25-49.9 Million
Emp.: 40
Mfr of Drilling Rigs
N.A.I.C.S.: 213111

Parker Drilling Company International Limited (1)
5 Greenway Plz Ste 100, Houston, TX 77046
Tel.: (281) 406-2000
Web Site: http://www.parkerdrilling.com
Sales Range: $125-149.9 Million
Emp.: 150
Offshore & Onshore Contract Drilling
N.A.I.C.S.: 213111

Parker Drilling Management Services, Inc. (1)
5 Greenway Plz Ste 100, Houston, TX 77046-0506
Tel.: (281) 406-2000
Investment Management Service
N.A.I.C.S.: 551112

Parker Drilling Netherlands BV (1)
Vlietweg 17/V, 2266 KA, Leidschendam, Netherlands
Tel.: (31) 703174470
Oil Rig & Platform Drilling Services
N.A.I.C.S.: 213112

Parker USA Drilling Company (1)
1110 Unifab Rd, New Iberia, LA 70560
Tel.: (337) 365-8154
Sales Range: $50-74.9 Million
Emp.: 50
Drilling Oil & Gas Well Services
N.A.I.C.S.: 213111

Quail Tools (1)
3805 Hwy 14, New Iberia, LA 70560 (100%)
Tel.: (337) 365-8154
Web Site: http://www.quailtools.com
Sales Range: $50-74.9 Million
Emp.: 70
N.A.I.C.S.: 213111

Quail Tools, L.P. (1)
3812 E Market St, Enid, OK 73701
Tel.: (580) 237-1039
Drilling Equipment Mfr
N.A.I.C.S.: 333132
Joshua Corkill (Reg Mgr-Mktg)

PARKERVISION, INC.

4446-1A Hendricks Ave Ste 354, Jacksonville, FL 32207
Tel.: (904) 732-6100   FL
Web Site:
https://www.parkervision.com
Year Founded: 1989
PRKR—(OTCQB)
Rev.: $925,000
Assets: $1,751,000
Liabilities: $52,440,000
Net Worth: ($50,689,000)
Earnings: ($9,813,000)
Emp.: 7
Fiscal Year-end: 12/31/22
Wireless Radio Frequency (RF) Designer, Developer & Mfr
N.A.I.C.S.: 334220
Jeffrey L. Parker (Chm & CEO)
Cynthia L. Poehlman (CFO & Sec)

PARKS! AMERICA, INC.

1300 Oak Grv Rd, Pine Mountain, GA 31822
Tel.: (706) 663-8744   NV
Year Founded: 1954
PRKA—(OTCIQ)
Rev.: $9,912,260
Assets: $19,194,071
Liabilities: $5,245,844
Net Worth: $13,948,227
Earnings: ($1,094,481)
Emp.: 43
Fiscal Year-end: 09/29/24
Theme Park Operator
N.A.I.C.S.: 713110
Jeffery Lococo (Sec)
Todd R. White (CFO)

Subsidiaries:

Wild Animal Safari, Inc. (1)
1300 Oak Grove Rd, Pine Mountain, GA 31822 (100%)
Tel.: (706) 663-8744
Web Site: http://www.animalsafari.com
Animal Theme Park
N.A.I.C.S.: 713110

Wild Animal, Inc. (1)
124 Jungle Dr, Strafford, MO 65757 (100%)
Tel.: (417) 859-5300
Emp.: 25
Animal Theme Park
N.A.I.C.S.: 713110
Dale W. Van Voorhis (VP)

PARKWAY, INC.

5847 San Felipe St Ste 2200, Houston, TX 77057
Tel.: (346) 200-3100   MD
Web Site: http://pky.com
Year Founded: 2016
PKY—(NYSE)
Real Estate Investment Trust
N.A.I.C.S.: 531390
Scott E. Francis (CFO & Chief Acctg Officer)
Mike Fransen (COO & Mng Dir)
Jason A. Bates (Chief Investment Officer)

Subsidiaries:

Parkway Properties LP (1)

390 N Orange Ave Ste 2400, Orlando, FL 32803
Tel.: (407) 650-0593
Web Site: http://www.pky.com
Real Estate Investment Services
N.A.I.C.S.: 531390

Parkway Property Investments, LLC (1)
5847 San Felipe St Ste 2200, Houston, TX 77057
Tel.: (346) 200-3100
Web Site: http://www.pky.com
Real Estate Investment Services
N.A.I.C.S.: 531390
James R. Heistand (Pres & CEO)

PARSEC CAPITAL ACQUISITION CORP.

320 W Main St, Lewisville, TX 75057
Tel.: (203) 524-6524   DE
Web Site:
http://www.parsecacquisition.com
Year Founded: 2021
PCXU—(NASDAQ)
Investment Services
N.A.I.C.S.: 523999
Paul Haber (CFO)
Kelly Kellner (CEO)
Terry Debono (Pres)

PARSONS CORPORATION

5875 Trinity Pkwy Ste 300, Centreville, VA 20120
Tel.: (703) 988-8500   DE
Web Site: https://www.parsons.com
Year Founded: 1944
PSN—(NYSE)
Rev.: $5,442,749,000
Assets: $4,804,061,000
Liabilities: $2,427,346,000
Net Worth: $2,376,715,000
Earnings: $161,149,000
Emp.: 18,500
Fiscal Year-end: 12/31/23
Engineering & Construction Services
N.A.I.C.S.: 237990
John Stasulli (CTO/VP-Defense & Space Engrg Solutions)
Matthew Ofilos (CFO)

Subsidiaries:

Argotek, Inc. (1)
1911 N Fort Myer Dr Ste 1100, Arlington, VA 22209-1618
Tel.: (703) 558-0036
Web Site: http://www.argotek.com
Sales Range: $200-249.9 Million
Emp.: 95
Information Assurance & Security Systems Engineering Services
N.A.I.C.S.: 561621

BCC Engineering, Inc. (1)
7300 N Kendall Dr Ste 400, Miami, FL 33156
Tel.: (305) 670-2350
Web Site: http://www.bcceng.com
Engineeering Services
N.A.I.C.S.: 541330
Jose A. Munoz (Pres)

Braxton Technologies, LLC (1)
559 E Pikes Peak Ave Ste 300, Colorado Springs, CO 80903-1500
Tel.: (719) 380-8488
Web Site: http://www.braxtontech.com
Sales Range: $10-24.9 Million
Emp.: 96
Custom Computer Programming Services for NASA & U.S. Air Force's GPS Systems
N.A.I.C.S.: 541511
Kevin O'Neil (Chm)
Rob Patterson (Chief Revenue Officer)
Jim Robinson (Dir-Information Technology)
Ken O'Neil (Pres & COO)

DZSP 21 LLC (1)
Naval Base Guam NFM Complex B100, Santa Rita, GU 96915
Tel.: (671) 339-3977
Web Site: https://dzsp21.com
Facility Support Management Services
N.A.I.C.S.: 561210

Wayne L. Cornell *(Dir, Pres & CEO)*
Shannon Quinata *(Dir)*
Mark Lopez *(Dir-Pub Works & Mgr-Utilities)*
Vincent J. Salas *(Project Mgr-Safety)*
Shiela Concepcion *(Bus Dir)*
Robert W. Jackson II *(Deputy Dir)*

Delcan Technologies, Inc. (1)
3577 Pkwy Ln Bldg V Ste 100, Peachtree
Corners, GA 30092
Tel.: (770) 446-4900
Web Site:
   https://www.delcantechnologies.com
Mobile Data Tracking Services
N.A.I.C.S.: 518210
Russ Brookshire *(Mgr-IOT-Standards)*
Larry Simmons *(Mgr-Business Development)*
Jon Wyott *(Sr Engr)*

IPKeys Power Partners, Inc (1)
44 Gilbert St W, Tinton Falls, NJ 07701
Tel.: (732) 389-8112
Web Site:
   http://www.ipkeyspowerpartners.com
Aggregation & Automated Demand Response Services
N.A.I.C.S.: 513210
Robert M. Nawy *(Founder & CEO)*
Mark Ponder *(Pres)*
Jennice Holtom *(VP-Customer Ops)*
Jim Boch *(Chief Engr-Smart Grid)*
David Paradis *(VP-Smart Grid Solutions)*
Ingrid Palmieri *(VP-Product Delivery)*
Erika Valentine *(VP-Software & Solution Implementation Svcs)*

Ingenicomm, LLC (1)
14120 Parke Long Ct Ste 210, Chantilly, VA
20151
Tel.: (703) 665-4333
Web Site: https://www.ingenicomm.net
Enterprise Engineering Services
N.A.I.C.S.: 541330

OGSystems LLC (1)
14291 Park Meadow Dr Ste 100, Chantilly,
VA 20151
Tel.: (703) 870-7552
Web Site: http://www.ogsystems.com
Sales Range: $10-24.9 Million
Emp.: 400
Intelligence & Surveillance Technology
N.A.I.C.S.: 513210
Garrett Pagon *(Co-CEO & Co-Founder)*
Omar Balkissoon *(Co-Founder & Chm)*
Dan Ehrmantraut *(CFO)*
Steven Martin *(COO)*
Aarish Gokaldas *(CEO)*
Rich Aves *(Chief Growth Officer)*
Lorinda Ayling *(Chief Svcs Officer)*
Karl Schwarz *(Partner)*
Laurie Ternes *(Partner)*
Michael Becker *(Partner)*
Richard J. D'Alessandro *(Partner)*
Gene Murphy *(Mng Partner)*
Hector Cuevas *(Mng Partner)*
Ken Krupa *(Mng Partner)*
Michelle Tobin *(Mng Partner)*
Tony DeGrand *(Mng Partner)*
Ben Tinker *(Assoc Partner)*
Claire LeSuer *(Assoc Partner)*
Elisa Soto *(Assoc Partner)*
Jonathan McColgan *(Assoc Partner)*
Ken McCall *(Assoc Partner)*
Michael Doll *(Assoc Partner)*
Pat Kelly *(Assoc Partner)*
Ralston Mitchell *(Assoc Partner)*
Rohan Miller *(Assoc Partner)*
Sarah Knapp *(Assoc Partner)*
Timothy Siems *(Assoc Partner)*
Tony Mehalic *(Assoc Partner)*
Victor Simonis *(Assoc Partner)*
Mark Tappan *(Chief Engr)*

Parsons Construction Group Inc. (1)
605 Norgal Dr Ste A, Lebanon, OH 45036
Tel.: (513) 278-2000
Web Site: http://www.justcallparsons.com
Construction Services
N.A.I.C.S.: 236210

**Parsons Group International
Limited** (1)
4 Grosvenor Pl, London, SW1X 7PG,
United Kingdom (100%)
Tel.: (44) 2072038440
Sales Range: $10-24.9 Million
Emp.: 40
Engineering & Construction

N.A.I.C.S.: 541330

**Parsons Infrastructure & Technology
Group Inc.** (1)
100 W Walnut St, Pasadena, CA
91124-0001 (100%)
Tel.: (626) 440-6000
Web Site: http://www.parsons.com
Sales Range: $100-124.9 Million
Emp.: 500
Engineeering Services
N.A.I.C.S.: 541330

**Parsons Transportation Group
Inc.** (1)
1133 15th St NW Ste 800, Washington, DC
20005-2710 (100%)
Tel.: (202) 775-3300
Web Site: http://www.parsons.com
Sales Range: $10-24.9 Million
Emp.: 50
Engineering Consultants
N.A.I.C.S.: 541330

**Polaris Alpha Advanced Systems,
Inc.** (1)
5450 Tech Ctr Dr Ste 400, Colorado
Springs, CO 80919
Tel.: (719) 452-7010
Web Site: http://www.polarisalpha.com
Technology Systems Design & Support
Services
N.A.I.C.S.: 541512

Subsidiary (Domestic):

Solidyn Solutions, LLC (2)
5445 DTC Prkwy Ste 1110, Greenwood Village, CO 80111
Tel.: (303) 945-4148
Engineeering Services
N.A.I.C.S.: 541330

SPARTA, Inc. (1)
25531 Commercentre Dr Ste 120, Lake
Forest, CA 92630
Tel.: (949) 768-8161
Web Site: http://www.sparta.com
Engineering & Construction Services
N.A.I.C.S.: 237990

Sealing Technologies, Inc. (1)
7134 Columbia Gateway Dr Ste 160, Columbia, MD 21046
Tel.: (443) 542-0040
Web Site: http://www.sealingtech.com
Emp.: 150
Security System Services
N.A.I.C.S.: 561621
Ed Sealing *(CEO)*
Brandon Whalen *(COO)*

Subsidiary (Domestic):

Quark Security Inc. (2)
4945 Montgomery Rd, Ellicott City, MD
21043-6748
Tel.: (443) 457-8275
Web Site: http://www.quarksecurity.com
Computer System Design Services
N.A.I.C.S.: 541512
Spencer Shimko *(Founder)*

Williams Electric Co. Inc. (1)
695 Denton Blvd, Fort Walton Beach, FL
32547
Tel.: (850) 862-1171
Control System Integration, Electrical &
General Contracting & Energy Infrastructure
Services
N.A.I.C.S.: 238210
Daniel Rucker *(Pres)*

Xator Corporation (1)
543 Harbor Blvd Ste 501, Destin, FL 32541
Tel.: (850) 460-2860
Web Site: http://www.xatorcorp.com
Process, Physical Distribution & Logistics
Consulting Services
N.A.I.C.S.: 541512
Gary Pseiffer *(Pres)*
Albert Stewart *(Sr VP-Bus Dev)*

Subsidiary (Domestic):

TSM Corp. (2)
7622 Bartlett Corporate Dr Ste 101, Bartlett,
TN 38133
Tel.: (901) 373-0300
Web Site: http://www.tsmcorporation.com
Rev.: $9,000,000

Emp.: 117
All Other Information Services
N.A.I.C.S.: 519290
Robert Green *(Pres)*

PARTNERS BANK OF CALIFORNIA
27201 Puerta Real Ste 160, Mission
Viejo, CA 92691
Tel.: (949) 732-4000
Web Site: https://www.pbofca.com
Year Founded: 2007
PBKX—(OTCIQ)
Commericial Banking
N.A.I.C.S.: 522110
Mike Ahmar *(Chm)*

PARTS ID, INC.
1 Corporate Dr Ste C, Cranbury, NJ
08512
Tel.: (609) 642-4700   DE
Web Site: https://www.partsidinc.com
Year Founded: 2016
ID—(NYSEAMEX)
Rev.: $340,596,365
Assets: $25,908,706
Liabilities: $53,403,886
Net Worth: ($27,495,180)
Earnings: ($17,923,880)
Emp.: 26
Fiscal Year-end: 12/31/22
Digital Commerce Company
N.A.I.C.S.: 561499
Mark Atwater *(VP-Vendor Rels)*
Prashant Pathak *(Chm)*
John Pendleton *(Exec VP-Legal-Corp
Affairs)*
Lev Peker *(CEO)*

PASITHEA THERAPEUTICS
CORP.
1111 Lincoln Rd Ste 500, Miami
Beach, FL 33139
Tel.: (702) 514-4174   DE
Web Site: https://www.pasithea.com
Year Founded: 2020
KTTA—(NASDAQ)
Rev.: $486,559
Assets: $45,180,089
Liabilities: $2,681,841
Net Worth: $42,498,248
Earnings: ($13,936,452)
Emp.: 15
Fiscal Year-end: 12/31/22
Research & Development in Biotechnology (except Nanobiotechnology)
N.A.I.C.S.: 541714
Tiago Reis Marques *(CEO)*
Lawrence Steinman *(Founder &
Chm)*
Daniel Schneiderman *(CFO)*

PASSAGE BIO, INC.
1 Commerce Sq 2005 Market St 39th
Fl, Philadelphia, PA 19103
Tel.: (267) 866-0311   DE
Web Site:
   https://www.passagebio.com
Year Founded: 2017
PASG—(NASDAQ)
Rev.: $2,269,000
Assets: $243,549,000
Liabilities: $42,183,000
Net Worth: $201,366,000
Earnings: ($136,125,000)
Emp.: 85
Fiscal Year-end: 12/31/22
Biotechnology Research & Development Services
N.A.I.C.S.: 541714
William Chou *(Pres & CEO)*
James M. Wilson *(Co-Founder)*
Eliseo Oreste Salinas *(Interim Chief
Medical Officer & Chief R&D Officer)*
Aditya Kohli *(Co-Founder)*
Kathleen Borthwick *(CFO, Principal
Acctg Officer & Sr VP)*

Edgar B. Cale *(Interim Pres, Gen
Counsel & Sec)*
Stuart Henderson *(Chief Bus Officer)*
Eden Fucci *(Sr VP-Technical Ops)*
Karl Whitney *(Sr VP-Global Regulatory Affairs)*
Susan Browne *(Chief Scientific Officer)*

PASSUR AEROSPACE, INC.
3452 Lake Lynda Dr Ste 190, Orlando, FL 32817
Tel.: (847) 241-8565   NY
Web Site: https://www.passur.com
Year Founded: 1967
PSSR—(OTCIQ)
Rev.: $6,157,185
Assets: $3,837,228
Liabilities: $14,879,176
Net Worth: ($11,041,948)
Earnings: $93,198
Emp.: 40
Fiscal Year-end: 10/31/21
Flight Tracking Information & Decision Support Software to the Aviation
Industry
N.A.I.C.S.: 513210
David Brukman *(CTO)*
Brian G. Cook *(Pres & CEO)*
Mark Libby *(VP-Collaborative Solutions)*
Evee Burgard *(VP-Mktg)*
Lucio Petroccione *(Sr VP)*
Allison O'Neill *(Exec VP-Fin & Admin)*
William A. Cranor Jr. *(VP)*

PATHFINDER BANCORP, INC.
214 W 1st St, Oswego, NY 13126
Tel.: (315) 343-0057   DE
Web Site:
   https://www.pathfinderbank.com
PBHC—(NASDAQ)
Rev.: $57,012,000
Assets: $1,399,921,000
Liabilities: $1,288,339,000
Net Worth: $111,582,000
Earnings: $12,932,000
Emp.: 160
Fiscal Year-end: 12/31/22
Bank Holding Company
N.A.I.C.S.: 551111
James A. Dowd *(Pres & CEO)*
Ronald G. Tascarella *(Exec VP)*
Robert G. Butkowski *(COO & Sr VP)*
Justin K. Bigham *(CFO & Sr VP)*
Daniel R. Phillips *(CIO & Sr VP)*
William D. O'Brien *(Chief Risk Officer,
Sec, Sr VP & First VP-Credit Admin)*

Subsidiaries:

Fitzgibbons Agency LLC (1)
44 E Bridge St, Oswego, NY 13126
Tel.: (315) 342-5000
Banking Services
N.A.I.C.S.: 522180

PathFinder Bank (1)
291 State Route 104 E, Oswego, NY
13126-2547
Tel.: (315) 343-4483
Web Site: https://www.pathfinderbank.com
Commercial Bank
N.A.I.C.S.: 522110
Ronald G. Tascarella *(First VP & Sls Mgr)*
Justin K. Bigham *(CFO & Sr VP)*
Amy Shaw *(Mgr-Mexico)*
John M. Andrews *(Mgr-Central Square)*
Beth Kesler Alfieri *(Officer-Bus Dev & VP)*
William Bower *(Officer-Bus Dev & VP)*
Alison Xuan Ha *(Officer-Bus Dev & VP)*
Craig Nessel *(Mgr-Oswego Plaza)*
David Cavallaro *(Mgr-Clay)*

PATHFINDER CELL THERAPY,
INC.
12 Bow St, Cambridge, MA 02138
Tel.: (617) 245-0289   DE

Pathfinder Cell Therapy, Inc.—(Continued)

PFND—(OTCEM)
Regenerative Medicine Mfr
N.A.I.C.S.: 325412
Richard L. Franklin *(Co-Founder, Pres & CEO)*
Joerg Gruber *(Co-Founder & Chm)*

PATHWARD FINANCIAL, INC.
5501 S Broadband Ln, Sioux Falls, SD 57108
Tel.: (605) 782-1767   DE
Web Site: https://www.pathward.com
Year Founded: 1993
CASH—(NASDAQ)
Rev.: $754,705,000
Assets: $7,549,336,000
Liabilities: $6,709,731,000
Net Worth: $839,605,000
Earnings: $168,357,000
Emp.: 1,239
Fiscal Year-end: 09/30/24
Bank Holding Company
N.A.I.C.S.: 551111
Douglas J. Hajek *(Chm)*
Gregory A. Sigrist *(CFO & Exec VP)*
Anthony M. Sharett *(Pres)*
Sonja A. Theisen *(Chief Governance, Risk & Compliance Officer & Exec VP)*
Becky S. Shulman *(Vice Chm)*
Brett L. Pharr *(CEO)*
Charles Ingram *(Chief Tech & Product Officer & Exec VP)*
Jennifer W. Warren *(Chief Acctg Officer & Sr VP)*
Kia Tang *(Chief People & Inclusion Officer & Exec VP)*

Subsidiaries:

MetaBank, N.A.   (1)
5501 S Broadband Ln, Sioux Falls, SD 57108
Tel.: (605) 362-2423
Web Site: http://www.metabank.com
Federal Savings Bank
N.A.I.C.S.: 522180
Douglas J. Hajek *(Chm & Vice Chm)*
Frederick V. Moore *(Executives, Bd of Dirs)*
Anthony M. Sharett *(Pres)*
Becky S. Shulman *(Vice Chm)*
Brett L. Pharr *(CEO)*
Kathryn M. Thorson *(Pres-Community Banking)*
Jon W. Wilcke *(Pres-Northwest Iowa Market)*
Glen W. Herrick *(CFO & Exec VP)*
Charles Ingram *(CIO & Exec VP)*
Shelly Schneekloth *(Chief Ops Officer & Exec VP)*
Sheree Thornsberry *(Exec VP & Head-Payments)*
Kathi Winter *(Chief People Officer & Exec VP)*

Division (Domestic):

AFS/IBEX   (2)
750 N Saint Paul St Ste 1500, Dallas, TX 75201
Tel.: (877) 237-4239
Web Site: http://www.afsibex.com
Emp.: 32
Insurance Premium Financing Services
N.A.I.C.S.: 522299
John F. Holsan *(Pres)*
Eric Sepci *(Exec VP)*
John P. Costa *(Exec VP & Head-Ops)*
Jerry L. Frith *(VP)*

Subsidiary (Domestic):

AFS/IBEX Financial Services Inc. of California   (3)
4100 Newport Pl Dr Ste 670, Newport Beach, CA 92660
Tel.: (949) 756-2600
Web Site: http://www.afsibex.com
Insurance Premium Financing Services
N.A.I.C.S.: 522299
Jerry L. Frith *(VP-Ops-Western Reg)*

Division (Domestic):

Crestmark   (2)
5480 Corporate Dr Ste 350, Troy, MI 48098
Tel.: (248) 641-5100
Web Site: http://www.crestmark.com
Asset Based Lending, Sales Financing & Factoring Services
N.A.I.C.S.: 522220
Michael K. Goik *(Pres & COO)*
Rick Pierman *(Pres/Sr VP-Crestmark Equipment Fin)*
Christopher Soupai *(Pres-Div)*

Subsidiary (Domestic):

EPS Financial, LLC   (2)
201 Ferry St #1484, Easton, PA 18042
Tel.: (484) 546-2240
Web Site: http://www.epsfinancial.net
Tax Preparation Services
N.A.I.C.S.: 541218
Clark Gill *(Founder)*

Technology Investment Partners, LLC   (2)
40950 Woodward Ave Ste 201, Bloomfield Hills, MI 48304
Tel.: (248) 593-3900
Web Site: http://www.tipcapital.com
Emp.: 45
Equipment Rental &Asset Management Services
N.A.I.C.S.: 532420
John Azzopardi *(CFO)*
Scott M. Grady *(Pres)*
Thomas R. Rutherford *(Founder)*

Pathward, N.A.   (1)
5501 S Broadband Ln, Sioux Falls, SD 57108-2253
Web Site: https://www.pathward.com
Banking Services
N.A.I.C.S.: 522110
Douglas J. Hajek *(Chm)*
Gregory A. Sigrist *(CFO & Exec VP)*

PATIENT ACCESS SOLUTIONS, INC.
2001 Marcus Ave, New Hyde Park, NY 11042
Tel.: (631) 241-9404   NV
Web Site: https://www.pashealth.com
Year Founded: 2006
PASO—(OTCIQ)
Rev.: $2,263,000
Assets: $1,702,000
Liabilities: $3,249,000
Net Worth: ($1,547,000)
Earnings: $670,000
Emp.: 14
Fiscal Year-end: 10/31/19
Web Portal System & POS Terminal Solutions for Electronic Medical Eligibility, Referrals, Service Authorizations & Claims Processing
N.A.I.C.S.: 541519
Bruce Weitzberg *(Pres & CEO)*

PATIENT PORTAL TECHNOLOGIES, INC.
8276 Willett Pkwy, Baldwinsville, NY 13027
Tel.: (315) 638-2030
PPRG—(OTCEM)
Health Care Srvices
N.A.I.C.S.: 622310
Kevin Kelly *(Pres)*

PATRICK INDUSTRIES, INC.
107 W Franklin St, Elkhart, IN 46515
Tel.: (574) 294-7511   IN
Web Site: https://www.patrickind.com
Year Founded: 1959
PATK—(NASDAQ)
Rev.: $4,881,872,000
Assets: $2,782,471,000
Liabilities: $1,827,302,000
Net Worth: $955,169,000
Earnings: $328,196,000
Emp.: 11,000
Fiscal Year-end: 12/31/22

Building Products & Materials Mfr
N.A.I.C.S.: 337110
Andrew L. Nemeth *(Chm & CEO)*
Jeffrey M. Rodino *(Pres-RV)*
Charlie Roeder *(Exec VP-Sls)*
Kip B. Ellis *(Pres-Powersports & Housing)*
Jacob R. Petkovich *(CFO, Principal Acctg Officer, Treas & Exec VP-Fin)*
Stacey Amundson *(Chief HR Officer)*
Doyle K. Stump *(Exec VP)*
Todd G. Gongwer *(Exec VP)*

Subsidiaries:

All Counties Glass, Inc.   (1)
210 S Center St, Santa Ana, CA 92703
Tel.: (714) 547-8021
Building Product & Equipment Distr
N.A.I.C.S.: 423390

Cana Inc.   (1)
29194 Phillips St, Elkhart, IN 46514
Tel.: (574) 262-4664
Web Site: https://www.componentsbycana.com
Doors & Door Parts & Trim, Wood
N.A.I.C.S.: 321911
David Geiger *(Pres)*

Creative Wood Designs   (1)
2632 Lincolnway E, Goshen, IN 46526
Tel.: (574) 642-4887
Sales Range: $25-49.9 Million
Emp.: 69
Framing Contractors
N.A.I.C.S.: 238130

Dehco, Inc.   (1)
3601 Charlotte Ave, Elkhart, IN 46517
Tel.: (574) 294-2684
Web Site: https://www.dehco.com
Recreational Motor Vechicle Parts, Manufactured Housing Supplies Mfr & Distr
N.A.I.C.S.: 423490

Dowco, Inc.   (1)
4230 Clipper Dr, Manitowoc, WI 54220
Tel.: (920) 682-7796
Web Site: http://www.dowco-inc.com
Liners & Boat Covers, Fabric Mfr & Supplier
N.A.I.C.S.: 314910

Engineered Metals & Composites, Inc.   (1)
2219 Fish Hatchery Ln, West Columbia, SC 29172
Tel.: (803) 939-4955
Web Site: http://www.emctowers.com
Prefabricated Metal Building & Component Mfr
N.A.I.C.S.: 332311
Sherry Forbes *(Pres)*
Ana Goodman *(Supvr-Production)*

Fresno Shower Door, Inc.   (1)
3603 W Gettysburg Ave, Fresno, CA 93722
Tel.: (559) 221-4100
Web Site: https://www.fresnoshowerdoor.com
Window & Door Mfr
N.A.I.C.S.: 321911

Front Range Stone, Inc.   (1)
2195 S Raritan St, Englewood, CO 80110
Tel.: (303) 761-4257
Web Site: https://www.denvergranitecountertop.com
Specialty Trade Contractors
N.A.I.C.S.: 238990
Brad Pearce *(Co-Founder)*

Frontline Manufacturing Inc.   (1)
2466 W 200 N, Warsaw, IN 46580
Tel.: (574) 453-2902
Web Site: http://diamondtubshowers.com
Shower Stalls, Fiberglass & Plastics Mfr
N.A.I.C.S.: 326191

G.G. Schmitt & Sons Inc.   (1)
2821 Old Tree Dr, Lancaster, PA 17603
Tel.: (717) 394-3701
Web Site: http://www.ggschmitt.com
Sales Range: $10-24.9 Million
Emp.: 65
Developers of Marine Hardware
N.A.I.C.S.: 332510

Geremarie Corporation   (1)

1275 Ensell Rd, Lake Zurich, IL 60047
Tel.: (847) 540-1154
Web Site: https://www.geremarie.com
High-Precision Aluminum Components Mfr
N.A.I.C.S.: 331315
Jim Schultz *(Founder)*

Great Lakes Boat Top, LLC   (1)
15 Quality Cir, Vonore, TN 37885
Web Site: https://www.greatlakesboattop.com
Marine Canvas Mfr
N.A.I.C.S.: 314910

Hyperform, Inc.   (1)
458 Gus Hipp Blvd, Rockledge, FL 32955
Tel.: (321) 632-6503
Web Site: http://www.hyperforminc.com
Sales Range: $1-9.9 Million
Emp.: 13
Sporting And Athletic Goods, Nec
N.A.I.C.S.: 339920
Kurt Wilson *(CEO)*

IMP Holdings LLC   (1)
409 Growth Pkwy, Angola, IN 46703-9323
Tel.: (260) 665-6112
Web Site: https://www.indianamarine.com
Motor Vehicle Electrical & Electronic Equipment Mfr
N.A.I.C.S.: 336320

Indiana Transport, Inc.   (1)
2311 S Nappanee St, Elkhart, IN 46517
Tel.: (574) 293-3642
Web Site: http://www.indianatransport.com
Transit & Ground Passenger Transportation
N.A.I.C.S.: 485999
Tom Roeder *(Bus Mgr)*
Kyle Pateros *(Dir-Ops)*
Brock Doty *(Acct Exec)*

Inland Plywood Company   (1)
375 Cass Ave, Pontiac, MI 48342
Tel.: (248) 334-4706
Web Site: https://www.inlandplywood.com
Whslr of Plywood
N.A.I.C.S.: 423310

KLS Doors, LLC   (1)
501 Kettering Dr, Ontario, CA 91761
Web Site: https://www.klsdoors.com
Metal Door Mfr
N.A.I.C.S.: 332321

KRA International, LLC   (1)
1810 Clover Rd, Mishawaka, IN 46545
Tel.: (574) 259-3550
Web Site: https://www.krainternational.com
PVC Insulated Wire Harness & Cable Products Mfr
N.A.I.C.S.: 335921

MEP Acquisition Corp   (1)
1401 Tower Rd, Lebanon, MO 65536
Tel.: (417) 588-3128
Web Site: https://marine-electrical.com
Ship Building & Repairing Services
N.A.I.C.S.: 336611

Maple City Woodworking Corp.   (1)
2948 Hackberry Dr, Goshen, IN 46526
Tel.: (574) 642-3342
Sales Range: $1-9.9 Million
Emp.: 30
Hardwood Cabinet Doors & Fascia Mfr
N.A.I.C.S.: 321911
Jeff Stine *(Pres)*

Marine Accessories Corporation   (1)
412 N Cedar Bluff Rd Ste 108, Knoxville, TN 37801
Tel.: (865) 229-1420
Web Site: https://www.marine-accessories.com
Marine Products Distr
N.A.I.C.S.: 423990
Richard N. Reyenger *(CEO)*
David Metz *(CFO)*
Jim Wilson *(Pres-Canvas Solutions)*
Tony Williams *(Pres-Tower Solutions)*

Marine Accessories Europe B.V.   (1)
Sweilandstraat 5, 2361 JA, Warmond, Netherlands
Tel.: (31) 713011220
Boat Building Mfr
N.A.I.C.S.: 336612

Medallion Plastics Inc.   (1)
21700 Protecta Dr, Elkhart, IN 46516

Tel.: (574) 522-7527
Web Site: http://www.medallionplastics.com
Plastics Including Thermoformers Mfr
N.A.I.C.S.: 326199
Bob Toth (Pres)

Metal Moulding Corp. (1)
1225 Northgate Bus Pkwy, Madison, TN 37115
Tel.: (615) 865-9867
Web Site: https://www.metalmoulding.com
Prefabricated Metal Building & Component Mfr
N.A.I.C.S.: 332311
Kevin Chambliss (Supvr-Shipping Dept)
Jackie Hester (Mgr-Production)
Phillip Wilson (Supvr-Paint Dept)
David Smallwood (VP & Gen Mgr)
Wade Lewis (Mgr-Plant)
Mack Blackwell (Asst Mgr-Plant)
Carol Smallwood (Office Mgr)
Jimmy Parrish (Founder)

Middlebury Hardwood Products (1)
101 Joan Dr, Middlebury, IN 46540
Tel.: (574) 825-9524
Web Site: http://www.mhpi.us
Sales Range: $25-49.9 Million
Emp.: 150
Wooden Cabinet Doors Mfr & Distr
N.A.I.C.S.: 337110

Mishawaka Sheet Metal, Inc. (1)
28505 County Rd 20 W, Elkhart, IN 46517
Tel.: (574) 294-5959
Web Site:
   http://www.mishawakasheetmetal.com
Rev.: $2,100,000
Emp.: 60
Sheet Metal Manufacturer
N.A.I.C.S.: 332322
Jeff Troyer (Pres)

Nickell Moulding Company Inc. (1)
3015 Mobile Dr, Elkhart, IN 46514
Tel.: (574) 264-3129
Web Site: https://www.nickellmoulding.com
Hardwood & Wrapped Mouldings & Trim & Custom Wood Frames Mfr & Marketer
N.A.I.C.S.: 321918
Scott McAfoos (Controller-Bus Unit)

North American Forest Products, Inc. (1)
27263 May St, Edwardsburg, MI 49112
Tel.: (269) 663-8500
Web Site: https://www.nafpinc.com
Sales Range: $1-9.9 Million
Emp.: 220
Mfr & Distr of Wood Products for Recreational Vehicles & Manufactured Housing
N.A.I.C.S.: 321999

Parkland Plastics (1)
104 Yoder Dr, Middlebury, IN 46540
Tel.: (574) 825-4336
Web Site: https://www.parklandplastics.com
Rev.: $6,700,000
Emp.: 50
All Other Miscellaneous Store Retailers, except Tobacco Stores
N.A.I.C.S.: 459999

Patrick Adorn Manufacturing (1)
57420 Nagy Dr, Elkhart, IN 46517
Tel.: (574) 295-5223
Web Site: http://www.patrickind.com
Sales Range: $200-249.9 Million
Emp.: 300
Hardwood Veneer & Plywood Distribution
N.A.I.C.S.: 327420

Rockford Corporation (1)
600 S Rockford Dr, Tempe, AZ 85281
Tel.: (480) 967-3565
Web Site: http://www.rockfordcorp.com
Household Audio & Video Equipment Mfr
N.A.I.C.S.: 334310
Richard G. Vasek (CFO, Sec & VP-Fin)
Peter H. Kamin (Chm)
Zach Luke (Mgr-Natl Sls-Fosgate)
Ronnie Brashear (Mgr-Reg Sls-Fosgate)
Greg Cobbs (Mgr-Reg Sls-Fosgate)

Subsidiary (Domestic):

Lightning Audio Corporation (2)
2055 E 6th St, Tempe, AZ 85281-2963
Tel.: (480) 966-8278
Web Site: http://www.lightningaudio.com
Electrical Appliances, Television & Radio

N.A.I.C.S.: 441330

SEI Manufacturing, Inc. (1)
100 Industrial Dr, Cromwell, IN 46732
Tel.: (260) 856-3800
Web Site: https://www.madebysei.com
Marine Product Mfr
N.A.I.C.S.: 336612

Sea-Dog Corporation (1)
3402 Smith Ave, Everett, WA 98201
Tel.: (425) 259-0194
Web Site: http://www.sea-dog.com
Sales Range: $1-9.9 Million
Emp.: 56
Marine Hardware & Supplies
N.A.I.C.S.: 423860
Mark Nysether (Pres)

Sea-Lect Plastic Corp. (1)
3420 Smith Ave, Everett, WA 98201
Tel.: (425) 339-0288
Web Site: http://www.sealectplastics.com
Sales Range: $1-9.9 Million
Emp.: 12
Plastic Injection, Molding, Design & Product Development
N.A.I.C.S.: 326199
Matt Poischbeg (VP)

Structural Composites of Indiana, Inc. (1)
1118 Gerber St, Ligonier, IN 46767-2417
Tel.: (260) 894-4083
Web Site: https://www.scindiana.com
Fiber Glass Products Mfr
N.A.I.C.S.: 326199

Structural Composites, Inc. (1)
360 E Dr, Melbourne, FL 32904
Tel.: (321) 951-9464
Web Site:
   https://www.structuralcomposites.com
Fabricated Structural Metal Mfr
N.A.I.C.S.: 332312

Transhield, Inc. (1)
2932 Thorne Dr, Elkhart, IN 46514-5028
Tel.: (574) 266-4118
Web Site: https://www.transhield-usa.com
Custom Fit Storage & Transportation Covers Mfr
N.A.I.C.S.: 313210
Matt Peat (Exec VP-Sls)
James Glick (Pres)
Brian McKenzie (VP-Ops)
Seckin Ozol (VP-Engrg & R&D)
Mark Schuck (VP-Supply Chain Mgmt)
Jeff Vold (VP-Govt Bus Dev & Indus)
Konrad Bereza (CFO)
Mindy Kruggel (Dir-Marketing & TopCure Sls)
Jorge Martinez (Acct Mgr)

Transport Indiana, LLC (1)
2311 S Nappanee St, Elkhart, IN 46517
Tel.: (574) 293-3642
Web Site: https://www.indianatransport.com
Specialized Freight Trucking Services
N.A.I.C.S.: 484230
Tom Roeder (Bus Mgr)
Kyle Pateros (Dir-Ops)
Patrick Hills (Mgr-Recruiting)

Williamsburg Furniture Inc. (1)
2096 Cheyenne St, Nappanee, IN 46550
Web Site:
   http://www.williamsburgfurnitureinc.com
Metal Household Furniture Mfr
N.A.I.C.S.: 337126
Gus Feiler (Founder & Pres)

PATRIOT GOLD CORP.
401 Ryland St Ste 180, Reno, NV 89502
Tel.: (702) 456-9565   NV
Web Site:
   https://www.patriotgoldcorp.com
Year Founded: 1998
PGOL—(OTCQB)
Rev.: $1,786,040
Assets: $4,212,625
Liabilities: $222,428
Net Worth: $3,990,197
Earnings: $621,511
Fiscal Year-end: 12/31/22
Gold Mining
N.A.I.C.S.: 212220

Robert D. Coale (Chm)
Trevor Newton (Founder, Pres, CEO, Treas & Sec)

PATRIOT NATIONAL BANCORP, INC.
900 Bedford St, Stamford, CT 06901
Tel.: (203) 252-5900   CT
Web Site:
   https://www.bankpatriot.com
Year Founded: 1994
PNBK—(NASDAQ)
Rev.: $47,617,000
Assets: $1,043,359,000
Liabilities: $983,776,000
Net Worth: $59,583,000
Earnings: $6,161,000
Emp.: 130
Fiscal Year-end: 12/31/22
Bank Holding Company
N.A.I.C.S.: 551111
Michael A. Carrazza (Chm)
David Lowery (Pres & CEO)
Al Botta Jr. (Chief Payments Officer & Exec VP)
Joseph Perillo (CFO & Exec VP)
Fred Staudmyer (Chief Admin Officer & Exec VP)
Steven Grunblatt (CIO & Exec VP)
Thomas E. Slater (Chief Credit Officer & Exec VP)

Subsidiaries:

Patriot Bank, N.A. (1)
900 Bedford St, Stamford, CT 06901
Tel.: (203) 252-5900
Web Site: http://www.bankpatriot.com
Sales Range: $25-49.9 Million
Federal Savings Bank
N.A.I.C.S.: 522180
Michael A. Carrazza (Chm)
David Lowery (Pres & CEO)
Al Botta Jr. (Chief Payments Officer & Exec VP)
Joseph Perillo (CFO & Exec VP)
Fred Staudmyer (Chief Admin Officer & Exec VP)
Thomas E. Slater (Chief Credit Officer & Exec VP)

PATTEN ENERGY SOLUTIONS GROUP, INC.
14753 Greenwood Rd, Dolton, IL 60419
Tel.: (312) 884-7626   NV
Year Founded: 2004
PTTN—(OTCIQ)
Sales Range: $1-9.9 Million
Holding Company; Downstream Oil Marketer; Waste Oil Collection, Recycling & Re-Distribution Services
N.A.I.C.S.: 551112
Robert Rosinski (Pres & CEO)
Ernest B. Remo (Chm)

Subsidiaries:

Patten Energy Enterprises, Inc. (1)
3437 S Main St, Los Angeles, CA 90007
Tel.: (323) 235-3500
Web Site: http://www.pattenenergy.com
Sales Range: $1-9.9 Million
Emp.: 25
Petroleum Product Whslr
N.A.I.C.S.: 424720
Ezekiel Patten Jr. (Founder)

PATTERSON COMPANIES, INC.
1031 Mendota Heights Rd, Saint Paul, MN 55120
Tel.: (651) 686-1600   MN
Web Site:
   https://www.pattersoncompanies.com
Year Founded: 1877
PDCO—(NASDAQ)
Rev.: $6,471,471,000
Assets: $2,879,146,000

Liabilities: $1,760,611,000
Net Worth: $1,118,535,000
Earnings: $207,557,000
Emp.: 7,600
Fiscal Year-end: 04/29/23
Dental Equipment & Supplies Distr
N.A.I.C.S.: 423450
Kevin Barry (CFO)
John M. Wright (VP-IR)
Donald J. Zurbay (Pres & CEO)
Les B. Korsh (Gen Counsel, Sec & VP)
Donald J. Zurbay (Pres & CEO)

Subsidiaries:

Aspen Veterinary Resources, Ltd (1)
2915 Rocky Mountain Ave Ste 400, Loveland, CO 80538
Tel.: (970) 353-2600
Web Site:
   https://www.aspenveterinaryresources.com
Animal Food Mfr & Distr.
N.A.I.C.S.: 311119

C.A.P.L. Limited (1)
Unit 6 Brock Way, Knutton, Newcastle-under-Lyme, ST5 6AZ, Staffordshire, United Kingdom
Tel.: (44) 1782948040
Web Site: http://www.capl.co.uk
Emp.: 120
Veterinary Laboratory Services
N.A.I.C.S.: 541940

County Footwear Limited (1)
Unit 2270 Parkway, Kettering, NN15 6XR, Northamptonshire, United Kingdom
Tel.: (44) 1536527201
Web Site: http://www.countyfootwear.com
Sales Range: $25-49.9 Million
Emp.: 50
Footwear Mfr
N.A.I.C.S.: 316210

Direct Dental Supply Co. (1)
1267 Spice Is Dr, Sparks, NV 89431   (100%)
Tel.: (775) 331-4300
Web Site: http://www.directdentalsupply.com
Sales Range: $25-49.9 Million
Emp.: 10
Mail Order Distributor of Dental Supplies
N.A.I.C.S.: 423450

Dolphin Imaging Systems, LLC (1)
9200 Oakdale Ave Ste 500, Chatsworth, CA 91311
Tel.: (818) 435-1368
Web Site: https://www.dolphinimaging.com
Emp.: 100
Diagnostic Imaging Center Services
N.A.I.C.S.: 621512
Sonya Lester (Dir-Ops)
Michael Quick (Mgr-IT)
Pamela Roberts (Mgr-Acctg & Admin)
Dewitt Blankenship (Mgr-Mgmt Software Products)
Ken Gladstone (Mgr-Imaging Software Products)
Matt Yamamato (Sls Dir-US & Canada)
Michael Zazucki (Mgr-Technical Support)

Hawaii Mega-Cor., Inc. (1)
99-940 Iwaena St Ste C, Aiea, HI 96701
Tel.: (808) 487-7711
Animal Pharmaceutical Product Distr
N.A.I.C.S.: 424210
Betty Liu (Mgr-Ops)

Medco Supply Co. (1)
500 Fillmore Ave, Tonawanda, NY 14150
Tel.: (716) 695-3244
Web Site: http://www.medco-athletics.com
Sales Range: $75-99.9 Million
Emp.: 23
Sports Medicine, First Aid & Medical Supplies Distr
N.A.I.C.S.: 456199

Metron Medical Australia Pty Limited (1)
3-4 Anzed court, Mulgrave, 3170, VIC, Australia
Tel.: (61) 397751234
Web Site: http://www.metron.com.au
Sales Range: $25-49.9 Million
Emp.: 5
Medical Equipment Whslr

Patterson Companies, Inc.—(Continued)

N.A.I.C.S.: 423450
Richard New (Mgr)

National Veterinary Services Limited (1)
Tel.: (44) 1782771100
Web Site: https://www.nvsweb.co.uk
Sales Range: $50-74.9 Million
Emp.: 500
Veterinary Professional Support Services
N.A.I.C.S.: 561499
Martin Riley (Mng Dir)
Greg Lorimer (Dir-Comml)
Danny Roberts (Dir-Ops)
Dave Howard (Dir-IT)
Mel Whittaker (Head-Sls-South)
Naomi McCallum (Dir-Buying)
Nik Watson (Head-Sls-North)

Unit (Domestic):

Dechra Laboratory Services (2)
Lancefield House 23 Mains Lane, Little Singleton, Poulton-le-Fylde, FY6 7LJ, Lancs, United Kingdom
Tel.: (44) 1253899215
Web Site: http://www.dechralabs.co.uk
Emp.: 50
Veterinary Diagnostic & Clinical Pathology Laboratory Services
N.A.I.C.S.: 621511
Diane Saffery (Dir-NWL)

National Veterinary Services Limited (2)
Unit 2 Sawston Trading Park London Road, Pampisford Sawston, Cambridge, CB22 3EE, United Kingdom
Tel.: (44) 1223 493 400
Web Site: http://www.thehormonelab.com
Sales Range: $10-24.9 Million
Emp.: 10
Veterinary Immunoassay Laboratory Services
N.A.I.C.S.: 621511

Patterson Dental (1)
N30 W22383 Green Rd Ste B, Waukesha, WI 53186
Tel.: (262) 506-2700
Sales Range: $10-24.9 Million
Emp.: 40
Dental Products & Services Supplier
N.A.I.C.S.: 423450
Cecile Schauer (VP-Mktg & Comml Software)

Patterson Dental Canada Inc. (1)
1205 Henri-Bourassa W, Montreal, H3M 3E6, QC, Canada (100%)
Tel : (514) 745-4040
Web Site: https://www.pattersondental.com
Sales Range: $75-99.9 Million
Emp.: 193
Dental Equipment & Supplies Distr
N.A.I.C.S.: 423450

Patterson Dental Supply, Inc. (1)
1031 Mendota Heights Rd, Saint Paul, MN 55120-1419 (100%)
Tel.: (651) 686-1600
Web Site: http://www.pattersondental.com
Sales Range: $1-4.9 Billion
Emp.: 1,400
Dental Equipment & Supplies Distr
N.A.I.C.S.: 423450
Tim E. Rogan (Pres)
Mark Walchirk (CEO)
Eric R. Shirley (Sr VP-Bus Dev)

Patterson Global Limited (1)
Nunn Brook Road, Huthwaite, Sutton in Ashfield, NG17 2HU, Nottinghamshire, United Kingdom
Tel.: (44) 1623448706
Web Site:
https://www.performancehealth.co.uk
Medical Equipment Distr
N.A.I.C.S.: 423450

Patterson Logistics Services, Inc. (1)
5000 Dahlia St Ste A, Denver, CO 80216
Tel.: (303) 377-2418
Emp.: 8
Hospital Equipment Whslr
N.A.I.C.S.: 423450

Patterson Office Supplies, Inc. (1)

3310 N Duncan Rd, Champaign, IL 61822-7892
Tel.: (217) 351-5400
Web Site:
http://www.pattersoncompanies.com
Medical Dental & Hospital Equipment Whslr
N.A.I.C.S.: 423450

Patterson Technology Center, Inc. (1)
1201 Althoff Dr, Effingham, IL 62401
Tel.: (217) 347-5964
Medical & Hospital Equipment Whslr
N.A.I.C.S.: 423450

Patterson Veterinary Supply, Inc. (1)
137 Barnum Rd, Devens, MA 01434
Tel.: (978) 353-6000
Web Site: http://www.pattersonvet.com
Sales Range: $150-199.9 Million
Emp.: 70
Veterinary Supplies Whslr
N.A.I.C.S.: 541940

Subsidiary (Domestic):

Animal Health International, Inc. (2)
2915 Rocky Mountain Ave Ste 400, Loveland, CO 80538
Tel.: (970) 353-2600
Web Site:
https://www.animalhealthinternational.com
Emp.: 320
Animal Health Product Distr
N.A.I.C.S.: 325412
Douglas E. Jones (Pres-Companion Animal)

Subsidiary (Non-US):

Kane Veterinary Supplies, Ltd. (3)
11204-186 Street, Edmonton, T5S 2W2, AB, Canada
Tel.: (780) 453-1516
Web Site: https://www.kanevet.com
Animal Health Products Distr
N.A.I.C.S.: 423450

Performance Health France (1)
Zone Industrielle de Montjoly Avenue de l'Industrie, 08013, Charleville-Mezieres, Cedex, France
Tel.: (33) 324529121
Web Site: http://www.pattersonmedical.fr
Medical Equipment Distr
N.A.I.C.S.: 423450

Tumble Forms Inc. (1)
1013 Barker Rd, Dolgeville, NY 13329
Tel.: (315) 429-3101
Sales Range: $25-49.9 Million
Emp.: 132
Medical Device Mfr
N.A.I.C.S.: 339112
Scott P. Anderson (CEO)

Turnkey Computer Systems, LLC (1)
2505 Lakeview Dr Ste 100, Amarillo, TX 79109
Tel.: (806) 372-1249
Web Site: https://www.turnkeynet.com
Emp.: 80
Electronic Store Operator
N.A.I.C.S.: 449210

PATTERSON-UTI ENERGY, INC.

10713 W Sam Houston Pkwy N Ste 800, Houston, TX 77064
Tel.: (281) 765-7100 DE
Web Site: https://www.patenergy.com
PTEN—(NASDAQ)
Rev.: $2,647,592,000
Assets: $3,143,823,000
Liabilities: $1,478,300,000
Net Worth: $1,665,523,000
Earnings: $154,658,000
Emp.: 6,500
Fiscal Year-end: 12/31/22
Onshore Contract Drilling Services for Oil & Gas Exploration
N.A.I.C.S.: 213111
William Andrew Hendricks Jr. (Pres & CEO)
Seth D. Wexler (Gen Counsel, Sec & Sr VP)

Robert Wayne Drummond Jr. (Vice Chm)
C. Andrew Smith (CFO & Exec VP)
James M. Holcomb (COO, Chief Bus Officer & Exec VP)
Kenneth N. Berns (Chief Comml Officer & Exec VP)
Diana Dotolo (Sr VP-Human Resources)
Kathryn Roark (Sr VP-Sustainability, Diversity, and Culture)
Marty Unrein (Sr VP-Sales & Marketing)
Matt Pye (Sr VP-Industry Affairs)

Subsidiaries:

Current Power Solutions, Inc. (1)
5050 W Greens Rd, Houston, TX 77066
Tel.: (281) 943-7700
Web Site: http://www.currentpsi.com
Power Electrical Equipment Mfr
N.A.I.C.S.: 335999

Great Plains Oilfield Rental, L.L.C. (1)
3401 S Radio Rd, El Reno, OK 73036
Tel.: (405) 345-4354
Web Site: https://gpor.com
Oil Field Rental Equipment Services
N.A.I.C.S.: 532412
Drew Parker (Pres)

MS Directional, LLC (1)
3335 Pollok Dr, Conroe, TX 77303
Tel.: (936) 442-2500
Web Site: https://msdir.com
Oil & Gas Drilling Services
N.A.I.C.S.: 213111

Multi-Shot, LLC (1)
7821 Will Rogers Blvd, Fort Worth, TX 76140
Tel.: (817) 568-1038
Web Site: http://www.msenergyservices.com
Directional Drilling Services
N.A.I.C.S.: 213111

NexTier Oilfield Solutions Inc. (1)
3990 Rogerdale Rd, Houston, TX 77042
Tel.: (713) 325-6000
Web Site: https://www.nextierofs.com
Rev.: $3,244,822,000
Assets: $1,727,168,000
Liabilities: $937,249,000
Net Worth: $789,919,000
Earnings: $314,969,000
Emp.: 4,302
Fiscal Year-end: 12/31/2022
Well Drilling Services
N.A.I.C.S.: 213111

Subsidiary (Non-US):

Mobile Data Technologies Ltd. (2)
101 14535-118 Avenue, Edmonton, T5L 2M7, AB, Canada
Tel.: (780) 452-4855
Web Site: https://www.mobiledatatech.com
Information Technology Services
N.A.I.C.S.: 541511
Davis McGregor (Pres)
Jesse Duncan (VP-Technology)
Jeremy Kozzy Koskewich (Ops Mgr)

Patterson-UTI Drilling Canada Limited (1)
1306-8th St, Nisku, T9E 7M1, AB, Canada
Tel.: (780) 955-7777
Oil & Gas Wells Drilling Contractor
N.A.I.C.S.: 213111

Patterson-UTI Drilling Company, LLC (1)
10713 W Sam Houston Pkwy N Ste 800, Houston, TX 77064
Tel.: (281) 765-7100
Web Site: https://www.patenergy.com
Oil & Natural Gas Production; Land-based Drilling Rigs
N.A.I.C.S.: 213111
Mike Holcomb (Pres)
Mike Garvin (Pres)

Patterson-UTI Management Services, LLC (1)
10713 W Sam Houston Pkwy N Ste 800, Houston, TX 77064

Tel.: (281) 765-7100
Contract Drilling & Pumping Services
N.A.I.C.S.: 213112

Phelps Drilling Co. (1)
101 6 Ave SW, Calgary, T2P 3P4, AB, Canada
Tel.: (403) 269-2858
Web Site: http://www.patenergy.com
Sales Range: $200-249.9 Million
Emp.: 150
Oil & Gas Wells Drilling
N.A.I.C.S.: 213111

Pioneer Energy Services Corp. (1)
1250 NE Loop 410 Ste 1000, San Antonio, TX 78209
Tel.: (210) 828-7689
Web Site: http://www.pioneeres.com
Rev.: $443,099,000
Assets: $439,913,000
Liabilities: $272,635,000
Net Worth: $167,278,000
Earnings: $4,841,000
Emp.: 1,451
Fiscal Year-end: 12/27/2019
Land Contract Drilling Services for Oil & Gas Production
N.A.I.C.S.: 213111
Dean A. Burkhardt (Chm)
Donald G. Lacombe (Sr VP-Marketing-Drilling Svcs)
Carlos R. Pena (Chief Strategy Officer & Exec VP)
W. Scott Keenen (Sr VP-Human Resources-Global)
Daniel Petro (Treas & VP-Investor Relations)
Bryce Seki (Officer-Compliance, Gen Counsel, Sec & VP)
John Locken (VP-Operations-Drilling Svcs)
Matthew S. Porter (Pres & CEO)

Subsidiary (Domestic):

Pioneer Coiled Tubing Services, LLC (2)
111 W Etienne Rd, Maurice, LA 70555
Tel.: (337) 892-5900
Oil & Gas Related Services
N.A.I.C.S.: 213112
Chip Boutte (Mgr-District)

Pioneer Energy Services Corp. - Coiled Tubing Services (2)
111 W Etienne Rd, Maurice, LA 70555
Tel.: (337) 892-5900
Web Site: http://www.pioneeres.com
Sales Range: $100-124.9 Million
Emp.: 200
Oil & Gas Coiled Tubing Services
N.A.I.C.S.: 213112

Pioneer Wireline Services, L.L.C. (2)
1401 Hwy 380, Graham, TX 76450
Tel.: (940) 549-7914
Oil & Gas Wells Drilling Services
N.A.I.C.S.: 213111

Ulterra Drilling Technologies, L.P. (1)
201 Main St Ste 1660, Fort Worth, TX 76102
Tel.: (817) 293-7555
Web Site: https://www.ulterra.com
Emp.: 500
Oil & Gas Well Drill Bits Mfr
N.A.I.C.S.: 333132
John Clunan (Pres & CEO)

Universal Pressure Pumping, Inc. (1)
6 Desta Dr Ste 4000, Midland, TX 79705
Tel.: (432) 682-9401
Oil & Gas Pumping Services
N.A.I.C.S.: 213112
Indya Kohutek (Coord-HS&E)
Eddie Noriega (Supvr-HS&E)
Joe Luman (Dir-Standards & Assurances)

Universal Well Services, Inc. (1)
201 Arch St, Meadville, PA 16335
Tel.: (814) 337-1983
Web Site: http://www.univwell.com
Sales Range: $75-99.9 Million
Emp.: 10
Well Pumping Services
N.A.I.C.S.: 213112

Warrior Rig Technologies Limited (1)

1515-28 Street NE, Calgary, T2A 3T1, AB, Canada
Tel.: (403) 291-6444
Web Site: http://www.warriorrig.com
Drilling Rig Equipment Mfr
N.A.I.C.S.: 333132

PAUL MUELLER COMPANY
1600 W Phelps St, Springfield, MO 65802
Tel.: (417) 575-9000　　　　MO
Web Site:
　https://www.paulmueller.com
Year Founded: 1940
MUEL—(OTCIQ)
Rev.: $229,156,000
Assets: $134,269,000
Liabilities: $70,753,000
Net Worth: $63,516,000
Earnings: ($9,890,000)
Emp.: 880
Fiscal Year-end: 12/31/23
Stainless Steel Processing Equipment Mfr
N.A.I.C.S.: 332313
David T. Moore (Pres & CEO)
John J. Ghirardelli (Chm)
Kenneth E. Jeffries (CFO)
Denise M. Silvey (Sec & Mgr-HR)

Subsidiaries:

Mueller Lichtenvoorde B.V.　　(1)
Nijverheidsstraat 14, Lichtenvoorde, 7131 PA, Netherlands
Tel.: (31) 544 356030
Web Site: http://www.muellerbv.com
Emp.: 120
Dairy Farm Equipment Mfr
N.A.I.C.S.: 333111
Harry Nigkamp (Plant Mgr)

Mueller Transportation, Inc.　　(1)
1600 W Phelps St, Springfield, MO 65802-4273　　　　(100%)
Tel.: (417) 831-3000
Web Site: http://www.muel.com
Sales Range: $100-124.9 Million
Emp.: 450
Distr & Transporter of Stainless Steel Products & Components
N.A.I.C.S.: 332420
Aaron L. Owen (Pres-Ops)

PAVMED INC.
360 Madison Ave Fl 25, New York, NY 10017
Tel.: (917) 813-1828　　　　DE
Web Site: https://www.pavmed.com
Year Founded: 2014
PAVM—(NASDAQ)
Rev.: $377,000
Assets: $53,980,000
Liabilities: $43,046,000
Net Worth: $10,934,000
Earnings: ($88,983,000)
Emp.: 124
Fiscal Year-end: 12/31/22
Medical Device Mfr
N.A.I.C.S.: 339112
Shaun M. O'Neil (COO & Exec VP)
Dennis M. McGrath (Pres & CFO)
Lishan Aklog (Founder, Chm & CEO)
Michael J. Glennon (Vice Chm)
Michael Gordon (Gen Counsel)
Deepika A. Lakhani (Chief Regulatory Officer)
Suman M. Verma (Chief Scientific Officer)
Victoria T. Lee (Chief Medical Officer)

Subsidiaries:

Lucid Diagnostics Inc.　　(1)
360 Madison Ave Fl 25, New York, NY 10017　　　　(79.99%)
Tel.: (917) 813-1828
Web Site: https://www.luciddx.com
Rev.: $377,000
Assets: $32,509,000
Liabilities: $9,462,000
Net Worth: $23,047,000

Earnings: ($56,171,000)
Emp.: 74
Fiscal Year-end: 12/31/2022
Medical Laboratories
N.A.I.C.S.: 621511
Shaun M. O'Neil (Pres & COO)

PAXMEDICA, INC.
303 S Broadway Ste 125, Tarrytown, NY 10591
Tel.: (914) 987-2876　　　　DE
Web Site:
　https://www.paxmedica.com
Year Founded: 2018
PXMD—(NASDAQ)
Assets: $2,204,318
Liabilities: $2,095,518
Net Worth: $108,800
Earnings: ($14,801,767)
Emp.: 3
Fiscal Year-end: 12/31/22
Research & Development in Biotechnology (except Nanobiotechnology)
N.A.I.C.S.: 541714
Howard J. Weisman (Chm & CEO)
Joseph Lucchese (CFO)
Michael L. Derby (Founder)
Stephen D. Sheldon (COO)

PAYCHEX, INC.
911 Panorama Trl S, Rochester, NY 14625-2396
Tel.: (585) 385-6666　　　　DE
Web Site: https://www.paychex.com
Year Founded: 1971
PAYX—(NASDAQ)
Rev.: $5,278,300,000
Assets: $10,383,100,000
Liabilities: $6,582,100,000
Net Worth: $3,801,000,000
Earnings: $1,690,400,000
Emp.: 16,500
Fiscal Year-end: 05/31/24
Payroll Processing, Human Resources & Benefits Outsourcing Solutions for Small to Medium-Sized Businesses
N.A.I.C.S.: 541214
Michael E. Gioja (Sr VP-IT & Product Dev)
Terry P. Mayotte (Pres-Insurance Agency)
B. Thomas Golisano (Founder)
Martin Mucci (Chm)
Mark A. Bottini (Sr VP-Sls)
Terrence Sukalski (VP-HR Svcs Sls)
Neal Collins (Mng Dir-Mergers & Acquisitions & VP-Corp Dev)
Frank Fiorille (VP-Risk, Compliance & Data Analytics)
Tom Hammond (VP-Corp Strategy & Product Mgmt)
Michael Jeffrey (VP-Major Market Svcs Sls)
Ted Jordan (VP-Svc)
Maureen Lally (VP-Mktg)
Mick Whittemore (VP-IT-Enterprise Ops)
Robert L. Schrader (CFO & Sr VP)
Tamara Duncan (VP-Sls-SMB)
Bradley Schaufenbuel (Chief Information Security Officer & VP)
Karen E. Saunders McClendon (Chief HR Officer & VP)
John Connors (VP-Software Dev)
Lisa Fleming (Mgr-PR)
Elizabeth Roaldsen (Sr VP-Ops & Customer Experience)
John B. Gibson Jr. (Pres & CEO)

Subsidiaries:

Advantage Payroll Services Inc.　　(1)
126 Merrow Rd, Auburn, ME 04211-1330
Tel.: (207) 784-0178
Web Site: http://www.paychex.com
Payroll Processing Services
N.A.I.C.S.: 541214

Expense Wire LLC　　(1)
1099 Akron Rd, Wooster, OH 44691
Tel.: (330) 264-9468
Web Site: http://www.expensewire.com
Software Development Services
N.A.I.C.S.: 541511

Nettime Solutions LLC　　(1)
8840 E Chaparral Rd Ste 145, Scottsdale, AZ 85250
Tel.: (480) 296-0400
Web Site: http://www.nettimesolutions.com
Emp.: 50
Software Product Development Services
N.A.I.C.S.: 541511

Oasis Outsourcing, Inc.　　(1)
2054 Vista Pkwy Ste 300, West Palm Beach, FL 33411
Tel.: (866) 709-9401
Web Site: http://www.oasisadvantage.com
Human Resources, Employee Benefits, Payroll, Workers' Compensation & Risk Management Professional Outsourcing Services
N.A.I.C.S.: 561330
Terry P. Mayotte (Founder & Pres)

Subsidiary (Domestic):

Diversified Human Resources, Inc.　　(2)
1600 N Desert Dr, Tempe, AZ 85016
Tel.: (480) 941-5588
Human Resource & Insurance Brokerage, Payroll Processing & Temporary Staffing Services
N.A.I.C.S.: 541612

Doherty Employer Services　　(2)
7625 Parklawn Ave, Edina, MN 55435
Tel.: (952) 835-8888
Web Site:
　http://www.dohertyemployment.com
Sales Range: $50-74.9 Million
Emp.: 57
Human Resources Management, Benefits Administration & Payroll Processing Services
N.A.I.C.S.: 541214

Fortune Industries Inc.　　(2)
9020 Overlook Blvd Ste 201, Brentwood, TN 37027
Tel.: (615) 665-9060
Sales Range: $50-74.9 Million
Human Resource, Employee Benefits & Risk Management Professional Outsourcing Services
N.A.I.C.S.: 561330

Subsidiary (Domestic):

Century II　　(3)
9020 Overlook Blvd Ste 201, Brentwood, TN 37027
Tel.: (615) 665-9060
Web Site: http://www.centuryii.net
Sales Range: $75-99.9 Million
Holding Company; Outsourced Human Resource Services
N.A.I.C.S.: 551112
Kim Troup (Exec VP)

Subsidiary (Domestic):

Century II Services, Inc.　　(4)
9020 Overlook Blvd Ste 201, Brentwood, TN 37027
Tel.: (615) 665-9060
Web Site: http://www.centuryii.net
Sales Range: $100-124.9 Million
Emp.: 25
Business Services
N.A.I.C.S.: 561499

Century II Staffing, Inc.　　(4)
9020 Overlook Blvd Ste 201, Brentwood, TN 37027
Tel.: (615) 665-9060
Web Site: http://www.centuryii.net
Sales Range: $10-24.9 Million
Emp.: 27
Human Resource Outsource Services
N.A.I.C.S.: 561499

Subsidiary (Domestic):

Century II Staffing TN, Inc.　　(5)
9020 Overlook Blvd Ste 201, Brentwood, TN 37027

Tel.: (615) 665-9060
Web Site: http://www.centuryii.net
Human Resource Consulting Services
N.A.I.C.S.: 541612

Subsidiary (Domestic):

Commercial Solutions, Inc.　　(3)
6402 Corporate Dr, Indianapolis, IN 46278
Tel.: (317) 532-1374
Web Site:
　http://www.commercialsolutions.com
Sales Range: $25-49.9 Million
Emp.: 25
Electronic Product Distr
N.A.I.C.S.: 423620
Dan Brooker (Pres)

Fortune Wireless, Inc.　　(3)
6402 Corporate Dr, Indianapolis, IN 46278
Tel.: (317) 532-1374
Web Site: http://www.fortune.com
Sales Range: $100-124.9 Million
Emp.: 50
Wireless Networks Turnkey Services
N.A.I.C.S.: 334220
Brad Riggs (Dir-Site Dev Svcs)
Robert Weeks (Dir-Construction Svcs)
Jason Riggs (VP-Site Dev Ops)
Mike Daubenmire (Sr Project Mgr-Site Dev)

James H. Drew Corporation　　(3)
8701 Zionsville Rd, Indianapolis, IN 46268
Tel.: (317) 876-3739
Web Site: https://www.jameshdrew.com
Sales Range: $250-299.9 Million
Fiber Optic, Smart Highway Systems, Traffic Signals, Street Signs, High Mast & Ornamental Lighting, Guardrail, Wireless Communications & Fabrications of Structural Steel Contractor
N.A.I.C.S.: 237130

Kingston Sales Corporation　　(3)
6402 Corporate Dr, Indianapolis, IN 46278
Tel.: (317) 532-1374
Web Site: http://www.kingstonsales.com
Sales Range: $50-74.9 Million
TV's, Digital Satellite Systems, CCTV, Sound Systems, Electronic Locking Systems, Intercom Systems, Wire & Fiber Optics Mfr Sales Representative
N.A.I.C.S.: 423620
Shawn Brovold (Pres)

Professional Staff Management, Inc.　　(3)
6801 Lk Plz Ste D 405, Indianapolis, IN 46220
Tel.: (317) 816-7007
Web Site: http://www.psmin.com
Sales Range: $1-9.9 Million
Emp.: 8
Professional Staff Management Services
N.A.I.C.S.: 561499
Scott Tant (Pres)

Subsidiary (Domestic):

PSM Financial Services, LLC　　(4)
1836 Sunningdale Ct, Oviedo, FL 32765-5832
Tel.: (407) 971-7657
Business Support Services; Financial Services
N.A.I.C.S.: 561499

Subsidiary (Domestic):

Oasis Outsourcing　　(2)
7675 Dagget St Ste 200, San Diego, CA 92111
Tel.: (858) 598-1800
Web Site: http://www.oasisadvantage.com
Sales Range: $25-49.9 Million
Human Resources, Payroll, Benefits & Risk Management Staffing Services
N.A.I.C.S.: 561330
Dolores Calicchio (Chief HR Officer & Exec VP-HR)

Staff One, Inc.　　(2)
8111 LBJ Freeway Ste 1350, Dallas, TX 75251
Tel.: (214) 461-1140
Web Site: http://www.staffone.com
Sales Range: $200-249.9 Million
Emp.: 40
Recruitment Services

Paychex, Inc.—(Continued)
N.A.I.C.S.: 541612
Anissa Wilson *(Dir-HR Svcs)*

Paychex Management Corp. **(1)**
911 Panorama Trl S, Rochester, NY 14625-2311
Tel.: (585) 385-6666
Payroll Processing Services
N.A.I.C.S.: 541214

Paychex Securities Corporation **(1)**
1175 John St, West Henrietta, NY 14586-9102
Tel.: (585) 336-7800
Securities Brokerage Services
N.A.I.C.S.: 523150

Paychex Time & Attendance Inc. **(1)**
1025 Greenwood Blvd Ste 301, Lake Mary, FL 32746
Tel.: (407) 333-1338
Web Site: http://www.paychex.com
Payroll Processing Services
N.A.I.C.S.: 541214

SurePayroll, Inc. **(1)**
911 Panorama Trl S, Rochester, NY 14625
Tel.: (847) 676-8420
Web Site: https://www.surepayroll.com
Sales Range: $10-24.9 Million
Emp.: 100
Online Payroll Services
N.A.I.C.S.: 541214

PAYCOR HCM, INC.
4811 Montgomery Rd, Cincinnati, OH 45212   **DE**
Web Site: https://www.paycor.com
Year Founded: 2018
PYCR—(NASDAQ)
Rev.: $654,948,000
Assets: $2,609,393,000
Liabilities: $1,322,467,000
Net Worth: $1,286,926,000
Earnings: ($58,942,000)
Emp.: 2,900
Fiscal Year-end: 06/30/24
Holding Company
N.A.I.C.S.: 551112
Sarah Haines *(Chief Acctg Officer)*
Jason A. Wright *(Chm)*
Adam Ante *(CFO)*
Alice Geene *(Chief Legal Officer & Sec)*
Charles Mueller *(Chief Revenue Officer)*
Ryan Bergstrom *(Chief Product & Tech Officer)*
Raul Villar Jr. *(CEO)*

PAYLOCITY HOLDING CORPORATION
1400 American Ln, Schaumburg, IL 60173
Tel.: (847) 463-3200   **DE**
Web Site: https://www.paylocity.com
Year Founded: 2013
PCTY—(NASDAQ)
Rev.: $1,402,515,000
Assets: $4,245,460,000
Liabilities: $3,212,396,000
Net Worth: $1,033,064,000
Earnings: $206,766,000
Emp.: 6,400
Fiscal Year-end: 06/30/24
Holding Company; Cloud-Based Payroll & Human Resource Management Software Solutions
N.A.I.C.S.: 551112
Steven R. Beauchamp *(Chm)*
Andrew Cappotelli *(VP-Client Tax Ops & Chief Compliance & Risk Officer)*
Toby J. Williams *(Pres & CEO)*
Steven I. Sarowitz *(Founder)*
Jay Schedler *(VP-Real Estate-Procurement)*
Rob Goldstein *(VP-Technical Svcs)*
Cheryl Johnson *(Chief HR Officer)*

John Taylor *(VP-Client Svcs)*
Holly Fulp *(VP & Head-Corp Dev)*
Ryan Glenn *(CFO & Treas)*
Josh Scutt *(VP-Sls)*
Dan Hassenplug *(VP-User Experience)*
Adam McElhinney *(Chief Data Science Officer & VP-Insights)*
Amber Livingston *(Gen Counsel & VP)*
Meera Mehta *(CMO)*
Christine Pellini *(VP-Product-Technology)*
Tauhidah Shakir *(Chief Diversity Officer & VP-Human Resources)*
Nicholas Rost *(Chief Acctg Officer & VP)*

Subsidiaries:

BeneFLEX HR Resources, Inc. **(1)**
10805 Sunset Office Dr Ste 401, Saint Louis, MO 63127
Tel.: (314) 909-6979
Web Site:
    https://planamendments.paylocity.com
Landscape Architectural Services
N.A.I.C.S.: 541320

Paylocity Corporation **(1)**
1400 American Ln, Schaumburg, IL 60173
Tel.: (847) 956-4850
Web Site: http://www.paylocity.com
Sales Range: $10-24.9 Million
Emp.: 208
Cloud-Based Payroll & Human Resource Management Software Solutions
N.A.I.C.S.: 541511
Steven R. Beauchamp *(CEO)*
Michael R. Haske *(Pres & COO)*
Steven I. Sarowitz *(Founder & Chm)*
Christina Moriarty *(VP-Tax Svcs)*
Rob Goldstein *(VP-Technical Svcs)*
Tauhidah Shakir *(Chief Diversity Officer & VP-HR)*

Samepage Labs Inc. **(1)**
1999 S Bascom Ste 700, Campbell, CA 95008
Web Site: https://www.samepage.io
Software Development Services
N.A.I.C.S.: 541511
Jan Jezek *(VP-Engrg)*
Scott Schreiman *(Co-Founder & CEO)*
Martin Viktora *(Co-Founder & CTO)*

VidGrid Inc. **(1)**
413 Wacouta St, Saint Paul, MN 55101
Tel.: (651) 560-6447
Web Site: https://www.vidgrid.com
Vidoo Broadcasting Services
N.A.I.C.S.: 516210

PAYMENTUS HOLDINGS, INC.
11605 N Community House Rd Ste 300, Charlotte, NC 28277   **DE**
Web Site:
    https://www.paymentus.com
Year Founded: 2011
PAY—(NYSE)
Rev.: $497,001,000
Assets: $461,539,000
Liabilities: $64,360,000
Net Worth: $397,179,000
Earnings: ($513,000)
Emp.: 1,260
Fiscal Year-end: 12/31/22
Holding Company
N.A.I.C.S.: 551112
Sanjay Kalra *(CFO & Sr VP)*
Gerasimos Portocalis *(Chief Comml Officer)*
Paul Seamon *(VP-Fin & Strategy)*
Dushyant Sharma *(Chm, Pres & CEO)*

PAYONEER GLOBAL INC.
195 Broadway, New York, NY 10007
Tel.: (212) 600-9272
Web Site: https://www.payoneer.com
PAYO—(NASDAQ)
Rev.: $627,623,000
Assets: $6,594,651,000

Liabilities: $6,049,395,000
Net Worth: $545,256,000
Earnings: ($11,970,000)
Emp.: 2,336
Fiscal Year-end: 12/31/22
Financial Services
N.A.I.C.S.: 523999
Beatrice Ordonez *(CFO)*
Scott Galit *(Co-CEO)*
John Caplan *(Co-CEO)*
Itai Perry *(Chief Acctg Officer)*

Subsidiaries:

FTAC Olympus Acquisition Corp. **(1)**
2929 Arch St Ste 1703, Philadelphia, PA 19104
Tel.: (215) 701-9555
Emp.: 3
Investment Services
N.A.I.C.S.: 523999
Douglas Listman *(CFO)*
Shami Patel *(COO)*

Payoneer, Inc. **(1)**
195 Broadway, New York, NY 10007
Tel.: (646) 658-3695
Web Site: https://www.payoneer.com
Sales Range: $25-49.9 Million
Emp.: 207
Global Payout Services
N.A.I.C.S.: 522320
Charles Rosenblatt *(Chief Strategy Officer)*

PAYPAL HOLDINGS, INC.
2211 North 1st St, San Jose, CA 95131
Tel.: (408) 967-1000   **DE**
Web Site: https://www.paypal.com
Year Founded: 1998
PYPL—(NASDAQ)
Rev.: $29,771,000,000
Assets: $82,166,000,000
Liabilities: $61,115,000,000
Net Worth: $21,051,000,000
Earnings: $4,246,000,000
Emp.: 27,200
Fiscal Year-end: 12/31/23
Holding Company; Payment Processing Services
N.A.I.C.S.: 551112
J. Alexander Chriss *(Pres & CEO)*
Blake Jorgensen *(CFO)*
Franz Paasche *(Chief Corp Affairs Officer & Sr VP)*
John Kunze *(Sr VP)*
Maryclaire Campbell *(Sr VP-Digital Commerce Sls & Global Pro Svcs)*
Wes Hummel *(VP)*
Jamie S. Miller *(CFO & Exec VP)*
Kausik Rajgopal *(Exec VP & Chief Strategy, Corporate Development & Partnerships Officer)*
Alfonso Villanueva *(Sr VP)*
Christopher Natali *(Chief Acctg Officer & VP)*
John Kim *(Chief Product Officer & Exec VP)*
Archana Deskus *(CIO)*
Sripada Shivananda *(CTO & Exec VP)*

Subsidiaries:

Hyperwallet Systems Inc. **(1)**
Suite 2600 Three Bentall Centre 595 Burrard Street, PO Box 49314, Vancouver, V7X 1L3, BC, Canada
Web Site: https://www.hyperwallet.com
Financial Services
N.A.I.C.S.: 523999

PayPal U.K. Ltd. **(1)**
Whittaker House Whittaker Avenue, Richmond Upon Thames, Surrey, TW9 1EH, United Kingdom
Tel.: (44) 2079494780
Financial Support Services
N.A.I.C.S.: 521110

PayPal, Inc. **(1)**
2211 N 1st St, San Jose, CA 95131
Tel.: (408) 967-1000

Web Site: http://www.paypal.com
Sales Range: Less than $1 Million
Internet Payment Services
N.A.I.C.S.: 518210
J. Alexander Chriss *(Pres & CEO)*

Subsidiary (Domestic):

Bill Me Later, Inc. **(2)**
9690 Deereco Rd 7th Fl, Timonium, MD 21093
Tel.: (443) 921-1900
Web Site: http://www.billmelater.com
Sales Range: $50-74.9 Million
Online Payment Processing Services
N.A.I.C.S.: 561499

Braintree, Inc. **(2)**
464 Bourbon Ln, Naperville, IL 60565-2497
Tel.: (630) 420-9728
Emp.: 9
Data Processing Services
N.A.I.C.S.: 518210

Subsidiary (Domestic):

Braintree Payment Solutions, LLC **(3)**
222 W Merchandise Mart Plz Ste 800, Chicago, IL 60654
Tel.: (312) 455-9540
Web Site:
    http://www.braintreepayments.com
Sales Range: $25-49.9 Million
Online Payment Gateway Services
N.A.I.C.S.: 522320

Subsidiary (Non-US):

PayPal (UK) Limited **(2)**
Whittaker House 2 Whittaker Avenue, Richmond, TW9 1EH, Surrey, United Kingdom
Tel.: (44) 2084392000
Management Consulting Services
N.A.I.C.S.: 541618

Subsidiary (Domestic):

PayPal Asset Management, Inc. **(2)**
2211 N 1st St, San Jose, CA 95131
Tel.: (408) 967-7500
Investment Advice Services
N.A.I.C.S.: 523940

Subsidiary (Non-US):

PayPal Australia Pty Limited **(2)**
Level 23 1 York Street, Sydney, 2000, NSW, Australia
Tel.: (61) 282239500
Web Site: https://www.paypal.com
Payroll Management Services
N.A.I.C.S.: 541214

PayPal Canada Co. **(2)**
661 University Avenue Suite 506, Toronto, M5G 1M1, ON, Canada
Financial Transaction Services
N.A.I.C.S.: 522320

Subsidiary (Domestic):

PayPal Charitable Giving Fund **(2)**
1250 I St NW Ste 1202, Washington, DC 20005
Tel.: (202) 551-9076
Web Site: https://www.paypal.com
Charity Organization
N.A.I.C.S.: 813211

Subsidiary (Non-US):

PayPal Nederlands B.V. **(2)**
Wibautstraat 224, Amsterdam, 1097, Netherlands
Tel.: (31) 204167248
Commercial Services
N.A.I.C.S.: 335132

PayPal Polska Sp z o.o. **(2)**
Emilii Plater 53 woj Mazowieckie, 00-113, Warsaw, Poland
Tel.: (48) 224582128
Management Consulting Services
N.A.I.C.S.: 541618

PayPal Pte. Ltd. **(2)**
5 Temasek Boulevard 09-01 Suntec Tower Five, Singapore, 38985, Singapore

Tel.: (65) 65104501
Telephone Communication Services
N.A.I.C.S.: 517121

Subsidiary (Domestic):

Paydiant, Inc. (2)
275 Grove St, Auburndale, MA 02466
Tel.: (617) 219-4200
Web Site: http://www.paydiant.com
Mobile Application Development Services
N.A.I.C.S.: 541511
Melinda Smith (CFO)

Swift Financial, LLC (2)
3505 Silverside Rd, Wilmington, DE 19810
Tel.: (302) 374-7000
Web Site: https://www.swiftfinancial.com
Consumer Lending
N.A.I.C.S.: 522291

Xoom Corporation (2)
425 Market St 12th Fl, San Francisco, CA
94105
Tel.: (415) 777-4800
Web Site: http://www.xoom.com
Emp.: 295
Online-to-Offline International Money Transfer Service
N.A.I.C.S.: 525990
Kevin E. Hartz (Co-Founder)

PAYSIGN, INC.

2615 St Rose Pkwy, Henderson, NV
89052
Tel.: (702) 453-2221 NV
Web Site: https://www.paysign.com
PAYS—(NASDAQ)
Rev.: $38,033,667
Assets: $108,244,253
Liabilities: $91,950,958
Net Worth: $16,293,295
Earnings: $1,027,775
Emp.: 110
Fiscal Year-end: 12/31/22
Payment Technology Solutions
N.A.I.C.S.: 522320
Mark R. Newcomer (Founder, Chm,
Pres & CEO)
Matthew Lanford (Chief Payments
Officer)
Joan M. Herman (Exec VP)
Eric Trudeau (Chief Compliance Officer)
Robert Strobo (Chief Legal Officer,
Gen Counsel & Sec)
Matthew Lanford (Pres & COO)
Matthew Turner (VP-Patient Affordability Svcs)
Jeffery B. Baker (CFO)
Alicia Ches (Mktg Dir)
Brad Cunningham (CTO)

PAZOO, INC.

34 DeForest Ave Unit 9, East Hanover, NJ 07936
Tel.: (973) 455-0970 NV
Web Site: http://www.pazoo.com
Year Founded: 2010
PZOO—(OTCIQ)
Sales Range: Less than $1 Million
Online Health & Wellness Products
Retailer
N.A.I.C.S.: 456199
Steven Basloe (Chm, Pres & Interim
CEO)
Ben Hoehn (CFO & COO)

PB BANKSHARES, INC.

185 E Lincoln Hwy, Coatesville, PA
19320
Tel.: (610) 384-8282 MD
Web Site:
https://www.presencebank.com
Year Founded: 2021
PBBK—(NASDAQ)
Rev.: $15,237,000
Assets: $386,547,000
Liabilities: $340,560,000
Net Worth: $45,987,000
Earnings: $2,114,000

Emp.: 35
Fiscal Year-end: 12/31/22
Offices of Bank Holding Companies
N.A.I.C.S.: 551111
Douglas L. Byers (Chief Banking Officer & Exec VP)
Larry Witt (COO, CIO & Exec VP)
Angela M. Krezmer (CFO & Sr VP)
Janak M. Amin (Pres & CEO)

PB FINANCIAL CORPORATION

450 N Winstead Ave, Rocky Mount,
NC 27804
Tel.: (252) 443-9477 NC
Web Site: https://www.pbknc.com
Year Founded: 2017
PBNC—(OTCQX)
Bank Holding Company
N.A.I.C.S.: 551111
Ted E. Whitehurst (Pres & CEO)
David Keul (CFO & Exec VP)
Robert Ladd III (Chief Lending Officer
& Exec VP)

Subsidiaries:

Providence Bank (1)
450 N Winstead Ave, Rocky Mount, NC
27804
Tel.: (252) 443-9477
Web Site: http://www.pbknc.com
Rev.: $13,625,995
Assets: $322,242,260
Liabilities: $280,827,508
Net Worth: $41,414,752
Earnings: $2,628,776
Fiscal Year-end: 12/31/2017
Commericial Banking
N.A.I.C.S.: 522110
Ted E. Whitehurst (Pres & CEO)
David Keul (CFO & Exec VP)
Richard C. Anderson (Chm)
Robert Ladd III (Chief Lending Officer &
Exec VP)

Providence Bank (1)
450 N Winstead Ave, Rocky Mount, NC
27804
Tel.: (252) 443-9477
Web Site: http://www.pbknc.com
Rev.: $13,625,995
Assets: $322,242,260
Liabilities: $280,827,508
Net Worth: $41,414,752
Earnings: $2,628,776
Fiscal Year-end: 12/31/2017
Commericial Banking
N.A.I.C.S.: 522110
Ted E. Whitehurst (Pres & CEO)
David Keul (CFO & Exec VP)
Richard C. Anderson (Chm)
Robert Ladd III (Chief Lending Officer &
Exec VP)

Providence Bank (1)
450 N Winstead Ave, Rocky Mount, NC
27804
Tel.: (252) 443-9477
Web Site: http://www.pbknc.com
Rev.: $13,625,995
Assets: $322,242,260
Liabilities: $280,827,508
Net Worth: $41,414,752
Earnings: $2,628,776
Fiscal Year-end: 12/31/2017
Commericial Banking
N.A.I.C.S.: 522110
Ted E. Whitehurst (Pres & CEO)
David Keul (CFO & Exec VP)
Richard C. Anderson (Chm)
Robert Ladd III (Chief Lending Officer &
Exec VP)

Providence Bank (1)
450 N Winstead Ave, Rocky Mount, NC
27804
Tel.: (252) 443-9477
Web Site: http://www.pbknc.com
Rev.: $13,625,995
Assets: $322,242,260
Liabilities: $280,827,508
Net Worth: $41,414,752
Earnings: $2,628,776
Fiscal Year-end: 12/31/2017
Commericial Banking
N.A.I.C.S.: 522110

Ted E. Whitehurst (Pres & CEO)
David Keul (CFO & Exec VP)
Richard C. Anderson (Chm)
Robert Ladd III (Chief Lending Officer &
Exec VP)

PBF ENERGY INC.

1 Sylvan Way 2nd Fl, Parsippany, NJ
07054
Tel.: (973) 455-7500 DE
Web Site: https://www.pbfenergy.com
Year Founded: 2008
PBF—(NYSE)
Rev.: $38,324,800,000
Assets: $14,387,800,000
Liabilities: $7,756,500,000
Net Worth: $6,631,300,000
Earnings: $2,140,500,000
Emp.: 3,776
Fiscal Year-end: 12/31/23
Petroleum Refiner & Supplier
N.A.I.C.S.: 324110
Thomas J. Nimbley (Exec Chm)
Timothy Paul Davis (Sr VP-Supply,
Trading & Optimization)
Thomas L. O'Connor (Sr VP-
Commodity Risk & Strategy)
Matthew C. Lucey (Pres & CEO)
Colin Murray (VP-IR)
Karen Berriman Davis (CFO & Sr VP)
Steven G. Steach (Sr VP)
Wendy Ho Tai (Sr VP)
Jim Fedena (Sr VP)
Trecia Canty (Sec & Sr VP)

Subsidiaries:

Chalmette Refining, L.L.C. (1)
500 W Saint Bernard Hwy, Chalmette, LA
70043 (100%)
Tel.: (504) 281-1212
Web Site: http://www.chalmetterefining.com
Petroleum Refinery Operator
N.A.I.C.S.: 324110

Delaware Pipeline Company LLC (1)
1 Sylvan Way 2nd Fl, Parsippany, NJ
07054
Tel.: (302) 836-6500
Emp.: 5
Pipeline Transportation Services
N.A.I.C.S.: 486910
Rich Fetters (Mgr)

PBF Energy Company LLC (1)
1 Sylvan Way 2nd Fl, Parsippany, NJ
07054
Tel.: (973) 455-7500
Web Site: https://www.pbfenergy.com
Rev.: $46,830,299,999
Assets: $13,547,300,000
Liabilities: $9,137,200,000
Net Worth: $4,410,100,000
Earnings: $3,766,100,000
Emp.: 3,616
Fiscal Year-end: 12/31/2022
Petroleum Refining Services
N.A.I.C.S.: 324110
Thomas J. Nimbley (CEO)
Timothy Paul Davis (Sr VP-Supply, Trading
& Optimization)
Thomas L. O'Connor (Sr VP-Commodity
Risk & Strategy)
Erik Young (CFO & Sr VP)
John Barone (Chief Acctg Officer)
Trecia Canty (Gen Counsel, Sec & Sr VP)

PBF Energy Western Region
LLC (1)
1 Sylvan Way Ste 2, Parsippany, NJ 07054
Tel.: (973) 455-7500
Petroleum Product Mfr
N.A.I.C.S.: 324110

PBF Holding Company LLC (1)
1 Sylvan Way 2nd Fl, Parsippany, NJ
07054 (100%)
Tel.: (973) 455-7500
Web Site: https://www.pbfenergy.com
Rev.: $46,780,600,000
Assets: $13,150,200,000
Liabilities: $7,533,100,000
Net Worth: $5,617,100,000
Earnings: $3,710,300,000
Emp.: 3,528
Fiscal Year-end: 12/31/2022

Holding Company; Oil Refineries
N.A.I.C.S.: 551112
Thomas J. Nimbley (CEO)
Timothy Paul Davis (Sr VP-Supply, Trading
& Optimization)
Thomas L. O'Connor (Sr VP-Commodity
Risk & Strategy)
Trecia Canty (Gen Counsel, Gen Counsel,
Sec, Sec, Sr VP & Sr VP)
Matthew C. Lucey (Pres)
Karen B. Davis (CFO)
Wendy Ho Tai (Sr VP)
Jim Fedena (Sr VP)
Colin Murray (VP)
Mike A. Bukowski (Sr VP)

Subsidiary (Domestic):

Delaware City Refining Company
LLC (2)
4550 Wrangle Hill Rd, Delaware City, DE
19706 (100%)
Tel.: (302) 834-6000
Web Site: http://www.pbfenergy.com
Petroleum Refiner
N.A.I.C.S.: 324110

PBF Finance Corporation (2)
1 Sylvan Way 2nd Fl, Parsippany, NJ
07054
Tel.: (973) 455-7500
Emp.: 3,638
Petroleum Product Refining Services
N.A.I.C.S.: 324110
Thomas J. Nimbley (CEO)

Paulsboro Refining Company
LLC (2)
800 Billingsport Rd, Paulsboro, NJ
08066 (100%)
Tel.: (856) 224-6000
Web Site: http://www.pbfenergy.com
Petroleum Refiner
N.A.I.C.S.: 324110

Toledo Refining Company LLC (2)
1819 Woodville Rd, Oregon, OH 43616-
3159
Tel.: (419) 698-6600
Web Site: http://www.pbfenergy.com
Petroleum Refiner
N.A.I.C.S.: 324110

Torrance Refining Company (2)
3700 W 190th St, Torrance, CA 90504
Tel.: (310) 505-3158
Web Site: https://www.torrancerefinery.com
Petroleum Refiner
N.A.I.C.S.: 324110

PBF Logistics LP (1)
1 Sylvan Way 2nd Fl, Parsippany, NJ
07054 (100%)
Tel.: (973) 455-7500
Web Site: http://www.pbflogistics.com
Rev.: $355,535,000
Assets: $901,297,000
Liabilities: $652,601,000
Net Worth: $248,696,000
Earnings: $153,287,000
Emp.: 89
Fiscal Year-end: 12/31/2021
Petroleum & Oil Terminals, Pipelines &
Storage Facilities Lessor, Owner & Acquirer
N.A.I.C.S.: 531190
Thomas J. Nimbley (Chm & CEO)

Paulsboro Natural Gas Pipeline Company LLC (1)
800 Billingsport Rd, Paulsboro, NJ 08066-
1035
Tel.: (856) 224-6019
Oil & Gas Field Drilling Services
N.A.I.C.S.: 213111

Toledo Terminaling Company
LLC (1)
1 Sylvan Way 2nd Fl, Parsippany, NJ
07054
Tel.: (973) 455-7500
Gas Storage Services
N.A.I.C.S.: 424710

PBS HOLDING, INC.

919 W 29th St, Cheyenne, WY 82001
Tel.: (214) 418-6940 NV
Year Founded: 1996
PBHG—(OTCIQ)

PBS Holding, Inc.—(Continued)

Digital Marketing Services
N.A.I.C.S.: 541613
Edward I. Vakser *(Founder, Chm & CEO)*

PC CONNECTION, INC.

730 Milford Rd, Merrimack, NH 03054
Tel.: (603) 683-2000   **DE**
Web Site:
   https://www.connection.com
Year Founded: 1982
CNXN—(NASDAQ)
Rev.: $3,124,996,000
Assets: $1,099,826,000
Liabilities: $333,651,000
Net Worth: $766,175,000
Earnings: $89,219,000
Emp.: 2,685
Fiscal Year-end: 12/31/22
Direct Marketer of Computer Products
N.A.I.C.S.: 423430
Patricia Gallup *(Co-Founder & Chief Admin Officer)*
Rick Gilligan *(Pres-Bus Solutions)*
Larry Kirsch *(Pres-Pub Sector Solutions)*
Cam Kelly *(CIO & Sr VP)*
Jay Bothwick *(Vice Chm & Sec)*
Robert Pratt *(Sr VP-Real Estate & Workplace Ops)*
Timothy J. McGrath *(Pres & CEO)*
Thomas C. Baker *(CFO, Treas & Sr. VP)*
Jamal Khan *(Chief Growth & Innovation Officer)*
Brian Hicks *(Sr VP-Product Mgmt & Ops)*
Joan Evans *(Sr VP-HR)*
Mickey Bland *(Pres-Enterprise Solutions Group)*
Dave Hall *(Gen Mgr-Tech Solutions)*
Kyle Reeb *(VP-Legal Svcs & Administration)*
Scott Sova *(CIO)*

Subsidiaries:

GlobalServe, Inc.   **(1)**
440 Sylvan Ave Ste 260, Englewood Cliffs, NJ 07632   **(100%)**
Tel.: (914) 729-6800
Web Site: http://www.global-serve.com
Sales Range: $10-24.9 Million
Emp.: 50
IT Procurement, IT Services & Software Development
N.A.I.C.S.: 541512
Jamal Khan *(CEO)*
Stan Boncic *(Dir-Tech)*
Chris Ryan *(VP-Fin)*
Peter Waters *(Dir-Enterprise & Direct Sls)*

MoreDirect, Inc.   **(1)**
1001 Yamato Rd Ste 200, Boca Raton, FL 33431-4403
Tel.: (561) 237-3300
Web Site: http://www.moredirect.com
Software Development Services
N.A.I.C.S.: 541511

PC Connection Sales Corporation   **(1)**
100 Main St Fl Mlls 3-2, Dover, NH 03820
Tel.: (603) 423-3360
Web Site: http://www.pcconnection.com
Computer Peripheral Equipment Whslr
N.A.I.C.S.: 423430

PCB BANCORP

3701 Wilshire Blvd Ste 900, Los Angeles, CA 90010-2871
Tel.: (213) 210-2000   **CA**
Web Site:
   https://www.mypcbbank.com
Year Founded: 2003
PCB—(NASDAQ)
Rev.: $116,250,000

Assets: $2,420,036,000
Liabilities: $2,084,594,000
Net Worth: $335,442,000
Earnings: $34,987,000
Emp.: 267
Fiscal Year-end: 12/31/22
Bank Holding Company
N.A.I.C.S.: 551111
Henry Kim *(Pres & CEO)*
David W. Kim *(Chief Banking Officer)*
Mimi Lee *(Sr VP)*
Michael Kwon *(CTO)*

Subsidiaries:

Pacific City Bank   **(1)**
3701 Wilshire Blvd Ste 900, Los Angeles, CA 90010-2871
Tel.: (213) 210-2000
Web Site: https://www.mypcbbank.com
Banking & Financial Services
N.A.I.C.S.: 522110
Henry Kim *(Pres & Grp CEO)*
Sang Young Lee *(Chm)*

PCM FUND, INC.

1633 Broadway, New York, NY 10019
Tel.: (212) 739-4000   **MD**
PCM—(NYSE)
Rev.: $11,891,000
Assets: $193,938,000
Liabilities: $75,757,000
Net Worth: $118,181,000
Earnings: $7,998,000
Fiscal Year-end: 06/30/19
Investment Management Service
N.A.I.C.S.: 525990

PCS EDVENTURES!.COM, INC.

11915 W Executive Dr Ste 101, Boise, ID 83713
Tel.: (208) 343-3110   **ID**
Web Site:
   https://www.edventures.com
Year Founded: 1994
PCSV—(OTCIQ)
Rev.: $9,094,466
Assets: $8,290,344
Liabilities: $634,527
Net Worth: $7,655,817
Earnings: $4,441,188
Emp.: 22
Fiscal Year-end: 03/31/24
Educational Support Services
N.A.I.C.S.: 611710
Robert Orson Grover *(Exec VP & Sec)*
Michael J. Bledsoe *(Pres)*
Alexandra Monjar *(Dir-Sls)*
Michelle Fisher *(Dir-Curriculum Dev)*

PCT LTD

4235 Commerce St, Little River, SC 29566
Tel.: (843) 390-7900   **NV**
Web Site: http://www.para-con.com
Year Founded: 1986
PCTL—(OTCIQ)
Rev.: $1,281,177
Assets: $4,254,258
Liabilities: $8,752,282
Net Worth: ($4,498,024)
Earnings: $088,610
Emp.: 16
Fiscal Year-end: 12/31/21
Investment Services
N.A.I.C.S.: 523999
Gary J. Grieco *(Chm, Pres & CEO)*
Arthur E. Abraham *(CFO)*

Subsidiaries:

Paradigm Convergence Technologies Corporation   **(1)**
4235 Commerce St, Little River, SC 29566
Tel.: (843) 390-7900
Web Site: http://www.para-con.com
Agricultural Chemical Product Mfr.
N.A.I.C.S.: 325320
Gary Grieco *(Co-Founder)*

PD-RX PHARMACEUTICALS, INC.

727 N Ann Arbor, Oklahoma City, OK 73127   **OK**
Web Site: https://www.pdrx.com
Year Founded: 1987
PDRX—(OTCIQ)
Rev.: $20,870,974
Assets: $8,658,557
Liabilities: $1,647,718
Net Worth: $7,010,839
Earnings: ($12,919)
Fiscal Year-end: 06/30/19
Health Care Srvices
N.A.I.C.S.: 621610
Jack L. McCall *(COO & Exec VP-Ops)*

PDF SOLUTIONS, INC.

2858 De La Cruz Blvd, Santa Clara, CA 95050
Tel.: (408) 280-7900   **DE**
Web Site: https://www.pdf.com
PDFS—(NASDAQ)
Rev.: $148,549,000
Assets: $278,671,000
Liabilities: $68,659,000
Net Worth: $210,012,000
Earnings: ($3,429,000)
Emp.: 458
Fiscal Year-end: 12/31/22
Custom Computer Programming Services
N.A.I.C.S.: 541511
John K. Kibarian *(Co-Founder, Pres & CEO)*
Kimon W. Michaels *(Co-Founder & Exec VP-Products & Solutions)*
Adnan Raza *(CFO & Exec VP-Fin)*

Subsidiaries:

Cimetrix Incorporated   **(1)**
6979 S High Tech Dr, Salt Lake City, UT 84047-3757
Tel.: (801) 256-6500
Web Site: https://www.cimetrix.com
Sales Range: $1-9.9 Million
Emp.: 33
Software Products for Electronics & Semiconductor Industries
N.A.I.C.S.: 513210
Robert H. Reback *(Pres, CEO, VP-Connectivity Grp & Gen Mgr)*
David Francis *(Dir-Product Mgmt)*
Brian Rubow *(Dir-Solutions Engrg)*
Richard Howard *(Dir-Technical Ops)*
David Warren *(Dir-Software Engrg)*
C. Alan Weber *(VP-New Product Innovations)*
Ranjan Chatterjee *(VP-Connectivity Grp)*
Brent Forsgren *(Dir-CCF Svcs)*
Kimberly Daich *(Mktg Dir)*
Alan Weber *(VP-New Product Innovations)*

Cimetrix Japan KK   **(1)**
Trojan Building 201-5-48-2 2F, Chojmachi Naka-ku, Yokohama, 231-0033, Kanagawa, Japan
Tel.: (81) 453410150
Software & Engineering Services
N.A.I.C.S.: 541330
Kerry Iwamoto *(Gen Mgr)*

Cimetrix Software (Shanghai) Co., Ltd.   **(1)**
Unit 1203 No 51 Zhengxue Road Yangpu Distric, Pudong New Area, Shanghai, China
Tel.: (86) 2161171616
Software & Engineering Services
N.A.I.C.S.: 541330

PDF Solutions GmbH   **(1)**
Schwanthalerstrasse 10, D-80336, Munich, Germany
Tel.: (49) 897670620
Intergrated Circuit Design Mfr & Services
N.A.I.C.S.: 541512

PDF Solutions KK   **(1)**
1-58-7 V H 401 Yoyogi, Shibuya-ku, Tokyo, 151-0053, Japan
Tel.: (81) 368244574
Software Application Development Services

N.A.I.C.S.: 513210

PDL COMMUNITY BANCORP

2244 Westchester Ave, Bronx, NY 10462
Tel.: (718) 931-9000   **NY**
Year Founded: 1960
PDLB—(NASDAQ)
Rev.: $66,586,000
Assets: $1,355,231,000
Liabilities: $1,195,687,000
Net Worth: $159,544,000
Earnings: $3,853,000
Emp.: 183
Fiscal Year-end: 12/31/20
Bank Holding Company
N.A.I.C.S.: 551111
Carlos P. Naudon *(Pres & CEO)*
Steven A. Tsavaris *(Chm)*
Frank Perez *(CFO & Exec VP)*

Subsidiaries:

Mortgage World Bankers, Inc.   **(1)**
32-75 Steinway St, Astoria, NY 11103
Tel.: (718) 274-1234
Web Site: http://www.mwbankers.com
Sales Range: $1-9.9 Million
Emp.: 50
Real Estate Mortgage Services
N.A.I.C.S.: 522292
Michael Lagoudis *(Pres & CEO)*
Steven A. Tsavaris *(Chm)*

PDS BIOTECHNOLOGY CORPORATION.

303A College Rd E, Princeton, NJ 08540
Tel.: (917) 797-7904   **DE**
Web Site:
   https://www.pdsbiotech.com
Year Founded: 2009
PDSB—(NASDAQ)
Rev.: $353,490
Assets: $14,491,252
Liabilities: $2,793,545
Net Worth: $11,697,707
Earnings: ($6,998,606)
Emp.: 15
Fiscal Year-end: 12/31/19
Pharmaceutical Preparation Manufacturing
N.A.I.C.S.: 325412
Kirk V. Shepard *(Chief Medical Officer)*
Lars Boesgaard *(CFO & Principal Acctg Officer)*
R. Loch MacDonald *(Founder)*
Stephan F. Toutain *(COO)*
Frank Bedu-Addo *(Pres & CEO)*
Gregory Conn *(Co-Founder & Chief Scientific Officer)*
Stephen Glover *(Chm)*

PEABODY ENERGY CORPORATION

701 Market St, Saint Louis, MO 63101-1826
Tel.: (314) 342-3400   **DE**
Web Site:
   https://www.peabodyenergy.com
Year Founded: 1883
BTU—(NYSE)
Rev.: $4,946,700,000
Assets: $5,962,100,000
Liabilities: $2,354,600,000
Net Worth: $3,607,500,000
Earnings: $815,600,000
Emp.: 5,400
Fiscal Year-end: 12/31/23
Coal Mining & Processing Services
N.A.I.C.S.: 212114
Darren Ronald Yeates *(COO & Exec VP)*
Mark A. Spurbeck *(CFO, Principal Acctg Officer & Exec VP)*

Marc E. Hathhorn (Pres-Ops-U.S.)
James C. Grech (Pres & CEO)
Jamie Frankcombe (Pres)

Subsidiaries:

American Land Development,
LLC   (1)
1150 1st Ave Ste 920, King of Prussia, PA
19406
Tel.: (610) 680-3500
Web Site: https://www.uslandev.com
Real Estate Development Services
N.A.I.C.S.: 531390

Burton Coal Pty Ltd   (1)
L 13 Boq Building 259 Queen St, Brisbane,
4000, QLD, Australia
Tel.: (61) 749405555
Coal Mining Services
N.A.I.C.S.: 212114

Coalsales, LLC   (1)
701 Market St, Saint Louis, MO 63101
Tel.: (314) 342-3400
Web Site: http://www.peabodyenergy.com
Sales Range: $150-199.9 Million
Emp.: 1,000
Coal Marketing Services
N.A.I.C.S.: 423520

Coaltrade International, LLC   (1)
701 Market St, Saint Louis, MO 63101
Tel.: (314) 342-3400
Web Site: http://www.peabodyenergy.com
Sales Range: $10-24.9 Million
Emp.: 1,000
Coal Products Sales
N.A.I.C.S.: 423520

Dalrymple Bay Coal Terminal Pty
Ltd   (1)
Martin Armstrong Drive, Hay Point, MacKay,
4740, QLD, Australia
Tel.: (61) 749438444
Web Site: https://www.dbct.com.au
Coal Mining Services
N.A.I.C.S.: 212114

Half-Tide Marine Pty Ltd   (1)
Martin Armstrong Dr, Mackay, 4740, QLD,
Australia
Tel.: (61) 749438444
Coal Ore Mining
N.A.I.C.S.: 212114

Independence Material Handling,
LLC   (1)
701 Market St Ste 840, Saint Louis, MO
63101-1826
Tel.: (314) 342-3400
Coal Mining Services
N.A.I.C.S.: 213113

Lee Ranch Coal Company   (1)
35 Miles N Milan, Grants, NM 87020-0757
Tel.: (505) 285-4651
Sales Range: $150-199.9 Million
Emp.: 250
Bituminous Coal & Lignite Mining Services
N.A.I.C.S.: 212114

Midco Supply and Equipment
Corporation   (1)
1141 N 11th St, Omaha, NE 68102
Tel.: (402) 345-6600
Coal Mining Services
N.A.I.C.S.: 213113

Middlemount Coal Pty Ltd   (1)
Level 4 100 Melbourne Street, Brisbane,
4000, QLD, Australia
Tel.: (61) 731792000
Web Site:
    http://www.middlemountcoal.com.au
Coal Mining Services
N.A.I.C.S.: 213113

Mount Thorley Coal Loading Pty
Ltd.   (1)
81 Mount Thorley Rd, Mount Thorley, 2330,
NSW, Australia
Tel.: (61) 2 6574 6553
Coal Mining Services
N.A.I.C.S.: 212114

Pacific Export Resources, LLC   (1)
701 Market St Ste 880, Saint Louis, MO
63101
Tel.: (314) 342-3406

Coal Mining Services
N.A.I.C.S.: 213113

Peabody (Bowen) Pty Ltd.   (1)
100 Melbourne Street, Brisbane, 4101,
QLD, Australia
Tel.: (61) 73 239 7650
Web Site: https://www.peabodyenergy.com
Emp.: 100
Coal Mine Operator
N.A.I.C.S.: 212115

Peabody (Wilkie Creek) Pty Ltd. (1)
100 Melbourne Street, Brisbane, 4101,
QLD, Australia
Tel.: (61) 732255500
Coal Mining Services
N.A.I.C.S.: 212114

Peabody Australia Holdco Pty
Ltd.   (1)
Peabody Building 100 Melbourne Street,
Brisbane, 4101, QLD, Australia
Tel.: (61) 732255500
Coal Mining Services
N.A.I.C.S.: 213113

Peabody COALTRADE Asia Private
Ltd.   (1)
1 Temasek Avenue Ste 21-03 Millenia
Tower 1, Singapore, 039192, Singapore
Tel.: (65) 66035900
Web Site: http://www.peabodyenergy.com
Coal Mining Services
N.A.I.C.S.: 212114

Peabody Capricorn Pty Ltd   (1)
L14 Bank Of Qld Bldg 259 Queen St, Bris-
bane, 4001, QLD, Australia
Tel.: (61) 732397232
Coal Mining Services
N.A.I.C.S.: 213113

Peabody Coaltrade GmbH   (1)
Ruhrallee 185, 45136, Essen, Germany
Tel.: (49) 2018945135
Coal Mining Services
N.A.I.C.S.: 213113

Peabody Coaltrade, LLC   (1)
Peabody Plaza 701 Market St Ste 860,
Saint Louis, MO 63101-1826
Tel.: (314) 342-3400
Web Site: http://www.peabodyenergy.com
Rev.: $90,000
Emp.: 300
Coal Mining & Marketing Services
N.A.I.C.S.: 423520

Peabody Development Company,
LLC   (1)
701 Market St, Saint Louis, MO 63101
Tel.: (314) 342-3400
Web Site: http://www.peabodyenergy.com
Sales Range: $10-24.9 Million
Emp.: 2
Coal Property Management Services
N.A.I.C.S.: 212115

Peabody Energy Australia Coal Pty
Ltd   (1)
Peabody Building 100 Melbourne Street,
Brisbane, 4101, QLD, Australia
Tel.: (61) 73 225 5500
Web Site: http://www.peabodyenergy.com
Sales Range: $1-4.9 Billion
Emp.: 7,400
Coal Producer & Manufacturer
N.A.I.C.S.: 324199

Peabody Energy Australia PCI
Limited   (1)
100 Melbourne Street, Brisbane, 4101,
QLD, Australia
Tel.: (61) 732217210
Emp.: 903
Coal Mining Services
N.A.I.C.S.: 212115
Julian D. Thornton (CEO)

Subsidiary (Domestic):

Moorvale Coal Pty Ltd   (2)
Peak Downs Highway, PO Box 193, Nebo,
4742, Queensland, Australia   (73%)
Tel.: (61) 7 4958 0250
Web Site: http://www.peabodyenergy.com
Coal Mining Services
N.A.I.C.S.: 212114

Peabody Coppabella Pty Ltd   (2)

Peak Downs Highway, Nebo, 4742, QLD,
Australia   (73%)
Tel.: (61) 74 958 0206
Web Site: http://www.peabodyenergy.com
Coal Mining Services
N.A.I.C.S.: 212114

Peabody Energy Midwest Group   (1)
7100 Eagle Crest Blvd, Evansville, IN
47715
Tel.: (812) 434-8500
Web Site: http://www.peabodyenergy.com
Rev.: $72,000,000
Emp.: 90
Coal Mining, Processing & Sales
N.A.I.C.S.: 212114

Peabody Holding Company Inc.   (1)
701 Market St Ste 900, Saint Louis, MO
63101-1826
Tel.: (314) 342-3400
Web Site: http://www.peabodyenergy.com
Sales Range: $100-124.9 Million
Emp.: 260
Holding Company
N.A.I.C.S.: 551112

Peabody Investment & Development
Business Services Beijing Co.
Ltd.   (1)
Suite 1537 Beijing Yintai Center Level 15
Tower C 2, Jianguomenwai Avenue Chaoy-
ang District, Beijing, 100022, China
Tel.: (86) 1065637898
Coal Mining Services
N.A.I.C.S.: 213114

Peabody Midwest Mining, LLC   (1)
3066 S 900 E, Cannelburg, IN 47519
Tel.: (812) 644-7323
Sales Range: $75-99.9 Million
Emp.: 100
Coal Mining Services
N.A.I.C.S.: 212114
Matt Ubeelhor (Mgr)

Peabody-Winsway Resources
BV   (1)
Johan V Oldenbarneveltln 9d, Hague, Neth-
erlands
Tel.: (31) 703229067
Bituminous Coal/Lignite Surface Mining
N.A.I.C.S.: 212114

Powder River Coal, LLC   (1)
1013 E Boxelder Rd, Gillette, WY 82718
Tel.: (307) 687-3900
Sales Range: $1-9.9 Million
Emp.: 60
Coal Mining & Processing
N.A.I.C.S.: 213113

RFC Corporate Finance, Inc.   (1)
Level 12, Gateway Macquarie Place, Syd-
ney, 2000, Australia
Tel.: (61) 292500000
Web Site: http://www.rfcambrian.com
Emp.: 13
Bituminous Coal Lignite Surface Mining
Services
N.A.I.C.S.: 212114

Riverview Terminal Company   (1)
17412 Us Route 23, Catlettsburg, KY 41129
Tel.: (606) 931-0300
Bituminous Coal Mining Services
N.A.I.C.S.: 212114

United Minerals Company, LLC   (1)
409 N Van Buren St, Huntingburg, IN
47542-1404
Tel.: (812) 683-4644
Coke Mfr
N.A.I.C.S.: 212114

Wambo Coal Terminal Pty Ltd   (1)
L 13 259 Queen St, Brisbane, 4000, Qld,
Australia
Tel.: (61) 265702200
Coal Mining Services
N.A.I.C.S.: 212114

PEAPACK-GLADSTONE FI-
NANCIAL CORPORATION
468 RT 206, Bedminster, NJ 07921
Tel.: (908) 234-0700   NJ
Web Site: https://www.pgbank.com
Year Founded: 1921

PGC—(NASDAQ)
Rev.: $211,875,000
Assets: $6,353,593,000
Liabilities: $5,820,613,000
Net Worth: $532,980,000
Earnings: $74,246,000
Emp.: 498
Fiscal Year-end: 12/31/22
Bank Holding Company
N.A.I.C.S.: 551111
Frank A. Cavallaro (CFO & Sr Exec
VP)
Douglas L. Kennedy (Pres & CEO)
Maureen E. Hemhauser (Chief Risk
Officer, Officer & Exec VP-Peapack-
Gladstone Bank & Head-Compliance)
Jeffrey J. Carfora (Sr Exec VP)
F. Duffield Meyercord (Chm)
Robert A. Plante (COO & Exec VP)
Gregory Martin Smith (Pres)
Lisa Chalkan (Chief Credit Officer)
Brydget Falk-Drigan (Chief HR Offi-
cer)
Thomas J. Ross Jr. (Pres)
Stuart Vorcheimer (Exec VP & Head-
Commercial & Industrial Lending)
Kevin Runyon (CIO, Chief Digital Offi-
cer & Exec VP)
Kate Sant'Angelo (Sr VP & Dir-
Personal Banking)

Subsidiaries:

Lassus Wherley & Associates,
P.C.   (1)
1 Academy St, New Providence, NJ 07974-
1842
Tel.: (908) 464-0102
Offices of Certified Public Accountants
N.A.I.C.S.: 541211

Murphy Capital Management Inc.   (1)
268 Main St, Gladstone, NJ 07934
Tel.: (908) 719-6430
Web Site: http://www.peapackprivate.com
Sales Range: $1-9.9 Million
Portfolio Management
N.A.I.C.S.: 523940

PGB Trust and Investments of
Delaware   (1)
Montchanin Corporate Ctr 20 Montchanin
Rd Ste 210, Greenville, DE 19807
Tel.: (302) 255-1506
Web Site: http://www.pgbank.com
Emp.: 2
Investment Management Service
N.A.I.C.S.: 523940
Lisa K. Berry (Mng Dir)

Peapack-Gladstone Bank   (1)
190 Main St, Gladstone, NJ 07934 (100%)
Tel.: (908) 234-0700
Web Site: https://www.pgbank.com
Sales Range: $150-199.9 Million
Emp.: 300
Banking Services
N.A.I.C.S.: 522110
Frank A. Cavallaro (CFO & Sr Exec VP)
Vincent A. Spero (Exec VP & Head-Comml
Real Estate)
Douglas L. Kennedy (Pres & CEO)
Birgitta Natale (Sr VP & Dir-Residential &
Consumer Lending)
Jeffrey J. Carfora (Sr Exec VP)
Rosanne Schwab (VP-PR & Comm Mgr)
John P. Babcock (Sr Exec VP)
Kevin Runyon (CIO, Chief Digital Officer &
Exec VP)
Robert A. Plante (COO & Exec VP)
Brydget Falk-Drigan (Chief HR Officer &
Exec VP)
Eric H. Waser (Exec VP & Head-Investment
Banking)
Gregory M. Smith (Exec VP & Head-Comml
Banking)
Rick DeBel (Chief Retail & Deposit Solu-
tions Officer & Exec VP)
Matthew Remo (Sr VP & Dir-Strategy &
Dev)

PEAR THERAPEUTICS, INC.
195 Church St 15th Fl, New Haven,
CT 06510

Pear Therapeutics, Inc.—(Continued)

Tel.: (203) 680-8543   DE
Year Founded: 2020
PEAR—(NASDAQ)
Rev.: $12,694,000
Assets: $95,129,000
Liabilities: $64,544,000
Net Worth: $30,585,000
Earnings: ($75,491,000)
Emp.: 200
Fiscal Year-end: 12/31/22
Investment Services
N.A.I.C.S.: 523999
Ellen E. Snow *(Chief Acctg Officer)*
Elon S. Boms *(Chm & CEO)*
Steven J. Benson *(COO)*

**PEARL HOLDINGS ACQUISI-
TION CORP.**
767 3rd Ave 11th Fl, New York, NY
10017
Tel.: (212) 457-1540   Ky
Web Site: https://www.pearlhac.com
Year Founded: 2021
PRLH—(NASDAQ)
Rev.: $2,887,145
Assets: $207,466,287
Liabilities: $214,114,263
Net Worth: ($6,647,976)
Earnings: $2,040,450
Emp.: 3
Fiscal Year-end: 12/31/22
Investment Services
N.A.I.C.S.: 523999
Craig E. Barnett *(CEO & Chm)*
Terry Duddy *(Vice Chm)*
Martin F. Lewis *(Mng Dir & CFO)*
Scott M. Napolitano *(Mng Dir)*

**PEBBLEBROOK HOTEL
TRUST**
4747 Bethesda Ave Ste 1100,
Bethesda, MD 20814
Tel.: (240) 507-1300   MD
Web Site:
   https://www.pebblebrookhotels.com
Year Founded: 2009
PEB—(NYSE)
Rev.: $1,391,891,000
Assets: $6,133,540,000
Liabilities: $3,048,997,000
Net Worth: $3,084,543,000
Earnings: ($87,171,000)
Emp.: 58
Fiscal Year-end: 12/31/22
Hospitality Real Estate Investment
Trust
N.A.I.C.S.: 525990
Jon E. Bortz *(Founder, Chm, Pres &
CEO)*
Raymond D. Martz *(CFO, Treas, Sec
& Exec VP)*

Subsidiaries:

Buckeyes Hotel Owner LP   **(1)**
2 Bethesda Metro Ctr, Bethesda, MD 20814
Tel.: (240) 507-1300
Real Estate Investment Services
N.A.I.C.S.: 531210

CHRC LLC   **(1)**
4710 E Falcon Dr Ste 125, Mesa, AZ 85215
Tel.: (480) 654-4606
Web Site: http://www.chrc4work.com
Staffing & Recruiting Services
N.A.I.C.S.: 561311

Golden Eagles Lessee LLC   **(1)**
422 SW Broadway, Portland, OR 97205
Tel.: (503) 412-6304
Hotel & Motel Management Services
N.A.I.C.S.: 561110

Hazel Lessee LLC   **(1)**
9891 Gulf Shore Dr, Naples, FL 34108
Tel.: (239) 597-3123
Web Site: https://www.laplayaresort.com
Hotel & Resort Operator
N.A.I.C.S.: 721120

Hoyas Lessee LLC   **(1)**
55 5th St, San Francisco, CA 94103
Tel.: (415) 543-8555
Hotel & Motel Management Services
N.A.I.C.S.: 561110

LaSalle Hotel Properties   **(1)**
7550 Wisconsin Ave 10th Fl, Bethesda, MD
20814
Tel.: (301) 941-1500
Web Site: http://www.lasallehotels.com
Rev.: $1,104,815,000
Assets: $3,814,941,000
Liabilities: $1,338,480,000
Net Worth: $2,476,461,000
Earnings: $195,034,000
Emp.: 36
Fiscal Year-end: 12/31/2017
Real Estate Investment Trust; Owner & Op-
erator of Hotel Properties
N.A.I.C.S.: 525990
Jon E. Bortz *(Founder)*
Michael D. Barnello *(Pres & CEO)*

Subsidiary (Domestic):

DC Six Lessee, L.L.C.   **(2)**
15 E St NW, Washington, DC 20001
Tel.: (202) 347-4200
Web Site: https://www.hotelgeorge.com
Hotel
N.A.I.C.S.: 721110

Dim Sum Lessee, Inc.   **(2)**
342 Grant Ave, San Francisco, CA 94108
Tel.: (415) 394-0500
Web Site: http://www.hoteltriton.com
Restaurant Operating Services
N.A.I.C.S.: 722511

Don't Look Back Lessee, LLC   **(2)**
215 Charles St, Boston, MA 02114
Tel.: (617) 224-4000
Web Site: http://www.libertyhotel.com
Restaurant & Lodging Services
N.A.I.C.S.: 721110
Nicole Gagnon *(Mgr-Public Relations-
Marketing)*

Hotel Rouge   **(2)**
1315 16th St NW, Washington, DC 20036-
2205
Tel.: (202) 232-8000
Web Site: http://www.rougehotel.com
Sales Range: $1-9.9 Million
Hotel
N.A.I.C.S.: 721110
Mike Defrino *(CEO)*
Kathleen Reidenbach *(Chief Comml Officer)*
Allison Reid *(Chief Dev Officer)*
Scott Gingerich *(Sr VP)*
Ben Timashenka *(VP-East)*
Danny Bortnick *(VP)*
Maria Streeby *(VP)*
Josh Mayo *(VP-West)*
Anthony Barone *(VP)*
Ginny Too *(Sr VP-People)*
Tiffany Cooper *(Sr VP-Development-West)*
Charlotte Dehaven *(VP-Development)*
Hari Jun *(Dir-Development-West)*
David Ruger *(Sr Dir-Development-West)*
Roger Doyle *(Sr VP-Finance)*
Sandy Babbitt *(Sr Dir)*
Ave Bradley *(Creative Dir & Sr VP)*
Telesa Via *(VP-Sales)*
Suzanne Halperin *(VP)*
Connor Smith *(VP-Marketing)*
Sarita Mallinger *(Sr Dir-Media)*
Nathan Bacher *(VP-Distribution)*
Nina Beizai *(VP-Communications-Content)*
Melinda Stier *(Gen Counsel & Sr VP)*

LHO Alexis Lessee, L.L.C.   **(2)**
1007 1st Ave, Seattle, WA 98104
Tel.: (206) 624-4844
Web Site: http://www.alexishotel.com
Hotels & Motels Services
N.A.I.C.S.: 721110

LHO Viking Hotel, L.L.C.   **(2)**
1 Bellevue Ave, Newport, RI 02840
Tel.: (401) 847-3300
Web Site: http://www.hotelviking.com
Hotels & Motels Services
N.A.I.C.S.: 721110

LHOberge Lessee, Inc.   **(2)**
1540 Camino Del Mar, Del Mar, CA 92014
Tel.: (858) 386-1336
Web Site: https://www.laubergedelmar.com

Restaurant Operating Services
N.A.I.C.S.: 722511

LaSalle Washington One Lessee,
Inc.   **(2)**
1733 N St, Washington, DC 20036-2801
Tel.: (202) 393-3000
Web Site: http://www.topazhotel.com
Hotels & Motels Services
N.A.I.C.S.: 721110

Unit (Domestic):

Park Central Hotel San
Francisco   **(2)**
50 3rd St, San Francisco, CA 94103
Tel.: (415) 974-6400
Web Site: http://www.parkcentralsf.com
Sales Range: $10-24.9 Million
Luxury Hotel Operator
N.A.I.C.S.: 721110

Subsidiary (Domestic):

Park Sunset, LLC   **(2)**
8462 W Sunset Blvd, West Hollywood, CA
90069-1912
Tel.: (323) 654-4600
Web Site: http://www.graftononsunset.com
Restaurant & Lodging Services
N.A.I.C.S.: 721110

Silver P Lessee, LLC   **(2)**
2121 P St NW, Washington, DC 20037
Tel.: (202) 448-1800
Web Site: http://www.hotelpalomar-dc.com
Restaurant Operating Services
N.A.I.C.S.: 722511

Sunset City, LLC   **(2)**
7073 W Sunset Blvd, Los Angeles, CA
90028-7509
Tel.: (818) 762-7000
Restaurant Operating Services
N.A.I.C.S.: 722511

Unit (Domestic):

Topaz Hotel   **(2)**
1733 N St NW, Washington, DC 20036-
2801
Tel.: (202) 393-3000
Web Site: http://www.topazhotel.com
Sales Range: $25-49.9 Million
Hotel
N.A.I.C.S.: 722511

PEDEVCO CORP.
575 N Dairy Ashford Energy Ctr II Ste
210, Houston, TX 77079
Tel.: (713) 221-1768   TX
Web Site: https://www.pedevco.com
Year Founded: 2000
PED—(NYSEAMEX)
Rev.: $30,034,000
Assets: $116,110,000
Liabilities: $19,651,000
Net Worth: $96,459,000
Earnings: $2,844,000
Emp.: 14
Fiscal Year-end: 12/31/22
Crude Petroleum Extraction Services
N.A.I.C.S.: 211120
Simon Kukes *(CEO)*
Frank C. Ingriselli *(Founder)*
Clark R. Moore *(Gen Counsel & Exec
VP)*
John J. Scelfo *(Chm)*
John Douglas Schick *(Pres)*

PEDRO'S LIST, INC.
11700 W Charleston Blvd Ste 170-
174, Las Vegas, NV 89135
Tel.: (702) 985-7544   NV
Year Founded: 2014
PDRO—(OTCIQ)
Assets: $23,518
Liabilities: $369,805
Net Worth: ($346,287)
Earnings: ($882,360)
Emp.: 1
Fiscal Year-end: 10/31/22
Investment Holding Company
N.A.I.C.S.: 551112

**PEGASUS PHARMACEUTI-
CALS, INC.**
4440 PGA Blvd Ste 308, Palm Beach
Gardens, FL 33410
Tel.: (561) 626-9901
PGUZ—(OTCIQ)
Pharmaceuticals Product Mfr
N.A.I.C.S.: 325412
Daniel P. Kesonen *(Chm & CEO)*

PEGASYSTEMS INC.
1 Main St, Cambridge, MA 02142
Tel.: (617) 374-9600   MA
Web Site: https://www.pega.com
PEGA—(NASDAQ)
Rev.: $1,432,616,000
Assets: $1,510,736,000
Liabilities: $1,156,898,000
Net Worth: $353,838,000
Earnings: $67,808,000
Emp.: 5,406
Fiscal Year-end: 12/31/23
Business Process Management Soft-
ware Solutions
N.A.I.C.S.: 513210
Christian Guttmann *(VP-Engrg, Deci-
sioning & AI)*
Katherine Parente *(Chief HR Officer)*
Judy Buchholz *(Sr VP)*
Don Schuerman *(CTO)*
Lisa Pintchman *(VP)*
Matt Cushing *(Chief Comml Officer)*
Frank Guerrera *(Chief Technical Sys
Officer)*
Paula Milton *(VP)*
Mary Tafuri *(VP)*
Deepak Visweswaraiah *(VP)*
Alan Trefler *(Founder, Chm & CEO)*

Subsidiaries:

Antenna Dexterra Asia Pacific PTY
Ltd.   **(1)**
93 Maltravers Road Ivanhoe East, Mel-
bourne, 3079, VIC, Australia
Tel.: (61) 413716444
Emp.: 10
Investment Management Service
N.A.I.C.S.: 523940

Antenna Software, LLC   **(1)**
111 Town Square Pl, Jersey City, NJ 07310
Tel.: (201) 239-2300
Mobile Application Development Services
N.A.I.C.S.: 513210
Jim Somers *(Chief Mktg & Strategy Officer)*
John Gannon *(Gen Partner)*
Bill H. Smith *(CFO)*
Ken Nicolson *(Exec VP-Global Sls & Bus
Dev)*

Openspan, Inc.   **(1)**
11175 Cicero Dr Ste 200, Alpharetta, GA
30022
Tel.: (678) 527-5400
Web Site: http://www.openspan.com
Rev.: $7,000,000
Emp.: 100
Intelligence Solutions for Better Customer
Engagement
N.A.I.C.S.: 513210
Francis Carden *(Founder)*

Pega Japan K.K.   **(1)**
Hirakawacho 1-1-1 Hirakawacho Court
Floor 9, Chiyoda-ku, Tokyo, 102-0093, Ja-
pan
Tel.: (81) 332212455
Software Development Services
N.A.I.C.S.: 513210
Nobuhiko Watanabe *(Pres & Mng Dir)*

Pegasystems AG   **(1)**
The Circle 6 Zurich Airport, 8058, Zurich,
Switzerland
Tel.: (41) 432100600
Business Process Management Software
Solutions
N.A.I.C.S.: 513210

Pegasystems B.V.   **(1)**
Atrium-Tower 1 Centre Building- 10th Floor
Strawinskylaan, Claude Debussylaan 20b,
1077 ZX, Amsterdam, Netherlands

Tel.: (31) 8000228968
Business Process Management Software
Solutions
N.A.I.C.S.: 513210

**Pegasystems Bilgi Teknolojileri
Anonim Sirketi** (1)
Palmiye Cad B39A No 20 Goksu Evleri An-
adolu, Hisari Beykoz, 34815, Istanbul, Tur-
kiye
Tel.: (90) 2164658600
Software Publishing Services
N.A.I.C.S.: 513210

Pegasystems Canada Inc. (1)
The Exchange Tower 130 King Street West
Suite 1800, Toronto, M5X 1E3, ON, Canada
Tel.: (416) 860-6233
Emp.: 5
Business Process Management Software
Solutions
N.A.I.C.S.: 513210

Pegasystems France, S.A.R.L. (1)
Centre d'Affaires Paris Trocadero 112 Av-
enue Kleber, 75116, Paris, France
Tel.: (33) 800904881
Business Process Management Software
Solutions
N.A.I.C.S.: 513210

Pegasystems GmbH (1)
Web Site: https://www.pega.com
Business Process Management Software
Solutions
N.A.I.C.S.: 513210
Walter Koehler (VP)
Carsten Rust (Sr Dir)
Harald Esch (Mng Dir & VP-Sales)
Ileana Honigblum (VP-Sales)

Pegasystems Japan K.K. (1)
Hirakawacho Court 8F 1 1 1 Hirakawacho,
Chiyoda ku, Tokyo, 102-0093, Japan
Tel.: (81) 3 3221 2455
Business Process Management Software
Solutions
N.A.I.C.S.: 513210

Pegasystems Limited (1)
3rd Floor 23 Forbury Road, Reading, RG1
3JH, Berkshire, United Kingdom (100%)
Tel.: (44) 8000148123
Sales Range: $50-74.9 Million
Emp.: 120
Business Process Management Software
Solutions
N.A.I.C.S.: 513210

Pegasystems Private Limited (1)
32-04 Millenia Tower One Temasek Avenue,
Singapore, 039192, Singapore
Tel.: (65) 8008523032
Business Process Management Software
Solutions
N.A.I.C.S.: 513210

Pegasystems Proprietary Limited (1)
Level 16 1 Margaret Street, Sydney, 2000,
NSW, Australia
Tel.: (61) 800763425
Business Process Management Software
Solutions
N.A.I.C.S.: 513210
Scott Leader (Exec Dir-Australia & New
Zealand)
Nick Vince (Dir-Alliances & Channels-
Australia & New Zealand)

Pegasystems Sp. Zoo (1)
Ilzecka 26, Warsaw, 02-135, Poland
Tel.: (48) 225 757 211
Business Process Management Software
Solutions
N.A.I.C.S.: 513210

Pegasystems Spain, S.L. (1)
C/ Jose Abascal 41 5th floor office 502,
28003, Madrid, Spain
Tel.: (34) 900998422
Business Process Management Software
Solutions
N.A.I.C.S.: 513210
Mariano Garrigues (Dir-Sls)

Pegasystems Thailand Limited (1)
Office 504 Bangkok Gaysorn Plaza No 999
Gaysorn Shopping Centre, 5th Floor Unit
5B-1 Ploenchit Road Lumpini Patumwan,
Bangkok, 10330, Thailand
Tel.: (66) 26240570

Software Publishing Services
N.A.I.C.S.: 513210

Pegasystems Worldwide Inc. (1)
1 Main St, Cambridge, MA 02142-1590
Tel.: (617) 374-9600
Web Site: https://www.pega.com
Business Management Software Provider
N.A.I.C.S.: 513210

**Pegasystems Worldwide India Private
Limited** (1)
3rd Floor Block 2 DLF Cyber City Gachi-
bowli, Hyderabad, 500 032, India
Tel.: (91) 40 3055 5600
Business Process Management Software
Solutions
N.A.I.C.S.: 513210

PEI WORLDWIDE HOLDINGS, INC.
101 E Park Blvd Ste 879, Plano, TX
75074
Tel.: (254) 214-5523
PEIW—(OTCIQ)
Building Materials Mfr
N.A.I.C.S.: 327120
Gifford Ludwigsen (Pres & CEO)

PEKIN LIFE INSURANCE CO
2505 Ct St, Pekin, IL 61558-0001
Web Site:
https://www.pekininsurance.com
Year Founded: 1921
PKIN—(OTCIQ)
Direct Life Insurance Carriers
N.A.I.C.S.: 524113
Neil Kaderabek (CIO)

PELOTON INTERACTIVE, INC.
441 9th Ave 6th Fl, New York, NY
10001
Tel.: (917) 671-9198 DE
Web Site:
https://www.onepeloton.com
Year Founded: 2012
PTON—(NASDAQ)
Rev.: $2,700,500,000
Assets: $2,185,200,000
Liabilities: $2,704,300,000
Net Worth: ($519,100,000)
Earnings: ($551,900,000)
Emp.: 2,257
Fiscal Year-end: 06/30/24
Exercise Equipment Designer & Mfr
N.A.I.C.S.: 339920
Tom Cortese (Co-Founder)
John Foley (Co-Founder)
Hisao Kushi (Co-Founder)
Tammy Albarran (Chief Legal Officer
& Sec)
Barry McCarthy (Pres & CEO)
Kevin Cornils (Chief Comml Officer)
Tom Cortese (Co-Founder & Chief
Product Officer)
Yony Feng (Co-Founder & CTO)
Allen Klingsick (Chief Acctg Officer)
Jennifer Cotter (Chief Content Offi-
cer)
Gwen Riley (Sr VP-Music)
Shari Eaton (Sr VP & Head-People-
Global)
Elizabeth Coddington (CFO)
Ben Boyd (Sr VP-Global Comm)
Mariana Garavaglia (COO)
Nick Caldwell (Chief Product Officer)
Peter Stern (Pres & CEO)

Subsidiaries:

Precor, Inc. (1)
20031 142nd Ave NE, Woodinville, WA
98072-4002 (100%)
Tel.: (425) 486-9292
Web Site: http://www.precor.com
Sales Range: $100-124.9 Million
Emp.: 400
Mfr of Exercise Equipment
N.A.I.C.S.: 339920
Rob Barker (Pres)

PENDRELL CORPORATION
2300 Carillon Point, Kirkland, WA
98033
Tel.: (425) 278-7100 WA
Web Site: https://www.pendrell.com
Year Founded: 2000
PCOA—(OTCIQ)
Sales Range: $25-49.9 Million
Emp.: 12
intellectual Property Asset Manage-
ment Services
N.A.I.C.S.: 541618
James Baker (VP-Licensing & Strate-
gic Dev)
Lee E. Mikles (Pres & CEO)
Steven A. Ednie (CFO & VP)

Subsidiaries:

ContentGuard, Inc. (1)
6900 Dallas Pkwy Ste 850, Plano, TX
75024
Tel.: (469) 331-9030
Web Site: http://www.contentguard.com
Software Development Services
N.A.I.C.S.: 541511

**Helsinki Memory Technologies
Oy** (1)
Hermiankatu 6-8D, 33720, Tampere, Fin-
land
Tel.: (358) 505827119
Web Site:
http://www.helsinkimemorytech.com
Memory Technology Research & Develop-
ment Services
N.A.I.C.S.: 541715
Kimmo Mylly (Mng Dir)

Ovidian Group LLC (1)
2030 Addison St Ste 640, Berkeley, CA
94704
Tel.: (510) 665-4305
Web Site: http://www.ovidian.com
Intellectual Property Solutions
N.A.I.C.S.: 541618
Steven Horowitz (Founder & Principal)

PENGUIN SOLUTIONS, INC.
1390 McCarthy Blvd, Milpitas, CA
95035
Tel.: (510) 623-1231 Ky
Web Site:
https://www.penguinsolutions.com
Year Founded: 1988
SGH—(NASDAQ)
Rev.: $1,170,796,000
Assets: $1,474,506,000
Liabilities: $1,075,298,000
Net Worth: $399,208,000
Earnings: ($41,785,000)
Emp.: 2,700
Fiscal Year-end: 08/30/24
Semiconductor & Related Device Mfr
& Distr
N.A.I.C.S.: 334413
Pete Manca (Pres-Intelligent Platform
Solutions)
Mark W. Adams (Pres & CEO)
Penelope A. Herscher (Chm)
Michael Wellman (Chief HR Officer)
Jack A. Pacheco (COO & Pres-
Memory Solutions)
Anne Kuykendall (Chief Legal Officer,
Gen Counsel, Sr VP & VP)
Joe Clark (Pres-LED Solutions)
Phil Pokorny (CTO)
Mark Seamans (VP-Global Mktg)
Nathan Olmstead (CFO & Sr VP)

Subsidiaries:

**Artesyn Embedded Computing,
Inc.** (1)
2900 S Diablo Way Ste 190, Tempe, AZ
85282
Tel.: (602) 438-5720
Web Site: http://www.artesyn.com
Sales Range: $100-124.9 Million
Emp.: 244
Designer, Mfr & Distr of Embedded Power
& Computing Products, Systems & Solu-
tions

N.A.I.C.S.: 334419
Stephen Dow (Pres)
Eric Gauthier (VP-Strategic Alliances &
Partnerships)
Todd Wynia (VP-Plng & Dev)

Penguin Computing Inc. (1)
45800 Northport Loop W, Fremont, CA
94538
Tel.: (415) 954-2800
Web Site:
http://www.penguincomputing.com
Computer Integrated Systems Design
N.A.I.C.S.: 541512
Kylee Stephens (Dir-Mktg)

**SMART Modular Technologies Sdn.
Bhd.** (1)
Plot 18 Lorong Jelawat 4, Kawasan Perin-
dustrian Seberang Jaya, 13700, Perai, Pen-
ang, Malaysia
Tel.: (60) 43880000
Software Development Services
N.A.I.C.S.: 541511

**SMART Modular Technologies,
Inc.** (1)
39870 Eureka Dr, Newark, CA 94560
Tel.: (510) 623-1231
Memory Module Mfr
N.A.I.C.S.: 334413
Ajay B. Shah (Founder)
Jack A. Pacheco (Pres)

SMART Worldwide Holdings, Inc. (1)
39870 Eureka Dr, Newark, CA 94560
Tel.: (510) 623-1231
Web Site: http://www.smartm.com
Sales Range: $700-749.9 Million
Holding Company; Memory Modules, Em-
bedded Computing Subsystems & Thin Film
Transistor Products Mfr
N.A.I.C.S.: 551112
Lionel Fernandez (Mgr-Mktg Comm)
Michael Rubino (VP-Worldwide Engrg)
Alan Marten (Chief Strategy Officer & Sr
VP)
KiWan Kim (Pres-SMART Brazil & Sr VP-
Emerging Markets)
Frank Perezalonso (VP-Bus Dev-Memory
Bus Unit)
Anjali Reddy (VP-Worldwide Matls)

**Stratus Technologies Ireland
Limited** (1)
Unit 275 Blanchardstown Corporate Park 2
Ballycoolin, Dublin, D15 TD61, Ireland
Tel.: (353) 18976000
Computer Software Development Services
N.A.I.C.S.: 541511

Stratus Technologies, Inc. (1)
5 Mill & Main Place Ste 500, Maynard, MA
01754-3409
Tel.: (978) 461-7000
Web Site: http://www.stratus.com
Sales Range: $250-299.9 Million
Emp.: 200
Computer Systems Mfr; Computer System
Design & Support Services
N.A.I.C.S.: 334111
David C. Laurello (Chm)
Delfi L. Nieto (VP-HR)
David Harrington (Officer-Corp Quality &
VP-Supply Chain)
Jim Robichaud (VP-Sls Ops)
Bob Kellegrew (Gen Counsel & VP)
Dara Ambrose (VP-Engrg)
Jason Andersen (VP-Bus Line Mgmt)
Eric-Jan Schmidt (VP-Global & Corp Mktg)
Duncan Cooke (Mgr-Bus Dev-UK & Europe)
John Vicente (CTO)
Walter Loh (CFO)

PENN BANCSHARES, INC.
170 S Broadway, Pennsville, NJ
08070
Tel.: (856) 678-6006 NJ
Web Site:
https://www.pennsvillenb.com
PEBA—(OTCIQ)
Banking Holding Company
N.A.I.C.S.: 522110
William Masten (Pres)

PENN ENTERTAINMENT, INC.

PENN Entertainment, Inc.—(Continued)

825 Berkshire Blvd Ste 200, Wyomissing, PA 19610
Tel.: (610) 373-2400   **PA**
Web Site:
https://www.pennentertainment.com
Year Founded: 1972
PENN—(NASDAQ)
Rev.: $6,362,900,000
Assets: $16,064,200,000
Liabilities: $12,864,600,000
Net Worth: $3,199,600,000
Earnings: $490,000,000
Emp.: 23,333
Fiscal Year-end: 12/31/23
Horse Racing & Casino Facilties
Owner & Operator
N.A.I.C.S.: 713290
Todd George *(Exec VP-Ops)*
D. Eric Schippers *(Sr VP-Pub Affairs)*
Richard Primus *(CIO & Sr VP)*
Jennifer Weissman *(CMO & Sr VP)*
Rafael Verde *(Sr VP-Reg Ops)*
Erin Chamberlin *(Sr VP-Reg Ops)*
Aaron Rosenthal *(Sr VP-Reg Ops)*
Harper H. Ko *(Chief Legal Officer, Sec & Exec VP)*
Felicia Hendrix *(CFO, Principal Acctg Officer & Exec VP)*
Justin Carter *(Sr VP-Reg Ops)*
Wendy Hamilton *(Chief HR Officer & Sr VP)*
Jay A. Snowden *(Pres & CEO)*

Subsidiaries:

Alton Casino, LLC   **(1)**
1 Piasa St, Alton, IL 62002
Tel.: (618) 474-7500
Web Site: https://www.argosyalton.com
Sales Range: $200-249.9 Million
Emp.: 350
Casino
N.A.I.C.S.: 713210

BTN, LLC   **(1)**
676 Bayview Ave, Biloxi, MS 39530
Tel.: (228) 435-7000
Web Site: https://www.boomtownbiloxi.com
Sales Range: $250-299.9 Million
Emp.: 980
Gaming Casino
N.A.I.C.S.: 713210

Belle of Sioux City, L.P.   **(1)**
100 Larsen Park Rd, Sioux City, IA 51102
Tel.: (712) 294-5600
Web Site: http://www.argosysiouxcity.com
Sales Range: $50-74.9 Million
Emp.: 380
Casinos Services
N.A.I.C.S.: 713210

Bossier Casino Venture, LLC   **(1)**
777 Margaritaville Way, Bossier City, LA 71111
Tel.: (318) 698-7177
Web Site:
http://www.margaritavillebossiercity.com
Casino & Hotel Services
N.A.I.C.S.: 721120

Central Ohio Gaming Ventures, LLC   **(1)**
200 Georgesville Rd, Columbus, OH 43228
Tel.: (614) 308-3333
Web Site:
https://www.hollywoodcolumbus.com
Casino Operator
N.A.I.C.S.: 713210

Danville Development, LLC   **(1)**
7351 S Union Park Ave Ste 250, Midvale, UT 84047
Tel.: (801) 316-1107
Web Site:
https://www.danvilledevelopment.com
Property Development Services
N.A.I.C.S.: 531390
Layla Misrasi *(Mgr-Acctg)*

Freehold Raceway Off Track LLC   **(1)**
130 Park Ave, Freehold, NJ 07728
Tel.: (732) 462-3800

Web Site: https://www.freeholdraceway.com
Casino & Hotel Operator
N.A.I.C.S.: 721120

Greektown Casino Hotel   **(1)**
555 E Lafayette Blvd, Detroit, MI 48226
Tel.: (313) 223-2999
Web Site:
http://www.greektowncasinohotel.com
Casino Hotels
N.A.I.C.S.: 721120

HC Aurora, LLC   **(1)**
1 W New York St Bridge, Aurora, IL 60506
Tel.: (630) 801-1234
Web Site:
https://www.hollywoodcasinoaurora.com
Casino Hotel Operator
N.A.I.C.S.: 721120

HC Bangor, LLC   **(1)**
500 Main St, Bangor, ME 04401
Web Site:
https://www.hollywoodcasinobangor.com
Emp.: 500
Racetrack, Hotel & Casino
N.A.I.C.S.: 721120

HWCC-Tunica, LLC   **(1)**
1150 Casino Strip Resort Blvd, Robinsonville, MS 38664
Tel.: (662) 357-7700
Web Site:
https://www.hollywoodcasinotunica.com
Emp.: 700
Casino Hotel Operator
N.A.I.C.S.: 721120

Indiana Gaming Company, LLC   **(1)**
777 Hollywood Blvd, Lawrenceburg, IN 47025
Tel.: (812) 539-6856
Web Site:
https://www.hollywoodindiana.com
Sales Range: $250-299.9 Million
Emp.: 2,400
Hotel & Casino Services
N.A.I.C.S.: 721120
Thomas P. Burke *(Sr VP-Reg Ops)*

LVGV, LLC   **(1)**
12300 Las Vegas Blvd S, Henderson, NV 89044
Tel.: (702) 797-1000
Web Site: https://www.themresort.com
Emp.: 100
Casino Hotels & Spa Operating Services
N.A.I.C.S.: 721120

PNGI Charles Town Gaming, LLC   **(1)**
580 E 5th Ave, Ranson, WV 25438
Tel.: (304) 725-7001
Sales Range: $300-349.9 Million
Emp.: 2,000
Thoroughbred Horse Racing
N.A.I.C.S.: 711219
Roger Ramey *(VP-Pub Affairs)*

Penn Cecil Maryland, Inc.   **(1)**
1201 Chesapeake Overlook Pkwy, Perryville, MD 21903
Tel.: (410) 378-8500
Web Site:
http://www.hollywoodcasinoperryville.com
Gambling Casino
N.A.I.C.S.: 713210

Pennsylvania National Turf Club, LLC   **(1)**
777 Hollywood Blvd, Grantville, PA 17028
Tel.: (717) 469-2211
Web Site: https://www.hollywoodpnrc.com
Racetrack & Casino Operator
N.A.I.C.S.: 711212

Pinnacle Entertainment, Inc.   **(1)**
3980 Howard Hughes Pkwy, Las Vegas, NV 89169
Tel.: (702) 541-7777
Web Site: http://www.pnk.com
Rev.: $2,561,848,000
Assets: $3,950,228,000
Liabilities: $4,271,199,000
Net Worth: ($320,971,000)
Earnings: $63,104,000
Emp.: 15,377
Fiscal Year-end: 12/31/2017
Holding Company; Casino Hotels & Resorts Operator

N.A.I.C.S.: 551112
Mickey Parenton *(Sr VP-Ops)*

Subsidiary (Domestic):

Ameristar Casino Black Hawk, LLC   **(2)**
111 Richman St, Black Hawk, CO 80422
Tel.: (720) 946-4000
Web Site:
https://www.ameristarblackhawk.com
Emp.: 98
Casino Hotel Operator
N.A.I.C.S.: 721120

Ameristar Casino Council Bluffs, LLC   **(2)**
2200 River Rd, Council Bluffs, IA 51501
Tel.: (712) 396-3056
Web Site:
https://www.ameristarcouncilbluffs.com
Sales Range: $900-999.9 Million
Hotel & Casino Operator
N.A.I.C.S.: 721120

Ameristar Casino East Chicago, LLC   **(2)**
777 Ameristar Blvd, East Chicago, IN 46312
Tel.: (219) 378-3000
Web Site:
https://www.ameristareastchicago.com
Emp.: 1,900
Casino Resort Operator
N.A.I.C.S.: 721120

Ameristar Casino Vicksburg, LLC   **(2)**
4116 Washington St, Vicksburg, MS 39180
Tel.: (601) 638-1000
Web Site:
https://www.ameristarvicksburg.com
Sales Range: $125-149.9 Million
Hotel & Casino Operations
N.A.I.C.S.: 721120

Boomtown, LLC   **(2)**
2100 Garson Rd, Reno, NV 89439
Tel.: (775) 345-6000
Web Site: https://www.boomtownreno.com
Sales Range: $200-249.9 Million
Emp.: 4,102
Hotel & Casino
N.A.I.C.S.: 721120

CCR Pennsylvania Racing, Inc.   **(2)**
210 Race Track Rd, Washington, PA 15301
Tel.: (724) 225-9300
Web Site: http://www.meadowsgaming.com
Racetrack & Casino Operator
N.A.I.C.S.: 711212

Cactus Pete's, LLC   **(2)** **(100%)**
1385 Hwy 93, Jackpot, NV 89825
Tel.: (775) 755-2321
Web Site: https://www.cactuspetes.com
Sales Range: $125-149.9 Million
Emp.: 900
Hotel & Casino Operations
N.A.I.C.S.: 721120

Unit (Domestic):

The Horseshu Hotel & Casino   **(3)** **(100%)**
1585 Hwy 98, Jackpot, NV 89825
Tel.: (775) 755-7777
Web Site: http://www.ameristar.com
Sales Range: $50-74.9 Million
Emp.: 800
Hotel & Casino Operations
N.A.I.C.S.: 721120

Subsidiary (Non-US):

Casino Magic Neuquen SA   **(2)**
Teodoro Planas 4005, Q8300, Neuquen, Argentina
Tel.: (54) 2994452600
Web Site: http://www.casinomagic.com
Sales Range: $125-149.9 Million
Casino
N.A.I.C.S.: 721120

Subsidiary (Domestic):

Double Bogey, LLC   **(2)**
825 Berkshire Blvd, Wyomissing, PA 19610-1247
Tel.: (469) 547-1094
Sales Range: $10-24.9 Million
Emp.: 4
Casinos & Hotels Operator
N.A.I.C.S.: 721120

Robyn Hamlin *(Gen Mgr)*

Ogle Haus, LLC   **(2)**
1013 W Main St, Vevay, IN 47043
Tel.: (812) 427-2020
Web Site: http://www.belterracasino.com
Sales Range: Less than $1 Million
Emp.: 15
Hotel, Banquet & Meeting Facilities
N.A.I.C.S.: 721110

Pinnacle Retama Partners, LLC   **(2)**
1 Retama Pkwy, Selma, TX 78154
Tel.: (210) 651-7000
Web Site: https://www.retamapark.com
Horse Racetrack
N.A.I.C.S.: 711212

Plainville Gaming and Redevelopment, LLC   **(1)**
301 Washington St, Plainville, MA 02762
Tel.: (508) 576-4500
Web Site:
https://www.plainridgeparkcasino.com
Hotel Services
N.A.I.C.S.: 721110

RIH Acquisitions MS II, LLC   **(1)**
1450 Jackpot Blvd, Robinsonville, MS 38664-9791
Tel.: (662) 357-1500
Web Site: https://www.1stjackpot.com
Casino Operator
N.A.I.C.S.: 713210

Raceway Park, Inc.   **(1)**
5700 Telegraph Rd, Toledo, OH 43612-3635
Tel.: (419) 476-7751
Web Site: http://www.toledo.com
Racetrack Operator
N.A.I.C.S.: 713990

SOKC, LLC   **(1)**
301 Dog Track Rd, Longwood, FL 32750
Tel.: (407) 831-1600
Web Site: http://www.orlando-otw.com
Emp.: 95
Dog Racetrack
N.A.I.C.S.: 711212
Mitch Cohen *(Gen Mgr)*
Cody Clonts *(Mgr-Mutuels)*
Steve Smith *(Dir-Racing)*

Score Media and Gaming Inc.   **(1)**
125 Queens Quay East, Toronto, M5A 0Z6, ON, Canada
Tel.: (416) 479-8812
Web Site:
https://www.scoremediaandgaming.com
Rev.: $16,208,059
Assets: $61,570,912
Liabilities: $38,725,207
Net Worth: $22,845,705
Earnings: ($29,671,880)
Emp.: 192
Fiscal Year-end: 08/31/2020
Sports Data Collection & Distribution Services
N.A.I.C.S.: 518210
Josh Sidsworth *(Chief Compliance Officer & Gen Counsel)*

Springfield Gaming and Redevelopment, LLC   **(1)**
825 Berkshire Blvd, Wyomissing, PA 19610
Tel.: (774) 215-5174
Gambling Industry Operator
N.A.I.C.S.: 713290

St. Louis Gaming Ventures, LLC   **(1)**
777 Casino Ctr Dr, Maryland Heights, MO 63043
Tel.: (314) 770-8100
Web Site:
https://www.hollywoodcasinostlouis.com
Sales Range: $75-99.9 Million
Emp.: 1,800
Hotel & Casino
N.A.I.C.S.: 721120

The Missouri Gaming Company, LLC   **(1)**
777 NW Argosy Casino Pkwy, Riverside, MO 64150
Tel.: (816) 746-3100
Web Site: http://www.argosykansascity.com
Sales Range: $250-299.9 Million
Emp.: 40
Casino Operator

N.A.I.C.S.: 713210
John Chaszar (Pres)

Toledo Gaming Ventures, LLC (1)
1968 Miami St, Toledo, OH 43605-3359
Tel.: (419) 661-5200
Web Site:
  https://www.hollywoodcasinotoledo.com
Emp.: 1,000
Casino Operator
N.A.I.C.S.: 713210

Tropicana Las Vegas Hotel & Casino, Inc. (1)
3801 Las Vegas Blvd S, Las Vegas, NV 89109
Tel.: (702) 739-3626
Web Site: http://www.troplv.com
Rev.: $109,660,000
Assets: $345,245,000
Liabilities: $93,017,000
Net Worth: $252,228,000
Earnings: ($19,255,000)
Emp.: 1,486
Fiscal Year-end: 12/31/2014
Holding Company; Casino Hotel & Resort Operator
N.A.I.C.S.: 551112
Jay A. Snowden (VP)

Subsidiary (Domestic):

Tropicana Las Vegas, Inc. (2)
3801 Las Vegas Blvd S, Las Vegas, NV 89109-4325
Tel.: (702) 739-2222
Web Site: https://casinos.ballys.com
Casino Hotel Operator
N.A.I.C.S.: 721120

PENNANTPARK FLOATING RATE CAPITAL LTD.
1691 Michigan Ave, Miami Beach, FL 33139
Tel.: (786) 297-9500   MD
Web Site:
  http://www.pennantpark.com
Year Founded: 2010
PFLT—(NYSE)
Rev.: $186,355,000
Assets: $2,108,845,000
Liabilities: $1,231,551,000
Net Worth: $877,294,000
Earnings: ($206,000)
Fiscal Year-end: 09/30/24
Closed-End Investment Fund
N.A.I.C.S.: 525990
Arthur H. Penn (CEO & Chm)
Richard T. Allorto Jr. (CFO & Treas)
Richard Cheung (CFO & Treas)

PENNANTPARK INVESTMENT CORPORATION
1691 Michigan Ave, Miami Beach, FL 33319
Tel.: (212) 905-1000   MD
Web Site:
  https://www.pennantpark.com
PNNT—(NYSE)
Rev.: $143,818,000
Assets: $1,389,086,000
Liabilities: $895,178,000
Net Worth: $493,908,000
Earnings: ($33,647,000)
Fiscal Year-end: 09/30/24
Closed-End Investment Fund
N.A.I.C.S.: 525990
Arthur H. Penn (CEO, Mng Partner & Chm)
Richard T. Allorto Jr. (CFO & Treas)
Richard Cheung (CFO & Treas)
Jose A. Briones Jr. (Sr Partner)
Michael Appelbaum (Mng Dir)
Terence Clerkin (Mng Dir)
James Heyer (Head-Capital Markets)
Dan Horn (Mng Dir-Chicago)
Colin Maguire (Principal)
Ryan Raskopf (Mng Dir)
James Stone (Mng Dir-Los Angeles)
Steve Winograd (Mng Dir)

Pete Mitchell (Mng Dir & Head-Private Capital Fundraising)
Glen Daci (VP)
Leonardo Marques (Asst VP)
Komal Merai (Asst VP)
Thomas Parry (Asst VP)
Reji Paul (VP)
Evan Rabin (VP)
Jeffrey Sion (Corp Counsel)
Jose A. Briones Jr. (Partner)

Subsidiaries:

PennantPark SBIC GP, LLC (1)
590 Madison Ave 15th Fl, New York, NY 10022
Tel.: (212) 905-1000
Investment Services
N.A.I.C.S.: 523910

Superior Digital Displays, LLC (1)
1350 Avenue of the Americas 2nd Fl, New York, NY 10019
Tel.: (646) 532-2953
Web Site:
  http://www.superiordigitaldisplays.com
Billboard Display Advertising Services
N.A.I.C.S.: 541850
William Mulder (CMO)
Wally Kelly (CEO)
Lou Formisano (Chief Revenue Officer)

PENNEXX FOODS, INC.
2420 Enterprise Rd Ste 107, Clearwater, FL 33763
Web Site: http://www.pennexx.net
Year Founded: 1999
PNNX—(NASDAQ)
Emp.: 4
Information Technology Services
N.A.I.C.S.: 513210
Vincent Risalvato (CTO)

PENNS WOODS BANCORP, INC.
300 Market St, Williamsport, PA 17703
Tel.: (570) 322-1111   PA
Web Site: https://www.pwod.com
Year Founded: 1983
PWOD—(NASDAQ)
Rev.: $73,641,000
Assets: $2,000,080,000
Liabilities: $1,832,415,000
Net Worth: $167,665,000
Earnings: $17,422,000
Emp.: 302
Fiscal Year-end: 12/31/22
Bank Holding Company
N.A.I.C.S.: 551111
Brian L. Knepp (CFO)
Michael J. Casale Jr. (Vice Chm)
Richard A. Grafmyre (CEO)
Christine M. Barto (Chief HR Officer)
Jack W. Jones (Chief Banking Officer)
Gerald J. Seman (Pres)

Subsidiaries:

Jersey Shore State Bank (1)
300 Market St, Williamsport, PA 17701
Tel.: (570) 322-1111
Web Site: https://www.jssb.com
Sales Range: $25-49.9 Million
Emp.: 181
Commericial Banking
N.A.I.C.S.: 522110
Michael J. Casale Jr. (Chm)
Richard A. Grafmyre (Pres & CEO)

Subsidiary (Domestic):

M Group Inc. (2)
1720 E 3rd St, Williamsport, PA 17701   (100%)
Tel.: (570) 322-4627
Web Site:
  https://www.comprehensivefinancial group.com
Sales Range: $10-24.9 Million
Emp.: 4
Retailer of Insurance & Investment Products

N.A.I.C.S.: 524210
Brian L. Knepp (CEO)

The Luzerne Bank (1)
118 Main St, Luzerne, PA 18709
Tel.: (570) 288-4511
Web Site: https://www.luzernebank.com
Emp.: 78
Commericial Banking
N.A.I.C.S.: 522110
Barbara Cassise (Reg Pres)
Jack W. Jones (Chief Banking Officer & Sr VP)
Robert O. Neher (Pres)
Rose Mahler (Officer-Mortgage Loan)

PENNSYLVANIA LUMBER-MENS MUTUAL INSURANCE COMPANY
One Commerce Sq 2005 Market St Ste 1200, Philadelphia, PA 19103
Web Site: https://www.plmins.com
Year Founded: 1895
SCTH—(OTC)
Insurance Services
N.A.I.C.S.: 524126
John K. Smith (Pres & CEO)

PENNSYLVANIA REAL ESTATE INVESTMENT TRUST
1 Commerce Sq 2005 Market St Ste 1000, Philadelphia, PA 19103
Tel.: (215) 875-0700   PA
Web Site: http://www.preit.com
Year Founded: 1960
PRET—(OTCQB)
Rev.: $296,028,000
Assets: $1,803,129,000
Liabilities: $1,927,565,000
Net Worth: ($124,436,000)
Earnings: ($148,318,000)
Emp.: 149
Fiscal Year-end: 12/31/22
Real Estate Investment Trust
N.A.I.C.S.: 551112
Joseph J. Aristone (Exec VP-Leasing)
Joseph F. Coradino (Chm & CEO)
Andrew M. Ioannou (Exec VP-Fin & Acquisitions)
Vince Vizza (First VP-Leasing)
Anthony DiLoreto (First VP-Leasing)
Daniel Herman (Sr VP-Dev)
Lisa M. Most (Gen Counsel & Exec VP)
Joshua Schrier (VP-Acquisitions)
Bradford Hughart (VP-IT)
Michael A. Khouri (First VP-Leasing)
Johanna Didio (VP-Legal)
Dan Pascale (VP-Dev)
Joshua Talley (First VP-Legal)
Paula M. Charles (VP-Leasing)
Sean Linehan (VP-Leasing)
Gene McCaffery (VP-Leasing)
Sathana Semonsky (Chief Acctg Officer & VP)
Nadine Salem (Dir-Leasing)
John Braithwaite (Dir-Leasing)
Clare Rose (Sr Dir-Specialty Leasing)
Dave Zamichielli (VP-Property Acctg)
Mario C. Ventresca Jr. (CFO & Exec VP)
Rudolph Alberts Jr. (Sr VP-Ops)

Subsidiaries:

Crossroads Mall (1)
2 Crossroads Mall, Mount Hope, WV 25880
Tel.: (304) 255-6176
Web Site: https://shopcrossroads.com
Commerical Buildings Rental & Leasing Services
N.A.I.C.S.: 531120

Cumberland Mall Associates (1)
3849 S Delsea Dr, Vineland, NJ 08360
Tel.: (856) 825-9507
Web Site:
  https://www.cumberlandmallnj.com
Commerical Buildings Rental & Leasing Services
N.A.I.C.S.: 531120

Moorestown Mall LLC (1)
400 Route 38, Moorestown, NJ 08057
Tel.: (856) 231-4444
Web Site: https://moorestown-mall.com
Commerical Buildings Rental & Leasing Services
N.A.I.C.S.: 531120

PR Exton Square Property L.P. (1)
260 Exton Sq, Exton, PA 19341
Tel.: (610) 363-7034
Web Site: https://www.extonsquare.com
Commerical Buildings Rental & Leasing Services
N.A.I.C.S.: 531120

PR Francis Scott Key LLC (1)
5500 Buckeystown Pike, Frederick, MD 21703
Tel.: (301) 662-5152
Web Site: https://www.shopfskmall.com
Commerical Buildings Rental & Leasing Services
N.A.I.C.S.: 531120

PR Gainesville LLC (1)
7340 Atlas Walk Way, Gainesville, VA 20155-2991
Tel.: (703) 754-2999
Emp.: 25
Commerical Buildings Rental & Leasing Services
N.A.I.C.S.: 531120
Reg Lass (Chm)

PR Jacksonville Limited Partnership (1)
375 Jacksonville Mall, Jacksonville, NC 28546
Tel.: (910) 353-2477
Web Site:
  https://www.shopjacksonvillemall.com
Commerical Buildings Rental & Leasing Services
N.A.I.C.S.: 531120

PR Logan Valley LLC (1)
5580 Goods Ln Ste 1, Altoona, PA 16602-2842
Tel.: (814) 949-8181
Web Site:
  http://www.shoploganvalleymall.com
Commerical Buildings Rental & Leasing Services
N.A.I.C.S.: 531120

PR North Dartmouth LLC (1)
200 Dartmouth Mall, Dartmouth, MA 02747
Tel.: (508) 999-4535
Web Site:
  https://www.shopdartmouthmall.com
Commerical Buildings Rental & Leasing Services
N.A.I.C.S.: 531120

PR Palmer Park Mall Limited Partnership (1)
2455 Park Ave, Easton, PA 18045
Tel.: (610) 258-6017
Web Site:
  http://www.shoppalmerparkmall.com
Commerical Buildings Rental & Leasing Services
N.A.I.C.S.: 531120

PR Springfield Town Center LLC (1)
6500 Springfield Mall, Springfield, VA 22150
Tel.: (703) 971-3000
Web Site:
  https://www.springfieldtowncenter.com
Shopping Mall Operator
N.A.I.C.S.: 445110

PR Valley View LLC (1)
3800 State Rd 16, La Crosse, WI 54601
Tel.: (608) 781-4700
Web Site: https://www.myvalleyview.com
Commerical Buildings Rental & Leasing Services
N.A.I.C.S.: 531120

PR Viewmont LLC (1)
100 Viewmont Mall, Scranton, PA 18508
Tel.: (570) 346-9165
Web Site:
  https://www.shopviewmontmall.com
Commerical Buildings Rental & Leasing Services
N.A.I.C.S.: 531120

PR Washington Crown Limited Partnership (1)

Pennsylvania Real Estate Investment Trust—(Continued)

1500 W Chestnut St, Washington, PA 15301-5864
Tel.: (724) 228-4270
Web Site:
  https://www.shopwashingtoncrown.com
Commerical Buildings Rental & Leasing Services
N.A.I.C.S.: 531120

PR Wiregrass Commons LLC (1)
900 Commons Dr, Dothan, AL 36303
Tel.: (334) 792-7734
Web Site:
  https://www.shopwiregrasscommons
  mall.com
Commerical Buildings Rental & Leasing Services
N.A.I.C.S.: 531120

PR Wyoming Valley Limited Partnership (1)
29 Wyoming Valley Mall, Wilkes Barre, PA 18702
Tel.: (570) 822-9944
Web Site:
  https://www.shopwyomingvalleymall.com
Commerical Buildings Rental & Leasing Services
N.A.I.C.S.: 531120

PREIT Gadsden Mall LLC (1)
1001 Rainbow Dr Ste 51, Gadsden, AL 35901
Tel.: (256) 547-0501
Web Site:
  https://www.shopgadsdenmall.com
Emp.: 3
Commerical Buildings Rental & Leasing Services
N.A.I.C.S.: 531120

Preit Associates, L.P. (1)
2005 Market St Ste 1000, Philadelphia, PA 19103
Tel.: (215) 875-0700
Web Site: https://www.preit.com
Holding Company (with Property Ownership)
N.A.I.C.S.: 531120

Preit-Rubin, Inc. (1)
200 S Broad St Fl 3, Philadelphia, PA 19102-3815
Tel.: (215) 875-0700
Web Site: https://www.preit.com
Sales Range: $50-74.9 Million
Emp.: 100
Real Estate Investment Trust, Development & Commercial Real Estate Broker
N.A.I.C.S.: 531210

Red Rose Commons Associates, L.P. (1)
350 Sentry Pkwy, Blue Bell, PA 19422
Tel.: (610) 397-1833
Management Consulting Services
N.A.I.C.S.: 541611

WG Park, LP (1)
2500 Moreland Rd, Willow Grove, PA 19090
Tel.: (215) 657-6000
Web Site:
  https://www.willowgroveparkmall.com
Commerical Buildings Rental & Leasing Services
N.A.I.C.S.: 531120

Walnut Street Abstract, L.P. (1)
1125 Ocean Ave, Lakewood, NJ 08701
Tel.: (732) 333-2607
Web Site:
  https://www.walnutstreetabstract.com
Insurance Management Services
N.A.I.C.S.: 524298

PENNYMAC FINANCIAL SERVICES, INC.

3043 Townsgate Rd Ste 200, Westlake Village, CA 91361
Tel.: (818) 224-7442   DE
Web Site:
  https://www.pennymacfinancial.com
Year Founded: 2008
PFSI—(NYSE)
Rev.: $1,401,656,000

Assets: $18,844,563,000
Liabilities: $15,305,960,000
Net Worth: $3,538,603,000
Earnings: $144,656,000
Emp.: 3,900
Fiscal Year-end: 12/31/23
Mortgage Lending Services
N.A.I.C.S.: 522310
Douglas Jones (Pres)
David A. Spector (Chm & CEO)
Derek W. Stark (Sr Mng Dir & Chief Legal Officer)
William Chang (Sr Mng Dir & Chief Capital Markets Officer)
Daniel Stanley Perotti (CFO)
Kevin Chamberlain (Exec VP)
Isaac Garden (Sr VP)
Steven R. Bailey (Sr Mng Dir)
Don White (Sr Mng Dir)

Subsidiaries:

PennyMac Loan Services, LLC (1)
3043 Townsgate Rd Ste 200, Westlake Village, CA 91361
Tel.: (818) 224-7442
Web Site: https://www.pennymac.com
Emp.: 6,500
Financial Management Services
N.A.I.C.S.: 541611

PENNYMAC MORTGAGE INVESTMENT TRUST

3043 Townsgate Rd Ste 200, Westlake Village, CA 91361
Tel.: (818) 224-7442   MD
Web Site: https://pmt.pennymac.com
Year Founded: 2009
PMT—(NYSE)
Rev.: $303,771,000
Assets: $13,921,564,000
Liabilities: $11,958,749,000
Net Worth: $1,962,815,000
Earnings: ($115,106,000)
Emp.: 4,000
Fiscal Year-end: 12/31/22
Mortgage Loan Investment Services
N.A.I.C.S.: 522310
Douglas Jones (Pres & Chief Mortgage Banking Officer)
David A. Spector (Chm & CEO)
Daniel Stanley Perotti (CFO)

Subsidiaries:

PennyMac Corp. (1)
3043 Townsgate Rd Ste 300, Westlake Village, CA 91361
Tel.: (818) 878-8416
Web Site: http://www.gopennymac.com
Sales Range: $350-399.9 Million
Emp.: 1,000
Investment Management Service
N.A.I.C.S.: 523940
Stanford L. Kurland (Chm & CEO)
David A. Spector (Pres & Chief Investment Officer)

PENSKE AUTOMOTIVE GROUP, INC.

1845 S Telegraph Rd, Bloomfield Hills, MI 48302-0954
Tel.: (248) 642-6565   DE
Web Site:
  https://www.penskeautomotive.com
Year Founded: 1990
PAG—(NYSE)
Rev.: $29,527,400,000
Assets: $15,671,500,000
Liabilities: $10,915,900,000
Net Worth: $4,755,600,000
Earnings: $1,053,200,000
Emp.: 28,000
Fiscal Year-end: 12/31/23
Holding Company; New & Used Car Dealerships Operator
N.A.I.C.S.: 551112
Anthony R. Pordon (Exec VP-IR & Corp Dev)
Robert H. Kurnick Jr. (Pres)

Shane M. Spradlin (Gen Counsel, Sec & Exec VP)
Bernie W. Wolfe (Exec VP-Ops-West)
Gregory W. Penske (Vice Chm)
John Cragg (Exec. VP-Ops-East)
Michelle Hulgrave (CFO & Exec VP)
Rich Hook (CIO & Exec VP)
Tyler Heard (Exec VP-Ops-Central)
George W. Brochick (Exec VP-Strategic Dev)
Tracy Cassady (Exec VP-Mktg)
Anthony Facione (VP)
Aaron Michael (Treas)
Randall Seymore (COO)
Roger S. Penske (Chm & CEO)
Claude H. Denker III (Exec VP-HR)

Subsidiaries:

Around The Clock Freightliner Group LLC (1)
3040 Irving Blvd, Dallas, TX 75247
Tel.: (214) 631-2620
Web Site: https://www.premiertruck.com
New & Used Truck Parts Dealership & Services
N.A.I.C.S.: 423110
Andy Baker (Sls Mgr-Fort Worth)
Steve Noland (Sls Mgr-Knoxville)
Jeff Bowling (Mgr-Oklahoma)
John Blevins (Sls Mgr-)
Ken Shumake (Mgr-Svc-Chattanooga)
Donald Ballance (Mgr-Svc-North Dallas)
Ron Beaver (Mgr-Svc-Tulsa)
Rob Elmore (Mgr-Parts-Amarillo)
Darren Hunt (Mgr-Parts-South Dallas)
Mike Leverington (Mgr-Midland)
Matthew Workman (Branch Mgr-Tremonton)
Brent Fryer (Mgr-Parts-Oklahoma City)
Brad Flatt (Mgr-Collision Center-Amarillo)
Randy Ogle (Mgr-Collision Center-Knoxville)
Terry Morrow (Mgr-Collision Center-Tulsa)
Becky Morris (Mgr-F&I-Amarillo)
Phillip Evans (Mgr-Chattanooga)
John Kerr (Mgr-F&I-Oklahoma City & Ardmore)
Marlon Todd (Mgr-F&I-Tulsa)
Peter Brakner (Mgr-F&I-North & South Dallas)
Anthony Shimkus (Mgr-Parts-North Dallas)
Jose Gonzales (Coord-CIC)
Joshua Jenkins (Coord-CIC)
Ron Long (Pres & CEO)

Subsidiary (Domestic):

Kansas City Freightliner Sales Inc. (2)
7800 NE 38th St, Kansas City, MO 64161-9454
Tel.: (816) 453-4400
Web Site: http://www.kcfreightliner.com
Sales Range: $100-124.9 Million
Emp.: 257
Automobiles & Other Motor Vehicles Parts & Accessories Mfr
N.A.I.C.S.: 441110
Mike Westfall (Sls Mgr & Gen Mgr)
Garrett Westfall (Sls Mgr)
Corey Boatman (Mgr)
Mike Slagle (Mgr)
Ryan Hoppe (Mgr)
Tim Shaw (Mgr)
Brandon Berrios (Mgr)
Garrett Westfall (Sls Mgr)
Corey Boatman (Mgr)
Mike Slagle (Mgr)
Ryan Hoppe (Mgr)
Tim Shaw (Mgr)
Brandon Berrios (Mgr)

River States Truck & Trailer (2)
3959 N Kinney Coulee Rd, La Crosse, WI 54601
Tel.: (608) 784-1149
Web Site: http://www.riverstates.com
Sales Range: $10-24.9 Million
Emp.: 46
Trucks, Tractors & Trailers: New & Used
N.A.I.C.S.: 441110
Joseph Laux (Chm)
Joel Laux (Pres)

Audi Zentrum Aachen Jacobs Auto GmbH (1)
Madrider Ring 19, 52078, Aachen, Germany

Tel.: (49) 2419203200
New Car Distr
N.A.I.C.S.: 441110

AutoVanti Brianza S.r.l. (1)
Via Milano 33, 20832, Desio, Italy
Tel.: (39) 03623981
Web Site: http://www.autovanti-brianza.it
Car Distr
N.A.I.C.S.: 441110

AutoVanti Monza S.r.l. (1)
Viale Sicilia 130, 20900, Monza, Italy
Tel.: (39) 03939391
Web Site: http://www.autovanti-monza.it
Car Distr
N.A.I.C.S.: 441110

Autohaus Augsburg GmbH (1)
Ammannstrasse 1, 86167, Augsburg, Germany
Tel.: (49) 82190090
Web Site: http://www.autohaus-augsburg.de
Automotive Retailer
N.A.I.C.S.: 441227

Autohaus Nix GmbH (1)
Frankfurter Str 1-7, 63607, Wachtersbach, Germany
Tel.: (49) 60538030
Web Site: https://www.auto-nix.de
Car Distr
N.A.I.C.S.: 441110

Automotive Media, LLC (1)
500 W Long Lk Rd, Troy, MI 48098
Tel.: (248) 537-8500
Web Site: https://www.imbranded.com
Emp.: 50
Food Transportation Services
N.A.I.C.S.: 488490
Jim Whitehead (Founder & CEO)
Rob Efurt (COO)
Leslie McLain (Creative Dir)
Kristofer Petruska (Mgr-Graphics Production)

Bill Brown Ford Inc. (1)
32222 Plymouth Rd, Livonia, MI 48150-1925
Tel.: (734) 421-7000
Web Site: http://www.billbrownford.com
Sales Range: $75-99.9 Million
Emp.: 250
Automobile Dealers
N.A.I.C.S.: 441110
David Tashman (Gen Mgr)
Jason Ellsworth (Mgr-Customer Rels)
Joe Hershey (Mgr-Body Shop)
John Houle (Dir-Fleet Ops)
Matt Garchow (Mgr-New Vehicle Sls)
Mike Ivey (Mgr-Sls Bus)
Mike Tabone (Mgr-Sls Bus)
Lou Zinzi (Mgr-Sls Bus)

Car Sense Inc. (1)
2801 Bethlehem Pike, Hatfield, PA 19440
Tel.: (844) 839-2750
Web Site: http://www.carsense.com
Used Car Whslr
N.A.I.C.S.: 441120
Jason Lief (Gen Mgr-Sls)
Jill Sedoris (Office Mgr-Pittsburgh)
Tim Janney (Mgr-Internal Svc)
Jason Seipt (Gen Sls Mgr)
Amy DiJenno (Mgr-Acctg)
Cory Ermold (Mgr-Inventory)
Sunny Sikhoumeuang (Gen Mgr-Sls)
Mike Driscoll (Mgr-Sls)
Ryan Addeo (Gen Mgr)
Stephen Bodnar (Gen Sls Mgr)
Kenny Yoder (Mgr-Detail)

Classic Auto Group, Inc. (1)
3400-H Route 42, Turnersville, NJ 08012
Tel.: (856) 499-5570
Web Site:
  https://www.turnersvillecollisioncenter.com
Automotive Retailer
N.A.I.C.S.: 441227

Classic Imports, Inc. (1)
18777 US Hwy 12, New Buffalo, MI 49117-9130
Tel.: (269) 469-2007
Automotive Retailer
N.A.I.C.S.: 441227

Cycle Holdings, LLC (1)
2555 Telegraph Rd, Bloomfield Hills, MI 48302

Tel.: (248) 648-2517
Holding Company
N.A.I.C.S.: 551112

DiFeo Leasing Partnership   **(1)**
585 State Rte 440, Jersey City, NJ 07305-4878
Tel.: (201) 435-2003
Automotive Part Whslr
N.A.I.C.S.: 441330

DiFeo Partnership, LLC   **(1)**
905 Communipaw Ave, Jersey City, NJ 07304-1317
Tel.: (201) 433-9500
Automotive Part Whslr
N.A.I.C.S.: 441330

Goodson North, LLC   **(1)**
17350 N Fwy, Houston, TX 77090-5010
Tel.: (281) 971-5586
Web Site: http://teamgillmanhondanorth.com
Motor Vehicle Dealers
N.A.I.C.S.: 441227
Lou Lawrence *(Gen Mgr)*

HBL, LLC   **(1)**
8598 Leesburg Pike, Vienna, VA 22182
Tel.: (703) 564-6100
Web Site: https://www.auditysonscorner.com
New & Used Car Dealer
N.A.I.C.S.: 441110

HT Automotive, LLC   **(1)**
8030 S Autoplex Loop, Tempe, AZ 85284
Tel.: (480) 893-7900
Web Site: https://www.tempehonda.com
Sales Range: $75-99.9 Million
Emp.: 150
Car Dealership
N.A.I.C.S.: 441110

HVPH Motor Corporation   **(1)**
Ave John F Kennedy Km 3 9 Marginal, San Juan, PR 00929
Tel.: (787) 273-3000
Motor Vehicle Dealers
N.A.I.C.S.: 441110
Jutith Parra *(Gen Mgr)*

Inskip Auto Mall   **(1)**
1515 Bald Hill Rd, West Warwick, RI 02886
Tel.: (401) 821-1510
Web Site: http://www.inskipautomall.com
Sales Range: $150-199.9 Million
Emp.: 375
Car Dealership
N.A.I.C.S.: 441110
Ralph Iacovone *(Pres)*

Jacobs Auto Laurensberg GmbH   **(1)**
Henricistrasse 29, 52072, Aachen, Germany
Tel.: (49) 241889990
Car Distr
N.A.I.C.S.: 441110

Jacobs Holding GmbH   **(1)**
Madrider Ring 10, 52078, Aachen, Germany
Tel.: (49) 2419777551
Web Site: http://www.jacobs-gruppe.de
Car Distr
N.A.I.C.S.: 441110

Landers Auto Sales, LLC   **(1)**
22615 Interstate 30, Bryant, AR 72022
Tel.: (501) 213-0744
Web Site: http://www.landersautosales.com
Car Distr
N.A.I.C.S.: 441110

Maranello Concessionaires Limited   **(1)**
Unit B8 Crabtree Road Thorpe Industrial Estate, Egham, TW20 8RN, Surrey, United Kingdom
Tel.: (44) 1784436222
Web Site: https://www.ferrariparts.co.uk
Emp.: 30
Genuine Ferrari Automotive Parts & Accessories Sales
N.A.I.C.S.: 441310

Maranello Sales Limited   **(1)**
Tower Garage A30 Bypass, Egham, TW20 0AX, Surrey, United Kingdom
Tel.: (44) 1784862468
Web Site: http://london-maranello.ferraridealers.com
Emp.: 20

New Car Dealers
N.A.I.C.S.: 441110
Jon Morgan *(Gen Mgr)*

McCoy Freightliner   **(1)**
2323 NE Columbia Blvd, Portland, OR 97211
Tel.: (503) 735-1970
Web Site: http://www.freightlinertrucks.com
Sales Range: $25-49.9 Million
Emp.: 11
Truck Tractors
N.A.I.C.S.: 441110
John Schmitz *(Gen Mgr)*
Robert McCoy *(Pres)*

Motorcars Acquisition IV, LLC   **(1)**
18151 Rockside Rd, Bedford, OH 44146-2039
Tel.: (440) 359-6125
Web Site: https://www.toyotaofbedford.com
Sales Range: $25-49.9 Million
Emp.: 100
New & Used Car Dealer
N.A.I.C.S.: 441110

Motorcars Acquisition, LLC   **(1)**
99 Broadway Ave, Bedford, OH 44146
Tel.: (440) 439-0100
Automotive Retailer
N.A.I.C.S.: 441110

Nicole Racing Japan, LLC   **(1)**
13F Yokohama Blue Avenue 4-4-2 Minatomirai, Nishi-ku, Yokohama, 220-0012, Kanagawa, Japan
Tel.: (81) 45 228 8360
Web Site: https://www.nicole.co.jp
Automotive Distr
N.A.I.C.S.: 423110

PAG Greenwich M1, LLC   **(1)**
261 W Putnam Ave, Greenwich, CT 06830
Tel.: (203) 717-4607
Web Site: https://www.mercedesbenzgreenwich.com
Car Distr
N.A.I.C.S.: 441110

PAG Madison L1, LLC   **(1)**
8000 Airport Rd, Middleton, WI 53562
Tel.: (608) 554-4436
Web Site: https://www.lexusofmadison.com
Emp.: 40
New & Used Automobiles Sales
N.A.I.C.S.: 441110
Jacob Schkirkie *(Mgr-Parts)*
Nate Riesen *(Gen Mgr)*
Gary Poduch *(Mgr-Svc)*
Josh Anderson *(Mgr-Sls & Bus)*
Jerry Ortega *(Sls Mgr-New Car)*

PAG Madison T1, LLC   **(1)**
3501 Lancaster Dr, Madison, WI 53718
Tel.: (608) 402-4063
Web Site: https://www.eastmadisontoyota.com
Sales Range: $125-149.9 Million
Emp.: 150
New & Used Automobiles Sales
N.A.I.C.S.: 441110

PAG Orlando Partnership, Ltd.   **(1)**
11020 S Orange Blossom Trl, Orlando, FL 32837
Tel.: (407) 792-4484
Web Site: https://www.centralfloridatoyota.com
Sales Range: $75-99.9 Million
Emp.: 150
Car Dealership
N.A.I.C.S.: 441110

PAG Santa Ana AVW, Inc.   **(1)**
4910 Kearny Mesa Rd, San Diego, CA 92111-2407
Tel.: (858) 279-8151
Web Site: http://www.kearnymesatoyota.com
Automotive Retailer
N.A.I.C.S.: 441227

PAG West, LLC   **(1)**
7111 E Chauncey Ln, Phoenix, AZ 85054-6143
Tel.: (480) 538-4300
Web Site: http://www.penskeautomotive.com
Emp.: 600
New & Used Car Dealers
N.A.I.C.S.: 441110

PPS Holdings Australia Pty. Ltd.   **(1)**
488 Blackshaws Rd, Altona, 3025, VIC, Australia
Tel.: (61) 1300688338
Holding Company
N.A.I.C.S.: 551112

Palm Beach Toyota   **(1)**
200 S Congress Ave, West Palm Beach, FL 33406
Tel.: (561) 855-3887
Web Site: https://www.palmbeachtoyota.com
Sales Range: $50-74.9 Million
Emp.: 100
Car Dealership
N.A.I.C.S.: 441110

Penske Australia Pty. Ltd.   **(1)**
72 Formation Street, Wacol, 4076, QLD, Australia
Tel.: (61) 73 271 7777
Web Site: https://penske.com.au
Machinery Mfr & Distr
N.A.I.C.S.: 333242
Hamish Christie-Johnston *(Mng Dir)*
Ben Buckland *(Gen Mgr-People)*
Leigh Henderson *(COO)*

Penske Automotive Europe Gmbh   **(1)**
Engstlatter Weg 18, Stuttgart, 70567, Baden-Wurttemberg, Germany
Tel.: (49) 7112204576
Emp.: 223
Car Distr
N.A.I.C.S.: 441110

Penske Automotive Group, Inc. - Arizona   **(1)**
7171 E Chauncey Ln, Phoenix, AZ 85054
Tel.: (480) 538-6200
Web Site: http://www.pagarizona.com
Sales Range: $250-299.9 Million
Automobile Sales
N.A.I.C.S.: 441110

Penske Automotive Group, Inc. - Southern California   **(1)**
5202 Kearny Mesa Rd, San Diego, CA 92111
Tel.: (858) 541-0200
Web Site: http://www.kearnymesaacura.com
Sales Range: $250-299.9 Million
Emp.: 20
Car Dealership
N.A.I.C.S.: 441110

Penske Cadillac of California, Inc.   **(1)**
186030 S Hawthorne Blvd, Torrance, CA 90504-5504
Tel.: (310) 697-1800
Web Site: http://www.penskecadillac.com
Truck, Utility Trailer & RV (Recreational Vehicle) Rental & Leasing
N.A.I.C.S.: 532120
Harout Boyadjian *(Gen Mgr)*
Caddy Munteanu *(Sls Mgr)*
Atto Sargon *(Floor Mgr)*
Ron Gorey *(Sls Mgr)*
Reynaldo Gonzalez *(Sls Mgr)*

Penske Car Rental Memphis, LLC   **(1)**
2495 Winchester Rd, Memphis, TN 38118
Tel.: (901) 345-5680
Car Rental Services
N.A.I.C.S.: 532111
Leigh Powell *(Mgr-Maintenance)*

Penske Commercial Vehicles Investments NZ Pty Ltd.   **(1)**
4 Langley Road Wuri, Auckland, 2104, New Zealand
Tel.: (64) 92507800
Car Dealer
N.A.I.C.S.: 441110

Penske Commercial Vehicles NZ   **(1)**
4 Langley Road, PO Box 4350, Wiri, 2104, New Zealand
Tel.: (64) 92504101
Web Site: http://www.tcv.co.nz
Automobile Maintenance Services
N.A.I.C.S.: 811198

Penske Honda of Indianapolis   **(1)**
4140 E 96th St, Indianapolis, IN 46240
Tel.: (317) 799-0135

Web Site: https://www.penskehondaindy.com
Emp.: 470
Car Dealership
N.A.I.C.S.: 441110

Penske New Zealand   **(1)**
4 Langley Road, Wiri, Auckland, 2104, New Zealand
Tel.: (64) 9 252 0910
Machinery Mfr
N.A.I.C.S.: 333242
Andrew Kerridge *(Gen Mgr-Information Technology)*
Tanya Myint *(Gen Mgr-)*
Kimberley Ruddock *(Gen Mgr-Marketing)*

Penske Power Systems Pty Ltd   **(1)**
78 - 82 Riverside Road, Chipping Norton, 2170, NSW, Australia
Tel.: (61) 297942600
Web Site: http://www.penskeps.com
Sales Range: $200-249.9 Million
Emp.: 100
Diesel & Gas Engines & Power Systems Distr
N.A.I.C.S.: 423830
Leigh Henderson *(Gen Mgr-Western Ops)*
Matthew Smith *(Gen Mgr-Off-Highway)*
Craig Lee *(Gen Mgr-On-Highway)*
Greg Dobe *(Gen Mgr-Remanufacturing & Production)*
Roger Gleeson *(Gen Mgr-Defence)*

Penske Sportwagen Hamburg GmbH   **(1)**
Merkurring 2, 22143, Hamburg, 22143, Germany
Tel.: (49) 405700300
Web Site: https://www.penske-hamburg.de
New Car Dealers
N.A.I.C.S.: 441110
Jens Werner *(Mng Dir)*

Penske Sportwagenzentrum GmbH   **(1)**
Elsa-Brandstrom-Strasse 11, 68229, Mannheim, Germany
Tel.: (49) 621483660
Web Site: https://www.porsche-mannheim.de
New & Used Dealers
N.A.I.C.S.: 441110
Sascha Pfeifer *(Mgr-Workshop)*
Hardy Langer *(Coord-Classic)*
Jens Werner *(Mng Dir)*

Penske Truck Leasing Company, L.P.   **(1)**
2675 Morgantown Rd, Reading, PA 19607
Tel.: (610) 775-6000
Web Site: http://www.pensketruckleasing.com
Commercial & Consumer Truck Leasing, Contract Maintenance & Rental Services
N.A.I.C.S.: 532120
Don Metcalf *(Dir-Product Mktg)*
Art Vallely *(Pres)*
Sherry Sanger *(Sr VP-Mktg)*
Michael Duff *(Chief Compliance Officer & Sr VP-Govt Rels)*

Subsidiary (Domestic):

Decarolis Truck Rental Inc.   **(2)**
333 Colfax St, Rochester, NY 14606-3107
Tel.: (585) 254-1169
Web Site: http://www.decarolis.com
Sales Range: $400-449.9 Million
Emp.: 500
Truck Rental & Leasing
N.A.I.C.S.: 532120
Paul DeCarolis *(Chm)*
Mark Williams *(VP-Fin)*
Michael Margarone *(Pres)*

Subsidiary (Domestic):

Monroe School Transportation Inc.   **(3)**
970 Emerson St, Rochester, NY 14606-2708   **(100%)**
Tel.: (585) 458-3230
Web Site: http://www.nellc.com
Sales Range: $25-49.9 Million
Emp.: 300
School Buses & Transportation
N.A.I.C.S.: 485410

Subsidiary (Domestic):

Kris-Way Truck Leasing Inc.   **(2)**

Penske Automotive Group, Inc.—(Continued)

43 Hemco Rd Ste 1, South Portland, ME 04106
Tel.: (207) 799-8593
Web Site: http://www.kris-way.com
Sales Range: $25-49.9 Million
Emp.: 150
Truck Leasing Services
N.A.I.C.S.: 532120
Thomas Keefer *(Pres)*
Evelyn Tonks *(CFO)*
Jim Ryan *(VP-Ops)*
Robert Coale *(VP-Sls)*

Division (Domestic):

Penske Truck Rental (2)
2675 Morgantown Rd, Reading, PA 19607
Tel.: (610) 775-6000
Web Site: http://www.pensketruckrental.com
Sales Range: $125-149.9 Million
Truck Rental Services
N.A.I.C.S.: 532120
Brian Hard *(Pres & CEO)*
Don Mikes *(Sr VP-Rental)*

Subsidiary (Domestic):

Star Truck Rentals Inc. (2)
3940 Eastern Ave SE, Grand Rapids, MI 49508
Tel.: (616) 243-7033
Web Site: http://www.starlease.com
Sales Range: $25-49.9 Million
Emp.: 130
Provider of Tranportation Services
N.A.I.C.S.: 532120
David Bylenga *(Exec VP)*
Brent Larson *(Mgr-Sls)*
Kyle Hillman *(Controller)*
Lonnie Vis *(Dir-Maintenance)*
Theresa Morris *(Mgr-Parts)*
Dave Donbrock *(Branch Mgr)*
Tom Bylenga *(Pres)*

Premier Truck Group (1)
4200 Port Blvd, Dallas, TX 75241
Tel.: (972) 225-4300
Web Site: https://www.premiertruck.com
Commercial Vehicles Dealer
N.A.I.C.S.: 532120

Premier Truck Group of Oshawa (1)
720 Wilson Road South, Oshawa, L1H 6E8, ON, Canada (100%)
Tel.: (905) 432-3838
Web Site: https://www.premiertruck.com
Transportation Services
N.A.I.C.S.: 481212

R Stratton & Co Limited (1)
2 Penman Way Grove Park Enderby, Leicester, LE19 1ST, Leicestershire, United Kingdom
Tel.: (44) 1162821000
Automotive Distr
N.A.I.C.S.: 441227
Laurence Vaughan *(CEO)*

SK Motors, LLC (1)
10805 Lanham Severn Rd, Lanham, MD 20706-2115
Tel.: (301) 464-0400
Web Site: http://www.skmotors.cc
Motor Vehicle Dealers
N.A.I.C.S.: 441227
David Zoloto *(Gen Mgr)*
Marcus Fortense *(Mgr-Sls)*
Brad Levine *(Mgr-Sls)*
Ed Hickman *(Mgr-Parts)*
Mike Rothery *(Mgr-Svc)*

Scottsdale Ferrari, LLC (1)
18118 N Scottsdale Rd, Phoenix, AZ 85054
Tel.: (480) 991-5322
Web Site: https://www.scottsdaleferrari.com
New Car Dealers
N.A.I.C.S.: 441110
Larry Isaacs *(Mgr)*
Chad Morgan *(Gen Mgr)*
Tim Cupp *(Mgr)*
David Mase *(Mgr-Mktg)*
Gary Simon *(Brand Mgr)*
Patrick O'Hara *(Sls Mgr)*

Scottsdale Paint & Body, LLC (1)
350 N Hayden Rd, Scottsdale, AZ 85257
Tel.: (480) 941-8800
Web Site: http://www.penskeautomotivegroup.com

Automobile Parts Distr
N.A.I.C.S.: 423120

Somerset Motors, Inc. (1)
1550 Rte 22 E, Bridgewater, NJ 08807-1137
Tel.: (732) 271-4000
Web Site: http://www.lexusofbridgewater.com
New & Used Car Dealers
N.A.I.C.S.: 441110

Sytner Group Limited (1)
2 Penman Way Grove Park, Meridian Business Park, Leicester, LE19 1ST, United Kingdom (100%)
Tel.: (44) 1162821000
Web Site: http://www.sytner.co.uk
Sales Range: $1-4.9 Billion
Emp.: 4,500
Operator of Luxury Automobile Dealerships
N.A.I.C.S.: 423110
Darren Edwards *(CEO)*

Subsidiary (Domestic):

Guy Salmon Honda Limited (2)
Manchester Rd, Knutsford, WA16 0ST, United Kingdom
Tel.: (44) 1565632525
New Car Dealers
N.A.I.C.S.: 441110

Guy Salmon Jaguar Stockport (2)
396 Wellington Road, Stockport, SK1 2AD, United Kingdom
Tel.: (44) 1616372021
Web Site: http://www.sytner.co.uk
Emp.: 200
Car Dealership
N.A.I.C.S.: 441110

Guy Salmon Limited (2)
2 Penman Way Grove Park, Leicester, LE19 1ST, Leicestershire, United Kingdom
Tel.: (44) 2083988966
Web Site: http://www.guysalmon.co.uk
New & Used Car Dealer
N.A.I.C.S.: 441110
David Edward *(Principal)*

Sytner Cars Limited (2)
2 Penman Way Grove Park, Leicester, LE19 1ST, Leicestershire, United Kingdom
Tel.: (44) 1274270570
Sales Range: $25-49.9 Million
Emp.: 45
New Car Dealers
N.A.I.C.S.: 441110
Sean Endeacott *(Mgr)*

Sytner Coventry Limited (2)
128 Holyhead Road, Coventry, CV5 8NA, West Midlands, United Kingdom
Tel.: (44) 2476600600
Web Site: http://www.sytnercoventrybmw.co.uk
Emp.: 120
New Car Dealers
N.A.I.C.S.: 441110

Sytner Finance Limited (2)
2 Penman Way Grove Park, Leicester, LE19 1ST, Leicestershire, United Kingdom
Tel.: (44) 1753887888
Web Site: http://www.sytner.co.uk
Emp.: 4
Automobile Financing Services
N.A.I.C.S.: 522220

Sytner Limited (2)
2 Penman Way Grove Park, Leicester, LE19 1ST, Leicestershire, United Kingdom
Tel.: (44) 1419431015
Sales Range: $25-49.9 Million
Emp.: 32
Automotive Retailer
N.A.I.C.S.: 441227

Sytner Retail Limited (2)
2 Penman Way Grove Park, Leicester, LE19 1ST, Leicestershire, United Kingdom
Tel.: (44) 1213089000
Automotive Retailer
N.A.I.C.S.: 441227

Sytner Sheffield Limited (2)
Brightside Way, Sheffield, S9 2RQ, South Yorkshire, United Kingdom
Tel.: (44) 1144932457
Web Site: http://www.sytner.co.uk

New & Used Car Dealer
N.A.I.C.S.: 441110

Sytner of Leicester Limited (2)
Meridian Business Park Meridian East, Leicester, LE19 1UY, Leicestershire, United Kingdom
Tel.: (44) 1162827700
Web Site: https://www.sytnerleicesterbmw.co.uk
New Car Dealers
N.A.I.C.S.: 441110

Toyota of Clovis (1)
895 W Shaw Ave, Clovis, CA 93612
Tel.: (559) 316-0431
Web Site: https://www.toyotaofclovis.com
Sales Range: $50-74.9 Million
Emp.: 80
Automobiles, New & Used
N.A.I.C.S.: 441110
Chris Royston *(Gen Mgr)*
Rudy Rivera *(Gen Sls Mgr)*
Karan Kanda *(Mgr-Sls)*
Merle Dasher *(Mgr-Parts)*
Matt Shergill *(Fin Dir)*
Marc Giusti *(Mgr-Fin)*
Daniel Gonzalez *(Mgr-Fin)*
Michelle Vue *(Mgr-Bus Dev)*
Eric Brincefield *(Mgr-Used Car)*

Turnersville Auto Mall (1)
3400 Rte 42, Turnersville, NJ 08012
Tel.: (856) 629-1900
Web Site: https://www.turnersvilleautomall.com
Sales Range: $250-299.9 Million
Emp.: 600
Car Dealership
N.A.I.C.S.: 441110

Turnersville Auto Outlet, LLC (1)
3751 Route 42, Blackwood, NJ 08012-1731
Tel.: (856) 629-8700
New & Used Car Dealers
N.A.I.C.S.: 441110

UAG Atlanta H1, LLC (1)
3699 Buford Dr NE, Buford, GA 30519
Tel.: (678) 318-3100
Web Site: https://www.hondamallofgeorgia.com
Sales Range: $50-74.9 Million
Emp.: 100
Car Dealership
N.A.I.C.S.: 441110

UAG Fairfield CA, LLC (1)
2555 Telegraph Rd, Bloomfield Hills, MI 48302-0954
Tel.: (248) 648-2500
Web Site: http://www.penskeautomotive.com
Emp.: 100
Car Distr
N.A.I.C.S.: 441110

UAG Fairfield CM, LLC (1)
102 Linwood Ave, Fairfield, CT 06824
Tel.: (203) 204-3011
Web Site: http://www.fairfieldmotorscollision.com
Car Repair Services
N.A.I.C.S.: 811121

UAG Fayetteville III, LLC (1)
1418 W Showroom Dr, Fayetteville, AR 72704
Tel.: (479) 324-2485
Web Site: https://www.acuraoffayetteville.com
Sales Range: $150-199.9 Million
Emp.: 300
Car Dealership
N.A.I.C.S.: 441110
Chris Everitt *(Gen Mgr)*
Joe Bittengle *(Gen Mgr)*
Ashley Wagler *(Mgr)*
David Howard *(Fin Mgr)*
Adam Meyer *(Mgr)*
Clark Rathe *(Sls Mgr)*
Payton Thomas *(Fin Mgr)*
Adam Meyer *(Mgr)*
Clark Rathe *(Sls Mgr)*
Payton Thomas *(Fin Mgr)*

UAG Landers Springdale, LLC (1)
1352 W Showroom Dr, Fayetteville, AR 72704-6806
Tel.: (479) 251-2100

New & Used Car Dealers
N.A.I.C.S.: 441110
John Robin *(Gen Mgr)*

UAG West Bay IA, LLC (1)
1095 Centerville Rd, Warwick, RI 02886
Tel.: (401) 821-1510
Web Site: http://www.lexusofwarwick.com
Sales Range: $25-49.9 Million
Emp.: 75
Automotive Retail Services
N.A.I.C.S.: 441227

Volkswagen Zentrum Aachen (VW) GmbH (1)
Trierer Strasse 169, 52078, Aachen, Germany
Tel.: (49) 24197770
Web Site: https://www.volkswagen.de
Car Distr
N.A.I.C.S.: 441110

Western Star Truck Centre Pty Ltd. (1)
72 Formation Street, PO Box 301, Godna, 4076, Wacol, Australia
Tel.: (61) 732717777
Web Site: http://www.westernstar.com.au
Emp.: 200
Car Distr
N.A.I.C.S.: 441110

Western Star Trucks Australia Pty. Ltd. (1)
72 Formation St, Wacol, 4076, QLD, Australia
Tel.: (61) 732717777
Web Site: http://www.westernstar.com.au
Sales Range: $50-74.9 Million
Emp.: 200
Heavy-Duty Class 8 Trucks & Truck Parts
N.A.I.C.S.: 423110

Subsidiary (Non-US):

MAN Automotive Imports (NZ) Ltd (2)
4 Langley Road, Wiri, Auckland, 2104, New Zealand
Tel.: (64) 92520910
Sales Range: $25-49.9 Million
Emp.: 40
Automobile Import & Distr
N.A.I.C.S.: 423110
Jason Cann *(Gen Mgr)*

Subsidiary (Domestic):

Man Automotive Imports Pty Ltd (2)
72 Formation Street, Wacol, 4076, QLD, Australia
Tel.: (61) 732717777
Web Site: http://www.man.com.au
Sales Range: $50-74.9 Million
Emp.: 100
Automotives Import & Distr
N.A.I.C.S.: 423120

Man Imports Pty Ltd (2)
72 Formation St, Wacol, 4076, QLD, Australia
Tel.: (61) 732717777
Emp.: 200
Waste Management Services
N.A.I.C.S.: 562998
Paul Glivic *(Gen Mgr)*

PENUMBRA, INC.

1 Penumbra Pl, Alameda, CA 94502
Tel.; (510) 748-3200 DE
Web Site: https://www.penumbrainc.com
Year Founded: 2004
PEN—(NYSE)
Rev.- $1,058,522,000
Assets: $1,556,305,000
Liabilities: $377,361,000
Net Worth: $1,178,944,000
Earnings: $90,954,000
Emp.: 4,200
Fiscal Year-end: 12/31/23
Surgical & Medical Instrument Mfr
N.A.I.C.S.: 339112
Ben Tompkins *(Exec VP-Dev)*
Sharon Hughes *(Sr VP-HR & Employee Dev)*

Johanna Roberts *(Gen Counsel, Sec & Exec VP)*
Ben Sorci *(Exec VP-Ops)*
Maggie S. Yuen *(CFO)*
Lambert Shiu *(Chief Acctg Officer)*
Jason Mills *(Exec VP-Strategy)*
James F. Benenati *(Chief Medical Officer)*
Adam Elsesser *(Co-Founder, Chm, Pres & CEO)*
Arani Bose *(Co-Founder)*

Subsidiaries:

Crossmed S.p.A. (1)
Corso Canonico Giuseppe Allamano 34, Grugliasco, 10095, Italy
Tel.: (39) 0114027301
Surgical & Medical Instrument Whslr
N.A.I.C.S.: 423450

Penumbra Europe GmbH (1)
Am Borsigturm 44, 13507, Berlin, Germany
Tel.: (49) 3020056760
Surgical Equipment Distr
N.A.I.C.S.: 423450

Penumbra Latin America Distribuidora de Equipamentos e Productos Medicos LTDA (1)
Av Brigadeiro Faria Lima 1336 cj 82, Sao Paulo, 01401-001, Brazil
Tel.: (55) 1128835825
Surgical Equipment Distr
N.A.I.C.S.: 423450

Penumbra Neuro Australia Pty. Ltd. (1)
Suite 3 Level 5 1 Oxford Street, Darlinghurst, 2010, NSW, Australia
Tel.: (61) 1300817025
Web Site: https://www.penumbrainc.com
Surgical Equipment Distr
N.A.I.C.S.: 423450

PEOPLES BANCORP INC.
138 Putnam St, Marietta, OH 45750
Tel.: (740) 373-3155 OH
Web Site:
https://www.peoplesbancorp.com
Year Founded: 1980
PEBO—(NASDAQ)
Rev.: $348,390,000
Assets: $7,207,304,000
Liabilities: $6,421,976,000
Net Worth: $785,328,000
Earnings: $101,292,000
Emp.: 1,267
Fiscal Year-end: 12/31/22
Bank Holding Company
N.A.I.C.S.: 551111
Tyler J. Wilcox *(Pres & CEO)*
Susan D. Rector *(Chm)*
Jason M. Eakle *(Chief Credit Officer & Exec VP)*
Kathryn Bailey *(CFO, Treas & Exec VP)*
Tyler Wilcox *(Exec VP-Community Banking)*
Mark J. Augenstein *(Exec VP-Ops)*
Ryan Kirkham *(Gen Counsel & Exec VP)*

Subsidiaries:

Limestone Bancorp, Inc. (1)
2500 Eastpoint Pkwy, Louisville, KY 40223
Tel.: (502) 499-4800
Web Site: https://www.limestonebank.com
Rev.: $66,687,000
Assets: $1,462,455,000
Liabilities: $1,328,597,000
Net Worth: $133,858,000
Earnings: $18,342,000
Emp.: 222
Fiscal Year-end: 12/31/2022
Bank Holding Company
N.A.I.C.S.: 551111

Subsidiary (Domestic):

PBI Bank (2)
2500 Eastpoint Pkwy, Louisville, KY 40223
Tel.: (502) 499-4800

Web Site: http://www.pbibank.com
Sales Range: $150-199.9 Million
Emp.: 60
Commercial Banking Services
N.A.I.C.S.: 522110
John T. Taylor *(Pres & CEO)*
Kevin Eskew *(VP)*

Peoples Bank (1)
138 Putnam St, Marietta, OH 45750 (100%)
Tel.: (740) 373-3155
Web Site: https://www.peoplesbancorp.com
Sales Range: $150-199.9 Million
Savings Bank
N.A.I.C.S.: 522180
Tyler J. Wilcox *(Pres & CEO)*
Susan D. Rector *(Chm)*
Jason M. Eakle *(Chief Credit Officer & Exec VP)*

Subsidiary (Domestic):

PBNA, LLC (2)
1100 N Market St 4th Fl, Wilmington, DE 19890
Tel.: (302) 778-2647
Investment Advisory Services
N.A.I.C.S.: 523940

Peoples Insurance Agency, LLC (2)
1700 8th St SW, Waverly, IA 50677 (100%)
Tel.: (319) 352-6327
Web Site: https://www.peoples-insurance.com
Sales Range: Less than $1 Million
Emp.: 100
Insurance Agents
N.A.I.C.S.: 524210

PEOPLES BANCORP OF NORTH CAROLINA, INC.
Tel.: (828) 464-5620 NC
Web Site:
https://www.peoplesbanknc.com
Year Founded: 1999
PEBK—(NASDAQ)
Rev.: $81,120,000
Assets: $1,620,927,000
Liabilities: $1,515,732,000
Net Worth: $105,195,000
Earnings: $16,123,000
Emp.: 279
Fiscal Year-end: 12/31/22
Bank Holding Company
N.A.I.C.S.: 522110
Lance A. Sellers *(Pres & CEO)*
Kimberly Boyd-Leaks *(Chief Banking Support Officer & Exec VP)*
James S. Abernethy *(Vice Chm)*
Jeffrey N. Hooper *(CFO & Exec VP)*
James O. Perry *(Chief Retail Officer & Exec VP)*
Timothy P. Turner *(Chief Credit Officer & Exec VP)*
William D. Cable Sr. *(Sec, Exec VP & Asst Treas)*

Subsidiaries:

Peoples Bank (1)
420 W A St, Newton, NC 28658
Tel.: (828) 464-5663
Web Site: https://www.peoplesbanknc.com
Sales Range: $25-49.9 Million
Emp.: 100
Banking Services
N.A.I.C.S.: 522110
Robert C. Abernethy *(Chm)*
Lance A. Sellers *(Pres & CEO)*
Kimberly Boyd-Leaks *(Chief Banking Support Officer & Exec VP)*

PEOPLES BANCORP WASH
Tel.: (740) 373-3155 OH
Year Founded: 1921
PPBB—(OTCIQ)
Banking Services
N.A.I.C.S.: 522110
Charles LeCocq *(CEO)*
Susan D. Rector *(Chm)*
Charles W. Sulerzyski *(Pres)*
Katie Bailey *(CFO, Treas & Exec VP)*

PEOPLES FINANCIAL CORPORATION
152 Lameuse St, Biloxi, MS 39530
Tel.: (228) 435-5511 MS
Web Site:
https://www.thepeoples.com
Year Founded: 1984
PFBX—(OTCQX)
Rev.: $30,603,000
Assets: $861,639,000
Liabilities: $806,445,000
Net Worth: $55,194,000
Earnings: $8,941,000
Emp.: 132
Fiscal Year-end: 12/31/22
Bank Holding Company
N.A.I.C.S.: 551111
Chevis C. Swetman *(Chm, Pres & CEO)*
A. Wes Fulmer *(Exec VP)*
J. Patrick Wild *(Second VP)*
Christy N. Ireland *(Sec & VP)*

Subsidiaries:

The Peoples Bank (1)
152 Lameuse St, Biloxi, MS 39530
Tel.: (228) 435-5511
Web Site: https://www.thepeoples.com
Rev.: $42,250,632
Emp.: 240
National Commercial Banks
N.A.I.C.S.: 522110
Chevis C. Swetman *(Chm, Pres & CEO)*
A. Wes Fulmer *(Exec VP)*
J. Patrick Wild *(Sr VP)*
Christy N. Ireland *(Sr VP)*
Liz Corso Joachim *(Vice Chm)*
A. Tanner Swetman *(Sr VP)*
Thomas H. Wicks *(Officer-Trust & Asst VP)*
Thomas E. Quave *(Officer-Trust & Asst VP)*

PEOPLES FINANCIAL SERVICES CORP.
150 N Washington Ave, Scranton, PA 18503
Tel.: (570) 346-7741 PA
Web Site: https://ir.psbt.com
Year Founded: 1986
PFIS—(NASDAQ)
Rev.: $123,179,000
Assets: $3,553,515,000
Liabilities: $3,238,165,000
Net Worth: $315,350,000
Earnings: $38,090,000
Emp.: 393
Fiscal Year-end: 12/31/22
Bank Holding Company
N.A.I.C.S.: 551111
Timothy H. Kirtley *(Chief Risk Officer, Sec & Exec VP)*
Craig W. Best *(CEO)*
Thomas P. Tulaney *(Pres & COO)*
John R. Anderson III *(CFO & Exec VP)*
Lynn M. Peters Thiel *(Chief Retail Officer & Exec VP)*
Laureen S. Cook *(Chief Acctg Officer)*
Thomas C. Cassidy *(Chief Investment Officer)*
Ian Matlack *(Pres & Pres-Greater Delaware Valley Market)*
Christopher Savena *(Pres & Pres-Greater Pittsburgh Valley Market)*
Susan L. Hubble *(CIO & Exec VP)*
Jeffrey A. Drobins *(Chief Lending Officer & Exec VP)*
Neal D. Koplin *(Chief Banking Officer & Sr Exec VP)*
Amy E. Vieney *(Chief HR Officer & Sr VP)*
Mary Griffin Cummings *(Gen Counsel & Exec VP)*
Donna Yanuzzi *(Officer-Equipment Fin & Exec VP)*
Edward O. Naab *(Pres-Central PA Market)*

Subsidiaries:

Peoples Security Bank and Trust Company (1)
150 N Washington Ave, Scranton, PA 18503
Tel.: (570) 346-7741
Web Site: https://www.psbt.com
Sales Range: $75-99.9 Million
Commercial Banking
N.A.I.C.S.: 522110
Craig W. Best *(CEO)*
Thomas P. Tulaney *(Pres & COO)*
Joseph M. Ferretti *(Pres-Market-Northeast & Exec VP)*
Jeffrey Solimine *(Officer-Mortgage Loan & VP)*
Sharon Byrne *(Officer-Corp Lending & Sr VP)*
J. Patrick Dietz *(Officer-Comml Lending & Sr VP)*
Amy Branning *(Officer-Comml Lending & VP)*
William Terrinoni *(Officer-Comml Lending & VP)*
Leigh A. Selden *(Sr VP-Comml Deposits & Treasury Svcs)*
Jill Zindle *(Sr VP & Mgr-Sls & Svcs)*

PEOPLES LTD.
76 Church St, Wyalusing, PA 18853
Tel.: (570) 746-1011 PA
Year Founded: 1987
PPLL—(OTCIQ)
Banking Holding Company
N.A.I.C.S.: 551111
Anthony J. Gabello *(Pres & CEO)*
Valerie W. Kinney *(Sr VP)*
Eli T. Tomlinson *(Sr VP)*
Drea M. Barbose *(Officer-Comml Loan)*
Janice M. Bevacqua *(Branch Mgr)*
Maylene V. Gregory *(Branch Mgr)*
Stacy L. Kaufmann *(Branch Mgr)*
Cynthia A. Miller *(Coord-Administrative Services & Human Resources)*
Jason D. Miller *(Officer-Mortgage Ops)*
Aimee O'Connor *(Branch Mgr)*
Tammy L. Schaeffer *(Supvr-Accounting)*
Sean Ann Schoen *(Dir-Marketing)*
George R. Spencer *(Officer-Comml Loan)*
William M. Joseph *(Sr VP)*
Jay W. Chadwick *(Chm)*
Andrew S. Ripic III *(Vice Chm)*
James L. Souto *(Sr VP)*
Marguerite M. Donato *(Sr VP)*

PEOPLES TRUST COMPANY OF ST. ALBANS
25 Kingman St, Saint Albans, VT 05478
Tel.: (802) 524-2196 VT
Web Site: https://www.ptcvt.com
Year Founded: 1886
PPAL—(OTCIQ)
Rev.: $10,617,295
Assets: $337,578,013
Liabilities: $301,055,808
Net Worth: $36,522,205
Earnings: $2,194,844
Fiscal Year-end: 12/31/20
State Commercial Banks
N.A.I.C.S.: 522110
Lyle D. Poirier *(VP)*
Danielle E. Manahan *(Sr VP)*
Barbara J. Toof *(Sr VP)*
Aaron A. Reynolds *(CFO & Sr Exec VP)*
Michael J. Elmore *(CIO & Sr VP)*
Jay C. Cummings *(Officer-Bus Dev & VP)*
Deidra Arel *(Officer-Comml Loan)*
Stacey M. Cauller *(Sr VP)*
Lloyd W. Larrow *(Sr VP)*
Carol C. Spillane *(Sr VP)*
Anne E. Gosselin *(Sr VP)*

Peoples Trust Company of St. Albans—(Continued)

Janice L. LaRocque *(Sr VP-BSA)*
Rachael A. Brown *(VP)*
Linda Lothian *(Branch Mgr)*
Carisa Ledoux *(Officer-Commercial & Residential Loan & VP)*
Travis Sweeney *(VP)*
Justin Wright *(Officer-Comml Loan)*
Linda M. LeBlanc Jr. *(COO, Sr Exec Officer & Sr Exec VP)*

PEOPLESWAY.COM, INC.

6033 Florence Ave Ste 200, Charlotte, NC 28212
Tel.: (704) 837-7971   NV
Web Site:
  http://www.peoplesway.com
Year Founded: 1999
PLWY—(OTCIQ)
Cosmetics Products Mfr
N.A.I.C.S.: 325620
Eugene A. Johnston *(CEO, CFO, Treas & Sec)*

PEPGEN INC.

321 Harrison Ave, Boston, MA 02118
Tel.: (781) 797-0979   DE
Web Site: https://www.pepgen.com
Year Founded: 2018
PEPG—(NASDAQ)
Rev.: $2,903,000
Assets: $217,440,000
Liabilities: $37,809,000
Net Worth: $179,631,000
Earnings: ($69,104,000)
Emp.: 45
Fiscal Year-end: 12/31/22
Biotechnology Research & Development Services
N.A.I.C.S.: 541714
Laurie B. Keating *(Chm)*
James McArthur *(Pres & CEO)*
Noel Donnelly *(CFO)*
Jaya Goyal *(Exec VP-)*
Michelle L. Mellion *(Chief Medical Officer, Sr VP & Head-)*
Mary Beth Delena *(Gen Counsel & Sec)*
Paul Streck *(Exec VP & Head-Research & Development)*
Dave Borah *(Sr VP-Investor Relations & Corporate Communications)*
Afsaneh Mohebbi *(Sr VP-Program Mgmt)*
Hayley Parker *(Sr VP-Global Regulatory Affairs)*
Niels Svenstrup *(Sr VP-Chemistry, Manufacturing, and Controls)*
Kyle Breidenstine *(VP-Finance & Controller)*
Jeffrey Foy *(VP-Toxicology)*
Patricia Fraser *(VP-Pharmacovigilance)*
Jane Larkindale *(VP-Clinical Science)*
Pallavi Lonkar *(VP-Bioanalytical, Biomarkers, and DMPK)*
Debra Sawyer *(VP-Quality Assurance)*

PEPPERLIME HEALTH ACQUISITION CORPORATION

548 Market St Ste 97425, San Francisco, CA 94104
Tel.: (415) 263-9939   Ky
Web Site:
  https://www.pepperlimehealth.com
Year Founded: 2021
PEPL—(NASDAQ)
Rev.: $2,441,119
Assets: $175,398,054
Liabilities: $180,796,814
Net Worth: ($5,398,760)
Earnings: $1,087,752
Emp.: 4
Fiscal Year-end: 12/31/22

Investment Services
N.A.I.C.S.: 523999
Ramzi Haidamus *(Chm & CEO)*
Eran Pilovsky *(CFO)*
Frank Ferrari *(Pres)*
Maurice Op de Beek *(Exec VP)*

PEPSICO, INC.

700 Anderson Hill Rd, Purchase, NY 10577
Tel.: (914) 253-2000   NC
Web Site: https://www.pepsico.com
Year Founded: 1965
PEP—(NASDAQ)
Rev.: $91,471,000,000
Assets: $100,495,000,000
Liabilities: $81,858,000,000
Net Worth: $18,637,000,000
Earnings: $9,074,000,000
Emp.: 318,000
Fiscal Year-end: 12/30/22
Snacks, Carbonated & Non-Carbonated Beverages & Food Mfr & Distr
N.A.I.C.S.: 312111
James Caulfield *(CFO & Exec VP)*
Ramon Luis Laguarta *(Chm & CEO)*
Katharina Stenholm *(Chief Sustainability Officer & Sr VP)*
Ramkumar Krishnan *(Chief Comml Officer & CEO-Intl Beverages)*
Jim Andrew *(Chief Sustainability Officer & Exec VP-Beyond the Bottle)*
Rene Lammers *(Chief Science Officer & Exec VP)*
Anne Fink *(Pres-Foodservice-Global)*
Seth Cohen *(CIO & Sr VP)*
Marie T. Gallagher *(Sr VP & Controller)*
Athina Kanioura *(Chief Strategy & Transformation Officer & Exec VP)*
Tina Bigalke *(Chief Diversity & Engagement Officer-Global)*
Vince Jones *(Head-eCommerce)*
Pietro Antonio Tataranni *(Chief Medical Officer & Sr VP-Life Sciences)*
Jane Wakely *(Chief Consumer & Mktg Officer, Chief Growth Officer-Intl Foods)*

Subsidiaries:

Alimentos del Istmo, S.A.   (1)
Apt 6-7 Ave Frangipany Corregimiento de Gurundu El Dorado, Panama, Panama
Tel.: (507) 2250115
Soft Drinks Mfr
N.A.I.C.S.: 312111

Anderson Hill Insurance Limited   (1)
Swan Building 3rd Fl 26 Victoria St, Hamilton, HM 12, Bermuda
Tel.: (441) 2959102
Web Site: http://www.pepsico.com
Emp.: 2
Alcoholic Beverages Mfr
N.A.I.C.S.: 722410
Mary-Lynn Robinson *(Mng Dir)*

Aradhana Foods and Juices Private Limited   (1)
6-3-905 4th Fl Saboo Towers Rajbhavan Rd Somaji Guda, Hyderabad, 500082, Andhra Pradesh, India
Tel.: (91) 4044584558
Sales Range: $10-24.9 Million
Emp.: 7
Alcoholic Beverages Mfr
N.A.I.C.S.: 722410
Desmond DSouza *(Gen Mgr)*

Beverages, Foods & Service Industries, Inc.   (1)
700 Anderson Hill Rd, Purchase, NY 10577
Tel.: (914) 253-2000
Web Site: http://www.pepsico.com
Soft Drink Distr
N.A.I.C.S.: 722515

Bluebird Foods Limited   (1)
124 Wiri Station Road, Manukau City, Auckland, New Zealand

Tel.: (64) 800730123
Web Site: https://www.bluebird.co.nz
Soft Drinks Mfr
N.A.I.C.S.: 312111

Bluebird Foods Limited   (1)
124 Wiri Station Road, Manukau, 2104, Auckland, New Zealand
Tel.: (64) 800730123
Web Site: http://www.bluebird.co.nz
Snack Food Mfr
N.A.I.C.S.: 311919

Bluejay Holdings LLC   (1)
30 N Gould St, Sheridan, WY 82801
Tel.: (307) 203-3505
Web Site: https://www.bluejayagents.com
Soft Drinks Mfr
N.A.I.C.S.: 312111

Border Properties, Inc.   (1)
1100 N Expy Ste E, Brownsville, TX 78521-1407
Tel.: (956) 546-3551
Alcoholic Beverages Services
N.A.I.C.S.: 722410
Barbara Eriksen *(Office Mgr)*
Mark Johnson *(Pres)*

Centro-Mediterranea de Bebidas Carbónicas PepsiCo, SL   (1)
Avenida de los Olmos 2, 01013, Vitoria, Alava, Spain
Tel.: (34) 900164164
Soft Drinks Mfr
N.A.I.C.S.: 312111

Chipsy For Food Industries SAE (Chipsy)   (1)
38 Mossadak Street Dokki, PO Box 27, El Mohandessin, Giza, Egypt
Tel.: (20) 23610093
Web Site: http://www.chipsyegypt.com
Snack Food Mfr
N.A.I.C.S.: 311919

Cipa Industrial de Produtos Alimentares Ltda.   (1)
Rodovia BR 153 Km 13 S/N, Jardim Paraiso, Aparecida de Goiania, 74984-431, GO, Brazil
Tel.: (55) 6240066213
Food Products Mfr
N.A.I.C.S.: 311991

Cipa Nordeste Industria de Produtos Alimentares Ltda.   (1)
Rodovia BR 101 Km 118 S/N/, Distrito Industrial Manoel Conde Sobral, Itaporanga d'Ajuda, 49120-000, SE, Brazil
Tel.: (55) 7332154751
Soft Drinks Mfr
N.A.I.C.S.: 312111

Cocina Autentica, LLC   (1)
7701 Legacy Dr, Plano, TX 75024-4002
Tel.: (972) 334-2587
Snack Food Mfr
N.A.I.C.S.: 311919

Comercializadora Nacional SAS Ltda.   (1)
Calle 110 No 9-25 Piso 4, Bogota, 1001, DC, Colombia
Tel.: (57) 15895111
Food Product Mfr & Distr
N.A.I.C.S.: 311919

Comercializadora Snacks, S.R.L.   (1)
Zona Industrial, Valera, Trujillo, Venezuela
Tel.: (58) 2712210190
Snack Food Distr
N.A.I.C.S.: 722515

CytoSport, Inc.   (1)
1340 Treat Blvd Ste 350, Walnut Creek, CA 94597
Tel.: (707) 751-3942
Web Site: http://www.cytosport.com
Nutritional Supplement Products Mfr, Distr & Online Retailer
N.A.I.C.S.: 311999
Lisa Selk *(CEO)*

Dark Green Australia Pty Limited   (1)
Twr A L 8 799 Pacific Hwy, Chatswood, 2067, NSW, Australia
Tel.: (61) 299511704
Snack Food Mfr
N.A.I.C.S.: 311919

Drinkfinity USA, Inc.   (1)
PO Box 1986, Horsham, PA 19044-9467
Web Site: http://www.drinkfinity.com
Soft Drinks Mfr
N.A.I.C.S.: 312111

Drinkstation, Inc.   (1)
1605 Lockness Pl, Los Angeles, CA 90501
Tel.: (310) 530-3859
Web Site: https://drinkstation.com
Water Purification Equipment Mfr & Distr
N.A.I.C.S.: 333413

Duyvis B.V.   (1)
Antwoordnummer 2460, 3600 VB, Maarssen, Netherlands
Tel.: (31) 8007377426
Web Site: https://www.duyvis.nl
Soft Drinks Mfr
N.A.I.C.S.: 312111

Duyvis Production B.V.   (1)
Diederik Sonoyweg 17, 1540 BR, Zaandam, Netherlands
Tel.: (31) 756514914
Web Site: https://www.duyvis.nl
Peanuts Mfr
N.A.I.C.S.: 722410

Electropura, S.R.L. de C.V.   (1)
Norte 45 No 709 Industrial Vallejo Azcapotzalco, Mexico, Mexico
Tel.: (52) 5511061500
Alcoholic Beverages Mfr
N.A.I.C.S.: 722410

Epic Enterprises Inc   (1)
11 Copeland Dr, Ayer, MA 01432-1790
Tel.: (978) 772-2340
Web Site: http://www.epicenterprisesinc.com
Soft Drinks Mfr
N.A.I.C.S.: 312111

Essentuksky plant of mineral waters on KMV Ltd.   (1)
141 Ul Pyatigorskaya, Yessentuki, Russia
Tel.: (7) 8793462325
Soft Drinks Mfr
N.A.I.C.S.: 312111

Euro-Juice G.m.b.H. Import and Vertrieb   (1)
Reiherstieg-Hauptdeich 39-47, 21107, Hamburg, 21107, Germany
Tel.: (49) 407527601
Soft Drinks Mfr
N.A.I.C.S.: 312111

Evercrisp Snack Productos de Chile S.A.   (1)
Avenida Cerillos N 999, commune of Cerillos, Santiago, Chile
Tel.: (56) 800395176
Web Site: http://www.pepsico.cl
Soft Drinks Mfr
N.A.I.C.S.: 312111

Frito-Lay Poland Sp.z.o.o.   (1)
ul Zamoyski 24/26, 03-801, Warsaw, Poland
Tel.: (48) 226707070
Web Site: http://www.pepsicopoland.com
Soft Drinks Mfr
N.A.I.C.S.: 312111

Frito-Lay Trading Company (Poland) GmbH   (1)
Spitalgasse 2, Bern, 3011, Switzerland
Tel.: (41) 313347000
Web Site: http://www.pepsico.com
Soft Drinks Mfr
N.A.I.C.S.: 312111

Fruko Mesrubat Sanayi, Ltd. Sti.   (1)
Tekfen Tower A Blok 209-3-4 Buyukdere Caddesi, Istanbul, 34394, Turkiye
Tel.: (90) 2123193000
Alcoholic Beverages Mfr
N.A.I.C.S.: 722410

GB International, Inc.   (1)
1800 112th Ave NE Ste 302E, Bellevue, WA 98004
Tel.: (425) 643-0500
Web Site: https://www.gbiworld.com
Soft Drinks Mfr
N.A.I.C.S.: 312111

Grupo Sabritas, S. de R.L. de C.V.   (1)
Norte 45 No 740 Industrial Vallejo Azcapot-

zalco, Mexico, 2300, Mexico
Tel.: (52) 5525823000
Alcoholic Beverages Mfr
N.A.I.C.S.: 722410

Hudson Valley Insurance Company (1)
99 W Main St, Walden, NY 12586
Tel.: (845) 778-2141
Web Site: http://www.hvagents.com
Emp.: 12
Insurance Agency Services
N.A.I.C.S.: 524210

Ignite Acquisition, Inc. (1)
5718 Westheimer Rd Ste 1000, Houston, TX 77057
Tel.: (713) 825-6599
Web Site: https://www.igniteacquisitionstx.com
Soft Drinks Mfr
N.A.I.C.S.: 312111

Industria de Refrescos Del Noreste, S.R.L. de C.V. (1)
Dr Coss No 815 Sur, Monterrey, 64000, Mexico
Tel.: (52) 8181270000
Soft Drinks Mfr
N.A.I.C.S.: 312111

Inversiones Borneo S.R.L. (1)
Calle Gonzales Prada No 174 Semi Rustica San Gregorio, Ate, 03, Peru
Tel.: (51) 12654231
Soft Drinks Mfr
N.A.I.C.S.: 312111

Inviting Foods LLC (1)
PO Box 049003, Chicago, IL 60604-9003
Web Site: https://hilolife.com
Soft Drinks Mfr
N.A.I.C.S.: 312111

Jordan Ice and Aerated Water Ltd. (1)
Zahran Street PepsiCo Bldg Bayader Area, PO Box 146, 11118, Amman, Jordan
Tel.: (962) 64892014
Soft Drinks Mfr
N.A.I.C.S.: 312111

KeVita, Inc. (1)
2220 Celsius Ave Ste A, Oxnard, CA 93030
Tel.: (888) 310-6106
Web Site: http://www.kevita.com
Soft Drinks Mfr
N.A.I.C.S.: 312111

Knjaz Milos a.d. (1)
Industrijska zona BB, 34300, Arandelovac, Serbia
Tel.: (381) 34700700
Web Site: http://www.knjaz.co.rs
Bottled Water & Juice Mfr & Whslr
N.A.I.C.S.: 312112
Zorica Vukcevic-Kljajic (Dir-Ops)
Zoran Dragas (Dir-Logistics)
Mihailo Jankovic (Gen Mgr)

Latvian Snacks SIA (1)
11c Katlakalna St, Riga, LV 1073, Latvia
Tel.: (371) 67320075
Alcoholic Beverages Mfr
N.A.I.C.S.: 722410

Marbo Product d.o.o. Beograd (1)
Dorda Stanojevica 14, Belgrade, 11070, Serbia
Tel.: (381) 113637000
Web Site: http://www.pepsico.com
Emp.: 100
Bakery Product Mfr & Distr
N.A.I.C.S.: 311812

Marbo d.o.o. Laktasi (1)
Bb Sportski Centar, Laktasi, 78250, Bosnia & Herzegovina
Tel.: (387) 51533215
Sales Range: $25-49.9 Million
Emp.: 30
Alcoholic Beverages Mfr
N.A.I.C.S.: 722410
Daniel Nadanic (Gen Mgr)

Matutano-Sociedade de Produtos Alimentares, Unipesoal Lda. (1)
Quinta Dos Conegos, Carregado, P-2580-465, Portugal
Tel.: (351) 263850500
Web Site: http://www.matutano.pt

Bakery Products Mfr & Sales
N.A.I.C.S.: 311919
Filipa Martines (Mgr)

One World Enterprises, LLC (1)
PO Box 6955, Bloomington, IN 47407
Tel.: (812) 339-2256
Web Site: https://bloomington.com
Soft Drinks Mfr
N.A.I.C.S.: 312111

P-Americas, LLC (1)
5733 Citrus Blvd, Harahan, LA 70123
Tel.: (504) 733-8705
Grocery Product Distr
N.A.I.C.S.: 424490

P.B.I. Fruit Juice Company BVBA (1)
Noordelijk Insteekdok-Zone 4 JP Verschaveweg 131 USA Kaai 411/412, 8380, Zeebrugge, West Flanders, Belgium
Tel.: (32) 50207207
Web Site: http://www.tropicana.de
Sales Range: $50-74.9 Million
Emp.: 250
Beverages Mfr
N.A.I.C.S.: 311919
Gerard Dekruijk (Gen Mgr)

PEPSI-COLA SR, s.r.o. (1)
Nadrazna 534, 901 01, Malacky, Slovakia
Tel.: (421) 347963110
Web Site: http://www.pepsico.sk
Soft Drinks Mfr
N.A.I.C.S.: 312111

PRS, Inc. (1)
10455 White Granite Dr Ste 400, Oakton, VA 22124
Tel.: (703) 536-9000
Web Site: https://prsinc.org
Soft Drinks Mfr
N.A.I.C.S.: 312111

Pepsi Foods Private Limited (1)
3B DLF Corporate Park S Block Qutab Enclave DLF Phase 3, Phase III, Gurgaon, 122002, Haryana, India (100%)
Tel.: (91) 1242880699
Web Site: http://www.pepsiindia.co.in
Sales Range: $50-74.9 Million
Emp.: 150
Snack Food Mfr
N.A.I.C.S.: 311919

Pepsi Logistics Company, Inc. (1)
5600 Headquarters Dr, Plano, TX 75024
Web Site: https://www.pepsilogistics.com
Soft Drinks Mfr
N.A.I.C.S.: 312111

Pepsi-Cola (Thai) Trading Company Limited (1)
Unit 2101 21st Floor, Two Pacific Place Building, 142 Sukhumvit Road Khlong Toey, Bangkok, 10110, Thailand
Tel.: (66) 26532110
Sales Range: $25-49.9 Million
Emp.: 34
Soft Drinks Mfr
N.A.I.C.S.: 312111

Pepsi-Cola Bottling Company of Ft. Lauderdale-Palm Beach, LLC (1)
7305 Garden Rd, Riviera Beach, FL 33404-3407
Tel.: (561) 848-1000
Web Site: http://www.pepsi.com
Emp.: 1,000
Soft Drink Distr
N.A.I.C.S.: 424490

Pepsi-Cola General Bottlers Poland SP, z.o.o. (1)
Ul Zamoyskiego 24/26, 03-801, Warsaw, Poland
Tel.: (48) 226707070
Web Site: http://www.pepsicopoland.com
Emp.: 2,850
Soft Drinks Mfr
N.A.I.C.S.: 312111

Pepsi-Cola GmbH (1)
Hugenottenallee 173, 63263, Neu-Isenburg, Germany
Tel.: (49) 61027490
Web Site: http://www.pepsico.com
Sales Range: $75-99.9 Million
Emp.: 200
Soft Drinks Mfr

N.A.I.C.S.: 312112
Andre Grube (Mng Dir)

Pepsi-Cola Interamericana de Guatemala S.A. (1)
5 Avenida 5-55 Zona 14, Guatemala, Guatemala
Tel.: (502) 23867800
Soft Drinks Mfr
N.A.I.C.S.: 312111

Pepsi-Cola International (PVT) Limited (1)
3B DLF Corporate Park S Block Qutab Enclave Phase III, Gurgaon, 122002, Haryana, India
Tel.: (91) 124 2355880
Web Site: http://www.pepsicoindia.co.in
Soft Drinks & Snacks Mfr
N.A.I.C.S.: 312112

Pepsi-Cola Manufacturing (Ireland) Unlimited Company (1)
Little Island Industrial Estate, Cork, Ireland (100%)
Tel.: (353) 214353921
Emp.: 160
Beverage Distr
N.A.I.C.S.: 424490

Pepsi-Cola Mexicana, S. de R.L. de C.V. (1)
Vasco de Quiroga 3000 Piso 4, Mexico, 1210, Mexico
Tel.: (52) 52614600
Web Site: http://mx.pepsimundo.com
Sales Range: $100-124.9 Million
Emp.: 250
Food Product Mfr & Distr
N.A.I.C.S.: 311919

Subsidiary (Domestic):

Embotelladora de Occidente S.A. de C.V. (2)
Av Mariano Otero 911 Col Del Fresno, Jardines De La Victoria Norte, 44900, Guadalajara, Mexico
Tel.: (52) 3336786600
Web Site: http://pepsico.com.mx
Soft Drinks Mfr
N.A.I.C.S.: 312111

Unit (Domestic):

Pepsi Beverages Company Mexico (2)
Avenida Acoxpa No 69 Col San Lorenzo Huipulco, Delegacion Tlalpan, 14370, Mexico, Mexico
Tel.: (52) 5556278600
Web Site: http://www.pepsico.com.mx
Soft Drink Bottler & Distr
N.A.I.C.S.: 312111

Pepsi-Cola Operating Company of Chesapeake & Indianapolis (1)
5411 W 78th St, Indianapolis, IN 46268
Tel.: (317) 876-3464
Soft Drinks Mfr
N.A.I.C.S.: 312111

Pepsi-Cola Products Philippines, Inc. (1)
Km 29 National Road Tunasan, Muntinlupa, 1773, Metro Manila, Philippines
Tel.: (63) 28873774
Web Site: http://www.pepsiphilippines.com
Sales Range: $600-649.9 Million
Emp.: 2,940
Soft Drinks Mfr
N.A.I.C.S.: 312111
Oscar S. Reyes (Chm)
Rosario C. Z. Nava (Compliance Officer & Sec)
Furqan Ahmed Syed (Co-Pres)
Imran Moid (CFO & Sr VP)
Angelica M. Dalupan (VP-Corp Affairs & Comm)
Domingo F. Almazan (Sr VP, Head-Natl Sls & Sr Gen Mgr-Metro Sls Ops)
Lyndon Cuadra (VP & Sr Gen Mgr-Visayas)
Robert Tongcua (VP & Sr Gen Mgr-Mindanao)
Jika Dalupan (VP-Corp Affair & Comm)
Samudra Bhattacharya (Co-Pres)
Celerino T. Grecia III (Sr VP-HR)
Allan A. Frias II (Sr VP-Mfg & Logistics)
Samuel A. Dalisay Jr. (VP-Supply Chain)

Pepsi-Cola of Corvallis, Inc. (1)
2636 NE Belvue St, Corvallis, OR 97330-4257
Tel.: (541) 758-1212
Soft Drink Distr
N.A.I.C.S.: 424490

PepsiCo (China) Co., Ltd. (1)
3 Jinhua Er Street Jinbi Road, Economic and Technological Development Zone, 510730, Guangzhou, China
Tel.: (86) 2082214888
Web Site: http://www.pepsico.com.cn
Soft Drinks Mfr
N.A.I.C.S.: 312111

PepsiCo (Ireland) (1)
Kilnagleary Crosshaven Road, Carrigaline, County Cork, Ireland
Tel.: (353) 214846100
Web Site: http://www.pepsico.ie
Soft Drinks Mfr
N.A.I.C.S.: 312111

PepsiCo Amacoco Bebidas Do Brasil Ltda. (1)
Avenida Presidente Juscelino Kubitschek n 180 9th floor, Vila Nova Conceicao, Sao Paulo, 04543-000, SP, Brazil
Tel.: (55) 1151887282
Web Site: http://www.pepsico.com.br
Soft Drink & Snack Food Whslr
N.A.I.C.S.: 424490

PepsiCo Americas Beverages (1)
1111 Westchester Ave, White Plains, NY 10604
Tel.: (914) 767-6000
Emp.: 66,800
Holding Company; Soft Drink Mfr & Distr
N.A.I.C.S.: 551112

Subsidiary (Domestic):

IZZE Beverage Company (2)
2990 Center Green Ct S, Boulder, CO 80301
Tel.: (303) 327-5515
Web Site: http://www.izze.com
Sales Range: $10-24.9 Million
Emp.: 18
Carbonated Fruit Juice Mfr
N.A.I.C.S.: 312111

Division (Domestic):

Pepsi Beverages Company (2)
700 Anderson Hill Rd, Purchase, NY 10577
Tel.: (914) 767-6000
Web Site: http://www.pepsico.com
Sales Range: $5-14.9 Billion
Soft Drink Mfr & Distr
N.A.I.C.S.: 312111

Subsidiary (Domestic):

Pepsi Northwest Beverages LLC (3)
3003 R W Johnson Rd Sw, Tumwater, WA 98512-6173
Tel.: (360) 357-9090
Soft Drinks Mfr
N.A.I.C.S.: 312111
Brian S. Charneski (Chm)
Tom Connolly (Reg Mgr)

Joint Venture (Domestic):

Pepsi Bottling Ventures LLC (2)
4141 ParkLake Ave Ste 600, Raleigh, NC 27612
Tel.: (919) 865-2300
Web Site: http://www.pepsibottlingventures.com
Sales Range: $200-249.9 Million
Soft Drinks Bottler; Owned by Suntory Ltd. & PepsiCo, Inc.
N.A.I.C.S.: 312111
Paul Finney (Pres & CEO)
Matthew Bucherati (Sr VP-Ops & Supply Chain)
Derek Hill (CFO)
Claire Niver (Sr VP-HR & Corp Affairs)
Mark Johnson (Sr VP-Sls & Mktg)

Plant (Domestic):

Pepsi Bottling - Raleigh (3)
Six Forks Ctr 4700 Homewood Ct Ste 380, Raleigh, NC 27609-5711
Tel.: (919) 782-9271

PepsiCo, Inc.—(Continued)

Sales Range: $250-299.9 Million
Emp.: 1,000
Bottles & Markets Pepsi Cola & Other
Drinks
N.A.I.C.S.: 312111
Rick Poillon *(Pres & CEO)*

Subsidiary (Domestic):

**Pepsi-Cola Bottling Co of Roxboro,
NC, Inc.**   **(3)**
605 S Morgan St, Roxboro, NC 27573
Tel.: (336) 599-2166
Rev.: $4,500,000
Emp.: 36
Other Grocery & Related Products Merchant Whslr
N.A.I.C.S.: 424490
Brantly T. Burnett *(Pres)*

Division (Domestic):

PepsiCo Beverages Americas   **(2)**
555 W Monroe St, Chicago, IL 60661
Tel.: (312) 821-1000
Web Site: http://www.pepsico.com
Sales Range: $250-299.9 Million
Regional Managing Office; Soft Drink Mfr &
Distr
N.A.I.C.S.: 551114

Subsidiary (Domestic):

Pepsi-Cola North America   **(3)**
700 Anderson Hill Rd, Purchase, NY 10577
Tel.: (914) 253-2000
Web Site: http://www.pepsico.com
Bottling Operations Management Services
N.A.I.C.S.: 561499

Plant (Domestic):

Pepsi-Cola Manufacturing International Ltd.   **(4)**
Cidra Industrial Park, Cidra, PR
00739   **(100%)**
Tel.: (787) 739-8411
Sales Range: $75-99.9 Million
Emp.: 160
Soft Drinks Mfr
N.A.I.C.S.: 312111
Martin Chacin *(Gen Mgr)*

Subsidiary (Domestic):

The Gatorade Company   **(3)**
555 W Monroe, Chicago, IL
60661-3605   **(100%)**
Tel.: (312) 821-1000
Web Site: http://www.gatorade.com
Sales Range: $550-600.0 Million
Emp.: 1,210
Energy Drink Mfr
N.A.I.C.S.: 312112

Subsidiary (Domestic):

**South Beach Beverage
Company**   **(2)**
700 Anderson Hill Rd, Purchase, NY
10577   **(100%)**
Tel.: (203) 899-7111
Web Site: http://www.sobeworld.com
Sales Range: $25-49.9 Million
Emp.: 1,500
Exotic Teas, Fruit Juices, Waters & Sports
Drinks Mfr & Distr
N.A.I.C.S.: 312111

PepsiCo Americas Foods   **(1)**
7701 Legacy Dr, Plano, TX 75024
Tel.: (972) 334-7000
Web Site: http://www.fritolay.com
Food & Snack Mfr & Distr
N.A.I.C.S.: 311919

Subsidiary (Domestic):

Frito-Lay, Inc.   **(2)**
7701 Legacy Dr, Plano, TX
75024-4002   **(100%)**
Tel.: (972) 334-7000
Web Site: https://www.fritolay.com
Sales Range: $5-14.9 Billion
Emp.: 3,000
Snack Food Mfr
N.A.I.C.S.: 311919

Subsidiary (Non-US):

Corina Snacks Limited   **(3)**
Limassol Industrial Estate Corner Delou &
Neftonos St, Limassol, 3056, Cyprus
Tel.: (357) 25391639
Web Site: http://www.pepsico.com
Emp.: 180
Snack Food Mfr
N.A.I.C.S.: 311919

Frito Lay Sp.z.o.o.   **(3)**
ul Zamoyskiego 24/26, 03-801, Warsaw,
Poland
Tel.: (48) 226707070
Web Site: http://www.pepsicopoland.com
Alcoholic Beverages Mfr
N.A.I.C.S.: 722410

**Frito-Lay Gida Sanayi Ve Ticaret
A.S.**   **(3)**
Tekfen Tower Buyukdere Cad No 209 A
Blok D 2 34394 4 Levent, Sisli, Istanbul,
Turkiye
Tel.: (90) 8502220737
Web Site: http://fritolay.com.tr
Alcoholic Beverages Mfr
N.A.I.C.S.: 722410

**Frito-Lay Netherlands Holding
B.V.**   **(3)**
Zonnebaan 35, 3542 EB, Utrecht, Netherlands
Tel.: (31) 302473811
Web Site: http://www.pepsico.nl
Soft Drinks Mfr
N.A.I.C.S.: 722410

Subsidiary (Domestic):

Frito-Lay North America, Inc.   **(3)**
7701 Legacy Dr, Plano, TX 75024
Tel.: (972) 334-7000
Web Site: http://www.fritolay.com
Savory Snack Mfr
N.A.I.C.S.: 311919
Joan Cetera *(VP-Comm)*
Michael Lindsey *(Chief Transformation &
Strategy Officer)*
Patrick McLaughlin *(Chief HR Officer & Sr
VP-HR)*
Leanne Oliver *(Gen Counsel & Sr VP)*
Gregg Roden *(Sr VP-Supply Chain)*
Stefano Sartoretti *(CFO & Sr VP)*
Dianne Sutter *(Officer-Market Supply & Sr
VP-Global Procurement)*
Rachel Ferdinando *(CMO & Sr VP)*
Mike Del Pozzo *(Chief Customer Officer &
Sr VP)*
Steve Llewellyn *(Sr VP & Gen Mgr-Field
Sls)*

Plant (Domestic):

Frito-Lay-Charlotte   **(4)**
2911 Nevada Blvd, Charlotte, NC 28273
Tel.: (704) 588-4150
Web Site: http://www.fritolay.com
Sales Range: $200-249.9 Million
Emp.: 450
Potato Chips & Snacks Mfr
N.A.I.C.S.: 311919

Subsidiary (Non-US):

**Frito-Lay Trading Company (Europe)
GmbH**   **(3)**
Spitalgasse 2, Bern, 3011, Switzerland
Tel.: (41) 313347000
Web Site: http://www.pepsico.co.uk
Sales Range: $250-299.9 Million
Emp.: 100
Snack Food Mfr
N.A.I.C.S.: 311919

Frito-Lay de Chile   **(3)**
Avenida Los Cerrillos 999, Cerrillos, Santiago, Chile
Tel.: (56) 22700400
Sales Range: $250-299.9 Million
Snack Food Mfr
N.A.I.C.S.: 311919

Joint Venture (Domestic):

Sabra Dipping Company LLC   **(3)**
777 Westchester Ave Fl 3, White Plains, NY
10604
Tel.: (718) 932-9000
Web Site: http://www.sabra.com

Sales Range: $50-74.9 Million
Dip & Spread Mfr
N.A.I.C.S.: 311919
Meiky Tollman *(VP-Growth & Capabilities-
Global)*
Eugenio Perrier *(CMO)*
John Boes *(Exec VP-Sls)*
Frank Armetta *(VP-Supply Chain-Global)*
Paula Fitzgerald *(CFO)*
Stacey Zeltner *(VP-HR)*
Cherie Floyd *(CTO)*
Joey Bergstein *(CEO)*

Subsidiary (Domestic):

Stacy's Pita Chip Company, Inc. **(3)**
121 Memorial Pkwy, Randolph, MA 02368
Tel.: (781) 963-6995
Web Site: http://www.stacyssnacks.com
Snack Food Mfr & Retailer
N.A.I.C.S.: 311919
Jennifer Saenz *(Pres)*

Subsidiary (Non-US):

**The Smith's Snackfood
Company**   **(3)**
Level 8 799 Pacific Highway, Chatswood,
2067, NSW, Australia
Tel.: (61) 1800025789
Web Site: http://www.smiths.com.au
Snack Foods Mfr & Distr
N.A.I.C.S.: 311919

Subsidiary (Non-US):

**Grupo Gamesa S. de R.L. de
C.V.**   **(2)**
Av Lazaro Cardenas No 2404 Edif E Col
Los Soles, San Pedro, 66270, Garza Garcia, Mexico
Tel.: (52) 8183995151
Web Site: http://www.gamesa.com.mx
Cookies & Snacks Mfr
N.A.I.C.S.: 311821

Division (Domestic):

Gamesa S. de R.L. de C.V.   **(3)**
Lazaro Cardenas No 2404 Pte Edificio
Soles Valle Oriente, Garza Garcia, 66270,
Mexico
Tel.: (52) 8183995151
Web Site: http://www.gamesa.com.mx
Sales Range: $250-299.9 Million
Emp.: 520
Food, Beverage & Tobacco Products Mfr
N.A.I.C.S.: 311919

Subsidiary (US):

Gamesa USA, Inc.   **(3)**
2850 E Cedar St, Ontario, CA 91761
Tel.: (909) 930-0886
Sales Range: $50-74.9 Million
Emp.: 60
Cookie Distr
N.A.I.C.S.: 424490

Subsidiary (Non-US):

Maizoro S.A. de C.V.   **(2)**
Norte 59 No 1100, Esquina Poniente 150,
Industrial Vallejo Azcapotzalco, 02300,
Mexico, DF, Mexico
Tel.: (52) 3333166840
Web Site: https://www.maizoro.com
Sales Range: $250-299.9 Million
Breakfast Cereal Mfr
N.A.I.C.S.: 311230

Sabritas, S.A. de R.L. de C.V.   **(2)**
Paseo de las Palmas 735 pisos 16 Y 17,
Colonia Lomas de Chapultepec, 11000,
Mexico, DF, Mexico
Tel.: (52) 5552027373
Web Site: http://www.sabritas.com.mx
Snack Food Mfr
N.A.I.C.S.: 311919

Subsidiary (Domestic):

The Quaker Oats Company   **(2)**
555 W Monroe Ste 16-01, Chicago, IL
60661-9001
Tel.: (312) 821-1000
Web Site: http://www.quakeroats.com
Grain-Based Foods & Beverages
N.A.I.C.S.: 311230

Holding (Non-US):

Quaker Holdings (UK) Ltd.   **(3)**
1600 Arlington Business Park Theale, PO
Box 24, Reading, RG7 4SA, Berkshire,
United Kingdom
Tel.: (44) 1189306666
Web Site: http://www.pepsico.co.uk
Sales Range: $250-299.9 Million
Emp.: 800
Holding Company
N.A.I.C.S.: 551112

Holding (Domestic):

Quaker Oats Limited   **(4)**
PO Box 7757, Leicester, LE4 5ZY, United
Kingdom   **(100%)**
Tel.: (44) 2038054817
Web Site: http://quaker.co.uk
Cereals & Snack Foods
N.A.I.C.S.: 311919

Holding (Non-US):

Quaker Oats B.V.   **(3)**
Brielselaan 7, 3081 AA, Rotterdam,
Netherlands   **(100%)**
Tel.: (31) 102906888
Web Site: http://www.quakeroats.com
Sales Range: Less than $1 Million
Emp.: 40
Cereal Mfr
N.A.I.C.S.: 311211
Menno Mackenbach *(Mng Dir)*

**Quaker Products (Malaysia) Sdn
Bhd**   **(3)**
15th Fl W Wing Wisma Consplant 2 No 7
Jalan Ss 16 1, 47500, Subang Jaya, Selangor Darul Ehsan, Malaysia
Tel.: (60) 356378000
Web Site:
     http://www.quakerproducts.com.my
Sales Range: $25-49.9 Million
Emp.: 27
Cereal & Beverage Mfr
N.A.I.C.S.: 311230

**PepsiCo Australia Holdings Pty
Limited**   **(1)**
Tower A Level 4 799 Pacific Highway,
Chatswood, 2067, NSW, Australia
Tel.: (61) 800025789
Web Site: https://www.pepsico.com.au
Soft Drinks Mfr
N.A.I.C.S.: 312111

**PepsiCo Azerbaijan Limited Liability
Company**   **(1)**
Bridge Plaza Floor 5 24 Bakikhanov str,
AZ1065, Baku, Azerbaijan
Tel.: (994) 124045552
Soft Drinks Mfr
N.A.I.C.S.: 312111
Rufat Shirinov *(Mgr-Bus Dev)*

PepsiCo BeLux BVBA   **(1)**
Da Vincilaan 3, 1930, Zaventem, Belgium
Tel.: (32) 27140540
Web Site: http://www.pepsico.be
Emp.: 180
Soft Drinks Mfr
N.A.I.C.S.: 312111
Japo Ouwerkerk *(Dir-Pub Policy, Govt Affairs & Comm)*
Wim Destoop *(VP & Gen Mgr)*
Jamie Newbury *(Sr Dir-Fin)*
Tim Mulder *(Sls Dir-Retail)*
Geoffroy Beaujean *(Sls Dir-Away From
Home)*
Tarok Wakod *(Dir Supply Chain)*
Meike Vorst *(Dir-Legal)*
Jose Senra *(Dir-IT)*
Hanneke van Aert *(Dir-HR)*
Barbara van Verseveld *(Comml Dir-Snacks)*
Joris van der Schoot *(Comml Dir-Nutrition)*

PepsiCo Beverages Italia S.r.l.   **(1)**
Via del Bosco Rinnovato 8 Edificio U4, Assago, 20057, Milan, Italy
Tel.: (39) 02434381
Web Site: http://www.pepsico.co.it
Sales Range: $25-49.9 Million
Emp.: 80
Soft Drinks Mfr
N.A.I.C.S.: 312111

**PepsiCo Beverages Switzerland
GmbH**   **(1)**

Genfergasse 4, 3011, Bern, Switzerland
Tel.: (41) 313347000
Web Site: http://www.pepsi.com
Soft Drinks Mfr
N.A.I.C.S.: 312111

PepsiCo CZ s.r.o. (1)
Kolbenova 50/510, 190 00, Prague, 9,
Czech Republic
Tel.: (420) 266191200
Web Site: http://www.pepsico.cz
Soft Drink Mfr & Distr
N.A.I.C.S.: 312111

PepsiCo Canada ULC (1)
5550 Explorer Drive 8th Floor, Mississauga,
L4W 0C3, ON, Canada
Tel.: (289) 374-5000
Web Site: http://www.pepsico.ca
Sales Range: $100-124.9 Million
Emp.: 200
Holding Company; Soft Drinks, Foods &
Snacks Mfr & Distr
N.A.I.C.S.: 551112

Unit (Domestic):

PepsiCo Beverages Canada (2)
5205 Satellite Drive, Mississauga, L4W 5J7,
ON, Canada
Tel.: (905) 212-7377
Web Site: http://www.pepsico.ca
Sales Range: $100-124.9 Million
Soft Drink Bottler & Distr
N.A.I.C.S.: 312111

PepsiCo Foods Canada (2)
5550 Explorer Drive 8th Floor, Mississauga,
L4W 0C3, ON, Canada
Tel.: (289) 374-5000
Web Site: http://www.pepsico.ca
Sales Range: $100-124.9 Million
Cereal & Snacks Mfr & Distr
N.A.I.C.S.: 311919

Plant (Domestic):

PepsiCo Foods Canada - Peterborough Plant (3)
14 Hunter Street E, PO Box 4100, Peterborough, K9J 7B2, ON, Canada
Tel.: (800) 433-2652
Web Site: http://www.pepsico.ca
Sales Range: $50-74.9 Million
Emp.: 125
Cereal & Snack Foods Mfr & Distr
N.A.I.C.S.: 311919

PepsiCo Deutschland GmBH (1)
Hugenottenallee 173, 63263, Neu-Isenburg,
Germany
Tel.: (49) 61027490
Web Site: https://www.pepsico.de
Soft Drinks Mfr
N.A.I.C.S.: 312111

PepsiCo Deutschland GmBH (1)
Hugenottenallee 173, 63263, Neu-Isenburg,
Germany
Tel.: (49) 61027490
Web Site: http://www.pepsico.de
Soft Drinks Mfr
N.A.I.C.S.: 312111

PepsiCo Eesti (1)
Tuglase 14, 51006, Tartu, Estonia
Tel.: (372) 5122689
Web Site: http://www.pepsico.ee
Emp.: 10
Snack Food & Beverages Mfr
N.A.I.C.S.: 311919

PepsiCo Finance (Antilles B) N.V. (1)
World Trade Center, 23 Piscadera Bay,
Willemstad, Curacao (100%)
Tel.: (599) 94636266
Web Site: http://www.pepsi.com
Sales Range: $125-149.9 Million
Emp.: 2
Financial Services
N.A.I.C.S.: 522320

PepsiCo Foods, A.I.E. (1)
Avenida de los Olmos 2, 01013, Vitoria,
Spain
Tel.: (34) 902115163
Web Site: http://www.pepsico.es
Soft Drinks Mfr
N.A.I.C.S.: 312111

PepsiCo France SNC (1)
15 boulevard Charles De Gaulle, 92705,
Colombes, Cedex, France
Tel.: (33) 155699000
Web Site: http://www.pepsi.fr
Emp.: 620
Bottled & Canned Soft Drinks Sales
N.A.I.C.S.: 424490
Christophe Laffont *(Dir-Fin, IT & Transformation)*
Jean-Paul Guichard *(Dir-Supply Chain)*
Thomas Decroix *(Dir-Comml)*
Sebastien Le Miere *(Dir-Beverage & Digital Div)*
Sophie Perrin *(Dir-Corp)*
Anne-Sophie Carrier *(Dir-Nutrition Div)*

PepsiCo India Holdings Private Limited (1)
Intellion Edge 1st Floor Office-01 5th and
6th Floor Tower - A, Southern Periphery
Road Sector-72, Gurgaon, 122 001, Haryana, India
Tel.: (91) 1800224020
Soft Drinks Mfr
N.A.I.C.S.: 312111

PepsiCo India Holdings Private Limited (1)
3B DLF Corporate Park S Block Qutab Enclave Phase-III, Gurgaon, 122002, Haryana,
India
Tel.: (91) 1242880699
Web Site: http://www.pepsicoindia.co.in
Holding Company
N.A.I.C.S.: 551112
Ahmed El-Sheikh *(Pres)*
George Kovoor *(Sr VP/Gen Mgr-Beverages)*

PepsiCo International Ltd. (1)
63 Kew Rd, Richmond, TW9 2QL, Surrey,
United Kingdom
Tel.: (44) 2083324000
Web Site: http://www.pepsi.co.uk
Sales Range: $75-99.9 Million
Emp.: 160
Soft Drinks Mfr
N.A.I.C.S.: 312111

PepsiCo Ireland Food & Beverages (1)
Unit A 3rd Floor Apex Business Centre
Blackthorn Road, Sandyford, Dublin, 18,
Ireland
Tel.: (353) 1293227
Web Site: http://www.walkerscrisps.ie
Sales Range: $25-49.9 Million
Emp.: 39
Snack Food Mfr
N.A.I.C.S.: 311919

PepsiCo Nederland B.V. (1)
Zonnebaan 35, 3542 EB, Utrecht, Netherlands
Tel.: (31) 302473811
Web Site: http://www.pepsico.nl
Emp.: 30
Soft Drinks Mfr
N.A.I.C.S.: 312111
Japo Ouwerkerk *(Mgr-Pub Policy, Govt Affairs & Comm)*
Wim Destoop *(VP & Gen Mgr)*
Barbara van Verseveld *(Dir-Comml-Snacks)*
Meike Vorst *(Dir-Legal)*

PepsiCo Nederland B.V. (1)
Stadsplateau 22-23, PO Box 1008, Kantoorgebouw Central Park, 3521 AZ, Utrecht,
Netherlands
Tel.: (31) 302473811
Web Site: http://www.pepsico.nl
Soft Drinks Mfr
N.A.I.C.S.: 312111

PepsiCo Nordic Finland OY (1)
Hiomotie 32, 00380, Helsinki, Finland
Tel.: (358) 96824450
Web Site: http://www.pepsico.com
Soft Drinks Mfr
N.A.I.C.S.: 312111

PepsiCo Puerto Rico, Inc. (1)
Cidra Industrial Park, Cidra, PR 00739
Tel.: (787) 739-8411
Web Site: http://www.pepsico.com
Soft Drinks Mfr
N.A.I.C.S.: 312111

PepsiCo Services Asia Ltd. (1)
622 Emporium Tower 17th & 22nd Floor

Sukhumvit Rd Klongton Klongtoey, Bangkok, 10110, Thailand
Tel.: (66) 26894600
Web Site: http://www.pepsithai.com
Soft Drinks Mfr
N.A.I.C.S.: 312111

PepsiCo de Argentina S.R.L. (1)
Cazadores de Coquimbo 2860, B1605BZ,
Munro, Buenos Aires, Argentina
Tel.: (54) 11 5533 5000
Web Site: http://www.pepsicoargentina.com
Soft Drinks Mfr
N.A.I.C.S.: 312111

PepsiCo do Brasil Holding Ltda. (1)
Rua Verbo Divino 1661, Sao Paulo, 04719-
002, Brazil
Tel.: (55) 1151887300
Holding Company
N.A.I.C.S.: 551112

PepsiCo do Brasil Ltda. (1)
Tel.: (55) 1151887000
Web Site: http://www.pepsico.com.br
Snack Food Mfr
N.A.I.C.S.: 311919

Pioneer Foods UK Ltd. (1)
40 Bradfield Road, Finedon Industrial Estate, Wellingborough, NN8 4HB, Northamptonshire, United Kingdom
Tel.: (44) 1933229139
Web Site: https://www.pioneer-foods-uk.com
Food Product Mfr & Distr
N.A.I.C.S.: 311991

Pipers Crisps Limited (1)
Pegasus Road Elsham Wold, Brigg, DN20
0SQ, North Lincolnshire, United Kingdom
Tel.: (44) 1652686960
Web Site: https://www.piperscrisps.com
Potato Chip Mfr & Whslr
N.A.I.C.S.: 311919
Simon Briggs *(Mgr-Dev-Intl)*

Prev PepsiCo Sociedade Previdenciaria (1)
Av Pres Juscelino Kubitschek 180 15 andar,
Itaim Bibi, Sao Paulo, Brazil
Tel.: (55) 8003260929
Web Site: https://www.prevpepsico.com.br
Soft Drinks Mfr
N.A.I.C.S.: 312111

Primrose, LLC (1)
724 Maple Grove Rd 127, Duluth, MN
55811
Tel.: (218) 724-4900
Web Site:
http://www.primroseretirement.com
Soft Drinks Mfr
N.A.I.C.S.: 312111

Procesos Plasticos S.R.L. de C.V. (1)
Av Hidalgo No 6, Parque Cartagena, Tultitlan, 54918, Hidalgo, Mexico
Tel.: (52) 5558881903
Soft Drinks Mfr
N.A.I.C.S.: 312111

Productos Industrializados Saltillo, S. de R.L. de C.V. (1)
Las Torres Parque Industrial Las Torres,
25114, Saltillo, Coahuila de Zaragoza,
Mexico
Tel.: (52) 8444382806
Web Site: http://www.pissacorp.com
Confectionary Product Mfr
N.A.I.C.S.: 311919

Punica Getranke GmbH (1)
Reiherstieg-Hauptdeich 39-47, Hamburg,
21107, Germany
Tel.: (49) 407527601
Web Site: http://www.punica.de
Soft Drinks Mfr
N.A.I.C.S.: 312111

Quadrant-Amroq Beverages S.R.L. (1)
Calea Vacaresti nr 391 etaj 4 Sectiunea 1
sector 4, Bucharest, 040069, Romania
Tel.: (40) 372377100
Web Site: http://www.pepsico.ro
Soft Drinks Mfr
N.A.I.C.S.: 312111

Quaker Manufacturing, LLC (1)
321 N Clark St, Chicago, IL 60654

Tel.: (312) 222-7111
Cereal Product Mfr
N.A.I.C.S.: 311230

Quaker Oats Australia Pty Ltd (1)
12 Carolyn Way, Forrestfield, 6058, WA,
Australia
Tel.: (61) 894548166
Web Site: http://www.quakeroats.com.au
Emp.: 45
Cereal Product Mfr
N.A.I.C.S.: 311230

Quaker Oats Europe, Inc. (1)
1105 N Market St, Wilmington, DE 19801
Tel.: (312) 821-1000
Web Site: http://www.quakeroats.com
Food Products Distr
N.A.I.C.S.: 424490

Quaker Peru S.R.L. (1)
Central Car S / N KM 11 5, Lima, Peru
Tel.: (51) 13560351
Breakfast Cereal Mfr
N.A.I.C.S.: 311230

Quaker Trading Limited (1)
Bridge Road, PO Box 24, Southall, UB2
4AG, Middlesex, United Kingdom
Tel.: (44) 2085742388
Grocery Product Distr
N.A.I.C.S.: 424490

Rockstar Inc. (1)
101 Convention Center Dr Ste 777, Las
Vegas, NV 89109
Tel.: (702) 939-5535
Web Site: http://rockstarenergy.com
Energy Drink Mfr & Marketer
N.A.I.C.S.: 312111

Sakata Rice Snacks Australia Pty Ltd (1)
145 Fitzgerald Road, Laverton, 3026, VIC,
Australia
Tel.: (61) 393694800
Web Site: http://www.pepsico.com.au
Emp.: 150
Snack Food Mfr
N.A.I.C.S.: 311919

Saudi Snack Foods Company Limited (1)
Tavaren Center King Fahad Road Tahlia
Street, Riyadh, 11455, Saudi Arabia
Tel.: (966) 12018888
Web Site: http://www.pepsico.com
Food & Beverage Mfr
N.A.I.C.S.: 312111

Shanghai PepsiCo Snacks Company Limited (1)
4th Floor Block B Victory Mansion 2200 Kai
Xuan Road, 200030, Shanghai, China
Tel.: (86) 2164687600
Snack Food Mfr
N.A.I.C.S.: 311919

Simba (Proprietary) Limited (1)
Andre Greyvenstein Avenue, Clearwater
Estate Office Park, Isando, 1600, Gauteng,
South Africa
Tel.: (27) 119286000
Web Site: http://www.simba.co.za
Soft Drinks Mfr
N.A.I.C.S.: 312111

Subsidiary (Domestic):

Pioneer Food Group Limited (2)
Ground Floor Building 1 Silver Stream Business Park 10 Muswell Road, Bryanston,
Johannesburg, 2191, South Africa
Tel.: (27) 219744000
Web Site: http://www.pioneerfoods.co.za
Rev.: $1,627,463,648
Assets: $1,174,336,975
Liabilities: $494,739,636
Net Worth: $679,597,338
Earnings: $86,987,727
Emp.: 9,239
Fiscal Year-end: 09/30/2018
Food & Beverage Services
N.A.I.C.S.: 311421
Tertius Alwyn Carstens *(CEO)*
Felix Lombard *(VP-Essential Foods)*
Jay-Ann Jacobs *(VP-Legal)*
Riaan Heyl *(VP-Go-to-Market)*
Bridgitte Backman *(VP-PPGA & Comm)*
Andreas Epiphaniou *(CFO & Sr VP)*

PepsiCo, Inc.—(Continued)

Annalize Van Der Waal *(VP-HR)*
Walter Todd *(Sr VP-Supply Chain-AMESA)*
Craig Weitz *(Sr VP-R&D)*
Roushay Swarts *(Sr Dir-IT)*

Subsidiary (Domestic):

Ceres Fruit Juices (Pty) Ltd **(3)**
Glacier Place 1 Sportica Crescent Tyger Valley, Bellville, 7530, South Africa
Tel.: (27) 219744000
Web Site: http://ceresfruitjuice.com
Sales Range: $25-49.9 Million
Emp.: 120
Fruit Juices Mfr
N.A.I.C.S.: 311421

Continental Beverages (Pty) Ltd **(3)**
32a Market St, Paarl, 7646, Western Cape, South Africa
Tel.: (27) 218070000
Web Site: http://www.pioneerfoods.co.za
Sales Range: $50-74.9 Million
Emp.: 430
Canned & Bottled Juices Distr
N.A.I.C.S.: 424490

Subsidiary (Non-US):

Pioneer Foods (UK) Limited **(3)**
40 Bradfield Road Finedon Industrial Estate, Wellingborough, NN8 4HB, Northamptonshire, United Kingdom
Tel.: (44) 1933229139
Web Site: https://www.pioneer-food-uk.com
Emp.: 70
Breakfast Cereal Mfr
N.A.I.C.S.: 311230

Plant (Domestic):

Bokomo Foods (UK) Ltd - Peterborough Factory **(4)**
Unit 2 Southgate Way Orton Southgate, Peterborough, PE2 6YG, Cambs, United Kingdom
Tel.: (44) 1733362900
Sales Range: $25-49.9 Million
Emp.: 80
Breakfast Cereal Mfr
N.A.I.C.S.: 311230

Subsidiary (Domestic):

Sasko Pasta (Pty) Ltd **(3)**
Rte 21 Corp Park Clockhouse Bldg 1st Fl W Wing 51 Sovereign Dr, Irene, Pretoria, 0062, Gauteng, South Africa
Tel.: (27) 123455975
Web Site: http://www.saskopasta.co.za
Sales Range: $25-49.9 Million
Emp.: 80
Pasta Mfr
N.A.I.C.S.: 311824

Simba Quix Swaziland (Pty) Limited **(1)**
30 Chris De Villiers St, PO Box 778, Ermelo, 2351, South Africa
Tel.: (27) 178113391
Grocery Product Distr
N.A.I.C.S.: 424490

Smartfoods, Inc. **(1)**
72 Wabash Ave, Clifton, NJ 07011
Tel.: (973) 778-7700
Web Site: https://www.smartfoodsinc.us
Soft Drinks Mfr
N.A.I.C.S.: 312111

Smiths Food Group, B.V. **(1)**
PO Box 1008, Maarssen, 3600 BA, Netherlands
Tel.: (31) 302473811
Web Site: http://www.smiths.nl
Snack Food Mfr
N.A.I.C.S.: 311919
Win Bitsnoop *(Gen Mgr)*

Snack Ventures S.A. **(1)**
Calle Tarragona 161 6, 08014, Barcelona, Spain
Tel.: (34) 934840500
Web Site: http://www.pepsico.com
Snack Food Mfr
N.A.I.C.S.: 311919

SodaStream Canada Ltd. **(1)**
325A Annagem Blvd, Mississauga, L5T

3A7, ON, Canada
Web Site: https://sodastream.ca
Soft Drinks Mfr
N.A.I.C.S.: 312111

SodaStream Enterprises N.V. **(1)**
Reduitlaan 42, 4814 DC, Breda, Netherlands
Tel.: (31) 8000223637
Soft Drinks Mfr
N.A.I.C.S.: 312111

SodaStream International Ltd. **(1)**
Gilboa Street, Airport City, Ben-Gurion Airport, 7019900, Israel
Tel.: (972) 39762317
Web Site: http://www.sodastream.com
Rev.: $543,371,000
Assets: $616,865,000
Liabilities: $115,689,000
Net Worth: $501,176,000
Earnings: $74,389,000
Emp.: 2,592
Fiscal Year-end: 12/31/2017
Sparkling Water & Flavored Sparkling Water Mfr
N.A.I.C.S.: 312111
Daniel Erdreich *(CFO)*
Eyal Shohat *(CEO)*
Idan Zu-Aretz *(COO)*
Galit Zucker *(Chief People Officer)*
Matti Yahav *(CMO)*
Roy Naaman *(VP-Growth Markets & Corp Dev)*
Ferdinand Barckhahn *(Gen Mgr-DACH)*

Subsidiary (Non-US):

SodaStream (SA) (Pty) Ltd. **(2)**
Route 21 Corporate Park 48 Sovereign Drive Irene Ext 30, PO Box 26849, Centurion, 1462, Gauteng, South Africa
Tel.: (27) 123459220
Web Site: http://www.sodastream.co.za
Home Beverage Carbonation System Mfr & Distr
N.A.I.C.S.: 333415

SodaStream (Switzerland) AG **(2)**
Bosch 67, 6331, Hünenberg, Switzerland
Tel.: (41) 417854444
Web Site: http://www.sodastream.ch
Sales Range: $25-49.9 Million
Emp.: 23
Home Beverage Carbonation System Mfr
N.A.I.C.S.: 332215

Subsidiary (US):

SodaStream Direct LLC **(2)**
1 Mall Dr, Cherry Hill, NJ 08002
Tel.: (800) 763-2258
Cooling & Dispensing Machinery Mfr
N.A.I.C.S.: 333415

Subsidiary (Domestic):

SodaStream Industries Ltd. **(2)**
1 Atir Yeda St, Kfar Saba, 4464301, Israel
Tel.: (972) 765996708
Home Beverage Carbonation System Mfr & Distr
N.A.I.C.S.: 333415

Subsidiary (Non-US):

SodaStream International B.V. **(2)**
Reduitlaan 42, 4814 DC, Breda, Netherlands
Web Site: http://www.sodastream.nl
Sales Range: $25-49.9 Million
Emp.: 20
Home Beverage Carbonation System Mfr
N.A.I.C.S.: 332215

Subsidiary (Domestic):

SodaStream Israel Ltd. **(2)**
Atir Yeda 1, Kfar Saba, Israel
Web Site: http://www.sodastream.co.il
Home Beverage Carbonation System Mfr
N.A.I.C.S.: 332215

Subsidiary (Non-US):

SodaStream Nordics AB **(2)**
Hammarby alle 150, 120 66, Stockholm, Sweden
Tel.: (46) 858630400
Web Site: https://www.sodastream.se

Sales Range: $25-49.9 Million
Emp.: 30
Home Beverage Carbonation System Mfr & Distr
N.A.I.C.S.: 332215

Subsidiary (US):

SodaStream USA, Inc. **(2)**
136 Gaither Dr Ste 200, Mount Laurel, NJ 08054
Tel.: (856) 755-3400
Web Site: https://www.sodastream.com
Sales Range: $25-49.9 Million
Emp.: 50
Home Beverage Carbonation Systems Mfr
N.A.I.C.S.: 335220
John Sheppard *(Pres)*
Bryan Welsh *(Gen Mgr)*

Subsidiary (Non-US):

Sodastream Australia Pty. Ltd. **(2)**
21 Henderson Road, Knoxfield, 3180, VIC, Australia
Tel.: (61) 387060200
Web Site: http://www.sodastream.com.au
Sales Range: $25-49.9 Million
Emp.: 40
Home Beverage Carbonation Systems Mfr
N.A.I.C.S.: 335220

Star Foods Bulgaria EOOD **(1)**
Sofia Airport Logistic Park 64 Haristofor Columb Blvd Fl 1 Bldg 1, Sofia, 1592, Bulgaria
Tel.: (359) 28035100
Web Site: http://www.pepsico.com
Sales Range: $25-49.9 Million
Emp.: 5
Soft Drinks Mfr
N.A.I.C.S.: 312111

Stratosphere Communications Pty Ltd **(1)**
1/278 Campbell Parade, PO Box 7226, Bondi Beach, Sydney, 2026, NSW, Australia
Tel.: (61) 404661833
Web Site: https://www.sodapressco.com
Soft Drinks Mfr
N.A.I.C.S.: 312111

Sun Foods Inc. **(1)**
1830 Gillespie Way Ste 101, El Cajon, CA 92020
Tel.: (619) 596-7979
Web Site: https://www.sunfood.com
Soft Drinks Mfr
N.A.I.C.S.: 312111

Tasty Foods S.A. **(1)**
Standardized Food Industry 22nd km Athens - Lamia, 145 65, Aylos Stefanos, Greece
Tel.: (30) 2106298000
Web Site: http://www.pepsico.com.gr
Snack Food Mfr
N.A.I.C.S.: 311919

The Concentrate Manufacturing Company of Ireland **(1)**
Little Ireland Business Park, Cork, Ireland
Tel.: (353) 214523100
Web Site: http://www.pepsico.com
Emp.: 500
Laboratory Testing Services
N.A.I.C.S.: 541380
David Murray *(Mng Dir)*

The Concentrate Mfr Company of Ireland **(1)**
Little Island Industrial Estate, Cork, Ireland
Tel.: (353) 214846100
Web Site: http://www.pepsico.ie
Soft Drinks Mfr
N.A.I.C.S.: 312111

The Gatorade Company of Australia Pty Limited **(1)**
L 5 55 Harrington St The Rocks, Sydney, 2000, NSW, Australia
Tel.: (61) 292414111
Business Support Services
N.A.I.C.S.: 561499

The Pepsi Bottling Group (Canada) ULC **(1)**
5205 Satellite Drive, Mississauga, L4W 5J7, ON, Canada

Tel.: (905) 212-7377
Web Site: http://www.pepsico.ca.com
Soft Drink Mfr & Distr
N.A.I.C.S.: 312111

The Radical Fruit Company of New York **(1)**
Enterprise Centre Hospital, Limerick, Ireland
Tel.: (353) 61383930
Web Site:
http://www.radicalfruitcompany.co.uk
Fruit Product Mfr
N.A.I.C.S.: 311411
Diarmuid Crowley *(Gen Mgr)*

Tropicana Alvalle S.L. **(1)**
Mayor Puente Tocinos 17, 30006, Murcia, Spain
Tel.: (34) 968230200
Soft Drinks Mfr
N.A.I.C.S.: 312111

Tropicana Europe N.V. **(1)**
Noordelijk Insteekdok - Zone 4 JP Verschaveweg 131 USA Kaai 411/412, 8380, Zeebrugge, Belgium
Tel.: (32) 50207207
Web Site: http://www.pepsico.be
Emp.: 180
Soft Drinks Mfr
N.A.I.C.S.: 312111

Tropicana Looza Benelux BVBA **(1)**
Imperiastraat 6, PO Box 2, Zaventem, 1930, Belgium
Tel.: (32) 27140540
Soft Drinks Mfr
N.A.I.C.S.: 312111
Win Destoop *(Gen Mgr)*

Tropicana Manufacturing Company, Inc. **(1)**
1001 13th Ave E, Bradenton, FL 34208
Tel.: (312) 821-1000
Fruit Juices Mfr
N.A.I.C.S.: 311411

UAB Lithuanian Snacks **(1)**
Zalgirio str 94, Vilnius, 09300, Lithuania
Tel.: (370) 52602444
Web Site: http://www.pepsico.lt
Emp.: 28
Snack Food Mfr
N.A.I.C.S.: 311919

Veurne Snack Foods BVBA **(1)**
Albert I laan 33, 8630, Veurne, Belgium
Tel.: (32) 58310111
Web Site: http://www.lays.be
Emp.: 480
Snack Food Mfr
N.A.I.C.S.: 311919

Walkers Group Limited **(1)**
Ashlar House 230 Cumberworth Lane, Denby Dale, Huddersfield, HD8 8PR, United Kingdom
Tel.: (44) 1484959595
Web Site: https://walker.group
Soft Drinks Mfr
N.A.I.C.S.: 312111

Walkers Snack Foods Limited **(1)**
FREEPOST 4 Leycroft Road, Leicester, LE4 5ZY, United Kingdom
Tel.: (44) 2038054817
Web Site: http://www.walkers.co.uk
Cookies, Crackers & Potato Chips Mfr
N.A.I.C.S.: 311821

Wimm-Bill-Dann JSC **(1)**
Dmitrovskoye shosse 108, 127591, Moscow, Russia
Tel.: (7) 4959370550
Web Site: http://www.wbd.ru
Dairy Products & Soft Drink Mfr & Whslr
N.A.I.C.S.: 424490

PERASO INC.
2309 Bering Dr, San Jose, CA 95131
Tel.: (408) 418-7500 **CA**
Web Site: https://www.perasoinc.com
Year Founded: 1991
PRSO—(NASDAQ)
Rev.: $14,868,000
Assets: $22,486,000
Liabilities: $7,229,000
Net Worth: $15,257,000
Earnings: ($32,398,000)

Emp.: 73
Fiscal Year-end: 12/31/22
Memory Technologies for Semiconductor Industry & Electronic Product Manufacturers
N.A.I.C.S.: 334413
Daniel L. Lewis (*VP & Gen Mgr-memory products*)
Ronald Glibbery (*CEO*)

Subsidiaries:

MoSys Inc. **(1)**
755 N Mathilda Ave, Sunnyvale, CA 94085
Tel.: (408) 731-1800
Web Site: http://www.mosysinc.com
Sales Range: $100-124.9 Million
Computer Electronic Parts Mfr
N.A.I.C.S.: 334419

MoSys International, Inc. **(1)**
Hachobori Kitajima Bldg 3F, 1 8 2 Shintomi Chuuoku, Tokyo, 104 0041, Japan
Tel.: (81) 335237018
Web Site: http://www.mosys.com
Sales Range: $100-124.9 Million
Electronic Parts Distr
N.A.I.C.S.: 334419

PERCEPTION CAPITAL CORP. III

3109 W 50th St Ste 207, Minneapolis, MN 55410
Tel.: (952) 456-5300   Ky
Web Site:
https://www.perceptioniii.com
Year Founded: 2021
PFTA—(NASDAQ)
Rev.: $11,277,331
Assets: $264,135,562
Liabilities: $270,713,392
Net Worth: ($6,577,830)
Earnings: $8,556,001
Emp.: 2
Fiscal Year-end: 12/31/22
Investment Holding Company
N.A.I.C.S.: 551112
Rick Gaenzle (*CEO*)
Tao Tan (*Pres*)

PERDOCEO EDUCATION CORPORATION

1750 E Golf Rd Ste 350, Schaumburg, IL 60173
Tel.: (847) 781-3600   DE
Web Site:
https://www.perdoceoed.com
Year Founded: 1994
PRDO—(NASDAQ)
Rev.: $710,004,000
Assets: $1,007,316,000
Liabilities: $165,895,000
Net Worth: $841,421,000
Earnings: $147,652,000
Emp.: 2,285
Fiscal Year-end: 12/31/23
Vocational Schools Operator
N.A.I.C.S.: 611710
Todd S. Nelson (*Pres & CEO*)
David C. Czeszewski (*CIO & Sr VP*)
Todd S. Nelson (*Chm*)
Elise Baskel (*Sr VP*)
Greg Jansen (*Gen Counsel*)
John Kline (*Sr VP*)
Jeffrey D. Ayers (*Gen Counsel, Sec & Sr VP*)

Subsidiaries:

American InterContinental University, Inc. **(1)**
6600 Peachtree-Dunwoody Rd 500 Embassy Row, Atlanta, GA 30328
Tel.: (404) 965-6500
Web Site: https://www.aiuniv.edu
Sales Range: $25-49.9 Million
Vocational Education Services
N.A.I.C.S.: 611310

Briarcliffe College **(1)**
1055 Stewart Ave, Bethpage, NY 11714

Tel.: (516) 918-3600
Web Site: http://www.briarcliffe.edu
Graduate & Undergraduate College
N.A.I.C.S.: 611310
George Santiago Jr. (*Pres*)

Brooks Institute **(1)**
5301 N Ventura Ave, Ventura, CA 93001
Tel.: (805) 585-8000
Web Site: http://www.brooks.edu
Sales Range: $25-49.9 Million
Emp.: 150
Vocational Education Services
N.A.I.C.S.: 611519
Chris Buckpitt (*Mgr-Building*)
Jesse Groves (*Dir-Gallery*)
Traci Jaslove (*Mgr-Santa Barbara Facilities*)

Brown College **(1)**
1345 Mendota Hts Rd, Mendota Heights, MN 55120
Tel.: (651) 905-3400
Web Site: http://www.mh.sanfordbrown.edu
Sales Range: $100-124.9 Million
Emp.: 30
Vocational Education Services
N.A.I.C.S.: 611519
Sheila Malewska (*Pres*)

CEC Insurance Agency, LLC **(1)**
7836 Church St Ste 1, Millington, TN 38053
Tel.: (901) 872-7060
Insurance Brokerage Services
N.A.I.C.S.: 524210

CEC Management, Inc. **(1)**
231 N Martingale Rd, Schaumburg, IL 60173
Tel.: (847) 781-3600
Web Site: http://www.cec.com
Sales Range: $150-199.9 Million
Emp.: 600
Business Services
N.A.I.C.S.: 561320
Gary E. McCullough (*CEO*)

Collins College **(1)**
4750 S 44th Pl 3100, Phoenix, AZ 85040
Tel.: (480) 966-3000
Web Site: http://www.collinscollege.edu
Sales Range: $50-74.9 Million
Emp.: 200
Provider of Vocational Education
N.A.I.C.S.: 611519

Colorado Technical University **(1)**
1575 Garden of the Gods Rd Ste 100, Colorado Springs, CO 80907
Tel.: (719) 598-0200
Web Site: https://www.coloradotech.edu
Colleges & Universities
N.A.I.C.S.: 611310
Harald Seidel (*Pres*)

Harrington College of Design **(1)**
200 W Madison St Lbby 2, Chicago, IL 60606-3593
Tel.: (312) 939-4975
Sales Range: $75-99.9 Million
Vocational Education Services
N.A.I.C.S.: 611310
Max S. Shangle (*Pres*)
Mitchell M. Obstfeld (*Chm*)
Dirk Fletcher (*Chm-Digital Photography Programs Dept*)
Gretchen Frickx (*Dir-Academic Svcs*)

Harrington Institute of Interior Design, Inc. **(1)**
200 W Madison St 2nd Fl, Chicago, IL 60606-3433
Tel.: (312) 939-4975
Web Site: http://www.harrington.edu
Schools & Universities Educational Service Provider
N.A.I.C.S.: 611310
Gretchen Frickx (*Pres*)

International Academy of Design & Technology **(1)**
1 N State St Ste 500, Chicago, IL 60602-3309
Tel.: (312) 980-9200
Sales Range: $75-99.9 Million
Emp.: 500
Vocational Education Services
N.A.I.C.S.: 611310
Antony Williams (*Pres*)

International Academy of Design & Technology Detroit, Inc. **(1)**

1850 Research Dr, Troy, MI 48083
Tel.: (248) 457-2700
Web Site: http://www.careered.com
Schools & Universities Educational Service Provider
N.A.I.C.S.: 611310

International Academy of Design & Technology-Nashville, LLC **(1)**
1 Bridgestone Park, Nashville, TN 37214
Tel.: (615) 232-7384
Web Site: http://www.iadt.edu
Schools & Universities Educational Service Provider
N.A.I.C.S.: 611310

International Academy of Design and Technology **(1)**
6039 S Rio Grande Ave, Orlando, FL 32809
Tel.: (407) 857-2300
Web Site: http://www.iadt.edu
Sales Range: $50-74.9 Million
Emp.: 300
Vocational Education Services
N.A.I.C.S.: 611310

International University of Monaco, SAM **(1)**
Le Stella 14 Rue Hubert Clerissi, 98000, Monaco, 98000, Monaco
Tel.: (377) 97986986
Web Site: https://www.monaco.edu
Sales Range: $10-24.9 Million
Emp.: 35
Schools & Universities Educational Service Provider
N.A.I.C.S.: 611310
Jean-philippe Muller (*Gen Dir*)
Marie-luce Torres (*Mgr-Digital Experience & Learning Resources*)
Jean-francois Vallauri (*Coord-Technical Svcs*)
Marjorie Bertschy (*Program Dir-Mktg-Luxury Goods & Svcs*)

Katharine Gibbs of Philadelphia, LLC **(1)**
2501 Monroe Blvd, Norristown, PA 19403-2422
Tel.: (610) 676-0500
Sales Range: $10-24.9 Million
Emp.: 15
Vocational Education Services
N.A.I.C.S.: 611110
Debra Weninger (*Pres*)

Kitchen Academy **(1)**
2800 W Higgins Rd, Hoffman Estates, IL 60169-2071
Web Site: http://www.kitchenacademy.com
Sales Range: $75-99.9 Million
Culinary Institute
N.A.I.C.S.: 611519

Le Cordon Bleu College of Culinary Arts **(1)**
8100 E Camelback Rd Ste 1001, Scottsdale, AZ 85251
Tel.: (480) 425-3000
Web Site: http://www.chefs.edu
Sales Range: $50-74.9 Million
Vocational Education Services
N.A.I.C.S.: 611699

Le Cordon Bleu College of Culinary Arts **(1)**
600 SW 10th Ave Ste 500, Portland, OR 09720
Tel.: (503) 223-2245
Web Site: http://www.chefs.edu
Sales Range: $1-9.9 Million
Vocational Education Services in Culinary Arts & Patisserie & Baking
N.A.I.C.S.: 611310
Julia Brooks (*Pres*)

Le Cordon Bleu College of Culinary Arts **(1)**
8511 Commodity Cir Ste 100, Orlando, FL 32819
Tel.: (407) 888-4000
Web Site: http://www.chefs.edu
Sales Range: $25-49.9 Million
Emp.: 100
Vocational Education Services in Culinary Arts & Patisserie & Baking
N.A.I.C.S.: 611310
James Bartholomew (*Pres-North America*)

Le Cordon Bleu College of Culinary Arts in Chicago **(1)**

361 W Chestnut, Chicago, IL 60610
Tel.: (312) 944-0882
Web Site: http://www.chefs.edu
Sales Range: $25-49.9 Million
Emp.: 100
Vocational Education Services
N.A.I.C.S.: 611699
Maegan Murphy (*Pres*)

Le Cordon Bleu North America, LLC **(1)**
1927 Lakeside Pkwy, Tucker, GA 30084
Tel.: (770) 938-4711
Web Site: http://www.chefs.edu
Sales Range: $25-49.9 Million
Emp.: 70
Education Services
N.A.I.C.S.: 611710

Missouri College, Inc. **(1)**
1405 S Hanley Rd, Brentwood, MO 63144
Tel.: (314) 768-7800
Web Site: http://www.cec.com
Sales Range: $50-74.9 Million
Vocational Education Services
N.A.I.C.S.: 611519

Sanford-Brown College - Boston **(1)**
126 Newbury St, Boston, MA 02116
Tel.: (617) 578-7100
Web Site: http://www.sanfordbrown.edu
Sales Range: $10-24.9 Million
Emp.: 20
Vocational Education Services
N.A.I.C.S.: 611210

Sanford-Brown College Inc. **(1)**
1345 Smizer Mill Rd, Fenton, MO 63026
Tel.: (636) 651-1600
Sales Range: $50-74.9 Million
Emp.: 200
Business & Secretarial Schools
N.A.I.C.S.: 611410

Sanford-Brown College, LLC **(1)**
1101 Eastport Plz Dr, Collinsville, IL 62234
Tel.: (618) 344-5600
Web Site: http://www.sanford-browncollege.com
Schools & Universities Educational Services
N.A.I.C.S.: 611710

The Katharine Gibbs Corporation-Melville **(1)**
320 S Service Rd, Melville, NY 11747-3201
Tel.: (631) 293-2460
Sales Range: $25-49.9 Million
Emp.: 50
Professional Schools & Universities Operator
N.A.I.C.S.: 611310

The Katharine Gibbs School of Norwalk, Inc. **(1)**
270 Farmington Ave Ste 245, Farmington, CT 06032
Tel.: (860) 882-1690
Sales Range: $10-24.9 Million
Emp.: 21
Vocational Education Services
N.A.I.C.S.: 611410

The Katharine Gibbs School of Piscataway, Inc. **(1)**
630 W Mount Pleasant Ave, Livingston, NJ 07039
Tel.: (732) 885-1580
Web Site: http://www.gibbseducation.com
Sales Range: $25-49.9 Million
Emp.: 61
Vocational Education Services
N.A.I.C.S.: 611410

Words of Wisdom, LLC **(1)**
231 N Martingale Rd, Schaumburg, IL 60173
Web Site:
https://www.wordsofwisdombooks.com
E Books & Educational Software Provider
N.A.I.C.S.: 513210

PEREGRINE INDUSTRIES, INC.

4525 W Reno Ave Ste A2-A4, Las Vegas, NV 89118

Peregrine Industries, Inc.—(Continued)

Tel.: (702) 888-1798   FL
Year Founded: 1995
PGID—(OTCIQ)
Rev.: $61,054
Assets: $1,668,408
Liabilities: $86,287
Net Worth: $1,582,121
Earnings: ($140,462)
Fiscal Year-end: 07/31/21
Industrial Products Mfr
N.A.I.C.S.: 333248
Miaohong Hanson (Pres & CEO)
Dong Hai Shi (Chm & Exec VP)
Lili Fan (CFO, Treas & Sec)

PERELLA WEINBERG PARTNERS LP
767 5th Ave, New York, NY 10153
Tel.: (212) 287-3200   DE
Web Site:
https://www.pwpartners.com
Year Founded: 2006
PWP—(NASDAQ)
Rev.: $648,652,000
Assets: $761,108,000
Liabilities: $492,862,000
Net Worth: $268,246,000
Earnings: ($111,840,000)
Emp.: 663
Fiscal Year-end: 12/31/23
Financial Advisory & Asset Management Services
N.A.I.C.S.: 523999
Robert Blumenfeld (Exec Dir)
Robert K. Steel (Vice Chm & Partner)
Peter A. Weinberg (Founder, Chm & CEO)
Kevin M. Cofsky (Partner)
Bruce Mendelsohn (Partner & Head-Restructuring)
Titus Leung (Partner)
Cem Koray (Partner)
Dietrich Becker (Pres, Partner & Head-European Advisory)
Jonathan Prather (Partner)
Riccardo Benedetti (Partner)
Kevin Lockhart (Partner)
Philip Pucciarelli (Partner)
Mauro Rossi (Partner & Mng Dir)
John M. Cesarz (Partner & Mng Dir)
Ridwan Obaray (Mng Dir)
Tulika Garg (Exec Dir)
Andrew Bednar (CEO & Partner)
Alexandra Gottschalk (Mng Dir & CFO)
Drew Ackert (Partner)
Jillian Colbert Alsheimer (Partner)
Christian Bradeen (Partner)
Kristin Carey (Partner)
Anthony Giuliano (Partner)
William Glass (Partner)
Michael J. Grace (Partner)
Ross Hammerman (Partner)
Timothy Kisling (Partner)
Philippe McAuliffe (Partner)
Douglas McGovern (Partner)
Nikhil V. Menon (Partner)
Christopher O'Connor (Partner)
Mark Polemeni (Partner)
Sam Tanzer (Partner)
Justin Kamen (Mng Dir & Chief Legal Officer)

Subsidiaries:

PWP Growth Equity LLC   (1)
767 5th Ave 10th Fl, New York, NY 10153
Tel.: (212) 287-3341
Web Site: http://www.pwpgrowthequity.com
Privater Equity Firm
N.A.I.C.S.: 523999
David Ferguson (Co-Founder & Mng Dir)
John McKee (Mng Dir)
Henry Heinerscheid (Mng Dir)
Santiago Nunez (Dir)
Dustin Price (Dir)
Dan Leever (Operating Partner)
Gilbert L. Baird III (Co-Founder & Partner)

Subsidiary (Domestic):

Alloy Die Casting Company   (2)
6550 Caballero Blvd, Buena Park, CA 90620
Tel.: (714) 521-9800
Web Site: http://www.alloydie.com
Sales Range: $25-49.9 Million
Emp.: 150
Die-Casting Services
N.A.I.C.S.: 331523
David W. Beddome (Pres)
Rick Simpson (Pres & CEO)

Subsidiary (Domestic):

Cast-Rite International Inc.   (3)
515 E Airline Way, Gardena, CA 90248
Tel.: (310) 532-2080
Web Site: https://www.cast-rite.com
Sales Range: $25-49.9 Million
Emp.: 114
Zinc & Zinc-Base Alloy Castings, Except Die-Castings
N.A.I.C.S.: 331529
Donald G. DeHaan (Pres)
Howard Watkins (Controller)

Perella Weinberg UK Limited   (1)
Third Floor 80 Charlotte Street, London, W1T 4DF, United Kingdom
Tel.: (44) 2072682800
Investment Financing Services
N.A.I.C.S.: 523999

Tudor, Pickering, Holt & Co. Securities-Canada ULC   (1)
Bow Valley Square IV Suite 2110 250 6th Avenue SW, Calgary, T2P 3H7, AB, Canada
Tel.: (403) 705-7830
Investment Financing Services
N.A.I.C.S.: 523999

Tudor, Pickering, Holt & Co., LLC   (1)
1111 Bagby St Ste 4900, Houston, TX 77002
Tel.: (713) 333-7100
Web Site: http://www.tphco.com
Energy Investment & Merchant Banking
N.A.I.C.S.: 523999
Bobby Tudor (Chm)
Maynard Holt (CEO)
Dan Pickering (Pres & Head-TPH Asset Mgmt)
Cameron Alguire (Mng Dir-Investment Banking)
Lance Gilliland (Mng Dir & Co-Head-M&A Investment Banking)
Paul Perea (Mng Dir & Co-Head-M&A Investment Banking)
Max Barrett (Exec Dir-Investment Banking)
Dean Burke (Exec Dir-Capital Solutions)
Jeff Tillery (Mng Dir & Head-Capital Solutions)
Chad Michael (Mng Dir & Head-Upstream Investment Banking)
Joe Amador (Mng Dir-Investment Banking)
Alex Andreichuk (Mng Dir-Investment Banking)
Aaron Blomquist (Mng Dir-Investment Banking)
Kirk Chatawanich (Mng Dir-Investment Banking)

PERF GO-GREEN HOLDINGS, INC.
12 E 52nd St 4th Fl, New York, NY 10022
Tel.: (212) 935-3550
Year Founded: 2005
PGOG—(OTCEM)
Biodegradable Plastic Product Retailer
N.A.I.C.S.: 423930
Michael Caridi (COO)

PERFORMANCE FOOD GROUP COMPANY
12500 W Creek Pkwy, Richmond, VA 23238
Tel.: (804) 484-7700   DE
Web Site: https://www.pfgc.com
Year Founded: 2002

PFGC—(NYSE)
Rev.: $58,281,200,000
Assets: $13,392,900,000
Liabilities: $9,266,000,000
Net Worth: $4,126,900,000
Earnings: $435,900,000
Emp.: 37,000
Fiscal Year-end: 06/29/24
Holding Company; Grocery Whslr & Distr
N.A.I.C.S.: 551112
Erika T. Davis (Chief HR Officer & Exec VP)
Craig H. Hoskins (Pres & COO)
H. Patrick Hatcher (CFO & Exec VP)
A. Brent King (Gen Counsel, Sec & Exec VP)
Robert D. Evans (Sr VP)
George Holm (CEO)
Jim Hope (Exec VP-Ops)
Mike Miller (Gen Counsel, Sec & Sr VP)
A. Brent King (Gen Counsel, Sec & Exec VP)
Donald S. Bulmer (CIO & Exec VP)
Erika T. Davis (Chief HR Officer & Exec VP)
Claudia Mills (VP-Diversity & Inclusion)
Bill Marshall (VP-IR)
Chasity Grosh (Chief Acctg Officer & Sr VP)
Scott E. McPherson (Chief Field Ops Officer & Exec VP)
Scott Golden (Dir-Comm & Engagement)
George L. Holm (Founder, Chm & CEO)

Subsidiaries:

AFFLINK, Inc.   (1)
1400 Afflink Pl, Tuscaloosa, AL 35406-2289
Tel.: (205) 345-4180
Web Site: https://www.afflink.com
Sales Range: $25-49.9 Million
Marketing Consulting Services
N.A.I.C.S.: 541613
Vince June (Sr VP-Supplier Dev & Mktg)
Michael Wilson (Pres & CEO)
Ron Wright (VP-Strategic Growth)
Peggy Cunningham (VP-Bus Svcs)

Caro Foods, Inc.   (1)
2324 Bayou Blue Rd, Houma, LA 70364
Tel.: (985) 872-1483
Sales Range: $125-149.9 Million
Food Products Distr
N.A.I.C.S.: 424410
Ralph Boudreau (Pres)
Brian Burchak (VP-Mdsg & Mktg)
Dirk Day (VP-Ops)

Carroll County Foods, Inc.   (1)
1333 Avondale Rd, New Windsor, MD 21776-8901
Tel.: (410) 876-2113
Web Site: http://www.psgc.com
Sales Range: $75-99.9 Million
Groceries Whslr
N.A.I.C.S.: 424410

Eby-Brown Company, LLC   (1)
1415 W Diehl Rd Ste 300N, Naperville, IL 60563
Web Site: http://www.eby-brown.com
Convenience Store Supplier & Wholesale Food Distr of Tobacco, Candy & Convenience Products
N.A.I.C.S.: 424410
Richard Wake (Co-Pres)
Tom Wake (Co-Pres)
Jode Bunce (Exec VP-Cigarettes)
Sharon Kuncl (VP-Mdsg)
Andy Batt (VP-Mdsg)
George Main (VP-Mdsg)
Cindy Dougherty (Mgr-Inventory Mgmt)

Division (Domestic):

Eby Brown Ohio   (2)
1982 Commerce Rd, Springfield, OH 45504   (100%)
Tel.: (937) 325-9254

Web Site: https://www.core-mark.com
Sales Range: $25-49.9 Million
Emp.: 300
General Line Grocery Distr
N.A.I.C.S.: 424940
Richard Wake (Pres)

Eby-Brown Co.   (2)
326 S Marble St, Rockmart, GA 30153-2622
Tel.: (770) 684-6524
Web Site: http://www.eby-brown.com
Sales Range: $25-49.9 Million
Emp.: 200
Wholesale Groceries Distr
N.A.I.C.S.: 424410

Eby-Brown Co.   (2)
2085 E Michigan Ave, Ypsilanti, MI 48197   (100%)
Tel.: (734) 487-8868
Web Site: http://www.eby-brown.com
Sales Range: $50-74.9 Million
Emp.: 350
General Line Groceries
N.A.I.C.S.: 424940
Richard Wake (Owner)
Steve Lindquist (VP-Ops)
Tom Wake (Owner)

Eby-Brown Co.   (2)
2051 Base Line Rd, Montgomery, IL 60538-1193   (100%)
Tel.: (630) 966-0300
Web Site: http://www.eby-brown.com
Emp.: 150
Warehouse Wholesale Distributor of Candy Tobacco Automotive Part & Grocery Distr
N.A.I.C.S.: 424450
Sean Jones (Gen Mgr)

Eby-Brown Co.   (2)
2516 Prospect Dr, Eau Claire, WI 54703-3872   (100%)
Tel.: (715) 874-4445
Web Site: http://www.eby-brown.com
Sales Range: $25-49.9 Million
Emp.: 100
General Line Groceries
N.A.I.C.S.: 424940

Eby-Brown Mid-Atlantic   (2)
6610 Cabot Dr, Baltimore, MD 21226-1754   (100%)
Tel.: (410) 360-6000
Web Site: http://www.eby-brown.com
Sales Range: $25-49.9 Million
Emp.: 200
Grocery Distr
N.A.I.C.S.: 424410

Liberty U.S.A., Inc.   (2)
920 Irwin Run Rd, West Mifflin, PA 15122
Tel.: (800) 289-5872
Web Site: http://www.libertyusa.com
Food Items Distr
N.A.I.C.S.: 311999
Kenny Sayers (Category Mgr-Foodsvc Deli)
Francesco Trama (Dir-Network Ops)
Mary Kohl (VP)
Ron Forney (Dir-Food Svc Sls)
Gary McGuirk Jr. (Pres & CEO)

Five Star Distributors Inc.   (1)
220 N Fairway Dr, Vernon Hills, IL 60061
Tel.: (847) 680-9900
Web Site: http://www.fivestardist.com
Sales Range: $10-24.9 Million
Vending Machine Product Distr
N.A.I.C.S.: 424450

Fox River Foods Inc.   (1)
5030 Baseline Rd, Montgomery, IL 60538-1125
Tel.: (630) 896-1991
Web Site:
http://www.performancefoodservice.com
Sales Range: $25-49.9 Million
Emp.: 300
Packaged Frozen Goods
N.A.I.C.S.: 424420

Hale Brothers Summit, LLC   (1)
5262 Air Park Blvd, Morristown, TN 37813
Tel.: (423) 318-8700
Web Site:
http://www.performancefoodservice.com
Sales Range: $450-499.9 Million
Food Service Industry Food Distr
N.A.I.C.S.: 424490

North Center Foodservice Corp. (1)
PO Box 2628, Augusta, ME 04338-2628
Tel.: (207) 623-8451
Web Site:
   http://www.performancefoodservice.com
Sales Range: $25-49.9 Million
Groceries Whslr
N.A.I.C.S.: 424410

Performance Food Group, Inc. (1)
188 Inverness Dr W Ste 800, Englewood,
CO 80112-3901
Tel.: (303) 662-7100
Web Site: https://www.vistar.com
Food Products & Related Supplies Distr
N.A.I.C.S.: 424410
Patrick T. Hagerty (CEO)
Jeff Fischer (VP-Strategic Dev)
Ann Reidy (Sr VP-Procurement & Pricing)
Steven Lewis (VP-Sls-Retail)
Cece Kramer (VP-Sls-Hospitality, Travel &
Value)
John Ochi (Sr VP-Ops)
Sean Mahoney (Sr VP-Sls & Mktg)
Sherri Hager (VP-Vending & OCS)

Subsidiary (Domestic):

PFG Florida, LLC (2)
3150 Gallagher Rd, Dover, FL 33527-0730
Tel.: (813) 659-0811
Web Site:
   http://www.performancefoodservice.com
Sales Range: $100-124.9 Million
Groceries Whslr
N.A.I.C.S.: 424410

Plant (Domestic):

PFG Miltons (2)
3501 Old Oakwood Rd, Oakwood, GA
30566
Tel.: (770) 532-7779
Web Site: http://www.pfgmiltons.com
Sales Range: $300-349.9 Million
Emp.: 550
Groceries Whslr
N.A.I.C.S.: 424410

Subsidiary (Domestic):

PFG-Lester Broadline Inc. (2)
401 Maddox Simpson Pkwy, Lebanon, TN
37090
Tel.: (615) 444-2010
Web Site:
   http://www.performancefoodservice.com
Sales Range: $150-199.9 Million
Grocery Whslr
N.A.I.C.S.: 424410

Plant (Domestic):

PFG-Middendorf (2)
3737 N Broadway, Saint Louis, MO 63147
Tel.: (314) 241-4800
Web Site: http://www.pfgc.com
Sales Range: $150-199.9 Million
Grocery Distr
N.A.I.C.S.: 424410
David Marsh (Pres)

PFG-Powell (2)
110 N Lee St, Thomasville, GA 31792-5484
Tel.: (229) 226-4331
Sales Range: $50-74.9 Million
Groceries & Related Products Whslr
N.A.I.C.S.: 424420

Subsidiary (Domestic):

PFG-Thoms Proestler Company (2)
8001 51st St W, Rock Island, IL 61201
Tel.: (309) 787-1234
Web Site: http://pfgc.com
Sales Range: $300-349.9 Million
Provider of Wholesale Food Distribution
Services
N.A.I.C.S.: 424490

Plant (Domestic):

Performance Food Group (2)
1 Performance Blvd, Springfield, MA 01104
Tel.: (413) 733-3053
Web Site: http://www.pfgspringfield.com
Sales Range: $75-99.9 Million
Groceries Whslr
N.A.I.C.S.: 424410
Robert Crory (Pres)

Unit (Domestic):

Performance Food Group AFI (2)
1 Ikea Dr, Elizabeth, NJ 07207-2906
Tel.: (908) 629-1800
Web Site:
   http://www.perfomancefoodservice.com
Sales Range: $150-199.9 Million
Groceries Whslr
N.A.I.C.S.: 424410
Mike Irwin (Pres)

Plant (Domestic):

**Performance Food Group Little
Rock** (2)
4901 Asher Ave, Little Rock, AR 72204-
7968
Tel.: (501) 568-3141
Web Site:
   http://www.performancefoodservice.com
Sales Range: $150-199.9 Million
Grocery Whslr
N.A.I.C.S.: 424410

**Performance Food Group
Victoria** (2)
204 N Brownson St, Victoria, TX 77901-
8535
Tel.: (361) 582-7500
Web Site: http://www.pfgvictoria.com
Sales Range: $75-99.9 Million
Groceries Whslr
N.A.I.C.S.: 424410

Subsidiary (Domestic):

**Performance Food Group of Texas,
LP** (2)
4141 Lucius McCelvey, Temple, TX 76504-
1226
Tel.: (254) 778-4519
Web Site:
   http://www.performancefoodservice.com
Sales Range: $150-199.9 Million
Emp.: 340
Groceries Whslr
N.A.I.C.S.: 424410

Division (Domestic):

**Performance Food Group, Inc. -
Broadline Division** (2)
12500 W Creek Pkwy, Richmond, VA 23238
Tel.: (804) 484-7700
Groceries Whslr & Distr
N.A.I.C.S.: 424410

**Performance Food Group, Inc. - Cus-
tomized Distribution** (2)
245 N Castle Heigths Ave, Lebanon, TN
37087
Tel.: (615) 444-2995
Web Site: https://www.pfgcustomized.com
Sales Range: $150-199.9 Million
Emp.: 150
Grocery Distr
N.A.I.C.S.: 424490

Unit (Domestic):

**Performance Food Group, Inc. -
Phoenix Specialty Distribution
Center** (2)
2434 S 10th St, Phoenix, AZ 85034-6521
Tel.: (602) 254-2500
Candy, Snacks & Beverages Whslr
N.A.I.C.S.: 424450
Don Bulmer (VP-IT)
Jeff Fischer (VP-Strategic Dev)
Steven Lewis (VP-Sls-Retail)
Ann Reidy (Sr VP-Procurement & Pricing)

Subsidiary (Domestic):

**Performance Foodservice-Somerset,
LLC** (2)
910 Hwy 461, Somerset, KY 42503
Tel.: (606) 274-4858
Web Site: http://www.somersetfoods.com
Sales Range: $25-49.9 Million
Broadline Food Distributor Services
N.A.I.C.S.: 424420

Preferred Snacks, LLC (1)
1919 US Hwy 34 Ste 600, Waco, NE 68450
Tel.: (402) 728-5398
Web Site: https://www.preferredsnacks.com
Popcorn Snack Mfr
N.A.I.C.S.: 311999

Reinhart FoodService, LLC (1)
6250 N River Rd Ste 9000, Rosemont, IL
60018
Tel.: (608) 782-2660
Web Site:
   http://www.reinhartfoodservice.com
Rev.: $1,400,000,000
Emp.: 400
Food & Nonfood Items Distr
N.A.I.C.S.: 424410

Subsidiary (Domestic):

CONCO Food Service (2)
2450 Severn Ave Ste 301, Metairie, LA
70001
Tel.: (504) 834-4082
Web Site: http://www.rfsdelivers.com
Sales Range: $75-99.9 Million
Food Distribution Services
N.A.I.C.S.: 424410

Earth Brothers, Ltd. (2)
449 River St, North Springfield, VT 05150
Tel.: (800) 228-5481
Web Site: http://www.blackriverproduce.com
Emp.: 200
Fresh Fruit & Vegetable Merchant Whslr
N.A.I.C.S.: 424480
Mark Curran (Co-Founder)
Steve Birge (Co-Founder)

Division (Domestic):

**Reinhart FoodService, LLC - Atlanta
Division** (2)
980 Six Flags Rd, Austell, GA 30168
Tel.: (678) 460-0355
Grocery Delivery Services
N.A.I.C.S.: 492210

**Reinhart FoodService, LLC - Burling-
ton Division** (2)
784 Hercules Dr, Colchester, VT 05446
Tel.: (802) 655-7595
Food Delivery Services
N.A.I.C.S.: 722310

**Reinhart FoodService, LLC - Cedar
Rapids Division** (2)
4100 44th Ave SW, Cedar Rapids, IA 52404
Tel.: (319) 396-1300
Food Delivery Services
N.A.I.C.S.: 492210
Rick Day (Gen Mgr)

**Reinhart FoodService, LLC - Chicago
Division** (2)
251 Central Ave, University Park, IL 60484
Tel.: (708) 672-1572
Food Delivery Services
N.A.I.C.S.: 492210

**Reinhart FoodService, LLC - Cincin-
nati Division** (2)
535 Shepherd Ave, Cincinnati, OH 45215
Tel.: (513) 421-9184
Food Delivery Services
N.A.I.C.S.: 492210

**Reinhart FoodService, LLC - Cleve-
land Division** (2)
6575 Davis Industrial Pkwy, Solon, OH
44139
Tel.: (440) 528-1275
Food Delivery Services
N.A.I.C.S.: 722310

**Reinhart FoodService, LLC - Detroit
Division** (2)
24838 Ryan Rd, Warren, MI 48091
Tel.: (586) 757-9998
Web Site: http://www.rfsdelivers.com
Emp.: 150
Grocery Delivery Services
N.A.I.C.S.: 492210

**Reinhart FoodService, LLC - Eastern
Pennsylvania Division** (2)
100 Industrial Park Rd, Coal Township, PA
17866
Tel.: (570) 644-1111
Web Site: http://www.rfsdelivers.com
Grocery Delivery Services
N.A.I.C.S.: 492210

**Reinhart FoodService, LLC - Jack-
sonville Division** (2)
7735 Westside Industrial Dr, Jacksonville,
FL 32219

Tel.: (904) 781-9888
Grocery Delivery Services
N.A.I.C.S.: 492210

**Reinhart FoodService, LLC - Johnson
City Division** (2)
2722 S Roan St, Johnson City, TN 37601
Tel.: (423) 979-1052
Web Site: http://www.rfsdelivers.com
Food Delivery Services
N.A.I.C.S.: 492210

**Reinhart FoodService, LLC - Kansas
City Division** (2)
290 SE Thompson Dr, Lees Summit, MO
64082
Tel.: (816) 246-0100
Web Site: http://www.rfsdelivers.com
Food Delivery Services
N.A.I.C.S.: 492210

**Reinhart FoodService, LLC - Knox-
ville Division** (2)
4721 Singleton Station Rd, Louisville, TN
37777
Tel.: (865) 970-7800
Web Site: http://www.rfsdelivers.com
Food Delivery Services
N.A.I.C.S.: 492210
Gary Rose (Pres-Div)

**Reinhart FoodService, LLC - La
Crosse Division** (2)
1500 St James St, La Crosse, WI 54602
Tel.: (608) 782-2660
Food Delivery Services
N.A.I.C.S.: 492210

**Reinhart FoodService, LLC - Lafay-
ette Division** (2)
1016 SW Evangeline Trwy, Lafayette, LA
70501
Tel.: (337) 232-5675
Food Delivery Services
N.A.I.C.S.: 492210

**Reinhart FoodService, LLC - Louis-
ville Division** (2)
2201 Ampere Dr, Louisville, KY 40299
Tel.: (502) 267-5464
Web Site: http://www.rfsdelivers.com
Food Delivery Services
N.A.I.C.S.: 492210

**Reinhart FoodService, LLC - Mar-
quette Division** (2)
881 County Rd 480, Marquette, MI 49855
Tel.: (906) 249-1428
Food Delivery Services
N.A.I.C.S.: 492210

**Reinhart FoodService, LLC - Milwau-
kee Division** (2)
9950 S Reinhart Dr, Oak Creek, WI 53154
Tel.: (414) 761-5011
Food Delivery Services
N.A.I.C.S.: 492210

**Reinhart FoodService, LLC - New
Bedford Division** (2)
214 Samuel Barnet Blvd, New Bedford, MA
02745
Tel.: (508) 985-2200
Grocery Delivery Services
N.A.I.C.S.: 492210

**Reinhart FoodService, LLC - New
Orleans Division** (2)
918 Edwards Ave, Harahan, LA 70123
Tel.: (504) 733-5200
Food Delivery Services
N.A.I.C.S.: 492210

**Reinhart FoodService, LLC - Pitts-
burgh Division** (2)
226 E View Dr, Mount Pleasant, PA 15666
Tel.: (724) 696-2200
Web Site: http://www.rfsdelivers.com
Grocery Delivery Services
N.A.I.C.S.: 492210

**Reinhart FoodService, LLC - Rich-
mond Division** (2)
8025 Quality Dr, Prince George, VA 23875
Tel.: (804) 861-1107
Food Delivery Services
N.A.I.C.S.: 722310

**Reinhart FoodService, LLC - Sha-
wano Division** (2)

Performance Food Group Company—(Continued)

1260 County Rd B, Shawano, WI 54166
Tel.: (715) 280-7070
Food Delivery Services
N.A.I.C.S.: 492210

Reinhart FoodService, LLC - Shreveport Division (2)
524 W 61st St, Shreveport, LA 71148
Tel.: (318) 869-3061
Food Delivery Services
N.A.I.C.S.: 722310

Reinhart FoodService, LLC - Springfield Division (2)
1620 N Packer Rd, Springfield, MO 65803
Tel.: (417) 862-6644
Food Delivery Services
N.A.I.C.S.: 722310

Reinhart FoodService, LLC - Tidewater Division (2)
1201 Progress Rd, Suffolk, VA 23434
Tel.: (757) 538-8000
Food Delivery Services
N.A.I.C.S.: 722310

Reinhart FoodService, LLC - Twin Cities Division (2)
13400 Commerce Blvd, Rogers, MN 55374
Tel.: (763) 428-6500
Web Site: http://www.rfsdelivers.com
Food Delivery Services
N.A.I.C.S.: 722310

Reinhart FoodService, LLC - Valdosta Division (2)
107 B Ave, Valdosta, GA 31603
Tel.: (229) 242-0867
Web Site: http://www.rfsdelivers.com
Food Delivery Services
N.A.I.C.S.: 492210

Subsidiary (Domestic):

The IJ Company (2)
4721 Singleton Sta Rd, Louisville, TN 37777-4746
Tel.: (865) 970-7800
Web Site: http://www.reinhart.com
Sales Range: $75-99.9 Million
Distr of Groceries
N.A.I.C.S.: 424410

Roma Food Enterprises Inc. (1)
12650 E Arapahoe Rd, Centennial, CO 80112
Tel.: (732) 463-7662
Web Site: http://www.romafood.com
Food Distr
N.A.I.C.S.: 424410

Sunrise Fresh Produce, LLC (1)
4229 Michael Avalon Dr, Jackson, MS 39209
Tel.: (601) 213-4008
Web Site: https://www.sunrisefreshproduce.com
Fruit Mfr & Distr
N.A.I.C.S.: 311421

T.F. Kinnealey & Co., Inc. (1)
1100 Pearl St, Brockton, MA 02301
Tel.: (508) 638-7700
Web Site: https://kinnealey.com
Meat & Meat Products Distr
N.A.I.C.S.: 445240
Robert Wallace (VP-Fin & Controller)

PERFORMANT FINANCIAL CORPORATION
333 N Canyons Pkwy Ste 100, Livermore, CA 94551
Tel.: (925) 960-4800   DE
Web Site:
   https://www.performantcorp.com
Year Founded: 1976
PFMT—(NASDAQ)
Rev.: $109,184,000
Assets: $118,833,000
Liabilities: $34,348,000
Net Worth: $84,485,000
Earnings: ($6,537,000)
Emp.: 1,023
Fiscal Year-end: 12/31/22

Technology-Based Recovery & Related Analytics
N.A.I.C.S.: 541519
Lisa C. Im (Exec Chm)
Simeon M. Kohl (CEO)
Simeon Kohl (Sr VP & Gen Mgr-Healthcare)
Ian Johnston (Chief Acctg Officer & VP)
Rohit Ramchandani (CFO)
Melissa Christ (Chief People Officer)
Christian Bass (VP)
Alan Coulter (VP)
Taylor Culberson (VP)
Ted Doyle (VP)
Amanda Purvis (VP)
Scott Putnam (VP)

Subsidiaries:

Performant Recovery, Inc. (1)
333 N Canyons Pkwy Ste 100, Livermore, CA 94551
Tel.: (209) 858-3500
Web Site: http://www.dcswins.com
Sales Range: $50-74.9 Million
Emp.: 750
Collection Agency
N.A.I.C.S.: 561440

PERIGEE HOLDINGS INC.
9605 W 49 Ave Ste 200, Wheat Ridge, CO 80033
Tel.: (303) 422-8127   NV
Web Site:
   http://www.crowdgather.com
Year Founded: 2005
PEHD—(OTCIQ)
Sales Range: Less than $1 Million
Emp.: 2
Internet Forum Hosting & Content Management Systems Services, Software & Applications
N.A.I.C.S.: 513210
Calvin Smiley (CEO)
Michael A. Littman (Sec)
Shelly Williams (Asst Sec)

PERIMETER SOLUTIONS, SA
10667 Jersey Blvd Rancho, Cucamonga, CA 91730
Tel.: (352) 2668621   LU
Web Site: https://www.perimeter-solutions.com
Year Founded: 2021
PRM—(NYSE)
Fire Retardant Product Mfr
N.A.I.C.S.: 325998

PERIPHAS CAPITAL PARTNERING CORPORATION
667 Madison Ave 15th Fl, New York, NY 10065
Tel.: (646) 876-6351   DE
Year Founded: 2020
PCPCU—(NYSE)
Investment Services
N.A.I.C.S.: 523999
Sanjeev Mehra (CEO)
Jeff Dodge (COO)
Anish Pathipati (Exec VP)

PERMA-FIX ENVIRONMENTAL SERVICES, INC.
8302 Dunwoody Pl Ste 250, Atlanta, GA 30350
Tel.: (770) 587-9898   DE
Web Site: https://www.perma-fix.com
Year Founded: 1990
PESI—(NASDAQ)
Rev.: $70,599,000
Assets: $70,898,000
Liabilities: $33,365,000
Net Worth: $37,533,000
Earnings: ($3,816,000)
Emp.: 287
Fiscal Year-end: 12/31/22
Environmental Services

N.A.I.C.S.: 562211
Richard Grondin (Exec VP-Waste Treatment Ops)
Louis Francis Centofanti (Founder & Exec VP/Exec VP-Strategic Initiatives)
Larry Morse Shelton (Chm)
Mark J. Duff (Pres & CEO)

Subsidiaries:

Diversified Scientific Services, Inc. (1)
657 Gallaher Rd, Kingston, TN 37763   (100%)
Tel.: (865) 376-0084
Sales Range: $50-74.9 Million
Emp.: 37
Providers of Treatment, Storage & Disposal Facilities for Liquid Hazardous & Radioactive Wastes
N.A.I.C.S.: 562112

East Tennessee Materials and Energy Corporation (1)
930 Perimeter Rd, Oak Ridge, TN 37830   (100%)
Tel.: (865) 251-2097
Web Site: http://www.perma-fix.com
Sales Range: $25-49.9 Million
Emp.: 90
Waste Treatment, Storage & Disposal Services
N.A.I.C.S.: 562920

Perma-Fix Environmental Services UK Limited (1)
Unit 5 Newburn Bridge Road, Blaydon, NE21 4NT, Tyne and Wear, United Kingdom
Tel.: (44) 7889252536
Nuclear Waste Management Services
N.A.I.C.S.: 562211

Perma-Fix Medical S.A (1)
Skarbowcow 23a, 53-025, Wroclaw, Poland
Tel.: (48) 717357005
Web Site: https://www.medical-isotope.com
Nuclear Medicine Mfr
N.A.I.C.S.: 325411

Perma-Fix Northwest, Inc. (1)
2025 Battelle Blvd, Richland, WA 99354
Tel.: (509) 375-5160
Hazardous Waste Treatment Services
N.A.I.C.S.: 562211

Perma-Fix of Florida, Inc. (1)
1940 NW 67th Pl, Gainesville, FL 32653   (100%)
Tel.: (352) 373-6066
Sales Range: $1-9.9 Million
Emp.: 50
Waste Treatment
N.A.I.C.S.: 562211
Randy Self (Gen Mgr)

SEC Radcon Alliance, LLC (1)
Business Ctr 2800 Solway Rd, Knoxville, TN 37931
Tel.: (865) 690-0501
Web Site: http://www.sec-tn.com
Environmental Services
N.A.I.C.S.: 541620

Safety & Ecology Corporation (1)
2800 Solway Rd, Knoxville, TN 37931
Tel.: (865) 690-0501
Web Site: http://www.sec-tn.com
Sales Range: $200-249.9 Million
Full-Service Environmental, Hazardous & Radiological Infrastructure Remediation & Advanced Construction Services
N.A.I.C.S.: 562910

PERMA-PIPE INTERNATIONAL HOLDINGS, INC.
24900 Pitkin Rd Ste 309, Spring, TX 77386
Tel.: (281) 598-6222   DE
Web Site:
   https://www.permapipe.com
Year Founded: 1993
PPIH—(NASDAQ)
Rev.: $142,569,000
Assets: $122,966,000
Liabilities: $65,182,000

Net Worth: $57,784,000
Earnings: $5,945,000
Emp.: 667
Fiscal Year-end: 01/31/23
Holding Company; Piping Systems Products
N.A.I.C.S.: 333413
David J. Mansfield (Pres & CEO)
David S. Barrie (Chm)
D. Bryan Norwood (CFO)
Will Leong (VP & Gen Mgr-PermAlert)
Jill Curry (VP-HR)
Matthew E. Lewicki (CFO, Treas, Sec & VP)

Subsidiaries:

Midwesco Filter Resources, Inc. (1)
309 N Braddock St, Winchester, VA 22601
Tel.: (540) 773-4780
Web Site: http://www.midwescofilter.com
Emp.: 350
Air Filtration Equipment Mfr
N.A.I.C.S.: 333413

Midwesco Mechanical and Energy, Inc. (1)
200 E Howard Ave, Des Plaines, IL 60018
Tel.: (847) 929-1700
Web Site: http://www.midwescoinc.com
Emp.: 10
Air Purification Equipment Mfr
N.A.I.C.S.: 333413

National Filter Media (1)
691 N 400 W, Salt Lake City, UT 84103
Tel.: (801) 363-6736
Web Site: http://www.nfm-filter.com
Air Purification Equipment Mfr
N.A.I.C.S.: 333413
Troy S. Robbs (Pres & CEO)

Perma-Pipe Canada, LTD. (1)
1600 407 2nd Street Southwest, Calgary, T2P 2Y3, AB, Canada
Tel.: (403) 264-4880
Steel Pole Mfr
N.A.I.C.S.: 332919

Perma-Pipe Egypt for Metal Fabrication & Insulation Industries (Perma-Pipe Egypt) S.A.E (1)
43KM Cairo Ismailia road Shorouk 3 City LMakan Compound Villa 4, Cairo, Egypt
Tel.: (20) 1202269110
Industrial Pipe Mfr
N.A.I.C.S.: 332996
Adham Sharkawy (Gen Mgr)

Perma-Pipe Middle East FZC (1)
Block A Suite AG 00A-07 Building, Dubai Silicon Oasis, Dubai, United Arab Emirates
Tel.: (971) 46072010
Web Site: http://www.permapipe.ae
Piping Mfr
N.A.I.C.S.: 332996

Perma-Pipe, Inc. (1)
2100 Golf Rd Ste 190, Rolling Meadows, IL 60008
Tel.: (847) 966-2235
Sales Range: $25-49.9 Million
Emp.: 45
Prefabricated Insulated Pipe
N.A.I.C.S.: 332996
D. Bryan Norwood (CFO)

Thermal Care Inc. (1)
5680 W Jarvis Ave, Niles, IL 00714-0401   (100%)
Tel.: (847) 966-2260
Web Site: http://www.thermalcare.com
Sales Range: $25-49.9 Million
Emp.: 80
Plastic Mold Chillers & Heaters Mfr
N.A.I.C.S.: 333415

PERMANENT TECHNOLOGIES, INC.
81 Boylston St, Brookline, MA 02445
Tel.: (617) 784-7466   NV
Web Site: http://www.tinelok.com
PERT—(OTCIQ)
Locking Fastener Assembly Mfr & Distr

N.A.I.C.S.: 332722
Frederick Barry II *(COO)*
Peter Dichiara *(Co-Sec)*
Ross D. Carmel *(Co-Sec)*
Robert Boyd Jr. *(Pres)*

PERMEX PETROLEUM COR-PORATION

2911 TURTLE CREEK BLVD, SUITE
925, DALLAS, TX 75219
Tel.: (604) 259-2525   BC
OIL—(CNSX)
Rev.: $688,827
Assets: $10,941,747
Liabilities: $3,772,955
Net Worth: $7,168,792
Earnings: ($4,483,195)
Emp.: 2
Fiscal Year-end: 06/30/23
Oil & Gas Exploration Services
N.A.I.C.S.: 213112

PERMIAN BASIN ROYALTY TRUST

3838 Oak Lawn Ave Ste 1720, Dal-
las, TX 75219   TX
Web Site: https://pbt-permian.com
Year Founded: 1980
PBT—(NYSE)
Rev.: $54,466,228
Assets: $3,134,877
Liabilities: $2,855,444
Net Worth: $279,433
Earnings: $53,543,824
Fiscal Year-end: 12/31/22
Miscellaneous Intermediation
N.A.I.C.S.: 523910

PERMIAN RESOURCES CORP

300 N Marienfeld St Ste 1000, Mid-
land, TX 79701
Tel.: (432) 695-4222   DE
Web Site: https://permianres.com
PR—(NYSE)
Rev.: $2,131,265,000
Assets: $8,492,592,000
Liabilities: $2,836,296,000
Net Worth: $5,656,296,000
Earnings: $749,840,000
Emp.: 218
Fiscal Year-end: 12/31/22
Holding Company; Petroleum & Natu-
ral Gas Exploration ,Development &
Extraction Services
N.A.I.C.S.: 551112
William M. Hickey III *(Co-CEO)*
James H. Walter *(Co-CEO)*
Steven D. Gray *(Chm)*
Guy Oliphint *(CFO & Exec VP)*
Brandon Gaynor *(Exec VP-Business
Development & Strategy)*
Ryan Gitomer *(Sr VP-Finance)*
Casey McCain *(Sr VP-Production
Ops)*
Clayton Smith *(Sr VP-Dev Ops)*
Kyle Bowzer *(VP-Engineering)*
Michelle Collette *(VP-Human Re-
sources)*
Will Ellison *(VP-Marketing & Mid-
stream)*
Patrick Godwin *(VP-Land)*
Sergio Ojeda *(VP-Geosciences)*
Charles Osborn *(CIO & VP)*

Subsidiaries:

Centennial Resource Production,
LLC   **(1)**
1401 17th St Ste 1000, Denver, CO
80202   **(89%)**
Tel.: (720) 441-5515
Web Site: http://www.cdevinc.com
Petroleum & Natural Gas Exploration ,De-
velopment & Extraction Services
N.A.I.C.S.: 211120

Earthstone Energy, LLC   **(1)**

1400 Woodloch Forest Dr Ste 300, The
Woodlands, TX 77380
Tel.: (281) 298-4246
Web Site:
    https://www.earthstoneenergy.com
Rev.: $1,695,154,000
Assets: $3,937,401,000
Liabilities: $1,613,384,000
Net Worth: $2,324,017,000
Earnings: $452,485,000
Emp.: 219
Fiscal Year-end: 12/31/2022
Oil & Gas Exploration & Extraction Services
N.A.I.C.S.: 211120
Timothy D. Merrifield *(Exec VP-Geology &
Geophysics)*
Tony Oviedo *(Exec VP-Acctg & Admin)*
Leonard W. Wood *(VP-Exploration & Dev)*
Bill Wiederkehr *(VP-Fin Reporting & Tax)*
Geoff Vernon *(VP-Reservoir Engrg & A&D)*
Shannon Klier *(VP-Completions & Produc-
tion)*
Robert W. Hunt *(Gen Counsel)*
Nick Goree *(VP)*
Lane T. McKinney *(VP-Land)*
Mark Lumpkin Jr. *(CFO & Exec VP)*

Subsidiary (Domestic):

Basic Petroleum Services, Inc.   **(2)**
PO Box 213, Bruni, TX 78344-0213
Tel.: (361) 747-5221
Petroleum Product Whslr
N.A.I.C.S.: 211120

Oak Valley Operating, LLC   **(2)**
1400 Woodloch Forest Dr Ste 300, The
Woodlands, TX 77380
Tel.: (281) 298-4246
Oil & Gas Field Operating Services
N.A.I.C.S.: 213112

PERMIANVILLE ROYALTY TRUST

601 Travis St 16th Fl, Houston, TX
77002
Tel.: (512) 236-6555   DE
Web Site:
    https://www.permianvilleroyalty
    trust.com
Year Founded: 2011
PVL—(NYSE)
Rev.: $15,027,041
Assets: $60,564,545
Net Worth: $60,564,545
Earnings: $13,480,500
Fiscal Year-end: 12/31/22
Oil & Gas Investment Services
N.A.I.C.S.: 213112
Sarah Newell *(VP)*

PERMROCK ROYALTY TRUST

3838 Oak Lawn Ave Ste 1720, Dal-
las, TX 75219   DE
Web Site: https://www.permrock.com
Year Founded: 2017
PRT—(NYSE)
Rev.: $13,177,436
Assets: $82,023,051
Liabilities: $1,981,938
Net Worth: $80,041,113
Earnings: $12,303,956
Fiscal Year-end: 12/31/22
Property Management Services
N.A.I.C.S.: 523910
Jana Egeler *(VP-Trust Administrator)*

PERNIX GROUP, INC.

151 E 22nd St, Lombard, IL 60148
Tel.: (630) 620-4787   DE
Web Site:
    http://www.pernixgroup.com
Year Founded: 1994
PRXG—(OTCIQ)
Sales Range: $150-199.9 Million
Emp.: 475
Engineering & Construction Services
N.A.I.C.S.: 237990
Grant G. McCullagh *(Exec VP)*
Nidal Z. Zayed *(Pres & CEO)*
Michael Frye *(VP-Power)*
Warren Bryant *(VP-Construction Ops)*

Subsidiaries:

BE&K Building Group, LLC   **(1)**
201 E McBee Ave Ste 400, Greenville, SC
29601-2410
Tel.: (864) 250-5000
Web Site: http://www.bekbg.com
Industrial, Commercial & Institutional Facility
Construction & Support Services
N.A.I.C.S.: 236220
Grant G. McCullagh *(Chm)*
William Mac Carpenter *(Pres)*
James Timothy Parker *(Sr VP-South Caro-
lina Reg)*
Anthony Harden *(Sr VP-Preconstruction)*
Chuck Lewis *(Gen Counsel)*
Candace Watson *(Dir-HR)*
Shawn Rodwell *(VP-Fin)*
Courtney Skunda *(Mgr-Bus Dev-Res Tri-
angle Park)*
Steve Olson *(COO)*
Jon Fayard *(VP)*
Dan Klancnik *(Sr VP-Innovation & Tech)*

Branch (Domestic):

BE&K Building Group, LLC -
Charlotte   **(2)**
5605 Carnegie Blvd Ste 200, Charlotte, NC
28209
Tel.: (704) 551-2700
Web Site: http://www.bekbg.com
Industrial, Commercial & Institutional Facility
Construction & Support Services
N.A.I.C.S.: 236220
G. Michael Baumbach *(Exec VP-Charlotte
Reg Ops)*
Jeffrey D. Thompson *(Sr VP-Bus Dev)*
Frank Holley *(Exec VP-Natl Sls)*
Garland Burton Jr. *(Dir-Diversity & Commu-
nity Affairs)*

Basic Industries Limited   **(1)**
Level 4 Ra Marama, 91 Gordon Street PO
Box 369, Suva, Fiji
Tel.: (679) 3311433
Producer And Supplier Of Cement

PERPETUA RESOURCES CORP.

Tel.: (208) 901-3060   BC
Web Site:
    https://www.perpetuaresources.com
PPTA—(NASDAQ)
Rev.: $618,328
Assets: $99,445,155
Liabilities: $13,614,633
Net Worth: $85,830,522
Earnings: ($28,713,531)
Emp.: 29
Fiscal Year-end: 12/31/22
Gold Mining Services
N.A.I.C.S.: 212220
Jonathan Cherry *(Pres & CEO)*
Jessica Largent *(CFO)*
Jess Largent *(VP-IR & Fin)*
Chris Fogg *(Mgr-IR)*
Michael Wright *(VP-Projects)*
Mckinsey Lyon *(VP-External Affairs)*

Subsidiaries:

Midas Gold, Inc.   **(1)**
15920 E Indiana Ave Ste 101, Spokane Val-
ley, WA 99216
Tel.: (509) 927-4653
Web Site: http://www.midasgoldcorp.com
Gold Ore Mining Services
N.A.I.C.S.: 212220

PERPETUAL INDUSTRIES INC.

2193 Rotunda Dr, Auburn, IN 46706
Tel.: (702) 707-9811   NV
Web Site:
    https://www.perpetualindustries.com
Year Founded: 2005
PRPI—(OTCIQ)
Rev.: $8,445,394
Assets: $11,514,967
Liabilities: $2,974,785
Net Worth: $8,540,182
Earnings: ($127,015)
Emp.: 13

Fiscal Year-end: 12/31/21
Research & Development in the
Physical, Engineering & Life Sciences
(except Nanotechnology & Biotech-
nology)
N.A.I.C.S.: 541715
Brent W. Bedford *(Chm, Pres & CEO)*
Carl Dilley *(COO)*
William Griffin Thomas *(CFO)*

PERSHING RESOURCES COMPANY, INC.

200 S Virginia St 8th Fl, Reno, NV
89501
Tel.: (775) 398-3124
Web Site:
    https://www.pershingpm.com
PSGR—(OTCIQ)
Assets: $317,000
Liabilities: $294,000
Net Worth: $23,000
Earnings: ($962,000)
Emp.: 2
Fiscal Year-end: 12/31/20
Other Metal Ore Mining
N.A.I.C.S.: 212290
Stephen D. Plumb *(Chm, Pres, CEO
& Treas)*
Richard Levychin *(CFO)*
Joel Adams III *(COO & Sec)*

PERSHING SQUARE TONTINE HOLDINGS, LTD.

787 11th Ave 9th Fl, New York, NY
10019
Tel.: (212) 813-3700   DE
Year Founded: 2020
PSTHU—(NYSE)
Emp.: 2
Investment Services
N.A.I.C.S.: 523999
William Albert Ackman *(Chm & CEO)*

PERSONALIS, INC.

6600 Dumbarton Cir, Fremont, CA
94555
Tel.: (650) 752-1300   DE
Web Site:
    https://www.personalis.com
Year Founded: 2011
PSNL—(NASDAQ)
Rev.: $65,047,000
Assets: $292,700,000
Liabilities: $74,561,000
Net Worth: $218,139,000
Earnings: ($113,315,000)
Emp.: 395
Fiscal Year-end: 12/31/22
Biotechnology Research & Develop-
ment Services
N.A.I.C.S.: 541714
Richard Chen *(Chief Medical Officer
& Exec VP-R&D)*
Aaron Tachibana *(CFO & COO)*
Christopher Hall *(Pres & CEO)*
James Azzaro *(VP-Diagnostic Sls)*
Aaron Tachibana *(CFO & COO)*
Euan Ashley *(Co-Founder)*
Russ Altman *(Co-Founder)*
Michael Snyder *(Co-Founder)*
Deepshikha Bhandari *(Sr VP-
Regulatory)*
Donald Brown *(VP-Laboratory Ops)*
Stephen Fairclough *(VP-Informatics)*
Ken Brunt *(VP-Client Experience)*

Subsidiaries:

Personalis (UK) Ltd.   **(1)**
Squires House 205A High Street, West
Wickham, Canterbury, BR4 0PH, Kent,
United Kingdom
Tel.: (44) 1708121888
Bio Technology Services
N.A.I.C.S.: 541714

Shanghai Personalis Biotechnology
Co., Ltd.   **(1)**

Personalis, Inc.—(Continued)

Building 2 juke biological park 218 yindu road, Xuhui District, Shanghai, China
Tel.: (86) 2180118168
Web Site: https://www.personalbio.cn
Biotechnology Research Services
N.A.I.C.S.: 541714

PERSPECTIVE THERAPEU-TICS, INC.

2401 Elliott Ave Ste 320, Seattle, WA 98121
Tel.: (509) 375-5329   **DE**
Web Site:
   https://perspectivetherapeutics.com
Year Founded: 1983
CATX—(NYSEAMEX)
Rev.: $10,053,000
Assets: $70,416,000
Liabilities: $3,010,000
Net Worth: $67,406,000
Earnings: ($3,387,000)
Emp.: 61
Fiscal Year-end: 06/30/21
Holding Company; Therapeutic Medical Isotope & Device Mfr
N.A.I.C.S.: 551112
Jonathan Hunt (CFO)

Subsidiaries:

IsoRay Medical, Inc.   (1)
350 Hills St Ste 106, Richland, WA 99354-5511
Tel.: (509) 375-5329
Web Site: http://www.isoray.com
Sales Range: $100-124.9 Million
Emp.: 40
Therapeutic Medical Isotope & Device Mfr
N.A.I.C.S.: 339112

PET ECOLOGY BRANDS, INC.

30 N Gould St Ste 5835, Sheridan, WY 82801
Tel.: (312) 481-6850   **TX**
Year Founded: 1996
PECD—(OTCIQ)
Pet Product Mfr
N.A.I.C.S.: 311111
Benjamin Robert Berry (Pres, CEO & CFO)

PETCO HEALTH AND WELL-NESS COMPANY, INC.

10850 Via Frontera, San Diego, CA 92127
Tel.: (858) 453-7845   **DE**
Web Site: https://www.petco.com
Year Founded: 2015
WOOF—(NASDAQ)
Rev.: $6,255,284,000
Assets: $5,363,152,000
Liabilities: $4,178,723,000
Net Worth: $1,184,429,000
Earnings: ($1,280,210,000)
Emp.: 29,000
Fiscal Year-end: 02/03/24
Holding Company
N.A.I.C.S.: 551112
Glenn K. Murphy (Chm)
Michelle Bonfilio (Chief HR Officer)
Ilene Eskenazi (Chief Legal Officer & Sec)
Tariq Hassan (CMO)
Justin Tichy (Chief Stores Officer)
John Zavada (Chief Information & Admin Officer)
Brian LaRose (CFO)
Joel D. Anderson (CEO)
Ilene Eskenazi (Chief Legal Officer & Sec)

PETLIFE PHARMACEUTICALS, INC.

8033 Sunset Blvd, Los Angeles, CA 90046
Tel.: (424) 216-6807   **NV**

Web Site:
   http://www.petlifepharma.com
PTLF—(OTCIQ)
Emp.: 1
Veterinary Pharmaceutical Mfr
N.A.I.C.S.: 325412
Vivek Ramana (Chief Medical Officer)

PETMED EXPRESS, INC.

420 S Congress Ave Ste 100, Delray Beach, FL 33445
Tel.: (561) 526-4444   **FL**
Web Site:
   https://www.petmedexpress.com
PETS—(NASDAQ)
Rev.: $281,064,000
Assets: $169,884,000
Liabilities: $73,153,000
Net Worth: $96,731,000
Earnings: ($7,464,000)
Emp.: 287
Fiscal Year-end: 03/31/24
Pet Pharmaceutical Sales
N.A.I.C.S.: 541940
Gian M. Fulgoni (Chm)
Christine Chambers (CFO)
Sandra Y. Campos (Pres & CEO)
Robyn M. D'Elia (COO)

Subsidiaries:

First Image Marketing, Inc.   (1)
1441 SW 29th Ave, Pompano Beach, FL 33069
Tel.: (954) 979-5995
Web Site: http://www.1800petmeds.com
Marketing Consulting Services
N.A.I.C.S.: 541613

Petcarerx.Com   (1)
52 Merton Ave, Lynbrook, NY 11563
Tel.: (516) 295-8780
Web Site: https://www.petcarerx.com
Sales Range: $1-9.9 Million
Emp.: 75
Miscellaneous Retail Stores, Nec, Nsk
N.A.I.C.S.: 459910
Natalie Bonacasa (Mgr-Mktg)

PETRO RIVER OIL CORP.

55 5th Ave Ste 1702, New York, NY 10003
Tel.: (469) 828-3900   **DE**
Web Site:
   http://www.petroriveroil.com
Year Founded: 2000
PTRC—(OTCEM)
Rev.: $1,645,170
Assets: $10,016,583
Liabilities: $5,955,731
Net Worth: $4,060,852
Earnings: ($5,105,107)
Emp.: 4
Fiscal Year-end: 04/30/19
Oil & Gas Exploration Services
N.A.I.C.S.: 211120
Scot J. Cohen (Exec Chm & CEO)
Stephen R. Brunner (Pres)
David Briones (CFO)

PETRO USA, INC.

7325 Oswego Rd, Liverpool, NY 13090
Tel.: (315) 451-7515   **NV**
Web Site:
   https://www.allstatepropertieshold ings.com
Year Founded: 2008
PBAJ—(OTCIQ)
Assets: $100
Liabilities: $128,506
Net Worth: ($128,406)
Earnings: ($23,863)
Fiscal Year-end: 06/30/23
Holding Company
N.A.I.C.S.: 551112
Joseph C. Passalaqua (Chm, Pres, CEO & Sec)

PETRO-VICTORY ENERGY CORP.

5960 Berkshire Ln 6th Fl, Dallas, TX 75225
Tel.: (214) 971-2647
Web Site:
   http://www.petrovictoryenergy.com
VRY—(TSXV)
Rev.: $297,065
Assets: $4,686,764
Liabilities: $7,229,762
Net Worth: ($2,542,998)
Earnings: $187,579
Fiscal Year-end: 12/31/20
Oil & Gas Producing Services
N.A.I.C.S.: 213112

PETROGAS COMPANY

200 Post Oak Blvd Ste 4100, Houston, TX 77056
Tel.: (832) 899-8597   **NV**
Year Founded: 2014
PTCO—(OTCIQ)
Liabilities: $799,228
Net Worth: ($799,228)
Earnings: ($90,588)
Fiscal Year-end: 03/31/24
Oil & Gas Exploration Services
N.A.I.C.S.: 213112
Huang Yu (Pres, CEO, CFO, Treas, Sec, Exec VP & Portfolio Mgr)

PETROLIA ENERGY CORPO-RATION

710 N Post Oak Rd Ste 400, Houston, TX 77024
Tel.: (832) 723-1266   **CO**
Web Site:
   https://www.petroliaenergy.com
Year Founded: 2002
BBLSQ—(OTCEM)
Sales Range: $1-9.9 Million
Emp.: 6
Oil & Gas Exploration
N.A.I.C.S.: 211120
James Edward Burns (Chm)
Mark M. Allen (Pres & CEO)

Subsidiaries:

Askarii Resources, LLC   (1)
710 N Post Oak Rd Ste 512, Houston, TX 77024
Tel.: (832) 941-0011
Web Site: http://www.askarii.com
Oil & Gas Exploration Services
N.A.I.C.S.: 211120

PETRONE WORLDWIDE, INC.

2200 N Commerce Pkwy, Weston, FL 33326
Web Site:
   http://www.petroneworldwide.com
PFWI—(OTCIQ)
Sales Range: Less than $1 Million
Emp.: 1
Furniture & Bathroom Accessories Distr
N.A.I.C.S.: 423210

PETROS PHARMACEUTICALS, INC.

4400 Route 9 S Ste 1000, Freehold, NJ 07728
Tel.: (973) 242-0005   **DE**
Web Site:
   https://www.petrospharma.com
Year Founded: 2020
PTPI—(NASDAQ)
Emp.: 24
Pharmaceutical Product Mfr & Distr
N.A.I.C.S.: 325412
Fady Boctor (Pres)
Joshua N. Silverman (Vice Chm)
Mitchell Arnold (Chief Acctg Officer)

PETROSHALE, INC.

303 E 17th Ave Ste 940, Denver, CO 80203
Tel.: (303) 297-1407
Web Site:
   http://www.petroshaleinc.com
Year Founded: 1994
PSH—(OTCIQ)
Rev.: $102,138,000
Assets: $502,877,000
Liabilities: $365,177,000
Net Worth: $137,700,000
Earnings: ($61,985,000)
Emp.: 14
Fiscal Year-end: 12/31/20
Oil & Gas Exploartion Services
N.A.I.C.S.: 213112
Bruce Chernoff (Chm)
Tony Izzo (Sr VP-Corp Dev)
Dominic Pallone (VP-Land & Acquisitions)
Jeff Haskins (Fin Dir)
Lauren Morahan (Mgr-Regulatory & Compliance)
Scott Pittman (CFO)
Richard Kessy (COO)
Stan Sprinkle (Chief Acctg Officer)

PETROSUN, INC.

2999 N 44th St Ste 620, Phoenix, AZ 85018
Tel.: (480) 425-4290
Web Site: https://www.petrosun.us
PSUD—(OTCIQ)
Crude Petroleum Extraction Services
N.A.I.C.S.: 211120
Gordon LeBlanc Jr. (CEO)

PETROTAL CORP.

11451 Katy Freeway Ste 500, Houston, TX 77079
Tel.: (713) 609-9101   **AB**
Web Site: http://www.petrotal-corp.com
Year Founded: 1979
TAL—(AIM)
Oil & Gas Exploration Services
N.A.I.C.S.: 213112
Douglas C. Urch (Chm)
Manuel Pablo Zuniga-Pflucker (Pres, CEO & Corp Sec)
Gregory E. Smith (CFO & Exec VP)
Estuardo Alvarez-Calderon (VP-Ops)

Subsidiaries:

PetroTal LLC   (1)
16225 Park Ten Pl Ste 200, Houston, TX 77084
Tel.: (713) 894-4156
Web Site: http://www.petrotalllc.com
Oil & Gas Exploration
N.A.I.C.S.: 213112
Manuel Pablo Zuniga-Pflucker (Pres & CEO)
Gregory E. Smith (CFO & Exec VP)
Estuardo Alvarez-Calderon (VP-Ops)
Charles R. Fetzner (VP-Asset Dev)

PetroTal Peru S.R.L.   (1)
Calle Andres Reyes 437 Piso 8 Edificio Platinum Plaza Torre II, San Isidro, Lima, Peru
Tel.: (51) 17158078
Oil & Gas Exploration & Production
N.A.I.C.S.: 211120

PETROTEQ ENERGY INC.

15315 W Magnolia Blvd Ste 120, Sherman Oaks, CA 91403   **ON**
Web Site: https://www.petroteq.com
Year Founded: 2012
PQEFF—(OTCIQ)
Rev.: $2,000,000
Assets: $81,034,566
Liabilities: $14,881,641
Net Worth: $66,152,925
Earnings: ($9,474,243)
Fiscal Year-end: 08/31/21

Crude Petroleum Extraction Services
N.A.I.C.S.: 211120
Aleksandr Blyumkin (Founder)
Robbie Grossman (Sec)
Vladimir Podlipskiy (Interim CEO)
Michael Hopkinson (CFO)

PETVIVO HOLDINGS, INC.

5151 Edina Industrial Blvd Ste 575,
Minneapolis, MN 55439
Tel.: (952) 405-6216   NV
Web Site: https://www.petvivo.com
Year Founded: 2009
PETV—(NASDAQ)
Rev.: $968,706
Assets: $3,115,253
Liabilities: $2,429,300
Net Worth: $685,953
Earnings: ($10,955,295)
Emp.: 20
Fiscal Year-end: 03/31/24
Pharmaceutical Preparation Manufac-
turing
N.A.I.C.S.: 325412
Randall A. Meyer (COO)
John Lai (CEO)
John Fitzgerald Dolan (Chief Bus Dev
Officer, Gen Counsel & Sec)
Russell Siakel (Mktg Dir)

Subsidiaries:

Gel-Del Technologies Inc.   (1)
1000 Westgate Dr Ste 127, Saint Paul, MN
55114   (100%)
Tel.: (651) 209-0707
Web Site: http://www.gel-del.com
Biomedical Material Mfr
N.A.I.C.S.: 541715
David B. Masters (Chm, Pres & CTO)

PFIZER INC.

66 Hudson Blvd E, New York, NY
10001-2192
Tel.: (212) 733-2323   DE
Web Site: https://www.pfizer.com
Year Founded: 1849
PFE—(NYSE)
Rev.: $58,496,000,000
Assets: $226,501,000,000
Liabilities: $137,213,000,000
Net Worth: $89,288,000,000
Earnings: $2,119,000,000
Emp.: 88,000
Fiscal Year-end: 12/31/23
Diversified, Research-Based Health
Care Company with Businesses in
Pharmaceuticals, Hospital Products,
Consumer Products & Animal Health
N.A.I.C.S.: 325412
Douglas M. Lankler (Gen Counsel &
Exec VP)
Rady A. Johnson (Chief Compliance,
Quality & Risk Officer & Exec VP)
David M. Denton (CFO & Exec VP)
Alvin Shih (Founder-Rare Disease
ResUnit)
Lidia L. Fonseca (Chief Digital &
Tech Officer & Exec VP)
Jennifer B. Damico (Principal Acctg
Officer, Sr VP & Controller)
Alexandra Kropotova (Head-Clinical
Respiratory-Analgesics-Global)
Payal Sahni (Chief HR Officer & Exec
VP)
Margaret M. Madden (Sec & Sr VP)
Maria Rivas (Chief Medical Affairs
Officer-Global & Head-Evidence Gen-
eration)
Michael McDermott (Chief Global
Supply Officer & Exec VP)
Angela Hwang (Head-
Biopharmaceuticals)
Payal Sahni Becher (Chief People
Experience Officer)
Dave M. Denton (CFO)
Chris Boshoff (Chief Oncology Res &
Dev Officer & Exec VP)

Corey S. Goodman (Founder-
Biotherapeutics & Bioinnovation Cen-
ter)
Albert Bourla (Chm & CEO)
Mikael Dolsten (Chief Scientific Offi-
cer & Pres-Research, Development &
Medical-Worldwide)

Subsidiaries:

AHP Holdings Pty. Limited   (1)
38-42 Wharf Rd, West Ryde, 2144, NSW,
Australia
Tel.: (61) 298503893
Holding Company
N.A.I.C.S.: 551112

Agouron Pharmaceuticals, Inc.   (1)
10777 Science Ctr Dr, San Diego, CA
92121-1111
Tel.: (858) 622-3000
Emp.: 991
Pharmaceutical Product Mfr & Distr
N.A.I.C.S.: 325412

Alacer Corp.   (1)
80 Icon, Foothill Ranch, CA 92610
Tel.: (949) 454-3900
Web Site: http://www.emergenc.com
Sales Range: $50-74.9 Million
Emp.: 100
Vitamin Drink Mix Mfr
N.A.I.C.S.: 312111

Alpharma Pharmaceuticals LLC   (1)
1 New England Ave, Piscataway, NJ 08854
Tel.: (732) 465-3600
Pharmaceuticals Product Mfr
N.A.I.C.S.: 325412

Amplyx Pharmaceuticals Inc.   (1)
12730 High Bluff Dr Ste 160, San Diego,
CA 92130
Tel.: (858) 345-1755
Web Site: http://www.amplyx.com
Drugs & Druggists' Sundries Merchant
Whslr
N.A.I.C.S.: 424210
Ciara Kennedy (Pres & CEO)
Robert Webb (VP)
Michael Hodges (Chief Medical Officer)
Karen Joy Shaw (Chief Scientific Officer)
Elizabeth Gordon (VP-Regulatory Affairs)
Carlos Sattler (Sr VP-Clinical Dev)
Chris LeMasters (COO)

Arena Pharmaceuticals, Inc.   (1)
136 Heber Ave Ste 204, Park City, UT
84060
Tel.: (128) 082-4200
Web Site:
    https://www.arenapharmaceuticals.co.uk
Rev.: $54,000
Assets: $784,705,000
Liabilities: $111,468,000
Net Worth: $673,237,000
Earnings: ($616,433,000)
Emp.: 448
Fiscal Year-end: 12/31/2021
Drug Discovery Technology Developer
N.A.I.C.S.: 325412
Derek T. Chalmers (Founder)
Vincent E. Aurentz (Chief Bus Officer &
Exec VP)
Garry A. Neil (Chm)
Vincent Aurentz (Chief Bus Officer & Exec
VP)
Douglas A. Bakan (Exec VP-Technical Ops)
Joan Schmidt (Gen Counsel, Sec & Exec
VP)
Laurie Stelzer (CFO & Exec VP)
Paul D. Streck (Chief Medical Officer)
Mike Paolucci (Exec VP-Human Capital)
Laurie D. Stelzer (CFO & Exec VP)

Array BioPharma Inc.   (1)
3200 Walnut St, Boulder, CO 80301
Tel.: (303) 381-6600
Web Site: http://www.arraybiopharma.com
Rev.: $173,768,000
Assets: $460,364,000
Liabilities: $240,621,000
Net Worth: $219,743,000
Earnings: ($147,346,000)
Emp.: 298
Fiscal Year-end: 06/30/2018
Disease Discovery & Treatment Pharma-
ceutical Development Services
N.A.I.C.S.: 325412

Rogan P. Nunn (Interim Gen Counsel)
Douglas E. Giordano (Pres & Treas)
Margaret M. Madden (Sec & VP)
Bryan Supran (VP)

Ayerst-Wyeth Pharmaceuticals
LLC   (1)
Km 142 Hm 1 Rr 3, Guayama, PR 00784
Tel.: (787) 864-4010
Pharmaceuticals Product Mfr
N.A.I.C.S.: 325412

Biohaven Pharmaceutical Holding
Company Ltd.   (1)
215 Church St, New Haven, CT 06510
Tel.: (203) 404-0410
Web Site: https://www.biohaven.com
Rev.: $462,509,000
Assets: $1,077,212,000
Liabilities: $1,820,221,000
Net Worth: ($743,009,000)
Earnings: ($846,586,000)
Emp.: 928
Fiscal Year-end: 12/31/2021
Biopharmaceutical Product Research & De-
velopment Services
N.A.I.C.S.: 325412
Vlad Coric (Chm & CEO)
John Tilton (Chief Comml Officer)
Charles Conway (Chief Scientific Officer)
Gregory H. Bailey (Executives, Bd of Dirs)
Douglas G. Gray (Sec)
Beth Morris (Exec Dir-Clinical Ops)
Lia Donahue (Sr Dir-Clinical Ops)
Meghan Lovegren (Dir-Clinical Ops)
Marianne Frost (Sr VP-Regulatory Affairs)
David Stock (VP-Biostatistics)
David Loomis (Controller)
Clifford Bechtold (Pres, Chief Compliance
Officer & Chief Compliance Officer & Gen
Mgr-Ireland)
Loren Aguiar (VP-R&D)
Irfan Qureshi (VP-Neurology)
Rajesh Kumar (VP-Chemistry, Mfg & Con-
trols)
Anthony Gentile (Dir-Clinical Ops & Pro-
gram Fin)
Andrea Ivans (Dir-Clinical Ops)
Ashwini Ghatpande (VP-Scientific Writing &
Regulatory)
Francine Healy (Exec Dir-Scientific Writing
& Regulatory Submissions)
Chris Jensen (Dir-Medical Affairs)
Gilbert L'italien (Sr VP & Head-Gheor &
Epidemiology)
Lisa Kamen (Dir-Clinical Ops)
Gene Dubowchik (VP-Chemistry & R&D)
Leena Philominathan (Assoc Dir-Scientific
Writing & Regulatory)
Lisa Stocking (Dir-Regulatory Affairs & Ops)
Melissa Beiner (Dir-R&D)
Nicole Carfora (Coord-Project)
Matthew DeLawder (Dir-Acctg)
Victoria Wirtz (Sr Dir-Biostatistics)
Shuai Li (Dir-Bus Dev)
Ajaya Kumar Reka (Sr Dir-CM&C)
Javier Gonzalez (Exec Dir-CMC)
Maryellen McQuade (Chief Talent & Sus-
tainability Officer)
Richard Bertz (VP-Pharmacology & Phar-
macometrics)
David Leahy (Sr Dir-Chemistry, Mfg & Con-
trols)
Megan Dow (Dir-Portfolio & Dev Strategy)
Sarah Ringuette (Exec Dir-Regulatory Af-
fairs)
Jenny Strauss (Mgr-Medical Information &
Comm)
Chris Barrett (Sr VP-Managed Markets &
Govt Affairs)
Chris Deluzio (Sr VP-Sls & Comml Ops)
Graham Goodrich (Sr VP-Brand Mktg)
Jimi Ayodele (VP-Fin)
Christine Lopez (Sr Dir-Employee Engage-
ment)
Amanda Ward (Sr Dir-Comml Insights &
Analytics)
Shari Dow (Dir-Comml Comm)
Michelle Mansilla (Dir-Sls, Analytics & Bus
Effectiveness)
Stephanie Gerome (Dir-Sls Force Effective-
ness)
Mike Gabriel (Dir-Comml Ops)
Sanjay Keshav (Sr Dir-Comml Ops)
Terry Luthman (Dir-Sls Trng)
Sharon Hanscom (Dir-Comml Learning &
Dev)
Christine Faith Oakley (Dir-Trng Ops)
Jane Ipsen (Assoc Dir-Comml Learning)

Paloma Fernandez-Montés Moraleda (Pres)
Gaston Araya Ortega (VP)

Capsugel Healthcare Limited   (1)
208/209 Kanakia Western Edge II Western
Express Highway Borivali East, Mumbai,
400 066, India
Tel.: (91) 2230111002
Pharmaceuticals Product Mfr
N.A.I.C.S.: 325412

Capsugel de Mexico, S. de R.L. de
C.V.   (1)
Blvd 18 de Noviembre 1030 A Col, Parque
Industrial Puebla 2000 Puebla Pue, 72270,
Mexico, Mexico
Tel.: (52) 2223721500
Web Site: http://www.capsugel.com
Pharmaceutical Preparation Mfr
N.A.I.C.S.: 325412

Carlerba - Produtos Quimicos e Far-
maceuticos, Lda.   (1)
Lagoas Park Edf Dez Porto Salvo, Lisbon,
2740-264, Portugal
Tel.: (351) 214235500
Pharmaceutical Products Distr
N.A.I.C.S.: 456110

Coley Pharmaceutical Group,
Ltd.   (1)
340 Terry Fox Drive Suite 200, K2K 3A2,
Ottawa, ON, Canada
Tel.: (613) 254-5622
Pharmaceuticals Product Mfr
N.A.I.C.S.: 325412

Compania Farmaceutica Upjohn,
S.A.   (1)
10 Av 4-58 Zona 1, Guatemala, Guatemala
Tel.: (502) 22305664
Sales Range: $500-549.9 Million
Emp.: 200
Pharmaceutical Preparation Mfr
N.A.I.C.S.: 325412
Gerardo Paic (Gen Mgr)

CovX Research LLC   (1)
Tel.: (858) 964-2000
Sales Range: $200-249.9 Million
Biopharmaceutical Developer
N.A.I.C.S.: 325412

Subsidiary (Non-US):

CovX Technologies Ireland
Limited   (2)
Tel.: (353) 214378701
Web Site: http://www.pfizer.ie
Biopharmaceutical Developer
N.A.I.C.S.: 325412

Encysive Pharmaceuticals Inc.   (1)
4848 Loop Central Dr 7th Fl, Houston, TX
77030-5400
Tel.: (713) 796-8822
Developer of Small-Molecule Drugs to Treat
Vascular Diseases
N.A.I.C.S.: 325412

FPZ Deutschland den Rucken
Starken GmbH   (1)
Gustav-Heinemann-Ufer 88a, 50968, Co-
logne, Germany
Tel.: (49) 221995300
Web Site: http://www.fpz.de
Pharmaceuticals Product Mfr
N.A.I.C.S.: 325412

Ferrosan A/S   (1)
Sydmarken 5, 2860, Soborg, Denmark
Tel.: (45) 70252860
Web Site:
    https://www.ferrosanmedicaldevices.com
Emp.: 140
Medical Device Whslr
N.A.I.C.S.: 423450

Global Blood Therapeutics, Inc.   (1)
181 Oyster Point Blvd, South San Fran-
cisco, CA 94080
Tel.: (650) 741-7700
Web Site: http://www.gbt.com
Rev.: $194,749,000
Assets: $939,208,000
Liabilities: $742,798,000
Net Worth: $196,410,000
Earnings: ($303,091,000)
Emp.: 457
Fiscal Year-end: 12/31/2021

Pfizer Inc.—(Continued)

Pharmaceuticals Mfr
N.A.I.C.S.: 325412
Jung E. Choi (Chief Bus Officer & Chief
Strategy Officer)
Tricia Suvari (Chief Legal Officer)
Jonathan Sorof (Sr VP & Head-Medical Af-
fairs)
Brian Cathers (Chief Scientific Officer)
Eric Fink (Chief HR Officer)
Nazila Habibizad (Sr VP-Ops)
David L. Johnson (Chief Comml Officer)
Jung E. Choi (Chief Strategy Officer & Chief
Bus Officer)

Godecke GmbH (1)
Mooswaldallee 1-9, 79090, Freiburg, Ger-
many
Tel.: (49) 7615180
Pharmaceuticals Whslr
N.A.I.C.S.: 424210

HOSPIRA INVICTA SA (1)
Europa 20 B Parque Empre La Moraleja,
28108, Alcobendas, Spain
Tel.: (34) 914909900
Web Site: http://www.hospira.es
Pharmaceuticals Mfr
N.A.I.C.S.: 325412

Hospira Slovakia, s.r.o. (1)
Pribinova 25, Bratislava, 811 09, Slovakia
Tel.: (421) 917497001
Pharmaceuticals Product Mfr
N.A.I.C.S.: 325412

Hospira, Inc. (1)
275 N Field Dr, Lake Forest, IL 60045
Tel.: (847) 937-6472
Web Site: https://www.hospira.com
Holding Company; Specialty Pharmaceuti-
cals & Delivery Systems Mfr
N.A.I.C.S.: 551112
Christopher B. Begley (Founder)
John Young (Pres)

Unit (Domestic):

Hospira - Austin (2)
3900 Howard Ln, Austin, TX 78728
Tel.: (512) 255-2000
Pharmaceutical Preparations
N.A.I.C.S.: 423450

Subsidiary (Non-US):

Hospira Aseptic Services Limited (2)
First Floor Horizon Building Honey Lane,
Hurley, SL6 6RJ, United Kingdom
Tel.: (44) 8000843474
Specialty Pharmaceuticals & Patient Care
Products Mfr
N.A.I.C.S.: 325412

Hospira Deutschland GmbH (2)
Linkstr 10, 10785, Berlin, Germany
Tel.: (49) 8001014206
Web Site: http://www.hospira.de
Pharmaceutical & Medication Delivery Pro-
vider
N.A.I.C.S.: 325412

Hospira Italia S.r.l. (2)
Via Orazio 20/22, 80122, Naples, Italy
Tel.: (39) 0812405911
Web Site: http://www.hospira.it
Pharmaceuticals & Patient Safety Care
Product Mfr
N.A.I.C.S.: 325412

Hospira Philippines, Inc. (2)
39/F Robinsons Equitable Tower ADB Av-
enue Corner Poveda Road, Ortigas Center,
Pasig, 1605, Metro Manila, Philippines
Tel.: (63) 27777000
Pharmaceuticals Product Mfr
N.A.I.C.S.: 325412

Hospira Pty Limited (2)
Level 3 500 Collins Street, Melbourne, 3000,
VIC, Australia
Tel.: (61) 387445200
Web Site: http://www.hospira.com.au
Holding Company; Regional Managing Of-
fice
N.A.I.C.S.: 551112

Subsidiary (Domestic):

Hospira Australia Pty. Ltd. (3)
Level 3 500 Collins Street, Melbourne,

3000, VIC, Australia
Tel.: (61) 387445200
Web Site: https://www.hospira.com.au
Specialty Medicine & Pharmaceutical Devel-
oper, Mfr & Distr
N.A.I.C.S.: 325412

Subsidiary (Non-US):

Hospira UK Limited (2)
Horizon Honey Lane, Maidenhead, Hurley,
SL6 6RJ, United Kingdom
Tel.: (44) 7035273887
Web Site: https://www.pfizer.com
Pharmaceutical & Biotechnology Products
Mfr
N.A.I.C.S.: 325412

Subsidiary (Domestic):

Hospira Worldwide, LLC (2)
275 N Field Dr, Lake Forest, IL 60045
Tel.: (224) 212-2000
Specialty Pharmaceuticals & Patient Safety
Care Products Mfr
N.A.I.C.S.: 325412

InnoPharma, Inc. (1)
10 Knightsbridge Rd, Piscataway, NJ 08854
Tel.: (732) 885-2939
Biological Product Mfr
N.A.I.C.S.: 325414
Navneet Puri (Co-Founder & VP-
Pharmaceutical Science)
Satish Pejaver (Scientific Officer & Exec
Dir)
Sriram J. Ramanathan (Co-Founder, Scien-
tific Officer & Exec Dir)
John C. Deighan (Sr Dir-Fin)

John Wyeth & Brother Limited (1)
Huntercombe Lane South Taplow, Maiden-
head, SL6 0PH, United Kingdom
Tel.: (44) 1628604377
Pharmaceuticals Product Mfr
N.A.I.C.S.: 325412

Kenfarma, S.A. (1)
Avenida De Europa 20 V, Alcobendas,
28108, Spain
Tel.: (34) 914909900
Web Site: http://www.pfizer.com
Sales Range: $250-299.9 Million
Emp.: 800
Pharmaceutical Preparation Mfr
N.A.I.C.S.: 325412

Laboratorios Parke Davis, S.L. (1)
Avenue of Europe 20B, Alcobendas, 28108,
Spain
Tel.: (34) 914909900
Web Site: http://www.pfizer.com
Pharmaceutical Preparation Mfr
N.A.I.C.S.: 325412

Laboratorios Pfizer Ltda. (1)
Rua Alexandre Dumas 1860 Chacara Santo
Antonio, Guuarulhos, Sao Paulo, CEP
04717-904, SP, Brazil
Tel.: (55) 1151858500
Web Site: https://www.pfizer.com.br
Sales Range: $800-899.9 Million
Emp.: 1,359
Pharmaceuticals Mfr
N.A.I.C.S.: 325412

Laboratorios Pfizer, Lda. (1)
Lagoas Park - Edificio 10, 2740-271, Porto
Salvo, Portugal
Tel.: (351) 214235500
Web Site: https://www.pfizer.pt
Sales Range: $50-74.9 Million
Emp.: 200
Pharmaceutical Services
N.A.I.C.S.: 325412

Orfi-Farma S.L. (1)
Carretera Nacional 1 km 23, 28700, San
Sebastian, Spain
Tel.: (34) 913346400
Web Site: http://www.Pfizer.es
Pharmaceutical Preparation Mfr
N.A.I.C.S.: 325412

PT. Capsugel Indonesia (1)
Jl Raya Bogor Km 42, PO Box 15/CBI, Cibi-
nong, Jakarta, 16916, Jawa Barat, Indone-
sia
Tel.: (62) 218752226
Web Site: https://www.capsugel.com
Pharmaceuticals Product Mfr

N.A.I.C.S.: 325412

PT. Pfizer Indonesia (1)
28th Floor World Trade Center 3 Jl Jendral
Sudirman Kav 29-31, Jakarta, 12920, Indo-
nesia
Tel.: (62) 2180861400
Web Site: https://www.pfizer.com
Emp.: 400
Pharmaceutical Products
N.A.I.C.S.: 325412

Parke-Davis & Company Limited (1)
B-2 Site, Karachi, 75700, Pakistan
Tel.: (92) 212570625
Web Site: http://www.pfizer.com.pk
Sales Range: $150-199.9 Million
Emp.: 350
Pharmaceutical Mfr & Marketer
N.A.I.C.S.: 325412

Pfizer (1)
23 25 Avenue du Docteur Lannelongue,
75014, Paris, France
Tel.: (33) 158073000
Web Site: https://www.pfizer.fr
Emp.: 1,100
Pharmaceuticals Product Mfr
N.A.I.C.S.: 325412

**Pfizer (China) Research and Devel-
opment Co. Ltd.** (1)
Building No 3 Lane 60 Naxian Road, Pu-
dong Zhangjiang Hi-Tech Park, Shanghai,
201210, China
Tel.: (86) 2128935888
Web Site: https://www.pfizer.com.cn
Pharmaceutical Preparation Mfr
N.A.I.C.S.: 325412

Pfizer (Perth) Pty Limited (1)
15 Brodie Hall Dr Technology Park, Bentley,
6102, WA, Australia
Tel.: (61) 893620666
Web Site: https://www.pfizer.com
Pharmaceuticals Mfr
N.A.I.C.S.: 325412

Pfizer (Thailand) Limited (1)
1 Park Silom Building 27th Floor Rooms
2701-2704 and 2707-2708, Silom Road Si-
lom Subdistrict Bang Rak District, Bangkok,
10500, Thailand (100%)
Tel.: (66) 27614555
Web Site: https://www.pfizer.co.th
Sales Range: $200-249.9 Million
Emp.: 500
Pharmaceuticals Mfr
N.A.I.C.S.: 325412

**Pfizer (Vietnam) Limited
Company** (1)
Floor 17 Unit 1701 Friendship Tower 31 Le
Duan, Ben Nghe Ward District 1, Ho Chi
Minh City, Vietnam
Tel.: (84) 2836224000
Web Site: https://www.pfizer.com.vn
Pharmaceuticals Product Mfr
N.A.I.C.S.: 325412

Pfizer - Middleton (1)
2232 Pleasantville Rd, Middleton, WI
53562-4241 (100%)
Tel.: (608) 836-3500
Web Site: http://www.pfizer.com
Sales Range: $25-49.9 Million
Emp.: 50
Pharmaceuticals Mfr & Distr
N.A.I.C.S.: 325414

Pfizer A/S (1)
Drammensveien 288, 0283, Oslo,
Norway (100%)
Tel.: (47) 67526100
Web Site: https://www.pfizer.no
Sales Range: $25-49.9 Million
Emp.: 85
Pharmaceuticals Mfr
N.A.I.C.S.: 325412

Pfizer AB (1)
Vetenskapsvagen 10, 191 90, Sollentuna,
Sweden (100%)
Tel.: (46) 85 505 2000
Web Site: https://www.pfizer.se
Sales Range: $200-249.9 Million
Emp.: 430
Pharmaceuticals Mfr
N.A.I.C.S.: 325412

Pfizer AG (1)

Scharenmoosstrasse 99, CH-8052, Zurich,
Switzerland (100%)
Tel.: (41) 434957111
Web Site: https://www.pfizer.ch
Sales Range: $150-199.9 Million
Emp.: 400
Pharmaceutical Services
N.A.I.C.S.: 325412

Pfizer AS (1)
Lilleakerveien 2b, 0283, Oslo, Norway
Tel.: (47) 67526100
Web Site: https://www.pfizer.com
Sales Range: $25-49.9 Million
Emp.: 100
Pharmaceutical Preparation Mfr
N.A.I.C.S.: 325412

Pfizer ApS (1)
Lautrupvang 8, 2750, Ballerup,
Denmark (100%)
Tel.: (45) 44201100
Web Site: https://www.pfizer.dk
Sales Range: $25-49.9 Million
Emp.: 95
Pharmaceuticals Mfr
N.A.I.C.S.: 325412

Pfizer Argentina (1)
Complejo Thames Office Park Colectora
Panamericana Piso 1, Sector B 1804 Lado
Sur, Buenos Aires, Argentina (99.99%)
Tel.: (54) 1147887000
Web Site: http://www.pfizer.com.ar
Sales Range: $150-199.9 Million
Pharmaceutical Preparation Mfr
N.A.I.C.S.: 325412

Pfizer Asia International B.V. (1)
Rivium Westlaan 142, 2909 LD, Capelle
aan den IJssel, Netherlands
Tel.: (31) 104064200
Web Site: https://www.pfizer.nl
Sales Range: $50-74.9 Million
Emp.: 250
Holding Company
N.A.I.C.S.: 551112

Pfizer Asia Pacific Pte Ltd. (1)
31 Tuas S Avenue 6, Singapore, 637578,
Singapore
Tel.: (65) 64190100
Web Site: http://www.pfizer-pappl-sg.com
Sales Range: $75-99.9 Million
Emp.: 240
Pharmaceuticals Mfr
N.A.I.C.S.: 325412

**Pfizer Australia Holdings Pty
Limited** (1)
Level 15-18 151 Clarence Street, Sydney,
2000, NSW, Australia
Tel.: (61) 298503333
Web Site: http://www.pfizer.com.au
Pharmaceutical Preparation Mfr
N.A.I.C.S.: 325412

Subsidiary (Domestic):

ResApp Health Limited (2)
Level 8 127 Creek St, Brisbane, 4000,
QLD, Australia
Tel.: (61) 8 6211 5099
Web Site: http://www.resapphealth.com.au
Rev.: $972,369
Assets: $7,231,501
Liabilities: $1,405,393
Net Worth: $5,826,108
Earnings: ($5,190,550)
Fiscal Year-end: 06/30/2021
Respiratory Disease Management Technol-
ogy Developer
N.A.I.C.S.: 541519
Nicki Farley (Sec)
Tony Keating (CEO & Mng Dir)
Brian Leedman (VP-Corp Affairs)
Kay Taylor (VP-Strategic Dev & Ops)
Rob Keniger (VP-Software Engrg)

**Pfizer Australia Investments Pty.
Ltd.** (1)
38-42 Wharf Rd, Sydney, 2114, NSW, Aus-
tralia
Tel.: (61) 298503333
Web Site: https://www.pfizer.com
Pharmaceutical Preparation Mfr
N.A.I.C.S.: 325412

Pfizer Australia Pty Limited (1)
Level 15-18 151 Clarence Street, Sydney,

2000, NSW, Australia **(100%)**
Tel.: (61) 298503333
Web Site: https://www.pfizer.com.au
Sales Range: $800-899.9 Million
Emp.: 1,200
Pharmaceuticals Mfr
N.A.I.C.S.: 325412

Pfizer B.V. **(1)**
Rivium Westlaan 142, 2909 LD, Capelle
aan den IJssel, Netherlands **(100%)**
Tel.: (31) 104064200
Web Site: https://www.pfizer.nl
Sales Range: $200-249.9 Million
Emp.: 250
Pharmaceutical Services & Mfr
N.A.I.C.S.: 325412

Pfizer Biotech Corporation **(1)**
177 Chung Cheng E Rd Sec 2, Tanshui
Chen, Taipei, 25159, Taiwan
Tel.: (886) 228097979
Web Site: http://www.pfizer.com
Emp.: 20
Pharmaceutical Preparation Mfr
N.A.I.C.S.: 325412

Pfizer Biotechnology Ireland **(1)**
Shanbally, Ringaskiddy, Ireland
Tel.: (353) 215007920
Pharmaceuticals Product Mfr
N.A.I.C.S.: 325412

Pfizer Canada Inc. **(1)**
17300 Trans-Canada Highway, Kirkland,
H9J 2M5, QC, Canada **(100%)**
Tel.: (514) 695-0500
Web Site: https://www.pfizer.ca
Sales Range: $300-349.9 Million
Emp.: 700
Pharmaceutical Preparations & Sales
N.A.I.C.S.: 325412

Pfizer Chile S.A. **(1)**
Cerro el Plomo 5680 Torre 6 Piso 16, Las
Condes, Santiago, Chile
Tel.: (56) 800392348
Web Site: https://www.pfizer.cl
Pharmaceuticals Product Mfr
N.A.I.C.S.: 325412

Pfizer Cia. Ltda. **(1)**
Av Simon Bolivar y calle Nayon Eko Park
Torre 5 Piso 6, 300 MTS Comdado, Quito,
170404, Ecuador
Tel.: (593) 23962100
Web Site: https://www.pfizer.com.ec
Pharmaceutical Preparation Mfr
N.A.I.C.S.: 325412

**Pfizer Consumer Healthcare
GmbH** **(1)**
Linkstrasse 10, Berlin, 10785,
Germany **(100%)**
Tel.: (49) 3055005501
Web Site: http://www.pfizer-
selbstmedikation.de
Sales Range: $25-49.9 Million
Emp.: 100
Pharmaceuticals Mfr
N.A.I.C.S.: 325412

Pfizer Corporation **(1)**
Albrook Park Ofc 106, Panama,
Panama **(100%)**
Tel.: (507) 2328888
Web Site: https://www.pfizer.com
Sales Range: $150-199.9 Million
Emp.: 60
Pharmaceutical Preparation Mfr
N.A.I.C.S.: 325412

**Pfizer Corporation Austria Gesell-
schaft m.b.H.** **(1)**
Floridsdorfer Hauptstrasse 1, Postfach 439,
1210, Vienna, Austria **(100%)**
Tel.: (43) 1521150
Web Site: https://www.pfizer.at
Sales Range: $50-74.9 Million
Emp.: 160
Pharmaceuticals Mfr
N.A.I.C.S.: 325412
Nicole Schlautmann *(Mng Dir)*

**Pfizer Corporation Hong Kong
Limited** **(1)**
21/F Kerry Centre 683 King's Road, Quarry
Bay, China (Hong Kong)
Tel.: (852) 28119711
Web Site: https://www.pfizer.com.hk

Sales Range: $50-74.9 Million
Emp.: 200
Pharmaceutical Preparation Mfr
N.A.I.C.S.: 325412

Pfizer Croatia d.o.o. **(1)**
Slavonska avenija 6, 10000, Zagreb, Croa-
tia
Tel.: (385) 13908777
Web Site: https://www.pfizer.hr
Pharmaceuticals Product Mfr
N.A.I.C.S.: 325412

Pfizer Croatia d.o.o. **(1)**
Slavonska avenija 6, 10000, Zagreb, Croa-
tia
Tel.: (385) 1 390 8777
Web Site: https://www.pfizer.hr
Pharmaceuticals Product Mfr
N.A.I.C.S.: 325412

Pfizer Deutschland GmbH **(1)**
Linkstrasse 10, 10785, Berlin, Germany
Tel.: (49) 3055005501
Web Site: https://www.pfizer.de
Sales Range: $25-49.9 Million
Emp.: 600
Pharmaceuticals Mfr
N.A.I.C.S.: 325412

Pfizer Dominicana, S.A. **(1)**
Av J F Kennedy 10 Sd Edf Pellerano &
Herrera P 1, Santo Domingo, Dominican
Republic
Tel.: (809) 2626500
Pharmaceutical Products Distr
N.A.I.C.S.: 456110

Pfizer Enterprises SARL **(1)**
51 Avenue J F Kennedy, Luxembourg,
1855, Luxembourg
Tel.: (352) 2609091
Web Site: http://www.pfizer.com
Sales Range: $25-49.9 Million
Emp.: 20
Pharmaceutical Preparation Mfr
N.A.I.C.S.: 325412

Pfizer Esbjerg A/S **(1)**
Lautrup Vant 8, 2750, Ballerup,
Denmark **(100%)**
Tel.: (45) 44201100
Web Site: http://www.pfizer.dk
Sales Range: $50-74.9 Million
Emp.: 170
Pharmaceuticals Mfr
N.A.I.C.S.: 325412

**Pfizer European Service Center
BVBA** **(1)**
Hoge Wei 10, 1930, Zaventem, Belgium
Tel.: (32) 27220211
Web Site: http://www.pfizer.be
Sales Range: $50-74.9 Million
Emp.: 165
Pharmaceuticals Mfr
N.A.I.C.S.: 325412

Pfizer Export Company **(1)**
Touche House Ln, Dublin, Ireland
Tel.: (353) 14484600
Pharmaceuticals Product Mfr
N.A.I.C.S.: 325412

**Pfizer France International Invest-
ments SAS** **(1)**
23-25 Avenue du Docteur Lannelongue,
75014, Paris, Cedex 14, France
Tel.: (33) 158073000
Web Site: https://www.pfizer.fr
Pharmaceuticals Product Mfr
N.A.I.C.S.: 325412

Pfizer Germany B.V. & Co. KG **(1)**
Linkstr 10, 10785, Berlin, Germany
Tel.: (49) 3055005501
Web Site: http://www.pfizer.com
Emp.: 600
Pharmaceutical Products Distr
N.A.I.C.S.: 456110

Pfizer Global Supply Japan Inc. **(1)**
681 Saedocho Tsuzuki-Ku, Yokohama, 224-
0054, Kanagawa, Japan
Tel.: (81) 459291403
Pharmaceuticals Product Mfr
N.A.I.C.S.: 325412

Pfizer Group Limited **(1)**
Ramsgate Rd, Sandwich, CT13 9ND, Kent,
United Kingdom **(100%)**

Tel.: (44) 1304616161
Web Site: http://www.pfizer.co.uk
Sales Range: $1-4.9 Billion
Emp.: 3,600
Pharmaceutical Research & Development
Services
N.A.I.C.S.: 325412

Pfizer Gulf FZ-LLC **(1)**
Sheikh Zayed Road Al Moosa Tower 2, PO
Box 29553, 12338, Dubai, United Arab
Emirates
Tel.: (971) 43322286
Web Site: https://www.pfizerprogulf.com
Pharmaceutical Product Whslr
N.A.I.C.S.: 424210

**Pfizer Gyogyszerkereskedelmi
Kft.** **(1)**
Alkotas u 53 MOM Park A epulet, 1123, Bu-
dapest, Hungary
Tel.: (36) 1 488 3700
Web Site: https://www.pfizer.hu
Pharmaceuticals Mfr
N.A.I.C.S.: 325412

**Pfizer HK Service Company
Limited** **(1)**
Ste 5207-08 52/F Central Plaza, Harbor Rd,
Wanchai, New Territories, China (Hong
Kong)
Tel.: (852) 24098181
Web Site: http://www.pfizer.com.hk
Sales Range: $125-149.9 Million
Emp.: 40
Pharmaceutical Preparation Mfr
N.A.I.C.S.: 325412

Pfizer Health AB **(1)**
Mariefredsvagen 39, Sodermanlands, 645
41, Strangnas, Sweden
Tel.: (46) 15227300
Emp.: 40
Pharmaceutical Preparation Mfr
N.A.I.C.S.: 325412

Pfizer Health Solutions Inc. **(1)**
235 E 42nd St, New York, NY
10017-5703 **(100%)**
Tel.: (212) 733-2323
Web Site: http://www.pfizer.com
Care Management & Technology Solutions
N.A.I.C.S.: 541690

**Pfizer Healthcare India Private
Limited** **(1)**
Emerald Building 237 Anna Salai, Chennai,
600 006, Tamil Nadu, India
Tel.: (91) 4461568000
Web Site: https://www.pfizerhealth.co.in
Pharmaceuticals Product Mfr
N.A.I.C.S.: 325412

Pfizer Healthcare Ireland **(1)**
The Pfizer Building 9 Riverwalk National
Digital Park, Ciywest Business Campus,
Dublin, 24, Ireland
Tel.: (353) 14676500
Web Site: https://www.pfizer.ie
Sales Range: $25-49.9 Million
Emp.: 7
Pharmaceutical Preparation Mfr
N.A.I.C.S.: 325412

Pfizer Hellas, A.E. **(1)**
Messoghion Ave 243 NEO, Psycaiko, 154
51, Athens, Greece **(100%)**
Tel.: (30) 2106785800
Web Site: https://www.pfizer.gr
Sales Range: $200-249.9 Million
Emp.: 100
Pharmaceuticals Mfr
N.A.I.C.S.: 325412

Pfizer Holding France (S.C.A.) **(1)**
23 Av Du Docteur Lannelongue, 75014,
Paris, France
Tel.: (33) 158073000
Sales Range: $25-49.9 Million
Emp.: 5
Pharmaceutical Preparation Mfr
N.A.I.C.S.: 325412

Pfizer Holding Italy S.p.A. **(1)**
Via Valbondione 113, Rome, 00188, Italy
Tel.: (39) 06331821
Pharmaceutical Preparation Mfr
N.A.I.C.S.: 325412

**Pfizer Holdings International Luxem-
bourg (PHIL) Sarl** **(1)**

Ave J-F Kennedy 51, Luxembourg, 1855,
Luxembourg
Tel.: (352) 2609091
Web Site: https://www.pfizer.com
Holding Company
N.A.I.C.S.: 551112

Pfizer Ilaclari Limited Sirketi **(1)**
Muallim Naci cad No 55, Ortakoy, 34347,
Istanbul, Turkiye
Tel.: (90) 2123107000
Web Site: http://www.pfizer.com.tr
Pharmaceuticals Product Mfr
N.A.I.C.S.: 325412
Tuncay Teksoz *(Dir-Corp Rels)*

Pfizer Ilaclari, A.S. **(1)**
Ortakoy 34347, 80840, Istanbul,
Turkiye **(100%)**
Tel.: (90) 2123107000
Web Site: http://www.pfizer.com.tr
Sales Range: $150-199.9 Million
Pharmaceuticals Mfr
N.A.I.C.S.: 325412

Pfizer International Corporation **(1)**
Pfizer Bldg Dubai Media City, 29553, Dubai,
United Arab Emirates
Tel.: (971) 44532000
Pharmaceutical Preparation Mfr
N.A.I.C.S.: 325412

Pfizer International LLC **(1)**
235 E 42nd St, New York, NY
10017 **(100%)**
Tel.: (212) 733-2323
Web Site: https://www.pfizer.com
Sales Range: $150-199.9 Million
Pharmaceuticals Mfr
N.A.I.C.S.: 325412

Subsidiary (Domestic):

Pfizer Overseas LLC **(2)**
235 E 42nd St, New York, NY
10017 **(100%)**
Tel.: (212) 733-2323
Web Site: https://www.pfizer.com
Holding Company
N.A.I.C.S.: 325412

**Pfizer International Trading (Shang-
hai) Limited** **(1)**
25-28/F and 36/F CITIC Square 1168 Nan
Jing Road W, Shanghai, 200041, China
Tel.: (86) 2160432500
Web Site: http://www.pfizer.com.cn
Pharmaceutical Preparation Mfr
N.A.I.C.S.: 325412

Pfizer Ireland Pharmaceuticals **(1)**
Ringaskiddy Active Pharmaceutical Ingredi-
ent Plant, PO Box 17, Ringaskiddy,
P43X336, County Cork, Ireland **(100%)**
Tel.: (353) 21 437 8701
Web Site: http://www.pfizer.ie
Sales Range: $200-249.9 Million
Emp.: 4,000
Pharmaceuticals Mfr
N.A.I.C.S.: 325412

Pfizer Italia S.r.l. **(1)**
Via Valbondione 113, 00188, Rome, Italy
Tel.: (39) 06331821
Web Site: https://www.pfizer.it
Emp.: 2,000
Pharmaceuticals Mfr
N.A.I.C.S.: 325412

Pfizer Japan Inc. **(1)**
3-22-7 Yoyogi Shinjuku Bunka Quint Build-
ing, Shibuya-ku, Tokyo, 151-8589,
Japan **(100%)**
Tel.: (81) 353097000
Web Site: https://www.pfizer.co.jp
Sales Range: $1-4.9 Billion
Emp.: 3,000
Pharmaceuticals Mfr
N.A.I.C.S.: 325412
Akihisa Harada *(CEO)*

Pfizer Laboratories (Pty) Limited **(1)**
85 Bute Lane, PO Box 783720, Sandton,
2146, Gauteng, South Africa
Tel.: (27) 86 073 4937
Web Site: https://www.pfizerpro.co.za
Pharmaceutical Preparation Mfr
N.A.I.C.S.: 325412

Pfizer Laboratories PFE (Pty) Ltd **(1)**
85 Bute Lane, Sandton, 2196, South Africa

Pfizer Inc.—(Continued)
Tel.: (27) 113206000
Pharmaceuticals Product Mfr
N.A.I.C.S.: 325412

Pfizer Limited (1)
The Capital 1802 / 1901 Plot No C-70 G
Block, Bandra Kurla Complex, Mumbai,
400051, India (52.03%)
Tel.: (91) 2266932000
Web Site: https://www.pfizerltd.co.in
Rev: $316,634,955
Assets: $445,795,350
Liabilities: $119,145,390
Net Worth: $326,649,960
Earnings: $67,923,765
Emp.: 2,358
Fiscal Year-end: 03/31/2021
Pharmaceutical Mfr & Distr
N.A.I.C.S.: 325412
Sandesh C. Seth (Dir-Compliance)
Prajeet Nair (Officer-Compliance & Sec)
R. A. Shah (Chm)
Vivek Dhariwal (Exec Dir-Technical Ops)
S. Sridhar (Mng Dir)
Sharad Goswani (Dir-Pub Affairs)
Samir Kazi (Sr Dir-Legal)
Milind Patil (CFO & Dir-Fin)
Arvind Jain (Dir-Vaccines)
V. C. Iyer (Sr Dir-Procurement)
Deepak Rakheja (Dir-Global Comml Ops)
Aninda Shome (Dir-Supply Chain)
Navin Singhania (Dir-Bus Tech)
Manish Paliwal (Dir-PEH Regulatory Affairs)
Madhav Joshi (Sr Dir-Internal Medicine)
Anil Pattanshetty (Dir-Inflammation & Immunology)
Sonali Dighe (Sr Dir-Medical Affairs)
Shilpi Singh (Dir-HR)

Pfizer Limited (1)
Walton Oaks Dorking Rd Walton-on-the-Hill,
Tadworth, KT20 7NS, Surrey, United
Kingdom (100%)
Tel.: (44) 1304616161
Web Site: http://www.pfizervaccines.co.uk
Sales Range: $150-199.9 Million
Pharmaceuticals Mfr
N.A.I.C.S.: 325412

Pfizer Limited (1)
The Capital 1802 / 1901 Plot No C-70 G
Block, Bandra Kurla Complex Bandra E,
Mumbai, 400 051, India
Tel.: (91) 2266932000
Web Site: https://www.pfizerltd.co.in
Pharmaceuticals Product Mfr
N.A.I.C.S.: 325412

Pfizer Limited (Taiwan) (1)
177 Chung Cheng E Rd Sec 2, Tamsui,
25114, Taiwan
Tel.: (886) 228097979
Web Site: http://www.pfizer.com.tw
Sales Range: $150-199.9 Million
Emp.: 350
Pharmaceuticals Mfr
N.A.I.C.S.: 325412

Pfizer Logistics Center (1)
1855 N Shelby Oaks Dr, Memphis, TN
38134
Tel.: (901) 387-5200
Sales Range: $75-99.9 Million
Emp.: 240
Pharmaceutical Services
N.A.I.C.S.: 517111

Pfizer Luxembourg SARL (1)
Rond-Point du Kirchberg 51 Avenue JF
Kennedy, 1855, Luxembourg, Luxembourg
Tel.: (352) 26114930
Emp.: 8
Pharmaceutical Preparation Mfr
N.A.I.C.S.: 325412

Pfizer Malaysia Sdn Bhd (1)
Level 10 11 Wisma Averis Tower 2 Avenue
5, Bangsar South No 8 Jalan Kerinchi,
59200, Kuala Lumpur, Malaysia (100%)
Tel.: (60) 322816000
Web Site: https://www.pfizer.com.my
Pharmaceuticals Mfr
N.A.I.C.S.: 325412

**Pfizer Manufacturing Austria
G.m.b.H.** (1)
Uferstrasse 15, A-2304, Orth an der Donau,
Austria

Tel.: (43) 2212323
Web Site: https://www.pfizer.com
Biological Product Mfr
N.A.I.C.S.: 325414

**Pfizer Manufacturing Belgium
N.V.** (1)
Rijksweg 12, 2870, Puurs, Belgium
Tel.: (32) 38909211
Sales Range: $300-349.9 Million
Emp.: 2,500
Pharmaceutical Preparation Mfr
N.A.I.C.S.: 325412

**Pfizer Manufacturing Deutschland
GmbH** (1)
Linkstrasse 10, 10785, Berlin, Germany
Tel.: (49) 7303120
Pharmaceuticals Product Mfr
N.A.I.C.S.: 325412

**Pfizer Manufacturing Deutschland
PFE GmbH** (1)
Mooswaldallee 1, 79108, Freiburg, Germany
Tel.: (49) 7615180
Biological Product Mfr
N.A.I.C.S.: 325414

Pfizer Medical Systems, Inc. (1)
235 E 42nd St, New York, NY
10017-5703 (100%)
Tel.: (212) 573-2323
Web Site: http://www.pfizer.com
Sales Range: $10-24.9 Million
Emp.: 25
Pharmaceutical Services
N.A.I.C.S.: 325412

**Pfizer Medical Technology Group
(Netherlands) B.V.** (1)
Rivium Westlaan 142, 2909 LD, Capelle
aan den IJssel, Netherlands (100%)
Tel.: (31) 104064200
Web Site: http://www.pfizer.nl
Sales Range: $150-199.9 Million
Emp.: 350
Pharmaceuticals Mfr
N.A.I.C.S.: 325412
Rob Van Aperen (Mng Dir)

Subsidiary (Non-US):

PGM European Logistics Center (2)
Hoge Wei 10, 1930, Zaventem,
Belgium (100%)
Tel.: (32) 27220211
Web Site: http://www.pfizer.com
Sales Range: $200-249.9 Million
Pharmaceutical Research Services
N.A.I.C.S.: 325412

**Pfizer Medicamentos Genericos e
Participacoes Ltda.** (1)
Rua Alexandre Dumas 1860 Chacara Santo
Antonio, Sao Paulo, 04717-904, SP, Brazil
Tel.: (55) 1151858500
Emp.: 300
Holding Company
N.A.I.C.S.: 551112
Vitor Mezei (Pres)

Pfizer N.V./S.A. (1)
Pleinlaan 17, Elsene, 1050, Brussels,
Belgium (100%)
Tel.: (32) 25546211
Web Site: https://www.pfizer.be
Sales Range: $900-999.9 Million
Emp.: 1,500
Pharmaceuticals Mfr
N.A.I.C.S.: 325412

Pfizer Netherlands B.V. (1)
Rivium Westlaan 142, 2909 LD, Capelle
aan den IJssel, Netherlands
Tel.: (31) 104064200
Web Site: https://www.pfizer.nl
Pharmaceuticals Product Mfr
N.A.I.C.S.: 325412

Pfizer New Zealand Limited (1)
Shortland Street, Grafton, Auckland, 1140,
New Zealand
Tel.: (64) 99503977
Web Site: https://www.pfizer.co.nz
Sales Range: $25-49.9 Million
Emp.: 130
Pharmaceuticals Product Mfr
N.A.I.C.S.: 325412
Anne Harris (Mng Dir)

Pfizer Norge AS (1)
Drammensveien 288, 0283, Oslo, Norway
Tel.: (47) 67526100
Web Site: http://www.pfizer.no
Emp.: 85
Pharmaceuticals Product Mfr
N.A.I.C.S.: 325412

Pfizer Oy (1)
Tietokuja 4, 00330, Helsinki,
Finland (100%)
Tel.: (358) 9430040
Web Site: https://www.pfizer.fi
Emp.: 120
Pharmaceuticals Mfr
N.A.I.C.S.: 325412

**Pfizer PFE (Malaysia) SDN.
BHD.** (1)
Level 10 & 11 Wisma Averis Tower 2, Avenue 5 Bangsar South No 8 Jalan Kerinchi,
59200, Kuala Lumpur, Malaysia
Tel.: (60) 322816000
Web Site: https://www.pfizer.com.my
Pharmaceuticals Product Mfr
N.A.I.C.S.: 325412

Pfizer PFE Ilaclari Anonim Sirketi (1)
Levent 199 No 199 Ic Kapi No 106 Floor
26, 34394, Istanbul, Turkiye
Tel.: (90) 2123107000
Web Site: https://privacycenter.pfizer.com
Biopharmaceutical Product Mfr
N.A.I.C.S.: 325414

**Pfizer PFE New Zealand Holding
B.V.** (1)
Rivium westlaan 142, 2909 LD, Capelle aan
den IJssel, Netherlands
Tel.: (31) 104064200
Web Site: http://www.pfizer.com
Holding Company
N.A.I.C.S.: 551112

Pfizer PFE, spol. s r.o. (1)
Stroupeznickeho 3191/ 17, Smichov, 150
00, Prague, Czech Republic
Tel.: (420) 283004111
Web Site: http://www.pfizer.cz
Emp.: 228
Pharmaceuticals Product Mfr
N.A.I.C.S.: 325412

Pfizer Pakistan Limited (1)
24th Floor Sky Tower East Wing Dolmen
City HC-3 Block-4 Scheme-5, Clifton, Karachi, 75600, Pakistan
Tel.: (92) 21325706215
Web Site: https://www.pfizer.com.pk
Pharmaceuticals Product Mfr
N.A.I.C.S.: 325412

Pfizer Pharma GmbH (1)
Friedrichstrasse 110, 10117, Berlin, Germany
Tel.: (49) 3055005501
Web Site: https://www.pfizer.de
Emp.: 2,500
Pharmaceutical Preparation Mfr
N.A.I.C.S.: 325412

Pfizer Pharma PFE GmbH (1)
Linkstrasse 10, 10785, Berlin, Germany
Tel.: (49) 8008535555
Web Site: http://www.pfizerpro.de
Pharmaceutical Product Whslr
N.A.I.C.S.: 424210

**Pfizer Pharmaceutical (Wuxi) Co.,
Ltd.** (1)
Bridge No 7 Mashan, Binhu District, Wuxi,
214092, Jiangsu, China
Tel.: (86) 51085960999
Pharmaceuticals Product Mfr
N.A.I.C.S.: 325412

**Pfizer Pharmaceuticals Israel
Ltd.** (1)
9 Shenkar Street, Herzliya, Israel (99%)
Tel.: (972) 99700500
Web Site: https://www.pfizer.co.il
Sales Range: $150-199.9 Million
Pharmaceutical Preparation Manufacturing
N.A.I.C.S.: 325412

**Pfizer Pharmaceuticals Korea
Ltd.** (1)
Pfizer Tower 110 Toegyero Road Jung-Gu,
Seoul, 004-631, Korea (South)
Tel.: (82) 23172114

Web Site: https://www.pfizer.co.kr
Pharmaceuticals Mfr
N.A.I.C.S.: 325412

Pfizer Pharmaceuticals Ltd. (1)
The Fifth Square Tower B 8-12/F No 3-7
Chaoyangmen North Avenue, Dongcheng
District, Beijing, 100010, China
Tel.: (86) 10 851 67000
Web Site: http://www.pfizer.com.cn
Sales Range: $50-74.9 Million
Emp.: 180
Pharmaceuticals Mfr
N.A.I.C.S.: 325412

**Pfizer Pharmaceuticals Tunisie
Sarl** (1)
Rue du Lac de Constance, 1053, Tunis,
Tunisia
Tel.: (216) 71961330
Sales Range: $25-49.9 Million
Emp.: 74
Pharmaceutical Preparation Mfr
N.A.I.C.S.: 325412

Pfizer Polska Sp. z.o.o. (1)
ul Zwirki i Wigury 16B, 02-092, Warsaw,
Poland
Tel.: (48) 223356100
Web Site: https://www.pfizer.com.pl
Emp.: 15
Pharmaceutical Preparation Mfr
N.A.I.C.S.: 325412

**Pfizer Prev-Sociedade de Previdencia
Privada** (1)
Rua Alexandre Dumas 1860-3 andar Chacara Santo Antonio, Sao Paulo, 07190-001,
Brazil
Tel.: (55) 8007277043
Web Site: https://pfizerprev.com.br
Pharmaceuticals Product Mfr
N.A.I.C.S.: 325412

Pfizer Products Inc. (1)
558 Eastern Point Rd, Groton, CT
06340 (100%)
Tel.: (860) 441-4100
Sales Range: $200-249.9 Million
Emp.: 32
Toiletries & Non Prescription Drug Mfr
N.A.I.C.S.: 325411

**Pfizer Products India Private
Limited** (1)
Pfizer Centre Patel Estate S, Mumbai,
400102, Maharashtra, India
Tel.: (91) 2266932000
Web Site: https://www.pfizerindia.com
Pharmaceutical Preparation Mfr
N.A.I.C.S.: 325412

Pfizer Pte. Ltd. (1)
Science Park Road Science Park II 04-01,
Singapore, 117528, Singapore (100%)
Tel.: (65) 6402 8888
Web Site: http://www.pfizer.com.sg
Sales Range: $75-99.9 Million
Emp.: 130
Pharmaceuticals Marketer
N.A.I.C.S.: 424210

Pfizer Research & Development (1)
4000 Centre Green Way, Cary, NC 27513-2125
Tel.: (919) 653-7001
Web Site: http://www.pfizer.com
Sales Range: $10-24.9 Million
Emp.: 10
Pharmaceutical Research & Development
Services
N.A.I.C.S.: 541715

**Pfizer Research Technology
Center** (1)
620 Memorial Dr, Cambridge, MA
02139 (100%)
Tel.: (617) 551-3000
Web Site: http://www.pfizer.com
Sales Range: $25-49.9 Million
Emp.: 100
Medical Research Services
N.A.I.C.S.: 541715

Pfizer Romania SRL (1)
Tel.: (40) 212072800
Web Site: https://www.pfizer.ro
Pharmaceutical Preparation Mfr
N.A.I.C.S.: 325412

Pfizer S.A. (1)
Avda De Europa 20B Business Park La Moraleja, 28108, Alcobendas, Spain (100%)
Tel.: (34) 914909900
Web Site: https://www.pfizer.es
Sales Range: $350-399.9 Million
Emp.: 1,100
Pharmaceuticals Mfr
N.A.I.C.S.: 325412

Pfizer S.A.S. (1)
23-25 avenue du Docteur Lannelongue,
Paris, 75014, France (100%)
Tel.: (33) 158073000
Web Site: https://www.pfizer.fr
Sales Range: $25-49.9 Million
Emp.: 1,000
Pharmaceutical Preparation Services
N.A.I.C.S.: 325412
Emmanuel Quiles (Pres)

Pfizer S.G.P.S. Lda. (1)
Lagoas Park - Edificio 10 Porto Salvo,
2740-271, Lisbon, Portugal
Tel.: (351) 214235500
Web Site: https://www.pfizer.pt
Pharmaceuticals Product Mfr
N.A.I.C.S.: 325412

Pfizer S.R.L. (1)
Colectora Panamericana 1804 Piso 1- Sector B - Lado Sur, Villa Adelina, CP
B1607EEV, Buenos Aires, Argentina
Tel.: (54) 1147887000
Web Site: https://www.pfizer.com.ar
Emp.: 600
Pharmaceutical Preparation Mfr
N.A.I.C.S.: 325412

Pfizer S.r.l. (1)
Via Isonzo 71, 04100, Latina, Italy
Tel.: (39) 06331821
Web Site: https://www.pfizer.it
Emp.: 2,000
Pharmaceuticals Product Mfr
N.A.I.C.S.: 325412

Pfizer SA (Belgium) (1)
Boulevard De La Plaine 17 Ixelles, 1050,
Brussels, Belgium (100%)
Tel.: (32) 25546211
Sales Range: $300-349.9 Million
Emp.: 250
Pharmaceuticals Mfr
N.A.I.C.S.: 325412

Subsidiary (Non-US):

Pfizer s.r.o. (2)
Stroupeznickeho Block 5, 150 00, Prague,
Czech Republic (100%)
Tel.: (420) 283004111
Web Site: http://www.pfizer.com
Sales Range: $100-124.9 Million
Emp.: 300
Pharmaceutical Preparation Mfr
N.A.I.C.S.: 325412

Pfizer SRB d.o.o. (1)
Tresnjinog cveta1/VI, 11000, Belgrade, Serbia
Tel.: (381) 113630000
Web Site: https://www.pfizer.rs
Pharmaceuticals Product Mfr
N.A.I.C.S.: 325412

Pfizer Saudi Limited (1)
Airport Road Business Gate Complex building no 7 2nd Floor, Qurtoba District, Riyadh,
Saudi Arabia
Tel.: (966) 122293500
Web Site: https://www.pfizersaudi.com.sa
Pharmaceuticals Product Mfr
N.A.I.C.S.: 325412

Pfizer Service Company BVBA (1)
Hoge Wei 10, 1930, Zaventem, Belgium
Tel.: (32) 27220211
Web Site: https://www.pfizer.be
Emp.: 200
Pharmaceutical Preparation Mfr
N.A.I.C.S.: 325412

Pfizer Service Company Ireland (1)
House Ifsc, Dublin, Ireland
Tel.: (353) 16700277
Pharmaceuticals Product Mfr
N.A.I.C.S.: 325412

Pfizer Shared Services (1)
Watermarque Ringsend Road, Ringsend,

Dublin, Ireland
Tel.: (353) 14807000
Web Site: https://www.pfizer.com
Sales Range: $150-199.9 Million
Emp.: 50
Pharmaceutical Preparation Mfr
N.A.I.C.S.: 325412

Pfizer Spain S.A. (1)
Plaza Europa 9-11 7th Floor, Pl Xavier Cugat Ed D, 08908, Barcelona, Spain (100%)
Tel.: (34) 932424621
Web Site: http://www.pfizer.es
Sales Range: $350-399.9 Million
Emp.: 725
Pharmaceuticals Mfr
N.A.I.C.S.: 325412

Pfizer Specialties Limited (1)
7th Floor Heritage Place 21 Lugard avenue,
Ikoyi PMB 80081 Victoria Island, Lagos,
Nigeria
Tel.: (234) 127039215
Pharmaceuticals Product Mfr
N.A.I.C.S.: 325412

Pfizer Taiwan Ltd. (1)
177 Chung Cheng East Rd Sec 2, Tamsui,
25114, Taiwan (100%)
Tel.: (886) 228097979
Web Site: http://www.pfizer.com.tw
Sales Range: $25-49.9 Million
Emp.: 100
Pharmaceutical Preparation Mfr
N.A.I.C.S.: 325412

Pfizer Trading Polska sp. z.o.o. (1)
ul Zwirki i Wigury 16B, 02-092, Warsaw,
Poland
Tel.: (48) 22 335 6100
Web Site: http://www.pfizer.com.pl
Pharmaceutical Products Distr
N.A.I.C.S.: 456110

Pfizer Venezuela, S.A. (1)
Edif Pfizer Av Principal de los Ruices entre
2da y 3era transversal DC, 1071, Caracas,
Venezuela
Tel.: (58) 2126302900
Web Site: https://www.pfizervenezuela.com
Pharmaceutical Product Mfr & Distr
N.A.I.C.S.: 325412

Pfizer, Inc. (1)
19F-20F 8 Rockwell Building Hidalgo Drive
Rockwell Center Poblacion, Makati, 1210,
Metro Manila, Philippines
Tel.: (63) 284519200
Web Site: https://www.pfizer.com.ph
Emp.: 384
Pharmaceuticals Product Mfr
N.A.I.C.S.: 325412

Pfizer, S.A. de C.V. (1)
Paseo de los Tamarindos No 40, Colonia
Bosques de las Lomas Alcaldia Cuajimalpa,
CP 05120, Mexico, Mexico
Tel.: (52) 8004012002
Web Site: https://www.pfizer.com.mx
Pharmaceuticals Product Mfr
N.A.I.C.S.: 325412

Pfizer, S.L. (1)
Avda Europa 20 B, Parque empresarial La
Moraleja, 28108, Alcobendas, Madrid,
Spain
Tel.: (34) 914909900
Web Site: https://www.pfizer.es
Pharmaceuticals Product Mfr
N.A.I.C.S.: 325412

Pfizer, spol. s r.o. (1)
Stroupeznickeho 3191/17, Smichov, 150
00, Prague, Czech Republic
Tel.: (420) 283004111
Web Site: https://www.pfizer.cz
Emp.: 200

Pharmacia & Upjohn LLC (1)
100 Route 206 N, Peapack, NJ 07977
Tel.: (908) 901-8000
Pharmaceutical Product Mfr & Distr
N.A.I.C.S.: 325412

**Pharmacia (South Africa) (Pty)
Ltd** (1)
85 Bute Lane, Sandton, 2196, South Africa
Tel.: (27) 113206000
Web Site: http://www.pfizer.co.za
Pharmaceuticals Product Mfr
N.A.I.C.S.: 325412

Pharmacia LLC (1)
1340 Smith Ave Ste A, Baltimore, MD
21209
Tel.: (443) 388-8710
Pharmaceutical Products Distr
N.A.I.C.S.: 456110

Quigley Company, Inc. (1)
8250 Mill St, Vanderbilt, MI 49795
Tel.: (212) 808-0644
Web Site: http://www.quigleytrust.com
Refractory Products Mfr
N.A.I.C.S.: 327120

Rinat Neuroscience Corp. (1)
230 E Grand Ave, South San Francisco, CA
94080
Tel.: (650) 615-7300
Web Site: https://www.pfizer.com
Emp.: 200
Research Development
N.A.I.C.S.: 541715

Site Realty, Inc. (1)
571 W Middle St, Gettysburg, PA 17325
Tel.: (717) 334-4674
Web Site: https://sitesrealtyinc.com
Pharmaceuticals Product Mfr
N.A.I.C.S.: 325412

Suzhou Capsugel Ltd. (1)
No 369 Suhong M Rd, Suzhou Industrial
Park, Suzhou, 215021, China
Tel.: (86) 51262585188
Web Site: http://www.Capsugelinc.com
Emp.: 40
Pharmaceuticals Product Mfr
N.A.I.C.S.: 325412

Trillium Therapeutics Inc. (1)
2488 Dunwin Drive, Mississauga, L5L 1J9,
ON, Canada (100%)
Tel.: (416) 595-0627
Web Site:
http://www.trilliumtherapeutics.com
Rev.: $148,000
Assets: $300,822,000
Liabilities: $21,975,000
Net Worth: $278,847,000
Earnings: ($59,346,000)
Emp.: 33
Fiscal Year-end: 12/31/2020
Pharmaceuticals Mfr
N.A.I.C.S.: 325412
Robert Uger (Chief Scientific Officer)
Penka Petrova (Chief Dev Officer)
Robert L. Kirkman (Chm)
Jan Skvarka (Pres & CEO)
Kathleen Large (Sr VP-Clinical Ops)
Ingmar Bruns (Chief Medical Officer)
Rosemary Harrison (Sr VP-Corp Dev &
Strategy)

Vesteralens Naturprodukter AB (1)
Uddevallavagen 3C, 452 31, Stromstad,
Sweden
Tel.: (46) 20474748
Web Site: http://www.vnp.se
Pharmaceutical Product Mfr
N.A.I.C.S.: 325412

Vesteralens Naturprodukter AS (1)
Strandgata 16, PO Box 154, 8400, Sortland, Norway
Tel.: (47) 80080818
Web Site: http://www.vnp.no
Emp.: 45
Pharmaceuticals Product Mfr
N.A.I.C.S.: 325412

ViiV Healthcare (1)
980 Great West Road, Brentford, TW8
9GS, Middlesex, United Kingdom
Tel.: (44) 2083806200
Web Site: https://www.viivhealthcare.com
Sales Range: $1-4.9 Billion
Emp.: 4,000
HIV Treatment Mfr; Joint Venture of Pfizer,
Inc. & GlaxoSmithKline plc
N.A.I.C.S.: 325412
Jill Anderson (CFO)
Harmony Garges (Chief Medical Officer)
Cheryl MacDiarmid (Head-Global Comml
Strategy)
Stephen Rea (Head-External Affairs &
Comm)
Andrew Stewart (Chief Compliance Officer
& Gen Counsel)

**Warner Lambert del Uruguay
S.A.** (1)

Dr Luis Bonavita 1266 Oficina 504 - WTC
Torre IV, 11300, Montevideo, Uruguay
Tel.: (598) 26261212
Web Site: https://www.pfizer.uy
Pharmaceuticals Product Mfr
N.A.I.C.S.: 325412

Wyeth (Malaysia) Sdn. Bhd. (1)
T1-12 Jaya 33 No 3 Lot 33 Jalan Semangat, Seksyen 13, Petaling Jaya, 46100, Selangor Darul Ehsan, Malaysia
Tel.: (60) 800885526
Web Site: http://www.wyethnutrition.com.my
Pharmaceuticals Product Mfr
N.A.I.C.S.: 325412

Wyeth Lederle S.r.l. (1)
Via Nettunense 90, Aprilia, 04011, Latina,
Italy
Tel.: (39) 06927151
Web Site: https://www.pfizer.com
Pharmaceutical Preparation Mfr
N.A.I.C.S.: 325412

**Wyeth Nutritional (China) Co.,
Ltd.** (1)
No 199 Fangzhou Rd, Suzhou, 215126,
China
Tel.: (86) 51267335000
Pharmaceuticals Product Mfr
N.A.I.C.S.: 325412

Wyeth Pakistan Limited (1)
Room No 002 003 PGS Admin Block First
Floor Plot No B-2 S I T E, Karachi, Pakistan
Tel.: (92) 2132570621
Web Site: https://www.wyethpakistan.com
Medicine Mfr
N.A.I.C.S.: 325412

Wyeth Pharmaceutical Co., Ltd. (1)
No 4 BaoDaiXi Road, Suzhou, 215128,
China
Tel.: (86) 51265270337
Pharmaceutical Preparation Mfr
N.A.I.C.S.: 325412

**Zydus Hospira Oncology Private
Limited** (1)
Zydus Tower Satellite Cross Roads,
Ahmedabad, 380 015, Gujarat, India
Tel.: (91) 7926868100
Web Site: http://www.zyduscadila.com
Health Care Srvices
N.A.I.C.S.: 621610

PFO GLOBAL, INC.
14401 Beltwood Pkwy W Ste 115,
Dallas, TX 75224
Tel.: (817) 251-4333   NV
Year Founded: 1993
PFGBQ—(OTCIQ)
Investment Services
N.A.I.C.S.: 523999
Thomas M. Rickards IV (Pres)

PG&E CORPORATION
300 Lakeside Dr Ste 210, Oakland,
CA 94612
Tel.: (415) 973-1000   CA
Web Site: https://www.pgecorp.com
Year Founded: 1905
PCG—(NYSE)
Rev.: $24,428,000,000
Assets: $125,698,000,000
Liabilities: $100,406,000,000
Net Worth: $25,292,000,000
Earnings: $2,242,000,000
Emp.: 28,010
Fiscal Year-end: 12/31/23
Holding Company; Energy Services
N.A.I.C.S.: 221122
John R. Simon (Chief Ethics & Compliance Officer)
Sumeet Singh (COO & Exec VP-Ops)
Julie M. Kane (Chief Ethics & Compliance Officer, Sr VP & Deputy Gen
Counsel)
Stephanie N. Williams (VP & Controller)
Patricia K. Poppe (CEO)

PG&E Corporation—(Continued)

Carolyn J. Burke *(CFO & Exec VP-Fin)*
Robert C. Flexon *(Chm)*
Jessica C. Hogle *(VP)*
Brian M. Wong *(Sec, Sr VP & Gen Counsel)*
Francisco Benavides *(Chief Safety Officer & Sr VP)*
Ajay Waghray *(CIO & Sr VP)*
Carla J. Peterman *(Chief Sustainability Officer & Exec VP)*
Mari Becker *(Treas)*
Yvonne A. McIntyre *(VP)*
Stephanie Williams *(VP)*

Subsidiaries:

PG&E Energy Recovery Funding LLC **(1)**
245 Market St Ste 424, San Francisco, CA 94105 **(100%)**
Tel.: (415) 973-6252
Investment Management Service
N.A.I.C.S.: 523999

PG&E Generating Company **(1)**
1 Market Plz, San Francisco, CA 94105
Tel.: (415) 267-7000
Web Site: http://www.pge-corp.com
Rev.: $280,000
Emp.: 100
Public Utility Holding Companies
N.A.I.C.S.: 221118

Pacific Gas & Electric Company **(1)**
300 Lakeside Dr, Oakland, CA 94612 **(100%)**
Tel.: (415) 973-1000
Web Site: https://www.pge.com
Rev.: $20,641,999,999
Assets: $103,177,000,000
Liabilities: $77,567,000,000
Net Worth: $25,610,000,000
Earnings: $138,000,000
Emp.: 25,999
Fiscal Year-end: 12/31/2021
Regulated Gas & Electric Utility
N.A.I.C.S.: 221122
John R. Simon *(Chief Ethics & Compliance Officer, Exec VP & Gen Counsel)*
Stephen J. Cairns *(Chief Audit Officer & VP)*
Sumeet Singh *(COO & Exec VP-Ops)*
Stephanie N. Williams *(CFO, VP & Controller)*
Patricia K. Poppe *(CEO)*
Andrew K. Williams *(VP-Shared Svcs)*
Laurie M. Giammona *(Sr VP-Customer Care)*
Mary K. King *(Chief Diversity Officer & Chief Diversity Officer-Human Resources)*
Keith F. Stephens *(Chief Comm Officer & VP)*
Ken Wells *(VP)*
Francisco Benavides *(Chief Safety Officer & Chief Safety Officer)*
Julius Cox *(Exec VP-People, Shared Svcs, and Supply Chain)*
David E. Hatton *(VP)*
Wade Smith *(Sr VP-Electric Ops)*
Angie Gibson *(VP, VP, VP & VP)*
David L. Leach *(VP, VP, VP, VP & VP)*
Meredith E. Allen *(VP)*

PGI INCORPORATED
212 S Central Ste 304, Saint Louis, MO 63105
Tel.: (314) 512-8650 **FL**
Web Site:
http://www.pgiincorporated.com
Year Founded: 1958
PGAI—(OTCEM)
Rev.: $4,000
Assets: $336,000
Liabilities: $92,900,000
Net Worth: ($92,564,000)
Earnings: ($1,568,000)
Fiscal Year-end: 12/31/19
Property Management Services
N.A.I.C.S.: 531311
Andrew S. Love *(Chm)*
Laurence A. Schiffer *(Vice Chm-, Pres, CEO, CFO & Chief Acctg Officer)*

Subsidiaries:

Burnt Store Marina, Inc. **(1)**
3192 Matecumbe Key Rd, Punta Gorda, FL 33955-1913
Tel.: (941) 637-0083
Web Site: http://www.burntstoremarina.com
Marina Boat Services
N.A.I.C.S.: 713930

PGIM GLOBAL HIGH YIELD FUND, INC.
655 Broad St 6th Fl, Newark, NJ 07102-4077
Tel.: (973) 802-5032
GHY—(NYSE)
Fund Management Services
N.A.I.C.S.: 523940
Stuart Sherman Parker *(Pres)*
Scott Edward Benjamin *(VP)*

PGIM HIGH YIELD BOND FUND, INC.
655 BRd St 6TH Fl, Newark, NJ 07102
Tel.: (973) 367-7530 **MD**
Web Site:
https://www.investment.prudential.com
Year Founded: 2012
ISD—(NYSE)
Closed-End Investment Fund
N.A.I.C.S.: 525990
Stuart Sherman Parker *(Pres)*
Scott Edward Benjamin *(VP)*
Paul Appleby *(Portfolio Mgr)*
Robert Cignarella *(Portfolio Mgr)*
Michael J. Collins *(Portfolio Mgr)*
Terence Wheat *(Portfolio Mgr)*
Robert Spano *(Portfolio Mgr)*
Ryan Kelly *(Portfolio Mgr)*
Brian Clapp *(Portfolio Mgr)*
Daniel Thorogood *(Portfolio Mgr)*
Ray Ahn *(CMO)*

PHARMA-BIO SERV, INC.
6 Carr 696, Dorado, PR 00646-3306
Tel.: (787) 278-2709 **DE**
Web Site:
https://www.pharmabioserv.com
PBSV—(OTCQB)
Rev.: $16,976,856
Assets: $19,902,061
Liabilities: $3,775,276
Net Worth: $16,126,785
Earnings: $1,310,180
Emp.: 100
Fiscal Year-end: 10/31/23
Regulatory Compliance Consulting Services; Microbiological & Chemical Testing Services; Information Technology Consulting Services & Technical Training
N.A.I.C.S.: 926150
Pedro J. Lasanta *(CFO, Sec & VP-Fin & Admin)*
Victor Sanchez *(Pres, CEO & Pres-Ops-Europe)*
Miriam Marrero *(Mgr-HR)*

Subsidiaries:

Pharma-Bio Serv Ltd. **(1)**
54 Newtown Park, Annacotty Co, Limerick, Ireland
Tel.: (353) 21 4619034
Medical Testing & Technology Consulting Services
N.A.I.C.S.: 926150
Fiona Gilchrist *(Gen Mgr)*

Pharma-Bio Serv PR, Inc. **(1)**
Dorado Industrial Zone Lot 14 St 1, Dorado, PR 00646
Tel.: (787) 278-2709
Web Site: www.pharmabioserv.com
Medical Testing & Technology Consulting Services
N.A.I.C.S.: 926150

Pharma-Bio Serv US, Inc. **(1)**
545 W Germantown Pike Ste 200, Plymouth Meeting, PA 19462
Tel.: (215) 997-3310
Administrative Management Consulting Services
N.A.I.C.S.: 541611
Elizabeth Plaza *(Pres-Global Ops & CEO)*

Pharma-Bio Serv, S.L. **(1)**
C/ Faraday 7, 28049, Madrid, Spain
Tel.: (34) 914529362
Web Site: http://www.pharmabioserv.com
Emp.: 10
Medical Testing & Technology Consulting Services
N.A.I.C.S.: 926150

harma-Bio Serv PR, Inc. **(1)**
6 Carr 696, Dorado, PR 00646-3306
Tel.: (787) 278-2709
Web Site: https://www.pharmabioserv.com
Pharmaceutical Consulting Services
N.A.I.C.S.: 541611

PHARMACYTE BIOTECH, INC.
3960 Howard Hughes Pkwy Ste 500, Las Vegas, NV 89169
Tel.: (917) 595-2850
Web Site:
https://www.pharmacyte.com
PMCB—(NASDAQ)
Rev.: $8,853,771
Assets: $59,903,883
Liabilities: $32,256,280
Net Worth: $27,647,603
Earnings: $333,763
Emp.: 2
Fiscal Year-end: 04/30/24
Pharmaceuticals Product Mfr
N.A.I.C.S.: 325412
Joshua N. Silverman *(Interim Chm, Interim Pres & Interim CEO)*
Carlos A. Trujillo *(CFO)*

PHASEBIO PHARMACEUTICALS, INC.
1 Great Valley Pkwy Ste 30, Malvern, PA 19355
Tel.: (610) 981-6500 **DE**
Web Site: http://www.phasebio.com
Year Founded: 2002
PHASQ—(NASDAQ)
Rev.: $10,831,000
Assets: $60,540,000
Liabilities: $153,574,000
Net Worth: ($93,034,000)
Earnings: ($131,071,000)
Emp.: 60
Fiscal Year-end: 12/31/21
Biopharmaceutical Product Mfr & Distr
N.A.I.C.S.: 325412
John S. Lee *(Chief Medical Officer)*
Lawrence Perkins *(Principal Fin Officer)*
Susan Arnold *(VP-Preclinical & CMC)*
Glen Burkhardt *(VP-HR)*
Kris Hanson *(VP & Head-Legal)*
Lauren Richardson *(Asst VP-Quality & Regulatory)*
Jonathan J. Birchall *(Chief Comml Officer)*
Jonathan P. Mow *(CFO)*
Clay Bernardin Thorp *(Chm)*

PHATHOM PHARMACEUTICALS, INC.
100 Campus Dr Ste 102, Florham Park, NJ 07932
Tel.: (650) 325-5156 **DE**
Web Site:
https://www.phathompharma.com
Year Founded: 2018
PHAT—(NASDAQ)
Rev.: $2,132,000
Assets: $164,810,000
Liabilities: $239,624,000
Net Worth: ($74,814,000)

Earnings: ($197,723,000)
Emp.: 112
Fiscal Year-end: 12/31/22
Biotechnology Research & Development Services
N.A.I.C.S.: 541714
David Socks *(Co-Founder)*
Aditya Kohli *(Co-Founder & Chief Bus Officer)*
Larry Miller *(Gen Counsel)*
Terrie Curran *(Pres & CEO)*
Azmi Nabulsi *(COO)*
Tom Harris *(Head-Regulatory Affairs)*
Eckhard Leifke *(Chief Medical Officer)*
Joseph Hand *(Chief Admin Officer)*
Martin Gilligan *(Chief Comml Officer)*
Molly Henderson *(Chief Fin & Bus Officer)*
Anthony Guzzo *(Chief Acctg Officer & VP)*

PHENIXFIN CORP.
445 Park Ave 10th Fl, New York, NY 10022
Tel.: (212) 859-0390 **DE**
Web Site: https://www.phenixfc.com
PFX—(NASDAQ)
Rev.: $36,485,013
Assets: $302,751,813
Liabilities: $142,444,040
Net Worth: $160,307,773
Earnings: $13,885,262
Emp.: 6
Fiscal Year-end: 09/30/24
Investment Services
N.A.I.C.S.: 523999
Min Kim *(Principal & Controller)*
David A. Lorber *(Chm & CEO)*
Ellida McMillan *(CFO)*
Chris Cannellos *(Controller)*
Ryan Phalen *(Mng Dir)*

Subsidiaries:

FlexFIN, LLC **(1)**
555 Madison Ave Ste 1400, New York, NY 10022
Tel.: (212) 994-2454
Web Site: https://flexfin.com
Jewelry Finance Services
N.A.I.C.S.: 541219

PHIBRO ANIMAL HEALTH CORPORATION
300 Frank W Burr Blvd Ste 21, Teaneck, NJ 07666-6712
Tel.: (201) 329-7300 **NY**
Web Site: https://www.pahc.com
Year Founded: 1947
PAHC—(NASDAQ)
Rev.: $1,017,679,000
Assets: $982,184,000
Liabilities: $725,543,000
Net Worth: $256,641,000
Earnings: $2,416,000
Emp.: 1,940
Fiscal Year-end: 06/30/24
Animal Health & Nutrition Products & Specialty Chemical Products Mfr & Marketer
N.A.I.C.S.: 311119
Glenn C. David *(CFO)*
Jonathan Bendheim *(Pres-MACIE Reg & Gen Mgr-Ops-Israel)*
Jack Clifford Bendheim *(Chm, Pres & CEO)*
Daniel M. Bendheim *(Exec VP-Corp Strategy, Pres-Performance Products & VP-Bus Dev)*
Thomas G. Dagger *(Gen Counsel, Sec & Sr VP)*
Larry L. Miller *(COO)*
Michael Giambalvo *(Pres-PhibroChem & Ethanol Performance Grp)*

Anthony Andolino *(Treas & VP-Fin)*
Lisa A. Escudero *(Sr VP-HR)*
Ramon Fuenmayor *(Pres-South America)*
Rob Aukerman *(Pres-North America)*
Jean-Christophe Filippi *(Pres-Asia Pacific)*

Subsidiaries:

ABIC Biological Laboratories Ltd.   **(1)**
3 Hayetzira Street, PO Box 489, West Industrial Zone, Beit Shemesh, 99100, Israel
Tel.: (972) 732700300
Veterinary Pharmaceutical Mfr
N.A.I.C.S.: 325412

Biotay S.A.   **(1)**
Rutherford 4503 Grand Bourg, B1615GYC, Buenos Aires, Argentina
Tel.: (54) 3327444567
Animal Food Product Mfr
N.A.I.C.S.: 311119

Ferro Metal & Chemical Corporation Ltd.
213 Regus House 400 Thames Valley Park Drive, Reading, RG6 1PT, Berkshire, United Kingdom   **(100%)**
Tel.: (44) 1189653868
Web Site: http://www.fmccorp.co.uk
Sales Range: $25-49.9 Million
Emp.: 4
Specialty Chemicals Marketer & Distr
N.A.I.C.S.: 424690
George Moffett *(Mng Dir)*

Koffolk Ltd.   **(1)**
PO Box 1098, Tel Aviv, 61010, Israel
Tel.: (972) 3 9273100
Web Site: http://www.koffolkfc.com
Fine Chemicals & Chemical Intermediates Mfr & Distr
N.A.I.C.S.: 325998

Division (Domestic):

Koffolk Animal Health & Nutrition   **(2)**
PO Box 1098, Tel Aviv, 61010, Israel
Tel.: (972) 3 9273100
Web Site: http://www.koffolkah.com
Veterinary Pharmaceuticals Mfr & Distr
N.A.I.C.S.: 325412

Osprey Biotechnics, Inc.   **(1)**
1833 57th St Ste A, Sarasota, FL 34243
Tel.: (941) 351-2700
Web Site: http://www.ospreybiotechnics.com
Biological Product Mfr
N.A.I.C.S.: 325414
Lauren Danielson *(Pres & CEO)*
Chris Reuter *(VP-Science)*

PB Animal Health de Mexico S. de R.L. de C.V.   **(1)**
Calle Francisco de Quevedo 117 Torre A Piso 6 Col Arcos Vallarta, Guadalajara, 44130, Jalisco, Mexico
Tel.: (52) 3338180529
Chemical Product Whslr
N.A.I.C.S.: 424690

Phibro Animal Health (Proprietary) Limited   **(1)**
63 Regency Drive Block B Technolink Route 21 Corporate Office Park, Irene, 0062, Gauteng, South Africa
Tel.: (27) 124500600
Chemical Product Whslr
N.A.I.C.S.: 424690

Phibro Animal Health Ltd.   **(1)**
3 Hamelacha St Western Industrial Zone, Beit Shemesh, Israel
Tel.: (972) 732700322
Chemical Product Whslr
N.A.I.C.S.: 424690

Phibro Animal Health Ltd.   **(1)**
1500-1874 Scarth Street, Regina, S4P 4E9, SK, Canada
Tel.: (306) 347-8475
Chemical Product Whslr
N.A.I.C.S.: 424690

Phibro Animal Health de Argentina SRL   **(1)**
Rutherford 4503, B1615GYC, Buenos Aires, Grand Bourg, Argentina
Tel.: (54) 1143141593

Chemical Product Whslr
N.A.I.C.S.: 424690

Phibro Animal PTY Limited   **(1)**
Suite 146 Lexington Drive, Bella Vista, 2153, NSW, Australia
Tel.: (61) 296163700
Chemical Product Whslr
N.A.I.C.S.: 424690

Phibro Hayvan Sagligi Urunleri Sanayi ve Ticaret A.S.   **(1)**
Ataturk Caddesi Esin Sokak Yazgan is Merkezi No 3/9 Kozyatagi, 34734, Istanbul, Turkiye
Tel.: (90) 2163012020
Web Site: https://www.pahc.com
Animal Food Product Mfr
N.A.I.C.S.: 311119

Phibro-Tech, Inc.   **(1)**
8851 Dice Rd, Santa Fe Springs, CA 90670
Tel.: (562) 698-8036
Specialty Chemicals Mfr & Marketer
N.A.I.C.S.: 325998

Prince Agri Products, Inc.   **(1)**
229 Radio Rd, Quincy, IL 62305
Tel.: (217) 222-8854
Web Site: http://www.princeagri.com
Animal Nutrition Ingredients Mfr
N.A.I.C.S.: 311119
Dean J. Warras *(Pres)*

Quimica Real Ltda.
Rua Nair Pentagna Guimaraes 762, Heliopolis, Belo Horizonte, CEP 31741-545, Minas Gerais, Brazil
Tel.: (55) 3130572000
Web Site: https://www.quimicareal.com.br
Chemicals Mfr
N.A.I.C.S.: 325998

PHIL-GOOD PRODUCTS INCORPORATED
3500 W Reno, Oklahoma City, OK 73107
Tel.: (405) 942-5527   **OK**
Web Site: http://www.philgood.com
Year Founded: 1959
PHGD—(OTCIQ)
Plastics Product Mfr
N.A.I.C.S.: 326199
Peggy V. Phillips *(Pres)*
Tim Cassil *(Exec VP)*

PHILIP MORRIS INTERNATIONAL INC.
677 Washington Blvd Ste 1100, Stamford, CT 06901
Tel.: (203) 905-2413   **VA**
Web Site: https://www.pmi.com
PM—(NYSE)
Rev.: $35,174,000,000
Assets: $65,304,000,000
Liabilities: $74,750,000,000
Net Worth: ($9,446,000,000)
Earnings: $7,813,000,000
Emp.: 82,700
Fiscal Year-end: 12/31/23
Holding Company; Cigarettes & Other Tobacco Products Mfr & Whslr
N.A.I.C.S.: 551112
Jacek Olczak *(CEO)*
Frederic de Wilde *(Pres-South & Southeast Asia, Commonwealth of Independent States, Middle East & Africa)*
Werner Barth *(Pres-Combustibles Category & Global Combustibles Mktg)*
Emmanuel Andre Marie Babeau *(CFO)*
Paul Riley *(Pres-East Asia, Australia & Duty Free Reg)*
Charles Bendotti *(Sr VP-People & Culture)*
Frank de Rooij *(VP-Treasury & Corp Fin)*
Devin Carey *(Dir-IR)*
Marian Salzman *(Sr VP-Comm-Global)*

Stacey Kennedy *(Pres-Americas & CEO-PMI's U.S. Bus)*
Badrul A. Chowdhury *(Chief Life Sciences Officer-Smoke-Free Products)*
Bin Li *(Chief Product Officer)*
Travis Parman *(Chief Comm Officer & VP)*
Jorge Insuasty *(Pres-Vectura Fertin Pharma)*
Gregoire Verdeaux *(Sr VP-External Affairs)*
Reginaldo Dobrowolski *(VP & Controller)*

Subsidiaries:

Fertin Pharma A/S   **(1)**
Dandyvej 19, 7100, Vejle, Denmark
Tel.: (45) 72151300
Web Site: https://www.fertin.com
Pharmaceuticals Product Mfr
N.A.I.C.S.: 325412

IPM India Wholesale Trading Private Limited   **(1)**
Unit No 20 Ground Floor Plot No D-1 Salcon Rasvilas, Saket District Centre Saket, New Delhi, 110 017, India
Tel.: (91) 1142195401
Cigarette Mfr
N.A.I.C.S.: 312230

Industrias del Tabaco, Alimentos y Bebidas S.A.   **(1)**
Chimborazo 705 y Pampite La Esquina Centro de Negocios Edificio 3, Cumbaya, Quito, Ecuador
Tel.: (593) 23969600
Emp.: 200
Cigarette Mfr
N.A.I.C.S.: 312230

Intertaba S.p.A.   **(1)**
Via Fratelli Rosselli 4, Zola Predosa, 40069, Italy
Tel.: (39) 0513517611
Emp.: 400
Cigarette Mfr
N.A.I.C.S.: 312230
Daniele Boanini *(Mgr-HR Svcs)*
Fabio Cantieri *(Mgr-Process Tech Dev)*

Limited Liability Company Philip Morris Sales & Distribution   **(1)**
30 Spaska st Podil Plaza 5th floor, Kiev, 04070, Ukraine
Tel.: (380) 443894600
Tobacco Product Distr
N.A.I.C.S.: 424940

Massalin Particulares S.A.   **(1)**
Antonio Malaver 550, Vicente Lopez, Buenos Aires, Argentina
Tel.: (54) 1147052200
Web Site: http://www.pmi.com
Emp.: 2,600
Cigarette Mfr
N.A.I.C.S.: 312230

PHILSA Philip Morris Sabanci Sigara ve Tutunculuk Sanayi ve Ticaret A.S.   **(1)**
Kucukcamlica Mahallesi Ord Prof Fahrettin Kerim Gokay Cad No 58-58/1, Kucukcamlica, 34696, Istanbul, Uskudar, Turkiye
Tel.: (90) 2165443000
Web Site: https://www.pmi.com
Emp.: 1,200
Tobacco Product Mfr
N.A.I.C.S.: 312230

PM Equity Partner Sarl   **(1)**
Avenue de Rhodanie 50, 1007, Lausanne, Switzerland
Tel.: (41) 582420000
Web Site: https://www.pmequitypartner.com
Venture Capital Services
N.A.I.C.S.: 523910
Dean Haworth *(Mgr-Investment)*
Jason Gao *(Mgr-Investment)*
Maria Serrador *(Mgr-Investment)*

PMI Global Services, Inc.   **(1)**
120 Park Ave 6th Fl, New York, NY 10017
Tel.: (917) 663-2233
Cigarettes & Other Tobacco Products Mfr & Whslr
N.A.I.C.S.: 312230

PMI Service Center Europe spolka z ograniczona odpowiedzialnoscia   **(1)**
Al Jana Pawla II 196, 31-982, Krakow, Poland
Tel.: (48) 126464646
Tobacco Mfr
N.A.I.C.S.: 312230

PT Hanjaya Mandala Sampoerna Tbk.   **(1)**
Jalan Rungkut Indusri Raya No 18, Surabaya, 60293, Indonesia
Tel.: (62) 318431699
Web Site: https://www.sampoerna.com
Rev.: $7,531,960,957
Assets: $3,592,238,184
Liabilities: $1,652,489,930
Net Worth: $1,939,748,254
Earnings: $525,806,906
Emp.: 20,453
Fiscal Year-end: 12/31/2023
Cigarette Mfr
N.A.I.C.S.: 312230

PT Philip Morris Indonesia   **(1)**
One Pacific Place 20th Floor, Sudirman Central Business District Jl Jend Sudirman Kav 52-531, Jakarta, 12190, Indonesia
Tel.: (62) 215151234
Emp.: 400
Cigarette Mfr
N.A.I.C.S.: 312230

PT SRC Indonesia Sembilan   **(1)**
One Pacific Place Lantai 18 Jl Jendral Sudirman Kav 52 - 53, Jakarta, 12190, Indonesia
Tel.: (62) 8041000234
Web Site: https://www.src.id
Grocery Whslr
N.A.I.C.S.: 445110

Papastratos Cigarette Manufacturing Company   **(1)**
Imeros Topos Location Kororemi, 19300, Aspropyrgos, 19300, Greece
Tel.: (30) 2104193000
Web Site: http://www.pmi.com
Emp.: 800
Tobacco Product Mfr
N.A.I.C.S.: 312230

Papastratos Cigarettes Manufacturing Company S.A.   **(1)**
Imeros Topos Location Kororemi, Aspropyrgos, 193 00, Greece
Tel.: (30) 2104193000
Emp.: 800
Tobacco Product Distr
N.A.I.C.S.: 424940

Philip Morris (Australia) Ltd   **(1)**
Level 5 30 Convention Centre Place, South Wharf, 3006, VIC, Australia
Tel.: (61) 385311000
Web Site:
  http://www.philipmorrisinternational.com
Sales Range: $1-4.9 Billion
Emp.: 800
Cigarette Mfr
N.A.I.C.S.: 312230
Paul Riley *(Pres)*

Philip Morris (New Zealand) Limited   **(1)**
46 Sale Street Auckland Central, Auckland, 1010, New Zealand
Tel.: (64) 95315060
Emp.: 70
Tobacco Mfr
N.A.I.C.S.: 312230

Philip Morris (Pakistan) Limited   **(1)**
Office 04 05 5th Floor Corporate office block Dolmen City Plot HC-3, Block 4 Clifton, Karachi, 75600, Pakistan
Tel.: (92) 213520960001
Web Site: https://www.pmi.com
Emp.: 739
Cigarette Mfr & Distr
N.A.I.C.S.: 312230
Joao Manuel *(Mng Dir)*
Kamran Y. Mirza *(Chm)*
Muhammad Zeeshan *(Exec Dir)*

Philip Morris ApS   **(1)**
Copenhagen Towers Orestads Boulevard 108 3sal, 2300, Copenhagen, Denmark
Tel.: (45) 70231021
Emp.: 90

Philip Morris International Inc.—(Continued)

Cigarette Distr
N.A.I.C.S.: 424940

Philip Morris Armenia Limited Liability Company (1)
2 Vazgen Sargsyan str, Yerevan, 0010, Armenia
Tel.: (374) 60656043
Tobacco Mfr
N.A.I.C.S.: 312230
Mihael Solter (Gen Mgr)

Philip Morris Asia Limited (1)
Suites 2402-2411 24/F Devon House Taikoo Place 979 King's Road, Quarry Bay, China (Hong Kong)
Tel.: (852) 28251600
Emp.: 300
Tobacco Mfr
N.A.I.C.S.: 312230

Philip Morris Austria GmbH (1)
Vorgartenstrasse 206 C / 6 Stock, 1020, Vienna, Austria
Tel.: (43) 1727861001
Emp.: 125
Tobacco Mfr
N.A.I.C.S.: 312230

Philip Morris Benelux B.V.B.A. (1)
Borsbeeksebrug 24, 2600, Berchem, Belgium
Tel.: (32) 80058089
Web Site: http://www.pmi.com
Tobacco Product Mfr
N.A.I.C.S.: 312230

Philip Morris Brands S.a.r.l. (1)
Quai Jeanrenaud 3, 2000, Neuchatel, 2000, Switzerland
Tel.: (41) 582421111
Cigarette Mfr
N.A.I.C.S.: 312230

Philip Morris Brasil Industria e Comercio Ltda. (1)
Avenida Brigadeiro Faria Lima 4055, Jardim Paulista, Sao Paulo, Brazil
Tel.: (55) 51 3909 3000
Web Site: http://www.pmi.com
Tobacco Product Mfr
N.A.I.C.S.: 312230

Philip Morris Bulgaria EOOD (1)
32 Atanas Dukov St, 1407, Sofia, Bulgaria
Tel.: (359) 28063100
Tobacco Mfr
N.A.I.C.S.: 312230

Philip Morris Chile Comercializadora Limitada (1)
Avenida Kennedy 5735 Torre Marriot Poniente Oficina 509, 7550000, Las Condes, Santiago, Chile
Tel.: (56) 223694300
Emp.: 9
Tobacco Mfr
N.A.I.C.S.: 312230

Philip Morris Costa Rica, Sociedad Anonima (1)
La Ribera de Belen Costado Norte de Industrias Firestone, Heredia, Costa Rica
Tel.: (506) 22983400
Cigarette Mfr
N.A.I.C.S.: 312230

Philip Morris Dominicana, S.A. (1)
Torre Acropolis piso 22 Av Winston Churchill esq, Rafael Augusto Sanchez Ensanche Piantini, Santo Domingo, Dominican Republic
Tel.: (809) 9202200
Tobacco Mfr
N.A.I.C.S.: 312230

Philip Morris Eesti Osauhing (1)
Tartu mnt 43 / F R Kreutzwaldi 24, 10147, Tallinn, Estonia
Tel.: (372) 6050400
Emp.: 14
Tobacco Mfr
N.A.I.C.S.: 312230

Philip Morris Egypt Limited Liability Company (1)
81st 90th Street, New Cairo, Cairo, Egypt
Tel.: (20) 226147700
Emp.: 200

Tobacco Mfr
N.A.I.C.S.: 312230

Philip Morris Finland OY (1)
Itamerenkatu 3, 00180, Helsinki, Finland
Tel.: (358) 207600600
Emp.: 15
Cigarette Mfr & Distr
N.A.I.C.S.: 312230
Tom Rasmussen (Mgr-Consumer Engagement)

Philip Morris France S.A.S. (1)
Defense Plaza 23 / 25 rue Delariviere, La Defense Lefoullon, 92064, Puteaux, France
Tel.: (33) 155916700
Tobacco Mfr
N.A.I.C.S.: 312230

Philip Morris GmbH (1)
Am Haag 14, 82166, Grafelfing, Germany
Tel.: (49) 8972470
Web Site: http://www.philipmorris.com
Sales Range: $1-4.9 Billion
Emp.: 1,400
Mfr of Cigarettes
N.A.I.C.S.: 312230

Philip Morris International Management SA (1)
Avenue De Rhodanie 50, 1007, Lausanne, Switzerland
Tel.: (41) 582420000
Web Site: http://www.pmi.com
Emp.: 3,000
Cigarette Goods Mfr
N.A.I.C.S.: 312230

Philip Morris Investments B.V. (1)
Marconilaan 20, 4622 RD, Bergen-op-Zoom, Netherlands
Tel.: (31) 164295000
Cigarette Mfr
N.A.I.C.S.: 312230

Philip Morris Italia S.r.l. (1)
Via Po 11-13-15, 00198, Rome, Italy
Tel.: (39) 06854451
Emp.: 700
Cigarette Distr
N.A.I.C.S.: 424940

Philip Morris Japan Godo-Kaisha Inc. (1)
Sanno Park Tower 22nd Floor 2-11-1, Nagata-cho Chiyoda-ku, Tokyo, 100-6190, Japan
Tel.: (81) 335097200
Emp.: 1,600
Tobacco Product Mfr & Distr
N.A.I.C.S.: 312230

Philip Morris Japan Kabushiki Kaisha (1)
Sanno Park Tower 22nd Floor 2-11-1, Nagata-cho, Chiyoda Ku, Tokyo, 100-6190, Japan
Tel.: (81) 335097200
Web Site: http://www.philipmorrisinternational.com
Sales Range: $1-4.9 Billion
Emp.: 1,900
Tobacco Mfr
N.A.I.C.S.: 312230

Philip Morris Kazakhstan LLP (1)
Zhansugurov Street 90, Otegen Batyr Village Ily District, 040700, Almaty, Kazakhstan
Tel.: (7) 7272588888
Cigarette Mfr
N.A.I.C.S.: 312230

Philip Morris Korea Inc. (1)
25th Floor One IFC 10 Gukjegeumyung-ro, Yeongdeungpo-gu, Seoul, 07326, Korea (South)
Tel.: (82) 237070700
Cigarette Mfr
N.A.I.C.S.: 312230

Philip Morris Korea Inc. (1)
25th Floor One IFC 10 Gukjegeumyung-ro, Yeongdeungpo-gu, Seoul, 07326, Korea (South)
Tel.: (82) 237070700
Web Site: http://www.pmi.com
Emp.: 1,100
Cigarette Mfr & Distr
N.A.I.C.S.: 312230

Chong Ilwoo (Mng Dir)

Philip Morris Latin America Services S.R.L. (1)
Juan Carlos Cruz 1960, Vicente Lopez, Pcia BA, Argentina
Tel.: (54) 1152963000
Emp.: 2,500
Tobacco Mfr
N.A.I.C.S.: 312230

Philip Morris Limited (1)
10 Hammersmith Grove, London, W6 7AP, United Kingdom
Tel.: (44) 2082220700
Cigarette Mfr
N.A.I.C.S.: 312230
Silviu Miron (Head-Comml Plng)

Philip Morris Ljubljana, Storitveno Podjetje, d.o.o. (1)
Letaliska cesta 29a, 1000, Ljubljana, Slovenia
Tel.: (386) 15863700
Emp.: 30
Tobacco Mfr
N.A.I.C.S.: 312230

Philip Morris Ltd. (1)
10 Hammersmith Grove, London, W6 7AP, United Kingdom
Tel.: (44) 2082220700
Web Site: https://www.pmi.com
Emp.: 350
Cigarette Mfr & Distr
N.A.I.C.S.: 312230

Philip Morris Maghreb SARL (1)
Bvd Sidi Mohamed Ben Abdellah Casablanca Marina Tour Ivoire 1, 6eme Etage, 20030, Casablanca, Morocco
Tel.: (212) 520205656
Emp.: 70
Tobacco Product Mfr & Distr
N.A.I.C.S.: 312230

Philip Morris Malaysia Sdn. Bhd. (1)
Level 25 1 Powerhouse No 1, Persiaran Bandar Utama Bandar Utama, 47800, Petaling Jaya, Selangor Darul Ehsan, Malaysia
Tel.: (60) 320805600
Emp.: 380
Cigarette Mfr
N.A.I.C.S.: 312230

Philip Morris Management Services (Middle East) Limited (1)
Floor 6 Bldg 2 The Gate District Dubai International Financial Centre, PO Box Number 506523, Dubai, United Arab Emirates
Tel.: (971) 43696000
Emp.: 145
Tobacco Mfr
N.A.I.C.S.: 312230

Philip Morris Manufacturing & Technology Bologna S.p.A. (1)
Via Giacomo Venturi 1-2 Localita Crespellano, Valsamoggia, 40056, Bologna, Italy
Tel.: (39) 0513517611
Emp.: 1,600
Tobacco Product Distr
N.A.I.C.S.: 424940

Philip Morris Manufacturing GmbH (1)
Neukollnische Allee 80, 12057, Berlin, Germany
Tel.: (49) 30683880
Cigarette Mfr
N.A.I.C.S.: 312230

Philip Morris Manufacturing Senegal S.A.R.L. (1)
Km 11 Route de Rufisque, BP 50596, Dakar, Senegal
Tel.: (221) 338798300
Emp.: 400
Tobacco Mfr
N.A.I.C.S.: 312230

Philip Morris Mexico Productos Y Servicios, S. de R.L. de C.V. (1)
Lago Zurich No 245 Edificio Presa Falcon Tercer Piso, Col Ampliacion Granada Del Miguel Hidalgo, 11529, Mexico, Mexico
Tel.: (52) 5591847000
Emp.: 1,800

Cigarette Mfr
N.A.I.C.S.: 312230

Philip Morris North Africa SARL (1)
Emeraude Palace Building - Offices BM1 and AM1, Rue du Lac Windermere Les Berges du Lac, 1504, Tunis, Tunisia
Tel.: (216) 71964274
Emp.: 20
Tobacco Mfr
N.A.I.C.S.: 312230

Philip Morris Norway AS (1)
Dronningens gate 8A, 0152, Oslo, Norway
Tel.: (47) 23100360
Web Site: https://www.pmi.com
Emp.: 21
Tobacco Product Mfr
N.A.I.C.S.: 312230

Philip Morris Operations a.d. (1)
Bulevar 12 februar 74, 18106, Nis, Serbia
Tel.: (381) 18554433
Cigarette Mfr
N.A.I.C.S.: 312230

Philip Morris Panama Sociedad en Comandita por Acciones (1)
Juan Diaz Via Jose Domingo Diaz Calle 117 Oeste Edif Fabrica Parker, Panama, Panama
Tel.: (507) 2179400
Cigarette Mfr
N.A.I.C.S.: 312230

Philip Morris Pazarlama ve Satis A.S. (1)
Kucukcamlica Mahallesi Ord Prof Fahrettin Kerim Gokay Cad No 58-58/1, Kucukcamlica Uskudar, 34696, Istanbul, Turkiye
Tel.: (90) 2165443000
Emp.: 500
Tobacco Product Mfr & Distr.
N.A.I.C.S.: 312230

Philip Morris Polska Distribution Sp. z o.o. (1)
ul Inflancka 4C Gdanski Business Center D, 00-189, Warsaw, Poland
Tel.: (48) 226062222
Tobacco Product Distr
N.A.I.C.S.: 424940
Tomasz Zuzlik (Mgr-PMO)

Philip Morris Polska S.A. (1)
Al Jana Pawla II 196, 31-982, Krakow, Poland
Tel.: (48) 126464646
Emp.: 3,000
Cigarette Mfr & Distr
N.A.I.C.S.: 312230
Magdalena Ignacek (Mgr-Logistics Support)

Philip Morris Polska Tobacco Spolka z ograniczona odpowiedzialnoscia (1)
Al Jana Pawla II 196, 31-982, Krakow, Poland
Tel.: (48) 801101000
Cigarette Mfr
N.A.I.C.S.: 312230

Philip Morris Products S.A. (1)
Quai Jeanrenaud 3, 2000, Neuchatel, Switzerland
Tel.: (41) 582421111
Web Site: http://www.pmi.com
Emp.: 400
Cigarette Mfr & Distr
N.A.I.C.S.: 312230

Philip Morris Reunion S.A.R.L. (1)
ZA Ravine a Marquet 4 bis rue Antanifotsy, 97419, La Possession, Reunion
Tel.: (262) 262711180
Cigarette Mfr
N.A.I.C.S.: 312230

Philip Morris Romania S.R.L. (1)
Strada Horea Closca si Crisan nr 83-105, Otopeni, Romania
Tel.: (40) 372823401
Tobacco Product Distr
N.A.I.C.S.: 424940

Philip Morris SA Philip Morris Sabanci Pazarlama ve Satis A.S. (1)
Kucukcamlica Mahallesi Ord Prof Fahrettin Kerim Gokay Cad No 58-58/1, Kucukcamlica - Uskudar, 34696, Istanbul, Turkiye

Tel.: (90) 2165443000
Emp.: 500
Tobacco Distr
N.A.I.C.S.: 459991

Philip Morris Sabanci Pazalarma Ve Satis A.S.   **(1)**
Kucukcamlica Mahallesi Ord Prof Fahrettin Kerim Gokay Cad No 58-58/1, Kucuk Camlica, 34696, Istanbul, Uskudar, Turkiye   **(75.25%)**
Tel.: (90) 216 544 30 00
Web Site: http://www.pmsa.com.tr
Sales Range: $50-74.9 Million
Emp.: 1,000
Tobacco Marketing & Distribution; Owned 75.25% by Philip Morris & 24.75% by Haci Omer Sabanci Holding A.S.
N.A.I.C.S.: 459991

Philip Morris Sabanci Sigara Ve Tutunculuk A.S.   **(1)**
Acibadem St Sahrettin Kerim Gokay St 58/1, Kucukcamlica Uskudar, 34696, Istanbul, Turkiye   **(75%)**
Tel.: (90) 2165443000
Web Site: http://www.pmicareers.com
Sales Range: $75-99.9 Million
Emp.: 285
Tobacco Factory; Owned 75% by Philip Morris & 25% by Sabanci A.S.
N.A.I.C.S.: 111910
Turhan Talu (Pres)

Philip Morris Sales and Marketing Ltd.   **(1)**
Tsvetnoy boulevard 2, Moscow, 127051, Russia
Tel.: (7) 4957059220
Cigarette Mfr
N.A.I.C.S.: 312230

Philip Morris Services d.o.o.   **(1)**
Bulevar Zorana Dindica 64a, 11070, Belgrade, Serbia
Tel.: (381) 112010800
Emp.: 900
Tobacco Mfr
N.A.I.C.S.: 312230

Philip Morris Seyahat Perakende Satis Anonim Sirketi   **(1)**
Kucuk Camlica Mahallesi Ord Prof Fahrettin Kerim Gokay Cad No 58, Kucukcamlica - Uskudar, 34696, Istanbul, Turkiye
Tel.: (90) 2165443460
Cigarette Mfr
N.A.I.C.S.: 312230

Philip Morris Singapore Pte. Ltd.   **(1)**
3791 Jalan Bukit Merah 08-18 E-Centre Redhill, Singapore, 159471, Singapore
Tel.: (65) 64130991
Emp.: 50
Tobacco Mfr
N.A.I.C.S.: 312230

Philip Morris South Africa (Proprietary) Limited   **(1)**
3 Bridgeway Road Bridgeways Precinct, Century City, Cape Town, 7441, South Africa
Tel.: (27) 215274840
Emp.: 600
Tobacco Mfr
N.A.I.C.S.: 312230

Philip Morris Spain, S.L.   **(1)**
Jose Lazaro Galdiano 6 Planta 4, 28036, Madrid, Spain
Tel.: (34) 917485500
Emp.: 700
Tobacco Mfr
N.A.I.C.S.: 312230

Philip Morris Switzerland Sarl   **(1)**
Avenue de Rhodanie 50, 1007, Lausanne, Switzerland
Tel.: (41) 582420000
Emp.: 3,000
Tobacco Mfr
N.A.I.C.S.: 312230

Philip Morris Trading (Thailand) Company Limited   **(1)**
689 Bhiraj Tower 39-40th Floor Sukhumvit Road, Klongton Nua Wattana, Bangkok, 10110, Thailand
Tel.: (66) 20659999
Web Site: https://www.pmi.com

Emp.: 300
Tobacco Product Distr
N.A.I.C.S.: 424940

Philip Morris Trading S.R.L.   **(1)**
Strada Nicolae Filipescu nr 28, Bucharest, Romania
Tel.: (40) 372823389
Web Site: https://www.pmi.com
Cigarette Distr
N.A.I.C.S.: 424940

Philip Morris Tutun Mamulleri Sanayi ve Ticaret A.S.   **(1)**
Kucukcamlica Mahallesi Ord Prof Fahrettin Kerim Gokay Cad No 58-58/1, Kucukcamlica Uskudar, 34696, Istanbul, Türkiye
Tel.: (90) 2165443000
Emp.: 1,200
Tobacco Product Mfr & Distr
N.A.I.C.S.: 312230

Philip Morris Vietnam Limited Liability Company   **(1)**
Level 11 The Metropolitan 235 Dong Khoi, District 1, Ho Chi Minh City, Vietnam
Tel.: (84) 838231333
Emp.: 350
Tobacco Mfr
N.A.I.C.S.: 312230

Philip Morris Zagreb d.o.o.   **(1)**
Heinzelova 70, 10000, Zagreb, Croatia
Tel.: (385) 16166900
Emp.: 120
Tobacco Product Mfr & Distr
N.A.I.C.S.: 312230

PrJSC Philip Morris Ukraine   **(1)**
30 Spaska st Podil Plaza 5th floor, Kiev, 04070, Ukraine
Tel.: (380) 443894600
Web Site: https://www.pmi.com
Emp.: 1,300
Tobacco Product Mfr
N.A.I.C.S.: 312230

PrJSC Philip Morris Ukraine   **(1)**
30 Spaska st Podil Plaza 5th floor, Kiev, 04070, Ukraine
Tel.: (380) 44 389 4600
Web Site: https://www.pmi.com
Emp.: 1,300
Cigarette Distr
N.A.I.C.S.: 312230

Reviti Limited   **(1)**
Scottish Friendly House 16 Blythswood Square, Glasgow, G2 4HJ, Lanarkshire, United Kingdom
Tel.: (44) 3333235433
Web Site: https://www.revitilife.com
Fire Insurance Services
N.A.I.C.S.: 524113

SIA Philip Morris Latvia   **(1)**
Krisjana Valdemara Street 62, Riga, 1013, Latvia
Tel.: (371) 167201201
Emp.: 24
Tobacco Mfr
N.A.I.C.S.: 312230

Swedish Match AB   **(1)**
Sveavagen 44, SE-118 85, Stockholm, Sweden
Tel.: (46) 101393000
Web Site: http://www.swedishmatch.com
Rev.: $2,099,618,796
Assets: $2,244,420,092
Liabilities: $2,440,641,771
Net Worth: ($196,221,679)
Earnings: $607,584,741
Emp.: 7,536
Fiscal Year-end: 12/31/2022
Matches, Lighters, Chewing Tobacco & Snuff
N.A.I.C.S.: 312230
Marie-Louise Heiman (Gen Counsel & Sr VP-Grp Legal Affairs)
Lars Olof Lofman (Sr VP-R&D-Europe Div)
Joakim Tilly (Pres-Europe Div)
Andrew Cripps (Deputy Chm)
Thomas Hayes (Co-CFO, Pres-US Div & Sr VP-Fin Grp)
Hakan Soderberg (Pres-Lights Div)
Anders Larsson (Co-CFO)
Lars Dahlgren (Pres & CEO)

Subsidiary (Non-US):

Domino Holdings France SARL   **(2)**

Za Du Bel Air 2 Rue Hippolyte Mege Mouries, 78120, Rambouillet, Yvelines, France
Tel.: (33) 130465678
Investment Management Service
N.A.I.C.S.: 523940

Subsidiary (Domestic):

Gotlands Snus AB   **(2)**
Sockerbruket Roma, Romakloster, 622 54, Gotland, Sweden
Tel.: (46) 498200990
Web Site: https://www.gotlandssnus.se
Cigarette Mfr
N.A.I.C.S.: 312230
Kind Regards (Co-Founder & Co-CEO)
Henrik Jakobsson (Co-Founder & Co-CEO)

Subsidiary (Non-US):

House of Oliver Twist A/S   **(2)**
Borstenbindervej 1, 5230, Odense, Denmark
Tel.: (45) 6 615 7117
Web Site: https://www.oliver-twist.dk
Cigarette Mfr
N.A.I.C.S.: 312230
Lars Dahlgren (CEO)

Subsidiary (US):

SM Cigars Inc.   **(2)**
700 Columbia Hwy, Dothan, AL 36301-1802   **(100%)**
Tel.: (334) 793-7289
Tobacco Processing & Cigar Mfr
N.A.I.C.S.: 312230
Tony Martin (Mgr)

Subsidiary (Non-US):

SM Deutschland GmbH   **(2)**
Am Rathaus 9, 94051, Hauzenberg, Germany
Tel.: (49) 15117222999
Web Site: https://www.smdeutschland.com
Transportation Services
N.A.I.C.S.: 485991

SM Lighters BV   **(2)**
AHG Fokkerstraat 5, 9400 AB, Assen, Netherlands
Tel.: (31) 592376888
Sales Range: $25-49.9 Million
Emp.: 100
Cigarette Lighters Mfr
N.A.I.C.S.: 339999
P. Verhoog (Dir)
J. L. Ravel (Mgr-Sls & Mktg)
W. Mulder (Mgr-Fin)

SM Norge A/S   **(2)**
Bryggegata 9, 0250, Oslo, Norway
Tel.: (47) 22 727240
Web Site: http://www.swedishmatch.com
Sales Range: $25-49.9 Million
Cigars & Matches Distr
N.A.I.C.S.: 424940

SM Philippines Inc.   **(2)**
104 Technology Avenue Laguna Technopark Special Economic Zone, Binan, 4024, Laguna, Philippines
Tel.: (63) 495440770
Lighter Mfr
N.A.I.C.S.: 339999
Maribel Umali (Head-HR)

Subsidiary (Domestic):

SMD Logistics AB   **(2)**
Box 2071, 196 02, Kungsangen, Sweden
Tel.: (46) 87642010
Web Site: https://www.smdlogistics.se
Cigarette Mfr
N.A.I.C.S.: 312230

Swedish Match Distribution AB   **(2)**
Matarvagen 41, 196 37, Kungsangen, Sweden   **(100%)**
Tel.: (46) 87642000
Sales Range: $50-74.9 Million
Emp.: 70
Tobacco Product Distr
N.A.I.C.S.: 424940

Subsidiary (Non-US):

Swedish Match Dominicana S.A.   **(2)**
Garcia y Vega Extension III, Industrial Free Zone Calle Las Palomas Zona Franca Industrial Parte 1, Santiago, Dominican Republic
Tel.: (809) 5754300
Cigarette Mfr
N.A.I.C.S.: 312230

Subsidiary (Domestic):

Swedish Match Industries AB   **(2)**
Vastra Drottningvagen 15, PO Box 84, 522 22, Tidaholm, Vastergotland, Sweden   **(100%)**
Tel.: (46) 101393500
Emp.: 158
Matches Mfr
N.A.I.C.S.: 339999

Subsidiary (US):

Swedish Match North America Inc.   **(2)**
7300 Beaufont Springs Dr Ste 400, Richmond, VA 23225
Tel.: (804) 302-1700
Sales Range: $50-74.9 Million
Emp.: 100
Tobacco Product Distr
N.A.I.C.S.: 424940

Subsidiary (Domestic):

Swedish Match North Europe AB   **(2)**
Maria Skolgata 83, 118 53, Stockholm, Sweden   **(100%)**
Tel.: (46) 86580200
Cigars & Matches Retailer
N.A.I.C.S.: 424940
Lars Gahlgren (Gen Mgr)

Subsidiary (Non-US):

Swedish Match do Brasil S/A   **(2)**
Rua Conselheiro Laurindo n 1425, Ipanema, Curitiba, 80230-180, Parana, Brazil   **(99.4%)**
Tel.: (55) 413 302 5225
Web Site: https://www.swedishmatch.com.br
Rev.: $80,000,000
Emp.: 700
Tobacco Product Mfr
N.A.I.C.S.: 312230

V2 Tobacco A/S   **(2)**
Georg Jensens Vej 7, 8600, Silkeborg, Denmark
Tel.: (45) 87706030
Web Site: https://www.swedishmatch.com
Cigarette Mfr
N.A.I.C.S.: 312230

Swedish Match Lighters BV   **(1)**
AHG Fokkerstraat 5, 9403 AM, Assen, Netherlands
Tel.: (31) 592376888
Web Site: https://www.cricketlighters.com
Lighter Mfr & Distr
N.A.I.C.S.: 339999

Swedish Match Norge AS   **(1)**
Bryggegata 9, 0250, Oslo, Norway
Tel.: (47) 22727240
Tobacco Product Mfr & Distr
N.A.I.C.S.: 312230

TabLabs Inc.   **(1)**
Unit D107-19720 94A Avenue, Langley, V1M 3B7, BC, Canada
Tel.: (672) 202-1900
Web Site: https://www.tablabs.ca
Emp.: 800
Pharmaceuticals Product Mfr
N.A.I.C.S.: 325412
John Stephen (CEO)

UAB Philip Morris Baltic   **(1)**
Jogailos street 4 B, LT-01116, Vilnius, Lithuania
Tel.: (370) 52109555
Emp.: 110
Tobacco Product Mfr & Distr
N.A.I.C.S.: 312230

UAB Philip Morris Lietuva   **(1)**
Vilniaus Plentas 16, 94104, Klaipeda, Lithuania
Tel.: (370) 46484444
Emp.: 550
Tobacco Product Distr
N.A.I.C.S.: 424940
Scott Coutts (Sr VP)

Philip Morris International Inc.—(Continued)

Vectura Fertin Pharma Research Laboratories Pte. Ltd. (1)
50 Science Park Road 02-07 The Kendall
Singapore Science Park II, Singapore,
117406, Singapore
Tel.: (65) 66314500
Web Site:
    https://www.vecturafertinpharmalabs.com
Pharmaceutical Laboratory Services
N.A.I.C.S.: 541380

Vectura GmbH (1)
Dingolfinger Strasse 15, 81673, Munich,
Germany
Tel.: (49) 898979690
Pharmaceuticals Product Mfr
N.A.I.C.S.: 325412

Vectura Group plc (1)
One Prospect West, Chippenham, SN14
6FH, Wilts, United Kingdom (74.77%)
Tel.: (44) 1249667700
Web Site: http://www.vectura.com
Rev.: $258,781,432
Assets: $904,241,520
Liabilities: $165,098,752
Net Worth: $739,142,768
Earnings: $166,184,928
Emp.: 502
Fiscal Year-end: 12/31/2020
Respiratory Therapies Research & Development Services
N.A.I.C.S.: 325412
Joanne Hombal (Exec VP-HR)
John Murphy (Gen Counsel & Sec)
Will Downie (CEO)
Mark Bridgewater (Chief Comml Officer)
Geraldine Venthoye (Chief Scientific Officer & Exec VP-Product Dev)
David Lescuyer (Exec VP-Oral Bus)
Antony Fitzpatrick (Exec VP-Ops)
Christina Olsen (Exec VP-Corp Strategy & Comm)
Sharon Johnson (Exec VP-Delivery Mgmt)

Subsidiary (Domestic):

Vectura Delivery Devices Ltd. (2)
205 Cambridge Science Park Milton Rd,
Cambridge, CB4 0GZ, Cambs, United Kingdom
Tel.: (44) 1223422900
Web Site: http://www.vectura.com
Emp.: 30
Respiratory Therapies Delivery Device Mfr
N.A.I.C.S.: 339112

Branch (Domestic):

Vectura Group plc - Nottingham (2)
1 Mere Way, Ruddington, Nottingham,
NG11 6JS, United Kingdom
Tel.: (44) 1159747474
Respiratory Therapies Research & Development Services
N.A.I.C.S.: 325412

Subsidiary (US):

Vectura Inc (2)
371 Turnpike Rd, Southborough, MA 01772
Tel.: (508) 573-5700
Pharmaceuticals Product Mfr
N.A.I.C.S.: 325412

ZAO Philip Morris Izhora (1)
7 Volkhonskoye shosse Industrial Zone
Gorelovo Block No 2, Lomonosov, 198323,
Russia
Tel.: (7) 8127184545
Cigarette Mfr
N.A.I.C.S.: 312230

PHILLIPS 66 COMPANY
2331 CityWest Blvd, Houston, TX
77042
Tel.: (832) 765-3010 DE
Web Site: https://www.phillips66.com
PSX—(NYSE)
Rev.: $149,890,000,000
Assets: $75,501,000,000
Liabilities: $43,851,000,000
Net Worth: $31,650,000,000
Earnings: $7,015,000,000
Emp.: 14,000
Fiscal Year-end: 12/31/23

Holding Company; Petroleum Refining & Sales
N.A.I.C.S.: 551112
Paula A. Johnson (Gen Counsel, Sec & Exec VP-Legal & Govt Affairs)
Donald A. Baldridge (Exec VP-Midstream & Chemicals)
Mark E. Lashier (Chm, Pres & CEO)
Tandra C. Perkins (Chief Admin Officer, Chief Digital Officer & Sr VP)
Sonya Reed (Sr VP-Corp Comm & HR)
Jeff Dietert (VP-IR)
Zhanna Golodryga (Exec VP-Emerging Energy & Sustainability)
Brian M. Mandell (Exec VP-Mktg & Comml)
Vanessa L. Allen Sutherland (Gen Counsel, Sec & Exec VP-Govt Affairs)
Sonya Reed (Sr VP-Corp Comm & HR)
Richard G. Harbison (Exec VP)
Vanessa Sutherland (Gen Counsel)
Todd Denton (Sr VP)

Subsidiaries:

Chevron Phillips Chemical Company LLC (1)
10001 6 Pines Dr, The Woodlands, TX
77380 (50%)
Tel.: (832) 813-4100
Web Site: https://www.cpchem.com
Sales Range: $5-14.9 Billion
Emp.: 4,800
Producer of Olefins & Polyolefins; Supplier of Aromatics, Alpha Olefins, Styrenics & Specialty Chemicals
N.A.I.C.S.: 325110
Tim Hill (Gen Counsel, Sec & Sr VP-Legal & Pub Affairs)
Mitch Eichelberger (Exec VP-Polymers & Specialties)
Carolyn Burke (CFO & Exec VP)
Maricela Caballero (Sr VP-HR)
Steve Prusak (Sr VP-Corp Plng & Tech)
Bryan Canfield (Sr VP-Mfg)
Justine Smith (Sr VP-Petrochemicals)
Allison Martinez (CIO)

Subsidiary (Non-US):

Chevron Phillips Chemicals International N.V. (2)
Brusselsesteenweg 355 BV, Overijse, 3090,
Belgium
Tel.: (32) 26891211
Web Site: http://www.cpch.net
Sales Range: $400-449.9 Million
Emp.: 75
Chemical Products Mfr
N.A.I.C.S.: 325998

DCP Midstream, LP (1)
2331 CityWest Blvd, Houston, TX 77042
Tel.: (303) 595-3331
Web Site: https://www.dcpmidstream.com
Rev.: $10,707,000,000
Assets: $13,380,000,000
Liabilities: $7,504,000,000
Net Worth: $5,876,000,000
Earnings: $395,000,000
Emp.: 1,788
Fiscal Year-end: 12/31/2021
Natural Gas Processing, Transporting, Storage & Distribution Services
N.A.I.C.S.: 221210
Jerry Barnhill (Chief Environmental, Health, Safety Officer & Grp VP)
Donald A. Baldridge (Interim CEO)
Tamara Bray (Chief HR Officer & Grp VP)
Richard A. Loving (Chief Acctg Officer)
George Green (Gen Counsel & Grp VP)

Subsidiary (Domestic):

DCP Michigan Pipeline & Processing, LLC (2)
6250 Old State Rd, Johannesburg, MI
49751
Tel.: (989) 939-8360
Web Site: https://www.dcpmidstream.com
Sales Range: $25-49.9 Million
Emp.: 20
Natural Gas Distribution Services

N.A.I.C.S.: 221210

DCP Midstream, LLC (2)
6900 E Layton Ave Ste 900, Denver, CO
80237
Tel.: (303) 595-3331
Web Site: https://www.dcpmidstream.com
Rev.: $6,893,000,000
Assets: $14,106,000,000
Liabilities: $7,212,000,000
Net Worth: $6,894,000,000
Earnings: $93,000,000
Fiscal Year-end: 12/31/2016
Holding Company; Natural Gas Processing, Transporting, Storage & Distribution Services
N.A.I.C.S.: 551112
Jerry Barnhill (Officer-Environmental, Health, Safety & Operational Risk)
George Green (Corp Counsel)

Marysville Hydrocarbons LLC (2)
2510 Busha Hwy, Marysville, MI 48040
Tel.: (586) 445-2300
Emp.: 40
Natural Gas Extraction Services
N.A.I.C.S.: 211130

JET Energy Trading GmbH (1)
Caffamacherreihe 1, 20355, Hamburg, Germany
Tel.: (49) 4063801504
Petroleum Product Whslr
N.A.I.C.S.: 424720

JET Tankstellen Austria GmbH (1)
Samergasse 27, 5020, Salzburg, Austria
Tel.: (43) 66 287 7880
Web Site: https://www.jet-tankstellen.at
Petroleum Product Whslr
N.A.I.C.S.: 424710

JET Tankstellen Deutschland GmbH (1)
Caffamacherreihe 1, 20355, Hamburg,
Germany (100%)
Tel.: (49) 40638010
Web Site: https://www.jet.de
Petroleum Product Whslr
N.A.I.C.S.: 424720
Georg Ober (Mng Dir)

Pester Marketing Company (1)
4643 S Ulster St Ste 350, Denver, CO
80237
Tel.: (303) 693-9331
Web Site: http://www.pestermarketing.com
Petroleum Merchant Whslr
N.A.I.C.S.: 424720
Rich Spresser (Pres & CEO)
Terry Lacy (CFO & VP)
R. Cloyd (Co-Founder)
Esther Pester (Co-Founder)

Phillips 66 Bantry Bay Terminal Limited (1)
Reenrour, Bantry, County Cork, Ireland
Tel.: (353) 2750346
Petroleum Product Whslr
N.A.I.C.S.: 424710

Phillips 66 Canada Ltd. (1)
1400-335 8 Ave SW, Calgary, T2P 1C9,
AB, Canada
Tel.: (587) 233-6600
Web Site: https://www.phillips66.com
Emp.: 35
Petroleum Product Whslr
N.A.I.C.S.: 424710
Doug Heinzer (Pres)

Phillips 66 Company (1)
PO Box 421959, Houston, TX 77242-1959
Tel.: (281) 293-6600
Web Site: https://www.phillips66.com
Petroleum Product Whslr
N.A.I.C.S.: 424710

Phillips 66 GmbH (1)
Industriestrasse 49, 6300, Zug, Switzerland
Tel.: (41) 417636456
Petroleum Product Whslr
N.A.I.C.S.: 424710

Phillips 66 International Trading Pte. Ltd. (1)
1 Temasek Avenue 40-01 Milenia Tower,
Singapore 039192, Singapore
Tel.: (65) 69334100
Trading Services for Crude & Refined Oil
Products

N.A.I.C.S.: 424720

Phillips 66 Limited (1)
7th Floor 200-202 Aldersgate Street, London, EC1A 4HD, United Kingdom
Tel.: (44) 2078224400
Web Site: https://www.phillips66.co.uk
Emp.: 180
Petroleum Product Whslr
N.A.I.C.S.: 424720

Phillips 66 Partners LP (1)
2331 City W Blvd, Houston, TX
77042 (99.99%)
Web Site: http://www.phillips66partners.com
Rev.: $1,754,000,000
Assets: $7,101,000,000
Liabilities: $4,164,000,000
Net Worth: $2,937,000,000
Earnings: $777,000,000
Emp.: 600
Fiscal Year-end: 12/31/2021
Oil & Gas Production
N.A.I.C.S.: 324199
J. Scott Pruitt (VP & Controller)

Phillips 66 Polypropylene Canada Inc. (1)
1400 S Park Ave, Linden, NJ 07036
Tel.: (918) 977-4923
Petroleum Product Whslr
N.A.I.C.S.: 424720
Greg Garlin (CEO)

Phillips Gas Company (1)
968 Phillips, Bartlesville, OK 74004
Tel.: (918) 661-6600
Petroleum Product Whslr
N.A.I.C.S.: 424720

Phillips Utility Gas Corporation (1)
PO Box 4428, Houston, TX 77210
Tel.: (832) 379-6255
Petroleum Product Whslr
N.A.I.C.S.: 424720

Pioneer Pipe Line Company (1)
90 Foothill Blvd, Rock Springs, WY 82901
Tel.: (307) 362-7541
Petroleum Product Whslr
N.A.I.C.S.: 424720

Seagas Pipeline Company (1)
PO Box 2197, Houston, TX 77079
Tel.: (281) 293-3227
Oil & Gas Drilling Services
N.A.I.C.S.: 213111

Sentinel Transportation LLC (1)
3521 Silverside Rd Ste 2A, Wilmington, DE
19810 (100%)
Tel.: (302) 477-1640
Web Site: https://www.sentineltrans.com
Long Distance Trucking Services
N.A.I.C.S.: 484110
Randy Bailey (VP-Operations)

Branch (Domestic):

Sentinel Transportation LLC - Belle (2)
901 W Dupont Ave, Belle, WV 25015
Tel.: (304) 949-6233
Trucking Service
N.A.I.C.S.: 484121

Sentinel Transportation LLC - Louisville (2)
2606 Millers Ln, Louisville, KY 40216
Tel.: (502) 774-9139
Transportation Services
N.A.I.C.S.: 484110

Sentinel Transportation LLC Washington (2)
WV 892, Washington, WV 26181
Tel.: (304) 863-3305
Trucking Service
N.A.I.C.S.: 484110

Sentinel Transportation LLC - Westlake (2)
3363 Bayou D'Inde Rd, Westlake, LA 70669
Tel.: (337) 882-6852
Trucking Service
N.A.I.C.S.: 484121

PHILUX GLOBAL GROUP INC
2323 Main St, Irvine, CA 92614
Tel.: (714) 793-9227 NV

Web Site: https://philuxglobal.com
Year Founded: 1982
PHIL—(OTCIQ)
Rev.: $5,000
Assets: $90,856
Liabilities: $9,744,823
Net Worth: ($9,653,967)
Earnings: ($8,195,380)
Fiscal Year-end: 06/30/24
Investment & Financial Services
N.A.I.C.S.: 523999
Henry D. Fahman *(Chm, Pres, CEO & Acting CFO)*
Tina T. Phan *(Treas)*
Steve Truong *(Chm-Audit Committee)*
Hoang Vo *(VP-Global Bus Dev)*

Subsidiaries:

PHI Capital Holdings, Inc.   **(1)**
5348 Vegas Dr Ste 1176, Las Vegas, NV 89108-2347
Tel.: (702) 475-5430
Web Site: http://www.phicapitalholdings.com
Financial Services
N.A.I.C.S.: 523999
Henry D. Fahman *(Chm)*
Hoang D. Vo *(Mng Dir)*
Henry Fahman *(CEO)*
Garry Mcdowall *(VP)*
Dan Dubell *(Mng Dir)*
Dang Le Nguyen *(Mng Dir)*
Michael Bennett *(Mng Dir)*

PHIO PHARMACEUTICALS CORP.

11 Apex Dr Ste 300A PMB 2006, Marlborough, MA 01752
Tel.: (508) 767-3861   DE
Web Site:
   https://www.phiopharma.com
PHIO—(NASDAQ)
Assets: $9,364,000
Liabilities: $1,634,000
Net Worth: $7,730,000
Earnings: ($10,826,000)
Emp.: 8
Fiscal Year-end: 12/31/23
Pharmaceuticals Mfr
N.A.I.C.S.: 325412
Robert M. Infarinato *(CFO, Principal Acctg Officer & VP)*
Geert Cauwenbergh *(Interim Principal Exec & Fin Officer)*
Robert J. Bitterman *(Chm)*
Linda Mahoney *(Sr VP)*
Caitlin Kontulis *(Sec & VP-Admin & Fin)*

PHOENIX BIOTECH ACQUISITION CORP.

2201 Broadway Ste 705, Oakland, CA 94612
Tel.: (215) 731-9450   DE
Year Founded: 2021
PBAX—(NASDAQ)
Rev.: $2,836,864
Assets: $42,367,032
Liabilities: $53,122,409
Net Worth: ($10,755,377)
Earnings: ($667,736)
Emp.: 3
Fiscal Year-end: 12/31/22
Investment Services
N.A.I.C.S.: 523999
Chris Ehrlich *(CEO)*
Daniel Geffken *(CFO)*
Douglas Fisher *(Pres)*

PHOENIX FOOTWEAR GROUP, INC.

2236 Rutherford Rd Ste 113, Carlsbad, CA 92008
Tel.: (760) 602-9688   DE
Web Site:
   https://www.phoenixfootwear.com
Year Founded: 1882

PXFG—(OTCIQ)
Rev.: $19,581,000
Assets: $13,546,000
Liabilities: $12,604,000
Net Worth: $942,000
Earnings: ($159,000)
Emp.: 45
Fiscal Year-end: 12/28/19
Men's & Women's Footwear & Apparel Designer, Developer, Mfr & Marketer
N.A.I.C.S.: 316210
James R. Riedman *(Chm & CEO)*
John Dillen *(CFO, Treas & Sec)*

PHOENIX MOTOR INC.

5112 New Bern Ave, Raleigh, NC 27610
Tel.: (919) 276-8877   DE
Web Site:
   https://www.phoenixmotorsnc.com
Year Founded: 2020
PEV—(NASDAQ)
Rev.: $4,330,000
Assets: $20,443,000
Liabilities: $8,161,000
Net Worth: $12,282,000
Earnings: ($12,705,000)
Emp.: 60
Fiscal Year-end: 12/31/22
Holding Company
N.A.I.C.S.: 551112
Wenbing Chris Wang *(CFO)*
Lewis W. Liu *(COO)*

PHONEX HOLDINGS, INC

150 Executive Dr Ste Q, Edgewood, NY 11717
Tel.: (212) 213-6805   DE
Web Site: http://www.usell.com
Year Founded: 2003
PXHI—(OTCIQ)
Rev.: $149,190,000
Assets: $17,018,000
Liabilities: $2,594,000
Net Worth: $14,424,000
Earnings: $7,916,000
Emp.: 85
Fiscal Year-end: 12/31/22
Electronics & Precious Metals Recycling & Sales
N.A.I.C.S.: 561499
Robert M. Averick *(Chm)*
Nik Raman *(CEO & CFO)*

PHOTRONICS, INC.

15 Secor Rd, Brookfield, CT 06804
Tel.: (203) 775-9000   CT
Web Site:
   https://www.photronics.com
Year Founded: 1969
PLAB—(NASDAQ)
Rev.: $866,946,000
Assets: $1,712,059,000
Liabilities: $231,300,000
Net Worth: $1,480,759,000
Earnings: $183,848,000
Emp.: 1,878
Fiscal Year-end: 10/31/24
Photomasks Mfr
N.A.I.C.S.: 334413
Constantine S. Macricostas *(Founder)*
Christopher J. Progler *(CTO-Strategic Plng & Exec VP)*
Richelle E. Burr *(Chief Admin Officer & Exec VP)*
R. Troy Dewar *(VP-IR)*
Eric Rivera *(Interim CFO, Chief Acctg Officer & Controller)*
Frank Lee *(Pres & CEO)*
Dennic Hu *(VP-Supply Chain-Global)*
Debbie Wierzbicki *(Sr VP)*

Subsidiaries:

PK, Ltd.   **(1)**
493-3 Sungsung-Dong, Cheonan, 330 300, Choong-Nam, Korea (South)

Tel.: (82) 415290400
Web Site: http://www.photronics.com
Sales Range: $75-99.9 Million
Emp.: 350
Photomasks Mfr
N.A.I.C.S.: 334413

Subsidiary (Non-US):

PKLT   **(2)**
13 Tongshan Rd, Daya Township, Taichung, 428, Taiwan
Tel.: (886) 43 705 5000
Web Site: https://www.pklt.com.tw
Sales Range: $25-49.9 Million
Emp.: 59
Photomasks & Other Electronic Component Mfr
N.A.I.C.S.: 334413

Photronics California, Inc.   **(1)**
830 Hillview Ct Ste 280, Milpitas, CA 95035
Tel.: (408) 935-6005
Web Site: http://www.photronics.com
Sales Range: $50-74.9 Million
Emp.: 10
Photomasks Mfr
N.A.I.C.S.: 334413

Photronics Idaho, Inc.   **(1)**
10136 S Federal Way, Boise, ID 83716-9636
Tel.: (208) 908-4000
Web Site: http://www.photronics.com
Photomasks & Reticles Mfr
N.A.I.C.S.: 333242

Photronics Korea, Ltd.   **(1)**
15 2Gongdan 3-ro, Seobuk Choong-Nam, Cheonan, 31075, Korea (South)
Tel.: (82) 415290460
Semiconductor Photomask Product Mfr & Distr
N.A.I.C.S.: 334413

Photronics MZD, GmbH   **(1)**
Maria-Reiche-Strasse 4, 01109, Dresden, Germany
Tel.: (49) 35 188 5280
Web Site: http://www.photronics.com
Sales Range: $10-24.9 Million
Emp.: 16
Photomasks Mfr
N.A.I.C.S.: 334413

Photronics Singapore Pte, Ltd.   **(1)**
33 Ubi Avenue 3 03-09 Vertex Building, Singapore, 408868, Singapore
Tel.: (65) 3 567 9933
Web Site: http://www.photronics.com
Emp.: 20
Photomasks Mfr
N.A.I.C.S.: 334413

Photronics UK, Ltd.   **(1)**
Technology Dr, Bridgend, CF31 3LU, United Kingdom
Tel.: (44) 1656674300
Emp.: 82
Photomasks Mfr
N.A.I.C.S.: 334413
Robert Lloyd *(Gen Mgr)*

Taichung Photronics Photomask Co., Ltd.   **(1)**
No 13 Tongshan Road, Daya Township, Taichung, 428, Taiwan
Tel.: (886) 437055000
Web Site: https://www.pklt.com.tw
Semiconductor Photomask Product Mfr & Distr
N.A.I.C.S.: 334413

PHREESIA, INC.   DE

Web Site: https://www.phreesia.com
Year Founded: 2005
PHR—(NYSE)
Rev.: $280,910,000
Assets: $370,057,000
Liabilities: $82,238,000
Net Worth: $287,819,000
Earnings: ($176,146,000)
Emp.: 1,576
Fiscal Year-end: 01/31/23
Healthcare Software Development Services
N.A.I.C.S.: 541511

Amy VanDuyn *(Sr VP-HR)*
David Linetsky *(Sr VP-Life Sciences)*
Allison Hoffman *(Gen Counsel)*
Sally Thayer *(VP-Product Mgmt)*
David Breton *(VP-Product Mgmt)*
Russell Thatcher *(VP-Engrg)*
Richard Greenwell *(VP-Engrg)*
Sara DiNardo *(VP-Customer Solutions & Health Sys)*
Danielle Lynch *(VP-Client Experience)*
Hilary Hatch *(Chief Clinical Officer)*
Maureen McKinney *(VP-Corp Comm)*
Matt Cardon *(VP)*
Kristin Roberts *(VP)*
Will Snow *(VP)*
Kharen Hauck *(VP-Marketing)*
Sandra Schittone *(VP)*
Nick Vissat *(VP)*
Derrick Deberry *(VP)*
Ashwin Uttamchandani *(VP)*
Alexandra Beneville *(VP)*
Evan Roberts *(Co-Founder & COO)*
Michael Weintraub *(Chm)*
Chaim Indig *(Co/Co-Founder, CEO & CEO)*
Balaji Gandhi *(CFO)*
Tiffany McGee *(Gen Counsel & Asst Gen Counsel)*
Alexis Lyons *(Gen Counsel, Sec & Asst Gen Counsel)*
Jack Callahan *(CTO & VP-Integration Engrg)*
Elizabeth Fox *(VP-Product Mgmt)*
Kristen Ballantine *(VP-Public Affairs)*
Melissa Mitchell *(Chief Privacy Officer)*
Yvonne Hui *(Principal Acctg Officer & VP)*

Subsidiaries:

Insignia Health, LLC   **(1)**
1 SW Columbia St Ste 700, Portland, OR 97258-2025
Tel.: (503) 299-2800
Web Site: http://www.insigniahealth.com
Ambulatory Health Care Services
N.A.I.C.S.: 621999
Traci Smolen *(Acct Mgr)*
Sherry McVey *(Mgr-Mktg Comm)*

PHUNWARE, INC.

1002 West Ave, Austin, TX 78701
Tel.: (512) 693-4199   DE
Web Site: https://www.phunware.com
PHUN—(NASDAQ)
Rev.: $21,794,000
Assets: $54,835,000
Liabilities: $29,954,000
Net Worth: $24,881,000
Earnings: ($50,894,000)
Emp.: 106
Fiscal Year-end: 12/31/22
Data Processing, Hosting & Related Services
N.A.I.C.S.: 518210
Michael Snavely *(CEO)*
Alan S. Knitowski *(Founder)*
Troy Reisner *(CFO)*
Jeremy Kidd *(Sr VP-Sls & Mktg & Gen Mgr-Software)*
Stephen Chen *(Chm)*
Chris Olive *(Chief Legal Officer, Gen Counsel & Exec VP)*
Andrew Soltan *(VP-Engineering)*
Suzy Elizondo *(VP-Product & Design)*
Chad Difuntorum *(VP-QA & Support)*
Jason Powell *(VP-Information Technology)*
Cody Wimbish *(VP-Program Mgmt & Customer Success)*

Subsidiaries:

Phunware Opco, Inc.   **(1)**
1002 West Ave, Austin, TX 78701
Tel.: (512) 693-4199
Web Site: http://www.phunware.com

Phunware, Inc.—(Continued)

Software Development Services
N.A.I.C.S.: 541511
Alan S. Knitowski *(CEO)*

PHX MINERALS INC.

1601 NW Expy Valliance Bank Tower
Ste 1100, Oklahoma City, OK 73118
Tel.: (405) 948-1560   **OK**
Web Site: https://www.phxmin.com
Year Founded: 1926
PHX—(NYSE)
Rev.: $37,749,044
Assets: $117,011,014
Liabilities: $38,302,275
Net Worth: $78,708,739
Earnings: ($6,217,237)
Emp.: 20
Fiscal Year-end: 09/30/21
Crude Petroleum Extraction Services
N.A.I.C.S.: 211120
Chad L. Stephens *(Pres & CEO)*
Raphael D'Amico *(CFO, Sec & VP)*
Chad D. True *(Principal Acctg Officer)*
Kenna D. Clapp *(Dir-Land)*
Danielle D. Mezo *(Dir-Engrg)*
Carl Vandervoort *(Dir-Geology)*

PICK-UPS PLUS, INC.

1718 Fry Rd Ste 175, Houston, TX
77084
Tel.: (281) 828-9995   **DE**
Web Site: https://pickupsplus.net
PUPS—(OTCIQ)
Asset Management Services
N.A.I.C.S.: 533110
James A. Clarke *(Pres)*

PIEDMONT COMMUNITY BANK GROUP, INC.

Tel.: (478) 986-5900   **GA**
PCBN—(OTCIQ)
Bank Holding Company
N.A.I.C.S.: 551111
John A. Hudson *(Chm)*
Julie Simmons *(CFO & Exec VP)*
R. Drew Hulsey Jr. *(CEO)*
Mickey C. Parker *(Pres)*
M. Cole Davis Jr. *(Exec VP)*

PIEDMONT LITHIUM INC.

42 E Catawba St, Belmont, NC
28012
Tel.: (704) 461-8000
Web Site:
  https://www.piedmontlithium.com
Year Founded: 1983
PLL—(NASDAQ)
Assets: $187,851,629
Liabilities: $7,440,918
Net Worth: $180,410,711
Earnings: ($19,993,848)
Emp.: 20
Fiscal Year-end: 06/30/21
Investment Services
N.A.I.C.S.: 523940
Keith D. Phillips *(Pres & CEO)*
Patrick H. Brindle *(COO & Exec VP)*
David Buckley *(VP)*
Bruce Czachor *(Chief Legal Officer, Sec & Exec VP)*
Jeffrey Armstrong *(Chm)*
Austin Devaney *(VP-Sls & Mktg)*
Brian Risinger *(VP-Corp Comm. & IR)*
Michael D. White *(CFO & Exec VP)*
Lamont Leatherman *(VP)*
Jim Nottingham *(Sr Project Mgr-Concentrate Ops)*
Binh Meador *(Sr Project Mgr-Chemical Ops)*
John Ray *(Production Mgr-Chemical Ops)*
Malissa Gordon *(Mgr-Community & Govt Rels)*
Erin Sanders *(VP-Corp Comm)*

PIEDMONT OFFICE REALTY TRUST, INC.

5565 Glenridge Connector Ste 450,
Atlanta, GA 30342
Tel.: (770) 418-8800
Web Site:
  https://www.piedmontreit.com
Year Founded: 1997
PDM—(NYSE)
Rev.: $577,756,000
Assets: $4,057,082,000
Liabilities: $2,334,110,000
Net Worth: $1,722,972,000
Earnings: ($48,387,000)
Emp.: 150
Fiscal Year-end: 12/31/23
Real Estate Investment Trust
N.A.I.C.S.: 525990
Robert E. Bowers *(CFO, Chief Admin Officer & Exec VP)*
Laura P. Moon *(Chief Acctg Officer & Sr VP)*
Christopher Brent Smith *(Pres & CEO)*
George M. Wells *(COO & Exec VP)*
Robert K. Wiberg *(Exec VP-Northeast Reg & Head-Dev)*
Dale H. Taysom *(Vice Chm)*
Christopher A. Kollme *(Exec VP-Fin & Strategy)*
Brad C. Pittman *(VP-Capital Transactions)*
Marie Worsham *(Reg Mgr)*
Patrick McGregor *(VP)*
Mike Hagmann *(Reg Mgr)*
David Ketcham *(Gen Mgr)*
Edward H. Guilbert III *(Treas & Exec VP-Fin)*

Subsidiaries:

Piedmont Government Services,
LLC   **(1)**
80 M St SE Ste 140, Washington, DC
20003-3550
Tel.: (202) 454-5860
Real Estate Agency & Brokerage Services
N.A.I.C.S.: 531210

Piedmont Power, LLC   **(1)**
12555 James Madison Hwy, Orange, VA
22960
Tel.: (540) 672-1111
Web Site: http://www.piedmontpower.com
New & Used Agricultural Equipment Dealer
N.A.I.C.S.: 532490

PIER 1 IMPORTS, INC.

100 Pier 1 Pl, Fort Worth, TX 76102
Tel.: (817) 252-8000   **DE**
Web Site: http://www.pier1.com
Year Founded: 1962
PIR—(NYSE)
Rev.: $1,552,938,000
Assets: $656,290,000
Liabilities: $566,761,000
Net Worth: $89,529,000
Earnings: ($198,833,000)
Emp.: 4,000
Fiscal Year-end: 03/02/19
Decorative Home Furnishings & Furniture Direct Import & Sales
N.A.I.C.S.: 449110
Daila D. Ramirez *(Principal Acctg Officer)*
William H. Savage *(Chief Supply Chain Officer & Exec VP)*
Donna Noce Colaco *(Pres & Chief Customer Officer)*
Lance Wills *(CIO & Exec VP)*
Christine C. Murray *(Chief HR Officer & Exec VP-HR)*
Robert E. Bostrom *(Chief Legal & Compliance Officer, Sec & Exec VP)*
Robert James Riesbeck *(CEO & CFO)*

Subsidiaries:

Pier 1 Imports (U.S.), Inc.   **(1)**

100 Pier 1 Pl, Fort Worth, TX
76102-2600   **(100%)**
Tel.: (817) 252-8000
Web Site: http://www.pier1.com
Sales Range: $300-349.9 Million
Emp.: 900
Direct Importer & Retailer of Decorative
Home Furnishings & Furniture
N.A.I.C.S.: 449129

Pier 1 Services Company   **(1)**
100 Pier 1 Pl, Fort Worth, TX 76102
Tel.: (817) 878-8000
Web Site: http://www.pier1.com
Interior Design Services
N.A.I.C.S.: 541410

PIERIS PHARMACEUTICALS, INC.

225 Franklin St Fl 26, Boston, MA
02110
Tel.: (857) 246-8998   **NV**
Web Site: https://www.pieris.com
Year Founded: 2013
PIRS—(NASDAQ)
Rev.: $25,902,000
Assets: $95,490,000
Liabilities: $67,561,000
Net Worth: $27,929,000
Earnings: ($33,277,000)
Emp.: 127
Fiscal Year-end: 12/31/22
Pharmaceuticals Mfr
N.A.I.C.S.: 325412
Stephen S. Yoder *(Pres & CEO)*
Shane Olwill *(Sr VP & Head-Translational Science)*
Hitto Kaufmann *(Chief Scientific Officer & Sr VP)*
Thomas Bures *(CFO & Sr VP)*
James A. Geraghty *(Chm)*

Subsidiaries:

Pieris Australia Pty Limited   **(1)**
1/12 Tierney Place, Tweed Heads, 2486,
NSW, Australia
Tel.: (61) 755361052
Web Site: https://www.pieris.com.au
Pharmaceutical Products Distr
N.A.I.C.S.: 424210

Pieris Pharmaceuticals GmbH   **(1)**
Zeppelinstrasse 3, 85399, Hallbergmoos,
Germany
Tel: (49) 811124470
Pharmaceutical Products Distr
N.A.I.C.S.: 424210
Eckhard Niemeier *(VP)*

PIMCO CA MUNI INCOME FUND II

1633 Broadway, New York, NY 10019
Tel.: (212) 739-4000   **MA**
PCK—(NYSE)
Rev.: $21,522
Assets: $528,155
Liabilities: $240,017
Net Worth: $288,138
Earnings: $15,885
Fiscal Year-end: 12/31/19
Investment Management Service
N.A.I.C.S.: 525990

PIMCO CORPORATE & IN- COME OPPORTUNITY FUND

1633 Broadway, New York, NY 10019
Tel.: (212) 739-4000   **MA**
PTY—(NYSE)
Rev.: $133,427,000
Assets: $1,885,281,000
Liabilities: $381,398,000
Net Worth: $1,503,883,000
Earnings: $33,475,000
Fiscal Year-end: 07/31/19
Investment Management Service
N.A.I.C.S.: 525990

PIMCO CORPORATE & IN- COME STRATEGY FUND

1633 Broadway, New York, NY 10019
Tel.: (212) 739-4000   **MA**
PCN—(NYSE)
Rev.: $57,330,000
Assets: $798,324,000
Liabilities: $182,868,000
Net Worth: $615,456,000
Earnings: $48,079,000
Fiscal Year-end: 07/31/19
Investment Management Service
N.A.I.C.S.: 525990

PIMCO DYNAMIC INCOME FUND

1633 Broadway, New York, NY 10019
Tel.: (212) 739-4000   **MA**
Web Site: http://www.pimco.com
PDI—(NYSE)
Sales Range: $150-199.9 Million
Investment Services
N.A.I.C.S.: 523999

PIMCO GLOBAL STOCK- SPLUS & INCOME FUND

1633 Broadway, New York, NY 10019
Tel.: (212) 739-4000   **MA**
PGP—(NYSE)
Rev.: $14,859,000
Assets: $273,903,000
Liabilities: $166,341,000
Net Worth: $107,562,000
Earnings: $12,052,000
Fiscal Year-end: 06/30/19
Investment Management Service
N.A.I.C.S.: 525990

PIMCO INCOME OPPORTU- NITY FUND

1633 Broadway, New York, NY 10019
PKO—(NYSE)
Rev.: $42,587,000
Assets: $627,451,000
Liabilities: $217,374,000
Net Worth: $410,077,000
Earnings: $31,333,000
Fiscal Year-end: 06/30/19
Investment Management Service
N.A.I.C.S.: 525990
Daniel J. Ivascyn *(Mgr-Fund)*

PIMCO INCOME STRATEGY FUND II

1633 Broadway, New York, NY 10019
Tel.: (212) 739-4000   **MA**
PFN—(NYSE)
Rev.: $60,843,000
Assets: $874,680,000
Liabilities: $154,328,000
Net Worth: $720,352,000
Earnings: $50,953,000
Fiscal Year-end: 07/31/19
Investment Management Service
N.A.I.C.S.: 525990

PIMCO MORTGAGE INCOME TRUST INC.

650 Newport Center Dr, Newport
Beach, CA 92660
Tel.: (949) 720-6000
PMTG—(NYSE)
Real Estate Investment Services
N.A.I.C.S.: 531210
Casey Newell *(CEO)*

PIMCO MUNICIPAL INCOME FUND II

1633 Broadway, New York, NY 10019
Tel.: (212) 739-4000   **MA**
PML—(NYSE)
Rev.: $63,541,000
Assets: $1,497,163,000
Liabilities: $416,206,000
Net Worth: $1,080,957,000
Earnings: $47,818,000
Fiscal Year-end: 12/31/19
Investment Management Service

N.A.I.C.S.: 525990

PIMCO NEW YORK MUNICIPAL INCOME FUND

1633 Broadway, New York, NY 10019
Tel.: (212) 739-4000 **MA**
PNF—(NYSE)
Rev.: $71,067,000
Assets: $181,118,000
Liabilities: $45,083,000
Net Worth: $136,035,000
Earnings: $5,332,000
Fiscal Year-end: 12/31/19
Investment Management Service
N.A.I.C.S.: 525990

PIMCO NEW YORK MUNICIPAL INCOME FUND III

1633 Broadway, New York, NY 10019
Tel.: (212) 739-4000 **MA**
PYN—(NYSE)
Rev.: $9,814,000
Assets: $246,914,000
Liabilities: $59,318,000
Net Worth: $187,596,000
Earnings: $882,000
Fiscal Year-end: 12/31/19
Investment Management Service
N.A.I.C.S.: 525990
Deborah A. DeCotis (Chm)

PINE ISLAND ACQUISITION CORP.

2455 E Sunrise Blvd Ste 1205, Fort Lauderdale, FL 33304
Tel.: (954) 526-4865 **DE**
Year Founded: 2020
PIPP—(NYSE)
Investment Services
N.A.I.C.S.: 523999
John A. Thain (Chm)
Philip A. Cooper (CEO)
Charles G. Bridge Jr. (CFO & Sec)

PINE TECHNOLOGY ACQUISITION CORP.

260 Lena Dr, Aurora, OH 44202
Tel.: (212) 402-8216 **DE**
Year Founded: 2020
PTOC—(NASDAQ)
Rev.: $647,416
Assets: $345,734,458
Liabilities: $381,033,826
Net Worth: ($35,299,368)
Earnings: ($1,661,915)
Emp.: 2
Fiscal Year-end: 12/31/21
Investment Services
N.A.I.C.S.: 523999
Christopher Longo (Co-Founder & CEO)
Robert Schwarz (CFO, Treas & Sec)
Adam Karkowsky (Co-Founder)

PINEAPPLE ENERGY INC.

10900 Red Cir Dr, Minnetonka, MN 55343
Tel.: (952) 996-1674 **MN**
Web Site:
https://www.pineappleenergy.com
Year Founded: 1969
PEGY—(NASDAQ)
Rev.: $27,522,099
Assets: $74,695,487
Liabilities: $47,473,195
Net Worth: $27,222,292
Earnings: ($10,352,240)
Emp.: 255
Fiscal Year-end: 12/31/22
Renewable Energy Semiconductor Mfr
N.A.I.C.S.: 221114
Roger H. D. Lacey (Chm & Exec Chm)
Scott Maskin (Interim CEO)

Kristin A. Hlavka (Principal Acctg Officer & Controller)
Kyle Udseth (Founder)

Subsidiaries:

Suttle Apparatus Corporation **(1)**
1001 E Hwy 212, Hector, MN 55342
Tel.: (320) 848-6711
Web Site: http://www.suttlesolutions.com
Emp.: 100
Telecommunications Equipment Mfr
N.A.I.C.S.: 334210

Suttle, Inc. **(1)**
1001 E Hwy 212, Hector, MN 55342
Tel.: (320) 848-6711
Broadband Network Services
N.A.I.C.S.: 517111

Transition Networks **(1)**
10900 Red Cir Dr, Minnetonka, MN 55343 **(100%)**
Tel.: (952) 941-7600
Web Site: http://www.transition.com
Sales Range: $25-49.9 Million
Emp.: 106
Distr Hardware-Based Connectivity Solutions
N.A.I.C.S.: 334118
Anita Kumar (Gen Mgr)

PINEAPPLE, INC.

12301 Wilshire Blvd Ste 302, Los Angeles, CA 90025 **NV**
Web Site:
https://www.pineappleinc.com
Year Founded: 1983
PNPL—(OTCIQ)
Assets: $2,358
Liabilities: $1,376,972
Net Worth: ($1,374,614)
Earnings: ($7,856,392)
Fiscal Year-end: 12/31/22
Management Consulting Services
N.A.I.C.S.: 541618
Shawn Credle (CEO)
Matthew Feinstein (Founder)

PINNACLE BANCSHARES, INC.

1811 2nd Ave, Jasper, AL 35501
Tel.: (205) 221-4111 **AL**
Web Site:
https://www.pinnaclebanc.com
Year Founded: 1935
PCLB—(OTCIQ)
Sales Range: $1-9.9 Million
Emp.: 82
Bank Holding Company
N.A.I.C.S.: 551111
Mary Jo Gunter (Sec & VP)
Robert B. Nolen Jr. (Pres & CEO)
Joe B. Adams (Treas)
Robbin Reed Allen (Chm)

Subsidiaries:

Pinnacle Bank **(1)**
1811 2nd Ave, Jasper, AL 35501 **(100%)**
Tel.: (205) 221-4111
Web Site: http://www.pinnaclebanc.com
Sales Range: $50-74.9 Million
Emp.: 150
Retail & Commercial Banking
N.A.I.C.S.: 522110
Mary Jo Gunter (Sec & Sr VP-Banking Svcs)
James W. Cannon (Chm)
Edward A. Davidson (Reg Pres)
Robert B. Nolen Jr. (Pres & CEO)

PINNACLE BANK

7597 Monterey St, Gilroy, CA 95020
Tel.: (408) 842-8200
Web Site: https://www.pinnacle.bank
Year Founded: 2006
PBNK—(OTCIQ)
Rev.: $2,786,621,000
Assets: $47,959,883,000
Liabilities: $41,924,095,000
Net Worth: $6,035,788,000

Earnings: $562,152,000
Emp.: 3,357
Fiscal Year-end: 12/31/23
Commercial Banking Services
N.A.I.C.S.: 522110
Susan K. Black (Chm)
Bruce H. Kendall (CFO & Exec VP)
Denise Brown (Chief Admin Officer & Exec VP)
Jessica Chavez (Chief Risk Officer & Exec VP)
Allen R. Greco (Vice Chm)
Harvey L. Blodgett (Officer-Lending & Exec VP)
Cliff Dennett (Chief Credit Officer)
Anthony Marandos (Reg Pres & Exec VP)
Doug Moffat (Reg Pres & Exec VP)
Michael Khan (Exec VP)
Jeffrey Johnson (Exec VP-Capital Fin Grp)
Kevin O'Hare (Exec VP)
Kimberly Raynal (Exec VP-Ops Admin)
Joe Servi (Sr VP & Sr Mgr-Relationship)
Jeffrey D. Payne (Pres, CEO & Member-Mgmt Bd)

PINNACLE BANK OF OREGON

8880 SW Nimbus Ave Ste D, Beaverton, OR 97008
Tel.: (503) 644-3000
PNNB—(OTCIQ)
Banking Services
N.A.I.C.S.: 522110
Ronald A. May (CEO)

PINNACLE BANKSHARES CORP.

622 Broad St, Altavista, VA 24517-1830
Tel.: (434) 369-3000 **VA**
Web Site: http://www.1stnatbk.com
Year Founded: 1997
PPBN—(OTCQX)
Rev.: $29,460,000
Assets: $860,514,000
Liabilities: $802,184,000
Net Worth: $58,330,000
Earnings: $3,062,000
Emp.: 187
Fiscal Year-end: 12/31/20
Bank Holding Company
N.A.I.C.S.: 551111
Donald W. Merricks (Vice Chm)
Bryan M. Lemley (CFO, Treas & Sec)
James E. Burton IV (Chm)
Aubrey H. Hall III (Pres & CEO)

Subsidiaries:

First National Bank of Altavista **(1)**
622 Broad St, Altavista, VA 24517
Tel.: (434) 369-3000
Web Site: http://www.1stnatbk.com
Sales Range: $25-49.9 Million
Emp.: 100
National Commercial Banks
N.A.I.C.S.: 522110
Timothy W. Holt (Chief Credit Officer & Sr VP)
Judith A. Clements (Chief HR Officer & Exec VP)
Vivian S. Brown (Chief Retail Officer & Exec VP)
Allison Daniels (COO & Exec VP)
Donald W. Merricks (Vice Chm)
Thomas R. Burnett Jr. (Chief Lending Officer & Exec VP)

PINNACLE FINANCIAL PARTNERS, INC.

150 3rd Ave S Ste 900, Nashville, TN 37201
Tel.: (615) 744-3700 **TN**
Web Site: https://www.pnfp.com
Year Founded: 2000

PNFP—(NASDAQ)
Rev.: $1,695,371,000
Assets: $47,959,883,000
Liabilities: $41,924,095,000
Net Worth: $6,035,788,000
Earnings: $546,960,000
Emp.: 3,357
Fiscal Year-end: 12/31/23
Bank Holding Company
N.A.I.C.S.: 551111
M. Terry Turner (Co-Founder, Pres & CEO)
Harold R. Carpenter (CFO)
Hugh M. Queener (Chief Admin Officer & Exec VP)
Patti Harris (Sr VP & Mgr-HR)
Mac Johnston (Chief Investment Officer)
Mike Hendren (Officer-Credit & Sr VP)
Randy Withrow (CIO & Sr VP)
Richard D. Callicutt II (Chm-Carolinas & Virginia)
Jerry Hampton (Exec VP)
Kim Jenny (Officer-Risk & Performance Mgmt & Exec VP)
M. Glenn Layne (Officer-Credit-Rutherford & Sr VP)
Gary Collier (Exec VP & Mgr-Pinnacle Asset Mgmt)
Mike Hammontree (Dir-Corp Svcs)
Karen Hargis (Sr VP & Mgr-Client Svcs Area)
Tim Huestis (Chief Credit Officer)
Dan Stubblefield (Sr VP & Controller)
Larry Whisenant (Sr VP & Mgr-Client Svcs)
Roger Osborne (Pres/CEO-PNFP Capital Markets)
Rick Arthur (Exec VP-Consumer & Small Bus)
Edwin Andrew Moats (Exec VP & Dir-Music, Sports & Entertainment)
Summer Yeiser (Sr VP & Mgr-Learning & Dev)
Heather Matkins (Mgr-Greensboro Area)
Linda Seiber (Mgr-Banking Ops)
David Willingham (Mgr-Client Advisory-Area)
Susan Rogers Apple (Mgr-Client Svcs-Central North Carolina Area)
Gerry Barber (Sr VP & Dir-Client Svc Center)
Rob Ellenburg (Pres-Charlotte)
Paul Neil (Officer-Credit)
Randy Nicely (Mgr-Client Svcs-Virginia Western Reg)
Rob Garcia (Pres-Atlanta)
Kent Cleaver (Exec VP)
Katie Elder (Mgr-Client Svcs-Southern North Carolina)
Mary Schneider (Chief Compliance Officer)
Michelle Sweeney (Mgr-Pur & Properties)
Greg Winkler (Mgr-Comml Banking Team)
Brian Gilbert (Sr VP & Mgr-Asset Liability)
Connie Arrington (Mgr-ACH Program-Corp Svcs)
Sammy Ballesteros (Exec VP & Mgr-Special Assets Grp)
Sam Belk (Officer-Lending)
Tim Bewley (Sr VP)
Mary Beth Brackman (Mgr-Client Svc Center)
Keith Davis (Mgr-Trust & Investments Svcs)
Sarah Sanders Teague (Officer-Credit)
Beth Hobbs (Mgr-Credit Svcs Process)
David Hoppenworth (Dir-SBA Lending)

Pinnacle Financial Partners, Inc.—(Continued)

Carla Jarrell *(Officer-Community Dev)*
Morgan Lyons *(Mng Dir-Loan Syndications)*
Tim McAuley *(Mgr-Small Bus Lending)*
LeeAnn McCoy-Tomlin *(Mgr-Client Svc Center)*
Andy Moats *(Exec VP & Dir-Music, Sports & Entertainment)*
Anne Rolman *(Mgr-Treasury Mgmt Svcs)*
Erik Sanford *(Mgr-Credit Svcs)*
Gary Shaffer *(Mgr-Loan Svcs)*
Linda Stewart *(Mgr-Consumer Underwriting)*
Steve Swain *(Sr VP & Mgr-Community Lending)*
Maria Trapp *(Mgr-Loan Svcs)*
Ted Simpson *(Officer-Credit-Memphis)*
Ted Simpson *(Officer-Credit-Memphis)*

Subsidiaries:

Advocate Capital, Inc. **(1)**
1 Vantage Way Ste C-200, Nashville, TN 37228
Tel.: (615) 377-6872
Web Site: https://www.advocatecapital.com
Litigation Funding Services
N.A.I.C.S.: 524292
Paul B. Myers *(Chief Credit Officer)*
Donna A. Jones *(Pres, Sr VP & Dir-Assoc & Client Experience)*
Tina R. Burns *(VP)*
Mary K. Berst *(COO)*
Jim Pacelli *(VP-Strategic Solutions)*
Todd Jackson *(VP)*
Rachel Minyard *(VP-Marketing)*

Pinnacle Bank **(1)**
150 3Rd Ave S Ste 900, Nashville, TN 37201 **(100%)**
Tel.: (615) 744-3700
Web Site: http://www.pnfp.com
Sales Range: $450-499.9 Million
Commericial Banking
N.A.I.C.S.: 522110
M. Terry Turner *(Founder, Pres & CEO)*
Harold R. Carpenter *(CFO)*
Richard D. Callicutt II *(Chm-Carolinas & Virginia)*

Subsidiary (Domestic):

HPB Insurance Group, Inc. **(2)**
801 N Elm St, High Point, NC 27262
Tel.: (336) 881-3500
Web Site: https://www.hpbinsurance.com
General Insurance Services
N.A.I.C.S.: 524210

Miller & Loughry, Inc. **(2)**
214 W College St, Murfreesboro, TN 37133-7001
Tel.: (615) 896-9292
Web Site: http://www.mlbins.com
Sales Range: $25-49.9 Million
Emp.: 35
Insurance Agencies & Brokerage Services
N.A.I.C.S.: 524210

PINNACLE WEST CAPITAL CORPORATION
400 N 5th St, Phoenix, AZ 85004
Tel.: (602) 371-7171 **AZ**
Web Site:
https://www.pinnaclewest.com
Year Founded: 1985
PNW—(NYSE)
Rev.: $4,695,991,000
Assets: $24,661,153,000
Liabilities: $18,376,291,000
Net Worth: $6,284,862,001
Earnings: $501,557,000
Emp.: 81
Fiscal Year-end: 12/31/23
Holding Company; Producer & Distr of Electricity & Energy-Related Products & Services to Retail & Wholesale Customers

N.A.I.C.S.: 551112
Elizabeth A. Blankenship *(Chief Acctg Officer, VP & Controller)*
Jeffrey B. Guldner *(Chm, Pres & CEO)*
Robert S. Aiken *(VP-Federal Affairs)*
Shirley Baum *(VP)*
James R. Hatfield *(Chief Admin Officer & Exec VP)*
James R. Hatfield *(Chief Admin Officer & Exec VP)*

Subsidiaries:

Arizona Public Service Company **(1)**
400 N 5th St, Phoenix, AZ 85072-3999 **(100%)**
Tel.: (602) 371-3614
Web Site: https://www.aps.com
Rev.: $4,324,384,000
Assets: $22,543,852,000
Liabilities: $15,490,897,000
Net Worth: $7,052,955,000
Earnings: $524,929,000
Emp.: 5,861
Fiscal Year-end: 12/31/2022
Generator & Electricity Supplier
N.A.I.C.S.: 237130
Theodore N. Geisler *(CFO & Sr VP)*
Jeffrey B. Guldner *(Chm & CEO)*
Elizabeth A. Blankenship *(Chief Acctg Officer, VP & Controller)*

El Dorado Investment Company **(1)**
400 N Fifth St, Phoenix, AZ 85004-2223 **(100%)**
Tel.: (602) 250-1000
Rev.: $940,000
Emp.: 2
National Venture Capital Firm
N.A.I.C.S.: 523910

Subsidiary (Domestic):

Arizona Professional Baseball Ltd Partnership **(2)**
401 E Jefferson St, Phoenix, AZ 85004
Tel.: (602) 462-6500
Sales Range: $100-124.9 Million
Professional Baseball Club
N.A.I.C.S.: 711211

Zolo Technologies **(2)**
4946 N 63rd St, Boulder, CO 80301
Tel.: (303) 604-5800
Web Site: http://www.zolotech.com
Laser Based Sensors Mfr
N.A.I.C.S.: 334513
John L. Skolds *(Chm)*

Highland Water Company, Inc. **(1)**
1127 Stockmens Rd, Ash Fork, AZ 86320
Tel.: (928) 699-4344
Container Trucking Services
N.A.I.C.S.: 484121

Rancho Viejo Properties **(1)**
26 Calle Ancla, Santa Fe, NM 87508
Tel.: (505) 473-7700
Web Site: https://www.ranchoviejo.com
Sales Range: $25-49.9 Million
Emp.: 6
Residential Building Construction Services
N.A.I.C.S.: 531110
Peter Kempf *(Dir-Sls & Mktg)*

Sedona Golf Resort LC **(1)**
35 Rdg Trl Dr, Sedona, AZ 86351
Tel.: (928) 284-9355
Web Site: https://www.sedonagolfresort.com
Golf Course & Club Management Services
N.A.I.C.S.: 713910
Jeremy Hayman *(Gen Mgr)*
Kathy Harmon *(Mgr-Mdse)*
Micah Filice *(Head-Golf Professional)*
Katie Cook *(Dir-Food, Beverage & Events)*

StoneRidge - Prescott Valley LLC **(1)**
1300 Stoneridge Dr, Prescott Valley, AZ 86314
Tel.: (928) 759-0048
Web Site: https://www.stoneridgeaz.com
Emp.: 25
Residential Building Rental & Leasing Services
N.A.I.C.S.: 531110

Subsidiary (Domestic):

StoneRidge Golf Course, LLC **(2)**

1601 N Bluff Top Dr, Prescott Valley, AZ 86314
Tel.: (928) 772-6500
Web Site: https://www.stoneridgegolf.com
Golf Course & Club Management Services
N.A.I.C.S.: 713910

SunRidge Canyon, LLC **(1)**
13100 N SunRidge Dr, Fountain Hills, AZ 85268
Tel.: (480) 837-5100
Web Site: http://www.sunridgegolf.com
Golf Course & Club Management Services
N.A.I.C.S.: 713910
Kris Starr *(Dir-Ops)*
Wes Neal *(Head-Golf Pro)*

PINTEREST, INC.
651 Brannan St, San Francisco, CA 94107
Tel.: (415) 762-7100 **DE**
Web Site: https://www.pinterest.com
Year Founded: 2008
PINS—(NYSE)
Rev.: $3,055,071,000
Assets: $3,594,405,000
Liabilities: $503,725,000
Net Worth: $3,090,680,000
Earnings: ($35,610,000)
Emp.: 4,014
Fiscal Year-end: 12/31/23
Online Content Sharing Application Developer
N.A.I.C.S.: 513210
Benjamin Silbermann *(Co-Founder)*
Julia Brau Donnelly *(CFO)*
Jon Kaplan *(Head)*
Jeremy King *(Sr VP & Head-Engrg)*
Aya Kanai *(Head-Content)*
Celestine Maddy *(Head)*
Waleed Ojeil *(Head)*
Malik Ducard *(Chief Content Officer)*
Nichole Barnes Marshall *(Head-Inclusion & Diversity-Global)*
Christine Deputy *(Chief People Officer)*
Bill Ready *(CEO)*
Bill Watkins *(Chief Revenue Officer)*
Paul Sciarra *(Co-Founder)*
Sabrina Ellis *(Chief Product Officer)*

PIONEER BANCORP, INC.
652 Albany Shaker Rd, Albany, NY 12211
Tel.: (518) 730-3025 **MD**
Web Site: https://www.pioneerny.com
Year Founded: 2019
PBFS—(NASDAQ)
Rev.: $104,646,000
Assets: $1,895,404,000
Liabilities: $1,598,876,000
Net Worth: $296,528,000
Earnings: $15,260,000
Emp.: 253
Fiscal Year-end: 06/30/24
Bank Holding Company
N.A.I.C.S.: 551111
Madeline D. Taylor *(Chm)*
Patrick J. Hughes *(CFO & Exec VP)*
Robert J. Nichols *(Chief Credit Officer & Exec VP)*
Thomas Signor *(Pres, Chief Admin Officer, Chief HR Officer, Sec & Exec VP)*

PIONEER BANKCORP, INC.
652 Albany Shaker Rd, Albany, NY 12211
Tel.: (518) 730-3025 **MD**
Web Site:
https://investors.pioneerny.com
Year Founded: 1922
PBKC—(OTCIQ)
Bank Holding Company
N.A.I.C.S.: 551111
Tom Amell *(Pres & CEO)*
Kelli Arnold *(Chief Strategy Officer, Chief Innovations Officer & Exec VP)*

Susan M. Hollister *(Chief HR Officer, Sec & Exec VP)*
Patrick J. Hughes *(CFO & Exec VP)*
James Murphy *(Chief Credit Officer & Exec VP)*
Thomas Signor *(Chief Admin Officer & Exec VP)*
Jesse A. Tomczak *(Chief Banking Officer & Exec VP)*

Subsidiaries:

First Bank **(1)**
300 E Sugarland Hwy, Clewiston, FL 33440
Tel.: (863) 983-3003
Web Site: http://www.first1bank.com
Rev.: $1,806,000
Emp.: 6
Commercial Banking
N.A.I.C.S.: 522110
Kim Abowd *(VP-BSA & Deposit Compliance)*
Deborah Van Sickle *(Chief Lending Officer, Officer-Lending Compliance & Sr VP)*
Susan Hill *(VP & Asst Mgr)*

PIONEER BANKSHARES, INC.
Tel.: (540) 778-2294 **VA**
Web Site:
https://www.pioneerbks.com
Year Founded: 1983
PNBI—(OTCIQ)
Bank Holding Company
N.A.I.C.S.: 551111
Mark N. Reed *(Pres & CEO)*
Loretta Lancaster *(Vice Pres & CIO)*
Melissa Campbell *(Vice Pres & Chief Admin Officer)*
Timothy Cash *(Vice Pres & Mgr-Bus Banking Acct)*
Michael Kane *(Vice Pres-Retail Banking & Bus Devt)*
Reid Young *(Sr VP-Comml Lending)*

Subsidiaries:

Pioneer Bank **(1)**
252 E Main St, Stanley, VA 22851
Tel.: (540) 778-2294
Web Site: http://www.pioneerbks.com
Sales Range: $10-24.9 Million
Emp.: 30
Commericial Banking
N.A.I.C.S.: 522110
Lori Hassott *(CFO & VP)*
Betty Purdham *(Sr VP-Lending)*

PIONEER DIVERSIFIED HIGH INCOME FUND, INC
60 State St, Boston, MA 02109
Tel.: (617) 742-7825 **MD**
HNW—(NYSEAMEX)
Rev.: $14,101,367
Assets: $200,629,479
Liabilities: $65,776,232
Net Worth: $134,853,247
Earnings: $10,073,684
Fiscal Year-end: 04/30/19
Investment Management Service
N.A.I.C.S.: 525990

PIONEER FLOATING RATE FUND, INC
60 State St 5th Fl, Boston, MA 02109
Tel.: (617) 742-7825 **MD**
PHD—(NYSE)
Rev.: $26,577,952
Assets: $461,715,070
Liabilities: $168,984,786
Net Worth: $292,730,284
Earnings: $17,994,475
Fiscal Year-end: 11/30/19
Investment Management Service
N.A.I.C.S.: 525990

PIONEER HIGH INCOME FUND, INC.

60 State St 5th Fl, Boston, MA 02109
Tel.: (617) 742-7825   MD
PHT—(NYSE)
Rev.: $30,372,952
Assets: $314,032,083
Liabilities: $102,170,705
Net Worth: $211,861,378
Earnings: $23,595,916
Fiscal Year-end: 03/31/20
Investment Management Service
N.A.I.C.S.: 525990

PIONEER MERGER CORP.
660 Madison Ave, New York, NY 10065
Tel.: (212) 803-9080   Ky
Year Founded: 2020
PACXU—(NASDAQ)
Investment Holding Company
N.A.I.C.S.: 551112
Jonathan N. Christodoro (Chm)
Rick Gerson (Co-Pres)
Oscar Salazar (Co-Pres)
Ryan Khoury (CEO)
Scott Carpenter (COO)
Matthew Corey (CFO)

PIONEER MUNICIPAL HIGH INCOME ADVANTAGE FUND, INC.
60 State St 5th Fl, Boston, MA 02109
Tel.: (617) 742-7825   MD
MAV—(NYSE)
Rev.: $19,239,061
Assets: $441,793,480
Liabilities: $160,421,474
Net Worth: $281,372,006
Earnings: $11,800,855
Fiscal Year-end: 03/31/20
Investment Management Service
N.A.I.C.S.: 525990

PIONEER MUNICIPAL HIGH INCOME FUND, INC.
60 State St 5th Fl, Boston, MA 02109
Tel.: (617) 742-7825   MD
MHI—(NYSE)
Rev.: $19,681,469
Assets: $413,407,115
Liabilities: $444,177
Net Worth: $412,962,938
Earnings: $16,757,405
Fiscal Year-end: 04/30/19
Investment Management Service
N.A.I.C.S.: 525990

PIONEER NATURAL RE-SOURCES COMPANY
777 Hidden Rdg, Irving, TX 75038
Tel.: (972) 444-9001   DE
Web Site: https://www.pxd.com
Year Founded: 1962
PXD—(NYSE)
Rev.: $19,362,000,000
Assets: $36,613,000,000
Liabilities: $13,442,000,000
Net Worth: $23,171,000,000
Earnings: $4,894,000,000
Emp.: 2,213
Fiscal Year-end: 12/31/23
Natural Gas Producer, Developer & Explorer
N.A.I.C.S.: 211130
Scott Douglas Sheffield (Founder)
Mark S. Berg (Exec VP-Corporate Ops)
Mark H. Kleinman (Gen Counsel & Exec VP)
James Kenneth Thompson (Chm)
John C. Distaso (Sr VP-Mktg)
Elizabeth A. McDonald (Sr VP-Strategic Plng, Field Dev & Mktg)
Thaddeus J. Owens (VP-Comm & Govt Rels)
Tom Fitter (Supvr-IR)
Bonnie S. Black (VP-Tech & Ops)

Craig Kuiper (VP-Production Ops)
Tyson Taylor (VP-HR)
Gerardo Torres (VP-Permian Completions)
Richard P. Dealy (CEO)
Christopher L. Washburn (Chief Acctg Officer & VP)
Tyson L. Taylor (Sr VP)
Akshar Patel (Sec)
Jerome D. Hall Jr. (Exec VP-Ops)

Subsidiaries:

Pioneer Natural Resources Tunisia Ltd.   (1)
La Residence Lakeo - 3rd Fl Rue Du Lac Michigan, Tunis, 1053, Tunisia
Tel.: (216) 71960885
Web Site: http://www.pioneer.com
Sales Range: $25-49.9 Million
Emp.: 30
Natural Gas Producer, Developer & Explorer
N.A.I.C.S.: 211130

Pioneer Natural Resources USA, Inc.   (1)
5205 N O'Connor Blvd Ste 200, Irving, TX 75039
Tel.: (432) 571-5010
Web Site: https://www.pxd.com
Oil & Gas Operations
N.A.I.C.S.: 213112

Pioneer PE Holding LLC   (1)
303 Colorado St Ste 3000, Austin, TX 78701
Tel.: (737) 704-2300
Web Site: http://www.parsleyenergy.com
Rev.: $1,958,814,000
Assets: $9,856,214,000
Liabilities: $3,333,566,000
Net Worth: $6,522,648,000
Earnings: $175,212,000
Emp.: 496
Fiscal Year-end: 12/31/2019
Oil & Gas Exploration
N.A.I.C.S.: 211110
Mark Timmons (VP-Field Ops)
Carrie Endorf (VP-Reservoir Engrg & Plng)
Paul Treadwell (Co-Founder & Sr VP-Production Ops)
Mike Hinson (Co-Founder & Sr VP-Corp Affairs)
Cecilia Camarillo (Sr VP-Acctg)
Stephanie Reed (Sr VP-Corp Dev, Land & Midstream)
Mark Brown (VP-Security & Risk Mgmt)
Kristin McClure (VP-HR)
Jody Jordan (VP-Mktg)
Rob Hembree (VP-IT)
Landon Martin (VP-Drilling & Completions)
Todd Peters (VP-Geoscience)
Kyle Rhodes (VP-IR)

Subsidiary (Domestic):

Jagged Peak Energy Inc.   (2)
1401 Lawrence St Ste 1800, Denver, CO 80202
Tel.: (720) 215-3700
Web Site:
http://www.jaggedpeakenergy.com
Rev.: $581,644,000
Assets: $1,767,141,000
Liabilities: $819,191,000
Net Worth: $947,950,000
Earnings: $165,458,000
Emp.: 94
Fiscal Year-end: 12/31/2018
Oil & Gas Field Development Services
N.A.I.C.S.: 213112
Joseph N. Jaggers (Founder)
Robert W. Howard (CFO & Exec VP)
Shonn D. Stahlecker (Controller)
Craig R. Walters (COO & Exec VP)
Ian T. Piper (VP-Fin & Corp Plng)
David F. Eckelberger (VP-Land)
Nathan P. Leonard (VP-Ops)

Parsley Energy Management, LLC   (2)
303 Colorado St Ste 3003, Austin, TX 78701
Tel.: (737) 704-2300
Crude Oil Merchant Whslr
N.A.I.C.S.: 424720
Jeffery Boggs (Sr Mgr-Drilling Engrg)

Parsley Energy Operations, LLC   (2)
550 W Texas Ave Ste 2, Midland, TX 79701
Tel.: (432) 818-2100
Web Site: https://www.parsleyenergy.com
Emp.: 200
Oil & Gas Field Operating Services
N.A.I.C.S.: 213112

Parsley Energy, LLC   (2)
500 W Texas Ave Ste 200, Midland, TX 79701
Tel.: (432) 818-2100
Oil Well Drilling Services
N.A.I.C.S.: 213111
Ryan Dalton (CFO & Exec VP)

Parsley Finance Corp.   (2)
303 Colorado St Ste 3003, Austin, TX 78701
Tel.: (737) 704-2300
Financial Services
N.A.I.C.S.: 541611

Premier Silica LLC   (1)
5205 N O'Connor Blvd Ste 200, Irving, TX 75039-3746
Tel.: (972) 444-9001
Web Site: http://www.premiersilica.com
Construction Materials Merchant Whslrning
N.A.I.C.S.: 423610
Dennis Dronzek (Pres)

Sendero Drilling Company, LLC   (1)
14 E Beauregard Ave, San Angelo, TX 76903
Tel.: (325) 655-7641
Web Site: https://www.senderodrilling.com
Emp.: 150
Oil Field Drilling Services
N.A.I.C.S.: 213112
Michael Benetich (Mgr-Ops)
Kirk Cleere (Pres)
Joey Davis (CFO)
Stacy Johnson (Chief Acctg Officer)
Valerie Canada (Mgr-HR)
Dennis Cobb (Dir-Safety)

PIONEER OIL & GAS
1206 W S Jordan Pkwy Unit B, South Jordan, UT 84095-5512
Tel.: (801) 566-3000   UT
Web Site: https://www.piol.com
POGS—(OTCIQ)
Oil & Gas Exploration Services
N.A.I.C.S.: 213112
Don A. Colton (Pres)

PIONEER POWER SOLU-TIONS, INC.
1 Parker Plz 400 Kelby St 12th Fl, Fort Lee, NJ 07024
Tel.: (212) 867-0700   NV
Web Site:
https://www.pioneerpowersolutions.com
Year Founded: 1995
PPSI—(NASDAQ)
Rev.: $41,493,000
Assets: $33,022,000
Liabilities: $18,804,000
Net Worth: $14,218,000
Earnings: ($1,898,000)
Emp.: 143
Fiscal Year-end: 12/31/23
Electronic Transformers & Wind Turbines Mfr
N.A.I.C.S.: 334416
Nathan J. Mazurek (Chm, Pres & CEO)
Walter Michalec (CFO, Treas & Sec)

Subsidiaries:

Titan Energy Systems Inc.   (1)
9210 Wyoming Ave N Ste 250, Minneapolis, MN 55445
Tel.: (952) 960-2371
Web Site:
https://www.pioneercriticalpower.com
Electric Equipment Mfr
N.A.I.C.S.: 423610
Richard Guerrero (Mgr-Equipment Sls & Svc)

PIPER SANDLER COMPANIES
800 Nicollet Mall Ste 900, Minneapolis, MN 55402
Tel.: (612) 303-6000   DE
Web Site:
https://www.pipersandler.com
Year Founded: 1895
PIPR—(NYSE)
Rev.: $1,435,118,000
Assets: $2,181,557,000
Liabilities: $927,529,000
Net Worth: $1,254,028,000
Earnings: $101,180,000
Emp.: 1,790
Fiscal Year-end: 12/31/22
Holding Company; Investment Banking & Institutional Securities Firm Services
N.A.I.C.S.: 551112
Thomas P. Schnettler (Vice Chm & Mng Dir-Merchant Banking Grp)
Mark Bradley (Chm-Fin Sponsor Coverage)
Gordon Dean (Vice Chm-Investment Banking)
Jonathan J. Doyle (Vice Chm & Head-Fin Svcs)
Mark F. Stierman (Mng Dir)
Jon W. Salveson (Chm-Healthcare Investment Banking Grp & Vice Chm-Investment Banking)
John Geelan (Mng Dir, Gen Counsel & Sec)
R. Scott LaRue (Vice Chm-Investment Banking)
Chad R. Abraham (Chm & CEO)
Steven Schmidt (Mng Dir -Tech & Head-Tech Investment Banking)
Jarrad Evans (Mng Dir-Hospitality Grp)
Leonard Sheer (Mng Dir & Head-Capital Advisory Grp)
Aamer Naseer (Mng Dir-Healthcare Investment Banking)
Jamie Lockhart (Mng Dir-Healthcare Investment Banking)
Melissa French (Mng Dir-Consumer Investment Banking)
Vincenzo di Nicola (Mng Dir-Healthcare Investment Banking Grp)
Robert A. DeSutter (Mng Dir-Healthcare Investment Banking)
Nick Osborne (Co-Head-Tech Investment Banking)
Peter Phillippi (Mng Dir & Grp Head-Hospitality)
Peter Fish (Mng Dir)
Tom Howland (Mng Dir & Head-Real Estate Investment Banking)
Mike Dillahunt (Co-Head)
Nick Hagen (Head)
John Henningsgard (Co-Head)
Keith Kleven (Co-Head)
Michael Cox (Co-Head)
Jeffrey Moen (Mng Dir)
Matt Morrell (Mng Dir)
Timothy Nasby (Mng Dir)
Wes Olson (Mng Dir)
Matt Patrick (Mng Dir)
Brent M. Rivard (Mng Dir)
Matt Schmitz (Mng Dir)
Amy Steele Gaylord (Mng Dir)
Bradley Wirt (Mng Dir)
Barbara Wolter (Mng Dir)
Bart Federak (Dir)
John Gast (Dir)
Trent Holland (VP)
Debbra L. Schoneman (Pres)
Pam Nightingale (Mng Dir-Investment Banking)

Subsidiaries:

DBO Partners Holding LLC   (1)
1 Embarcadero Ctr Ste 3700, San Francisco, CA 94111
Tel.: (415) 367-6000

Piper Sandler Companies—(Continued)

Web Site: http://www.dbopartners.com
Financial Advisory Services
N.A.I.C.S.: 523940
Kristin F. Gannon *(Partner)*
Bryan Andrzejewski *(Partner)*
Robert Berner *(Partner)*

Edgeview Partners L.P.　　　　**(1)**
201 S College St Ste 2000, Charlotte, NC
28244
Tel.: (704) 602-3900
Web Site: http://www.edgeview.com
Investment Banking & Securities Dealing
N.A.I.C.S.: 523150

Piper Jaffray Companies-Seattle　**(1)**
1420 5th Ave Ste 1425, Seattle, WA 98101
Tel.: (206) 628-5463
Web Site: http://www.seattlenorthwest.com
Sales Range: $50-74.9 Million
Emp.: 88
Financial Services
N.A.I.C.S.: 523150

Piper Jaffray Ltd.　　　　　　**(1)**
88 Wood Street 13th Floor, London, EC2V
7RS, United Kingdom
Tel.: (44) 2077968400
Web Site: http://www.piperjaffray.com
Investment Banking, Equity Research &
Equity Sales & Trading
N.A.I.C.S.: 523150

Subsidiary (Domestic):

**Simmons & Company International
Limited**　　　　　　　　　　　**(2)**
13th Floor 88 Wood Street, London, EC2V
7RS, United Kingdom
Tel.: (44) 2077968400
Web Site: http://www.simmonspjc.com
Investment Banking Services
N.A.I.C.S.: 523150

Piper Sandler & Co.　　　　　**(1)**
800 Nicollet Mall Ste 900, Minneapolis, MN
55402
Tel.: (612) 303-6000
Investment Management Service
N.A.I.C.S.: 523940
James J. Dunne III *(Sr Mng Principal)*
Jonathan J. Doyle *(Sr Mng Principal)*
James J. Dunne III *(Sr Mng Principal)*

Sandler, O'Neill & Partners, L.P.　**(1)**
1251 Avenue of the Americas 6th Fl, New
York, NY 10020
Tel.: (212) 466-7800
Web Site: http://www.sandleroneill.com
Sales Range: $10-24.9 Million
Emp.: 300
Investment Services
N.A.I.C.S.: 523150

Subsidiary (Domestic):

**Sandler O'Neill Mortgage Finance
L.P.**　　　　　　　　　　　　　**(2)**
6363 Poplar Ave Ste 330, Memphis, TN
38119
Tel.: (901) 682-5656
Web Site: http://www.sandleroneill.com
Sales Range: $10-24.9 Million
Emp.: 10
Investment Services
N.A.I.C.S.: 523999

**Simmons & Company
International**　　　　　　　　　**(1)**
700 Louisiana St Ste 1900, Houston, TX
77002
Tel.: (713) 236-9999
Web Site: http://www.simmonspjc.com
Investment Bankers
N.A.I.C.S.: 523150
Frederick W. Charlton *(Chm & Mng Dir-
Energy Investment Banking)*
Michael Beveridge *(Mng Dir)*
Andrew C. Schroeder *(Mng Dir & Co-Head-
Energy Investment Banking)*
Ira H. Green *(Mng Dir & Head-Energy Capi-
tal Markets)*
Paul R. Steier *(Mng Dir)*
Nicholas J. Dalgarno *(Mng Dir)*
James P. Baker *(Mng Dir & Co-Head-
Investment Banking & Capital Markets-
Global)*

Sanjiv Shah *(Mng Dir & Co-Head-Energy
Investment Banking)*
Spencer W. Rippstein *(Mng Dir & Co-Head-
Energy Investment Banking)*
Daniel J. Camper *(Dir-Engrg)*
Spencer English *(Dir)*
Nabeel Siddiqui *(Mng Dir)*
Ross Atkinson *(Dir-Investment Banking)*
Victoria B. Beard *(Dir-Mktg & Bus Dev)*
Tim McEuen *(Dir-Investment Banking)*
Vinu S. Iyengar *(Dir)*
Vijayeta Desai *(VP)*
Ian Falik *(VP)*
Matt Guyton *(VP)*
Ryan Oatman *(VP)*
Billy H. O'Neil *(Mng Dir)*
Terry Padden *(Mng Dir)*
Doug Reynolds *(Mng Dir)*
Chris B. Starr *(VP)*
Robert Urquhart *(Mng Dir)*
William S. Nichols IV *(Dir)*

Simmons Private Equity II, L.P.　**(1)**
22 Waverley Place, Aberdeen, AB10 1XP,
United Kingdom
Tel.: (44) 1224202300
Investment Banking Services
N.A.I.C.S.: 523150

Stamford Partners LLP　　　　**(1)**
First Floor 4 St Paul's Churchyard, London,
EC4M 8AY, United Kingdom
Tel.: (44) 2079079400
Web Site: http://www.stamford-partners.com
Investment Banking & Securities Dealing
Services
N.A.I.C.S.: 523150
Simon Milne *(Partner)*
Damian Thornton *(Partner)*
Alastair Mathieson *(Partner)*
Alison Paul *(Office Mgr)*
Robert Iseman *(Principal)*
James Rogers *(Principal)*

The Valence Group, LLC　　　**(1)**
90 Park Ave 27th Fl, New York, NY 10016
Tel.: (212) 764-8756
Web Site: http://www.valencegroup.com
Financial Investment Activities
N.A.I.C.S.: 523999
Peter Hall *(Co-Founder)*

Weeden & Co., LP　　　　　　**(1)**
145 Mason St, Greenwich, CT 06830
Tel.: (203) 861-7600
Web Site: http://www.weedenco.com
Sales Range: $25-49.9 Million
Emp.: 125
Security Brokers & Dealers
N.A.I.C.S.: 523150
Lance Lonergan *(CEO)*

PITNEY BOWES INC.

3001 Summer St, Stamford, CT
06926
Tel.: (203) 356-5000　　**DE**
Web Site:
　https://www.pitneybowes.com
Year Founded: 1920
PBI—(NYSE)
Rev.: $3,538,042,000
Assets: $4,741,355,000
Liabilities: $4,680,702,000
Net Worth: $60,653,000
Earnings: $36,940,000
Emp.: 11,000
Fiscal Year-end: 12/31/22
Mailing, Shipping, Copying, Commu-
nications Recording & Facsimile Sys-
tems; Item Identification & Tracking
Systems & Supplies; Mailroom, Re-
prographics & Related Management
Services
N.A.I.C.S.: 334519
Christopher Johnson *(Pres-Fin Svcs
& Sr VP)*
Lance E. Rosenzweig *(Interim CEO)*
Debbie Pfeiffer *(Pres-Presort Svcs)*
James Fairweather *(Chief Innovation
Officer & Sr VP)*
Shemin Nurmohamed *(Pres, Pres-
Sending Tech Solutions & Exec VP)*
Gregg S. Zegras *(Pres-Ecommerce
Pitney Bowes-Global & Exec VP)*

Judy Morris *(Chief HR Officer)*
Lauren Freeman-Bosworth *(Gen
Counsel, Sec & Exec VP)*
Geoff Kupferschmid *(Treas & VP)*

Subsidiaries:

Borderfree Limited　　　　　　**(1)**
51/52 Fitzwilliam Square West, Dublin, Ire-
land
Tel.: (353) 15134134
Loan Brokerage Services
N.A.I.C.S.: 522310

Compulit Inc.　　　　　　　　**(1)**
4460 44th St Se, Grand Rapids, MI 49512
Tel.: (616) 285-9590
Sales Range: $10-24.9 Million
Emp.: 100
Provider of Computer Services For Law
Firms
N.A.I.C.S.: 513210

Emtex Software, Inc.　　　　　**(1)**
901 Yamato Rd Ste 120, Boca Raton, FL
33431
Tel.: (561) 241-7229
Sales Range: $25-49.9 Million
Emp.: 24
Computer Related Product & Software Ser-
vices
N.A.I.C.S.: 423430

Miller's Presort, Inc.　　　　　**(1)**
1147 Sweitzer Ave, Akron, OH 44301
Tel.: (330) 434-9200
Web Site:
　http://www.millersprintandmail.com
Direct Mail Advertising
N.A.I.C.S.: 541860
Stephen Shamblin *(Owner)*

**Montgomery Office Equipment
Co.**　　　　　　　　　　　　　**(1)**
380 Arba St, Montgomery, AL 36104
Tel.: (334) 265-9578
Sales Range: $50-74.9 Million
Emp.: 30
Mfr of Photocopy Machines
N.A.I.C.S.: 459999

Newgistics, Inc.　　　　　　　**(1)**
7171 SW Pkwy Bldg 300 Ste 400, Austin,
TX 78735
Tel.: (512) 225-6000
Web Site: http://www.newgistics.com
Parcel & Freight Transportation Solutions
N.A.I.C.S.: 488510

**Pitney Bowes (Asia Pacific) Pte.
Ltd**　　　　　　　　　　　　　**(1)**
1 Wallich Street Guoco Tower Level 14-01,
Singapore, 078881, Singapore
Tel.: (65) 64033928
Web Site: https://www.pitneybowes.com
Sales Range: $25-49.9 Million
Emp.: 40
Machines & Equipment Distr
N.A.I.C.S.: 333248

Pitney Bowes (Ireland) Limited　**(1)**
Cedarhurst Building Arkle Road, Sandyford,
D18 X6N2, Dublin, 18, Ireland　　**(100%)**
Tel.: (353) 14608700
Web Site: https://www.pitneybowes.com
Sales Range: $25-49.9 Million
Mailing & Management Systems
N.A.I.C.S.: 333310

Pitney Bowes (Switzerland) AG　**(1)**
Vogelsangstrasse 17, Effretikon, 8307, Swit-
zerland
Tel.: (41) 520545757
Sales Range: $25-49.9 Million
Emp.: 20
Office Paper Handling & Mailing Machines
N.A.I.C.S.: 423420

Pitney Bowes (Thailand) Limited　**(1)**
19f Kpn Tower Rama 9 Rd Bangkapi
Huaykwan, Bangkok, 10310,
Thailand　　　　　　　　　　　**(100%)**
Tel.: (66) 27170588
Web Site: http://www.pb.com
Sales Range: $10-24.9 Million
Emp.: 13
Office & Mailing Machines
N.A.I.C.S.: 333310

**Pitney Bowes Australia Pty
Limited**　　　　　　　　　　　**(1)**

Level 1 68 Waterloo Road, Macquarie Park,
2113, NSW, Australia
Tel.: (61) 132363
Web Site: https://www.pitneybowes.com
Integrated Mail Provider Services
N.A.I.C.S.: 541715

Subsidiary (Domestic):

**Pitney Bowes Australia FAS Pty.
Limited**　　　　　　　　　　　**(2)**
Level 1 68 Waterloo Road, Sydney, 2113,
NSW, Australia
Tel.: (61) 294753500
Web Site: https://www.pitneybowes.com
Emp.: 80
Office Machinery Mfr
N.A.I.C.S.: 333310
Steven Darracott *(CEO)*

**Pitney Bowes Credit Australia
Limited**　　　　　　　　　　　**(2)**
95a St Hilliers Rd, Auburn, 2144, NSW,
Australia
Tel.: (61) 13 2363
Web Site: http://www.pitneybowes.com.au
Office Administrative Services
N.A.I.C.S.: 561110

**Pitney Bowes Brasil Equipamentos e
Servicos Ltda**　　　　　　　　**(1)**
Alameda Tocantins 630-Galpao 3-Bloco
Tocantins-Condominio Multiplo 3, Bairro Al-
phaville Centro Industrial e Empresarial,
Sao Paulo, 06455-020, Brazil
Tel.: (55) 1123488860
Web Site: http://www.pitneybowes.com
Emp.: 63
Ecommerce Solution Provider
N.A.I.C.S.: 333310

**Pitney Bowes Business Supplies &
Services**　　　　　　　　　　**(1)**
3001 Summer St, Stamford, CT 06905
Tel.: (203) 356-5000
Web Site: http://www.pd.com
Sales Range: $250-299.9 Million
Emp.: 800
Global Technology, Customer Engagement,
Shipping & Mailing Services
N.A.I.C.S.: 561910

Pitney Bowes Danmark A/S　　**(1)**
Marielundvej 46C st, 2730, Herlev,
Denmark　　　　　　　　　　　**(100%)**
Tel.: (45) 70221223
Web Site: https://azolver.dk
Emp.: 50
Document Management Services
N.A.I.C.S.: 561499
Antre Lasen *(Mng Dir)*

**Pitney Bowes Deutschland
G.m.b.H.**　　　　　　　　　　**(1)**
Poststrasse 4-6, 64293, Darmstadt,
Germany　　　　　　　　　　　**(100%)**
Tel.: (49) 61 515 2020
Web Site: https://www.pitneybowes.com
Global E-Commerce, Mailing, Shipping So-
lutions
N.A.I.C.S.: 513210

Pitney Bowes France　　　　　**(1)**
Immeuble Le Triangle, La Plaine, 93456,
Saint Denis, France
Tel.: (33) 825850825
Web Site: https://www.pitneybowes.fr
Customer Information Management &
Global Ecommerce;Mail Handling & Busi-
ness Solutions
N.A.I.C.S.: 561499

Subsidiary (Domestic):

Pitney Bowes Asterion SAS　　**(2)**
Perspective Seine Building Hall A, 84 rue
Charles Michels, Saint Denis, 93284,
France
Tel.: (33) 155844040
Printing & Processing Services
N.A.I.C.S.: 323111

Secap Groupe Pitney Bowes　　**(2)**
11 Rue Des Bretons, Cedex, 93218, Paris,
France　　　　　　　　　　　　**(100%)**
Tel.: (33) 149467373
Web Site: http://www.secap.fr
Sales Range: $10-24.9 Million
Emp.: 160
Postal & Franking Services

N.A.I.C.S.: 491110

Pitney Bowes International Holdings, Inc. (1)
801 N West St Fl 2, Wilmington, DE 19801-1525
Tel.: (302) 656-8595
Investment Holding Services
N.A.I.C.S.: 523940

Pitney Bowes Italia S.r.l. (1)
Via Paracelso 16, Agrate Brianza, MI 20864, Milan, Italy (100%)
Tel.: (39) 0295009228
Web Site: http://www.pitneybowes.it
Sales Range: $100-124.9 Million
Business & Office Mailing Solutions
N.A.I.C.S.: 561499

Pitney Bowes Japan (1)
Gotenyama Trust Tower 12th floor 4-7-35 Kitashinagawa, Shinagawa-ku, Tokyo, 140-0001, Japan (50%)
Tel.: (81) 35 657 1200
Web Site: https://www.pitneybowes.com
Sales Range: $50-74.9 Million
Business Equipment
N.A.I.C.S.: 423420
Takuya Tanabe (CEO)

Pitney Bowes Limited (1)
Building 5 Trident Place, Hatfield Business Park Mosquito Way, Hatfield, AL10 9UJ, Hertfordshire, United Kingdom
Tel.: (44) 844 499 2992
Web Site: https://www.pitneybowes.com
Business Equipment Whslr
N.A.I.C.S.: 423420

Subsidiary (Domestic):

OLDEMT LIMITED (2)
Building 600 Floor 2, Watford, WD25 7GS, Hertfordshire, United Kingdom
Tel.: (44) 1923279300
Ecommerce Solution Provider
N.A.I.C.S.: 333310

Unit (Domestic):

Pitney Bowes Business Systems-International (2)
The Pinnacles, Harlow, CM19 5BD, Essex, United Kingdom (100%)
Tel.: (44) 8444992992
Web Site: http://www.pitneybowes.co.uk
Sales Range: $150-199.9 Million
Emp.: 250
Global Technology, Customer Engagement, Shipping & Mailing Services
N.A.I.C.S.: 561431

Subsidiary (Domestic):

Pitney Bowes UK LP (2)
Building 5 Trident Place, Hatfield Business Park Mosquito Way, Hatfield, AL10 9UJ, Hertfordshire, United Kingdom
Tel.: (44) 8444992992
Web Site: https://www.pitneybowes.com
Ecommerce Solution Provider
N.A.I.C.S.: 513210

Quadstone Paramics Ltd (2)
The Smith Centre, Henley-on-Thames, RG9 6AB, United Kingdom
Tel.: (44) 1491416600
Web Site: http://www.paramics-online.com
Emp.: 8
Computer & Software Related Services
N.A.I.C.S.: 541511
Kevin Malone (Mng Dir)

Pitney Bowes Oy (1)
PL 109, Italahdenkatu 22A, 00211, Helsinki, Finland (100%)
Tel.: (358) 96824060
Sales Range: $1-9.9 Million
Emp.: 25
Business Equipment
N.A.I.C.S.: 423420

Pitney Bowes Presort Services, Inc. (1)
10110 I St, Omaha, NE 68127-1116
Tel.: (402) 339-6500
Sales Range: $350-399.9 Million
Emp.: 250
National Mail Presorting Services
N.A.I.C.S.: 561499

Debbie Pfeiffer (Pres)
Tracey Evans (VP-Ops)

Pitney Bowes Software Inc. (1)
4200 Parliament Pl Ste 600, Lanham, MD 20706-1844
Tel.: (770) 833-1649
Web Site: http://www.g1.com
Sales Range: $100-124.9 Million
Emp.: 599
Computer Softwares Mfr
N.A.I.C.S.: 513210

Subsidiary (Non-US):

Pitney Bowes Software Australia Pty. Ltd. (2)
Level 1 68 Waterloo Rd Macquarie Park, Sydney, 2113, NSW, Australia
Tel.: (61) 294753500
Web Site: http://www.pitneybowes.com
Sales Range: $10-24.9 Million
Emp.: 50
Location Software
N.A.I.C.S.: 334610

Pitney Bowes Software Europe Limited (2)
6 Hercules Way Leavesden Park, Watford, WD25 7GS, Herts, United Kingdom
Tel.: (44) 1923279100
Web Site: http://www.pitneybowes.com
Sales Range: $100-124.9 Million
Emp.: 80
Computer Softwares Mfr
N.A.I.C.S.: 334610

Subsidiary (Non-US):

Pitney Bowes Software GmbH (3)
Kelsterbacher Str 23, Raunheim, 65479, Germany
Tel.: (49) 6142203400
Web Site: http://www.pitneybowes.com
Location Software
N.A.I.C.S.: 513210

Subsidiary (Domestic):

Pitney Bowes Software Limited (3)
Minton Place, Windsor, SL4 1EG, United Kingdom
Tel.: (44) 1753848200
Web Site: http://www.pbinsight.com
Sales Range: $25-49.9 Million
Emp.: 248
Location Software Mfr
N.A.I.C.S.: 513210

Subsidiary (Non-US):

Pitney Bowes Software K. K. (2)
Ebisu Prime Square Tower 13th Floor 1-1-39 Hiroo, Shibuya-ku, Tokyo, 150-0012, Japan
Tel.: (81) 354686881
Web Site: http://www.nextmarketing.jp
Data Management Services
N.A.I.C.S.: 518210

Pitney Bowes Svenska AB (1)
Hammarbacken 12, PO Box 408, 191 24, Sollentuna, Sweden (100%)
Tel.: (46) 87341711
Web Site: http://www.pitneybowes.se
Sales Range: $50-74.9 Million
Emp.: 160
Business Equipment Mfr
N.A.I.C.S.: 333310

Pitney Bowes Technology Center (1)
35 Waterview Dr, Shelton, CT 06484-4301
Tel.: (203) 924-3500
Web Site: http://www.pitneybowes.com
Sales Range: $125-149.9 Million
Emp.: 500
Global Technology, Customer Engagement, Shipping & Mailing Services
N.A.I.C.S.: 339940

Pitney Bowes of Canada Ltd. (1)
5500 Explorer Drive, Mississauga, L4W 5C7, ON, Canada (100%)
Tel.: (905) 219-3000
Web Site: http://www.pitneybowes.com
Sales Range: $250-299.9 Million
Emp.: 300
Mail & Document Management Services
N.A.I.C.S.: 334519

Subsidiary (Domestic):

Pitney Bowes Canada LP (2)
200-314 Harwood Avenue, Ajax, L1S 2J1, ON, Canada
Tel.: (905) 427-9772
Ecommerce Solution Provider
N.A.I.C.S.: 333310

Division (Domestic):

Pitney Bowes of Canada Ltd.-Leasing Division (2)
5500 Explorer Dr, Mississauga, L4W 5C7, ON, Canada (100%)
Tel.: (905) 219-3000
Web Site: http://www.pitneybowes.ca
Sales Range: $75-99.9 Million
Emp.: 275
Equipment Leasing
N.A.I.C.S.: 532412

Print, Inc. (1)
11335 Northeast 122nd Way Ste 275, Kirkland, WA 98034
Tel.: (425) 629-2433
Web Site: http://www.printinc.com
Sales Range: $25-49.9 Million
Emp.: 250
Developer of Document Management Infrastructure Products & Services
N.A.I.C.S.: 561499

PIVOT TECHNOLOGY SOLUTIONS, INC.
15461 Springdale St, Huntington Beach, CA 92649
Tel.: (741) 861-2200   ON
Web Site: http://www.pivotts.com
Year Founded: 2011
PTG—(TSXV)
Rev.: $1,373,630,000
Assets: $421,319,000
Liabilities: $414,071,000
Net Worth: $7,248,000
Earnings: ($4,591,000)
Emp.: 829
Fiscal Year-end: 12/31/18
Holding Company; Information Technology Services
N.A.I.C.S.: 551112
John Flores (VP-Mktg)
Cory Reid (CIO)
Kevin Shank (CEO)
Mary Tullao (Controller)
Matthew Girardot (Sec)
Matt Olsen (Chief Strategy Officer)
Mike Flanagan (Exec VP-Unified Portfolio Tech)
Wade Dawe (Chm)
David Toews (CFO)
Matt Olson (COO)
Bob Pike (Interim CEO-SmartEdge.com, Inc)
Wendy Coticchia (Chief Compliance Officer)
Scott Ward (Exec VP-Partners & Alliances)

Subsidiaries:

Austin Ribbon & Computer Supplies, Inc. (1)
9211 Waterford Centre Blvd Ste 125, Austin, TX 78758
Tel.: (512) 452-0651
Web Site: http://www.arc-is.com
Emp.: 35
Computer Peripheral Equipment & Software Merchant Whslr
N.A.I.C.S.: 423430
Ashley Ambroso (Mgr-Relationship)
Brandie Reed (Coord-Recruiting)
Britta Butler (VP-Sls & Staffing)
Efren Garcia (Gen Counsel)
Erin Werley (Coord-Recruiting)
Jeremy Kling (Mgr-Mobility Acct)
Juli Primeaux (Mgr-Relationships)
Kiera Talbott (Mgr-Relationship)
Scott Sizemore (Exec VP)

Pivot Technology Solutions, Ltd. (1)
15461 Springdale St, Huntington Beach, CA 92649

Tel.: (714) 861-2200
Web Site: http://www.acsacs.com
Emp.: 800
Holding Company; Information Technology Assessment & Consulting Services
N.A.I.C.S.: 551112
Corbet Lancaster (VP-Fin)
Kevin Prahm (VP-Sls & Ops)

Affiliate (Domestic):

Applied Computer Solutions (2)
15461 Springdale St, Huntington Beach, CA 92649 (40%)
Tel.: (714) 861-2200
Web Site: http://www.acsacs.com
Information Technology Assessment & Consulting Services
N.A.I.C.S.: 541519
Kurt Steinhauer (Pres)
Corbet Lancaster (VP-Fin)
Kevin Prahm (VP-Sls & Ops)

Sigma Technology Solutions, Inc. (1)
607 E Sonterra Blvd Ste 250, San Antonio, TX 78258
Tel.: (210) 348-9876
Web Site: http://www.sigmasolinc.com
Sales Range: $10-24.9 Million
Emp.: 100
Information Technology Service Company
N.A.I.C.S.: 519290
Scott Gruendler (CEO)
Frank Jarzombek (Exec VP)
Whitney Deal (Coord-Mktg Events)
Cynthia Brodsky (Coord-Sls)
Christopher Bell (Engr-Sys)
James Smith (Dir-Solutions Engrg)
Joe Barrett (Dir-Sls-Dallas)
John Flores (VP-Mktg & Bus Dev)
Mike Clesceri (Dir-Sls-Chicago)
Mike Moates (VP-Sls)
Rob Jezek (Dir-Sls-Oklahoma)

PIXELWORKS, INC.
16760 SW Upper Boones Ferry Rd Ste 101, Portland, OR 97224
Tel.: (503) 601-4545   OR
Web Site:
https://www.pixelworks.com
Year Founded: 1997
PXLW—(NASDAQ)
Rev.: $70,146,000
Assets: $102,323,000
Liabilities: $58,992,000
Net Worth: $43,331,000
Earnings: ($16,030,000)
Emp.: 222
Fiscal Year-end: 12/31/22
System-On-Chip Semiconductors & Software Developer & Marketer
N.A.I.C.S.: 334413
Todd A. DeBonis (Pres & CEO)
Elias N. Nader (CFO)
Haley F. Aman (COO)
Sean Keohane (Exec VP-Business Development & Operations)
Linna Liu (VP)
Hongmin B. Zhang (Chief Technical Officer)
Tzoyao Chan (Exec VP-Engrg)
Wallace Pai (CIO & Exec VP)

Subsidiaries:

Pixelworks Corporation (1)
226 Airport Pkwy Ste 595, San Jose, CA 95110-1095
Tel.: (408) 200-9200
Rev.: $5,100,000
Emp.: 51
Integrated Circuits, Semiconductor Networks, Etc.
N.A.I.C.S.: 334413

Pixelworks Semiconductor Technology (Shanghai) Co. Ltd. (1)
Rm 301-303 No 88 Lane 887 Zuchongzhi Road, Zhangjiang Hi-Tech Park, Shanghai, 201203, China
Tel.: (86) 2151314777
Sales Range: $25-49.9 Million
Emp.: 150
Develops & Markets System-On-Chip Semiconductors & Software

Pixelworks, Inc.—(Continued)

N.A.I.C.S.: 334413
John Lau (Sr Mgr)

Pixelworks Semiconductor Technology (Taiwan) Inc. **(1)**
11F No 22 Lane 407 Sec 2 Tiding Blvd, Neihu Dist, Taipei, 11493, Taiwan
Tel.: (886) 287976600
Sales Range: $10-24.9 Million
Emp.: 60
Develops & Markets Semiconductors & Software
N.A.I.C.S.: 334413

ViXS Systems Inc. **(1)**
1210 Sheppard Ave East Suite 800, Toronto, M2K 1E3, ON, Canada
Tel.: (416) 646-2000
Web Site: http://www.pixelworks.com
Fabless Semiconductor Mfr
N.A.I.C.S.: 334413
Indra Laksono (Founder)

PJT PARTNERS INC.
280 Park Ave, New York, NY 10017
Tel.: (212) 364-7810 DE
Web Site:
https://www.pjtpartners.com
Year Founded: 2015
PJT—(NYSE)
Rev.: $1,153,182,000
Assets: $1,434,978,000
Liabilities: $573,814,000
Net Worth: $861,164,000
Earnings: $145,682,000
Emp.: 1,012
Fiscal Year-end: 12/31/23
Investment Advisory Services
N.A.I.C.S.: 523940
Mark Buschmann (Partner-Restructuring & Special Situations Grp)
Christopher M. Harland (Partner-Strategic Advisory Grp)
Paul J. Taubman (Chm & CEO)
Helen T. Meates (Partner & CFO)
Ji-Yeun Lee (Mng Partner)
Borja Arteaga (Partner-Strategic Advisory Grp-Madrid)
Jamie Baird (Partner-Restructuring & Special Situations Grp)
Ivan Brockman (Partner-Strategic Advisory Grp-San Francisco)
K. Don Cornwell (Partner)
Paige Costigan (Partner & COO)
Tom Davidson (Partner-Strategic Advisory Grp)
Rob Friedsam (Partner-Strategic Advisory Grp)
Basil Geoghegan (Partner-Strategic Advisory Grp-London)
Johannes Groeller (Partner-Strategic Advisory Grp-London)
Martin Gudgeon (Partner & Head-European Restructuring & Special Situations Grp)
Suzanne L. Stefany (Partner)
Dayan Abeyaratne (Partner-Strategic Advisory Grp)
Jacques E. Brand (Partner-Strategic Advisory Grp)
Karl Knapp (Partner & Head-Global Industrials-Strategic Advisory Grp)
James C. Murray (Partner-Strategic Advisory Grp)
Larry Nath (Partner-Strategic Advisory Grp)
Michael Gilbert (Partner-Strategic Advisory Grp)
Emmanuel Gueroult (Partner-Strategic Advisory Grp-London)
Jessica Kearns (Partner-Strategic Advisory Grp)
Peter Laurinaitis (Partner-Restructuring & Special Situations Grp)
Scott Matlock (Partner-Strategic Advisory Grp)

Ben Monaghan (Partner-Strategic Advisory Grp-London)
Jason Noble (Partner-Strategic Advisory Grp)
David Perdue (Partner-Strategic Advisory Grp)
John Trousdale (Partner)
Amish Barot (Partner-Strategic Advisory Grp)
Erik Lisher (Partner & COO-Restructuring & Special Situations Grp)
Jamie O'Connell (Partner-Restructuring & Special Situations Grp)
Michel Antakly (Partner-Strategic Advisory Grp-London)
John Singh (Partner-Restructuring & Special Situations Grp)
Laurence Whittemore (Partner-Strategic Advisory Grp)
Antonin Baladi (Partner-Strategic Advisory Grp-London)
Pierre Bourderye (Partner-Strategic Advisory Grp-London)
Peter Chang (Partner-Hong Kong)
Christopher Dimsey (Partner-Strategic Advisory Grp)
Laurie Fitch (Partner-Strategic Advisory Grp-London)
Celeste Guth (Partner-Strategic Advisory Grp)
Shirish Joshi (Partner-Restructuring & Special Situations Grp-London)
Simon Lyons (Partner-Strategic Advisory Grp-London)
Kathleen McCabe (Partner-Strategic Advisory Grp)
Guy A. Nachtomi (Partner-Strategic Advisory Grp-Los Angeles)
Michael O'Donovan (Partner-Strategic Advisory Grp)
Matthew J. Parr (Partner-Strategic Advisory Grp-Chicago)
Rakesh Patel (Partner-Strategic Advisory Grp-London)
Sara Price (Partner-Strategic Advisory Grp)
Eri Kakuta (Partner-Strategic Advisory Grp)
Paul Sheaffer (Partner-Restructuring & Special Situations Grp)
Josh Abramson (Partner-Restructuring & Special Situations Grp)
Hoke Slaughter (Partner-Strategic Advisory Grp)
Gregory Dalvito (Partner-Strategic Advisory Grp)
Paul Hudson (Partner-Park Hill's Hedge Fund & Private Credit Team)
Tarek Aguizy (Partner)
Christopher Areson (Partner)
Hugo Baring (Partner)
Allison Bennington (Partner)
Damali Bond (Partner)
Matthew Casper (Partner)
David Cecil (Partner)
Matt Cino (Partner)
Earl Dowling (Partner)
Michael J. Freudenstein (Partner)
Abe M. Friedman (Partner)
Richard Govers (Partner)
Javier Grana (Partner)
Brent Herlihy (Partner)
Doug Jarrett (Partner)
Sean Keene (Co-Founder)
Joe Lenehan (Co-Founder)
Brian Levine (Co-Founder)
Johanna Lottmann (Partner)
Max Mayer-Eming (Partner)
Alexander Moomjy (Partner)

Steve Zelin (Partner & Head-Restructuring & Special Situations Grp-Americas)
Steve Zelin (Partner & Head-Restructuring & Special Situations Grp-Americas)

Subsidiaries:

PJT Partners (France) SAS **(1)**
32-34 Avenue Kleber, 75116, Paris, France
Tel.: (33) 170701550
Investment Banking Services
N.A.I.C.S.: 523150

PJT Partners (UK) Limited **(1)**
1 Curzon Street, London, W1J 5HD, United Kingdom
Tel.: (44) 2036501100
Investment Advisory Services
N.A.I.C.S.: 523940

PJT Partners Japan K.K. **(1)**
Roppongi Hills Mori Tower 16F 6-10-1, Roppongi Minato-ku, Tokyo, 106-6116, Japan
Tel.: (81) 345654848
Investment Banking Services
N.A.I.C.S.: 523150

PLAINS ALL AMERICAN PIPE-LINE, L.P.
333 Clay St Ste 1600, Houston, TX 77002
Tel.: (713) 646-4100 DE
Web Site: https://www.plains.com
Year Founded: 1998
PAA—(NASDAQ)
Rev.: $57,342,000,000
Assets: $27,892,000,000
Liabilities: $14,567,000,000
Net Worth: $13,325,000,000
Earnings: $1,037,000,000
Emp.: 4,100
Fiscal Year-end: 12/31/22
Crude Oil, Refined Petroleum & Natural Gas Transportation, Storage & Marketing
N.A.I.C.S.: 423860
Wilfred C. W. Chiang (Chm & CEO)
Chris R. Chandler Sr. (COO & Exec VP)
Gregory L. Armstrong (Co-Founder)
Harry N. Pefanis (Pres)
Wilfred C. W. Chiang (Chm & CEO)
Will Abney (VP Mergers, Acquisitions, and Strategic Planning)
Kevin Cantrell (VP-Internal Audit)
Mark Eilerman (VP-Lease Supply)
Blake Fernandez (VP-Investor Relations)
Jimmy Ferrell (VP-Supply Chain Management)
Patrick Hodgins (VP-Health, Safety, and Environmental)
Robert Nobles (VP-US Facilities & Rail)
Mark Odom (VP-Crude Oil Bus Dev & Outside the Permian Basin)
James Pinchback (VP-Pipeline Comml)
Jim Tillis (VP-Human Resources)
Al Swanson (CFO & Exec VP)
Jeremy Goebel (Chief Comml Officer & Exec VP)
Richard McGee (Gen Counsel, Sec & Exec VP)
Sharon Spurlin (Treas & Sr VP)
Russ Montgomery (VP & Controller)
Dean Liollio (Sr VP-Special Projects)
Drew Engstrom (VP-Ops South Region)

Subsidiaries:

BridgeTex Pipeline Company, LLC **(1)**

Capline Pipeline Company LLC **(1)**
539 S Main St, Findlay, OH 45840
Tel.: (419) 672-6740
Web Site: http://www.cappl.com

Crude Oil Pipeline System Services
N.A.I.C.S.: 486110

PAA Natural Gas Storage, L.P. **(1)**
333 Clay St Ste 1500, Houston, TX 77002-4101 **(100%)**
Tel.: (713) 646-4100
Sales Range: $350-399.9 Million
Natural Gas Storage Services
N.A.I.C.S.: 213112
Allan D. Swanson (CFO & Sr VP)

Pine Prairie Energy Center, LLC **(1)**
333 Clay St Ste 1300, Houston, TX 77002-4101
Tel.: (713) 652-3669
Web Site:
http://www.pineprairieenergycenter.com
Sales Range: $50-74.9 Million
Emp.: 50
Gas Storage Services
N.A.I.C.S.: 213112
Ben Reese (Sr VP-Comml)

Plains All American, Inc. **(1)**
3600 Bowman Ct, Bakersfield, CA 93308-5019
Tel.: (661) 587-2080
Web Site: http://www.paalp.com
Sales Range: $150-199.9 Million
Emp.: 60
Crude Oil, Refined Products & LPG
N.A.I.C.S.: 211120

Plains Gas Solutions, LLC **(1)**
333 Clay St Ste 1600, Houston, TX 77002
Tel.: (713) 646-4100
Web Site: http://www.plainsallamerican.com
Natural Gas Processing Services
N.A.I.C.S.: 213112
Kevin Cofer (Mgr-Bus Dev)

Plains LPG Services GP LLC **(1)**
3875 Stiegel Pike Sta Rte 501 S, Newmanstown, PA 17073
Tel.: (717) 949-3469
Web Site: http://www.plainsmidstream.com
Emp.: 8
Technical Services
N.A.I.C.S.: 541990

Plains Marketing GP Inc. **(1)**
333 Clay St Ste 1600, Houston, TX 77002
Tel.: (713) 646-4100
Web Site: http://www.plainsallamerican.com
Oil Support Services
N.A.I.C.S.: 213112

Subsidiary (Domestic):

Plains Marketing, LP **(2)**
333 Clay Ste 1600, Houston, TX 77002-4804
Tel.: (713) 646-4100
Web Site: http://www.paalp.com
Sales Range: $75-99.9 Million
Emp.: 500
Marketing Transportation & Storage of Crude Oil
N.A.I.C.S.: 424720

Plains Midstream Canada ULC **(1)**
Suite 1400 607 Eighth Avenue S W, Calgary, T2P 0A7, AB, Canada
Tel.: (403) 298-2100
Web Site: http://www.plainsmidstream.com
Emp.: 1,200
Oil Storage Services
N.A.I.C.S.: 213112
Constantine S. Liollio (Pres)
Tyler Knowler (VP-Fin)
Sterling Koch (VP-Legal & Land)
Neil Lyons (VP-Comml)
Brent Nadeau (VP-HR)
Michelle Podavin (Sr VP-NGL Comml Assets)
Dan Reinbold (VP-Information Svcs-North America)
Dean Liollio (Pres)

PLAINS GP HOLDINGS, L.P.
333 Clay St Ste 1600, Houston, TX 77002
Tel.: (713) 646-4100 DE
Web Site: https://www.plains.com
Year Founded: 2013
PAGP—(NASDAQ)
Rev.: $57,341,999,999
Assets: $29,207,000,000

Liabilities: $14,569,000,000
Net Worth: $14,638,000,000
Earnings: $168,000,000
Emp.: 4,100
Fiscal Year-end: 12/31/22
Holding Company; Oil & Gas Operations
N.A.I.C.S.: 551112
Wilfred C. W. Chiang (Chm & CEO)
Blake Fernandez (VP-Investor Relations)
Chris Chandler (COO & Exec VP)

Subsidiaries:

5D Marketing LLC   (1)
5 Winged Foot Way, Littleton, CO 80123
Tel.: (720) 922-3445
Miscellaneous Financial Investment Services
N.A.I.C.S.: 523999

Plains Gas Solutions, LLC   (1)
333 Clay St Ste 1600, Houston, TX 77002
Tel.: (713) 652-3602
Web Site: http://www.paalp.com
Natural Gas Extraction Services
N.A.I.C.S.: 211130

Plains Marketing, L.P.   (1)
333 Clay St Ste 1600, Houston, TX 77210-4648
Tel.: (713) 646-4460
Crude Oil & Natural Gas Liquid Logistic Services
N.A.I.C.S.: 541614

PLANET 13 HOLDINGS, INC.

4850 W Sunset Rd, Las Vegas, NV 89118
Tel.: (702) 815-1313
Web Site: https://planet13.com
PLTH—(CNSX)
Rev.: $104,574,377
Assets: $233,629,973
Liabilities: $42,741,108
Net Worth: $190,888,865
Earnings: ($48,980,300)
Emp.: 567
Fiscal Year-end: 12/31/22
Offices of Other Holding Companies
N.A.I.C.S.: 551112
Larry Scheffler (Chm & CEO)

Subsidiaries:

Next Green Wave Holdings, Inc.   (1)
300-1055 West Hastings Street, Vancouver, V6E 2E9, BC, Canada
Tel.: (604) 609-6180
Web Site: http://www.nextgreenwave.com
Rev.: $12,627,677
Assets: $20,293,691
Liabilities: $3,307,870
Net Worth: $16,985,821
Earnings: $3,455,748
Fiscal Year-end: 12/31/2020
Cannabis Product Distr
N.A.I.C.S.: 424210
Mike Jennings (Co-Founder & CEO)
Paul Chow (Co-Founder)
Robert Dzisiak (Chm)
Matthew Jewell (CFO)
Ryan Lange (CMO)

PLANET FITNESS, INC.

4 Liberty Ln W, Hampton, NH 03842
Tel.: (603) 750-0001   DE
Web Site:
  https://www.planetfitness.com
Year Founded: 1992
PLNT—(NYSE)
Rev.: $1,071,326,000
Assets: $2,969,693,000
Liabilities: $3,088,684,000
Net Worth: ($118,991,000)
Earnings: $147,035,000
Emp.: 3,797
Fiscal Year-end: 12/31/23
Physical Fitness Facilities
N.A.I.C.S.: 713940
Brian O'Donnell (Chief Acctg Officer & VP)

Colleen Keating (CEO)
Kathy Gentilozzi (Chief People Officer)
McCall Gosselin (Sr VP-Comm & Corp Social Responsibility)
Sherrill Kaplan (Chief Digital Officer)
Jamie Medeiros (Chief Brand Officer)
Paul Barber (CIO)

Subsidiaries:

Edison Fitness Group LLC   (1)
561 US Highway 1, Edison, NJ 08817
Tel.: (732) 339-1730
Fitness Center Operator
N.A.I.C.S.: 713940

PF Derry LLC   (1)
55 Crystal Ave Ste 402, Derry, NH 03038
Tel.: (603) 421-2990
Emp.: 12
Fitness Center Operator
N.A.I.C.S.: 713940

PF Erie LLC   (1)
Tel.: (814) 866-0110
Fitness Center Operator
N.A.I.C.S.: 713940

PF Greensburg LLC   (1)
5280 Route 30 Ste 01A, Greensburg, PA 15601
Tel.: (724) 834-0700
Fitness Center Operator
N.A.I.C.S.: 713940

PF Vallejo, LLC   (1)
3505 Sonoma Blvd No 40, Vallejo, CA 94590
Tel.: (707) 643-1041
Fitness Center Operator
N.A.I.C.S.: 713940

Pla-Fit Holdings, LLC   (1)
26 Fox Run Rd, Newington, NH 03801
Tel.: (603) 750-0001
Holding Company
N.A.I.C.S.: 551112

Planet Fitness Holdings, LLC   (1)
775 Lafayette Rd, Portsmouth, NH 03801
Tel.: (603) 436-5797
Holding Company
N.A.I.C.S.: 551112

PLANET GREEN HOLDINGS CORP.

130 30 31st Ave Ste 512, Flushing, NY 11354
Tel.: (718) 799-0380   NV
Web Site:
  https://www.planetgreenhold
  ings.com
Year Founded: 1986
PLAG—(NYSEAMEX)
Rev.: $44,756,826
Assets: $60,720,386
Liabilities: $20,133,888
Net Worth: $40,586,498
Earnings: ($25,808,418)
Emp.: 143
Fiscal Year-end: 12/31/22
Holding Company; Processed Convenience Foods & Chestnut Products Mfr & Whslr
N.A.I.C.S.: 551112
Lili Hu (CFO)
Bin Zhou (Chm & CEO)
Yiming Qian (Deputy Dir-Tech)
Huiying Jin (Gen Mgr-Tea Grp)

Subsidiaries:

Fast Approach Inc.   (1)
3600 Steeles Avenue East, Markham, L3R 9Z7, ON, Canada
Tel.: (416) 388-2888
Web Site: https://www.fastapproach.ca
Internet Marketing Services
N.A.I.C.S.: 541613
Yong Yang (CEO)
Yiming Qian (Founder)

Jilin Chuangyuan Chemical Co., Ltd.   (1)
1 Yinhe Street, Economic and Technological

Development Zone, Meihekou, 135000, Jilin, China
Tel.: (86) 4354227709
Web Site: https://www.jlsgchem.com
Chemical Products Mfr
N.A.I.C.S.: 325998

PLANET LABS PBC

645 Harrison St 4th Fl, San Francisco, CA 94107
Tel.: (702) 781-4313   DE
Web Site: https://www.planet.com
PL—(NYSE)
Emp.: 930
Fiscal Year-end: 12/31/23
Software Publr
N.A.I.C.S.: 513210
Harry L. You (Chm)
Ashley Fieglein Johnson (Pres & CFO)
David Chung (VP)
Niccolo M. de Masi (CEO)
Niccolo de Masi (CEO)

PLANET RESOURCE RECOVERY, INC.

8815 Industrial Dr, Pearland, TX 77584
Tel.: (281) 213-5622   NV
PRRY—(OTCIQ)
Organic Chemical Mfr
N.A.I.C.S.: 325199
Enrique A. Salinas III (Pres & CEO)

PLANET SIGNAL, INC.

3938 Smith St Ste B, Union City, CA 94587
Tel.: (510) 493-2446
PLNE—(OTCIQ)
Online Shopping Services
N.A.I.C.S.: 541511
Karla V. Montenegro (Pres & CEO)

PLASTIC2OIL, INC.

20 Iroquois St, Niagara Falls, NY 14303
Tel.: (716) 278-0015   NV
Web Site: https://www.plastic2oil.com
PTOI—(OTCIQ)
Assets: $703,000
Liabilities: $19,278,000
Net Worth: ($18,575,000)
Earnings: ($1,789,000)
Emp.: 4
Fiscal Year-end: 12/31/20
Chemical Process Products
N.A.I.C.S.: 325998
Richard W. Heddle (Pres, Pres & CEO)

PLATEAU MINERAL DEVELOPMENT, INC.

51221 Industrial Dr, Macomb, MI 48042
Tel.: (586) 781-3000
PMDP—(OTCIQ)
Oil & Gas Field Exploration Services
N.A.I.C.S.: 213112
Alan L. Jacobs (CEO)

PLATINUM STUDIOS, INC.

815 Moraga Dr Ste 207, Los Angeles, CA 90049
Tel.: (310) 807-8100   CA
Web Site:
  https://www.platinumstudios.com
Year Founded: 1997
PDOS—(OTCIQ)
Sales Range: Less than $1 Million
All Other Publishers
N.A.I.C.S.: 513199
Scott Mitchell Rosenberg (Chm & CEO)

PLAYAGS, INC.

6775 S Edmond St Ste 300, Las Vegas, NV 89118-3502
Tel.: (702) 722-6700   NV
Web Site: https://www.playags.com
Year Founded: 2013
AGS—(NYSE)
Rev.: $309,436,000
Assets: $684,751,000
Liabilities: $635,390,000
Net Worth: $49,361,000
Earnings: ($8,035,000)
Emp.: 659
Fiscal Year-end: 12/31/22
Electronic Gaming Machines Mfr & Distr
N.A.I.C.S.: 339930
David Lopez (Pres & CEO)
Kimo Akiona (CFO, Chief Acctg Officer & Treas)
Victor Gallo (Gen Counsel & Sec)
Sigmund Lee (CTO)
Drew Pawlak (VP & Gen Mgr-Latin America)
John Hemberger (Sr VP-Table Products)
Julia Boguslawski (CMO)
Robert Blair (Deputy Gen Counsel)
Kris Morishige (Sr VP-Fin)
Rob Ziems (Chief Legal Officer & Sec)
Nikki Davis (Dir-Mktg & Comm)
Brad Boyer (Sr VP-IR & Corp Ops)

Subsidiaries:

Integrity Gaming ULC   (1)
800 West Pender Street Suite 1430, Vancouver, V6C 2V6, BC, Canada
Tel.: (604) 683-8393
Rev.: $14,077,217
Assets: $32,917,917
Liabilities: $34,187,849
Net Worth: ($1,269,932)
Earnings: $8,467,582
Fiscal Year-end: 12/31/2017
Investment Services
N.A.I.C.S.: 523999
Adam Kniec (CFO)
Jason Lowry (VP-Ops)
James Kim (VP-Corp Dev & Co-Sec)
Philip Bowden (Pres-Integrity Companies)
Robert Moore (VP-Integrity Companies)
Dan Zurcher (Dir-New Market Dev)

Subsidiary (US):

AGS Capital, LLC   (2)
9850 E 30th St, Indianapolis, IN 46229
Tel.: (317) 396-5932
Web Site: https://www.ags-capital.com
Business Investment Management Services
N.A.I.C.S.: 561110
Alan Symons (Chm & CEO)
Steve Blackburn (Pres)
Jayseph Richardson (Dir-IT)
Maria Rafet (Dir-HR)
Josie Henneke (VP)

Platform 9 Corporation   (1)
84 W Santa Clara St Ste 800, San Jose, CA 95113
Tel.: (650) 898-7369
Web Site: https://www.platform9.com
Information Technology Services
N.A.I.C.S.: 541511
Sirish Raghuram (Co/Co-Founder, Co-CEO & Chief Growth Officer)
Amrish Kapoor (VP-Engrg)
Ravi Jacob (CFO)
Madhura Maskasky (Co-Founder)
Roopak Parikh (Co-Founder)
Emilia A'Bell (Chief Revenue Officer)
Vishwa Kapadia (Chief People Officer)
Ron Haberman (VP-Customer Operations)

Playags Mexico, S. De R.L. De C.V.   (1)
Jaime Balmes 8 Piso 6 Oficina 601-A Col Los Morales Polanco Del, CP 11510, Acuamanala de Miguel Hidalgo, Mexico
Tel.: (52) 5552505450
Gaming Equipment Distr
N.A.I.C.S.: 423920

PlayAGS, Inc.—(Continued)

PLAYERS NETWORK

1771 E Flamingo Rd Ste 201-A, Las
Vegas, NV 89119
Tel.: (702) 840-3270
Web Site:
  http://www.playersnetwork.com
Year Founded: 1993
PNTV—(OTCIQ)
Sales Range: Less than $1 Million
Emp.: 2
Internet Broadcasting Services
N.A.I.C.S.: 516210
Mark Bradley (Chm & CEO)
Remus Bleahu (Creative Dir)
David Berry (Dir-Bus Dev)
Bryan Garabrandt (Dir-Mktg & Analytics)
Yunnie Lin (Asst Dir-Creative)
David Kavanagh (Engr-Lead Software)
Peter Kelesis (Editor)
Madeline Schrenkeisen (Editor)
David Wilson (Editor)

PLAYSTUDIOS, INC.

10150 Covington Cross Dr, Las Vegas, NV 89144
Tel.: (725) 877-7000   Ky
Web Site:
  https://www.playstudios.com
Year Founded: 2020
MYPS—(NASDAQ)
Rev.: $290,309,000
Assets: $352,009,000
Liabilities: $49,696,000
Net Worth: $302,313,000
Earnings: ($17,783,000)
Emp.: 752
Fiscal Year-end: 12/31/22
Investment Services
N.A.I.C.S.: 523999
James J. Murren (Chm)
Daniel Fetters (Co-CEO)
Edward King (Co-CEO)
Christopher Grove (Exec VP)

Subsidiaries:

PlayStudios, Inc.   (1)
10300 W Charleston Blvd Ste 13272, Las
Vegas, NV 89135
Tel.: (702) 800-5716
Emp.: 51
Game Software Development Services
N.A.I.C.S.: 541511
Andrew Pascal (Co-Founder, Chm & CEO)
Chad Hansing (Co-Founder)
Monty Kerr (Co-Founder)
Nicholas Koenig (Co-Founder & Chief Creative Officer)
Paul Mathews (Co-Founder & COO)
Michael P. Rolnick (Co-Founder)
Stephanie Rosol (Chief People Performance Officer)
Jason Hahn (Exec VP & Head-Corp & Bus Dev)

PLBY GROUP, INC.

1 Montgomery St Ste 3700, San
Francisco, CA 94104
Tel.: (415) 887-2311   DE
Web Site: https://www.plbygroup.com
Year Founded: 2019
PLBY—(NASDAQ)
Rev.: $266,933,000
Assets: $552,463,000
Liabilities: $397,211,000
Net Worth: $155,252,000
Earnings: ($277,704,000)
Emp.: 497
Fiscal Year-end: 12/31/22
Holding Company; Adult Magazine,
Calendar & Internet Media Publisher;
Adult Entertainment Programming &
Home Video Production & Distribution
N.A.I.C.S.: 523999
Rachel Webber (Chief Brand Officer
& Pres-Corp Strategy)

Marc Crossman (CFO & COQ)
Ashley Kechter (Pres)
Chris Riley (Gen Counsel & Sec)
Ben Kohn (Pres & CEO)
Suhail Rizvi (Chm)

Subsidiaries:

Playboy Enterprises, Inc.   (1)
10960 Wilshire Blvd Ste 2200, Los Angeles,
CA 90024
Tel.: (702) 751-8000
Sales Range: $200-249.9 Million
Emp.: 547
Holding Company; Adult Magazine, Calendar & Internet Media Publisher; Adult Entertainment Programming & Home Video Production & Distribution
N.A.I.C.S.: 551112

Subsidiary (Non-US):

Lake Shore Press, Inc.   (2)
Tel.: (312) 751-8000
Sales Range: $25-49.9 Million
Emp.: 100
Adult Material Periodical, Book & Internet
Publisher
N.A.I.C.S.: 513120

Unit (Non-US):

Playboy Special Editions   (3)
                                 (100%)
Tel.: (312) 751-8000
Sales Range: $75-99.9 Million
Special Edition Periodical & Calendar Publisher
N.A.I.C.S.: 513120

Subsidiary (Domestic):

Playboy Entertainment Group,
Inc.   (2)
2706 Media Center Dr, Los Angeles, CA
90065-1733   (100%)
Tel.: (323) 276-4000
Web Site: http://www.playboy.com
Sales Range: $50-74.9 Million
Emp.: 160
Film Production; Cable
N.A.I.C.S.: 516210
Daniel Smith (Pres-Domestic Home Video)
Steve Smith (Mng Dir)

Subsidiary (Domestic):

Alta Loma Productions, Inc.   (3)
2706 Media Center Dr, Los Angeles, CA
90065   (100%)
Tel.: (323) 276-4000
Sales Range: $25-49.9 Million
Emp.: 150
Syndicated Television
N.A.I.C.S.: 516120
Jason Burns (VP-Dev)

Unit (Domestic):

Playboy Studio West   (3)
2112 Broadway Ave, Santa Monica, CA
90404   (100%)
Tel.: (310) 264-6600
Web Site: http://www.playboy.com
Sales Range: $10-24.9 Million
Emp.: 12
Photography Studio
N.A.I.C.S.: 541921
Gary Cole (Editor-Photo)

Subsidiary (Domestic):

Playboy TV & Video Enterprises,
Inc.   (3)
2706 Media Ctr Dr, Los Angeles, CA
90065-3732   (100%)
Tel.: (323) 276-4000
Web Site: http://www.playboy.com
Video Production Services
N.A.I.C.S.: 512110

Subsidiary (Domestic):

Playboy Franchisings Inc.   (2)
680 North Lk Shore Dr, Chicago, IL 60611
Tel.: (312) 751-8000
Web Site: http://www.playboy.com
Sales Range: $10-24.9 Million
Emp.: 50
Franchising, Selling & Licensing

N.A.I.C.S.: 512110

PLEXUS CORP.

1 Plexus Way, Neenah, WI 54957
Tel.: (920) 969-6000   WI
Web Site: https://www.plexus.com
Year Founded: 1980
PLXS—(NASDAQ)
Rev.: $3,960,827,000
Assets: $3,153,821,000
Liabilities: $1,828,996,000
Net Worth: $1,324,825,000
Earnings: $111,815,000
Emp.: 20,000
Fiscal Year-end: 09/28/24
Mfr of Electronic Products for Medical, Telecommunications, Industrial &
Computer Markets
N.A.I.C.S.: 334412
Scott Theune (Pres-AMER)
Angelo M. Ninivaggi (Chief Admin
Officer, Gen Counsel, Sec & Exec
VP)
Todd P. Kelsey (Pres & CEO)
Oliver K. Mihm (COO & Exec VP)
Patrick John Jermain (CFO & Exec
VP)
Heather Beresford (VP-Aftermarket
Svcs)
Andy Hyatt (Sr VP-Customer
Solutions-Global)
Rob Michalkiewicz (Controller)
Mike Running (Sr VP-Aftermarket
Svcs & Engrg Solutions-Global)
Victor Tan (Pres-APAC)
Kyle Mcmillan (Sr VP-Global Ops)
Steve Rogers (Treas & VP-Tax)
Pat Rothe (CIO)
Scott Anderson (VP-Quality & Regulatory)
Jamie Crouse (VP-HR)
Shawn Harrison (VP-Comm & IR)
Chris Hood (Pres, CEO, Exec VP &
Sr VP)
Megan Schleicher (Sr Dir, Pres, CEO,
Exec VP & Sr VP)

Subsidiaries:

PTL Information Technology Services
Corp.   (1)
120 Main St, Neenah, WI 54956-0677
Tel.: (920) 722-8748
Web Site: http://www.plexus.com
Electronics Manufacturing Services
N.A.I.C.S.: 334412

Plexus (Hangzhou) Co., Ltd.   (1)
No 66 Dongxindadao Road Building D,
Hangzhou, 310053, Zhejiang, China
Tel.: (86) 57189822800
Web Site: http://www.plexus.com
Emp.: 400
Electric Equipment Mfr
N.A.I.C.S.: 335999

Plexus Aerospace, Defense & Security Services, LLC   (1)
1 Plexus Way, Neenah, WI 54956
Tel.: (920) 722-3451
Electronic Engineering Services
N.A.I.C.S.: 541330
William Peterson (Dir-
Defense/Security/Aerospace Solutions)

Plexus Deutschland GmbH   (1)
Heinrich-Hertz-Str 2A, 64295, Darmstadt,
Germany
Tel.: (49) 615113775500
Web Site: https://www.plexus.com
Electric Equipment Mfr
N.A.I.C.S.: 335999

Plexus International Services,
Inc.   (1)
55 Jewelers Park Dr, Neenah, WI 54957
Tel.: (920) 751-3612
Web Site: http://www.plexus.com
Sales Range: $300-349.9 Million
Emp.: 1,800
Holding Company for International Operations
N.A.I.C.S.: 334412

Subsidiary (Non-US):

Plexus Asia, Ltd.   (2)
Plot 40 Hilir Sungai Keluang 4 Bayan Lepas
Free Industrial Zone, Phase IV Bayan
Lepas, 11900, Penang, Malaysia
Tel.: (60) 46326000
Holding Company
N.A.I.C.S.: 551112

Subsidiary (Non-US):

Plexus (Xiamen) Co., Ltd.   (3)
No 6 Xiangxing 2 Road, Xiamen Area of
China Pilot Free Trade Zone, Xiamen,
361006, Fujian, China
Tel.: (86) 5925757000
Sales Range: $150-199.9 Million
Emp.: 700
Mfr of Electronic Products for Medical, Telecommunications, Industrial & Computer
Markets
N.A.I.C.S.: 334513

Subsidiary (Domestic):

Plexus Manufacturing Sdn. Bhd.   (3)
Bayan Lepas Free Industrial Zone, Phase II
Bayan Lepas, 11900, Penang, Malaysia
Tel.: (60) 46321000
Sales Range: $900-999.9 Million
Emp.: 5,000
Mfr & Engineering of Electronic Products for
Medical, Telecommunications, Industrial &
Computer Markets
N.A.I.C.S.: 334513

Subsidiary (Non-US):

Plexus Corp. Limited   (2)
Lee Forbes Way Pinnacle Hill Industrial Estate, Kelso, TD5 8XX, Roxburghshire,
United Kingdom   (100%)
Tel.: (44) 1573223601
Web Site: http://www.plexus.com
Sales Range: $50-74.9 Million
Emp.: 340
Mfr of Electronic Products for Medical, Telecommunications, Industrial & Computer
Markets
N.A.I.C.S.: 334513
Oliver Mihm (COO & Exec VP)

Subsidiary (Non-US):

Plexus Corp. (UK) Limited   (3)
Emp.: 280
Mfr of Electronic Products for Medical, Telecommunications, Industrial & Computer
Markets
N.A.I.C.S.: 334513
Alan Hutchison (Mgr-Test Engrg)

Subsidiary (Non-US):

Plexus Corp. Services (UK)
Limited   (2)
Lee Forbes Way, Pinnacle Hill Industrial Estate, Kelso, TD5 8XX, Roxburghshire,
United Kingdom
Tel.: (44) 1573223601
Bare Printed Circuit Board Mfr
N.A.I.C.S.: 334412

Plexus Services Corp.   (1)
One Plexus Way, Neenah, WI 54956
Tel.: (920) 722-3451
Web Site: http://www.plexus.com
Rev.: $375,000,000
Emp.: 400
Mfr of Printed Circuit Boards
N.A.I.C.S.: 334412

Plant (Domestic):

Plexus   (2)
16399 Franklin Rd, Nampa, ID 83687-9393
Tel.: (208) 898-2600
Web Site: http://www.plexus.com
Sales Range: $100-124.9 Million
Emp.: 400
Electronics Manufacturing Services
N.A.I.C.S.: 334412

Subsidiary (Non-US):

Plexus Servicios S. de R.L. de
C.V.   (2)
Avenida de las Torres 2304, Col Lote Bravo
Zona Sur CD, Ciudad Juarez, 32574, Chihuahua, Mexico

Tel.: (52) 16 49 19 00
Web Site: http://www.plexus.com
Sales Range: $100-124.9 Million
Mfr of Electronic Products for Medical, Tele-
communications, Industrial & Computer
Markets
N.A.I.C.S.: 334513

Plexus Services RO S.R.L.   (1)
Eugeniu Carada Street No 2-4, Bihor,
410610, Oradea, Romania
Tel.: (40) 259400500
Electric Equipment Mfr
N.A.I.C.S.: 335999

PLIANT THERAPEUTICS, INC.
331 Oyster Point Blvd, South San
Francisco, CA 94080
Tel.: (650) 481-6770   DE
Web Site: https://www.pliantrx.com
Year Founded: 2015
PLRX—(NASDAQ)
Rev.: $9,685,000
Assets: $350,613,000
Liabilities: $37,271,000
Net Worth: $313,342,000
Earnings: ($123,321,000)
Emp.: 124
Fiscal Year-end: 12/31/22
Biotechnology Research & Develop-
ment Services
N.A.I.C.S.: 541714
Hans Hull (Chief Bus Officer)
Eric Lefebvre (Chief Medical Officer)
Keith Cummings (CFO)
Barbara Howes (Chief HR Officer)
Katerina Leftheris (VP-Chemistry)
Scott Turner (Sr VP-Res)
Marzena Jurek (VP-Clinical Ops)
Eve-Irene Lepist (VP-Non-Clinical
Dev)
Dean Sheppard (Co-Founder)
Rik Derynck (Co-Founder)
Bill DeGrado (Co-Founder)
Hal Chapman (Co-Founder)
Hoyoung Huh (Chm)
S. Mishima Gerhart (Chief Regulatory
Officer)
Gregory P. Cosgrove (VP-Clinical
Dev)
Christopher Keenan (VP-IR & Corp
Comm)
Monica Sandberg (VP-Regulatory
Affairs)
Fernando Rock (VP-Drug Discovery)
Scott Peters (VP-Fin & Controller)
Mike Ouimette (Gen Counsel & Sec)
Bernard Coulie (Pres & CEO)

PLUG POWER INC.
968 Albany Shaker Rd, Latham, NY
12110
Tel.: (518) 782-7700   DE
Web Site:
    https://www.plugpower.com
Year Founded: 1997
PLUG—(NASDAQ)
Rev.: $891,340,000
Assets: $4,902,738,000
Liabilities: $2,004,613,000
Net Worth: $2,898,125,000
Earnings: ($1,368,833,000)
Emp.: 3,687
Fiscal Year-end: 12/31/23
Designer & Developer of On-Site
Electricity Generation Systems
N.A.I.C.S.: 221122
Paul B. Middleton (CFO)
Sanjay Shrestha (Chief Strategy Offi-
cer & Gen Mgr-Energy Solutions)
Chris Suriano (Exec VP-Svc)
Gerard L. Conway Jr. (Gen Counsel)
Preeti Pande (CMO)
David Mindnich (Exec VP)
Meryl Mallery (VP)
George C. McNamee (Founder &
Chm)
Andrew J. Marsh (Pres & CEO)

Subsidiaries:

Applied Cryo Technologies, Inc.   (1)
7150 Almeda Genoa Rd, Houston, TX
77075
Tel.: (281) 888-3884
Web Site: https://www.appliedcryotech.com
Storage Tank Mfr & Distr
N.A.I.C.S.: 332420

Frames Holding BV   (1)
Eikenlaan 23, 2404 BP, Alphen aan den
Rijn, Netherlands
Tel.: (31) 172461600
Web Site: https://www.frames-group.com
Natural Gas Distribution Services
N.A.I.C.S.: 221210

United Hydrogen Group, Inc.   (1)
1900 Main St Ste 223, Canonsburg, PA
15317-5861
Tel.: (866) 942-7763
Oil & Gas Dist.
N.A.I.C.S.: 221210

PLUM ACQUISITION CORP. III
2021 Fillmore St Ste 2089, San Fran-
cisco, CA 94115
Tel.: (929) 529-7125   Ky
Web Site: https://www.aptmspac.com
Year Founded: 2021
PLMJ—(NASDAQ)
Rev.: $4,074,730
Assets: $287,503,867
Liabilities: $298,221,482
Net Worth: ($10,717,615)
Earnings: $9,055,597
Emp.: 2
Fiscal Year-end: 12/31/22
Investment Services
N.A.I.C.S.: 523999
Steven Handwerker (CFO)
Kanishka Roy (Chm, Pres & CEO)

PLUMAS BANCORP
5050 Meadowood Mall Cir, Reno, NV
89502
Tel.: (775) 786-0907   CA
Web Site:
    https://www.plumasbank.com
PLBC—(NASDAQ)
Rev.: $70,808,000
Assets: $1,621,044,000
Liabilities: $1,502,040,000
Net Worth: $119,004,000
Earnings: $26,444,000
Emp.: 193
Fiscal Year-end: 12/31/22
Bank Holding Company
N.A.I.C.S.: 551111
Andrew J. Ryback (Pres & CEO)
Robert J. McClintock (Vice Chm)
Richard L. Belstock (Exec VP)
B. J. North (Chief Banking Officer &
Exec VP-Plumas Bank)
Michonne R. Ascuaga (Sec)

Subsidiaries:

Plumas Bank   (1)
336 W Main St, Quincy, CA 95971 (100%)
Tel.: (530) 283-6800
Web Site: https://www.plumasbank.com
Sales Range: $125-149.9 Million
Emp.: 197
Commercial Banking Services
N.A.I.C.S.: 522210
Elizabeth Kuipers (VP & Mgr-Mktg)
Terrance J. Reeson (Vice Chm & Sec)
Andrew J. Ryback (Pres & CEO)
Richard L. Belstock (Exec VP)
B. J. North (Chief Banking Officer & Exec
VP)
Aaron M. Boigon (CIO & Exec VP)
Jeffrey T. Moore (Chief Credit Officer &
Exec VP)

PLURALSIGHT, INC.
42 Future Way, Draper, UT 84020
Tel.: (801) 784-9007   DE
Web Site: http://www.pluralsight.com
Year Founded: 2017

PS—(NASDAQ)
Rev.: $391,865,000
Assets: $1,151,133,000
Liabilities: $949,363,000
Net Worth: $201,770,000
Earnings: ($128,080,000)
Emp.: 1,700
Fiscal Year-end: 12/31/20
Holding Company; Online Technical
Training Services
N.A.I.C.S.: 551112
Aaron B. Skonnard (Co-Founder &
CEO)
Mark K. Miller (CFO)
Brandon Peay (Exec VP-Pluralsight
Skills)
Matthew Forkner (Chief Legal Officer)
Frederick Onion (Co-Founder)
Ben Veghte (Sr Dir-Comm)
Kathryn Murphy (Exec VP-Pluralsight
Flow)
Christopher Oliver (Exec VP-Corp
Strategy)
Chris Tonas (CTO)
Lindsay Bayuk (CMO)
Will Clive (Chief People Officer)
Gary Eimerman (Gen Mgr-Pluralsight
Skills)
Dan Sorensen (Dir-Comm)

Subsidiaries:

Pluralsight, LLC   (1)
42 Future Way, Draper, UT 84020
Tel.: (801) 784-9007
Web Site: http://www.pluralsight.com
Online Technical Training Services
N.A.I.C.S.: 518210
Joseph M. DiBartolomeo (Chief Revenue
Officer)
Heather Zynczak (CMO)
Aaron B. Skonnard (Founder & CEO)
Nate Walkingshaw (Chief Experience Offi-
cer)
Anita Grantham (Chief People Officer)
Mariangel Babbel (Dir-Comm)
James W. Budge (CFO)
Lindsey Kneuven (Head-Social Impact)
D. J. Anderson (VP-Comm)
Fritz Onion (Founder)
Brandon Peay (Sr VP-Strategy & Bus Ops)
Matthew Forkner (Gen Counsel)

Subsidiary (Domestic):

DevelopIntelligence LLC   (2)
980 West Dillon Rd, Louisville, CO 80027
Tel.: (720) 445-4360
Web Site:
    http://www.developintelligence.com
Software Publisher
N.A.I.C.S.: 513210
Kelby Zorgdrager (Founder & CEO)

Smarterer, Inc.   (2)
500 Harrison Ave Ste 3R, Boston, MA
02118
Tel.: (857) 268-5263
Web Site: http://www.smarterer.com
Software Publisher
N.A.I.C.S.: 513210
Shimon Rura (Product Dir-Mgmt)
Dave Balter (Co-Founder)

PLUS PRODUCTS INC
340 S Lemon Ave, Walnut, CA 91789
Web Site:
    http://www.plusproductscbd.com
PLUS—(CNSX)
Rev.: $13,850,351
Assets: $29,254,971
Liabilities: $20,955,763
Net Worth: $8,299,208
Earnings: ($30,226,462)
Fiscal Year-end: 12/31/19
Cannabis Product Mfr
N.A.I.C.S.: 325411
Jake Heimark (Co-Founder & CEO)
Justin Gwin (Co-Founder)

PLUS THERAPEUTICS, INC.

4200 Marathon Blvd Ste 200, Austin,
TX 78756
Tel.: (210) 974-6900   DE
Web Site:
    https://www.plustherapeutics.com
PSTV—(NASDAQ)
Rev.: $224,000
Assets: $23,867,000
Liabilities: $17,422,000
Net Worth: $6,445,000
Earnings: ($20,275,000)
Emp.: 17
Fiscal Year-end: 12/31/22
Biopharmaceutical Technologies De-
veloper, Mfr & Whslr
N.A.I.C.S.: 325412
Marc H. Hedrick (Pres & CEO)
Russ Havranek (VP-Corp Strategy &
New Product Plng)
Melissa Moore (VP)
Pius Maliakal (VP-Clinical Ops)

**PLUTONIAN ACQUISITION
CORP.**
1441 Broadway 3rd 5th & 6th Fl, New
York, NY 10018
Tel.: (646) 969-0946   DE
Year Founded: 2021
PLTN—(NASDAQ)
Assets: $59,305,317
Liabilities: $55,682,414
Net Worth: $3,622,903
Earnings: $126,217
Fiscal Year-end: 12/31/22
Investment Management Service
N.A.I.C.S.: 523999
Wei Kwang Ng (Chm, Pres & CEO)

PLX PHARMA INC.
9 Fishers Ln Ste E, Sparta, NJ 07871
Tel.: (973) 409-6541   DE
Web Site: http://www.plxpharma.com
Year Founded: 2010
PLXP—(NASDAQ)
Rev.: $8,208,000
Assets: $76,642,000
Liabilities: $40,976,000
Net Worth: $35,666,000
Earnings: ($48,650,000)
Emp.: 16
Fiscal Year-end: 12/31/21
Holding Company; Pharmaceutical
Mfr & Whslr
N.A.I.C.S.: 551112
Steven Valentino (VP-Trade Sls)
Natasha Giordano (Pres & CEO)
Michael J. Valentino (Chm)
Rita M. O'Connor (CFO & Head-Mfg
& Supply Chain)
Joanne Cotignola (VP-Mktg)

Subsidiaries:

PLx OpCo Inc.   (1)
8285 El Rio Ste 130, Houston, TX 77054-
4654
Tel.: (713) 842-1249
Web Site: http://www.plxpharma.com
Pharmaceuticals Mfr
N.A.I.C.S.: 325412

**PLYMOUTH INDUSTRIAL REIT,
INC.**
20 Custom House St 11th Fl, Boston,
MA 02110
Tel.: (617) 340-3814   MD
Web Site:
    https://www.plymouthreit.com
Year Founded: 2011
PLYM—(NYSE)
Rev.: $183,536,000
Assets: $1,521,318,000
Liabilities: $1,044,937,000
Net Worth: $476,381,000
Earnings: ($16,886,000)
Emp.: 44
Fiscal Year-end: 12/31/22
Real Estate Investment Trust

Plymouth Industrial REIT, Inc.—(Continued)

N.A.I.C.S.: 525990
Jeffrey E. Witherell (Chm & CEO)
Pendleton P. White Jr. (Co-Founder)
Anne Alger Hayward (Gen Counsel & Sr VP)
James M. Connolly (Exec VP-Asset Mgmt)
Anthony Saladino (CFO & Exec VP)
Lyndon Blakesley (Chief Acctg Officer)
Benjamin P. Coues (Sr VP)
Scott L. Robinson (Sr VP)

PMV CONSUMER ACQUISITION CORP.

249 Royal Palm Way Ste 503, Palm Beach, FL 33480
Tel.: (561) 318-3766   DE
Web Site: https://www.pmv-consumer.com
Year Founded: 2020
PMVC—(OTCIQ)
Rev.: $9,869,389
Assets: $1,368,044
Liabilities: $638,783
Net Worth: $729,261
Earnings: $8,622,353
Fiscal Year-end: 12/31/22
Investment Services
N.A.I.C.S.: 523999
Timothy Foufas (Co-Pres & Sec)
Robert LaPenta Jr. (Co-Chm)
Joseph A. Gabelli (Co-Pres)
John N. Givissis (Chief Acctg Officer & Sr VP)
Nathan Miller (CFO)
Marc J. Gabelli (Chm & Co-CEO)

PMV PHARMACEUTICALS, INC.

1 Research Way, Princeton, NJ 08540
Tel.: (609) 642-6670   DE
Web Site: https://www.pmvpharma.com
Year Founded: 2013
PMVP—(NASDAQ)
Rev.: $3,714,000
Assets: $270,308,000
Liabilities: $24,280,000
Net Worth: $246,028,000
Earnings: ($73,317,000)
Emp.: 62
Fiscal Year-end: 12/31/22
Research & Development in Biotechnology (except Nanobiotechnology)
N.A.I.C.S.: 541714
David H. Mack (Co-Founder, Pres & CEO)
Deepika Jalota (Chief Dev Officer)
Michael Carulli (CFO & Principal Acctg Officer)
Robert Ticktin (Gen Counsel)
Richard A. Heyman (Chm)
Arnold Levine (Co-Founder)
Laura De Leon (VP & Head-Clinical Ops)
Thomas Shenk (Co-Founder)
Tim Smith (Sr VP & Head-Corp Dev & IR)
Marc Fellous (Sr VP & Head-Clinical Dev & Medical Affairs)
Arshad Haque (VP)
J. D. Kern (VP)
Crystal Zuckerman (VP)
Shibu Sleeba (VP)
David H. Mack (Co-Founder, Pres & CEO)
Arnold Levine (Co-Founder)

POEMA GLOBAL HOLDINGS CORP.

101 Natoma St 2F, San Francisco, CA 94105

Tel.: (415) 432-8880   Ky
Year Founded: 2020
PPGHU—(NASDAQ)
Investment Services
N.A.I.C.S.: 523999
Emmanuel DeSousa (Co-Chm)
Joaquin Rodriguez Torres (Co-Chm)
Homer Sun (CEO)
Marc Chan (Pres)

POINT TO POINT METHODICS, INC.

999 S Shady Grove Rd Ste 103, Memphis, TN 38120
Tel.: (901) 761-2159   NV
Web Site: https://mail.ppmhinc.com
Year Founded: 1997
PPMH—(OTCIQ)
Software Development Services
N.A.I.C.S.: 541511
Paul Baioni (Pres & CEO)
John Miller (CFO & Exec VP)

POINT.360

2701 Media Center Dr, Los Angeles, CA 90065
Tel.: (323) 987-9444   CA
Web Site: http://www.point360.com
Year Founded: 1990
PTSX—(OTCIQ)
Sales Range: $25-49.9 Million
Emp.: 380
Video Duplication & Distribution; Distributor of National Television Spot Advertising, Trailers, Infomercials, Syndicated Programming & Electronic Press Kits to Broadcast Outlets
N.A.I.C.S.: 512199
Haig S. Bagerdjian (Chm, Pres, CEO & CFO)

Subsidiaries:

Modern Videofilm, Inc.   (1)
2300 W Empire Ave, Burbank, CA 91504
Tel.: (818) 840-1700
Web Site: http://www.point360.com
Emp.: 500
Services Allied To Motion Pictures
N.A.I.C.S.: 334610
Wendy Canto (Dir-Ops)

Point.360-Highland   (1)
1147 Vine St, Hollywood, CA 90038-1207   (100%)
Tel.: (323) 957-5500
Sales Range: $25-49.9 Million
Emp.: 25
Making Copies of Video Tapes
N.A.I.C.S.: 334610
Dave Tuszynski (Gen Mgr)

POLAR POWER, INC.

249 E Gardena Blvd, Gardena, CA 90248
Tel.: (310) 830-9153   CA
Web Site: https://www.polarpower.com
POLA—(NASDAQ)
Rev.: $16,056,000
Assets: $24,188,000
Liabilities: $6,007,000
Net Worth: $18,181,000
Earnings: ($5,584,000)
Emp.: 113
Fiscal Year-end: 12/31/22
Motor & Generator Mfr
N.A.I.C.S.: 335312
Arthur D. Sams (Pres, CEO, Chm & Sec)
Luis Zavala (CFO & VP)
Christopher Sabo (Dir-Telecom Sls & Bus Dev-North America)
Andre Herbst (Dir-Telecom Sls & Bus Dev-Africa)
Raj Hira (Dir-Telecom Sls-Asia Pacific)
Michael Mullen (Mgr-Key Acct-MEA)
Cristian Tapliuc (Product Mgr-Romania)

POLARIS INTERNATIONAL HOLDINGS, INC.

391 E Las Colinas Blvd Ste 130, Irving, TX 75039
Tel.: (970) 279-3478   DE
PIHN—(OTCIQ)
Metal Mining & Exploration Services
N.A.I.C.S.: 213114
Kunimitsu Misawa (Pres & CEO)

POLARIS, INC.

2100 Hwy 55, Medina, MN 55340
Tel.: (763) 542-0500   MN
Web Site: https://www.polaris.com
Year Founded: 1954
PII—(NYSE)
Rev.: $8,934,400,000
Assets: $5,516,300,000
Liabilities: $4,095,500,000
Net Worth: $1,420,800,000
Earnings: $502,800,000
Emp.: 18,500
Fiscal Year-end: 12/31/23
All-Terrain Vehicles, Snowmobiles & Motorcycles Mfr & Marketer
N.A.I.C.S.: 336110
James P. Williams (Chief HR Officer & Sr VP)
Stephen L. Eastman (Pres-Parts, Garments, and accessories Div)
Pam Kermisch (Chief Customer Engagement & Growth Officer & VP-ORV Mktg)
Ben Duke (Pres-Marine)
Pamela L. Kermisch (Chief Customer Growth Officer)
Benjamin D. Duke (Pres)
J. C. Weigelt (VP)
Lucy Clark Dougherty (Officer-Compliance, Gen Counsel, Sec & Sr VP)
Michael T. Speetzen (CEO)

Subsidiaries:

Aixam Lusitana Sociedad De Comercializacae de Automoveis, S.A. (1)
Largo das Fontainhas 29, 1300-255, Lisbon, Portugal
Tel.: (351) 219609111
Web Site: http://www.aixam.pt
Motor Vehicle Mfr & Distr
N.A.I.C.S.: 336999

Aixam Mega Italia S.R.L.   (1)
Via Del Lavoro 9, Roreto Di Cherasco, 12002, Cuneo, Italy
Tel.: (39) 0172499186
Web Site: https://www.aixam-mega.it
Motor Vehicle Mfr & Distr
N.A.I.C.S.: 336999

Aixam Mega Nederland BV   (1)
Linie 15, 5405 AR, Uden, Netherlands
Tel.: (31) 41 324 7250
Web Site: https://www.aixam.nl
Motor Vehicle Mfr & Distr
N.A.I.C.S.: 336999

Aixam Mega S.A.S.   (1)
56 Route de Pugny, BP 70112, Pugny, 73101, Aix-les-Bains, Cedex, France
Tel.: (33) 47 961 4245
Web Site: https://www.aixam.com
Motor Vehicle Mfr & Distr
N.A.I.C.S.: 336999

Aixam-Mega Iberica, S.L.   (1)
Sant Cugat Business Park Av Via Augusta 15-25 B1 Planta 1 of 18-19, St Cugat del Valles, 08174, Barcelona, Spain
Tel.: (34) 90 205 2900
Web Site: https://www.aixam-mega.com
Motor Vehicle Mfr & Distr
N.A.I.C.S.: 336999

Global Electric Motorcars LLC   (1)
1900 Hwy 71, Spirit Lake, IA 51360
Tel.: (712) 336-3797
Web Site: http://www.gemcar.com
Sales Range: $25-49.9 Million
Emp.: 80
Electric-Powered Motor Vehicle Mfr
N.A.I.C.S.: 336110

Goupil Industrie S.A.   (1)
2445 Avenue de la Vallee du Lot, 47320, Bourran, France
Tel.: (33) 553793939
Web Site: http://www.goupil-ev.fr
Sales Range: $25-49.9 Million
Electric Vehicle Mfr
N.A.I.C.S.: 336320

Kolpin Outdoors, Inc.   (1)
9955 59th Ave N, Plymouth, MN 55442
Tel.: (763) 478-5800
Web Site: https://www.kolpin.com
Sales Range: $1-9.9 Million
ATV & UTV Accessories Mfr, Whslr & Retailer
N.A.I.C.S.: 339920

Larson Boats LLC   (1)
790 Markham Dr, Pulaski, WI 54162
Tel.: (320) 632-5481
Web Site: http://www.larsonboatgroup.com
Boat Mfr
N.A.I.C.S.: 336612
Jeff Olson (Pres)

Polaris Acceptance Inc.   (1)
2100 Hwy 55, Medina, MN 55340
Tel.: (763) 542-0500
Web Site: http://www.cdf.wf.com
Financial Services
N.A.I.C.S.: 522220

Polaris Britain Limited   (1)
Forge Mills Park Station Road, Industrial Estate Coleshill, Birmingham, B46 1HT, Warwickshire, United Kingdom
Tel.: (44) 330 041 5145
Web Site: https://www.polarisbritain.com
All-Terrain Vehicles, Snowmobiles, Motorcycles & Personal Watercraft Mfr & Marketer; Replacement Parts, Garments & Accessories Marketer
N.A.I.C.S.: 336991

Polaris Direct Inc.   (1)
2100 Hwy 55, Medina, MN 55340
Tel.: (763) 542-0500
Web Site: http://www.polarisindustries.com
Sales Range: $100-124.9 Million
Emp.: 250
All-Terrain Vehicles, Snowmobiles, Motorcycles & Personal Watercraft Direct Sales & Marketer
N.A.I.C.S.: 336999

Polaris Finland Oy   (1)
Porraskuja 3, 01740, Vantaa, Finland
Tel.: (358) 102872000
Web Site: http://www.polaris.fi
Motorcycle Parts Mfr
N.A.I.C.S.: 336991

Polaris France S A   (1)
50 rue du President Sadate, 29000, Quimper, France
Tel.: (33) 298548420
Web Site: https://www.polaris.fr
Sales Range: $10-24.9 Million
All-Terrain Vehicles, Snowmobiles, Motorcycles & Personal Watercraft Mfr & Marketer; Replacement Parts, Garments & Accessories Marketer
N.A.I.C.S.: 336991
Emmanuel Pean (Mng Dir)

Polaris Industries Ltd.   (1)
1445 Church Avenue, Winnipeg, R2X 2X9, MB, Canada
Tel.: (204) 925-7100
Motor Vehicle Body Mfr
N.A.I.C.S.: 336211

Polaris Industries Manufacturing LLC   (1)
2100 Hwy 55, Medina, MN 55340
Tel.: (763) 542-0500
Web Site: http://www.polarisind.com
Sales Range: $150-199.9 Million
Emp.: 400
All-Terrain Vehicles, Snowmobiles, Motorcycles & Personal Watercraft Mfr
N.A.I.C.S.: 336999

Polaris Industries Of Canada   (1)
50 Praire Way, Winnipeg, R2J 3J8, MB, Canada
Tel.: (204) 925-7100
Web Site: https://www.polaris.com
Sales Range: $10-24.9 Million
Emp.: 16

All-Terrain Vehicles, Snowmobiles, Motorcycles & Personal Watercraft Mfr, Sales & Marketer; Replacement Parts, Garments & Accessories Marketer
N.A.I.C.S.: 336991

Polaris Norway AS (1)
Kirkerudveien 1, PO Box 484, 1831, Askim, Norway (100%)
Tel.: (47) 69816888
Web Site: http://www.polarisind.com
Sales Range: $10-24.9 Million
All-Terrain Vehicles, Snowmobiles, Motorcycles & Personal Watercraft Mfr & Marketer; Related Replacement Parts, Garments & Accessories Marketer
N.A.I.C.S.: 336991

Polaris Sales Australia Pty Ltd. (1)
36 Grimes Court, Derrimut, 3030, VIC, Australia
Tel.: (61) 393945610
Web Site:
    http://www.polarisindustries.com.au
Sales Range: $10-24.9 Million
All-Terrain Vehicles, Snowmobiles, Motorcycles & Personal Watercraft Mfr & Marketer; Replacement Parts, Garments & Accessories Marketer
N.A.I.C.S.: 336991

Polaris Sales Inc. (1)
2100 Hwy 55, Medina, MN 55340
Tel.: (763) 542-0500
Web Site: http://www.polarisindustries.com
Sales Range: $125-149.9 Million
Emp.: 400
All-Terrain Vehicles, Snowmobiles, Motorcycles & Personal Watercraft Sales
N.A.I.C.S.: 336999

Polaris Scandinavia AB (1)
Brittsbovagen 1, Jamtland, 831 52, Ostersund, Sweden (100%)
Tel.: (46) 6 319 9560
Web Site:
    http://www.polarisscandinavia.com
Sales Range: $25-49.9 Million
Emp.: 20
All-Terrain Vehicles, Snowmobiles, Motorcycles & Personal Watercraft Mfr & Marketer; Related Replacement Parts, Garments & Accessories Marketer
N.A.I.C.S.: 336991

Primordial, Inc. (1)
1021 Bandana Sq Ste 225, Saint Paul, MN 55108
Tel.: (651) 395-6200
Web Site: http://www.primordial.com
Motor Vehicle Body Mfr
N.A.I.C.S.: 336211

TAP Manufacturing, LLC (1)
400 W Artesia Blvd, Compton, CA 90220
Tel.: (310) 900-5500
Web Site:
    http://www.transamericanautoparts.com
Automobile Parts Mfr
N.A.I.C.S.: 336999
Scott Ward (Pres)

TAP Worldwide, LLC (1)
400 W Artesia Blvd, Compton, CA 90220
Tel.: (310) 900-5500
Web Site:
    https://transamericanautoparts.com
Automotive Parts Mfr & Distr
N.A.I.C.S.: 336999
Greg Adler (Pres & CEO)

Taylor-Dunn Manufacturing Company (1)
2114 W Ball Rd, Anaheim, CA 92804
Tel.: (714) 956-4040
Web Site: http://www.taylor-dunn.com
Gas & Electric Vehicles Mfr
N.A.I.C.S.: 333924

Teton Outfitters, LLC (1)
3753 E County Line Rd, Rigby, ID 83442
Tel.: (208) 745-2728
Web Site: https://www.klim.com
Motor Vehicle Body Mfr
N.A.I.C.S.: 336211

Transamerican Auto Parts Co. (1)
400 W Artesia Blvd, Compton, CA 90220
Tel.: (310) 900-5500
Web Site:
    https://transamericanautoparts.com

Automotive Part Whslr
N.A.I.C.S.: 441330
Greg Adler (Vice Chm)

Victory Motorcycles Australia Pty Ltd (1)
544-554 Elizabeth Street, Melbourne, 3000, VIC, Australia
Tel.: (61) 393423888
Web Site:
    http://www.victorymotorcycles.com.au
Emp.: 20
Motor Cycles Design & Mfr
N.A.I.C.S.: 336991

WSI Industries, Inc. (1)
213 Chelsea Rd, Monticello, MN 55362
Tel.: (763) 295-9202
Web Site: http://www.wsiindustries.com
Rev.: $30,641,082
Assets: $24,485,368
Liabilities: $11,048,794
Net Worth: $13,436,574
Earnings: ($814,297)
Fiscal Year-end: 08/27/2017
Precision Contract Machining Services
N.A.I.C.S.: 332710
Michael J. Pudil (Chm, Pres & CEO)

Subsidiary (Domestic):

Bowman Tool & Machining Inc. (2)
660 37th St Nw, Rochester, MN 55901-3400 (100%)
Tel.: (507) 286-1400
Web Site: https://www.btmcnc.com
Sales Range: $25-49.9 Million
Emp.: 80
Precision Machining Company Serving the Construction & Forestry Industries
N.A.I.C.S.: 332710

POLARITYTE, INC.
1960 S 4250 W, Salt Lake City, UT 84104
Tel.: (385) 237-2279   DE
Web Site: https://www.polarityte.com
PTE—(NASDAQ)
Rev.: $814,000
Assets: $22,847,000
Liabilities: $6,229,000
Net Worth: $16,618,000
Earnings: ($7,833,000)
Emp.: 42
Fiscal Year-end: 12/31/22
Bio Technology Services
N.A.I.C.S.: 541714
Edward Winslow Swanson (Founder)
Cameron Hoyler (Gen Counsel & Exec VP-Corp Dev & Strategy)
Nikolai Sopko (Chief Scientific Officer & VP-R&D)
Richard Hague (Pres & CEO)
Jacob Patterson (CFO-Interim)
Peter Anthony Cohen (Chm)

POLYMERIC RESOURCES CORP.
55 Haul Rd, Wayne, NJ 07470-6677
Tel.: (973) 694-4141   NJ
Year Founded: 1976
PLYR—(OTCEM)
Sales Range: $25-49.9 Million
Emp.: 25
Mfr of Resins
N.A.I.C.S.: 325991

Subsidiaries:

Custom Resins Inc. (1)
55 Haul Rd, Wayne, NJ 07470-6612
Tel.: (973) 694-4141
Web Site: http://www.customresins.com
Sales Range: $10-24.9 Million
Provider of Plastic Products
N.A.I.C.S.: 325211

PONIARD PHARMACEUTI-CALS, INC.
300 Elliott Ave W Ste 530, Seattle, WA 98119
Tel.: (206) 281-7001   WA
Web Site: http://www.poniard.com

Year Founded: 1984
PARD—(OTCIQ)
Emp.: 12
Monoclonal Antibody Based Pharmaceutical Mfr
N.A.I.C.S.: 325412
Anna Lewak Wight (VP-Legal & Sec)

PONO CAPITAL TWO, INC.
643 Ilalo St Ste 102, Honolulu, HI 96813
Tel.: (808) 892-6611   DE
Year Founded: 2022
PTWO—(NASDAQ)
Asset Management Services
N.A.I.C.S.: 523999
Darryl Nakamoto (CEO)
Allison Van Orman (CFO)
Dustin Shindo (Chm)
Trisha Nomura (Chm-Audit Committee)

PONTEM CORPORATION
2170 Buckthorne Pl Ste 320, The Woodlands, TX 77380
Tel.: (212) 457-9077   Ky
Year Founded: 2020
PNTM—(NYSE)
Rev.: $9,953,496
Assets: $700,219,019
Liabilities: $733,074,840
Net Worth: ($32,855,821)
Earnings: $34,843,375
Emp.: 2
Fiscal Year-end: 12/31/22
Investment Services
N.A.I.C.S.: 523999
Hubertus Muehlhaeuser (Chm & CEO)
Nina Murphy (CFO)

PONTIAC BANCORP, INC.
300 W Washington St, Pontiac, IL 61764
Tel.: (815) 844-6155   DE
Web Site:
    http://www.bankofpontiac.com
Year Founded: 1982
PONT—(OTCIQ)
Bank Holding Company
N.A.I.C.S.: 551111
Christopher Clement (Sec)
Mark Donovan (VP)
Michelle Schultz (Treas)

Subsidiaries:

Bank of Pontiac (1)
300 W Washington St, Pontiac, IL 61764-1746 (100%)
Tel.: (815) 844-6155
Web Site: http://www.bankofpontiac.com
Sales Range: $10-24.9 Million
Emp.: 60
Full Banking Services
N.A.I.C.S.: 522110
John A. Marshall (VP)
Chris Clement (Asst VP-Agricultural Svcs)
Mark Donovan (Asst VP-Installment Lending)

POOL CORPORATION
109 Northpark Blvd, Covington, LA 70433-5521
Tel.: (985) 892-5521   DE
Web Site: https://www.poolcorp.com
Year Founded: 1980
POOL—(NASDAQ)
Rev.: $5,541,595,000
Assets: $3,428,068,000
Liabilities: $2,115,281,000
Net Worth: $1,312,787,000
Earnings: $523,229,000
Emp.: 6,000
Fiscal Year-end: 12/31/23
Swimming Pool Supplies & Related Products Distr
N.A.I.C.S.: 423910

Manuel J. Perez de la Mesa (Vice Chm)
Jennifer M. Neil (Chief Legal Officer & VP)
Melanie M. Hart (CFO, Treas & VP)
Donna K. Williams (CMO, VP & Gen Mgr)
Peter D. Arvan (Pres & CEO)
Curtis J. Scheel (Dir-IR)
Todd Marshall (CIO)
Walker F. Saik (Chief Acctg Officer & Controller)
Kendall Large (VP)
Ike Mihaly (VP)
Luther Willems (Chief HR Officer)

Subsidiaries:

Horizon (1)
4055 W Saturn Way, Chandler, AZ 85226
Tel.: (480) 961-3311
Web Site: https://www.horizononline.com
Sales Range: $125-149.9 Million
Emp.: 300
Farm & Garden Machinery
N.A.I.C.S.: 423820

Horizon Distributors, Inc. (1)
109 Northpark Blvd, Covington, LA 70433-5521
Tel.: (480) 337-6700
Web Site: https://www.horizononline.com
Sales Range: $25-49.9 Million
Emp.: 25
Landscape & Irrigation Products Distr
N.A.I.C.S.: 423820

Subsidiary (Domestic):

Turf & Garden, Inc. (2)
5445 Nansemond Pkwy, Suffolk, VA 23435
Tel.: (757) 638-0132
Farm Supplies Whslr
N.A.I.C.S.: 424910

Jet-Line Products Inc. (1)
55 Jacobus Ave, Kearny, NJ 07032-4512
Tel.: (973) 690-2999
Web Site: http://www.jetlineonline.com
Swimming Pools, Equipment & Supplies
N.A.I.C.S.: 423910

Branch (Domestic):

Jet Line Products Long Island (2)
1325 Suffolk Ave, Islandia, NY 11749
Tel.: (631) 348-3600
Web Site: http://www.jetlineprod.com
Sales Range: $25-49.9 Million
Emp.: 25
Swimming Pools, Equipment & Supplies
N.A.I.C.S.: 423910
Andrew Levinson (Pres)

Subsidiary (Domestic):

Jet Line Products Texas, LLC (2)
850 Freeport Pkwy, Coppell, TX 75019
Tel.: (972) 745-7946
Swimming Pool Equipments Distr
N.A.I.C.S.: 423910

Jet Line Products of South Jersey, LLC (2)
1400 Taylors Ln, Cinnaminson, NJ 08077
Tel.: (856) 786-0099
Web Site: http://www.jetlineonline.com
Swimming Pool Equipments Distr
N.A.I.C.S.: 423910

Pool Distributors Colombia S.A.S. (1)
Carrera 10 128 70 In 2, Bogota, 1004, Colombia
Tel.: (57) 13268600
Swimming Pool Cover & Other Product Mfr
N.A.I.C.S.: 326199

Pool Systems Pty. Ltd. (1)
27 Strathwyn Street, Brendale, 4500, QLD, Australia
Tel.: (61) 130 036 6020
Web Site: https://www.poolsystems.com.au
Swimming Pool Cover & Other Product Mfr
N.A.I.C.S.: 326199

SCP Benelux SA (1)
21 Maalbeekweg, 1930, Zaventem, Belgium
Tel.: (32) 23860340

Pool Corporation—(Continued)

Web Site: http://www.scpeurope.nl
Emp.: 10
Swimming Pool Equipment Whslr
N.A.I.C.S.: 423910

SCP Distributors LLC (1)
109 Northpark Blvd, Covington, LA 70433-5521
Tel.: (985) 892-5521
Web Site: http://www.scppool.com
Emp.: 2,000
Swimming Pool Supplies Whslr
N.A.I.C.S.: 423910

SCP France SAS (1)
8 Ave Des Metiers, La Primaube, 12000, France
Tel.: (33) 565733240
Web Site: http://www.scpeurope.fr
Swimming Pool Equipment & Supplies Whslr
N.A.I.C.S.: 423910

SCP Pool Distributors Spain S.L. (1)
Poligono Industrial El Molino Calle los Nardos 16, 28970, Madrid, Spain
Tel.: (34) 916169560
Swimming Pool Equipment Whslr
N.A.I.C.S.: 423910

Superior Pool Products, Inc. (1)
109 Northpark Blvd, Covington, LA 70433
Tel.: (985) 892-5521
Web Site:
http://www.superiorpoolproducts.com
Sales Range: $50-74.9 Million
Emp.: 800
Distr of Pool Chemicals & Accessories
N.A.I.C.S.: 423910

POPULAR, INC.
209 Munoz Rivera Ave, Hato Rey, PR 00918
Tel.: (787) 765-9800   PR
Web Site: https://www.popular.com
Year Founded: 1893
BPOP—(NASDAQ)
Rev.: $3,896,031,000
Assets: $70,758,155,000
Liabilities: $65,611,202,000
Net Worth: $5,146,953,000
Earnings: $539,930,000
Emp.: 9,237
Fiscal Year-end: 12/31/23
Commercial Banking Services
N.A.I.C.S.: 551111
Richard L. Carrion Rexach (Chm)
Ignacio Alvarez (CEO)
Javier D. Ferrer-Fernandez (Pres & COO)
Manuel Chinea (Exec VP)
Jorge J. Garcia (CFO & Exec VP)
Eduardo J. Negron (Exec VP-Admin Grp)
Lidio V. Soriano (Chief Risk Officer & Exec VP-Corp Risk Mgmt Grp)
Camille Burckhart (CIO, Chief Digital Officer & Exec VP-Innovation, Tech & Ops Grp)
Juan O. Guerrero (Exec VP-Fin & Insurance Svcs Grp)
Gilberto Monzon (Exec VP-Individual Credit Grp)
Luis E. Cestero (Exec VP-Retail Banking Grp)
Eli S. Sepulveda (Exec VP-Comml Credit Grp)
Beatriz Castellvi Armas (Chief Security Officer & Exec VP-Corp Security Grp)
Manuel Chinea (Exec VP)
Maria Cristina Gonzalez-Noguera (Chief Comm & Pub Affairs Officer & Exec VP)
Jose R. Coleman Tio (Chief Legal Officer)

Subsidiaries:

Banco Popular S.A. (1)

Velasques St No 34, 28001, Madrid, Spain   (50%)
Tel.: (34) 902301000
Web Site: http://www.bancopopular.es
Sales Range: $150-199.9 Million
Commercial & Retail Banking
N.A.I.C.S.: 522299

Banco Popular de Puerto Rico (1)
209 Ave Ponce De Leon, San Juan, PR 00918
Tel.: (787) 724-3650
Web Site: http://www.bppr.com
Sales Range: $1-4.9 Billion
Emp.: 10,651
Full Banking Services
N.A.I.C.S.: 522110
Ignacio Alvarez (Pres & CEO)
Javier D. Ferrer-Fernandez (Pres)

Branch (Domestic):

Banco Popular Puerto Rico - Virgin Islands Regional Office (2)
193 Altona & Wegunst, Saint Thomas, VI 00802
Tel.: (787) 706-4111
Sales Range: $100-124.9 Million
Emp.: 235
Regional Managing Office; Commercial Banking
N.A.I.C.S.: 551114

Division (Domestic):

Banco Popular de Puerto Rico - Trust Division (2)
153 Ponce de Leon Ave - 8th Fl, San Juan, PR 00918
Tel.: (787) 764-1893
Sales Range: $1-4.9 Billion
Plan Administration Services; Investment Management
N.A.I.C.S.: 522180

Subsidiary (Domestic):

Popular Auto LLC (2)
153 Ave Ponce De Leon, Hato Rey, PR 00918
Tel.: (787) 763-4848
Web Site:
https://www.popularautorentals.com
Automobile Leasing Services
N.A.I.C.S.: 532112

Popular Bank (1)
85 Broad St 10th Fl, New York, NY 10004
Tel.: (212) 246-4385
Web Site: https://www.popularbank.com
Sales Range: $400-449.9 Million
Emp.: 1,379
Commericial Banking
N.A.I.C.S.: 522110
Ignacio Alvarez (Pres & CEO)
Javier D. Ferrer-Fernandez (Pres)

Subsidiary (Domestic):

E-LOAN, Inc. (2)
85 Broad St 10th Fl, New York, NY 10004
Tel.: (925) 847-6200
Web Site: http://www.eloan.com
Sales Range: $125-149.9 Million
Mortgages, Auto Loans, Credit Cards & Small Business Loans
N.A.I.C.S.: 522310

POPULATION HEALTH INVESTMENT CO., INC.
1 World Financial Center, New York, NY 10281
Tel.: (212) 993-3113   Ky
Year Founded: 2020
PHIC—(NASDAQ)
Investment Services
N.A.I.C.S.: 523999
Ian C. Read (Co-Founder & Chm)
Christopher T. Cox (Sr VP)
Clive Meanwell (Co-Founder & CEO)
Chris Visioli (CFO)
Whit Bernard (Sr VP)
Christopher T. Cox (Sr VP)

PORCH GROUP, INC.
411 1st Ave S Ste 501, Seattle, WA 98104

Tel.: (847) 477-7963   DE
Web Site:
https://www.porchgroup.com
Year Founded: 2019
PRCH—(NASDAQ)
Rev.: $275,948,000
Assets: $1,049,057,000
Liabilities: $969,704,000
Net Worth: $79,353,000
Earnings: ($156,559,000)
Emp.: 1,800
Fiscal Year-end: 12/31/22
Investment Services
N.A.I.C.S.: 523999
Shawn Tabak (CFO & Principal Acctg Officer)
Janet Zimmermann (VP-People)
Emily Lear (Head-IR)
Sofia Rossato (Pres-Floify LLC & Gen Mgr-Floify LLC)
Matthew Ehrlichman (Founder, Chm & CEO)

Subsidiaries:

Americas Call Center, LLC (1)
1221 W 103rd St Ste 304, Kansas City, MO 64114
Web Site:
https://www.americascallcenter.com
Telecommunication Servicesb
N.A.I.C.S.: 517810

Elite Insurance Group, Inc. (1)
169 S Main St, Reidsville, GA 30453
Tel.: (912) 557-1065
Web Site: https://www.elite-insgroup.com
Insurance Services
N.A.I.C.S.: 524210
David Wilson (Pres & CEO)
Hunter Davis (COO)
Will Dykes (VP-Sls & Mktg)
Meagan Ryals (Office Mgr-Contracting)

Homeowners of America Holding Corporation (1)
1333 Corporate Dr Ste 325, Irving, TX 75038
Tel.: (972) 607-4241
Web Site: http://www.hoaic.com
Sales Range: $75-99.9 Million
Emp.: 56
Holding Company; Property & Casualty Insurance
N.A.I.C.S.: 551112
Spencer W. Tucker (Exec VP)
Michael C. Rosentraub (CFO, Treas & Sec)
Debbie L. Carter (Sr VP-Ops)
Michael S. Cox (VP & Dir-Sls & Mktg)
Brent W Parker (VP & Dir-Claims)
Don Capik (Sls Mgr-Georgia)
Adam Kornick (Pres)

MovingPlace, LLC (1)
2200 1st Ave S, Seattle, WA 98134
Web Site: https://www.movingplace.com
Self Services
N.A.I.C.S.: 812310

Residential Warranty Services, Inc. (1)
698 Pro-Med Ln, Carmel, IN 46032
Web Site: http://www.residentialwarrantyservices.com
Reinsurance Carriers
N.A.I.C.S.: 524130
P. Nathan Thornberry (Pres)

SML Relocation, LLC (1)
1400 Corporate Dr Ste 300, Irving, TX 75038
Web Site:
https://www.simplemovinglabor.com
Household Moving Services
N.A.I.C.S.: 484210
Lisa Dias (CEO)

iRoofing, LLC (1)
3127 W Hallandale Beach Blvd Ste 107, Hallandale Beach, FL 33009
Web Site: https://www.iroofing.org
Software Services
N.A.I.C.S.: 541511
Daniel Meridor (Co-Founder)
Oded Shemla (Co-Founder)

PORTILLO'S, INC.

2001 Spring Rd Ste 400, Oak Brook, IL 60523
Tel.: (630) 954-3773   DE
Web Site: https://www.portillos.com
Year Founded: 2021
PTLO—(NASDAQ)
Rev.: $587,104,000
Assets: $1,280,083,000
Liabilities: $847,182,000
Net Worth: $432,901,000
Earnings: $10,851,000
Emp.: 8,040
Fiscal Year-end: 12/25/22
Holding Company
N.A.I.C.S.: 551112
Michael Osanloo (Pres & CEO)
Michelle Hook (CFO & Treas)
Susan Shelton (Gen Counsel & Sec)
Jill Waite (Chief HR Officer)
Rick Cook (Sr VP-Tech)
Nick Scarpino (Sr VP-Mktg & Off Premise Dining)
Michael A. Miles Jr. (Chm)
Mike Ellis (Chief Dev Officer)

PORTLAND GENERAL ELECTRIC COMPANY
121 SW Salmon St, Portland, OR 97204
Tel.: (503) 464-8000   OR
Web Site:
https://www.portlandgeneral.com
Year Founded: 1889
POR—(NYSE)
Rev.: $2,923,000,000
Assets: $11,208,000,000
Liabilities: $7,889,000,000
Net Worth: $3,319,000,000
Earnings: $228,000,000
Emp.: 2,842
Fiscal Year-end: 12/31/23
Electric Power Distribution Services
N.A.I.C.S.: 221122
Brad Jenkins (VP-Utility Ops)
Brett Sims (VP-Strategy, Regulation & Energy Supply)
Benjamin F. Felton (COO & Exec VP)
Joseph R. Trpik Jr. (CFO & Sr VP-Finance)
Angelica Espinosa (Chief Legal Officer, Chief Compliance Officer, Gen Counsel & Sr VP)
Anne Mersereau (VP-HR, Diversity, Equity, and Inclusion)
Debbie Powell (VP-Utility Ops)

PORTMAN RIDGE FINANCE CORPORATION
650 Madison Ave 23rd Fl, New York, NY 10022
Tel.: (212) 891-2880   DE
Web Site:
https://www.portmanridge.com
Year Founded: 2006
PTMN—(NASDAQ)
Rev.: $69,614,000
Assets: $619,486,000
Liabilities: $387,363,000
Net Worth: $232,123,000
Earnings: $28,890,000
Fiscal Year-end: 12/31/22
Investment Management Service
N.A.I.C.S.: 523999
Brandon Satoren (CFO, Treas & Sec)
Patrick Schafer (Chief Investment Officer)
David Held (Chief Compliance Officer)
Edward Goldthorpe (Chm, Pres & CEO))

Subsidiaries:

OHA Investment Corporation (1)
1114 Ave of the Americas 27th Fl, New York, NY 10036
Tel.: (212) 852-1900

Web Site:
http://www.ohainvestmentcorporation.com
Rev.: $8,468,000
Assets: $84,777,000
Liabilities: $48,868,000
Net Worth: $35,909,000
Earnings: $671,000
Fiscal Year-end: 12/31/2018
Financial Investment Services for Energy
Industry
N.A.I.C.S.: 523999
Cory E. Gilbert (CFO & Treas)
Lisa R. Price (Chief Compliance Officer)
Steven T. Wayne (Pres & CEO)

POSABIT SYSTEMS CORP.

15 Lake Bellevue Dr Ste 101, Belle-
vue, WA 98005
Web Site: https://www.posabit.com
POSAF—(OTCQX)
Rev.: $49,772,117
Assets: $17,996,874
Liabilities: $9,773,852
Net Worth: $8,223,022
Earnings: $8,063,603
Fiscal Year-end: 12/31/22
Custom Computer Programming Ser-
vices
N.A.I.C.S.: 541511
Matthew Fowler (CFO)
Chris Baker (Chief Strategy Officer)
Ryan Hamlin (Founder & CEO)
Sarah Mirsky-Terranova (Chief Com-
pliance Officer)

POSEIDA THERAPEUTICS, INC.

9390 Towne Centre Dr Ste 200, San
Diego, CA 92121
Tel.: (858) 779-3100   DE
Web Site: https://www.poseida.com
Year Founded: 2014
PSTX—(NASDAQ)
Rev.: $130,492,000
Assets: $351,837,000
Liabilities: $164,242,000
Net Worth: $187,595,000
Earnings: ($64,002,000)
Emp.: 312
Fiscal Year-end: 12/31/22
Biotechnology Research & Develop-
ment Services
N.A.I.C.S.: 541714
Mark J. Gergen (Pres & Chief Bus
Officer)
Kristin Martin (Chief HR Officer)
Devon J. Shedlock (Sr VP-R&D)
Johanna Mylet (CFO)
Harry J. Leonhardt (Chief Compliance
Officer, Gen Counsel & Sec)
Jeffrey W. Winkelman (VP-Intellectual
Property)
Karen Basbaum (VP-Bus Dev)
Mark J. Gergen (Exec Chm)
Kristin Yarema (Pres & CEO)

POSITIVE PHYSICIANS HOLD-INGS, INC.

100 Berwyn Park Ste 220, Berwyn,
PA 19312   PA
Web Site:
http://www.positivephysicians.com
Year Founded: 2018
PPHI—(OTCEM)
Rev.: $27,965,606
Assets: $156,620,361
Liabilities: $83,426,956
Net Worth: $73,193,405
Earnings: ($238,951)
Fiscal Year-end: 12/31/19
Holding Company
N.A.I.C.S.: 551112
Matthew T. Popoli (Chm)
Duncan McLaughlin (Bd of Dirs &
Vice Chm)
Michael George Roque (Pres & CEO)

Subsidiaries:

Positive Physicians Insurance
Company   (1)
850 Cassatt Rd 100 Berwyn Park Ste 220,
Berwyn, PA 19312
Web Site: http://www.positivephysicians.com
Medical Liability Insurance Services
N.A.I.C.S.: 524114
Lewis Sharps (Founder, Pres & CEO)
Leslie Latta (COO)
Daniel Payne (Treas)
Jason Sharps (Dir-Sls, Mktg & Broker Rels)
Debbie Gass (Dir-Underwriting)

POST HOLDINGS PARTNER-ING CORPORATION

2503 S Hanley Rd, Saint Louis, MO
63144
Tel.: (314) 644-7600   DE
Web Site: https://www.postpspc.com
Year Founded: 2021
PSPC—(NYSE)
Assets: $350,536,227
Liabilities: $360,515,999
Net Worth: ($9,979,772)
Earnings: $11,892,175
Emp.: 2
Fiscal Year-end: 12/31/22
Investment Services
N.A.I.C.S.: 523999
Robert V. Vitale (Pres & Chief Invest-
ment Officer)
Jeff A. Zadoks (Chm)
Bradly A. Harper (CFO)

POST HOLDINGS, INC.

2503 S Hanley Rd, Saint Louis, MO
63144
Tel.: (314) 644-7600   MO
Web Site:
https://www.postholdings.com
Year Founded: 2012
POST—(NYSE)
Rev.: $6,226,700,000
Assets: $12,414,700,000
Liabilities: $9,355,500,000
Net Worth: $3,059,200,000
Earnings: $166,700,000
Emp.: 10,735
Fiscal Year-end: 09/30/21
Holding Company; Breakfast Cereal
Mfr
N.A.I.C.S.: 551112
Robert V. Vitale (Pres & CEO)
Jeff A. Zadoks (COO & Exec VP)
Darcy Horn Davenport (Pres/CEO-
BellRing Brands)
Matthew J. Mainer (CFO, Treas & Sr
VP)
Diedre J. Gray (Chief Admin Officer,
Gen Counsel & Exec VP)
Sally Abbott (Mng Dir-Weetabix-UK &
Ireland)
Bradly A. Harper (Chief Acctg Officer
& Sr VP)
Mark A. Delahanty (Pres/CEO-Post
Refrigerated Retail)

Subsidiaries:

8th Avenue Food & Provisions,
Inc.   (1)
1400 S Hwy Dr Ste 402, Fenton, MO 63026
Tel.: (314) 282-4746
Web Site: https://www.8ave.com
Food Mfr
N.A.I.C.S.: 311230
Scott McNair (Pres & CEO)
Craig Cohen (CFO)
Marcel Tayssoun (VP-IT)
Hitesh Ruparel (Sr VP-Supply Chain)
Mike Petrie (Gen Mgr-Pasta)
Deepashri Khare (Chief HR Officer)
Jim Donzelli (Sr VP)
Amy Michtich (COO)

Alpen Food Company South Africa
(Pty) Ltd.   (1)
1 Melck Street, Maitland, 7405, South Africa
Tel.: (27) 215063240

Web Site: https://www.alpenfood.co.za
Breakfast Cereal Mfr
N.A.I.C.S.: 311230

BellRing Brands, Inc.   (1)
Tel.: (314) 644-7600
Web Site: https://www.bellring.com
Rev.: $1,666,800,000
Assets: $691,600,000
Liabilities: $1,015,100,000
Net Worth: ($323,500,000)
Earnings: $165,500,000
Emp.: 420
Fiscal Year-end: 09/30/2023
Nutrition Product Whslr
N.A.I.C.S.: 456191
Robert V. Vitale (Chm)
Darcy Horn Davenport (Pres & CEO)
Paul A. Rode (CFO & Treas)
Eric Hunn (VP-People)
Craig L. Rosenthal (Gen Counsel, Sec & Sr
VP)
Ching-Yee Hu (Sr VP)

Bob Evans Farms, LLC   (1)
8200 Walton Pkwy, New Albany, OH
43054   (100%)
Web Site:
https://www.bobevansgrocery.com
Sausage & Other Food Products Mfr & Distr
N.A.I.C.S.: 311999

Casa Trucking, Inc.   (1)
120 Tower St, Gaylord, MN 55334
Tel.: (507) 237-4600
Food Store Operator
N.A.I.C.S.: 445298

Dakota Growers Pasta Company,
Inc.   (1)
1 Pasta Ave, Carrington, ND 58421
Tel.: (701) 652-2855
Web Site: http://www.dakotagrowers.com
Sales Range: $100-124.9 Million
Emp.: 300
Pasta Mfr & Whslr
N.A.I.C.S.: 311824

Dymatize Enterprises, Inc.   (1)
111 Leslie St, Dallas, TX 75207
Tel.: (972) 732-1990
Web Site: http://www.dymatize.com
Sales Range: $150-199.9 Million
Emp.: 20
Nutritional & Sports Supplements Mfr &
Marketer
N.A.I.C.S.: 325412

Golden Boy Foods Ltd.   (1)
7725 Lougheed Highway, Burnaby, V5A
4V8, BC, Canada
Tel.: (604) 433-2200
Web Site: http://www.goldenboyfoods.com
Sales Range: $250-299.9 Million
Nut & Dried Fruit Product Mfr
N.A.I.C.S.: 311911

Subsidiary (US):

American Blanching Company   (2)
155 Rip Wiley Rd, Fitzgerald, GA 31750-
1028
Tel.: (229) 423-4098
Web Site:
http://www.americanblanching.com
Emp.: 400
Roasted Nuts & Peanut Butter Mfr
N.A.I.C.S.: 311911
Jack Warden (Pres & CEO)

Golden Boy Nut Corporation   (1)
101 Hudson St, Troy, AL 36079
Tel.: (334) 674-0037
Web Site: http://www.goldenboyfoods.com
Food Store Operator
N.A.I.C.S.: 445298

Golden Boy Portales, LLC   (1)
2503 S Hanley Rd, Saint Louis, MO 63144
Tel.: (314) 644-7600
Food Preparation Whslr
N.A.I.C.S.: 424420

Golden Nut Company (USA) Inc.   (1)
1555 Odell St, Blaine, WA 98230
Tel.: (360) 332-1990
Food Preparation Whslr
N.A.I.C.S.: 424420

Latimer Group Limited   (1)
Top Fl 3-5 Hardwidge Street, London, SE1

3SY, United Kingdom
Tel.: (44) 2079989150
Web Site: http://www.latimergroup.org
Grocery & Related Product Distr
N.A.I.C.S.: 424490

MFI Holding Corporation   (1)
200 West St, New York, NY 10282-2198
Tel.: (212) 902-1000
Holding Company
N.A.I.C.S.: 551112

MOM Brands Company, LLC   (1)
20802 Kensington Blvd, Lakeville, MN
55044
Tel.: (952) 322-8000
Web Site: http://www.mombrands.com
Breakfast Cereal Mfr
N.A.I.C.S.: 311230

MOM Brands Ssales, LLC   (1)
20802 Kensington Blvd, Lakeville, MN
55044
Tel.: (952) 322-8000
Web Site: http://www.mombrands.com
Food Preparation Whslr
N.A.I.C.S.: 424420

Michael Foods Group, Inc.   (1)
301 Carlson Pkwy Ste 400, Minnetonka,
MN 55305
Tel.: (952) 258-4000
Web Site: http://www.michaelfoods.com
Sales Range: $1-4.9 Billion
Emp.: 3,675
Egg, Potato, Cheese & Other Dairy Case
Products Mfr & Distr
N.A.I.C.S.: 311999
Adrian M. Jones (Chm)

Subsidiary (Domestic):

Michael Foods, Inc.   (2)
9350 Excelsior Blvd Ste 300, Hopkins, MN
55343
Tel.: (952) 258-4000
Web Site: https://www.michaelfoods.com
Sales Range: $1-4.9 Billion
Refrigerated Grocery Products, Non-Frozen
Potato Products & Fresh, Frozen & Dried
Egg Products Producer & Distr
N.A.I.C.S.: 311999

Subsidiary (Domestic):

Crystal Farms Refrigerated Distribu-
tion Company   (3)
301 Carlson Pkwy Ste 400, Minnetonka,
MN 55305
Tel.: (952) 544-8101
Web Site: http://www.microfoods.com
Sales Range: $25-49.9 Million
Emp.: 100
Refrigerated Dairy Case Items Mfr
N.A.I.C.S.: 424430

Farm Fresh Foods, Inc.   (3)
3840 N Civic Center Dr Ste B, North Las
Vegas, NV 89030-7534
Tel.: (702) 643-5238
Sales Range: $25-49.9 Million
Emp.: 30
Potato Products Mfr
N.A.I.C.S.: 311999

Papetti's Hygrade Egg Products,
Inc.   (3)
1 Papetti Plz, Elizabeth, NJ 07206
Tel.: (908) 282-7900
Web Site: http://www.papetti.com
Sales Range: $25-49.9 Million
Emp.: 50
Egg Products Mfr & Distr
N.A.I.C.S.: 311999
Charles Bailey (Gen Mgr)

Willamette Egg Farms LLC   (3)
31348 S Hwy 170, Canby, OR 97013-9557
Tel.: (503) 651-0000
Web Site: http://www.willametteegg.com
Commercial Egg Farm
N.A.I.C.S.: 112310
Greg Satrum (Co-Owner)
Gordon Satrum (Co-Owner)

Michael Foods of Delaware, Inc.   (1)
301 Carlson Pkwy Ste 400, Minnetonka,
MN 55305
Tel.: (952) 258-4000
Web Site: http://michaelfoods.com
Food Store Operator

Post Holdings, Inc.—(Continued)

N.A.I.C.S.: 445298

Subsidiary (Domestic):

Henningsen Foods, Inc. (2)
14334 Industrial Rd, Omaha, NE 68144-3334
Tel.: (402) 330-2500
Web Site: http://www.henningsenfoods.com
Dehydrated Food Products; Custom Dehydration
N.A.I.C.S.: 311999
Gina Blankenau (Mgr-Logistics)

Pineland Farms Potato Company, Inc. (1)
115 Presque Isle Rd, Mars Hill, ME 04758
Web Site: http://www.pinelandpotatoes.com
Potato Farming Services
N.A.I.C.S.: 111211
Laurie Nelson (Mgr-HR)

Post Brands Pet Care, LLC (1)
1111 N Miller Park Ct, Visalia, CA 93291
Tel.: (916) 452-8823
Web Site: http://www.perfectionpetfoods.com
Dog & Cat Food Mfr
N.A.I.C.S.: 311111
Don Hill (Dir-Tech Svcs)

Post Consumer Brands, LLC (1)
20802 Kensington Blvd, Lakeville, MN 55044
Web Site: https://www.postconsumerbrands.com
Grocery & Related Product Distr
N.A.I.C.S.: 424490

Post Foods, LLC (1)
Tel.: (314) 644-7600
Web Site: https://www.postconsumerbrands.com
Emp.: 4,600
Breakfast Cereal Mfr, Distr & Marketer
N.A.I.C.S.: 311230
Robert V. Vitale (Pres & CEO)

Subsidiary (Non-US):

Post Foods Canada Corp. (2)
5651 Lewis Avenue, PO Box 450, Niagara Falls, L2E 6T8, ON, Canada
Tel.: (905) 374-7111
Web Site: http://www.postfoods.ca
Sales Range: $100-124.9 Million
Breakfast Cereal Mfr
N.A.I.C.S.: 311230

Plant (Domestic):

Post Foods, LLC - Battle Creek Plant (2)
275 Cliff St, Battle Creek, MI 49014-6354
Tel.: (269) 966-1000
Web Site: http://www.postfoods.com
Sales Range: $125-149.9 Million
Breakfast Cereal Mfr
N.A.I.C.S.: 311230

Post Foods, LLC - Jonesboro Plant (2)
5800 CW Post Rd, Jonesboro, AR 72401
Tel.: (870) 933-4100
Web Site: http://www.postfoods.com
Sales Range: $50-74.9 Million
Breakfast Cereal Mfr
N.A.I.C.S.: 311230

Post Foods, LLC - Modesto Plant (2)
901 E Whitmore Ave, Modesto, CA 95353-0390
Tel.: (209) 541-3400
Sales Range: $50-74.9 Million
Breakfast Cereal Mfr
N.A.I.C.S.: 311230

Branch (Domestic):

Post Foods, LLC - Parsippany Administrative Office (2)
1 Upper Pond Rd Bldg E 2nd Fl, Parsippany, NJ 07054
Tel.: (973) 658-2300
Web Site: http://www.postfoods.com
Administrative Services
N.A.I.C.S.: 561110

PowerBar Inc. (1)
445 State St, Fremont, MI 49413
Tel.: (800) 587-6937
Web Site: http://www.powerbar.com
Sales Range: $75-99.9 Million
Emp.: 300
Energy & Protein Bars Mfr
N.A.I.C.S.: 311340

Subsidiary (Non-US):

Active Nutrition International GmbH (2)
Zielstattstrasse 42, 81379, Munich, Germany
Tel.: (49) 895020070
Web Site: http://www.active-nutrition-international.com
Energy & Protein Bars Mfr
N.A.I.C.S.: 311340

Premier Nutrition Company, LLC (1)
PO Box 933, Kings Mountain, NC 28086
Web Site: http://www.premiernutrition.com
Nutrition Product Whslr
N.A.I.C.S.: 456191
Kathleen Beckert (VP-Fin)
Michael Sparda (VP-Sls)
Darcy Horn Davenport (Pres)
Robin Singh (Sr VP)
Marc Mollere (Sr VP)
Brain Hofmeister (VP)
Eric Hunn (Sr VP)
Ching-Yee Hu (Sr VP)

Primo Piatto, Inc. (1)
7300 36th Ave N, Minneapolis, MN 55427-2001
Tel.: (763) 531-5340
Food Preparation Whslr
N.A.I.C.S.: 424420

Weetabix Company, LLC (1)
20802 Kensington Blvd, Lakeville, MN 55044
Web Site: http://www.weetabixusa.com
Nutrition Wheat Product Mfr
N.A.I.C.S.: 311999

Weetabix East Africa Limited (1)
GATE A Lungalunga Rd GATE B Lusingeti Rd Off Likoni Rd, PO Box 78633, Industrial Area, 00507, Nairobi, Kenya
Tel.: (254) 206652377
Web Site: https://www.weetabixea.com
Breakfast Cereal Mfr
N.A.I.C.S.: 311230

Weetabix Foods Limited (1)
Station Road Burton Latimer, Kettering, NN15 5JR, United Kingdom
Tel.: (44) 1536722181
Web Site: http://www.weetabix.co.uk
Breakfast Cereal Mfr
N.A.I.C.S.: 311230

Weetabix Limited (1)
Station Road, Burton Latimer, Kettering, NN15 5JR, Northamptonshire, United Kingdom (100%)
Tel.: (44) 1536722181
Web Site: https://www.weetabix.co.uk
Cereal Mfr
N.A.I.C.S.: 311230
Richard Martin (CFO)
Bruce Condon (Dir-Fin)

Subsidiary (Non-US):

Weetabix of Canada Limited (2)
751 D'Arcy St, Cobourg, K9A 4B1, ON, Canada
Tel.: (000) 040-0500
Web Site: http://www.weetabix.ca
Cereal Mfr
N.A.I.C.S.: 311230

POSTAL REALTY TRUST, INC.

75 Columbia Ave, Cedarhurst, NY 11516
Tel.: (516) 295-7820   MD
Web Site: https://www.postalrealtytrust.com
Year Founded: 2018
PSTL—(NYSE)
Rev.: $53,330,000
Assets: $501,303,000
Liabilities: $217,592,000

Net Worth: $283,711,000
Earnings: $3,854,000
Emp.: 42
Fiscal Year-end: 12/31/22
Other Activities Related to Real Estate
N.A.I.C.S.: 531390
Andrew Spodek (CEO)
Jeremy Garber (Pres, Treas & Sec)
Matt Brandwein (Chief Acctg Officer & Sr VP)
Carrie Herz (Corp Counsel & Sr VP)
Raphael Harel (Sr VP-Acquisitions)
Isaac Richter (Exec VP & Head-Asset Mgmt)
Marc Lefkovich (VP & Controller-Property)
Nicole Subrati (Coord-Acquisitions)
Josh Anand (Project Mgr)
Nathan Barry (VP & Sr Project Mgr)
Brandon Burrell (Project Mgr)
Daniel Hazelton (Project Mgr)
Robert B. Klein (CFO)
David Loss (Exec VP & Head-Real Estate)
Jie Chai (Corp Counsel & Sr VP)
Amy Collins (VP-Asset Mgmt)
Andrea Gritser (VP & Controller)
Michael Marino (VP-Acquisitions)
Cindy Kelly (Controller-Asst Property)
Jonathan Gerzon (Mgr-Property Acctg)
Sebastian Fileccia (Project Mgr)
Peter Boucher (Project Mgr)
Peter Vavalle (Project Mgr)
Robert Fontana (Project Mgr)
Richard Broderick (Project Mgr)
Jordan Cooperstein (VP)

Subsidiaries:

A&J Assets LLC (1)
PO Box 293091, Lewisville, TX 75067
Tel.: (469) 209-5512
Web Site: https://www.ajassets.com
Real Estate Services
N.A.I.C.S.: 531390

POTBELLY CORPORATION

111 N Canal St Ste 325, Chicago, IL 60606
Tel.: (312) 951-0600   DE
Web Site: https://www.potbelly.com
PBPB—(NASDAQ)
Rev.: $491,409,000
Assets: $252,160,000
Liabilities: $238,367,000
Net Worth: $14,093,000
Earnings: $5,577,000
Emp.: 5,000
Fiscal Year-end: 12/31/23
Holding Company; Sandwich Shops Owner, Operator & Franchisor
N.A.I.C.S.: 551112
Steven W. Cirulis (CFO, Chief Strategy Officer & Sr VP)
Robert D. Wright (Pres & CEO)
Adam Noyes (COO & Sr VP)
Larry Strain (Chief Dev Officer)

Subsidiaries:

Potbelly Franchising, LLC (1)
222 Merchandise Mart Plz, Chicago, IL 60654
Tel.: (312) 836-1007
Web Site: http://www.potbelly.com
Sandwich Shop Franchisor
N.A.I.C.S.: 533110

Potbelly Sandwich Works, LLC (1)
111 N Canal St Ste 325, Chicago, IL 60606
Tel.: (312) 836-1007
Web Site: http://www.potbelly.com
Emp.: 100
Sandwich Shops Operator
N.A.I.C.S.: 722513

POTLATCHDELTIC CORPORATION

601 W 1st Ave Ste 1600, Spokane, WA 99201
Tel.: (509) 835-1500   DE
Web Site: https://www.potlatchdeltic.com
Year Founded: 1903
PCH—(NASDAQ)
Rev.: $1,330,780,000
Assets: $3,550,555,000
Liabilities: $1,287,402,000
Net Worth: $2,263,153,000
Earnings: $333,900,000
Emp.: 1,330
Fiscal Year-end: 12/31/22
Paper Mfr & Dist, Pulp & Lumber Products
N.A.I.C.S.: 525990
Eric J. Cremers (Pres & CEO)
Glen F. Smith (Chief Acctg Officer)
William R. DeReu (VP-Real Estate Div)
Robert L. Schwartz (VP-HR)
Anna E. Torma (VP-Pub Affairs)
Michele L. Tyler (Gen Counsel, Sec & VP)
Ashlee Cribb (VP-Wood Products)
Ashlee Townsend Cribb (VP-)
Darin R. Ball (VP-)

Subsidiaries:

CatchMark Timber Trust, Inc. (1)
5 Concourse Pkwy Ste 2650, Atlanta, GA 30328
Web Site: http://www.catchmark.com
Rev.: $102,161,000
Assets: $507,310,000
Liabilities: $323,314,000
Net Worth: $183,996,000
Earnings: $58,262,000
Emp.: 21
Fiscal Year-end: 12/31/2021
Real Estate Investment Services
N.A.I.C.S.: 523999
Donald L. Warden (VP-Real Estate & Alternative Income)
John D. Capriotti (VP-Acquisitions)
Todd P. Reitz (Chief Resources Officer)
Lesley H. Solomon (Gen Counsel & Sec)
Ursula A. Godoy-Arbelaez (CFO, Treas & Sr VP)

Chenal Country Club (1)
10 Chenal Club Blvd, Little Rock, AR 72223
Tel.: (501) 821-4141
Web Site: https://www.chenalcc.com
Country Club
N.A.I.C.S.: 713910
Shannon Webre (Dir-Member Rels)
Crystal Herring (Mgr-Sls-Catering)
Tandy Hunjan (Mgr-HR)
Jed Spencer (Head-Golf Course Superintendent)
Augie Barrios (Gen Mgr)
Aubrey de Matthaeis (Dir-Member Enrollment)

Chenal Properties, Inc. (1)
7 Chenal Blvd, Little Rock, AR 72223 (100%)
Tel.: (501) 821-5555
Web Site: https://www.chenal.com
Sales Range: Less than $1 Million
Emp.: 7
Residential & Commercial Real Estate Development
N.A.I.C.S.: 531190

Potlatch Corporation Wood Products Group (1)
601 W Burst, Spokane, WA 99201 (100%)
Tel.: (509) 328-0930
Web Site: http://www.potlatchcorp.com
Rev.: $506,247,008
Emp.: 13
Lumber, Plywood & Particle Board Sales
N.A.I.C.S.: 423310

Potlatch Minnesota Timberlands, LLC (1)
601 W 1st Ave Ste 1600, Spokane, WA 99201
Tel.: (509) 835-1500
Timber Wood Product Distr
N.A.I.C.S.: 423990

The Prescott & Northwestern Railroad Co. (1)

PO Box 390, Warren, AR
71671-0390 **(100%)**
Tel.: (870) 887-3103
Web Site: http://www.potlatchcorp.com
Sales Range: $1-9.9 Million
Emp.: 7
Providing Railroad Services
N.A.I.C.S.: 482111

POTOMAC BANCSHARES INC.

111 E Washington St, Charles Town,
WV 25414
Tel.: (304) 725-8431
Web Site: https://www.mybct.bank
PTBS—(OTCIQ)
Rev.: $41,533,000
Assets: $830,714,000
Liabilities: $763,840,000
Net Worth: $66,874,000
Earnings: $7,264,000
Emp.: 122
Fiscal Year-end: 12/31/23
State Commercial Banks
N.A.I.C.S.: 522110
Dean J. Cognetti *(CFO & Exec VP)*
Keith B. Berkeley *(Chm)*
Raymond F. Goodrich *(Chief Lending Officer & Exec VP)*
Tim E. Lewis *(Exec VP & Dir-Retail & Tech Ops)*
Alice P. Frazier *(Pres & CEO)*

POWELL INDUSTRIES, INC.

8550 Mosley Rd, Houston, TX 77075-
1180
Tel.: (713) 944-6900 DE
Web Site: https://www.powellind.com
Year Founded: 1947
POWL—(NASDAQ)
Rev.: $1,012,356,000
Assets: $928,180,000
Liabilities: $445,107,000
Net Worth: $483,073,000
Earnings: $149,848,000
Emp.: 2,748
Fiscal Year-end: 09/30/24
Electrical Power Generators & Control Equipment Mfr, Designer & Marketer
N.A.I.C.S.: 221122
Brett A. Cope *(Chm, Pres & CEO)*
Michael W. Metcalf *(CFO, Principal Acctg Officer, Treas, Sec & Exec VP)*

Subsidiaries:

Nextron Corporation **(1)**
14-6120 11th Street SE, Calgary, T2H 2L7,
AB, Canada
Tel.: (403) 735-9555
Web Site: https://www.nextron.ca
Temperature Monitoring Devices & Controllers
N.A.I.C.S.: 334513

Powell (UK) Limited **(1)**
Ripley Rd, Bradford, BD4 7EH, Yorkshire,
United Kingdom **(100%)**
Tel.: (44) 1274734221
Sales Range: $100-124.9 Million
Emp.: 300
Mfr & Designer of Instrumentation Panels,
Switchgear & Controls
N.A.I.C.S.: 335313
Robin Graham *(Mgr-Pur)*
Mike Galley *(Mng Dir)*

Powell Canada Inc. **(1)**
10960 274 Street, Acheson, T7X 6P7, AB,
Canada
Tel.: (780) 948-3300
Web Site: http://www.powellind.ca
Emp.: 300
Metal Fabricating Services
N.A.I.C.S.: 423830
Thomas W. Powell *(Chm)*
Brett A. Cope *(Pres & CEO)*

Powell ESCO Company **(1)**
8550 Mosley, Houston, TX 77075 **(100%)**
Tel.: (713) 944-6900
Web Site: http://www.powellesco.com
Rev.: $9,000,000

Emp.: 50
Electric Service Company
N.A.I.C.S.: 335311

Powell Electrical Manufacturing
Company **(1)**
8550 Mosley Rd, Houston, TX
77075-1116 **(100%)**
Tel.: (713) 944-6900
Web Site: http://www.powellelectric.com
Sales Range: $400-449.9 Million
Emp.: 1,200
Mfr, Designer & Marketer of Electrical
Power Generators & Control Equipment
N.A.I.C.S.: 335314

Powell Electrical Systems, Inc. **(1)**
8550 Mosley Rd, Houston, TX 77075
Tel.: (713) 944-6900
Emp.: 400
Custom Engineered Electrical Systems Mfr
N.A.I.C.S.: 335313

Powell Industries Asia, Pte. Ltd. **(1)**
350 Orchard Road 11-08 Shaw House, Singapore, 238882, Singapore
Tel.: (65) 96625698
Electrical Apparatus & Equipment Distr
N.A.I.C.S.: 423610

Unibus, Inc. **(1)**
515 Railroad Ave, Northlake, IL
60164-1652 **(100%)**
Tel.: (708) 409-1200
Web Site: http://www.unibus.com
Rev.: $9,000,000
Emp.: 90
Mfr, Designer & Marketer of Electrical
Power Generators & Control Equipment
N.A.I.C.S.: 335311

POWER & DIGITAL INFRA-STRUCTURE ACQUISITION CORP.

321 N Clark St Ste 2440, Chicago, IL
60654
Tel.: (312) 374-6932 DE
Web Site: http://www.xpdispac.com
Year Founded: 2020
XPDI—(NASDAQ)
Investment Services
N.A.I.C.S.: 523999
Theodore J. Brombach *(Chm)*
Patrick C. Eilers *(CEO)*
Benjamin W. Atkins *(VP)*
Jesse Peltan *(VP)*
James P. Nygaard Jr. *(CFO)*

POWER INTEGRATIONS, INC.

5245 Hellyer Ave, San Jose, CA
95138
Tel.: (408) 414-9200 CA
Web Site: https://www.power.com
Year Founded: 1988
POWI—(NASDAQ)
Rev.: $444,538,000
Assets: $819,868,000
Liabilities: $67,627,000
Net Worth: $752,241,000
Earnings: $55,735,000
Emp.: 819
Fiscal Year-end: 12/31/23
High-Voltage Analog Integrated Circuit Mfr
N.A.I.C.S.: 334413
Sandeep Nayyar *(CFO & VP-Fin)*
Steven J. Sharp *(Executives)*
Balu Balakrishnan *(Chm, Pres & CEO)*
Clifford Walker *(VP-Corp Dev)*
Douglas G. Bailey *(VP-Mktg)*
Radu M. Barsan *(VP-Tech)*
Mike Matthews *(VP-Product Dev)*
Thomas Simonis *(VP)*
Sunny Gupta *(VP-Ops)*
Klas Eklund *(Co-Founder)*
Art Fury *(Co-Founder)*
Yang Chiah Yee *(VP-Global)*

Subsidiaries:

Odyssey Semiconductor Technologies, Inc. **(1)**

9 Brown Rd, Ithaca, NY 14850
Tel.: (607) 882-2754
Web Site: https://www.odysseysemi.com
Rev.: $321,049
Assets: $4,172,682
Liabilities: $5,746,994
Net Worth: ($1,574,312)
Earnings: ($5,693,612)
Emp.: 13
Fiscal Year-end: 12/31/2022
Semiconductor & Related Device Manufacturing
N.A.I.C.S.: 334413
Richard J. Brown *(Co-Founder & CEO)*
James R. Shealy *(Co-Founder, Treas & Sec)*
Alfred Schremer *(VP-R&D)*

Power Integrations (Europe)
Limited **(1)**
1st Floor Saint James's House, East Street,
Farnham, GU9 7TJ, Surrey, United Kingdom
Tel.: (44) 1252730140
Web Site: http://www.powerint.com
Sales Range: $1-9.9 Million
Emp.: 4
High-Voltage Analog Integrated Circuit Mfr
N.A.I.C.S.: 334413

Subsidiary (Non-US):

Power Integrations GmbH **(2)**
Ruckerstrasse 3, Munich, 80336, Germany
Tel.: (49) 8955273910
High-Voltage Analog Integrated Circuit Mfr
N.A.I.C.S.: 334413

Power Integrations Singapore Pte.
Limited **(1)**
51 Newton Road 20-01/03 Goldhill Plaza,
Singapore, 308900, Singapore
Tel.: (65) 63582160
Web Site: http://www.powerintegrations.com
Sales Range: $10-24.9 Million
High-Voltage Analog Integrated Circuit Mfr
N.A.I.C.S.: 334413

Subsidiary (Non-US):

Power Integrations, K.K. **(2)**
Yusen Shin-Yokohama 1-chome Bldg 1-7-9
Shin-Yokohama, Kohoku-Ku, Yokohama,
222-0033, Kanagawa, Japan
Tel.: (81) 454711021
High-Voltage Analog Integrated Circuit Mfr
N.A.I.C.S.: 334413
Gagan Jain *(Mng Dir)*

Power Integrations Switzerland Holding GmbH **(1)**
Langfeldweg 87, 2504, Biel/Bienne, Switzerland
Tel.: (41) 323444747
Web Site: https://www.power.com
Holding Company
N.A.I.C.S.: 551112

POWER REIT

301 Winding Rd, Old Bethpage, NY
11804
Tel.: (212) 750-0371 MD
Web Site: https://www.pwreit.com
PW—(NYSEAMEX)
Rev.: $2,357,695
Assets: $70,210,240
Liabilities: $48,746,184
Net Worth: $21,464,056
Earnings: ($15,018,342)
Emp.: 2
Fiscal Year-end: 12/31/23
Real Estate Investment Trust
N.A.I.C.S.: 525990
David H. Lesser *(Chm, CEO, Treas & Sec)*
Susan P. Hollander *(Chief Acctg Officer)*

Subsidiaries:

Pittsburgh & West Virginia
Railroad **(1)**
2 Port Amherst Dr, Charleston, WV 25306-
6699
Tel.: (304) 926-1124
Railroad Real Estate Investment Trust
N.A.I.C.S.: 525990

David H. Lesser *(Chm & CEO)*

POWER SOLUTIONS INTER-NATIONAL, INC.

201 Mittel Dr, Wood Dale, IL 60191
Tel.: (630) 350-9400 DE
Web Site:
https://www.psiengines.com
Year Founded: 2011
PSIX—(NASDAQ)
Rev.: $481,333,000
Assets: $319,913,000
Liabilities: $350,285,000
Net Worth: ($30,372,000)
Earnings: $11,270,000
Emp.: 800
Fiscal Year-end: 12/31/22
High Performance, Low Emission
Power Mfr & Distr
N.A.I.C.S.: 333613
Kenneth J. Winemaster *(Co-Founder)*
Constantine Dino Xykis *(CEO & Chief Technical Officer)*
Kenneth Xun Li *(CFO)*
Matthew Thomas *(Controller)*

Subsidiaries:

Bi-Phase Technologies, LLC **(1)**
201 Mittel St, Wood Dale, IL 60191
Tel.: (630) 350-9400
Web Site: https://www.bi-phase.com
Motor Vehicle Fuel Injection Systems &
Components Mfr
N.A.I.C.S.: 336310

Power Great Lakes, Inc **(1)**
201 Mittel Dr, Wood Dale, IL 60191
Tel.: (630) 350-9400
Motor Vehicle Supplies & New Parts Merchant Whlsr
N.A.I.C.S.: 423120

Powertrain Integration LLC **(1)**
32505 Industrial Dr, Madison Heights, MI
48071-5004
Tel.: (248) 577-0010
General Motor Engine Mfr
N.A.I.C.S.: 336310

Professional Power Products,
Inc. **(1)**
448 W Madison St, Darien, WI 53114
Tel.: (262) 882-9000
Web Site:
http://www.professionalpowerproducts.com
Sales Range: $25-49.9 Million
Emp.: 90
Switchgear & Switchboard Apparatus Mfr
N.A.I.C.S.: 335313

POWERDYNE INTERNA-TIONAL, INC.

45 Main St, North Reading, MA
01867
Tel.: (401) 739-3300 DE
Web Site:
https://www.powerdyneinternatio
nal.com
Year Founded: 2006
PWDY—(OTCIQ)
Rev.: $1,207,168
Assets: $317,536
Liabilities: $316,420
Net Worth: $1,116
Earnings: ($1,342,016)
Emp.: 7
Fiscal Year-end: 12/31/22
Electrical Generation Technology &
Equipment Mfr
N.A.I.C.S.: 333611
James F. O'Rourke *(CEO & Principal Acctg Officer)*
Arthur M. Read II *(Gen Counsel & Exec VP)*

POWERED BRANDS

292 Madison Ave Fl 8, New York, NY
10017
Tel.: (212) 756-3508 Ky
Year Founded: 2020

Powered Brands—(Continued)

POWRU—(NASDAQ)
Rev.: $4,080,746
Assets: $276,949,725
Liabilities: $294,525,545
Net Worth: ($17,575,820)
Earnings: $2,845,235
Emp.: 3
Fiscal Year-end: 12/31/21
Investment Services
N.A.I.C.S.: 523999
Mito Yamada (COO)
Katherine Power (CEO)
Dana Settle (Chm)
Brianna Mobrem (CFO)

POWERFLEET, INC.
123 Tice Blvd Ste 101, Woodcliff
Lake, NJ 07677
Tel.: (201) 996-9000   DE
Web Site:
https://www.powerfleet.com
Year Founded: 1993
AIOT—(NASDAQ)
Rev.: $135,157,000
Assets: $217,435,000
Liabilities: $134,620,000
Net Worth: $82,815,000
Earnings: ($11,905,000)
Emp.: 795
Fiscal Year-end: 12/31/22
Radio & Television Broadcasting &
Wireless Communications Equipment
Manufacturing
N.A.I.C.S.: 334220
Steve Towe (CEO)
Michael Benjamin Brodsky (Chm)
Offer Lehmann (COO)
David Wilson (CFO)

Subsidiaries:

Asset Intelligence, LLC   (1)
18552 Macarthur Blvd Ste 450, Irvine, CA
92612
Tel.: (800) 968-8021
Software Development Services
N.A.I.C.S.: 513210

Complete Innovations Inc.   (1)
18 King Street East Suite 1800, Toronto,
ON, Canada
Tel.: (416) 994-0863
Web Site: https://www.fleetcomplete.com
Wireless Communications Equipment
Manufacturing
N.A.I.C.S.: 334220

I.D. Systems (UK) Ltd   (1)
10 St Ann Street, Salisbury, SP1 2DN,
United Kingdom
Tel.: (44) 190888850
Web Site: http://www.id-systems.com
Sales Range: $10-24.9 Million
Emp.: 6
Vehicle Management & Tracking Systems
Mfr
N.A.I.C.S.: 334519

Keytroller, LLC   (1)
3907 W Martin Luther King Blvd, Tampa, FL
33614
Tel.: (813) 877-4500
Web Site: http://www.keytroller.com
Electronic Instruments & Related Products
Mfr
N.A.I.C.S.: 334513

MiX Telematics Limited   (1)
Howick Close Waterfall Park, Midrand,
1686, South Africa
Tel.: (27) 116548000
Web Site: http://www.mixtelematics.com
Rev.: $144,993,000
Assets: $176,563,000
Liabilities: $67,746,000
Net Worth: $108,817,000
Earnings: $4,522,000
Emp.: 1,029
Fiscal Year-end: 03/31/2023
Fleet & Mobile Asset Management Software
N.A.I.C.S.: 513210
Stefan B. Joselowitz (Founder, Pres &
CEO)

Gert Pretorius (Mng Dir & Exec VP)
Catherine Lewis (Exec VP-Tech & Mng Dir-
Central Services Organisation)
Paul Dell (CFO & Chief Acctg Officer)
Jonathan Bates (Exec VP-Mktg)

Subsidiary (Domestic):

Matrix Vehicle Tracking   (2)
Waterfall Park Bus Bekker Road Vorna Val-
ley, Bekker Street, Johannesburg, South
Africa
Tel.: (27) 116548000
Web Site: http://www.matrix.co.za
Sales Range: $75-99.9 Million
Emp.: 500
Vehicle Tracking Services
N.A.I.C.S.: 541519
Gert Pretorius (Mng Dir-Africa)

MiX Telematics International (Pty)
Ltd.   (2)
Blaauwklip Office Park 2, Cnr Strand & We-
bersvallei Road, Stellenbosch, South Africa
Tel.: (27) 218805500
Web Site: https://www.mixtelematics.com
Sales Range: $25-49.9 Million
Emp.: 250
Fleet Management Services
N.A.I.C.S.: 541519

Pointer Argentina S.A.   (1)
Av Olazabal 1515, 1428, Buenos Aires,
Argentina
Tel.: (54) 8108885522
Wireless Communication Equipment Mfr
N.A.I.C.S.: 334220

Pointer Logistica y Monitoreo, S.A. de
C.V.   (1)
Tecoyotitla 412 Local 102 Colonia Exhaci-
enda De Guadalupe Chimalistac, Delega-
cion Alvaro Obregon, Mexico, Mexico
Tel.: (52) 5515201270
Wireless Communication Equipment Mfr
N.A.I.C.S.: 334220

Pointer SA (PTY) Ltd.   (1)
Block C Belvedere Office Park Pasita
Street, Bellville, South Africa
Tel.: (27) 219156500
Wireless Communication Equipment Mfr
N.A.I.C.S.: 334220
Denis Human (Dir-Customer Svcs)

Pointer Telocation Ltd.   (1)
14 Hamelacha Street, Rosh Ha'Ayin,
4809133, Israel
Tel.: (972) 35723111
Web Site: http://www.pointer.com
Rev.: $77,786,000
Assets: $90,084,000
Liabilities: $23,948,000
Net Worth: $66,136,000
Earnings: $6,927,000
Emp.: 724
Fiscal Year-end: 12/31/2018
Vehicle Recovery & Security Systems &
Services
N.A.I.C.S.: 561621
David Mahlab (Pres & CEO)
Avi Magid (Pres)
Ilan Goldstein (CEO)

Subsidiary (Non-US):

Pointer Localizacion Y Asistencia
S.A   (2)
Carlos Pellegrini 675, Buenos Aires,
Argentina   (86.45%)
Tel.: (54) 1150773700
Web Site: http://www.pointer.com.ar
Sales Range: $50-74.9 Million
Emp.: 16
Insurance Services
N.A.I.C.S.: 524298

Pointer Recuperacion de Mexico S.A.
de C.V.   (2)
Tecoyotitla 412 Local 102 Colonia Ex Haci-
enda De Guadalupe Chimalistac, Delega-
tion Alvaro Obregon, 01050, Mexico, DF,
Mexico   (74%)
Tel.: (52) 551 520 1270
Web Site: http://www.pointer.mx
Sales Range: $25-49.9 Million
Emp.: 120
Security Systems
N.A.I.C.S.: 561621

Subsidiary (Domestic):

Shagrir Motor Vehicle Systems
Ltd.   (2)
8 Hanapach St, 58117, Holon, Israel
Tel.: (972) 35579555
Web Site: http://www.shagrir.co.il
Sales Range: $25-49.9 Million
Emp.: 80
Security System Services
N.A.I.C.S.: 561621

Pointer do Brasil Comercial Ltda.   (1)
Condominio Empresarial Araguaia Alameda
Araguaia 1142 Bloco 2 3 Andar, Barueri,
Sao Paulo, Brazil
Tel.: (55) 1136605600
Wireless Communication Equipment Mfr
N.A.I.C.S.: 334220
Henrique Vogler (CFO)

Pointer, Inc.   (1)
1027 N Stadem Dr, Tempe, AZ 85281
Tel.: (480) 966-1674
Web Site: https://www.pointerinc.com
Rev.: $1,100,000
Emp.: 12
Transmitter Product Mfr
N.A.I.C.S.: 334511

PowerFleet GmbH   (1)
Am Seestern 4, 40547, Dusseldorf, Ger-
many
Tel.: (49) 211310545460
Wireless Communication Equipment Mfr
N.A.I.C.S.: 334220
Ute Filippone (Mng Dir)

PowerFleet Systems Ltd.   (1)
10 St Ann Street, Salisbury, SP1 2DN,
United Kingdom
Tel.: (44) 1908888250
Fleet Management Services
N.A.I.C.S.: 561110

**POWERLOCK INTERNA-
TIONAL CORP.**
17571 Griffin Ln Ste B, Huntington
Beach, CA 92647
Web Site: http://www.powerlock.com
Year Founded: 2005
PWLK—(OTCIQ)
Vehicle Anti Theft Product Distr
N.A.I.C.S.: 423110
Rick Fass (Pres)
James Cooper (CFO)

**POWERUP ACQUISITION
CORP.**
188 Grand St Ste 195, New York, NY
10013
Tel.: (754) 282-1865   Ky
Web Site:
https://www.powerupacq.com
Year Founded: 2021
PWUP—(NASDAQ)
Rev.: $4,316,583
Assets: $300,182,005
Liabilities: $310,119,906
Net Worth: ($9,937,901)
Earnings: $3,340,238
Emp.: 3
Fiscal Year-end: 12/31/22
Investment Services
N.A.I.C.S.: 523999
Howard Doss (CFO)
Surendra Ajjarapu (Chm)
Bruce Hack (Vice Chm)
Jack Tretton (CEO)
Michael Olson (COO)
Gabriel Schillinger (Pres)
Matthew Ball (Chief Strategy Officer)

**POWIN ENERGY CORPORA-
TION**
20550 SW 115th Ave, Tualatin, OR
97062
Tel.: (503) 598-6659   NV
Web Site: http://powinenergy.com
Year Founded: 1989
PWON—(OTCIQ)
Sales Range: $1-9.9 Million

Emp.: 18
Original Equipment Mfr
N.A.I.C.S.: 423830
Joseph Lu (Chm)
Geoffrey L. Brown (CEO)
Stuart Statman (Head-Product & En-
grg)
Mike Wietecki (Sec & VP-Bus Opera-
tion)
Anthony Carroll (Pres)

PPG INDUSTRIES, INC.
PO Box 30170, College Station, TX
77842-3170
Tel.: (412) 434-3131   PA
Web Site: https://www.ppg.com
Year Founded: 1883
PPG—(NYSE)
Rev.: $18,246,000,000
Assets: $21,647,000,000
Liabilities: $13,624,000,000
Net Worth: $8,023,000,000
Earnings: $1,270,000,000
Emp.: 53,000
Fiscal Year-end: 12/31/23
Paints, Flat Glass, Auto & Aircraft
Glass, Fiberglass & Chemicals Mfr &
Supplier
N.A.I.C.S.: 325510
Vincent J. Morales (CFO & Sr VP)
Anne M. Foulkes (Gen Counsel & Sr
VP)
Xudong Sharon Feng (Dir-Science &
Technology-Global Analytical Sci-
ences)
Kevin D. Braun (Sr VP-Industrial
Coatings Segment)
Jeffrey C. Davies (VP-Corp Dev)
Adriana Macouzet (VP/Gen Mgr-
Protective & Marine Coatings-Latin
America)
Alisha Bellezza (VP-Automotive
Coatings-Global)
Jaime A. Irick (Sr VP-Architectural
Coatings & Global Traffic Solutions
Bus-US & Canada)
Daniel G. J. Korte (VP–Global)
John A. Bruno (VP-Fin)
Jerome Zamblera (VP-Automotive
Refinish-Europe, Middle East & Af-
rica)
Roald Johannsen (VP-Automotive
Coatings-Europe, Middle East & Af-
rica)
Mark Cancilla (VP-Environment,
Health & Safety)
John A. Jankowski (Treas & VP)
David S. Bem (CTO & VP-Science &
Tech)
Chancey E. Hagerty (Sr VP-
Automotive Refinish Coatings)
Juan J. Ardid (VP-Protective & Ma-
rine Coatings-Canada)
Kumar Nandan (VP-Tax)
Steven Pocock (VP-Architectural
Coatings-EMEA North & East)
Kevin R. Walling (Chief HR Officer &
VP)
Tony Wu (VP-Automotive Refinish-
Asia)
Pascal Tisseyre (VP-Architectural
Coatings-Europe, Middle East & Af-
rica South)
Jaime A. Irick (VP-Architectural
Coatings-Canada)
Melissa Wills (VP-Fin Admin)
Brian R. Williams (Chief Acctg Officer,
VP & Controller)
Joe Gette (Sec, VP & Deputy Gen
Counsel)
Brad Budde (Chief Digital Officer &
VP)
John A. Bruno (VP-Fin)
Xiaodong Wu (VP)
Melissa A. Wills (VP)
Joseph R. Gette (Sec)

Bradley J. Budde *(VP)*
K. Henrik Bergstrom *(VP)*
Emmanuelle Guerin *(VP)*
Nianbin Li *(VP)*
Xiaobing Nie *(Pres-Asia Pacific)*
Javier Sosa Mejia *(VP)*
Meri M. Vainikka *(VP)*
Jonathan Edwards *(Dir-IR)*
Bhaskar Ramachandran *(CIO & VP-Global)*
Timothy M. Knavish *(Chm, Pres & CEO)*

Subsidiaries:

A P Resinas, S.A. de C.V. (1)
Centro Comercial City Shops Blvd Manuel Avila Camacho No 3130 Piso 7, Tlalnepantla, 54020, Estado de Mexico, Mexico
Tel.: (52) 16693700
Web Site: http://www.apquimica.com.mx
Industrial Coating Product Mfr
N.A.I.C.S.: 325510

Alermac Inversiones, S.A. de C.V. (1)
Blvd Manuel Avila Camacho No 138, Mexico, 11560, Distrito Federal, Mexico
Tel.: (52) 5552841700
Emp.: 1,200
Coating Product Whslr
N.A.I.C.S.: 424950

Alpha Coating Technologies, LLC (1)
1725 Western Dr, West Chicago, IL 60185
Tel.: (630) 268-8787
Web Site: http://www.alphacoatingtech.com
Paint & Coating Mfr
N.A.I.C.S.: 325510

Belletech Corp. (1)
700 W Lake Ave, Bellefontaine, OH 43311-0790
Tel.: (937) 599-3774
Web Site: http://www.belletechcorp.com
Sales Range: $75-99.9 Million
Automotive Glass Assemblies; Owned 60% by Asahi Glass Co., Ltd. & 40% by PPG Industries, Inc.
N.A.I.C.S.: 327215

Brown Brothers Distribution Limited (1)
Needham Rd, Stowmarket, IP14 2AD, Suffolk, United Kingdom
Tel.: (44) 1245266736
Web Site: https://www.ppgrefinishdistribution.co.uk
Paint & Coating Mfr
N.A.I.C.S.: 325510

Comex Industrial Coatings, S.A. de C.V. (1)
Avenida Gustavo Baz No 3999 Centro Industrial, Tlalnepantla, 54030, Mexico
Tel.: (52) 5516692500
Web Site: http://www.comex.com.mx
Architectural Coating Product Mfr
N.A.I.C.S.: 325510

Consorsio Comex, S.A. de C.V. (1)
Blvd Manuel Avila Camacho 138 PH 1 2 Col, Distrito Federal, Lomas de Chapultepec, 11650, Mexico
Tel.: (52) 5552841600
Web Site: http://www.comex.com.mx
Industrial Coating Product Mfr
N.A.I.C.S.: 325510

Cristacol S.A. (1)
Callao 1430 - Villa Madero, B1768AGL, Buenos Aires, Argentina
Tel.: (54) 1151394100
Web Site: https://www.cristacol.com.ar
Construction Building Material Whslr
N.A.I.C.S.: 423390

Dexmet Corporation (1)
22 Barnes Industrial Rd S, Wallingford, CT 06492
Tel.: (203) 294-4440
Web Site: http://www.dexmet.com
Precision Expanded Metals, Foils & Polymers Mfr
N.A.I.C.S.: 331315
Mark Murdoch *(VP-Engrg)*
Moe Rahamat *(COO)*
Tim Poor *(CEO)*
Ken Burtt *(VP-Sls & Mktg)*

Distribuidora Korma, S.A. de C.V. (1)
Aut Mex- Qro Km 33 5 No 104 Lote 2 Col Lecheria, Tultitlan, 54940, Estado de Mexico, Mexico
Tel.: (52) 58640600
Coating Product Whslr
N.A.I.C.S.: 424950
Feliciano Solis *(Bus Mgr-Indus & Mgr-Retail Sls)*

Dongguan Huajia Surface Technology Co., Ltd. (1)
Wanjiang Dist, Dongguan, Guangdong, China
Tel.: (86) 76922288858
Thermoplastic Powder Coating Mfr & Distr
N.A.I.C.S.: 325998

Dyrup A/S (1)
Gladsaxevej 300, 2860, Soborg, Denmark (100%)
Tel.: (45) 39579300
Web Site: http://www.dyrup.com
Sales Range: $250-299.9 Million
Emp.: 250
Paint & Wood Care Products Mfr
N.A.I.C.S.: 325510

Subsidiary (Non-US):

Dyrup GmbH (2)
Klosterhofweg 64, Postfach 30 02 63, 41199, Monchengladbach, Germany
Tel.: (49) 21669646
Web Site: http://www.dyrup.de
Sales Range: $25-49.9 Million
Emp.: 100
Paint & Varnish Removers Mfr
N.A.I.C.S.: 325510

Dyrup SAS (2)
Industrial Zone Montplaisir 25 Rue Jean-Rond d Alembert, 81030, Albi, Cedex, France
Tel.: (33) 563782010
Paint Coating & Material Mfr
N.A.I.C.S.: 325510
Delphine Maillet Rigolet *(Mgr-Demand)*

Dyrup Sp. z o.o. (2)
ul Dabrowskiego 238, 93-231, Lodz, Poland
Tel.: (48) 422531377
Web Site: https://dyrup.polandtrade.pl
Sales Range: $25-49.9 Million
Emp.: 60
Paint & Varnish Removers Mfr
N.A.I.C.S.: 325510

Pinturas Dyrup, S.A. (2)
Poligono Industrial Santiga Pla Dels Avellaners 4, Barbera del Valles, 08210, Barcelona, Spain
Tel.: (34) 937293000
Web Site: http://www.dyrup.es
Sales Range: $25-49.9 Million
Emp.: 60
Paint & Wood Care Products Mfr
N.A.I.C.S.: 325510

Tintas Dyrup, S.A. (2)
Rua Cidade De Goa 26, Sacavem, 2685-038, Portugal
Tel.: (351) 218410200
Web Site: http://www.dyrup.pt
Sales Range: $50-74.9 Million
Emp.: 200
Paint & Coating Mfr & Whslr
N.A.I.C.S.: 325510

Electra-Finish, Inc. (1)
201 Art Bryan Dr, Asheboro, NC 27203
Tel.: (336) 672-0754
Web Site: http://www.electra-finish.com
Spraying & Coating Services
N.A.I.C.S.: 238160

Ennis - Flint New Zealand (1)
9 Akatea Road, Glendene, Auckland, 0602, New Zealand
Tel.: (64) 98186410
Design Pavement Marking Material & Traffic Safety Product Mfr
N.A.I.C.S.: 333120

Ennis Traffic Safety Solutions Pty Ltd (1)
69-77 Williamson Road, Ingleburn, 2565, NSW, Australia
Tel.: (61) 298294275

Web Site: http://www.ennisflintapac.com
Design Pavement Marking Material & Traffic Safety Product Mfr
N.A.I.C.S.: 333120

Ennis-Flint, Inc. (1)
4161 Piedmont Pkwy Ste 370, Greensboro, NC 27410
Traffic Paint Product Mfr
N.A.I.C.S.: 325510

Fabrica de Pinturas Universales, S.A. de C.V. (1)
Roberto Fulton No 4, Colonia San Nicolas, Tlalnepantla, 54030, Estado de Mexico, Mexico
Tel.: (52) 5516691800
Web Site: http://www.ppg.com
Industrial Coating Product Distr & Mfr
N.A.I.C.S.: 325510

Hemmelrath Automotive Coatings (Jilin) Co., Ltd. (1)
No 336 Kunlun Road, Jilin, 132101, China
Tel.: (86) 43265083366
Paint & Coating Mfr
N.A.I.C.S.: 325510

Hodij Coatings B.V. (1)
Tel.: (31) 52 827 1916
Web Site: https://hodijcoatings.com
Paint Coating & Material Mfr
N.A.I.C.S.: 325510
Egbert Oosterhof *(CEO)*

Huangshan Huajia Surface Technology Co., Ltd. (1)
No 109 Yongjia Avenue, Huizhou District, Huangshan, Anhui, China
Tel.: (86) 5593515170
Web Site: https://www.hjchem.com
Emp.: 700
Thermoplastic Powder Coating Mfr & Distr
N.A.I.C.S.: 325998

IVC Industrial Coatings Inc. (1)
2831 E Industrial Park Dr, Brazil, IN 47834
Tel.: (812) 442-5080
Web Site: http://www.teamivc.com
Sales Range: $100-124.9 Million
Emp.: 300
Paint & Coating Merchant Whslr
N.A.I.C.S.: 424950

Industria Chimica Reggiana I.C.R. SPA (1)
Street M Gasparini 7, 42124, Reggio Emilia, Italy
Tel.: (39) 0522517803
Web Site: https://www.icrsprint.it
Paint Mfr & Distr
N.A.I.C.S.: 325510

Jinan Huajia Surface Technology Co., Ltd. (1)
No 76 Xinglong Ave, Jiyang Dist, Jinan, Shandong, China
Tel.: (86) 53184230907
Thermoplastic Powder Coating Mfr & Distr
N.A.I.C.S.: 325998

Karl Woerwag Lack-und Farbenfabrik GmbH & Co. KG (1)
Kornwesthelmer Strasse 49, 70825, Korntal-Munchingen, Germany
Tel.: (49) 7 118 2960
Web Site: https://www.woerwag.com
Emp.: 1,100
Paint & Coating Mfr
N.A.I.C.S.: 325510

MetoKote Corporation, Inc. (1)
1340 Neubrecht Rd, Lima, OH 45801
Tel.: (419) 996-7800
Web Site: https://www.ppgcoatingsservices.com
Protective Coating Applications Mfr
N.A.I.C.S.: 325510
Jon Barrett *(Bus Dir)*
Mark Blasiman *(Acct Mgr-Sls-Equipment Inquiries & Major Programs)*
Paul Tipple *(Acct Mgr-Sls-Illinois & Iowa)*
Doug Sanders *(Acct Mgr-Sales)*
Justin McMillen *(Acct Mgr-Sales)*

Subsidiary (Non-US):

MetoKote Canada Ltd. (2)
50 Raglin Road, Cambridge, N1T 1Z5, ON, Canada

Tel.: (519) 621-2884
Web Site: http://www.metokote.com
Protective Coating Applications Mfr
N.A.I.C.S.: 325510
Rudy Bowers *(Acct Mgr-Sales)*

MetoKote Deutschland GmbH (2)
Werner-Heisenberg-Strasse 19, Mannheim, 68169, Germany
Tel.: (49) 621 460 8610
Web Site: http://www.metokote.com
Protective Coating Applications Mfr
N.A.I.C.S.: 325510
Patrick Lammertyn *(Acct Mgr-Sls)*

MetoKote U.K. Limited (2)
Hackwood Road, High March Industrial Estate, Daventry, NN11 4ES, United Kingdom
Tel.: (44) 132 770 3745
Web Site: http://www.metokote.com
Emp.: 70
Protective Coating Applications Mfr
N.A.I.C.S.: 325510

Milamar Coatings, LLC (1)
311 NW 122nd St Ste 100, Oklahoma City, OK 73114
Tel.: (405) 755-8448
Web Site: https://www.milamar.com
Coating Metal Product Mfr
N.A.I.C.S.: 332812

One Shot LLC (1)
1701 E 122nd St, Chicago, IL 60633 (100%)
Tel.: (773) 646-5900
Web Site: http://www.1shot.com
Rev.: $2,400,000
Emp.: 20
Mfr Paints & Allied Products
N.A.I.C.S.: 325510

PPG (Austria) Handels GmbH (1)
Siezenheimerstr 31, Salzburg, 5020, Austria
Tel.: (43) 6624204250
Web Site: http://www.au.ppgrefinish.com
Paints & Coatings Mfr
N.A.I.C.S.: 325510

PPG AP Resinas, S.A. de C.V. (1)
Norte 4 No 3 Nuevo Parque Industrial San Juan del Rio, 76809, Queretaro, Mexico
Tel.: (52) 4271393200
Web Site: https://www.apresinas.com
Paint Mfr & Distr
N.A.I.C.S.: 325510

PPG Aerospace (1)
12780 San Fernando Rd, Sylmar, CA 91342
Tel.: (818) 362-6711
Web Site: https://www.ppgaerospace.com
Emp.: 1,200
Aerospace Coatings, Sealants & Aircraft Windshield Mfr
N.A.I.C.S.: 325510

Subsidiary (Domestic):

Cuming Microwave Corporation (2)
264 Bodwell St, Avon, MA 02322
Tel.: (508) 521-6700
Web Site: https://www.cumingmicrowave.com
Emp.: 160
Microwave Absorber Technology & Materials Mfr
N.A.I.C.S.: 326150

Deft, Inc. (2)
17451 Von Karman Ave, Irvine, CA 92614
Tel.: (949) 474-0400
Web Site: http://www.ppg.com
Sales Range: $50-74.9 Million
Emp.: 140
Aerospace Coating Mfr
N.A.I.C.S.: 325510

Plant (Domestic):

Deft, Inc. of Ohio (3)
411 East Keystone St, Alliance, OH 44601
Tel.: (330) 821-5500
Web Site: http://www.deftfinishes.com
Emp.: 18
Paint & Coating Mfr
N.A.I.C.S.: 325510

Subsidiary (Domestic):

Sierracin Corporation (2)

PPG Industries, Inc.—(Continued)

12780 San Fernando Rd, Sylmar, CA
91342-3728
Tel.: (818) 362-6711
Web Site: http://www.sierracin.com
Sales Range: $300-349.9 Million
Emp.: 600
Aircraft Windshield, Window & Canopy Mfr
N.A.I.C.S.: 336413

Subsidiary (Domestic):

PRC-DeSoto International, Inc. (3)
12780 San Fernando Rd, Sylmar, CA
91342 (100%)
Tel.: (818) 362-6711
Web Site: http://www.ppg.com
Sales Range: $150-199.9 Million
Emp.: 550
Aerospace Equipment Sealants & Coatings
Supplier
N.A.I.C.S.: 325510

Unit (Domestic):

**PRC-DeSoto International, Inc. -
Mount Laurel** (4)
823 E Gate Dr Ste 4, Mount Laurel, NJ
08054
Tel.: (856) 234-1600
Sales Range: $1-9.9 Million
Emp.: 17
Coating & Sealant Mfr
N.A.I.C.S.: 325510
Sally Neher (Mgr)
Mary Ready (Mgr-Customer Svc)

**PPG Aerospace Materials (Suzhou)
Co. Ltd.**
No 155 Hua Shan Road, Suzhou New Dis-
trict, Suzhou, 215129, China
Tel.: (86) 51266615858
Paint Mfr & Distr
N.A.I.C.S.: 325510

**PPG Architectural Coatings
EMEA** (1)
Amsterdamseweg 14, Uithoorn, Netherlands
Tel.: (31) 297541700
Web Site:
http://www.corporateportal.ppg.com
Sales Range: $150-199.9 Million
Emp.: 1,800
Paint & Other Liquid Architectural Coatings
Mfr
N.A.I.C.S.: 325510

Subsidiary (Non-US):

PPG Architectural Coatings (2)
Parc Industriel Zone D 5, 7170, Manage,
Belgium
Tel.: (32) 64517611
Sales Range: $100-124.9 Million
Emp.: 300
Paint & Other Liquid Architectural Coatings
Mfr
N.A.I.C.S.: 325510

PPG Architectural Coatings (2)
1 Rue De I Union, Rueil-Malmaison, 92565,
France
Tel.: (33) 157610000
Web Site: http://www.ppg.com
Sales Range: $25-49.9 Million
Emp.: 80
Paint & Other Liquid Architectural Coatings
Mfr
N.A.I.C.S.: 325510

**PPG Architectural Coatings UK
Limited** (2)
Huddersfield Road, Batley, Birstall, WF17
9XA, West Yorkshire, United Kingdom
Tel.: (44) 1924354000
Web Site: http://www.ppg.com
Emp.: 800
Paint & Coatings Mfr
N.A.I.C.S.: 325510

PPG Architectural Finishes, Inc. (1)
1 PPG Pl, Pittsburgh, PA 15272-0001
Tel.: (412) 434-3131
Web Site: http://www.ppg.com
Rev.: $400,000,000
Emp.: 100
Mfr of Paints, Stains & Specialty Coatings
N.A.I.C.S.: 325510

Subsidiary (Domestic):

Homax Products, Inc. (2)
200 Westerly Rd, Bellingham, WA 98226
Tel.: (360) 733-9029
Web Site: http://www.homaxproducts.com
Sales Range: $25-49.9 Million
Emp.: 434
Architectural Finishing Products Mfr & Whslr
N.A.I.C.S.: 325510

Subsidiary (Non-US):

**PPG Architectural Coatings Canada,
Inc.** (2)
3280 Boulevard Sainte-Anne Beauport,
Quebec, G1E 3K9, QC, Canada
Tel.: (418) 663-9886
Web Site: http://www.sico.ca
Emp.: 95
Paint Distr
N.A.I.C.S.: 424950
Henrik Bergstrom (CEO & VP)

PPG CEE Premazi (1)
Kolicevo 65, 1230, Domzale, Slovenia
Tel.: (386) 17224739
Coating Product Mfr
N.A.I.C.S.: 325510

PPG CEE Premazi (d.o.o.) (1)
Kolicevo 65, Domzale, 1230, Slovenia
Tel.: (386) 17224730
Coating Product Mfr
N.A.I.C.S.: 325510
Tatjana Juvanc (Coord-Customer Svc & Sls
Office)

PPG Cameroun SA (1)
Zi Magzi-Bassa Bp 1028, Douala, Camer-
oon
Tel.: (237) 33375923
Paint Coating & Material Mfr
N.A.I.C.S.: 325510

PPG Canada Inc. (1)
8200 Keele Street Concord, Concord, L4K
2A5, ON, Canada
Tel.: (905) 669-1020
Rev.: $660,000,000
Emp.: 2,100
Flat Glass, Coatings & Chemicals Mfr
N.A.I.C.S.: 327211

**PPG Coatings (Hong Kong) Co.,
Limited** (1)
Suite 1010-1015 Cityplaza One 1111 Kings
Road, Taikoo Shing, Hong Kong, China
(Hong Kong)
Tel.: (852) 0028604500
Paint & Coating Mfr
N.A.I.C.S.: 325510

**PPG Coatings (Kunshan) Co.,
Ltd.** (1)
53 Jinyang Rd Kunshan Economic Develop-
ment Zone, Kunshan, 215331, Jiangsu,
China
Tel.: (86) 512576788
Paint & Coating Mfr
N.A.I.C.S.: 325510

**PPG Coatings (Singapore) Pte
Ltd** (1)
1 Tuas Basin Close, Singapore, 638803,
Singapore
Tel.: (65) 68653737
Web Site: http://corporate.ppg.com
Paint & Coating Mfr
N.A.I.C.S.: 325510

**PPG Coatings (Suzhou) Company
Ltd.** (1)
66 Xiang Yang Rd, Suzhou New District,
Suzhou, 215011, Jiangsu, China
Tel.: (86) 51268251299
Web Site: http://www.ppg.com
Emp.: 1,010
Protective & Decorative Automotive Coat-
ings Mfr
N.A.I.C.S.: 811121

**PPG Coatings (Thailand) Co.,
Ltd.** (1)
1617 Pattanakarn Rd Kwaeng Suanluang,
Khet Suanluang, Bangkok, 10250, Thailand
Tel.: (66) 2 319 4190
Web Site: http://www.ppg.com
Sales Range: $25-49.9 Million
Emp.: 100
Paint & Coating Mfr

N.A.I.C.S.: 327910

PPG Coatings (Tianjin) Co., Ltd. (1)
No 192 Huanghia Road TEDA, Tianjin,
300457, China
Tel.: (86) 2225323470
Paint & Coating Mfr
N.A.I.C.S.: 325510

PPG Coatings BV (1)
Papesteeg 95, 4006 WC, Tiel,
Netherlands (100%)
Tel.: (31) 344672922
Web Site: http://www.quickbase.com
Sales Range: $10-24.9 Million
Emp.: 44
Coating Mfr
N.A.I.C.S.: 325510

PPG Coatings Belgium BV (1)
Tweemontstraat 104, 2100, Deurne, Bel-
gium
Tel.: (32) 33606511
Paint & Coating Mfr
N.A.I.C.S.: 325510

PPG Coatings Belux N.V. (1)
Genkersteenweg 311, Hasselt, 3500, Bel-
gium
Tel.: (32) 1 127 87 01
Emp.: 165
Paint & Coating Mfr
N.A.I.C.S.: 325510

PPG Coatings Danmark AS (1)
Gladsaxevej 300, 2860, Soborg, Denmark
Tel.: (45) 3 957 9300
Web Site: https://ppgpro.dk
Paint Distr
N.A.I.C.S.: 424950

**PPG Coatings Deutschland
GmbH** (1)
An der Halde 1, 44805, Bochum, Germany
Tel.: (49) 2348690
Web Site: http://www.ppg.com
Paint Distr
N.A.I.C.S.: 424950

PPG Coatings Europe B.V. (1)
Oceanenweg 2, Amsterdam, 1047 BB,
Netherlands
Tel.: (31) 204075050
Paint & Coating Mfr
N.A.I.C.S.: 325510

**PPG Coatings Manufacturing
SARL** (1)
7 Allee de la Plaine Seine-Maritime, 76700,
Gonfreville-l'Orcher, France
Tel.: (33) 235535400
Web Site: http://www.ppgcoatings.com
Emp.: 160
Paint & Coating Mfr
N.A.I.C.S.: 325510

PPG Coatings Nederland BV (1)
Amsterdamseweg 14, 1422 AD, Uithoorn,
Netherlands
Tel.: (31) 297541911
Web Site: http://www.ppg.com
Paint Distr
N.A.I.C.S.: 424950

PPG Coatings S.A. (1)
7 Allee De La Plaine Seine-Maritime,
76700, Gonfreville-l'Orcher, 76700, France
Tel.: (33) 235535400
Paint & Coating Mfr
N.A.I.C.S.: 325510

**PPG Coatings South Africa (Pty)
Ltd.** (1)
9 Arnold St Alberton, 1448, Alrode, Gau-
teng, South Africa
Tel.: (27) 118641755
Paint Distr
N.A.I.C.S.: 424950

**PPG Daihan Packaging Coatings,
Ltd.** (1)
615 Pakdal-Dong, Manan-Gu, Anyang, Ko-
rea (South)
Tel.: (82) 34346660778
Sales Range: $150-199.9 Million
Coating Mfr
N.A.I.C.S.: 325510

PPG Deco Czech a.s. (1)
Brasy cp 223, 338 24, Brasy, Czech Republic

Tel.: (420) 37 179 1081
Web Site: https://www.ppgdeco.cz
Emp.: 60
Paint & Coating Mfr
N.A.I.C.S.: 325510

PPG Deco Slovakia, s.r.o. (1)
Sad SNP 667/10, Zilina, 010 01, Slovakia
Tel.: (421) 417078733
Web Site: https://www.ppgdeco.sk
Chemical Products Distr
N.A.I.C.S.: 332999

**PPG Deutschland Business Suport
GmbH** (1)
Stackenbergstrasse 34, 42329, Wuppertal,
Germany
Tel.: (49) 2027883000
Web Site: http://www.ppg.com
Paint & Coating Product Mfr
N.A.I.C.S.: 325510

**PPG Deutschland Sales Services
GmbH** (1)
Dusseldorfer Strasse 80, 40721, Hilden,
Germany
Tel.: (49) 21037911
Web Site: https://de.ppgrefinish.com
Paint & Varnish Products Distr
N.A.I.C.S.: 424950

PPG Guadeloupe SAS (1)
ZA de Petit Perou, Abymes, 97176, Guade-
loupe
Tel.: (590) 834052
Paint Coating & Material Mfr
N.A.I.C.S.: 325510

PPG Hellas S.A. (1)
45 Tatoiou str, Acharnai, 136 77, Athens,
Greece
Tel.: (30) 2102402975
Web Site: http://www.gr.ppgrefinish.com
Paint & Coating Whslr
N.A.I.C.S.: 424950

**PPG Hemmelrath Lackfabrik
GmbH** (1)
Jakob-Hemmelrath-Strasse 1, 63911, Klin-
genberg, Germany
Tel.: (49) 9 372 1360
Web Site: https://www.hemmelrath.de
Emp.: 540
Paint & Coating Mfr
N.A.I.C.S.: 325510

PPG Iberica, S.A. (1)
Ctra Gracia Manresa Km 19 2 Apartado De
Correos 22, Rubi, 08191, Spain
Tel.: (34) 935867400
Paint & Coating Mfr
N.A.I.C.S.: 325510

PPG Industrial Coatings B.V. (1)
Antennestraat 3, Veenendaal, 3903 LZ,
Netherlands
Tel.: (31) 318567800
Paint & Coatings Mfr
N.A.I.C.S.: 325510

PPG Industries (Korea) Ltd. (1)
128-7 Yongdang-Dong, Busan, 608-829,
Korea (South)
Tel.: (82) 516208111
Paint & Coating Mfr
N.A.I.C.S.: 325510

PPG Industries (UK) Ltd. (1)
Darlington Road, Durham, DL4 2QP, United
Kingdom (100%)
Tel.: (44) 1388772541
Web Site: http://www.ppg.com
Sales Range: $25-49.9 Million
Emp.: 100
Coating Mfr
N.A.I.C.S.: 325510
Charles E. Bunch (Chm)

**PPG Industries Australia Pty.
Limited** (1)
14 McNaughton Road, Clayton, 3168, VIC,
Australia
Tel.: (61) 132424
Web Site: https://www.ppgrefinish.com.au
Sales Range: $125-149.9 Million
Emp.: 400
Paint & Industrial Coating Mfr & Supplier

N.A.I.C.S.: 325510

Subsidiary (Domestic):

Protec Pty. Ltd. (2)
14 McNaughton Rd, Clayton, 3169, VIC, Australia (100%)
Tel.: (61) 180 007 6466
Web Site: https://www.protec.com.au
Automotive Paint & Industrial Coating Mfr
N.A.I.C.S.: 325510

PPG Industries Belgium S.A./N.V. (1)
Blarenberglaan A 21B, 2800, Mechelen, Flanders, Belgium
Tel.: (32) 15 40 90 03
Web Site: http://www.ppg-info.com
Automotive Refinish & Industrial Coatings Distr
N.A.I.C.S.: 424950

PPG Industries Chemicals B.V. (1)
Valgenweg 1-3, 9936 HV, Delfzijl, Netherlands
Tel.: (31) 596676710
Web Site: http://www.ppg.com
Emp.: 60
Paints Mfr
N.A.I.C.S.: 325510

PPG Industries Colombia Ltda. (1)
Calle 51 40-13, Itagui, Antioquia, Colombia
Tel.: (57) 43787400
Web Site: https://colombia.ppg.com
Automotive Painting Services
N.A.I.C.S.: 424950

PPG Industries Europe Sarl (1)
Route de Gilly 32, Vaud, 1180, Rolle, Switzerland
Tel.: (41) 218223000
Web Site: http://www.ppg.com
Emp.: 70
Paints Mfr
N.A.I.C.S.: 325510

PPG Industries France SAS (1)
Route D Estreux, PO Box 6, Saultain, 59990, France (100%)
Tel.: (33) 327149700
Web Site: http://www.ppg.com
Sales Range: $100-124.9 Million
Emp.: 300
Coatings & Paint Mfr
N.A.I.C.S.: 325510
Charles E. Bunch *(Chm)*

PPG Industries Italia S.p.A. (1)
Strada Statale 87 KM 16 460, Caivano, 80023, Naples, Italy
Tel.: (39) 081835111
Paint & Coating Mfr
N.A.I.C.S.: 325510

PPG Industries Italia Srl (1)
Strada Statale 87 Km 16 460, Caivano, 80023, Italy (100%)
Tel.: (39) 0818358111
Sales Range: $150-199.9 Million
Emp.: 100
Coating Mfr
N.A.I.C.S.: 325510
Charles E. Bunch *(Chm)*

PPG Industries Kimya Sanayi ve Ticaret Anonim Sirketi (1)
Pembe Cad No 2 Org San Bolg, Bursa, 16159, Turkiye (100%)
Tel.: (90) 2242424290
Web Site: http://www.ppg.com
Sales Range: $150-199.9 Million
Emp.: 50
Paint & Coatings Mfr
N.A.I.C.S.: 325510
Charles E. Bunch *(Chm)*

PPG Industries LLC (1)
Kazinka Village, Gryazinskiy District, Lipetsk, 399071, Russia
Tel.: (7) 4742423000
Paint Coating & Material Mfr
N.A.I.C.S.: 325510

PPG Industries Lackfabrik GmbH (1)
Werner-Siemens Stasse 1 Baden, Weingarten, D-76356, Germany (100%)
Tel.: (49) 7244640
Web Site: http://www.ppgindustries.com
Sales Range: $25-49.9 Million
Emp.: 100
Coating Mfr

N.A.I.C.S.: 325510
Charles E. Bunch *(Chm)*

PPG Industries Lipetsk LLC (1)
Lipetsk Special Economic Zone Gryazi District, Gryazi District, Lipetsk, 399071, Russia
Tel.: (7) 4742515180
Web Site: http://www.sezlipetsk.com
Coating Product Distr
N.A.I.C.S.: 424950

PPG Industries Netherlands B.V. (1)
Copernicusstraat 10, Wijchen, 6604 CR, Netherlands
Tel.: (31) 24 645 63 03
Web Site: http://www.ppgindustries.com
Emp.: 20
Automotive Coating Mfr
N.A.I.C.S.: 325510

PPG Industries New Zealand Limited (1)
5 Monahan Rd Mt Wellington, PO Box 22122, Otahuhu, Auckland, New Zealand
Tel.: (64) 95731620
Web Site: https://www.ppgnz.co.nz
Paint & Coatings Mfr
N.A.I.C.S.: 325510

PPG Industries Ohio, Inc. (1)
3800 W 143rd St, Cleveland, OH 44111-4901 (100%)
Tel.: (216) 671-0050
Web Site: http://www.ppg.com
Sales Range: $300-349.9 Million
Emp.: 660
Mfr & Wholsale Automoted Coating
N.A.I.C.S.: 325510

PPG Industries Poland Sp. z o.o. (1)
Ul Bodycha 47, 05-816, Warsaw, Poland
Tel.: (48) 227530310
Web Site: https://ceb.ppgrefinish.com
Paints Mfr
N.A.I.C.S.: 325510

Subsidiary (Domestic):

PPG Deco Polska Sp. z o.o. (2)
ul Kwidzynska 8, 51-416, Wroclaw, Lower Silesian, Poland
Tel.: (48) 80 111 3311
Web Site: https://www.dekoral.pl
Emp.: 700
Paint Mfr & Distr
N.A.I.C.S.: 325510

PPG Industries Securities, Inc. (1)
1886 Lynnbury Woods Rd, Dover, DE 19904-1801 (100%)
Tel.: (302) 678-9800
Web Site: http://www.pppg.com
Rev.: $110,000
Emp.: 3
Holding Company
N.A.I.C.S.: 551112

PPG Industries de Mexico, SA de CV (1)
Libramiento A Tequisquiapan 66, Zona Industrial, San Juan del Rio, 76800, Queretaro, Mexico (100%)
Tel.: (52) 80022639426
Web Site: http://www.ppg.com
Sales Range: $150-199.9 Million
Emp.: 800
Coating Mfr
N.A.I.C.S.: 325510
Charles E. Bunch *(Chm)*
Adriana E. Macouzet-Flores *(VP-Latin America)*

Subsidiary (Domestic):

Consorcio Comex, S.A. de C.V. (2)
Blvd Manuel Avila Camacho 138 PH 1 & 2 Col, 11650, Lomas de Chapultepec, DF, Mexico
Tel.: (52) 5516691600
Web Site: http://www.comex.com.mx
Holding Company; Paint & Coatings Mfr, Distr & Retailer
N.A.I.C.S.: 551112

Subsidiary (Domestic):

Comercial Mexicana de Pinturas, S.A. de C.V. (3)
Marcos Achar Lobation No 6, Col Tepexpan Mpo Acolman, CP 55885, Mexico, Mexico

Tel.: (52) 159 4957 0211
Web Site: http://www.comex.com.mx
Paint Mfr & Whslr
N.A.I.C.S.: 325510

PPG Industries, Inc. - Monroeville Chemical Center (1)
440 College Park Dr, Monroeville, PA 15146
Tel.: (724) 325-5100
Web Site: http://www.ppg.com
Sales Range: $75-99.9 Million
Emp.: 202
Commodity Chemicals, Optical Dyes & Specialty Materials Mfr
N.A.I.C.S.: 325998

PPG Italia Business Support S.r.l (1)
Via Comasina 121, 20161, Milan, Italy (100%)
Tel.: (39) 0264041
Web Site: http://corporate.ppg.com
Business Support Services
N.A.I.C.S.: 561499

PPG Italia Sales & Services Srl (1)
Via Comasina 121, 20161, Milan, Italy (100%)
Tel.: (39) 0264042238
Web Site: http://www.ppgpmc.com
Paint, Coatings & Specialty Products Mfr
N.A.I.C.S.: 325510

PPG Kansai Automotive Finishes Canada, LP (1)
834 Caledonia Rd, Toronto, M6B 3X9, ON, Canada
Tel.: (905) 855-5667
Automotive Painting Services
N.A.I.C.S.: 424950

PPG Korea Ltd. (1)
128-7 Yongdang Dong, Busan, 608-829, Korea (South)
Tel.: (82) 51 620 8111
Web Site: http://www.ppg.com
Chemicals, Paints & Coatings Mfr
N.A.I.C.S.: 325510

PPG Luxembourg Finance S.a.R.L. (1)
6C Rue Gabriel Lippmann, L-5365, Munsbach, Luxembourg
Tel.: (352) 26478730
Web Site: http://www.ppg.com
Paint & Coatings Mfr
N.A.I.C.S.: 325510

PPG Management (Shanghai) Co., Ltd (1)
25/F Cloud Nine Plaza 1118 West Yan An Road, Shanghai, China
Tel.: (86) 2160918500
Paint & Coating Mfr
N.A.I.C.S.: 325510

PPG Mexico, S.A. de C.V. (1)
Av 1 de Mayo No 229 Col Industrial Atoto, Naucalpan, 53100, Mexico, Mexico
Tel.: (52) 5550930470
Automotive Refinish Coating Services
N.A.I.C.S.: 811121
Mario Najera Valle *(Mgr-Territory-Refinish Automotive)*

PPG PMC Japan Co Ltd (1)
8F Shintetus Bldg 1-1 Daikaidori 1-Chome, Kobe, 652-0803, Japan
Tel.: (81) 785742777
Web Site: http://www.ppg-amercoat.com
Emp.: 20
Paint & Coatings Mfr
N.A.I.C.S.: 325510

PPG Packaging Coatings (Suzhou) Co., Ltd. (1)
66 Xiang Yang Road, Suzhou New District, Suzhou, 215011, China
Tel.: (86) 51268251299
Paint & Coating Mfr
N.A.I.C.S.: 325510

PPG Paints Trading (Shanghai) Co., Ltd. (1)
Room 607 BM Tower No 218 Wusong Road, Shanghai, 200080, China
Tel.: (86) 2163578290
Paint Distr
N.A.I.C.S.: 424950

PPG Performance Coatings (Malaysia) Sdn. Bhd. (1)

Lot 9 & 11 Jalan Tukang 16/4, PO Box 7079, Shah Alam, 40702, Selangor Darul Ehsan, Malaysia
Tel.: (60) 355193062
Paint & Coating Mfr
N.A.I.C.S.: 325510

PPG Premazi CEE (d.o.o.) (1)
Kolicevo 65, 1230, Domzale, Slovenia
Tel.: (386) 17224739
Emp.: 10
Industrial Coating Product Mfr
N.A.I.C.S.: 325510
Tatjana Juvanc *(Asst Dir-Comml)*

PPG Protective & Marine Coatings (1)
11605 Vimy Ridge Rd, Alexander, AR 70202 (100%)
Tel.: (501) 455-4500
Web Site: https://www.ppgpmc.com
Sales Range: $200-249.9 Million
Emp.: 150
Protective & Marine Coating Mfr
N.A.I.C.S.: 325510

Affiliate (Non-US):

Oasis-Ameron Company Ltd. (2)
PO Box 4926, Al Khobar, 31952, Saudi Arabia (40%)
Tel.: (966) 38121300
Web Site: https://www.oasisamercoat.com
Sales Range: $25-49.9 Million
Emp.: 100
Protective Coatings, Marine & Industrial Paints, Tank Linings & Surfacers Mfr
N.A.I.C.S.: 325510
Toufic Zeidan *(VP)*
Raed Sleiman *(Mgr-Pur & Coord-Sls)*

PPG Retail France SAS (1)
Zi Route De Thennes, 80110, Moreuil, France
Tel.: (33) 322353535
Emp.: 240
Coating Product Distr
N.A.I.C.S.: 424950

PPG Reunion SAS (1)
ZAC Finette II, Sainte Clotilde, Reunion
Tel.: (262) 296969
Paint Coating & Material Mfr
N.A.I.C.S.: 325510

PPG Romania S.A. (1)
Catanoaia Street No 33, 3rd district, Bucharest, Romania
Tel.: (40) 21 256 0385
Web Site: https://www.ppgromania.ro
Paint Coating & Material Mfr
N.A.I.C.S.: 325510
Gemma Ranga *(Mgr-Sls Export)*

PPG SSC Co., Ltd. (1)
4th 5th Fl Haeundae B/D 29 Jungdong 2-ro 10beon-gil, Haeundae-Gu, Busan, 612-847, Korea (South)
Tel.: (82) 51 749 8500
Web Site: http://www.ppgpmc.com
Emp.: 60
Paint & Coating Mfr
N.A.I.C.S.: 325510

PPG Switzerland GmbH (1)
Fabrikweg 6-8, Bern, Burgdorf, 3401, Switzerland
Tel.: (41) 344214242
Emp.: 35
Chemical Products Distr
N.A.I.C.S.: 332999

PPG Trilak Kft. (1)
Grassalkovich ut 4, 1238, Budapest, Hungary
Tel.: (36) 14216100
Web Site: https://www.ppgtrilak.hu
Paint Coating & Material Mfr
N.A.I.C.S.: 325510

PPG Univer S.P.A. (1)
Via Monte Rosa 7, 28010, Novara, Cavallirio, Italy
Tel.: (39) 0163806611

N.A.I.C.S.: 325510
Charles E. Bunch *(Chm)*

PPG Industries, Inc.—(Continued)

Web Site: http://www.univer.it
Paint Mfr & Distr
N.A.I.C.S.: 325510

PPG Worwag Coatings GmbH & Co. KG (1)
Kornwestheimer Str 49, 70825, Korntal-Munchingen, Germany
Tel.: (49) 71182960
Web Site: https://www.woerwag.com
Emp.: 1,100
Powder Coating Product Mfr & Distr
N.A.I.C.S.: 325510

PRC-Desoto Australia Pty Ltd. (1)
21/23 Ovata Dr, Tullamarine, 3043, VIC, Australia
Tel.: (61) 393351557
Web Site: http://www.ppgaerospace.com
Emp.: 25
Adhesive Mfr
N.A.I.C.S.: 325520

PT. PPG Coatings Indonesia (1)
Jalan Rawa Gelam III No 1, Jakarta Industrial Estate Pulo Gadung Jakarta, Jakarta Timur, 13960, Indonesia
Tel.: (62) 21 4605710
Web Site: http://www.ppg.com
Emp.: 100
Paint & Coating Mfr
N.A.I.C.S.: 325510

Paintzen Inc. (1)
242 W 30th St Ste 500, New York, NY 10001
Web Site: https://www.paintzen.com
Painting & Wall Covering Contractor
N.A.I.C.S.: 238320
Eric Fitzgerald *(VP-Sales)*
Garon Benner *(Dir)*
Kristen Chuber *(Sr Dir-Marketing-Communications)*
Anna Monzon *(Dir)*
Edward Zebrowski *(Controller)*

Peinture de Paris SAS (1)
41 Bis rue du Chateau, 92500, Rueil-Malmaison, France
Tel.: (33) 147492020
Web Site: http://www.peinturesdeparis.com
Paint & Coating Mfr
N.A.I.C.S.: 325510

Plasticos Envolventes, S.A. de C.V. (1)
Calle Ano 1857 No 12 Colonia Santa Maria Ticoman Gustavo A Madero, Gustavo A Madero, Mexico, 07330, Mexico
Tel.: (52) 5516692600
Architectural Coating Product Mfr
N.A.I.C.3.: 325510
Jose Leal *(Head-Engrg)*

Primalex a.s. (1)
Brasy C P 223, Plzen, Brasy, 338 24, Czech Republic
Tel.: (420) 371 791 081
Web Site: http://www.primalex.cz
Emp.: 8
Paints Mfr
N.A.I.C.S.: 325510

ProCoatings B.V. (1)
Oliemolenstraat 73, 1333 DB, Almere, Netherlands
Tel.: (31) 365370099
Web Site: https://www.procoatings.nl
Paint Whslr
N.A.I.C.S.: 424950

Revocoat France SAS (1)
2 Rue D Oresmeaux - ZI Nord, 60130, Saint-Just-en-Chaussee, France
Tel.: (33) 344776100
Coating Product Mfr
N.A.I.C.S.: 325510
Carlos Goncalves *(Mgr-Ops & Site)*

Revocoat Iberica SL (1)
C/ Camino Del Corral 7 Pol Alcamar, Camarma de Esteruelas, 28816, Madrid, Spain
Tel.: (34) 918866143
Coating Product Mfr
N.A.I.C.S.: 325510
Carlos Garcia *(Mgr-Supply Chain)*

Road Infrastructure Investment Holdings, Inc. (1)

4161 Piedmont Pkwy Ste 370, Greensboro, NC 27410
Tel.: (336) 308-3798
Web Site: https://www.ennisflint.com
Road Safety Product Mfr
N.A.I.C.S.: 333120
Paul J. Carlson *(CTO)*

Schoch Holding AG (1)
Fabrikweg 6-8, Burgdorf, CH3401, Switzerland
Tel.: (41) 344214242
Emp.: 16
Holding Company
N.A.I.C.S.: 551112

Sealants Europe SAS (1)
84 Rue Salvador Allende, 95870, Bezons, France
Tel.: (33) 134233423
Coating Product Mfr
N.A.I.C.S.: 325510
Xavier Parra *(Engr-Sls & Technical-Aerospace Sealants-France, Swiss & Belgium)*

Sigma Coatings Proprietary Limited (1)
9 Arnold Street Alrode, Alberton, South Africa
Tel.: (27) 113894800
Web Site: https://www.sigmacoatings.co.za
Paint Mfr & Distr
N.A.I.C.S.: 325510

Sigma Marine & Protective Coatings Holding B.V (1)
Amsterdamseweg 14 North Holland, 1422 AD, Uithoorn, 1422 AD, Netherlands
Tel.: (31) 297541911
Investment Management Service
N.A.I.C.S.: 523999

Sigma Samsung Coatings Co., Ltd (1)
Haeundae Buiding 4 & 5Th Floor 29 Jung Gond 2-Ro 10 Peon-Jil, Haeundae-gu, Busan, 612-851, Korea (South)
Tel.: (82) 517498500
Web Site: http://www.ppgpmc.com
Sales Range: $25-49.9 Million
Emp.: 60
Coating Mfr
N.A.I.C.S.: 325510
Stephan Jeong *(Pres)*

SigmaKalon Nigeria Limited (1)
1a Professor Tiamiyu Belo-Osagie Street Parkveiw Estate, Ikoyi, Lagos, Nigeria
Tel.: (234) 12717385
Paint Distr
N.A.I.C.S.: 424950

Solarlens Co., Ltd. (1)
Nos 371-373 Chalongkrung Road Kwaeng Lum-Pra-Teuw Khet Lardkraban, Bangkok, Thailand
Tel.: (66) 23260578
Chemical Products Distr
N.A.I.C.S.: 332999

Spraylat Coatings (Shanghai) Limited (1)
No 655 Baofeng Road Xuhang Town, Jiading District, Shanghai, 201808, China
Tel.: (86) 2139978111
Paint & Coating Mfr
N.A.I.C.S.: 325510

Strongsville Automotive Coatings (1)
19699 Progress Dr, Strongsville, OH 44149
Tel.: (440) 572-2800
Web Site: http://www.ppg.com
Emp.: 117
Automotive Primer & Specialty Powder Coatings Mfr
N.A.I.C.S.: 325510

Plant (Domestic):

PPG Decorative Coatings-Carolina (2)
630 Calle Feria, Carolina, PR 00987
Tel.: (787) 641-8900
Web Site: http://www.ppg.com
Rev.: $30,000,000
Emp.: 150
Paints & Coatings Mfr
N.A.I.C.S.: 325510

PPG Decorative Coatings-Carrollton (2)
1900 N Josey Ln Bldg 1, Carrollton, TX 75006
Tel.: (972) 417-7400
Web Site: http://www.ppg.com
Sales Range: $25-49.9 Million
Emp.: 200
Decorative Paints Mfr
N.A.I.C.S.: 325510

PPG Decorative Coatings-Huron (2)
300 Sprowl Rd, Huron, OH 44839
Tel.: (419) 433-5664
Web Site: http://www.ppg.com
Decorative Paints, Colorants, Resins & Packaging Coatings Mfr
N.A.I.C.S.: 325510

TRIGA COLOR, a.s. (1)
Marikova 42, Brno, 1152, Czech Republic
Tel.: (420) 5 3219 3923
Web Site: http://www.trigacolor.cz
Emp.: 50
Paint Distr
N.A.I.C.S.: 424950

Texstars LLC (1)
802 Ave J E, Grand Prairie, TX 75050 **(100%)**
Tel.: (972) 647-1366
Web Site: http://www.texstars.com
Sales Range: $25-49.9 Million
Emp.: 200
Mfr of Plastic & Composite Components & Assemblies for Aerospace Industry
N.A.I.C.S.: 336413
Nicholas Scarsella *(Pres & CEO)*

The Crown Group Co. (1)
2111 Walter P Reuther Dr, Warren, MI 48091-6108
Tel.: (586) 575-9800
Web Site: http://www.thecrowngrp.com
Custom Coatings Application Mfr
N.A.I.C.S.: 332812

The Homax Group, Inc. (1)
200 Westerly Rd, Bellingham, WA 98226
Tel.: (360) 733-9029
Housing Development Services
N.A.I.C.S.: 238390
Ray Mazur *(CIO)*

Tikkurila Oyj (1)
Kuninkaalantie 1, PO Box 53, FI-01301, Vantaa, Finland
Tel.: (358) 201912000
Web Site: http://www.tikkurilagroup.com
Rev.: $635,096,123
Assets: $489,447,131
Liabilities: $296,916,321
Net Worth: $192,530,811
Earnings: $37,225,266
Emp.: 2,607
Fiscal Year-end: 12/31/2019
Paints & Coatings Mfr
N.A.I.C.S.: 325510
Petteri Wallden *(Vice Chm)*
Jari Paasikivi *(Chm)*
Meri Vainikka *(Sr VP-Offering)*
Melisa Barholm *(Sr VP-HR)*
Elisa Markula *(CEO)*
Fredrik Linde *(Sr VP-Ops)*
Markus Melkko *(CFO)*
Anders Rotkirch *(Sr VP-Transformation & ICT)*
Oskari Vidman *(Sr VP-Sls)*
Roman Ivashko *(Sr VP-Sls-East Div)*

Subsidiary (Non-US):

A3 Tikkurila (2)
Liimi 5, EE-10621, Tallinn, Estonia
Tel.: (372) 6501100
Web Site: http://www.vivacolor.ee
Paints Mfr
N.A.I.C.S.: 325510

Alcro-Beckers AB (2)
Textilgatan 31, SE 120 86, Stockholm, Sweden
Tel.: (46) 87756000
Web Site: http://www.alcro-beckers.com
Emp.: 140
Paints Mfr
N.A.I.C.S.: 325510

Subsidiary (Non-US):

Tikkurila Danmark A/S (3)

Gejlhavegard 5, 6000, Kolding, Denmark **(100%)**
Tel.: (45) 43631611
Web Site: http://www.tikkurila.dk
Paints Mfr
N.A.I.C.S.: 325510

Tikkurila Norge A/S (3)
Stanseveien 25C, 0976, Oslo, Norway **(100%)**
Tel.: (47) 22803290
Web Site: https://www.tikkurila.no
Paints Mfr
N.A.I.C.S.: 325510

Subsidiary (Non-US):

OOO Gamma Industrial Coatings (2)
ul Boksitogorskaya 9 letter K, 195248, Saint Petersburg, Russia **(100%)**
Tel.: (7) 8123133836
Web Site: http://www.gammalkm.spb.ru
Industrial Coatings Mfr & Distr
N.A.I.C.S.: 325510

OOO Tikkurila (2)
Ave Building 15 building 3, Devyatogo Yanvarya, 192289, Saint Petersburg, Russia
Tel.: (7) 8123803399
Web Site: https://www.tikkurila.ru
Household & Structural Paint Mfr
N.A.I.C.S.: 325510

Pigrol Farben GmbH (2)
Hospitalstrasse 39/71, Postfach 1622, 91522, Ansbach, Germany
Tel.: (49) 98165060
Web Site: http://www.pigrol.de
Decorative Paints & Industrial Coatings Mfr & Marketer
N.A.I.C.S.: 325510

SIA Tikkurila (2)
Kruzes Iela 23 k-3, Riga, 1046, Latvia **(100%)**
Tel.: (371) 67611135
Web Site: http://www.vivacolor.lv
Sales Range: $25-49.9 Million
Emp.: 30
Paints Mfr
N.A.I.C.S.: 325180

TOO Tikkurila (2)
Kabdolov str 16 4th floor, 050062, Almaty, Kazakhstan **(100%)**
Tel.: (7) 727 333 5888
Web Site: http://www.kz.tikkurila.com
Emp.: 3
Decorative Paints Sales & Marketing
N.A.I.C.S.: 424950

Tikkurila (China) Paints Co., Ltd. (2)
Room T2-B-1808 Wangjing SOHO No 1 Futong East Street, Chaoyang District, Beijing, 1000102, China **(100%)**
Tel.: (86) 1067875756
Web Site: https://www.tikkurila.cn
Decorative Paints & Industrial Coatings Sales & Marketing
N.A.I.C.S.: 424950

Tikkurila AB (2)
Textilgatan 31, 120 86, Stockholm, Sweden **(100%)**
Tel.: (46) 87756000
Web Site: https://www.tikkurila.se
Emp.: 50
Industrial Coatings Sales & Marketing
N.A.I.C.S.: 424950

Tikkurila Coatings Sp. z.o.o. (2)
Ul Ksiedza Kujota 16, PL 70 605, Szczecin, Poland **(100%)**
Tel.: (48) 914624606
Web Site: http://www.tikkurila.pl
Sales Range: $25-49.9 Million
Emp.: 50
Paint & Coatings Mfr & Whslr
N.A.I.C.S.: 424950
Aleksander Truszczynski *(Head)*

Tikkurila Polska S.A. (2)
Ul Ignacego Moscickiego 23, 39-200, Debica, Poland **(100%)**
Tel.: (48) 146805600
Web Site: https://www.tikkurila.pl
Decorative Paints & Industrial Coatings Mfr, Marketer & Distr
N.A.I.C.S.: 325510

Tikkurila Zorka d.o.o. (2)

Hajduk Veljkova b b, 15000, Sabac,
Serbia   **(100%)**
Tel.: (381) 15 368 800
Web Site: http://www.tikkurilagroup.com
Decorative Paints & Industrial Coatings Mfr,
Marketer & Distr
N.A.I.C.S.: 325510

Tikkurila d.o.o.e.l.   **(2)**
1550 16 kacanicki pat vizbegovo, 1000,
Skopje, North Macedonia   **(100%)**
Tel.: (389) 22549050
Decorative Paints & Industrial Coatings
Sales & Marketing
N.A.I.C.S.: 424950
Vladimir Kuzmanovski *(Gen Mgr)*

UAB Tikkurila   **(2)**
Sietyno G 8, 04304, Vilnius, Lithuania
Tel.: (370) 52706413
Web Site: http://www.vivacolor.lt
Sales Range: $25-49.9 Million
Emp.: 20
Paint Whslr
N.A.I.C.S.: 424950

Tikkurila Sverige AB   **(2)**
Textilgatan 31, 12086, Stockholm, Sweden
Tel.: (46) 87756000
Web Site: https://tikkurila.se
Emp.: 200
Paint Mfr & Distr
N.A.I.C.S.: 325510

Vanex, Inc.   **(1)**
1700 S Shawnee St, Mount Vernon, IL
62864-0020
Tel.: (618) 244-1413
Industrial Coating Product Mfr
N.A.I.C.S.: 325510
Walter Rexing *(VP-Technical Svc)*

Varossieau Suriname NV   **(1)**
Mastanaweg 4, Paramaribo, Suriname
Tel.: (597) 484447
Web Site: https://www.varossieau-
paints.com
Paint Distr
N.A.I.C.S.: 424950

VersaFlex, Inc.   **(1)**
686 S Adams St, Kansas City, KS 66105
Tel.: (913) 321-9000
Web Site: https://versaflex.com
Emp.: 130
Paint & Coating Mfr
N.A.I.C.S.: 325510
David Cerchie *(Pres)*

Whitford Jiangmen Ltd.   **(1)**
No 308 Jin Ou Road, Jiangmen, 52900,
Guangdong, China
Tel.: (86) 7503866689
Paint & Coating Mfr
N.A.I.C.S.: 325510

Whitford Ltd.   **(1)**
11 Stuart Road, Manor Park, Runcorn, WA7
1TH, Cheshire, United Kingdom
Tel.: (44) 1928571000
Paint & Coating Mfr
N.A.I.C.S.: 325510
Mike Knowles *(Sls Mgr)*

Whitford Ltd.   **(1)**
Units 923A-928 9th Floor Trade Square 681
Cheung Sha Wan Road, Kowloon, China
(Hong Kong)
Tel.: (852) 21546000
Paint & Coating Mfr
N.A.I.C.S.: 325510
Philip P. H. Wong *(Mktg Mgr-Asia Pacific)*

Whitford Worldwide Company   **(1)**
47 Park Ave, Elverson, PA 19520
Tel.: (610) 286-3500
Web Site: http://www.whitfordww.com
Sales Range: $25-49.9 Million
Emp.: 700
Mfr of Fluoropolymer Coatings
N.A.I.C.S.: 325520
David P. Willis Jr. *(Founder & Chm)*

Subsidiary (Domestic):

Alpha Coatings Inc   **(2)**
622 S Corporate Dr, Fostoria, OH 44830
Tel.: (419) 436-1255
Web Site: http://www.alpha-coatings.com
Adhesive Coating Mfr
N.A.I.C.S.: 325510

Subsidiary (Non-US):

HP Polymers, Ltd.   **(2)**
32 Kerr Crescent, Puslinch, N0B 2J0, ON,
Canada
Tel.: (519) 826-0374
Web Site: http://www.hppolymers.com
Emp.: 10
Plastic Materials Mfr
N.A.I.C.S.: 325211
Darren Van neck *(Pres)*

Subsidiary (Domestic):

Polymeric Systems, Inc.   **(2)**
47 Park Ave, Elverson, PA 19520
Tel.: (610) 286-2500
Web Site:
https://www.polymericsystems.com
Adhesive Mfr
N.A.I.C.S.: 325520

Whitford Corporation   **(2)**
47 Park Ave, Elverson, PA 19520
Tel.: (610) 286-3500
Web Site: http://www.whitfordww.com
Adhesives & Sealants
N.A.I.C.S.: 325520
David P. Willis *(Pres)*

Subsidiary (Non-US):

Whitford Espana S.L.   **(2)**
Centro Industrial Santiga Passatge
d'Arraona 4-6 Local 6, 08210, Barbera del
Valles, Spain
Tel.: (34) 93 718 8512
Fluoropolymer Coating Mfr
N.A.I.C.S.: 325510

Whitford GmbH   **(2)**
Robert-Bosch-Strasse 11, 65582, Diez, Ger-
many
Tel.: (49) 6432 50 79 0
Emp.: 14
Fluoropolymer Coating Mfr
N.A.I.C.S.: 325510
Anne Willis *(Mng Dir)*
Joan Peris *(Mng Dir)*

Whitford India Private Limited   **(2)**
Plot No 86 M&N KIADB Industrial Area Ji-
gani 1st Phase, Anekal Taluka, Bengaluru,
562 105, India
Tel.: (91) 8028017500
Emp.: 23
Fluoropolymer Coating Mfr
N.A.I.C.S.: 325510

Whitford Pte Ltd   **(2)**
No 1 Tuas Basin Close, Singapore, 638803,
Singapore
Tel.: (65) 6861 6877
Web Site: http://www.whitfordww.com
Emp.: 100
Coating Mfr
N.A.I.C.S.: 325510

Whitford S.r.l.   **(2)**
Verziano 109 127, 25131, Brescia, Italy
Tel.: (39) 030 358 0113
Fluoropolymer Coating Mfr
N.A.I.C.S.: 325510

Whitford SARL   **(2)**
75 Boulevard Haussmann, 75008, Paris,
France
Tel.: (33) 142685235
Emp.: 2
Fluoropolymer Coating Mfr
N.A.I.C.S.: 325510
Joan Peris *(Gen Mgr)*

Whitford do Brasil Ltda.   **(2)**
Avenida Sao Carlos 620 1 Distrito Industrial
Americao Brasiliense, Sao Paulo, 14820-
000, Brazil
Tel.: (55) 16 2108 6800
Web Site: http://www.whitfordww.com
Chemical Products Mfr
N.A.I.C.S.: 325998

**Worwag Coatings (Langfang) Co.,
Ltd.**   **(1)**
9 Quanxing Road, ETDZ, Langfang,
065001, Hebei, China
Tel.: (86) 3165919502
Chemical Coating Product Mfr & Distr
N.A.I.C.S.: 325998

**PPJ HEALTHCARE ENTER-
PRISES, INC.**
401 E Jackson St Ste 2340, Tampa,
FL 33602
Tel.: (813) 723-1206   NV
Web Site:
http://www.ppjenterprise.com
Year Founded: 2000
PPJE—(OTCIQ)
Health Care Srvices
N.A.I.C.S.: 621999
Chandana Basu *(CEO)*

PPL CORPORATION
2 N Ninth St, Allentown, PA 18101-
1179
Tel.: (610) 774-5151   PA
Web Site: https://www.pplweb.com
Year Founded: 1920
PPL—(NYSE)
Rev.: $8,312,000,000
Assets: $39,236,000,000
Liabilities: $25,303,000,000
Net Worth: $13,933,000,000
Earnings: $740,000,000
Emp.: 6,629
Fiscal Year-end: 12/31/23
Holding Company; Electric Power
Generation & Distribution
N.A.I.C.S.: 551112
Vincent Sorgi *(Pres & CEO)*
Gregory N. Dudkin *(Exec VP)*
Marlene C. Beers *(VP & Controller)*
Christine M. Martin *(Pres-Electric
Utilities)*
Andy Ludwig *(VP-IR)*
Andrew Elmore *(VP-Tax)*
Francis X. Sullivan *(COO & Exec VP)*
Joseph P. Bergstein Jr. *(CFO)*
Andrew W. Elmore *(VP)*
Angela K. Gosman *(Chief HR Officer)*
John R. Crockett *(Pres-LG&E & KU
Energy)*
David J. Bonenberger *(Pres-Rhode
Island Energy)*
Angie McDonald Evans *(VP)*
Matthew B. Green *(Sr VP)*

Subsidiaries:

CEP Reserves, Inc.   **(1)**
3993 Howard Hughes Pkwy, Las Vegas, NV
89169-0961
Tel.: (702) 866-2281
Elctric Power Generation Services
N.A.I.C.S.: 221118

LG&E and KU Energy LLC   **(1)**
220 W Main St, Louisville, KY 40202-1377
Tel.: (502) 589-1444
Web Site: https://www.lge-ku.com
Rev.: $3,106,000,000
Assets: $16,277,000,000
Liabilities: $11,161,000,000
Net Worth: $5,116,000,000
Earnings: $450,000,000
Emp.: 1,016
Fiscal Year-end: 12/31/2020
Electric & Natural Gas Distr
N.A.I.C.S.: 221122
John R. Crockett III *(Pres, Chief Compli-
ance Officer, Sec & Gen Counsel)*
Lonnie E. Bellar *(COO)*
Kent W. Blake *(CFO)*
Robert M. Conroy *(VP-State Regulation &
Rates)*
Tom Jessee *(VP-Gas Ops)*
Beth McFarland *(VP-Transmission)*
David Sinclair *(VP-Energy Supply & Analy-
sis)*
Eileen L. Saunders *(VP-Customer Svcs)*
Steven Turner *(VP-Power Production)*
Peter Waldrab *(VP)*
David J. Freibert Jr. *(VP-External Affairs)*

Subsidiary (Domestic):

Kentucky Utilities Company   **(2)**
1 Quality St, Lexington, KY 40507-1462
Tel.: (502) 627-2000
Web Site: http://www.lge-ku.com
Rev.: $1,884,000,000
Assets: $9,714,000,000

Liabilities: $5,562,000,000
Net Worth: $4,152,000,000
Earnings: $312,000,000
Emp.: 759
Fiscal Year-end: 12/31/2023
Regulated Electric Utility
N.A.I.C.S.: 221111
John R. Crockett III *(Pres, Chief Compli-
ance Officer, Sec & Gen Counsel)*
Kent W. Blake *(CFO)*
Robert M. Conroy *(VP)*
David J. Freibert Jr. *(VP)*
Chris Garrett *(VP)*
Tom Jessee *(VP)*
Beth McFarland *(VP)*
Eileen L. Saunders *(VP)*
David Sinclair *(VP)*
Scott Straight *(VP)*
Steven Turner *(VP)*
Peter Waldrab *(VP)*
Chris Whelan *(VP)*

**Louisville Gas and Electric
Company**   **(2)**
220 W Main St, Louisville, KY
40202-1377   **(100%)**
Tel.: (502) 627-2000
Web Site: http://www.lge-ku.com
Rev.: $1,613,000,000
Assets: $7,753,000,000
Liabilities: $4,581,000,000
Net Worth: $3,172,000,000
Earnings: $266,000,000
Emp.: 927
Fiscal Year-end: 12/31/2023
Electric & Natural Gas Distr
N.A.I.C.S.: 221122
John R. Crockett III *(Pres, Chief Compli-
ance Officer, Sec & Gen Counsel)*
Kent W. Blake *(CFO)*
Christopher M. Garrett *(VP)*
Robert M. Conroy *(VP)*
David J. Freibert Jr. *(VP)*
Tom Jessee *(VP)*
Beth McFarland *(VP)*
Eileen L. Saunders *(VP)*
Scott Straight *(VP)*
Steven Turner *(VP)*
Peter Waldrab *(VP)*

PPL Development Corporation   **(1)**
2 N 9th St, Allentown, PA 18101
Tel.: (610) 774-5151
Web Site: http://www.pplweb.com
Sales Range: $100-124.9 Million
Business Services Focusing on Acquisition
& Divestiture
N.A.I.C.S.: 561499

PPL Electric Utilities Corporation   **(1)**
2 N 9th St, Allentown, PA
18101-1179   **(100%)**
Tel.: (610) 774-5151
Web Site: http://www.pplelectric.com
Rev.: $3,008,000,000
Assets: $14,294,000,000
Liabilities: $8,391,000,000
Net Worth: $5,903,000,000
Earnings: $519,000,000
Emp.: 1,438
Fiscal Year-end: 12/31/2023
Electric Power & Natural Gas Distr
N.A.I.C.S.: 221122
Gregory N. Dudkin *(Pres)*
John R. Crockett III *(Pres)*
David J. Bonenberger *(Pres)*
David K. Arthur *(VP)*
W. Mark Brooks *(VP)*
Andrew W. Elmore *(VP)*
Angie McDonald Evans *(VP)*
Matthew B. Green *(Sr VP)*
Tadd J. Henninger *(Treas)*
Andrew Ludwig *(VP)*
Christine M. Martin *(Chief Sustainability Of-
ficer)*
Steven D. Phillips *(Chief Compliance Offi-
cer)*

PPL Energy Funding Corporation   **(1)**
2 N 9th St, Allentown, PA 18101-1170
Tel.: (610) 774-5151
Web Site: http://www.pplweb.com
Energy Related Financial Services
N.A.I.C.S.: 921130

PPL Generation, LLC   **(1)**
2 N 9th St, Allentown, PA 18101-1139
Tel.: (610) 774-5151
Web Site: http://www.pplweb.com

PPL Corporation—(Continued)

Sales Range: $200-249.9 Million
Power Generation Services
N.A.I.C.S.: 221118

Subsidiary (Domestic):

PPL Montana Holdings, LLC (2)
303 N 28th St, Billings, MT 59101-1255
Tel.: (406) 237-6900
Web Site: http://www.pplmontana.com
Sales Range: $500-549.9 Million
Emp.: 550
Energy Generation Services
N.A.I.C.S.: 221122

Subsidiary (Domestic):

PPL Montana, LLC (3)
303 N Broadway Ste 400, Billings, MT 59101-1255
Tel.: (406) 237-6900
Eletric Power Generation Services
N.A.I.C.S.: 221118
Steve Craig *(Supvr-Sourcing)*

Subsidiary (Domestic):

PPL Montour, LLC (2)
209th St, Allentown, PA 18101
Tel.: (610) 774-5151
Web Site: http://www.pplweb.com
Sales Range: $200-249.9 Million
Emp.: 325
Power Generation Services
N.A.I.C.S.: 221118

PPL Susquehanna LLC (2)
1190 E Mountain Blvd, Wilkes Barre, PA 18702-7938 **(90%)**
Tel.: (570) 831-6286
Sales Range: $10-24.9 Million
Emp.: 1,000
Nuclear Power Services
N.A.I.C.S.: 221113

PPL Global, LLC (1)
2 N Ninth St, Allentown, PA 18101-1179
Tel.: (610) 774-5997
Web Site: http://www.pplweb.com
Holding Company
N.A.I.C.S.: 551112

Subsidiary (Non-US):

PPL UK Investments Limited (2)
Avonbank Feeder Road, Bristol, BS2 0TB, United Kingdom
Tel.: (44) 12715651062
Investment Management Service
N.A.I.C.S.: 523940

PPL WW Holdings Limited (2)
Emp.: 2,634
Holding Company

Subsidiary (Non-US):

Western Power Distribution (3)
(100%)
Tel.: (44) 2070043000
Web Site: https://www.nationalgrid.com
Sales Range: $700-749.9 Million
Emp.: 2,552
Electricity Distribution Services
N.A.I.C.S.: 335311

PRA GROUP, INC.
150 Corporate Blvd, Norfolk, VA 23502
Tel.: (757) 519-9300   DE
Web Site: https://www.pragroup.com
Year Founded: 1996
PRAA—(NASDAQ)
Rev.: $802,554,000
Assets: $4,525,354,000
Liabilities: $3,285,978,000
Net Worth: $1,239,376,000
Earnings: $66,754,000
Emp.: 3,155
Fiscal Year-end: 12/31/23
Debt Collection Services
N.A.I.C.S.: 561440
Steven D. Fredrickson *(Chm)*
Vikram A. Atal *(Pres & CEO)*
Martin Sjolund *(Pres-PRA Grp-Europe)*

Elizabeth Kersey *(Sr VP-Comm & Pub Policy)*
Jan Husby *(CIO)*
Owen James *(Officer)*
Latisha Tarrant *(Chief HR Officer)*
Najim Mostamand *(VP-IR)*
Rakesh Sehgal *(CFO & Exec VP)*

Subsidiaries:

Claims Compensation Bureau, LLC (1)
130 Corporate Blvd, Norfolk, VA 23502
Tel.: (610) 834-9010
Web Site: https://www.claimscompensation.com
Sales Range: $25-49.9 Million
Emp.: 15
Claim Recovery Services
N.A.I.C.S.: 524292
Leah Stolker Jordan *(VP)*
Marc Richman *(Mgr-Ops)*
Jennifer Foster *(VP-Sls & Bus Dev)*
Robert Rey *(Pres)*
Mark Schneider *(VP-Ops)*
Heather Shain Hall *(VP-Claim Filing & Client Services)*

PRA Group Europe AS (1)
PO Box 9137, Gronland, NO-0133, Oslo, Norway
Tel.: (47) 24103100
Sales Range: $150-199.9 Million
Emp.: 700
Credit Administrative & Financial Services
N.A.I.C.S.: 522390

Subsidiary (Domestic):

Aktiv Kapital Financial Services AS (2)
Christian Krohgs gate 16, 0186, Oslo, Norway **(100%)**
Tel.: (47) 24103100
Emp.: 421
Financial Management Services
N.A.I.C.S.: 525990

Subsidiary (Non-US):

AK Sverige AB (3)
Forsta langgatan 21, 413 27, Gothenburg, Sweden
Tel.: (46) 317041600
Debt Collection Services
N.A.I.C.S.: 561440

Subsidiary (Domestic):

Aktiv Kapital Investment AS (3)
Idrettsveien 9, 1400, Ski, Norway
Tel · (47) 24103100
Debt Collection Services
N.A.I.C.S.: 561440

Subsidiary (Non-US):

PRA Group (UK) Limited (2)
Halo Enterprise & Innovation Centre Hill Street, Kilmarnock, KA3 1HA, Kent, United Kingdom **(100%)**
Tel.: (44) 8081965550
Web Site: https://pragroup.co.uk
Sales Range: $25-49.9 Million
Emp.: 100
Debt Collection Services
N.A.I.C.S.: 561440

PRA Group Canada Inc. (2)
200 - 244 Pall Mall St, London, N6A 5P6, ON, Canada **(100%)**
Web Site: https://www.pra-group.ca
Emp.: 60
Credit Administrative & Financial Services
N.A.I.C.S.: 522390

PRA Group Deutschland GmbH (2)
Landfermannstrasse 6, 47051, Duisburg, Germany
Tel.: (49) 203289260
Web Site: https://www.pragroup.de
Credit Services & Collection Agency
N.A.I.C.S.: 522390
Godfrey Mbawala *(Mng Dir)*
Marcel Kochling *(Mng Dir)*

Subsidiary (Domestic):

PRA Group Norge AS (2)

Dronning Eufemias gate 6, 0191, Oslo, Norway
Tel.: (47) 24103150
Emp.: 54
Debt Collection & Credit Administrative Services
N.A.I.C.S.: 561440

PRA Group Norge AS (2)
Dronning Eufemias gate 6, 0191, Oslo, Norway
Tel.: (47) 24103150
Web Site: https://www.pragroup.no
Emp.: 54
Debt Collection & Credit Administrative Services
N.A.I.C.S.: 561440

PRA Group Norge AS (2)
Dronning Eufemias gate 6, 0191, Oslo, Norway
Tel.: (47) 24103150
Web Site: https://www.pragroup.no
Emp.: 54
Debt Collection & Credit Administrative Services
N.A.I.C.S.: 561440

PRA Group Norge AS (2)
Dronning Eufemias gate 6, 0191, Oslo, Norway
Tel.: (47) 24103150
Web Site: https://www.pragroup.no
Emp.: 54
Debt Collection & Credit Administrative Services
N.A.I.C.S.: 561440

Subsidiary (Non-US):

PRA Group Osterreich Inkasso GmbH (2)
Marktstrasse 3, 7000, Eisenstadt, Austria **(100%)**
Tel.: (43) 268290313000
Web Site: https://www.pragroup.at
Sales Range: $25-49.9 Million
Emp.: 60
Credit Administrative & Financial Services
N.A.I.C.S.: 522390
Werner Ringhofer *(Mng Dir)*
Martin Sjolund *(Mng Dir)*

PRA Group Poland sp. Z oo (2)
Proximo 1 ul Prosta 68, 00-838, Warsaw, Poland
Tel.: (48) 222766600
Web Site: https://www.pragroup.pl
Receivables Management Services
N.A.I.C.S.: 525990

PRA Group Sverige AB (2)
S T Persgatan 0, 750 20, Uppsala, Sweden
Tel.: (46) 855121714
Web Site: https://www.pragroup.se
Debt Collection & Credit Administrative Services
N.A.I.C.S.: 561440

PRA Iberia SLU (2)
C/Albasanz n 16 3 Planta, 28037, Madrid, Spain
Tel.: (34) 90 080 0673
Web Site: https://pragroup.es
Debt Collection & Credit Administrative Services
N.A.I.C.S.: 561440

PRA Suomi OY (2)
Yliopistonkatu 7, 100, Helsinki, Finland
Tel.: (358) 80096400
Web Site: https://www.pragroup.fi
Debt Collection & Credit Administrative Services
N.A.I.C.S.: 561440

PRA Suomi OY (2)
Yliopistonkatu 7, 100, Helsinki, Finland
Tel.: (358) 80096400
Web Site: https://www.pragroup.fi
Debt Collection & Credit Administrative Services
N.A.I.C.S.: 561440

PRA Suomi OY (2)
Yliopistonkatu 7, 100, Helsinki, Finland
Tel.: (358) 80096400
Web Site: https://www.pragroup.fi
Debt Collection & Credit Administrative Services
N.A.I.C.S.: 561440

PRA Suomi OY (2)
Yliopistonkatu 7, 100, Helsinki, Finland
Tel.: (358) 80096400
Web Site: https://www.pragroup.fi
Debt Collection & Credit Administrative Services
N.A.I.C.S.: 561440

PRA Group Europe Financial Services AS (1)
Dronning Eufemias Gate 6, PO Box 9106, 0191, Oslo, Norway
Tel.: (47) 24103100
Credit Reporting Services
N.A.I.C.S.: 561450

PRA Group Europe Portfolio AS (1)
Bishop Gunnerus' gate 14A, 0185, Oslo, Norway
Tel.: (47) 24103100
Debt Collection Services
N.A.I.C.S.: 561440

PRA Group Osterreich Portfolio GmbH (1)
Marktstrasse 3, 7000, Eisenstadt, Austria
Tel.: (43) 268290313000
Web Site: http://pragroup.at
Debt Collection Services
N.A.I.C.S.: 561440

PRA Receivables Management, LLC (1)
150 Corporate Blvd, Norfolk, VA 23502
Bankrupt Account Management Services
N.A.I.C.S.: 525920

RCB Planejamento Financeiro LTDA. (1)
Av Paulista 1048-CJ 101-Bela Vista, Sao Paulo, 1310-100, SP, Brazil
Tel.: (55) 1138078649
Collection Agency Services
N.A.I.C.S.: 561440

RCB Portfolios LTDA. (1)
Pc General Gentil Falcao 108 Conj 132 Do Centro Empresarial, E Cultural Joao Domingues De Araujo Cidade Moncoes, Sao Paulo, 04571-150, SP, Brazil
Tel.: (55) 28741129
Collection Agency Services
N.A.I.C.S.: 561440

PRAETORIAN PROPERTY, INC,
7702 E Doubletree Ranch Rd Ste 300, Scottsdale, AZ 85258
Tel.: (480) 902-3399   NV
Year Founded: 2011
PRRE—(OTCIQ)
Sales Range: $10-24.9 Million
Emp.: 2
Investment Services
N.A.I.C.S.: 523999

PRAIRIE OPERATING CO.
602 Sawyer St Ste 710, Houston, TX 77007
Tel.: (713) 424-4247   DE
Web Site:
https://www.prairieopco.com
Year Founded: 2001
PROP—(OTCQB)
Rev.: $517,602
Assets: $6,793,097
Liabilities: $13,318,156
Net Worth: ($6,525,059)
Earnings: ($13,783,198)
Emp.: 2
Fiscal Year-end: 12/31/22
All Other Business Support Services
N.A.I.C.S.: 561499
Robert Craig Owen *(CFO)*
Edward Kovalik *(Chm & CEO)*
Jeremy Ham *(Chief Comml Officer)*
Gary C. Hanna *(Pres)*

PRAXIS PRECISION MEDICINES, INC.

99 High St 30th Fl, Boston, MA
02110
Tel.: (617) 300-8460   DE
Web Site:
   https://www.praxismedicines.com
Year Founded: 2015
PRAX—(NASDAQ)
Rev.: $957,000
Assets: $115,128,000
Liabilities: $39,022,000
Net Worth: $76,106,000
Earnings: ($214,029,000)
Emp.: 109
Fiscal Year-end: 12/31/22
Research & Development in Biotech-
nology (except Nanobiotechnology)
N.A.I.C.S.: 541714
Steven Petrou (Co-Founder & Chief
Scientific Officer)
Alex Nemiroff (Gen Counsel & Sec)
David Goldstein (Co-Founder)
Kelly McCue (Chief People Officer)
Megan Sniecinski (Chief Bus Officer)
Lauren Mastrocola (Chief Acctg Offi-
cer)
Marcio Souza (Pres & CEO)

PRECICION TRIM, INC.

17011 Beach Blvd 9th Fl, Huntington
Beach, CA 92647
Tel.: (657) 378-7981   NV
PRTR—(OTCIQ)
Robotic Machine Mfr & Distr
N.A.I.C.S.: 336110
Richie Kerwin Lim (CEO)

PRECIGEN, INC.

20358 Seneca Meadows Pkwy, Ger-
mantown, MD 20876
Tel.: (301) 556-9900   VA
Web Site: https://precigen.com
Year Founded: 1998
PGEN—(NASDAQ)
Rev.: $6,225,000
Assets: $151,043,000
Liabilities: $32,545,000
Net Worth: $118,498,000
Earnings: ($95,904,000)
Emp.: 202
Fiscal Year-end: 12/31/23
Synthetic Biological Products
N.A.I.C.S.: 325998
Randal J. Kirk (Chm)
Donald P. Lehr (Chief Legal Officer)
Helen Sabzevari (Pres & CEO)
Rutul R. Shah (COO)
Amy R. Lankford (VP)
Harry Thomasian Jr. (CFO)

Subsidiaries:

Exemplar Genetics, LLC   (1)
PO Box 829, North Liberty, IA 52317
Tel.: (712) 722-2767
Web Site:
   https://www.exemplargenetics.com
Emp.: 20
Biotechnology Research & Development
Services
N.A.I.C.S.: 541714

GenVec, Inc.   (1)
910 Clopper Road Ste 220N, Gaithersburg,
MD 20878
Tel.: (240) 632-0740
Web Site: http://www.dna.com
Sales Range: Less than $1 Million
Clinical-Stage Biopharmaceutical Mfr
N.A.I.C.S.: 325412
Lenore Reid (Head-HR)

Genomatix, Inc.   (1)
3025 Boardwalk Ste 160, Ann Arbor, MI
48108
Software Development Services
N.A.I.C.S.: 541511

Intrexon BioInformatics Germany
GmbH   (1)
Bayerstr 85a, 80335, Munich, Germany
Tel.: (49) 895997660

Web Site: http://www.genomatix.de
Software Development Services
N.A.I.C.S.: 541511

Okanagan Specialty Fruits Inc.   (1)
12033 Loomer Road, Summerland, V0H
1Z0, BC, Canada
Tel.: (250) 404-0101
Synthetic Biological Product Mfr
N.A.I.C.S.: 325998

Oxitec Ltd.   (1)
71 Innovation Dr Milton Park, Abingdon,
OX14 4RQ, United Kingdom
Tel.: (44) 1235832393
Web Site: https://www.oxitec.com
Emp.: 60
Biological Insect Control Products Devel-
oper
N.A.I.C.S.: 325320
Grey Frandsen (CEO)
Kevin Gorman (Chief Dev Officer)
Nathan Rose (Head-Regulatory Affairs)
Meredith Fensom (Head-Pub Affairs-Global)
Eva Darrington (CFO)

Oxitec do Brasil Tecnologia de Inse-
tos Ltda   (1)
Av Alexander Grahan Bell 200 Bloco C
Modulo 3 Techno Park, Campinas, 13069-
330, Brazil
Tel.: (55) 1935140100
Pesticide Mfr
N.A.I.C.S.: 325320

ViaGen, L.C.   (1)
715 Discovery Blvd Ste 410 A, Cedar Park,
TX 78613
Tel.: (512) 986-7212
Web Site: http://www.viagenpets.com
Biotechnology Research & Development
Services
N.A.I.C.S.: 541714

PRECIPIO, INC.

4 Science Park 3rd Fl, New Haven,
CT 06511
Tel.: (203) 787-7888   DE
Web Site:
   https://www.precipiodx.com
Year Founded: 1997
PRPO—(NASDAQ)
Rev.: $9,412,000
Assets: $21,504,000
Liabilities: $5,137,000
Net Worth: $16,367,000
Earnings: ($12,203,000)
Emp.: 53
Fiscal Year-end: 12/31/22
Diagnostic Products & Services
N.A.I.C.S.: 334516
Ilan Danieli (CEO)
A. Zaki Sabet (COO)
Richard A. Sandberg (Chm)
Ayman Mohamed (Founder)
Matthew Gage (Interim CFO)

Subsidiaries:

Precipio Diagnostics LLC   (1)
4 Science Park 3rd Fl, New Haven, CT
06511-1962
Tel.: (203) 787-7888
Web Site: https://www.precipiodx.com
Medical Laboratory Specializing in Cancer
Research & Development
N.A.I.C.S.: 541713

Transgenomic Ltd.   (1)
40 Watt Rd Hillington Pk Pacal, Glasgow,
G52 OOYY, United Kingdom
Tel.: (44) 1418928800
Web Site: http://www.transgenomic.com
Sales Range: $100-124.9 Million
Emp.: 10
Developer of Genetic Variation Detection
Products
N.A.I.C.S.: 339112

PRECISION BIOSCIENCES, INC.

302 E Pettigrew St, Durham, NC
27701
Tel.: (919) 314-5512   DE

Web Site:
   https://www.precisionbioscien
   ces.com
Year Founded: 2006
DTIL—(NASDAQ)
Rev.: $25,098,000
Assets: $238,169,000
Liabilities: $177,736,000
Net Worth: $60,433,000
Earnings: ($111,637,000)
Emp.: 198
Fiscal Year-end: 12/31/22
Biotechnology Research & Develop-
ment Services
N.A.I.C.S.: 541714
John Alexander Kelly (CFO & Princi-
pal Acctg Officer)
Matthew Kane (Co-Founder)
Derek Jantz (Co-Founder & Chief
Scientific Officer)
David Thomson (Co-Founder)
Jeff Smith (Co-Founder & CTO)
Dario Scimeca (Gen Counsel)
Cindy Atwell (Sr VP-Bus Dev & Alli-
ance Mgmt)
Alex Kelly (CIO)
Maurissa Messier (Sr Dir-Corp
Comm)
Juli Blanche (Chief People Officer)
Mei Burris (Dir-Fin & IR)
Michael Amoroso (Pres & CEO)

Subsidiaries:

Elo Life Systems, Inc.   (1)
3054 E Cornwallis Rd, Durham, NC 27709
Tel.: (919) 514-1107
Web Site: https://elolife.com
Bio Technology Services
N.A.I.C.S.: 541714
Abid Ansari (VP-Fin)
Derek Jantz (Co-Founder)
Jeff Smith (Co-Founder)
Matt Kane (Co-Founder)
Alec Hayes (VP-Tech & Products)

PRECISION OPTICS CORPO-RATION, INC.

22 E Broadway, Gardner, MA 01440
Tel.: (978) 630-1800   MA
Web Site: https://www.poci.com
Year Founded: 1989
POCI—(NASDAQ)
Rev.: $19,104,350
Assets: $16,912,574
Liabilities: $6,844,786
Net Worth: $10,067,788
Earnings: ($2,951,377)
Emp.: 83
Fiscal Year-end: 06/30/24
Commercial & Service Industry Ma-
chinery Manufacturing
N.A.I.C.S.: 333310
Richard E. Forkey (Founder)
Joseph N. Forkey (Pres & CEO)
Peter H. Woodward (Chm)
Jonathan Everett (VP-Engrg)
Richard Cyr (Gen Mgr-Optics Lab)
Robert Ross (Dir-Product Design &
Dev)
Bruce Radl (Dir-Tech Dev)
John Hargraves (Dir-Ops)
Terri Moore (Dir-Quality & Regulatory
Affairs)
Mahesh Lawande (COO)
Wayne M. Coll (CFO)

Subsidiaries:

Lighthouse Imaging LLC   (1)
765 Roosevelt Trail Ste 9, Windham, ME
04062
Tel.: (207) 893-8233
Web Site: http://www.lighthouseoptics.com
Surgical & Medical Instrument Mfr
N.A.I.C.S.: 339112
Dennis Leiner (CTO)
Tom Snyder (CEO)
Robert Austring (Chief Comml Officer)
Benjamin Gray (CTO)

Ross Optical Industries, Inc.   (1)
1410 Gail Borden Pl Ste A-3, El Paso, TX
79935
Tel.: (915) 595-5417
Web Site: http://www.rossoptical.com
Optical Instrument & Lens Mfr
N.A.I.C.S.: 333310
Edward Ross (Founder)
Lisa Yang (Mgr-Engrg)
Divi Mangadu (Pres)

PREDICTIVE ONCOLOGY INC.

2915 Commers Dr Ste 900, Eagan,
MN 55121
Tel.: (651) 389-4800   DE
Web Site: https://www.predictive-
oncology.com
Year Founded: 2002
POAI—(NASDAQ)
Rev.: $1,505,459
Assets: $25,734,644
Liabilities: $3,968,752
Net Worth: $21,765,892
Earnings: ($25,737,634)
Emp.: 31
Fiscal Year-end: 12/31/22
Research & Development in Biotech-
nology (except Nanobiotechnology)
N.A.I.C.S.: 541714
Josh Blacher (Interim CFO & Princi-
pal Acctg Officer)
Raymond F. Vennare (Chm & CEO)
Theresa Ferguson (Sr Dir-Mktg)
Larry DeLucas (Sr VP)
Arlette H. Uihlein (Sr VP)

Subsidiaries:

Soluble Biotech Inc.   (1)
200 Riverhills Business Park Ste 250, Bir-
mingham, AL 35242
Tel.: (651) 389-4839
Web Site: http://www.solublebiotech.com
Research & Development Services
N.A.I.C.S.: 541714
Larry DeLucas (Founder & CEO)
Bob Myers (CFO)
Keith Champion (Dir-Ops)
Chrysanty Weaver (Dir-Res)

Soluble Therapeutics, Inc.   (1)
1500 1st Ave N, Birmingham, AL 35203
Tel.: (205) 206-4600
Pharmaceutical Preparation Mfr
N.A.I.C.S.: 325412

TumorGenesis Inc.   (1)
4 Technology Way, Salem, MA 01970
Tel.: (781) 883-6639
Web Site: http://www.tumorgenesis.net
Laboratory Testing Services
N.A.I.C.S.: 541380

PREDICTIVE TECHNOLOGY GROUP, INC.

2735 Parleys Way Ste 205, Salt Lake
City, UT 84109
Tel.: (801) 980-7720   NV
Web Site:
   http://www.predtechgroup.com
Year Founded: 2005
PRED—(OTCEM)
Rev.: $24,441,424
Assets: $83,842,415
Liabilities: $28,919,133
Net Worth: $54,923,282
Earnings: ($85,769,266)
Emp.: 62
Fiscal Year-end: 06/30/20
Biotechnology Research & Develop-
ment Services
N.A.I.C.S.: 541714
Bradley C. Robinson (CEO)
Paul Evans (COO)
John E. Sorrentino (Chm)

Subsidiaries:

Cellsure, L3C   (1)
615 Arapeen Dr Ste 300, Salt Lake City, UT
84108
Web Site: http://www.cellsure.com
Healtcare Services

Predictive Technology Group, Inc.—(Continued)

N.A.I.C.S.: 621491

Predictive Laboratories, Inc. **(1)**
2749 E Parleys Way Ste 100, Salt Lake City, UT 84109
Web Site: http://www.predictivelabs.com
Diagnostic Laboratory Services
N.A.I.C.S.: 621511
Allen Ward *(Pres)*
Lesa Nelson *(COO)*
Tom Holm *(Dir-Sls & Mktg Support)*
Shane Rowley *(Dir-Fin)*
Ken Neff *(Dir-IT)*

Predictive Therapeutics, LLC **(1)**
2735 Parleys Way Ste 205, Salt Lake City, UT 84109
Web Site: http://www.predrx.com
Diagnostic Product Mfr & Distr
N.A.I.C.S.: 334510

PREFERRED BANK
601 S Figueroa St 48th Fl, Los Angeles, CA 90017
Tel.: (213) 891-1188
Web Site:
  https://www.preferredbank.com
Year Founded: 1991
PFBC—(NASDAQ)
Rev.: $234,187,000
Assets: $4,628,481,000
Liabilities: $4,158,466,000
Net Worth: $470,015,000
Earnings: $78,371,000
Emp.: 279
Fiscal Year-end: 12/31/19
Commericial Banking
N.A.I.C.S.: 522110
Nick Pi *(Chief Credit Officer & Exec VP)*
Johnny Hsu *(Deputy COO & Exec VP)*
Clark Hsu *(Vice Chm)*
Wellington Chen *(Pres & COO)*
Edward J. Czajka *(CFO & Exec VP)*
Li Yu *(Chm & CEO)*
Edward J. Czajka *(CFO & Exec VP)*

PREFERRED COMMERCE, INC.
1655 Palm Beach Lakes Blvd Ste 800, West Palm Beach, FL 33401
Tel.: (561) 752-2250
Web Site: http://www.growums.com
Year Founded: 1999
OCBM—(OTCIQ)
Sales Range: $1-9.9 Million
Emp.: 17
Software
N.A.I.C.S.: 513210

PREFORMED LINE PRODUCTS COMPANY
660 Beta Dr, Cleveland, OH 44143
Tel.: (440) 461-5200   OH
Web Site: https://www.plp.com
Year Founded: 1947
PLPC—(NASDAQ)
Rev.: $637,021,000
Assets: $568,479,000
Liabilities: $209,563,000
Net Worth: $358,624,000
Earnings: $54,395,000
Emp.: 3,261
Fiscal Year-end: 12/31/22
Mfr of Products for Constructing Electrical Power Lines & Telecommunications Systems
N.A.I.C.S.: 237130
John M. Hofstetter *(Exec VP-Ops-US)*
Dennis F. McKenna *(CEO)*
R. Steven Kestner *(Executives, Bd of Dirs)*
J. Ryan Ruhlman *(Pres)*
Tim O'Shaughnessy *(VP-HR)*
Andrew S. Klaus *(CFO)*
William Koh *(VP-Asia Pacific)*

Subsidiaries:

APRESA - PLP Spain, S. A. **(1)**
Av Roberto Osborne 11, 41007, Seville, Spain
Tel.: (34) 954997223
Web Site: https://www.plp-spain.com
Sales Range: $100-124.9 Million
Emp.: 50
Wire Devices & Communications Equipment
N.A.I.C.S.: 335931

Beijing PLP Conductor Line Products, Ltd. **(100%)**
1 Guohuai Jie Development Zone, Liangxiang, Beijing, 102488, China
Tel.: (86) 1089360860
Web Site: https://www.plp.com.cn
Sales Range: $25-49.9 Million
Emp.: 80
Wire Devices & Communications Equipment
N.A.I.C.S.: 335931

Direct Power and Water Corporation **(100%)**
4000 Vassar Dr NE B, Albuquerque, NM 87107
Tel.: (505) 889-3585
Web Site: http://www.power-fab.com
Solar Racking Structure & Equipment Mfr
N.A.I.C.S.: 334413

Electropar Ltd. **(1)**
35 Lady Ruby Drive, Manukau, East Tamaki, 2013, Auckland, New Zealand
Tel.: (64) 92742000
Web Site: http://www.electropar.co.nz
Emp.: 80
Electric Power Transmission Equipment & Supplies Mfr
N.A.I.C.S.: 237130
Brett Hewitt *(Mng Dir)*
Peter Stern *(CEO)*
Simon Pratt *(Exec Mgr-Sls)*
Ivan Haeane *(Exec Mgr-Energy)*
Kamlesh Prasad *(Mgr-Engrg)*
Murray Howell *(Mgr-Mktg)*

Helix Uniformed Ltd. **(1)**
1600 46 th Avenue, Lachine, H8T 3J9, QC, Canada
Tel.: (514) 828-0057
Web Site: https://www.helix-uni.ca
Emp.: 40
Power Transmission Component Mfr
N.A.I.C.S.: 333613

MICOS TELCOM s.r.o. **(1)**
Haj 365, Kralice na Hane, 798 12, Olomouc, Czech Republic
Tel.: (420) 60 422 2657
Web Site: https://www.micostelcom.com
Telecommunication Cable Mfr & Distr
N.A.I.C.S.: 335929
Jiri Novak *(Mgr-New Market Dev)*

PLP Argentina SRL **(1)**
Parque Industrial del Oeste Ruta 25 cruce con Ruta 24, Moreno, 1744, Buenos Aires, Argentina
Tel.: (54) 91135834413
Web Site: https://plpargentina.com.ar
Electrical Equipment Distr
N.A.I.C.S.: 423610

PLP Produtos Para Linhas Proformados Ltda. **(1)**
Av Tenente Marques 1112 - Empresarial Mirante de Cajamar, Cajamar, 07790-260, SP, Brazil **(100%)**
Tel.: (55) 1144488000
Web Site: https://www.plp.com.br
Sales Range: $50-74.9 Million
Emp.: 170
Mfr of Electrical Equipment, Wiring & Supplies
N.A.I.C.S.: 335931
Geraldo Mendonca *(Dir-Comml)*

PLP Russia Ltd. **(1)**
Raketny Bulvar d 16 office 1601, 129164, Moscow, Russia
Tel.: (7) 4952520314
Web Site: http://www.plp-russia.ru
Electrical Equipment Distr
N.A.I.C.S.: 423610

PT Preformed Line Products Indonesia **(1)**
Tel.: (62) 2185933899

Web Site: https://plp.com
Emp.: 300
Power Transmission Supplies Mfr & Distr
N.A.I.C.S.: 237130

Preformados De Mexico SA **(1)**
Leibnitz No 11-102, Col Anzures Delegacion Miguel Hidalgo, 15590, Mexico, Mexico
Tel.: (52) 5552031602
Web Site: https://www.plpmexico.com
Sales Range: $25-49.9 Million
Emp.: 150
Mfr of Wire
N.A.I.C.S.: 331318
Salvador Naranjo *(Mng Dir)*
Miguel Angel Guerrero *(Mgr-Energy Sls)*

Preformed Line Products (Australia) Pty Ltd. **(1)**
190 Power Street, Glendenning, 2761, NSW, Australia **(100%)**
Tel.: (61) 288050000
Web Site: https://www.preformed.com.au
Emp.: 85
Electrical Equipment Mfr & Distr
N.A.I.C.S.: 335313
Matthew Greely *(Gen Mgr-Engrg & Strategic Sourcing)*
Stephen Haller *(Mng Dir)*
Ikesh Tharmarajah *(Gen Mgr-Fin)*
Adam Talbot *(Gen Mgr-Sls & Mktg)*
Ali Sohanian *(Gen Mgr-Supply Chain)*
Malcolm Stewart *(Mng Dir)*

Preformed Line Products (France) SAS **(1)**
1bis rue des Champs Odes, 78200, Buchelay, France
Tel.: (33) 177492800
Web Site: https://www.plp-france.fr
Electrical Equipment Distr
N.A.I.C.S.: 423610
Bruno Maiano *(Mng Dir)*

Preformed Line Products (Great Britain) Ltd. **(1)**
East Portway, Andover, SP10 3LH, Hampshire, United Kingdom **(100%)**
Tel.: (44) 1264366234
Web Site: https://www.plp.com
Sales Range: $25-49.9 Million
Emp.: 100
Mfr of Overhead Transmission Fittings
N.A.I.C.S.: 333613
Martin Spayes *(Dir-Sls)*
Trevor Taljaard *(Mgr-Export Sls)*

Preformed Line Products (Malaysia) Sdn. Bhd **(1)**
No 3 Jalan BK 1/11, Kinrara Industrial Park Bandar Kinrara, 47100, Puchong, Selangor Darul Ehsan, Malaysia
Tel.: (60) 380755922
Web Site: https://www.preformed.asia
Sales Range: $25-49.9 Million
Emp.: 50
Power Transmission Equipment Mfr & Distr
N.A.I.C.S.: 221121

Preformed Line Products (South Africa) Pty. Ltd. **(1)**
180 Ohrtmann Road, Willowton, Pietermaritzburg, 3201, KwaZulu-Natal, South Africa **(100%)**
Tel.: (27) 333975800
Web Site: https://plp.com
Sales Range: $25-49.9 Million
Emp.: 150
Wire Devices, Cable Anchoring & Control Hardware
N.A.I.C.S.: 335931
David Muller *(Mgr-Comml & Bus Dev)*

Preformed Line Products (Vietnam) Ltd. **(1)**
No 9A Street 53 Zone 5, Tan Phong Ward District 7, Ho Chi Minh City, Vietnam
Tel.: (84) 2839339927
Electric Power Distr
N.A.I.C.S.: 221122
Do Hong Lam *(Gen Mgr)*
Ngo Kim Dung *(Product Mgr)*

Preformed Line Products Canada Ltd. **(1)**
1711 Bishop St N, Cambridge, N1T 1N5, ON, Canada
Tel.: (519) 740-6666
Web Site: https://www.preformed.ca

Sales Range: $10-24.9 Million
Emp.: 50
Mfr of Pole Line Hardware
N.A.I.C.S.: 335932
Wade Cutting *(Product Mgr)*
Phil Jones *(Mng Dir)*

PRELUDE THERAPEUTICS INCORPORATED
175 Innovation Blvd, Wilmington, DE 19805
Tel.: (302) 467-1280   DE
Web Site: https://www.preludetx.com
Year Founded: 2016
PRLD—(NASDAQ)
Rev.: $8,102,000
Assets: $220,500,000
Liabilities: $25,063,000
Net Worth: $195,437,000
Earnings: ($115,438,000)
Emp.: 122
Fiscal Year-end: 12/31/22
Biotechnology Research & Development Services
N.A.I.C.S.: 541714
Jane E. Huang *(Pres & Chief Medical Officer)*
Bryant D. Lim *(Interim CFO, Chief Legal Officer, Principal Acctg Officer & Sec)*
Kris Vaddi *(CEO)*
Peggy Scherle *(Chief Scientific Officer)*
Andrew Combs *(Exec VP & Head-Chemistry)*
Aimee Crombie *(Sr VP & Head-Strategic Plng & Ops)*
Adam Shilling *(VP-Early Dev & Regulatory Affairs)*
Madhu Pudipeddi *(VP-Technical Ops)*
Paul A. Friedman *(Chm)*

PREMIER BIOMEDICAL, INC.
1150 S 8th St, El Centro, CA 92243
Tel.: (442) 270-2302   NV
Web Site:
  http://www.premierbiomedical.com
Year Founded: 2010
BIEI—(OTCIQ)
Rev.: $14,281
Assets: $100,943
Liabilities: $1,933,761
Net Worth: ($1,832,818)
Earnings: ($374,470)
Fiscal Year-end: 12/31/10
Pharmaceutical Researcher & Developer
N.A.I.C.S.: 325412
Mitchell S. Felder *(Founder)*
David Caplan *(Chm, Pres, Treas & Sec)*
Ivan Mendez *(CEO)*

PREMIER EXHIBITIONS, INC.
3045 Kingston Ct Ste I, Peachtree Corners, GA 30071
Tel.: (404) 842-2600   FL
Web Site:
  http://www.premierexhibitions.com
PRXIQ—(OTCIQ)
Special Exhibition Operator
N.A.I.C.S.: 713990
Jerome Henshall *(CFO)*
Daoping Bao *(Chm, Pres & CEO)*

Subsidiaries:

Premier Vision, LLC **(1)**
2049 Wells St Ste 1, Wailuku, HI 96793
Tel.: (808) 244-8034
Web Site: http://www.premiervisionllc.com
Eye Care Service
N.A.I.C.S.: 456199

RMS Titanic Inc **(1)**
3340 Peachtree Rd NE Ste 900, Atlanta, GA 30326
Tel.: (404) 842-2600
Web Site: http://www.rmstitanic.net

Sales Range: $50-74.9 Million
Shipwreck Salvage Services
N.A.I.C.S.: 713990
Michael Little *(CFO & COO)*

Worldwide Licensing & Merchandising, Inc. **(1)**
7324 International Dr, Orlando, FL 32819
Tel.: (407) 248-1166
Web Site: http://titanicorlando.com
Amusement & Recreation Industries
N.A.I.C.S.: 713990

PREMIER FINANCIAL BAN-CORP, INC.
2883 5th Ave, Huntington, WV 25702
Tel.: (304) 525-1600 **KY**
Web Site:
http://www.premierbankinc.com
PFBI—(NASDAQ)
Rev.: $82,917,000
Assets: $1,945,822,000
Liabilities: $1,685,915,000
Net Worth: $259,907,000
Earnings: $22,438,000
Emp.: 337
Fiscal Year-end: 12/31/20
Bank Holding Company
N.A.I.C.S.: 551111
J. Mark Bias *(Pres & CEO-Premier Bank)*
Robert W. Walker *(Pres & CEO)*
Brien M. Chase *(CFO & Sr VP)*

Subsidiaries:

Citizens Deposit Bank & Trust Company **(1)**
10 2nd St, Vanceburg, KY 41179
Tel.: (606) 796-3001
Web Site: http://www.cdbt.com
Sales Range: $10-24.9 Million
Emp.: 116
Commercial Banking
N.A.I.C.S.: 522110
Michael R. Mineer *(Pres & CEO)*

Premier Bank, Inc. **(1)**
2883 5th Ave, Huntington, WV 25702
Tel.: (304) 525-1600
Web Site: http://www.premierbankinc.com
Sales Range: $50-74.9 Million
Emp.: 230
Commercial Banking
N.A.I.C.S.: 522110
J. Mark Bias *(Pres & CEO)*

PREMIER FINANCIAL CORP.
601 Clinton St, Defiance, OH 43512
Tel.: (419) 785-8700 **OH**
Web Site:
https://www.premierfincorp.com
Year Founded: 1995
PFC—(NASDAQ)
Rev.: $339,872,000
Assets: $8,455,342,000
Liabilities: $7,567,621,000
Net Worth: $887,721,000
Earnings: $102,187,000
Emp.: 1,206
Fiscal Year-end: 12/31/22
Bank Holding Company
N.A.I.C.S.: 551111
Donald P. Hileman *(Exec Chm)*
Sharon L. Davis *(Chief HR Officer & Exec VP)*
Paul D. Nungester Jr. *(CFO)*
Richard J. Schiraldi *(Vice Chm)*
Jason Gendics *(Exec VP-Retail & Bus Banking)*
Gary M. Small *(Pres & CEO)*
Varun Chandhok *(CIO & Exec VP)*
Kathy Bushway *(CMO & Sr VP)*
Dennis E. Rose Jr. *(Chief Strategy Officer & Exec VP)*
Shannon M. Kuhl *(Chief Legal Officer & Exec VP)*
Tina M. Shaver *(Chief Risk Officer & Exec VP)*

Rick Hull *(Exec VP & Head-Commercial Banking)*
Jennifer Scroggs *(Sr VP & Dir-Wealth Mgmt)*

Subsidiaries:

First Federal Bank of the Midwest **(1)**
25600 Elliott Rd, Defiance, OH 43512-9003 **(100%)**
Tel.: (419) 538-7100
Web Site: http://www.first-fed.com
Sales Range: $100-124.9 Million
Emp.: 450
Financial Services
N.A.I.C.S.: 523940
Donald P. Hileman *(CFO)*
Sharon L. Davis *(Chief HR Officer & Exec VP)*
Paul D. Nungester Jr. *(CFO)*
Vincent J. Liuzzi III *(Pres)*

PREMIER HOLDING CORP.
1382 Valencia Ave Unit F, Tustin, CA 92780
Tel.: (949) 260-8070 **NV**
Web Site: http://www.prhlcorp.com
PRHL—(OTCIQ)
Sales Range: $1-9.9 Million
Emp.: 1
Investment Holding Company; Energy Products
N.A.I.C.S.: 551112
Lawrence Young *(VP)*
Patrick Farah *(Mng Partner-The Power Company)*
Tarek Elmani *(Sec)*
Scott Dinsmoor *(CEO)*

PREMIER POWER RENEW-ABLE ENERGY, INC.
4961 Windplay Dr Ste 100, El Dorado Hills, CA 95762
Tel.: (916) 939-0400 **DE**
Web Site:
http://www.premierpower.com
Year Founded: 2006
PPRW—(OTCEM)
Sales Range: $50-74.9 Million
Emp.: 48
Solar Power Equipment Design, Integration & Installation Services
N.A.I.C.S.: 221118

PREMIER PRODUCT GROUP, INC.
1700 W Sunn Fjord Ln L209, Bremerton, WA 98312
Tel.: (360) 620-4397 **DE**
Web Site: http://www.pmpginc.com
Year Founded: 1979
PMPG—(OTCIQ)
Liabilities: $1,427,634
Net Worth: ($1,427,634)
Earnings: ($763,000)
Fiscal Year-end: 12/31/20
Holding Company
N.A.I.C.S.: 551112
Darrell A. Calloway *(Pres)*
Tony Hicks *(Chm & CEO)*

PREMIER, INC.
13034 Ballantyne Corporate Pl, Charlotte, NC 28277
Tel.: (704) 357-0022 **DE**
Web Site:
https://www.premierinc.com
Year Founded: 1969
PINC—(NASDAQ)
Rev.: $1,346,361,000
Assets: $3,401,449,000
Liabilities: $1,439,218,000
Net Worth: $1,962,231,000
Earnings: $106,719,000
Emp.: 2,900
Fiscal Year-end: 06/30/24

Healthcare Management Supply Services
N.A.I.C.S.: 541611
Michael J. Alkire *(Pres & CEO)*
Richard J. Statuto *(Chm)*
Leigh Anderson *(COO)*
Blair Childs *(Sr VP-Pub Affairs)*
Andy Brailo *(Chief Comml Officer)*
Leigh Anderson *(Pres-Performance Svcs)*
David Klatsky *(Gen Counsel)*
David Alfred Hargraves *(Sr VP-Supply Chain)*
Angie McCabe *(VP-IR)*
Ben Krasinski *(Dir-IR)*
Joe Machicote *(Chief Diversity & Inclusion Officer)*
Lindsay Powers *(Sr VP-People)*
Glenn G. Coleman *(CFO & Chief Admin Officer)*

Subsidiaries:

Acro Pharmaceutical Services LLC **(1)**
313 Henderson Dr, Sharon Hill, PA 19079-1034
Tel.: (800) 906-7798
Web Site: http://www.acropharmacy.com
Pharmaceuticals Whslr
N.A.I.C.S.: 424210
Brett Furchner *(Pres-Specialty Pharmacy Payer Networks)*
Greg Isaak *(CEO)*
Robert Raffalo *(COO)*
Glen Farmer *(Fin Dir)*
Susan Castillo *(VP-Specialty Pharmacy Product Dev)*
Anthony Mottola *(VP-Pharmacy Trade Rels)*
Acacia Strachan *(Dir-Clinical Pharmacy)*
Sue Anne Donnelly *(Dir-Receivable & Reimbursement)*
Chris Duffy *(Dir-Pharmacy)*

Cecity.com, Inc. **(1)**
285 E Waterfront Dr Ste 100, Homestead, PA 15120
Tel.: (412) 338-0366
Web Site: http://www.cecity.com
Sales Range: $1-9.9 Million
Emp.: 65
Wired Telecommunications Carriers
N.A.I.C.S.: 517111

Innovatix, LLC **(1)**
13034 Ballantyne Corporate Pl, Charlotte, NC 28277
Web Site: https://www.innovatix.com
Medical Management Consulting Services
N.A.I.C.S.: 541611
Lisa Walsh *(Sr VP)*

MEMdata, LLC **(1)**
1601 Sebesta Rd, College Station, TX 77845
Tel.: (979) 695-1950
Web Site: http://www.memdata.com
Emp.: 32
Equipment Planning & Analytics Business for Medical Facilities
N.A.I.C.S.: 541690

Meddius, LLC **(1)**
455 2nd St SE Ste 101, Charlottesville, VA 22902-5697
Tel.: (434) 977-5154
Health Care Services
N.A.I.C.S.: 621610

Premier Healthcare Alliance, L.P. **(1)**
13034 Ballantyne Corporate Pl, Charlotte, NC 28277
Tel.: (704) 357-0022
Emp.: 700
Healthcare Products
N.A.I.C.S.: 423450
Michael J. Alkire *(Pres)*

Subsidiary (Domestic):

Premier Healthcare Solutions Inc **(2)**
1 W Lakeshore Dr Ste 250, Birmingham, AL 35209
Tel.: (205) 502-7241
Web Site: https://www.premierhealthcare.com
Health Care Services

N.A.I.C.S.: 621610

Subsidiary (Domestic):

Premier Research Institute, Inc. **(3)**
444 N Capitol St NW Ste 625, Washington, DC 20001
Tel.: (202) 879-8018
Healthcare Services
N.A.I.C.S.: 541715

Stanson Health, Inc. **(3)**
13034 Ballantyne Corporate Pl, Charlotte, NC 28277
Web Site: http://www.stansonhealth.com
Healthcare Management Supply Services
N.A.I.C.S.: 541611
Alex Tatiyants *(CTO)*
Ryan M. Nellis *(VP & Gen Mgr)*
Marika E. Repasi *(Dir-Fin & Admin)*

Subsidiary (Domestic):

Premier Supply Chain Improvement, Inc. **(2)**
13034 Balntyn Corp Pl, Charlotte, NC 28277
Tel.: (704) 357-0022
Residential Buildings & Dwellings Leasing Services
N.A.I.C.S.: 531110

Subsidiary (Domestic):

MedPricer.com, Inc. **(3)**
2351 Boston Post Rd, Guilford, CT 06437
Tel.: (203) 453-4554
Web Site: http://www.medpricer.com
Healthcare Industry Electronic Sourcing Services
N.A.I.C.S.: 518210
Chris Gormley *(CEO)*
Steve Piotraczk *(Chief Revenue Officer)*

Nexera, LLC **(3)**
555 W 57th St, New York, NY 10019
Healtcare Services
N.A.I.C.S.: 621610

Premier Insurance Management Services, Inc. **(1)**
12707 High Bluff Dr Ste 140, San Diego, CA 92130
Tel.: (619) 699-3073
Office Administrative Services
N.A.I.C.S.: 561110
Tom Green *(VP-Sls & Mktg)*

Premier Services, LLC **(1)**
1210 Gateway Rd Ste 1, Lake Park, FL 33403
Tel.: (561) 881-0840
Web Site: http://www.premiersvs.com
Professional Scientific & Technical Services
N.A.I.C.S.: 541990

Symmedrx, LLC **(1)**
10955 Lowell Ave Ste 600, Overland Park, KS 66210
Tel.: (913) 338-4900
Health Care Srvices
N.A.I.C.S.: 621610

TheraDoc, Inc. **(1)**
257 E 200 S Ste 600, Salt Lake City, UT 84111 **(100%)**
Tel.: (801) 415-4400
Web Site: https://www.theradoc.com
Clinical Surveillance System Services
N.A.I.C.S.: 541511

PRESIDENTIAL REALTY COR-PORATION
1430 Broadway Ste 503, New York, NY 10018
Tel.: (914) 948-1300 **DE**
Web Site: https://www.presrealty.com
Year Founded: 1911
PDNLA—(OTCIQ)
Rev.: $1,100,817
Assets: $1,022,274
Liabilities: $2,043,344
Net Worth: ($1,021,070)
Earnings: ($119,688)
Emp.: 4
Fiscal Year-end: 12/31/22
Real Estate Investment Trust
N.A.I.C.S.: 523999

Presidential Realty Corporation—(Continued)

Alexander Ludwig *(Pres, CFO, COO & Sec)*
Nickolas W. Jekogian III *(Chm & CEO)*

Subsidiaries:

Preston Lake Realty   **(1)**
6168 S Norcross Tucker Rd, Tucker, GA 30084
Tel.: (770) 493-3675
Sales Range: $1-9.9 Million
Emp.: 13
Real Estate Investment Company
N.A.I.C.S.: 531110

PRESIDIO PROPERTY TRUST, INC.
4995 Murphy Canyon Rd Ste 300, San Diego, CA 92123
Tel.: (760) 471-8536
Web Site: https://www.presidiopt.com
Year Founded: 1999
SQFT—(NASDAQ)
Rev.: $17,635,614
Assets: $175,962,638
Liabilities: $114,661,757
Net Worth: $61,300,881
Earnings: $13,177,526
Emp.: 15
Fiscal Year-end: 12/31/23
Real Estate Investment Services
N.A.I.C.S.: 531390
Jack Kendrick Heilbron *(Chm, Pres & CEO)*
Gary M. Katz *(Chief Investment Officer)*
Steve Hightower *(Pres-Model Home)*
Edward H. Bentzen IV *(Chief Acctg Officer)*

PRESSURE BIOSCIENCES, INC.
480 Neponset St Unit 10B, Canton, MA 02021
Tel.: (508) 230-1828   MA
Web Site:
   https://www.pressurebioscien ces.com
Year Founded: 1986
PBIO—(OTCQB)
Rev.: $1,977,763
Assets: $1,049,676
Liabilities: $33,803,505
Net Worth: ($32,753,829)
Earnings: ($29,314,298)
Emp.: 15
Fiscal Year-end: 12/31/23
Analytical Laboratory Instrument Manufacturing
N.A.I.C.S.: 334516
Richard T. Schumacher *(Founder, Pres, CEO, Interim CFO & Treas)*
Edmund Ting *(Sr VP-Engrg)*
Alexander Lazarev *(Chief Science Officer)*

PRESTIGE CARS INTERNATIONAL, INC.
1013 W Sunrise Blvd, Fort Lauderdale, FL 33311
Tel.: (954) 779-1000
Web Site:
   https://www.prestigiouseuro cars.com
PREC—(OTCIQ)
Used Car Dealers
N.A.I.C.S.: 441120

PRESTIGE CONSUMER HEALTHCARE INC.
4615 Murray Pl, Lynchburg, VA 24502
Tel.: (914) 524-6800   DE
Web Site:
   https://www.prestigebrands.com

PBH—(NYSE)
Rev.: $1,125,357,000
Assets: $3,318,417,000
Liabilities: $1,663,333,000
Net Worth: $1,655,084,000
Earnings: $209,339,000
Emp.: 570
Fiscal Year-end: 03/31/24
Over-the-Counter Drugs, Household Cleaning & Personal Care Products
N.A.I.C.S.: 325412
Ronald M. Lombardi *(Chm, Pres & CEO)*
Christine Sacco *(CFO)*
Adel Mekhail *(Exec VP-Marketing-Sales)*
Jeff Zerillo *(Sr VP-Operations)*
Mary Beth Fritz *(Sr VP-Quality-Regulatory Affairs)*
Jeff Thompson *(VP-Manufacturing-Operations)*

Subsidiaries:

C.B. Fleet Company, Inc.   **(1)**
4615 Murray Pl, Lynchburg, VA 24502
Tel.: (434) 528-4000
Web Site: https://www.fleetlabs.com
Beauty & Healthcare Products Mfr
N.A.I.C.S.: 325620

Unit (Domestic):

Fleet Laboratories   **(2)**
4615 Murray Pl, Lynchburg, VA 24502
Tel.: (434) 528-4000
Web Site: https://www.fleetlabs.com
Health Care Srvices
N.A.I.C.S.: 621999

Care Pharmaceuticals Pty Limited   **(1)**
PO Box 1674, Bondi Junction, 1355, NSW, Australia
Tel.: (61) 293001900
Web Site:
   https://www.carepharmaceuticals.com.au
Health Care Srvices
N.A.I.C.S.: 621610

Medtech Holdings, Inc.   **(1)**
660 White Plains Rd, Tarrytown, NY 10591
Tel.: (914) 524-6800
Pharmacies & Drug Retailer
N.A.I.C.S.: 456110

Prestige Services Corp.   **(1)**
90 N Broadway, Irvington, NY 10533
Tel.: (914) 524-6879
Pharmaceutical Preparation Mfr
N.A.I.C.S.: 325412

The Spic & Span Company   **(1)**
90 N Broadway, Irvington, NY 10533-1235
Tel.: (914) 524-6800
Web Site: http://www.spicnspan.com
Rev.: $30,000,000
Emp.: 75
Household Cleaning Products Mfr & Sales
N.A.I.C.S.: 325611

PRESTO AUTOMATION, INC.
985 Industrial Rd. Ste 205, San Carlos, CA 94070
Tel.: (650) 817-9012   DE
Web Site: https://www.presto.com
Year Founded: 2008
PRST—(NASDAQ)
Rev.: $26,135,000
Assets: $46,687,000
Liabilities: $91,914,000
Net Worth: ($45,227,000)
Earnings: ($34,480,000)
Emp.: 137
Fiscal Year-end: 06/30/23
Software Devolopment
N.A.I.C.S.: 513210
Krishna Gupta *(Interim CEO)*
Katherine Hoffman-Flynt *(COO)*

PRESTON HOLLOW COMMUNITY CAPITAL, INC.
1717 Main St Ste 3900, Dallas, TX 75201

Tel.: (214) 389-0813   MD
Web Site: http://www.phcllc.com
Year Founded: 2014
PHCC—(NYSE)
Emp.: 35
Investment Services
N.A.I.C.S.: 523999
Jim Thompson *(Co-Founder, Chm & CEO)*
Cliff Weiner *(Co-Founder & Head-Fixed Income)*
Paige Deskin *(CFO)*
Ramiro Albarran *(Co-Head-Originations)*
Charlie Visconsi *(Co-Head-Originations)*

PRICESMART INC.
9740 Scranton Rd, San Diego, CA 92121
Tel.: (858) 404-8800   DE
Web Site:
   https://www.pricesmart.com
Year Founded: 1997
PSMT—(NASDAQ)
Rev.: $4,913,898,000
Assets: $2,022,694,000
Liabilities: $899,729,000
Net Worth: $1,122,965,000
Earnings: $138,875,000
Emp.: 34,913
Fiscal Year-end: 08/31/24
Warehouse Membership Discount Services
N.A.I.C.S.: 455219
Rodrigo Calvo *(Exec VP-Real Estate)*
Francisco Velasco *(Chief Ethics & Compliance Officer, Gen Counsel, Sec & Exec VP)*
John D. Hildebrandt *(Pres & COO)*
Robert E. Price *(Founder, Chm & Interim CEO)*
David R. Snyder *(Vice Chm)*
Michael L. McCleary *(Exec VP)*
David N. Price *(Exec VP)*

Subsidiaries:

Aeropost Colombia, SAS   **(1)**
Calle 25 99 - 29, Fontibon, Bogota, Colombia
Tel.: (57) 3336026200
Electronic Trading Services
N.A.I.C.S.: 492210

Aeropost International Services, Inc.   **(1)**
1 Aeropost Way MIA 4567, Miami, FL 33206-3206
Tel.: (305) 592-5534
Freight Transportation Arrangement
N.A.I.C.S.: 488510

PSMT (Jamaica), Ltd.   **(1)**
111 Red Hills Road, Kingston, Jamaica   **(67.5%)**
Tel.: (876) 19691242
Sales Range: $25-49.9 Million
Emp.: 150
Retailer of General Merchandise
N.A.I.C.S.: 455211

PriceSmart (Guatelmala), S.A.   **(1)**
22 Ave 18-46 Zona 10 Pradera, Guatemala, Guatemala   **(100%)**
Tel.: (502) 23013000
Web Site: http://www.shop.pricesmart.com
Grocery Services
N.A.I.C.S.: 492210

PriceSmart (Guatemala), S.A.   **(1)**
21 Avenida 7-90 Zona 11, Miraflores, Guatemala, Guatemala
Tel.: (502) 23015000
Web Site: https://www.pricesmart.com
Shopping Club Operator
N.A.I.C.S.: 455211
Jorge Vargas *(Mgr-Club)*

PriceSmart (Jamaica) Limited   **(1)**
111 Red Hills Road, Kingston, 19, Jamaica
Tel.: (876) 9691242
Shopping Club Operator
N.A.I.C.S.: 455211

PriceSmart (Trinidad) Ltd.   **(1)**
Sales Range: $200-249.9 Million
Grocery Stores
N.A.I.C.S.: 445110

PriceSmart Colombia SAS   **(1)**
Avenida Calle 26 No 71A, Bogota, Colombia
Tel.: (57) 17424114
Web Site: http://www.pricesmart.com
Sales Range: $25-49.9 Million
Emp.: 25
Membership Warehouse Club Operator
N.A.I.C.S.: 455219

PriceSmart Dominicana, S.A.   **(1)**
Charles Sumner Avenue No 54, Los Prados, Santo Domingo, Dominican Republic
Tel.: (809) 3343333
Web Site: http://www.pricesmart.com
Sales Range: $200-249.9 Million
Grocery Stores
N.A.I.C.S.: 445110
Francisco Medina *(Mgr-HR)*

PriceSmart El Salvador, S.A. de C.V.   **(1)**
Urbanizacion Madre Selva Calle Cortez Blanco y Ave El Pepeto 86, Antiguo Cuscatlan, La Libertad, El Salvador   **(100%)**
Tel.: (503) 22467400
Grocery Store Services
N.A.I.C.S.: 492210

PriceSmart Honduras, S.A. de C.V.   **(1)**
100 Mts al Sur de Curn El Playon, San Pedro Sula, Honduras   **(100%)**
Tel.: (504) 25120390
Sales Range: $75-99.9 Million
Emp.: 200
Grocery Warehouse Club & Services
N.A.I.C.S.: 455211

PriceSmart Panama, S.A.   **(1)**
sobre el Km 443 Via Panamericana/Carretera hacia Concepcion David, Corregimiento San Pablo Viejo Distrito de David, Panama, Chiriqui, Panama   **(100%)**
Tel.: (507) 7880250
Web Site: http://www.pricesmart.com
Sales Range: $25-49.9 Million
Emp.: 70
Grocery Stores
N.A.I.C.S.: 445110

Prismar de Costa Rica, S.A.   **(1)**
Frente Al Registro Nacional, Curridabat, 11801, San Jose, Costa Rica   **(100%)**
Tel.: (506) 40351500
Web Site: http://shop.pricesmart.com
Wholesale Price Club Services
N.A.I.C.S.: 455211

PRIMARY BANK
207 Route 101, Bedford, NH 03110
Tel.: (603) 310-7200   NH
Web Site:
   https://www.primarybanknh.com
Year Founded: 2015
PRMY—(OTCIQ)
Commercial Banking Services
N.A.I.C.S.: 522110
William E. Stone *(Pres & CEO)*
Joseph B. Bator *(Exec VP)*
William Greiner *(Chm)*
Crystal A. Dionne *(Pres, CEO, CFO & Sr VP)*
Renate Wallem *(COO, Exec VP & Sr VP)*
Phil Taub *(Vice Chm)*
Thomas Conaton *(Officer-Loan & Exec VP)*

PRIME MEDICINE, INC.
21 Erie St, Cambridge, MA 02139
Tel.: (617) 564-0013   DE
Web Site: https://primemedicine.com
Year Founded: 2019
PRME—(NASDAQ)
Rev.: $1,903,000

Assets: $360,314,000
Liabilities: $44,044,000
Net Worth: $316,270,000
Earnings: ($142,014,000)
Emp.: 175
Fiscal Year-end: 12/31/22
Biotechnology Research & Development Services
N.A.I.C.S.: 541714
Allan Reine (CFO)
Ann L. Lee (Chief Technical Officer)
Richard Brudnick (Chief Bus Officer)
Keith Gottesdiener (Pres & CEO)
Jeremy Duffield (Chief Scientific Officer)
Ann Lee (Chief Technical Officer)
Carman Alenson (Chief Acctg Officer)
Richard Brudnick (Chief Bus Officer)
David Liu (Co-Founder)
Niamh Alix (Chief HR Officer)
Mohammed Asmal (Chief Medical Officer)
Karen Brown (Sr VP-Intellectual Property & Legal Affairs)
Andrew Anzalone (Co-Founder & Head)
Meredith Goldwasser (Sr VP & Head)
Fubao Wang (Sr VP & Head)

PRIME MERIDIAN HOLDING COMPANY

Tel.: (850) 907-2300   FL
Web Site:
    https://www.primemeridianbank.com
Year Founded: 2010
PMHG—(OTCQX)
Rev.: $41,821,000
Assets: $854,528,000
Liabilities: $774,552,000
Net Worth: $79,976,000
Earnings: $8,708,000
Emp.: 110
Fiscal Year-end: 12/31/23
Bank Holding Company
N.A.I.C.S.: 551111
Richard A. Weidner (Chm)
Susan Payne Turner (Chief Risk Officer & Exec VP)
Clint F. Weber (CFO, Principal Acctg Officer & Exec VP)
Monte L. Ward (CIO & Exec VP)
Sammie D. Dixon Jr. (Vice Chm, Pres & CEO)
Chris L. Jensen Jr. (Exec VP)

Subsidiaries:

Prime Meridian Bank   (1)
1897 Capital Cir NE, Tallahassee, FL 32308
Tel.: (850) 907-2301
Web Site:
    http://www.primemeridianbank.com
Banking Services
N.A.I.C.S.: 522110
Katie Proctor (Sr VP)
Mesha Ware (VP)
Tyler Harris (VP & Mgr-Customer Rels)
Philip Pomeroy (VP & Mgr-Customer Rels)
Christine Brooks (VP)
Erika Moran (Assoc Mgr-Relationship)
Sarah Zambetti (Assoc Mgr-Relationship)
Laura Jo Hewitt (VP & Mgr-Mortgage Lending)
Adrienne Granger (Officer-Mortgage Loan)
Christie Powis (Officer-Mortgage Loan)
Angela Walden (Officer-Mortgage Loan)
Sammie D. Dixon Jr. (Vice Chm, Pres & CEO)

PRIMECARE SYSTEMS, INC.

5 Aerial Way, Syosset, NY 11791
Tel.: (757) 591-0323   DE
Web Site: https://pcare.com
PCYS—(OTCIQ)
Software Development Services
N.A.I.C.S.: 541511
Dave Bennett (Exec VP-Healthcare)
Pat Barilla (VP-Operations & Healthcare)

Mark Cortina (VP-Enterprise Solutions-Healthcare)
Stefanie Cadogan (VP-Customer Sls)

PRIMEENERGY RESOURCES CORPORATION

9821 Katy Fwy, Houston, TX 77024
Tel.: (713) 735-0000   DE
Web Site: https://primeenergy-resources-corporation.ir.rdgfilings.com
Year Founded: 1973
PNRG—(NASDAQ)
Rev.: $125,087,000
Assets: $247,137,000
Liabilities: $106,784,000
Net Worth: $140,353,000
Earnings: $48,664,000
Emp.: 114
Fiscal Year-end: 12/31/22
Oil & Gas Field Services
N.A.I.C.S.: 211120
Beverly A. Cummings (CFO, Treas & Exec VP)
Charles E. Drimal Jr. (Chm, Pres & CEO)
Virginia M. Forese (Sec)

Subsidiaries:

EOWS Midland Company   (1)
3520 E Garden City Hwy, Midland, TX 79701
Tel.: (432) 682-2727
Web Site: http://www.primeenergy.com
Oil & Gas Field Services
N.A.I.C.S.: 213112

Eastern Oil Well Service Company   (1)
1 Landmark Sq Ste 1100, Stamford, CT 06901   (100%)
Tel.: (203) 358-5700
Web Site: http://www.primeenergy.com
Sales Range: $1-9.9 Million
Emp.: 35
Performs Well Service Activities
N.A.I.C.S.: 237120
Beverly A. Cummings (VP)
Charles E. Drimal Jr. (CEO)

Prime Offshore L.L.C.   (1)
9821 Katy Fwy Ste 1050, Houston, TX 77024
Tel.: (713) 461-7221
Sales Range: $50-74.9 Million
Emp.: 50
Oil & Gas Exploration Services
N.A.I.C.S.: 211120
Jim R. Brock (Pres & CFO)

Prime Operating Company   (1)
9821 Katy Fwy Ste 1050, Houston, TX 77024
Tel.: (713) 735-0000
Web Site: http://www.primeenergy.com
Oil & Gas Drilling & Production
N.A.I.C.S.: 532412

Southwest Oilfield Construction Company   (1)
PO Box 376, Kingfisher, OK 73750-0376
Tel.: (405) 375-5203
Rev.: $108,000
Performs Well Services
N.A.I.C.S.: 213112

PRIMERICA, INC.

1 Primerica Pkwy, Duluth, GA 30099-0001
Tel.: (770) 381-1000   DE
Web Site: https://www.primerica.com
Year Founded: 2009
PRI—(NYSE)
Rev.: $2,815,691,000
Assets: $15,027,732,000
Liabilities: $12,961,765,000
Net Worth: $2,065,967,000
Earnings: $576,601,000
Emp.: 2,849
Fiscal Year-end: 12/31/23
Financial Holding Company
N.A.I.C.S.: 551111

Peter W. Schneider (Pres)
Glenn J. Williams (CEO)
Gregory C. Pitts (COO & Exec VP)
Jeffrey S. Fendler (Chief Compliance Officer, Chief Risk Officer & Exec VP)
Kathryn E. Kieser (Chief Reputation Officer & Exec VP)
Brett A. Rogers (Gen Counsel & Exec VP)
Lisa A. Brown (Chief Admin Officer & Exec VP)
Tracy Tan (CFO)

Subsidiaries:

Primerica Financial Services, Inc.   (1)
1 Primerica Pkwy, Duluth, GA 30099   (100%)
Tel.: (770) 381-1000
Web Site: http://www.primerica.com
Emp.: 1,500
Insurance & Asset Management Services
N.A.I.C.S.: 524210

Subsidiary (Domestic):

PFS Investments, Inc.   (2)
3120 Breckenridge Blvd, Duluth, GA 30099   (100%)
Tel.: (770) 381-1000
Web Site: http://www.primerica.com
Asset Management Services
N.A.I.C.S.: 523999
Estee Faranda (CEO)

Subsidiary (Non-US):

Primerica Financial Services (Canada) Ltd.   (2)
1550 South Gateway Rd Ste 319, Mississauga, L4W 5G6, ON, Canada   (100%)
Tel.: (905) 614-0009
Sales Range: Less than $1 Million
Emp.: 7,000
Insurance Services
N.A.I.C.S.: 524210

Subsidiary (Domestic):

PFSL Investments Canada Ltd.   (3)
2000 Argentia, Mississauga, L5N 1P7, ON, Canada
Tel.: (905) 812-2900
Web Site: http://www.primerica.com
Investment Services
N.A.I.C.S.: 523999

Primerica Life Insurance Company of Canada   (3)
Suite 400 6985 Financial Drive, Mississauga, L5N 0G3, ON, Canada   (100%)
Tel.: (905) 812-2900
Web Site: https://www.primericacanada.ca
Fire Insurance Services
N.A.I.C.S.: 524113

Primerica Life Insurance Company of Canada   (3)
Suite 400 6985 Financial Drive, Mississauga, L5N 0G3, ON, Canada   (100%)
Tel.: (905) 812-2900
Web Site: https://www.primericacanada.ca
Fire Insurance Services
N.A.I.C.S.: 524113

Primerica Life Insurance Company of Canada   (3)
Suite 400 6985 Financial Drive, Mississauga, L5N 0G3, ON, Canada   (100%)
Tel.: (905) 812-2900
Web Site: https://www.primericacanada.ca
Fire Insurance Services
N.A.I.C.S.: 524113

Primerica Life Insurance Company of Canada   (3)
Suite 400 6985 Financial Drive, Mississauga, L5N 0G3, ON, Canada   (100%)
Tel.: (905) 812-2900
Web Site: https://www.primericacanada.ca
Fire Insurance Services
N.A.I.C.S.: 524113

Subsidiary (Domestic):

Primerica Life Insurance Company   (2)

1 Primerica Pkwy, Duluth, GA 30099   (100%)
Tel.: (770) 381-1000
Individual Life Insurance Services
N.A.I.C.S.: 524113

Subsidiary (Domestic):

National Benefit Life Insurance Company   (3)
30-30 47th Ave Ste 625, Long Island City, NY 11101   (100%)
Tel.: (212) 615-7500
Web Site:
    https://www.nationalbenefitlife.com
Fire Insurance Services
N.A.I.C.S.: 524113

PRIMIS FINANCIAL CORP.

6830 Old Dominion Dr, McLean, VA 22101
Tel.: (703) 893-7400   VA
Web Site:
    https://www.primisbank.com
Year Founded: 2005
FRST—(NASDAQ)
Rev.: $237,868,000
Assets: $3,856,546,000
Liabilities: $3,458,953,000
Net Worth: $397,593,000
Earnings: ($10,112,000)
Emp.: 528
Fiscal Year-end: 12/31/23
Bank Holding Company
N.A.I.C.S.: 551111
Matthew A. Switzer (CFO & Exec VP)
Dennis J. Zember Jr. (Pres & CEO)

Subsidiaries:

Primis Bank   (1)
291 Virginia St, Urbanna, VA 23175
Tel.: (804) 758-3096
Banking Services
N.A.I.C.S.: 522110
Dennis J. Zember Jr. (CEO)

Sonabank   (1)
6830 Old Dominion Dr, McLean, VA 22101
Tel.: (703) 893-7400
Web Site: https://primisbank.com
Commericial Banking
N.A.I.C.S.: 522110

PRIMO WATER CORPORATION

1150 Assembly Dr Ste 800, Tampa, FL 33607
Tel.: (813) 544-8515   Ca
Web Site:
    https://www.primowatercorp.com
Year Founded: 1955
PRMW—(NYSE)
Rev.: $2,073,300,000
Assets: $3,723,400,000
Liabilities: $2,403,300,000
Net Worth: $1,320,100,000
Earnings: ($3,200,000)
Emp.: 9,230
Fiscal Year-end: 01/01/22
Holding Company; Soft Drinks Mfr & Marketer
N.A.I.C.S.: 551112
Robbert Rietbroek (CEO)
Marni Morgan Poe (Chief Legal Officer & Sec)
Jason Ausher (Chief Acctg Officer)
David Hass (CFO)
William Jamieson (CIO-Global)
Mercedes Romero (Chief Procurement Officer)
Anne Melaragni (Chief HR Officer)
David Hass (Chief Strategy Officer)

Subsidiaries:

Clear Mountain Refreshment Service, LLC   (1)
4713 W Bethany Rd, North Little Rock, AR 72117-3448
Tel.: (501) 664-6700

Primo Water Corporation—(Continued)

Web Site:
http://www.premiumrefreshment.com
Bottled Water, Coffee & Refreshments
Products Mfr
N.A.I.C.S.: 312112
Lisa Burns *(CFO)*

Cott Corporation - US Corporate Headquarters **(1)**
5519 W Idlewild Ave, Tampa, FL 33634
Tel.: (813) 313-1854
Web Site: http://www.cott.com
Corporate Office
N.A.I.C.S.: 551114

Subsidiary (Non-US):

AquaTerra Corporation **(2)**
1200 Britannia Road East, Mississauga,
L4W 4T5, ON, Canada
Tel.: (905) 795-6500
Web Site: http://www.aquaterracorp.ca
Snack & Nonalcoholic Beverage Services
N.A.I.C.S.: 722515

Subsidiary (Domestic):

Caroline LLC **(2)**
607 Highland Colony Pkwy Ste 300, Ridgeland, MS 39157
Tel.: (601) 605-4458
Web Site: https://www.carolinems.com
Business Support Services
N.A.I.C.S.: 561499

Cliffstar LLC **(2)**
1 Cliffstar Ave, Dunkirk, NY 14048 **(100%)**
Tel.: (716) 366-6100
Web Site: http://www.cliffstar.com
Sales Range: $650-699.9 Million
Emp.: 1,200
Juice Mfr
N.A.I.C.S.: 311411

Subsidiary (Non-US):

Cott Limited **(2)**
Citrus Grove Sideley, Kegworth, DE74 2FJ,
Derbs, United Kingdom
Tel.: (44) 1509 674915
Web Site: http://www.cott.co.uk
Emp.: 100
Holding Company; Soft Drink Mfr & Whslr
N.A.I.C.S.: 551112

Cott Maquinaria y Equipo, S.A. de C.V. **(2)**
Calle De Los Palos No 35, San Pablo
Xochimehuacan, Puebla, Mexico
Tel.: (52) 2223721400
Web Site: http://www.cott.com.mx
Sales Range: $100-124.9 Million
Emp.: 300
Soft Drinks Mfr
N.A.I.C.S.: 312111

Subsidiary (Domestic):

Cott Vending Inc. **(2)**
10838 Ambassador Blvd, Saint Louis, MO
63132-1708
Tel.: (314) 994-7545
Web Site: http://www.cott.com
Sales Range: $25-49.9 Million
Emp.: 14
Soft Drink Vending Machine Mfr
N.A.I.C.S.: 445132

DS Services of America, Inc. **(2)**
200 Eagles Landing Dr, Lakeland, FL
33810
Tel.: (770) 933-1400
Web Site: https://www.water.com
Emp.: 200
Bottled Water & Sports Drinks Mfr
N.A.I.C.S.: 312112

Unit (Domestic):

DS Services of America, Inc. - Crystal Springs **(3)**
200 Eagles Landing Dr, Lakeland, FL
33810
Web Site: https://www.crystal-springs.com
Bottled Water Distr
N.A.I.C.S.: 312112

DS Services of America, Inc. - Deep Rock Water Co. **(3)**

200 Eagles Landing Dr, Lakeland, FL
33810
Web Site: https://www.deeprockwater.com
Bottled Water Retailer
N.A.I.C.S.: 312112

DS Services of America, Inc. - Hinckley Springs **(3)**
200 Eagles Landing Dr, Lakeland, FL
33810
Tel.: (773) 586-8600
Web Site: https://www.hinckleysprings.com
Pure Drinking, Distilled, Nursery & Artesian
Spring Bottled Water & Water Coolers, Instant Beverages & Coffee Service
N.A.I.C.S.: 312112

DS Services of America, Inc. - Mount Olympus **(3)**
200 Eagles Landing Dr, Lakeland, FL
33810
Tel.: (863) 940-6800
Web Site:
https://www.mountolympuswater.com
Bottled Water Mfr
N.A.I.C.S.: 312112

Subsidiary (Domestic):

Highland Mountain Water **(3)**
1596 Fullenwider Rd, Gainesville, GA
30507-8450
Tel.: (770) 534-0093
Web Site:
http://www.highlandmountainwater.com
Bottled Water Supplier
N.A.I.C.S.: 312112

Mountain Valley Spring Company, LLC **(3)**
150 Central Ave, Hot Springs National Park,
AR 71902
Tel.: (501) 624-1635
Web Site:
http://www.mountainvalleyspring.com
Bottled Water Mfr & Distr
N.A.I.C.S.: 312112
Bradley K. Frieberg *(CFO)*

Subsidiary (Domestic):

GW Services, LLC **(2)**
1385 Park Ctr Dr, Vista, CA 92081
Web Site: http://glacierwater.com
Bottled Water Mfr
N.A.I.C.S.: 312112

Subsidiary (Non-US):

Mexico Bottling Services, S.A. de C.V. **(2)**
Calle De Los Palos 35, San Pablo
Xochimehuacan, Puebla, 72014, Mexico
Tel.: (52) 2223721400
Web Site: http://www.cott.com.mx
Sales Range: $75-99.9 Million
Emp.: 30
Soft Drinks Mfr
N.A.I.C.S.: 312111

Eden Springs Espana S.A.U **(1)**
Avenida Sistema Solar 7 Nave-D, San Fernando de Henares, 28830, Madrid, Spain
Tel.: (34) 90 012 2000
Web Site: https://www.aguaeden.es
Water Dispenser Distr
N.A.I.C.S.: 424490

Eden Springs International S.A. **(1)**
Chemin Du Tresi 6B, 1028, Preverenges,
Switzerland
Tel.: (41) 80 080 5000
Web Site: https://www.edensprings.ch
Water Dispenser Distr
N.A.I.C.S.: 424490

Eden Springs Scandinavia AB **(1)**
Fosievagen 15, 214 31, Malmo, Sweden
Tel.: (46) 2 052 1521
Web Site: https://www.edensprings.se
Water Dispenser Distr
N.A.I.C.S.: 424490

Eden Springs sp. z o.o. **(1)**
ul Dzialkowa 56a, 02-234, Warsaw, Poland
Tel.: (48) 80 122 2444
Web Site: https://www.eden.pl
Water Dispenser Distr
N.A.I.C.S.: 424490

Garraways Ltd **(1)**

Unit 42 Bradley Court Bradley Fold Trading
Estate Radcliffe Moor Road, Bolton, BL2
6RT, Lancashire, United Kingdom
Tel.: (44) 8719769788
Web Site: https://www.garraways.co.uk
Soft Drink Distr
N.A.I.C.S.: 424490

Mountain Glacier LLC **(1)**
709 Oak Hill Rd, Evansville, IN 47711-7711
Web Site: http://www.mountainglacier.com
Bottled Water Mfr
N.A.I.C.S.: 312112

Water Coolers (Scotland) Limited **(1)**
76 Hamilton Road, Motherwell, ML1 3BY,
Lanarkshire, United Kingdom
Tel.: (44) 155 566 6438
Web Site:
https://www.watercoolersscotland.com
Water Dispenser Distr
N.A.I.C.S.: 424490

PRIMORIS SERVICES CORPORATION
2300 N Field St Ste 1900, Dallas, TX
75201
Tel.: (214) 740-5600   DE
Web Site: https://www.prim.com
PRIM—(NYSE)
Rev.: $5,715,309,000
Assets: $3,827,427,000
Liabilities: $2,591,335,000
Net Worth: $1,236,092,000
Earnings: $126,145,000
Emp.: 2,773
Fiscal Year-end: 12/31/23
Holding Company; Specialty Contractors & Engineering Services
N.A.I.C.S.: 551112
Thomas Edward McCormick *(Pres & CEO)*
Kenneth M. Dodgen *(CFO & Exec VP)*
James Pratt *(Pres-Power Delivery)*
Colt Moedl *(Pres-Utilities)*
Michael Luckey *(Sr VP-Major Projects)*
Rachel Weiss *(Mgr)*
Rhonda Anderson *(Chief HR Officer)*
Chad Haxton *(CIO)*

Subsidiaries:

ARB Structures **(1)**
26000 Commercentre Dr, Lake Forest, CA
92630
Tel.: (949) 598-9242
Web Site: http://www.arbino.com
Sales Range: $350-399.9 Million
Emp.: 1,200
Provider of Contracting Services
N.A.I.C.S.: 237120

ARB, Inc. **(1)**
26000 Commercentre Dr, Lake Forest, CA
92630-8816
Tel.: (949) 598-9242
Web Site: http://www.arbinc.com
Sales Range: $50-74.9 Million
Emp.: 1,000
Provider of Construction Services
N.A.I.C.S.: 236220
Maurice W. Gallarda *(Pres-Infrastructure)*

Cardinal Contractors, Inc. **(1)**
10405 Technology Ter, Lakewood Ranch,
FL 34211-1023
Tel.: (941) 377-8555
General Contractor Engaged in Water
Sewer & Gas Main & Industrial Construction
N.A.I.C.S.: 236220

Cardinal Mechanical, Inc. **(1)**
14455 Primoris Way, Houston, TX 77048
Tel.: (281) 478-5100
Web Site: http://www.cardinalmech.com
Emp.: 90
Civil & Mechanical Engineering Services
N.A.I.C.S.: 541330

GML Coatings, LLC **(1)**
10315 Technology Ter, Lakewood Ranch,
FL 34211 **(100%)**
Tel.: (941) 755-2176
Web Site: https://www.gmlcoatings.com

Emp.: 20
Containment & Protective Coatings Mfr
N.A.I.C.S.: 325510

James Construction Group LLC **(1)**
18484 Petroleum Dr, Baton Rouge, LA
70809
Tel.: (225) 465-2192
Web Site: http://jamesconstructiongroup.net
Sales Range: $800-899.9 Million
Emp.: 1,500
Heavy Civil Engineering, Industrial Infrastructure & Maintenance Services
N.A.I.C.S.: 237990

Juniper Rock Corporation **(1)**
26000 Commercentre Dr, Lake Forest, CA
92630
Tel.: (949) 598-9242
General Building Contractors Services
N.A.I.C.S.: 236115

OnQuest Canada, ULC **(1)**
200-6025 11 Street SE, Calgary, T2H 2Z2,
AB, Canada
Tel.: (403) 252-2676
Web Site: http://www.onquest.com
Engineering Services
N.A.I.C.S.: 541330

Onquest, Inc. **(1)**
180 E Arrow Hwy, San Dimas, CA
91773 **(100%)**
Tel.: (909) 451-0500
Web Site: http://www.onquest-inc.com
Sales Range: $25-49.9 Million
Emp.: 45
Petrochemical Furnace Engineering Services
N.A.I.C.S.: 333994

Subsidiary (Non-US):

Born Heaters Canada, ULC **(2)**
3582 118th Ave SE, Calgary, T2Z 3X1, AB,
Canada
Tel.: (403) 252-2676
Web Site: http://www.borncanada.com
Petrochemical Funrance Engineering
N.A.I.C.S.: 333994

PFMG Solar Tustin, LLC **(1)**
7777 Center Ave Ste 200, Huntington
Beach, CA 92647
Tel.: (714) 408-2982
Web Site: http://www.pfmgsolar.com
Solar Panels Installation Services
N.A.I.C.S.: 238210
Sam Houston *(CEO)*

PLH Group, Inc. **(1)**
400 E Las Colinas Blvd Ste 800, Irving, TX
75039
Tel.: (214) 272-0500
Web Site: http://www.plhgroupinc.com
Construction Services
N.A.I.C.S.: 237130

Subsidiary (Domestic):

Power Line Services, Inc. **(2)**
2100 Great SW Pkwy, Fort Worth, TX
76106
Tel.: (469) 513-6764
Web Site: https://www.powerlinesinc.com
Sales Range: $10-24.9 Million
Construction Services
N.A.I.C.S.: 237130
Mark A. Crowson *(CEO)*

Subsidiary (Domestic):

Air2, LLC **(3)**
1 Texas Sta Ct Ste 325, Timonium, MD
21093
Tel.: (410) 560-5620
Web Site: https://www.air2.com
Emp.: 5
Helicopter-Assisted Construction, Maintenance & Inspection Services to Electric Utility Industry
N.A.I.C.S.: 237130
Mark Camus *(VP-Technical Procedures)*
Sunita Khorana *(Pres)*
Jonna Sole *(VP)*

Auger Services, Inc. **(3)**
524 W Hwy 30, Gonzales, LA 70737
Tel.: (225) 647-9233
Web Site: https://www.augerservices.com

Sales Range: $50-74.9 Million
Transmission Line Construction, Substations, Industrial/ Petrochemical, Highway, Cellular Towers, Rock Drilling & Vibratory Caissons
N.A.I.C.S.: 237130
Michael J. Cutrone *(Pres)*
Ed Radford *(Sr VP)*

R.B. Hinkle Construction, Inc. **(3)**
21595 Cedar Ln Unit 6, Sterling, VA 20166
Tel.: (703) 430-0200
Web Site: https://www.rbhinkle.com
Emp.: 150
Underground Utility Installation Services
N.A.I.C.S.: 237130
Robbie Hinkle *(Pres)*
Pedro Hernandez *(Sr VP)*

Snelson Companies Inc. **(3)**
638 Sunset Park Dr Ste 115, Sedro Woolley, WA 98284
Tel.: (360) 856-6511
Web Site: https://www.snelsonco.com
Full Service Industrial & Utility Contractor
N.A.I.C.S.: 236210
Jeff Knapp *(VP & Mgr-Pipeline Svcs)*

Subsidiary (Domestic):

SIS Northwest, Inc. **(4)**
913 Maple St, Sedro Woolley, WA 98284
Tel.: (360) 854-0074
Energy & Marine Steel Assemblies
N.A.I.C.S.: 238120

Division (Domestic):

Snelson Companies Inc. Gas Distribution Division **(4)**
638 Sunset Park Dr Ste 115, Sedro Woolley, WA 98284
Tel.: (360) 856-6511
Web Site: http://www.snelsonco.com
Sales Range: $50-74.9 Million
Emp.: 25
Gas Distribution Systems
N.A.I.C.S.: 221210
Michael Woodmansee *(CFO & Exec VP)*

Snelson Companies Inc. Pipeline Division **(4)**
638 Sunset Park Dr Ste 115, Sedro Woolley, WA 98284
Tel.: (360) 856-6511
Web Site: http://www.snelson.com
Sales Range: $25-49.9 Million
Wire Line Services
N.A.I.C.S.: 237120
Brian Ganske *(Exec VP)*

Snelson Stations & Facilities Division **(4)**
638 Sunset Park Dr Ste 115, Sedro Woolley, WA 98284
Tel.: (360) 856-6511
Web Site: http://www.snelsonco.com
Sales Range: $50-74.9 Million
Natural Gas Facilities Repair & Maintenance
N.A.I.C.S.: 213112

Subsidiary (Domestic):

Sun Electric Services, Inc. **(3)**
1103 Market Ave, Odessa, TX 79761
Tel.: (432) 580-9500
Web Site: https://www.sunelectric.com
High-Voltage Transmission Construction & Maintenance Services
N.A.I.C.S.: 237130
Chrissy Smith *(Office Mgr)*

Total Electrical Service & Supply Co. **(3)**
1031 Andrews Hwy, Midland, TX 79702
Tel.: (432) 682-1991
Web Site: https://www.tesscoenergy.com
Electrical Construction & Maintenance Services to Electric Utility & Oil & Natural Gas Markets
N.A.I.C.S.: 237130

Pipe Jacking Trenchless, Inc. **(1)**
11858 Bernard Plz Ste 100, San Diego, CA 92128
Tel.: (909) 880-8446
Tunnel Construction Services
N.A.I.C.S.: 237990
Evan Wheeler *(Project Mgr)*

Primoris Aevenia, Inc. **(1)**
3030 24th Ave S, Moorhead, MN 56560
Tel.: (218) 284-9500
Web Site: http://www.aevenia.com
Sales Range: $25-49.9 Million
Emp.: 250
Energy & Electrical Construction Services
N.A.I.C.S.: 237130

Division (Domestic):

Mueller Concrete Construction Company **(2)**
245 Business Park Dr, Postville, IA 52162 **(100%)**
Tel.: (563) 864-7203
Web Site: http://www.muellertower.com
Rev.: $3,000,000
Emp.: 18
Poured Concrete Foundation & Structure Contractors
N.A.I.C.S.: 238110

Primoris Design & Construction, Inc. **(1)**
6101 S Broadway Ave Ste 200, Tyler, TX 75703
Tel.: (903) 730-9400
Engineering Design Services
N.A.I.C.S.: 541330
Kevin Maloney *(Pres)*

Primoris Distribution Services, Inc. **(1)**
10518 US Hwy 301, Dade City, FL 33525
Tel.: (813) 996-0019
Pipeline Construction Services
N.A.I.C.S.: 237120
Lisa Judge *(VP-Ops, Safety, and Compliance)*

Primoris Electric, Inc. **(1)**
3500 Pegasus Dr, Bakersfield, CA 93308
Tel.: (661) 833-4400
Electrical Contracting Services
N.A.I.C.S.: 238210

Primoris Energy Services Corporation **(1)**
1010 CR 59, Rosharon, TX 77583
Tel.: (281) 431-5900
Engineeering Services
N.A.I.C.S.: 541330

Primoris T&D Services, LLC **(1)**
115 W 7th St Ste 1410, Fort Worth, TX 76102
Tel.: (682) 233-9016
Engineering Consulting Services
N.A.I.C.S.: 541330
John Pinkerton *(VP-Ops-West)*

Q3 Contracting, Inc. **(1)**
53 S Owasso Blvd W, Little Canada, MN 55117
Tel.: (651) 224-2424
Web Site: http://q3contracting.com
Emp.: 1,500
Electrical Contracting Services
N.A.I.C.S.: 238210

Stellaris, LLC **(1)**
26000 Commercenter Dr, Lake Forest, CA 92630
Tel.: (949) 454-7162
Sales Range: $350-399.9 Million
Emp.: 2,000
Civil & Infrastructure Construction Services
N.A.I.C.S.: 541330

Vadnais Trenchless Services, Inc. **(1)**
11858 Bernardo Plaza Ct Ste 100, San Diego, CA 92128
Tel.: (858) 550-1460
Web Site: http://www.vadnaistrenchless.com
Engineeering Services
N.A.I.C.S.: 541330

Willbros Group, Inc. **(1)**
4400 Post Oak Pkwy Ste 1000, Houston, TX 77027
Tel.: (713) 403-8000
Web Site: http://primoriscorp.com
Oil, Gas & Power Industries Contracting Services
N.A.I.C.S.: 211120
Linnie A. Freeman *(Chief Compliance Officer, Gen Counsel & Sr VP)*
Mark Grosskopf *(Dir-Technical Svcs)*
Debra Mitchell *(Coord-HR)*

Subsidiary (Domestic):

Scelerin Heaters LLC **(2)**
7633 E 63rd Pl Ste 270, Tulsa, OK 74133
Tel.: (918) 499-2700
Web Site: http://www.scelerin.com
Industrial Construction & Engineering Services
N.A.I.C.S.: 236210
Richard Terral *(Project Mgr)*

Subsidiary (Non-US):

The Oman Construction Company LLC **(2)**
1st Floor - Landmark Building No 5115/3/3 Way No 4557 Complex No 245, PO Box 142, Opposite to Al Ameen Mosque North Al Khuwair, PC 100, Muscat, Oman
Tel.: (968) 22056000
Web Site: https://www.toco.com.om
Oil Field Maintenance Services, Field Gathering & Processing Construction, Mainline Pipeline Construction & Maintenance
N.A.I.C.S.: 237120
Mark Dean *(CEO)*

Willbros Construction Services (Canada) L.P. **(2)**
1103 95 Street SW, Edmonton, T6X0P8, AB, Canada
Tel.: (780) 400-4200
Web Site: http://www.primoriscorp.com
Construction Engineering Services
N.A.I.C.S.: 237990
Jeremy Kinch *(Pres)*

Subsidiary (Domestic):

Willbros T&D Services, LLC **(2)**
115 W 7th St Ste 1410, Fort Worth, TX 76102
Tel.: (682) 233-9016
Oil & Gas Fields Contract Services
N.A.I.C.S.: 213112
Johnny M. Priest *(Pres)*

PRINCETON BANCORP, INC.
183 Bayard Ln, Princeton, NJ 08540
Tel.: (609) 921-1700
Web Site:
https://www.thebankofprinceton.com
Year Founded: 2007
BPRN—(NASDAQ)
Sales Range: $50-74.9 Million
Commericial Banking
N.A.I.C.S.: 522110
Ross E. Wishnick *(Vice Chm)*
Edward J. Dietzler *(Pres & CEO)*
Stephen A. Distler *(Vice Chm)*
Robert N. Ridolfi *(Sec)*

Subsidiaries:

Cornerstone Financial Corporation **(1)**
6000 Midlantic Dr Ste 120 S, Mount Laurel, NJ 08054
Tel.: (856) 439-0300
Web Site: http://www.cornerstonebank.net
Bank Holding Company
N.A.I.C.S.: 551111
Eugene D'Orazio *(COO & Exec VP)*

Subsidiary (Domestic):

Cornerstone Bank **(2)**
6000 Midlantic Dr Ste 120S, Mount Laurel, NJ 08054
Tel.: (856) 439-0300
Web Site: http://www.cornerstonebank.net
Sales Range: $25-49.9 Million
Emp.: 35
Commericial Banking
N.A.I.C.S.: 522110
Fred Lopez *(VP & MgrRelationship)*

PRINCETON CAPITAL CORPORATION
800 Turnpike St Ste 300, North Andover, MA 01845
Tel.: (978) 794-3366 MD
Web Site:
https://www.princetoncapital corp.com
Year Founded: 1959

PIAC—(OTCIQ)
Rev.: $2,480,893
Assets: $32,314,195
Liabilities: $409,633
Net Worth: $31,904,562
Earnings: ($178,900)
Fiscal Year-end: 12/31/23
Financial Services
N.A.I.C.S.: 523999
Mark S. DiSalvo *(Interim Pres & Interim CEO)*
Florina Klingbaum *(Chief Compliance Officer)*
Darren Stainrod *(Chm)*

PRINCIPAL FINANCIAL GROUP, INC.
711 High St, Des Moines, IA 50392
Tel.: (515) 247-5111 DE
Web Site: https://www.principal.com
Year Founded: 1879
PFG—(NASDAQ)
Rev.: $13,665,800,000
Assets: $305,046,700,000
Liabilities: $294,085,000,000
Net Worth: $10,961,700,000
Earnings: $623,200,000
Emp.: 19,800
Fiscal Year-end: 12/31/23
Financial Products & Services Including Retirement & Investment Services, Life & Health Insurance, Mortgage Banking to Businesses, Individuals & Institutional Clients
N.A.I.C.S.: 551112
Karen E. Shaff *(Chief Legal Officer, Sec & Exec VP)*
John Egan *(VP-IR)*
Barbara A. McKenzie *(Sr Exec Dir-Investments)*
Amy C. Friedrich *(Pres-Insurance Solutions)*
Dennis Menken *(Chief Investment Officer & Sr VP)*
Roberto Walker *(Pres-Latin America & Exec VP)*
Patrick Gregory Halter *(Pres-Asset Mgmt-Global & Principal Global Investors)*
Ellen W. Shumway *(Sr Exec Dir-Strategy & Investments-Principal Global Investors)*
Beth Wood *(CMO & Sr VP)*
Srinivas D. Reddy *(Sr VP-Retirement & Income Solutions)*
Kenneth A. McCullum *(Chief Risk Officer & Sr VP)*
Kara Hoogensen *(Sr VP-Specialty Benefits)*
Vivek Agrawal *(Chief Growth Officer & Exec VP)*
Dennis J. Menken *(Chief Investment Officer)*
Bethany A. Wood *(CMO)*
Kara M. Hoogensen *(Sr VP)*
Noreen M. Fierro *(Chief Compliance Officer)*
Teresa Hassara *(Sr VP)*
Joel M. Pitz *(Sr VP)*
Nate Schelhaas *(Sr VP)*
Anthony Shea Treadway *(Sr VP)*
Humphrey Lee *(VP)*
Deanna D. Strable-Soethout *(Pres, CEO & COO)*
Daniel J. Houston *(Exec Chm)*

Subsidiaries:

BrasilPrev Previdencia Privada S.A. **(1)**
Verbo Divino Chacara Sto Antonio, 04717-004, Sao Paulo, SP, Brazil
Tel.: (55) 1140047170
Web Site: http://www2.brasilprev.com.br
Sales Range: $1-4.9 Billion
Investment Services
N.A.I.C.S.: 523940

Principal Financial Group, Inc.—(Continued)

CIMB-Principal Asset Management Berhad (1)
10th Floor Bangunan CIMB Jalan Semantan, Damansara Heights, Kuala Lumpur, 50490, Malaysia
Tel.: (60) 3 2084 2000
Web Site: http://www.cimb-principal.com.my
Emp.: 185
Asset Management
N.A.I.C.S.: 523940
Munirah Khairuddin (CEO)

Subsidiary (Domestic):

CIMB Wealth Advisors Berhad (2)
50 52 54 Jalan ss 21/39 Damansara Utama, 47400, Petaling Jaya, Selangor, Malaysia
Tel.: (60) 3 7718 3000
Web Site:
http://www.cwealthadvisors.com.my
Financial Advisory Services
N.A.I.C.S.: 523999

Subsidiary (Non-US):

CIMB-Principal Asset Management (Singapore) Pte Ltd (2)
50 Raffles Place 22-03A Singapore Land Tower, Singapore, 48623, Singapore
Tel.: (65) 6210 8488
Web Site: http://www.principal.com.sg
Emp.: 1
Asset Management Services
N.A.I.C.S.: 523940

CIMB-Principal Asset Management Company Limited (2)
44 CIMB THAI Bank Building 16th Floor Langsuan Road, Lumpini Pathumwan, Bangkok, 10330, Thailand
Tel.: (66) 26869595
Web Site: http://www.principal.th
Emp.: 100
Financial Management Services
N.A.I.C.S.: 523999

Claritas Administracao de Recursos Ltda. (1)
Av Brigadeiro Faria Lima 4221-4 andar Itaim Bibi, Sao Paulo, 04538-133, SP, Brazil
Tel.: (55) 1121314900
Web Site: http://en.claritas.com.br
Asset Management Services
N.A.I.C.S.: 531390

Delaware Charter Guarantee & Trust Co. (1)
1013 Center Rd, Wilmington, DE 19899
Tel.: (302) 006-2131
Web Site: http://www.principaltrust.com
Sales Range: $50-74.9 Million
Emp.: 94
Pension Management
N.A.I.C.S.: 525120

Diversified Dental Services Inc (1)
7312 W Cheyenne Ave Ste 7, Las Vegas, NV 89129-7425
Tel.: (702) 869-6200
Insurance Agencies
N.A.I.C.S.: 524210

Edge Asset Management Inc (1)
2 Union Sq 601 Union St Ste 2200, Seattle, WA 98101-1377
Tel.: (206) 913-5800
Web Site: https://www.edgeassetmgt.com
Emp.: 30
Investment Management Service
N.A.I.C.S.: 523999

Employers Dental Services, Inc. (1)
3430 E Sunrise Ste 160, Tucson, AZ 85718
Tel.: (520) 696-4343
Web Site: https://www.employersdental.com
Sales Range: $75-99.9 Million
Pre-Paid Dental Plan Services
N.A.I.C.S.: 524298

Finisterre Capital LLP (1)
10 New Burlington Street, London, W1S 3BE, United Kingdom
Tel.: (44) 2032066910
Web Site: http://www.finisterrecapital.com
Emp.: 40
Investment Management Service

N.A.I.C.S.: 523940
Damien Buchet (Chief Investment Officer-Total Return Grp)

Health Risk Resource Group Inc (1)
18200 Von Karman Ste 300, Irvine, CA 92612
Web Site: http://www.hrgi.com
Sales Range: $10-24.9 Million
Emp.: 40
Hospital & Medical Plan Services
N.A.I.C.S.: 541611
John Crumpton (CMO & Chief Sls Officer)

Hipotecaria Cruz del Sur Principal, S.A. (1)
Avda El Golf 150 Piso 2, Las Condes, Chile
Tel.: (56) 6004618000
Web Site: http://www.cruzdelsurprincipal.cl
Financial Services
N.A.I.C.S.: 541611

Hipotecaria Security Principal, S.A. (1)
Av El Golf 150 Piso 2, Las Condes, Chile
Tel.: (56) 6004618000
Web Site: http://www.securityprincipal.cl
Mortgage Financing Services
N.A.I.C.S.: 522310

Kofstad Agency Inc. (1)
505 Main St, Presque Isle, ME 04769
Tel.: (207) 764-4422
Rev.: $380,000
Emp.: 7
Insurance Agents Brokers & Service
N.A.I.C.S.: 524210
Ronald Kofstad (Pres)

Liongate Capital Management Inc. (1)
711 High St, Des Moines, IA 50392
Tel.: (515) 248-2611
Web Site: https://www.principalam.com
Investment Management Service
N.A.I.C.S.: 523940

Liongate Capital Management LLP (1)
103 Mount Street 4th Floor, London, W1K 2TJ, United Kingdom
Tel.: (44) 2070734600
Web Site: http://www.liongatecapital.com
Investment Management Service
N.A.I.C.S.: 523940
Paul Bentley (Mng Dir)
Tim Stumpff (Pres)
Matthew Annenberg (Mng Dir & Co-CIO)
Rick Teisch (Co-CIO)
Francisco Garrido (Mng Dir & Head-Operational Due Diligence)
Tzvety Petrova (Mng Dir & Head-Res-Europe)
Sandeep Shah (Mng Dir & Head-Quantitative Res)
Matthew Elstrop (Asst Portfolio Mgr)
Julian Lopez-Portillo (Asst Portfolio Mgr)
Dustin Mommen (CTO)

Morley Financial Services (1)
1300 SW 5th Ave Ste 3300, Portland, OR 97201
Tel.: (503) 484-9300
Web Site: https://www.morley.com
Sales Range: $100-124.9 Million
Emp.: 28
Investment Advisory Services
N.A.I.C.S.: 523940

Origin Asset Management LLP (1)
One Carey Lane, London, EC2V 8AE, United Kingdom
Tel.: (44) 2078128500
Web Site: https://www.originam.com
Emp.: 12
Investment Management Service
N.A.I.C.S.: 523940
Tarlock Randhawa (Mng Partner)
Paul Gibson (Mgr-Investment Admin)
Nishil Patel (Partner & COO)
Kunal Shah (Asst Mgr-Investment Ops)

PT Principal Asset Management (1)
Revenue Tower District 8 5th Floor Jl Jend Sudirman No 52-53, Sudirman No 28, Jakarta, 12190, Indonesia (60%)
Tel.: (62) 215 088 9988
Web Site: https://www.principal.co.id
Commercial Banking Services
N.A.I.C.S.: 522110

Priyanto Soedarsono (CIO)
Agung Budiono (CEO)
Rudi Hermanto Sagala (COO)
Diah Sofiyanti (CMO)

Petula Associates, LLC (1)
711 High St, Des Moines, IA 50392
Tel.: (515) 244-7801
Emp.: 12
Land Subdivision & Development Services
N.A.I.C.S.: 237210

Preferred Product Network, Inc. (1)
711 High St, Des Moines, IA 50392
Tel.: (515) 247-5111
Web Site: http://www.principal.com
Sales Range: $150-199.9 Million
Life & Health Insurance Services
N.A.I.C.S.: 524113

Principal Asset Management Berhad (1)
10th floor Bangunan CIMB, Jalan Semantan Damansara Heights, 50490, Lumpur, Malaysia
Tel.: (60) 37 723 7260
Web Site: https://www.principal.com.my
Investment Management Service
N.A.I.C.S.: 523999
Munirah Khairuddin (Exec Dir & CEO)
Patrick Chang (Chief Investment Officer)
Ng Jit Seng (COO)
Harry Leong (Head)
Lim Khai Qi (Head-Risk Management)

Principal Asset Management Company Private Limited (1)
Exchange Plaza B wing Ground Floor NSE Building Bandra Kurla Complex, Bandra E, Mumbai, 400051, India
Tel.: (91) 2267720555
Web Site: http://www.principalindia.com
Sales Range: $75-99.9 Million
Retirement Consulting Services
N.A.I.C.S.: 541618
Pedro Borda (Assoc Dir)
Rajat Jain (Chief Investment Officer)
Hariharan Iyer (Head-Ops & Customer Svcs)
Richa Parasrampuria (Head-Compliance)
Bekxy Kuriakose (Head-Fixed Income)
Gaurav Goyal (Head-Sls & Distr-Natl)
Ragesh Renganathan (Head-Fund Acctg, Commission & MIS)
Siddharth Singh (Head-Products & Bank Alliances)
Gurvinder Singh Wasan (Mgr-Fund)
Siddarth Mohta (Assoc Mgr-Fund)
Jane Ann Conway (Assoc Dir)
Venkata Surya Bharat Ravuri (Mng Dir)
Sudhir Kedia (Mgr-Fund)
Ashish Aggarwal (Assoc Mgr-Fund)

Principal Bank (1)
711 High St, Des Moines, IA 50392
Tel.: (515) 248-0555
Web Site: http://www.principalbank.com
Sales Range: $50-74.9 Million
Financial Services, Checking, Savings Accounts, CDs, IRAs, Credit Cards, Home Equity, Consumer & Student Loans
N.A.I.C.S.: 522180

Principal Chile Limitada (1)
Apoquindo 3600 Piso 10, Las Condes, Santiago, Chile
Tel.: (56) 224137017
Web Site: http://www.principal.cl
Financial Services
N.A.I.C.S.: 541611

Subsidiary (Domestic):

Administradora de Fondos de Pensiones Argentum S.A. (2)
Apoquindo 3600 Piso 8, Las Condes, Santiago, Chile
Tel.: (56) 224137060
Emp.: 400
Financial Services
N.A.I.C.S.: 541611

Administradora de Fondos de Pensiones Cuprum S.A. (2)
Bandera 236 Piso 9, Santiago, Chile (97.97%)
Tel.: (56) 226744101
Web Site: https://www.cuprum.cl
Sales Range: Less than $1 Million
Fund Management Services
N.A.I.C.S.: 525190

Maria Angelica Valenzuela Correa (Deputy Dir)
Christian Urzua Infante (Deputy Dir)
Felipe Balmaceda Mahns (Deputy Dir)
O. Martin Mujica (Gen Mgr)
L. Andres Garcia (Mgr-Investment)
C. Daniela Varas (Mgr-Corp Affairs & Sustainability)
G. Alejandro Arellano (Fin Mgr)
P. Andrea Mellado (Mgr-Compliance)
E. Daniela Novoa (Mgr-People)
S. Mariano Navarrete (Sls Mgr & Mgr-Branch)
G. Rodrigo Lopez (Ops Mgr & Mgr-Administration)
R. Mariana Sanchez (Mgr-Digital Sls)
N. Felipe Aguilera (Mgr-Legal)
K. Mauricio Sanhueza (Mgr-Technology)

Principal Commercial Funding, LLC (1)
711 High St, Des Moines, IA 50392
Tel.: (515) 247-6582
Web Site: http://www.principal.com
Sales Range: $650-699.9 Million
Asset Management Services
N.A.I.C.S.: 523940
James P. McCaughan (CEO)

Principal Compania de Seguros de Vida Chile S.A. (1)
Av Apoquindo 3600 Piso 10, Las Condes, Santiago, Chile (100%)
Tel.: (56) 22 810 7017
Web Site: https://www.principal.cl
Sales Range: $150-199.9 Million
Emp.: 300
Life Insurance & Retirement Planning Products
N.A.I.C.S.: 524113

Principal Development Investors, LLC (1)
711 High St, Des Moines, IA 50392
Tel.: (515) 247-5111
Web Site: http://www.principal.com
Sales Range: $300-349.9 Million
Asset Management Services
N.A.I.C.S.: 523940

Principal Enterprise Capital, LLC (1)
6701 Westown ParkwaySte200, West Des Moines, IA 50266
Tel.: (515) 246-4000
Web Site: http://www.principal.com
Sales Range: $650-699.9 Million
Asset Management Services
N.A.I.C.S.: 523940
Dan Schulte (Pres & Mng Partner)

Principal Financial Advisors, Inc. (1)
711 High St, Des Moines, IA 50392
Tel.: (515) 247-5111
Web Site: http://www.principal.com
Asset Management Services
N.A.I.C.S.: 523940

Principal Financial Group (Australia) Pty. Ltd. (1)
Level 43 50 Bridge St, Sydney, 2000, NSW, Australia
Tel.: (61) 282269000
Web Site: http://www.principal.com
Sales Range: $10-24.9 Million
Emp.: 22
Financial Products & Services Including Retirement & Investment Services, Life & Health Insurance, Mortgage Banking to Businesses, Individuals & Institutional Clients
N.A.I.C.S.: 524114

Principal Financial Group, Inc. - Appleton (1)
1837 W Wisconsin Ave, Appleton, WI 54914
Tel.: (920) 832-3821
Web Site: http://www.principal.com
Sales Range: $25-49.9 Million
Emp.: 90
Consulting & Administration Services for Employee Benefit Plans
N.A.I.C.S.: 524292

Principal Financial Group, Inc. - Indianapolis (1)
8910 Purdue Rd Ste 705, Indianapolis, IN 46268
Tel.: (317) 874-3802
Web Site: http://www.principal.com

Sales Range: $125-149.9 Million
Emp.: 450
Insurance Claims Processing & Consulting
Services
N.A.I.C.S.: 524298

**Principal Financial Group, Inc. -
Raleigh** (1)
4141 Parklake Ave Ste 450, Raleigh, NC
27612
Tel.: (919) 745-2040
Web Site: http://www.ebsnq.com
Rev.: $190,000
Emp.: 90
Insurance Services
N.A.I.C.S.: 524298
Keith E. Mays *(Reg Mng Dir)*

Principal Financial Services, Inc. (1)
711 High St, Des Moines, IA 50392
Tel.: (515) 247-5111
Web Site: http://www.principal.com
Financial Products & Services Including Re-
tirement & Investment Services, Life &
Health Insurance, Mortgage Banking to
Businesses, Individuals & Institutional Cli-
ents
N.A.I.C.S.: 524114

Principal Genera S.A. de C.V. (1)
4116 16 de Septiembre, 72534, Puebla,
Mexico
Tel.: (52) 12222407978
Web Site: http://www.principal.com
Sales Range: $25-49.9 Million
Emp.: 40
Financial Products & Services Including Re-
tirement & Investment Services, Life &
Health Insurance, Mortgage Banking to
Businesses, Individuals & Institutional Cli-
ents
N.A.I.C.S.: 524114

Principal Global Investors (1)
711 High St, Des Moines, IA
50392-0490 **(100%)**
Tel.: (515) 248-2611
Web Site: https://www.principalam.com
Sales Range: $75-99.9 Million
Emp.: 150
Investment Advisor
N.A.I.C.S.: 525990
Barbara A. McKenzie *(COO-Boutique Ops
& Sr Exec Dir)*
Matthew Minnetian *(Portfolio Mgr)*

Affiliate (Domestic):

Post Advisory Group, LLC (2)
2049 Century Park E Ste 3050, Los Ange-
les, CA 90067
Tel.: (310) 996-9600
Web Site: https://www.postadvisory.com
Sales Range: $100-124.9 Million
Asset Management Services
N.A.I.C.S.: 523940
Eileen Mancera *(Mng Dir & Head-Sls &
Mktg)*
Jeffrey Stroll *(Chief Investment Officer)*

Subsidiary (Domestic):

**Principal Global Columbus Circle,
LLC** (2)
Metro Ctr 1 Sta Pl 8th Fl S, Stamford, CT
06902
Tel.: (203) 353-6000
Web Site: http://www.columbuscircle.com
Sales Range: $100-124.9 Million
Emp.: 45
Asset Management Services
N.A.I.C.S.: 523940

**Principal Real Estate Investors,
LLC** (2)
711 High St, Des Moines, IA 50392
Tel.: (515) 248-9289
Web Site: https://www.principalglobal.com
Sales Range: $250-299.9 Million
Real Estate Investment Services
N.A.I.C.S.: 525990

**Principal Global Investors (Australia)
Service Company Pty Limited** (1)
Level 43 Amp Centre 50 Bridge Street, PO
Box 4169, Sydney, 2000, NSW, Australia
Tel.: (61) 282269000
Web Site: http://www.principalglobal.com
Sales Range: $100-124.9 Million
Emp.: 65
Asset Management Services

N.A.I.C.S.: 523940
Grant Forster *(CEO)*

Subsidiary (Domestic):

**Principal Global Investors (Australia)
Limited** (2)
Level 30 Chifley Tower 2 Chifley Square,
Sydney, 2000, NSW, Australia
Tel.: (61) 282269000
Web Site: https://www.principalam.com
Sales Range: $75-99.9 Million
Asset Management Services
N.A.I.C.S.: 523940

**Principal Global Investors (Europe)
Limited** (1)
1 Wood Street, London, EC2V 7JB, United
Kingdom
Tel.: (44) 2077100220
Web Site: http://www.principal.com
Sales Range: $1-9.9 Million
Emp.: 70
The Provision of Fund Management Ser-
vices
N.A.I.C.S.: 523940
Tim Stumpff *(CEO)*

**Principal Global Investors (Singa-
pore), Ltd** (1)
One Raffles Quay 19-01 North Tower, Sin-
gapore, 048583, Singapore
Tel.: (65) 63320683
Web Site: http://www.principalglobal.com
Sales Range: $650-699.9 Million
Institutional Asset Managers
N.A.I.C.S.: 523160

Principal Global Investors, LLC (1)
711 High St, Des Moines, IA 50392
Tel.: (515) 247-5594
Web Site: https://www.principalglobal.com
Asset Management Services
N.A.I.C.S.: 531390
Patrick Gregory Halter *(CEO)*
Kamal Bhatia *(Pres & CEO)*

**Principal Global Services Private
Limited** (1)
Level 6 7 Cyber City, Pune, 411013, Maha-
rashtra, India
Tel.: (91) 2066214000
Web Site: http://www.principal.com
Emp.: 1,000
Insurance Agencies
N.A.I.C.S.: 524210
Kaushik Majumdar *(Mng Dir)*

**Principal International (Asia)
Limited** (1)
Unit 1-2 10/F Central Plaza 18 Harbour Rd
Wanchai, Hong Kong, China (Hong
Kong) **(100%)**
Tel.: (852) 28271628
Web Site: http://www.principal.com.hk
Sales Range: $75-99.9 Million
Emp.: 300
Holding Company; Owner of Retirement &
Insurance Products
N.A.I.C.S.: 551112

Subsidiary (Domestic):

**Principal Asset Management Com-
pany Asia, Ltd.** (2)
30/F Millennium City 6 392 Kwun Tong
Road Kwun Tong, Kowloon, Hong Kong,
China (Hong Kong)
Tel.: (852) 28271233
Web Site: http://www.principal.com.hk
Sales Range: $100-124.9 Million
Emp.: 75
Investment Management Service
N.A.I.C.S.: 523940
Rex Pak-Kuen Au Yeung *(Pres & CEO)*

**Principal Global Investors (Asia)
Limited** (2)
Unit 1001-1003 Central Plz 18 Harbor
Road, Wanchai, China (Hong Kong)
Tel.: (852) 28271234
Web Site: http://www.principal.com.hk
Emp.: 300
Investment Fund Services
N.A.I.C.S.: 523940
Art Bacci *(CEO)*

**Principal Insurance Company (Hong
Kong) Limited** (2)

Ste 1001 1003 Central Plz 18 Harbour Rd,
Wanchai, China (Hong Kong) **(53%)**
Tel.: (852) 28271234
Web Site: http://www.principal.com.hk
Sales Range: $50-74.9 Million
Emp.: 350
Trustee, Administration & Investment Man-
agement Services for MPF Products & Re-
tirement Schemes in Hong Kong
N.A.I.C.S.: 541611
Stanley Yip *(CEO)*

**Principal Trust Company (Asia)
Limited** (2)
30/F Millennium City 6 392 Kwun Tong
Road, Kwun Tong, Kowloon, China (Hong
Kong)
Tel.: (852) 28271233
Web Site: http://www.principal.com.hk
Sales Range: $250-299.9 Million
Professional Trustee Services
N.A.I.C.S.: 523160

**Principal International Argentina,
S.A.** (1)
Sarmiento 663 4th Fl, Buenos Aires,
Argentina **(100%)**
Tel.: (54) 1143480900
Web Site: http://www.principal.com.ar
Sales Range: $25-49.9 Million
Emp.: 75
Holding Company; Owner of Life Insurance
& Annuities
N.A.I.C.S.: 524128

Principal International, Inc. (1)
711 High St, Des Moines, IA 50392-0420
Tel.: (515) 247-5111
Web Site: https://www.principal.com
Holding Company; Life & Health Insurance,
Mortgage Banking, Retirement & Invest-
ment Services
N.A.I.C.S.: 551112

**Principal Investment & Retirement
Services Limited** (1)
392 Kwun Tong Rd Kwun Tong, Wan Chai,
Kowloon, China (Hong Kong)
Tel.: (852) 28271233
Investment & Pension Fund Services
N.A.I.C.S.: 523940
Carmen Lam *(CEO)*

**Principal Islamic Asset Management
Sdn. Bhd.** (1)
10th floor Bangunan CIMB Jalan Seman-
tan, Damansara Heights, 50490, Kuala
Lumpur, Malaysia
Tel.: (60) 320848888
Web Site: https://www.principalislamic.com
Asset Management Services
N.A.I.C.S.: 523940

**Principal Life Insurance
Company** (1)
711 High St, Des Moines, IA 50392-0420
Tel.: (515) 247-5111
Web Site: http://www.principal.com
Life Insurance
N.A.I.C.S.: 524113
Dennis Menken *(Chief Investment Officer &
Sr VP)*

Division (Domestic):

Design Benefits Inc. (2)
1155 Seminole Trl, Charlottesville, VA
22906
Tel.: (434) 296-1122
Web Site:
   https://www.designbenefitsinc.com
Rev.: $950,000
Emp.: 20
Insurance Brokers
N.A.I.C.S.: 524210
P D Cockrell *(Owner)*
David Cockrell *(Pres)*

Elan Group Inc. (2)
2910 W Bay to Bay Blvd, Tampa, FL 33629-
8172
Tel.: (813) 839-1530
Web Site: https://www.elan-group.com
Rev.: $1,200,000
Emp.: 17
Providing Insurance
N.A.I.C.S.: 524210
Ross Hays *(Co-Pres)*
Duffy Thaxton *(Co-Pres)*
Suzy Mendelson *(VP)*
David Thaxton *(VP)*

G&G Agency Ltd. (2)
330 Motor Pkwy Ste 105, Hauppauge, NY
11788
Tel.: (631) 237-4600
Web Site: http://www.goldiscompanies.com
Insurance Agents
N.A.I.C.S.: 524210

**Greater NY Financial
Consultants** (2)
400 W Main St Ste 101, Riverhead, NY
11901
Tel.: (631) 506-0444
Web Site:
   http://www.financialconsultants.com
Rev.: $370,000
Emp.: 3
Life Insurance Agency
N.A.I.C.S.: 561499

Herman Agency Inc. (2)
715 Enterprise Dr, Oak Brook, IL 60523-
1907
Tel.: (630) 571-2200
Web Site: https://www.hermanagency.com
Rev.: $1,900,000
Emp.: 35
Fire Insurance Services
N.A.I.C.S.: 524113
Leslie Herman *(Office Mgr)*
Pat Stolfi *(Mgr-Case)*
Coleen Zeri *(Mgr-Case & LTCI Product
Support)*
Burt Herman *(Founder & Chm)*

J. Dempsey Inc. (2)
1304 S Main St, Ann Arbor, MI 48104
Tel.: (734) 761-1700
Web Site: https://www.dempseyinc.com
Rev.: $610,000
Emp.: 7
Insurance Agents
N.A.I.C.S.: 524210
Kim Phillips *(VP)*

Affiliate (Domestic):

Jonathan Hind Financial Group (2)
4760 White Bear Pkwy Ste 100, White Bear
Lake, MN 55110
Tel.: (651) 429-3868
Web Site: http://www.jhfg.com
Rev.: $635,000
Emp.: 8
Life Insurance
N.A.I.C.S.: 524113
Erik Young *(Pres)*
Dayna Geisbauer *(Mgr-New Bus)*

Division (Domestic):

**Metro Accident & Health Agency,
Inc.** (2)
500 N Broadway Ste 243, Jericho, NY
11753
Tel.: (516) 364-5111
Web Site: https://www.metrodi.com
Rev.: $870,000
Emp.: 10
Insurance Agents
N.A.I.C.S.: 524210

PPI Benefits Solutions (2)
10 Research Pkwy Ste 200, Wallingford, CT
06492
Tel.: (203) 793-1200
Web Site: https://www.ppibenefits.com
Sales Range: $10-24.9 Million
Emp.: 200
Life Insurance Carrier
N.A.I.C.S.: 541611

**Principal Mexico Compania de Se-
guros S.A. de C.V.** (1)
Ave Universidad 1571-2 Piso, Florida Alvaro
Obregon, CP 01030, Mexico, DF,
Mexico **(80%)**
Tel.: (52) 5554228400
Web Site: http://www.principal.com.mx
Sales Range: $100-124.9 Million
Emp.: 120
Fire Insurance Services
N.A.I.C.S.: 524113

**Principal Pensiones, S.A. de
C.V.** (1)
Calzada del Valle no 112 Ote Col Del Valle,
San Pedro, Garza Garcia, 66220, NL,
Mexico
Tel.: (52) 8002774624

Principal Financial Group, Inc.—(Continued)

Web Site: http://www.principal.com.mx
Emp.: 5,000
Investment Services
N.A.I.C.S.: 523999
Luis Valdez (Pres)

Principal Real Estate B.V. (1)
WTC Schiphol A Tower 4th Floor Schiphol
Boulevard 127, 1118 BG, Schiphol, Nether-
lands
Tel.: (31) 206765060
Financial Services
N.A.I.C.S.: 523940

**Principal Real Estate Europe
Limited** (1)
65 Grosvenor Street, London, W1K 3JH,
United Kingdom
Tel.: (44) 2073558800
Web Site: http://www.principalreeurope.com
Financial Services
N.A.I.C.S.: 523940

Principal Real Estate GmbH (1)
Taunusanlage 16, 60325, Frankfurt am
Main, Germany
Tel.: (49) 6950506690
Financial Services
N.A.I.C.S.: 523940

**Principal Real Estate Kapitalverwal-
tungsgesellschaft mbH** (1)
Taunusanlage 16, 60325, Frankfurt am
Main, Germany
Tel.: (49) 6950506690
Financial Services
N.A.I.C.S.: 523940

Principal Real Estate S.L. (1)
Calle Maria de Molina 40 1 dcha, 28006,
Madrid, Spain
Tel.: (34) 915648622
Financial Services
N.A.I.C.S.: 523940

Principal Real Estate S.a.r.l. (1)
6 Rue Jean Monnet, 2180, Luxembourg,
Luxembourg
Tel.: (352) 26754108
Financial Services
N.A.I.C.S.: 523940

Principal Real Estate SAS (1)
36 Avenue Hoche Batiment A, 75008, Paris,
France
Tel.: (33) 140155300
Financial Services
N.A.I.C.S.: 523940

**Principal Retirement Advisors Private
Limited** (1)
Exchange Plaza B Wing Ground Floor NSE
Building Bandra Kurla Complex, Bandra
East, Mumbai, 400 051, India
Tel.: (91) 2267720555
Web Site:
http://www.principalretirementindia.com
Pension Fund Management Services
N.A.I.C.S.: 525110
Venkata Surya Bharat Ravuri (Mng Dir)

Professional Pensions, Inc. (1)
10 Research Pkwy Ste 200, Wallingford, CT
06492
Tel.: (203) 793-1200
Web Site: https://www.ppibenefits.com
Sales Range: $25-49.9 Million
Emp.: 52
Group Insurance & Retirement Program
Services
N.A.I.C.S.: 524298

RobustWealth, Inc. (1)
204 N Union St, Lambertville, NJ 08530
Tel.: (609) 483-8101
Web Site: http://www.robustwealth.com
Real Estate Investment Services
N.A.I.C.S.: 525990
Mike Kerins (Founder & Co-CEO)
Matthew Schafer (CFO)
Rob Cavallaro (Chief Investment Officer)
Chris Kerins (CTO)
Ryan Downing (Co-CEO)
Jessica Wooke (Head-Product Dev)
Andrew Donohue (Chief Compliance Offi-
cer)
Robert Redican (Chief Revenue Officer)

**Spectrum Asset Management,
Inc.** (1)

2 High Rdg Park Ste 2, Stamford, CT
06905
Tel.: (203) 322-0189
Web Site: https://www.samipfd.com
Sales Range: Less than $1 Million
Asset Management Services
N.A.I.C.S.: 523940
Fernando Diaz (VP & Portfolio Mgr)
Joseph J. Urciuoli (Head-Res)
Chad Stogel (VP-Res)
Albano Tunnera (VP-NYSE Trading)
Roberto Giangregorio (VP & Portfolio Mgr)
Kevin Nugent (VP & Portfolio Mgr)
John Kriz (Sr VP-Res)
Manu Krishnan (Sr VP & Portfolio Mgr)
James Hodapp (Sr VP)
Steven Solmonson (Sr VP)
Patricia Tyler (Mgr-Office)
Matthew Byer (COO)
Jennifer Simpson (Controller)
Joseph Hanczor (Chief Compliance Officer)
Satomi Yarnell (Asst VP-Portfolio Admin &
Client Svc)
Thomas Kuna (Asst VP-Back Office Ops)
L. Phillip Jacoby IV (Chief Investment Offi-
cer)

PRINCIPAL SOLAR, INC.
100 Cres Ct Ste 700, Dallas, TX
75201
Tel.: (214) 885-0032   DE
Web Site: https://pswwenergy.com
Year Founded: 2011
PSWW—(OTCIQ)
Sales Range: Less than $1 Million
Solar Electric Power Generation Ser-
vices
N.A.I.C.S.: 221114
K. Bryce Toussaint (CEO)
Anthony Lerner (COO)

PRINEVILLE BANCORPORA-
TION
555 NW Third St, Prineville, OR
97754
Tel.: (541) 447-4106
PNVL—(OTCIQ)
Commercial Banking Services
N.A.I.C.S.: 522110
Robin B. Freeman (CEO)

PRIORITY TECHNOLOGY
HOLDINGS, INC.
2001 Wside Pkwy Ste 155, Al-
pharetta, GA 30004
Tel.: (404) 952-2107
Web Site:
https://prioritycommerce.com
Year Founded: 2015
PRTH—(NASDAQ)
Rev.: $663,641,000
Assets: $1,373,363,000
Liabilities: $1,476,149,000
Net Worth: ($102,786,000)
Earnings: ($39,030,000)
Emp.: 863
Fiscal Year-end: 12/31/22
Investment Services
N.A.I.C.S.: 523999
John V. Priore (Co-Founder)
Thomas C. Priore (Co-Founder, Chm
& CEO)
Ranjana Ram (COO)
David Faupol (CMO)
Bradley J. Miller (Chief Risk Officer &
Gen Counsel)
Rajiv Kumar (Chief Acctg Officer & Sr
VP)
Tim O'Leary (CFO)

PRISM TECHNOLOGIES
GROUP, INC.
101 Parkshore Dr Ste 100, Folsom,
CA 95630
Tel.: (916) 932-2860   DE
Web Site: http://www.przmgroup.com
Year Founded: 1995
PRZM—(OTCEM)
Sales Range: $1-9.9 Million

Emp.: 4
Patent Licensing Services
N.A.I.C.S.: 561499
Eric Loewe (Gen Counsel & Sec)

Subsidiaries:

**Goldrush Insurance Services,
Inc.** (1)
11290 Pyrites Way Ste 200, Gold River, CA
95670
Tel.: (916) 853-3300
Sales Range: $75-99.9 Million
Insurance Services
N.A.I.C.S.: 524298

Prism Technologies, LLC (1)
2323 S 171st Street Ste 106, Omaha, NE
68130
Tel.: (402) 934-2020
Web Site: http://www.prsmip.com
Software Development Services
N.A.I.C.S.: 541511
Gregory J. Duman (Pres & CFO)
Andre J. Bahou (Chief Legal Officer & VP)
Richard L. Gregg (Founder, CTO & VP)

PRISMONE GROUP, INC.
207 W Plant St Unit 770447, Winter
Garden, FL 34777
Tel.: (321) 293-1000   NV
Web Site: https://www.prismone.com
Year Founded: 2007
PMOZ—(OTCEM)
Communications, Multimedia & Other
Network Systems Design, Consulting,
Installation, Integration, Support &
Management Services
N.A.I.C.S.: 541990
Samir A. Burshan (Founder, Pres &
CEO)
Stefanie Vaught (CFO)
Douglas Vaught (COO & VP)
Jerry Jackson (VP)
Lori Jensen Burshan (VP)

PRIVATE BANCORP OF
AMERICA, INC.
9404 Genesee Ave Ste 100, La Jolla,
CA 90237
Tel.: (858) 875-6900   CA
Web Site:
https://www.calprivate.bank
Year Founded: 2015
PBAM—(OTCQX)
Rev.: $130,584,000
Assets: $2,152,468,000
Liabilities: $1,966,685,000
Net Worth: $185,783,000
Earnings: $40,856,000
Emp.: 207
Fiscal Year-end: 12/31/23
Bank Holding Company
N.A.I.C.S.: 551111
Thomas V. Wornham (CEO)
Rick A. Sowers (Pres & CEO)
Cory Stewart (CFO)
Selwyn Isakow (Chm)

Subsidiaries:

CalPrivate Bank (1)
9404 Genesee Ave Ste 100, La Jolla, CA
92037
Tel.: (858) 875-6900
Web Site: http://www.calprivate.bank
Sales Range: $10-24.9 Million
Commericial Banking
N.A.I.C.S.: 522110
Thomas V. Wornham (CEO)
Steve Rippe (Chief Credit Officer)
Eric Larson (CFO)
Rick Sowers (Pres)

PRIVETERRA ACQUISITION
CORP. II
1 Park Plz, Irvine, CA 92614
Tel.: (212) 616-9600   DE
Year Founded: 2020
PMGM—(NASDAQ)
Rev.: $3,862,680

Assets: $30,361,378
Liabilities: $46,968,768
Net Worth: ($16,607,390)
Earnings: $7,097,636
Emp.: 5
Fiscal Year-end: 12/31/22
Investment Holding Company
N.A.I.C.S.: 551112
David Pace (Co-CEO)
Daniel Fleischmann (Chief Strategy
Officer)

PRIVIA HEALTH GROUP, INC.
950 N Glebe Rd Ste 700, Arlington,
VA 22203
Tel.: (571) 366-8850   DE
Web Site:
https://www.priviahealth.com
Year Founded: 2007
PRVA—(NASDAQ)
Rev.: $1,356,660,000
Assets: $792,813,000
Liabilities: $273,764,000
Net Worth: $519,049,000
Earnings: ($8,585,000)
Emp.: 964
Fiscal Year-end: 12/31/22
Women Healthcare Services
N.A.I.C.S.: 621610
Edward C. Fargis (Chief Legal Offi-
cer, Gen Counsel, Sec & Exec VP)
Parth Mehrotra (CEO)
David Mountcastle (CFO & Principal
Acctg Officer)
David King (Chm)
Jeffrey S. Sherman (CFO & Exec VP)

PRO-DEX, INC.
2361 McGaw Ave, Irvine, CA 92614
Tel.: (949) 769-3200   CO
Web Site: https://www.pro-dex.com
Year Founded: 1978
PDEX—(NASDAQ)
Rev.: $53,844,000
Assets: $52,477,000
Liabilities: $21,610,000
Net Worth: $30,867,000
Earnings: $2,127,000
Emp.: 148
Fiscal Year-end: 06/30/24
Dental Product Mfr
N.A.I.C.S.: 423450
Richard Lee Van Kirk (Pres & CEO)
Nicholas John Swenson (Chm)
Alisha K. Charlton (CFO)
Daniel Santos (Dir-Research & De-
velopment & Business Development)
Chris Jackson (Dir-Operations)
Jorge Cuervo (Dir-Project Mgmt)

PROASSURANCE CORPORA-
TION
100 Brookwood Pl Ste 300, Birming-
ham, AL 35209
Tel.: (205) 877-4400   DE
Web Site:
https://www.proassurance.com
PRA—(NYSE)
Rev.: $1,106,688,000
Assets: $5,699,999,000
Liabilities: $4,595,981,000
Net Worth: $1,104,018,000
Earnings: ($402,000)
Emp.: 1,083
Fiscal Year-end: 12/31/22
Holding Company; Medical Liability
Insurance
N.A.I.C.S.: 551112
Jeffrey Patton Lisenby (Gen Counsel,
Sec & Exec VP)
Edward Lewis Rand Jr. (Pres & CEO)
Dana Shannon Hendricks (CFO,
Treas & Exec VP)
Noreen Lynn Dishart (Chief HR Offi-
cer & Exec VP)
Kevin Merrick Shook (Pres)

Subsidiaries:

Eastern Insurance Holdings, Inc. (1)
25 Race Ave, Lancaster, PA 17603-3179
Tel.: (717) 396-7095
Holding Company; Workers' Compensation Insurance & Reinsurance Products & Services
N.A.I.C.S.: 551112

Subsidiary (Domestic):

Eastern Alliance Insurance Company (2)
25 Race Ave, Lancaster, PA 17603
Tel.: (717) 396-7095
Web Site: http://www.easternalliance.com
Sales Range: $50-74.9 Million
Emp.: 140
Workers' Compensation Insurance & Reinsurance Products & Services
N.A.I.C.S.: 524126
Kevin Merrick Shook (Pres)

Employers Security Insurance Company (2)
12911 N Meridian St Sre 100, Carmel, IN 46032
Tel.: (317) 573-4884
Web Site: http://www.esic.com
Sales Range: $10-24.9 Million
Emp.: 25
Workers' Compensation Insurance & Reinsurance Products & Services
N.A.I.C.S.: 524126
Michael Leonard Boguski (Chief Underwriting Officer)

Medmarc Casualty Insurance Company (1)
4795 Meadow Wood Ln Ste 335 W, Chantilly, VA 20151-2219
Tel.: (703) 652-1300
Web Site: https://www.medmarc.com
Sales Range: $10-24.9 Million
Emp.: 75
Administrative Management & General Management Consulting Services
N.A.I.C.S.: 541611
Karen Murphy (Pres)
Sara Dyson (VP-Underwriting Ops & Risk Management)
Sonia Valdes (VP)

NORCAL Mutual Insurance Co. (1)
560 Davis St Fl 2, San Francisco, CA 94111-1902
Tel.: (415) 397-9700
Web Site: http://www.norcalmutual.com
Sales Range: $50-74.9 Million
Emp.: 200
Surety Insurance & Liability Insurance Company
N.A.I.C.S.: 524126
Scott Diener (CEO)
Kara Ricci (Chief Legal Officer, Sec & Sr VP)
Michael Perkins (VP-Information Technology)
Jaan E. Sidorov (Chm)
Patricia A. Dailey (Dir)
Mark D. Johnson (CFO & Sr VP)
Joy E. Corso (VP-Marketing-Communications)
Neil E. Simons (VP-Product Development)
Dustin A. Shaver (VP-Risk Management)
Michael G. Roque (VP-Business Development)
Steven Packer (Sec)
Julie L. Burns (Chief HR Officer & Sr VP)
Ronald C. Rumin (COO & Sr VP)

Subsidiary (Domestic):

PMSLIC Insurance Company (2)
1700 Bent Creek Blvd, Mechanicsburg, PA 17050-1865
Tel.: (717) 791-1212
Web Site: http://www.pmslic.com
Medical Insurance Services
N.A.I.C.S.: 524114
Scott Diener (Chm)

PACO Assurance Company, Inc. (1)
3000 Meridian Blvd Ste 400, Franklin, TN 37067
Tel.: (615) 371-8776
Web Site: http://www.picagroup.com
Sales Range: $50-74.9 Million
Emp.: 100
Professional Liability Insurance Services

N.A.I.C.S.: 524210

Podiatry Insurance Company of America (1)
3000 Merridian Blvd Ste 400, Franklin, TN 37067
Tel.: (615) 371-8776
Web Site: https://www.picagroup.com
Sales Range: $10-24.9 Million
Emp.: 120
Liability Insurance
N.A.I.C.S.: 524210
Ross Taubman (Pres & Chief Medical Officer)
Margaret Christian (Sr VP-Bus Ops)
Daniel Shrode (VP)

ProAssurance (1)
670 Morrison Rd Ste 210, Columbus, OH 43230
Tel.: (614) 751-1000
Web Site: http://www.proassurance.com
Sales Range: $10-24.9 Million
Emp.: 4
Liability Insurance
N.A.I.C.S.: 524126

ProAssurance - Birmingham (1)
100 Brookwood Pl, Birmingham, AL 35209
Tel.: (205) 877-4400
Web Site: https://www.proassurance.com
Professional Liability Insurance Services
N.A.I.C.S.: 524210

ProAssurance Corporation (1)
2801 SW 149th Ave Ste 200, Miramar, FL 33027
Tel.: (954) 442-3113
Web Site: http://www.proassurance.com
Sales Range: $150-199.9 Million
Insurance Services
N.A.I.C.S.: 524126

ProAssurance Corporation (1)
1242 E Independence St Ste 100, Springfield, MO 65804
Tel.: (417) 887-3120
Web Site: http://www.proassurance.com
Sales Range: $10-24.9 Million
Emp.: 15
Liability Insurance
N.A.I.C.S.: 524126

ProAssurance Corporation (1)
1250 23rd St NW Ste 250, Washington, DC 20037   (100%)
Tel.: (202) 969-1866
Web Site: http://www.proassurance.com
Sales Range: $75-99.9 Million
Emp.: 107
Medical Malpractice Insurance & Practice Management Services
N.A.I.C.S.: 524210

ProAssurance Corporation - Mobile (1)
3658 College Ln S, Mobile, AL 36608
Tel.: (251) 343-6801
Web Site: http://www.proassurance.com
Liability Insurance Carrier
N.A.I.C.S.: 524126

ProAssurance Indemnity Company Inc (1)
100 Brookwood Pl Ste 500, Birmingham, AL 35209
Tel.: (205) 877-4400
Insurance Brokerage Services
N.A.I.C.S.: 524210

ProAssurance Indemnity LLC (1)
965 Emerson Pkwy Ste H, Greenwood, IN 46143
Tel.: (317) 884-5650
Web Site: http://www.proassurance.com
Sales Range: $25-49.9 Million
Emp.: 38
Medical Liability Insurance Services
N.A.I.C.S.: 524126

ProAssurance Mid-Continent Underwriters, Inc. (1)
3131 Eastside Ste 425, Houston, TX 77098
Tel.: (713) 965-6900
Web Site: http://www.proassurancemidcontinent.com
Healthcare Professional Liability Insurance Services
N.A.I.C.S.: 524114

ProAssurance Wisconsin Insurance Company (1)
1002 Deming Way, Madison, WI 53744-5650
Tel.: (608) 831-8331
Web Site: http://www.picwisconsin.com
Sales Range: $25-49.9 Million
Emp.: 75
Disability Insurance Services
N.A.I.C.S.: 524210

ProNational Insurance Company (1)
2600 Professionals Dr, Okemos, MI 48864
Tel.: (517) 349-6500
Web Site: http://www.proassurance.com
Sales Range: $25-49.9 Million
Emp.: 70
Medical Malpractice Insurance
N.A.I.C.S.: 524126
William Stancil Starnes (Chm, Pres & CEO)

Branch (Domestic):

ProAssurance Casualty Company (2)
1250 E Diehl Rd Ste 302, Naperville, IL 60563-9388
Tel.: (630) 577-0760
Web Site: http://www.proassurance.com
Sales Range: Less than $1 Million
Emp.: 8
Casualty Insurance Services
N.A.I.C.S.: 524210

ProAssurance Indemnity Company (2)
965 Emerson Pkwy Ste H, Greenwood, IN 46143
Tel.: (317) 884-5650
Web Site: http://www.proassurance.com
Sales Range: $10-24.9 Million
Emp.: 28
Insurance Company
N.A.I.C.S.: 524298

ProNational Insurance Company (2)
13919 Carrollwood Vlg Run, Tampa, FL 33618-2746
Tel.: (813) 969-2010
Web Site: http://www.proassurance.com
Sales Range: $10-24.9 Million
Emp.: 13
Insurance Company
N.A.I.C.S.: 524126

The Medical Assurance Company, Inc. (1)
100 Brookwood Pl, Birmingham, AL 35209   (100%)
Tel.: (205) 877-4400
Web Site: http://www.medicalassurance.com
Sales Range: $75-99.9 Million
Emp.: 170
Medical Malpractice Insurance
N.A.I.C.S.: 524126

Branch (Domestic):

The Medical Assurance Company (2)
113 St Clair Bldg Ste 500, Cleveland, OH 44114   (100%)
Tel.: (216) 515-1300
Web Site: http://www.proassurance.com
Sales Range: $10-24.9 Million
Emp.: 5
Liability Insurance
N.A.I.C.S.: 524126

PROBILITY MEDIA CORPORATION

4400 Sample Rd STE 136, Coconut Creek, FL 33073
Tel.: (281) 806-5000   NV
Web Site:
http://www.probilitymedia.com
Year Founded: 2011
PBYA—(OTCEM)
Sales Range: $1-9.9 Million
Emp.: 47
Investment Services
N.A.I.C.S.: 523999
Evan M. Levine (Chm & CEO)
Noah I. Davis (Pres & COO)
Richard Corbin Jr. (Vice Chm)

Subsidiaries:

Cranbury International LLC (1)
1517 San Jacinto St, Houston, TX 77002
Tel.: (802) 622-1475
Web Site:
http://www.cranburyinternational.com
Educational Book Exporter & Publisher
N.A.I.C.S.: 513130
Ethan Atkin (Pres)

One Exam Prep LLC (1)
4400 W Sample Rd Ste 136, Coconut Creek, FL 33073
Tel.: (877) 804-3959
Web Site: http://www.1examprep.com
Education Services
N.A.I.C.S.: 611710
Rob Estell (Pres)
Charlie Bennett (Sls Mgr)

Premier Purchasing and Marketing Alliance LLC (1)
178 BRd St, Glens Falls, NY 12801
Tel.: (800) 833-8788
Web Site: http://www.premierpma.com
Software Development Services
N.A.I.C.S.: 513210

PubCo Reporting Services, Inc. (1)
6800 SW 40th St Ste 213, Miami, FL 33155
Tel.: (305) 396-1415
Web Site: http://www.pubcoreporting.com
Electronic Reporting & Filing Solutions for Publicly Traded Companies on EDGAR & SEDAR Systems
N.A.I.C.S.: 518210
Christopher Ellerbeck (Pres)

W Marketing Inc. (1)
30 Oser Ave Ste 500, Hauppauge, NY 11788
Tel.: (888) 226-7052
Web Site: http://www.wmarketingonline.com
Construction Materials Distr
N.A.I.C.S.: 423390

PROCEPT BIOROBOTICS CORPORATION

900 Island Dr, Redwood City, CA 94065
Tel.: (650) 232-7200   DE
Web Site: https://www.procept-biorobotics.com
Year Founded: 2007
PRCT—(NASDAQ)
Rev.: $75,014,000
Assets: $309,329,000
Liabilities: $112,257,000
Net Worth: $197,072,000
Earnings: ($87,154,000)
Emp.: 428
Fiscal Year-end: 12/31/22
Medical & Surgical Equipment Mfr
N.A.I.C.S.: 339112
Kevin Waters (CFO & Sr VP)
Sham Shiblaq (Sr VP-Commercialization)
Surag Mantri (Sr VP-R&D)
Alaleh Nouri (Gen Counsel, Sec & Sr VP)
Bijesh Chandran (VP-Regulatory Affairs & QA)
Matthew Salkeld (VP-Health, Economic & Reimbursement)
Mohan Sancheti (VP-Ops)
Barry Templin (VP-Clinical & Medical Affairs)
Minni Vittal (VP-People)
Frederic Moll (Chm)
Reza Zadno (Pres & CEO)

PROCESSA PHARMACEUTICALS, INC.

7380 Coca Cola Dr Ste 106, Hanover, MD 21076
Tel.: (443) 776-3133   DE
Web Site:
https://www.processapharmaceuticals.com
Year Founded: 2011

Processa Pharmaceuticals, Inc.—(Continued)

PCSA—(NASDAQ)
Rev.: $335,541
Assets: $5,786,643
Liabilities: $797,484
Net Worth: $4,989,159
Earnings: ($11,121,520)
Emp.: 13
Fiscal Year-end: 12/31/23
Pharmaceuticals Product Mfr
N.A.I.C.S.: 325412
David Young (Pres-R&D)
George K. Ng (CEO)
David Young (Chm & CEO)
Patrick Lin (Chief Strategy & Bus Officer)
Sian Bigora (Co-Founder & Chief Dev Officer)
Wendy Guy (Co-Founder & Chief Admin Officer)
Yvonne Madden (VP-Project Mgmt)
Helen Pentikis (VP-Clinical Pharmacology)
Chang-Rung Chen (Co-Founder & Sr Dir-Translational Science)
Mary G. Nyberg (Sr Dir-Clinical Ops)
Justin Yorke (Chm)
Russell L. Skibsted (CFO)

PROCORE TECHNOLOGIES, INC.
6309 Carpinteria Ave, Carpinteria, CA 93013   CA
Web Site: https://www.procore.com
Year Founded: 2002
PCOR—(NYSE)
Rev.: $950,010,000
Assets: $1,893,568,000
Liabilities: $737,958,000
Net Worth: $1,155,610,000
Earnings: ($189,694,000)
Emp.: 3,694
Fiscal Year-end: 12/31/23
Software Development Services
N.A.I.C.S.: 541511
Tooey Courtemanche (Founder, Co-Pres & Co-CEO)
Steve Zahm (Chief Culture Officer)
Paul E. Lyandres (Pres-Fintech)
Benjamin C. Singer (Chief Legal Officer & Sec)
Olga Kibler (Chief People Officer)
Steve Davis (Pres-Product & Tech)
Howard Fu (CFO & Treas)
Sarah Hodges (CMO)
Joy Durling (Chief Data Officer)
Kevin Walker (Chief Security Officer)
Linden Hillenbrand (Sr VP)
Kim Chamberlain (Sr VP)
Bill F. Fleming Jr. (Sr VP)
Rubiena Duarte (VP)
Craig F. Courtemanche Jr. (Founder, Chm, Pres & CEO)

PROCYON CORP.
164 Douglas Rd, Oldsmar, FL 34677   CO
Tel.: (727) 447-2998
Web Site:
    https://www.procyoncorp.com
Year Founded: 1987
PCYN—(OTCIQ)
Rev.: $4,984,433
Assets: $3,204,412
Liabilities: $917,122
Net Worth: $2,287,290
Earnings: ($341,140)
Emp.: 19
Fiscal Year-end: 06/30/24
Pharmaceutical & Medical Products Mfr
N.A.I.C.S.: 325412
Regina W. Anderson (Chm)
Justice W. Anderson (Pres & CEO)
James B. Anderson (CFO)

PROFESSIONAL DIVERSITY

NETWORK, INC.
55 E Monroe St Ste 2120, Chicago, IL 60603
Tel.: (312) 614-0950   DE
Web Site: http://www.prodivnet.com
IPDN—(NASDAQ)
Rev.: $8,314,088
Assets: $6,836,133
Liabilities: $4,527,109
Net Worth: $2,309,024
Earnings: ($2,602,722)
Emp.: 37
Fiscal Year-end: 12/31/22
Professional & Career Oriented Website Owner & Operator
N.A.I.C.S.: 513140
Hao Zhang (Chm)
Chad Hoersten (CTO)

Subsidiaries:

Expo Experts, LLC   (1)
7770 Cooper Rd Ste 3B, Cincinnati, OH 45242-7727
Tel.: (513) 561-5422
Web Site: https://www.expoexpertsllc.com
All Other Support Services
N.A.I.C.S.: 561990
Carrie Dunham (VP)

NAPW, Inc.   (1)
1305 Franklin Ave Ste 300, Garden City, NY 11530
Tel.: (516) 877-5500
Web Site: http://www.napw.com
Professional Development Training Services
N.A.I.C.S.: 611430

Noble Voice LLC   (1)
8255 Lemont Rd Ste 200, Darien, IL 60561-1803
Tel.: (630) 541-8917
Web Site: http://www.noblevoice.com
Call Center Services
N.A.I.C.S.: 561422

PROFESSIONAL HOLDING CORP.
396 Alhambra Cir Ste 255, Coral Gables, FL 33134
Tel.: (786) 483-1757   FL
Web Site: http://proholdco.com
PFHD—(NASDAQ)
Rev.: $85,808,000
Assets: $2,664,111,000
Liabilities: $2,432,587,000
Net Worth: $231,524,000
Earnings: $21,364,000
Fiscal Year-end: 12/31/21
Bank Holding Company
N.A.I.C.S.: 551111
Mary Usategui (CFO)
Abel L. Iglesias (Pres & CEO)

Subsidiaries:

Professional Bank   (1)
396 Alhambra Cir Ste 255, Coral Gables, FL 33134
Tel.: (786) 483-1757
Web Site: http://www.professionalbankfl.com
Banking Services
N.A.I.C.S.: 522110
Mary Usategui (CFO & Exec VP)
Abel L. Iglesias (Pres & CEO)

PROFICIENT ALPHA ACQUISITION CORP.
40 Wall St 29th Fl, New York, NY 10005
Tel.: (917) 289-0932   NV
Web Site: http://www.paac-us.com
Year Founded: 2018
PAAC—(NASDAQ)
Rev.: $925,742
Assets: $117,909,571
Liabilities: $97,378,432
Net Worth: $20,531,139
Earnings: $190,391
Emp.: 2
Fiscal Year-end: 09/30/19
Investment Services

N.A.I.C.S.: 523999
Kin Sze (Pres, CEO & Sec)
Weixuan Luo (CFO)

PROFICIENT AUTO LOGISTICS, INC.
12276 San Jose Blvd Ste 426, Jacksonville, FL 32223
Tel.: (904) 506-7918   DE
Web Site:
    https://proficientautologistics.com
Year Founded: 2023
PAL—(NASDAQ)
Emp.: 680
Transportation Services
N.A.I.C.S.: 484230

PROFIRE ENERGY, INC.
321 S 1250 W Ste 1, Lindon, UT 84042
Tel.: (801) 796-5127   NV
Web Site:
    https://www.profireenergy.com
Year Founded: 2003
PFIE—(NASDAQ)
Rev.: $58,208,060
Assets: $66,293,845
Liabilities: $9,455,619
Net Worth: $56,838,226
Earnings: $10,776,714
Emp.: 118
Fiscal Year-end: 12/31/23
Oil & Gas Industry Burner Management Products Developer
N.A.I.C.S.: 333132
Cameron Tidball (Co-Pres & Co-CEO)
Patrick Fisher (VP-Product Dev)
Ryan Northcott (Dir)
Daren Haws (Dir)
Ryan W. Oviatt (Co-Pres, Co-CEO, CFO & Treas)

Subsidiaries:

Midflow Services, LLC   (1)
812 S Washington St, Millersburg, OH 44654
Tel.: (330) 674-2399
Web Site: http://www.midflow.net
Oil & Natural Gas Services
N.A.I.C.S.: 213112

Profire Combustion, Inc.   (1)
55 Alberta Ave, Bay 12 55 Alberta Ave, Spruce Grove, T7X 3A6, AB, Canada
Tel.: (780) 960-5278
Emp.: 30
Oil & Gas Industry Burner Management Systems Marketing
N.A.I.C.S.: 333132
Cameron Tidball (VP-Sls & Mktg)

PROFIT PLANNERS MANAGEMENT, INC.
104 W 40th St 5th Fl, New York, NY 10701
Tel.: (646) 289-5358   NV
Web Site:
    http://www.profitplannersmgt.com
Year Founded: 2009
PPMT—(OTCIQ)
Sales Range: $1-9.9 Million
Emp.: 5
Business & Financial Services
N.A.I.C.S.: 523999
Wesley Ramjeet (CEO)
Jyoti Hardat (VP)
Bradley L. Steere II (Sec)

PROFRAC HOLDING CORP.
333 Shops Blvd Ste 301, Willow City, TX 76087
Tel.: (254) 776-3722   DE
Web Site:
    https://www.pfholdingscorp.com
Year Founded: 2021
ACDC—(NASDAQ)
Rev.: $2,425,600,000

Assets: $2,933,600,000
Liabilities: $4,045,800,000
Net Worth: ($1,112,200,000)
Earnings: $91,500,000
Emp.: 3,664
Fiscal Year-end: 12/31/22
Offices of Other Holding Companies
N.A.I.C.S.: 551112
Ladd Wilks (CEO)
Coy Randle (COO)
Matthew D. Wilks (Chm)

Subsidiaries:

U.S. Well Services, Inc.   (1)
1360 Post Oak Blvd Ste 1800, Houston, TX 77056
Tel.: (832) 562-3730
Web Site: http://www.uswellservices.com
Rev.: $250,463,000
Assets: $243,557,000
Liabilities: $372,660,000
Net Worth: ($129,103,000)
Earnings: ($80,045,000)
Emp.: 414
Fiscal Year-end: 12/31/2021
Investment Services
N.A.I.C.S.: 523999
Kyle O'Neill (Pres & CEO)
Jasper Antolin (Principal Acctg Officer & Controller)
Josh Shapiro (CFO & Sr VP)

PROG HOLDINGS, INC.
256 W Data Dr, Draper, UT 84020-2315
Tel.: (385) 351-1369   GA
Web Site:
    https://www.progholdings.com
PRG—(NYSE)
Rev.: $2,408,264,000
Assets: $1,491,255,000
Liabilities: $899,924,000
Net Worth: $591,331,000
Earnings: $138,838,000
Emp.: 1,606
Fiscal Year-end: 12/31/23
Holding Company
N.A.I.C.S.: 551112
Steven A. Michaels (Pres & CEO)
Sridhar Nallani (CTO)
John A. Baugh (VP-IR)
Todd King (Chief Legal Officer & Chief Compliance Officer)
Debra Fiori (Chief People Officer)
Brian Garner (CFO)
Nate Roe (Chief Comml Officer)

PROGRESS ACQUISITION CORP.
50 Milk St 16th Fl, Boston, MA 02109
Tel.: (617) 401-2700   DE
Year Founded: 2020
PGRW—(NASDAQ)
Rev.: $2,033,373
Assets: $172,900,991
Liabilities: $175,457,050
Net Worth: ($2,556,059)
Earnings: $1,041,478
Emp.: 2
Fiscal Year-end: 12/31/21
Investment Services
N.A.I.C.S.: 523999
David Arslanian (Pres & CEO)

PROGRESS SOFTWARE CORPORATION
15 Wayside Rd Ste 400, Burlington, MA 01803
Tel.: (781) 280-4000   MA
Web Site: https://www.progress.com
Year Founded: 1981
PRGS—(NASDAQ)
Rev.: $602,013,000
Assets: $1,411,479,000
Liabilities: $1,012,975,000
Net Worth: $398,504,000

Earnings: $95,069,000
Emp.: 2,071
Fiscal Year-end: 11/30/22
Business Application Infrastructure
Software Developer, Marketer & Distr
N.A.I.C.S.: 513210
Yogesh K. Gupta *(Pres & CEO)*
Katie Kulikoski *(Chief HR Officer & Exec VP)*
Jennifer Ortiz *(Exec VP-Corporate Marketing)*
Sundar Subramanian *(Exec VP & Gen Mgr)*
Anthony Folger *(CFO & Exec VP)*
Jeremy Segal *(Sr VP-Corp Dev)*
Domenic LoCoco *(Chief Acctg Officer)*
Shirley Knowles *(Chief Diversity Officer & Chief Inclusion Officer)*
Ian Pitt *(Co-CIO)*
Richard Barretto *(Co-CIO, Chief Information Security Officer, Sr VP & VP)*
Stephanie YuFan Wang *(Chief Legal Officer, Sec & Exec VP)*
Loren Jarrett *(Exec VP & Gen Mgr-Digital Experience)*
Dinara Doyle *(VP)*

Subsidiaries:

Corticon Technologies, Inc.   **(1)**
400 S El Camino Real, San Mateo, CA 94402
Tel.: (650) 212-2424
Web Site: http://www.corticon.com
Emp.: 323
Business Rules Management Systems Software Developer
N.A.I.C.S.: 513210

DataDirect Technologies Corp.   **(1)**
3005 Carrington Mill Blvd Ste 400, Morrisville, NC 27560
Tel.: (919) 461-4200
Web Site: http://www.datadirect.com
Sales Range: $75-99.9 Million
Emp.: 200
Computer Peripheral Equipment
N.A.I.C.S.: 334118

Subsidiary (Non-US):

DataDirect Technologies Ltd.   **(2)**
3rd Floor 3 Arlington Square Downshire Way, Bracknell, RG12 1WA, Berkshire, United Kingdom
Tel.: (44) 1344360444
Web Site: http://www.datadirect-tech.co.uk
Sales Range: $10-24.9 Million
Emp.: 15
Computer Software
N.A.I.C.S.: 334610

DataDirect Technologies NV   **(2)**
A Stocletlaan 202 B, 2570, Duffel, Belgium
Tel.: (32) 15307700
Web Site: http://www.datadirect.com
Sales Range: $10-24.9 Million
Emp.: 28
Computer Software
N.A.I.C.S.: 334610

DataRPM LLC   **(1)**
201 Redwood Shores Pkwy Ste 125, Redwood City, CA 94065
Tel.: (650) 227-1957
Web Site: http://www.datarpm.com
Software Development & Deployment Services
N.A.I.C.S.: 513210

Ipswitch, Inc.   **(1)**
15 Wayside Rd 4th Fl, Burlington, MA 01803
Tel.: (781) 676-5700
Web Site: http://www.ipswitch.com
Internet Productivity Software Developer & Retailer
N.A.I.C.S.: 513210
Roger Greene *(Founder & Chm)*

KEMP Technologies Inc.   **(1)**
3 Huntington Quadrangle, Melville, NY 11747
Tel.: (631) 345-5292
Web Site: https://kemptechnologies.com

Sales Range: $25-49.9 Million
Emp.: 200
Other Management Consulting Services
N.A.I.C.S.: 541618
Ray Downes *(CEO)*
Simon Roach *(CTO)*
Peter Melerud *(Founder & Chief Strategy Officer)*
George Lo *(CFO)*
Tony Thompson *(Chief Mktg Officer)*
Marguerite Leen *(Mng Dir)*
Tony Sandberg *(Dir-Asia Pacific)*

Kemp Technologies India Private Limited   **(1)**
516-520 5th Floor International Trade Tower Nehru Place, New Delhi, 110019, India
Tel.: (91) 9818147766
Information Technology Services
N.A.I.C.S.: 541511

Kemp Technologies Limited   **(1)**
Mary Rosse Centre Holland Road National Technology Park, Limerick, Ireland
Tel.: (353) 6 126 0101
Information Technology Services
N.A.I.C.S.: 541511

Kemp Technologies Pte. Ltd.   **(1)**
3 Church Street 12-01 Samsung Hub, Singapore, 049483, Singapore
Tel.: (65) 6 580 2188
Information Technology Services
N.A.I.C.S.: 541511

Kinvey LLC   **(1)**
1 Beacon St 15th Fl, Boston, MA 02108
Tel.: (617) 505-4096
Web Site: http://www.kinvey.com
Mobile Application Development Services
N.A.I.C.S.: 541511
Sravish Sridhar *(Founder)*

NuSphere Corporation   **(1)**
59 Damonte Ranch Pkwy Ste B 412, Reno, NV 89521
Tel.: (408) 416-5353
Web Site: http://shop.nusphere.com
Sales Range: $75-99.9 Million
Open Source Software & Services
N.A.I.C.S.: 513210

Pantero Corporation   **(1)**
300 5th Ave Ste 630, Waltham, MA 02451
Tel.: (781) 890-2890
Application Software Development Services
N.A.I.C.S.: 513210

Progress OpenEdge   **(1)**
14 Oak Park Dr, Bedford, MA 01730
Tel.: (781) 280-4000
Web Site: http://www.progress.com
Sales Range: $75-99.9 Million
Data Management Platform which Simplifies the Development, Deployment, Integration & Management of Business Applications
N.A.I.C.S.: 541511

Progress Security Corporation   **(1)**
14 Oak Park, Bedford, MA 01730-1414
Tel.: (781) 280-4000
Business Application Software Development Services
N.A.I.C.S.: 513210

Progress Software Corporation of Canada Ltd.   **(1)**
5001 Yonge St, North York, M2N 6P6, ON, Canada
Tel.: (416) 250-0823
Emp.: 10
Application Software Development Services
N.A.I.C.S.: 513210

Progress Software Europe B.V.   **(1)**
Prins Alexanderplein 12, 3067 GC, Rotterdam, Netherlands
Tel.: (31) 102865700
Web Site: http://www.progress.com
Holding Company; Business Application Infrastructure Software Marketer, Distr & Support Services
N.A.I.C.S.: 551112
Mark Armstrong *(Mng Dir & VP-EMEA)*

Subsidiary (Non-US):

Progress Software   **(2)**
Alexandra House the Sweepstakes, Ballsbridge, Dublin, Ireland
Tel.: (353) 866008154

Web Site: http://www.progress.com
Sales Range: $75-99.9 Million
Emp.: 20
Software Publisher
N.A.I.C.S.: 513210

Progress Software A/S   **(2)**
Lautruphoej 1-3, 2750, Ballerup, Denmark
Tel.: (45) 44830300
Business Application Software Distr
N.A.I.C.S.: 423430

Progress Software AG   **(2)**
Chateau de Vaumarcus SA, Le Chateau Vaumarcus, Boudry, CH-2028, Switzerland
Tel.: (41) 447443944
Web Site: http://www.progress.com
Business Application Software Distr
N.A.I.C.S.: 423430

Progress Software AS   **(2)**
CJ Hambros Plass 2C, Oslo, 0164, Norway
Tel.: (47) 22996280
Web Site: http://www.progress.no
Business Application Software Distr
N.A.I.C.S.: 423430

Subsidiary (Domestic):

Progress Software B.V.   **(2)**
Prins Alexanderplein 11, 3067 GC, Rotterdam, Netherlands   **(100%)**
Tel.: (31) 102351111
Web Site: http://www.progress.com
Sales Range: $25-49.9 Million
Emp.: 60
Business Application Software Distr
N.A.I.C.S.: 423430

Subsidiary (Non-US):

Progress Software EAD   **(2)**
54B Tsarigradsko Shose Blvd, Sofia, 1784, Bulgaria
Tel.: (359) 28099850
Web Site: http://www.telerik.com
Software Developer
N.A.I.C.S.: 513210

Progress Software GesmbH   **(2)**
Campus 21 Businesspark Wien Sud, Liebermannstrasse F05 3 02, Brunn am Gebirge, 2345, Austria
Tel.: (43) 2236379837
Software Development Services
N.A.I.C.S.: 541511

Progress Software GmbH   **(2)**
Christophstr 15-17, 50670, Cologne, Germany
Tel.: (49) 2219357900
Web Site: http://www.progress.com
Sales Range: $25-49.9 Million
Emp.: 50
Business Application Software Distr
N.A.I.C.S.: 423430
Olf Jannsch *(Mng Dir)*

Branch (Domestic):

Progress Software GmbH   **(3)**
Christophstr 15-17, 50670, Cologne, Germany
Tel.: (49) 2219357900
Web Site: http://www.progress.de
Business Application Software Distr
N.A.I.C.S.: 513210

Subsidiary (Non-US):

Progress Software Italy S.r.l.   **(2)**
Piazzale Biancamano 8, 20121, Milan, Italy
Tel.: (39) 0262033036
Web Site: http://www.progress.com
Sales Range: $10-24.9 Million
Business Application Software Distr
N.A.I.C.S.: 423430

Progress Software Limited   **(2)**
Venture House 2 Arlington Square, Bracknell, RG12 1WA, Berkshire, United Kingdom
Tel.: (44) 1344360444
Web Site: http://www.progress.com
Business Application Software Distr
N.A.I.C.S.: 423430

Subsidiary (Domestic):

Apama (UK) Limited   **(3)**
200 Rustat House Clifton Road, Cambridge, CB1 7EG, United Kingdom

Tel.: (44) 8703517212
Web Site: http://www.progress.com
Business Application Software Development Services
N.A.I.C.S.: 513210

Telerik UK Ltd.   **(3)**
Highland Court Tollgate Chandlers Ford, Eastleigh, SO53 3TY, Hants, United Kingdom
Tel.: (44) 1344360444
Web Site: http://www.telerik.com
Software Developer
N.A.I.C.S.: 513210

Subsidiary (Non-US):

Progress Software NV   **(2)**
Avenue Marnix 23 5th Floor, PO Box 59, 1000, Brussels, Belgium
Tel.: (32) 15307700
Web Site: http://www.progress.com
Business Application Software Distr
N.A.I.C.S.: 423430

Progress Software Oy   **(2)**
Keilaranta 16, 02150, Espoo, Finland
Tel.: (358) 925107310
Web Site: http://www.progress.com
Sales Range: $10-24.9 Million
Business Application Software Distr
N.A.I.C.S.: 423430

Progress Software S.A.S.   **(2)**
5 place de la Pyramide, 92088, Puteaux, France
Tel.: (33) 155681111
Web Site: http://www.progress.com
Sales Range: $25-49.9 Million
Business Application Software Distr
N.A.I.C.S.: 423430

Progress Software S.L.U.   **(2)**
Calle Nanclares de oca 1-B, 28022, Madrid, Spain
Tel.: (34) 917102169
Web Site: http://www.progress.com
Sales Range: $10-24.9 Million
Emp.: 10
Business Application Software Distr
N.A.I.C.S.: 423430

Branch (Domestic):

Progress Software S.L.   **(3)**
Oficina N 111 C/Francisco Silvela 42 1 Planta, 28028, Madrid, Spain
Tel.: (34) 917102169
Web Site: http://www.progress.com
Sales Range: $10-24.9 Million
Business Application Software Distr
N.A.I.C.S.: 423430

Subsidiary (Non-US):

Progress Software Sp. z o.o.   **(2)**
Wierzbowa 9/11, 00-094, Warsaw, Poland
Tel.: (48) 692422771
Web Site: http://www.progress.pl
Sales Range: $10-24.9 Million
Emp.: 4
Business Application Software Distr
N.A.I.C.S.: 423430
Leszesk Lewoc *(CEO)*

Progress Software Svenska AB   **(2)**
Ostermalmstorg 1, 114 42, Stockholm, Sweden
Tel.: (46) 850256606
Web Site: http://www.progress.com
Business Application Software Distr
N.A.I.C.S.: 423430

Progress Software Japan KK   **(1)**
Minami Azabu T F Building 8F 4-11-22, Minami Azabu Mintao-ku, Tokyo, 106-0047, Japan
Tel.: (81) 368265720
Computer Peripheral Equipment Distr
N.A.I.C.S.: 423440

Progress Software Pty. Ltd.   **(1)**
100 Miller st Suite 30 02 North, Sydney, 2060, NSW, Australia
Tel.: (61) 398058600
Business Application Infrastructure Software Marketer & Distr
N.A.I.C.S.: 423430

Subsidiary (Non-US):

Progress Japan KK   **(2)**

Progress Software Corporation—(Continued)

Kawakita Memorial Building 18 Ichiban-cho, Chiyoda-Ku, Tokyo, 102-0082, Japan
Tel.: (81) 335567610
Web Site: http://www.progress-japan.co.jp
Business Application Software Development Services
N.A.I.C.S.: 513210

Progress Software Corporation (S) Pte. Ltd. **(2)**
Spaces Clarke Quay 4th Floor 21 Merchant Road, Gateway West, Singapore, 058267, Singapore
Tel.: (65) 68281400
Web Site: http://www.progress.com
Business Application Infrastructure Software Marketer & Distr
N.A.I.C.S.: 423430

Progress Software Corporation Limited **(2)**
33 Hysan Ave 45/F the Lee Gardens, 255-257 Gloucester Rd, Causeway Bay, China (Hong Kong)
Tel.: (852) 28248712
Web Site: http://www.progress.com
Sales Range: $10-24.9 Million
Emp.: 10
Business Application Software Distr
N.A.I.C.S.: 423430

Progress Solutions India Private Limited **(2)**
8th Floor R-Tech Park Goregaon East, Nir-Ion Complex Opposite Western Express Highway, Mumbai, 400 063, India
Tel.: (91) 2240837000
Business Application Software Development Services
N.A.I.C.S.: 513210

Subsidiary (Domestic):

Progress Software Development Private Limited **(3)**
Plot No 1 No 83 1, Raidurg Panmaktha, Hyderabad, 500019, India
Tel.: (91) 4045106000
Web Site: http://www.progress.com
Sales Range: $50-74.9 Million
Business Application Software Development Services
N.A.I.C.S.: 513210

Telerik India Private Limited **(3)**
Unit No 505 Tower A Spaze iTech Park Gurgaon Sohna Road Sector 49, Gurgaon, 122002, Haryana, India
Tel.: (91) 9899115375
Web Site: http://www.telerik.com
Software Developer
N.A.I.C.S.: 513210

Progress Software do Brasil Ltda. **(1)**
Rua Irma Gabriela n 51 4th floor - room 416 - Spaces Berrini, Sao Paulo, 04171-130, Brazil
Tel.: (55) 1137976220
Web Site: http://www.progress.com
Sales Range: $25-49.9 Million
Business Application Software Distr
N.A.I.C.S.: 423430

Savvion, Inc. **(1)**
5104 Old Ironsides Dr Ste 205, Santa Clara, CA 95054
Tel.: (408) 330-3400
Application Software Development Services
N.A.I.C.S.: 513210

PROGRESSIVE GREEN SOLUTIONS, INC.
445 County Rd 101 Ste E, Yaphank, NY 11980
Tel.: (631) 775-8920   **NV**
Year Founded: 2011
PGSC—(OTCIQ)
Investment Services
N.A.I.C.S.: 523999
Eugene Fernandez (Pres, Interim CFO & VP-Bus Dev)
Michael Cox (COO & VP-Ops)

Subsidiaries:

Green Remanufacturing LLC   **(1)**

---

445 County Rd 101 Ste E, Yaphank, NY 11980
Tel.: (631) 775-8920
Web Site: http://www.greenrsus.com
Consumer Electronic Equipment Repair & Maintenance Services
N.A.I.C.S.: 811210
Robert Madden (Exec VP-Bus Dev)

PROGYNY, INC.
1359 Broadway, New York, NY 10018
Tel.: (212) 888-3124   **DE**
Web Site: https://www.progyny.com
Year Founded: 2008
PGNY—(NASDAQ)
Rev.: $786,913,000
Assets: $542,986,000
Liabilities: $166,018,000
Net Worth: $376,968,000
Earnings: $30,358,000
Emp.: 393
Fiscal Year-end: 12/31/22
Health Care Srvices
N.A.I.C.S.: 621610
Peter Anevski (CEO)
David Schlanger (Chm)
Peter Anevski (Pres & COO)
Mark Livingston (CFO)
Michael Sturmer (Chief Growth & Strategy Officer & Exec VP)
Janet Choi (Chief Medical Officer)
Arielle Bogorad (Sr VP-Employer Market Strategy)
Allison Swartz (Gen Counsel)
Julie Stadlbauer (Chief Bus Dev Officer & Exec VP)
Cassandra Pratt (Chief HR Officer & Sr VP-People)
Katie Higgins (Chief Comml Officer)
Steven Leist (CTO)

PROJECT ENERGY REIMAGINED ACQUISITION CORP.
1280 El Camino Real Ste 200, Menlo Park, CA 94025
Tel.: (415) 205-7937   **Ky**
Web Site: https://www.pegyr.com
Year Founded: 2021
PEGR—(NASDAQ)
Rev.: $3,699,187
Assets: $268,217,415
Liabilities: $278,391,603
Net Worth: ($10,174,188)
Earnings: $13,274,685
Emp.: 6
Fiscal Year-end: 12/31/22
Miscellaneous Financial Investment Activities
N.A.I.C.S.: 523999
Srinath Narayanan (Pres & CEO)
Michael Browning (Chm)
David Roberts (COO)
Prakash Ramachandran (CFO)
Tim Dummer (Head-Bus Strategy)
Kathy Liu (Head-Tech Strategy)
David Michail (Corp Counsel)

PROKIDNEY CORP.
2000 Frontis Plz Blvd, Winston Salem, NC 27103
Tel.: (336) 999-7028   **Ky**
Web Site: https://www.prokidney.com
Year Founded: 2015
PROK—(NASDAQ)
Rev.: $5,983,000
Assets: $517,996,000
Liabilities: $1,614,612,000
Net Worth: ($1,096,616,000)
Earnings: ($40,103,000)
Emp.: 87
Fiscal Year-end: 12/31/22
Biotechnology Research & Development Services
N.A.I.C.S.: 541714
Lucio Tozzi (Sr VP-Global Clinical Ops)
Timothy Bertram (CEO)

Nikhil Pereira-Kamath (Chief Bus Officer)
Bruce Culleton (CEO)
James Coulston (CFO)
Pablo Legorreta (Chm)
Tim Bertram (CEO)
Todd C. Girolamo (Sec)
Pablo Legorreta (Co-Founder & Chm)

PROLIANCE INTERNATIONAL, INC.
100 Gando Dr, New Haven, CT 06513
Tel.: (203) 401-6450   **DE**
PLNTQ—(OTCIQ)
Automobile Part Mfr & Distr
N.A.I.C.S.: 336390
Charles E. Johnson (Pres & CEO)
Arlen F. Henock (CFO & Exec VP)

PROLOGIS, INC.
Pier 1 Bay 1, San Francisco, CA 94111
Tel.: (415) 394-9000   **MD**
Web Site: https://www.prologis.com
Year Founded: 1991
PLD—(NYSE)
Rev.: $8,023,469,000
Assets: $93,020,840,000
Liabilities: $35,197,120,000
Net Worth: $57,823,720,000
Earnings: $3,053,373,000
Emp.: 2,574
Fiscal Year-end: 12/31/23
Industrial Real Estate Investment Trust
N.A.I.C.S.: 525990
Hamid R. Moghadam (Co-Founder, Chm & CEO)
Eugene F. Reilly (Vice Chm)
Tracy Ward (Sr VP-IR)
Martina Malone (Mng Dir & Head-Capital Raising-Global)
Edward S. Nekritz (Chief Legal Officer & Gen Counsel)
Michael S. Curless (Chief Customer Officer)
Colleen McKeown (Chief HR Officer)
Angeli Stirbei (VP-Strategic Capital Bus)
Susan Uthayakumar (Chief Energy & Sustainability Officer)
Mahvash Yazdi (Chm-Energy Advisory Bd)
Uzo Akotaobi (VP-Human Resources)
Timothy D. Arndt (CFO)
Jason Bennett (Mng Dir)
Eric Brown (Mng Dir-Ops-Global)
Chris Caton (Mng Dir-Strategy & Analytics-Global)
Liz Dunn (Sr VP-Customer Led Innovation)
Sineesh Keshav (CTO)
Daniel Letter (Pres)
Rafat Shehadeh (Head-Construction, Procurement & Essentials-Global)
Aki Tanizumi (Mng Dir & Head-Investor & PR, HR, Administration & IT)
Lisa Vincent (Sr VP-Operational Excellence)
Patrick Gemma (Head-West Reg)
Alison M. Hill (Mng Dir-Strategic Capital)

Subsidiaries:

DCT Industrial Trust Inc.   **(1)**
555 17th St Ste 3700, Denver, CO 80202
Tel.: (303) 597-2400
Web Site: http://www.dctindustrial.com
Rev.: $424,468,000
Assets: $4,010,672,000
Liabilities: $1,961,209,000
Net Worth: $2,049,463,000
Earnings: $103,494,000
Emp.: 145
Fiscal Year-end: 12/31/2017

Real Estate Investment Services
N.A.I.C.S.: 525990

Subsidiary (Domestic):

DCT MEXICO REIT LLC   **(2)**
518 17th St Ste 800, Denver, CO 80202
Tel.: (303) 597-2400
Real Estate Services
N.A.I.C.S.: 525990
Alex Mergl (Mgr)

DCT PAN AMERICAN LLC   **(2)**
518 17th St, Denver, CO 80202
Tel.: (303) 597-2400
Real Estate Investment Services
N.A.I.C.S.: 531210

DIVIDEND CAPITAL ADVISORS LLC   **(2)**
518 17th St Ste 1200, Denver, CO 80202-4108
Tel.: (303) 228-2200
Web Site: http://www.dividendcapital.com
Real Estate Services
N.A.I.C.S.: 525990
Dawn Rogers (Mgr)

STIRLING CAPITAL PROPERTIES, LLC   **(2)**
18499 Phantom St 8, Victorville, CA 92394
Tel.: (760) 246-2954
Real Estate Asset Management Services
N.A.I.C.S.: 531390

Duke Realty Corporation   **(1)**
8711 River Xing Blvd, Indianapolis, IN 46240
Tel.: (317) 808-6000
Web Site: http://www.dukerealty.com
Rev.: $1,105,923,000
Assets: $10,445,655,000
Liabilities: $4,306,694,000
Net Worth: $6,138,961,000
Earnings: $852,895,000
Emp.: 340
Fiscal Year-end: 12/31/2021
Commercial Real Estate Services
N.A.I.C.S.: 522292
Mark Milnamow (Chief Acctg Officer & Sr VP)
Samuel O'Briant (Exec VP-East Reg)
Steven W. Schnur (COO & Exec VP)
Mark A. Denien (CFO & Exec VP)
Nick Anthony (Chief Investment Officer & Exec VP)
Chris Burns (Exec VP-West & Central Reg)
Pete Harrington (Exec VP-Construction)
Jenny Bean (Chief HR Officer)

Subsidiary (Domestic):

AD West End, LLC   **(2)**
1621 W End Blvd, Saint Louis Park, MN 55416
Tel.: (763) 450-0554
Web Site: http://www.theshopsatwestend.com
Emp.: 50
Real Estate Development Services
N.A.I.C.S.: 531210

BremnerDuke McKinney Development I, LLC   **(2)**
600 E 96th St Ste 100, Indianapolis, IN 46240
Tel.: (317) 808-6000
Web Site: http://www.dukerealty.com
Real Estate Development Services
N.A.I.C.S.: 531210

Duke Realty Limited Partnership   **(2)**
8711 River Crossing Blvd, Indianapolis, IN 46240
Tel.: (317) 808-6000
Rev.: $1,105,922,999
Assets: $10,445,654,999
Liabilities: $4,306,694,000
Net Worth: $6,138,960,999
Earnings: $861,617,999
Emp.: 339
Fiscal Year-end: 12/31/2021
Real Estate Asset Management Services
N.A.I.C.S.: 531390
James B. Connor (Chm & CEO)

Duke Realty Ohio   **(2)**
4555 Lk Forest Dr Ste 400, Blue Ash, OH 45242-3785
Tel.: (513) 956-4400

Real Estate Agents & Brokerage Services
N.A.I.C.S.: 531210
Dennis D. Oklak (Chm & CEO)

Duke/Hulfish, LLC (2)
47 Hulfish St Ste 210, Princeton, NJ 08542
Tel.: (609) 683-4900
Real Estate Development Services
N.A.I.C.S.: 531210

Lafayette Real Estate LLC (2)
853 Broadway 5th Fl, New York, NY 10003
Tel.: (212) 677-7356
Web Site: http://www.lafayette-re.com
Real Estate Development Services
N.A.I.C.S.: 531210
Thibault Adrien (CEO & Founder)
Heidi Coppola (Sr VP-Operations)
Maylis de Lacoste (Dir-Marketing-Investor Relations)
Isabelle Levilain (Dir-Human Resources)
Andy Mieles (Controller-Property)
Jesus Nunez-Unda (Partner)
Melissa Fort (Office Mgr)
Christopher Mataja (COO)
Josh Nathan (Principal)
Dennis Cisterna (Chief Investment Officer-for,rent)
Liya Mo (VP)
Cristina Rudiez (VP-Business Development)
Michael Bergh (Sr Mgr)
Jackie Lee (CEO)
Neven Simikic (Mgr)

Industrial Property Trust Inc. (1)
518 17th St 17th Fl, Denver, CO 80202
Tel.: (303) 228-2200
Web Site:
   http://www.industrialpropertytrust.com
Rev.: $241,299,000
Assets: $2,831,624,000
Liabilities: $1,651,266,000
Net Worth: $1,180,358,000
Earnings: ($6,837,000)
Fiscal Year-end: 12/31/2018
Real Estate Investment Trust
N.A.I.C.S.: 525990
Evan H. Zucker (Chm)
Dwight L. Merriman III (CEO & Mng Dir)

Liberty Property Trust (1)
650 E Swedesford Rd Ste 400, Wayne, PA 19087
Tel.: (610) 648-1700
Web Site: http://www.libertyproperty.com
Real Estate Investment Trust
N.A.I.C.S.: 531390

Subsidiary (Non-US):

Blythe Valley Innovation Centre Ltd. (2)
Central Boulevard, Blythe Valley Park, Solihull, B90 8AJ, United Kingdom
Tel.: (44) 1215069000
Web Site: http://www.bvic.co.uk
Emp.: 4
Real Estate Brokerage Services
N.A.I.C.S.: 531210

Kings Hill Estate Management Company Limited (2)
The Conrtol Tower 29 liberty Sq, West Malling, ME19 4RL, Kent, United Kingdom
Tel.: (44) 1732870375
Web Site: http://www.kings-hill.com
Sales Range: $25-49.9 Million
Emp.: 25
Real Estate Brokerage Services
N.A.I.C.S.: 531210
Andrew Blavins (Pres)
Caroline Binns (Assoc Dir-Mktg & Leasing)
James Leech (Sr Mgr-Property)

Subsidiary (Domestic):

Liberty AIPO Limited Partnership (2)
255 S Orange Ave Ste 1500, Orlando, FL 32801
Tel.: (407) 649-1200
Web Site: http://www.prologis.com
Real Estate Brokerage Services
N.A.I.C.S.: 531210

Liberty Durham, LLC (2)
500 Chesterfield Pkwy, Malvern, PA 19355-8707
Tel.: (610) 648-1736
Web Site: http://www.libertyproperty.com
Emp.: 10

Real Estate Brokerage Services
N.A.I.C.S.: 531210

Subsidiary (Non-US):

Liberty Property Trust UK Limited (2)
11 Tower View, Kings Hill, West Malling, ME19 4RL, Kent, United Kingdom
Tel.: (44) 1732870375
Web Site: http://www.kings-hill.com
Sales Range: $1-9.9 Million
Emp.: 30
Real Estate Services
N.A.I.C.S.: 531390
Andrew Belvins (Mng Dir)
Caroline Binns (Assoc Dir)

Subsidiary (Domestic):

Kings Hill Property Management Limited (3)
The Control Tower 29 Liberty Square, West Malling, ME19 4RG, Kent, United Kingdom
Tel.: (44) 1732870375
Web Site: http://www.kings-hill.com
Sales Range: $1-9.9 Million
Emp.: 30
Real Estate Services
N.A.I.C.S.: 531390
Elizabeth Roche (Dir-Fin)

Kings Hill Residential Estate Management Company Limited (3)
The Control Tower 29 Liberty Square Kings Hill, West Malling, ME19 4RG, Kent, United Kingdom
Tel.: (44) 1732870375
Web Site: http://www.kings-hills.com
Sales Range: $1-9.9 Million
Emp.: 25
Real Estate Services
N.A.I.C.S.: 531390
Elizabeth Roche (Dir-Fin)

Rouse Kent (Central) Limited (3)
29 Tower View, Kings Hill, West Malling, ME19 4RL, Kent, United Kingdom
Tel.: (44) 1732870375
Web Site: http://www.kings-hill.com
Emp.: 25
Real Estate & Property Development Services
N.A.I.C.S.: 531210

Rouse Kent (Residential) Limited (3)
29 Liberty Square Kings Hill, West Malling, ME19 4RG, Kent, United Kingdom
Tel.: (44) 1732223400
Web Site: http://www.king-hill.com
Emp.: 20
Real Estate Services
N.A.I.C.S.: 531390
Andrew Blevins (Mng Dir)

Prologis, L.P. (1)
Pier 1 Bay 1, San Francisco, CA 94111
Tel.: (415) 394-9000
Web Site: https://www.prologis.com
Rev.: $8,023,468,999
Assets: $93,020,839,999
Liabilities: $35,197,119,999
Net Worth: $57,823,719,999
Earnings: $3,130,647,000
Emp.: 2,573
Fiscal Year-end: 12/31/2023
Holding Company
N.A.I.C.S.: 551112
Hamid R. Moghadam (Chm & CEO)
Gary E. Anderson (COO)
Tim Arndt (CFO)
Michael S. Curless (Chief Customer Officer)
Dan Letter (Pres)
Colleen McKeown (Chief HR Officer)
Edward S. Nekritz (Chief Legal Officer)
Eugene F. Reilly (Vice Chm)
Lori A. Palazzolo (Mng Dir)

Subsidiary (Domestic):

AMB/AFCO Cargo, LLC (2)
Pier 1 Bay 1, San Francisco, CA 94111
Tel.: (415) 394-9000
Web Site: http://www.prologis.com
Logistics; Air Cargo & Package Express Service
N.A.I.C.S.: 541614

Joint Venture (Domestic):

KTR Capital Partners, LLC (2)

1001 Conshohocken State Rd, West Conshohocken, PA 19428-2908 **(55%)**
Tel.: (484) 530-1280
Web Site: http://www.ktrcapital.com
Emp.: 89
Industrial Real Estate Investment, Development, Property Management & Leasing Services
N.A.I.C.S.: 531390
Jeffrey E. Kelter (Chm)
Tracey Swienton (Mgr)
J. Peter Lloyd (Partner & CFO)
Stephen J. Butte (Partner)
John P. DiCola (Partner)
Francis K. Ryan (Partner)
A. Donald Chase Jr. (Partner)

Subsidiary (Non-US):

Prologis B.V. (2)
Symphony Offices Gustav Mahlerplein 17-21, Schiphol Airport, 1082 MS, Amsterdam, Netherlands
Tel.: (31) 206556666
Web Site: http://www.prologis.com
Sales Range: $50-74.9 Million
Real Estate Management Services
N.A.I.C.S.: 531390

Prologis Canada Incorporated (2)
2810 Matheson Blvd E Suite 200, Mississauga, L4W 4X7, ON, Canada
Tel.: (905) 290-1702
Web Site: http://www.prologis.com
Sales Range: $300-349.9 Million
Emp.: 3
Real Estate Agents & Managers
N.A.I.C.S.: 531210

Prologis Japan Incorporated (2)
Tokyo Building 21st Floor 2-7-3 Marunouchi, Chiyoda-ku, Tokyo, 100-6421, Japan
Tel.: (81) 368609000
Web Site: https://www.prologis.co.jp
Sales Range: $300-349.9 Million
Emp.: 136
Real Estate Development
N.A.I.C.S.: 531210

Prologis Property France S.a.r.l. (2)
3 Avenue Hoche, 75008, Paris, France
Tel.: (33) 1 48145555
Web Site: http://www.prologis.com
Sales Range: $25-49.9 Million
Emp.: 45
Industrial Real Estate Investment Trust
N.A.I.C.S.: 525990
Francois Rispe (Pres)

Prologis UK Holdings S.A. (2)
34-38 Avenue de la Liberte L, 1930, Luxembourg, Luxembourg
Tel.: (352) 26205740
Investment Management Service
N.A.I.C.S.: 523940

Prologis UK Limited (2)
Prologis House Blythe Gate, Blythe Valley Park, Solihull, B90 8AH, West Midlands, United Kingdom
Tel.: (44) 1212248700
Web Site: https://www.prologis.co.uk
Investment Management Service
N.A.I.C.S.: 523940
Robin Woodbridge (Sr VP & Head-Capital Deployment)
Phil Oakley (VP-Customer Led Dev)
Melissa Brand (Dir-Investment Svcs)
Mark Shepherd (VP-Project Mgmt)
David Storer (VP-Project Mgmt)
Jamie West (VP-Project Mgmt)
Martin Cooper (VP-Project Mgmt)
Dave Mellor (Dir-Project Mgmt)
Julie Bunce (Office Mgr)
Charlie Rickard (Partner-Fin Bus)
Ian Romano (VP-Capital Deployment & Leasing)
Sally Duggleby (VP-Capital Deployment & Leasing)
David Ribbands (Dir-Project Mgmt)
Sarah Stanniland (Coord-Real Estate & Customer Experience)
Andrew Blevins (Sr VP)

PROPEL MEDIA, INC.
2010 Main St Ste 900, Irvine, CA 92614
Tel.: (949) 251-0640 **DE**
Year Founded: 2014

PROM—(OTCEM)
Sales Range: $75-99.9 Million
Emp.: 54
Holding Company
N.A.I.C.S.: 551112
Marvin Tseu (CEO)

Subsidiaries:

DeepIntent Technologies, Inc. (1)
1460 Broadway Fl 15, New York, NY 10036-7306
Tel.: (646) 827-9524
Digital Marketing Services
N.A.I.C.S.: 541810
Amit Chaturvedi (COO)
Chris Paquette (Founder & CEO)

PROPETRO HOLDING CORP.
303 W Wall St Ste 102, Midland, TX 79701
Tel.: (432) 688-0012 **TX**
Web Site:
   https://www.propetroservices.com
Year Founded: 2007
PUMP—(NYSE)
Rev.: $1,279,701,000
Assets: $1,335,786,000
Liabilities: $381,753,000
Net Worth: $954,033,000
Earnings: $203,000,000
Emp.: 2,000
Fiscal Year-end: 12/31/22
Oil Field Services
N.A.I.C.S.: 213112
Celina A. Davila (Chief Acctg Officer)
Samuel D. Sledge (CEO)
Adam Munoz (Pres & COO)
David S. Schorlemer (CFO & Principal Acctg Officer)
Shelby Fietz (Chief Comml Officer)
Matt Augustine (Dir-Corp Dev & IR)

PROPHASE LABS, INC.
711 Stewart Ave Ste 200, Garden City, NY 11530
Tel.: (516) 464-6121 **NV**
Web Site:
   https://www.prophaselabs.com
Year Founded: 1989
PRPH—(NASDAQ)
Rev.: $122,647,000
Assets: $87,648,000
Liabilities: $24,017,000
Net Worth: $63,631,000
Earnings: $18,463,000
Emp.: 129
Fiscal Year-end: 12/31/22
Cold-Remedy, Nutrition & Weight Management Products Mfr, Marketer & Developer
N.A.I.C.S.: 325412
Ted William Karkus (Chm & CEO)
Robert A. Morse (Principal Acctg Officer & Controller)

Subsidiaries:

Pharmaloz Manufacturing Inc. (1)
500 N 15th Ave, Lebanon, PA 17046
Tel.: (717) 274-9800
Web Site: https://www.pharmaloz.com
Pharmaceuticals Product Mfr
N.A.I.C.S.: 325412
Tom Kaufman (Mgr)

ProPhase Diagnostics, Inc. (1)
42 Throckmorton Ln, Old Bridge, NJ 08857
Tel.: (732) 705-6400
Laboratory Testing Services
N.A.I.C.S.: 541380

ProPhase Digital Media, Inc. (1)
621 N Shady Retreat Rd, Doylestown, PA 18901
Tel.: (215) 345-4005
Web Site: http://prophasedigitalmedia.com
Marketing & Advertising Services
N.A.I.C.S.: 541613

PROS HOLDINGS, INC.

PROS Holdings, Inc.—(Continued)

3200 Kirby Dr Ste 600, Houston, TX
77098
Tel.: (713) 335-5105   DE
Web Site: https://www.pros.com
Year Founded: 1985
PRO—(NYSE)
Rev.: $303,708,000
Assets: $421,833,000
Liabilities: $499,706,000
Net Worth: ($77,873,000)
Earnings: ($56,354,000)
Emp.: 1,486
Fiscal Year-end: 12/31/23
Pricing & Revenue Optimization Soft-
ware
N.A.I.C.S.: 513210
Andres D. Reiner *(Pres & CEO)*
Craig C. Zawada *(Chief Visionary
Officer)*
Stefan B. Schulz *(CFO & Exec VP)*
Scott Cook *(Chief Acctg Officer & Sr
VP)*
Todd McNabb *(Chief Revenue Offi-
cer)*
Grad Conn *(CMO)*
Sunil John *(Chief Product Officer)*

Subsidiaries:

Cameleon Software SA   (1)
Le Galilee 185 Rue Galilee, PO Box 87270,
Labege, 31672, France   **(83.4%)**
Tel.: (33) 811707878
Sales Range: $10-24.9 Million
Emp.: 86
Computer Software Developer
N.A.I.C.S.: 513210
Jacques Soumeillan *(Pres & CEO)*
Thibault de Bouville *(CFO)*
Sylvie Rouge *(Sr VP-Product Mktg)*
Francoise Asparre *(Deputy CEO & Sr VP-
Pro Svc)*
Jerome Amilhastre *(Head-R&D)*
Lionel Chapurlat *(VP-Alliances & Bus Dev)*

Cameleon Software USA, Inc.   (1)
5215 Old Orchard Rd Ste 505, Skokie, IL
60077
Tel.: (847) 583-8450
Software Development Services
N.A.I.C.S.: 541511

EveryMundo LLC   (1)
25 SE 2nd Ave 9th Fl, Miami, FL 33131
Tel.: (305) 375-0045
Web Site: https://www.everymundo.com
Sales Range: $25-49.9 Million
Emp.: 24
Marketing Consulting Services
N.A.I.C.S.: 541613
Anton Diego *(CEO & Founder)*

PROS Bulgaria EOOD   (1)
1 Alabin Str Telus Tower 16th Floor Mace-
donia Square, Sofia, 1000, Bulgaria
Tel.: (359) 29580595
Web Site: https://pros.com
Software Development Services
N.A.I.C.S.: 541511

PROS France SAS   (1)
6 rue Louis Pasteur, Boulogne-Billancourt,
92100, Paris, France
Tel.: (33) 811707878
Software Development Services
N.A.I.C.S.: 541512

PROS Revenue Management,
L.P.   (1)
3100 Main St Ste 900, Houston, TX 77002-
9320
Tel.: (713) 335-5151
Web Site: http://www.pros.com
Emp.: 300
Custom Computer Software Programming
Services
N.A.I.C.S.: 541511

SignalDemand, Inc.   (1)
101 Montgomery Stt Ste 400, San Fran-
cisco, CA 94104
Tel.: (415) 356-0800
Web Site: http://www.signaldemand.com
Sales Range: $1-9.9 Million
Emp.: 25
Custom Computer Programming Services

N.A.I.C.S.: 541511

PROSOMNUS, INC.
5675 Gibraltar Dr, Pleasanton, CA
94588   DE
Web Site:
   https://httwww.prosomnus.com
Year Founded: 2006
OSA—(NASDAQ)
Rev.: $19,393,343
Assets: $33,196,641
Liabilities: $53,691,070
Net Worth: ($20,494,429)
Earnings: ($7,145,320)
Emp.: 129
Fiscal Year-end: 12/31/22
Medical Device Mfr
N.A.I.C.S.: 339112
Brian Dow *(CFO)*
Laing Rikkers *(Chm)*
Len Liptak *(CEO)*

**PROSPECT CAPITAL CORPO-
RATION**
10 E 40th St 42nd Fl, New York, NY
10016
Tel.: (212) 448-0702   MD
Web Site:
   https://www.prospectstreet.com
Year Founded: 1988
PSEC—(NASDAQ)
Rev.: $861,662,000
Assets: $7,857,092,000
Liabilities: $2,559,171,000
Net Worth: $5,297,921,000
Earnings: $147,416,000
Fiscal Year-end: 06/30/24
Non-Control Debt Financing to Low
Performing Energy Companies
N.A.I.C.S.: 551111
John Francis Barry III *(Chm & CEO)*
Alexandra Krasinets *(VP-Acctg)*
Jason Wilson *(Mng Dir)*
John W. Kneisley *(Mng Dir)*
Steven Stone *(Chief Credit Officer)*
Theodore V. Fowler *(Mng Dir)*
Michael Grier Eliasek *(Pres & COO)*
David L. Belzer *(Mng Dir)*
Bart J. Debie *(Mng Dir)*
David Moszer *(Mng Dir)*
John G. Burges *(Mng Dir)*
Colin McGinnis *(Mng Dir)*
Maury Cartine *(Mng Dir)*
Kristin Lea Van Dask *(CFO, Chief
Compliance Officer, Treas & Sec)*
Al Faella *(CTO)*
Jonathan J. Li *(Chief Compliance Of-
ficer & Deputy Gen Counsel)*
Steven F. Elliott *(Chief Information
Security Officer)*
Robert Melman *(Mng Dir & Principal)*
Edward Shuman *(Principal)*
Angel Solis *(Principal)*
Justin R. Martini *(Principal & Sr VP)*
Matthew Barry *(Principal & VP)*
Aderly Kor *(Sr VP & VP)*
Benjamin Bloom *(Sr VP & VP)*
Vivian Chen *(VP-Tax)*
Gabe Lewis *(VP)*
Effie Tzirtziropoulos *(VP-Fin)*
Nick Bodurian *(Principal & VP)*
Samuel Jolly *(Principal & VP)*
Daria Becker *(Head-Admin)*
Trisha Blackman *(Sr VP-
Administration & Head-HR)*
Lindsey Harrison *(Controller)*
Kelly Riley *(Controller)*
Rosa Mark-Brown *(VP-Human Re-
sources & Asst VP-HR)*
Danielle Altier *(Asst VP-Fin)*
Michael Manzella *(Dir/Sr Mgr-Tax)*
Kenneth Kessler *(Mgr-Tax)*
Ryan Tumelty *(Mgr-Acctg)*
Pauline Livaditis *(Mgr-Fin)*
Leah Toribio *(Mgr-Recruitment)*
Joshua Jaffe *(Mgr-Tax)*

Justin H. Wertman *(Deputy Gen
Counsel)*
Roman Troitsky *(Deputy Gen Coun-
sel)*
Russell Wininger *(Chief Compliance
Officer-Prospect Capital Mgmt & As-
soc Gen Counsel)*
Miles Burns *(VP)*
Mariella Capuano *(Mgr-
Administration)*
Mike Cosentino *(VP-Technology)*
Sean Feng *(VP)*
Sarah Fitzmartin *(Controller-Valuation
& Due Diligence)*
Drew Gieger *(VP)*
Zachary Goldstein *(VP)*
Carlos Hammer *(VP)*
Matt Krugman *(Sr VP)*
Jon Lin *(VP)*
JoAnna Povlas *(Fin Mgr)*
Joseph Ryu *(Principal)*
Josh Soffer *(Principal)*
Chris Wang *(VP-Originations)*
James Warren *(VP)*
Neil Zieses *(VP)*

Subsidiaries:

CP Energy Services, Inc.   (1)
23937 E 1010 Rd, Weatherford, OK 73096
Tel.: (580) 225-2672
Web Site: http://www.prohal.com
Sales Range: $25-49.9 Million
Emp.: 6
Oil & Gas Exploration Services
N.A.I.C.S.: 213111
Joe Don Selman *(Pres)*

Subsidiary (Domestic):

CP Well Testing LLC   (2)
3600 S Hwy 183, Clinton, OK 73601
Tel.: (580) 225-2672
Emp.: 50
Support Activities for Oil & Gas Operations
N.A.I.C.S.: 213112
Craig Wright *(CEO)*

Tower Loan of Mississippi, Inc.   (1)
406 Liberty Park Ct, Flowood, MS 39232
Tel.: (601) 939-8813
Web Site: http://www.towerloan.com
Rev.: $8,843,000
Emp.: 98
Personal Credit & Consumer Lending Ser-
vices
N.A.I.C.S.: 522291

**PROSPERITY BANCSHARES,
INC.**
4295 San Felipe, Houston, TX 77027
Tel.: (281) 269-7199   TX
Web Site:
   https://www.prosperitybankusa.com
Year Founded: 1983
PB—(NYSE)
Rev.: $1,597,808,000
Assets: $38,547,877,000
Liabilities: $31,468,547,000
Net Worth: $7,079,330,000
Earnings: $419,316,000
Emp.: 3,850
Fiscal Year-end: 12/31/23
Bank Holding Company
N.A.I.C.S.: 551111
Robert E. Dowdell *(Exec VP)*
David Zalman *(Chm & CEO)*
Kevin J. Hanigan *(Pres & COO)*
Randy D. Hester *(Chief Lending Offi-
cer & Exec VP)*
Charlotte M. Rasche *(Gen Counsel &
Exec VP)*
Edward Z. Safady *(Vice Chm)*
Asylbek Osmonov *(CFO)*
Mays Davenport *(Exec VP & Dir-Corp
Strategy)*
Mike Marshall *(Chm-West Texas)*

Subsidiaries:

Citizens Insurance Agency of Texas,
Inc.   (1)

101 S Main St, Victoria, TX 77901
Tel.: (361) 573-6321
Emp.: 4
Insurance Agents
N.A.I.C.S.: 524210

LegacyTexas Financial Group,
Inc.   (1)
5851 Legacy Cir, Plano, TX 75024
Tel.: (972) 578-5000
Web Site:
   http://www.legacytexasfinancialgroup.com
Rev.: $381,749,000
Assets: $9,051,142,000
Liabilities: $7,956,775,000
Net Worth: $1,094,367,000
Earnings: $154,189,000
Emp.: 851
Fiscal Year-end: 12/31/2018
Holding Company
N.A.I.C.S.: 551111

Subsidiary (Domestic):

LegacyTexas Insurance Services,
Inc.   (2)
707 E Arapaho Rd Ste 200, Richardson, TX
75081
Tel.: (972) 461-7300
Banking Services
N.A.I.C.S.: 522110

LegacyTexas Title Co.   (2)
5949 Sherry Ln Ste 100, Dallas, TX 75225
Tel.: (214) 272-5400
Web Site: https://www.legacytexastitle.com
Insurance Related Services
N.A.I.C.S.: 524298
Laurence Henry *(Pres)*

Lone Star State Bancshares, Inc.   (1)
6220 Milwaukee Ave, Lubbock, TX 79424
Tel.: (806) 771-7717
Web Site: http://www.lonestarwtx.com
Sales Range: $25-49.9 Million.
Emp.: 72
Bank Holding Company
N.A.I.C.S.: 551111
Alan L. Lackey *(Pres-West Texas)*
Edmund W. McGee *(CFO)*
Melisa Roberts *(VP-West Texas)*

Subsidiary (Domestic):

Lone Star State Bank of West
Texas   (2)
6220 Milwaukee Ave, Lubbock, TX 79424
Tel.: (806) 771-7717
Web Site: http://www.lonestarwtx.com
Emp.: 35
Retail & Commercial Banking
N.A.I.C.S.: 522110
Alan L. Lackey *(Chm & CEO)*
Jonathan Ruth *(VP)*
Kirk Thomas *(Pres)*

Prosperity Bank   (1)
1301 N Mechanic, El Campo, TX 77437
Tel.: (979) 543-2200
Web Site: https://www.prosperity.bank
Commericial Banking
N.A.I.C.S.: 522110
Robert E. Dowdell *(Exec VP)*
David Zalman *(Chm & CEO)*
Kevin J. Hanigan *(Pres)*
H. E. Timanus Jr. *(Chm & COO)*

Branch (Domestic):

Prosperity Bank - Central Oklahoma
Regional Office   (2)
3333 NW Expy, Oklahoma City, OK 73112
Tel.: (405) 810-4920
Web Site: http://www.prosperitybanktx.com
Regional Managing Office: Commercial
Banking
N.A.I.C.S.: 551114

Prosperity Bank - East Texas/Tyler
Regional Office   (2)
1200 S Beckham Ave, Tyler, TX 75701
Tel.: (903) 593-1767
Web Site:
   http://www.prosperitybankusa.com
Sales Range: $10-24.9 Million
Emp.: 24
Regional Managing Office: Commercial
Banking
N.A.I.C.S.: 551114

Prosperity Bank - South Texas/Victoria Regional Office (2)

101 S Main St, Victoria, TX 77901
Tel.: (361) 573-6321
Web Site:
http://www.prosperitybankusa.com
Regional Managing Office; Commercial
Banking
N.A.I.C.S.: 551114
M. Russell Marshall (Pres-West Texas)

Prosperity Bank - West Texas Regional Office (2)

1401 Ave Q, Lubbock, TX 79401
Tel.: (806) 767-7000
Web Site: http://www.prosperitybanktx.com
Regional Managing Office; Commercial
Banking
N.A.I.C.S.: 551114
David Zalman (CEO)

PROTAGENIC THERAPEU-TICS, INC.

149 5th Ave Ste 500, New York, NY
10010
Tel.: (212) 994-8200   DE
Web Site: https://protagenic.com
Year Founded: 1994
PTIX—(NASDAQ)
Rev.: $185,790
Assets: $8,037,420
Liabilities: $1,119,862
Net Worth: $6,917,558
Earnings: ($3,555,505)
Emp.: 1
Fiscal Year-end: 12/31/22
Research & Development in Biotech-
nology (except Nanobiotechnology)
N.A.I.C.S.: 541714

Subsidiaries:

Protagenic Therapeutics, Inc. (1)
149 5th Ave, New York, NY 10010-6801
Tel.: (212) 994-8200
Web Site: http://www.protagenic.com
Biotechnology Research & Development
Services
N.A.I.C.S.: 541714
David A. Lovejoy (Co-Founder)
Robert B. Stein (Chief Medical Officer)
Andrew Slee (COO)
Garo H. Armen (Exec Chm)

SendTraffic.com, Inc. (1)
450 7th Ave, New York, NY 10123
Tel.: (212) 273-1141
Web Site: http://www.sendtraffic.com
Sales Range: $1-9.9 Million
Emp.: 25
Internet Marketing Services
N.A.I.C.S.: 541810
Nathan Fong (CFO)

Traffix, Inc. (1)
469 7th Ave, New York, NY 10018
Tel.: (212) 716-1977
Web Site: http://www.atrinsic.com
Sales Range: $50-74.9 Million
Emp.: 93
Online Marketing Services
N.A.I.C.S.: 541890
Nathan Fong (CFO)

PROTAGONIST THERAPEU-TICS, INC.

7707 Gateway Blvd Ste 140, Newark,
CA 94560-1160
Tel.: (510) 474-0170   DE
Web Site: https://www.protagonist-
inc.com
Year Founded: 2009
PTGX—(NASDAQ)
Rev.: $26,581,000
Assets: $247,928,000
Liabilities: $32,320,000
Net Worth: $215,608,000
Earnings: ($127,393,000)
Emp.: 105
Fiscal Year-end: 12/31/22
Biopharmaceutical Research & De-
velopment Services
N.A.I.C.S.: 541715

Tracy M. Woody (Exec VP-Comml
Strategy)
Matthew Gosling (Gen Counsel &
Exec VP)
Mohammad Masjedizadeh (CTO &
Exec VP)
Arturo Molina (Chief Medical Officer)
Asif Ali (CFO & Exec VP)
Suneel K. Gupta (Chief Dev Officer)
Carter King (Exec VP-Business De-
velopment & Sr VP-Bus Dev)
Dinesh V. Patel (Pres & CEO)

PROTALIX BIOTHERAPEU-TICS, INC.

2 University Plz Ste 100, Hacken-
sack, NJ 07601
Tel.: (201) 696-9345   FL
Web Site: https://www.protalix.com
Year Founded: 1993
PLX—(NYSEAMEX)
Rev.: $47,638,000
Assets: $55,787,000
Liabilities: $66,427,000
Net Worth: ($10,640,000)
Earnings: ($14,927,000)
Emp.: 193
Fiscal Year-end: 12/31/22
Plant Cell Therapy Biopharmaceutical
Mfr
N.A.I.C.S.: 325412
Yaron Naos (Sr VP-Ops)
William Taylor (VP-Bus Dev)
Eliot Richard Forster (Chm)
Dror Bashan (Pres & CEO)
Eyal Rubin (CFO & Sr VP)
Yael Hayon (VP-R&D)
Yael Fellous (VP)
Tanya Gershanik (VP)

PROTARA THERAPEUTICS, INC.

345 Park Ave S 3rd Fl, New York, NY
10010
Tel.: (646) 844-0337   DE
Web Site: https://www.protaratx.com
Year Founded: 2001
TARA—(NASDAQ)
Rev.: $1,110,000
Assets: $113,290,000
Liabilities: $11,207,000
Net Worth: $102,083,000
Earnings: ($65,952,000)
Emp.: 25
Fiscal Year-end: 12/31/22
Biopharmaceutical Mfr
N.A.I.C.S.: 325412
Luke M. Beshar (Chm)
Patrick Fabbio (CFO)
Jesse Shefferman (Co-Founder, Pres
& CEO)
Hannah Fry (Principal Acctg Officer &
Controller)
Mary Grendell (Gen Counsel)
Kristy Rosse (Chief People Officer)
Justine O'Malley (Sr VP)

PROTECT PHARMACEUTICAL CORPORATION

12465 S Fort St Ste 240, Draper, UT
84020
Tel.: (347) 692-8942   NV
Year Founded: 1987
PRTT—(OTCIQ)
Holding Company; Pharmaceutical
Mfr
N.A.I.C.S.: 551112
Ali Yildiz (Pres)
Sergio Velasquez (Mgr)

PROTECTIVE CAPITAL STRUCTURES CORP.

1313 N Market St Ste 302, Wilmington, DE 19801
Tel.: (646) 450-1467   FL

Web Site: http://www.pcso1.com
PCSO—(OTCIQ)
Banking Holding Company
N.A.I.C.S.: 551111
Charles F. Johnson II (Vice Chm)

PROTEIN REACTOR COM-BINED FUELS, INC.

5824 E 32nd Ave, Tampa, FL 33619
Tel.: (813) 507-2971   DE
Year Founded: 2011
PRCF—(OTCIQ)
Food Products Mfr
N.A.I.C.S.: 311999
Nestor C. Buenaflor (Founder, Chm,
CEO & CFO)

PROTEK CAPITAL, INC.

232 Dell Range Blvd, Cheyenne, WY
82001
Tel.: (302) 553-5205   WY
Year Founded: 2005
PRPM—(OTCIQ)
Investment Services
N.A.I.C.S.: 523999
Eddie Vasker (CEO)
Edward I. Vakser (CEO)

PROTEO, INC.

2102 Business Ctr Dr, Irvine, CA
92612
Tel.: (949) 253-4155   NV
Web Site: http://www.proteo.us
PTEO—(OTCIQ)
Rev.: $23,939
Assets: $238,437
Liabilities: $891,313
Net Worth: ($652,876)
Earnings: ($218,167)
Emp.: 5
Fiscal Year-end: 12/31/19
Pharmaceuticals Mfr
N.A.I.C.S.: 325412
Birge Bargmann (CEO-PBAG)
Juergen Paal (COO-PBAG)

Subsidiaries:

Proteo Biotech AG (1)
Am Kiel-Kanal 44, 24106, Kiel, Germany
Tel.: (49) 4318888462
Web Site: http://www.proteo.de
Biotechnology Research & Development
Services
N.A.I.C.S.: 541714

PROTERRA, INC.

1815 Rollins Rd, Burlingame, CA
94010
Tel.: (864) 438-0000   Ky
Web Site: https://www.proterra.com
Year Founded: 2020
PTRA—(NASDAQ)
Rev.: $309,364,000
Assets: $840,459,000
Liabilities: $323,601,000
Net Worth: $516,858,000
Earnings: ($237,950,000)
Emp.: 1,247
Fiscal Year-end: 12/31/22
Investment Services
N.A.I.C.S.: 523999
Gareth T. Joyce (Pres & CEO)
John J. Allen (Chm)
Amy E. Ard (CFO)
JoAnn Covington (Chief Legal Officer,
Head-Govt Relations & Sec)
Julian R. Soell (COO)
Jeffrey D. Embt (Chief Acctg Officer)

Subsidiaries:

Proterra, Inc. (1)
1815 Rollins Rd, Burlingame, CA 94010
Tel.: (864) 438-0000
Web Site: http://www.proterra.com
Automobile Mfr
N.A.I.C.S.: 336110

Roger M. Nielsen (Chm)
Ryan C. Popple (Founder)
John Walsh (Sr VP-Sls)
Richard Huibregtse (Sr VP-Engrg)
Dustin Grace (CTO)
Kelly Scheib (VP-HR)
Chris Bailey (Pres-Powered & Energy)
Jeffrey Mitchell (Interim Gen Counsel & In-
terim Sec)

PROTIDE PHARMACEUTI-CALS, INC.

505 Oakwood Rd Ste 200, Lake Zu-
rich, IL 60047
Tel.: (847) 726-3100
Web Site:
http://www.protidepharma.com
PPMD—(OTCIQ)
Sales Range: Less than $1 Million
Emp.: 3
Pharmaceuticals Mfr
N.A.I.C.S.: 325412

PROTO LABS, INC.

5540 Pioneer Creek Dr, Maple Plain,
MN 55359
Tel.: (763) 479-3680   MN
Web Site: https://www.protolabs.com
Year Founded: 1999
PRLB—(NYSE)
Injection Molding Mfr
N.A.I.C.S.: 333511
Sarah Ekenberg (Mktg Mgr-PR & Me-
dia)

PROTO LABS, INC.

5540 Pioneer Creek Dr, Maple Plain,
MN 55359
Tel.: (763) 479-7240   MN
Web Site: https://www.protolabs.com
Year Founded: 1999
PRLB—(NYSE)
Rev.: $503,877,000
Assets: $772,353,000
Liabilities: $77,058,000
Net Worth: $695,295,000
Earnings: $17,220,000
Emp.: 2,415
Fiscal Year-end: 12/31/23
Custom Prototypes & Plastic Prod-
ucts Mfr
N.A.I.C.S.: 326199
Robert Bodor (Pres & CEO)
Bjoern Klaas (Mng Dir-Europe,
Middle East & Africa, VP & Gen Mgr)
Dan Schumacher (CFO)
Dan Schumacher (CFO)
Ryan Johnsrud (Mgr)

Subsidiaries:

Alphaform Ltd (1)
450 Brook Drive Green Park, Reading, RG2
6UU, Berkshire, United Kingdom
Tel.: (44) 1183340335
Web Site: http://www.alphaform.co.uk
Emp.: 200
Rapid Prototyping & Metal Coating Services
N.A.I.C.S.: 332812

FineLine Prototyping, Inc. (1)
9310 Focal Pt, Raleigh, NC 27617
Tel.: (919) 781-7702
Web Site:
http://www.finelineprototyping.com
Sales Range: $1-9.9 Million
Emp.: 39
Custom Prototype & Plastic Products Mfr
N.A.I.C.S.: 326199

PGC Wire and Cable, LLC (1)
17 Hampshire Dr, Hudson, NH 03051
Tel.: (603) 821-7300
Web Site: http://www.pgcwirecable.com
Wire Harnesses Mfr
N.A.I.C.S.: 334419

PL Finland Oy (1)
Aholantie 17, 21290, Rusko, Finland
Tel.: (358) 290091001
Web Site: https://prod-www.protolabs.com
Prototypes & Models Mfr

Proto Labs, Inc.—(Continued)

N.A.I.C.S.: 339930

Proto Labs Eschenlohe GmbH   **(1)**
Blauanger 6, 82438, Eschenlohe, Germany
Tel.: (49) 8824910330
Fabricated Metal Products Mfr
N.A.I.C.S.: 332999
Oliver Rebele (Gen Mgr)

Proto Labs GmbH   **(1)**
Kapellenstrasse 10, 85622, Feldkirchen,
Germany
Tel.: (49) 89905002089
Plastic Prototype Product Mfr & Distr
N.A.I.C.S.: 326160
Michael Meier (Dir-Fin)

Proto Labs Tooling GmbH   **(1)**
Blauanger 6, 82438, Eschenlohe, Germany
Tel.: (49) 882 491 0330
Industrial Machinery Mfr
N.A.I.C.S.: 333242
Bjorn Klaas (Co-Mng Dir)
Lee Ball (Co-Mng Dir)

Proto Labs, G.K.   **(1)**
2-10-8 Hironodai, Zama, 252-0012, Kana-
gawa, Japan
Tel.: (81) 46 203 9100
Web Site: https://www.protolabs.co.jp
Emp.: 50
Custom Prototypes & Plastic Products Mfr
N.A.I.C.S.: 326199

Proto Labs, Ltd.   **(1)**
Halesfield 8, Telford, TF7 4QN, Shropshire,
United Kingdom
Tel.: (44) 195 268 3047
Web Site: https://www.protolabs.co.uk
Emp.: 250
Custom Prototypes & Plastic Products Mfr
N.A.I.C.S.: 326199

Rapid Sheet Metal LLC   **(1)**
104 Perimeter Rd, Nashua, NH 03063
Tel.: (603) 821-5300
Web Site:
  http://www.rapidmanufacturing.com
Sheet Metal Parts Mfr
N.A.I.C.S.: 332999

PROTO SCRIPT PHARMACEU-TICAL CORP.

9830 6th St Ste 103, Rancho Cu-
camonga, CA 91730
PSCR—(OTCEM)
Medical Equipment Repair Services
N.A.I.C.S.: 811210
Michelle Rico (Pres, CEO, CFO &
Treas)

PROTOKINETIX, INC.

109 W Main St, Dalton, OH 44618
Tel.: (330) 455-4971   **NV**
Web Site:
  https://www.protokinetix.com
PKTX—(OTCQB)
Assets: $480,557
Liabilities: $44,696
Net Worth: $435,861
Earnings: ($415,479)
Fiscal Year-end: 12/31/23
Bio-technology Research & Develop-
ment Services
N.A.I.C.S.: 541715
Clarence E. Smith (Chm, Pres &
CEO)
Michael Richard Guzzetta (CFO)

PROTOSOURCE CORP.

2300 Tulare St Ste 210, Fresno, CA
93721
Tel.: (310) 314-9801   **CA**
PSCO—(OTCIQ)
Software Development Services
N.A.I.C.S.: 541511

PROVECTUS BIOPHARMA-CEUTICALS, INC.

800 S Gay St Ste 1610, Knoxville,
TN 37929
Tel.: (865) 769-4011   **NV**

Web Site:
  https://www.provectusbio.com
PVCT—(OTCQB)
Rev.: $989,042
Assets: $2,037,246
Liabilities: $8,265,756
Net Worth: ($6,228,510)
Earnings: ($3,554,683)
Emp.: 4
Fiscal Year-end: 12/31/22
Pharmaceutical & Medical Device Mfr
N.A.I.C.S.: 325412
Eric A. Wachter (CTO)
Dominic Rodrigues (Pres)
Edward Pershing (CEO)
Heather Raines (CFO)

PROVIDENCE RESOURCES, INC.

700 Lavaca St Ste 1400, Austin, TX
78701
Tel.: (210) 807-4204   **TX**
PVDRS—(OTCIQ)
Emp.: 1
Well Drilling
N.A.I.C.S.: 213111
Markus Mueller (Chm)
Zonghan Wu (Sec)

PROVIDENT FINANCIAL HOLDINGS, INC.

3756 Central Ave, Riverside, CA
92506
Tel.: (951) 686-6060   **DE**
Web Site:
  https://www.myprovident.com
Year Founded: 1956
PROV—(NASDAQ)
Rev.: $58,671,000
Assets: $1,272,200,000
Liabilities: $1,142,259,000
Net Worth: $129,941,000
Earnings: $7,351,000
Emp.: 160
Fiscal Year-end: 06/30/24
Banking Holding Company
N.A.I.C.S.: 551111
Donavon P. Ternes (Pres, CEO, CFO
& COO)

Subsidiaries:

Provident Financial Corp   **(1)**
3756 Central Ave, Riverside, CA
92506   **(100%)**
Tel.: (951) 000-0000
Web Site:
  http://www.providentsavingsbank.com
Sales Range: $150-199.9 Million
Emp.: 300
Provider of Annuities, Brokerage Services &
Insurance
N.A.I.C.S.: 522110

Subsidiary (Domestic):

Provident Savings Bank, F.S.B.   **(2)**
3756 Central Ave, Riverside, CA
92506   **(100%)**
Tel.: (951) 686-6060
Web Site: https://www.myprovident.com
Sales Range: $125-149.9 Million
Provider of Banking Services
N.A.I.C.S.: 522180
Donavon P. Ternes (Pres, CEO, CFO &
COO)
Gwendolyn L. Wertz (Sr VP-Retail Banking)
David S. Weiant (Chief Lending Officer & Sr
VP)
Deborah L. Hill (Chief Admin Officer, Chief
HR Officer & Sr VP)
Lilian Salter (CIO & Sr VP)
R. Scott Ritter (Sr VP-Mortgage Banking)
Kenneth R. Fisher (Acting CFO)

PROVIDENT FINANCIAL SER-VICES, INC.

111 Wood Ave S Ste 200, Iselin, NJ
08830
Tel.: (732) 590-9200   **DE**
Web Site: https://www.provident.bank

Year Founded: 2002
PFS—(NYSE)
Rev.: $553,970,000
Assets: $13,783,436,000
Liabilities: $12,185,733,000
Net Worth: $1,597,703,000
Earnings: $175,648,000
Emp.: 1,124
Fiscal Year-end: 12/31/22
Offices of Bank Holding Companies
N.A.I.C.S.: 551111
Thomas J. Shara (Vice Chm)
Thomas M. Lyons (CFO & Sr Exec
VP)
Christopher P. Martin (Exec Chm)
Anthony J. Labozzetta (Pres & CEO)
Adriano Duarte (Chief Acctg Officer &
Exec VP)
John Kuntz (Gen Counsel, Sec & Sr
Exec VP)
Bennett MacDougall (Deputy Gen
Counsel)

Subsidiaries:

Lakeland Bancorp, Inc.   **(1)**
250 Oak Ridge Rd, Oak Ridge, NJ 07438
Tel.: (973) 697-2000
Web Site: https://www.lakelandbank.com
Rev.: $395,642,000
Assets: $10,783,840,000
Liabilities: $9,675,253,000
Net Worth: $1,108,587,000
Earnings: $107,369,000
Emp.: 860
Fiscal Year-end: 12/31/2022
Bank Holding Company
N.A.I.C.S.: 551111

Subsidiary (Domestic):

1st Constitution Bancorp   **(2)**
2650 Route 130, Cranbury, NJ 08512
Tel.: (609) 655-4500
Web Site: http://www.1stconstitution.com
Rev.: $83,789,000
Assets: $1,806,909,000
Liabilities: $1,619,252,000
Net Worth: $187,657,000
Earnings: $18,086,000
Emp.: 211
Fiscal Year-end: 12/31/2020
Bank Holding Company
N.A.I.C.S.: 551111
Stephen J. Gilhooly (CFO, Treas & Sr VP)
Charles S. Crow III (Chm)
Naqi A. Naqvi (Chief Acctg Officer & Sr VP)

Highlands Bancorp, Inc.   **(2)**
310 Rte 94, Vernon, NJ 07462
Tel.: (973) 764-3200
Web Site:
  http://www.highlandsstatebank.com
Rev.: $20,455,000
Assets: $449,016,000
Liabilities: $420,506,000
Net Worth: $28,510,000
Earnings: $1,957,000
Emp.: 45
Fiscal Year-end: 12/31/2017
Bank Holding Company
N.A.I.C.S.: 551111

Subsidiary (Domestic):

Highlands State Bank   **(3)**
310 Rte 94, Vernon, NJ 07462
Tel.: (973) 764-3200
Web Site:
  http://www.highlandsstatebank.com
Sales Range: $25-49.9 Million
Emp.: 18
Commericial Banking
N.A.I.C.S.: 522110

Subsidiary (Domestic):

Lakeland Bank   **(2)**
250 Oak Ridge Rd, Oak Ridge, NJ 07438
Tel.: (973) 697-2000
Web Site: https://www.lakelandbank.com
Retail & Commercial Banking
N.A.I.C.S.: 522110
Thomas J. Shara (Pres & CEO)
Mary Ann Deacon (Chm)

Subsidiary (Domestic):

1st Constitution Bank   **(3)**

2650 Rte 130 & Dey Rd, Cranbury, NJ
08512
Tel.: (609) 655-4500
Web Site: http://www.1stconstitution.com
Sales Range: $10-24.9 Million
Emp.: 55
Commericial Banking
N.A.I.C.S.: 522110
William J. Barrett (Dir)
Charles S. Crow III (Chm)

The Provident Bank   **(1)**
239 Washington St, Jersey City, NJ 07302
Tel.: (732) 590-9200
Web Site: https://www.provident.bank
Sales Range: $250-299.9 Million
Commericial Banking
N.A.I.C.S.: 522110
Thomas M. Lyons (CFO & Sr Exec VP)
Christopher P. Martin (Exec Chm)
Anthony J. Labozzetta (Pres & CEO)
Anthony J. Labozzetta (Pres & CEO)
Ravi Vakacherla (Chief Digital & Innovation
Officer & Exec VP)

Subsidiary (Domestic):

Beacon Trust Company   **(2)**
163 Madison Ave Ste 600, Morristown, NJ
07960
Tel.: (973) 377-8090
Web Site: http://www.beacontrust.com
Portfolio Management
N.A.I.C.S.: 523940
Leonard G. Gleason (Gen Counsel)
Christopher Martin (Chm)
Charles Pawlik (VP & Portfolio Mgr)
Valerie O. Murray (Pres)
Brian McGann (Exec Mng Dir-Investment
Strategy & Head-Investment Strategy)
John Longo (Chief Investment Officer)
Kenneth Lenskold (Chief Compliance Offi-
cer)
Antonia Pancel-Cipric (Chief Fiduciary Offi-
cer)
Zoie Silver (Sr VP & Mgr-Client Svcs)
Denis Belinskiy (Officer-Tech & Sr VP)
Diane Allard (VP & Portfolio Mgr)
William Butler (Mng Dir & Dir-Res)
Richard Cawthorne (Mng Dir & Portfolio
Mgr)
Erman Civelek (Sr VP)
John J. Corcoran (Portfolio Mgr)
Maria Di Zio (VP & Portfolio Mgr)
Howard Friedner (Exec Mng Dir & Portfolio
Mgr)
Susan Hayes (Mng Dir & Portfolio Mgr-
Fixed Income)
Joseph F. Healy (Mng Dir & Dir-Res)
Jeffrey Loewy (Founder & Portfolio Mgr)
Spencer Marsh (Sr Mng Dir & Portfolio Mgr)
Christopher C. Perrine (VP & Portfolio Mgr)
Christopher Shagawat (VP & Portfolio Mgr)
Stefan Hermann (Mng Dir)
Dawn M. Avallone (Officer-Trust & VP)
Lauren Cecala (Officer-Trust & Asst VP)
Jake Clemens (Mgr-Customer Rels)
Caitlin DeGroat (Asst VP & Mgr-Customer
Relation)
Adam Goldberg (Mgr-Customer Rels)

Subsidiary (Domestic):

Tirschwell & Loewy, Inc.   **(3)**
400 Park Ave 16th Fl, New York, NY 10022
Tel.: (212) 888-7940
Financial Investment Activities
N.A.I.C.S.: 523999

PROVISION HOLDING, INC.

9253 Eton Ave, Chatsworth, CA
91311
Tel.: (818) 775-1624   **NV**
Web Site: http://www.provision.tv
Year Founded: 2004
PVHO—(OTCIQ)
Sales Range: $1-9.9 Million
Emp.: 8
Holding Company; Interactive Display
Technology Solutions
N.A.I.C.S.: 551112
Jeffrey Lynn Vrachan (VP-Engrg)
Joseph Turner (VP-Media Sls)
Mark Leonard (Pres & CEO)
Curt Thornton (Chm & COO)
Robert J. Ostrander Jr. (Exec VP-Bus
Dev & Sls)

PROVISION OPERATION SYSTEMS, INC.

121 Agate Ave, Newport Beach, CA 92662   OK
Web Site:
    http://www.provisionholdings.com
PVNO—(OTCIQ)
Real Estate Development Services
N.A.I.C.S.: 531390
Hassan Kassir *(Chm & CEO)*
William S. Stewart *(CFO)*

PROXIM WIRELESS CORPORATION

2114 Ringwood Ave, San Jose, CA 95131
Tel.: (408) 383-7600   DE
Web Site: https://www.proxim.com
Year Founded: 1982
PRXM—(OTCIQ)
Sales Range: $25-49.9 Million
Emp.: 203
Radio & Television Broadcasting & Wireless Communications Equipment Manufacturing
N.A.I.C.S.: 334220
Lee M. Gopadze *(Chm)*
Gregory Marzullo *(Pres & CEO)*
David Sumi *(Sr VP-Mktg & Product Mgmt)*
Dael A. Bartlett *(VP-Mktg)*

PRUDENTIAL FINANCIAL, INC.

751 Broad St, Newark, NJ 07102
Tel.: (973) 802-6000   NJ
Web Site: https://www.prudential.com
Year Founded: 1875
PRU—(NYSE)
Rev.: $53,979,000,000
Assets: $721,123,000,000
Liabilities: $691,336,000,000
Net Worth: $29,787,000,000
Earnings: $2,488,000,000
Emp.: 40,366
Fiscal Year-end: 12/31/23
Insurance, Real Estate & Financial Investment Services
N.A.I.C.S.: 524113
Salene Hitchcock-Gear *(Pres-Individual Life Insurance)*
Robert Michael Falzon *(Vice Chm)*
Ann M. Kappler *(Gen Counsel & Exec VP)*
Yanela C. Frias *(CFO & Exec VP)*
Lucien A. Alziari *(Chief HR Officer & Exec VP)*
Candace J. Woods *(Chief Actuary & Sr VP)*
Caroline Feeney *(CEO-Insurance & Retirement Bus)*
Andrew F. Sullivan *(Exec VP & Head-Intl Businesses & PGIM)*
Timothy Lee Schmidt *(Chief Investment Officer & Sr VP)*
Caroline A. Feeney *(Exec VP & Head-U.S. Businesses)*
Stacey Goodman *(CIO & Exec VP)*
Charles Frederick Lowrey Jr. *(Chm & CEO)*

Subsidiaries:

ASPF II - Verwaltungs - GmbH & Co. KG   (1)
Wittelsbacherplatz 1, Munich, Germany
Tel.: (49) 89286450
Fire Insurance Services
N.A.I.C.S.: 524113

Assurance IQ, LLC   (1)
920 5th Ave Ste 3600, Seattle, WA 98104
Web Site: https://assurance.com
Fire Insurance Services
N.A.I.C.S.: 524113
Michael Rowell *(Co-Founder)*
Mike Paulus *(Co-Founder)*
Allison Arzeno *(CEO)*
Nick Howard *(Sr VP-Technology)*
Gulliver Swenson *(Chief People Officer)*

Grant Fisher *(CFO)*
Suzanne Sainato *(Chief Compliance Officer)*
Doug Morrin *(Chief Legal Officer)*
Jaymee Johnson *(CMO)*
Nick Howard *(Sr VP-Technology)*
Doug Morrin *(Chief Legal Officer)*

Broad Street Global Advisors LLC   (1)
340 US 202, Somers, NY 10589
Tel.: (914) 427-8037
Web Site: https://www.broadstreetglobaladvisors.com
Fire Insurance Services
N.A.I.C.S.: 524113

Cottage Street Investments LLC   (1)
2020 Fulmer St, Philadelphia, PA 19115
Tel.: (215) 715-7994
Emp.: 4
Investment Management Service
N.A.I.C.S.: 523940

EuroCore GP S.a r.l.   (1)
2 Boulevard de la Foire 2nd Floor, 1528, Luxembourg, Luxembourg
Tel.: (352) 27623410
Life Insurance & Retirement Related Services
N.A.I.C.S.: 524113

Everbright PGIM Fund Management Co., Ltd.   (1)
222 46th Floor Bund Center Shanghai Yan an East Road, Shanghai, 200002, China
Tel.: (86) 2133074700
Asset Management Services
N.A.I.C.S.: 523940

Financial Assurance Japan, Inc.   (1)
2-13-10 Nagatacho, Chiyoda, Tokyo, 100-0014, Japan
Tel.: (81) 355016466
Emp.: 4
Investment Management Service
N.A.I.C.S.: 523940
Tomoyuki Inoue *(Pres)*

GAM Consultoria Economica Ltda.   (1)
Av Ataulfo De Paiva 1251 Sala 801 Parte Leblon, Rio de Janeiro, 22440-034, Brazil
Tel.: (55) 2121141977
Web Site: http://www.gapassets.com.br
Emp.: 45
Insurance Management Services
N.A.I.C.S.: 524298
Ivan Gueta *(Mng Dir)*

GAP Prudential Alocacao de Recursos Ltda.   (1)
Rua Tabapua 422 Sl 42 Ch Itaim, Vila Nova Conceicao, Sao Paulo, 04533-001, Brazil
Tel.: (55) 1130730014
Insurance Management Services
N.A.I.C.S.: 524298

Gibraltar Properties, Inc.   (1)
11625 Custer Rd 110-212, Frisco, TX 75035
Tel.: (905) 963-9153
Emp.: 7
Real Estate Investment Services
N.A.I.C.S.: 531390
Jude Cherilus *(Gen Mgr)*

Jennison Associates LLC   (1)
466 Lexington Ave, New York, NY 10017-3149
Tel.: (212) 421-1000
Web Site: https://www.jennison.com
Sales Range: $200-249.9 Million
Emp.: 361
Investment Advisory Services
N.A.I.C.S.: 523930
Spiros Segalas *(Founder)*
Peter Clark *(Head-Product & Strategy)*
Guillaume Mascotto *(Mng Dir & Head-Environmental, Social & Governance Strategy)*

Montana Capital Partners AG   (1)
Oberneuhofstrasse 1, 6340, Baar, Switzerland
Tel.: (41) 415117950
Web Site: https://www.montana-capital-partners.eu
Investment Management Service
N.A.I.C.S.: 525910

PGIM (Australia) Pty. Ltd.   (1)
Level 23 Deutsche Bank Place 126 Philip St, Sydney, 2000, NSW, Australia
Tel.: (61) 282489700
Real Estate Services
N.A.I.C.S.: 531390

PGIM (Hong Kong) Ltd.   (1)
Rooms 4202-4203 42nd Floor Gloucester Tower, The Landmark 15 Queen's Road, Central, China (Hong Kong)
Tel.: (852) 37698288
Real Estate Services
N.A.I.C.S.: 531390

PGIM (Shanghai) Company Ltd.   (1)
Unit 2357 Level 23 Five Corporate Avenue 150 Hubin Road, Shanghai, 200021, China
Tel.: (86) 2180135002
Real Estate Services
N.A.I.C.S.: 531390

PGIM (Singapore) Pte. Ltd.   (1)
88 Market Street 43-06 CapitaSpring, Singapore, 048948, Singapore
Tel.: (65) 67352833
Real Estate Services
N.A.I.C.S.: 531390

PGIM India Asset Management Private Limited   (1)
4th Floor C Wing Laxmi Towers Bandra Kurla Complex, Bandra East, Mumbai, 400 051, India
Tel.: (91) 2261593131
Web Site: https://www.pgimindiapms.com
Mutual Fund Services
N.A.I.C.S.: 525910
Surjitt Singh Arora *(Portfolio Mgr)*
Adam Broder *(Assoc Dir)*

PGIM Ireland Limited   (1)
Pramerica Drive Letterkenny Business Technology Park, Letterkenny, F92 W8CY, Co Donegal, Ireland
Tel.: (353) 749170236
Fire Insurance Services
N.A.I.C.S.: 524113

PGIM Limited   (1)
Grand Buildings 1-3 Strand Trafalgar Square, London, WC2N 5HR, United Kingdom
Tel.: (44) 2077662400
Fire Insurance Services
N.A.I.C.S.: 524113

PGIM Quantitative Solutions LLC   (1)
655 Broad St, Newark, NJ 07102
Tel.: (973) 367-5604
Web Site:
    https://www.pgimquantitativesolutions.com
Investment Management Service
N.A.I.C.S.: 523999
Linda T. Gibson *(Chm & CEO)*
George N. Patterson *(Chief Investment Officer)*
Marco Aiolfi *(Co-Head-)*
Richard L. Crist *(Head-)*

PGIM Real Estate (Japan) Ltd.   (1)
The Prudential Tower 16th Floor 2-13-10 Nagata-cho, Chiyoda-ku, Tokyo, 100-0014, Japan
Tel.: (81) 362058222
Fire Insurance Services
N.A.I.C.S.: 524113

PGIM Real Estate (UK) Limited   (1)
Grand Buildings 1-3 Strand Trafalgar Square, London, WC2N 5HR, United Kingdom
Tel.: (44) 2077662400
Fire Insurance Services
N.A.I.C.S.: 524113

PGIM Real Estate France SAS   (1)
15 avenue Matignon, 75008, Paris, France
Tel.: (33) 153300102
Real Estate Investment Services
N.A.I.C.S.: 531390

PGIM Real Estate Germany AG   (1)
Wittelsbacherplatz 1, 80333, Munich, Germany
Tel.: (49) 89286450
Real Estate Investment Services
N.A.I.C.S.: 531390

PGIM Real Estate Luxembourg S.A.   (1)

2 Boulevard de la Foire 2nd Floor, 1528, Luxembourg, Luxembourg
Tel.: (352) 27623410
Fire Insurance Services
N.A.I.C.S.: 524113

PGIM Real Estate Mexico S.C.   (1)
Paseo de la Reforma 412 - 18th Floor Col Juarez, 06600, Mexico, Mexico
Tel.: (52) 5550932770
Fire Insurance Services
N.A.I.C.S.: 524113

PGIM Real Estate S. de R.L. de C.V.   (1)
Paseo de la Reforma No 412 18th floor Col Juarez, 06600, Mexico, Mexico
Tel.: (52) 5550932770
Real Estate Investment Services
N.A.I.C.S.: 531390

PGIM Wadhwani LLP   (1)
9th Floor Orion House 5 Upper St Martin's Lane, London, WC2H 9EA, United Kingdom
Tel.: (44) 2076633400
Web Site: https://www.pgimwadhwani.com
Investment Management Service
N.A.I.C.S.: 523999

PGIM, Inc.   (1)
655 Broad St 8th Fl, Newark, NJ 07102
Web Site: https://www.pgim.com
Fire Insurance Services
N.A.I.C.S.: 524113

PRICOA Capital Management Limited   (1)
Grand Buildings 1-3 Strand Trafalgar Square, London, WC2N 5HR, United Kingdom
Tel.: (44) 2077662400
Fire Insurance Services
N.A.I.C.S.: 524113

PRICOA Consulting (Shanghai) Co., Ltd.   (1)
30/F Raffliers Plaza No 268 Xizang, Middle Road Huangpu Distr, Shanghai, 200001, China
Tel.: (86) 2161226058
Insurance Agencies Brokerage Services
N.A.I.C.S.: 524210

PRICOA Relocation Asia Pte. Ltd.   (1)
3 Anson Rd 20-02 Springleaf Tower, Singapore, 079909, Singapore
Tel.: (65) 65361966
Sales Range: $50-74.9 Million
Emp.: 50
Insurance Agencies Brokerage Services
N.A.I.C.S.: 531210

PRICOA Relocation France SAS   (1)
15 Rue Croix Castel BP 70, 78602, Maisons-Laffitte, France
Tel.: (33) 139120060
Web Site: http://www.helma-international.com
Emp.: 30
Mobility Management Services
N.A.I.C.S.: 541618

PT PFI Mega Life Insurance   (1)
GKM GREEN TOWER Lantai 17 Jl TB Simatupang Kav 89G RT 10/RW 002, Kel Kebagusan Kec Pasar Minggu, Jakarta Selatan, 12520, Indonesia
Tel.: (62) 2129545555
Web Site: https://www.pfimegalife.co.id
Fire Insurance Services
N.A.I.C.S.: 524113
Hani Kusumowardhani *(Dir-Compliance)*
Anton Pranayama *(CIO)*

Pramerica Fosun Life Insurance Co., Ltd.   (1)
Room 01 02 03 05 06 & 07 17-18F Building A LCM Plaza No 1-2 Lane 2389, Zhang Yang Road China Shanghai Pilot Free Trade Zone, Shanghai, 200135, China
Tel.: (86) 2120692888
Fire Insurance Services
N.A.I.C.S.: 524113

Pramerica Life Insurance Company Limited   (1)
4th Floor Building No 9 B Cyber City DLF City Phase III, Gurgaon, 122002, India
Tel.: (91) 18605007070

Prudential Financial, Inc.—(Continued)

Web Site: https://www.pramericalife.in
Emp.: 2,250
Insurance Services
N.A.I.C.S.: 524210
Karthik Chakrapani (Chief Bus Officer)
Sharad K. Sharma (Chief HR & Ethics Officer)
Abhishek Das (Chief Investment Officer)

Pramerica SGR S.p.A (1)
via Monte di Pieta 5, 20121, Milan, Italy
Tel.: (39) 02430241
Web Site: http://www.pramericasgr.it
Asset Management Services
N.A.I.C.S.: 523940
Angelo Sigismondi (CFO & COO)

**Pramerica Systems Ireland
Limited** (1)
Pramerica Drive Letterkenny Business &
Technology Park, Letterkenny, Donegal,
F92 W8CY, Ireland
Tel.: (353) 749167600
Web Site: http://www.pramerica.ie
Sales Range: $1-4.9 Billion
Emp.: 1,400
Financial Services
N.A.I.C.S.: 523999
Ciaran Harvey (Sr Mng Dir & CIO)
Andrea McBride (Head-Software Engrg Solutions)
Gerard Grant (Head-Tech, Innovation &
Support Svcs)
Chris Lynch (Head-Professional Bus Svcs)
Naomi Hegarty (VP-Risk Mgmt)
Paul McEldowney (VP-Fin Reporting)
Shawn Ollis (VP-Ops)
Mary Bradshaw (VP-HR)

Pruco Securities, LLC (1)
751 Broad St, Newark, NJ 07102
Tel.: (973) 802-6000
Investment Advisory Services
N.A.I.C.S.: 523940

**Prudential Agricultural Credit,
Inc.** (1)
6750 Poplar Ave Ste 708, Memphis, TN
38138-5644
Tel.: (901) 758-1352
Insurance Agencies Brokerage Services
N.A.I.C.S.: 524210

**Prudential Agricultural Investments,
Inc.** (1)
801 Warrenville Rd Ste 150, Lisle, IL
60532-4328 (100%)
Tel.: (630) 810-1700
Web Site: http://www.prudential.com
Sales Range: $1-9.9 Million
Emp.: 12
Agricultural Finance Services
N.A.I.C.S.: 522299

Subsidiary (Domestic):

Flor-Ag Corporation (2)
201 S Orange Ave Ste 795, Orlando, FL
32801
Tel.: (407) 649-9601
Sales Range: Less than $1 Million
Emp.: 2
Agricultural Insurance Services
N.A.I.C.S.: 524298
Charles Allison (VP)

Prudential Agricultural Property Holding Company, LLC (1)
1209 Orange St, Wilmington, DE 19801
Tel.: (302) 658-7581
Insurance Agencies Brokerage Services
N.A.I.C.S.: 524210

Prudential Annuities (1)
1 Corporate Dr, Shelton, CT
06484 (100%)
Tel.: (203) 926-1888
Web Site:
http://www.annuities.prudential.com
Financial Investment Consultants
N.A.I.C.S.: 523999
Lisa M. Bennett (VP-Communications-Global)

Subsidiary (Domestic):

**American Skandia Marketing,
Incorporated** (2)

PO Box 7960, Philadelphia, PA 19176
Tel.: (203) 926-1888
Web Site:
http://www.annuities.prudential.com
Sales Range: $650-699.9 Million
Securities Products Distr
N.A.I.C.S.: 523150

Prudential Asset Resources, Inc. (1)
2100 Ross Ave Ste 2500, Dallas, TX
75201-6732
Tel.: (214) 777-4500
Web Site: http://www.prudential.com
Emp.: 150
Mortgage & Nonmortgage Loans Broking
Services
N.A.I.C.S.: 522310
Joni Brown-Haas (Pres)

Prudential Bank & Trust, FSB (1)
280 Trumbull St, Hartford, CT 06103
Sales Range: $125-149.9 Million
Banking Services
N.A.I.C.S.: 522110
Jamie Kalamarides (CEO)

Prudential Capital & Investment Services, LLC (1)
2 Prudential Plz 5600, Chicago, IL 60601
Tel.: (312) 540-4221
Investment Management Service
N.A.I.C.S.: 523940

Prudential Capital Group, L.P. (1)
180 N Stetson Ave 2 Prudential Plz Ste
5600, Chicago, IL 60601
Tel.: (312) 540-4235
Web Site: http://www3.prudential.com
Sales Range: $100-124.9 Million
Emp.: 50
Investment Services
N.A.I.C.S.: 523150

Joint Venture (Domestic):

AmeriMark Direct, LLC (2)
6864 Engle Rd, Cleveland, OH 44130
Tel.: (847) 748-2201
Web Site: https://www.amerimark.com
Sales Range: $50-74.9 Million
Direct Marketing; Women's Apparel; Cosmetics & Fragrances; Jewelry, Watches &
Accessories; Health Related Merchandise
N.A.I.C.S.: 541860
Gareth Giesler (Chm & CEO)
Louis Giesler (Pres)
Diane Huzar (Exec VP)

Subsidiary (Domestic):

Harriet Carter Gifts, Inc. (3)
425 Stump Rd, North Wales, PA 19454
Tel.: (215) 361-5100
Web Site: http://www.harrietcarter.com
Household Accessories & Gifts Mail Order
N.A.I.C.S.: 459420
George Feenie (Dir-Ops)
Lowell Bergey (CTO & CIO)
Mary Norton (Mgr-Mail List)

**Prudential Defined Contribution
Services** (1)
751 Broad St, Newark, NJ 07102 (100%)
Tel.: (973) 802-4757
Web Site: http://www.prudential.com
Sales Range: $75-99.9 Million
Emp.: 150
Sells Prudentials Investment Activities to
Pension Funds & Foundations; Administers
Pension Plans for Corporate Clients
N.A.I.C.S.: 524113

Prudential Equity Group, LLC (1)
1 New York Plz 15th Fl, New York, NY
10292-2015
Tel.: (212) 778-1000
Sales Range: $1-4.9 Billion
Emp.: 500
Financial Services
N.A.I.C.S.: 523999

Prudential Financial (1)
8401 Greensboro Dr, McLean, VA 22102
Tel.: (703) 821-1319
Web Site: http://www.prudential.com
Mortgage Bankers & Correspondents
N.A.I.C.S.: 522292

Prudential Financial (1)
1270 Avenue of the Americas Ste 1000,
New York, NY 10020

Tel.: (212) 459-1300
Web Site: http://www.prudential.com
Sales Range: $650-699.9 Million
Dealers Security; Owned (62%) Wachovia
Corporation & (38%) Prudential Financial,
Inc.
N.A.I.C.S.: 523150

Prudential Florida WCI Realty (1)
1150 S US Hwy 1, Jupiter, FL 33477
Tel.: (561) 354-1700
Sales Range: $750-799.9 Million
Real Estate Services
N.A.I.C.S.: 531210

Prudential Funding LLC (1)
2 Gateway Ctr Ste 201, Newark, NJ
07102 (100%)
Tel.: (973) 802-7294
Web Site: https://www.prudential.com
Sales Range: $75-99.9 Million
Emp.: 25
Financial Management Services
N.A.I.C.S.: 561110

**Prudential Gibraltar Agency Co.,
Ltd.** (1)
8F Win Gotanda Building 1-30-2 Nishigotanda, Shinagawa-ku, Tokyo, 141-0031,
Japan
Tel.: (81) 357406730
Web Site: https://www.pg-agency.co.jp
Insurance Agencies Brokerage Services
N.A.I.C.S.: 524210

Prudential Global Funding, LLC (1)
2 Gateway Ctr Fl 5, Newark, NJ
07102-5003 (100%)
Tel.: (973) 802-6000
Web Site: https://www.prudential.com
Sales Range: $1-4.9 Billion
Emp.: 375
Foreign Trade & International Banks
N.A.I.C.S.: 523150
Gary Nebeck (Pres)
Frank Digaetano (VP)
Tom Kolefas (Mng Dir)

**Prudential Huntoon Paige Associates,
Ltd.** (1)
8 100 Mulberry St, Newark, NJ
07102 (100%)
Tel.: (732) 767-8700
Web Site: http://www.prudential.com
Sales Range: $25-49.9 Million
Emp.: 13
Mortgage Bankers & Correspondents
N.A.I.C.S.: 522292

Prudential Insurance (1)
101 W Big Beaver Ste 705, Troy, MI
48084 (100%)
Tel.: (248) 088-3089
Web Site: http://www.prudential.com
Sales Range: $50-74.9 Million
Emp.: 100
Direct Life Insurance Carriers
N.A.I.C.S.: 524113

**Prudential International Insurance
Holdings, Ltd.** (1)
751 Broad St, Newark, NJ 07102
Tel.: (973) 802-6000
Web Site: https://www.prudential.com
Sales Range: $25-49.9 Million
Emp.: 10
International Insurance Services Holding
Company
N.A.I.C.S.: 551112

Subsidiary (Non-US):

Prudential Seguros Mexico, S.A. (2)
Av Santa Fe 428 piso 7 DownTown Torre II,
Col Santa Fe Cuajimalpa Cuajimalpa de
Morelos, 05348, Mexico, Mexico
Tel.: (52) 11037000
Web Site:
https://www.prudentialseguros.com.mx
Insurance Management Services
N.A.I.C.S.: 524298

**Prudential Servicios, S. de R.L. de
C.V.** (2)
Ejercito Nacional No 843 B Acceso A Piso
1, Mexico, 11520, Distrito Federal, Mexico
Tel.: (52) 5552680800
Insurance Management Services
N.A.I.C.S.: 524298

**Prudential International Investments
Corporation** (1)
655 Broad St 8th Fl, Newark, NJ 07102
Tel.: (973) 802-9634
Web Site: http://www.pgim.com
Holding Company; Investment Management
Services
N.A.I.C.S.: 551112

Subsidiary (Non-US):

**DHFL Pramerica Asset Managers
Private Limited** (2)
2nd Floor Nirlon House Dr Annie Besant
Road, Worli, Mumbai, 400 030,
India (50%)
Tel.: (91) 2261593000
Web Site: http://www.dhflpramericamf.com
Investment Management Service
N.A.I.C.S.: 523940

PGIM Japan Co., Ltd. (2)
Prudential Tower 2-13-10, Nagatacho
Chiyoda-ku, Tokyo, 100-0014, Japan
Tel.: (81) 368327000
Web Site: https://www.pgimjp.com
Emp.: 80
Insurance Management Services
N.A.I.C.S.: 524298

**Pramerica Asia Fund Management
Limited** (2)
Rooms 4202-4203 42nd Floor Gloucester
Tower, The Landmark 15 Queen's Road,
Central, China (Hong Kong)
Tel.: (852) 25095700
Web Site: http://www.pramericarei.com
Insurance Agencies Brokerage Services
N.A.I.C.S.: 524210

**Pramerica Investment Management
Limited** (2)
Grand Buildings 1-3 Strand Trafalgar
Square, London, 5HRWC2N, United Kingdom
Tel.: (44) 2077662570
Investment Management Service
N.A.I.C.S.: 523999

**Prudential Investment Management,
Inc.** (1)
655 Broad St 8th Fl, Newark, NJ
07102 (100%)
Tel.: (973) 802-6000
Web Site:
http://www.investmentmanagement.pru
dential.com
Rev.: $962,000,000,000
Emp.: 40,000
Investment Services
N.A.I.C.S.: 522310
Catherine Marcus (Co-CEO & COO)
David Hunt (CEO)
Joanna Drew (Head-Comm-EMEA)
Ted Smith (Head-Global Comm)

Subsidiary (Non-US):

Everbright Pramerica Fund Management Co., Ltd. (2)
46-47/F Wai Tan Center 222 East Yan An
Avenue, Shanghai, China
Tel.: (86) 2133074700
Web Site: http://www.epf.com.cn
Financial Management Services
N.A.I.C.S.: 541611

Subsidiary (Domestic):

PREI International, Inc. (2)
7 Giralda Farms, Madison, NJ 07940
Tel.: (973) 734-1300
Web Site:
https://www.investmentmanagement.
prudential.com
Sales Range: $200-249.9 Million
Emp.: 200
Real Estate Investment Services
N.A.I.C.S.: 531390
Lee Menifee (Mng Dir & Head-America)

Subsidiary (Non-US):

**Pramerica Fixed Income (Asia)
Limited** (3)
50 Raffles Place 27-04 Singapore Land
Tower, Singapore, 48623, Singapore
Tel.: (65) 66229280
Sales Range: $25-49.9 Million
Emp.: 9
Insurance Agencies Brokerage Services
N.A.I.C.S.: 524210

Clifford Lau *(Gen Mgr)*

Pramerica Real Estate Investors (Asia) Pte. Ltd. **(3)**
88 Market Street 43-06 CapitaSpring, Singapore, 48948, Singapore
Tel.: (65) 67352833
Web Site: http://www.pramerica.com
Sales Range: $10-24.9 Million
Emp.: 50
Real Estate Investment Services
N.A.I.C.S.: 531390

Prudential Real Estate Investors, Sociedad Responsabilidad Limitada De Capital Variable **(3)**
paseo de la resorome 412 Fl 18, 06600, Mexico, Mexico
Tel.: (52) 5550932770
Web Site: http://www.prudentialfinancial.com
Sales Range: $200-249.9 Million
Emp.: 200
Real Estate Investment Services
N.A.I.C.S.: 531390

Subsidiary (Domestic):

Prudential Private Placement Investors L.P. **(2)**
655 Broad St, Newark, NJ 07102
Tel.: (973) 802-8608
Investment Advisory Services
N.A.I.C.S.: 523940

Subsidiary (Non-US):

Prudential Real Estate Investors (Japan) K. K. **(2)**
3-20-1 minamiazabu, Minato-ku, Tokyo, 106-0047, Japan
Tel.: (81) 357393920
Real Estate Investment Services
N.A.I.C.S.: 531390

Prudential Real Estate Investors Investimentos Imobiliarios Ltda. **(2)**
Pres Wilson 231 6 & Centro, 20030-021, Rio de Janeiro, Brazil
Tel.: (55) 2122173400
Real Estate Investment Services
N.A.I.C.S.: 531390

Subsidiary (Domestic):

Quantitative Management Associates LLC **(2)**
2 Gateway Ctr 6th Fl, Newark, NJ 07102
Tel.: (973) 856-5709
Web Site: https://www.pgimquantitativesolutions.com
Investment Management Service
N.A.I.C.S.: 523940
George N. Patterson *(Co-Chief Investment Officer)*
Peter Xu *(Co-Head-Quantitative Equities)*
Adam Broder *(Head-Distr-Global)*
Andrew Dyson *(CEO & Chm)*
Larry Marchese *(Chief Tech & Ops Officer)*
John Gee-Grant *(Head-Intl Distr & Global Consultant Rels)*
Frances Orabona *(Head-Global Client Relationship Mgmt)*
Brad Zenz *(Head-Sls-North American)*
Edward L. Campbell *(Dir-Dynamic Asset Allocation)*
Richard L. Crist *(Head-Trading-Global)*
Lorne Johnson *(Dir-Institutional Solutions)*
Stacie L. Mintz *(Co-Head-Quantitative Equities)*
John W. Moschberger *(Portfolio Mgr)*
John Praveen *(Portfolio Mgr)*
Gavin Smith *(Head-Equity Res)*
Linda Gibson *(Chief Bus Officer)*
Marco Aiolfi *(Dir-Systematic Multi-Asset Strategies)*
Stephen Brundage *(Dir-Affiliate Solutions)*
Yesim Tokat-Acikel *(Dir-Multi-Asset Res)*
Adam Kloczkowski *(CFO)*

Prudential Investments LLC **(1)**
100 Mulberry St 14th Fl Gateway Ctr 3, Newark, NJ 07102-4077
Tel.: (973) 802-6000
Investment Management Service
N.A.I.C.S.: 523940
Stuart Sherman Parker *(Pres & CEO)*

Prudential Mortgage Capital Company, LLC **(1)**

8401 Greensboro Dr Ste 200, McLean, VA 22102 **(100%)**
Tel.: (703) 610-1400
Web Site: http://www.prudential.com
Sales Range: $75-99.9 Million
Emp.: 40
Commercial Mortgage Financial Services Company
N.A.I.C.S.: 522299

Subsidiary (Domestic):

Prudential Mortgage Capital Company II, LLC **(2)**
100 Mulberry St, Newark, NJ 07102
Tel.: (312) 565-6274
Insurance Agencies Brokerage Services
N.A.I.C.S.: 524210

Prudential Mutual Fund Services LLC **(1)**
4400 Computer Dr, Westborough, MA 01581
Tel.: (973) 367-3529
Web Site: http://www.pgim.com
Mutual Fund Management Services
N.A.I.C.S.: 523940

Prudential Real Estate Affiliates, Inc. **(1)**
18500 Von Karman Ave Ste 400, Irvine, CA 92612 **(100%)**
Tel.: (949) 794-7900
Web Site: http://www.prea.prudential.com
Sales Range: $1-4.9 Billion
Emp.: 43,000
Real Estate Services
N.A.I.C.S.: 531210

Prudential Relocation Ltd. **(1)**
5700 Yonge St Suite 1110, Toronto, 4K2M2M, ON, Canada
Tel.: (416) 221-5900
Insurance Agencies Brokerage Services
N.A.I.C.S.: 524210

Prudential Retirement Insurance and Annuity Company **(1)**
280 Trumbull St, Hartford, CT 06103-3513
Tel.: (860) 534-2000
Web Site: http://www.prudential.com
Insurance Agencies Brokerage Services
N.A.I.C.S.: 524210

Prudential Seguros, S.A. **(1)**
Av Leandro N Alem 855 5 Piso, CP1001, Buenos Aires, Argentina
Tel.: (54) 4 891 5000
Web Site: https://www.prudentialseguros.com.ar
Emp.: 390
Fire Insurance Services
N.A.I.C.S.: 524113
Mauricio Zanatta *(Pres & CEO)*

Prudential Trust Company **(1)**
30 Scranton Office Park, Scranton, PA 18507-1796
Tel.: (570) 341-6000
Web Site: http://www.prudential.com
Investment Advice
N.A.I.C.S.: 523940

Prudential do Brasil Seguros de Vida S.A. **(1)**
Rua Mena Barreto no 114, Botafogo, Rio de Janeiro, 22271-100, Brazil **(99.9%)**
Tel.: (55) 2130037783
Web Site: https://www.prudential.com.br
Sales Range: $75-99.9 Million
Emp.: 150
Holding Company; Insurance Services
N.A.I.C.S.: 551112

QMA Wadhwani LLP **(1)**
9th Floor Orion House 5 Upper Street Martins Lane, London, WC2H 9EA, United Kingdom
Tel.: (44) 2076633400
Web Site: https://www.pgimwadhwani.com
Asset Management Services
N.A.I.C.S.: 523940
Sushil Wadhwani *(Chief Investment Officer)*

Rockstone Co., Ltd. **(1)**
3-6-5 Jingumae, Shibuya-ku, Tokyo, 150-0001, Japan
Tel.: (81) 36 271 1619
Web Site: https://www.rockstone.co.jp
Emp.: 12

Furniture Whslr
N.A.I.C.S.: 423490
Kenji Matsunari *(Pres & CEO)*

SMP Holdings, Inc. **(1)**
913 N Market St, Wilmington, DE 19801-3019
Tel.: (302) 656-0200
Insurance Agencies Brokerage Services
N.A.I.C.S.: 524210

The Gibraltar Life Insurance Company, Ltd. **(1)**
2-13-10 Nagatacho, Chiyoda-ku, Tokyo, 100-8953, Japan **(100%)**
Tel.: (81) 355016001
Web Site: https://www.gib-life.co.jp
Sales Range: $1-4.9 Billion
Emp.: 6,000
Individual Life & Indemnity Health Coverage, Individual Annuities, Group Life Insurance & Group Annuities
N.A.I.C.S.: 524128
Takeshi Soeda *(Pres)*
Peter Kravitz *(Gen Counsel-Automotive Retailer & VP-Bus Affairs)*

Subsidiary (Domestic):

AIG Star Life Insurance Co., Ltd. **(2)**
4-1-3 Taihei Sumida, Meguro ku, Tokyo, 130-8660, Japan
Tel.: (81) 120160414
Fire Insurance Services
N.A.I.C.S.: 524113
Norio Tomono *(Pres & CEO)*

CLIS Co., Ltd. **(2)**
Omori Bellport A Building 6-26-1 Minamioi, Shinagawa-ku, Tokyo, 140-0013, Japan
Tel.: (81) 368628400
Web Site: https://www.clis.co.jp
Emp.: 344
Financial Management Services
N.A.I.C.S.: 541611
Takahiko Iwahashi *(Pres)*

Subsidiary (Non-US):

Gibraltar BSN Life Berhad **(2)**
Level G Mercu 2 KL Eco City No 3 Jalan Bangsar, 59200, Kuala Lumpur, Malaysia
Tel.: (60) 32 298 2000
Web Site: https://www.gibraltarbsn.com
Emp.: 7,000
Fire Insurance Services
N.A.I.C.S.: 524210
Roslin Asther *(Head-Human Resources)*
Jonathan Graybill *(Exec Dir)*
Kamil Khalid Ariff *(Chm)*
Kok Wah Lee *(CEO)*
Rangam Bir *(Pres & CEO)*
Soon Chua Kim *(COO)*
Su-En Yap Suat Yen *(Chief Partnership Officer)*
Susan Ong Char Kwee *(CMO)*
Tuck Wai Chan *(Chief Risk & Compliance Officer)*
Wei Lai *(Chief Actuary)*
Ganesh Sivarajah *(Head-Internal Audit)*
Daniel Toh *(Chief Sls Officer)*
Chua E. Long *(COO)*
Chua E. Long *(COO)*

Kyoei do Brasil Companhia de Seguros **(2)**
Av Paulista 475 1 & 6, Bela Vista, Sao Paulo, 01311-000, SP, Brazil **(85%)**
Tel.: (55) 1131713199
Sales Range: $25-49.9 Million
Emp.: 40
Life Insurance Products & Services
N.A.I.C.S.: 524113

Subsidiary (Domestic):

Oriental Life Insurance Cultural Development Center **(2)**
The Prudential Tower 9F 2-13-10 Nagatacho, Chiyoda Ku, Tokyo, 100-0014, Japan **(100%)**
Tel.: (81) 355016570
Web Site: https://www.olis.or.jp
Sales Range: $10-24.9 Million
Emp.: 8
Insurance Services
N.A.I.C.S.: 524128
Yoshihiro Syuto *(Pres)*

Subsidiary (Non-US):

P.T. Jakarta Kyoai Medical Center **(2)**

Wisma Keiai 6th floor Jl Jend Sudirman kav 3, Jakarta, 10220, Indonesia **(76.3%)**
Tel.: (62) 215724330
Sales Range: $25-49.9 Million
Emp.: 40
Medical Check-up Service
N.A.I.C.S.: 524114
Harrianto Folichin *(Pres)*

Affiliate (Domestic):

The Kyoei Annuity Home Co., Ltd. **(2)**
4-4-1 Hongoku-cho Nihonbashi, Chuo-ku, Tokyo, Japan **(10%)**
Tel.: (81) 3327 08511
Sales Range: $50-74.9 Million
Emp.: 120
Management of Annuity Homes
N.A.I.C.S.: 524128

Subsidiary (Domestic):

Sanei Collection Service Co., Ltd. **(3)**
Higashi-Ikebukuro 4-24-3 Ikebukuro Gibraltar Life Building 4F, Toshima, Tokyo, 170-0013, Japan
Tel.: (81) 339805211
Web Site: https://sanei-cs.jp
Financial Management Services
N.A.I.C.S.: 541611

Affiliate (Domestic):

The Kyoei Building Management Co., Ltd. **(2)**
4-4-1 Hongoku-cho Nihonbashi, Chuo-ku, Tokyo, Japan **(10%)**
Tel.: (81) 3327 08511
Sales Range: $250-299.9 Million
Emp.: 459
Insurance Services
N.A.I.C.S.: 524128

Subsidiary (Domestic):

Toho Shinyo Hosho Company **(2)**
4-4 Omachi Toho Square Bldg 6f, Fukushima, 960-8041, Japan
Tel.: (81) 245258828
Specialty Finance Services
N.A.I.C.S.: 522220

The Prudential Gibraltar Financial Life Insurance Co., Ltd. **(1)**
2-13-10 Nagatacho, Chiyoda-Ku, Tokyo, 100-0014, Japan
Tel.: (81) 367405000
Web Site: https://www.pgf-life.co.jp
Insurance Agencies Brokerage Services
N.A.I.C.S.: 524210
Ryunosuke Shiba *(CFO)*

The Prudential Insurance Company of America **(1)**
751 Broad St, Newark, NJ 07102-3777
Tel.: (973) 802-3654
Web Site: https://www.prudential.com
Sales Range: $125-149.9 Million
Life Insurance Carrier & Services
N.A.I.C.S.: 524113

Subsidiary (Domestic):

PRUCO Life Insurance Company **(2)**
213 Washington St, Newark, NJ 07102 **(100%)**
Tel.: (973) 802-6000
Web Site: http://www.prudential.com
Rev.: $3,554,498,000
Assets: $189,299,841,000
Liabilities: $184,936,310,000
Net Worth: $4,363,531,000
Earnings: $341,749,000
Emp.: 363
Fiscal Year-end: 12/31/2022
Life Insurance Carrier & Services
N.A.I.C.S.: 524128
Dylan J. Tyson *(Pres & CEO)*
Susan M. Mann *(CFO, Chief Acctg Officer & VP)*

The Prudential Life Insurance Co. Ltd. **(1)**
Prudential Tower 1F general reception 2-13-10, Nagatacho Chiyoda-ku, Tokyo, 100-0014, Japan **(100%)**
Tel.: (81) 355015500
Web Site: https://www.prudential.co.jp

Prudential Financial, Inc.—(Continued)

Sales Range: $100-124.9 Million
Emp.: 200
Traditional & Variable Life Insurance Products
N.A.I.C.S.: 524113
Motofusa Hamada (CEO)

Subsidiary (Domestic):

Prudential General Services of Japan Y.K. (2)
The Prudential Tower 2-13-10 Nagata-cho, Chiyoda, Tokyo, 100-0014, Japan
Tel.: (81) 355015500
Information Retrieval Services
N.A.I.C.S.: 541513

The Prudential Life Realty Group (1)
751 Broad St, Newark, NJ 07102-3714 (100%)
Tel.: (973) 802-6000
Web Site: http://www.prudential.com
Sales Range: $1-4.9 Billion
Emp.: 375
Real Estate Manager, Developer, Mortgage Lender
N.A.I.C.S.: 531210

Subsidiary (Domestic):

Capital Agricultural Property Services, Inc. (2)
801 Warrenville Rd Ste 150, Lisle, IL 60532 (100%)
Tel.: (630) 434-9150
Web Site: https://capitalag.com
Sales Range: $25-49.9 Million
Emp.: 12
Agricultural Management Services
N.A.I.C.S.: 531210

The Relocation Freight Corporation of America (1)
2420 N Coliseum Blvd, Fort Wayne, IN 46805-3139
Tel.: (260) 496-9648
Freight Transportation Services
N.A.I.C.S.: 488510

Washington Street Investments LLC (1)
12165 SW Ames Ln, Tigard, OR 97224
Tel.: (503) 380-5462
Web Site: http://www.washingtonstreetinvestments.com
Investment Management Service
N.A.I.C.S.: 523940
Bryce D. Peterson (Pres)

PSB HOLDINGS, INC.
1905 W Stewart Ave, Wausau, WI 54401
Tel.: (715) 842-2191 **WI**
Web Site:
https://www.psbholdingsinc.com
PSBQ—(OTCQX)
Sales Range: $25-49.9 Million
Emp.: 161
Bank Holding Company
N.A.I.C.S.: 551111
Scott M. Cattanach (Pres & CEO)
Katie Tolokken (COO & VP)
Jessica Barnes (CFO & Sr VP)
Robert McPherson (VP-Risk Management)
Jeffrey Saxton (VP)
Tina Seidl (VP-Human Resources)
Erik Rajek (Chief Credit Officer & Sr VP)

Subsidiaries:

Peoples State Bank (1)
1905 Stewart Ave, Wausau, WI 54401
Tel.: (715) 842-2191
Web Site: http://www.psbwi.com
Sales Range: $10-24.9 Million
Federal Savings Institutions
N.A.I.C.S.: 522180
Scott Cattanach (Pres & CEO)
Chuck Winegarden (Chief Credit Officer)
Adam Siewert (Asst VP-Comml Banking-Stevens Point)
Dale Sankey (Asst VP-Comml Banking)
Jessica Brown (CFO & Sr VP)

PSH GROUP HOLDINGS, INC.
1955 Baring Blvd, Sparks, NV 89434
Tel.: (400) 066-6359 **NV**
Year Founded: 2004
GLHD—(OTCIQ)
Seafood Product Mfr
N.A.I.C.S.: 311710
Xin Min Tian (Pres)
Yu Shan Zhang (Fin Dir)
Shifu Jiang (Fin Dir)
Qun Wang (Treas)

PSYC CORPORATION
28 Laura Ln, Kiamesha Lake, NY 12751
Tel.: (845) 309-9573 **NV**
Web Site:
http://www.globaltracsolutions.com
PSYC—(OTCIQ)
Rev.: $1,412,156
Assets: $227,589
Liabilities: $6,408,360
Net Worth: ($6,180,771)
Earnings: ($3,793,666)
Fiscal Year-end: 12/31/19
Holding Company
N.A.I.C.S.: 551112
David Flores (CEO)
Daniel Joseph Jaros (CEO)
Daniel Andrews-Cutright (Dir)

PSYCHEMEDICS CORPORATION
5220 Spring Valley Rd Ste 230, Dallas, TX 75254
Tel.: (978) 206-8220 **DE**
Web Site:
https://www.psychemedics.com
PMD—(NASDAQ)
Rev.: $25,240,000
Assets: $18,732,000
Liabilities: $7,961,000
Net Worth: $10,771,000
Earnings: ($1,084,000)
Emp.: 133
Fiscal Year-end: 12/31/22
Hair Analysis for Substance Abuse Detection
N.A.I.C.S.: 621512
Brian Hullinger (Pres & CEO)
Shannon Shoemaker (Chief Revenue Officer)
Daniella Mehalik (Principal Fin Officer, Principal Acctg Officer, Treas & VP-Fin)

PTC INC.
121 Seaport Blvd, Boston, MA 02210
Tel.: (781) 370-5000 **MA**
Web Site: https://www.ptc.com
Year Founded: 1985
PTC—(NASDAQ)
Rev.: $2,097,053,000
Assets: $6,288,842,000
Liabilities: $3,611,552,000
Net Worth: $2,677,290,000
Earnings: $245,540,000
Emp.: 7,231
Fiscal Year-end: 09/30/23
Software Publisher
N.A.I.C.S.: 513210
Kristian P. Talvitie (CFO & Exec VP)
Aaron C. von Staats (Gen Counsel & Exec VP)
Kristian Talvitie (CFO & Exec VP)
Steve Dertien (CTO & Exec VP)
Craig Melrose (Exec VP-Digital Transformation Solutions)
Jon Hirschtick (Gen Mgr-Onshape & Atlas)
Kevin Wrenn (Exec VP-Products)
Catherine A. Kniker (Chief Strategy Officer, Chief Sustainability Officer & Exec VP)
Jamie Pappas (Exec VP-Global Sls)
Janice Durbin Chaffin (Chm)
Neil Barua (Pres & CEO)

Subsidiaries:

Arena Solutions, Inc. (1)
989 E Hillsdale Blvd Ste 250, Foster City, CA 94404
Tel.: (650) 513-3500
Custom Computer Programming Services
N.A.I.C.S.: 541511
Craig Livingston (CEO)
Andrea Pitts (Sr VP-Sls-Global)
Nathan Martin (VP-Customer Success)
Wenxiang Ma (CTO & Exec VP-Engrg)
Fred Waugh (VP-Mktg)

Atego Group Ltd. (1)
701 Eagle Tower, Montpellier Drive, Cheltenham, GL50 1TA, United Kingdom
Tel.: (44) 1242229300
Web Site: http://www.atego.com
Software Publishing Services
N.A.I.C.S.: 513210
Quentin Baer (Chm)

Atego SAS (1)
5-7 rue de la Gare, 92130, Issy-les-Moulineaux, France
Tel.: (33) 141461999
Software Publishing Services
N.A.I.C.S.: 513210

ColdLight Solutions, LLC (1)
550 E Swedesford Rd Ste 260, Wayne, PA 19087
Tel.: (877) 493-7186
Web Site: http://www.coldlight.com
Sales Range: $1-9.9 Million
Emp.: 18
Predictive Analytics Software Developer
N.A.I.C.S.: 513210

IOXP GmbH (1)
Julius-Hatry-Strasse 1, 68163, Mannheim, Germany
Tel.: (49) 62115028580
Web Site: http://www.ioxp.de
Information Technology Services
N.A.I.C.S.: 541519
Holger Mengay-Eckstein (Mng Dir)

Logistics Business Systems Limited (1)
6 Sceptre Way Sceptre Point, Bamber Bridge, Preston, PR5 6AW, United Kingdom
Tel.: (44) 1772315050
Software Product Development Services
N.A.I.C.S.: 513210

MCA Solutions BVBA (1)
Pegasuslaan 5, Machelen, 1831, Vlaams Brabant, Belgium
Tel.: (32) 22518542
Software Product Development Services
N.A.I.C.S.: 541511

OnShape Inc. (1)
One Alewife Ctr Ste 130, Cambridge, MA 02140
Web Site: http://www.onshape.com
Application Software Services
N.A.I.C.S.: 541511

PTC (Canada) Inc. (1)
3773 Cote Vertu Office 200, Montreal, H4R 2M3, QC, Canada (100%)
Tel.: (514) 333-4010
Sales Range: $1-9.9 Million
Emp.: 8
Prepackaged Software
N.A.I.C.S.: 334610

Unit (Domestic):

Parametric Technology (Canada) Ltd. - Waterloo (2)
410 Albert Street, Waterloo, N2L 3V3, ON, Canada
Tel.: (519) 884-2251
Web Site: http://www.ptc.com
Software Configuration Management & UNIX to Windows Cross Platform Development Tools Services
N.A.I.C.S.: 541512

PTC (SSI) Limited (1)
12 Camden Row, Dublin, 8, Ireland
Tel.: (353) 14793207
Software Product Development Services
N.A.I.C.S.: 541511
Eamonn Clarke (Gen Mgr)

PTC Eastern Europe Limited S.R.L. (1)
Tel.: (40) 312255440
Web Site: http://www.ptc.ro
Emp.: 200
Software Publisher
N.A.I.C.S.: 513210

PTC Inc. - Fairfax (1)
12701 Fair Lakes Cir Ste 350, Fairfax, VA 22033-4910
Tel.: (703) 803-3343
Web Site: http://www.ptc.com
Sales Range: $10-24.9 Million
Emp.: 30
Software Products & Consulting Services
N.A.I.C.S.: 513210

PTC Inc. - Fort Collins (1)
3801 Automation Way Ste 110, Fort Collins, CO 80525-3434
Tel.: (970) 267-8000
Web Site: http://www.ptc.com
Sales Range: $75-99.9 Million
Flexible CAD & Collaborative PLM Applications Developer
N.A.I.C.S.: 541511

PTC Inc. - Needham (1)
140 Kendrick St, Needham, MA 02494
Tel.: (781) 370-5000
Web Site: http://www.ptc.com
Sales Range: $10-24.9 Million
Emp.: 100
Math, Science & Engineering Software Mfr & Marketer for Business, Academia, Research & Government
N.A.I.C.S.: 541511

PTC International Limited Liability Company (1)
Rusakovaskaya Street 13, 107140, Moscow, Russia
Tel.: (7) 4999739598
Software Publisher
N.A.I.C.S.: 513210

PTC Japan KK (1)
37 Flr Shinjuku Oak Tower 6-8-1 Nishishinjuku, Shinjuku-ku, Tokyo, 163-6037, Japan
Tel.: (81) 333468100
Web Site: http://www.ja.ptc.com
Emp.: 100
Software Publisher
N.A.I.C.S.: 513210

PTC Software (India) Private Limited (1)
Marisoft-II Survey No 15 Vadgaonsheri, Kalyaninagar, Pune, 411 014, Maharashtra, India
Tel.: (91) 2066053000
Sales Range: $200-249.9 Million
Emp.: 1,500
Software Publisher
N.A.I.C.S.: 513210

Parametric Tech Brasil Ltda. (1)
Rua Samuel Morse 120 3 Andar CJ 33 34, 04576-060, Sao Paulo, SP, Brazil (100%)
Tel.: (55) 1155011279
Web Site: http://www.ptc.com
Sales Range: $1-9.9 Million
Emp.: 15
Prepackaged Software
N.A.I.C.S.: 334610

Parametric Technology (Denmark) A/S (1)
Tel.: (45) 43270600
Sales Range: $25-49.9 Million
Emp.: 12
Software Development Services
N.A.I.C.S.: 541511

Parametric Technology (Hong Kong) Limited (1) (100%)
Tel.: (852) 28028982
Web Site: http://www.ttc.com
Sales Range: $10-24.9 Million
Emp.: 45
Prepackaged Software
N.A.I.C.S.: 334610

Parametric Technology (India) Private Ltd. (1)
Marisoft - II Survey No 15 Vadgaonsheri Kalyani Nagar, Pune, 411 014, India
Tel.: (91) 2066053000

Web Site: http://www.ptc.com
Computer Software Publishing Services
N.A.I.C.S.: 513210

Parametric Technology Australia Pty. Limited (1)
Level 17 9 Castlereagh Street, Botany, Sydney, 2000, NSW, Australia
Tel.: (61) 291528770
Computer Peripheral Equipment & Software Whslr
N.A.I.C.S.: 423430

Parametric Technology Corporation (Malaysia) Sdn. Bhd. (1)
Level 28 The Gardens South Tower Mid Valley City Lingkaran Syed Putra, Kuala Lumpur, 59200, Malaysia
Tel.: (60) 322987360
Information Technology Consulting Services
N.A.I.C.S.: 541618

Parametric Technology Espana, S.A. (1)
Tel.: (34) 934751200
Software Publisher
N.A.I.C.S.: 513210

Parametric Technology Europe B.V. (1)
Beta Technology & Business Accelerator Unit K119, 5656 AE, Eindhoven, Netherlands (100%)
Tel.: (31) 408519240
Sales Range: $100-124.9 Million
Prepackaged Software
N.A.I.C.S.: 334610

Subsidiary (Non-US):

Parametric Technology (Schweiz) AG (2)
Badenerstrasse 15, 8004, Zurich, Switzerland (100%)
Tel.: (41) 448243434
Sales Range: $10-24.9 Million
Emp.: 10
Prepackaged Software
N.A.I.C.S.: 334610

Parametric Technology (UK) Ltd. (2)
(100%)
Tel.: (44) 1252410008
Sales Range: $10-24.9 Million
Emp.: 60
Prepackaged Software
N.A.I.C.S.: 334610

Parametric Technology GmbH (2)
(100%)
Tel.: (49) 89321060
Web Site: https://www.ptc.com
Sales Range: $25-49.9 Million
Emp.: 130
Prepackaged Software
N.A.I.C.S.: 334610
Rolf Seifert (Mng Dir)

Unit (Domestic):

Parametric Technology GmbH - Sindelfingen (3)
Posener Strasse 1, Sindelfingen, 71065, Germany
Tel.: (49) 7031 951 0
Web Site: http://www.ptc.com
Developer of Collaboration Software
N.A.I.C.S.: 334610

Subsidiary (Non-US):

Parametric Technology S.A. (2)
350 JRGG de la Lauziere 70543, CS 70543, 13594, Aix-en-Provence, Cedex, France (100%)
Tel.: (33) 442970000
Sales Range: $25-49.9 Million
Emp.: 150
Prepackaged Software
N.A.I.C.S.: 334610

Parametric Technology Gesellschaft, m.b.H. (1)
Munchner Bundesstrasse 142, Salzburg, 5020, Austria
Tel.: (43) 6624266240
Computer Peripheral Equipment & Software Whslr
N.A.I.C.S.: 423430

Parametric Technology Israel Ltd. (1)
HaMada St 9 Gav-Yam Park North, PO Box 12471, Herzliyya, 46733, Israel
Tel.: (972) 99614300
Software Publisher
N.A.I.C.S.: 513210

Parametric Technology Mexico, S.A. de C.V. (1)
Paseo de la Reforma 350 piso 10, Colonia Juarez, Chihuahua, 06600, Chihuahua, Mexico
Tel.: (52) 5591711592
Electronic Components Mfr
N.A.I.C.S.: 334417

Parametric Technology Singapore Pte. Ltd. (1)
Tel.: (65) 62322080
Software Publisher
N.A.I.C.S.: 513210

Qualcomm Connected Experiences Switzerland AG (1)
Forrlibuckstrasse 178, Zurich, 8005, Switzerland
Tel.: (41) 439608686
Software Publishing Services
N.A.I.C.S.: 513210

ServiceMax Australia Pty. Ltd. (1)
2 Morven Gardens, Greenwich, 2065, NSW, Australia
Tel.: (61) 1300000629
Web Site: https://servicemax.com.au
Field Service Management Software Development Services
N.A.I.C.S.: 541511

ServiceMax Global Ltd. (1)
14 Garrick Street, London, WC2E 9BJ, United Kingdom
Tel.: (44) 2038467320
Field Service Management Software Development Services
N.A.I.C.S.: 518210

ServiceMax Technologies (India) Private Limited (1)
1 & 2 Murphy Road The Millenia Tower A Level 1 and 2, Halasuru, Bengaluru, 560008, India
Tel.: (91) 8049298000
Field Service Management Software Development Services
N.A.I.C.S.: 518210

TWNKLS B.V. (1)
Stationsplein 45 Unit B1 036, 3013 AK, Rotterdam, Netherlands
Tel.: (31) 102600200
Web Site: http://www.twnkls.com
Application Software Services
N.A.I.C.S.: 541511

ThingWorx, Inc. (1)
350 Eagleview Blvd Ste 200, Exton, PA 19341
Tel.: (610) 594-6200
Web Site: http://www.thingworx.com
Emp.: 92
Software Development Services
N.A.I.C.S.: 513210

pure-systems GmbH (1)
Carl-Miller-Str 6, 39112, Magdeburg, Germany
Tel.: (49) 3915445690
Web Site: https://www.pure-systems.com
Enterprise Software Development Services
N.A.I.C.S.: 541511

PTC THERAPEUTICS, INC.
500 Warren Corporate Ctr Dr, Warren, NJ 07080
Tel.: (908) 222-7000   DE
Web Site: https://www.ptcbio.com
Year Founded: 1998
PTCT—(NASDAQ)
Rev.: $698,801,000
Assets: $1,705,619,000
Liabilities: $2,052,705,000
Net Worth: ($347,086,000)
Earnings: ($559,017,000)
Emp.: 1,410
Fiscal Year-end: 12/31/22

Pharmaceutical Developer
N.A.I.C.S.: 325412
Pierre Gravier (CFO)
Stuart W. Peltz (Founder)
Mark E. Boulding (Chief Legal Officer & Exec VP)
Michael Schmertzler (Chm)
Allan Steven Jacobson (Executives)
Martin Rexroad (Chief Culture & Community Officer)
Mary Frances Harmon (Sr VP-Corp & Patient Rels)
Matthew B. Klein (Pres & CEO)
Hege Sollie-Zetlmayer (Sr VP-HR)
Golden Lee (Chief Medical Officer)
Kylie O'Keefe (Chief Comml Officer)
Ellen Welch (Chief Scientific Officer)
Eric Pauwels (Chief Bus Officer)
Eric Pauwels (Chief Bus Officer)

Subsidiaries:

PTC Therapeutics International Limited (1)
5th Floor 3 Grand Canal Plaza Grand Canal Street Upper, Dublin, D04 EE70, Ireland
Tel.: (353) 1 906 8700
Web Site: https://www.ptcbio.ie
Pharmaceutical Developer
N.A.I.C.S.: 325412

PTK ACQUISITION CORP.
4601 Wilshire Blvd Ste 240, Los Angeles, CA 90010
Tel.: (213) 625-8886   DE
Web Site: http://www.ptktech.com
Year Founded: 2019
PTKU—(NYSEAMEX)
Assets: $115,403,470
Liabilities: $110,403,469
Net Worth: $5,000,001
Earnings: ($724,516)
Fiscal Year-end: 12/31/20
Investment Services
N.A.I.C.S.: 523999
Peter Kuo (Co-Founder & CEO)
Timothy Chen (Co-Founder & CFO)
Ker Zhang (Co-Founder & Sec)
John Hui (Co-Founder)
Vincent Tsai (Mng Dir)
Sumeet Mehra (Mng Dir)

PTS, INC.
1318-B Putman Dr, Huntsville, AL 35816
Tel.: (256) 539-6787   AL
Web Site: https://pts-inc.com
Year Founded: 1996
PTSH—(OTCIQ)
Technical Services
N.A.I.C.S.: 541990

PUBLIC COMPANY MANAGEMENT CORPORATION
9350 Wilshire Blvd Ste 203, Beverly Hills, CA 90212
Tel.: (310) 862-1957   NV
Web Site:
https://www.pubcomanagement.com
PCMC—(OTCIQ)
Assets: $58,766
Liabilities: $555,593
Net Worth: ($496,827)
Earnings: ($35,808)
Fiscal Year-end: 09/30/23
Management Consulting Services
N.A.I.C.S.: 541611
Patrick McMahon (Pres)

PUBLIC POLICY HOLDING COMPANY
800 N Capitol St, NW Ste 800, Washington, DC 20002
Tel.: (202) 688-0020
Web Site: https://pphcompany.com
Year Founded: 2014
PPHC—(AIM)

Holding Company
N.A.I.C.S.: 551112

Subsidiaries:

Multistate Associates Inc. (1)
515 King St Ste 300, Alexandria, VA 22314-3137
Tel.: (703) 368-1110
Web Site: http://www.multistate.com
Scientific & Technical Consulting Services
N.A.I.C.S.: 541690
Paul Hallman (Pres)

PUBLIC SERVICE CO OF NEW MEXICO
Tel.: (505) 241-2750
Web Site: https://www.pnm.com
Year Founded: 1917
PNM—(NYSE)
Rev.: $1,766,825,000
Assets: $6,272,166,000
Liabilities: $4,311,842,000
Net Worth: $1,960,324,000
Earnings: $103,898,000
Emp.: 751
Fiscal Year-end: 12/31/22
Natural Gas Distr
N.A.I.C.S.: 221210
Robert J. Schoen (Mng Dir)
Pat Vincent-Collawn (Chm & CEO)
Don Tarry (Pres & CEO)
Brian Iverson (Gen Counsel, Sec & Sr VP)
Lisa Eden (CFO & Sr VP)
Mike Mertz (Sr VP-Operations)
Sabrina Greinel (Treas & VP)
Kathleen Larese (VP-Customer Ops)
Sheila Mendez (CIO & VP)
Omni Warner (VP-Operations & Engineering)
Laurie Williams (VP-Integrated Plng)
Henry E. Monroy (VP-Regulatory)
Julie Rowey (Chief Customer Officer & VP)
Becky Teague (VP-Human Resources)

PUBLIC SERVICE ENTERPRISE GROUP INCORPORATED
80 Park Plz, Newark, NJ 07102
Tel.: (973) 430-7000   NJ
Web Site: https://nj.pseg.com
Year Founded: 1903
PEG—(NYSE)
Rev.: $11,237,000,000
Assets: $50,741,000,000
Liabilities: $35,264,000,000
Net Worth: $15,477,000,000
Earnings: $2,563,000,000
Emp.: 12,543
Fiscal Year-end: 12/31/23
Diversified Energy & Energy Services Holding Company
N.A.I.C.S.: 221210
Grace Park (Gen Counsel & Exec VP)
Ralph A. Larossa (Chm, Pres & CEO)
Shahid Malik (Pres-PSEG Energy Resources & Trade)
Lathrop Craig (VP-ISO Ops-PSEG Energy Resources & Trade)
Tamara L. Linde (Chief Legal Officer & Exec VP)
Daniel J. Cregg (CFO & Exec VP)
Richard T. Thigpen (Sr VP-Corp Citizenship)
Rose M. Chernick (VP & Controller)
Sheila J. Rostiac (Chief HR Officer, Chief Diversity Officer & Sr VP-HR)
Zeeshan Sheikh (Chief Information & Digital Officer & Sr VP)

Subsidiaries:

PSEG Energy Holdings LLC (1)
80 Park Plz, Newark, NJ 07102 (100%)
Tel.: (973) 430-7000

Public Service Enterprise Group Incorporated—(Continued)

Web Site: http://www.pseg.com
Sales Range: $1-4.9 Billion
Emp.: 200
Non-Utility Holdings
N.A.I.C.S.: 221111

Subsidiary (Domestic):

PSEG Energy Resources & Trade LLC (2)
80 Park Plz, Newark, NJ 07102
Tel.: (973) 430-7000
Web Site: http://www.pseg.com
Sales Range: $650-699.9 Million
Asset Based Trading
N.A.I.C.S.: 522299

PSEG Global LLC (2)
80 Park Plz, Newark, NJ 07102
Tel.: (973) 430-7000
Web Site: http://www.pseg.com
Sales Range: $100-124.9 Million
Develops, Acquires, Owns, Operates & Invests in Independent Power Generators
N.A.I.C.S.: 335312

PSEG Resources LLC (2)
80 Park Plaza Ste 3, Newark, NJ 07102 (100%)
Tel.: (973) 430-7000
Web Site: http://www.pseg.com
Sales Range: $200-249.9 Million
Emp.: 14
Energy Related Financial Transactions
N.A.I.C.S.: 221111

PSEG Power LLC (1)
80 Park Plz, Newark, NJ 07102 (100%)
Tel.: (973) 430-7000
Web Site: http://www.pseg.com
Rev.: $3,634,000,000
Assets: $12,704,000,000
Liabilities: $5,100,000,000
Net Worth: $7,604,000,000
Earnings: $594,000,000
Emp.: 2,033
Fiscal Year-end: 12/31/2020
Electric Power Distr
N.A.I.C.S.: 221122
Tamara L. Linde (Gen Counsel & Exec VP)
Daniel J. Cregg (CFO & Exec VP)
Tamara L. Linde (Gen Counsel & Exec VP)
Rose M. Chernick (VP & Controller)
Brian J. Clark (Sr VP-Fossil Ops)
Carl J. Fricker (VP-Power Ops Support)

Subsidiary (Domestic):

PSEG Power Fossil LLC (2)
80 Park Plz Ste 3, Newark, NJ 07102
Tel.: (973) 430-7000
Web Site: http://www.pseg.com
Sales Range: $650-699.9 Million
Emp.: 169
Natural Gas, Coal & Oil Fired Generating Units Operator
N.A.I.C.S.: 211120

Public Service Electric & Gas Company (1)
80 Park Plz, Newark, NJ 07102
Tel.: (973) 430-7000
Web Site: https://investor.pseg.com
Rev.: $7,807,000,000
Assets: $42,873,000,000
Liabilities: $25,825,000,000
Net Worth: $17,048,000,000
Earnings: $1,515,000,000
Emp.: 7,240
Fiscal Year-end: 12/31/2023
Electric & Gas Distribution & Generation Services
N.A.I.C.S.: 221112
Daniel J. Cregg (CFO & Exec VP)
Kim C. Hanemann (Pres & COO)
Eric Carr (Pres)

Subsidiary (Domestic):

PSEG Services Corp. (2)
80 Park Plaza - T11, Newark, NJ 07102
Tel.: (973) 430-7842
Web Site: http://nj.pseg.com
Sales Range: $200-249.9 Million
Emp.: 1,500
Electronic Services
N.A.I.C.S.: 561110

PUBLIC STORAGE
701 Western Ave, Glendale, CA 91201-2349
Tel.: (818) 244-8080 MD
Web Site:
    https://www.publicstorage.com
Year Founded: 1972
PSA—(NYSE)
Rev.: $4,517,690,000
Assets: $19,809,216,000
Liabilities: $9,702,270,000
Net Worth: $10,106,946,000
Earnings: $1,948,741,000
Emp.: 6,200
Fiscal Year-end: 12/31/23
Real Estate Investment Trust; Self-Storage Facility Owner & Operator
N.A.I.C.S.: 525990
Nathaniel A. Vitan (Chief Legal Officer, Sec & Sr VP)
H. Thomas Boyle III (CFO)
Natalia N. Johnson (Chief Admin Officer)
Joseph D. Russell Jr. (Pres & CEO)

Subsidiaries:

PS Orangeco, Inc. (1)
701 Western Ave, Glendale, CA 91201-2349 (100%)
Tel.: (818) 244-8080
Web Site: http://www.publicstorage.com
Sales Range: $50-74.9 Million
Emp.: 6
Portable Self-Storage, Truck Leasing & Storage Products Sales
N.A.I.C.S.: 531130

Public Storage OP, LP (1)
653 Jefferic Blvd, Dover, DE 19901
Tel.: (302) 760-9238
Storage Unit Services
N.A.I.C.S.: 531130

Public Storage Properties (1)
701 Western Ave, Glendale, CA 91201-2349
Tel.: (818) 244-8080
Web Site: http://www.publicstorage.com
Sales Range: $1-9.9 Million
Emp.: 300
Commercial Real Estate Properties Acquisition & Development
N.A.I.C.S.: 531390

Shurgard Self Storage S.C.A. (1)
Breedveld 31, 1702, Groot-Bijgaarden, Belgium (49%)
Tel.: (32) 24642990
Web Site: https://www.shurgard.com
Sales Range: $25-49.9 Million
Emp.: 65
Self-Storage Facilities Owner & Operator
N.A.I.C.S.: 531130
Marc Oursin (CEO)
Jean-Louis Reinalda (VP-Real Estate)
Ammar Kharouf (VP-HR & Legal)
Duncan Bell (VP-Ops)
Jean Kreusch (CFO)

Simply Storage Management LLC (1)
7932 W Sand Lake Rd Ste 108, Orlando, FL 32819
Tel.: (407) 248-7878
Web Site: http://www.simplyss.com
Sales Range: $25-49.9 Million
Emp.: 27
Self Storage Facilities Owner & Operator
N.A.I.C.S.: 531130

ezStorage Corp. of Maryland (1)
5329 Westbard Ave, Bethesda, MD 20816
Tel.: (301) 718-4600
Web Site: http://www.ezstorage.com
Rev.: $3,000,000
Emp.: 50
General Warehousing & Storage
N.A.I.C.S.: 493110
Anthony Manganaro (Owner)

PUBLICSQ. INC.
250 S Australian Ave Ste 1300, West Palm Beach, FL 33401
Tel.: (561) 805-3588 DE

Web Site:
    https://investors.publicsq.com
Year Founded: 2021
PSQH—(NYSE)
Holding Company
N.A.I.C.S.: 551112
Michael Seifert (Founder, Chm, Pres & CEO)

PUBMATIC INC.
601 Marshall St, Redwood City, CA 94063
Tel.: (650) 331-3485
Web Site: https://www.pubmatic.com
Year Founded: 2006
PUBM—(NASDAQ)
Rev.: $256,380,000
Assets: $642,175,000
Liabilities: $329,987,000
Net Worth: $312,188,000
Earnings: $28,705,000
Emp.: 875
Fiscal Year-end: 12/31/22
Digital Media Platform Developer
N.A.I.C.S.: 513210
Mukul Kumar (Co-Founder & Pres-Engrg)
Anand Das (Co-Founder)
Steven Pantelick (CFO)
Paulina Klimenko (Chief Growth Officer)
Jason Barnes (Chief Revenue Officer-Asia Pacific)
Emma Newman (Chief Revenue Officer-Europe, Middle East & Africa)
Kyle Dozeman (Chief Revenue Officer-Americas)
Johanna Bauman (CMO)
Michael Van Der Zweep (Controller)
Nishant Khatri (Sr VP-Product Mgmt)
Lorrie Dougherty (Sr VP-HR)
Lisa Gimbel (Chief Acctg Officer)
Jaan Janes (VP)
Andrew Woods (Gen Counsel)
Franck Lewkowicz (Country Mgr-France)
Cristian Coccia (Reg VP-Southern Europe)
Rajeev K. Goel (Co-Founder & CEO)
Amar K. Goel (Co-Founder, Chm & Chief Innovation Officer)

PUGET TECHNOLOGIES, INC.
1200 N Federal Hwy Ste 200-A, Boca Raton, FL 33432
Tel.: (614) 246-0070 NV
Web Site:
    http://www.pugettechnologies.com
Year Founded: 2010
PUGE—(OTCIQ)
Assets: $55
Liabilities: $324,147
Net Worth: ($324,092)
Earnings: ($1,378,110)
Emp.: 2
Fiscal Year-end: 10/31/20
Wool Bedding Products Distr
N.A.I.C.S.: 423220
Hermann Burckhardt (Chm, Pres & CEO)
Victor German Quintero (CTO)
Thomas M. Jaspers (CFO, Treas & Sec)

PUISSANT INDUSTRIES, INC.
480 Lexington Rd, Lexington, KY 40383
Tel.: (423) 994-0352 FL
Web Site: http://www.psss.co
Year Founded: 2009
PSSS—(OTCIQ)
Oil & Gas Exploration Services
N.A.I.C.S.: 211120
Mark E. Holbrook (Founder & Pres)
Marshall E. Holbrook (Founder & VP)
Cora J. Holbrook (Founder, CFO, Treas & Sec)

PULMATRIX, INC.
945 Concord St Ste 1217, Framingham, MA 01701
Tel.: (781) 357-2333 DE
Web Site: https://www.pulmatrix.com
Year Founded: 2013
PULM—(NASDAQ)
Rev.: $6,071,000
Assets: $40,953,000
Liabilities: $9,844,000
Net Worth: $31,109,000
Earnings: ($18,836,000)
Emp.: 28
Fiscal Year-end: 12/31/22
Pharmaceuticals Mfr
N.A.I.C.S.: 325412
Teofilo David Raad (Pres & CEO)
Michael J. Higgins (Chm)
Richard P. Batycky (Sr VP-R&D)
Michelle S. Siegert (Treas, Sec & VP-Fin)
David A. Edwards (Bd of Dirs & Co-Founder)
Steven Kramer (VP-Quality)

Subsidiaries:

Pulmatrix Operating Company (1)
99 Hayden Ave Ste 390, Lexington, MA 02421
Tel.: (781) 357-2333
Web Site: http://www.pulmatrix.com
Sales Range: $1-9.9 Million
Emp.: 30
Pulmonary Medical Instrument Developer
N.A.I.C.S.: 339112

PULMONX CORPORATION
700 Chesapeake Dr, Redwood City, CA 94063
Tel.: (650) 364-0400 DE
Web Site: https://www.pulmonx.com
Year Founded: 1995
LUNG—(NASDAQ)
Rev.: $53,662,000
Assets: $193,676,000
Liabilities: $39,669,000
Net Worth: $154,007,000
Earnings: ($58,923,000)
Emp.: 269
Fiscal Year-end: 12/31/22
Medical Device Mfr & Distr
N.A.I.C.S.: 339112
Steven S. Williamson (Pres & CEO)
John McKune (VP & Controller)
John McKune (VP & Controller)
Mehul Joshi (CFO & Principal Acctg Officer)
Beran Rose (Chief Comml Officer)
Sri Radhakrishnan (Chief Technical Officer)
David Lehman (Gen Counsel)
Jerome Erath (Sr VP & Gen Mgr-Europe, The Middle East, and Africa)
Narinder S. Shargill (VP-Global Medical Affairs)
Kelly M. Shriner (VP-Patient Access)
Lauren Cristina (VP-Fin & Admin)
Marcee Maroney (VP-Mktg)
Lisa Paul (Chief People Officer)
Sarah Huber (VP-Sales)
Anna Gawlicka (VP-Clinical Affairs)
Bryan Hix (VP-Comml Ops)

Subsidiaries:

PulmonX International Sarl (1)
Rue de la Treille 4, 2000, Neuchatel, Switzerland
Tel.: (41) 324752076
Surgical & Medical Instrument Mfr
N.A.I.C.S.: 339112

Pulmonx Australia Pty Ltd (1)
Suite 5 Level 6 65 York Street, Sydney, 2000, NSW, Australia
Tel.: (61) 1300785666
Web Site: https://www.pulmonx.com.au
Surgical & Medical Instrument Mfr
N.A.I.C.S.: 339112

PULSE BIOSCIENCES, INC.

3957 Point Eden Way, Hayward, CA 94545
Tel.: (510) 906-4600   NV
Web Site:
  https://www.pulsebiosciences.com
Year Founded: 2014
PLSE—(NASDAQ)
Rev.: $700,000
Assets: $77,877,000
Liabilities: $80,125,000
Net Worth: ($2,248,000)
Earnings: ($58,505,000)
Emp.: 61
Fiscal Year-end: 12/31/22
Biological Research & Development Services
N.A.I.C.S.: 541715
Darrin R. Uecker (CTO)
Niv Ad (Chief Science Officer-Cardiac Surgery)
Mitchell E. Levinson (Chief Strategy Officer)
Richard Nuccitelli (Chief Science Officer)
David Danitz (VP-Engrg)
Robert Tyson (VP-Sls-North America)
Holly Hartman (VP-Bus Dev & Corp Strategy)
William Knape (VP-Regulatory, Clinical & Quality Affairs)
Edison Manuel (VP-Ops)
Patty Perla (VP-HR)
Ken Stratton (Gen Counsel & Co-Sec)
Kevin P. Danahy (Chief Comml Officer)
Joe Talarico (VP-Bus Dev)
Gansevoort Dunnington (Chief Medical Officer)
Robert W. Duggan (Exec Chm)
Burke T. Barrett (Pres, CEO & Principal Financial Officer)

PULSE EVOLUTION CORPORATION

11450 SE Dixie Hwy, Hobe Sound, FL 33455
Tel.: (772) 545-9050
Year Founded: 2013
PLFX—(NASDAQ)
Emp.: 40
Information Technology Services
N.A.I.C.S.: 513210

PULTEGROUP, INC.

3350 Peachtree Rd NE, Atlanta, GA 30326
Tel.: (404) 978-6400   MI
Web Site:
  https://www.pultegroupinc.com
Year Founded: 1950
PHM—(NYSE)
Rev.: $16,061,578,000
Assets: $16,087,050,000
Liabilities: $5,703,793,000
Net Worth: $10,383,257,000
Earnings: $2,602,372,000
Emp.: 6,382
Fiscal Year-end: 12/31/23
Holding Company; New Housing Operative Builder, Real Estate Brokerage, Sales & Mortgage Services
N.A.I.C.S.: 551112
Robert T. O'Shaughnessy (Exec VP)
Kevin A. Henry (Chief People Officer & Exec VP)
Manish M. Shrivastava (CMO & VP)
Ryan R. Marshall (Pres & CEO)
Joseph L. Drouin (CIO & VP)
Kimberly M. Hill (VP-Tax & Asst Sec)
Todd N. Sheldon (Gen Counsel, Sec & Exec VP)
D. Bryce Langen (Treas & VP)
Brien P. O'Meara (Principal Acctg Officer, VP & Controller)

Michelle Hairston (Sr VP-HR)
Macey Kessler (Mgr-Corp Comm)
Tommy Oswald (Mgr-Procurement-Northeast Florida)
Matthew W. Koart (COO & Exec VP)
Michelle Gregorec (Pres-Arizona)
Chris Edgar (Pres-West)
James L. Ossowski (CFO & Exec VP)

Subsidiaries:

Bay Vista At Meadow Park, L.P. (1)
5 Hutchins Way Ste 100, Novato, CA 94949
Tel.: (415) 382-0801
Web Site: http://www.jsco.net
Residential Construction
N.A.I.C.S.: 236220

Butterfield Properties LLC (1)
477 E Bttrfeld Rd, Lombard, IL 60148
Tel.: (630) 691-9999
Web Site:
  http://www.butterfieldproperties.com
Real Estate Management Services
N.A.I.C.S.: 531390

Conestoga Golf Club LLC (1)
1499 Falcon Rdg Pkwy, Mesquite, NV 89034
Tel.: (702) 346-4292
Web Site: http://www.conestogagolf.com
Sales Range: $25-49.9 Million
Emp.: 35
Golf Course Services
N.A.I.C.S.: 713910
Mark Whetzel (Dir-Golf)

Del Webb Communities of Virginia, Inc. (1)
201 Castle Hill Dr, Fredericksburg, VA 22406
Tel.: (540) 374-8700
Web Site: http://www.delwebb.com
Sales Range: $10-24.9 Million
Emp.: 3
Home Building & Community Services
N.A.I.C.S.: 624229

Del Webb Corporation (1)
100 Bloomfield Hills Pkwy Ste 300, Bloomfield Hills, MI 48304
Tel.: (248) 647-2750
Web Site: http://www.pulte.com
Sales Range: $1-4.9 Billion
Emp.: 300
Retirement Community Housing Operative Builder & Brokerage Services
N.A.I.C.S.: 236117
William J. Pulte (Chm)

Holding (Domestic):

Sun City Hilton Head (2)
25 Thurmond Way, Bluffton, SC 29910   (100%)
Tel.: (843) 757-5857
Web Site: https://www.suncityhiltonhead.org
Sales Range: $50-74.9 Million
Adult Community
N.A.I.C.S.: 623312

Sun City Huntley (2)
12880 Del Webb Blvd, Huntley, IL 60142   (100%)
Tel.: (847) 515-7650
Web Site: http://www.sccah.com
Sales Range: $50-74.9 Million
Adult Community
N.A.I.C.S.: 623312

Sun City Texas (2)
1501 Sun City Blvd, Georgetown, TX 78633-4987
Tel.: (512) 931-6900
Web Site: http://www.pulte.com
Sales Range: $75-99.9 Million
Emp.: 20
Adult Community
N.A.I.C.S.: 623312

Del Webb Texas Limited Partnership (1)
Tel.: (512) 729-1228
Web Site: http://www.delwebb.com
Residential Construction
N.A.I.C.S.: 236115

DiVosta Building, LLC (1)

4500 PGA Blvd, Palm Beach Gardens, FL 33418-3994
Tel.: (561) 627-2112
Web Site: http://www.divosta.com
Civil Engineering Services
N.A.I.C.S.: 541330

Hillcrest Golf & Country Club, Ltd. (1)
4600 Hillcrest Dr, Hollywood, FL 33021   (100%)
Tel.: (954) 987-5000
Web Site: http://www.hillcrestgcc.com
Sales Range: $1-9.9 Million
Emp.: 70
Golf Course & Country Club
N.A.I.C.S.: 713910

Innovative Construction Group, LLC (1)
5216 Shad Rd, Jacksonville, FL 32257
Tel.: (904) 398-5690
Web Site: http://www.icgbuilds.com
Construction Contracting Services
N.A.I.C.S.: 236220
Ryan Melin (Pres)
Andrew Melin (VP-Continuous Improvement)
Chris Pisano (Mgr-Bus Dev)

John Wieland Homes & Neighborhoods, Inc. (1)
360 Concord St, Alpharetta, GA 30009
Tel.: (678) 839-9528
Web Site: http://www.jwhomes.com
Single-family Residential Construction
N.A.I.C.S.: 236117

LCD Communications LLC (1)
1511 Imperial Crown Dr, Houston, TX 77043-3348
Tel.: (713) 467-9156
Telephone Services
N.A.I.C.S.: 517121

PCD Realty LLC (1)
16767 N Perimeter Dr Ste 100, Scottsdale, AZ 85260
Tel.: (480) 860-5332
Real Estate Services
N.A.I.C.S.: 531210
Taylor Mize (Gen Sls Mgr)

Pulte Arizona Services, Inc. (1)
12339 N 93rd Wy, Scottsdale, AZ 85260   (100%)
Tel.: (480) 631-2914
Residential Construction Services
N.A.I.C.S.: 236117

Pulte Georgia (1)
360 Concord St, Alpharetta, GA 30009   (100%)
Tel.: (678) 839-9528
Web Site: http://www.pulte.com
Sales Range: $25-49.9 Million
Emp.: 100
Residential Construction Services
N.A.I.C.S.: 541611

Pulte Home Company, LLC (1)
100 Bloomfield Hills Pkwy Ste 300, Bloomfield Hills, MI 48304
Tel.: (248) 647-2750
Web Site: http://www.pulte.com
Emp.: 300
Building Construction Services
N.A.I.C.S.: 236115

Pulte Homes - Cary (1)
1000 Pyrenees Way, Cary, NC 27519
Tel.: (919) 759-6380
Web Site: http://www.pulte.com
Sales Range: $50-74.9 Million
Emp.: 100
Residential Construction Services
N.A.I.C.S.: 236115

Pulte Homes - Southwest Florida (1)
18405 Parksville Dr, Estero, FL 33928-3501
Tel.: (239) 356-0122
Sales Range: $150-199.9 Million
Residential Construction Services
N.A.I.C.S.: 236115

Pulte Homes - St. Louis (1)
16640 Chesterfield Grove Ste 200, Chesterfield, MO 63005
Tel.: (636) 537-7000
Rev.: $189,826,879
Emp.: 100

New Construction, Single-Family Houses
N.A.I.C.S.: 236115

Pulte Homes - Tampa (1)
3810 Northdale Blvd Ste 100, Tampa, FL 33624-1870   (100%)
Tel.: (813) 265-3343
Web Site: http://www.pulte.com
Sales Range: $50-74.9 Million
Emp.: 80
Residential Construction Services
N.A.I.C.S.: 236115

Pulte Homes - Washington, DC (1)
3047 Rittenhouse Cir, Fairfax, VA 22031-6208
Tel.: (703) 218-8134
Web Site: http://www.pulte.com
Sales Range: $50-74.9 Million
Emp.: 100
Residential Construction Services
N.A.I.C.S.: 236115

Pulte Homes Tennessee, Inc. (1)
1801 Ivy Crest Dr, Brentwood, TN 37027
Tel.: (866) 201-0092
Residential Construction
N.A.I.C.S.: 236118

Pulte Homes of Michigan, LLC (1)
100 Bloomfield Hills Pkwy Ste 150, Bloomfield Hills, MI 48304
Tel.: (248) 593-6699
Sales Range: $50-74.9 Million
Emp.: 35
Residential Construction Services
N.A.I.C.S.: 236115

Pulte Homes of New England LLC (1)
115 Flanders Rd Ste 200, Westborough, MA 01581-1089
Tel.: (508) 870-9999
Construction Services
N.A.I.C.S.: 236220

Pulte Homes of PA, Limited Partnership (1)
100 Bloomfield Hill Pkwy Ste 300, Bloomfield Hills, MI 48304
Tel.: (248) 647-2750
Web Site: http://www.pultehome.com
Emp.: 346
Residential Construction
N.A.I.C.S.: 236115

Pulte Homes of Texas, L.P. (1)
1234 Lake Shore Dr Ste 750A, Coppell, TX 75019-2484   (100%)
Tel.: (972) 304-2800
Web Site: http://www.pultehomes.com
Sales Range: $150-199.9 Million
Emp.: 170
Residential Construction
N.A.I.C.S.: 237210

Branch (Domestic):

Pulte Homes of Texas, L.P. - Dallas (2)
4800 Regent Blvd Ste 100, Irving, TX 75063-2439
Tel.: (972) 304-2805
Web Site: http://www.pulte.com
New Housing Operative Builder & Sales
N.A.I.C.S.: 236117

Pulte Homes of Texas, L.P. - Houston (2)
16670 Park Row Blvd Ste 100, Houston, TX 77084-6866
Tel.: (281) 749-8000
Web Site: http://www.pultegroup.com
Sales Range: $25-49.9 Million
Emp.: 160
Residential Construction Services
N.A.I.C.S.: 561612
Lindy Oliva (Pres)

Pulte International Corporation (1)
100 Bloomfield Hills Pkwy Ste 300, Bloomfield Hills, MI 48304-2950
Tel.: (248) 647-2750
Web Site: http://www.pultehomes.com
Emp.: 2
Residential Construction
N.A.I.C.S.: 236117

Pulte Mortgage LLC (1)

PulteGroup, Inc.—(Continued)

7390 S Lola St, Englewood, CO
80112 **(100%)**
Tel.: (303) 740-8800
Sales Range: $150-199.9 Million
Emp.: 500
Mortgage Banking & Sales Financing Services
N.A.I.C.S.: 522310

Pulte Payroll Corporation **(1)**
3350 Peachtree Road NE, Atlanta, GA
30326
Tel.: (248) 647-2750
Construction Services
N.A.I.C.S.: 236220

Pulte.com, Inc. **(1)**
100 Bloomfield Hills Pkwy, Bloomfield Hills,
MI 48304-2949
Tel.: (248) 644-7300
Web Site: http://www.pulte.com
Emp.: 300
Residential Construction
N.A.I.C.S.: 236116

PUMA BIOTECHNOLOGY, INC.
10880 Wilshire Blvd Ste 2150, Los
Angeles, CA 90024
Tel.: (424) 248-6500 **DE**
Web Site:
https://www.pumabiotechnolo
gy.com
Year Founded: 2010
PBYI—(NASDAQ)
Rev.: $228,031,000
Assets: $222,059,000
Liabilities: $200,451,000
Net Worth: $21,608,000
Earnings: $2,000
Emp.: 192
Fiscal Year-end: 12/31/22
Pharmaceutical Preparation Manufacturing
N.A.I.C.S.: 325412
Alan H. Auerbach (Chm, Pres &
CEO)
Douglas Hunt (Sr VP-Regulatory Affairs, Medical Writing & Project Mgmt)
Maximo F. Nougues (CFO)
Jeff J. Ludwing (Chief Comml Officer)

PURE BIOSCIENCE, INC.
771 Jamacha Rd Ste 512, El Cajon,
CA 92019
Tel.: (619) 596-8600 **CA**
Web Site: https://www.purebio.com
Year Founded: 1992
PURE—(OTCIQ)
Rev.: $3,927,000
Assets: $4,303,000
Liabilities: $970,000
Net Worth: $3,333,000
Earnings: ($2,319,000)
Emp.: 10
Fiscal Year-end: 07/31/21
Pharmaceutical Preparation Manufacturing
N.A.I.C.S.: 325412
Robert F. Bartlett (Pres & CEO)
Tom Myers (Exec VP-Dev & Tech)
Ivan Chen (Chm)
Dolana Blount (VP-Tech Dev & Regulatory Affairs)
Jason Kawata (VP-Food Div)
Zhinong Yan (Exec VP)
John Kasperski (VP)
Tim Steffensmeier (VP)
Tyler Mattson (VP)
Tucker Reigner (Reg Mgr)

PURE CAPITAL SOLUTIONS INC.
3800 American Blvd W Ste 1500,
Minneapolis, MN 55431
Tel.: (612) 584-0590 **UT**
Year Founded: 2010
PCST—(OTCIQ)
Television Broadcasting Services

N.A.I.C.S.: 516120
Christopher W. Allen (COO)
David Conley (CFO)
Steve Autrey (Pres)
Joseph C. Horvath (CEO)
Melissa Potts (Sec)

PURE CYCLE CORPORATION
34501 E Quincy Ave Bldg 65, Watkins, CO 80137
Tel.: (303) 292-3456 **CO**
Web Site:
https://www.purecyclewater.com
PCYO—(NASDAQ)
Rev.: $14,586,000
Assets: $133,216,000
Liabilities: $14,982,000
Net Worth: $118,234,000
Earnings: $4,699,000
Emp.: 38
Fiscal Year-end: 08/31/23
Water Utility Services
N.A.I.C.S.: 221310
Mark W. Harding (Pres & CEO)
Kevin B. McNeill (CFO, Principal
Acctg Officer & VP)
Scott E. Lehman (VP-Engrg)
Patrick J. Beirne (Chm)
Dirk Lashnits (VP-Land Dev)

PURE HARVEST CORPORATION GROUP, INC.
8879 Forrest Dr, Highlands Ranch,
CO 80126
Tel.: (303) 915-2027 **CO**
Web Site:
http://www.pureharvestcanna
bis.com
Year Founded: 2003
PHCG—(OTCIQ)
Rev.: $2,332,140
Assets: $11,039,983
Liabilities: $7,020,045
Net Worth: $4,019,938
Earnings: ($6,346,859)
Emp.: 25
Fiscal Year-end: 12/31/20
Medicinal Product Mfr
N.A.I.C.S.: 621511
Matthew Gregarek (Chm & CEO)

PURE STORAGE, INC.
650 Castro St Ste 400, Mountain
View, CA 94041 **DE**
Web Site:
https://www.purestorage.com
Year Founded: 2009
PSTG—(NYSE)
Rev.: $2,830,621,000
Assets: $3,655,760,000
Liabilities: $2,385,666,000
Net Worth: $1,270,094,000
Earnings: $61,311,000
Emp.: 5,600
Fiscal Year-end: 02/04/24
Computer Storage Device Mfr
N.A.I.C.S.: 334112
Scott Dietzen (Vice Chm)
John Colgrove (Founder & CTO)
Dan FitzSimons (Chief Revenue Officer)
Joseph Pinto (Chief Customer Experience Officer)
Kevan Krysler (CFO)
Ajay Singh (Chief Product Officer)
Todd Claverie (VP-Integrated Ops)
Mona Chu (Chief Acctg Officer & VP)
Charles H. Giancarlo (Chm & CEO)

Subsidiaries:

Pure Storage (RUS) Limited Liability
Company **(1)**
BC Zubovsky 21-23 bld 1 Zubovsky blvd,
Moscow, Russia
Tel.: (7) 9859995994
Computer Related Equipment Distr
N.A.I.C.S.: 423430

Pure Storage HK Ltd. **(1)**
Unit 37 23/F One Island East, Quarry Bay,
China (Hong Kong)
Tel.: (852) 37507835
Computer Software Services
N.A.I.C.S.: 541511
Jeff Ko (Mgr-Technical)

Pure Storage Ltd. **(1)**
3 Lotus Park The Causeway, Staines-upon-
Thames, TW18 3AG, Surrey, United Kingdom
Tel.: (44) 8002088116
Computer Software Services
N.A.I.C.S.: 541511
Lorrayne Gilbert (Sr Mgr-Mktg-Global)

Pure Storage New Zealand
Limited **(1)**
The Generator Level 10 11 Britomart Place,
Auckland, New Zealand
Tel.: (64) 800578302
Computer Related Equipment Distr
N.A.I.C.S.: 423430

PUREBASE CORPORATION
8631 Hwy 124, Ione, CA 95640
Tel.: (209) 274-9143 **NV**
Web Site: https://www.purebase.com
Year Founded: 2010
PUBC—(OTCIQ)
Rev.: $325,875
Assets: $811,521
Liabilities: $3,040,031
Net Worth: ($2,228,510)
Earnings: ($9,087,329)
Emp.: 7
Fiscal Year-end: 11/30/23
Investment Services
N.A.I.C.S.: 523999
Arthur Scott Dockter (Chm, Pres &
CEO)

PURECYCLE TECHNOLOGIES, INC.
4651 Salisbury Rd Ste 400, Jacksonville, FL 32256 **DE**
Web Site: https://www.purecycle.com
Year Founded: 2020
PCT—(NASDAQ)
Rev.: $2,641,000
Assets: $861,336,000
Liabilities: $350,453,000
Net Worth: $510,883,000
Earnings: ($84,746,000)
Emp.: 177
Fiscal Year-end: 12/31/22
Holding Company; Polypropylene
Plastic Mfr
N.A.I.C.S.: 551112
Dustin Olson (CEO)
Jaime Vasquez (CFO)
Tamsin Ettefagh (Chief Sustainability
Officer & Chief Comml Officer)
Brad Kalter (Gen Counsel & Sec)
Brett Hafer (Exec VP-Manufacturing)

PURERAY CORPORATION
3490 Piedmont Rd Ste 1120, Atlanta,
GA 30305
Tel.: (404) 869-6242 **WA**
Web Site:
http://www.puroraycorp.com
PURY—(OTCIQ)
Sales Range: $50-74.9 Million
Solar Charging & Lighting Systems
Mfr
N.A.I.C.S.: 335139
Jefrey M. Wallace (Pres, CEO & Sec)
Derek Blackburn (CFO & Treas)
John McIlwaine (COO)

PURETECH HEALTH PLC
6 Tide St, Boston, MA 02210
Tel.: (617) 482-2333 **UK**
Web Site:
https://www.puretechhealth.com
Year Founded: 2015

PRTC—(NASDAQ)
Rev.: $15,618,000
Assets: $702,647,000
Liabilities: $155,058,000
Net Worth: $547,589,000
Earnings: ($37,065,000)
Emp.: 201
Fiscal Year-end: 12/31/22
Biopharmaceutical Product Mfr &
Distr
N.A.I.C.S.: 325412
John L. LaMattina (Sr Partner)
Daphne Zohar (Bd of Dirs, Co-
Founder & CEO)
Bharatt Chowrira (Pres & CEO)
Eric Elenko (Co-Founder, Pres &
Chief Innovation Officer)
Charles Sherwood (Gen Counsel)
Spencer Ball (Sr VP-Human Resources)
Michael Inbar (Sr VP-Finance)
Frank Salisbury (Sr VP-Commercial &
Product Strategy)
Allison Mead Talbot (Head-
Communications)
Anita Terpstra (Sr VP-Intellectual
Property)

Subsidiaries:

Sonde Health, Inc. **(1)**
1 Washington Mall Ste 3072, Boston, MA
02108
Tel.: (617) 456-0982
Web Site: https://www.sondehealth.com
Health Care Equipment Mfr
N.A.I.C.S.: 339112
David Liu (CEO)
Anya Gupta (VP-Bus Dev)

Vedanta Biosciences, Inc. **(1)**
19 Blackstone St, Cambridge, MA 02139
Tel.: (857) 706-1427
Web Site: https://www.vedantabio.com
Health Care Equipment Mfr
N.A.I.C.S.: 339112
Bernat Olle (Founder & CEO)
Dan Couto (COO)
Debra Winslow (VP-Program Mgmt & Ops
Plng)
Mark Mullikin (CFO)

PURPLE INNOVATION, INC.
4100 N Chapel Rdg Rd Ste 200,
Lehi, UT 84043
Tel.: (801) 756-2600 **DE**
Web Site: https://www.purple.com
Year Founded: 2015
PRPL—(NASDAQ)
Rev.: $575,692,000
Assets: $433,333,000
Liabilities: $254,443,000
Net Worth: $178,890,000
Earnings: ($89,689,000)
Emp.: 1,600
Fiscal Year-end: 12/31/22
Holding Company; Mattress & Bedding Accessories Mfr & Marketer
N.A.I.C.S.: 551112
Keira Krausz (CMO)
Tricia McDermott (Chief Legal Officer)
Jack Roddy (Chief People Officer)
Jeff Hutchings (Chief Innovation Officer)
Todd E. Vogensen (CFO)
Eric Haynor (COO)
Robert T. DeMartini (CEO)

Subsidiaries:

Intellibed, LLC **(1)**
1680 S Distribution Dr, Salt Lake City, UT
84104
Web Site: https://intellibed-mattress.com
Mattress Mfr & Distr
N.A.I.C.S.: 337910

PURTHANOL RESOURCES LIMITED
2711 Centreville Rd Ste 400, Wilmington, DE 19808

Tel.: (302) 288-0658   DE
Web Site:
   http://www.purthanolbiofuel.net
Year Founded: 1998
PURT—(OTCEM)
Sales Range: Less than $1 Million
Emp.: 4
Ethanol Fuel Alternative Producer
N.A.I.C.S.: 221118

PUTNAM COUNTY NATIONAL BANK

43 Gleneida Ave, Carmel, NY 10512
Tel.: (845) 225-3688
Web Site:
   http://www.putnamcountynational
   bank.com
Year Founded: 1865
PUNB—(OTCIQ)
Commercial Banking Services
N.A.I.C.S.: 522110

PVH CORP.

285 Madison Ave, New York, NY 10017
Tel.: (212) 381-3500   DE
Web Site: https://www.pvh.com
Year Founded: 1881
PVH—(NYSE)
Rev.: $9,217,700,000
Assets: $11,172,900,000
Liabilities: $6,054,000,000
Net Worth: $5,118,900,000
Earnings: $663,600,000
Emp.: 17,000
Fiscal Year-end: 02/04/24
Apparel & Accessories Designer, Mfr,
Distr & Retailer
N.A.I.C.S.: 315250
Amba Subrahmanyam *(Chief People Officer)*
Mark D. Fischer *(Gen Counsel, Sec & Exec VP)*
Michael M. Calbert *(Chm)*
James W. Holmes *(Exec VP & Controller)*
Eileen Mahoney *(CIO & Exec VP)*
Martijn Hagman *(CEO-Tommy Hilfiger-Global & CEO-PVH Europe)*
Stefan Larsson *(CEO)*
Tommy Hilfiger *(Founder-Tommy Hilfiger)*
Zac Coughlin *(CFO & Exec VP)*
Michael Calbert *(Chm)*
Sophia Hwang-Judiesch *(Pres)*

Subsidiaries:

Arrow Shirt Co.   (1)
200 Madison Ave, New York, NY 10016-3903
Tel.: (212) 381-3500
Web Site: http://www.arrowshirt.com
Sales Range: $150-199.9 Million
Emp.: 75
Apparels Mfr
N.A.I.C.S.: 315250

CK Stores Belgium BVBA   (1)
Square De L'Atomium 1, Brussels, 1020, Belgium
Tel.: (32) 24799116
Apparel Clothing & Accessorie Whslr
N.A.I.C.S.: 313210

CK Stores Denmark ApS   (1)
Trangravsvej 2, 1436, Copenhagen, Denmark
Tel.: (45) 32624645
Apparel Clothing & Accessorie Whslr
N.A.I.C.S.: 313210

Calvin Klein, Inc.   (1)
205 W 39th St, New York, NY 10018
Web Site: https://www.calvinklein.us
Apparel Clothing & Accessorie Whslr
N.A.I.C.S.: 424110

Confezioni Moda Italia S.r.l.   (1)
Via Giulio Catoni 147, Trento, 38123, TN, Italy
Tel.: (39) 0461943234

Apparel Clothing & Accessorie Whslr
N.A.I.C.S.: 424340

Gazal Corporation Limited   (1)
3-7 McPherson Street, Banksmeadow, 2019, NSW, Australia
Tel.: (61) 293162800
Web Site: http://www.gazal.com.au
Rev.: $9,944,223
Assets: $107,149,570
Liabilities: $34,283,804
Net Worth: $72,865,766
Earnings: $8,872,610
Emp.: 900
Fiscal Year-end: 02/03/2018
Wholesale & Retail of Branded Apparel & Accessories
N.A.I.C.S.: 424350
Peter James Wood *(Sec)*
G. Griffiths *(CFO)*

Subsidiary (Domestic):

Body Art Australia Pty Limited   (2)
40 Oxford St, Collingwood, 3066, VIC, Australia
Tel.: (61) 384129999
Web Site: http://www.gazal.com.au
Sales Range: $25-49.9 Million
Emp.: 20
Apparel Mfr & Whslr
N.A.I.C.S.: 458110

Subsidiary (Non-US):

Gazal (NZ) Limited   (2)
Morgan St New Market, PO Box 58266, Greenmount, Auckland, 1023, New Zealand   (100%)
Tel.: (64) 92725850
Web Site: http://www.gazal.com.au
Sales Range: $25-49.9 Million
Emp.: 2
Casual Wear Suppliers
N.A.I.C.S.: 458110
Paul Cleminson *(Mgr-Sls-Natl)*

Subsidiary (Domestic):

Gazal Apparel Pty Limited   (2)
3 Macpherson St, Banksmeadow, 2019, NSW, Australia
Tel.: (61) 293162800
Web Site: http://www.gazal.com.au
Sales Range: $25-49.9 Million
Emp.: 200
Apparel & Accessories Mfr
N.A.I.C.S.: 315990
Michael Gazal *(Mng Dir)*

Gazal Clothing Company Pty Limited   (2)
3 7 Macpherson St, Banksmeadow, 2019, NSW, Australia
Tel.: (61) 293162800
Web Site: http://www.gazal.com.au
Sales Range: $50-74.9 Million
Emp.: 200
Apparel Mfr & Whslr
N.A.I.C.S.: 458110

Hilfiger Stores Denmark Aps   (1)
Danneskiold-Samsoes Alle 55, 1434, Copenhagen, Denmark
Tel.: (45) 70208073
Web Site: http://dk.tommy.com
Apparel Clothing & Accessorie Whslr
N.A.I.C.S.: 458110

Hilfiger Stores SRO   (1)
Chvalovice-Hate 196 75, 669 02, Znojmo, Czech Republic
Tel.: (420) 515294245
Web Site: http://www.tommy.com
Apparel Clothing & Accessorie Whslr
N.A.I.C.S.: 458110

Hilfiger Stores SpZoo   (1)
ul Emilii Plater 53, 00-113, Warsaw, Poland
Tel.: (48) 223237753
Apparel Clothing & Accessorie Whslr
N.A.I.C.S.: 458110
Wojciech Ploski *(Gen Mgr)*

Izod   (1)
1001 Frontier Rd MS No 44, Bridgewater, NJ 08807   (100%)
Tel.: (800) 866-7292
Web Site:
   http://www.izod.partnerbrands.com

Sales Range: $250-299.9 Million
Emp.: 750
Sportswear Mfr
N.A.I.C.S.: 315250

PVH Finland OY   (1)
Lintulahdenkuja 10, 00500, Helsinki, Finland
Tel.: (358) 977450700
Web Site: http://www.tommy.com
Emp.: 12
Apparel Clothing & Accessorie Whslr
N.A.I.C.S.: 424350

PVH Neckwear, Inc.   (1)
1735 S Santa Fe Ave, Los Angeles, CA 90021
Tel.: (213) 892-8569
Web Site:
   http://www.pvhneckweargroup.com
Apparel Clothing & Accessorie Whslr
N.A.I.C.S.: 458110

PVH Osterreich GesmbH   (1)
Wickenburgallee 2, 5101, Bergheim, Austria
Tel.: (43) 662458906
Apparel Clothing & Accessorie Whslr
N.A.I.C.S.: 313210

PVH Superba/Insignia Neckwear, Inc.   (1)
200 Madison Ave, New York, NY 10016   (100%)
Tel.: (212) 381-3500
Web Site: http://www.pvh.com
Sales Range: $300-349.9 Million
Emp.: 350
Men's & Boys' Neckwear Mfr & Distr
N.A.I.C.S.: 424350

PVH Wholesale Corp.   (1)
200 Madison Ave, New York, NY 10016   (100%)
Tel.: (212) 381-3500
Web Site: http://www.pvh.com
Sales Range: $150-199.9 Million
Emp.: 500
Men's & Boys' Clothing & Accessories Distr
N.A.I.C.S.: 424350

Phillips-Van Heusen Canada, Inc.   (1)
555 Richmond St W Ste 1106, Toronto, M5V 3B1, ON, Canada
Tel.: (416) 363-1500
Emp.: 20
Mens Clothing Store Operator
N.A.I.C.S.: 315210
Richard Deck *(Exec VP)*

TH Denmark Aps   (1)
Kongens Nytorv 13 1050, 1050, Copenhagen, Denmark
Tel.: (45) 33917710
Family Clothing Store Operator
N.A.I.C.S.: 458110

The Warnaco Group, Inc.   (1)
501 7th Ave, New York, NY 10018
Tel.: (212) 287-8000
Emp.: 7,136
Apparel Clothing & Accessorie Whslr
N.A.I.C.S.: 313210

Tommy Hilfiger (HK) Ltd.   (1)
Tel.: (852) 21780518
Apparel Clothing & Accessorie Whslr
N.A.I.C.S.: 458110

Tommy Hilfiger (Shanghai) Apparel Co. Ltd.   (1)
Rm201c No 118 Xinling Rd Waiga, Shanghai, 200052, China
Tel.: (86) 2162820366
Apparel & Accessory Retailer
N.A.I.C.S.: 458110

Tommy Hilfiger Corporation   (1)
9/F Novel Industrial Building 850-870 Lai Chi Kok Road, Cheung Sha Wan, Kowloon, China (Hong Kong)
Tel.: (852) 2216 0668
Web Site: http://www.tommy.com
Sales Range: $1-4.9 Billion
Emp.: 5,800
Apparel Clothing & Accessorie Whslr
N.A.I.C.S.: 315250
Sophia Hwang-Judiesch *(Pres-North America)*
Thomas J. Hilfiger *(Founder & Designer)*

Tommy Hilfiger Europe B.V.   (1)

Stadhouderskade 6, Amsterdam, 1054 ES, Netherlands
Tel.: (31) 207194788
Web Site: http://www.global.tommy.com
Sales Range: $150-199.9 Million
Emp.: 600
Apparel Clothing & Accessorie Whslr
N.A.I.C.S.: 458110
Avery Baker *(Pres & Brand Dir-Global)*
Virginia Ritchie *(VP-Comm)*
Alegra O'Hare *(CMO-Global)*

True & Co.   (1)
222 W Mission Ave Ste 10, Spokane, WA 99201-2341
Tel.: (509) 326-1743
Web Site: http://www.trueandco.com
Womens' Undergarments Mfr
N.A.I.C.S.: 315250

PWRCOR, INC.

60 E 42nd St Ste 4600, New York, NY 10165
Tel.: (212) 796-4097   DE
Web Site: https://www.pwrcor.com
Year Founded: 1983
PWCO—(OTCIQ)
Rev.: $189,965
Assets: $224,632
Liabilities: $701,442
Net Worth: ($476,810)
Earnings: ($112,056)
Emp.: 4
Fiscal Year-end: 12/31/20
Energy Conversion Technology Services & Mfr
N.A.I.C.S.: 221122
Thomas Telegades *(CEO & Interim CFO)*
Peter Fazio *(COO)*
James A. Valentino *(Chm)*

PYROPHYTE ACQUISITION CORP.

3262 Westheimer Rd Ste 706, Houston, TX 77098
Tel.: (281) 701-4234   Ky
Web Site:
   https://www.pyrophytespac.com
Year Founded: 2021
PHYT—(NYSE)
Rev.: $83
Assets: $210,012,487
Liabilities: $221,055,535
Net Worth: ($11,043,048)
Earnings: $10,643,117
Emp.: 2
Fiscal Year-end: 12/31/22
Investment Services
N.A.I.C.S.: 523999
Bernard J. Duroc-Danner *(Chm & CEO)*
Sten L. Gustafson *(Pres, CEO & CFO)*

PYXIS ONCOLOGY, INC.

321 Harrison Ave 11 th Fl Ste 1, Boston, MA 02118
Tel.: (617) 221-9059   DE
Web Site: https://pyxisoncology.com
Year Founded: 2018
PYXS—(NASDAQ)
Rev.: $23,000
Assets: $280,021,000
Liabilities: $18,708,000
Net Worth: $261,313,000
Earnings: ($75,975,000)
Emp.: 56
Fiscal Year-end: 12/31/21
Research & Development in Biotechnology (except Nanobiotechnology)
N.A.I.C.S.: 541714
Ken Kobayashi *(Chief Medical Officer)*
Jan Pinkas *(Chief Scientific Officer)*
Pamela Yanchik Connealy *(CFO & COO)*
Lara S. Sullivan *(Pres & CEO)*
Pamela Connealy *(CFO)*

Pyxis Oncology, Inc.—(Continued)

Martina Molsbergen *(Interim Chief Bus Officer)*
John Flavin *(Chm)*
Jitendra Wadhane *(Chief Acctg Officer, Sr VP-Fin & Controller)*

Subsidiaries:

Apexigen, Inc. **(1)**
75 Shoreway Rd Ste C, San Carlos, CA 94070
Tel.: (650) 931-6236
Web Site: https://www.apexigen.com
Biotechnology Research
N.A.I.C.S.: 541714

PYXUS INTERNATIONAL, INC.
6001 Hospitality Ct Ste 100, Morrisville, NC 27560-2009
Tel.: (919) 379-4300   VA
Web Site: https://www.pyxusintl.com
Year Founded: 2020
PYYX—(OTCIQ)
Rev.: $2,032,559,000
Assets: $1,657,913,000
Liabilities: $1,511,090,000
Net Worth: $146,823,000
Earnings: $3,184,000
Emp.: 3,000
Fiscal Year-end: 03/31/24
Holding Company; Tobacco Products Distr
N.A.I.C.S.: 551112
J. Pieter Sikkel *(Pres & CEO)*
Scott A. Burmeister *(COO & Exec VP)*
William L. O'Quinn Jr. *(Chief Legal Officer, Sec & Sr VP)*
Tracy G. Purvis *(Exec VP-Info Sys & Global Bus)*
Flavia B. Landsberg *(CFO & Exec VP)*
Dustin Styons *(Exec VP-Bus Strategy & Sls)*
Fernanda Goncalves *(Chief HR Officer & Sr VP)*
Miranda Kinney *(Sr VP-Global Comm & Sustainability)*

Subsidiaries:

AOSP Investments, LLC **(1)**
8001 Aerial Ctr Pkwy, Morrisville, NC 27560
Tel.: (919) 379-4300
Financial Investment Services
N.A.I.C.S.: 523940
Peter Sikkel *(CEO)*

Alliance One Brasil Exportadora de Tabacos Ltda. **(1)**
Rua Coronel Agra 1767 Bairro Centro, Venancio Aires, 95800-000, Rio Grande do Sul, Brazil
Tel.: (55) 5137931400
Web Site: https://www.aointl.com
Leaf Tobacco Products & Cigarette Mfr
N.A.I.C.S.: 312230

Alliance One Brasil Exportadora de Tabacos Ltda. **(1)**
Rua Coronel Agra 1767 Bairro Centro, Venancio Aires, 95800-000, Rio Grande do Sul, Brazil
Tel.: (55) 5137931400
Web Site: https://www.aointl.com
Leaf Tobacco Products & Cigarette Mfr
N.A.I.C.S.: 312230

Alliance One Brasil Exportadora de Tabacos Ltda. **(1)**
Rua Coronel Agra 1767 Bairro Centro, Venancio Aires, 95800-000, Rio Grande do Sul, Brazil
Tel.: (55) 5137931400
Web Site: https://www.aointl.com
Leaf Tobacco Products & Cigarette Mfr
N.A.I.C.S.: 312230

Alliance One Brasil Exportadora de Tabacos Ltda. **(1)**
Rua Coronel Agra 1767 Bairro Centro, Venancio Aires, 95800-000, Rio Grande do

Sul, Brazil
Tel.: (55) 5137931400
Web Site: https://www.aointl.com
Leaf Tobacco Products & Cigarette Mfr
N.A.I.C.S.: 312230

Alliance One International A.G. **(1)**
Hauptstrasse 53, PO Box 230, Birsfelden, 4127, Basel, Switzerland
Tel.: (41) 613199319
Tobacco Product Distr
N.A.I.C.S.: 424940

Alliance One International Services Limited **(1)**
Building A Riverside Way, Camberley, GU15 3YL, Surrey, United Kingdom
Tel.: (44) 1276404600
Web Site: http://www.aointl.com
Emp.: 20
Tobacco Distr
N.A.I.C.S.: 424940

Alliance One International Singapore Pte Ltd. **(1)**
78 Shenton Way 28-01, Singapore, 079120, Singapore
Tel.: (65) 63271155
Web Site: http://www.aointl.com
Emp.: 7
Tobacco Distr
N.A.I.C.S.: 424940

Alliance One International Tabak B.V. **(1)**
Schiphol Boulevard 359D Tower 11T, 1118 BJ, Schiphol, Netherlands
Tel.: (31) 202382400
Tobacco Leaf Distr
N.A.I.C.S.: 424590

Alliance One Macedonia AD **(1)**
Zapaden Bulevar 105, 1430, Kavadarci, North Macedonia
Tel.: (389) 43421800
Web Site: http://www.aointl.com
Sales Range: $75-99.9 Million
Emp.: 300
Leaf Tobacco Products
N.A.I.C.S.: 424940

Alliance One Myanmar Co., Ltd. **(1)**
N 81B Kam Baw Za Street, Thit Taw Yard, Taunggyi, Shan State, Myanmar
Tel.: (95) 812124469
Tobacco Products Whslr
N.A.I.C.S.: 424940
Kyaw Thet *(Coord-Ops-Tobacco Project)*

Alliance One Rotag AG **(1)**
Hardeckstrasse 2a, 76185, Karlsruhe, Germany
Tel.: (49) 721509010
Web Site: http://www.aointl.com
Sales Range: $50-74.9 Million
Emp.: 50
Distr of Leaf Tobacco Products
N.A.I.C.S.: 459991

Alliance One Services (Thailand) Limited **(1)**
Airport Business Park Building Suite 211-213 90 Mahidol Road, T Haiya A Muang, Chiang Mai, 50100, Thailand
Tel.: (66) 53203337
Web Site: http://www.aointl.com
Sales Range: $25-49.9 Million
Emp.: 22
Tobacco Product Distr
N.A.I.C.S.: 424940

Alliance One Specialty Products LLC **(1)**
2305 Baldree Rd, Wilson, NC 27893
Tel.: (252) 206-3200
Emp.: 100
Cigarette Mfr
N.A.I.C.S.: 312230

Alliance One Tabaco Guatemala S.A. **(1)**
1a Avenida 15-46 Zona 10, Guatemala, Guatemala
Tel.: (502) 22441122
Web Site: http://www.aointl.com
Leaf Tobacco Products
N.A.I.C.S.: 459991

Alliance One Tabaco Mexico S.A. de C.V. **(1)**

Calle Jalisco 211, Colonia Valle de Matatipac, 63195, Tepic, Mexico
Tel.: (52) 3112147882
Web Site: http://www.aointl.com
Sales Range: $50-74.9 Million
Emp.: 37
Tobacco Products
N.A.I.C.S.: 459991

Alliance One Tobacco (Kenya) Limited **(1)**
PO Box 4721, Garissa Road, 1002, Thika, Kenya
Tel.: (254) 202426066
Tobacco Product Distr
N.A.I.C.S.: 424940

Alliance One Tobacco (Malawi) Limited **(1)**
Tel.: (265) 1710255
Web Site: http://www.aointl.com
Tobacco Products
N.A.I.C.S.: 312230

Alliance One Tobacco (Malawi) Limited **(1)**
Tel.: (265) 1710255
Web Site: http://www.aointl.com
Tobacco Products
N.A.I.C.S.: 312230

Alliance One Tobacco (Malawi) Limited **(1)**
Tel.: (265) 1710255
Web Site: http://www.aointl.com
Tobacco Products
N.A.I.C.S.: 312230

Alliance One Tobacco (Malawi) Limited **(1)**
Tel.: (265) 1710255
Web Site: http://www.aointl.com
Tobacco Products
N.A.I.C.S.: 312230

Alliance One Tobacco (Uganda) Limited **(1)**
Plot 46 Upper Kololo Terrace, PO Box 12599, Nakasero, Kampala, Uganda
Tel.: (256) 393012599
Tobacco Products Whslr
N.A.I.C.S.: 424940

Alliance One Tobacco Argentina S.A. **(1)**
Estacion Zuviria, El Carril, A4421XAU, Salta, Argentina
Tel.: (54) 3874908018
Web Site: http://www.aointl.com
Emp.: 600
Tobacco Product Distr
N.A.I.C.S.: 424940

Alliance One Tobacco Bulgaria EOOD **(1)**
62 Saedinenie Blvd, 6300, Haskovo, Bulgaria
Tel.: (359) 38661800
Web Site: http://www.aointl.com
Sales Range: $200-249.9 Million
Emp.: 100
Leaf Tobacco Products
N.A.I.C.S.: 459991
Alex Strohschoen *(Pres)*

Alliance One Tobacco Canada, Inc. **(1)**
252 Power Street, PO Box 201, Delhi, N4B 1J2, ON, Canada
Tel.: (519) 688-1086
Web Site: http://www.aointl.com
Sales Range: $25-49.9 Million
Emp.: 8
Tobacco
N.A.I.C.S.: 459991

Alliance One Tobacco Guatemala, S.A. **(1)**
Tel.: (502) 22441122
Web Site: http://www.aointl.com
Emp.: 30
Tobacco Product Distr
N.A.I.C.S.: 424940

Alliance One Tobacco Tanzania Ltd. **(1)**
Kinglowira, PO Box 1595, Morogoro, Tanzania
Tel.: (255) 232603494

Tobacco Product Distr
N.A.I.C.S.: 424940

Alliance One Tutun A.S. **(1)**
Yedi Eylul Mahallesi Philsa Caddesi No 50, Torbali, 35860, Izmir, Turkiye
Tel.: (90) 2323767700
Web Site: http://www.eng.allianceone.com.tr
Sales Range: $75-99.9 Million
Emp.: 90
Tobacco
N.A.I.C.S.: 459991

Alliance One Zambia Ltd. **(1)**
3140 Buyantanshi Road, PO Box 30994, Industrial Area, Lusaka, Zambia
Tel.: (260) 211266847
Tobacco Product Distr
N.A.I.C.S.: 424940

Alliance OneTobacco Argentina S.A. **(1)**
Estacion Zuviria El Carril, A4421XAU, Salta, Argentina
Tel.: (54) 3874908018
Web Site: http://www.aointl.com
Sales Range: $150-199.9 Million
Leaf Tobacco Products
N.A.I.C.S.: 459991

Canada's Island Gardens, Inc. **(1)**
7 Innovation Way, Charlottetown, C1E 0B7, PE, Canada
Web Site: http://canadasislandgarden.com
Tobacco Leaf Distr
N.A.I.C.S.: 424590

Criticality LLC **(1)**
1900-A Stantonsburg Rd SE, Wilson, NC 27893
Tel.: (252) 640-3440
Web Site: https://www.criticalitync.com
Food Farming Services
N.A.I.C.S.: 111419

FIGR Cannabis Inc. **(1)**
3400 One First Canadian Place, PO Box 130, Toronto, M5X 1A4, ON, Canada
Tel.: (416) 863-1200
Web Site: http://figrcannabis.com
Security Software Development Services
N.A.I.C.S.: 541511

Gadora Tobacco P.S.C. **(1)**
SFB 2 Building ADC Warehousing and Industries Park Aqaba Back Road, ASEZA AQABA Special Economic Zone, Al Aqabah, Jordan
Tel.: (962) 32035970
Web Site: http://www.aointl.com
Emp.: 70
Tobacco Product Distr
N.A.I.C.S.: 424940

Goldleaf Pharm, Inc. **(1)**
11 Grigg Drive, Simcoe, N3Y 4L1, ON, Canada
Tel.: (519) 428-1088
Tobacco Leaf Distr
N.A.I.C.S.: 424590

Humble Juice Co., LLC **(1)**
2455 Conejo Spectrum St Unit 100, Thousand Oaks, CA 91320
Tel.: (805) 375-0153
Web Site: https://www.humblejuiceco.com
E-liquid Product Mfr & Distr
N.A.I.C.S.: 312230

Leaf Trading Company Ltd. **(1)**
Tel.: (7) 8124497470
Web Site: https://www.ltcservice.com
Emp.: 14
Freight Forwarding Services
N.A.I.C.S.: 327910

Mashonaland Tobacco Company **(1)**
No 4 Simon Mazorodze Rd, PO Box 1297, Harare, Zimbabwe
Tel.: (263) 8677007545
Sales Range: $50-74.9 Million
Emp.: 49
Tobacco
N.A.I.C.S.: 459991

Mashonaland Tobacco Holdings (Pvt) Ltd. **(1)**
No 4 Simon Mazorodze Road, PO Box 1297, Harare, Zimbabwe
Tel.: (263) 8677007545
Agricultural Product Services

N.A.I.C.S.: 926140

P.T. Indonesia Tri Sembilam **(1)**
Jl Ngoro Industri Persada Block S-1, Ngoro, Mojokerto, 61385, Indonesia
Tel.: (62) 321618999
Tobacco Product Distr
N.A.I.C.S.: 424940

P.T. Indonesia Tri Sembilan **(1)**
Jl Ngoro Industri Persada Block S-1, Ngoro, Mojokerto, 61385, Indonesia
Tel.: (62) 3216818999
Agricultural Product Services
N.A.I.C.S.: 926140

P.T. Mayangsari **(1)**
Jl Hayam Wuruk 6, Jember, 68133, Indonesia
Tel.: (62) 331485800
Web Site: http://www.mayangsari.co.id
Sales Range: $150-199.9 Million
Tobacco Products
N.A.I.C.S.: 459991

Zip Fulfillment LLC **(1)**
200 Forsyth Hall Dr Ste E, Charlotte, NC 28273
Tel.: (704) 322-3737
Web Site: http://www.zipfulfillment.com
Logistic Software Development Services
N.A.I.C.S.: 541511

PZENA INVESTMENT MANAGEMENT, INC.
320 Park Ave, New York, NY 10022
Tel.: (212) 355-1600   DE
Web Site: http://www.pzena.com
PZN—(NYSE)
Rev.: $199,334,000
Assets: $264,300,000
Liabilities: $86,246,000
Net Worth: $178,054,000
Earnings: $18,679,000
Emp.: 140
Fiscal Year-end: 12/31/21
Investment Services
N.A.I.C.S.: 523940
Richard S. Pzena (Chm, CEO & Co-Chief Investment Officer)
John Paul Goetz (Co-Pres & Co-Chief Investment Officer)
William Louis Lipsey (Pres)
Jessica R. Doran (CFO & Treas)
Caroline Chenyu Cai (Co-Portfolio Mgr-Intl, Global & European)
Evan K. Fire (COO)

Subsidiaries:

Pzena Financial Services, LLC **(1)**
320 Park Ave 8th Fl, New York, NY 10022
Tel.: (212) 583-1291
Investment Services
N.A.I.C.S.: 525990

Pzena Investment Management Pty Ltd **(1)**
Level 8 350 Collins Street, Melbourne, 3000, VIC, Australia
Tel.: (61) 386760617
Investment Management Service
N.A.I.C.S.: 523940

Pzena Investment Management, Ltd **(1)**
34-37 Liverpool Street, London, EC2M 7PP, United Kingdom
Tel.: (44) 2039592375
Investment Advisory Services
N.A.I.C.S.: 523940
Adrian Jackson (Dir-Bus Dev & Client Svcs)

Q BIOMED INC.
366 Madison Ave 3rd Fl, New York, NY 10017
Tel.: (212) 588-0022   NV
Web Site: https://www.qbiomed.com
QBIO—(OTCQB)
Rev.: $195,597
Assets: $809,480
Liabilities: $5,494,842
Net Worth: ($4,685,362)
Earnings: ($8,741,274)

Emp.: 9
Fiscal Year-end: 11/30/21
Biotechnology Research & Development Services
N.A.I.C.S.: 541714
David Laskow-Pooley (VP-Product Dev)
Denis D. Corin (Chm, Chm, CEO & CEO)
William Rosenstadt (Chief Legal Officer & Gen Counsel)
Robert Derham (VP-Orphan Products)
Ari Jatwes (Dir-Fin)
Kristin Marvin Keller (Chief Comml Officer)
Geoff Fatzinger (Head-Regulatory Affairs-Global)

Q-GOLD RESOURCES LTD.
121 E Birch Ave Ste 508, Flagstaff, AZ 86001
Tel.: (928) 779-0166
Web Site:
     http://www.qgoldresources.com
E6Q—(TSXV)
Sales Range: Less than $1 Million
Gold & Silver Ore Mining Services
N.A.I.C.S.: 212220
Deborah Battiston (CFO)
J. Bruce Carruthers II (Chm & CEO)

Q.E.P. CO., INC.
1001 Broken Sound Pkwy NW, Boca Raton, FL 33487
Tel.: (561) 994-5550   DE
Web Site:
     https://www.qepcorporate.com
Year Founded: 1979
QEPC—(OTCQX)
Rev.: $445,531,000
Assets: $206,356,000
Liabilities: $126,954,000
Net Worth: $79,402,000
Earnings: $9,648,000
Emp.: 735
Fiscal Year-end: 02/28/22
Saw Blade & Handtool Manufacturing
N.A.I.C.S.: 332216
Lewis Gould (Exec Chm)
Jamie L. Clingan (Sr VP-Mktg)
Leonard Gould (Pres & CEO)
Enos Brown (CFO & Exec VP)

Subsidiaries:

Boiardi Products Corporation **(1)**
453 Main St, Little Falls, NJ 07424
Tel.: (973) 256-1100
Web Site: http://www.boiardiproducts.com
Sales Range: $10-24.9 Million
Emp.: 10
Commercial Mortar Products Distr
N.A.I.C.S.: 325520
John J. Mezzone (Mgr)

Imperial Industries, Inc. **(1)**
1259 NW 21st St, Pompano Beach, FL 33069
Tel.: (954) 917-4114
Web Site: http://www.imperialindustries.com
Sales Range: $25-49.9 Million
Emp.: 25
Building Materials Mfr
N.A.I.C.S.: 327910

Subsidiary (Domestic):

Premix-Marbletite Mfg. Co. **(2)**
1259 NW 21st St, Pompano Beach, FL 33069
Tel.: (954) 917-7665
Web Site: http://www.premixmarbletite.com
Sales Range: $125-149.9 Million
Mfr & Distr of Building Materials
N.A.I.C.S.: 444180

Nupla Corporation **(1)**
11912 Sheldon St, Sun Valley, CA 91352-1509
Tel.: (818) 827-0718
Web Site: http://www.nuplacorp.com

Sales Range: $25-49.9 Million
Emp.: 125
Industrial Surface Protective Hammers & Related Products Mfr
N.A.I.C.S.: 332216
Sumi Gandhi (Mgr-Intl Sls)
Dan Harold (Dir-Mktg & Sls)

Subsidiary (Domestic):

HISCO, Inc. **(2)**
4320 N Cooper Ave, Oklahoma City, OK 73118
Tel.: (405) 524-2700
Web Site: http://www.hisco-okc.com
Sales Range: $10-24.9 Million
Emp.: 10
Hand Tool Mfr
N.A.I.C.S.: 332216

Q.E.P. Australia Pty Limited **(1)**
68 Prosperity Way, Dandenong South, 3175, VIC, Australia
Tel.: (61) 3 9797 1888
Web Site: http://www.qep.com
Flooring & Flooring Tools Mfr & Sales
N.A.I.C.S.: 321918

Roberts Consolidated Industries Inc. **(1)**
1001 Broken Sound Pkwy NW Ste A, Boca Raton, FL 33487   **(100%)**
Tel.: (561) 994-5550
Web Site:
     http://www.robertsconsolidated.com
Sales Range: $100-124.9 Million
Emp.: 60
Flooring Installation Tools & Accessories Mfr & Distr
N.A.I.C.S.: 332216
Lewis Gould (CEO)

Subsidiary (Non-US):

Roberts Company Canada Limited **(2)**
2070 Steeles Avenue, Bramalea, L6T 1A7, ON, Canada
Tel.: (905) 791-4444
Web Site:
     http://www.robertsconsolidated.com
Sales Range: $25-49.9 Million
Emp.: 35
Flooring Installation Tools Whslr
N.A.I.C.S.: 423440

Southern Cross Building Products, LLC **(1)**
361 High Rdg Rd, Boynton Beach, FL 33426
Tel.: (561) 932-0300
Flooring Accessories, Tile & Other Related Items Distr
N.A.I.C.S.: 238330

Vitrex Limited **(1)**
Everest Road, Lytham Saint Anne's, FY8 3AZ, Lancashire, United Kingdom
Tel.: (44) 1253789180
Web Site: http://www.vitrex.co.uk
Sales Range: $25-49.9 Million
Emp.: 16
Tiling Tools & Accessories Mfr & Distr
N.A.I.C.S.: 332216
Sandra Miller (Mgr-Ops)

Q2 HOLDINGS, INC.
10355 Pecan Park Blvd, Austin, TX 78729
Tel.: (512) 275-0072   DE
Web Site: https://www.q2.com
Year Founded: 2005
QTWO—(NYSE)
Rev.: $624,624,000
Assets: $1,201,425,000
Liabilities: $752,946,000
Net Worth: $448,479,000
Earnings: ($65,384,000)
Emp.: 2,312
Fiscal Year-end: 12/31/23
Holding Company
N.A.I.C.S.: 551112
Matthew P. Flake (Chm & CEO)
Robert H. Seale III (Founder)
Adam D. Blue (CTO)
John E. Breeden (COO)

Lou Senko (Chief Availability Officer)
Kim Rutledge (Exec VP-People)
Carlos Carvajal (CMO)
Mike Volanoski (Chief Revenue Officer)
Kirk L. Coleman (Pres)
Scott Kerr (Gen Counsel)
Jonathan A. Price (CFO, Principal Acctg Officer & Exec VP-Strategy & Emerging Bus)

Subsidiaries:

Cloud Lending, Inc. **(1)**
13785 Research Blvd Ste 150, Austin, TX 78750
Tel.: (650) 918-0499
Web Site: http://www.cloudlendinginc.com
Financial Services
N.A.I.C.S.: 523940

Q2 Software, Inc. **(1)**
10355 Pecan Park Blvd, Austin, TX 78729
Tel.: (512) 275-0072
Web Site: https://www.q2.com
Sales Range: $25-49.9 Million
Emp.: 120
Electronic Banking Platform Software Developer & Publisher
N.A.I.C.S.: 513210
Matthew P. Flake (Pres & CEO)
Kirk Coleman (Pres)
David Mehok (CFO)
Kim Rutledge (Exec VP)
Adam Blue (CTO)
John Breeden (COO)
Mike Volanoski (Chief Revenue Officer)
Jonathan Price (Exec VP)
Scott Kerr (Sr VP)

Subsidiary (Domestic):

SmartyPig, L.L.C. **(2)**
175 S W Temple Ste 600, Salt Lake City, UT 84101
Tel.: (515) 256-2086
Web Site: https://www.smartypig.com
Banking Services
N.A.I.C.S.: 522110

Sensibill Inc. **(1)**
2967 Dundas St W 660, Toronto, M6P 1Z2, ON, Canada
Web Site: https://getsensibill.com
Finance Investment Services
N.A.I.C.S.: 523999

Q32 BIO INC.
830 Winter St 2nd Fl, Waltham, MA 02451
Tel.: (781) 999-0232   DE
Web Site: https://www.q32bio.com
Year Founded: 2015
QTTB—(NASDAQ)
Rev.: $1,156,000
Assets: $84,564,000
Liabilities: $11,573,000
Net Worth: $72,991,000
Earnings: $112,961,000
Emp.: 7
Fiscal Year-end: 12/31/23
Genetic Medicine Development Services
N.A.I.C.S.: 541714
Lee Kalowski (Pres & CFO)
Jason Campagna (Chief Medical Officer)
Paul Alloway (Pres & COO)
Shelia Violette (Founding Partner & Chief Scientific Officer)
Saul W. Fink (Chief Technical Officer)
David S. Grayzel (Co-Founder)
Jodie Pope Morrison (CEO)

QC HOLDINGS, INC.
8208 Melrose Dr, Lenexa, KS 66214
Tel.: (913) 234-5000   KS
Web Site: https://www.qchi.com
Year Founded: 1984
QCCO—(OTCIQ)
Sales Range: $125-149.9 Million
Emp.: 1,000
Payday Loan Store Operator

QC Holdings, Inc.—(Continued)
N.A.I.C.S.: 522291
Darrin J. Andersen (Pres & CEO)
Don Early (Chm)
Douglas E. Nickerson (CFO)
Mary Lou Andersen-Early (Founder)
Wayne S. Wood (VP-Ops)
Frank Gocinski (CIO)
Mark Sesler (COO)
Cathy Tharp (Chief Acctg Officer, Treas & Controller)

Subsidiaries:

Direct Credit Atlantic Inc.   (1)
1959 Uppr Water St Ste 1700, Halifax, B3J
3N2, NS, Canada
Tel.: (902) 482-1395
Mortgage & Nonmortgage Loan Brokers
N.A.I.C.S.: 522310

QC Financial Services of Texas, Inc.   (1)
7021 Alameda Ave, El Paso, TX 79915-3454
Tel.: (915) 778-4574
Investment Management Service
N.A.I.C.S.: 523940

QC Financial Services, Inc.   (1)
9401 Indian Creek Pkwy Ste 1500, Shawnee Mission, KS 66210
Tel.: (913) 439-1100
Web Site: http://www.qcholding.com
Investment Management Service
N.A.I.C.S.: 523940
Darrin J. Andersen (VP)

Subsidiary (Domestic):

Express Check Advance of South Carolina, LLC   (2)
10050 Dorchester Rd Ste 107, Summerville, SC 29485-8534
Tel.: (843) 832-9965
Financial Consulting Services
N.A.I.C.S.: 522291

QCR HOLDINGS, INC.
3551 7th St, Moline, IL 61265
Tel.: (309) 277-2657   DE
Web Site: https://www.qcrh.com
Year Founded: 1993
QCRH—(NASDAQ)
Rev.: $373,300,000
Assets: $7,948,837,000
Liabilities: $7,176,113,000
Net Worth: $772,724,000
Earnings: $99,066,000
Emp.: 924
Fiscal Year-end: 12/31/22
Multi-Bank Holding Company
N.A.I.C.S.: 551111
Larry J. Helling (CEO)
Todd A. Gipple (Pres & CFO)
Nick W. Anderson (Chief Acctg Officer & Sr VP)
Pamela J. Goodwin (Sr VP & Mgr-Loan Ops)
Todd C. Kerska (Chm-Best In Class Initiatives & Exec VP)
James M. Field (Vice Chm)
Robert M. Eby (Chief Credit Officer & Exec VP)
Reba K. Winter (COO & Exec VP)
Monte C. McNew (Chief Lending Officer)
John R. Oakes (Treas & Sr VP)
R. Timothy Harding (Exec VP & Dir-Internal Audit)

Subsidiaries:

Bates Financial Advisors, Inc.   (1)
8437 Northern Ave, Rockford, IL 61107
Tel.: (815) 332-4020
Web Site:
   https://www.batesfinancialadvisors.com
Financial Services
N.A.I.C.S.: 523940
George E. Bates (Founder, Pres & Chief Compliance Officer)
Felicia Gulotta-Johnson (Office Mgr & Mgr-HR)

Cedar Rapids Bank & Trust Company   (1)
500 1st Ave NE, Cedar Rapids, IA 52401
Tel.: (319) 862-2728
Web Site: https://crbt.bank
Commericial Banking
N.A.I.C.S.: 522110
Larry J. Helling (Founder, Pres & CEO)
Fred G. Timko (Chm)
John Rodriguez (COO & Exec VP)
Dana Nichols (Founder)
Deborah Gertsen (Sr VP-Trust & Investments)
Jamie Jonas (VP-Comml Banking)
Kevin Bruns (Exec VP-Wealth Mgmt)
Rand Westlund (Chief Investment Officer)
Ruth Nebergall (VP-Comml Banking)
Sue Lowder (Officer-Comml Real Estate & VP)
Theresa Blong (VP & Mgr-Credit Dept)
Trish Ellison (Chief Credit Officer & Exec VP)
Rick Seger (Officer-Trust & Sr VP)
Grant Luebe (Investment Officer & Asst VP)
James D. Klein (Pres)
John Hall (Chief Lending Officer & Exec VP)
Brittney Clarke (Sr VP & Mgr-Retail)
Ashley Rodemeyer (Officer-Retail & Branch Mgr)
Allie Jackson (Officer-Retail & Branch Mgr)
Liz Posekany (Asst VP & Branch Mgr)
Virginia Wilts (Officer-Retail & Branch Mgr)
Matt Carlisle (Officer-Retail & Branch Mgr)
Cody Ritter (VP & Mgr-Real Estate)
Ben Weber (VP-Comml Banking)
Brad Holub (VP-Comml Banking)
Dave Stoltenberg (First VP-Comml Banking)
Gary Becker (Sr VP & Mgr-Comml Real Estate)
Josh Burgett (Asst VP-Comml Banking)
Josh Moore (Sr VP & Mgr-Comml Real Estate)
Tyler Clark (Asst VP-Comml Banking)
Pauline Herb (First VP-Treasury Mgmt)
Amanda Opfer (VP-Treasury Mgmt)

Division (Domestic):

Community Bank & Trust   (2)
422 Commercial St, Waterloo, IA 50701
Tel.: (319) 291-2000
Web Site: https://communitybt.bank
Commericial Banking
N.A.I.C.S.: 522110
Stacey J. Bentley (Pres & CEO)
Rand Westlund (Chief Investment Officer)
Bob Seymour (Officer-Bus Dev & Asst VP)
Kevin Bruns (Sr VP-Wealth Mgmt & Trust)
Mitch Dellamuth (Officer-Investment)
Todd Kerska (Exec VP)
Pauline Herb (VP)
Amanda Opfer (VP)
Jen Welton (VP)

Community State Bank   (1)
817 N Ankeny Blvd, Ankeny, IA 50023
Tel.: (515) 331-3100
Web Site: http://www.bankcsb.com
Commericial Banking
N.A.I.C.S.: 522110

Guaranty Federal Bancshares, Inc.   (1)
2144 E Republic Rd Ste F200, Springfield, MO 65804
Tel.: (417) 520-4333
Web Site: http://www.gbankmo.com
Rev.: $50,943,320
Assets: $1,146,252,939
Liabilities: $1,057,284,573
Net Worth: $88,968,366
Earnings: $6,832,214
Fiscal Year-end: 12/31/2020
Bank Holding Company
N.A.I.C.S.: 551111
Carter M. Peters (CFO & Exec VP)
Sheri D. Biser (Chief Credit Officer & Exec VP-Guaranty Bank)

Subsidiary (Domestic):

Guaranty Bank   (2)
1341 W Battlefield, Springfield, MO 65807
Tel.: (417) 520-4333
Web Site: https://www.gbankmo.com
Sales Range: $50-74.9 Million
Emp.: 7,200
Banking Services

N.A.I.C.S.: 522110
Guaranty Realty, Inc.   (1)
624 Eiserman Ave, Branson, MO 65616
Tel.: (417) 337-0310
Banking Services
N.A.I.C.S.: 522110

Quad City Bank & Trust Company   (1)
2118 Middle Rd, Bettendorf, IA 52722
Tel.: (563) 344-0600
Web Site: http://www.qcbt.bank
Commericial Banking
N.A.I.C.S.: 522110
Mark C. Kilmer (Chm)
John H. Anderson (Pres & CEO)
Chris Johnson (VP)
Cynthia Carlson (Exec VP-Wealth Mgmt Div)
Tracy Brashears (First VP-Wealth Mgmt-Trust Svcs)
Todd Larsen (Officer-Wealth Mgmt & VP)
Brenda Heisch (Officer-Wealth Mgmt & VP)
Rick Jennings (Sr VP-Tax-Special Svcs)
Paul Schmitt (Officer-Wealth Mgmt & VP)
Randolph Westlund (Chief Investment Officer & Exec VP)
Dan Zude (Officer-Investment & VP)
Trisha Townsend (Officer-Investment & VP)
DeAnna Smith (Officer-Trust Ops & Asst VP)
Kathy Francque (Exec VP)
D. Clay Boatman (Sr VP)
Amy Braack (Sr VP)
Jay Johnson (Sr VP)
Sarah Dolan (VP)
Kristin D. King (VP)
Kevin Volker (Officer-Correspondent Banking)
Kate Johnson (VP & Mgr-Correspondent Banking)
Lynne Haines (Officer-Correspondent Banking Ops)
Olivia Ortega (Officer-Items Processing & VP)
Tyler Edwards (VP-Investment Center)
Dave Howell (First VP-Investment Center)
John Nagle (Sr VP)
Eileen Roethler (First VP)
Beth Dunn (VP)
Amanda Boyer (VP)
Chad Manternach (VP)
Suzanne Jahns (VP)
Therese Gerwe (Sr VP-Treasury Mgmt)
Janelle Carter (VP-Treasury Mgmt)
Maria Peeters (Mgr-Relationship)

Springfield First Community Bank   (1)
2006 S Glenstone Ave, Springfield, MO 65804
Tel.: (417) 882-8111
Web Site: http://www.sfcbank.com
Community Bank Services
N.A.I.C.S.: 522110
Monte C. McNew (Pres & CEO)

m2 Equipment Finance, LLC   (1)
175 N Patrick Blvd Ste 140, Brookfield, WI 53045-5819
Tel.: (262) 789-6670
Web Site:
   https://www.m2equipmentfinance.com
Finance & Leasing Services
N.A.I.C.S.: 522220
John Engelbrecht (Founder & Chm)
Richard W. Couch (Pres & CEO)
Christine Kennedy (CFO)
David Houser (Sr VP)
Paul Celentani (Officer)
John O'Connor (Sr VP)
Richard Popp (Sr VP)
Bruce Volk (Sr VP)
Donna Welter (Sr VP)
Michael Wilkins (VP)
Rusty Long (Sr VP)

m2 Lease Funds, LLC   (1)
175 N Patrick Blvd Ste 140, Brookfield, WI 53045
Tel.: (262) 781-4809
Web Site: http://www.m2lease.com
Commercial & Industrial Equipment Leasing Services
N.A.I.C.S.: 532490
Gary Stang (Sr VP)
Chip David Houser (Sr VP)
Brian Besler (Exec VP)

John R. Engelbrecht (Founder & Chm)
Richard W. Couch (Pres & CEO)
Christine Kennedy (CFO)
John O'Connor (VP & Mgr-Bus Dev-Natl)
Paul Celentani (Officer-Leasing)
Jacqueline Flynn (Sr VP)
Richard Popp (Sr VP)
James Rogers (Sr VP-Sls & Bus Dev)
Bruce Volk (Sr VP)
Donna Welter (Sr VP)
Michael Wilkins (VP)
Jennifer Carstens (Dir-Tax)
Rusty Long (Gen Counsel & Sr VP)

QELL ACQUISITION CORP.
505 Montgomery St Ste 1100, San Francisco, CA 94111
Tel.: (415) 874-3000   Ky
Year Founded: 2020
QELLU—(NASDAQ)
Emp.: 2
Investment Services
N.A.I.C.S.: 523999
Barry Engle (CEO)
Sam Gabbita (CFO)

QENEX COMMUNICATIONS, INC.
1112 Links Cir Ste 10, Jonesboro, AR 72404
Tel.: (870) 323-0094   CO
Year Founded: 1988
QNXC—(OTCIQ)
Communication Equipment Mfr
N.A.I.C.S.: 334290
John A. Bush (CEO)
Christian Morrison (COO)
Denton Guthrie (CFO)

QHSLAB, INC.
901 Northpoint Pkwy Ste 302, West Palm Beach, FL 33407
Tel.: (929) 379-6503   DE
Web Site: https://www.qhslab.com
Year Founded: 1983
USAQ—(OTCQB)
Rev.: $1,243,186
Assets: $1,957,453
Liabilities: $1,881,208
Net Worth: $76,245
Earnings: ($996,001)
Emp.: 4
Fiscal Year-end: 12/31/22
Real Estate Asset Management Services
N.A.I.C.S.: 531390
Troy Grogan (Chm, Pres, CEO & CFO)
Cyndi Cole (Controller-Fin)
Jesus Davila (Dir-Corp Strategy & Dev)
Olivia Giamanco (Mktg Dir)
Janeane Perry (Creative Dir)
Marcos A. Sanchez-Gonzalez (VP-Medical & Scientific Affairs)

QHY GROUP
1501 Bdwy Ste 1515, New York, NY 10036
Tel.: (212) 324-1876   NV
Web Site:
   http://www.americanqhygroup.com
Year Founded: 2007
QHYG—(OTCIQ)
Rev.: $7,000
Assets: $2,203,661
Liabilities: $2,169,626
Net Worth: $34,035
Earnings: ($819,516)
Emp.: 5
Fiscal Year-end: 12/31/20
Wastewater Treatment Equipments Mfr
N.A.I.C.S.: 237110
Max Mao (Chm, Pres, CEO & Co-CFO)

Roy Teng *(Exec Dir)*
Coco Kou *(Co-CFO)*
Vincent McGill *(VP)*

QIAN YUAN BAIXING, INC.

5422 Carrier Dr Ste 309, Orlando, FL 32819
Tel.: (407) 363-5633
QYBX—(OTCIQ)
Health Care Srvices
N.A.I.C.S.: 621999
Dan Valladao *(Chm, Pres & CEO)*

QIANSUI INTERNATIONAL GROUP CO., LTD.

86 Broad St 19th Fl, New York, NY 10004
Tel.: (347) 690-5187   DE
Year Founded: 1992
QIAN—(OTCIQ)
Assets: $1,588
Liabilities: $117,560
Net Worth: ($115,972)
Earnings: ($76,373)
Emp.: 1
Fiscal Year-end: 12/31/21
Investment Services
N.A.I.C.S.: 523999
Yu Yang *(Pres, CEO, CFO & Treas)*

QNB CORP.

15 N 3rd St, Quakertown, PA 18951-9005
Tel.: (215) 538-5600   PA
Web Site: https://www.qnbbank.com
Year Founded: 1984
QNBC—(OTCIQ)
Rev.: $58,152,000
Assets: $1,668,497,000
Liabilities: $1,597,539,000
Net Worth: $70,958,000
Earnings: $15,921,000
Emp.: 190
Fiscal Year-end: 12/31/22
Bank Holding Company
N.A.I.C.S.: 551111
David W. Freeman *(Pres & CEO)*
Mary E. Liddle *(Chief Acctg Officer)*
Jeffrey Lehocky *(CFO & Exec VP)*
Scott G. Orzehoski *(Chief Lending Officer & Exec VP)*
Courtney L. Covelens *(Chief Bus Banking Officer)*
Christina S. McDonald *(CMO)*

Subsidiaries:

QNB   (1)
PO Box 9005, Quakertown, PA 18951-9005
Tel.: (215) 538-5600
Web Site: https://www.qnbbank.com
Sales Range: $25-49.9 Million
Emp.: 70
National Commercial Banks
N.A.I.C.S.: 522110
David W. Freeman *(Pres & CEO)*

QNB Bank   (1)
320 W Broad St, Quakertown, PA 18951-9005
Tel.: (215) 538-5600
Web Site: https://www.qnbbank.com
Emp.: 200
Commercial Banking Services
N.A.I.C.S.: 522110
David W. Freeman *(Pres & CEO)*
David W. Freeman *(Pres & CEO)*
Jonas Homa *(Officer/Officer-Comml Loan, Sr VP & VP)*
Alex Lipyanik *(Officer-Comml Loan & VP)*
Justin Hartrum *(Officer-Comml Loan & Sr VP)*
Tom Klee *(Officer-Comml Loan & Sr VP)*
April Donahue *(Sr VP-Retail Lending Manager)*
Brian Adzema *(Assoc VP)*
Brian Lawrence *(Sr VP)*
Bruce Knipe *(Sr VP)*
Christopher Berg *(VP)*
Donald States *(VP)*
Maria Friendshuh *(Assoc VP)*

Nicholas Yelicanin *(Sr VP)*
Scott Orzehoski *(Exec VP)*
Stephanie Zajkowski *(VP)*

QOMOLANGMA ACQUISITION CORP.

1178 Broadway 3rd Fl, New York, NY 10001
Tel.: (626) 757-4601   DE
Year Founded: 2021
QOMO—(NASDAQ)
Rev.: $1,925,395
Assets: $9,378,339
Liabilities: $13,861,552
Net Worth: ($4,483,213)
Earnings: ($138,905)
Fiscal Year-end: 12/31/23
Investment Management Service
N.A.I.C.S.: 523999
Hao Shen *(CFO)*
Jonathan P. Myers *(Chm, CEO & CFO)*

QORVO, INC.

7628 Thorndike Rd, Greensboro, NC 27409-9421
Tel.: (336) 664-1233   DE
Web Site: https://www.qorvo.com
QRVO—(NASDAQ)
Rev.: $3,769,506,000
Assets: $6,554,635,000
Liabilities: $2,998,263,000
Net Worth: $3,556,372,000
Earnings: ($70,322,000)
Emp.: 8,700
Fiscal Year-end: 03/30/24
Holding Company; Radio Frequency Technologies Designer, Mfr & Whslr
N.A.I.C.S.: 551112
Paul J. Fego *(VP-Ops-Global)*
Paul J. Fego *(VP-Ops-Global)*
Walden C. Rhines *(Chm)*
Philip Chesley *(Pres-Infrastructure & Defense Products)*
Brent Dietz *(Dir-Corporate Communications)*
Gina B. Harrison *(VP & Controller)*
Douglas Delieto *(VP-Investor Relations)*
J. K. Givens *(Gen Counsel, Sec & VP)*
Steven Eric Creviston *(Pres-Mobile Products & VP)*
Grant A. Brown *(CFO & Sr VP)*
Robert A. Bruggeworth *(Pres & CEO)*

Subsidiaries:

Cavendish Kinetics B.V.   (1)
Emmaplein 4c, 5211 VW, 's-Hertogenbosch, Netherlands
Tel.: (31) 736249110
Mobile Device Mfr
N.A.I.C.S.: 334210

Cavendish Kinetics, Inc.   (1)
2960 N 1st St, San Jose, CA 95134
Tel.: (408) 457-1940
Web Site: http://www.cavendish-kinetics.com
Electronic Components Mfr
N.A.I.C.S.: 334419
Richard Knipe *(CTO & VP-Engrg)*
Paul Dal Santo *(Pres & CEO)*
Patrick Murray *(CFO)*
Atul Shingal *(Exec VP-Ops)*
Dan Smith *(CMO)*
Paul Tornatta *(VP-RF Sys & Antenna Engrg)*

Custom MMIC Design Services, Inc.   (1)
1 Park Dr Ste 12, Westford, MA 01886-3535
Tel.: (978) 467-4290
Web Site: http://www.custommmic.com
Engineeering Services
N.A.I.C.S.: 541330

Decawave (Shenzhen) Limited   (1)
No 2127 1st Floor Fortune Building No 88 Fuhua 3rd Road, Futian District, Shenzhen,

518000, China
Tel.: (86) 18676380238
Semiconductor Mfr
N.A.I.C.S.: 333242

Decawave Limited   (1)
Adelaide Chambers Peter Street, Dublin, D08 T6YA, Ireland
Tel.: (353) 1 6975030
Web Site: http://www.decawave.com
Semiconductor Mfr
N.A.I.C.S.: 334413
Ciaran Connell *(Co-Founder & CEO)*
Michael McLaughlin *(Co-Founder & CTO)*
Graeme N. Walker *(CFO)*
William McFadden *(COO)*
Luc Darmon *(Gen Mgr-Secure Transactions)*
Bob Twomey *(Chief Revenue Officer)*
Paul Kettle *(Chief Innovation Officer)*

Nextinput, Inc.   (1)
980 Linda Vista Ave, Mountain View, CA 94043
Tel.: (650) 963-9310
Web Site: http://www.nextinput.com
Computer Related Services
N.A.I.C.S.: 541519
Ryan Diestelhorst *(Founder & CTO)*
Ali Foughi *(CEO)*

Qorvo (Beijing) Co., Ltd.   (1)
No 17 Tongji Middle Road, Beijing Economic and Technological Development Area, Beijing, 100176, China
Tel.: (86) 1067879977
Web Site: http://www.qorvo.com
Supplier of Integrated Circuits
N.A.I.C.S.: 334413

Qorvo Belgium NV   (1)
Spinnerijstraat 14, 9240, Zele, Belgium
Tel.: (32) 52454400
Integrated Chip Distr
N.A.I.C.S.: 423690

Qorvo Costa Rica S.R.L.   (1)
Zona Franca Metropolitana, Barreal De Heredia, 40104, Heredia, Costa Rica
Tel.: (506) 22098900
Web Site: http://www.qorvocr.com
Sales Range: $100-124.9 Million
Emp.: 250
Semiconductor Mfr & Testing
N.A.I.C.S.: 334413

Qorvo Denmark ApS   (1)
Bejlerholm 1, 9400, Norresundby, Denmark
Tel.: (45) 96730441
Semiconductor Component Whslr
N.A.I.C.S.: 423690

Qorvo Dezhou Co., Ltd.   (1)
Dongfanghong East Road 6868, Industrial Park of Dezhou Economic & Technological Development Area, Dezhou, 253084, China
Tel.: (86) 5342276868
Integrated Chip Distr
N.A.I.C.S.: 423690

Qorvo Germany Holding GmbH   (1)
Loeffelholzstrasse 20, 90441, Nuremberg, Germany
Tel.: (49) 9119411233
Semiconductor Design & Manufacturing
N.A.I.C.S.: 334413

Qorvo International Pte. Ltd.   (1)
1 Changi Business Park Avenue 1 04-01, Singapore, 486058, Singapore
Tel.: (65) 66328300
Web Site: http://www.qorvo.com
Sales Range: $25-49.9 Million
Emp.: 17
Radio Communication System Component Mfr
N.A.I.C.S.: 334419

Qorvo Japan YK   (1)
Grand Front Osaka Tower B 3-1 Ofuka-cho, Kita-ku, Osaka, 530-0011, Japan
Tel.: (81) 357195210
Sales Range: $10-24.9 Million
Emp.: 5
Radio Communication System Component Mfr
N.A.I.C.S.: 334413
Yoshi Koizumi *(Office Mgr)*

Qorvo Korea Ltd.   (1)
10F Haesung 1 Bldg 504 Teheran-ro,

Gangnam-gu, Seoul, 06178, Korea (South)
Tel.: (82) 234497000
Web Site: http://www.rfmd.com
Supplier of Integrated Circuits
N.A.I.C.S.: 334413

Qorvo Munich GmbH   (1)
Konrad-Zuse-Platz 1, 81829, Munich, Germany   (100%)
Tel.: (49) 89996282600
Sales Range: $100-124.9 Million
Emp.: 60
Electronic Components & Devices Mfr & Marketer
N.A.I.C.S.: 334413
Oskar Guthardt *(Reg Mgr-Sls)*

Qorvo Shanghai Ltd.   (1)
Room 1101 Yong Da International Tower 2277 Long Yang Road, Pu Dong District, Shanghai, 201204, China
Tel.: (86) 2150117290
Network & Radio Frequency Solution Provider
N.A.I.C.S.: 334413

Qorvo UK Limited   (1)
3 Waterside Drive Arlington Business Park, Theale, RG7 4SW, Reading, United Kingdom
Tel.: (44) 89167250
Supplier of Integrated Circuits
N.A.I.C.S.: 334413
Thomas Eichhorst *(Reg Mgr-Sls-Central & Eastern Europe)*

Qorvo US, Inc.   (1)
7628 Thorndike Rd, Greensboro, NC 27409
Tel.: (336) 664-1233
Web Site: https://www.qorvo.com
Sales Range: $800-899.9 Million
Emp.: 3,109
Holding Company; Radio Frequency Technologies Designer, Mfr & Whslr
N.A.I.C.S.: 551112
Robert A. Bruggeworth *(CEO)*

Subsidiary (Domestic):

Qorvo California, Inc.   (2)
950- A Lawrence Dr, Thousand Oaks, CA 91320
Tel.: (805) 480-5099
Microwave, Radio Frequency Amplifiers & Amplifier-Based Subsystems Designer & Mfr
N.A.I.C.S.: 334413
Ralph G. Quinsey *(Pres)*

Qorvo Florida, Inc.   (2)
1818 S Orange Blossom Trl, Apopka, FL 32703-9419   (100%)
Tel.: (407) 886-8860
Web Site: http://www.qorvo.com
Sales Range: $75-99.9 Million
Emp.: 280
Telecommunication Related Products Mfr
N.A.I.C.S.: 334416

Qorvo Oregon, Inc.   (2)
63140 Britta St Bldg C, Bend, OR 97703
Tel.: (541) 640-8686
Web Site: http://www.qorvo.com
Emp.: 45
Electronic Components Mfr
N.A.I.C.S.: 334419

Qorvo Texas, LLC   (2)
500 W Renner Rd, Richardson, TX 75080
Tel.: (972) 994-8200
Web Site: http://www.qorvo.com
Sales Range: $25-49.9 Million
Emp.: 100
Semiconductor Design & Manufacture
N.A.I.C.S.: 334413

Qorvo Utrecht, B.V.   (1)
Leidseveer 10, 3511 SB, Utrecht, Netherlands
Tel.: (31) 302621157
Integrated Chip Distr
N.A.I.C.S.: 423690

QRONS INC.

28-10 Jackson Ave Ste 26N, Long Island City, NY 11101
Tel.: (212) 945-2080   WY
Web Site: https://qrons.com
Year Founded: 2016

Qrons Inc.—(Continued)

QRON—(OTCQB)
Assets: $3,069
Liabilities: $1,282,351
Net Worth: ($1,279,282)
Earnings: ($733,517)
Emp.: 2
Fiscal Year-end: 12/31/22
Biotechnology Research & Development Services
N.A.I.C.S.: 541713
Jonah Meer (Co-Founder, CEO, CFO & Sec)
Ido Merfeld (Co-Founder & Pres)
Liat Hammer (Dir-Res)

QRS MUSIC TECHNOLOGY, INC.
269 Quaker Dr, Seneca, PA 16346
Tel.: (786) 279-8989   DE
Web Site: https://www.qrsmusic.com
Year Founded: 1900
QRSM—(OTCIQ)
Musical Instrument Manufacturing
N.A.I.C.S.: 339992
Thomas Dolan (Pres & CEO)

QS ENERGY, INC.
23902 FM 2978, Tomball, TX 77375
Tel.: (775) 300-7647   NV
Web Site: https://www.qsenergy.com
Year Founded: 1998
QSEP—(OTCIQ)
Assets: $158,000
Liabilities: $4,848,000
Net Worth: ($4,690,000)
Earnings: ($1,548,000)
Emp.: 2
Fiscal Year-end: 12/31/22
Oil & Natural Gas Extraction Services
N.A.I.C.S.: 211130
Cecil Bond Kyte (Chm, CEO & CFO)

QSAM BIOSCIENCES, INC.
9442 Capital of Texas Hwy N Plz 1 Ste 500, Austin, TX 78759
Tel.: (512) 343-4558   DE
Web Site: http://www.qsambio.com
QSAM—(OTCQB)
Assets: $364,621
Liabilities: $1,580,030
Net Worth: ($1,936,609)
Earnings: ($5,481,291)
Emp.: 4
Fiscal Year-end: 12/31/22
Compost & Engineered Soils Mfr
N.A.I.C.S.: 115112
Douglas R. Baum (Pres & CEO)
C. Richard Piazza (Chm)
Adam King (CFO)

Subsidiaries:

George B. Wittmer Associates, Inc. (1)
500 Palmer St, Green Cove Springs, FL 32043
Tel.: (904) 879-0220
Web Site: http://www.wittmer-agricycle.com
Waste Management Services
N.A.I.C.S.: 562998

Organics By Gosh (1)
13602 FM 969, Austin, TX 78724-6396
Tel.: (512) 276-1211
Web Site: http://www.organicsbygosh.com
Organic Mulch, Compost & Garden Soil Maker & Seller
N.A.I.C.S.: 115112

QT IMAGING HOLDINGS, INC.
3 Hamilton Landing, Ste 160, Novato, CA 94949
Tel.: (650) 276-7040   DE
Web Site: https://www.qtimaging.com
QTI—(NYSE)
Rev.: $1,526,860
Assets: $23,398,562

Liabilities: $12,690,494
Net Worth: ($12,514,886)
Earnings: ($5,132,332)
Fiscal Year-end: 12/31/23
Diagnostic Imaging Centers
N.A.I.C.S.: 621512
Andrea Betti-Berutto (Chief Technical Officer)
Avi S. Katz (Mng Partner)
Brad Weightman (Treas)
Peter Wang (Chief Technical Officer)
Raluca Dinu (Pres)

QUAD COUNTY CORN PROCESSORS COOPERATIVE
6059 159th St, Galva, IA 51020
Tel.: (712) 282-4628
Web Site: https://www.quad-county.com
Year Founded: 2000
QCCP—(OTCIQ)
Corn Oil & Grain Services
N.A.I.C.S.: 111199
Brian Friedrichsen (Pres)

QUAD M SOLUTIONS, INC.
115 River Rd Ste 151, Edgewater, NJ 07020
Tel.: (723) 423-5520   ID
Web Site:
    https://www.quadmsolutions.com
Year Founded: 1932
MMMM—(OTCIQ)
Rev.: $54,892,679
Assets: $10,748,095
Liabilities: $10,194,060
Net Worth: $554,035
Earnings: ($4,212,053)
Emp.: 18
Fiscal Year-end: 12/31/22
Mineral Exploration & Mining Services
N.A.I.C.S.: 213115
Pat Dileo (CEO, Interim CFO & Chm)
Joseph Frontiere (Interim CEO & Interim CFO)

QUAD/GRAPHICS, INC.
N61 W23044 Harry's Way, Sussex, WI 53089-3995
Tel.: (414) 566-6000   WI
Web Site: https://www.quad.com
Year Founded: 1971
QUAD—(NYSE)
Rev.: $3,217,000,000
Assets: $1,701,800,000
Liabilities: $1,528,900,000
Net Worth: $172,900,000
Earnings: $9,300,000
Emp.: 15,300
Fiscal Year-end: 12/31/22
Commercial Printing Services
N.A.I.C.S.: 323111
J. Joel Quadracci (Chm, Pres & CEO)
Joel Quadracci (Chm, Pres & CEO)
David J. Honan (COO & Exec VP)
Anthony C. Staniak (CFO)
Maura Packham (VP-Corp Comm)
Eric N. Ashworth (Exec VP-Product Solutions & Market Strategy)
Don McKenna (Sr VP-Sls Admin)
Dana B. Gruen (Chief Compliance Officer, Chief Risk Officer, Gen Counsel & Sec)
Julie Currie (Chief Revenue Officer & Exec VP)
Joshua J. Golden (CMO)
Robert H. Quadracci (Chief HR Officer)
Alicia Alston (VP-Mktg & Comm)

Subsidiaries:

Anselmo L. Morvillo, S.A. (1)
Av Francisco Pienovi 317, B1868DRG, Avellaneda, Buenos Aires, Argentina

Tel.: (54) 114 135 9900
Web Site: http://www.morvillo.com.ar
Sales Range: $75-99.9 Million
Emp.: 280
Commercial Printing Services
N.A.I.C.S.: 323111

Encoda Systems Inc. (1)
525 Plymouth Rd Ste 307, Plymouth Meeting, PA 19462
Tel.: (610) 397-1632
Web Site: http://www.encoda.com
Sales Range: $75-99.9 Million
Emp.: 400
Computer Software Mfr & Computer Consulting Services
N.A.I.C.S.: 541511

Ivie & Associates, Inc. (1)
601 Silveron Blvd, Flower Mound, TX 75028
Tel.: (972) 899-5000
Advetising Agency
N.A.I.C.S.: 541810
Warren Ivie (Co-Founder & CEO)
Kay Ivie (Co-Founder)

Subsidiary (Domestic):

CLM LLC (1)
588 W Idaho St Ste 200, Boise, ID 83702
Tel.: (208) 342-2525
Web Site: https://www.clmnorthwest.com
Marketing, Branding, Public Relations & Stategic Planning Services
N.A.I.C.S.: 541613
Max White (Dir-Creative)
Mike Gerhardt (Sr Acct Mgr)
Della Fencl (Controller)
Becky L. Erickson (Mgr-Production)
Jill Moore (Sr Mgr-Acct)
Megan Miller (Acct Mgr)
Maddie Brady (Coord-Media)
Antonio Gallegos (Acct Coord)
Laura Munsil (Project Mgr-Creative)
Vanessa Almaraz (Coord)
Antonio Gallegos (Acct Coord)
Laura Munsil (Project Mgr-Creative)
Vanessa Almaraz (Coord)
Antonio Gallegos (Acct Coord)
Laura Munsil (Project Mgr-Creative)
Vanessa Almaraz (Coord)

RD&F Advertising, Inc. (2)
14901 Quorum Dr Ste 400, Dallas, TX 75254
Tel.: (214) 459-0116
Advertising & Marketing Services
N.A.I.C.S.: 541890
Mark Davis (Pres)

Marin's Deutschland GmbH (1)
Rather Str 49 d, 40476, Dusseldorf, Germany
Tel.: (49) 21138541719
Web Site:
    https://www.wp.marinsdeutschland.de
Marketing Agent Services
N.A.I.C.S.: 541613

Periscope (Asia) Limited (1)
Unit 3-4 1/F The Whitney 183 Wai Yip Street, Kowloon, Kwun Tong, China (Hong Kong)
Tel.: (852) 35259900
Information Technology Services
N.A.I.C.S.: 541511
Gilbert Lee (Mng Dir)

Periscope Printing & Packaging India Private Limited (1)
Apartment V - 406 Atrium Hotel Shooting Range Road, Unit 805 Pinnacle Tower, Faridabad, 121 001, Haryana, India
Tel.: (91) 1294001805
Paper Mfr
N.A.I.C.S.: 322299

Periscope, Inc. (1)
921 Washington Ave S, Minneapolis, MN 55415
Tel.: (612) 399-0500
Web Site: http://www.periscope.com
Advertising Agencies
N.A.I.C.S.: 541810
Bill Simpson (Chm)
Virginia Hines (CFO & COO)
Jenifer Anhorn (Exec VP-Bus Dev)
Victor Kimble (Exec VP-Strategy)
Chris Hiland (Exec VP-Client Leadership)

John Keenan (Exec VP-Mktg & Analytics)
Ryan Peck (Creative Dir)
Scott O'Leary (Creative Dir)
Jen Stocksmith (Grp Creative Dir)
Heath Pochucha (Exec Creative Dir)
Jason Bottenus (Exec Creative Dir)

Subsidiary (Domestic):

Anthem Marketing, LLC (2)
549 W Randolph Ste 700, Chicago, IL 60661
Tel.: (312) 441-0382
Web Site: https://www.anthemedge.com
Marketing Consulting Services
N.A.I.C.S.: 541613
Lori Piest (Sr Dir-Human Resources-Operations)

Plural Grafica E Editora Ltda (1)
Av Marcos Penteado de Ulhoa Rodrigues 700 Santana de Parnaiba, 06543-001, Sao Paulo, Brazil
Tel.: (55) 1141529425
Web Site: http://www.plural.com.br
Sales Range: $250-299.9 Million
Emp.: 1,000
Commercial Lithographic Printing Services
N.A.I.C.S.: 323111

Q/G Holland B.V. (1)
Flevolaan 9, 1382 JX, Weesp, Netherlands
Tel.: (31) 294496222
Control System Design & Mfr
N.A.I.C.S.: 334511

Quad/Graphics Europe Sp. z o.o (1)
ul Pultuska 120, 07-200, Wyszkow, Poland
Tel.: (48) 223367005
Web Site: https://www.quadgraphics.pl
Control System Design & Mfr
N.A.I.C.S.: 334511

Quad/Graphics Querataro S.A. de C.V. (1)
Lote 37 Fracc Agroindustrial La Cruz, PO Box 512, El Marques, Queretaro, 76240, Mexico
Tel.: (52) 4422781300
Web Site: http://www.quadgraphics.com
Sales Range: $125-149.9 Million
Emp.: 200
Printing Services
N.A.I.C.S.: 323111

Quad/Graphics, Inc. - Atglen (1)
4581 Lower Valley Rd, Atglen, PA 19310
Tel.: (414) 208-2700
Sales Range: $125-149.9 Million
Emp.: 350
Print Production Services
N.A.I.C.S.: 323111

Quad/Graphics, Inc. - Chicago Premedia (1)
1201 Wiley Rd 100, Schaumburg, IL 60173
Tel.: (847) 882-2810
Web Site: http://www.qg.com
Sales Range: $25-49.9 Million
Emp.: 15
Commercial Printing Services
N.A.I.C.S.: 323111

Quad/Graphics, Inc. - Dickson (1)
1665 Old Columbia Rd, Dickson, TN 37055
Tel.: (615) 446-6700
Sales Range: $125-149.9 Million
Emp.: 400
Commercial Printing
N.A.I.C.S.: 323111

Quad/Graphics, Inc. - Effingham (1)
420 W Industrial Ave, Effingham, IL 62401-0250
Tel.: (414) 622-2500
Sales Range: $250-299.9 Million
Emp.: 765
Commercial Printing Services
N.A.I.C.S.: 323111
Bob Walls (Dir-Pur)

Quad/Graphics, Inc. - Enfield (1)
96 Phoenix Ave, Enfield, CT 06082-4408
Tel.: (860) 741-0150
Web Site: http://www.qg.com
Sales Range: $50-74.9 Million
Emp.: 115
Offset Printing
N.A.I.C.S.: 323111

Quad/Graphics, Inc. - Fairfield (1)

100 N Miller St, Fairfield, PA 17320-9707
Tel.: (414) 208-2800
Web Site: http://www.qg.com
Sales Range: $150-199.9 Million
Emp.: 500
Print Production Services
N.A.I.C.S.: 323111

Quad/Graphics, Inc. - Fernley (1)
2200 Newlands Dr E, Fernley, NV 89408
Tel.: (775) 575-1400
Web Site: http://www.qg.com
Sales Range: $50-74.9 Million
Emp.: 150
Print Production Services
N.A.I.C.S.: 323111

Quad/Graphics, Inc. - Franklin (1)
1 World Packaging Cir, Franklin, WI 53132
Tel.: (414) 855-9100
Sales Range: $150-199.9 Million
Emp.: 500
Commercial Printing Services
N.A.I.C.S.: 323111

Quad/Graphics, Inc. - Hazleton (1)
594 Can Do Expy, Hazleton, PA 18202
Tel.: (570) 459-5700
Web Site: http://www.qg.com
Sales Range: $75-99.9 Million
Emp.: 499
Commercial Printing Services
N.A.I.C.S.: 323111

Quad/Graphics, Inc. - Leominster (1)
27 Nashua St, Leominster, MA 01453-3311
Tel.: (978) 534-8351
Web Site: http://www.qg.com
Sales Range: $50-74.9 Million
Emp.: 200
Commercial Printing Services
N.A.I.C.S.: 323111

Quad/Graphics, Inc. - Midland (1)
1700 James Savage Rd, Midland, MI 48642
Tel.: (989) 496-3333
Sales Range: $150-199.9 Million
Emp.: 600
Commercial Printing Services
N.A.I.C.S.: 323111

Quad/Graphics, Inc. - Pewaukee (1)
W2224 N3322 Duplainville Rd, Pewaukee, WI 53072
Tel.: (414) 566-7500
Web Site: http://www.qg.com
Sales Range: $25-49.9 Million
Emp.: 2,300
Print Production Services
N.A.I.C.S.: 323111

Quad/Graphics, Inc. - St. Cloud (1)
660 NE Mayhew Lake Rd, Saint Cloud, MN 56304
Tel.: (320) 654-2400
Web Site: http://www.qg.com
Sales Range: $75-99.9 Million
Emp.: 280
Commercial Printing Services
N.A.I.C.S.: 323111

Quad/Graphics, Inc. - Taunton (1)
1133 County St, Taunton, MA 02780
Tel.: (508) 823-4581
Sales Range: $100-124.9 Million
Emp.: 325
Commercial Printing Services
N.A.I.C.S.: 323111
Michael Agnew (Plant Mgr)

Quad/Graphics, Inc. - Waukee (1)
250 NW 10th St, Waukee, IA 50263
Tel.: (515) 987-5100
Web Site: http://www.qg.com
Sales Range: $50-74.9 Million
Emp.: 135
Commercial Printing Services
N.A.I.C.S.: 323111

Quad/Graphics, Inc. - Woburn (1)
110 Commerce Way, Woburn, MA 01801
Tel.: (781) 231-7200
Sales Range: $25-49.9 Million
Emp.: 140
Printing Services
N.A.I.C.S.: 323111

Quad/Tech Europe, Inc. (1)
Short Muiderweg 2, 1382 LR, Weesp, Netherlands
Tel.: (31) 294496222

Sales Range: $25-49.9 Million
Emp.: 30
Commercial Printing Services
N.A.I.C.S.: 323111
Stephan Doppelhammer (Global Mgr-Market-Pkg)

Quad/Winkowski Sp. zoo (1)
ul Gwiazdzista 5, 01-651, Warsaw, Mazowieckie, Poland
Tel.: (48) 22 460 53 30
Web Site: http://www.winkowski.pl
Printing Services
N.A.I.C.S.: 323111

Subsidiary (Non-US):

QuadWinkowski (2)
Linnes vag 2, 191 35, Sollentuna, Sweden
Tel.: (46) 854445150
Web Site: http://www.quadwinkowski.co.uk
Sales Range: $25-49.9 Million
Emp.: 2
Printing Services
N.A.I.C.S.: 323111

Winkowski Deutschland GmbH (2)
Georg-Weiss-Weg 3, 53125, Bonn, Germany
Tel.: (49) 2282891952
Web Site: http://www.winkowski-druck.de
Printing Services
N.A.I.C.S.: 323111

QuadTech (Shanghai) Trading Company Limited (1)
Room 1605 Ben Ben Mansion 300 Xikang Road, Jing'an, Shanghai, 200040, China
Tel.: (86) 2162882525
Emp.: 20
Commercial Printing Services
N.A.I.C.S.: 323111

QuadTech Europe (1)
Flevolaan 9, Weesp, 1382 JX, Netherlands
Tel.: (31) 294 496222
Web Site: http://www.quadtechworld.com
Sales Range: $25-49.9 Million
Emp.: 25
Commercial Printing Services
N.A.I.C.S.: 323111

QuadTech Ireland (1)
Holland Road National Technology Park, Limerick, Ireland
Tel.: (353) 61336900
Commercial Printing Services
N.A.I.C.S.: 323111

Reproducciones Fotomecanicas S.A. de C.V. (1)
Democracias No 116, San Miguel de Allende, 02700, Guanajuato, Mexico
Tel.: (52) 5553581055
Commercial Printing Services
N.A.I.C.S.: 323111

Rise Interactive Media & Analytics, LLC (1)
1 S Wacker Dr Fl 3, Chicago, IL 60606
Tel.: (312) 281-9933
Web Site: http://www.riseinteractive.com
Marketing Agent Services
N.A.I.C.S.: 541613
Jon Morris (Founder)
Larry Fisher (CEO)
David Zuaiter (CFO)
Howard Diamond (Chief Strategy Officer)
Brent Laufenberg (CTO)
Lou Amodeo (VP-Digital Strategy)
Ruth Ayres (VP-Bus Dev)
Ashmita Chatterjee (VP-Acct Mgmt)
Doug Durkalski (VP-Acct Mgmt)
Justin Garvin (VP-Media Strategy)
Alison Golin (VP-Project Mgmt)
Aaron Horowitz (VP-Bus Dev)
Mitch Perkal (VP-Digital Strategy)
Daniel Ripes (VP-Acct Mgmt)
Rob Sauter (VP-Acct Mgmt)
Natalie Scherer (Sr VP-Mktg)
David Schmidt (Sr VP-Legal)
Nicole Skaluba (Sr VP-Employee Svcs)
Jeff Teitelbaum (Sr VP-Client Svcs)
Joy Wilson (VP-Product Mgmt)
Jean Zhang (VP-Customer Experience)

Rise Interactive SRL (1)
El Salvador 5218, C1414BPV, Buenos Aires, Argentina
Tel.: (54) 3122819933

Web Site: http://www.riseinteractive.com
Advertising & Marketing Services
N.A.I.C.S.: 541810
Larry Fisher (CEO)

Unigraphic, Inc. (1)
110 Commerce Way Bldg J, Woburn, MA 01801
Tel.: (781) 231-7200
Web Site: http://www.uni-graphic.com
Control System Design & Mfr
N.A.I.C.S.: 334511

QUADRO ACQUISITION ONE CORP.

2685 Nottingham Ave, Los Angeles, CA 90027
Tel.: (302) 738-6680   Ky
Year Founded: 2020
QDRO—(NASDAQ)
Assets: $233,338,881
Liabilities: $236,507,869
Net Worth: ($3,168,988)
Earnings: $8,721,564
Emp.: 1
Fiscal Year-end: 12/31/22
Investment Management Service
N.A.I.C.S.: 523999
Dimitri Elkin (CEO)
Konstantin Tourevski (Chm)

QUAINT OAK BANCORP, INC.

501 Knowles Ave, Southampton, PA 18966
Tel.: (215) 364-4059   PA
Web Site: https://www.quaintoak.com
QNTO—(OTCQB)
Rev.: $59,802,000
Assets: $754,118,000
Liabilities: $702,553,000
Net Worth: $51,565,000
Earnings: $1,670,000
Emp.: 124
Fiscal Year-end: 12/31/23
Bank Holding Company
N.A.I.C.S.: 551111
Robert T. Strong (Pres & CEO)
John J. Augustine (CFO & Exec VP)
Diane J. Colyer (Sec & Sr VP)
William R. Gonzalez (Exec VP-Quaint Oak Bank)

Subsidiaries:

Quaint Oak Bank (1)
501 Knowles Ave, Southampton, PA 18966
Tel.: (215) 364-4059
Web Site: https://www.quaintoak.com
Commercial Banking Services
N.A.I.C.S.: 522110
Robert T. Strong (Pres & CEO)
John J. Augustine (CFO, Treas & Exec VP)

QUAKER CHEMICAL CORPORATION

1 Quaker Park 901 E Hector St, Conshohocken, PA 19428-2380
Tel.: (610) 832-4000   PA
Web Site:
  https://www.quakerhoughton.com
Year Founded: 1918
KWR—(NYSE)
Rev.: $1,943,585,000
Assets: $2,821,622,000
Liabilities: $1,543,037,000
Net Worth: $1,278,585,000
Earnings: ($15,931,000)
Emp.: 5,200
Fiscal Year-end: 12/31/22
Custom-Formulated Chemical Specialty Products & Fluid Management Services for the Steel, Automotive & Can Industries
N.A.I.C.S.: 325199
Robert T. Traub (Gen Counsel, Sec & Sr VP)
Jeewat Bijlani (Chief Strategy Officer & Exec VP)

Wilbert Platzer (Sr VP-EHS, Procurement & Ops-Global)
Andrew E. Tometich (Pres & CEO)
Dave Slinkman (CTO & Sr VP)
Jeffrey J. Kutz (Chief Acctg Officer & VP)
Melissa Leneis (Chief HR Officer & Exec VP)
Jeff L. Fleck (Chief Supply Chain Officer & Sr VP)
Joseph Berquist (Chief Comml Officer & Exec VP)
Tom Coler (CFO & Exec VP)
Anna Ransley (Chief Digital Information Officer & Sr VP)

Subsidiaries:

AC Products, Inc. (1)
9930 Painter Ave, Whittier, CA 90605-2759   **(100%)**
Tel.: (714) 630-7311
Web Site: https://www.acpmaskants.com
Sales Range: $10-24.9 Million
Emp.: 29
Adhesive & Liquid Rubber Coatings Mfr
N.A.I.C.S.: 325520

Binol AB (1)
Vastra Kajen 8, 374 31, Karlshamn, Blekinge, Sweden
Tel.: (46) 45482800
Sales Range: $25-49.9 Million
Emp.: 22
Lubricant Mfr
N.A.I.C.S.: 324191

Commonwealth Oil Corporation (1)
2080 Ferriss Road North, Harrow, N0R 1G0, ON, Canada
Tel.: (519) 738-3503
Chemical Products Mfr
N.A.I.C.S.: 325199

DA Stuart India Private Limited (1)
502&503 Montreal Business Centre 5th Floor, Baner, Pune, 411045, Maharashtra, India
Tel.: (91) 2067245300
Inorganic Chemical Mfr
N.A.I.C.S.: 325180

DA Stuart Shanghai Co. (1)
No 139 Zhuyuan Road, Pujiang Industrial Area Minhang, Shanghai, 201112, China
Tel.: (86) 2167742570
Lubricant & Metalworking Fluid Mfr
N.A.I.C.S.: 324191

ECLI Products, LLC (1)
3851 Exchange Ave, Aurora, IL 60504
Tel.: (630) 449-5000
Web Site: https://www.ecllube.com
Oil & Grease Mfr
N.A.I.C.S.: 324191

Engineered Custom Lubricants GmbH (1)
Im Bruckerfeld 8, 42799, Leichlingen, Germany
Tel.: (49) 21759905530
Web Site: http://www.ecllube.com
Oil & Grease Mfr
N.A.I.C.S.: 324191

GHI Asia Pacific Pte. Ltd. (1)
22 Boon Lay Way 01-61, Trade Hub 21, Singapore, 609968, Singapore
Tel.: (65) 62351544
Lubricant & Metalworking Fluid Mfr
N.A.I.C.S.: 324191

Houghton International Inc. (1)
945 Madison Ave, Norristown, PA 19403
Tel.: (610) 666-4000
Web Site: http://www.houghtonintl.com
Specialty Chemical Oil & Lubricant Mfr
N.A.I.C.S.: 325998
Jeewat Bijlani (Sr VP)
David Slinkman (Sr VP-Res & Tech-Global)
Kym Johnson (Chief HR Officer & Sr VP)
Kevin Smith (Pres-EMEA & Sr VP)

Subsidiary (Non-US):

Houghton (Shanghai) Specialty Industrial Fluids Co. Ltd. (2)
No 188 Jiangtian East Road, Songjiang In-

Quaker Chemical Corporation—(Continued)

dustrial Area, Shanghai, 201613, China
Tel.: (86) 21 67742570
Web Site: http://www.houghtonintl.com
Specialty Chemicals Mfr
N.A.I.C.S.: 325998

Houghton Asia Pacific Co., Ltd. (2)
Units A-B 15F Neich Tower 128 Gloucester
Rd, Wanchai, China (Hong Kong)
Tel.: (852) 27708211
Web Site: http://www.houghtonintl.com
Specialty Chemicals Distr
N.A.I.C.S.: 424690

Houghton Australia Pty. Ltd. (2)
287 Wickham Road, Moorabbin, 3189, VIC,
Australia
Tel.: (61) 3 9555 0344
Web Site: http://www.houghton.com.au
Specialty Chemicals, Oils & Lubricants Mfr
N.A.I.C.S.: 325998

Houghton Brazil Ltda. (2)
Rua Alpont 170 Capuava, Maua, Sao
Paulo, 09380-908, SP, Brazil
Tel.: (55) 1145128200
Web Site: http://www.houghtonintl.com
Specialty Chemicals & Lubricants Mfr
N.A.I.C.S.: 325998

Houghton Canada Inc. (2)
915 Meyerside Drive, Mississauga, L5T
1R8, ON, Canada
Web Site: http://www.houghtonintl.com
Specialty Industrial Processing Chemicals
Whslr
N.A.I.C.S.: 424690

Houghton Japan Co., Ltd. (2)
Yokohama Kanazawa High Tech Center
Techno-core 2F Room C br, Minato-ku, Yo-
kohama, 236-0004, Kanagawa, Japan
Tel.: (81) 453499010
Web Site: http://www.houghton.co.jp
Specialty Chemicals Distr
N.A.I.C.S.: 424690

Houghton Mexico S.A. de C.V. (2)
Efrain Gonzalez Luna 2007 Dept O19, Col
Americana, Guadalajara, CP 44160,
Jalisco, Mexico
Tel.: (52) 333 615 9331
Web Site: http://www.houghtonintl.com
Specialty Chemicals Distr
N.A.I.C.S.: 424690

**Houghton Oil (Malaysia) Sdn,
Bhd.** (2)
313 Block E Kelana Parkview No 1 Jalan
SS 6/2, Kelana Jaya, 47301, Petaling Jaya,
Selangor Darul Ehsan, Malaysia
Tel.: (60) 37/8054633
Web Site: http://www.houghtonintl.com
Specialty Chemicals Distr
N.A.I.C.S.: 424690

Houghton Plc (2)
Beacon Road, Trafford Park, Manchester,
MI7 IAF, United Kingdom
Tel.: (44) 1618745000
Specialty Metal Processing Chemicals Mfr
N.A.I.C.S.: 325998

Subsidiary (Non-US):

Houghton CZ s.r.o. (3)
Bartosova 3, 602 00, Brno, Czech Republic
Tel.: (420) 542213332
Web Site: http://www.houghtonintl.com
Specialty Chemicals Distr
N.A.I.C.S.: 424690

Houghton Denmark A/S (3)
Energiens Energivej 3, 4180, Soro, Den-
mark
Tel.: (45) 45852300
Web Site: http://www.houghtonintl.com
Specialty Chemicals Distr
N.A.I.C.S.: 424690

Houghton Deutschland GmbH (3)
Giselherstrasse 57, 44339, Dortmund, Ger-
many
Tel.: (49) 800 7435562
Web Site: http://www.houghtonintl.com
Specialty Chemicals & Lubricants Mfr
N.A.I.C.S.: 325998

Houghton Iberica S.A. (3)

Avenida Arraona 73-79, Pol Ind Can
Salvatella-Torre Mateu, 08210, Barbera del
Valles, Spain
Tel.: (34) 937188500
Web Site: http://www.houghtonintl.com
Specialty Chemicals & Lubricants Mfr
N.A.I.C.S.: 325998

Houghton Italia S.p.A. (3)
Via F Postiglione 30, 10024, Moncalieri,
Italy
Tel.: (39) 0116475811
Web Site: http://www.houghtonintl.com
Specialty Metal Processing Chemicals Mfr
N.A.I.C.S.: 325998

Houghton Kimya San A.S. (3)
Kosuyolu Mah Asma Dali Sok No 14
Kadikoy, 34718, Istanbul, Turkiye
Tel.: (90) 2163251515
Web Site: http://www.houghtonintl.com
Specialty Chemicals Distr
N.A.I.C.S.: 424690

Houghton Polska Sp. z o.o. (3)
ul Kapelanka 17, 30-347, Krakow, Poland
Tel.: (48) 123475650
Web Site: http://www.houghtonintl.com
Specialty Chemicals Distr
N.A.I.C.S.: 424690

Houghton Sverige AB (3)
Vastra Kajen 8, 374 31, Karlshamn, Swe-
den
Tel.: (46) 42295510
Web Site: http://www.houghtonintl.com
Specialty Chemicals Distr
N.A.I.C.S.: 424690

Houghton Ukraine Ltd. (3)
13 Prirechnaya St, Kiev, 04213, Ukraine
Tel.: (380) 443601024
Web Site: http://www.houghtonintl.com
Specialty Chemicals Distr
N.A.I.C.S.: 424690

Subsidiary (Non-US):

Houghton Romania S.R.L. (3)
2A Jiului Street 4th floor Room 2, 013219,
Bucharest, Romania
Tel.: (40) 21 667 06 15
Web Site: http://www.houghtonintl.com
Lubricant Oil Distr
N.A.I.C.S.: 424720

Houghton Taiwan Co. Ltd. (2)
8/F-1 No 115 Keelung Rd Sec 2, Taipei,
Taiwan
Tel.: (886) 2 2739 3707
Web Site: http://www.houghtonintl.com
Specialty Chemicals Distr
N.A.I.C.S.: 424690

Korea Houghton Corporation (2)
19th floor Professional Construction Asso-
ciation Building, Dongjak-gu, Seoul, 156-
010, Korea (South)
Tel.: (82) 232843300
Web Site: http://www.tectylasia.com
Lubricant Oil Mfr
N.A.I.C.S.: 324191

Thai Houghton 1993 Co., Ltd. (2)
Branch 001/BKK office 77/105-106 25th
Floor Sinn Sathorn Tower, Krungdhonburi
Road Klongsarn, Bangkok, 10600, Thailand
Tel.: (66) 24401262
Specialty Chemicals, Oils & Lubricants Mfr
N.A.I.C.S.: 325998

Houghton Singapore (1)
22 Boon Lay Way 01-61 Trade Hub 21, Sin-
gapore, 609968, Singapore
Tel.: (65) 62351544
Chemical Product Mfr & Distr
N.A.I.C.S.: 325998

**Internationale Metall Impragnier
GmbH** (1)
Daimlerstrasse 12, 40789, Monheim am
Rhein, Germany
Tel.: (49) 2173499850
Web Site: https://www.imp-sealants.de
Chemical Products Mfr
N.A.I.C.S.: 325199

Kelko Quaker Chemical, S.A. (1)
Edif Parque Cristal Piso 7, Torre Este Los
Palos Grandes, Caracas, 1060A,
Venezuela (50%)

Tel.: (58) 2122854044
Web Site: http://www.quakerchem.com
Sales Range: $10-24.9 Million
Emp.: 15
Chemicals Mfr
N.A.I.C.S.: 325998

Lubricor, Inc. (1)
475 Conestogo Road, Waterloo, N2L 4C9,
ON, Canada
Tel.: (519) 884-8455
Synthetic Oil Mfr
N.A.I.C.S.: 325199
Jorma Braks (Chm)

Maldaner GmbH (1)
Max-Planck-Ring 3, D-40764, Langenfeld,
Germany
Tel.: (49) 2173984990
Web Site: https://www.maldaner.de
Porous Metal Component Mfr
N.A.I.C.S.: 332312
Gary Roy Lloyd (Mng Dir)
Nicholas Anthony Ogden (Mng Dir)
Bernd Wendinger (Mng Dir)

Nippon Quaker Chemical, Ltd. (1)
2-1-3 Shibukawa-cho, Yao, 581-0075,
Osaka, Japan (50%)
Tel.: (81) 729921650
Web Site: https://www.quakerchem.co.jp
Sales Range: $25-49.9 Million
Emp.: 60
Chemical Mfr & Whslr
N.A.I.C.S.: 325998
Takeo Mizuki (Pres & CEO)

Norman Hay Engineering Ltd. (1)
Lyons Park, West Midlands, Coventry, CV5
9PF, United Kingdom
Tel.: (44) 2476253099
Web Site: https://www.nhe.uk.com
Chemical Products Mfr
N.A.I.C.S.: 325199

Q2 Technologies, LLC (1)
14729 Hwy 105 W Ste 200, Montgomery,
TX 77356
Tel.: (936) 588-2242
Web Site: http://www.q2technologies.com
Sales Range: $25-49.9 Million
Emp.: 3
Basic Inorganic Chemical Mfr
N.A.I.C.S.: 325180

**Quaker Chemical (Australasia) Pty.
Ltd.** (1)
287 Wickham Road, Moorabbin, 3189, VIC,
Australia (100%)
Tel.: (61) 28 336 8532
Web Site: http://www.quaker.com.au
Sales Range: $10-24.9 Million
Emp.: 12
Chemicals Whslr
N.A.I.C.S.: 424690

**Quaker Chemical (China) Co.,
Ltd.** (1)
No 619 Tian Ying Road, Qingpu Industrial
Park, Shanghai, 201700, China (100%)
Tel.: (86) 2139201666
Web Site: http://zh.quakerchem.com
Chemicals Whslr
N.A.I.C.S.: 424690

Quaker Chemical B.V. (1)
Industrieweg 7, 1422 AH, Uithoorn,
Netherlands (100%)
Tel.: (31) 297544644
Web Site: http://www.quakerchem.com
Sales Range: $50-74.9 Million
Emp.: 200
Chemicals Mfr
N.A.I.C.S.: 325998

**Quaker Chemical Corp. - Manufactur-
ing & Logistics - Steel Products** (1)
3431 Yankee Rd, Middletown, OH 45044
Tel.: (513) 422-9600
Web Site: http://www.quakerchem.com
Sales Range: $10-24.9 Million
Emp.: 35
Processing Lubricants, Maintenance Prod-
ucts, Metal Working Fluids & Surface Treat-
ment Products Mfr
N.A.I.C.S.: 324191

Quaker Chemical Europe B.V. (1)
Industrieweg 1 13, 1422 AH, Uithoorn,
Netherlands

Tel.: (31) 297544669
Chemical Products Mfr
N.A.I.C.S.: 325998

Quaker Chemical India Ltd. (1)
Unit 11/3 Acropolis 1858/1 Rajdanga Main
Road, Kolkata, 700107, India (55%)
Tel.: (91) 3340464500
Web Site: http://www.quakerchemindia.com
Sales Range: $1-9.9 Million
Emp.: 20
Chemicals Mfr
N.A.I.C.S.: 325998

**Quaker Chemical Industria e Comer-
cio Ltda.** (1)
Avenida Brasil no 44 178 Industrial District
of Campo Grande, 23078-001, Rio de Ja-
neiro, RJ, Brazil (100%)
Tel.: (55) 2133051800
Sales Range: $10-24.9 Million
Emp.: 110
Chemicals Mfr
N.A.I.C.S.: 325998
Alexandre Jacome (Gen Mgr)

Quaker Chemical Limited (1)
5th floor 6 St Andrew Street, London, EC4A
3AE, Gloucestershire, United
Kingdom (100%)
Tel.: (44) 1453820800
Web Site: http://www.quakerchem.com
Sales Range: $25-49.9 Million
Emp.: 18
Chemicals Whslr
N.A.I.C.S.: 424690

Quaker Chemical MEA FZE (1)
Office N LB 13118, Jebel Ali, Dubai, United
Arab Emirates
Tel.: (971) 48870718
Chemical Products Mfr
N.A.I.C.S.: 325998

**Quaker Chemical Participacoes,
Ltda.** (1)
Av Brasil 44178 Sala A Campo Grande, Rio
de Janeiro, 23078-001, Brazil
Tel.: (55) 212240095
Chemical Products Mfr
N.A.I.C.S.: 325998

Quaker Chemical S.A. (1)
Libertad 1039 - 7th floor, Buenos Aires,
Argentina (100%)
Tel.: (54) 1152448004
Custom Formulated Chemical Distr
N.A.I.C.S.: 424690

**Quaker Chemical South Africa (Pty.)
Ltd.** (1)
169 Tedstone Road, Wadeville, Johannes-
burg, Kwa Zulu Natal, South Africa (51%)
Tel.: (27) 11 820 7111
Web Site: http://www.quakerchem.com
Sales Range: $10-24.9 Million
Emp.: 10
Chemicals Mfr
N.A.I.C.S.: 325998

Quaker Chemical, S.A. (1)
Pol Ind Can Bernades-Subira C/ Ripolles 5,
Santa Perpetua de Mogoda, 08130, Barce-
lona, Spain (100%)
Tel.: (34) 935742700
Web Site: http://www.quakerchem.com
Sales Range: $25-49.9 Million
Emp.: 50
Chemicals Whslr
N.A.I.C.S.: 424690

Quaker Chemical, S A (1)
52 rue de la Victoire TMF Pole, Paris, Ce-
dex, France (100%)
Tel.: (33) 156536399
Web Site: http://www.quakerchemical.com
Sales Range: $10-24.9 Million
Emp.: 40
Chemicals Whslr
N.A.I.C.S.: 424690

Quaker Chemical, S.r.l. (1)
Via Carlo Magni 6 Zona Industriale, 21049,
Tradate, VA, Italy
Tel.: (39) 0331829901
Web Site: http://www.quakerchem.com
Chemical Products Mfr
N.A.I.C.S.: 327110

Quaker Russia B.V. (1)

Industrieweg 7, 1422 AH, Uithoorn, Netherlands
Tel.: (31) 297544644
Chemical Products Mfr
N.A.I.C.S.: 325998

Sterr & Eder Industrieservice GmbH (1)
Waldkirchener Str 12, 84030, Landshut, Germany
Tel.: (49) 8719748190
Web Site: https://www.sterr-eder.de
Logistics Management Services
N.A.I.C.S.: 541614

Summit Lubricants, Inc. (1)
4D Treadeasy Ave, Batavia, NY 14020-9567
Tel.: (585) 344-4301
Web Site: https://www.summitlubricants.com
Sales Range: $25-49.9 Million
Emp.: 50
Petroleum Lubricating Oil & Grease Mfr
N.A.I.C.S.: 324191

Surface Technology (Coventry) Ltd. (1)
Lyons Park, Coventry, CV5 9PF, United Kingdom
Tel.: (44) 2476253099
Web Site: https://www.surfacetechnology.co.uk
Electronic Parts Mfr
N.A.I.C.S.: 334419

Surface Technology (East Kilbride) Ltd. (1)
15-17 Colvilles Place, Kelvin Industrial Estate, East Kilbride, G75 0PZ, United Kingdom
Tel.: (44) 1355248223
Electronic Parts Mfr
N.A.I.C.S.: 334419

Surface Technology (Leeds) Ltd. (1)
Long Causeway Cross Green, Leeds, LS9 0NY, United Kingdom
Tel.: (44) 8454500870
Electronic Parts Mfr
N.A.I.C.S.: 334419

Surface Technology Aberdeen Ltd. (1)
Site 14 Greenbank Rd, East Tullos, Aberdeen, AB12 3BQ, United Kingdom
Tel.: (44) 1224515320
Electronic Parts Mfr
N.A.I.C.S.: 334419

Surface Technology Australia (1)
7 Marriott Road, Jandakot, 6164, WA, Australia
Tel.: (61) 894174047
Electronic Parts Mfr
N.A.I.C.S.: 334419

Tecniquimia Mexicana S.A. de C.V. (1)
Beta 8023 Col Industrial Mitras, Garcia, 66000, Monterrey, NL, Mexico (100%)
Tel.: (52) 8181587100
Web Site: http://www.quakerchem.com
Chemicals Mfr
N.A.I.C.S.: 325998

Ultraseal Chongqing Limited (1)
6 Feng Dian Road, Degan Industrial Road Jiang Jin District, Chongqing, China
Tel.: (86) 2347852200
Chemical Products Mfr
N.A.I.C.S.: 325199

Ultraseal International Group Ltd. (1)
Lyons Park, Coventry, CV5 9PF, United Kingdom
Tel.: (44) 2476258444
Web Site: https://www.ultraseal-impregnation.com
Chemical Products Mfr
N.A.I.C.S.: 325199

Ultraseal Shanghai Limited (1)
51 Taizhong Road, Anting Town Jiading District, Shanghai, 201814, China
Tel.: (86) 2169160313
Chemical Products Mfr
N.A.I.C.S.: 325199
Kevin Ng (Mng Dir)

Ultraseal USA Inc. (1)

4343 Concourse Dr Ste 340, Ann Arbor, MI 48108
Tel.: (734) 222-9478
Sealant Mfr & Distr
N.A.I.C.S.: 325520

Unitek Servicios De Asesoiria Especializad S.A. (1)
Avenida Loma Alta 2623 Loma Larga Monterey, Nuevo Leon, 64710, Mexico
Tel.: (52) 8183444353
Emp.: 10
Transportation Services
N.A.I.C.S.: 488999

Verkol S.A. (1)
Poligono Industrial Zalain 23, 31780, Bera, Spain
Tel.: (34) 94 863 0811
Web Site: https://www.verkol.es
Emp.: 65
Engineeering Services
N.A.I.C.S.: 541330

Wallover Oil Company Incorporated (1)
21845 Drake Rd, Strongsville, OH 44149
Tel.: (440) 238-9250
Web Site: http://www.wallover.com
Chemical Products Mfr
N.A.I.C.S.: 325199

QUALCOMM INCORPORATED
5775 Morehouse Dr, San Diego, CA 92121-1714
Tel.: (858) 587-1121   DE
Web Site:
  https://www.qualcomm.com
Year Founded: 1985
QCOM—(NASDAQ)
Rev.: $38,962,000,000
Assets: $55,154,000,000
Liabilities: $28,880,000,000
Net Worth: $26,274,000,000
Earnings: $10,142,000,000
Emp.: 49,000
Fiscal Year-end: 09/29/24
Telecommunication Servicesb
N.A.I.C.S.: 517112
Mark D. McLaughlin (Chm)
Cristiano Renno Amon (Pres & CEO)
James H. Thompson (CTO)
Akash Palkhiwala (CFO & COO)
Heather Ace (Chief HR Officer)
Don McGuire (CMO & Sr VP)
Ann Cathcart Chaplin (Gen Counsel & Sec)
Neil Martin (Chief Acctg Officer & Sr VP)
Jim Cathey (Chief Comml Officer)
Christian Block (Sr VP)
Roawen Chen (Sr VP)
Nakul Duggal (Sr VP)
Alex Katouzian (Sr VP)
Jeff Torrance (Sr VP)
Durga Malladi (Sr VP)
Rahul Patel (Sr VP)

Subsidiaries:

Arriver US, Inc. (1)
27000 Meadowbrook Rd Ste 201, Novi, MI 48377
Tel.: (248) 200-3090
Web Site: https://arriverusa.teamtailor.com
Software Development Services
N.A.I.C.S.: 541511

QUALCOMM (UK) Limited (1)
Spectrum Point 279 Farnborough Rd, Farnborough, GU14 7LS, United Kingdom
Tel.: (44) 1252363100
Web Site: http://www.qualcomm.com
Wireless Technology & Services
N.A.I.C.S.: 517111

QUALCOMM Atheros, Inc. (1)
1700 Technology Dr, San Jose, CA 95110
Tel.: (408) 773-5200
Web Site: http://www.qca.qualcomm.com
Sales Range: $900-999.9 Million
Emp.: 1,778
Semiconductor System Solutions Mfr for Wireless & Other Network Communications Products

N.A.I.C.S.: 334413

Subsidiary (Non-US):

QUALCOMM Atheros Canada Corporation (2)
144 Front St W Suite 385, Toronto, M5J 2L7, ON, Canada
Tel.: (416) 217-0451
Wireless Technology & Services
N.A.I.C.S.: 517111

QUALCOMM Atheros Hong Kong (2)
PO Box 333, Fo Tan, Hong Kong, NT, China (Hong Kong)
Tel.: (852) 82061131
Web Site: http://www.qca.qualcomm.com
Sales Range: $100-124.9 Million
Mfr & Sales of Semiconductor System Solutions for Wireless & Other Network Communications Products
N.A.I.C.S.: 334413

QUALCOMM Atheros Taiwan (2)
12f No 407 Ruiguang Rd, Neihu District, Taipei, 11492, Taiwan
Tel.: (886) 287516385
Web Site: http://www.qualcomm.com
Mfr of Semiconductor System Solutions for Wireless & Other Network Communications Products
N.A.I.C.S.: 334413

QUALCOMM Atheros Technology (Macao Commercial Offshore) Limited (2)
Alameda Drive Carlos D'Assumpcao 181-187 Centro Comercial do Grupo, Brilhantismo, 17 Andar West, Macau, China (Macau)
Tel.: (853) 28750670
Web Site: http://www.qca.qualcomm.com
Sales Range: $10-24.9 Million
Emp.: 5
Sales of Semiconductor System Solutions for Wireless & Other Network Communications Products
N.A.I.C.S.: 334413

QUALCOMM CDMA Technologies (1)
5775 Morehouse Dr, San Diego, CA 92121-1714
Tel.: (858) 587-1121
Web Site: http://www.qualcomm.com
Sales Range: $100-124.9 Million
Mfr of Wireless Chipsets & Software Solutions
N.A.I.C.S.: 334413

Subsidiary (Non-US):

QUALCOMM CDMA Technologies (Korea) Y.H. (2)
17th Fl Popa Gangnam Tower 119 Nonhyeon Tong, Seoul, 135 090, Kangnam-Ku, Korea (South) (100%)
Tel.: (82) 234041114
Web Site: http://www.cdmatech.com
Sales Range: $10-24.9 Million
Emp.: 250
Telecommunication Servicesb
N.A.I.C.S.: 517112

Division (Domestic):

Rapid Bridge LLC (2)
9710 Scranton Rd Ste 160, San Diego, CA 92121
Tel.: (858) 410-5950
Web Site: http://www.rapidbridge.com
Internet Protocol Semiconductors Designer & Mfr
N.A.I.C.S.: 334413

Subsidiary (Domestic):

SnapTrack, Inc. (2)
675 Campbell Technology Pkwy Ste 200, Campbell, CA 95008
Tel.: (408) 626-0500
Sales Range: $10-24.9 Million
Emp.: 80
GPS Tracking Services
N.A.I.C.S.: 541511

QUALCOMM CDMA Technologies Asia-Pacific Pte. Ltd. (1)
6 Serangoon North Avenue 5, Singapore,

554910, Singapore
Tel.: (65) 64030935
Communication Equipment Parts Mfr
N.A.I.C.S.: 334220

QUALCOMM Communication Technologies Ltd. (1)
22F NO 11 Songgao Rd Sinyi District, Taipei, 11073, Taiwan
Tel.: (886) 2 66334000
Wireless Technology & Services
N.A.I.C.S.: 517111

QUALCOMM Firethorn Holdings, LLC (1)
3333 Piedmont Ave Ste 300, Atlanta, GA 30305
Tel.: (678) 507-2500
Web Site: http://www.firethornmobile.com
Sales Range: $50-74.9 Million
Emp.: 200
Intergrated Mobile Phone Banking & Payment Services
N.A.I.C.S.: 513210
Rocco J. Fabiano (Pres)

QUALCOMM Global Trading, Inc. (1)
5775 Morehouse Dr, San Diego, CA 92121
Tel.: (858) 587-1121
Web Site: http://www.qualcomm.com
Wireless Technology & Services
N.A.I.C.S.: 517111

QUALCOMM Government Technologies (1)
5775 Morehouse Dr, San Diego, CA 92121
Tel.: (858) 587-1121
Web Site: http://www.qualcomm.com
Develops, Markets & Sells Products & Technologies Tailored to US Government & Homeland Security Applications
N.A.I.C.S.: 517112

QUALCOMM India Private Limited (1)
Unit No 1102 Platina Building G block 11th Fl Plot C-59 Bandra Kurla C, Mumbai, 400050, Maharashtra, India
Tel.: (91) 2267041400
Wireless Technology & Services
N.A.I.C.S.: 517111
Larry M. Paulson (Pres & VP)
Jim Cathey (Pres-Asia Pacific & India & Sr VP)
Parag Kar (VP-Govt Affairs)
Rajen Vagadia (Country Mgr)

QUALCOMM Innovation Center, Inc. (1)
5775 Morehouse Dr, San Diego, CA 92121-1714 (100%)
Tel.: (858) 587-1121
Web Site: http://www.quicinc.com
Computer Engineering & Software Development Services
N.A.I.C.S.: 541519

Subsidiary (Domestic):

iSkoot Technologies, Inc. (2)
501 2nd St Ste 216, San Francisco, CA 94107
Tel.: (415) 684-1011
Web Site: http://www.iskoot.com
Software Programming Services for Mobile Products & Internet
N.A.I.C.S.: 541512

QUALCOMM Internet Services (1)
5775 Morehouse Dr, San Diego, CA 92121
Tel.: (858) 587-1121
Web Site: http://www.qualcomm.com
Mobile Telecommunications Services
N.A.I.C.S.: 517112

QUALCOMM Israel Ltd (1)
Omega Center Matam Postal Agency, Haifa, 31905, Israel
Tel.: (972) 48506506
Communication Equipment Mfr
N.A.I.C.S.: 334220

QUALCOMM Japan (1)
Shin Aoyama Bldg W 18th Fl 1-1-1 Minami-Aoyama, Minato-Ku, Tokyo, 107-0062, Japan (100%)
Tel.: (81) 354128900
Web Site: http://www.qualcomm.co.jp

QUALCOMM Incorporated—(Continued)

Sales Range: $25-49.9 Million
Emp.: 70
Digital Wireless Communications Products,
Technologies & Services
N.A.I.C.S.: 517112

QUALCOMM MEMS Technologies, Inc. (1)
5775 Morehouse Dr, San Diego, CA
92121 (100%)
Tel.: (858) 587-1121
Web Site: http://www.qualcomm.com
Sales Range: $250-299.9 Million
Emp.: 1,500
Development of Micro-Electrical Mechanical
System (MEMS) Display for Mobile Devices
N.A.I.C.S.: 334419

QUALCOMM Services Labs, Inc. (1)
5775 Morehouse Dr, San Diego, CA 92121
Tel.: (858) 587-1121
Web Site: http://www.qualcomm.com
Research & Development of New Services
& Applications for Mobile Technology
N.A.I.C.S.: 541715

QUALCOMM Technologies International, Ltd. (1)
Churchill House Cambridge Business Park,
Cambridge, CB4 0WZ, United
Kingdom (100%)
Tel.: (44) 1223692000
Sales Range: $250-299.9 Million
Emp.: 700
Electronic Components Mfr
N.A.I.C.S.: 334413
Anthony Murray (Sr VP & Gen Mgr-Voice &
Music)

Subsidiary (Non-US):

CSR India Private Limited (2)
7th Flr Wing A Etamin Blk Prestige Tech
Park II, Marthahalli-Sarjapur Outer Ring
Road, Marathahalli, Bengaluru, 560 103,
India (100%)
Tel.: (91) 8025183000
Sales Range: $25-49.9 Million
Emp.: 200
Wireless Devices Mfr
N.A.I.C.S.: 334413
Prabhakar Shastry (Gen Mgr)

CSR Technology (India) Private Limited (2)
7th Flr Wing A Etamin Blk Prestige Tech
Park II, Marthahalli-Sarjapur Outer Ring
Road, Marthahalli, Bengaluru, 560 103,
India
Tel.: (91) 8025183000
Global Positioning System Semiconductor
Products Developer & Mfr
N.A.I.C.S.: 334413

Subsidiary (Domestic):

UbiNetics (VPT) Limited (2)
Cambridge Technology Centre, Melbourn,
SG8 6DP, United Kingdom
Tel.: (44) 1763 262,222
Sales Range: $200-249.9 Million
Emp.: 600
Mobile Communications Services
N.A.I.C.S.: 517112

QUALCOMM Technology Licensing (1)
5775 Morehouse Dr, San Diego, CA 92121
Tel.: (858) 587-1121
Web Site: http://www.qualcomm.com
Technology & Intellectual Property Licensing
Services
N.A.I.C.S.: 533110
Alex Rogers (Pres & Exec VP)

QUALCOMM Ventures (1)
5775 Morehouse Dr, San Diego, CA 92121-
1714
Tel.: (858) 587-1121
Web Site: http://www.qualcomm.com
Sales Range: $650-699.9 Million
Venture Capital Investment Services
N.A.I.C.S.: 523999

QUALCOMM Wireless Semi Conductor Technologies Limited (1)
Units 2101-2105 North Tower Beijing Kerry
Center 1 Guanghua Road, Chaoyang, Bei-

jing, 100020, China
Tel.: (86) 1085296529
Semiconductor Devices Mfr
N.A.I.C.S.: 334413
Frank Meng (Chm)

RF360 Europe GmbH (1)
Anzinger Strasse 13, 81671, Munich, Germany
Tel.: (49) 89208052751
Web Site: http://www.en.rf360.com
Next Generation Mobile Technology Mfr
N.A.I.C.S.: 334413
Uli Wehr (Sr Dir-IT)

Spike Technologies LLC (1)
698 Gibraltar Ct, Milpitas, CA 95035
Tel.: (408) 635-8700
Electronic Components Mfr
N.A.I.C.S.: 334419

Xiam Technologies Limited (1)
Block S 2nd Floor East Point Business
Park, Fairview, Dublin, 3, Ireland
Tel.: (353) 14832000
Web Site: http://www.xiam.com
Sales Range: $10-24.9 Million
Emp.: 35
Personalized Targeting & Recommendations Software Developer
N.A.I.C.S.: 513210

QUALIGEN THERAPEUTICS, INC.
2042 Corte del Nogal Ste B, Carlsbad, CA 92011
Tel.: (760) 452-8111 DE
Web Site: https://qlgntx.com
Year Founded: 2004
QLGN—(NASDAQ)
Rev.: $4,983,556
Assets: $19,083,491
Liabilities: $10,316,901
Net Worth: $8,766,590
Earnings: ($18,640,543)
Emp.: 31
Fiscal Year-end: 12/31/22
Pharmaceuticals Mfr
N.A.I.C.S.: 325412
Michael S. Poirier (Chm & CEO)
Amy S. Broidrick (Chief Strategy Officer & Exec VP)

QUALSTAR CORPORATION
15707 Rockfield Blvd Ste 105, Irvine,
CA 92618
Tel.: (805) 583-7744 CA
Web Site: https://www.qualstar.com
Year Founded: 1984
QBAK—(OTCIQ)
Rev.: $13,439,000
Assets: $10,038,000
Liabilities: $3,295,000
Net Worth: $6,743,000
Earnings: ($7,000)
Emp.: 15
Fiscal Year-end: 12/31/19
Data Storage Mfr
N.A.I.C.S.: 334112
Louann Negrete (CFO)
David J. Wolenski (Chm)
Steven N. Bronson (CEO)

Subsidiaries:

Qualstar Sales and Service Corporation (1)
3990-B Heritage Oak Ct, Simi Valley, CA
93063
Tel.: (805) 583-7744
Sales Range: $25-49.9 Million
Office Equipment Sales & Servicing
N.A.I.C.S.: 423420

QUALTEK SERVICES INC.
475 Sentry Pkwy E Ste 200, Blue
Bell, PA 19422
Tel.: (484) 804-4585 DE
Web Site:
https://www.qualtekservices.com
QTEK—(NASDAQ)
Rev.: $753,856,000

Assets: $688,927,000
Liabilities: $789,647,000
Net Worth: ($100,720,000)
Earnings: ($36,420,000)
Emp.: 1,947
Fiscal Year-end: 12/31/22
Investment Services
N.A.I.C.S.: 523999
Christopher S. Hisey (CEO)
Andrew S. Weinberg (Chm)
Matthew J. McColgan (CFO)

Subsidiaries:

Concurrent Group LLC (1)
475 Sentry Pkwy E Ste 200, Blue Bell, PA
19422
Tel.: (484) 804-4500
Web Site:
https://www.concurrentgroupllc.com
Emergency Restoration Services
N.A.I.C.S.: 541620

QualSat, LLC (1)
9495 E Lochnay Ln, Tucson, AZ 85747
Tel.: (248) 320-6248
Web Site: https://qualsat.com
Telecommunication Servicesb
N.A.I.C.S.: 517121

QualTek, LLC (1)
475 Sentry Pkwy E Ste 200, Blue Bell, PA
19422
Tel.: (484) 804-4500
Web Site: http://www.qualtekservices.com
Telecommunication Servicesb
N.A.I.C.S.: 517810
Tom Mix (Pres-Recovery Logistics)
Scott Hisey (CEO)
Adam Spittler (CFO)
Elizabeth Downey (Chief Admin Officer)
Michael B. Williams (Chief Bus Officer)
Paul Kestenbaum (Gen Counsel)
Kevin Doran (Pres-Wireless)
Jay Heaberlin (Pres-Renewables & Wireline)

Subsidiary (Domestic):

Broken Arrow Communications, Inc. (2)
8316 Corona Loop NE, Albuquerque, NM
87113
Tel.: (505) 877-2100
Web Site: http://www.bacom-inc.com
Wireless Telecommunications Systems &
Facility Engineering, Construction, Maintenance & Repair Services
N.A.I.C.S.: 237990
Ryan Calhoun (Pres)
Erin Schlagel (Controller)
Shawn Armijo (Mgr-HR & Payroll)
Dan Filler (CFO & Sr Exec Officer)

Fiber Network Solutions, Inc. (2)
21262 US Hwy 69 S, Tyler, TX 75703-9104
Tel.: (903) 894-4640
Web Site: http://www.fnsolutions.net
Custom Computer Programming Services
N.A.I.C.S.: 541511
Tim Hooker (Owner)

Urban Cable Technology Inc. (2)
36 S Vlg Ave, Exton, PA 19341-1213
Tel.: (610) 280-9400
Web Site: http://www.urbancable.com
Electrical Contractor
N.A.I.C.S.: 238210
Phil Digiore (Owner)

Vertical Limit Construction, LLC (2)
825 3rd Ave S, Wanamingo, MN 55983
Tel.: (507) 824-1222
Construction, Technical & Engineering Services
N.A.I.C.S.: 237130

Vinculums Services, Inc. (2)
10 Pasteur Ste 100, Irvine, CA 92618-3815
Tel.: (949) 783-3550
Web Site: http://www.vinculums.com
Sales Range: $50-74.9 Million
Emp.: 155
Engineering Services
N.A.I.C.S.: 541330
Bart Van Aardenne (Chm)
Paul Foster (CEO)
Brian Woodward (COO)

QUALYS, INC.
919 E Hillsdale Blvd 4F, Foster City,
CA 94404
Tel.: (650) 801-6100 DE
Web Site: https://www.qualys.com
Year Founded: 1999
QLYS—(NASDAQ)
Rev.: $554,458,000
Assets: $812,618,000
Liabilities: $444,444,000
Net Worth: $368,174,000
Earnings: $151,595,000
Emp.: 2,188
Fiscal Year-end: 12/31/23
On-Demand IT Security Risk & Compliance Management Solutions
N.A.I.C.S.: 513210
Rima Touma-Bruno (Chief HR Officer)
Dilip Bachwani (Sr VP-Engrg & Cloud
Ops)
Pinkesh Shah (Chief Product Officer)
Ishpreet Singh (CIO)
Dino DiMarino (Chief Revenue Officer)
Jeffrey P. Hank (Chm)
Sumedh S. Thakar (Pres & CEO)

Subsidiaries:

Qualys Australia Pty Ltd. (1)
39/2 Park Street, Sydney, 2000, NSW, Australia
Tel.: (61) 284172152
Security System Services
N.A.I.C.S.: 561621

Qualys GmbH (1)
Terminalstrasse Mitte 18, 85356, Munich,
Germany
Tel.: (49) 8997007146
Security System Services
N.A.I.C.S.: 561621
Jannis Utz (Acct Mgr-Technical)

Qualys Hong Kong Limited (1)
Suite 08 20/F One International Finance
Centre, 1 Harbour View Street Central,
Hong Kong, China (Hong Kong)
Tel.: (852) 30085642
Security System Services
N.A.I.C.S.: 561621

Qualys International, Inc. (1)
1600 Bridge Pkwy Ste 201, Redwood City,
CA 94065
Tel.: (650) 801-6131
Security System Services
N.A.I.C.S.: 561621

Qualys Japan K.K. (1)
Pacific Century Place 8F 1-11-1,
Marunouchi Chiyoda-Ku, Tokyo, 100-6208,
Japan
Tel.: (81) 368608296
Web Site: https://www.qualys.com
Security System Services
N.A.I.C.S.: 561621

Qualys Ltd. (1)
100 Brook Drive Green Park, Reading, RG2
6UJ, Berkshire, United Kingdom
Tel.: (44) 1189131500
Security System Services
N.A.I.C.S.: 561621

Qualys Middle East FZE (1)
Dubai Silicon Oasis HQ Block B Office B2-
206, PO Box 341439, Dubai, United Arab
Emirates
Tel.: (971) 43712561
Web Site: https://www.qualys.com
Security System Services
N.A.I.C.S.: 561621

Qualys Security TechServices Private Ltd. (1)
10th to 16th Floor Tower B Panchshil Business Park Survey No 20, Balewadi, Pune,
411045, India
Tel.: (91) 2061300600
Security System Services
N.A.I.C.S.: 561621
Rishikesh Bhide (Engr-Software)

Qualys Technologies, S.A. (1)
Maison de la Defense 7 Place de la Defense, 92400, Courbevoie, France

Tel.: (33) 141973570
Web Site: https://www.qualys.com
Emp.: 40
Security System Services
N.A.I.C.S.: 561621

QUANERGY SYSTEMS, INC.
433 Lakeside Dr, Sunnyvale, CA 94085
Tel.: (408) 245-9500   DE
Web Site: https://quanergy.com
Year Founded: 2019
QNGYQ—(OTCQX)
Rev.: $1,845,877
Assets: $278,844,071
Liabilities: $273,844,070
Net Worth: $5,000,001
Earnings: $1,283,657
Emp.: 2
Fiscal Year-end: 12/31/20
LiDAR Sensor & Other Electronic Products Mfr
N.A.I.C.S.: 334511
Simon Alexander Vine *(Chm)*
Enzo Signore *(CEO)*
Enzo Signore *(CMO)*

Subsidiaries:

Quanergy Perception Technologies, Inc.   **(1)**
433 Lakeside Dr, Sunnyvale, CA 94085
Tel.: (408) 245-9500
Web Site: https://quanergy.com
Light Detection & Ranging Device Developer
N.A.I.C.S.: 334511

QUANEX BUILDING PRODUCTS CORP.
945 Bunker Hill Rd Ste 900, Houston, TX 77024
Tel.: (713) 961-4600
Web Site: https://www.quanex.com
NX—(NYSE)
Rev.: $1,277,862,000
Assets: $2,319,788,000
Liabilities: $1,309,042,000
Net Worth: $1,010,746,000
Earnings: $33,059,000
Emp.: 7,068
Fiscal Year-end: 10/31/24
Engineered Building Product Materials Mfr
N.A.I.C.S.: 331315
Bob Daniels *(Pres-North American Fenestration)*
George L. Wilson *(Chm, Pres & CEO)*
Paul B. Cornett *(Gen Counsel, Sec & Sr VP)*
Scott M. Zuehlke *(CFO, Treas & Sr VP)*
John Sleva *(Pres-North American Cabinet Components)*
Kim Garcia *(Chief HR Officer)*
Louis Ventura *(CIO)*
Jim Nixon *(VP)*
Elan Zehavi *(VP)*
Karen Ettredge *(Principal Acctg Officer, VP & Controller)*

Subsidiaries:

Edgetech (UK) LTD   **(1)**
Stonebridge House Rowley Drive, Stonebridge Trading Estate, Coventry, CV3 4FG, United Kingdom
Tel.: (44) 2476639931
Web Site: www.edgetechig.co.uk
Glass Products Mfr
N.A.I.C.S.: 327211
Chris Alderson *(Mng Dir)*
Charlotte Mercer *(Head-Mktg)*
John Stark *(Head-Ops)*
Tony Palmer *(Head-Sls)*
Emma Leaney *(Controller-Fin)*

Edgetech Europe GmbH   **(1)**
Gladbacher Strasse 23, 52525, Heinsberg, Germany

Tel.: (49) 2452964910
Web Site: https://en.superspacer.com
Emp.: 100
Glass Protection & Window Spacers Mfr
N.A.I.C.S.: 339999

HL Plastics Ltd.   **(1)**
Flamstead House, Denby Hall Business Park, Ripley, DE5 8JX, Derbyshire, United Kingdom
Tel.: (44) 1332883800
Web Site: http://www.hlplastics.co.uk
Plastic Material & Resin Mfr
N.A.I.C.S.: 325211

Liniar Ltd.   **(1)**
Flamstead House Denby Hall Business Park, Derby, DE5 8JX, United Kingdom
Tel.: (44) 1332883900
Web Site: https://www.liniar.co.uk
Window & Door Mfr
N.A.I.C.S.: 321911
Adam Cook *(Mgr-Transport)*
Amanda Walker *(Mgr-Warehouse, Logistics & Admin)*
Charlotte Curtis *(Mgr-Bus Dev)*
Martin Thurley *(Mng Dir)*
Sue Davenport *(Mktg Dir)*

Mikron Industries, Inc.   **(1)**
1034 6th Ave N, Kent, WA 98032
Tel.: (253) 854-8020
Web Site: https://www.quanex.com
Vinyl Windows & Door Systems Mfr & Design
N.A.I.C.S.: 321911

Quanex Homeshield, LLC   **(1)**
32140 E 830 N Rd, Chatsworth, IL 60921
Tel.: (815) 635-3171
Mfr of Aluminum Building Products, Fascia, Exterior Trim & Soffit
N.A.I.C.S.: 332321

Plant (Domestic):

Quanex Homeshield LLC - Rice Lake Screens Plant   **(2)**
311 W Coleman St, Rice Lake, WI 54868-2407
Tel.: (715) 234-9061
Sales Range: $75-99.9 Million
Emp.: 200
Windows Screen Manufacturers
N.A.I.C.S.: 332321

Quanex Homeshield LLC - Richmond Plant   **(2)**
451 Industrial Pkwy, Richmond, IN 47374
Tel.: (765) 966-0322
Sales Range: $75-99.9 Million
Emp.: 130
Components for Doors & Windows Mfr
N.A.I.C.S.: 332321

Quanex IG Systems, Inc.   **(1)**
800 Cochran Ave, Cambridge, OH 43725
Tel.: (740) 439-2338
Web Site: https://www.quanex.com
Glass Protection Systems Product Mfr
N.A.I.C.S.: 325520

Quanex Screens LLC   **(1)**
4545 W Camelback Rd, Phoenix, AZ 85031
Tel.: (602) 455-0200
Glass Products Mfr
N.A.I.C.S.: 327211

Tyman plc   **(1)**
29 Queen Anne s Gate, London, SW1H 9BU, United Kingdom
Tel.: (44) 2079768000
Web Site: www.tymanplc.com
Rev.: $777,702,016
Assets: $1,089,434,528
Liabilities: $487,828,796
Net Worth: $601,605,732
Earnings: $50,507,184
Emp.: 4,035
Fiscal Year-end: 12/31/2020
Building Product Mfr
N.A.I.C.S.: 444180
Martin Towers *(Chm)*
Jeff Graby *(Pres & CEO-AmesburyTruth)*
Carolyn Gibson *(Sec)*
Jason Ashton *(Interim CEO)*

Subsidiary (US):

Amesbury Truth   **(2)**

700 W Bridge St, Owatonna, MN 55060
Web Site: http://www.amesburytruth.com
Block & Tackle Mfr
N.A.I.C.S.: 333923
Bob Burns *(Pres)*
Brian Rea *(Chief HR Officer)*
Dave Piet *(Sr VP-Sls)*
Michelle Nissen *(VP-Product Mgmt)*

Subsidiary (Domestic):

Ashland Hardware Systems   **(3)**
545 E John Carpenter Fwy Ste 610, Irving, TX 75062
Tel.: (469) 621-9830
Web Site:
    https://www.ashlandhardware.com
Emp.: 400
Window & Door Hardware Mfr
N.A.I.C.S.: 326199
James Prete *(Pres)*
Mark Murphy *(VP)*
Craig Heinberg *(Mktg)*

Overland Products Company, Inc.   **(3)**
1687 N Airport Rd, Fremont, NE 68025
Tel.: (402) 721-7270
Web Site: http://www.amesburytruth.com
Sales Range: $10-24.9 Million
Emp.: 55
Metal Stamping
N.A.I.C.S.: 332119

Subsidiary (Domestic):

Balance UK Limited   **(2)**
30-32 Martock Business Park Great Western Road, Martock, TA12 6HB, Somerset, United Kingdom
Tel.: (44) 1935826960
Web Site: http://www.eraeverywhere.com
Sales Range: $25-49.9 Million
Emp.: 45
Window Hardware & Accessories Mfr
N.A.I.C.S.: 321911

Subsidiary (US):

Bandlock Corporation Inc.   **(2)**
1734 S Vineyard Ave, Ontario, CA 91761
Tel.: (909) 947-7500
Web Site: http://www.amesbury.com
Plastic Extrusions & Industrial Vacuum Couplers Distr
N.A.I.C.S.: 424610

Subsidiary (Domestic):

Bilco UK Ltd.   **(2)**
Park Farm Business Centre Fornham St Genevieve, Bury Saint Edmunds, IP28 6TS, Suffolk, United Kingdom
Tel.: (44) 1284701696
Web Site: http://www.bilcouk.co.uk
Roofing Retailer
N.A.I.C.S.: 444180
James Fisher *(Mng Dir)*
Stan Winfield *(Mgr-Northern Reg Sls)*
Warren Tyce *(Mgr-Production)*

ERA Products Limited   **(2)**
Straight Road Short Heath, Willenhall, WV12 5RA, West Midlands, United Kingdom
Tel.: (44) 1922490000
Web Site: http://www.era-security.com
Emp.: 100
Door Locks Mfr
N.A.I.C.S.: 332321

Subsidiary (US):

Fastek Products Inc.   **(2)**
515 Noid Rd, Canton, SD 57013
Tel.: (605) 987-4361
Emp.: 80
Injection Molded Plastic Products & Zinc Die Cast Components Distr
N.A.I.C.S.: 423310
Alphonse Strubbe *(Gen Mgr)*

Subsidiary (Non-US):

Giesse Group Hellas S.A.   **(2)**
Kolonou 1-3, 12131, Peristeri, Greece
Tel.: (30) 2105582045
Metal Products Mfr
N.A.I.C.S.: 332312

Giesse S.p.A.   **(2)**

Via Tubertini 1, 40054, Budrio, BO, Italy
Tel.: (39) 0518850000
Web Site: http://www.giesse.it
Metal Products Mfr
N.A.I.C.S.: 332312

Jatec GmbH   **(2)**
Carl-Zeiss-Str 37, 63322, Rodermark, Germany
Tel.: (49) 60748960
Web Site: http://www.jatechandles.com
Metal Products Mfr
N.A.I.C.S.: 332312
Marco Pialors *(Mng Dir)*

Regiutti S.p.A.   **(2)**
Loc Fondi n 33 Zona Industriale, Agnosine, 25071, Brescia, BS, Italy
Tel.: (39) 0365896186
Web Site: http://www.reguitti.it
Metal Products Mfr
N.A.I.C.S.: 332312

Subsidiary (US):

Schlegel Systems, Inc.   **(2)**
700 W Bridge St, Owatonna, MN 55060
Tel.: (585) 427-7200
Web Site: http://www.amesburytruth.com
Sales Range: $250-299.9 Million
Emp.: 650
Engineered Perimeter Sealing Systems
N.A.I.C.S.: 326299

Subsidiary (Non-US):

Schlegel Australia Pty Limited   **(3)**
44 Riverside Road, Chipping Norton, 2170, NSW, Australia
Tel.: (61) 287072000
Web Site: http://www.schlegel.com
Sales Range: $25-49.9 Million
Emp.: 30
Foam & Pile Weatherstrip Mfr & Distr
N.A.I.C.S.: 332321

Schlegel BVBA   **(3)**
Rochesterlaan 4, 8470, Gistel, Belgium   **(100%)**
Tel.: (32) 59270312
Web Site: http://www.schlegel.com
Sales Range: $10-24.9 Million
Emp.: 35
Sealing Components Mfr
N.A.I.C.S.: 339991

Schlegel Belgium BVBA   **(3)**
Rochesterlaan 4, Gistel, 8470, West Flanders, Belgium
Tel.: (32) 59270300
Web Site: http://www.schlegel.com
Sales Range: $25-49.9 Million
Emp.: 80
Weatherstrips Mfr
N.A.I.C.S.: 332321

Schlegel Engineering KK   **(3)**
4th Floor Iwanami Shoten Annex 3-1 Kanda Jinbo Cho, 2 Chome Chiyoda Ku, Tokyo, 101 0051, Japan   **(100%)**
Tel.: (81) 332639621
Silo Mfr
N.A.I.C.S.: 332618

Schlegel Far East Ltd   **(3)**
Unit 8 3 F Block A New Trade Plz, 6 On Ping St, Sha Tin, China (Hong Kong)   **(100%)**
Tel.: (852) 26869872
Web Site: http://www.schlegelemi.com.hk
Sales Range: $25-49.9 Million
Emp.: 200
Gaskets Mfr
N.A.I.C.S.: 339991

Schlegel Germany GmbH   **(3)**
Bredowstrasse 33, 22113, Hamburg, Germany   **(100%)**
Tel.: (49) 40733290
Web Site: http://www.schlegel.de
Sales Range: $25-49.9 Million
Emp.: 50
Sealing Components Mfr
N.A.I.C.S.: 339991

Schlegel Pty Ltd   **(3)**
44 Riverside Road - Chipping Norton, PO Box 813, Liverpool, 2170, NSW, Australia   **(100%)**
Tel.: (61) 287072000
Web Site: http://www.schlegel.com

Quanex Building Products Corp.—(Continued)

Sales Range: $25-49.9 Million
Emp.: 50
Sealing Products Mfr
N.A.I.C.S.: 339991

Schlegel SRL (3)
Via Miglioli 20 40, 20090, Segrate,
Italy (100%)
Tel.: (39) 022136115
Sales Range: $1-9.9 Million
Emp.: 10
Sealing Components Mfr
N.A.I.C.S.: 339991

Schlegel Taliana SL (3)
Pol Industrial Sta Margarida Anoia 9, Ter-
rassa, 08223, Barsillona, Spain (100%)
Tel.: (34) 937863264
Web Site: http://www.schlegel.com
Sales Range: $25-49.9 Million
Emp.: 80
Sealing Components Mfr
N.A.I.C.S.: 339991
Peter Santo (CEO)

Schlegel UK (2006) Limited (3)
Henlow Industrial Estate, Henlow Camp,
SG16 6DS, Beds, United Kingdom
Tel.: (44) 1462815500
Web Site: http://www.schlegel.com
Sales Range: $25-49.9 Million
Emp.: 80
Holding Company
N.A.I.C.S.: 551112

Subsidiary (Domestic):

Schlegel (UK) Limited (4)
Henlow Industrial Estate, Henlow Camp,
SG16 6DS, Beds, United Kingdom (100%)
Tel.: (44) 1462815500
Sales Range: $25-49.9 Million
Emp.: 60
Window & Door Sealing Systems Mfr
N.A.I.C.S.: 339991
Peter Santo (CEO)

Subsidiary (Domestic):

Securidor Limited (2)
Station Industrial Estate, Bromyard, HR7
4HP, Herefordshire, United Kingdom
Tel.: (44) 8452190800
Web Site: http://www.securidor.ltd.uk
Composite Doors Mfr
N.A.I.C.S.: 321911

Subsidiary (US):

The Bilco Company (2)
PO Box 1203, New Haven, CT 06505
Tel.: (203) 934-6363
Web Site: http://www.bilco.com
Construction Supplies & Fixtures Mfr
N.A.I.C.S.: 332321
Tom Crowley (Pres)

Truth Hardware Inc. (2)
700 W Bridge St, Owatonna, MN 55060
Tel.: (507) 451-5620
Web Site: http://www.truth.com
Sales Range: $10-24.9 Million
Emp.: 700
Residential & Commercial Door & Window
Hardware Mfr
N.A.I.C.S.: 332510

Subsidiary (Domestic):

Ventrolla Limited (2)
Ventrolla House Crimple Ct Hornbeam Bus
Pk, Harrogate, HG2 8PB, North Yorkshire,
United Kingdom
Tel.: (44) 1423859323
Web Site: http://www.ventrolla.co.uk
Sales Range: $10-24.9 Million
Emp.: 50
Window Renovation Services
N.A.I.C.S.: 561720

Woodcraft Industries, Inc. (1)
525 Lincoln Ave SE, Saint Cloud, MN
56304
Tel.: (320) 252-1503
Web Site: https://www.woodcraftind.com
Cabinet & Furniture Components Mfr
N.A.I.C.S.: 337110
John Fitzpatrick (CEO)

Subsidiary (Domestic):

Brentwood Corp. (2)
453 Industrial Way, Molalla, OR 97038
Tel.: (503) 829-7366
Web Site: http://www.brentwoodcorp.com
Cabinet & Furniture Components Mfr
N.A.I.C.S.: 337110

Plant (Domestic):

**Woodcraft Industries Inc. - Mounds
View Plant** (2)
2270 Woodale Dr, Mounds View, MN 55112
Tel.: (763) 231-4000
Sales Range: $50-74.9 Million
Emp.: 200
Wood Component Mfr
N.A.I.C.S.: 321999
Dan Welch (Plant Mgr)

QUANTA SERVICES, INC.

2727 N Loop W, Houston, TX 77008
Tel.: (713) 629-7600 DE
Web Site:
https://www.quantaservices.com
Year Founded: 1997
PWR—(NYSE)
Rev.: $20,882,206,000
Assets: $16,237,225,000
Liabilities: $9,953,870,000
Net Worth: $6,283,355,000
Earnings: $744,689,000
Emp.: 52,500
Fiscal Year-end: 12/31/23
Holding Company; Electric, Fuel &
Water Infrastructure Contracting Ser-
vices
N.A.I.C.S.: 551112
Derrick A. Jensen (Exec VP-Bus
Ops)
Redgie Probst (COO)
Donald Wayne (Gen Counsel & Exec
VP)
Jayshree Desai (Chief Corp Dev Offi-
cer)
Redgie Probst (Pres-Electric Power)
Paul M. Nobel (Chief Acctg Officer)
Jayshree S. Desai (CFO)
Earl C. Austin Jr. (Pres & CEO)

Subsidiaries:

1 Diamond, LLC (1)
801 Seaco Ave, Deer Park, TX 77536
Tel.: (281) 241-8111
Web Site:
http://www.1diamondtoohnology.com
Diamond Mining Services
N.A.I.C.S.: 212390

Advanced Electric Systems, LLC (1)
441 W Power Line Rd, Heber City, UT
84032
Tel.: (860) 623-3406
Web Site: https://www.quantaservices.com
Electrical Contractor Services
N.A.I.C.S.: 238210

All Power Products Inc. (1)
6035 97 St NW, Edmonton, T6E 3J3, AB,
Canada
Tel.: (780) 434-0023
Web Site: http://www.allpowr.com
Electrical & Telecommunications Infrastruc-
ture Construction Tools Whslr
N.A.I.C.S.: 423610

Allteck Limited Partnership (1)
2555 Gilmore Ave, Burnaby, V5C 4T6, BC,
Canada
Tel.: (604) 857-6600
Web Site: http://www.allteck.com
Eletric Power Generation Services
N.A.I.C.S.: 221118
Mike Scott (Pres)
Rob Beard (CFO)
Patty Edwards (Sr VP-Bus Mgmt)

Allteck Line Contractors Inc. (1)
18750 96 Ave, Surrey, V4N 3P9, BC,
Canada
Tel.: (604) 857-6600
Web Site: https://allteck.com
Emp.: 60

Electrical Infrastructure Contracting Ser-
vices
N.A.I.C.S.: 238210
Chris Grajek (Dir-Health & Safety)
Patty Edwards (Sr VP-Bus Mgmt)
Bruce Scott (VP-Support Svcs)
Mike Scott (Pres)
Rob Beard (CFO)

**American Eagle Ready Mix Utah,
LLC** (1)
7811 W 2100 S, Magna, UT 84044
Tel.: (801) 438-8490
Web Site: https://www.aermut.com
Sweeper Services
N.A.I.C.S.: 561720

Arizona Trench Company, LLC (1)
2140 W Williams Dr, Phoenix, AZ 85027
Tel.: (623) 877-9728
Web Site:
https://arizonatrenchcompany.com
Construction Management Services
N.A.I.C.S.: 236220

**Arnett & Burgess Energy Services
LP** (1)
2930-715 5th Avenue SW, Calgary, T2P
2X6, AB, Canada
Tel.: (403) 265-0900
Web Site: https://www.abenergyservices.com
Pipeline Construction Services
N.A.I.C.S.: 237120

**Arnett & Burgess Oil Field Construc-
tion Limited** (1)
Hwy 55 RR 195A, PO Box 209, Athabasca,
T9S 2A3, AB, Canada
Tel.: (780) 689-3580
Web Site: http://www.abpipeliners.com
Oil & Gas Field Engineering Services
N.A.I.C.S.: 333132
Carey Arnett (Pres)
Jamie Arnett (VP-Fin)
Steve Arnett (Sr Mgr-Equipment)
Mark McPherson (VP-Integrity)
David Hampshire (Project Mgr-Execution)
Clif Lett (Mgr-Construction Div)
Graham Hunt (Mgr-Corp Dev & HR)
Bob Cantwell (Mgr-Quality Control)
Cathy Forester (Accountant)

**Arnett & Burgess Pipeliners (Rockies)
LLC** (1)
605 11Th Ave SW, Watford City, ND 58854
Tel.: (701) 444-4738
Web Site: http://www.abpipeliners.com
Oil & Gas Field Machinery Mfr
N.A.I.C.S.: 333132

Arnett & Burgess Pipeliners Ltd. (1)
Suite 2930 715 5th Avenue SW, Calgary,
T2P 2X6, AB, Canada
Tel.: (403) 265-0900
Web Site: https://www.abpipeliners.com
Oil & Gas Field Engineering Services
N.A.I.C.S.: 333132
Steve Arnett (Sr Mgr-Equipment)
Carey Arnett (Pres)
Jamie Arnett (CFO & VP-Fin)
Mark McPherson (VP-Integrity)
Tyler Featherstone (VP-Construction)
Derek Britton (Exec VP)

**B&N Clearing and Environmental,
LLC** (1)
438 E Millsap Rd Ste 102, Fayetteville, AR
72703
Tel.: (479) 313-6377
Leading Infrastructure Contracting Services
N.A.I.C.S.: 237120
Robert Bendure (Pres)

**Banister Pipelines Constructors
Corp.** (1)
502-24 Ave, Nisku, T9E 8G3, AB, Canada
Tel.: (780) 955-7167
Web Site: https://www.banister.ca
Pipeline Construction Services
N.A.I.C.S.: 237120

**Blackbox Technologies International
LLC** (1)
8050 Leesa Ln, Pasadena, TX 77507
Tel.: (713) 947-6469
Web Site: https://www.blackboxtech.com
Oil & Gas Drilling Services
N.A.I.C.S.: 213111

Blattner Energy, LLC (1)

392 County Rd 50, Avon, MN 56310
Tel.: (320) 356-7351
Web Site: https://www.blattnerenergy.com
Construction Management Services
N.A.I.C.S.: 236220

Blattner Holding Company, LLC (1)
392 County Rd 50, Avon, MN 56310
Tel.: (320) 356-7351
Web Site: https://www.blattnercompany.com
Renewable Energy Services
N.A.I.C.S.: 541690

Brent Woodward, inc. (1)
307 SW 2Nd St, Redmond, OR 97756
Tel.: (541) 504-5538
Web Site:
https://www.brentwoodwardinc.com
Electrical Contractor Services
N.A.I.C.S.: 238210

CAN-FER Utility Services, LLC (1)
3340 Roy Orr Blvd, Grand Prairie, TX
75050
Tel.: (972) 484-4344
Web Site: https://www.can-fer.com
Electrical & Telecommunications Infrastruc-
ture Contracting Services
N.A.I.C.S.: 238210
Jim Switzer (CEO)

CanACRE Ltd. (1)
18750 96th Ave, Surrey, V4N 3P9, BC,
Canada
Tel.: (416) 548-8602
Web Site: https://www.canacre.com
Construction Management Services
N.A.I.C.S.: 236220

**Canadian Utility Construction
Limited** (1)
18750 96 Ave, Surrey, V4N 3P9, BC,
Canada
Tel.: (604) 576-9358
Web Site: https://www.canadianutility.com
Natural Gas Distr
N.A.I.C.S.: 486210

Cat Spec, Ltd. (1)
225 S 16Th St, La Porte, TX 77571
Tel.: (281) 867-1125
Web Site:
https://www.strongholdspecialtyltd.com
Electrical Contractor Services
N.A.I.C.S.: 238210

Catalyst Changers Inc. (1)
19-5431 Tshp Rd 325B, Sundre, T0M 1X0,
AB, Canada
Tel.: (403) 638-2241
Web Site: http://catalystchangers.ca
Pipeline Construction Services
N.A.I.C.S.: 237120
Steve Green (Sr VP)

Coe Drilling Pty Ltd. (1)
Level 2 22 Cordelia Street, Brisbane, 4101,
QLD, Australia
Tel.: (61) 730291300
Web Site: http://www.coedrilling.com.au
Oil & Gas Wells Drilling Services
N.A.I.C.S.: 213111

**Consolidated Power Projects Austra-
lia Ltd** (1)
205 Halifax Street, Adelaide, 5000, SA,
Australia
Tel.: (61) 882917800
Web Site: https://www.conpower.com.au
Electrical Engineering Services
N.A.I.C.S.: 541330
Eric Winn (VP-Engrg)

Crux Subsurface Inc. (1)
4308 N Barker Rd, Spokane Valley, WA
99027
Tel.: (509) 892-9409
Web Site: https://www.cruxsub.com
Sales Range: $1-9.9 Million
Emp.: 40
Electrical & Telecommunications Infrastruc-
ture Contracting Services
N.A.I.C.S.: 238210

Cupertino Electric, Inc. (1)
1132 N 7th St, San Jose, CA 95112
Tel.: (408) 808-8000
Web Site: https://www.cei.com
Sales Range: $125-149.9 Million
Emp.: 260
Electrical Contracting

N.A.I.C.S.: 238210
Tom Schott *(Pres & CEO)*
Brett Boncher *(COO)*
Debra Olson *(Chief Legal Officer)*
William Slakey *(CFO)*
Estrella Parker *(Chief People Officer)*

Subsidiary (Domestic):

Cupertino Electric, Inc. (2)
1740 Cesar Chavez St, San Francisco, CA
94124-1134
Tel.: (415) 970-3400
Web Site: http://www.ceei.com
Sales Range: $10-24.9 Million
Emp.: 65
Electrical Contracting Services
N.A.I.C.S.: 238210
Talin Andonians *(Chief People Officer)*
Bruce Baxter *(Sr VP-Ops)*
Brett Boncher *(Sr VP-Ops)*
Debra Olson *(Chief Legal Officer)*
William Slakey *(CFO)*
Adam Spillane *(Sr VP-Ops)*
Rob Thome *(Sr VP-Ops)*

Cupertino Electric, Inc. (2)
2020 W Guadalupe Rd, Gilbert, AZ
85233-8327 (100%)
Tel.: (480) 503-2530
Web Site: http://www.cei.com
Sales Range: $10-24.9 Million
Emp.: 4
Electrical Contracting
N.A.I.C.S.: 238210
John Boncher *(Pres & CEO)*

DNR Pressure Welding Ltd. (1)
PO Box 1330, Stettler, T0C 2L0, AB,
Canada
Tel.: (403) 742-2859
Web Site: http://dnrwelding.ca
Oil & Gas Pipeline Construction Services
N.A.I.C.S.: 237120

Dacon Corporation (1)
16 Huron Dr, Natick, MA 01760
Tel.: (508) 651-3600
Web Site: https://www.dacon1.com
Commercial Building Construction Services
N.A.I.C.S.: 236220
Kevin W. Quinn *(Pres & CEO)*
Armand A. Souliere *(COO & VP)*
Renee L. Laskey *(CFO & Treas)*
Charles D. Reilly *(VP-Bus Dev)*
John D. Bradshaw *(Project Mgr-
Construction)*
Karla A. Brewster *(Accountant-Project-
Construction)*
Daryl R. Carter *(Dir-Architecture)*
Joy M. Shapiro *(Dir-Bus Dev)*
Lisa M. Springer *(Accountant-Project)*
Renny Schofield *(Dir-Construction Ops)*
Ken Hyszczak *(Dir-Design)*

Dashiell Corporation (1)
12301 Kurland Dr 4th Fl, Houston, TX
77034
Tel.: (713) 558-6600
Web Site: https://www.dashiell.com
Emp.: 300
Electrical & Telecommunications Infrastruc-
ture Contracting Services
N.A.I.C.S.: 238210

Digco Utility Construction, L.P. (1)
200 Ida Rd, Broussard, LA 70518
Tel.: (337) 837-5447
Web Site: http://www.rangerdirectional.com
Emp.: 30
Water & Sewer Line Construction Services
N.A.I.C.S.: 237110
Lyle Girouard *(Pres)*

Domino Highvoltage Supply Inc. (1)
20800 Lougheed Hwy, PO Box 38, Maple
Ridge, V2X 7E9, BC, Canada
Tel.: (866) 887-8617
Web Site: http://dominohighvoltage.com
Industrial Equipment Distr
N.A.I.C.S.: 423830
Grant Lockhart *(Pres)*

EHV Power ULC (1)
21 Cardico Drive, Stouffville, L4A 2G5, ON,
Canada
Tel.: (905) 888-7266
Web Site: http://www.ehvpower.com
Electrical & Telecommunications Infrastruc-
ture Contracting Services

Energy Consulting Group, LLC (1)
1 Overton Park 3625 Cumberland Blvd Ste
260, Atlanta, GA 30339
Tel.: (770) 763-4900
Web Site: https://www.ecg-llc.com
Energy Resource Management Services
N.A.I.C.S.: 541690

Enscope Pty Ltd (1)
7/50 Oxford Close, West Leederville, 6007,
WA, Australia
Tel.: (61) 862296500
Web Site: https://enscope.com.au
Oil & Gas Pipeline Construction Services
N.A.I.C.S.: 237120
Kane Ramsay *(Pres)*
Yorick Van Dommelen *(VP-Project Delivery)*
Matthew Sawyer *(Reg Mgr-Queensland)*

FiberTel, LLC (1)
893 N 450 W, Springville, UT 84663
Tel.: (801) 489-0659
Web Site: https://www.fibertelllc.com
Construction Services
N.A.I.C.S.: 236220

**First Infrastructure Capital Advisors,
LLC** (1)
2707 N Loop W Ste 130, Houston, TX
77008
Tel.: (713) 337-7980
Web Site:
https://www.firstinfrastructurecapital.com
Electrical Contractor Services
N.A.I.C.S.: 238210
Cyrus Aghili *(Sr VP)*

Flare Construction, LLC (1)
300 N Industrial Park Rd, Coalville, UT
84017
Tel.: (435) 336-2888
Web Site: https://www.flareconstruction.com
Construction Services
N.A.I.C.S.: 236220
Chris Boyer *(Pres)*

**Fueling Systems Contractors,
LLC** (1)
185 Devlin Rd, Napa, CA 94558
Tel.: (707) 280-3911
Construction Engineering Services
N.A.I.C.S.: 541330

**H.L. Chapman Pipeline Construction,
Inc.** (1)
9250 FM 2243, Leander, TX 78641
Tel.: (512) 259-7662
Web Site: https://www.hlchapman.com
Emp.: 200
Trenching & Mass Rock Excavating Ser-
vices
N.A.I.C.S.: 238910

Subsidiary (Domestic):

Sullivan Welding (2)
16102 NE 10th St, Gainesville, FL 32609
Tel.: (352) 485-2949
Emp.: 6
Machinery & Equipment Maintenance Ser-
vices
N.A.I.C.S.: 811310

HBK Engineering, LLC (1)
921 W Van Buren St, Chicago, IL 60607
Tel.: (312) 432-0076
Web Site: https://www.hbkengineering.com
Engineeering Services
N.A.I.C.S.: 541330
Roger Rehayem *(Sr VP)*
Sandra Arredondo *(Sr VP-HR & Admin)*

Hargrave Power, LLC (1)
3340 Roy Orr Blvd Ste 203, Grand Prairie,
TX 75050
Tel.: (214) 308-6927
Web Site: http://www.hargravepower.com
Industrial Transmission Supplies Distr
N.A.I.C.S.: 423840

**Haverfield International
Incorporated** (1)
1750 Emmitsburg Rd, Gettysburg, PA
17325
Tel.: (717) 334-1826
Web Site: https://www.haverfield.com
Power Line Construction & Maintenance
Services

N.A.I.C.S.: 237130

InfraSource, LLC (1)
14103 Stewart Rd, Sumner, WA 98390
Tel.: (734) 434-2000
Web Site: https://www.quantaservices.com
Sales Range: $50-74.9 Million
Emp.: 2,000
Holding Company; Fuel, Power, Telecom-
munications & Water Infrastructure Con-
struction Services
N.A.I.C.S.: 551112

Subsidiary (Domestic):

InfraSource Construction, LLC (2)
2311 Green Rd, Ann Arbor, MI 48105
Tel.: (734) 434-2000
Web Site: https://www.infrasourceus.com
Emp.: 2,000
Fuel, Power, Telecommunications & Water
Infrastructure Construction Services
N.A.I.C.S.: 237990

InfraSource Installation, LLC (2)
5051 Westheimer Rd Ste 1650, Houston,
TX 77056
Tel.: (713) 629-7600
Web Site: https://www.mears.net
Emp.: 2,500
Electrical & Telecommunications Infrastruc-
ture Contracting Services
N.A.I.C.S.: 238210

M.J. Electric, LLC (2)
200 W Frank Pipp Dr, Iron Mountain, MI
49801-1419
Tel.: (906) 774-8000
Web Site: https://www.mjelectric.com
Electrical & Instrumentation Construction &
Maintenance
N.A.I.C.S.: 238210
Tony Broccolo *(Exec VP-Industrial, Power &
Controls Div)*
Tom Nagy *(Exec VP-Utility Div)*
David Houle *(VP-Safety, Health & Environ-
mental)*
Paul Randby *(Sr VP-Western Ops)*
David Hoyt *(VP-Industrial, Power & Controls
Div)*
Marty Sutinen *(VP-Industrial, Power & Con-
trols Div)*
Dan Hinds *(VP-North Central Ops)*
Steve Feira *(VP-HR)*
Bill Shaw *(Sr VP-Eastern Ops)*
Jim Voss *(VP-Industrial, Power & Controls
Div)*

Sunesys, LLC (2)
202 Titus Ave, Warrington, PA 18976
Tel.: (215) 343-6300
Web Site: http://www.sunesys.com
Sales Range: $25-49.9 Million
Emp.: 100
Computer Networking Services
N.A.I.C.S.: 541519

**Innoversa Mobile Solutions GP
Ltd.** (1)
280 Applewood Crescent Unit 1, Concord,
L4K4E5, ON, Canada
Tel.: (647) 298-7528
Web Site: https://innoversa.com
Energy Supply Equipment Mfr & Distr
N.A.I.C.S.: 335999

Intermountain Electric, Inc. (1)
5050 Osage St Ste 500, Denver, CO 80221
Tel.: (303) 733-7248
Web Site: http://imelect.com
Emp.: 425
Electrical & Specialty Contractor
N.A.I.C.S.: 238210
Tom Allen *(Pres)*

Subsidiary (Domestic):

IM Electric, Inc. (2)
2920 Tuxedo Ave, West Palm Beach, FL
33405
Tel.: (561) 357-7756
Web Site: https://www.imelectric.com
Electrical Engineering Services
N.A.I.C.S.: 541330
Greg L. Mandor *(Pres)*

IME Intermountain Electric, Inc. (2)
5050 Osage St Ste 500, Denver, CO 80221
Tel.: (303) 733-7248
Web Site: http://www.imelect.com

Emp.: 425
Industrial Electrical Product Mfr & Distr
N.A.I.C.S.: 334513
Tom Allen *(Pres)*

Irby Construction Company (1)
318 Old Hwy 49 S, Richland, MS 39218-
9449
Tel.: (601) 709-4729
Web Site: https://www.irbyconstruction.com
Electrical Contractor
N.A.I.C.S.: 238210
Margaret Rushing *(CFO)*

Division (Domestic):

Okay Construction Company (2)
9774 18th St W, Princeton, MN 55371
Tel.: (763) 633-8724
Web Site: http://www.okayconstruction.us
Sales Range: $25-49.9 Million
Emp.: 37
Electrical Infrastructure Contracting Ser-
vices
N.A.I.C.S.: 238210
Betsey Slepica *(Office Mgr)*

Island Mechanical Corporation (1)
91-2461 Coral Sea Rd, Kapolei, HI 96707
Tel.: (808) 682-5363
Web Site:
https://www.islandmechanical.com
Oil & Gas Pipeline Construction Services
N.A.I.C.S.: 237120

J&R Underground LLC (1)
916 Blake St, Blanchardville, WI 53516
Tel.: (608) 523-4290
Web Site: https://www.jrundergroundllc.com
Sales Range: $10-24.9 Million
Emp.: 90
Underground Utilites Contractor
N.A.I.C.S.: 238990

J. W. Didado Electric, LLC (1)
1033 Kelly Ave, Akron, OH 44306
Tel.: (330) 374-0070
Web Site: https://www.jwdidado.com
Emp.: 700
Emergency Electrical Power Services
N.A.I.C.S.: 335132

J.C.R. Construction Co., Inc. (1)
181 Route 27, Raymond, NH 03077
Tel.: (603) 895-4062
Web Site: https://jcrutility.com
Emp.: 90
Electrical Contractor Services
N.A.I.C.S.: 238210

JBT Electric, LLC (1)
8876 Winzer Rd, Beaumont, TX 77705
Tel.: (409) 794-2722
Web Site: https://www.quantaservices.com
Electrical Contractor Services
N.A.I.C.S.: 238210

JET Tank Service, LLC (1)
501 Mike W Powers Ln, Inola, OK 74036
Tel.: (918) 543-2555
Web Site:
http://www.tankrepairservices.com
Storage Tank Mfr
N.A.I.C.S.: 332420
Jerry D. LaValley *(Pres)*

Lee Electrical Construction, LLC (1)
12828 Hwy 15-501 S, Aberdeen, NC
28315-0055
Tel.: (910) 944-9728
Web Site: https://www.lee-electrical.com
Power Line Construction Services
N.A.I.C.S.: 237130

Lex Engineering Ltd. (1)
Suite 110 - 4321 Still Creek Drive, Burnaby,
V5C 6S7, BC, Canada
Tel.: (604) 205-9900
Web Site: https://lexengineering.com
Electrical Contractor Services
N.A.I.C.S.: 238210

M. G. Dyess, Inc. (1)
7159 Hwy 35, Bassfield, MS 39421
Tel.: (601) 943-6663
Web Site: https://www.mgdyess.com
Oil & Gas Field Machinery Mfr
N.A.I.C.S.: 333132
Grant Dyess *(Pres)*
Mike Dyess *(VP-Construction)*
Hunter Dyess *(Mgr-Growth Svcs)*

Quanta Services, Inc.—(Continued)

Brian McRaney *(Mgr-Tech Svcs)*
Jeremy Miller *(Mgr-Supoort Svcs)*
Jeff Glenn *(Mgr-Ops)*
Aaron Crowell *(Dir-Safety)*

MTS Quanta, LLC (1)
10551 Barkley Ste 200, Overland Park, KS 66212
Tel.: (913) 383-0800
Web Site: http://www.mtsquanta.com
Power Line Maintenance Services
N.A.I.C.S.: 237130

Mears Group Inc. (1)
4500 N Mission Rd, Rosebush, MI 48878
Tel.: (989) 433-2929
Web Site: http://www.mearscorrosion.com
Sales Range: $125-149.9 Million
Emp.: 500
Electrical & Telecommunications Infrastructure Contracting Services
N.A.I.C.S.: 238210
Kevin Garrity *(Exec VP)*

Subsidiary (Non-US):

Mears Canada Corp. (2)
402-22nd Avenue, Nisku, T9E-7W8, AB, Canada
Tel.: (780) 518-3475
Web Site: http://www.mearshdd.net
HDD & DP Project & Services
N.A.I.C.S.: 486990

Mears Inline Inspection Services (1)
14411 West Rd, Houston, TX 77041
Tel.: (832) 634-2800
Emp.: 3
Oil & Gas Pipeline Construction Services
N.A.I.C.S.: 237120
William Garrow *(VP)*

N.J. Construction Pty Ltd (1)
PO Box 1940, Queanbeyan, 2620, NSW, Australia
Tel.: (61) 262329400
Web Site: http://www.njconstruction.com.au
Electrical Contractor Services
N.A.I.C.S.: 238210

Nacap Australia Pty Ltd. (1)
599 Doncaster Rd, Doncaster, 3108, VIC, Australia
Tel.: (61) 388481888
Web Site: http://www.nacap.com.au
Electric Power Transmission Services
N.A.I.C.S.: 221121

Nacap Pty Ltd. (1)
599 Doncaster Rd, Doncaster, 3108, VIC, Australia
Tel.: (61) 388481888
Web Site: http://www.nacap.com.au
Oil & Gas Construction Services
N.A.I.C.S.: 237120
Matthew O'Connell *(Pres)*
Paul Whyte *(Head-HSE)*

North Houston Pole Line, L.P. (1)
1608 Margaret St, Houston, TX 77093
Tel.: (713) 691-3616
Web Site: https://www.nhplc.com
Emp.: 30
Electrical & Telecommunications Infrastructure Contracting Services
N.A.I.C.S.: 238210

NorthStar Energy Services, Inc. (1)
15025 E Fwy, Channelview, TX 77530
Tel.: (281) 452-2355
Web Site: https://www.nses.com
Emp.: 70
Oil & Gas Pipeline Construction Services
N.A.I.C.S.: 237120

Northern Powerline Constructors, Inc. (1)
7941 Sandlewood Pl, Anchorage, AK 99507-3135
Tel.: (907) 344-3436
Web Site:
  https://www.northernpowerline.com
Power Line Construction Services
N.A.I.C.S.: 237130

Northstar Sharps Foundation Specialists Ltd. (1)
1511 Sparrow Drive, Nisku, T9E 8H9, AB, Canada

Tel.: (780) 955-2108
Web Site: http://www.northstarsharps.com
Electrical Contractor Services
N.A.I.C.S.: 238210

Nova Constructors LLC (1)
267 Ihei Chatan Cho Park Side Ihei 1st Floor 101, Okinawa, 904-0102, Japan
Tel.: (81) 9082910053
Construction Engineering Services
N.A.I.C.S.: 541330

Nova Constructors LTD (1)
1305 Lumsden Rd, Port Orchard, WA 98367
Tel.: (707) 260-1656
Web Site: http://www.novagrp.com
Construction Engineering Services
N.A.I.C.S.: 541330
Walt Schwartz *(VP-Ops-Pacific Northwest & Ops Mgr-Northwest)*

Nova Group, Inc. (1) **(100%)**
185 Devlin Rd, Napa, CA 94558
Tel.: (707) 265-1100
Web Site: https://www.novagrp.com
Emp.: 200
Engineering & Heavy Construction Services
N.A.I.C.S.: 237110
Scott R. Victor *(Pres & COO)*
Dee Fedrick *(VP-Preconstruction Svcs)*
Walt Schwartz *(VP-Ops-Pacific Northwest)*

O.J. Pipelines Canada Limited Partnership (1)
1409 4 Street, Nisku, T9E 7M9, AB, Canada
Tel.: (780) 955-3900
Web Site: http://www.ojpipelines.com
Pipeline Construction Services
N.A.I.C.S.: 237120

Unit (Domestic):

O.J. Industrial Maintenance (2)
PO Box 6309, Fort McMurray, T9H 5N3, AB, Canada
Tel.: (780) 955-5217
Web Site: http://www.ojindustrial.ca
Emp.: 100
Oil & Gas Pipeline Construction Services
N.A.I.C.S.: 237120
Chad Eusanio *(Mng Dir)*

P.J. Helicopters, Inc. (1)
903 Langley Way, Red Bluff, CA 96080
Tel.: (530) 527-5059
Web Site: https://www.pjhelicopters.com
Transportation Services
N.A.I.C.S.: 481111
Greg Stine *(Dir-Safety)*
Justin Gunsauls *(VP)*

PAH Electrical Contractors, Inc. (1)
4770 N Belleview Ave Ste 300, Kansas City, MO 64116-2188
Tel.: (816) 474-9340
Web Site: https://www.parelectric.com
Emp.: 2,500
Electrical Contractor
N.A.I.C.S.: 238210

Unit (Domestic):

Computapole (2)
5776 Stoneridge Mall Rd Ste 290, Pleasanton, CA 94588
Web Site: http://www.computapole.com
Mobile & Database Software Provider
N.A.I.C.S.: 541511

Pennsylvania Transformer Technology Inc. (1)
201 Carolina Dr, Raeford, NC 28376-9272
Tel.: (910) 875-7600
Web Site: http://www.patransformer.com
Sales Range: $25-49.9 Million
Emp.: 300
Provider of Power Distribution & Transformer Services
N.A.I.C.S.: 335311
Ravi Rahangdale *(Pres)*
Shashi Rahangdale *(Controller)*

Performance Energy Services, L.L.C (1)
132 Valhi Lagoon Xing, Houma, LA 70360
Tel.: (985) 850-9555
Web Site: https://www.pesllc.com
Electric & Mechanical Engineering Services

N.A.I.C.S.: 541330

Phoenix Power Group, Inc. (1)
220 Park Ave Ste 110, Florham Park, NJ 07932
Tel.: (631) 492-1803
Web Site: https://www.phoenixpg.com
Electrical Contractor Services
N.A.I.C.S.: 238210

Potelco, Inc. (1)
14103 Stewart Rd, Sumner, WA 98390
Tel.: (253) 863-0484
Web Site: https://www.potelco.net
Emp.: 900
Electrical & Telecommunications Infrastructure Contracting Services
N.A.I.C.S.: 238210
Gary Tucci *(CEO)*
Craig Davis *(Sr VP)*
Bryan Sabari *(VP-Safety & Trng)*
George Coleman *(Pres)*
Mark Honeysett *(VP)*
Scott Keaton *(VP)*
Luke Loder *(VP)*
Michael Ritter *(VP)*
Tom Falskow *(CFO)*

Price Gregory International, Inc. (1)
24275 Katy Fwy Ste 500, Katy, TX 77494
Tel.: (713) 780-7500
Web Site: https://www.pricegregory.com
Oil & Gas Pipeline Construction Services
N.A.I.C.S.: 237120
Tommy N. Jones *(Sr VP)*
Irene E. Schaffer *(CFO & Exec VP)*
David Hopkins *(VP)*
Mike Thibodeaux *(Sr VP)*
Jimmy Burns *(VP-Western Ops)*
Caleb Scheve *(Dir-Safety & Health)*
Bobby Merritt *(VP)*
Robert E. Bell Jr. *(Pres & CEO)*

QP Energy Services, LLC (1)
1221 S Main St Ste 208, Boerne, TX 78006
Tel.: (361) 563-3360
Web Site:
  https://www.qpenergyservices.com
Electrical Contractor Services
N.A.I.C.S.: 238210

QPS Engineering LTD. (1)
2900-715 5 Ave Sw, Calgary, T2P 2X6, AB, Canada
Tel.: (403) 910-3866
Leading Infrastructure Contracting Services
N.A.I.C.S.: 237120

QPS Engineering, LLC (1)
4500 S Garnett Rd Ste 100, Tulsa, OK 74146
Tel.: (918) 858-7620
Web Site: http://www.qpse.com
Emp.: 250
Pipeline Construction Services
N.A.I.C.S.: 237120
Bryan Moses *(Pres)*

Quanta Government Solutions, Inc. (1)
2800 Post Oak Blvd Ste 2600, Houston, TX 77056
Tel.: (713) 629-7600
Web Site: http://www.quantaservices.com
Sales Range: $1-9.9 Million
Government Contracting Project Management Services
N.A.I.C.S.: 561499

Quanta Infrastructure Solutions Group, LLC (1)
2707 N Loop W Ste 500, Houston, TX 77008
Tel.: (713) 335-7755
Web Site: https://quantaisg.com
Engineering Construction Services
N.A.I.C.S.: 541330

Quanta Lines Pty. Ltd. (1)
Level 1 601 Doncaster Road, PO Box 105, Doncaster, 3108, VIC, Australia
Tel.: (61) 388481855
Web Site: http://quantalines.com.au
Construction Services
N.A.I.C.S.: 237990
Mark Gould *(Pres)*
Chris Connell *(VP-Bus Dev & Strategy)*
Barney Manga *(VP-Ops)*
Rob Appleton *(VP-Solutions & Dev)*

Quanta Marine Services, LLC (1)

2000 W Sam Houston Pkwy Ste 500, Houston, TX 77042
Tel.: (281) 897-1500
Web Site: http://www.quantamarine.com
Electrical Engineering Services
N.A.I.C.S.: 541330

Quanta Subsurface, LLC (1)
4308 N Barker Rd, Spokane Valley, WA 99027
Tel.: (509) 789-7747
Web Site: http://www.quantasubsurface.com
Engineering Construction Services
N.A.I.C.S.: 237990

Quanta Technology, LLC (1)
4020 Westchase Blvd Ste 300, Raleigh, NC 27607
Tel.: (919) 334-3000
Web Site: https://www.quanta-technology.com
Electric Power Transmission Services
N.A.I.C.S.: 221121
Damir Novosel *(Pres)*
H. Lee Willis *(Partner & Sr VP)*
Farid Katiraei *(VP-Advanced Tech Integration)*
Carl L. Wilkins *(VP-Distr)*
David Elizondo *(VP-Bus Dev-Global & Intl Ops)*
Gregg Lemler *(VP-Asset Mgmt)*
Scott Hammond *(CFO)*
Kevin Curtis *(Exec VP)*

Quanta Telecom Canada Ltd. (1)
9595 Enterprise Way SE, Calgary, T3S 0A1, AB, Canada
Tel.: (587) 620-0201
Web Site: http://www.quantatelecom.ca
Telecommunication Contractor Services
N.A.I.C.S.: 238210
Victor Budzinski *(Pres)*

Quanta Telecommunication Services, LLC (1)
2707 N Loop W Ste 400, Houston, TX 77008
Tel.: (832) 634-0010
Web Site: https://www.quantatelcom.com
Telecommunication Contractor Services
N.A.I.C.S.: 238210

Quanta Telecommunication Solutions, LLC (1)
2707 N Loop W Ste 400, Houston, TX 77008
Tel.: (832) 634-0010
Web Site: https://www.quantatelcom.com
Engineering Construction Services
N.A.I.C.S.: 541330

Quanta Utility Engineering Services, Inc. (1)
4770 N Belleview Ave Ste 100, Kansas City, MO 64116-2190
Tel.: (816) 414-1100
Web Site: https://www.ques.com
Electrical Contractor Services
N.A.I.C.S.: 238210

RP Construction Services, LLC (1)
305 Dela Vina Ave, Monterey, CA 93940
Web Site: https://www.rpcs.com
Solar Equipment Mfr & Distr
N.A.I.C.S.: 334413

Realtime Utility Engineers, Inc. (1)
2908 Marketplace Dr, Fitchburg, WI 53719
Tel.: (608) 906-7800
Web Site:
  https://www.realtimeutilityengineers.com
Emp.: 100
Electrical & Telecommunications Infrastructure Contracting Services
N.A.I.C.S.: 238210
David Herbst *(Dir-Field Svcs)*

Robinson Brothers Construction, LLC (1)
6150 NE 137th Ave, Vancouver, WA 98682
Tel.: (360) 576-5359
Web Site: https://www.rbc-utility.com
Construction Services
N.A.I.C.S.: 236220

Service Electric Company (1)
1631 E 25th St, Chattanooga, TN 37404
Tel.: (423) 265-3161
Web Site: https://www.serviceelectricco.com
Emp.: 2,000

Electrical Power Line Construction & Engineering Services
N.A.I.C.S.: 237130

Southern Electric Corporation (1)
PO Box 320398, Flowood, MS 39232
Tel.: (601) 939-2333
Web Site: https://www.secofms.com
Electrical Contractor Services
N.A.I.C.S.: 238210

Stronghold, Ltd. (1)
225 S 16th St, La Porte, TX 77571
Tel.: (281) 867-1125
Web Site:
   https://www.thestrongholdcompanies.com
Sales Range: $500-549.9 Million
Emp.: 2,800
Holding Company; Oil, Gas & Petrochemical Industry Contract Engineering & Fabricating Services
N.A.I.C.S.: 551112
Chris Box (COO)
Blake Stoehr (CFO)
Jack Sutherland (VP)
Chad Edgar (Sr VP)
Cole Mercer (VP)
Cheryl Wyatt (VP)
Amanda Cange (Gen Counsel)

Summit Line Construction, Inc. (1)
441 W Power Line Rd, Heber City, UT 84032
Tel.: (435) 657-0721
Web Site:
   https://www.summitlineconstruction.com
Electric Power Transmission Services
N.A.I.C.S.: 221121

Sumter Utilities, Inc. (1)
1151 N Pike W, Sumter, SC 29153   **(100%)**
Tel.: (803) 469-8585
Web Site: https://www.sumter-utilities.com
Sales Range: $300-349.9 Million
Emp.: 750
Power Line Construction; Electrical Contractor; Wholesale Electrical Apparatus & Tools
N.A.I.C.S.: 237130
Mikell Murray (Exec VP)
Mark Martines (VP)
James Barbee (VP)
Jennifer Sonntag (CFO)

T. G. Mercer Consulting Services, Inc. (1)
PO Box 1870, Aledo, TX 76008
Tel.: (817) 489-7100
Web Site: https://www.tgmercer.com
Pipeline Construction Services
N.A.I.C.S.: 237120

TC Infrastructure Services Ltd. (1)
28 Strathmoor Way, Sherwood Park, T8H 2A5, AB, Canada
Tel.: (780) 467-1367
Web Site: https://tcinfrastructure.com
Electrical Contractor Services
N.A.I.C.S.: 238210
Roger Ethier (Gen Mgr)
Ryan Harker (Mgr-Subdivision Shallow Utilities)
Lance Premak (Sr Project Mgr-Utility Construction)
Claude Ethier (Mgr-Traffic Controls & Rentals)

The Hallen Construction Co. Inc. (1)
11 Commercial St, Plainview, NY 11803
Tel.: (516) 432-8300
Web Site: http://www.hallen.com
Gas Utility Contracting services
N.A.I.C.S.: 213112
Thomas B. Poole (Chm)
Dennis J. Springer (Sr VP-Fin)
Stuart H. Buhrendorf (Sr VP-EHS & Risk Mgmt)
Edward Fitzgerald (VP-Ops)
Linda Birkeland (Treas & VP-Fin)
Eugene Hickey (Sr VP-Ops)
Pascale J. Ambrosio (Exec VP-Engrg & Estimating)
Mike Hickey (Exec VP-Ops)
James P. Small Jr. (VP-Pur)

The Ryan Company, Inc. (1)
15 Commerce Way, Norton, MA 02766
Tel.: (508) 742-2500
Web Site: https://www.ryancompany.net
Utility Construction Services

N.A.I.C.S.: 237130

Subsidiary (Domestic):

Ryan Company Inc. (2)
3361 Republic Ave, Saint Louis Park, MN 55426
Tel.: (952) 915-6475
Web Site: https://www.ryancompanyinc.com
Heating Equipment Installation Services
N.A.I.C.S.: 238220
Mike Rocheford (Pres)
Matt Kiemen (Gen Mgr & Engr-Mechanical)
Ryan Thill (Mgr-Inside Sls & Project)

Ultimate Powerline Contracting Ltd. (1)
117 Shorthorn St, North Battleford, S0M 0E0, SK, Canada
Tel.: (306) 446-2355
Electrical Engineering Services
N.A.I.C.S.: 541330

Underground Construction Co., Inc. (1)
5145 Industrial Way, Benicia, CA 94510
Tel.: (707) 746-8800
Web Site:
   https://www.undergroundconstruction.com
Sales Range: $200-249.9 Million
Emp.: 380
Heavy Construction, Water Sewer & Utility Lines; General Engineering Contractors; General Contractors of Non-Residential & Industrial Buildings & Warehouses
N.A.I.C.S.: 237110
Chris Ronco (Pres)
Jason Bowen (CFO)
Andrew Nortz (VP)
Chad Hardesty (VP)

Utility Line Management Services, Inc. (1)
2345 W Foothill Blvd, Upland, CA 91786
Tel.: (909) 920-0812
Web Site: https://ulm-services.com
Electrical & Telecommunications Infrastructure Contracting Services
N.A.I.C.S.: 238210

Valard Construction Australia Pty. Ltd. (1)
L1 599 Doncaster Road, Doncaster, 3108, VIC, Australia
Tel.: (61) 459054632
Water & Sewer Line Construction Services
N.A.I.C.S.: 237110
Brett Smit (VP)

Valard Construction LP (1)
4209 - 99 Street, Edmonton, T6E 5V7, AB, Canada
Tel.: (780) 436-9876
Web Site: http://www.valard.com
Emp.: 1,400
Electrical & Telecommunications Infrastructure Contracting Services
N.A.I.C.S.: 238210
Victor Wearden (CFO)
Dave Torgerson (COO)
Jessie Feniuk (Gen Counsel-Acting)
Jeff Rogers (VP-Distr)
Brett Smit (VP-Professional Svcs)

Subsidiary (Domestic):

Phasor Engineering Inc. (2)
1st Floor 10774 42 St SE, Calgary, T2C 0L5, AB, Canada
Tel.: (403) 238-3695
Web Site: http://www.phasorengineering.ca
Emp.: 50
Electrical Power Distribution Equipment Repair, Maintenance & Engineering Services
N.A.I.C.S.: 811310
Harvir Mann (Pres-Acting)
Ed Ng (VP-Bus Dev)

Sharp's Construction Services 2006 Ltd. (2)
7331 34 St NW, Edmonton, T6B 2W6, AB, Canada
Tel.: (780) 466-1255
Web Site:
   http://www.sharpsconstruction.com
Foundation Drilling Services
N.A.I.C.S.: 238910

Subsidiary (Non-US):

VALARD Polska sp. z o.o. (2)

ul Bonifraterska 17, Warsaw, Poland
Tel.: (48) 880442341
Power Line Construction & Maintenance Services
N.A.I.C.S.: 237130

Subsidiary (Domestic):

Valard Geomatics Ltd. (2)
4209 - 99 Street, Edmonton, T6E 5V7, AB, Canada
Tel.: (780) 436-9876
Web Site: http://www.valardgeomatics.com
Electric Power Transmission Services
N.A.I.C.S.: 221121

Valard Geomatics BC, Ltd. (1)
4321 Still Creek Drive Suite 110, c/o Phasor Engineering sister co, Burnaby, V5C 6S7, BC, Canada
Tel.: (604) 681-7621
Water & Sewer Line Construction Services
N.A.I.C.S.: 237110
Shilo Neveu (Exec VP)
Keith Sones (Exec VP)
Jeff Rogers (VP)
Gilles Pelletier (VP)
Dave Robb (VP)

Winco, Inc. (1)
22300 NE Yellow Gate Ln, Aurora, OR 97002
Tel.: (503) 678-6060
Web Site: https://www.wincoservices.com
Emp.: 7
Power Line Construction Services
N.A.I.C.S.: 237130
Mike Patton (COO & VP)

QUANTA, INC.
632 S Glenwood Pl, Burbank, CA 91506
Tel.: (818) 659-8052   **NV**
Year Founded: 2016
QNTA—(NASDAQ)
Rev.: $673,407
Assets: $887,549
Liabilities: $5,498,863
Net Worth: ($4,611,314)
Earnings: ($8,253,124)
Emp.: 4
Fiscal Year-end: 12/31/21
Applied Science Company
N.A.I.C.S.: 541715
Phillip Sands (Pres)
Arthur Grant Mikaelian (Chm, CEO, CFO & Exec VP)

QUANTERIX CORPORATION
900 Middlesex Tpke Bldg 1, Billerica, MA 01821
Tel.: (617) 301-9400   **DE**
Web Site: https://www.quanterix.com
Year Founded: 2007
QTRX—(NASDAQ)
Rev.: $105,522,000
Assets: $434,199,000
Liabilities: $75,259,000
Net Worth: $358,940,000
Earnings: ($96,700,000)
Emp.: 125
Fiscal Year-end: 12/31/22
Research & Development in Biotechnology (except Nanobiotechnology)
N.A.I.C.S.: 541714
David R. Walt (Co-Founder)
Michael Miller (COO)
Masoud Toloue (Pres & CEO)
Erica Bell (Chief People Officer)
Laurie Churchill (Gen Counsel)
Darrin Crisitello (Chief Comml Officer)
Alexandra Phillips (CIO)
Vandana Sriram (CFO)

Subsidiaries:

Aushon Biosystems, Inc. (1)
43 Manning Rd, Billerica, MA 01821
Tel.: (978) 436-6400
Web Site: http://www.aushon.com
Biotechnology Product Mfr Services
N.A.I.C.S.: 541714
Peter Honkanen (Founder)

UmanDiagnostics AB (1)
Tvistevagen 48 C, 907 36, Umea, Sweden
Tel.: (46) 90777880
Web Site: https://www.umandiagnostics.se
Medical Research Services
N.A.I.C.S.: 541715
Niklas Norgren (CEO)

QUANTGATE SYSTEMS INC.
99 Wall St Ste 1701, New York, NY 10005
Tel.: (416) 479-0880   **NV**
Web Site:
   http://www.quantgatesystems.com
Year Founded: 2009
QGSI—(OTCQB)
Rev.: $6,193
Assets: $2,554,376
Liabilities: $1,087,187
Net Worth: $1,467,189
Earnings: ($215,532)
Emp.: 2
Fiscal Year-end: 05/31/20
Algorithmic Securities Trading Systems Developer; Software & Interactive Games Developer
N.A.I.C.S.: 513210
Ilan Yosef (COO & CTO)
Allan J. Bezanson (CEO)

QUANTRX BIOMEDICAL CORP.
10190 SW 90th Ave, Tualatin, OR 97123
Tel.: (212) 980-2235   **NV**
Web Site: http://www.quantrx.com
Year Founded: 1993
QTXB—(OTCIQ)
Assets: $5,950
Liabilities: $2,647,047
Net Worth: ($2,641,097)
Earnings: ($260,042)
Fiscal Year-end: 12/31/21
Medical Diagnostic Instrument Mfr
N.A.I.C.S.: 339112
Shalom Z. Hirschman (Chm, CEO & Principal Acctg Officer)

QUANTUM COMPUTING INC.
5 Marine View Plz Ste 214, Hoboken, NJ 07030
Tel.: (703) 436-2161   **DE**
Web Site:
   https://quantumcomputinginc.com
Year Founded: 2017
QUBT—(NASDAQ)
Rev.: $358,047
Assets: $78,728,275
Liabilities: $5,459,722
Net Worth: $73,268,553
Earnings: ($29,730,672)
Emp.: 39
Fiscal Year-end: 12/31/23
Custom Computer Programming Services
N.A.I.C.S.: 551112
Robert P. Liscouski (Chm)
William J. McGann (Pres & CEO)
Yuping Huang (Chief Quantum Officer)
Christopher Boehmler (CFO)

QUANTUM CORPORATION
224 Airport Pkwy Ste 550, San Jose, CA 95110
Tel.: (408) 944-4000   **DE**
Web Site: https://www.quantum.com
Year Founded: 1980
QMCO—(NASDAQ)
Rev.: $311,600,000
Assets: $187,615,000
Liabilities: $309,113,000
Net Worth: ($121,498,000)
Earnings: ($41,286,000)
Emp.: 770
Fiscal Year-end: 03/31/24
Data Storage Systems

Quantum Corporation—(Continued)

N.A.I.C.S.: 334112
Henk Jan Spanjaard *(Chief Revenue Officer)*
Kenneth P. Gianella *(CFO)*
James J. Lerner *(Chm, Pres & CEO)*
Natasha Beckley *(CMO)*
Bruno Hald *(VP/Gen Mgr-Secondary Storage)*
Ed Fiore *(VP/Gen Mgr-Primary Storage)*
Brian Pawlowski *(Chief Dev Officer)*
Laura A. Nash *(Chief Acctg Officer)*

Subsidiaries:

Quantum Corp. - Irvine   (1)
141 Innovation Dr, Irvine, CA 92617
Tel.: (949) 856-7800
Web Site: http://www.quantum.com
Sales Range: $50-74.9 Million
Emp.: 110
Data Storage Systems
N.A.I.C.S.: 334112

Quantum Corp. - Pikes Peak
Operations   (1)
10125 Federal Dr, Colorado Springs, CO
80908-4508
Tel.: (719) 536-5000
Web Site: http://www.quantum.com
Sales Range: $100-124.9 Million
Emp.: 400
Data Storage Systems
N.A.I.C.S.: 334112

Quantum Corp. - Santa Maria   (1)
1290 W McCoy Ln, Santa Maria, CA 93455-1049
Tel.: (805) 349-1234
Sales Range: $100-124.9 Million
Tape Heads Mfr
N.A.I.C.S.: 334419

Quantum SARL   (1)
1 Rue du Debarcadere Ste 53 54 47 49,
92700, Colombes, France
Tel.: (33) 141434900
Data Storage Device Mfr
N.A.I.C.S.: 334112
Patrick Morel *(Sr Mgr-Channel-Scale Out Storage-EMEA)*

Quantum Storage Australia Pty,
Ltd.   (1)
Level 2 Ann Place 895 Ann St, Fortitude
Valley, 4006, QLD, Australia
Tel.: (61) 738539440
Web Site: http://www.quantum.com
Data Storage Systems
N.A.I.C.S.: 334112

Quantum Storage Japan
Corporation   (1)
S Shinotsuka Bldg 9th Fl, Tokyo, 170-0005,
Japan
Tel.: (81) 359780070
Web Site: http://www.quantum.co.jp
Sales Range: Less than $1 Million
Emp.: 20
Data Storage Systems
N.A.I.C.S.: 334118

Quantum Storage Singapore Pte.
Ltd.   (1)
229 Mountbatten Road 02 20-22, Singapore, 398007, Singapore
Tel.: (65) 67259010
Web Site: http://www.quantum.com
Data Storage Systems
N.A.I.C.S.: 334112

Quantum Storage UK, Ltd.   (1)
First FL The Lightbox Willoughby Road,
Bracknell, RG12 8FB, Berkshire, United
Kingdom   (100%)
Tel.: (44) 1344353500
Web Site: http://www.quantum.com
Sales Range: $10-24.9 Million
Emp.: 14
Data Storage Systems
N.A.I.C.S.: 334112

Violin Memory, Inc.   (1)
2560 N First St Ste 300, San Jose, CA
95131
Tel.: (650) 396-1500
Web Site: http://www.vmem.com

Computer Memory Array Mfr
N.A.I.C.S.: 334112
James P. Curley *(CFO)*
Mark Lewis *(Exec Chm)*
Todd Oseth *(COO)*
Richard N. Nottenburg *(Chm)*
Ebrahim Abbasi *(Pres & CEO)*

Subsidiary (Non-US):

Violin Memory Data Storage System
Company, Ltd.   (2)
6F Tower 2 West Prosper Centre No 5
Guanghua Road, Chaoyang District, Beijing,
100020, China
Tel.: (86) 1085731521
Computer Storage Device Mfr
N.A.I.C.S.: 334112

Violin Memory EMEA Ltd.   (2)
Quatro House Lyon Way, Camberley, GU16
7ER, Surrey, United Kingdom
Tel.: (44) 1276 804620
Web Site: http://www.violin-memory.com
Computer Memory Array Mfr
N.A.I.C.S.: 334112
Garry Veale *(Mng Dir)*
Vince Blackall *(VP-Channels)*
Carlo Wolf *(VP-Sls)*

Subsidiary (Domestic):

Violin Memory Federal Systems,
Inc.   (2)
4555 Great America Pkwy, Baltimore, MD
21228
Tel.: (650) 396-1500
Emp.: 10
Semiconductor & Related Device Mfr
N.A.I.C.S.: 334413

Subsidiary (Non-US):

Violin Memory K.K.   (2)
Level 8 Pacific Century Place Marunouchi
1-11-1 Marunouchi, Chiyoda-ku, Tokyo,
100-6208, Japan
Tel.: (81) 368608239
Computer Storage Device Mfr
N.A.I.C.S.: 334112
Masakazu Toi *(Country Mgr)*

Violin Memory Singapore Pte.
Ltd.   (2)
80 Raffles Place No 36 30 32 UOB Plaza 1,
Singapore, 048624, Singapore
Tel.: (65) 62484941
Computer Storage Device Mfr
N.A.I.C.S.: 334112

QUANTUM ENERGY, INC.
3825 Rockbottom, Henderson, NV
89030
Tel.: (602) 612-7404   NV
Year Founded: 2004
QREE—(OTCIQ)
Rev.: $324,240
Assets: $18,490,088
Liabilities: $21,007,525
Net Worth: ($2,517,437)
Earnings: ($47,604,051)
Emp.: 7
Fiscal Year-end: 02/28/22
Fuel Distr
N.A.I.C.S.: 424720
Anthony T. J. Ker *(Treas & Sec)*
Harry Ewert *(CEO)*
Will Westbrook *(CFO)*
William Hinz *(Chm)*

QUANTUM FINTECH ACQUISITION CORPORATION
4221 W Boy Scout Blvd Ste 300,
Tampa, FL 33607
Tel.: (813) 257-9366   DE
Web Site: http://www.qftacorp.com
Year Founded: 2020
QFTA—(NYSE)
Rev.: $14,606,651
Assets: $204,207,681
Liabilities: $209,217,520
Net Worth: ($5,009,839)
Earnings: $11,045,567
Emp.: 3

Fiscal Year-end: 12/31/22
Investment Services
N.A.I.C.S.: 523999
John Schaible *(Chm & CEO)*
Miguel Leon *(CFO)*

QUANTUM FUEL SYSTEMS TECHNOLOGIES WORLD-WIDE, INC.
25245 Arctic Ocean Dr, Lake Forest,
CA 92630
Tel.: (949) 930-3400   DE
Web Site: http://www.qtww.com
Year Founded: 2002
QTWWQ—(OTCIQ)
Fuel Control Systems, Pressure
Regulators & Storage Cylinders Mfr
N.A.I.C.S.: 336211
Brian Olson *(CFO)*

Subsidiaries:

Schneider Power Inc.   (1)
49 Bathurst Street Ste 101, Toronto, M5V
2P2, ON, Canada
Tel.: (416) 847-3724
Web Site: http://www.schneiderpower.com
Renewable Power Generation System Design Services
N.A.I.C.S.: 221118

QUANTUM INTERNATIONAL CORP.
6434 So Quebec St, Greenwood Village, CO 90111
Tel.: (720) 984-0488   TX
Web Site:
https://quantuminternational
corp.com
Year Founded: 2001
QUAN—(OTCIQ)
Machinery Mfr
N.A.I.C.S.: 333998
Justin Waiau *(Pres, CEO, Treas & Sec)*

QUANTUM MEDICAL TRANSPORT, INC.
14090 SW Fwy Ste 300, Sugar Land,
TX 77478
Tel.: (832) 521-1880   DE
Web Site:
http://www.quantummedicaltransport.com
DRWN—(OTCIQ)
Sales Range: Less than $1 Million
Medical Transportation Services
N.A.I.C.S.: 488999
Ricky Bernard *(Pres)*

QUANTUM-SI INCORPORATED
530 Old Whitfield St, Guilford, CT
06437
Tel.: (646) 793-3510   DE
Web Site: https://www.quantum-si.com
Year Founded: 2020
QSI—(NASDAQ)
Rev.: $5,301,000
Assets: $391,485,000
Liabilities: $32,779,000
Net Worth: $358,706,000
Earnings: ($132,442,000)
Emp.: 202
Fiscal Year-end: 12/31/22
Investment Services
N.A.I.C.S.: 523999
Kevin L. Rakin *(Co-Founder & Partner)*
Jonathan M. Rothberg *(Co-Founder)*
Jeffrey Hawkins *(Pres & CEO)*
Claudia Napal Drayton *(CFO)*
Jennifer Barretta *(Partner)*
Johan Denecke *(Sr VP-Ops)*

QUANTUMKORE INC.

7712 Bougainvillea Ct, West Palm
Beach, FL 33412
Tel.: (954) 294-2313   NV
Web Site:
https://www.qkinnovation.com
Year Founded: 1999
SBOX—(OTCIQ)
Sales Range: Less than $1 Million
Media & Entertainment Product Developer
N.A.I.C.S.: 541512
Claudio Mirella *(CEO)*
Andrea Piazzoli *(Pres)*
Daniele de Molli *(COO)*
Bruno Polistina *(CFO)*
Enrico Carlo Fumagalli *(CTO)*
Richard C. Weiner *(Sec-Consultant)*
Suneel Anant Sawant *(Chm)*

QUANTUMSCAPE CORPORATION
1730 Technology Dr, San Jose, CA
95110
Tel.: (408) 452-2000   DE
Web Site:
https://ir.quantumscape.com
Year Founded: 2020
QS—(NYSE)
Rev.: $866,378,000
Assets: $3,051,040,000
Liabilities: $1,268,763,000
Net Worth: $1,782,277,000
Earnings: ($92,476,000)
Emp.: 2,325
Fiscal Year-end: 12/31/23
Investment Services
N.A.I.C.S.: 523999
Jagdeep Singh *(Founder)*
Siva Sivaram *(Pres & CEO)*
Robert Remenar *(Vice Chm)*
Simon Boag *(CTO)*
Daniel Huber *(CFO)*

QUANTUMSPHERE, INC.
2905 Tech Ctr Dr, Santa Ana, CA
92705
Tel.: (714) 545-6266   CA
Web Site: http://www.qsinano.com
Year Founded: 2002
QSIM—(OTCIQ)
Sales Range: Less than $1 Million
Emp.: 7
Metal-Air Battery Systems Designer &
Mfr
N.A.I.C.S.: 335910
Kevin D. Maloney *(Chm, Pres & CEO)*
SangKeun Park *(VP-Mfg)*
Vito A. Canuso *(VP-Intellectual Property)*
Brendan McKenney *(Mgr-Production)*
Matthew Griffith *(VP-Ops)*
Bill Collins *(VP-Bus Dev)*

QUARTA-RAD, INC.
1201 N Orange St Ste 700, Wilmington, DE 19801-1186
Tel.: (201) 877-2002   DE
Web Site: https://www.quartarad.com
Year Founded: 2011
QURT—(OTCIQ)
Rev.: $508,316
Assets: $683,314
Liabilities: $289,721
Net Worth: $393,593
Earnings: $44,492
Fiscal Year-end: 12/31/23
General Merchandise Retailer
N.A.I.C.S.: 455219
Victor Shvetsky *(Chm, Pres, CEO, CFO, Principal Acctg Officer & Sec)*

QUEEN CITY INVESTMENTS, INC.
302 Pine Ave, Long Beach, CA
90802

Tel.: (562) 290-3727   CA
Year Founded: 1972
QUCT—(OTCIQ)
Investment Management Service
N.A.I.C.S.: 523940
W. Henry Walker *(Exec VP)*
Kevin M. Tiber *(VP)*
Lina Oba *(Accountant)*
Bud Terrell *(Accountant)*
Daniel K. Walker *(Chm & Pres)*
Christine M. Walker-Bowman *(COO & Exec VP)*
Christie Mainberger *(Treas & Sec)*
Sandra Gifford *(Asst Sec & Asst Treas)*

QUEEN'S GAMBIT GROWTH CAPITAL
55 Hudson Yards 44th Fl, New York, NY 10001
Tel.: (917) 907-4618   Ky
Year Founded: 2020
GMBTU—(NASDAQ)
Emp.: 2
Investment Services
N.A.I.C.S.: 523999
Victoria Grace *(CEO)*
Anastasia Nyrkovskaya *(CFO)*

QUEENCH, INC.
131 Jericho Tpke, Jericho, NY 11753
Tel.: (516) 333-3890   UT
QENC—(OTCIQ)
Bottled & Canned Soft Drink Mfr
N.A.I.C.S.: 312111
Lyndell Parris *(Pres & CEO)*

QUEST DIAGNOSTICS, INC.
500 Plaza Dr, Secaucus, NJ 07094
Tel.: (973) 520-2700   DE
Web Site:
   https://www.questdiagnostics.com
Year Founded: 1967
DGX—(NYSE)
Rev.: $9,252,000,000
Assets: $14,022,000,000
Liabilities: $7,680,000,000
Net Worth: $6,342,000,000
Earnings: $854,000,000
Emp.: 40,000
Fiscal Year-end: 12/31/23
Medical Testing Laboratories
N.A.I.C.S.: 621511
Cecilia K. McKenney *(Chief HR Officer & Sr VP)*
Michael E. Prevoznik *(Gen Counsel & Sr VP)*
Dermot Shorten *(Sr VP-Strategy, M&A & Ventures)*
Sam A. Samad *(CFO & Exec VP)*
Michael J. Deppe *(Chief Acctg Officer, VP & Controller)*
Gabrielle Wolfson *(Chief Info & Digital Officer & Sr VP)*
James E. Davis *(Chm, Pres & CEO)*
Cecilia McKenney *(Chief HR Officer & Sr VP)*
Robert Gorman *(VP-Ops-U.S)*
Yuri Fesko *(Chief Medical Officer & Sr VP)*

Subsidiaries:

AmeriPath Consulting Pathology Services, P.A.   (1)
568 Ruin Creek Rd Ste 5, Henderson, NC 27536
Tel.: (252) 492-4477
Sales Range: $10-24.9 Million
Emp.: 14
Pathology Laboratory Services
N.A.I.C.S.: 621511

AmeriPath Indianapolis, P.C.   (1)
2560 N Shadeland Ave Ste A, Indianapolis, IN 46219
Tel.: (317) 275-8000
Web Site: https://www.ameripath.com

Sales Range: $25-49.9 Million
Emp.: 200
Medical Laboratory Services
N.A.I.C.S.: 621511

AmeriPath Pittsburgh, P.C.   (1)
875 Greentree Rd 4 Pkwy Ctr Ste 325, Pittsburgh, PA 15220
Tel.: (412) 682-3083
Web Site: http://www.ameripath.com
Emp.: 30
Medical Laboratory Services
N.A.I.C.S.: 621511

AmeriPath, Inc.   (1)
7111 Fairway Dr Ste 101, Palm Beach Gardens, FL 33418
Tel.: (561) 712-6200
Web Site: https://www.ameripath.com
Sales Range: $750-799.9 Million
Emp.: 10
Anatomic Pathology & Molecular Diagnostic Services
N.A.I.C.S.: 621511
Stephen W. Aldred *(Reg Pres)*

Subsidiary (Domestic):

AmeriPath Consolidated Labs, Inc.   (2)
895 SW 30th Ave Ste 201, Pompano Beach, FL 33069
Medical Research Services
N.A.I.C.S.: 621511

Diagnostic Pathology Services, Inc.   (2)
3300 Northwest Expy, Oklahoma City, OK 73112
Tel.: (405) 842-2061
Diagnostic Services
N.A.I.C.S.: 621512

Specialty Laboratories, Inc.   (2)
27027 Tourney Rd, Valencia, CA 91355-5386
Tel.: (661) 799-6543
Web Site: http://www.specialtylabs.com
Clinical & Reference Laboratory Testing Services
N.A.I.C.S.: 621511

Arlington Pathology Association 5.01(a) Corporation   (1)
908 Wright St, Arlington, TX 76012-4730
Tel.: (817) 460-4366
Medical Laboratory Services
N.A.I.C.S.: 621511

Associated Clinical Laboratories   (1)
1526 Peach St, Erie, PA 16501-2190
Tel.: (814) 461-2420
Web Site:
   https://www.associatedclinicallab.com
Medical Laboratory Services
N.A.I.C.S.: 621511

Athena Diagnostics, Inc.   (1)
200 Forest St 2nd Fl, Marlborough, MA 01752
Tel.: (508) 756-2886
Web Site:
   https://www.athenadiagnostics.com
Sales Range: $100-124.9 Million
Emp.: 300
Diagnostic Testing Products Mfr
N.A.I.C.S.: 325413
Robert E. Flaherty *(Pres & CEO)*

BluePrint Genetics Oy   (1)
Keilaranta 16 A-B, 02150, Espoo, Finland
Tel.: (358) 402511372
Web Site: https://www.blueprintgenetics.com
Diagnostic Services
N.A.I.C.S.: 621512
Riitta Pelli *(CFO)*

Celera Corporation   (1)
1401 Harbor Bay Pkwy, Alameda, CA 94502
Tel.: (510) 749-4200
Web Site: http://www.celera.com
Sales Range: $125-149.9 Million
Emp.: 490
Disease Testing, Treatment & Management Products & Services
N.A.I.C.S.: 621511
Peter Barrett *(Co-Founder)*

Subsidiary (Domestic):

Berkeley HeartLab, Inc.   (2)

468 Littlefield Ave, South San Francisco, CA 94080-6105
Tel.: (650) 651-3100
Web Site: http://www.bhlinc.com
Sales Range: $75-99.9 Million
Emp.: 300
Cardiovascular Disease Testing & Management Services
N.A.I.C.S.: 621511

Cleveland HeartLab, Inc.   (1)
6701 Carnegie Ave Ste 500, Cleveland, OH 44103
Tel.: (216) 426-6085
Web Site:
   https://www.clevelandheartlab.com
Healtcare Services
N.A.I.C.S.: 622310

Colorado Pathology Consultants, P.C.   (1)
6750 W 52nd Ave Ste F, Arvada, CO 80002-3957
Tel.: (720) 898-3300
Sales Range: $25-49.9 Million
Emp.: 200
Pathology Laboratory Services
N.A.I.C.S.: 621511

Dermpath Diagnostics   (1)
7485 E Tanque Verde Rd, Tucson, AZ 85715
Tel.: (520) 320-7681
Web Site:
   https://www.dermpathdiagnostics.com
Sales Range: $10-24.9 Million
Emp.: 25
Healtcare Services
N.A.I.C.S.: 621399

Diagnostic Laboratory of Oklahoma LLC   (1)
225 NE 97th St, Oklahoma City, OK 73114
Tel.: (405) 608-6100
Web Site: http://www.dlolab.com
Emp.: 200
Medical Laboratory Services
N.A.I.C.S.: 621511
R'nee Mullen *(CEO)*

Diagnostic Pathology Services, P.C.   (1)
Memorial Missionary Rdg Tower 725 Glenwood Ave Ste E-690, Chattanooga, TN 37404-1161
Tel.: (423) 629-7688
Web Site:
   https://www.diagnosticpathologyservices.com
Emp.: 15
Pathology Services
N.A.I.C.S.: 621511

Diagnostic Reference Services Inc.   (1)
1 Malcolm Ave, Teterboro, NJ 07608
Tel.: (201) 393-5143
Diagnostic Services
N.A.I.C.S.: 621512

HemoCue Holding AB   (1)
Box 1204, Angelholm, 262 23, Skane, Sweden
Tel.: (46) 731458200
Testing Lab Services
N.A.I.C.S.: 621511

LabOne Canada, Inc.   (1)
25 Valleywood Dr Unit 7, Markham, L3R 5L9, ON, Canada
Tel.: (905) 947-9797
Web Site: http://www.examone.com
Sales Range: $1-9.9 Million
Emp.: 10
Laboratory Testing Services for the Life & Health Insurance Industry
N.A.I.C.S.: 621512

Subsidiary (Domestic):

ExamOne Canada, Inc.   (2)
209-1119 Fennell Ave E, Hamilton, L8T 1S2, ON, Canada
Tel.: (905) 574-3033
Web Site: https://www.examone.com
Medical Laboratory Services
N.A.I.C.S.: 621511

Med Fusion, LLC   (1)

2501 S State Hwy 121 Ste 1100, Lewisville, TX 75067-8188
Tel.: (972) 966-7000
Web Site: https://medfusionservices.com
Laboratory Diagnostic Testing Services
N.A.I.C.S.: 621511

PACK Health, LLC   (1)
110 12Th St N, Birmingham, AL 35203
Web Site: https://www.packhealth.com
Healthcare Management Consulting Services
N.A.I.C.S.: 621498

PhenoPath Laboratories, PLLC   (1)
1737 Airport Way S Ste 201, Seattle, WA 98134-1636
Tel.: (206) 374-9000
Web Site: https://www.phenopath.com
Diagnostic Laboratory Testing Services
N.A.I.C.S.: 621511
Allen M. Gown *(Founder & Assoc Dir-Medical)*

Quest Diagnostics Clinical Laboratories, Inc.   (1)
1 Malcolm Ave, Teterboro, NJ 07608
Tel.: (201) 393-5000
Web Site: http://www.questdiagnostics.com
Sales Range: $50-74.9 Million
Emp.: 1,500
Laboratory Services
N.A.I.C.S.: 621511

Unit (Domestic):

Quest Diagnostics - Houston   (2)
5850 Rogerdale, Houston, TX 77072
Tel.: (713) 667-5829
Web Site: http://www.questdiagnostics.com
Sales Range: $100-124.9 Million
Emp.: 600
Laboratory Testing
N.A.I.C.S.: 621511

Quest Diagnostics - Lenexa   (2)
10101 Renner Blvd, Lenexa, KS 66219
Tel.: (913) 888-1770
Substance Abuse Testing
N.A.I.C.S.: 621511

Quest Diagnostics - Nashville   (2)
525 Mainstream Dr, Nashville, TN 37228
Tel.: (615) 687-2000
Web Site: https://www.questdiagnostics.com
Rev.: $200,000,000
Emp.: 100
Testing Services, Clinical Labs
N.A.I.C.S.: 621511

Quest Diagnostics - San Antonio   (2)
607 E Sontarra Ste 306, San Antonio, TX 78258
Tel.: (210) 225-5101
Web Site: http://www.questdiagnostics.com
Sales Range: $25-49.9 Million
Clinical Laboratory
N.A.I.C.S.: 621511

Quest Diagnostics - Schaumberg   (2)
808 Woodfield Rd Ste 400, Schaumburg, IL 60173-4538
Tel.: (224) 301-7530
Provider of Clinical Laboratory Services
N.A.I.C.S.: 621511

Quest Diagnostics - Seattle   (2)
1737 Airport Way S Ste 200, Seattle, WA 60173-4538
Tel.: (206) 623-8100
Web Site: http://www.questdiagnostics.com
Clinical Laboratory
N.A.I.C.S.: 621511

Quest Diagnostics - Syosset   (2)
269 Jericho Tpke, Syosset, NY 11791-3426
Tel.: (516) 677-5355
Web Site: http://www.questdiagnostics.com
Sales Range: $25-49.9 Million
Emp.: 350
Clinical Laboratory
N.A.I.C.S.: 621511

Quest Diagnostics - West Hills   (2)
8401 Fallbrook Ave, West Hills, CA 91304
Tel.: (818) 737-6000
Web Site: http://www.questdiagnostics.com
Clinical Laboratory Services
N.A.I.C.S.: 621511

Quest Diagnostics Incorporated   (1)
1901 Sulphur Spring Rd, Baltimore, MD 21227

Quest Diagnostics, Inc.—(Continued)

Tel.: (410) 247-9100
Diagnostic Services
N.A.I.C.S.: 621512

Quest Diagnostics Incorporated (1)
4444 Giddings Rd, Auburn Hills, MI 48326
Tel.: (248) 373-9120
Diagnostic Services
N.A.I.C.S.: 621512
John Newton (Coord-Hardware)

Quest Diagnostics Incorporated (1)
4230 Burnham Ave, Las Vegas, NV 89119
Tel.; (702) 236-7041
Diagnostic Services
N.A.I.C.S.: 621512
Albert Miller (Sr Dir-Pricing Infrastructure)

**Quest Diagnostics Ireland
Limited** (1)
Unit 20 Northwood House Santry, D09
EK40, Dublin, 9, Ireland
Tel.: (353) 16090800
Web Site: http://www.questdiagnostics.com
Medical Laboratory Services
N.A.I.C.S.: 621511

Quest Diagnostics Limited (1)
Unit B1 Parkway West Cranford Lane Hes-
ton, London, TW5 9QA, United Kingdom
Tel.: (44) 2083773300
Medical Laboratory Services
N.A.I.C.S.: 621511

**Quest Diagnostics Nichols
Institute** (1)
33608 Ortega Hwy, San Juan Capistrano,
CA 92675-2042
Tel.: (949) 728-4000
Web Site: http://www.questdiagnostics.com
Laboratory Testing Services
N.A.I.C.S.: 621511

Subsidiary (Domestic):

**Quest Diagnostics Nichols Institute,
Inc.** (2)
14225 Newbrook Dr, Chantilly, VA 20151-
2228
Tel.: (703) 802-6900
Web Site: http://www.nicholsinstitute.com
Clinical & Esoteric Testing Services
N.A.I.C.S.: 621511

ReproSource, Inc. (1)
200 Forest St 2nd Fl Ste B, Marlborough,
MA 01752
Tel.: (781) 937-8893
Web Site: http://www.reprosource.com
Testing Laboratory Services
N.A.I.C.S.: 541380

Shiel Medical Laboratory, Inc. (1)
63 Flushing Ave Unit 336 Bldg 292, Brook-
lyn, NY 11205-1010
Tel.: (718) 552-1000
Diagnostic Imaging Centers
N.A.I.C.S.: 621512

**St. Luke's Pathology Associates,
P.A.** (1)
10330 Hickman Mills Dr, Kansas City, MO
64137
Tel.: (816) 412-7004
Web Site: http://www.questdiagnostics.com
Laboratory Services
N.A.I.C.S.: 621511

Summit Health, Inc. (1)
27175 Haggerty Rd, Novi, MI 48377
Tel : (248) 799-8303
Web Site: http://www.summithealth.com
Emp.: 12,000
Health Care Srvices
N.A.I.C.S.: 621498

QUEST PATENT RESEARCH
CORPORATION
411 Theodore Fremd Ave Ste 206S,
Rye, NY 10580-1411   DE
Web Site: https://www.qprc.com
Year Founded: 1986
QPRC—(OTCQB)
Rev.: $451,194
Assets: $1,227,076
Liabilities: $9,789,903
Net Worth: ($8,562,827)

Earnings: ($753,516)
Emp.: 2
Fiscal Year-end: 12/31/22
Asset Management Services
N.A.I.C.S.: 523940
Jon C. Scahill (Pres, CEO, Acting
CFO & Sec)
Timothy J. Scahill (CTO)
William Ryall Carroll (Chm)

QUEST RESOURCE HOLDING
CORPORATION
3481 Plano Pkwy Ste 100, The
Colony, TX 75056
Tel.: (972) 464-0004   NV
Web Site: https://investors.qrhc.com
Year Founded: 2002
QRHC—(NASDAQ)
Rev.: $284,037,823
Assets: $181,491,049
Liabilities: $110,352,001
Net Worth: $71,139,048
Earnings: ($6,047,986)
Emp.: 197
Fiscal Year-end: 12/31/22
Recycling & Waste Management Ser-
vices
N.A.I.C.S.: 562998
Daniel M. Friedberg (Chm)
Brett Johnston (CFO & Sr VP)
S. Ray Hatch (Pres & CEO)
Perry W. Moss (Chief Revenue Offi-
cer & Sr VP-Sls)
Dave Sweitzer (COO)

Subsidiaries:

Earth911, Inc. (1)
3481 Plano Pkwy, The Colony, TX 75056
Tel.: (480) 889-2650
Web Site: http://www.earth911.com
Software Development Services
N.A.I.C.S.: 541511

Global Alerts LLC (1)
1375 N Scottsdale Rd Ste 330, Scottsdale,
AZ 85257
Tel.: (480) 337-3326
Web Site:
    http://www.globalpatentsolutions.com
Environmental Consulting & Management
Services
N.A.I.C.S.: 541620

**Quest Resource Management Group,
LLC** (1)
3481 Plano Pkwy Ste 100, The Colony, TX
75056
Tel.: (972) 464-0004
Web Site: https://www.questrmg.com
Environmental Consulting & Management
Services
N.A.I.C.S.: 541620

**Sustainable Resources Management,
LLC** (1)
30722 Kingston Rd, Easton, MD 21601
Tel.: (410) 770-4502
Web Site:
    http://www.sustainableresourcemanage
    mentinc.com
Environmental Consulting & Management
Services
N.A.I.C.S.: 541620
Brian Knox (Pres)

QUETTA ACQUISITION COR-
PORATION
1185 Avenue of the Americas Ste
301, New York, NY 10036
Tel.: (212) 612-1400   DE
Year Founded: 2023
QETA—(NASDAQ)
Investment Management Service
N.A.I.C.S.: 523999

QUICK-MED TECHNOLOGIES,
INC.
904 NW 4th St, Gainesville, FL
32601-4285
Tel.: (352) 379-0611   NV

Web Site:
    http://www.quickmedtech.com
Year Founded: 1997
QMDT—(OTCIQ)
Sales Range: Less than $1 Million
Emp.: 5
Pharmaceutical Preparation Mfr
N.A.I.C.S.: 325412
Bernd Liesenfeld (Pres)
Kristen Lee Kempfert (Sec)

QUICKLOGIC CORPORATION
2220 Lundy Ave, San Jose, CA
95131
Tel.: (408) 990-4000   CA
Web Site: https://www.quicklogic.com
Year Founded: 1988
QUIK—(NASDAQ)
Rev.: $16,180,000
Assets: $32,586,000
Liabilities: $20,691,000
Net Worth: $11,895,000
Earnings: ($4,267,000)
Emp.: 45
Fiscal Year-end: 01/01/23
Programmable Logic Semiconductors
Mfr & Marketer
N.A.I.C.S.: 334413
Elias N. Nader (CFO & Sr VP-Fin)
Timothy Saxe (CTO & Sr VP-Engrg)
Brian C. Faith (Pres & CEO)
Rajiv Jain (VP-Worldwide Ops)

Subsidiaries:

QuickLogic International Inc. (1)
Hersham Place Technology Park Molesey
Rd, Hersham, Walton-on-Thames, KT12
4RZ, Surrey, United Kingdom   (100%)
Tel.: (44) 1932213160
Web Site: https://www.quicklogic.com
Customizable Semiconductors for Mobile
Devices
N.A.I.C.S.: 334413

**QuickLogic Software (India) Private
Ltd.** (1)
Brindavan 3rd Floor 10 Yashoda nagar Jak-
kurPlantation, Yashoda Nagar Main Road,
Bengaluru, 560064, India   (100%)
Tel.: (91) 8030479000
Sales Range: $25-49.9 Million
Emp.: 25
Semiconductors Mfr & Marketer
N.A.I.C.S.: 334413

SensiML Corporation (1)
4900 SW Griffith Dr Ste256, Beaverton, OR
97005
Tel.: (503) 567-2143
Web Site: https://www.sensiml.com
Software Services
N.A.I.C.S.: 541511
Chris Rogers (Co-Founder & CEO)
Chris Knorowski (Co-Founder & CTO)
Marc Giroux (Co-Founder)

QUIDELORTHO CORPORA-
TION
9975 Summers Ridge Rd, San Diego,
CA 92121
Tel.: (858) 552-1100   DE
Web Site:
    https://www.quidelortho.com
Year Founded: 2021
QDEL—(NASDAQ)
Rev.: $2,997,800,000
Assets: $8,563,100,000
Liabilities: $3,557,200,000
Net Worth: $5,005,900,000
Earnings: ($10,100,000)
Emp.: 7,100
Fiscal Year-end: 12/31/23
Holding Company; Diagnostic Prod-
ucts Mfr
N.A.I.C.S.: 551112
Brian J. Blaser (Pres & CEO)
Joseph M. Busky (CFO)
Michael S. Iskra (Interim CEO, Chief
Comml Officer & Exec VP)

Robert J. Bujarski (Interim Pres, COO
& Exec VP)
Kenneth F. Buechler (Chm)
Werner Kroll (Sr VP-R&D)
Michelle A. Hodges (Gen Counsel,
Sec & Sr VP)

Subsidiaries:

**Ortho Clinical Diagnostics Holdings
plc** (1)
1001 Route 202, Raritan, NJ 08869
Tel.: (908) 218-8000
Web Site:
    http://www.orthoclinicaldiagnostics.com
Rev.: $2,042,800,000
Assets: $3,363,800,000
Liabilities: $2,953,300,000
Net Worth: $410,500,000
Earnings: ($54,300,000)
Emp.: 4,800
Fiscal Year-end: 01/02/2022
Holding Company; Vitro Diagnostics
N.A.I.C.S.: 551112
Chris Smith (Chm & CEO)

Subsidiary (Domestic):

Ortho-Clinical Diagnostics, Inc. (2)
1001 US Hwy 202, Raritan, NJ 08869
Tel.: (908) 218-8000
Web Site: http://www.orthoclinical.com
Sales Range: $1-4.9 Billion
Emp.: 4,500
In-Vitro Diagnostic Products Mfr
N.A.I.C.S.: 325413
Alex Socarras (Chief Comml Officer)
Robert Yates (Chm)
Chris Smith (CEO)

Subsidiary (Non-US):

Ortho-Clinical Diagnostics (3)
50 100 Holmers Farm Way, High Wy-
combe, HP12 4DP, Bucks, United Kingdom.
Tel.: (44) 1494658631
Web Site: http://www.orthoclinical.com
Sales Range: $125-149.9 Million
Emp.: 600
In-Vitro Diagnostic Products Mfr
N.A.I.C.S.: 325413

Ortho-Clinical Diagnostics GmbH (3)
Karl-Landsteiner-Strasse 1, Neckargemund,
69151, Germany   (100%)
Tel.: (49) 6223770
Web Site: http://www.orthoclinical.com
Sales Range: $50-74.9 Million
Emp.: 200
In-Vitro Diagnostic Products Mfr
N.A.I.C.S.: 325413
Wolfgang Stier (Mgr-Mktg)

Ortho-Clinical Diagnostics K.K. (3)
16F Gate City Osaki East Tower 1-11-2
Osaki, Shinagawa-Ku, Tokyo, 141-0032,
Japan   (100%)
Tel.: (81) 120036527
Web Site: http://www.ocd.co.jp
Sales Range: $25-49.9 Million
Emp.: 180
In-Vitro Diagnostic Products Mfr
N.A.I.C.S.: 325413
Otsuka Ichiro (Mgr-Cellular Tech)

Ortho-Clinical Diagnostics N.V. (3)
Parklaan 22 Bus 10, 2300, Turnhout,
Belgium   (100%)
Tel.: (32) 4 60 03 03
Web Site: http://www.orthoclinical.com
Sales Range: $50-74.9 Million
Emp.: 150
In-Vitro Diagnostic Products Mfr
N.A.I.C.S.: 325413

Ortho-Clinical Diagnostics S.A. (3)
24 Boulevard SebastienBrant TSA 40007,
67400, Illkirch-Graffenstaden,
France   (100%)
Tel.: (33) 388663682
Web Site: http://www.orthoclinical.com
Sales Range: $150-199.9 Million
Emp.: 375
In-Vitro Diagnostic Products Mfr
N.A.I.C.S.: 325413
Hubert Guyot (Dir-Product Mgmt)

Ortho-Clinical Diagnostics S.p.A. (3)
Viale dell Innovazione 3, 20126, Milan, Italy
Tel.: (39) 0287103546

Web Site: http://www.orthoclinical.com
Sales Range: $50-74.9 Million
Emp.: 240
In-Vitro Diagnostic Products Mfr
N.A.I.C.S.: 325413
Enrico Sebastiano (Mgr-Strategic Sls)

Plant (Domestic):

Ortho-Clinical Diagnostics, Inc. -
Rochester **(3)**
100 Indigo Creek Dr, Rochester, NY 14626
Tel.: (585) 453-3000
Web Site: http://www.orthoclinical.com
Sales Range: $900-999.9 Million
Emp.: 409
In-Vitro Diagnostic Products Mfr
N.A.I.C.S.: 325413

Quidel Corporation **(1)**
9975 Summers Ridge Rd, San Diego, CA
92121
Tel.: (858) 552-1100
Web Site: http://www.quidel.com
Rev.: $1,698,551,000
Assets: $2,430,374,000
Liabilities: $501,012,000
Net Worth: $1,929,362,000
Earnings: $704,226,000
Emp.: 1,600
Fiscal Year-end: 12/31/2021
Rapid Immuno-Diagnostic Products Mfr
N.A.I.C.S.: 325413
Ratan Borkar (Sr VP-Intl Comml Ops)
Edward K. Russell (Sr VP-Bus Dev)
Karen C. Gibson (Sr VP-Digital Health Bus
Unit)
Ruben Argueta (Dir-IR)
William J. Ferenczy (Sr VP-Cardiometabolic
Bus Unit)
Tamara A. Ranalli (Sr VP-Molecular Bus
Unit)
Michael Donald Abney Jr. (Sr VP-Sls &
Distr-North America)

Subsidiary (Domestic):

Diagnostic Hybrids, Inc. **(2)**
2005 E State St Ste 100, Athens, OH
45701
Tel.: (858) 552-1100
Sales Range: $25-49.9 Million
Emp.: 215
Cell Cultures for Medical Testing
N.A.I.C.S.: 325413

Branch (Domestic):

Quidel Corporation - Santa Clara **(2)**
2981 Copper Rd, Santa Clara, CA 95051
Tel.: (408) 616-4301
Diagnostic Tests Mfr
N.A.I.C.S.: 325412

Subsidiary (Non-US):

Quidel Ireland Limited **(2)**
2nd Floor Merchants Square Merchants
Road, Galway, H91 ETN2, Ireland
Tel.: (353) 91412474
Pharmaceutical Products Distr
N.A.I.C.S.: 424210

QUINCE THERAPEUTICS, INC.
611 Gateway Blvd Ste 273, South
San Francisco, CA 94080
Tel.: (415) 910-5717   DE
Web Site: https://www.quincetx.com
Year Founded: 2012
QNCX—(NASDAQ)
Rev.: $1,068,000
Assets: $103,910,000
Liabilities: $3,317,000
Net Worth: $100,593,000
Earnings: ($51,660,000)
Emp.: 21
Fiscal Year-end: 12/31/22
Research & Development in Biotech-
nology (except Nanobiotechnology)
N.A.I.C.S.: 541714
Charles S. Ryan (Pres)
Ted Monohon (Chief Acctg Officer,
VP-Fin & Principle Fin Officer)
Casey C. Lynch (Co-Founder)
Stephen S. Dominy (Co-Founder)
Kristen Gafric (Co-Founder)

David Hennings (VP-CMC)
Caryn Gordon McDowell (Chief Legal
& Admin Officer & Sec)

QUINSTREET, INC.
950 Tower Ln Ste 1200, Foster City,
CA 94404
Tel.: (650) 578-7632   CA
Web Site: https://www.quinstreet.com
Year Founded: 1999
QNST—(NASDAQ)
Rev.: $613,514,000
Assets: $368,546,000
Liabilities: $151,721,000
Net Worth: $216,825,000
Earnings: ($31,331,000)
Emp.: 899
Fiscal Year-end: 06/30/24
Online Vertical Marketing & Media
Services
N.A.I.C.S.: 541613
Douglas Valenti (Founder, Chm &
CEO)
Nina Bhanap (Pres-Product & Tech)
Tim Stevens (COO)
Gregory Wong (CFO)
Martin J. Collins (Chief Legal & Pri-
vacy Officer)

Subsidiaries:

Modernize, Inc. **(1)**
804 Congress Ave Ste 400, Austin, TX
78701
Tel.: (888) 296-0170
Web Site: http://www.modernize.com
Home Improvement Services
N.A.I.C.S.: 444110
Alan Godfrey (Sr VP-Home Svcs)
Jeff Barnes (VP & Gen Mgr-Core Svcs)
Josh Smykal (Sr Dir-Bus Ops)
Jamie Smith (Dir-Client Acquisition Svcs)
Robert Skorpil (Dir-Organic Mktg)

QuinStreet Europe Ltd. **(1)**
10 Accommodation Rd, Colchester, CO4
5HR, Essex, United Kingdom
Tel.: (44) 1206271162
Custom Computer Programming Services
N.A.I.C.S.: 541511

QuinStreet Insurance Agency,
Inc. **(1)**
950 Tower Ln 6th Fl, Foster City, CA 94404
Tel.: (855) 430-7753
Web Site: http://www.carinsurance.com
Auto Insurance
N.A.I.C.S.: 524298

QUIPT HOME MEDICAL CORP.
1019 Town Dr, Wilder, KY 41076
Tel.: (859) 878-2220   BC
Web Site:
    https://quipthomemedical.com
QIPT—(NASDAQ)
Rev.: $245,915,000
Assets: $247,248,000
Liabilities: $140,057,000
Net Worth: $107,191,000
Earnings: ($6,763,000)
Emp.: 1,200
Fiscal Year-end: 09/30/24
Durable Medical Equipment Distr
N.A.I.C.S.: 423450
Gregory Crawford (Chm & CEO)
Hardik Mehta (CFO)
Will Childers (VP-Bus Dev)
Jerry Kirn (VP-Ops)
Mark Miles (VP-IT)
Cole Stevens (VP-Corp Dev)

Subsidiaries:

Access Respiratory Home Care,
LLC **(1)**
4031 Veterans Memorial Blvd, Metairie, LA
70002-5501
Tel.: (504) 889-7878
Web Site: http://www.accessrespiratory.com
Health Practitioners
N.A.I.C.S.: 621399

Black Bear Medical, Inc. **(1)**

275 Marginal Way, Portland, ME 04101
Tel.: (207) 871-0008
Web Site: http://www.blackbearmedical.com
Sales Range: $1-9.9 Million
Medical & Hospital Equipment & Supplies
Whslr
N.A.I.C.S.: 423450

Central Oxygen Inc. **(1)**
1019 Town Dr, Wilder, KY 41076
Tel.: (765) 284-6404
Medical, Dental & Hospital Equipment &
Supplies Merchant Whslr
N.A.I.C.S.: 423450

Coastal Med Tech, Inc. **(1)**
1113 Stillwater Ave, Bangor, ME 04401
Tel.: (207) 848-7730
Web Site: http://www.coastalmedtech.com
Emp.: 45
Home Medical Equipment Distr
N.A.I.C.S.: 532283
Catherine Hamilton (CFO)

Cooley Medical Equipment, Inc. **(1)**
1184 S Lk Dr, Prestonsburg, KY 41653
Tel.: (606) 886-9267
Web Site: http://www.cooleymedical.com
Emp.: 25
Home Medical Equipment Distr
N.A.I.C.S.: 423450

Health Technology Resources,
LLC **(1)**
1400 E Lake Cook Rd Ste 170, Buffalo
Grove, IL 60089
Tel.: (847) 947-8044
Web Site: http://yourhtr.com
Rev.: $1,200,000
Emp.: 8
Medical, Dental & Hospital Equipment &
Supplies Merchant Whslr
N.A.I.C.S.: 423450
Greg Schoonover (Pres & CEO)

Legacy Oxygen & Home Care Equip-
ment, LLC **(1)**
126 Lone Oak Rd, Paducah, KY 42001-
4442
Tel.: (270) 442-7887
Web Site: http://www.legacyoxygen.com
Sales Range: $1-9.9 Million
Emp.: 14
Surgical Appliance & Supplies Mfr
N.A.I.C.S.: 339113
Tony Wave (CEO)

Norcal Respiratory Inc. **(1)**
3075 Crossroads Dr Ste A, Redding, CA
96003-8018
Tel.: (530) 246-1200
Web Site: http://www.norcalrespiratory.com
Chemical & Allied Products Merchant Whslr
N.A.I.C.S.: 424690
Jim Rehmann (Owner)

Patient-Aids, Inc. **(1)**
10032 Montgomery Rd, Cincinnati, OH
45242
Tel.: (513) 984-8876
Sales Range: $10-24.9 Million
Home Care Health Services & Equipment
N.A.I.C.S.: 423450
Greg Crawford (Pres)
Jerry Kirn (VP-Ops)

West Home Health Care, Inc. **(1)**
2085 Dabney Rd, Richmond, VA 23230-
3335
Tel.: (804) 353-7703
Web Site: http://www.whhci.com
Sales Range: $1-9.9 Million
Emp.: 5
Home Medical Equipment Retailer
N.A.I.C.S.: 456199
Joseph Groux (Gen Mgr)

QUOTEMEDIA, INC.
17100 E Shea Blvd Ste 230, Foun-
tain Hills, AZ 85268
Tel.: (480) 905-7311   NV
Web Site:
    http://www.quotemedia.com
QMCI—(OTCQB)
Rev.: $17,527,605
Assets: $6,562,093
Liabilities: $7,790,768
Net Worth: ($1,228,675)

Earnings: $444,470
Emp.: 121
Fiscal Year-end: 12/31/22
Financial Stock Market Data, Market
News Feeds, Market Research Infor-
mation & Financial Software Solu-
tions
N.A.I.C.S.: 491110
David M. Shworan (Co-Pres)
Amy Newhard (Mgr-Compliance)
Venous Ghassemi (Mgr-DevOps,
Quality & Release)
Madhu Acharya (Engr-Software)
Robert J. Thompson (Chm)
Keith J. Randall (Co/Co-Pres, CEO,
CFO & CFO)
Christian Amott (CTO)
David Hay (Sr VP-Corp Accounts &
Sls Dir)
Jon Lazzarino (Sr VP-Sls Ops)
Alex Smigoc (Dir-Software Dev & Cli-
ent Support)
Josh Haywood (Dir-Ops)
Matthew Green (Mgr-Technical Sup-
port)

QURATE RETAIL, INC.
12300 Liberty Blvd, Englewood, CO
80112
Tel.: (720) 875-5300   DE
Web Site:
    https://www.qurateretail.com
Year Founded: 1991
QRTEA—(NASDAQ)
Rev.: $10,915,000,000
Assets: $11,368,000,000
Liabilities: $10,879,000,000
Net Worth: $489,000,000
Earnings: ($145,000,000)
Emp.: 20,300
Fiscal Year-end: 12/31/23
Offices of Other Holding Companies
N.A.I.C.S.: 551112
Gregory B. Maffei (Exec Chm)
Courtnee Alice Chun (Chief Portfolio
Officer)
Courtnee Alice Chun (Chief Portfolio
Officer)
Brian J. Wendling (CFO & Chief
Acctg Officer)
Renee L. Wilm (Chief Admin Officer
& Chief Legal Officer)
David L. Rawlinson II (Pres & CEO)

Subsidiaries:

Bodybuilding.com, LLC **(1)**
431 Railroad Ave, Camp Hill, PA 17011
Tel.: (717) 761-5041
Web Site: http://www.bodybuilding.com
Health Fitness Services
N.A.I.C.S.: 713940

City Cycle, Inc. **(1)**
2607 S 3200, West Valley City, UT 84119
Tel.: (801) 736-6396
Web Site: http://www.competitivecyclist.com
Internet Bike Retailer
N.A.I.C.S.: 441227

ER Marks, Inc. **(1)**
3411 Silverside Rd 205BC, Wilmington, DE
19810-4895
Tel.: (302) 478-4371
Cable & Other Subsription Services
N.A.I.C.S.: 516210

Giftco, Inc. **(1)**
1237 S Victoria Ave Ste 162, Oxnard, CA
93035
Tel.: (805) 773-9200
Web Site: https://www.giftco.com
Sales Range: $150-199.9 Million
Online Gift Retailer
N.A.I.C.S.: 459420

Higher Power Inc. **(1)**
9169 W State St Ste 510, Boise, ID 83714
Tel.: (208) 377-9002
Web Site: https://www.bodybuilding.com
Sales Range: $100-124.9 Million
Emp.: 180
Bodybuilding Information Website

Qurate Retail, Inc.—(Continued)

N.A.I.C.S.: 519290

Liberty Interactive LLC (1)
12300 Liberty Blvd, Englewood, CO
80112 **(100%)**
Tel.: (720) 875-5400
Web Site: http://www.libertymedia.com
Holding Company; Entertainment, Communications & Media Services
N.A.I.C.S.: 551112

Subsidiary (Domestic):

KSI Inc. (2)
301 N Rehoboth Blvd, Milford, DE 19963
Tel.: (302) 422-4014
Web Site: https://www.ksiinc.org
Cable & Other Subsription Services
N.A.I.C.S.: 516210
Jayson Crouch (VP)

MotoSport, LLC (1)
15353 SW Sequoia Pkwy Ste 140, Portland, OR 97224
Tel.: (503) 783-5600
Web Site: https://www.motosport.com
Motorcycle Parts & Accessories Retailer
N.A.I.C.S.: 441227

Qurate Retail Group, Inc. (1)
1200 Wilson Dr, West Chester, PA 19380
Tel.: (484) 701-1000
Holding Company; Online Shopping & Mail-Order Services
N.A.I.C.S.: 551112
Scott Barnhart (COO)
Mary Elizabeth Campbell (Executives)
David Rawlinson II (Pres)
Mike Fitzharris (Pres)
Rob Muller (Pres)
Aidan O'Meara (Pres)
Terry Boyle (Pres)
Ryan McKelvey (Pres)
Karen Etzkorn (CIO)
Linda Aiello (Chief People Officer)
Bill Wafford (CFO)

Subsidiary (Domestic):

Affiliate Sales & Marketing, Inc (2)
1200 Wilson Dr, West Chester, PA 19380
Tel.: (484) 701-8113
Web Site: https://asm.qvc.com
Home Shopping Services
N.A.I.C.S.: 541613

HSN, Inc. (2)
1 HSN Dr, Saint Petersburg, FL
33729 **(100%)**
Tel.: (727) 872-1000
Web Site: https://www.hsn.com
Sales Range: $1 4.0 Billion
Electronic Shopping Services
N.A.I.C.S.: 516210
Rob Muller (Pres)

Subsidiary (Domestic):

Contract Decor, Inc. (3)
72-184 N Shore St, Thousand Palms, CA
92276
Tel.: (760) 343-4444
Web Site: https://www.contractdecor.net
Interior Design Services
N.A.I.C.S.: 541410

Cornerstone Brands, Inc. (3)
5568 W Chester Rd, West Chester, OH
45069
Tel.: (513) 603-1000
Catalog Retailer
N.A.I.C.S.: 449129

Subsidiary (Domestic):

Garnet Hill, Inc. (4)
231 Main St, Franconia, NH 03580
Tel.: (603) 823-5545
Web Site: https://www.garnethill.com
Women's Clothing & Bedding Mail Order
Retailer
N.A.I.C.S.: 458110

The Territory Ahead (4)
5345 Creek Rd, Blue Ash, OH 45242
Tel.: (513) 466-0727
Web Site: https://www.territoryahead.com
Men's & Women's Casual Clothing Store &
Catalog Retailer

N.A.I.C.S.: 458110

Subsidiary (Domestic):

HSN Catalog Services, Inc. (3)
23297 Commerce Park, Cleveland, OH
44122-5808
Tel.: (216) 662-6553
Mail Order & Catalog Sales Operator
N.A.I.C.S.: 425120

HSN Improvements, LLC (3)
5568 W Chester Rd, West Chester, OH
45069
Tel.: (727) 872-1000
Web Site:
http://www.improvementscatalog.com
Home Accessory Distr
N.A.I.C.S.: 455219

Ingenious Designs LLC (3)
2060 9th Ave, Ronkonkoma, NY 11779
Mops Floor & Dust
N.A.I.C.S.: 541613

Subsidiary (Domestic):

QVC, Inc. (2)
1200 Wilson Dr, West Chester, PA
19380 **(98%)**
Tel.: (484) 701-1000
Web Site: https://www.qvc.com
Rev.: $9,887,000,000
Assets: $12,404,000,000
Liabilities: $7,832,000,000
Net Worth: $4,572,000,000
Earnings: ($1,867,000,000)
Emp.: 20,800
Fiscal Year-end: 12/31/2022
Electronic Retailing Services
N.A.I.C.S.: 455219
Mike Fitzharris (Pres)
David L. Rawlinson (Pres)
James M. Hathaway (CFO)

Subsidiary (Domestic):

QVC Chesapeake, Inc. (3)
1553 River Birch Run N, Chesapeake, VA
23320
Tel.: (757) 448-4300
Electronic Shopping Services
N.A.I.C.S.: 455219

QVC Delaware, Inc. (3)
3226 Kirkwood Hwy, Wilmington, DE 19808
Tel.: (484) 701-8972
Emp.: 30
Online Product Distr
N.A.I.C.S.: 425120

Subsidiary (Non-US):

QVC Deutschland Inc. & Co. KG (3)
Plockstrasse 30, 40221, Dusseldorf, Germany
Tel.: (49) 21130070
Advetising Agency
N.A.I.C.S.: 541810

**QVC Grundstucksverwaltungs
GmbH** (3)
Plockstr 30, 40221, Dusseldorf, Germany
Tel.: (49) 21130070
Web Site: http://www.qvc.de
Cable Channel Operating Services
N.A.I.C.S.: 516210

QVC Handel S.a r.l. & Co. KG (3)
Rhein Studios Plockstrasse 30, 40221, Dusseldorf, Germany
Tel.: (49) 21130070
Online Commerce Services
N.A.I.C.S.: 423620

QVC eService LLC & Co. KG (3)
Unterneustadter Kirchplatz 5, 34123, Kassel, Germany
Tel.: (49) 56189060
Online Commerce Services
N.A.I.C.S.: 423620

Sincerely Incorporated (1)
1625 N Market Blvd Ste N 112, Sacramento, CA 95834
Tel.: (916) 445-1254
Web Site: https://www.sincerely.com
Emp.: 15
Software Publishing Services
N.A.I.C.S.: 513210

**The Cornerstone Brands Group,
Inc.** (1)
5568 W Chester Rd, West Chester, OH
45069
Tel.: (513) 603-1000
Online Commerce Services
N.A.I.C.S.: 455110

e-Style, LLC (1)
1249 Climbing Rose Dr, Orlando, FL 32818
Tel.: (321) 436-6369
Courier Service
N.A.I.C.S.: 492210

QXO, INC.
5 American Ln, Greenwich, CT 06831
Tel.: (973) 396-1720 DE
Web Site: https://www.qxo.com
Year Founded: 2002
QXO—(NASDAQ)
Rev.: $44,985,276
Assets: $21,438,067
Liabilities: $11,885,603
Net Worth: $9,552,464
Earnings: ($282,219)
Emp.: 172
Fiscal Year-end: 12/31/22
Holding Company; Business Consulting & Financial Software Developer
N.A.I.C.S.: 551112
Mark Meller (Chm, Pres & CEO)
Joseph P. Macaluso (CFO)

Subsidiaries:

SWK Technologies, Inc. (1)
120 Eagle Rock Ave Ste 330, East Hanover, NJ 07936 **(100%)**
Tel.: (973) 758-6100
Web Site: http://www.swktech.com
Business Consulting & Financial Software
Developer
N.A.I.C.S.: 513210
Mark Meller (CEO)
Michelle Paparo (Sr VP-Sage 100)
Diana Kyser (COO)
Antonio Carrion (CMO)
John Shepperson (Sr VP-Bus Dev-Enterprise Sls)
B. J. O'Reilly (CTO)

Subsidiary (Domestic):

2000 Soft Inc. (2)
200 Sandpointe Ave Ste 560, Santa Ana,
CA 92707
Tel.: (949) 699-1777
Web Site: http://www.teamacctech.com
Accounting Software Distr
N.A.I.C.S.: 423400
Karen Espinoza (Founder)

ESC, Inc. (2)
1620 W Fountainhead Pkwy Ste 507,
Tempe, AZ 85282
Tel.: (480) 784-1622
Web Site: http://www.escsoftware.com
Sales Range: $1-9.9 Million
Emp.: 15
Business Management Software Developer
& Publisher
N.A.I.C.S.: 513210

JCS Computer Resource Corp. (2)
726 W Algonquin Rd, Arlington Heights, IL
60005-4416
Tel.: (847) 364-0835
Web Site: http://www.jcscomputer.com
Software Development Services
N.A.I.C.S.: 513210
Marilyn Longbein (Mgr)

Oates & Company, LLC. (2)
2309 W Cone Blvd Ste 220, Greensboro,
NC 27408
Tel.: (336) 230-0200
Software Publishing Services
N.A.I.C.S.: 513210

R1 RCM INC.
433 W Ascension Way Ste 200, Murray, UT 84123
Tel.: (312) 324-7820 DE
Web Site: https://www.r1rcm.com
Year Founded: 2022

RCM—(NASDAQ)
Rev.: $2,254,200,000
Assets: $4,960,200,000
Liabilities: $2,208,800,000
Net Worth: $2,751,400,000
Earnings: $3,300,000
Emp.: 29,400
Fiscal Year-end: 12/31/23
Healthcare Revenue Cycle Management Services
N.A.I.C.S.: 541611
Lee Rivas (CEO)
Kyle Hicok (Chief Comml Officer &
Exec VP)
John Sparby (Pres)
Jennifer Williams (CFO)
Kyle Hicok (Chief Comml Officer &
Exec VP)
Brian Gambs (CTO)
Kristina Bourke (Exec VP)

Subsidiaries:

Acclara Solutions, LLC (1)
13201 Northwest Freeway Ste 600, Houston, TX 77040
Tel.: (713) 429-6000
Web Site: http://www.acclara.com
Insurance Agencies & Brokerages
N.A.I.C.S.: 524210
Chuck Zacney (VP-Client Services)
Tom DuBrul (CEO)

Cloudmed, LLC (1)
1100 Peachtree St Ste 1550, Atlanta, GA
30309
Tel.: (484) 840-1984
Web Site: http://revintsolutions.com
Administrative Management & General
Management Consulting Service
N.A.I.C.S.: 541611
Lee Rivas (CEO)
Kathryn Stalmack (Gen Counsel)
Tiffany Lewis (Chief People Officer)

R1 RCM Holdco Inc. (1)
434 W Ascension Way 6th Fl, Murray, UT
84123 **(100%)**
Tel.: (312) 324-7820
Web Site: https://www.r1rcm.com
Rev.: $1,474,600,000
Assets: $1,449,300,000
Liabilities: $1,102,600,000
Net Worth: $346,700,000
Earnings: $97,200,000
Emp.: 10,200
Fiscal Year-end: 12/31/2021
Holding Company; Healthcare Revenue
Cycle Management Services
N.A.I.C.S.: 551112
Corey Perman (Exec VP-Compliance &
Risk)
Kate Sanderson (Chief HR Officer & Exec
VP)
Sean Radcliffe (Gen Counsel & Exec VP)
Logan Johnston (Exec VP-Central Ops)
Vijay Kotte (Chief Solutions Officer & Exec
VP-Strategy & Corp Dev)

Subsidiary (Domestic):

SCI Solutions Inc. (2)
720 3rd Ave Ste 1000 Pacific Bldg, Seattle,
WA 98104
Healthcare Software Developer
N.A.I.C.S.: 513210
Joel French (CEO & Mng Partner)

Subsidiary (Domestic):

DatStat, Inc. (3)
720 3rd Ave Ste 1000, Seattle, WA 98104
Tel.: (206) 526-9985
Web Site: https://www.datstat.com
Software & Technology Development Services
N.A.I.C.S.: 513210

RA GLOBAL SERVICES, INC.
325 N Saint Paul St Ste 2460, Dallas,
TX 75201
Tel.: (214) 965-8230 DE
RAGL—(OTCIQ)
Holding Company
N.A.I.C.S.: 551112
Davis Martin (CFO)

RACKSPACE TECHNOLOGY, INC.
19122 Hwy 281 N Ste 128, San Antonio, TX 78258-7667
Tel.: (210) 312-4000   DE
Web Site:
https://www.rackspace.com
Year Founded: 1998
RXT—(NASDAQ)
Rev.: $3,122,300,000
Assets: $5,456,700,000
Liabilities: $4,827,200,000
Net Worth: $629,500,000
Earnings: ($804,800,000)
Emp.: 6,800
Fiscal Year-end: 12/31/22
Software Development Services
N.A.I.C.S.: 541511
Kellie Teal-Guess (*Chief HR Officer*)
Srini Koushik (*CTO*)

RADIAN GROUP, INC.
550 E Swedesford Rd Ste 350, Wayne, PA 19087
Tel.: (215) 231-1000   DE
Web Site: https://www.radian.com
Year Founded: 1977
RDN—(NYSE)
Rev.: $1,190,726,000
Assets: $7,063,729,000
Liabilities: $3,144,402,000
Net Worth: $3,919,327,000
Earnings: $742,934,000
Emp.: 1,400
Fiscal Year-end: 12/31/22
Credit Risk Management Services
N.A.I.C.S.: 524126
Edward J. Hoffman (*Gen Counsel, Sec & Sr Exec VP*)
Derek V. Brummer (*Pres-Mortgage*)
Emily Riley (*Chief Mktg & Comm Officer & Sr VP*)
Richard G. Thornberry (*CEO*)
Robert J. Quigley (*Chief Acctg Officer, Exec VP & Controller*)
Mary Dickerson (*COO, Chief People Officer & Sr Exec VP*)
Sumita Pandit (*CFO & Sr Exec VP*)

Subsidiaries:

Clayton Group Holdings Inc.   (1)
2638 S Falkenburg Rd, Riverview, FL 33578
Tel.: (215) 231-1563
Web Site: https://www.clayton.com
Emp.: 550
Mortgage & Real Estate Management Services
N.A.I.C.S.: 561110

Clayton Holdings UK, Ltd.   (1)
Summerton Road, Oldbury, Warley, B69 2EL, West Midlands, United Kingdom
Tel.: (44) 1215111190
Web Site: https://www.claytonholdings.com
Emp.: 6
Holding Company
N.A.I.C.S.: 551112
Leslie Hickens (*Mgr-Grp Quality*)

Subsidiary (Domestic):

Clayton Euro Risk, Ltd.   (2)
40 Queen Square, Bristol, BS1 4QP, United Kingdom
Tel.: (44) 1173155800
Emp.: 200
Investment Advisory Services
N.A.I.C.S.: 523940

Clayton Holdings, Inc.   (1)
100 Beard Saw Mill Rd Ste 200, Shelton, CT 06484
Tel.: (203) 926-5600
Web Site: http://www.clayton.com
Sales Range: $150-199.9 Million
Emp.: 700
Mortgage-Related Loan & Securities Transaction Management, Credit Risk Monitoring & Management Services
N.A.I.C.S.: 561499
Robert A. Harris (*Gen Counsel & Sr VP*)

Subsidiary (Domestic):

Clayton Fixed Income Services, Inc.   (2)
1700 Lincoln St Ste 1600, Denver, CO 80203
Tel.: (720) 947-6947
Web Site: http://www.clayton.com
Sales Range: $100-124.9 Million
Emp.: 250
Credit Risk Management & Analysis Services
N.A.I.C.S.: 522390

Red Bell Real Estate, LLC   (2)
1415 S Main St, Salt Lake City, UT 84115
Tel.: (801) 483-4300
Web Site: http://www.redbellre.com
Real Estate Services
N.A.I.C.S.: 531210
Jeffrey Jonas (*Founder*)

ValuAmerica, Inc.   (2)
113 Technology Dr, Pittsburgh, PA 15275
Tel.: (412) 494-0400
Web Site: http://www.valuamerica.com
Sales Range: $1-9.9 Million
Emp.: 45
Real Estate Information & Technology Services
N.A.I.C.S.: 531390

Entitle Insurance Company   (1)
6100 Oak Tree Blvd Ste 200, Independence, OH 44131
Web Site: http://www.entitledirect.com
Title Insurance Services
N.A.I.C.S.: 524127
Lee Baskey (*Sr VP-Underwriting Ops*)

Five Bridges Advisors LLC   (1)
7315 Wisconsin Ave Ste 750 W, Bethesda, MD 20814-3202
Tel.: (301) 841-6447
General Management Consulting Services
N.A.I.C.S.: 541611

GR Financial LLC   (1)
2691 S Decker Lake Ln, West Valley City, UT 84119
Tel.: (801) 456-2168
Investment Advisory Services
N.A.I.C.S.: 523940

Homegenius Real Estate LLC   (1)
7730 S Union Park Ave Ste 400, Midvale, UT 84047
Web Site: https://homegeniusrealestate.com
Real Estate Development Services
N.A.I.C.S.: 531210

Independent Settlement Services, LLC   (1)
1000 GSK Dr Ste 210, Coraopolis, PA 15108
Tel.: (412) 788-1740
Web Site: http://www.isspgh.net
Real Estate Services
N.A.I.C.S.: 531390

Pyramid Platform, LLC   (1)
7730 S Union Park Ave Ste 400, Midvale, UT 84047
Web Site: http://www.pyramidplatform.com
Software Development Services
N.A.I.C.S.: 541511

Radian Guaranty Inc.   (1)
1500 Maerket St, Philadelphia, PA 19102
Tel.: (215) 564-6600
Web Site: http://www.radian.com
Mortgage Insurance Services
N.A.I.C.S.: 524298

Subsidiary (Domestic):

Radian Services LLC   (2)
1601 Market St, Philadelphia, PA 19103
Tel.: (800) 523-1988
Web Site: http://www.radian.biz.com
Direct Property & Casualty Insurance Services
N.A.I.C.S.: 524126

Radian Investor Surety Inc.   (1)
1601 Market St, Philadelphia, PA 19103
Tel.: (215) 231-1225
Financial Services
N.A.I.C.S.: 523910

Radian Title Insurance Inc.   (1)
1500 Market St, Philadelphia, PA 19102
Tel.: (203) 724-1150
Web Site: http://www.radian.com
Insurance Agencies & Brokerages
N.A.I.C.S.: 524210

RADIANT LOGISTICS, INC.
Triton Towers 2 700 S Renton Village Place 7th Fl, Renton, WA 98057
Tel.: (425) 462-1094   DE
Web Site:
https://www.radiantdelivers.com
Year Founded: 2001
RLGT—(NYSEAMEX)
Rev.: $802,470,000
Assets: $371,185,000
Liabilities: $161,676,000
Net Worth: $209,509,000
Earnings: $8,197,000
Emp.: 909
Fiscal Year-end: 06/30/24
Holding Company; Transportation & Supply Chain Management Services
N.A.I.C.S.: 551112
Bohn H. Crain (*Founder, Chm & CEO*)
Todd E. Macomber (*CFO & Sr VP*)
Noel Howard (*VP-Domestic Svcs*)
Arnold Goldstein (*Chief Comml Officer & Sr VP*)
Randy Briggs (*VP-Intl Svcs*)
Harry Smit (*Sr VP & Mgr-Canada*)
Mark Rowe (*Sr VP-Tech*)
Susan Carr (*VP-Financial Shared Svcs*)
Tim O'Brien (*Sr VP & Gen Mgr-Forwarding*)
Christopher Brach (*Sr VP & Gen Mgr-Brokerage*)

Subsidiaries:

Adcom Express, Inc.   (1)
Tel.: (425) 462-1094
Web Site: http://www.adcomworldwide.com
Sales Range: $50-74.9 Million
Emp.: 200
Freight Transportation Arrangement
N.A.I.C.S.: 488510
Bohn H. Crain (*Pres*)

Cascade Transportation, Inc.   (1)
855 S 192nd St Ste 500, Seattle, WA 98148
Tel.: (206) 431-8642
Sales Range: $1-9.9 Million
Emp.: 10
Freight Transportation Arrangement
N.A.I.C.S.: 488510

DBA Distribution Services, Inc.   (1)
701 Cottontail Ln, Somerset, NJ 08875
Tel.: (732) 764-6780
Web Site: http://www.dbaco.com
Rev.: $36,900,257
Emp.: 55
Freight Forwarding
N.A.I.C.S.: 488510

Don Cameron & Associates, Inc.   (1)
396 American Blvd E, Bloomington, MN 55420
Tel.: (952) 884-0070
Sales Range: $1-9.9 Million
Emp.: 50
Freight Transportation Arrangement
N.A.I.C.S.: 488510
Don Cameron (*Pres*)

Highways & Skyways, Inc.   (1)
1150 Aviation Blvd Ste A, Hebron, KY 41048
Tel.: (859) 371-3656
Web Site:
https://www.highwaysandskyways.com
Logistics Management Services
N.A.I.C.S.: 488510
Larry Widlowski (*Gen Mgr*)

Subsidiary (Domestic):

Highways & Skyways of NC, Inc.   (2)
7617 Bentley Rd Ste A, Greensboro, NC 27409
Tel.: (336) 668-3433

Emp.: 50
Logistics Management Services
N.A.I.C.S.: 488510

International Freight Systems (of Oregon), Inc.   (1)
5440 SW Westgate Dr Ste 325, Portland, OR 97221
Tel.: (503) 239-0107
Web Site: https://www.ifs-pdx.com
Freight Transportation Services
N.A.I.C.S.: 488510

Navegate Logistics, Ltd.   (1)
1300 Mendota Hts Rd, Mendota Heights, MN 55120
Tel.: (651) 379-5030
Web Site: https://www.navegate.com
Transportation & Logistics Services
N.A.I.C.S.: 541614

Navegate Supply Chain (Shanghai) Co., Ltd.   (1)
425 Yishan Road Room 1001, Shanghai, 200235, China
Tel.: (86) 2164696096
Transportation & Logistics Services
N.A.I.C.S.: 541614

On Time Express, Inc.   (1)
733 W 22nd St, Tempe, AZ 85282
Tel.: (480) 634-9190
Web Site: http://www.otexp.com
Air Freight Transportation Services
N.A.I.C.S.: 488510

Radiant Customs Services, Inc.   (1)
182-09 149th Rd, Jamaica, NY 11413
Tel.: (718) 995-3850
Customs Brokerage Services
N.A.I.C.S.: 561499
Michael von Loesch (*VP-Intl Svcs*)

Radiant Global Logistics (HK) Limited   (1)
Tel.: (852) 35860505
Freight Transportation Services
N.A.I.C.S.: 488510

Radiant Global Logistics (Shanghai) Ltd.   (1)
1223 Xie Tu Road Unit 1406 Zhijun Building, Shanghai, 200032, China
Tel.: (86) 8008434784
Transportation & Logistics Services
N.A.I.C.S.: 541614

Radiant Global Logistics, Inc.   (1)
700 S Renton Village Pl Fl 7, Renton, WA 98057
Tel.: (425) 462-1094
Sales Range: $200-249.9 Million
Emp.: 320
Freight Transportation Arrangement
N.A.I.C.S.: 488510

Subsidiary (Non-US):

Radiant Global Logistics Ltd.   (2)
5090 Orbitor Drive, Mississauga, L4W 5B5, ON, Canada
Tel.: (905) 602-2700
Web Site:
http://www.radiantgloballogistics.com
Holding Company
N.A.I.C.S.: 551112

Radiant Logistics Partners LLC   (1)
7402 Coho Dr Ste 106, Huntington Beach, CA 92648
Tel.: (310) 387-9204
Logistics Consulting Servies
N.A.I.C.S.: 541614
Craig Sloss (*Mgr-Sls*)

Subsidiary (Non-US):

Wheels Group Inc.   (2)
1280 Courtneypark Drive E, Mississauga, L5T 1N6, ON, Canada
Tel.: (905) 602-2700
Web Site: https://radiantdelivers.com
Holding Company; Integrated Logistics, Freight Transportation & Warehousing Services
N.A.I.C.S.: 551112
Tim Boyce (*CMO & Pres-Wheels Clipper-US*)

Subsidiary (US):

Wheels Clipper Inc.   (3)

Radiant Logistics, Inc.—(Continued)

9014 Heritage Pkwy Ste 300, Woodridge, IL 60517
Tel.: (630) 739-0700
Web Site: https://www.clippergroup.com
Contract Freight & Trailers Services
N.A.I.C.S.: 484230
Walter Whitt (Exec VP-US & Strategic Alliances)

Subsidiary (Non-US):

Radiant Global Logistics (CA), Inc. (4)
Tel.: (562) 921-2188
Web Site: http://www.wheelsgroup.com
Freight Forwarding & Logistics Management Services
N.A.I.C.S.: 488510

Subsidiary (Domestic):

Wheels Logistics Inc. (3)
1280 Courtneypark Drive E, Mississauga, L5T 1N6, ON, Canada
Tel.: (905) 565-1212
Web Site: http://www.thewheelsgroup.com
Emp.: 200
Freight Forwarding & Logistics Management Services
N.A.I.C.S.: 488510
Tim Boyce (COO)

Wheels MSM Canada Inc. (3)
1280 Courtney Park Drive E, Mississauga, L5T 1N6, ON, Canada
Tel.: (905) 951-6800
Freight Forwarding & Logistics Management Services
N.A.I.C.S.: 488510

Radiant Road & Rail, Inc. (1)
9014 Heritage Pkwy Ste 300, Woodridge, IL 60517
Web Site: https://rrs.radiantdelivers.com
Dry & Refrigerated Shipping Services
N.A.I.C.S.: 484230

Service By Air, Inc. (1)
752 A Hempstead Tpke Ste 203, Franklin Square, NY 11010
Tel.: (516) 576-0500
Web Site: http://www.sbaglobal.com
Sales Range: $125-149.9 Million
Freight Transportation Arrangement
N.A.I.C.S.: 488510

RADIOIO, INC.
475 Pk Ave S 4th Fl, New York, NY 10016
Tel.: (212) 486-3364 NY
Web Site: http://www.radioio.com
Year Founded: 1995
RAIO—(OTCEM)
Sales Range: $1-9.9 Million
Emp.: 10
Media Content Distribution Services
N.A.I.C.S.: 513199

RADIUM RESOURCES CORP.
3422 Old Capitol Trl, Wilmington, DE 19808 DE
Year Founded: 2006
RADR—(OTCIQ)
Mineral Exploration Services
N.A.I.C.S.: 213114
Nadeem Shahid (Pres)

RADIUS RECYCLING, INC.
299 SW Clay St Ste 400, Portland, OR 97201
Tel.: (503) 224-9900 OR
Web Site:
https://www.radiusrecycling.com
Year Founded: 1906
RDUS—(NASDAQ)
Rev.: $2,738,692,000
Assets: $1,533,769,000
Liabilities: $908,029,000
Net Worth: $625,740,000
Earnings: ($266,224,000)
Emp.: 3,011
Fiscal Year-end: 08/31/24

Scrap Steel & Iron Processor
N.A.I.C.S.: 562920
Tamara L. Adler Lundgren (Chm, Pres & CEO)
Richard D. Peach (Chief Strategy Officer & Exec VP)
Michael R. Henderson (Pres-Ops & Sr VP)
Stefano R. Gaggini (CFO & Sr VP)
Erich D. Wilson (Chief HR Officer & Sr VP)
James Matthew Vaughn (Chief Compliance Officer, Gen Counsel & Sr VP)
Brian Souza (Chief Ops Mgmt Officer & Sr VP)
Steven Heiskell (Pres-Products & Svcs & Sr VP)
Erika Kelley (Chief Acctg Officer & VP)

Subsidiaries:

Cascade Steel Rolling Mills, Inc. (1)
3200 NE Highway 99W, McMinnville, OR 97128 (100%)
Tel.: (503) 472-4181
Web Site: http://www.cascadesteel.com
Sales Range: $200-249.9 Million
Emp.: 440
Producer of Steel
N.A.I.C.S.: 331110

Crawford Street Corp. (1)
3200 NW Yeon St, Portland, OR 97210
Tel.: (503) 224-9900
Sales Range: $300-349.9 Million
Recycler & Distributor of Scrap & Waste Metals
N.A.I.C.S.: 531120

General Metals of Tacoma, Inc. (1)
1902 Marine View Dr, Tacoma, WA 98422
Tel.: (253) 572-4000
Sales Range: $50-74.9 Million
Emp.: 130
Scrap & Waste Metals Recycler & Distr
N.A.I.C.S.: 423930

Metals Recycling, L.L.C.
30 Green Earth Way, Johnston, RI 02919
Tel.: (401) 943-0683
Sales Range: $25-49.9 Million
Emp.: 65
Metal Scrap Whslr
N.A.I.C.S.: 423930
Andrew Naporano (Gen Mgr)

Millis Industries, Inc. (1)
167 Water St, Laconia, NH 03246
Tel.: (603) 528-4217
Web Site: https://www.millsind.com
Plastic Corrugated Container Mfr
N.A.I.C.S.: 326160

Mormil Corp. (1)
3200 NW Yeon Ave, Portland, OR 97210
Tel.: (503) 224-9900
Sales Range: $50-74.9 Million
Emp.: 100
Recycler & Distributor of Scrap & Waste Metals
N.A.I.C.S.: 423930

Oregon Rail Marketing Co. (1)
299 SW Clay St Suite 350, Portland, OR 97201
Tel.: (503) 224-9900
Web Site: http://www.schnitzersteel.com
Sales Range: $75-99.9 Million
Management Consulting Services
N.A.I.C.S.: 541611

Pick-N-Pull Auto Dismantlers (1)
10850 Gold Ctr Dr Ste 330, Rancho Cordova, CA 95670
Tel.: (916) 689-2000
Sales Range: $1-9.9 Million
Emp.: 20
Waste Metals Recycling & Distr
N.A.I.C.S.: 423930
Spence Enterprises (Principal)

Pick-n-Pull Auto & Truck Dismantlers (1)
3419 Sunrise Blvd, Rancho Cordova, CA 95742
Tel.: (916) 635-2027

Web Site: https://www.picknpull.com
Sales Range: $800-899.9 Million
Emp.: 2,000
Automobile Scrap & Waste Material Services
N.A.I.C.S.: 423930

Proleride Transport Systems, Inc. (1)
3200 NW Yeon Ave, Portland, OR 97210-1524 (100%)
Tel.: (503) 224-9900
Web Site: http://www.schnitzersteel.com
Sales Range: $100-124.9 Million
Holding Company
N.A.I.C.S.: 488999

Prolerized New England Company LLC (1)
69 Rover St, Everett, MA 02149-5514
Tel.: (617) 389-8300
Sales Range: $50-74.9 Million
Emp.: 100
Scrap Metal Recycling
N.A.I.C.S.: 423930
Barry Isaacs (Controller)
Bonnie Gessner (Dir-HR)
Elmer Flordeliza (Mgr-Network)
Daniel Shapiro (Mgr-Ops)

SSI International, Inc. (1)
1902 Marine View Dr, Tacoma, WA 98422
Tel.: (253) 572-4000
Web Site: http://www.schnitzersteel.com
Sales Range: $50-74.9 Million
Emp.: 100
Recycler & Distributor of Scrap & Waste Metals
N.A.I.C.S.: 423930

SSP Reclamation Co. (1)
299 SW Clay St Ste 350, Portland, OR 97201
Tel.: (503) 224-9900
Web Site: http://www.schnitzersteel.com
Reclamation Services
N.A.I.C.S.: 236210

Schnitzer Fresno, Inc. (1)
2727 S Chestnut Ave, Fresno, CA 93725
Tel.: (559) 233-3211
Metal Recycling Services
N.A.I.C.S.: 423930

Schnitzer Northeast-Concord (1)
25 Sandquist St, Concord, NH 03301
Tel.: (603) 225-2267
Metal Recycling Services
N.A.I.C.S.: 423930

Schnitzer Puerto Rico, Inc. (1)
Rd 2 KM 7 7 Corujo Industrial Park Lot 22, Bayamon, PR 00960
Tel.: (787) 619-9138
Ferrous Metal Whslr
N.A.I.C.S.: 423510

Schnitzer Southeast - Atlanta (1)
906 Adamson St SW, Atlanta, GA 30315
Tel.: (404) 332-0000
Scrap Metal Recycling Services
N.A.I.C.S.: 423930

Schnitzer Southeast - Macon (1)
1645 7th St, Macon, GA 31206-1037
Tel.: (478) 743-6773
Web Site: http://www.thescrapmarket.com
Sales Range: $10-24.9 Million
Emp.: 60
Scrap Metal Recycling Services
N.A.I.C.S.: 423930

Schnitzer Southeast, LLC (1)
1301 E Gordon Ave, Albany, GA 31705
Tel.: (229) 432-6255
Web Site: https://www.schnitzersteel.com
Metal Cable Mfr & Distr
N.A.I.C.S.: 332618

Schnitzer Steel BC, Inc. (1)
12195 Musqueam Drive, Surrey, V3V 3T2, BC, Canada
Tel.: (604) 580-0251
Scrap Metal Recycling Services
N.A.I.C.S.: 331491

Schnitzer Steel Billings (1)
1100 6th Ave N, Billings, MT 59101
Tel.: (406) 252-8080
Sales Range: $25-49.9 Million
Emp.: 15
Scrap Metal Recycling

N.A.I.C.S.: 423930

Schnitzer Steel Hawaii Corp. (1)
91-056 Hanua St, Kapolei, HI 96707
Tel.: (808) 682-5810
Web Site:
http://www.hawaiimetalrecycling.com
Emp.: 30
Metal Recycling Services
N.A.I.C.S.: 423930

Schnitzer Steel Industries, Inc.-Woodinville (1)
23711 63rd Ave SE, Woodinville, WA 98072
Tel.: (425) 481-1828
Metal Recycling Services
N.A.I.C.S.: 423930

RADNET, INC.
1510 Cotner Ave, Los Angeles, CA 90025
Tel.: (310) 478-7808 NY
Web Site: https://www.radnet.com
Year Founded: 1984
RDNT—(NASDAQ)
Rev.: $1,430,061,000
Assets: $2,433,907,000
Liabilities: $1,942,455,000
Net Worth: $491,452,000
Earnings: $10,650,000
Emp.: 6,946
Fiscal Year-end: 12/31/22
Diagnostic Imaging Centers
N.A.I.C.S.: 621512
Ranjan Jayanathan (CIO)
Howard G. Berger (Co-Founder, Chm, Pres & CEO)
Norman R. Hames (Pres & COO-Western Ops)
Stephen M. Forthuber (Pres & COO-Eastern Ops)
Michael Murdock (Chief Dev Officer & Exec VP)
Laura Foster (Sr VP-Compliance & Regulatory Affairs)
Terri Herrick (Sr VP-Contracting & Network Strategy)
Mital Patel (Chief Admin Officer & Exec VP-Fin Plng & Analysis)
Mark D. Stolper (CFO & Exec VP)
Charles H. Shaw III (Sr VP-HealthCare Network Strategy & Bus Dev-Eastern Ops)
Ruth Villiger-Wilson (Sr VP-HR)
A. Gregory Sorensen (Chief Science Officer & Exec VP)
Cornelic Woodorp (Proc/CEO Digital Health)

Subsidiaries:

Advanced Radiology, LLC (1)
1700 Reisterstown Rd Ste 112, Baltimore, MD 21208
Tel.: (410) 580-2100
Web Site:
https://www.advancedradiology.com
Emp.: 80
Diagnostic Imaging Services
N.A.I.C.S.: 621512

American Radiology Services of Delaware, Inc. (1)
3700 Fleet St Ste 110, Baltimore, MD 21224
Tel.: (410) 910-0150
Emp.: 800
Diagnostic Imaging Center Operator
N.A.I.C.S.: 621512

American Radiology Services, LLC (1)
8820 Columbia 100 Pkwy Ste 100, Columbia, MD 21045
Tel.: (410) 298-0454
Diagnostic Imaging Services
N.A.I.C.S.: 621512
Christina Mielke (Mgr)

Carroll County Radiology, LLC (1)
291 Stoner Ave, Westminster, MD 21157
Tel.: (410) 848-4945
Emp.: 3
Diagnostic Imaging Center Operator

N.A.I.C.S.: 621512

Diagnostic Imaging Associates (1)
10700 E Geddes Ave, Englewood, CO
80112
Tel.: (303) 761-9190
Web Site: http://www.invisionsallyjobe.com
Sales Range: $1-9.9 Million
Emp.: 30
Radiology & Associated Diagnostic Testing
Services
N.A.I.C.S.: 621512

East Bergen Imaging, LLC (1)
401 Sylvan Ave, Englewood Cliffs, NJ
07632
Tel.: (201) 541-5401
Diagnostic Imaging Services
N.A.I.C.S.: 621512
Marcel Pirovano (Mng Dir)

Garden State Radiology Network,
LLC (1)
157 Fries Mill Rd, Turnersville, NJ 08012
Tel.: (856) 677-1010
Healtcare Services
N.A.I.C.S.: 621512

Mid Rockland Imaging Partners,
Inc. (1)
18 Squadron Blvd, New City, NY 10956
Tel.: (845) 634-9729
Emp.: 100
Diagnostic Imaging Services
N.A.I.C.S.: 621512

Montgomery Community Magnetic
Imaging Center Limited
Partnership (1)
18103 Prince Philip Dr, Olney, MD 20832
Tel.: (301) 924-4625
Diagnostic Imaging Center Operator
N.A.I.C.S.: 621512

Mount Airy Imaging Center, LLC (1)
504 E Ridgeville Blvd Ste 130, Mount Airy,
MD 21771
Healtcare Services
N.A.I.C.S.: 621512

New Jersey Imaging Network,
LLC (1)
772 Northfield Ave, West Orange, NJ
07052-1008
Tel.: (973) 325-0002
Web Site: https://www.radnet.com
Diagnostic Imaging Center Operator
N.A.I.C.S.: 621512

Nulogix Health, Inc. (1)
745 Atlantic Ave, Boston, MA
02111 **(100%)**
Tel.: (617) 352-1230
Artificial Intelligence Services
N.A.I.C.S.: 541715
Paul Berger (Pres)

Orange County Radiation Oncology,
LLC (1)
1100-A N Tustin Ave, Santa Ana, CA 92705
Tel.: (714) 835-8520
Web Site: https://www.ocroc.net
Medical Practice Services
N.A.I.C.S.: 621111

RMIS Imaging Services, Inc. (1)
Suite 302-250 Holman Centre, Summer-
side, C1N 1B6, PE, Canada
Tel.: (902) 724-3317
Diagnostic Imaging Center Operator
N.A.I.C.S.: 621512

RadNet Managed Imaging Services,
Inc. (1)
1510 Cotner Ave, Los Angeles, CA 90025
Tel.: (310) 445-2800
Emp.: 106
Diagnostic Imaging Services
N.A.I.C.S.: 621512

RadNet Management Inc. (1)
1510 Cotner Ave, Los Angeles, CA 90025-
3303
Tel.: (310) 445-2800
Web Site: http://www.radnet.com
Sales Range: $400-449.9 Million
Emp.: 100
Accounting & Auditing Services
N.A.I.C.S.: 541219

Radiology Alliance Delivery System,
LLC (1)
412 Malcolm Dr, Westminster, MD 21157
Tel.: (410) 751-7631
Diagnostic Imaging Center Operator
N.A.I.C.S.: 621512

Radsite LLC (1)
326 1st St Ste 28, Annapolis, MD 21403
Tel.: (443) 440-6007
Medicare & Medicaid Services
N.A.I.C.S.: 923130
Garry Carneal (Pres & CEO)

Rolling Oaks Radiology, Inc. (1)
415 Rolling Oaks Dr Ste 125 160 230,
Thousand Oaks, CA 91361
Tel.: (805) 778-1513
Emp.: 70
Diagnostic Imaging Services
N.A.I.C.S.: 621512

Scriptsender, LLC (1)
10664 W Forest Hill Blvd, Wellington, FL
33414
Tel.: (561) 293-8700
Web Site: https://scriptsender.com
Software Development Services
N.A.I.C.S.: 541511

Turner Imaging Systems, Inc. (1)
1119 S 1680 W, Orem, UT 84058
Tel.: (801) 796-2951
Web Site: https://turnerxray.com
Diagnostic Products Mfr
N.A.I.C.S.: 325413
Tom Youd (COO)
Roberto Scorcia (VP-Sls & Mktg)

Valley Imaging Partners Inc. (1)
690 Main St S, Southbury, CT 06488
Tel.: (408) 358-6881
Web Site: https://draxray.com
Diagnostic Imaging Services
N.A.I.C.S.: 621512
Maria Thornton (Reg Mgr)

eRad, Inc. (1)
201 Brookfield Pkwy Ste 160, Greenville,
SC 29607
Tel.: (864) 234-7430
Web Site: https://erad.com
Sales Range: $25-49.9 Million
Emp.: 21
Medical Diagnostic Software Publisher
N.A.I.C.S.: 541511
Gabor Ligeti (CTO)
Jim Connors (VP-Product Dev)
Dave Cunningham (VP-Sls)
Michael Remkus (VP-Ops)
Brian Huff (Dir-Technical Svcs)
Dave Perry (Dir-Software Dev)
Brooke Incontrera (Mgr-Mktg Comm)

RAFAEL HOLDINGS, INC.
520 Broad St, Newark, NJ 07102
Tel.: (212) 658-1450　　　　DE
Web Site:
　https://www.rafaelholdings.com
RFL—(NYSE)
Rev.: $637,000
Assets: $96,832,000
Liabilities: $10,574,000
Net Worth: $86,258,000
Earnings: ($65,003,000)
Emp.: 28
Fiscal Year-end: 07/31/24
Holding Company
N.A.I.C.S.: 551112
Howard S. Jonas (Exec Chm)
William Conkling (CEO)
Ashok Marin (Chief Legal Officer)
Melissa Lozner (Chief Compliance &
Ethics Officer)
Brandi Robinson (Chief Corp Affairs
Officer)
David A. Polinsky (CFO)

RAINFOREST RESOURCES,
INC.
936 SW 1ST AVE Ste 299, Miami, FL
33130
Tel.: (593) 600-8121

Web Site:
　https://www.rainforestresources
　inc.com
RRIF—(OTCIQ)
Forestry Land Services
N.A.I.C.S.: 115310
Michael Nilsson (Pres & CEO)

RAINMAKER SYSTEMS, INC.
1821 S Bascom Ave Ste 385, Camp-
bell, CA 95008
Tel.: (408) 659-1800　　　　DE
Year Founded: 1999
VCTL—(OTCIQ)
Management Consulting Services
N.A.I.C.S.: 541618
Terry Lydon (Pres & CEO)
Bryant Tolles (CFO & Sec)

RALLYBIO CORPORATION
234 Church St Ste 1020, New Haven,
CT 06510
Tel.: (203) 859-3820　　　　DE
Web Site: https://www.rallybio.com
Year Founded: 2018
RLYB—(NASDAQ)
Rev.: $2,305,000
Assets: $180,435,000
Liabilities: $11,118,000
Net Worth: $169,317,000
Earnings: ($66,654,000)
Emp.: 41
Fiscal Year-end: 12/31/22
Research & Development in Biotech-
nology (except Nanobiotechnology)
N.A.I.C.S.: 541714
Stephen Uden (Co-Founder, Pres &
CEO)
Martin W. Mackay (Co-Founder)
Jonathan I. Lieber (CFO & Treas)
Stephen Uden (Pres, COO & Chief
Scientific Officer)
Jeffrey M. Fryer (Co-Founder)
Steven Ryder (Chief Medical Officer)
Ami Bavishi (Head-IR & Corp Comm)

RALPH LAUREN CORPORA-
TION
650 Madison Ave, New York, NY
10022
Tel.: (212) 318-7000　　　　DE
Web Site:
　https://www.ralphlauren.com
Year Founded: 1967
RL—(NYSE)
Rev.: $6,631,400,000
Assets: $6,602,600,000
Liabilities: $4,152,300,000
Net Worth: $2,450,300,000
Earnings: $646,300,000
Emp.: 14,800
Fiscal Year-end: 03/30/24
Men's, Women's & Children's Cloth-
ing & Accessories, Fragrances, Home
Furnishings, Luggage & Furs Mfr &
Sales
N.A.I.C.S.: 315250
Jane Hamilton Nielsen (CFO & COO)
Ralph Lauren (Exec Chm & Chief
Creative Officer)
David Lauren (Vice Chm & Chief In-
novation Officer)
Christopher L. Clipper (CFO-
Innovation & Go-To-Market strategies
& Sr VP)
Patrice Louvet (Pres & CEO)

Subsidiaries:

Acqui Polo Espana SL (1)
C / Serrano 26, Madrid, 28001, Spain
Tel.: (34) 915402013
Sales Range: $100-124.9 Million
Emp.: 35
Textiles & Footwear Mfr & Whslr
N.A.I.C.S.: 458110

Acqui Polo SAS (1)

2 Place De La Madeleine, 75008, Paris,
France
Tel.: (33) 144775300
Mens Clothes Mfr & Whslr
N.A.I.C.S.: 424350

Club Monaco Corp. (1)
157 Bloor Street West, Toronto, M5S 1P7,
ON, Canada
Tel.: (416) 591-8837
Web Site: http://www.clubmonaco.com
Emp.: 60
Men's Clothing Stores
N.A.I.C.S.: 458110

Club Monaco Inc. (1)
403 Queen Street West, Toronto, M5V 2A5,
ON, Canada
Tel.: (416) 979-5633
Web Site: http://www.clubmonaco.com
Clothing & Cosmetics Retailer
N.A.I.C.S.: 458110

Club Monaco U.S., LLC (1)
160 5th Ave, New York, NY 10010
Tel.: (212) 352-0936
Web Site:
　http://www.clubmonaco.borderfree.com
Family Clothing Stores
N.A.I.C.S.: 458110
Francis Pierrel (CEO & Pres-Brand-Global)

PRL Portugal, Unipessoal LDA (1)
Avenida Fonte Cova, Modivas, Vila do
Conde, 4485-592, Portugal
Tel.: (351) 229288900
Web Site: http://www.ralphlauren.com
Sales Range: $25-49.9 Million
Emp.: 40
Retail Clothing Adults Specialized Stores
N.A.I.C.S.: 459999

Polo Ralph Lauren Milan S.r.l. (1)
Via San Barnaba 27, 20122, Milan, Italy
Tel.: (39) 02550571
Clothing & Textiles Retailer
N.A.I.C.S.: 459999

Polo/Ralph Lauren (1)
54 Nassau St, Princeton, NJ 08542
Tel.: (609) 497-6441
Web Site: http://www.polo.com
Sales Range: $300-349.9 Million
Emp.: 777
Apparel & Accessories
N.A.I.C.S.: 315990

Poloco USA, Inc. (1)
8001 Terrace Ave, Middleton, WI 53562
Tel.: (608) 709-8683
Web Site: http://info.polco.us
Online Community Engagement Services
N.A.I.C.S.: 517810
Alec Vice (Specialist-Bus Dev)
Alex Pedersen (CFO & CTO)
Alyssa Brunner (Specialist-Program)
Ann Michelle Hill (Office Mgr)
Angelica Wedell (Dir-Mktg & Comm)

RL Retail France S.A.S. (1)
Vallee Outlet Shopping Vil, 77700, Serris,
France
Tel.: (33) 160427990
Apparel Retailer
N.A.I.C.S.: 315990

Ralph Lauren Belgium S.p.r.l. (1)
Komedieplaats 12, Antwerp, 2000, Belgium
Tel.: (32) 32012600
Cloth Retailer
N.A.I.C.S.: 458110

Ralph Lauren France S.A.S. (1)
23 Rue de Vienne, Polo Ralph Lauren,
75008, Paris, France
Tel.: (33) 157324775
Web Site: https://www.ralphlauren.fr
Emp.: 300
Clothing & Footwear Whslr
N.A.I.C.S.: 424350

Ralph Lauren Germany GmbH (1)
Maximilianstrasse 23, 80539, Munich, Ger-
many
Tel.: (49) 89223731
Web Site: https://www.ralphlauren.de
Family Clothing Retailer
N.A.I.C.S.: 458110

Ralph Lauren London Ltd. (1)
105-109 Fulham Road, London, SW3 6RL,
United Kingdom
Tel.: (44) 20 7590 7990
Web Site: http://www.ralphlauren.co.uk
Emp.: 15

Ralph Lauren Corporation—(Continued)

Footwear Whslr
N.A.I.C.S.: 459999

Ralph Lauren Netherlands BV (1)
Bataviaplein 265, 8242 PV, Lelystad, Neth-
erlands
Tel.: (31) 202035212
Web Site: https://www.ralphlauren.nl
Family Clothing Retailer
N.A.I.C.S.: 458110

Ralph Lauren Scandinavia AB (1)
Biblioteksgatan 10, 11146, Stockholm, Swe-
den
Tel.: (46) 854501140
Web Site: https://www.ralphlauren.com
Fashion Apparels Mfr
N.A.I.C.S.: 315990

The Ralph Lauren Womenswear
Company, L.P. (1)
40 Kero Rd, Carlstadt, NJ 07072-2604
Tel.: (201) 531-6300
Womens Apparel Whslr
N.A.I.C.S.: 424350

RAMACO RESOURCES, INC.
250 W Main St Ste 1900, Lexington,
KY 40507
Tel.: (859) 244-7455　　　DE
Web Site:
　https://www.ramacoresources.com
Year Founded: 2016
METC—(NASDAQ)
Rev.: $565,688,000
Assets: $596,339,000
Liabilities: $287,141,000
Net Worth: $309,198,000
Earnings: $116,042,000
Emp.: 725
Fiscal Year-end: 12/31/22
Coal Exploration Services
N.A.I.C.S.: 213113
Randall Whittaker Atkins *(Founder,*
Chm & CEO)
Jeremy R. Sussman *(CFO, Exec VP*
& Asst Sec)
John C. Marcum *(Chief Acctg Officer)*
Paul Horn *(Chief Mine Dev Officer)*
Scott Kreutzer *(Chief Admin Officer)*
Scott Spears *(Sr VP)*
Toby Edwards *(Sr VP)*

RAMBUS INC.
4453 N 1st St Ste 100, San Jose, CA
95134
Tel.: (408) 462-8000　　　DE
Web Site: https://www.rambus.com
Year Founded: 1990
RMBS—(NASDAQ)
Rev.: $454,793,000
Assets: $1,012,594,000
Liabilities: $233,297,000
Net Worth: $779,297,000
Earnings: ($14,310,000)
Emp.: 765
Fiscal Year-end: 12/31/22
High-Speed Chip Interface Inventor &
Designer
N.A.I.C.S.: 334413
John K. Allen *(Chief Acctg Officer &*
VP-Acctg)
Luc Seraphin *(Pres & CEO)*
Sean Fan *(COO & Sr VP)*
Cliff Burnette *(Chief HR Officer & Sr*
VP)
Jeffry Moore *(Sr VP-Ops-Global)*
I. Nong Chao *(VP)*
Kendra De Berti *(VP)*
Tina Faris *(Deputy Gen Counsel)*

Subsidiaries:

Cryptography Research, Inc. (1)
425 Market St 11th Fl, San Francisco, CA
94105
Tel.: (415) 397-0123
Web Site: http://www.cryptography.com

Sales Range: $10-24.9 Million
Emp.: 60
Data Security Solutions
N.A.I.C.S.: 541512

Northwest Logic, Inc. (1)
1100 NE Compton Dr Ste 100, Hillsboro,
OR 97006
Tel.: (503) 533-5800
Web Site: http://www.nwlogic.com
Semiconductors Mfr; High-performance,
Silicon-proven, Easy-to-use IP Cores Mfr
N.A.I.C.S.: 541330

Rambus Canada Inc. (1)
4950 Yonge Street Suite 1812, Toronto,
M2N 6K1, ON, Canada
Tel.: (416) 925-5643
Semiconductor Product Distr
N.A.I.C.S.: 423690

Rambus Delaware LLC (1)
6611 W Snowville Rd, Brecksville, OH
44141
Tel.: (440) 397-2600
Web Site: http://www.rambus.com
Emp.: 50
Electronic Products Mfr
N.A.I.C.S.: 334419

Rambus K.K. (1)
Shiroyama Trust Tower 33th Floor 4-3-1
Toranomon, Minato-ku, Tokyo, 105-6034,
Japan (100%)
Tel.: (81) 345806800
Web Site: http://www.rambus.co.jp
Sales Range: $75-99.9 Million
Emp.: 4
Computer System Design Services
N.A.I.C.S.: 541512

Rambus Korea, Inc. (1)
KT Seolleung Tower West 420 Teheran-ro
12F, Gangnam-gu, Seoul, 06611, Korea
(South)
Tel.: (82) 269538007)
Semiconductors & Related Devices Mfr
N.A.I.C.S.: 334413

Unity Semiconductor Corporation (1)
1050 Enterprise Way Ste 700, Sunnyvale,
CA 94089
Tel.: (408) 462-8000
Semiconductor Devices Mfr
N.A.I.C.S.: 334413
Ronald Black *(Pres & CEO)*

RAND CAPITAL CORPORA-
TION
14 Lafayette Sq Ste 1405, Buffalo,
NY 14203
Tel.: (716) 853-0802　　　NY
Web Site:
　https://www.randcapital.com
Year Founded: 1969
RAND—(NASDAQ)
Rev.: $5,765,181
Assets: $63,481,192
Liabilities: $5,759,872
Net Worth: $57,721,320
Earnings: $4,430,410
Emp.: 4
Fiscal Year-end: 12/31/22
Venture Capital Firm
N.A.I.C.S.: 523999
Daniel P. Penberthy *(Pres & CEO)*

Subsidiaries:

Rand Capital SBIC, Inc. (1)
2200 Rand Bldg, Buffalo, NY 14203
Tel.: (716) 853-0802
Web Site: http://www.randcapital.com
Sales Range: $650-699.9 Million
Business Investment Company
N.A.I.C.S.: 523999

RAND WORLDWIDE, INC.
11201 Dolfield Blvd Ste 112 Owings
Mills, Baltimore, MD 21117
Tel.: (410) 581-8080　　　DE
Web Site: https://www.rand.com
Year Founded: 1997
RWWI—(OTCIQ)
Emp.: 430

Design Automation & Product Life-
cycle Management Solutions
N.A.I.C.S.: 423430
Chantale Marchand *(VP-Mktg)*
Peter H. Kamin *(Chm)*
Scott Hale *(VP-IMAGINiT Svcs)*
John Kuta *(CFO)*
Nedim Celik *(CIO & VP-Info Sys)*
Kathy Herold *(VP-HR)*
Lawrence Rychlak *(Pres & CEO)*

Subsidiaries:

Avatech of Florida Inc. (1)
7880 Woodland Ctr Blvd, Tampa, FL 33614
Tel.: (813) 496-8882
Rev.: $560,000
Emp.: 12
Prepackaged Software
N.A.I.C.S.: 449210

Avatech of Nebraska Inc. (1)
11422 Miracle Hills Dr Ste 420, Omaha, NE
68154
Tel.: (402) 451-6669
Web Site: http://www.rand.com
Rev.: $5,800,000
Emp.: 14
Computers, Peripherals & Software Mfr
N.A.I.C.S.: 423430

IMAGINiT Technologies (1)
11201 Dolfield Blvd Ste 112, Owings Mills,
MD 21117
Tel.: (216) 834-8300
Web Site: http://www.imaginit.com
Computer System Design Services
N.A.I.C.S.: 541512
Lawrence Rychlak *(Pres & CEO)*

RANGE IMPACT, INC.
1901 Ave of the Stars 2nd Fl, Los
Angeles, CA 90067
Tel.: (530) 231-7800　　　NV
Web Site: https://rangeimpact.com
Year Founded: 2007
RNGE—(OTCIQ)
Rev.: $4,832,278
Assets: $8,230,465
Liabilities: $5,291,022
Net Worth: $2,939,443
Earnings: ($1,072,176)
Emp.: 40
Fiscal Year-end: 12/31/22
Agricultural Biotechnology Services
N.A.I.C.S.: 541715
Robert T. Brooke *(Co-Founder)*
Avtar S. Dhillon *(Co-Founder)*
Brandon Zipp *(Co-Founder & Chief*
Science Officer-Graphium Biosci-
ences, Inc.)
Richard McKilligan *(CFO-Graphium*
Biosciences, Inc)
Edward Feighan *(Chm)*
Michael R. Cavanaugh *(CEO)*
Reef Karim *(Chief Medical Officer-*
Vitality Healthtech)

RANGE RESOURCES CORPO-
RATION
100 Throckmorton St Ste 1200, Fort
Worth, TX 76102
Tel.: (817) 870-2601　　　DE
Web Site:
　https://www.rangeresources.com
Year Founded: 1981
RRC—(NYSE)
Rev.: $3,374,418,000
Assets: $7,203,885,000
Liabilities: $3,438,334,000
Net Worth: $3,765,551,000
Earnings: $871,142,000
Emp.: 548
Fiscal Year-end: 12/31/23
Oil & Gas Exploration, Property Ac-
quisition, Drilling & Extraction
N.A.I.C.S.: 211120
Alan W. Farquharson *(Sr VP-*
Reservoir Engrg & Economics)
Dennis L. Degner *(Pres & CEO)*
Mark S. Scucchi *(CFO & Exec VP)*

Laith Sando *(VP-IR)*
Mark Windle *(Dir-Corp Comm)*
Erin W. McDowell *(Gen Counsel, Sec*
& Sr VP)

Subsidiaries:

Range Resources-Appalachia,
LLC (1)
100 Throckmorton St Ste 1200, Fort Worth,
TX 76102
Tel.: (817) 870-2601
Oil & Natural Gas Exploration Services
N.A.I.C.S.: 211120
Mike Mitchell *(Engr-Network)*

Range Resources-Louisiana, Inc. (1)
500 Dallas St Ste 1800, Houston, TX 77002
Tel.: (713) 588-8300
Rev.: $732,189,000
Assets: $5,082,849,000
Liabilities: $3,614,928,000
Net Worth: $1,467,921,000
Earnings: ($297,890,000)
Emp.: 484
Fiscal Year-end: 12/31/2015
Holding Company; Oil & Gas Exploration &
Extraction
N.A.I.C.S.: 551112
Jeffrey L. Ventura *(CEO)*
Roger S. Manny *(CFO)*
Dori A. Ginn *(Sr VP & Controller)*

RANGER ENERGY SERVICES,
INC.
10350 Richmond Ave Ste 550, Hous-
ton, TX 77042
Tel.: (713) 935-8900　　　DE
Web Site:
　https://www.rangerenergy.com
Year Founded: 2017
RNGR—(NYSE)
Rev.: $608,500,000
Assets: $381,600,000
Liabilities: $115,400,000
Net Worth: $266,200,000
Earnings: $15,100,000
Emp.: 2,000
Fiscal Year-end: 12/31/22
Oil & Gas Exploration Services
N.A.I.C.S.: 333132
J. Matt Hooker *(Sr VP)*
Melissa Cougle *(CFO)*
Stuart N. Bodden *(Pres & CEO)*
Jim Kulis *(VP)*
Jason Perry *(VP)*
Shelley M. Weimer *(VP)*
Justin Whitley *(Gen Counsel)*

Subsidiaries:

Ranger Energy Equipment, LLC (1)
800 Gessner Rd Ste 1000, Houston, TX
77024-4257
Tel.: (713) 935-4152
Oil & Gas Exploration Services
N.A.I.C.S.: 237120

Ranger Energy Services, LLC (1)
10350 Richmond Ave Ste 550, Houston, TX
77042
Tel.: (713) 935-8900
Web Site: https://www.rangerenergy.com
Oil & Gas Exploration Services
N.A.I.C.S.: 237120

RANI THERAPEUTICS HOLD-
INGS, INC.
2051 Ringwood Ave, San Jose, CA
95131
Tel.: (408) 457-3700　　　DE
Web Site:
　https://www.ranitherapeutics.com
Year Founded: 2021
RANI—(NASDAQ)
Assets: $108,027,000
Liabilities: $34,023,000
Net Worth: $74,004,000
Earnings: ($30,588,000)
Emp.: 163
Fiscal Year-end: 12/31/22

Offices of Other Holding Companies
N.A.I.C.S.: 551112
Talat Imran (CEO)
Svai Sanford (CFO)
Mir Hashim (Chief Scientific Officer)
Mir Imran (Founder & Chm)

RANPAK HOLDINGS CORP.
7990 Auburn Rd, Concord, OH 44077
Tel.: (440) 354-4445   Ky
Web Site: https://www.ranpak.com
Year Founded: 2017
PACK—(NYSE)
Rev.: $326,500,000
Assets: $1,133,500,000
Liabilities: $520,700,000
Net Worth: $612,800,000
Earnings: ($41,400,000)
Emp.: 819
Fiscal Year-end: 12/31/22
Investment Services
N.A.I.C.S.: 523999
Omar Marwan Asali (Chm & CEO)
William E. Drew (Mng Dir, Co-CFO & Sr VP)
David Murgio (COO & Gen Counsel)
Michael S. Gliedman (CTO)
Jason Cho (Mng Dir)
Ritwik Chatterjee (Mng Dir)
Daniel Naccarella (Co-CFO)

Subsidiaries:

Ranpak Corp. (1)
7990 Auburn Rd Concord Twp, Painesville, OH 44077-9701
Tel.: (440) 354-4445
Web Site: http://www.ranpak.com
Protective Paper Packaging Material Mfr
N.A.I.C.S.: 322299

Subsidiary (Non-US):

Ranpak BV (2)
Rimburgerweg 40, Eygelshoven, 6471 XX, Kerkrade, Netherlands
Tel.: (31) 882551111
Web Site: https://www.ranpak.com
Packaging Services
N.A.I.C.S.: 561910

Unit (Domestic):

Ranpak Corp. - Reno (2)
4681 Aircenter Cir, Reno, NV 89502
Tel.: (775) 972-1400
Web Site: http://www.ranpak.com
Protective Paper Packaging Material Mfr
N.A.I.C.S.: 322299

Ranpak Pte. Ltd. (1)
456 Alexandra Road 04-07 Fragrance Empire Building, Singapore, 119962, Singapore
Tel.: (65) 69087390
Protecting Product Mfr
N.A.I.C.S.: 339113

RAPID MICRO BIOSYSTEMS, INC.
1001 Pawtucket Blvd W Ste 280, Lowell, MA 01854
Tel.: (978) 349-3200   DE
Web Site:
https://www.rapidmicrobio.com
Year Founded: 2006
RPID—(NASDAQ)
Rev.: $17,133,000
Assets: $190,650,000
Liabilities: $26,481,000
Net Worth: $164,169,000
Earnings: ($60,806,000)
Emp.: 177
Fiscal Year-end: 12/31/22
All Other Miscellaneous Waste Management Services
N.A.I.C.S.: 562998
Robert Spignesi (Pres & CEO)
Steve Furlong (CFO)
Wendy Hinchey (VP-Global Sls & Mktg)
Andrew Khouri (Dir-Bus Dev & Strategy)

Steven Raters (VP-Global Technical Svcs)
Phil Stewart (VP-Mfg)
Ed Ognibene (VP-Product Dev)
Gurinder Grewal (Sr VP-Strategy)
Mike Noyes (VP-Ops)
Andy Keys (Chief Comml Officer)

RAPID THERAPEUTIC SCIENCE LABORATORIES, INC.
1008 E Jefferson Ave Ste 132, Whitney, TX 76692
Tel.: (858) 987-4910   NV
Web Site: https://www.rtslco.com
Year Founded: 2013
RTSL—(OTCIQ)
Assets: $2,254,580
Liabilities: $5,396,063
Net Worth: ($3,141,483)
Earnings: ($1,794,726)
Emp.: 3
Fiscal Year-end: 12/31/22
Investment Services
N.A.I.C.S.: 523999
Donal R. Schmidt Jr. (Pres & CEO)
D. Hughes Watler Jr. (CFO)

RAPID7, INC.
120 Causeway St Ste 400, Boston, MA 02114
Tel.: (617) 247-1717   DE
Web Site: https://www.rapid7.com
Year Founded: 2000
RPD—(NASDAQ)
Rev.: $685,083,000
Assets: $1,358,991,000
Liabilities: $1,479,065,000
Net Worth: ($120,074,000)
Earnings: ($124,717,000)
Emp.: 2,623
Fiscal Year-end: 12/31/22
Security Data & Analytics Solutions
N.A.I.C.S.: 513210
Timothy M. Adams (CFO & Principal Acctg Officer)
Corey E. Thomas (Chm & CEO)
Tas Giakouminakis (Founder & CTO)
Christina Luconi (Chief People Officer)
Conan Reidy (Sr VP-Corp Dev & Strategic Alliances)
Sunil Shah (VP-IR)
Tim Adams (CFO)
Larry D'Angelo (Chief Customer Officer)
Jaya Baloo (Chief Security Officer)
Lisa Agrella (Sr VP)
David Boffa (Sr VP)
Jeremiah Deway (Sr VP)
Raisa Litmanovich (Gen Counsel)
Jen Renna (Sr VP)
Raj Samani (Sr VP)
Julian Waits (Sr VP)

Subsidiaries:

Rapid7 Canada, Inc. (1)
1 Toronto St, Toronto, M5A 1K4, ON, Canada
Tel.: (617) 247-1717
Data Processing & Management Services
N.A.I.C.S.: 541513
Corey E. Thomas (CEO)

Rapid7 Singapore Pte. Ltd. (1)
51 Cuppage Road 06-06, Singapore, 229469, Singapore
Tel.: (65) 68177056
Software Development Services
N.A.I.C.S.: 541511

RAPT THERAPEUTICS, INC.
561 Eccles Ave, South San Francisco, CA 94080
Tel.: (650) 489-9000   DE
Web Site: https://www.rapt.com
Year Founded: 2015

RAPT—(NASDAQ)
Rev.: $1,527,000
Assets: $266,209,000
Liabilities: $21,043,000
Net Worth: $245,166,000
Earnings: ($83,838,000)
Emp.: 97
Fiscal Year-end: 12/31/22
Biotechnology Research & Development Services
N.A.I.C.S.: 541714
Juan Carlos Jaen (Co-Founder)
Brian Wong (Pres & CEO)
William Ho (Chief Medical Officer)
Michael Listgarten (Gen Counsel)
Rodney Young (CFO, Principal Acctg Officer & Sec)
Dirk Brockstedt (Chief Scientific Officer)
David Wustrow (Sr VP-Drug Discovery & Preclinical Dev)
Paul Kassner (Sr VP-Quantitative & Computational Biology)
Lisa Moore (VP-Bus Dev & Strategy)
Gwen Carscadden (Chief HR Officer)
Jennifer Nicholson (Sr VP-Regulatory Affairs & Quality Assurance)
Adnan Rahman (VP-Commercial)
Nipun Davar (Sr VP-Technical Ops)

RARE ELEMENT RESOURCES LTD.
PO Box 271049, Littleton, CO 80127
Tel.: (720) 278-2460   BC
Web Site:
https://www.rareelementresources.com
Year Founded: 2003
REEMF—(OTCQB)
Rev.: $258,000
Assets: $18,867,000
Liabilities: $1,932,000
Net Worth: $16,935,000
Earnings: ($9,426,000)
Emp.: 2
Fiscal Year-end: 12/31/22
Mining Resources & Development Services
N.A.I.C.S.: 212390
Gerald W. Grandey (Chm)
Wayne E. Rich (CFO)
Kenneth J. Mushinski (Pres & CEO)
Kelli C. Kast-Brown (Chief Admin Officer, Gen Counsel & VP)

Subsidiaries:

Rare Element Resources, Inc. (1)
2009 E Cleveland St, Sundance, WY 82729-8272
Tel.: (307) 283-3500
Metal Mining Services
N.A.I.C.S.: 213114
Richard Larsen (Mgr-Engrg)

RAVE RESTAURANT GROUP, INC.
3551 Plano Pkwy, The Colony, TX 75056
Tel.: (469) 384-5000   MO
Web Site: https://www.raverg.com
Year Founded: 1958
RAVE—(NASDAQ)
Rev.: $12,150,000
Assets: $15,819,000
Liabilities: $3,117,000
Net Worth: $12,702,000
Earnings: $2,473,000
Emp.: 21
Fiscal Year-end: 06/30/24
Pizza Restaurant Operator & Franchisor
N.A.I.C.S.: 722511
Brandon L. Solano (CEO)
Mark E. Schwarz (Chm)

Subsidiaries:

Pie Five Pizza Company, Inc. (1)

15250 Dallas Pkwy, Dallas, TX 75248
Tel.: (972) 726-7435
Web Site: http://www.piefivepizza.com
Emp.: 16
Specialty Foods Mfr
N.A.I.C.S.: 311412
Aaron Archuleta (Dir-Ops)

Pizza Inn, Inc. (1)
300 N Main St, Clarkton, MO 63837
Tel.: (573) 448-3737
Specialty Foods Mfr
N.A.I.C.S.: 311412
Justin Smith (Sr Dir-Ops)

RAYMOND JAMES FINANCIAL, INC.
880 Carillon Pkwy, Saint Petersburg, FL 33716
Tel.: (727) 567-1000   FL
Web Site:
https://www.raymondjames.com
Year Founded: 1962
RJF—(NYSE)
Rev.: $14,923,000,000
Assets: $82,992,000,000
Liabilities: $71,325,000,000
Net Worth: $11,667,000,000
Earnings: $2,068,000,000
Emp.: 19,000
Fiscal Year-end: 09/30/24
Investment & Financial Planning Services
N.A.I.C.S.: 551112
Tash Elwyn (Pres-Private Client Grp)
Scott A. Curtis (COO)
Jonathan W. Oorlog Jr. (Chief Acctg Officer, Sr VP & Controller)
Paul M. Shoukry (Pres & CFO)
Mike White (CMO)
George Catanese (Chief Risk Officer)
Shannon Reid (Sr VP/Dir-Div-Independent Contractors Div)
Jonathan N. Santelli (Gen Counsel, Sec & Exec VP)
Chris Aisenbrey (Chief HR Officer)
Heather Knable (Sr VP-Fin Ops & Strategy)
Andy Zolper (Chief IT Security Officer & Sr VP)
Erik Fruland (Pres-Asset Mgmt Svcs)
Stephen Liverpool (Asst Gen Counsel)
Gala Wan (Sr VP-Risk Mgmt)
Calvin Sullivan (Chief Strategy Officer-Fixed Income)
Horace Carter (Pres-Fixed Income)
Jodi Perry (Head-Advisor Recruiting-Natl)
David Allen (Sr VP)
Leslie Ann Curry (Chief Experience Officer)
Bob Kendall (Pres-Investment Mgmt)
Steve LaBarbera (Chief Compliance Officer)
Vicki Mazur (Sr VP)
Jeffrey A. Dowdle (Vice Chm)
Scott A. Curtis (COO)
James E. Bunn (Pres-Capital Mkts Segment)
Paul Christopher Reilly (Chm & CEO)
Katherine H. Larson (Chief Acctg Officer & Controller)

Subsidiaries:

Carillon Tower Advisers, Inc. (1)
880 Carillon Pkwy, Saint Petersburg, FL 33716
Tel.: (727) 567-4656
Web Site: http://www.carillontower.com
Investment Management Service
N.A.I.C.S.: 523940
Cooper Abbott (Chm & Pres)
Damian Sousa (Chief Compliance Officer)
Eric Wilwant (COO)
Robert D. Kendall (Pres)
Ludmila Chwazik (Chief Compliance Officer)
Carolyn Gill (Treas)

Affiliate (Domestic):

Eagle Asset Management, Inc. (2)

Raymond James Financial, Inc.—(Continued)

880 Carillon Pkwy, Saint Petersburg, FL 33716
Tel.: (727) 573-2453
Web Site: http://www.eagleasset.com
Rev.: $27,800,000,000
Emp.: 180
Investment Management Service
N.A.I.C.S.: 523940
Thomas Alan James (Chm)

Subsidiary (Domestic):

Carillon Fund Distributors, Inc. (3)
880 Carillon Pkwy, Saint Petersburg, FL 33716-1102
Tel.: (727) 573-2453
Investment Management Service
N.A.I.C.S.: 523940

ClariVest Asset Management, LLC (3)
3611 Valley Centre Dr Ste 100, San Diego, CA 92130 (100%)
Tel.: (858) 480-2440
Web Site: http://www.clarivest.com
Sales Range: $1-9.9 Million
Emp.: 19
Investment Management Service
N.A.I.C.S.: 523999
Stacey R. Nutt (CEO, Chief Investment Officer, Principal & Portfolio Mgr)
David Vaughn (Chief Investment Officer-Non-US & Global Strategies)
Todd Wolter (Chief Investment Officer-US & Alternatives Strategies)
Tiffany Ayres (Pres)

Eagle Fund Services, Inc. (3)
The Raymond James Fin Ctr 880 Carillon Pkwy, Saint Petersburg, FL 33716 (100%)
Tel.: (727) 567-1000
Web Site: http://www.eagleasset.com
Sales Range: $50-74.9 Million
Emp.: 100
Asset Management Services
N.A.I.C.S.: 523940

Subsidiary (Domestic):

Scout Investments, Inc. (2)
928 Grand Blvd, Kansas City, MO 64106 (100%)
Tel.: (816) 860-7000
Web Site: http://www.scoutinv.com
Investment Advisory & Management Services
N.A.I.C.S.: 523940

Charles Stanley Group PLC (1)
55 Bishopsgate, London, EC2N 3AS, United Kingdom
Web Site: http://www.charles-stanley.co.uk
Rev.: $232,373,778
Assets: $505,745,269
Liabilities: $338,293,588
Net Worth: $167,451,681
Earnings: $14,219,402
Emp.: 747
Fiscal Year-end: 03/31/2021
Stock Broking Services
N.A.I.C.S.: 523940
Julie M. Ung (Sec-Grp & Head-Legal)
Glenn Baker (Dir-Bus Dev)
Nicholas Muston (Dir-Private Clients & Charities)
Bob Campion (Head-Fiduciary Mgmt)
Daniel Riddaway (Portfolio Mgr)
Jon Cunliffe (CIO)
Ross Brookes (Head-Collectives Res)
Jane Bransgrove (Dir-Asset Mgmt)
Chris Ainscough (Dir-Asset Mgmt)
Michael Bennett (COO)
Steve Jones (Head-Compliance)
Peter Kelk (Chief Risk Officer)
Andrew Meigh (Mng Dir-Financial Plng)
Kate Griffiths-lambeth (Dir-HR)
Chris Harris-deans (Dir-Investment Mgmt Dev)
John Porteous (Head-Distr-Grp)

Subsidiary (Domestic):

Charles Stanley & Co. Ltd. (2)
55 Bishopsgate, London, EC2N 3AS, United Kingdom
Tel.: (44) 207 739 8200
Web Site: https://www.charles-stanley.co.uk

Sales Range: $400-449.9 Million
Emp.: 800
Brokerage Services, Investment Advice & Asset Management
N.A.I.C.S.: 523940

Subsidiary (Domestic):

Rock (Nominees) Limited (3)
25 Luke Street, London, EC2A 4AR, United Kingdom
Tel.: (44) 2071496000
Web Site: http://charlesstanley.co.uk
Sales Range: $300-349.9 Million
Securities Brokerage Services
N.A.I.C.S.: 523150
David Howard (Mng Dir)

Cougar Global Investments Limited (1)
200 King Street West Suite 1901, Toronto, M5H 3T4, ON, Canada
Tel.: (416) 368-5255
Web Site: https://www.cougarglobal.com
Investment Management Service
N.A.I.C.S.: 523940
James Breech (Founder)

Financo Limited (1)
7 Vigo Street, London, W1S 3HF, United Kingdom
Tel.: (44) 2037009653
Investment Management Service
N.A.I.C.S.: 523940

Financo, LLC (1)
540 Madison Ave 3rd Fl, New York, NY 10022
Tel.: (212) 593-9000
Web Site: http://www.financo.com
Sales Range: $1-9.9 Million
Emp.: 38
Investment Management Service
N.A.I.C.S.: 561110
Colin Welch (Pres & COO)
Gilbert W. Harrison (Founder)

Gay-Lussac Gestion (1)
45 Avenue George V, 75008, Paris, France
Tel.: (33) 145616490
Web Site: https://www.gaylussacgestion.com
Emp.: 24
Asset Management Services
N.A.I.C.S.: 531390
Aurelia De La Malene (Mng Dir)
Louis de Fels (Mng Dir)
Adrien Blum (Mng Dir)

Howe Barnes Capital Management, Inc. (1)
222 S Riverside Plz 7th Fl, Chicago, IL 60606
Tel.: (312) 655-2771
Investment Management Service
N.A.I.C.S.: 523940

MOR Associates, LP (1)
8601 Robert Fulton Dr Ste 200, Columbia, MD 21046
Tel.: (410) 290-1400
Financial Service Provider
N.A.I.C.S.: 522320

Morgan Properties, LLC (1)
50 Front St, Memphis, TN 38103
Tel.: (901) 579-4243
Emp.: 3
Real Estate Management Services
N.A.I.C.S.: 531210
Jim Dieck (Gen Counsel)
Laurel Hillocks (VP-Washington)
Jillian Fikkert (Dir-Property Mktg)
Kimberly Boland (Dir-Digital Mktg)
Tracy Fauntleroy (Dir-Corp Brand Mktg & Comm)

RJ Equities, Inc. (1)
880 Carillon Pkwy, Saint Petersburg, FL 33716-1102
Tel.: (727) 573-3800
Securities Brokerage Services
N.A.I.C.S.: 523150

Raymond James & Associates, Inc. (1)
The Raymond James Fin Ctr 880 Carillon Pkwy, Saint Petersburg, FL 33716 (100%)
Tel.: (727) 573-3800
Web Site: http://www.raymondjames.com

Sales Range: $1-4.9 Billion
Emp.: 5,000
Investment Services & Securities Brokerage
N.A.I.C.S.: 523150
Thomas Alan James (Chm & CEO)

Raymond James Affordable Housing Investments (1)
880 Carillon Pkwy, Saint Petersburg, FL 33716-1102 (100%)
Tel.: (727) 573-3800
Web Site: http://www.rjtcf.com
Sales Range: $200-249.9 Million
Emp.: 75
Low Income Housing Subsidy Services
N.A.I.C.S.: 523150

Subsidiary (Domestic):

Gateway Institutional Tax Credit Fund II, Ltd (2)
880 Carillon Pkwy, Saint Petersburg, FL 33716
Tel.: (727) 567-1000
Investment Management Service
N.A.I.C.S.: 523940

Raymond James Bank, National Association (1)
710 Carillon Pkwy, Saint Petersburg, FL 33716
Tel.: (727) 567-8000
Web Site: http://www.raymondjamesbank.com
Federal Savings Bank
N.A.I.C.S.: 522180
Jeffrey P. Julien (Chm)
Steven M. Raney (Pres & CEO)
Ken Ginel (CFO, Treas & Exec VP)
Thomas Macina (Exec VP-Corp & Real Estate Banking)
Suzanne Manganiello Cosper (Sr VP)
Mark Moody (Exec VP-Credit Risk)
Frederick C. Hosken (Mng Dir-Fixed Income)
Bill Geis (Exec VP-Retail Banking)
Carolynn Rosse (Chief Compliance Officer & Sr VP)
Amanda Stevens (COO, Chief Strategy Officer & Exec VP)
Will Guthrie (VP)
Michael Kosup (VP)

Subsidiary (Domestic):

Raymond James Mortgage Company, Inc. (2)
710 Carillon Pkwy, Saint Petersburg, FL 33716
Web Site: http://rjbank.mortgagewebcenter.com
Mortgage Lending Services
N.A.I.C.S.: 522292

Raymond James Capital, Inc. (1)
The Raymond James Fin Ctr 880 Carillon Pkwy, Saint Petersburg, FL 33716-2749 (100%)
Tel.: (727) 567-5575
Web Site: http://www.raymondjamescapital.com
Emp.: 4
Private Equity & Merchant Banking Services
N.A.I.C.S.: 523999
Gene J. Ostrow (Mng Dir)
David E. Thomas Jr. (Mng Dir)

Raymond James Corporate Finance GmbH (1)
Theresienstrasse 1, 80333, Munich, Germany
Tel.: (49) 8923237770
Financial Investment Services
N.A.I.C.S.: 523940

Raymond James Financial International, Ltd. (U.K.) (1)
25 Ropemaker St 13th Floor Ropemaker Place, London, EC2Y 9LY, United Kingdom
Tel.: (44) 2037985600
Web Site: http://www.raymondjames.com
Sales Range: $25-49.9 Million
Emp.: 35
Investment Management Service
N.A.I.C.S.: 523940

Raymond James Financial Planning Ltd. (1)

38 Prospect St, Newmarket, L3Y 3S9, ON, Canada
Tel.: (905) 898-0489
Investment Management Service
N.A.I.C.S.: 523940

Raymond James Financial Services Advisors, Inc. (1)
880 Carillon Pkwy, Saint Petersburg, FL 33716 (100%)
Tel.: (727) 567-3800
Web Site: http://www.raymondjames.com
Sales Range: $1-4.9 Billion
Emp.: 2,700
Investment Advisory Services
N.A.I.C.S.: 523940

Raymond James Geneva S.A. (1)
4 Cours De Rive, 1204, Geneva, Switzerland
Tel.: (41) 228182828
Web Site: http://www.raymondjames.com
Sales Range: $25-49.9 Million
Emp.: 15
Investment Management Service
N.A.I.C.S.: 523940

Raymond James Insurance Group, Inc. (1)
880 Carillon Pkwy, Saint Petersburg, FL 33716 (100%)
Tel.: (727) 567-1000
Web Site: http://www.raymondjames.com
Sales Range: $75-99.9 Million
Insurance & Annuity Products Brokerage Services
N.A.I.C.S.: 524210
Scott Stolz (Pres)

Raymond James Investment Services Limited (1)
Ropemaker Place 25 Ropemaker St, London, EC2Y 9LY, United Kingdom
Tel.: (44) 2037983000
Web Site: http://www.raymondjames.uk.com
Emp.: 200
Investment Management Service
N.A.I.C.S.: 523940
Peter Moores (CEO)
Cynthia Poole (Dir-Rels Mgmt & Bus Support)
Naz Islam (CFO)
Stuart Wright (Head-Ops & Product Mgmt)
Mark de Ste Croix (Head-Compliance & Legal)
David Strydom (Head-Tech & Facilities)
Erin Eckhouse (Head-HR)
Kerry Nicholls (Deputy Head-Relationship Mgmt & Trng)
Tracy Speechley (Deputy Head-Ops)
Mark Filipponi (Deputy Head-Tech & Facilities)

Raymond James Latin Advisors Limited (1)
Ruta 8 Km 17 500 Zonamerica, Aroba Building 1 Office 215, Montevideo, 91600, Uruguay
Tel.: (598) 25182033
Web Site: http://www.raymondjames.com
Sales Range: $25-49.9 Million
Emp.: 30
Investment Management Service
N.A.I.C.S.: 523940
Tom James (CEO)

Raymond James Ltd. (1)
2100 925 West Georgia Street Cathedral Place, Vancouver, V6C 3L2, BC, Canada (100%)
Tel.: (604) 659-8000
Web Site: https://www.raymondjames.ca
Sales Range: $150-199.9 Million
Emp.: 150
Investment Banking Services
N.A.I.C.S.: 523150
Tom Williams (Sr VP-Growth & Dev-Private Client Grp)
Paul Allison (Chm)
Richard Rousseau (Vice Chm-Private Client Grp-Quebec)
Lloyd Costley (COO)
Jamie Coulter (CEO)
Anne Meyer (CFO & Sr VP)
Bob McDonald (Sr Mng Dir & Head-Institutional Trading)
Craig McDougall (Sr Mng Dir & Head-Investment Banking & M&A)
Thomas Raidl (Chief Admin Officer)

Daryl Swetlishoff *(Head-Res)*
Sybil Verch *(Exec VP & Head-Private Client Solutions)*
Adam Kauffman *(Mng Dir-Private Capital Solutions & Recapitalization)*
Sean C. Martin *(Mng Dir-Investment Banking & Head-Fin Institutions & Fin Tech)*
Gavin McOuat *(Mng Dir-Investment Banking & Head-Mining & Metals)*

Subsidiary (Domestic):

Raymond James Investment Counsel Ltd.
200 King Street West Suite 1903, Toronto, M5H 3T4, ON, Canada
Tel.: (416) 777-6418
Web Site:
    https://www.raymondjamesinvestment
    counsel.ca
Financial Investment Advice Services
N.A.I.C.S.: 523940
David Tasker *(Pres)*
Harvey Sliwowicz *(Sr VP)*
Adrian Weiss *(Chief Compliance Officer)*

Raymond James South American Holdings, Inc. (1)
880 Carillon Pkwy, Saint Petersburg, FL 33716-1102
Tel.: (727) 567-5575
Investment Management Service
N.A.I.C.S.: 551112

Subsidiary (Non-US):

RJ Delta Capital S.A. (2)
Cerrito 1186 Piso 5, C1010AAX, Buenos Aires, Argentina
Tel.: (54) 1152762546
Investment Management Service
N.A.I.C.S.: 523940

RJ Delta Fund Management S.A. (2)
Cerrito 1186 Piso 11, C1010AAX, Buenos Aires, Argentina
Tel.: (54) 1152762525
Web Site: http://www.rjdelta.com
Emp.: 30
Investment Management Service
N.A.I.C.S.: 523940

Raymond James Argentina Sociedad De Bolsa, S.A.
San Martin 344 Floor 22, C1004AAH, Buenos Aires, Argentina
Tel.: (54) 1148502500
Web Site: http://www.raymondjames.com.ar
Sales Range: $25-49.9 Million
Emp.: 45
Investment Management Service
N.A.I.C.S.: 523940

Raymond James Uruguay, S.A. (1)
Luis A de Herrera 1248 Torre 1 Piso 15 Oficina 1501, World Trade Center, Montevideo, 11300, Uruguay
Tel.: (598) 26227558
Sales Range: $25-49.9 Million
Emp.: 11
Investment Management Service
N.A.I.C.S.: 523940

SLG Partners, LP II (1)
880 Carillon Pkwy Twr III 7th Fl, Saint Petersburg, FL 33716
Tel.: (727) 567-5066
Financial Service Provider
N.A.I.C.S.: 522320

Silver Lane Advisors LLC (1)
3 Columbus Cir 22nd Fl, New York, NY 10019
Tel.: (212) 883-9400
Web Site: http://www.silverlane.com
Financial Brokerage Services
N.A.I.C.S.: 523999

Sumridge Partners, LLC (1)
111 Town Sq Pl Ste 320, Jersey City, NJ 07310
Tel.: (201) 898-2525
Web Site: http://www.sumridge.com
Financial Investment Activities
N.A.I.C.S.: 523999
Tom O. Brien *(Partner)*
Paul Scotto *(Dir-Credit Sls)*
Adam Braham *(Dir-Credit Sls)*

The Producers Choice LLC (1)
1152 E Long Lake Rd, Troy, MI 48085-4965
Tel.: (248) 498-7500
Web Site:
    http://www.producerschoicenetwork.com
Life Insurance Related Service Providers
N.A.I.C.S.: 524113

TriState Capital Holdings, Inc. (1)
1 Oxford Ctr 301 Grant St Ste 2700, Pittsburgh, PA 15219
Tel.: (412) 304-0304
Web Site: http://www.tristatecapitalbank.com
Rev.: $289,943,000
Assets: $13,004,852,000
Liabilities: $12,168,130,000
Net Worth: $836,722,000
Earnings: $78,060,000
Emp.: 361
Fiscal Year-end: 12/31/2021
Bank Holding Company
N.A.I.C.S.: 551111

Subsidiary (Domestic):

Chartwell Investment Partners, L.P. (2)
1205 Westlakes Dr Ste 100, Berwyn, PA 19312
Tel.: (610) 296-1400
Web Site: http://www.chartwellip.com
Rev.: $7,500,000,000
Emp.: 50
Institutional & Private Asset Management Services
N.A.I.C.S.: 523940
Joseph A. Barilotti *(VP-Mktg & Client Svcs)*
Timothy J. Riddle *(CEO & Mng Partner)*
Douglas W. Kugler *(Sr Portfolio Mgr)*
Peter M. Schofield *(Sr Portfolio Mgr)*
Andrew S. Toburen *(Sr Portfolio Mgr)*
Edward Nishan Antoian *(Mng Partner & Chief Investment Officer)*
T. Ryan Harkins *(Sr Portfolio Mgr)*
Mark D. Tindall *(Portfolio Mgr)*
Michael P. Magee *(COO)*
Joseph A. Barilotti Jr. *(VP)*
Allen A. Chapracki *(Dir)*

TriState Capital Bank (2)
1 Oxford Centre 301 Grant St Ste 2700, Pittsburgh, PA 15219
Tel.: (412) 304-0304
Web Site: http://www.tristatecapitalbank.com
Commercial Banking
N.A.I.C.S.: 522110
Brian S. Fetterolf *(Co-Pres & CEO)*
A. William Schenck III *(Vice Chm)*
James F. Getz *(Chm)*
James E. Mele *(Sr VP & Mgr-Treasury Mgmt)*
Bob Kane *(VP & Mgr-Relationship-Comml Real Estate)*
Thomas M. Groneman *(Chief Credit Officer & Exec VP)*
Cynthia Meyer *(Chief Risk Officer)*
Melvin M. Washington *(Chief Audit Officer)*
Craig Coffey *(Natl Sls Mgr)*
Tai Park *(Sr VP & Mgr-Relationship-Private Banking)*

RAYONIER ADVANCED MATERIALS INC.
1301 Riverplace Blvd Ste 2300, Jacksonville, FL 32207
Tel.: (904) 357-4600   DE
Web Site: https://www.ryam.com
Year Founded: 1926
RYAM—(NYSE)
Rev.: $1,717,267,000
Assets: $2,347,528,000
Liabilities: $1,518,215,000
Net Worth: $829,313,000
Earnings: $(14,919,000)
Emp.: 2,500
Fiscal Year-end: 12/31/22
Chemical Product Mfr & Distr
N.A.I.C.S.: 325998
DeLyle W. Bloomquist *(Pres & CEO)*
Gabriela Garcia *(Chief Acctg Officer, VP & Controller)*
Michael Osborne *(VP-Mfg)*
Joshua C. Hicks *(Sr VP-High Purity Cellulose)*
Christian Ribeyrolle *(Pres & Sr VP-Biomaterials)*

Marcus J. Moeltner *(CFO & Sr VP-Fin)*
Mickey Walsh *(Treas & VP-Investor Relations)*
Kenneth J. Duffy *(Sr VP-Paperboard & High Yield Pulp & VP)*
Whitney K. McGuire *(VP & Asst Gen Counsel)*
Chris Sittard *(VP-Sourcing)*
James L. Posze Jr. *(Chief Admin Officer & Sr VP-HR)*

Subsidiaries:

Rayonier Performance Fibers, LLC (1)
4470 Savannah Hwy, Jesup, GA 31545
Tel.: (912) 427-5000
Cellulose Products Mfr
N.A.I.C.S.: 326113

RAYONIER INC.
1 Rayonier Wy, Yulee, FL 32097
Tel.: (904) 357-9100   NC
Web Site: https://www.rayonier.com
Year Founded: 1926
RYN—(NYSE)
Rev.: $1,056,933,000
Assets: $3,647,585,000
Liabilities: $1,769,983,000
Net Worth: $1,877,602,000
Earnings: $173,493,000
Emp.: 438
Fiscal Year-end: 12/31/23
Timber, Performance Fiber & Wood Products; Real Estate Investment Trust
N.A.I.C.S.: 525990
Mark D. McHugh *(Pres & CEO)*
Dod A. Fraser *(Chm)*
Douglas M. Long *(Chief Resource Officer & Exec VP)*
April J. Tice *(CFO, Chief Acctg Officer & Sr VP)*
Christopher T. Corr *(Sr VP-Real Estate Dev)*

Subsidiaries:

Pope Resources Limited Partnership (1)
19950 7th Ave NE Ste 200, Poulsbo, WA 98370
Tel.: (360) 697-6626
Web Site: http://www.poperesources.com
Rev.: $109,903,000
Assets: $493,549,000
Liabilities: $174,556,000
Net Worth: $318,993,000
Earnings: $2,435,000
Emp.: 61
Fiscal Year-end: 12/31/2019
Timberland Managers
N.A.I.C.S.: 113110
Jonathan P. Rose *(VP-Real Estate)*
Kevin C. Bates *(VP-Timberland Investment)*
Mike Mackelwich *(VP-Timberland Ops)*
Daemon P. Repp *(CFO & VP)*
Adrian W. Miller *(VP-Corp Affairs & Admin)*

Subsidiary (Domestic):

ORM Timber Fund II, Inc. (2)
19950 7th Avenue NE Ste 200, Poulsbo, WA 98370
Tel.: (360) 697-6626
Emp.: 4
Investment Management Service
N.A.I.C.S.: 523940

Olympic Resource Management (2)
19245 10th Ave NE, Poulsbo, WA 98370-7456
Tel.: (360) 697-6626
Web Site: http://www.orm.com
Sales Range: $1-9.9 Million
Emp.: 25
Real Estate Management
N.A.I.C.S.: 531210

Raydient LLC (1)
1 Rayonier Way, Yulee, FL 32097
Web Site: http://www.raydientplaces.com
Real Estate Services

N.A.I.C.S.: 531390
John Weidenhaft *(Sr Mgr-Real Estate)*
Jason Shearer *(Sr Mgr-Rural Products)*

Rayonier Mississippi Timberlands Company (1)
225 Water St Ste 1400, Jacksonville, FL 32202
Tel.: (904) 357-9100
Forestry Related Services
N.A.I.C.S.: 115310

Rayonier New Zealand Ltd. (1)
Level 5 32-34 Mahuhu Crescent, Auckland, 1010, New Zealand   (100%)
Tel.: (64) 93022988
Forest Products Ownership & Sales
N.A.I.C.S.: 113110

Subsidiary (Domestic):

Matariki Forestry Group (2)
Level 5 32-34 Mahuhu Crescent, PO Box 9283, Newmarket, Auckland, 1149, New Zealand   (65%)
Tel.: (64) 9 302 2988
Web Site: http://www.matarikiforests.co.nz
Emp.: 90
Timberland Holdings
N.A.I.C.S.: 115310

Subsidiary (Domestic):

Matariki Forests (3)
Level 5 32-34 Mahuhu Crescent, Auckland, 1010, New Zealand   (100%)
Tel.: (64) 93022988
Web Site: http://www.matarikiforests.co.nz
Emp.: 100
Timberland Tracts
N.A.I.C.S.: 113110

Rayonier TRS Forest Operations, LLC (1)
29650 Comstock Rd, Elberta, AL 36530
Tel.: (251) 986-5210
Web Site: http://www.rayonierseedlings.com
Emp.: 4
Tree Seedlings Supplier
N.A.I.C.S.: 111421

Rayonier Timberlands, L.P. (1)
50 N Laura St, Jacksonville, FL 32202   (100%)
Tel.: (904) 357-9100
Web Site: http://www.rayonier.com
Sales Range: $1-9.9 Million
Emp.: 50
Forestry Services
N.A.I.C.S.: 115310

TerraPointe LLC (1)
1901 Is Walkway, Fernandina Beach, FL 32034
Tel.: (904) 261-0833
Web Site:
    http://www.terrapointelandsales.com
Sales Range: $50-74.9 Million
Emp.: 100
Real Estate Manangement Services
N.A.I.C.S.: 531390

RBAZ BANCORP, INC.
645 E Missouri Ave Ste 108, Phoenix, AZ 85012
Tel.: (602) 277-2500
RBAZ—(OTCIQ)
Banking Services
N.A.I.C.S.: 551111

Subsidiaries:

Republic Bank of Arizona (1)
645 E Missouri Ave Ste 108, Phoenix, AZ 85012-1314
Tel.: (602) 277-2500
Web Site: https://www.republicbankaz.com
Commercial Banking Services
N.A.I.C.S.: 522110
Amy Lou Blunt *(Chief Credit Officer & Exec VP)*
Jonathan Olson *(Sr VP)*
Greg Barrett *(VP)*
Alan L. Sparks *(Chm)*
Brian Ruisinger *(Pres & CEO)*
Melissa Roberson *(Officer-Loan Documentation & Asst VP)*
Christine Haugen *(CFO & Exec VP)*
Frank Smith *(Sr VP-Operations)*

Ben Van Horn *(Sr VP-Comml Banker)*
Karen Vitkovich *(Officer-Treasury Mgmt & Sr VP)*
Jennie Timlin *(VP & Mgr-MRB Banking)*
Patrick Sutter *(VP & Portfolio Mgr)*
Kayla Ortega *(VP & Mgr-Deposit Ops)*
Cathy Mireles *(VP & Asst Mgr-Branch)*
Kristen McLean *(VP-Comml Banker)*
Nicole Kleinschmidt *(VP & Mgr-Scottsdale Branch)*
Rhonda Kaiser *(Officer-Compliance & VP)*
Karen Hanson *(VP & Mgr-Gilbert Branch)*
Todd Grady *(VP & Portfolio Mgr)*

RBB BANCORP

1055 Wilshire Blvd Ste 1200, Los Angeles, CA 90017
Tel.: (213) 627-9888　　　　　**CA**
Web Site:
　https://www.royalbusinessbank usa.com
Year Founded: 2008
RBB—(NASDAQ)
Rev.: $192,222,000
Assets: $3,919,058,000
Liabilities: $3,434,495,000
Net Worth: $484,563,000
Earnings: $64,327,000
Emp.: 379
Fiscal Year-end: 12/31/22
Bank Holding Company
N.A.I.C.S.: 551111
Lynn M. Hopkins *(CFO & Exec VP)*
David R. Morris *(CEO)*
Johnny Lee *(Pres & Chief Banking Officer)*
Diana C. Hanson *(Chief Acctg Officer & Sr VP)*
I-Ming Liu *(Chief Risk Officer & Exec VP)*
Simon Pang *(Chief Strategy Officer & Exec VP)*
Jeffrey Yeh *(Chief Credit Officer & Exec VP)*
Tsu Te Huang *(Exec VP & Dir-Private Banking)*
Tammy Song *(Chief Lending Officer & Exec VP)*
Ashley Chang *(Exec VP)*
Shalom Chang *(Chief Acctg Officer)*

Subsidiaries:

Gateway Bank, F.S.B.　　　　　　　(1)
360 8th St, Oakland, CA 94607
Tel.: (510) 268-8108
Web Site: http://www.gatewayfsb.com
Commercial Banking Services
N.A.I.C.S.: 522110
Glen Terry *(CEO)*
Fiona Ngan *(Mktg Mgr)*

Royal Business Bank　　　　　　　(1)
1055 Wilshire Blvd Ste 200, Los Angeles, CA 90017
Tel.: (213) 627-9888
Web Site:
　https://www.royalbusinessbankusa.com
Commericial Banking
N.A.I.C.S.: 522110
Gary Fan *(Chief Admin Officer & Exec VP)*
Lynn M. Hopkins *(CFO & Exec VP)*
David R. Morris *(CEO)*
Johnny Lee *(Pres & Chief Banking Officer)*
Diana C. Hanson *(Chief Acctg Officer & Sr VP)*
Huichian Lin Wang *(Officer-Loan)*
Kyky Ko *(Officer-Loan)*
Amy Lee *(Officer-Loan)*
Dan Watanabe *(Sr VP & Dir-Mortgage Production)*

RBC BEARINGS INCORPORATED

1 Tribology Ctr, Oxford, CT 06478
Tel.: (203) 267-7001　　　　**DE**
Web Site:
　https://www.rbcbearings.com
Year Founded: 1919

RBC—(NYSE)
Rev.: $1,560,300,000
Assets: $4,678,600,000
Liabilities: $1,926,700,000
Net Worth: $2,751,900,000
Earnings: $209,900,000
Emp.: 5,302
Fiscal Year-end: 03/30/24
Industrial Machinery & Equipment Mfr
N.A.I.C.S.: 332991
Michael J. Hartnett *(Chm, Pres & CEO)*
Daniel A. Bergeron *(COO)*
Richard J. Edwards *(VP & Gen Mgr)*
Robert M. Sullivan *(CFO, Chief Acctg Officer & VP)*
John J. Feeney *(Chief Legal Officer, Gen Counsel, Sec & VP)*

Subsidiaries:

All Power Manufacturing Co.　　　(1)
13141 Molette St, Santa Fe Springs, CA 90670
Tel.: (562) 802-2640
Web Site: https://www.rbcbearings.com
Sales Range: $25-49.9 Million
Emp.: 70
Ball & Roller Bearing Mfr
N.A.I.C.S.: 332991
Brad Haywood *(Office Mgr)*

Climax Metal Products Company　(1)
8141 Tyler Blvd, Mentor, OH 44060
Tel.: (440) 585-0300
Web Site: https://www.climaxmetal.com
Sales Range: $10-24.9 Million
Emp.: 50
Shaft Collar, Rigid Coupling & Keyless Locking Device Mfr & Whslr
N.A.I.C.S.: 332510

Dodge Industrial Australia Pty Ltd.　　　　　　　　　　　　(1)
Tel.: (61) 401860080
Mounted Bearing Mfr
N.A.I.C.S.: 332991

Dodge Industrial Canada Inc.　　(1)
Mounted Bearing Mfr
N.A.I.C.S.: 332991

Dodge Industrial India Private Limited　　　　　　　　　　(1)
Office No 1&2 Casablanca 1st Floor Opp Karishma Complex, Kothrud, Pune, 411038, India
Tel.: (91) 9175138733
Mounted Bearing Mfr
N.A.I.C.S.: 332991

Dodge Mechanical Power Transmission Mexico, S. de R.L. de C.V.　(1)
Av Punto Sur 312 Piso 04 Ste 123, Los Gavilanes, 45645, Jalisco, Mexico
Tel.: (52) 3310171749
Mounted Bearing Mfr
N.A.I.C.S.: 332991

Heim Bearings Company　　　　(1)
60 Round Hill Rd, Fairfield, CT 06824
Tel.: (203) 255-1512
Web Site: https://www.rbcbearings.com
Sales Range: $25-49.9 Million
Emp.: 15
Spherical Bearing & Industrial Metal Component Mfr
N.A.I.C.S.: 332991

Industrial Tectonics Bearing Corp.　　　　　　　　　　(1)
18301 S Santa Fe Ave, Rancho Dominguez, CA 90221
Tel.: (310) 537-3750
Web Site: https://www.rbcbearings.com
Sales Range: $25-49.9 Million
Emp.: 250
Mfr of Ball & Roller Bearings
N.A.I.C.S.: 332991

Industrial Tectonics Bearings Corporation　　　　　　　(1)
18301 S Santa Fe Ave, Rancho Dominguez, CA 90221
Tel.: (310) 537-3750
Precision Product Mfr
N.A.I.C.S.: 332721

Nice Ball Bearings Inc.　　　　(1)
400 Sulivan Way, West Trenton, NJ 08628
Tel.: (609) 882-5050
Web Site: http://www.rbcbearings.com
Ball & Roller Bearing Mfr
N.A.I.C.S.: 332991

PIC Design Inc.　　　　　　　(1)
86 Benson Rd, Middlebury, CT 06762-3215
Tel.: (203) 758-8272
Web Site: https://www.pic-design.com
Rev.: $10,000,000
Emp.: 50
Mfr of Standard & Special Precision Mechanical Components
N.A.I.C.S.: 333519

Phoenix Bearings, Ltd.　　　　(1)
Northway Lane, Tewkesbury, GL20 8JG, Gloucestershire, United Kingdom
Tel.: (44) 1684298294
Web Site: http://www.phoenix-bearings.co.uk
Emp.: 50
Ball & Roller Bearing Mfr
N.A.I.C.S.: 332991

RBC Aerostructures LLC　　　(1)
123 Commerce Way, Westminster, SC 29693
Tel.: (864) 886-4600
Emp.: 13
Industrial Supplies Whslr
N.A.I.C.S.: 423840
Alex Belch *(Engr-Mfg)*

RBC Aircraft Products, Inc.　　(1)
2788 Winstead Rd, Torrington, CT 06790
Tel.: (860) 626-7800
Web Site: https://www.rbcbearings.com
Ball & Roller Bearing Mfr
N.A.I.C.S.: 332991

RBC Bearings Inc. - Linear Precision Products Division　　　　(1)
1298 Thunderbolt Dr, Walterboro, SC 29488
Tel.: (843) 538-5040
Web Site: http://www.rbcbearings.com
Sales Range: $1-9.9 Million
Emp.: 30
Bolt, Nut, Screw, Rivet & Washer Mfr
N.A.I.C.S.: 332722
Michael J. Hartnett *(Chm, Pres & CEO)*

RBC Bearings Polska sp. z o.o.　(1)
Wojska Polskiego 16A, 39-300, Mielec, Poland
Tel.: (48) 177464800
Web Site: https://www.rbcpolska.pl
Motor Vehicle Bearing Mfr
N.A.I.C.S.: 336350

RBC Nice Bearings, Inc.　　　(1)
400 Sullivan Way, West Trenton, NJ 08628
Tel.: (609) 882-5050
Ball & Roller Bearing Mfr
N.A.I.C.S.: 332991

RBC Precision Products - Plymouth　　　　　　　　　　(1)
2928 Gary Dr, Plymouth, IN 46563
Tel.: (574) 935-3027
Web Site: https://www.rbcbearings.com
Ball & Roller Bearings Mfr
N.A.I.C.S.: 332991

RBC Precision Products-Bremen, Inc.　　　　　　　　　　(1)
225 Industrial Dr, Bremen, IN 46506
Tel.: (574) 546-4455
Web Site: http://www.rbcbearings.com
Emp.: 15
Ball & Roller Bearing Mfr
N.A.I.C.S.: 332991

RBC Precision Products-Plymouth, Inc.　　　　　　　　　　(1)
2928 Gary Dr, Plymouth, IN 46563
Tel.: (574) 935-3027
Web Site: https://www.rbcbearings.com
Sales Range: $25-49.9 Million
Emp.: 50
Ball & Roller Bearing Mfr
N.A.I.C.S.: 332991
Paul Larsen *(Mgr-Sls)*
Mike Hartnett *(Pres)*

RBC Southwest Products, Inc.　(1)
5001 B Commerce Dr, Baldwin Park, CA 91706

Tel.: (626) 358-0181
Web Site: https://www.rbcbearings.com
Ball & Roller Bearing Mfr
N.A.I.C.S.: 332991

RBC Transport Dynamics Corporation　　　　　　　　(1)
3131 W Segerstrom Ave, Santa Ana, CA 92704-9998
Tel.: (714) 546-3131
Web Site: https://www.rbcbearings.com
Sales Range: $10-24.9 Million
Emp.: 150
Mfr Of Bearings
N.A.I.C.S.: 333613

RBC de Mexico S DE RL DE CV　(1)
Avenida 16 de Septiembre Lote 11, Parque Industrial, Reynosa, Tamps, Mexico
Tel.: (52) 8999581271
Ball & Roller Bearing Mfr
N.A.I.C.S.: 332991

Roller Bearing Company of America Inc.　　　　　　　　　　(1)
1 Tribology Ctr 102 Willenbrock Rd, Oxford, CT 06478
Tel.: (203) 267-7001
Web Site: http://www.rbcbearings.com
Sales Range: $25-49.9 Million
Mfr Ball & Roller Bearings
N.A.I.C.S.: 332991
Michael J. Hartnett *(Chm, Pres & CEO)*

Sargent Aerospace & Defense, LLC　　　　　　　　　　(1)
5675 W Burlingame Rd, Tucson, AZ 85743-9453
Tel.: (520) 744-1000
Web Site:
　https://www.sargentaerospace.com
Sales Range: $150-199.9 Million
Emp.: 750
Hydraulic & Mechanical Actuators & Valves Mfr
N.A.I.C.S.: 332721

Schaublin GmbH　　　　　　　(1)
Birkenweiher Strasse 12, 63505, Langenselbold, Germany
Tel.: (49) 6184932720
Web Site: https://www.schaublin.de
Lathe Tool Mfr
N.A.I.C.S.: 333515

Specline, Inc.　　　　　　　　(1)
2230 Mouton Dr, Carson City, NV 89706
Tel.: (775) 882-7717
Web Site: http://www.specline.com
Rev.: $6,666,666
Emp.: 35
Ball & Roller Bearing Mfr
N.A.I.C.S.: 332991

Swiss Tool Systems AG　　　　(1)
Wydenstrasse 28, Burglen, 8575, Weinfelden, Switzerland
Tel.: (41) 716348520
Web Site: https://www.swisstools.org
HSK-Turning Tool Product Distr
N.A.I.C.S.: 423840
Peter Heinemann *(Dir-Engrg & Product Mgmt)*
Michael Brusch *(Mgr-Mfr)*

TPE de Mexico, S. de R.L. de C.V.　　　　　　　　　　(1)
Km 127 366 5 Manzana 7 Lote 4 Y 5 Parq, Tecate, 21430, Mexico
Tel.: (52) 6656550700
Electronic Components Mfr
N.A.I.C.S.: 334419

Western Precision Aero LLC　　(1)
11600 Monarch St, Garden Grove, CA 92841
Tel.: (714) 893-7999
Web Site: https://www.rbcbearings.com
Automobile Parts Distr
N.A.I.C.S.: 423120
Ed McKenna *(Pres & CEO)*

RBC LIFE SCIENCES, INC.

2301 Crown Ct, Irving, TX 75038
Tel.: (972) 893-4000　　　　**NV**
Web Site:
　https://www.rbclifesciences.com
Year Founded: 1991
RBCL—(OTCIQ)
Sales Range: $1-9.9 Million

Nutritional Supplements & Personal Care Products Mfr & Distr
N.A.I.C.S.: 456199
Clinton H. Howard *(Founder & Chm)*
Steven E. Brown *(Pres & CEO)*
Don Clark *(CIO)*
Wayne Holbrook *(Pres)*
Jerry Phelps *(VP-Science & Technology)*
Ken Sabot *(Sr VP-Operations)*
Trevor Scofield *(VP-Intl Ops)*

RBID.COM, INC.
895 Dove St 3rd Fl, Newport Beach, CA 92660
Tel.: (949) 851-4733   FL
Web Site: http://www.rbid.com
Year Founded: 1988
RBDC—(OTCIQ)
Online Shopping Services
N.A.I.C.S.: 519290
Alan Rothman *(Pres)*
Mairead Howe *(VP)*
David A. Howe *(Treas)*

RCF ACQUISITION CORP.
1400 Wewatta St Ste 850, Denver, CO 80202
Tel.: (720) 946-1444   Ky
Year Founded: 2021
RCFA—(NYSE)
Rev.: $16,134,963
Assets: $238,350,858
Liabilities: $244,915,320
Net Worth: ($6,564,462)
Earnings: $13,843,499
Emp.: 2
Fiscal Year-end: 12/31/22
Investment Services
N.A.I.C.S.: 523999
James McClements *(Co-Founder & Chm)*
James McClements *(Co-Founder & Chm)*
Sunny S. Shah *(CEO)*
Thomas M. Boehlert *(CFO)*

RCI HOSPITALITY HOLDINGS, INC.
10737 Cutten Rd, Houston, TX 77066
Tel.: (281) 397-6730   TX
Web Site:
   https://www.rcihospitality.com
Year Founded: 1994
RICK—(NASDAQ)
Rev.: $295,604,000
Assets: $584,364,000
Liabilities: $321,254,000
Net Worth: $263,110,000
Earnings: $3,018,000
Emp.: 3,613
Fiscal Year-end: 09/30/24
Holding Company; Gentlemen's Clubs & Sports Bars Owner & Operator
N.A.I.C.S.: 551112
Eric Scott Langan *(Chm, Pres & CEO)*
Travis Reese *(Exec VP)*
Bradley Chhay *(CFO & Principal Acctg Officer)*
Dean Reardon *(VP)*

Subsidiaries:

BMB Dining Services (Stemmons), Inc.   **(1)**
7501 N Stemmons Fwy Ste 140, Dallas, TX 75247
Tel.: (214) 267-2662
Web Site: https://www.4bombshells.com
Sales Range: $1-9.9 Million
Restaurant & Sports Bar Operator
N.A.I.C.S.: 722511

Cabaret East   **(1)**
12325 Calloway Cemetery Rd, Fort Worth, TX 76040
Tel.: (817) 354-5247

Web Site: http://www.cabareteast.com
Sales Range: $1-9.9 Million
Real Estate Agency & Brokerage Services
N.A.I.C.S.: 531210

California Grill LLC   **(1)**
7117 Avignon Dr, Round Rock, TX 78681-5332
Tel.: (512) 388-0221
Restaurant Operators
N.A.I.C.S.: 722513

Club Onyx Houston   **(1)**
3113 Bering Dr, Houston, TX 77057
Tel.: (713) 785-0444
Web Site: http://www.clubonyxhouston.com
Sales Range: $1-9.9 Million
Gentlemen's Club Operator
N.A.I.C.S.: 722410

E. D. Publications, Inc.   **(1)**
2431 Estancia Blvd Bldg B, Clearwater, FL 33761
Tel.: (727) 726-3592
Publishing Services
N.A.I.C.S.: 513120
Don Waitt *(Publr)*
Dave Manack *(Assoc Publr & Editor)*
Caroline Ashe *(Coord-Database)*
Teresa Tearno *(Mgr-AR)*
Kevin Pennington *(Dir-Art)*

E.D. Publications, Inc.   **(1)**
2431 Estancia Blvd Bldg B, Clearwater, FL 33761
Tel.: (727) 726-3592
Web Site: http://www.edpublications.com
Emp.: 8
Adult Nichtclub Industry Trade Magazine Publisher
N.A.I.C.S.: 513120
Don Waitt *(Publr)*
Dave Manack *(Assoc Publr & Editor)*
Teresa Tearno *(Mgr-AR)*
Caroline Ashe *(Coord-Database)*
Kevin Pennington *(Art Dir)*

JAI Dining Services (Edinburg), Inc.   **(1)**
5021 W St Hwy 107, Edinburg, TX 78541
Tel.: (956) 381-4117
Web Site: https://www.jaguarsedinburg.com
Sales Range: $1-9.9 Million
Gentlemen's Club Operator
N.A.I.C.S.: 722410

JAI Dining Services (Harlingen), Inc.   **(1)**
14286 US Hwy 83, Harlingen, TX 78552
Tel.: (956) 428-3500
Web Site: https://www.jaguarsharlingen.com
Sales Range: $1-9.9 Million
Gentlemen's Club Operator
N.A.I.C.S.: 713990

Miami Gardens Square One, Inc.   **(1)**
150 NW 183rd St, Miami, FL 33169
Tel.: (305) 651-5822
Web Site: https://www.tootsiescabaret.com
Sales Range: $10-24.9 Million
Gentlemen's Club Operator
N.A.I.C.S.: 722410

RCI Dining Services (16328 I-35), Inc.   **(1)**
16328 N Interstate Hwy 35, Austin, TX 78728
Tel.: (512) 252-7079
Web Site:
   http://www.downintexassaloonatx.com
Sales Range: $1-9.9 Million
Gentlemen's Club Operator
N.A.I.C.S.: 722410
Rich Marez *(Mgr)*

RCI Dining Services (37th Street), Inc.   **(1)**
61 W 37th St, New York, NY 10018
Tel.: (646) 669-9678
Web Site: https://www.vividcabaretny.com
Gentlemen's Club Operator
N.A.I.C.S.: 722410
Shaun Kevlin *(Reg Mgr)*

RCI Dining Services (Airport Freeway), Inc.   **(1)**
15000 Airport Fwy, Fort Worth, TX 76155
Tel.: (817) 399-0500
Web Site: https://www.ricksdfw.com

Sales Range: $1-9.9 Million
Gentlemen's Club Operator
N.A.I.C.S.: 722410

RCI Dining Services (Glenwood), Inc.   **(1)**
15 Glenwood Ave, Minneapolis, MN 55403
Tel.: (612) 465-8777
Web Site: https://www.thesevilleclub.com
Pub Operator
N.A.I.C.S.: 722410

RCI Dining Services (New York), Inc.   **(1)**
50 W 33rd St, New York, NY 10001
Tel.: (212) 372-0855
Web Site: http://www.ricksnewyorkcity.com
Sales Range: $10-24.9 Million
Gentlemen's Club Operator
N.A.I.C.S.: 722410

RCI Dining Services (Round Rock), Inc.   **(1)**
3105 S Interstate 35, Round Rock, TX 78664
Tel.: (512) 218-8012
Web Site: https://www.ricksnorthaustin.com
Sales Range: $1-9.9 Million
Gentlemen's Club Operator
N.A.I.C.S.: 722410

RCI Dining Services (Sulphur), Inc.   **(1)**
3260 S Cities Service Hwy, Westlake, LA 70665
Tel.: (337) 882-1556
Web Site:
   https://www.temptationssulphur.com
Sales Range: $1-9.9 Million
Gentlemen's Club Operator
N.A.I.C.S.: 722410

RCI Entertainment (Fort Worth), Inc.   **(1)**
7101 Calmont Ave, Fort Worth, TX 76116
Tel.: (817) 732-0000
Web Site: https://www.ricksfortworth.com
Sales Range: $1-9.9 Million
Gentlemen's Club Operator
N.A.I.C.S.: 722410

RCI Entertainment (Minnesota), Inc.   **(1)**
300 S 3rd St, Minneapolis, MN 55415
Tel.: (612) 321-0488
Web Site: https://www.ricksminneapolis.com
Sales Range: $1-9.9 Million
Gentlemen's Club Operator
N.A.I.C.S.: 722410

RCI Entertainment (San Antonio), Inc.   **(1)**
5418 Brewster St, San Antonio, TX 78233
Tel.: (210) 657-2800
Web Site: https://www.rickssanantonio.com
Sales Range: $1-9.9 Million
Gentlemen's Club Operator
N.A.I.C.S.: 722410

Seville Operations LLC   **(1)**
15 Glenwood Ave, Minneapolis, MN 55403
Tel.: (612) 465-8777
Web Site: http://www.thesevilleclub.com
Sales Range: $1-9.9 Million
Emp.: 100
Gentlemen's Club Operator
N.A.I.C.S.: 722410

StorErotica Magazine, Inc.   **(1)**
2431 Estancia Blvd Bldg B, Clearwater, FL 33761
Tel.: (727) 723-8827
Web Site: http://www.storerotica.com
Emp.: 9
Erotic Retail Industry Trade Magazine Publisher
N.A.I.C.S.: 513120
Dave Manack *(Assoc Publr & Editor)*
Don Waitt *(Publr)*
Teresa Tearno *(Mgr-AR)*
Caroline Ashe *(Coord-Database)*

The End Zone, Inc.   **(1)**
2908 S Columbus Blvd, Philadelphia, PA 19148-5106
Tel.: (215) 218-1040
Web Site: http://www.onyxclubs.com
Sales Range: $1-9.9 Million
Gentlemen's Club Operator
N.A.I.C.S.: 722410

Top Shelf Entertainment, LLC   **(1)**
5300 Old Pineville Rd, Charlotte, NC 28217
Tel.: (704) 525-7050
Web Site:
   https://www.clubonyxcharlotte.com
Sales Range: $1-9.9 Million
Gentlemen's Club Operator
N.A.I.C.S.: 722410

XTC Cabaret (Dallas), Inc.   **(1)**
8550 N Stemmons Fwy, Dallas, TX 75247
Tel.: (214) 267-8550
Web Site: https://www.xtcdallas.com
Sales Range: $1-9.9 Million
Gentlemen's Club Operator
N.A.I.C.S.: 713990

XTC Cabaret, Inc.   **(1)**
3501 Andtree Blvd, Austin, TX 78724-2503
Tel.: (512) 929-3558
Web Site: https://www.xtcaustin.com
Sales Range: $1-9.9 Million
Emp.: 25
Gentlemen's Club Operator
N.A.I.C.S.: 713990

RCM TECHNOLOGIES, INC.
2500 McClellan Ave Ste 350, Pennsauken, NJ 08109-4613
Tel.: (856) 356-4500   NV
Web Site: https://www.rcmt.com
Year Founded: 1971
RCMT—(NASDAQ)
Rev.: $203,875,000
Assets: $72,852,000
Liabilities: $46,883,000
Net Worth: $25,969,000
Earnings: $10,989,000
Emp.: 250
Fiscal Year-end: 01/01/22
Holding Company; Information Technology & Engineering Services
N.A.I.C.S.: 551112
Kevin D. Miller *(CFO, Treas & Sec)*
Michael Saks *(Pres-Health Care Svcs Div)*
Bradley S. Vizi *(Pres & Chm)*
Tina Ciocca *(Exec VP-Aerospace)*
Marc Chafetz *(VP)*
William Gargano *(Sr VP)*

Subsidiaries:

PSR Engineering Solutions d.o.o.   **(1)**
Kralja Vladimira 54, 11000, Belgrade, Serbia
Tel.: (381) 11 406 6670
Web Site: https://www.psr.co.rs
Engineeering Services
N.A.I.C.S.: 541512

Point Comm, Inc.   **(1)**
2600 Skymark Ave Build 11 Suite 201, Mississauga, L4W 5B2, ON, Canada
Tel.: (905) 270-4996
Web Site: http://www.pointcomm.ca
Electric Equipment Mfr
N.A.I.C.S.: 423610

RCM Technologies (USA), Inc.   **(1)**
2500 McClellan Ave Ste 350, Pennsauken, NJ 08109   **(100%)**
Tel.: (856) 356-4500
Web Site: http://www.rcmt.com
Sales Range: $10-24.9 Million
Emp.: 50
Information Technology & Engineering Services
N.A.I.C.S.: 561499
Leon Kopyt *(Chm)*

RDE, INC.
1500 W Shure Dr Ste 600, Arlington Heights, IL 60004
Tel.: (847) 506-9680   DE
Web Site:
   https://www.rdeholdings.com
Year Founded: 2011
RSTN—(OTCQB)
Rev.: $4,444,595
Assets: $1,574,804
Liabilities: $4,623,821
Net Worth: ($3,049,017)

RDE, Inc.—(Continued)

Earnings: ($1,278,524)
Emp.: 27
Fiscal Year-end: 12/31/22
Restaurant Operators
N.A.I.C.S.: 722511
Aaron Horowitz *(Pres)*
Ketan Thakker *(CEO)*
Steve Handy *(CFO)*

RE/MAX HOLDINGS, INC.

5075 S Syracuse St, Denver, CO
80237
Tel.: (303) 770-5531   DE
Web Site:
   https://www.remaxholdings.com
Year Founded: 2013
RMAX—(NYSE)
Rev.: $325,671,000
Assets: $577,150,000
Liabilities: $653,211,000
Net Worth: ($76,061,000)
Earnings: ($69,022,000)
Emp.: 544
Fiscal Year-end: 12/31/23
Holding Company; Real Estate
Agency Operator & Franchisor
N.A.I.C.S.: 551112
David L. Liniger *(Co-Founder)*
Gail A. Liniger *(Co-Founder)*
W. Erik Carlson *(CEO)*
Karri R. Callahan *(CFO)*
Grady Ligon *(CIO)*
Leah Jenkins *(Chief Acctg Officer &
VP)*
Rob Fuchs *(Exec VP-Human Re-
sources & Administration)*
Amy Lessinger *(Pres)*
Susie Winders *(Chief Compliance
Officer, Gen Counsel, Sec & Exec
VP)*

Subsidiaries:

First Leads, LLC   (1)
12 Shirley Rd, Andover, MA 01810
Tel.: (978) 296-4322
Web Site: http://www.1stleads.com
Call Center Services
N.A.I.C.S.: 561422
Mike Sheehy *(Pres & CEO)*

Gadberry Group, LLC   (1)
11101 Anderson Dr Ste 300, Little Rock, AR
72212
Tel.: (501) 907-7100
Web Site: http://www.g73data.com
Sales Range: $1-9.9 Million
Emp.: 15
Computer System Design Services
N.A.I.C.S.: 541512
Adam Gadberry *(Co-Founder)*
Larry Martin *(Co-VP)*
Chris Tackett *(Exec Dir-Tech)*

Motto Franchising, LLC   (1)
5075 S Syracuse St Ste 1200, Denver, CO
80237
Real Estate Agency Operator
N.A.I.C.S.: 531210
Ward Morrison *(Pres & CEO)*
Chris Erickson *(VP-Product Dev & Strategy)*

RE/MAX Bench Realty Group   (1)
626 E Main St, Middletown, NY 10940
Tel.: (845) 341-0004
Web Site: http://www.benchmark-realty-
   group-new-windsor-ny.remax.com
Real Estate Services
N.A.I.C.S.: 531210

RE/MAX Ontario-Atlantic Canada,
Inc.   (1)
340 1060 Manhattan Drive, Kelowna, V1Y
9X9, BC, Canada
Tel.: (250) 860-3628
Web Site: https://www.remax.ca
Real Estate Services
N.A.I.C.S.: 531110

RE/MAX, LLC   (1)
5075 S Syracuse St, Denver, CO 80237
Tel.: (303) 770-5531

Web Site: https://www.remax.com
Sales Range: $125-149.9 Million
Emp.: 250
Real Estate Agency Operator & Franchisor
N.A.I.C.S.: 531210
Christopher Alexander *(Pres-)*

Wemlo, LLC   (1)
5400 S University Dr Ste 210, Davie, FL
33328
Web Site: http://www.wemlo.io
Software Development Services
N.A.I.C.S.: 541511
Ward Morrison *(Pres & CEO)*
Chris Erickson *(VP-Product Dev & Strategy)*

booj, LLC   (1)
1095 S Monaco Pkwy, Denver, CO 80224
Tel.: (303) 290-7440
Web Site: https://www.booj.com
Website Design Services
N.A.I.C.S.: 541714
John Sable *(Mng Partner)*

READING INTERNATIONAL, INC.

189 2nd Av Ste 2S, New York, NY
10003
Tel.: (213) 235-2240   NV
Web Site: https://www.readingrdi.com
Year Founded: 1999
RDI—(NASDAQ)
Rev.: $203,115,000
Assets: $587,055,000
Liabilities: $523,776,000
Net Worth: $63,279,000
Earnings: ($36,184,000)
Emp.: 97
Fiscal Year-end: 12/31/22
Holding Company; Movie Theater
Owner
N.A.I.C.S.: 551112
Ellen Marie Cotter *(Pres, CEO & Vice
Chm)*
Steve Lucas *(Controller)*
Sandra Herrera *(Sec & Assoc Gen
Counsel)*
Margaret Cotter *(Chm & Exec VP-
Dev & Dev-New York)*
Gilbert Avanes *(CFO, Treas & Exec
VP)*
S. Craig Tompkins *(Gen Counsel &
Exec VP)*
Mark Douglas *(Mng Dir-Australia &
New Zealand-Australia,New Zealand)*
Andrzej Matyczynski *(Exec VP-Global
Ops)*
Guy W. Adams *(Dir-Cyber Risk)*
Guy W. Adams *(Dir-Cyber Risk)*

Subsidiaries:

Consolidated Entertainment, Inc.   (1)
1044 Auahi St, Honolulu, HI 96814
Tel.: (808) 594-7035
Motion Picture Exhibitor
N.A.I.C.S.: 512131

Hotel Newmarket Pty Ltd   (1)
133 Charleston Rd, Bendigo, 3550, VIC,
Australia
Tel.: (61) 354433042
Home Management Services
N.A.I.C.S.: 721110

Minetta Live, LLC   (1)
18 Minneta Lane, New York, NY 10012
Tel.: (213) 235-2244
Entertainment Services
N.A.I.C.S.: 512131

Reading Rouse Hill Pty Ltd   (1)
Rouse Hill Town Centre 10-14 Market Lane,
Rouse Hill, Sydney, 2155, NSW, Australia
Tel.: (61) 29 830 2800
Web Site:
   http://www.readingcinemas.com.au
Motion Picture Exhibitor
N.A.I.C.S.: 512131

Rialto Distribution Ltd   (1)
122 Queen Street, PO Box 47-045,
Northcote Point, Auckland, 0627, New Zealand
Tel.: (64) 93763373

Web Site: http://www.rialtodistribution.com
Sales Range: $10-24.9 Million
Theatrical Film Distr
N.A.I.C.S.: 512199

Westlakes Cinema Pty Ltd   (1)
111 West Lakes Boulevard, West Lakes,
Adelaide, 5021, SA, Australia
Tel.: (61) 88 159 0800
Web Site:
   http://www.readingcinemas.com.au
Emp.: 4
Motion Picture Exhibitor
N.A.I.C.S.: 512131

READY CREDIT CORP.

10340 Viking Dr Ste 125, Eden Prai-
rie, MN 55344
Tel.: (612) 466-7360   NV
Web Site:
   http://www.readycreditcorp.com
Year Founded: 2006
RCTC—(OTCIQ)
Financial Management Services
N.A.I.C.S.: 523999
Brian A. Niebur *(CFO)*

REAL AMERICAN CAPITAL CORPORATION

8 Exchange Blvd Ste 610, Rochester,
NY 14614-1804
Tel.: (585) 967-3198   DE
Web Site: http://www.rlabco.com
Year Founded: 1999
RLAB—(OTCIQ)
Clothing Products Distr
N.A.I.C.S.: 458110

REAL BRANDS, INC.

12 Humbert St, North Providence, RI
02911
Tel.: (781) 366-7400
Web Site:
   https://www.realbrands.com
RLBD—(OTCIQ)
Rev.: $11,133
Assets: $1,161,859
Liabilities: $1,914,754
Net Worth: ($752,895)
Earnings: ($905,944)
Emp.: 3
Fiscal Year-end: 12/31/22
All Other Miscellaneous Food Manu-
facturing
N.A.I.C.S.: 311999
Jerry Pearring *(CEO)*

Subsidiaries:

Canadian American Standard Hemp
Inc.   (1)
815 Jefferson Ave, Warwick, RI 02886
Tel.: (617) 725-8900
Web Site:
   https://americanstandardhemp.com
Spectrum Oil Whslr
N.A.I.C.S.: 424690

REAL GOOD FOOD COMPANY, INC.

3 Executive Campus Ste 155, Cherry
Hill, NJ 08002
Tel.: (856) 644-5624   DE
Web Site:
   https://www.realgoodfoods.com
Year Founded: 2021
RGF—(NASDAQ)
Rev.: $141,588,000
Assets: $131,439,000
Liabilities: $139,541,000
Net Worth: ($8,102,000)
Earnings: ($10,983,000)
Emp.: 130
Fiscal Year-end: 12/31/22
Frozen Food Distr
N.A.I.C.S.: 424420
Jim Behling *(CFO)*
Tim Zimmer *(CEO)*
Bryan Freeman *(Chm)*
Andrew J. Stiffelman *(CMO)*

REALPHA TECH CORP.

6515 Longshore Loop Ste 100, Dub-
lin, OH 43017
Tel.: (707) 732-5742   DE
Web Site: https://www.realpha.com
Year Founded: 2021
AIRE—(NASDAQ)
Emp.: 9
Information Technology Services
N.A.I.C.S.: 541512
Jorge Aldecoa *(Chief Product Officer)*
Giri Devanur *(Founder, Chm & CEO)*
Brent Miller *(Co-CFO)*
William Brent Miller *(Co-CFO & Prin-
cipal Acctg Officer)*

REALTY INCOME CORPORA-TION

11995 El Camino Real, San Diego,
CA 92130
Tel.: (858) 284-5000   MD
Web Site:
   https://www.realtyincome.com
Year Founded: 1969
O—(NYSE)
Rev.: $4,078,993,000
Assets: $57,779,357,000
Liabilities: $24,672,388,000
Net Worth: $33,106,969,000
Earnings: $872,309,000
Emp.: 418
Fiscal Year-end: 12/31/23
Real Estate Investment Trust
N.A.I.C.S.: 525990
Gregory J. Whyte *(COO & Exec VP)*
Sumit Roy *(Pres & CEO)*
Sean P. Nugent *(Sr VP & Controller)*
Neale W. Redington *(Chief Acctg Of-
ficer & Sr VP)*
Jonathan Pong *(CFO, Treas & Exec
VP)*
Mark E. Hagan *(Chief Investment Of-
ficer & Exec VP)*
Michelle Bushore *(Chief Legal Officer,
Gen Counsel, Sec & Exec VP)*
Christie Kelly *(CFO)*

Subsidiaries:

ARC PA-QRS Trust   (1)
106 York Rd, Jenkintown, PA 19046
Tel.: (212) 415-6500
Emp.: 6
Trust Management & Fiduciary Services
N.A.I.C.S.: 523991

ARC TITUCAZ001, LLC   (1)
5421 E Williams Blvd, Tucson, AZ 85711
Tel.: (520) 747-1248
Real Estate Development Services
N.A.I.C.S.: 531390

Tau Atlantic, LLC   (1)
600 La Terraza Blvd, Escondido, CA 92025
Tel.: (804) 267-7220
Real Estate Development Services
N.A.I.C.S.: 531390

VEREIT, Inc.   (1)
2325 E Camelback Rd 9th Fl, Phoenix, AZ
85016
Tel.: (602) 778-6000
Web Site: http://www.vereit.com
Rev.: $1,161,366,000
Assets: $13,324,408,000
Liabilities: $6,512,840,000
Net Worth: $6,811,568,000
Earnings: $201,128,000
Emp.: 160
Fiscal Year-end: 12/31/2020
Real Estate Investment Trust
N.A.I.C.S.: 525990

Subsidiary (Domestic):

Cole Capital Corporation   (2)
900 Rr620 S Ste C101-182, Lakeway, TX
78734
Web Site:
   https://www.colecapitalcorporation.com
Building & Construction Services
N.A.I.C.S.: 236116

VEREIT Operating Partnership, L.P. (2)
2325 E Camelback Rd 9th Fl, Phoenix, AZ 85016
Rev.: $1,161,365,999
Assets: $13,324,407,999
Liabilities: $6,512,839,999
Net Worth: $6,811,567,999
Earnings: $201,278,000
Emp.: 159
Fiscal Year-end: 12/31/2020
Real Estate Investment Services
N.A.I.C.S.: 531210
Michael J. Bartolotta (CFO & Exec VP)

REBORN COFFEE, INC.
580 N Berry St, Brea, CA 92821
Tel.: (714) 784-6369   FL
Web Site: https://reborncoffee.com
Year Founded: 2015
REBN—(NASDAQ)
Rev.: $3,240,523
Assets: $8,457,541
Liabilities: $4,171,012
Net Worth: $4,286,529
Earnings: ($3,554,897)
Emp.: 2
Fiscal Year-end: 12/31/22
Commercial Bakery Services
N.A.I.C.S.: 311812
Jay Kim (CEO)
Farooq Mahmood Arjomand (Chm)
Dennis R. Egidi (Vice Chm)

REBUS HOLDINGS INC.
2629 Townsgate Rd Ste 215, Westlake Village, CA 91361
Tel.: (818) 597-7552   DE
Web Site:
   http://www.inspyrtherapeutics.com
Year Founded: 2003
RBSH—(OTCIQ)
Assets: $5,000
Liabilities: $5,242,000
Net Worth: ($5,237,000)
Earnings: ($1,020,000)
Fiscal Year-end: 12/31/22
Pharmaceutical Researcher, Developer & Mfr
N.A.I.C.S.: 325412
Robert A. Scherne (Accountant)

Subsidiaries:

Lewis & Clark Pharmaceuticals, Inc. (1)
1180 Seminole Trl Ste 495, Charlottesville, VA 22901-5713
Tel.: (434) 963-4000
Web Site: https://www.lncpharma.com
Pharmacies & Drug Stores
N.A.I.C.S.: 456110
Larry Rodman (Chief Science Officer)
Robert Thompson (Founder, Chm & CEO)

RECHARGE ACQUISITION CORP.
1900 Main St Ste 201, Sarasota, FL 34236
Tel.: (937) 610-4057   DE
Year Founded: 2020
RCHGU—(NASDAQ)
Rev.: $20,199,111
Assets: $203,132,838
Liabilities: $218,698,261
Net Worth: ($15,565,423)
Earnings: $19,129,061
Emp.: 2
Fiscal Year-end: 12/31/21
Investment Services
N.A.I.C.S.: 523999
Rajesh Soin (Chm)
Anthony Kenney (CEO)
Michael Gearhardt (CFO)

RECONDITIONED SYSTEMS, INC.
235 S 56th St, Chandler, AZ 85226
Tel.: (480) 968-1772   AZ

Web Site: http://www.resy.net
Year Founded: 1987
RESY—(OTCIQ)
Office Workstations Remanufacturer
N.A.I.C.S.: 337214
Dirk D. Anderson (Pres & CEO)

RECURSION PHARMACEUTICALS, INC.
41 S Rio Grande St, Salt Lake City, UT 84101
Tel.: (385) 269-0203   DE
Web Site: https://www.recursion.com
Year Founded: 2013
RXRX—(NASDAQ)
Rev.: $39,843,000
Assets: $701,288,000
Liabilities: $215,482,000
Net Worth: $485,806,000
Earnings: ($239,476,000)
Emp.: 500
Fiscal Year-end: 12/31/22
Biotechnology Research & Development Services
N.A.I.C.S.: 541714
David J. Mauro (Chief Medical Officer)
R. Martin Chavez (Chm)
Michael Secora (CFO)
Tina Marriott Larson (Pres & COO)
Louisa Daniels (Chief Legal Officer & Gen Counsel)
Heather Kirkby (Chief People Officer)
Benjamin Mabey (CTO)
Mason Victors (Chief Product Officer)
Lina Nilsson (VP-Product)
Ron Alfa (Sr VP-Translational Discovery)
Yolanda Chong (Sr VP-Biology)
Mike Genin (VP-Chemistry)
Imran Haque (VP-Data Science)
Nathan Hatfield (VP-Legal & Assoc Gen Counsel)
Matt Kinn (VP-Bus Dev & Corp Initiatives)
Adeline Low (Vp-Core Ops)
Kristen Rushton (VP-Bus Ops)
Blake Borgeson (Co-Founder)
Dean Y. Li (Co-Founder)
Christopher Gibson (Co-Founder & CEO)

RED CAT HOLDINGS, INC.
15 Ave Munoz Rivera Ste 5, San Juan, PR 00901-2510   NV
Web Site:
   https://www.redcatholdings.com
Year Founded: 1984
RCAT—(NASDAQ)
Rev.: $17,836,382
Assets: $48,537,612
Liabilities: $4,973,082
Net Worth: $43,564,530
Earnings: ($24,052,629)
Emp.: 89
Fiscal Year-end: 04/30/24
Investment Holding Company
N.A.I.C.S.: 551112
Jeffrey M. Thompson (Founder, Chm, Pres & CEO)
Teal Drones (CTO)

Subsidiaries:

Skypersonic, Inc. (1)
269 Executive Dr Ste A, Troy, MI 48083
Tel.: (248) 850-7439
Web Site: https://www.skypersonic.net
Indoor Drone Mfr
N.A.I.C.S.: 333310

RED CELL DRM ACQUISITION CORP.
345 N Maple Dr, Beverly Hills, CA 90210
Tel.: (310) 361-0450   DE
Year Founded: 2021

RCDAU—(NASDAQ)
Investment Services
N.A.I.C.S.: 523999
Joshua A. Lobel (Chm)
Gavin Hood (CEO)
Kenneth L. Bedingfield (CFO)

RED MILE ENTERTAINMENT, INC.
223 San Anselmo Way Ste 3, San Anselmo, CA 94960
Tel.: (415) 339-4240   DE
RDML—(OTCIQ)
Software Development Services
N.A.I.C.S.: 541511
Ben Zadik (CFO)

RED RIVER BANCSHARES, INC.
1412 Centre Ct Dr Ste 101, Alexandria, LA 71301
Tel.: (318) 561-4000   LA
Web Site:
   https://www.redriverbank.net
Year Founded: 1998
RRBI—(NASDAQ)
Rev.: $113,122,000
Assets: $3,082,686,000
Liabilities: $2,816,933,000
Net Worth: $265,753,000
Earnings: $36,916,000
Emp.: 340
Fiscal Year-end: 12/31/22
Bank Holding Company
N.A.I.C.S.: 551111
R. Blake Chatelain (Pres & CEO)
Isabel V. Carriere (CFO, Exec VP & Asst Sec)
Andrew B. Cutrer (Sr VP)

Subsidiaries:

Red River Bank (1)
1412 Centre Ct Dr Ste 101, Alexandria, LA 71301
Tel.: (318) 561-4000
Web Site: https://www.redriverbank.net
Commericial Banking
N.A.I.C.S.: 522110
R. Blake Chatelain (Pres & CEO)
Debra Mckinney (Asst VP & Mgr-Down Town Banking Center)
Carla George (Asst VP-Mortgage Lending)
Mike Murphy (CIO)
Jennifer Wells (Mgr-Consumer Loan Processing)
Willie Spears (Sr VP-Pub Affairs)
Rae Hair (VP & Branch Mgr)
Jannease F. Seastrunk (VP-Community Rels)
David K. Thompson (Pres-Baton Rouge)
Meghan Donelon (Pres-New Orleans)

RED ROBIN GOURMET BURGERS, INC.
10000 E Geddes Ave Ste 500, Englewood, CO 80112
Tel.: (303) 846-6000   DE
Web Site: https://www.redrobin.com
Year Founded: 1969
RRGB—(NASDAQ)
Rev.: $1,162,078,000
Assets: $928,998,000
Liabilities: $852,024,000
Net Worth: $76,974,000
Earnings: ($50,002,000)
Emp.: 22,483
Fiscal Year-end: 12/26/21
Hamburger Restaurant Chain
N.A.I.C.S.: 722511
Todd Allan Penegor (Pres & CEO)
Gerard Johan Hart (Pres & CEO)
Robyn Arnell Brenden (Chief Acctg Officer)
Raphael Gross (Mng Dir)
Todd Wilson (CFO & Exec VP)
Wayne Davis (Sr VP)
Sarah Mussetter (Chief Legal Officer)

Subsidiaries:

Red Robin Frederick County, LLC (1)
5582 Spectrum Dr, Frederick, MD 21703
Tel.: (301) 620-1081
Restaurant Services
N.A.I.C.S.: 722310

Red Robin International, Inc. (1)
1080 Brea Mall, Brea, CA 92821
Tel.: (714) 529-6766
Web Site: https://www.redrobin.com
Sales Range: $1-9.9 Million
Emp.: 70
Chain Restaurant
N.A.I.C.S.: 722511

Red Robin West, Inc. (1)
6312 S Fiddlers Green Cir, Englewood, CO 80111
Tel.: (303) 846-6000
Web Site: http://www.redrobin.com
Sales Range: $50-74.9 Million
Emp.: 200
Restaurant Chain
N.A.I.C.S.: 722511

Red Robin of Baltimore County, Inc. (1)
8200 Perry Hall Blvd, Baltimore, MD 21236
Tel.: (410) 933-1768
Restaurant Services
N.A.I.C.S.: 722310

Red Robin of Charles County, Inc. (1)
200 Baltimore St, La Plata, MD 20646
Tel.: (301) 645-0550
Web Site: https://www.charlescountymd.gov
Restaurant Services
N.A.I.C.S.: 722310

RED ROCK RESORTS, INC.
1505 S Pavilion Center Dr, Las Vegas, NV 89135
Tel.: (702) 495-3550   DE
Web Site:
   https://www.redrockresorts.com
Year Founded: 2015
RRR—(NASDAQ)
Rev.: $1,724,086,000
Assets: $3,954,512,000
Liabilities: $3,710,625,000
Net Worth: $243,887,000
Earnings: $176,004,000
Emp.: 9,385
Fiscal Year-end: 12/31/23
Holding Company; Casino Hotels & Resorts Owner & Operator
N.A.I.C.S.: 551112
Stephen L. Cootey (CFO, Treas & Exec VP)
Jeffrey T. Welch (Chief Legal Officer & Exec VP)
Lorenzo J. Fertitta (Vice Chm)
Frank J. Fertitta III (Chm & CEO)

Subsidiaries:

Station Casinos LLC (1)
1505 S Pavilion Center Dr, Las Vegas, NV 89135
Tel.: (702) 862-3154
Web Site: https://www.stationcasinos.com
Assets: $3,269,967,000
Liabilities: $2,633,502,000
Net Worth: $636,465,000
Earnings: $163,892,000
Fiscal Year-end: 12/31/2016
Holding Company; Casinos Hotels & Resorts Developer & Operator; Other Leisure & Entertainment Assets Operator
N.A.I.C.S.: 551111

Subsidiary (Domestic):

Fertitta Entertainment, LLC (2)
1505 S Pavilion Center Dr, Las Vegas, NV 89135
Tel.: (702) 495-3000
Web Site:
   https://www.fertittaentertainment.com
Casino Hotels, Restaurants & Sports Organization Operator
N.A.I.C.S.: 561110

Red Rock Resorts, Inc.—(Continued)

Frank J. Fertitta III *(Chm & CEO)*

NP Fiesta LLC   **(2)**
777 W Lake Mead Pkwy, Henderson, NV
89015
Tel.: (702) 631-7000
Web Site:
  https://www.fiestahenderson.sclv.com
Casino Hotel Operator
N.A.I.C.S.: 721120

NP Palace LLC   **(2)**
2411 W Sahara Ave, Las Vegas, NV 89102
Tel.: (702) 367-2411
Web Site: https://www.palacestation.com
Emp.: 1,300
Casino Hotel Operator
N.A.I.C.S.: 721120

NP Rancho LLC   **(2)**
2400 N Rancho Dr, Las Vegas, NV 89130
Tel.: (702) 631-7000
Web Site: https://www.fiestarancho.sclv.com
Casino Hotel Operator
N.A.I.C.S.: 721120

NP Red Rock LLC   **(2)**
1505 S Pavilion Ctr Dr, Las Vegas, NV
89135
Tel.: (702) 495-3000
Web Site: https://www.redrocklasvegas.com
Casino Hotel Operator
N.A.I.C.S.: 721120

NP Santa Fe LLC   **(2)**
4949 N Rancho Dr, Las Vegas, NV 89130
Tel.: (702) 658-4900
Web Site: https://www.santafestation.com
Casino Hotel Operator
N.A.I.C.S.: 721120

NP Sunset LLC   **(2)**
1301 W Sunset Rd, Henderson, NV 89014-
6607
Tel.: (702) 547-7777
Web Site: https://www.sunsetstation.com
Casino Hotel Operator
N.A.I.C.S.: 721120

NP Texas LLC   **(2)**
2101 Texas Star Ln, North Las Vegas, NV
89032-3562
Tel.: (702) 631-1000
Web Site: https://www.texasstation.com
Casino Hotel Operator
N.A.I.C.S.: 721120

Red Rock Resort   **(2)**
4111 Boulder Hwy, Las Vegas, NV 89121-
2510
Tel.: (702) 432-7777
Web Site:
  http://www.boulderstation.sclv.com
Casino Hotel Operator
N.A.I.C.S.: 721120

RED TRAIL ENERGY, LLC
3682 Hwy 8 S, Richardton, ND 58652
Tel.: (701) 974-3308   **ND**
Web Site: https://redtrailenergy.com
Year Founded: 2003
REGX—(NASDAQ)
Rev.: $199,645,418
Assets: $116,790,200
Liabilities: $33,418,468
Net Worth: $83,371,732
Earnings: $5,561,255
Emp.: 49
Fiscal Year-end: 09/30/23
Methanol Mfr
N.A.I.C.S.: 325193
Sidney A. Mauch *(Chm)*
Dirs)
Mike Appert *(Vice Chm)*
Ambrose R. Hoff *(Sec)*

RED VIOLET, INC.
2650 N Military Trl Ste 300, Boca Ra-
ton, FL 33431
Tel.: (561) 757-4000   **DE**
Web Site: https://www.redviolet.com
Year Founded: 2017
RDVT—(NASDAQ)
Rev.: $53,318,000

Assets: $77,414,000
Liabilities: $6,321,000
Net Worth: $71,093,000
Earnings: $616,000
Emp.: 186
Fiscal Year-end: 12/31/22
Holding Company; Data & Analytics
Services
N.A.I.C.S.: 551112
Derek Dubner *(Chm & CEO)*
Daniel MacLachlan *(CFO)*
James Reilly *(Pres)*
Jeffrey Dell *(CIO)*
Angus Macnab *(CTO)*

Subsidiaries:

IDI Holdings, LLC   **(1)**
2650 N Military Trail Ste 300, Boca Raton,
FL 33431
Tel.: (561) 962-2160
Holding Company
N.A.I.C.S.: 551112

Whoodle, LLC   **(1)**
Schoolside Plaza 5 S Centre Ave, Leesport,
PA 19533
Tel.: (484) 671-2571
Web Site: http://www.whoodles61.net
Dog Trainer Services
N.A.I.C.S.: 812910

Subsidiary (Domestic):

Interactive Data, LLC   **(2)**
3057 Peachtree Industrial Blvd Ste 100,
Duluth, GA 30097-8619
Web Site: https://www.ididata.com
Software Development Services
N.A.I.C.S.: 541511
Derek Dubner *(CEO)*

**REDBALL ACQUISITION
CORP.**
667 Madison Ave 16th Fl, New York,
NY 10065
Tel.: (212) 235-1000   **Ky**
Year Founded: 2020
RBACU—(NYSE)
Rev.: $13,243,374,000
Assets: $576,057,835,000
Liabilities: $653,841,290,000
Net Worth: ($77,783,455,000)
Earnings: $6,777,102,000
Fiscal Year-end: 12/31/21
Investment Services
N.A.I.C.S.: 523999
Billy Beane *(Co-Chm)*
Gerald Cardinale *(Co-Chm)*
Alec Scheiner *(CEO)*
David Grochow *(CFO)*
Luke Bornn *(Exec VP)*

REDEFY CORPORATION
2675 S Abilene St 215, Aurora, CO
80014
Tel.: (720) 504-8000   **FL**
Web Site: http://www.redefy.com
Year Founded: 2011
RDCO—(OTCIQ)
Real Estate Brokerage Services
N.A.I.C.S.: 531390
Chris Rediger *(CEO)*

Subsidiaries:

Redefy, Inc.   **(1)**
2675 S Abilene St Ste 200, Aurora, CO
80014
Tel.: (888) 323-4465
Web Site: http://www.redefy.com
Real Estate Brokerage Services
N.A.I.C.S.: 531210
Jordan Connett *(Chm)*
Chris Rediger *(Founder, CEO & CTO)*
Carrie Aversano *(Dir-Market Launch)*
Mike Perry *(Dir-Mktg)*
Joel Boyd *(Dir-Ops-West)*
Stephanie Gaudreau *(Dir-HR)*
Victor Navarro *(Mgr-Acctg)*
Suzanne Collins *(Mgr-Media)*
Robert Rudey *(Sr Engr-Sys)*

Susha Roberts *(Mgr-Content)*
Michelle Adcock *(Accountant)*
William Passan *(VP-Bus Dev)*

REDFIN CORPORATION
1715 114th Ave SE Ste 220, Belle-
vue, WA 98004
Tel.: (206) 576-8610   **DE**
Web Site: https://www.redfin.com
Year Founded: 2002
RDFN—(NASDAQ)
Rev.: $2,284,442,000
Assets: $1,574,204,000
Liabilities: $1,510,251,000
Net Worth: $63,953,000
Earnings: ($321,143,000)
Emp.: 5,572
Fiscal Year-end: 12/31/22
Offices of Real Estate Agents & Bro-
kers
N.A.I.C.S.: 531210
Chris Nielsen *(CFO)*
Bridget Frey *(CTO)*
Keith Broxterman *(Sr VP-Real Estate
Support)*
Meg Nunnally *(Head-IR)*
Mariam Sughayer *(Head)*
Jason Aleem *(Sr VP)*
Jon Ziglar *(CEO)*
Glenn Kelman *(CEO)*

Subsidiaries:

**Forward Settlement Solutions,
Inc.**   **(1)**
1628 John F Kennedy Blvd 8 Penn Ctr Ste
700, Philadelphia, PA 19103
Web Site: https://www.titleforward.com
Insurance Services
N.A.I.C.S.: 524127

Redfin Mortgage, LLC   **(1)**
5830 Granite Pkwy Ste 100 - 202, Plano,
TX 75024
Real Estate Services
N.A.I.C.S.: 531390

RentPath, LLC   **(1)**
950 E Paces Ferry Rd NE Ste 2600, At-
lanta, GA 30326
Tel.: (678) 421-3000
Web Site: http://www.rentpath.com
Online Media Publisher; Apartment, Condos
& House Search & Rental Services
N.A.I.C.S.: 531390
Kim Payne *(CFO & Sr VP)*
Carl F. Salas *(Treas & Sr VP)*
J. Michael Barber *(Chief Acctg Officer & Sr
VP)*
Arlene Mayfield *(Sr VP-Sales)*
Michael Shaw *(VP-Tax)*
Mark Brooks *(VP-Audit-Internal)*
Scott Asher *(VP)*
David A. Bell *(Chief Strategy Officer & VP-
Corp Dev & Transformation)*
Marc Lefar *(Pres & CEO)*
Marlon Starr *(Gen Counsel, Gen Counsel &
Gen Counsel)*
Mike Child *(CTO)*
Krista Nordlund *(VP)*
Ryan Davis *(VP-Marketing)*
Stephanie Haigh *(Dir)*
Dhiren Fonseca *(Pres & CEO)*
Jon Ziglar *(CEO)*
Sean Barry *(COO)*
Bijoy Verghese *(CFO)*
Nishant Phadnis *(Chief Product Officer)*
David Sommers *(CTO)*
Will Byrum *(Sr Dir-Corporate Development-
Strategy)*
Kathy Neumann *(CMO)*

Group (Domestic):

Consumer Source Inc.   **(2)**
3585 Engineering Dr Ste 100, Norcross, GA
30092   **(100%)**
Tel.: (678) 421-3000
Web Site: http://www.apartmentguide.com
Sales Range: $100-124.9 Million
Emp.: 400
Consumer Directory Publisher
N.A.I.C.S.: 513199
Charles Stubbs *(CEO)*

Division (Domestic):

DistribuTech   **(3)**
1908 Lynx Pl, Ontario, CA 91761-7801
Tel.: (909) 923-6213
Web Site: http://www.distributech.com
Sales Range: $1-9.9 Million
Emp.: 3
Advertising Material Distr
N.A.I.C.S.: 541870

DistribuTech   **(3)**
8298 Arville Ste 104, Las Vegas, NV
89139   **(100%)**
Tel.: (702) 253-9551
Web Site: http://www.distributech.net
Sales Range: $10-24.9 Million
Emp.: 6
Publication Distr
N.A.I.C.S.: 513199
Tom Clauer *(Grp Dir)*
Rodney Barton *(VP)*
Don Karbowski *(Co-CEO)*
Ryan Ritchie *(Co-CEO)*
Sarah Curry *(Natl Dir)*
Eric Danziger *(Gen Mgr)*
Melissa Jandebeur *(Dir-Human Resources)*
Jon Garber *(Gen Mgr)*
Jose Lopez *(Gen Mgr)*
Ryan Ritchie *(Co-CEO)*
Sarah Curry *(Natl Dir)*
Eric Danziger *(Gen Mgr)*
Melissa Jandebeur *(Dir-Human Resources)*
Jon Garber *(Gen Mgr)*
Jose Lopez *(Gen Mgr)*

DistribuTech - Southwest Region   **(3)**
Ste 150 4635 W McDowell Rd, Phoenix, AZ
85035-4152
Tel.: (602) 484-0894
Web Site: http://www.distributech.net
Sales Range: $1-9.9 Million
Emp.: 2
Circular & Handbill Distribution
N.A.I.C.S.: 541870

DistribuTech Inc.   **(3)**
8026 Sunport Dr Ste 304, Orlando, FL
32809   **(100%)**
Tel.: (407) 888-0745
Web Site: http://www.distributech.net
Sales Range: $1-9.9 Million
Emp.: 4
Free Consumer Guides Distr
N.A.I.C.S.: 541870

REDHAWK HOLDINGS CORP.
100 Petroleum Dr Ste 200, Lafayette,
LA 70508
Tel.: (337) 269-5933   **NV**
Web Site:
  http://www.redhawkholdings
  corp.com
Year Founded: 2005
SNDD—(OTCIQ)
Rev.: $1,134,192
Assets: $1,968,539
Liabilities: $3,901,130
Net Worth: ($1,932,591)
Earnings: ($1,813,702)
Fiscal Year-end: 06/30/20
Holding Company
N.A.I.C.S.: 551112
G. Darcy Klug *(Chm, CFO & Sec)*
Phillip C. Spizale *(CEO)*

Subsidiaries:

EcoGen Europe Ltd.   **(1)**
1 Lewis Court Grove Park, Leicester, LE19
1SD, United Kingdom
Tel.: (44) 1162897162
Web Site: http://www.ecogen-europe.co.uk
Pharmaceutical Product Retailer
N.A.I.C.S.: 424210

**RedHawk Medical Products UK
Ltd.**   **(1)**
Office 7 5 Museum Square, Leicester, LE1
6UF, United Kingdom
Tel.: (44) 1162897162
Web Site: http://www.redhawkmedical.co.uk
Medical Device Mfr & Distr
N.A.I.C.S.: 334510

REDWIRE CORPORATION

8226 Philips Hwy Ste 101, Jackson-
ville, FL 32256
Tel.: (203) 504-7835   Ky
Web Site:
  https://www.redwirespace.com
Year Founded: 2020
RDW—(NYSE)
Rev.: $160,549,000
Assets: $257,698,000
Liabilities: $264,173,000
Net Worth: ($6,475,000)
Earnings: ($130,617,000)
Emp.: 700
Fiscal Year-end: 12/31/22
Search, Detection, Navigation, Guid-
ance, Aeronautical & Nautical System
& Instrument Manufacturing
N.A.I.C.S.: 334511
Peter Cannito *(Chm, Pres & CEO)*
Al Tadros *(CTO)*
William Read *(CFO)*
Jonathan E. Baliff *(CFO)*
Chris Edmunds *(Chief Acctg Officer &
Sr VP)*
Peter Cannito *(Chm, Pres & CEO)*
Jonathan E. Baliff *(CFO)*

Subsidiaries:

QinetiQ Space NV   (1)
Hogenakkerhoekstraat 9, 9150, Kruibeke,
Belgium
Tel.: (32) 32501414
Advanced Small Satellites, Advanced
Space Mechanisms & Structures, Instru-
ments & Facilities for Micro Gravity Re-
search
N.A.I.C.S.: 927110
Erik Masure *(Mng Dir)*

Redwire,LLC   (1)
669 Forest St, Marlborough, MA 01752
Tel.: (508) 485-9100
Web Site: http://redwirespace.com
Aerospace Equipment Mfr
N.A.I.C.S.: 334511
Al Tadros *(Chief Growth Officer & Exec VP-
Space Infrastructure)*
Peter Cannito *(Chm & CEO)*
Mike Gold *(Exec VP-Civil Space Bus Dev &
External Affairs)*
Dean Bellamy *(Exec VP-Security Space-
Natl)*

Subsidiary (Domestic):

Adcole Maryland Aerospace,
LLC   (2)
669 Forest St, Marlborough, MA 01752
Tel.: (508) 485-9100
Web Site: http://www.adcolemai.com
Small Satellites & Spacecraft Attitude Con-
trol Components Mfr
N.A.I.C.S.: 336412
Dwight Barefoot *(Program Mgr)*

Subsidiary (Domestic):

Maryland Aerospace, Inc.   (3)
2145 Priest Bridge Ct Ste 15, Crofton, MD
21114-2477
Tel.: (410) 451-2505
Web Site: http://www.adcolemai.com
Small Satellite Components Mfr
N.A.I.C.S.: 927110

Subsidiary (Domestic):

Deep Space Systems, Inc.   (2)
8802 S Holland Ct, Littleton, CO 80128-
6997
Tel.: (720) 922-1276
Web Site:
  http://www.deepspacesystems.com
Rev.: $1,000,000
Engineeering Services
N.A.I.C.S.: 541330
Michelle C. Bailey *(Pres)*

Deployable Space Systems, Inc.   (2)
153 Castilian Dr, Goleta, CA 93117
Tel.: (805) 722-8090
Web Site: http://www.dss-space.com
Research & Development in the Physical,
Engineering & Life Sciences
N.A.I.C.S.: 541715

Brian Spence *(Co-Founder & Pres)*
Steve White *(Co-Founder & VP)*

Loadpath, LLC   (2)
11428 Academy Rdg Rd NE, Albuquerque,
NM 87111-6896
Web Site: http://www.loadpath.com
Research & Development in the Physical,
Engineering & Life Sciences
N.A.I.C.S.: 541715
Karin Avery *(Mgr-Quality)*

Oakman Aerospace, Inc.   (2)
9092 S Ridgeline Blvd, Littleton, CO 80129
Tel.: (303) 904-6060
Web Site: http://www.oak-aero.com
Research & Development in the Physical,
Engineering & Life Sciences
N.A.I.C.S.: 541715
Maureen O'Brien *(CEO)*
Stanley Kennedy Jr. *(Pres)*

Roccor LLC   (2)
2602 Clover Basin Dr Ste D, Longmont, CO
80503
Tel.: (303) 200-0068
Web Site: http://www.roccor.com
Engineeering Services
N.A.I.C.S.: 541330
Douglas Campbell *(Founder)*
Chris Pearson *(Pres)*

Techshot, Inc.   (2)
7200 Hwy 150, Greenville, IN 47124
Tel.: (812) 923-9591
Web Site: http://www.techshot.com
Electromedical & Electrotherapeutic Appara-
tus Mfr
N.A.I.C.S.: 334510
Dominic Foster *(CTO)*
John Vellinger *(Co-Founder & Pres)*

REDWOOD CAPITAL BANK
402 G St, Eureka, CA 95501
Tel.: (707) 444-9800   CA
Web Site:
  https://www.redwoodcapital
  bank.com
Year Founded: 2004
RWCB—(OTCQX)
Rev.: $21,641,339
Assets: $521,440,083
Liabilities: $475,731,450
Net Worth: $45,708,633
Earnings: $7,043,798
Fiscal Year-end: 12/31/23
Commericial Banking
N.A.I.C.S.: 522110
John E. Dalby *(Pres & CEO)*

REDWOOD FINANCIAL, INC.
1000 E Cook St, Redwood Falls, MN
56283
Tel.: (507) 637-1000   MN
Year Founded: 1995
REDW—(OTCIQ)
Financial Investment Services
N.A.I.C.S.: 523999
Daryl L. Karsky *(CEO)*
Catherine L. Prouty *(Sec)*
Stephanie Seely *(Treas)*
Thomas W. Stotesbery *(Chm)*
John Scott Nelson *(Vice Chm)*

REDWOOD TRUST, INC.
1 Belvedere Pl Ste 300, Mill Valley,
CA 94941
Tel.: (415) 389-7373   MD
Web Site:
  https://www.redwoodtrust.com
RWT—(NYSE)
Rev.: $707,854,000
Assets: $13,030,899,000
Liabilities: $11,946,914,000
Net Worth: $1,083,985,000
Earnings: ($163,520,000)
Emp.: 347
Fiscal Year-end: 12/31/22
Other Financial Vehicles
N.A.I.C.S.: 525990
Douglas B. Hansen Jr. *(Founder)*
Christopher J. Abate *(CEO)*

Collin Lee Cochrane *(Chief Acctg Of-
ficer & Principal Acctg Officer)*
Carlene A. Graham *(COO)*
Dashiell I. Robinson *(Pres)*
Sasha G. Macomber *(Chief HR Offi-
cer)*
Andrew M. Gillmer *(Mng Dir & Portfo-
lio Mgr)*
Jonathan M. Groesbeck *(Mng Dir &
Head-Bus Dev)*
John H. Isbrandtsen *(Mng Dir &
Treas)*
David P. Monks *(Mng Dir-Fin)*
Lucy D. Ruiz *(Mng Dir & Controller)*
Shawnda D. Merriman *(Mng Dir-Post
Purchase Ops)*
Matthew J. Pope *(Mng Dir & Deputy
Gen Counsel)*
Nathan S. Charles *(Mng Dir-
Application Dev & Support)*
Brooke E. Carillo *(CFO)*
John Arens *(Mng Dir)*
John J. Arens *(Head)*
Emil J. Fanelli *(Mng Dir)*
Cara L. Newman *(Mng Dir)*
Jeremy P. Strom *(Mng Dir)*
Gina Sykes *(Mng Dir)*
Emilian Halloran *(Mng Dir)*

Subsidiaries:

CoreVest American Finance Lender
LLC   (1)
1920 Main St Ste 850, Irvine, CA 92614
Web Site: http://www.corevestfinance.com
Real Estate Investment Services
N.A.I.C.S.: 531390

Sequoia Residential Funding,
Inc.   (1)
1 Belvedere Pl Ste 330, Mill Valley, CA
94941
Tel.: (415) 389-7373
Real Estate Mortgage Services
N.A.I.C.S.: 531190
Christopher J. Abate *(Pres)*

REDWOODS ACQUISITION
CORP.
1115 Broadway 12th Fl, New York,
NY 10010
Tel.: (646) 916-5315   DE
Year Founded: 2021
RWOD—(NASDAQ)
Assets: $118,246,636
Liabilities: $122,291,148
Net Worth: ($4,044,512)
Earnings: $1,233,352
Emp.: 2
Fiscal Year-end: 12/31/22
Investment Services
N.A.I.C.S.: 523999
Jiande Chen *(CEO)*
Edward Cong Wang *(CFO)*

Subsidiaries:

Strategic Asset Leasing, Inc.   (1)
545 8th Ave Ste 401, New York, NY 10018
Tel.: (212) 613-5453
Web Site: https://www.anewmeds.com
Oil & Gas Field Equipment Mfr
N.A.I.C.S.: 333132
William Lieberman *(Pres)*

REED'S, INC.
201 Merritt 7, Norwalk, CT 06851
Tel.: (310) 217-9400   DE
Web Site:
  https://www.drinkreeds.com
Year Founded: 1987
REED—(OTCQX)
Rev.: $49,599,000
Assets: $26,321,000
Liabilities: $22,118,000
Net Worth: $4,203,000
Earnings: ($16,407,000)
Emp.: 31
Fiscal Year-end: 12/31/21

Natural Carbonated Beverages,
Candy, Ice Cream & Various Other
Food Beverage & Food Products Mfr
N.A.I.C.S.: 312111
Neal Cohane *(Chief Sls Officer)*
John J. Bello *(Chm)*
Norman E. Snyder Jr. *(CEO)*
Joann Tinnelly *(CFO)*

REELTIME RENTALS, INC.
19930 68th Ave N E, Kenmore, WA
98028
Tel.: (206) 579-0222
Web Site: https://www.reeltime.com
RLTR—(OTCIQ)
Public Relations Agencies
N.A.I.C.S.: 541820
Barry Henthorn *(CEO & CTO)*

REFLECT SCIENTIFIC, INC.
1266 S 1380 W, Orem, UT 84058
Tel.: (801) 226-4100   UT
Web Site:
  https://www.reflectscientific.com
RSCF—(OTCQB)
Rev.: $2,041,297
Assets: $2,446,194
Liabilities: $149,592
Net Worth: $2,296,602
Earnings: $89,396
Emp.: 7
Fiscal Year-end: 12/31/22
Scientific Equipment Mfr
N.A.I.C.S.: 334516
William G. Moon *(VP-Engrg)*
Kim Boyce *(Chm, Pres, CEO & CFO)*
Thomas Tait *(VP)*

REFOCUS GROUP, INC.
6A Liberty Ste 100, Aliso Viejo, CA
92656   DE
Web Site: http://www.refocus-
group.com
RFCS—(OTCIQ)
Medical Device Mfr
N.A.I.C.S.: 339112
Thomas Loarie *(Chm)*
Mike Judy *(CEO)*
George Hampton *(VP-Mktg & Bus
Dev)*
David Ozinga *(VP-Mfg Ops)*
Selene Burke *(VP-Clinical Affairs)*

REGAL REXNORD CORPORA-
TION
111 W Michigan St, Milwaukee, WI
53203
Tel.: (608) 364-8800   WI
Web Site:
  https://www.regalrexnord.com
Year Founded: 1955
RRX—(NYSE)
Rev.: $6,250,700,000
Assets: $15,431,400,000
Liabilities: $9,066,300,000
Net Worth: $6,365,100,000
Earnings: ($57,400,000)
Emp.: 32,100
Fiscal Year-end: 12/31/23
Power Transmission Systems & High-
Speed Steel Rotary Cutting Tools Mfr
N.A.I.C.S.: 335312
Robert J. Rehard *(CFO & VP)*
Louis Vernon Pinkham *(CEO)*
Rakesh Sachdev *(Chm)*
John M. Avampato *(CIO & VP)*
Scott D. Brown *(Pres-Comml Sys
Segment)*
Cheryl A. Lewis *(Chief HR Officer &
VP)*
Alexander P. Scarpelli *(Chief Acctg
Officer, VP & Controller)*
Kevin J. Zaba *(Pres)*
Justin D. Baier *(VP)*
Gennaro J. Colacino *(VP)*

Regal Rexnord Corporation—(Continued)

Roger Fei *(Pres)*
Yvette Henry *(VP)*
Hugo Dubovoy Jr. *(Gen Counsel, Sec & Exec VP)*

Subsidiaries:

A.O. Smith Electrical Products GmbH **(1)**
Jagerstrasse 10, 41239, Monchengladbach, Germany
Tel.: (49) 2166134872
Web Site: http://www.aosmith.co
Industrial & Commerical Electric Motor Distr
N.A.I.C.S.: 423610

Air-Con Technologies, Inc. **(1)**
385 Admiral Blvd, Mississauga, L5T 2M8, ON, Canada
Tel.: (905) 564-8171
Heating Equipment Mfr & Distr
N.A.I.C.S.: 333414

Altra Industrial Motion Corp. **(1)**
300 Granite St Ste 201, Braintree, MA 02184
Tel.: (781) 917-0600
Web Site: https://www.altramotion.com
Rev.: $1,945,500,000
Assets: $3,676,600,000
Liabilities: $1,674,200,000
Net Worth: $2,002,400,000
Earnings: $127,000,000
Emp.: 9,300
Fiscal Year-end: 12/31/2022
Holding Company; Mechanical Power Transmission Products Designer, Mfr & Marketer
N.A.I.C.S.: 551112
Glenn E. Deegan *(Gen Counsel, Sec & Exec VP-Legal & HR)*

Subsidiary (Non-US):

ALTRA INDUSTRIAL MOTION, INC. **(2)**
(100%)
Tel.: (781) 917-0600
Web Site: http://www.altramotion.com
Sales Range: $25-49.9 Million
Emp.: 40
Power Transmission & Motion Control Products Designer, Mfr & Marketer
N.A.I.C.S.: 333613

Subsidiary (Non-US):

Ameridrives Couplings **(3)**
Tel.: (814) 480-5000
Web Site: https://www.ameridrives.com
Sales Range: $25-49.9 Million
Emp.: 200
Mfr of Mechanical Power Transmission Products
N.A.I.C.S.: 334513

Ameridrives International, LLC **(3)**
Tel.: (814) 480-5000
Web Site: https://www.ameridrives.com
Sales Range: $25-49.9 Million
Gear Couplings & Mill Spindles Heavy Duty High Torque Applications Products Mfr
N.A.I.C.S.: 333613

Boston Gear **(3)**
Tel.: (781) 917-0600
Web Site: http://www.bostongear.com
Sales Range: $25-49.9 Million
Emp.: 38
Bearings, Pillow Blocks, Gears, Sprockets, Fluid Power Components, Roller Chain, Speed Reducers, Electric Motors, Clutch Brakes & Universal Joints
N.A.I.C.S.: 333612

Kilian Manufacturing Corporation **(3)**
Tel.: (315) 432-0700
Web Site: https://www.kilianbearings.com
Custom Bearings & Assemblies Mfr
N.A.I.C.S.: 332991

Group (Non-US):

Marland Clutch Products **(3)**
Tel.: (630) 455-1752
Web Site: http://www.marland.com
Sales Range: $1-9.9 Million
Emp.: 1

Mfr & Designer of Overrunning Clutches, Back-Stop Clutches & Clutch Couplings
N.A.I.C.S.: 811114

Nuttall Gear LLC **(3)**
Tel.: (716) 298-4100
Web Site: https://www.nuttallgear.com
Sales Range: $50-74.9 Million
Enclosed Gear Drives Mfr
N.A.I.C.S.: 333612

Subsidiary (Non-US):

TB Wood's Corporation **(3)**
Tel.: (717) 264-7161
Web Site: https://www.tbwoods.com
Power Transmission Product Mfr
N.A.I.C.S.: 333613

TB Wood's Incorporated **(3)**
Tel.: (717) 264-7161
Web Site: https://www.tbwoods.com
Sales Range: $100-124.9 Million
Electronic & Mechanical Industrial Power Transmission Equipment
N.A.I.C.S.: 333613

Warner Electric, Inc. **(3)**
Tel.: (815) 389-3771
Web Site: http://www.warnerelectric.com
Mfr of Electric Brakes, Clutches & Controls for Transportation, Industry & Agriculture, Photoelectrics, Linear Actuators & Ball Bearing Screws
N.A.I.C.S.: 336340

Subsidiary (Non-US):

Altra Industrial Motion India Private Ltd. **(2)**
Gat No 448/14 Shinde Vasti Tal Khed Nighoje, Pune, 410 501, Nighoje Tal Khed, India
Tel.: (91) 2135622100
Mechanical Power Transmission Distr
N.A.I.C.S.: 423840
Prashant Khadangle *(Asst Gen Mgr)*

Altra Industrial Motion Russia OOO **(2)**
Volokolamskoye sh 142 bldg 6 Business Center Irbis, 125464, Moscow, Russia
Tel.: (7) 4956420468
Web Site: http://www.altramotion.com
Gear Motor & Adapter Mfr
N.A.I.C.S.: 333612

Altra Industrial Motion South Africa (Pty.) Ltd. **(2)**
Unit 11 Middle Park Cnr Craig and Dormehl St, Anderbolt, Boksburg, 1459, Gauteng, South Africa
Tel.: (27) 119184270
Web Site: http://www.altramotion.co.za
Mechanical Power Transmission Distr
N.A.I.C.S.: 423840

Aluminium Die Casting S.r.l. **(2)**
Viale Veneto 48, Saonara, 35020, Padua, Italy
Tel.: (39) 0498798011
Mechanical Power Equipment Mfr
N.A.I.C.S.: 333613

Bauer Gear Motor Finland Oy Ab **(2)**
Teknobulevardi 3-5, 01530, Vantaa, Finland
Tel.: (358) 207189700
Web Site: http://www.bauergears.com
Sales Range: $10-24.9 Million
Gear Motor & Adapter Mfr
N.A.I.C.S.: 333612
Lauri Svinhufvud *(Mng Dir)*

Bauer Gear Motor Limited **(2)**
Unit 1, Nat lane Business Park, Winsford, CW7 3BS, Cheshire, United Kingdom
Tel.: (44) 1606868600
Web Site: http://www.bauergears.com
Emp.: 6
Gear Motor & Adapter Mfr
N.A.I.C.S.: 333612

Elsim Elektroteknik Sistemler Sanayi ve Ticaret A.S. **(2)**
Salkim Sogut Sok No 30/A Dikmen, 06460, Ankara, Turkiye
Tel.: (90) 31247 984 7273
Web Site: https://www.elsim.com.tr
Alarm Panel Security Services
N.A.I.C.S.: 561621

Subsidiary (Domestic):

Guardian Couplings LLC **(2)**
300 Indiana Hwy 212, Michigan City, IN 46360
Tel.: (219) 874-5248
Web Site: http://www.guardiancouplings.com
Mechanical Power Transmission Mfr & Distr
N.A.I.C.S.: 333613

Guardian Ind., Inc. **(2)**
300 Indiana Hwy 212, Michigan City, IN 46360
Tel.: (219) 874-5248
Web Site: https://www.guardiancouplings.com
Sales Range: $1-9.9 Million
Power Transmission Component Mfr
N.A.I.C.S.: 333613

Kollmorgen Corporation **(2)**
203A W Rock Rd, Radford, VA 24141
Tel.: (540) 633-3545
Web Site: https://www.kollmorgen.com
Electronic Motion Control Stabilized Systems Mfr
N.A.I.C.S.: 334417

Subsidiary (Non-US):

KOLLMORGEN Europe GmbH **(3)**
Pempelfurtstrasse 1, 40880, Ratingen, Germany
Tel.: (49) 210293940
Web Site: http://www.kollmorgen.com
Medicinal Product Mfr
N.A.I.C.S.: 339112

Kollmorgen Automation AB **(3)**
Kongegardsgatan 7, 431 90, Molndal, Sweden
Tel.: (46) 31938000
Web Site: http://www.kollmorgen.com
Industrial Machinery Mfr
N.A.I.C.S.: 333248

Kollmorgen srl **(3)**
Via per Cinisello 95/97, 20834, Nova Milanese, MB, Italy
Tel.: (39) 0362594260
Web Site: http://www.kollmorgen.com
Industrial Machinery Mfr
N.A.I.C.S.: 333248

Subsidiary (Domestic):

Motion Engineering Incorporated **(3)**
33 S La Patera Ln, Santa Barbara, CA 93117
Tel.: (805) 681-3300
Web Site: https://www.motioneng.com
Electrical Equipment & Component Mfr
N.A.I.C.S.: 005000

Subsidiary (Non-US):

Portescap Co., Ltd. **(2)**
Toyohashi Science Core 405 333-9 Hamaike Aza Nishimiyukicho, Kudankita Chiyoda-Ku, Toyohashi, 441-8113, Aichi, Japan
Tel.: (81) 532219226
Miniature Motor Mfr
N.A.I.C.S.: 335312

Stromag Dessau GmbH **(2)**
Dessauer Str 10, Rosslau, 06844, Dessau, Germany
Tel.: (49) 3402190206
Web Site: http://www.stromag.com
Electromagnetic Clutch & Brake Mfr
N.A.I.C.S.: 005014

Stromag France SAS **(2)**
20 allee des Erables C D G, PO Box 40004, Villepinte, 95934, Roissy-en-France, Cedex, France
Tel.: (33) 149903220
Web Site: http://www.stromagfrance.com
Electromagnetic Clutch & Brake Mfr & Distr
N.A.I.C.S.: 333613

Stromag GmbH **(2)**
Hansastr 120, 59425, Unna, Germany
Tel.: (49) 23031020
Web Site: https://www.stromag.com
Electromagnetic Clutch & Brake Mfr
N.A.I.C.S.: 335314

Svendborg Brakes ApS **(2)**

Jernbanevej 9, 5882, Vejstrup, Denmark
Tel.: (45) 63255255
Web Site: https://www.svendborg-brakes.com
Mechanical Power Transmission Mfr & Distr
N.A.I.C.S.: 333613

Subsidiary (Non-US):

Svendborg Brakes Peru S.A.C. **(3)**
Urb Villa Corpac Mz A Lote1A, Cerro Colorado, Arequipa, Peru
Tel.: (51) 959223653
Mechanical Power Equipment Mfr
N.A.I.C.S.: 333613

Subsidiary (Domestic):

Thomson Linear LLC **(2)**
203A W Rock Rd, Radford, VA 24141
Tel.: (540) 633-3549
Web Site: http://www.thomsonlinear.com
Logistic Services
N.A.I.C.S.: 541614

Subsidiary (Non-US):

Thomson Neff GmbH **(3)**
Greifswalder Str 9, 16515, Oranienburg, Germany
Tel.: (49) 33015717152
Web Site: https://www.tgadeutschland.de
Industrial Machinery Mfr
N.A.I.C.S.: 333248

Tollo Linear AB **(3)**
Bredbandsvagen 12, 29162, Kristianstad, Sweden
Tel.: (46) 445902400
Industrial Machinery Components Mfr
N.A.I.C.S.: 333248

Subsidiary (Non-US):

Twiflex Ltd. **(2)**
317-319 Ampthill Road, Bedford, MK42 9RD, Middlesex, United Kingdom
Tel.: (44) 1234350311
Web Site: https://www.twiflex.com
Sales Range: $25-49.9 Million
Emp.: 75
Disc Brake Calipers & Rubberelement Couplings Mfr
N.A.I.C.S.: 336340
Neil Wright *(VP & Dir-HDCB)*

Warner Electric (Singapore) Pty, Ltd. **(2)**
30 Pioneer Road, Singapore, 627725, Singapore
Tel.: (65) 64874464
Web Site: http://www.warnerelectric.com
Sales Range: $10-24.9 Million
Emp.: 7
Power Transmission Products Mfr & Distr
N.A.I.C.S.: 333613

Warner Electric (Taiwan) Ltd. **(2)**
3rd Fl No 35 Lane 32 Kwang-Fu South Road, Taipei, 00105, Taiwan
Tel.: (886) 225778156
Web Site: http://www.warnerelectric.com.tw
Power Transmission Products Mfr & Marketer
N.A.I.C.S.: 333613

Warner Electric (Thailand) Ltd. **(2)**
178 Soi Anamai Srinakarin Rd, Suanluang, Bangkok, 10250, Thailand
Tel.: (66) 23225527
Web Site: http://www.warnerelectric.co.th
Power Transmission Products Mfr & Marketer
N.A.I.C.S.: 333613

Benshaw Inc. **(1)**
615 Alpha Dr, Pittsburgh, PA 15238
Tel.: (412) 968-0100
Web Site: https://benshaw.com
Sales Range: $50-74.9 Million
Emp.: 75
Motor Starters & Controllers, Electric
N.A.I.C.S.: 335314
Pete Morgan *(Pres)*

Subsidiary (Domestic):

Excel Industrial Electronics, Inc. **(2)**
44360 Reynolds Dr, Clinton Township, MI 48036
Tel.: (586) 463-3811

Sales Range: $1-9.9 Million
Emp.: 25
Engineeering Services
N.A.I.C.S.: 541330
Carolyn Beck (CEO)

CMG Electric Motors (Malaysia) Sdn. Bhd. (1)
6536A Jalan Bukit Kemuning Batu 6
Seksyen 34, 40470, Shah Alam, Selangor Darul Ehsan, Malaysia
Tel.: (60) 351249217
Web Site: http://www.cmggroup.com.au
Emp.: 60
Motor & Generator Mfr
N.A.I.C.S.: 335312

CMG Electric Motors (NZ) Limited (1)
18 Jomac Place, PO Box 71142, Avondale, -1348, New Zealand
Tel.: (64) 98203550
Web Site: http://www.cmggroup.co.nz
Sales Range: $10-24.9 Million
Emp.: 20
Electric & Gear Motor Mfr
N.A.I.C.S.: 335312

Changzhou REGAL-BELOIT Sinya Motor Co. Ltd. (1)
25 Hengluo Road henglin Town, Henglin Town, Changzhou, 213101, China
Tel.: (86) 51988526518
Web Site: http://www.sinyamotor.com
Sales Range: $200-249.9 Million
Emp.: 900
Electric Motor Mfr & Distr
N.A.I.C.S.: 335312

Durst (1)
5560 E Buss Rd, Clinton, WI 53525   (100%)
Tel.: (608) 365-2563
Web Site: http://www.durstdrives.com
Sales Range: $75-99.9 Million
Emp.: 190
Mfr of Speed Reducers & Gear Drives
N.A.I.C.S.: 333612

Elco Do Brazil Ltda. (1)
Avenida Armando De Andrade 549, Taboao Da Serra, Sao Paulo, 06754-210, Brazil
Tel.: (55) 1147019337
Web Site: https://www.elco-spa.com
Emp.: 175
Heating Equipment Mfr & Distr
N.A.I.C.S.: 333414

Elco E-Trade Srl (1)
Via Marconi 1, 20065, Inzago, Italy
Tel.: (39) 02953191
Web Site: http://www.elco-spa.it
Sales Range: $25-49.9 Million
Emp.: 200
Motor & Generator Mfr
N.A.I.C.S.: 335312

Elco Motors Asia PTE Limited (1)
22 Kallang Ave 07-06 Hong Aik Ind Bldg, Singapore, 339413, Singapore
Tel.: (65) 62989169
Web Site: http://www.regalbeloit.com
Emp.: 2
Motor & Generator Mfr
N.A.I.C.S.: 335312

Elco de Colombia SAS (1)
Av Cra 129 No 22 B- 57 Bodega No 26 Parque Industrial de Occidente, Fontibon, Bogota, Colombia
Tel.: (57) 17440959
Web Site: http://www.elco.com.co
Motor & Generator Mfr
N.A.I.C.S.: 335312

Fasco Australia Pty. Ltd. (1)
1/14 Monterey Road Dandenong South, Melbourne, 3175, VIC, Australia
Tel.: (61) 387872100
Web Site: http://www.fasco.com
Electric Motor & Blower Mfr
N.A.I.C.S.: 333996

Fasco Motors Thailand Ltd. (1)
29/7-8 Moo3 Bangkruay-Sainoi Rd Bangkrang, Muang Nonthaburi, Nonthaburi, 11000, Thailand
Tel.: (66) 29232277
Web Site: http://www.fascomotors.co.th
Sales Range: $200-249.9 Million
Emp.: 900
Electric Motor Mfr

N.A.I.C.S.: 335312

Hub City, Inc. (1)
2914 Industrial Ave, Aberdeen, SD 57402-1089   (100%)
Tel.: (605) 225-0360
Web Site: http://www.hubcityinc.com
Sales Range: $50-74.9 Million
Emp.: 450
Mechanical Power Transmission Component Mfr
N.A.I.C.S.: 333613

IG-Mex, S. de R.L. de C.V. (1)
Blvd Thomas Fernandez y Farenheit Parque Industrial Bermudez, 32180, Ciudad Juarez, Chihuahua, Mexico
Tel.: (52) 6566880300
Electrical & Motion Control Product Mfr
N.A.I.C.S.: 333515

Jakel, Incorporated (1)
201 S Madison Ave, Aurora, MO 65605
Tel.: (417) 678-7264
Sales Range: $100-124.9 Million
Subfractional Motors & Blowers
N.A.I.C.S.: 335312

LEESON Electric - Grove Gear (1)
1524 15th Ave, Union Grove, WI 53182
Tel.: (262) 878-1221
Web Site: http://www.grovegear.com
Sales Range: $100-124.9 Million
Emp.: 200
Mfr of Standard & Special Worm Gear Speed Reducers, Custom Gearing & Gearmotors
N.A.I.C.S.: 333612

Milwaukee Gear Company (1)
5150 N Port Washington Rd, Milwaukee, WI 53217
Tel.: (414) 962-3532
Web Site: http://www.milwaukeegear.com
Sales Range: $50-74.9 Million
Emp.: 125
Speed Changers, Drives & Gears Mfr
N.A.I.C.S.: 333612

Morrill Motors, Inc.1946 (1)
229 S Main Ave, Erwin, TN 37650 (100%)
Tel.: (423) 743-6000
Web Site: http://www.morrillmotors.com
Rev.: $35,187,232
Emp.: 433
Electric Motors & Fan Blades
N.A.I.C.S.: 335312

Subsidiary (Non-US):

Morrill Motors (Jiaxing) Co., Ltd. (2)
Canada Technological Industrial Park Honggao Rd, Xiuzhou District, Jiaxing, 314001, Zhejiang, China
Tel.: (86) 57383939168
Emp.: 200
Motor & Generator Mfr
N.A.I.C.S.: 335312
Leo Liu (Gen Mgr)

Nicotra Gebhardt S.p.A (1)
24040 Ciserano, Via Modena 18, Zingonia, Loc Zingonia Bg, Italy
Tel.: (39) 035873111
Web Site: http://www.nicotra-gebhardt.com
Industrial Fans Mfr
N.A.I.C.S.: 333413

Subsidiary (Non-US):

Nicotra Gebhardt AB (2)
Kraketorpsgatan 30, PO Box 237, 431 53, Molndal, Sweden
Tel.: (46) 311302610
Web Site: http://www.nicotra-gebhardt.com
Industrial Fans Mfr
N.A.I.C.S.: 333413

Nicotra Gebhardt GmbH (2)
Gebhardtstrasse 19 25, 74638, Waldenburg, Germany
Tel.: (49) 79421010
Web Site: https://www.nicotra-gebhardt.com
Fans & Air Conditioners Mfr
N.A.I.C.S.: 333415

Nicotra Gebhardt Ltd. (2)
Unit D Parkgate Business Park Rail Mill Way, Rotherham, S62 6JQ, S Yorks, United Kingdom
Tel.: (44) 1709780760

Industrial Fans Mfr
N.A.I.C.S.: 333413

Nicotra Gebhardt NV (2)
Heiveldekens 16, B-2550, Kontich, Belgium
Tel.: (32) 3 610 01 53
Industrial Fan Distr
N.A.I.C.S.: 423730

Nicotra Gebhardt Pte Ltd (2)
12 Tuas Loop, Singapore, 637346, Singapore
Tel.: (65) 68633473
Industrial Fans Mfr
N.A.I.C.S.: 333413

Nicotra Gebhardt Pvt. Ltd. (2)
Plot no 28F & 29 Sector-31, Kasna, Noida, 201 308, Uttar Pradesh, India
Tel.: (91) 120 4783400
Industrial Fans Mfr
N.A.I.C.S.: 333413

Nicotra Gebhardt S.A. (2)
Calle Jamaica 5, Alcala de Henares, 28806, Madrid, Spain
Tel.: (34) 918 84 6110
Industrial Fans Mfr
N.A.I.C.S.: 333413

Productos Electricos Aplicados, S. de R.L. de C.V. (1)
Carretera Presa La Amistad Km 6 Parque Industrial Amistad, Acuna, 26220, Mexico
Tel.: (52) 8777730227
Electrical & Motion Control Product Mfr
N.A.I.C.S.: 333515

RBC Manufacturing Corporation (1)
100 E Randolph St, Wausau, WI 54401   (100%)
Tel.: (715) 675-3359
Web Site: http://www.marathonelectric.com
Sales Range: $400-449.9 Million
Emp.: 400
Mfr Electric Motors, Generators & Wiring Devices
N.A.I.C.S.: 335312

Subsidiary (Non-US):

Marathon Electric Far East Pte Ltd. (2)
12 Tuas Loop, Singapore, 637346, Singapore
Tel.: (65) 62661851
Web Site: http://www.marathonelectric.com
Sales Range: $10-24.9 Million
Emp.: 3
Motor & Generator Mfr
N.A.I.C.S.: 335312

Subsidiary (Domestic):

Marathon Special Products Corp. (2)
427 Van Camp Rd, Bowling Green, OH 43402   (100%)
Tel.: (419) 352-8441
Web Site: https://www.marathonsp.com
Sales Range: $50-74.9 Million
Emp.: 175
Mfr of Current Carrying Wiring Devices
N.A.I.C.S.: 335313

Regal Australia Pty Ltd. (1)
19 Corporate Avenue, Rowville, 3178, Australia
Tel.: (61) 392374000
Web Site: http://www.regalaustralia.com.au
Commercial & Industrial Machinery Equipment Rental Services
N.A.I.C.S.: 532490

Regal Beloit (Wuxi) Co., Ltd. (1)
No 6 Xiangge Rd Hudai Town, Binghu District, Wuxi, 214161, China
Tel.: (86) 51081831600
Cutting Tool & Machine Tool Accessory Mfr
N.A.I.C.S.: 333515

Regal Beloit America, Inc. (1)
200 State St, Beloit, WI 53511
Tel.: (956) 664-4200
Motor & Generator Mfr
N.A.I.C.S.: 335312

Subsidiary (Non-US):

Regal Beloit Spain, S.A. (2)
Ernio bidea s/n, 20159, Zizurkil, Gipuzkoa, Spain

Tel.: (34) 943690054
Web Site: http://www.regalpts.com
Couplings & Transmission Elements Mfr
N.A.I.C.S.: 333517

Regal Beloit Canada, an Alberta Limited Partnership (1)
320 Superior Boulevard, Mississauga, L5T 2N7, ON, Canada
Tel.: (905) 670-4770
Web Site: http://www.leeson.ca
Emp.: 50
Electric Motor Mfr & Distr
N.A.I.C.S.: 335312

Regal Beloit FZE (1)
JAFZA 20 Suite 111, PO Box 262629, Jebel Ali, Dubai, United Arab Emirates
Tel.: (971) 48812666
Web Site: http://www.regalbeloit.com
Emp.: 50
Electric Motor Distr
N.A.I.C.S.: 423610

Regal Beloit Spain SA (1)
Ernio Bidea s/n, 20159, Zizurkil, Spain
Tel.: (34) 943690054
Wireless Communication Equipment Mfr
N.A.I.C.S.: 334220

Regal Power Transmission Solutions (1)
7120 New Buffington Rd, Florence, KY 41042
Tel.: (859) 342-7900
Web Site: http://www.regalpts.com
Power Transmission Equipment Sales
N.A.I.C.S.: 423610

Rotor B.V. (1)
Mors 1-5, PO Box 45, 7151 MX, Eibergen, Netherlands
Tel.: (31) 545464640
Web Site: https://www.rotor.nl
Electric Motor Mfr & Distr
N.A.I.C.S.: 335312

Subsidiary (Non-US):

Rotor U.K. Limited (2)
16 Everitt Close Denington Industrial Estate, Wellingborough, NN8 2QF, United Kingdom
Tel.: (44) 1933230900
Web Site: http://www.rotor.co.uk
Sales Range: $10-24.9 Million
Emp.: 12
Electric Motor Mfr & Distr
N.A.I.C.S.: 335312

Shanghai Marathon GeXin Electric Co. Ltd. (1)
767 Baoqi Road, Baoshan District, Shanghai, 200444, China
Tel.: (86) 2156681618
Web Site: http://www.shmgec.com
Sales Range: $25-49.9 Million
Emp.: 160
Motor & Generator Mfr
N.A.I.C.S.: 335312

Torin Industries (Malaysia) Sdn. Bhd. (1)
6536a Jalan Bukit Kemuning Batu 6 Seksyen 34, Seksyen, Shah Alam, 40470, Selangor Darul Ehsan, Malaysia
Tel.: (60) 351246157
Web Site: http://www.torin.com.au
Emp.: 100
Heating Equipment Mfr & Distr
N.A.I.C.S.: 335312

Transmission Australia Pty., Ltd. (1)
22 Corporate Ave, Rowville, 3178, VIC, Australia
Tel.: (61) 397554444
Power Transmission Component Distr
N.A.I.C.S.: 423610

Subsidiary (Non-US):

Regal Beloit New Zealand Ltd. (2)
Findex Level 29 188 Quay Street, Auckland Central, Auckland, 1010, New Zealand
Tel.: (64) 98203550
Web Site: http://www.regalaustralia.com.au
Sales Range: $25-49.9 Million
Emp.: 50
Electrical & Thermal Insulating Material Supplier

Regal Rexnord Corporation—(Continued)

N.A.I.C.S.: 238210

Unico, Inc. (1)
3725 Nicholson Rd, Franksville, WI
53126-0505 (100%)
Tel.: (262) 886-5678
Web Site: https://www.unicous.com
Sales Range: $50-74.9 Million
Emp.: 250
Industrial Motion-Controls & Drive Products
Developer & Mfr
N.A.I.C.S.: 335314

Subsidiary (Non-US):

Unico (UK) Ltd. (2)
Garamonde Drive, Wymbush, Milton
Keynes, MK8 8LF, United Kingdom
Tel.: (44) 1908260000
Web Site: https://www.unicouk.com
Sales Range: $10-24.9 Million
Emp.: 400
Motor & Drive Mfr
N.A.I.C.S.: 333996
Christopher Hutt (Gen Mgr)
Sean Brady (Mgr-Customer Svcs)
Ylenia Ponsillo (Coord-Spares)

Unico China Automation Co. Ltd. (2)
1018 Building A 11 Xinghuo St Science City,
Fengtai District, Beijing, 100070, China
Tel.: (86) 1083681846
Web Site: http://www.unicocn.com
Emp.: 10
Motor & Generator Mfr
N.A.I.C.S.: 335312

Unico Deutschland GmbH (2)
Dortmunder Strasse 7, 57234, Wilnsdorf,
Germany
Tel.: (49) 27393030
Web Site: https://unicous.com
Sales Range: $25-49.9 Million
Emp.: 55
Motor & Drive Mfr
N.A.I.C.S.: 333996
Heribert Huwer (Mng Dir)

Unico Japan Co. Ltd. (2)
1-4-3 Tokuicho, Chuo-ku, Osaka, 540-0025,
Japan
Tel.: (81) 669450077
Web Site: http://www.unicojp.co.jp
Sales Range: $10-24.9 Million
Emp.: 20
Motor & Generator Mfr
N.A.I.C.S.: 335312

Unicoven C. A. (2)
8va Carrera Sur Casa No 102 Entre Calle
14 Y 15, Pueblo Nuevo Sur, El Tigre, Anzo-
ategui, Venezuela
Tel.: (58) 5218787889877
Web Site: http://www.unicous.com
Electric Motor Mfr & Distr
N.A.I.C.S.: 335312

Velvet Drive (1)
1208 Old Norris Rd, Liberty, SC 29657-
3508
Tel.: (864) 843-9231
Web Site: https://www.velvetdrive.com
Sales Range: $50-74.9 Million
Emp.: 60
Hi-Performance Ring & Pinion, Custom
Geardrives & Speed Reducers Mfr
N.A.I.C.S.: 333612

REGENCY AFFILIATES, INC.
1890 Palmer Ave Ste 303, Larch-
mont, NY 10538
Tel.: (212) 644-3450　　　**DE**
Web Site:
　　https://www.regencyaffiliates.com
RAFI—(OTCIQ)
Rev.: $5,234,781
Assets: $87,454,662
Liabilities: $24,713,614
Net Worth: $62,741,048
Earnings: ($2,042,242)
Fiscal Year-end: 12/31/23
Asset & Financial Services
N.A.I.C.S.: 523999
Laurence S. Levy (Chm, CEO &
CFO)
Carol Zelinski (Sec)

REGENCY CENTERS CORPORATION
1 Independent Dr Ste 114, Jackson-
ville, FL 32202
Tel.: (904) 598-7000　　　**FL**
Web Site:
　　https://www.regencycenters.com
Year Founded: 1993
REG—(NASDAQ)
Rev.: $1,322,466,000
Assets: $12,426,913,000
Liabilities: $5,234,978,000
Net Worth: $7,191,935,000
Earnings: $359,500,000
Emp.: 492
Fiscal Year-end: 12/31/23
Real Estate Investment Trust
N.A.I.C.S.: 525990
Lisa Palmer (Pres & CEO)
Alan T. Roth (COO & Pres-East Re-
gion)
Martin E. Stein Jr. (Exec Chm)
Michael J. Mas (CFO & Exec VP)
Thomas C. Paul (VP-Internal Audit)
Nicholas A. Wibbenmeyer (Chief In-
vestment Officer & Pres-West Re-
gion)
Dale Johnston (CIO & Sr VP)
Terah L. Devereaux (Principal Acctg
Officer & Sr VP)
Amy D'Olimpio (Sr VP-HR)
Mark Peternell (VP-Sustainability-
Denver)
Andrew Mumford (VP-Joint Ventures
Portfolio Mgmt)
Ernst A. Bell (VP & Assoc Gen Coun-
sel)
Jack deVilliers (VP-Investments-New
York & Connecticut)
Jan Hanak (VP-Mktg & Comm)
Stephanie Waidner (VP & Assoc Gen
Counsel)
Jamie Conroy (VP-HR)
Michael R. Herman (Gen Counsel,
Sec & Sr VP)
Christy McElroy (Sr VP-Capital Mar-
kets)
Terah Devereaux (Chief Acctg Offi-
cer)
Jill Caffey (VP)
Matt Lee (VP)
Joanne Mondares (VP)

Subsidiaries:

**East Meadow Plaza Regency,
LLC** (1)
1897-1899 Front St, East Meadow, NY
11554
Tel.: (203) 635-5561
Shopping Mall Operator
N.A.I.C.S.: 531120

**FW IL-Riverside/Rivers Edge,
LLC** (1)
1 Independent Dr Ste 114, Jacksonville, FL
32202
Tel.: (904) 598-7000
Real Estate Investment Services
N.A.I.C.S.: 531110

King Farm Center, LLC (1)
403 Redland Blvd, Rockville, MD 20850
Tel.: (703) 442-4300
Web Site: http://kingfarmvillagecenter.com
Nursery & Farm Supply Store Operator
N.A.I.C.S.: 444240

Marketplace Center, Inc. (1)
1411 W Covell Blvd, Davis, CA 95616
Tel.: (925) 279-1800
Web Site:
　　http://www.shopmarketplacedavis.com
Grocery Product Distr
N.A.I.C.S.: 445110

Midway Shopping Center, L.P. (1)
Midway Shopping Ctr, Scarsdale, NY 10583
Tel.: (203) 862-5422
Shopping Mall Operator
N.A.I.C.S.: 531120

REG-UB Properties, LLC (1)

321 Railroad Ave, Greenwich, CT 06830
Tel.: (203) 863-8200
Web Site: http://www.ubproperties.com
Rev.: $143,103,000
Assets: $997,326,000
Liabilities: $423,024,000
Net Worth: $574,302,000
Earnings: $39,704,000
Emp.: 55
Fiscal Year-end: 10/31/2022
Real Estate Investment Trust
N.A.I.C.S.: 525990
Michael R. Herman (Gen Counsel, Sec &
Sr VP)
Linda L. Lacey (Sr VP & Dir-Leasing)
James M. Aries (Sr VP & Dir-Acquisitions)
John T. Hayes (CFO, Treas & Sr VP)
Diane Midollo (VP & Controller)
Stephan A. Rapaglia (COO, Sr VP & Asst
Sec)
Andrew R. Albrecht (VP & Dir-Mgmt & Con-
struction)
Suzanne M. Moore (VP & Dir-Accounts Re-
ceivables)
Nicholas Capuano (VP)
Joseph J. Allegretti (VP-Leasing)
Miyun Sung (Chief Legal Officer, Sec & Sr
VP)
Christopher Perez (VP & Controller)

Subsidiary (Domestic):

UB Orangeburg, LLC (2)
321 Railroad Ave, Greenwich, CT 06830
Tel.: (203) 863-8260
Web Site: http://www.ubproperties.com
Emp.: 50
Residential Property Management Services
N.A.I.C.S.: 531390
Willing L. Biddle (Pres)

Regency Centers, L.P. (1)
1 Independent Dr Ste 114, Jacksonville, FL
32202-5019
Tel.: (904) 598-7000
Web Site: https://www.regencycenters.com
Rev.: $1,322,465,999
Assets: $12,426,912,999
Liabilities: $5,234,977,999
Net Worth: $7,191,934,999
Earnings: $359,499,999
Emp.: 491
Fiscal Year-end: 12/31/2023
Shopping Center Leasing Services
N.A.I.C.S.: 531120
Nicholas A. Wibbenmeyer (Pres)
Mkie Mas (CFO)
Alan Roth (Pres)
Nick Wibbenmeyer (Pres)
Barry Argalas (Mng Dir)
Patrick Conway (Mng Dir)
Kirsta Di Iaconi (Mng Dir)
Andre Kolcozar (Mng Dir)
Patrick Krejs (Mng Dir)
Scottt Prigge (Mng Dir)
Ernst Bell (VP)
Lauren Borronari (VP)
Anne Brettingen (VP)
Jill Caffey (VP)
Jamie Conroy (VP)
Amy D'Olimpio (Sr VP)
Will Damrath (VP)
Terah Devereaux (Chief Acctg Officer)
Jack De Villiers (Sr VP)
Meghan Dones (VP)
Steve Felderman (VP)
Gary Fields (VP)
John Fitzpatrick (VP)
Jason Gibson (VP)
Jan Hanak (VP)
Mike Herman (Gen Counsel)
Patrick Johnson (Sr VP)
Andrew Kabat (Sr VP)
Ray Kayacan (VP)
Mike Kinsella (Sr VP)
Nick Koglin (VP)
Matt Lee (VP)
Peggy McDermott (VP)
Christy McElroy (Sr VP)
Patrick McKinley (Sr VP)
Dave McNulty (VP)
John Mehigan (Sr VP)
Joanne Mondares (VP)
Andrew Mumford (VP)
Abe Pacetti (Sr VP)
Tom Paul (VP)
Mark Peternell (VP)
Chris Sanchez (VP)
Doug Shaffer (Sr VP)

Nate Smith (VP)
Sam Steible (VP)
Erik Tompkins (VP)
Kurt Utterback (VP)
Stephanie Wainder (VP)
Chris Widmayer (Sr VP)
Rebecca Wing (VP)

Subsidiary (Domestic):

Belmont Chase, LLC (2)
19800-19890 Belmont Chase Dr, Ashburn,
VA 20147-3414
Tel.: (703) 442-4300
Restaurant Operators
N.A.I.C.S.: 722511

Regency-Kleban Properties, LLC (2)
1189 Post Rd, Fairfield, CT 06824
Tel.: (203) 955-1978
Web Site: https://www.klebanproperties.com
Real Estate Management Services
N.A.I.C.S.: 531210
Kenneth W. Kleban (Pres)
Deborah Coba (Sr Mgr-Property)
April Clyne (Sr Mgr-Property)
Al Kleban (Chm)
Evan Kleban (VP-Dev)
Jan Kmiec (Mgr-Construction & Mainte-
nance)
Bailey Kleban (Mgr-Ventures)
Jeff Campbell (Mgr-Facilities)
Sasha Hemingway (Controller)

Waverly Regency, LLC (2)
1122 Kenilworth Dr Ste 502, Baltimore, MD
21204
Tel.: (410) 825-0996
Web Site:
　　http://www.waverlymanagement.com
Administrative Management Services
N.A.I.C.S.: 561110
Seth A. McDonnell (CEO & Founder)
Eleanor Shriver Magee (Mgr-Business De-
velopment)

**Serramonte Center Holding Co.,
LLC** (1)
3 Serramonte Ctr, Daly City, CA 94015
Tel.: (650) 301-3360
Web Site:
　　https://www.serramontecenter.com
Shopping Mall Services
N.A.I.C.S.: 531120

**The Center at Slatten Ranch,
LLC** (1)
5779 Lone Tree Way, Antioch, CA 94531
Tel.: (925) 757-5930
Beauty Salon Operator
N.A.I.C.S.: 812111

Willows Center Concord, Inc. (1)
1975 Diamond Blvd, Concord, CA 94520
Tel.: (925) 825-4001
Web Site: http://www.willowsshopping.com
Shopping Mall Services
N.A.I.C.S.: 531120

REGENERON PHARMACEUTICALS, INC.
777 Old Saw Mill River Rd, Tarry-
town, NY 10591-6707
Tel.: (914) 847-7000　　　**NY**
Web Site:
　　https://www.regeneron.com
Year Founded: 1988
REGN—(NASDAQ)
Rev.: $13,117,200,000
Assets: $33,080,200,000
Liabilities: $7,107,100,000
Net Worth: $25,973,100,000
Earnings: $3,953,600,000
Emp.: 13,450
Fiscal Year-end: 12/31/23
Developer of Protein-Based Drugs for
Treatment of Diseases & Conditions
N.A.I.C.S.: 325412
Joseph J. LaRosa (Gen Counsel, Sec
& Exec VP)
Nouhad Husseini (Sr VP-Bus Dev)
Neil Stahl (Exec VP-R&D)
Daniel Van Plew (Exec VP & Gen
Mgr-Industrial Ops & Product Supply)
Andrew Murphy (Exec VP-Res)

Christopher R. Fenimore *(CFO & Sr VP-Fin)*
Ned Braunstein *(Exec VP-Regulatory Affairs-Global Patient Safety)*
Hanne Bak *(Sr VP-Preclinical Mfg & Process Dev)*
Gerald Carreau *(Sr VP-Comml Scale Mfg & Mfg Tech)*
Scott Carver *(Sr VP-Mfg & Process Sciences)*
Israel Lowy *(Sr VP-Translational Sciences & Oncology)*
Hala Mirza *(Sr VP-Corporate Communications)*
Brian Zambrowicz *(Sr VP-Functional Genomics)*
Aris Baras *(Sr VP-Regeneron Genetics Center)*
Maya Bermingham *(Sr VP-Pub Policy & Govt Affairs)*
Bob McCowan *(CIO & Sr VP-IT)*
Smita Pillai *(Chief Diversity, Equity & Inclusion Officer)*
Kerry Reinertsen *(Sr VP-Strategic Alliances)*
Deborah Tegan *(Sr VP-Strategic Sourcing & Procurement)*
Gregory Geba *(Sr VP-Global Dev Scientific Council)*
Gary Herman *(Sr VP-Early Clinical Dev & Experimental Sciences)*
Johnathan M. Lancaster *(Sr VP-Medical Affairs-Global)*
John Lin *(Sr VP-Immuno-Oncology & Head-Bispecifics)*
William Olson *(Sr VP-Therapeutic Proteins)*
L. Andres Sirulnik *(Sr VP-Translational & Clinical Sciences-Hematology)*
Randy Soltys *(Sr VP-Drug Safety & Pharmacometrics)*
Gavin Thurston *(Sr VP-Oncology Res)*
Patrice Gilooly *(Sr VP-Quality Assurance & Ops)*
Jennifer McNay *(Sr VP-CMC Regulatory Sciences & Industrial Affairs)*
Niall O'Leary *(Sr VP & Head-Site-IOPS Raheen)*
Gerald Underwood *(Sr VP-Technical Ops)*
Ron Wang *(Sr VP-Quality Control)*
Christina Chan *(Sr VP-Corporate Communications)*
David Snow *(Sr VP & Head-Global)*
Mark Volpe *(Sr VP-Tax)*
David Simon *(Sr VP-Finance)*
George D. Yancopoulos *(Founder, Co-Chm, Co-Pres & Chief Scientific Officer)*
Leonard S. Schleifer *(Co-Chm, Pres & CEO)*

Subsidiaries:

Checkmate Pharmaceuticals, Inc. **(1)**
245 Main St 2nd Fl, Cambridge, MA 02142
Tel.: (617) 682-3625
Web Site:
  http://www.checkmatepharma.com
Rev.: $65,000
Assets: $78,838,000
Liabilities: $9,379,000
Net Worth: $69,459,000
Earnings: ($61,405,000)
Emp.: 30
Fiscal Year-end: 12/31/2021
Biotechnology Research & Development Services
N.A.I.C.S.: 541714
Katherine A. Eade *(Gen Counsel)*
Kleem Chaudhary *(Chief Bus Officer)*
Art Krieg *(Founder & Chief Scientific Officer)*
James Wooldridge *(Chief Medical Officer)*
Robert Dolski *(CFO & Principal Acctg Officer)*
Alan Bash *(Pres & CEO)*

Decibel Therapeutics, Inc. **(1)**
1325 Boylston St Ste 500, Boston, MA 02215
Tel.: (617) 370-8701
Web Site: https://www.decibeltx.com
Rev.: $1,192,000
Assets: $123,373,000
Liabilities: $41,580,000
Net Worth: $81,793,000
Earnings: ($63,005,000)
Emp.: 68
Fiscal Year-end: 12/31/2022
Biotechnology Research & Development Services
N.A.I.C.S.: 541714
Robert E. Landry *(CFO)*
Joseph J. LaRosa *(Sec)*
Nouhad Husseini *(Mng Dir)*
Leonard N. Brooks *(Treas)*

Regeneron **(1)**
777 Old Saw Mill River Rd, Tarrytown, NY 10591
Tel.: (914) 847-7000
Web Site: http://www.regeneron.com
Sales Range: $150-199.9 Million
Mfr of Pharmaceuticals
N.A.I.C.S.: 325412

Regeneron Canada Company **(1)**
Lower Water Street, PO Box 997, Halifax, B3J 0J2, NS, Canada
Web Site: https://www.regeneron.ca
Pharmaceutical & Medicine Mfr
N.A.I.C.S.: 325412

Regeneron France SAS **(1)**
33 rue Francois 1er, 75008, Paris, France
Tel.: (33) 800906738
Web Site: https://www.regeneron.fr
Medicine Transformation & Drug Development Services
N.A.I.C.S.: 621999

Regeneron Ireland **(1)**
Raheen Business Park, Limerick, V94 Y7Y3, Ireland
Tel.: (353) 61782000
Pharmaceutical Products Distr
N.A.I.C.S.: 424210

Regeneron Ireland Designated Activity Company **(1)**
One Warrington Place, Dublin, DO2 HH27, Ireland
Tel.: (353) 14112200
Web Site: https://www.regeneron.ie
Emp.: 1,400
Biopharmaceutical Drug Mfr
N.A.I.C.S.: 325412
Muriel O'Byrne *(VP & Head-Regulatory Affairs & European Bus Office)*

Regeneron Italy S.r.l. **(1)**
Via Pietro Paleocapa 1, 20121, Milan, Italy
Tel.: (39) 0800180052
Web Site: https://www.regeneron.it
Medicine Transformation & Drug Development Services
N.A.I.C.S.: 621999

Regeneron Japan KK **(1)**
Tekko Building 4F 1-8-2, Marunouchi Chiyoda-ku, Tokyo, 100-0005, Japan
Tel.: (81) 8001239172
Web Site: https://www.regeneron.co.jp
Medicine Transformation & Drug Development Services
N.A.I.C.S.: 621999

Regeneron NL B.V. **(1)**
Herikerbergweg 88, 1101 CM, Amsterdam, Netherlands
Tel.: (31) 850644034
Web Site: https://www.regeneron.nl
Pharmaceutical & Medicine Mfr
N.A.I.C.S.: 325412

REGENERX BIOPHARMACEUTICALS INC.

15245 Shady Grove Rd Ste 470, Rockville, MD 20850
Tel.: (301) 208-9191   DE
Web Site: https://www.regenerx.com
Year Founded: 1982
RGRX—(OTCQB)
Rev.: $76,761
Assets: $382,177

Liabilities: $3,827,648
Net Worth: ($3,445,471)
Earnings: ($1,727,455)
Emp.: 2
Fiscal Year-end: 12/31/22
Biopharmaceutical Researcher & Mfr
N.A.I.C.S.: 325412
Allan L. Goldstein *(Chm & Chief Scientific Officer)*
J. J. Finkelstein *(Pres)*
Dane Saglio *(CFO)*

REGENICIN, INC.

10 High Ct, Little Falls, NJ 07424
Tel.: (973) 557-8914   NV
Web Site: https://www.regenicin.com
RGIN—(OTCIQ)
Assets: $5,315
Liabilities: $3,733,000
Net Worth: ($3,727,685)
Earnings: ($758,456)
Emp.: 3
Fiscal Year-end: 09/30/19
Cell Therapy & Biotechnology Products Developer
N.A.I.C.S.: 325414
John J. Weber *(CFO & Chief Acctg Officer)*
Randall E. McCoy *(Pres & CEO)*
J. Roy Nelson *(Chief Science Officer)*

REGENXBIO INC.

9804 Medical Ctr Dr, Rockville, MD 20850
Tel.: (240) 552-8181   DE
Web Site: https://www.regenxbio.com
Year Founded: 2008
RGNX—(NASDAQ)
Rev.: $112,724,000
Assets: $833,268,000
Liabilities: $317,073,000
Net Worth: $516,195,000
Earnings: ($280,321,000)
Emp.: 401
Fiscal Year-end: 12/31/22
Biotechnology Products Focusing on Gene Therapy Mfr
N.A.I.C.S.: 325413
Allan M. Fox *(Co-Founder)*
Olivier Danos *(Chief Scientific Officer & Sr VP)*
Shiva G. Fritsch *(Chief Comm Officer & Chief People Officer)*
Curran M. Simpson *(COO)*
Ram Palanki *(Comml, Ops & Strategy)*
Steve Pakola *(Chief Medical Officer)*
Kenneth T. Mills *(Co-Founder)*
Patrick J. Christmas II *(Chief Legal Officer)*
Mitchell Chan *(CFO, Principal Acctg Officer & Exec VP)*
Curran M. Simpson *(Pres, CEO & COO)*

REGIONAL BRANDS INC.

6060 Parkland Blvd Ste 200, Mayfield Heights, OH 44124
Tel.: (216) 825-4005   DE
Web Site:
  https://www.regionalbrandsinc.com
RGBD—(OTCIQ)
Rev.: $36,977,125
Assets: $25,172,201
Liabilities: $8,395,644
Net Worth: $16,776,557
Earnings: $256,725
Emp.: 84
Fiscal Year-end: 12/31/20
Offices of Other Holding Companies
N.A.I.C.S.: 551112
Carl J. Grassi *(Chm)*

Subsidiaries:

B.R. Johnson, LLC **(1)**

6960 Fly Rd, East Syracuse, NY 13057   **(76.17%)**
Tel.: (315) 437-1070
Web Site: http://www.brjohnson.com
Sales Range: $1-9.9 Million
Construction Products Distr & Installation Contractor
N.A.I.C.S.: 423310

REGIONAL HEALTH PROPERTIES, INC.

1050 Crown Pointe Pkwy Ste 720, Atlanta, GA 30338
Tel.: (678) 869-5116   GA
Web Site:
  https://regionalhealthproperties.com
Year Founded: 2017
RHE—(NYSEAMEX)
Rev.: $17,164,000
Assets: $62,181,000
Liabilities: $61,996,000
Net Worth: $185,000
Earnings: ($3,888,000)
Emp.: 114
Fiscal Year-end: 12/31/23
Healthcare Real Estate Investment Trust
N.A.I.C.S.: 525990
Brent S. Morrison *(Chm, Pres, CEO & Sec)*
Heather L. Pittard *(Chief Acctg Officer)*
Paul J. O'Sullivan *(Sr VP)*

Subsidiaries:

ADK Lumber City Operator, LLC **(1)**
245 Hwy 19, Lumber City, GA 31549-9779
Tel.: (912) 363-2484
Nursing Care Facility Services
N.A.I.C.S.: 623110

ADK Oceanside Operator, LLC **(1)**
7 Rosewood Ave, Tybee Island, GA 31328-9435
Tel.: (912) 786-4511
Nursing Care Facility Services
N.A.I.C.S.: 623110
Brian Nutter *(Head-HR)*

ADK Powder Springs Operator, LLC **(1)**
3460 Powder Springs Rd, Powder Springs, GA 30127-2322
Tel.: (770) 439-9199
Nursing Care Facility Services
N.A.I.C.S.: 623110

Assured Health Care, Inc. **(1)**
1250 W Dorothy Ln Ste 204, Kettering, OH 45409
Tel.: (937) 294-2803
Sales Range: $10-24.9 Million
Emp.: 50
Health Care Srvices
N.A.I.C.S.: 621610
Barbette Spitler *(Exec Dir)*

Benton Nursing, LLC **(1)**
224 S Main St, Bentonville, AR 72712-5963
Tel.: (479) 273-3373
Nursing Care Facility Services
N.A.I.C.S.: 623110
Boyd Gentry *(Pres & CEO)*

Coosa Nursing ADK, LLC **(1)**
513 Pineview Ave, Glencoe, AL 35905-1803
Tel.: (256) 492-5350
Nursing Care Facility Services
N.A.I.C.S.: 623110

Eaglewood Village, LLC **(1)**
2000 Villa Rd, Springfield, OH 45503-1700
Tel.: (937) 399-7195
Nursing Care Facility Services
N.A.I.C.S.: 623110

Hearth & Care of Greenfield, LLC **(1)**
238 S Washington St, Greenfield, OH 45123-1467
Tel.: (937) 981-3349
Web Site: http://www.hearth-and-care.com
Nursing Care Facility Services
N.A.I.C.S.: 623110

Hearth & Home of Urbana, LLC **(1)**

Regional Health Properties, Inc.—(Continued)

1579 E State Route 29, Urbana, OH 43078-9554
Tel.: (937) 653-5263
Web Site:
https://www.hearthandhomeurbana.com
Nursing & Personal Care Services
N.A.I.C.S.: 623311

Hearth & Home of Van Wert, LLC (1)
1118 Westwood Dr, Van Wert, OH 45891
Tel.: (419) 232-2450
Web Site:
https://www.hearthandhomevanwert.com
Nursing & Personal Care Services
N.A.I.C.S.: 623311

Hearth & Home of Vandalia, Inc. (1)
55 Great Hill Dr, Dayton, OH 45414
Tel.: (937) 264-1100
Web Site:
https://www.hearthandhomevandalia.com
Emp.: 40
Nursing & Personal Care Services
N.A.I.C.S.: 623311

Homestead Nursing, LLC (1)
826 N St, Stamps, AR 71860-4522
Tel.: (870) 533-4444
Sales Range: $10-24.9 Million
Emp.: 65
Nursing Care Facility Services
N.A.I.C.S.: 623110

Mountain View Nursing, LLC (1)
706 Oak Grove St, Mountain View, AR 72560-8601
Tel.: (870) 269-5835
Sales Range: $25-49.9 Million
Emp.: 85
Nursing Facility Services
N.A.I.C.S.: 623110

The Pavilion Care Center, LLC (1)
705 Fulton St, Sidney, OH 45365-3203
Tel.: (937) 492-9591
Emp.: 63
Nursing Care Facility Services
N.A.I.C.S.: 623110
Troy Hutchinson (Reg Mgr)

Valley River Nursing, LLC (1)
5301 Wheeler Ave, Fort Smith, AR 72901-8339
Tel.: (479) 646-3454
Nursing Care Facility Services
N.A.I.C.S.: 623110

REGIONAL MANAGEMENT CORP.

979 Batesville Rd Ste B, Greer, SC 29651
Tel.: (864) 448-7000   DE
Web Site:
https://www.regionalmanagement.com
Year Founded: 1987
RM—(NYSE)
Rev.: $551,399,000
Assets: $1,794,527,000
Liabilities: $1,472,254,000
Net Worth: $322,273,000
Earnings: $15,958,000
Emp.: 2,081
Fiscal Year-end: 12/31/23
Consumer Finance Management Services
N.A.I.C.S.: 522291
Brian J. Fisher (Chief Strategy & Dev Officer)
Catherine Atwood (Gen Counsel, Sec & Sr VP)
Robert W. Beck (Pres, CEO & Dir)
Harpreet Rana (CFO & Exec VP)
Manish Parmar (Chief Credit Risk Officer & Exec VP)

Subsidiaries:

Credit Recovery Associates, Inc. (1)
PO Box 1228, Mauldin, SC 29662
Tel.: (864) 546-3401
Web Site:
https://www.creditrecoveryassociates.com

Account Collection Services
N.A.I.C.S.: 561440

RMC Reinsurance, LTD (1)
4125 Tamiami Trail N, Naples, FL 34103
Tel.: (239) 298-8210
Web Site: https://www.rmcgp.com
Emp.: 15
Insurance Agencies & Brokerage Services
N.A.I.C.S.: 524210

Regional Finance Company of New Mexico, LLC (1)
200 1st St Ste C, Alamogordo, NM 88310
Tel.: (575) 437-2461
Mortgage & Nonmortgage Loan Brokerage Services
N.A.I.C.S.: 522310

Regional Finance Company of Oklahoma, LLC (1)
1500 Hoppe Blvd Ste 6, Ada, OK 74820
Tel.: (580) 279-0021
Web Site:
https://branches.regionalfinance.com
Mortgage & Nonmortgage Loan Brokerage Services
N.A.I.C.S.: 522310

Regional Finance Corporation of Alabama (1)
458 1st St SW, Alabaster, AL 35007
Tel.: (205) 419-4309
Web Site:
https://branches.regionalfinance.com
Mortgage & Nonmortgage Loan Brokerage Services
N.A.I.C.S.: 522310
Crystal Jordan-Cross (Branch Mgr)

Regional Finance Corporation of Georgia (1)
3421-6 Cypress Mill Rd, Brunswick, GA 31520
Tel.: (912) 261-2882
Mortgage & Nonmortgage Loan Brokerage Services
N.A.I.C.S.: 522310

Regional Finance Corporation of North Carolina (1)
1337 C E Dixie Dr, Asheboro, NC 27203
Tel.: (336) 625-3232
Mortgage & Nonmortgage Loan Brokerage Services
N.A.I.C.S.: 522310

Regional Finance Corporation of South Carolina (1)
1309 W Poinsett St, Greer, SC 29650
Tel.: (864) 801-9800
Web Site:
https://branches.regionalfinance.com
Sales Range: $25-49.9 Million
Emp.: 40
Licensed Loan Companies, Small
N.A.I.C.S.: 522291

Regional Finance Corporation of Tennessee (1)
1321 Bell Rd, Antioch, TN 37013
Tel.: (615) 942-6951
Web Site:
https://branches.regionalfinance.com
Emp.: 3
Mortgage & Nonmortgage Loan Brokerage Services
N.A.I.C.S.: 522310

Regional Finance Corporation of Texas (1)
3182 Catclaw Dr, Abilene, TX 79606
Tel.: (325) 307-6626
Mortgage & Nonmortgage Loan Brokerage Services
N.A.I.C.S.: 522310

Regional Management Receivables, LLC (1)
509 W Butler Rd, Greenville, SC 29607
Tel.: (864) 422-8011
Business Management Services
N.A.I.C.S.: 561110

REGIONS FINANCIAL CORPORATION

1900 5th Ave N, Birmingham, AL 35203

Tel.: (205) 581-7890   DE
Web Site: https://www.regions.com
Year Founded: 1971
RF—(NYSE)
Rev.: $9,153,000,000
Assets: $152,194,000,000
Liabilities: $134,701,000,000
Net Worth: $17,493,000,000
Earnings: $1,976,000,000
Emp.: 20,101
Fiscal Year-end: 12/31/23
Bank Holding Company
N.A.I.C.S.: 551111
David R. Keenan (Chief Admin Officer, Chief HR Officer & Sr Exec VP)
William D. Ritter (Sr Exec VP & Head-Wealth Mgmt Grp)
Kate Randall Danella (Chief Strategy & Client Experience Officer & Sr Exec VP)
Karin Allen (Chief Acctg Officer & Asst Controller)
Karin Allen (Chief Acctg Officer & Asst Controller)
Karin K. Allen (Chief Acctg Officer)
David J. Turner Jr. (CFO & Sr Exec VP)
John M. Turner Jr. (Pres & CEO)

Subsidiaries:

BlackArch Partners LP. (1)
227 W Trade St Ste 2200, Charlotte, NC 28202
Tel.: (704) 414-6300
Web Site:
https://www.blackarchpartners.com
Miscellaneous Financial Services
N.A.I.C.S.: 522299
Adam M. Tindel (Mng Dir)
R. Ches Riley (Co-Founder & Mng Dir)
Charles Thompson (Mng Dir)
Brandon Boor (VP)
Ryan Jackson (Mng Dir)
Nhan Nguyen (VP)
Zach Daniels (VP)
Chris Lyons (VP)
Patrick J. Martin II (Mng Dir)

Clearsight Advisors Inc. (1)
1650 Tysons Blvd Ste 710, McLean, VA 22102
Tel.: (703) 672-3100
Web Site: https://clearsightadvisors.com
Finance Investment Services
N.A.I.C.S.: 523999

Highland Associates, Inc. (1)
2545 Highland Ave S Ste 200, Birmingham, AL 35205-2478
Tel.: (205) 933-8664
Web Site: https://www.highlandassoc.com
Management Consulting Services
N.A.I.C.S.: 541611
Amanda H. Poe (Chief Compliance Officer)

RFC Financial Services Holding LLC (1)
3050 Peachtree Rd NW Ste 400, Atlanta, GA 30305
Tel.: (404) 279-7400
Financial Management Consulting Services
N.A.I.C.S.: 541611

Regions Asset Company (1)
3501 Silverside Rd Ste 209, Wilmington, DE 19810-4910
Tel.: (302) 478-3061
Auto Parts & Equipment Mfr
N.A.I.C.S.: 423110

Regions Bank (1)
1900 5th Ave N, Birmingham, AL 35203
Tel.: (205) 944-1300
Web Site: http://www.regions.com
Commercial Banking
N.A.I.C.S.: 522110
David J. Turner Jr. (CFO & Sr Exec VP)
John M. Turner Jr. (Pres & CEO)
Clara Green (Head-Diversity & Inclusion)
Robert S. Heffes (Mng Dir & Head-Credit Distr)
Mike Mauldin (Head-Healthcare Grp)
Ward Cheatham (Head-Corp Banking)
Dan Massey (Chief Enterprise Ops &Tech Officer)

Tom Speir (Head-Strategy & Corp Dev)
Nikki Stephenson (Head-Credit Products-Corp Banking Grp)
Sean Creedon (Sr VP & Mgr-Relationship)
Victor Sostar (Co-Head-Originationson)
Anna Brackin (Chief Compliance Officer)
Gary Walton (Chief Risk Officer-Consumer Banking & Wealth Mgmt)
Matt Lusco (Chief Risk Officer)

Subsidiary (Domestic):

Ascentium Capital LLC (2)
23970 Highway 59 N, Kingwood, TX 77339-1535
Web Site: https://www.ascentiumcapital.com
Equipment Finance Services
N.A.I.C.S.: 522310
Thomas Depping (CEO)
Richard Baccaro (Sr VP-Vendor Sls)
David Pederson (Sr VP-Tech)
Evan Wilkoff (Sr VP-Capital Markets)
Hernan Traversone (Sr VP-Credit)
Eric Lemire (Sr VP-Ops)
Daniel Bocash (Sr VP-Asset Mgmt)
Ben Earthman (Sec & Sr VP-Legal)
Bob Neagle (Sr VP & Gen Mgr-Merchant Fin)
Ozgen Sayginsoy (Sr VP-Risk Mgmt)
David Lyder (Sr VP-Sls & Mktg)

EnerBank USA (2)
1245 Brickyard Rd Ste 600, Salt Lake City, UT 84106   (100%)
Tel.: (801) 832-0700
Web Site: http://www.enerbank.com
Sales Range: $125-149.9 Million
Unsecured Home Improvement & Home Energy Loans
N.A.I.C.S.: 522310
Kristin B. Dittmer (CFO & Exec VP)
Robb Kerry (Chief Credit Officer, Officer-Enterprise Risk & Exec VP)
Charles E. Knadler (Pres & CEO)
Rejji Hayes (Chm)
Allyson Torsak (Sr VP)

Regions Investment Management, Inc. (2)
1901 6th Ave N, Birmingham, AL 35203
Tel.: (205) 264-5523
Web Site: https://www.regions.com
Investment Advisory & Management Services
N.A.I.C.S.: 523940

Regions Business Capital Corporation (1)
599 Lexington Ave 45th Fl, New York, NY 10022
Tel.: (212) 935-6398
Investment Management Service
N.A.I.C.S.: 523940

Regions Commercial Equipment Finance, LLC (1)
1900 5th Ave N St 2400, Birmingham, AL 35203
Tel.: (205) 326-4666
Financial Management Consulting Services
N.A.I.C.S.: 541611

Regions Mortgage, Inc. (1)
PO Box 18001, Hattiesburg, MS 39404-8001   (100%)
Web Site: http://www.regionsmortgage.com
Sales Range: $200-249.9 Million
Emp.: 700
Mortgage Banking
N.A.I.C.S.: 522292

Revolution Partners, LLC (1)
300 Boylston St, Boston, MA 02116
Tel.: (901) 421-6300
Web Site:
https://www.revolutionpartners.com
Investment Banking Service
N.A.I.C.S.: 523940
Lauren Sekerke (Dir-Investments)

Trilogy Risk Specialists, Inc. (1)
3325 Paddocks Pkwy Ste 200, Suwanee, GA 30024
Tel.: (678) 845-6500
Web Site: http://www.trilogyrisk.com
Insurance Agency Services
N.A.I.C.S.: 524210

REGIS CORPORATION

3701 Wayzata Blvd Ste 600, Minneapolis, MN 55416
Tel.: (952) 947-7777 MN
Web Site: https://www.regiscorp.com
Year Founded: 1954
RGS—(NASDAQ)
Rev.: $202,982,000
Assets: $530,496,000
Liabilities: $473,709,000
Net Worth: $56,787,000
Earnings: $91,060,000
Emp.: 275
Fiscal Year-end: 06/30/24
Salons, Beauty Schools & Hair Restoration Centers Owner & Operator
N.A.I.C.S.: 812112
David J. Grissen (Chm)
Kersten D. Zupfer (CFO & Exec VP)
Matthew Doctor (Pres & CEO)
John Davi (CTO & Exec VP)
Michelle DeVore (Sr VP & Head-Mktg)
Jim B. Lain (Exec VP-Brand Ops, Supercuts, and Cost Cutters)
Michael Ferranti (Exec VP-Brand Ops, SmartStyle, First Choice Haircutters, Roosters, and Portfolio Brands)

Subsidiaries:

BeautyFirst Inc. (1)
10610 E 26th Cir N, Wichita, KS 67216
Tel.: (316) 529-1430
Rev.: $65,000,000
Emp.: 75
Cosmetic Store Operator
N.A.I.C.S.: 456120

Fiesta Salons, Inc. (1)
7201 Metro Blvd, Minneapolis, MN 55439 (100%)
Tel.: (952) 947-7777
Web Site: http://www.fiestasalons.com
Sales Range: $100-124.9 Million
Emp.: 2,000
Beauty Salons Owner & Operator
N.A.I.C.S.: 812112
Dan Hanrahan (Pres)

First Choice Haircutters, Ltd (1)
540-4915 130th Ave Se, Calgary, T2Z 4J2, AB, Canada
Tel.: (587) 295-4570
Web Site: https://www.firstchoice.com
Beauty Salon Operator
N.A.I.C.S.: 812112

Pro-Cuts, Inc. (1)
7201 Metro Blvd, Minneapolis, MN 55439
Tel.: (952) 947-7777
Web Site: http://www.procuts.com
Sales Range: $50-74.9 Million
Hair Salons Franchiser
N.A.I.C.S.: 812112

SmartStyle Family Hair Salons (1)
7201 Metro Blvd, Minneapolis, MN 55439 (100%)
Tel.: (952) 947-7777
Web Site: http://www.smartstyle.com
Sales Range: $75-99.9 Million
Hair Salons Operator
N.A.I.C.S.: 812112

Supercuts Corporate Shops, Inc. (1)
1732 Marsh Rd, Wilmington, DE 19810-4606
Tel.: (302) 551-6227
Web Site: https://www.supercuts.com
Beauty Salon Operator
N.A.I.C.S.: 812112

Supercuts, Inc. (1)
7201 Metro Blvd, Minneapolis, MN 55439
Tel.: (952) 947-7777
Web Site: http://www.supercuts.com
Sales Range: $300-349.9 Million
Emp.: 4,000
Haircare Retailer & Franchisor
N.A.I.C.S.: 812112

REGNUM CORP.
600 3rd Ave 19th Fl, New York, NY 10016
Tel.: (310) 881-6954 NV

Web Site:
https://www.regnumcorp.com
Year Founded: 2016
RGMP—(OTCIQ)
Rev.: $45,000
Assets: $864,677
Liabilities: $2,025,387
Net Worth: ($1,160,710)
Earnings: ($780,887)
Emp.: 2
Fiscal Year-end: 12/31/22
Commercial Property Managing Services
N.A.I.C.S.: 531312
Robert J. Stubblefield (CFO)

REGO PAYMENT ARCHITECTURES, INC.
325 Sentry Pkwy Ste 200, Blue Bell, PA 19422
Tel.: (267) 465-7530 DE
Web Site:
https://www.regopayments.com
Year Founded: 2008
RPMT—(OTCQB)
Rev.: $2,073
Assets: $6,376,625
Liabilities: $40,363,981
Net Worth: ($33,987,356)
Earnings: ($17,630,704)
Emp.: 4
Fiscal Year-end: 12/31/22
Online Parental Monitoring System Services
N.A.I.C.S.: 513210
Peter S. Pelullo (CEO)
Gerald Hannahs (Chm)
Denise Tayloe (Pres & CEO)

REGULUS THERAPEUTICS, INC.
4224 Campus Pt Ct Ste 210, San Diego, CA 92121
Tel.: (858) 202-6300 DE
Web Site: https://www.regulusrx.com
Year Founded: 2007
RGLS—(NASDAQ)
Rev.: $605,000
Assets: $46,716,000
Liabilities: $13,425,000
Net Worth: $33,291,000
Earnings: ($28,323,000)
Emp.: 30
Fiscal Year-end: 12/31/22
Biopharmaceutical Research & Development Services
N.A.I.C.S.: 541715
Preston S. Klassen (Pres & Head-R&D)
Moh Ahmadian (VP-Chemistry & Pharmaceutical Dev)
Brian K. Campion (VP-Business Development)
Amin Kamel (VP-Drug Metabolism & Pharmacokinetics)
Tate Owen (Sr Dir-Drug Metabolism & Pharmacokinetics)
Cris Calsada (CFO)
Christopher Aker (Gen Counsel & Sr VP)
Rekha Garg (Chief Medical Officer & Sr VP-Clinical Dev & Regulatory)
Claire Padgett (Sr VP-Clinical Ops)
Morgan Carlson (VP-Biology)
Edmund Lee (VP-Translational Medicine)
Curtis Monnig (VP-CMC)
Daniel Penksa (VP-Finance & Controller)
Joseph P. Hagan (CEO & principal executive officer)

REINSURANCE GROUP OF AMERICA, INC.
16600 Swingley Rdge Rd, Chesterfield, MO 63017

Tel.: (636) 736-7000 MO
Web Site: https://www.rgare.com
Year Founded: 1973
RGA—(NYSE)
Rev.: $18,567,000,000
Assets: $97,623,000,000
Liabilities: $88,452,000,000
Net Worth: $9,171,000,000
Earnings: $902,000,000
Emp.: 3,900
Fiscal Year-end: 12/31/23
Fire Insurance Services
N.A.I.C.S.: 524113
Jonathan Porter (Chief Risk Officer-Global & Exec VP)
J. Jeffrey Hopson (Sr VP-IR)
Tony Cheng (Pres & CEO)
William L. Hutton (Gen Counsel, Sec & Exec VP)
Lynn Phillips (VP-Comm)
Rene Cotting (Sr VP-Asset-Intensive-Global Fin Solutions)
Jeff Nordstrom (Chief Risk Officer & Sr VP-Global Fin Solutions)
Lizzie Curry (Dir-PR)
Leslie Barbi (Chief Investment Officer & Exec VP)
Tony Cheng (Pres)
Axel Andre (CFO & Exec VP)

Subsidiaries:

Arch Solutions Agency LLC (1)
16600 Swingley Ridge Rd, Chesterfield, MO 63017-1706
Tel.: (319) 573-7743
Reinsurance Services
N.A.I.C.S.: 524130

Castlewood Reinsurance Company (1)
16600 Swingley Ridge Rd, Chesterfield, MO 63017-1706
Tel.: (636) 736-7000
Emp.: 5,000
Reinsurance Services
N.A.I.C.S.: 524130

Elite Sales Processing, Inc. (1)
11205 Wright Cir Ste 120, Omaha, NE 68144
Tel.: (402) 933-1758
Web Site:
http://www.elitesalesprocessing.com
Reinsurance Services
N.A.I.C.S.: 524130
Carla Brown (COO)
Chad Gracey (CMO)
Dennis Gunderson (Chief Underwriting Officer)
Quinn Jones (CIO)

LOGiQ3 INC. (1)
60 Adelaide Street East Suite 1300, Toronto, M5C 3E4, ON, Canada
Tel.: (416) 340-7435
Web Site: http://www.logiq3.com
Reinsurance Services
N.A.I.C.S.: 524130

Leidsche Verzekering Maatschapij N.V. (1)
Bouwmeesterplein 1, 2801 BX, Gouda, Netherlands
Tel.: (31) 180555255
Web Site:
https://www.leidscheverzekeringen.nl
General Insurance Services
N.A.I.C.S.: 524210

Omnilife Insurance Company, Limited (1)
24 Chiswell Street, London, EC1 4TY, United Kingdom
Tel.: (44) 2073740123
Web Site: http://www.omnilife.co.uk
Fire Insurance Services
N.A.I.C.S.: 524113
Jonathan Plumtree (CEO)
Dan High (Ops Mgr)
Nathan Beverley (CFO)
Mark Hutchins (Mgr-Actuarial)
Doreen Aroussian (Mgr-Fin & HR)

RGA Capital Limited U.K. (1)
16th Floor 5 Aldermanbury Square, London,

EC2V 7HR, United Kingdom
Tel.: (44) 2077106700
Reinsurance Services
N.A.I.C.S.: 524130

RGA Global Reinsurance Company, Ltd. (1)
Rua Surubim 577 Conj 212 Cidade Moncoes, Sao Paulo, 04571-050, Brazil
Tel.: (55) 1148625000
Reinsurance Services
N.A.I.C.S.: 524130
Ronald Poon Affat (CEO)

RGA International Reinsurance Company (1)
3rd Floor Block C Central Park, Leopardstown, Dublin, D18 X5T1, Ireland
Tel.: (353) 12902900
Web Site: http://www.rgare.com
Emp.: 22
Insurance Services
N.A.I.C.S.: 524298
William Briffaut (Mng Dir)

RGA International Reinsurance Company Limited (1)
3rd Floor Block C Central Park, Leopardstown, Dublin, Ireland
Tel.: (353) 12902900
Reinsurance Services
N.A.I.C.S.: 524130
Enda Murphy (Exec VP & Head-Global Bus Ops)
Paul Nitsou (Chm)

RGA Life Reinsurance Company of Canada (1)
1981 McGill College Avenue 13th Floor, Montreal, H3A 3A8, QC, Canada (100%)
Tel.: (514) 985-5260
Web Site: http://www.rgare.ca
Sales Range: $50-74.9 Million
Emp.: 150
Fire Insurance Services
N.A.I.C.S.: 524113
Alka Gautam (Pres & CEO)
Brian Louth (CMO & Sr VP-Dev)

RGA Life Reinsurance Company of Canada (1)
161 Bay Street Suite 4220, Toronto, M5J 2S1, ON, Canada (100%)
Tel.: (416) 682-0000
Web Site: http://www.rgare.com
Sales Range: $10-24.9 Million
Emp.: 25
Fire Insurance Services
N.A.I.C.S.: 524113
Alka Gautam (Pres & CEO)
Robert Mallette (Chief Product & Pricing Officer & Sr VP)
Gay Burns (Exec VP)
Jonathan Porter (Chief Risk Officer)
Lawrence S. Carson (Exec VP)
Leslie Barbi (CIO)
Olav Cuiper (Chief Client Officer)
Ray Kleeman (Chief HR Officer)
Timothy L. Rozar (CEO)
Todd C. Larson (CFO)
William L. Hutton (Exec VP)

RGA Reinsurance Company (1)
16600 Swingley Ridge Rd, Chesterfield, MO 63017-1706
Tel.: (636) 736-7000
Web Site: https://www.rgare.com
Reinsurance Services
N.A.I.C.S.: 524130
Lawrence S. Carson (Exec VP)
Ron Herrmann (Exec VP)
Senan O'Loughlin (Sr VP)

RGA Reinsurance Company Middle East Limited (1)
Office No 1801 18th Floor Al Fattan Currency House Tower - II, PO Box 506539, Dubai International Financial Centre, Dubai, United Arab Emirates
Tel.: (971) 43896000
Web Site: https://www.rgare.com
Reinsurance Services
N.A.I.C.S.: 524130
Ashraf Al Azzouni (Mng Dir)
Dennis Sebastian (Reg Dir-Health)

RGA Reinsurance Company of Australia Limited (1)
Grosvenor Place Level 23 225 George

Reinsurance Group of America, Inc.—(Continued)

Street, Sydney, 2000, NSW, Australia
Tel.: (61) 282645800
Web Site: http://www.rgare.com
Reinsurance Services
N.A.I.C.S.: 524130

RGA Reinsurance Company of South Africa, Limited (1)
7th Floor The Terraces Black River Park 2
Fir Street, Observatory, Cape Town, 7925, South Africa
Tel.: (27) 214861700
Emp.: 100
Reinsurance Services
N.A.I.C.S.: 524130

RGA Reinsurance UK Limited (1)
16th Floor 5 Aldermanbury Square, London, EC2V 7HR, United Kingdom
Tel.: (44) 20 7710 6700
Web Site: http://www.rgare.com
Insurance Services
N.A.I.C.S.: 524298
Simon Wainwright (Mng Dir)
Calvin Cole (Head-Underwriting)
Hamish Galloway (Sr VP-Global Fin Solutions)

RGA Services (Singapore) Pte. Ltd. (1)
5 Temasek Blvd 04-03 Suntec Tower Five, Singapore, 038985, Singapore
Tel.: (65) 66929380
Reinsurance Services
N.A.I.C.S.: 524130
SooHwee Tan (Dir-Pricing & Global Fin Sol)

RGA Services India Private Limited (1)
302 Akruti Center Point MIDC Central Road Andheri E, Mumbai, 400 093, Maharashtra, India
Tel.: (91) 2267092590
Web Site: http://www.rgare.com
Sales Range: $25-49.9 Million
Emp.: 45
Reinsurance & Financial Services
N.A.I.C.S.: 524130

RGA UK Services Limited (1)
45th Floor 22 Bishopsgate, London, EC2N 4BQ, United Kingdom
Tel.: (44) 2077106700
Reinsurance Services
N.A.I.C.S.: 524130

RGAx LLC (1)
16600 Swingley Ridge Rd, Chesterfield, MO 63017-1706
Tel.: (636) 736-7000
Web Site: https://www.rgax.com
Fire Insurance Services
N.A.I.C.S.: 524113
Dennis Barnes (CEO)
Sandi Hubert (COO & Sr VP)
Alisha Harb (VP)
Andre Dreyer (VP)
Peter Rodes (VP)
Sherry Du (Mng Dir)
Todd Seabaugh (VP)

Subsidiary (Domestic):

My Life Covered LLC (2)
16600 Swingley Ridge Rd Ste 1300, Chesterfield, MO 63017
Tel.: (314) 339-1990
Web Site: http://www.mylifecoveredagency.com
Fire Insurance Services
N.A.I.C.S.: 524113

SALT Associates LLC (1)
42 US Route 1 Ste 1, Cumberland Foreside, ME 04110
Tel.: (207) 846-9779
Web Site: http://www.saltassociates.biz
Insurance Services
N.A.I.C.S.: 524113
Don Russell (Founder & Pres)
Jeff Verrill (Principal)
Jennifer Daigle (VP-Ops)
Julie Spugnardi (Dir-Mktg)
Mark Beagle (Exec Dir)

REJUVEL BIO-SCIENCES, INC.

325 SW 15th Ave, Pompano Beach, FL 33069
Tel.: (954) 354-2678　　FL
Web Site: http://rejuvel.com
Year Founded: 2009
NUUU—(OTCEM)
Sales Range: Less than $1 Million
Emp.: 1
Skin Care Product Mfr
N.A.I.C.S.: 325620
Charles J. Scimeca (Pres, CEO, Treas & Sec)

REKOR SYSTEMS, INC.
6721 Columbia Gateway Dr Ste 400, Columbia, MD 21046
Tel.: (410) 762-0800　　DE
Web Site: https://www.rekor.ai
Year Founded: 2017
REKR—(NASDAQ)
Rev.: $19,920,000
Assets: $83,840,000
Liabilities: $34,503,000
Net Worth: $49,337,000
Earnings: ($83,115,000)
Emp.: 267
Fiscal Year-end: 12/31/22
Holding Company
N.A.I.C.S.: 551112
Eyal Hen (CFO)
Bulent Ozcan (Dir-IR)
Robert Alan Berman (Exec Chm)
Riaz Latifullah (Exec VP-Corp Dev)
Matthew Hill (Chief Science Officer)
Charles A. Degliomini (Exec VP-Govt Rels & Corp Comm)
Chris Kadoch (CTO)
Scott Rutherford (Chief Innovation Officer)
Michael Dunbar (Chief Revenue Officer)
David Desharnais (Pres, CEO & COO)

Subsidiaries:

All Traffic Data Services, LLC (1)
9660 W 44th Ave., Wheat Ridge, CO 80033
Tel.: (916) 771-8700
Web Site: http://www.alltrafficdata.net
Management Consulting Services
N.A.I.C.S.: 541618
Bill Nichols (Mgr)

Subsidiary (Domestic):

Traffic Research & Analysis, Inc. (2)
3844 E Indian School Rd, Phoenix, AZ 85018
Tel.: (602) 840-1500
Web Site: http://www.tra-inc.com
Sales Range: $1-9.9 Million
Emp.: 60
Scientific & Technical Consulting Services
N.A.I.C.S.: 541690
Susan Medland (Pres)
Lisa Walters (Office Mgr)

Firestorm Solutions, LLC (1)
1000 Holcomb Woods Pkwy Ste 130, Roswell, GA 30076
Tel.: (800) 321-2219
Web Site: http://www.firestorm.com
General Management Consulting Services
N.A.I.C.S.: 541611
Jason Russell (Pres)

Global Public Safety, LLC (1)
7449 Race Rd Ste 100, Hanover, MD 21076
Tel.: (443) 557-0200
Web Site: https://www.globalpublicsafety.us
Public Safety Services
N.A.I.C.S.: 922190

Keystone Solutions, Inc. (1)
6901 Shawnee Mission Pkwy Ste 215, Overland Park, KS 66202-4005
Tel.: (913) 381-1012
Web Site: http://www.ksi-usa.com
Computer Related Services
N.A.I.C.S.: 541519
Ben Orth (CEO)

OpenALPR Software Solutions, LLC (1)
7020 Dorsey Rd Bldg C, Hanover, MD 21076
Web Site: http://www.openalpr.com
Software Development Services
N.A.I.C.S.: 513210

Rekor Recognition Systems (1)
7020 Dorsey Rd, Hanover, MD 21076　　(100%)
Tel.: (410) 762-0800
Web Site: http://www.brekford.com
Sales Range: $1-9.9 Million
Motor Vehicle Video & Communications Products Mfr
N.A.I.C.S.: 334310
Scott Rutherford (Chief Strategic Officer)
Brad Schaeffer (Sr Mng Dir)
Maurice R. Nelson (Mng Dir)

Southern Traffic Services, Inc. (1)
2911 Westfield Rd, Gulf Breeze, FL 32563
Tel.: (850) 934-5732
Web Site: http://www.southerntrafficservices.com
Sales Range: $1-9.9 Million
Emp.: 40
Business Consulting Services Whol Industrial Equipment
N.A.I.C.S.: 541690

RELAY THERAPEUTICS, INC.
399 Binney St 2nd Fl, Cambridge, MA 02142
Tel.: (617) 370-8837　　DE
Web Site: https://www.relaytx.com
Year Founded: 2015
RLAY—(NASDAQ)
Rev.: $25,546,000
Assets: $843,980,000
Liabilities: $91,977,000
Net Worth: $752,003,000
Earnings: ($341,973,000)
Emp.: 323
Fiscal Year-end: 12/31/23
Biotechnology Research & Development Services
N.A.I.C.S.: 541714
Brian Adams (Gen Counsel)
Tom Catinazzo (Sr VP-Fin)
Pascal Fortin (Sr VP & Head-Early Res)
Mary Mader (VP-Chemistry)
Iain Martin (VP-Drug Metabolism & Pharmacokinetics)
Jamie Nichols (Head-Genetic Diseases)
Mahesh Padval (Sr VP-Pharmaceutical Drug Dev)
Andy Porter (Chief People Experience Officer & Exec VP)
Imogen Pryce (Sr VP-R&D Ops & Strategy)
Peter Rahmer (Sr VP-Corp Affairs & IR)
Pat Walters (Sr VP-Computation)
Jim Watters (Sr VP & Head-Late Res)
Ben B. Wolf (Chief Medical Officer)
Alexis Borisy (Chm)
Tara O'Meara (Sr VP-Clinical Dev Ops)
Charles Ferte (VP)
Donald A. Bergstrom (Exec VP & Head-R&D)
Tom McLean (VP-Intellectual Property)
Patrick Riley (Sr VP-Artificial Intelligence)
Sanjiv K. Patel (Pres & CEO)
Mark Murcko (Co-Founder)

RELIABILITY INCORPORATED
2505 Gateway Ctr Dr, Clarksburg, MD 20871
Tel.: (202) 965-1100　　TX
Web Site: https://www.rlby.com
RLBY—(OTCIQ)
Rev.: $25,725,000

Assets: $13,490,000
Liabilities: $4,819,000
Net Worth: $8,671,000
Earnings: ($739,000)
Emp.: 266
Fiscal Year-end: 12/31/22
Investment Services
N.A.I.C.S.: 523999
Hannah M. Bible (Chm)
Nick Tsahalis (Pres, Pres & CEO)
Terry McKenzie (VP-HR)

Subsidiaries:

The Maslow Media Group, Inc. (1)
22 Baltimore Rd, Rockville, MD 20850　　(94%)
Tel.: (202) 965-1100
Web Site: http://www.maslowmedia.com
Sales Range: $25-49.9 Million
Emp.: 1,639
Video Production & Staffing Services
N.A.I.C.S.: 512110

RELIANCE GLOBAL GROUP, INC.
300 Blvd of the Americas Ste 105, Lakewood, NJ 08701
Tel.: (732) 380-4600　　FL
Web Site: https://www.relianceglobalgroup.com
Year Founded: 2013
RELI—(NASDAQ)
Rev.: $16,755,884
Assets: $38,427,729
Liabilities: $29,516,690
Net Worth: $8,911,039
Earnings: $6,466,162
Emp.: 78
Fiscal Year-end: 12/31/22
Holding Company; Insurance Agencies & Real Estate
N.A.I.C.S.: 551112
Ezra Beyman (Chm & CEO)
Yaakov Beyman (Exec VP-Insurance Div)
Mark Sisson (COO-US Benefits Alliance)
Moshe Fishman (Dir-Insurance Ops)
Jonathan Fortman (COO-Fortman Insurance Svcs)
Joel Markovitz (Chief Acctg Officer)
Joel Markovits (Chief Acctg Officer)

Subsidiaries:

Altruis Benefits Consulting, Inc. (1)
30600 Telegraph Rd Ste 1225, Bingham Farms, MI 48025
Web Site: https://www.altruisbenefit.com
Insurance Services
N.A.I.C.S.: 524210

Barra & Associates LLC (1)
1051 Perimeter Dr Ste 290, Schaumburg, IL 60173
Tel.: (630) 206-9660
Web Site: http://www.ifsbrokerage.com
Sales Range: $1-9.9 Million
Emp.: 65
Financial Brokerage Services
N.A.I.C.S.: 523999
Grant M. Barra (CEO & Mng Partner)
Michael Dobek (Partner)
Rachel Butler (Partner)
Christian Salgado (Mgr-Social Media)
Brandon Johnson (Mgr-Asset & Underwriting)

Fortman Insurance Agency, Inc. (1)
614 N Perry St, Ottawa, OH 45875
Tel.: (419) 523-4500
Web Site: http://www.fortmanins.com
Insurance Agencies & Brokerages
N.A.I.C.S.: 524210
John Fortman (Co-Founder)

US Benefits Alliance, LLC (1)
272 Bell Ave, Cadillac, MI 49601
Web Site: https://usbenefitsalliance.com
Insurance Services
N.A.I.C.S.: 524210

RELIANCE STEEL & ALUMINUM CO.

16100 N 71st St Ste 400, Scottsdale, AZ 85254
Tel.: (480) 564-5700   DE
Web Site: https://reliance.com
Year Founded: 1939
RS—(NYSE)
Rev.: $14,805,900,000
Assets: $10,480,300,000
Liabilities: $2,747,500,000
Net Worth: $7,732,800,000
Earnings: $1,335,900,000
Emp.: 15,000
Fiscal Year-end: 12/31/23
Metal Products Mfr
N.A.I.C.S.: 332999
Karla R. Lewis *(Pres & CEO)*
Stephen P. Koch *(COO & Exec VP)*
Arthur Ajemyan *(CFO, Principal Acctg Officer & Sr VP)*
Jeffrey W. Durham *(Sr VP-Ops)*
Suzanne M. Bonner *(CIO & Sr VP)*
Sean M. Mollins *(Sr VP-Ops)*
Michael R. Hynes *(Sr VP)*
William A. Smith II *(Gen Counsel, Sec & Sr VP)*

Subsidiaries:

AMI Metals Europe SPRL   (1)
Rue Louis Bleriot 23, 6041, Gosselies, Belgium
Tel.: (32) 7 137 6799
Web Site: http://www.amimetals.com
Emp.: 3
Metal Service Center & Distr
N.A.I.C.S.: 423510

AMI Metals France SAS   (1)
Batiment B11 Zone artisanale de laiguille, 46100, Figeac, France
Tel.: (33) 565503460
Metal Product Distr
N.A.I.C.S.: 423510

AMI Metals UK Limited   (1)
Unit 3 Vauxhall Supply Park North Road, Ellesmere Port, CH65 1BL, United Kingdom
Tel.: (44) 8458536149
Metal Product Distr
N.A.I.C.S.: 423510

AMI Metals, Inc.   (1)
1738 General George Patton Dr, Brentwood, TN 37027   (100%)
Tel.: (615) 377-0400
Web Site: https://www.amimetals.com
Sales Range: $200-249.9 Million
Emp.: 40
Metal Service Centers for Aerospace Industry
N.A.I.C.S.: 423510
Scott Smith *(Pres)*

All Metal Services (Malaysia) Sdn. Bhd.   (1)
No 2a Jalan Hakim, Hicom-glenmarie Industrial Park, 40150, Shah Alam, Selangor Darul Ehsan, Malaysia
Tel.: (60) 37 806 1325
Web Site: http://www.allmetal.co.uk
Metal Product Distr
N.A.I.C.S.: 423510

All Metal Services India Private Limited   (1)
437/A Aequs Special Economic Zone, Hattargi Village, Belgaum, 591243, Karnataka, India
Tel.: (91) 8028379124
Metal Services
N.A.I.C.S.: 423510
Prasad R. S. *(Gen Mgr)*

All Metal Services Limited   (1)
Suite 2D Landmark Place 1-5 Windsor Road, Slough, SL1 1JL, United Kingdom
Tel.: (44) 1895444066
Web Site: http://www.allmetal.co.uk
Metal Services
N.A.I.C.S.: 423510

All Metal Services Ltd.   (1)
12th Feng Cheng Road, Shaanxi Xian Export Processing Zone, Xi'an, 710016, China

Tel.: (86) 2986125300
Metal Services
N.A.I.C.S.: 423510

All Metal Services Ltd.   (1)
12th Feng Cheng Road Shaanxi Xian Export Processing Zone, Xian, 710016, China
Tel.: (86) 2986125300
Metal Services
N.A.I.C.S.: 423510

All Metals Processing & Logistics, Inc.   (1)
115 Coastline Rd, Spartanburg, SC 29301-9301
Tel.: (864) 574-8050
Web Site: http://www.allmetals.com
Fabricated Pipe & Pipe Fitting Mfr
N.A.I.C.S.: 332996
Stephanie Duncan *(VP-Sls)*
Richard Sigmon *(CFO)*

Allegheny Steel Distributors, Inc.   (1)
900 Rte 910, Indianola, PA 15051   (100%)
Tel.: (412) 767-5000
Web Site: https://alleghenysteel.com
Sales Range: $10-24.9 Million
Emp.: 75
Metals Service Center
N.A.I.C.S.: 423510
Bernie Herrmann *(Pres)*

Aluminium Services UK Limited   (1)
Unit 6 Horton Industrial Park Horton Road, West Drayton, UB7 8JD, Middlesex, United Kingdom
Tel.: (44) 1895444066
Coke Oven Product Mfr
N.A.I.C.S.: 324199

Aluminum and Stainless, Inc.   (1)
101 Thruway Park, Lafayette, LA 70502   (100%)
Tel.: (337) 837-4381
Web Site: http://www.aluminumandstainless.com
Sales Range: $25-49.9 Million
Emp.: 50
Metals Service Center
N.A.I.C.S.: 423510
Joseph Wolf *(Pres)*

American Metals Corporation   (1)
1499 Parkway Blvd, West Sacramento, CA 95691-5019   (100%)
Tel.: (916) 371-7700
Web Site: http://www.american-metals.com
Sales Range: $50-74.9 Million
Emp.: 145
Metals Service Center
N.A.I.C.S.: 423510
Ryan Mollins *(COO & VP)*
Nicole Heater *(Pres & CEO)*
Paul Worden *(CFO)*
Ray Garr *(Mgr-Plate)*
Troy Trosin *(Mgr-Sls)*
Dan Nethaway *(Gen Mgr-Fresno)*

Subsidiary (Domestic):

Alaska Steel Co.   (2)
6180 Electron Dr, Anchorage, AK 99518   (100%)
Tel.: (907) 561-1188
Web Site: https://www.alaskasteel.com
Sales Range: $25-49.9 Million
Emp.: 50
Processes & Distributes Steel & Aluminum Products
N.A.I.C.S.: 331513
Maynard Gates *(Pres & CEO)*
Chris Glover *(Mgr-Project & Sls)*
Joe Pavlas *(Dir-Sls)*
Mike Galyon *(Mgr-Rebar)*
Will Bolz *(Branch Mgr)*

Best Manufacturing, Inc.   (1)
4929 Krueger Dr, Jonesboro, AR 72401   (100%)
Tel.: (870) 931-9533
Web Site: https://www.bestmanufacturinginc.com
Sales Range: $10-24.9 Million
Emp.: 20
Fabricated Structural Metal
N.A.I.C.S.: 332312
James Best *(Pres)*

Bralco Metals   (1)
410 Mars Dr, Garland, TX 75040

Tel.: (972) 276-2676
Web Site: http://www.rsac.com
Rev.: $26,600,000
Emp.: 34
Metal Products Mfr
N.A.I.C.S.: 332999

Bralco Metals (Australia) Pty Ltd.   (1)
26 Lillee Crescent, Tullamarine, 3043, VIC, Australia
Tel.: (61) 393105566
Web Site: https://www.airportmetals.com.au
Aircraft Parts Distr
N.A.I.C.S.: 423860

Chapel Steel Canada, Ltd.   (1)
91 Eastport Boulevard, Hamilton, L8H 7S3, ON, Canada
Tel.: (289) 780-0570
Web Site: http://www.chapelsteel.com
Metal Product Distr
N.A.I.C.S.: 423510

Chapel Steel Corp.   (1)
590 N Bethlehem Pike, Lower Gwynedd, PA 19002
Tel.: (215) 793-0899
Web Site: http://www.chapelsteel.com
Metal Product Distr
N.A.I.C.S.: 423510
Patrick Jones *(CFO)*

Chatham Steel Corporation   (1)
501 W Boundary St, Savannah, GA 31401-3105   (100%)
Tel.: (912) 233-5751
Web Site: http://www.chathamsteel.com
Sales Range: $50-74.9 Million
Emp.: 100
Metals Service Center
N.A.I.C.S.: 423510

Clayton Metals, Inc.   (1)
546 Clayton Ct, Wood Dale, IL 60191
Tel.: (630) 860-7000
Web Site: https://www.claytonmetals.com
Sales Range: $100-124.9 Million
Emp.: 50
Aluminum & Stainless Steel Products Processing & Distr
N.A.I.C.S.: 423510
William Hall *(Gen Mgr)*

Continental Alloys & Services (Delaware) LLC   (1)
18334 Stuebner-Airline Rd, Spring, TX 77379
Tel.: (281) 376-9600
Web Site: http://www.contalloy.com
Metal Product Mfr & Distr
N.A.I.C.S.: 331210

Continental Alloys & Services (Malaysia) Sdn. Bhd.   (1)
Jalan Persiaran Teknologi Taman Teknologi Johor, PO Box 39, 81400, Senai, Malaysia
Tel.: (60) 75999975
Web Site: http://www.contalloy.com
Steel Products Mfr
N.A.I.C.S.: 332999

Continental Alloys & Services Inc.   (1)
18334 Stuebner-Airline Rd Spring, Houston, TX 77379
Tel.: (281) 376-9600
Web Site: http://www.contalloy.com
Steel Products Mfr
N.A.I.C.S.: 332999
Randy Zajicek *(Pres)*

Continental Alloys & Services Inc.   (1)
Suite 1440 530 8th Avenue SW, Calgary, T2P 3S8, AB, Canada
Tel.: (403) 216-5150
Web Site: http://www.contalloy.com
Steel Products Mfr
N.A.I.C.S.: 332999

Continental Alloys & Services Limited   (1)
South View, Peterhead, AB42 3GZ, United Kingdom
Tel.: (44) 177 948 0420
Web Site: http://www.contalloy.com
Steel Products Mfr
N.A.I.C.S.: 332999

Continental Alloys & Services Pte. Ltd.   (1)

16 Tuas West Avenue, Singapore, 638441, Singapore
Tel.: (65) 6 690 0178
Web Site: http://www.contalloy.com
Steel Products Mfr
N.A.I.C.S.: 332999

Continental Alloys Middle East FZE   (1)
PO Box 263040, Jebel Ali, United Arab Emirates
Tel.: (971) 4 880 9770
Web Site: http://www.contalloy.com
Steel Products Mfr
N.A.I.C.S.: 332999

Cooksey Iron & Metal Co. Inc.   (1)
801 2nd St E, Tifton, GA 31794
Tel.: (229) 382-4680
Rev.: $20,000,000
Emp.: 50
Steel
N.A.I.C.S.: 423510
Mike Cooksey *(Pres)*

Crest Steel Corp.   (1)
6580 General Rd, Riverside, CA 92509
Tel.: (951) 727-2600
Web Site: https://www.creststeel.com
Sales Range: $1-9.9 Million
Emp.: 125
Steel Distr
N.A.I.C.S.: 331110
Phil Steinberg *(Founder)*

Delta Steel, L.P.   (1)
7355 Roundhouse Ln, Houston, TX 77078
Tel.: (713) 635-1200
Web Site: http://www.deltasteel.com
Sales Range: $25-49.9 Million
Emp.: 20
Steel Service Centers & Metal Processing Services
N.A.I.C.S.: 423510

Subsidiary (Domestic):

Smith Pipe & Steel Company   (2)
735 N 19th Ave, Phoenix, AZ 85009
Tel.: (602) 257-9494
Web Site: https://www.smithpipe.com
Steel Service Centers & Processing Services
N.A.I.C.S.: 423510

Dubose National Energy Services, Inc.   (1)
900 Industrial Dr, Clinton, NC 28328
Tel.: (910) 590-2151
Web Site: https://www.dubosenes.com
Metal & Metal Products Whlsr
N.A.I.C.S.: 423510
Carl M. Rogers *(Pres & CEO)*

Durrett Sheppard Steel Company, Inc.   (1)
6800 E Baltimore St, Baltimore, MD 21224   (100%)
Tel.: (410) 633-6800
Web Site: https://durrettsheppard.com
Sales Range: $50-74.9 Million
Emp.: 80
Metals Service Center
N.A.I.C.S.: 423510

Earle M. Jorgensen Company   (1)
10650 S Alameda St, Lynwood, CA 90262
Tel.: (323) 567-1122
Web Site: http://www.emjmetals.com
Sales Range: $1-4.9 Billion
Emp.: 103
Metal Bar & Tubular Products Distr
N.A.I.C.S.: 423510
Gil Leon *(CFO & VP)*
Stephen Ghoens *(VP-Eastern Reg)*
Ed King *(VP-Southern Reg)*
Rob Roy *(VP-Western Reg)*
Crofford Lane *(VP-Mdsg)*

Subsidiary (Non-US):

Earle M. Jorgensen Canada, Inc.   (2)
1255 Ave Laplace, Laval, H7C 2N6, QC, Canada
Tel.: (450) 661-5181
Web Site: http://www.emjmetal.com
Sales Range: $25-49.9 Million
Emp.: 40
Steel & Aluminum Distr
N.A.I.C.S.: 423510

Reliance Steel & Aluminum Co.—(Continued)

Earle M. Jorgensen Canada, Inc. **(2)**
305 Pendant Dr, Mississauga, L5T 2W9, ON, Canada
Tel.: (905) 564-0866
Web Site: http://www.emjmetals.com
Sales Range: $25-49.9 Million
Emp.: 50
Steel & Aluminum Distr
N.A.I.C.S.: 423510

Unit (Domestic):

Earle M. Jorgensen Co. - Honing Center/Tulsa **(2)**
7313 E Pine, Tulsa, OK 74110
Tel.: (918) 835-1511
Web Site: http://www.emjmetals.com
Sales Range: $25-49.9 Million
Emp.: 23
Metal & Mining Products Distr
N.A.I.C.S.: 423510

Earle M. Jorgensen Co. - Specialty Tubing/Eldridge **(2)**
325 N 16th Ave, Eldridge, IA 52748
Tel.: (563) 285-5340
Web Site: http://www.emjmetals.com
Sales Range: $25-49.9 Million
Emp.: 40
Metal Tubing Distr
N.A.I.C.S.: 423510

Feralloy Corporation **(1)**
8755 W Higgins Rd Ste 970, Chicago, IL 60631
Tel.: (773) 380-1500
Web Site: http://www.feralloy.com
Sales Range: $25-49.9 Million
Emp.: 17
Flat Rolled Steel Products Processor & Distr
N.A.I.C.S.: 423510
Jack D. Love (CFO & VP-Fin)
John A. Hirt (VP-Employee Dev)
Carlos Rodriguez-Borjas (Pres)
Jeffery B. Diener (COO)
Steve Milanoski (Gen Mgr-Dev & Tech)

Subsidiary (Domestic):

Feralloy Indiana Corp. **(2)**
8755 W Higgins Rd Ste 970, Chicago, IL 60631
Tel.: (773) 380-1500
Web Site: http://www.feralloy.com
Sales Range: $25-49.9 Million
Emp.: 17
Holding Company
N.A.I.C.S.: 551112

Joint Venture (Domestic):

Feralloy Processing Company **(3)**
600 George Nelson Dr, Portage, IN 46368
Tel.: (219) 787-8773
Web Site: http://www.feralloy.com
Flat Rolled Steel Products Processor & Distr; Owned 51% by Feralloy Corporation & 49% by United States Steel Corporation
N.A.I.C.S.: 423510

Affiliate (Domestic):

Indiana Pickling & Processing Company **(3)**
6650 Nautical Dr, Portage, IN 46368
Tel.: (219) 787-8889
Web Site: http://www.feralloy.com
Sales Range: $25-49.9 Million
Steel Hydrochloric Pickling & Processing Services
N.A.I.C.S.: 332813

Division (Domestic):

Feralloy Midwest (Portage) Division **(2)**
6755 Waterway, Portage, IN 46368
Tel.: (219) 787-9698
Web Site: http://www.feralloy.com
Sales Range: $75-99.9 Million
Emp.: 75
Flat Rolled Steel Products Processor & Distr
N.A.I.C.S.: 423510

Subsidiary (Domestic):

Feralloy Ohio Corp. **(2)**

8755 W Higgins Rd Ste 970, Chicago, IL 60631
Tel.: (773) 380-1500
Web Site: http://www.feralloy.com
Sales Range: $25-49.9 Million
Emp.: 15
Holding Company
N.A.I.C.S.: 551112

Feralloy Oregon Corp. **(2)**
8755 W Higgins Rd Ste 970, Chicago, IL 60631
Tel.: (773) 380-1500
Web Site: http://www.feralloy.com
Sales Range: $25-49.9 Million
Emp.: 20
Holding Company
N.A.I.C.S.: 551112

Joint Venture (Domestic):

Oregon Feralloy Partners **(3)**
14400 N Rivergate Blvd, Portland, OR 97203 **(40%)**
Tel.: (503) 286-8869
Web Site: https://www.feralloy.com
Flat Rolled Steel Products Processor & Distr
N.A.I.C.S.: 423510

Division (Domestic):

Feralloy Southern Division **(2)**
1435 Red Hat Rd, Decatur, AL 35601
Tel.: (256) 301-0500
Web Site: http://www.feralloy.com
Sales Range: $50-74.9 Million
Flat Rolled Steel Products Processor & Distr
N.A.I.C.S.: 423510

Division (Domestic):

Feralloy Charleston Division **(3)**
1020 N Steel Cir, Huger, SC 29450
Tel.: (843) 336-4107
Web Site: http://www.feralloy.com
Sales Range: $50-74.9 Million
Emp.: 15
Flat Rolled Steel Products Processor & Distr
N.A.I.C.S.: 423510

Division (Domestic):

Feralloy St. Louis Division **(2)**
2500 Century Dr, Granite City, IL 62040
Tel.: (618) 452-2500
Web Site: http://www.feralloy.com
Sales Range: $50-74.9 Million
Flat Rolled Steel Products Processor & Distr
N.A.I.C.S.: 423510

Feralloy Western Division **(2)**
936 Performance Dr, Stockton, CA 95206
Tel.: (209) 234-0548
Web Site: http://www.feralloy.com
Sales Range: $75-99.9 Million
Flat Rolled Steel Products Processor & Distr
N.A.I.C.S.: 423510

Subsidiary (Domestic):

GH Metal Solutions, Inc. **(2)**
2890 Airport Rd NW, Fort Payne, AL 35968
Tel.: (256) 845-5411
Web Site: https://www.ghmetalsolutions.com
Sales Range: $25-49.9 Million
Carbon Steel Products Processor & Fabricator
N.A.I.C.S.: 331110

Ferguson Perforating Company **(1)**
130 Ernest St, Providence, RI 02905
Tel.: (401) 941-8876
Web Site: https://www.fergusonperf.com
Perforated Metal, Perforated Plastic & Perforated Composite Solutions
N.A.I.C.S.: 332119

Fox Metals & Alloys, Inc. **(1)**
12660 FM 529, Houston, TX 77041 **(100%)**
Tel.: (281) 890-6666
Web Site: https://www.foxmetals.com
Sales Range: $50-74.9 Million
Metal Distr
N.A.I.C.S.: 423510

Fry Steel Company **(1)**
13325 Molette St, Santa Fe Springs, CA 90670-5568
Tel.: (562) 802-2721
Web Site: http://www.frysteel.com
Metal Service Centers & Other Metal Merchant Whslr
N.A.I.C.S.: 423510

Hagerty Steel & Aluminum Co. **(1)**
601 N Main, East Peoria, IL 61611-8130 **(100%)**
Tel.: (309) 699-7251
Web Site: https://www.hagertysteel.com
Sales Range: $50-74.9 Million
Emp.: 85
Metals Service Centers & Offices
N.A.I.C.S.: 423510

Infra-Metals Co. **(1)**
4501 Curtis Ave, Baltimore, MD 21225
Tel.: (410) 355-2550
Web Site: http://www.infra-metals.com
Sales Range: $150-199.9 Million
Structural Steel Service Centers
N.A.I.C.S.: 423510
Mark Haight (Pres)

Division (Domestic):

Infra-Metals Co. **(2)**
8 Pent Hwy, Wallingford, CT 06492-2336
Tel.: (203) 294-2980
Web Site: http://www.infra-metals.com
Sales Range: $150-199.9 Million
Structural Steel Service Centers
N.A.I.C.S.: 423510
Mark Haight (Pres-Northern Reg)

KMS FAB, LLC **(1)**
100 Parry St, Luzerne, PA 18709
Tel.: (570) 338-0200
Metal Products Mfr
N.A.I.C.S.: 332999

KMS South, Inc. **(1)**
3401 Platt Springs Rd, West Columbia, SC 29170
Tel.: (803) 796-9995
Metal Products Mfr
N.A.I.C.S.: 332999

Lampros Steel, Inc. **(1)**
9040 N Burgard Way, Portland, OR 97203
Tel.: (503) 285-6667
Web Site: http://www.lamprossteel.com
Emp.: 20
Structural Steel Products Distr
N.A.I.C.S.: 238120

Liebovich Bros., Inc. **(1)**
2116 Preston St, Rockford, IL 61102 **(100%)**
Tel.: (815) 987-3200
Web Site: https://www.liebovich.com
Sales Range: Less than $1 Million
Emp.: 300
Steel Fabrications
N.A.I.C.S.: 331513

McKey Perforating Co., Inc. **(1)**
3033 S 166th St, New Berlin, WI 53151-3555
Tel.: (262) 786-2700
Web Site: https://www.mckeyperforatedmetal.com
Sales Range: $10-24.9 Million
Emp.: 70
Metal Stamping
N.A.I.C.S.: 332119

Merfish Pipe & Supply, Co. **(1)**
83 Turnpike Rd, Ipswich, MA 01938
Tel.: (800) 869-5731
Web Site: http://www.merfish.com
Metals Service Center Whol Industrial Supplies
N.A.I.C.S.: 423510
Robert Setzekorn (VP & Gen Mgr)
Patrick Starkey (Sls Mgr-West)

Subsidiary (Domestic):

United Pipe & Steel Corp. **(2)**
83 Tpke Rd, Ipswich, MA 01938
Tel.: (978) 356-9300
Web Site: http://www.united-pipe.com
Steel Pipe Distr
N.A.I.C.S.: 423510
Joe Kelly (VP-Pur)
Corey Lowsky (VP-Sls)
Michael Blair (VP-Natl Accts)
Lee Goldman (Dir-IT)

Metalcenter, Inc. **(1)**
12034 Greenstone Ave, Santa Fe Springs, CA 90670-0101 **(100%)**
Tel.: (562) 944-3322
Web Site: https://www.rsac.com
Sales Range: $25-49.9 Million
Emp.: 85
Metals Processing & Distribution
N.A.I.C.S.: 423510

Metals USA Holdings Corp. **(1)**
2400 E Commercial Blvd Ste 905, Fort Lauderdale, FL 33308 **(100%)**
Tel.: (954) 202-4000
Web Site: http://www.metalsusa.com
Rev.: $1,983,600,000
Assets: $1,003,900,000
Liabilities: $693,700,000
Net Worth: $310,200,000
Earnings: $52,700,000
Emp.: 2,550
Fiscal Year-end: 12/31/2012
Holding Company; Metal Processor & Distr
N.A.I.C.S.: 551112

Subsidiary (Domestic):

Flag Intermediate Holdings Corporation **(2)**
2400 E Commercial Blvd Ste 905, Fort Lauderdale, FL 33308
Tel.: (954) 202-4000
Emp.: 2,200
Investment Management Service
N.A.I.C.S.: 551112

Subsidiary (Domestic):

Metals USA, Inc. **(3)**
4901 NW 17th Way Ste 405, Fort Lauderdale, FL 33309
Tel.: (954) 202-4000
Web Site: http://www.metalsusa.com
Metal Processing & Distribution Services
N.A.I.C.S.: 423510
David A. Martens (Pres-Plates & Shapes-West)
Scott Sharp (VP-Sls & Ops)
Randall Lapp (Dir-HR & Corp Comm)
Peter Szoke (Sr Dir-IT)
Frank Koons (CEO)
John Frazier (COO)
David Carter (Pres)

Subsidiary (Domestic):

Gregor Technologies LLC **(4)**
529 Technology Park Dr, Torrington, CT 06790
Tel.: (860) 482-2569
Web Site: https://www.gregortech.com
Sheet Metal Fabrication Services
N.A.I.C.S.: 332312

Instrument Cases LLC **(4)**
529 Technology Park Dr, Torrington, CT 06790
Tel.: (860) 489-6977
Web Site: http://www.instrumentcasesllc.com
Sheet Metal Fabrication Services
N.A.I.C.S.: 332312

Subsidiary (Non-US):

Metals USA Building Products, Canada Inc. **(4)**
Highway No 3 No 581, Courtland, N0J 1E0, ON, Canada
Tel.: (519) 688-2200
Sales Range: $25-49.9 Million
Emp.: 25
Steel Products Mfr
N.A.I.C.S.: 331110
Francis Underhill (Gen Mgr)

Subsidiary (Domestic):

Metals USA Carbon Flat Rolled, Inc. **(4)**
1070 W Liberty St, Wooster, OH 44691
Tel.: (330) 264-8416
Web Site: http://www.metalsusa.com
Steel Products Mfr
N.A.I.C.S.: 331110

Metals USA Plate Processing L.L.C. **(4)**
1900 Kitty Hawk Ave, Philadelphia, PA 19112-1806

Tel.: (215) 599-0535
Web Site: http://www.metalsusa.com
Steel Products Mfr
N.A.I.C.S.: 331110

Metals USA Plates and Shapes Northeast, L.P. (4)
50 Cabot Blvd, Langhorne, PA 19047
Tel.: (267) 580-2100
Web Site: http://www.metalsusa.com
Metal Service Center Operator
N.A.I.C.S.: 423510

Metals USA Plates and Shapes Southeast, Inc. (4)
1251 Woodland Ave Bldg 1 2 3 4 5 6, Mobile, AL 36652
Tel.: (251) 456-4531
Web Site: http://www.metalsusa.com
Metal Service Centers & Steel Products Mfr
N.A.I.C.S.: 423510
Mickey Marshall (Pres)

Metals USA Specialty Metals North-central, Inc. (4)
3000 Shermer Rd, Northbrook, IL 60065
Tel.: (847) 291-2400
Web Site: http://www.metalsusa.com
Steel Products Mfr
N.A.I.C.S.: 331110

Ohio River Metal Services, Inc. (4)
5150 Loop Rd, Jeffersonville, IN 47130
Tel.: (812) 282-4770
Sales Range: $25-49.9 Million
Emp.: 80
Rolled Steel Shape Manufacturing Services
N.A.I.C.S.: 331221

The Richardson Trident Company, L.L.C. (4)
405 N Plano Rd, Richardson, TX 75081
Tel.: (972) 231-5176
Web Site: https://www.trident-metals.com
Sales Range: $125-149.9 Million
Emp.: 510
Sales & Distribution of Metals
N.A.I.C.S.: 423510
Jennifer Kennealy (Dir-Pur)
Brian Monaghan (Sls Dir)
Tim Williamson (VP)

i-Solutions Direct, Inc. (4)
1300 Virginia Dr Ste 320, Fort Washington, PA 19034-3223
Tel.: (215) 540-8004
Steel Products Mfr
N.A.I.C.S.: 331110

National Specialty Alloys, Inc. (1)
18250 Kieth Harrow, Houston, TX 77084
Tel.: (281) 345-2115
Web Site: https://www.nsalloys.com
Metal Processing & Distr
N.A.I.C.S.: 423510
Mark Russ (Pres & COO)
Eileen Casiraghi (VP-Ops)
Anthony Kosler (VP-Specialty Products)
Harold Vance (Asst VP-Information Sys)
Heather Thomas (Mgr-Quality)
Alfonso Nino (Mgr-Warehouse)
Jim Rauch (VP-Strategic Sls & Bus Dev-Natl)
Brad Poole (VP-Sls-Natl)
Ron Haynie (VP-Sls)
Henry Borrero (Sls Dir-Intl)
Katherine Herrera (Supvr-Sls Ops-Intl)

Northern Illinois Steel Supply Company (1)
24005 S Northern Illinois Dr, Channahon, IL 60410
Tel.: (815) 467-9000
Web Site: https://www.nisteel.com
Sales Range: $10-24.9 Million
Emp.: 47
Steel Product & Precision Fabrication Services
N.A.I.C.S.: 331511

Olympic Metals, Inc. (1)
5775 Monaco St, Commerce City, CO 80022 **(100%)**
Tel.: (303) 286-9700
Web Site: http://www.rsac.com
Sales Range: $25-49.9 Million
Emp.: 21
Wholesale of Non-Ferrous Metals
N.A.I.C.S.: 423510

PDM Steel Service Centers, Inc. (1)
3535 E Myrtle St, Stockton, CA 95205 **(100%)**
Tel.: (209) 943-0513
Web Site: http://www.pdmsteel.com
Sales Range: $75-99.9 Million
Emp.: 150
Metals Service Center
N.A.I.C.S.: 423510

Subsidiary (Domestic):

Liebovich/PDM Steel & Aluminum Company (2)
155 50th Ave SW, Cedar Rapids, IA 52406 **(100%)**
Tel.: (319) 366-8431
Web Site: http://www.liebovich.com
Sales Range: $25-49.9 Million
Emp.: 55
Warehousing, Processing & Distribution of Steel
N.A.I.C.S.: 423510

Branch (Domestic):

PDM - Woodland (2)
1785 Schurman Way, Woodland, WA 98674 **(100%)**
Tel.: (360) 225-1133
Web Site: http://www.pdmsteel.com
Sales Range: $25-49.9 Million
Emp.: 45
Warehousing, Processing & Distributing of Steel
N.A.I.C.S.: 423510

PDM Steel Service Center-Fresno (2)
4005 E Church Ave, Fresno, CA 93725 **(100%)**
Tel.: (559) 442-1410
Web Site: http://www.pdmsteel.com
Sales Range: $25-49.9 Million
Emp.: 49
Warehousing, Processing & Distributing Steel
N.A.I.C.S.: 423510

PDM Steel Service Center-Santa Clara (2)
3500 Bassett St, Santa Clara, CA 95054 **(100%)**
Tel.: (408) 988-3000
Web Site: http://www.pdmsteel.com
Sales Range: $25-49.9 Million
Emp.: 50
Warehousing, Processing & Distributing of Steel
N.A.I.C.S.: 423510

PDM Steel Service Center-Spanish Fork (2)
1100 N 300 W, Spanish Fork, UT 84660-9501 **(100%)**
Tel.: (801) 798-8676
Web Site: http://www.pdmsteel.com
Sales Range: $25-49.9 Million
Emp.: 75
Warehousing, Processing & Distributing of Steel
N.A.I.C.S.: 423510
Galen Littleton (Gen Mgr)
Joe Anderson (Mgr-Sls)
Brant Ludwig (Mgr-Inside Sls)
Michael Hunsaker (Mgr-Ops)
Rob Mower (Mgr-Credit)
Shad Hansen (Mgr-Pur)

PDM Steel Service Center-Sparks (2)
1250 Kleppe Ln, Sparks, NV 89431 **(100%)**
Tel.: (775) 358-1441
Web Site: http://www.pdmsteel.com
Sales Range: $25-49.9 Million
Emp.: 45
Warehousing, Processing & Distributing of Steel
N.A.I.C.S.: 423510

Pacific Metal Co (1)
10700 SW Manhasset Dr, Tualatin, OR 97062-8608
Tel.: (503) 454-1051
Web Site: https://www.pacificmetal.com
Sales Range: $25-49.9 Million
Emp.: 75

Mfr of Aluminum Bars, Rods, Ingots, Sheets, Pipes, Steel Plates & Nonferrous Products
N.A.I.C.S.: 423510

Phoenix Corporation (1)
4685 Buford Hwy, Norcross, GA 30071
Tel.: (770) 447-4211
Metal Processing Services
N.A.I.C.S.: 423510

Phoenix Metals Company (1)
201 Donovan Rd, Kansas City, KS 66115-1426 **(100%)**
Tel.: (913) 321-5200
Web Site: http://www.phoenixmetals.com
Steel Service Center
N.A.I.C.S.: 423510

Division (Domestic):

Central Plains Steel Co. (2)
3900 Comotara St, Wichita, KS 67226 **(100%)**
Tel.: (316) 636-4500
Web Site: http://cpsteel.com
Rev.: $25,500,000
Emp.: 35
Steel Service Center
N.A.I.C.S.: 425120

Phoenix Metals Company (1)
4685 Buford Hwy, Norcross, GA 30071 **(100%)**
Tel.: (770) 447-4211
Web Site: http://www.phoenixmetals.net
Metals Service Center
N.A.I.C.S.: 423510
Philip Abernathy (Mgr-Sls)

Subsidiary (Domestic):

Steel Bar (2)
1120 Tarrant Rd, Greensboro, NC 27409 **(100%)**
Tel.: (336) 294-0053
Web Site: http://www.reliance.com
Sales Range: $25-49.9 Million
Emp.: 10
Metals Service Center
N.A.I.C.S.: 423510

Precision Flamecutting and Steel, Inc. (1)
14500 Wagg Way Rd, Houston, TX 77041
Tel.: (281) 477-1600
Web Site: https://www.pflame.com
Metal Plate Cutting & Forging Services
N.A.I.C.S.: 423510

Reliance Metalcenter Asia Pacific Pte. Ltd. (1)
42D Penjuru Road 02-01, Singapore, 609162, Singapore
Tel.: (65) 62651211
Steel & Metal Whslr
N.A.I.C.S.: 423510

Reliance Metals (Shanghai) Co., Ltd. (1)
388 Huigang Road Unit 4 1st Floor No.10 Warehou, Shanghai, 201308, China
Tel.: (86) 2120966052
Steel Product Distr
N.A.I.C.S.: 423510

Reliance Metals Canada Limited (1)
6925 8th Street Northwest, Edmonton, T6P 1T9, AB, Canada
Tel.: (780) 801-4114
Web Site: http://www.rmcl.com
Sales Range: $200-249.9 Million
Metal Distr
N.A.I.C.S.: 331210
Barbara Zemblowski (Controller-Grp)
Cora Zhang (Mgr-Fin)
Natasha Burns (Mgr-Corp Credit-Western Canada)
James Murphy (Mgr-HS & Quality Assurance)
Sari MacPherson (Mgr-Comm & Bus Rels)
David Sapunjis (Pres)
Lorenzo Prete (VP)
Sergio Pace (Mgr-Credit-Eastern Canada)
Brad Williams (Mgr-Corp Pur)

Subsidiary (Domestic):

Encore Metals, Inc. (2)
9810-39th Avenue, Edmonton, T6E 0A1, AB, Canada

Tel.: (780) 436-6660
Web Site: https://www.encoremetals.com
Sales Range: $25-49.9 Million
Emp.: 23
Metals Processing & Distr Services
N.A.I.C.S.: 423510

Division (US):

Encore Metals (3)
789 N 400 W, North Salt Lake, UT 84054
Tel.: (801) 383-3808
Web Site: http://www.encoremetals.com
Sales Range: $25-49.9 Million
Emp.: 10
Whslr of Steel
N.A.I.C.S.: 423510

Encore Metals (3)
10250 SW N Dakota St, Tigard, OR 97223
Tel.: (503) 620-8810
Web Site: http://www.encoremetals.com
Sales Range: $25-49.9 Million
Emp.: 12
Distribution of Steel
N.A.I.C.S.: 333923

Encore Metals (3)
2225 6th Ave S, Seattle, WA 98134
Tel.: (206) 623-6672
Web Site: http://www.encoremetals.com
Steel Distr
N.A.I.C.S.: 331210

Division (Domestic):

Encore Metals (3)
7805-51st Street S E, Calgary, T2C 2Z3, AB, Canada
Tel.: (403) 236-1418
Web Site: https://www.encoremetals.com
Steel Distr
N.A.I.C.S.: 331210

Encore Metals (3)
7470 Vantage Way Tilbury Industrial Park, Delta, V4G 1H1, BC, Canada
Tel.: (604) 940-0439
Web Site: https://www.encoremetals.com
Steel Distr
N.A.I.C.S.: 331210

Team Tube (3)
9810-39th Avenue, Edmonton, T6E 0A1, AB, Canada
Tel.: (780) 462-7222
Web Site: http://www.teamtube.com
Metal Distr
N.A.I.C.S.: 331210
Brian Marchand (Branch Mgr)

Service Steel Aerospace Corporation (1)
4609 70th Ave E, Fife, WA 98424 **(100%)**
Tel.: (253) 627-2910
Web Site: https://www.ssa-corp.com
Sales Range: $25-49.9 Million
Emp.: 30
Metals Service Center
N.A.I.C.S.: 423510
Dave Johnson (VP-Admin)
Doug Nesbitt (Pres)
Erich Thompson (VP-Sls & Mktg)
Rich Mallette (Dir-Procurement)
Charles Steward (Mgr-Safety & Corp Ops)
Dan Bergstrom (Mgr-Corp Quality)
Beth Collobert (Mgr-Corp Credit)
Mike Hightower (Gen Mgr-Seattle Branch)

Siskin Steel and Supply Co., Inc. (1)
1901 Riverfront Pkwy, Chattanooga, TN 37408-1037 **(100%)**
Tel.: (423) 756-3671
Web Site: https://www.siskin.com
Sales Range: $200-249.9 Million
Emp.: 525
Metals Service Center
N.A.I.C.S.: 423510
Betty Anne Nall (CFO)

Southern Steel Supply, LLC (1)
475 N Dunlap St, Memphis, TN 38105-2201
Tel.: (901) 523-1170
Web Site:
http://www.southernsteelsupply.com
Metal Service Centers & Other Metal Merchant Whslr
N.A.I.C.S.: 423510
Michael Wexler (CFO)

Toma Metal, Inc. (1)

Reliance Steel & Aluminum Co.—(Continued)

740 Cooper Ave, Johnstown, PA 15906-1033 (100%)
Tel.: (814) 536-3596
Web Site: https://tomametalsinc.com
Sales Range: $10-24.9 Million
Emp.: 50
Metals Service Center
N.A.I.C.S.: 423510
Mark Borstnar (Gen Mgr)
Donald Shovestull (Mgr-Traffic)

Toma Metals, Inc. (1)
740 Cooper Ave, Johnstown, PA 15906-1033
Tel.: (814) 536-3596
Web Site: https://www.tomametalsinc.com
Metal Service Centers & Distr
N.A.I.C.S.: 423510

Tubular Steel, Inc. (1)
1031 Executive Pkwy Dr, Saint Louis, MO 63141-6351
Tel.: (314) 851-9200
Web Site: https://www.tubularsteel.com
Steel Distr
N.A.I.C.S.: 423510
Todd Roberts (Pres, COO & VP)

Valex Corp. (1)
6080 Leland St, Ventura, CA 93003 (97%)
Tel.: (805) 658-0944
Web Site: https://www.valex.com
Sales Range: $50-74.9 Million
Emp.: 90
Mfr of Stainless Steel Tubing & Components
N.A.I.C.S.: 332813
Fred Apodaca (Mgr-Western Reg)

Valex Korea Co., Ltd. (1)
281 2F Gate4 Kimpo Int'l Airport Freight Terminal GongHang-dong, KangSeo-ku, Seoul, kyonggi-do, Korea (South)
Tel.: (82) 27070203
Web Site: http://www.valex.co.kr
Steel Product Distr
N.A.I.C.S.: 423510

Viking Materials, Inc. (1)
11305 Franklin Ave, Franklin Park, IL 60131 (100%)
Tel.: (847) 451-7171
Web Site: http://www.vikingmaterials.com
Sales Range: Less than $1 Million
Emp.: 45
Metals Service Center
N.A.I.C.S.: 423510

RELIANT HOLDINGS, INC.
Tel.: (724) 465-6075 NV
Web Site:
   https://www.reliantholdings.com
Year Founded: 2014
RELT—(OTCQB)
Rev.: $4,616,404
Assets: $751,246
Liabilities: $649,240
Net Worth: $102,006
Earnings: $333,876
Emp.: 3
Fiscal Year-end: 12/31/22
Holding Company
N.A.I.C.S.: 551112
Robert Kane (Founder, Pres & CEO)
Rich McDonald (Exec VP)
Pat Bowman (VP-Marketing)
Bruce Charles (VP-Information Technology)
Judy Hill (VP & Controller)
Kelly LaPorte (VP-Operations)
Dee-Ann Bollinger (VP-Compliance & Human Resources)
Shannon Rugolsky (Mgr-Contact Center Department)
Brenda Gray (Accountant)
Tom Kane (Mgr-Property)
Tom Swab (Mktg Mgr-Affiliate)
Matt Yohe (Mktg Mgr-Affiliate)
Jim White (Mgr-Fulfillment Department)

Subsidiaries:

Reliant Pools, Inc. (1)

12343 Hymeadow Dr Ste 3-A, Austin, TX 78750
Tel.: (512) 407-2623
Web Site: https://www.reliantpools.com
Building Design Services
N.A.I.C.S.: 541310

RELIV INTERNATIONAL, INC.
136 Chesterfield Ind Blvd, Chesterfield, MO 63005
Tel.: (636) 537-9715 DE
Web Site: https://www.reliv.com
Year Founded: 1988
RELV—(OTCIQ)
Rev.: $35,055,315
Assets: $15,306,996
Liabilities: $4,205,353
Net Worth: $11,101,643
Earnings: ($444,357)
Emp.: 91
Fiscal Year-end: 12/31/19
Nutritional Supplements, Weight-Management Products, Sports Drink Mixes, Nutritional Bars, Dietary Fiber Products, Functional Foods & Skin Care Products Mfr & Marketer
N.A.I.C.S.: 325411
Robert L. Montgomery (Founder & Chm)
Stephen M. Merrick (Gen Counsel & Sec)
Steven D. Albright (CFO & Sr VP)
Ryan A. Montgomery (CEO)
Tina Van Horn (Dir-Product Dev & Fit3 Trainer)
Debra P. Hellweg (COO & Sr VP)
Susan Stone (Mng Dir-Asia Pacific)
Michelle Robles-Devnani (Mng Dir-Philippines)
Kerri Toy (Mng Dir-Reliv Europe)
Jason Gregory (Sls Mgr-Reliv Europe)
Jo Anne Sy (Mgr-Sales & Marketing-Reliv Philippines)
Jim Lahm (VP-IT)
Claudia Jimenez (Mgr-Sls & Mktg-Mexico)

Subsidiaries:

Reliv Australia Pty, Limited (1)
Building I Unit 18 22 Powers Road Seven Hills, Po Box 70, Sydney, 2147, NSW, Australia
Tel.: (61) 298527000
Web Site: http://reliv.com.au
Nutrition Foods & Products Wlslr
N.A.I.C.S.: 456191
Sue Stone (Mng Dir)

Reliv Europe Limited (1)
Unit 10 Colemeadow Road North Moons Moat, Redditch, B98 9PB, Worcestershire, United Kingdom
Tel.: (44) 1527592878
Web Site: http://www.reliv.co.uk
Nutrition Food Product Whslr
N.A.I.C.S.: 456191

Reliv, Inc. (1)
136 Chesterfield Industrial Blvd, Chesterfield, MO 63005
Tel.: (636) 537-9715
Web Site: http://www.reliv.com
Sales Range: $50-74.9 Million
Emp.: 170
Pharmaceutical Preparation Mfr
N.A.I.C.S.: 325412

RELM HOLDINGS, INC.
1719 Delaware Ave, Wilmington, DE 19806
Tel.: (302) 824-7064
RELM—(OTCIQ)
Information Technology Management Services
N.A.I.C.S.: 541512
Susan Fast (VP)

RELMADA THERAPEUTICS, INC.
2222 Ponce de Leon Blvd Fl 3, Coral Gables, FL 33134
Tel.: (786) 629-1376 NV
Web Site: https://www.relmada.com
Year Founded: 2011
RLMD—(NASDAQ)
Rev.: $4,205,253
Assets: $152,905,179
Liabilities: $12,468,877
Net Worth: $140,436,302
Earnings: ($157,043,823)
Emp.: 14
Fiscal Year-end: 12/31/22
Pharmaceutical Preparation Manufacturing
N.A.I.C.S.: 325412
Charles S. Ence (Chief Acctg & Compliance Officer)
Sergio C. Traversa (CEO)
Maged S. Shenouda (CFO)
Paolo Manfredi (Chief Scientific Officer-Acting)
Marco Pappagallo (Chief Medical Officer-Acting)

REMARK HOLDINGS, INC.
800 S Commerce St, Las Vegas, NV 89106
Tel.: (702) 701-9514 DE
Web Site:
   https://www.remarkholdings.com
Year Founded: 2006
MARK—(NASDAQ)
Rev.: $11,666,000
Assets: $14,436,000
Liabilities: $34,861,000
Net Worth: ($20,425,000)
Earnings: ($55,483,000)
Emp.: 88
Fiscal Year-end: 12/31/22
Online Publishing Services
N.A.I.C.S.: 551112
Kai-Shing Tao (Chm)

Subsidiaries:

Banks.com, Inc. (1)
425 Market St Ste 2200, San Francisco, CA 94108
Tel.: (415) 962-9700
Web Site: http://www.banks.com
Sales Range: $10-24.9 Million
Emp.: 10
Internet Search Services
N.A.I.C.S.: 516210

Subsidiary (Domestic):

MyStockFund Securities, Inc (2)
13700 US Hwy 1st Ste 202E, Juno Beach, FL 33408-1600
Tel.: (561) 626-0407
Web Site: https://www.mystockfund.com
Securities Brokerage Services
N.A.I.C.S.: 523150

Casino Travel & Tours, LLC (1)
6225 S Valley View Blvd Ste L, Las Vegas, NV 89118-6811
Web Site: http://www.casinotravel.com
Travel Management Services
N.A.I.C.S.: 561510

INTAC International, Inc. (1)
Units 6-7 32/F Laws Commercial Plaza, 788 Cheung Sha Wan Road, Kowloon, China (Hong Kong)
Tel.: (852) 23858789
Web Site: http://www.intac-international.com.cn
Sales Range: $1-9.9 Million
Wireless Handsets Mfr & Distr; Educational Software Developer
N.A.I.C.S.: 334220

Remark Entertainment (Shanghai) Co. Ltd. (1)
21F No 268 Middle Xizang Road, Huang Pu District, Shanghai, China
Tel.: (86) 2162403065
Web Site: https://www.remark-entertainment.cn
Entertainment Broadcasting Services
N.A.I.C.S.: 516210

Wesley Wu (Dir-Client Svc)
Karen Ge (Controller-Fin)

REMITLY GLOBAL, INC.
1111 3rd Ave Ste 2100, Seattle, WA 98101 DE
Web Site: https://www.remitly.com
Year Founded: 2018
RELY—(NASDAQ)
Rev.: $653,560,000
Assets: $695,953,000
Liabilities: $215,866,000
Net Worth: $480,087,000
Earnings: ($114,019,000)
Emp.: 2,700
Fiscal Year-end: 12/31/22
Holding Company
N.A.I.C.S.: 551112
Joshua Hug (Co-Founder & Chm)
Vishal Ghotge (Exec VP-North America)
Robert Kaskel (Exec VP-People)
Karim Meghji (CEO)
Robert Singer (CIO)
Saema Somalya (Gen Counsel & Sec)
Matthew Oppenheimer (Co-Founder & Pres)
Vikas Mehta (CFO)
Ankur Sinha (CTO)
Rina Hahn (CMO)
Nick Moiseff (Exec VP-FinTech Platform)
Pankaj Sharma (Chief Bus Officer)
Milkana Brace (Exec VP-Consumer Product)
Gail Miller (Chief Acctg Officer)

Subsidiaries:

Remitly U.K., Ltd. (1)
90 Whitfield Street, London, W1T 4EZ, United Kingdom
Tel.: (44) 8081692816
Web Site: https://www.remitly.com
Investment Financing Services
N.A.I.C.S.: 523999

REMSLEEP HOLDINGS, INC.
14175 ICOT Blvd Ste 300, Clearwater, FL 33760
Tel.: (727) 955-4465
Web Site: https://www.remsleep.com
RMSL—(OTCQB)
Rev.: $320,710
Assets: $3,360,900
Liabilities: $652,362
Net Worth: $2,708,538
Earnings: ($1,486,574)
Emp.: 2
Fiscal Year-end: 12/31/22
Surgical & Medical Instrument Manufacturing
N.A.I.C.S.: 339112
Tom Wood (Co-Founder, CEO & Designer)
Russell Bird (Co-Founder)

RENASANT CORPORATION
209 Troy St, Tupelo, MS 38804-4827
Tel.: (662) 680-1001 MS
Web Site:
   https://investors.renasant.com
Year Founded: 1982
RNST—(NASDAQ)
Rev.: $691,063,000
Assets: $16,988,176,000
Liabilities: $14,852,160,000
Net Worth: $2,136,016,000
Earnings: $166,068,000
Emp.: 2,334
Fiscal Year-end: 12/31/22
Bank Holding Company
N.A.I.C.S.: 551111
Edward Robinson McGraw (Exec Chm)

C. Mitchell Waycaster *(Vice Chm & CEO)*
James C. Mabry IV *(CFO & Exec VP)*
David L. Meredith *(Chief Credit Officer & Exec VP)*
Curtis J. Perry *(Chief Corp Banking Officer & Exec VP)*
Jimmy R. Baxter III *(Chief Risk Officer & Exec VP)*
W. Mark Williams *(Chief Banking Ops Officer & Sr Exec VP)*
Mark W. Jeanfreau *(Chief Governance Officer, Gen Counsel & Sr Exec VP)*
Tracey Morant Adams *(Chief Community Dev Officer & Sr Exec VP)*

Subsidiaries:

Renasant Bank (1)
209 Troy St, Tupelo, MS 38804 **(100%)**
Tel.: (662) 680-1362
Sales Range: $300-349.9 Million
Emp.: 1,400
Commercial Banking Services
N.A.I.C.S.: 522110
Edward Robinson McGraw *(Exec Chm)*
C. Mitchell Waycaster *(Vice Chm & CEO)*

Subsidiary (Domestic):

Nashville Capital Corp. (2)
1820 W End Ave 2nd Fl, Nashville, TN 37203
Tel.: (615) 259-9084
Web Site: https://parkplacecapital.com
Investment Advisory Services
N.A.I.C.S.: 523940
Paul B. Ordonio *(Chief Compliance Officer)*

Renasant Bank - Alabama Region Headquarters (2)
2001 Park Pl N Ste 100, Birmingham, AL 35203
Tel.: (205) 716-3475
Web Site: http://www.renasantbank.com
Sales Range: $125-149.9 Million
Regional Managing Office; Commercial Banking
N.A.I.C.S.: 551114

Renasant Bank - Georgia Region Headquarters (2)
721 N Westover Blvd, Albany, GA 31707
Tel.: (229) 878-2041
Web Site: http://www.renasantbank.com
Regional Managing Office; Commercial Banking
N.A.I.C.S.: 551114

Renasant Bank - Tennessee Region Headquarters (2)
1820 W End Ave, Nashville, TN 37203
Tel.: (615) 340-3000
Web Site: http://www.renasantbank.com
Regional Managing Office; Commercial Banking
N.A.I.C.S.: 551114

RENAVOTIO, INC.
601 S Boulder Ave Ste 600, Tulsa, OK 74119
Tel.: (260) 490-9990 NV
Web Site: http://renavotio.com
Year Founded: 2013
RIII—(OTCIQ)
Rev.: $4,124,300
Assets: $4,665,955
Liabilities: $3,975,847
Net Worth: $690,108
Earnings: ($1,752,529)
Emp.: 3
Fiscal Year-end: 12/31/20
Internet Movie & Film Producer
N.A.I.C.S.: 512110
William C. Robinson *(Chm, Pres, CEO, CFO, Treas & Sec)*
Robert Mackey *(COO)*

Subsidiaries:

Utility Management & Construction, LLC (1)
396301 W Rd 3000, Ochelata, OK 74051

Web Site: http://www.umcco.com
Emp.: 15
Construction Services
N.A.I.C.S.: 236220

RENEWABLE ENERGY & POWER, INC.
3395 W Cheyenne Ave Ste 111, North Las Vegas, NV 89032
Tel.: (702) 685-9524 NV
Web Site:
https://reappower.weebly.com
Year Founded: 2012
RBNW—(OTCIQ)
Sales Range: Less than $1 Million
Emp.: 5
Lighting Equipment Mfr
N.A.I.C.S.: 335139
Donald MacIntyre *(Chm, Pres & CEO)*
Bruce Parsons *(CFO & Treas)*
Bruce MacIntyre *(Sec & VP-Mktg)*
Perry Barker *(VP-Sls)*

RENEWABLE ENERGY SOLUTION SYSTEMS, INC.
2030 Powers Ferry Rd SE Ste 212, Atlanta, GA 30339
Tel.: (404) 816-9220 DE
RESS—(OTCIQ)
Renewable Energy Services
N.A.I.C.S.: 221114
Erik Nelson *(Pres)*

RENEWAL FUELS, INC.
8 The Green Suite, Dover, DE 19901
Web Site: http://www.rnwfmerger.com DE
RNWF—(OTCIQ)
Financial Investment Services
N.A.I.C.S.: 523999
Carey W. Cooley *(CEO & Pres)*

RENN FUND, INC.
470 Park Ave S, New York, NY 10016
Tel.: (914) 703-6904 TX
Web Site: http://www.rencapital.com
RCG—(NYSEAMEX)
Rev.: $115,062
Assets: $13,661,534
Liabilities: $1,305,405
Net Worth: $12,356,129
Earnings: ($106,856)
Fiscal Year-end: 12/31/19
Closed-End Investment Fund
N.A.I.C.S.: 525990
Jay Kesslen *(Chief Compliance Officer & VP)*

RENNOVA HEALTH, INC.
400 S Australian Ave 8th Fl, West Palm Beach, FL 33401
Tel.: (561) 855-1626 DE
Web Site:
https://www.rennovahealth.com
RNVA—(OTCIQ)
Rev.: $13,036,172
Assets: $20,572,762
Liabilities: $49,667,350
Net Worth: ($29,094,588)
Earnings: ($3,293,055)
Emp.: 85
Fiscal Year-end: 12/31/22
Holding Company; Medical Technologies Platform Developer & Data Services; Clinical Laboratory Testing Services
N.A.I.C.S.: 551112
Seamus Lagan *(Pres, CEO & Interim CFO)*
Thomas Laussermair *(VP-IT Engrg-Rennova Health Technology Solutions)*
Karen Taylor *(Dir-HR)*
Kristi Dymond *(Treas)*

Subsidiaries:

Clinlab, Inc. (1)
296 Treemont Dr, Orange City, FL 32763
Web Site: http://www.clinlabinc.com
Healthcare Support Services
N.A.I.C.S.: 621610

CollabRx (1)
44 Montgomery St Ste 800, San Francisco, CA 94104
Tel.: (415) 248-5350
Web Site: http://www.collabrx.com
Cloud-Based Medical Platform Software Developer & Services
N.A.I.C.S.: 518210

Epinex Diagnostics Laboratories, Inc. (1)
14351 Myford Rd, Tustin, CA 92780
Tel.: (949) 660-7770
Web Site: https://www.epinex.com
Healthcare Support Services
N.A.I.C.S.: 621610

Genomas Inc. (1)
67 Jefferson St, Hartford, CT 06106
Tel.: (860) 972-4574
Web Site: http://www.genomas.com
Biomedical Mfr
N.A.I.C.S.: 325414
Gualberto Ruano *(Founder, Pres, CEO & Dir-Medical)*

Health Technology Solutions, Inc. (1)
400 S Australian Ave Ste 800, West Palm Beach, FL 33401
Tel.: (561) 666-9814
Web Site:
http://www.healthtechnologysolutions.com
Software Development Services
N.A.I.C.S.: 541511

International Technologies, LLC (1)
71 Franklin Tpke, Waldwick, NJ 07463
Tel.: (201) 857-3914
Healthcare Support Services
N.A.I.C.S.: 621610

Jellico Medical Center, Inc. (1)
188 Tennessee Ln, Jellico, TN 37762
Tel.: (423) 784-7252
Web Site: http://www.jellicohospital.com
Healthcare Support Services
N.A.I.C.S.: 621610
Gene Miller *(CEO-Interim)*
Evelyn Ghulam *(Controller)*
Jean Kidd *(Dir-HR)*
Mikal Hensarling *(Dir-IT)*
Allen McClary *(Chm)*
Kaye Marantette *(Chief Nursing Officer)*

Medical Billing Choices, Inc. (1)
814 Tyvola Rd Ste 116, Charlotte, NC 28217
Tel.: (704) 527-8010
Web Site:
https://www.medicalbillingchoices.com
Healthcare Support Services
N.A.I.C.S.: 621610

Medical Mime, Inc. (1)
7960 Central Industrial Dr Ste 120, Riviera Beach, FL 33404
Tel.: (561) 666-9814
Web Site: http://www.medicalmime.com
Healthcare Support Services
N.A.I.C.S.: 621610

Medytox Diagnostics, Inc. (1)
400 S Australian Ave Ste 800, West Palm Beach, FL 33401
Tel.: (561) 855-1626
Web Site: http://www.rennovahealth.com
Clinical Laboratory Testing Services
N.A.I.C.S.: 541380

Mountain View Physician Practice, Inc. (1)
Mountain View PP 114 No Duncan St, Jamestown, TN 38556
Tel.: (931) 879-6293
Web Site: http://www.mountainviewpp.com
Healthcare Support Services
N.A.I.C.S.: 621610

RENOVACARE, INC.

9375 E Shea Blvd Suite 107A, Scottsdale, AZ 85260 NV
Web Site:
https://www.renovacareinc.com
RCAR—(OTCIQ)
Rev.: $931,276
Assets: $3,652,134
Liabilities: $1,305,245
Net Worth: $2,346,889
Earnings: ($4,471,723)
Emp.: 1
Fiscal Year-end: 12/31/21
Cell Deposition Device Mfr
N.A.I.C.S.: 339112
Roger Esteban-Vives *(VP-Res & Product Dev)*
Robin A. Robinson *(Chief Scientific Officer)*
Rodney Sparks *(VP-Intellectual Property)*
Jo Ellen Schweinle *(Chief Medical Officer)*
Justin Frere *(CFO)*
Harmel S. Rayat *(Founder & Pres)*
Kaiyo Nedd *(Pres & CEO)*
Amit Singh *(VP-Investor Rel)*
Lucy Wu *(Controller)*

RENOVARE ENVIRONMENTAL, INC.
80 Red Schoolhouse Rd, Chestnut Ridge, NY 10977
Tel.: (845) 262-1081 DE
Web Site: https://www.biohitech.com
Year Founded: 2013
RENO—(NASDAQ)
Rev.: $12,347,529
Assets: $42,336,371
Liabilities: $52,438,381
Net Worth: ($10,102,010)
Earnings: ($21,596,998)
Emp.: 34
Fiscal Year-end: 12/31/21
Online Computer Programming Courses
N.A.I.C.S.: 541519
Brian C. Essman *(CFO & Treas)*
Nicholaus Rohleder *(Interim Chm)*

Subsidiaries:

Entsorga West Virginia LLC (1)
870 Grapevine Rd, Martinsburg, WV 25405
Tel.: (845) 262-1081
Web Site: http://www.entsorgawv.com
Computer Disaster Recovery Services
N.A.I.C.S.: 541519

RENOVARO BIOSCIENCES INC.
2080 Century Park E Ste 906, Los Angeles, CA 90067
Tel.: (305) 918-1980 DE
Web Site:
https://www.renovarobio.com
Year Founded: 2011
RENB—(NASDAQ)
Rev.: $989,124
Assets: $163,129,450
Liabilities: $31,152,306
Net Worth: $131,977,144
Earnings: ($80,650,172)
Emp.: 25
Fiscal Year-end: 06/30/24
Pharmaceuticals Mfr
N.A.I.C.S.: 325412
Serhat Gumrukcu *(Co-Founder)*
Greg Duczynski *(Sr VP-Clinical Ops)*
Rene Sindlev *(Chm)*
Mark R. Dybul *(CEO)*
Argist Karapetyan *(VP-Finance & Controller-Corp)*
Saleem Mahammad *(Head-Research & Development)*
Elango Kathirvel *(Head-Analytical Dev)*

RENOVATE NEIGHBORHOODS, INC.

Renovate Neighborhoods, Inc.—(Continued)

621 Sturges Rd, Fortson, GA 31808
Tel.: (561) 562-2956　　　　NV
Web Site: http://www.renovate-
neighborhoods.com
Year Founded: 1995
RNVT—(OTCIQ)
Construction Consulting Services
N.A.I.C.S.: 541330
Paul L. Strozier *(Pres, Treas & Sec)*

RENOVORX, INC

4546 El Camino Real Ste B1, Los
Altos, CA 94022
Tel.: (650) 284-4433　　　　DE
Web Site: https://www.renovorx.com
Year Founded: 2012
RNXT—(NASDAQ)
Rev.: $61,000
Assets: $7,265,000
Liabilities: $1,102,000
Net Worth: $6,163,000
Earnings: ($9,889,000)
Emp.: 9
Fiscal Year-end: 12/31/22
Research & Development in Biotech-
nology (except Nanobiotechnology)
N.A.I.C.S.: 541714
Shaun R. Bagai *(CEO)*
Ramtin Agah *(Founder, Chm & Chief
Medical Officer)*
Paul Manners *(VP-Fin)*
Joe Paraschac *(VP-Ops)*
Nicole Lama *(Sr Dir-Clinical Ops &
Research)*
Imtiaz Qureshi *(Dir-Imaging)*
Ronald B. Kocak *(Principal Acctg Of-
ficer, Principal Fin Officer, VP & Con-
troller)*
Leesa Gentry *(Chief Clinical Officer)*

RENT THE RUNWAY, INC.

10 Jay St, Brooklyn, NY 11201
Web Site:
https://www.renttherunway.com
Year Founded: 2009
RENT—(NASDAQ)
Rev.: $296,400,000
Assets: $336,200,000
Liabilities: $371,500,000
Net Worth: ($35,300,000)
Earnings: ($138,700,000)
Emp.: 880
Fiscal Year-end: 01/31/23
Designer Fashion & Accessories
Rental Services
N.A.I.C.S.: 532281
Jennifer Y. Hyman *(Founder, Chm,
Pres, CEO & Principal Operating Offi-
cer)*
Larry Steinberg *(CTO)*
Brian Donato *(Chief Revenue Officer)*
Drew Rau *(Sr VP-Supply Chain &
Inventory)*
Jennifer Fleiss *(Head-Bus Dev)*

REO PLASTICS, INC.

11850 93rd Ave N, Maple Grove, MN
55369
Tel.: (763) 425-4171　　　　MN
Web Site:
https://www.reoplastics.com
Year Founded: 1960
REOP—(OTCIQ)
All Other Plastics Product Manufac-
turing
N.A.I.C.S.: 326199
Greg King *(Production Mgr)*

REOSTAR ENERGY CORPO-
RATION

87 N Raymond Ave, Pasadena, CA
91103
Tel.: (310) 999-3506　　　　NV
Web Site:
https://reostarenergycorp.com

Year Founded: 2004
REOS—(OTCIQ)
Sales Range: $1-9.9 Million
Emp.: 13
Support Activities for Oil & Gas Op-
erations
N.A.I.C.S.: 213112

REPAY HOLDINGS CORPORA-
TION

3 W Paces Ferry Rd Ste 200, Atlanta,
GA 30305
Tel.: (404) 504-7472　　　　Ky
Web Site: https://www.repay.com
Year Founded: 2017
RPAY—(NASDAQ)
Rev.: $279,227,000
Assets: $1,626,800,000
Liabilities: $698,507,000
Net Worth: $928,293,000
Earnings: $12,836,000
Emp.: 579
Fiscal Year-end: 12/31/22
Investment Services
N.A.I.C.S.: 523999
Shaler Alias *(Co-Founder & Pres)*
Tim Murphy *(CFO)*
Shaler Alias *(Co-Founder & Pres)*
Tyler Dempsey *(Gen Counsel)*
Naomi Barnett *(Exec VP-HR)*
David Guthrie *(CTO)*
Darin Horrocks *(Exec VP)*
John Morris *(Co-Founder & CEO)*

Subsidiaries:

CPS Payment Services, LLC　　(1)
12400 N Meridian St Ste 185, Carmel, IN
46032
Web Site:
http://www.cpspaymentservices.com
Financial Services
N.A.I.C.S.: 523999
Wade Eckman *(Pres & CEO)*
Ken Barrett *(Exec VP-Ops)*
Richard Otruba *(Exec VP-Tech)*
Scott Saltmarsh *(Exec VP-Bus Dev)*
Jeff Wiesinger *(Exec VP-Fin)*

Electronic Payment Providers,
Inc.　　(1)
8800 E Raintree Dr Ste 210, Scottsdale, AZ
85260
Tel.: (602) 443-5900
Web Site: http://www.mybillingtree.com
Rev.: $3,800,000
Emp.: 35
Financial Transactions Processing, Reserve
& Clearinghouse Activities
N.A.I.C.S.: 522320
Dan Willis *(CFO)*

Mesa Acquirer LLC　　(1)
5646 E Main St Ste 5, Mesa, AZ 85205
Web Site: http://www.apspayments.com
Financial Services
N.A.I.C.S.: 523999

Repay Holdings LLC　　(1)
3 W Paces Ferry Rd Ste 200, Atlanta, GA
30305
Tel.: (855) 369-5578
Web Site: http://www.repayonline.com
Sales Range: $10-24.9 Million
Emp.: 11
Electronic Financial Transactions Process-
ing
N.A.I.C.S.: 522320

Sigma Acquisition LLC　　(1)
7660 Fay Ave Ste H263, La Jolla, CA
92037
Tel.: (858) 605-1587
Web Site:
https://www.sigmaacquisitions.com
Professional Services
N.A.I.C.S.: 541990

Trisource Solutions, LLC　　(1)
405 Utica Ridge Rd 208, Davenport, IA
52807
Tel.: (563) 359-9564
Web Site: https://www.repay.com
Financial Transactions Processing, Reserve
& Clearinghouse Activities

N.A.I.C.S.: 522320

REPLIGEN CORPORATION

41 Seyon St Bldg 1 Ste 100,
Waltham, MA 02453
Tel.: (781) 250-0111　　　　DE
Web Site: https://www.repligen.com
Year Founded: 1981
RGEN—(NASDAQ)
Rev.: $638,764,000
Assets: $2,824,411,000
Liabilities: $853,208,000
Net Worth: $1,971,203,000
Earnings: $41,577,000
Emp.: 1,783
Fiscal Year-end: 12/31/23
Drugs for Autoimmune & Neurological
Disorder Treatment
N.A.I.C.S.: 325414
Paul R. Schimmel *(Co-Founder)*
Anthony J. Hunt *(Pres & CEO)*
Ralf Kuriyel *(Sr VP-R&D)*
Christine Gebski *(Sr VP-Filtration &
Chromatography)*
Sondra S. Newman *(Head-IR-Global)*
James R. Bylund *(COO)*
Kola Otitoju *(Sr VP-Strategy & Bus
Dev)*
Kimberly Cornwell *(Gen Counsel)*
Leslie Golvin *(VP)*
Jamie M. Humara *(Sr VP)*
Keith Robison Lee *(CIO)*
Mark Salerno *(VP)*
Neil Whitfield *(VP)*
Olivier Loeillot *(Pres & Chief Comml
Officer)*
Jason K. Garland *(CFO & Principal
Acctg Officer)*

Subsidiaries:

ARTeSYN Biosolutions Estonia
OU　　(1)
Kesk Tee 10a Juri Alevik, Harju, Maakond,
75301, Estonia
Tel.: (372) 53502901
Biological Drug Mfr
N.A.I.C.S.: 325412

ARTeSYN Biosolutions Ireland
Limited　　(1)
Six Cross Roads, Kilbarry, Waterford, X91
YR27, Ireland
Tel.: (353) 51508431
Web Site:
https://www.artesynbiosolutions.com
Biological Drug Mfr
N.A.I.C.S.: 325412

ARTeSYN Biosolutions USA,
LLC　　(1)
1771 S Sutro Ter, Carson City, NV 89706-
0364
Tel.: (775) 235-5200
Biological Drug Mfr
N.A.I.C.S.: 325412

Bio-Flex Solutions, L.L.C.　　(1)
119 Fredon Springdale Rd, Newton, NJ
07860
Tel.: (973) 383-1232
Web Site: https://www.bflex.co
Molded Component Product Distr
N.A.I.C.S.: 424610

C Technologies, Inc.　　(1)
685 Route 202/206, Bridgewater, NJ 08807
Tel.: (908) 707-1009
Web Site: https://ctech.repligen.com
Fiber Optic Cable Mfr
N.A.I.C.S.: 335921
Craig Harrison *(Pres)*
Mark Salerno *(VP-Ops)*
Larry Russo *(Dir-Intl Sls)*
Glenn Giffin *(Dir-Service Excellence)*
Marina Lopez *(Dir-Quality & Organizational
Knowledge)*
Mary Ann Vernieri *(Mgr-Inside Sls)*
Eric Shih *(Mgr-Engrg)*
Dodd Weisenberger *(Mgr-Software Engrg)*
Vincent Romano *(Assoc Dir-Analytical Sup-
port)*
Joe Ferraiolo *(Assoc Dir-Bioanalytics Appli-
cations)*

Luis Costa *(Mgr-Quality Assurance)*
Donna Cassano *(Ops Mgr)*
Pablo Olivares *(Production Mgr)*
John Sirico *(Mgr-IT)*
Greg Flohs *(Mgr-Acctg)*

Engineered Molding Technology
LLC　　(1)
1 Fairchild Sq Ste 111, Clifton Park, NY
12065
Tel.: (518) 406-5276
Web Site:
http://www.engineeredmolding.com
Silicone Molded Product Mfr
N.A.I.C.S.: 333511

Metenova AB　　(1)
Norra Agatan 32, 43135, Molndal, Sweden
Tel.: (46) 313359500
Web Site: https://www.metenova.com
Biotech & Pharmaceutical Product Mfr
N.A.I.C.S.: 325412

Non-Metallic Solutions, Inc.　　(1)
440 Washington St, Auburn, MA 01501
Tel.: (508) 832-5400
Web Site: http://www.nmsbio.com
Non Metallic Product Mfr
N.A.I.C.S.: 327999

Polymem S.A.　　(1)
3 Rue de L'industrie - Zone de VIC, 31320,
Castanet-Tolosan, France
Tel.: (33) 561317866
Web Site: https://www.polymem.fr
Water Treatment Equipment Mfr
N.A.I.C.S.: 312112

Repligen (Shanghai) Biotechnology
Co. Ltd.　　(1)
Suite GH 2nd Floor Tower 1 Hengyue Inter-
national Edifice, Lane 1238 Zhangjiang
Road Pudong District, Shanghai, 201210,
China
Tel.: (86) 2168810228
Research & Development Biotechnology
Services
N.A.I.C.S.: 541714

Repligen Estonia OU　　(1)
Uus-Ringi Tee 10, Harju Maakond, 75301,
Juri, Estonia
Tel.: (372) 53502901
Biotechnology Research & Development
Services
N.A.I.C.S.: 541714

Repligen GmbH　　(1)
Parkstr 10, 88212, Ravensburg, Germany
Tel.: (49) 751561210
Web Site: https://www.repligen.com
Pharmaceutical Preparation Mfr & Distr
N.A.I.C.S.: 325411

Repligen India Private Limited　　(1)
3rd Floor No 2/55 Outer Ring Road Veeran-
napalya Hebbal, Bengaluru, 560 045, Kar-
nataka, India
Tel.: (91) 8042077396
Research & Development Biotechnology
Services
N.A.I.C.S.: 541714

Repligen Ireland Limited　　(1)
Six Cross Roads, Kilbarry, Waterford, X91
YR27, Ireland
Tel.: (353) 51508431
Biologic Drug Mfr & Distr
N.A.I.C.S.: 325412

Repligen Japan LLC　　(1)
2-6-8 Anyoji Spectrum Bldg 5th Floor, Ritto,
520-3015, Shiga, Japan
Tel.: (81) 775527820
Research & Development Biotechnology
Services
N.A.I.C.S.: 541714

Repligen Korea Co. Ltd.　　(1)
602-1ho 9-22 Pangyo-ro 255beon-gil,
Bundang-gu, Seongnam, 13486, Gyeonggi-
do, Korea (South)
Tel.: (82) 316288771
Research & Development Biotechnology
Services
N.A.I.C.S.: 541714

Repligen Sweden AB　　(1)
Sankt Lars Vag 47, 222 70, Lund, Sweden
Tel.: (46) 462801700

Sales Range: $25-49.9 Million
Emp.: 50
Biological Product Mfr
N.A.I.C.S.: 325414

Spectrum Labs India Pvt. Ltd. **(1)**
No 839 1st Floor A Block Damodaran Road
Sahakara Nagar, Bengaluru, 560 092, Kar-
nataka, India
Tel.: (91) 8042077396
Pharmaceutical Preparation Mfr & Distr
N.A.I.C.S.: 325411

REPLIMUNE GROUP, INC.
500 Unicorn Park Dr 3rd Fl, Woburn,
MA 01801
Tel.: (781) 222-9600 DE
Web Site: https://www.replimune.com
Year Founded: 2017
REPL—(NASDAQ)
Rev.: $23,356,000
Assets: $487,722,000
Liabilities: $113,214,000
Net Worth: $374,508,000
Earnings: ($215,794,000)
Emp.: 331
Fiscal Year-end: 03/31/24
Biotechnology Research & Develop-
ment Services
N.A.I.C.S.: 541714
Emily Hill *(CFO)*
Philip Astley-Sparke *(Co-Founder &
Exec Chm)*
Robert Coffin *(Co-Founder & Chief
Scientist)*
Colin Love *(Co-Founder)*
Sushil Patel *(CEO)*
Andrew Schwendenman *(Chief Acctg
Officer)*

REPOSITRAK INC
5282 S Commerce Dr Ste D292,
Murray, UT 84107
Tel.: (435) 645-2000 NV
Web Site: https://repositrak.com
TRAK—(NYSE)
Rev.: $19,098,910
Assets: $50,583,431
Liabilities: $4,701,500
Net Worth: $45,881,931
Earnings: $5,590,289
Emp.: 69
Fiscal Year-end: 06/30/23
Operations Management Software
N.A.I.C.S.: 513210
Randall K. Fields *(Pres, CEO & Chm)*
Edward L. Clissold *(Gen Counsel)*
Derek Hannum *(Sr VP-Customer
Success)*
John Merrill *(CFO)*
Joe Meherg *(Sr VP-Sls)*
Cerina Hrasko *(VP-Development)*
Bruce Bruce Christiansen *(Sr VP-
Strategy & Product)*

Subsidiaries:

Prescient Applied Intelligence,
Inc. **(1)**
3160 Pinebrook Rd, Park City, UT 84098-
5380
Tel.: (610) 719-1600
Web Site: http://www.prescient.com
Sales Range: $1-9.9 Million
Emp.: 40
Retail Supply Chain & Replenishment Ser-
vices
N.A.I.C.S.: 425120

REPUBLIC BANCORP, INC.
601 W Market St, Louisville, KY
40202
Tel.: (502) 584-3600 KY
Web Site:
https://www.republicbank.com
Year Founded: 1998
RBCAA—(NASDAQ)
Rev.: $333,994,000
Assets: $5,835,543,000,000
Liabilities: $4,978,930,000,000

Net Worth: $856,613,000,000
Earnings: $91,106,000
Emp.: 984
Fiscal Year-end: 12/31/22
Bank Holding Company
N.A.I.C.S.: 551111
A. Scott Trager *(Vice Chm & Pres)*
Steven E. Trager *(Exec Chm & CEO)*
Kevin D. Sipes *(CFO, Chief Acctg
Officer & Exec VP)*
Anthony T. Powell *(Chief Lending Of-
ficer & Exec VP)*

Subsidiaries:

Republic Bank & Trust Company **(1)**
Republic Corporate Ctr 601 W Market St,
Louisville, KY 40202-2700
Tel.: (502) 584-3600
Web Site: https://www.republicbank.com
Sales Range: $150-199.9 Million
Emp.: 650
Commercial Banking
N.A.I.C.S.: 522110
Logan M. Pichel *(Pres & CEO)*
A. Scott Trager *(Vice Chm)*
Steven E. Trager *(Exec Chm & CEO)*
Kevin D. Sipes *(CFO & Exec VP)*
Andrew Trager-Kusman *(Chief Strategy Of-
ficer & Sr VP)*
Kathy Pleasant *(VP)*
Jim Ensign *(Chief Brand Officer & Sr VP)*
Pedro Bryant *(Exec VP & Mng Dir-
Community Lending)*
Lisa Butcher *(Dir-Private Banking)*
Steve McWilliams *(Pres-Metro Philadelphia)*
Kelly Trimble *(VP & Mgr-Relationship)*

Subsidiary (Domestic):

CBank **(2)**
8050 Hosbrook Rd Ste 220, Cincinnati, OH
45236
Tel.: (513) 651-3000
Web Site: http://www.cbankusa.com
Sales Range: $1-9.9 Million
Emp.: 2
Trust, Fiduciary & Custody Activity Services
N.A.I.C.S.: 523991
Erick K. Harback *(Chief Credit Officer & Sr
VP)*
Jeffrey L. Wyler *(Chm)*
J. Vonderhaar *(CFO & Sr VP)*

REPUBLIC FIRST BANCORP, INC.
50 S 16th St, Philadelphia, PA 19102
Tel.: (215) 735-4422 PA
Web Site:
http://www.myrepublicbank.com
Year Founded: 1987
FRBK—(NASDAQ)
Rev.: $151,185,000
Assets: $5,065,735,000
Liabilities: $4,757,622,000
Net Worth: $308,113,000
Earnings: $5,054,000
Emp.: 467
Fiscal Year-end: 12/31/20
Bank Holding Company
N.A.I.C.S.: 523940
Michael T. LaPlante *(Chief Acctg Offi-
cer & Sr VP)*
Harry D. Madonna *(Founder)*
Thomas X. Geisel *(Pres & CEO)*
Tracie A. Young *(Chief Risk Officer &
Exec VP-Republic Bank)*
Jay Neilon *(Chief Credit Officer &
Exec VP-Republic Bank)*
Linda Sanchez *(Chief People Officer
& Exec VP)*
Thomas X. Geisel *(Pres & CEO)*
Michael W. Harrington *(CFO)*
Brian F. Doran *(Gen Counsel & Exec
VP)*
Francis Mitchell *(Chief Investment
Officer, Treas & Sr VP)*

Subsidiaries:

Republic First Bank **(1)**
Two Liberty Place 50 S 16th St Ste 2400,
Philadelphia, PA 19102 **(100%)**

Web Site: http://www.myrepublicbank.com
Sales Range: $50-74.9 Million
Commercial Bank
N.A.I.C.S.: 522110
Michael T. LaPlante *(Chief Acctg Officer &
Sr VP)*
Harry D. Madonna *(Chm)*
Thomas X. Geisel *(Pres & CEO)*
Tracie A. Young *(Chief Risk Officer & Exec
VP)*
Michael W. Harrington *(CFO)*
Krista Collings *(Mgr-Store-Glassboro)*
Frank Cavallaro *(CFO & Exec VP)*
Jay Neilon *(Chief Credit Officer & Exec VP)*
Tricia Blair *(Mgr-Store-Medford)*
Anthony Dragani *(Officer-Loan)*
Casey Patrick Coyle *(Officer-Loan)*
Christine Laufer *(Officer-Loan)*
Dominic John Sardo *(Officer-Loan)*
Donna Hoffman *(Officer-Loan & Mgr-Client
Rels)*
Vincent Reilly *(Officer-Loan)*
Gregory Waters *(Officer-Loan)*
Stephen Aslanian *(Officer-Loan)*
James O. Mazzola *(Officer-Loan)*
Janice Ramsey *(Officer-Loan)*
Joe Conlin *(Officer-Loan)*
Sangkung Choi *(Officer-Loan)*
Joe McGuckin *(Sls Mgr)*
John O'Neal *(Officer-Loan)*
Joshua Lerman *(Officer-Loan)*
Kathie Seymour *(Officer-Loan)*
Kevin N. MacDonald *(Officer-Loan)*
Lori M. Boiler *(Officer-Loan)*
Marc Cramer *(Officer-Loan)*
Michael Badessa *(Officer-Loan)*
Michael McNamee *(Officer-Loan)*
Robert Angradi *(Sr VP)*
Robert Nepa *(Officer-Loan)*
Robyn Clancy-Merwede *(Officer-Loan)*
Rosemary Lance *(Officer-Loan)*
Sheryl Simon *(Sr VP & Sr Mgr-Relationship-
New York)*
Dan Markus *(Reg VP)*
Peter Musumeci *(Pres-Metro New York)*
Steve McWilliams *(Pres-Metro Philadelphia)*
Donald Greenleaf *(VP-Comml Lending-
Bucks County)*
Francis Mitchell *(Chief Investment Officer,
Treas & Sr VP)*

Subsidiary (Domestic):

Oak Mortgage Company, LLC **(2)**
525 Rte 73 N Ste 101, Marlton, NJ 08053
Tel.: (856) 988-8100
Web Site: http://www.oakmortgageusa.com
Sales Range: $1-9.9 Million
Emp.: 64
Residential Mortgage Services
N.A.I.C.S.: 522310
Robert Angradi *(Sr VP)*
Anthony Dragani *(Officer-Loan)*
Casey Patrick Coyle *(Officer-Loan)*
Christine Laufer *(Officer-Loan)*
Dominick John Sardo *(Officer-Loan)*
Donald Werner *(Officer-Loan)*
Donna Hoffman *(Officer-Loan & Mgr-Client
Rels)*
Eugene Park *(Officer-Loan)*
Gregory Waters *(Officer-Loan)*
James Cha *(Mgr-Mortgage Center)*
James Mazzola *(Officer-Loan)*
Janice Ramsey *(Officer-Loan)*
Joe Jackson *(Officer-Loan)*
Joe McGuckin *(Asst VP & Mgr-Mktg Div)*
John O'Neal *(Officer-Loan)*
Joshua I. Lerman *(Officer-Loan)*
Kathie Seymour *(Officer-Loan)*
Kevin MacDonald *(Officer-Loan)*
Lori Boiler *(Officer-Loan)*
Marc Cramer *(Officer-Loan)*
Michael Badessa *(Officer-Loan)*
Michael McNamee *(Officer-Loan)*
Philip Giangiordano *(Branch Mgr)*
Robert Nepa *(Officer-Loan)*
Robyn Clancy-Merwede *(Officer-Loan)*
Ronson Quick *(Officer-Loan)*

REPUBLIC SERVICES, INC.
18500 N Allied Way, Phoenix, AZ
85054
Tel.: (480) 627-2700 DE
Web Site:
https://www.republicservices.com
Year Founded: 1998
RSG—(NYSE)
Rev.: $14,964,500,000

Assets: $31,410,100,000
Liabilities: $20,866,600,000
Net Worth: $10,543,500,000
Earnings: $1,731,000,000
Emp.: 41,000
Fiscal Year-end: 12/31/23
Waste Recycling Services
N.A.I.C.S.: 562211
Catharine D. Ellingsen *(Chief Legal
Officer, Chief Ethics & Compliance
Officer & Sec)*
Brian M. DelGhiaccio *(CFO & Exec
VP)*
Jon Vander Ark *(Pres & CEO)*
Jeff Hughes *(Chief Admin Officer &
Exec VP)*
Gregg Brummer *(COO & Exec VP)*

Subsidiaries:

AWIN Leasing Company, Inc. **(1)**
2011 College Dr, Lake Havasu City, AZ
86403
Tel.: (928) 855-9441
Environmental Consulting Services
N.A.I.C.S.: 541620

Agri-Tech, Inc. of Oregon **(1)**
1214 Montgomery St SE, Albany, OR
97322-3266
Tel.: (541) 926-7738
Environmental Consulting Services
N.A.I.C.S.: 541620

Allied Waste Environmental Manage-
ment Group, LLC **(1)**
5011 S Lilley Rd, Canton, MI 48188
Tel.: (734) 397-2790
Web Site: http://www.republicservices.com
Sales Range: $25-49.9 Million
Emp.: 20
Environmental Consulting Services
N.A.I.C.S.: 541620

Allied Waste Industries, Inc **(1)**
18500 N Allied Way, Phoenix, AZ 85054-
5156
Tel.: (480) 627-2700
Emp.: 22,800
Waste Management Services
N.A.I.C.S.: 562213

Allied Waste Services of Fort Worth,
LLC **(1)**
6100 Elliott Reeder Rd, Fort Worth, TX
76117
Tel.: (817) 332-7301
Environmental Consulting Services
N.A.I.C.S.: 541620

Allied Waste Services of Massachu-
setts, LLC **(1)**
1080 Airport Rd, Fall River, MA 02720-4736
Tel.: (508) 676-1091
Environmental Consulting Services
N.A.I.C.S.: 541620

Allied Waste Services of Page,
Inc. **(1)**
3004 Coppermine Rd, Page, AZ 86040
Tel.: (928) 645-3885
Waste Management Services
N.A.I.C.S.: 562998

Allied Waste Services of Stillwater,
Inc. **(1)**
2417 N Marine Rd, Stillwater, OK 74075
Tel.: (405) 377-3880
Environmental Consulting Services
N.A.I.C.S.: 541620

Allied Waste Systems of Arizona,
LLC **(1)**
2011 College Dr, Lake Havasu City, AZ
86403-1953
Tel.: (928) 854-9154
Web Site: http://www.republicservices.com
Environmental Consulting Services
N.A.I.C.S.: 541620

Allied Waste, Inc. **(1)**
808 S Joliet St, Joliet, IL 60436
Tel.: (847) 429-7370
Web Site: http://www.alliedwaste.com
Sales Range: $1-9.9 Million
Emp.: 30
Refuse Collection & Disposal Services
N.A.I.C.S.: 562211

Republic Services, Inc.—(Continued)

American Disposal Services of West Virginia, Inc. (1)
258 N Fork Rd, Wheeling, WV 26003
Tel.: (304) 336-7800
Web Site: http://www.disposal.com
Environmental Consulting Services
N.A.I.C.S.: 541620

American Sanitation, Inc. (1)
1729 Action Ave, Napa, CA 94559
Tel.: (707) 554-8258
Web Site: https://www.american-sanitation.com
Environmental Consulting Services
N.A.I.C.S.: 541620
Sam Javorina (Pres)

Apache Junction Landfill Corporation (1)
4050 S Tomahawk Rd, Apache Junction, AZ 85119
Tel.: (480) 982-7003
Environmental Consulting Services
N.A.I.C.S.: 541620

Atlas Transport, Inc. (1)
3433 35th St N, Birmingham, AL 35207-3855
Tel.: (205) 849-9455
Environmental Consulting Services
N.A.I.C.S.: 541620

BFI Transfer Systems of Georgia, LLC (1)
3125 S Martin St, Atlanta, GA 30344-4377
Tel.: (770) 861-0724
Sales Range: $25-49.9 Million
Emp.: 5
Environmental Consulting Services
N.A.I.C.S.: 541620

BFI Waste Systems of Georgia, LLC (1)
5691 S Richland Creek Rd, Buford, GA 30518-2249
Tel.: (770) 271-3575
Web Site: http://www.republicservices.com
Emp.: 25
Environmental Consulting Services
N.A.I.C.S.: 541620

BFI Waste Systems of Kentucky, LLC (1)
100 Ellis Smeathers Rd, Owensboro, KY 42303-9701
Tel.: (270) 926-3255
Emp.: 26
Environmental Consulting Services
N.A.I.C.S.: 541620

BFI Waste Systems of Virginia, LLC (1)
1000 Iris Rd, Little Plymouth, VA 23091-9701
Tel.: (804) 785-2140
Emp.: 16
Waste Treatment & Disposal Services
N.A.I.C.S.: 562211

Benfield Sanitation Services, Inc. (1)
282 Scotts Creek Rd, Statesville, NC 28625-2342
Tel.: (704) 872-2668
Web Site: http://www.bsstrash.com
Recyclable Material Merchant Whslr
N.A.I.C.S.: 423930

Berkeley Sanitary Service, Inc. (1)
3260 Blume Dr Ste 115, Richmond, CA 94800
Tel.: (510) 262-7100
Solid Waste Collection, Recycling & Disposal Services
N.A.I.C.S.: 562219

Broadhurst Environmental, Inc. (1)
4800 Broadhurst Rd W, Screven, GA 31560 (100%)
Tel.: (912) 530-7050
Web Site: http://www.broadhurstlandfill.com
Sales Range: $10-24.9 Million
Emp.: 120
Solid Waste Management Services
N.A.I.C.S.: 562212

CECOS International, Inc. (1)
5600 Niagara Falls Blvd, Niagara Falls, NY 14304

Tel.: (716) 282-2676
Sales Range: $25-49.9 Million
Emp.: 4
Environmental Consulting Services
N.A.I.C.S.: 541620
Jay Dojka (Supvr-Ops)

Camelot Landfill TX, LP (1)
580 Huffines Blvd, Lewisville, TX 75056-9551
Tel.: (215) 646-4347
Environmental Consulting Services
N.A.I.C.S.: 541620

Celina Landfill, Inc. (1)
6141 Depweg Rd, Celina, OH 45822
Tel.: (419) 925-4592
Web Site: http://www.republicservices.com
Sales Range: $25-49.9 Million
Emp.: 4
Environmental Consulting Services
N.A.I.C.S.: 541620

Central Sanitary Landfill, Inc. (1)
21545 W Cannonsville Rd, Pierson, MI 49339
Tel.: (616) 636-4096
Web Site: https://centrallandfill.com
Emp.: 78
Solid Waste Landfill Services
N.A.I.C.S.: 562212

Citizens Disposal, Inc. (1)
2361 W Grand Blanc Rd, Grand Blanc, MI 48439
Tel.: (810) 655-4207
Environmental Consulting Services
N.A.I.C.S.: 541620
Bob Thornton (Gen Mgr)

Clinton County Landfill Partnership (1)
2700 N State Rd 39, Frankfort, IN 46041
Tel.: (765) 654-8144
Sales Range: $50-74.9 Million
Emp.: 100
Real Estate Services
N.A.I.C.S.: 522292

Copper Mountain Landfill, Inc. (1)
34853 E County 12th St, Wellton, AZ 85356
Tel.: (928) 785-3797
Web Site: http://www.republicservices.com
Emp.: 11
Environmental Consulting Services
N.A.I.C.S.: 541620

Courtney Ridge Landfill, LLC (1)
2001 N State Route 291, Independence, MO 64058-2823
Tel.: (816) 257-7999
Environmental Consulting Services
N.A.I.C.S.: 541620

Delta Container Corporation (1)
1145 W Charter Way, Stockton, CA 95206
Tel.: (209) 466-5192
Waste Collection & Recycling Services
N.A.I.C.S.: 562119

Devens Recycling Center, LLC (1)
45 Independence Dr, Devens, MA 01434
Tel.: (978) 772-6500
Web Site: http://www.devensrecycling.com
Recycling Services
N.A.I.C.S.: 562920
W. Kurt Macnamara (Founder & Principal)
Jack Curtin (CFO)
Bob Fico (Sls Mgr)
Darlene Duval (Office Mgr)
James M. Benson (Partner)

ECOFLO Field Services, LLC (1)
2750 Patterson St, Greensboro, NC 27407
Web Site: https://www.ecoflo.com
Environmental Consulting Services
N.A.I.C.S.: 541620

East Carolina Environmental, LLC (1)
1922 Republican Rd, Aulander, NC 27805 (100%)
Tel.: (252) 348-3322
Web Site: http://www.republicservices.com
Sales Range: $10-24.9 Million
Emp.: 15
Land Fill Services
N.A.I.C.S.: 562212

Ellis County Landfill TX, LP (1)
5703 N I 45, Ennis, TX 75119-0910

Tel.: (972) 875-5374
Environmental Consulting Services
N.A.I.C.S.: 541620

Envirocycle, Inc. (1)
849 SW 21st Ter, Fort Lauderdale, FL 33312
Tel.: (954) 792-8177
Web Site: http://www.republicservices.com
Sales Range: $25-49.9 Million
Emp.: 30
Environmental Consulting Services
N.A.I.C.S.: 541620

Envotech-Illinois L.L.C. (1)
2782 Landfill Trl, Litchfield, IL 62056
Tel.: (217) 324-2811
Emp.: 4
Environmental Consulting Services
N.A.I.C.S.: 541620

Epperson Waste Disposal, Inc. (1)
2360 Cynthiana Rd, Williamstown, KY 41097
Tel.: (859) 824-5208
Web Site: http://www.eppersonwaste.com
Sales Range: $200-249.9 Million
Emp.: 14
Solid Waste Management Services
N.A.I.C.S.: 562212
Jake Wilson (Gen Mgr)

FCR, LLC (1)
2911 Tennyson Ave Ste 304, Eugene, OR 97408
Tel.: (541) 957-8654
Web Site: http://www.gofcr.com
Emp.: 2,000
Business Process Outsourcing Services
N.A.I.C.S.: 561422
Jennifer Babbin Clark (VP-Security & Technology)
Matthew Achak (Co-Founder & Pres)
John Stadter (Co-Founder & Chm)
Katheryn Carnahan (COO)

GDS Cleveland (1)
1160 Airport Rd, Shelby, NC 28151 (100%)
Tel.: (704) 482-7916
Sales Range: $10-24.9 Million
Emp.: 39
Solid Waste Collection & Disposal Services
N.A.I.C.S.: 621111

Grants Pass Sanitation, Inc. (1)
1381 Redwood Ave, Grants Pass, OR 97527
Tel.: (541) 479-5335
Waste Management Services
N.A.I.C.S.: 562213

Greenridge Waste Services, LLC (1)
232 Landfill Rd, Scottdale, PA 15000
Tel.: (724) 887-9400
Environmental Consulting Services
N.A.I.C.S.: 541620

Gulf West Landfill TX, LP (1)
2601 S Jenkins Rd, Anahuac, TX 77514
Tel.: (409) 267-6666
Waste Management Services
N.A.I.C.S.: 562998

Illiana Disposal Partnership (1)
865 Wheeler St, Crown Point, IN 46307-2751
Tel.: (219) 662-8600
Environmental Consulting Services
N.A.I.C.S.: 541620

Illinois Landfill, Inc. (1)
16310 E 1000 N Rd, Hoopeston, IL 60942
Tel.: (217) 283-5968
Emp.: 7
Environmental Consulting Services
N.A.I.C.S.: 541620
Kenny Samet (Gen Mgr)

Imperial Landfill, Inc. (1)
3354 Dogwood Rd, Imperial, CA 92251
Tel.: (760) 355-0004
Environmental Consulting Services
N.A.I.C.S.: 541620

Lake Norman Landfill, Inc. (1)
7099 Quarry Ln, Stanley, NC 28164-6799
Tel.: (704) 822-3033
Web Site: http://www.republicservices.com
Emp.: 3
Environmental Consulting Services

N.A.I.C.S.: 541620

Lee County Landfill SC, LLC (1)
1431 Sumter Hwy, Bishopville, SC 29010-8934
Tel.: (803) 484-5341
Web Site: https://www.leecountysc.org
Emp.: 50
Environmental Consulting Services
N.A.I.C.S.: 541620
Lee Postao (Gen Mgr)

Lee County Landfill, Inc. (1)
1214 S Bataan Rd, Dixon, IL 61021-8308
Tel.: (815) 288-4607
Web Site: http://www.republicservices.com
Sales Range: $25-49.9 Million
Emp.: 20
Environmental Consulting Services
N.A.I.C.S.: 541620

Lemons Landfill, LLC (1)
15250 Old Bloomfield Rd, Dexter, MO 63841-9724
Tel.: (573) 624-8135
Sales Range: $25-49.9 Million
Emp.: 6
Waste Management Services
N.A.I.C.S.: 562998

Lewisville Landfill TX, LP (1)
801 E College St, Lewisville, TX 75057
Tel.: (972) 436-4217
Waste Management Services
N.A.I.C.S.: 562998

Mid America Contractors, L.L.C. (1)
3900 E Pkwy, Groves, TX 77619
Tel.: (409) 962-3600
Web Site: http://www.midamericacontractors.net
Sales Range: $1-9.9 Million
Emp.: 14
Construction Services
N.A.I.C.S.: 236220
Elizabeth Cravens (Principal)

New Morgan Landfill Company, Inc. (1)
420 Quarry Rd, Morgantown, PA 19543
Tel.: (610) 286-6844
Web Site: http://www.republicservices.com
Sales Range: $25-49.9 Million
Emp.: 33
Environmental Consulting Services
N.A.I.C.S.: 541620

Northwest Tennessee Disposal Corporation (1)
518 Beech Chapel Rd, Union City, TN 38261-8039
Tel.: (731) 885-1941
Environmental Consulting Services
N.A.I.C.S.: 541620
David Bragg (Mgr-Facility)

Oklahoma City Landfill, L.L.C. (1)
7600 SW 15th St, Oklahoma City, OK 73128
Tel.: (405) 745-3002
Web Site: https://www.wasteconnections.com
Solid Waste Landfill Services
N.A.I.C.S.: 562212

Organix Solutions, LLC (1)
7455 France Ave S Ste 363, Edina, MN 55435
Tel.: (612) 916-5296
Web Site: http://www.organixsolutions.com
Crop Protection Services
N.A.I.C.S.: 115112

Pine Hill Farms Landfill TX, LP (1)
1102 Forest Industrial Blvd, Longview, TX 75603
Tel.: (903) 984-3922
Emp.: 29
Waste Management Services
N.A.I.C.S.: 562998

Pleasant Oaks Landfill TX, LP (1)
3031 Farm Rd 3417, Mount Pleasant, TX 75455
Tel.: (903) 577-3100
Waste Collection Services
N.A.I.C.S.: 562111
Rob Hedges (Gen Mgr)

Port Clinton Landfill, Inc. (1)
530 N Camp Rd, Port Clinton, OH 43452

Tel.: (419) 635-2367
Web Site: http://www.republicservices.com
Sales Range: $25-49.9 Million
Emp.: 5
Waste Management Services
N.A.I.C.S.: 562998

Rabanco Companies (1)
54 S Dawson St, Seattle, WA 98134
Tel.: (206) 332-7700
Web Site: http://www.rabanco.com
Sales Range: $25-49.9 Million
Emp.: 60
Environmental Consulting Services
N.A.I.C.S.: 541620

Rainbow Environmental Services, LLC (1)
17121 Nichols St, Huntington Beach, CA 92647
Tel.: (714) 847-3581
Web Site: http://www.rainbowes.com
Environmental Consulting Services
N.A.I.C.S.: 541620

Rainbow Transfer/Recycling, Inc. (1)
17121 Nichols Ln, Huntington Beach, CA 92647
Tel.: (714) 847-5818
Emp.: 165
Solid Waste Landfill Services
N.A.I.C.S.: 562212

Republic Environmental Technologies, Inc. (1)
770 E Sahara Ave, Las Vegas, NV 89104
Tel.: (702) 734-5400
Waste Management Services
N.A.I.C.S.: 562998

Republic Services Vasco Road, LLC (1)
4001 N Vasco Rd, Livermore, CA 94551
Tel.: (925) 447-0491
Environmental Consulting Services
N.A.I.C.S.: 541620

Republic Services of Canada, Inc. (1)
14 Pirie Dr, Dundas, L9H 6X5, ON, Canada
Tel.: (905) 628-9825
Web Site: http://www.republicservices.com
Environmental Consulting Services
N.A.I.C.S.: 541620

Republic Services of Colorado Hauling, LLC (1)
7475 E 84th Ave, Commerce City, CO 80022-5040
Tel.: (303) 289-9045
Web Site: http://www.republicservices.com
Environmental Consulting Services
N.A.I.C.S.: 541620

Republic Services of Georgia, Limited Partnership (1)
84 Clifton Blvd, Savannah, GA 31408-9601
Tel.: (912) 963-5630
Sales Range: $25-49.9 Million
Emp.: 30
Environmental Consulting Services
N.A.I.C.S.: 541620
Tim Laux *(Gen Mgr)*

Republic Services of Indiana Transportation, LLC (1)
832 Langsdale Ave, Indianapolis, IN 46202
Tel.: (317) 917-7300
Environmental Consulting Services
N.A.I.C.S.: 541620

Republic Services of Iowa, LLC (1)
6449 Valley Dr, Bettendorf, IA 52722
Tel.: (563) 332-0050
Waste Recycling Services
N.A.I.C.S.: 562112

Republic Services of Kentucky, LLC (1)
451 Conway Ct, Lexington, KY 40511-1007
Tel.: (859) 273-8305
Web Site: http://www.republicservices.com
Environmental Consulting Services
N.A.I.C.S.: 541620

Republic Services of Murfreesboro - Allied Waste Div (1)
750 E Jefferson Pike, Murfreesboro, TN 37130-8777
Tel.: (615) 782-5500

Web Site: http://www.republicservices.com
Sales Range: $25-49.9 Million
Emp.: 30
Waste Management Services
N.A.I.C.S.: 562998

Republic Services of New Jersey, LLC (1)
4100 Church Rd, Mount Laurel, NJ 08054-2221
Tel.: (856) 234-4000
Web Site: http://www.republicservices.com
Environmental Consulting Services
N.A.I.C.S.: 541620

Republic Services of North Carolina, LLC (1)
1220 Commerse St SW, Dunn, NC 28613
Tel.: (828) 695-2057
Web Site: http://www.republicservices.com
Environmental Consulting Services
N.A.I.C.S.: 541620

Republic Services of Ohio Hauling, LLC (1)
2800 S Erie St, Massillon, OH 44646
Tel.: (330) 830-9050
Web Site: http://www.republicservices.com
Emp.: 100
Environmental Consulting Services
N.A.I.C.S.: 541620

Republic Services of Pennsylvania, LLC (1)
Berkshire Industrial Park 3730 Sandhurst Dr, York, PA 17406
Waste Management Services
N.A.I.C.S.: 562998

Republic Services of South Carolina, LLC (1)
109 Josephine Dr, Beaufort, SC 29906
Tel.: (843) 524-1485
Environmental Consulting Services
N.A.I.C.S.: 541620

Republic Services, Inc. - Grants Pass (1)
1920 NW Washington Blvd, Grants Pass, OR 97526-3470
Tel.: (541) 479-3371
Sales Range: $25-49.9 Million
Emp.: 20
Waste Management Services
N.A.I.C.S.: 562998
Don Moss *(Site Mgr)*

Republic Waste Services of Texas LP, Inc. (1)
10554 Tanner Rd, Houston, TX 77041
Tel.: (281) 446-2030
Sales Range: $25-49.9 Million
Emp.: 1,000
Solid Waste Disposal & Recyling Services
N.A.I.C.S.: 562219
Donald W. Slager *(Pres)*

Republic Waste Services of Texas, Ltd. (1)
1212 Harrison Ave, Arlington, TX 76011
Tel.: (817) 317-2000
Environmental Consulting Services
N.A.I.C.S.: 541620

Republic/CSC Disposal and Landfill, Inc. (1)
101 Republic Way, Avalon, TX 76623 **(100%)**
Tel.: (972) 627-3413
Sales Range: $25-49.9 Million
Emp.: 2
Solid Waste Collection & Disposal Services
N.A.I.C.S.: 562111

Republic/Maloy Landfill & Sanitation (1)
2811 FM 1568, Campbell, TX 75422-2239 **(100%)**
Tel.: (903) 886-7832
Solid Waste Collection & Landfill Disposal Services
N.A.I.C.S.: 562212

Resource Recovery Systems, LLC (1)
12409 NE San Rafael St, Portland, OR 97230
Tel.: (503) 256-8865
Waste Recycling Services

N.A.I.C.S.: 562111
Jim Weatherford *(Mgr)*

Richmond Sanitary Service, Inc. (1)
12615 Hoffman Rd, Marcellus, MI 49067
Tel.: (269) 646-5368
Web Site: https://www.richmondsanitaryservices.com
Environmental Consulting Services
N.A.I.C.S.: 541620

Roosevelt Associates (1)
3535 Bayshore Blvd NE, Saint Petersburg, FL 33703
Tel.: (904) 354-3008
Apartment Construction Services
N.A.I.C.S.: 236210

Royal Holdings, Inc. (1)
2001 W Washington St, South Bend, IN 46628
Tel.: (574) 246-5000
Environmental Consulting Services
N.A.I.C.S.: 541620

Sangamon Valley Landfill, Inc. (1)
2565 Sand Hill Rd, Springfield, IL 62707-6922
Tel.: (217) 528-9256
Emp.: 100
Waste Management Services
N.A.I.C.S.: 562998
Dan Winters *(Gen Mgr)*

Santek Waste Services LLC (1)
650 25th St NW 100, Cleveland, TN 37311
Tel.: (423) 476-9160
Web Site: http://www.santekenviro.com
Rev.: $6,510,000
Emp.: 30
Hazardous Waste Treatment & Disposal
N.A.I.C.S.: 562211
Cheryl L. Dunson *(Exec VP-Mktg)*
Matt Dillard *(Exec VP-Ops)*
Tim Watts *(COO)*

Solano Garbage Company (1)
2901 Industrial Ct, Fairfield, CA 94533
Tel.: (707) 437-8900
Web Site: http://www.republicservices.com
Environmental Consulting Services
N.A.I.C.S.: 541620

Southeast (OKC) Landfill (1)
7001 S Bryant Ave, Oklahoma City, OK 73149-7207
Tel.: (405) 672-7379
Web Site: http://www.republicservices.com
Sales Range: $25-49.9 Million
Emp.: 18
Waste Management Services
N.A.I.C.S.: 562998

Southwest Disposal Service, Inc. (1)
3001 N Fm 866, Odessa, TX 79764
Tel.: (432) 385-1899
Solid Waste Landfill Services
N.A.I.C.S.: 562212

Southwest Landfill TX, LP (1)
20700 Helium Rd, Canyon, TX 79015-5651
Tel.: (806) 342-6245
Web Site: https://southwestlandfilltx.com
Waste Management Services
N.A.I.C.S.: 562998

Sunrise Sanitation Service, Inc. (1)
105 S 2nd St Ste 4, Oakland, MD 21550
Tel.: (301) 389-5697
Web Site: https://www.sunrisesanitation.com
Environmental Consulting Services
N.A.I.C.S.: 541620
Stuart G. Thayer Jr. *(Founder)*

Sycamore Landfill, Inc. (1)
8514 Mast Blvd, Santee, CA 92071
Tel.: (760) 508-5119
Environmental Consulting Services
N.A.I.C.S.: 541620

Tayman Industries, Inc. (1)
5692 Eastgate Dr, San Diego, CA 92121
Tel.: (858) 453-8878
Web Site: http://www.taymaninc.com
Sales Range: $1-9.9 Million
Waste Collection & Recycling Services
N.A.I.C.S.: 562111
Lawrence Chapman *(Owner)*

Tervita, LLC (1)
10845 LA-1, Shreveport, LA 71115
Tel.: (318) 797-0087

Salt Water Disposal Services
N.A.I.C.S.: 213112

Trash Butler, LLC (1)
4411 W Tampa Bay Blvd, Tampa, FL 33614
Tel.: (813) 701-2020
Web Site: https://www.trashbutler.com
Facility Providing Services
N.A.I.C.S.: 561210
Steve Dobrowolski *(Reg Mgr)*

US Ecology, Inc. (1)
101 S Capitol Blvd Ste 1000, Boise, ID 83702
Tel.: (208) 331-8400
Web Site: http://www.usecology.com
Rev.: $988,001,000
Assets: $1,805,398,000
Liabilities: $1,181,074,000
Net Worth: $624,324,000
Earnings: $5,337,000
Emp.: 3,600
Fiscal Year-end: 12/31/2021
Holding Company; Radioactive & Hazardous Waste Treatment & Disposal Services
N.A.I.C.S.: 551110
Steven D. Welling *(Exec VP-Sls & Mktg)*
Simon G. Bell *(COO & Exec VP)*
Eric L. Gerratt *(CFO, Treas & Exec VP)*
Andrew P. Marshall *(Exec VP-Regulatory Compliance & Safety)*

Subsidiary (Domestic):

EQ Alabama, Inc. (2)
51328 AL Hwy 17, Sulligent, AL 35586
Tel.: (205) 698-8915
Emp.: 3
Refuse Collection Services
N.A.I.C.S.: 562111
Shanda Murff *(Mgr-Facility)*

EQ Detroit, Inc. (2)
1923 Frederick St, Detroit, MI 48211
Tel.: (313) 347-1300
Refuse Collection Services
N.A.I.C.S.: 562111
Gail Detweiler *(Coord-Approvals)*

EQ Florida, Inc. (2)
7202 E 8th Ave, Tampa, FL 33619
Tel.: (813) 623-5302
Web Site: http://www.usecology.com
Emp.: 60
Hazardous Waste Treatment Services
N.A.I.C.S.: 562211

EQ Holdings, Inc. (2)
201 General Mills Blvd, Golden Valley, MN 55426
Tel.: (612) 435-6800
Web Site: https://www.eqh.com
Holding Company
N.A.I.C.S.: 551112

Subsidiary (Domestic):

EQ Terminal Services LLC (3)
4 Hook Rd, Bayonne, NJ 07002
Tel.: (201) 436-3500
Industrial Cleaning Services
N.A.I.C.S.: 561790

EQ The Environmental Quality Company (3)
17440 College Pkwy Ste 300, Livonia, MI 48152
Tel.: (734) 521-8000
Sales Range: $350-399.9 Million
Waste Management Services
N.A.I.C.S.: 562998

Subsidiary (Domestic):

Allstate Power Vac, Inc. (4)
928 E Hazelwood Ave, Rahway, NJ 07065
Tel.: (732) 815-0220
Web Site: http://www.aspvac.com
Sales Range: $25-49.9 Million
Emp.: 300
Waste Management, Disposal Services & Other Environmental Services
N.A.I.C.S.: 562998
Mike Dello *(Gen Mgr)*
Andrew Shackett *(Pres & CEO)*
Kevin Sheppard *(Chief Dev Officer)*
Jay Marcotte *(CIO)*
Terry Earnest *(VP-Treatment & Disposal Svcs)*

Republic Services, Inc.—(Continued)

Donna Miller *(Sr VP-Environmental, Health & Safety)*
Tasha Perez *(VP-HR & Dir-HR)*

EQ Industrial Services, Inc. **(4)**
26705 Northline Rd, Taylor, MI 48180
Tel.: (734) 941-4397
Web Site: http://www.eqonline.com
Sales Range: $25-49.9 Million
Emp.: 35
Turnkey Environmental & Waste Services
N.A.I.C.S.: 562998

Branch (Domestic):

EQ Industrial Services Inc. - Indianapolis **(5)**
2650 N Shadeland, Indianapolis, IN 46219
Tel.: (317) 247-7100
Sales Range: $1-9.9 Million
Hazardous Waste Treatment & Disposal
N.A.I.C.S.: 562211
James Treloar *(Gen Mgr)*

Subsidiary (Domestic):

EQ Resource Recovery, Inc. **(4)**
36345 Van Born Rd, Romulus, MI 48174-4057
Tel.: (734) 727-5500
Sales Range: $1-9.9 Million
Emp.: 100
Materials Recovery Facilities
N.A.I.C.S.: 562920
Mario Romero *(VP-Ops)*
Tom Schuck *(Exec VP)*

Envirite, Inc. **(4)**
2050 Central Ave SE, Canton, OH 44707
Tel.: (330) 456-6238
Web Site: http://www.usecology.com
Sales Range: $25-49.9 Million
Emp.: 135
Refuse System Services
N.A.I.C.S.: 541611

Subsidiary (Domestic):

Envirite of Illinois, Inc. **(5)**
16435 Center Ave, Harvey, IL 60426-6078
Tel.: (708) 596-7040
Web Site: http://www.usecology.com
Sales Range: $25-49.9 Million
Emp.: 25
Treatment of Inorganic Wastes & Metals Recycling Services
N.A.I.C.S.: 562219

Envirite of Pennsylvania, Inc. **(5)**
730 Vogelsong Rd, York, PA 17404-1763
Tel.: (717) 846-1900
Nonhazardous Waste Treatment & Disposal
N.A.I.C.S.: 562219

Subsidiary (Domestic):

Michigan Disposal, Inc. **(3)**
49350 N I-94 Service Dr, Belleville, MI 48111
Web Site: http://www.usecology.com
Hazardous Waste Treatment Services
N.A.I.C.S.: 562211

Subsidiary (Domestic):

EQ Northeast, Inc. **(2)**
185 Industrial Rd, Wrentham, MA 02093-9878
Tel.: (508) 384-6151
Hazardous Waste Treatment Services
N.A.I.C.S.: 562211
Thomas Vine *(VP)*

EQ Oklahoma, Inc. **(2)**
2700 S 25th W Ave, Tulsa, OK 74107
Tel.: (918) 582-9595
Hazardous Waste Treatment Services
N.A.I.C.S.: 562211

Envirite Transportation, LLC **(2)**
2050 Central Ave, Canton, OH 44707
Tel.: (330) 456-6238
Transportation Support Services
N.A.I.C.S.: 485210

Subsidiary (Non-US):

NRC Environmental Services (UK) Limited **(2)**
25 Clarke Road Mount Farm, Milton

Keynes, MK1 1LG, United Kingdom
Tel.: (44) 1908467800
Oil Spill Cleanup Services
N.A.I.C.S.: 562910
Challis Neil *(Sr VP)*

Subsidiary (Domestic):

NRC Group Holdings Corp. **(2)**
3500 Sunrise Highway Ste 200 Bldg 200, Great River, NY 11739
Tel.: (631) 224-9141
Web Site: http://www.nrcc.com
Rev.: $360,170,000
Assets: $376,127,000
Liabilities: $407,671,000
Net Worth: ($31,544,000)
Earnings: ($47,257,000)
Emp.: 1,564
Fiscal Year-end: 12/31/2018
Investment Services
N.A.I.C.S.: 523999
Mike Reese *(Sr VP)*

Subsidiary (Domestic):

NRC Group Holdings, LLC **(3)**
3500 Sunrise Hwy Ste 200 Bldg 200, Great River, NY 11739
Tel.: (800) 337-7455
Web Site: http://nrcc.com
Holding Company
N.A.I.C.S.: 551112
Paul Taveira *(Pres & CEO)*
Joe Peterson *(CFO)*
Lou O'Brien *(Sr VP)*
Bob George *(Sr VP)*
Mike Reese *(Sr VP)*
Neil Challis *(Sr VP-Intl)*
Ken Koppler *(Dir-HSEQ)*

Subsidiary (Domestic):

National Response Corporation **(4)**
3500 Sunrise Hwy Ste 200 Bldg 200, Great River, NY 11739
Tel.: (631) 224-9141
Web Site: https://nrcc.com
Sales Range: $50-74.9 Million
Emp.: 920
Oil Spill Removal & Emergency Response Services
N.A.I.C.S.: 624230

Subsidiary (Domestic):

NRC NY Environmental Services, Inc. **(5)**
1 Adler Dr, East Syracuse, NY 13057
Tel.: (315) 437-2065
Environmental Cleanup Services
N.A.I.C.S.: 924110

Specialized Response Solutions, LP **(5)**
411 Bolliger Blvd, Fort Worth, TX 76108
Tel.: (817) 246-3338
Web Site: http://www.specializedresponse.com
Emp.: 27
Emergency Response Services for Hazardous Materials
N.A.I.C.S.: 562211

Subsidiary (Non-US):

Sureclean Limited **(5)**
Barra Business Park Mounie Drive, Oldmeldrum, AB51 0GX, United Kingdom
Tel.: (44) 7825363808
Web Site: https://www.sureclean.com
Emp.: 135
Specialty Industrial & Environmental Solutions to Oil & Gas, Petrochemical, Renewables, Utilities, Civil Engineering & Construction Sectors
N.A.I.C.S.: 238990

Subsidiary (Domestic):

Sprint Energy Services **(4)**
1700 N E St, La Porte, TX 77571
Tel.: (281) 867-9131
Web Site: http://www.sprintenergy.com
Waste Management, Cleaning Services, Field Support & Equipment Provider & Services
N.A.I.C.S.: 562998
Philip Bowman *(CFO)*

Subsidiary (Non-US):

National Response Corporation (Angola) LDA **(2)**
Travessa Jose Anchieta No 1 Villa Clotilde, Luanda, Angola
Tel.: (244) 932650567
Web Site: https://nrcc.com
Oil Spill Cleanup Services
N.A.I.C.S.: 562910
Klaus Holst Jensen *(Ops Mgr)*

National Response Corporation (NRC) Environmental Services UAE L LC
WH 06 Plot 27A15 ICAD 3, PO Box 12945, Mussafah South, Abu Dhabi, United Arab Emirates
Tel.: (971) 25549550
Web Site: https://nrcc.com
Oil Spill Cleanup Services
N.A.I.C.S.: 562910

Subsidiary (Domestic):

Quail Run Services, LLC **(2)**
952 Echo Ln Ste 460, Houston, TX 77024
Tel.: (832) 767-4749
Web Site: https://www.quailrunservices.com
Wastewater Treatment Facility Services
N.A.I.C.S.: 221320
Alex Epley *(Pres)*

US Ecology Houston, Inc. **(2)**
1700 N E St, La Porte, TX 77571
Tel.: (281) 867-9131
Waste Management Services
N.A.I.C.S.: 562112

US Ecology Idaho, Inc. **(2)**
20400 Lemley Rd, Grand View, ID 83624
Tel.: (208) 834-2275
Web Site: http://www.americanecology.com
Radioactive & Hazardous Waste Treatment & Disposal Services
N.A.I.C.S.: 562211

US Ecology Illinois, Inc. **(2)**
13279 350 E St, Sheffield, IL 61361
Tel.: (815) 454-2342
Radioactive Waste Processing & Recycling Services
N.A.I.C.S.: 562211

US Ecology Karnes County Disposal, LLC **(2)**
900 S County Rd 153, Kenedy, TX 78119
Tel.: (830) 307-8015
Web Site: https://www.usecology.com
Hazardous Waste Treatment & Disposal Services
N.A.I.C.S.: 562211

US Ecology Michigan, Inc. **(2)**
49350 N I-94 Service Dr, Belleville, MI 48111
Web Site: http://www.usecology.com
Processor of Waste Chemicals
N.A.I.C.S.: 562211

US Ecology Nevada, Inc. **(2)**
Hwy 95 11 Miles S of Beatty, Beatty, NV 89003
Tel.: (775) 553-2203
Web Site: https://www.usecology.com
Radioactive & Hazardous Waste Treatment & Disposal Services
N.A.I.C.S.: 562211

US Ecology Romulus, Inc. **(2)**
36345 Van Born Rd, Romulus, MI 48174-4057
Tel.: (704) 727-5500
Web Site: https://www.usecology.com
Waste Management Services
N.A.I.C.S.: 562219

US Ecology Sulligent, Inc. **(2)**
51328 AL Hwy 17, Sulligent, AL 35586
Tel.: (205) 698-8915
Web Site: https://www.usecology.com
Waste Management Services
N.A.I.C.S.: 562219

US Ecology Tampa, Inc. **(2)**
7202 E 8th Ave, Tampa, FL 33619
Web Site: https://www.usecology.com
Waste Management Services
N.A.I.C.S.: 562219

US Ecology Taylor, Inc. **(2)**

26705 Northline Rd, Taylor, MI 48180
Tel.: (734) 941-4397
Environmental Remediation Services
N.A.I.C.S.: 562910

US Ecology Texas, Inc. **(2)**
3277 County Rd 69, Robstown, TX 78380
Tel.: (361) 387-3518
Web Site: http://www.usecology.com
Sales Range: $25-49.9 Million
Emp.: 60
Radioactive & Hazardous Waste Treatment & Disposal Services
N.A.I.C.S.: 562211

US Ecology Tulsa, Inc. **(2)**
2700 S 25th W Ave, Tulsa, OK 74107
Tel.: (918) 582-9595
Web Site: https://www.usecology.com
Waste Management Services
N.A.I.C.S.: 562219

US Ecology Vernon, Inc. **(2)**
5375 S Boyle Ave, Vernon, CA 90058
Web Site: https://www.usecology.com
Holding Company
N.A.I.C.S.: 551112

US Ecology Washington, Inc. **(2)**
1777 Terminal Dr Ste A, Richland, WA 99354
Tel.: (509) 377-2411
Web Site: https://www.usecology.com
Emp.: 21
Radioactive & Hazardous Waste Treatment & Disposal Services
N.A.I.C.S.: 562211

US Ecology Winnie, LLC **(2)**
26400 Wilber Rd, Winnie, TX 77665
Tel.: (409) 794-3119
Web Site: https://www.usecology.com
Waste Management Services
N.A.I.C.S.: 562219

Vac-All Service, Inc. **(2)**
26705 Northline Rd, Taylor, MI 48180
Tel.: (734) 941-4397
Sales Range: $1-9.9 Million
Emp.: 75
Industrial Support Services
N.A.I.C.S.: 561990

Wayne Disposal, Inc. **(2)**
49350 N I-94 Service Dr, Belleville, MI 48111
Tel.: (734) 697-2200
Hazardous Waste Treatment Services
N.A.I.C.S.: 562211
Kerry Durnen *(Mgr)*

Upper Rock Island County Landfill, Inc. **(1)**
17201 20th Ave N, East Moline, IL 61244
Tel.: (309) 496-2396
Environmental Consulting Services
N.A.I.C.S.: 541620

Uwharrie Environmental **(1)**
500 Landfill Rd, Mount Gilead, NC 27306-8935
Tel.: (910) 576-3697
Web Site: http://uwharrieenvironmental.tbu.com
Sales Range: $25-49.9 Million
Emp.: 35
Landfill
N.A.I.C.S.: 562920

Victoria Landfill TX, LP **(1)**
18500 N Allied Way, Phoenix, AZ 85054
Tel.: (480) 627-2700
Environmental Consulting Services
N.A.I.C.S.: 541620

WDTR, Inc. **(1)**
2215 N Front St, Woodburn, OR 97071
Tel.: (503) 981-1278
Emp.: 50
Environmental Consulting Services
N.A.I.C.S.: 541620

Wasatch Regional Landfill, Inc. **(1)**
18500 N Allied way, Phoenix, AZ 85054
Tel.: (801) 924-8454
Waste Management Services
N.A.I.C.S.: 562998
Kirk Krappe *(Gen Mgr)*

West Contra Costa Sanitary Landfill, Inc. **(1)**

Foot of Parr Blvd, Richmond, CA 94801
Tel.: (510) 970-7260
Environmental Consulting Services
N.A.I.C.S.: 541620

Willamette Resources, Inc.   (1)
10295 SW Ridder Rd, Wilsonville, OR 97070
Tel.: (503) 570-0626
Emp.: 18
Environmental Consulting Services
N.A.I.C.S.: 541620

RESCAP LIQUIDATING TRUST

8400 Nomandale Lake Blvd, Minneapolis, MN 55437
Tel.: (215) 734-4400   DE
Web Site:
http://www.rescapliquidatingtrust.com
RESCU—(OTCIQ)
Investment Management Service
N.A.I.C.S.: 525990

RESEARCH FRONTIERS INCORPORATED

240 Crossways Park Dr, Woodbury, NY 11797
Tel.: (516) 364-1902   DE
Web Site:
https://www.smartglass.com
Year Founded: 1965
REFR—(NASDAQ)
Rev.: $539,686
Assets: $5,366,451
Liabilities: $569,586
Net Worth: $4,796,865
Earnings: ($2,669,349)
Emp.: 6
Fiscal Year-end: 12/31/22
Glass Production & Glass Technology Research Services
N.A.I.C.S.: 327212
Joseph M. Harary *(Pres, CEO, Interim CFO, Gen Counsel & Sec)*
Michael R. Lapointe *(VP-Aerospace Products)*

RESEARCH SOLUTIONS, INC.

10624 S Eern Ave Ste A 614, Henderson, NV 89052
Tel.: (310) 477-0354   NV
Web Site:
https://www.researchsolutions.com
Year Founded: 2006
RSSS—(NASDAQ)
Rev.: $32,934,152
Assets: $17,026,276
Liabilities: $12,142,558
Net Worth: $4,883,718
Earnings: ($1,632,384)
Emp.: 131
Fiscal Year-end: 06/30/22
Marketing Research & Public Opinion Polling
N.A.I.C.S.: 541910
Peter Victor Derycz *(Co-Founder)*
Scott Ahlberg *(COO)*
Marc Nissan *(CTO)*
Roy W. Olivier *(Pres & CEO)*
Rogier van Erkel *(Chief Revenue Officer)*
Shane Hunt *(Chief Customer Success Officer)*
Michiel van der Heijden *(Chief Product Officer)*
Tedd Adams *(Dir-Sls)*
Eric Aguirre *(Dir-Prospecting)*
Frank Buckley *(Acct Mgr)*
Stefan Bungartz *(Dir-EMEA Customer Engagement)*
Yoally Castellanos *(Mgr-Customer Engagement)*
Karina Chavez *(Product Mgr)*
Matthew Daugherty *(Mgr-Customer Engagement)*
Marco dela Torre *(Mgr-Data Information)*
Andreas Dorsch *(Sls Dir-GSA)*

Pete Dunning *(Sr Mgr-Customer Engagement)*
Curt Edwards-Neff *(Dir-Customer Support)*
Todd Everett *(VP-Product Dev)*
Kenji Fujita *(Dir-Tech Ops)*
Nayle Gomez Cordero *(Mgr-Customer Engagement)*
Lourdes Gracia *(Production Mgr)*
Maria Hatfield *(Sr Mgr-Bus Dev)*
Tony Landolt *(Head-Academic Bus Dev)*
Bob Lydon *(Sr Mgr-Digital Mktg)*
Melanie Mack *(Mgr-Key Acct & Library Svc)*
Marie Martin *(Coord-Tech Project)*
Gabriela Martinez *(Mktg Mgr)*
Sharon Mattern Buttiker *(Dir-Content Mgmt)*
Paulina Isabel Mora *(Coord-Customer Happiness)*
Leah Rodriguez *(VP-Mktg)*
Giovanni Rosales *(Mgr-CRM Database)*

RESERVOIR MEDIA, INC.

200 Varick Ste 801A, New York, NY 10014
Tel.: (212) 675-0541   DE
Web Site: https://www.reservoir-media.com
Year Founded: 2007
RSVR—(NASDAQ)
Rev.: $122,286,530
Assets: $754,082,929
Liabilities: $404,420,406
Net Worth: $404,420,406
Earnings: $2,539,201
Emp.: 92
Fiscal Year-end: 03/31/23
Media Representatives
N.A.I.C.S.: 541840
Rell Lafargue *(Pres)*

RESHAPE LIFESCIENCES INC.

18 Technology Dr Ste 110, Irvine, CA 92618
Tel.: (949) 429-6680   DE
Web Site:
https://www.reshapelifesciences.com
Year Founded: 2008
RSLS—(NASDAQ)
Rev.: $11,240,000
Assets: $11,142,000
Liabilities: $7,481,000
Net Worth: $3,661,000
Earnings: ($46,214,000)
Emp.: 40
Fiscal Year-end: 12/31/22
Surgical & Medical Instrument Manufacturing
N.A.I.C.S.: 339112
Thomas Stankovich *(CFO)*
Dan W. Gladney *(Exec Chm)*
Michael Bordainick *(Sr VP-Comml Ops)*
Paul F. Hickey *(Pres & CEO)*

Subsidiaries:

ReShape Lifesciences Inc.   (1)
1001 Calle Amanecer, San Clemente, CA 92673
Tel.: (949) 429-6680
Web Site:
http://www.reshapelifesciences.com
Rev.: $11,299,000
Assets: $37,061,000
Liabilities: $22,573,000
Net Worth: $14,488,000
Earnings: ($21,630,000)
Emp.: 37
Fiscal Year-end: 12/31/2020
Implantable Systems Developer to Treat Obesity & Other Gastrointestinal Disorders
N.A.I.C.S.: 339112
Thomas Stankovich *(CFO & Sr VP)*
Raj Nihalani *(CTO-Bus Dev)*

Kevin Condrin *(Sr VP-Comml)*
Vipul Shah *(Sr VP-Ops & R&D)*
Dov Gal *(Compliance Officer & VP-Regulatory & Clinical Affairs)*
Brendan O'Connell *(VP-Fin & Controller)*

RESIDEO TECHNOLOGIES, INC.

16100 N 71st St Ste 550, Scottsdale, AZ 85254
Tel.: (480) 573-5340   DE
Web Site: https://www.resideo.com
Year Founded: 2018
REZI—(NYSE)
Rev.: $6,242,000,000
Assets: $6,645,000,000
Liabilities: $3,896,000,000
Net Worth: $2,749,000,000
Earnings: $210,000,000
Emp.: 14,000
Fiscal Year-end: 12/31/23
Home Electronic Security Device Distr
N.A.I.C.S.: 423610
Michael Carlet *(CFO & Exec VP)*
Thomas A. Surran *(Pres-Products & Solutions)*
Jeannine Lane *(Chief Compliance Officer, Gen Counsel, Sec & Exec VP)*
Steve Kelly *(Chief HR Officer & Exec VP)*
Tina Beskid *(Chief Acctg Officer & VP)*
Jay L. Geldmacher *(Pres & CEO)*

Subsidiaries:

ADI Global Distribution AB   (1)
Tillgangligheten 3, 417 01, Gothenburg, Sweden
Tel.: (46) 101302400
Web Site: http://www.adiglobal.se
Electrical Products Distr
N.A.I.C.S.: 423610

Ademco (Pty) Ltd.   (1)
North Gate Ext 7 1609 5 Platinum Dr, Dr Longmeadow Business Estate, Moddersfontein, 2090, Guateng, South Africa
Tel.: (27) 115742500
Web Site: http://www.adiglobal.co.za
Electronic Component Retailer
N.A.I.C.S.: 423690

Ademco 1 GmbH   (1)
Hardhofweg 40, 74821, Mosbach, Germany
Tel.: (49) 6261810
Electronic Parts & Equipment Distr
N.A.I.C.S.: 423690

Ademco 1 Limited   (1)
200 Berkshire Place Triangle, Winnersh, RG41 5RD, Berkshire, United Kingdom
Tel.: (44) 3001301299
Electronic Parts & Equipment Distr
N.A.I.C.S.: 423690

Ademco Austria GmbH   (1)
Thomas Klestil Platz 13, 1030, Vienna, Austria
Tel.: (43) 810200213
Electronic Parts & Equipment Distr
N.A.I.C.S.: 423690

Ademco CZ s.r.o.   (1)
Turanka 1236/96, Slatina, 627 00, Brno, Czech Republic
Tel.: (420) 545501333
Web Site: https://homecomfort.resideo.com
Electronic Parts & Equipment Distr
N.A.I.C.S.: 423690

Ademco Otomasyon Limited Sirketi   (1)
Barbaros Mahallesi Halk Cad Palladium Residence A Blok Apt No 8 A/2, Atasehir, 34746, Istanbul, Turkiye
Tel.: (90) 2166636033
Web Site: https://ev.honeywellhome.com.tr
Electronic Parts & Equipment Distr
N.A.I.C.S.: 423690

Ademco Supply S.r.l.   (1)
Str George Constantinescu 3 Sector 2, Bucharest, Romania

Tel.: (40) 312243000
Electronic Parts & Equipment Distr
N.A.I.C.S.: 423690

BRK Brands, Inc.   (1)
3901 Liberty St Rd, Aurora, IL 60504-8122
Tel.: (800) 323-9005
Web Site: http://www.brkelectronics.com
Smoke & Carbon Monoxide Alarms, Home Safety Products & Health Products Mfr
N.A.I.C.S.: 334290

Buoy Labs, Inc.   (1)
125 McPherson St, Santa Cruz, CA 95060
Web Site: http://www.buoy.ai
Software Development Services
N.A.I.C.S.: 541511

Electronic Custom Distributors, Inc.   (1)
4747 Westpark Dr, Houston, TX 77027
Tel.: (713) 525-3206
Web Site: http://www.ecdcom.com
Electronic Part Distr & Whslr
N.A.I.C.S.: 423690
Tom Hart *(Mgr-Sls)*
Allan Doris *(Mgr-Distr)*
Bob Harrell *(Branch Mgr)*
Michelle Provenzano *(Coord-Mktg)*
Rick Tucker *(Branch Mgr)*
Travis Garza *(Asst Mgr-Distr)*

First Alert, Inc.   (1)
3901 Liberty St, Aurora, IL 60504
Tel.: (800) 323-9005
Web Site: http://www.firstalert.com
Smoke Detectors, Carbon Monoxide Detectors & Power Generators Mfr
N.A.I.C.S.: 334290

Herman Integration Services LLC   (1)
13400 Wright Cir Unit E6, Tampa, FL 33626
Web Site: https://www.herman-is.com
System Integration Services
N.A.I.C.S.: 541512
Chris Bianchet *(Gen Mgr)*
Richard Andrade *(VP-Ops)*

LifeWhere, LLC   (1)
106 Isabella St, Pittsburgh, PA 15212
Web Site: http://www.lifewhere.com
Software Development Services
N.A.I.C.S.: 541511
Brian Courtney *(CEO)*
James Gillespie *(Chm)*
Bob Boehmer *(VP-IoT)*
Scott Glover *(VP-Acct Growth)*

Pittway 3 GmbH   (1)
La Piece 6 6, 1180, Rolle, Switzerland
Tel.: (41) 449450101
Electronic Parts & Equipment Distr
N.A.I.C.S.: 423690

Pittway BVBA   (1)
Hermes Plaza Hermeslaan 1H, 1831, Diegem, Belgium
Tel.: (32) 24042311
Electronic Parts & Equipment Distr
N.A.I.C.S.: 423690

Pittway Homes Systems, S.L.   (1)
Av De Italia 7 2a planta, 28821, Coslada, Madrid, Spain
Tel.: (34) 914143315
Electronic Parts & Equipment Distr
N.A.I.C.S.: 423690

Resideo International (India) Pvt. Ltd.   (1)
6th Floor Unitech Trade Center Sector - 43 Block C, Sushant Lok Phase - I, Gurgaon, 122002, Haryana, India
Tel.: (91) 8001039744
Web Site: http://www.resideoindia.com
Electronic Parts & Equipment Distr
N.A.I.C.S.: 423690
Vipin Arora *(Sr Dir-HR)*

Resideo Korlatolt Felelossegu Tarsasag   (1)
Dozsa Gyorgy ut 147, 8800, Nagykanizsa, Hungary
Tel.: (36) 680021331
Web Site: https://homecomfort.resideo.com
Electronic Parts & Equipment Distr
N.A.I.C.S.: 423690
Geza Hoffman *(Mgr-Bus Dev)*

Resideo Life Care Solutions LLC   (1)

Resideo Technologies, Inc.—(Continued)

3400 Intertech Dr Ste 200, Brookfield, WI 53045
Web Site:
   http://www.lifecaresolutions.resideo.com
Electronic Parts & Equipment Distr
N.A.I.C.S.: 423690

Resideo S.r.l.   (1)
Via Philips 12, 20900, Monza, MB, Italy
Tel.: (39) 0399590900
Web Site: https://www.resideo.com
Electronic Parts & Equipment Distr
N.A.I.C.S.: 423690
Massimiliano Sala (Sr Mgr-Sls)

Resideo Sarl   (1)
1198 avenue du Dr Maurice Donat, 06250, Mougins, France
Tel.: (33) 450316730
Web Site: https://www.resideo.com
Electronic Parts & Equipment Distr
N.A.I.C.S.: 423690

Resideo s.r.o.   (1)
Mlynske Nivy 71, 821 05, Bratislava, Slovakia
Tel.: (421) 232262211
Web Site: https://homecomfort.resideo.com
Electronic Parts & Equipment Distr
N.A.I.C.S.: 423690
Jan Filip (Mgr-Solution)

Snap One Holdings Corp   (1)
1800 Continental Blvd Ste 200, Charlotte, NC 28273
Tel.: (704) 927-7620
Web Site: https://www.snapone.com
Rev.: $1,123,811,000
Assets: $1,652,521,000
Liabilities: $895,350,000
Net Worth: $757,171,000
Earnings: ($8,626,000)
Emp.: 1,652
Fiscal Year-end: 12/30/2022
Offices of Other Holding Companies
N.A.I.C.S.: 551112
John H. Heyman (CEO)
John Heyman (CEO)
Jefferson Dungan (COO)
G. Paul Hess (Chief Product Officer)
JD Ellis (Chief Legal Officer)
Abigail Hanlon (Dir-PR & Mktg Events)

Subsidiary (Domestic):

Snap One, LLC   (2)
1800 Continental Blvd Ste 200, Charlotte, NC 28273
Tel.: (704) 927-7620
Web Site: https://snapone.com
Audio/Video, Security, Networking & Automation Products
N.A.I.C.S.: 334310
Michael Carlet (CFO)
John H. Heyman (CEO)
Kathleen Creech (Chief HR Officer)

Subsidiary (Domestic):

Control4 Corporation   (3)
11734 S Election Rd, Salt Lake City, UT 84020
Tel.: (801) 523-3100
Web Site: http://www.control4.com
Rev.: $272,458,000
Assets: $252,548,000
Liabilities: $46,201,000
Net Worth: $206,347,000
Earnings: $43,840,000
Fiscal Year-end: 12/31/2018
Home Audio, Video & Lighting Controls Mfr & Sales
N.A.I.C.S.: 334220
J. D. Ellis (Gen Counsel)
John Heyman (CEO)
Michael Carlet (CFO)

Subsidiary (Non-US):

Control4 APAC Pty. Ltd.   (4)
66-68 Wedgewood Rd, Hallam, 3803, VIC, Australia
Tel.: (61) 387951700
Home Automation Product Mfr
N.A.I.C.S.: 334419
Andrew Starow (Gen Mgr)

Control4 EMEA Ltd   (4)
Greenpark Business Centre, York, YO61

1ET, United Kingdom
Tel.: (44) 1347812300
Web Site: http://www.control4.com
Emp.: 10
Automation & Control System Distr
N.A.I.C.S.: 423830
Robert Fuller (Gen Mgr)

Control4 Europe doo Belgrade   (4)
Omladinskih brigada 90d Airport City, Belgrade, 11073, Serbia
Tel.: (381) 113111049
Home Automation Product Mfr
N.A.I.C.S.: 334419

Control4 Germany GmbH   (4)
Unterschweinstiege 2-14, 60549, Frankfurt, Germany
Tel.: (49) 6934873395
Web Site: http://www.control4germany.gmbh
Home Automation Product Mfr
N.A.I.C.S.: 334419
Wolfgang Hoehne (Mgr-Mktg)

Nexus Technologies Pty Ltd   (4)
66-68 Wedgewood Road, Hallam, 3803, VIC, Australia
Tel.: (61) 387951700
Web Site:
   http://www.nexuscomparators.com
Emp.: 20
Automation & Control System Distr
N.A.I.C.S.: 423830

Subsidiary (Domestic):

Pakedge Device & Software Inc.   (4)
3847 Breakwater Ave, Hayward, CA 94545
Tel.: (650) 385-8702
Web Site: http://www.pakedge.com
Network Integration Services
N.A.I.C.S.: 541512
Lindsay Miller (Dir-Fin & HR)

Triad Speakers, Inc.   (4)
15835 NE Cameron Blvd, Portland, OR 97230
Tel.: (503) 256-2600
Web Site: http://www.triadspeakers.com
Home Theater & Stereo Loudspeakers Mfr
N.A.I.C.S.: 334310
Paul Teixeira (Mgr-Mktg)

Subsidiary (Domestic):

Custom Plus Distributing, LLC   (3)
49 37th St NW, Auburn, WA 98001
Tel.: (253) 859-1159
Web Site:
   http://www.customplusdistributing.com
A/V, Surveillance, Networking & Remote Management Products
N.A.I.C.S.: 334310
Mike Munger (VP)

Subsidiary (Non-US):

Staub Electronics Ltd.   (2)
160-11791 Hammersmith Way, Richmond, V7A 5C6, BC, Canada
Tel.: (604) 270-7316
Web Site: https://www.staub.ca
Electronic Components Distr
N.A.I.C.S.: 423690
Scott Trotter (Pres)
Brian Crowe (Mgr-Business Development)
Phil Heck (Mgr-Business Development)

bk-electronic GmbH   (1)
Ludwig-Roebel-Strasse 11, 68309, Mannheim, Germany
Tel.: (49) 62139181396
Web Site: https://www.bkelektronik.de
Electronic Components Mfr
N.A.I.C.S.: 334419

RESMED INC.
9001 Spectrum Center Blvd, San Diego, CA 92123
Tel.: (858) 836-5000   DE
Web Site: https://www.resmed.com
Year Founded: 1989
RMD—(NYSE)
Rev.: $4,685,297,000
Assets: $6,872,394,000
Liabilities: $2,008,351,000
Net Worth: $4,864,043,000
Earnings: $1,020,951,000
Emp.: 9,980

Fiscal Year-end: 06/30/24
Surgical & Medical Instrument Manufacturing
N.A.I.C.S.: 339112
Bobby Ghoshal (Pres-SaaS)
Peter C. Farrell (Founder)
Brett A. Sandercock (CFO)
Michael J. Farrell (Chm & CEO)
Carlos M. Nunez (Chief Medical Officer)
Justin Leong (Chief Product Officer)
Hemanth Reddy (Chief Strategy Officer)
Andrew Price (Pres-Ops-Global)
Katrin Pucknat (CMO)
Lucile Blaise (Sr VP-Strategy & Bus Dev)
Michael Rider (Corp Counsel-Global & Sec)
Dawn Haake (Chief Quality Officer)
Amy Wakeham (Chief Comm & IR Officer)

Subsidiaries:

Brightree LLC   (1)
125 Technology Pkwy, Peachtree Corners, GA 30092
Tel.: (678) 243-1800
Web Site: https://www.brightree.com
Home Medical Equipment Billing & Business Management Software Solutions Services
N.A.I.C.S.: 541219
Liz Brown (VP-Customer Satisfaction)
Nick Knowlton (VP-Bus Dev)
Doug Brandberg (Head-Fin)
Nupura Kolwalkar (Chief Product Officer)
Sunil Krishnan (VP-Revenue Cycle Mgmt Svcs Bus)
Trish Nettleship (CMO)

Subsidiary (Domestic):

Apacheta Corporation   (2)
53 W Baltimore Pike Ste 200, Media, PA 19063
Tel.: (610) 558-5852
Custom Computer Programming Services
N.A.I.C.S.: 541511

Brightree Patient Collections Llc   (1)
10800 Farley St, Overland Park, KS 66210
Tel.: (913) 744-3360
Software Development Services
N.A.I.C.S.: 513210

Brightree Services LLC   (1)
7137 236th Ave, Paddock Lake, WI 53168-8975
Tel.: (678) 243-1800
Web Site: http://www.brightree.com
Emp.: 6
Landscaping Services
N.A.I.C.S.: 561730

Curative Medical Devices GmbH   (1)
Blasewitzer Strasse 41, 01307, Dresden, Germany
Tel.: (49) 3514504510
Web Site: http://www.curativemedical.com
Medical Device Mfr & Distr
N.A.I.C.S.: 334510

Curative Medical Inc.   (1)
3327 Kifer Rd, Santa Clara, CA 95051-0719
Tel.: (408) 414-2188
Medical Device Mfr & Distr
N.A.I.C.S.: 334510
Jiango Sun (Pres)
Jessica Chiu (CEO)

Curative Medical Technology (Suzhou) Ltd   (1)
No 9 Pei Yuan Road Science And Technology City, New District, Suzhou, 215163, China
Tel.: (86) 51269217308
Web Site: http://www.curativemedical.com
Electromedical Device Mfr & Distr
N.A.I.C.S.: 334510

EdenSleep New Zealand Limited   (1)
131 Cobham Drive Hamilton East, Hamilton, 3216, New Zealand
Tel.: (64) 78582568
Web Site: http://www.edensleep.co.nz

Sleep Disorder Center Operator
N.A.I.C.S.: 621498

Gruendler GmbH   (1)
Karneolstr 4, 72250, Freudenstadt, Germany
Tel.: (49) 744191460
Web Site: http://www.gruendler-medical.de
Sales Range: $25-49.9 Million
Emp.: 45
Innovative Medical Products Design & Mfr
N.A.I.C.S.: 334510
Markus Grundler (CEO)

Healthcarefirst, Inc.   (1)
1343 E Kingsley St Ste A, Springfield, MO 65804
Web Site: https://www.healthcarefirst.com
Electronic Health Record Software Services
N.A.I.C.S.: 513210
Amy Anderson (VP-Product)

Inova Labs, Inc.   (1)
3500 Comsouth Dr Ste 100, Austin, TX 78744
Tel.: (512) 617-1700
Web Site: http://www.inovalabs.com
Emp.: 200
Medical Device Mfr & Distr
N.A.I.C.S.: 334510

Maribo Medico A/S   (1)
Kidnakken 11, 4930, Maribo, Denmark
Tel.: (45) 54757549
Web Site: http://www.resmedmaribo.dk
Medical Device Mfr & Distr
N.A.I.C.S.: 334510

MatrixCare, Inc.   (1)
1550 American Blvd E 9th Fl, Bloomington, MN 55425
Tel.: (952) 995-9800
Web Site: https://www.matrixcare.com
Senior Care Software Developer & Marketer
N.A.I.C.S.: 513210
John Damgaard (Pres & CEO)
Gary Pederson (Exec VP-Facilities Div)
Kevin Whitehurst (Sr VP-Skilled Nursing Solutions)
Peter Goepfrich (CFO)
Eric Grunden (Chief Customer Officer)
Lynn Mandle (VP-People)
Wendy Roberts (VP-Bus Dev & Partnerships)
Denise Spillane (VP-Mktg)
Ingrid Svensson (Chief Product Officer)
John Weatherbie (CTO)

Subsidiary (Domestic):

eHealth Solutions, Inc.   (2)
575 8th Ave 15th Fl, New York, NY 10018
Tel.: (212) 268-4242
Web Site: http://www.sigmacare.com
Software Developer; Mobile, Point-of-care Solutions
N.A.I.C.S.: 513210

Mediserv Sp. Zoo   (1)
ul Leszno 34/36, 01 199, Warsaw, Poland
Tel.: (48) 25392200
Web Site: http://www.mediserv.pl
Medical Equipment Mfr
N.A.I.C.S.: 334519

Reciprocal Labs Corporation   (1)
1 S Pinckney St Ste 610, Madison, WI 53703
Tel.: (608) 251-0470
Web Site: https://www.propellerhealth.com
Healthcare Equipment Distr
N.A.I.C.S.: 423450
Ted Burns (VP-Product)
V. J. Bala (Sr VP-Mktg)
Annie Lorenzo (VP)
Jack Edwards (VP)
Jason Gorman (VP)

ResMed (Beijing) Trading Co., Ltd.   (1)
Room 1201-2 Floor 12 Building 12 Taiyanggong Middle Road, Chaoyang District, Beijing, 100028, China
Tel.: (86) 4006690050
Web Site: https://www.resmed.com.cn
Medical Equipment Distr
N.A.I.C.S.: 423450

ResMed CZ s.r.o.   (1)
Hvezdova 1689/2A, 140 00, Prague, Czech Republic

Tel.: (420) 244471299
Web Site: http://www.resmed.cz
Medical Equipment Distr
N.A.I.C.S.: 424210

ResMed Deutschland GmbH (1)
Haferwende 40, 28357, Bremen, Germany
Tel.: (49) 421489930
Web Site: http://www.resmed.de
Sales Range: $50-74.9 Million
Emp.: 200
Mfr of Medical Equipment to Treat Sleep-Disordered Breathing
N.A.I.C.S.: 339112

ResMed Finland Oy (1)
Hevosenkenka 3, 02600, Espoo, Finland
Tel.: (358) 98676820
Web Site: http://www.resmed.fi
Sales Range: $1-9.9 Million
Emp.: 15
Mfr of Medical Equipment to Treat Sleep-Disordered Breathing
N.A.I.C.S.: 339112
Jussi Vuorela *(Mng Dir & Gen Mgr)*

ResMed Germany Saas Holdings GmbH (1)
Fraunhoferstrasse 16, 82152, Martinsried, Germany
Tel.: (49) 89990100
Web Site: https://www.resmed.de
Medical Equipment Retailer
N.A.I.C.S.: 423450

ResMed Holdings Ltd. (1)
1 Elizabeth Macarthur Drive, Bella Vista, 2153, NSW, Australia
Tel.: (61) 288841000
Web Site: http://www.resmed.com
Sales Range: $100-124.9 Million
Mfr of Medical Equipment to Treat Sleep-Disordered Breathing
N.A.I.C.S.: 339112

Subsidiary (Non-US):

ResMed (Beijing) Medical Device Co., Ltd (2)
Room 2505 25/F Building B Landgent Center, Chaoyang, Beijing, 100022, China
Tel.: (86) 1067786887
Medical Devices Design & Mfr
N.A.I.C.S.: 334510
Leo Yang *(Gen Mgr)*

ResMed (UK) Limited (2)
Quad 1 First Floor Becquerel Ave Harwell Campus, Didcot, OX11 0RA, United Kingdom
Tel.: (44) 1235862997
Web Site: https://www.resmed.co.uk
Mfr of Medical Equipment to Treat Sleep-Disordered Breathing
N.A.I.C.S.: 339112

ResMed India Private Ltd (2)
Coworks Aerocity First Floor Worldmark 1 Asset Area 11, Aerocity Hospitality District Igi Airport, New Delhi, 110037, Delhi, India
Tel.: (91) 1147613100
Web Site: http://www.resmed.com
Emp.: 100
Medical Device Mfr
N.A.I.C.S.: 334510
Aparajito Mukherjee *(Mng Dir)*

Subsidiary (Domestic):

ResMed Ltd. (2)
1 Elizabeth Macarthur Dr, Bella Vista, 2153, NSW, Australia
Tel.: (61) 288841000
Web Site: http://www.resmed.com.au
Emp.: 1,200
Distr of Medical Equipment to Treat Sleep-Disordered Breathing
N.A.I.C.S.: 423450

Subsidiary (Domestic):

ResMed Asia Operations Pty Ltd (3)
1 Elizabeth Macarthur Dr, Bella Vista, 2153, NSW, Australia
Tel.: (61) 288841000
Web Site: http://www.resmed.com.au
Sales Range: $450-499.9 Million
Emp.: 1,200
Medical Equipment Mfr & Distr
N.A.I.C.S.: 423450

Subsidiary (Non-US):

ResMed Sensor Technologies Ltd. (3)
Termini 3 Arkle Rd, Sandyford Business Park Sandyford, Dublin, D18 T6T7, Ireland
Tel.: (353) 12243777
Sales Range: $25-49.9 Million
Emp.: 35
Medical Device Mfr
N.A.I.C.S.: 334510

Subsidiary (Non-US):

ResMed Norway AS (2)
Fjordveien 1, 1363, Hovik, Norway
Tel.: (47) 67118850
Web Site: http://www.resmed.no
Sales Range: $10-24.9 Million
Emp.: 14
Medical Equipments Mfr & Distr
N.A.I.C.S.: 334510
Knut Valland *(Gen Mgr)*

ResMed Taiwan Co., Ltd (2)
4F-6 No 9 Sec 2 Beitou Rd, Beitou District, Taipei, 112, Taiwan
Tel.: (886) 225568707
Medical Equipment Mfr
N.A.I.C.S.: 334519

ResMed KK (1)
7F Nihon Seimei Kasugacho Building 1-33-13 Hongo, Bunkyo-ku, Tokyo, 113-0033, Japan
Tel.: (81) 358406781
Web Site: http://www.resmed.com
Treat Sleep-Disordered Breathing Medical Equipment Mfr
N.A.I.C.S.: 339112

ResMed Maribo A/S (1)
Kidnakken 11, 4930, Maribo, Denmark
Tel.: (45) 54757549
Software Development Services
N.A.I.C.S.: 513210
Mette Toxvaerd Larsen *(CEO)*

ResMed New Zealand Limited (1)
PO Box 51-048, Pakuranga, Auckland, New Zealand
Tel.: (64) 274737633
Mfr of Medical Equipment to Treat Sleep-Disordered Breathing
N.A.I.C.S.: 339112

ResMed Polska Sp Zoo (2)
Ul Pokorna 2 Lok U18A, 00-199, Warsaw, Poland
Tel.: (48) 668662424
Web Site: http://www.zdrowysen.info
Medical Instrument Distr
N.A.I.C.S.: 423450

ResMed SAS (1)
Technologique De Lyon - 292 Allee Jacques Monod, 69792, Saint Priest, Cedex, France
Tel.: (33) 426100209
Web Site: https://www.resmed.fr
Medical Equipment to Treat Sleep-Disordered Breathing Mfr
N.A.I.C.S.: 339112

Subsidiary (Domestic):

ResMed Paris SAS (2)
240 rue de la Motte, Moissy-Cramayel, 77550, France
Tel.: (33) 160183600
Web Site: http://www.resmed.com
Emp.: 25
Medical Device & Equipment Mfr
N.A.I.C.S.: 334510

ResMed Schweiz AG (1)
Viaduktstrasse 40, 4051, Basel, Switzerland
Tel.: (41) 615647000
Web Site: http://www.resmed.com
Sales Range: $100-124.9 Million
Emp.: 50
Mfr of Medical Equipment to Treat Sleep-Disordered Breathing
N.A.I.C.S.: 339112

ResMed Sleep Solutions Limited (1)
96 Jubilee Avenue Milton Park, Abingdon, OX14 4RW, United Kingdom
Tel.: (44) 1235862997
Medical Product Distr
N.A.I.C.S.: 424210

ResMed Sweden AB (1)
Jan Stenbecks Square 17, 164 40, Kista, Sweden
Tel.: (46) 84771000
Web Site: http://www.resmed.com
Sales Range: $10-24.9 Million
Emp.: 20
Mfr of Medical Equipment to Treat Sleep-Disordered Breathing
N.A.I.C.S.: 339112
Peter Anderson *(Mng Dir)*

SG Medical Pte Ltd (1)
304 04 05A Orchard Road, 238880, Singapore, Singapore
Tel.: (65) 62847177
Web Site: http://www.sgmedical.org
Sales Range: $1-9.9 Million
Emp.: 7
Mfr of Medical Equipment to Treat Sleep-Disordered Breathing
N.A.I.C.S.: 339112
Sam Chow *(Mng Dir)*

Salve Wohngruppen GmbH (1)
Alleestrasse 75, 42853, Remscheid, Germany
Tel.: (49) 21912019970
Web Site: http://www.salvewohngruppen.de
Emp.: 300
Health Care Srvices
N.A.I.C.S.: 621999

Sleeptech Limited (1)
12/477 Devon Street East Strandon, New Plymouth, 4312, New Zealand
Tel.: (64) 800333675
Web Site: https://www.edensleep.co.nz
Medical Equipment Distr
N.A.I.C.S.: 423450

RESONATE BLENDS, INC.

26565 Agoura Rd Ste 200, Calabasas, CA 91302
Tel.: (916) 445-1254   NV
Web Site:
   https://www.resonateblends.com
Year Founded: 1984
KOAN—(OTCQB)
Rev.: $16,468
Assets: $992,341
Liabilities: $3,127,913
Net Worth: ($2,135,572)
Earnings: ($1,415,979)
Emp.: 6
Fiscal Year-end: 12/31/23
Mobile Marketing
N.A.I.C.S.: 541613
Geoffrey Selzer *(Co-Founder)*
Henry Steingieser *(Co-Founder & Creative Dir)*
Skyler Quisenberry *(Co-Founder & Dir-Product Dev)*
Sian Seligman *(Dir-Mktg)*
James Morrison *(Pres & Sec)*

RESOURCE SOLUTIONS GROUP, INC.

7621 Little Ave Ste 100, Charlotte, NC 28226
Tel.: (704) 643-0676   NV
Web Site:
   https://www.resourcesolutions
   group.com
Year Founded: 2005
RSGX—(OTCIQ)
Management Consulting Services
N.A.I.C.S.: 541618
Gary Musselman *(Pres & CEO)*
Marcia Sartori *(VP)*
Michael Peterson *(VP)*
Antoinette Peterson *(VP)*
Kevin Callinan *(Controller)*

RESOURCES CONNECTION, INC.

17101 Armstrong Ave Ste 100, Irvine, CA 92614
Tel.: (714) 430-6400   DE
Web Site: https://www.rgp.com

RGP—(NASDAQ)
Rev.: $632,801,000
Assets: $510,914,000
Liabilities: $92,151,000
Net Worth: $418,763,000
Earnings: $21,034,000
Emp.: 791
Fiscal Year-end: 05/25/24
Employment Services
N.A.I.C.S.: 561311
Kate W. Duchene *(Pres & CEO)*
Tom Schember *(Exec VP-Client Svcs-Global)*
Venkat Ramaswamy *(Sr VP & Head-Europe)*
Katy Conway *(Chief People Officer)*
Jennifer Y. Ryu *(Exec VP)*
Bhadresh Patel *(COO)*
Keith Golden *(CIO)*
Julie Shaver *(Sr VP-Corporate Development & Strategy)*
Lauren Elkerson *(Chief Legal Officer)*
Donald B. Murray *(Founder)*

Subsidiaries:

Resources Connection LLC (1)
17101 Armstrong Ave Ste 100, Irvine, CA 92614
Tel.: (714) 430-6400
Sales Range: $10-24.9 Million
Emp.: 50
Contract Employment Services
N.A.I.C.S.: 561311

Resources Connection Mexico S de RL de CV (1)
Ave Ejercito Nacional 769 L 07-C Colonia Granada, Mayor's Office Miguel Hidalgo, 11520, Mexico, Mexico
Tel.: (52) 5520006500
Web Site: http://www.rgt.com
Emp.: 12
Business Management Consulting Services
N.A.I.C.S.: 541611

Resources Global Professionals (Europe) BV (1)
Secoya Building E Papendorpseweg 91, 3528 BJ, Utrecht, Netherlands
Tel.: (31) 306867000
Web Site: http://www.resources.nl
Emp.: 60
Business Management Consulting Services
N.A.I.C.S.: 541611
Hans Wichink *(VP-Revenue)*

Resources Global Professionals (France) SAS (1)
125 Avenue des Champs Elysees, 75008, Paris, France
Tel.: (33) 170080360
Web Site: http://www.resourcesglobal.fr
Sales Range: $25-49.9 Million
Emp.: 17
Business Management Consulting Services
N.A.I.C.S.: 541611
Kate W. Duchene *(VP-HR)*

Resources Global Professionals (Germany) GmbH (1)
Hochstrasse 53, 60313, Frankfurt, Germany
Tel.: (49) 69244458540
Web Site: http://www.rgp.com
Business Management Consulting Services
N.A.I.C.S.: 541611

Resources Global Professionals (Hong Kong) Limited (1)
4/F Lee Garden Three 1 Sunning Road, Causeway Bay, China (Hong Kong)
Tel.: (852) 28787711
Web Site:
   http://www.resourcesglobalhk.com
Sales Range: $25-49.9 Million
Emp.: 80
Business Management Consulting Services
N.A.I.C.S.: 541611
Mary Lam *(VP-Talent)*

Resources Global Professionals (India) Private Ltd. (1)
1116 Unit no - 1102 Level 11 Tower B Peninsula Business Park, S B Road Lower Parel, Mumbai, 400 013, Maharashtra, India
Tel.: (91) 2266879400

Resources Connection, Inc.—(Continued)

Web Site: http://www.rgp.com
Sales Range: $25-49.9 Million
Emp.: 10
Business Management Consulting Services
N.A.I.C.S.: 541611
Ganesh Chandrasekaran (VP-Revenue)

Resources Global Professionals (Ireland) Ltd. (1)
2 Grand Canal Square Grand Canal Harbour, Dublin, Ireland
Tel.: (353) 14867800
Web Site: http://www.rgp.com
Emp.: 8
Business Management Consulting Services
N.A.I.C.S.: 541611
Anne Gallagher (Dir-Talent)

Resources Global Professionals (Japan) K.K.
Pacific Century Place Marunouchi 13th floor
1-11-1, Marunouchi Chiyoda-ku, Tokyo,
100-6213, Japan
Tel.: (81) 367759168
Web Site: http://www.rgp.com
Sales Range: $25-49.9 Million
Emp.: 100
Business Management Consulting Services
N.A.I.C.S.: 541611
Tsuguhito Shimada (VP-Revenue)

Resources Global Professionals (Korea) Ltd. (1)
14-120 416 Hangang-daero, Jung-gu,
Seoul, 04637, Korea (South)
Tel.: (82) 27610999
Web Site: http://www.rgp.com
Sales Range: $25-49.9 Million
Emp.: 3
Business Management Consulting Services
N.A.I.C.S.: 541611
Chloe Jun (Dir-Talent)

Resources Global Professionals (Norway) AS (1)
Fridtjof Nansen Square 6, Oslo, 160, Norway
Tel.: (47) 23310400
Web Site: http://www.resourcesglobal.no
Business Management Consulting Services
N.A.I.C.S.: 541611
Charlott Laurell (Dir-Talent)
Peter Stenbrink (VP-Revenue)

Resources Global Professionals (Singapore) Pte. Ltd. (1)
5 Shenton Way UIC Building 11-01, Singapore, 068808, Singapore
Tel.: (65) 65519388
Web Site: http://www.rgp.com
Emp.: 8
Business Management Consulting Services
N.A.I.C.S.: 541611
Joan Lee (Dir-Talent)
Sachin Shah (Reg VP-Digital Asia)

Resources Global Professionals (Taiwan) Co. Ltd. (1)
13F-2 No 6 Sec 4 Xin Yi Road, Taipei, 106,
Taiwan
Tel.: (886) 227006049
Management Consulting Services
N.A.I.C.S.: 541611

Resources Global Professionals Sweden AB (1)
Sveavagen 13, 111 57, Stockholm, Sweden
Tel.: (46) 7824360800
Web Site: http://www.rgp.com
Sales Range: $25-49.9 Million
Emp.: 70
Business Management Consulting Services
N.A.I.C.S.: 541611

Resources Global Professionals, Inc. (1)
121 King Street West Suite 2130, Toronto,
M5H 3T9, ON, Canada
Tel.: (416) 364-3360
Web Site: http://www.resourcesglobal.com
Sales Range: $25-49.9 Million
Emp.: 9
Business Management Services
N.A.I.C.S.: 561110
Donald B. Murray (Chm)
Susan Paterson (Dir-Revenue)

Veracity Consulting Group, LLC (1)

4800 Cox Rd Ste 100, Glen Allen, VA
23060
Tel.: (804) 585-0310
Web Site: http://www.meetveracity.com
Information Technology & Services
N.A.I.C.S.: 541519
Laura Aldred (Mgr-HR & Ops)

RESPIRERX PHARMACEUTICALS INC.
126 Vly Rd Ste C, Glen Rock, NJ
07452
Tel.: (917) 834-7206   DE
Web Site: https://www.respirerx.com
Year Founded: 1987
RSPI—(OTCIQ)
Assets: $22,781
Liabilities: $11,903,101
Net Worth: ($11,880,320)
Earnings: ($3,972,993)
Emp.: 2
Fiscal Year-end: 12/31/22
Pharmaceutical Preparation Developer
N.A.I.C.S.: 325412
Arnold S. Lippa (Chm, Interim Pres, Interim CEO & Chief Scientific Officer)
Jeff Eliot Margolis (CFO, Treas, Sec & Sr VP)
Richard Purcell (Sr VP-R&D)
David Dickason (Sr VP-Preclinical Product Dev)

REST EZ, INC.
1398 W Mason Hollow Dr, Riverton,
UT 84065
Tel.: (801) 300-2542   WY
Web Site: https://www.restez.net
Year Founded: 2016
RTEZ—(OTCEM)
Assets: $2,594
Liabilities: $173,158
Net Worth: ($170,564)
Earnings: ($428,706)
Fiscal Year-end: 03/31/23
Pharmaceutical Product Mfr & Distr
N.A.I.C.S.: 325412
Brandon Sosa (CEO)

RETAIL OPPORTUNITY INVESTMENTS CORP.
11250 El Camino Real Ste 200, San
Diego, CA 92130
Tel.: (858) 677-0900   DE
Web Site: https://www.roireit.net
Year Founded: 2007
ROIC—(NASDAQ)
Rev.: $312,929,000
Assets: $3,004,279,000
Liabilities: $1,619,681,000
Net Worth: $1,384,598,000
Earnings: $51,869,000
Emp.: 70
Fiscal Year-end: 12/31/22
Real Estate Investment Services
N.A.I.C.S.: 523999
Stuart A. Tanz (Pres & CEO)
Richard K. Schoebel (COO)
Michael B. Haines (CFO)
Lauren N. Silveira (Chief Acctg Officer)

Subsidiaries:

Retail Opportunity Investments Partnership, LP (1)
11250 El Camino Real, San Diego, CA
92130
Tel.: (858) 677-0900
Web Site: https://www.roireit.net
Rev.: $312,928,999
Assets: $3,004,278,999
Liabilities: $1,619,680,999
Net Worth: $1,384,597,999
Earnings: $55,460,000
Emp.: 69
Fiscal Year-end: 12/31/2022
Real Estate Asset Management Services

N.A.I.C.S.: 531390
Stuart A. Tanz (Pres & CEO)

RETAIL VALUE INC.
3300 Enterprise Pkwy, Beachwood,
OH 44122
Tel.: (216) 755-5500   OH
Web Site:
http://www.retailvalueinc.com
RVI—(NYSE)
Rev.: $55,658,000
Assets: $144,398,000
Liabilities: $77,384,000
Net Worth: $67,014,000
Earnings: ($17,699,000)
Fiscal Year-end: 12/31/21
Commercial Property Rental Services
N.A.I.C.S.: 531120
David R. Lukes (Chm, Pres & CEO)
Christa A. Vesy (CFO & Chief Acctg Officer)
Aaron M. Kitlowski (Sec & Exec VP)
John M. Cattonar (Sr VP-Investments)
Joseph E. Chura (Sr VP-Property Ops)
Eric C. Cotton (Compliance Officer & Deputy Gen Counsel)
Maria Manley-Dutton (Deputy Gen Counsel)
Conor M. Fennerty (Exec VP)
Michael S. Owendoff (Deputy Gen Counsel)
Kim M. Scharf (Sr VP-Tech)
Jeff Scott (Sr VP-Property Reporting)
Robert Siebenschuh (Sr VP-Property Acctg Ops)
Steve Bakke (Sr VP-Capital Markets)

RETRACTABLE TECHNOLOGIES, INC.
511 Lobo Ln, Little Elm, TX 75068-
5295
Tel.: (972) 294-1010   TX
Web Site:
https://www.retractable.com
Year Founded: 1994
RVP—(NYSEAMEX)
Rev.: $94,818,938
Assets: $195,665,665
Liabilities: $89,128,856
Net Worth: $106,536,809
Earnings: $5,078,557
Emp.: 190
Fiscal Year-end: 12/31/22
Safety Needle Devices Designer, Developer, Mfr & Marketer
N.A.I.C.S.: 339112
Thomas J. Shaw (Founder, Chm, Pres & CEO)
Russell B. Kuhlman (VP-Sls Dev)
Lawrence G. Salerno (Dir-Ops)
Kathryn M. Duesman (VP-Clinical Affairs)
Michele M. Larios (Gen Counsel & VP)
Judy Ni Zhu (Mgr-R&D)
R. John Maday (Mgr-Production)
John W. Fort III (CFO, Treas & VP)

RETRIEVE MEDICAL HOLDINGS, INC.
376 Main St Ste 100, Bedminster, NJ
07921
Tel.: (908) 510-3247   NV
Web Site: https://retrievemedical.com
Year Founded: 2007
RMHI—(OTCIQ)
Assets: $130,349
Liabilities: $621,503
Net Worth: ($491,154)
Earnings: ($164,969)
Emp.: 1
Fiscal Year-end: 09/30/22
Phytocannabinnoid Pharmaceutical
Mfr

N.A.I.C.S.: 325412
Donald Thomas III (Chief Medical Officer)
Joerg Klaube (CFO)
Harriet L. Donnelly (CMO)
James J. Noonan (Dir-Operations & Training)
Thomas Swon (Dir-Business Development)
Mark Rosenberg (Co-Founder & Chm)
Jerry E. Swon (Co-Founder & CEO)

REVANCE THERAPEUTICS, INC.
1222 Demonbreun St 20th Fl, Nashville, TN 37203
Tel.: (510) 742-3400   DE
Web Site: https://www.revance.com
Year Founded: 1999
RVNC—(NASDAQ)
Rev.: $132,565,000
Assets: $581,900,000
Liabilities: $569,300,000
Net Worth: $12,600,000
Earnings: ($356,422,000)
Emp.: 534
Fiscal Year-end: 12/31/22
Biopharmaceutical Developer & Mfr
N.A.I.C.S.: 325412
Mark J. Foley (CEO)
Tobin C. Schilke (CFO & Principal Acctg Officer)
David A. Hollander (Chief Medical Officer)
Dwight Moxie (Gen Counsel, Sec & Sr VP)
Jessica Serra (Head-IR & ESG)
David A. Hollander (Chief Medical Officer)
Amie Krause (Chief People Officer)

REVASUM, INC.
825 Buckley Rd, San Luis Obispo,
CA 93401
Tel.: (805) 541-6424
Web Site: https://www.revasum.com
RVS—(ASX)
Microelectronic Equipment Mfr
N.A.I.C.S.: 334413
Jerry Cutini (Pres & CEO)

REVELATION BIOSCIENCES, INC.
4660 La Jolla Vlg Dr Ste 100, San
Diego, CA 92122
Tel.: (650) 800-3717   DE
Web Site:
https://www.revbiosciences.com
Year Founded: 2019
REVB—(NASDAQ)
Rev.: $34,962
Assets: $5,503,415
Liabilities: $4,450,962
Net Worth: $1,052,453
Earnings: ($10,829,549)
Emp.: 6
Fiscal Year-end: 12/31/22
Investment Services
N.A.I.C.S.: 523999
James Rolke (CEO)
Sandra Vedrick (VP-IR & PR)
Chester Zygmont III (CFO)
Robin Marsden (VP-Biology)
Carol Odle (VP-Clinical Ops)
George Tidmarsh (Chm)

REVELSTONE CAPITAL ACQUISITION CORP.
14350 Myford Rd, Irvine, CA 92606
Tel.: (949) 751-7518   DE
Year Founded: 2021
RCAC—(NASDAQ)
Rev.: $2,534,942

Assets: $169,625,495
Liabilities: $174,872,273
Net Worth: ($5,246,778)
Earnings: $1,137,756
Emp.: 2
Fiscal Year-end: 12/31/22
Investment Services
N.A.I.C.S.: 523999
Morgan Callagy (Co-CEO)
Daniel Neukomm (Co-CEO)

REVERENCE ACQUISITION CORP.
10 E 53rd St 14th Fl, New York, NY 10022
Tel.: (212) 804-8025   Ky
Year Founded: 2021
RCPIU—(NYSE)
Investment Services
N.A.I.C.S.: 523999
Milton Berlinski (Chm & CEO)
David Sloane (CFO)

REVIV3 PROCARE COMPANY
901 S Fremont Ave Unit 158, Alhambra, CA 91803
Tel.: (888) 638-8883   DE
Web Site:
   https://www.reviveprocare.com
Year Founded: 2015
AXIL—(NYSEAMEX)
Rev.: $27,498,539
Assets: $10,974,361
Liabilities: $3,278,575
Net Worth: $7,695,786
Earnings: $2,003,134
Emp.: 14
Fiscal Year-end: 05/31/24
Hair Care Product Mfr & Distr
N.A.I.C.S.: 325620
Jeff Toghraie (Chm & CEO)
Christopher Go (Sec)
Jeff Brown (COO)
Donald Starace (Pres)
Monica Diaz Brickell (CFO)

REVIVA PHARMACEUTICALS HOLDINGS, INC.
10080 N Wolfe Rd Ste SW3 200, Cupertino, CA 95014
Tel.: (408) 501-8881   DE
Web Site:
   https://www.revivapharma.com
Year Founded: 2018
RVPH—(NASDAQ)
Rev.: $182,802
Assets: $18,923,675
Liabilities: $6,607,279
Net Worth: $12,316,396
Earnings: ($24,339,292)
Emp.: 10
Fiscal Year-end: 12/31/22
Clinical-stage Biopharmaceutical Company
N.A.I.C.S.: 325412
Laxminarayan Bhat (Pres & CEO)
Narayan Prabhu (CFO)
Parag Saxena (Chm)

REVOLUTION HEALTHCARE ACQUISITION CORP.
20 University Rd, Cambridge, MA 02138
Tel.: (617) 234-7000   DE
Year Founded: 2021
REVH—(NASDAQ)
Investment Services
N.A.I.C.S.: 523999
Jay Markowitz (CEO)
Mark McDonnell (CFO)
Jason Doren (Chief Admin Officer)
Jeff Leiden (Chm)
Paul Fielding (COO)

REVOLUTION LIGHTING

TECHNOLOGIES, INC.
177 Broad St 12th Fl, Stamford, CT 06901
Tel.: (203) 504-1111   DE
Web Site: http://www.rvlti.com
Year Founded: 1993
RVLT—(NASDAQ)
Sales Range: $150-199.9 Million
Emp.: 270
Light Emitting Diode (LED) Lighting Mfr & Distr
N.A.I.C.S.: 335921
Joan Atkinson Nano (CFO & Principal Acctg Officer)
Brian L. Daley (Sr VP-Sls & Mktg)
Robert V. LaPenta Sr. (Chm, Pres & CEO)

Subsidiaries:

Array Lighting   (1)
124 Floyd Smith Dr Ste 300, Charlotte, NC 28262
Tel.: (704) 405-9740
Web Site: http://www.arraylighting.com
Sales Range: $10-24.9 Million
Emp.: 50
Lighting Systems Mfr
N.A.I.C.S.: 335139
Marolyn Merrell (Mgr-Intl Sls)

Energy Source, LLC   (1)
311 Bdwy, Providence, RI 02909
Tel.: (401) 270-4600
Web Site: http://www.energysource.cc
Rev.: $2,132,000
Emp.: 13
Electrical Contractor
N.A.I.C.S.: 238210

Lumificient Corporation   (1)
8752 Monticello Ln N, Maple Grove, MN 55369
Tel.: (763) 424-3702
Web Site: http://www.lumificient.com
Sales Range: $100-124.9 Million
Lighting Systems Mfr
N.A.I.C.S.: 335139

Nexxus Lighting-Pool & Spa   (1)
9400 Southridge Park Ct, Orlando, FL 32819
Tel.: (407) 857-9900
Sales Range: $10-24.9 Million
Emp.: 25
Lighting Systems Mfr
N.A.I.C.S.: 335139

Relume Technologies, Inc.   (1)
1795 N Lapeer Rd, Oxford, MI 48371   (100%)
Tel.: (248) 969-3800
Web Site: http://www.relume.com
Sales Range: $10-24.9 Million
Emp.: 9
LED Lighting Products Designer & Mfr
N.A.I.C.S.: 335139

Subsidiary (Domestic):

All Around Lighting, Inc.   (2)
10005 Muirlands Blvd Ste I, Irvine, CA 92618
Tel.: (949) 458-5999
Web Site: http://www.allaroundlighting.com
Sales Range: $1-9.9 Million
Emp.: 10
Home Furnishing Store Operator
N.A.I.C.S.: 449129

Sentinel System, LLC   (2)
1795 N Lapeer Rd, Oxford, MI 48371
Tel.: (248) 289-4725
Web Site: http://www.sentinelcontrols.com
Professional Wireless Equipment & Supply Whslr
N.A.I.C.S.: 423490

SV Lighting   (1)
9400 Southridge Park Ct Ste 200, Orlando, FL 32819   (100%)
Tel.: (407) 857-9900
Web Site: http://www.svlighting.com
Sales Range: $100-124.9 Million
Light Emitting Diode (L.E.D.) Manufacturing Facility
N.A.I.C.S.: 335132

Value Lighting, Inc.   (1)
1110 Allgood Industrial Ct, Marietta, GA 30066
Tel.: (770) 874-2191
Web Site: http://www.valuelightinginc.com
Scientific & Technical Consulting Services
N.A.I.C.S.: 541690

REVOLUTION MEDICINES, INC.
700 Saginaw Dr, Redwood City, CA 94063
Tel.: (650) 481-6801   DE
Web Site: https://www.revmed.com
Year Founded: 2014
RVMD—(NASDAQ)
Rev.: $35,380,000
Assets: $811,930,000
Liabilities: $126,742,000
Net Worth: $685,188,000
Earnings: ($248,705,000)
Emp.: 246
Fiscal Year-end: 12/31/22
Pharmaceutical Product Mfr & Distr
N.A.I.C.S.: 325412
Margaret Horn (COO)
Luan M. Wilfong (Chief HR Officer)
Xiaolin Wang (Exec VP-Clinical Dev)
Jack Anders (CFO & Principal Acctg Officer)
Adrian Gill (Sr VP-Medicinal Chemistry)
Walter Reiher (CIO)
Jan Smith (Sr VP-Biology)
Zhengping Wang (VP-Non-Clinical Dev & Clinical Pharmacology)
Martin Burke (Co-Founder)
Michael Fischbach (Co-Founder)
Kevan Shokat (Co-Founder)
Shaoling Li (VP-CMC & Quality)
Stephen M. Kelsey (Pres-R&D)
Jeff Cislini (Gen Counsel, VP & Deputy Gen Counsel)
Elena Koltun (VP-Medicinal Chemistry)
Mallika Singh (VP-Translational Res)
Margaret A. Horn (COO)
Mark A. Goldsmith (Chm, Pres & CEO)

Subsidiaries:

EQRx, Inc.   (1)
50 Hampshire St, Cambridge, MA 02139
Tel.: (617) 315-2255
Web Site: https://www.eqrx.com
Rev.: $186,788,000
Assets: $1,455,016,000
Liabilities: $66,154,000
Net Worth: $1,388,862,000
Earnings: ($169,089,000)
Emp.: 362
Fiscal Year-end: 12/31/2022
Biotechnology Research & Development Services
N.A.I.C.S.: 541714
Alexis Borisy (Chm)
Dina Ciarimboli (Sec)
Melanie Nallicheri (Founder)
Jami Rubin (CFO)
Rona Anhalt (Chief People Officer)

REVOLVE GROUP, INC.
12889 Moore St, Cerritos, CA 90703
Tel.: (562) 926-5672   DE
Web Site: https://www.revolve.com
Year Founded: 2012
RVLV—(NYSE)
Rev.: $1,101,416,000
Assets: $579,318,000
Liabilities: $199,745,000
Net Worth: $379,573,000
Earnings: $58,697,000
Emp.: 1,384
Fiscal Year-end: 12/31/22
Fashion Apparels Retailer
N.A.I.C.S.: 458110
Jesse Timmermans (CFO)
Raissa Gerona (Chief Brand Officer)
Ray Lingao (Chief Plng Officer)

Mitch Moseley (CEO-Owned Brands)
Divya Mathur (Chief Merchandising Officer & Dir-Fashion)
Jodi Lumsdaine Chapin (Gen Counsel & Sec)
Michael Karanikolas (Co-Founder, Chm & Co-CEO)
Michael Mente (Co-Founder & Co-CEO)

Subsidiaries:

Forward by Elyse Walker, LLC   (1)
12889 Moore St, Cerritos, CA 90703
Tel.: (562) 926-5672
Web Site: https://www.fwrd.com
Clothing Material Distr
N.A.I.C.S.: 458110

REVVITY, INC.
940 Winter St, Waltham, MA 02451
Tel.: (781) 663-6900   MA
Web Site: https://www.revvity.com
Year Founded: 1937
RVTY—(NYSE)
Rev.: $2,750,571,000
Assets: $13,564,665,000
Liabilities: $5,691,926,000
Net Worth: $7,872,739,000
Earnings: $693,094,000
Emp.: 11,500
Fiscal Year-end: 12/31/23
Instruments, Optoelectronics, Life Sciences & Fluid Sciences Products Mfr
N.A.I.C.S.: 334516
Joel S. Goldberg (Gen Counsel, Sec & Sr VP-Admin)
Daniel Tereau (Sr VP-Strategy & Bus Dev)
Prahlad R. Singh (Pres & CEO)
Tajinder Vohra (Sr VP-Global Ops)
Miriame Victor (Chief Comml Officer & Sr VP)
Maxwell Krakowiak (CFO & Sr VP)

Subsidiaries:

Beijing Huaan Magnech Bio-Tech Co., Ltd.   (1)
No 6 Chaoqian Road, Chnapging District, Beijing, 102200, China
Tel.: (86) 1089710920
Medicine Research Development Services
N.A.I.C.S.: 541714

Beijing Meizheng Bio-Tech Co., Ltd.   (1)
No 2 Building No 8 Courtyard Fenggusilu Road, Yanqing District, Beijing, 102101, China
Tel.: (86) 1081197003
Medicine Research Development Services
N.A.I.C.S.: 541714

Biolegend, Inc.   (1)
9727 Pacific Heights Blvd, San Diego, CA 92121
Tel.: (858) 455-9588
Web Site: http://www.biolegend.com
Emp.: 50
Commercial Physical Research, Nsk
N.A.I.C.S.: 541720
Gene Lay (Founder, Pres & CEO)
Craig Monell (VP-Bus Ops)

Bioo Scientific Corporation   (1)
7050 Burleson Rd, Austin, TX 78744
Tel.: (512) 707-8993
Web Site: http://www.biooscientific.com
Food & Feed Safety Product Mfr
N.A.I.C.S.: 541715

Caliper Life Sciences, Inc.   (1)
68 Elm St, Hopkinton, MA 01748   (100%)
Tel.: (508) 435-9500
Web Site: http://www.caliperls.com
Sales Range: $100-124.9 Million
Emp.: 469
Research Tools for Drug Discovery & Development
N.A.I.C.S.: 334516

Ceiba Solutions, Inc.   (1)
10 Post Office Sq 8th Fl, Boston, MA 02109

Revvity, Inc.—(Continued)

Tel.: (617) 692-2988
Web Site: http://www.ceibasolutions.com
Emp.: 5
Sciences & Laboratory IT Software & Services
N.A.I.C.S.: 513210

Cisbio Bioassays SAS (1)
Parc Marcel Boiteux, BP 84175, Codolet,
30200, Bagnols-sur-Ceze, Cedex, France
Tel.: (33) 46 679 6705
Web Site: https://www.fre.cisbio.eu
Pharmaceuticals Product Mfr
N.A.I.C.S.: 325412

Control Development Inc. (1)
2633 Foundation Dr, South Bend, IN 46628
Tel.: (574) 288-7338
Web Site:
   https://www.controldevelopment.com
Measuring & Controlling Device Mfr
N.A.I.C.S.: 334519

Covaris, Inc. (1)
14h Gill St, Woburn, MA 01801
Tel.: (781) 932-3959
Web Site: https://www.covaris.com
Rev.: $3,800,000
Emp.: 25
Analytical Laboratory Instrument Mfr
N.A.I.C.S.: 334516
Justine Laugharn (VP-Fin & Admin)
Simon Price (VP-Sls & Mktg)

DNA Laboratories Sdn. Bhd. (1)
B1-3 & B1-4 Block Plasma UKM-MTDC
Technology Centre, Universiti Kebangsaan
Malaysia, 43650, Bangi, Selangor, Malaysia
Tel.: (60) 389252700
Web Site: http://www.dna-laboratories.com
Testing Laboratory Services
N.A.I.C.S.: 621511

EUROIMMUN (South East Asia) Pte
Ltd (1)
No 01-01/05 Ultro Building No 1 Changi
Business Park Avenue 1, Singapore,
486058, Singapore
Tel.: (65) 68050399
Laboratory Diagnostic Equipment Mfr &
Distr
N.A.I.C.S.: 334516

EUROIMMUN Diagnostics Espana,
S.L.U. (1)
Avda Somosierra N 22 Nave 15A, San Sebastian de los Reyes, 28703, Madrid, Spain
Tel.: (34) 916591369
Web Site: http://www.euroimmun.es
Laboratory Diagnostic Equipment Mfr &
Distr
N.A.I.C.S.: 334516

EUROIMMUN France SAS (1)
Espace Villa Parc - L'Erable 1 avenue
Marne et Gondoire, 77600, Bussy-Saint-
Martin, France
Tel.: (33) 164616666
Web Site: https://www.bio-advance.com
Laboratory Diagnostic Equipment Mfr &
Distr
N.A.I.C.S.: 334516

EUROIMMUN Italia Diagnostica
Medica S.r.l. (1)
Corso United States 4 - Scala F Padua PD,
Pediatric Research Institute City of Hope,
35127, Padova, Italy
Tel.: (39) 049 780 0178
Web Site: https://www.euroimmun.it
Emp.: 37
Laboratory Diagnostic Equipment Mfr &
Distr
N.A.I.C.S.: 334516

EUROIMMUN Medical Diagnostics
(China) Co., Ltd (1)
Room 1908-1910 Building No 1 8 Beichen
East Road, Chaoyang District, Beijing,
100101, China
Tel.: (86) 1058045000
Laboratory Diagnostic Equipment Mfr &
Distr
N.A.I.C.S.: 334516

EUROIMMUN Medical Diagnostics
Canada Inc. (1)
2566 Meadowpine Boulevard, Mississauga,

L5N 6P9, ON, Canada
Tel.: (905) 542-8828
Laboratory Diagnostic Equipment Mfr &
Distr
N.A.I.C.S.: 334516

EUROIMMUN Medical Laboratory
Diagnostics South Africa (Pty)
Ltd. (1)
5 Winton Close, Cape Town, 7441, South
Africa
Tel.: (27) 215577666
Laboratory Diagnostic Equipment Mfr &
Distr
N.A.I.C.S.: 334516
Jason Rogers (Head-Technical)

EUROIMMUN Polska Spolka z
o.o. (1)
ul Widna 2a, 50-543, Wroclaw, Poland
Tel.: (48) 713730808
Web Site: http://www.euroimmun.pl
Laboratory Diagnostic Equipment Mfr &
Distr
N.A.I.C.S.: 334516

EUROIMMUN Portugal Unipessoal
Lda. (1)
Mr Emanuel Sa Miranda Taguspark Edificio
Tecnologia 2 2 47, 2740-122, Porto Salvo,
Portugal
Tel.: (351) 218750000
Laboratory Diagnostic Equipment Mfr &
Distr
N.A.I.C.S.: 334516

EUROIMMUN Schweiz AG (1)
Ringstrasse 37, 6010, Kriens, Switzerland
Tel.: (41) 3609000
Web Site: https://www.euroimmun.ch
Laboratory Diagnostic Equipment Mfr &
Distr
N.A.I.C.S.: 334516

EUROIMMUN UK Ltd. (1)
Ashville House 131-139 The Broadway,
Wimbledon, London, SW19 1QJ, United
Kingdom
Tel.: (44) 208 540 7058
Web Site: https://www.euroimmun.co.uk
Laboratory Diagnostic Equipment Mfr &
Distr
N.A.I.C.S.: 334516

EURQIMMUN US Inc. (1)
1 Bloomfield Ave, Mountain Lakes, NJ
07046
Tel.: (973) 656-1000
Web Site: https://www.euroimmun.us
Pharmaceutical Preparation Mfr
N.A.I.C.S.: 325412
Hamid Erfanian (Chief Comml Officer)

Euroimmun Japan Co. Ltd. (1)
1-9-10 Nihonbashihoridome - cho, Chuo-ku,
Tokyo, 103-0012, Japan
Tel.: (81) 366612117
Web Site: https://euroimmun.co.jp
Medical Laboratory Services
N.A.I.C.S.: 621511

Euroimmun Turkey Tibbi Laboratuar
Teshisleri A.S. (1)
No 10 NEF09 A Blok Kat 10 Daire 108-118,
Kagithane, 34415, Istanbul, Türkiye
Tel.: (90) 2123258504
Medical Laboratory Services
N.A.I.C.S.: 621511

Geospiza, Inc. (1)
100 W Harrison N Tower Ste 330, Seattle,
WA 98119
Tel.: (206) 633-4403
Web Site: http://www.geospiza.com
Sales Range: $10-24.9 Million
Emp.: 18
Genetic Analysis & Laboratory Workflow
Software Developer
N.A.I.C.S.: 513210

Horizon Discovery Group, plc (1)
8100 Cambridge Research Park, Water-
beach, Cambridge, CB25 9TL, United King-
dom
Tel.: (44) 1223976000
Web Site: http://www.horizondiscovery.com
Rev.: $76,404,635
Assets: $203,881,662
Liabilities: $37,263,868
Net Worth: $166,617,794

Earnings: ($6,039,918)
Emp.: 416
Fiscal Year-end: 12/31/2019
Biological Product Mfr
N.A.I.C.S.: 325414
Chris Lowe (Head-Res Ops)
Terry Pizzie (CEO)
Jayesh Pankhania (CFO & Sec)

Nexcelom Bioscience LLC (1)
360 Merrimack St Ste 200, Lawrence, MA
01843
Tel.: (978) 327-5340
Web Site: http://www.nexcelom.com
Sales Range: $10-24.9 Million
Emp.: 130
Cell-based Assays Device Designer, Devel-
oper & Mfr
N.A.I.C.S.: 339112
Peter Li (Pres & CEO)
Bo Lin (Dir-Application Dev)

Omni International, Inc. (1)
935 Cobb Place Blvd, Kennesaw, GA
30144
Tel.: (770) 421-0058
Web Site: https://www.omni-inc.com
Laboratory Equipment Mfr & Distr
N.A.I.C.S.: 334516

Oxford Immunotec Global
Limited (1)
94C Innovation Drive, Milton Park, Abing-
don, OX14 4RZ, United Kingdom
Tel.: (44) 1235442780
Web Site: http://www.oxfordimmunotec.com
Rev.: $73,710,000
Assets: $235,252,000
Liabilities: $21,561,000
Net Worth: $213,691,000
Earnings: ($1,809,000)
Emp.: 243
Fiscal Year-end: 12/31/2019
In-Vitro Diagnostics
N.A.I.C.S.: 325413

Division (US):

Imugen, Inc. (2)
315 Norwood Park S, Norwood, MA 02062
Tel.: (781) 255-0770
Web Site: http://www.imugen.com
Emp.: 13
Clinical & Research Laboratory Diagnostics
N.A.I.C.S.: 541715

Subsidiary (Non-US):

Oxford Immunotec K.K. (2)
8F Nisso Bldg No16 3-8-8 Shinyokohama,
Kohoku-ku, Yokohama, 222-0033, Japan
Tel.: (81) 454738005
Pharmaceutical Preparation Mfr
N.A.I.C.S.: 325412
Kazutaka Fujiaara (Dir-Sls)

Subsidiary (Domestic):

Oxford Immunotec Ltd (2)
143 Park Drive Milton, Abingdon, OX14
4SE, Oxfordshire, United Kingdom
Tel.: (44) 1235442780
Pharmaceutical Preparation Mfr
N.A.I.C.S.: 325412

Subsidiary (US):

Oxford Immunotec, Inc. (2)
293 Boston Post Rd W Ste 210, Marlbor-
ough, MA 01752
Tel.: (508) 481-4648
Web Site: http://www.oxfordimmunotec.com
Emp.: 16
In-Vitro Diagnostics
N.A.I.C.S.: 325413

Subsidiary (Domestic):

Immunetics, Inc. (3)
27 Drydock Ave 6th Fl, Boston, MA 02210
Tel.: (617) 896-9100
Web Site: http://www.immunetics.com
Rev.: $1,000,000
Emp.: 15
Surgical & Medical Instrument Mfr
N.A.I.C.S.: 339112

Ozmen Tibbi Laboratuar Teshisleri
A.S. (1)
Sultan Selim Mahallesi Lalegul Sokak No
10 NEF09 A Blok Kat 10, Daire 108-118

Kagithane, 34415, Istanbul, Türkiye
Tel.: (90) 2123258504
Analytical Laboratory Instrument Mfr
N.A.I.C.S.: 334516
Ilknur Sen (Acct Mgr)

Perkin Elmer de Mexico, S.A. (1)
Macedonio Alcala 54 Col Guadalupe Inn,
Alvaro Obregon, 01020, Mexico, Mexico
Tel.: (52) 559 990 3660
Web Site: https://perkinelmermx.com.mx
Analytical Laboratory Instrument Mfr
N.A.I.C.S.: 334516

Subsidiary (Domestic):

Inochem S.A. de C.V. (2)
La Gloria No 5 San Miguel Ajusco Tlalpan,
14700, Mexico, Mexico
Tel.: (52) 5558464878
Web Site: https://www.inochem.com.mx
Chemical Products Mfr
N.A.I.C.S.: 325998

Perkin-Elmer Instruments (Philip-
pines) Corporation (1)
Unit 409-410 Common Goal Tower Finance
Corner Industry Streets, Madrigal Business
Park Alabang, Muntinlupa, 1780, Philippines
Tel.: (63) 8220511
Medical Equipment Whslr
N.A.I.C.S.: 423450

PerkinElmer (Hong Kong) Ltd. (1)
Room 1803 Aitken Vanson Centre 61 Hoi
Yuen Rd, Hoi Yuen Road, Kwun Tong,
China (Hong Kong)
Tel.: (852) 26201881
Analytical Laboratory Instrument Mfr
N.A.I.C.S.: 334516

PerkinElmer BioSignal, Inc. (1)
1744 Rue William, Montreal, H3J 1R4, QC,
Canada
Tel.: (514) 937-1010
Analytical Laboratory Instrument Mfr
N.A.I.C.S.: 334516

Subsidiary (Domestic):

PerkinElmer Health Sciences Canada
Inc. (2)
501 Rowntree Dairy Rd Unit 6, Woodbridge,
L4L 8H1, ON, Canada
Tel.: (905) 851-4585
Web Site: http://www.perkinelmer.com
Sales Range: $25-49.9 Million
Emp.: 40
Analytical Laboratory Instrument Mfr
N.A.I.C.S.: 334516

PerkinElmer Danmark A/S (1)
Tonsbakken 16-18, Skovlunde, 2740, Den-
mark
Tel.: (45) 80884236
Web Site: http://www.perkinelmer.com
Sales Range: $10-24.9 Million
Emp.: 20
Analytical Laboratory Instrument Mfr
N.A.I.C.S.: 334516

PerkinElmer Espana, S.L. (1)
Ronda de Poniente 19 - Building Fiteni VI,
Tres Cantos, 28760, Madrid, Spain
Tel.: (34) 91 806 1200
Web Site: https://www.perkinelmer.com
Analytical Laboratory Instrument Mfr
N.A.I.C.S.: 334516

PerkinElmer Finland Oy (1)
Mustionkatu 6, 20750, Turku, Finland
Tel.: (358) 2 267 8111
Web Site: https://www.perkinelmerfinland.fi
Sales Range: $10-24.9 Million
Emp.: 600
Analytical Laboratory Instrument Mfr
N.A.I.C.S.: 334516

PerkinElmer Genomics, Inc. (1)
90 Emerson Ln, Bridgeville, PA
15017 **(100%)**
Tel.: (412) 220-2300
Web Site:
   http://www.perkinelmergenetics.com
Sales Range: $10-24.9 Million
Emp.: 53
Newborn Metabolic Screening Facilities
N.A.I.C.S.: 621511

PerkinElmer Health Sciences,
Inc. (1)

940 Winter St, Waltham, MA 02451
Tel.: (781) 663-6900
Web Site: http://www.perkinelmer.com
Sales Range: $75-99.9 Million
Emp.: 500
Scientific Instrument Mfr
N.A.I.C.S.: 334516

Subsidiary (Domestic):

Perten Instruments, Inc.   (2)
6444 S 6th St Rd, Springfield, IL 62712
Tel.: (217) 585-9440
Web Site: http://www.perten.com
Emp.: 40
Analytical Instrument Distr
N.A.I.C.S.: 334516

PerkinElmer Healthcare Diagnostics
(Shanghai) Co., Ltd.   (1)
No 1670 Zhangheng Road, Zhangjiang
High-Tech Park, Shanghai, 201203, China
Tel.: (86) 216 064 5888
Web Site: https://www.perkinelmer.com.cn
Medical Equipment Whslr
N.A.I.C.S.: 423450

PerkinElmer Holding GmbH   (1)
Ferdinand-Porsche-Ring 17, 63110, Rod-
gau, Germany
Tel.: (49) 61066100
Web Site: http://www.perkinelmer.com
Sales Range: $25-49.9 Million
Emp.: 100
Biotechnology Research & Development
Services
N.A.I.C.S.: 551112

PerkinElmer Informatics, Inc.   (1)
940 Winter St, Waltham, MA 02451
Tel.: (203) 925-4602
Web Site: http://www.cambridgesoft.com
Scientific Solution Software Provider
N.A.I.C.S.: 541511

PerkinElmer Japan Co. Ltd.   (1)
4F Technical Center Yokohama Business
Park, 134 Kobe-cho Hodogaya-ku, Yoko-
hama, 240-0005, Kanagawa, Japan
Tel.: (81) 45 339 5862
Web Site: https://www.perkinelmer.co.jp
Emp.: 130
Analytical Laboratory Instrument Mfr
N.A.I.C.S.: 334516
Mutsuo Aoki (Pres)

PerkinElmer Nederland B.V.   (1)
Rigaweg 22, 9723 TH, Groningen, Nether-
lands
Tel.: (31) 8000234490
Analytical Laboratory Instrument Mfr
N.A.I.C.S.: 334516

PerkinElmer Pty. Ltd.   (1)
Lvl 2 Bldg 5 Brandon Office Park 530-540
Springvale Road, Glen Waverley, Mel-
bourne, 3150, VIC, Australia
Tel.: (61) 80 003 3391
Web Site: https://www.perkinelmer.com
Analytical Laboratory Instrument Mfr
N.A.I.C.S.: 334516

PerkinElmer Saglik ve Cevre Bilimleri
Ltd.   (1)
Sti Merkez Mahallesi Baglar Caddesi
Kagithane Ofis Park N14, Kagithane, Istan-
bul, Turkiye
Tel.: (90) 2123121100
Medical Equipment Whslr
N.A.I.C.S.: 423450

PerkinElmer Saolyk ve Cevre Bilimleri
Ltd.   (1)
Sti Merkez Mahallesi Baglar Caddesi
Kagithane Ofis Park N 14 Kagithane, Istan-
bul, Turkiye
Tel.: (90) 2123121100
Laboratory Instruments Distr
N.A.I.C.S.: 423450

PerkinElmer Singapore Pte Ltd.   (1)
2 Tukang Innovation Grove 04-01 JTC
MedTech Hub MedTech Park, Singapore,
618305, Singapore
Tel.: (65) 6 868 1688
Web Site: http://www.perkinelmer.com.sg
Analytical Laboratory Instrument Mfr
N.A.I.C.S.: 334516

Subsidiary (Non-US):

PerkinElmer Instruments (Shanghai)
Co. Ltd.   (2)

No 1670 Zhangheng Road, Zhangjiang
High-Tech Park, 201203, Shanghai, China
Tel.: (86) 2160645888
Web Site: http://www.perkinelmer.com.cn
Analytical Laboratory Instrument Mfr
N.A.I.C.S.: 334516

PerkinElmer South Africa (Pty)
Ltd.   (1)
Thornhill Office Park Unit 21 94 Bekker
Road, Midrand, 2196, South Africa
Tel.: (27) 115640600
Medical Equipment Whslr
N.A.I.C.S.: 423450

PerkinElmer Taiwan Corporation   (1)
8F No 1091 Yuu Cheng Rd, Gushan Dist,
Kaohsiung, 804, Taiwan
Tel.: (886) 75521030
Web Site: http://www.perkinelmer.com
Analytical Laboratory Instrument Mfr
N.A.I.C.S.: 334516

PerkinElmer Vertriebs GmbH   (1)
Feldstrasse 34, 2345, Brunn am Gebirge,
Austria
Tel.: (43) 800111933
Sales Range: $25-49.9 Million
Emp.: 30
Analytical Laboratory Instrument Mfr
N.A.I.C.S.: 334516

PerkinElmer chemagen Technologie
GmbH   (1)
Arnold-Sommerfeld-Ring 2, 52499, Baes-
weiler, Germany
Tel.: (49) 240 180 5500
Web Site: https://www.chemagen.com
Sales Range: $25-49.9 Million
Emp.: 30
Analytical Laboratory Instrument Mfr
N.A.I.C.S.: 334516

Perten Instruments AB   (1)
Instrumentvagen 31, PO Box 9006, 126 09,
Hagersten, Sweden
Tel.: (46) 85 058 0900
Web Site: http://www.perten.com
Analytical Instrument Mfr
N.A.I.C.S.: 334516

Subsidiary (Non-US):

Delta Instruments B.V.   (2)
Kelvinlaan 3, 9207 JB, Drachten, Nether-
lands
Tel.: (31) 512 58 22 22
Web Site: http://www.deltainstruments.com
Sales Range: $10-24.9 Million
Emp.: 42
Analytical Instrument Mfr & Distr
N.A.I.C.S.: 334516

Perten Instruments France
SASU   (2)
2 rue Maurice Koechlin ZAC les Jesuites,
67500, Haguenau, France
Tel.: (33) 388930516
Analytical Instrument Mfr
N.A.I.C.S.: 334516

Perten Instruments GmbH   (2)
Schnackenburgallee 116a, 22525, Ham-
burg, Germany
Tel.: (49) 407662630
Laboratory Equipment Whslr
N.A.I.C.S.: 423450

Subsidiary (Domestic):

Perten Instruments Inc.   (2)
Instrumentvagen 31, 126 53, Hagersten,
Sweden
Tel.: (46) 850580900
Advanced Food Instrument Whslr
N.A.I.C.S.: 423830
Sven Holmlund (CEO)

Subsidiary (Non-US):

Perten Instruments Inc.   (2)
Unit B 112 Scurfield Boulevard, Winnipeg,
R3Y 1G4, MB, Canada
Tel.: (204) 487-1125
Laboratory Instruments Distr
N.A.I.C.S.: 423450

Perten Instruments Italia Srl   (2)
Via Vincenzo Gioberti 4, 20123, Milan, Italy
Tel.: (39) 0800906642
Industrial Equipment Distr

N.A.I.C.S.: 423610

Perten Instruments of Australia Pty
Ltd   (2)
Unit 13 2 Eden Park Drive, Macquarie Park,
2113, NSW, Australia
Tel.: (61) 298703400
Analytical Instrument Mfr & Whslr
N.A.I.C.S.: 334516

SOCOMA-PERTEN SAS   (1)
44 Avenue Jean Moulin, 31320, Castanet-
Tolosan, France
Tel.: (33) 561734002
Laboratory Equipment Whslr
N.A.I.C.S.: 423450

Shanghai Haoyuan Biotech Co.,
Ltd.   (1)
Building 2 Lane 2933 Huqingping Road
Zhaoxiang, Qingpu District, Shanghai,
215234, China
Tel.: (86) 215 975 5611
Web Site: http://www.haoyuansh.com
Medical Research & Development Services
N.A.I.C.S.: 541715

Solus Scientific Solutions Ltd.   (1)
9 Mansfield Network Centre, Millennium
Business Park Concorde Way, Mansfield,
NG19 7JZ, Nottinghamshire, United King-
dom
Tel.: (44) 1623429701
Testing Laboratory Services
N.A.I.C.S.: 541380

Solus Scientific Solutions, Inc.   (1)
Ste 350 Townview Business Crt Gest St,
Cincinnati, OH 45203
Tel.: (513) 381-3207
Testing Laboratory Services
N.A.I.C.S.: 541380

Tulip Diagnostics Pvt Ltd.   (1)
16/278/2 Flat No 7 & 8 Ashirwad Plaza
Sector 17 Sabzi Mandi Road, Indira Nagar,
Lucknow, 226 016, India
Web Site: https://www.tulipgroup.com
Diagnostic Substance Mfr
N.A.I.C.S.: 325413

Subsidiary (Domestic):

Biosense Technologies Pvt. Ltd.   (2)
A-233 Road No 21-Y, Wagle Industrial Es-
tate, Thane, 400604, Maharashtra, India
Tel.: (91) 18001237890
Web Site: http://www.biosense.in
Medical Equipment Whslr
N.A.I.C.S.: 423450

Orchid Biomedical Systems Pvt
Ltd.   (2)
Office No 805 Excellencia Lodha Supremus
Road No 22 Wagle Estate, Thane, 400 604,
MH, India
Tel.: (91) 6682000
Diagnostic Substance Mfr
N.A.I.C.S.: 325413
Vinod Kadam (Mgr-Production)

ViaCord, LLC   (1)
930 Winter St Ste 2500, Waltham, MA
02451
Tel.: (617) 914-3900
Web Site: http://www.viacord.com
Sales Range: $25-49.9 Million
Emp.: 100
Biological Research Services
N.A.I.C.S.: 541714
Cynthia A. Fisher (Founder)

REX AMERICAN RESOURCES
CORPORATION
7720 Paragon Rd, Dayton, OH 45459
Tel.: (937) 276-3931   DE
Web Site:
        https://www.rexamerican.com
Year Founded: 1984
REX—(NYSE)
Rev.: $855,000,000
Assets: $579,579,000
Liabilities: $68,585,000
Net Worth: $510,994,000
Earnings: $27,697,000
Emp.: 122
Fiscal Year-end: 01/31/23
Investment Services

N.A.I.C.S.: 523999
Stuart Alan Rose (Chm & Head-Corp
Dev)
Zafar A. Rizvi (Pres & CEO)
Douglas L. Bruggeman (CFO)
Edward M. Kress (Sec)

Subsidiaries:

NuGen Energy, LLC   (1)
27283 447th Ave, Marion, SD 57043
Tel.: (605) 648-2100
Web Site: https://www.nugenmarion.com
Sales Range: $25-49.9 Million
Emp.: 20
Ethyl Alcohol Mfr
N.A.I.C.S.: 325193

One Earth Energy, LLC   (1)
202 N Jordan Dr, Gibson City, IL 60936
Tel.: (217) 784-5321
Web Site: https://www.oneearthenergy.com
Emp.: 50
Basic Organic Chemical Mfr
N.A.I.C.S.: 325199
Jack Murray (Treas, Treas, Sec & Dir-
Secretary)
Steven Kelly (Pres & CEO)
Ben Kurtenbach (CFO)
Phillip Moritz (VP)

Rex Radio and Television, Inc.   (1)
2875 Needmore Rd, Dayton, OH 45414
Tel.: (937) 276-3931
Home Appliance Whslr
N.A.I.C.S.: 449210

REXFORD INDUSTRIAL RE-
ALTY, INC.
11620 Wilshire Blvd Ste 1000, Los
Angeles, CA 90025
Tel.: (310) 966-1680   MD
Web Site:
        https://www.rexfordindustrial.com
REXR—(NYSE)
Rev.: $797,826,000
Assets: $10,929,829,000
Liabilities: $2,785,924,000
Net Worth: $8,143,905,000
Earnings: $238,016,000
Emp.: 242
Fiscal Year-end: 12/31/23
Real Estate Services
N.A.I.C.S.: 531390
Laura Clark (CFO)
Howard Schwimmer (Co-CEO)
Michael S. Frankel (Co-CEO)
Richard S. Ziman (Co-Founder)
David E. Lanzer (Gen Counsel &
Sec)

REZOLUTE, INC.
275 Shoreline Dr Ste 500, Redwood
City, CA 94065
Tel.: (650) 206-4507   DE
Web Site:
        https://www.rezolutebio.com
Year Founded: 2010
RZLT—(NASDAQ)
Rev.: $4,203,000
Assets: $123,721,000
Liabilities: $7,549,000
Net Worth: $116,172,000
Earnings: ($51,787,000)
Emp.: 51
Fiscal Year-end: 06/30/23
Biopharmaceutical Product Mfr
N.A.I.C.S.: 325412
Daron G. Evans (CFO)
Brian Roberts (Chief Medical Officer)
Michael R. Deperro (VP-Ops)
Erin O'Boyle (VP-Clinical Ops)
Davelyn Eaves Hood (Head-Scientific
& Patient Affairs)
Rajat Agrawal (VP-Clinical Dev)
Michael Covarrubias (VP-CMC)
Chris Milks (VP-Fin)
Nevan Charles Elam (Pres & CEO)

RF INDUSTRIES, LTD.

RF Industries, Ltd.—(Continued)

16868 Via Del Campo Ct Ste 200, San Diego, CA 92127
Tel.: (858) 549-6340   NV
Web Site:
   https://www.rfindustries.com
RFIL—(NASDAQ)
Rev.: $72,168,000
Assets: $82,278,000
Liabilities: $42,516,000
Net Worth: $39,762,000
Earnings: ($3,078,000)
Emp.: 321
Fiscal Year-end: 10/31/23
Electronic Connector Manufacturing
N.A.I.C.S.: 334417
Christophe Massenet (VP-Tech & Engrg)
Robert D. Dawson (Pres & CEO)
Peter Yin (CFO & Sec)
Ray Bibisi (COO)

Subsidiaries:

AVIEL ELECTRONICS   (1)
3060 N Walnut Ste 150, Las Vegas, NV 89115
Tel.: (702) 739-8155
Web Site: http://www.avielelectronics.com
Sales Range: $10-24.9 Million
Emp.: 10
Microwave & RF Connector Mfr
N.A.I.C.S.: 334417

C Enterprises, L.P.   (1)
2445 Cades Way, Vista, CA 92081
Tel.: (760) 599-5111
Web Site: http://www.centerprises.com
Telecommunications & Data Communications Equipment & Solutions Mfr & Distr
N.A.I.C.S.: 334290
Steven Yamasaki (COO)
Arne Jensen (Dir-Mfg Ops)
Trevor Turner (Dir-Sls-Natl)

Cables Unlimited, Inc.   (1)
3 Old Dock Rd, Yaphank, NY 11980
Tel.: (631) 563-6363
Web Site: http://www.cables-unlimited.com
Communication & Energy Wire Mfr
N.A.I.C.S.: 335929
Darren Clark (Pres)

Microlab/FXR LLC   (1)
25 Eastmans Rd, Parsippany, NJ 07054
Tel.: (862) 328-1101
Wob Site: https://microlabtech.com
Microwave Component Mfr & Distr
N.A.I.C.S.: 334419

RF Cable Assemblies Division   (1)
7610 Miramar Rd, San Diego, CA 92126
Tel.: (858) 549-6340
Web Site: http://www.rfcables.com
Sales Range: $25-49.9 Million
Emp.: 100
Coaxial Cable Assemblies Mfr
N.A.I.C.S.: 334417
Howard F. Hill (CEO)

RF Connectors Division   (1)
7610 Miramar Rd, San Diego, CA 92126
Tel.: (858) 549-6340
Web Site: http://www.rfcoaxconnectors.com
Sales Range: $100-124.9 Million
Emp.: 100
Coaxial Connectors, Adapters, Assembly & Test Kit Prod Mfr
N.A.I.C.S.: 334417
Howard F. Hill (CEO)

Rel-Tech Electronics, Inc.   (1)
215 Pepes Farm Rd, Milford, CT 06460
Tel.: (203) 877-8770
Web Site: http://www.rel-tech.com
Sales Range: $1-9.9 Million
Radio & Television Broadcasting & Wireless Communications Equipment Mfr
N.A.I.C.S.: 334220
Bill LeBlanc (Co-Founder)
Ralph Palumbo (Co-Founder)

Schroff Technologies International, Inc.   (1)
376 Dry Bridge Rd Bldg H1, North Kingstown, RI 02852
Tel.: (401) 667-2773

Thermal System Wireless Telecom Mfr
N.A.I.C.S.: 334220

Worswick Industries, Inc.   (1)
7642 Clairemont Mesa Blvd, San Diego, CA 92111-1535
Tel.: (858) 571-5400
Web Site: http://www.oddcables.com
Sales Range: $10-24.9 Million
Emp.: 15
Computer Cables & Wire Harnesses Mfr
N.A.I.C.S.: 334417

RGC RESOURCES, INC.
519 Kimball Ave, Roanoke, VA 24016
Tel.: (540) 777-4427   VA
Web Site:
   https://www.rgcresources.com
RGCO—(NASDAQ)
Rev.: $75,174,779
Assets: $310,109,193
Liabilities: $210,407,484
Net Worth: $99,701,709
Earnings: $10,102,062
Emp.: 99
Fiscal Year-end: 09/30/21
Holding Company; Natural Gas Distr
N.A.I.C.S.: 551112
John B. Williamson III (Chm)
Paul W. Nester (Pres & CEO)
Lawrence T. Oliver (Sec & Sr VP-Regulatory & External Affairs)
C. Brooke Miles (VP-HR, Asst Treas & Asst Sec)
Timothy J. Mulvaney (CFO, Treas & VP)
Jason Field (CFO, Principal Acctg Officer, Treas & VP)

Subsidiaries:

RGC Ventures of Virginia, Inc.   (1)
519 Kimball Ave NE, Roanoke, VA 24016
Tel.: (540) 777-4427
Sales Range: $600-649.9 Million
Application Solutions Services
N.A.I.C.S.: 541990

Roanoke Gas Company   (1)
519 Kimball Ave NE, Roanoke, VA 24016-2103   (100%)
Tel.: (540) 777-4427
Sales Range: $200-524.9 Million
Natural Gas Utility Services & Propane Distr
N.A.I.C.S.: 221210
Carl James Shockley Jr. (COO & VP)
Paul W. Nester (Pres & CEO)
Lawrence T. Oliver (Sec & Sr VP-Regulatory & External Affairs)
C. Brooke Miles (VP-HR)
Robert L. Wells II (CIO, VP, Asst Sec & Asst Treas)

RH
15 Koch Rd, Corte Madera, CA 94925
Tel.: (415) 924-1005   DE
Web Site: https://www.rh.com
Year Founded: 1979
RH—(NYSE)
Rev.: $3,029,126,000
Assets: $4,143,897,000
Liabilities: $4,441,291,000
Net Worth: ($297,394,000)
Earnings: $127,561,000
Emp.: 5,960
Fiscal Year-end: 02/03/24
Holding Company; Home Furnishings
N.A.I.C.S.: 551112
Eri Chaya (Co-Pres)
Jack Preston (CFO)
Christina Hargarten (Chief Acctg Officer)

Subsidiaries:

Dmitriy & Company LLC   (1)
437 W 16th St 5th Fl, New York, NY 10011
Tel.: (212) 243-4800
Web Site: https://www.dmitriyco.com
Furniture Distr
N.A.I.C.S.: 449110

JEUP Inc.   (1)
4171 Luxe Court SE, Grand Rapids, MI 49512
Tel.: (616) 669-0427
Web Site: http://www.jeupfurniture.com
Rev.: $4,000,000
Emp.: 20
Furniture Retailer
N.A.I.C.S.: 449110
Joseph Jeup (Mgr)

RH Build & Design, Inc.   (1)
1951 Bowen St, Oshkosh, WI 54901
Tel.: (920) 231-1619
Web Site: https://www.rhdesignbuild.com
Architectural Design Services
N.A.I.C.S.: 541310
Dennis Ruedinger (Partner)
Susan Hirschberg (Partner)

RH F&B Minnesota, LLC   (1)
6801 France Ave S, Edina, MN 55435
Tel.: (952) 206-6307
Interior Design Services
N.A.I.C.S.: 541410

RH San Francisco F&B, LLC   (1)
590 20th St, San Francisco, CA 94103
Tel.: (415) 865-0407
Interior Design Services
N.A.I.C.S.: 541410

RH Yountville F&B, LLC   (1)
6725 Washington St, Yountville, CA 94599
Tel.: (707) 339-4654
Interior Design Services
N.A.I.C.S.: 541410

Restoration Hardware Canada, Inc.   (1)
100 Anderson Road Suite 302, Calgary, T2J 3V1, AB, Canada
Tel.: (403) 271-2122
Home Furniture Distr
N.A.I.C.S.: 423210

Subsidiary (Domestic)

RH F&B Operations Canada, Inc.   (2)
2555 Granville St Ste 110, Vancouver, V6H 3G7, BC, Canada
Tel.: (604) 731-3918
Interior Design Services
N.A.I.C.S.: 541410

Restoration Hardware, Inc.   (1)
1700 Redwood Hwy, Corte Madera, CA 94925-1249
Tel.: (628) 266-2040
Web Site:
   http://www.restorationhardware.com
Sales Range: $1-4.9 Billion
Home Furnishings, Functional & Decorative Hardware & Related Merchandise Retailer; Owned by Catterton Partners & Three Towers Partners LLC
N.A.I.C.S.: 449110

Waterworks Operating Company LLC   (1)
60 Backus Ave, Danbury, CT 06810
Web Site: http://www.waterworks.com
Plumbing Fittings & Supplies Mfr
N.A.I.C.S.: 423720

RHINEBECK BANCORP, INC.
Tel.: (845) 454-8555   MD
Web Site:
   https://www.rhinebeckbank.com
Year Founded: 2018
RBKB—(NASDAQ)
Rev.: $54,488,000
Assets: $1,335,977,000
Liabilities: $1,227,845,000
Net Worth: $108,132,000
Earnings: $6,997,000
Emp.: 182
Fiscal Year-end: 12/31/22
Bank Holding Company
N.A.I.C.S.: 551111
Michael J. Quinn (Pres & CEO)

RHINO NOVI, INC.
2831 Saint Rose Pkwy Ste 200, Henderson, NV 89052
Tel.: (775) 981-0270   NV

Web Site:
   http://www.rhinointernational
corp.com
RNOV—(OTCIQ)
Financial Management Services
N.A.I.C.S.: 523999
Itav Avital (CEO)

RHYTHM PHARMACEUTICALS, INC.
222 Berkeley St 12th Fl, Boston, MA 02116
Tel.: (857) 264-4280   DE
Web Site: https://www.rhythmtx.com
Year Founded: 2008
RYTM—(NASDAQ)
Rev.: $77,428,000
Assets: $332,745,000
Liabilities: $162,986,000
Net Worth: $169,759,000
Earnings: ($184,678,000)
Emp.: 226
Fiscal Year-end: 12/31/23
Biotechnology Research & Development Services
N.A.I.C.S.: 541714
Christopher German (Principal Acctg Officer & Controller)
Hunter C. Smith (CFO & Treas)
David Connolly (Head-IR & Comm)
Jennifer Chien (Exec VP & Head-North America)
Yann Mazabraud (Exec VP & Head-Intl)
Brieana Buckley (VP-Medical Affairs)
Jim Flaherty (Gen Counsel & Sr VP)
Pam Cramer (Chief HR Officer)
Dana Washburn (Sr VP)
Elisabeth Cronert-Bendell (Sr VP)
David P. Meeker (Chm, Pres & CEO)

RIBBIT LEAP, LTD.
364 University Ave, Palo Alto, CA 94301
Tel.: (650) 485-3758   Ky
Web Site: http://www.ribbitleap.com
Year Founded: 2020
LEAPU—(NYSE)
Investment Services
N.A.I.C.S.: 523999
Meyer Malka (Co-Founder, Chm & CEO)
Cynthia McAdam (Co-Founder & COO)

RIBBON COMMUNICATIONS INC.
6500 Chase Oaks Blvd Ste 100, Plano, TX 75023
Tel.: (978) 614-8100   DE
Web Site:
   https://ribboncommunications.com
Year Founded: 2017
RBBN—(NASDAQ)
Rev.: $819,760,000
Assets: $1,255,564,000
Liabilities: $737,137,000
Net Worth: $518,427,000
Earnings: ($98,083,000)
Emp.: 3,394
Fiscal Year-end: 12/31/22
Holding Company; VoIP Telecommunications Services
N.A.I.C.S.: 551112
Bruce W. McClelland (Pres & CEO)
Patrick W. Macken (Chief Legal Officer & Exec VP)
Dan Redington (Exec VP-Global Sls)
Joni Roberts (CMO & Sr VP)
Sam Bucci (COO, Exec VP & Gen Mgr-IP Optical Networks Bus Unit)
Petrena Ferguson (Sr VP-HR)
Miguel A. Lopez (CFO & Exec VP)

Subsidiaries:

ECI Telecom Ltd.   (1)

30 Hasivim Street, Petah Tiqwa, 49517, Israel **(10%)**
Tel.: (972) 39266555
Sales Range: $650-699.9 Million
Telecommunications Systems Marketer & Mfr
N.A.I.C.S.: 334210

Holding (Non-US):

ECI Telecom **(2)**
Espace Velizy Le Nugesser 13 Ave Morane Saulnier, Lathail Beadr, 78140, Velizy-Villacoublay, France
Tel.: (33) 134630480
Web Site: http://www.ecitele.com
Sales Range: $25-49.9 Million
Emp.: 25
Telecom Network Hardware Mfr
N.A.I.C.S.: 517810

ECI Telecom (Philippines), Inc. **(2)**
27/F Unit 2702 Antel 2000 Building 121 Valero St, Salcedo Vlg, Makati, 1226, Metro Manila, Philippines
Tel.: (63) 28452333
Web Site: http://www.ecitele.com
Sales Range: $1-9.9 Million
Emp.: 50
Telecom Network Hardware Mfr
N.A.I.C.S.: 334418

ECI Telecom (Singapore) **(2)**
150 Beach Rd Ste 28 07 Gateway W, Singapore, 189720, Singapore
Tel.: (65) 62977335
Web Site: http://www.ecitele.com
Sales Range: $25-49.9 Million
Emp.: 14
N.A.I.C.S.: 334418

Subsidiary (US):

ECI Telecom Americas Inc. **(2)**
5100 NW 33rd Ave Ste 150, Fort Lauderdale, FL 33309-6362
Tel.: (954) 772-3070
Web Site: http://www.ecitele.com
Sales Range: $25-49.9 Million
Emp.: 70
Telecommunication Servicesb
N.A.I.C.S.: 541512

Holding (Non-US):

ECI Telecom GmbH **(2)**
Bueropark Oberursel In der Au 27, Oberursel, Germany
Tel.: (49) 617162090
Web Site: http://www.ecitele.com
Sales Range: $25-49.9 Million
Emp.: 50
Provider of Digital Telecommunications & Data Transmission Systems to Network Service Providers
N.A.I.C.S.: 517111

ECI Telecom Iberica S.A. **(2)**
Josefa Valcarcel 3 5, 28027, Madrid, Spain
Tel.: (34) 917434950
Web Site: http://www.dominion.es
Sales Range: $25-49.9 Million
Emp.: 9
Telecom Network Hardware Mfr
N.A.I.C.S.: 334418

ECI Telecom Ltd. - China **(2)**
7/F East Communication Bldg No 398 Wensan Road, Dongcheng District, Hangzhou, 100007, China
Tel.: (86) 57188865127
Web Site: http://www.ecitele.com
Sales Range: $25-49.9 Million
Emp.: 10
Telecom Network Hardware Mfr
N.A.I.C.S.: 334418

ECI Telecom Ukraine LLC **(1)**
Packet Optical Business Unit 1 Laboratorny Pereulok, Kiev, Ukraine
Tel.: (380) 672358566
Telecommunication Servicesb
N.A.I.C.S.: 517810

Ribbon Communications Israel Limited **(1)**
30 Hasivim Street, PO B 7387, Petach Tikva, 49250, Israel
Tel.: (972) 39266555
Telecommunication Servicesb
N.A.I.C.S.: 517810

Ribbon Communications Operating Company, Inc. **(1)**
4 Technology Park Dr, Westford, MA 01886
Tel.: (978) 614-8100
Web Site: https://www.ribboncommunications.com
Sales Range: $250-299.9 Million
Holding Company
N.A.I.C.S.: 551112
Jamie Gibson *(VP-Technology-Sls Engrg)*

Subsidiary (Domestic):

GENBAND US LLC **(2)**
3605 E Plano Pkwy, Plano, TX 75074 **(100%)**
Tel.: (833) 742-2661
Web Site: http://ribboncommunications.com
IP Multimedia Application & Infrastructure Products & Solutions Supplier
N.A.I.C.S.: 517810
Daryl E. Raiford *(CFO & Exec VP)*

Subsidiary (Domestic):

Ureach Technologies, Inc. **(3)**
Holmdel Corporate Plaza 2137 State Hwy 35 & Union Ave, Holmdel, NJ 07733
Tel.: (732) 335-5400
Web Site: http://www.ureach.com
Communications Products & Services
N.A.I.C.S.: 517112

Subsidiary (Domestic):

Network Equipment Technologies, Inc. **(2)**
4 Technology Park Dr, Westford, MA 01886
Tel.: (877) 412-8867
Voice, ATM & IP Development Services
N.A.I.C.S.: 334210

Subsidiary (Non-US):

Ribbon Communications Czech Republic s.r.o. **(2)**
Katerinska 466/40 -2nd floor, Nove Mesto na Morave, 120 00, Prague, Czech Republic
Tel.: (420) 222119604
Emp.: 40
Network Communications Infrastructure Design Services
N.A.I.C.S.: 541512

Subsidiary (Domestic):

Ribbon Communications Federal Inc. **(2)**
21660 Ridgetop Cir Ste 100, Dulles, VA 20166
Tel.: (703) 948-1800
Sales Range: $25-49.9 Million
Emp.: 50
Government Sales of Communication Equipment
N.A.I.C.S.: 423690

Subsidiary (Non-US):

Ribbon Communications France EURL **(2)**
13-15 Rue Jeanne Braconnier, Meudon La Foret, 92360, Meudon, France
Tel.: (33) 184196030
Network Communications Infrastructure Design Services
N.A.I.C.S.: 541512

Ribbon Communications Germany GmbH **(2)**
Ginqo 11th Floor - Hahnstr 31-35, 60528, Frankfurt, Germany
Tel.: (49) 6990732269
Software Development Services
N.A.I.C.S.: 541511

Ribbon Communications Hong Kong Limited **(2)**
29/F Sun Life Tower Suite A152 AT-LASPACE The Gateway, Harbour City, Kowloon, China (Hong Kong)
Tel.: (852) 39215247
Software Development Services
N.A.I.C.S.: 541511

Ribbon Communications K.K. **(2)**
13F Shibuya Prime Plaza 19-1 Maruyamacho, Shibuya-ku, Tokyo, 150-0044, Japan
Tel.: (81) 36 455 2100

Web Site: http://www.ribboncommunications.com
Telecommunication Servicesb
N.A.I.C.S.: 517810

Ribbon Communications Malaysia Sdn. Bhd. **(2)**
Suite 12-2 Level 12 The Vertical Corporate Tower B Avenue 10, Bangsar South City No 8 Jalan Kerinchi, 59200, Kuala Lumpur, Malaysia
Tel.: (60) 320359661
Data Communications Equipment Mfr
N.A.I.C.S.: 334210
Cindy Lim *(Sec)*

Ribbon Communications Singapore Pte. Ltd. **(2)**
1 Fullerton Road 02-01 One Fullerton, Singapore, 049213, Singapore
Tel.: (65) 68325589
Telecommunication Servicesb
N.A.I.C.S.: 517810

Ribbon Communications Switzerland GmbH **(2)**
Seefeldstrasse 69, 8008, Zurich, Switzerland
Tel.: (41) 435081077
Software Development Services
N.A.I.C.S.: 541511

Sonus Networks (India) Private Limited **(2)**
Alpha and Delta Blocks Embassy Tech Square Outer Ring Road, Kadubeesanahalli Village Varthur Hobli, Bengaluru, 560 066, Karnataka, India
Tel.: (91) 8067895100
Web Site: http://www.sonux.com
Sales Range: $50-74.9 Million
Emp.: 400
Telecommunication Servicesb
N.A.I.C.S.: 517810

Sonus Networks Australia Pty Ltd. **(2)**
Suite 1303 - Level 13 - Tower 1 475 Victoria Avenue, Chatswood, 2067, NSW, Australia
Tel.: (61) 280695850
Networking & Communications Equipment Mfr
N.A.I.C.S.: 334210

Subsidiary (Domestic):

Taqua LLC **(2)**
1130 E Arapaho Ste 200, Richardson, TX 75081
Tel.: (855) 467-6687
Web Site: http://www.sonus.net
Mobile & Fixed IP Convergence Solutions
N.A.I.C.S.: 517810

Ribbon Communications Rus Limited Liability Company **(1)**
Office 9021 Smolensky Passage Smolenskaya sq 3, 121099, Moscow, Russia
Tel.: (7) 4959378350
Telecommunication Servicesb
N.A.I.C.S.: 517810

Ribbon Communications do Brasil Ltda **(1)**
Condominio West Towers Tower B Alameda Rio Negro 500, 18 Andar - Sala 1801 Alphaville Barueri, Sao Paulo, 06454-000, Brazil
Tel.: (55) 1139588654
Telecommunication Servicesb
N.A.I.C.S.: 517810

Ribbon Networks Ltd. Co. **(1)**
TIOC Business Center 6F No 6 Sec 4 Hsinyi Rd Offices 615 and 616, Da-an District, Taipei, 10683, Taiwan
Tel.: (886) 255562377
Telecommunication Servicesb
N.A.I.C.S.: 517810

RICEBRAN TECHNOLOGIES
25420 Kuykendahl Rd Ste B300, Tomball, TX 77375
Tel.: (646) 971-8899 **CA**
Web Site:
https://www.ricebrantech.com
Year Founded: 1998

RIBT—(NASDAQ)
Rev.: $41,617,000
Assets: $27,433,000
Liabilities: $14,524,000
Net Worth: $12,909,000
Earnings: ($7,858,000)
Emp.: 94
Fiscal Year-end: 12/31/22
Rice Milling
N.A.I.C.S.: 311212
Robert DePaul *(VP-Ops)*
Eric Tompkins *(Chm)*
William J. Keneally *(Interim CFO)*

Subsidiaries:

Golden Ridge Rice Milles, Inc. **(1)**
1784 Hwy 1, Wynne, AR 72396
Tel.: (870) 208-8808
Web Site: http://www.goldenridgerice.com
Rice Milling Mfr
N.A.I.C.S.: 311212

Healthy Natural Inc. **(1)**
3000 Skyway Cir N, Irving, TX 75038
Tel.: (972) 570-4600
Web Site: http://www.healthynatural.com
Nutrition Food Supplement Store Operator
N.A.I.C.S.: 456191

RICHARDSON ELECTRONICS, LTD.
40W267 Keslinger Rd, Lafox, IL 60147-0393
Tel.: (630) 208-2200 **DE**
Web Site: https://www.rell.com
Year Founded: 1947
RELL—(NASDAQ)
Rev.: $196,460,000
Assets: $192,445,000
Liabilities: $34,493,000
Net Worth: $157,952,000
Earnings: $61,000
Emp.: 407
Fiscal Year-end: 06/01/24
Electronic Components, Equipment & Assemblies Distr for Industrial Applications
N.A.I.C.S.: 423690
Edward J. Richardson *(Chm, Pres & CEO)*
Kathleen M. McNally *(Sr VP-Supply Chain-Global)*
Wendy S. Diddell *(COO & Exec VP)*
Jens Ruppert *(Exec VP & Gen Mgr-Canvys)*
Robert J. Ben *(CFO, Chief Acctg Officer, Sec & Exec VP)*

Subsidiaries:

Cetron Electronics Manufacturing Division **(1)**
40 W 267 Keslinger Rd, Lafox, IL 60147
Tel.: (630) 208-2300
Web Site: http://www.rell.com
Sales Range: $400-449.9 Million
Mfr of Electron Tubes
N.A.I.C.S.: 334419
Edward J. Richardson *(Chm, CEO & Acting Gen Mgr-Electron Device Grp)*

International Medical Equipment & Service, Inc. **(1)**
8190 Regent Pkwy, Fort Mill, SC 29715-8366
Tel.: (704) 739-3597
Web Site: http://www.imesimaging.com
Emp.: 16
Diagnostic Imaging Equipment Supplier
N.A.I.C.S.: 423450

Richardson Electronics Benelux B.V. **(1)**
Kruisweg 811 Building IV, 2132 NG, Hoofddorp, Netherlands
Tel.: (31) 854878287
Web Site: http://www.rell.com
Emp.: 2
Industrial Electronic Component Distr
N.A.I.C.S.: 423690

Richardson Electronics GmbH **(1)**

Richardson Electronics, Ltd.—(Continued)

Boschstr 8, 82178, Puchheim,
Germany   **(100%)**
Tel.: (49) 8981891280
Web Site: https://www.rellaser.de
Sales Range: $10-24.9 Million
Emp.: 4
Sales & Marketing
N.A.I.C.S.: 449210

Richardson Electronics Iberica
S.A.   **(1)**
C/ Maestro Arbos 9, 28045, Madrid, Spain
Tel.: (34)-915283700
Electronic Parts & Equipment Whslr
N.A.I.C.S.: 423690

Richardson Electronics India Private
Limited   **(1)**
WeWork DD-23 10th Floor Tower 1 Sea-
woods Grand Central Sector 40, Navi Mum-
bai, 400 706, Maharashtra, India
Tel.: (91) 7777042682
Web Site: http://www.richardsonrfpd.com
Emp.: 3
Industrial Electronic Component Distr
N.A.I.C.S.: 423690

Richardson Electronics Italy,
S.r.l.   **(1)**
Via Di Pratignone 65-67, Calenzano, 50041,
Florence, Italy   **(100%)**
Tel.: (39) 055420831
Sales Range: $10-24.9 Million
Emp.: 15
Distr of Electron Tubes & Power Semicon-
ductors
N.A.I.C.S.: 449210
Ed Richardson *(Gen Mgr)*

Richardson Electronics Japan Co.,
Ltd.   **(1)**
Ichigaya MS Building 8F 4-1-9 Kudankita,
Chiyoda-ku, Tokyo, 102-0073,
Japan   **(100%)**
Tel.: (81) 363808441
Sales Range: $10-24.9 Million
Emp.: 15
Sales & Marketing
N.A.I.C.S.: 449210

Richardson Electronics
Ltd.-Central   **(1)**
40W267 Keslinger Rd, Lafox, IL
60147-0393   **(100%)**
Tel.: (630) 208-2200
Web Site: http://www.rell.com
Sales Range: $125-149.9 Million
Emp.: 300
Sales & Marketing
N.A.I.C.S.: 423690
Edward J. Richardson *(Chm, Pres, CEO &
COO)*

Richardson Electronics
Ltd.-Northeastern   **(1)**
701 1 Koehler Ave, Ronkonkoma, NY
11779
Tel.: (631) 468-3900
Web Site:http://www.rell.com
Sales Range: $25-49.9 Million
Emp.: 150
Sales & Marketing
N.A.I.C.S.: 449210
Edward J. Richardson *(Chm, Pres, CEO &
COO)*

Richardson Electronics S.R.L.   **(1)**
Via Di Pratignone 65-67, Calenzano, 50041,
Florence, Italy
Tel.: (39) 055420831
Web Site: http://www.rell.com
Electronic Equipment Distr
N.A.I.C.S.: 423690

Richardson Electronics do Brasil
Ltda.   **(1)**
Rua Visconde De Taunay 709, Sao Paulo,
04726-010, SP, Brazil
Tel.: (55) 1151869655
Web Site: https://www.rellaser.com.br
Emp.: 80
Electronic Components Distr
N.A.I.C.S.: 423690

Richardson Electronics, Ltd.   **(1)**
Unit 1 - 22 The Green Nettleham, Lincoln,
LN2 2NR, United Kingdom   **(100%)**
Tel.: (44) 1522548598

Web Site: http://www.rell.com
Sales Range: $10-24.9 Million
Emp.: 35
Electronic Parts & Equipment
N.A.I.C.S.: 449210

Richardson Electronics, Ltd. -
Spain   **(1)**
Avenida Manoteras 30 A217, Madrid,
28050, Spain   **(100%)**
Tel.: (34) 915283700
Web Site: http://www.rell.com
Electronics Mfr & Distr
N.A.I.C.S.: 449210

Richardson Electronique SAS   **(1)**
2 Rue Jean Lantier, 75001, Paris, France
Tel.: (33) 178958790
Sales Range: $25-49.9 Million
Emp.: 15
Distribution & Marketing
N.A.I.C.S.: 335311
M. R. Lucannu *(Pres)*

RICHSPACE ACQUISITION
CORP.

1633 Old Bayshore Hwy Ste 280,
Burlingame, CA 94010
Tel.: (650) 380-0355   Ky
Year Founded: 2021
RICHU—(NASDAQ)
Investment Services
N.A.I.C.S.: 523999
Bo Wu *(CEO)*
Jianyong Zhang *(CFO)*

RIDGEFIELD ACQUISITION
CORP.

Tel.: (805) 484-8855   NV
Web Site:
     https://www.ridgefieldacquisi
     tion.com
Year Founded: 1983
RDGA—(OTCIQ)
Assets: $24,415
Liabilities: $159,418
Net Worth: ($135,003)
Earnings: ($72,982)
Emp.: 1
Fiscal Year-end: 12/31/23
Investment Services
N.A.I.C.S.: 523999
Steven N. Bronson *(Chm, Pres, CEO
& CFO)*

RIGEL PHARMACEUTICALS,
INC.

611 Gateway Blvd Ste 900, South
San Francisco, CA 94080
Tel.: (650) 624-1100   DE
Web Site: https://www.rigel.com
Year Founded: 1996
RIGL—(NASDAQ)
Rev.: $120,242,000
Assets: $134,279,000
Liabilities: $147,895,000
Net Worth: $13,616,000)
Earnings: ($58,573,000)
Emp.: 155
Fiscal Year-end: 12/31/22
Pharmaceutical Preparation Manufac-
turing
N.A.I.C.S.: 325412
Raul R. Rodriguez *(Pres & CEO)*
Esteban S. Masuda *(Exec VP-Res)*
Joseph Lasaga *(Sr VP-Corp Dev)*
Dean L. Schorno *(CFO & Exec VP)*
Dave Santos *(Chief Comml Officer &
Exec VP)*
Raymond J. Furey *(Gen Counsel)*
Julie Patel *(Sr VP)*
Garry Nolan *(Founder)*
Thomas A. Raffin *(Founder)*

RIGEL RESOURCE ACQUISI-
TION CORP.

1045 Ave of the Americas 25th Fl,
New York, NY 10018

Tel.: (646) 453-2672   Ky
Web Site:
     https://www.rigelresource.com
Year Founded: 2021
RRAC—(NYSE)
Rev.: $17,673,218
Assets: $311,080,023
Liabilities: $327,069,871
Net Worth: ($15,989,848)
Earnings: $16,278,508
Emp.: 4
Fiscal Year-end: 12/31/22
Investment Services
N.A.I.C.S.: 523999
Oskar Lewnowski *(Chm)*
Jonathan Lamb *(CEO)*
Nathanael Abebe *(Pres)*
Jeff Feeley *(CFO)*

RIGETTI COMPUTING, INC.

775 Heinz Ave, Berkeley, CA 94710
Tel.: (510) 210-5550   DE
Web Site: https://www.rigetti.com
Year Founded: 2013
RGTI—(NASDAQ)
Rev.: $13,102,000
Assets: $203,442,000
Liabilities: $53,218,000
Net Worth: $150,224,000)
Earnings: ($71,521,000)
Emp.: 144
Fiscal Year-end: 12/31/22
Software Development Services
N.A.I.C.S.: 541511
Thomas J. Iannotti *(Chm)*
Cathy L. McCarthy *(Vice Chm)*
David Rivas *(CTO)*
Jeffrey Bertelsen *(CFO)*
Rick Danis *(Gen Counsel)*
Subodh Kulkarni *(Pres)*

RIGHT ON BRANDS, INC.

6501 Dalrock Rd Ste 100, Rowlett,
TX 75089
Tel.: (214) 736-7252   NV
Web Site:
     https://www.rightonbrands.com
Year Founded: 2011
RTON—(OTCIQ)
Rev.: $1,135,939
Assets: $206,829
Liabilities: $703,888
Net Worth: ($497,059)
Earnings: $8,726
Fiscal Year-end: 03/31/23
Consumer Brand Company; Hemp-
based Foods
N.A.I.C.S.: 311999
A. David Youssefyeh *(CFO)*
Jerry Grisaffi *(CEO & Chm)*
B. K. Turner *(Controller)*

RIGHTSCORP, INC.

3100 Donald Douglas Loop N, Santa
Monica, CA 90405
Tel.: (775) 881-8091   NV
Web Site: https://www.rightscorp.com
Year Founded: 2010
RIHT—(OTCIQ)
Sales Range: Less than $1 Million
Emp.: 8
Intellectual Property & Copyright Pro-
tection Services
N.A.I.C.S.: 561499
Cecil Bond Kyte *(Chm, CEO & CFO)*

RIGHTSMILE, INC.

8251 La Palma Ave 432, Buena Park,
CA 90620   WY
Year Founded: 2001
RIGH—(OTCIQ)
Health Care Srvices
N.A.I.C.S.: 621999
Angel Stanz *(CEO)*

RILEY EXPLORATION PERM-
IAN, INC.

29 E Reno Ave Ste 500, Oklahoma
City, OK 73104
Tel.: (405) 415-8699   TN
Web Site:
     https://www.rileypermian.com
REPX—(NYSEAMEX)
Rev.: $3,038,000
Assets: $5,371,000
Liabilities: $2,656,000
Net Worth: $2,715,000
Earnings: ($3,648,000)
Emp.: 12
Fiscal Year-end: 12/31/20
Oil & Natural Gas Exploration, Pro-
duction & Pipeline Transportation
Services
N.A.I.C.S.: 211120
Bobby D. Riley *(Chm, Pres & CEO)*
Jeffrey M. Gutman *(Chief Acctg Offi-
cer)*
Corey Riley *(CIO & Chief Compliance
Officer)*
Philip Riley *(CFO)*
John P. Suter *(COO)*
Michael Palmer *(Exec VP-Corp Land)*
Beth Di Santo *(Gen Counsel & Sec)*

Subsidiaries:

Riley Exploration - Permian, LLC   **(1)**
29 E Reno Ave Ste 500, Oklahoma City,
OK 73104
Tel.: (405) 415-8699
Web Site: http://www.rileypermian.com
Oil & Gas Exploration & Extraction
N.A.I.C.S.: 213112
Kevin L. Riley *(COO & Exec VP)*

Riley Permian Operating Company,
LLC   **(1)**
29 E Reno Ave Ste 500, Oklahoma City,
OK 73104
Tel.: (405) 415-8699
Oil & Gas Operation Services
N.A.I.C.S.: 213112

Tengasco Pipeline Corporation   **(1)**
11121 Kingston Pike Ste E, Knoxville, TN
37934   **(100%)**
Tel.: (865) 675-1554
Web Site: http://www.tengasco.com
Sales Range: $200-249.9 Million
Emp.: 10
Owns & Operates Pipeline for Natural Gas
Transport
N.A.I.C.S.: 486210

RIMINI STREET, INC.

1700 S Pavilion Ctr Dr Ste 330, Las
Vegas, NV 89135
Tel.: (702) 839-9671   DE
Web Site:
     https://www.riministreet.com
Year Founded: 2005
RMNI—(NASDAQ)
Rev.: $409,662,000
Assets: $391,041,000
Liabilities: $468,211,000
Net Worth: ($77,170,000)
Earnings: ($2,480,000)
Emp.: 1,920
Fiscal Year-end: 12/31/22
Other Computer Related Services
N.A.I.C.S.: 541519
Steven Salaets *(Exec VP-Special
Projects)*
Seth A. Ravin *(Chm & CEO)*
Yorio Wakisaka *(Gen Mgr-Japan)*
Andrew Terry *(Grp VP & Assoc Gen
Counsel-Corp)*
Judy Stubbington *(VP-Fin-Ops)*
Kien Phung *(VP-Global Svc Delivery-
Siebel & Salesforce)*
Pat Phelan *(VP-Market Res)*
Craig Mackereth *(Sr VP-Global Sup-
port)*
William Allen *(VP-Sls-NA-Southwest
& Southern Reg)*

Joshua Blair *(VP-Sls Enablement-Global & Effectiveness)*
Jason Hardiman *(Grp VP & Assoc Gen Counsel-Intellectual Property)*
Paul Henville *(Sr VP-Product Delivery-Global)*
David Miller *(VP-Global Client Onboarding-Grp)*
Dean Pohl *(VP-IR)*
Prashant Tenkale *(VP-Enterprise Applications)*
Renee Wells *(VP-Product Strategy)*
Satish Narasimhan *(VP-Fin-FP&A)*
Greg Leiner *(VP-SAP Svcs Solution Architects)*
Edenize Maron *(Gen Mgr-Latin America)*
Michael L. Perica *(CFO & Exec VP)*
Jeff Spicer *(CMO)*
Yusuf Abdul-Rehman *(VP)*
Tiago Achcar *(VP)*
Brian Almas *(Sr VP)*
Mina Almassi *(VP)*
Daniel Benad *(Grp VP)*
Eneas de Lima Bernardo *(VP)*
Matthew Bingham *(VP)*
Anita Blackwood *(VP)*
Michael Cannon *(VP)*
Kristen Cardinalli *(VP)*
Gray Chapman *(VP)*
Phil Cullen *(Sr VP)*
Michelle Davenport *(VP)*
Michael Davichick *(VP)*
Bruno Faustino *(VP)*
Barry Ghotra *(VP)*
Nobutake Gohdo *(CTO)*
Guy Guiffre *(VP)*
Bill Carslay *(Grp VP)*

Subsidiaries:

Rimini Street Australia Pty. Limited **(1)**
Level 10 20 Martin Place, Sydney, 2000, NSW, Australia
Tel.: (61) 282160960
Web Site: http://www.riministreet.com
Software Support Services
N.A.I.C.S.: 541519

Rimini Street Brazils Servicos de Tecnologia Ltda. **(1)**
19 Torre D Av Pres Juscelino Kubitschek 2041 - Vila Nova Conceicao, Sao Paulo, 04543-011, Brazil
Tel.: (55) 1131974711
Web Site: http://www.riministreet.com
Software Support Services
N.A.I.C.S.: 541519

Rimini Street Canada Inc. **(1)**
161 Bay Street 27th Floor, Toronto, M5J 2S1, ON, Canada
Tel.: (416) 572-2240
Software Development Services
N.A.I.C.S.: 541511

Rimini Street FZ, LLC **(1)**
Tel.: (971) 600575283
Software Support Services
N.A.I.C.S.: 541519

Rimini Street GmbH **(1)**
Westhafenplatz 1, 60327, Frankfurt, Germany
Tel.: (49) 69710456230
Web Site: https://www.riministreet.com
Software Support Services
N.A.I.C.S.: 541519

Rimini Street, Ltd. **(1)**
Level 37 1 Canada Square, London, E14 5AA, United Kingdom
Tel.: (44) 2037637463
Web Site: http://www.riministreet.com
Software Support Services
N.A.I.C.S.: 541519

RIMROCK GOLD CORP.

3651 Lindell Rd Ste D155, Las Vegas, NV 89103 NV
Web Site:
https://www.rimrockgold.com

Year Founded: 2007
RMRK—(OTCIQ)
Emp.: 2
Cannabis Product Mfr & Distr
N.A.I.C.S.: 325411
Jordan Starkman *(Pres & CEO)*

RING ENERGY, INC.

1725 Hughes Landing Blvd Ste 900, The Woodlands, TX 77380
Tel.: (281) 397-3699 NV
Web Site:
https://www.ringenergy.com
Year Founded: 2004
REI—(NYSEAMEX)
Rev.: $361,056,001
Assets: $1,376,496,392
Liabilities: $589,913,492
Net Worth: $786,582,900
Earnings: $104,864,641
Emp.: 108
Fiscal Year-end: 12/31/23
Crude Petroleum Extraction Services
N.A.I.C.S.: 211120
Paul D. McKinney *(Chm & CEO)*
Alexander Dyes *(Exec VP-Engrg & Corp Strategy)*
Travis T. Thomas *(CFO, Treas, Sec & Exec VP)*

RINGCENTRAL, INC.

20 Davis Dr, Belmont, CA 94002
Tel.: (650) 472-4100 DE
Web Site:
https://www.ringcentral.com
Year Founded: 1999
RNG—(NYSE)
Rev.: $2,202,429,000
Assets: $1,944,913,000
Liabilities: $2,447,482,000
Net Worth: ($502,569,000)
Earnings: ($165,240,000)
Emp.: 4,084
Fiscal Year-end: 12/31/23
Software Publisher
N.A.I.C.S.: 513210
Vladimir G. Shmunis *(Co-Founder, Exec Chm & CEO)*
John Marlow *(Chief Admin Officer & Gen Counsel)*
Vladimir Vendrow *(Co-Founder & CTO)*
Kira Makagon *(Chief Innovation Officer & Exec VP)*
Sonalee Parekh *(CFO)*
Srini Raghavan *(Chief Product Officer)*

Subsidiaries:

Connect First, Inc. **(1)**
2545 Central Ave Ste 200, Boulder, CO 80301
Web Site: https://www.connectfirst.com
Software Development Services
N.A.I.C.S.: 513210

Dimelo, SA **(1)**
Residence Idolem 57 Rue de l'Etang de Chevrise Mont Vernon I, 97150, Saint-Martin, France
Tel.: (33) 177372757
Web Site: http://www.dimelo.com
Software Development Services
N.A.I.C.S.: 513210
Stephane Lee *(Founder)*

RingCentral Australia Pty Ltd **(1)**
Level 28-WeWork 161 Castlereagh Street, Sydney, 2000, NSW, Australia
Tel.: (61) 280738499
Web Site: https://www.ringcentral.com
Software Publishing Services
N.A.I.C.S.: 513210

RingCentral CH GmbH **(1)**
Stockerstrasse 43, 8002, Zurich, Switzerland
Tel.: (41) 8839036
VoIP Service Provider
N.A.I.C.S.: 517810

RingCentral France **(1)**
3 Rue Saint-Georges, 75009, Paris, France
Tel.: (33) 185640349
Web Site: https://www.ringcentral.com
Computer Design Services
N.A.I.C.S.: 541512
Stephane Lee *(Mng Dir)*

RingCentral Germany GmbH **(1)**
Poststrasse 33 Hamburg Business Center, 20354, Hamburg, Germany
Tel.: (49) 4082212906
Unified Communication Services
N.A.I.C.S.: 517410

RingCentral Ireland Ltd. **(1)**
Skybridge House Corballis Road, Dublin, Ireland
Tel.: (353) 14869027
Web Site: https://www.ringcentral.com
Software Publishing Services
N.A.I.C.S.: 513210

RIOT PLATFORMS, INC.

3855 Ambrosia St Ste 301, Castle Rock, CO 80109
Tel.: (303) 794-2000 CO
Web Site:
https://www.riotplatforms.com
Year Founded: 2000
RIOT—(NASDAQ)
Rev.: $280,678,000
Assets: $2,051,080,000
Liabilities: $163,058,000
Net Worth: $1,888,022,000
Earnings: ($49,472,000)
Emp.: 534
Fiscal Year-end: 12/31/23
Cryptocurrency Mining Operations
N.A.I.C.S.: 339990
Philip J. McPherson *(VP-Capital Markets)*
Jason Les *(CEO)*
Benjamin Yi *(Chm)*
William Jackman *(Gen Counsel)*
Jason Chung *(Head)*
Ghazaleh Barman *(VP)*
Lyle Theriot *(Head)*
Ashton Harris *(Head)*
David Schatz *(Sr VP)*

RISKON INTERNATIONAL, INC.

Tel.: (479) 259-2977 NV
Web Site: https://www.bitnile.com
Year Founded: 2007
ROII—(OTCIQ)
Rev.: $14,365,276
Assets: $23,775,517
Liabilities: $37,719,641
Net Worth: ($13,944,124)
Earnings: ($87,361,603)
Emp.: 16
Fiscal Year-end: 03/31/23
Holding Company; Thin Film Solar Cells Developer
N.A.I.C.S.: 551112
Douglas Gintz *(CTO)*
Randy Scott May *(Founder)*
Jimmy R. Galla *(Chief Acctg Officer)*
Milton C. Ault III *(Chm & CEO)*

Subsidiaries:

Eco360, LLC **(1)**
11955 Freedom Dr Ste 700, Reston, VA 20190
Tel.: (703) 667-7500
Web Site: http://www.echo360.com
Education Development Services
N.A.I.C.S.: 611710
Fred Singer *(CEO)*

Ecoark, Inc. **(1)**
3333 Pinnacle Hills Pkwy Ste 220, Rogers, AR 72758
Tel.: (479) 259-2977
Web Site: http://www.ecoarkusa.com
Solar Cell Technologies Developer
N.A.I.C.S.: 334413

Magnolia Solar, Inc. **(1)**

54 Cummings Park Ste 316, Woburn, MA 01801 **(100%)**
Tel.: (781) 497-2900
Web Site: https://www.magnoliasolar.com
Solar Cells Design & Development
N.A.I.C.S.: 334413
E. James Egerton *(Exec VP)*
Roger E. Welser *(CTO)*

Sable Polymer Solutions, LLC **(1)**
4350 Avery Dr, Flowery Branch, GA 30542
Tel.: (770) 965-8970
Web Site: http://www.sablepolymer.com
Recycled Plastic Product Mfr
N.A.I.C.S.: 325991

Zest Labs, Inc **(1)**
2349 Bering Dr, San Jose, CA 95131
Tel.: (408) 200-6500
Web Site: http://www.zestlabs.com
Fresh Food Post Harvest Services
N.A.I.C.S.: 115114
Peter A. Mehring *(Founder & CEO)*
Russell Shikami *(Sr VP-Ops)*
Scott Durgin *(CTO)*
Tom Reese *(VP-Bus & Program Mgmt)*
Tom Solomon *(VP-Retail Sls)*
Kevin Payne *(VP-Mktg)*
Dean Kawaguchi *(Dir-Tech)*

RITHM CAPITAL CORP.

799 Broadway 8th Fl, New York, NY 10003
Tel.: (212) 850-7770 DE
Web Site: https://www.rithmcap.com
Year Founded: 2011
RITM—(NYSE)
Rev.: $3,715,496,000
Assets: $35,311,785,000
Liabilities: $28,210,747,000
Net Worth: $7,101,038,000
Earnings: $532,678,000
Emp.: 6,570
Fiscal Year-end: 12/31/23
Real Estate Investment Trust
N.A.I.C.S.: 525990
Charles Sorrentino *(Mng Dir)*
Varun Wadhawan *(Mng Dir)*
Sanjeev Khanna *(Mng Dir)*
William Magee Jr. *(Mng Dir)*
Jeff Gravelle *(Mng Dir)*
Joseph Celentano *(Mng Dir)*
John Ryan *(Mng Dir)*
Danny Knight *(Mng Dir)*
Kenneth Bruce *(Mng Dir)*
Andrew Vinci *(Mng Dir)*
Paul Gross *(Mng Dir)*
Satish Mansukhani *(Mng Dir)*
Leah Fischler *(Dir)*
Tad Wolkin *(Dir)*
Paul Saake *(Sr VP)*
Sarah Zichlin *(Sr VP)*
Evonne Huang *(Sr VP)*
Donald Chan *(Sr VP)*
Lindsay Goldenberg *(Sr VP)*
Celestina Leung *(Sr VP)*
Tyler Peterson *(VP)*
Janice-Marie Pecache *(VP)*
Emma Bolla *(Assoc Gen Counsel)*
Nicola Santoro Jr. *(CFO, Chief Acctg Officer & Treas)*
Michael Nierenberg *(Chm, Pres & CEO)*

Subsidiaries:

Avenue 365 Lender Services, LLC **(1)**
1 Oxford Vly 2300 E Lincoln Hwy, Langhorne, PA 19047
Web Site: https://www.avenue365.com
Insurance Services
N.A.I.C.S.: 524210
Mike Alen *(VP)*
Marsha Dulaney *(Acct Mgr)*
Randi McEwing *(VP-Operations)*
Shawnna Sorenson *(Dir-Closing)*
Shawnna Sorenson *(Dir-Closing)*
Mike Allen *(VP)*

Caliber Home Loans, Inc. **(1)**
1525 S Belt Line Rd, Coppell, TX 75019
Tel.: (855) 808-2124

Rithm Capital Corp.—(Continued)

Web Site: http://www.caliberhomeloans.com
Emp.: 3,500
Home Loans & Mortgages
N.A.I.C.S.: 522291
Sanjiv Das (CEO)
Russ Smith (COO & Exec VP)
Patricia Shumate (Exec VP)
Gregg Smallwood (Gen Counsel & Gen Counsel)
Ann Thorn (Chief Loan Admin Officer & Chief Loan Admin Officer)
James Hecht (Exec VP & Head)
John Gibson (Exec VP)
Jennifer Corcoran (Sr VP)
Julie Richtel (Chief Risk Officer & Exec VP)
Sean Harding (Chief HR Officer)
Manoj Satnaliwala (Sr VP & Head-Audit)

Capital Partners Mortgage, LLC (1)
1515 N University Dr Ste 102D, Coral Springs, FL 33071
Tel.: (954) 905-1152
Web Site:
    http://www.capitalpartnersmtg.com
Financial Services
N.A.I.C.S.: 541611
Mark Pearlstein (Officer-Loan)
Craig Garcia (Pres)
Marta Figueredo (Officer-Loan)

Carnegie Mortgage Partners, LLC (1)
74 Godwin Ave Ste 116, Ridgewood, NJ 07450
Web Site:
    https://www.carnegiemortgagepart ners.com
Mortgage Service Provider
N.A.I.C.S.: 522310

Carolina One Mortgage, LLC (1)
4024 Salt Pointe Pkwy Ste A, North Charleston, SC 29405
Tel.: (843) 202-2074
Web Site: https://www.carolinaonemtg.com
Mortgage Bank Services
N.A.I.C.S.: 522310
Kim Shelpman (Branch Mgr & Sr VP)
Trip Ritchie (Sls Mgr)
Trip Ritchie (Sls Mgr)

Coast One Mortgage LLC (1)
30400 Detroit Rd Ste 106, Westlake, OH 44145
Web Site:
    https://www.coastonemortgage.com
Mortgage Service Provider
N.A.I.C.S.: 522310

Conway Financial Services, LLC (1)
183 Columbia Rd, Hanover, MA 02339
Tel.: (781) 871-5588
Web Site: https://www.conwayfinancial.com
Financial Services
N.A.I.C.S.: 541611

Ditech Financial LLC (1)
1100 Virginia Dr, Fort Washington, PA 19034
Tel.: (800) 700-9212
Web Site: http://www.ditech.com
Financial Services; Home Loans, Refinance & Mortgage
N.A.I.C.S.: 522310
Evelyn Caetano (Ops Mgr)

E Street Appraisal Management LLC (1)
6041 Wallace Rd Extension Ste 210, Wexford, PA 15090
Web Site: https://www.estreetamc.com
Commercial Appraisal Services
N.A.I.C.S.: 531320
Barbara Ford (Pres & CEO)
Joseph Kasler (VP)

Genesis Capital Real Estate Advisors, Inc. (1)
15303 Ventura Blvd Ste 700, Sherman Oaks, CA 91403
Web Site: https://www.genesiscapital.com
Financial Services
N.A.I.C.S.: 523999

Landed Home Loans LLC (1)
3601 Walnut St 5th Fl Office 134, Denver, CO 80205
Web Site:
    https://www.landedhomeloans.com

Mortgage Bank Services
N.A.I.C.S.: 522310

Milestone Home Lending, LLC (1)
236 E Carmel Dr, Carmel, IN 46032
Tel.: (317) 343-3108
Web Site: https://www.milestonehl.com
Mortgage Bank Services
N.A.I.C.S.: 522310
Brittany Wineinger (Pres)

NewRez LLC (1)
1100 Virginia Dr Ste 125, Fort Washington, PA 19034
Web Site: https://www.newrez.com
Financial Banking Services
N.A.I.C.S.: 522110
Bob Johnson (COO)
Baron Silverstein (Pres)
Dart Budz (CFO)
Kedar Sathe (CIO)
Gena Coursen (Chief Admin Officer)
Julie Raisch (Chief Strategy Officer)
Spencer Mosness (Chief Risk Officer)
Felicia Grumet (COO)
Matthew Cluney (CMO)

Partners United Financial, LLC (1)
250 E Wilson Bridge Rd Ste 110, Worthington, OH 43085
Web Site:
    https://www.partnersunitedfinancial.com
Financial Banking Services
N.A.I.C.S.: 522110
Mike Mulgrew (Pres)
Sean Morrow (Reg Mgr)
Sarah Graf (Officer-Loan)
Jennifer Carey (Sls Mgr)
Shane Gilmet (Officer-Loan)
Eric Sanders (Sls Mgr)
Darcy Conkle (Officer-Loan)
Emad Bastawros (Sls Mgr)
Emad Bertan (Sls Mgr)
Viken Shirinian (Officer-Loan)
Doug Waldman (Officer-Loan)
Eric Porter (Officer-Loan)
Lindsay Einer (Officer)
Ashley Burridge (Officer-Loan)
Sarah Graf (Officer-Loan)
Jennifer Carey (Sls Mgr)
Shane Gilmet (Officer-Loan)
Eric Sanders (Sls Mgr)
Darcy Conkle (Officer-Loan)
Emad Bastawros (Sls Mgr)
Emad Bertan (Sls Mgr)
Viken Shirinian (Officer-Loan)
Doug Waldman (Officer-Loan)
Eric Porter (Officer-Loan)
Lindsay Einer (Officer)
Ashley Burridge (Officer-Loan)

Platinum Eagle Mortgage, LLC (1)
465 W President George Bush Hwy Ste 103, Richardson, TX 75080
Web Site:
    https://www.platinumeaglemortgage.com
Finance Investment Services
N.A.I.C.S.: 523999

Plus Relocation Mortgage, LLC (1)
600 Hwy 169 S Ste 450, Saint Louis Park, MN 55426
Web Site:
    https://www.plusrelocationmortgage.com
Mortgage Bank Services
N.A.I.C.S.: 522310
Drew Lightowler (Pres)
Bruce Carberry (Officer-Loan)
David Bashel (Officer-Loan)
Jared Johnson (Officer-Loan)
Jill Sebik (Officer-Loan)
Mike Johnson (Officer-Loan)
Mark Schenkelberg (Officer-Loan)

Preferred Lending Services, LLC (1)
15310 Amberly Dr Ste 250, Tampa, FL 33647
Web Site: https://www.flpls.com
Mortgage Bank Services
N.A.I.C.S.: 522310

Sanctuary Home Mortgage LLC (1)
3350 Northlake Pkwy Ste 15M, Atlanta, GA 30345
Web Site:
    https://www.sanctuaryhomemortgage.com
Home Mortgage Services
N.A.I.C.S.: 522310

Sculptor Capital Management, Inc. (1)

9 W 57th St, New York, NY 10019
Tel.: (212) 790-0000
Web Site: https://www.sculptor.com
Rev.: $419,002,000
Assets: $1,652,206,000
Liabilities: $1,265,623,000
Net Worth: $386,583,000
Earnings: ($16,210,000)
Emp.: 343
Fiscal Year-end: 12/31/2022
Institutional Asset Management Services
N.A.I.C.S.: 523940
David M. Levine (Exec Mng Dir & Chief Legal Officer)
Dava E. Ritchea (Exec Mng Dir & CFO)
Steve Orbuch (Founder)
Peter Wallach (Exec Mng Dir)

Subsidiary (Domestic):

OZ Management II LP (2)
9 W 57th St 39th Fl, New York, NY 10019
Tel.: (212) 790-0041
Web Site: http://www.ozcap.com
Emp.: 550
Investment Management Service
N.A.I.C.S.: 523940

Subsidiary (Non-US):

Och-Ziff Capital Management Hong Kong Limited (2)
Suite 2002 Level 20 One Pacific Place 88 Queensway, Hong Kong, China (Hong Kong)
Tel.: (852) 22972580
Investment Management Service
N.A.I.C.S.: 523940

Och-Ziff Management Europe Limited (2)
40 Argyll Street 2nd Floor, London, W1F 7EB, United Kingdom
Tel.: (44) 2077584400
Investment Management Service
N.A.I.C.S.: 523940

Sculptor Capital Management Europe Limited (2)
40 Argyll Street 2nd Floor, London, W1F 7EB, United Kingdom
Tel.: (44) 2077584400
Financial Investment Services
N.A.I.C.S.: 523999

Sculptor Capital Management Hong Kong Limited (2)
Suite 2002 Level 20 One Pacific Place 88 Queensway, Hong Kong, China (Hong Kong)
Tel.: (852) 22972580
Asset Management Services
N.A.I.C.S.: 523940
Adrian Colberg (Mng Dir & Head-IR)
Robert Johnston (Mng Dir & Gen Counsel)

Shellpoint Partners LLC (1)
2 Grand Central Tower 140 E 45th St 37th Fl, New York, NY 10017
Tel.: (212) 850-7700
Web Site: http://www.shellpointllc.com
Finance Company Focused on Residential Mortgage Market
N.A.I.C.S.: 523999
Bruce Williams (CEO)
Joe McSherry (CFO)

Subsidiary (Domestic):

NewRez LLC (2)
1100 Virginia Dr Ste 125, Fort Washington, PA 19034
Tel.: (484) 594-1300
Web Site: https://www.newrez.com
Mortgage Lender
N.A.I.C.S.: 522310

Subsidiary (Domestic):

Shelter Mortgage Company, LLC (3)
1245 Cheyenne Ave Ste 304B/304C, Grafton, WI 53024 **(100%)**
Tel.: (414) 721-2800
Web Site: https://www.sheltermortgage.com
Mortgage Loan Services
N.A.I.C.S.: 522310
Randy Vanden Houten (CFO)

Shelter Home Mortgage, LLC (1)

1770 Indian Trail Lilburn Rd NW Ste 400, Norcross, GA 30093
Tel.: (678) 205-5849
Web Site:
    https://www.shelterhomemortgage.com
Mortgage Bank Services
N.A.I.C.S.: 522310
James Williamson (Pres)
Karen Skiba (VP)
Geoff Beene (Mgr-Closing)
Kassondra Lewis (Mgr-Processing)
Amanda Beene (Mgr-Underwriting)
Erin De Armas (Officer-Loan)
Kim Pounders (Officer-Loan)
Darrell Edquist (Officer-Loan)
Allison Watson (Officer-Loan)
Dominic Landry (Officer-Loan)
Jim Scheu (Officer-Loan)
Alicia Justice (Officer-Loan)
Brett Kiker (Officer-Loan)
Robbie Crozier (Officer-Loan)
Susan Sharp (Officer-Loan)
Brandon Dainas (Officer-Loan)
Marquis L. Shipley (Officer-Loan)
Tammy Mills (Officer-Loan)
Kathy Vitali (Officer-Loan)
Alec Jones (Officer-Loan)
Nancy Grieve (Officer-Loan)
Joanne Rotella (Officer-Loan)
Julie Wilson (Officer-Loan)
Ann Falconer (Officer-Loan)
Stanley Caldwell (Officer-Loan)
Luanne Smith (Officer-Loan)
Matt Kuglin (Officer-Loan)

Shelter Mortgage TJV LLC (1)
601 Office Center Dr Ste 100, Fort Washington, PA 19034
Web Site: https://www.sheltermortgage.com
Mortgage Service Provider
N.A.I.C.S.: 522310

Spring Equity, LLC (1)
2929 Arch St Ste 500, Philadelphia, PA 19104
Web Site: https://mortgage.springeq.com
Mortgage Bank Services
N.A.I.C.S.: 522310
Jerry Schiano (CEO)
Curt James (CFO)
Anthony Battaglia (Mktg Dir)

Summit Home Mortgage, LLC (1)
414 W Milham Ave, Portage, MI 49024
Tel.: (269) 488-1606
Web Site: https://www.summithomemtg.com
Mortgage Lending Services
N.A.I.C.S.: 522292

Synergy Home Mortgage, LLC (1)
1100 Caughlin Crossing Ste 1A, Reno, NV 89519
Tel.: (775) 800 7036
Web Site: https://www.synergyhm.com
Mortgage Bank Services
N.A.I.C.S.: 522310
Dereck Bowlen (Branch Mgr)
Angela Welsh (Officer-Loan)
Angela Welsh (Officer-Loan)

Your Home Financial LLC (1)
26615 Center Ridge Rd Unit 4, Westlake, OH 44145
Web Site:
    https://www.yourhomefinancial.com
Mortgage Bank Services
N.A.I.C.S.: 522310
Paul Mckelvey (Pres)
Amy Terrell (Officer-Loan)

RIVAL TECHNOLOGIES, INC.
3773 Howard Hughes Pkwy Ste 500, Las Vegas, NV 89169
Tel.: (702) 751-8846   NV
Web Site: http://www.rvti.com
RVTI—(OTCIQ)
Sales Range: Less than $1 Million
Diesel Engine Water Injection Systems
N.A.I.C.S.: 333618
Perry Guglielmi (Pres & CEO)

RIVER CITY BANK INC.
2480 Natomas Park Dr Ste 150, Sacramento, CA 95833-2937
Tel.: (916) 567-2600

Web Site:
https://www.rivercitybank.com
Year Founded: 1973
RCBC—(OTCIQ)
Sales Range: $50-74.9 Million
Emp.: 146
State Commercial Banking Services
N.A.I.C.S.: 522110
Shawn L. Devlin (Chm)
Pat Lewis (COO & Exec VP)
Stephen Fleming (Pres & CEO)
Rosa Cucicea (CFO)
Dan Franklin (Sr VP & Dir-Comml Banking-Bay Area)
Matthew Cheeseman (VP-Walnut Creek)
Brian Killeen (CFO & Exec VP)
Rebecca Fabisch Miller (Exec VP & Dir-Commercial Banking)
Tony Eyer (Sr VP & Dir-Information Technology)
Ken Imwinkelried (Chief Credit Officer & Sr VP)
Jeremy Spencer (Sr VP & Dir-Internal Audit & Regulatory Relations)

RIVER FINANCIAL CORPORATION
2611 Legends Dr, Prattville, AL 36066
Tel.: (334) 290-1012   AL
Web Site:
https://www.riverbankandtrust.com
Year Founded: 2012
RVRF—(OTCIQ)
Rev.: $101,115,000
Assets: $2,833,382,000
Liabilities: $2,695,196,000
Net Worth: $138,186,000
Earnings: $27,929,000
Emp.: 305
Fiscal Year-end: 12/31/22
Bank Holding Company
N.A.I.C.S.: 551111
James M. Stubbs (CEO)
Gerald Ray Smith Jr. (Pres)
W. Murray Neighbors (Vice Chm)
Alex Leishman (Founder)
Julia Duzon (COO)
Bill Mongan (Gen Counsel)
James Page (Dir)
Laura Christiansen (Dir)
Ellen Weaver (Dir)
Louie Liang (Dir)
Alexandra Gaiser (Dir)

RIVER VALLEY COMMUNITY BANK
1629 Colusa Ave, Yuba City, CA 95993
Tel.: (530) 755-0418
Web Site: https://www.myrvcb.com
RVCB—(OTCIQ)
Rev.: $15,560,689
Assets: $442,309,682
Liabilities: $404,512,290
Net Worth: $37,797,392
Earnings: $4,159,074
Fiscal Year-end: 12/31/19
Commericial Banking
N.A.I.C.S.: 522110
John M. Jelavich (Pres & CEO)
Luke Parnell (Chief Credit Officer & Exec VP)
Michael Finn (CFO & Exec VP)
Greg Heckman (Sr VP & Mgr-Relationship)
Sarah Davocato-Carvalho (VP & Controller)

RIVERDALE OIL & GAS CORP.
1700 7th Ave Ste 2300, Seattle, WA 98101   NV
RVDO—(OTCIQ)
Oil & Gas Exploration Services
N.A.I.C.S.: 213112
Richard Hawkins (CEO)

RIVERNORTH OPPORTUNITIES FUND, INC.
1290 Broadway Ste 1100, Denver, CO 80203
Tel.: (561) 484-7185
Web Site: https://www.rivernorth.com
RIV—(NYSE)
Other Financial Vehicles
N.A.I.C.S.: 525990
John S. Oakes (Chm)

RIVERNORTH/DOUBLELINE STRATEGIC OPPORTUNITY FUND, INC.
360 S Rosemary Ave Ste 1420, West Palm Beach, FL 33401
Tel.: (312) 832-1440   MD
OPP—(NYSE)
Rev.: $16,586,712
Assets: $274,300,979
Liabilities: $75,087,970
Net Worth: $199,213,009
Earnings: $10,300,601
Fiscal Year-end: 06/30/19
Investment Management Service
N.A.I.C.S.: 525990

RIVERVIEW BANCORP, INC.
900 Washington St Ste 900, Vancouver, WA 98660
Tel.: (360) 693-6650   WA
Web Site:
https://www.riverviewbank.com
RVSB—(NASDAQ)
Rev.: $66,797,000
Assets: $1,521,529,000
Liabilities: $1,365,941,000
Net Worth: $155,588,000
Earnings: $3,799,000
Emp.: 226
Fiscal Year-end: 03/31/24
Bank Holding Company
N.A.I.C.S.: 551111
Gerald L. Nies (Chm)
Daniel D. Cox (Acting Pres, Acting CEO & COO)
Bradley J. Carlson (Vice Chm)
David Lam (CFO & Exec VP)
Michael Sventek (Chief Lending Officer & Exec VP)
Robert Benke (Chief Credit Officer & Exec VP)
Daniel D. Cox (Chief Credit Officer & Exec VP)
B. Nicole Sherman (Pres & CEO)

Subsidiaries:

Riverview Community Bank   (1)
900 Washington St Ste 100, Vancouver, WA 98660
Tel.: (360) 693-7086
Web Site: https://www.riverviewbank.com
Commericial Banking
N.A.I.C.S.: 522110
Krista Holland (Dir-HR)
Gerald L. Nies (Vice Chm)
Daniel D. Cox (Acting Pres, Acting CEO & COO)
Michael Sventek (Chief Lending Officer & Exec VP)
Robert Benke (Chief Credit Officer & Exec VP)
Tracie Jellison (Chief Retail Banking Officer & Exec VP)
Cody Ritter (Sr VP)

Subsidiary (Domestic):

Riverview Asset Management Corp.   (2)
900 Washington St Ste 900, Vancouver, WA 98660
Tel.: (360) 693-7442
Web Site: http://riverviewtrust.com
Emp.: 18
Wealth Management Services
N.A.I.C.S.: 523940
Lori M. Hawkins (Sr VP & Dir-Trusts & Estates)
Christopher Cline (Pres & CEO)

Colleen Sisson (Officer-Trust & VP)
Maggie Traverso (Sr VP & Dir-Private Wealth)
Margaret Dent (Officer-Trust & VP)
Lori Hawkins (Sr VP)
Evan Sowers (Pres)
Jon Trause (VP)
Kara Stoddart (VP)
Matt Bayley (Sr VP)
Molly Filbin (Sr VP)

RIVEX TECHNOLOGY CORP.
1001 S Main St Ste 4036, Kalispell, MT 59901
Tel.: (406) 601-3532   NV
Year Founded: 2014
RIVX—(OTCIQ)
Liabilities: $31,550
Net Worth: ($31,550)
Earnings: ($55,982)
Emp.: 2
Fiscal Year-end: 03/31/19
Mobile Software Development Services
N.A.I.C.S.: 513210
Koong Wai Loon (Pres, CEO, Treas & Sec)

RIVIAN AUTOMOTIVE, INC.
14600 Myford Rd, Irvine, CA 92606   DE
Year Founded: 2015
RIVN—(NASDAQ)
Rev.: $4,434,000,000
Assets: $16,778,000,000
Liabilities: $7,637,000,000
Net Worth: $9,141,000,000
Earnings: ($5,432,000,000)
Emp.: 16,790
Fiscal Year-end: 12/31/23
Automobile Mfr
N.A.I.C.S.: 336310
Michael Callahan (Chief Legal Officer)
Mike Johnson (Chief Info Security Officer)
Robert J. Scaringe (Founder, Chm & CEO)
Helen Russell (Chief HR Officer)
Neil Sitron (Gen Counsel)
Martin Huelder (VP-Comml Ops-Europe)
Anthony Sanger (VP-Facilities-Georgia)
Sarah O'Brien (Chief Comm Officer)
Claire McDonough (CFO & Interim Principal Acctg Officer)
Robert J. Scaringe (CEO, Founder & Chm)
Jiten Behl (Chief Growth Officer)

Subsidiaries:

Rivian Automotive Canada, Inc.   (1)
1038 Homer Street, Vancouver, V6B 2W9, BC, Canada
Electric Vehicle Mfr & Distr
N.A.I.C.S.: 336320

RJD GREEN, INC.
5151 S Mingo Ste F, Tulsa, OK 74146
Tel.: (918) 551-7883   NV
Web Site: https://www.rjdgreen.com
Year Founded: 2009
RJDG—(OTCIQ)
Other Construction Material Merchant Wholesalers
N.A.I.C.S.: 423390
Ron Brewer (CEO)
Jerry Niblett (COO)
John Rabbitt (CFO)
Richard Billings (Dir-Tech)

RLI CORP.
9025 N Lindbergh Dr, Peoria, IL 61615
Tel.: (309) 692-1000   DE

Web Site: https://www.rlicorp.com
Year Founded: 2017
RLI—(NYSE)
Rev.: $1,511,994,000
Assets: $5,180,221,000
Liabilities: $3,766,707,000
Net Worth: $1,413,514,000
Earnings: $304,611,000
Emp.: 1,099
Fiscal Year-end: 12/31/23
Insurance Services
N.A.I.C.S.: 524298
Craig W. Kliethermes (Bd of Dirs, Pres & CEO)
Kevin S. Horwitz (VP-Innovation Mgmt & Policy Dev)
Lisa T. Gates (VP-Comm & Mktg)
Matthew R. Campen (VP-Claim)
Nicolas C. Mesco (VP-Claim)
Kathleen M. Kappes (VP-HR)
Patrick D. Ferrell (VP-Internal Audit)
Phil Brodeur (VP-Risk Svcs)
Todd Bryant (CFO)
Marcos Cancio (VP-Claim Counsel)
Aaron Diefenthaler (Chief Investment Officer & Treas)
Jeff Fick (Chief Legal Officer & Sec)
Cory Figiel (VP-Claim)
Bryan Fowler (CIO)
Bob Handzel (Chief Claim Officer)
Deb Millum (VP-Claim)
Kathleen Taylor (VP-Acctg & Branch Ops)
Bret Stone (VP-Data & Analytics)
Seth A. Davis (VP & Controller)
Thomas J. Ward (VP-Risk Svcs)
Jennifer L. Klobnak (COO)

Subsidiaries:

Contractors Bonding and Insurance Company   (1)
3101 Western Ave Ste 300, Seattle, WA 98121
Web Site: http://www.cbic.com
Sales Range: $50-74.9 Million
Emp.: 70
Property & Casualty Insurance Services
N.A.I.C.S.: 524126

Data & Staff Service Co.   (1)
1213 Valley St, Seattle, WA 98109
Tel.: (206) 624-8312
Sales Range: $100-124.9 Million
Emp.: 200
Property & Casualty Insurance Services
N.A.I.C.S.: 524126
Donna Paluch (Program Mgr)

RLI Atlanta - P/C   (1)
2970 Claremont Rd Ste 1000, Atlanta, GA 30329-4422
Tel.: (404) 638-1855
Web Site: http://www.rlicorp.com
Sales Range: $10-24.9 Million
Emp.: 52
Provider of Insurance Coverage
N.A.I.C.S.: 541110

RLI Insurance Company   (1)
9025 N Lindbergh Dr, Peoria, IL 61615
Tel.: (309) 692-1000
Web Site: http://www.rlicorp.com
Sales Range: $150-199.9 Million
Emp.: 400
Fire, Marine & Casualty Insurance
N.A.I.C.S.: 524126
Craig W. Kliethermes (Pres & CEO)

Subsidiary (Domestic):

Mt. Hawley Insurance Company   (2)
9025 N Lindbergh Dr, Peoria, IL 61615   (100%)
Tel.: (309) 692-1000
Web Site: http://www.rlicorp.com
Sales Range: $100-124.9 Million
Emp.: 400
Surplus Lines Insurance
N.A.I.C.S.: 524126

Division (Domestic):

RLI & Hawaii Product Lines   (2)

RLI Corp.—(Continued)

700 Bishops St, Honolulu, HI
96813   **(100%)**
Tel.: (808) 533-1515
Web Site: http://www.rlicorp.com
Sales Range: $10-24.9 Million
Emp.: 9
Specializing in Personal Property Insurance
N.A.I.C.S.: 488510

RLI Chicago Regional Office   **(2)**
525 W Van Buren St Congress Ctr Ste 350,
Chicago, IL 60607-4103
Tel.: (312) 360-1566
Web Site: http://www.rlicorp.com
Sales Range: $10-24.9 Million
Emp.: 55
Insurance, Specializing in Primary General
Liability, Commercial Umbrella, Excess Liability & Commercial Property
N.A.I.C.S.: 926150

RLI Los Angeles Regional Office   **(2)**
801 S Figueroa St Ste 900, Los Angeles,
CA 90017-2531
Tel.: (213) 683-0838
Web Site: http://www.rlicorp.com
Sales Range: $1-9.9 Million
Emp.: 30
Insurance, Specializing in Commercial
Property, DIC & Inland Marine
N.A.I.C.S.: 531210

RLI Northern California Regional
Office   **(2)**
1277 Treat Blvd Ste 600, Walnut Creek, CA
94597   **(100%)**
Tel.: (510) 891-0118
Web Site: http://www.rli.com
Sales Range: $10-24.9 Million
Emp.: 16
Insurance, Specializing in Property, DIC &
Commercial Package
N.A.I.C.S.: 524126

RLI Southeast Regional Office   **(2)**
3655 North Point Pkwy Preston Ridge I Ste
400, Alpharetta, GA 30005
Tel.: (770) 754-0100
Web Site: http://www.rlicorp.com
Sales Range: $75-99.9 Million
Emp.: 40
Insurance, Specializing in Primary & Excess
General Liability, Commercial & Excess
Umbrella
N.A.I.C.S.: 524210

RLI Special Risk   **(2)**
200 N Glastonbury Blvd Ste 301, Glastonbury, CT 06033   **(100%)**
Tel.: (860) 652-3044
Web Site: http://www.rlicorp.com
Sales Range: $10-24.9 Million
Emp.: 15
Commercial Insurance Services
N.A.I.C.S.: 524126

RMG ACQUISITION CORP.
1411 Broadway 16th Fl, New York,
NY 10018
Tel.: (212) 220-9503   **DE**
Web Site:
  http://www.rmgacquisition.com
Year Founded: 2018
RMG—(NYSE)
Rev.: $12,602
Assets: $234,584,340
Liabilities: $229,584,339
Net Worth: $5,000,001
Earnings: $2,086,083
Emp.: 5
Fiscal Year-end: 12/31/19
Investment Services
N.A.I.C.S.: 523999
D. James Carpenter *(Chm)*
Robert S. Mancini *(CEO)*
Philip Kassin *(Pres & COO)*

ROADRUNNER TRANSPORTA-TION SYSTEMS, INC.
1431 Opus Pl Ste 530, Downers
Grove, IL 60515
Tel.: (414) 615-1500   **DE**

Web Site:
  https://www.shiproadrunner
  freight.com
Year Founded: 1984
RRTS—(OTCIQ)
Rev.: $1,847,862,000
Assets: $670,397,000
Liabilities: $614,565,000
Net Worth: $55,832,000
Earnings: ($340,937,000)
Emp.: 3,600
Fiscal Year-end: 12/31/19
Offices of Other Holding Companies
N.A.I.C.S.: 551112
Christopher W. Jamroz *(Exec Chm & CEO)*
Patrick K. McKay *(Sr VP-Enterprise Fleet Svcs)*
Robert M. Milane *(Chief Compliance Officer & Gen Counsel)*
Frank L. Hurst *(Pres-Roadrunner Freight)*
William R. Goodgion *(Pres-Ascent International)*
Michael K. Rapken *(CIO)*
Christopher W. Jamroz *(Chm)*
Patrick J. Unzicker *(CFO & Exec VP)*
Douglas J. Smith *(Chief Compliance Officer & Sr VP-HR)*

Subsidiaries:

A&A Express, LLC   **(1)**
1015 N 9th Ave, Brandon, SD 57005
Tel.: (605) 582-2402
Web Site: http://www.aaexpressinc.com
Sales Range: $25-49.9 Million
Emp.: 70
Trucking Service
N.A.I.C.S.: 484121

A&A Logistics, LLC   **(1)**
1703 S Angeline St, Seattle, WA 98108
Tel.: (206) 334-2983
Transportation & Logistics Services
N.A.I.C.S.: 484230

Active Aero Group, Inc.   **(1)**
2068 E St, Belleville, MI 48111
Tel.: (734) 547-7200
Web Site: http://www.activeaero.com
Sales Range: $250-299.9 Million
Emp.: 300
Air Freight Transportation Services
N.A.I.C.S.: 481112

Subsidiary (Domestic):

Active Aero Motor Carrier, LLC   **(2)**
2068 E St, Belleville, MI 48111
Tel.: (734) 547-8715
Aircraft Maintenance & Repair Services
N.A.I.C.S.: 811198

Active Aero Services, LLC   **(2)**
2068 E St, Belleville, MI 48111
Tel.: (734) 547-7359
Web Site:
  http://www.activeaeroservices.com
Aircraft Maintenance & Repair Services
N.A.I.C.S.: 811198

USA Jet Airlines, Inc.   **(2)**
2068 E St, Belleville, MI 48111
Tel.: (734) 547-7200
Web Site: http://usajet.aero
Passenger Air Transportation Services
N.A.I.C.S.: 481111
Christopher W. Jamroz *(CEO)*

Big Rock Transportation, LLC   **(1)**
304 Dawnridge Ln, Troutville, VA 24175
Tel.: (540) 977-4090
Emp.: 4
Transportation & Logistics Services
N.A.I.C.S.: 484230

Combi Maritime Corporation.   **(1)**
709 Hindry Ave, Inglewood, CA 90301
Tel.: (310) 216-0239
Web Site: http://www.combimaritime.com
Freight Transportation Services
N.A.I.C.S.: 484121
Fred Saxer *(Owner)*

Consolidated Transportation World,
LLC   **(1)**

147 Summit St Bldg 3a Summit Industrial
Park, Peabody, MA 01960
Tel.: (978) 977-0081
Transportation & Logistics Services
N.A.I.C.S.: 484230

D&E Transport Inc.   **(1)**
4141 150th St NW, Clearwater, MN 55320
Tel.: (763) 878-2880
Web Site: http://www.detransportinc.com
Sales Range: $10-24.9 Million
Emp.: 30
Food & Agricultural Freight Trucking Services
N.A.I.C.S.: 484121

Everett Logistics, LLC   **(1)**
2615 N Prickett Rd Ste 9 72089, Bryant, AR
72089
Tel.: (501) 569-9910
Logistics Consulting Servies
N.A.I.C.S.: 541614

Expedited Freight Systems, LLC   **(1)**
4801 68th Ave, Kenosha, WI 53144
Tel.: (262) 605-3375
Web Site: http://www.expedited.org
General Freight Trucking, Long-Distance,
Truckload
N.A.I.C.S.: 484121

Group Transportation Services,
Inc.   **(1)**
5876 Darrow Rd, Hudson, OH 44236
Tel.: (330) 342-8700
Sales Range: $25-49.9 Million
Emp.: 71
Transportation & Logistics Services
N.A.I.C.S.: 484230
Paul Kithcart *(Pres)*

Subsidiary (Domestic):

Capital Transportation Logistics,
LLC   **(2)**
2068 E St, Belleville, MI 48111
Tel.: (603) 881-3350
Web Site: http://www.ascentgl.com
Sales Range: $25-49.9 Million
Emp.: 25
Freight Transportation Arrangement
N.A.I.C.S.: 488510
Erin Verranault *(Pres)*

Great Northern Transportation Services, LLC   **(2)**
PO Box 347, Nashua, NH 03061
Tel.: (603) 672-1275
Web Site: http://gntsnh.com
Sales Range: $25-49.9 Million
Emp.: 6
Transportation & Logistics Services
N.A.I.C.S.: 484230
Chris M. Cook *(Pres-Domestic Freight Mgmt)*
Micah Holst *(Pres-Intl Freight Forwarding)*
William Vechiarella *(Pres-Retail Consolidation)*

ISI Logistics South, LLC   **(1)**
6801 S 33rd St Ste 2, McAllen, TX 78503
Tel.: (956) 661-8300
Logistics Consulting Servies
N.A.I.C.S.: 541614
Kenn Hardley *(Pres)*

Integrated Services Inc.   **(1)**
2758 Commerce Dr, Kokomo, IN 46902
Tel.: (765) 454-0500
Web Site: http://www.isiwarehouse.com
General Freight Trucking Services, Warehousing & Logistics Services
N.A.I.C.S.: 484110

M. Bruenger & Co., Inc.   **(1)**
6250 N Broadway, Wichita, KS 67219-1102
Tel.: (316) 744-0494
Web Site: http://www.bruenger.net
Sales Range: $100-124.9 Million
Emp.: 215
Interstate Trucking Services
N.A.I.C.S.: 484121

Marisol International, LLC   **(1)**
100 E Royal Dr Ste 224, Irving, TX 75039
Tel.: (469) 420-9800
Web Site: http://www.marisolintl.com
Freight Transportation & Logistics Consulting Services
N.A.I.C.S.: 484121

Chris M. Cook *(Pres-Domestic Freight Mgmt)*
Micah Holst *(Pres-Logistics Intl Freight Forwarding-Global)*
William Vechiarella *(Pres-Retail Consolidation)*

Midwest Carriers, LLC   **(1)**
3165 Dodd Rd A, Saint Paul, MN 55121
Tel.: (651) 686-6700
Transportation & Logistics Services
N.A.I.C.S.: 484230

Midwest Transit, Inc.   **(1)**
707 Malenfant Blvd, Dieppe, E1A 5T8, NB,
Canada
Tel.: (506) 854-4010
Web Site: http://www.midwesttransit.com
Sales Range: $25-49.9 Million
Emp.: 5
Transportation & Logistics Services
N.A.I.C.S.: 484230

Roadrunner Carriers, LLC   **(1)**
4900 S Pennsylvania Ave, Cudahy, WI
53110
Tel.: (414) 615-1500
Freight Transportation Services
N.A.I.C.S.: 484121

Roadrunner Transportation Systems,
Inc.   **(1)**
4501 E Washington Blvd Ste 2, Los Angeles, CA 90040
Tel.: (323) 780-3488
Web Site: http://www.rrts.com
Transportation, Shipping & Logistics Services
N.A.I.C.S.: 484121

The Meadowlark Group, LLC   **(1)**
6277 Spinnaker Ridge Ln, Clinton, WA
98236-9546
Tel.: (206) 817-3401
Transportation & Logistics Services
N.A.I.C.S.: 484230

World Transport Services, LLC   **(1)**
5 Wade St, Augusta, ME 04332
Tel.: (207) 622-4032
Sales Range: $25-49.9 Million
Emp.: 20
Transportation & Logistics Services
N.A.I.C.S.: 484230
Noah Wilmot *(Gen Mgr)*

YES Trans, Inc.   **(1)**
6 Main St, Salisbury, MA 01952
Tel.: (978) 465-5556
Sales Range: $1-9.9 Million
Emp.: 50
Refrigerated Freight Trucking Services
N.A.I.C.S.: 484220

ROADZEN, INC.
111 Anza Blvd, Suite 109, Burlingame, CA 94010
Tel.: (650) 414-3530   **VG**
Web Site: https://roadzen.ai
Year Founded: 2021
RDZN—(NASDAQ)
Rev.: $46,724,287
Assets: $58,136,346
Liabilities: $68,636,212
Net Worth: ($10,499,866)
Earnings: ($99,669,335)
Emp.: 368
Fiscal Year-end: 03/31/24
Insurance Services
N.A.I.C.S.: 524298

ROBERT HALF INC.
2884 Sand Hill Rd Ste 200, Menlo
Park, CA 94025
Tel.: (650) 234-6000   **DE**
Web Site: https://www.roberthalf.com
Year Founded: 1948
RHI—(NYSE)
Rev.: $6,392,517,000
Assets: $3,010,789,000
Liabilities: $1,422,438,000
Net Worth: $1,588,351,000
Earnings: $411,146,000
Emp.: 15,000
Fiscal Year-end: 12/31/23

Holding Company; Specialized Staffing & Administrative Support Placement Services
N.A.I.C.S.: 551112
Michael Keith Waddell (Vice Chm, Pres & CEO)
Robert W. Glass (Exec VP-Corp Dev)
Michael C. Buckley (CFO & Exec VP)
Paul F. Gentzkow (Pres-Talent Solutions & CEO-Talent Solutions)
Lynne C. Smith (Sr VP-HR & Compensation)
Colin S. Mooney (Chief Digital Officer & Sr VP)
Ryan Sutton (Exec Dir-Tech Practice Grp)
Katherine Spencer Lee (Chief Admin Officer)
Christopher C. Nelson (CMO)

Subsidiaries:

Protiviti Inc. **(1)**
2884 Sand Hill Rd Ste 200, Menlo Park, CA 94025
Tel.: (650) 234-6000
Web Site: https://www.protiviti.com
Sales Range: $75-99.9 Million
Emp.: 100
Independent Internal Auditing & Risk Consulting Services
N.A.I.C.S.: 541618
Joseph A. Tarantino (Pres & CEO)
Brian Christensen (Exec VP-Global)
Andrew Clinton (Exec VP-Intl Ops)
Cory Gunderson (Exec VP-Global Solutions)
Shelley Metz-Galloway (Mng Dir)
Barbara Rothenstein (Exec VP-Global Fin & Ops)
Susan Haseley (Exec VP-Global Diversity & Inclusion)
Scott Redfearn (Exec VP-Global HR)
Patrick Scott (Exec VP-Global Industry, Client Programs & Mktg)
Tom McClune (Officer-Risk-Global & Exec VP)
Tom McClune (Officer-Risk-Global & Exec VP)
Tom McClune (Officer-Risk-Global & Exec VP)
Ana Amato (Mng Dir)

Subsidiary (Domestic):

Identropy, Inc. **(2)**
7600 Burnet Rd Ste 505, Austin, TX 78757
Tel.: (201) 580-2700
Web Site: http://www.identropy.com
Emp.: 40
Software Publisher
N.A.I.C.S.: 513210
Frank Villavicencio (Head-Product)
Ashraf Motiwala (Co-Founder & Mng Partner)
Bill Aliferis (Dir-PS)
Chad Wolcott (VP-Professional Svcs)
Christa Bradley (Sr Mgr-Project)
Dave Redmond (Mgr-Pre-Sls)
Diane Spinelli (Sr Dir-PS)
Jeff Chang (Mng Partner & VP-Sls)
Kevin Harrington (Mgr-PS)
Kristen Beenders (Dir-HR)
Mark Gyorey (Sr Dir-Professional Svcs)
Victor Barris (Co-Founder & Mng Partner)
Wayne Cissell (VP-Ops & Emerging Technologies)

Subsidiary (Non-US):

Protiviti B.V. **(2)**
SOM 1 Building Floor M Gustav Mahlerlaan 32, 1082 MC, Amsterdam, Netherlands
Tel.: (31) 203460400
Web Site: https://www.protiviti.com
Emp.: 30
Global Business Consulting & Internal Audit Services
N.A.I.C.S.: 541611
Jaap Gerkes (Mng Dir)

Protiviti BVBA **(2)**
Westpoint t Hofveld 6 East, Groot-Bijgaarden, 1702, Belgium
Tel.: (32) 24821240
Web Site: http://www.roberthalfinternational.com

Global Business Consulting & Internal Audit Services
N.A.I.C.S.: 541611

Protiviti Consulting Private Limited **(2)**
15th Floor Tower A DLF Building No 5 DLF Phase III DLF Cyber City, Gurgaon, 122002, Haryana, India
Tel.: (91) 1246618600
Web Site: https://www.protiviti.com
Global Business Consulting & Internal Audit Services
N.A.I.C.S.: 541611

Protiviti GmbH **(2)**
Mainzer Landstrasse 50, 60325, Frankfurt am Main, Germany
Tel.: (49) 69963768100
Web Site: https://www.protiviti.com
Staffing & Risk Consulting Services
N.A.I.C.S.: 541618

Subsidiary (Domestic):

Protiviti Government Services, Inc. **(2)**
1640 King St Ste 400, Alexandria, VA 22314
Tel.: (703) 299-3444
Web Site: https://www.protivitigovernmentservices.com
Emp.: 25
Internal Audit & Management Consulting Services
N.A.I.C.S.: 541611

Subsidiary (Non-US):

Protiviti Hong Kong Co. Ltd. **(2)**
9th Floor Nexxus Building 41 Connaught Road, Central, China (Hong Kong)
Tel.: (852) 22380499
Web Site: http://www.protiviti.cn
Emp.: 30
Professional Staffing & Consulting Services
N.A.I.C.S.: 561311

Protiviti Pte. Ltd. **(2)**
9 Raffles Place 40-02 Republic Plaza I, Singapore, 048619, Singapore
Tel.: (65) 62200666
Web Site: https://www.protiviti.com.sg
Global Business Consulting & Internal Audit Services
N.A.I.C.S.: 541611
Sam Bassett (Mng Dir-Tech Consulting)
Ann Chi Koh (Mng Dir-Fin Advisory & Internal Audit)
Marek Kosmowski (Dir-Digital Transformation)
Gregor Neveling (Dir-Compliance & Risk)

Protiviti Pty. Limited **(2)**
Level 21 Rialto South Tower 525 Collins Street, Melbourne, 3000, VIC, Australia
Tel.: (61) 399481200
Web Site: https://www.protiviti.com
Emp.: 30
Global Business Consulting & Internal Audit Services
N.A.I.C.S.: 541611

Protiviti S.r.l. **(2)**
Via Tiziano 32, 20145, Milan, MI, Italy
Tel.: (39) 0265506301
Web Site: https://www.protiviti.com
Global Business Consulting & Internal Audit Services
N.A.I.C.S.: 541611
Alberto Carnevale (Mng Dir)

Protiviti SAS **(2)**
15-19 rue des Mathurins, 75009, Paris, France
Tel.: (33) 142962277
Web Site: https://www.protiviti.com
Sales Range: $25-49.9 Million
Global Business Consulting & Internal Audit Services
N.A.I.C.S.: 541611
Arnaud Floquet (Mng Dir)

Protiviti Shanghai Co., Ltd. **(2)**
Rm 1915-16 Bldg 2 International Commerce Centre, No 288 South Shaanxi Road Xuhui Dist, Shanghai, 200030, China
Tel.: (86) 2151536900
Web Site: https://www.protiviti.cn

Specialized Staffing Services
N.A.I.C.S.: 561320

Subsidiary (Domestic):

R2integrated **(2)**
509 S Exeter St, Ste 300, Baltimore, MD 21202
Tel.: (410) 327-0007
Web Site: http://www.r2integrated.com
Advertising Agencies
N.A.I.C.S.: 541810
Matt Goddard (CEO)
David Taub (Mng Dir-Baltimore)
Chris Chodnicki (Exec Dir-Strategic Partnerships)
Jody Stoehr (Mng Dir-Seattle)
Walter Starr (CFO)
Cindy Nowicki (Sr Dir-Strategy & Content)
Dennis Totah (Exec VP-Ops-US)
Kara Alcamo (Sr Dir-Digital Mktg)
Lara Poncia (Sr Dir-Ops)
Marianne Fromm (Dir-HR)
Mike Onalfo (Dir-Data Svcs)
Natalie Staines (Dir-Mktg)
Nick Christy (Sr VP-Enterprise Tech)
Steve Hill (Sr Dir-Brand Strategy)
Tom Beck (Mng Dir)
Steve Karr (Sr Dir-Mktg Cloud)

Protiviti Switzerland GmbH **(1)**
Bahnhofpl 9, 8001, Zurich, Switzerland
Tel.: (41) 433447641
Web Site: https://www.protiviti.com
Consulting Services
N.A.I.C.S.: 541611

RHHC LLC **(1)**
16 N Evans St, Pottstown, PA 19464
Tel.: (267) 406-7890
Web Site: https://www.royaltyhomecare.net
Health Care Srvices
N.A.I.C.S.: 621610

Robert Half Assessoria Em Recursos Humanos Ltda. **(1)**
Avenida Doutor Cardoso de Melo 1184 Vila Olimpia, Sao Paulo, 04548-004, Brazil
Tel.: (55) 1133820145
Web Site: http://www.roberthalf.com.br
Sales Range: $25-49.9 Million
Emp.: 150
Professional Staffing & Consulting Services
N.A.I.C.S.: 561320
Fernando Mantovani (Mng Dir)

Robert Half Australia Pty. Ltd. **(1)**
Level 24 1 Martin Place, Sydney, 2000, NSW, Australia
Tel.: (61) 279088834
Web Site: https://www.roberthalf.com.au
Emp.: 60
Specialised Recruitment Services
N.A.I.C.S.: 561320
Michael Keith Waddell (Vice Chm- & CFO)
Michael C. Buckley (CFO)

Robert Half Austria GmbH **(1)**
Herrengasse 1-3, Vienna, 1010, Austria
Tel.: (43) 15337479
Web Site: https://www.roberthalf.at
Sales Range: $25-49.9 Million
Emp.: 7
Specialized Staffing Services
N.A.I.C.S.: 561320

Robert Half BVBA **(1)**
Stationsstraat 34, PO Box 1, 1702, Groot-Bijgaarden, Belgium
Tel.: (32) 24817575
Web Site: http://www.roberthalf.be
Emp.: 250
Employment Placement Services
N.A.I.C.S.: 561311

Robert Half Canada Inc. **(1)**
181 Bay Street Suite 820, Toronto, M5J 2T3, ON, Canada
Tel.: (647) 957-7004
Web Site: https://www.roberthalf.com
Sales Range: $25-49.9 Million
Specialized Staffing Services
N.A.I.C.S.: 561320

Robert Half Consulting Services BVBA **(1)**
Jan Van Gentstraat 1 Bus 301, Antwerp, 2000, Belgium
Tel.: (32) 26400370
Professional Staffing & Consulting Services

N.A.I.C.S.: 561311

Robert Half Corporation **(1)**
2884 Sand Hill Rd, Menlo Park, CA 94025
Tel.: (650) 234-6000
Web Site: http://www.roberthalf.com
Specialized Staffing & Administrative Support Placement Services
N.A.I.C.S.: 561320

Division (Domestic):

Robert Half Corporation - Accountemps Division **(2)**
2884 Sand Hill Rd, Menlo Park, CA 94025-7072
Tel.: (650) 234-6000
Web Site: http://www.accountemps.com
Finance & Accounting Temporary Help Services
N.A.I.C.S.: 561320
Harold Max Messmer Jr. (Chm & CEO)

Robert Half Corporation - Finance & Accounting Division **(2)**
2884 Sand Hill Rd, Menlo Park, CA 94025
Tel.: (650) 234-6000
Web Site: http://www.roberthalffinance.com
Finance & Accounting Professional Employment Placement Services
N.A.I.C.S.: 561311
Jason Parma (Dir-Permanent Placement Svcs)

Robert Half Corporation - Legal Division **(2)**
2884 Sand Hill Rd Ste 200, Menlo Park, CA 94025-7072
Tel.: (650) 234-6000
Web Site: http://www.roberthalflegal.com
Legal Staffing Services
N.A.I.C.S.: 561320
Harold Max Messmer Jr. (Chm & CEO)

Robert Half Corporation - Management Resources Division **(2)**
2884 Sand Hill Rd Ste 200, Menlo Park, CA 94025-7072
Tel.: (925) 598-5000
Web Site: http://www.rhimr.com
Senior-Level Project-Based Financial Staffing Services
N.A.I.C.S.: 561320

Robert Half Corporation - OfficeTeam Division **(2)**
2884 Sand Hill Rd Ste 200, Menlo Park, CA 94025
Tel.: (650) 234-6000
Web Site: http://www.officeteam.com
Specialized Temporary Administrative Support Staffing
N.A.I.C.S.: 561320
Harold Max Messmer Jr. (Chm & CEO)

Robert Half Corporation - Technology Division **(2)**
2884 Sand Hill Rd Ste 200, Menlo Park, CA 94025
Tel.: (650) 234-6000
Web Site: http://www.roberthalf.com
Technology & Information Technology Staffing Services
N.A.I.C.S.: 561320
Catherine Hamilton (Dir)

Robert Half Corporation - The Creative Group Division **(2)**
2884 Sand Hill Rd, Menlo Park, CA 94025
Tel.: (650) 234-6000
Web Site: http://www.roberthalf.com
Creative, Advertising, Marketing & Internet Professional Staffing Services
N.A.I.C.S.: 561320
Harold Max Messmer Jr. (Chm & CEO)

Robert Half Deutschland Beteiligungsgesellschaft GmbH **(1)**
Mainzer Landstrasse 50, 60325, Frankfurt am Main, Germany
Tel.: (49) 69256247401
Web Site: http://www.roberthalf.de
Sales Range: $25-49.9 Million
Specialized Staffing Services
N.A.I.C.S.: 561320

Robert Half Hong Kong Limited **(1)**
9th Floor Nexxus Building 41 Connaught Road, Central, China (Hong Kong)
Tel.: (852) 36537300
Web Site: https://www.roberthalf.com.hk

Robert Half Inc.—(Continued)

Specialised Recruitment Services
N.A.I.C.S.: 561320

Robert Half Human Resources
Shanghai Company Limited   **(1)**
Room 1912-14 19th Floor 288 Shanxi
South Road Phase II, IMCO Plaza Office
Building Xuhui District, Shanghai, 200031,
China
Tel.: (86) 2160320555
Web Site: https://www.roberthalf.cn
Sales Range: $25-49.9 Million
Specialised Recruitment Services
N.A.I.C.S.: 561320

Robert Half International (Dubai)
Ltd.   **(1)**
Gate Village 1 Level 1 Office Unit 104, PO
Box 482100, Dubai International Financial
Centre DIFC, Dubai, United Arab Emirates
Tel.: (971) 43826700
Web Site: https://www.roberthalf.ae
Emp.: 20
Professional Staffing Services
N.A.I.C.S.: 561320

Robert Half International B.V.   **(1)**
Quarter Plaza-2nd floor Transformatorweg,
82 1014 AK, Amsterdam, Netherlands
Tel.: (31) 205106767
Web Site: https://www.roberthalf.com
Emp.: 50
Specialized Staffing Services
N.A.I.C.S.: 561320

Robert Half International Ireland
Limited   **(1)**
25-28 North Wall Quay IFSC, Dublin, 1,
Ireland
Tel.: (353) 15746770
Web Site: https://www.roberthalf.ie
Employment Placement Agency Services
N.A.I.C.S.: 561311

Robert Half International Pte.
Ltd.   **(1)**
9 Raffles Place 40-02 Republic Plaza I, Sin-
gapore, 048619, Singapore
Tel.: (65) 65337778
Web Site: https://www.roberthalf.com.sg
Emp.: 20
Specialized Staffing Services
N.A.I.C.S.: 561320

Robert Half International
S.A./N.V.   **(1)**
Alfons Gossetlaan 28 A, PO Box 8, 1702,
Groot-Bijgaarden, Belgium
Tel.: (32) 24816620
Sales Range: $10-24.9 Million
Emp.: 70
Employment Agencies
N.A.I.C.S.: 561311

Robert Half Japan Ltd.   **(1)**
Level 19 Hilton Plaza West Office Tower
2-2-2 Umeda, Kita-ku, Osaka, 530-0001,
Japan
Tel.: (81) 345630710
Web Site: https://www.roberthalf.com
Emp.: 92
Specialized Staffing Services
N.A.I.C.S.: 561320
Yewki Tomita (Mng Dir)

Robert Half Limited   **(1)**
10th Floor The Shard 32 London Bridge
Street, London, SE1 9SG, United
Kingdom   **(100%)**
Tel.: (44) 2073896900
Web Site: https://www.roberthalf.com
Staffing Services
N.A.I.C.S.: 561311

Robert Half Nederland B.V.   **(1)**
Gatwickstraat 17, 1043 GL, Amsterdam,
Netherlands
Tel.: (31) 205106767
Web Site: https://www.roberthalf.nl
Specialized Staffing Services
N.A.I.C.S.: 561320

Robert Half S.r.l.   **(1)**
Via Marche 54, 00187, Rome, Italy
Tel.: (39) 0642049611
Web Site: http://www.roberthalf.it
Sales Range: $25-49.9 Million
Emp.: 20
Staffing & Management Consulting Services

N.A.I.C.S.: 541611

Robert Half Sarl   **(1)**
Spaces Place de la Gare 5, 1616, Luxem-
bourg, Luxembourg
Tel.: (352) 26730630
Web Site: https://www.roberthalf.lu
Sales Range: $25-49.9 Million
Specialized Staffing Services
N.A.I.C.S.: 561320

ROBINHOOD MARKETS, INC.
85 Willow Rd, Menlo Park, CA
94025   DE
Web Site: https://www.robinhood.com
Year Founded: 2013
HOOD—(NASDAQ)
Rev.: $1,865,000,000
Assets: $32,332,000,000
Liabilities: $25,636,000,000
Net Worth: $6,696,000,000
Earnings: ($541,000,000)
Emp.: 2,200
Fiscal Year-end: 12/31/23
Brokerage Services
N.A.I.C.S.: 524210
Daniel Gallagher (Chief Legal Officer)
Christina Smedley (Chief Mktg &
Comm Officer)
Jason Warnick (CFO)
Vladimir Tenev (Co-Founder, Chm,
Pres & CEO)
Baiju Bhatt (Co-Founder)

ROBLOX CORPORATION
970 Park Pl, San Mateo, CA 94403
Tel.: (888) 858-2569
Web Site:
  https://www.corp.roblox.com
Year Founded: 2006
RBLX—(NYSE)
Rev.: $2,799,274,000
Assets: $6,168,078,000
Liabilities: $6,099,452,000
Net Worth: $68,626,000
Earnings: ($1,151,946,000)
Emp.: 2,457
Fiscal Year-end: 12/31/23
Gaming Software Development Ser-
vices
N.A.I.C.S.: 541511
Tami Bhaumik (VP-Mktg)
Scott Rubin (Sr VP-Bus Dev)
Jared Shapiro (VP-Engrg & Platform)
Hans Gunawan (VP-Fin)
Mike Guthrie (CFO)
Manuel Bronstein (Chief Product Offi-
cer)
Nick Tornow (VP-Engrg-Dev)
David Baszucki (Founder & CEO)

Subsidiaries:

Speechly Oy   **(1)**
Kaisaniemenkatu 1 D 124, 00100, Helsinki,
Finland
Tel.: (358) 961815180
Web Site: https://www.speechly.com
Software Development Services
N.A.I.C.S.: 541511

ROBOSERVER SYSTEMS
CORP.
3440 E Russell Rd Ste 217, Las Ve-
gas, NV 89120
Tel.: (801) 575-8073   DE
Year Founded: 2000
RBSY—(OTCIQ)
Computer Equipment Mfr
N.A.I.C.S.: 334118
Delmar A. Janovec (CEO)
Richard Surber (Pres & CEO)

ROCHESTER COMMUNITY
BASEBALL, INC.
1 Morrie Silver Way, Rochester, NY
14608
Tel.: (716) 454-1001   NY
Web Site: http://www.milb.com

RCCB—(OTCIQ)
Sports Club Operator
N.A.I.C.S.: 711211

ROCK CREEK PHARMACEUTI-
CALS, INC.
2040 Whitfield Ave Ste 300, Sara-
sota, FL 34243
Tel.: (844) 727-0727   DE
Web Site:
  http://www.rockcreekpharmaceu
  ticals.com
Year Founded: 1998
RCPIQ—(OTCIQ)
Sales Range: Less than $1 Million
Emp.: 5
Pharmaceuticals Mfr
N.A.I.C.S.: 325412
Michael John Mullan (Chm, Pres &
CEO)
Theodore Jenkins (VP-Corp Strategy,
Dev & IR)
Ryan K. Lanier (Chief Scientific Offi-
cer)

Subsidiaries:

RCP Development Inc.   **(1)**
177 Patton Rd, Jasper, AL 35503
Tel.: (205) 522-6775
Surveying & Mapping Services
N.A.I.C.S.: 541370
Robert Patton (Pres)

ROCK RIDGE RESOURCES,
INC.
PO Box 1927, Blue Jay, CA 92317
Tel.: (972) 677-7690   NV
Web Site:
  http://www.rockridgeresources
  inc.com
Year Founded: 2010
RRRI—(OTCIQ)
Business Development Services
N.A.I.C.S.: 561499
Ryan Moller (COO)
Daniel Voorhees (Chm, Pres & CEO)

ROCKET COMPANIES, INC.
1050 Woodward Ave, Detroit, MI
48226
Tel.: (313) 373-7990   DE
Web Site:
  https://www.rocketcompanies.com
Year Founded: 1985
RKT—(NYSE)
Rev.: $3,799,269,000
Assets: $19,231,740,000
Liabilities: $10,930,030,000
Net Worth: $8,301,710,000
Earnings: ($15,514,000)
Emp.: 14,700
Fiscal Year-end: 12/31/23
Financial Investment Services
N.A.I.C.S.: 523999
Varun Krishna (CEO & CEO-Rocket
Mortgage)
Daniel Gilbert (Chm)
Brian Brown (CFO & Treas)
Tina V. John (Gen Counsel & Sec)
Bill Emerson (Pres)
Daniel Gilbert (Founder & Chm)

Subsidiaries:

Amrock Title Insurance Company   **(1)**
662 Woodward Ave 10th Fl, Detroit, MI
48226
Web Site: https://www.amrocktic.com
Insurance Services
N.A.I.C.S.: 524210

Amrock, LLC   **(1)**
662 Woodward Ave, Detroit, MI 48226
Web Site: https://www.amrock.com
Real Estate Services
N.A.I.C.S.: 531390
Rob Sayre (CIO)
Steve Nadolski (VP-Commercial-Natl)
Jason Hall (VP-Sales-Natl)

Edison Financial ULC   **(1)**
156 Chatham St W Suite 2, Windsor, N9A
5M6, ON, Canada
Web Site: https://rocketmortgage.ca
Financial Mortgage Services
N.A.I.C.S.: 522310

Nexsys Technologies LLC   **(1)**
1054 Woodward Ave, Detroit, MI 48226
Web Site: http://www.nexsystech.com
Information & Communication Technology
Services
N.A.I.C.S.: 541430

RockLoans Marketplace LLC   **(1)**
1274 Library St 2nd Fl, Detroit, MI 48226
Tel.: (313) 230-5233
Web Site: https://www.rocketloans.com
Financial Loan Services
N.A.I.C.S.: 522390

ROCKET LAB USA, INC.
3881 McGowen St, Long Beach, CA
90808
Tel.: (714) 465-5737   DE
Web Site:
  https://www.rocketlabusa.com
Year Founded: 2006
RKLB—(NASDAQ)
Rev.: $210,996,000
Assets: $989,123,000
Liabilities: $315,917,000
Net Worth: $673,206,000
Earnings: ($135,944,000)
Emp.: 1,400
Fiscal Year-end: 12/31/22
Guided Missile & Space Vehicle
Manufacturing
N.A.I.C.S.: 336414
Andrew Bunker (VP-Govt Ops & Bus
Strategy)
Peter Beck (Founder, Chm, Pres &
CEO)

Subsidiaries:

Advanced Solutions, Inc.   **(1)**
7815 Shaffer Pkwy, Littleton, CO 80127
Tel.: (303) 979-2417
Web Site: http://www.go-asi.com
Sales Range: $1-9.9 Million
Emp.: 27
Engineering Services
N.A.I.C.S.: 541330
John A. Cuseo (Founder & CEO)
Kyle Andringa (Engr-Aerospace & Controls)
Susan Babcock (Engr-Software & Sys)
Jeff Bone (Engr-Aerospace & Controls)
James Bradley (Engr-Software & Sys)
Clint DeHerrera (Engr-Software & Sys)
Laurie Delphia (Mgr-Acctg, Contracts &
Benefits)
Andy Gerrie (Engr-Software & Sys)
Troy Gray (Engr-Electrical)
Dennis Griffin (Engr-Aerospace & Controls)
Ashton Halladay (Engr-Software & Sys)
Robert Leonard (Engr-Software & Sys)
Mike Morris (Engr-Software & Electrical)
Jeff Robbins (Mgr-Bus Dev)
Josh Russell (Mgr-Bus Dev)
Brandon Smith (Engr-Software & Sys)
Bruce Bieber (Engr-Integration & Test)
Drew Ackerman (Engr-Software & Sys)
Jamie Mouw (Engr-Embedded Software)
Jeremy Byrne (Engr-Software & Sys)
Michael Chaffin (Engr-Software & Sys)
Nicole Ramos (Engr-Software & Sys)
Tim Rood (Engr-Aerospace & Controls)
Zach Cuseo (Engr-Aerospace & Controls)
Atoughi Abo (Mng Partner)

Planetary Systems Corp.
2303 Kansas Ave, Silver Spring, MD 20910-
1904
Tel.: (301) 495-0737
Web Site:
  http://www.planetarysystemscorp.com
Emp.: 25
Other Guided Missile & Space Vehicle Parts
& Auxiliary Equipment Manufacturing
N.A.I.C.S.: 336419
Christopher Flood (Engr-Mechanical)
Mike Whalen (Pres & CEO)

SolAero Technologies Corp.   **(1)**
10420 Research Rd SE, Albuquerque, NM
87123
Tel.: (505) 332-5000
Emp.: 250

Solar Cells & Solar Panels Mfr & Supplier
N.A.I.C.S.: 334413
Brad Clevenger (Pres & CEO)

ROCKET PHARMACEUTICALS, INC.

The Empire State Bldg 350 5th Ave
Ste 7530, New York, NY 10118
Tel.: (646) 440-9100
Web Site:
  http://www.rocketpharma.com
9IP1—(STU)
Health Care Srvices
N.A.I.C.S.: 621999
Gaurav Shah (Pres & CEO)
Roderick Wong (Chm)
Carlos Garcia-Parada (CFO)
John Militello (Principal Acctg Officer, Treas, VP-Fin & Controller)
Martin L. Wilson (Chief Compliance Officer, Gen Counsel & Sr VP)
Kevin Giordano (Dir-Corp Comm)
Mayur Kasetty (Dir-Bus Dev & Ops)

ROCKET PHARMACEUTICALS, INC.

9 Cedarbrook Dr, Cranbury, NJ 08512
Tel.: (646) 440-9100   DE
Web Site:
  https://www.rocketpharma.com
Year Founded: 1999
RCKT—(NASDAQ)
Rev.: $3,889,000
Assets: $551,807,000
Liabilities: $62,121,000
Net Worth: $489,686,000
Earnings: ($221,863,000)
Emp.: 240
Fiscal Year-end: 12/31/22
Pharmaceutical Preparation Manufacturing
N.A.I.C.S.: 325412
Aaron Ondrey (CFO)
Gaurav Shah (CEO)
Jonathan Schwartz (Chief Gene Therapy Officer)
Mark White (Chief Medical Officer)
Mark White (Chief Medical Officer)
Kinnari Patel (Pres)
Mayo Pujols (Chief Technical Officer)
Isabel Carmona (Chief HR Officer)
Carlos Martin (Chief Comml Officer)
Raj Prabhakar (Chief Bus Officer)
Gayatri R. Rao (Chief Dev Officer)
Martin Wilson (Chief Compliance Officer)
John C. Militello (Principal Acctg Officer)
Jessie Yeung (VP)

ROCKETFUEL BLOCKCHAIN, INC.

201 Spear St Ste 1100, San Francisco, CA 94105
Tel.: (424) 256-8560   NV
Web Site: https://rocketfuel.inc
Year Founded: 2018
RKFL—(OTCQB)
Rev.: $203,199
Assets: $1,216,367
Liabilities: $1,039,991
Net Worth: $176,376
Earnings: ($3,778,424)
Emp.: 21
Fiscal Year-end: 03/31/23
Software Development Services
N.A.I.C.S.: 541511
Peter M. Jensen (CEO)
Gert Funk (Chm)
Bennett J. Yankowitz (CFO & Sec)
Rohan Hall (CTO)
Kurt Kumar (VP-Mktg & Bus Dev)

ROCKWELL AUTOMATION, INC.

1201 S 2nd St, Milwaukee, WI 53204
Tel.: (414) 382-2000   DE
Web Site:
  https://www.rockwellautomation.com
Year Founded: 1903
ROK—(NYSE)
Rev.: $8,264,200,000
Assets: $11,232,100,000
Liabilities: $7,556,900,000
Net Worth: $3,675,200,000
Earnings: $947,300,000
Emp.: 27,000
Fiscal Year-end: 09/30/24
Auto Parts Mfr
N.A.I.C.S.: 334513
Christopher Nardecchia (CIO & Sr VP-IT)
Blake D. Moret (Chm, Pres & CEO)
Rebecca W. House (Chief People & Legal Officer, Sec & Sr VP)
Alejandro Cesar Capparelli (VP-Global Comml Lifecycle Svcs)
Elik I. Fooks (Sr VP-Corp Dev)
Alejandro Capparelli (VP-Global Comml Lifecycle Svcs)
Tessa M. Myers (Sr VP-Intelligent Devices)
Terry L. Riesterer (Principal Acctg Officer, VP & Controller)
Susana Gonzalez (Pres-Europe, Middle East & Africa)
Isaac Woods (Treas & VP)
Scott Wooldridge (Pres-Asia Pacific)
Cyril Perducat (CTO & Sr VP)
Veena M. Lakkundi (Sr VP-Strategy & Corp Dev)
Marci Pelzer (Dir-External Comm)
Scott Genereux (Chief Revenue Officer & Sr VP)
Gina Ayala Claxton (Pres-Americas)
Nicole Darden Ford (Chief Info Security Officer & VP)
Ed Moreland (Head-Govt Affairs & External Comm)
Aijana Zellner (Head-IR & Market Strategy)
Brad Skogman (VP)
Christian E. Rothe (CFO & Sr VP)

Subsidiaries:

Asem, S.r.l.   (1)
Via Buia 4, Artegna, 33011, Udine, Italy
Tel.: (39) 04329671
Web Site: http://www.asem.it
Emp.: 204
Industrial Automation Equipments Mfr
N.A.I.C.S.: 333998
Fabrizio Scovenna (Chm)
Renzo Guerra (Pres)

CUBIC Modulsystem A/S   (1)
Skjoldborgsgade 21, DK-9700, Bronderslev, Denmark
Tel.: (45) 98822400
Web Site: https://www.cubic.eu
Electrical Panels Mfr & Distr
N.A.I.C.S.: 335313

ESC Services, Inc.   (1)
1201 S 2nd St, Milwaukee, WI 53588
Tel.: (866) 773-7541
Web Site: http://www.escservices.com
Industrial Automation Power, Control & Information Products Mfr
N.A.I.C.S.: 334513

ICS Triplex ISaGRAF Inc.   (1)
9975 Catania Ave Ste U, Brossard, J4Z 3V6, QC, Canada
Tel.: (450) 445-3353
Web Site: http://www.isagraf.com
Sales Range: $25-49.9 Million
Emp.: 50
Software Publisher
N.A.I.C.S.: 513210

Kalypso, LP   (1)
3659 Green Rd Ste 100, Beachwood, OH 44122
Tel.: (216) 378-4290
Web Site: http://www.kalypso.com
Emp.: 50

Management Consulting Services
N.A.I.C.S.: 541611
George Young (CEO)
Emily Adams (Dir-Ops-Global)
Trey Allen (Dir-IT-Global)

Subsidiary (Domestic):

Palladius, Inc.   (2)
1001 E Harmony Rod Ste A 414, Fort Collins, CO 80525
Tel.: (970) 282-0400
Web Site: http://www.integware.com
Emp.: 15
Scientific & Technical Consulting Services
N.A.I.C.S.: 541690
Christopher Kay (CEO)

MAVERICK Technologies, LLC   (1)
265 Admiral Trost Rd, Columbia, IL 62236
Tel.: (618) 281-9100
Web Site: http://www.mavtechglobal.com
Industrial Automation & IT Consulting Services
N.A.I.C.S.: 541690
Paul J. Galeski (Founder)
John Mills (Pres)
Jim Huff (Reg VP-Global Process Sls)
Sathiyanarayanan Ramanathan (Sr Engr)
Chrystal Kiefer (Coord-Mktg)
James Miller (Dir-Process Sls-North America)
Nancy Lux (Dir-HR)
Brian Batts (Dir-Consulting & Solutions)
Joel Boisselle (Dir-Design & Field Ops)

MagneMotion Inc.   (1)
139 Barnum Rd, Devens, MA 01434
Tel.: (978) 757-9100
Web Site: http://www.magnemotion.com
Electro-Magnetic Systems & Machinery Mfr
N.A.I.C.S.: 333998
Todd S. Webber (Pres)

PT Rockwell Automation
Indonesia   (1)
Mid Plaza 2 Building 22nd Floor Kav 10-11, Jalan Jendral Sudirman, Jakarta, 10220, Pusat, Indonesia
Tel.: (62) 2125545200
Drives, Industrial Systems, Motion Control Products Distr
N.A.I.C.S.: 334513

Rockwell Automation (China) Company Limited   (1)
Unit 603 - 606 Tower C COFCO Plaza No 8 Jian Guo Men Nei Da Jie, Dongcheng Beijing District, Beijing, 100005, China
Tel.: (86) 1065182535
Measuring, Medical & Controlling Device Mfr
N.A.I.C.S.: 334512
Robert Ninker (Dir-Bus Solutions)

Rockwell Automation (Malaysia) Sdn. Bhd.   (1)
Enterpise Square 4 Lot L3-E 10A & Ie-E-11, Technology Park, Kuala Lumpur, 57000, Malaysia   (100%)
Tel.: (60) 389976688
Web Site:
  http://www.rockwellautomation.com.my
Sales Range: $10-24.9 Million
Emp.: 40
Automation Products Distr
N.A.I.C.S.: 238210

Rockwell Automation (N.Z.) Ltd.   (1)
2B Pacific Rise Mt Wellington, Mt Wellington, Auckland, 1060, New Zealand (100%)
Tel.: (64) 92763070
Web Site:
  http://www.rockwellautomation.co.nz
Sales Range: $25-49.9 Million
Emp.: 30
Soft Starters, Sensor, PLC & Drive Products Distr; Industrial Automation Systems Engineering, Training & Support Services
N.A.I.C.S.: 333310
Scott Wooldridge (Mng Dir)

Rockwell Automation (Philippines) Inc.   (1)
W 5th Avenue Building 9th Fl Units D & E, Makati, 1634, Philippines
Tel.: (63) 27056400
Web Site:
  http://www.locator.rockwellautomation.com
Industrial Automation Products Mfr

N.A.I.C.S.: 335314

Rockwell Automation (Xiamen) Ltd.   (1)
Finance & Logistics Services
N.A.I.C.S.: 541614

Rockwell Automation A/S   (1)
Herstedostervej 27 29, DK 2620, Albertslund, Denmark   (100%)
Tel.: (45) 70110109
Web Site: http://www.rockwellautomation.dk
Sales Range: $25-49.9 Million
Emp.: 150
Industrial Automation Products, Systems & Services
N.A.I.C.S.: 333310

Rockwell Automation AB   (1)
Hammarbacken 6A, Sollentuna, Sweden   (100%)
Tel.: (46) 771219219
Web Site: http://www.rockwellautomation.se
Sales Range: $10-24.9 Million
Emp.: 65
Industrial Automation Equipment & Software Distr
N.A.I.C.S.: 423830

Rockwell Automation Argentina S.A.   (1)
Av Leandro N Alem 1050 5th floor, C1001AAS, Buenos Aires, Argentina   (100%)
Tel.: (54) 1155544000
Web Site:
  http://www.rockwellautomation.com.ar
Sales Range: $25-49.9 Million
Emp.: 51
Window Regulators, Sunroofs, Latches, Seat Adjusting Systems & Automobile Parts Supplier
N.A.I.C.S.: 423110

Rockwell Automation Asia Pacific Limited   (1)
Level 14 Core F Cyberport 3 100 Cyberport Rd, Hong Kong, China (Hong Kong)   (100%)
Tel.: (852) 28874788
Web Site:
  http://www.rockwellautomation.com.cn
Sales Range: $25-49.9 Million
Emp.: 100
Industrial Automation Products, Systems & Services, Power Products & Programmable Controllers
N.A.I.C.S.: 238210

Rockwell Automation Australia Ltd.   (1)
841 Mountain Highway, Bayswater, 3153, VIC, Australia   (100%)
Tel.: (61) 800431011
Web Site:
  https://www.rockwellautomation.com
Sales Range: $25-49.9 Million
Emp.: 130
Industrial Control Systems Supplier & Distr
N.A.I.C.S.: 335314
Scott Wooldridge (Mng Dir)

Rockwell Automation B.V.   (1)
Fascinatio Boulevard 350, 3065 WB, Rotterdam, Netherlands
Tel.: (31) 102665555
Web Site:
  https://www.rockwellautomation.com
Industrial Automation Equipment & Software Distr
N.A.I.C.S.: 423830

Rockwell Automation Canada Ltd.   (1)
135 Dundas Street North, Cambridge, N1R 5N9, ON, Canada   (100%)
Tel.: (519) 623-1810
Industrial Automation & Power Products, Systems & Services
N.A.I.C.S.: 334513
Jim Hardy (Controller)

Rockwell Automation Caribbean LLP   (1)
Carr 2 Km 123 7 Bo Caimit St Ca, Aguadilla, PR 00603
Tel.: (787) 706-3940
Engineeering Services
N.A.I.C.S.: 541330

Rockwell Automation, Inc.—(Continued)

Rockwell Automation Chile S.A. (1)
(100%)
Tel.: (56) 22900700
Industrial Automation Mfr
N.A.I.C.S.: 333248

Rockwell Automation Drives Systems (1)
6400 W Enterprise Dr, Mequon, WI 53092-4400
Tel.: (262) 512-8200
Web Site: http://www.ab.com
Sales Range: $400-449.9 Million
Emp.: 1,000
Drive Systems Mfr
N.A.I.C.S.: 334513

Rockwell Automation European Headquarters S.A./N.V. (1)
De Kleetlaan 12 A, 1831, Diegem, Belgium (99.6%)
Tel.: (32) 26630600
Web Site: http://www.rockwellautomation.be
Sales Range: $25-49.9 Million
Emp.: 130
Aircraft Manufacturing
N.A.I.C.S.: 336411

Rockwell Automation G.m.b.H. (1)
Parsevalstrasse 11, Dusseldorf, Germany
Tel.: (49) 21141553620
Web Site:
http://www.rockwellautomation.com
Measuring, Medical & Controlling Device Mfr
N.A.I.C.S.: 334512

Rockwell Automation Germany G.m.b.H. & Co. KG (1)
Westring 222, 42329, Wuppertal, Germany
Tel.: (49) 20273910
Electronics Products & Safety Relays Distr
N.A.I.C.S.: 423690

Rockwell Automation GesmbH (1)
Kotzina strasse 9, 4030, Linz, Austria (100%)
Tel.: (43) 732389090
Web Site: http://www.rockwellautomation.at
Sales Range: $10-24.9 Million
Emp.: 30
Automation Products Distr & Mfr
N.A.I.C.S.: 238210
Ludwig Haslauer *(Mng Dir & Country Dir-Sls)*

Rockwell Automation India Ltd. (1)
C-11 Site-IV Industrial Area, Sahibabad, 201 010, Ghaziabad, Uttar Pradesh, India (100%)
Tel.: (91) 8000504090
Sales Range: $75-99.9 Million
Emp.: 200
Industrial Automation Products Supplier
N.A.I.C.S.: 423830

Rockwell Automation Japan Co., Ltd. (1)
Shinkawa Sanko Building 1-3-17 Shinkawa, Chuo-ku, Tokyo, 104 0033, Japan (100%)
Tel.: (81) 332062784
Web Site:
http://www.automation.rockwell.co.jp
Sales Range: $25-49.9 Million
Emp.: 50
Automation & Industrial Control Products Supplier
N.A.I.C.S.: 423830

Rockwell Automation Korea Ltd. (1)
(100%)
Tel.: (82) 221884400
Web Site:
http://www.rockwellautomation.co.kr
Sales Range: $10-24.9 Million
Emp.: 80
Industrial Automation Products, Systems & Services, LV Power Products, Logic Component & Programmable Controllers; AC/DC Drive Systems, Motors & Spare Parts
N.A.I.C.S.: 334513

Rockwell Automation L.L.C. (1)
18th Floor Al Wahda Commercial City Tower 1, Sheikh Hazza Bin Zayed The First Street, Abu Dhabi, United Arab Emirates (49%)
Tel.: (971) 26948100

Industrial Equipment Distr
N.A.I.C.S.: 423830

Rockwell Automation Limited (1)
(100%)
Web Site:
http://www.rockwellautomation.com
Sales Range: $10-24.9 Million
Emp.: 8
Distr of Automation Products
N.A.I.C.S.: 238210

Rockwell Automation Ltd. (1)
Pitfield Kiln Farm, Milton Keynes, MK11 3DR, Buckinghamshire, United Kingdom (100%)
Tel.: (44) 8702425004
Web Site:
http://www.rockwellautomation.co.uk
Sales Range: $75-99.9 Million
Emp.: 200
Industrial Controls Distr
N.A.I.C.S.: 336411

Rockwell Automation Middle East (1)
Al Wahda Commercial Tower City Tower 1 18th Floor Hazaa Biyed n ZaThe, Abu Dhabi, 35274, United Arab Emirates
Tel.: (971) 26948100
Web Site: http://www.rockwellautomation.ae
Sales Range: $25-49.9 Million
Automation Controls & Drive Systems Distr
N.A.I.C.S.: 334513

Rockwell Automation Proprietary Limited (1)
Janadel Ave Riverview Pk, Halfway Gdn, Midrand, 1685, South Africa (74.99%)
Tel.: (27) 116549700
Web Site:
http://www.rockwellautomation.co.za
Sales Range: $25-49.9 Million
Emp.: 254
Automation Products Distr
N.A.I.C.S.: 449210

Rockwell Automation Puerto Rico, Inc. (1)
Calle 1 Metro Office 6, Guaynabo, PR 00968
Tel.: (787) 300-6228
Web Site:
http://www.rockwellautomation.com
Industrial Machinery Equipment Merchant Whslr
N.A.I.C.S.: 423830

Rockwell Automation S.A. (1)
(100%)
Tel.: (34) 932959000
Web Site: http://www.rockwellautomation.es
Sales Range: $50-74.9 Million
Emp.: 100
Electrical Component Distr
N.A.I.C.S.: 336340

Subsidiary (Non-US):

Rockwell Automation LDA (2)
Tel.: (351) 214225500
Web Site:
http://www.domino.automation.rockwell.com
Sales Range: $10-24.9 Million
Emp.: 11
Automation Products Distr & Mfr
N.A.I.C.S.: 334220

Division (Domestic):

Rockwell Automation S.A. (2)
Josep Pla 101, 08019, Barcelona, Spain (100%)
Tel.: (34) 914810808
Web Site: http://www.rockwellautomation.es
Aircraft Mfr
N.A.I.C.S.: 336411
Jose Paredes *(Gen Dir & Country Dir-Sls)*

Rockwell Automation S.A. (1)
36 Ave De L'Europe, F 78941, Velizy-Villacoublay, Cedex, France (100%)
Tel.: (33) 130677200
Web Site: http://www.rockwellautomation.fr
Sales Range: $75-99.9 Million
Emp.: 200
Automation Products Distr & Mfr
N.A.I.C.S.: 238210

Rockwell Automation S.A./N.V. (1)
De Kleetlaan 12 A, Diegem, 1831, Belgium (100%)
Tel.: (32) 27168411
Web Site: http://www.rockwellautomation.be
Sales Range: $10-24.9 Million
Emp.: 60
Industrial Control Mfr
N.A.I.C.S.: 335314

Rockwell Automation S.R.O. (1)
(100%)
Tel.: (420) 221500111
Web Site: http://www.rockwellautomation.cz
Sales Range: $10-24.9 Million
Emp.: 150
Electronic Connectors Researcher
N.A.I.C.S.: 334512
Jan Bevzicek *(Mng Dir)*

Subsidiary (Non-US):

Rockwell Automation (2)
Bolshoy Strochenovsky Pereulok 22 25, 115054, Moscow, Russia
Tel.: (7) 4959560464
Web Site: http://www.rockwellautomation.ru
Sales Range: $10-24.9 Million
Emp.: 31
Automation Products Consulting
N.A.I.C.S.: 238210
Boris Mourhgorv *(Mng Dir)*

Rockwell Automation S.r.l. (1)
(100%)
Tel.: (39) 02334471
Web Site:
http://www.rockwellautomation.com
Sales Range: $50-74.9 Million
Emp.: 100
Electronic Controls & Communications Products Distr
N.A.I.C.S.: 336411

Rockwell Automation SAS (1)
4 Bis Rue Brindejonc des Moulinais, ZAC de la Grande Plaine, 31500, Toulouse, France (100%)
Tel.: (33) 562477575
Web Site: http://www.rockwellautomation.fr
Sales Range: $10-24.9 Million
Emp.: 20
Automation System Mfr
N.A.I.C.S.: 541513

Rockwell Automation Services S.R.O. (1)
Argentinska 1610 4, 170 00, Prague, Czech Republic
Tel.: (420) 221500111
Web Site:
http://www.rockwellautomation.com
Engineering Services & System Integration
N.A.I.C.S.: 541512

Rockwell Automation Soft Switching Technologies (1)
8155 Forsythia St, Middleton, WI 53562
Tel.: (608) 662-7200
Web Site:
http://www.rockwellautomation.com
Motor & Generator Mf
N.A.I.C.S.: 335312
Jason Doescher *(CFO)*

Rockwell Automation Solutions GmbH (1)
Zur Giesserei 19-27, 76227, Karlsruhe, Germany (100%)
Tel.: (49) 72196506
Web Site:
http://www.rockwellautomation.com
Sales Range: $25-49.9 Million
Emp.: 150
Automation Products
N.A.I.C.S.: 541512

Rockwell Automation Southeast Asia Pte. Ltd. (1)
No 2 Corporation Road 04-05/06 Corporation Place, Singapore, 618494, Singapore (100%)
Tel.: (65) 65106688
Sales Range: $100-124.9 Million
Telecommunications Equipment Mfr
N.A.I.C.S.: 335314

Rockwell Automation Sp. z.o.o. (1)
Powazkowska 44C, Warsaw, Poland (100%)

Tel.: (48) 224596690
Web Site:
http://www.rockwellautomation.com
Sales Range: $10-24.9 Million
Emp.: 20
Industrial Control Mfr
N.A.I.C.S.: 335314

Rockwell Automation Switzerland GmbH (1)
Industriestrasse 20, Aarau, Aargau, Switzerland
Tel.: (41) 628897777
Web Site:
http://www.rockwellautomation.com
Industrial Automation Products Distr
N.A.I.C.S.: 335314

Rockwell Automation Taiwan Co., Ltd. (1)
14F No 120 Sec 2 Jianguo North Rd, Taipei, 104, Taiwan (100%)
Tel.: (886) 2 6618 8288
Web Site:
http://www.rockwellautomation.com
Sales Range: $10-24.9 Million
Emp.: 30
Industrial Automation Control Mfr
N.A.I.C.S.: 333248

Rockwell Automation Thai Co. Ltd. (1)
(100%)
Web Site:
http://www.rockwellautomation.com
Sales Range: $25-49.9 Million
Emp.: 45
Electrical Equipment
N.A.I.C.S.: 336411

Rockwell Automation de Mexico, S.A. de C.V. (1)
Avenida Santa Fe 481 Piso 3 Colonia Cruz manca, Mexico, Mexico (100%)
Tel.: (52) 5552462000
Web Site:
https://www.rockwellautomation.com
Sales Range: $50-74.9 Million
Emp.: 200
Industrial Automation Products, Systems & Services Reseller
N.A.I.C.S.: 335314

Branch (Domestic):

Rockwell Automation de Mexico, S.A. de C.V. (2)
Av Manuel Gomez Morin Num 3870 Segundo Piso Col Centro Sur, Queretaro, 76090, Qro, Mexico (100%)
Tel.: (52) 442 309 5300
Web Site:
http://www.rockwellautomation.com
Window Regulators & Sunroofs
N.A.I.C.S.: 336340

Rockwell Automation do Brasil Ltda. (1)
1488 Verbo Divino St 1 floor Charcara Antonio, Sao Paulo, Brazil (100%)
Tel.: (55) 1151899500
Web Site:
http://www.rockwellautomation.com.br
Sales Range: $75-99.9 Million
Emp.: 300
Industrial Automation Control Products, Systems & Services Distr
N.A.I.C.S.: 335314

Rockwell Automation of Ohio, Inc. (1)
1700 Edison Dr, Milford, OH 45150-2729 (100%)
Tel.: (513) 576-6151
Web Site:
http://www.rockwellautomation.com
Industrial Automation
N.A.I.C.S.: 238290

Rockwell Colombia S.A (1)
North Point II Building Carrera 7 No 156-78 Piso 19, Bogota, Colombia (100%)
Tel.: (57) 16499600
Web Site:
http://www.rockwellautomation.com
Automation Control Products Mfr
N.A.I.C.S.: 335314

Rockwell Commercial Holdings, Ltd. (1)

Pitfield Kiln Farm, Milton Keynes, MK11
3DR, Bucks, United Kingdom
Tel.: (44) 1908838800
Electrical Equipment Whslr
N.A.I.C.S.: 335999

Rockwell Otomasyon Ticaret
A.S.   **(1)**
Karaman Ciftlik Yolu Caddesi Kar Plaza is
Merkezi No 47 E Block Fl 6, Icerenkoy Dis-
trict Atasehir, 34752, Istanbul,
Turkiye   **(100%)**
Tel.: (90) 4444940
Sales Range: $10-24.9 Million
Emp.: 10
Industrial Machinery Mfr
N.A.I.C.S.: 335314
Suma Atali *(Mgr-Fin)*

Rockwell Software, Inc.   **(1)**
1201 S 2nd St, Milwaukee, WI
53204   **(100%)**
Web Site:
    http://www.rockwellautomation.com
Sales Range: $150-199.9 Million
Emp.: 600
Industrial Automated Software
N.A.I.C.S.: 334610

Sensia LLC   **(1)**
Web Site: http://www.sensiaglobal.com
Industrial Automation Equipments Mfr
N.A.I.C.S.: 333998
Allan Rentcome *(CEO)*
Adam Nightingale *(VP-HR)*
Neil Enright *(VP-Sls & Mktg)*
Melissa Nandi *(VP)*
Rajesh Puri *(VP)*
Stephanie Baril *(CFO)*
Paul Krause *(VP)*
Andrea Monte *(VP)*
Tami Haggard *(VP)*
Yasser El-Khazindar *(CEO)*

Silvertech Middle East FZCO   **(1)**
Shed Area Jebel Ali Freezone, Dubai,
17910, United Arab Emirates
Tel.: (971) 48837070
Web Site: http://www.silvertech-dubai.com
Emp.: 15
System Automation Services
N.A.I.C.S.: 513210

Sprecher & Schuh, Inc.   **(1)**
15910 Intl Plz Dr, Houston, TX
77032-2439   **(100%)**
Tel.: (281) 442-9000
Sales Range: $25-49.9 Million
Emp.: 30
Motor Control Mfr
N.A.I.C.S.: 336411
David Wiltse *(Mgr-Sls-Southern)*
Brent Triplett *(Reg Mgr-Bus Dev-Southern)*
Richard Henley *(Mgr-Sls-West & Central)*
Brian Zoldan *(Reg Mgr-Bus Dev-West Cen-
tral)*
Joseph Lamendola *(Mgr-Sls-Northeast)*
Michael Carr *(Mgr-Bus Dev-Northeast)*

ThinManager   **(1)**
1220 Old Alpharetta Rd Ste 300, Alpharetta,
GA 30005
Web Site: http://www.thinmanager.com
Automation Software Development Services
N.A.I.C.S.: 541511
Tom Jordan *(VP-Mktg)*
Paul Burns *(Dir-Trng & Technical Svcs)*
Mark Westol *(Sls Dir-Midwest & Western
Canada)*
Jamie Blanchard *(Sls Dir-Northeast & East-
ern Canada)*
Keith Jones *(Sls Dir-West)*
Nick Putman *(Sr Engr-Comml)*
Todd Garmon *(Engr-Application)*

ROCKWELL MEDICAL, INC.
30142 S Wixom Rd, Wixom, MI
48393
Tel.: (248) 960-9009   MI
Web Site:
    https://www.rockwellmed.com
Year Founded: 1995
RMTI—(NASDAQ)
Rev.: $72,810,000
Assets: $46,635,000
Liabilities: $32,529,000
Net Worth: $14,106,000

Earnings: ($18,679,000)
Emp.: 253
Fiscal Year-end: 12/31/22
Hemodialysis, Concentrates, Dialysis
Kits & Other Hemodialysis Products
Mfr
N.A.I.C.S.: 334510
Timothy T. Chole *(Sr VP-Sales-
Marketing)*
Mark Strobeck *(Pres & CEO)*
Heather R. Hunter *(Chief Corp Affairs
Officer & Sr VP)*
Jesse Neri *(Sr VP-Finance)*
Megan Timmins *(Chief Legal Officer,
Sec & Exec VP)*

Subsidiaries:

Rockwell Transportation, Inc.   **(1)**
30142 Wixom Rd, Wixom, MI 48393
Tel.: (248) 960-9009
Sales Range: $150-199.9 Million
Trucking Service
N.A.I.C.S.: 484122

ROCKY BRANDS, INC.
39 E Canal St, Nelsonville, OH 45764
Tel.: (740) 753-1951   OH
Web Site:
    https://www.rockybrands.com
Year Founded: 1932
RCKY—(NASDAQ)
Rev.: $615,475,000
Assets: $582,390,000
Liabilities: $366,917,000
Net Worth: $215,473,000
Earnings: $20,465,000
Emp.: 2,490
Fiscal Year-end: 12/31/22
Men's & Women's Footwear & Ap-
parel Designer, Mfr & Marketer
N.A.I.C.S.: 316210
Curtis A. Loveland *(Sec)*
Thomas D. Robertson *(CFO, COO,
Principal Acctg Officer & Treas)*
Jason S. Brooks *(Chm & CEO)*

Subsidiaries:

Durango Boot Company, LLC   **(1)**
45 E Canal St, Nelsonville, OH 45764
Tel.: (740) 753-3130
Web Site: http://www.rockybrands.com
Sales Range: $125-149.9 Million
Emp.: 260
Outdoor & Occupational Footwear De-
signer, Mfr & Distr
N.A.I.C.S.: 316210

Georgia Boot, LLC   **(1)**
39 E Canal St, Nelsonville, OH 45764
Tel.: (740) 753-1951
Web Site: http://www.rockybrands.com
Sales Range: $450-499.9 Million
Outdoor & Occupational Footwear De-
signer, Mfr & Distr
N.A.I.C.S.: 316210

Lehigh Outfitters, LLC   **(1)**
39 E Canal St, Nelsonville, OH 45764
Tel.: (740) 753-9100
Web Site: https://www.lehighoutfitters.com
Sales Range: $400-449.9 Million
Emp.: 250
Safety Footwear & Apparel Mfr
N.A.I.C.S.: 316210
Mike Brooks *(Chm)*

Lifestyle Footwear, Inc.   **(1)**
Carr 125 Km 3/8 Bo Pueblo St Ca, Moca,
PR 00676
Tel.: (787) 877-5050
Footwear Mfr & Distr
N.A.I.C.S.: 326299
Aurora Gonzalez *(Coord-Shipping)*

Rocky Brands Canada, Inc.   **(1)**
50 Northland Rd Unit 3, Waterloo, N2V
1N3, ON, Canada
Tel.: (519) 883-8226
Emp.: 12
Footwear Whslr
N.A.I.C.S.: 424340

Rocky Brands US, LLC   **(1)**

37601 Rocky Boots Way, Logan, OH 43138
Tel.: (740) 753-1951
Footwear Mfr
N.A.I.C.S.: 316210

Rocky Canada, Inc.   **(1)**
50 Northland Rd Unit 3, Waterloo, N2V
1N3, ON, Canada
Tel.: (519) 883-8226
Emp.: 12
Footwear Whslr
N.A.I.C.S.: 424340

Rocky Outdoor Gear   **(1)**
45 E Canal St, Nelsonville, OH 45764
Tel.: (740) 753-3130
Web Site: https://rockyoutlet.com
Sales Range: $125-149.9 Million
Emp.: 40
Outdoor & Occupational Footwear De-
signer, Mfr & Distr
N.A.I.C.S.: 316210

Rocky Outdoor Gear Store, LLC   **(1)**
45 E Canal St, Nelsonville, OH 45764
Tel.: (740) 753-3130
Web Site: http://www.rockyoutlet.com
Apparel Mfr & Distr
N.A.I.C.S.: 315210

ROCKY MOUNTAIN CHOCO-
LATE FACTORY, INC.
265 Turner Dr, Durango, CO 81303
Tel.: (970) 259-0554   DE
Web Site: https://www.rmcf.com
Year Founded: 2014
RMCF—(NASDAQ)
Rev.: $27,950,687
Assets: $20,577,218
Liabilities: $9,941,059
Net Worth: $10,636,159
Earnings: ($4,171,883)
Emp.: 135
Fiscal Year-end: 02/29/24
Holding Company; Chocolate Candy
& Confections Mfr
N.A.I.C.S.: 551112
Ryan R. McGrath *(Sr VP-IT)*
Jeffrey Richart Geygan *(Interim CEO)*
Carrie E. Cass *(Executives)*

Subsidiaries:

Rocky Mountain Chocolate Factory,
Inc.   **(1)**
265 Turner Dr, Durango, CO 81303
Tel.: (970) 259-0554
Web Site: https://www.rmcf.com
Chocolate Candy & Confections Mfr
N.A.I.C.S.: 311351
Ryan R. McGrath *(Sr VP-IT)*
Jeffrey Richart Geygan *(Interim CEO)*
Franklin E. Crail *(Founder)*
Donna L. Coupe *(VP-Franchise Support &
Trng)*
Kara Conklin *(VP-Franchise Dev)*
Andy Black *(VP-Supply Chain)*
Kelsea Schmidt *(VP-Mktg)*
Tyson Snider *(VP-Mfg)*
Starlette B. Johnson *(Chm)*

Subsidiary (Domestic):

Aspen Leaf Yogurt, LLC   **(2)**
265 Turner Dr, Durango, CO 81303
Tel.: (702) 586-8700
Web Site: https://www.aspenleafyogurt.com
Emp.: 15
Ice Cream & Frozen Dessert Mfr
N.A.I.C.S.: 311520

Subsidiary (Non-US):

U-Swirl, Inc.   **(2)**
                 (60%)
Tel.: (702) 586-8700
Web Site: https://www.u-swirl.com
Emp.: 18
Holding Company; Frozen Yogurt Restau-
rant Owner, Operator & Franchisor
N.A.I.C.S.: 551112
Bryan J. Merryman *(Chm & CEO)*

Subsidiary (Domestic):

U-Swirl International, Inc.   **(3)**
265 Turner Dr, Durango, CO 81303

Tel.: (702) 586-8700
Web Site: https://www.u-swirl.com
Emp.: 18
Snack & Nonalcoholic Beverage Bar Opera-
tor
N.A.I.C.S.: 722515
Alan Stribling *(Pres)*

ROCKY MOUNTAIN HIGH
BRANDS, INC.
3540 14th St Ste 200, Plano, TX
75074
Tel.: (972) 833-1584   NV
Web Site:
    http://www.rockymountainhigh
    brands.com
Year Founded: 2014
RMHB—(OTCIQ)
Rev.: $205,250
Assets: $545,959
Liabilities: $3,168,310
Net Worth: ($2,622,351)
Earnings: ($5,266,794)
Emp.: 3
Fiscal Year-end: 12/31/19
Beverage Product Mfr & Distr
N.A.I.C.S.: 312111
Charles Smith *(Chm)*
David M. Seeberger *(Pres, CEO &
Gen Counsel)*
Imran F. Kaiser *(Sr VP)*
Zia Mehar *(Mgr-Development)*

ROCKY MOUNTAIN INDUSTRI-
ALS, INC.
6200 S Syracuse Way Ste 450,
Greenwood Village, CO 80111
Tel.: (720) 614-5213   NV
Web Site:
    https://www.rockymountainindus
    trials.com
RMRI—(OTCIQ)
Rev.: $827,515
Assets: $25,502,773
Liabilities: $25,528,714
Net Worth: ($25,941)
Earnings: ($8,349,750)
Emp.: 13
Fiscal Year-end: 03/31/23
All Other Miscellaneous Nonmetallic
Mineral Product Manufacturing
N.A.I.C.S.: 327999
Gregory M. Dangler *(CEO)*

RODEDAWG INTERNATIONAL
INDUSTRIES, INC.
1968 S Coast Hwy 190, Laguna
Beach, CA 92651   NV
Year Founded: 1999
RWGI—(OTCIQ)
Sport Utility Vehicle Mfr
N.A.I.C.S.: 339920

ROGERS CORPORATION
2225 W Chandler Blvd, Chandler, AZ
85224
Tel.: (480) 917-6026   MA
Web Site:
    https://www.rogerscorp.com
Year Founded: 1832
ROG—(NYSE)
Rev.: $971,171,000
Assets: $1,646,214,000
Liabilities: $473,748,000
Net Worth: $1,172,466,000
Earnings: $116,629,000
Emp.: 3,800
Fiscal Year-end: 12/31/22
Bare Printed Circuit Board Manufac-
turing
N.A.I.C.S.: 334412
Jay B. Knoll *(Gen Counsel, Sec & Sr
VP- Corp Dev)*
Mark D. Weaver *(Chief Acctg Officer
& Controller)*
Jonathan J. Rowntree *(Sr VP/Gen
Mgr-Advanced Connectivity Solu-
tions)*

Rogers Corporation—(Continued)

Randall Colin Gouveia (Pres & CEO)
Amy Kweder (Dir-Corp Comm)
Steve Haymore (Dir-IR)
Larry Schmid (Sr VP-Global Ops &
Supply Chain)
Jessica Morton (Gen Counsel, Sec &
VP)
Brian Larabee (VP)

Subsidiaries:

Curamik Electronics GmbH   (1)
Am Stadtwald 2, 92676, Eschenbach, Germany
Tel.: (49) 964592220
Web Site: http://www.curamik.com
Sales Range: $25-49.9 Million
Emp.: 600
Direct Bonded Copper Substrates Mfr
N.A.I.C.S.: 331420

Subsidiary (US):

Curamik Electronics, Inc.   (2)
3770 Arapaho Rd, Addison, TX 75001-4311
Tel.: (214) 615-1533
Ceramic Circuit Boards Distr
N.A.I.C.S.: 334412

DeWAL Industries, Inc.   (1)
15 Ray Trainor Dr, Narragansett, RI
02882   (100%)
Tel.: (401) 789-9736
Polymer Films & Pressure Sensitive Tapes
Mfr
N.A.I.C.S.: 326113

Diversified Silicone Products,
Inc.   (1)
13937 Rosecrans Ave, Santa Fe Springs,
CA 90670-5209
Tel.: (562) 404-8942
Web Site: http://www.diversifiedsilicone.net
Rubber Products Mfr
N.A.I.C.S.: 326299

Griswold, LLC.   (1)
1 River St, Moosup, CT 06354
Tel.: (860) 564-3321
Web Site: http://www.griswoldllc.com
Engineered Cellular Rubber Mfr
N.A.I.C.S.: 326299
Dan Mahoney (CEO)

Rogers (Shanghai) International Trading Co. Ltd.   (1)
Rm 1003 Want Want Building No 211 Shi
Men Yi Road, Jing An District, Shanghai,
200041, China   (100%)
Tel.: (06) 21 6217 5500
Sales of Electronic Components
N.A.I.C.S.: 423690

Rogers B.V.B.A.   (1)
Afrikalaan 188, 9000, Gent, Belgium
Tel.: (32) 92353611
Web Site: http://www.rogers.be
Emp.: 150
Textile Material Manufacturer
N.A.I.C.S.: 313310

Rogers Corp. - Advanced Circuit Materials Division - Flexible
Products   (1)
100 S Roosevelt Ave, Chandler, AZ 85226-3436
Tel.: (480) 917-5270
Web Site: http://www.rogerscorp.com
Sales Range: $100-124.9 Million
Emp.: 4
Mfr of Electronic Insulation Materials
N.A.I.C.S.: 334419

Rogers Corp. - Advanced Circuit Materials Division - High Frequency
Products   (1)
100 S Roosevelt Ave, Chandler, AZ 85226-3415
Tel.: (480) 961-1382
Web Site: http://www.rogerscorp.com
Sales Range: $125-149.9 Million
Emp.: 250
Mfr of Microwave Dielectric Materials
N.A.I.C.S.: 334419

Rogers Corp. - Durel Division   (1)

2225 W Chandler Blvd, Chandler, AZ
85224-6155   (100%)
Tel.: (480) 917-6000
Web Site: http://www.rogerscorp.com
Sales Range: $50-74.9 Million
Emp.: 200
Mfr of Electric Lamps
N.A.I.C.S.: 335139

Rogers Corp. - High Performance
Foams Division - Bisco Silicones (1)
171 W St Charles Rd, Carol Stream, IL
60188
Tel.: (630) 784-6200
Web Site: http://www.rogerscorporation.com
Sales Range: $200-249.9 Million
Mfr of High Performance Silicone Rubber,
Sponge, Foam & Foam Substrate Combination Materials
N.A.I.C.S.: 325211

Rogers Corp. - High Performance
Foams Division - Composite
Materials   (1)
1 Technology Dr, Rogers, CT 06263-0217
Tel.: (860) 779-5735
Web Site: http://www.rogerscorp.com
Sales Range: $25-49.9 Million
Emp.: 100
Mfr & Marketer of Air-Laid, Needle-
Punched, Highloft Nonwoven Fabrics Used
for Padding, Thermal Insulation, Dampening
& Ductor Sleeves & Prefilter Applications
N.A.I.C.S.: 325211

Rogers Corp. - High Performance
Foams Division - Poron
Urethanes   (1)
245 Woodstock Rd, Woodstock, CT 06281-1815
Tel.: (860) 928-3622
Web Site: http://www.rogerscorp.com
Sales Range: $50-74.9 Million
Emp.: 100
Mfr of Polyurethane-Based Microcellular
Materials
N.A.I.C.S.: 325211

Rogers Corporation - Delaware
Facility   (1)
1100 Governor Lea Rd, Bear, DE 19701-1998
Tel.: (302) 834-2100
Web Site: http://www.rogerscorp.com
Emp.: 120
Silicone Products Mfr
N.A.I.C.S.: 325212

Rogers Germany GmbH   (1)
Am Stadtwald 2, 92676, Eschenbach, Germany
Tel.: (49) 964592220
Web Site: http://www.curamik.com
Energy Efficiency Services
N.A.I.C.S.: 541614

Rogers Inoac Corporation   (1)
9-117 Nashinoki, Chita-gun, Taketoyo, 470-
2309, Aichi, Japan   (50%)
Tel.: (81) 569741811
Web Site: https://www.poron.jp
Sales Range: $25-49.9 Million
Emp.: 80
Polyurethane Material Mfr
N.A.I.C.S.: 325211
Takashi Ishi (Mgr-Mktg)

Rogers Japan Inc.   (1)
4-2-16 Nihonbashi Hongokucho Daiwa Ni-
honbashi Hongokucho Building 8F, Chuo-
ku, Tokyo, 103-0021, Japan
Tel.: (81) 352002700
Web Site: https://www.rogerscorp.jp
Sales Range: $10-24.9 Million
Emp.: 9
Sales of Interconnection Products
N.A.I.C.S.: 449210

Rogers Korea, Inc.   (1)
407ho A-dong Pyeongchon Acro Tower 230
Simin-daero, Dongan-gu, Anyang, 445 896,
Gyeonggi-Do, Korea (South)   (100%)
Tel.: (82) 313603622
Web Site: http://www.rogerscorp.com
Sales Range: $25-49.9 Million
Emp.: 6
Polymer & Electronic Materials Sales
N.A.I.C.S.: 423690

Rogers N.V.   (1)

Noorwegenstraat 3, 9940, Evergem,
Belgium   (100%)
Tel.: (32) 92353611
Web Site: http://www.rogerscorp.com
Sales Range: $75-99.9 Million
Emp.: 150
Printed Circuit Board Mfr
N.A.I.C.S.: 334412

Rogers Taiwan, Inc.   (1)
11F-1 No 345 Chung-Ho Road, Yung-Ho
District, New Taipei City, 23447,
Taiwan   (100%)
Tel.: (886) 286609056
Web Site: http://www.rogerscorporation.com
Emp.: 40
Polymer & Electronic Materials Sales
N.A.I.C.S.: 423690

Rogers Technologies (Suzhou) Co.,
Ltd.   (1)
No 28 West Shenhu Road, Suzhou Indus-
trial Park, Suzhou, 215122, Jiangsu, China
Tel.: (86) 51262582700
Plastic Material & Resin Mfr
N.A.I.C.S.: 325211
Roger Leng (Mgr-Mfr)

Rogers Technologies Singapore,
Inc.   (1)
60 Kaki Bukit Place 03-04 Eunos Techpark
Lobby B, Singapore, 415979,
Singapore   (100%)
Tel.: (65) 67473521
Web Site: http://www.rogerscorp.com
Sales Range: $25-49.9 Million
Emp.: 5
Polymer & Electronic Materials Sales
N.A.I.C.S.: 423690

Rogers Technology (Suzhou) Co.,
Ltd.   (1)
338 Shen Hu road, Suzhou Industrial Park,
Suzhou, 215122, China
Tel.: (86) 512 6258 2700
Mfr of Polyurethane-Based Microcellular
Materials
N.A.I.C.S.: 325211

Utis Co., Ltd   (1)
349 Haean-ro, Danwon-gu, Ansan, 15613,
Gyeonggi-do, Korea (South)
Tel.: (82) 313653320
Web Site: http://www.utis-co.com
Mobile Internet Devices & Consumer Elec-
tronics Product Mfr
N.A.I.C.S.: 334419

**ROGUE STATION COMPANIES,
INC.**
806 Oneal Ln, Baton Rouge, LA
70616
Tel.: (214) 769-0247   DE
RGST—(OTCIQ)
Telecommunication Servicesb
N.A.I.C.S.: 517810

ROKU, INC.
1173 Coleman Ave, San Jose, CA
95110
Tel.: (408) 556-9040   DE
Web Site: https://www.roku.com
Year Founded: 2002
ROKU—(NASDAQ)
Rev.: $3,484,619,000
Assets: $4,261,792,000
Liabilities: $1,935,459,000
Net Worth: $2,326,333,000
Earnings: ($709,561,000)
Emp.: 3,150
Fiscal Year-end: 12/31/23
Electronic Entertainment Device Mfr
N.A.I.C.S.: 334310
Scott de Haas (Sr VP-Product Engrg
& Ops)
Stephen Kay (Gen Counsel & Sr VP)
Ilya Asnis (Sr VP-Roku OS)
Mustafa Ozgen (Sr VP & Gen Mgr-
Acct Acquisition)
Charlie Collier (Pres)
Kamilah Mitchell-Thomas (Sr VP-
People)
Dan Jedda (CFO)

Brian Pinkerton (Sr VP-Advanced
Dev)
Gidon Katz (Sr VP)
Mustafa Ozgen (Pres-Devices)
Gidon Katz (Pres-Consumer Experi-
ence)
Matthew Banks (Chief Acctg Officer,
VP & Controller)
Gil Fuchsberg (Sr VP)
John Kelly (Sr VP)
Matthew Banks (Chief Acctg Officer,
VP & Controller)
Anthony Wood (Founder, Chm, Pres
& CEO)

Subsidiaries:

DataXu, Inc.   (1)
53 Stat St 25th Fl, Boston, MA 02109
Tel.: (857) 244-6200
Web Site: http://www.dataxu.com
Emp.: 201
Information Technology Consulting Services
N.A.I.C.S.: 541512
Sandro Catanzaro (Co-Founder)
Manjula Kandasamy (Sr Dir-Sls)

This Old House Ventures, LLC   (1)
135 W 50th St 10th Fl, New York, NY
10020
Tel.: (212) 522-9465
Web Site: http://www.thisoldhouse.com
Home Improvement Magazine Publisher,
Television Programming & Other Media
Publishing
N.A.I.C.S.: 513199
Eric Thorkilsen (CEO & Mng Partner)
Susan Wyland (Editor-in-Chief-Magazine)
Joe Brady (CFO)
Michael Burton (Chief Revenue Officer)
Michael Gutkowski (Chief Digital Officer)
Chris Wolfe (Gen Mgr)

Division (Domestic):

This Old House Magazine   (2)
135 W 50th St 10th Fl, New York, NY
10020
Tel.: (212) 522-7861
Web Site: http://www.thisoldhouse.com
Home Improvement Magazine Publisher
N.A.I.C.S.: 513100
Susan Wyland (Editor-in-Chief)
Mark Powers (Editor)

ROLLINS, INC.
2170 Piedmont Rd NE, Atlanta, GA
30324
Tel.: (404) 888-2000   DE
Web Site: https://www.rollins.com
Year Founded: 1948
ROL—(NYSE)
Rev.: $3,073,278,000
Assets: $2,595,460,000
Liabilities: $1,439,893,000
Net Worth: $1,155,567,000
Earnings: $434,957,000
Emp.: 19,031
Fiscal Year-end: 12/31/23
Pest Control Services
N.A.I.C.S.: 561710
Gary W. Rollins (Exec Chm)
Kenneth D. Krause (CFO, Treas &
Exec VP)
John F. Wilson (Vice Chm)
Jerry E. Gahlhoff Jr. (Pres & CEO)

Subsidiaries:

AMES Group Limited   (1)
Units 7-8 Acorn Park Vernon Road, Black-
heath, Birmingham, B62 8EG, United King-
dom
Tel.: (44) 3301910005
Web Site: http://www.amesgroup.uk.com
Pest Control Services
N.A.I.C.S.: 561710

Aardwolf Pestkare (Singapore) Pte.
Ltd.   (1)
26 Third Lok Yang Road, Singapore,
628015, Singapore
Tel.: (65) 62681771
Web Site: https://aardwolfpestkare.com
Pest Management Services

N.A.I.C.S.: 115310

Adams Pest Control Pty Ltd (1)
252 Normanby Road, South Melbourne,
3205, VIC, Australia
Tel.: (61) 396452388
Web Site:
    https://www.adamspestcontrol.com.au
Pest Control Services
N.A.I.C.S.: 561710
Peter Taylor *(Gen Mgr)*

**Albany Environmental Services
Ltd.** (1)
44 Russell Square, London, WC1B 4JP,
United Kingdom
Tel.: (44) 2072878845
Web Site:
    https://www.albanypestcontrol.co.uk
Pest Control Services
N.A.I.C.S.: 561710

Baroque (S.W.) Limited (1)
Orchard Cottage Down Thomas, Plymouth,
PL9 0DY, United Kingdom
Tel.: (44) 1752862908
Web Site:
    http://www.baroquepestcontrol.co.uk
Pest Control Services
N.A.I.C.S.: 561710

**Clark Pest Control of Stockton
Inc.** (1)
555 N Guild Ave, Lodi, CA 95240-2023
Tel.: (209) 368-7152
Web Site: http://www.clarkpest.com
Sales Range: $25-49.9 Million
Emp.: 630
Provider of Pest Control Services
N.A.I.C.S.: 561710

Subsidiary (Domestic):

**Clark Pest Control of Nevada,
LLC** (2)
690 Kresge Ln, Sparks, NV 89431
Tel.: (775) 359-8215
Web Site: http://www.clarkpest.com
Consumer Services
N.A.I.C.S.: 561990

Clark Pest Control, Inc. (2)
1700 K St Ste 200, Bakersfield, CA 93301
Tel.: (661) 635-3535
Web Site: http://www.clarkpest.com
Exterminating & Pest Control Services
N.A.I.C.S.: 561710

Jeff's Pest Control Service, Inc. (2)
4606 Mtn Lakes Blvd Ste E, Redding, CA
96003-1449
Tel.: (530) 247-1802
Web Site: http://www.jeffspest.com
Exterminating & Pest Control Services
N.A.I.C.S.: 561710
Jeff De Rosa *(Founder)*

**Clark Pest Control of Nevada,
LLC** (1)
690 Kresge Ln, Sparks, NV 89431
Tel.: (775) 262-7594
Pest Exterminating & Control Services
N.A.I.C.S.: 561710

Crane Pest Control, Inc. (1)
2700 Geary Blvd, San Francisco, CA
94118-3498
Tel.: (415) 922-1666
Web Site: http://www.cranepestcontrol.com
Sales Range: $10-24.9 Million
Emp.: 100
Pest Control Services
N.A.I.C.S.: 561710
Harold S. Stein *(Pres & CEO)*

Enviropest Control Services Ltd. (1)
Prince of Wales House 62 Prince of Wales
Lane, Birmingham, B14 4JY, West Mid-
lands, United Kingdom
Tel.: (44) 1216936616
Web Site: http://www.enviropest.co.uk
Pest Control Services
N.A.I.C.S.: 561710

**Europest Environmental Services
Limited** (1)
Unit G Trecenydd Business Park, Caer-
philly, CF83 2RZ, United Kingdom
Tel.: (44) 2920868961
Web Site: https://www.theeurogroup.co.uk

Pest Exterminating & Control Services
N.A.I.C.S.: 561710

Fox Pest Control - Albany LLC (1)
431 New Karner Rd Ste 170, Albany, NY
12205
Tel.: (518) 300-4732
Pest Exterminating & Control Services
N.A.I.C.S.: 561710

**Fox Pest Control - Long Island,
LLC** (1)
66 S 2nd St Unit D, Bay Shore, NY 11706
Tel.: (631) 458-5003
Pest Exterminating & Control Services
N.A.I.C.S.: 561710

**Fox Pest Control - Louisiana
LLC** (1)
4545 Sherwood Commons Blvd Ste 4B,
Baton Rouge, LA 70816
Tel.: (225) 228-4757
Pest Exterminating & Control Services
N.A.I.C.S.: 561710

**Fox Pest Control - McAllen TX,
LLC** (1)
200 E Expressway 83 Unit Ste L-1, Pharr,
TX 78577
Tel.: (956) 435-7142
Pest Exterminating & Control Services
N.A.I.C.S.: 561710

**Fox Pest Control - Orlando West,
LLC** (1)
2836 County Rd 523 Ste F7, Wildwood, FL
34785
Tel.: (407) 863-3592
Pest Exterminating & Control Services
N.A.I.C.S.: 561710

**Fox Pest Control - Pittsburgh,
LLC** (1)
377 Northgate Dr, Warrendale, PA 15086
Tel.: (724) 384-7071
Pest Exterminating & Control Services
N.A.I.C.S.: 561710

**Fox Pest Control - Rhode Island,
LLC** (1)
1300 Jefferson Blvd, Warwick, RI 02886
Tel.: (401) 655-2922
Pest Exterminating & Control Services
N.A.I.C.S.: 561710

**Fox Pest Control - Virginia Beach,
LLC** (1)
908 Ventures Way Ste A, Chesapeake, VA
23320
Tel.: (757) 206-2718
Pest Exterminating & Control Services
N.A.I.C.S.: 561710

Fox Pest Services, LLC (1)
755 S Main St, Logan, UT 84321
Web Site: https://fox-pest.com
Pest Exterminating & Control Services
N.A.I.C.S.: 561710

**Guardian Hygiene Services
Limited** (1)
Unit 11 Lincoln Enterprise Park Newark
Road, Lincoln, LN5 9FP, United Kingdom
Tel.: (44) 1522688180
Web Site: https://guardian-group.co.uk
Pest Control Services
N.A.I.C.S.: 561710

Guardian Pest Control Limited (1)
Unit 11 Lincoln Enterprise Park Newark
Road, Lincoln, LN5 9FP, United Kingdom
Tel.: (44) 1522705511
Pest Control Services
N.A.I.C.S.: 115112

HomeTeam Pest Defense, LLC (1)
1341 W Mockingbird Ln Ste 850W, Dallas,
TX 75247 **(100%)**
Tel.: (214) 665-8700
Web Site: https://www.pestdefense.com
Sales Range: $125-149.9 Million
Emp.: 1,900
Pest Control Management Services
N.A.I.C.S.: 561710
Brady Camp *(Pres)*
Russ Horton *(VP-Technical Svcs)*
Ken Hylkema *(VP-Residential Sls)*
Debbie Silver *(VP-Builder Sls)*
Kathy Zielinski *(VP-Mktg, Comm & Trng)*

Mike Johnson *(VP-Operations)*
Suzanne Scott *(VP-Marketing)*
Toby Schafer *(VP-Human Resources &)*

Industrial Fumigant Company (1)
13420 W 99th St, Lenexa, KS 66215-1365
Tel.: (913) 782-6399
Web Site: https://www.indfumco.com
Rev.: $26,000,000
Emp.: 140
Pest Control Services
N.A.I.C.S.: 561710

Subsidiary (Domestic):

**International Food Consultants,
LLC** (2)
2088 Tocobaga Ln, Nokomis, FL 34275
Tel.: (201) 738-4700
Pest Control Services
N.A.I.C.S.: 561710

Kestrel Pest Control Limited (1)
Unit 19 Monks Brook Industrial Park School
Close, Chandlers Ford, SO53 4RA, Hamp-
shire, United Kingdom
Tel.: (44) 2380083679
Web Site: http://www.kestrelpestcontrol.com
Pest Control Services
N.A.I.C.S.: 561710

Kinro Investments, Inc. (1)
1105 N Market St 1300, Wilmington, DE
19801
Tel.: (302) 429-2600
Pest Control Services
N.A.I.C.S.: 561710

NBC Environment Limited (1)
The Grove Kenninghall Road, Banham,
Norfolk, NR16 2HE, United Kingdom
Tel.: (44) 3335672020
Web Site:
    https://www.nbcenvironment.co.uk
Pest Exterminating & Control Services
N.A.I.C.S.: 561710

Northwest Exterminating, LLC (1)
830 Kennesaw Ave NW, Marietta, GA
30060
Tel.: (888) 466-7849
Web Site: http://www.callnorthwest.com
Pest Control Services
N.A.I.C.S.: 561710

Subsidiary (Domestic):

Jody Millard Pest Control, LLC (2)
1906 Hamill Rd Ste 112, Hixson, TN 37343
Tel.: (423) 799-2731
Web Site:
    https://www.jodymillardpestcontrol.com
Pest Control Services
N.A.I.C.S.: 561710

Sawyer Exterminating, Inc. (2)
401 Alamance Rd, Burlington, NC 27215
Tel.: (336) 226-1448
Web Site:
    http://www.sawyerexterminating.com
Exterminating & Pest Control Services
N.A.I.C.S.: 561710
Marty Stadler *(Coord-Mktg & Ops)*

Target Pest Control, Inc. (2)
7830 AL-157, Cullman, AL 35057
Tel.: (205) 942-9009
Web Site: http://www.targetpestcontrol.com
Exterminating & Pest Control Services
N.A.I.C.S.: 561710

OPC Pest Control, Inc. (1)
5800 Poplar Level Rd, Louisville, KY 40228
Tel.: (502) 969-9635
Web Site: http://www.opcpest.com
Pest Control Services
N.A.I.C.S.: 561710
Kevin Mills *(Co-Pres)*
Kassandra Mills *(Co-Pres)*

Orkin, Inc. (1)
2170 Piedmont Rd NE, Atlanta, GA
30324-4135 **(100%)**
Tel.: (404) 888-2000
Web Site: http://www.orkin.com
Sales Range: $900-999.9 Million
Emp.: 4,715
Termite & Pest Control Services
N.A.I.C.S.: 561710
Gary W. Rollins *(Chm)*

Subsidiary (Non-US):

Orkin Canada (2)
5840 Falbourne Street, Mississauga, L5R
4B5, ON, Canada **(100%)**
Tel.: (905) 502-9700
Web Site: http://www.orkincanada.ca
Sales Range: $10-24.9 Million
Emp.: 50
Disinfecting & Pest Control Services
N.A.I.C.S.: 561710
Sean Rollo *(Mgr-Technical Bus Dev)*
Rob Quinn *(Pres)*
Bruno Levesque *(VP)*
Steve Leavitt *(Pres)*

PCO Acqusitions, Inc. (1)
1105 N Market St Ste 1500, Wilmington, DE
19801
Tel.: (302) 656-2030
Pest Control Services
N.A.I.C.S.: 561710

**PermaTreat Pest Control Company
Inc.** (1)
6420 Seminole Trl, Barboursville, VA 22923
Tel.: (434) 985-3800
Web Site: http://www.permatreat.com
Emp.: 10
Pest Control Services
N.A.I.C.S.: 561710
Jack Broome *(Pres)*

Division (Non-US):

Orkin Canada (2)
11312-163 Street NW, Edmonton, T5M
1Y6, AB, Canada
Tel.: (780) 483-3070
Web Site: http://www.orkincanada.ca
Emp.: 40
Pest Control Services
N.A.I.C.S.: 561710

Orkin Canada (2)
101-84 North Bend Street Unit 101, Coquit-
lam, V3K 6H1, BC, Canada
Tel.: (604) 409-4522
Web Site: http://www.orkincanada.ca
Pest Control Services
N.A.I.C.S.: 561710

Pestproof Limited (1)
Mitre Street, Failsworth, Manchester, M35
9BY, United Kingdom
Tel.: (44) 1616849451
Web Site: https://pestproof.co.uk
Pest Control & Cleaning Services
N.A.I.C.S.: 561710

Rollins Supply, Inc. (1)
2170 Piedmont Rd NE, Atlanta, GA
30324-4135 **(100%)**
Tel.: (404) 888-2000
Web Site: http://www.rollins.com
Sales Range: $10-24.9 Million
Emp.: 15
Pest Control Services
N.A.I.C.S.: 325320

**Safeguard Pest Control and Environ-
mental Services Limited** (1)
Unit 6 Churchill Business Park The Flyers
Way, Westerham, TN16 1BT, Kent, United
Kingdom
Tel.: (44) 330 191 0486
Web Site:
    https://www.safeguardpestcontrol.co.uk
Pest Control Services
N.A.I.C.S.: 561710

**Scientific Pest Management
(Australia/Pacific) Pty. Ltd.** (1)
2A/62 Secam Street, Mansfield, 4122, QLD,
Australia
Tel.: (61) 300467546
Web Site: https://www.scientificpest.com.au
Pest Management Services
N.A.I.C.S.: 115310

Statewide Rollins Pty Ltd (1)
34 Old Dookie Rd, Shepparton, 3630, VIC,
Australia
Tel.: (61) 358316200
Web Site:
    http://www.statewidepestcontrol.com.au
Pest Control Services
N.A.I.C.S.: 561710

**Van Vynck Environmental Services
Ltd.** (1)

Rollins, Inc.—(Continued)

Riverside Business Centre Fort Road, Til-
bury, RM18 7ND, Essex, United Kingdom
Tel.: (44) 8081689447
Web Site: https://www.vvenv.co.uk
Pest Control Services
N.A.I.C.S.: 561710

Waltham Services LLC (1)
9 Erie Dr, Natick, MA 01760
Tel.: (781) 893-1810
Web Site: http://www.walthamservices.com
Sales Range: $10-24.9 Million
Emp.: 200
Termite & Pest Control Services
N.A.I.C.S.: 561710
Mark Bretz (VP & Gen Mgr)

Subsidiary (Domestic):

Expert Pest Control, Inc. (2)
967 S St, Fitchburg, MA 01420-7019
Web Site: http://www.expertpestcontrol.net
Exterminating & Pest Control Services
N.A.I.C.S.: 561710

Unit (Domestic):

Flower City Pest Elimination (2)
2975 Brighton Hen Tl Rd Ste 200, Roches-
ter, NY 14623 (100%)
Tel.: (585) 263-2847
Web Site: http://www.flowercitypest.com
Termite & Pest Control Service
N.A.I.C.S.: 561710

Western Pest Services (1)
800 Lanidex Plz, Parsippany, NJ 07054
Tel.: (973) 515-0100
Web Site: http://www.westernpest.com
Sales Range: $25-49.9 Million
Emp.: 750
Pest Control Services
N.A.I.C.S.: 561710
Pat Porcella (VP)

ROOSHINE, INC.
1617 Florida Ave, West Palm Beach,
FL 33401
Tel.: (347) 642-1434 NV
Web Site: http://www.chooserain.com
Year Founded: 1998
RSAU—(OTCIQ)
Bottled Water & Hydroponics
N.A.I.C.S.: 312112
Maximo A. Gomez (CEO)
Les Brian McCall (Chm)

ROOSTER ENERGY LTD.
16285 Park Ten Pl Ste 120, Houston,
TX 77084
Tel.: (832) 772-6313 BC
Web Site:
    http://www.roosterenergyltd.com
Year Founded: 1988
3P4A—(DEU)
Sales Range: $25-49.9 Million
Oil & Gas Exploration Services
N.A.I.C.S.: 213112
Tod Darcey (Sr VP-Ops)
Chester F. Morrison Jr. (Chm)
Kenneth F. Tamplain Jr. (Interim Pres
& CEO)
Leroy F. Guidry Jr. (Interim CFO)

ROOT, INC.
80 E Rich St Ste 500, Columbus, OH
43215 DE
Web Site: https://www.joinroot.com
Year Founded: 2015
ROOT—(NASDAQ)
Rev.: $455,000,000
Assets: $1,347,700,000
Liabilities: $1,182,000,000
Net Worth: $165,700,000
Earnings: ($147,400,000)
Emp.: 680
Fiscal Year-end: 12/31/23
Property Insurance Services
N.A.I.C.S.: 524126

ROOT9B HOLDINGS, INC.

102 N Cascade Ave Ste 220, Colo-
rado Springs, CO 80919
Tel.: (602) 889-1137 NV
Web Site:
    http://www.root9bholdings.com
Year Founded: 2000
RTNB—(NASDAQ)
Sales Range: $10-24.9 Million
Emp.: 154
Computer Related Consulting Ser-
vices
N.A.I.C.S.: 541690

Subsidiaries:

GreenHouse Holdings, Inc. (1)
1775 Hancock St Ste 160, San Diego, CA
92110
Tel.: (858) 273-2626
Sales Range: $1-9.9 Million
Emp.: 30
Holding Company
N.A.I.C.S.: 551112

Subsidiary (Domestic):

Control Engineering, Inc. (2)
2306 Newport Blvd, Costa Mesa, CA 92627
Tel.: (714) 535-5590
Web Site:
    http://www.controlengineering.com
Sales Range: $1-9.9 Million
Emp.: 20
Engineering Services
N.A.I.C.S.: 541330
Carlos Carrillo (VP-Engrg)

ROPER TECHNOLOGIES, INC.
6496 University Pkwy, Sarasota, FL
34240
Tel.: (941) 556-2601 DE
Web Site: https://www.ropertech.com
Year Founded: 1981
ROP—(NYSE)
Rev.: $6,177,800,000
Assets: $28,167,500,000
Liabilities: $10,722,700,000
Net Worth: $17,444,800,000
Earnings: $1,384,200,000
Emp.: 16,800
Fiscal Year-end: 12/31/23
Energy, Analytical Instrumentation,
Fluid Handling, Medical & Industrial
Control Equipment Mfr
N.A.I.C.S.: 334513
Jason P. Conley (CFO & Exec VP)
Jason P. Conley (VP & Controller)
John K. Stipancich (Gen Counsel,
Sec & Exec VP)
John K. Stipancich (Gen Counsel,
Sec & Exec VP)
Laurence Neil Hunn (Pres & CEO)

Subsidiaries:

AC Analytical Controls B.V. (1)
Kiotoweg 555, 3047 BG, Rotterdam, Neth-
erlands
Tel.: (31) 10 462 4811
Web Site: https://www.paclp.com
Sales Range: $25-49.9 Million
Emp.: 70
Analytical Laboratory Instrument Mfr
N.A.I.C.S.: 334516

Aderant Holdings, Inc. (1)
500 Northridge Rd Ste 800, Atlanta, GA
30350
Tel.: (404) 720-3600
Web Site: https://www.aderant.com
Software Business Solutions
N.A.I.C.S.: 513210
Chris Cartrett (Pres & CEO)
Karen Ross (VP-Admin & Fin)
Matt Graywood (VP-Pro Svcs-Global)
Samantha Rouse (VP-Customer Support-
Global)
Doug Matthews (Chief Product Officer)
Andrew Hoyt (CTO)
Shira Aharoni (Chief People Officer)
George Seymour (Chief Revenue Officer)

Subsidiary (Domestic):

Aderant North America, Inc. (2)

1760 Summit Lake Dr Ste 105, Tallahassee,
FL 32317
Tel.: (850) 224-2200
Web Site: https://www.aderant.com
Provider of Software, E-Commerce & Con-
sulting Services
N.A.I.C.S.: 541511

**Aderant Legal Holdings (AUS) Pty
Ltd** (1)
Level 5 112 Castlereagh Street, Sydney,
2000, NSW, Australia
Tel.: (61) 285071600
Software Development Services
N.A.I.C.S.: 541511

Advanced Sensors Limited (1)
8 Meadowbank Road, Carrickfergus, Antrim,
BT38 8YF, United Kingdom
Tel.: (44) 289 332 8922
Web Site:
    https://www.advancedsensors.co.uk
Analytical Instrument Mfr
N.A.I.C.S.: 334516

Alpha Technologies GmbH (1)
Pfaffenstr 21, 74078, Heilbronn, Germany
Tel.: (49) 71313824800
Web Site: http://www.alpha-
technologies.com
Electric Equipment Mfr
N.A.I.C.S.: 335999

Alpha Trust Corporation (1)
8226 Douglas Ave Ste 625, Dallas, TX
75225
Tel.: (214) 234-9200
Web Site: https://www.alphatrust.com
Financial Services
N.A.I.C.S.: 523999

Amot Controls Corporation (1)
8824 Fallbrook Dr, Houston, TX 77064
Tel.: (281) 940-1800
Sales Range: $25-49.9 Million
Emp.: 100
Mfr of Thermostatic Valves, Switches, Elec-
tronics, Engine Controls, Panels & Sensors
N.A.I.C.S.: 334513

Amot Controls GmbH (1)
Rondenbarg 25, 22525, Hamburg, Germany
Tel.: (49) 408 537 1298
Web Site: https://www.amot.com
Emp.: 5
Electronic Control Systems & Condition
Monitoring Equipment Mfr
N.A.I.C.S.: 334513

Amtech World Corporation (1)
8158 Adams Dr, Hummelstown, PA 17036
Tel.: (717) 561-2400
Medical & Industrial Control Equipment Mfr
N.A.I.C.S.: 334513

**Ascension Technology
Corporation** (1)
120 Graham Way Ste 130, Shelburne, VT
05482
Tel.: (802) 985-1114
Web Site: https://www.ascension-tech.com
Electromagnetic Tracking Device Mfr
N.A.I.C.S.: 335314

Atlantic Health Partners, LLC (1)
301 W Atlantic Ave Ste 5, Delray Beach, FL
33444
Tel.: (860) 674-9785
Web Site:
    https://www.atlantichealthpartners.com
Emp.: 6
Vaccine Purchasing Organization & Distr
N.A.I.C.S.: 424210
Kim Thompson (Sr Mgr-Acct)

**Atlas Healthcare Software India Pri-
vate Limited** (1)
Bipl Omega Building 5th Floor Block Ep
And Gp Sector - V Salt Lake, Kolkata, 700
091, West Bengal, India
Tel.: (91) 3323573000
Software Development Services
N.A.I.C.S.: 541511

Avitru, LLC (1)
175 W 200 S Ste 100, Salt Lake City, UT
84101
Web Site: http://www.deltek.com
Software Publishing & Solution Finding Services

N.A.I.C.S.: 513210

BidClerk, Inc. (1)
3825 Edwards Rd Ste 800, Cincinnati, OH
45209
Tel.: (877) 737-6482
Web Site: https://www.bidclerk.com
Construction Data Provider
N.A.I.C.S.: 541990

**CIVCO Medical Instruments Co.,
Inc.** (1)
102 1st St S, Kalona, IA 52247-9589
Tel.: (319) 248-6757
Web Site: https://www.civco.com
Sales Range: $25-49.9 Million
Emp.: 180
Medical Equipment Mfr
N.A.I.C.S.: 339112
Robin Therme (Pres)
Mike Marshall (VP-Corp Svcs)
Lisa Johnson (VP-Fin)
Kevin Cleary (VP-Global Commercialization)
Brad Dunlap (VP-Bus Dev)
Alexas Swartz (Gen Mgr-Guidance BU &
Infection Control)

Division (Domestic):

CIVCO Medical Solutions (2)
12 Bridge St, Deep River, CT 06417
Tel.: (860) 526-2862
Web Site: http://www.pcimedical.com
Medical Probe & Scope Disinfection Ser-
vices
N.A.I.C.S.: 562211

CIVCO Medical Solutions B.V. (1)
Kiotoweg 407, 3047 BG, Rotterdam, Neth-
erlands
Tel.: (31) 103036600
Cancer Treatment Services
N.A.I.C.S.: 622310
Sven Vlasblom (Mgr-Ops)

Cambridge Viscosity, Inc (1)
50 Redfield St Ste 204, Boston, MA 02122
Tel.: (781) 393-6500
Web Site:
    https://www.cambridgeviscosity.com
Measuring Device Mfr
N.A.I.C.S.: 334519

Chalwyn Limited (1)
Western Way, Bury Saint Edmunds, IP33
3SZ, Suffolk, United Kingdom
Tel.: (44) 1284715739
Web Site: http://www.chalwyn.co.uk
Diesel Engine Safety Product Design & Mfr
N.A.I.C.S.: 333618

CliniSys Group Limited (1)
Culverdon House Abbotts Way, Chertsey,
KT16 9LF, Surrey, United Kingdom
Tel.: (44) 1932581200
Web Site: http://www.clinisys.co.uk
Emp.: 100
Holding Company
N.A.I.C.S.: 551112
Andrew Darby (CFO)
Michael Simpson (CEO-Grp)

Subsidiary (Non-US):

MIPS (2)
Sluisweg 2 bus 5, 9000, Gent, Belgium
Tel.: (32) 92202321
Web Site: https://www.clinisys.com
Medical Laboratory Services
N.A.I.C.S.: 621511

Clinisys Deutschland GmbH (1)
Am Klingenweg 6, 65396, Walluf, Germany
Tel.: (49) 612370160
Diagnostic Research & Testing Services
N.A.I.C.S.: 541380

Clinisys N.V. (1)
Sluisweg 2 Bus 5, 9000, Gent, Belgium
Tel.: (32) 92202321
Laboratory Research & Testing Services
N.A.I.C.S.: 541380

Clinisys Scotland Limited (1)
24 St Vincent Place, Glasgow, G1 2EU,
United Kingdom
Tel.: (44) 1413529000
Clinical Laboratory Services
N.A.I.C.S.: 621511

**Compressor Controls
Corporation** (1)

4745 121st St, Des Moines, IA 50323-2316
Tel.: (515) 270-0857
Web Site: https://www.cccglobal.com
Sales Range: $50-74.9 Million
Emp.: 160
Turbomachinery Control Mfr
N.A.I.C.S.: 335314
Ed Maslak (Pres)
Ryan Eicher (VP-Fin)
Richard Hall (VP-Marketing)
Serge Staroselsky (CTO)
Shawn Olson (Gen Mgr)
Lucy Detzel (VP)

Subsidiary (Non-US):

Compressor Controls (Beijing) Corporation Ltd. (2)
Rm 1508C Baosteel Mansion No12 Jianguomen Wai Street, Chaoyang Dist, Beijing, 100020, China
Tel.: (86) 1065070590
Emp.: 20
Turbomachinery Control Mfr
N.A.I.C.S.: 335314

Compressor Controls Corporation B.V. (2)
Weerenweg 10, 1161 AH, Zwanenburg, Netherlands
Tel.: (31) 20 407 0000
Web Site: https://www.cccglobal.com
Turbomachinery Control Mfr
N.A.I.C.S.: 335314

Compressor Controls Corporation S.r.l. (2)
Via Matteotti 62, 20092, Cinisello Balsamo, MI, Italy
Tel.: (39) 02 611 1151
Web Site: https://www.cccglobal.com
Emp.: 45
Turbomachinery Control Mfr
N.A.I.C.S.: 335314

Compressor Controls Pty. Ltd. (2)
Level 11 125 St Georges Terrace, Perth, 6000, WA, Australia
Tel.: (61) 86 189 4930
Web Site: https://www.cccglobal.com
Emp.: 1
Turbomachinery Control Mfr
N.A.I.C.S.: 335314

Compressor Controls Saudi Arabia, LLC (1)
Adeer Tower Floor 3 Unit 1 7383 Prince Turkey St, PO Box 34413-2212, Al Khobar, Saudi Arabia
Tel.: (966) 504996551
Turbo Machinery Optimization Services
N.A.I.C.S.: 541330

Construction Market Data Group LLC (1)
30 Technology Pkwy S Ste 10, Norcross, GA 30092
Tel.: (770) 417-4000
Construction Data Services
N.A.I.C.S.: 518210

Cornell Pump Company (1)
16261 SE 130th Ave, Clackamas, OR 97015
Tel.: (503) 653-0330
Web Site: https://www.cornellpump.com
Sales Range: $25-49.9 Million
Emp.: 5
Pumps & Pumping Equipment Mfr
N.A.I.C.S.: 333914
Marcus Davi (VP-Sls)

DAT Solutions, LLC (1)
8405 SW Nimbus Ave, Beaverton, OR 97008
Tel.: (972) 875-3824
Web Site: https://www.dat.com
Emp.: 275
Transportation Solutions
N.A.I.C.S.: 488999
Tony Salazar (CFO & VP)
Jeff Hopper (CMO & VP)
Satish Maripuri (CEO)
Jeff Clementz (Chief Product Officer)
Brian Gill (CTO)
Ken Adamo (VP-Strategy & Business Development)

Deltek Nederland B.V. (1)

Papendorpseweg 99, 3528 BJ, Utrecht, Netherlands
Tel.: (31) 307430014
Software Services
N.A.I.C.S.: 513210

Deltek Philippines LLC (1)
2291 Wood Oak Dr, Herndon, VA 20171-2823
Web Site: https://www.deltek.com
Software Development Services
N.A.I.C.S.: 541511

Deltek Systems (Philippines) Ltd. (1)
950 N Washington St Ste 213, Alexandria, VA 22314
Software Publishing & Solution Finding Services
N.A.I.C.S.: 513210

Deltek, Inc. (1)
2291 Wood Oak Dr, Herndon, VA 20171-2823
Tel.: (703) 734-8606
Web Site: http://www.deltek.com
Project Management Software & Services
N.A.I.C.S.: 541511
Michael P. Corkery (Pres & CEO)
Dean Tilsley (CFO & Sr VP)
Brian Daniell (Chief Customer Officer & Sr VP)
Ed Hutner (Sr VP-Human Resources)
Warren Linscott (Chief Product Officer & Sr VP)
Pete Mann (Sr VP-Corporate Development)
Kevin Plexico (Sr VP)
Natasha Engan (Sr VP)
Perry Hardt (CMO & Sr VP)
Tracy Schampers (Sr VP & Gen Counsel)
Matt Strazza (Sr VP-Sales-Global)
Ronda Cilsick (CIO & Grp VP)
Margo Martin (Grp VP-Customer Success)
Caleb Merriman (Chief Information Security Officer & VP)
Dinakar Hituvalli (CTO & Sr VP)

Subsidiary (Domestic):

ComputerEase Software Inc. (2)
6460 Harrison Ave, Cincinnati, OH 45247
Tel.: (513) 481-5800
Web Site: http://www.construction-software.com
Computer & Software Stores
N.A.I.C.S.: 449210

Subsidiary (Non-US):

Deltek Danmark A/S (2)
Vordingborggade 18-22, 2100, Copenhagen, Denmark
Tel.: (45) 3 527 7900
Web Site: https://www.deltek.com
Emp.: 209
Project Management Software & Services
N.A.I.C.S.: 513210

Deltek GB Limited (2)
The Aircraft Factory 100 Cambridge Grove, London, W6 0LE, United Kingdom
Tel.: (44) 2075185010
Project Management Software & Services
N.A.I.C.S.: 541611
Neil Davidson (VP-Enterprise)

Deltek Netherlands B.V. (2)
Papendorpseweg 99, 3528 BJ, Utrecht, Netherlands
Tel.: (31) 30 743 0014
Web Site: https://www.deltek.com
Project Management Software & Services
N.A.I.C.S.: 541611

Deltek Norge AS (2)
Grundingen 6, 0250, Oslo, Norway
Tel.: (47) 2 201 3800
Web Site: https://www.deltek.com
Business Management Solutions
N.A.I.C.S.: 541611

Deltek Sverige AB (2)
Hollandargatan 11, 111 36, Stockholm, Sweden
Tel.: (46) 85 870 7700
Web Site: https://www.deltek.com
Business Management Solutions
N.A.I.C.S.: 541611

Subsidiary (Domestic):

Executive Business Services, Inc. (2)

43398 Business Park Dr, Temecula, CA 92590-0000
Tel.: (951) 693-0440
Web Site: http://www.propricer.com
Software Publisher
N.A.I.C.S.: 513210
Joseph Shurance (CEO)

Subsidiary (Non-US):

Replicon Inc. (2)
910 7th Ave SW Ste 800, Calgary, T2P 3N8, AB, Canada
Tel.: (403) 262-6519
Web Site: http://www.replicon.com
Sales Range: $25-49.9 Million
Emp.: 100
Web-Based Time & Expense Solutions & Productivity Software Producer
N.A.I.C.S.: 513210
Raj Narayanaswamy (Co-Founder & Co-CEO)
Lakshmi Raj (Co-Founder & Co-CEO)
Peter Kinash (CFO)
Suresh Kuppahally (COO)
Scott Bales (VP)
Shelly Davenport (Sr VP)

Subsidiary (Non-US):

Replicon Australia Pty Ltd (3)
Level 32 101 Miller Street, North Sydney, 2060, NSW, Australia
Tel.: (61) 283104797
Software Development Services
N.A.I.C.S.: 541511
John Kearney (VP-Sls)

Replicon Europe LTD (3)
3000 Hillswood Drive Hillswood Business Park, Chertsey, KT16 0RS, United Kingdom
Tel.: (44) 2035145511
Software Development Services
N.A.I.C.S.: 541511

Subsidiary (Domestic):

Tip Technologies, Inc. (2)
N14 W24200 Tower Place Suite 100, Waukesha, WI 53188
Tel.: (262) 544-1211
Web Site: http://www.tiptech.com
Sales Range: $1-9.9 Million
Emp.: 23
Custom Computer Programming Services
N.A.I.C.S.: 541511
Michael Miller (CEO)

Dynisco Instruments LLC (1)
38 Forge Pkwy, Franklin, MA 02038
Tel.: (508) 541-9400
Web Site: https://www.dynisco.com
Sales Range: $50-74.9 Million
Emp.: 300
Electronic Pressure Transducers Mfr
N.A.I.C.S.: 334519

Subsidiary (Domestic):

Alpha Technologies Services LLC (2)
6279 Hudson Crossing Pkwy Ste 200, Hudson, OH 44236
Tel.: (330) 745-1641
Web Site: https://www.alpha-technologies.com
Sales Range: $10-24.9 Million
Emp.: 100
Process Control Instruments
N.A.I.C.S.: 334513

Subsidiary (Non-US):

Dynisco Europe GmbH (2)
Pfaffenstr 21, 74078, Heilbronn, Germany
Tel.: (49) 71312970
Web Site: https://www.dynisco.com
Sales Range: $10-24.9 Million
Emp.: 24
Sales of Measurement Instruments
N.A.I.C.S.: 334513

Dynisco Instruments S.a.r.l. (2)
466 Rue Du Marche Rollay, 94500, Champigny-sur-Marne, France
Tel.: (33) 148818459
Web Site: http://www.dynisco.com
Melt Pressure & Temperature Sensor Mfr
N.A.I.C.S.: 326199

Dynisco S.r.l. (2)

Via Matteotti 62, 20092, Cinisello Balsamo, MI, Italy
Tel.: (39) 026 604 5158
Web Site: https://www.dynisco.com
Sales Range: $100-124.9 Million
Emp.: 2
Testing Instruments Mfr
N.A.I.C.S.: 334515

Dynisco SPOL, SRO (2)
C P 579A, Dolni Becva, 75655, Zlin, Czech Republic
Tel.: (420) 571647228
Measuring & Controlling Equipment Mfr
N.A.I.C.S.: 334519

Dynisco Shanghai Sensor and Instrument Co., Ltd. (1)
Bldg 7A No 568 Longpan Rd, Malu Jiading, Shanghai, 201801, China
Tel.: (86) 2134074072819
Web Site: http://www.dynisco.com
Analytical Instrument Mfr
N.A.I.C.S.: 334516

Dynisco-Viatran Instrument Sdn Bhd (1)
Lot 3615 Jalan SM 6/8, Seri Manjung, 32040, Perak, Malaysia
Tel.: (60) 5 688 4014
Plastics Product Mfr
N.A.I.C.S.: 326111

FTI Flow Technology, Inc. (1)
8930 S Beck Ave Ste 107, Tempe, AZ 85284
Tel.: (480) 240-3400
Web Site: https://www.ftimeters.com
Emp.: 40
Analytical Instrument & Industrial Control Equipment Mfr
N.A.I.C.S.: 334516

Frontline Technologies Group LLC (1)
1400 Atwater Dr, Malvern, PA 19355
Tel.: (610) 722-9745
Web Site: http://www.frontlineeducation.com
Web-Based Solutions Services
N.A.I.C.S.: 513210
Mark Gruzin (CEO)
Jim Catalino (Chief Revenue Officer)
Elizabeth Combs (Mng Dir-Frontline Research & Learning Institute)
Greg Doran (CFO)
Kevin Haugh (Chief Product Officer)
David Reiling (Chief Client Officer)

Subsidiary (Domestic):

Excent Corporation (2)
60 King St, Roswell, GA 30075-4414 (100%)
Tel.: (678) 735-4210
Data Management Software Developer & Student Curriculums
N.A.I.C.S.: 541511
Greg Chisholm (VP-Customer Care & Svcs)

Hayes Software Systems, Inc. (2)
12007 Research Blvd Ste 103, Austin, TX 78759
Tel.: (512) 219-7610
Web Site: http://www.hayessoft.com
Software Development Services
N.A.I.C.S.: 541511
Michael Hayes (Founder & Chm)
Matt Winebright (CEO)
Laura Sager (VP-Res & Dev)
Debbie Disler (VP-Customer Support & Trng)
Anna Maxin (COO)
Sara Arthrell (Dir-Mktg)
John Mellios (Dir-Client Svcs)
Brad Moore (VP-Sls)
Mario Torres (Chief Revenue Officer)
Kunal Ashar (CTO)
Diana Richie (Dir-Strategic Accts)
Rebecca Rosas (Dir-Mktg)

Gatan U.K. Limited (1)
25 Nuffield Way, Oxfordshire, Abingdon, OX14 1RL, United Kingdom
Tel.: (44) 1235540160
Tem & Stem Product Mfr
N.A.I.C.S.: 335991

Innovative Product Achievements LLC (1)

Roper Technologies, Inc.—(Continued)

3059 Premiere Pkwy Ste 200, Duluth, GA 30097
Tel.: (770) 814-6060
Web Site: https://www.thinkipa.com
Emp.: 30
Automated Distribution Process Services
N.A.I.C.S.: 334513

Inovonics Corporation (1)
397 S Taylor Ave, Louisville, CO 80027
Tel.: (303) 939-9336
Web Site: http://www.inovonics.com
Emp.: 70
Commercial Grade Wireless Security Product Mfr
N.A.I.C.S.: 561612
Craig Dever (VP-Mktg & Sls)
Tom Bjorkman (VP-Acctg & Fin)
Chris Allen (Reg Sls Mgr-Northeast)
Steve Rulis (Mgr-OEM & Sls)
Lalit Pandit (VP-Engrg)
Rob McMaster (VP-Supply Chain & Operations)

Integrated Designs L.P. (1)
2853 Dickerson Pkwy Ste 114, Carrollton, TX 75007
Tel.: (972) 975-9774
Web Site: https://www.idi-cybor.com
Digital Valves & Pumps Mfr
N.A.I.C.S.: 333914
Jack Laessle (Pres)

Internet Pipeline, Inc. (1)
222 Valley Creek Blvd Ste 300, Exton, PA 19341
Tel.: (484) 348-6555
Web Site: http://www.ipipeline.com
Software Developer
N.A.I.C.S.: 513210
Bill Atlee (Founder & Chief Strategy Officer)
Larry Berran (CEO)
Ian Teague (Mng Dir-UK)
Daphne Thomas (COO)
Chris Nichols (Exec VP-R&D)
Maureen Kincade (Chief Transformation Officer)
Kevin Baer (Chief HR Officer)
Roy Goodart (VP-Product Mgmt)
Eric Rea (Exec VP-Bus Dev)
Bill Hunter (Sr VP-Sls)
Jessica Brown (Asst VP-Mktg)
Joe Paddock (VP-Sls)
Robert Powell (VP-Sls & Wealth Mgmt)
Jay Marshall (VP-Client Svcs)
Michael Hirl (Asst VP-Client Svcs)
Stu Feldman (Asst VP-Professional Svcs)
Chris Samuel (Dir-Bus Ops-UK)
Deane Price (CEO)
Kimberly Beck (VP-Marketing)
Riad Hasan (Asst VP)
Tim Parsons (Sr VP-Research & Development)
Martin Redington (Sr VP-Technology)
David Libesman (VP)
Bill Brice (Exec VP)
John Bryner (CFO)
Dan Dayanim (Asst VP-Compliance)
Deane Price (CEO)
Kimberly Beck (VP-Marketing)
Riad Hasan (Asst VP)
Tim Parsons (Sr VP-Research & Development)
Martin Redington (Sr VP-Technology)
David Libesman (VP)
Bill Brice (Exec VP)
John Bryner (CFO)
Dan Dayanim (Asst VP-Compliance)
Deane Price (CEO)
Kimberly Beck (VP-Marketing)
Riad Hasan (Asst VP)
Tim Parsons (Sr VP-Research & Development)
Martin Redington (Sr VP-Technology)
David Libesman (VP)
Bill Brice (Exec VP)
John Bryner (CFO)
Dan Dayanim (Asst VP-Compliance)

Subsidiary (Domestic):

Impact Financial Systems (2)
721 Jetton St Ste 300, Davidson, NC 28036
Tel.: (704) 894-9331
Web Site: http://www.ifsautomation.com
Financial Services
N.A.I.C.S.: 522310

Tim Parsons (Pres & CEO)
Jeff Deming (CFO & COO)
Ray Mulligan (Mng Dir-Product Strategy)
Travis Champion (Mng Dir-Bus Dev)
Mary Paige Kistler (Dir-Solution Delivery)
Randy Barnes (Dir-Product Mgmt)

Laser App Software, Inc. (2)
3190 Shelby St Bldg D-100, Ontario, CA 91764
Web Site: https://www.laserapp.com
Sales Range: $1-9.9 Million
Emp.: 25
Custom Computer Programming Services
N.A.I.C.S.: 541511
Edward Beggs (Founder)

Logitech Limited (1)
Erskine Ferry Road, Old Kilpatrick, Glasgow, G60 5EU, United Kingdom
Tel.: (44) 138 987 5444
Web Site: https://www.logitech.uk.com
Emp.: 50
Precision Sawing & Polishing Equipment Design & Mfr
N.A.I.C.S.: 333517
Mark Kennedy (Head-Sls & Process Dev)
Stephen Slack (Head-Engrg)
John McCrossan (Engr-Process Dev)
Tom McGroggan (Engr-Process Dev)

MEDTEC, Inc. (1)
2301 Jones Blvd, Coralville, IA 52241
Tel.: (319) 248-6757
Web Site: http://www.civco.com
Surgical & Medical Instruments
N.A.I.C.S.: 339112
Robin Therme (Pres)
Lisa Johnson (VP-Finance)
Mike Marshall (VP-Corp Svcs)
Alexas Swartz (Gen Mgr-Infection Control-Guidance BU)
Michael McVey (VP-Operations-Kalona)
Kevin Cleary (VP-Global)
Brad Dunlap (VP-Business Development)
Ryan Swartz (Gen Mgr-High-Level Disinfection,Men's Health BU)

MIPS Austria GesmbH (1)
Europaplatz 2/1/2, 1150, Vienna, Austria
Tel.: (43) 18909086
Industrial Valve Mfr
N.A.I.C.S.: 332911

Managed Health Care Associates, Inc. (1)
25-A Vreeland Rd Ste 200, Florham Park, NJ 07932-0789
Tel.: (973) 966-9200
Web Site: https://www.mhainc.com
Sales Range: $10-24.9 Million
Emp.: 50
Healthcare Software Services & Solutions
N.A.I.C.S.: 513210
Teresa DiCaro (Exec VP)
Gloria P. Barr (Gen Counsel & Exec VP)
Walter Gramley (Sr VP)
Fred Bonaccorso (Exec VP)
John Lees (Sr VP-Ops)
Tom Hermey (Exec VP-Technology-Operations)
Tom Hermey (Exec VP-Technology-Operations)
Tom Hermey (Exec VP-Technology-Operations)
David Holladay (CEO)
Michael Ansel (Chief Growth Officer)
Carl T. Bertram (Exec VP)
Deane Price (CEO)
Daphne Thomas (COO)
Bil Atlee (Founder)
Ian Teague (Mng Dir)
John Peart (Sr VP)
Bill Hunter (Sr VP)
Joe Paddock (VP)
Maureen Kincade (Sr VP)
Jay Marshall (Sr VP)
Chris Nichols (CTO)
Tim Parsons (Sr VP)
Martin Redington (VP)
Roy Goodart (VP)
Stephen Slocum (VP)
David Libesman (VP)
John Bryner (CFO)
Clifford A. Farren Jr. (Exec VP-Finance)

Subsidiary (Domestic):

SoftWriters, Inc. (2)

5800 Corporate Dr, Pittsburgh, PA 15237
Tel.: (412) 492-9841
Web Site: https://frameworkltc.com
Sales Range: $1-9.9 Million
Emp.: 23
Pharmacy Management Software Developer & Distr
N.A.I.C.S.: 513210
Jackie Maitland (VP-Customer Success)
Scott Beatty (Co-Pres)
Deepika Devarajan (VP)
Joshua Porter (VP-Sales)
Beth Davis (VP-People)
Jason Yablinsky (VP)
Deepika Devarajan (VP)
Joshua Porter (VP-Sales)
Beth Davis (VP-People)
Jason Yablinsky (VP)
Deepika Devarajan (VP)
Joshua Porter (VP-Sales)
Beth Davis (VP-People)
Jason Yablinsky (VP)
Danielle Greer (VP)
Mike Steffek (VP)

Media Cybernetics Inc. (1)
1700 Rockville Pike Ste 240, Rockville, MD 20852
Tel.: (301) 495-3305
Web Site: https://www.mediacy.com
Sales Range: $10-24.9 Million
Emp.: 25
Image Analysis & Image Processing Software Developer
N.A.I.C.S.: 513210

Medical Equipment Distributors, Inc. (1)
2200-109 E Millbrook Rd, Raleigh, NC 27604
Tel.: (919) 873-9168
Web Site: https://www.medicaldists.com
Medical Equipment Distr
N.A.I.C.S.: 423450

Medical Information Professional Systems NV (1)
Industriepark-Zwijnaarde 3A, Gent, 9052, Belgium
Tel.: (32) 92202321
Industrial Valve Mfr
N.A.I.C.S.: 332911

Metrix Instrument Co., LP (1)
8824 Fallbrook Dr, Houston, TX 77064
Tel.: (281) 940-1802
Web Site: https://www.metrixvibration.com
Sales Range: $10-24.9 Million
Emp.: 90
Mfr & Developer of Solid-State Vibration Detection & Monitoring Equipment
N.A.I.C.S.: 334515

NDI Europe GmbH (1)
Guttinger Strasse 37, 78315, Radolfzell, Germany
Tel.: (49) 77 328 2340
Web Site: https://www.ndieurope.com
Medical & Industrial Control Equipment Mfr
N.A.I.C.S.: 334513

Neptune Technology Group (Canada) Limited (1)
7275 West Credit Avenue, Mississauga, L5N 5M9, ON, Canada
Tel.: (905) 858-4211
Web Site: https://www.neptunetg.com
Water Metering & Automatic Meter Reading Equipment Mfr
N.A.I.C.S.: 334514

Neptune Technology Group Inc. (1)
1600 Alabama Hwy 229, Tallassee, AL 36078
Tel.: (334) 283-6555
Web Site: https://www.neptunetg.com
Water Measurement & Data Collection Systems Supplier
N.A.I.C.S.: 333310

Northern Digital Inc. (1)
103 Randall Drive, Waterloo, N2V 1C5, ON, Canada
Tel.: (519) 884-5142
Web Site: https://www.ndigital.com
Sales Range: $25-49.9 Million
Emp.: 250
Medical & Industrial Control Measuring Equipment Mfr
N.A.I.C.S.: 334513

On Center Software, Inc. (1)
8708 Technology Forest Pl Ste 175, The Woodlands, TX 77381
Tel.: (281) 297-9000
Web Site: https://www.oncenter.com
Sales Range: $1-9.9 Million
Emp.: 50
Custom Computer Programming Services
N.A.I.C.S.: 541511

PAC Instruments (Thailand) Company Limited (1)
Bhiraj Tower at EmQuartier Room No 3034 Level 30, 689 Sukhumvit Road Soi 35 Klongton Nuea Vadhana, Bangkok, 10110, Thailand
Tel.: (66) 20172802
Pac Equipment Whslr
N.A.I.C.S.: 423830

Petroleum Analyzer Company (1)
8824 Fallbrook Dr, Houston, TX 77064-4855 (100%)
Tel.: (281) 940-1803
Web Site: https://www.paclp.com
Sales Range: $25-49.9 Million
Emp.: 100
Process Instruments for Physical Property Analysis of Petroleum Products
N.A.I.C.S.: 334516

Subsidiary (Non-US):

Walter Herzog GmbH (2)
Badstrasse 3-5, PO Box 1241, 97912, Lauda-Konigshofen, Germany (100%)
Tel.: (49) 93436400
Web Site: http://www.paclp.com
Sales Range: $25-49.9 Million
Mfr of Process Instruments for Petroleum Products
N.A.I.C.S.: 334513

Phase Analyzer Company Ltd. (1)
11168 Hammersmith Gate, Richmond, V7A 5H8, BC, Canada
Tel.: (604) 241-9568
Web Site: https://www.phase-technology.com
Test Instrument Mfr
N.A.I.C.S.: 334513

Photometrics UK Limited (1)
Beech House 27 Little Marlow Road, Buckinghamshire, Marlow, SL7 1HA, Buckinghamshire, United Kingdom
Tel.: (44) 1628477025
Web Site: http://www.photometrics.de
Emp.: 6
CCD & EMCCD Camera System Mfr
N.A.I.C.S.: 333310

PowerPlan Operations ANZ Pty. Ltd. (1)
Level 28 303 Collins Street, Melbourne, 3000, VIC, Australia
Tel.: (61) 396789268
Tem & Stem Product Mfr
N.A.I.C.S.: 335991

PowerPlan Operations Ltd. (1)
Golden Cross House 8 Duncannon Street, London, WC2N 4JF, United Kingdom
Tel.: (44) 2039117625
Tem & Stem Product Mfr
N.A.I.C.S.: 335991

PowerPlan, Inc. (1)
300 Galleria Pkwy Ste 2100, Atlanta, GA 30339
Tel.: (678) 223-2800
Web Site: https://www.powerplan.com
Accounting, Tax & Budgeting Software Developer & Publisher
N.A.I.C.S.: 513210
Sarah Park (VP-HR)
Joe Gomes (CEO)
Neal Tisdale (CTO & Sr VP)
Marc Bortniker (Sr VP-Sls-Global)
Suzanne Ward (Sr VP-Product Mgmt)
Kevin Janflone (CFO)
Paresh Patel (Sr VP)

RF IDeas, Inc. (1)
425 N Martingale Rd Ste 1680, Schaumburg, IL 60173
Tel.: (847) 870-1723
Web Site: https://investors.ropertech.com
Sales Range: $10-24.9 Million
Emp.: 45
Identification Card Technologies Mfr

N.A.I.C.S.: 334511
Tod Besse *(Sr VP-Sls & Mktg-Global)*
Nicholas Low *(Dir-Sales-Asia Pacific)*

Redlake Inc. (1)
6295 Ferris Sq Ste A, San Diego, CA
92121-3248
Tel.: (858) 481-8182
Web Site: http://www.redlake.com
Sales Range: $25-49.9 Million
Emp.: 100
Mfr of Electronic Parts & Equipment
N.A.I.C.S.: 334516

Roda Deaco Valve, Inc. (1)
4320 Roper Rd NW, Edmonton, T6B 3T8,
AB, Canada
Tel.: (780) 465-4429
Web Site: http://www.rodadeaco.com
Industrial Valve & Control Equipment Mfr
N.A.I.C.S.: 334513

**Roper Brasil Comercio E Promocao
De Productos E Servicos LTDA** (1)
Av Rio Branco Centro, 20090-003, Rio de
Janeiro, Brazil
Tel.: (55) 2135147506
Analytical Instrument Mfr
N.A.I.C.S.: 334516

Roper Engineering s.r.o. (1)
Struers Building Vystavni 3374/40a, 702 00,
Ostrava, Czech Republic
Tel.: (420) 55 888 9933
Web Site: https://roper.cz
Laboratory Equipment Design & Mfr
N.A.I.C.S.: 334516

Roper Industries Limited (1)
Western Way, Bury Saint Edmunds, IP33
3SZ, Suffolk, United Kingdom
Tel.: (44) 128 471 5739
Web Site: https://www.amot.com
Sales Range: $25-49.9 Million
Emp.: 90
Pressure & Temperature Sensor Product
Mfr
N.A.I.C.S.: 334516

Roper Middle East Ltd. (1)
Dubai Airport Free Zone, PO Box 293724,
Dubai, United Arab Emirates
Tel.: (971) 42045754
Analytical Instrument Mfr
N.A.I.C.S.: 334516
Munther Juma *(Mng Dir)*

Roper Pump Company (1)
3475 Old Maysville Rd, Commerce, GA
30529
Tel.: (706) 335-5551
Web Site: https://www.roperpumps.com
Industrial Pump Design & Mfr
N.A.I.C.S.: 333914

Roper Scientific GmbH (1)
Einsteinstrasse Nr 39a, 82152, Martinsried,
Germany
Tel.: (49) 896607793
Web Site: http://www.roperscientific.de
Sales Range: $10-24.9 Million
Emp.: 10
Image Analysis Product & Software Mfr
N.A.I.C.S.: 333310

Roper Scientific SAS (1)
Z I Petite Montagne Sud Lisses 8 Rue De
Forez C E 1702, 91017, Evry, Cedex,
France
Tel.: (33) 160860365
Web Site: http://www.ropertech.com
Ccd & Emccd Camera System Mfr
N.A.I.C.S.: 333310

Sinmed B.V. (1)
Pasteurstraat 6, Reeuwijk, 2811 DX, South
Holland, Netherlands
Tel.: (31) 182394495
Analytical Instrument & Industrial Control
Equipment Mfr
N.A.I.C.S.: 334513

Strata Decision Technology India Private Limited (1)
CO 01 to 04 World Trade Centre Tower 4
Level 2 Dholepatil Farm Road, Opp EON
Free Zone MIDC Knowledge Park Kharadi,
Pune, 411014, Maharashtra, India
Tel.: (91) 2249705184
Software Development Services
N.A.I.C.S.: 541511

Strata Decision Technology LLC (1)
200 E Randolph St 49th Fl, Chicago, IL
60601-6463
Tel.: (312) 726-1227
Web Site: https://www.stratadecision.com
IT Services
N.A.I.C.S.: 541511
Dan Michelson *(CEO)*
Liz Kirk *(Sr VP-Strategic Svcs)*
John Martino *(CFO & COO)*
Heidi Farrell *(Sr VP-People Ops)*
Martin Luethi *(CTO)*
Jennifer Rauworth *(Sr VP-Client Services)*
John Gragg *(Exec Dir & Sr VP)*
Steve Lefar *(Exec Dir)*
John Gragg *(Exec Dir & Sr VP)*
Steve Lefar *(Exec Dir)*

Subsidiary (Domestic):

**Enterprise Performance Systems,
Inc.** (2)
16090 Swingley Ridge Rd, Chesterfield, MO
63017
Tel.: (636) 532-8907
Web Site: http://www.eclipsys.com
Sales Range: $1-9.9 Million
Emp.: 20
Software Publisher
N.A.I.C.S.: 513210

**Strata Decision Technology,
L.L.C.** (1)
200 E Randolph St 49th Fl, Chicago, IL
60601-6463
Tel.: (312) 726-1227
Web Site: https://www.stratadecision.com
Software Publisher
N.A.I.C.S.: 513210
Heidi Farrell *(Sr VP-People Ops)*
John Gragg *(Exec Dir & Sr VP)*
Steve Lefar *(Exec Dir)*
Jennifer Rauworth *(Sr VP-Client Services)*
John Gragg *(Exec Dir & Sr VP)*
Steve Lefar *(Exec Dir)*
Jennifer Rauworth *(Sr VP-Client Services)*
John Gragg *(Exec Dir & Sr VP)*
Steve Lefar *(Exec Dir)*
Jennifer Rauworth *(Sr VP-Client Services)*
Dan Dunham *(CFO)*
Joel Gerber *(VP)*
Ryan Self *(VP)*
Frank Stevens *(Chief Growth Officer)*
John Martino *(CEO)*

Subsidiary (Domestic):

**Syntellis Performance Solutions,
LLC** (2)
320 N Sangamon St Ste 700, Chicago, IL
60607
Tel.: (847) 441-0022
Web Site: https://www.syntellis.com
Emp.: 360
IT Consulting & Services
N.A.I.C.S.: 541690

Subsidiary (Domestic):

Stratasan, LLC (3)
450 10th Cir N, Nashville, TN 37203
Web Site: http://www.stratasan.com
Sales Range: $1-9.9 Million
Emp.: 50
Software Development Services
N.A.I.C.S.: 541511
Jason Moore *(Co-Founder & CEO)*
Brian Dailey *(Co-Founder & CTO)*
Carrie Nall *(Sr VP-Fin & Admin)*
Haley Devlin *(Sr VP-Bus Ops)*
Tom Snarsky *(Sr VP-Sls)*

**Strategic Healthcare Programs,
LLC** (1)
6500 Hollister Ave Ste 210, Santa Barbara,
CA 93117
Tel.: (805) 963-9446
Web Site: https://www.shpdata.com
Emp.: 25
Data Analytics & Benchmarking Dashboard
Services
N.A.I.C.S.: 541511
Christopher M. Attaya *(VP-Product Strategy)*
Zeb Clayton *(VP-Client Svcs)*
John Shewell *(VP-)*

Struers A/S (1)
Pederstrupvej 84, 2750, Ballerup, Denmark

Tel.: (45) 4 460 0800
Web Site: https://www.struers.com
Sales Range: $25-49.9 Million
Emp.: 210
Analytical Laboratory Instrument Mfr
N.A.I.C.S.: 334516

Struers GmbH (1)
Carl-Friedrich-Benz-Strasse 5, 47877, Willich, Germany
Tel.: (49) 2 154 4860
Web Site: https://www.struers.com
Sales Range: $25-49.9 Million
Emp.: 40
Analytical Laboratory Instrument Mfr
N.A.I.C.S.: 334516

Struers Inc. (1)
24766 Detroit Rd Westlake, Cleveland, OH
44145
Tel.: (440) 871-0071
Web Site: https://www.struers.com
Laboratory Semi-automatic & Automatic
Equipment Mfr
N.A.I.C.S.: 334516
Steen Jensen *(Pres)*

Struers Ltd. (1)
Unit 11 Evolution the Amp Whittle Way, Catcliffe, Rotherham, S60 5BL, South Yorkshire, United Kingdom
Tel.: (44) 8456046664
Web Site: https://www.struers.com
Sales Range: $10-24.9 Million
Emp.: 16
Analytical Laboratory Instrument Mfr
N.A.I.C.S.: 334516

Struers SARL (1)
370 Rue Du Marche Rollay, 94507,
Champigny-sur-Marne, France
Tel.: (33) 155091430
Web Site: http://www.struers.com
Emp.: 30
Laboratory Semi-automatic & Automatic
Equipment Mfr
N.A.I.C.S.: 334516

**Sunquest Information Systems,
Inc.** (1)
3300 E Sunrise Dr, Tucson, AZ 85718
Tel.: (520) 570-2000
Web Site: https://www.sunquestinfo.com
Sales Range: $75-99.9 Million
Emp.: 400
Healthcare Industry Diagnostic & Laboratory
Information Systems Developer
N.A.I.C.S.: 541512
Jonathan Pierson *(COO)*
Paul Stinson *(Chief Growth Officer)*
Tamera Millington Bhatti *(VP-People Ops)*
Andrew Branski *(VP-Fin)*
Michael Simpson *(Pres)*
Anthony Ventress *(Sr VP-Product Dev)*

Subsidiary (Non-US):

Sunquest Information Systems (Europe) Limited (2)
Parkview House 82 Oxford Road, Uxbridge,
UB8 1UX, United Kingdom
Tel.: (44) 845 519 4010
Web Site: http://www.sunquestinfo.com
Healthcare Industry Diagnostic & Laboratory
Information Systems Developer
N.A.I.C.S.: 541511

**Sunquest Information Systems (India)
Private Limited** (2)
3rd Floor Indraprastha Equinox No 23, 100
Feet Inner Ring Rd Ejipura, Bengaluru, 560
095, India
Tel.: (91) 80 4048 4048
Emp.: 150
Healthcare Industry Diagnostic & Laboratory
Information Systems Developer
N.A.I.C.S.: 541511
A.B. Baskar *(Gen Mgr)*

Technolog Limited (1)
Ravenstor Road, Wirksworth, DE4 4FY,
Derbyshire, United Kingdom
Tel.: (44) 162 982 3611
Web Site: https://www.technolog.com
Sales Range: $25-49.9 Million
Emp.: 100
Meter Reading & Pressure Control Products
Design & Mfr
N.A.I.C.S.: 334512

The CBORD Group Inc. (1)
950 Danby Rd Ste 100C,-Ithaca, NY 14850
Tel.: (607) 257-2410
Web Site: https://www.cbord.com
Sales Range: $10-24.9 Million
Emp.: 450
Card Systems, Food Service Management
Software & Security Solutions
N.A.I.C.S.: 513210
Larry Delaney *(Sr VP)*
Sarah Hayes *(VP-Customer Care)*
Aric Alibrio *(Sr VP-Sales)*
Jon Lawrence *(VP-)*
Corey Jensen *(VP-Human Resources)*
Aric Alibrio *(Sr VP-Sales)*
Dan Park *(CEO)*
Ken Chow *(Interim CFO)*
Mamie Hodnett *(VP-Human Resources)*

Subsidiary (Domestic):

**Horizon Software International
LLC** (2)
2850 Premiere Pkwy Ste 100, Duluth, GA
30097
Tel.: (770) 554-6353
Web Site: https://www.horizonsoftware.com
Rev.: $10,090,665
Emp.: 70
Food Service Software Developer
N.A.I.C.S.: 541511

Student Advantage LLC (2)
950 Danby Rd Ste 100C, Ithaca, NY 14850
Tel.: (617) 912-2011
Web Site: https://studentadvantage.com
Media & Commerce Company Focused on
the Higher Education Market
N.A.I.C.S.: 611710

**The Foundry Visionmongers
Limited** (1)
5 Golden Square, London, W1F 9HT,
United Kingdom
Tel.: (44) 20 7479 4350
Web Site: http://www.thefoundry.co.uk
Visual Effect Software Developer
N.A.I.C.S.: 513210
Bill Collis *(Pres)*
Simon Robinson *(Founder)*
Richard Shackleton *(Head-Strategy)*
Lucy Cooper *(Head-Marketing)*
Jon Starck *(Head)*
Phil Parsonage *(Head-Engineering)*
Jody Madden *(Chief Customer Officer)*
Martin Franks *(CFO)*
Jon Wadelton *(CTO)*
Jack Greasely *(Head)*
Michael Ephraim *(Head-Sales-The Americas)*
Charlotte Dawson *(Mgr)*
Najeeb Khan *(Mgr)*
Nikki Morris *(Mgr)*
Karen Slatford *(Chm)*
Mike Pilcher *(Chief Sls Officer)*
Jill Ezard *(Chief HR Officer)*
Kenneth Knobel *(Reg Sls Mgr)*
Craig Rodgerson *(CEO)*
Christy Anzelmo *(Chief Product Officer)*
Jess Barlow *(Chief HR Officer)*
Alex Foulds *(Chief Revenue Officer)*
James France *(CFO)*
Jason Gagnon *(Supvr)*
Sam Lucas *(Head)*

TransCore Holdings Inc. (1)
3721 Tecport Dr Suite 102, Harrisburg, PA
17111
Tel.: (717) 561-2400
Web Site: http://www.transcore.com
Sales Range: $300-349.9 Million
Emp.: 1,800
Computer Software, Supplies & Services
N.A.I.C.S.: 513210

Subsidiary (Domestic):

TransCore, LP (2)
8158 Adams Dr Bldg 200, Hummelstown,
PA 17036
Tel.: (214) 461-6435
Web Site: http://www.transcore.com
Sales Range: $300-349.9 Million
Emp.: 1,800
Radio Frequency Identification Technology
Services
N.A.I.C.S.: 334220

Subsidiary (Domestic):

Intellitrans, LLC (3)

Roper Technologies, Inc.—(Continued)

756 W Peachtree St NW, Atlanta, GA 30308
Web Site: http://www.intellitrans.com
Fiscal Year-end: 12/31/2004
Goods Transportation Arrangement Services
N.A.I.C.S.: 488510

TransCore Commercial Services, LLC (3)
2700 S Kaufman, Ennis, TX 75119
Tel.: (888) 888-2100
Sales Range: $10-24.9 Million
Emp.: 17
Analytical Laboratory Instrument Mfr
N.A.I.C.S.: 334516

Subsidiary (Non-US):

TransCore Link Logistics Corporation (3)
2 Robert Speck Parkway Ste 900, Mississauga, L4Z 1H8, ON, Canada
Tel.: (905) 795-0580
Web Site: http://www.transcore.ca
Transportation Technology Solutions Provider
N.A.I.C.S.: 488510

Subsidiary (Domestic):

TransCore Marketing Communications (3)
3410 Midcourt Rd Ste 102, Carrollton, TX 75006
Tel.: (214) 461-6443
Web Site: http://www.transcore.com
Sales Range: $1-9.9 Million
Emp.: 8
Wireless Data Technologies for Intelligent Transportation Systems
N.A.I.C.S.: 238210

United Controls Group, Inc. (1)
400 Lazelle Rd Ste 13, Columbus, OH 43240
Tel.: (740) 326-1007
Web Site: http://www.unitedcontrolsgroup.com
Sales Range: $25-49.9 Million
Emp.: 33
Engine Control System Design & Mfr
N.A.I.C.S.: 334513

Uson LP (1)
8640 N Elbridge Pkwy, Houston, TX 77041
Tel.: (281) 671-2000
Web Site: https://www.uson.com
Sales Range: $50-74.9 Million
Emp.: 200
Mfr Of Leak And Flow Testing Equipment
N.A.I.C.S.: 334513

Verathon Inc. (1)
20001 N Creek Pkwy, Bothell, WA 98011
Tel.: (425) 867-1348
Web Site: https://www.verathon.com
Sales Range: $100-124.9 Million
Emp.: 380
Electromedical & Electrotherapeutic Apparatus Mfr
N.A.I.C.S.: 334510
Earl Thompson (Pres)
Parimal Shah (Sr VP)
Chad Ludwig (Sr VP-)
Tracy Olson (VP-Finance)
Jamie Valliant (VP)
Jeff Clark (VP-Operations)
Fredrik Consson (VP-Corporate Marketing)
Jon Stevens (VP-Quality & Regulatory)
Mark Humphrey (VP-People)
Moira Galvin (VP)
Pawan Singh (VP)
Dan Morgan (VP)
Travis Bonnor (VP-)

Subsidiary (Non-US):

Verathon Medical (Austrailia) Pty Limited (2)
Unit 9 39 Herbert Street, Saint Leonards, 2065, NSW, Australia
Tel.: (61) 294312000
Web Site: http://www.verathon.com
Medical Equipment Distr
N.A.I.C.S.: 423450

Verathon Medical (Canada) ULC (2)

2227 Douglas Road, Burnaby, V5C 5A9, BC, Canada
Tel.: (604) 439-3009
Web Site: https://www.verathon.com
Sales Range: $25-49.9 Million
Emp.: 60
Medical Device & Instrument Mfr
N.A.I.C.S.: 334510

Verathon Medical (Europe) B.V. (2)
Willem Fenengastraat 13, 1096 BL, Amsterdam, Netherlands
Tel.: (31) 20 210 3091
Web Site: http://www.verathon.nl
Sales Range: $25-49.9 Million
Emp.: 25
Medical Device & Instrument Mfr
N.A.I.C.S.: 334510

Verathon Medical (France) S.a.r.l. (2)
Espace Europeen de l'Entreprise 16 avenue de l'Europe, 67300, Schiltigheim, France
Tel.: (33) 36 878 0079
Web Site: http://www.verathon.fr
Sales Range: $10-24.9 Million
Emp.: 6
Medical Device & Instrument Mfr
N.A.I.C.S.: 334510

Vertafore, Inc. (1)
999 18th St 4th Fl, Denver, CO 80202
Web Site: http://www.vertafore.com
Insurance Software & Information Solutions
N.A.I.C.S.: 513210
Amy Zupon (CEO)
Cassidy Smirnow (Chief Revenue Officer)
Greg Ingino (CTO & Sr VP)
Steve Tucker (CFO)
Jon Newpol (Sr VP & Gen Mgr-Distr & Compliance)
James Thom (Chief Product Officer & Sr VP)
Maggie Warren (Gen Counsel & Sr VP)
Kristin Nease (VP-HR)
C. Andrew Ballard (Co-Founder)

Subsidiary (Domestic):

MGA Systems, Inc. (2)
105 Maxess Rd Ste 202B, Melville, NY 11747-4401
Web Site: http://www.mgasystems.com
Computer System Design Services
N.A.I.C.S.: 541512
John Bennis (Pres)

Subsidiary (Domestic):

Netrate Systems, Inc. (3)
3493 Woods Edge, Okemos, MI 48864
Tel.: (517) 347-6739
Web Site: http://www.netrate.com
Software Develoment
N.A.I.C.S.: 541512
David Jordan (CEO)
Tom Rahl (VP-Sls)
Jason Barlow (Pres)
Jadalyn Devries (COO-Transportation Insurance Svcs)
Tina Land (COO-Venture Insurance Programs)
Richard Trezza (Pres-Core Programs)
Jeff Lewis (Dir-Client Svcs)
Paul Areida (CEO)

Subsidiary (Domestic):

QQ Solutions, Inc. (2)
350 Fairway Dr Ste 101, Deerfield Beach, FL 33441
Tel.: (877) 809-2509
Web Site: http://www.qqsolutions.com
Insurance Agency Management Software Services
N.A.I.C.S.: 518210

Viastar Services, LP (1)
2700 S Kaufman St, Ennis, TX 75119-7131
Tel.: (972) 875-3824
Truck Repair & Maintenance Services
N.A.I.C.S.: 811310

Viatran Corporation (1)
199 Fire Tower Dr, Tonawanda, NY 14150
Tel.: (716) 629-3800
Web Site: http://www.viatran.com
Sales Range: $10-24.9 Million
Emp.: 51

Instrument Manufacturing for Measuring & Testing Electricity & Electrical Signals
N.A.I.C.S.: 334515

Workbook Software A/S (1)
GI Lundtoftevej 5 4th Floor, 2800, Lyngby, Denmark
Tel.: (45) 70203318
Web Site: https://www.workbook.net
Advertising Services
N.A.I.C.S.: 541810

Zetec (Shanghai) Co., Ltd. (1)
Rm 4102-4104 1468 Nanjing Road West United Plaza, Shanghai, 200040, China
Tel.: (86) 2162797700
Electric Equipment Mfr
N.A.I.C.S.: 335999
Gibson Wu (Mgr-Engrg)

Zetec France (2)
Mini Parc du Verger Bat G 1 rue de Terre Neuve ZA de Courtaboeuf, 91940, Les Ulis, France
Tel.: (33) 160923939
Electric Equipment Mfr
N.A.I.C.S.: 335999

Zetec, Inc. (1)
8226 Bracken Pl SE Ste #100, Snoqualmie, WA 98065
Tel.: (425) 974-2700
Web Site: http://www.zetec.com
Supplier of Eddy Equipment, Supplies & Software Products
N.A.I.C.S.: 334519
Wayne Wilkinson (Pres)
Steve Kingma (VP-Fin)
Shane Campbell (VP-Ops & Supply Chain)
Kihang Choi (VP-Power Generation)

iPipeline Limited (1)
Second Floor The Quadrangle Building Imperial Promenade, Cheltenham, GL50 1PZ, United Kingdom
Tel.: (44) 3454084022
Web Site: https://www.uk.ipipeline.com
Information Technology Services
N.A.I.C.S.: 541512
Pat O'Donnell (CEO)

iPipeline, Inc. (1)
222 Valley Creek Blvd Ste 300, Exton, PA 19341
Tel.: (484) 348-6555
Web Site: https://ipipeline.com
Life Insurance & Financial Services
N.A.I.C.S.: 524210

iSqFt Parent Corporation (1)
3825 Edwards Rd Ste 800, Cincinnati, OH 45209
Tel.: (513) 645-8004
Web Site: http://www.constructconnect.com
Holding Company; Construction, Engineering & Contracting Professional Connection Services
N.A.I.C.S.: 551112
Dave Conway (Pres & CEO)
Julie Storm (Chief HR Officer-People)
Jennifer Johnson (Chief Experience Officer)
Robert Ven (CIO & CTO)
Mark Casaletto (Pres-Canada)
Howard H. Atkins (Exec VP)
Buck Brody (CFO)
Todd Ciganek (Exec VP)
Jim Hill (Chief Revenue Officer, Chief Revenue Officer & Chief Revenue Officer-Market)
Jonathan Kost (Chief Strategy Officer, Exec VP & Gen Mgr)
Matt Strazza (Pres & CEO)
Doug Dockery (CTO)
Hope Needham (Chief People & Culture Officer)
Matt Strazza (Pres & CEO)
Doug Dockery (CTO)
Hope Needham (Chief People & Culture Officer)

Subsidiary (Domestic):

CMD Group, LLC (2)
30 Technology Pkwy S Ste 100, Norcross, GA 30092
Tel.: (770) 417-4000
Construction Market Data & Building Product Information Publisher & Market Analytics Services
N.A.I.C.S.: 518210

iTradeNetwork, Inc. (1)
4160 Dublin Blvd Ste 300, Dublin, CA 94568
Tel.: (925) 660-1100
Web Site: https://www.itradenetwork.com
Sales Range: $25-49.9 Million
Emp.: 55
Products, Services & Information for the Perishable Foods Industry
N.A.I.C.S.: 541618
Nathan Romney (Chief Product Officer)
Amer Akhtar (CEO)
Jeanette Pereira (Chief Information Security Officer)
Cynthia Bergallo (VP-Human Resources)
Ryan Licari (Exec VP-)
Lamia Barrington (Sr VP-Customer Success)
Keith Woodward (CMO)

Subsidiary (Non-US):

iTradeNetwork, Ltd. (2)
9-10 Market Place, London, W1W 8AQ, Bucks, United Kingdom
Tel.: (44) 8700100228
Web Site: http://www.itradenetwork.com
Products, Services & Information for the Perishable Foods Industry
N.A.I.C.S.: 541618

RORINE INTERNATIONAL HOLDING CORPORATION
Ste 325 7582 Las Vegas Blvd S, Las Vegas, NV 89123
Tel.: (702) 560-4373 NV
RIHC—(OTCIQ)
Investment Services
N.A.I.C.S.: 523999
Hau-Ran Tsau (Pres, CEO & Treas)
Bruce Michael Smith (CFO)
David Patrick Novak (Exec VP)

ROSE HILL ACQUISITION CORPORATION
981 Davis Dr NW, Atlanta, GA 30327
Tel.: (404) 973-7681 Ky
Web Site: http://www.rosehillacq.com
Year Founded: 2021
ROSE—(NASDAQ)
Rev.: $7,316,926
Assets: $148,968,685
Liabilities: $157,482,908
Net Worth: ($8,514,223)
Earnings: $6,210,140
Emp.: 5
Fiscal Year-end: 12/31/22
Investment Services
N.A.I.C.S.: 523999
Udi O. Margulies (CEO)

ROSS STORES, INC.
5130 Hacienda Dr, Dublin, CA 94568-7579
Tel.: (925) 965-4400 DE
Web Site: https://www.rossstores.com
Year Founded: 1957
ROST—(NASDAQ)
Rev.: $18,695,829,000
Assets: $13,416,463,000
Liabilities: $9,127,880,000
Net Worth: $4,288,583,000
Earnings: $1,512,041,000
Emp.: 101,000
Fiscal Year-end: 01/28/23
Department Store Retailer
N.A.I.C.S.: 458110
Michael Balmuth (Exec Chm)
Barbara Rentler (Vice Chm & CEO)
Michael K. Kobayashi (Pres-Ops & Tech)
Michael J. Hartshorn (Grp Pres & COO)
Stephen Brinkley (Pres-Ops)
Adam M. Orvos (CFO & Exec VP)
Connie Kao (Grp VP-IR)
Jeffrey Burrill (Chief Acctg Officer, Sr VP & Controller)

Subsidiaries:

Ross Dress for Less, Inc. (1)
5412 Ygnacio Valley Rd, Concord, CA 94521
Tel.: (925) 524-0276
Apparel & Accessories Whslr
N.A.I.C.S.: 315250
Bernard Brautigan (Pres-Mdsg)

ROTATE BLACK, INC.
201 E Mitchell St, Petoskey, MI 49770
Tel.: (231) 347-0777
Year Founded: 2005
ROBK—(OTCEM)
Hotel & Restaurant Operator
N.A.I.C.S.: 721110
John Paulsen (CEO)

ROTECH HEALTHCARE HOLDINGS INC.
3600 Vineland Rd, Orlando, FL 32811
Tel.: (407) 822-4600 DE
Year Founded: 2018
ROTK—(NASDAQ)
Rev.: $503,183,000
Assets: $668,510,000
Liabilities: $638,752,000
Net Worth: $29,758,000
Earnings: $119,160,000
Fiscal Year-end: 12/31/20
Holding Company
N.A.I.C.S.: 551112
Timothy C. Pigg (Chm, Pres & CEO)
Thomas J. Koenig (CFO & Treas)
Robin Menchen (COO)
Steven Burres (Gen Counsel & Sec)

ROTH CH ACQUISITION CO.
2340 Collins Ave Ste 402, Miami Beach, FL 33141
Tel.: (949) 720-7133 Ky
Web Site: https://www.rothch.com
Year Founded: 2021
USCT—(NASDAQ)
Rev.: $7,003,413
Assets: $23,531,337
Liabilities: $25,379,151
Net Worth: ($1,847,814)
Earnings: $2,586,752
Fiscal Year-end: 12/31/23
Investment Management Service
N.A.I.C.S.: 523999
Byron Roth (Chm & Co-CEO)
John Lipman (Co-CEO)
Aaron Gurewitz (Co-Pres)
Rick Hartfiel (Co-Pres)
Joseph Tonnos (CFO & CIO)
Ryan Hultstrand (Co-COO)
Matthew Day (Co-COO)

ROUCHON INDUSTRIES, INC.
3729 San Gabriel River Pkwy Ste C, Pico Rivera, CA 90660
Tel.: (562) 821-5924 CA
Web Site: https://www.swiftech.com
Year Founded: 1994
RCHN—(OTCIQ)
Rev.: $3,730,000
Assets: $2,215,000
Liabilities: $465,000
Net Worth: $1,750,000
Earnings: $658,000
Emp.: 32
Fiscal Year-end: 12/31/19
Totalizing Fluid Meter & Counting Device Mfr
N.A.I.C.S.: 334514
Gabriel Rouchon (Founder)

ROYAL CARIBBEAN CRUISES LTD.
1050 Caribbean Way, Miami, FL 33132
Tel.: (305) 539-6000 LR

Web Site:
https://www.royalcaribbean.com
Year Founded: 1968
RCL—(NYSE)
Rev.: $13,900,000,000
Assets: $35,131,000,000
Liabilities: $30,232,000,000
Net Worth: $4,899,000,000
Earnings: $1,697,000,000
Emp.: 98,200
Fiscal Year-end: 12/31/23
Cruise Line & Tour Operator
N.A.I.C.S.: 483112
Donna J. Hrinak (Sr VP-Corp Affairs)
Richard D. Fain (Chm)
Harri U. Kulovaara (Exec VP-Maritime & Newbuilding)
Jason T. Liberty (Pres & CEO)
Henry J. Pujol (Chief Acctg Officer & Sr VP)
Naftali Holtz (CFO)
Silvia Garrigo (Chief Environmental, Social & Governance Officer & Sr VP)
Dana Ritzcovan (Exec VP)
Laura Hodges Bethge (Exec VP)
R. Alexander Lake (Chief Legal Officer)

Subsidiaries:

Pullmantur SA (1)
Calle Mahonia 2, Madrid, 28043, Spain (49%)
Tel.: (34) 915561114
Web Site: http://www.pullmantur.es
Tour Operator
N.A.I.C.S.: 483112
Richard Vogel (Pres & CEO)

RCL (UK) Ltd. (1)
Building 3 The Heights Brooklands, Weybridge, KT13 0NY, Surrey, United Kingdom
Tel.: (44) 8444934005
Web Site: http://www.rcl-uk.com
Sales Range: $350-399.9 Million
Emp.: 159
Cruise Vessel Leasing; Sales & Marketing Operators for Cruise Line
N.A.I.C.S.: 561599

RCL Cruises Ltd. (1)
7 The Heights Brooklands, Weybridge, KT13 0XW, Surrey, United Kingdom
Tel.: (44) 3444934005
Cruise Operator
N.A.I.C.S.: 483112
Adam Armstrong (Mng Dir)
Kathryn Valk (Dir-Sls & Mktg-Australia & New Zealand)
Adam Armstrong (Mng Dir)
Cameron Mannix (Mgr-Bus Dev-Celebrity Cruises-Australia & New Zealand)
Wendy Anderson (Mgr-Sls-Victoria & Tasmania)

Royal Caribbean Cruise Lines AS (1)
Mustadsvei 1, PO Box 114, Lilleaker, 0216, Oslo, Norway
Tel.: (47) 80253252
Web Site: http://www.royalcaribbean.no
Sales Range: $25-49.9 Million
Emp.: 11
Cruise Ship Operator
N.A.I.C.S.: 487210

Royal Caribbean Cruises (Asia) Pte. Ltd. (1)
3 Anson Road 13-02 Springleaf Tower, Singapore, 079909, Singapore
Tel.: (65) 66750413
Cruise Operator
N.A.I.C.S.: 483112

Royal Caribbean Cruises (Australia) Pty. Ltd (1)
Level 2 80 Arthur Street, North Sydney, 2060, NSW, Australia
Tel.: (61) 243315400
Cruise Operator
N.A.I.C.S.: 483112
Adam Armstrong (Dir-Comml-Intl)
Sean Treacy (Dir-Comml-Asia Pacific)
Gavin Smith (Mng Dir-Australia & New Zealand)

Royal Celebrity Tours Inc. (1)
8440 154th Ave NE, Redmond, WA 98052
Tel.: (425) 376-4000
Sales Range: $10-24.9 Million
Emp.: 20
Tour Operator
N.A.I.C.S.: 561520

Silversea Cruises Australia Pty. Ltd. (1)
Suite 1 Level 8 8 Spring Street, Sydney, 2000, NSW, Australia
Tel.: (61) 292550600
Travel & Tourism Services
N.A.I.C.S.: 561510

Silversea Cruises Ltd. (1)
(100%)
Tel.: (377) 97702424
Web Site: https://www.silversea.com
Luxury Cruise Line Operator
N.A.I.C.S.: 483112

Representative Office (US):

Silversea Cruises Ltd. - The Americas Regional Office (2)
333 Ave f the Americas Ste 2600, Miami, FL 33131
Web Site: http://www.silversea.com
Luxury Cruise Line Operator
N.A.I.C.S.: 483112
Mark Conroy (Mng Dir)
Joseph Leon (VP-Field Sls)
Marcus Kenny (Dir-Bus Dev & Agency Sls)

TUI Cruises GmbH (1)
Heidenkampsweg 58, 20097, Hamburg, Germany
Tel.: (49) 40600015000
Web Site: https://www.meinschiff.com
Cruise Line & Tour Operator
N.A.I.C.S.: 483112
Wybcke Meier (Chm)

Subsidiary (Domestic):

Hapag-Lloyd Kreuzfahrten GmbH (2)
Ballindamm 25, 20095, Hamburg, Germany
Tel.: (49) 403070300
Web Site: http://www.hl-cruises.com
Ship Chartering Services
N.A.I.C.S.: 483112

ROYAL ENERGY RESOURCES, INC.
56 Broad St Ste 2, Charleston, SC 29401
Tel.: (843) 900-7693 DE
Web Site: https://www.royalenergy.us
Year Founded: 1999
ROYE—(OTCIQ)
Sales Range: $200-249.9 Million
Emp.: 702
Oil & Gas Exploration Services
N.A.I.C.S.: 211120
William L. Tuorto (Chm)

Subsidiaries:

Rhino Resource Partners LP (1)
424 Lewis Hargett Cir Ste 250, Lexington, KY 40503
Tel.: (859) 389-6500
Web Site: http://www.rhinolp.com
Rev.: $181,036,000
Assets: $194,547,000
Liabilities: $158,832,000
Net Worth: $35,715,000
Earnings: ($99,519,000)
Emp.: 605
Fiscal Year-end: 12/31/2019
Coal Producer & Marketer
N.A.I.C.S.: 212115
William L. Tuorto (Chm)

ROYAL FINANCIAL, INC.
9226 S Commercial Ave, Chicago, IL 60617
Tel.: (773) 768-4800 DE
Web Site:
http://www.royalbankweb.com
Year Founded: 1887
RYFL—(OTCIQ)
Rev.: $19,130,350

Assets: $404,987,634
Liabilities: $365,151,231
Net Worth: $39,836,403
Earnings: $3,704,181
Emp.: 76
Fiscal Year-end: 06/30/19
Bank Holding Company
N.A.I.C.S.: 551111
Leonard S. Szwajkowski (Pres & CEO)
James A. Fitch Jr. (Chm)

Subsidiaries:

Royal Savings Bank (1)
9226 S Commercial Ave, Chicago, IL 60617
Tel.: (773) 768-4800
Web Site: http://www.royalbankweb.com
Emp.: 14
Savings Bank
N.A.I.C.S.: 522180
Leonard S. Szwajkowski (Pres & CEO)
Judy Johnson (Asst VP)
Toni Gonzalez (COO & Sr VP)
Richard Nichols (VP-Comml Banking)
Colleen Thomiszer (CFO & Sr VP)

ROYAL GOLD, INC.
1144 15th St Ste 2500, Denver, CO 80202
Tel.: (303) 573-1660 DE
Web Site: https://www.royalgold.com
Year Founded: 1981
RGLD—(NASDAQ)
Rev.: $605,717,000
Assets: $3,361,057,000
Liabilities: $460,416,000
Net Worth: $2,900,641,000
Earnings: $239,440,000
Emp.: 30
Fiscal Year-end: 12/31/23
Precious Metal Royalty Acquisition & Management Services
N.A.I.C.S.: 523999
William H. Heissenbuttel (Pres & CEO)
William M. Zisch (Executives)
Paul K. Libner (CFO & Treas)
Daniel K. Breeze (VP-Corp Dev)
Alistair Baker (VP-IR & Bus Dev-Royal Gold Corp)
Randy Shefman (Gen Counsel & VP)
Allison Forrest (VP)
Laura B. Gill (Chief Compliance Officer)
Martin Raffield (VP)

Subsidiaries:

Denver Mining Finance Company, Inc. (1)
1660 Wynkoop St Ste 1000, Denver, CO 80202 (100%)
Tel.: (303) 573-1660
Web Site: http://www.royalgold.com
Sales Range: $75-99.9 Million
Gold & Silver Mining Services
N.A.I.C.S.: 541611

High Desert Mineral Resources, Inc. (1)
1660 Wynkoop St Ste 1000, Denver, CO 80202 (100%)
Tel.: (303) 573-1660
Web Site: http://www.royalgold.com
Sales Range: $150-199.9 Million
Gold & Silver Mining
N.A.I.C.S.: 423940

International Royalty Corporation (1)
10 Inverness Dr E Ste 104, Englewood, CO 80112
Tel.: (303) 799-9015
Gold Exploration & Mining Services
N.A.I.C.S.: 212220

Royal Crescent Valley, Inc. (1)
1660 Wynkoop St Ste 1000, Denver, CO 80202 (100%)
Tel.: (303) 573-1660
Web Site: http://www.royalgold.com
Sales Range: $150-199.9 Million
Gold & Silver Mining Services
N.A.I.C.S.: 423840

Royal Gold, Inc.—(Continued)

ROYAL MINES & MINERALS CORP.

1080 Wigwam Pkwy, Henderson, NV 89072
Tel.: (702) 429-7451   NV
Web Site: http://www.royalmmc.com
Year Founded: 2005
RYMM—(OTCIQ)
Emp.: 3
Metal Mining Services
N.A.I.C.S.: 212290
K. Ian Matheson (CEO)

ROYALE ENERGY, INC.

1530 Hilton Head Rd Ste 205, El Cajon, CA 92019
Tel.: (619) 383-6600   CA
Web Site: https://www.royl.com
Year Founded: 1986
ROYL—(OTCQB)
Rev.: $1,718,664
Assets: $10,786,780
Liabilities: $43,357,023
Net Worth: ($32,570,243)
Earnings: ($3,598,418)
Emp.: 11
Fiscal Year-end: 12/31/21
Crude Petroleum Extraction Services
N.A.I.C.S.: 211120
Johnny Jordan (Pres, CEO & COO)
Ronald Lipnick (Interim CFO & Interim Principal Acctg Officer)
John Sullivan (Chm)
Jonathan Gregory (Vice Chm)
Stephen M. Hosmer (Co-Founder & Sec)

Subsidiaries:

Matrix Oil Corp.   (1)
104 W Anapamu St, Santa Barbara, CA 93101
Crude Petroleum & Natural Gas Extraction
N.A.I.C.S.: 211120
Jeff Kerns (Founder & Partner)

ROYALTY PHARMA PLC

110 E 59th St Fl 33, New York, NY 10022
Tel.: (212) 883-0200   UK
Web Site:
    https://www.royaltypharma.com
Year Founded: 1990
RPRX—(NASDAQ)
Rev.: $2,354,554,000
Assets: $16,381,851,000
Liabilities: $6,297,562,000
Net Worth: $10,084,289,000
Earnings: $1,134,834,000
Emp.: 89
Fiscal Year-end: 12/31/23
Holding Company
N.A.I.C.S.: 551112
Pablo Legorreta (Co-Founder, Chm & CEO)
Terrance Coyne (CFO & Exec VP)
Arthur McGivern (Gen Counsel)
Kristin Stafford (Chief Acctg Officer & Sr VP)

ROYCE GLOBAL VALUE TRUST, INC.

745 5th Av Ste 2400, New York, NY 10151
Tel.: (212) 355-7311
RGT—(NYSE)
Rev.: $2,485,829
Assets: $151,739,460
Liabilities: $8,929,239
Net Worth: $142,810,221
Earnings: $584,483
Fiscal Year-end: 12/31/19
Investment Management Service
N.A.I.C.S.: 525990

Christopher D. Clark (Pres, CEO, Mng Dir & Co-Chief Investment Officer)

ROYCE MICRO-CAP TRUST, INC.

745 5th Ave, New York, NY 10151
Tel.: (212) 408-4587   MD
RMT—(NYSE)
Rev.: $4,956,455
Assets: $427,497,290
Liabilities: $22,690,294
Net Worth: $404,806,996
Earnings: $382,166
Fiscal Year-end: 12/31/19
Investment Management Service
N.A.I.C.S.: 525990
Christopher D. Clark (Pres)

RPC, INC.

2801 Buford Hwy NE Ste 300, Atlanta, GA 30329
Tel.: (404) 321-2140   DE
Web Site: https://www.rpc.net
Year Founded: 1984
RES—(NYSE)
Rev.: $1,601,762,000
Assets: $1,129,013,000
Liabilities: $271,278,000
Net Worth: $857,735,000
Earnings: $218,363,000
Emp.: 2,732
Fiscal Year-end: 12/31/22
Holding Company: Oilfield Services Consisting of Equipment Rental, Well Completion, Control Services & Transportation, Storage & Inspection Services for Oilfield Tubular Goods
N.A.I.C.S.: 213112
Richard A. Hubbell (Exec Chm)
Ben M. Palmer (Pres & CEO)
Timothy C. Rollins (VP)
James C. Landers (VP-Corp Svcs)
Sharon A. Gardner (Mgr-IR & Corp Comm)

Subsidiaries:

Patterson Services, Inc.   (1)
2828 Technology Forest Blvd, The Woodlands, TX 77381
Tel.: (281) 875-4006
Web Site:
    https://www.pattersonservices.com
Sales Range: $100-124.9 Million
Oilfield Equipment Rental Services Including Drill Pipe, Drill Collars & Blowout Preventers
N.A.I.C.S.: 532412

Patterson Truck Line, Inc.   (1)
8032 Main St, Houma, LA 70360
Tel.: (985) 851-5541
Freight Transportation Services
N.A.I.C.S.: 484110

RPC Energy Services of Canada, Ltd   (1)
130 469 McCoy Drive, Red Deer, T4E 0A4, AB, Canada
Tel.: (403) 346-5550
Web Site: http://www.thrutubing.com
Emp.: 5
Industrial Equipment Rental & Leasing Services
N.A.I.C.S.: 532490

Thru Tubing Solutions   (1)
2033 N Main St, Newcastle, OK 73065
Tel.: (405) 692-1900
Web Site: https://www.thrutubing.com
Sales Range: $10-24.9 Million
Emp.: 15
Coiled Tubing Equipment Mfr
N.A.I.C.S.: 333132

RPM INTERNATIONAL INC.

2628 Pearl Rd, Medina, OH 44256
Tel.: (330) 273-5090   DE
Web Site: https://www.rpminc.com
Year Founded: 1947

RPM—(NYSE)
Rev.: $7,335,277,000
Assets: $6,586,543,000
Liabilities: $4,074,318,000
Net Worth: $2,512,225,000
Earnings: $589,442,000
Emp.: 17,207
Fiscal Year-end: 05/31/24
Holding Company; Paint Mfr
N.A.I.C.S.: 551112
Russell L. Gordon (CFO & VP)
Lonny R. DiRusso (CIO)
Randell McShepard (Chief Talent Officer)
Timothy R. Kinser (VP-Ops)
Gordon Hyde (VP-Mfg)
Matthew Franklin (VP-IT)
Scott Copeland (VP-Financial Plng & Analysis)
Mark T. Rankin (VP-Sys-Global)
Lee A. Bowers (VP-Environmental, Health, and Safety)
Michael J. Laroche (Chief Acctg Officer, CFO-Specialty Products Group, VP & Controller)
Bryan R. Gillette (VP-Internal Audit)
Frank C. Sullivan (Founder, Chm & CEO)

Subsidiaries:

2002 Perlindustria, S.L.U.   (1)
Poligono can Prunera, Vallirana, 08759, Barcelona, Spain
Tel.: (34) 936834400
Web Site: https://www.perlindustria.com
Sales Range: $25-49.9 Million
Emp.: 50
Paint & Coating Mfr
N.A.I.C.S.: 325510

AD Fire Protection Systems Inc.   (1)
420 Tapscott Road, Scarborough, M1B 1Y4, ON, Canada
Tel.: (416) 292-2361
Web Site: http://www.adfire.com
Fire Protection Material Mfr
N.A.I.C.S.: 325998
Ron van Frankfoort (Dir-Sls Comml Fireproofing)

Argos Gestion, S.L.U.   (1)
Josepila Bosch 5 and 7, Barcelona, 08034, Spain
Tel.: (34) 932096019
Web Site: http://www.argosgestion.com
Sales Range: $25-49.9 Million
Emp.: 50
Fire Protection Equipment Mfr
N.A.I.C.S.: 339999

Betumat Quimica Ltda.   (1)
Rodovia BA 522, Distrito Industrial CEP, 43813-300, Candeias, Brazil
Tel.: (55) 7131182000
Web Site: http://www.betumat.com.br
Waterproof Mfr
N.A.I.C.S.: 324122

Bomat, Inc.   (1)
150 Puuhale Rd, Honolulu, HI 96819
Tel.: (808) 832-1155
Web Site: http://www.bondedmaterials.com
Construction Material Mfr & Whslr
N.A.I.C.S.: 327390

CFM Consolidated, Inc.   (1)
7009 45th St Ct E, Fife, WA 98424-3700
Tel.: (253) 922-2700
Web Site: http://www.cfmconsolidated.com
Plastics Product Mfr
N.A.I.C.S.: 326150

Carboline (Dalian) Paint Company Ltd.   (1)
Room 2405 Gugeng International Business Building 138 Junma Road, Jinzhou New Edz, Dalian, 116600, China
Tel.: (86) 41187060166
Chemical Distr
N.A.I.C.S.: 424690

Carboline (India) Private Limited   (1)
605 Town Centre II Andheri Kurla Road Marol Andheri East, Mumbai, 400059, India
Tel.: (91) 2228500321

Chemical Distr
N.A.I.C.S.: 424690

Carboline Global, Inc.   (1)
2150 Schuetz Rd, Saint Louis, MO 63146
Tel.: (314) 644-1000
Web Site: https://www.carboline.com
Paint & Coating Mfr
N.A.I.C.S.: 325510

Chemspec Europe Limited   (1)
Tong Park Otley Road, Shipley, BD17 7QD, West Yorkshire, United Kingdom
Tel.: (44) 1274597333
Web Site: http://www.chemspec-europe.com
Sales Range: $10-24.9 Million
Emp.: 12
Carpet Cleaning Equipment Mfr
N.A.I.C.S.: 333310

Chemtec Chemicals B.V.   (1)
Breevaartstraat 71, Rotterdam, 3044 AG, Netherlands
Tel.: (31) 104120974
Web Site: http://www.chemtec.nl
Sales Range: $10-24.9 Million
Emp.: 16
Cleaning Equipment Mfr
N.A.I.C.S.: 332813

Citadel Restoration and Repair, Inc.   (1)
2271 2nd St N Ste 100, Saint Paul, MN 55109
Tel.: (651) 289-8110
Web Site: https://www.citadelfloors.com
Floor Coating Mfr
N.A.I.C.S.: 324122

DAP Global, Inc.   (1)
2400 Boston St Ste 200, Baltimore, MD 21224
Web Site: https://www.dap.com
Waterproof Sealant Mfr & Distr
N.A.I.C.S.: 325520

Dane Color UK Limited   (1)
7 Stanley Street, Stalybridge, SK15 1SS, Cheshire, United Kingdom
Tel.: (44) 1613044000
Web Site: http://www.danecolor.com
Sales Range: $25-49.9 Million
Emp.: 60
Specialist Pigment & Ink Mfr
N.A.I.C.S.: 325130
Fintan McGrath (CEO)

Dri-Eaz Products Limited   (1)
22 Plover Close Interchange Park, Newport Pagnell, MK16 9PS, United Kingdom
Tel.: (44) 1908611211
Web Site: https://dri-eaz.hae.org.uk
Emp.: 6
Water & Fire Damage Restoration Product Mfr
N.A.I.C.S.: 236118

Dri-Eaz Products, Inc.   (1)
15180 Josh Wilson Rd, Burlington, WA 98233
Tel.: (360) 757-7776
Web Site: http://www.dri-eaz.com
Dehumidifier & Airmover Equipment Mfr
N.A.I.C.S.: 333415

Ecoloc NV   (1)
Motstraat 54-8, Mechelen, 2800, Belgium
Tel.: (32) 36332323
Web Site: http://www.ecolocflooring.com
Sales Range: $25-49.9 Million
Emp.: 5
Polyvinyl Chloride Flooring Mfr
N.A.I.C.S.: 325211

Ekspan Limited   (1)
Compass Works 410 Brightside Lane, Sheffield, S9 2SP, United Kingdom
Tel.: (44) 1142611126
Bearing Mfr
N.A.I.C.S.: 333613
John Senior (Sls Mgr-Technical)

Euclid Admixture Canada Inc.   (1)
595 Canarctic Dr, Toronto, M3J 2P9, ON, Canada
Tel.: (416) 747-7107
Web Site: http://www.euclidchemical.com
Sales Range: $25-49.9 Million
Emp.: 15
Concrete Additive Mfr
N.A.I.C.S.: 325998

F T Morrell & Company Limited (1)
Wellington Works Mill Lane, Woodley,
Stockport, SK6 1RN, United Kingdom
Tel.: (44) 1614065300
Web Site: http://www.morrells.co.uk
Wood Coating Mfr
N.A.I.C.S.: 324122

FibreGrid Limited (1)
Unit 2 Civic Industrial Estate Homefield
Road Central, Haverhill, CB9 8QP, Suffolk,
United Kingdom
Tel.: (44) 1440712722
Web Site: http://www.fibregrid.com
Emp.: 15
Anti-Slip Safety Product Mfr & Whslr
N.A.I.C.S.: 423390

**HiChem Paint Technologies Pty.
Limited** (1)
level 2/307 Ferntree Gully Rd, Mount Wa-
verley, 3149, VIC, Australia
Tel.: (61) 1300784476
Web Site: http://www.hichem.com.au
Paint & Coating Mfr
N.A.I.C.S.: 325510

Holton Food Products Company (1)
1151 Timber Dr, Elgin, IL 60123
Tel.: (708) 352-5599
Web Site: https://www.holtonfp.com
Emp.: 9
Food Product Mfr & Distr
N.A.I.C.S.: 311999

Key Resin Co. (1)
4050 Clough Woods Dr, Batavia, OH 45103
Tel.: (513) 943-4225
Web Site: https://www.keyresin.com
Sales Range: $1-9.9 Million
Emp.: 20
Polymer Flooring & Coating System Mfr
N.A.I.C.S.: 325998
Eric Borglum *(Pres)*

Kirker Enterprises, Inc. (1)
55 E 6th St, Paterson, NJ 07524
Tel.: (973) 754-9000
Web Site: http://www.kirkerent.com
Cosmetics Mfr
N.A.I.C.S.: 325620

Krud Kutter, Inc. (1)
1535 Oak Industrial Ln, Cumming, GA
30041
Tel.: (770) 888-8827
Cleaning Product Mfr
N.A.I.C.S.: 325612
Jason Roussel *(Dir-Mktg)*

Legend Brands, Inc. (1)
15180 Josh Wilson Rd, Burlington, WA
98233
Tel.: (360) 757-7776
Web Site: http://www.legendbrands.com
Facility Maintenance & Cleaning Product
Mfr & Distr
N.A.I.C.S.: 325612
Gary Lambert *(Mgr-Pur)*

Mantrose UK Limited (1)
7B Northfield Farm, Great Shefford, RG17
7BY, Berkshire, United Kingdom
Tel.: (44) 1488648988
Web Site: http://www.mantrose.com
Emp.: 17
Edible Coatings & Specialty Product Mfr
N.A.I.C.S.: 311351

Martin Mathys NV (1)
Kolenbergstraat 23, 3545, Zelem, Halen,
Belgium
Tel.: (32) 13460200
Web Site: http://www.mathyspaints.eu
Sales Range: $25-49.9 Million
Emp.: 100
Paint & Coating Mfr
N.A.I.C.S.: 325510

Miracle Sealants Company, LLC (1)
12318 Lower Azusa Rd, Arcadia, CA 91006-
5872
Tel.: (626) 443-6433
Web Site: http://www.miraclesealants.com
Cleaning Preparation Mfr & Distr
N.A.I.C.S.: 325612

Morrells Woodfinishes Limited (1)
Wellington Works Mill Lane, Woodley,
Stockport, SK6 1RN, Cheshire, United King-
dom

Tel.: (44) 1614065300
Web Site: http://www.morrells.co.uk
Paint & Coating Product Mfr
N.A.I.C.S.: 325510

NatureSeal, Inc. (1)
100 Nyala Farms Rd, Westport, CT 06880
Tel.: (203) 454-1800
Web Site: https://www.natureseal.com
Processed Food Mfr & Distr
N.A.I.C.S.: 311991
Tim Grady *(Asst Dir-Sls)*

Nudura Inc. (1)
27 Hooper Rd, Barrie, L4N 9S3, ON,
Canada
Tel.: (705) 726-9499
Web Site: https://www.nudura.com
Building Construction Services
N.A.I.C.S.: 236220

**Pipeline and Drainage Systems
Limited** (1)
Cavendish House Unit 1 Enterprise 36,
Tankersley, Barnsley, S75 3DZ, United
Kingdom
Tel.: (44) 1138418861
Web Site: https://www.pdsenviro.com
Sales Range: $25-49.9 Million
Emp.: 20
Bridge & Channel Drainage Construction
Services
N.A.I.C.S.: 237990

Pitchmastic PMB Limited (1)
Cavendish House Unit 1 Enterprise 36,
Tankersley, Barnsley, S75 3DZ, South York-
shire, United Kingdom
Tel.: (44) 1138418861
Web Site: https://www.pitchmasticpmb.co.uk
Structural Waterproofing System Mfr
N.A.I.C.S.: 313320

Profile Food Ingredients, LLC (1)
1151 Timber Dr, Elgin, IL 60123
Tel.: (847) 622-1700
Web Site:
  https://www.profilefoodingredients.com
Food Processing & Mfr
N.A.I.C.S.: 311999
Ted Benic *(CEO)*

Pure Air Control Services, Inc. (1)
4911 Creekside Dr Ste C, Clearwater, FL
33760
Tel.: (727) 572-4550
Web Site: http://www.pureaircontrols.com
Sales Range: $1-9.9 Million
Emp.: 30
Indoor Environmental Consulting & Building
Inspection Services
N.A.I.C.S.: 541620
Francisco Aguirre *(Dir-Building Sciences)*

**RPM Consumer Holding
Company** (1)
2628 Pearl Rd, Medina, OH 44256 **(100%)**
Tel.: (330) 273-5090
Web Site: https://www.rpminc.com
Holding Company
N.A.I.C.S.: 551112

Subsidiary (Domestic):

DAP Products, Inc. (2)
2400 Boston St Ste 200, Baltimore, MD
21224-4723
Tel.: (410) 675-2100
Web Site: https://www.dap.com
Emp.: 110
Caulks, Sealants, Adhesives, Spacklings &
General Patch & Repair Products Mfr
N.A.I.C.S.: 325520
Darlene Blackwell *(Sec-Regulatory & Envi-
ronmental)*

Subsidiary (Non-US):

DAP Canada Corp. (3)
475 Finchdene Square Unit 5, Scarbor-
ough, M1X 1B7, ON, Canada **(100%)**
Tel.: (416) 321-1522
Web Site: http://www.dap.com
Sales Range: $50-74.9 Million
Emp.: 15
Adhesives & Sealants Whslr
N.A.I.C.S.: 424690
John McLaughlin *(Pres)*

Subsidiary (Domestic):

Mohawk Finishing Products, Inc. (2)

2220 US Hwy 70 SE Ste 100, Hickory, NC
28602 **(100%)**
Tel.: (828) 261-0325
Web Site: https://www.mohawk-
  finishing.com
Sales Range: $75-99.9 Million
Wood, Metal & Vinyl Substrates Repair
Products Mfr
N.A.I.C.S.: 325510

Rust-Oleum Corporation (2)
11 Hawthorn Pkwy, Vernon Hills, IL
60061-1402 **(100%)**
Tel.: (847) 367-7700
Web Site: http://www.rustoleum.com
Rust-Preventive, General Purpose, Decora-
tive, Specialty & Professional Paints Mfr
N.A.I.C.S.: 325510
Bill Spaulding *(Pres)*

Unit (Domestic):

Ali Industries, Inc. (3)
747 E Xenia Dr, Fairborn, OH 45324
Tel.: (937) 878-3946
Web Site: http://www.gatorfinishing.com
Emp.: 200
Abrasive Product Mfr
N.A.I.C.S.: 327910
Michael Kilbourne *(Dir-Creative Svcs)*

Subsidiary (Domestic):

Rust-Oleum International, LLC (3)
11 Hawthorn Pkwy, Vernon Hills, IL 60061-
1402
Tel.: (847) 367-7700
Web Site: http://www.rustoleum.com
Sales Range: $250-299.9 Million
Holding Company
N.A.I.C.S.: 551112

Subsidiary (Domestic):

ROC Sales, Inc. (4)
11 Hawthorn Pkwy, Vernon Hills, IL 60061
Tel.: (847) 367-7700
Web Site: http://www.rust-oleum.com
Sales Range: $75-99.9 Million
Emp.: 100
Protective Coatings, Specialty Chemicals &
Flooring Products Whslr
N.A.I.C.S.: 449121

Rust-Oleum Sales Co., Inc. (4)
11 Hawthorn Pkwy, Vernon Hills, IL 60061-
1402
Tel.: (847) 367-7700
Web Site: https://www.rustoleum.com
Sales Range: $75-99.9 Million
Emp.: 200
Paints, Varnishes & Supplies Whslr
N.A.I.C.S.: 425120

The Flecto Company, Inc. (4)
11 Hawthorn Pkwy, Vernon Hills, IL 60061-
1402
Tel.: (847) 367-7700
Web Site: http://www.flecto.com
Sales Range: $25-49.9 Million
Emp.: 80
Specialty Wood Coatings Mfr
N.A.I.C.S.: 325510

Subsidiary (Non-US):

Rust-Oleum Japan Corporation (3)
JAPAN R-O Corporation Shinmi Bld 1-3-4
Mineoka-cho, In Hirado Yokohama Com-
pany Hodogaya-ku, Yokohama, 240-0064,
Japan
Tel.: (81) 457448940
Web Site: http://www.rustoleum.com
Sales Range: $150-199.9 Million
Emp.: 5
Rust-Preventive, General Purpose, Decora-
tive, Specialty & Professional Paints Mfr
N.A.I.C.S.: 325510

Subsidiary (Domestic):

Seal-Krete Inc. (3)
PO Box 1527, Auburndale, FL 33823-1527
Tel.: (863) 967-1535
Web Site: http://www.seal-krete.com
Adhesive Mfr
N.A.I.C.S.: 325520

Whink Products Company (3)
1901 15th Ave, Eldora, IA 50627
Tel.: (641) 939-2353

Polish & Other Sanitation Good Mfr
N.A.I.C.S.: 325612

Subsidiary (Domestic):

The Testor Corporation (2)
440 Blackhawk Ave, Rockford, IL
61104 **(100%)**
Tel.: (815) 962-6654
Web Site: http://www.testors.com
Sales Range: $100-124.9 Million
Model Paints, Adhesives, Tools & Plastic
Kits Mfr
N.A.I.C.S.: 325510

Zinsser Co., Inc. (2)
173 Belmont Dr, Somerset, NJ
08875 **(100%)**
Tel.: (732) 469-8100
Web Site: http://www.zinsser.com
Sales Range: $50-74.9 Million
Primers, Wallcovering Removal Products,
Wallcovering Application Products, Clear
Finishes & Mildew-Proofing Products Mfr
N.A.I.C.S.: 325510

Subsidiary (Domestic):

OKON, Inc. (3)
173 Belmont Dr, Somerset, NJ 08875
Tel.: (732) 469-8100
Web Site: http://www.okoninc.com
Sales Range: $10-24.9 Million
Emp.: 12
Water Repellant Sealer Mfr
N.A.I.C.S.: 325520

Zinsser Brands Company (3)
11 Hawthorn Pkwy, Vernon Hills, IL 60061
Tel.: (847) 367-7700
Paint & Coating Mfr
N.A.I.C.S.: 325510
Ann Gearty *(Sr Mgr-Brand)*

Zinsser Holdings, LLC (3)
173 Belmont Dr, Somerset, NJ 08875
Tel.: (732) 469-8100
Web Site: http://www.zinsser.com
Holding Company
N.A.I.C.S.: 551112

Subsidiary (Domestic):

Mantrose-Haeuser Co. (4)
100 Nyala Farms Rd, Westport, CT
06880 **(100%)**
Tel.: (203) 454-1800
Web Site: https://www.mantrose.com
Sales Range: $25-49.9 Million
Emp.: 80
Shellac-Based Specialty Coatings Products
Mfr
N.A.I.C.S.: 325510

Modern Masters Inc. (4)
9380 San Fernando Rd, Sun Valley, CA
91352
Tel.: (818) 683-0201
Web Site: http://www.modernmasters.com
Sales Range: $10-24.9 Million
Emp.: 30
Decorative Specialty Paint Products Mfr
N.A.I.C.S.: 325998

RPM Industrial Holding Co. (1)
2628 Pearl Rd PO Box 777, Medina, OH
44258 **(100%)**
Tel.: (330) 273-5090
Web Site: http://www.rpmintl.com
Sales Range: $50-74.9 Million
Emp.: 100
Holding Company
N.A.I.C.S.: 551112

Subsidiary (Domestic):

Republic Powdered Metals, Inc. (2)
2628 Pearl Rd, Medina, OH 44256
Tel.: (330) 273-8712
Web Site: http://www.rpmrepublic.com
Sales Range: $25-49.9 Million
Emp.: 35
Roof & Wall Restoration Products Mfr
N.A.I.C.S.: 325510

Tremco Incorporated (2)
3735 Green Rd, Beachwood, OH
44122 **(100%)**
Tel.: (216) 292-5000
Web Site: http://www.tremcoinc.com
Emp.: 500

RPM International Inc.—(Continued)

Protective Coatings, Sealants & Roofing Materials Mfr; Building Maintenance & Construction Industries
N.A.I.C.S.: 325520

Subsidiary (Domestic):

Paramount Technical Products (3)
2600 Paramount Dr, Spearfish, SD 57783-3208
Tel.: (605) 642-4787
Sales Range: $10-24.9 Million
Emp.: 15
Plastic Waterproofing Products Mfr
N.A.I.C.S.: 325998
Allan DiJone *(Plant Mgr)*

Subsidiary (Non-US):

RPM Canada (3)
220 Wicksteed Ave, Toronto, M4H 1G7, ON, Canada
Tel.: (416) 421-3300
Web Site: http://www.tremco.com
Sealant, Weatherproofing, Residential Waterproofing & Passive Fire Control Products Whslr
N.A.I.C.S.: 325510

Subsidiary (Domestic):

Schul International Co., LLC (3)
1 Industrial Park Dr, Pelham, NH 03076-2160
Tel.: (603) 889-6872
Web Site: https://www.schul.com
Adhesives/Sealants Mfr
N.A.I.C.S.: 325520

The Euclid Chemical Company (3)
19215 Redwood Rd, Cleveland, OH 44110
Tel.: (216) 531-9222
Web Site: https://www.euclidchemical.com
Sales Range: $125-149.9 Million
Emp.: 250
Concrete Construction Specialty Products & Services
N.A.I.C.S.: 325520

Subsidiary (Domestic):

Increte Systems Inc. (4)
1611 Gunn Hwy, Odessa, FL 33556
Tel.: (813) 886-8811
Web Site: http://www.increte.com
Sales Range: $10-24.9 Million
Emp.: 60
Concrete Floor & Walkway Product Mfr
N.A.I.C.S.: 327390

J W Brett, Inc. (4)
9660 71st St NE, Albertville, MN 55301
Tel.: (763) 497-7351
Sales Range: $1-9.9 Million
Emp.: 22
Brick, Stone & Related Construction Material Merchant Whslr
N.A.I.C.S.: 423320
John Brett *(Pres)*
Wendy Fong *(Pres)*

The Euclid Chemical Company (4)
19215 Redwood Rd, Cleveland, OH 44110
Tel.: (216) 531-9222
Web Site: https://www.euclidchemical.com
Sales Range: $10-24.9 Million
Emp.: 55
Concrete Restoration, Curing, Coating, Grouting, Waterproofing & Traffic Deck Products & Systems Mfr
N.A.I.C.S.: 325510

Subsidiary (Non-US):

Tremco Asia Pte. Ltd. (3)
60 Paya Lebar Road 05-53 Paya Lebar Square, Singapore, 409051, Singapore
Tel.: (65) 62466804
Web Site: http://www.tremcoinc.com
Sales Range: $25-49.9 Million
Emp.: 6
Protective Coatings & Sealants Mfr for Building Maintenance & Construction Industries
N.A.I.C.S.: 325520

Tremco Australia (3)
Unit 1 2 Park Rd, Rydalmere, 2116, NSW, Australia

Tel.: (61) 296382755
Web Site: http://www.tremco.com.au
Protective Coatings & Sealants Mfr for Building Maintenance & Construction Industries
N.A.I.C.S.: 325520
Steven Miller *(Mng Dir)*

Subsidiary (Domestic):

Tremco Pty. Ltd. (4)
Unit 1 2 Park Rd, Rydalmere, 2116, NSW, Australia
Tel.: (61) 296382755
Web Site: http://www.tremco.com.au
Sales Range: $25-49.9 Million
Emp.: 35
Protective Coatings & Sealants Mfr for Building Maintenance & Construction Industries
N.A.I.C.S.: 325520
Steven Miller *(Mng Dir)*

Subsidiary (Domestic):

Tremco Barrier Solutions, Inc. (3)
3735 Green Rd, Beachwood, OH 44122
Tel.: (800) 876-5624
Web Site: http://www.tremcobarriersolutions.com
Waterproofing Systems Mfr
N.A.I.C.S.: 325520

Weatherproofing Technologies, Inc. (3)
3735 Green Rd, Beachwood, OH 44122
Tel.: (216) 292-5000
Web Site: http://www.wtiservices.com
Sales Range: $125-149.9 Million
Emp.: 300
Roofing & General Contracting Services
N.A.I.C.S.: 238390

RPM Lux Enterprises S.ar.l. (1)
9 rue du Laboratoire, Luxembourg, 1911, Luxembourg
Tel.: (352) 27125335
Construction Materials Mfr
N.A.I.C.S.: 423390
Mark Albertus *(CEO)*

RPM Performance Coatings Group, Inc. (1)
1000 E Park Ave, Maple Shade, NJ 08052
Tel.: (856) 779-7500
Web Site: http://www.rpmperformancecoatings.com
Sales Range: $1-4.9 Billion
Polymer Wall & Lining System Mfr
N.A.I.C.S.: 325211
David C. Dennsteadt *(Pres)*

Subsidiary (Non-US):

A.P.I. Applicazioni Plastiche Industriali S.p.A. (2)
via Dante Alighieri 27, Mussolente, 36065, Vicenza, Italy
Tel.: (39) 0424579711
Web Site: http://www.apiplastic.com
Protective Coatings & Resin Flooring Mfr & Installer
N.A.I.C.S.: 325510

Subsidiary (US):

API USA, Inc. (3)
2025 NW 102 Ave Ste 107, Miami, FL 33172
Tel.: (305) 592-8115
Web Site: http://www.apiusa.com
Protective Coatings & Sealants Mfr
N.A.I.C.S.: 325510

Subsidiary (Domestic):

Arnette Polymers, LLC (2)
8905 Wollard Blvd, Richmond, MO 64085
Tel.: (816) 776-3005
Web Site: https://www.arnettepolymers.com
Thermoset Polymer Mfr
N.A.I.C.S.: 325211

Carboline Company (2)
2150 Schuetz Rd, Saint Louis, MO 63146 **(100%)**
Tel.: (314) 644-1000
Web Site: http://www.carboline.com
Sales Range: $100-124.9 Million
Emp.: 300
Protective Coatings Mfr

N.A.I.C.S.: 325510
Rick Brown *(VP-Sls-US)*
Darrin Andrews *(Exec VP-Sls-North America)*

Subsidiary (Domestic):

Carboline Corp. (3)
2150 Schetz Rd, Saint Louis, MO 63146
Tel.: (314) 644-1000
Web Site: http://www.carboline.com
Sales Range: $50-74.9 Million
Emp.: 105
Holding Company
N.A.I.C.S.: 551112

Carboline Dubai Corporation (3)
2150 Scheutz Rd, Saint Louis, MO 63146
Tel.: (314) 644-1000
Web Site: http://www.carboline.com
Sales Range: $25-49.9 Million
Emp.: 100
Paint & Coating Mfr
N.A.I.C.S.: 325510
Randy Rotch *(Pres)*

Subsidiary (Non-US):

Carboline France S.A.S. (3)
Immeuble Le Newton C 7 Mail B Thimonnier, Lognes, 77185, Paris, France
Tel.: (33) 160065566
Web Site: https://www.carboline.fr
Sales Range: $25-49.9 Million
Emp.: 9
Paint & Coating Mfr
N.A.I.C.S.: 325510

Carboline Italia S.p.A. (3)
Carboline Via Margherita De Vizzi 77, Cinisello Balsamo, 20092, Milan, Italy
Tel.: (39) 0294759236
Web Site: https://it.carboline.com
Emp.: 25
Paint & Coating Mfr
N.A.I.C.S.: 325510

Carboline Norge AS (3)
Husebysletta 7-9, PO Box 593, 3412, Lierstranda, Norway
Tel.: (47) 32857300
Web Site: https://www.carboline.no
Emp.: 67
Paint & Coating Mfr
N.A.I.C.S.: 325510

Subsidiary (Domestic):

Dudick, Inc. (3)
1818 Miller Pkwy, Streetsboro, OH 44241
Tel.: (330) 562-1970
Web Site: http://www.dudick.com
Sales Range: $1-9.9 Million
Emp.: 55
Paint & Coating Mfr
N.A.I.C.S.: 325510
Amy Nelson *(Purchasing Agent)*

Subsidiary (Domestic):

Expanko, Inc. (2)
1000 E Park Ave, Maple Shade, NJ 08052
Tel.: (610) 380-0300
Web Site: https://www.expanko.com
Sales Range: $10-24.9 Million
Emp.: 18
Cork Flooring & Terrazzo Tile Mfr
N.A.I.C.S.: 449121

Subsidiary (Non-US):

Hummervoll Industribelegg AS (2)
Sanddalsringen 3, Nesttun, 5225, Bergen, Norway
Tel.: (47) 55922700
Web Site: https://www.hummervoll.no
Sales Range: $10-24.9 Million
Emp.: 48
Supplier & Installer of Industrial Flooring Systems
N.A.I.C.S.: 238330

Perlita Y Vermiculita, S.L.U. (2)
Polygon Can Prunera C/ Garraf s/n, 08759, Barcelona, Spain
Tel.: (34) 932096019
Web Site: http://www.perlitayvermiculita.com
Emp.: 40
Paint & Coating Mfr
N.A.I.C.S.: 325510

Specialty Polymer Coatings Inc. (2)
100 5350 - 272nd Street, Langley, V4W 1S3, BC, Canada
Tel.: (604) 514-9711
Web Site: http://www.spc-net.com
Rev.: $7,687,104
Emp.: 200
Liquid Epoxy & Polyurethane Coatings Mfr, Formulator & Distr
N.A.I.C.S.: 325510
Brett Planzer *(Sls Dir-Technical)*

Subsidiary (Domestic):

StonCor Group, Inc. (2)
1000 E Park Ave, Maple Shade, NJ 08052
Tel.: (856) 779-7500
Web Site: https://www.stonhard.com
Sales Range: $750-799.9 Million
Emp.: 200
Industrial & Commercial Polymer-Based Floors, Walls, Coatings, Linings & Construction Products Mfr & Retailer
N.A.I.C.S.: 325510

Subsidiary (Domestic):

Fibergrate Composite Structures, Inc. (3)
5151 Beltline Rd Ste 1212, Dallas, TX 75254
Tel.: (972) 250-1633
Web Site: https://www.fibergrate.com
Sales Range: $75-99.9 Million
Emp.: 200
Plastic Hardware & Building Materials Mfr
N.A.I.C.S.: 326199

Subsidiary (Non-US):

Fibergrate Composite Structures Limited (4)
Wass Way Durham Lane Industrial Park, Eaglescliffe, Stockton-on-Tees, TS16 0RG, United Kingdom
Tel.: (44) 1642784747
Web Site: http://www.fibergrate.co.uk
Emp.: 50
Glass Reinforced Plastic Product Mfr
N.A.I.C.S.: 326220

Subsidiary (Non-US):

Flowcrete Group Ltd. (3)
The Flooring Technology Centre Booth Lane, Sandbach, CW11 3QF, Cheshire, United Kingdom
Tel.: (44) 1942929903
Web Site: http://www.flowcrete.co.uk
Sales Range: $75-99.9 Million
Emp.: 60
Commercial & Industrial Flooring Mfr
N.A.I.C.S.: 326199
Kevin Potter *(Mng Dir)*

Subsidiary (Non-US):

Flowcrete (Hong Kong) Ltd (4)
Unit 805-807 8/F Kin Sang Commercial Centre, 49 King Yip Street Kwun Tong, Kowloon, China (Hong Kong)
Tel.: (852) 27950478
Web Site: http://www.flowcrete.com
Sales Range: $10-24.9 Million
Emp.: 5
Industrial Floor & Wall Coating Mfr
N.A.I.C.S.: 326199

Flowcrete Asia Sdn. Bhd. (4)
The Flooring Technology Centre Lot 37631 37632 Jalan 6/37A, Taman Bukit Maluri Industrial Area Kepong, 52100, Kuala Lumpur, Malaysia
Tel.: (60) 362779575
Web Site: http://www.flowcrete.com
Sales Range: $25-49.9 Million
Emp.: 100
Specialist Flooring Product Mfr
N.A.I.C.S.: 332322

Flowcrete Australia Pty. Limited (4)
63 Radley Street, Virginia, 4014, QLD, Australia
Tel.: (61) 38899222
Web Site: http://www.flowcreteaustralia.com.au
Sales Range: $10-24.9 Million
Emp.: 7
Specialist Flooring Product Mfr
N.A.I.C.S.: 332322

Sean Tinsley (Natl Mgr-Flooring)
Tony Girolamo (Sls Mgr)
Emma Hollywood (Coord-Sls Support)
Ryan Mulquin (Coord-NSW Warehouse)

Flowcrete France S.A.S. (4)
12 rue du Parc Oberhausbergen, 67033,
Strasbourg, Cedex 2, France
Tel.: (33) 971008000
Web Site: http://www.flowcrete.fr
Specialist Flooring Product Mfr
N.A.I.C.S.: 332322

Flowcrete India Private Limited (4)
Ganesh Tower Door No B-1 1st floor 1st
Avenue Ashok Nagar, Chennai, 600083,
TamilNadu, India
Tel.: (91) 4440176600
Web Site: http://www.flowcrete.in
Sales Range: $10-24.9 Million
Emp.: 15
Specialist Flooring Product Mfr
N.A.I.C.S.: 332322
V. Srinivasan (Sls Dir)
A. Anjanappa (Exec Dir)

Flowcrete Middle East FZCO (4)
22th Floor Suite 2207 Jafza View 18, PO
Box 17641, Jebel Ali Free Zone, Dubai,
17641, United Arab Emirates
Tel.: (971) 48864728
Web Site: http://www.flowcrete.ae
Sales Range: $10-24.9 Million
Emp.: 13
Specialist Flooring Product Mfr
N.A.I.C.S.: 332322

Subsidiary (US):

Flowcrete North America Inc. (4)
4050 Clough Woods Dr, Batavia, OH 45103
Tel.: (513) 943-4225
Web Site: http://www.flowcrete.com
Sales Range: $50-74.9 Million
Emp.: 25
Industrial Floor & Wall Coating Mfr
N.A.I.C.S.: 326199

Subsidiary (Non-US):

Flowcrete Norway AS (4)
Berghagan 7, 1405, Langhus, Norway
Tel.: (47) 64860830
Web Site: https://www.flowcrete.eu
Emp.: 6
Specialist Flooring Product Mfr
N.A.I.C.S.: 332322
Liv Totland Lund (Mgr-Customer Svcs)

Flowcrete Polska Sp. z .o.o. (4)
ul Marywilska 34, 03-228, Warsaw, Poland
Tel.: (48) 228798907
Web Site: https://www.flowcrete.eu
Sales Range: $10-24.9 Million
Emp.: 20
Industrial Floor & Wall Coating Mfr
N.A.I.C.S.: 326199
Miroslaw Rosinski (Reg Dir-Sls)
Artur Wojtowicz (Reg Sls Mgr)
Jaroslaw Chelstowski (Reg Dir)
Piotr Jakobczak (Dir-Sls)
Yan Sevin (Mgr-Export)
Elena Kucharenko (Mgr-Export)

Flowcrete SA (Pty) Ltd (4)
Trio Industrial Park 8 Qashana Khuzwayo
Road, Jacobs, New Germany, 4025, South
Africa
Tel.: (27) 317059386
Web Site: http://www.flowcrete.com
Sales Range: $50-74.9 Million
Emp.: 40
Industrial Wall & Floor Coating Mfr
N.A.I.C.S.: 326199
Rob Weyers (Mgr-Bus Unit)

Flowcrete Sweden AB (4)
Perstorp Industripark, 284 80, Perstorp,
Sweden
Tel.: (46) 31570010
Web Site: http://www.flowcrete.se
Industrial Wall & Floor Coating Mfr
N.A.I.C.S.: 326199
Jukka Kaikkonen (Mng Dir)

Subsidiary (Domestic):

Flowcrete UK Limited (4)
The Flooring Technology Centre Booth
Lane, Sandbach, CW11 3QF, Cheshire,
United Kingdom

Tel.: (44) 1270753000
Web Site: http://www.flowcrete.co.uk
Emp.: 60
Specialist Flooring Product Mfr
N.A.I.C.S.: 332322
Emma Phillips (Sls Mgr-Specification-North)

Subsidiary (Non-US):

StonCor (Deutschland) GmbH (3)
Schumanstr 18, 52146, Wurselen, Germany
Tel.: (49) 240541740
Web Site: https://www.stonhard.de
Emp.: 15
Polymer Industrial Flooring Mfr
N.A.I.C.S.: 238330

StonCor Africa Pty. Ltd. (3)
Midrand Industrial Park 8 Cresset Rd,
Edenvale, 1685, Chloorkop, South Africa
Tel.: (27) 112545500
Web Site: https://www.pro-struct.co.za
Sales Range: $50-74.9 Million
Protective Coatings Mfr & Whslr
N.A.I.C.S.: 325510
Grant Boonzaier (Mng Dir)

StonCor Benelux B.V. (3)
Braak 1, 4704 RJ, Roosendaal, Nether-
lands
Tel.: (31) 165585230
Web Site: http://www.stoncor.com
Emp.: 25
Polymer Industrial Flooring Mfr
N.A.I.C.S.: 238330

**StonCor Corrosion Specialists Group
Ltda.** (3)
Av Eid Mansur 382, Parque Sao Jorge,
06700-000, Cotia, SP, Brazil
Tel.: (55) 1146129797
Web Site: http://www.stoncor.com.br
Sales Range: $25-49.9 Million
Emp.: 65
Industrial & Commercial Polymer-Based
Floors, Walls, Coatings, Linings & Construc-
tion Products Mfr & Retailer
N.A.I.C.S.: 238330

StonCor Espana SL (3)
Avda Diagonal 520 6th Low, 8006, Barce-
lona, Spain
Tel.: (34) 933623785
Web Site: https://www.stonhard.es
Emp.: 8
Polymer Industrial Flooring Mfr
N.A.I.C.S.: 238330

StonCor South Cone S.A. (3)
Einstein 1095, Parque OKS, B1619JWA,
Garin, Buenos Aires, Argentina
Tel.: (54) 1150323113
Web Site: https://www.stoncor.com.ar
Corrosion Protection Coatings Whslr
N.A.I.C.S.: 423840

Stonhard (U.K.) Limited (3)
Unit G Taylor Business Park Warrington
Road, Risley, Warrington, WA3 6BL, Hamp-
shire, United Kingdom
Tel.: (44) 1925649458
Web Site: https://www.stonhard.co.uk
Sales Range: $10-24.9 Million
Emp.: 15
Specialist Flooring Product Mfr
N.A.I.C.S.: 332322

Stonhard Nederland B.V. (3)
Zilverenberg 18, 5234 GM, 's-
Hertogenbosch, Netherlands
Tel.: (31) 165585200
Web Site: https://www.stonhard.nl
Emp.: 4
Polymer Industrial Flooring Mfr
N.A.I.C.S.: 238330

Stonhard S.A.S. (3)
7 mail B Thimonnier Immeuble le Newton
C, 77185, Lognes, France
Tel.: (33) 160064419
Web Site: https://www.stonhard.fr
Sales Range: $10-24.9 Million
Emp.: 23
Specialist Flooring Product Mfr
N.A.I.C.S.: 332322
Michel Nolis (Pres-Europe)

RPM, Inc. (1)
2628 Pearl Rd, Medina, OH 44256
Tel.: (330) 273-5090
Web Site: http://www.rpminc.com

Sales Range: $1-4.9 Billion
Emp.: 80
Protective Coatings Mfr
N.A.I.C.S.: 325510

Subsidiary (Domestic):

**Chemical Specialties Manufacturing
Corp.** (2)
901 N Newkirk St, Baltimore, MD 21205-
3013
Tel.: (410) 675-4800
Web Site: http://www.chemspecworld.com
Sales Range: $50-74.9 Million
Emp.: 70
Upholstery Cleaning Products Mfr
N.A.I.C.S.: 325612

Day-Glo Color Corp. (2)
4515 St Clair Ave, Cleveland, OH
44103-1203 (100%)
Tel.: (216) 391-7070
Web Site: https://www.dayglo.com
Sales Range: $100-124.9 Million
Emp.: 300
Fluorescent Color Mfr
N.A.I.C.S.: 325130

Dryvit Holdings, Inc. (2)
1 Energy Way, West Warwick, RI 02893
Tel.: (401) 822-4100
Web Site: http://www.dryvit.com
Sales Range: $150-199.9 Million
Emp.: 100
Holding Company
N.A.I.C.S.: 551112

Subsidiary (Domestic):

Dryvit Systems, Inc. (3)
1 Energy Way, West Warwick, RI
02893 (100%)
Tel.: (401) 822-4100
Web Site: http://www.dryvit.com
Sales Range: $200-249.9 Million
Emp.: 150
Exterior Insulation & Finish Systems Mfr
N.A.I.C.S.: 325998

Subsidiary (Non-US):

Dryvit Systems Canada Ltd. (4)
129 Ringwood Dr, Stouffville, L4A 8A2, ON,
Canada (100%)
Tel.: (905) 642-0444
Web Site: http://www.dryvit.com
Sales Range: $10-24.9 Million
Emp.: 50
Exterior Insulation & Finish Systems Mfr
N.A.I.C.S.: 238310

**Dryvit Systems USA (Europe) Sp. z
o.o.** (4)
ul Postepu 6, Warsaw, 02-676, Poland
Tel.: (48) 223582870
Web Site: http://www.dryvit.com.pl
Sales Range: $75-99.9 Million
Emp.: 100
Exterior Insulation & Finish Systems Mfr
N.A.I.C.S.: 325998

Subsidiary (Non-US):

Dryvit UK Limited (3)
Unit 4 Wren Park Hitchin Road, Shefford,
SG17 5JD, Bedfordshire, United Kingdom
Tel.: (44) 1462819555
Web Site: https://www.dryvit.com
Emp.: 9
Exterior Insulation & Finish System Con-
tractor
N.A.I.C.S.: 238310
Joe Gribben (Sls Mgr-Area)

Subsidiary (Domestic):

Kop-Coat, Inc. (2)
3040 William Pitt Way, Pittsburgh, PA
15238
Tel.: (412) 227-2426
Web Site: https://www.kop-coat.com
Sales Range: $25-49.9 Million
Emp.: 150
Marine Coatings, Wood Treatments & Fuel
Compounds Mfr & Marketer
N.A.I.C.S.: 325510

Subsidiary (Non-US):

Agpro (N.Z.) Ltd. (3)
10 Polaris Place East Tamaki, Auckland,

2013, New Zealand
Tel.: (64) 508536536
Web Site: https://www.agpro.co.nz
Sales Range: $10-24.9 Million
Emp.: 15
Herbicides, Fungicides & Fertilizer Products
Mfr
N.A.I.C.S.: 325110
Peter Thomas (Mgr-Farming)
Trevor Hayde (Mgr-Sls)
Mark Freeman (Mgr-Horticultural)
Wayne Binney (Gen Mgr)
Justin Casey (Mgr-Sth Island Bus)
Danny Varsanyi (Mgr-Customer Svc)

Kop-Coat New Zealand Ltd. (3)
Kot-Coat House 2 Te Papa Tipu Innovation
Park, 49 Sala Street, Rotorua, 3010, New
Zealand
Tel.: (64) 73436304
Sales Range: $10-24.9 Million
Emp.: 10
Marine Coatings, Wood Treatments & Fuel
Compounds Mfr & Marketer
N.A.I.C.S.: 325510
Cameron Scott (Gen Mgr)

Subsidiary (Domestic):

Pettit Paint Company (3)
36 Pine St, Rockaway, NJ 07866
Tel.: (973) 625-3100
Web Site: http://www.pettitpaint.com
Sales Range: $25-49.9 Million
Emp.: 50
Marine Paint Mfr
N.A.I.C.S.: 325510

Subsidiary (Domestic):

RPM Wood Finishes Group, Inc. (2)
2220 Hwy 70 SE Ste 100, Hickory, NC
28602
Tel.: (828) 261-0325
Web Site: https://rpmicg.com
Sales Range: $150-199.9 Million
Emp.: 340
Holding Company; Furniture, Cabinetry &
Decorative Wood Coatings
N.A.I.C.S.: 551112

Subsidiary (Domestic):

Chemical Coatings, Inc. (3)
22 S Ctr St, Hickory, NC 28603-0220
Tel.: (828) 261-0325
Web Site: http://www.rpminc.com
Sales Range: $100-124.9 Million
Emp.: 150
Coating Mfr
N.A.I.C.S.: 321114
Ronnie Holman (Pres)

Westfield Coatings Corp. (3)
221 Union St, Westfield, MA 01086
Tel.: (413) 562-9655
Web Site: http://www.rpmwfg.com
Sales Range: $10-24.9 Million
Emp.: 25
Custom-Formulated Coatings Mfr
N.A.I.C.S.: 325510

Subsidiary (Domestic):

TCI, Inc. (2)
300 Martin Marietta Dr, Americus, GA
31719 (100%)
Tel.: (229) 937-1248
Web Site: https://tcipowder.com
Sales Range: $50-74.9 Million
Emp.: 14,000
Powder Coating Mfr
N.A.I.C.S.: 325510

RPM/Belgium N.V. (1)
Henri Dunantstraat 11B, Industriepark
Noord, 8700, Tielt, Belgium
Tel.: (32) 51403801
Web Site: http://www.rpm-belgium.be
Sales Range: $10-24.9 Million
Emp.: 30
Industrial Flooring & Specialty Waterproof-
ing Systems Mfr & Distr
N.A.I.C.S.: 324122
David Chapman (Pres)

Subsidiary (Non-US):

Alteco Technik GmbH (2)
Raiffeisenstrasse 16, 27239, Twistringen,
Germany

RPM International Inc.—(Continued)

Tel.: (49) 424392950
Web Site: https://www.alteco-technik.de
Emp.: 30
Specialist Flooring Product Mfr
N.A.I.C.S.: 332322

Radiant Color N.V. (1)
Europark 1046, 3530, Houthalen,
Belgium (100%)
Tel.: (32) 11520740
Web Site: https://www.radiantcolor.be
Sales Range: $25-49.9 Million
Emp.: 60
Fluorescent Pigments & Ink Bases Mfr &
Marketer
N.A.I.C.S.: 325510
Jan Van Speybroeck *(Dir-Sls)*
Patrizia Vigna *(Officer-Fin)*
Patrick Cheval *(Mgr-Fin)*
Hubrecht Peeters *(Area Mgr-Sls)*
Erik Bovens *(Area Mgr-Sls)*
Olivier Frederix *(Area Mgr-Sls)*
Chantal Zwerts *(Officer-Customer Svc)*
Inge Schols *(Officer-Customer Svc)*
Jolanda Kemps *(Officer-Customer Svc)*
Keith Hui *(Mgr-Bus Dev-Asia Pacific)*
Everard Nys *(Dir-Mfg & Ops)*
Ingrid Pollers *(Dir-R&D)*
Miranda Sidarow *(Mgr-Regulatory Affairs &
Environment)*
Stefan Detremmerie *(Mgr-QC)*
Carine Haesen *(Officer-Procurement)*
Martin Horrobin *(Mgr-Technical)*
Greet Steegmans *(Officer-Customer Svc)*
Robby Ballet *(Supvr-Logistics)*
Peggy Boelanders *(Mgr-HR)*

**Rust-Oleum Australia & New Zealand
Pty. Ltd.** (1)
Level 2/307 Ferntree Gully Rd, Mount Wa-
verley, 3149, VIC, Australia
Tel.: (61) 1300784476
Paint Product Mfr
N.A.I.C.S.: 325510

**Rust-Oleum Australia Pty.
Limited** (1)
level 2/307 Ferntree Gully Rd, Mount Wa-
verley, 3149, VIC, Australia
Tel.: (61) 1300784476
Web Site: http://www.rustoleum.com.au
Emp.: 20
Paint & Coating Mfr & Distr
N.A.I.C.S.: 325510
Jack Hurst *(Dir-Sls)*

Rust-Oleum France S.A.S. (1)
11 Rue Jules Verne B P 39, 95322, Saint
Leu-la-Foret, France
Tel.: (33) 130400044
Sales Range: $25-49.9 Million
Emp.: 40
Specialist Flooring Product Mfr
N.A.I.C.S.: 332322
Colin Carter *(Mng Dir)*

Rust-Oleum UK Limited (1)
Rotterdam House 116 Quayside,
Newcastle, NE1 3DY, United Kingdom
Tel.: (44) 2476717329
Web Site: http://www.rust-oleum.eu
Paint & Coating Mfr
N.A.I.C.S.: 325510

SPS B.V. (1)
Zilverenberg 16, 5234 GM, 's-
Hertogenbosch, Netherlands
Tel.: (31) 736422710
Web Site: https://www.spsbv.com
Coating Mfr & Distr
N.A.I.C.S.: 325510

Sapphire Scientific Inc. (1)
2604 Liberator, Prescott, AZ 86301
Tel.: (928) 445-3030
Web Site:
   https://www.legendbrandscleaning.com
Carpet Cleaning Accessories Mfr
N.A.I.C.S.: 333310

Siamons International Inc. (1)
48 Galaxy Blvd Unit 413, Toronto, M9W
6C8, ON, Canada
Tel.: (416) 213-0219
Web Site: http://www.concrobium.com
Mold Remediation Chemical Mfr
N.A.I.C.S.: 325320

**Specialty Polymer Coatings USA,
Inc.** (1)

22503 FM 521, Angleton, TX 77515
Tel.: (281) 595-3530
Industrial Chemical Distr
N.A.I.C.S.: 424690
Tracy Menard *(VP)*
Mike Musslewhite *(Mgr-Bus Dev)*
Troy Marshall *(Sls Mgr-Engrg)*

TCI Powder Coating Canada Inc. (1)
903 Barton St, Stoney Creek, L8E 5P5,
ON, Canada
Tel.: (905) 643-0306
Powder Coating Mfr
N.A.I.C.S.: 325510
Drew Spencer *(Acct Mgr-Ohio, Western
Pennsylvania & New York Territory)*
Jack Bostock *(VP-Sls)*

**TCI Powder Coatings de Mexico,
S.A. de C.V.** (1)
The Juarez No 26, San Jose del Cabo,
03900, Mexico
Tel.: (52) 5556780762
Powder Coating Mfr
N.A.I.C.S.: 325510

Tevco Enterprises, Inc. (1)
110 Pomponio Ave, South Plainfield, NJ
07080
Tel.: (908) 754-7306
Web Site: http://www.tevco.com
Cosmetics Mfr
N.A.I.C.S.: 325620

Tor Coatings Limited (1)
Unit 21 White Rose Way Follingsby Park,
Chester-Le-Street, Gateshead, NE10 8YX,
Durham, United Kingdom
Tel.: (44) 1483791398
Web Site: https://www.tor-coatings.com
Sales Range: $50-74.9 Million
Emp.: 180
Paint & Coating Material Mfr
N.A.I.C.S.: 325510

Toxement, S.A. (1)
Parque Industrial Gran Sabana, Cundi-
namarca, 11001, Tocancipa, Colombia
Tel.: (57) 6018698787
Web Site: https://www.toxement.com.co
Powder Coating Mfr
N.A.I.C.S.: 325510

**Tremco CPG (India) Private
Limited** (1)
Ganesh Towers Door no B-1 1st Floor 1st
Avenue Ashok Nagar, Chennai, 600 083,
Tamilnadu, India
Tel.: (91) 4440176600
Web Site: https://www.tremcocpg-india.in
Construction Product & Coating Mfr
N.A.I.C.S.: 332812

Tremco CPG Germany GmbH (1)
Werner-Haepp-Str 1, 92439, Schwandorf,
Germany
Tel.: (49) 94342080
Construction Product Mfr
N.A.I.C.S.: 332812

Tremco CPG Sweden AB (1)
Polhemsplatsen 5, 411 03, Gothenburg,
Sweden
Tel.: (46) 31570010
Construction Equipment Mfr & Distr
N.A.I.C.S.: 333120

Tremco illbruck Dis Ticaret A.S. (1)
Tekstilkent Koza Plaza B Blok Kat 21 No
78, Maltepe, 34235, Istanbul, Türkiye
Tel.: (90) 2124384466
Web Site: http://www.tremco-illbruck.com.tr
Emp.: 50
Powder Coating Mfr
N.A.I.C.S.: 325510

Tremco illbruck GmbH (1)
Campus 21 Liebermannstrasse A02 401,
2345, Brunn am Gebirge, Austria
Tel.: (43) 22363124470
Web Site: http://www.tremco-illbruck.com
Sales Range: $25-49.9 Million
Emp.: 15
Coating Material Mfr

N.A.I.C.S.: 324122

Tremco illbruck Group GmbH (1)
Von-der-Wettern-Str 27, 51149, Cologne,
Germany
Tel.: (49) 2203575500
Web Site: http://www.tremco-illbruck.com
Construction Equipment Mfr
N.A.I.C.S.: 325520
Daniel Johnson *(Mng Dir)*

Tremco illbruck Limited (1)
Coupland Road Hindley Green, Wigan,
WN2 4HT, United Kingdom
Tel.: (44) 1942251400
Web Site: http://www.tremco-illbruck.com
Emp.: 75
Powder Coating Mfr
N.A.I.C.S.: 325510

Tremco illbruck Production SAS (1)
66 Route de Gray, 21850, Saint Apollinaire,
France
Tel.: (33) 971001830
Web Site: http://www.tremcoillbruck.com
Emp.: 24
Powder Coating Mfr
N.A.I.C.S.: 325510

**Tremco illbruck Produktion
GmbH** (1)
Niederlassung Traunreut Traunring 65,
83301, Traunreut, Germany
Tel.: (49) 866934100
Powder Coating Mfr
N.A.I.C.S.: 325510

Tremco illbruck SAS (1)
12 rue du Parc, Valparo, 67205, Oberhaus-
bergen, France
Tel.: (33) 97100140
Powder Coating Mfr
N.A.I.C.S.: 325510

Tremco illbruck Swiss AG (1)
Sihlbruggstrasse 144, 6340, Baar, Switzer-
land
Tel.: (41) 417601212
Web Site: http://www.tremco-illbruck.ch
Sales Range: $25-49.9 Million
Emp.: 26
Powder Coating Mfr
N.A.I.C.S.: 325510

Tremco illbruck kft (1)
Puskas Tivadar u 3, 2040, Budaors, Hun-
gary
Tel.: (36) 23428218
Web Site: http://www.tremco-illbruck.com
Emp.: 2
Powder Coating Mfr
N.A.I.C.S.: 325510

Tremco illbruck ooo (1)
Zarichnaya str 2, Klimovsk, Moscow,
142180, Russia
Tel.: (7) 4956440299
Web Site: http://www.tremco-illbruck.com
Sales Range: $25-49.9 Million
Emp.: 15
Powder Coating Distr
N.A.I.C.S.: 325510
Pyak Leonid *(CEO)*

Tremco illbruck s.r.o. (1)
Slezska 2526/113, 130 00, Prague, 3,
Czech Republic
Tel.: (420) 296565333
Web Site: http://www.tremco-illbruck.cz
Emp.: 20
Powder Coating Mfr
N.A.I.C.S.: 325510

Tremco illbruck, S.L.U. (1)
Ronda Maiols 1 Edificio BMC Local 135-
137, Sant Quirze del Valles, 08192, Barce-
lona, Spain
Tel.: (34) 937197005
Web Site: http://www.tremco-illbruck.es
Emp.: 3
Powder Coating Mfr
N.A.I.C.S.: 325510

Universal Sealants (U.K.) Limited (1)
Kingston House 3 Walton Road Pattinson
North, Washington, NE38 8QA, Tyne &
Wear, United Kingdom
Tel.: (44) 1914161530
Web Site: https://www.uslgroup.com
Emp.: 250
Construction Products & Services

N.A.I.C.S.: 237990

Subsidiary (US):

Prime Resins, Inc. (2)
2291 Plunkett Rd, Conyers, GA 30012-3433
Tel.: (770) 388-0626
Web Site: https://www.primeresins.com
Sales Range: $1-9.9 Million
Emp.: 22
Plastics Material & Resin Mfr
N.A.I.C.S.: 325211
David L. Barton *(Founder & Pres)*

Viapol Ltda. (1)
Rodovia Vito Ardito n 6401 - Km 118 5 - Jd
Campo Grande, Cacapava, 12282-535, Sao
Paulo, Brazil
Tel.: (55) 1232213000
Web Site: http://www.viapol.com.br
Construction Product Mfr
N.A.I.C.S.: 237990
Amilton Oliveira *(CEO)*

Watco GmbH (1)
Krankelsweg 14, 41748, Viersen, Germany
Tel.: (49) 21625301717
Web Site: https://www.watco.de
Sales Range: $25-49.9 Million
Emp.: 10
Paint & Coating Material Mfr
N.A.I.C.S.: 325510

Watco S.ar.l. (1)
Arteparc coworking space 9 rue des Boule-
aux, 59810, Lesquin, France
Tel.: (33) 320527777
Web Site: https://www.watco.fr
Paint & Coating Distr
N.A.I.C.S.: 325510
Charlotte Dubois *(Sec-Comml)*

Watco UK Limited (1)
Eastgate Court 195-205 High Street, Guild-
ford, GU1 3AW, Surrey, United Kingdom
Tel.: (44) 1483418418
Web Site: https://www.watco.co.uk
Sales Range: $25-49.9 Million
Emp.: 50
Paint & Coating Mfr
N.A.I.C.S.: 325510

RTS OIL HOLDINGS, INC.
2319 Foothill Dr Ste 160, Salt Lake
City, UT 84109
Tel.: (801) 810-4662   UT
RTSO—(OTCIQ)
Crude Oil Retailers
N.A.I.C.S.: 457210

RTW RETAILWINDS, INC.
330 W 34th St 9th Fl, New York, NY
10001
Tel.: (212) 884-2000   IN
Web Site:
   http://www.cardinalethanol.com
Year Founded: 2005
RTW—(NYSE)
Rev.: $826,990,000
Assets: $411,984,000
Liabilities: $396,027,000
Net Worth: $15,957,000
Earnings: ($61,623,000)
Emp.: 1,413
Fiscal Year-end: 02/01/20
Methanol Mfr
N.A.I.C.S.: 325193
Grace A. Nichols *(Chm)*

Subsidiaries:

Fashion to Figure, LLC (1)
330 West 34th St, New York, NY 10001
Web Site: http://www.fashiontofigure.com
Fashion Apparel Distr
N.A.I.C.S.: 458110
Jennifer Schmitt *(Dir-E-Commerce)*

RTX CORPORATION
1000 Wilson Blvd, Arlington, VA
22209
Tel.: (781) 522-3000   DE
Web Site: https://www.rtx.com
Year Founded: 1934

RTX—(NYSE)
Rev.: $68,920,000,000
Assets: $161,869,000,000
Liabilities: $100,424,000,000
Net Worth: $61,445,000,000
Earnings: $3,195,000,000
Emp.: 185,000
Fiscal Year-end: 12/31/23
Holding Company; Power, Building
Systems & Aerospace Products Mfr
N.A.I.C.S.: 551112
Gregory J. Hayes *(Chm)*
Robin Diamonte *(Chief Investment Officer)*
Dantaya M. Williams *(Chief HR Officer & Exec VP)*
Henry F. Brooks *(Pres-Power & Controls-Collins Aerospace)*
Amy L. Johnson *(Principal Acctg Officer, VP & Controller)*
Steven A. Forrest *(VP & Asst Controller)*
Amy L. Johnson *(VP & Controller)*
Vince Campisi *(Chief Digital Officer)*
Barbara Borgonovi *(Sr VP-Corp Strategy & Dev)*
Pamela Erickson *(Chief Comm Officer)*
Neil G. Mitchill Jr. *(CFO)*
Juan M. de Bedout *(CTO & Sr VP)*
Christopher T. Calio *(Pres, CEO & COO)*

Subsidiaries:

Blades Technology Ltd.   **(1)**
PO Box 330, Nahariyya, 22102, Israel
Tel.: (972) 49878888
Web Site: http://www.btl.co.il
Industrial Machinery Mfr
N.A.I.C.S.: 333924

Collins Aerospace   **(1)**
4 Coliseum Ctr 2730 W Tyvola Rd, Charlotte, NC 28217-4578
Tel.: (704) 423-7000
Web Site: http://www.collinsaerospace.com
Emp.: 70,000
Holding Company; Executive Office; Aerospace Vehicles & Components Mfr
N.A.I.C.S.: 551112
Steve Timm *(Pres)*
Troy Brunk *(Pres-Avionics)*
Maya Raichelson *(VP-Mission Sys Ops)*
Conn Doherty *(VP/Gen Mgr-BMC2 & Autonomy Solutions)*

Unit (Non-US):

Collins Aerospace - Aerostructures, Prestwick Service Center   **(2)**
1 Dow Avenue, Prestwick, KA9 2SA, South Ayrshire, United Kingdom
Tel.: (44) 1292670200
Aerostructure Maintenance, Overhaul & Repair Services
N.A.I.C.S.: 488190

Unit (Domestic):

Collins Aerospace - Air Management Systems   **(2)**
1 Hamilton Rd, Windsor Locks, CT 06096
Tel.: (860) 654-6000
Aerospace Fans, Compressors & Vapor Cycle Systems Mfr
N.A.I.C.S.: 336413

Plant (Domestic):

Collins Aerospace - Cheshire   **(2)**
250 Knotter Dr, Cheshire, CT 06410
Tel.: (203) 250-3500
Aerospace Sensory Equipment Mfr
N.A.I.C.S.: 334511

Unit (Domestic):

Collins Aerospace - Electric Systems   **(2)**
4747 Harrison Ave, Rockford, IL 61108
Tel.: (815) 226-6000
Aerospace Electric Systems & Auxiliary Equipment Mfr
N.A.I.C.S.: 336419

Collins Aerospace - ISR Systems   **(2)**
7 Technology Park Dr, Westford, MA 01886
Tel.: (978) 490-2141
Aerospace Intelligence, Surveillance & Reconnaissance Equipment Mfr
N.A.I.C.S.: 336413

Subsidiary (Domestic):

Cloud Cap Technology, Inc.   **(3)**
205 Wasco Loop, Hood River, OR 97031
Tel.: (541) 387-2120
Web Site: http://www.cloudcaptech.com
Unmanned Aerospace Vehicle Systems Developer & Mfr
N.A.I.C.S.: 334511

N2 Imaging Systems, LLC   **(3)**
14440 Myford Rd, Irvine, CA 92606
Tel.: (714) 573-8800
Web Site: http://www.n2imaging.com
Sales Range: $10-24.9 Million
Military Visible & Infrared Imaging Systems Designer & Mfr
N.A.I.C.S.: 334511

Sensors Unlimited, Inc.   **(3)**
330 Carter Rd, Princeton, NJ 08540
Tel.: (609) 333-8000
Web Site: http://www.sensorsinc.com
Emp.: 115
Short Wave Infrared Sensing Products Developer & Mfr
N.A.I.C.S.: 334511

Unit (Domestic):

Collins Aerospace - Landing Gear   **(2)**
6225 Oak Tree Blvd, Independence, OH 44131
Tel.: (216) 341-1700
Aircraft Landing Gear Mfr
N.A.I.C.S.: 336413

Plant (Non-US):

UTC Aerospace Systems - Landing Gear, Burlington   **(3)**
5415 North Service Road, Burlington, L7L 5H7, ON, Canada
Tel.: (905) 319-3006
Web Site: http://www.utcaerospacesystems.com
Aircraft Landing Gear Overhaul & Repair Services
N.A.I.C.S.: 488190

UTC Aerospace Systems - Landing Gear, Oakville   **(3)**
1400 South Service Road West, Oakville, L6L 5Y7, ON, Canada
Tel.: (905) 827-7777
Web Site: http://www.utcaerospacesystems.com
Aircraft Landing Gear Mfr, Maintenance, Overhaul & Repair Services
N.A.I.C.S.: 336413

Plant (Domestic):

Collins Aerospace - Riverside   **(2)**
8200 Arlington Ave, Riverside, CA 92503
Tel.: (951) 351-5400
Aircraft Engine & Engine Components Mfr
N.A.I.C.S.: 336412

Collins Aerospace - San Marcos   **(2)**
2005 Technology Way, San Marcos, TX 78666
Tel.: (512) 754-3600
Aircraft Engine Mfr & Assembly Services
N.A.I.C.S.: 336412

Unit (Domestic):

Collins Aerospace - Wheels & Brakes   **(2)**
101 Waco St, Troy, OH 45373
Tel.: (937) 339-3811
Aircraft Wheel & Brake Equipment Mfr
N.A.I.C.S.: 336413

Unit (Non-US):

Collins Aerospace – Actuation Systems   **(2)**
Stafford Road Fordhouses, Wolverhampton, WV10 7EH, United Kingdom
Tel.: (44) 1189359000

Aircraft Actuation Systems & Components Mfr
N.A.I.C.S.: 336413

Subsidiary (Domestic):

Crompton Technology Group Limited   **(3)**
Chalker Way, Banbury, OX16 4XD, Oxon, United Kingdom
Tel.: (44) 1295755100
Web Site: http://www.ctgltd.com
Sales Range: $25-49.9 Million
Emp.: 150
Aerospace Composite Components & Systems Mfr
N.A.I.C.S.: 336413

Unit (Non-US):

UTC Aerospace Systems - Actuation Systems, Buc   **(3)**
106 rue Fourny, 78530, Buc, France
Tel.: (33) 139205200
Web Site: http://www.utcaerospacesystems.com
Aircraft Actuation Systems & Components Mfr
N.A.I.C.S.: 336413

Subsidiary (Domestic):

Hamilton Sundstrand Corporation   **(2)**
1 Hamilton Rd, Windsor Locks, CT 06096   **(100%)**
Tel.: (860) 654-6000
Web Site: http://www.utcaerospacesystems.com
Sales Range: $5-14.9 Billion
Emp.: 42,000
Building System & Aerospace Product Mfr
N.A.I.C.S.: 551112

Subsidiary (Non-US):

CT Group Limited   **(3)**
6 Chesterfield Gardens, London, W1J 5BQ, United Kingdom
Tel.: (44) 2073185770
Aircraft Part Mfr
N.A.I.C.S.: 336413

Subsidiary (Domestic):

Dynamic Controls HS, Inc.   **(3)**
1 Hamilton Rd, Windsor Locks, CT 06096
Tel.: (860) 654-6000
Web Site: http://www.utcaerospacesystems.com
Aerospace Electronic Control Systems Mfr
N.A.I.C.S.: 336413

Subsidiary (Non-US):

HS Marston Aerospace Limited   **(4)**
Wobaston Road, Fordhouses, Wolverhampton, WV10 6QJ, United Kingdom
Tel.: (44) 1902572777
Web Site: http://www.hsmarston.co.uk
Sales Range: $50-74.9 Million
Emp.: 300
Aerospace Heat Transfer & Fluid Management Components Mfr
N.A.I.C.S.: 336413

Subsidiary (Non-US):

Goodrich Aerospace Europe GmbH   **(3)**
Hein-Sass-Stieg 10, 21129, Hamburg, Germany
Tel.: (49) 40743130
Aircraft Part Mfr
N.A.I.C.S.: 336413

Goodrich Lighting Systems GmbH & Co. KG   **(3)**
Bertramstrasse 8, 59557, Lippstadt, Germany
Tel.: (49) 294176760
Aircraft Part Mfr
N.A.I.C.S.: 336413

Subsidiary (Domestic):

Hamilton Sundstrand Space Systems International, Inc.   **(3)**
1 Hamilton Rd, Windsor Locks, CT 06096-1010
Tel.: (860) 654-6000

Web Site: http://www.utcaerospacesystems.com
Space Systems & Auxiliary Equipment Mfr
N.A.I.C.S.: 336419

Subsidiary (Non-US):

Ratier-Figeac SA   **(3)**
Avenue Ratier, 46101, Figeac, France
Tel.: (33) 565505050
Web Site: http://www.ratier-figeac.com
Sales Range: $300-349.9 Million
Emp.: 1,273
Aircraft Propeller Designer & Mfr
N.A.I.C.S.: 336413
Francois Mestre *(Mgr-Maintenance)*
David Ravello *(Mgr-Repair Sls)*
Corinne Dayde *(Mgr-Technical Support)*
Stephanie Maniaval *(Mgr-Spares Sls)*
Jean-Francois Chanut *(Pres)*
Gilles Tremoulet *(Mgr-Customer Support)*

Subsidiary (Domestic):

Rohr, Inc.   **(3)**
850 Lagoon Dr, Chula Vista, CA 91910-2098
Tel.: (619) 691-4111
Web Site: http://www.utcaerospacesystems.com
Emp.: 4,600
Aircraft Nacelles, Thrust Reversers & Pylons Mfr
N.A.I.C.S.: 336413

Subsidiary (Non-US):

Goodrich Aerostructures Service Center - Asia Pte. Ltd.   **(4)**
41 Changi North Crescent, Singapore, 499638, Singapore
Tel.: (65) 65806262
Web Site: http://www.utcaerospacesystems.com
Aerostructure Maintenance, Overhaul & Repair Services
N.A.I.C.S.: 488190

Plant (Non-US):

UTC Aerospace Systems - Aerostructures, Colomiers   **(4)**
36 Avenue Jean Monnet, PO Box 152, 31774, Colomiers, France
Tel.: (33) 561 305 959
Web Site: http://www.utcaerospacesystems.com
Emp.: 700
Aerospace Engine Mfr & Nacelle Integration Services
N.A.I.C.S.: 336412

UTC Aerospace Systems - Aerostructures, Hamburg   **(4)**
Hein-Sass-Stieg 10, Hamburg, D-21129, Germany
Tel.: (49) 4074 313 103
Web Site: http://www.utcaerospacesystems.com
Emp.: 120
Aircraft Engine Assembly & Maintenance Services
N.A.I.C.S.: 336412

UTC Aerospace Systems - Aerostructures, Tianjin   **(4)**
B-1 Area No 15 West 15th Avenue, Tianjin Airport Industrial Park, Tianjin, 300308, China
Tel.: (86) 225 8211 309
Web Site: http://www.utcaerospacesystems.com
Aerostructure Maintenance, Overhaul & Repair Services; Aircraft Engine Build-up & Supply Chain Management Services
N.A.I.C.S.: 488190

Subsidiary (Domestic):

Rosemount Aerospace Inc.   **(3)**
14300 Judicial Rd, Burnsville, MN 55306
Tel.: (952) 892-4000
Web Site: http://www.utcaerospacesystems.com
Sales Range: $200-249.9 Million
Emp.: 850
Aerospace Sensors & Integrated Systems Developer & Mfr
N.A.I.C.S.: 334511
Justin Keppy *(Pres)*

RTX Corporation—(Continued)

Subsidiary (Domestic):

Kidde Technologies Inc. (4)
4200 Airport Dr NW, Wilson, NC
27896 (100%)
Tel.: (252) 237-7004
Web Site: http://kiddetechnologies.com
Sales Range: $200-249.9 Million
Aviation & Ground Vehicle Fire Protection,
Fire Supression & Safety Systems Mfr
N.A.I.C.S.: 339999

Division (Domestic):

Kidde Aerospace (5)
4200 Airport Dr NW, Wilson, NC 27896-
8630
Tel.: (252) 237-7004
Web Site: http://www.kiddeaerospace.com
Aircraft Fire Detection & Suppression Sys-
tems Mfr
N.A.I.C.S.: 336413

Subsidiary (Non-US):

Kidde Graviner Ltd. (5)
Mathisen Way Poyle Road, Colnbrook, SL3
0HF, Berks, United Kingdom
Tel.: (44) 1753 683 245
Web Site: http://www.kiddegraviner.com
Sales Range: $25-49.9 Million
Emp.: 156
Fire Detection & Suppression Systems Mfr
N.A.I.C.S.: 333998

**Kidde-Deugra Brandschutzsysteme
GmbH** (5)
Kaiserswerther Str 115, 40880, Ratingen,
Germany
Tel.: (49) 2102405131
Web Site: http://www.kidde-deugra.com
Sales Range: $10-24.9 Million
Emp.: 52
Fire Protection Products Mfr
N.A.I.C.S.: 333998

L'Hotellier (5)
4 Rue Henri Poincare, 92160, Antony,
France
Tel.: (33) 146660808
Web Site: http://www.lhotellier.net
Sales Range: $25-49.9 Million
Emp.: 80
Fire Detection & Suppression Equipment &
Control Systems Mfr
N.A.I.C.S.: 339999

Plant (Domestic):

**Rosemount Aerospace Inc. -
Union** (4)
225 Stringtown Rd, Union, WV 24983
Tel.: (304) 772-3062
Emp.: 390
Aerospace Ice Detection, Protection &
Heating Systems Mfr
N.A.I.C.S.: 334511
Pat Appleman *(Plant Mgr)*

Subsidiary (Non-US):

Rosemount Aerospace Limited (4)
Clittaford Rd, Southway, Plymouth, PL6
6DE, Devon, United Kingdom
Tel.: (44) 1752695695
Web Site:
http://www.utcaerospacesystems.com
Aerospace Sensor Developer & Mfr
N.A.I.C.S.: 334511

Subsidiary (Domestic):

**Simmonds Precision Products
Inc.** (4)
100 Panton Rd, Vergennes, VT 05491
Tel.: (802) 877-4000
Aircraft Sensing & Control Systems Mfr
N.A.I.C.S.: 334511
Erin Wollam-Berens *(Mgr-Quality & Con-
figuration Mgmt)*
Elizabeth Barrett Bracchitta *(Mgr-Quality-
Product & Supplier)*

Subsidiary (Domestic):

Walbar Inc. (3)
1 5th St Peabody Industrial Park, Peabody,
MA 01960-4944
Tel.: (978) 532-2350

Emp.: 75
Jet Engine Turbine Blades, Vanes & Com-
ponents Repair & Overhaul Services
N.A.I.C.S.: 811210
Cheryl Ruelle *(Mgr-HR)*

**Winslow Marine Products
Corporation** (3)
11700 Winslow Dr, Arcadia, FL 34269
Tel.: (941) 613-6666
Web Site: http://www.winslowliferaft.com
Sales Range: $10-24.9 Million
Emp.: 70
Life Raft Mfr
N.A.I.C.S.: 326299

Subsidiary (Domestic):

Rockwell Collins, Inc. (2)
400 Collins Rd NE, Cedar Rapids, IA 52498
Tel.: (319) 378-3500
Web Site: http://www.rockwellcollins.com
Aviation Electronic & Communications Com-
ponents Mfr
N.A.I.C.S.: 334290
Wayne Flory *(VP)*

Subsidiary (Domestic):

B/E Aerospace, Inc. (3)
1400 Corporate Ctr Way, Wellington, FL
33414
Tel.: (561) 791-5000
Web Site: http://www.beaerospace.com
Commercial & General Aviation Aircraft
Cabin Interior Products & Equipment Mfr,
Designer & Retailer
N.A.I.C.S.: 336360

Subsidiary (Non-US):

ATS Korea (4)
68-1 Baek-Ri Jeongnam-Myeon, Hwaseong,
445-962, Kyeonggi-Do, Korea (South)
Tel.: (82) 3180595380
Web Site: http://www.atschiller.com
Semiconductor Equipment Distr
N.A.I.C.S.: 423690
K. S. Lee *(Mng Dir)*

Subsidiary (Domestic):

Aerospace Lighting Corporation (4)
355 Knickerbocker Ave, Bohemia, NY
11716
Tel.: (631) 563-6400
Web Site: http://www.beaerospace.com
Aircraft Interior Product Mfr
N.A.I.C.S.: 336360

Altis Aero Systems LLC (4)
101 Coleman Blvd Ste G, Savannah, GA
31408
Tel.: (912) 748-1800
Web Site: http://www.altisaero.com
Aircraft Machinery Mfr
N.A.I.C.S.: 332510

Subsidiary (Non-US):

**B/E Aerospace Canada
Company** (4)
25 Dunlop Ave, Winnipeg, R2X 2V2, MB,
Canada
Tel.: (204) 783-5402
Web Site: http://www.belspace.com
Aircraft Machinery Mfr
N.A.I.C.S.: 332510

B/E Aerospace Fischer GmbH (4)
Muller-Armack-Str 4, 84034, Landshut, Ger-
many
Tel.: (49) 971992400
Web Site: http://www.fischer-seats.com
Aircraft Seat Mfr
N.A.I.C.S.: 316990

B/E Aerospace Holdings GmbH (4)
Focksweg 36a, 21129, Hamburg, Germany
Tel.: (49) 4031979190
Web Site: http://beaerospace.com
Holding Company
N.A.I.C.S.: 551112

Subsidiary (Domestic):

**B/E Aerospace (Germany)
GmbH** (5)
Focksweg 36A, 21129, Hamburg, Germany
Tel.: (49) 4031979190
Aircraft Interior Product Mfr

N.A.I.C.S.: 336360

Plant (Domestic):

B/E Aerospace Inc. (4)
10800 Pflumm Rd, Lenexa, KS 66215-4061
Tel.: (913) 338-9800
Web Site: http://www.beaerospace.com
Aircraft Interior Products Distr
N.A.I.C.S.: 423450

Subsidiary (Domestic):

**B/E Aerospace Machined Products,
Inc.** (4)
7155 Fenwick Ln, Westminster, CA 92683
Tel.: (714) 896-9001
Web Site: http://www.beaerospace.com
Aircraft Equipment Mfr
N.A.I.C.S.: 336413

Subsidiary (Non-US):

B/E Aerospace Systems GmbH (4)
Revalstrasse 1, 23560, Lubeck, Germany
Tel.: (49) 45140930
Aircraft Part Mfr
N.A.I.C.S.: 336413

Group (Domestic):

**B/E Aerospace Thermal & Power
Management** (4)
216 Lafayette Rd, North Hampton, NH
03862
Tel.: (603) 964-9780
Web Site: http://www.beaerospace.com
Thermal Management & Interconnect Solu-
tions
N.A.I.C.S.: 333415
Pamela Ruebusch *(Founder & CEO)*

Subsidiary (Domestic):

**Advanced Thermal Sciences
Corporation** (5)
3355 E La Palma Ave, Anaheim, CA 92806
Tel.: (714) 688-4200
Web Site: http://www.atschiller.com
Temperature Control Systems Mfr
N.A.I.C.S.: 334512
Masashi Iwao *(VP & Gen Mgr)*

Subsidiary (Non-US):

ATS Japan Corp. (6)
7-2-4 Nishiarai, Adachi-ku, Tokyo, 123-
0841, Japan
Tel.: (81) 356470511
Web Site: http://www.atschiller.com
Semiconductor Equipment Distr
N.A.I.C.S.: 423690

ATS Japan Kabushiki Kaisha (6)
627-1 Fukuroyama, Saitama-Ken, Koshi-
gaya, 343-0032, Japan
Tel.: (81) 489775155
Web Site: http://www.atschiller.com
Aircraft Equipment Mfr
N.A.I.C.S.: 336413

Subsidiary (Non-US):

**Advanced Thermal Sciences Taiwan
Corp.** (7)
4F No 198 Xingong 2nd Rd, 30244, Zhubei,
Hsinchu, Taiwan
Tel.: (886) 35520088
Web Site: http://www.atschiller.com
Temperature Control Equipment Mfr
N.A.I.C.S.: 336412

Subsidiary (Domestic):

**American Avionic Technologies
Corporation** (5)
25 Industrial Blvd, Medford, NY 11763
Tel.: (631) 924-8200
Web Site: http://beaerospace.com
Electronic Assembly & Component Mfr
N.A.I.C.S.: 335999

Brazonics, Inc. (5)
94 Tide Mill Rd, Hampton, NH 03842
Tel.: (603) 926-5700
Web Site: http://www.beaerospace.com
Electronics Packaging & Thermal Manage-
ment Product Mfr
N.A.I.C.S.: 331318

Woven Electronics LLC (5)

N.A.I.C.S.: 336360

Plant (Domestic):

B/E Aerospace Inc. (4)
1001 Old Stage Rd, Simpsonville, SC
29681
Tel.: (864) 963-5131
Electronic Components
N.A.I.C.S.: 334419

Subsidiary (Non-US):

**BE Aerospace (Netherlands)
B.V.** (4)
Galvanibaan 5, 3439 MG, Nieuwegein,
Netherlands
Tel.: (31) 306029200
Web Site: http://www.beaerospace.com
Aircraft Interior Product Mfr
N.A.I.C.S.: 336360

**BE Aerospace Holdings (UK)
Limited** (4)
Nissen House Grovebury Road, Leighton
Buzzard, LU7 4TB, United Kingdom
Tel.: (44) 1525854854
Web Site: http://www.collinsaerospace.com
Aircraft Freights Mfr
N.A.I.C.S.: 336413

**BE Engineering Services India Pri-
vate Limited** (4)
6-3-902/A 2nd Floor Central Plaza Near
Yashoda, Hyderabad, 500082, Andhra
Pradesh, India
Tel.: (91) 4040218000
Engineering Services
N.A.I.C.S.: 541330

**Boeing Distribution Services Sp
z.o.o** (4)
ul Zaleska 96, Rzeszow, 35-322, Poland
Tel.: (48) 178554726
Web Site: http://www.boeingdistribution.com
Aircraft Fastener & Consumable Product
Distr
N.A.I.C.S.: 423710

EMTEQ Europe GmbH (4)
Bitzibergstrasse 5, 8184, Bachenbulach,
Switzerland
Tel.: (41) 442181200
Web Site: http://www.beaerospace.com
Switching Products Mfr
N.A.I.C.S.: 335313
Tolta Bayrav *(Mng Dir)*

Subsidiary (Domestic):

J.A. Reinhardt & Co., Inc. (4)
3319 Spruce Cabin Rd, Mountainhome, PA
18342
Tel.: (570) 595-7491
Web Site: http://www.beaerospace.com
Aerospace Product & Parts Mfr
N.A.I.C.S.: 336413

Macrolink, Inc. (4)
1500 N Kellogg Dr, Anaheim, CA 92807-
1902
Tel.: (714) 777-8800
Electronic Products Mfr
N.A.I.C.S.: 334419

Thermal Solutions LLC (4)
PO Box 3244, Lancaster, PA 17604-3244
Tel.: (717) 239-7642
Web Site: https://www.thermalsolutions.com
Aircraft Part Mfr
N.A.I.C.S.: 336413

Subsidiary (Non-US):

**Wessex Advanced Switching Prod-
ucts Limited** (4)
Alexandria Park Penner Road, Havant, PO9
1QY, Hampshire, United Kingdom
Tel.: (44) 2392457000
Web Site: http://www.waspswitches.co.uk
Emp.: 100
Switching Products Mfr
N.A.I.C.S.: 335313

Subsidiary (Non-US):

**Ensambladores Electronicos de
Mexico, S. de R.L. de C.V.** (3)
Sierra San Agustin No 2498, Mexicali, Baja
California, Mexico
Tel.: (52) 6868373400
Web Site: http://www.rockwellcollins.com
Electronic Equipment Distr
N.A.I.C.S.: 449210

Subsidiary (Domestic):

Intertrade Limited (3)
400 Collins Road NE, Cedar Rapids, IA 52498
Tel.: (319) 378-3500
Web Site: http://www.intertrade-collins.com
Aircraft Equipment Buyer & Supplier
N.A.I.C.S.: 423510

Subsidiary (Non-US):

Kaiser Optical Systems SARL (3)
5 Allee du moulin Berger, 69130, Ecully, France
Tel.: (33) 437499073
Optical Instrument Mfr
N.A.I.C.S.: 333310

Rockwell Collins Australia Pty Limited (3)
2-8 Allied Drive, Tullamarine, 3043, VIC, Australia
Tel.: (61) 383188000
Web Site: http://www.rockwellcollins.com
Navigation Equipment Mfr
N.A.I.C.S.: 334511

Rockwell Collins Canada Inc. (3)
30 Edgewater St Ste 104, Ottawa, K2L 1V8, ON, Canada
Tel.: (613) 595-2200
Web Site: http://www.rockwellcollins.com
Aerospace Product & Parts Mfr
N.A.I.C.S.: 335314

Rockwell Collins China (3)
Unit 1606-1610 Tower A City Center Of Shanghai 100 Zun Yi Road, Shanghai, 200051, China
Tel.: (86) 2162195507
Web Site: http://www.rockwellcollins.com
Avionics & Marine Inertial Navigation & Telecommunications Equipment & Systems
N.A.I.C.S.: 517111

Subsidiary (Domestic):

Rockwell Collins Control Technologies, LLC (3)
3721 Macintosh Dr Vint Hill Tech Park, Warrenton, VA 20187
Tel.: (540) 428-3300
Web Site: http://www.rockwellcollins.com
Aerospace Navigation Systems Developer & Mfr
N.A.I.C.S.: 334511

Subsidiary (Non-US):

Rockwell Collins Deutschland GmbH (3)
Grenzhoefer Weg 36, D 69123, Heidelberg, Germany
Tel.: (49) 62215120
Web Site: http://www.collinsaerospace.com
Communication & Navigation Equipment for Airborne & Aerospace Platforms
N.A.I.C.S.: 334511

Rockwell Collins Deutschland Holdings GmbH (3)
Grenzhofer Weg 36, Heidelberg, 69123, Baden-Wurttemberg, Germany
Tel.: (49) 62215120
Web Site: http://www.rockwellcollins.com
Investment Management Service
N.A.I.C.S.: 541618

Rockwell Collins France, S.A.S. (3)
6 Ave Didier Daurat, BP 20083, F 31701, Blagnac, Cedex, France
Tel.: (33) 561717700
Web Site: http://www.rockwellcollins.com
Avionics & Marine Inertial Navigation & Telecommunications Systems Mfr
N.A.I.C.S.: 423420
Pierre Roumagnac (Mng Dir)

Subsidiary (Domestic):

Rockwell Collins Optronics, Inc. (3)
2752 Loker Ave W, Carlsbad, CA 92010
Tel.: (760) 438-9255
Web Site: http://www.rockwellcollins.com
Aviation Electronics Mfr & Supplier
N.A.I.C.S.: 333310

Rockwell Collins Simulation & Training Solutions LLC (3)

22626 Sally Ride Dr, Sterling, VA 20164
Tel.: (703) 234-2100
Web Site: http://www.rockwellcollins.com
Simulation & Training Systems & Related Services
N.A.I.C.S.: 333310

Subsidiary (Non-US):

Rockwell Collins Southeast Asia Pte. Ltd. (3)
18 Loyang Lane Loyang Industrial Estate, Singapore, 508918, Singapore
Tel.: (65) 65422078
Web Site: http://www.collinsaerospace.com
Aircraft Maintenance Services
N.A.I.C.S.: 488190
David Tan (Mng Dir)

Rockwell Collins UK Limited (3)
730 Wharfedale Rd, Winnersh, RG41 5TP, Wokingham, United Kingdom
Tel.: (44) 1189359000
Web Site: http://www.collinsaerospace.com
Ground Positioning Systems & Aviation Electronics Mfr & Supplier
N.A.I.C.S.: 336413

Subsidiary (Domestic):

Rockwell Collins UK Ltd. - Information Management Services (4)
Pegasus One Pegasus Place, Gatwick Road, Crawley, RH10 9AY, West Sussex, United Kingdom
Tel.: (44) 1293641200
Web Site: http://www.collinsaerospace.com
Aerospace Diagnostics, Transportation Communication Systems & Systems Engineering Services
N.A.I.C.S.: 541330
Paul Hickox (Mng Dir)

Subsidiary (Non-US):

Rockwell Collins do Brasil Ltda. (3)
Sao Jose dos Campos Rua Ambrosio Molina 1090-Bloco D / Bloco F, Eugenio de Melo - Sao Jose dos Campos, Sao Jose dos Campos, 12247-000, Brazil
Tel.: (55) 1239086200
Web Site: http://www.rockwellcollins.com
Navigation Equipment Mfr
N.A.I.C.S.: 334511

Unit (Non-US):

UTC Aerospace Systems - Engine Control Services (2)
The Radleys Marston Green, Birmingham, B33 0HZ, United Kingdom
Tel.: (44) 1217885000
Aerospace Engine Technical Support Services
N.A.I.C.S.: 541990

Subsidiary (Non-US):

Goodrich Control Systems GmbH (3)
Bataverstrasse 80, 41462, Neuss, Germany
Tel.: (49) 21319530
Web Site: http://www.utcaerospacesystems.com
Aerospace Engine Technical Support Services
N.A.I.C.S.: 541990

Devonshire Switzerland Holdings GmbH (1)
Matthofstrand 6, Lucerne, 6005, Switzerland
Tel.: (41) 419840101
Holding Company
N.A.I.C.S.: 551112

IAE International Aero Engines AG (1)
400 Main St, East Hartford, CT
Tel.: (860) 565-4321
Web Site: https://links.prattwhitney.com
Aerospace Product Mfr & Distr
N.A.I.C.S.: 336412

NSI, Inc. (1)
100 Cambridge St Ste 1400, Boston, MA 02114
Tel.: (719) 439-0618
Web Site: https://nsiteam.com
Aircraft Part Mfr

N.A.I.C.S.: 336413

Polskie Zaklady Lotnicze Sp. zo.o (1)
ul Wojska Polskiego 3, 39-300, Mielec, Poland
Tel.: (48) 177431900
Web Site: http://www.pzlmielec.pl
Emp.: 1,600
Aircraft Machinery Mfr
N.A.I.C.S.: 332510
Janusz Zakrecki (Pres & Gen Dir)
Artur Wojtas (Dir-Aftermarket & Flight Ops)
Pawel Wojtasik (Fin Dir)
Marta Rokoszak (Dir-HR)
Wojciech Stromczynski (VP & Dir-Legal Svcs)
Piotr Niedbala (Dir-Bus Dev & Programs)
Marek Chojecki (Mgr-Bus Dev-Aircraft)
Anita Tabor (Mgr-Bus Dev-Aerostructures)
Stanislaw Kwarciany (Mgr-Aftermarket Section & Sls Svc)
Andrzej Predki (Dir-Quality)
Tomasz Kiec (Mgr-Bus Dev & Aftermarket)
Tomasz Krason (Office Mgr-Pur & Supply Mgmt)

Pratt & Whitney (1)
400 Main St, East Hartford, CT 06118   **(100%)**
Tel.: (860) 565-4321
Web Site: https://prattwhitney.com
Sales Range: $5-14.9 Billion
Emp.: 38,442
Design, Development, Marketing & Support of Commercial Aircraft Engines
N.A.I.C.S.: 336412
Matthew F. Bromberg (Pres-Military Engines)
Jill M. Albertelli (Sr VP-Transformation & Strategy)
Christopher T. Calio (Pres)
Shane Eddy (Officer-Ops & Sr VP)
Dave Emmerling (VP-Comml Aftermarket)
Geoff Hunt (Sr VP-Engrg)
Lisa Szewczul (VP-Environment, Health & Safety)
Maureen Waterston (Chief HR Officer & VP)
Rick Deurloo (Chief Comml Officer)
Ashmita Sethi (Mng Dir-India)
Paul E. Nye (VP-Quality)
Candace Kronholm (Gen Counsel & VP)
David Porter (CFO & VP)
Jeana Thomas (CIO-Global & VP)
Tizz Weber (Chief Comm Officer & VP)

Subsidiary (Domestic):

Homogeneous Metals Inc. (2)
2395 Main St, Clayville, NY 13322
Tel.: (315) 839-5421
Web Site: http://www.hmipowder.com
Sales Range: $25-49.9 Million
Emp.: 100
Steel Powders & Alloys
N.A.I.C.S.: 331110
John Lapinski (Controller-Quotations & Pur Orders)
Nancy Rudnitski (Mgr-HR)
Rusty Moore (Mgr-Quality)
Jim Baron (Mgr-Production Ops)
Nathan Wells (Mgr-Facilities & Maintenance)
Ryan Forthofer (Gen Mgr)

Joint Venture (Domestic):

International Aero Engines AG (2)
400 Main St, East Hartford, CT 06118
Tel.: (860) 565-0140
Web Site: http://www.i-a-e.com
Sales Range: $75-99.9 Million
Emp.: 400
Aircraft Engine Mfr
N.A.I.C.S.: 336412
Earl E. Exum (Executives)

Subsidiary (Non-US):

Japan Turbine Technologies Co., Ltd. (2)
Taiei Kogyo Danchi Kichioka, Narita, 287-0225, Japan   **(100%)**
Tel.: (81) 476735450
Sales Range: $50-74.9 Million
Emp.: 150
Aircraft Maintenance Services
N.A.I.C.S.: 488119

Subsidiary (Domestic):

Pratt & Whitney Auto-Air Composites, Inc. (2)
5640 Enterprise Dr, Lansing, MI 48911-4103   **(100%)**
Tel.: (517) 393-4040
Web Site: http://www.autoair.com
Sales Range: $25-49.9 Million
Emp.: 260
Aerospace Composite Parts, Specializing in Jet Engine Components & Jet Engine Ground Support Equipment
N.A.I.C.S.: 336412

Subsidiary (Non-US):

Pratt & Whitney Canada Holdings Corp. (2)
1000 Boul Marie-Victorin, Longueuil, J4G 1A1, QC, Canada
Tel.: (450) 677-9411
Web Site: http://www.pwc.ca
Investment Management Service
N.A.I.C.S.: 523940

Subsidiary (Domestic):

Pratt & Whitney Canada Corp. (3)
1000 Marie-Victorin Blvd, Longueuil, J4G 1A1, QC, Canada   **(100%)**
Tel.: (450) 677-9411
Web Site: https://www.prattwhitney.com
Sales Range: $1-4.9 Billion
Emp.: 8,650
Aircraft Engine & Engine Parts Mfr
N.A.I.C.S.: 336412
Maria Della Posta (Pres)
Nicolas Amyot (VP-Fin)

Pratt & Whitney Canada Leasing, Limited Partnership (3)
1000 Marie-Victorin Blvd, Longueuil, J4G 1A1, QC, Canada
Tel.: (450) 677-9411
Web Site: https://www.pwc.ca
Jet Propulsion Parts Mfr
N.A.I.C.S.: 336412

Subsidiary (Domestic):

Pratt & Whitney Component Solutions, Inc. (2)
400 Main St, East Hartford, CT 06118
Tel.: (860) 565-4321
Web Site: http://prattwhitney.com
Aircraft Machinery Mfr
N.A.I.C.S.: 332510

Pratt & Whitney Engine Services, Inc. (2)
1525 Midway Park Rd, Bridgeport, WV 26330-9688   **(100%)**
Tel.: (304) 842-5421
Web Site: http://www.pwc.ca
Sales Range: $25-49.9 Million
Emp.: 450
Aircraft & Heavy Equipment Repair Services
N.A.I.C.S.: 811210

Pratt & Whitney Military Aftermarket Services, Inc. (2)
1177 N Great SW Pkwy, Grand Prairie, TX 75050-2629   **(100%)**
Tel.: (972) 343-1300
Web Site: http://www.pw.utc.com
Sales Range: $1-9.9 Million
Emp.: 16
Military Aircraft Turbine Engine Mfr
N.A.I.C.S.: 336412

Unit (Domestic):

Dallas Aerospace Operations (3)
1875 North Interstate 35 E, Carrollton, TX 75006-3786   **(100%)**
Tel.: (972) 245-9633
Mfr of Engines, Engine Parts & Expendables
N.A.I.C.S.: 423860

Subsidiary (Domestic):

Pratt & Whitney PSD Inc. (2)
275 E Robinson Ave, Springdale, AR 72764
Tel.: (479) 750-3600
Sales Range: $25-49.9 Million
Emp.: 200
Repair of Aircraft Engines & Engine Parts

RTX Corporation—(Continued)

N.A.I.C.S.: 336412

Subsidiary (Non-US):

Pratt & Whitney Rzeszow S.A.   **(2)**
ul Hetmanska 120, 35-078, Rzeszow, Poland
Tel.: (48) 178546100
Web Site: http://www.pwrze.com
Emp.: 3,700
Aircraft Engine Mfr
N.A.I.C.S.: 336412

Pratt & Whitney Services Pte Ltd   **(2)**
18 Loyang Crescent, Singapore, 508982, Singapore
Tel.: (65) 65454866
Web Site: http://www.pw.utc.com
Sales Range: $75-99.9 Million
Emp.: 200
Aircraft Engine Mfr
N.A.I.C.S.: 336412

Subsidiary (Domestic):

Precision Components Intl. Inc.   **(2)**
8801 Macon Rd, Columbus, GA 31908
Tel.: (706) 568-5400
Web Site: http://www.pciga.com
Rev.: $46,900,000
Emp.: 550
Metal & Wood Aircraft Propeller Blades
N.A.I.C.S.: 336413

Range Generation Next, LLC   **(1)**
6905 N Wickham Rd Ste 301, Melbourne, FL 32940
Tel.: (321) 428-3454
Web Site: https://www.rgnext.com
Aircraft Part Mfr
N.A.I.C.S.: 336413

Raytheon Company   **(1)**
870 Winter St, Waltham, MA 02451-1449
Tel.: (781) 522-3000
Web Site: http://www.raytheon.com
Rev.: $29,176,000,000
Assets: $34,566,000,000
Liabilities: $22,343,000,000
Net Worth: $12,223,000,000
Earnings: $3,343,000,000
Emp.: 70,000
Fiscal Year-end: 12/31/2019
Defense & Aerospace Technologies Developer & Mfr
N.A.I.C.S.: 334511
Rebecca B. Rhoads (Pres-Bus Svcs-Global)
Pamela A. Wickham (VP-Corp Affairs & Comm)
Michael J. Wood (Chief Acctg Officer, VP & Controller)
Mark E. Russell (VP-Engrg, Tech & Mission Assurance)
David Wilkins (VP-Contracts & Supply Chain)
Randa G. Newsome (VP-HR & Security-Global)
Frank R. Jimenez (Gen Counsel, Sec & VP)
Kevin G. DaSilva (Treas & VP)
Wesley D. Kremer (Co-Pres)
Ralph H. Acaba (VP)
Ed Fortunato (VP-Govt Rels)
Roy Azevedo (Co-Pres)
Jeanette Hughes (VP-Internal Audit)
Amanda Sorensen (Sr VP-HR)

Subsidiary (Domestic):

Blackbird Technologies, Inc.   **(2)**
13900 Lincoln Park Dr Ste 400, Herndon, VA 20171
Tel.: (703) 796-1420
Web Site: http://www.blackbirdtech.com
Sales Range: $1-9.9 Million
Emp.: 99
Custom Computer Programming Services
N.A.I.C.S.: 541511

Henggeler Computer Consultants, Inc.   **(2)**
10010 Junction Dr 113s, Annapolis Junction, MD 20701
Tel.: (301) 317-8995
Web Site:
    http://www.henggelerconsulting.com
Rev.: $5,495,000
Emp.: 35
Custom Computer Programming Services
N.A.I.C.S.: 541511

Richard Henggeler (Owner)

Subsidiary (Non-US):

Raytheon Australia Pty Ltd   **(2)**
4 Brindabella Cct Brindabella Business Park, Canberra Airport, Canberra, 2609, ACT, Australia
Tel.: (61) 261220200
Web Site:
    https://www.raytheonaustralia.com.au
Sales Range: $600-649.9 Million
Emp.: 1,500
Defence Contractors
N.A.I.C.S.: 334511
Michael Ward (Mng Dir)
Ohad Katz (Head-Contracts & Supply Chain)
Gerard Foley (Head-Strategy & Bus Dev)
Sarah Valentine (Head-Bus Ops)
Des McNicholas (Head-Bus Assurance)
Geoff Gillespie (COO)
Gerry Wheeler (Head-Pub Affairs)
Jim Gardener (Gen Mgr-Joint Battlespace Sys)
Rod Equid (Head-Campaigns & Captures)
Murray Hundleby (Head-Legal Affairs)
Christian Herring (Head-IT)
Janette Coulton (Head-HR)
David Hewish (Head-Engrg)
Warren Latham (Gen Mgr-Submarines)
Julie Brown (Gen Mgr-Mission Solutions)
Andrew Whittaker (Gen Mgr-Maritime)
Sam MacMillan (CFO)

Unit (Domestic):

Raytheon Australia Air Warfare Destroyer   **(3)**
620 Mersey Road North, 620 Mersey Rd, Osborne, 5017, SA, Australia
Tel.: (61) 881657000
Web Site: http://www.raytheon.com.au
Air Warfare Destroyers Combat Systems Engineering Services
N.A.I.C.S.: 541990

Raytheon Australia Integrated Solutions   **(3)**
Building C 5 Talavera Road, Macquarie Park, 2113, NSW, Australia
Tel.: (61) 288706555
Web Site: http://www.raytheon.com.au
Emp.: 200
Mission System Integrator & Support Services
N.A.I.C.S.: 541519

Raytheon Australia Mission Support   **(3)**
2nd Floor Building 5 Gateway Office Park, 747 Lytton Road, Murarrie, 4172, QLD, Australia
Tel.: (61) 7 3908 5200
Web Site: http://www.raytheon.com
Solutions & Support Services; Force Platforms, Systems & Products
N.A.I.C.S.: 541990

Raytheon Australia Security Solutions   **(3)**
14 Wales Street, Belconnen, 2617, ACT, Australia
Tel.: (61) 262534344
Web Site: http://www.raytheon.com.au
Information Security Solutions for Defense & Intelligence
N.A.I.C.S.: 541990

Subsidiary (Non-US):

Raytheon Canada Limited   **(2)**
1640-360 Albert Street, Ottawa, K1R 7X7, ON, Canada   **(100%)**
Tel.: (613) 233-4121
Web Site: http://www.raytheon.com
Sales Range: $10-24.9 Million
Emp.: 12
Technology Solutions, Engineering Services, Surveillance & Navigation Systems, Air Traffic Control Radars & Systems, Highway Traffic Management & Maritime Surveillance
N.A.I.C.S.: 334511

Division (Domestic):

Raytheon Canada Limited - Waterloo   **(3)**

400 Phillip Street, Waterloo, N2L 6R7, ON, Canada   **(100%)**
Tel.: (519) 885-0110
Web Site: http://www.raytheon.ca
Radar Systems, Signal Processing & Air Traffic Control Equipment Mfr
N.A.I.C.S.: 334511

Raytheon Canada Limited Support Services Division   **(3)**
919 72nd Avenue NE, Calgary, T2E 8N9, AB, Canada
Tel.: (403) 295-6600
Web Site: http://www.raytheon.ca
Defense & Aerospace Support Solutions Services for Technology Systems
N.A.I.C.S.: 541990

Raytheon ELCAN Optical Technologies   **(3)**
450 Leitz Road, Midland, L4R 5B8, ON, Canada
Tel.: (705) 526-5401
Web Site: http://www.elcan.com
Emp.: 650
Optical & Electronic Products & Applications Developer
N.A.I.C.S.: 333310

Unit (Domestic):

Raytheon Civil Communications Solutions   **(2)**
1001 Boston Post Rd, Marlborough, MA 01752
Tel.: (919) 790-1011
Web Site: http://www.raytheon.com
Information Sharing Services Through Telecommunication & Service-Oriented Architecture Solutions
N.A.I.C.S.: 541519

Raytheon Combat Systems   **(2)**
2501 W University Dr, McKinney, TX 75071
Tel.: (972) 952-2000
Web Site: http://www.raytheon.com
Sales Range: $300-349.9 Million
Emp.: 1,900
Developer & Producer of Integrated Ground Combat Surveillance & Target Engagement Solutions
N.A.I.C.S.: 541519

Branch (Domestic):

Raytheon Company   **(2)**
1100 Wilson Blvd, Arlington, VA 22209   **(100%)**
Tel.: (703) 525-1550
Web Site: http://www.raytheon.com
Sales Range: $50-74.9 Million
Emp.: 200
Business Development & Government Relations
N.A.I.C.S.: 541613

Subsidiary (Non-US):

Raytheon Deutschland GmbH   **(2)**
Kulturstrasse 105, 85356, Freising, Germany
Tel.: (49) 81619020
Web Site: http://www.raytheon.com
Sales Range: $25-49.9 Million
Emp.: 50
Development of Digital Receivers for Radar Systems
N.A.I.C.S.: 334511
Andreas Radermacher (Mng Dir)

Unit (Domestic):

Raytheon Integrated Communications Systems   **(2)**
1001 Boston Post Road, Marlborough, MA 01752
Tel.: (919) 790-1011
Web Site: http://www.raytheon.com
Military Communications Solutions for Defense
N.A.I.C.S.: 517810

Subsidiary (Domestic):

Raytheon BBN Technologies   **(3)**
10 Moulton St, Cambridge, MA 02138   **(100%)**
Tel.: (617) 873-8000
Web Site: http://www.bbn.com

Technical, Scientific Research & Computer Services
N.A.I.C.S.: 541511
Ed Campbell (Pres)

Unit (Domestic):

Raytheon Integrated Defense Systems   **(2)**
50 Apple Hill Dr, Tewksbury, MA 01876
Tel.: (978) 858-5000
Web Site: http://www.raytheon.com
Sales Range: $5-14.9 Billion
Emp.: 15,000
Inspection & Testing Services
N.A.I.C.S.: 334511

Subsidiary (Domestic):

Raytheon Solipsys   **(3)**
8170 Maple Lawn Blvd Ste 300, Fulton, MD 20759   **(100%)**
Tel.: (240) 554-8100
Web Site: http://www.solipsys.com
Sales Range: $25-49.9 Million
Emp.: 130
Mfr of Defense Application Products
N.A.I.C.S.: 513210

Unit (Domestic):

Raytheon Intelligence, Information & Services   **(2)**
1200 S Jupiter Rd, Garland, TX 75042-7711
Tel.: (972) 272-0515
Web Site: http://www.raytheon.com
Sales Range: $1-4.9 Billion
Emp.: 8,900
High Technology Intelligence & Information Solutions
N.A.I.C.S.: 541990

Subsidiary (Non-US):

Raytheon International, Inc.   **(2)**
Akasaka Intercity 12F 1-11-44 Akasaka Minato-ku, Minato-ku, Tokyo, 107 0052, Japan
Tel.: (81) 335688050
Defense Electronics & Systems Integration
N.A.I.C.S.: 334511
Mark Nicol (Pres-Canada)
Christopher J. Davis (Pres)

Subsidiary (Domestic):

Raytheon Ktech   **(2)**
1300 Eubank Blvd SE, Albuquerque, NM 87123
Tel.: (505) 998-5830
Sales Range: $75-99.9 Million
Emp.: 400
Electronic Research Services
N.A.I.C.S.: 541715
Mary S. Rice (Mgr-Contracts Dept)
Peter Duselis (Mgr-Pulsed Power)

Unit (Domestic):

Raytheon Missile Systems   **(2)**
1151 E Hermans Rd, Tucson, AZ 85756   **(100%)**
Tel.: (520) 794-3000
Web Site: http://www.raytheon.com
Sales Range: $5-14.9 Billion
Emp.: 12,500
Designs, Develops & Produces Missile Systems
N.A.I.C.S.: 336414

Subsidiary (Domestic):

Raytheon Pikewerks Corporation   **(2)**
105 A Church St, Madison, AL 35758
Tel.: (256) 325-0010
Web Site: http://www.pikewerks.com
Sales Range: $1-9.9 Million
Emp.: 42
Cyber Security & Software Protection
N.A.I.C.S.: 423430

Raytheon SI Government Solutions   **(2)**
4450 W Eau Gallie Blvd, Melbourne, FL 32934
Tel.: (321) 253-7841
Sales Range: $25-49.9 Million
Emp.: 20
Security Software & System Design Services
N.A.I.C.S.: 541512

Gordon Burns *(Chm)*

Unit (Domestic):

**Raytheon Space & Airborne
Systems** **(2)**
2000 E El Segundo Blvd, El Segundo, CA
90245 **(100%)**
Tel.: (310) 647-1000
Web Site: http://www.raytheon.com
Sales Range: $1-4.9 Billion
Emp.: 12,400
Technology Solutions to Enhance Success
in Critical Space & Airborne Missions
N.A.I.C.S.: 334511
Roy Azevedo *(Pres)*

Subsidiary (Domestic):

**Raytheon Applied Signal Technology,
Inc.** **(3)**
460 W California Ave, Sunnyvale, CA 94086
Tel.: (408) 749-1888
Web Site: http://www.appsig.com
Sales Range: $200-249.9 Million
Emp.: 856
Signal Processing Equipment Designer, De-
veloper, Mfr & Marketer
N.A.I.C.S.: 334290

Division (Domestic):

Applied Signal Technology **(4)**
306 Sentinel Dr Ste 100, Annapolis Junc-
tion, MD 20701
Tel.: (301) 327-2331
Web Site: http://www.appsig.com
Sales Range: $10-24.9 Million
Emp.: 260
Designer, Developer, Mfr & Marketer of Sig-
nal Processing Equipment
N.A.I.C.S.: 334290

Applied Signal Technology **(4)**
1128 W 2400 S, Salt Lake City, UT 84119
Tel.: (801) 908-7555
Web Site: http://www.raytheon.com
Sales Range: $1-9.9 Million
Emp.: 42
Designer, Developer, Mfr & Marketer of Sig-
nal Processing Equipment
N.A.I.C.S.: 334290

Subsidiary (Domestic):

Applied Signal Technology, Inc. **(4)**
20101 Hamilton Ave Ste 150, Torrance, CA
90502
Tel.: (310) 436-7000
Web Site: http://www.appsig.com
Sales Range: $10-24.9 Million
Emp.: 33
Engineering Laboratory, Except Testing
N.A.I.C.S.: 541715

Subsidiary (Non-US):

Raytheon Spain **(2)**
Parque Tecnologico de Andalucía Avda
Juan Lopez de Penalver 12, Campanillas,
29590, Malaga, Spain
Tel.: (34) 95 224 92 00
Web Site: http://www.raytheon.com
Sales Range: $25-49.9 Million
Emp.: 200
Optical & Electronic Products & Applications
Developer
N.A.I.C.S.: 333310

Raytheon Systems Limited **(2)**
The Pinnacles, Elizabeth Way, Harlow,
CM19 5BB, Essex, United
Kingdom **(100%)**
Tel.: (44) 1279426862
Sales Range: $500-549.9 Million
Emp.: 1,350
Mfr of Air Traffic Control Equipment, Radar
Display Equipment
N.A.I.C.S.: 334511

Subsidiary (Domestic):

**Raytheon Technical Services Com-
pany LLC** **(2)**
12160 Sunrise Valley Dr, Reston, VA
20191 **(100%)**
Tel.: (703) 295-2000
Web Site: http://www.raytheon.com
Sales Range: $1-4.9 Billion
Emp.: 9,500

Technical, Scientific & Professional Services
for Defense, Federal & Commercial Customers
N.A.I.C.S.: 541990

Unit (Domestic):

**Customized Engineering & Depot
Support** **(3)**
6125 E 21st St, Indianapolis, IN 46219
Tel.: (317) 306-8471
Web Site: http://www.raytheon.com
Sales Range: $250-299.9 Million
Emp.: 1,200
Engineeering Services
N.A.I.C.S.: 541330

Unit (Domestic):

**Raytheon Analysis & Test
Laboratory** **(4)**
6125 E 21st St, Indianapolis, IN 46219
Tel.: (317) 306-3433
Web Site: http://www.raytheon.com
Sales Range: $25-49.9 Million
Emp.: 20
Engineering Analysis & Testing
N.A.I.C.S.: 541380

Subsidiary (Domestic):

**Raytheon Professional Services
LLC** **(3)**
1200 S Jupiter Rd, Garland, TX
75042 **(100%)**
Tel.: (972) 205-5100
Web Site: http://www.raytheon.com
Sales Range: $250-299.9 Million
Emp.: 950
Training, Learning & Outsourcing Services
N.A.I.C.S.: 611430

Unit (Domestic):

**Raytheon Technical Services Com-
pany LLC - Mission Support
Operations** **(3)**
12160 Sunrise Valley Dr Ste 500, Reston,
VA 20191
Tel.: (703) 295-2000
Web Site: http://www.raytheon.com
Development & Support for Engineering &
Integration Services, Global Security Solu-
tions, Civil Aviation Solutions & Operations,
Training & Logistics
N.A.I.C.S.: 541330

Subsidiary (Non-US):

Raytheon United Kingdom **(2)**
Kao One Kao Park, Harlow, CM17 9NA,
Essex, United Kingdom
Tel.: (44) 1895816207
Web Site: http://www.raytheon.co.uk
Emp.: 300
Software Development Services
N.A.I.C.S.: 541511
Lord Strathclyde *(Chm)*

Unit (Domestic):

Raytheon Vision Systems **(2)**
75 Coromar Dr, Goleta, CA 93117
Tel.: (805) 562-4363
Web Site: http://www.raytheon.com
Sales Range: $25-49.9 Million
Emp.: 90
Develops & Produces Detection & Imaging
Devices
N.A.I.C.S.: 334511

Subsidiary (Domestic):

**Thales-Raytheon Systems Company
LLC** **(2)**
1801 Hughes Dr, Fullerton, CA
92834-9455 **(100%)**
Tel.: (714) 446-3118
Web Site: http://www.thalesraytheon.com
Air Command, Control & Defense Systems
Developer & Mfr
N.A.I.C.S.: 334511

Raytheon Intelligence & Space **(1)**
1100 Wilson Blvd, Arlington, VA 22209
Tel.: (703) 284-4305
Advanced Sensors, Training & Cyber &
Software Solutions Developer
N.A.I.C.S.: 513210
Roy Azevedo *(Pres)*

Riello S.P.A. **(1)**
Via Ing Pilade Riello 7, Legnago, 37045,
Verona, Italy
Tel.: (39) 0442548900
Web Site: http://www.riello.it
Air Conditioning & Refrigeration Mfr & Distr
N.A.I.C.S.: 333415

UTC (US) LLC **(1)**
7201 N Lindbergh Blvd, Hazelwood, MO
63042
Tel.: (314) 731-4422
Web Site: https://www.utc-usa.com
Aircraft Part Mfr
N.A.I.C.S.: 336413

UTC Canada Corporation **(1)**
1515 Drew Road, Mississauga, L5S 1Y8,
ON, Canada
Tel.: (905) 405-3209
Air Conditioning System Mfr
N.A.I.C.S.: 333415

UTCL Investments B.V. **(1)**
Terminalweg 27, Amersfoort, 3821AJ, Neth-
erlands
Tel.: (31) 337502100
Aerospace Product & Parts Mfr
N.A.I.C.S.: 336411

**United Technologies Australia Hold-
ings Limited** **(1)**
5-9 Ricketty St, Mascot, 2020, NSW, Australia
Tel.: (61) 1300727041
Holding Company
N.A.I.C.S.: 551112

**United Technologies Canada,
Ltd.** **(1)**
Suite 1410 18 kenaston Gardens, North
York, M2K 3C7, ON, Canada
Tel.: (416) 222-4416
Search Detection Equipment Mfr
N.A.I.C.S.: 334511

**United Technologies International
Corporation-Asia Private Limited** **(1)**
72 Anson Rd Suite 09-00 Anson House
Downtown, Singapore, 079911, Singapore
Tel.: (65) 65496751
Sales Range: $25-49.9 Million
Emp.: 30
Human Resouce Services
N.A.I.C.S.: 541612
N. Bala *(Gen Mgr)*

**United Technologies Research
Center** **(1)**
411 Silver Ln, East Hartford, CT 06108
Tel.: (860) 610-7000
Web Site: http://www.utrc.utc.com
Sales Range: $75-99.9 Million
Emp.: 450
Basic & Applied Technology Research
N.A.I.C.S.: 541720

RUBICON TECHNOLOGIES, INC.
100 W Main St Ste 610, Lexington,
KY 40507 **DE**
Web Site: https://www.rubicon.com
Year Founded: 2008
RBT—(NYSE)
Rev.: $675,388,000
Assets: $204,029,000
Liabilities: $358,481,000
Net Worth: ($154,452,000)
Earnings: ($281,771,000)
Emp.: 434
Fiscal Year-end: 12/31/22
Cloud-based Waste & Recycling So-
lutions
N.A.I.C.S.: 518210
Kevin Schubert *(Pres & CFO)*
Tom Owston *(Chief Comml Officer)*
Chris Spooner *(Exec VP-Finance)*
Lauren Guilbeau *(Head-Human Re-
sources)*
Paula Henderson *(Chief Sls Officer &
Exec VP)*
Osman H. Ahmed *(Interim CEO)*

Subsidiaries:

**Rubicon Technologies Holdings,
LLC** **(1)**

100 W Main St Ste 610, Lexington, KY
40507
Tel.: (844) 479-1507
Web Site: https://www.rubicon.com
Software Publr
N.A.I.C.S.: 518210

RUBICON TECHNOLOGY, INC.
900 E Green St Unit A, Bensenville,
IL 60106
Tel.: (847) 295-7000 **DE**
Web Site:
https://www.rubicontechnology.com
Year Founded: 2000
RBCN—(OTCQB)
Rev.: $3,587,000
Assets: $5,959,000
Liabilities: $2,755,000
Net Worth: $3,204,000
Earnings: $935,000
Emp.: 12
Fiscal Year-end: 12/31/22
Monocrystalline Sapphire & Other
Crystalline Products Mfr & Whslr
N.A.I.C.S.: 333242
Michael E. Mikolajczyk *(Chm)*

Subsidiaries:

Rubicon Worldwide LLC **(1)**
900 E Green St, Bensenville, IL 60106
Tel.: (847) 295-7000
Web Site: http://www.rubicontechnology.com
Electronic Material Development & Mfr
N.A.I.C.S.: 334419

RUBIUS THERAPEUTICS, INC.
124 Washington St Ste 101, Foxbor-
ough, MA 02035
Tel.: (508) 543-1720 **DE**
Web Site: https://www.rubiustx.com
Year Founded: 2013
RUBY—(NASDAQ)
Rev.: $819,000
Assets: $23,070,000
Liabilities: $7,939,000
Net Worth: $15,131,000
Earnings: ($179,666,000)
Emp.: 6
Fiscal Year-end: 12/31/22
Biotechnology Research & Develop-
ment Services
N.A.I.C.S.: 541714
Noubar B. Afeyan *(Founder)*
Pablo J. Cagnoni *(Chm)*
Lori Melancon *(VP-Corp Affairs)*
Dannielle Appelhans *(Pres, CEO, In-
terim Principal Fin Officer & Principal
Acctg Officer)*

RUMBLE INC.
444 Gulf of Mexico Dr, Longboat Key,
FL 34228
Tel.: (941) 210-0196 **DE**
Web Site: https://corp.rumble.com
Year Founded: 2013
RUM—(NASDAQ)
Rev.: $39,384,284
Assets: $366,982,638
Liabilities: $27,347,859
Net Worth: $339,634,779
Earnings: ($11,403,994)
Emp.: 70
Fiscal Year-end: 12/31/22
Advertising Agency Services
N.A.I.C.S.: 541810
Chris Pavlovski *(Founder, Chm &
CEO)*

RUMBLEON, INC.
1007 State Hwy 121, Allen, TX 75013
Tel.: (214) 495-0259 **NV**
Web Site: https://www.rumbleon.com
Year Founded: 2013
RMBL—(NASDAQ)
Rev.: $1,793,368,000
Assets: $1,027,210,000
Liabilities: $821,195,000
Net Worth: $206,015,000

RumbleON, Inc.—(Continued)

Earnings: ($261,513,000)
Emp.: 2,717
Fiscal Year-end: 12/31/22
Investment Services
N.A.I.C.S.: 523999
Steven J. Pully (Chm)
Tiffany B. Kice (CFO)
Thomas E. Aucamp (Chief Admin Officer & Sec)
Beverley Rath (Principal Acctg Officer & Controller)
Michael W. Kennedy (CEO)

Subsidiaries:

Autosport USA, Inc.   (1)
8040 Belvedere Rd, West Palm Beach, FL 33411
Tel.: (561) 471-7300
Web Site: http://www.autosportusacars.com
Used Luxury Car Distr
N.A.I.C.S.: 441110

RMBL Missouri, LLC   (1)
2100 E Outer Rd, Scott City, MO 63780-7114
Tel.: (469) 534-2828
Investment Services
N.A.I.C.S.: 523999

Wholesale Express, LLC   (1)
1528 E Williams Field Rd Ste 205, Gilbert, AZ 85295
Tel.: (615) 392-4100
Web Site:
  https://www.wholesaleexpress247.com
Transportation Services
N.A.I.C.S.: 484220

Wholesale,Inc   (1)
8037 Eastgate Blvd, Mount Juliet, TN 37122-3150
Tel.: (615) 449-0388
Web Site:
  https://wholesaleinc.rumbleon.com
Used Car Dealers
N.A.I.C.S.: 441120

RUNNING FOX RESOURCE CORP.
8148 Carr Cr, Arvada, CO 80005
Tel.: (403) 775-9089
Web Site:
  http://www.runningfoxresource.com
Year Founded: 1981
RUN—(TSXV)
Rev.: $765
Assets: $716,265
Liabilities: $32,140
Net Worth: $684,125
Earnings: ($189,780)
Fiscal Year-end: 11/30/19
Oil Field Services
N.A.I.C.S.: 213114
Michael Meyers (CEO)
Steven Schurman (CFO)

RUNWAY GROWTH FINANCE CORP.
205 N Michigan Ave Ste 4200, Chicago, IL 60601
Tel.: (312) 698-6902   **MD**
Web Site:
  https://investors.runwaygrowth.com
Year Founded: 2015
RWAY—(NASDAQ)
Rev.: $108,552,000
Assets: $1,141,766,000
Liabilities: $565,714,000
Net Worth: $576,052,000
Earnings: $59,796,000
Fiscal Year-end: 12/31/22
Financial Lending Services
N.A.I.C.S.: 522291
R. David Spreng (Founder, Chm, Pres, CEO & Chief Investment Officer)
Thomas B. Raterman (CFO, COO, Principal Acctg Officer, Treas & Sec)
Ted Cavan (Mng Dir-Tech)

RUSH ENTERPRISES, INC.
555 IH 35 S, New Braunfels, TX 78130
Tel.: (830) 302-5200   **TX**
Web Site:
  https://www.rushenterprises.com
Year Founded: 1965
RUSHA—(NASDAQ)
Rev.: $7,925,024,000
Assets: $4,364,241,000
Liabilities: $2,473,825,000
Net Worth: $1,890,416,000
Earnings: $347,055,000
Emp.: 7,860
Fiscal Year-end: 12/31/23
Holding Company; Commercial Motor Vehicles & Equipment Retailer
N.A.I.C.S.: 551112
W. M. Rush (Chm, Pres & CEO)
Steven L. Keller (CFO & Treas)
Corey Lowe (Sr VP-Peterbilt Dealerships)
Michael J. McRoberts (COO)
Jody Pollard (Sr VP-Truck Sls & Aftermarket Sls)
Jason T. Wilder (Sr VP-Navistar Dealerships)

Subsidiaries:

Associated Acceptance, Inc.   (1)
1020 NE Loop 410 Ste 630, San Antonio, TX 78209
Tel.: (210) 901-5500
Web Site:
  https://www.rushtruckinsurance.com
Truck Insurance Services
N.A.I.C.S.: 524298

Central California Truck and Trailer Sales, LLC   (1)
2345 Evergreen Ave, West Sacramento, CA 95691
Tel.: (916) 617-4348
Web Site: http://www.wtrucksales.net
Truck Distr
N.A.I.C.S.: 423110

Dallas Peterbilt, Inc.   (1)
515 N Loop 12, Irving, TX 75061-8709
Tel.: (469) 706-5200
Web Site: http://www.rushtruckcenters.com
Sales Range: $100-124.9 Million
Emp.: 185
Truck Sales
N.A.I.C.S.: 441227

Idealease of Chicago LLC   (1)
4655 S Ctr Ave, Chicago, IL 60638
Tel.: (708) 295-5940
Vehicle Leasing Services
N.A.I.C.S.: 532120

Nashville Peterbilt Inc.   (1)
515 N Loop 12, Irving, TX 75061-8709
Tel.: (615) 220-7777
Web Site: http://www.rushtruckcenters.com
Sales Range: $100-124.9 Million
Emp.: 150
New & Used Truck Dealer
N.A.I.C.S.: 441227

RTC Nevada, LLC   (1)
600 S Grand Central Pkwy Ste 350, Las Vegas, NV 89106
Tel.: (702) 676-1500
Transportation Services
N.A.I.C.S.: 488490

Rush Accessories Corporation   (1)
900 Expo Dr, Smyrna, TN 37167
Tel.: (615) 220-7730
Web Site: https://www.chromecountry.com
Emp.: 5
Automotive Parts & Accessories Whslr
N.A.I.C.S.: 441330

Rush Administrative Services, Inc.   (1)
1480 NE loop 820, Fort Worth, TX 76106
Tel.: (830) 626-5286
Emp.: 500
Transportation Management Services
N.A.I.C.S.: 541611

Rush GMC Truck Center of El Paso, Inc.   (1)

12253 Gateway Blvd W, El Paso, TX 79936
Tel.: (915) 778-6435
Automotive Retailer
N.A.I.C.S.: 441110

Rush GMC Truck Center of Tucson, Inc.   (1)
755 E 44th St, Tucson, AZ 85713
Tel.: (520) 205-8500
Web Site: http://www.rushtruckcenters.com
Sales Range: $25-49.9 Million
Emp.: 30
Truck Rental & Leasing Services
N.A.I.C.S.: 532120

Rush Logistics, Inc.   (1)
634 W Webster Ave, Chicago, IL 60614
Tel.: (773) 296-9390
Web Site: https://www.rushlogistics.com
Logistics & Distribution Services
N.A.I.C.S.: 541614

Rush Medium Duty Truck Centers of Colorado, Inc.   (1)
6800 E 50th Ave, Commerce City, CO 80022
Tel.: (720) 508-7700
Web Site:
  https://www.rushfordenterprices.com
Automotive Parts & Accessories Whslr
N.A.I.C.S.: 441330
Justin Goree (Gen Mgr-Reg)
Tim Trom (Reg Sls Mgr-Truck)
Rodney Haberer (Mgr-Medium-Duty Svc)
Justin Ertle (Mgr-Mobile Svc)

Rush Peterbilt Truck Center   (1)
8922 Interstate 10 E, San Antonio, TX 78219
Tel.: (210) 901-7100
Web Site: http://www.rushtruckcenters.com
Sales Range: $25-49.9 Million
Emp.: 150
Heavy Construction Equipment Rental
N.A.I.C.S.: 532412

Rush Truck Center of Albuquerque, Inc.   (1)
6521 Hanover Rd NW, Albuquerque, NM 87121
Tel.: (505) 839-3600
Web Site: http://www.rushtruckcenters.com
Automobiles & Other Motor Vehicles Retailer
N.A.I.C.S.: 423110

Rush Truck Centers - Kansas City   (1)
7700 NE 38th St, Kansas City, MO 64161
Tel.: (816) 455-1833
Web Site: https://www.rushtruckcenters.com
Commercial Truck Sales & Service
N.A.I.C.S.: 423110
David Spinner (Gen Mgr)

Rush Truck Centers - Lowell   (1)
807 S Bloomington St, Lowell, AR 72745
Tel.: (479) 770-1200
Web Site: https://www.rushtruckcenters.com
Emp.: 60
Commercial Truck Sales & Service
N.A.I.C.S.: 423110
Katrina Newman (Branch Mgr)

Rush Truck Centers - Memphis   (1)
1750 E Brooks Rd, Memphis, TN 38116-3606
Tel.: (901) 345-6275
Web Site: https://www.rushtruckcenters.com
Sales Range: $25-49.9 Million
Emp.: 100
Commercial Truck Sales & Service
N.A.I.C.S.: 423110
Carl Hayes (VP & Gen Mgr)

Rush Truck Centers - North Little Rock   (1)
11401 Diamond Dr, North Little Rock, AR 72117
Tel.: (501) 945-8400
Web Site: https://www.rushtruckcenters.com
Sales Range: $25-49.9 Million
Emp.: 100
Commercial Truck Sales & Service
N.A.I.C.S.: 423110
Jerry Schaefer (Gen Mgr)

Rush Truck Centers of Arizona, Inc.   (1)

3382 E Gila Ridge Rd, Yuma, AZ 85365
Tel.: (928) 336-9700
Sales Range: $25-49.9 Million
Emp.: 30
SMI Truck Whslr
N.A.I.C.S.: 333924

Rush Truck Centers of California Inc.   (1)
8830 E Slauson Ave, Pico Rivera, CA 90660   (100%)
Tel.: (830) 626-5232
Web Site: https://www.rushtruckcenters.com
Sales Range: $100-124.9 Million
Emp.: 140
Service Centers & On-Road Services for Automobiles & Other Motor Vehicles
N.A.I.C.S.: 811111

Rush Truck Centers of Colorado Inc.   (1)
5165 Vasqez Blvd, Denver, CO 80216-2241   (100%)
Tel.: (303) 292-3170
Web Site: https://www.rush-enterprises.com
Sales Range: $50-74.9 Million
Emp.: 120
Sales & Services of Automobiles & Other Motor Vehicles
N.A.I.C.S.: 423110
Justin Goree (Gen Mgr-Reg)
Tori Keller (Mgr-Parts)
Mike Adams (Reg Sls Mgr-Heavy-Duty New Truck)
Todd LaPenna (Mgr-Svc)
Bill Maki (Mgr-Used Truck Sls)
Danny McGilvray (Mgr-Body Shop)

Rush Truck Centers of Florida, Inc.   (1)
9401 Bachman Rd, Orlando, FL 32824
Tel.: (407) 403-5300
Web Site: https://www.peterbiltcfl.com
Sales Range: $75-99.9 Million
Emp.: 50
Trucks, Tractors & Trailers: New & Used
N.A.I.C.S.: 441110

Rush Truck Centers of Georgia, Inc.   (1)
2120 Atlanta Rd SE, Smyrna, GA 30080
Tel.: (678) 718-3000
Web Site: https://www.rushtruckcenters.com
Heavy & Medium Duty Truck Dealer
N.A.I.C.S.: 423110

Rush Truck Centers of Idaho, Inc.   (1)
770 W Amity Rd, Boise, ID 83705
Tel.: (208) 401-2200
Sales Range: $25-49.9 Million
Emp.: 179
Automobile & Motor Vehicle Whslr
N.A.I.C.S.: 423110

Rush Truck Centers of Illinois, Inc.   (1)
575 Saint Paul Blvd, Carol Stream, IL 60188
Tel.: (630) 909-2400
Web Site: https://www.rushtruckcenters.com
Automotive Distr
N.A.I.C.S.: 423110
Timothy Fanter (Mgr-Gen)

Rush Truck Centers of Indiana, Inc.   (1)
1325 W Thompson Rd, Indianapolis, IN 46217
Tel.: (317) 677-9200
Web Site: https://www.rushtruckcenters.com
Industrial Equipment & Truck Distr
N.A.I.C.S.: 423120
Shelby Howard (Gen Mgr & Reg Mgr)

Rush Truck Centers of Kansas, Inc.   (1)
11525 S Rogers Rd, Olathe, KS 66062
Tel.: (913) 815-2400
Web Site: https://www.rushtruckcenters.com
Emp.: 23
Industrial Equipment & Truck Distr
N.A.I.C.S.: 423120
Nick Hunt (Mgr-Gen)

Rush Truck Centers of Kentucky, Inc. (1)
251 New Porter Pike Rd, Bowling Green, KY 42103
Tel.: (270) 936-7000
Web Site: https://www.rushtruckcenters.com
Truck Whslr
N.A.I.C.S.: 423110

Rush Truck Centers of Missouri, Inc. (1)
3701 Chouteau Ave, Saint Louis, MO 63110
Tel.: (314) 449-7200
Web Site: https://www.rushtruckcenters.com
Industrial Equipment & Truck Distr
N.A.I.C.S.: 423110

Rush Truck Centers of Nevada, Inc, (1)
4120 Donovan Way, North Las Vegas, NV 89030
Tel.: (702) 970-5000
Web Site: https://www.rushtruckcenters.com
Truck Whslr
N.A.I.C.S.: 423110

Rush Truck Centers of New Mexico, Inc. (1)
6521 Hanover Rd NW, Albuquerque, NM 87121
Tel.: (505) 839-3600
Sales Range: $25-49.9 Million
Emp.: 40
Transportation & Construction Equipment Retailer
N.A.I.C.S.: 484110
Kevin Walker (Gen Mgr)

Rush Truck Centers of Ohio, Inc. (1)
11775 Hwy Dr, Cincinnati, OH 45241
Tel.: (513) 372-8800
Web Site: https://www.rushtruckcenters.com
Operation of Commercial Vehicle Dealerships
N.A.I.C.S.: 423110
Derrek Weaver (Asst Sec)

Rush Truck Centers of Oregon, Inc. (1)
588 SE 1st Ave, Ontario, OR 97914-2904
Tel.: (541) 889-8681
Web Site: http://www.rushtruckcenters.com
Sales Range: $25-49.9 Million
Emp.: 7
Automobile & Other Motor Vehicle Merchant Whslr
N.A.I.C.S.: 423110

Rush Truck Centers of Tennessee, Inc. (1)
900 Expo Dr, Smyrna, TN 37167
Tel.: (615) 220-7600
Web Site: https://www.rushenterprises.com
Emp.: 100
Duty Truck Distr
N.A.I.C.S.: 423110

Rush Truck Centers of Texas, L.P. (1)
4515 Ave A, Lubbock, TX 79404
Tel.: (806) 686-3600
Web Site: https://www.rushtruckcenters.com
Sales Range: $25-49.9 Million
Emp.: 45
Truck & Bus Retailer
N.A.I.C.S.: 441110

Rush Truck Centers of Utah, Inc. (1)
964 S 3800 W, Salt Lake City, UT 84104
Tel.: (801) 972-5320
Automobiles & Other Motor Vehicles Retailer
N.A.I.C.S.: 423110

Rush Truck Leasing, Inc. (1)
601 Republic Cir, Birmingham, AL 35214
Tel.: (205) 578-4400
Web Site: https://www.rushtruckleasing.com
Sales Range: $25-49.9 Million
Emp.: 5
Truck Leasing Services
N.A.I.C.S.: 532120

Rush Truck Leasing-Jacksonville (1)
718 Ln Ave N, Jacksonville, FL 32254
Tel.: (904) 559-4900
Web Site: http://www.rushtruckcenter.com
Commercial Trucks Distr
N.A.I.C.S.: 423110

Rushco, Inc. (1)
1 Warehouse St, Rushville, NY 14544
Tel.: (405) 262-1938
Fuel Oil Distr
N.A.I.C.S.: 424720

RUSH STREET INTERACTIVE, INC.
900 N Michigan Ave Ste 950, Chicago, IL 60611
Tel.: (773) 893-5855   DE
Web Site:
    https://www.rushstreetinteractive.com
Year Founded: 2019
RSI—(NYSE)
Rev.: $592,212,000
Assets: $350,346,000
Liabilities: $159,472,000
Net Worth: $190,874,000
Earnings: ($38,631,000)
Emp.: 700
Fiscal Year-end: 12/31/22
Online Casinos Operator
N.A.I.C.S.: 713210
Kyle L. Sauers (CFO)
Einar Roosileht (CEO)
Mattias Stetz (COO & Exec VP)
Paul Wierbicki (Chief Legal Officer & Gen Counsel)
Neil Bluhm (Exec Chm)
Richard Schwartz (Co-Founder & CEO)

RUSHNET, INC.
12725 W Indian School Rd Ste E 101, Avondale, AZ 85392
Tel.: (916) 616-7037   CO
Web Site: http://www.rushnetinc.com
Year Founded: 2018
RSHN—(OTCIQ)
Alcoholic Beverages Mfr
N.A.I.C.S.: 312111
Michael A. Cunha (Pres, CEO & Sec)
Chris Russell (Gen Counsel)

RVL PHARMACEUTICALS PLC
400 Crossing Blvd, Bridgewater, NJ 08807
Tel.: (908) 809-1300   IE
Web Site: https://www.rvlpharma.com
Year Founded: 2017
RVLP—(NASDAQ)
Rev.: $49,721,000
Assets: $128,510,000
Liabilities: $77,417,000
Net Worth: $51,093,000
Earnings: ($51,692,000)
Emp.: 125
Fiscal Year-end: 12/31/22
Pharmaceutical Product Mfr & Distr
N.A.I.C.S.: 325412
Christopher Klein (Gen Counsel & Sec)
Jarret Miller (Exec VP-HR)
James Schaub (COO & Exec VP)
Michael J. DePetris (Principal Acctg Officer)

Subsidiaries:

Osmotica Kereskedelmi es Szolgaltato Kft (1)
Berlini u 47-49 III ep I em, Budapest, 1045, Hungary
Tel.: (36) 17000690
Pharmaceuticals Product Mfr
N.A.I.C.S.: 325412

Subsidiary (Non-US):

Osmotica Argentina, S.A. (2)
Francisco Acuna de Figueroa 821, C1180AAO, Buenos Aires, Argentina
Tel.: (54) 1143794100
Pharmaceuticals Product Mfr
N.A.I.C.S.: 325412

Trigen Laboratories, LLC (1)

1880 McFarland Pkwy, Alpharetta, GA 30005
Web Site: https://www.osmotica.com
Pharmaceuticals Product Mfr
N.A.I.C.S.: 325412

Vertical Pharmaceuticals, LLC (1)
400 Crossing Blvd, Bridgewater, NJ 08807
Tel.: (908) 809-1300
Web Site: https://www.verticalpharma.com
Pharmaceutical Products Distr
N.A.I.C.S.: 424210

RXO INC.
11215 N Community House Rd, Charlotte, NC 28277
Tel.: (980) 308-6058   DE
Web Site: https://www.rxo.com
Year Founded: 2022
RXO—(NYSE)
Rev.: $3,927,000,000
Assets: $1,825,000,000
Liabilities: $1,231,000,000
Net Worth: $594,000,000
Earnings: $4,000,000
Emp.: 6,051
Fiscal Year-end: 12/31/23
Transportation Services
N.A.I.C.S.: 488510
Mary E. Kissel (Vice Chm)
Heidi Ratti (Chief HR Officer)
Jamie Harris (CFO)
Drew Wilkerson (CEO)

Subsidiaries:

Coyote Logistics, LLC (1)
2545 W Diversey Ave 3rd Fl, Chicago, IL 60647
Web Site: https://www.coyote.com
Truckload, Intermodal, Air, Ocean & Supply Chain Services
N.A.I.C.S.: 488510

RXR ACQUISITION CORP.
625 RXR plaza, Uniondale, NY 11556
Tel.: (516) 506-6797   DE
Year Founded: 2021
RXRAU—(NASDAQ)
Investment Services
N.A.I.C.S.: 523999
Scott H. Rechler (Chm & CEO)
Michael Maturo (CFO)
Jason Barnett (Gen Counsel)
Matthew Boras (Sr VP-Investment)

RXSIGHT, INC.
100 Columbia, Aliso Viejo, CA 92656
Tel.: (949) 521-7830   CA
Web Site: https://www.rxsight.com
Year Founded: 1997
RXST—(NASDAQ)
Rev.: $89,077,000
Assets: $182,550,000
Liabilities: $22,188,000
Net Worth: $160,362,000
Earnings: ($48,608,000)
Emp.: 374
Fiscal Year-end: 12/31/23
Information Technology Services
N.A.I.C.S.: 541512
Matt Haller (CTO)
Chris Sandstedt (VP-IOL Dev & RxSight Fellow)
Debe Deck (VP-Regulatory Affairs)
Jeremy Dong (VP-Advanced Engrg)
Victoria Piunova (VP-LAL Chemistry)
Caroline Vaughn (VP-Human Resources)
J. Andy Corley (Chm)
Ron Kurtz (Pres & CEO)
Shelley Thunen (Co-Pres & CFO)
Ilya Goldshleger (Co-Pres & COO)
Eric Weinberg (Co-Pres & Chief Comml Officer)
Pat Cullen (VP-Quality & Quality)
Steve Everly (Sr VP-Sales & VP)
Roy Freeman (Sr VP-Marketing & Professional Rels & VP)

Jeffrey Ha (VP-Medical Affairs)
Oliver Moravcevic (VP-Investor Relations)
Shea Sudol (VP-Information Technology & Cybersecurity)
Yi Young (VP-Quality Assurance)
Ronald Kurtz (Pres & CEO)

RYAN SPECIALTY HOLDINGS, INC.
2 Prudential Plz, Chicago, IL 60601
Tel.: (312) 784-6001   DE
Web Site:
    https://www.ryanspecialty.com
Year Founded: 2021
RYAN—(NYSE)
Rev.: $2,077,549,000
Assets: $7,247,209,000
Liabilities: $6,267,565,000
Net Worth: $979,644,000
Earnings: $194,480,000
Emp.: 4,350
Fiscal Year-end: 12/31/23
Holding Company
N.A.I.C.S.: 551112
Timothy W. Turner (Pres)
Michael L. Conklin (Chief HR Officer & Exec VP)
Patrick G. Ryan (Founder, Chm & CEO)
Jeremiah R. Bickham (CFO & Exec VP)
Mark S. Katz (Gen Counsel & Exec VP)
Michael Blackshear (Chief Compliance & Privacy Officer & Head-Diversity, Equity & Inclusion)
Waleed K. Husain (Chief Risk Officer)
Alice Phillips Topping (Chief Mktg & Comm Officer & Sr VP)
Nicholas Mezick (Dir-IR)

Subsidiaries:

Accurisk Solutions LLC (1)
10 S LaSalle St Ste 2350, Chicago, IL 60603
Tel.: (312) 857-9100
Web Site: http://www.accurisksolutions.com
Risk Solution Services
N.A.I.C.S.: 524298
Daniel Boisvert (Pres & CEO)

Keystone Risk Partners, LLC (1)
1 Tower Bridge, Conshohocken, PA 19428-2873
Tel.: (610) 941-7751
Web Site: http://www.keystonerisk.com
Insurance Agencies & Brokerages
N.A.I.C.S.: 524210
Betsy Mallon (Sr VP)

Ryan Specialty Group, LLC (1)
Prudential Plaza 180 N Stetson Ave Ste 4600, Chicago, IL 60601
Tel.: (312) 784-6001
Web Site: http://www.ryansg.com
Holding Company; Insurance Brokerage Services
N.A.I.C.S.: 551112
Patrick G. Ryan (Founder, Chm & CEO)
Edward F. McCormack (Pres & Gen Counsel-RT Specialty)
Miles Wuller (Pres & CEO-Ryan Specialty Underwriting Managers)
Kieran T. Dempsey (Mng Dir & Chief Underwriting Officer)
Brendan M. Mulshine (Chief Revenue Officer)
Jeremiah R. Bickham (CFO & Exec VP)
Kathleen M. Burns (Chief Digital Officer)
Lisa J. Paschal (Chief HR Officer & Sr VP)
Alice P. Topping (CMO & Chief Comm Officer)
Jamie Bouloux (CEO-Emergin Risk)
David S. De Berry (CEO-Concord Specialty Risk)
Mark S. Katz (Gen Counsel & Exec VP)
John Zern (Pres/CEO-Ryan Specialty Benefits)
Kathy Guerville (Chief Underwriting Officer-Underwriting Management Specialty)

Subsidiary (Domestic):

All Risks, Ltd. (2)

Ryan Specialty Holdings, Inc.—(Continued)

10150 York Rd 5th Fl, Hunt Valley, MD
21030
Tel.: (410) 828-5810
Web Site: http://www.allrisks.com
Emp.: 550
Insurance & Brokerage Services
N.A.I.C.S.: 524210
Ryan Grimes (Sr VP-Ops-Northeast &
Western Reg)
Christopher McGovern (Sr VP-Specialty
Programs-Natl)
Rex Regan (Sr VP-Ops-Virginia & North
Carolin)
Matthew D. Nichols (Pres)
Lee Branson (VP-Personal Lines)
Abby Daugherty (Asst VP-Phoenix)
Chris Kelleher (VP-Specialty Programs-Natl)
Don Deising (VP & Branch Mgr-Orlando,
Ormond Beach-FL)
Glenn Hargrove (Mng Dir-South Central)
Hugh Mooney (Sr VP & Branch Mgr-Atlanta,
GA & Jupiter-FL)
Jim Vajda (VP-Pub Livery)
Joe Quigley (VP)
Lora Robbins (VP-Charlotte-NC)
Marcus Payne (Mng Dir)
Mark Melander (Chief Admin Officer)
Richard Lang (Asst VP-Marine)
Steve Kass (VP & Branch Mgr-Ft. Lauder-
dale, Miami, Tampa-FL)
Marya Propis (Sr VP & Dir-Distr & Broker
Partnerships)

Atlantic Specialty Lines, Inc. **(2)**
9020 Stony Point Pkwy Ste 450, Richmond,
VA 23235
Tel.: (804) 320-9500
Web Site: http://www.atlanticspecial.com
Sales Range: $10-24.9 Million
Emp.: 75
Specialty Insurance Brokerage
N.A.I.C.S.: 524210
Robert Bryan (Pres)
Lindsey Harris (Coord-Claims & London
Contract)
Eunice Hucker (Sr VP)
Greg Provenzo (Sr VP)

Subsidiary (Domestic):

Specialty Lines of Pennsylvania,
LLC **(3)**
600 W Germantown Pike Ste 400, Plym-
outh Meeting, PA 19462
Tel.: (610) 940-1662
Web Site: http://www.atlanticspecial.com
Specialty Insurance Brokerage
N.A.I.C.S.: 524210

Subsidiary (Domestic):

Global Special Risks, LLC **(2)**
9821 Katy Fwy Ste 750, Houston, TX
77024
Tel.: (713) 952-2774
Web Site: http://www.gsrum.com
Marine & Energy Insurance Services
N.A.I.C.S.: 524210
Chris Zuniga (Manager-Claims)

Griffin Underwriting Services **(2)**
2375 130th Ave NE Ste 200, Bellevue, WA
98005
Tel.: (425) 453-8599
Web Site: https://www.gogus.com
Insurance Agencies & Brokerages
N.A.I.C.S.: 524210
Jason Griffin (Pres)
Van Griffin (Pres)
Steve Mitchell (VP)

International Specialty Insurance **(2)**
105 W Main St, Elkin, NC 28621-3432
Tel.: (336) 835-2230
Web Site: http://www.isinsurance.com
Insurance Agencies & Brokerages
N.A.I.C.S.: 524210
Dave Ferraro (Owner)

R-T Specialty, LLC **(2)**
6450 Transit Rd Depew, New York, NY
14043
Tel.: (716) 856-3065
Web Site: https://www.rtspecialty.com
Insurance Brokerage Services
N.A.I.C.S.: 524210
Michael T. VanAcker (Exec VP)
Peter Costolnick (Sr VP)

Division (Domestic):

RSG Underwriting Managers,
LLC **(2)**
Prudential Plz 180 N Stetson Ave Ste 4600,
Chicago, IL 60601
Tel.: (312) 784-6001
Web Site: http://ryansg.com
Specialty Property & Casualty Management
N.A.I.C.S.: 524298
Nicholas D. Cortezi (Chm & CEO)
Alan Belthoff (VP-Global Special Risks)
Miles Wuller (Exec VP)
Matt Nichols (Pres)

Subsidiary (Domestic):

Interstate Insurance Management,
Inc. **(3)**
2307 Menoher Blvd, Johnstown, PA 15905
Tel.: (814) 255-7878
Web Site: https://www.interstate-
insurance.com
Insurance Management
N.A.I.C.S.: 524210

Subsidiary (Domestic):

RT New Day **(2)**
2465 Kuser Rd Ste 202, Hamilton, NJ
08960
Tel.: (609) 298-3516
Web Site: http://rtspecialty.com
Insurance Agencies & Brokerages
N.A.I.C.S.: 524210

Subsidiary (Non-US):

Ryan Specialty Group, LLC -
Denmark **(2)**
Strandvejen 125, 2900, Hellerup, Denmark
Tel.: (45) 72301240
Web Site: http://www.ryansg.com
Insurance Underwriting Services
N.A.I.C.S.: 524126
Thomas Harrild (Mng Dir)

Ryan Specialty Group, LLC -
Sweden **(2)**
Brahegatan 2, 114 37, Stockholm, Sweden
Tel.: (46) 841026881
Web Site: http://www.ryansg.com
Insurance Services
N.A.I.C.S.: 524298
Sverker Edstrom (Mng Dir)

Socius Insurance Services Inc. **(1)**
Tel.: (205) 746-1075
Web Site: http://www.sociusinsurance.com
Insurance Agencies & Brokerages
N.A.I.C.S.: 524210
Hank Slickley (VP)
Patrick Hanley (Pres & CEO)

RYDER SYSTEM, INC.

2333 Ponce de Leon Blvd Ste 700,
Coral Gables, FL 33134
Tel.: (305) 500-3726 **FL**
Web Site: https://www.ryder.com
Year Founded: 1933
R—(NYSE)
Rev.: $11,783,000,000
Assets: $15,778,000,000
Liabilities: $12,709,000,000
Net Worth: $3,069,000,000
Earnings: $406,000,000
Emp.: 47,500
Fiscal Year-end: 12/31/23
Holding Company; Commercial Truck
Leasing & Rental & Logistics Ser-
vices
N.A.I.C.S.: 551112
Robert E. Sanchez (Chm & CEO)
Robert D. Fatovic (Chief Legal Offi-
cer, Sec & Exec VP)
Karen M. Jones (CMO & Sr VP)
John J. Diez (CFO & Exec VP)
Steve W. Martin (Sr VP-Dedicated
Transportation Solutions)
Frank Lopez (Chief HR Officer &
Exec VP)
John J. Gleason (Chief Sls Officer &
Exec VP)

Subsidiaries:

Bedford Logistics, LLC **(1)**
1812 High Grove Ln Ste 101, Naperville, IL
60540
Tel.: (630) 357-9700
Web Site: https://www.bedfordlogistics.com
Logistic Services
N.A.I.C.S.: 484110

Bullwell Trailer Solutions Limited **(1)**
100 Burton Road, Streethay, Lichfield,
WS13 8LN, United Kingdom
Tel.: (44) 1543416665
Trailer Repair Services
N.A.I.C.S.: 811121

Cardinal Logistics Management
Corp **(1)**
5333 Davidson Hwy, Concord, NC 28027-
8478
Tel.: (704) 786-6125
Web Site: http://www.cardlog.com
Sales Range: $150-199.9 Million
Emp.: 250
Long-Distance Delivery Services
N.A.I.C.S.: 484110
Tom Hostetler (CEO)
Jerry Bowman (Pres & COO)
Michael Robert (CFO)

Dallas Service Center, Inc. **(1)**
5115 S Cockrell Hill Rd, Dallas, TX 75236
Tel.: (214) 330-4661
Web Site: http://www.dsctruck.com
Truck Repair & Maintenance & Mechanical
Repairs
N.A.I.C.S.: 811111

Dotcom Distribution **(1)**
300 Nixon Ln, Edison, NJ 08837-3831
Tel.: (732) 287-2300
Web Site: http://www.dotcomdist.com
Wired Telecommunications Carriers
N.A.I.C.S.: 517111
William Follett (Pres)

Maple Mountain Co-Packers LLC **(1)**
3596 Mtn Vista Pkwy Ste 2, Provo, UT
84606
Tel.: (801) 960-3387
Web Site: https://www.gommcp.com
Packaging & Labeling Services
N.A.I.C.S.: 561910

Ryder (Shanghai) Logistics, Co.,
Ltd. **(1)**
Room 1806 Hi-Shanghai New City Block 8
No 950 Dalian Road, Yang Pu District,
Shanghai, 200092, China
Tel.: (86) 21 3653 7799
Supply Chain & Logistics Services
N.A.I.C.S.: 541614
Tina Cheung (Gen Mgr)
Sammy Wong (Mgr-Ops)

Ryder Container Terminals **(1)**
1275 Kingsway Ave, Port Coquitlam, V3C
1S2, BC, Canada
Tel.: (604) 941-0266
Web Site: http://reservations.ryder.com
Truck Transportation Services
N.A.I.C.S.: 532120
Nathan Redman (Mgr-Warehouse)

Ryder Energy Distribution
Corporation **(1)**
11690 NW 105 St, Miami, FL 33178
Tel.: (305) 500-3726
Web Site: https://www.ryder.com
Sales Range: $400-449.9 Million
Emp.: 6
Petroleum Products
N.A.I.C.S.: 424720

Ryder Fuel Services, LLC **(1)**
11200 Hempstead Rd, Houston, TX 77092
Tel.: (713) 956-0473
Web Site: https://www.ryderfs.com
Truck Rental & Leasing Services
N.A.I.C.S.: 532120

Ryder Integrated Logistics, Inc. **(1)**
11690 NW 105th St, Miami, FL 33178
Tel.: (305) 500-3726
Web Site: https://www.lms.ryder.com
Sales Range: $450-499.9 Million
Emp.: 1,000
Logistics & Freight Transportation Services
N.A.I.C.S.: 484121

Ryder Limited **(1)**
2610 The Crescent Birmingham Business
Park, Solihull Parkway, Birmingham, B37
7YE, United Kingdom
Tel.: (44) 121 407 5290
Web Site: http://www.ryder.com
Commercial Truck Leasing & Rental Ser-
vices
N.A.I.C.S.: 532120

Ryder Puerto Rico, Inc. **(1)**
Carretera 865 Km 06 Bo Camp, Toa Baja,
PR 00949
Tel.: (787) 794-2410
Web Site: http://www.ryder.com
Sales Range: $1-9.9 Million
Emp.: 30
Logistics Transportation Services
N.A.I.C.S.: 541614

Ryder System Holdings (UK)
Limited **(1)**
Fell Bank Birtley, Newcastle, DH3 2SP,
United Kingdom
Tel.: (44) 1914106464
Truck Transportation Services
N.A.I.C.S.: 488999

Ryder Truck Rental, Inc. **(1)**
11690 NW 105th St, Miami, FL
33178 **(100%)**
Tel.: (305) 500-3726
Web Site: https://www.ryder.com
Sales Range: $350-399.9 Million
Emp.: 1,000
Truck Leasing, Rental, Maintenance & Re-
pair
N.A.I.C.S.: 532120

Subsidiary (Non-US):

Ryder Truck Rental Canada Ltd. **(2)**
700 Creditstone Road, Concord, L4K 5A5,
ON, Canada **(100%)**
Tel.: (905) 826-8777
Web Site: https://canada.ryder.com
Sales Range: $10-24.9 Million
Emp.: 65
Commercial Truck Leasing, Rental & Logis-
tical Services
N.A.I.C.S.: 532120

Ryder de Mexico S.A. de C.V. **(1)**
Alfonso Napoles Gandara No 50 Primer
Piso Col Santa Fe Pena Blanca, Delega-
cion Alvaro Obregon, Mexico, 01210,
Mexico
Tel.: (52) 5552576900
Web Site: http://www.ryder.com
Sales Range: $1-9.9 Million
Emp.: 20
Commercial Truck Leasing, Rental & Logis-
tical Services
N.A.I.C.S.: 532120

Ryder, Inc. of Florida **(1)**
11690 NW 105th St, Miami, FL 33178-1103
Tel.: (305) 500-3726
Web Site: http://www.ryder.com
Truck Utility Trailer Recreational Vehicle
Rental Leasing
N.A.I.C.S.: 532120

Hyder-Ascent Logistics Pte Ltd. **(1)**
24 Penjuru Road 10-01, Singapore,
609128, Singapore **(100%)**
Tel.: (65) 68622188
Web Site: http://www.asia.ryder.com
Sales Range: $50-74.9 Million
Emp.: 550
Supply Chain & Logistical Services
N.A.I.C.S.: 541614

RYERSON HOLDING CORPO-
RATION

6201 15th Ave, Brooklyn, NY 11219
Tel.: (312) 292-5033 **DE**
Web Site: https://ir.ryerson.com
Year Founded: 2007

Ryder CRSA Logistics (HK)
Limited **(1)**
Unit 1713 17th Floor Miramar Tower 132
Nathan Road, Tsimshatsui, Kowloon, China
(Hong Kong)
Tel.: (852) 2235 9100
Truck Rental & Leasing Services
N.A.I.C.S.: 532120

RYI—(NYSE)
Rev.: $6,323,600,000
Assets: $2,334,300,000
Liabilities: $1,441,300,000
Net Worth: $893,000,000
Earnings: $391,000,000
Emp.: 4,200
Fiscal Year-end: 12/31/22
Holding Company; Metal Processor & Distr
N.A.I.C.S.: 551112
Edward J. Lehner *(Pres & CEO)*
Mike Burbach *(COO)*
Mark Silver *(Chief HR Officer, Gen Counsel & Exec VP)*
John Orth *(Exec VP-Ops)*
Molly D. Kannan *(Chief Acctg Officer & Controller)*
James Claussen *(CFO & Exec VP)*
Srini Sundararajan *(CIO)*

Subsidiaries:

Excelsior Metals, Inc.   (1)
2597 N Fordham Ave, Fresno, CA 93727
Tel.: (559) 346-0932
Web Site: http://www.excelsiormetals.com
Sales Range: $1-9.9 Million
Emp.: 27
Fabricated Structural Metal Mfr
N.A.I.C.S.: 332312
Gus Benson *(VP)*
Ray Roush *(Founder, Owner & CEO)*
Mark J. Allen *(VP-Dev)*

Fanello Industries, Inc.   (1)
50 East Main St, Lavonia, GA 30553
Tel.: (706) 356-5359
Web Site: http://www.fanelloindustries.com
Metal Stamping
N.A.I.C.S.: 332119
Vince Fanello *(Pres)*

Ford Tool Steels, Inc.   (1)
5051 Pattison Ave, Saint Louis, MO 63110
Tel.: (314) 772-3322
Web Site: https://www.fordtoolsteels.com
Metals Service Center
N.A.I.C.S.: 423510
Susan Gasser *(Owner)*

Howard Precision Metals, Inc.   (1)
8058 N 87th St, Milwaukee, WI 53224
Tel.: (414) 355-9611
Web Site: http://www.howardprecision.com
Sales Range: $1-9.9 Million
Emp.: 47
Aluminum Sheet, Plate, And Foil, Nsk
N.A.I.C.S.: 331315

Hudson Tool Steel Corporation   (1)
17871 Park Pl Dr Ste #135, Cerritos, CA 90703
Tel.: (800) 996-0411
Web Site: http://www.hudsontoolsteel.com
Sales Range: $1-9.9 Million
Emp.: 100
Tool Steels, Carbon Steels & Alloy Steels Distr
N.A.I.C.S.: 423510
Sean Weidenhammer *(Gen Mgr)*
Rick Resner *(Pres)*

Norlen, Inc.   (1)
900 Grossman Dr, Schofield, WI 54476-0000
Web Site: http://www.norlen.com
Plate Work Mfr
N.A.I.C.S.: 332313
Gary Gebert *(Mgr-Mktg)*

Ryerson Canada, Inc.   (1)
7525 Financial Drive, Brampton, L6Y 5P4, ON, Canada
Tel.: (905) 792-1414
Emp.: 200
Metal Product Whslr
N.A.I.C.S.: 423510
Grant McFater *(Asst Gen Mgr)*

Ryerson Inc.   (1)
227 W Monroe 27th Fl, Chicago, IL 60606
Tel.: (312) 292-5000
Web Site: http://www.ryerson.com
Metal Machining & Welding & Fabrication Shops Operator & Products Whslr
N.A.I.C.S.: 332710
Edward J. Lehner *(Pres & CEO)*

Subsidiary (Domestic):

Central Steel & Wire Company   (2)
3000 W 51st St, Chicago, IL 60632-2122
Tel.: (773) 471-3800
Web Site: http://www.centralsteel.com
Processed & Unprocessed Ferrous & Non-ferrous Metals Mfr & Distr
N.A.I.C.S.: 423510

Fay Industries, Inc.   (2)
17200 Foltz Pkwy, Strongsville, OH 44149
Tel.: (440) 572-5030
Web Site: http://www.fayindustries.com
Sales Range: $25-49.9 Million
Emp.: 65
Steel Service Center
N.A.I.C.S.: 423510
Conley Schnaterbeck *(VP)*
Craig Notarianni *(VP)*

Laserflex Corporation   (2)
3649 Parkway Ln, Hilliard, OH 43026-3026
Tel.: (614) 850-9600
Web Site: http://www.laserflex-inc.com
Sales Range: $25-49.9 Million
Emp.: 100
Fabricated Metal Products Mfr
N.A.I.C.S.: 332999
Ken Kinkopf *(Pres)*
Rick Sulc *(Gen Mgr)*
Mike Shirley *(Mgr-Sls)*
M. Beth Hagerty *(Mgr-HR & Acctg)*

Plant (Domestic):

Ryerson Inc. - Atlanta   (2)
4400 Peachtree Industrial Blvd, Norcross, GA 30071-1648
Tel.: (770) 368-4200
Web Site: http://www.ryerson.com
Sales Range: $75-99.9 Million
Emp.: 100
Metal Machining, Welding & Fabrication Services & Whslr
N.A.I.C.S.: 332710
Doug Britt *(Mgr-Fabrication)*

Ryerson Inc. - Burns Harbor   (2)
310 Tech Dr, Burns Harbor, IN 46304-8843
Tel.: (219) 764-3500
Web Site: http://www.ryerson.com
Sales Range: $75-99.9 Million
Emp.: 100
Metal Machining, Welding & Fabrication Services & Whslr
N.A.I.C.S.: 332710
Jeff Redfield *(Gen Mgr)*

Ryerson Inc. - Coon Rapids   (2)
455 85th Ave NW, Minneapolis, MN 55433-6026
Tel.: (763) 717-9000
Web Site: http://www.ryerson.com
Sales Range: $100-124.9 Million
Emp.: 150
Metal Machining Welding & Fabrication Mfr
N.A.I.C.S.: 332710
Edward J. Lehner *(Pres & CEO)*
Erich S. Schnaufer *(CFO)*
Mark Silver *(Gen Counsel, Sec & Exec VP)*
John Orth *(Exec VP-Ops)*
Kevin Richardson *(Pres-South-East Reg)*

Ryerson Inc. - Little Rock   (2)
771 Lindsey Rd, Little Rock, AR 72206
Tel.: (501) 490-2255
Web Site: http://www.ryerson.com
Sales Range: $100-124.9 Million
Emp.: 150
Metal Machining, Welding & Fabrication Services & Whslr
N.A.I.C.S.: 332710
John Crews *(Gen Mgr)*
Jon Clark *(Mgr-Outside Sls)*

Ryerson Inc. - Memphis   (2)
3779 Knight Rd, Memphis, TN 38118-6331
Tel.: (901) 541-6540
Web Site: http://www.ryerson.com
Sales Range: $25-49.9 Million
Emp.: 30
Metal Machining, Welding & Fabrication Services & Whslr
N.A.I.C.S.: 332710
Guy Carter *(Gen Mgr)*
Teddy Cavitt *(Mgr-Inside Sls)*
Edward J. Lehner *(Pres & CEO)*

Kevin Richardson *(Pres-South-East)*
Erich Schnaufer *(CFO)*
Mark Silver *(Gen Counsel, Sec & Exec VP)*

Ryerson Inc. - Minneapolis   (2)
1605 N Hwy 169, Minneapolis, MN 55441
Tel.: (763) 544-4401
Web Site: http://www.ryerson.com
Emp.: 50
Metal Machining, Welding & Fabrication Services & Whslr
N.A.I.C.S.: 332710
John Rich *(Gen Mgr)*

Ryerson Inc. - Seattle   (2)
600 SW 10th St, Renton, WA 98057
Tel.: (206) 624-2300
Web Site: http://www.ryerson.com
Sales Range: $75-99.9 Million
Emp.: 65
Metal Machining, Welding & Fabrication Services & Whslr
N.A.I.C.S.: 332710
Scott McCullough *(VP & Gen Mgr)*

Subsidiary (Domestic):

Southern Tool Steel, Inc.   (2)
2726 Kanasita Dr, Hixson, TN 37343
Tel.: (423) 870-7888
Web Site: http://www.southerntoolsteel.com
Rev.: $5,000,000
Emp.: 16
Metal Service Centers & Other Metal Merchant Whslr
N.A.I.C.S.: 423510
Kathy McClung *(Mgr-Accts Receivable)*

Turret Steel Industries, Inc.   (2)
105 Pine St, Imperial, PA 15126
Tel.: (724) 266-8200
Web Site: http://www.turretsteel.com
Steel Bars Distr
N.A.I.C.S.: 423510
Wendell MacDonald *(Mgr-Sls-Natl)*
Karthik Krishnasamy *(Mgr-Ops)*
Larry R. Weir *(Mgr-Credit)*
Dean G. Eriks *(Reg Mgr-Sls)*
Jeff Redfield *(Gen Mgr)*
Neil M. Stein *(Mgr-Sls-Natl)*
Fred L. Olmsted Jr. *(VP-Pur & Reg Mgr)*

Subsidiary (Domestic):

Sunbelt-Turret Steel, Inc.   (3)
527 Atando Ave, Charlotte, NC 28206   (100%)
Tel.: (704) 342-4321
Web Site: http://www.sunbeltturretsteel.com
Sales Range: $10-24.9 Million
Emp.: 52
Carbon & Alloy Steel Bar Mfr & Distr
N.A.I.C.S.: 423510
Steve Atkinson *(Mgr-Sls)*
Vince Higlesias *(Mgr-Dos Palos)*
Ken Tantare *(Mgr-Portland)*

Wilcox Steel, LLC   (3)
1240 Contract Dr, Green Bay, WI 54304
Tel.: (920) 347-4730
Web Site: http://www.wilcoxsteel.com
Sales Range: $1-9.9 Million
Emp.: 27
Steel Products Mfr
N.A.I.C.S.: 331221
Fran Larson *(Gen Mgr)*

TSA Processing Dallas, LLC   (1)
1625 W Sam Houston Pkwy N, Houston, TX 77043
Tel.: (630) 860-5900
Web Site: http://www.tsaprocessing.com
Iron & Steel Mills Mfr
N.A.I.C.S.: 331110
Bobby Medus *(Mgr)*

RYMAN HOSPITALITY PROPERTIES, INC.

1 Gaylord Dr, Nashville, TN 37214
Tel.: (615) 316-6000   DE
Web Site: https://www.rymanhp.com
Year Founded: 1991
RHP—(NYSE)
Rev.: $1,805,969,000
Assets: $4,040,623,000
Liabilities: $3,944,722,000
Net Worth: $95,901,000
Earnings: $134,948,000

Emp.: 689
Fiscal Year-end: 12/31/22
Hospitality Real Estate Investment Trust
N.A.I.C.S.: 525990
Colin V. Reed *(Chm)*
Mark Fioravanti *(Pres & CEO)*
Jennifer Hutcheson *(CFO, Chief Acctg Officer, Exec VP & Controller)*
Patrick Chaffin *(COO-Hotels & Exec VP)*
Scott J. Lynn *(Gen Counsel, Sec & Exec VP)*
Shannon Sullivan *(VP-Corp & Brand Comm)*
Patrick Q. Moore *(CEO-Opry Entertainment Grp)*

Subsidiaries:

300 Broadway, LLC   (1)
300 Broadway, Dobbs Ferry, NY 10522
Tel.: (914) 693-1882
Apartment Rental Services
N.A.I.C.S.: 531110

GPSI, Inc.   (1)
1425 Whitlock Ln Ste 108, Carrollton, TX 75006
Tel.: (972) 446-0037
Web Site: https://gpsiwater.com
Transportation Services
N.A.I.C.S.: 484121

Grand Ole Opry, LLC   (1)
600 Opry Mills Dr, Nashville, TN 37214
Tel.: (615) 871-6779
Web Site: https://www.opry.com
Sales Range: $450-499.9 Million
Emp.: 1,000
Entertainment & Hospitality Services
N.A.I.C.S.: 713110

Unit (Domestic):

WSM-AM   (2)
2644 Mcgavock Pike, Nashville, TN 37214-1202
Tel.: (615) 737-9650
Web Site: https://wsmradio.com
Rev.: $300,000,000
Emp.: 30
Radio Broadcasting Stations
N.A.I.C.S.: 516110
Jason Cooper *(Chief Engr)*
J. Patrick Tinnell *(Dir-Content & Programming)*
Jason Mayes *(Mgr-Sls)*
Lexi Carter *(Dir-Music)*

Ole Red Gatlinburg, LLC   (1)
511 Pkwy, Gatlinburg, TN 37738
Tel.: (865) 325-3101
Web Site: https://olered.com
Restaurant Services
N.A.I.C.S.: 722511

RHP Hotel Properties, LP   (1)
1 Gaylord Dr, Nashville, TN 37214
Tel.: (615) 316-6000
Web Site: https://www.rymanhp.com
Emp.: 50
Real Estate Investment Management Services
N.A.I.C.S.: 525990
Colin V. Reed *(Pres)*

RHP Investments, Inc.   (1)
145 E 57th St Fl 4, New York, NY 10022
Tel.: (212) 371-4380
Emp.: 9
Investment Management Service
N.A.I.C.S.: 523940

RHP Partner, LLC   (1)
1 Gaylord Dr, Nashville, TN 37214
Tel.: (615) 316-6000
Web Site: https://www.rymanhp.com
Real Estate Investment Management Services
N.A.I.C.S.: 531390

RYVYL INC.

3131 Camino Del Rio N Ste 1400,
San Diego, CA 92108
Tel.: (415) 433-3777   NV

Ryvyl Inc.—(Continued)

Web Site: https://www.ryvyl.com
Year Founded: 2007
RVYL—(NASDAQ)
Rev.: $32,909,112
Assets: $97,657,142
Liabilities: $99,580,095
Net Worth: ($1,922,953)
Earnings: ($49,235,698)
Emp.: 110
Fiscal Year-end: 12/31/22
Digital Banking Services
N.A.I.C.S.: 523150
George Oliva (CFO)
Ben Errez (Chm, Chief Acctg Officer & Exec VP)
Fredi Nisan (CEO)
Kenneth Haller (Pres-Payments)

Subsidiaries:

Northeast Merchant Systems Inc (1)
24 New Boston Rd, Sturbridge, MA 01566
Tel.: (508) 347-5922
Web Site: http://www.nemerchant.com
Rev.: $1,400,000
Emp.: 8
Credit Bureaus
N.A.I.C.S.: 561450
Aaron Dewar (Pres)
Nola Ruel (Treas & VP-Fin)

S&P GLOBAL INC.

55 Water St, New York, NY 10041
Tel.: (212) 438-1000   **NY**
Web Site: https://www.spglobal.com
Year Founded: 1860
SPGI—(NYSE)
Rev.: $12,497,000,000
Assets: $60,589,000,000
Liabilities: $22,489,000,000
Net Worth: $38,100,000,000
Earnings: $2,626,000,000
Emp.: 40,450
Fiscal Year-end: 12/31/23
Holding Company; Business Market Intelligence, Ratings & Information Products & Services
N.A.I.C.S.: 551112
John L. Berisford (Pres-S&P Global Ratings)
Steven J. Kemps (Gen Counsel & Gen Counsel)
Courtney Geduldig (Chief Pub & Govt Affairs Officer)
David R. Guarino (Chief Comm Officer)
Ewout L. Steenbergen (CFO & Exec VP)
Swamy Kocherlakota (CIO & Exec VP)
Dimitra Manis (Chief Purpose Officer & Exec VP)
Christopher F. Craig (Chief Acctg Officer, Sr VP & Controller)
Christopher Krantz (Sr Dir-Communications)
Christina Twomey (Head-Enterprise Comm-S&P Global Ratings)
Jason Feuchtwanger (Dir)
Chip Merritt (VP-Investor Relations)
Mark Réchtin (Exec Dir & Exec Editor-Mobility)
Sally Moore (Exec VP)
Martina L. Cheung (Pres & CEO)

Subsidiaries:

451 Research, LLC (1)
20 W 37th St 6th Fl, New York, NY 10018   (100%)
Tel.: (212) 505-3030
Web Site: http://www.451research.com
Emp.: 100
Information Technology Research & Development
N.A.I.C.S.: 541715
Simon Carruthers (COO)
Brett Azuma (Chief Res Officer & Exec VP-San Francisco)

Kiran Shah (Head-Professional Svcs-Global)
Daniel Kennedy (Dir-Res-Information Security)
Melanie Posey (VP-Res & Gen Mgr)

BENTEK Energy LLC (1)
1800 Larimer St Ste 2000, Denver, CO 80202
Tel.: (303) 988-1320
Web Site: http://www.bentekenergy.com
Sales Range: $25-49.9 Million
Emp.: 150
Information Services
N.A.I.C.S.: 519290

BRC Investor Services S.A. (1)
CRA 19 A 90-13 Oficina 708, Bogota, Colombia
Tel.: (57) 3904259
Web Site: http://www.brc.com.co
Credit Rating Services
N.A.I.C.S.: 561450

CME Information Services (Beijing) Co., Ltd. (1)
15F China World Tower No 3 Jianguomen-wai Avenue, Chaoyang, Beijing, 100004, China
Tel.: (86) 1057372634
Web Site: http://www.djindexes.com
Emp.: 1
Financial Risk Management Services
N.A.I.C.S.: 523150

CRISIL Irevna Information Technology (Hangzhou) Company Ltd. (1)
1603 & 1606 Hengxin Mansion 588 Jiang-Nan Road, Binjiang, Hangzhou, 310052, China
Tel.: (86) 57181069801
Marketing Data Analysis Services
N.A.I.C.S.: 541910

CRISIL Irevna UK Limited (1)
St Clements House, 27-28 Clements Lane, London, EC4N 7AE, United Kingdom
Tel.: (44) 8703336336
Financial Management Services
N.A.I.C.S.: 541611

CRISIL Irevna US LLC (1)
880 3rd Ave 12th Fl, New York, NY 10022
Tel.: (646) 292-3520
Financial Management Services
N.A.I.C.S.: 541611

CRISIL Ratings Limited (1)
Crisil House Central Avenue Hiranandani Business Park, Powai, Mumbai, 400076, India
Tel.: (91) 2233423000
Web Site: https://www.crisilratings.com
Financial Investment Services
N.A.I.C.S.: 523999
Gurpreet Chhatwal (Mng Dir)
Holly Kulka (Chm)
Subodh Rai (Pres & Chief Rating Officer)

Coalition Development Ltd. (1)
Ropemaker Place 25 Ropemaker Street, London, EC2Y 9LY, United Kingdom
Tel.: (44) 2071761400
Web Site: http://www.coalition.com
Business Consulting Services
N.A.I.C.S.: 541611
Kate Joicey-Cecil (Head-Client Relationships & Dev)

Coalition Development Systems (India) Private Limited (1)
International InfoTech Park Tower 4 Vashi Railway Station Complex, Vashi Sec30A, Navi Mumbai, 400705, India
Tel.: (91) 2239116464
Business Consulting Services
N.A.I.C.S.: 541611
A. Arun Kumar (Assoc VP)

Coalition Singapore Pte. Ltd. (1)
60 Robinson Road, 11-01 BEA Building, Singapore, 068892, Singapore
Tel.: (65) 62221845
Web Site: http://www.coalition.com
Credit Rating Services
N.A.I.C.S.: 561450

DJI Opco LLC (1)
55 Water St, New York, NY 10041
Tel.: (212) 438-3544

Financial Management Services
N.A.I.C.S.: 541611

Greenwich Associates Canada, ULC (1)
14 Prince Arthur Avenue Suite 208, Toronto, M5R 1A9, ON, Canada
Tel.: (647) 264-9581
Information Services
N.A.I.C.S.: 519290

Greenwich Associates Japan K.K. (1)
8-6-9-414 Akasaka, Minato-ku, Tokyo, 107-0052, Japan
Tel.: (81) 334755212
Information Services
N.A.I.C.S.: 519290

Greenwich Associates Singapore Pte. Ltd. (1)
1 George Street 10-01, Singapore, 049145, Singapore
Tel.: (65) 62360142
Information Services
N.A.I.C.S.: 519290

Greenwich Associates UK Limited (1)
90 Basinghall Street, London, EC2V 5AY, United Kingdom
Tel.: (44) 2077269400
Information Services
N.A.I.C.S.: 519290

IHS Markit Ltd. (1)
4th Floor Ropemaker Place 25 Ropemaker Street, London, EC2Y 9LY, United Kingdom
Tel.: (44) 2072602000
Web Site: http://www.ihsmarkit.com
Rev.: $4,658,100,000
Assets: $16,913,900,000
Liabilities: $7,424,500,000
Net Worth: $9,489,400,000
Earnings: $1,206,800,000
Emp.: 16,000
Fiscal Year-end: 11/30/2021
Financial Data, Portfolio Valuations & Derivatives Trade Processing Services
N.A.I.C.S.: 522320
Yaacov Mutnikas (CTO & Chief Data Scientist)
Ronnie West (Chief People Officer & Exec VP)
Eric Boyer (Sr VP-IR)
Zion Hilelly (Mng Dir & Head-Operations-Client Support)
Brian Crotty (Exec VP-Global Energy & Natural Resources)

Subsidiary (US):

IHS Inc. (2)
15 Inverness Way E, Englewood, CO 80112
Tel.: (303) 397-7956
Web Site: http://global.ihs.com
Business Support Services
N.A.I.C.S.: 561499

Irevna Limited (1)
1 Giltspur Street, Farringdon, London, EC1A 9DD, United Kingdom
Tel.: (44) 8703336336
Web Site: http://www.irevna.com
Sales Range: $200-249.9 Million
Emp.: 1,400
Data Research Services
N.A.I.C.S.: 519290

MEI LLC (1)
3838 Western Way NE, Albany, OR 97321
Tel.: (541) 917-0020
Web Site:
    https://www.meiriggingcrating.com
Semiconductor & Solar Product Mfr
N.A.I.C.S.: 334413
Jim Simer (Mgr-Inside Sls & Svc)

McGraw Hill Australia Pty Ltd (1)
Level 2 Everglade Bldg 82 Water Loo Rd, North Ryde, 2113, NSW, Australia (100%)
Tel.: (61) 299001800
Web Site: http://www.mcgraw-hill.com.au
Sales Range: $25-49.9 Million
Emp.: 265
Books & Educational Materials, Professional Information, Training Systems
N.A.I.C.S.: 513130

McGraw-Hill (Germany) GmbH (1)

Opernturm Bockenheimer Landstrase 2-4, 60306, Frankfurt am Main, Germany
Tel.: (49) 69339990
Web Site: http://www.stglobal.com
Sales Range: $25-49.9 Million
Emp.: 120
Book Publishing & Media Service
N.A.I.C.S.: 513130

McGraw-Hill Book Publishing Company (1)
New Statesman House Stafferton Way, Maidenhead, SL6 1AD, Berks, United Kingdom (100%)
Tel.: (44) 1628502500
Web Site: http://www.mcgraw-hill.co.uk
Sales Range: $50-74.9 Million
Emp.: 150
Books & Educational Materials
N.A.I.C.S.: 513130

McGraw-Hill Finance (UK) Ltd. (1)
McGraw Hill Building, Canary Wharf, London, E14 5LH, United Kingdom
Tel.: (44) 2077167000
Book Retailer
N.A.I.C.S.: 459210

McGraw-Hill Financial Japan K.K. (1)
1-6-5 Marunouchi, Chiyoda City, Tokyo, 100-0005, Japan
Tel.: (81) 345508000
Financial Management Services
N.A.I.C.S.: 541611

McGraw-Hill Financial Singapore Pte. Limited (1)
12 Marina Boulevard 23-01 Marina Bay Financial Centre Tower 3, Singapore, 018982, Singapore
Tel.: (65) 306401
Financial Management Consulting Services
N.A.I.C.S.: 541611
Bang Wen Wu (Sr Mgr-Tax)

McGraw-Hill Indices U.K. Limited (1)
The Mcgraw-hill Companies 20 Canada Square Canary Wharf, London, E14 5LH, United Kingdom
Tel.: (44) 14365017150
Financial Management Consulting Services
N.A.I.C.S.: 541611

McGraw-Hill Interamericana do Brasil Ltda. (1)
Brigadeiro Faria Lima 201 Conj 181 E 182, Sao Paulo, 05426-100, Brazil
Tel.: (55) 1130399700
Web Site: http://www.spglobal.com
Sales Range: $25-49.9 Million
Emp.: 5
Book Retailer
N.A.I.C.S.: 513130

McGraw-Hill International (U.K.) Limited (1)
25 Ropemaker Street, London, EC2Y 9LY, United Kingdom
Tel.: (44) 2071763800
Web Site: http://www.mhfi.com
Emp.: 800
Books Publishing Services
N.A.I.C.S.: 513130

McGraw-Hill Korea, Inc (1)
3F Ji-Woo Building 376-12 Seokyo-Dong, Mapo-Ku, Seoul, 121-210, Korea (South)
Tel.: (82) 2 325 2351
Book Publishers
N.A.I.C.S.: 513130

McGraw-Hill Professional (1)
1325 Avenue of the Americas 7th Fl, New York, NY 10019
Tel.: (212) 904-2000
Web Site: https://www.mhprofessional.com
Sales Range: $75-99.9 Million
Emp.: 250
Publishing for Professionals
N.A.I.C.S.: 513130
Scott Grillo (VP & Grp Publr)
Lara Zoble (Sr Editor-Electrical & Electronics Engrg)

Christopher Brown *(Publr)*
Lauren Sapira *(Dir-Editorial-Access Engrg & Access Science)*
Elizabeth Houde *(Coord-Editorial)*
Bob O'Sullivan *(Assoc Publr)*
Diane Grayson *(Assoc Editor)*

McGraw-Hill/Interamericana de Chile Limitada (1)
Calle Evaristo Lillo 112 Piso 7, Las Condes, Santiago, Chile
Tel.: (56) 2 6613000
Book Publishers
N.A.I.C.S.: 513130

McGraw-Hill/Interamericana, S.A. (1)
Aquilino de la Guardia Calle 8 Edificio Igra, Panama, Panama
Tel.: (507) 2056000
Books Publishing Services
N.A.I.C.S.: 513130

Panjiva, Inc. (1)
55 Water St 42nd Fl, New York, NY 10041
Tel.: (646) 205-0594
Web Site: https://panjiva.com
Web Search Portal Operator
N.A.I.C.S.: 519290
Josh Green *(Co-Founder & CEO)*

Private Market Connect LLC (1)
3 Bala Plz W Ste 700, Bala Cynwyd, PA 19004
Tel.: (610) 340-3450
Web Site: http://www.privatemarketconnect.com
Investment Management Service
N.A.I.C.S.: 523940
Ed D'Onofrio *(CEO & Mng Dir)*
Jamie Krakow *(VP & Bus Mgr)*
Bob Havardansky *(Supvr-Reporting & Metrics)*
Matt Leonard *(Supvr-Data Capture)*
Vince Leventis *(Supvr-Data Entry & IT Projects)*
Kurtis Lerma *(Supvr-Transitions)*
Chris Moore *(Supvr-Controls & Transitions)*

S&P DJ Indices UK Ltd (1)
20 Canada Square, Canary Wharf, London, E14 5LH, United Kingdom
Tel.: (44) 2071768888
Investment Advisory Services
N.A.I.C.S.: 523940

S&P Global Commodities UK Limited (1)
Peek House 20 Eastcheap, London, EC3M 1EB, United Kingdom
Tel.: (44) 2076260600
Marketing Data Analysis Services
N.A.I.C.S.: 541910

S&P Global Germany GmbH (1)
Opernturm Bockenheimer Landstrase 2-4, 60306, Frankfurt, Germany
Tel.: (49) 69339990
Marketing Data Analysis Services
N.A.I.C.S.: 541910

S&P Global Italy S.r.l (1)
Vicolo San Giovanni Sul Muro 1, 20121, Milan, 20121, Italy
Tel.: (39) 03357428128
Marketing Data Analysis Services
N.A.I.C.S.: 541910

S&P Global Market Intelligence Inc. (1)
55 Water St, New York, NY 10041
Web Site: https://www.spglobal.com
Collects, Standardizes & Disseminates Relevant Corporate, Financial, Market & M&A Data for Various Industries
N.A.I.C.S.: 518210
Martina Cheung *(Pres)*
Ellen Boyle *(Chief Comml Officer)*
Warren Breakstone *(Chief Product Officer-Data Mgmt Solutions)*
Sarah Cottle *(Head-New & Res)*
Greg Gartland *(Chief Product Officer)*
Farhan Husain *(Head-Comm)*
Di Hirji *(Sr VP-People)*
Balaji Krishnamurthy *(CTO-Platform)*
Adam Marchuck *(Chief Legal Officer)*
Suvankar Mazumdar *(CTO)*
Whit McGraw *(Head-Credit Risk Solutions-Global)*
Jason Gibson *(CFO)*
Abhishek Tomar *(Chief Data Officer)*
Lauren Seay *(Editor-US Banking Coverage)*

S&P Global Market Intelligence Information Management Consulting (Beijing) Co., Ltd. (1)
Fortune Financial Centre 49th Floor 23 E 3rd Ring Rd N, Guomao Chaoyang District, Beijing, 100001, China
Tel.: (86) 1065692929
Financial Information Services
N.A.I.C.S.: 519290

S&P Global Ratings France SAS (1)
40 Rue De Courcelles, 75008, Paris, France
Tel.: (33) 144206650
Emp.: 50
Credit Rating Services
N.A.I.C.S.: 561450
Tracy Cook *(Editor-Digital Content)*

S&P Global Ratings Singapore Pte. Ltd. (1)
12 Marina Boulevard, Singapore, 018982, Singapore
Tel.: (65) 65306401
Credit Rating Services
N.A.I.C.S.: 561450

S&P Global Sweden AB (1)
Master Samuelsgatan 6, PO Box 1753, 111 44, Stockholm, 111 44, Sweden
Tel.: (46) 84405900
Credit Rating Services
N.A.I.C.S.: 561450

SAM Sustainable Asset Management AG (1)
Josefstrasse 218, Zurich, CH-8005, Switzerland (100%)
Tel.: (41) 446531010
Web Site: http://www.robecosam.com
Sustainable Investment, Asset Management & Private Equity Services
N.A.I.C.S.: 523940

SP Global Financial Iberia, S.L.U. (1)
Paseo De La Castellana 7, 28046, Madrid, Spain
Tel.: (34) 913896969
Credit Rating Services
N.A.I.C.S.: 561450

Standard & Poor's Financial Services LLC (1)
55 Water St, New York, NY 10041-0016
Tel.: (212) 438-2000
Web Site: http://www.standardandpoors.com
Sales Range: $1-4.9 Billion
Emp.: 7,500
Statistical Reports, Credit Ratings & Risk Solutions
N.A.I.C.S.: 541690

Subsidiary (Non-US):

CRISIL Ltd. (2)
Central Avenue Hiranandani Business Park, Powai, Mumbai, 400 076, India
Tel.: (91) 2233423000
Web Site: http://www.crisil.com
Sales Range: $10-24.9 Million
Business & Financial Services
N.A.I.C.S.: 561499
Ashu Suyash *(CEO & Mng Dir)*
Douglas L. Peterson *(Chm)*
Pawan Agarwal *(Chief Risk Officer)*
John L. Berisford *(Chm)*
Priti Arora *(Chief Strategy Officer & Head-Bus-Global Analytical Centre)*
Sanjay Chakravarti *(Pres & CFO)*
Dimitri Londos *(Co-Pres & Head-Bus-Global Risk & Analytics)*
Vivek Saxena *(Gen Counsel)*
Zak Murad *(Chief Tech & Information Officer)*
Ashish Vora *(Pres)*
Andre Cronje *(Pres)*
Jan Larsen *(Pres)*

Subsidiary (Non-US):

CRISIL Irevna Poland Sp. Z.o.o. (3)
Renaissance Business Centre Sw Mikolaja 7 6th floor, 50-125, Wroclaw, Poland
Tel.: (48) 713232660
Web Site: http://www.crisil.com
Emp.: 56
Book Publishers
N.A.I.C.S.: 513130

Gas Strategies Group Ltd (3)
10 St Bride Street, London, EC4A 4AD, United Kingdom
Tel.: (44) 2073329900
Web Site: https://www.gasstrategies.com
Business Services for Gas Industry
N.A.I.C.S.: 561499

Subsidiary (Domestic):

Gas Strategies Consulting Ltd. (4)
35 New Bridge St, London, EC4V 6BW, United Kingdom
Tel.: (44) 2073329900
Web Site: http://www.gas-strategies.com
Sales Range: $10-24.9 Million
Emp.: 50
Gas Information & Dissemination
N.A.I.C.S.: 519290
Chris Walters *(Dir-Consulting)*

Subsidiary (Domestic):

Global Data Services of India Limited (3)
1187/17crisil House Ghole Road, 411005, Pune, Maharashtra, India
Tel.: (91) 2025539064
Web Site: http://www.crisil.com
Sales Range: $10-24.9 Million
Emp.: 100
Research, Risk, Policy Advisory & Analytical Services
N.A.I.C.S.: 561499

Subsidiary (US):

Greenwich Associates LLC (3)
6 High Ridge Park, Stamford, CT 06905
Tel.: (203) 625-5038
Web Site: https://www.greenwich.com
Emp.: 400
Marketing Research Service
N.A.I.C.S.: 541910
Steven Busby *(CEO)*

Joint Venture (Domestic):

India Index Services and Products Limited (3)
Exchange Plaza C-1 Block G Bandra Kurla Complex Bandra East, Mumbai, 400051, India
Tel.: (91) 2226598386
Web Site: http://www.nseindia.com
Index-Related Services & Products; Owned 50% by National Stock Exchange of India Limited & 50% by CRISIL Ltd.
N.A.I.C.S.: 561499

Subsidiary (US):

Pipal Research Corporation (3)
601 Randolph W Ste 400, Chicago, IL 60661
Tel.: (312) 798-2100
Web Site: http://www.pipalresearch.com
Emp.: 203
Financial & Business Research Services
N.A.I.C.S.: 518210

Subsidiary (Domestic):

S&P Dow Jones Indices LLC (2)
55 Water St, New York, NY 10041
Tel.: (212) 438-2600
Web Site: https://www.spglobal.com
Investment Advisory Services
N.A.I.C.S.: 523940
Joe DePaolo *(Chief Legal Officer)*
Raj Varadarajan *(CTO)*
Dan Draper *(CEO)*
Gina Gavini *(COO)*

Division (Domestic):

S&P Global Platts (2)
55 Water St, New York, NY 10041
Tel.: (212) 438-1000
Web Site: http://www.platts.com
Commodity Markets Information Publishing & Benchmark Pricing Assessment Services
N.A.I.C.S.: 519290
Martin Fraenkel *(Pres)*
Sue Avinir *(COO)*
Jane Wood *(VP-People)*
Dave Ernsberger *(Head-Commodities Pricing-Global)*
Stan Guzik *(CTO)*

Silvina Aldeco-Martinez *(Chief Product Officer)*
Pierre Davis *(Chief Legal Officer)*
Martin Gijssel *(Chief Comml Officer)*
Saugata Saha *(CFO)*

Subsidiary (Domestic):

Petroleum Industry Research Associates, Inc. (3)
3 Park Ave 26th Fl, New York, NY 10016 (100%)
Tel.: (212) 686-6808
Web Site: http://www.pira.com
Sales Range: $1-9.9 Million
Emp.: 60
Energy Research Products
N.A.I.C.S.: 541715

Subsidiary (Non-US):

Capital IQ Information Systems (India) Pvt. Ltd. (4)
9th Floor Tower A DL Building 5 DLF Cyber City DLF Phase III, Gurgaon, 122002, India
Tel.: (91) 1246127000
Web Site: http://www.spcapitaliq.com
Financial Services
N.A.I.C.S.: 522320

Branch (Non-US):

Capital IQ, Inc. - Canada Branch (4)
130 King Street West Suite 1100, Toronto, M5X 1E5, ON, Canada
Tel.: (416) 507-2515
Software Whslr
N.A.I.C.S.: 423430

Subsidiary (Non-US):

Standard & Poor's (Australia) Pty Ltd. (2)
L 45 120 Collins St, Melbourne, 3000, VIC, Australia
Tel.: (61) 396312128
Web Site: https://www.spglobal.com
Book Publishers
N.A.I.C.S.: 513130

Standard & Poor's (Dubai) Limited (2)
Office No 209 Level 5, Gate Precinct Building 1, DIFC, PO Box 506650, Dubai, United Arab Emirates
Tel.: (971) 4 372 7100
Web Site: http://www.spglobal.com
Emp.: 54
General Financial Services
N.A.I.C.S.: 522320

Subsidiary (Domestic):

Standard & Poor's Compustat Services, Inc. (2)
7400 S Alton Ct Centennial, Englewood, CO 80112
Tel.: (303) 721-4551
Web Site: http://www.compustat.com
Sales Range: $400-449.9 Million
Emp.: 300
Financial Database Services
N.A.I.C.S.: 523940

Subsidiary (Non-US):

Standard & Poor's Credit Market Services Italy S.r.l. (2)
1 Vc San Giovanni Sul Muro, 20121, Milan, Italy
Tel.: (39) 02 72111
Web Site: http://www.standardandpoors.com
Emp.: 35
Book Publishers
N.A.I.C.S.: 513130

Standard & Poor's Maalot Ltd. (2)
12 Abba Hillel Silver St, Ramat Gan, 52506, Israel
Tel.: (972) 37539700
Web Site: http://www.maalotco.il
Emp.: 30
Financial Services
N.A.I.C.S.: 522320
Ronit Harel *(CEO)*

Standard & Poor's S.A. de C.V. (2)
1015 Torre A Piso 15 Edificio Punta Santa Fe Col Santa Fe, Mexico, 1376, Mexico
Tel.: (52) 5550814400

S&P Global Inc.—(Continued)

Web Site: http://www.standardandpoor.com
Sales Range: $25-49.9 Million
Emp.: 70
Financial Services
N.A.I.C.S.: 921130
Victor Herrera (Gen Dir)

Taiwan Ratings Corporation   (2)
2F No 167 Dunhua N Rd, Songshan Dist,
Taipei, 105, Taiwan
Tel.: (886) 221756800
Web Site: https://www.taiwanratings.com
Sales Range: $25-49.9 Million
Book Publishers
N.A.I.C.S.: 513130
Lih-Chung Chien (Chm)
Grace Lee (Pres & CEO)
Andy Chang (Sr Dir-Fin Svcs Ratings Dept)
Daniel Hsiao (Dir-Corp Ratings Dept)
Joe Lin (Dir-Structured Fin & Funds Ratings
Dept)
Simon Chen (Assoc Dir-Media & Digital
Content Dept)
Diana Kuo (Assoc Dir-Admin & Fin Dept)

**Standard & Poors Hong Kong
Limited**   (1)
Unit 6901 Level 69 Icc Kowloon, 1 Austin
Road West Kowloon, Hong Kong, China
(Hong Kong)
Tel.: (852) 6562396387
Credit Rating Services
N.A.I.C.S.: 561450

**Standard & Poors Singapore Pte.
Ltd.**   (1)
12 Marina Boulevard, 23-01 Marina Bay
Financial Centre Tower 3, Singapore,
018982, Singapore
Tel.: (65) 64382881
Credit Rating Services
N.A.I.C.S.: 561450
Ritesh Maheshwari (Mng Dir)

**The McGraw-Hill Companies,
S.r.l.**   (1)
Via Ripamonti 89, 20139, Milan, Italy
Tel.: (39) 025357181
Web Site: http://www.mcgraw-hill.it
Sales Range: $10-24.9 Million
Emp.: 40
Book Publishing
N.A.I.C.S.: 513130

The Steel Index Limited   (1)
20 Canada Square 12th Floor, Canary
Wharf, London, E14 5LH, United Kingdom
Tel.: (44) 2071767667
Web Site: http://www.thesteelindex.com
Price Providing Services
N.A.I.C.S.: 926150

Visallo, LLC   (1)
7900 Tysons 1 Pl Ste 270, McLean, VA
22102
Web Site: https://www.visallo.com
Software Development Services
N.A.I.C.S.: 513210

S&T BANCORP, INC.
800 Philadelphia St, Indiana, PA
15701
Tel.: (724) 465-0599   PA
Web Site: https://www.stbancorp.com
Year Founded: 1983
STBA—(NASDAQ)
Rev.: $399,010,000
Assets: $9,110,567,000
Liabilities: $7,925,908,000
Net Worth: $1,184,659,000
Earnings: $135,520,000
Emp.: 1,182
Fiscal Year-end: 12/31/22
Bank Holding Company
N.A.I.C.S.: 551111
David G. Antolik (Pres)
Mark Kochvar (CFO & Sr Exec VP)
Christopher J. McComish (CEO)
Melanie A. Lazzari (Exec VP & Con-
troller)
Mary Anne Dornetto (Chief Credit
Officer-Interim & Exec VP)
Steve Drahnak (Chief Comml Bank-
ing Officer)

Jim Michie (Chief Credit Officer)
Susan Nicholson (Chief HR Officer)
Rachel Smydo (Gen Counsel)
LaDawn Yesho (Chief Risk Officer)

Subsidiaries:

DNB Financial Corporation   (1)
4 Brandywine Ave, Downingtown, PA 19335
Tel.: (610) 269-1040
Web Site: http://www.dnbfirst.com
Rev.: $46,175,000
Assets: $1,158,235,000
Liabilities: $1,046,389,000
Net Worth: $111,846,000
Earnings: $10,684,000
Emp.: 156
Fiscal Year-end: 12/31/2018
Bank Holding Company
N.A.I.C.S.: 551111
Gerald F. Sopp (CFO, Sec & Exec VP)

S&T Bank   (1)
800 Philadelphia St, Indiana, PA 15701
Tel.: (724) 349-0599
Web Site: https://www.stbank.com
Sales Range: $200-249.9 Million
Commericial Banking
N.A.I.C.S.: 522110
David G. Antolik (Pres)
Mark Kochvar (CFO, Sr Exec VP & Mgr-Fin
Div)
Stephen A. Drahnak (Pres-Western PA &
Exec VP)
Christopher J. McComish (CEO)
Eric Huff (Dir-Asset-Based Lending)
Chad Carroll (Chief Admin Officer & Exec
VP)
Jonathan Costello (Exec VP-Bank Ops &
Mgr-Div)
Jordyn Kemats (Exec VP & Dir-Sls, Strat-
egy & Transition)
Kevin Doods (Chief Security Officer & Exec
VP)
Jim Michie (Exec VP)
Rachel Smydo (Exec VP)
Erik Taylor (Exec VP)
Meg Johnson (Exec VP)
Kristin Rombaugh (Exec VP)
Stephanie Kline (Exec VP)

Subsidiary (Domestic):

S&T Insurance Group, LLC   (2)
3135 New Germany Rd Ste 45, Ebensburg,
PA 15931   (100%)
Tel.: (814) 472-4711
Web Site: http://www.stbank.com
Holding Company; Insurance Products &
Services
N.A.I.C.S.: 551112

Subsidiary (Domestic):

S&T-Evergreen Insurance, LLC   (3)
416 S Ctr St Ste 2 And 3, Ebensburg, PA
15931
Tel.: (814) 472-7961
Web Site:
  https://www.evergreeninsurance.net
Emp.: 35
Insurance Products & Services
N.A.I.C.S.: 524298
Gregory C. Holsinger (Mgr-Personal Lines
& Acct Exec)
Michele A. Turner (Mgr-Comml Lines)
Aimee Altimore (Mgr-Comml Lines Acct
Svc)
Crystal G. Eckman (Mgr-Comml Lines Acct
Svc)
Nicole L. Killian (Mgr-Comml Lines Acct
Svc)

Subsidiary (Domestic):

Stewart Capital Advisors, LLC   (2)
800 Philadelphia St, Indiana, PA 15701
Tel.: (724) 465-3458
Web Site: https://www.stewartcap.com
Investment Advisory & Wealth Management
Services
N.A.I.C.S.: 523940
Malcolm E. Polley (Pres & Chief Investment
Officer)
David A. Finui (Sr VP & Sr Advisor-Wealth
Mgmt)
John Stoddart (VP)
Helena Rados-Derr (COO)

S&W SEED CO.
2101 Ken Pratt Blvd Ste 201, Long-
mont, CO 80501-6085
Tel.: (720) 506-9191   NV
Web Site: https://www.swseedco.com
Year Founded: 1980
SANW—(NASDAQ)
Rev.: $73,521,291
Assets: $151,989,828
Liabilities: $83,166,395
Net Worth: $68,823,433
Earnings: $14,410,078
Emp.: 134
Fiscal Year-end: 06/30/23
Alfalfa & Wheat Grower Farming
N.A.I.C.S.: 111140
Mark James Harvey (Bd of Dirs, Ex-
ecutives)
Dennis Charles Jury (Sr VP-Supply
Chain & Production-Intl)
Mark Herrmann (Pres & CEO)
Alan D. Willits (Chm)
David Thomas Callachor (Exec VP-
Intl)
Donald M. Panter (Exec VP-
Americas)
Steve Calhoun (VP-R&D)
Mike Eade (VP-Sls & Mktg-Americas)
Andrea McFarlane (Dir-HR-Global)
Elizabeth Horton (CFO & Sec)
Cameron Henley (Mng Dir)
Brent Johnson (VP)

Subsidiaries:

Chromatin, Inc.   (1)
10 S LaSalle St Ste 2100, Chicago, IL
60603
Tel.: (312) 292-5400
Web Site: http://www.chromatininc.com
Seed & Feedstock Products for Agriculture
& Bio-Industrial Processes
N.A.I.C.S.: 541715
Jeff Widder (Exec VP)
Anne Pansard (Gen Counsel)
Mike Battin (VP-Bus Dev & Sls-Natl)
Charles Miller (VP-Bus Dev & Intl Sls)
Larry McDowell (Dir-Field Ops)
Larry Lambright (Dir-Sorghum Breeding)
Scott Staggenborg (VP-R&D)
Troy Randolph (CFO)
Yale Peebles (VP-Strategy & Corp Dev)

Subsidiary (Domestic):

Production Seeds Plus, Inc.   (2)
800 E 6th St, Plainview, TX 79072
Tel.: (806) 293-3103
Web Site: http://www.proplusseed.com
Sales Range: $1-9.9 Million
Emp.: 48
Seed & Feedstock Products for Agriculture
& Bio-Industrial Processes
N.A.I.C.S.: 115114
Mark Leach (Mgr-Sls & Ops)
Gary Martin (Mgr-Sls & Production)

Pasture Genetics Pty Ltd   (1)
14-16 Hakkinen Road, Wingfield, Adelaide,
5013, SA, Australia
Tel.: (61) 884451111
Web Site: http://www.pasturegenetics.com
Seed Distr
N.A.I.C.S.: 424910
Ann Damin (Exec Dir)

**S&W Seed Company Australia Pty
Ltd**   (1)
Office 2 7 Pomona Road, PO Box 69,
Stirling, 5152, SA, Australia
Tel.: (61) 882716000
Web Site: http://www.sgiseeds.com
Emp.: 100
Seed Production Services
N.A.I.C.S.: 111140
Dennis Charles Jury (Gen Mgr)
Walter Van Leeuwen (Mgr-Sls & Mktg)
Shane Bradfield (Mgr-Logistics)
Michelle Lench (Mgr-Intl Shipping)
Peter Gibbs (Mgr-Production)
Andrew Carthew (Controller-Fin)

Seed Vision (Pty) Ltd.   (1)
PO Box 414, Krugersdorp, 1740, South
Africa

Tel.: (27) 728656813
Web Site: http://www.seedvision.co.za
Seed Farming Services
N.A.I.C.S.: 111199

**Sorghum Solutions South Africa (Pty)
Ltd.**   (1)
37 Eagle Street, Brackenfell, 7560, South
Africa
Tel.: (27) 873545604
Web Site: http://www.sorghumafrica.com
Seed Farming Services
N.A.I.C.S.: 111199

S.B.C.P. BANCORP, INC.
1205 Main St, Cross Plains, WI
53528
Tel.: (608) 798-3961   WI
Web Site: http://www.sbcp.bank
Year Founded: 1995
SBBI—(OTCIQ)
Rev.: $60,546,000
Assets: $1,322,875,000
Liabilities: $1,216,624,000
Net Worth: $106,251,000
Earnings: $9,673,000
Emp.: 235
Fiscal Year-end: 12/31/19
Bank Holding Company
N.A.I.C.S.: 551111
Charles L. Saeman (Chm & Pres)
James L. Tubbs (Pres/CEO-State
Bank of Cross Plains, Sec & Exec
VP)
Stephen J. Eager (Exec Dir)

Subsidiaries:

State Bank of Cross Plains   (1)
1205 Main St, Cross Plains, WI 53528
Tel.: (608) 798-3961
Web Site: http://www.sbcp.bank
Sales Range: $50-74.9 Million
Commericial Banking
N.A.I.C.S.: 522110
Charles L. Saeman (Chm)
Dan Savage (Sr VP-Fin)
James L. Tubbs (Pres & CEO)
Stephen J. Eager (Market Pres)
Suzanne M. Loken (CFO & Sr VP)
Kevin G. Piette (COO & Sr VP)
Scott P. Ducke (Chief Lending Officer &
Exec VP)
Paul Manchester (Chief Retail Officer & Sr
VP)

**S.H. RESOURCES & DEVEL-
OPMENT CORP.**
650 Williams Ln, Beverly Hills, CA
90210
Tel.: (310) 271-6215   UT
Year Founded: 1978
SDAD—(OTCIQ)
Real Estate Manangement Services
N.A.I.C.S.: 531390
Arie Ovadia (Pres)
Eli Schneidman (Sec & VP)

SAASMAX CORP.
7770 Regents Rd Ste 113-129, San
Diego, CA 92122   NV
Web Site: http://www.saasmax.com
SAAX—(OTCIQ)
Software Development Services
N.A.I.C.S.: 541511
Disa Moskowitz (Founder & CEO)
Clinton Gatewood (VP-Bus Dev &
Sls)
Richard Allen Hoke (Sr Dir & Partner-
Discovery)
Ted Finch (CMO & Partner-Portals)
Chris Gardner (Partner-Optimizer)

SAB BIOTHERAPEUTICS, INC.
2100 E 54th St N, Sioux Falls, SD
57104
Tel.: (605) 679-6980   DE
Web Site: https://www.sab.bio
Year Founded: 2020

SABS—(NASDAQ)
Rev.: $23,904,181
Assets: $50,904,927
Liabilities: $19,846,785
Net Worth: $31,058,142
Earnings: ($18,740,804)
Emp.: 56
Fiscal Year-end: 12/31/22
Investment Services
N.A.I.C.S.: 523999
Samuel J. Reich *(Chm & CEO)*
Eddie J. Sullivan Jr. *(Co-Founder, Pres & CEO)*
Lucy To *(CFO)*
Christoph Bausch *(COO & Exec VP)*
Alexandra Kropotova *(Chief Medical Officer & Exec VP)*
Edward Hamilton *(Co-Founder)*

SABINE ROYALTY TRUST

3838 Oak Lawn Ave Ste 1720, Dallas, TX 75219   TX
Web Site: https://www.sbr-sabine.com
Year Founded: 1982
SBR—(NYSE)
Rev.: $125,981,293
Assets: $16,282,983
Liabilities: $4,873,477
Net Worth: $11,409,506
Earnings: $122,693,873
Fiscal Year-end: 12/31/22
Venture Capital Services
N.A.I.C.S.: 523910

SABLE OFFSHORE CORP.

845 Texas Ave Ste 2900, Houston, TX 77002
Tel.: (713) 579-6106   DE
Web Site: https://sableoffshore.com
Year Founded: 2020
SOC—(NYSE)
Assets: $63,922,821
Liabilities: $55,985,970
Net Worth: $55,582,703
Earnings: ($32,180,557)
Emp.: 106
Fiscal Year-end: 12/31/23
Oil Operations
N.A.I.C.S.: 213112
Anthony Duenner *(Gen Counsel, Sec & Exec VP)*
Doss R. Bourgeois *(COO & Exec VP)*
James C. Flores *(Chm & CEO)*
Gregory D. Patrinely *(CFO & Exec VP)*
J. Caldwell Flores *(Pres)*

SABRA HEALTH CARE REIT, INC.

1781 Flight Way, Tustin, CA 92782
Tel.: (949) 679-0410   MD
Web Site:
https://www.sabrahealth.com
Year Founded: 2010
SBRA—(NASDAQ)
Rev.: $624,811,000
Assets: $5,747,672,000
Liabilities: $2,691,277,000
Net Worth: $3,056,395,000
Earnings: ($77,605,000)
Emp.: 42
Fiscal Year-end: 12/30/22
Other Financial Vehicles
N.A.I.C.S.: 525990
Brent P. Chappell *(Exec VP-Portfolio Mgmt)*
Richard K. Matros *(Chm, Pres & CEO)*
Peter W. Nyland *(Exec VP-Asset Mgmt)*
Brent P. Chappell *(Exec VP-Portfolio Mgmt)*
Michael Costa *(CFO, Sec & Exec VP)*
Darrin Smith *(Exec VP-Investments)*

Lukas Hartwich *(Sr VP)*
Talya Nevo-Hacohen *(Chief Investment Officer, Treas & Exec VP)*

Subsidiaries:

Healthtrust, L.L.C.   **(1)**
6801 Energy Ct Ste 200, Sarasota, FL 34240
Tel.: (941) 363-7500
Web Site: https://www.healthtrust.com
Health & Safety Certification Services
N.A.I.C.S.: 541611
Alan C. Plush *(CEO)*
Colleen Blumenthal *(COO)*
Ilya N. Gaev *(Partner-Boston)*
Samantha Medred *(Partner)*
Samantha Medred *(Partner)*
David Salinas *(Partner)*

SABRE CORPORATION

3150 Sabre Dr, Southlake, TX 76092
Tel.: (682) 605-1000   DE
Web Site: https://www.sabre.com
Year Founded: 2006
SABR—(NASDAQ)
Rev.: $2,537,015,000
Assets: $4,962,875,000
Liabilities: $5,835,702,000
Net Worth: ($872,827,000)
Earnings: ($435,448,000)
Emp.: 7,461
Fiscal Year-end: 12/31/22
Travel & Tourism Industry Software & Technical Support Services
N.A.I.C.S.: 541519
David J. Shirk *(Pres-Travel Solutions & Exec VP)*
David J. Shirk *(Pres-Travel Solutions & Exec VP)*
Kurt Joseph Ekert *(Pres & CEO)*
Jami B. Cordell Kindle *(Sr VP-Fin & Controlling)*
Joe DiFonzo *(CIO)*
Sundar Narasimhan *(Pres-Product Labs & Strategy & Sr VP)*
Shawn Williams *(Chief People Officer & Exec VP)*
Garry R. Wiseman *(Interim CTO, Chief Product Officer-Travel Solutions & Exec VP)*
Michael O. Randolfi *(CFO & Exec VP)*
Chadwick Ho *(Chief Legal Officer & Exec VP)*
Rochelle Boas *(Chief Legal Officer & Exec VP)*

Subsidiaries:

Airpas Aviation GmbH   **(1)**
Theodor-Heuss-Str 2, 38122, Braunschweig, Germany
Tel.: (49) 53188529100
Web Site: http://www.airpas.com
Software Services
N.A.I.C.S.: 541511
Brian Scott Evans *(Mng Dir, Treas & VP-Finance-Planning)*
David Jaqua *(Mng Dir & VP)*
Rene Koark *(COO)*
Sigurd Meyer-Hess *(Head-Customer Support)*
Immo Zech *(CIO)*
Klaus-Peter Warnke *(CEO)*
Philip Grindley *(CFO)*
Laszlo Keresztes *(CTO)*
Mike Charalambous *(Chief Compliance Officer)*

IHS GmbH   **(1)**
Hans-Bredow-Strasse 2, 71522, Backnang, Germany
Tel.: (49) 719134140
Web Site: https://www.ihs-gmbh.de
Industrial Equipment Mfr
N.A.I.C.S.: 333248

Sabre Asia Pacific Pte. Ltd.   **(1)**
1 Paya Lebar Link 05-05 Plq 2 Paya Lebar Quarter, Singapore, 408533, Singapore
Tel.: (65) 64260066
Travel Agency Services
N.A.I.C.S.: 561510

Frank Trampert *(Mng Dir & Chief Comml Officer)*
Anupam Bokil *(VP-Professional Svcs & Consulting-APAC)*

Sabre Austria GmbH   **(1)**
Wiedner Hauptstrasse 120-124/5 3, 1050, Vienna, Austria
Tel.: (43) 152522
Travel Agency Services
N.A.I.C.S.: 561510
Jonathan P. Ewbank *(Mng Dir)*
Zoran Savic *(Mng Dir)*
Christoph Berndt *(Mgr-Technical Application Support)*
Martin Kossiba *(Principal-Data Svcs)*

Sabre Belgium SA   **(1)**
Inter Access Park Pontbeekstraat 2/4 - Building 2 2nd Floor, 1702, Groot-Bijgaarden, Belgium
Tel.: (32) 24640500
Travel Agency Services
N.A.I.C.S.: 561510

Sabre Deutschland Marketing GmbH   **(1)**
Tauentzienstrasse 13, 10789, Berlin, Germany
Tel.: (49) 30408176990
Travel Agency Services
N.A.I.C.S.: 561510

Sabre Holdings Corporation   **(1)**
3150 Sabre Dr, Southlake, TX 76092   **(100%)**
Tel.: (682) 605-1000
Web Site: http://www.sabre.com
Holding Company
N.A.I.C.S.: 551112

Subsidiary (Domestic):

Radixx Solutions International, Inc.   **(2)**
20 N Orange Ave Ste 150, Orlando, FL 32801
Tel.: (407) 856-9009
Web Site: https://www.radixx.com
Airline Reservation System Provider
N.A.I.C.S.: 561599
Michael Barrera *(VP-Product Mgmt & Tech Strategy)*
Jamie Schulze *(VP-Strategic Bus Ops & Plng)*
Blair Hughes *(VP-Sls)*
Ludvik Olason *(VP-Software Engrg)*
Shankar Mishra *(VP-Product Mgmt & Innovation)*

Division (Domestic):

Sabre Airline Solutions   **(2)**
3150 Sabre Dr, Southlake, TX 76092
Tel.: (682) 605-1000
Web Site:
http://www.sabreairlinesolutions.com
Software Products, Passenger Solutions & Consulting Services for Airlines
N.A.I.C.S.: 488190
David J. Shirk *(Pres-Travel Solutions)*
David J. Shirk *(Pres-Travel Solutions)*

Subsidiary (Domestic):

Flightline Data Services, Inc.   **(3)**
138 Peachtree Ct, Fayetteville, GA 30215
Tel.: (770) 487-3482
Web Site: http://www.flightline.com
Airline Crew Member Schedule Management Solutions
N.A.I.C.S.: 518210

PRISM Group, Inc.   **(3)**
1380 Rio Rancho Blvd SE Ste 199, Rio Rancho, NM 87124
Tel.: (505) 897-7800
Web Site: http://www.prism-grp.com
Airline Corporate Customer Management Software & Services
N.A.I.C.S.: 513210

Subsidiary (Domestic):

Sabre Hospitality Solutions   **(2)**
3150 Sabre Dr, Southlake, TX 76092
Tel.: (682) 605-1000
Web Site: https://www.sabrehospitality.com
Hospitality Industry Software & Technical Support Services
N.A.I.C.S.: 541519

Frank Trampert *(Sr VP & Mng Dir-Global)*
Justin Ricketts *(Chief Product & Dev Officer & Sr VP)*
Scott Wilson *(Pres)*
Chris Boyle *(Sr VP)*
Gene Guhne *(Sr VP)*
Ashok Pinto *(Sr VP)*

Division (Domestic):

Sabre Travel Network   **(2)**
3150 Sabre Dr, Southlake, TX 76092
Tel.: (682) 605-1000
Web Site:
http://www.sabretravelnetwork.com
Sales Range: $1-4.9 Billion
Markets & Distributes Travel-Related Products & Services Through Travel Agency & Corporate Channels
N.A.I.C.S.: 561599
David J. Shirk *(Pres)*
Sean E. Menke *(CEO)*
Lawrence W. Kellner *(Chm)*
Roshan Mendis *(Chief Comml Officer & Exec VP)*
Abdul-razzaq Iyer *(VP-Middle East)*
Sean McDonald *(VP-Online Travel)*

Sabre Italia S.r.l.   **(1)**
Via Spina 9, Isola Vicentina, 36033, Rome, Vicenza, Italy
Tel.: (39) 044 497 7655
Web Site: https://www.sabreitalia.com
Industrial Equipment Whsr
N.A.I.C.S.: 423830

Sabre Marketing Nederland B.V.   **(1)**
Randstad 20-03, 1314 BA, Almere, Netherlands
Tel.: (31) 367999270
Travel Agency Services
N.A.I.C.S.: 561510
Angelique Lucas *(Office Mgr)*

Sabre Polska Sp. z o.o.   **(1)**
Ul Wadowicka 6D wejscie 9, 30-415, Krakow, Poland
Tel.: (48) 122967000
Travel Agency Services
N.A.I.C.S.: 561510
Sebastian Drzewiecki *(Mng Dir & VP-Global Dev Center)*

Sabre Seyahat Dagitim Sisternleri A.S.   **(1)**
19 Mayis Mah Buyukdere Cad Beytem Plaza No 20 K 11, Sisli, 34363, Istanbul, Turkiye
Tel.: (90) 2126660800
Travel Agency Services
N.A.I.C.S.: 561510

Sabre Sverige AB   **(1)**
Kungsgatan 15 6 tr, 111 43, Stockholm, Sweden
Tel.: (46) 850525944
Travel Agency Services
N.A.I.C.S.: 561510

Sabre Technology Holdings Pte. Ltd.   **(1)**
3015A Ubi Road 1 06-09, Singapore, 408705, Singapore
Tel.: (65) 62932003
Web Site: http://www.sabre.com.sg
Semiconductor Product Mfr
N.A.I.C.S.: 334413

Sabre Travel Network (Central Asia) LLP **(1)**
6th Floor 52 Abay Avenue, Almaty, 050008, Kazakhstan
Tel.: (7) 7273121717
Travel Agency Services
N.A.I.C.S.: 561510
Bakhtiyar Djalilov *(Mgr-IT Support Dept)*

Sabre Travel Network (Hong Kong) Limited **(1)**
Suites 10B-12 17th Floor Tower 3 33 Canton Road, Tsim Sha Tsui, Hong Kong, China (Hong Kong)
Tel.: (852) 29608888
Travel Agency Services
N.A.I.C.S.: 561510
Sam Tang *(Asst Mgr-Sls)*

Sabre Travel Network (Malaysia) Sdn. Bhd. **(1)**
Office Suite 02 Level 7 Ilham Tower No 8

Sabre Corporation—(Continued)

Jalan Binjai, 50450, Kuala Lumpur, Malaysia
Tel.: (60) 326034900
Travel Agency Services
N.A.I.C.S.: 561510
Rahim Abu Bakar (Acct Mgr)

Sabre Travel Network (Thailand) Ltd. (1)
No 2 Jasmine City Building 26 Floor Soi Prasarnmitr Sukhumvit 23, Sukhumvit Road Klongtoey-Nua Wattana, Bangkok, 10110, Thailand
Tel.: (66) 26841700
Travel Agency Services
N.A.I.C.S.: 561510

Sabre Travel Network Jordan LLC (1)
Esam Al Ajlouni Street Next to Marriott Hotel, Taib Commercial Building No66, 11192, Amman, Jordan
Tel.: (962) 65668777
Travel Agency Services
N.A.I.C.S.: 561510

Sabre Travel Network Middle East W.L.L. (1)
17th Floor Harbour Tower East Building No 1398 Road No 4626 Block 346, PO Box 3163, Manama, Bahrain
Tel.: (973) 17201000
Travel Agency Services
N.A.I.C.S.: 561510
Amira Abdulazim (Sr Mgr)

Sabre Travel Network Romania S.R.L. (1)
Plata Charles de Gaulle Nr 15 Cladirea Charles de Gaulle Plaza Etaj 3, Biroul 342Sectorul 1, Bucharest, Romania
Tel.: (40) 318604750
Travel Agency Services
N.A.I.C.S.: 561510

Sabre Ukraine LLC (1)
Street Turgenevskaya Building 15 Office 802, Kiev, Ukraine
Tel.: (380) 442388298
Software Services
N.A.I.C.S.: 541511
Sergii Kravets (Gen Mgr)
Yevgeniya Kirichek (Deputy Gen Mgr)

TVL Australia Pty Ltd (1)
Unit 8 137-145 Rooks Road, Nunawading, 3131, VIC, Australia
Tel.: (61) 398735610
Industrial Equipment Mfr
N.A.I.C.S.: 333248

SACHEM ACQUISITION CORP.
698 Main St, Branford, CT 06405
Tel.: (203) 433-4737   MD
Year Founded: 2021
SCEMU—(NYSE)
Investment Services
N.A.I.C.S.: 523999
John L. Villano (Chm, Pres, CEO, CFO, Treas & Sec)
Peter J. Cuozzo (Exec VP & COO)
William C. Haydon (Exec VP)

SACHEM CAPITAL CORP.
568 E Main St, Branford, CT 06405
Tel.: (203) 433-4736   NY
Web Site:
   https://www.sachemcapitalcorp.com
Year Founded: 2016
SACH—(NYSEAMEX)
Rev.: $52,276,025
Assets: $565,661,862
Liabilities: $347,954,508
Net Worth: $217,707,354
Earnings: $17,221,589
Emp.: 31
Fiscal Year-end: 12/31/22
Real Estate Investment Services
N.A.I.C.S.: 531210
John L. Villano (Chm, Pres, CEO, Interim CFO & Treas)
Peter Giannotti (Corp Counsel & Sec)

Nick Marcello (CFO & VP-Fin & Ops)
Eric O'Brien (Sr VP-Asset Mgmt)
Ralph Sylvester (VP-Asset Mgmt)

SACK LUNCH PRODUCTIONS INC.
569 N 300 W, Salt Lake City, UT 84103
Tel.: (801) 580-7172   NV
Web Site:
   http://sacklunchproductions.com
SAKL—(OTCIQ)
Investment Services
N.A.I.C.S.: 523999

SACKS PARENTE GOLF, INC.
551 Calle San Pablo, Camarillo, CA 93012   DE
Web Site:
   https://www.sacksparente.com
Year Founded: 2018
SPGC—(NASDAQ)
Emp.: 7
Sporting & Athletic Goods Manufacturing
N.A.I.C.S.: 339920
Tim Triplett (Founder & Pres)
Greg Campbell (Exec Chm)
Michael Ferris (Chief Strategy Officer)
Michael Keller (CFO)
Douglas W. Samuelson (CFO)

SADDLE RANCH MEDIA, INC.
19200 Von Karman Ave Ste 425, Irvine, CA 92612
Tel.: (949) 296-7501   UT
Year Founded: 1988
SRMX—(OTCIQ)
Entertainment Media Services
N.A.I.C.S.: 541840
Alan Bailey (CFO)
Max Chin Li (CEO)

SAFE & GREEN HOLDINGS CORP.
990 Biscayne Blvd, Miami, FL 33132
Tel.: (646) 240-4235   DE
Web Site:
   https://www.safeandgreenholdings.com
Year Founded: 1993
SGBX—(NASDAQ)
Rev.: $24,393,946
Assets: $26,555,680
Liabilities: $12,116,118
Net Worth: $14,439,562
Earnings: ($8,319,048)
Emp.: 85
Fiscal Year-end: 12/31/22
Holding Company; Modular Facilities Mfr
N.A.I.C.S.: 551112
Paul M. Galvin (Chm & CEO)
Stevan Armstrong (CTO)
William Rogers (COO)
James Henderson (Dir-Medical Bus Dev)
Patricia Kaelin (CFO)

Subsidiaries:

SG Residential, Inc. (1)
2247 Central Dr, Bedford, TX 76021
Web Site: https://www.sg-residential.com
Residential Remodeling Services
N.A.I.C.S.: 236118

Safe and Green Development Corporation (44.3%)
990 Biscayne Blvd Ste 501 Ofc 12, Miami, FL 33132
Tel.: (904) 496-0027
Web Site: https://www.sgdevco.com
Assets: $9,559,966
Liabilities: $7,672,189
Net Worth: $1,887,777
Earnings: ($4,200,541)
Emp.: 2
Fiscal Year-end: 12/31/2023

Residential Real Estate Investment & Development
N.A.I.C.S.: 531390
Paul M. Galvin (Chm)
David Villarreal (Pres & CEO)
Nicolai Brune (CFO)

SAFEGUARD SCIENTIFICS, INC.
150 N Radnor Chester Rd Ste F-200, Radnor, PA 19087
Tel.: (610) 293-0600   PA
Web Site: https://www.safeguard.com
Year Founded: 1953
SFE—(NASDAQ)
Rev.: $794,000
Assets: $37,692,000
Liabilities: $3,116,000
Net Worth: $34,576,000
Earnings: ($14,263,000)
Emp.: 26
Fiscal Year-end: 12/31/22
Holding Company; Investment Services Focused on Growth-Stage Life Sciences & Technology Businesses
N.A.I.C.S.: 551112
Joseph M. Manko Jr. (Chm)
G. Matthew Barnard (Gen Counsel & Sec)

Subsidiaries:

EnerTech Capital Partners (1) (100%)
One Tower Bridge 100 Front St Ste 1225 W, Conshohocken, PA 19428
Tel.: (416) 515-2759
Web Site: https://www.enertechcapital.com
Sales Range: $400-449.9 Million
Emp.: 8
Venture Capital Opportunities Investments
N.A.I.C.S.: 523940
Scott B. Ungerer (Founder & Mng Dir)
Wally Hunter (Mng Dir)
Jarett Carson (Mng Dir)
Dean Sciorillo (Mng Dir)
Gian Vergnetti (Principal)
Colleen Pale (Dir-Fin & Admin)

SCP Private Equity Partners (1)
7 Great Vly Pkwy Ste 190, Malvern, PA 19355
Tel.: (610) 995-2900
Web Site: https://www.scppartners.com
Sales Range: $75-99.9 Million
Emp.: 20
Invests in Post-Venture Stage & Growing Companies
N.A.I.C.S.: 523150
Winston J. Churchill Jr. (Mng Gen Partner)

SAFEHOLD INC.
1114 Avenue of the Americas 39th Fl, New York, NY 10036
Tel.: (212) 930-9400   MD
Web Site:
   https://www.safeholdinc.com
Year Founded: 1993
SAFE—(NYSE)
Rev.: $352,578,000
Assets: $6,548,314,000
Liabilities: $4,271,649,000
Net Worth: $2,276,665,000
Earnings: ($54,973,000)
Emp.: 86
Fiscal Year-end: 12/31/23
Commercial Real Estate Investment Services
N.A.I.C.S.: 531390
Jay S. Sugarman (Founder, Chm & CEO)
Elisha J. Blechner (Exec VP & Head-Portfolio Mgmt)
Timothy Doherty (Chief Investment Officer)
Douglas Heitner (Chief Legal Officer)
Garett Rosenblum (Chief Acctg Officer & Sr VP)
Kyle Curtin (Chief Admin Officer)
Brett Asnas (CFO)
Adam Cohen (Sr VP-Tax)

Ash Jogi (Sr VP & Head-Bus Solutions)
Carrie Brown (Sr VP-CRE Transaction Svcs)
Lori Schwartz (Head-Risk Mgmt)
Troy Stephan (Sr VP & Dir-Real Estate Technical Svcs)
Geoffrey Dugan (Gen Counsel)
Nicole McCarthy (Sr VP)
Pearse Hoffmann (Sr VP)
Steve Wylder (Exec VP & Head-Investments)

Subsidiaries:

ASTAR Pima RoadScottsdale LLC (1)
8745 E Mcdowell Rd, Scottsdale, AZ 85257
Tel.: (678) 297-0100
Emp.: 99
Real Estate Services
N.A.I.C.S.: 531210

Asbury Partners, LLC (1)
1100 Ocean Ave, Asbury Park, NJ 07712
Tel.: (732) 774-1143
Real Estate Services
N.A.I.C.S.: 531210
Jeffrey Dewey (VP)

Avenida Naperville Partners LLC (1)
504 Commons Rd, Naperville, IL 60563
Tel.: (331) 213-2808
Web Site: http://www.avenidapartners.com
Apartment Building Construction Services
N.A.I.C.S.: 236116
Michael Murphy (Project Mgr)
Michele Clemen (Exec Dir)
Kathy Fezzuoglio (Dir-Sls & Mktg)
Tom Vander Velde (Dir-Sls & Mktg)
Jane Abe (Dir-Residential Enrichment)
Alan Reyes (Dir-Maintenance)
Hyacinth Waranimman (Dir-Bus Office)
Carrie Tuma (Coord-Move In)

Jade Eight Properties LLC (1)
737 Bishop St Ste 2800, Honolulu, HI 96813
Tel.: (808) 548-0686
Emp.: 3
Nonresidential Property Management Services
N.A.I.C.S.: 531312

Magnolia Green Development Partners LLC (1)
17301 Memorial Tournament Dr, Moseley, VA 23120
Tel.: (804) 818-6900
Web Site: http://www.magnoliagreen.com
Real Estate Services
N.A.I.C.S.: 531390

SFI Waipouli LLC (1)
1114 Avenue of the Americas 39th Fl, New York, NY 10036
Tel.: (949) 567-2412
Real Estate Services
N.A.I.C.S.: 531210

iStar Apartment Holdings LLC (1)
1114 Avenue of the Americas, New York, NY 10036
Tel.: (212) 930-9406
Holding Company
N.A.I.C.S.: 551112

iStar Asset Services, Inc. (1)
180 Glastonbury Blvd Ste 201, Glastonbury, CT 06033
Tel.: (860) 815-5900
Real Estate Services
N.A.I.C.S.: 531210
Mark Paparella (Mgr-Comml Loan Servicing)

iStar Marlin LLC (1)
1114 Ave of the Americas 39th Fl, New York, NY 10036
Tel.: (212) 930-9400
Real Estate Services
N.A.I.C.S.: 531210

SAFETY INSURANCE GROUP, INC.
20 Custom House St, Boston, MA 02110

Tel.: (617) 951-0600   DE
Web Site:
   https://www.safetyinsurance.com
Year Founded: 1979
SAFT—(NASDAQ)
Rev.: $797,559,000
Assets: $1,972,569,000
Liabilities: $1,160,570,000
Net Worth: $811,999,000
Earnings: $46,561,000
Emp.: 538
Fiscal Year-end: 12/31/22
Automobile, Homeowner & Umbrella Insurance
N.A.I.C.S.: 524126
George M. Murphy *(Chm, Pres & CEO)*
Stephen A. Varga *(VP-Mgmt Information Sys)*
Paul J. Narciso *(VP-Claims)*
John P. Drago *(VP-Mktg)*
Christopher T. Whitford *(CFO, Chief Acctg Officer, Sec & VP)*
Glenn R. Hiltpold *(VP-Actuarial Svcs)*

Subsidiaries:

Safety Insurance Co., Inc.   (1)
20 Custom House St, Boston, MA 02110-3513
Tel.: (617) 951-0600
Web Site: http://www.safetyinsurance.com
Auto & Home Insurance
N.A.I.C.S.: 524126

SAFETY SHOT, INC.
1061 E Indiantown Rd Ste 110, Jupiter, FL 33477
Tel.: (561) 244-7100   DE
Web Site:
   https://safetyshotofficial.com
Year Founded: 2018
SHOT—(NASDAQ)
Rev.: $6,196,743
Assets: $8,690,763
Liabilities: $5,025,169
Net Worth: $3,665,594
Earnings: ($15,223,028)
Emp.: 10
Fiscal Year-end: 12/31/22
Pharmaceutical Product Mfr & Distr
N.A.I.C.S.: 325412
Jordan Schur *(Pres)*
Jarrett A. Boon *(CEO)*
Brian S. John *(Founder)*
Danielle De Rosa-Diaz *(CFO)*
David Sandler *(COO)*
Josh Wagner *(Chief Revenue Officer)*

SAGA COMMUNICATIONS, INC.
73 Kercheval Ave, Grosse Pointe Farms, MI 48236
Tel.: (313) 886-7070   DE
Web Site: https://www.sagacom.com
SGA—(NASDAQ)
Rev.: $114,893,000
Assets: $240,753,000
Liabilities: $62,224,000
Net Worth: $178,529,000
Earnings: $9,202,000
Emp.: 585
Fiscal Year-end: 12/31/22
Broadcast Company; Developer & Operator of Radio & Television Stations
N.A.I.C.S.: 516210
Samuel D. Bush *(CFO, Treas & Sr VP)*
Catherine A. Bobinski *(Chief Acctg Officer, Sr VP-Fin & Controller)*
Christopher S. Forgy *(Pres & CEO)*
Tom Atkins *(VP-Engrg)*
Tracy Cleeton *(Chief Technical Officer)*
Angela Parks *(VP-Design & Facilities)*
Wayne Leland *(Sr VP-Ops)*
Annette Calcaterra *(VP)*

Subsidiaries:

Franklin Communications, Inc.   (1)
4401 Carriage Hill Ln, Columbus, OH 43220
Tel.: (614) 451-2191
Web Site:
   https://www.columbusradiogroup.com
Emp.: 100
Radio Broadcasting Services
N.A.I.C.S.: 516210
Erik Schmidt *(VP & Gen Mgr)*
Michelle Matthews *(Mgr-Ops & Brand)*
Ross Wagner *(Gen Sls Mgr)*

M. Belmont Ver Standig, Inc.   (1)
1820 Heritage Ctr Way, Harrisonburg, VA 22801
Tel.: (540) 434-0331
Web Site: http://harrisonburgradiogroup.com
Radio Broadcasting Stations
N.A.I.C.S.: 516110

Saga Broadcasting Corporation   (1)
73 Kercheval Ave Ste 201, Grosse Pointe Farms, MI 48236
Tel.: (313) 886-7070
Web Site: http://sagacom.com
Sales Range: $400-449.9 Million
Television Broadcasting
N.A.I.C.S.: 516120

Saga Communications of Iowa   (1)
1416 Locust St, Des Moines, IA 50309
Tel.: (515) 280-1350
Web Site: https://www.dsmradio.com
Sales Range: $10-24.9 Million
Emp.: 50
Television Broadcasting
N.A.I.C.S.: 516120

Saga Communications of South Dakota, LLC   (1)
501 S Ohlman St, Mitchell, SD 57301
Tel.: (605) 996-9667
Web Site: https://www.kmit.com
Sales Range: $10-24.9 Million
Emp.: 20
Radio Broadcasting Services
N.A.I.C.S.: 516210
Steve Morgan *(Program Dir)*
Matt Spaulding *(Dir-Sales)*

Saga Communications, Inc. - Columbus Radio Group   (1)
4401 Carriage Hill Ln, Columbus, OH 43220
Tel.: (614) 451-2191
Web Site: https://columbusradiogroup.com
Emp.: 50
Radio Broadcasting Stations
N.A.I.C.S.: 516110

Saga Radio Networks, LLC   (1)
100 N 6th St Ste 476A, Minneapolis, MN 55403
Tel.: (612) 321-7200
Web Site:
   http://www.minnesotanewsnetwork.com
Sales Range: $1-9.9 Million
Emp.: 17
Radio Broadcasting Stations
N.A.I.C.S.: 516110

Tidewater Communications, LLC   (1)
870 Greenbrier Cir Ste 399, Chesapeake, VA 23320
Tel.: (757) 366-9900
Sales Range: $200-249.9 Million
Emp.: 10
Radio Broadcasting
N.A.I.C.S.: 516210
Wayne Leland *(Gen Mgr)*
Carol Commander *(Dir-Sls)*
Mike Beck *(Mgr-Ops)*
Sonja Morrell *(Dir-Mktg)*

SAGALIAM ACQUISITION CORP.
1800 Avenue of the Stars Ste 1475, Los Angeles, CA 90067
Tel.: (213) 616-0011   DE
Year Founded: 2021
SAGA—(NASDAQ)
Investment Services
N.A.I.C.S.: 523999
Barry M. Kostiner *(CEO)*
Jane Liu *(VP-Bus Dev)*
Gabriel Del Virginia *(Sec)*

SAGE THERAPEUTICS, INC.
55 Cambridge Pkwy, Cambridge, MA 02142
Tel.: (617) 299-8380   DE
Web Site: https://www.sagerx.com
Year Founded: 2010
SAGE—(NASDAQ)
Rev.: $86,455,000
Assets: $882,277,000
Liabilities: $82,747,000
Net Worth: $799,530,000
Earnings: ($541,489,000)
Emp.: 487
Fiscal Year-end: 12/31/23
Pharmaceuticals Mfr
N.A.I.C.S.: 325412
Barry E. Greene *(CEO)*
Vanessa Procter *(Sr VP-External Affairs)*
Mark Pollack *(Sr VP-Global Medical Affairs)*
Kimi E. Iguchi *(CFO)*
Matt Lasmanis *(CTO & Chief Innovation Officer)*
Laura Gault *(Chief Medical Officer)*
Heinrich Schlieker *(Sr VP-Technical Ops)*
Mike Quirk *(Chief Scientific Officer & Sr VP)*
Pamela Herbster *(VP & Head-People)*
Steven M. Paul *(Co-Founder)*
Anne Marie Cook *(Gen Counsel & Sr VP)*
Anne Marie Cook *(Gen Counsel & Sr VP)*

SAGIMET BIOSCIENCES INC.
155 Bovet Rd Ste 303, San Mateo, CA 94402
Tel.: (650) 561-8600   DE
Web Site: https://www.sagimet.com
Year Founded: 2006
SGMT—(NASDAQ)
Rev.: $30,000
Assets: $68,959,000
Liabilities: $204,869,000
Net Worth: ($135,910,000)
Earnings: ($11,370,000)
Emp.: 6
Fiscal Year-end: 12/31/20
Biotechnology Research & Development Services
N.A.I.C.S.: 541714
David Happel *(Pres & CEO)*
George Kemble *(Exec Chm)*
Beth Seidenberg *(Chm)*
Thierry Chauche *(CFO, Principal Financial Officer & Principal Acctg Officer)*
Elizabeth Rozek *(Chief Compliance Officer & Gen Counsel)*
David Happel *(CEO)*
George Kemble *(Chm)*
Marie O'Farrell *(Sr VP-Research & Development & VP-R&D)*
Robert D'Urso *(Sr VP-New Products)*
Eduardo Bruno Martins *(Chief Medical Officer)*

SAIA, INC.
11465 Johns Creek Pkwy Ste 400, Johns Creek, GA 30097
Tel.: (770) 232-5067   DE
Web Site: https://www.saia.com
SAIA—(NASDAQ)
Rev.: $2,881,433,000
Assets: $2,583,565,000
Liabilities: $642,071,000
Net Worth: $1,941,494,000
Earnings: $354,857,000
Emp.: 14,000
Fiscal Year-end: 12/31/23
Truck Transportation
N.A.I.C.S.: 484121
Raymond R. Ramu *(Chief Customer Officer & Exec VP)*

Frederick J. Holzgrefe III *(Pres & CEO)*
Patrick D. Sugar *(Exec VP-Ops)*
Anthony Norwood *(Chief HR Officer & Exec VP)*
Kelly W. Benton *(Principal Acctg Officer)*
Rohit Lal *(CIO & Exec VP)*

Subsidiaries:

Linkex, Inc.   (1)
1621 Hutton Dr Ste 140, Dallas, TX 75006
Tel.: (972) 481-9900
Web Site: https://linkex.us
Freight Transportation Arrangement
N.A.I.C.S.: 488510

Saia Logistics Services, LLC   (1)
11465 Johns Creek Pkwy Ste 400, Johns Creek, GA 30097
Tel.: (770) 662-5008
Web Site: http://www.saialogistics.com
Administrative & General Management Consulting Services
N.A.I.C.S.: 541611

Saia Motor Freight Line, Inc.   (1)
11465 Johns Creek Pkwy Ste 400, Johns Creek, GA 30097
Tel.: (770) 232-5067
Web Site: http://www.saia.com
Sales Range: $450-499.9 Million
Emp.: 5,100
Regional Trucking Services
N.A.I.C.S.: 484121

Branch (Domestic):

Saia Motor Freight Line, Inc.   (2)
812 Blimp Rd, Houma, LA 70363
Tel.: (985) 851-2316
Web Site: http://www.saia.com
Sales Range: $100-124.9 Million
Emp.: 270
Regional Trucking Services
N.A.I.C.S.: 484121

Saia Motor Freight Line, Inc.   (2)
4423 S 67th St, Omaha, NE 68117
Tel.: (402) 592-7110
Web Site: http://www.saia.com
Sales Range: $1-9.9 Million
Emp.: 334
Trucking Service
N.A.I.C.S.: 484121

Saia Motor Freight Line, Inc.   (2)
900 Uniek Dr, Waunakee, WI 53597
Tel.: (608) 849-6371
Web Site: http://www.saia.com
Sales Range: $10-24.9 Million
Emp.: 200
Trucking Service
N.A.I.C.S.: 484121

Saia TL Plus   (1)
11465 Johns Creek Pkwy Ste 300, Johns Creek, GA 30097
Tel.: (770) 662-5008
Web Site: https://www.saialogistics.com
Sales Range: $10-24.9 Million
Emp.: 52
Freight Trucking Services
N.A.I.C.S.: 484121

SAKER AVIATION SERVICES, INC.
20 S St Pier 6 E River, New York, NY 10004
Tel.: (212) 776-4046   NV
Web Site:
   https://www.sakeraviation.com
SKAS—(OTCQB)
Rev.: $7,598,597
Assets: $6,912,925
Liabilities: $1,130,400
Net Worth: $5,782,525
Earnings: $1,246,621
Emp.: 12
Fiscal Year-end: 12/31/22
Aviation Services, Including Fueling, Hangaring & Aircraft Maintenance
N.A.I.C.S.: 488190
Judy B. Smulowitz *(Mgr-HR)*
Samuel D. Goldstein *(Acting Principal Exec Officer)*
Brian Tolbert Sr. *(Mgr-FBO Heliport)*

Saker Aviation Services, Inc.—(Continued)

Subsidiaries:

Phoenix Rising Aviation Inc. (1)
406 NW Wiley Post Hangr 6, Bartlesville, OK 74003
Tel.: (918) 337-0200
Web Site: https://www.praviation.com
Sales Range: $25-49.9 Million
Emp.: 25
Airport Operations
N.A.I.C.S.: 488119
Warren A. Peck (Co-Founder, Owner & Pres)
John Thompson (Mgr-Shop)
Pam Peck (Mgr-Accounts)

SALARIUS PHARMACEUTI-CALS, INC.
2450 Holcombe Blvd Ste X, Houston, TX 77021
Tel.: (832) 834-9144   DE
Web Site:
   https://www.salariuspharma.com
Year Founded: 2014
SLRX—(NASDAQ)
Rev.: $218,730
Assets: $14,650,799
Liabilities: $4,266,191
Net Worth: $10,384,608
Earnings: ($31,607,956)
Emp.: 12
Fiscal Year-end: 12/31/22
Biopharmaceutical Researcher, Developer & Mfr
N.A.I.C.S.: 325412
William K. McVicar (Chm)
Bruce J. McCreedy (Chief Scientific Officer-Interim)
Rebecca Griffith-Eskew (VP-Clinical Dev & Ops)
David J. Arthur (Pres, Pres, CEO & CEO)
Mark J. Rosenblum (CFO)
Nadeem Q. Mirza (Sr VP-Clinical Dev)

SALEM MEDIA GROUP, INC.
6400 N Belt Line Rd Ste 200, Irving, TX 75063
Tel.: (972) 831-1920   DE
Web Site:
   https://www.salemmedia.com
SALM—(NASDAQ)
Rev.: $266,966,000
Assets: $505,122,000
Liabilities: $329,765,000
Net Worth: $175,357,000
Earnings: ($3,236,000)
Emp.: 1,147
Fiscal Year-end: 12/31/22
Broadcasting Services
N.A.I.C.S.: 516110
Edward G. Atsinger III (Exec Chm)
David A. R. Evans (COO)
Evan D. Masyr (CFO & Exec VP)
David P. Santrella (CEO)
Edward C. Atsinger Jr. (Executives, Bd of Dirs)
Christopher J. Henderson (Gen Counsel, Sec & Exec VP-Legal & HR)
Allen Power (Pres-Brdcst Media)
David Howard (Gen Mgr-Washington DC)
Chuck Olmstead (Mgr-WAVA-AM & FM & Sirius XM Family Talk)
Andy Massingill (Sr Dir-Digital Sls)
Chris Gould (Sr VP-Natl Programming & Ministry Rels)
Dan Nelson (VP-Salem Events & Mktg)
Carolyn Cassidy (Gen Mgr-Salem Surround-Tampa & Sarasota)
Val Carolin (Reg VP)

Subsidiaries:

KFAX San Francisco (1)

39650 Liberty St Ste 340, Fremont, CA 94538
Tel.: (510) 897-1879
Web Site: https://www.kfax.com
Rev.: $5,200,000
Emp.: 22
Radio Broadcasting Stations
N.A.I.C.S.: 516110
Edward G. Atsinger III (Pres & CEO)

KPRZ 1210AM Radio Inc (1)
9255 Towne Centre Dr Ste 535, San Diego, CA 92121
Tel.: (858) 535-1210
Web Site: https://www.kprz.com
Rev.: $2,300,000
Emp.: 25
Christian Talk Radio Broadcasting
N.A.I.C.S.: 516110

New Inspiration Broadcasting Co. Inc. (1)
500 E Esplanade Dr Ste 1500, Oxnard, CA 93036
Tel.: (805) 288-3872
Web Site: http://983fmtheword.com
Sales Range: $200-249.9 Million
Radio Broadcasting Stations
N.A.I.C.S.: 516110

One Place Llc (1)
3759 Georgetown Rd NW, Cleveland, TN 37312
Tel.: (423) 614-5006
Web Site: http://www.oneplace.com
Rev.: $2,800,000
Emp.: 40
Computer Graphics Service
N.A.I.C.S.: 516110

Oneplace Llc (1)
9401 Courthouse Rd Ste 307, Chesterfield, VA 23832
Tel.: (804) 768-9404
Web Site: http://www.oneplace.com
Sales Range: $10-24.9 Million
Emp.: 15
Religious Website
N.A.I.C.S.: 513199

Pennsylvania Media Associates (1)
4880 Santa Rosa Rd Ste 300, Camarillo, CA 93012
Tel.: (805) 384-4502
Web Site: http://www.srnonline.com
Rev.: $1,700,000
Emp.: 30
Radio Broadcasting Stations
N.A.I.C.S.: 516110
Edward G. Atsinger III (Pres)

Radio 780 Inc (1)
1901 N Moore St 200, Arlington, VA 22209
Tel.: (703) 534-2000
Web Site: http://www.wavaam.com
Rev.: $740,000
Emp.: 40
Radio Broadcasting Stations
N.A.I.C.S.: 516110

Reach Satellite Network Inc. (1)
402 BNA Dr Ste 400, Nashville, TN 37217
Tel.: (615) 367-2210
Web Site:
   http://www.salemmusicnetwork.com
Sales Range: Less than $1 Million
Emp.: 40
Radio Broadcasting Stations
N.A.I.C.S.: 516110
Edward G. Atsinger III (Pres)

SRN News (1)
1901 N Moore St Ste 201, Arlington, VA 22209
Tel.: (703) 528-6213
Web Site: http://www.srnnews.com
Rev.: $420,000
Emp.: 15
Radio Broadcasting Stations
N.A.I.C.S.: 516110

Salem Communications Holding Corporation (1)
4880 Santa Rosa Rd, Camarillo, CA 93012
Tel.: (805) 987-0400
Sales Range: $25-49.9 Million
Emp.: 100
Radio Communication Services
N.A.I.C.S.: 517112
Edward G. Atsinger III (CEO)

Salem Communications Tampa/Sarasota (1)
5211 W Laurel St Ste A, Tampa, FL 33607
Tel.: (813) 639-1903
Web Site: http://www.salemtampa.com
Emp.: 25
Radio Stations
N.A.I.C.S.: 516110

Salem Media of Colorado, Inc. (1)
3131 S Vaughn Way, Aurora, CO 80014-3511
Tel.: (303) 750-5687
Web Site: http://www.710knus.com
Sales Range: $10-24.9 Million
Emp.: 30
Radio Broadcasting Services
N.A.I.C.S.: 516110
Brian Taylor (VP & Gen Mgr)
Kelly Michaels (Dir-Ops)
Rebecca Gibbs (Office Mgr)

Salem Media of Hawaii, Inc. (1)
1160 N King St Fl 2nd, Honolulu, HI 96817
Tel.: (808) 533-0065
Web Site: http://www.salem.cc
Sales Range: $10-24.9 Million
Emp.: 30
Radio Broadcasting Services
N.A.I.C.S.: 516110

Salem Media of Massachusetts, LLC (1)
26501 Renaissance Pkwy, Cleveland, OH 44128
Tel.: (216) 901-0921
Broadcasting Services
N.A.I.C.S.: 516110

Salem Media of Oregon, Inc. (1)
6400 SE Lk Rd Ste 350, Portland, OR 97222
Tel.: (503) 652-8172
Web Site: http://www.1041thefish.com
Sales Range: $1-9.9 Million
Emp.: 45
Radio Broadcasting Stations
N.A.I.C.S.: 516110

Salem Media of Pennsylvania (1)
7 Pkwy Ctr Ste 625, Pittsburgh, PA 15220-3707
Tel.: (412) 937-1958
Web Site: https://www.wordfm.com
Rev.: $2,500,000
Emp.: 40
Radio Broadcasting Stations
N.A.I.C.S.: 516110
Gary Dickson (Dir-Program)
Mike Howard (Gen Mgr-Sls)

Salem Media of Texas, Inc. (1)
4880 Santa Rosa Rd, Camarillo, CA 93012
Tel.: (805) 233-3235
Web Site: http://www.salemmedia.com
Sales Range: $25-49.9 Million
Emp.: 100
Radio Broadcasting Services
N.A.I.C.S.: 516110

Salem Music Networks Inc (1)
402 BNA Dr Ste 400, Nashville, TN 37217
Tel.: (615) 367-2210
Web Site: https://salemmusicnetwork.com
Rev.: $1,000,000
Emp.: 30
Contemporary
N.A.I.C.S.: 516110
Stuart W. Epperson Sr. (Chm)

Salem Publishing, Inc. (1)
402 BNA Dr Ste 400, Nashville, TN 37217
Tel.: (615) 386-3011
Web Site: http://www.salempublishing.com
Magazine Publisher
N.A.I.C.S.: 513120

Salem Radio Network Incorporated (1)
6400 N Belt Line Rd Ste 210, Irving, TX 75063
Tel.: (972) 707-6885
Web Site: https://www.srnonline.com
Radio Broadcasting Stations
N.A.I.C.S.: 516210

Salem Radio Representatives (1)
6400 N Belt Ln Rd, Irving, TX 75063
Tel.: (972) 402-8800
Web Site: http://www.srnonline.com

Sales Range: $10-24.9 Million
Emp.: 20
Radio Broadcasting Stations
N.A.I.C.S.: 516110

Salem Web Network, LLC (1)
111 Virginia St Ste 500, Richmond, VA 23219
Tel.: (804) 205-9700
Web Site: http://www.salemwebnetwork.com
Sales Range: $25-49.9 Million
Emp.: 120
Online Advertising Services
N.A.I.C.S.: 541890

South Texas Broadcasting, Inc. (1)
6161 Savoy Dr STE 1200, Houston, TX 77036-3363
Tel.: (713) 260-6137
Web Site: https://www.kkht.com
Sales Range: $10-24.9 Million
Emp.: 25
Radio Broadcasting Services
N.A.I.C.S.: 516110
Chuck Jewell (Gen Mgr)

SALESFORCE, INC.
415 Mission St 3rd Fl, San Francisco, CA 94105
Tel.: (415) 901-7000   DE
Web Site:
   https://www.salesforce.com
Year Founded: 1999
CRM—(NYSE)
Rev.: $34,857,000,000
Assets: $99,823,000,000
Liabilities: $40,177,000,000
Net Worth: $59,646,000,000
Earnings: $4,136,000,000
Emp.: 72,682
Fiscal Year-end: 01/31/24
Software Development Services
N.A.I.C.S.: 551112
Marc Russell Benioff (Co-Founder, Chm & CEO)
Stephen Fisher (Exec VP & Gen Mgr-Next Gen CRM & Unified Data Services)
Brian Millham (COO)
Parker Harris (CTO)
Clara Shih (CEO/Gen Mgr-Service Cloud)
Juan R. Perez (CIO)
Shaka Rasheed (Sr VP-Strategic Banking & Wealth Management)
Juan Perez (CIO)

Subsidiaries:

ATKA US, LLC (1)
723 Western Ave Ste 1, Holmen, WI 54636
Tel.: (608) 526-2178
Software Publishing Services
N.A.I.C.S.: 513210

Buddy Media, Inc. (1)
155 6th Ave 12th Fl, New York, NY 10013
Tel.: (212) 634-1494
Web Site:
   http://www.salesforcemarketingcloud.com
Sales Range: $50-74.9 Million
Emp.: 300
Social Marketing Software
N.A.I.C.S.: 513210

ClickSoftware Technologies Ltd. (1)
Azorim Park Oren Building 94 Em-Hamoshavot Road, Petah Tiqwa, 49527, Israel
Tel.: (972) 3 7659 400
Web Site: http://www.clicksoftware.com
Sales Range: $125-149.9 Million
Workforce & Service Management Software Products & Services
N.A.I.C.S.: 513210
Mark Cattini (CEO)

Subsidiary (Non-US):

ClickSoftware Australia Pty Limited (2)
Level 12 277 William Street, Melbourne, 3000, VIC, Australia
Tel.: (61) 399466400
Web Site: http://www.clicksoftware.com

Workforce & Service Management Software
Products & Services
N.A.I.C.S.: 513210

**ClickSoftware Central Europe
GmbH** (2)
HanauerLandstrasse 293 A, 60314, Frankfurt am Main, Germany
Tel.: (49) 69 48981300
Web Site: http://www.clicksoftware.com
Workforce & Service Management Software
Products & Services
N.A.I.C.S.: 513210

ClickSoftware Europe Limited (2)
The Priory Stomp Road, Burnham,
SL17LW, Bucks, United Kingdom
Tel.: (44) 1628 60 7000
Web Site: http://www.clicksoftware.com
Workforce & Service Management Software
Products & Services
N.A.I.C.S.: 513210

Subsidiary (US):

ClickSoftware, Inc. (2)
35 Corporate Dr Ste 400, Burlington, MA
01803
Tel.: (781) 272-5903
Web Site: http://www.clicksoftware.com
Workforce & Service Management Software
Products & Services
N.A.I.C.S.: 513210

CloudConnect, LLC (1)
1 Harbour Pl Ste 330, Portsmouth, NH
03801
Tel.: (508) 651-3900
Web Site: https://www.cloudconnect.net
Software Development Services
N.A.I.C.S.: 541511
Adam Gross (Co-Founder)

Datorama GmbH (1)
Domstrasse 10, 20095, Hamburg, Germany
Tel.: (49) 40822178222
Marketing & Advertising Services
N.A.I.C.S.: 541613

EntropySoft S.A.S. (1)
10 Rue D uzes, Paris, 75002, France
Tel.: (33) 170611040
Software Development Services
N.A.I.C.S.: 541511

ExactTarget A.B. (1)
Box 180, 101 23, Stockholm, Sweden
Tel.: (46) 850573100
Software Development Services
N.A.I.C.S.: 541511

ExactTarget GmbH (1)
Theresienhoehe 28, 80339, Munich, Germany
Tel.: (49) 89244407066
Web Site: http://www.exacttarget.com
Software Development Services
N.A.I.C.S.: 541511

ExactTarget Pte. Ltd. (1)
5 Temasek Boulevard 13-01 Suntec Tower
5, Singapore, 038985, Singapore
Tel.: (65) 63025700
Software Development Services
N.A.I.C.S.: 541511

ExactTarget S.A.S. (1)
28 Rue de Londres, 75009, Paris, France
Tel.: (33) 184883291
Web Site: http://exacttarget.com
Software Development Services
N.A.I.C.S.: 541511

ExactTarget Tecnologia, Ltda. (1)
Avenida Copacabana 190 7 andar, Alphaville, Sao Paulo, 06472-001, Brazil
Tel.: (55) 1121103100
Web Site: http://www.salesforce.com
Emp.: 200
Software Development Services
N.A.I.C.S.: 541511

ExactTarget, Inc. (1)
20 N Meridian St Ste 200, Indianapolis, IN
46204
Tel.: (317) 423-3928
Web Site: http://www.exacttarget.com
Rev.: $292,272,000
Assets: $387,066,000
Liabilities: $105,449,000
Net Worth: $281,617,000

Earnings: ($20,958,000)
Emp.: 1,673
Fiscal Year-end: 12/31/2012
Software Products Mfr
N.A.I.C.S.: 513210

Subsidiary (Domestic):

Pardot LLC (2)
950 E Paces Ferry Rd Ste 3300, Atlanta,
GA 30326
Tel.: (404) 492-6845
Web Site: http://www.pardot.com
Sales Range: $25-49.9 Million
Emp.: 100
Marketing Automation Software
N.A.I.C.S.: 513210

Subsidiary (Non-US):

Pardot EMEA (3)
Heron Tower Floor 26, 110 Bishopsgate,
London, EC2N 4AY, United Kingdom
Tel.: (44) 20 3147 7600
Web Site: http://www.pardot.com
Marketing Automation Software
N.A.I.C.S.: 513210

Pardot Nordic (3)
Drottninggatan 78, 111 36, Stockholm, Sweden
Tel.: (46) 8 534 815 70
Web Site: http://www.pardot.com
Emp.: 15
Marketing Automation Software
N.A.I.C.S.: 513210

Heroku, Inc. (1)
650 7th St, San Francisco, CA 94103
Web Site: http://www.heroku.com
Software Design Services
N.A.I.C.S.: 513210

Heywire, Inc. (1)
1 Canal Park Ste 1130, Cambridge, MA
02141
Tel.: (617) 758-6200
Web Site: http://heywire.com
Software Publisher
N.A.I.C.S.: 513210

MapAnything, Inc. (1)
5200 77 Ctr Dr Ste 400, Charlotte, NC
28217
Tel.: (866) 547-8016
Web Site: http://www.mapanything.com
Geo-Analytics & Mapping
N.A.I.C.S.: 541360
Ben Brantly (Chief Product Officer)
John Stewart (CEO)
Chris Rosbrook (CFO)
Thomas DiVittorio (Chief Customer Officer)
Brian Bachofner (CMO)
Abraham Reyes (CTO)
Marc Silberstrom (Chief Revenue Officer)
Peter James (Sr VP-Sls)
Chris Groer (Sr VP-Routing & Optimization)
Ken Kramer (Sr VP-Product Strategy & Enablement)
Amy Matthews (VP-Customer Success)
Rich Holmes (Gen Counsel & Corp Sec)
Michelle Tucker (Dir-HR)

Subsidiary (Domestic):

The TerrAlign Group, Inc. (2)
5200 77 Ctr Dr Ste 400, Charlotte, NC
28217
Tel.: (703) 485-4560
Web Site: http://www.terralign.com
Sales Resource Optimization & Revenue-based Territory Designs
N.A.I.C.S.: 541611
Jim Brown (Pres)

MuleSoft Inc. (1)
415 Mission St, San Francisco, CA 94105
Tel.: (415) 229-2009
Web Site: https://www.mulesoft.com
Software Publisher
N.A.I.C.S.: 513210
Ross Mason (Founder)
Mark Dao (Co-Chief Product Officer)
Brent Hayward (Sr VP-Channels &
Alliances-Global)
Meir Amiel (Co-Chief Product Officer)
Rick Laner (Sr VP-Svcs & Support-Global)
David Egts (CTO-Pub Sector)

Subsidiary (Non-US):

MuleSoft Argentina (2)

Juana Manso 999 6th & 5th Floor,
C1107CBS, Buenos Aires, Argentina
Tel.: (54) 1153534497
Web Site: http://www.mulesoft.com
Software Publisher
N.A.I.C.S.: 513210

MuleSoft Australia (2)
Three Darling Park 12 Tower/201 Sussex
St, Sydney, 2000, NSW, Australia
Tel.: (61) 288545603
Web Site: http://www.mulesoft.com
Software Publisher
N.A.I.C.S.: 513210
Jonathan Stern (Reg VP)

SFDC Australia Pty. Ltd. (1)
Level 12 Darling Park Tower 3 201 Sussex
Street, Sydney, 2000, NSW, Australia
Tel.: (61) 29 394 7300
Web Site: https://www.salesforce.com
Sales Range: $50-74.9 Million
Emp.: 100
Customer Relationship Management (CRM)
Services
N.A.I.C.S.: 513210

SFDC Mexico S. de R.L. de C.V. (1)
Alfonso Napoles Gandara 50 4th Fl, Colonia Pena Blanca Santa Fe, Mexico, 01210,
Mexico
Tel.: (52) 5591711857
Web Site: http://www.salesforce.com
Sales Range: $900-999.9 Million
Customer Relationship Management (CRM)
Services
N.A.I.C.S.: 513210

SFDC Netherlands B.V. (1)
The Edge Gustav Mahlerlaan 2970, 1081
LA, Amsterdam, Netherlands
Tel.: (31) 307671000
Web Site: http://www.salesforce.com
Sales Range: $450-499.9 Million
Emp.: 3,000
Customer Relationship Management (CRM)
Services
N.A.I.C.S.: 513210

SFDC Norway AS (1)
Henrik Ibsens gate 90, 0255, Oslo, Norway
Tel.: (47) 24140479
Software Development Services
N.A.I.C.S.: 541511

SFDC Sweden AB (1)
Master Samuelsgatan 42 13tr, 111 57,
Stockholm, Sweden
Tel.: (46) 85 057 3100
Web Site: https://www.salesforce.com
Sales Range: $25-49.9 Million
Emp.: 50
Customer Relationship Management (CRM)
Services
N.A.I.C.S.: 513210

Branch (Non-US):

SFDC Sweden AB (Finland) (2)
Keilaranta 1, 02150, Espoo, Finland
Tel.: (358) 925108670
Customer Relationship Management Services
N.A.I.C.S.: 513210

SFDC UK Ltd. (London) (1)
Tower 42 Level 27A 25 Old Broad Street,
London, EC2N, United Kingdom
Tel.: (44) 2031477600
Web Site: http://www.salesforce.co.uk
Sales Range: $1-4.9 Billion
Customer Relationship Management (CRM)
Services
N.A.I.C.S.: 513210

Branch (Domestic):

SFDC UK Ltd. (Staines) (2)
Block Two Lotus Park, The Causeway,
Staines-upon-Thames, TW183AG, United
Kingdom
Tel.: (44) 1784607000
Web Site: http://www.salesforce.com
Sales Range: $75-99.9 Million
Emp.: 70
Customer Relationship Management (CRM)
Services
N.A.I.C.S.: 513210

Salesforce Argentina S.R.L. (1)

Juana Manso 999 - piso 6, Buenos Aires,
Argentina
Tel.: (54) 91151667050
Software Development Services
N.A.I.C.S.: 541511

Salesforce Commerce Cloud (1)
5 Wall St, Burlington, MA 01803
Tel.: (877) 540-3032
Web Site: http://www.demandware.com
Software Publisher
N.A.I.C.S.: 513210

Subsidiary (Non-US):

Demandware GmbH (2)
Leutragraben 2-4, 07743, Jena, Germany
Tel.: (49) 36417691000
Web Site: http://www.demandware.com
Software Design Services
N.A.I.C.S.: 541511
Timothy M. Adams (Mng Dir)

Salesforce Systems Spain, S.L. (1)
Paseo de la Castellana 79 Planta 7a,
28046, Madrid, Spain
Tel.: (34) 80 030 0229
Web Site: https://www.salesforce.com
Customer Relationship Management Services
N.A.I.C.S.: 334610

**Salesforce Technologies
Morocco** (1)
Boulevard Sidi Mohamed Ben Abdellah
Casablanca Marina Tour Cristal 1, Etage 4,
20100, Casablanca, Morocco
Tel.: (212) 522423640
Data Hosting Services
N.A.I.C.S.: 518210
Marouane Lamrani (Sr Mgr-Functional Consulting)

Salesforce UK Limited (1)
Village 9 Floor 26 Salesforce Tower 110
Bishopsgate, London, EC2N 4AY, United
Kingdom
Tel.: (44) 2031477600
Data Hosting Services
N.A.I.C.S.: 518210

**Salesforce.com Canada
Corporation** (1)
10 Bay Street Suite 400, Toronto, M5J 2R8,
ON, Canada
Tel.: (647) 256-4126
Web Site: https://www.salesforce.com
Sales Range: $750-799.9 Million
Customer Relationship Management (CRM)
Services
N.A.I.C.S.: 513210

**Salesforce.com Danmark, filial af
SFDC Sweden AB** (1)
Kampmannsgade 2, 1604, Copenhagen,
Denmark
Tel.: (45) 80830613
Software Development Services
N.A.I.C.S.: 541511

Salesforce.com France S.A.S. (1)
3 Avenue Octave Greard, 75007, Paris,
France
Tel.: (33) 17 210 9400
Web Site: https://www.salesforce.com
Sales Range: $25-49.9 Million
Emp.: 60
Customer Relationship Management (CRM)
Services
N.A.I.C.S.: 513210

Salesforce.com Germany GmbH (1)
Erika-Mann-Str 31, 80636, Munich, Germany
Tel.: (49) 800 182 2338
Web Site: https://www.salesforce.com
Sales Range: $75-99.9 Million
Customer Relationship Management (CRM)
Services
N.A.I.C.S.: 513210
Joachim Wettermark (Mng Dir)

Salesforce.com Italy S.r.l. (1)
Piazza Filippo Meda 5, 20121, Milan, Italy
Tel.: (39) 080 078 2619
Web Site: https://www.salesforce.com
Customer Relationships Management Services
N.A.I.C.S.: 541990

Salesforce.com Korea Limited (1)

Salesforce, Inc.—(Continued)

1st Basement Level 1st Floor Autoway Tower Yeongdong-daero 417, Gangnam-gu, Seoul, 06182, Korea (South)
Tel.: (82) 234986200
Software Development Services
N.A.I.C.S.: 541511

Salesforce.com Sarl   (1)
Route de la Longeraie 9, 1110, Morges, Switzerland
Tel.: (41) 216953700
Web Site: http://www.salesforce.com
Sales Range: $75-99.9 Million
Customer Relationship Management (CRM) Services
N.A.I.C.S.: 513210

Subsidiary (Non-US):

SFDC Ireland Ltd.   (2)
Level 1 Block A Nova Atria North, Sandyford Business Park, Dublin, 18, Ireland
Tel.: (353) 1 440 3500
Web Site: http://www.salesforce.com
Customer Relationship Management (CRM) Services
N.A.I.C.S.: 513210

Salesforce.com Singapore Pte. Ltd.   (1)
5 Temasek Boulevard 13-01 Suntec Tower 5, Singapore, 038985, Singapore
Tel.: (65) 6 302 5700
Web Site: http://www.salesforce.com
Sales Range: $25-49.9 Million
Emp.: 200
Customer Relationship Management (CRM) Services
N.A.I.C.S.: 513210

Salesforce.org EMEA Limited   (1)
100 New Bridge Street, London, EC4V 6JA, United Kingdom
Tel.: (44) 8000921223
Data Hosting Services
N.A.I.C.S.: 518210
Rob Acker (Mng Dir)
Nasi Jazayeri (Chief Technology & Product Officer)
Allyson Fryhoff (Chief Strategic Engagement Officer)
Marc Ferris (Sr VP-Nonprofit Sls)
Bijan Bedroud (Sr VP & Gen Mgr)

Slack Technologies, Inc.   (1)
50 Fremont St, San Francisco, CA 94105
Tel.: (415) 630-7943
Web Site: https://www.slack.com
Rev.: $902,610,000
Assets: $2,433,700,000
Liabilities: $1,576,259,000
Net Worth: $857,441,000
Earnings: ($300,422,000)
Emp.: 2,545
Fiscal Year-end: 01/31/2021
Software Development Services
N.A.I.C.S.: 541511
David Schellhase (Gen Counsel & Sec)
Ali Rayl (VP-Customer Experience)
Brad Armstrong (VP-Bus Dev & Corp Dev)
Brandon Zell (Chief Acctg Officer)
Julie Liegl (CMO)
Robert Frati (Sr VP-Sls & Customer Success)
Nadia Rawlinson (Chief People Officer)
Sean Catlett (Chief Security Officer)
Jonathan Prince (VP-Comm & Policy)
Megan Cristina (Chief Privacy Officer)
Brian Elliott (VP-Future Forum)
Allan Leinwand (Sr VP-Engrg)
Tamar O. Yehoshua (Chief Product Officer)

Tableau Software, Inc.   (1)
1621 N 34th St, Seattle, WA 98103
Tel.: (206) 633-3400
Web Site: http://www.tableau.com
Rev.: $1,155,352,000
Assets: $1,634,725,000
Liabilities: $621,140,000
Net Worth: $1,013,585,000
Earnings: ($77,042,000)
Fiscal Year-end: 12/31/2018
Developer of Data Analysis & Visualization Software
N.A.I.C.S.: 513210
Dan Miller (Exec VP-Sls, Svcs & Support)
Jay Peir (Exec VP-Corp Strategy)
Andrew Beers (CTO)

Michele Yetman (Exec VP-HR)
Jennifer Nowell (Reg VP-Federal Civilian Sls)
Steve Krepich (VP)
Brian Matsubara (Regl VP-Global Technology Alliances)
Tom Walker (Exec VP-Cloud)

Subsidiary (Domestic):

Agiloft, Inc.   (2)
460 Seaport Ct Ste 200, Redwood City, CA 94063-5548
Tel.: (650) 459-5637
Web Site: http://www.agiloft.com
Software Publisher
N.A.I.C.S.: 513210
Richard Morgan (VP-Engrg)
Elisabeth Bykoff (VP-Global Alliances)
Nicole Milstead (CMO)
Eric Laughlin (CEO)

Subsidiary (Non-US):

Tableau (China) Co., Ltd.   (2)
Suite 5103 51/F Raffles City 268 Xizang Zhong Road, Huangpu Qu, Shanghai, 200001, China
Tel.: (86) 2123127591
Software Development Services
N.A.I.C.S.: 541511
Stanley Zhang (Partner & Mgr)

Tableau Asia Pacific Pte. Ltd.   (2)
South Beach Tower Level 10 38 Beach Road, Singapore, 189767, Singapore
Tel.: (65) 67685000
Software Development Services
N.A.I.C.S.: 541511
Benaga Virgantara (Mgr-Area-Sls-Enterprise)

Tableau France S.A.S.   (2)
255 boulevard Pereire, 75017, Paris, France
Tel.: (33) 186760944
Software Development Services
N.A.I.C.S.: 541511
Sebastien Cassar (Mgr-Acct)

Tableau Germany GmbH   (2)
Ulmenstrasse 30, 60325, Frankfurt am Main, Germany
Tel.: (49) 69589976700
Software Development Services
N.A.I.C.S.: 541511

Tableau Japan K.K.   (2)
Nissey Marunouchi Garden Tower 1-1-3 Marunouchi, Chiyoda-ku, Tokyo, 100-0005, Japan
Tel.: (81) 368992500
Software Development Services
N.A.I.C.S.: 541511
Shun Hamada (Pres & Country Mgr)

Tableau Software UK   (2)
Blue Fin Building 110 Southwark Street, London, SE1 0SU, Surrey, United Kingdom
Tel.: (44) 2033104500
Data Analysis & Visualization Software
N.A.I.C.S.: 513210

Vlocity AR SRL   (1)
Avenida Beliera 3025 Parque Austral Edificio M4, B1629WWA, Pilar, Buenos Aires, Argentina
Tel.: (54) 91151667050
Computer Software Services
N.A.I.C.S.: 541511

Vlocity Australia Pty Ltd   (1)
Level 12 Tower 3 Darling Park 201 Sussex Street, Sydney, 2000, NSW, Australia
Tel.: (61) 293947300
Computer Software Services
N.A.I.C.S.: 541511

Vlocity Cloud Applications India Private Limited   (1)
Torrey Pines Third Floor Embassy Golf Links Business Park, Varthur Hobli Chalaghatta Village, Bengaluru, 560 071, Karnataka, India
Tel.: (91) 8068363700
Computer Software Services
N.A.I.C.S.: 541511

Vlocity Cloud Applications Mexico S. de R.L. de C.V.   (1)
Montes urales 424 lomas de chapultepec v.

seccion, 11000, Mexico, Mexico
Tel.: (52) 18664508123
Computer Software Services
N.A.I.C.S.: 541511

Vlocity Cloud Computing Israel Ltd.   (1)
114 Yigal Alon Street, Tel Aviv, 6744320, Israel
Tel.: (972) 18003873285
Computer Software Services
N.A.I.C.S.: 541511

Vlocity Japan K.K.   (1)
Nippon Life Marunouchi Garden Tower Salesforce Tower, 1-1-3 Marunouchi, Chiyoda-ku, Tokyo, 100-0005, Japan
Tel.: (81) 342221000
Computer Software Services
N.A.I.C.S.: 541511

Vlocity Singapore Pte. Ltd.   (1)
5 Temasek Boulevard 13-01 Suntec Tower 5, Singapore, 038985, Singapore
Tel.: (65) 63025700
Computer Software Services
N.A.I.C.S.: 541511

SALLY BEAUTY HOLDINGS, INC.

3001 Colorado Blvd, Denton, TX 76210
Tel.: (940) 297-4594   DE
Web Site:
https://www.sallybeautyholdings.com
Year Founded: 1964
SBH—(NYSE)
Rev.: $3,717,031,000
Assets: $2,792,899,000
Liabilities: $2,164,364,000
Net Worth: $628,535,000
Earnings: $153,414,000
Emp.: 12,000
Fiscal Year-end: 09/30/24
Professional Beauty Supplies Distr
N.A.I.C.S.: 423850
Denise Paulonis (Pres & CEO)
Diana S. Ferguson (Chm)
Marlo M. Cormier (CFO & Sr VP)
Mary Beth Edwards (CIO, Chief Transformation Officer & Sr VP)
Jeff Harkins (VP-IR & Strategic Plng)
Scott C. Sherman (Chief Legal Officer, Chief HR Officer & Sr VP)
Mark G. Spinks (Pres-Beauty Systems Group LLC)
John Goss (Pres-Sally Beauty Supply)
Olivier Badezet (Sr VP & Mng Dir-Europe)
Joe Bowe (Chief Supply Chain Officer, Sr VP & Grp VP-Supply Chain, Logistics, and Real Estate)
Bryan DeYoung (VP-Grp)
Natalie Lockhart (VP-Grp Strategy, Customer Insights, and Digital Experience)

Subsidiaries:

Generic Value Products, Inc.   (1)
11222 I St, Omaha, NE 68137
Tel.: (402) 537-9276
Beauty Supply Distr
N.A.I.C.S.: 456120

High Intensity Products, Inc.   (1)
2425 Olympic Blvd, Santa Monica, CA 90404
Tel.: (310) 828-2993
Cosmetics Retailer & Distr
N.A.I.C.S.: 456120

Ogee Limited   (1)
Broadway 1, Accrington, BB51JZ, Lancashire, United Kingdom
Tel.: (44) 1254391002
Web Site: http://www.sallyexpress.com
Beauty Supply Distr
N.A.I.C.S.: 456120

Pro-Duo Deutschland GmbH   (1)

Moselstrasse 27, 60329, Frankfurt, Germany
Tel.: (49) 69233836
Web Site: http://www.pro-duo.de
Cosmetics Retailer & Distr
N.A.I.C.S.: 456120

Pro-Duo NV   (1)
Traktaatweg 1, 9000, Gent, Belgium
Tel.: (32) 9 216 30 00
Web Site: http://www.pro-duo.be
Sales Range: $25-49.9 Million
Emp.: 4
Cosmetics Retailer & Distr
N.A.I.C.S.: 456120

Pro-Duo Spain SL   (1)
Poligono Industrial n 1, Arroyomolinos, 28938, Mostoles, Madrid, Spain
Tel.: (34) 916852568
Web Site: http://www.pro-duo.es
Emp.: 15
Beauty Supply Distr
N.A.I.C.S.: 456120

SBCBSG Company de Mexico, s. de R.I. de C.V.   (1)
Eloy Cavazos No 2623, Cerro de la Silla, Guadalupe, 67170, Nuevo Leon, Mexico
Tel.: (52) 8113407028
Cosmetics Retailer & Distr
N.A.I.C.S.: 456120

Sally Beauty Netherlands BV   (1)
De Witbogt 9, Eindhoven, 5652AG, Netherlands
Tel.: (31) 402114479
Beauty Supply Distr
N.A.I.C.S.: 456120

Sally Chile Holding SpA   (1)
Calle Estoril 50 Of 1003, Las Condes, Santiago, Chile
Tel.: (56) 225962400
Web Site: http://www.intersalon.cl
Beauty Supply Distr
N.A.I.C.S.: 456120

Sally Holdings LLC   (1)
3001 Colorado Blvd, Denton, TX 76210-6802
Tel.: (940) 898-7500
Cosmetics Retailer & Distr
N.A.I.C.S.: 456120

Subsidiary (Domestic):

Beauty Systems Group LLC   (2)
3001 Colorado Blvd, Denton, TX 76210-6802
Tel.: (940) 898-7500
Web Site:
http://www.sallybeautyholdings.com
Beauty Product Distr
N.A.I.C.S.: 456120
Mark G. Spinks (Pres)

Subsidiary (Domestic):

Aerial Company Inc.   (3)
2300 Aerial Dr, Marinette, WI 54143
Tel.: (715) 735-9323
Salon Equipment & Supplies
N.A.I.C.S.: 423850

Armstrong McCall Holdings, Inc.   (3)
4115 Freidrich Ln Ste 300, Austin, TX 78744-2315
Tel.: (512) 444-1757
Web Site: http://www.armstrongmccall.com
Holding Company; Cosmetics & Beauty Supplies
N.A.I.C.S.: 551112

Subsidiary (Domestic):

Armstrong McCall, L.P.   (4)
4115 Freidrich Ln Ste 300, Austin, TX 78744
Tel.: (512) 444-1757
Web Site: http://www.armstrongmccall.com
Beauty Supply Distr
N.A.I.C.S.: 456120
Dean McCall (Founder)

Subsidiary (Non-US):

Beauty Systems Group (Canada), Inc.   (3)
330 Laird Rd Unit 10, Guelph, N1G 3X7, ON, Canada   (100%)
Tel.: (519) 576-5700
Web Site: http://www.bsgcanada.com

Beauty Supplies
N.A.I.C.S.: 456120

Subsidiary (Domestic):

Loxa Beauty LLC   **(3)**
5750 Castle Creek Pkwy, Indianapolis, IN
46250-4336
Tel.: (317) 716-1848
Web Site: http://www.loxabeauty.com
Professional, Scientific & Technical Services
N.A.I.C.S.: 541990

My Best Friend's Hair, LLC   **(3)**
12523 Jeffries Pl, Carmel, IN 46033-9139
Tel.: (317) 716-1848
Web Site: http://mybestfriendshair.com
Beauty Supply Distr
N.A.I.C.S.: 456120

Pacific Salon Systems Inc.   **(3)**
2900 37th Ave SW, Tumwater, WA 98512
Tel.: (360) 357-5822
Sales Range: $25-49.9 Million
Emp.: 25
Distr of Beauty Parlor Equipment & Supplies
N.A.I.C.S.: 423850
Michael Heines *(Pres)*

Subsidiary (Domestic):

Sally Beauty Military Supply LLC   **(2)**
3001 Colorado Blvd, Denton, TX 76210
Tel.: (940) 898-7500
Professional, Scientific & Technical Services
N.A.I.C.S.: 541990

Sally Salon Services Ltd   **(1)**
Unit 3 The Arc 25 Colquhoun Avenue, Hillington, Glasgow, G52 4BN, United Kingdom
Tel.: (44) 3301231907
Web Site: http://www.salon-services.com
Sales Range: $350-399.9 Million
Emp.: 1,638
Cosmetics Retailer & Distr
N.A.I.C.S.: 456120

Salon Services Franchising Ltd   **(1)**
Kelvin Avenue 82-90, Glasgow, G524LT,
United Kingdom
Tel.: (44) 1418823355
Web Site: http://www.sallyexpress.com
Beauty Supply Distr
N.A.I.C.S.: 456120

Salon Success Limited   **(1)**
1-2 Millennium Point Broadfields, Aylesbury,
HP19 8YH, Buckinghamshire, United Kingdom
Tel.: (44) 8456590011
Web Site: http://www.salon-success.co.uk
Emp.: 85
Beauty Supply Distr
N.A.I.C.S.: 456120
Simon Tickler *(Mng Dir)*
Zoe Vears *(Dir-Publicity)*
Ken West *(Dir-Education)*
Emma Stallard *(Dir-Education & Key Accounts)*
Catherine Bell *(Dir-Full Svc Sls)*

Schoeneman Beauty Supply Inc.   **(1)**
210 Industrial Park Rd, Pottsville, PA
17901-9126
Tel.: (570) 429-1189
Sales Range: $75-99.9 Million
Emp.: 500
Salon Professional Equipment & Supplies
N.A.I.C.S.: 456120
Gary G. Winterhalter *(Pres & CEO)*

Silk Elements, Inc.   **(1)**
10733 Alpharetta Hwy, Roswell, GA 30076-
1424
Tel.: (770) 552-8000
Beauty Supply Distr
N.A.I.C.S.: 456120

Sinelco International BVBA   **(1)**
Klein Frankrijkstraat 37, 9600, Ronse, Belgium
Tel.: (32) 55334141
Web Site: http://www.sinelco.com
Sales Range: $25-49.9 Million
Emp.: 4
Cosmetics Retailer & Distr
N.A.I.C.S.: 456120

Subsidiary (Non-US):

Sinelco Italiana SRL   **(2)**

Via Bandoli 16, Bagnacavallo, Ravenna,
48012, Italy
Tel.: (39) 054547106
Beauty Supply Distr
N.A.I.C.S.: 456120

Venique, Inc.   **(1)**
3001 Colorado Blvd, Denton, TX 76210
Tel.: (940) 898-7500
Web Site: http://www.veniquenails.com
Beauty Supply Distr
N.A.I.C.S.: 456120

SALON MEDIA GROUP, INC.
870 Market St, San Francisco, CA
94102
Tel.: (415) 870-7566
Web Site: http://www.salon.com
Year Founded: 1995
SLNM—(OTCIQ)
Online News & Social Networking
Services
N.A.I.C.S.: 516210
Elizabeth Hambrecht *(CFO)*

SAMSARA INC.
1 De Haro St, San Francisco, CA
94107
Tel.: (415) 985-2400   **DE**
Year Founded: 2015
IOT—(NYSE)
Rev.: $937,385,000
Assets: $1,734,845,000
Liabilities: $819,698,000
Net Worth: $915,147,000
Earnings: ($286,726,000)
Emp.: 2,895
Fiscal Year-end: 02/03/24
Software Development Services
N.A.I.C.S.: 541511
J. Andrew Munk *(Chief Acctg Officer)*
Sanjit Biswas *(Co-Founder & CEO)*
John Bicket *(Co-Founder & CTO)*
Dominic Phillips *(CFO & Exec VP)*
Kiren Sekar *(Chief Strategy Officer)*
Sarah Patterson *(CMO)*
Jeffrey Hausman *(Chief Product Officer)*
Lara Caimi *(Pres-Worldwide Field
Ops)*

Subsidiaries:

Samsara Networks Limited   **(1)**
1 Alie Street Fourth Floor, London, E1 8DE,
United Kingdom
Tel.: (44) 2039652700
Software Development Services
N.A.I.C.S.: 541511

SAMSARA LUGGAGE, INC.
6 Broadway Ste 934, New York, NY
10004   **NV**
Web Site:
     https://www.samsaraluggage.com
Year Founded: 2007
SAML—(OTCIQ)
Rev.: $361,000
Assets: $12,000
Liabilities: $2,130,000
Net Worth: ($2,118,000)
Earnings: ($144,000)
Emp.: 2
Fiscal Year-end: 12/31/23
Luggages & Travel Necessities Mfr
N.A.I.C.S.: 458320
John-Paul Backwell *(CEO)*

**SAN JUAN BASIN ROYALTY
TRUST**
3838 Oak Lawn Ave Ste 1720, Dallas, TX 75219   **TX**
Web Site: https://www.sjbrt.com
Year Founded: 1980
SJT—(NYSE)
Rev.: $79,066,171
Assets: $8,456,901
Liabilities: $5,488,194
Net Worth: $2,968,707

Earnings: $77,599,453
Fiscal Year-end: 12/31/22
Portfolio Management & Investment
Advice
N.A.I.C.S.: 523940

SANA BIOTECHNOLOGY, INC.
188 E Blaine St Ste 400, Seattle, WA
98102
Tel.: (206) 701-7914   **DE**
Web Site: https://www.sana.com
Year Founded: 2018
SANA—(NASDAQ)
Rev.: $3,762,000
Assets: $822,720,000
Liabilities: $323,405,000
Net Worth: $499,315,000
Earnings: ($269,476,000)
Emp.: 421
Fiscal Year-end: 12/31/22
Biotechnology Research & Development Services
N.A.I.C.S.: 541714
Steven D. Harr *(Pres & CEO)*
Robin Andrulevich *(Chief People Officer & Exec VP)*
Farah Anwar *(Head-Dev Ops)*
Ed Rebar *(CTO & Sr VP)*
Richard Mulligan *(Vice Chm & Head-
SanaX)*
Christian Hordo *(Chief Bus Officer &
Sr VP)*
James J. MacDonald *(Gen Counsel,
Sec & Exec VP)*
Terry Fry *(Sr VP & Head-TCell Therapeutics)*
Steven Goldman *(Sr VP & Head-CNS
Therapy)*
Chuck Murry *(Sr VP & Head-
Cardiometabolic Cell Therapy)*
Sonja Schrepfer *(Sr VP & Head-
Hypoimmune Platform)*
Snehal Patel *(Sr VP & Head-Mfg)*
Julie Lepin *(Sr VP & Head-Quality,
Regulatory & Safety)*
Gary Meininger *(Chief Medical Officer)*
Steven D. Harr *(Co-Founder, Pres &
CEO)*
Hans Edgar Bishop *(Chm)*
Richard C. Mulligan *(Vice Chm)*

SANARA MEDTECH INC.
1200 Summit Ave Ste 414, Fort
Worth, TX 76102
Tel.: (817) 529-2300   **TX**
Web Site:
     https://www.sanaramedtech.com
Year Founded: 2001
SMTI—(NASDAQ)
Rev.: $45,842,845
Assets: $61,035,386
Liabilities: $19,315,411
Net Worth: $41,719,975
Earnings: ($7,937,497)
Emp.: 101
Fiscal Year-end: 12/31/22
Collagen-Based Wound Care Products Mfr & Distr
N.A.I.C.S.: 339113
Michael D. McNeil *(CFO)*
Seth Yon *(VP)*
Prodromos Ververeli *(VP)*
Ryan Phillips *(Pres)*
Rebecca E. McMahon *(Pres)*
W. David Lee *(Pres)*
Ronald T. Nixon *(Exec Chm & CEO)*

SANDBRIDGE X2 CORP.
725 5th Ave 23rd Fl, New York, NY
10022
Tel.: (212) 292-7870   **DE**
Web Site:
     http://www.sandbridgex2.com
Year Founded: 2021
SBII—(NYSE)

Investment Services
N.A.I.C.S.: 523999
Ken Suslow *(Chm & CEO)*
Richard Henry *(CFO)*
Joseph Lamastra *(COO)*

SANDRIDGE ENERGY, INC.
1 E Sheridan Ste 500, Oklahoma
City, OK 73104
Tel.: (405) 429-5500   **DE**
Web Site:
     https://www.sandridgeenergy.com
Year Founded: 1984
SD—(NYSE)
Rev.: $254,258,000
Assets: $600,497,000
Liabilities: $112,575,000
Net Worth: $487,922,000
Earnings: $242,168,000
Emp.: 102
Fiscal Year-end: 12/31/22
Crude Petroleum Extraction Services
N.A.I.C.S.: 211120
Jonathan Frates *(Chm)*
Grayson Pranin *(Pres & CEO)*
Dean Parrish *(COO & Sr VP)*

Subsidiaries:

Dynamic Offshore Resources,
LLC   **(1)**
1301 McKinney St Ste 900, Houston, TX
77010
Tel.: (713) 728-7840
Web Site: http://www.dynamicosr.com
Oil & Gas Exploration & Development Services
N.A.I.C.S.: 213112

Lariat Services, Inc.   **(1)**
123 Robert S Kerr Ave, Oklahoma City, OK
73102-6406   **(100%)**
Tel.: (405) 429-5500
Web Site: http://www.lariatservices.com
Drilling & Oilfield Services
N.A.I.C.S.: 213111

MidCon Midstream, LP   **(1)**
123 Robert S Kerr Ave, Oklahoma City, OK
73102
Tel.: (405) 425-5500
Oil & Gas Services
N.A.I.C.S.: 213112
Kevin C. Clement *(Pres)*
James D. Bennett *(CEO)*
Philip T. Warman *(Gen Counsel, Sec & Sr
VP)*
Eddie M. LeBlanc III *(Chief Acctg Officer)*

SandRidge CO2, LLC   **(1)**
6 Desta Dr Ste 6300, Midland, TX 79705
Tel.: (432) 687-4242
Crude Oil Pipeline Transportation Services
N.A.I.C.S.: 486110

SandRidge Exploration and Production, LLC
1601 Northwest Expy Ste 1600, Oklahoma
City, OK 73118
Tel.: (405) 753-5500
Crude Petroleum & Natural Gas Extraction
Services
N.A.I.C.S.: 211120

SandRidge Holdings, Inc.   **(1)**
123 Robert S Kerr Ave, Oklahoma City, OK
73102
Tel.: (405) 429-5500
Holding Company
N.A.I.C.S.: 551112

SandRidge Midstream, Inc.   **(1)**
123 Robert S Kerr Ave, Oklahoma City, OK
73102-6406
Tel.: (405) 429-5500
Web Site: http://www.sandridgeenergy.com
Emp.: 300
Gathering, Compression, Processing &
Treating Services of Natural Gas
N.A.I.C.S.: 211120

SandRidge Mississippian Trust I   **(1)**
601 Travis St 16F, Houston, TX 77002
Tel.: (512) 236-6555
Rev.: $3,272,000
Assets: $8,743,000
Net Worth: $8,743,000

SandRidge Energy, Inc.—(Continued)

Earnings: $743,000
Fiscal Year-end: 12/31/2020
Investment Services
N.A.I.C.S.: 523999
Sarah Newell (VP)

SandRidge Mississippian Trust II (1)
601 Travis St 16F, Houston, TX 77002
Tel.: (512) 236-6555
Web Site:
    http://sandridgesdr.investorhq.business
    wire.com
Rev.: $10,147,000
Assets: $17,390,000
Net Worth: $17,390,000
Earnings: $5,877,000
Fiscal Year-end: 12/31/2019
Oil & Gas Investment Services
N.A.I.C.S.: 523999
Sarah Newell (VP)

SandRidge Permian Trust (1)
601 Travis St 16F, Houston, TX 77002
Tel.: (512) 236-6555
Rev.: $14,578,000
Assets: $17,330,000
Net Worth: $17,330,000
Earnings: $6,597,000
Fiscal Year-end: 12/31/2020
Oil & Gas Services
N.A.I.C.S.: 213112
Sarah Newell (VP)

SANDSTON CORPORATION
1496 Business Park Dr Ste A, Traverse City, MI 49686
Tel.: (231) 943-2221   MI
Year Founded: 1983
SDON—(OTCIQ)
Assets: $22
Liabilities: $33,197
Net Worth: ($33,175)
Earnings: ($33,145)
Fiscal Year-end: 12/31/22
Holding Company
N.A.I.C.S.: 551112

SANDY SPRING BANCORP, INC.
17801 Georgia Ave, Olney, MD 20832
Tel.: (301) 774-6400   MD
Web Site:
    https://www.sandyspringbank.com
Year Founded: 1988
SASR—(NASDAQ)
Rev.: $582,686,000
Assets: $13,833,119,000
Liabilities: $12,349,351,000
Net Worth: $1,483,768,000
Earnings: $166,299,000
Emp.: 1,134
Fiscal Year-end: 12/31/22
Offices of Bank Holding Companies
N.A.I.C.S.: 551111
Daniel J. Schrider (Chm, Pres & CEO)
Joseph J. O'Brien Jr. (Chief Banking Officer & Exec VP)
Kevin Slane (Chief Risk Officer & Exec VP)
Gary Fernandes (Chief HR Officer)
Joseph J. O'Brien (Chief Banking Officer)

Subsidiaries:

Sandy Spring Bank (1)
17801 Georgia Ave, Olney, MD 20832   (100%)
Tel.: (301) 774-6400
Web Site: https://www.sandyspringbank.com
Sales Range: $350-399.9 Million
Commericial Banking
N.A.I.C.S.: 522110
Daniel J. Schrider (Pres & CEO)
Mark Gunder (Chief Bus Dev Officer & Sr VP)
Philip Fish (VP)
Erika Clore (VP & Mgr)
Ann Conger (VP & Mgr)

Ellen Cunningham (VP & Mgr)
Victor Emeogo (VP & Mgr)
Erin Adams (Officer-Treasury Mgmt)
Cheryl Settlemyer (Sr VP & Mgr-Relationship)
Alia Sherwani (VP & Mgr-Market Relationship)
Clark A. Snow (VP-Comml Banking)
Monica Tressler (Sr VP-Comml Banking & Treasury Mgmt)
Joyce Wilker (Sr VP-Comml & Mgr-Industrial & Institutional Relationship)
Lauren Storm (Asst VP)
Lauren Storm (Asst VP)
Joseph J. O'Brien Jr. (Exec VP)

Subsidiary (Domestic):

Sandy Spring Insurance Corporation (2)
170 Jennifer Rd Ste 200, Annapolis, MD 21401
Tel.: (410) 897-5800
Web Site: http://www.sandyspringbank.com
Sales Range: $100-124.9 Million
Insurance Services
N.A.I.C.S.: 524210

West Financial Services, Inc. (2)
2010 Corporate Ridge Rd Ste 530, McLean, VA 22102   (100%)
Tel.: (703) 847-2500
Web Site: https://www.westfinancial.com
Sales Range: Less than $1 Million
Financial Planning, Asset Management & Wealth Consulting Services
N.A.I.C.S.: 523940
Glenn A. Robinson (Chief Investment Officer)
Kristan L. Anderson (Dir-Fin Plng & Retirement Plan Svcs)
Leslie J. Helfgott (Mgr-Event & Project)
Laurie M. Kramer (Mng Dir)
Anh N. Lam (Chief Compliance Officer)
Glenn M. Guard (Mgr-Relationship)

SANGAMO THERAPEUTICS, INC.
7000 Marina Blvd, Brisbane, CA 94005
Tel.: (510) 970-6000   DE
Web Site: https://www.sangamo.com
Year Founded: 1995
SGMO—(NASDAQ)
Rev.: $111,299,000
Assets: $562,509,000
Liabilities: $267,551,000
Net Worth: $294,958,000
Earnings: ($192,278,000)
Emp.: 478
Fiscal Year-end: 12/31/22
Medical Research & Development Services
N.A.I.C.S.: 541713
Prathyusha Duraibabu (CFO & Sr VP)
Jason Fontenot (Chief Scientific Officer)
Jaspreet Gill (Chief Quality Officer & Sr VP)
Whitney Jones (Chief People Officer & Sr VP)
Lisa Rojkjaer (Chief Medical Officer)
Louise Wilkie (Head)
Scott Willoughby (Gen Counsel)

Subsidiaries:

Sangamo Therapeutics France S.A.S. (1)
Les Cardoulines HT1 Allee de la Nertiere, Sophia Antipolis, 06560, Valbonne, France   (100%)
Tel.: (33) 497218300
Rev.: $2,676,019
Assets: $17,709,162
Liabilities: $11,516,226
Net Worth: $6,192,936
Earnings: ($13,069,850)
Emp.: 46
Fiscal Year-end: 12/31/2017
Cell Immunotherapy Developer
N.A.I.C.S.: 541715

SANMINA CORPORATION

2700 N 1st St, San Jose, CA 95134
Tel.: (408) 964-3500   DE
Web Site: https://www.sanmina.com
SANM—(NASDAQ)
Rev.: $6,756,643,000
Assets: $4,206,719,000
Liabilities: $2,328,091,000
Net Worth: $1,878,628,000
Earnings: $268,998,000
Emp.: 32,000
Fiscal Year-end: 10/02/21
Consumer Electronics & Appliances Rental
N.A.I.C.S.: 532210
Jure Sola (Co-Founder, Chm, Pres & CEO)
Paige Melching (Sr VP-Investor Comm)
Jonathan Faust (CFO & Exec VP)

Subsidiaries:

AV BreconRidge Limited (1)
6/F Enterprise Square Three 39 Wang Chiu Road, Kowloon, 200050, China (Hong Kong)
Tel.: (852) 23347334
Web Site: http://www.avconcept.com.hk
Emp.: 100
Electrical Component Mfr
N.A.I.C.S.: 335999
Than Hueng (Gen Mgr)

Hadco Corporation (1)
12A Manor Pkwy, Salem, NH 03079
Tel.: (603) 898-8000
Electrical Lighting Product Mfr
N.A.I.C.S.: 335132

Masterpiece Machine & Manufacturing Company (1)
10245 W Airport Blvd, Stafford, TX 77477
Tel.: (713) 952-4102
Web Site:
    http://www.masterpiecemachine.com
Emp.: 25
Industrial Machinery & Equipment Merchant Whslr
N.A.I.C.S.: 423830
Michael Cheatwood (Gen Mgr)

Primary Sourcing Corporation (1)
2930 Rogerdale Rd, Houston, TX 77042
Tel.: (713) 952-5405
Web Site: http://www.primarys.com
Industrial Machinery & Equipment Merchant Whslr
N.A.I.C.S.: 423830
Georgios Varsamis (Pres)

SCI Technology, Inc. (1)
13000 Memorial Pkwy SW, Huntsville, AL 35803
Tel.: (256) 882-4800
Web Site: http://www.sci.com
Military & Commercial Aviation Design & Manufacturing Services
N.A.I.C.S.: 336419
Max Klein (CTO)
Lori Sabino (Sr Dir-Contracts, Pricing, and Proposals)
Mike Sedgwick (VP-Products)
Bob Schassie (Pres)
Peter Cianfaglione (VP)
Andrea Hill (Controller)
David Roeloffs (VP)
Steve Young (VP)

Sanmina Corporation (1)
1201 W Crosby Rd, Carrollton, TX 75006-6905   (100%)
Tel.: (469) 675-2300
Sales Range: $100-124.9 Million
Emp.: 340
Custom Cable & Wire Harness Assemblies Mfr
N.A.I.C.S.: 335931

Sanmina Corporation - Kunshan (1)
No 18 Zijin Road, Zhangpu Town, Kunshan, Jiangsu, China
Tel.: (86) 51257714449
Web Site: http://www.sanmina.com
Electrical Component Mfr
N.A.I.C.S.: 334419

Sanmina France SAS (1)
260 Street Hazel, 50110, Tourlaville, France

Tel.: (33) 233888888
Electronic Parts Mfr
N.A.I.C.S.: 334419

Sanmina SAS (1)
1 Rue Michael Faraday, Montigny-le-Bretonneux, 78180, France
Tel.: (33) 130811700
Emp.: 50
Electronic Components Mfr
N.A.I.C.S.: 334419

Sanmina-SCI (Shenzhen) Limited (1)
No 1 Nan Ling Road, Shenzhen, 518125, Guangdong, China
Tel.: (86) 75527250088
Web Site: http://www.sanmina.com
Electric Equipment Mfr
N.A.I.C.S.: 335999

Sanmina-SCI AB (1)
Svedjevagen 12, Sjalevad, 894 35, Ornskoldsvik, Sweden
Tel.: (46) 660266600
Web Site: http://www.sanmina.com
Printed Circuit Board Assemblies Mfr & Testing & Electronics Systems & Sub Systems Assembler
N.A.I.C.S.: 334412

Sanmina-SCI EMS Haukipudas OY (1)
Teollisuustie 1, Haukipudas, Finland
Tel.: (358) 207700100
Web Site: http://www.sanmina.com
Electronic Technology Services
N.A.I.C.S.: 811310

Sanmina-SCI Enclosure Systems (Asia) Ltd. (1)
5/F Kader Indl Bldg 22 Kai Cheung Rd, Kowloon, Hong Kong, China (Hong Kong)
Tel.: (852) 23051800
Web Site: http://www.sanmina.com
Electronic Technology Services
N.A.I.C.S.: 811310

Sanmina-SCI Enclosure Systems (Shenzhen) Ltd. (1)
Bldg 1-4 Hongtian Jinyuan Industrial Zone, Huangpu Village Sha, Shenzhen, 518125, Guangdong, China
Tel.: (86) 75527226622
Communication Equipment Mfr
N.A.I.C.S.: 334290

Sanmina-SCI Enclosure Systems OY (1)
Joensuunkatu 3, Salo, 24100, Varsinais-Suomi, Finland
Tel.: (358) 2777110
Sales Range: $25-49.9 Million
Emp.: 130
Sheet Metal Parts Mfr
N.A.I.C.S.: 335999

Sanmina-SCI Germany GmbH (1)
Lerchenstrasse 1, 91710, Gunzenhausen, Germany
Tel.: (49) 9831510
Sales Range: $50-74.9 Million
Emp.: 200
Printed Circuit Board Assemblies Mfr & Testing & Assembly of Electronics Systems & Sub Systems
N.A.I.C.S.: 334412
Dietmar Gunther (Mng Dir)

Sanmina-SCI GmbH (1)
Lerchenstr 1, Gunzenhausen, 91710, Germany
Tel.: (49) 9831510
Web Site: http://www.sanmina.com
Sales Range: $25-49.9 Million
Emp.: 15
Bare Printed Circuit Board Mfr
N.A.I.C.S.: 334412

Sanmina-SCI Holding GmbH & Co. KG (1)
Lerchenstr 1, Gunzenhausen, 91710, Germany
Tel.: (49) 9831514060
Electronic Products Mfr
N.A.I.C.S.: 335999

Sanmina-SCI Hungary Electronics Manufacturing Limited Liability Company (1)

Kota Jozsef Ut 2, 2800, Tatabanya, Hungary
Tel.: (36) 34515600
Web Site: http://www.sanminasci.com
Sales Range: $100-124.9 Million
Emp.: 15
Printed Circuit Board Assemblies Mfr & Testing & Assembly of Electronics Systems & Sub Systems
N.A.I.C.S.: 334412
Karoly Hoffman *(Dir-Pur)*

Sanmina-SCI Ireland **(1)**
Rathealy Road Fermoy, Cork, 361 SX24, Ireland
Tel.: (353) 2582400
Sales Range: $150-199.9 Million
Emp.: 500
Printed Circuit Board Assemblies Mfr & Testing & Assembly of Electronics Systems & Sub Systems
N.A.I.C.S.: 334412
Mark Kaiser *(Pres)*

Sanmina-SCI Israel Medical Systems, Ltd. **(1)**
5 Industrial Area, Ma'alot-Tarshiha, 21570, Israel
Tel.: (972) 49079222
Web Site: http://www.sanmina-sci.com
Sales Range: $125-149.9 Million
Emp.: 400
Printed Circuit Board Assemblies Mfr & Testing & Assembly of Electronics Systems & Sub Systems
N.A.I.C.S.: 334412
Mark Kaiser *(Pres)*

Sanmina-SCI Manchester Plant **(1)**
140 Abby Rd, Manchester, NH 03103 **(100%)**
Tel.: (603) 621-1800
Sales Range: $75-99.9 Million
Emp.: 300
Mfr of Printed Circuit Boards
N.A.I.C.S.: 334412

Sanmina-SCI Optical Technology (Shenzhen) Ltd. **(1)**
No 3 Hongmian Road Free Trade Zone, Futian Dist, Shenzhen, 518100, China
Tel.: (86) 75583599988
Bare Printed Circuit Board Mfr
N.A.I.C.S.: 334412

Sanmina-SCI RSP de Mexico S.A. de C.V. **(1)**
Carr Guadalajara - Chapala, Tlajomulco de Zuniga, 45640, JAL, Mexico
Tel.: (52) 3336689800
Web Site: http://www.sanmina.com
Emp.: 10,000
Bare Printed Circuit Board Mfr
N.A.I.C.S.: 334412

Sanmina-SCI Systems (Malaysia) SND BHD **(1)**
202 Lorong Perusahaan Maju 9, Bukit Tengah Industrial Park, Perai, 13600, Malaysia
Tel.: (60) 45081228
Bare Printed Circuit Board Mfr
N.A.I.C.S.: 334412

Sanmina-SCI Systems (Thailand) Limited **(1)**
90 Moo 1 Tiwanon Road, Muang, Pathumthani, 12000, Thailand
Tel.: (66) 28337100
Sales Range: $200-249.9 Million
Emp.: 100
Bare Printed Circuit Board Mfr
N.A.I.C.S.: 334412

Sanmina-SCI Systems Japan, Ltd. **(1)**
6F Shinagawa Grand Central Tower 2-16-4 Konan, Minato-Ku, Tokyo, 108-0075, Japan
Tel.: (81) 368635351
Web Site: http://www.sanmina.com
Emp.: 40
Bare Printed Circuit Board Mfr
N.A.I.C.S.: 334412

Sanmina-SCI Systems Singapore Pte. Ltd. **(1)**
2 Chai Chee Drive Adaptec Building, Singapore, 469044, Singapore
Tel.: (65) 62457300
Web Site: http://www.sanmina.com
Emp.: 1,000

Bare Printed Circuit Board Mfr
N.A.I.C.S.: 334412

Sanmina-SCI Systems de Mexico S.A. de C.V. **(1)**
Av Solidaridad Iberoamericana No 7020, El Salto, 45680, JAL, Mexico
Tel.: (52) 3336689700
Bare Printed Circuit Board Mfr
N.A.I.C.S.: 334412

Sanmina-SCI Technology India Private Limited **(1)**
Plot No Oz-1 Sipcot Hi-Tech Sez Oragadam Sriperumbudur Tal, Sriperumbudur, 602105, Tamilnadu, India
Tel.: (91) 4437196000
Web Site: http://www.sanmina.com
Sales Range: $350-399.9 Million
Emp.: 2,200
Bare Printed Circuit Board Mfr
N.A.I.C.S.: 334412
Muthu Sivan *(Mng Dir)*

Sanmina-SCI de Mexico S.A. de C.V. **(1)**
Carretera Guadalajara-Chapala 15 5 No 97, Tlajomulco de Zuniga, 45640, JAL, Mexico
Tel.: (52) 3332846100
Web Site: http://www.sanmina.com
Emp.: 2,000
Electronic Components Mfr
N.A.I.C.S.: 334419

Sanmina-SCI do Brazil Ldta. **(1)**
Rod SP 101 trecho Campinas-Monte Mor Km 12-Bairro Tera Preta, Hortolandia, Brazil
Tel.: (55) 1938659100
Industrial Machinery & Equipment Merchant Whslr
N.A.I.C.S.: 423830

Sanminade Mexico S.A. de C.V. **(1)**
Carretera guadalajara-Chapala K15 5 N 29, Tlajomulco de Zuniga, Jalisco, 45640, Mexico
Tel.: (52) 3332846100
Web Site: http://www.sanmina.com
Sales Range: $200-249.9 Million
Emp.: 700
Mfr of Printed Circuit Board Assemblies
N.A.I.C.S.: 334412

Sensorwise, Inc. **(1)**
2908 Rogerdale Rd, Houston, TX 77042
Tel.: (713) 952-3350
Web Site: http://www.sensorwise.com
Industrial Machinery & Equipment Merchant Whslr
N.A.I.C.S.: 423830
Abbas Arian *(VP-Engrg)*
Georgios Varsamis *(VP-Bus Dev)*
Laurence Wisniewski *(Pres)*

Viking Enterprise Solutions **(1)**
2700 N 1st St, San Jose, CA 95134
Tel.: (408) 964-3730
Web Site:
   https://www.vikingenterprisesolutions.com
Sales Range: $1-9.9 Million
Emp.: 100
Designer of Enterprise Servers
N.A.I.C.S.: 541715

Viking Technology **(1)**
20091 Ellipse, Foothill Ranch, CA 92610-3001
Tel.: (949) 643-7255
Web Site: http://www.vikingtechnology.com
Sales Range: $75-99.9 Million
Emp.: 167
Designer & Mfr of DRAM Modules, Flash Memory Products, Solid-State Drives (SSDs) & Mixed Technology Devices
N.A.I.C.S.: 334118

SANTA FE GOLD CORP.
Tel.: (505) 255-4852 DE
Web Site:
   https://www.santafegoldcorp.com
Year Founded: 1991
SFEG—(OTCIQ)
Sales Range: $1-9.9 Million
Emp.: 2
Gold Mining & Exploration Services
N.A.I.C.S.: 212220

Subsidiaries:

Azco Mica Inc. **(1)**

7239 N El Mirage Rd, Glendale, AZ 85382
Tel.: (623) 935-0774
Web Site: http://www.azco.com
Sales Range: $25-49.9 Million
Mining & Exploration Company
N.A.I.C.S.: 212290
W. Pierce Carson *(Chm, Pres & CEO)*

SANTEON GROUP, INC.
9108 Church St Unit 292, Manassas, VA 20108
Tel.: (703) 970-9200 DE
Web Site: http://www.santeon.com
SANT—(OTCIQ)
Internet Broadcasting Services
N.A.I.C.S.: 516210
Ashraf M. Rofail *(Pres & CEO)*

SANUWAVE HEALTH, INC.
11495 Valley View Rd, Eden Prairie, MN 55344
Tel.: (770) 419-7525 NV
Web Site: https://www.sanuwave.com
SNWV—(OTCQB)
Rev.: $16,742,000
Assets: $19,873,000
Liabilities: $60,883,000
Net Worth: ($41,010,000)
Earnings: ($10,293,000)
Emp.: 38
Fiscal Year-end: 12/31/22
Medical Device Mfr
N.A.I.C.S.: 339112
Kevin A. Richardson II *(Chief Strategy Officer)*
Peter Stegagno *(COO)*
Iulian Cioanta *(CTO & Chief Science Officer)*
Morgan C. Frank *(Chm & CEO)*
Andrew Walko *(Pres)*

Subsidiaries:

SANUWAVE AG **(1)**
Kreuzlingerstrasse 5, 8574, Lengwil, Switzerland
Tel.: (41) 716868900
Hospital & Medical Equipment Whslr
N.A.I.C.S.: 423450

SARATOGA INVESTMENT CORP.
535 Madison Ave 4th Fl, New York, NY 10022
Tel.: (212) 906-7800 MD
Web Site:
   https://www.saratogainvestment
   corp.com
SAR—(NYSE)
Rev.: $143,719,906
Assets: $1,191,205,835
Liabilities: $820,981,727
Net Worth: $370,224,108
Earnings: $56,874,308
Fiscal Year-end: 02/29/24
Other Financial Vehicles
N.A.I.C.S.: 525990
Christian L. Oberbeck *(Chm, Pres & CEO)*
Joseph S. Burkhart *(Mng Dir & Head-Bus Dev)*
Henri J. Steenkamp *(CFO, Chief Compliance Officer, Treas & Sec)*
John MacMurray *(Mng Dir & Portfolio Mgr)*
Charles Phillips *(Mng Dir & Portfolio Mgr)*
Christine Ramdihal *(Asst Controller)*
Rochelle Kracoff *(Mgr-Compliance & Accounts Payable)*
Jeannette Hill *(Controller)*
Petal Valme *(Mgr-Facilities)*
Marissa Mann *(VP)*
Thomas V. Inglesby *(Mng Dir & Portfolio Mgr)*
Thomas V. Inglesby *(Mng Dir & Portfolio Mgr)*

SAREPTA THERAPEUTICS, INC.
215 1st St Ste 415, Cambridge, MA 02142
Tel.: (617) 274-4000 OR
Web Site: https://www.sarepta.com
SRPT—(NASDAQ)
Rev.: $1,243,336,000
Assets: $3,264,576,000
Liabilities: $2,405,239,000
Net Worth: $859,337,000
Earnings: ($535,977,000)
Emp.: 1,314
Fiscal Year-end: 12/31/23
Pharmaceutical Development & Research
N.A.I.C.S.: 325412
Douglas S. Ingram *(Pres & CEO)*
Ian M. Estepan *(CFO & Exec VP)*
Bilal Arif *(Chief Technical Ops Officer)*
Louise R. Rodino-Klapac *(Chief Scientific Officer)*
Alison Nasisi *(Chief People Officer)*
Will Tilton *(Sr VP)*

Subsidiaries:

AVI BioPharma International Limited **(1)**
Mazars 30 Old Bailey, London, EC4M 7AU, United Kingdom
Tel.: (44) 2070634000
Pharmaceuticals Product Mfr
N.A.I.C.S.: 325412

SARISSA CAPITAL ACQUISITION CORP.
660 Steamboat Rd, Greenwich, CT 06830
Tel.: (203) 302-2330 Ky
Year Founded: 2020
SRSAU—(NASDAQ)
Rev.: $20,181,058
Assets: $200,634,152
Liabilities: $217,220,443
Net Worth: ($16,586,291)
Earnings: $19,396,370
Emp.: 6
Fiscal Year-end: 12/31/21
Investment Services
N.A.I.C.S.: 523999
Mark A. DiPaolo *(Founder)*
Odysseas D. Kostas *(Partner, Sr Mng Dir & Head-Research)*
Mark DiPaolo *(Sr Mng Dir)*
Simos Simeonidis *(Sr Mng Dir)*
Alexander J. Denner *(Founder & Chief Investment Officer)*

SATELLOGIC INC.
210 Delburg St, Davidson, NC 28036
Tel.: (704) 894-4482 VG
Web Site: https://www.satellogic.com
Year Founded: 2010
SATL—(NASDAQ)
Rev.: $6,012,000
Assets: $143,855,000
Liabilities: $37,657,000
Net Worth: $106,198,000
Earnings: ($36,641,000)
Emp.: 382
Fiscal Year-end: 12/31/22
Custom Computer Programming Services
N.A.I.C.S.: 541511
Emiliano Kargieman *(CEO)*
Gerardo Richarte *(CTO)*
Rick Dunn *(CFO)*

SATIVUS TECH CORP.
3 Bethesda Metro Center Ste 700, Bethesda, MD 20814
Tel.: (203) 307-1179 DE
Web Site: https://sativustech.com
Year Founded: 2015
SATT—(OTCIQ)
Assets: $1,150,000

Sativus Tech Corp.—(Continued)

Liabilities: $3,719,000
Net Worth: ($2,569,000)
Earnings: ($1,813,000)
Fiscal Year-end: 12/31/22
Electronic Technology Solutions
N.A.I.C.S.: 334112
Tal Wilk-Glazer (CEO)
Uri Ben-Or (CFO)

SAUL CENTERS, INC.

7501 Wisconsin Ave Ste 1500E,
Bethesda, MD 20814
Tel.: (301) 986-6200   MD
Web Site:
   https://www.saulcenters.com
Year Founded: 1993
BFS—(NYSE)
Rev.: $245,860,000
Assets: $1,833,302,000
Liabilities: $1,311,500,000
Net Worth: $521,802,000
Earnings: $50,194,000
Emp.: 129
Fiscal Year-end: 12/31/22
Real Estate Credit
N.A.I.C.S.: 522292
Philip D. Caraci (Vice Chm)
John F. Collich (Chief Acquisitions &
Dev Officer & Sr VP)
Bernard Francis Saul II (Chm & CEO)
Patrick T. Connors (VP-Fin)
Christine Nicolaides Kearns (Chief
Legal & Admin Officer & Exec VP)
Don Hachey (Sr VP-Construction)
Ken Kovach (Sr VP-HR)
Amelia Overton (Sr VP & Controller)
Willoughby B. Laycock (Sr VP-
Residential Design & Market Res)
D. Todd Pearson (Pres & COO)
Tricia Culpepper (Sr VP-Property
Mgmt)
Bettina T. Guevara (Gen Counsel,
Sec & Sr VP)
Judi Garland (Sr VP-Office & Retail)
Lori Godby (Sr VP-Residential)
Keith Brown (CIO)
Ben Nelson (VP)
Robert Rubin (VP)
Charles W. Sherren Jr. (Sr VP-
Property Mgmt)

Subsidiaries:

1500 Rockville Pike LLC   (1)
1500 Rockville Pike, Rockville, MD 20852
Tel.: (301) 986-6116
Web Site: http://www.partycity.com
Costume Store Operator
N.A.I.C.S.: 458110

Beacon Center, LLC   (1)
1298 Bay Dale Dr Ste 211, Arnold, MD
21012
Tel.: (410) 919-4904
Web Site:
   https://www.thebeaconcenterllc.com
Health Care Srvices
N.A.I.C.S.: 621420

Clarendon Center LLC   (1)
1200 N Garfield St, Arlington, VA 22201
Tel.: (703) 562-1600
Property Management Services
N.A.I.C.S.: 525990

Rockville Pike Holdings, LLC   (1)
7501 Wisconsin Ave 1500 E, Bethesda, MD
20814
Tel.: (301) 986-6077
Holding Company
N.A.I.C.S.: 551112

Seabreeze Plaza, LLC   (1)
30535 Us Hwy 19 N, Palm Harbor, FL
34684-3128
Tel.: (727) 787-8802
Web Site: https://www.saulcenters.com
Grocery Store Operator
N.A.I.C.S.: 445110

Seven Corners Center, LLC   (1)

6201 7 Corners Ctr, Falls Church, VA
22044
Tel.: (703) 237-4850
Web Site: https://www.saulcenters.com
Restaurant Operators
N.A.I.C.S.: 722511
Len Battifarano (Dir-Bus Dev)

Shops at Fairfax LLC   (1)
10730-10782 Lee Hwy, Fairfax, VA 22030
Tel.: (301) 986-7713
Supermarket Operator
N.A.I.C.S.: 445110

Washington Square Center   (1)
9585 SW Washington Square Rd, Portland,
OR 97223
Tel.: (503) 639-8860
Shopping Store Services
N.A.I.C.S.: 812990

SAVARA INC.

1717 Langhorne Newtown Rd Ste
300, Langhorne, PA 19047
Tel.: (512) 614-1848   DE
Web Site: https://savarapharma.com
Year Founded: 2000
SVRA—(NASDAQ)
Rev.: $689,000
Assets: $139,777,000
Liabilities: $31,999,000
Net Worth: $107,778,000
Earnings: ($38,150,000)
Emp.: 28
Fiscal Year-end: 12/31/22
Cancer & Viral Disease Drugs Devel-
oper
N.A.I.C.S.: 325412
Dave Lowrance (CFO)
Kate McCabe (Sr VP-Legal Affairs)
Robert M. Lutz (COO)
Anne Erickson (Sr VP)
Matt Pauls (Chm & CEO)
Ray Pratt (Chief Medical Officer)
Sid Advant (EVP-Global Technical
Ops)
Scott Wilhoit (EVP-Global Comml)
Charles LaPree (Sr VP-Global Regu-
latory Affairs & Quality)
Brian Robinson (Sr VP-Global Medi-
cal Affairs)
Matthew Pauls (Chm & CEO)

SAVERS VALUE VILLAGE, INC.

11400 SE 6th St Ste 125, Bellevue,
WA 98004
Tel.: (425) 462-1515   DE
Web Site:
   https://www.valuevillage.com
Year Founded: 2019
SVV—(NYSE)
Holding Company
N.A.I.C.S.: 551112
Michael W. Maher (CFO & Treas)
Jubran Tanious (COO)
Richard Medway (Chief Compliance
Officer, Gen Counsel & Sec)
Michael Maher (CFO)
Mindy Geisser (Chief People Svcs
Officer)
Sara Gaugl (VP-Marketing & Commu-
nications)
Chad Buscho (VP-Ops Svcs)
Gary Zardas (VP-Supply)
David Sibert (VP-Real Estate)
Mark Walsh (CEO)

SAVI FINANCIAL CORPORA-TION

208 E Blackburn Ste 101, Mount Ver-
non, WA 98273
Tel.: (360) 399-7000   WA
Year Founded: 2005
SVVB—(OTCIQ)
Financial Investment Services
N.A.I.C.S.: 523999

Rob Woods (CFO, Chief Acctg Officer, Principal Acctg Officer & VP)
Michal D. Cann (Chm & Pres)

SAVOY ENERGY CORPORA-TION

2100 W Loop S Ste 900, Houston,
TX 77027
Tel.: (713) 243-8788   NV
Year Founded: 1982
SNVP—(OTCIQ)
Oil & Gas Exploration Services
N.A.I.C.S.: 213112

SAXON CAPITAL GROUP, INC.

7580 E Gray Rd Ste 103, Scottsdale,
AZ 85260
Tel.: (602) 946-4246   NV
Web Site:
   https://energyglasssolar.com
Year Founded: 2003
SCGX—(OTCIQ)
Assets: $1,167
Liabilities: $153,739
Net Worth: ($152,572)
Earnings: ($111,002)
Fiscal Year-end: 12/31/21
Advertising Agency Services
N.A.I.C.S.: 541850

SB FINANCIAL GROUP, INC.

401 Clinton St, Defiance, OH 43512
Tel.: (419) 785-3663   OH
Web Site:
   https://www.yourstatebank.com
Year Founded: 1983
SBFG—(NASDAQ)
Rev.: $62,800,000
Assets: $1,335,633,000
Liabilities: $1,217,205,000
Net Worth: $118,428,000
Earnings: $12,521,000
Emp.: 268
Fiscal Year-end: 12/31/22
Bank Holding Company
N.A.I.C.S.: 551111
Mark A. Klein (Chm, Pres & CEO)
Anthony V. Cosentino (CFO & Exec
VP)
Ernesto Gaytan (Chief Tech Innova-
tion & Ops Officer & Exec VP)

Subsidiaries:

Rurbanc Data Services, Inc.   (1)
7622 State Route 66 N, Defiance, OH
43512-2662   (100%)
Tel.: (419) 783-8800
Web Site: http://www.rdsiweb.com
Sales Range: $10-24.9 Million
Emp.: 4
Bank Data Processing
N.A.I.C.S.: 518210

Subsidiary (Domestic):

Diverse Computer Marketers,
Inc.   (2)
3101 Technology Blvd Ste B, Lansing, MI
48910
Tel.: (517) 324-9512
Web Site: http://www.dcminc.com
Sales Range: $10-24.9 Million
Emp.: 10
Image & Remote Processing Services
N.A.I.C.S.: 561499

The State Bank and Trust
Company   (1)
401 Clinton St, Defiance, OH 43512-2662
Tel.: (419) 783-8950
Web Site: http://www.yourstatebank.com
Sales Range: $50-74.9 Million
Emp.: 137
Commericial Banking
N.A.I.C.S.: 522110
Mark A. Klein (Chm, Pres & CEO)
David A. Anderson (Officer-Bus Dev, Sr VP
& Mgr-Customer Rels)
Brandon S. Gerken (Mgr-SBA Lending)
Timothy P. Moser (Mgr-Agri Svcs)
Lesley L. Parrett (Dir-Treasury Mgmt)

Logan C. Wolfrum (Officer-Comml Svcs &
Asst VP)
Christopher P. Jakyma (Chief Wealth Mgmt
Officer)
Kelly W. Cleveland (Chief Investment Offi-
cer)
Michelle L. Zeedyk (Dir-Private Banking)
Pamela K. Benedict (Sr VP & Mgr-
Residential Mortgage)
David A. Homoelle (Reg Pres)
Clinton Beasley (Officer-Treasury Mgmt)
Brandon J. McGaharan (Officer-Bus Dev)
David A. Bell (Mgr-Retirement Svcs)
Richard Smith (Sls Mgr-Residential Real
Estate)
Steven J. Watson (Mgr-Residential Mort-
gage)
Daniel R. Prond (Sls Mgr-Residential)

SBA COMMUNICATIONS COR-PORATION

8051 Congress Ave, Boca Raton, FL
33487
Tel.: (561) 995-7670   FL
Web Site: https://www.sbasite.com
Year Founded: 1989
SBAC—(NASDAQ)
Rev.: $2,711,584,000
Assets: $10,178,441,000
Liabilities: $15,349,323,000
Net Worth: ($5,170,882,000)
Earnings: $501,812,000
Emp.: 1,787
Fiscal Year-end: 12/31/23
Real Estate Manangement Services
N.A.I.C.S.: 531390
Mark R. Ciarfella (Exec VP-Ops)
Richard Cane (Pres-Intl & Exec VP)
Joshua M. Koenig (Chief Admin Offi-
cer)
Brian M. Allen (Sr VP)
Elvis T. Clemetson (CIO)
Donald E. Day (Exec VP-Site Leas-
ing)
Michelle Eisner (Chief HR Officer)
Larry Harris (Sr VP)
David J. Porte (Sr VP)
Neil H. Seidman (Sr VP)
Brendan T. Cavanagh (Pres & CEO)

Subsidiaries:

SBA Network Services, Inc.   (1)
2530 NE 36th Ave, Ocala, FL
34470-3119   (100%)
Tel.: (352) 629-1774
Web Site: http://www.sba.com
Sales Range: $1-9.9 Million
Emp.: 20
Provider of Communication Services
N.A.I.C.S.: 237130

SBA Telecommunications, Inc.   (1)
8051 Congress Ave, Boca Raton, FL
33487-2797
Tel.: (561) 995-7670
Web Site: http://www.sbasite.com
Wireless Communication Services
N.A.I.C.S.: 517112

SBA Towers IV, LLC   (1)
5900 Broken Sound Pkwy NW, Boca Raton,
FL 33487
Tel.: (561) 226-9384
Real Estate Management Services
N.A.I.C.S.: 531210

SC HOLDINGS CORP.

30 Wall St, New York, NY 10005
Tel.: (212) 517-0858   CO
Year Founded: 2012
SCNG—(OTCIQ)
Financial Investment Services
N.A.I.C.S.: 523999
Timo Bernd Strattner (CEO)

SCANDIA, INC.

11415 NW 123 Ln, Reddick, FL
32686
Tel.: (786) 236-6434   DE

SDNI—(OTCIQ)
Building Construction Services
N.A.I.C.S.: 236220
Richard Astrom (Pres)

**SCANDIUM INTERNATIONAL
MINING CORP**
2011 Phaeton Ln, Reno, NV 89521
Tel.: (775) 355-9500   BC
Web Site:
    https://www.scandiummining.com
Year Founded: 2006
SCY—(TSX)
Assets: $2,601,003
Liabilities: $1,507,724
Net Worth: $1,093,279
Earnings: $850,596
Emp.: 5
Fiscal Year-end: 12/31/22
Gold Ore & Silver Ore Mining
N.A.I.C.S.: 212220
Willem P. C. Duyvesteyn (CTO)
William Bruce Harris (Chm)
George F. Putnam (Pres & CEO)
John Thompson (VP-Project Dev)

Subsidiaries:

The Technology Store, Inc.   (1)
2287 Route 112, Medford, NY 11763
Tel.: (631) 569-4440
Web Site:
    https://www.ttsthetechnologystore.com
Industrial Machinery Mfr
N.A.I.C.S.: 333248

SCANSOURCE, INC.
6 Logue Ct, Greenville, SC 29615
Tel.: (864) 288-2432   SC
Web Site:
    https://www.scansource.com
Year Founded: 1992
SCSC—(NASDAQ)
Rev.: $3,259,809,000
Assets: $1,779,032,000
Liabilities: $854,777,000
Net Worth: $924,255,000
Earnings: $77,060,000
Emp.: 2,300
Fiscal Year-end: 06/30/24
Distr of Specialty Technology Prod-
ucts, Including Automatic Identifica-
tion, Point of Sale & Telephony
Equipment
N.A.I.C.S.: 423430
Michael L. Baur (Founder, Chm &
CEO)
Shana C. Smith (Chief Legal Officer
& Sr Exec VP)
Brandy Ford (Chief Acctg Officer & Sr
VP)
Steve Jones (CFO & Sr Exec VP)
Rachel Hayden (CIO & Sr Exec VP)

Subsidiaries:

Advantix Solutions Group, Inc.   (1)
9355 John W Elliott Dr #25, Frisco, TX
75033
Tel.: (866) 238-2684
Web Site: http://www.advantixsolutions.com
Sales Range: $1-9.9 Million
Emp.: 35
Telecommunications Resellers
N.A.I.C.S.: 517121
Nathan Brown (Co-Pres)
Natasha R. Coons (Co-Pres)
Jodi Flanagan (Acct Mgr-Enterprise)
Chuck Taylor (Mgr-Fixed Telecom)
Kevin Richardson (Mgr-Client Support)
Matt Milhauser (Dir-Bus Dev)
Adrian Padilla (Acct Mgr)
Allen Brown (Office Mgr)
Sandra Durham-Richardson (Acct Dir-Mgmt
Svcs)

Canpango, S.A.   (1)
9 Pommern Street Unit 05 Humerail, Port
Elizabeth, 6001, South Africa
Tel.: (27) 875507129
Electronic Part & Equipment Distr
N.A.I.C.S.: 423690

Intelisys Communications, Inc.   (1)
1318 Redwood Way Ste 120, Petaluma, CA
94954   (100%)
Tel.: (707) 792-4900
Web Site: http://www.intelisys.com
Sales Range: $10-24.9 Million
Emp.: 120
Radio, Television & Other Electronics
Stores
N.A.I.C.S.: 449210
Michael Ketchum (Sr VP-Fin & Ops)
Mike McKenney (VP-Supplier Sls)
Brandon Smith (Sr VP-Sls-Natl)
J. R. Cook (Sr VP-West)
Rick Dellar (Co-Founder)
Rick Sheldon (Co-Founder)
Dana Topping (Owner)
Stacey Pompei (Gen Counsel, VP-Supplier
Mgmt & Atty)
Karla Roarty (Dir-Partner Sls-Southeast)
Eddie Acosta (Dir-Partner Sls-Southwest
Reg)
Elise Wolcott (Exec Mgr-Admin)
Monica Lutes (Mgr-HR-West Coast)
Samantha Zuniga-Juarez (Sr Dir-Supplier
Svcs-Nationwide)
Mark Morgan (Pres)
Tracy Hali (VP-Sls Ops)
Paul Constantine (Exec VP-Supplier Svcs)

Outsourcing Unlimited, Inc.   (1)
Sales Range: $75-99.9 Million
Outsourcing Solutions
N.A.I.C.S.: 541690

POS Portal, Inc.   (1)
180 Promenade Cir Ste 215, Sacramento,
CA 95834
Tel.: (916) 563-0111
Web Site: https://posportal.scansource.com
Sales Range: $1-9.9 Million
Emp.: 28
Electronic Payment Device Distr
N.A.I.C.S.: 423440
Benjamin Smith (CIO)
Buzz Stryker (Founder, Pres & CEO)
Gus Constancio (VP-Ops)
Joe Villamil (VP-Bus Dev)
Scott Agatep (COO)
Evamarie K. Ghiggeri (VP-Client Solutions)
Jennifer Schon (VP-Distr Control)

ScanSource Communications,
Inc.   (1)
6 Logue Ct, Greenville, SC
29615-5725   (100%)
Tel.: (864) 288-2432
Web Site: http://www.scansourcecommunica
    tions.com
Sales Range: $100-124.9 Million
Emp.: 625
Distr of Voice, Video & Converged Commu-
nications Solutions
N.A.I.C.S.: 517810

ScanSource Europe BV   (1)
Esp 260-C Industrienummer 2185, 5633
AC, Eindhoven, Netherlands
Tel.: (31) 8000223152
Web Site: http://www.scansource.com
Automatic Data Collection & Telecommuni-
cations Services
N.A.I.C.S.: 517121

ScanSource Europe Limited   (1)
2 Iridium Court 1St Floor Owen Avenue,
Hessle, HU13 9PF, E Yorkshire, United
Kingdom
Tel.: (44) 2070056555
Web Site: http://www.scansource.com
Cloud, Telecom & Technology Products &
Services
N.A.I.C.S.: 541512

ScanSource Europe SPRL   (1)
Avenue Du Bourget Bourgetlaan 44, Brus-
sels, 1130, Belgium   (100%)
Tel.: (32) 27634070
Web Site: http://www.scansource.eu
Sales Range: $25-49.9 Million
Emp.: 120
Converged Communications & Computer
Telephony Integration Solutions
N.A.I.C.S.: 541512

ScanSource Latin America   (1)
1935 NW 87th Ave, Miami, FL 33172
Tel.: (305) 398-4000
Web Site: http://www.scansource.com

Sales Range: $25-49.9 Million
Emp.: 60
Provider of Accessories & Supplies Com-
munications Components & Upgrades
N.A.I.C.S.: 423430

ScanSource Security, Inc.   (1)
8650 Commerce Dr Ste 100, Southaven,
MS 38671   (100%)
Tel.: (662) 342-3700
Web Site: http://www.scansource.com
Sales Range: $150-199.9 Million
Emp.: 4
Distr of Electronic Security Products
N.A.I.C.S.: 423690

ScanSource de Mexico S de RL de
CV   (1)
Calle 4 - 27 Frac Ind Alce Blanco, Naucal-
pan, 53370, Mexico   (100%)
Tel.: (52) 5536403500
Sales Range: $100-124.9 Million
Converged Communications & Computer
Telephony Integration Solutions
N.A.I.C.S.: 541512
Yvette McKenzie (Pres)

SCEPTER HOLDINGS, INC.
7260 W Azure Dr Ste 140 1200, Las
Vegas, NV 89130
Tel.: (702) 482-8593   NV
Web Site:
    https://www.scepterbrands.com
Year Founded: 2007
BRZL—(OTCIQ)
Offices of Other Holding Companies
N.A.I.C.S.: 551112
Robert Van Boerum (Chm)
Adam Nicosia (VP-Sls)

SCHEID VINEYARDS INC.
305 Hilltown Rd, Salinas, CA 93908
Tel.: (831) 455-9990   DE
Web Site:
    https://www.scheidvineyards.com
Year Founded: 1972
SVIN—(OTCIQ)
Rev.: $51,028,000
Assets: $150,721,000
Liabilities: $120,414,000
Net Worth: $30,307,000
Earnings: ($12,873,000)
Fiscal Year-end: 02/29/20
Wine Producer
N.A.I.C.S.: 111332
Al Scheid (Founder & Chm)
Scott Scheid (Pres & CEO)
Heidi Scheid (Exec VP)
Kurt Gollnick (COO)

SCHLUMBERGER LIMITED
5599 San Felipe 17th Fl, Houston,
TX 77056
Tel.: (713) 513-2000   CW
Web Site: https://www.slb.com
Year Founded: 1926
SLB—(NYSE)
Rev.: $33,135,000,000
Assets: $47,957,000,000
Liabilities: $26,598,000,000
Net Worth: $21,359,000,000
Earnings: $4,203,000,000
Emp.: 111,000
Fiscal Year-end: 12/31/23
Holding Company; Oilfield Services,
Electronic Equipment & Components
N.A.I.C.S.: 551112
Mark G. Papa (Chm)
Howard Guild (Chief Acctg Officer)
Miguel M. Galuccio (Executives, Bd
of Dirs)
Alexander C. Juden (Sec)
Khaled Al Mogharbel (Exec VP-
Geographies)
Stephane Biguet (CFO & Exec VP)
Rajeev Sonthalia (Pres-Digital & Inte-
gration)
Demosthenis Pafitis (CTO)
Vijay Kasibhatla (Dir-Mergers & Ac-
quisitions)

Saul R. Laureles (Dir & Asst Sec)
Dianne Ralston (Chief Legal Officer)
Ndubuisi Maduemezia (VP-IR)
James R. McDonald (Sr VP)
Katharina Beumelburg (Chief Strat-
egy & Sustainability Dev Officer)
Carmen Rando Bejar (Chief HR Offi-
cer)
Olivier Le Peuch (CEO)

Subsidiaries:

Cameron International
Corporation   (1)
1333 W Loop S Ste 1700, Houston, TX
77027
Tel.: (713) 513-3300
Web Site: https://www.slb.com
Oil & Gas Pressure Control Equipment Mfr
N.A.I.C.S.: 333132

Subsidiary (Non-US):

Cameron Argentina S.A.I.C.   (2)
Avenue Antartida Argentina 2711 CC No 2
2800, Zarate, Argentina
Tel.: (54) 3487422297
Drilling Machines Mfr
N.A.I.C.S.: 423810

Cameron Flow Control Technology
(UK) Limited   (2)
100 New Bridge Street, London, EC4V 6JA,
United Kingdom
Tel.: (44) 1243826741
Oil & Gas Pressure Control Equipment Distr
N.A.I.C.S.: 423830

Cameron Norge AS   (2)
Mekjarvik 1, Randaberg, 4070, Norway
Tel.: (47) 51415000
Construction Mining Machinery Equipment
Merchant Whslr
N.A.I.C.S.: 423810
Nicklus Stanton Cune (Mng Dir)

Cameron Norge Holding AS   (2)
Mekjarvik 1, Randaberg, 4070, Norway
Tel.: (47) 51415000
Holding Company; Oil & Gas Pressure Con-
trol Equipment Mfr
N.A.I.C.S.: 551112

Cameron Petroleum (UK)
Limited   (2)
100 New Bridge Street, London, EC4V 6JA,
United Kingdom
Tel.: (44) 1224282000
Oil & Gas Pressure Control Equipment Mfr
N.A.I.C.S.: 333132

Subsidiary (Domestic):

Cameron Rig Solutions LLC   (2)
6500 Brittmoore Rd, Houston, TX 77041
Tel.: (832) 782-6500
Oil & Gas Pressure Control Equipment Mfr
N.A.I.C.S.: 333132

Subsidiary (Non-US):

Cameron Sense AS   (2)
Andoyfaret 3, Kristiansand, 4623, Norway
Tel.: (47) 38034000
Marine Oil & Gas Drilling Equipment Mfr
N.A.I.C.S.: 333132

Cameron Services International Pty
Ltd   (2)
450 Belmont Avenue, Kewdale, 6105, WA,
Australia
Tel.: (61) 861899100
Oil & Gas Pressure Control Equipment Mfr
N.A.I.C.S.: 333132

Cameron Systems Limited   (2)
100 New Bridge Street, London, EC4V 6JA,
United Kingdom
Tel.: (44) 1276681107
Gas & Oil Exploration Services
N.A.I.C.S.: 213112

Group (Domestic):

Cameron Valves & Measurement (2)
4580 W Wall St, Midland, TX 79703
Tel.: (432) 694-9644
Web Site: http://www.products.slb.com
Valves & Related Equipment
N.A.I.C.S.: 423840

Schlumberger Limited—(Continued)

Plant (Domestic):

Cameron Valves & Measurement - Little Rock (3)
7200 Interstate 30, Little Rock, AR 72209-3163
Tel.: (501) 568-6000
Web Site: http://www.products.slb.com
Valves & Pipe Fittings
N.A.I.C.S.: 332919

Subsidiary (Domestic):

Max-Torque Ltd. (3)
2180 Corporate Ln Ste 116, Naperville, IL 60563
Tel.: (630) 369-9600
Web Site: http://www.maxtorque.com
Clutches Mfr
N.A.I.C.S.: 336350

Newmans Valve LLC (3)
4655 Wright Rd Ste 250, Stafford, TX 77477
Tel.: (832) 944-5930
Web Site: http://www.newmansvalves.com
Industrial Valves, Oil & Gas Valves & Downstream Valves Distr
N.A.I.C.S.: 332911
Sara Alford *(Gen Mgr)*
Steve Mines *(CEO)*
Major Coles *(Sls Mgr-Inside)*

Subsidiary (Domestic):

Cameron West Coast Inc. (2)
4315 Yeager Way, Bakersfield, CA 93313-2018
Tel.: (661) 837-4980
Pressure Control & Rig Systems
N.A.I.C.S.: 213112
Joseph Berry *(Gen Mgr)*

Subsidiary (Non-US):

Douglas Chero S.p.A. (2)
Localita Pradaglie, Carpaneto Piacentino, 29013, Piacenza, Italy
Tel.: (39) 0523854011
Web Site: http://www.douglas-chero.com
Mechanical Valve Mfr
N.A.I.C.S.: 332911

EAB Engineering AS (2)
Studievegen 16, 2815, Gjovik, Norway
Tel.: (47) 61184140
Web Site: http://www.eabeng.no
Oil & Gas Pressure Control Equipment Mfr & Subsea Services
N.A.I.C.S.: 333132

Luster Mekaniske Industri AS (2)
Gaupnegrandane, 6868, Gaupne, Norway
Tel.: (47) 57682240
Web Site: http://www.lmi-as.no
High Technology Welding & Pipelines Prefabrication
N.A.I.C.S.: 333132

Maskinering og Sveiseservice AS (2)
Vardheiveien 66, 4340, Bryne, Norway
Tel.: (47) 51770300
Web Site: http://www.maskinering-sveiseservice.no
Machining & Welding Services
N.A.I.C.S.: 332999
Hans Ingvar Kvia *(Mgr-Pur)*

Subsidiary (Domestic):

Newco Valves, LLC (2)
13127 Trinity Dr, Stafford, TX 77477
Tel.: (832) 944-5930
Web Site: http://www.newmansvalve.com
Mechanical Valve Mfr
N.A.I.C.S.: 332911

Subsidiary (Non-US):

OneSubsea GmbH (2)
Luckenweg 1, Celle, 29227, Germany
Tel.: (49) 51418060
Web Site: http://www.onesubsea.slb.com
Oil & Gas Offshore Products & Services
N.A.I.C.S.: 333132

Subsidiary (Domestic):

OneSubsea LLC (2)

4646 W Sam Houston Pkwy N, Houston, TX 77041
Tel.: (713) 939-2211
Web Site: http://www.onesubsea.slb.com
Subsea Oil & Gas Field Equipment Mfr
N.A.I.C.S.: 333132

Subsidiary (Non-US):

OneSubsea Malaysia Systems Sdn Bhd (2)
Lot D33-35 Jalan Dpb/6 Pelabuhan Tanjung Pelepas, Gelang Patah, 81560, Malaysia
Tel.: (60) 75043113
Web Site: http://www.onesubsea.com
Oil & Gas Pressure Control Equipment Mfr & Subsea Services
N.A.I.C.S.: 333132

OneSubsea Operations Limited (2)
Badentoy Avenue, Portlethen, Aberdeen, AB12 4YB, United Kingdom
Tel.: (44) 1224282000
Web Site: http://www.onesubsea.slb.com
Swivel & Marine Systems & Subsea Services
N.A.I.C.S.: 237990

OneSubsea Processing AS (2)
Sandslikroken 140, Sandsli, 5254, Norway
Tel.: (47) 55928800
Web Site: http://www.onesubsea.slb.com
Oil & Gas Pressure Control Equipment Mfr
N.A.I.C.S.: 333132

OneSubsea Processing Asia Pacific Sdn. Bhd. (2)
Suite 18-5 18th Floor Wisma UOA II 21, Jalan Pinang, 50450, Kuala Lumpur, Malaysia
Tel.: (60) 323824400
Web Site: http://www.onesubsea.com
Oil & Gas Offshore Products & Services
N.A.I.C.S.: 333132

OneSubsea UK Limited (2)
100 New Bridge St, London, EC4V 6JA, United Kingdom
Tel.: (44) 1132701144
Web Site: http://www.onesubsea.slb.com
Oil & Gas Field Equipment Mfr & Subsea Services
N.A.I.C.S.: 333132

RJB Engineering (UK) Limited (2)
Unit 5 Oak Industrial Park Chelmsford Road, Great Dunmow, CM6 1XN, United Kingdom
Tel.: (44) 1371876377
Web Site: http://www.rjbengineering.co.uk
Engineeering Services
N.A.I.C.S.: 541330

TEST International (2)
3C Albert Court Peasehill Road, Ripley, DE5 3AQ, United Kingdom
Tel.: (44) 1773749539
Web Site: http://www.testinternational.co.uk
Civil Engineering Materials Testing Equipment & Supplies
N.A.I.C.S.: 423490

GeoKnowledge AS (1)
Thunesvei 2, Oslo, 0274, Norway
Tel.: (47) 22941120
Web Site: http://www.geoknowledge.com
Oil & Gas Industry Software Solutions
N.A.I.C.S.: 513210

Subsidiary (US):

GeoKnowledge USA, Inc. (2)
2925 Briarpark Dr, Houston, TX 77042
Tel.: (832) 552-7624
Web Site: http://www.geoknowledge.com
Sales Range: $1-9.9 Million
Emp.: 15
Oil & Gas Industry Software Solutions
N.A.I.C.S.: 513210

Gyrodata, Inc. (1)
23000 NW Lake Dr, Houston, TX 77095
Tel.: (281) 213-6300
Web Site: https://www.gyrodata.com
Sales Range: $10-24.9 Million
Emp.: 1,200
Oil & Gas Exploration Services
N.A.I.C.S.: 213112
Martyn Greensmith *(VP-Global Ops)*
Gina Faludi *(Mgr-HR)*
Adel Sulais *(Project Mgr-IT)*

Ahmad Alhajami *(Coord-Ops-MWD)*
Robert Trainer *(Pres & CEO)*
Rob Shoup *(VP-Special Projects)*
Alana Kobayashi Pakkala *(COO)*

M-I Holdings BV (1)
Pannekeetweg 19, Heerhugowaard, 1704 PL, Netherlands
Tel.: (31) 725763120
Web Site: http://www.slb.com
Emp.: 11
Investment Management Service
N.A.I.C.S.: 551112

MegaDiamond, Inc. (1)
275 W 2230 N, Provo, UT 84604
Tel.: (801) 377-3474
Web Site: http://www.megadiamond.com
Sales Range: $50-74.9 Million
Designs, Manufactures & Markets Ultra-hard Materials for Mining, Tools, Construction, Oil & Gas Drilling
N.A.I.C.S.: 333131

PathFinder - A Schlumberger Company (1)
23500 Colonial Pkwy, Katy, TX 77493-3592
Tel.: (713) 996-1299
Web Site: http://www.pathfinderlwd.com
Directional Drilling Product Mfr
N.A.I.C.S.: 213112

Branch (Domestic):

PathFinder (2)
9200 W Reno Ave, Oklahoma City, OK 73127
Tel.: (405) 682-2284
Web Site: http://www.schlumberger.com
Sales Range: $600-649.9 Million
Emp.: 100
Drilling Oil & Gas Wells
N.A.I.C.S.: 213112
Philip P. Scala *(Co-Founder)*

Subsidiary (Non-US):

PathFinder Energy Services, Canada Ltd. (2)
1202 10th St, Nisku, T9E 8K2, AB, Canada
Tel.: (780) 955-7513
Web Site: http://www.pathfinderlwd.com
Sales Range: $25-49.9 Million
Emp.: 10
Directional Drilling Product Mfr
N.A.I.C.S.: 213112

Saxon Energy Services Inc. (1)
700 4th Avenue Southwest, Calgary, T2P 3J4, AB, Canada
Tel.: (403) 716-4150
Oil Well Drilling & Maintenance Services
N.A.I.C.S.: 213111

Subsidiary (Non-US):

Saxon Energy Services del Ecuador S.A. (2)
Calle 98 # 22 24 Oficina 214, Edificio Calle 100, Bogota, Colombia
Tel.: (57) 16444810
Sales Range: $200-249.9 Million
Oil Well Drilling & Maintenance Services
N.A.I.C.S.: 213111

Schlumberger (1)
125 Industrial Blvd, Sugar Land, TX 77478-3127
Tel.: (281) 285-8500
Web Site: http://www.schlumberger.com
Oil & Gas Exploration Services
N.A.I.C.S.: 517121

Schlumberger (1)
16115 Park Row Ste 190, Houston, TX 77084-5132
Tel.: (281) 285-6370
Web Site: http://www.sobs.com
Sales Range: $10-24.9 Million
Emp.: 11
Research Laboratory
N.A.I.C.S.: 334515

Schlumberger (1)
PO Box 340070, Prudhoe Bay, AK 99734-0070
Tel.: (907) 659-2800
Web Site: http://www.schlumberger.com
Sales Range: $10-24.9 Million
Emp.: 8

Mfr & Installation of Oil Well Completion Equipment
N.A.I.C.S.: 213112

Schlumberger (1)
5599 San Felipe St Ste 100, Houston, TX 77056-1708
Tel.: (713) 513-2000
Web Site: http://www.slm.com
Custom Computer Programming Services
N.A.I.C.S.: 213112

Schlumberger B.V. (1)
Van Houten Industriepark 11, Postbus 143, 1380 AC, Weesp, Netherlands
Tel.: (31) 294239500
Web Site: http://www.slb.com
Emp.: 80
N.A.I.C.S.: 213111

Schlumberger Canada Limited (1)
200 - 125 9 Avenue SE, Calgary, T2E 0P6, AB, Canada
Tel.: (403) 509-4000
Web Site: http://connect.slb.com
N.A.I.C.S.: 213111

Schlumberger Completion Systems (1)
4104 53rd Ave, Provost, T0B 3S0, AB, Canada
Tel.: (780) 753-2220
Sales Range: $10-24.9 Million
Emp.: 3
Oil & Gas Field Machinery
N.A.I.C.S.: 333132

Schlumberger Conveyence and Delivery Technology Corp. (1)
300 Schlumberger Dr, Sugar Land, TX 77478-2817
Tel.: (281) 285-8500
Web Site: http://www.slb.com
Emp.: 1,000
Cable Manufacturing for Drilling Oil
N.A.I.C.S.: 213112

Schlumberger Drilling and Measurement (1)
135 Rousseau Rd, Youngsville, LA 70592
Tel.: (337) 330-2340
Web Site: http://www.schlumberger.com
Well Logging
N.A.I.C.S.: 213112

Schlumberger GmbH & Co. KG (1)
Buchstrasse 20, Meckenheim, 53340, Germany
Tel.: (49) 22259250
Web Site: http://www.schlumberger-onwine.de
Sales Range: $50-74.9 Million
Emp.: 70
Oil Field Services
N.A.I.C.S.: 213112
Rudolf Knickenberg *(Mng Dir)*

Schlumberger International (1)
5091 Booker Ln, Jay, FL 32565
Tel.: (850) 675-6363
Sales Range: $10-24.9 Million
Emp.: 10
Servicing Oil & Gas Wells
N.A.I.C.S.: 213112

Schlumberger International (1)
7030 Ardmore St, Houston, TX 77054-2302
Tel.: (713) 747-4000
Web Site: http://www.slb.com
Sales Range: $25-49.9 Million
Emp.: 9
Mfr of Oil Fields Completion System
N.A.I.C.S.: 213112

Schlumberger International (1)
4709 Seminole Dr, Midland, TX 79703-6857
Tel.: (432) 699-2424
Sales Range: $50-74.9 Million
Emp.: 50
Petroleum & Machinery Industry
N.A.I.C.S.: 213112
Foluke Ajisafe *(Engr-Production & Stimulation)*

Schlumberger International (1)
1515 Poydras St Ste 900, New Orleans, LA 70112-4516
Tel.: (504) 592-5200
Web Site: http://www.slb.com
Sales Range: $10-24.9 Million
Emp.: 45
Servicing Oil & Gas Wells

N.A.I.C.S.: 213112

Schlumberger International (1)
1901 Commerce St, Hobbs, NM 88240
Tel.: (575) 392-0363
Web Site: http://www.slb.com
Sales Range: $10-24.9 Million
Emp.: 5
Retail of Diamond & Drill Bits
N.A.I.C.S.: 213111

Schlumberger Limited (1)
555 Industrial Blvd, Sugar Land, TX 77478-2817
Tel.: (281) 285-7700
Web Site: http://www.slb.com
Sales Range: $75-99.9 Million
Mfr Cable Wire for Oil Drilling
N.A.I.C.S.: 517121
Vill Poates *(Pres)*

Schlumberger Limited (1)
713 Market Dr, Oklahoma City, OK 73114-8132
Tel.: (405) 840-1621
Web Site: http://www.schlumberger.com
Sales Range: $25-49.9 Million
Oil Field Services
N.A.I.C.S.: 213112

Schlumberger Limited (1)
783 22 Rd, Grand Junction, CO 81505-9727
Tel.: (970) 257-0230
Web Site: http://www.slb.com
Sales Range: $25-49.9 Million
Emp.: 35
Well Logging
N.A.I.C.S.: 213112

Schlumberger Limited (1)
740 Honey Branch Industrial Park, Debord, KY 41214-8913
Tel.: (304) 269-1939
Web Site: http://www.slb.com
Sales Range: $75-99.9 Million
Emp.: 90
Oil Fields
N.A.I.C.S.: 213112

Schlumberger Limited (1)
1515 Poydras St Ste 900, New Orleans, LA 70112
Tel.: (504) 592-5200
Web Site: http://www.slb.com
Sales Range: $25-49.9 Million
Emp.: 34
Servicing Oil And Gas Wells
N.A.I.C.S.: 213112

Schlumberger Limited (1)
110 Schlumberger Dr, Sugar Land, TX 77478
Tel.: (281) 285-8500
Web Site: http://www.slb.com
Sales Range: $50-74.9 Million
Emp.: 50
Oil Field Services
N.A.I.C.S.: 213112

Schlumberger Limited (1)
600 S Tyler St, Amarillo, TX 79101
Tel.: (806) 373-5743
Web Site: http://www.slb.com
Sales Range: $10-24.9 Million
Emp.: 3
Well Logging
N.A.I.C.S.: 213112

Schlumberger Limited (1)
201 S Concord Rd Bldg 2, Belle Chasse, LA 70037-4430
Tel.: (504) 394-0550
Web Site: http://www.schlumberger.com
Sales Range: $25-49.9 Million
Emp.: 27
Servicing Oil And Gas Wells
N.A.I.C.S.: 213112

Schlumberger Limited - Coiled Tubing Services (1)
3530 Arundell Cir, Ventura, CA 93003-4922
Tel.: (805) 644-8160
Web Site: http://www.slb.com
Sales Range: $10-24.9 Million
Emp.: 10
Oil Field Services
N.A.I.C.S.: 213112

Schlumberger Limited - Drill Bits (1)
1310 Rankin Rd, Houston, TX 77073

Tel.: (281) 443-3370
Web Site: http://www.slb.com
Drilling Equipment Tools Mfr
N.A.I.C.S.: 333132

Schlumberger Limited - Houma (1)
101 Southwood Dr, Houma, LA 70364
Tel.: (985) 872-0438
Sales Range: $50-74.9 Million
Oil Field Related Services
N.A.I.C.S.: 237120

Schlumberger Network Solutions (1)
5599 San Felipe St, Houston, TX 77056-2724
Tel.: (713) 513-2000
Web Site: http://www.slb.com
Sales Range: $50-74.9 Million
Communication Service
N.A.I.C.S.: 517810

Schlumberger Norge AS (1)
Risabergvegen 3, PO Box 8013, Tananger, 4068, Norway
Tel.: (47) 51946000
Web Site: http://www.slb.com
Oil & Gas Field Equipment & Service Provider
N.A.I.C.S.: 213112

Schlumberger Oilfield Corp. (1)
5599 San Felipe St, Houston, TX 77056-2724
Tel.: (713) 513-2000
Sales Range: $100-124.9 Million
Meters: Electric Pocket Portable Panelboard, Etc.
N.A.I.C.S.: 541512

Schlumberger Oilfield Services (1)
300 Schlumberger Dr, Sugar Land, TX 77478
Tel.: (281) 285-8400
Construction Repair And Dismantling Services
N.A.I.C.S.: 517121
Stephen Fulgham *(CEO)*

Schlumberger Oilfield Services (1)
205 Industrial Blvd, Sugar Land, TX 77478-3168
Tel.: (281) 285-8500
Web Site: http://www.slb.com
Mfr Cable for Drilling Oil
N.A.I.C.S.: 213112

Schlumberger Oilfield Services (1)
200 125-9th Avenue SE, Calgary, T2G0P6, AB, Canada
Tel.: (403) 509-4000
Web Site: http://www.slb.com
Oil & Gas Extraction, Services
N.A.I.C.S.: 211120

Schlumberger Oilfield UK Plc (1)
Victory House Churchill Rd Manor Royal, Crawley, RH10 9LU, United Kingdom
Tel.: (44) 1293556655
Oil & Gas Field Equipment & Service Provider
N.A.I.C.S.: 213112

Schlumberger SA (1)
42 Rue Saint Dominique, Paris, 75007, France
Tel.: (33) 140621000
Oilfield Equipments & Service Provider
N.A.I.C.S.: 213112

Schlumberger Technology Corporation (1)
300 Schlumberger Dr, Sugar Land, TX 77478-3155
Tel.: (281) 285-8500
Web Site: http://www.slb.com
Geophysical Exploration Oil & Gas Field
N.A.I.C.S.: 213112

Branch (Domestic):

Schlumberger Technology Corp. (2)
525 S Main St, Tulsa, OK 74103-4509
Tel.: (918) 584-6651
Web Site: http://www.slb.com
Sales Range: $10-24.9 Million
Emp.: 8
Oil Field Services
N.A.I.C.S.: 213112

Schlumberger Technology Corp. (2)
3535 S Choctaw Ave, El Reno, OK 73036

Tel.: (405) 262-6580
Web Site: http://www.slb.com
Sales Range: $125-149.9 Million
Emp.: 150
Oil Field Services
N.A.I.C.S.: 213112

Schlumberger Technology Corp. (2)
1710 Callens Rd, Ventura, CA 93003-5611
Tel.: (805) 642-8230
Web Site: http://www.slb.com
Sales Range: $25-49.9 Million
Emp.: 16
Servicing Oil & Gas Wells
N.A.I.C.S.: 213112

Schlumberger Technology Corp. (2)
1700 Research Pkwy Dr Ste 100, College Station, TX 77845
Tel.: (979) 268-5600
Web Site: http://www.slb.com
Sales Range: $25-49.9 Million
Emp.: 17
Drilling Oil & Gas Wells
N.A.I.C.S.: 213112

Schlumberger Technology Corp. (2)
110 Schlumberger Dr, Sugar Land, TX 77478
Tel.: (281) 285-8500
Web Site: http://www.slb.com
Sales Range: $150-199.9 Million
Geophysical Exploration Services
N.A.I.C.S.: 213112

Schlumberger Technology Corp. (2)
101 Southwood Dr, Houma, LA 70364
Tel.: (985) 872-0438
Web Site: http://www.slb.com
Sales Range: $150-199.9 Million
Emp.: 200
Oil Field Services
N.A.I.C.S.: 213112

Schlumberger Technology Corp. (2)
2841 Pegasus Dr, Bakersfield, CA 93308
Tel.: (661) 864-4800
Web Site: http://www.slb.com
Sales Range: $10-24.9 Million
Emp.: 80
Oil Well Servicing
N.A.I.C.S.: 237120

Schlumberger Technology Corp. (2)
210 Schlumberger Dr, Sugar Land, TX 77478-3157
Tel.: (281) 285-8400
Web Site: http://www.slb.com
Sales Range: $50-74.9 Million
Emp.: 3,000
Geophysical Exploration Oil & Gas Field
N.A.I.C.S.: 213112

Schlumberger Technology Corp. (2)
3806 E Rio Grande St, Victoria, TX 77901
Tel.: (361) 575-8285
Web Site: http://www.slb.com
Sales Range: $50-74.9 Million
Emp.: 50
Servicing Oil & Gas Wells
N.A.I.C.S.: 213112

Schlumberger Technology Corp. (2)
473 N FM 772, Kingsville, TX 78363-2738
Tel.: (361) 592-5642
Web Site: http://www.slb.com
Sales Range: $25-49.9 Million
Emp.: 40
Oil Field Services
N.A.I.C.S.: 213112

Schlumberger Technology Corp. (2)
1350 E Burnett St, Long Beach, CA 90806-3512
Tel.: (562) 426-3329
Web Site: http://www.slb.com
Sales Range: $10-24.9 Million
Emp.: 5
Oil Field Services
N.A.I.C.S.: 213112

Schlumberger Technology Corp. (2)
369 Tristar Dr, Webster, TX 77598
Tel.: (281) 480-2000
Web Site: http://www.slb.com
Sales Range: $75-99.9 Million
Emp.: 75
Oil Field Services
N.A.I.C.S.: 213112

Schlumberger Technology Corp. (2)

3750 Industrial Blvd, Laurel, MS 39440
Tel.: (601) 428-0377
Web Site: http://www.slb.com
Sales Range: $25-49.9 Million
Emp.: 15
Oil Field Services
N.A.I.C.S.: 213112

Schlumberger Technology Corp. (2)
1815 Aguila Azteca, Laredo, TX 78043-9749
Tel.: (956) 722-4682
Web Site: http://www.slb.com
Sales Range: $25-49.9 Million
Emp.: 45
Well Logging
N.A.I.C.S.: 213112

Schlumberger Technology Corp. (2)
107 S Concord Rd, Belle Chasse, LA 70037
Tel.: (504) 394-0550
Web Site: http://www.slb.com
Sales Range: $25-49.9 Million
Emp.: 28
Oil Field Services
N.A.I.C.S.: 213112

Schlumberger Technology Corp. (2)
300 Industrial Rd, Liberty, TX 77575
Tel.: (936) 336-2291
Web Site: http://www.slb.com
Sales Range: $1-9.9 Million
Emp.: 20
Oil & Gas Wells Services
N.A.I.C.S.: 237120

Schlumberger Technology Corp. (2)
7604 N Hwy 81, Duncan, OK 73533
Tel.: (580) 255-5516
Web Site: http://www.slb.com
Sales Range: $25-49.9 Million
Emp.: 35
Oil Field Services
N.A.I.C.S.: 213112

Schlumberger Technology Corp. (2)
4212 W Admiral Doyle Dr, New Iberia, LA 70560-9131
Tel.: (337) 367-9998
Web Site: http://www.slb.com
Sales Range: $50-74.9 Million
Emp.: 80
Oil Sampling Service for Oil Companies
N.A.I.C.S.: 213112

Schlumberger Technology Corp. (2)
Spine Rd, Prudhoe Bay, AK 99734
Tel.: (907) 659-2487
Web Site: http://www.slb.com
Sales Range: $150-199.9 Million
Emp.: 200
Oil Field Services
N.A.I.C.S.: 213112

Schlumberger Technology Corp. (2)
49420 Kenai Spur Hwy, Kenai, AK 99611-9567
Tel.: (907) 776-8155
Web Site: http://www.slb.com
Sales Range: $25-49.9 Million
Emp.: 45
Oil Field Services
N.A.I.C.S.: 213112

Schlumberger Technology Corp. (2)
135 Rousseau Rd, Youngsville, LA 70592 (100%)
Tel.: (337) 330-2340
Web Site: http://www.slb.com
Oil Field Services
N.A.I.C.S.: 213112

Schlumberger Technology Corp. (2)
2005 Coteau Rd, Houma, LA 70364
Tel.: (985) 876-3066
Web Site: http://www.schlumberger.com
Sales Range: $25-49.9 Million
Emp.: 33
Oil Field Services
N.A.I.C.S.: 213112

Schlumberger Technology Corp. (2)
525 S Main St, Tulsa, OK 74103-4509
Tel.: (918) 584-6651
Web Site: http://www.schlumberger.com
Sales Range: $10-24.9 Million
Emp.: 8
Oil Field Services
N.A.I.C.S.: 213112

Schlumberger Technology Corp. (2)

Schlumberger Limited—(Continued)

1126 Airport Rd, Alice, TX 78332
Tel.: (361) 664-3458
Web Site: http://www.slb.com
Sales Range: $100-124.9 Million
Emp.: 125
Oil Field Services
N.A.I.C.S.: 213112

Schlumberger Technology Corp. (2)
311 Culbertson Ave, Worland, WY 82401
Tel.: (307) 347-3251
Web Site: http://www.slb.com
Sales Range: $50-74.9 Million
Emp.: 55
Oil Field Services
N.A.I.C.S.: 213112

Schlumberger Technology Corp. (2)
300 Schlumberger Dr, Sugar Land, TX 77478
Tel.: (281) 285-8500
Web Site: http://www.slb.com
Sales Range: $25-49.9 Million
Emp.: 25
Oil & Gas Line & Compressor Station Construction Services
N.A.I.C.S.: 213112

Schlumberger Technology Corp. (2)
301 Capacity Dr, Longview, TX 75604-5339
Tel.: (903) 297-4505
Web Site: http://www.schlumberger.com
Sales Range: $200-249.9 Million
Emp.: 230
Oil Field Services
N.A.I.C.S.: 213112

Schlumberger Technology Corp. (2)
1510 Wells Fargo, Corpus Christi, TX 78477
Tel.: (361) 882-5601
Sales Range: $25-49.9 Million
Emp.: 20
Oil Field Services
N.A.I.C.S.: 213112

Schlumberger Technology Corp. (2)
14131 Midway Rd 3700, Addison, TX 75001
Tel.: (972) 385-6470
Web Site: http://www.schlumberger.com
Sales Range: $50-74.9 Million
Emp.: 60
Oil Field Services
N.A.I.C.S.: 213112

Schlumberger Technology Corp. (2)
2527 W Bender, Hobbs, NM 88240
Tel.: (505) 325-5006
Web Site: http://www.schlumberger.com
Sales Range: $10-24.9 Million
Emp.: 35
Oil & Gas Exploration Services
N.A.I.C.S.: 213112

Schlumberger Technology Corp. (2)
1515 Poydras St Ste 900, New Orleans, LA 70112-4505
Tel.: (504) 592-5200
Web Site: http://www.slb.com
Sales Range: $25-49.9 Million
Emp.: 48
Oil Field Services
N.A.I.C.S.: 213112

Schlumberger Technology Corp. (2)
8321 Las Cruces Dr, Laredo, TX 78045
Tel.: (956) 724-4461
Web Site: http://www.schlumberger.com
Sales Range: $75-99.9 Million
Emp.: 250
Oil Field Services
N.A.I.C.S.: 213112

Schlumberger Technology Corp. (2)
9 Covington Rd, Natchez, MS 39120-2773
Tel.: (601) 442-7481
Sales Range: $1-9.9 Million
Emp.: 15
Construction Repair & Dismantling Services
N.A.I.C.S.: 237120

Schlumberger Technology Corp. (2)
12 E Dakota Pkwy, Williston, ND 58801-6131
Tel.: (701) 572-8393
Web Site: http://www.schlumberger.com
Sales Range: $25-49.9 Million
Emp.: 150
Oil Field Services

N.A.I.C.S.: 213112

Schlumberger Technology Corp. (2)
6411 A St, Anchorage, AK 99518
Tel.: (907) 273-1700
Web Site: http://www.slb.com
Sales Range: $25-49.9 Million
Emp.: 40
Oil Field Services
N.A.I.C.S.: 213112

Schlumberger Technology Corp. (2)
6120 Snow Rd, Bakersfield, CA 93308-9531
Tel.: (661) 864-4750
Web Site: http://www.slb.com
Sales Range: $50-74.9 Million
Emp.: 50
Well Logging
N.A.I.C.S.: 213112

Schlumberger Technology Corp. (2)
13812 W Main St, Larose, LA 70373-3002
Tel.: (985) 693-3161
Web Site: http://www.schlumberger.com
Sales Range: $100-124.9 Million
Emp.: 120
Well Logging
N.A.I.C.S.: 213112

Schlumberger Technology Corp. (2)
16879 W 141st St S, Kellyville, OK 74039-4623
Tel.: (918) 247-1300
Sales Range: $25-49.9 Million
Emp.: 45
Training & Development Consulting
N.A.I.C.S.: 213112

Schlumberger Technology Corp. (2)
1819 W Pinhook Rd Ste 250, Lafayette, LA 70508
Tel.: (337) 237-5944
Web Site: http://www.slb.com
Sales Range: $25-49.9 Million
Emp.: 12
Construction & Other Repairs
N.A.I.C.S.: 213112

Schlumberger Well Completions (1)
7030 Ardmore St, Houston, TX 77054
Tel.: (713) 747-4000
Web Site: http://www.slb.com
Emp.: 85,000
Oilfield Equipment, Tools & Pumps Mfr
N.A.I.C.S.: 213112

Unit (Domestic):

Schlumberger Bartlesville Product Center (2)
509 W Hensley Blvd, Bartlesville, OK 74003-2518 **(100%)**
Tel.: (918) 661-2000
Web Site: http://www.slb.com
Rev.: $335,000,000
Emp.: 200
Mfr of Electric Submersible Pumping Systems
N.A.I.C.S.: 213112

Division (Domestic):

Schlumberger Completions & Productivity (2)
7030 Ardmore St, Houston, TX 77054-2302 **(100%)**
Tel.: (713) 747-4000
Web Site: http://www.schlumberger.com
Sales Range: $600-649.9 Million
Emp.: 400
Mfr of Oilfield Equipment
N.A.I.C.S.: 213112

Unit (Domestic):

Schlumberger REDA Production Systems (2)
2400 Packer Rd, Lawrence, KS 66049-8903
Tel.: (785) 841-5610
Web Site: http://www.camco.com
Sales Range: $150-199.9 Million
Emp.: 157
Electric Cable For Powering Submersible Oil Pumps
N.A.I.C.S.: 213112

Schlumberger Reservoir Completions Center (2)

N.A.I.C.S.: 213112

14910 Airline Rd, Rosharon, TX 77583-1590
Tel.: (281) 285-5200
Web Site: http://www.slb.com
Sales Range: $125-149.9 Million
Emp.: 600
Oil Well Design Research & Development & Technologies Mfr
N.A.I.C.S.: 541715
Eric Larson *(Pres)*

Schlumberger Well Services (1)
531 Commerce Ave, Fort Morgan, CO 80701
Tel.: (970) 867-5361
Web Site: http://www.schlumberger.com
Sales Range: $25-49.9 Million
Emp.: 30
Well Logging
N.A.I.C.S.: 213112

Schlumberger Wireline & Testing (1)
1111 Madison Ln, Farmington, NM 87401
Tel.: (505) 325-5006
Sales Range: $25-49.9 Million
Emp.: 16
Oil Field Services
N.A.I.C.S.: 484121
Modhar Khan *(Gen Mgr)*

Services Petroliers Schlumberger S.A. (1)
42 Rue Saint Dominique, Paris, 75007, France
Tel.: (33) 899868243
Web Site: http://www.slb.com
Sales Range: $75-99.9 Million
Emp.: 100
N.A.I.C.S.: 213111
Andre B. Erlich *(CIO)*

Unit (Domestic):

Schlumberger Industries (2)
Le Palatin 1, 1 Cour Du Trianle La Defense, 92936, Montrouge, Cedex, France **(100%)**
Tel.: (33) 171776000
Web Site: http://www.slb.com
N.A.I.C.S.: 213111

Sweco (1)
8029 Dixie Hwy, Florence, KY 41042-2903
Tel.: (859) 283-8400
Web Site: http://www.sweco.com
Sales Range: $125-149.9 Million
Vibrating Screen Separators, Grinding Mills, Finishing Mills, Water Filters, Turbo Screen Air Classifiers, Stationary Screens, Hydrocyclones, Replacement Screens, Centrifugal Sifters Mfr
N.A.I.C.S.: 333248

Division (Non-US):

Sweco Europe S.A. (2)
Rue De La Recherche 8, Parc Industriel Sud Zone 1, Nivelles, 1400, Belgium **(100%)**
Tel.: (32) 67893434
Web Site: http://www.sweco.com
Sales Range: $25-49.9 Million
Emp.: 50
Energy, Process & Metalworking Equipment
N.A.I.C.S.: 333519

Swequipos, S.A. de C.V. (2)
Fernando Montes de Oca 21 Piso 1 Col Industrial San Nicolas, 54030, Tlalnepantla, Mexico **(100%)**
Tel.: (52) 55553219800
Web Site: http://www.sweco.com
Sales Range: $25-49.9 Million
Emp.: 20
Mfr of Vibratory Separating & Finishing Equipment; Separators, Finishing Mills, Industrial Screens & Air & Water Filters, Centrifugal Sifters, Heat Exchangers & Pressure Vessels
N.A.I.C.S.: 333414

WesternGeco LLC (1)
10001 Richmond Ave, Houston, TX 77042
Tel.: (713) 789-9600
Web Site: http://www.westerngeco.com
Sales Range: $10-24.9 Million
Emp.: 22
Geophysical Reservoir Imaging, Monitoring & Development Services
N.A.I.C.S.: 541360

WesternGeco Limited (1)
Schlumberger House Buckingham Gate Gatwick Airport, Gatwick, RH6 0NZ, West Sussex, United Kingdom
Tel.: (44) 1293556655
Web Site: http://www.slb.com
Sales Range: $75-99.9 Million
Emp.: 500
Geophysical Reservoir Imaging, Monitoring & Development Services
N.A.I.C.S.: 541360

Subsidiary (Non-US):

WesternGeco A/S (2)
Rifabergveien 3, PO Box 8013, Stavanger, 4068, Norway **(100%)**
Tel.: (47) 51946000
Web Site: http://www.westerngeco.com
Sales Range: $75-99.9 Million
Emp.: 300
Geophysical Reservoir Imaging, Monitoring & Development Services
N.A.I.C.S.: 541360

SCHMITT INDUSTRIES, INC.

2765 NW Nicolai St, Portland, OR 97210
Tel.: (503) 227-7908   **OR**
Web Site:
https://schmittindustries.com
SMIT—(NASDAQ)
Rev.: $7,864,350
Assets: $21,173,930
Liabilities: $17,404,347
Net Worth: $3,769,583
Earnings: ($8,089,672)
Emp.: 138
Fiscal Year-end: 05/31/21
Computerized Balancing Equipment Mfr for Rotating Devices
N.A.I.C.S.: 334513
Michael R. Zapata *(Exec Chm, Pres & CEO)*

Subsidiaries:

Schmitt Europe, Ltd. (1)
Unit 2 Leofric Court Progress Way Binley Industrial Estate, Coventry, CV3 2NT, United Kingdom **(100%)**
Tel.: (44) 24 7665 1774
Web Site: http://www.schmitt.co.uk
Sales Range: $25-49.9 Million
Emp.: 4
Sales of Precision Manufacturing Systems
N.A.I.C.S.: 333248

SCHNEIDER NATIONAL, INC.

3101 S Packerland Dr, Green Bay, WI 54313
Tel.: (920) 592-2000   **WI**
Web Site: https://www.schneider.com
Year Founded: 1935
SNDR—(NYSE)
Rev.: $5,498,900,000
Assets: $4,557,200,000
Liabilities: $1,600,400,000
Net Worth: $2,956,800,000
Earnings: $238,500,000
Fiscal Year-end: 12/31/23
Freight Forwarding & Logistics Management Services
N.A.I.C.S.: 551112
Shelly A. Dumas-Magnin *(VP & Controller)*
Mark B. Rourke *(Pres & CEO)*
Darrell Campbell *(CFO & Exec VP)*
Thomas G. Jackson *(Gen Counsel & Exec VP)*
Robert Reich *(Chief Admin Officer & Exec VP)*
Kara Leiterman *(Mgr-Media Rels)*

Subsidiaries:

Schneider Finance, Inc. (1)
911 Glory Rd, Green Bay, WI 54304
Tel.: (920) 592-2000
Web Site: https://www.sfitrucks.com
Emp.: 26
Truck Financial Leasing Services
N.A.I.C.S.: 522220

Schneider Logistics, Inc. **(1)**
3101 S Packerland Dr, Green Bay, WI
54313-6187 **(100%)**
Tel.: (920) 592-2000
Web Site: http://www.schneiderlogistics.com
Sales Range: $100-124.9 Million
Emp.: 750
Freight Management Services
N.A.I.C.S.: 488510

Subsidiary (Domestic):

**Schneider Logistics Transloading and
Distribution, Inc.** **(2)**
3101 S Packerland Dr, Green Bay, WI
54313-6187
Tel.: (920) 592-2000
Logistics Consulting Servies
N.A.I.C.S.: 541614

**Schneider National Bulk Carriers,
Inc.** **(1)**
3101 S Packerland Dr, Green Bay, WI
54313-6187
Tel.: (920) 592-2000
Bulk Freight Trucking Services
N.A.I.C.S.: 484230

Schneider Transport, Inc. **(1)**
Tel.: (920) 592-5900
General Freight Trucking Services
N.A.I.C.S.: 488510
Erin Van Zeeland (Sr VP & Gen Mgr-
Transportation Mgmt)

Turnkey Ventures LLC **(1)**
833 Front St Ste 201, Santa Cruz, CA
95060
Web Site: https://www.turnkeyventures.com
Real Estate Management Services
N.A.I.C.S.: 531390

**Watkins and Shepard Trucking,
Inc.** **(1)**
N 6400 Hwy 10 W, Missoula, MT 59808
Tel.: (406) 532-6121
Web Site: http://www.wksh.com
Freight Transportation Services
N.A.I.C.S.: 488510
Patrick Foran (CIO)

deBoer Transportation, Inc. **(1)**
8814 Hwy F, Blenker, WI 54415
Tel.: (715) 652-2911
Web Site: http://www.deboertrans.com
Sales Range: $25-49.9 Million
Emp.: 350
Transportation & Logistics
N.A.I.C.S.: 484121
Rick Crosson (COO)
Kay DeBoer (Co-Pres)
Dale DeBoer (Co-Pres)
Tom DeBoer (VP-Sls)
Jeremiah Montag (Dir-Maintenance)

SCHOLAR ROCK HOLDING CORPORATION
301 Binney St 3rd Fl, Cambridge, MA
02142
Tel.: (857) 259-3860 DE
Web Site:
https://www.scholarrock.com
Year Founded: 2017
SRRK—(NASDAQ)
Rev.: $33,193,000
Assets: $358,168,000
Liabilities: $97,933,000
Net Worth: $260,235,000
Earnings: ($134,502,000)
Emp.: 114
Fiscal Year-end: 12/31/22
Research & Development in Biotech-
nology (except Nanobiotechnology)
N.A.I.C.S.: 541714
Junlin Ho (Gen Counsel & Sec)
Jay T. Backstrom (Pres & CEO)
Mo Qatanani (Chief Scientific Officer)
Jing L. Marantz (Chief Medical Offi-
cer)
Caryn Parlavecchio (Chief HR Offi-
cer)
Tracey M. Sacco (Chief Comml Offi-
cer)
Mo Qatanani (Sr VP)
Timothy A. Springer (Co-Founder)

SCHOLASTIC CORPORATION
557 Broadway, New York, NY 10012
Tel.: (212) 343-6100 DE
Web Site: https://www.scholastic.com
Year Founded: 1920
SCHL—(NASDAQ)
Rev.: $1,589,700,000
Assets: $1,671,200,000
Liabilities: $653,100,000
Net Worth: $1,018,100,000
Earnings: $12,100,000
Emp.: 4,770
Fiscal Year-end: 05/31/24
Holding Company; Educational Multi-
media Publisher
N.A.I.C.S.: 551112
Mary Beech (CMO & Chief Transfor-
mation Officer)
Iole Lucchese (Chm, Chief Strategy
Officer & Exec VP)
Sasha Quinton (Pres-School Reading
Events & Exec VP)
Ellie Berger (Exec VP)
Peter Warwick (Pres & CEO)
Andrew S. Hedden (Gen Counsel,
Sec & Exec VP)
Kenneth J. Cleary (Pres-Intl)
Paul Hukkanen (Chief Acctg Officer &
VP)
Sasha Quinton (Pres-Scholastic Book
Fairs & Exec VP)
Elizabeth Polcari (Pres-Education So-
lutions & Exec VP)

Subsidiaries:

Scholastic Inc. **(1)**
557 Broadway, New York, NY 10012-3919
Tel.: (212) 343-6726
Web Site: https://www.scholastic.com
Sales Range: $50-74.9 Million
Emp.: 150
Educational Materials Publisher
N.A.I.C.S.: 513120
Sasha Quinton (Pres-School Reading
Events & Exec VP)
Ellie Berger (Pres-Trade Publ & Exec VP)
Peter Warwick (Pres & CEO)

Subsidiary (Domestic):

Grolier Incorporated **(2)**
90 Sherman Tpke, Danbury, CT 06816
Tel.: (203) 797-3500
Sales Range: $25-49.9 Million
Emp.: 45
Publisher of Children's Books
N.A.I.C.S.: 513130
Robert Horton (Pres)

Subsidiary (Domestic):

Caribe Grolier Inc. **(3)**
601 Del Parque St Pesquera Bldg Ste 701,
San Juan, PR 00909
Tel.: (787) 724-2590
Web Site: http://www.caribegrolier.com
House-To-House Encyclopedias
N.A.I.C.S.: 459210

Subsidiary (Non-US):

Grolier International, Inc. **(3)**
81 Ubi Ave 4 #02-30, Singapore, 408830,
Singapore
Tel.: (65) 90995800
Web Site: http://www.grobooks.com
Emp.: 6
Educational Support Services
N.A.I.C.S.: 611710
Frank Wong (Mng Dir)

Subsidiary (Non-US):

**Grolier International Private
Limited** **(4)**
Unit no 10 11 and 14 US Complex Main
Mathura Road, Adjacent to Jasola Apollo
Metro Station, New Delhi, 110076, India
Tel.: (91) 11612800000
Web Site: http://www.grolier-asia.com
Sales Range: $25-49.9 Million
Emp.: 150
Educational Support Services
N.A.I.C.S.: 611710

Subsidiary (Domestic):

Orchard Books, Inc. **(3)**
2222 N Orchard St, Chicago, IL 60657
Tel.: (773) 528-6200
Web Site: http://www.orchardbooksinc.com
Book Publishers
N.A.I.C.S.: 513130
Celia Lee (Sr Editor)

Scholastic Library Publishing Inc. **(3)**
90 Old Sherman Tpke, Danbury, CT 06816-
0001
Tel.: (203) 797-3500
Web Site:
http://www.scholasticlibrary.digital.scho
lastic.com
Book Publishers
N.A.I.C.S.: 513130

Scholastic at Home Inc. **(3)**
90 Old Sherman Tpke, Danbury, CT 06816-
0001
Tel.: (203) 797-3500
Book Club Mail Order
N.A.I.C.S.: 459210

Subsidiary (Non-US):

Ooka Island Inc. **(2)**
PO Box 25013, Charlottetown, C1A 9N4,
PE, Canada
Tel.: (877) 307-3616
Web Site: http://www.ookaisland.com
Learning Services
N.A.I.C.S.: 513199

Scholastic Australia Pty. Ltd. **(2)**
76-80 Railway Crescent, Lisarow, 2250,
NSW, Australia **(100%)**
Tel.: (61) 243283555
Web Site: https://www.scholastic.com.au
Emp.: 500
Educational Publisher
N.A.I.C.S.: 513130
David Peagram (Mng Dir)

Subsidiary (Domestic):

Scholastic Book Clubs, Inc. **(2)**
557 Broadway, New York, NY
10012-3919 **(100%)**
Tel.: (212) 343-6100
Web Site: https://clubs.scholastic.com
Mail Order Book Retailer
N.A.I.C.S.: 459210

Scholastic Book Fairs, Inc. **(2)**
38 Skyline Dr, Lake Mary, FL 32746-5404
Tel.: (407) 829-2665
Web Site: https://bookfairs.scholastic.com
Sales Range: $1-9.9 Million
Emp.: 48
Book Fair Organizer
N.A.I.C.S.: 711320
Sasha Quinton (Pres)
Stacy Lellos (Sr VP & Gen Mgr)
Tracy Van Straaten (VP)

Subsidiary (Domestic):

**Mrs. Nelson's Book Fair
Company** **(3)**
1648 W Orange Grove Ave, Pomona, CA
91768
Tel.: (909) 865-8550
Web Site: http://www.mrsnelsons.com
Sales Range: $1-9.9 Million
Emp.: 17
Book Stores
N.A.I.C.S.: 459210
Judy Nelson (Principal)

Subsidiary (Non-US):

Scholastic Book Fairs, Ltd. **(2)**
Westfield Rd, Southam, CV47 0RA, War-
wickshire, United Kingdom **(100%)**
Tel.: (44) 800212281
Web Site: http://www.scholastic.co.uk
Sales Range: $25-49.9 Million
Emp.: 65
Arranges Fairs for Sale of Books
N.A.I.C.S.: 561599
Steve Thompson (Mng Dir)

Scholastic Canada Ltd. **(2)**
175 Hillmount Road, Markham, L6C 1Z7,
ON, Canada **(100%)**
Tel.: (905) 887-7323
Web Site: https://www.scholastic.ca

Sales Range: $100-124.9 Million
Emp.: 800
Book Publishers
N.A.I.C.S.: 513130
Linda Gosnell (Pres)

Subsidiary (Domestic):

Scholastic Bookfairs Canada Ltd. **(3)**
945 Meyerside Dr, Mississauga, L5T 1P9,
ON, Canada
Tel.: (905) 670-0990
Book Publishers
N.A.I.C.S.: 513130

Subsidiary (Domestic):

Scholastic Entertainment Inc. **(2)**
524 Broadway, New York, NY 10012-4408
Tel.: (212) 343-6100
Educational Film Production Services
N.A.I.C.S.: 512110
Iole Lucchese (Pres)

Subsidiary (Domestic):

SE Distribution Inc. **(3)**
1311 S Hill St, Los Angeles, CA 90015-
3012
Tel.: (213) 745-6677
Web Site: http://www.sedisplayfixture.com
Sales Range: $10-24.9 Million
Emp.: 10
Children Video Distr
N.A.I.C.S.: 512120

Subsidiary (Non-US):

Scholastic Hong Kong Limited **(2)**
2001-2 20th Floor Top Glory Tower 262
Gloucester Road, Hong Kong, China (Hong
Kong)
Tel.: (852) 27226161
Web Site: http://www.scholastic.asia
Sales Range: $10-24.9 Million
Emp.: 15
English Language Reference Materials Pub-
lisher
N.A.I.C.S.: 513130
Frank Wong (Pres-Asia)

Unit (Domestic):

**Scholastic Inc. Information
Center** **(2)**
100 Plz Dr Ste 4, Secaucus, NJ
07094-3677 **(100%)**
Tel.: (201) 633-2400
Web Site: http://www.scholastic.com
Sales Range: $100-124.9 Million
Publishing
N.A.I.C.S.: 513120

**Scholastic Inc. National Distribution
Center** **(2)**
2931 E McCarty St, Jefferson City, MO
65101-4431 **(100%)**
Tel.: (573) 636-5271
Web Site: http://www.scholastic.com
Distribution Services
N.A.I.C.S.: 424920
Donald R. Stertzer (COO & VP)

Subsidiary (Non-US):

Scholastic New Zealand Ltd. **(2)**
21 Lady Ruby Drive, East Tamaki, Auck-
land, 2013, New Zealand **(100%)**
Tel.: (64) 92748112
Web Site: https://www.scholastic.co.nz
Sales Range: $10-24.9 Million
Emp.: 80
Educational Publisher
N.A.I.C.S.: 513130
Chris Cowan (Mgr-Territory-Christchurch &
Upper South Island)
Julie Smart (Mgr-Territory-Wellington &
Lower North Island)
Jules O'Malley (Mgr-Territory-North, West
Auckland & Northland)
Rachael Hobson (Mgr-Territory-South &
East Auckland)
Sandie Haddock (Mgr-Territory-Waikato &
Bay-Plenty)

Scholastic UK Limited **(2)**
1 London Bridge, London, SE1 9BG, United
Kingdom
Tel.: (44) 2070461630
Web Site: https://www.scholastic.co.uk
Book Publishers

Scholastic Corporation—(Continued)

N.A.I.C.S.: 513130

Subsidiary (Domestic):

Chicken House Publishing Ltd.   (3)
2 Palmer Street, Frome, BA11 1DS, Somerset, United Kingdom
Tel.: (44) 1373454488
Web Site:
   http://www.chickenhousebooks.com
Emp.: 9
Children Book Publisher
N.A.I.C.S.: 513130
Rachel Hickman (Deputy Mng Dir)
Elinor Bagenal (Dir-Rights)
Rachel Leyshon (Dir-Editorial)
Esther Waller (Mgr-Publ)
Laura Myers (Mgr-Publ)

Scholastic Limited   (3)
Westfield Road, Southam, CV47 0RA, Warwickshire, United Kingdom
Tel.: (44) 01926813910
Web Site: https://www.scholastic.co.uk
Sales Range: $10-24.9 Million
Emp.: 80
Book & Journal Publisher
N.A.I.C.S.: 513130

Subsidiary (Domestic):

The Scholastic Store, Inc.   (2)
557 Broadway, New York, NY 10012
Tel.: (212) 343-6166
Web Site: http://store.scholastic.com
Children Book Publisher
N.A.I.C.S.: 513130

SCHOOL SPECIALTY, INC.
W6316 Design Dr, Greenville, WI 54942
Tel.: (419) 589-1425   **WI**
Web Site:
   https://www.schoolspecialty.com
Year Founded: 1959
SCOO—(OTCIQ)
Rev.: $626,073,000
Assets: $234,742,000
Liabilities: $215,958,000
Net Worth: $18,784,000
Earnings: ($49,548,000)
Emp.: 1,136
Fiscal Year-end: 12/28/19
Non-Textbook Educational Supplies & Furniture Distr
N.A.I.C.S.: 424120
Gus D. Halas (Chm)
Kevin L. Baehler (CFO & Exec VP)
Ryan M. Bohr (COO & Exec VP)
Laura Vartanian (Sr VP-HR)
Stacey Rubin (Sr VP-Mktg)
Bodie Marx (Sr VP-Curriculum)
Allen Hoeppner (Sr VP-Mdsg & Category Mgmt)
Joseph Geltz (Sr VP-Ops & Process Excellence)
Michael Buenzow (Interim CEO)

Subsidiaries:

Califone International, Inc.   (1)
9135 Alabama Ave Ste B, Chatsworth, CA 91311
Tel.: (818) 407-2400
Web Site: http://www.califone.com
Emp.: 10
Audio & Video Equipment Mfr
N.A.I.C.S.: 334310
Grace Sun (Mgr-Product Sls & Mktg)

Childcraft Education Corporation   (1)
1156 4 Star Dr, Mount Joy, PA 17552   (100%)
Tel.: (717) 653-7500
Web Site:
   http://www.childcrafteducation.com
Sales Range: $50-74.9 Million
Emp.: 200
Catalog & Direct Mail Early Childhood Educational Toys & Classroom Materials
N.A.I.C.S.: 611710

Delta Education, LLC   (1)

80 Northwest Blvd, Nashua, NH 03061-3000
Tel.: (603) 579-3400
Web Site: http://www.deltaeducation.com
Sales Range: $50-74.9 Million
Emp.: 250
Elementary School Science & Math Materials Publisher
N.A.I.C.S.: 339930

Frey Scientific, Inc.   (1)
80 Northwest Blvd, Nashua, NH 03061-3000
Web Site: http://www.freyscientific.com
Educational Products Retailer
N.A.I.C.S.: 423490

Sax Arts & Crafts, Inc.   (1)
W6316 Design Dr, Greenville, WI 54942
Tel.: (800) 558-6696
Web Site: http://www.saxarts.com
Arts & Craft Items Whslr
N.A.I.C.S.: 459120

School Specialty Canada, Ltd.   (1)
103 - 20230 64th Avenue, Langley, V2Y 1N3, BC, Canada
Stationery Product Whslr
N.A.I.C.S.: 424120

Triumph Learning, LLC   (1)
136 Madison Ave, New York, NY 10016
Tel.: (212) 652-0200
Teaching Aids, Educational Content & Materials Provider
N.A.I.C.S.: 513199

SCHRODINGER, INC.
1540 Broadway 24th Fl, New York, NY 10036
Tel.: (212) 295-5800   **DE**
Web Site:
   https://www.schrodinger.com
Year Founded: 1990
SDGR—(NASDAQ)
Rev.: $180,955,000
Assets: $688,587,000
Liabilities: $240,682,000
Net Worth: $447,905,000
Earnings: ($149,186,000)
Emp.: 787
Fiscal Year-end: 12/31/22
Software Development Services
N.A.I.C.S.: 541511
Robert Abel (Exec VP)
Shane Brauner (CIO & Exec VP)
Mathew D. Halls (Sr VP-Materials Science)
Patrick Lorton (CTO & Exec VP)
Matt Repasky (Sr VP-Life Sciences Products)
Jenny Herman (Principal Acctg Officer, Sr VP-Fin & Controller)
Mike Beachy (Sr VP-Software Dev)
Jaren Madden (Sr VP-IR & Comm)
Geoffrey Porges (CFO & Exec VP)
Nathalie Lacoste (Sr VP)
Raghu Rangaswamy (VP)
Tomoko Satoh (VP)
Robert K. Suto (VP)
Frank Taffy (Sr VP)
Ramy Farid (Pres & CEO)
Richard A. Friesner (Co-Founder)
Karen Akinsanya (Pres-R&D & Therapeutics)

SCHULTZE SPECIAL PURPOSE ACQUISITION CORP.
800 Westchester Ave Ste 632, Rye Brook, NY 10573
Tel.: (914) 701-5260   **DE**
Web Site:
   http://www.samcospac.com
Year Founded: 2018
SAMA—(NASDAQ)
Rev.: $2,946,660
Assets: $133,061,140
Liabilities: $128,061,136
Net Worth: $5,000,004
Earnings: $1,812,272
Fiscal Year-end: 12/31/19

Investment Services
N.A.I.C.S.: 523999
George J. Schultze (Chm, Pres & CEO)
Gary M. Julien (Exec VP)
Jeffrey M. Glick (CFO)
Scarlett Du (Sec)
Bill Skolnick (VP-Bus Dev)

SCI ENGINEERED MATERIALS, INC.
2839 Charter St, Columbus, OH 43228
Tel.: (614) 486-0261   **OH**
Web Site:
   https://www.sciengineeredmaterials.com
Year Founded: 1987
SCIA—(OTCQB)
Rev.: $27,984,083
Assets: $17,486,420
Liabilities: $6,506,387
Net Worth: $10,980,033
Earnings: $2,193,899
Emp.: 23
Fiscal Year-end: 12/31/23
Semiconductor & Related Device Mfr
N.A.I.C.S.: 334413
Michael A. Smith (Sec)
Gerald S. Blaskie (CFO & VP)
Laura F. Shunk (Chm)
Jeremiah R. Young (Pres & CEO)

SCIENCE APPLICATIONS INTERNATIONAL CORPORATION
12010 Sunset Hills Rd, Reston, VA 20190
Tel.: (703) 676-4300
Web Site: https://www.saic.com
SAIC—(NYSE)
Rev.: $7,444,000,000
Assets: $5,314,000,000
Liabilities: $3,529,000,000
Net Worth: $1,785,000,000
Earnings: $477,000,000
Emp.: 24,000
Fiscal Year-end: 02/02/24
Technical Engineering & Enterprise Information Technology Services
N.A.I.C.S.: 541512
Nazzic S. Keene (Bd of Dirs, Executives)
Michelle A. O'Hara (Chief HR Officer & Exec VP)
Mark Escobar (Exec VP)
Josh Jackson (Sr VP-Naval Bus Unit)
Gabe Camarillo (Sr VP-Army Bus Unit)
Bridget Chatman (VP-Inclusion, Diversity & Corp Social Responsibility)
Prabu Natarajan (CFO & Exec VP)
David Ray (Sr VP-Space Bus)
Blake Nelson (VP-Platforms & Cloud Solutions)
Hilary L. Hageman (Gen Counsel, Sec & Exec VP)
Shane Sims (VP-Logistics & Supply Chain)
Collin Lee (VP-Bus Dev-Space)
Lauren Knausenberger (Chief Innovation Officer & Exec VP)
Toni Townes-Whitley (CEO)

Subsidiaries:

Engility Holdings, Inc.   (1)
4803 Stonecroft Blvd, Chantilly, VA 20151
Tel.: (703) 633-8300
Sales Range: $5-14.9 Billion
Holding Company; Systems Engineering Services
N.A.I.C.S.: 551112

Subsidiary (Domestic):

Engility Corporation   (2)
4803 Stonecroft Blvd, Chantilly, VA 20151
Tel.: (703) 633-8300
Financial Investment Services

N.A.I.C.S.: 523999

Halfaker & Associates, LLC   (1)
2900 S Quincy St Unit 410, Arlington, VA 22206-2281
Tel.: (703) 434-3900
Web Site: https://www.halfaker.com
Computer Facilities Management Services
N.A.I.C.S.: 541513
Dawn Halfaker (Pres & CEO)

Kinsey Technical Services, Inc.   (1)
14900 Bogle Dr Ste 103, Chantilly, VA 20151
Tel.: (703) 961-0046
Web Site: http://www.ktsi.net
Emp.: 50
Engineering Services
N.A.I.C.S.: 541330

Science Applications International Corporation - Huntsville   (1)
300 Voyager Way, Huntsville, AL 35806-3560
Tel.: (256) 837-7610
Sales Range: $200-249.9 Million
Emp.: 800
Computer Integrated Systems Design Services
N.A.I.C.S.: 541512

Science Applications International Corporation - Huntsville   (1)
4901 D Corporate Dr Northwest, Huntsville, AL 35805
Tel.: (256) 722-0190
Web Site: http://www.saic.com
Sales Range: $50-74.9 Million
Emp.: 4,000
Software Programming Applications
N.A.I.C.S.: 541511

SCIENCE STRATEGIC ACQUISITION CORP. ALPHA
1447 2nd St, Santa Monica, CA 90401
Tel.: (310) 393-3024   **DE**
Web Site: http://www.science-inc.com
Year Founded: 2020
SSAAU—(NASDAQ)
Investment Services
N.A.I.C.S.: 523999
Michael Jones (Chm & CEO)
Peter Pham (Pres)
Thomas Dare (CFO)
Priscilla Guevara (Head-IR)
April V. Henry (Exec VP-Corp Dev)

SCIENT, INC.
79 5th Ave, New York, NY 10003
Tel.: (212) 500-4900   **DE**
SCNTQ—(OTCIQ)
Information Technology Services
N.A.I.C.S.: 541511
Christopher Formant (CEO)
Jaques Tortoroli (CFO)

SCIENTIFIC ENERGY, INC.
27 Weldon St, Jersey City, NJ 07306
Tel.: (852) 253-0208   **UT**
SCGY—(OTCIQ)
Rev.: $44,111,814
Assets: $81,182,776
Liabilities: $14,251,827
Net Worth: $66,930,949
Earnings: ($3,766,129)
Emp.: 549
Fiscal Year-end: 12/31/22
Graphite Products Distr
N.A.I.C.S.: 423520
Stanley Chan (Chm, Pres, CEO, CFO & Sec)

SCIENTIFIC INDUSTRIES, INC.
80 Orville Dr Ste 102, Bohemia, NY 11716
Tel.: (631) 567-4700   **DE**
Web Site:
   https://www.scientificindustries.com
Year Founded: 1954
SCND—(OTCIQ)
Rev.: $9,775,200
Assets: $29,006,400

Liabilities: $2,781,600
Net Worth: $26,224,800
Earnings: ($3,672,500)
Emp.: 55
Fiscal Year-end: 06/30/21
Analytical Laboratory Instrument
Manufacturing
N.A.I.C.S.: 334516
Helena R. Santos *(Pres, CEO &
Treas)*

Subsidiaries:

Altamira Instruments, Inc.   (1)
149 Delta Dr, Pittsburgh, PA 15238
Tel.: (412) 963-6385
Web Site:
   http://www.altamirainstruments.com
Rev.: $5,000,000
Emp.: 12
Analytical Laboratory Instrument Mfr.
N.A.I.C.S.: 334516
Brook March *(Mgr-Mktg)*
Sharon Kiesel *(Office Mgr)*

SCIENTURE HOLDINGS, INC.
6308 Benjamin Rd Ste 708, Tampa,
FL 33634   DE
Web Site: https://scienture.com
Year Founded: 2005
SCNX—(NASDAQ)
Rev.: $8,272,214
Assets: $12,532,913
Liabilities: $11,990,560
Net Worth: $542,353
Earnings: ($17,843,574)
Emp.: 8
Fiscal Year-end: 12/31/23
Web Based Pharmaceutical Market-
place
N.A.I.C.S.: 551112
Yvonne Farrell *(Mgr-Client Relation-
ship)*
Jeff Davies *(Engr-Computer Sys Soft-
ware)*
Surendra Ajjarapu *(Chm & CEO)*
Prashant Patel *(Pres & COO)*

Subsidiaries:

Bonum Health, LLC   (1)
3840 Land O Lake Blvd, Land O Lakes, FL
34639
Health Care Srvices
N.A.I.C.S.: 621999

Community Specialty Pharmacy,
LLC   (1)
6308 Benjamin Rd Ste 709, Tampa, FL
33634
Tel.: (727) 896-0001
Web Site: http://www.comsprx.com
Medicine Distr
N.A.I.C.S.: 424210

Pinnacle Tek, Inc.   (1)
8913 Regents Park Dr Ste 680, Tampa, FL
33647
Tel.: (813) 601-3533
Web Site: http://www.pinnacle-tek.com
Information Technology Consulting Services
N.A.I.C.S.: 541512

Scienture, LLC   (1)
20 Austin Blvd, Commack, NY 11725
Tel.: (631) 670-6039
Web Site: https://scienture.com
Biopharmaceutical Developer
N.A.I.C.S.: 325412

Subsidiary (Domestic):

Scienture, Inc.   (2)
20 Austin Blvd, Commack, NY 11725
Tel.: (631) 670-6039
Web Site: https://scienture.com
Biopharmaceutical Developer
N.A.I.C.S.: 325412

SCILEX HOLDING COMPANY
960 San Antonio Rd, Palo Alto, CA
94303
Tel.: (650) 516-4310   DE

Web Site:
   https://www.scilexholding.com
Year Founded: 2020
SCLX—(NASDAQ)
Rev.: $38,034,000
Assets: $86,527,000
Liabilities: $50,288,000
Net Worth: $36,239,000
Earnings: ($23,364,000)
Emp.: 100
Fiscal Year-end: 12/31/22
Holding Company
N.A.I.C.S.: 551112
Henry H. Ji *(Exec Chm)*
Jaisim Shah *(Pres & CEO)*
Suketu D. Desai *(CTO & Sr VP)*
Dmitri Lissin *(Chief Medical Officer &
Sr VP)*
Suresh Khemani *(Chief Comml Offi-
cer & Sr VP)*
Steve Lincoln *(Chief Compliance Offi-
cer & Gen Counsel)*
Stephen Ma *(CFO & Sr VP)*
Elaine K. Chan *(Head-Medical Affairs
& Exec Dir)*
Gigi DeGuzman *(Head-Human Re-
sources & Exec Dir-Admin Ops)*
Mike Ciaffi *(Sls Dir-Natl)*
Sumant Rajendran *(Exec Dir-
Marketing)*

SCOOBEEZ GLOBAL, INC.
3463 Foothill Blvd, La Crescenta, CA
91214
Tel.: (818) 302-0100   ID
Web Site:
   http://www.abtholdings.com
Year Founded: 1957
SCBZ—(OTCIQ)
Sales Range: $25-49.9 Million
Investment Services
N.A.I.C.S.: 523999
Shahan Ohanessian *(Pres & CEO)*

SCOPUS BIOPHARMA INC.
420 Lexington Ave, New York, NY
10170
Tel.: (212) 479-2513   DE
Web Site:
   https://www.scopusbiopharma.com
Year Founded: 2017
SCPS—(OTCQB)
Assets: $392,265
Liabilities: $7,454,434
Net Worth: ($7,062,169)
Earnings: ($11,609,827)
Emp.: 13
Fiscal Year-end: 12/31/22
Biotechnology Research & Develop-
ment Services
N.A.I.C.S.: 541714
Joshua R. Lamstein *(Chm)*
Robert J. Gibson *(Vice Chm, Treas &
Sec)*
Ashish P. Sanghrajka *(Pres)*

SCORES HOLDING COMPANY,
INC.
34-35 Steinway St, Long Island City,
NY 11101
Tel.: (212) 246-9090   UT
Year Founded: 1981
SCRH—(OTCEM)
Rev.: $241,001
Assets: $211,404
Liabilities: $1,126,783
Net Worth: ($915,379)
Earnings: ($147,022)
Emp.: 3
Fiscal Year-end: 12/31/21
Holding Company; Gentleman's
Clubs
N.A.I.C.S.: 551112
Howard Rosenbluth *(CFO & Treas)*
Robert M. Gans *(Pres & CEO)*

Subsidiaries:

Scores Licensing Corp.   (1)
533 W 27th St Ste 535, New York, NY
10001
Tel.: (212) 868-4900
License Issuing Services
N.A.I.C.S.: 561990

SCORPIUS HOLDINGS, INC.
1305 E Houston St, San Antonio, TX
78205
Tel.: (919) 240-7133   DE
Web Site:
   https://www.scorpiusbiologics.com
Year Founded: 2008
SCPX—(NYSEAMEX)
Rev.: $6,383,169
Assets: $104,396,912
Liabilities: $31,960,244
Net Worth: $72,436,668
Earnings: ($43,434,706)
Emp.: 77
Fiscal Year-end: 12/31/22
Pharmaceuticals Mfr
N.A.I.C.S.: 325412
Jeffrey Alan Wolf *(Chm, Pres & CEO)*
Gary Vinson *(VP-Chemistry & Mfg
Controls)*
Matthew M. Seavey *(Exec Dir-Special
Projects)*
Guillermo Arana *(Exec Dir-Clinical
Dev)*

SCOTT'S LIQUID GOLD-INC.
470 Park Ave S, New York, NY
10016
Tel.: (646) 495-7333   CO
Web Site: https://horizonkinetics.com
Year Founded: 1954
SLGD—(OTCIQ)
Rev.: $16,570,000
Assets: $10,731,000
Liabilities: $7,911,000
Net Worth: $2,820,000
Earnings: ($8,851,000)
Emp.: 22
Fiscal Year-end: 12/31/22
Mfr of Wood Preservatives, Fine Fur-
niture & Wood Polish & Room Air
Fresheners
N.A.I.C.S.: 325611
Murray Stahl *(Co-Founder, Chm,
CEO & Chief Investment Officer)*
Steven Bregman *(Co-Founder &
Pres)*
Thomas Ewing *(Co-Founder & Mng
Dir)*
John Meditz *(Co-Founder & Sr Port-
folio Mgr)*
Alun Williams *(COO)*
Mark Herndon *(CFO)*
Jay Kesslen *(Mng Dir & Gen Coun-
sel)*
Darryl Monasebian *(Sr Portfolio Mgr)*
Brandon Colavita *(Portfolio Mgr)*
Andrew Parker *(Mng Dir)*
Aya Hirota Weissman *(Dir-Asia Strat-
egy & Sr Portfolio Mgr)*
Steven Tuen *(Portfolio Mgr-Res Ana-
lyst)*
Alan Swimmer *(Mng Dir)*
Eric Sites *(Portfolio Mgr-Res Analyst)*
Matthew Houk *(Portfolio Mgr-Res
Analyst)*
Andrea DeMichele *(Portfolio Mgr-
Client)*
James Davolos *(Portfolio Mgr-Res
Analyst)*
Rich Begun *(Sr Portfolio Mgr)*
Paul Abel *(Sr Portfolio Mgr)*
Chris McCarthy *(Mng Dir & Head-
Institutional Sls)*
Agustin Krisnawahjuesa *(Dir-Client
Service & Business Development)*
Chris Bell *(Mng Dir & Natl Sls Mgr)*
John Becker *(Sr VP)*

Kevin McRae *(Chief Information Se-
curity Officer & Dir-Technology)*
Russell Grimaldi *(Chief Compliance
Officer & Assoc Gen Counsel)*

Subsidiaries:

Colorado Product Concepts, Inc.   (1)
4880 Havana St, Denver, CO
80239-2416   (100%)
Tel.: (303) 373-4860
Web Site: http://www.scottsliquidgold.com
Sales Range: $50-74.9 Million
Mfr of Household Chemical Products, Skin
Care Products & Contract Packaging
N.A.I.C.S.: 325620

SLG Chemicals, Inc.   (1)
720 S Colorado Blvd PH N, Denver, CO
80246   (100%)
Tel.: (303) 373-4860
Web Site: https://www.slginc.com
Sales Range: $50-74.9 Million
Mfr of Household Chemical Products
N.A.I.C.S.: 325998

SLG Plastics, Inc.   (1)
4880 Havana St, Denver, CO
80239-2416   (100%)
Tel.: (303) 373-4860
Web Site: http://www.scottsliquidgold.com
Sales Range: $25-49.9 Million
Mfr of Injection Molded Plastics
N.A.I.C.S.: 326199

Scott's Liquid Gold- Advertising Pro-
motions, Inc.   (1)
4880 Havana St, Denver, CO
80239-2416   (100%)
Tel.: (303) 373-4860
Web Site: http://www.scottsliquidgold.com
Sales Range: $25-49.9 Million
In House Advertising Agency
N.A.I.C.S.: 325620

SCP & CO HEALTHCARE AC-
QUISITION COMPANY
2909 W Bay to Bay Blvd Ste 300,
Tampa, FL 33629
Tel.: (813) 318-9600   DE
Year Founded: 2020
SHACU—(NASDAQ)
N.A.I.C.S.:
Scott Feuer *(CEO)*
Bryan Crino *(Pres)*
Joseph Passero *(CFO)*

SCPHARMACEUTICALS, INC.
25 Mall Rd Ste 203, Burlington, MA
01803
Tel.: (617) 517-0730   DE
Web Site:
   https://www.scpharmaceuticals.com
Year Founded: 2013
SCPH—(NASDAQ)
Rev.: $1,203,000
Assets: $124,195,000
Liabilities: $51,762,000
Net Worth: $72,433,000
Earnings: ($36,838,000)
Emp.: 96
Fiscal Year-end: 12/31/22
Biotechnology Research & Develop-
ment Services
N.A.I.C.S.: 541714
Mike Hassman *(Sr VP-Technical
Ops)*
John Mohr *(Sr VP-Clinical Dev &
Medical Affairs)*
John H. Tucker *(Pres & CEO)*

SCREAMING EAGLE ACQUISI-
TION CORP.
955 5th Ave, New York, NY 10075
Tel.: (310) 209-7280   Ky
Year Founded: 2021
SCRM—(NASDAQ)
Rev.: $9,962,942
Assets: $760,412,422
Liabilities: $786,736,279
Net Worth: ($26,323,857)

Screaming Eagle Acquisition Corp.—(Continued)

Earnings: $22,511,785
Emp.: 3
Fiscal Year-end: 12/31/22
Investment Services
N.A.I.C.S.: 523999
Eli Baker *(CEO)*
Ryan O'Connor *(VP-Finance)*
Harry Evans Sloan *(Founder & Chm)*

SCRYPT CORPORATION

9050 N Capital of Texas Hwy Ste III-250, Austin, TX 78759
Tel.: (512) 493-6228
Web Site: http://www.scrypt.com
Year Founded: 1998
SYPT—(OTCIQ)
Sales Range: $1-9.9 Million
Document Management & Delivery Solutions
N.A.I.C.S.: 513210
Rich Trevivian *(VP-UX)*
Mike Walls *(VP-Dev)*
Sheri Cox *(Acct Mgr)*
Ruthie Gonzales *(Acct Mgr)*
Neil Burley *(CFO)*
Aleks Szymanski *(CEO)*
Nick Basil *(CTO)*
Paul Mise Jr. *(Mgr-Technical Support)*

Subsidiaries:

Scrypt Inc. **(1)**
2468 Historic Decatur Rd Suite 100, San Diego, CA 92106
Tel.: (858) 427-4301
Web Site: http://www.scrypt.com
Sales Range: $1-9.9 Million
Emp.: 15
Document Management Software Solutions
N.A.I.C.S.: 513210
Traci Basil *(Pres)*
Aleks Szymanski *(CEO)*

SCVX CORP.

1220 L St NW Ste 100-397, Washington, DC 20005
Tel.: (202) 681-8461 Ky
Web Site: http://www.scvx.com
Year Founded: 2019
SCVXU—(NYSE)
Rev.: $548,847
Assets: $231,527,508
Liabilities: $226,527,499
Net Worth: $5,000,009
Earnings: ($971,593)
Emp.: 3
Fiscal Year-end: 12/31/20
Investment Services
N.A.I.C.S.: 523999
Michael Doniger *(Chm & CEO)*
Hank Thomas *(CTO)*
Chris Ahern *(CFO & Sec)*
Abbie Ginis *(Mgr-Mktg & Ops)*

SCWORX CORP.

590 Madison Ave 21st Fl, New York, NY 10022
Tel.: (212) 739-7825 DE
Web Site: https://www.scworx.com
Year Founded: 2015
WORX—(NASDAQ)
Rev.: $3,804,943
Assets: $6,278,215
Liabilities: $2,424,766
Net Worth: $3,853,449
Earnings: ($3,981,144)
Emp.: 7
Fiscal Year-end: 12/31/23
Heath Care Software Solutions
N.A.I.C.S.: 513210
Alton F. Irby III *(Chm)*
Timothy A. Hannibal *(Pres & CEO)*
Christopher J. Kohler *(CFO)*

SCYNEXIS, INC.

1 Evertrust Plz 13th Fl, Jersey City, NJ 07302

Tel.: (201) 884-5485 DE
Web Site: https://www.scynexis.com
Year Founded: 1999
SCYX—(NASDAQ)
Rev.: $5,091,000
Assets: $87,810,000
Liabilities: $84,577,000
Net Worth: $3,233,000
Earnings: ($62,809,000)
Emp.: 36
Fiscal Year-end: 12/31/22
Pharmaceuticals Mfr
N.A.I.C.S.: 325412
David Angulo *(Pres & CEO)*
Yves Joseph Ribeill *(Executives)*
Ivor Macleod *(CFO & Principal Acctg Officer)*
Glen D. Park *(VP-Regulatory Affairs & Quality Assurance)*

SEABOARD CORPORATION

9000 W 67th St, Merriam, KS 66202
Tel.: (913) 676-8928 DE
Web Site:
https://www.seaboardcorp.com
Year Founded: 1918
SEB—(NYSEAMEX)
Rev.: $9,562,000,000
Assets: $7,566,000,000
Liabilities: $2,932,000,000
Net Worth: $4,634,000,000
Earnings: $226,000,000
Emp.: 12,847
Fiscal Year-end: 12/31/23
Diversified Agribusiness & Transportation Services
N.A.I.C.S.: 424470
Robert L. Steer *(Pres & CEO)*
David M. Becker *(Gen Counsel, Sec & Exec VP)*
Edward A. Gonzalez *(CEO-Marine-Seaboard Ops)*
Andriana N. Hoskins *(Treas & VP)*
Ty A. Tywater *(Sr VP-Audit Svcs)*
David H. Rankin *(CFO & Exec VP)*
Benjamin R. Hodes *(VP-Fin)*
Elizabeth A. Loudon *(VP-Tax)*
Emma A. Vacas Jacques *(Asst Treas)*
Peter Brown *(CEO-Pork-Seaboard Ops)*
Barbara M. Smith *(Principal Acctg Officer, VP & Controller)*

Subsidiaries:

Beira Grain Terminal, S.A. **(1)**
Praco Do CFM Behind Quayside 10, Beira, Mozambique
Tel.: (258) 843039203
Commodity Trading Services
N.A.I.C.S.: 523160
Miguel de Jenga *(CFO)*

Belarina Alimentos S.A. **(1)**
Rua Do Rocio 220 Conj 11 Sao Paulo, Vila Olimpia, 04552-000, Brazil
Tel.: (55) 40584500
Web Site: http://belarina.com.br
Emp.: 300
Wheat Milling & Whslr
N.A.I.C.S.: 311211

Butterball, LLC **(1)**
1 Butterball Ln, Garner, NC 27529 **(50%)**
Tel.: (919) 255-7900
Web Site: https://www.butterballcorp.com
Sales Range: $1-4.9 Billion
Turkey Processing
N.A.I.C.S.: 112330
Ron Tomaszewski *(VP-HR)*
Brett Worlow *(Gen Counsel & Sec)*

Subsidiary (Domestic):

Butterball, LLC **(2)**
411 N Main St, Carthage, MO 64836-1327
Tel.: (417) 423-8801
Web Site: http://www.butterballcorp.com
Sales Range: $50-74.9 Million
Emp.: 800
Turkey Processing
N.A.I.C.S.: 112330

Shawnda Doerr *(Mgr-Logistics)*

Butterball, LLC **(2)**
1240 E Diehl Rd, Naperville, IL 60563
Tel.: (630) 955-3000
Web Site: https://www.butterball.com
Sales Range: $10-24.9 Million
Emp.: 70
Turkey Processing
N.A.I.C.S.: 112330

Gusto Packing Co., Inc. **(2)**
2125 Rochester Dr, Montgomery, IL 60538
Tel.: (630) 896-8608
Web Site: http://www.gustopack.com
Sales Range: $10-24.9 Million
Emp.: 500
Packaged Meats Distr
N.A.I.C.S.: 311611
Ryan Ruettiger *(Mgr-Territory Sls)*
Dennis Keene *(VP-Sls & Mktg)*

Cape Fear Railways Inc. **(1)**
5519 Knox St Bldg 5, Fort Bragg, NC 28307
Tel.: (910) 396-7683
Sales Range: $1-9.9 Million
Emp.: 7
Railroads Line-Haul operating
N.A.I.C.S.: 482111

Eurafrique **(1)**
11Bis Cours Sextius, Aix-en-Provence, France
Tel.: (33) 442931951
Commodity Trading Services
N.A.I.C.S.: 523160

Fill-More Seeds Inc. **(1)**
1 Railway Ave, PO Box 70, Fillmore, S0G 1N0, SK, Canada
Tel.: (306) 722-3353
Web Site: http://www.fillmoreseeds.com
Sales Range: $25-49.9 Million
Crop Preparation & Shipping Services
N.A.I.C.S.: 325998

Flour Mills of Ghana Limited **(1)**
Gafco Industrial Complex Tema Port Area, Tema, Ghana
Tel.: (233) 50401200
Logistics Consulting Servies
N.A.I.C.S.: 541614

High Plains Bioenergy, LLC **(1)**
3291 Desert Rd, Guymon, OK 73942
Tel.: (580) 468-3790
Organic Chemical Mfr
N.A.I.C.S.: 325199

High Plains Transport LLC **(1)**
5964 Hwy 410, Mountain View, WY 82939
Tel.: (307) 782-6900
Emp.: 17
Local Trucking Services
N.A.I.C.S.: 484110
Blake Rinker *(Owner)*

Ingenio y Refineria San Martin del Tabacal S.A. **(1)**
Av Leandro N Alem 986 Piso 9, C1001AAR, Buenos Aires, Argentina **(100%)**
Tel.: (54) 1151672100
Web Site: http://www.tabacal.com.ar
Sales Range: $25-49.9 Million
Emp.: 50
Cane Sugar Refining
N.A.I.C.S.: 311314
Hugo Rossi *(Pres)*

InterAfrica Grains (Proprietary) Limited **(1)**
Coldstream Office Park Unit 18 Coldstream Street, Roodepoort, South Africa
Tel.: (27) 119581291
Logistics Consulting Servies
N.A.I.C.S.: 541614

Interra International Mexico, S. de R.L. de C.V. **(1)**
Av Ricardo Margain 575 Torre D Int 5644 Col Santa Engracia, San Pedro, 66267, Garza Garcia, Nuevo Leon, Mexico
Tel.: (52) 8180007541
Food Products Distr
N.A.I.C.S.: 424490

JacintoPort International LLC **(1)**
16398 Jacintoport Blvd, Houston, TX 77015
Tel.: (713) 673-7000
Web Site: https://www.jacintoport.com

Emp.: 300
Harbor Operations Services
N.A.I.C.S.: 488310

Les Grands Moulins de Dakar **(1)**
Avenue Felix Eboue, PO Box 2068, Dakar, Senegal
Tel.: (221) 338399797
Web Site: http://www.gmd.sn
Flour Milling Services
N.A.I.C.S.: 311211

Lesotho Flour Mills Limited **(1)**
44 Lioli Road Industrial Area, Maseru, 9300, Lesotho
Tel.: (266) 22313498
Web Site: http://www.lesothoflourmills.com
Flour Milling Services
N.A.I.C.S.: 311211
Ron Mills *(Mng Dir)*

Moderna Alimentos, S.A. **(1)**
Valderrama Oe7 Ycuero Caicedo, Guayaquil, Guayas, Ecuador
Tel.: (593) 994025981
Web Site: https://modernaalimentos.com.ec
Flour Milling & Marketing Services
N.A.I.C.S.: 311211

Mount Dora Farms, Inc. **(1)**
16398 Jacintoport Blvd, Houston, TX 77015-6586
Tel.: (713) 821-7439
Web Site: https://www.mountdorafarms.com
Sales Range: $50-74.9 Million
Emp.: 3
Jalapeno Pepper Producer & Distr
N.A.I.C.S.: 424480
Chris Corette *(Gen Mgr)*
Mario Velasquez *(Gen Mgr-Operations-Honduras)*
Julisa Alvarado *(Coord-Logistics)*
Alejandro Garrido *(Controller)*
Urania Erazo *(Plant Mgr)*
Alejandro Garrido *(Controller)*
Urania Erazo *(Plant Mgr)*

Subsidiary (Non-US):

Mount Dora Farms de Honduras SRL **(2)**
150 Metros Carretera Hacia Ajuterique, Comayagua, Honduras
Tel.: (504) 7720825
Web Site: http://www.mountdorafarms.com
Jalapeno Pepper Producer & Exporter
N.A.I.C.S.: 424480

PS International, LLC **(1)**
5309 E Ryan Pl, Sioux Falls, SD 57110
Tel.: (605) 332-1885
Web Site: http://www.psinternational.com
Industrial Commodity Trading Serviooo
N.A.I.C.S.: 523160

PSI Guyana Inc. **(1)**
Providence and McDoom, Georgetown, Guyana
Tel.: (592) 2330514
Web Site: https://www.psigyinvest.com
Seafood Whslr
N.A.I.C.S.: 424460

PSS Commodities, S. de R.L. de C.V. **(1)**
Tihuatlan No 15 Interior 904 San Jeronimo Aculco, Tecamachalco, 10400, Mexico, Mexico
Tel.: (52) 56069331
Web Site: http://www.psinternational.net
Logistics Consulting Servies
N.A.I.C.S.: 541614

Plum Grove Pty Ltd. **(1)**
Office 24 Manning Buildings 135 High Street Mall, Fremantle, 6160, WA, Australia
Tel.: (61) 894351022
Web Site: https://www.plumgrove.com.au
Farming Services
N.A.I.C.S.: 111998
Kate Rebeiro *(Sec)*
Pete Rees *(Mgr)*
Hayley Hobbs *(Mgr)*
Rikki Foss *(Gen Mgr & Mgr-Comm & Mktg)*
Tony Smith *(Dir)*

STI Holdings Inc. **(1)**
1831 Hardcastle Blvd, Purcell, OK 73080
Tel.: (405) 694-4418
Web Site: https://www.stoughtontrailers.com

Trailer Chas & Cargo Container Chas Mfr
N.A.I.C.S.: 336212

**Seaboard Energias Renovables y
Alimentos S.R.L.**   **(1)**
Encarnacion Ezcurra 365- Primer piso B,
C1107CLA, Buenos Aires, Argentina
Tel.: (54) 1151672100
Web Site: https://www.seaboard.com.ar
Sugar Distr
N.A.I.C.S.: 424490

Seaboard Energy Kansas, LLC   **(1)**
1043 Rd P, Hugoton, KS 67951
Tel.: (620) 604-0001
Web Site: https://seaboardenergy.com
Renewable Diesel Mfr
N.A.I.C.S.: 324199

**Seaboard Energy Oklahoma,
LLC**   **(1)**
3291 Desert Rd, Guymon, OK 73942
Tel.: (580) 468-3790
Pork Processing Services
N.A.I.C.S.: 311612

Seaboard Energy, LLC   **(1)**
9000 W 67th St, Shawnee Mission, KS
66202
Tel.: (913) 676-8800
Web Site: https://seaboardenergy.com
Renewable Energy Services
N.A.I.C.S.: 221118

**Seaboard Farms of Oklahoma
Inc.**   **(1)**
424 North Main St Ste 200, Guymon, OK
73942   **(100%)**
Tel.: (580) 338-1470
Web Site: http://www.seaboardfoods.com
Sales Range: $10-24.9 Million
Emp.: 865
Hogs
N.A.I.C.S.: 112210

Seaboard Foods LLC   **(1)**
2801 Hurliman Rd, Guymon, OK 73942
Tel.: (913) 261-2600
Web Site: https://www.seaboardfoods.com
Food Service Contractors
N.A.I.C.S.: 722310
Chad Groves (Pres & CEO)

Seaboard Foods Services Inc.   **(1)**
9000 W 67th St, Merriam, KS 66202
Tel.: (913) 261-2600
Web Site: https://www.seaboardfoods.com
Farrowing & Weanling Pig Services
N.A.I.C.S.: 112210

Seaboard Foods of Iowa, LLC   **(1)**
411 Lawler St, Iowa Falls, IA 50126
Tel.: (641) 648-5020
Emp.: 25
Commodity Trading Services
N.A.I.C.S.: 523160
Steve Huegerich (Mgr-Bus Dev)

Seaboard Marine Ltd. Inc.   **(1)**
8001 NW 79th Ave, Miami, FL
33166-2154   **(100%)**
Tel.: (305) 863-4444
Web Site: http://www.seaboardmarine.com
Sales Range: $200-249.9 Million
Deep Sea Foreign Transportation Of Freigh
N.A.I.C.S.: 483111
Edward Gonzales (Pres)

Seaboard Marine of Florida, Inc.   **(1)**
8001 NW 79th Ave, Miami, FL 33166-2154
Tel.: (305) 863-4444
Web Site: http://www.seaboardmarine.com
Sales Range: $350-399.9 Million
Shipping Consulting Services
N.A.I.C.S.: 488330

Seaboard Overseas Ltd.   **(1)**
9000 W 67th St Ste 300, Shawnee Mission,
KS 66202-3631   **(100%)**
Tel.: (913) 676-8800
Web Site:
    http://www.seaboardoverseas.com
Sales Range: $200-249.9 Million
Emp.: 200
Provider of Sea Freight Transport Services
N.A.I.C.S.: 523160

Seaboard Overseas Peru S.A.   **(1)**
Av Victor Andres Belaunde 332 Oficina 302,
Torre Cromo, San Isidro, Peru
Tel.: (51) 13777030

Animal Feed Mfr
N.A.I.C.S.: 311119

**Seaboard Overseas Trading and
Shipping (PTY) Ltd.**   **(1)**
1st Floor Milkwood West Building 1 Milk-
wood Crescent, Milkwood Park Douglas
Saunders Drive La Lucia, Durban, 4319,
South Africa
Tel.: (27) 315814500
Web Site:
    http://www.seaboardoverseas.com
Emp.: 55
Shipping Services
N.A.I.C.S.: 488330

Seaboard Sales Corp.   **(1)**
9000 W 67th St, Shawnee Mission, KS
66202-3631
Tel.: (913) 676-8800
Web Site: http://www.seaboard.com
Sales Range: $25-49.9 Million
Emp.: 45
Industrial Supplies
N.A.I.C.S.: 423840

Seaboard Ship Management Inc.   **(1)**
2825 N University Dr Ste 240, Coral
Springs, FL 33065
Tel.: (954) 846-1377
Web Site: http://www.seaboard.com
Sales Range: $10-24.9 Million
Emp.: 24
Management Consulting Services
N.A.I.C.S.: 541618
Claudio Dabelic (VP)

**Seaboard Trading & Shipping Ltd.
Inc.**   **(1)**
9000 W 67th St, Shawnee Mission, KS
66202
Tel.: (913) 722-2769
Web Site:
    http://www.seaboardoverseas.com
Sales Range: $200-249.9 Million
Emp.: 200
Commodity Contracts Brokers, Dealers
N.A.I.C.S.: 523160

Seaboard Transport LLC   **(1)**
9000 W 67th St, Shawnee Mission, KS
66202
Tel.: (913) 261-2600
Web Site: http://www.seaboardtransport.net
Transportation Services
N.A.I.C.S.: 488510

Seaboard de Colombia, S.A.   **(1)**
Cra 12 No 79-43 Officina 701, Santa Fe,
Bogota, Colombia
Tel.: (57) 13130513
Web Site: http://www.seaboardmarine.com
Shipping Agents
N.A.I.C.S.: 488330
Gabriel Majia (Gen Mgr)

Seaboard de Nicaragua, S.A.   **(1)**
Km 9 Carretera Norte Contiguo a Texaco
La Subasta, Managua, Nicaragua
Tel.: (505) 22337201
Web Site: http://www.seaboardmarine.com
Marine Shipping Services
N.A.I.C.S.: 488330
Mauricio Barberena (Country Mgr)

**Unga Farmcare (East Africa)
Limited**   **(1)**
Ngano House Commercial Street, PO Box
41788 - 00100, Dakar Road Industrial Area,
Nairobi, 100, Kenya
Tel.: (254) 207603170
Web Site: http://ungagroup.com
Animal Feed Mfr
N.A.I.C.S.: 311119

SEACHANGE INTERNA-
TIONAL, INC.
177 Huntington Ave Ste 1703, Bos-
ton, MA 02115-3153
Tel.: (978) 897-0100   DE
Web Site:
    https://www.seachange.com
Year Founded: 1993
SEAC—(NASDAQ)
Rev.: $32,493,000
Assets: $42,659,000
Liabilities: $11,448,000
Net Worth: $31,211,000

Earnings: ($11,404,000)
Emp.: 108
Fiscal Year-end: 01/31/23
Radio & Television Broadcasting &
Wireless Communications Equipment
Manufacturing
N.A.I.C.S.: 334220
Mark P. Szynkowski (CFO, Treas &
Sr VP)
Chris Klimmer (Pres & CEO)
Peter D. Aquino (Exec Chm)

Subsidiaries:

**Sea Change Asia Pacific Operations
Pte. Ltd.**   **(1)**
20 Jalan Afifi 08-06 Cisco Center, Singa-
pore, 409179, Singapore   **(100%)**
Tel.: (65) 68423531
Sales Range: $1-9.9 Million
Emp.: 5
N.A.I.C.S.: 334413

SeaChange India Private, Ltd.   **(1)**
3rd Floor Gujrals CST Road, Kalina Santa-
cruz, Mumbai, 400098, Maharashtra, India
Tel.: (91) 2267104190
Sales Range: $10-24.9 Million
Emp.: 8
Audio & Video Equipment Mfr
N.A.I.C.S.: 334310

SeaChange NLG B.V.   **(1)**
Flight Forum 3200 Geb C, 5657EW, Eind-
hoven, Netherlands
Tel.: (31) 402488176
Web Site: http://www.seachange.com
Financial Management Consulting Services
N.A.I.C.S.: 541611

SeaChange Polska Sp zoo   **(1)**
ul Przesok 2 Astoria, 00-032, Warsaw, Ma-
zowieckie, Poland
Tel.: (48) 222131665
Electronic System Whslr
N.A.I.C.S.: 423690

Xstream North America, Inc.   **(1)**
50 Nagog Pk, Acton, MA 01720
Tel.: (508) 897-0100
Web Site: http://www.xstream.net
Television Broadcasting Services
N.A.I.C.S.: 334220

Xstream Sp. z o.o.   **(1)**
Ul Przesok 2 ASTORIA Premium Offices,
00032, Warsaw, Poland
Tel.: (48) 222131665
Television Broadcasting Services
N.A.I.C.S.: 334220

SEACOAST BANKING COR-
PORATION OF FLORIDA
815 Colorado Ave, Stuart, FL 34994
Tel.: (772) 287-4000   FL
Web Site:
    https://www.seacoastbanking.com
Year Founded: 1983
SBCF—(NASDAQ)
Rev.: $446,585,000
Assets: $12,145,762,000
Liabilities: $10,537,987,000
Net Worth: $1,607,775,000
Earnings: $106,507,000
Emp.: 1,490
Fiscal Year-end: 12/31/22
Bank Holding Company
N.A.I.C.S.: 551111
Juliette P. Kleffel (COO)
Charles M. Shaffer (Chm, Pres &
CEO)
Joseph M. Forlenza (Chief Risk Offi-
cer & Exec VP)
Juliette P. Kleffel (Chief Banking Offi-
cer)
Daniel G. Chappell (Chief HR Officer
& Exec VP)
Tracey L. Dexter (CFO & Exec VP)
Austen Carroll (Chief Lending Officer
& Exec VP)
Jennifer Reissman (CMO & Exec VP)
James Stallings (Chief Credit Officer)

Subsidiaries:

Apollo Bancshares, Inc.   **(1)**
1150 S Miami Ave, Miami, FL 33130
Tel.: (305) 398-9000
Web Site: https://www.apollobank.com
Bank Holding Company
N.A.I.C.S.: 551111
Eddy Arriola (Chm & CEO)

Subsidiary (Domestic):

Apollo Bank   **(2)**
1150 S Miami Ave, Miami, FL 33130
Tel.: (305) 398-9000
Web Site: http://www.apollobank.com
Sales Range: $25-49.9 Million
Emp.: 48
Banking Services
N.A.I.C.S.: 522110
Eduardo J. Arriola (Chm & CEO)
German Olivera (Sr VP)
Joaquin Medina (Sr VP-Client Mgmt)
Miguel Lavastia (Mgr-IT)

Seacoast National Bank   **(1)**
815 Colorado Ave, Stuart, FL 34994-3053
Tel.: (772) 221-2760
Web Site: https://www.seacoastbank.com
Sales Range: $200-249.9 Million
Commericial Banking
N.A.I.C.S.: 522110
Juliette P. Kleffel (Pres-Reg Market-Central
Florida)
Christine Woods (Officer-Trust & Sr VP)
Carl Newton (Sr VP)
Steve Compton (VP-Private Advisor)
Tobias Meek (Sr VP)
Dennis Nolte (Sr VP-Financial Advisor)
Sam Fragale (VP-Private Advisor)
Justin Hardy (Sr VP)
Luis Vera (VP-Private Advisor)

Subsidiary (Domestic):

Legacy Bank of Florida   **(2)**
2300 Glades Rd Ste 120w, Boca Raton, FL
33431
Tel.: (561) 347-1970
Web Site: http://www.legacybankfl.com
Sales Range: $1-9.9 Million
Emp.: 32
Commercial Banks, Not Chartered
N.A.I.C.S.: 522110
Dennis Bedley (Chm & CEO)
Richard A. Simpson (Pres-West Palm
Beach Market)
Becky Buchanan (Sr VP)
Bradley R. Meredith (CFO & Exec VP)
Marcia K. Snyder (COO, Chief Lending Offi-
cer & Exec VP)
Cassandra Walker (VP-Sls & Mktg)
Marilyn Wilson (Sr VP)
John W. Lowery Jr. (Chief Credit Officer &
Exec VP)

SEACOR MARINE HOLDINGS
INC.
Corporate Secretary, Houston, TX
77079
Tel.: (346) 980-1700   DE
Web Site:
    https://www.seacormarine.com
Year Founded: 2014
SMHI—(NYSE)
Rev.: $217,325,000
Assets: $815,630,000
Liabilities: $436,484,000
Net Worth: $379,146,000
Earnings: ($71,650,000)
Emp.: 1,286
Fiscal Year-end: 12/31/22
Offices of Other Holding Companies
N.A.I.C.S.: 551112
John M. Gellert (Pres & CEO)
Jesus Llorca (CFO & Exec VP)
Andrew H. Everett (Gen Counsel,
Sec & Sr VP)
Gregory S. Rossmiller (Chief Acctg
Officer & Sr VP)
Tim Clerc (VP-Engrg)

SEAFARER EXPLORATION
CORP.

Seafarer Exploration Corp.—(Continued)

14497 N Dale Mabry Hwy Ste 209-N, Tampa, FL 33618
Tel.: (813) 448-3577 **DE**
Web Site:
https://www.seafarerexploration corp.com
SFRX—(OTCIQ)
Rev.: $12,972
Assets: $343,384
Liabilities: $1,839,081
Net Worth: ($1,495,697)
Earnings: ($2,616,601)
Fiscal Year-end: 12/31/22
Archaeologically-Sensitive Exploration & Recovery Services
N.A.I.C.S.: 488390
Kyle Kennedy (Founder, Chm, Pres & CEO)
Tim Reynolds (Head & Engr)
Dante Volpe (Sr Engr)

SEAGEN INC.
21823 30th Dr SE, Bothell, WA 98021
Tel.: (425) 527-4000 **WA**
Web Site: https://www.seagen.com
Year Founded: 1998
SGEN—(NASDAQ)
Rev.: $1,962,412,000
Assets: $3,674,532,000
Liabilities: $870,713,000
Net Worth: $2,803,819,000
Earnings: ($610,308,000)
Emp.: 3,256
Fiscal Year-end: 12/31/22
Monoclonal Antibodies Developer for the Treatment of Cancer
N.A.I.C.S.: 325414
Felix J. Baker (Chm)
Christopher Pawlowicz (Exec VP-HR)
Vaughn B. Himes (Chief Technical Officer)
Charles R. Romp (Exec VP-Comml)
Todd E. Simpson (CFO)
Nancy Whiting (Exec VP-Corp Strategy, Alliances & Comm)
Tuomo Patsi (Exec VP-Commercial-Intl)
Roger D. Dansey (Pres-R&D)
Lee Heeson (Exec VP)
Karin Tollefson (Sr VP & Head-Global Medical Affairs)
Clay B. Siegall (Co-Founder)
Jean I. Liu (Gen Counsel & Exec VP-Legal Affairs)
Albert Bourla (Chm & CEO)

Subsidiaries:

Cascadian Therapeutics, Inc. (1)
21823 30th Dr SE, Seattle, WA 98021
Tel.: (206) 801-2100
Web Site: http://www.seattlegenetics.com
Cancer Treatment Biotechnology Services
N.A.I.C.S.: 325412

Seagen Austria GmbH (1)
Teinfaltstrasse 8/4, 1010, Vienna, Austria
Tel.: (43) 72 077 8105
Web Site: https://www.seagen.at
Pharmaceuticals Product Mfr
N.A.I.C.S.: 325412

Seagen B.V. (1)
Evert van de Beekstraat 1-104, 1118 CL, Schiphol, Netherlands
Tel.: (31) 20 241 9041
Biotechnology Research Services
N.A.I.C.S.: 541714

Seagen Spain, S.L. (1)
Avenida de Bruselas 7, Alcobendas, 28108, Madrid, Spain
Tel.: (34) 919011012
Pharmaceuticals Product Mfr
N.A.I.C.S.: 325412

SEALED AIR CORPORATION

2415 Cascade Pointe Blvd, Charlotte, NC 28208
Tel.: (980) 221-3235 **DE**
Web Site: https://www.sealedair.com
Year Founded: 1960
SEE—(NYSE)
Rev.: $5,488,900,000
Assets: $7,200,600,000
Liabilities: $6,651,100,000
Net Worth: $549,500,000
Earnings: $341,600,000
Emp.: 17,000
Fiscal Year-end: 12/31/23
Food & Protective Packaging Products & Systems Mfr & Sales
N.A.I.C.S.: 326111
Sergio A. Pupkin (Chief Growth & Strategy Officer & Sr VP)
Angel Shelton Willis (Gen Counsel, Sec & VP)
Sergio Pupkin (Sr VP)
Veronika Johnson (Chief Acctg Officer & Controller)
Patrick M. Kivits (CEO)
Emile Z. Chammas (COO & Sr VP)
Dustin J. Semach (Pres & CFO)

Subsidiaries:

AFP (Shanghai) Limited (1)
Room 2602 Summit Center 1088 Yanan West Road, Shanghai, 200052, China
Tel.: (86) 2162487677
Publish Newsletter & Book Services
N.A.I.C.S.: 813910

APS Verwaltungs-GmbH (1)
Wallenrodstr 1, 91126, Schwabach, Germany
Tel.: (49) 912293930
Web Site: http://www.aps-immobilien.com
Real Estate Services
N.A.I.C.S.: 531390

Aconcagua Distribuciones SRL (1)
Libertad 940, Buenos Aires, Argentina
Tel.: (54) 48160741
Web Site: https://www.aconcagua-srl.com.ar
Healthcare Product Distr
N.A.I.C.S.: 424490

Automated Packaging Systems Comercial Importacao do Brasil Ltda. (1)
EZ Tower Office Tower B - 22 andar, R Arquiteto Olavo Redig de Campos 105, Sao Paulo, 04711-905, Brazil
Tel.: (55) 1938474847
Web Site: http://www.autobag.com.br
Plastic Bag Product Mfr
N.A.I.C.S.: 326111

Automated Packaging Systems Europe (1)
Leuvensesteenweg 542 Unit D, 1930, Zaventem, Belgium
Tel.: (32) 2 725 3100
Web Site: https://www.autobag.be
Plastic Bag Product Mfr
N.A.I.C.S.: 326111
Guy Van Acker (Gen Mgr)

Automated Packaging Systems GmbH & Co. KG (1)
Heinrich-Eberhardt-Str 10, 38304, Wolfenbuttel, Germany
Tel.: (49) 5331903830
Web Site: https://www.autobag.de
Plastic Bag Product Mfr
N.A.I.C.S.: 326111
Thomas Prautsch (Sls Mgr)

Automated Packaging Systems Inc. (1)
10175 Philipp Pkwy, Streetsboro, OH 44241-4706
Tel.: (330) 342-2000
Web Site: http://www.autobag.com
Mfr of Packaging Equipment & Plastic Bags
N.A.I.C.S.: 326111
Hershey Lerner (Co-Founder)
Bernie Lerner (Co-Founder)

Automated Packaging Systems Limited (1)
Enigma Business Park Sandys Road,

Malvern, WR14 1JJ, Worcestershire, United Kingdom
Tel.: (44) 168 489 1400
Web Site: https://www.autobag.co.uk
Plastic Bag Product Mfr
N.A.I.C.S.: 326111
Andy Pretious (Mgr-Sales-Marketing)

B+ Equipment SAS (1)
465 Avenue du Col de l'Ange, 13420, Gemenos, France
Tel.: (33) 442361500
Web Site: https://www.bplus-equip.com
Industrial Equipment Mfr & Distr
N.A.I.C.S.: 333993

Cryovac Londrina Ltda. (1)
Rua Francisca Hosken de Farias Castro 235, Parque Industrial Kiugo Takata, Londrina, 86042-400, Parana, Brazil
Tel.: (55) 4333427812
Food Packaging & Bubble Wrap Mfr
N.A.I.C.S.: 311999

Cryovac, Inc. (1)
100 Rogers Bridge Rd Bldg A, Duncan, SC 29334 (100%)
Tel.: (864) 433-2000
Web Site: http://www.cryovac.com
Sales Range: $250-299.9 Million
Emp.: 930
Flexible Plastic Packaging Materials & Equipment Mfr & Sales
N.A.I.C.S.: 326150

Subsidiary (Domestic):

Cryovac International Holdings, Inc. (2)
100 Rogers Bridge Rd Bldg A, Duncan, SC 29334
Tel.: (864) 433-2000
Emp.: 200
Holding Company
N.A.I.C.S.: 551112
Karl Deily (Pres)

Subsidiary (Non-US):

Cryovac Australia Pty. Ltd. (3)
1126 Sydney Rd, Fawkner, 3060, VIC, Australia (100%)
Tel.: (61) 393582244
Web Site: http://www.sealedair.com
Food Packaging Mfr
N.A.I.C.S.: 322219

Diversey (Malaysia) Sdn. Bhd. (1)
No 6 Jalan Utarid U5/14 Seksyen U5, 40150, Shah Alam, Selangor Darul Ehsan, Malaysia
Tel.: (60) 378597223
Web Site: https://diversey.com.my
Chemical Products Distr
N.A.I.C.S.: 424690
Janice Wong (Dir-Fin)

Diversey (Private) Limited (1)
12-D Commercial 1st Floor E M E Sector DHA, Lahore, Pakistan
Tel.: (92) 4235254603
Chemical Products Distr
N.A.I.C.S.: 424690

Diversey Acting Off-shore Capital Management Limited Liability Company (1)
Puskas Tivadar u 6, 2040, Budaors, Hungary
Tel.: (36) 23509100
Cleaning & Sanitation Product Distr
N.A.I.C.S.: 423720

Diversey Brasil Industria Quimica Ltda. (1)
Rua Nossa Senhora Do Socorro 125, Sao Paulo, 04764-020, Brazil
Tel.: (55) 1156811300
Soap & Detergents Distr
N.A.I.C.S.: 424690

Diversey Danmark ApS (1)
Teglbuen 10, Niva, Fredensborg, 2990, Denmark
Tel.: (45) 70106611
Web Site: http://www.sealedair.com
Emp.: 50
Chemical Products Distr
N.A.I.C.S.: 424690

Diversey Egypt Limited (1)

Block 1258 D Plot 1 2 Masaken, Sheraton Heliopolis, Cairo, Egypt
Tel.: (20) 222650100
Janitorial Services
N.A.I.C.S.: 561720
Mahmoud Khoder (District Mgr-Sls)

Diversey Espana Production, S.L. (1)
Parque de Negocios Viladecans Calle Antonio Machado 78-80, Viladecans, 08840, Spain
Tel.: (34) 902010602
Web Site: http://www.diverseysolutions.com
Cleaning & Sanitation Product Distr
N.A.I.C.S.: 423720

Diversey France Services S.A.S. (1)
201 rue Carnot, 94120, Fontenay-sous-Bois, France
Tel.: (33) 145147676
Web Site: https://diversey.fr
Cleaning & Sanitation Product Distr
N.A.I.C.S.: 423720

Diversey Germany Production OHG (1)
Mallaustrasse 50-56, 68219, Mannheim, Germany
Tel.: (49) 62187570
Web Site: https://diversey.com
Cleaning & Sanitation Product Distr
N.A.I.C.S.: 423720

Diversey Hellas Societe Anonyme Cleaning and Trading Systems (1)
5 Heimarras, 15125, Maroussi, Greece
Tel.: (30) 2106385900
Web Site: http://www.diverseysolutions.com
Cleaning & Sanitation Product Distr
N.A.I.C.S.: 423720
George Vassilakos (Mng Dir)

Diversey Hungary Manufacture and Trade Limited Liability Company (1)
Puskas Tivadar u 6, 2040, Budaors, Hungary
Tel.: (36) 23509100
Cleaning & Sanitation Product Distr
N.A.I.C.S.: 423720

Diversey Hygiene (Thailand) Co., Ltd. (1)
33/4 The Nine Tower Grand Rama 9 27th Floor Building B, Rama 9 Road Huai Khwang Subdistrict Huai Khwang District, Bangkok, 10310, Thailand
Tel.: (66) 21088100
Web Site: https://diversey.co.th
Chemical Products Distr
N.A.I.C.S.: 424690
Piyada Pannak (Acct Mgr)

Diversey India Private Limited (1)
501 5th Floor Ackruti Centre Point MIDC Central Road, Andheri E, Mumbai, India
Tel.: (91) 2266444222
Soap & Detergent Mfr
N.A.I.C.S.: 325611

Diversey Israel Ltd. (1)
North Ind Zone 14 Dotan St HaMerkaz, PO Box 13260, Yavne, Israel
Tel.: (972) 9323700
Soap & Detergent Mfr
N.A.I.C.S.: 325611
Miki Alterman (Mgr-IT Ops & Svcs)

Diversey Italy Production s.r.l. (1)
Strada St 235, 26010, Bagnolo Cremasco, Italy
Tel.: (39) 03732051
Web Site: http://www.sealedair.com
Emp.: 64
Soap & Detergent Mfr
N.A.I.C.S.: 325611

Diversey Jamaica Limited (1)
83 Hagley Park Road, Kingston, 10, Jamaica
Tel.: (876) 9268678
Chemical Products Distr
N.A.I.C.S.: 424690

Diversey Kimya Sanayi ve Ticaret A.S. (1)
Muallimkoy Sapagi Serenlikuyu Mevkii No 10, Gebze, Turkiye
Tel.: (90) 2626485000
Chemical Products Distr
N.A.I.C.S.: 424690

Diversey LLC **(1)**
Leningradskaya 39 bldg 6 7th floor/B,
141400, Moscow, Russia
Tel.: (7) 4959701797
Janitorial Services
N.A.I.C.S.: 561720

Diversey Maroc S.A. **(1)**
Bd Ahl Loughlam side road 1015 Indusparc
Imm B2 1st floor, Sidi Moumen, Casa-
blanca, Morocco
Tel.: (212) 522756506
Toilet Preparation Mfr
N.A.I.C.S.: 325620

**Diversey Netherlands Production
B.V.** **(1)**
Rembrandtlaan 414, 7545 ZW, Enschede,
Netherlands
Tel.: (31) 534887766
Soap & Detergent Mfr
N.A.I.C.S.: 325611
Rood Niglant *(Plant Mgr)*

Diversey New Zealand Limited **(1)**
3 Diversey Lane Manukau Central, Glen-
dene, Auckland, 2025, New Zealand
Tel.: (64) 800803615
Cleaning & Sanitation Product Mfr
N.A.I.C.S.: 332999

Diversey Peru S.A.C. **(1)**
Av Avenida Oscar R Benavides Ste 5849,
Entre Universitaria Y Colonial, 1, Callao,
Peru
Tel.: (51) 16145900
Cleaning & Sanitation Product Mfr
N.A.I.C.S.: 332999

Diversey Philippines, Inc. **(1)**
8th Floor Bankmer Building 6756 Ayala Av-
enue, Makati, 1226, Philippines
Tel.: (63) 282712400
Chemical Products Distr
N.A.I.C.S.: 424690
Orlando Solano *(Mgr-Sector)*

**Diversey Portugal - Sistemas de
Higiene e Limpeza, Unipessoal,
Lda.** **(1)**
Avenida Dr Luis De Sa 6/8/10 Zona Indus-
trial Da Abrunheira, 2714-505, Sintra, Portu-
gal
Tel.: (351) 219157000
Chemical Products Distr
N.A.I.C.S.: 424690

Diversey Romania S.R.L. **(1)**
Banul Antonache Office Center 5th floor
Banul Antonache Street 40 - 44, Bucharest,
Romania
Tel.: (40) 212333894
Web Site: https://diversey.com.ro
Emp.: 34
Janitorial Services
N.A.I.C.S.: 561720

Diversey Singapore Pty. Ltd. **(1)**
ICON IBP Tower B 3A International Busi-
ness Park Road 06 18, Singapore, 609935,
Singapore
Tel.: (65) 31650891
Web Site: https://diversey.com.sg
Chemical Products Distr
N.A.I.C.S.: 424690
Doreen Tay *(Sr Mgr-C&B)*

Diversey Slovakia, s.r.o. **(1)**
Rybnicna 40, 831 06, Bratislava, Slovakia
Tel.: (421) 249289111
Web Site: https://diversey.sk
Chemical Products Distr
N.A.I.C.S.: 424690

Diversey South Africa (Pty.) Ltd. **(1)**
Cnr Nagington & Rossouw Streets, PO Box
X037, Wadeville, 1422, South Africa
Tel.: (27) 118719000
Web Site: https://diversey.co.za
Emp.: 500
Chemical Products Distr
N.A.I.C.S.: 424690
Sanjay Hoolasi *(Mng Dir)*

Diversey Suomi Oy **(1)**
Kaurakatu 48 B, 20740, Turku, Finland
Tel.: (358) 207474220
Web Site: https://diversey.fi
Emp.: 30
Chemical Products Distr

N.A.I.C.S.: 424690

Diversey Sverige AB **(1)**
Liljeholmsstrande 3 6 tr, Box 47313, 117 43,
Stockholm, Sweden
Tel.: (46) 87799300
Cleaning & Sanitation Product Distr
N.A.I.C.S.: 423720

Diversey Sweden Services AB **(1)**
Liljeholmsvagen 18, 117 61, Stockholm,
Sweden
Tel.: (46) 87799369
Management Consulting Services
N.A.I.C.S.: 541618

**Diversey Switzerland Production
GmbH** **(1)**
Eschlikonerstrasse, 9542, Munchwilen,
Switzerland
Tel.: (41) 719692727
Cleaning & Sanitation Product Distr
N.A.I.C.S.: 423720

Entapack Pty. Ltd. **(1)**
4 Advantage Drive, Dandenong, 3175, VIC,
Australia
Tel.: (61) 39 767 5600
Web Site: https://www.entapack.com.au
Emp.: 10
Liquid Packaging Mfr
N.A.I.C.S.: 339999
Laurie Lovela *(Mng Dir)*

**FAGERDALA (LEAMCHABUNG)
LTD.** **(1)**
213/11 Leamchabung Industrial Estate Moo
3 Sukhumvit Road, Tungsukha Sub-District
Sriracha District, Chon Buri, 20230, Thai-
land
Tel.: (66) 38491530
Food Packaging Plastic Product Mfr
N.A.I.C.S.: 326150

**FAGERDALA (SUZHOU) PACKAG-
ING CO., LTD.** **(1)**
No 151 Jinling East Road, Weiting Town
Suzhou Industrial Park, Suzhou, 215121,
China
Tel.: (86) 51262745950
Food Packaging Plastic Product Mfr
N.A.I.C.S.: 326150

FAGERDALA (THAILAND) LTD. **(1)**
9/36 Moo 5 Phaholyothin Road, Klongnueng Klongluang, Pathumthani, 12120, Thailand
Tel.: (66) 29021433
Food Packaging Plastic Product Mfr
N.A.I.C.S.: 326150

**Fagerdala (Chengdu) Packaging Co.,
Ltd.** **(1)**
No 38 Gang Bei Er Road Chengdu Modern
Industrial Park North District, Pixian, Sich-
uan, 611731, China
Tel.: (86) 2861778162
Food Packaging Plastic Product Mfr
N.A.I.C.S.: 326150

**Fagerdala (Chongqing) Packaging
Co., Ltd.** **(1)**
No 10 Tongshan Road Biquan Street,
Bishan District, Chongqing, 402760, China
Tel.: (86) 2341661919
Food Packaging Plastic Product Mfr
N.A.I.C.S.: 326150

**Fagerdala (Huiyang) Packaging Co.,
Ltd.** **(1)**
Ching Ling Road North Shi Wei Huiyang
Economic Development Zone, Huiyang Dis-
trict, Huizhou, 516213, Guangdong, China
Tel.: (86) 7523277479
Food Packaging & Bubble Wrap Mfr
N.A.I.C.S.: 311999

**Fagerdala (Shanghai) Foams Co.
Ltd.** **(1)**
2nd Fl A Bld 17 No 33 Xiya Road Pilot Free
Trade Zone, Shanghai, 200131, China
Tel.: (86) 2150643298
Food Packaging & Bubble Wrap Mfr
N.A.I.C.S.: 311999

**Fagerdala (Shanghai) Polymer Co.
Ltd.** **(1)**
Bld 12 No 588 Yuanzhong Road, Huinan
Town Pudong District, Shanghai, 201300,
China

Tel.: (86) 2120961031
Food Packaging Plastic Product Mfr
N.A.I.C.S.: 326150

**Fagerdala (Xiamen) Packaging Co.
Ltd.** **(1)**
No 6 Butang Mid Rd Tongxiang Industrial
Base, Torch Hi-tech Industrial Development
Zone, Xiamen, 361100, China
Tel.: (86) 5925734666
Food Packaging & Bubble Wrap Mfr
N.A.I.C.S.: 311999

Fagerdala Malaysia Sdn. Bhd. **(1)**
Plot 36 Lorong Perusahaan Maju 7 Ka-
wasan Perindustrian Perai 4, 13600, Prai,
Penang, Malaysia
Tel.: (60) 45086588
Food Packaging & Bubble Wrap Mfr
N.A.I.C.S.: 311999

Fagerdala Mexico S.A. de C.V. **(1)**
Avenida Ramon Rayon 9942 Centro Indus-
trial Juarez, Hacienda de las Torres Ciudad
Juarez, 32695, Chihuahua, Mexico
Tel.: (52) 6562573626
Food Packaging Plastic Product Mfr
N.A.I.C.S.: 326150
Ramon Vizcaino *(Engr-Quality)*

Fagerdala Packaging Inc. **(1)**
2532 Airwest Blvd Airwest-Bldg V, Plain-
field, IN 46168
Tel.: (317) 782-3626
Food Packaging & Bubble Wrap Mfr
N.A.I.C.S.: 311999

Fagerdala Singapore Pte. Ltd. **(1)**
No 6 Penjuru Lane, Singapore, 609187,
Singapore
Tel.: (65) 63795000
Web Site: http://www.fagerdalagroup.com
Plastic & Foam Products
N.A.I.C.S.: 326140

**Holmes Packaging Australia Pty.
Ltd** **(1)**
Block L 391 Park Road, Regents Park,
2143, NSW, Australia
Tel.: (61) 297218913
Web Site: http://www.holmespackaging.com
Food & Protective Packaging Materials Mfr
N.A.I.C.S.: 322299

**KRIS Automated Packaging Systems
Private Limited** **(1)**
65 Shanti Industrial Estate S N Road, Mu-
lund West, Mumbai, 400080, Maharastra,
India
Tel.: (91) 2225649652
Web Site: https://www.autobag.co.in
Plastic Bag Product Mfr
N.A.I.C.S.: 326111
Karishma Mehta *(Fin Mgr)*

Kevothermal LLC **(1)**
3721 Spirit Dr SE, Albuquerque, NM 87106
Tel.: (505) 224-9373
Web Site: http://www.kevothermal.com
Vacuum Insulation Panel Mfr
N.A.I.C.S.: 326140

Kevothermal Limited **(1)**
Unit G Moreton Business Park, Moreton-on-
Lugg, Hereford, HR4 8DS, Herefordshire,
United Kingdom
Tel.: (44) 143 276 0200
Web Site: https://www.kevothermal.co.uk
Emp.: 15
Vacuum Insulation Panels Mfr
N.A.I.C.S.: 238310

Liqui-Box Corporation **(1)**
480 Schrock Rd Ste G, Columbus, OH
43229
Tel.: (614) 888-9280
Web Site: https://www.liquibox.com
Sales Range: $150-199.9 Million
Mfr of Flexible Liquid Packaging Systems
N.A.I.C.S.: 326111

Subsidiary (Domestic):

DS Smith Plastics Ltd. **(2)**
1201 Windham Pkwy Ste D, Romeoville, IL
60446
Tel.: (630) 296-2000
Web Site: http://www.dssmith-plastics.com
Plastic Container Mfr
N.A.I.C.S.: 326199

Salvador Servera *(Dir-Sls-Flexible Pkg-
Europe)*

Subsidiary (Non-US):

DS Smith Replen **(3)**
Madleaze Industrial Estate Bristol Rd,
Gloucester, GL1 5SG, United Kingdom
Tel.: (44) 1452 316565
Web Site: http://www.dssmithreplen.com
Sales Range: $25-49.9 Million
Emp.: 7
Injection Molded Plastic Products Mfr
N.A.I.C.S.: 326199

DS Smith Worldwide Dispensers **(3)**
Lee Road Merton Park Estate, Merton, Lon-
don, SW19 3WD, United Kingdom **(100%)**
Tel.: (44) 2085457500
Web Site: http://www.worldwide-
dispensers.com
Sales Range: $25-49.9 Million
Plastic Container Mfr
N.A.I.C.S.: 326160

DW Plastics NV **(3)**
Nijverheidsstraat 26, 3740, Bilzen, Belgium
Tel.: (32) 89412291
Web Site: http://www.dwplastics.com
Sales Range: $25-49.9 Million
Emp.: 75
Plastic Pallet Mfr
N.A.I.C.S.: 326199
Paul Baeyens *(Mng Dir-Injection Moulded
Products)*

Subsidiary (Domestic):

David S. Smith America Inc **(3)**
78 2nd Ave S, Lester Prairie, MN 55354
Tel.: (320) 395-2553
Web Site:
    http://www.worldwidedispensers.com
Injection Molded Plastic Products Mfr
N.A.I.C.S.: 326199

Subsidiary (Domestic):

Rapak, LLC **(4)**
1201 Windham Pkwy Ste D, Romeoville, IL
60446
Tel.: (630) 296-2000
Emp.: 200
Corrugated Board & Boxes Mfr
N.A.I.C.S.: 322211

Plant (Domestic):

Rapak, LLC - Indianapolis Plant **(5)**
7430 New Augusta Rd, Indianapolis, IN
46268
Tel.: (317) 872-0172
Plastic Bags & Films Mfr
N.A.I.C.S.: 326111
Garry Bledsoe *(Mgr-Sls & Mktg)*
Rick Smith *(Pres)*
Brent Todd *(VP-Sls & Mktg)*
Gary Smith *(CEO)*
Jim Becker *(Mgr-Integration)*

Rapak, LLC - Union City Plant **(5)**
2995 Ahern Ave, Union City, CA 94587
Tel.: (510) 324-0170
Corrugated & Solid Fiber Box Mfr
N.A.I.C.S.: 322211

Subsidiary (Non-US):

Liqui-Box Germany GmbH **(3)**
Dortmunder Strasse 6, 68723, Schwetzin-
gen, Germany
Tel.: (49) 620220970
Corrugated Board & Boxes Mfr
N.A.I.C.S.: 322211

Rapak AD **(3)**
Industrialna Str 45, Shumen, 9704, Bulgaria
Tel.: (359) 54 851045
Corrugated Board & Box Mfr
N.A.I.C.S.: 322211

Rapak Asia Pacific Limited **(3)**
373 Neilson Street Building C1 The Gate
Onehunga, Onehunga, Auckland, 1061,
New Zealand
Tel.: (64) 96362660
Web Site: http://www.rapak.com
Sales Range: $25-49.9 Million
Emp.: 100
Corrugated Board & Boxes Mfr
N.A.I.C.S.: 322211

Sealed Air Corporation—(Continued)

Plant (Domestic):

Liqui-Box Corp. **(2)**
519 Raybestos Dr, Upper Sandusky, OH
43351-9666
Tel.: (419) 294-3884
Sales Range: $75-99.9 Million
Injection Molding
N.A.I.C.S.: 326199
Dennis Rollason (Supvr-Maintenance)
Neal Blake (VP-Ops)
Brad Westlake (Engr-Mechanical Design)
Brenda Bretz-Rickle (Mgr-HR)
Kim Spath (Mgr-Sls & Mktg-United States)
Tim Frazier (Product Mgr-Lab)
Andrew McLeland (COO)
Ken Swanson (Pres & CEO)

PT Diversey Indonesia **(1)**
Menara Duta 6th floor Wing A Jalan HR Ra-
suna Said Kav B 9, Jakarta, 12190, Sela-
tan, Indonesia
Tel.: (62) 2152901961
Web Site: https://diversey.co.id
Chemical Products Distr
N.A.I.C.S.: 424690
Kurnia Ningsih (Mgr-Supply Chain)

Pack-Tiger GmbH **(1)**
Tel.: (41) 523153601
Paper Packing Products Distr
N.A.I.C.S.: 322299

Polypride, Inc. **(1)**
2150 Brevard Rd, High Point, NC
27263 **(100%)**
Tel.: (336) 889-8334
Web Site: http://www.polyprideinc.com
Sales Range: $10-24.9 Million
Emp.: 18
Plastic Film Packaging Mfr
N.A.I.C.S.: 322220

**Producembal-Producao de Embala-
gens, Ltda** **(1)**
Estrada Nacional 85 Lugar de Vala, 2450-
303, Valado Dos Frades, Portugal **(100%)**
Tel.: (351) 262570030
Web Site: http://www.sealedair.com
Sales Range: $10-24.9 Million
Emp.: 14
Food Containers Mfr
N.A.I.C.S.: 322219

Proxy Biomedical Ltd. **(1)**
Coilleach Co Galway, Spiddal, H91 C2NF,
Ireland
Tel.: (353) 91896900
Web Site: https://www.aranbiomedical.com
Medical Device Mfr & Distr
N.A.I.C.S.: 334510

Reflectix, Inc. **(1)**
1 School St, Markleville, IN 46056 **(100%)**
Tel.: (765) 533-4332
Web Site: https://www.reflectixinc.com
Sales Range: $75-99.9 Million
Emp.: 80
Polyethylene Bubble Pack Aluminum Foil
Faced Insulation & Related Products Mfr,
Distr & Sales
N.A.I.C.S.: 423330

Sealed Air (Asia) Holdings B.V. **(1)**
Lindenhoutseweg 45, 6545 AH, Nijmegen,
Netherlands
Tel.: (31) 243710111
Emp.: 100
Holding Company
N.A.I.C.S.: 551112

Sealed Air (Canada) Co. **(1)**
95 Glidden Rd, Brampton, L6T 2H8, ON,
Canada **(100%)**
Tel.: (905) 456-0701
Web Site: https://www.sealedair.com
Sales Range: $10-24.9 Million
Emp.: 50
Packaging Materials Mfr
N.A.I.C.S.: 322220

Sealed Air (China) Co., Ltd. **(1)**
6988 Songze Ave, Qingpu Industrial Park,
Shanghai, 201706, China
Tel.: (86) 213 920 2988
Web Site: https://www.sealedair.com.cn
Packaging Product Mfr & Distr
N.A.I.C.S.: 326199

Sealed Air (Israel) Ltd. **(1)**
14/15 Dotan, Yavne, 8122533,
Israel **(100%)**
Tel.: (972) 89323737
Web Site: http://www.sealedair.com
Sales Range: $10-24.9 Million
Emp.: 25
Packaging Materials Sales & Distr
N.A.I.C.S.: 561910

Sealed Air (New Zealand) **(1)**
24 Bancroft Crescent Glendene Waitakere,
Auckland, 0602, New Zealand **(100%)**
Tel.: (64) 98139800
Web Site: http://www.sealedair.com
Sales Range: $50-74.9 Million
Emp.: 150
Packaging Mfr
N.A.I.C.S.: 322220

Plant (Domestic):

Sealed Air (New Zealand) **(2)**
3 Foreman Road, PO Box 3085, 3216,
Hamilton, New Zealand **(100%)**
Tel.: (64) 78500100
Web Site: http://www.sealedair.com
Sales Range: $25-49.9 Million
Emp.: 300
Food Packaging Mfr
N.A.I.C.S.: 322219

Sealed Air (New Zealand) **(2)**
Prosser Street Wellington, Elsdon, 5022,
New Zealand **(100%)**
Tel.: (64) 42376069
Web Site: http://www.sealedair.com
Sales Range: $50-74.9 Million
Emp.: 150
Food Packaging Mfr
N.A.I.C.S.: 322219
Elen Heathcote (Mng Dir)

Sealed Air (Philippines) Inc. **(1)**
6756 Ayala Avenue, Metro Manila, 1226,
Makati, Philippines
Tel.: (63) 28459400
Web Site: http://www.sealedair.com
Packaging Products
N.A.I.C.S.: 322220

Sealed Air (Singapore) Pte. Ltd. **(1)**
2 Tuas Avenue 6, Singapore, 639293,
Singapore **(100%)**
Tel.: (65) 68611828
Web Site: http://www.sealedair.com
Sales Range: $10-24.9 Million
Emp.: 60
Packaging Material Distr
N.A.I.C.S.: 561910

Sealed Air (Taiwan) Limited **(1)**
Mittle Bldg No 1 Lane 2 Neisin Road Luhu
Township, Taoyuan, 00339, Taiwan **(100%)**
Tel.: (886) 33242988
Web Site: http://www.sealedair.com
Emp.: 27
Packaging Product Distr
N.A.I.C.S.: 561910

Sealed Air (Thailand) Ltd. **(1)**
9 29 Moo 5 Phaholyothin Road, Klong 1
Klong Luang, Pathumthani, 12120,
Thailand **(100%)**
Tel.: (66) 29020579
Web Site: http://www.sealedair.com
Sales Range: $1-9.9 Million
Emp.: 35
Packaging Materials
N.A.I.C.S.: 561910

Sealed Air Africa (Pty) Ltd. **(1)**
64 Rigger Rd Kempton Park, PO Box 2256,
Johannesburg, 1620, South Africa **(100%)**
Tel.: (27) 119234600
Web Site: http://www.emea.com
Sales Range: $25-49.9 Million
Emp.: 120
Packaging Materials Mfr & Sales
N.A.I.C.S.: 322220

**Sealed Air Americas Manufacturing S.
de R.L. de C.V** **(1)**
Av Parque Industrial Monterrey No 506,
Apodaca, Mexico
Tel.: (52) 8181949500
Rubber Products Mfr
N.A.I.C.S.: 333248

Sealed Air Argentina S.A. **(1)**
Primera Junta 550 1878 Quilmes, Buenos
Aires, B1878IPL, Argentina
Tel.: (54) 1142290100
Food Packaging Plastic Product Mfr
N.A.I.C.S.: 326150
Fabian Colli (Sr Engr-Sls)

**Sealed Air Australia (Holdings) Pty.
Limited** **(1)**
1126 Sydney Rd, Fawkner, 3060, Australia
Tel.: (61) 393592244
Emp.: 400
Plastic Food Packaging Products Mfr
N.A.I.C.S.: 322299
Jhon Newman (Head-HR)

Sealed Air Australia Pty. Limited **(1)**
1126 Sydney Road, Fawkner, 3060,
Australia **(100%)**
Tel.: (61) 295507888
Web Site: http://www.sealedair.com
Sales Range: $350-399.9 Million
Emp.: 9,700
Packaging Mfr
N.A.I.C.S.: 322220

Sealed Air B.V. **(1)**
Lindenhoutseweg 45, 6545 AH, Nijmegen,
Netherlands **(100%)**
Tel.: (31) 243710111
Sales Range: $25-49.9 Million
Emp.: 120
Packaging Products Mfr
N.A.I.C.S.: 326140

Sealed Air Corporation (US) **(1)**
200 Riverfront Blvd, Elmwood Park, NJ
07407 **(100%)**
Tel.: (201) 703-4161
Web Site: http://www.sealedair.com
Holding Company
N.A.I.C.S.: 551112

**Sealed Air Corporation -
Danbury** **(1)**
10 Old Sherman Tpke, Danbury, CT 06810-
4124
Tel.: (203) 791-3500
Web Site: http://www.sealedair.com
Sales Range: $75-99.9 Million
Emp.: 200
Mfr of Foam-In-Place Packaging Systems &
Materials
N.A.I.C.S.: 326140

Sealed Air Denmark A/S **(1)**
Teglbuen 10, DK 2730, Nivaa,
Denmark **(100%)**
Tel.: (45) 44853700
Web Site: http://www.sealedair.com
Sales Range: $10-24.9 Million
Emp.: 23
Container Sealing Compounds & Applica-
tion Equipment, Flexible Packaging Materi-
als & Equipment Sales
N.A.I.C.S.: 326199

Sealed Air GmbH **(1)**
Park 4, Root, 6039, Lucerne,
Switzerland **(100%)**
Tel.: (41) 3494500
Web Site: http://www.emiei.com
Sales Range: $25-49.9 Million
Emp.: 120
Packaging Materials Sales & Distr
N.A.I.C.S.: 561910

Sealed Air GmbH **(1)**
Erlengang 31, 22844, Norderstedt,
Germany **(100%)**
Tel.: (10) 1 062 6010
Web Site: https://sealedair.de
Sales Range: $100-124.9 Million
Emp.: 300
Packaging Materials Mfr
N.A.I.C.S.: 326199

Sealed Air Hong Kong Limited **(1)**
Rm 2301-7 23/F Millennium City Tower 1,
388 Kwun Tong Road, Kowloon, China
(Hong Kong) **(100%)**
Tel.: (852) 21787878
Web Site: http://www.sealedair.com
Sales Range: $10-24.9 Million
Emp.: 30
Packaging Product Distr
N.A.I.C.S.: 561910

Sealed Air Hungary Kft. **(1)**

**Amerikai Ut 1, Ujhartyan, 2367,
Hungary** **(100%)**
Tel.: (36) 29573300
Web Site: http://www.sealedair.com
Sales Range: $50-74.9 Million
Emp.: 300
Packaging Materials Sales
N.A.I.C.S.: 561910

Sealed Air Japan G.K. **(1)**
1-7 Nihonbashi Kodenmacho Square Nihon-
bashi, Chuo-ku, Tokyo, 103-0001,
Japan **(100%)**
Tel.: (81) 35 644 1141
Web Site: https://www.sealedair-japan.com
Sales Range: $25-49.9 Million
Emp.: 80
Plastic & Paper Packaging Products Distr
N.A.I.C.S.: 322220
Yagmur Sagnak (Pres)

Sealed Air Korea Limited **(1)**
757 1 Munhyung-li Opo-Eup, Gwangju,
464-894, Korea (South) **(100%)**
Tel.: (82) 317631716
Web Site: http://www.sealedair.com
Sales Range: $10-24.9 Million
Emp.: 30
Packaging Materials Mfr
N.A.I.C.S.: 322220

Sealed Air Limited **(1)**
Telford Way, Kettering, NN16 8UN,
Northants, United Kingdom **(100%)**
Tel.: (44) 1536315700
Web Site: http://www.sealedair.com
Sales Range: $50-74.9 Million
Emp.: 160
Packaging Products Mfr
N.A.I.C.S.: 326140

Plant (Domestic):

Sealed Air Limited **(2)**
Saxon Way, Royston, SG8 6DN, Hertford-
shire, United Kingdom **(100%)**
Tel.: (44) 1763261900
Web Site: http://www.sealedair.com
Sales Range: $25-49.9 Million
Emp.: 85
Packaging Sales & Mfr
N.A.I.C.S.: 322220

Sealed Air Luxembourg S.a.r.l **(1)**
14-16 Ave Pasteur, 2310, Luxembourg,
Luxembourg
Tel.: (352) 26196444
Plastic Food Packaging Products Mfr
N.A.I.C.S.: 322299
Barbara Mazur (Mgr)

**Sealed Air Netherlands Holdings IV
Cooperatief U.A,** **(1)**
De Boelelaan 32, 1083 HJ, Amsterdam,
Netherlands
Tel.: (31) 202589700
Holding Company
N.A.I.C.S.: 551112

Sealed Air Norge AS **(1)**
Stolvstadlia 16, Hedmark, 2360,
Norway **(100%)**
Tel.: (47) 62330200
Web Site: http://www.sealedaircorp.com
Sales Range: $10-24.9 Million
Emp.: 40
Packaging Mfr
N.A.I.C.S.: 322220
Rex Hincliffe (Mng Dir)

Sealed Air Oy **(1)**
Tyopajankatu 6a, Helsinki, 00580, Uusimaa,
Finland
Tel.: (358) 972574411
Sales Range: $25-49.9 Million
Emp.: 7
Packaging Products Mfr
N.A.I.C.S.: 322220

**Sealed Air Packaging (Shanghai) Co.
Ltd.** **(1)**
Songve Road 6988, Huang Pi North Rd,
Shanghai, 201706, China **(100%)**
Tel.: (86) 2139202988
Sales Range: $25-49.9 Million
Emp.: 30
Packaging Materials Mfr
N.A.I.C.S.: 322220

Sealed Air Packaging S.R.L. **(1)**

Via Europa 15, 20040, Milan, Bellusco,
Italy   **(100%)**
Tel.: (39) 03968351
Web Site: http://www.sealedaircorp.com
Sales Range: $25-49.9 Million
Emp.: 130
Packaging Products Mfr
N.A.I.C.S.: 322220

Sealed Air Polska Sp. z.o.o.   **(1)**
Duchnice ul Ozarowska 28A, 05-850,
Ozarow Mazowiecki, Poland   **(100%)**
Tel.: (48) 22 731 5901
Web Site: https://sealedair.com.pl
Sales Range: $10-24.9 Million
Emp.: 200
Packaging Mfr
N.A.I.C.S.: 322220

Sealed Air S.A.S.   **(1)**
53 Rue St Denis, 28230, Epernon, France
Tel.: (33) 237189100
Food Packaging Plastic Product Mfr
N.A.I.C.S.: 326150

Sealed Air S.L.   **(1)**
Calle Antonio Machado 78 - 80 BJ ED AUS-
TRALIA, Viladecans, 08840, Spain **(100%)**
Tel.: (34) 936352000
Web Site: http://www.sealedair.com
Sales Range: $25-49.9 Million
Emp.: 200
Packaging Products Mfr & Sales
N.A.I.C.S.: 326140

Sealed Air S.R.L   **(1)**
Via Trento 7, Passirana di Rho, Milan,
20040, Italy
Tel.: (39) 029332415
Sales Range: $125-149.9 Million
Emp.: 40
Plastic Food Packaging Products Mfr
N.A.I.C.S.: 322299

Sealed Air Shrink Equipment   **(1)**
100 Westford Rd, Ayer, MA 01432 **(100%)**
Tel.: (978) 772-3200
Web Site: http://www.shrink-pkg.com
Sales Range: $125-149.9 Million
Packaging Machinery Mfr
N.A.I.C.S.: 333993

Sealed Air Svenska A.B.   **(1)**
Patortsvagen 2, PO Box 146, Aneby, 578
32, Sweden   **(100%)**
Tel.: (46) 38047100
Web Site: http://www.sealedair.com
Sales Range: $25-49.9 Million
Emp.: 70
Packaging Materials Mfr
N.A.I.C.S.: 326140

Sealed Air Uruguay S.A.   **(1)**
Calle Ciguena No 7 Barrio Airopuerto,
Canelones, 14000, Uruguay
Tel.: (598) 26000961
Packaging & Labeling Services
N.A.I.C.S.: 561910

Sealed Air Verpackungen GmbH **(1)**
                                         (100%)
Tel.: (49) 663196680
Sales Range: $25-49.9 Million
Emp.: 180
Packaging Materials Mfr
N.A.I.C.S.: 322220

Sealed Air Vitembal S.L.   **(1)**
Poligono Industrial El Rincon Sector 5, Bu-
nol, 46360, Valencia, Spain
Tel.: (34) 962502775
Web Site: http://www.sealedair.com
Sales Range: $25-49.9 Million
Emp.: 80
Plastic Food Packaging Products Mfr
N.A.I.C.S.: 322299

Sealed Air de Mexico S. de R.L. de
C.V   **(1)**
Vuelta A La Cerca S/N Bugambilias, Jiute-
pec, 62550, Morelos, Mexico
Tel.: (52) 7773205528
Plastic Food Packaging Products Mfr
N.A.I.C.S.: 322299

Sealed Air s.r.o   **(1)**
V Sadech 4/15, 16000, Prague, Czech
Republic   **(100%)**
Tel.: (420) 220199551
Web Site: http://www.sealedair.com

Sales Range: $10-24.9 Million
Emp.: 15
Packaging Material Distr
N.A.I.C.S.: 561499

Shanklin Corporation   **(1)**
100 Westford Rd, Ayer, MA 01432
Tel.: (978) 772-3200
Web Site: http://www.shrink-pkg.com
Emp.: 165
Packaging Machinery Mfr
N.A.I.C.S.: 333993

SumaChem LLC   **(1)**
International City, Dubai, United Arab Emir-
ates
Tel.: (971) 506559413
Chemical Product Mfr & Distr
N.A.I.C.S.: 325199

Tart s.r.o   **(1)**
Vinohradska 91, Cernovice, 618 00, Brno,
Czech Republic   **(49%)**
Tel.: (420) 548210500
Web Site: https://www.tart.cz
Sales Range: $75-99.9 Million
Emp.: 150
Packaging Machines & Materials Mfr, Sales
& Consulting Services
N.A.I.C.S.: 322220
Michal Hort *(Founder)*

Teneo SAS   **(1)**
71 BD Mission Marchand La Garenne Co-
lombes, 92250, Paris, France
Tel.: (33) 155513038
Web Site: https://www.teneo.net
Management Consulting Services
N.A.I.C.S.: 541611
Jerome Sarrasin *(Mgr-Acct)*

SEALIFE CORP.

5601 W Slauson Ave Ste 283, Culver
City, CA 90230
Tel.: (310) 338-9757
SLIF—(OTCIQ)
Chemical Products Mfr
N.A.I.C.S.: 325998
George Shen *(CEO)*

SEAPORT CALIBRE MATERI-
ALS ACQUISITION CORP.

360 Madison Ave 20th Fl, New York,
NY 10017
Tel.: (212) 616-7700   DE
Year Founded: 2021
SCMA—(NASDAQ)
Rev.: $2,822,802
Assets: $133,332,548
Liabilities: $142,938,101
Net Worth: ($9,605,553)
Earnings: $2,045,199
Emp.: 3
Fiscal Year-end: 12/31/21
Investment Services
N.A.I.C.S.: 523999
Stephen Smith *(Chm)*
Jim Tumulty *(CEO)*
Ed Siegel *(CFO)*

SEARCHLIGHT MINERALS
CORP.

7582 Hawks Landing Dr, West Palm
Beach, FL 33412
Tel.: (201) 390-5790   NV
Web Site:
   http://www.searchlightminerals.com
Year Founded: 1999
SRCH—(OTCIQ)
Mineral Exploration Services
N.A.I.C.S.: 213115
Martin B. Oring *(Chm, Pres & CEO)*

SEARS HOMETOWN AND
OUTLET STORES, INC.

5500 Trillium Blvd Ste 501, Hoffman
Estates, IL 60192
Tel.: (847) 286-7000   DE
Web Site: http://www.shos.com
SHOS—(NASDAQ)
Rev.: $1,449,948,000
Assets: $343,771,000

Liabilities: $223,815,000
Net Worth: $119,956,000
Earnings: ($53,464,000)
Emp.: 2,992
Fiscal Year-end: 02/02/19
Holding Company; Home Appliance,
Lawn & Garden Equipment, Hard-
ware & Sporting Goods Retailer; Dis-
count Outlet Stores Operator
N.A.I.C.S.: 551112
Ephraim J. Bird *(CFO & Sr VP)*
William A. Powell *(Pres & CEO)*
Charles J. Hansen *(Gen Counsel,
Sec & VP)*
Michael A. Gray *(COO & Sr VP)*
Lauri Joffe Turjeman *(Sr VP-Mktg,
eCommerce & IT)*

Subsidiaries:

Sears Authorized Hometown Stores,
LLC   **(1)**
3333 Beverly Rd, Hoffman Estates, IL
60179   **(100%)**
Tel.: (847) 286-2500
Web Site:
   http://www.searshometownstores.com
Small Electronics, Tools, Appliance & Out-
door Power Equipment Stores Operator
N.A.I.C.S.: 455219

Sears Home Appliance Showrooms,
LLC   **(1)**
3333 Beverly Rd, Hoffman Estates, IL
60179
Tel.: (847) 286-2500
Web Site:
   http://www.searshomeapplianceshow
   room.com
Household Appliance Store Operator
N.A.I.C.S.: 449210

Sears Outlet Stores, LLC   **(1)**
2065 George St, Melrose Park, IL 60160
Tel.: (708) 216-2870
Web Site: http://www.searsoutlet.com
Factory Direct or Refurbished Merchandise
Stores Operator
N.A.I.C.S.: 455219

SEASTAR MEDICAL HOLDING
CORPORATION

3513 Brighton Blvd Ste 410, Denver,
CO 80216   CO
Web Site: https://seastarmedical.com
Year Founded: 2020
ICU—(NASDAQ)
Assets: $4,767,000
Liabilities: $13,002,000
Net Worth: ($8,235,000)
Earnings: ($23,013,000)
Emp.: 9
Fiscal Year-end: 12/31/22
Medical Device Mfr
N.A.I.C.S.: 339112
David A. Green *(CFO)*
Bruce Rodgers *(Chm & Pres)*
Rick Barnett *(Vice Chm)*
Eric Schlorff *(CEO)*
Kevin Chung *(Chief Medical Officer)*
Sai P. Iyer *(VP-Medical Affairs & Res)*
Tom Mullen *(VP-Operations & Prod-
uct Development)*
Tim Varacek *(Sr VP-Commercial &
Bus Ops)*

SECTOR 10, INC.

10900 NE 4th St Ste 2300, Bellevue,
WA 98004
Tel.: (425) 331-9620   DE
Web Site: http://www.sector10.com
Year Founded: 1992
SECI—(OTCEM)
Emp.: 2
Development Stage Company; Pre-
deployed Emergency & Disaster Re-
sponse Equipment Mfr
N.A.I.C.S.: 339999

Pericles DeAvila *(Chm & Acting
Pres/CEO)*
Laurence A. Madison *(Acting CFO,
Treas & Sec)*

SECTOR 5, INC.

2000 Duke St Ste 110, Alexandria,
VA 22314
Tel.: (571) 348-1005   NV
Web Site: http://www.sector-five.com
Year Founded: 2012
SFIV—(OTCIQ)
Sales Range: Less than $1 Million
Electronic Products Mfr
N.A.I.C.S.: 334111
Erick Kuvshinikov *(Pres, CEO &
CFO)*

SECURCAPITAL HOLDINGS
CORP.

5256 S Mission Rd, Bonsall, CA
92003   NV
CQER—(OTCIQ)
Financial Investment Services
N.A.I.C.S.: 523999
Eric Littman *(Gen Counsel)*

SECURED SERVICES, INC.

11490 Commerce Park Dr Ste 240,
Reston, VA 20191
Tel.: (703) 476-7127   DE
Web Site: http://www.secured-
   services.com
SSVC—(OTCEM)
Sales Range: $1-9.9 Million
Emp.: 62
Network Security Design & Managed
Security Services
N.A.I.C.S.: 541512
Dale Quick *(CEO)*

SECURITY BANCORP, INC.

306 W Main St, McMinnville, TN
37110
Tel.: (931) 473-4483   TN
Web Site:
   http://www.securitybancorptn.com
Year Founded: 1997
SCYT—(OTCIQ)
Bank Holding Company
N.A.I.C.S.: 551111
Michael D. Griffith *(Pres & CEO)*
LeAnn Cartwright *(Accountant)*
Lisa Hillis *(Sr VP & Exec Asst)*
Thomas L. Foster *(Dir)*

Subsidiaries:

Security Federal Savings Bank of
McMinnville   **(1)**
306 W Main St, McMinnville, TN 37110
Tel.: (931) 473-4483
Web Site: http://www.secfed.net
Sales Range: $1-9.9 Million
Federal Savings Bank
N.A.I.C.S.: 522180
Joe H. Pugh *(Pres & CEO)*
Larry E. Brown *(Exec VP)*
Ray Spivey Jr. *(Sec)*

SECURITY FEDERAL CORPO-
RATION

Tel.: (803) 641-3000   SC
Web Site:
   https://www.securityfederalbank.com
SFDL—(OTCIQ)
Rev.: $52,190,000
Assets: $1,381,366,000
Liabilities: $1,221,133,000
Net Worth: $160,233,000
Earnings: $10,228,000
Emp.: 247
Fiscal Year-end: 12/31/22
Bank Holding Company
N.A.I.C.S.: 551111

Security Federal Corporation—(Continued)

Roy G. Lindburg *(Pres)*
J. Chris Verenes *(CEO)*
Darrell Rains *(CFO)*
Robert E. Alexander *(Sec)*

Subsidiaries:

Security Federal Bank   (1)
2587 Whiskey Rd, Aiken, SC 29803
Tel.: (803) 641-3000
Web Site:
  https://www.securityfederalbank.com
Federal Savings Bank
N.A.I.C.S.: 522180
Roy G. Lindburg *(Executives, Bd of Dirs)*
J. Chris Verenes *(Chm & CEO)*

Subsidiary (Domestic):

Security Federal Insurance, Inc.   (2)
1705 Whiskey Rd, Aiken, SC 29803
Tel.: (803) 641-3001
Web Site:
  https://www.securityfederalinsurance.com
Insurance Services
N.A.I.C.S.: 524210

SECURITY FIRST INTERNATIONAL HOLDINGS, INC.
501 E Las Olas Blvd, Fort Lauderdale, FL 33301
Tel.: (954) 546-1501   **NV**
Year Founded: 1990
SCFR—(OTCIQ)
Financial Investment Services
N.A.I.C.S.: 523210
Brian Fowler *(Pres)*

SECURITY NATIONAL FINANCIAL CORPORATION
433 W Ascension Way, Salt Lake City, UT 84123
Tel.: (801) 264-1060   **UT**
Web Site:
  https://www.securitynational.com
Year Founded: 1979
SNFCA—(NASDAQ)
Rev.: $389,652,328
Assets: $1,461,112,892
Liabilities: $1,168,325,965
Net Worth: $292,786,927
Earnings: $25,690,302
Emp.: 1,422
Fiscal Year-end: 12/31/22
Direct Life Insurance Carriers
N.A.I.C.S.: 524113
S. Andrew Quist *(Gen Counsel & VP-Ops & Mortgage)*
Jeffrey R. Stephens *(Gen Counsel & Sec)*
Stephen C. Johnson *(VP-Mortgage Ops)*
Scott M. Quist *(Chm, Pres & CEO)*
Jason G. Overbaugh *(VP & Dir-Natl Mktg-Life Insurance)*
Adam G. Quist *(Gen Counsel, VP-Memorial Svcs & Asst Sec)*

Subsidiaries:

Affordable Funerals and Cremations of America, Inc.   (1)
4387 3 500 W, Murray, UT 84123
Tel.: (801) 287-8233
Web Site: http://www.affordablefandc.com
Funeral & Cremation Services
N.A.I.C.S.: 812210

American Funeral Financial, LLC (1)
6000 Pelham Rd Ste B, Greenville, SC 29615
Tel.: (864) 232-4233
Web Site:
  http://www.americanfuneralfinancial.com
Insurance Services
N.A.I.C.S.: 524210

Beta Capital Corp.   (1)
200 Market Way, Rainbow City, AL 35906
Tel.: (757) 488-6960
Web Site: http://www.betacapitalcorp.com

Insurance Assignment Services
N.A.I.C.S.: 524113
Ronald D. Maxson *(Pres & CEO)*

Bluebonnet Properties, LLC   (1)
2012 Lake Air Dr Ste D, Waco, TX 76710
Tel.: (254) 776-3090
Web Site: https://www.bluebonnetprop.com
Property Management & Rental Services
N.A.I.C.S.: 522299

C & J Financial, LLC   (1)
200 Market Way, Rainbow City, AL 35906
Tel.: (256) 442-0020
Web Site: https://www.cjf.com
Sales Range: $10-24.9 Million
Emp.: 30
Insurance Services
N.A.I.C.S.: 524113
Jamie Meredith *(Exec VP)*
Kathryn Kilgore *(VP-Operations)*
Angie Keener *(Dir-Customer Loyalty)*
Brooke Breeden *(Dir-Customer Care)*
Chuck Gallagher *(VP-Sales)*
Jackie Hood *(Coord-Marketing)*
Jeff Harbeson *(Dir-Cash Flow Solutions)*
Jennifer Hill *(Dir-Resolution)*
Jennifer Oliver *(Sr Dir-Customer Loyalty)*
John Mitchell *(CTO)*
Kelly Tyson *(Coord-Assignment)*
Michael Mostofsky *(Dir-Business Development)*
Rob Brice *(Dir-Strategic Partnerships)*
Robert Jackowitz *(Dir-Client Rels)*
Tam Turner *(Coord-Assignment)*
Tandy Blackwell *(Dir-Customer Loyalty)*

Care Management Group, LLC   (1)
PO Box 1037, Rockville, MD 20849
Tel.: (202) 215-9209
Web Site: https://caremgroup.net
Health Care Management Services
N.A.I.C.S.: 621999
Betty J. Mizek *(Founder & Pres)*

Cottonwood Mortuary, Inc.   (1)
Tel.: (801) 278-2801
Web Site: http://www.memorialutah.com
Funeral Services
N.A.I.C.S.: 812210

Crystal Rose Funeral Home, Inc. (1)
9155 W Van Buren St, Tolleson, AZ 85353-2942
Tel.: (623) 936-3637
Funeral Homes & Funeral Services
N.A.I.C.S.: 812210

Deseret Memorial, Inc.   (1)
36 E 700 S, Salt Lake City, UT 84111
Tel.: (801) 364-6528
Web Site: http://www.memorialutah.com
Emp.: 4
Funeral Services
N.A.I.C.S.: 812210

EverLEND Mortgage Company (1)
2455 Parleys Way Ste 150, Salt Lake City, UT 84109
Tel.: (801) 713-4800
Web Site: https://www.everlend.com
Banking Services
N.A.I.C.S.: 522292

First Guaranty Insurance, Co. (1)
1044 River Oaks Dr Ste B, Flowood, MS 39232-9594
Web Site: https://www.first-gic.com
Emp.: 20
Insurance Brokerage Services
N.A.I.C.S.: 551112

Greer-Wilson Funeral Home, Inc. (1)
5921 W Thomas Rd, Phoenix, AZ 85033
Tel.: (623) 245-0994
Web Site:
  http://www.funerariasdelangel.com
Emp.: 15
Funeral Services
N.A.I.C.S.: 812210

Holladay Memorial Park, Inc. (1)
4900 S Memory Ln, Holladay, UT 84117-6231
Tel.: (801) 278-2803
Web Site: http://www.memorialutah.com
Funeral Services
N.A.I.C.S.: 812210

Memorial Estates, Inc.   (1)
Tel.: (801) 268-8771

Funeral Services
N.A.I.C.S.: 812210
Adam Quist *(Gen Mgr)*

Paradise Chapel Funeral Home, Inc.   (1)
3934 E Indian School Rd, Phoenix, AZ 85018
Tel.: (602) 955-1600
Web Site:
  http://www.paradisesunsetchapel.com
Funeral Homes & Funeral Services
N.A.I.C.S.: 812210

Security National Capital, Inc. (1)
5300 S 360 W Ste 310, Salt Lake City, UT 84123
Tel.: (800) 760-3384
Web Site: http://www.sncloans.com
Emp.: 50
Mortgage & Non Mortgage Loan Services
N.A.I.C.S.: 522310
Steve Johnson *(Pres)*

Security National Life Insurance Company   (1)
433 Ascension Way Ste 600, Salt Lake City, UT 84123   **(100%)**
Web Site:
  https://www.securitynationallife.com
Sales Range: $50-74.9 Million
Emp.: 100
Insurance Services
N.A.I.C.S.: 524113

SecurityNational Mortgage Company   (1)
Tel.: (801) 264-8111
Web Site: https://snmc.com
Commercial Mortgage Services
N.A.I.C.S.: 522310
Stephen C. Johnson *(Pres)*

SEELOS THERAPEUTICS, INC.
300 Park Ave, New York, NY 10022
Tel.: (646) 293-2100   **NV**
Web Site:
  https://www.seelostherapeutics.com
Year Founded: 1987
SEEL—(NASDAQ)
Rev.: $121,000
Assets: $22,746,000
Liabilities: $33,357,000
Net Worth: ($10,611,000)
Earnings: ($73,534,000)
Emp.: 16
Fiscal Year-end: 12/31/22
Pharmaceutical Mfr, Researcher & Developer
N.A.I.C.S.: 325412
Raj Mehra *(Founder, Chm, Pres, CEO & CFO-Interim)*
Michael Golembiewski *(CFO)*
Tim Whitaker *(Chief Medical Officer)*
Gopal Krishna *(Head-Mfg & Technical Ops)*
Karen Fusaro *(Sr VP)*

SEER, INC.
3800 Bridge Pkwy, Redwood City, CA 94065
Tel.: (650) 453-0000   **DE**
Web Site: https://www.seer.bio
Year Founded: 2017
SEER—(NASDAQ)
Rev.: $15,493,000
Assets: $487,929,000
Liabilities: $40,936,000
Net Worth: $446,993,000
Earnings: ($92,966,000)
Emp.: 164
Fiscal Year-end: 12/31/22
Biotechnology Research & Development Services
N.A.I.C.S.: 541714
Omid Farokhzad *(Co-Founder, Chm & CEO)*
David R. Horn *(Pres & CFO)*
Martin Goldberg *(VP-Product Dev)*
Damian Harris *(VP-Engrg)*
Jen Maggio *(VP & Controller)*

Asim Siddiqui *(VP-Software & Applications)*
Serafim Batzoglou *(VP)*
Elona Kogan *(Gen Counsel & Sec)*
Marissa Dixon *(Chief People Officer & VP)*
Shashanka Muppaneni *(VP-Corp Dev)*
Karen Possemato *(VP-Corp Mktg & Comm)*
Scott D. Thomas *(Chief Comml Officer)*
Philip Ma *(Co-Founder)*
Omid C. Farokhzad *(Co-Founder, Chm & CEO)*

SEI INVESTMENTS COMPANY
1 Freedom Valley Dr, Oaks, PA 19456
Tel.: (610) 676-1000   **PA**
Web Site: https://www.seic.com
Year Founded: 1968
SEIC—(NASDAQ)
Rev.: $1,919,793,000
Assets: $2,520,003,000
Liabilities: $388,175,000
Net Worth: $2,131,828,000
Earnings: $462,258,000
Emp.: 5,061
Fiscal Year-end: 12/31/23
Outsourced Investment & Fund Processing for Banks, Trust Companies & Investment Managers
N.A.I.C.S.: 522320
Alfred P. West Jr. *(Founder & Chm)*
Paul F. Klauder *(Exec VP & Head-Institutional Grp)*
Mary Jane Bobyock *(Mng Dir-Nonprofit Advisory Team-Institutional Grp)*
Randy Cusick *(Portfolio Mgr-Client-Institutional Grp)*
Ryan P. Hicke *(CEO)*
Sean Denham *(CFO)*
Michael Peterson *(Gen Counsel & Exec VP)*
Sneha Shah *(Exec VP & Head-New Bus Ventures)*
Sanjay Sharma *(Exec VP)*

Subsidiaries:

Archway Finance & Operations, Inc.   (1)
8888 N Keystone Crossing Ste 1400, Indianapolis, IN 46240
Tel.: (317) 819-5500
Web Site: http://www.archwayfo.com
Fund Management Services
N.A.I.C.S.: 523940
Paul Freeland *(Pres)*
Mike Landis *(VP-Fin & Ops)*
Scott Lederman *(VP-Bus Dev)*
Natalie Peters *(VP-Bus Dev & IR)*
Laura Leininger *(Sr Mgr-Investment Acctg)*

SEI Archway Technology Partners, LLC   (1)
8888 Keystone Crossing Ste 1400, Indianapolis, IN 46240
Tel.: (317) 819-5500
Web Site:
  https://www.archwaytechnology.net
Accounting & Management Software Solutions
N.A.I.C.S.: 513210
Brad Holifield *(Dir-Product Dev)*

SEI European Services Limited (1)
1st Floor Alphabeta 14-18 Finsbury Square, London, EC2A 1BR, United Kingdom
Tel.: (44) 2038108000
Sales Range: $75-99.9 Million
Emp.: 250
Financial Management Services
N.A.I.C.S.: 523999

SEI Financial Management Corporation   (1)
1 Freedom Valley Dr, Oaks, PA 19456
Tel.: (610) 676-1000
Web Site: http://www.seic.com

Sales Range: $200-249.9 Million
Emp.: 1,500
Administrative & Processing Services &
Software Systems
N.A.I.C.S.: 541611
Alfred P. West Jr. *(Chm & CEO)*

SEI Financial Services Company (1)
1 Freedom Vly Dr, Oaks, PA
19456   (100%)
Tel.: (610) 676-1000
Web Site: http://www.seic.com
Rev.: $31,791,000
Emp.: 1,200
Distribution & Management of Mutual Funds
& Other Financial Products
N.A.I.C.S.: 624410
Alfred P. West Jr. *(Chm & CEO)*

SEI Institutional Transfer Agent,
Inc.   (1)
1 Freedom Vly Dr, Oaks, PA 19456-9989
Tel.: (610) 676-1000
Investment Management Service
N.A.I.C.S.: 523940

SEI Investments (Asia), Limited (1)
The Hong Kong Club Building Suite 904 3
Jackson Road, Central, China (Hong Kong)
Tel.: (852) 3 515 7500
Web Site: https://www.seic.com
Emp.: 6
Wealth Management & Investment Advisory
Services
N.A.I.C.S.: 523940

SEI Investments (South Africa)
Limited   (1)
3 Melrose Boulevard 1st Floor, Melrose
Arch, Johannesburg, 2196, South Africa
Tel.: (27) 11 994 4200
Web Site: https://www.seic.com
Investment Management Service
N.A.I.C.S.: 523940

SEI Investments - Guernsey
Limited   (1)
1st & 2nd Floors Elizabeth House Les Ru-
ettes Brayes, PO Box 285, Saint Peter Port,
Guernsey
Tel.: (44) 1481737208
Financial Investment Services
N.A.I.C.S.: 523940

SEI Investments Canada
Company   (1)
130 King Street West Suite 2810, PO Box
433, Toronto, M5X 1E3, ON, Canada
Tel.: (416) 777-9700
Web Site: https://www.seic.com
Investment Management Service
N.A.I.C.S.: 523940
Ryan Hicke *(CEO)*
Sean Denham *(Exec VP)*
Jay Cipriano *(Exec VP)*
Sandy Ewing *(Exec VP)*
Paul F. Klauder *(Exec VP)*
Phil McCabe *(Exec VP)*
Sneha Shah *(Exec VP)*
Sanjay Sharma *(Exec VP)*
Michael Peterson *(Gen Counsel)*

SEI Investments Europe Limited (1)
1st Floor Alphabeta 14-18 Finsbury Square,
London, EC2A 1BR, United
Kingdom   (100%)
Tel.: (44) 203 810 8000
Web Site: http://www.seicorporation.com
Sales Range: $25-49.9 Million
Emp.: 150
Management Consulting Services
N.A.I.C.S.: 541611
Patrick Disney *(Chm)*

SEI Investments Global Funds
Services   (1)
1 Freedom Vly Dr, Oaks, PA 19456
Tel.: (610) 676-1000
Web Site: http://www.seic.com
Investment Management Service
N.A.I.C.S.: 523940

SEI Investments Global, Limited (1)
Styne House Upper Hatch Street, Dublin,
Ireland
Tel.: (353) 16382400
Web Site: http://www.seic.com
Sales Range: $50-74.9 Million
Emp.: 120
Investment Fund Management Services

N.A.I.C.S.: 523999
Alfred P. West Jr. *(Chm & CEO)*

SEI Investments Trustee & Custodial
Services (Ireland) Limited (1)
Styne House Upper Hatch St, Dublin, Ire-
land
Tel.: (353) 16382446
Web Site: http://www.seic.com
Emp.: 120
Investment Management Service
N.A.I.C.S.: 523940

SEI Novus UK (1)
1st Floor Alphabeta 14-18 Finsbury Square,
London, EC2A 1BR, United Kingdom
Tel.: (44) 2038108000
Financial Services
N.A.I.C.S.: 523999

SEI Trust Company (1)
1 Freedom Valley Dr, Oaks, PA 19456-9989
Tel.: (610) 676-1000
Investment Management Service
N.A.I.C.S.: 523940

SELECT MEDICAL HOLDINGS CORPORATION

4714 Gettysburg Rd, Mechanicsburg,
PA 17055
Tel.: (717) 920-4016   DE
Web Site:
   https://www.selectmedical.com
Year Founded: 2004
SEM—(NYSE)
Rev.: $6,664,058,000
Assets: $7,689,631,000
Liabilities: $6,141,913,000
Net Worth: $1,547,718,000
Earnings: $243,491,000
Emp.: 38,400
Fiscal Year-end: 12/31/23
Holding Company; Specialty Hospi-
tals & Outpatient Rehabilitation Clin-
ics Owner & Operator
N.A.I.C.S.: 551112
Martin F. Jackson *(Sr Exec VP-*
Strategic Fin & Ops)
Michael E. Tarvin *(Gen Counsel, Sec*
& Sr Exec VP)
Robert G. Breighner Jr. *(Sr VP-*
Compliance & Audit)
Robert A. Ortenzio *(Co-Founder &*
Exec Chm)
John A. Saich *(Co-Pres)*
Shelly Eckenroth *(Chief Comm, Mktg*
& Branding Officer & Sr VP)
Thomas P. Mullin *(Co-Pres)*
Joel T. Veit *(Treas & Sr VP)*
Michael F. Malatesta *(CFO & Exec*
VP)
David S. Chernow *(CEO)*
Robert G. Breighner Jr. *(Officer-Corp*
Compliance & VP-Compliance & Au-
dit Svcs)

Subsidiaries:

Advantage Rehabilitation Clinics,
Inc.   (1)
804 Ryder Ln, East Brunswick, NJ 08816
Tel.: (732) 238-4010
Outpatient Rehabilitation Services
N.A.I.C.S.: 623110

American Current Care of Arizona,
P.A.   (1)
7119 E Broadway Blvd, Tucson, AZ 85710
Tel.: (520) 881-0050
Web Site: https://www.concentra.com
Health Care Srvices
N.A.I.C.S.: 622110

American Current Care of Arkansas,
P.A.   (1)
3470 Landers Rd, North Little Rock, AR
72117
Tel.: (501) 945-0661
Web Site: https://www.concentra.com
Health Care Srvices
N.A.I.C.S.: 622110

American Current Care of Massachu-
setts, P.C.   (1)

140 Carando Dr, Springfield, MA 01104-
3296
Tel.: (413) 746-4006
Web Site: https://www.concentra.com
Health Care Srvices
N.A.I.C.S.: 622110

American Current Care of Michigan,
P.C.   (1)
1915 N Perry St, Pontiac, MI 48340-2237
Tel.: (248) 276-3999
Web Site: https://www.concentra.com
Health Care Srvices
N.A.I.C.S.: 622110

American Current Care of Nebraska,
P.C.   (1)
9602 M St, Omaha, NE 68127
Tel.: (402) 331-8555
Web Site: https://www.concentra.com
Health Care Srvices
N.A.I.C.S.: 622110

American Current Care of New Jer-
sey PA   (1)
210 Benigno Blvd Ste 202, Bellmawr, NJ
08031-2514
Tel.: (856) 931-0691
Web Site: https://www.concentra.com
Health Care Srvices
N.A.I.C.S.: 622110

American Current Care of North
Carolina, P.C.   (1)
4917 S Blvd, Charlotte, NC 28217
Tel.: (704) 395-0064
Health Care Srvices
N.A.I.C.S.: 622110

California Rehabilitation Institute,
LLC   (1)
2070 Century Park E, Los Angeles, CA
90067
Tel.: (424) 522-7100
Web Site:
   https://www.californiarehabinstitute.com
Health Care Srvices
N.A.I.C.S.: 622110
Alex Jawharjian *(COO)*
Pamela Roberts *(Sr Dir-Quality Outcomes &*
Res)

Caritas Rehab Services, LLC (1)
4402 Churchman Ave Ste 103, Louisville,
KY 40215
Tel.: (502) 361-5253
Web Site: https://www.kort.com
Sales Range: $10-24.9 Million
Emp.: 20
Outpatient Rehabilitation Services
N.A.I.C.S.: 622110

Cleveland Clinic Rehabilitation Hospi-
tals, LLC   (1)
33355 Health Campus Blvd, Avon, OH
44011
Tel.: (440) 937-9099
Web Site: https://my.clevelandclinic.org
Health Care Srvices
N.A.I.C.S.: 622110
Maureen Shepherd *(Mgr-HR)*

Concentra Inc.   (1)
5080 Spectrum Dr Ste 1200W, Addison, TX
75001-6484
Tel.: (972) 364-8000
Web Site: https://www.concentra.com
Holding Company; Healthcare Services
N.A.I.C.S.: 551112
Giovanni Gallara *(Chief Clinical Svcs Officer*
& Exec VP)
Dani Kendall *(Sr VP-Human Resources)*
Michael Kosuth *(COO-East Reg & Sr VP)*
Tom Devasia *(Chief Innovation Officer)*
Mike Rhine *(Exec VP)*

Subsidiary (Domestic):

Concentra Akron, LLC   (2)
1450 Firestone Pkwy, Akron, OH 44301
Tel.: (330) 724-3345
Web Site: https://www.concentra.com
Emp.: 25
Insurance & Healthcare Services
N.A.I.C.S.: 524114

Concentra Health Services, Inc. (2)
5080 Spectrum Dr W Tower Ste 400, Addison, TX 75001
Tel.: (972) 364-8000

Insurance Carrier
N.A.I.C.S.: 524114
Pedro Marzocca *(Dir-Reimbursement Pri-*
mary Care)
Mary Turner *(Assoc Gen Counsel)*

Concentra Occupational Health Re-
search Institute   (2)
5080 Spectrum Dr Ste 1200 W Tower, Addi-
son, TX 75001
Tel.: (512) 467-7232
Web Site: https://www.cohri.net
Medical Education & Research Services
N.A.I.C.S.: 541720

Concentra Operating Corporation (2)
5080 Spectrum Dr Ste 1200 W, Addison,
TX 75001-6484
Tel.: (972) 364-8000
Web Site: https://www.concentra.com
Emp.: 500
Occupational, Auto & Group Healthcare
Cost Containment, Case Management &
Workers Compensation Services
N.A.I.C.S.: 621399
Keith Newton *(Pres & CEO)*
John Anderson *(Chief Medical Officer & Sr*
VP)
John deLorimier *(CMO, Chief Sls Officer &*
Exec VP)
Greg Gilbert *(Sr VP-Reimbursement & Govt*
Affairs)
Jim Talalai *(CIO & Sr VP)*
Su Zan Nelson *(CFO)*
Jon Conser *(Sr VP-Sls)*
Matthew DiCanio *(Sr VP-Strategy & Corp*
Dev)
Dani Kendall *(Sr VP-HR)*
Giovanni Gallara *(Sr VP & Dir-Natl Therapy)*
Michael Kosuth *(Sr VP-Ops-East Reg)*
Doug McAndrew *(Sr VP-Ops-West Reg)*

Subsidiary (Domestic):

Concentra Medical Center   (3)
3580 Atlanta Ave, Hapeville, GA 30354-
1706
Tel.: (404) 768-3351
Web Site: http://www.concentra.com
Emp.: 30
Occupational Medicine & Health Care Ser-
vices
N.A.I.C.S.: 621111

Subsidiary (Domestic):

Concentra Solutions, Inc.   (2)
500 Sugar Mill Rd Bldg A Ste 130, Sandy
Springs, GA 30350
Web Site:
   https://www.concentrasolutions.com
Marketing Consulting Services
N.A.I.C.S.: 541618
Rica Askew *(VP-Sales-Marketing)*
Kim Christmas *(VP-HR)*

U.S. HealthWorks Medical Group,
Prof. Corp.   (2)
28035 Ave Stanford W, Valencia, CA 91355
Tel.: (661) 678-2300
Web Site: http://www.ussouthworks.com
Occupational Medicine & Urgent Care Ser-
vices
N.A.I.C.S.: 621999
Don Bopp *(Reg Dir-Sls)*

Concentra Primary Care of New Jer-
sey PA   (1)
6701 Bergenline Ave, West New York, NJ
07093
Tel.: (201) 758-9100
Health Care Srvices
N.A.I.C.S.: 622110

Crowley Physical Therapy Clinic,
Inc.   (1)
1455 Wright Ave, Crowley, LA 70526-2220
Tel.: (337) 788-1480
Outpatient Physical Therapy Services
N.A.I.C.S.: 621340

Dade Prosthetics & Orthotics,
Inc.   (1)
7800 SW 87th Ave Ste B205, Miami, FL
33173
Tel.: (305) 596-9821
Web Site: https://www.opcenters.com
Outpatient Rehabilitation Services
N.A.I.C.S.: 622110

Select Medical Holdings Corporation—(Continued)

Douglas Avery & Associates, Ltd. (1)
320-B Charles H Dimmock Pky Ste 6, Colonial Heights, VA 23834
Tel.: (804) 524-0533
Outpatient Physical Therapy Services
N.A.I.C.S.: 621340

Georgia Physical Therapy, Inc. (1)
2000 Village Professional Dr Ste 300, Canton, GA 30114
Tel.: (678) 880-9472
Web Site: https://www.georgiapt.com
Outpatient Physical Therapy Services
N.A.I.C.S.: 621340

Great Lakes Specialty Hospital-Hackley, LLC (1)
1700 Clinton St S 3, Muskegon, MI 49443
Web Site:
  https://www.selectspecialtyhospitals.com
Outpatient Rehabilitation Services
N.A.I.C.S.: 622110

Hand Therapy Associates, Inc. (1)
Post Ofc Plz Ste 173 150 Midway Rd, Cranston, RI 02920
Tel.: (401) 942-3343
Web Site:
  http://www.handtherapyassoc.com
Physiotherapy Clinic Operator
N.A.I.C.S.: 621340

Indianapolis Physical Therapy and Sports Medicine, Inc. (1)
3830 Shore Dr Ste A, Indianapolis, IN 46254-5657
Tel.: (317) 298-9746
Emp.: 4
Outpatient Physical Therapy Services
N.A.I.C.S.: 621340

Integrity Physical Therapy, Inc. (1)
3840 New Vision Dr, Fort Wayne, IN 46845
Tel.: (260) 483-2422
Medical Rehabilitation Hospital Services
N.A.I.C.S.: 622310

Joyner Sportsmedicine Institute, Inc. (1)
5400 Chambers Hill Rd Ste C, Harrisburg, PA 17111
Tel.: (717) 558-4333
Outpatient Physical Therapy Services
N.A.I.C.S.: 621340

KORT Rehabilitation at Home, LLC (1)
3626 Grant Line Rd Ste 105, New Albany, IN 47150-6417
Tel.: (812) 944-1377
Web Site: https://www.kort.com
Outpatient Rehabilitation Services
N.A.I.C.S.: 623110

Kentucky Orthopedic Rehabilitation, LLC (1)
1700 Envoy Cir, Louisville, KY 40299
Web Site: https://www.kort.com
Emp.: 500
Outpatient Physical Therapy Services
N.A.I.C.S.: 621340

Kentucky Rehabilitation Services, Inc. (1)
340 Thomas More Pkwy Ste 220, Crestview Hills, KY 41017
Tel.: (859) 341-6654
Health Care Srvices
N A I C S.: 622110

Kessler Institute for Rehabilitation, Inc. (1)
1199 Pleasant Valley Way, West Orange, NJ 07052
Tel.: (973) 731-3600
Outpatient Rehabilitation Services
N.A.I.C.S.: 622110
Michael D. Stubblefield (Dir-Cancer Rehabilitation)
Joseph P. Valenza (Dir-Pain Mgmt)
Yekyung Kong (Dir-Outpatient Stroke Svcs)
Neil N. Jasey (Dir-Medical)

Kessler Orthotic & Prosthetic Services, Inc. (1)
11 Microlab Rd, Livingston, NJ 07039
Tel.: (973) 992-9700

General Medical Services
N.A.I.C.S.: 623110

Kessler Rehab Centers, Inc. (1)
1465 Route 31, Annandale, NJ 08801
Tel.: (908) 735-6866
Web Site:
  https://www.kesslerrehabilitationcenter.com
Emp.: 6
Outpatient Rehabilitation Services
N.A.I.C.S.: 623110

Louisville Physical Therapy, P.S.C. (1)
4430 Crawford Ave, Louisville, KY 40258
Tel.: (502) 995-2705
Web Site: http://louisvillept.com
Physiotherapy Clinic Operator
N.A.I.C.S.: 621340
Jay Becht (Owner)

Madison Rehabilitation Center, Inc. (1)
141 Durham Rd Ste 14, Madison, CT 06443
Tel.: (203) 245-0001
Outpatient Rehabilitation Services
N.A.I.C.S.: 623110

NovaCare Occupational Health Services, Inc. (1)
4714 Gettysburg Rd, Mechanicsburg, PA 17055
Tel.: (717) 972-8199.
Web Site: https://www.novacare.com
Outpatient Physical Rehabilitation Services
N.A.I.C.S.: 622310

NovaCare Outpatient Rehabilitation, Inc. (1)
1855 S Rock Rd, Wichita, KS 67207
Tel.: (316) 682-6333
Emp.: 4
Outpatient Physical Rehabilitation Services
N.A.I.C.S.: 622310
Darci Needham (Mgr-Admin Svc)

NovaCare Rehabilitation (1)
150 E Huron Ste 803, Chicago, IL 60611-2999
Tel.: (312) 640-2473
Web Site: https://www.novacare.com
Outpatient Physical Therapy Services
N.A.I.C.S.: 621340

NovaCare Rehabilitation Services, Inc. (1)
559 Ctr View Blvd Cambridge Sq, Crestview Hills, KY 41017
Tel.: (859) 341-6654
Web Site: http://www.novacare.com
Outpatient Rehabilitation Services
N.A.I.C.S.: 622110

NovaCare Rehabilitation of Ohio, Inc. (1)
5 Severance Cir Ste 115, Cleveland Heights, OH 44118-1513
Tel.: (216) 381-0300
Web Site: https://www.novacare.com
Sales Range: $10-24.9 Million
Emp.: 5
Outpatient Physical Rehabilitation Services
N.A.I.C.S.: 622310

OSR Louisiana, LLC (1)
2614 Jefferson Hwy, New Orleans, LA 70121
Tel.: (717) 972-1100
Hospital Management Services
N.A.I.C.S.: 622110

Occspecialists Corp., A Medical Corporation (1)
9439 Archibald Ave Ste 101, Rancho Cucamonga, CA 91730-7946
Tel.: (909) 484-7701
Health Care Srvices
N.A.I.C.S.: 622110

Occupational Health Centers of California, A Medical Corporation (1)
5333 Mission Ctr Rd Ste 100, San Diego, CA 92108-1302
Tel.: (619) 295-3355
Health Care Srvices
N.A.I.C.S.: 622110

Occupational Health Centers of Michigan, P.C. (1)
30800 Telegraph Rd Ste 3900, Bingham Farms, MI 48025
Tel.: (248) 712-2100
Health Care Srvices
N.A.I.C.S.: 622110

Occupational Health Centers of Nebraska, P.C. (1)
4900 N 26th St Ste 104, Lincoln, NE 68521
Tel.: (402) 465-0010
Web Site:
  https://www.nebraskaocchealth.com
Health Care Srvices
N.A.I.C.S.: 622110

Occupational Health Centers of Ohio, P.A., Co. (1)
19000 E Eastland Ctr Ct Ste 200, Independence, OH 64055
Tel.: (816) 478-9299
Health Care Srvices
N.A.I.C.S.: 622110

Occupational Health Centers of The Southwest, P.A. (1)
1818 E Sky Harbor Cir N, Phoenix, AZ 85034
Tel.: (972) 364-8000
Emp.: 5
Health Care Srvices
N.A.I.C.S.: 622110

OnSite OccMed, P.A. (1)
1345 Valwood Pkwy Ste 306, Carrollton, TX 75006
Tel.: (972) 484-6435
Health Care Srvices
N.A.I.C.S.: 622110

P&O Services, Inc. (1)
24293 Telegraph Rd Ste 140, Southfield, MI 48033
Tel.: (248) 809-3072
Web Site: https://www.pandoservices.com
Personalized Care Product Distr
N.A.I.C.S.: 456199
Zia Ur Rahman (Pres)
Cindy Winter (Office Mgr-Billing)

PHS Physical Therapy, LLC (1)
3025 Market St, Camp Hill, PA 17011-4518
Tel.: (717) 737-7903
Health Care Srvices
N.A.I.C.S.: 622110

PTSMA, Inc. (1)
240 E St Ste C, Plainville, CT 06062
Tel.: (860) 793-6882
Health Care Srvices
N.A.I.C.S.: 622110

Physio at Hammonds Centre, LLC (1)
4523 Forsyth Rd, Macon, GA 31210
Tel.: (478) 254-7010
Medical Rehabilitation Hospital Services
N.A.I.C.S.: 622310

Physiotherapy Associates NRH Rehab, LLC (1)
16900 Science Dr Ste 104-106, Bowie, MD 20715
Tel.: (301) 805-7110
Medical Rehabilitation Hospital Services
N.A.I.C.S.: 622310

Physiotherapy Associates, Inc. (1)
680 American Ave, King of Prussia, PA 19406
Tel.: (678) 401-2952
Web Site: https://www.physiopt.com
Outpatient Physical, Occupational, Hand & Speech Therapy Services
N.A.I.C.S.: 621340

Pro Active Therapy of North Carolina, Inc. (1)
3301 Benson Dr Ste 135-A, Raleigh, NC 27609-7332
Tel.: (919) 872-8511
Outpatient Physical Therapy Services
N.A.I.C.S.: 621340

Pro Active Therapy of South Carolina, Inc. (1)
154-101 Amendment Ave, Rock Hill, SC 29732
Tel.: (803) 366-9990
Emp.: 9
Outpatient Therapy Centers & Clinics

N.A.I.C.S.: 621498
Adam Stickley (Mgr-Center)

Pro Active Therapy of Virginia, Inc. (1)
4521 Brambleton Ave 105, Roanoke, VA 24018
Tel.: (540) 989-8974
Outpatient Physical Therapy Services
N.A.I.C.S.: 621340

RCI (Michigan), Inc. (1)
1535 44th St SW Ste 300, Wyoming, MI 49509-4481
Tel.: (616) 530-1977
Web Site: https://www.hjphysavithirapy.com
Outpatient Physical Therapy Services
N.A.I.C.S.: 621340

RCI (WRS), Inc. (1)
326 E Main St, West Frankfort, IL 62896
Tel.: (618) 937-6200
Sales Range: $10-24.9 Million
Emp.: 6
Outpatient Physical Therapy Services
N.A.I.C.S.: 621340

Regency Hospital Company of Macon, LLC (1)
535 Coliseum Dr, Macon, GA 31217
Tel.: (478) 803-7300
Web Site:
  https://macon.regencyhospital.com
Outpatient Rehabilitation Services
N.A.I.C.S.: 623110
Lorraine A. Smith (CEO)

Regency Hospital Company of Meridian, L.L.C. (1)
1102 Constitution Ave 2nd Fl, Meridian, MS 39301-4001
Tel.: (601) 484-7900
Web Site:
  https://meridian.regencyhospital.com
Outpatient Rehabilitation Services
N.A.I.C.S.: 623110
Carolyn McKee (Chief Nursing Officer)
Eliza Gavin (CEO)

Regency Hospital Company of South Atlanta, L.L.C. (1)
1170 Cleveland Ave 4th Fl, East Point, GA 30344-3615
Tel.: (404) 466-4600
Web Site: http://www.regencyhospital.com
Outpatient Rehabilitation Services
N.A.I.C.S.: 623110

Regency Hospital Company of South Carolina, L.L.C. (1)
805 Pamplico Hghwy 2nd & 3rd Fl, Florence, SC 29505
Tel.: (843) 674-6200
Web Site:
  https://florence.regencyhospital.com
Inpatient Rehabilitation Clinic Operating Services
N.A.I.C.S.: 623110
Robbie Strickland (Chief Nursing Officer)
Amy Metz (CEO)

Regency Hospital of Cincinnati, LLC (1)
10500 Montgomery Rd Ground Fl, Cincinnati, OH 45242
Tel.: (513) 865-5300
Web Site: https://www.regencyhospital.com
Emp.: 200
Outpatient Rehabilitation Services
N.A.I.C.S.: 623110
Sue Glenn (Pres)

Regency Hospital of Columbus, LLC (1)
1430 S High St, Columbus, OH 43207-1045
Tel.: (614) 456-0300
Web Site:
  https://columbussouth.selectspecialty
  hospitals.com
Outpatient Rehabilitation Services
N.A.I.C.S.: 623110

Regency Hospital of Covington, LLC (1)
195 Highland Park Entrance, Covington, LA 70433
Tel.: (985) 867-3977
Web Site: http://www.regencyhospital.com
Outpatient Rehabilitation Clinic Operating Services

N.A.I.C.S.: 623110

Regency Hospital of Fort Worth, LLLP (1)
6801 Oakmont Blvd, Fort Worth, TX 76132
Tel.: (817) 840-0880
Web Site: http://www.regencyhospital.com
Sales Range: $25-49.9 Million
Emp.: 2
General Medical Services
N.A.I.C.S.: 622110

Regency Hospital of Greenville, LLC (1)
1 Saint Francis Dr 4th Fl, Greenville, SC 29601-3955
Tel.: (864) 255-1401
Web Site:
http://greenville.regencyhospital.com
Outpatient Rehabilitation Services
N.A.I.C.S.: 623110

Regency Hospital of Jackson, LLC (1)
969 Lakeland Dr Fl 6, Jackson, MS 39216
Tel.: (601) 364-6200
Web Site: https://www.regencyhospital.com
Outpatient Rehabilitation Services
N.A.I.C.S.: 623110

Regency Hospital of Minneapolis, LLC (1)
1300 Hidden Lakes Pkwy, Golden Valley, MN 55422-4286
Tel.: (763) 588-2750
Web Site:
https://minneapolis.regencyhospital.com
Outpatient Rehabilitation Services
N.A.I.C.S.: 623110
Sean Stricker (CEO)
Haddy Ceesay (Chief Nursing Officer)

Regency Hospital of North Central Ohio, LLC (1)
4200 Interchange Corporate Center Rd, Warrensville Heights, OH 44128-5631
Tel.: (216) 910-3800
Web Site:
https://clevelandeast.regencyhospital.com
Outpatient Rehabilitation Services
N.A.I.C.S.: 623110
Lisa Deering (CEO)
Arun Gupta (Chief Medical Officer)
Judith McCoy (Chief Nursing Officer)

Regency Hospital of Northwest Arkansas, LLC (1)
609 W Maple Ave 6th Fl, Springdale, AR 72764
Tel.: (479) 757-2600
Web Site: https://www.regencyhospital.com
Nursing Care Services
N.A.I.C.S.: 623110

Regency Hospital of Northwest Indiana, LLC (1)
4321 Fir St 4th Fl, East Chicago, IN 46312-3049
Tel.: (219) 392-7799
Web Site:
https://northwestindiana.regencyhos
pital.com
General Medical Services
N.A.I.C.S.: 623110

Regency Hospital of Southern Mississippi, LLC (1)
6051 Hwy 49 5th FL, Hattiesburg, MS 39401
Tel.: (601) 288-8510
Web Site: https://www.selectmedical.com
General Medical Services
N.A.I.C.S.: 623110

Rehab Associates of Jackson Hospital, LLC (1)
1215 Mulberry St, Montgomery, AL 36106
Tel.: (334) 262-6161
Web Site: https://www.rehab-
associates.com
Medical Rehabilitation Hospital Services
N.A.I.C.S.: 622310

Rehab Provider Network-East I, Inc. (1)
3301 Benson Dr Ste 135B, Raleigh, NC 27609-6842
Tel.: (919) 878-9996
Web Site: https://rehabprovidernetwork.com

Outpatient Rehabilitation Services
N.A.I.C.S.: 623110

Rehab Provider Network-Michigan, Inc. (1)
6978 Hillsdale Ct, Indianapolis, IN 46250-2040
Tel.: (800) 566-7764
Outpatient Rehabilitation Services
N.A.I.C.S.: 623110

Rehab Provider Network-Pennsylvania, Inc. (1)
2270 Douglas Blvd Ste 216, Roseville, CA 95661
Tel.: (888) 806-3096
Outpatient Rehabilitation Services
N.A.I.C.S.: 623110

Rehab Xcel, LLC (1)
441 Moosa Blvd, Eunice, LA 70535
Tel.: (337) 457-8164
Medical Rehabilitation Hospital Services
N.A.I.C.S.: 622310

RehabClinics (SPT), Inc. (1)
570 Egg Harbor Rd Ste B6, Sewell, NJ 08080
Tel.: (856) 218-8050
General Medical Services
N.A.I.C.S.: 623110

Rehabilitation Center of Washington, D.C., Inc. (1)
1776 Eye St NW, Washington, DC 20006
Tel.: (202) 775-5951
Outpatient Rehabilitation Services
N.A.I.C.S.: 623110

Rehabilitation Institute of Denton, LLC (1)
2620 Scripture St, Denton, TX 76201
Tel.: (940) 297-6500
Web Site: https://www.selectrehab-
denton.com
Outpatient Physical Therapy Services
N.A.I.C.S.: 621340

SLMC Finance Corporation (1)
103 Foulk Rd, Wilmington, DE 19803
Tel.: (302) 575-0603
Emp.: 4
Financial Services
N.A.I.C.S.: 521110

SSM Select Rehab St. Louis, LLC (1)
1027 Bellevue Ave 3rd Fl, Saint Louis, MO 63117
Tel.: (314) 768-5202
Web Site: https://www.ssm-rehab.com
General Medical Services
N.A.I.C.S.: 622110

Saco Bay Orthopaedic and Sports Physical Therapy, Inc. (1)
45 Western Ave, South Portland, ME 04106
Tel.: (207) 772-2625
Web Site: https://www.sacobaypt.com
Outpatient Physical Therapy Services
N.A.I.C.S.: 621340

Saco Bay Orthopedic and Sports Physical Therapy, Inc. (1)
55 Main St Ste B, Bridgton, ME 04009
Tel.: (207) 468-7115
Web Site: https://www.sacobaypt.com
Health Care Srvices
N.A.I.C.S.: 622110

Select Medical Corporation (1)
4714 Gettysburg Rd, Mechanicsburg, PA 17055 **(100%)**
Tel.: (717) 972-1100
Web Site: https://www.selectmedical.com
Sales Range: $5-14.9 Billion
Health Care Facilities Services
N.A.I.C.S.: 622310
Robert A. Ortenzio (Chm)
Rocco A. Ortenzio (Co-Founder & Vice Chm)
John A. Saich (Chief Admin Officer & Exec VP)
Thomas P. Mullin (Co-Pres)
Michael F. Malatesta (Exec VP)
Brian R. Rusignuolo (Exec VP)
Christopher S. Weigl (Chief Acctg Officer)

Subsidiary (Domestic):

NovaCare Rehabilitation (2)

680 American Ave, King of Prussia, PA 19406
Tel.: (610) 992-7200
Web Site: http://www.novacare.com
Sales Range: $10-24.9 Million
Emp.: 30
Physical Rehabilitation Clinics
N.A.I.C.S.: 621498
Dan Bradley (Pres-Outpatient Div)
Alan Evans (VP-Clinical Education)

Select Medical of Maryland, Inc. (1)
680 American Ave, King of Prussia, PA 19406
Tel.: (717) 972-1139
General Medical Services
N.A.I.C.S.: 623110

Select Physical Therapy - Avon (1)
34 Dale Rd Ste 203, Avon, CT 06001
Tel.: (860) 678-8655
Web Site:
http://www.selectphysicaltherapy.com
Outpatient Physical Therapy Services
N.A.I.C.S.: 621340
Ashley Neal (Mgr-Center)

Select Physical Therapy Texas Limited Partnership (1)
711 W 38th St, Austin, TX 78705-1125
Tel.: (512) 450-0909
Web Site: https://www.selectmedical.com
Sales Range: $10-24.9 Million
Emp.: 6
Outpatient Physical Therapy Services
N.A.I.C.S.: 621340

Select Physical Therapy of Albuquerque, Ltd. (1)
2113 Golf Course Rd, Rio Rancho, NM 87124
Tel.: (505) 898-9700
Web Site:
https://www.selectphysicaltherapy.com
Outpatient Physical Therapy Services
N.A.I.C.S.: 621340

Select Physical Therapy of Blue Springs Limited Partnership (1)
732 -734 N 7 Hwy, Blue Springs, MO 64014-2425
Tel.: (816) 229-6622
Sales Range: $10-24.9 Million
Emp.: 5
Outpatient Physical Therapy Services
N.A.I.C.S.: 621340

Select Physical Therapy of Chicago, Inc. (1)
150 E Huron St 803, Chicago, IL 60611-2999
Tel.: (312) 640-2473
Medical Rehabilitation Hospital Services
N.A.I.C.S.: 622310

Select Physical Therapy of Colorado Springs Limited Partnership (1)
15 S Weber Ste A, Colorado Springs, CO 80903-1920
Tel.: (719) 630-7774
Web Site: https://www.selectmedical.com
Physical Therapy Services
N.A.I.C.S.: 621340

Select Physical Therapy of Connecticut Limited Partnership (1)
9 Dog Ln Ste 108, Storrs Mansfield, CT 06268-2239
Tel.: (860) 429-0899
Web Site: https://www.selectmedical.com
Emp.: 20
Outpatient Physical Therapy Services
N.A.I.C.S.: 621340

Select Physical Therapy of Denver, Ltd. (1)
3102 S Parker Rd Ste A15, Aurora, CO 80014
Tel.: (303) 338-8598
Outpatient Physical Therapy Services
N.A.I.C.S.: 621340

Select Physical Therapy of Kendall, Ltd. (1)
11140 SW 88th St Ste 200, Miami, FL 33176-0901
Tel.: (305) 271-3223
Outpatient Physical Therapy Services
N.A.I.C.S.: 621340

Select Physical Therapy of Louisville, Ltd. (1)
1227 Goss Ave, Louisville, KY 40217-1239
Tel.: (502) 636-1200
Web Site: http://www.selectmedical.com
Outpatient Physical Therapy Services
N.A.I.C.S.: 621340

Select Physical Therapy of Portola Valley Limited Partnership (1)
454 Forest Ave, Palo Alto, CA 94301-2608
Tel.: (650) 331-3700
Web Site: https://www.selectmedical.com
Outpatient Physical Therapy Services
N.A.I.C.S.: 621340

Select Physical Therapy of St. Louis Limited Partnership (1)
1001 S Kirkwood Rd, Saint Louis, MO 63122-7251
Tel.: (314) 821-7554
Web Site: https://www.selectmedical.com
Outpatient Physical Therapy Services
N.A.I.C.S.: 621340

Select Physical Therapy of West Denver Limited Partnership (1)
7777 W 38th Ave Ste A-124, Wheat Ridge, CO 80033-6168
Tel.: (303) 940-0757
Web Site:
https://www.selectphysicaltherapy.com
Emp.: 7
Outpatient Physical Therapy Services
N.A.I.C.S.: 621340

Select Specialty Hospital - Daytona Beach, Inc. (1)
301 Memorial Medical Pkwy, Daytona Beach, FL 32117
Tel.: (386) 231-3470
Web Site:
https://daytonabeach.selectspecialtyhos
pitals.com
Health Care Srvices
N.A.I.C.S.: 622110
Adriane Lutes (CEO)

Select Specialty Hospital - Spectrum Health (1)
1840 Wealthy St SE, Grand Rapids, MI 49506
Tel.: (616) 774-3800
Web Site:
http://grandrapids.selectspecialtyhos
pitals.com
Outpatient Rehabilitation Services
N.A.I.C.S.: 623110
Jason Popma (Pres)

Select Specialty Hospital-Akron, LLC (1)
200 E Market St, Akron, OH 44308
Tel.: (330) 761-7500
Web Site:
https://akron.selectspecialtyhospitals.com
Emp.: 100
General Medical Services
N.A.I.C.S.: 622110
Sonda Burns (CEO)

Select Specialty Hospital-Ann Arbor, Inc. (1)
5301 E Huron River Dr 7 N, Ypsilanti, MI 48197
Tel.: (734) 337-1100
Web Site:
https://annarbor.selectspecialtyhos
pitals.com
General Medical Services
N.A.I.C.S.: 622110

Select Specialty Hospital-Arizona, Inc. (1)
7400 E Osborn Rd, Scottsdale, AZ 85251
Tel.: (480) 882-4360
Web Site:
https://www.selectspecialtyhospitals.com
Emp.: 99
General Medical Services
N.A.I.C.S.: 622110

Select Specialty Hospital-Augusta, Inc. (1)
1537 Walton Way, Augusta, GA 30904
Tel.: (706) 731-1200
Web Site: https://augusta.selectspecialtyhos
pitals.com
General Medical Services

Select Medical Holdings Corporation—(Continued)

N.A.I.C.S.: 622110

Select Specialty Hospital-Belhaven, LLC (1)
1225 N State St 5th Fl, Jackson, MS 39202
Tel.: (601) 968-1052
Web Site:
    https://www.belhaven.selectspecialty
    hospitals.com
Health Care Srvices
N.A.I.C.S.: 622110
Shannon Canard (CEO)

Select Specialty Hospital-Boardman, Inc. (1)
8049 S Ave, Youngstown, OH 44512
Tel.: (330) 726-5000
Physical Therapy Services
N.A.I.C.S.: 621340

Select Specialty Hospital-Central Pennsylvania, L.P. (1)
503 N 21st St 5th Fl, Camp Hill, PA 17011
Tel.: (717) 972-4575
General Medical Services
N.A.I.C.S.: 622110

Select Specialty Hospital-Charleston, Inc. (1)
3200 MacCorkle Ave SE, Charleston, WV 25604
Tel.: (681) 273-7100
Web Site:
    https://charleston.selectspecialtyhos
    pitals.com
General Medical Services
N.A.I.C.S.: 622110

Select Specialty Hospital-Cleveland, LLC (1)
11900 Fairhill Rd, Cleveland, OH 44120
Tel.: (216) 983-8030
Web Site:
    https://www.selectspecialtyhospitals.com
Emergency Care Hospital Services
N.A.I.C.S.: 621493

Select Specialty Hospital-Colorado Springs, Inc. (1)
6001 E Woodmen Rd 6th Fl, Colorado Springs, CO 80923
Tel.: (719) 571-6000
Web Site:
    https://www.selectspecialtyhospital.com
Emp.: 50
General Medical Services
N.A.I.C.S.: 622110
Dawn Johangges (CEO)

Select Specialty Hospital-Columbus, Inc. (1)
1087 Dennison Ave, Columbus, OH 43201
Tel.: (614) 458-9000
Web Site:
    https://columbusvictorianvillage.select
    specialtyhospitals.com
Emp.: 500
General Medical Services
N.A.I.C.S.: 622110
Lisa Pettrey (CEO)

Select Specialty Hospital-Dallas, Inc. (1)
2329 W Parker Rd, Carrollton, TX 75010
Tel.: (469) 892-1400
Web Site: https://www.selectmedical.com
General Medical Services
N.A.I.C.S.: 622110

Select Specialty Hospital-Danville, Inc. (1)
100 N Academy Ave Internal Mail Code 42-10, Danville, PA 17822
Tel.: (570) 214-9657
Web Site:
    http://danville.selectspecialtyhospitals.com
Emp.: 45
General Medical Services
N.A.I.C.S.: 622110

Select Specialty Hospital-Denver, Inc. (1)
1719 E 19th Ave 5B, Denver, CO 80218
Tel.: (303) 563-3700
Web Site:
    https://www.selectspecialtyhospital.com
General Medical Services

Select Specialty Hospital-Des Moines, Inc. (1)
1111 6th Ave 4th Fl Main, Des Moines, IA 50314
Tel.: (515) 247-4400
Web Site:
    https://desmoines.selectspecialtyhos
    pitals.com
Health Care Srvices
N.A.I.C.S.: 622110

Select Specialty Hospital-Durham, Inc. (1)
3643 N Roxboro St 6th Fl, Durham, NC 27704
Tel.: (984) 569-4040
Web Site:
    https://durham.selectspecialtyhospi
    tals.com
Emp.: 100
General Medical Services
N.A.I.C.S.: 622110

Select Specialty Hospital-Erie Inc. (1)
252 W 11th St, Erie, PA 16501
Tel.: (814) 874-5300
Web Site:
    https://erie.selectspecialtyhospitals.com
General Medical Services
N.A.I.C.S.: 622110

Select Specialty Hospital-Evansville, Inc. (1)
400 SE 4th St, Evansville, IN 47713
Tel.: (812) 421-2500
Web Site:
    https://evansville.selectspecialtyhos
    pitals.com
Emp.: 225
General Medical Services
N.A.I.C.S.: 622110

Select Specialty Hospital-Evansville, LLC (1)
400 SE 4th St, Evansville, IN 47713
Tel.: (812) 421-2500
General Medical Services
N.A.I.C.S.: 622110

Select Specialty Hospital-Flint, Inc. (1)
401 S Ballenger Hwy 5th Fl Central Tower, Flint, MI 48532
Tel.: (810) 342-4545
Web Site:
    https://flint.selectspecialtyhospitals.com
General Medical Services
N.A.I.C.S.: 622110

Select Specialty Hospital-Fort Myers, Inc. (1)
3050 Champion Ring Rd, Fort Myers, FL 33905
Tel.: (239) 313-2900
Web Site:
    https://www.selectspecialtyhospitals.com
Hospital Care Services
N.A.I.C.S.: 622110

Select Specialty Hospital-Fort Smith, Inc. (1)
1001 Towson Ave 6th Fl, Fort Smith, AR 72901
Tel.: (479) 441-3980
Web Site:
    https://fortsmith.selectspecialtyhos
    pitals.com
General Medical Services
N.A.I.C.S.: 622110
Zack Dawson (CEO)

Select Specialty Hospital-Fort Wayne, Inc. (1)
700 Broadway, Fort Wayne, IN 46802
Tel.: (260) 425-3810
Web Site:
    http://www.selectspecialtyhospitals.com
Hospital Services
N.A.I.C.S.: 622110

Select Specialty Hospital-Gainesville, Inc. (1)
1600 SW Archer Rd 5th Fl, Gainesville, FL 32610
Tel.: (352) 265-0055
Web Site:
    https://gainesville.selectspecialtyhos
    pitals.com

General Medical Services
N.A.I.C.S.: 622110
Ronnie Wagley (CEO)

Select Specialty Hospital-Greensboro, Inc. (1)
1200 N Elm St, Greensboro, NC 27401
Tel.: (336) 832-5700
Web Site:
    https://greensboro.selectspecialtyhos
    pitals.com
General Medical Services
N.A.I.C.S.: 622110

Select Specialty Hospital-Grosse Pointe, Inc. (1)
22101 Moross Rd 6th Fl, Detroit, MI 48236
Tel.: (313) 343-7560
Web Site:
    https://www.selectspecialtyhospitals.com
General Medical Services
N.A.I.C.S.: 622110

Select Specialty Hospital-Gulf Coast, Inc. (1)
4500 13th St 3rd Fl Wings C & D, Gulfport, MS 39501
Tel.: (228) 575-7500
Web Site:
    https://www.selectspecialtyhospitals.com
General Medical Services
N.A.I.C.S.: 622110

Select Specialty Hospital-Houston, L.P. (1)
3414 Ella Blvd, Houston, TX 77018-6100
Tel.: (713) 686-8408
Web Site: http://www.selectmedical.com
General Medical Services
N.A.I.C.S.: 622110

Select Specialty Hospital-Jackson, Inc. (1)
5903 Ridgewood Rd, Jackson, MS 39211
Tel.: (601) 899-3800
Web Site:
    https://jackson.selectspecialtyhospi
    tals.com
General Medical Services
N.A.I.C.S.: 622110

Select Specialty Hospital-Johnstown, Inc. (1)
320 Main St 3rd Fl, Johnstown, PA 15901
Tel.: (814) 534-7360
Web Site:
    https://johnstown.selectspecialtyhospi
    tals.com
Emp.: 150
General Medical Services
N.A.I.C.S.: 622110

Select Specialty Hospital-Kalamazoo, Inc. (1)
300 N Ave 6th Fl, Battle Creek, MI 49017
Tel.: (269) 245-4675
Emergency Care Hospital Services
N.A.I.C.S.: 621493

Select Specialty Hospital-Kansas City, Inc. (1)
1731 N 90th St, Kansas City, KS 66112
Tel.: (913) 732-5900
Web Site:
    https://kansascity.selectspecialtyhospi
    tals.com
General Medical Services
N.A.I.C.S.: 622110

Select Specialty Hospital-Knoxville, Inc. (1)
501 19th St Trustee Tower 7th Fl, Knoxville, TN 37916
Tel.: (865) 370-2830
Web Site:
    https://www.selectspecialtyhospitals.com
Emp.: 200
General Medical Services
N.A.I.C.S.: 622110

Select Specialty Hospital-Laurel Highlands, Inc. (1)
1 Mellon Way 3rd Fl, Latrobe, PA 15650
Tel.: (724) 539-3870
Web Site:
    https://laurelhighlands.selectspecialty
    hospitals.com
General Medical Services
N.A.I.C.S.: 622110

Select Specialty Hospital-Lexington, Inc. (1)
310 S Limestone St 3rd Fl, Lexington, KY 40508
Tel.: (859) 226-7321
Web Site: https://www.selectmedical.com
Emp.: 100
General Medical Services
N.A.I.C.S.: 622110

Select Specialty Hospital-Lincoln, Inc. (1)
2300 S 16th St 7th Fl, Lincoln, NE 68502-3704
Tel.: (402) 483-8444
Web Site:
    http://lincoln.selectspecialtyhospitals.com
Health Care Srvices
N.A.I.C.S.: 622110

Select Specialty Hospital-Little Rock, Inc. (1)
2 St Vincent Cir 6th Fl, Little Rock, AR 72205
Tel.: (501) 265-0600
Web Site:
    https://www.selectspecialtyhospitals.com
General Medical Services
N.A.I.C.S.: 622110

Select Specialty Hospital-Longview, Inc. (1)
700 E Marshall Ave Ground and 1st Fl W Wing, Longview, TX 75601
Tel.: (903) 315-1100
Web Site:
    https://longview.selectspecialtyhos
    pitals.com
Emp.: 40
General Medical Services
N.A.I.C.S.: 622110

Select Specialty Hospital-Macomb County, Inc. (1)
215 N Ave Ground and 5th Fl, Mount Clemens, MI 48043
Tel.: (586) 307-9010
Web Site:
    https://macomb.selectspecialtyhospi
    tals.com
General Medical Services
N.A.I.C.S.: 622110

Select Specialty Hospital-Madison, Inc. (1)
801 Braxton Pl, Madison, WI 53715
Tel.: (608) 260-2700
Web Site:
    https://madison.selectspecialtyhospi
    tals.com
Sales Range: $25-49.9 Million
Emp.: 200
General Medical Services
N.A.I.C.S.: 622110

Select Specialty Hospital-McKeesport, Inc. (1)
1500 5th Ave 6th Fl Crawford Bldg, McKeesport, PA 15132
Tel.: (412) 927-5700
Web Site:
    https://mckeesport.selectspecialtyhos
    pitals.com
Emp.: 94
General Medical Services
N.A.I.C.S.: 622110

Select Specialty Hospital-Memphis, Inc. (1)
1265 Union Ave 10th Fl Thomas Wing, Memphis, TN 38104
Tel.: (901) 546-2400
Web Site:
    https://memphis.selectspecialtyhospi
    tals.com
General Medical Services
N.A.I.C.S.: 622110

Select Specialty Hospital-Miami Lakes, Inc. (1)
14001 NW 82nd Ave, Miami Lakes, FL 33016
Tel.: (786) 609-9200
Web Site:
    https://www.selectspecialtyhospitals.com
Hospital Care Services
N.A.I.C.S.: 622110

Select Specialty Hospital-Midland, Inc. (1)

4214 Andrews Hwy Ste 320, Midland, TX
79703
Tel.: (432) 522-3044
Web Site:
http://www.selectspecialtyhospitals.com
General Medical Services
N.A.I.C.S.: 622110

**Select Specialty Hospital-Midtown
Atlanta, LLC** (1)
705 Juniper St NE, Atlanta, GA 30308
Tel.: (404) 873-2871
Web Site:
https://www.midtownatlanta.selectspe
cialtyhospitals.com
Healtcare Services
N.A.I.C.S.: 621999

**Select Specialty Hospital-Milwaukee,
Inc.** (1)
8901 W Lincoln Ave 2nd Fl, West Allis, WI
53227
Tel.: (414) 328-7700
Web Site:
https://milwaukeewestallis.selectspecial
tyhospitals.com
General Medical Services
N.A.I.C.S.: 622110

**Select Specialty Hospital-Nashville,
Inc.** (1)
2000 Hayes St Ste 1502, Nashville, TN
37203
Tel.: (615) 284-4599
Web Site:
https://nashville.selectspecialtyhospi
tals.com
General Medical Services
N.A.I.C.S.: 622110

**Select Specialty Hospital-North Knox-
ville, Inc.** (1)
1901 Clinch Ave 4 N, Knoxville, TN 37916
Tel.: (865) 331-2600
Web Site:
http://knoxville.selectspecialtyhospi
tals.com
Emp.: 100
General Medical Services
N.A.I.C.S.: 622110

**Select Specialty Hospital-Northeast
New Jersey, Inc.** (1)
96 Parkway, Rochelle Park, NJ 07662
Tel.: (201) 221-2352
Web Site:
https://northeastnewjersey.selectspe
cialtyhospitals.com
General Medical Services
N.A.I.C.S.: 622110

**Select Specialty Hospital-Northeast
Ohio, Inc.** (1)
2600 6th St SW 4th Fl, Canton, OH 44710
Tel.: (234) 364-4290
Web Site: https://www.selectmedical.com
General Medical Services
N.A.I.C.S.: 622110

**Select Specialty Hospital-Northern
Kentucky, LLC** (1)
85 N Grand Ave 3rd Fl, Fort Thomas, KY
41075
Tel.: (859) 572-3880
Web Site:
https://northernkentucky.selectspecial
tyhospitals.com
General Medical Services
N.A.I.C.S.: 622110

**Select Specialty Hospital-Northwest
Detroit, Inc.** (1)
6071 W Outer Dr 7th Fl, Detroit, MI 48235
Tel.: (313) 966-3939
Web Site:
https://www.selectspecialtyhospitals.com
General Medical Services
N.A.I.C.S.: 622110

**Select Specialty Hospital-Oklahoma
City, Inc.** (1)
3524 NW 56th St, Oklahoma City, OK
73112
Tel.: (405) 606-6937
Web Site:
https://oklahomacity.selectspecialtyhos
pitals.com
General Medical Services
N.A.I.C.S.: 622110

**Select Specialty Hospital-Omaha,
Inc.** (1)
1870 S 75th St, Omaha, NE 68124
Tel.: (402) 361-5700
Web Site:
https://omaha.selectspecialtyhospitals.com
General Medical Services
N.A.I.C.S.: 622110

**Select Specialty Hospital-Palm
Beach, Inc.** (1)
3060 Melaleuca Ln, Lake Worth, FL 33461
Tel.: (561) 357-7200
Web Site:
https://palmbeach.selectspecialtyhospi
tals.com
General Medical Services
N.A.I.C.S.: 622110

**Select Specialty Hospital-Panama
City, Inc.** (1)
615 N Bonita Ave 3rd Fl, Panama City, FL
32401
Tel.: (850) 767-3180
Web Site:
https://panamacity.selectspecialtyhospi
tals.com
General Medical Services
N.A.I.C.S.: 622110

**Select Specialty Hospital-Pensacola,
Inc.** (1)
7000 Cobble Creek Dr, Pensacola, FL
32504
Tel.: (850) 473-4800
Web Site:
https://pensacola.selectspecialtyhospi
tals.com
General Medical Services
N.A.I.C.S.: 622110

**Select Specialty Hospital-Phoenix,
Inc.** (1)
350 W Thomas Rd 3rd Fl Main, Phoenix,
AZ 85013
Tel.: (602) 406-6810
Web Site:
https://phoenix.selectspecialtyhospi
tals.com
General Medical Services
N.A.I.C.S.: 622110

**Select Specialty Hospital-
Pittsburgh/UPMC, Inc.** (1)
200 Lothrop St UPMC Montefiore-8 S MUH
E824, Pittsburgh, PA 15213
Tel.: (412) 586-9819
Web Site:
https://pittsburghupmc.selectspecialty
hospitals.com
Sales Range: $25-49.9 Million
Emp.: 110
General Medical Services
N.A.I.C.S.: 622110

**Select Specialty Hospital-Pontiac,
Inc.** (1)
44405 Woodward Ave 8th Fl, Pontiac, MI
48341
Tel.: (248) 452-5202
Web Site:
https://www.selectspecialtyhospitals.com
General Medical Services
N.A.I.C.S.: 622110

**Select Specialty Hospital-Quad Cities,
Inc.** (1)
1227 E Rusholme St, Davenport, IA 52803
Tel.: (563) 468-2000
Web Site:
https://quadcities.selectspecialtyhospi
tals.com
General Medical Services
N.A.I.C.S.: 622110

**Select Specialty Hospital-Richmond,
Inc.** (1)
2220 Edward Holland Dr, Richmond, VA
23230
Tel.: (804) 678-7000
Physical Therapy Services
N.A.I.C.S.: 621340

**Select Specialty Hospital-Saginaw,
Inc.** (1)
1447 N Harrison St 8th Fl Harrison Campus, Saginaw, MI 48602
Tel.: (989) 583-4850

Web Site:
https://saginaw.selectspecialtyhospi
tals.com
General Medical Services
N.A.I.C.S.: 622110

**Select Specialty Hospital-San Anto-
nio, Inc.** (1)
111 Dallas 4C Fl, San Antonio, TX 78205
Tel.: (210) 297-7170
Web Site: https://www.selectmedical.com
Emp.: 100
General Medical Services
N.A.I.C.S.: 622110

**Select Specialty Hospital-Savannah,
Inc.** (1)
5353 Reynolds St 4 S, Savannah, GA
31405
Tel.: (912) 819-7982
General Medical Services
N.A.I.C.S.: 622110

**Select Specialty Hospital-Sioux Falls,
Inc.** (1)
1305 W 18th St 2400 Fl Central Patient
Bldg, Sioux Falls, SD 57105
Tel.: (605) 312-9500
General Medical Services
N.A.I.C.S.: 622110

**Select Specialty Hospital-Springfield,
Inc.** (1)
1630 E Primrose, Springfield, MO 65804
Tel.: (417) 885-4700
General Medical Services
N.A.I.C.S.: 622110

**Select Specialty Hospital-Tallahassee,
Inc.** (1)
1554 Surgeons Dr, Tallahassee, FL 32308
Tel.: (850) 219-6800
Sales Range: $25-49.9 Million
Emp.: 175
General Medical Services
N.A.I.C.S.: 622110

**Select Specialty Hospital-The Vil-
lages, Inc.** (1)
5050 County Rd 472, Oxford, FL 34484
Tel.: (352) 689-6400
Web Site:
https://www.selectspecialtyhospitals.com
Hospital Care Services
N.A.I.C.S.: 622110
Nancy Howard (Mgr-Laboratory)

**Select Specialty Hospital-TriCities,
Inc.** (1)
1 Medical Park Blvd 5 W, Bristol, TN 37620
Tel.: (423) 844-5916
Emp.: 200
General Medical Services
N.A.I.C.S.: 622110

**Select Specialty Hospital-Tulsa,
Inc.** (1)
744 W 9th St 5th Fl & 6th W, Tulsa, OK
74127
Tel.: (918) 932-3700
Web Site: https://www.selectmedical.com
Emp.: 55
General Medical Services
N.A.I.C.S.: 622110

**Select Specialty Hospital-
Tulsa/Midtown, LLC** (1)
2300 E 14th St Ste 104, Tulsa, OK 74104
Tel.: (918) 982-6800
Web Site:
https://www.selectphysicaltherapy.com
General Medical Services
N.A.I.C.S.: 622110

**Select Specialty Hospital-Western
Missouri, Inc.** (1)
2316 E Meyer Blvd 3 W, Kansas City, MO
64132
Tel.: (816) 276-9444
Web Site: http://www.selectmedical.com
General Medical Services
N.A.I.C.S.: 622110

**Select Specialty Hospital-Wichita,
Inc.** (1)
929 N St Francis St N Tower 6th Fl,
Wichita, KS 67214
Tel.: (316) 261-8303
General Medical Services

N.A.I.C.S.: 622110

**Select Specialty Hospital-Wilmington,
Inc.** (1)
501 W 14th St 9th Fl, Wilmington, DE
19801
Tel.: (302) 295-9100
General Medical Services
N.A.I.C.S.: 622110

**Select Specialty Hospital-Winston-
Salem, Inc.** (1)
3333 Silas Creek Pkwy 6th Fl, Winston Sa-
lem, NC 27103-3013
Tel.: (336) 718-6300
Web Site:
https://www.selectspecialtyhospitals.com
General Medical Services
N.A.I.C.S.: 622110

**Select Specialty Hospital-
Youngstown, Inc.** (1)
1044 Belmont Ave 4th Fl, Youngstown, OH
44501
Tel.: (330) 480-3488
General Medical Services
N.A.I.C.S.: 622110

**Select Specialty Hospital-Zanesville,
Inc.** (1)
2000 Tamarack Rd 2nd Fl, Newark, OH
43055
Tel.: (220) 564-2600
Web Site:
https://www.selectspecialtyhospitals.com
Emp.: 100
General Medical Services
N.A.I.C.S.: 622110
Armand A. Bermudez (Dir-Medical)

Select Specialty-Downriver, LLC (1)
2333 Biddle Ave 8th Fl, Wyandotte, MI
48192
Tel.: (734) 246-5500
Web Site: http://www.selectmedical.com
General Medical Services
N.A.I.C.S.: 622110

Select Synergos, Inc. (1)
4716 Old Gettysburg Rd, Mechanicsburg,
PA 17055
Tel.: (717) 972-1100
Web Site: https://www.selectmedical.com
General Medical Services
N.A.I.C.S.: 622110

Special Care Hospital, LLC (1)
1840 Wealthy St SE, Grand Rapids, MI
49506-2921
Tel.: (616) 774-3800
Web Site:
https://www.selectspecialtyhospitals.com
Medical Rehabilitation Hospital Services
N.A.I.C.S.: 622310

**St. Mary's Medical Park Pharmacy,
Inc.** (1)
10860 N Mavinee Dr, Oro Valley, AZ 85737
Tel.: (520) 837-0161
Web Site: https://stmarysmpp.com
Emp.: 20
Health Care Srvices
N.A.I.C.S.: 622110

**Swanson Orthotic and Prosthetic
Center, Inc.** (1)
3436A Mckelvey Rd, Bridgeton, MO 63044
Tel.: (314) 231-1156
Web Site: https://www.novacare.com
Medical Rehabilitation Hospital Services
N.A.I.C.S.: 622310

The Rehab Center (1)
2610 E 7th St, Charlotte, NC 28204
Tel.: (704) 375-8900
Web Site: https://www.therehabcenter.com
Physical Rehabilitation Hospital Services
N.A.I.C.S.: 622310

**U.S. HealthWorks Medical Group of
Kansas City, P.A.** (1)
6501 E Commerce Ave, Kansas City, MO
64120-2171
Tel.: (816) 483-5550
Medical Rehabilitation Hospital Services
N.A.I.C.S.: 622310

**U.S. HealthWorks Medical Group of
Maine, Inc.** (1)

Select Medical Holdings Corporation—(Continued)

11 Medical Ctr Dr, Brunswick, ME 04011-2690
Tel.: (207) 725-2697
Medical Rehabilitation Hospital Services
N.A.I.C.S.: 622310

U.S. HealthWorks Medical Group of Minnesota, P.C. (1)
7550 34th Ave S, Minneapolis, MN 55450-1124
Tel.: (612) 727-1167
Medical Rehabilitation Hospital Services
N.A.I.C.S.: 622310

U.S. HealthWorks Medical Group of North Carolina, P.C. (1)
10616 Metromont Pkwy Ste 102, Charlotte, NC 28269-7656
Tel.: (704) 597-7228
Medical Rehabilitation Hospital Services
N.A.I.C.S.: 622310

U.S. HealthWorks Medical Group of Ohio, Inc. (1)
7117 Orchard Centre Dr, Holland, OH 43528
Tel.: (419) 866-9675
Medical Rehabilitation Hospital Services
N.A.I.C.S.: 622310

U.S. HealthWorks Medical Group of Tennessee, P.C. (1)
1616 Gallatin Pike N, Madison, TN 37115-2104
Tel.: (615) 865-8547
Medical Rehabilitation Hospital Services
N.A.I.C.S.: 622310

U.S. HealthWorks Medical Group of Washington, P.S. (1)
3726 Broadway, Everett, WA 98201-5030
Tel.: (425) 259-0300
Medical Rehabilitation Hospital Services
N.A.I.C.S.: 622310

U.S. HealthWorks Provider Network of Colorado, Inc. (1)
8200 E Belleview Ave Ste 428 C, Greenwood Village, CO 80111-2803
Tel.: (303) 741-1166
Medical Rehabilitation Hospital Services
N.A.I.C.S.: 622310

U.S. HealthWorks of Indiana, Inc. (1)
700 E Beardsley Ave Ste 100, Elkhart, IN 46514-3365
Tel.: (574) 206-8010
Medical Rehabilitation Hospital Services
N.A.I.C.S.: 622310

U.S. HealthWorks of Washington, Inc. (1)
4320 196th St SW Ste D, Lynnwood, WA 98036-6753
Tel.: (425) 774-8758
Medical Rehabilitation Hospital Services
N.A.I.C.S.: 622310

U.S. HealthWorks, Inc. (1)
25124 Springfield Ct Ste 200, Valencia, CA 91355
Tel.: (661) 678-2600
Medical Rehabilitation Hospital Services
N.A.I.C.S.: 622310

U.S. Medgroup Of Kansas, P.A. (1)
14809 W 95th St, Lenexa, KS 66215
Tel.: (913) 894-6664
Health Care Srvices
N.A.I.C.S.: 622110

U.S. Medgroup of Illinois, P.C. (1)
102 E Sunbridge Dr Ste 3, Fayetteville, AR 72703
Tel.: (479) 900-9807
Health Care Srvices
N.A.I.C.S.: 622110

U.S. Medgroup of Michigan, P.C. (1)
102 E Sunbridge Dr Ste 3, Fayetteville, AR 72703
Tel.: (479) 900-9807
Health Care Srvices
N.A.I.C.S.: 622110

U.S. Medgroup, P.A. (1)
12808 N Black Canyon Hwy, Phoenix, AZ 85029

Tel.: (602) 375-1155
Health Care Srvices
N.A.I.C.S.: 622110

U.S. Medgroup, P.A. (1)
580 Spectrum Dr Ste 120, Addison, TX 75001
Tel.: (972) 755-1838
Emp.: 3
Business Support Services
N.A.I.C.S.: 561499

U.S. Regional Occupational Health II of NJ, P.C. (1)
368 Lakehurst Rd Ste 206, Burlington, NJ 08080
Tel.: (717) 972-1100
Health Care Srvices
N.A.I.C.S.: 622110

U.S. Regional Occupational Health II, P.C. (1)
1800 Byberry Rd Ste 701, Huntingdon Valley, PA 19006-3518
Tel.: (215) 938-0800
Health Care Srvices
N.A.I.C.S.: 622110

Vibra Hospital of San Diego, LLC (1)
555 Washington St, San Diego, CA 92103
Tel.: (619) 389-3002
Web Site: https://www.vibrahealthcare.com
Health Care Srvices
N.A.I.C.S.: 622110

Victoria Healthcare, Inc. (1)
955 NW 3rd St Victoria Center, Miami, FL 33128-1274
Tel.: (305) 548-4020
Web Site: https://victorianursing.net
Healtcare Services
N.A.I.C.S.: 621610

West Gables Rehabilitation Hospital, LLC (1)
2525 SW 75th Ave, Miami, FL 33155
Tel.: (305) 262-6800
Web Site:
https://www.westgablesrehabhospital.com
Sales Range: $1-9.9 Million
Emp.: 150
Physical Therapy & Rehabilitation Services
N.A.I.C.S.: 621340
Walter Concepcion *(CEO)*
Mike De Cardenas *(Founder)*
Giselle Vivaldi *(Dir-Medical-Brain Injury)*
Natasha Peat *(Chief Nursing Officer)*

SELECT WATER SOLUTIONS, INC.
19350 Ste Hwy 249 Ste 600, Houston, TX 77070
Tel.: (713) 235-9500   DE
Web Site:
https://www.selectwater.com
Year Founded: 2016
WTTR—(NYSE)
Rev.: $1,585,353,000
Assets: $1,218,190,000
Liabilities: $326,018,000
Net Worth: $892,172,000
Earnings: $74,403,000
Emp.: 4,200
Fiscal Year-end: 12/31/23
Water Sollution Provider
N.A.I.C.S.: 213112
John D. Schmitz *(Chm, Pres & CEO)*
Cody Ortowski *(Exec VP-Bus Strategy)*
Nicholas L. Swyka *(CFO & Sr VP)*
Michael C. Skarke *(COO)*
Suzanne J. Colbert *(CTO)*
Christina Ibrahim *(Chief Compliance Officer)*

Subsidiaries:

Benchmark Energy Products, LLC (1)
3420 Executive Ctr Dr Ste 250, Austin, TX 78731
Tel.: (512) 481-4200
Web Site: https://www.benchmark-energy.com

Oil & Gas Equipment Mfr
N.A.I.C.S.: 333132

Nuverra Environmental Solutions, Inc. (1)
6720 N Scottsdale Rd Ste 190, Scottsdale, AZ 85253
Tel.: (602) 903-7802
Web Site: http://www.nuverra.com
Rev.: $110,287,000
Assets: $191,066,000
Liabilities: $58,783,000
Net Worth: $132,283,000
Earnings: ($44,143,000)
Emp.: 517
Fiscal Year-end: 12/31/2020
Environmental Solutions
N.A.I.C.S.: 541620
Joseph M. Crabb *(Chief Legal Officer & Exec VP)*
Stephen K. London *(VP-Bus Dev)*
Charles K. Thompson *(Chm)*
Patrick L. Bond *(CEO)*
Roger L. Mendelovitz *(Principal Acctg Officer & Controller)*

Subsidiary (Domestic):

Badlands Leasing, LLC (2)
14624 N Kierland Blvd Suite-300, Scottsdale, AZ 85254
Tel.: (602) 903-7802
Web Site: http://www.nuverra.com
Emp.: 20
Oil & Gas Field Services
N.A.I.C.S.: 213112

Badlands Power Fuels, LLC (2)
3711 4th Ave NE, Watford City, ND 58854
Tel.: (701) 842-3618
Web Site: http://www.nuverra.com
Emp.: 200
Oil & Gas Field Services
N.A.I.C.S.: 213112

Heckmann Water Resources (CVR), Inc. (2)
1607 NE Loop, Carthage, TX 75633-1964
Tel.: (903) 694-9913
Sales Range: $25-49.9 Million
Emp.: 35
Waste Treatment Services
N.A.I.C.S.: 562219

Peak Oilfield Services, LLC (1)
1820 I-35 Frontage Rd, Gainesville, TX 76240
Tel.: (940) 683-1600
Web Site: https://www.peakoilservices.com
Oil Field Services
N.A.I.C.S.: 213112
John D. Schmitz *(Founder)*
Abel Alvarez *(Area Mgr-South Texas)*
Matt Brennan *(Area Mgr-West Texas)*
Greg Hess *(Area Mgr-West Texas & Oklahoma)*

Rockwater Energy Solutions, Inc. (1)
1515 W Sam Houston Pkwy N Ste 100, Houston, TX 77043
Tel.: (713) 986-2500
Web Site: http://www.rockwaterenergy.com
Environmental Energy Solutions & Services
N.A.I.C.S.: 541620
Greg Steer *(Ops Mgr)*

Subsidiary (Domestic):

Rockwater Energy Solutions, Inc. - Midland (2)
4113 W Industrial, Midland, TX 79703
Tel.: (432) 697-9171
Oil Field Chemicals Whslr
N.A.I.C.S.: 213112

Select Energy Services LLC (1)
1400 Post Oak Blvd Ste 400, Houston, TX 77056
Tel.: (713) 296-1000
Web Site:
http://www.selectenergyservices.com
Support Activities for Oil & Gas Operations
N.A.I.C.S.: 213112

Tidal Logistics, Inc. (1)
12319 Business Hwy 287, Fort Worth, TX 76179
Web Site: http://www.tidallogistics.com
Logistic Services
N.A.I.C.S.: 488510

Ariel Rice *(Dir-Operations)*
Kyle Wanjura *(Dir-Operations)*
Don Pittmon *(Mgr)*
Carlos Lujan *(Mgr-HSSE)*
Charles Joey Fanguy Jr. *(Pres)*

SELECTIS HEALTH, INC.
8480 E Orchard Rd Ste 4900, Greenwood Village, CO 80111
Tel.: (720) 680-0808   UT
Web Site: http://www.gbcsreit.com
GBCS—(OTCIQ)
Rev.: $40,599,517
Assets: $42,490,042
Liabilities: $41,537,207
Net Worth: $952,835
Earnings: ($2,395,813)
Emp.: 655
Fiscal Year-end: 12/31/22
Real Estate Investment Trust
N.A.I.C.S.: 531390
Adam Desmond *(Bd of Dirs & CEO)*
James Creamer *(CFO)*

SELECTIVE INSURANCE GROUP, INC.
40 Wantage Ave, Branchville, NJ 07890-1000
Tel.: (973) 948-3000   NJ
Web Site: https://www.selective.com
Year Founded: 1977
SIGI—(NASDAQ)
Rev.: $3,558,062,000
Assets: $10,802,261,000
Liabilities: $8,274,697,000
Net Worth: $2,527,564,000
Earnings: $224,886,000
Emp.: 2,520
Fiscal Year-end: 12/31/22
Holding Company
N.A.I.C.S.: 551112
John J. Marchioni *(Chm, Pres & CEO)*
Anthony D. Harnett *(Chief Acctg Officer & Sr VP)*
Susan R. Perretta *(Sec)*
Vincent M. Senia *(Chief Actuary & Exec VP)*
John Bresney *(CIO & Exec VP)*
Paul Kush *(Chief Claims Officer & Exec VP)*
Rohan Pai *(Sr-VP & Treasury)*
Cyndi Bennett *(Chief HR Officer & Exec VP)*
Joe Eppers *(Chief Investment Officer)*
Rohit Mull *(Exec VP)*
Patrick S. Brennan *(CFO & Exec VP)*
Michael H. Lanza *(Chief Compliance Officer & Exec VP)*

Subsidiaries:

Mesa Underwriters Specialty Insurance Company (1)
6263 N Scottsdale Rd Ste 300, Scottsdale, AZ 85250
Tel.: (480) 306-8300
Web Site: http://www.music-ins.com
Sales Range: $25-49.9 Million
Insurance Services
N.A.I.C.S.: 524298
Eva Gonzalez *(VP-Product Dev)*

Selective Auto Insurance Company of New Jersey (1)
40 Wantage Ave, Branchville, NJ 07890
Tel.: (973) 948-3000
Automobile Insurance Services
N.A.I.C.S.: 524126

Selective Casualty Insurance Company (1)
40 Wantage Ave, Branchville, NJ 07890-1000
Tel.: (973) 948-3000
Insurance Management Services
N.A.I.C.S.: 524298
John J. Marchioni *(Pres)*

Selective Insurance Company of America (1)

40 Wantage Ave, Branchville, NJ 07890-1000
Tel.: (973) 948-3000
Web Site: http://www.selective.com
Sales Range: $700-749.9 Million
Emp.: 2,000
Automobile, Property, Workers' Compensation & General Liability Insurance & Fidelity & Surety Bonds
N.A.I.C.S.: 524126

Selective Insurance Company of South Carolina   (1)
3426 Toringdon Way Ste 200, Charlotte, NC 46032
Tel.: (704) 341-7474
Web Site:
    http://www.selectiveinsurance.com
Property & Casualty Insurance Products & Services
N.A.I.C.S.: 524126

Selective Insurance Company of the Southeast   (1)
3426 Toringdon Way Ste 200, Charlotte, NC 28277
Tel.: (704) 341-7474
Web Site: http://www.selective.com
Sales Range: $10-24.9 Million
Automobile, Property, Workers Compensation & General Liability Insurance & Fidelity & Surety Bonds
N.A.I.C.S.: 524210

Wantage Avenue Holding Company, Inc.   (1)
40 Wantage Ave, Branchville, NJ 07890
Tel.: (973) 948-3000
Web Site:
    http://www.selectiveinsurance.com
Sales Range: $75-99.9 Million
Emp.: 150
Holding Company; Insurance Services
N.A.I.C.S.: 551112

SELECTQUOTE, INC.
6800 W 115th St Ste 2511, Overland Park, KS 66211
Tel.: (913) 274-1994   DE
Web Site:
    https://www.selectquote.com
Year Founded: 1999
SLQT—(NYSE)
Rev.: $1,321,776,000
Assets: $1,193,908,000
Liabilities: $877,107,000
Net Worth: $316,801,000
Earnings: ($34,125,000)
Emp.: 4,292
Fiscal Year-end: 06/30/24
Holding Company
N.A.I.C.S.: 551112
William Grant II (Vice Chm)
Donald L. Hawks III (Chm)
Timothy Danker (CEO)
Ryan M. Clement (CFO)
Stephanie Fisher (Chief Acctg Officer)

Subsidiaries:

ChoiceMark Insurance Services, Inc.   (1)
8700 State Line Rd Ste 300, Leawood, KS 66206
Web Site:
    http://www.choicemarkinsurance.com
Insurance Services
N.A.I.C.S.: 524210

Simple Meds, LLC   (1)
6810 Hillsdale Ct, Indianapolis, IN 46250
Tel.: (615) 645-6337
Web Site: https://www.simplemeds.com
Medical Insurance Services
N.A.I.C.S.: 524114
Kyle Decker (VP)

SELLAS LIFE SCIENCES GROUP, INC.
7 Times Sq Ste 2503, New York, NY 10036
Tel.: (646) 200-5278   DE
Web Site:
    https://www.sellaslifesciences.com

Year Founded: 2006
SLS—(NASDAQ)
Rev.: $1,000,000
Assets: $20,943,000
Liabilities: $16,092,000
Net Worth: $4,851,000
Earnings: ($41,301,000)
Emp.: 17
Fiscal Year-end: 12/31/22
Biopharmaceutical Research & Development
N.A.I.C.S.: 325414
John T. Burns (CFO & Sr VP)
Angelos M. Stergiou (Founder, Pres, Pres, CEO & CEO)
Dragan Cicic (Sr VP-Clinical Dev)
Jane Wasman (Chm)

SEMLER SCIENTIFIC, INC.
2344 Walsh Ave, Santa Clara, CA 95051   DE
Web Site:
    https://www.semlerscientific.com
Year Founded: 2007
SMLR—(NASDAQ)
Rev.: $56,686,000
Assets: $62,693,000
Liabilities: $7,017,000
Net Worth: $55,676,000
Earnings: $14,325,000
Emp.: 127
Fiscal Year-end: 12/31/22
Medicinal Product Mfr
N.A.I.C.S.: 339112
Douglas Murphy-Chutorian (Pres & Interim CEO)
Jennifer Oliva Herrington (COO)
Herbert J. Semler (Founder)
Eric H. Semler (Chm)
Renae Cormier (CFO, Principal Acctg Officer & Head-Corp Comm & Bus Strategy)
Shane Reid (CTO & Sr VP)

SEMPER PARATUS ACQUISITION CORPORATION
767 3rd Ave 38th Fl, New York, NY 10017
Tel.: (646) 807-8832   Ky
Year Founded: 2021
LGST—(NASDAQ)
Rev.: $5,361,444
Assets: $357,138,356
Liabilities: $371,921,704
Net Worth: ($14,783,348)
Earnings: $4,408,361
Emp.: 3
Fiscal Year-end: 12/31/22
Investment Services
N.A.I.C.S.: 523999
Jeffrey A. Rogers (Pres, CFO & Sec)
Richard N. Peretz (Chm)
Hooman Yazhari (Vice Chm)
Ben Baldanza (CEO)

SEMPRA
488 8th Ave, San Diego, CA 92101
Tel.: (619) 696-2000   CA
Web Site: https://www.sempra.com
Year Founded: 1998
SRE—(NYSE)
Rev.: $16,720,000,000
Assets: $87,181,000,000
Liabilities: $53,527,000,000
Net Worth: $33,654,000,000
Earnings: $3,030,000,000
Emp.: 16,835
Fiscal Year-end: 12/31/23
Energy Services Holding Company; Provider of Electricity, Natural Gas & Value-Added Products & Services
N.A.I.C.S.: 551112
Jeffrey Walker Martin (Chm, Pres & CEO)
Peter R. Wall (Chief Acctg Officer, Sr VP & Controller)

Brian L. Kelly (VP-Govt Affairs)
Robert J. Borthwick (Deputy Gen Counsel)
Bruce E. MacNeil (Treas & VP)
Karen L. Sedgwick (Chief HR Officer & Sr VP)
Trevor Mihalik (CFO)
Karen Sedgwick (Chief HR Officer)
Diana Day (Deputy Gen Counsel)
Mitch Mitchell (Sr VP)
Glen Donovan (VP)
Deborah Martin (VP)
Christy Ihrig (VP)
Joy Gao (VP)
Toby Jack (VP)
April Robinson (Sec)
Kathryn J. Collier (VP-Audit Svcs)

Subsidiaries:

Infraestructura Energetica Nova, S.A.B. de C.V.   (1)
Torre New York Life Paseo de la Reforma 342 Piso 24 Col Juarez, 06600, Mexico, Mexico   (100%)
Tel.: (52) 5591380100
Web Site: https://www.ienova.com.mx
Rev.: $1,379,256,000
Assets: $9,552,506,000
Liabilities: $4,595,269,000
Net Worth: $4,957,237,000
Earnings: $467,685,000
Emp.: 1,300
Fiscal Year-end: 12/31/2019
Electricity & Natural Gas Supplier
N.A.I.C.S.: 221122
Carlos Ruiz Sacristan (Chm & Exec VP)
Tania Ortiz Mena Lopez Negrete (CEO)
Rene Buentello Carbonell (Chief Compliance Officer & Gen Counsel)
Juan Rodriguez Castaneda (Chief Natural Gas Operating Officer)
Carlos Mauer Barriga (CFO)
Abraham Zamora Torres (Chief Sustainability, Corp & Pub Affairs Officer)
Carlos Francisco Barajas Sandoval (Chief Power & Storage Operating Officer)
Jorge Molina Casellas (Chief Dev Officer)

Luz del Sur S.A.A   (1)
Av Canaval y Moreyra 380, San Isidro, Lima, Peru
Tel.: (51) 198676134
Web Site: https://www.luzdelsur.com.pe
Electric Power Distribution Services
N.A.I.C.S.: 221122
Mile Cacic (CEO)

San Diego Gas & Electric Company   (1)
8330 Century Park Ct, San Diego, CA 92123
Tel.: (619) 696-2000
Web Site: https://www.sdge.com
Rev.: $5,838,000,000
Assets: $26,422,000,000
Liabilities: $17,355,000,000
Net Worth: $9,067,000,000
Earnings: $915,000,000
Emp.: 4,633
Fiscal Year-end: 12/31/2022
Natural Gas & Electric Distr
N.A.I.C.S.: 221113
Bruce A. Folkmann (Pres & CFO)
Caroline A. Winn (CEO)
Diana Day (Chief Risk Officer, Gen counsel & Sr VP)
Valerie A. Bille (Chief Acctg Officer, VP & Controller)

Sempra Energy Holdings XI B.V.   (1)
Muiderstraat 7, 1011 PZ, Amsterdam, Netherlands
Tel.: (31) 205214777
Holding Company
N.A.I.C.S.: 551112

Sempra Energy Services   (1)
2500 Citywest Blvd Ste 1800, Houston, TX 77042-3035
Tel.: (713) 361-7600
Sales Range: $10-24.9 Million
Emp.: 79
Mechanical Contractor
N.A.I.C.S.: 238990

Sempra Energy Trading Corp.   (1)

58 Commerce Rd, Stamford, CT 06902-4506   (100%)
Tel.: (203) 355-5000
Rev.: $875,000,000
Emp.: 650
Gas Power Marketers & Energy Traders
N.A.I.C.S.: 221122

Sempra Pipelines & Storage Corp.   (1)
Tel.: (619) 696-2034
Sales Range: $1-4.9 Billion
Natural Gas Pipelines & Storage Facilities Operator
N.A.I.C.S.: 486210

Subsidiary (Non-US):

Mobile Gas Service Corporation   (2)
                                   (100%)
Tel.: (251) 450-4730
Web Site: http://www.mobile-gas.com
Sales Range: $50-74.9 Million
Emp.: 220
Natural Gas Distr
N.A.I.C.S.: 221210

Sempra Midstream, Inc.   (2)
                                   (100%)
Tel.: (281) 423-2700
Sales Range: $100-124.9 Million
Emp.: 75
Holding Company; Natural Gas Storage & Pipeline Transportation Services
N.A.I.C.S.: 551112

Sempra Texas Holdings Corp.   (1)
211 7th St SDte620, Austin, TX 78701   (100%)
Tel.: (214) 812-4600
Energy Services Holding Company
N.A.I.C.S.: 551112

Subsidiary (Domestic):

Oncor Electric Delivery Company LLC   (2)
1616 Woodall Rodgers Fwy, Dallas, TX 75202
Tel.: (214) 486-2000
Web Site: https://www.oncor.com
Rev.: $5,243,000,000
Assets: $33,038,000,000
Liabilities: $19,576,000,000
Net Worth: $13,462,000,000
Earnings: $905,000,000
Emp.: 4,561
Fiscal Year-end: 12/31/2022
Electric Power Distr
N.A.I.C.S.: 221118
James A. Greer (COO & Exec VP)
Walter Mark Carpenter (Sr VP-T&D Ops)
Don J. Clevenger (CFO & Sr VP)
Debbie Dennis (Chief HR Officer, Chief Customer Officer & Sr VP)
Joel Austin (Chief Digital Officer & Sr VP)
Matt C. Henry (Gen Counsel, Sec & Sr VP)
Angela Y. Guillory (Sr VP-HR & Corp Affairs)
Malia Hodges (CIO & Sr VP)
E. Allen Nye Jr. (CEO)

Subsidiary (Domestic):

Oncor NTU Holdings Company LLC   (3)
1616 Woodall Rodgers Fwy, Dallas, TX 75202
Tel.: (214) 486-2000
Web Site: http://www.oncor.com
Real Estate Investment Services
N.A.I.C.S.: 525990

Southern California Gas Company   (1)
555 W 5th St, Los Angeles, CA 90013   (100%)
Tel.: (213) 244-1200
Web Site: https://www.socalgas.com
Rev.: $6,840,000,000
Assets: $22,346,000,000
Liabilities: $15,648,000,000
Net Worth: $6,698,000,000
Earnings: $599,000,000
Emp.: 8,460
Fiscal Year-end: 12/31/2022
Natural Gas Distr
N.A.I.C.S.: 221210
Scott D. Drury (CEO)
Jimmie I. Cho (COO)

Sempra—(Continued)

Mia L. DeMontigny (CFO, Treas & Sr VP)
Maryam Sabbaghian Brown (Pres)
David Buczkowski (VP-Gas Distr)
Paul Goldstein (VP-Gas Transmission & Storage)
Kent Kauss (Reg VP-External Rels)
Gina Orozco-Mejia (VP-Gas Engrg & System Integrity)
Rodger R. Schwecke (Chief Infrastructure Officer & Sr VP)
Dan Skopec (Chief Regulatory Officer & Sr VP-State Govt Affairs)
Gillian Wright (Chief Customer Officer & Sr VP)
Ben Gordon (CIO, Chief Digital Officer & Sr VP)
Sandra Hrna (VP-Supply Chain & Ops Support)
Jeffery L. Walker (Chief Sys & Tech Officer & Sr VP)
Andy Carrasco (VP-Comm, Local Govt & Community Affairs)
Deana M. Ng (Chief Risk Officer & VP)
Erin M. Smith (Chief Talent & Culture Officer)
Devin Zornizer (VP-Construction)
Sara P. Mijares (Chief Acctg Officer, VP, Controller & Asst Treas)
Elsa Valay-Paz (VP)
Don Widjaja (VP)

Willmut Gas & Oil Company (1)
315 S Main St, Hattiesburg, MS 39401-2242
Tel.: (601) 544-6001
Web Site: http://www.willmut.com
Sales Range: $25-49.9 Million
Emp.: 45
Natural Gas Distribution
N.A.I.C.S.: 221210

SEMRUSH HOLDINGS, INC.
800 Boylston St Ste 2475, Boston, MA 02199   DE
Web Site: https://www.semrush.com
Year Founded: 2012
SEMR—(NYSE)
Rev.: $254,316,000
Assets: $298,690,000
Liabilities: $98,786,000
Net Worth: $199,904,000
Earnings: ($33,848,000)
Emp.: 1,316
Fiscal Year-end: 12/31/22
Offices of Other Holding Companies
N.A.I.C.S.: 551112
David Mason (Gen Counsel & Sec)
Oleg Shchegolev (CEO)
Eugene Levin (Pres)
Vitalii Obishchenko (COO)
Dmitry Melnikov (Founder)
Channing Ferrer (Chief Sls Officer)
Bob Gujavarty (VP-IR)
Jesse Platz (VP-PR)
Brian Mulroy (CFO)

SEMTECH CORPORATION
200 Flynn Rd, Camarillo, CA 93012-8790
Tel.: (805) 498-2111   DE
Web Site: https://www.semtech.com
Year Founded: 1960
SMTC—(NASDAQ)
Rev.: $756,533,000
Assets: $2,569,628,000
Liabilities: $1,813,593,000
Net Worth: $756,035,000
Earnings: $61,380,000
Emp.: 2,248
Fiscal Year-end: 01/29/23
Analog & Mixed-Signal Semiconductor Products Mfr
N.A.I.C.S.: 334413
Michael J. Wilson (Chief Quality Officer & Exec VP)
Asaf Silberstein (COO & Exec VP)
Madhu Rayabhari (VP & Gen Mgr-Protection Products Grp)
Paul H. Pickle (Pres & CEO)
Rockell Nathan Hankin (Chm)

Hong Q. Hou (Pres & CEO)
Ellen Bancroft (Chief Legal Officer & Exec VP)
Ross Gray (Sr VP & Gen Mgr-IoT Sys & Connectivity)
Mark Lin (CFO & Exec VP)
Mark P. Russell (Sr VP-Global Sls & Marketing)
Imran Sherazi (Sr VP & Gen Mgr-Signal Integrity Products Grp)

Subsidiaries:

Cycleo SAS (1)
510 Chemin des Varciaux, Saint Ismier, 38330, France
Tel.: (33) 674455268
Semiconductor Components Mfr
N.A.I.C.S.: 334413

EnVerv Inc. (1)
680 N McCarthy Blvd Ste 220, Milpitas, CA 95035
Tel.: (408) 457-8642
Web Site: http://www.enverv.com
Semiconductor Machinery Mfr
N.A.I.C.S.: 333242
Farrokh Farrokhi (Founder)

Semtech (International) AG (1)
Neue Jonastrasse 60, 8640, Rapperswil, Switzerland
Tel.: (41) 555881120
Web Site: http://www.semtech.com
Sales Range: $10-24.9 Million
Emp.: 12
Semiconductor Devices Mfr
N.A.I.C.S.: 334413
Jeffrey Gutierrez (Mng Dir)

Semtech Advanced Systems India Private Limited (1)
Block-B 4th Floor Fortune Towers, Chandrasekharpur, Bhubaneswar, 751023, Odisha, India
Tel.: (91) 6743531400
Emp.: 25
Semiconductor Components Mfr
N.A.I.C.S.: 334413

Semtech Canada Corporation (1)
4281 Harvester Rd, Burlington, L7L 5M4, ON, Canada
Tel.: (289) 856-9200
Silicon Integrated Circuits & Modules Designer, Mfr & Marketer
N.A.I.C.S.: 334515

Unit (Domestic):

Gennum Corp. - Ottawa Design Center (2)
4017 Carling Ave Suite 302, Kanata, K2K 2A3, ON, Canada
Tel.: (613) 270-0458
Web Site: http://www.gennum.com
N.A.I.C.S.: 334118

Subsidiary (Non-US):

Gennum UK Limited (2)
25 Long Garden Walk, Farnham, GU9 7HX, Hants, United Kingdom   (100%)
Tel.: (44) 1252747000
Web Site: http://www.gennum.com
Sales Range: $10-24.9 Million
Emp.: 7
N.A.I.C.S.: 334118

Semtech Corpus Christi S.A. de C.V. (1)
Principal B Sin Numero Edificio 7 Parque Industrial Sur, 88787, Reynosa, Tamaulipas, Mexico   (100%)
Tel.: (52) 8999580398
Web Site: http://www.semtech.com
Sales Range: $10-24.9 Million
Emp.: 25
Silicon Rectifiers, Zeners, Transient Voltage Suppressors, Multipliers, High Voltage Capacitors, Wafer Foundry & Linear & Switching Regulators Mfr
N.A.I.C.S.: 334413

Semtech EMEA Limited (1)
St James Court B Great Park Road, Bristol, BS32 4QJ, United Kingdom
Tel.: (44) 1454462200
Semiconductor Devices Mfr

N.A.I.C.S.: 334413

Semtech Europe Limited (1)
Units 2-3 Park Court Premier Way Abbey Park, Industrial estate, Romsey, SO51 9DN, Hampshire, United Kingdom
Tel.: (44) 1279714170
Semiconductor Components Mfr
N.A.I.C.S.: 334413

Semtech Germany GmbH (1)
Tel.: (49) 918797380
Web Site: https://www.semtech.de
Emp.: 10
Semiconductor Devices Mfr
N.A.I.C.S.: 334413

Semtech Ltd. (1)
Unit 3 Park Court Premier Way, Abbey Park Industrial Estates, Romsey, SO51 9DN, Hampshire, United Kingdom
Tel.: (44) 1794527602
Web Site: http://www.semtech.com
Semiconductor Products Mfr & Distr
N.A.I.C.S.: 334413

Semtech Netherlands BV (1)
Evert van de Beekstraat 310, 1118 CX, Schiphol, Netherlands
Tel.: (31) 205214777
Semiconductor Components Mfr
N.A.I.C.S.: 334413

Semtech San Diego (1)
10301 Meanley Dr Ste 100, San Diego, CA 92131   (100%)
Tel.: (858) 614-6700
Web Site: https://www.semtech.com
Sales Range: $10-24.9 Million
Emp.: 24
Semiconductors & Related Devices
N.A.I.C.S.: 334413

Semtech Semiconductor (Shanghai) Co. Ltd. (1)
Units 706/708/709 No 425 Yishan Road, Pudong New Area, Shanghai, 200235, China
Tel.: (86) 2163910830
Semiconductor Devices Mfr
N.A.I.C.S.: 334413

Semtech Semiconductor (Shenzhen) Company Limited (1)
Suite A401-403 A406-412 TCL Building Gaoxin South First Street, Nanshan District, Shenzhen, 518057, Guangdong, China
Tel.: (86) 75582828515
Semiconductor Devices Mfr
N.A.I.C.S.: 334413

Snowbush Mexico S.A.P.I. de C.V. (1)
Monto Blanoo 612 Trojoo do Orionto 1a Seccion, 20115, Aguascalientes, Mexico
Tel.: (52) 4499182823
Semiconductor Components Mfr
N.A.I.C.S.: 334413
Lizeth Hernandez (Engr-Physical Design)

Triune IP, LLC (1)
681 N Plano Rd Ste 121, Richardson, TX 75081
Tel.: (972) 231-1606
Emp.: 5
Semiconductor Components Mfr
N.A.I.C.S.: 334413

Triune Systems, LLC (1)
681 Plano Rd Ste 121, Richardson, TX 75081
Tel.: (972) 231-1606
Wireless Charging & Power Management Platforms
N.A.I.C.S.: 334413

SENECA FINANCIAL CORP.
35 Oswego St, Baldwinsville, NY 13027
Tel.: (315) 638-0233   NY
Web Site:
https://www.senecasavings.com
Year Founded: 2017
SNNF—(OTCIQ)
Rev.: $12,805,000
Assets: $256,725,000
Liabilities: $234,076,000
Net Worth: $22,649,000

Earnings: $755,000
Fiscal Year-end: 12/31/23
Holding Company
N.A.I.C.S.: 551111
Joseph G. Vitale (Pres & CEO)
Vincent J. Fazio (CFO & Exec VP)
William M. Le Beau (Chm)
Mark A. Zames (Pres-Infusion Bus Solutions)
Laurie Ucher (Sr VP-Retail Banking)
Angelo Testani (Sr VP-Comml Lending)
Jamie Nastri (Sr VP-Operations)
Ken Jardin (VP-Comml Lending)
Earl Monday (Officer-Marketing)
Rebecca Smith (Asst VP-Residential Lending)
Rebecca Derouin (Officer-BSA)
Scott Turner (Dir-Human Resources)
Jillian Manning (Asst VP-Operations)
Rachel Siderine (Officer-Business Development)
Francis Valchine III (Asst VP-Acctg Asst)
Cynthia Bunnell (Asst VP-Credit Analyst)
Tim Hanno (Branch Mgr)
Tom Mavretish (VP & Controller)
John James Pagan (Officer & Coord)

Subsidiaries:

Seneca Savings (1)
35 Oswego St, Baldwinsville, NY 13027
Tel.: (315) 638-0233
Web Site: http://www.senecasavings.com
Commercial Banking Services
N.A.I.C.S.: 522110
Joseph G. Vitale (Pres & CEO)
Vincent J. Fazio (CFO & Exec VP)
Tammy Purcell (VP-Lending)
Tom Mavretish (VP & Controller)
Angelo Testani (VP-Comml Lending)

SENECA FOODS CORPORATION
350 Willowbrook Office Park, Fairport, NY 14450
Tel.: (585) 495-4100   NY
Web Site:
https://www.senecafoods.com
Year Founded: 1949
SENEA—(NASDAQ)
Rev.: $1,458,603,000
Assets: $1,383,997,000
Liabilities: $801,104,000
Net Worth: $582,893,000
Earnings: $63,318,000
Emp.: 2,900
Fiscal Year-end: 03/31/24
Food Processor & Fruit & Vegetable Canning Services
N.A.I.C.S.: 311421
Paul L. Palmby (Pres & CEO)
Cynthia L. Fohrd (Chief Admin Officer & Sr VP)
Carl A. Cichetti (CIO & Sr VP-Tech & Plng)
Sarah S. Mortensen (Asst Sec)
Matt J. Henschler (Sr VP-Technical Svcs & Contract Mfg)
Dean E. Erstad (Sr VP-Sls & Mktg)
Aaron M. Girard (Sr VP-Logistics)
Timothy R. Nelson (Pres-Fruit & Snack & Sr VP-Ops)
Gregory R. Ide (VP, Controller & Sec)
Michael Wolcott (CFO & Sr VP-Fin)

Subsidiaries:

Marion Foods, Inc. (1)
213 Sturgis Rd, Marion, KY 42064-1235
Tel.: (270) 965-4261
Canned Fruit & Vegetable Producer
N.A.I.C.S.: 311421

Seneca Flight Operations (1)
2262 Airport Dr, Penn Yan, NY 14527-9590   (100%)
Tel.: (315) 536-4471

Web Site: http://www.senecaflight.com
Sales Range: $350-399.9 Million
Emp.: 20
Air Charter Services
N.A.I.C.S.: 481111
Rich Leppert *(Pres & Gen Mgr)*
Dave Fleming *(Dir-Maintenance)*
Sue Kline *(Accountant)*

Seneca Foods (1)
PO Box 460, Payette, ID 83661-0460
Tel.: (208) 642-9061
Sales Range: $250-299.9 Million
Emp.: 500
Cans Meat & Vegetable Products
N.A.I.C.S.: 311421

Seneca Foods (1)
229 W Waupun St, Oakfield, WI 53065-9741
Tel.: (920) 583-3161
Sales Range: $25-49.9 Million
Emp.: 37
Producer of Canned & Jarred Vegetables
N.A.I.C.S.: 311421

Seneca Foods (1)
N6889 State Rd 146, Cambria, WI 53923-9774
Tel.: (920) 348-2208
Sales Range: $10-24.9 Million
Emp.: 2
Producer of Canned & Jarred Vegetables
N.A.I.C.S.: 311421

Seneca Foods (1)
W13380 Chicago Ave, Hancock, WI 54943-9523
Tel.: (715) 228-3691
Sales Range: $25-49.9 Million
Emp.: 40
Canned Fruits & Specialties
N.A.I.C.S.: 311421

Seneca Foods (1)
3732 S Main St, Marion, NY
14505-9751   (100%)
Tel.: (315) 926-4277
Web Site: http://www.senecafoods.com
Sales Range: $50-74.9 Million
Emp.: 15
Mfr of Food Processor, Vegetables & Fruits
N.A.I.C.S.: 311421

Seneca Foods L.L.C. (1)
3736 S Main St, Marion, NY 14505
Tel.: (315) 926-8125
Canned Fruit & Vegetable Producer
N.A.I.C.S.: 311421

Seneca Foods-Central Div. (1)
418 Conde St, Janesville, WI
53546-2937   (100%)
Tel.: (608) 757-6000
Web Site: http://www.senecafoods.com
Sales Range: $300-349.9 Million
Emp.: 600
Mfr Of Processed Canned Vegetables
N.A.I.C.S.: 311421

Seneca Foods-Ripon (1)
477 S Douglas St, Ripon, WI 54971
Tel.: (920) 745-3111
Web Site: http://www.senecafoods.com
Sales Range: $50-74.9 Million
Emp.: 150
Producer of Canned & Jarred Vegetables
N.A.I.C.S.: 311421

Truitt Bros., Inc. (1)
1105 Frnt St NE, Salem, OR
97301   (100%)
Tel.: (503) 362-3674
Web Site: http://www.truittbros.com
Canned Fruits, Vegetables & Specialties
Producer
N.A.I.C.S.: 311421
Gwen Marr *(Sr Acct Mgr)*

SENESTECH, INC.
23460 N 19th Ave Ste 110, Phoenix,
AZ 85027
Tel.: (928) 779-4143   DE
Web Site:
   https://www.senestech.com
Year Founded: 2004
SNES—(NASDAQ)
Rev.: $1,193,000
Assets: $7,293,000

Liabilities: $942,000
Net Worth: $6,351,000
Earnings: ($7,710,000)
Emp.: 25
Fiscal Year-end: 12/31/23
Research & Development in Biotechnology
N.A.I.C.S.: 541714
Thomas C. Chesterman *(CFO, Treas, Exec VP & Asst Sec)*
Jamie Bechtel *(Chm)*
Joel Fruendt *(CEO)*
Dan Palasky *(Chief Technical Officer)*

SENSATA TECHNOLOGIES HOLDING PLC
529 Pleasant St, Attleboro, MA 02703
Tel.: (508) 236-3800   UK
Web Site: https://www.sensata.com
Year Founded: 2006
ST—(NYSE)
Rev.: $4,054,083,000
Assets: $7,680,987,000
Liabilities: $4,684,711,000
Net Worth: $2,996,276,000
Earnings: ($3,909,000)
Emp.: 19,400
Fiscal Year-end: 12/31/23
Holding Company; Sensors & Controls Mfr
N.A.I.C.S.: 551112
Jeffrey J. Cote *(Pres & CEO)*
Brian K. Roberts *(CFO & Exec VP)*
Hans Lidforss *(Chief Strategy & Corp Dev Officer)*
Alexia Taxiarchos *(Head-Media Rels)*
Jing Chang *(Sr VP-Performance Sensing & Sensing Solutions-Asia)*
Jacquie Boyer *(Chief Comml Officer & Sr VP)*
Hans G. Lidforss *(Sr VP)*
David Stott *(Corp Counsel)*
Jacob Sayer *(VP-Fin)*
Lynne J. Caljouw *(Chief Admin Officer)*
Andrew C. Teich *(Chm)*

Subsidiaries:

BEI Sensors SAS (1)
9 rue de Copenhague Espace Europeen de l'Entreprise-Schiltgheim, PO Box 70044, 67013, Strasbourg, Cedex, France
Tel.: (33) 388208080
Web Site: http://www.beisensors.com
Electronic Components Mfr
N.A.I.C.S.: 334419

CurbSoft, LLC (1)
PO Box 7387, Prospect Heights, IL 60070
Tel.: (331) 333-7036
Web Site: https://www.curbsoft.com
Sensor Installation Services
N.A.I.C.S.: 561621

Cynergy3 Components LLC (1)
11642 Knott Ave E-5, Garden Grove, CA 92841
Tel.: (310) 561-8092
Float Switch Mfr
N.A.I.C.S.: 335313
Robert Manus *(Mgr-Sls-Natl)*

Cynergy3 Components Ltd. (1)
7 Cobham Road, Ferndown Industrial Estate, Wimborne, BH21 7PE, Dorset, United Kingdom
Tel.: (44) 1202897969
Web Site: https://www.cynergy3.com
Float Switch Mfr
N.A.I.C.S.: 335313
Lee Burton *(Mgr-Technical)*

Dynapower Company, LLC (1)
85 Meadowland Dr, South Burlington, VT 05403
Tel.: (802) 860-7200
Web Site: https://www.dynapower.com
Power Conversion Products & Transformers Mfr
N.A.I.C.S.: 335311
Peter Pollak *(Pres)*
Adam M. Knudsen *(Pres)*

Pete Abele *(Sr Engr-Sls Applications)*
George Viola *(Sr Engr-Sls)*
Mary Duncan *(Supvr-Admin)*
Jason McGahey *(Engr-Sls-Indus Sys)*
Jason James *(Gen Mgr)*
Curthbert Serenje *(Gen Mgr)*
Abdoulaye Diallo *(Mgr-Sls)*
Chip Palombini *(Dir-Storage)*

Gigavac, LLC (1)
6382 Rose Ln, Carpinteria, CA 93013
Tel.: (805) 684-8401
Web Site: http://www.gigavac.com
Industrial Control Mfr
N.A.I.C.S.: 335314

Impress Sensors & Systems Limited (1)
Regency House 22-25 Kingsclere Park, Kingsclere, RG20 4SW, Hampshire, United Kingdom
Tel.: (44) 1635291600
Web Site: http://www.impress-sensors.co.uk
Sensor & Control Mfr
N.A.I.C.S.: 334513
Les Butler *(Mgr-Production)*

Industrial Interface Limited (1)
Unit 2 Deer Park Business Centre Eckington, Pershore, WR10 3DN, Worcestershire, United Kingdom
Tel.: (44) 1684628064
Web Site:
   https://www.industrialinterface.co.uk
Signal Conditioning & Control Instrument Mfr
N.A.I.C.S.: 334513

Lithium Balance A/S (1)
Lyskaer 3B, 2730, Herlev, Denmark
Tel.: (45) 58515104
Web Site: https://lithiumbalance.com
Electrical & Electronic Component Mfr
N.A.I.C.S.: 335999
Stephen Millen *(Dir-Engineering)*
Ayoe Pilak *(Partner-HR Business)*

Preco Electronics, LLC (1)
10335 Emerald St Ste 100, Boise, ID 83704
Tel.: (208) 323-1000
Web Site: http://www.preco.com
Vehicle Safety Equipment Mfr
N.A.I.C.S.: 334290
Jim Bean *(Pres & CEO)*

Schrader-Bridgeport International, Inc. (1)
205 Frazier Rd, Altavista, VA 24517
Tel.: (434) 369-4741
Web Site:
   http://www.schraderinternational.com
Sensor Mfr
N.A.I.C.S.: 334413

Sendyne Corp. (1)
250 W Broadway, New York, NY 10013
Tel.: (212) 966-0600
Web Site: https://www.sendyne.com
Semiconductor Product Mfr
N.A.I.C.S.: 334413
John Milios *(CEO)*
Nicolas Clauvelin *(CFO & Exec VP)*
Ellen Gooch *(Mktg Dir)*
Victor Marten *(Dir-Engineering)*

Sensata Technologies B.V. (1)
Kolthofsingel 8, 7602 EM, Almelo, 7602 EM, Netherlands
Tel.: (31) 546879555
Web Site: http://www.sensata.com
Sales Range: $1-4.9 Billion
Holding Company; Sensors & Control Instruments Mfr
N.A.I.C.S.: 551112

Subsidiary (Non-US):

August France Holding Company S.A.S. (2)
48 Rue De Salins, Pontarlier, 25300, France
Tel.: (33) 892976484
Holding Company
N.A.I.C.S.: 551112

DeltaTech Controls GmbH (2)
Freiheit 8, 13597, Germany
Tel.: (49) 30439990
Electronic Component Mfr & Distr
N.A.I.C.S.: 334419

Sensata Technologies Automotive Sensors (Shanghai) Co., Ltd. (2)
No 8 Lane 55 Fenggong Road, Shanghai, 201801, China
Tel.: (86) 2169155818
Sensor Mfr
N.A.I.C.S.: 334512

Sensata Technologies Baoying Co., Ltd. (2)
9 East Taishan Rd Baoying Economic Development Zone, Baoying, 225800, China
Tel.: (86) 51488873000
Electronic Components Mfr
N.A.I.C.S.: 334419

Sensata Technologies Changzhou Co., Ltd. (2)
18 Chuangxin Avenue, Xinbei District, Changzhou, 213031, China
Tel.: (86) 51985161188
Electronic Components Mfr
N.A.I.C.S.: 334419

Sensata Technologies China Co., Ltd. (2)
BM Intercontinental Business Centre 30th Floor 100 YuTong Road, Shanghai, 200070, China
Tel.: (86) 2123061500
Electronic Components Distr
N.A.I.C.S.: 423690

Sensata Technologies Dominicana, S.r.L. (2)
Carretera Sanchez Km 18 12, San Cristobal, 91000, Dominican Republic
Tel.: (809) 8095474836
Web Site: http://www.sensata.com
Emp.: 46
Relay & Industrial Control Mfr
N.A.I.C.S.: 335314

Sensata Technologies Germany GmbH (2)
Freiheit 8, 13597, Berlin, Germany
Tel.: (49) 30439990
Sensor Mfr
N.A.I.C.S.: 334512

Subsidiary (Domestic):

Sensata Technologies Holland B.V. (2)
Jan Tinbergenstraat 80, PO Box 43, 7559 SP, Hengelo, Netherlands
Tel.: (31) 743578000
Web Site: https://www.sensata.com
Sensor Mfr
N.A.I.C.S.: 334512

Subsidiary (Non-US):

Sensata Technologies Korea Limited (2)
Pan-Gyo Office 7th floor of U-space 2 A Building 670, Daewangpangyo-Ro Bundang-Gu, Seongnam, 13494, Gyeonggi-Do, Korea (South)
Tel.: (82) 316012000
Sensor Mfr
N.A.I.C.S.: 334512

Sensata Technologies Malaysia Sdn. Bhd. (2)
Lot 84 Persiaran Subang Indah Taman Perindustrian Subang USJ 1, 47600, Subang Jaya, Selangor, Malaysia
Tel.: (60) 355666188
Sensor Mfr
N.A.I.C.S.: 334512

Sensata Technologies Mex Distribution, S.A. de C.V. (2)
Aguascalientes Sur Ave, No 401 E Morelos I Ii and Ii Stage north Industrial park, Aguascalientes, 20298, Mexico
Tel.: (52) 4499105000
Electronic Components Mfr
N.A.I.C.S.: 334419

Sensata Technologies Sensores e Controles do Brasil Ltda. (2)
Tel.: (55) 1937541111
Sensor Mfr
N.A.I.C.S.: 334512

Sensata Technologies Singapore Pte. Ltd. (2)

Sensata Technologies Holding plc—(Continued)

3 Bishan Place Suite 02-04 Cpf Bishan
Building, Singapore, 579838, Singapore
Tel.: (65) 64786861
Sensor Mfr
N.A.I.C.S.: 334512

**Sensata Technologies Taiwan Co.,
Ltd.** (2)
7F No 163 Sec 1 Keelung Rd, Sinyi, Taipei,
Taiwan
Tel.: (886) 227602006
Web Site: http://www.sensata.com
Sensor Mfr & Distr
N.A.I.C.S.: 334512

Subsidiary (US):

Sensata Technologies, Inc. (2)
529 Pleasant St, Attleboro, MA
02703 (100%)
Tel.: (508) 236-3800
Web Site: https://www.sensata.com
Sales Range: $75-99.9 Million
Emp.: 200
Sensors & Control Instruments Designer,
Mfr & Marketer
N.A.I.C.S.: 334519

Subsidiary (Domestic):

BEI Sensors North America (3)
1461 Lawrence Dr, Thousand Oaks, CA
91320
Tel.: (805) 716-0322
Web Site: http://www.sensata.com
Electronic Components Mfr
N.A.I.C.S.: 334419

Control Devices, Inc. (3)
1801 N Juniper Ave, Broken Arrow, OK
74012
Tel.: (918) 258-6068
Web Site: https://www.pigging.com
Emp.: 48
Modern Pipeline Pig Tracking & Communi-
cations Equipment Mfr
N.A.I.C.S.: 486210
Jason Farque (VP)

Crydom, Inc. (3)
2475 Paseo de las Americas Ste201, San
Diego, CA 92154
Tel.: (619) 210-1550
Web Site: http://www.crydom.com
Solid State Relay Mfr
N.A.I.C.S.: 335314

Subsidiary (Non-US):

Crydom SSR Limited (4)
Everdene House Deansleigh Road, Wessex
Fields, Bournemouth, BH7 7DU, Dorset,
United Kingdom
Tel.: (44) 1202416170
Web Site: http://www.crydom.com
Solid State Relay Mfr
N.A.I.C.S.: 335314

Subsidiary (Domestic):

DeltaTech Controls USA, LLC (3)
5775 W Old Shakopee Rd, Bloomington,
MN 55379-1818
Tel.: (952) 403-7400
Web Site: http://www.deltatechcontrols.com
Sales Range: $50-74.9 Million
Emp.: 70
Electronic Operator Control Components &
Systems Developer & Distr
N.A.I.C.S.: 423610

Newall Electronics Inc. (3)
1803 O'Brien, Columbus, OH 43228-3845
Tel.: (614) 771-0213
Web Site: https://www.newall.com
Measuring Instruments Mfr
N.A.I.C.S.: 334513

Subsidiary (Non-US):

**Newall Measurement Systems
Ltd.** (4)
Unit 1 Wharf Way Business Park, Glen
Parva, Leicester, LE2 9UT, United Kingdom
Tel.: (44) 1162642730
Web Site: https://www.newall.co.uk
Measurement & Display Systems
N.A.I.C.S.: 334513
Chris Lawler (Sls Mgr-EMEA)

Subsidiary (Domestic):

Schrader International, Inc. (3)
205 Frazier Rd, Altavista, VA 24517
Tel.: (434) 369-4741
Web Site:
http://www.schraderinternational.com
Sales Range: $450-499.9 Million
Valve Products & Tire Hardware Mfr & Distr
N.A.I.C.S.: 332912

Subsidiary (Non-US):

Schrader Electronics Limited (4)
11 Technology Park Belfast Rd, Antrim,
BT41 1QS, N Ireland, United Kingdom
Tel.: (44) 2894461300
Tire Pressure Monitoring Systems, Valve
Products & Tire Hardware Mfr & Distr
N.A.I.C.S.: 336320

**Schrader International Brasil
Ltda.** (4)
Av Malek Assad 1600 Meia Lua, Jacarei,
CEP 12328-900, Sao Paulo, Brazil
Tel.: (55) 1239546500
Web Site:
http://www.schraderinternational.com
Valve Products & Tire Hardware Mfr & Distr
N.A.I.C.S.: 332912

Schrader SAS (4)
48 rue de Salins, BP 29, 25301, Pontarlier,
25301, France
Tel.: (33) 381385656
Web Site:
http://www.schraderinternational.com
Emp.: 400
Valve Products & Tire Hardware Mfr & Distr
N.A.I.C.S.: 332912

Subsidiary (Non-US):

Sensata Germany GmbH (3)
Postdamer Strasse 14, 32423, Minden,
Germany
Tel.: (49) 57138590
Pressure Sensor Mfr
N.A.I.C.S.: 334413

Subsidiary (Domestic):

**Sensata Technologies Indiana,
Inc.** (3)
529 Pleasant St, Attleboro, MA 02703
Tel.: (508) 236-3800
Emp.: 615
Electronic Components Mfr
N.A.I.C.S.: 334419

Unit (Domestic):

**Sensata Technologies Power
Controls** (3)
807 Woods Rd, Cambridge, MD 21613
Tel.: (410) 228-4600
Web Site: http://www.sensata.com
Power Management Sensor & Control Prod-
ucts Mfr
N.A.I.C.S.: 334519

Subsidiary (Non-US):

Nihon Airpax Co., Ltd. (4)
6-3 Chiyoda 5-chome, Sakado-shi, Saitama,
350-0214, Japan (100%)
Tel.: (81) 492837771
Web Site: http://www.airpax.jp
Sales Range: $10-24.9 Million
Circuit Protectors, Pickup Sensors, Thermo-
stats & Fuses Mfr
N.A.I.C.S.: 334519

Subsidiary (Non-US):

**Sensata Technologies de Mexico S
de RL de CV** (3)
Av Aguascalientes Sur 401 Ex Ejido Salto
de Ojocaliente, 20290, Aguascalientes,
Mexico
Tel.: (52) 4499105500
Automotive Sensor Mfr
N.A.I.C.S.: 334413

Unit (Domestic):

**Sensata Technologies, Inc. -
Dimensions** (3)
4467 White Bear Pkwy, Saint Paul, MN
55110-7626
Tel.: (651) 653-7000

Web Site:
http://www.dimensions.sensata.com
Sales Range: $25-49.9 Million
Emp.: 90
Power Inverters Mfr
N.A.I.C.S.: 335999

Subsidiary (Domestic):

Wabash Technologies, Inc. (3)
1375 Swan St, Huntington, IN 46750
Tel.: (260) 355-4100
Web Site: http://www.wabashtech.com
Sales Range: $100-124.9 Million
Emp.: 75
Sensor Technology Products Mfr
N.A.I.C.S.: 334416

Subsidiary (Non-US):

**Wabash Technologies De Mexico, S
De R L De C V** (4)
Av De La Eficiencia, Suite 2700 Pimsa IV,
Mexicali, 21210, Baja California, Mexico
Tel.: (52) 6869055900
Electronic Component Mfr & Whslr
N.A.I.C.S.: 334419

Plant (Domestic):

**Wabash Technologies, Inc. - Troy
Plant** (4)
3155 W Big Beaver Rd Ste 209, Troy, MI
48084
Tel.: (248) 220-5400
Emp.: 1,200
Holding Company
N.A.I.C.S.: 551112

Subsidiary (Domestic):

Xirgo Technologies, Inc. (3)
188 Camino Ruiz 2nd Fl, Camarillo, CA
93012
Tel.: (805) 319-4079
Web Site: http://www.xirgotech.com
Wireless IoT Communication Devices
N.A.I.C.S.: 517112
Joel Young (CTO)

Subsidiary (Non-US):

Swindon Silicon Systems Limited (2)
Interface House Interface Business Park
Bincknoll Lane, Royal Wootton Bassett,
Swindon, SN4 8SY, Wiltshire, United King-
dom
Tel.: (44) 1793649400
Web Site: https://www.swindonsilicon.com
Emp.: 135
Electronic Component Mfr & Distr
N.A.I.C.S.: 334419

Sensata Technologies GmbH (1)
Freiheit 8, 13597, Berlin, Germany
Tel.: (49) 30439990
Sensor & Control Mfr
N.A.I.C.S.: 334513

SmartWitness USA LLC (1)
1016 Lunt Ave, Schaumburg, IL 60193
Tel.: (312) 981-8774
Web Site: https://www.smartwitness.com
Electronic Components Mfr
N.A.I.C.S.: 334419

Spear Power Systems AS (1)
Tveiterasvegen 12, 5232, Paradis, Norway
Tel.: (47) 33767168
Energy Storage System Mfr
N.A.I.C.S.: 335910

Spear Power Systems, LLC (1)
2901 NE Hagan Rd, Lees Summit, MO
64064-2333
Tel.: (816) 272-7094
Web Site: http://www.spearps.com
Storage Battery Mfr
N.A.I.C.S.: 335910
Jeff Kostos (Pres & CEO)
Ryan Kostos (Mgr-Applications Engrg)

ThinGap Holdings, LLC (1)
2064 Eastman Ave Ste 109, Ventura, CA
93003-7787
Tel.: (805) 477-9741
Emp.: 10
Holding Company
N.A.I.C.S.: 551112
Sarah Gallagher (Pres & CEO)
Evan Frank (CTO)

Nancy Wong Johnson (Mgr-Ops)
Charles Descoteaux (Engr-Sls)
George Holbrook (Chm)

UAB Xirgo Global (1)
Tel.: (370) 70033335
Web Site: https://www.xirgoglobal.com
Emp.: 90
Electric Equipment Mfr
N.A.I.C.S.: 335311
Andrius Miglinas (Dir)
Edvinas Sakalinskas (Mgr)

**Wabash Technologies Mexico S. de
R.L. de C.V.** (1)
Av de la Eficiencia 2700 Pimsa IV, Mexicali,
21210, Baja California, Mexico
Tel.: (52) 6869055900
Sensor & Control Mfr
N.A.I.C.S.: 334513

**Wabash Technologies de Mexico
Technologies S. de R.L. de C.V.** (1)
Av De La Eficiencia No 2700 Alamitos,
21210, Mexicali, Baja California, Mexico
Tel.: (52) 6869055900
Motor Vehicle Parts Mfr
N.A.I.C.S.: 336211
Marco Ornelas (Mgr-HR)

SENSE TECHNOLOGIES INC.
2535 Carleton Ave Ste B, Grand Is-
land, NE 68803
Tel.: (308) 381-1355 BC
Web Site:
https://sensenaturalproducts.com
SNSGF—(OTCIQ)
Sales Range: Less than $1 Million
Other Motor Vehicle Parts Manufac-
turing
N.A.I.C.S.: 336390
Bruce E. Schreiner (Pres & CEO)
Bev Hummel (Sec)

**SENSEI BIOTHERAPEUTICS,
INC.**
1405 Research Blvd Ste 125, Rock-
ville, MD 20850
Tel.: (240) 243-8000 DE
Web Site: https://www.senseibio.com
Year Founded: 1999
SNSE—(NASDAQ)
Rev.: $1,783,000
Assets: $118,375,000
Liabilities: $14,968,000
Net Worth: $103,407,000
Earnings: ($48,588,000)
Emp.: 28
Fiscal Year-end: 12/31/22
Biotechnology Research & Develop-
ment Services
N.A.I.C.S.: 541714
John K. Celebi (Pres & CEO)
Edward van der Horst (Chief Scien-
tific Officer)

SENSEONICS HOLDINGS, INC.
20451 Seneca Meadows Pkwy, Ger-
mantown, MD 20876-7005
Tel.: (301) 515-7260 NV
Web Site:
https://www.senseonics.com
Year Founded: 2014
SENS—(NYSEAMEX)
Rev.: $22,390,000
Assets: $138,220,000
Liabilities: $102,424,000
Net Worth: $35,796,000
Earnings: ($60,392,000)
Emp.: 132
Fiscal Year-end: 12/31/23
Glucose Monitoring Systems Devel-
oper
N.A.I.C.S.: 325412
Timothy T. Goodnow (Pres & CEO)
Mukul Jain (COO)
Abhi Chavan (VP-Engrg & R&D)
Francine R. Kaufman (Chief Medical
Officer)

Rick Sullivan *(CFO)*
Katherine S. Tweden *(VP-Clinical Sciences)*

SENSIENT TECHNOLOGIES CORPORATION

777 E Wisconsin Ave, Milwaukee, WI
53202-5304
Tel.: (414) 271-6755   **WI**
Web Site: https://www.sensient.com
Year Founded: 1882
SXT—(NYSE)
Rev.: $1,437,039,000
Assets: $1,981,614,000
Liabilities: $982,016,000
Net Worth: $999,598,000
Earnings: $140,887,000
Emp.: 4,094
Fiscal Year-end: 12/31/22
Colors, Flavors, Yeast, Dehydrated
Vegetables & Seasonings Developer,
Mfr & Marketer
N.A.I.C.S.: 311930
Paul Manning *(Chm, Pres & CEO)*
Michael C. Geraghty *(Pres-Color Grp)*
John J. Manning *(Gen Counsel, Sec & Sr VP)*
Tobin Tornehl *(CFO, VP & Controller)*
Amy M. Agallar *(Treas & VP)*
Amy Schmidt Jones *(VP-HR)*
Thierry Hoang *(VP-Asia Pacific Grp)*

Subsidiaries:

SENSIENT COLORS EUROPE GMBH   (1)
Geesthachter Str 103, 21502, Geesthacht,
Germany
Tel.: (49) 415280000
Web Site: http://sensientfoodcolors.com
Food Color Mfr
N.A.I.C.S.: 311942

SENSIENT COSMETIC TECHNOLOGIES   (1)
7-9 rue de l'Industrie, 95310, Saint-Ouen-
l'Aumone, France
Tel.: (33) 13 448 5700
Web Site: http://www.sensient-
cosmetics.com
Sales Range: $50-74.9 Million
Emp.: 136
Cosmetic Colors & Ingredients Mfr
N.A.I.C.S.: 325620

SENSIENT COSMETIC TECHNOLOGIES E CORANTES, IMPORTACAO E EXPORTACAO DO   (1)
Alameda Oceania 149 - Polo empresarial
Tambore, Santana de Parnaiba, 06543-308,
Sao Paulo, Brazil
Tel.: (55) 1131613799
Cosmetic Ingredient Mfr
N.A.I.C.S.: 325620

SENSIENT COSMETIC TECHNOLOGIES POLAND, SP. Z.O.O.   (1)
Wojciech 10/1, 61-749, Poznan, Poland
Tel.: (48) 618550910
Cosmetic Ingredient Mfr
N.A.I.C.S.: 325620
Jowita Bober *(Acct Mgr-Sls)*

SENSIENT DEHYDRATED FLAVORS SAS   (1)
Le Mont De Monceau, 02350, Marchais,
France
Tel.: (33) 323223570
Web Site: http://www.sensient.com
Sales Range: $25-49.9 Million
Emp.: 50
Dehydrated Vegetable Ingredients Mfr
N.A.I.C.S.: 311942

SENSIENT FLAVORS & FRAGRANCES INDUSTRY & TRADE LIMITED COMPANY   (1)
Tel.: (90) 2124657871
Web Site:
    https://sensientflavorsandextracts.com
Emp.: 7
Flavor Extract Mfr
N.A.I.C.S.: 311942

SENSIENT FLAVORS AND FRAGRANCES SOUTH AFRICA (PROPRIETARY) LTD   (1)
11 Mastiff Rd Long Lake Ext 1 Linbro Business Park, Sandton, 1608, Gauteng, South
Africa
Tel.: (27) 110535200
Web Site: http://www.sensient.com
Emp.: 7
Flavor Extract Mfr
N.A.I.C.S.: 311942

SENSIENT FLAVORS AUSTRIA GMBH   (1)
Simmeringer Hauptstrasse 24, Cityport 11,
Vienna, 1110, Austria
Tel.: (43) 6641689484
Colors,Flavors & Fragrances Mfr
N.A.I.C.S.: 311942

SENSIENT FLAVORS ITALY S.R.L.   (1)
Via Firenze 11, Ornago, 20063, Cernusco
sul Naviglio, MI, Italy
Tel.: (39) 029 262 6009
Web Site: http://www.sensientflavors.com
Sales Range: $25-49.9 Million
Emp.: 50
Food Flavouring Products Mfr
N.A.I.C.S.: 311942

SENSIENT FOOD COLORS ITALY S.R.L.   (1)
Via della Stazione 22, Cade, 42100, Reggio
Emilia, Italy
Tel.: (39) 052 294 2134
Web Site: https://www.sensient.com
Emp.: 30
Colors, Flavors & Fragrances Mfr
N.A.I.C.S.: 311942

SENSIENT FOOD COLORS POLAND SP.ZO.O.   (1)
Aleje Jerozolimskie 81, 00-001, Warsaw,
Poland
Tel.: (48) 226950400
Emp.: 3
Colors, Flavors & Fragrances Mfr
N.A.I.C.S.: 311942
Roland Back *(Gen Mgr)*

SENSIENT FOOD COLORS ROMANIA S.R.L.   (1)
Sos Borsului Nr 40, 410605, Oradea, Bihor,
Romania
Tel.: (40) 259427218
Web Site: http://www.sensient-fce.com
Sales Range: $25-49.9 Million
Emp.: 4
Colors, Flavors & Fragrances Mfr
N.A.I.C.S.: 311942

SENSIENT FOOD COLORS THE NETHERLANDS BV   (1)
Amsterdamsestraatweg 19 B, Naarden,
1411 AW, Netherlands
Tel.: (31) 356997920
Sales Range: $25-49.9 Million
Emp.: 3
Colors,Flavors & Fragrances Mfr
N.A.I.C.S.: 311942

SENSIENT FRAGRANCES MEXICO, S.A. DE C.V.   (1)
Ayuntamiento 136-A Col Centro, Tlal-
nepantla, 54000, Estado de Mexico, Mexico
Tel.: (52) 53840040
Fragrances,Essential Oils & Aroma Chemicals Mfr
N.A.I.C.S.: 325199

SENSIENT FRAGRANCES, S.A.   (1)
Complejo Ecourban Edificio Azul Almogavers 119-123 Planta 4 Local 2, 08018, Barcelona, Spain
Tel.: (34) 932177477
Web Site:
    http://www.sensientfragrances.com
Emp.: 100
Fragrances,Essential Oils & Aroma Chemicals Mfr
N.A.I.C.S.: 325199

SENSIENT HOLDINGS UK   (1)
Bilton Road, Bletchley, Milton Keynes, MK1
1HP, Bucks, United Kingdom
Tel.: (44) 1908270270
Web Site: https://www.sensientflavorsandfra
    grances.com

Emp.: 120
Food Flavorings
N.A.I.C.S.: 311930

SENSIENT IMAGING TECHNOLOGIES INC.   (1)
2724 Loker Ave W, Carlsbad, CA 92010
Tel.: (760) 930-1600
Printing Ink Mfr
N.A.I.C.S.: 325910

SENSIENT IMAGING TECHNOLOGIES S.A. DE C.V.   (1)
Inkjet Privada Misiones 1119, Parque
Industrial Misiones, Tijuana, 22425, Mexico
Tel.: (52) 6646833655
Web Site: http://www.sensientpharma.com
Specialty Inks & Colors Mfr
N.A.I.C.S.: 325998

SENSIENT TECHNOLOGIES CORP. (CHINA) LTD   (1)
17 Junda Road East Zone GETDD,
Guangzhou, 51053, China
Tel.: (86) 2082226218
Web Site: http://www.sensient.cn
Sales Range: $25-49.9 Million
Emp.: 100
Colors, Flavors & Fragrances Mfr
N.A.I.C.S.: 311942

SENSIENT TECHNOLOGIES CORPORATION (JAPAN)   (1)
Toho Tokyo Shiba Building 2nd Floor 29-12
Shiba 2-Chome, Minato-ku, Tokyo, 105-
0014, Ibaragi, Japan
Tel.: (81) 364003270
Web Site: http://www.sensientpharma.com
Colors, Flavors & Fragrances Mfr
N.A.I.C.S.: 311942

Sensient Colors Canada Ltd.   (1)
30 River St, PO Box 818, Kingston, K7L
4X6, ON, Canada   **(100%)**
Tel.: (613) 546-5509
Web Site: https://www.sensient.com
Sales Range: $25-49.9 Million
Emp.: 20
Food Colors & Organic Pigments Mfr
N.A.I.C.S.: 311930

Sensient Colors LLC   (1)
2515 N Jefferson, Saint Louis, MO
63106-1939   **(100%)**
Tel.: (314) 889-7600
Web Site: https://sensientfoodcolors.com
Food Colors & Organic Pigments Mfr
N.A.I.C.S.: 311930

Sensient Colors SA de CV   (1)
Rodolfo Patron No 12 Parque Industrial
Lerma, PO Box 17, 5200, Lerma,
Mexico   **(100%)**
Tel.: (52) 722 265 1100
Web Site: http://www.sensient-tech.com
Sales Range: $100-124.9 Million
Emp.: 220
Food Colors & Organic Pigments Mfr
N.A.I.C.S.: 311930

Sensient Colors UK Ltd.   (1)
Oldmedow Road, Hardwick Industrial Estate, King's Lynn, PE30 4LA, Norfolk,
United Kingdom   **(100%)**
Tel.: (44) 1553669444
Web Site:
    https://www.sensientindustrial.com
Sales Range: $50-74.9 Million
Emp.: 100
Food Colors & Organic Pigments Mfr
N.A.I.C.S.: 325130

Sensient Cosmetic Technologies USA   (1)
300 Atrium Dr Ste 101, Somerset, NJ
08873   **(100%)**
Tel.: (908) 757-4500
Web Site: http://www.sensient-
cosmetics.com
Sales Range: $10-24.9 Million
Emp.: 50
Cosmetic Ingredients & Colorants Mfr
N.A.I.C.S.: 325130

Sensient Flavors & Fragrances SAS   (1)
1150 Boulevard Sebastien Brant Parc d Innovation, 67400, Illkirch-Graffenstaden,
France
Tel.: (33) 388795898

Food Products Distr
N.A.I.C.S.: 424490

Sensient Flavors International, Inc.   (1)
2800 W Higgins Rd Ste 900, Hoffman Estates, IL 60169
Tel.: (847) 755-5300
Web Site:
    https://www.sensientflavorsandfragran
    ces.com
Colors, Flavors & Fragrances Mfr
N.A.I.C.S.: 311942

Sensient Flavors Ltd.   (1)
Bilton Road, Bletchley, MK1 1HP, Milton
Keynes, United Kingdom
Tel.: (44) 1908270270
Web Site:
    https://www.sensientflavorsandfragran
    ces.com
Food & Beverage Flavorings Mfr
N.A.I.C.S.: 311930

Sensient Flavors, LLC   (1)
2800 W Higgins Rd Ste 900, Hoffman Estates, IL 60169   **(100%)**
Tel.: (847) 755-5300
Web Site: http://www.sensient.com
Sales Range: $650-699.9 Million
Emp.: 350
Food & Beverage Flavorings Mfr
N.A.I.C.S.: 311930

Sensient Food Colors Czech Republic CZ S.R.O.   (1)
Belohorska 47, 16900, Prague, Czech Republic
Tel.: (420) 233351703
Food & Beverage Mfr
N.A.I.C.S.: 311999

Sensient Natural Extraction Inc.   (1)
7901 Progress Way, Delta, V4G 1A3, BC,
Canada
Tel.: (604) 337-1578
Web Site: https://www.mazzainnovation.com
Food Products Mfr
N.A.I.C.S.: 311999

Sensient Natural Ingredients   (1)
BP 27, 02350, Marchais, France
Tel.: (33) 323223570
Dehydrated Food Mfr
N.A.I.C.S.: 311423
Jean-Christophe Soubeyrand *(Mgr-Bus Dev)*

Sensient Natural Ingredients LLC   (1)
151 S Walnut Rd, Turlock, CA 95380
Tel.: (209) 667-2777
Web Site:
    https://www.sensientnaturalingredi
    ents.com
Vegetable Mfr
N.A.I.C.S.: 311411

Sensient Natural Technologies LLC   (1)
151 S Walnut Rd, Turlock, CA 95380
Tel.: (209) 667-2777
Web Site: http://www.sensientnaturalingredi
    ents.com
Dehydrated Food Mfr
N.A.I.C.S.: 311423

Sensient Technologies Asia Pacific Pte. Ltd.   (1)
11 Biopolis Way Helios 06-01/02, Singapore, 138667, Singapore
Tel.: (65) 67767900
Sales Range: $25-49.9 Million
Emp.: 30
Colors, Flavors, Yeast, Dehydrated Vegetables & Seasonings Mfr & Marketer
N.A.I.C.S.: 311930

Sensient Technologies Australia Pty Ltd.   (1)
30-40 Kirkham Road West, Keysborough,
3173, VIC, Australia   **(100%)**
Tel.: (61) 397983011
Sales Range: $25-49.9 Million
Emp.: 70
Colors, Flavors, Yeast, Dehydrated Vegetables & Seasonings Mfr & Marketer
N.A.I.C.S.: 311930

Sensient Technologies Europe GmbH   (1)
Geesthachter Str 103, 21502, Geesthacht,
Germany
Tel.: (49) 415280000

Sensient Technologies
Corporation—(Continued)

Food Products Mfr
N.A.I.C.S.: 311999
David Hanson *(Mng Dir)*
Andreas Klingenberg *(Mng Dir)*
Leroy C. Watson *(Mng Dir)*

Sensient Turkey Dogal Maddeler
A.S. **(1)**
Sensient Koku Ve Parfumleri End Ve Tic Ltd
Sti, Instanbul World Trade Center A2 Block
Level 4 No 181 Yesilkoy, 34149, Istanbul,
Turkiye
Tel.: (90) 2124657871
Food & Beverage Mfr
N.A.I.C.S.: 311930

SENSUS HEALTHCARE, INC.
851 Broken Sound Pkwy NW Ste
215, Boca Raton, FL 33487
Tel.: (561) 922-5808 DE
Web Site:
https://www.sensushealthcare.com
Year Founded: 2010
SRTS—(NASDAQ)
Rev.: $44,532,000
Assets: $56,735,000
Liabilities: $8,666,000
Net Worth: $48,069,000
Earnings: $24,244,000
Emp.: 42
Fiscal Year-end: 12/31/22
Irradiation Apparatus Mfr
N.A.I.C.S.: 334517
Joseph C. Sardano *(Chm, CEO &
CEO)*
Michael J. Sardano *(Pres, Gen Counsel & Sec)*
Javier Rampolla *(CFO)*
Magdalena Martinez *(COO)*

Subsidiaries:

Aesthetic Mobile Laser Services,
Inc. **(1)**
905 E Hillsboro Blvd, Deerfield Beach, FL
33441-3523
Tel.: (954) 522-8477
Web Site:
http://www.aestheticmobilelaser.com
Offices of Physicians (except Mental Health
Specialists)
N.A.I.C.S.: 621111

SENTAIDA TIRE COMPANY LTD.
2901 W Coast I lwy Ste 140, Newport
Beach, CA 92663 NV
SDTC—(OTCIQ)
Tire Distr
N.A.I.C.S.: 441340
Robert Thompson *(Pres)*

SENTI BIOSCIENCES, INC.
2 Corporate Dr First Fl, South San
Francisco, CA 94080
Tel.: (650) 239-2030 DE
Web Site: https://www.sentibio.com
Year Founded: 2021
SNTI—(NASDAQ)
Rev.: $4,286,000
Assets: $180,792,000
Liabilities: $53,529,000
Net Worth: $127,263,000
Earnings: ($58,210,000)
Emp.: 122
Fiscal Year-end: 12/31/22
Biotechnology Research
N.A.I.C.S.: 541714
Kanya Rajangam *(Pres, Chief Medial
Officer & Head-Res & Dev)*
Yvonne Li *(Interim CFO, Principal
Acctg Officer & Treas)*
Kanya Rajangam *(Chief Medial Officer & Head-Res & Dev)*
Timothy Lu *(Co-Founder, CEO, Interim Principal Acctg Officer & Interim
Principal Financial Officer)*
Philip Lee *(Co-Founder)*

SENTINELONE, INC.
444 Castro St Ste 400, Mountain
View, CA 94041 DE
Web Site:
https://www.sentinelone.com
Year Founded: 2013
S—(NYSE)
Rev.: $621,154,000
Assets: $2,321,407,000
Liabilities: $727,364,000
Net Worth: $1,594,043,000
Earnings: ($338,693,000)
Emp.: 2,300
Fiscal Year-end: 01/31/24
Software Development Services
N.A.I.C.S.: 541511
Robin Tomasello *(Chief Acctg Officer)*
Nicholas Warner *(Pres-Security)*
Tomer Weingarten *(CEO)*
Nicholas Warner *(Pres-Security)*
Eran Ashkenazi *(Sr VP-Support &
Svcs)*
Divya Ghatak *(Chief People Officer)*
Mark Parrinello *(Sr VP-Sls)*
Raj Rajamani *(Chief Product Officer)*
Keenan Conder *(Chief Legal Officer
& Sec)*
Rob Salvagno *(Sr VP-Dev)*
Narayanan Srivatsan *(Chief Bus Officer)*
Richard Smith Jr. *(CTO)*
Barbara A. Larson *(CFO)*

SENTRY PETROLEUM LTD.
999 18th St Ste 3000, Denver, CO
80202 WY
Web Site:
http://www.sentrypetroleum.com
Year Founded: 2006
SPLM—(OTCQB)
Oil & Gas Exploration
N.A.I.C.S.: 211120
Raj Rajeswaran *(Pres & CEO)*

SENTRY TECHNOLOGY CORPORATION
1881 Lakeland Ave, Ronkonkoma,
NY 11779
Tel.: (631) 739-2000 NY
Web Site:
https://www.sentrytechnology.com
Year Founded: 1997
SKVY—(OTCIQ)
Sales Range: $1-9.9 Million
Emp.: 35
Other Communications Equipment
Manufacturing
N.A.I.C.S.: 334290
Joan E. Miller *(VP-Fin)*
Peter L. Murdoch *(Chm, Pres &
CEO)*
Elizabeth A. Heyder *(Sec)*

Subsidiaries:

Custom Security Industries Inc. **(1)**
25 Kinnear Court Unit 3, Richmond Hill,
L4B 1H9, ON, Canada **(51%)**
Tel.: (905) 886-0338
Web Site: https://www.csi-labels.com
Electronic Article Surveillance (EAS) Anti-
Shoplifting Tags & Labels Mfr
N.A.I.C.S.: 334419

Sentry Technology Canada Inc. **(1)**
25 Kinnear Court Unit 3, Richmond Hill,
L4B 1H9, ON, Canada **(100%)**
Tel.: (416) 574-4788
Web Site: https://sentrytechnology.com
Sales Range: $1-9.9 Million
Emp.: 10
Electronic Anti-Pilferage Security Devices &
Closed Circuit Televisions
N.A.I.C.S.: 561621

SEP ACQUISITION CORP.
3737 Buffalo Speedway Ste 1750,
Houston, TX 77098
Tel.: (713) 715-6820 DE

Web Site:
https://www.mercuryfund.com
Year Founded: 2021
SEPA—(NASDAQ)
Rev.: $9,393,376
Assets: $23,977,972
Liabilities: $31,229,415
Net Worth: ($7,251,443)
Earnings: $7,712,607
Emp.: 4
Fiscal Year-end: 12/31/22
Miscellaneous Financial Investment
Activities
N.A.I.C.S.: 523999
M. Blair Garrou *(Chm)*
R. Andrew White *(Pres & CEO)*

SEQUENTIAL BRANDS GROUP, INC.
1407 Broadway 38th Fl, New York,
NY 10018
Tel.: (646) 564-2577 DE
Web Site:
http://www.sequentialbrands
group.com
Year Founded: 1982
SQBG—(NASDAQ)
Rev.: $89,811,000
Assets: $565,909,000
Liabilities: $493,330,000
Net Worth: $72,579,000
Earnings: ($89,420,000)
Emp.: 19
Fiscal Year-end: 12/31/20
Holding Company; Branded Apparel
Designer & Marketer
N.A.I.C.S.: 551112
Silvia Mazzucchelli *(Chm)*
Lorraine DiSanto *(CFO)*

Subsidiaries:

Gaiam Americas, Inc. **(1)**
833 W South Boulder Rd Bldg G, Louisville,
CO 80027
Web Site: http://www.gaiam.com
Audio Tapes & Compact Discs Mfr & Distr
N.A.I.C.S.: 512250

Subsidiary (Non-US):

Gaiam PTY **(2)**
431 Warringah Road Frenchs Forest, Sydney, 2086, NSW, Australia
Tel.: (61) 1300301200
Web Site: http://gaiam.innovations.com.au
Emp.: 10
Catalog Shopping Services
N.A.I.C.S.: 459110

Galaxy Brands LLC **(1)**
1407 Broadway, New York, NY 10018
Tel.: (212) 425-2999
Brand Name Licensing Services
N.A.I.C.S.: 533110

Heelys, Inc. **(1)**
3200 Belmeade Dr Ste 100, Carrollton, TX
75006
Tel.: (214) 390-1831
Web Site: http://www.heelys.com
Sales Range: $25-49.9 Million
Emp.: 47
Holding Company; Sports Products Designer, Marketer & Distr
N.A.I.O.O.: 551112

Subsidiary (Domestic):

Heeling Holding Corporation **(2)**
3200 Belmeade Dr Ste 100, Carrollton, TX
75006
Tel.: (214) 390-1831
Holding Company
N.A.I.C.S.: 551112

Heeling Sports Limited **(2)**
3200 Belmeade Dr Ste 100, Carrollton, TX
75006
Tel.: (214) 390-1831
Web Site: http://www.heelys.com
Sales Range: $75-99.9 Million
Management Services
N.A.I.C.S.: 541611

SQBG, Inc. **(1)**
601 W 26th St 30th Fl, New York, NY
10001
Tel.: (646) 564-2577
Branded Apparel Designer Services
N.A.I.C.S.: 541490

The Franklin Mint, LLC **(1)**
486 Thomas Jones Way Ste 240, Exton, PA
19341-2897
Tel.: (610) 884-4800
Web Site: http://www.franklinmint.com
Sales Range: $150-199.9 Million
Emp.: 300
Mfr & Direct Marketing of Heirloom Quality
Collectibles
N.A.I.C.S.: 423940

SERA PROGNOSTICS, INC.
2749 E Parleys Way Ste 200, Salt
Lake City, UT 84109
Tel.: (801) 990-6605
Web Site:
https://www.seraprognostics.com
Year Founded: 2008
SERA—(NASDAQ)
Emp.: 57
Professional Equipment & Supplies
Merchant Whslr
N.A.I.C.S.: 423490
Steven W. Graves *(Founder)*
Douglas Carl Fisher *(Chief Bus Officer)*
Austin Aerts *(Interim CFO)*
Robert G. Harrison *(CIO)*
Jay Boniface *(Chief Scientific Officer)*
Paul Kearney *(Chief Data Officer)*
Benjamin G. Jackson *(Gen Counsel)*
Angie Fox *(VP-Clinical Ops)*
Doug Roach *(VP-Commercial)*
Nikki Martin *(VP-Quality & Regulatory)*
Eric Gourley *(Sr Dir-Project Mgmt)*
Evguenia Lindgardt *(Pres & Interim
CEO)*

SERES THERAPEUTICS, INC.
1 Haverhill Rd, Amesbury, MA 01913
Tel.: (617) 945-9626 DE
Web Site:
https://www.serestherapeutics.com
Year Founded: 2010
MCRB—(NASDAQ)
Rev.: $7,128,000
Assets: $348,784,000
Liabilities: $338,001,000
Net Worth: $10,783,000
Earnings: ($250,157,000)
Emp.: 431
Fiscal Year-end: 12/31/22
Pharmaceutical Preparation Manufacturing
N.A.I.C.S.: 325412
Noubar B. Afeyan *(Founder)*
Eric D. Shaff *(Pres & CEO)*
Matthew Henn *(Chief Scientific Officer & Exec VP)*
Lisa von Moltke *(Chief Medical Officer & Exec VP)*
Teresa L. Young *(Chief Comml &
Strategy Officer & Exec VP)*
David S. Ege *(CTO & Exec VP)*
Paula Cloghessy *(Chief People Officer)*
Lisa von Moltke *(Chief Medical Officer & Exec VP)*
Marella Thorell *(CFO, Principal Acctg
Officer & Exec VP)*
Thomas J. DesRosier *(Chief Legal
Officer, Sec & Exec VP)*
Thomas J. Desrosier *(Chief Legal
Officer, Sec & Exec VP)*

SERINA THERAPEUTICS, INC.
601 Genome Way Ste 2001, Huntsville, AL 35806
Tel.: (256) 327-9630
Web Site: http://www.agexinc.com
Year Founded: 2017

SER—(NYSEAMEX)
Rev.: $34,000
Assets: $3,241,000
Liabilities: $20,556,000
Net Worth: ($17,315,000)
Earnings: ($10,462,000)
Emp.: 5
Fiscal Year-end: 12/31/22
Biological Product Mfr
N.A.I.C.S.: 325414
Hal Sternberg *(VP-Res)*
Michael D. West *(Founder, Pres & CEO)*
Nafees Malik *(COO)*
Andrea E. Park *(CFO)*
Joanne Hackett *(Chm)*
Steven Ledger *(CEO)*

Subsidiaries:

Serina Therapeutics, Inc.   **(1)**
601 Genome Way Ste 3400, Huntsville, AL 35806
Tel.: (256) 327-0566
Web Site:
   http://www.serinatherapeutics.com
Research & Development in Biotechnology
N.A.I.C.S.: 541714
Tacey Viegas *(COO)*

SERITAGE GROWTH PROPERTIES

500 5th Ave Ste 1530, New York, NY 10110
Tel.: (212) 355-7800   **MD**
Web Site: https://www.seritage.com
Year Founded: 2014
SRG—(NYSE)
Rev.: $107,055,000
Assets: $1,841,721,000
Liabilities: $1,119,122,000
Net Worth: $722,599,000
Earnings: ($73,945,000)
Emp.: 32
Fiscal Year-end: 12/31/22
Real Estate Investment Trust
N.A.I.C.S.: 525990
Matthew E. Fernand *(Chief Legal Officer)*
John Garilli *(Interim CFO)*
Nino Cammalleri *(Sr VP)*
Eric Dinenberg *(COO)*
Andrea L. Olshan *(Pres & CEO)*

SERVICE CORPORATION INTERNATIONAL

1929 Allen Pkwy, Houston, TX 77019
Tel.: (713) 522-5141   **TX**
Web Site: https://www.sci-corp.com
Year Founded: 1962
SCI—(NYSE)
Rev.: $4,099,778,000
Assets: $16,355,400,000
Liabilities: $14,813,927,000
Net Worth: $1,541,473,000
Earnings: $537,317,000
Emp.: 17,612
Fiscal Year-end: 12/31/23
Holding Company; Funeral Homes & Cemeteries Operator
N.A.I.C.S.: 551112
Eric D. Tanzberger *(CFO & Sr VP)*
Elisabeth G. Nash *(Sr VP-Ops Svcs)*
Tammy R. Moore *(VP & Controller)*
John H. Faulk *(Sr VP-Revenue & Bus Dev)*
Gerry D. Heard *(VP-Sls)*
Steven A. Tidwell *(Sr VP-Sls & Mktg)*
Aaron G. Foley *(Treas & VP)*
Sarah E. Adams *(VP-Tax)*
Jamie Pierce *(CMO & VP)*
Lori Spilde *(Gen Counsel, Sec & Sr VP)*
Thomas Luke Ryan *(Chm, Pres & CEO)*
Sumner James Waring III *(COO & Sr VP)*
John Del Mixon II *(VP-IT)*

Subsidiaries:

A.B. Coleman Mortuary, Inc.   **(1)**
5660 Moncrief Rd, Jacksonville, FL 32209
Tel.: (904) 768-0507
Web Site:
   https://www.abcolemanmortuary.net
Funeral & Cremation Services
N.A.I.C.S.: 812210

Burgee-Henss-Seitz Funeral Home, Inc.   **(1)**
3631 Falls Rd, Baltimore, MD 21211
Tel.: (410) 889-3735
Web Site: http://www.dignitymemorial.com
Funeral & Cremation Services
N.A.I.C.S.: 812210
Michael B. Carpenter *(Mgr)*

Camellia Memorial Lawn, Inc.   **(1)**
10221 Jackson Rd, Sacramento, CA 95827
Tel.: (916) 363-9431
Funeral Homes & Funeral Services
N.A.I.C.S.: 812210

Carl Barnes Funeral Home, Inc.   **(1)**
746 W 22nd St, Houston, TX 77008
Tel.: (713) 869-4529
Web Site: http://www.dignitymemorial.com
Funeral & Cremation Services
N.A.I.C.S.: 812210

CemCare, Inc.   **(1)**
1030 Chicago Rd, Troy, MI 48083
Tel.: (248) 589-0660
Web Site: http://www.cemcare.com
Restoration & Cleaning Services
N.A.I.C.S.: 236118

Charles S. Zeiler & Son, Inc.   **(1)**
6224 Eastern Ave, Baltimore, MD 21224
Tel.: (410) 276-3588
Web Site: http://www.dignitymemorial.com
Funeral & Cremation Services
N.A.I.C.S.: 812210

Chas. Peter Nagel, LLC   **(1)**
352 E 87th St, New York, NY 10128
Tel.: (212) 289-2221
Funeral & Cremation Services
N.A.I.C.S.: 812210

Chicago Cemetery Corporation   **(1)**
11900 S Kedzie Ave, Chicago, IL 60803
Tel.: (708) 445-5401
Funeral & Cremation Services
N.A.I.C.S.: 812210

College Park Cemetery, Inc.   **(1)**
3600 Adams St, College Park, GA 30337
Tel.: (404) 761-5400
Web Site:
   http://www.collegeparkcemetery.com
Emp.: 9
Funeral & Cremation Services
N.A.I.C.S.: 812210

Cremation Society of Windsor & Essex County, Inc.   **(1)**
3260 Dougall Ave, Windsor, N9E 1S6, ON, Canada
Tel.: (519) 969-5449
Web Site: https://www.cremationsociety.ca
Cremation Services
N.A.I.C.S.: 812220

Crest Lawn Memorial Park, Inc.   **(1)**
2000 Marietta Blvd NW, Atlanta, GA 30318
Tel.: (404) 355-3380
Web Site:
   http://www.crestlawnmemorialpark.com
Sales Range: $10-24.9 Million
Emp.: 6
Funeral & Cremation Services
N.A.I.C.S.: 812210
Matthew Whaley *(Pres)*

Dale-Riggs Funeral Home, Inc.   **(1)**
572 Nebraska Ave, Toledo, OH 43604   **(90%)**
Tel.: (419) 248-4254
Web Site: https://www.dalefh.com
Funeral & Cremation Services
N.A.I.C.S.: 812210
Sheryl Anderson Riggs *(Mng Dir)*
Deborah Sandridge-Hall *(Office Mgr)*
Douglas Dunklin *(Plant Mgr-Physical)*
Kandice Saulsberry *(Mng Dir)*

Danzansky-Goldberg Memorial Chapels, Inc.   **(1)**

1091 Rockville Pike, Rockville, MD 20852
Tel.: (301) 340-1400
Web Site: http://www.sagelbloomfield.com
Funeral & Cremation Services
N.A.I.C.S.: 812210

East Lawn Palms Mortuary & Cemetery   **(1)**
5801 E Grant Rd, Tucson, AZ 85712
Tel.: (520) 885-6741
Web Site: http://www.dignitymemorial.com
Emp.: 25
Funeral & Cremation Services
N.A.I.C.S.: 812210
Michelle S. Green *(Mgr)*

Edward Sagel Funeral Direction, Inc.   **(1)**
1091 Rockville Pike, Rockville, MD 20852
Tel.: (301) 340-1400
Web Site: https://www.sagelbloomfield.com
Funeral & Cremation Services
N.A.I.C.S.: 812210
Edward Sagel *(Co-Owner, Mng Partner & Dir-Funeral)*
Max Bloomfield *(Mgr-Media Content)*
Scott Massingill *(Gen Mgr)*
Debbie Sagel *(Dir-Social Media)*
Larry Shor *(Dir-Monument Sls & Svc Div)*
Ron Rivenburgh *(Dir-Licensed Funeral-USN)*
Tisha Reid *(Dir-Licensed Funeral)*
Steve Fantl *(Dir)*
Angela Eiss *(Dir-Licensed Funeral)*
Kurt Blake *(Dir-Licensed Funeral)*
Lisa Vandewalle *(Dir)*
Andrew Linthicum *(Dir-Advanced Plng)*
Albert Bloomfield *(Co-Owner, Mng Partner & Dir-Funeral)*
Shane Seglin *(Coord)*
Edwin Vega *(Coord-Funeral Care)*
Joseph Bloomfield *(Coord-Funeral Care)*
Sammy Sagel *(Coord-Funeral Care)*
Sydnie Rivenburgh *(Coord-Funeral Care)*
Dorothy Bramble *(Controller)*
Linda Fox Lehman *(Controller)*
Max Carazo *(Coord)*

Families First Funeral Home & Tribute Centre, Inc.   **(1)**
3260 Dougall Ave, Windsor, N9E 1S6, ON, Canada
Tel.: (519) 969-5841
Web Site: https://www.familiesfirst.ca
Cremation Services
N.A.I.C.S.: 812220
Tara Breckles *(Mng Dir)*
Jennifer Wells *(Gen Mgr)*
Kate Laub *(Dir-Funeral)*
Mary-Lynn Parent *(Founder)*

Franklin-Strickland Funeral Home, Inc.   **(1)**
1724 Mccallie Ave, Chattanooga, TN 37404
Tel.: (423) 267-8361
Funeral & Cremation Services
N.A.I.C.S.: 812210

Gary L. Kaufman Funeral Home at Meadowridge Memorial Park, Inc.   **(1)**
7250 Washington Blvd, Elkridge, MD 21075
Tel.: (410) 796-8024
Web Site: http://www.dignitymemorial.com
Funeral & Cremation Services
N.A.I.C.S.: 812210

George Washington Cemetery Company, LLC   **(1)**
9500 Riggs Rd, Adelphi, MD 20783
Tel.: (301) 434-4640
Web Site: http://www.dignitymemorial.com
Funeral & Cremation Services
N.A.I.C.S.: 812210

Graceland Cemetery Development Co.   **(1)**
4814 White Horse Rd, Greenville, SC 29611
Tel.: (864) 269-1556
Funeral & Cremation Services
N.A.I.C.S.: 812210

Gracelawn Memorial Park, Inc   **(1)**
2220 N Dupont Hwy, New Castle, DE 19720
Tel.: (302) 654-6158
Web Site: http://www.dignitymemorial.com
Funeral Homes & Funeral Services

N.A.I.C.S.: 812210

H. P. Brandt Funeral Home, Inc.   **(1)**
1032 Perry Hwy, Pittsburgh, PA 15237
Tel.: (412) 364-4444
Web Site: http://www.dignitymemorial.com
Sales Range: $10-24.9 Million
Funeral Home Services
N.A.I.C.S.: 812210

Hamilton Funeral Chapel, Inc.   **(1)**
726 S Tarboro, Wilson, NC 27893
Tel.: (252) 291-0234
Web Site:
   http://www.hamiltonfuneralchapel.com
Sales Range: $10-24.9 Million
Emp.: 40
Funeral & Cremation Services
N.A.I.C.S.: 812210

Hawaiian Memorial Life Plan, Ltd.   **(1)**
1330 Maunakea St, Honolulu, HI 96817-4134
Tel.: (808) 522-9309
Funeral & Cremation Services
N.A.I.C.S.: 812210

Heaven's Pets at Lakelawn Metairie, LLC   **(1)**
5100 Pontchartrain Blvd Ave W, New Orleans, LA 70124
Tel.: (504) 482-7387
Web Site: https://www.heavenspets.com
Pet Death Care & Memorialization Services
N.A.I.C.S.: 812210
Jennifer Melius *(Founder)*
Patrick McCausland *(Pres)*
Deya Rairan *(Dir-Ops)*

Holmes Funeral Directors, Inc.   **(1)**
601 Claude E Holmes Sr Ave, Haines City, FL 33844
Tel.: (863) 419-2700
Web Site: https://www.holmesfd.com
Emp.: 14
Funeral Home Services
N.A.I.C.S.: 812210

I. J. Morris, LLC   **(1)**
21 E Deer Park Rd, Dix Hills, NY 11746
Tel.: (631) 499-6060
Web Site: http://www.dignitymemorial.com
Funeral & Cremation Services
N.A.I.C.S.: 812210
Matthew Gerald Fetter *(Dir-Funeral)*
Eric Michael Rubin *(Dir-Funeral)*
John Zuilkowski *(Dir-Funeral)*
David M. Rubin *(Gen Mgr)*

Kennedy Memorial Gardens, Inc.   **(1)**
2500 River Rd, Ellenwood, GA 30294
Tel.: (404) 243-8900
Web Site:
   http://www.kennedymemorialgardens.com
Emp.: 15
Funeral & Cremation Services
N.A.I.C.S.: 812210

Ker-Westerlund Funeral Home, Inc.   **(1)**
57 High St, Brattleboro, VT 05301
Tel.: (802) 254-5655
Web Site: http://phaneuf.net
Funeral & Cremation Services
N.A.I.C.S.: 812210

Lake View Memorial Gardens, Inc.   **(1)**
5000 N Illinois St, Fairview Heights, IL 62208
Tel.: (618) 233-7200
Web Site: http://www.dignitymemorial.com
Funeral & Cremation Services
N.A.I.C.S.: 812210
Holly L. Walker *(Mgr)*
Ryan D. Zinke *(Gen Mgr)*
Timothy Shawn Gibbons *(Dir)*
Melissa Nicole Pezza *(Dir)*

Lemmon Funeral Home of Dulaney Valley, Inc.   **(1)**
10 W Padonia Rd, Timonium, MD 21093
Tel.: (410) 252-6000
Web Site: http://www.dignitymemorial.com
Funeral & Cremation Services
N.A.I.C.S.: 812210
Bryan W. Clary *(Dir-Funeral)*
Michael J. Flagle *(Dir-Funeral)*

Service Corporation International—(Continued)

Lincoln Funeral Home, Inc. (1)
8100 Fireside Dr, Dallas, TX 75217
Tel.: (214) 398-8133
Funeral & Cremation Services
N.A.I.C.S.: 812210
Ron Kelly (Dir-In-Charge-Funeral & Gen Mgr-Funeral Home Ops)

Lincoln Memorial Park (1)
1311 Murdock Rd, Dallas, TX 75217
Tel.: (214) 398-8133
Funeral & Cremation Services
N.A.I.C.S.: 812210

M. J. Edwards Funeral Home, Inc. (1)
1165 Airways Blvd, Memphis, TN 38114-2249
Tel.: (901) 327-9360
Web Site: http://www.mjedwards.com
Sales Range: $10-24.9 Million
Emp.: 25
Funeral & Cremation Services
N.A.I.C.S.: 812210

Mainland Funeral Home, Inc. (1)
2711 Texas Ave, La Marque, TX 77568
Tel.: (409) 938-8123
Web Site: http://www.dignitymemorial.com
Funeral & Cremation Services
N.A.I.C.S.: 812210

Making Everlasting Memories, L.L.C. (1)
11475 Northlake Dr, Cincinnati, OH 45249
Web Site: https://www.mem.com
Online Publishing Services
N.A.I.C.S.: 513199
Steve Sefton (Pres)

McHugh Funeral Home, Inc. (1)
283 Hanover St, Manchester, NH 03104-4920
Tel.: (603) 622-0962
Web Site: http://www.dignitymemorial.com
Funeral & Cremation Services
N.A.I.C.S.: 812210

Miller-Dippel Funeral Home, Inc. (1)
9705 Belair Rd, Nottingham, MD 21236
Tel.: (410) 426-7171
Web Site: http://www.dignitymemorial.com
Funeral & Cremation Services
N.A.I.C.S.: 812210

Morris-Bates Funeral Home, Inc. (1)
1700 Evans, Fort Worth, TX 76104
Tel.: (817) 926-6263
Web Site:
    http://www.morrisbatesfuneralhome.com
Emp.: 14
Funeral & Cremation Services
N.A.I.C.S.: 812210
G. Wilson (CEO)

Mount Vernon Memorial Park & Mortuary (1)
8201 Greenback Ln, Fair Oaks, CA 95628 **(100%)**
Tel.: (916) 969-1251
Web Site: http://www.dignitymemorial.com
Emp.: 60
Funeral & Cremation Services
N.A.I.C.S.: 812210

Mourning Glory Funeral Services Inc. (1)
1201 8th Street East, Saskatoon, S7H 0S5, SK, Canada
Tel.: (306) 978-5200
Web Site: https://www.dignitymemorial.com
Funeral Services
N.A.I.C.S.: 812210

National Cremation Service, Inc. (1)
41-45 58th St, Woodside, NY 11377
Tel.: (718) 639-0488
Funeral & Cremation Services
N.A.I.C.S.: 812210

New York Funeral Chapels, LLC (1)
448 W Main St, Babylon, NY 11702
Tel.: (631) 669-3800
Emp.: 8
Funeral & Cremation Services
N.A.I.C.S.: 812210
Charles Spencer (Gen Mgr)

Oak Woods Management Company (1)

1035 E 67th St, Chicago, IL 60637
Tel.: (773) 288-3800
Web Site:
    http://www.oakwoodssummetry.net
Emp.: 25
Funeral & Cremation Services
N.A.I.C.S.: 812210
John D. Wymer (Pres & CEO)
Dane Moore (VP-Property Mgmt)
Mary Sadowski (Controller)
Kara Thompson (Ops Mgr)
Teresa Tata (Dir-HR)
Robert Hanshaw (Dir-Resident Svcs)
Deborah Pizzurro (Reg Mgr-New Dev)
Rose Gore (Reg Mgr)
Vic Steinfels (Reg Mgr)
Helen Zahler (Reg Mgr)
Xavier Sanchez (Reg Mgr)
Christy Smith (Reg Mgr)
Joanie McLain (Reg Mgr)
Michael Tyler II (Mktg Dir)

Oaklawn Cemetery Association (1)
4801 San Jose Blvd, Jacksonville, FL 32207
Tel.: (904) 737-7171
Web Site: http://www.dignitymemorial.com
Emp.: 20
Funeral & Cremation Services
N.A.I.C.S.: 812210

Palm Mortuary Inc. (1)
1325 N Main St, Las Vegas, NV 89101
Tel.: (702) 464-8300
Web Site: http://www.palmmortuary.com
Sales Range: $25-49.9 Million
Emp.: 130
Funeral Home
N.A.I.C.S.: 812210

Paradise Funeral Home, Inc. (1)
10401 W Montgomery, Houston, TX 77088
Tel.: (281) 445-1201
Web Site: http://www.dignitymemorial.com
Funeral & Cremation Services
N.A.I.C.S.: 812210

Phoenix Memorial Park Association (1)
200 W Beardsley Rd, Phoenix, AZ 85027
Tel.: (623) 434-7000
Web Site:
    http://www.phoenixmemorialpark.com
Sales Range: $10-24.9 Million
Emp.: 25
Funeral & Cremation Services
N.A.I.C.S.: 812210
Jennifer Lynn Peers (Dir-Funeral)

Pineview Memorial Park, Inc. (1)
450 W Five Notch Rd, North Augusta, SC 29841
Tel.: (803) 279-1508
Web Site:
    http://www.pineviewmemorialpark.com
Funeral & Cremation Services
N.A.I.C.S.: 812210

Rabenhorst Life Insurance Company (1)
833 Government St, Baton Rouge, LA 70802
Tel.: (225) 372-4439
Web Site: http://www.dignitymemorial.com
Direct Life Insurance Carriers
N.A.I.C.S.: 531210

Ridgewood Cemetery Company, Inc. (1)
9900 N Milwaukee Ave, Des Plaines, IL 60016
Tel.: (847) 824-4145
Web Site: http://www.dignitymemorial.com
Funeral & Cremation Services
N.A.I.C.S.: 812210

Robert L. Hendricks Funeral Home, Inc. (1)
3218 Philadelphia Ave, Chambersburg, PA 17201
Tel.: (717) 263-9123
Funeral & Cremation Services
N.A.I.C.S.: 812210

Rohland Funeral Home (1)
508 Cumberland St, Lebanon, PA 17042
Tel.: (717) 272-6673
Web Site: http://www.dignitymemorial.com
Funeral & Cremation Services
N.A.I.C.S.: 812210

Rose Hills Company (1)
3888 Workman Mill Rd, Whittier, CA 90601
Tel.: (562) 699-0921
Web Site: http://www.rosehills.com
Sales Range: $50-74.9 Million
Funeral Services
N.A.I.C.S.: 812220

Rosedale Cemetery Company (1)
917 Cemetery Rd, Martinsburg, WV 25404
Tel.: (304) 263-4922
Funeral & Cremation Services
N.A.I.C.S.: 812210

SCI Alabama Funeral Services, LLC (1)
1800 Oxmoor Rd, Birmingham, AL 35209
Tel.: (205) 879-3401
Funeral & Cremation Services
N.A.I.C.S.: 812210
Scott McBrayer (Mgr)

SCI Colorado Funeral Services, LLC (1)
7777 W 29th Ave, Denver, CO 80033
Tel.: (303) 445-4100
Sanitation & Mortuary Services
N.A.I.C.S.: 812210
Mike Skolaut (Gen Mgr)

Subsidiary (Domestic):

Allnutt Funeral Service, Inc. (2)
702 13th St, Greeley, CO 80631
Tel.: (970) 352-3366
Web Site: http://www.allnutt.com
Funeral Support Services
N.A.I.C.S.: 812210
Rick Allnutt (Pres)
Adam Findley (Gen Mgr)
Bill Smith (Mgr)
Michael R. Puckett (Mgr)
Julieen Jannel Burnham (Mgr)
Samantha Catherine French (Dir)

SCI Direct, Inc. (1)
7800 Whipple Ave NW, North Canton, OH 44720
Tel.: (330) 494-5504
Emp.: 570
Advertising Agency Services
N.A.I.C.S.: 541810

SCI Louisiana Funeral Services, Inc. (1)
2413 Highway 378, Westlake, LA 70669
Tel.: (337) 436-5507
Web Site: http://www.dignitymemorial.com
Funeral & Cremation Services
N.A.I.C.S.: 812210

SCI Missouri Funeral Services, Inc. (1)
611 Chestnut St, Belton, MO 64012
Tel.: (816) 966-9070
Web Site: http://www.funeralhome.com
Emp.: 5
Funeral & Cremation Services
N.A.I.C.S.: 812210

SCI Ohio Funeral Services, Inc. (1)
1985 S Taylor Rd, Cleveland, OH 44118-2158
Tel.: (216) 932-7900
Funeral & Cremation Services
N.A.I.C.S.: 812210

SCI Oklahoma Funeral Services, Inc. (1)
6001 NW Grand Blvd, Oklahoma City, OK 73118
Tel.: (405) 843-5771
Emp.: 30
Funeral & Cremation Services
N.A.I.C.S.: 812210

Subsidiary (Domestic):

Sunset Memorial Park Cemetery Trust (2)
2301 E Indian Hills Rd, Norman, OK 73071
Tel.: (405) 329-2553
Sales Range: $10-24.9 Million
Emp.: 4
Cemetery Management Services
N.A.I.C.S.: 812220
John Davendort (Gen Mgr)

SCI Pennsylvania Funeral Services, Inc. (1)

214 Modern Ave, Carnegie, PA 15106
Tel.: (412) 276-9488
Funeral & Cremation Services
N.A.I.C.S.: 812210

Subsidiary (Domestic):

Cremation Society of Pennsylvania, Inc. (2)
4100 Jonestown Rd, Harrisburg, PA 17109
Tel.: (717) 910-6507
Web Site:
    http://cremationofpennsylvania.com
Funeral Care & Funeral Flower Services
N.A.I.C.S.: 812210

Saul-Gabauer Funeral Home, Inc. (2)
273 Route 68, Rochester, PA 15074
Tel.: (724) 728-2456
Web Site: http://www.dignitymemorial.com
Sales Range: $10-24.9 Million
Funeral & Cremation Services
N.A.I.C.S.: 812210

SCI South Carolina Funeral Services, Inc. (1)
7784 Augusta, Greenville, SC 29604
Tel.: (864) 277-0078
Sales Range: $10-24.9 Million
Emp.: 70
Funeral & Cremation Services
N.A.I.C.S.: 812210
Pat Eskew (Gen Mgr)

SCI Texas Funeral Services, Inc. (1)
1929 Allen Pkwy, Houston, TX 77019-2506
Tel.: (713) 522-5141
Funeral & Cremation Services
N.A.I.C.S.: 812210

Subsidiary (Domestic):

Eubank Funeral Home, Inc. (2)
27532 State Highway 64, Canton, TX 75103
Tel.: (903) 567-4111
Funeral Homes & Funeral Services
N.A.I.C.S.: 812210
Theresa Tidwell (Sec)

Van Zandt County Haven of Memories, Inc. (2)
27532 State Hwy 64, Canton, TX 75103-3482
Tel.: (903) 567-4219
Funeral Homes & Funeral Services
N.A.I.C.S.: 812210

SCI West Virginia Funeral Services, Inc. (1)
State Rte 95 W, Parkersburg, WV 26103
Tel.: (304) 863-6011
Emp.: 12
Funeral & Cremation Services
N.A.I.C.S.: 812210
Cole Waybright (Office Mgr)

SCI Wisconsin Funeral Services, Inc. (1)
11030 W Forest Home Ave, Milwaukee, WI 53130
Tel.: (414) 476-2010
Funeral & Cremation Services
N.A.I.C.S.: 812210
John Klein (Mgr-Location)

Schimunek Funeral Home, Inc. (1)
610 W MacPhail Rd, Bel Air, MD 21014
Tel.: (410) 638-5360
Web Site: http://www.dignitymemorial.com
Funeral & Cremation Services
N.A.I.C.S.: 812210
John J. Evans (Gen Mgr)

Sherwood Memorial Park & Mausoleum, Inc. (1)
6841 Tara Blvd, Jonesboro, GA 30236
Tel.: (770) 478-5001
Web Site:
    http://www.sherwoodmemorialpark
    mausoleum.com
Sales Range: $10-24.9 Million
Emp.: 10
Funeral & Cremation Services
N.A.I.C.S.: 812210

St. Laurent Funeral Home, Inc. (1)
26 Kinsley St, Nashua, NH 03060
Tel.: (603) 882-1771
Web Site: http://www.dignitymemorial.com

Funeral & Cremation Services
N.A.I.C.S.: 812210

Sterling-Ashton-Schwab Funeral Home, Inc. (1)
1630 Edmondson Ave, Catonsville, MD 21228
Tel.: (410) 744-8600
Emp.: 15
Funeral & Cremation Services
N.A.I.C.S.: 812210
Mary Hackman (Gen Mgr)

Sterling-Ashton-Schwab-Witzke Funeral Home of Catonsville, Inc. (1)
1630 Edmondson Ave, Catonsville, MD 21228
Tel.: (410) 744-8600
Web Site: http://www.dignitymemorial.com
Funeral & Cremation Services
N.A.I.C.S.: 812210
Anna Lyn Kalb Newman (Dir-Funeral)

Stewart Enterprises, Inc. (1)
1333 S Clearview Pkwy, Jefferson, LA 70121 (100%)
Tel.: (504) 729-1400
Sales Range: $500-549.9 Million
Holding Company; Funeral & Cemetery Operations
N.A.I.C.S.: 551112

Subsidiary (Domestic):

Casdorph & Curry Funeral Home, Inc. (2)
110 B St, Saint Albans, WV 25177
Tel.: (304) 727-4351
Web Site: http://www.casdorphandcurry.com
Emp.: 7
Funeral Homes & Funeral Services
N.A.I.C.S.: 812210

Cedar Hill Cemetery Company, Inc. (2)
5829 Ritchie Hwy, Baltimore, MD 21225
Tel.: (410) 789-0150
Web Site: http://www.dignitymemorial.com
Cemetery Operator
N.A.I.C.S.: 812220

Chapel of the Valley Funeral Home, Inc. (2)
2065 Upper River Rd, Grants Pass, OR 97526
Tel.: (541) 479-7581
Web Site: http://www.dignitymemorial.com
Funeral Homes & Funeral Services
N.A.I.C.S.: 812210

Crest Lawn Memorial Gardens, Inc. (2)
2150 Mt View Rd, Marriottsville, MD 21104
Tel.: (410) 442-5700
Web Site: http://www.dignitymemorial.com
Funeral Homes & Funeral Services
N.A.I.C.S.: 812210

D.W. Newcomer's Sons Funeral Homes (2)
11200 Metcalfe Avenue Shawnee Mission, Kansas City, MO 66210
Tel.: (816) 931-7777
Web Site: http://www.dwnewcomers.com
Sales Range: $25-49.9 Million
Emp.: 25
Funeral Home & Cemeteries
N.A.I.C.S.: 812210

Druid Ridge Cemetery (2)
7900 Park Heights Ave, Baltimore, MD 21208
Tel.: (410) 486-5300
Web Site: http://www.dignitymemorial.com
Emp.: 13
Funeral Homes & Funeral Services
N.A.I.C.S.: 812210

Dunbar Funeral Home (2)
3926 Devine St, Columbia, SC 29205
Tel.: (803) 771-7990
Web Site: http://www.dignitymemorial.com
Funeral Homes & Funeral Services
N.A.I.C.S.: 812210

Emerald Hills Funeral Home & Memorial Park (2)
500 Kennedale Sublett Rd, Kennedale, TX 76060
Tel.: (817) 572-1681

Web Site:
https://www.emeraldhillsfuneralhome.com
Funeral Homes & Funeral Services
N.A.I.C.S.: 812210

Fort Lincoln Cemetery, Inc. (2)
3401 Bladensburg Rd, Brentwood, MD 20722
Tel.: (301) 864-5090
Web Site: http://www.dignitymemorial.com
Funeral Homes & Funeral Services
N.A.I.C.S.: 812210

Griffin-Leggett Healey & Roth Funeral Home (2)
5800 W 12th St, Little Rock, AR 72204
Tel.: (501) 661-9111
Web Site: http://www.dignitymemorial.com
Emp.: 12
Funeral Homes & Funeral Services
N.A.I.C.S.: 812210
Philip S. Copeland (Mgr)

Guardian Funeral Home (2)
5704 James Ave, Fort Worth, TX 76134
Tel.: (817) 293-8477
Web Site:
https://www.guardiancremation.com
Funeral Homes & Cremation Services
N.A.I.C.S.: 812210

Hines-Rinaldi Funeral Home, Inc. (2)
11800 New Hampshire Ave, Silver Spring, MD 20904
Tel.: (301) 622-2290
Web Site: http://www.dignitymemorial.com
Funeral Homes & Funeral Services
N.A.I.C.S.: 812210

John M. Taylor Funeral Home, Inc. (2)
147 Duke of Gloucester St, Annapolis, MD 21401
Tel.: (410) 263-4422
Web Site:
http://www.johnmtaylorfuneralhome.com
Funeral Homes & Funeral Services
N.A.I.C.S.: 812210

Klingel-Carpenter Mortuary, Inc. (2)
328 6th Ave, Huntington, WV 25701
Tel.: (304) 525-8121
Web Site: https://www.klingelcarpenter.com
Emp.: 25,000
Funeral Homes & Funeral Services
N.A.I.C.S.: 812210

Loudon Park Funeral Home, Inc. (2)
3620 Wilkens Ave, Baltimore, MD 21229 (100%)
Tel.: (410) 644-1900
Web Site:
http://www.loudonparkfuneralhome.com
Emp.: 220
Funeral Homes & Funeral Services
N.A.I.C.S.: 812210
Patrik M. Fleming (Gen Mgr)

McLaurin's Funeral Home, LLC (2)
721 E Morehead St, Reidsville, NC 27320 (100%)
Tel.: (336) 349-8286
Web Site: https://www.mclaurinfh.com
Funeral Homes & Funeral Services
N.A.I.C.S.: 812210
Gail Arunta (Sec)

National Harmony Memorial Park, Inc. (2)
7101 Sheriff Rd, Hyattsville, MD 20785 (100%)
Tel.: (301) 772-0900
Web Site: http://www.dignitymemorial.com
Funeral Homes & Cremation Services
N.A.I.C.S.: 812210

Pasadena Funeral Home, Inc. (2)
2203 Pasadena Blvd, Pasadena, TX 77502 (100%)
Tel.: (713) 473-6206
Web Site: http://www.dignitymemorial.com
Funeral Homes & Cremation Services
N.A.I.C.S.: 812210

Simple Tribute Funeral and Cremation Center (2)
1040 Rockville Pike Edmonston Shopping Ctr, Rockville, MD 20852
Tel.: (301) 545-0960
Web Site: http://www.dignitymemorial.com

Sales Range: $10-24.9 Million
Emp.: 2
Funeral Homes & Cremation Services
N.A.I.C.S.: 812210

The Parkwood Cemetery Company (2)
3310 Taylor Ave, Baltimore, MD 21234
Tel.: (410) 444-5474
Web Site:
http://www.parkwoodcemetery.com
Funeral Homes & Funeral Services
N.A.I.C.S.: 812210

Wilson Funeral Home, Inc. (2)
513 bTennessee Ave, Charleston, WV 25302
Tel.: (304) 343-5196
Web Site:
http://www.wilsonfuneralandcremation.com
Funeral Homes & Funeral Services
N.A.I.C.S.: 812210
W. Keith Garren (Mgr & Dir-Funeral)

Sunset Memorial Park Company (1)
110 Veterans Memorial Blvd, Metairie, LA 70005
Tel.: (504) 837-5880
Funeral Homes & Funeral Services
N.A.I.C.S.: 812210

Theo. C. Auman, Inc (1)
247 Penn St, Reading, PA 19601
Tel.: (610) 374-4505
Web Site: http://www.dignitymemorial.com
Funeral & Cremation Services
N.A.I.C.S.: 812210
Kyle Leroy Blankenbiller (Gen Mgr)
Rochelle P. Hess (Dir-Funeral)
Bianca Christina Rodriguez (Dir-Funeral)

Subsidiary (Domestic):

Auman's, Inc. (2)
390 W Neversink Rd, Reading, PA 19606
Tel.: (610) 370-0200
Web Site: http://www.dignitymemorial.com
Sales Range: $10-24.9 Million
Funeral & Cremation Services
N.A.I.C.S.: 812210
Kyle Leroy Blankenbiller (Gen Mgr)
Rochelle P. Hess (Dir-Funeral)
Bianca Christina Rodriguez (Dir-Funeral)

Thomas Amm GmbH (1)
Gartenstr 15, 37412, Herzberg, Germany
Tel.: (49) 552185070
Web Site: http://www.thomasamm-bestattungen.de
Funeral & Cremation Service
N.A.I.C.S.: 812210

Thomas M. Quinn & Sons, LLC (1)
41-45 58th St, Woodside, NY 11377
Tel.: (718) 721-9200
Web Site: http://www.dignitymemorial.com
Funeral & Cremation Services
N.A.I.C.S.: 812210
Michael Heredia (Gen Mgr)

Thompson Funeral Home, Inc. (1)
126 S 9th St, Lebanon, PA 17042
Tel.: (717) 272-0701
Web Site:
https://www.thompsonfuneralhomelebanon.com
Funeral Homes & Funeral Services
N.A.I.C.S.: 812210
Stephen P. Thompson (Owner)
Megan E. Mathewson (Dir-Funeral)
Teresa Brungart (Dir-Admin)

Vancouver Funeral Chapel, Inc. (1)
110 E 11th St, Vancouver, WA 98660-3226
Tel.: (360) 693-3633
Web Site: http://www.dignitymemorial.com
Sales Range: $10-24.9 Million
Funeral & Cremation Services
N.A.I.C.S.: 812210
Vera Marie Lewis (Mgr-Office)
Pamela J. De Mers (Dir-Funeral)

WFG-Cristo Rey Funeral Home, Inc. (1)
235 N Sampson, Houston, TX 77003
Tel.: (713) 237-1777
Web Site:
http://www.cristoreyfuneralhome.com
Sales Range: $10-24.9 Million
Funeral & Cremation Services
N.A.I.C.S.: 812210

WFG-Fuller Funerals, Inc. (1)
3100 Cutting Blvd, Richmond, CA 94804
Tel.: (510) 237-5473
Web Site: http://www.dignitymemorial.com
Funeral & Cremation Services
N.A.I.C.S.: 812210

WFG-Lockwood Funeral Home, Inc. (1)
9402 Lockwood Dr, Houston, TX 77016
Tel.: (713) 633-1421
Web Site: http://www.dignitymemorial.com
Funeral & Cremation Services
N.A.I.C.S.: 812210

Waco Memorial Park, Inc. (1)
6623 S Interstate Hwy 35, Waco, TX 76706
Tel.: (254) 662-1051
Funeral & Cremation Services
N.A.I.C.S.: 812210

Warford-Walker Mortuary, Inc. (1)
509 N Hughes, Amarillo, TX 79107
Tel.: (806) 374-5206
Web Site: https://www.warfordmortuary.com
Emp.: 1
Funeral & Cremation Services
N.A.I.C.S.: 812210
Freda Powell (Office Mgr)
Norris Jackson (Dir-Funeral)
Elizabeth Overstreet Hampton (VP-Ops & Community Rels)
Charles Emmett Warford (Founder)

Weerts Funeral Home, Inc. (1)
3625 Jersey Ridge Rd, Davenport, IA 52807
Tel.: (563) 355-4433
Web Site: http://www.dignitymemorial.com
Funeral Home & Funeral Services
N.A.I.C.S.: 812210

Westminster Gardens, Inc. (1)
3601 Whitehurst Rd, Greensboro, NC 27410
Tel.: (336) 288-7329
Web Site: http://www.dignitymemorial.com
Sales Range: $10-24.9 Million
Funeral & Cremation Services
N.A.I.C.S.: 812210

Wien & Wien, Inc. (1)
402 Park St, Hackensack, NJ 07601
Web Site: http://www.dignitymemorial.com
Funeral & Cremation Services
N.A.I.C.S.: 812210
Charles Costello (Gen Mgr)
Frederick M. Bennis (Dir-Funeral)
David S. Torley (Dir-Funeral)

Wilson Financial Group, Inc. (1)
15915 Katy Fwy, Houston, TX 77094
Tel.: (281) 579-2760
Investment Advisory Services
N.A.I.C.S.: 523940
Earl Harrison (VP)
Gerald Wilson (CEO)

Subsidiary (Domestic):

Southern Funeral Home, Inc. (2)
202 E Lafayette St, Winnfield, LA 71483
Tel.: (318) 628-6921
Web Site:
https://www.southernfuneralhome.com
Funeral & Cremation Services
N.A.I.C.S.: 812210
Donna Spangler (Office Mgr)
Lamar Tarver (Controller)
Bryan Price (Dir-Funeral)
Clyde Albritton (Dir)
Matt Miller (Dir)
Carla Peters (Office Mgr)
Patrick Price (Dir)
Jerry Price (Dir)
Samantha Shows (Dir)
Bill Staples (Dir)
Bruce Wilson (Asst Dir)

Wilson Holdings, Inc. (1)
15915 Katy Fwy Ste 500, Houston, TX 77094
Tel.: (281) 579-2760
Emp.: 25
Holding Company
N.A.I.C.S.: 551112

Woodlawn Cemetery of Chicago, Inc. (1)
7750 W Cermak Rd, Forest Park, IL 60130

Service Corporation International—(Continued)
Tel.: (708) 442-8500
Web Site: http://www.dignitymemorial.com
Funeral & Cremation Services
N.A.I.C.S.: 812210

Zimmerman- Auer Funeral Home, Inc. (1)
4100 Jonestown Rd, Harrisburg, PA 17109-2293
Tel.: (717) 545-4001
Web Site: http://www.zimmerman-auer.com
Funeral, Obituaries & Funeral Flower Services
N.A.I.C.S.: 812210

SERVICE PROPERTIES TRUST
2 Newton Pl 255 Washington St, Newton, MA 02458-1634
Tel.: (617) 964-8389 **MD**
Web Site: https://www.svcreit.com
Year Founded: 1995
SVC—(NASDAQ)
Rev.: $1,863,011,000
Assets: $7,488,191,000
Liabilities: $6,099,399,000
Net Worth: $1,388,792,000
Earnings: ($132,381,000)
Emp.: 600
Fiscal Year-end: 12/31/22
Real Estate Investment Trust
N.A.I.C.S.: 525990
Jennifer B. Clark (Sec)
Todd W. Hargreaves (Pres & Chief Investment Officer)
Brian E. Donley (CFO & Treas)
Jesse Abair (VP)

SERVICE TEAM INC.
18482 Park Villa Pl, Villa Park, CA 92861
Tel.: (714) 538-5214 **NV**
Web Site:
http://www.serviceteam.com
Year Founded: 2011
TISI—(NYSE)
Rev.: $3,913,174
Assets: $568,638
Liabilities: $382,603
Net Worth: $186,035
Earnings: $876
Emp.: 35
Fiscal Year-end: 08/31/19
Truck Bodies & Custom Parts Mfr
N.A.I.C.S.: 336110

SERVICENOW, INC.
2225 Lawson Ln, Santa Clara, CA 95054
Tel.: (408) 501-8550 **DE**
Web Site: http://www.servicenow.com
Year Founded: 2004
NOW—(NYSE)
Rev.: $8,971,000,000
Assets: $17,387,000,000
Liabilities: $9,759,000,000
Net Worth: $7,628,000,000
Earnings: $1,731,000,000
Emp.: 22,668
Fiscal Year-end: 12/31/23
Custom Computer Programming Products & Services
N.A.I.C.S.: 541511
Kelley Steven-Waiss (Chief Transformation Officer)
Alan L. Marks (Chief Mktg & Comm Officer)
Russ Elmer (Gen Counsel)
Gina Mastantuono (CFO)
Gabrielle Toledano (Chief Talent Officer)
Dan Wallace (VP)
Jacqui Canney (Chief People Officer)
Karen Pavlin (Chief Equity & Inclusion Officer)
Paul Smith (Chief Comml Officer)
Kevin T. McBride (Chief Acctg Officer, Sr VP & Controller)

Michael Park (CMO)
Chris Bedi (Interim Chief Product Officer)
William R. McDermott (Chm & CEO)
Manish H. Shah (Chief Digital Transformation Officer)
Frederic B. Luddy (Founder)

Subsidiaries:

DotWalk, Inc. (1)
990 Highland Dr Ste 204, Solana Beach, CA 92075
Web Site: https://www.dotwalk.io
Software Development Services
N.A.I.C.S.: 541511

ITapp Inc. (1)
4633 Old Ironsides Dr Ste 280, Santa Clara, CA 95054
Tel.: (408) 759-4827
Software Development Services
N.A.I.C.S.: 541511

Lightstep, Inc. (1)
101 Green St, San Francisco, CA 94111
Tel.: (415) 630-2411
Web Site: https://lightstep.com
Software Solutions Services
N.A.I.C.S.: 541511

ServiceNow A.B. Israel Ltd (1)
Hamerton House 18-20 Aharon Barth St Bldg A, Kiryat Aryeh, Petah Tiqwa, 49514, Israel
Tel.: (972) 36252200
Software Development Services
N.A.I.C.S.: 541511

ServiceNow Australia Pty Ltd (1)
123 Eagle Street Office 08-117, Brisbane, 4000, QLD, Australia
Tel.: (61) 732218777
Emp.: 8
Software Development Services
N.A.I.C.S.: 541511
Brent Paterson (Head-Alliances & Channels-Australia & New Zealand)

ServiceNow Belgium BVBA (1)
Luchthaven Brussel Nationaal 1K, Zaventem, 1930, Brussels, Belgium
Tel.: (32) 27092000
Software Development Services
N.A.I.C.S.: 541511

ServiceNow Brasil Gerenciamento De Servicos Ltda. (1)
Av Paulista 1079 - 7 andar, Sao Paulo, 01311-200, Brazil
Tel.: (55) 1127876342
Software Development Services
N.A.I.C.S.: 541511

ServiceNow Finland Oy (1)
Ruoholahti 3 Energiakatu 4, 00180, Helsinki, Finland
Tel.: (358) 92510700
Software Development Services
N.A.I.C.S.: 541511

ServiceNow France SAS (1)
Dueo Building 5 Boulevard Gallieni 5th Floor, 92130, Issy-les-Moulineaux, France
Tel.: (33) 176431100
Software Development Services
N.A.I.C.S.: 541511

ServiceNow Hong Kong Limited (1)
Lee Garden One 33 Hysan Avenue 44/F Causeway Bay, Hong Kong, China (Hong Kong)
Tel.: (852) 37085762
Software Development Services
N.A.I.C.S.: 541511

ServiceNow Italy (1)
4 Via Filippo Turati, 20121, Milan, Italy
Tel.: (39) 0200697100
Software Development Services
N.A.I.C.S.: 541511

ServiceNow Japan KK (1)
Ark Mori 1-12-32 Akasaka, Minato-ku, Tokyo, 107-0052, Japan
Tel.: (81) 352191400
Software Development Services
N.A.I.C.S.: 541511
Emi Kasahara (Sr Engr-Security)
Apurva Chikhalikar (Chief Strategy Officer-Asia Pacific & Japan)

ServiceNow Nederland BV (1)
Hoekenrode 3, 1102 BR, Amsterdam, Netherlands
Tel.: (31) 205655500
Software Development Services
N.A.I.C.S.: 541511
Barbara Forte (Mgr-Acctg)

ServiceNow Norway AS (1)
Professor Kohts vei 9, Lysaker, 1366, Norway
Tel.: (47) 21084740
Software Development Services
N.A.I.C.S.: 541511

ServiceNow Operations Mexico (1)
Paseo de la Reforma 350 Piso 11 Suite 1109, Colonia Juarez, 06600, Mexico, DF, Mexico
Tel.: (52) 5591711474
Software Development Services
N.A.I.C.S.: 541511

ServiceNow Poland Sp. Z.O.O. (1)
Ul Szyperska 14, 61-754, Poznan, Poland
Tel.: (48) 616232164
Web Site: http://www.spoc.pl
Information Technology Consulting Services
N.A.I.C.S.: 541512

ServiceNow Pte. Ltd. (1)
Suntec Tower 4 6 Temasek Boulevard Suite 40-01, Singapore, 038986, Singapore
Tel.: (65) 68090900
Software Development Services
N.A.I.C.S.: 541511
Angeline Lim (Reg Mgr-HR)

ServiceNow South Africa (Pty) Ltd. (1)
Ground 1st Floor 22 Magwa Crescent Gateway West, Johannesburg, 2066, South Africa
Tel.: (27) 112588500
Software Development Services
N.A.I.C.S.: 541511

ServiceNow Spain S.L. (1)
La Finca First Paseo Club Deportivo 1st Floor Edificio 4, Deportivo 1, 28223, Madrid, Spain
Tel.: (34) 912979700
Software Development Services
N.A.I.C.S.: 541511

ServiceNow Sweden AB (1)
Kungsportsavenyen 21 3rd Floor, 411 36, Gothenburg, Sweden
Tel.: (46) 86552600
Software Development Services
N.A.I.C.S.: 541511

ServiceNow Switzerland GmbH (1)
Glatthrugg Cherstrasse 4 1st Floor, Glattbrugg, 8152, Zurich, Switzerland
Tel.: (41) 443603040
Software Development Services
N.A.I.C.S.: 541511

ServiceNow Turkey Bilisim Sanayive Ticaret Ltd (1)
Buyükdere Caddesi No 185 Kanyon Plaz Kat 6, Levent, 34394, Istanbul, Türkiye
Tel.: (90) 2123197625
Software Development Services
N.A.I.C.S.: 541511

Servicenow UK Ltd. (1)
3rd Floor 150 Cheapside, London, EC2V 6ET, United Kingdom
Tel.: (44) 1784 221600
Web Site: http://www.servicenow.com
Custom Computer Programming Products & Services
N.A.I.C.S.: 541511

SERVISFIRST BANCSHARES, INC.
2500 Woodcrest Pl, Birmingham, AL 35209
Tel.: (205) 949-0302 **DE**
Web Site:
https://www.servisfirstbank.com
Year Founded: 2007
SFBS—(NYSE)
Rev.: $843,663,000
Assets: $16,129,668,000
Liabilities: $14,689,263,000

Net Worth: $1,440,405,000
Earnings: $206,791,000
Emp.: 591
Fiscal Year-end: 12/31/23
Bank Holding Company
N.A.I.C.S.: 551111
Thomas Ashford Broughton III (Chm, Pres & CEO)
Rodney E. Rushing (COO & Exec VP)

Subsidiaries:

ServisFirst Bank (1)
2500 Woodcrest Pl, Birmingham, AL 35209 **(100%)**
Tel.: (205) 949-0302
Web Site: https://www.servisfirstbank.com
Sales Range: $100-124.9 Million
Commercial Banking
N.A.I.C.S.: 522110
Thomas Ashford Broughton III (Chm, Pres & CEO)
Kirk P. Pressley (CFO, Exec VP-Strategic Plng & Exec VP)
Kary Keasler (Officer-Mortgage Loan & VP)
Karen Grahn (Sr VP & Mgr-Credit Card Div)
J. David Jordan (Chief Correspondent Ops Officer)
Daniel Fontaine (VP & Dir-Merchant Svcs)
Brian Atkins (VP & Dir-Merchant Svcs)
William Mellown (Asst VP-Correspondent Svcs)
Clare Vansant (Asst VP-Agent Card Programs)
Andy Kattos (CEO-Huntsville)

SERVOTRONICS, INC.
1110 Maple Rd, Elma, NY 14059
Tel.: (716) 655-5990 **DE**
Web Site:
https://www.servotronics.com
Year Founded: 1959
SVT—(NYSEAMEX)
Rev.: $43,821,000
Assets: $45,294,000
Liabilities: $10,182,000
Net Worth: $35,112,000
Earnings: ($2,117,000)
Emp.: 303
Fiscal Year-end: 12/31/22
Mfr & Marketer of Precision Control Components
N.A.I.C.S.: 333995
Robert A. Fraass (CFO)
William F. Farroll Jr. (CEO)

SES AI CORPORATION
35 Cabot Rd, Woburn, MA 01801
Tel.: (339) 298-8750 **MA**
Web Site: https://ses.ai
Year Founded: 2020
SES—(NYSE)
Rev.: $29,835,000
Assets: $440,439,000
Liabilities: $48,900,000
Net Worth: $391,539,000
Earnings: ($50,993,000)
Emp.: 200
Fiscal Year-end: 12/31/22
Renewable Energy Semiconductor Mtr
N.A.I.C.S.: 335910
Jing Liu Nealis (CFO)
Kyle Pilkington (Chief Legal Officer)
Hong Gan (Chief Science Officer)
Daniel Li (Chief Mfg Officer)
Winston Wang (Sr VP-Hardware Engrg)
Qichao Hu (Founder, Chm & CEO)

SETO HOLDINGS, INC.
2245 Texas Dr Ste 300, Sugar Land, TX 77479
Tel.: (281) 566-2500 **NV**
Year Founded: 1985

SETO—(OTCIQ)
Health Care Srvices
N.A.I.C.S.: 621999
Carey W. Cooley (CEO, Treas & Sec)

SEVEN ARTS ENTERTAIN-MENT INC.

3440 Oakcliff Rd Ste 104, Atlanta, GA 30340
Tel.: (770) 866-6250   WY
Web Site:
   https://www.sevenartsentertainment.com
Year Founded: 2014
SAPX—(OTCIQ)
Sales Range: $1-9.9 Million
Emp.: 8
Motion Picture & Recorded Music Production & Distribution
N.A.I.C.S.: 512110
Jason Black (CEO)

SEVEN ISLANDS, INC.

363 Lafayette St, New York, NY 10012
Tel.: (212) 433-4765   Ky
Year Founded: 2021
SVNIU—(NASDAQ)
Investment Services
N.A.I.C.S.: 523999
James Murdoch (Co-Chm)
Uday Shankar (Co-Chm)
Jeffrey Palker (Gen Counsel)
Nitin Kukreja (Pres)
Eleni Lionaki (CFO)

SEVIER COUNTY BANCSHARES, INC.

111 E Main St, Sevierville, TN 37862
Tel.: (865) 453-6101   TN
Web Site: http://www.bankscb.com
Year Founded: 1983
SVRH—(OTCIQ)
Bank Holding Company
N.A.I.C.S.: 551111
John M. Presley (Chm)
Bobby R. Stoffle (Pres & CEO)

Subsidiaries:

Sevier County Bank   (1)
111 E Main St, Sevierville, TN 37862
Tel.: (865) 453-6101
Web Site: http://www.bankscb.com
Commericial Banking
N.A.I.C.S.: 522110
John M. Presley (Chm)
Allen Bell (Sr VP & Dir-Ops & Retail Banking)
Cindy Latham (Sec & Asst VP)
Ashley A. McGhee (VP-Audit & Compliance)
Randy Roberson (Dir-Lending)
Bobby R. Stoffle (Pres & CEO)

SEYCHELLE ENVIRONMENTAL TECHNOLOGIES, INC.

22 Journey, Aliso Viejo, CA 92656
Tel.: (949) 234-1999   NV
Web Site: https://www.seychelle.com
Year Founded: 1998
SYEV—(OTCEM)
Rev.: $3,086,408
Assets: $4,180,750
Liabilities: $858,295
Net Worth: $3,322,455
Earnings: ($118,999)
Emp.: 9
Fiscal Year-end: 02/29/20
Water Filtration Systems Mfr
N.A.I.C.S.: 221310
Lena Smith (Sec)
Cari Beck (Pres, CEO, CFO & Mgr-HR)

SEZZLE INC.

700 Nicollet Mall Ste 640, Minneapolis, MN 55402
Tel.: (651) 504-5294   DE
Web Site: https://sezzle.com
Year Founded: 2016
SEZL—(NASDAQ)
Rev.: $159,356,772
Assets: $212,645,283
Liabilities: $190,550,959
Net Worth: $22,094,324
Earnings: $7,098,022
Fiscal Year-end: 12/31/23
Payment Management Services
N.A.I.C.S.: 522320
Amin Sabzivand (COO)
Josh Bohde (CTO)
Karen Hartje (CFO)
Paul Paradis (Co-Founder & Pres)

SFB BANCORP INC.

632 E Elk Ave, Elizabethton, TN 37643
Tel.: (423) 543-1000   TN
SFBK—(OTCIQ)
Banking Holding Company
N.A.I.C.S.: 551111
Peter W. Hampton (Pres)

SFSB, INC.

1614 Churchville Rd, Bel Air, MD 21015
Tel.: (443) 265-5570
SFBI—(OTCIQ)
Bank Holding Company
N.A.I.C.S.: 551111
Philip A. Logan (Pres)
Sophie A. Wittelsberger (CEO)

SHAKE SHACK INC.

225 Varick St Ste 301, New York, NY 10014
Tel.: (646) 747-7200   DE
Web Site:
   https://www.shakeshack.com
Year Founded: 2001
SHAK—(NYSE)
Rev.: $739,893,000
Assets: $1,457,570,000
Liabilities: $1,021,970,000
Net Worth: $435,600,000
Earnings: ($8,655,000)
Emp.: 9,695
Fiscal Year-end: 12/29/21
Fast Food Restaurant Operator
N.A.I.C.S.: 722513
Jeffrey Amoscato (Sr VP-Supply Chain & Menu Innovation)
Michael Kark (Chief Global Licensing Officer)
Andrew McCaughan (Chief Dev Officer)
Jay Livingston (CMO)
Dave Harris (CIO)
Katherine Fogertey (CFO)
Ronald Palmese Jr. (Chief Legal Officer)
Stephanie Sentell (Chief Operations Officer)
Robert M. Lynch (CEO)

Subsidiaries:

Shake Shack Enterprises, LLC   (1)
225 Varick St Ste 301, New York, NY 10014
Tel.: (646) 747-7189
Emp.: 196
Restaurant Operators
N.A.I.C.S.: 722511

SHAPEWAYS HOLDINGS, INC.

Tel.: (734) 422-6060   DE
Web Site:
   https://www.galileospac.com
SHPW—(NYSE)
Rev.: $33,157,000
Assets: $79,528,000
Liabilities: $11,737,000
Net Worth: $67,791,000
Earnings: ($20,221,000)
Emp.: 191

Fiscal Year-end: 12/31/22
Printing Manufacturing Solutions
N.A.I.C.S.: 323111
Luca Giacometti (Co-Founder & Chm)
Alberto Recchi (Co-Founder, CFO & Principal Acctg Officer)
Alberto Pontonio (Co-Founder)
Greg Kress (CEO)

Subsidiaries:

Shapeways, Inc.   (1)
419 Park Ave S, New York, NY 10016
Tel.: (646) 470-3576
Emp.: 100
Printing Services
N.A.I.C.S.: 323111

SHARING SERVICES GLOBAL CORPORATION

5200 Tennyson Pkwy Ste 400, Plano, TX 75024
Tel.: (469) 304-9400   NV
Web Site: https://www.shrginc.com
Year Founded: 2015
SHRG—(OTCIQ)
Rev.: $10,878,242
Assets: $6,634,914
Liabilities: $9,407,349
Net Worth: ($2,772,435)
Earnings: ($6,711,537)
Emp.: 32
Fiscal Year-end: 03/31/24
Diversified Holdings Company; Direct Selling Industry
N.A.I.C.S.: 551112
John Thatch (Interim Chm, Pres & CEO)
Chan Heng Fai Ambrose (Chm)
Heng Fai Chan (Chm)

Subsidiaries:

Elepreneurs U.S., LLC   (1)
1700 Coit Rd Ste 100, Plano, TX 75075
Web Site: http://www.elepreneur.com
Marketing Services
N.A.I.C.S.: 541613
Keith Halls (CEO)
Cathy McCain (Exec VP)
Garrett McGrath (Pres)
Clare Holbrook (CMO)
Sylvia McGrath (Chief Experience Officer)
Carolyn Rachaner (Dir-Product Dev & Compliance)

Elevacity U.S., LLC   (1)
1700 Coit Rd Ste 100, Plano, TX 75075
Web Site: http://www.elevacity.com
Beverage & Supplement Product Distr
N.A.I.C.S.: 456191
John Ortman (Sr Dir-Fulfillment)
Bo Short (CEO)

LEH Insurance Group, LLC   (1)
5200 Tennyson Pkwy Ste 400, Plano, TX 75024
Tel.: (469) 991-6332
Web Site: https://lehinsurance.com
Insurance & Finance Services
N.A.I.C.S.: 524210

SHARKNINJA, INC.

89 A St Ste 100, Needham, MA 02494
Tel.: (617) 243-0235   Ky
Web Site: https://ir.sharkninja.com
Year Founded: 2017
SN—(NYSE)
Rev.: $3,717,366,000
Assets: $3,294,891,000
Liabilities: $1,466,602,000
Net Worth: $1,828,289,000
Earnings: $232,354,000
Emp.: 2,800
Fiscal Year-end: 12/31/22
Holding Company; Small Home Appliance Mfr & Whslr
N.A.I.C.S.: 551112
Mark A. Barrocas (CEO)
Neil Shah (Chief Comml Officer & Exec VP)

Pedro J. Lopez-Baldrich (Chief Legal Officer)
Larry Flynn (Interim CFO & Chief Acctg Officer)
C. J. Xuning Wang (Chm)

Subsidiaries:

SharkNinja Appliance LLC   (1)
13007 E 8 Mile Rd, Warren, MI 48089
Tel.: (586) 775-1110
Small Appliance Designer & Mfr
N.A.I.C.S.: 541490

SharkNinja Co., Ltd.   (1)
3-3-18 Shimbashi Tsao Hibiya 11F, Minato-ku, Tokyo, 105-0004, Japan
Tel.: (81) 120522552
Web Site: https://www.shark.co.jp
Cleaning Appliance Mfr
N.A.I.C.S.: 335210

SharkNinja Europe Limited   (1)
3150 Century Way, Leeds, LS15 8ZB, United Kingdom
Web Site: http://www.sharkclean.co.uk
Small Appliance Whslr
N.A.I.C.S.: 423620

SharkNinja Operating LLC   (1)
89 A St Ste 100, Needham, MA 02494
Tel.: (617) 243-0235
Web Site: https://www.sharkninja.com
Emp.: 2,800
Home Appliance Designer, Mfr & Whslr
N.A.I.C.S.: 335220
Mark Barrocas (CEO)
Adam Petrick (CMO)
Arvind Bhatia (VP-IR)
Neil Shah (Chief Comml Officer)
Patraic Reagan (CFO)
Pedro J. Lopez-Baldrich (Chief Legal Officer)
Ross Richardson (Chief Design Officer)
Kim Smolko (COO)
Elizabeth Norberg (Chief People Officer)
Velia Carboni (CIO)

SHARPLINK GAMING, INC.

333 Washington Ave N Ste 104, Minneapolis, MN 55401
Tel.: (612) 293-0619   DE
Web Site: https://www.sharplink.com
Year Founded: 2022
SBET—(NASDAQ)
Online & Mobile Video Advertising Software & Services
N.A.I.C.S.: 513210

Subsidiaries:

SharpLink Gaming Ltd.   (1)
333 Washington Ave N, Ste104, Minneapolis, MN 55401
Tel.: (612) 293-0619
Web Site: https://www.sharplink.com
Rev.: $7,288,029
Assets: $65,045,491
Liabilities: $62,058,974
Net Worth: $2,986,517
Earnings: ($15,233,378)
Emp.: 62
Fiscal Year-end: 12/31/2022
Online & Mobile Video Advertising Software & Services
N.A.I.C.S.: 513210
Haim Mer (Chm)

Subsidiary (Non-US):

MTS Asia Ltd.   (2)
Room B-4 8 F Kwong Loong Tai Building 1026-1018 Tai Nan West Street, Cheung Sha Wan, Kowloon, China (Hong Kong)   (100%)
Tel.: (852) 24132802
Web Site: http://www.mtsasia.com
Sales Range: $25-49.9 Million
Emp.: 4
Operations Support Systems & Business Support Systems for Telecommunications Expense Management, Customer Care & Billing Solutions

SharpLink Gaming, Inc.—(Continued)

N.A.I.C.S.: 561499

Subsidiary (Domestic):

SportsHub Games Network Inc. (2)
323 Washington Ave N Ste 320, Minneapolis, MN 55401
Tel.: (612) 568-8698
Web Site: http://www.shgn.com
Entertainment; eSports Media Channels
N.A.I.C.S.: 513210
Rob Phythian (Pres & CEO)

Subsidiary (Domestic):

LeagueSafe, LLC (3)
3021 Harbor Ln N Ste 205, Plymouth, MN 55447
Tel.: (763) 269-3609
Web Site: https://www.leaguesafe.com
Finance Management & Payment Solutions
N.A.I.C.S.: 522320
Paul Charchian (Owner)

SHARPS TECHNOLOGY, INC.
105 Maxess Rd Ste 124, Melville, NY 11747
Tel.: (631) 574-4436 NV
Web Site:
https://www.sharpstechnology.com
Year Founded: 2017
STSS—(NASDAQ)
Assets: $11,839,656
Liabilities: $2,198,522
Net Worth: $9,641,134
Earnings: ($4,639,662)
Emp.: 58
Fiscal Year-end: 12/31/22
Surgical & Medical Instrument Manufacturing
N.A.I.C.S.: 339112
Robert M. Hayes (CEO)
Andrew R. Crescenzo (CFO)
Soren Bo Christiansen (Chm)
Ben Scheu (Sr Dir-Sls)

SHARPSPRING, INC.
5001 Celebration Pointe Ave Ste 410, Gainesville, FL 32608
Tel.: (877) 705-9362 DE
Web Site:
http://www.sharpspring.com
Year Founded: 1998
SHSP—(NASDAQ)
Rev.: $29,287,882
Assets: $56,745,746
Liabilities: $17,056,941
Net Worth: $39,688,805
Earnings: ($5,829,029)
Emp.: 250
Fiscal Year-end: 12/31/20
Internet-Based Email Delivery Services
N.A.I.C.S.: 513210
Richard Alan Carlson (Co-Founder, Pres & CEO)
Travis Whitton (Co-Founder & CTO)

SHATTUCK LABS, INC.
500 W 5th St Ste 1200, Austin, TX 78701
Tel.: (512) 900-4690 DE
Web Site:
https://www.shattucklabs.com
Year Founded: 2016
STTK—(NASDAQ)
Rev.: $652,000
Assets: $205,324,000
Liabilities: $29,167,000
Net Worth: $176,157,000
Earnings: ($101,945,000)
Emp.: 105
Fiscal Year-end: 12/31/22
Biotechnology Research & Development Services
N.A.I.C.S.: 541714
Taylor H. Schreiber (Co-Founder & CEO)

Taylor H. Schreiber (Co-Founder & CEO)
Josiah C. Hornblower (Co-Founder)
Lini Pandite (Chief Medical Officer)
Casi DeYoung (Chief Bus Officer)
Andrew R. Neill (VP-Fin & Corp Strategy)
George Fromm (VP-R&D)
Erin Ator Thomson (Gen Counsel)
Thomas Lampkin (VP-Regulatory Affairs)
Fatima Rangwala (VP-Clinical Dev)
Suresh de Silva (VP-Product Dev)
James Stout (VP-Chemistry, Mfg & Controls)
George Golumbeski (Chm)
Abhinav A. Shukla (Chief Technical Officer)
Kelli Collin (VP-Quality)
Bo Ma (VP-Biometrics)
Sanjay Khandekar (VP-Strategic Mktg)
Conor Richardson (Sr Dir-Fin & IR)

SHELBY AMERICAN INC.
6405 Ensworth St, Las Vegas, NV 89119
Tel.: (702) 942-7325 NV
Web Site: https://www.shelby.com
Year Founded: 1962
CSBI—(OTCIQ)
Automobile Mfr & Distr
N.A.I.C.S.: 336110
Joe E. Conway (Pres & Co-CEO)
M. Neil Cummings (Co-CEO)
Aaron Shelby (Co-Pres)
Tracey Smith (Exec VP-Licensing & Media Relations)
Gary Patterson (Co-Pres)
Vince Laviolette (VP-Production & Research & Development)

SHENANDOAH TELECOMMU-NICATIONS CO.
500 Shentel Way, Edinburg, VA 22824
Tel.: (540) 984-4141 VA
Web Site: https://www.shentel.com
Year Founded: 1981
SHEN—(NASDAQ)
Rev.: $267,371,000
Assets: $977,719,000
Liabilities: $339,712,000
Net Worth: $638,007,000
Earnings: ($8,379,000)
Emp.: 842
Fiscal Year-end: 12/31/22
Wired Telecommunications Carriers
N.A.I.C.S.: 517111
Christopher E. French (Chm, Pres & CEO)
Tracy Fitzsimmons (Vice Chm)
Christopher S. Kyle (VP-Industry Affairs & Regulatory)
Edward H. McKay (COO & Exec VP)
James J. Volk (CFO & Sr VP)
Heather K. Banks (Chief HR Officer & VP)
Elaine M. Cheng (CIO & VP)
Craig R. Venable (VP-Comml Sls)
Richard W. Mason Jr. (Sr VP)
Dara Leslie (Sr VP)
Derek C. Rieger (Gen Counsel)
Julie S. Wagoner (VP)
Mark C. Watkins (VP)
Raymond B. Ostroski (Sec & VP-Legal)

Subsidiaries:

Shenandoah Cable Television, LLC (1)
Shentel Center 500 Shentel Wy, Edinburg, VA 22824 (100%)
Tel.: (540) 984-5224
Web Site: http://www.shentel.com

Sales Range: $25-49.9 Million
Cable & Other Pay Television Services
N.A.I.C.S.: 516210
Christopher E. French (Chm, Pres & CEO)

Shenandoah Long Distance Co. Inc. (1)
500 Shentel Way, Edinburg, VA 22824 (100%)
Tel.: (540) 984-4141
Web Site: http://www.shentel.com
Sales Range: $1-9.9 Million
Emp.: 300
Telegraph & Other Communications
N.A.I.C.S.: 517111
Christopher E. French (Chm, Pres & CEO)

Shenandoah Mobile Co., Inc. (1)
PO Box 459, Edinburg, VA 22824 (100%)
Tel.: (540) 984-4149
Web Site: http://www.shentel.com
Sales Range: $10-24.9 Million
Radiotelephone Communication
N.A.I.C.S.: 517112
Christopher E. French (Chm, Pres & CEO)

Shenandoah Network Company Inc. (1)
124 S Main St, Edinburg, VA 22824 (100%)
Tel.: (540) 984-4149
Web Site: http://www.shentel.net
Sales Range: $50-74.9 Million
Emp.: 200
Telephone Communication, Except Radio Telephone
N.A.I.C.S.: 517121
Christopher E. French (Chm, Pres & CEO)

Shenandoah Telephone Company Inc. (1)
500 Shentel Way, Edinburg, VA 22824 (100%)
Tel.: (540) 984-5224
Web Site: http://www.shentel.com
Sales Range: $25-49.9 Million
Emp.: 400
Telephone Communication, Except Radio Telephone
N.A.I.C.S.: 517121
Christopher E. French (Chm, Pres & CEO)

Shentel Management Company (1)
106 S Main St, Edinburg, VA 22824
Tel.: (540) 984-5263
Telecommunication Management Consulting Services
N.A.I.C.S.: 541618

SHENZHEN YIDIAN DOUBLE WAY OF INNOVATION CUL-TURE MEDIA CORP.
136-20 38th Ave, Flushing, NY 11354
Tel.: (718) 395-8285 NV
Year Founded: 2008
SYDW—(OTCIQ)
Strategic, Financial & Operational Consulting Services
N.A.I.C.S.: 541611

SHF HOLDINGS, INC.
1526 Cole Blvd STE 250, Golden, CO 80401
Tel.: (303) 431-3435 DE
Web Site: https://ir.shfinancial.org
Year Founded: 2021
SHFS—(NASDAQ)
Bank Holding Company; Cannabis Industry Banking & Lending Services
N.A.I.C.S.: 551111
Sundie Seefried (CEO)

Subsidiaries:

SHF, LLC (1)
1526 Cole Blvd Ste 250, Golden, CO 80410
Tel.: (303) 431-3435
Web Site: https://shfinancial.org
Cannabis Industry Banking & Lending Services
N.A.I.C.S.: 522320

SHIFT TECHNOLOGIES, INC.
290 Division St Ste 400, San Francisco, CA 94103-4893 DE

Web Site: http://www.shift.com
Year Founded: 2018
SFTGQ—(NASDAQ)
Rev.: $670,753,000
Assets: $248,018,000
Liabilities: $307,804,000
Net Worth: ($59,786,000)
Earnings: ($172,042,000)
Emp.: 360
Fiscal Year-end: 12/31/22
Auto E-commerce Platform
N.A.I.C.S.: 441120
George Arison (Founder)
Ayman Moussa (CEO)
Keith Vertrees (Chief Product Officer & Chief Tech Officer)

Subsidiaries:

CarLotz, Inc. (1)
611 Bainbridge St Ste 100, Richmond, VA 23224
Tel.: (804) 728-3833
Web Site: http://www.carlotz.com
Rev.: $258,534,000
Assets: $290,289,000
Liabilities: $76,778,000
Net Worth: $213,511,000
Earnings: ($39,879,000)
Emp.: 492
Fiscal Year-end: 12/31/2021
Used Car & Consignment Dealer
N.A.I.C.S.: 441120
Thomas W. Stoltz (CFO)
Susan Lewis (VP-IR)
Ozan Kaya (Pres)
Eugene Kovshilovsky (CTO)

SHIFT4 PAYMENTS, INC.
3501 Corporate Pkwy, Center Valley 18034
Tel.: (888) 276-2108 DE
Web Site: https://www.shift4.com
Year Founded: 2019
FOUR—(NYSE)
Rev.: $2,564,800,000
Assets: $3,387,800,000
Liabilities: $2,519,400,000
Net Worth: $868,400,000
Earnings: $122,900,000
Emp.: 3,030
Fiscal Year-end: 12/31/23
Holding Company
N.A.I.C.S.: 551112
Jared Isaacman (Founder, Chm & CEO)
James J. Whalen (Chief Acctg Officer)

Subsidiaries:

Shift4 Payments, LLC (1)
2202 N Irving St, Allentown, PA 18109
Web Site: http://www.shift4.com
Point-of-Sale Secure Payment Processing Technologies Developer, Distr & Services
N.A.I.C.S.: 522320
Jared Isaacman (Chm & CEO)
Jared Isaacman (Founder)
Nancy Disman (CFO)
Taylor Lauber (Pres, Chief Strategy Officer & Sr VP-Strategic Projects)
Michael Husso (CIO)
Jordan Frankel (Gen Counsel)
Doug Demko (COO)
Michael Isaacman (Chief Comml Officer)
Dave Hoffman (Chief Product Officer)
Daniel Drasin (Chief Dev Officer)
Samantha Weeks (Chief Transformation Officer)
Nate Hirshberg (VP-Mktg)
Thomas McCrohan (Exec VP-Strategy & IR)
Sloan Bohlen (Mng Dir)

Subsidiary (Domestic):

IRN Payment Systems LLC (2)
800 Shames Dr, Westbury, NY 11590-1727
Tel.: (516) 333-3888
Computer Software Services

N.A.I.C.S.: 513210

POSitouch, LLC (2)
491 Kilvert St Ste 100, Warwick, RI 02886-1385
Tel.: (401) 732-5700
Web Site: http://www.positouch.com
Point-of-Sale Technologies & Software Designer, Distr & Services
N.A.I.C.S.: 423440
Bill Fuller (Co-Founder)
Ted Fuller (Co-Founder)

Shift4 Corporation (2)
1551 Hillshire Dr, Las Vegas, NV 89134
Tel.: (702) 597-2480
Web Site: http://www.shift4.com
Secure Payment Processing Technologies Developer & Services
N.A.I.C.S.: 541511

Vectron Systems AG (1)
Willy-Brandt-Weg 41, 48155, Munster, Germany
Tel.: (49) 25128560
Web Site: https://www.vectron-systems.com
Rev.: $35,184,712
Assets: $33,738,877
Liabilities: $5,760,283
Net Worth: $27,978,594
Earnings: ($2,536,457)
Emp.: 205
Fiscal Year-end: 12/31/2020
Computer System Design Services
N.A.I.C.S.: 541512
Christian Ehlers (Chm-Supervisory Bd)
Maurice Martin Oosenbrugh (Deputy Chm-Supervisory Bd)

Subsidiary (Domestic):

BonVito GmbH (2)
Willy-Brandt-Weg 41, 48155, Munster, Germany
Tel.: (49) 2512856112
Web Site: https://www.bonvito.net
Food Retailer
N.A.I.C.S.: 445298
Jens Reckendorf (Mng Dir)

Posmatic GmbH (2)
Willy-Brandt-Weg 41, 48155, Munster, Germany
Tel.: (49) 2512856155
Web Site: https://www.posmatic.de
Computer System Design Services
N.A.I.C.S.: 541512

SHIFTPIXY, INC.
4101 NW 25th St, Miami, FL 33131   WY
Web Site: https://www.shiftpixy.com
Year Founded: 2015
PIXY—(NASDAQ)
Rev.: $17,129,000
Assets: $6,500,000
Liabilities: $57,625,000
Net Worth: ($51,125,000)
Earnings: ($33,626,000)
Emp.: 31
Fiscal Year-end: 08/31/23
Mobile Application Development Services
N.A.I.C.S.: 541511
Scott W. Absher (Co-Founder, Chm, Pres & CEO)
Patrice H. Launay (CFO)
Mark A. Absher (Sec)
Douglas Beck (CTO)
J. Stephen Holmes (Co-Founder)
Timothy Papp (Gen Counsel)
Eddy Dominguez (COO)

SHIMMICK CORPORATION
530 Technology Dr Ste 300, Irvine, CA 92618
Tel.: (510) 777-5000   DE
Web Site: https://www.shimmick.com
Year Founded: 2019
SHIM—(NASDAQ)
Rev.: $664,158,000
Assets: $446,799,000
Liabilities: $395,204,000
Net Worth: $51,595,000

Earnings: $3,760,000
Emp.: 1,500
Fiscal Year-end: 12/30/22
Engineeering Services
N.A.I.C.S.: 541330

SHOALS TECHNOLOGIES GROUP, INC.
1400 Shoals Way, Portland, TN 37148
Tel.: (615) 451-1400   DE
Web Site: https://www.shoals.com
Year Founded: 1996
SHLS—(NASDAQ)
Rev.: $488,939,000
Assets: $843,993,000
Liabilities: $298,997,000
Net Worth: $544,996,000
Earnings: $39,974,000
Emp.: 1,309
Fiscal Year-end: 12/31/23
Electrical Product Mfr & Distr
N.A.I.C.S.: 335999
Dean Solon (Founder)
Jeffery Tolnar (Pres)
Brandon Moss (CEO)
Dominic Bardos (CFO)
Ben Macias (Chief Revenue Officer)
Jessica Uecker (Chief HR Officer)
John Hass (Chief Product Officer)

SHOE CARNIVAL, INC.
7500 E Columbia St, Evansville, IN 47715
Tel.: (812) 867-6471   IN
Web Site:
    https://www.shoecarnival.com
Year Founded: 1978
SCVL—(NASDAQ)
Rev.: $1,262,235,000
Assets: $989,781,000
Liabilities: $464,213,000
Net Worth: $525,568,000
Earnings: $110,068,000
Emp.: 2,500
Fiscal Year-end: 01/28/23
Footwear Retailer
N.A.I.C.S.: 458210
J. Wayne Weaver (Chm)
Marc A. Chilton (COO)
Carl N. Scibetta (Chief Mdsg Officer & Sr Exec VP)
Kent A. Zimmerman (VP-Consumer Tech & Innovation)
Patrick C. Edwards (CFO, Chief Acctg Officer, Treas, Sec & Sr VP)
Clifton E. Sifford (Vice Chm)
Mark J. Worden (Pres & CEO)

Subsidiaries:

Rogan Shoes Incorporated (1)
1750 Ohio St, Racine, WI 53405-3626
Tel.: (262) 637-3613
Web Site: http://www.roganshoes.com
Rev.: $28,700,000
Emp.: 25
Shoe Stores
N.A.I.C.S.: 458210
Pat Rogan (CEO)

SCHC, Inc. (1)
103 Foulk Rd, Wilmington, DE 19803-3742   (100%)
Tel.: (302) 421-7361
Footwear Products Whslr
N.A.I.C.S.: 424340

Subsidiary (Domestic):

SCLC, Inc. (2)
913 N Market St, Wilmington, DE 19801-3019   (100%)
Tel.: (302) 576-2899
Footwear Products Whslr
N.A.I.C.S.: 424340

Shoe Carnival Ventures, LLC (1)
7500 E Columbia St, Evansville, IN 47715   (100%)
Tel.: (812) 867-6471
Footwear Products Whslr

N.A.I.C.S.: 424340

Shoe Station Inc. (1)
720 Executive Park Dr, Mobile, AL 36606
Tel.: (251) 476-7472
Web Site: http://www.shoestation.com
Rev.: $37,000,000
Emp.: 28
Shoe Stores
N.A.I.C.S.: 458210
Terry S. Barkin (Founder)
Richard Ellison (Controller)
Charles Whiteside (VP)

SHORE BANCSHARES, INC.
18 E Dover St, Easton, MD 21601
Tel.: (410) 763-7800   MD
Web Site:
    https://www.shorebancshares.com
Year Founded: 1996
SHBI—(NASDAQ)
Rev.: $136,931,000
Assets: $3,477,276,000
Liabilities: $3,112,991,000
Net Worth: $364,285,000
Earnings: $31,177,000
Emp.: 469
Fiscal Year-end: 12/31/22
Bank Holding Company
N.A.I.C.S.: 551111
James M. Burke (Pres & CEO)
Vance W. Adkins (CFO, Treas & Exec VP)
Austin Joseph Slater Jr. (Vice Chm)
Donna J. Stevens (COO & Exec VP)

Subsidiaries:

Elliott Wilson Insurance, LLC (1)
106 N Harrison St, Easton, MD 21601-6005
Tel.: (410) 820-7797
Web Site:
    http://www.elliottwilsoninsurance.com
Sales Range: $10-24.9 Million
Emp.: 50
Commercial Banking Services
N.A.I.C.S.: 522110

Mubell Finance, LLC (1)
784 Wall St Ste 110, O'Fallon, IL 62269
Tel.: (314) 421-3637
Web Site: http://www.costfinancial.com
Sales Range: $75-99.9 Million
Insurance Premium Finance Services
N.A.I.C.S.: 524298

Severn Bancorp, Inc. (1)
200 Westgate Cir Ste 200, Annapolis, MD 21401
Tel.: (410) 260-2000
Web Site: http://www.severnbank.com
Rev.: $49,725,000
Assets: $952,553,000
Liabilities: $842,906,000
Net Worth: $109,647,000
Earnings: $6,706,000
Emp.: 187
Fiscal Year-end: 12/31/2020
Bank Holding Company
N.A.I.C.S.: 522110

Subsidiary (Domestic):

Severn Savings Bank, FSB (2)
200 Westgate Cir Ste 200, Annapolis, MD 21401
Tel.: (410) 260-2000
Web Site: http://www.severnbank.com
Sales Range: $25-49.9 Million
Emp.: 29
Banking Services
N.A.I.C.S.: 522180
Alan J. Hyatt (Chm, Pres & CEO)

Shore United Bank (1)
18 E St, Easton, MD 21601
Tel.: (410) 822-1400
Web Site: https://www.shoreunitedbank.com
Banking Services
N.A.I.C.S.: 522110
Vance W. Adkins (CFO, Treas & Exec VP)
Jeffrey E. Thompson (Vice Chm)
Clyde V. Kelly III (Chm)
Lloyd L. Beatty Jr. (Pres, Pres, CEO & CEO)
Kelly Sylvester (Officer-Loan & Branch Mgr-Milford)

Laura Newton (Officer-Loan)
Jennifer Annis (Officer-Loan)
John Augustus (Officer-Loan)
Casey Baynard (Officer-Loan)
Ross Bergey (Officer-Loan)
Diane Brandt (Officer-Loan)
Dawn Brode (Officer-Loan)
Wendy Buckler (Officer-Loan)
Eric A. Buono (Officer-Loan)
Brian Cannelongo (Officer-Loan)
Michael Cavey (Chief Lending Officer, Officer-Loan & Exec VP)
Chris Clough (Officer-Loan)
Chad Cronshaw (Officer-Loan)
Edward D. Dillon (Officer-Loan)
Vicki Ebaugh (Officer-Loan)
Gail Foltz (Officer-Loan)
Mary Foster (Officer-Loan)
Celynda Frank (Officer-Loan)
Lynn Hancock (Officer-Loan)
Chris Honeman (Officer-Loan)
Christine Hudson (Officer-Loan)
M. Neil Brownawell II (Officer-Loan & Sr VP-Bus Dev)
Lloyd L. Beatty Jr. (Pres & CEO)

The Community Financial Corporation (1)
3035 Leonardtown Rd, Waldorf, MD 20601
Tel.: (301) 645-5601
Web Site: https://www.cbtc.com
Rev.: $89,100,000
Assets: $2,410,017,000
Liabilities: $2,223,006,000
Net Worth: $187,011,000
Earnings: $28,317,000
Emp.: 196
Fiscal Year-end: 12/31/2022
Bank Holding Company
N.A.I.C.S.: 551111
John Chappelle (Chief Digital Officer)
Daryl Motley (Treas)
B. Scot Ebron (Chief Banking Officer)
Karrie Wood (Exec VP)
Ernie Williams (Exec VP)
Lacey Pierce (Chief Admin Officer)
Anthony Farland (Exec VP)
Thomas Erickson (Exec VP)
Talal Tay (Chief Risk Officer)

Holding (Domestic):

Community Bank of the Chesapeake (2)
3035 Leonardtown Rd, Waldorf, MD 20601
Tel.: (301) 645-5601
Web Site: http://www.cbtc.com
Banking Services
N.A.I.C.S.: 522110
James M. Burke (Pres & CEO)
Todd L. Capitani (CFO & Exec VP)
Christy M. Lombardi (COO & Exec VP)
Lacey Pierce (Chief Admin Officer & Exec VP)
Talal Tay (Chief Risk Officer & Exec VP)
Scot Ebron (Chief Banking Officer & Exec VP)
Austin Joseph Slater Jr. (Chm)

SHOREPOWER TECHNOLO-GIES, INC.
5291 NE Elam Young Pkwy Ste 180, Hillsboro, OR 97124-7560
Tel.: (503) 892-7345   DE
Web Site:
    https://www.shorepower.com
Year Founded: 1984
SPEV—(OTCIQ)
Rev.: $19,610
Assets: $209,379
Liabilities: $1,520,021
Net Worth: ($1,310,642)
Earnings: ($661,965)
Emp.: 1
Fiscal Year-end: 02/29/24
Electric Power Vehicle Charging Stations Designer, Mfr & Marketer
N.A.I.C.S.: 336999
Jeff Kim (Pres & CEO)

SHOULDERUP TECHNOLOGY ACQUISITION CORP.
125 Townpark Dr Ste 300, Kennesaw, GA 30144
Tel.: (970) 924-0446   DE

ShoulderUP Technology Acquisition
Corp.—(Continued)

Web Site:
https://www.shoulderupacquisi
tion.com
Year Founded: 2021
SUAC—(NYSE)
Rev.: $4,409,987
Assets: $310,398,693
Liabilities: $321,426,240
Net Worth: ($11,027,547)
Earnings: $2,428,020
Emp.: 2
Fiscal Year-end: 12/31/22
Investment Services
N.A.I.C.S.: 523999
Phyllis W. Newhouse (CEO)
Vincent Stewart (Chm)
Grace Vandecruze (CFO)
Shawn Henry (Vice Chm)

SHUTTERSTOCK, INC.
350 5th Ave 20th Fl, New York, NY
10118
Tel.: (646) 710-3417   DE
Web Site:
https://www.shutterstock.com
Year Founded: 2003
SSTK—(NYSE)
Rev.: $827,826,000
Assets: $881,184,000
Liabilities: $433,702,000
Net Worth: $447,482,000
Earnings: $76,103,000
Emp.: 1,328
Fiscal Year-end: 12/31/22
Online Royalty Free Subscription
Based Stock Photography Agency
N.A.I.C.S.: 541922
Sejal Amin (CTO)
Jarrod Yahes (CFO)
Steven Ciardiello (Chief Acctg Officer)
Rachel Mahoney (CMO)
Aimee Egan (Chief Enterprise Officer)
Jonathan Oringer (Chm)
Paul J. Hennessy (CEO)

Subsidiaries:

Envato Pty Ltd.   (1)
121 King Street, Melbourne, 3000, VIC,
Australia
Tel.: (61) 3 8376 6284
Web Site: http://www.envato.com
Website Development & Support Services
N.A.I.C.S.: 541512
Chaman Sidhu (Dir-Legal)
James Law (Dir-HR)
Ben Chan (Chief Comml Officer)

Pond5 Inc.   (1)
350 5th Ave 21st Fl, New York, NY 10118
Tel.: (646) 233-2155
Web Site: http://www.pond5.com
Software & Technology Development Ser-
vices
N.A.I.C.S.: 513210

Rex Features Ltd.   (1)
3rd Floor Counting House Hays Galleria
51-57 Tooley Street, London, SE1 2QN,
United Kingdom
Tel.: (44) 2072787294
Web Site: https://www.rexfeatures.com
Emp.: 3
Commercial Photography Services
N.A.I.C.S.: 551112

Shutterstock (UK) Ltd.   (1)
Third Floor Counting House Hays Galleria
51-57 Tooley Street, London, SE1 2QN,
United Kingdom
Tel.: (44) 2070234958
Commercial Photography Services
N.A.I.C.S.: 541922

TurboSquid, Inc.   (1)
935 Gravier St Ste 1600, New Orleans, LA
70112
Tel.: (504) 525-0990
Web Site: http://www.turbosquid.com
Rev.: $2,198,000
Emp.: 14

Custom Computer Programming Services
N.A.I.C.S.: 541511
Andrew Wisdom (VP-HR & IT)
Beau Perschall (VP-Bus Dev)
Eric Arvidson (CFO)
Michele Bousquet (VP-Mktg)
Matt Wisdom (CEO)

SHUTTLE PHARMACEUTI-
CALS HOLDINGS, INC.
401 Professional Dr Ste 260, Gaith-
ersburg, MD 20879
Tel.: (240) 403-4212   DE
Web Site: https://shuttlepharma.com
Year Founded: 2012
SHPH—(NASDAQ)
Assets: $8,653,545
Liabilities: $975,676
Net Worth: $7,677,869
Earnings: ($3,099,457)
Emp.: 7
Fiscal Year-end: 12/31/22
Holding Company
N.A.I.C.S.: 551112
Anatoly Dritschilo (CEO, Co-Founder
& Chm)
Peter Dritschilo (Pres & COO)
Mira Jung (Co-Founder & Chief Sci-
entific Officer-)
Michael P. Vander Hoek (CFO & VP-
Operations & Regulatory)
Tyvin A. Rich (Chief Medical Officer)
Milton Brown (Chief Scientific Officer)
Timothy Lorber (CTO)

SI-BONE, INC.
471 El Camino Real Ste 101, Santa
Clara, CA 95050
Tel.: (408) 207-0700   DE
Web Site: https://www.si-bone.com
Year Founded: 2008
SIBN—(NASDAQ)
Rev.: $106,409,000
Assets: $157,552,000
Liabilities: $59,250,000
Net Worth: $98,302,000
Earnings: ($61,256,000)
Emp.: 357
Fiscal Year-end: 12/31/22
Medical Device Mfr & Distr
N.A.I.C.S.: 334510
Jeffrey W. Dunn (Chm)
Laura A. Francis (CEO)
Michael A. Pisetsky (Chief Legal Offi-
cer & Sr VP-Ops & Admin)
W. Carlton Reckling (Chief Medical
Officer & VP-Medical Affairs)
Anthony J. Recupero (Pres-Comml
Ops)
Scott A. Yerby (CTO & Sr VP-Engrg)
Daniel J. Cher (Sr VP-Clinical &
Regulatory Affairs)
Nikolas F. Kerr (Sr VP-Product, Strat-
egy & Bus Dev)
Andrea Mercanti (VP-Ops-EMEA)
Joseph W. Powers (VP-Corp Mktg)
Mark A. Reiley (Founder)
Michael C. Blanchard (VP-Ops)
Troy S. Wahlenmaier (VP-Sls)
Jeffrey D. Zigler (VP-Market Access
& Reimbursement)
Anshul Maheshwari (Co-CFO)
Brian Broveleit (VP-Digital Mktg)
Robyn Capobianco (VP-Clinical Af-
fairs)
Joyce Goto (VP & Controller)
Roxanne Simon (VP-Project Mgmt)

Subsidiaries:

SI-BONE Deutschland GmbH   (1)
Steubenstrasse 46, 68163, Mannheim, Ger-
many
Tel.: (49) 62197686000
Web Site: http://www.si-bone.de
Medical Equipment Distr
N.A.I.C.S.: 423450
Si-Bone S.R.L.   (1)

Via Postcastello 6, 21013, Gallarate, Italy
Tel.: (39) 03311561179
Medical Equipment Distr
N.A.I.C.S.: 423450

Si-Bone Uk Ltd.   (1)
Unit 7b St James Business Park, Knares-
borough, HG5 8QB, North Yorkshire, United
Kingdom
Tel.: (44) 1423860025
Medical Equipment Distr
N.A.I.C.S.: 423450

SIBANNAC, INC.
9535 E Doubletree Ranch Rd Ste
120, Scottsdale, AZ 85258
Tel.: (480) 407-6445   NV
Web Site: https://snncinc.com
Year Founded: 1999
SNNC—(OTCIQ)
Sales Range: Less than $1 Million
Emp.: 1
Investment Services
N.A.I.C.S.: 523999
Kirk Kimerer (Pres-Media Div)
David Mersky (CEO)
Eric Stoll (Founder-Creative Strate-
gist)

SIDDHI ACQUISITION CORP.
The Chrysler Bldg 405 Lexington
Ave, New York, NY 10174
Tel.: (212) 818-8800   DE
Year Founded: 2020
SDHI—(NYSE)
Investment Services
N.A.I.C.S.: 523999
Brian D. Finn (Chm)
Melissa Facchina (Co-CEO)
Steven Finn (Co-CEO)
Amy Salerno (CFO)
Sam S. Potter (VP-Corp Dev)
Lauri Kien Kotcher (Vice Chm)

SIDECHANNEL, INC.
146 Main St Ste 405, Worcester, MA
01608
Tel.: (508) 925-0114   TX
Web Site: https://sidechannel.com
Year Founded: 1953
SDCH—(OTCQB)
Rev.: $7,400,000
Assets: $3,951,000
Liabilities: $1,247,000
Net Worth: $2,704,000
Earnings: ($904,000)
Emp.: 20
Fiscal Year-end: 09/30/24
Medical Billing Software Publisher
N.A.I.C.S.: 513210
Nicholas Hnatiw (CTO)
Brian Haugli (CEO)
Deborah MacConnel (Chm)
Ryan L. Polk (CFO)
Matt Klein (COO)

SIDNEY RESOURCES CORP.
Web Site:
http://www.sidneyresourcescorpo
ration.com
SDRC—(OTCIQ)
Metal Mining
N.A.I.C.S.: 212290
Gregg Lindner (Pres)
Dan Hally (COO, Treas & VP-Ops)
Sue Patti (Sec & VP-Fin)
Sean-Rae Zalewski (CEO)
Cameron Curriden (Dir)
Ryan Norman (Dir)

SIDUS SPACE, INC.
150 N Sykes Creek Pkwy Ste 200,
Merritt Island, FL 32953
Tel.: (321) 450-5633   DE
Web Site: https://sidusspace.com
Year Founded: 2012
SIDU—(NASDAQ)
Rev.: $7,293,408

Assets: $10,297,575
Liabilities: $6,422,362
Net Worth: $3,875,213
Earnings: ($12,839,968)
Emp.: 64
Fiscal Year-end: 12/31/22
Satellite Mfr
N.A.I.C.S.: 334220
Bill J. White (CFO)
Carol Craig (Founder, Chm & CEO)
Scott Silverman (COO)

SIEBERT FINANCIAL CORP.
300 Vesey St Ste 501, New York, NY
10282
Tel.: (212) 644-2400   NY
Web Site: https://www.siebert.com
Year Founded: 1996
SIEB—(NASDAQ)
Rev.: $50,102,000
Assets: $728,048,000
Liabilities: $678,128,000
Net Worth: $49,920,000
Earnings: ($2,990,000)
Emp.: 117
Fiscal Year-end: 12/31/22
Financial Services
N.A.I.C.S.: 523910
Andrew H. Reich (CFO, COO, Sec &
Exec VP)
John J. Gebbia (Chm & CEO)

Subsidiaries:

Muriel Siebert & Co., Inc.   (1)
15 Exchange Pl Ste 800, Jersey City, NJ
07302
Tel.: (201) 459-7250
Web Site: http://www.siebertnet.com
Sales Range: $10-24.9 Million
Financial Services
N.A.I.C.S.: 561499

Siebert AdvisorNXT, Inc.   (1)
120 Wall St Fl 25, New York, NY 10022
Tel.: (855) 299-1980
Web Site: http://www.advisornxt.com
Investment Advisory Services
N.A.I.C.S.: 523940

Weeden Prime Services, LLC   (1)
1500 Broadway Ste 1107, New York, NY
10036
Tel.: (646) 227-5518
Web Site: http://www.weedenprime.com
Security Brokerage Services
N.A.I.C.S.: 523150
Mike Mayerhofer (COO, Chief Compliance
Officer & Head-Ops)

SIENTRA, INC.
3333 Michelson Dr Ste 650, Irvine,
CA 92612
Tel.: (805) 562-3500   DE
Web Site: https://www.sientra.com
Year Founded: 2003
SIEN—(NASDAQ)
Rev.: $90,549,000
Assets: $165,421,000
Liabilities: $165,830,000
Net Worth: ($409,000)
Earnings: ($73,307,000)
Emp.: 304
Fiscal Year-end: 12/31/22
Surgical & Medical Instrument Mfr
N.A.I.C.S.: 339112
Deborah Bettencourt (VP-HR & Corp
Admin)
JoAnn Kuhne (VP-Regulatory Affairs,
Quality Assurance & Clinical Ops)
Caroline Van Hove (Chm)
Jeff Jones (VP-Ops)
Ronald Menezes (Pres & CEO)

Subsidiaries:

Vesta Inc.   (1)
9900 S 57th St, Franklin, WI 53132
Tel.: (414) 423-0550
Web Site: http://www.vestainc.com
Silicone Medical Devices & Accessories Mfr
N.A.I.C.S.: 326299

Vojna Andrle *(VP-Quality & Regulatory)*

SIERRA BANCORP
86 N Main St, Porterville, CA 93257
Tel.: (559) 782-4900   CA
Web Site:
    https://www.sierrabancorp.com
Year Founded: 2001
BSRR—(NASDAQ)
Rev.: $152,589,000
Assets: $3,608,590,000
Liabilities: $3,305,008,000
Net Worth: $303,582,000
Earnings: $33,659,000
Emp.: 442
Fiscal Year-end: 12/31/22
Bank Holding Company
N.A.I.C.S.: 551111
James C. Holly *(Vice Chm)*
Kevin J. McPhaill *(Pres & CEO)*
Michael W. Olague *(Chief Banking Officer & Exec VP)*
Matthew P. Hessler *(Sr VP & Dir-Mktg-Bank of the Sierra)*
Hugh F. Boyle *(Chief Credit Officer & Exec VP)*
Natalia Coen *(Chief Risk Officer & Exec VP)*
Cindy L. Dabney *(Chief Acctg Officer & Sr VP)*
Christopher G. Treece *(CFO & Exec VP)*

Subsidiaries:

Bank of the Sierra   (1)
61 N 2nd St, Porterville, CA 93257
Tel.: (559) 782-4900
Web Site: https://www.bankofthesierra.com
Sales Range: $75-99.9 Million
Commericial Banking
N.A.I.C.S.: 522110
James C. Holly *(Vice Chm)*
Kevin J. McPhaill *(Pres & CEO)*
Michael W. Olague *(Chief Banking Officer & Exec VP)*
Matthew P. Hessler *(Sr VP & Dir-Mktg)*
Hugh F. Boyle *(Chief Credit Officer & Exec VP)*
Natalia Coen *(Chief Risk Officer & Exec VP)*
C. Thomas Elford *(VP & Sr Loan Officer)*
Pamela J. Galli *(VP & Compliance Officer)*
Richard H. Schmid *(VP & Chief Appraiser)*
K. Kyle Amos *(Applications Admin Officer)*
Mark L. Anderson *(Special Assets Center Supvr)*
Grace M. Delgado *(Mgr-Opers)*
Timothy B. Dennis *(Phoenix Sys Admin Officer)*
Richard E. Tipton *(Mgr-Network Svcs)*
Mona M. Carr *(Sr VP & Dir-Process Ops)*
Cindy L. Dabney *(Chief Acctg Officer & Sr VP)*
Mark Bernal *(Sr VP & Dir-Branch Admin)*
Donna Richardson *(Sr VP & Dir-Svc Ops)*
Michell Hart *(Sr VP & Dir-Product Mgmt)*

SIERRA LAKE ACQUISITION CORP.
625 W Adams St, Chicago, IL 60661
Tel.: (331) 305-4319   DE
Year Founded: 2021
SIERU—(NASDAQ)
Investment Services
N.A.I.C.S.: 523999
Charles Alutto *(CEO)*
Robert Ryder *(CFO & Sec)*
Richard Burke *(Co-Chm)*
Kenneth L. Campbell *(Co-Chm)*
Ross Berner *(COO)*
Scott Daum *(Pres)*

SIERRA NEVADA GOLD INC.
5470 Louie Ln Ste 101, Reno, NV 89511
Tel.: (775) 507-7166   NV
Web Site: https://www.sngold.com.au
Year Founded: 2011
SNX—(ASX)

Assets: $15,888,371
Liabilities: $662,542
Net Worth: $15,225,829
Earnings: ($1,539,523)
Fiscal Year-end: 12/31/23
Gold Exploration Services
N.A.I.C.S.: 212220
Tony Panther *(Sec)*

SIFCO INDUSTRIES, INC.
970 E 64th St, Cleveland, OH 44103
Tel.: (216) 881-8600   OH
Web Site: https://www.sifco.com
Year Founded: 1913
SIF—(NYSEAMEX)
Rev.: $87,022,000
Assets: $95,993,000
Liabilities: $61,658,000
Net Worth: $34,335,000
Earnings: ($8,692,000)
Emp.: 368
Fiscal Year-end: 09/30/23
Jet Engine & Aerospace Components Production & Repair Services
N.A.I.C.S.: 336412
George Scherff *(CEO)*
Norman E. Wells Jr. *(Chm)*

Subsidiaries:

C Blade S.p.A. Manufacturing & Forging   (1)
Via Genova 1, 33085, Maniago, Italy
Tel.: (39) 042 773 5411
Web Site: https://www.cblade.it
Aircraft Engine & Engine Parts Mfr
N.A.I.C.S.: 336412
Giancarlo Sclabi *(CEO)*

General Aluminum Forgings, LLC   (1)
1140 Garden of the Gods Rd, Colorado Springs, CO 80907-3498
Tel.: (719) 598-4854
Aluminum Forging Services
N.A.I.C.S.: 332112

Quality Aluminum Forge, LLC   (1)
793 N Cypress St, Orange, CA 92867
Tel.: (714) 639-8191
Aluminum Forging Services
N.A.I.C.S.: 332112

SIFCO Applied Surface Concepts   (1)
5708 E Schaaf Rd, Independence, OH 44131-1308   (100%)
Tel.: (216) 524-0099
Web Site: http://www.sifcoasc.com
Sales Range: $50-74.9 Million
Emp.: 45
Brush Plating Mfr & Sales
N.A.I.C.S.: 332813
Tony Arana *(Sls Mgr-Southwest)*
Thomas Chapman *(Sls Mgr-Northeast)*
Tom DiCillo *(Sls Mgr-Midwest)*
Bill Kozane *(Sls Mgr-Southeast)*
Rob Wachtler *(Sls Mgr-West)*
Scott Peterson *(Sr Mgr-Trng)*
Chic Allen *(Gen Mgr)*
Kristi Baker *(Mgr-Gen Acctg)*
Sherri Beedles *(Mgr-HR)*
Chris Bzdusek *(Mgr-Ops)*
Mark Meyer *(Sls Mgr-North America)*
Danijela Milosevic-Popovich *(Mgr-R&D)*
Todd Romanski *(Mgr-Market-Intl)*
Lillian Smereczynsky *(Mgr-Quality)*

Subsidiary (Non-US):

SIFCO ASC - France   (2)
2 rue de la Noue guimante Lots 22/23 Parc d Activite de la Courtill, Saint-Thibault des Vignes, 77400, Paris, France
Tel.: (33) 160940787
Web Site: http://www.sifcoasc.fr
Electroplating & Anodizing Services
N.A.I.C.S.: 332813

SIFCO Applied Surface Concepts (UK), Limited   (2)
Aston Field Trading Estate, Bromsgrove, B60 3EX, Worcs, United Kingdom
Tel.: (44) 1527557740
Web Site: http://www.sifcoasc.co.uk

Sales Range: $100-124.9 Million
Emp.: 13
Brush Plating Systems Mfr & Sales
N.A.I.C.S.: 332813
Carl Hamilton *(Gen Mgr)*
Mark Cattle *(Dir-Sls)*
Mark Dorgan *(Mgr-Sls & Technical)*
Johnathan Hands *(Production Mgr)*
Ani Zhecheva Brain *(Coord-Reach & Quality Sys)*

SIFCO Applied Surface Concepts Sweden AB   (2)
PO Box 149, SE 795 22, Rattvik, Sweden
Tel.: (46) 24812525
Web Site: http://www.sifco.se
Sales Range: $50-74.9 Million
Brush Plating Systems Mfr & Sales
N.A.I.C.S.: 332813

SIFCO Forge Group   (1)
970 E 64th St, Cleveland, OH 44103-1694
Tel.: (216) 881-8600
Web Site: http://www.sifco.com
Sales Range: $100-124.9 Million
Mfr of Closed Impression Die Forging
N.A.I.C.S.: 332111

SIFCO Turbine Component Services   (1)
2430 N Winnetka Ave, Minneapolis, MN 55427   (100%)
Tel.: (763) 544-3511
Web Site: http://www.sifco.com
Sales Range: $25-49.9 Million
Emp.: 55
Repair & Modification of Jet Engine Components & Components for Stationary Combustion Turbine Engine
N.A.I.C.S.: 333611

T&W Forge, LLC   (1)
562 W Ely St, Alliance, OH 44601
Tel.: (330) 821-5740
Web Site: http://www.twforge.com
Aerospace & Turbine Components Mfr
N.A.I.C.S.: 336412

SIGHT SCIENCES, INC.
4040 Campbell Ave Ste 100, Menlo Park, CA 94025   DE
Web Site:
    https://www.sightsciences.com
Year Founded: 2010
SGHT—(NASDAQ)
Rev.: $71,331,000
Assets: $213,073,000
Liabilities: $52,997,000
Net Worth: $160,076,000
Earnings: ($86,242,000)
Emp.: 250
Fiscal Year-end: 12/31/22
Medical Device Mfr
N.A.I.C.S.: 334510
Reay H. Brown *(Chief Medical Officer)*
Paul Badawi *(Co-Founder & CEO)*
David Badawi *(Co-Founder & CTO)*
Alison Bauerlein *(CFO, Principal Acctg Officer & Treas)*
Sam Park *(COO)*
Jeremy Hayden *(Chief Legal Officer)*
Matthew W. Link *(Chief Comml Officer)*

SIGMABROADBAND CO.
2690 Cobb Pkwy Ste A5-284, Smyrna, GA 30080
Tel.: (706) 744-6222   GA
Web Site:
    https://www.sigmabbco.com
Year Founded: 2012
SGRB—(OTCIQ)
Assets: $15,002,000
Liabilities: $180,000
Net Worth: $14,822,000
Earnings: ($35,000)
Emp.: 12
Fiscal Year-end: 12/31/20
Voice, Data & Digital Video Services
N.A.I.C.S.: 517810

Jeffrey A. Brown *(Pres & CEO)*
Mark A. Bailey *(COO & VP)*

SIGMATA ELECTRONICS, INC.
640 Douglas Ave, Dunedin, FL 34698
Tel.: (727) 424-3277   DE
Year Founded: 2016
SMGE—(OTCIQ)
Assets: $3,000
Liabilities: $5,000
Net Worth: ($2,000)
Earnings: ($6,000)
Electronic Product Distr
N.A.I.C.S.: 449210

SIGMATRON INTERNATIONAL, INC.
2201 Landmeier Rd, Elk Grove Village, IL 60007
Tel.: (847) 956-8000   DE
Web Site:
    https://www.sigmatronintl.com
SGMA—(NASDAQ)
Rev.: $373,883,821
Assets: $223,793,975
Liabilities: $157,721,722
Net Worth: $66,072,253
Earnings: ($2,486,157)
Emp.: 2,750
Fiscal Year-end: 04/30/24
Electronic Components, Printed Circuit Board Assemblies & Box Build Electronic Products Mfr
N.A.I.C.S.: 423690
Rajesh B. Upadhyaya *(Exec VP-Ops-West Coast)*
John P. Sheehan *(Pres-EMS Ops)*
Gary R. Fairhead *(Chm & CEO)*
Dennis P. McNamara *(VP-Engrg)*
Curtis W. Campbell *(VP-Sls-West Coast Ops)*
James J. Reiman *(CFO, Treas, Sec & VP-Fin)*
Hom-Ming Chang *(VP-Ops-China)*
Keith D. Wheaton *(VP-Bus Dev-West Coast Ops)*
Michael Schillaci *(VP-Information Technology)*

Subsidiaries:

AbleMex, S.A. de C.V.   (1)
Calle Hacienda del Colorado No 21603 T-1, Parque Industrial Presidentes, 22215, Tijuana, BC, Mexico
Tel.: (52) 6646268680
Emp.: 390
Electronic Components Mfr
N.A.I.C.S.: 334419

Digital Appliance Controls de Mexico, S.A. de C.V.   (1)
Miguel de Cervantes No 151, Complejo Industrial Chihuahua, Chihuahua, Chih, Mexico
Tel.: (52) 6144420200
Emp.: 445
Electronic Components Mfr
N.A.I.C.S.: 334419

SigmaTron Electronic Technology Co., Ltd.   (1)
386 Hua Hong Road, Suzhou, 215200, Jiangsu, China
Tel.: (86) 51263408518101
Electronic Components Mfr
N.A.I.C.S.: 334419

SigmaTron US - West Coast   (1)
30000 Eigenbrodt Way, Union City, CA 94587
Tel.: (510) 477-5000
Web Site: http://www.sigmatronintl.com
Rev.: $30,000,000
Emp.: 80
Surface Burner Controls & Temperature Controls Mfr
N.A.I.C.S.: 334512
Rajesh B. Upadhyaya *(Exec Officer & Exec VP)*

Spitfire Controls (Vietnam) Co.
Ltd.   (1)
No 13 Plot 103/4 Street No 5, Amata Indus-
trial Park, Bien Hoa, Dong Nai, Vietnam
Tel.: (84) 613936801
Emp.: 291
Electronic Appliance Controls Mfr
N.A.I.C.S.: 334419
Peter Sognefest (Chm)

Standard Components de Mexico
S.A.   (1)
Carretera Presa La Amistad KM 6 5 S/N
Parque Industrial, y Camino a Santa Eula-
lia, CP 26248, Acuna, Coahuila, Mexico
Tel.: (52) 8307747216
Emp.: 785
Electronic Components Mfr
N.A.I.C.S.: 334419

Wujiang SigmaTron Electronics Co.,
Ltd.   (1)
386 Hua Hong Road, Suzhou, 215200, Ji-
angsu, China
Tel.: (86) 51263408518101
Electronic Components Mfr
N.A.I.C.S.: 334419

SIGNAL ADVANCE, INC.
2520 County Rd 81, Rosharon, TX
77583
Tel.: (713) 510-7445   TX
Web Site:
    https://www.signaladvance.com
Year Founded: 1992
SIGL—(OTCIQ)
Measuring & Controlling Devices Mfr
N.A.I.C.S.: 334519
Chris M. Hymel (Pres, Treas & Dir)
Ron A. Stubbers (VP & Dir)
Richard C. Seltzer (Sec & Dir)

SIGNAL HILL ACQUISITION
CORP.
2810 N Church St Ste 94644, Wilm-
ington, DE 19802-8172
Tel.: (646) 504-8172   DE
Year Founded: 2021
SGHL—(NASDAQ)
Rev.: $2,022,080
Assets: $104,194,119
Liabilities: $103,553,914
Net Worth: $640,205
Earnings: $863,201
Emp.: 2
Fiscal Year-end: 12/31/22
Investment Services
N.A.I.C.S.: 523999
Jonathan Bond (CEO)
Grainne Coen (Pres, CFO, Treas &
Sec)
Paul Roberts (Chm)

SIGNATURE BANK OF GEOR-
GIA
6065 Roswell Rd Ste 110, Sandy
Springs, GA 30328
Tel.: (404) 609-0674
Web Site:
    https://www.signaturebankga.com
Year Founded: 2005
SGBG—(OTCIQ)
Sales Range: $1-9.9 Million
Emp.: 24
Commericial Banking
N.A.I.C.S.: 522110
Debi Davidoff (Dir-Deposit Ops)
Freddie J. Deutsch (Pres & CEO)
Stephanie Vickers (CFO)
Angela Buckler (Dir-Sls & Mktg)
Karen Klotz (VP)
Allen Brock (Chm)
Matt Horsman (Asst VP & Portfolio
Mgr-Credit)
Blake Tibbitts (Sr VP)
Lawanna Saxon (Mng Dir-Mktg)
Amie Bowden (Mgr-Client Support)

Nicole Klein (Dir-Private Banking)
David Perlis (Mng Dir-Retail Banking
& Sr VP)
Tareasa Harrell (Mng Dir-SBA Lend-
ing & Sr VP)
Steve Reagin (Chief Lending Officer)

SIGNATURE DEVICES, INC.
36 Shadow Brook Ln, Lander, WY
82850
Tel.: (650) 654-4800   NV
Web Site:
    https://www.signaturedevices.com
SDVI—(OTCIQ)
Information Technology Services
N.A.I.C.S.: 541512
Inas Azzam (Pres & CEO)
Charles H. Townsend (Chm)
Roger Arias (Pres)

SIGNATURE EYEWEAR, INC.
498 N Oak St, Inglewood, CA 90302
Tel.: (310) 330-2700   CA
Web Site:
    http://www.signatureeyewear.com
Year Founded: 1983
SEYE—(OTCIQ)
Sales Range: $10-24.9 Million
Emp.: 105
Prescription Eyeglass Frames De-
signer, Marketer & Distr
N.A.I.C.S.: 339115
Michael Prince (CEO)

SIGNATURE LEISURE, INC.
1111 N Orlando Ave, Winter Park, FL
32789
Tel.: (407) 970-8460
SGLS—(OTCIQ)
Business Management Consulting
Services
N.A.I.C.S.: 541611
Stephen W. Carnes (Pres & CEO)

SIGNING DAY SPORTS, INC.
7272 E Indian School Rd Ste 101,
Scottsdale, AZ 85251
Tel.: (480) 220-6814   DE
Web Site:
    https://www.signingdaysports.com
Year Founded: 2019
SGN—(NYSEAMEX)
Rev.: $307,578
Assets: $4,704,611
Liabilities: $2,960,480
Net Worth: $1,744,131
Earnings: ($5,478,120)
Emp.: 14
Fiscal Year-end: 12/31/23
Sports Club Operator
N.A.I.C.S.: 711211

SIGNPATH PHARMA INC.
3477 Corporate Pkwy Ste 100, Cen-
ter Valley, PA 18034
Tel.: (215) 538-9996   DE
Web Site:
    http://www.signpathpharma.com
Year Founded: 2006
SGTH—(OTCIQ)
Sales Range: Less than $1 Million
Emp.: 2
Curcumin-Based Pharmaceuticals
Researcher, Developer & Mfr
N.A.I.C.S.: 325412
Lawrence Helson (Pres, CEO &
CFO)
Kai P. Larson (COO, Sec & VP-Corp
Dev)

SIGYN THERAPEUTICS, INC.
2468 Historic Decatur Rd Ste 140,
San Diego, CA 92106
Tel.: (619) 353-0800   DE
Web Site:
    https://www.sigyntherapeutics.com

Year Founded: 2013
SIGY—(OTCIQ)
Assets: $321,806
Liabilities: $3,734,306
Net Worth: ($3,412,500)
Earnings: ($4,145,936)
Emp.: 5
Fiscal Year-end: 12/31/23
Blood & Organ Banks
N.A.I.C.S.: 621991
James A. Joyce (Co-Founder, Chm &
CEO)
Craig P. Roberts (Co-Founder &
CTO)
Eric Lynam (Dir-Clinical Affairs)
Charlene R. Owen (Dir-Ops)
Jerry DeCiccio (CFO)

SILGAN HOLDINGS, INC.
4 Landmark Sq, Stamford, CT 06901
Tel.: (203) 975-7110   DE
Web Site:
    https://www.silganholdings.com
Year Founded: 1987
SLGN—(NYSE)
Rev.: $5,988,205,000
Assets: $7,611,236,000
Liabilities: $5,721,878,000
Net Worth: $1,889,358,000
Earnings: $325,965,000
Emp.: 14,400
Fiscal Year-end: 12/31/23
Holding Company; Metal Cans &
Plastic Bottles Mfr
N.A.I.C.S.: 332431
D. Greg Horrigan (Founder)
Robert B. Lewis (Exec VP-Admin &
Corp Dev)
Kimberly I. Ulmer (CFO, Treas & Sr
VP)
Adam J. Greenlee (Pres & CEO)
B. Frederik Prinzen (Sr VP-Corp Dev)
Frank W. Hogan III (Gen Counsel)
Alexander G. Hutter (VP)
Stacey J. McGrath (VP)
Daniel P. Murphy (VP)
Michelle D. Wilkes (VP)
Thomas J. Snyder (Pres)

Subsidiaries:

Cobra Plastics, Inc.   (1)
1244 E Highland Rd, Macedonia, OH 44056
Tel.: (330) 425-4260
Web Site: http://www.cobraplastics.com
Plastic Overcap Mfr
N.A.I.C.S.: 326199

ELSA Silgan Metal Packaging
S.A.   (1)
200 Thivon St, PO Box 80107, 18233, Ag-
ios Ioannis Rentis, Greece
Tel.: (30) 2104916611
Packaging Products Mfr
N.A.I.C.S.: 326112

Elsa - Silgan Metal Packaging
S.A.   (1)
Deer Ala Traffic Sign 23 KM Beside Military
Camp Wady Al Rayan, Amman, Jordan
Tel.: (962) 26570200
Metal Products Mfr
N.A.I.C.S.: 332999
Faisal Al Rashdan (Officer Slo)

Gateway Plastics, Inc.   (1)
5650 W County Line Rd, Mequon, WI
53092
Tel.: (262) 242-2020
Web Site: http://www.gatewayplastics.com
Sales Range: $1-9.9 Million
Emp.: 110
Plastics Products, Nec, Nsk
N.A.I.C.S.: 326199
Rick Robinson (Mgr-Plant)

Ruma Industrieverpackung Leipzig
GmbH   (1)
Merseburger Str 207, 4178, Leipzig, Ger-
many
Tel.: (49) 341446850
Web Site: http://www.silcon.com

Packaging Products Mfr
N.A.I.C.S.: 326112

Silgan Can Company   (1)
2120 NC 71 Hwy N Unit A, Maxton, NC
28364
Tel.: (910) 844-4141
Web Site: http://www.silgancontainers.com
Sales Range: $10-24.9 Million
Emp.: 18
Metal Tank Mfr
N.A.I.C.S.: 332431

Silgan Closures GmbH   (1)
Riesstrasse 16, 80992, Munich, Germany
Tel.: (49) 51179050
Web Site: https://www.silgan-closures.com
Metal Cap Mfr
N.A.I.C.S.: 332119

Silgan Closures UK Limited   (1)
3 Carriage Drive White Rose Way, Don-
caster, DN4 5NT, S Yorks, United Kingdom
Tel.: (44) 1302552400
Metal & Plastic Closure & Container Mfr
N.A.I.C.S.: 326160

Silgan Containers Manufacturing
Corporation   (1)
21600 Oxnard St Ste 600, Woodland Hills,
CA 91367   (100%)
Tel.: (818) 710-3700
Web Site: https://www.silgancontainers.com
Sales Range: $50-74.9 Million
Emp.: 100
Can Mfr
N.A.I.C.S.: 332431

Plant (Domestic):

Silgan Containers   (2)
21600 Oxnard St Ste 1600, Woodland Hills,
CA 91367
Tel.: (818) 710-3700
Web Site: https://www.silgancontainers.com
Sales Range: $50-74.9 Million
Emp.: 100
Metal Tank Mfr
N.A.I.C.S.: 332431

Silgan Containers Manufacturing
Puerto Rico LLC   (1)
Las Piedras S Industrial Park Rd 183 KM
21 2 St A, Las Piedras, PR 00771
Tel.: (787) 716-7880
Plastics Product Mfr
N.A.I.C.S.: 326199
Jorge Ramos (Controller)

Silgan Dispensing Systems & Pack-
aging do Brasil Industria de Embala-
gens Ltda.   (1)
Rod Dom Gabriel Paulino Bueno Couto S/N
KM 3 5, Distrito Industrial, Jundiai, 13212-
240, Sao Paulo, Brazil
Tel.: (55) 1121529800
Dispensing Equipment Distr
N.A.I.C.S.: 423830

Silgan Dispensing Systems (Wuxi)
Co., Ltd.   (1)
19 Xindu Road, Wuxi-Singapore Industrial
Park, Wuxi, 214028, China
Tel.: (86) 51085282008
Dispensing Pump Equipment Mfr & Distr
N.A.I.C.S.: 333914

Silgan Dispensing Systems Alkmaar
B.V.   (1)
Ivoorstraat 9, 1812 KA, Alkmaar, Nether-
lands
Tel.: (31) 725414666
Dispensing Equipment Distr
N.A.I.C.S.: 423830

Silgan Dispensing Systems Alkmaar
B.V.   (1)
Ivoorstraat 9, 1812 KA, Alkmaar, Nether-
lands
Tel.: (31) 725414666
Dispensing Equipment Distr
N.A.I.C.S.: 423830

Silgan Dispensing Systems Alkmaar
B.V.   (1)
Ivoorstraat 9, 1812 KA, Alkmaar, Nether-
lands
Tel.: (31) 725414666
Dispensing Equipment Distr
N.A.I.C.S.: 423830

Silgan Dispensing Systems Alkmaar B.V. **(1)**
Ivoorstraat 9, 1812 KA, Alkmaar, Netherlands
Tel.: (31) 725414666
Dispensing Equipment Distr
N.A.I.C.S.: 423830

Silgan Dispensing Systems Barcelona, S.L. **(1)**
25 Via Trajana, 08020, Barcelona, Spain
Tel.: (34) 933149111
Dispensing Pump Equipment Mfr & Distr
N.A.I.C.S.: 333914
Albert Deu (Mgr-IT Applications & Maintenance)

Silgan Dispensing Systems Canada Ltd. **(1)**
1 Gateway Blvd Suite 303, Brampton, L6T 0G3, ON, Canada
Tel.: (365) 230-9081
Dispensing Pump Equipment Mfr & Distr
N.A.I.C.S.: 333914

Silgan Dispensing Systems Corporation **(1)**
11901 Grandview Rd, Grandview, MO 64030
Tel.: (816) 986-6000
Web Site: https://www.silgandispensing.com
Sales Range: $400-449.9 Million
Emp.: 6,000
Sprayers & Dispensers for Liquid Dispensing Systems Mfr
N.A.I.C.S.: 326199

Silgan Dispensing Systems France S.A.S. **(1)**
10 rue de Chevreul, 92150, Suresnes, France
Tel.: (33) 139481270
Dispensing Pump Equipment Mfr & Distr
N.A.I.C.S.: 333914

Silgan Dispensing Systems Hemer GmbH **(1)**
Ernst - Stenner - Strasse 17, 58675, Hemer, Germany
Tel.: (49) 23725040
Dispensing Pump Equipment Mfr & Distr
N.A.I.C.S.: 333914

Silgan Dispensing Systems India Private Limited **(1)**
Office 314 Workafella Banjara Hills Irrum Manzil Colony Banjara Hill, Hyderabad, 500082, Telangana, India
Tel.: (91) 9920443356
Dispensing Pump Equipment Mfr & Distr
N.A.I.C.S.: 333914

Silgan Dispensing Systems Lacrost S.A.S. **(1)**
Chemin des Croux, CS 50008, Lacrost, 71700, Bourgogne, France
Tel.: (33) 385327900
Dispensing Equipment Distr
N.A.I.C.S.: 423830

Silgan Dispensing Systems Le Treport S.A.S. **(1)**
15 Bis Route Nationale, 76470, Le Treport, France
Tel.: (33) 235504953
Dispensing Equipment Distr
N.A.I.C.S.: 423830

Silgan Dispensing Systems Mexico Operadora, S.A. de C.V. **(1)**
Boulevard Insurgentes No 18895-3 Cerro Colorado, 22590, Tijuana, Mexico
Tel.: (52) 6646268305
Dispensing Pump Equipment Mfr & Distr
N.A.I.C.S.: 333914

Silgan Dispensing Systems Mexico, S.A. de C.V. **(1)**
Circuito Exportaciones 371 Parque Industrial Tres Naciones, 78395, San Luis Potosi, Mexico
Tel.: (52) 4448701100
Dispensing Pump Equipment Mfr & Distr
N.A.I.C.S.: 333914

Silgan Dispensing Systems Milano S.r.l. **(1)**
Strada Statale 35 dei Giovi 1, Zibido San Giacomo, 20080, Milan, Italy
Tel.: (39) 029041461
Dispensing Pump Equipment Mfr & Distr
N.A.I.C.S.: 333914

Silgan Dispensing Systems Netherlands B.V. **(1)**
16 Professor Asserweg, North Brabant, 5144 NC, Waalwijk, Netherlands
Tel.: (31) 416321600
Metal & Plastic Closure Distr
N.A.I.C.S.: 423840

Silgan Dispensing Systems Statersville LLC **(1)**
110 Graham Dr, Slatersville, RI 02876
Tel.: (401) 767-2400
Dispensing Pump Equipment Mfr & Distr
N.A.I.C.S.: 333914

Silgan Dispensing Systems Thomaston Corporation **(1)**
60 Electric Ave, Thomaston, CT 06787
Tel.: (860) 283-2000
Dispensing Equipment Distr
N.A.I.C.S.: 423830

Silgan Dispensing Systems Vicenza S.r.l. **(1)**
Via Monte Tomba 28a, 36060, Romano d'Ezzelino, VI, Italy
Tel.: (39) 0424839111
Dispensing Pump Equipment Mfr & Distr
N.A.I.C.S.: 333914

Silgan Equipment Company **(1)**
1301 W Dugdale Rd, Waukegan, IL 60085
Tel.: (847) 336-0552
Web Site: http://www.silganequipment.com
Emp.: 40
Closure Equipment Whslr
N.A.I.C.S.: 423440

Silgan Holdings Austria GmbH **(1)**
Landskrongasse 5/2, A-1010, Vienna, Austria
Tel.: (43) 385823410
Web Site: http://www.silganmp.com
Can Mfr
N.A.I.C.S.: 332119

Silgan Metal Packaging Enem o.o.o. **(1)**
36/6 Perova Str, 385130, Enem, Russia
Tel.: (7) 9010147660
Packaging Products Mfr
N.A.I.C.S.: 326112

Silgan Metal Packaging Germany GmbH **(1)**
Zscheilaer Strasse 45, D - 01662, Meissen, Germany
Tel.: (49) 352172010
Metal & Plastic Closure Distr
N.A.I.C.S.: 423840

Silgan Metal Packaging Leipzig GmbH **(1)**
Merserburgerstrasse 207, 04178, Leipzig, Germany
Tel.: (49) 341446850
Fabricated Metal Packaging Mfr
N.A.I.C.S.: 332999

Silgan Metal Packaging Stupino o.o.o. **(1)**
Krylova str 14, Stupino, 142802, Moscow, Russia
Tel.: (7) 4966479070
Sales Range: $25-49.9 Million
Emp.: 50
Metal Products Mfr
N.A.I.C.S.: 332431
Filippo Baldisserotto (Deputy Mgr)

Silgan Metal Packaging Tczew S.A. **(1)**
Ul Rokicka 13, PL - 83-110, Tczew, Poland
Tel.: (48) 587625903
Web Site: http://www.silganmp.com
Emp.: 150
Metal Products Mfr
N.A.I.C.S.: 332431

Silgan Plastic Closure Solutions **(1)**
185 Northgate Cir, New Castle, PA 16105
Tel.: (724) 658-3004
Web Site: http://www.silganplastics.com
Capping Equipment Mfr
N.A.I.C.S.: 326199

Silgan Plastics Corporation **(1)**
14515 N Outer 40 Ste 210, Chesterfield, MO 63017-5746 **(100%)**
Tel.: (314) 542-9223
Web Site: https://www.silganplastics.com
Sales Range: $25-49.9 Million
Emp.: 70
Plastics Bottle Mfr
N.A.I.C.S.: 326160

Silgan Tubes LLC **(1)**
1005 Courtaulds Dr, Woodstock, IL 60098-7390
Tel.: (815) 334-1200
Web Site: http://www.silganplastics.com
Sales Range: $300-349.9 Million
Emp.: 150
Plastic Tank Mfr
N.A.I.C.S.: 322220

Silgan White Cap (Shanghai) Co., Ltd. **(1)**
No 28 Bao Sheng Rd Songjiang Industrial Zone Songjiang, Shanghai, 201613, China
Tel.: (86) 2157741105134
Crown & Closure Mfr
N.A.I.C.S.: 332119

Silgan White Cap Americas LLC **(1)**
140 31st St, Downers Grove, IL 60515-1212
Tel.: (630) 515-8383
Web Site: https://www.silgan-closures.com
Sales Range: $150-199.9 Million
Emp.: 1,800
Closures & Sealing Systems for Rigid Containers
N.A.I.C.S.: 423840

Silgan White Cap Belgium N.V. **(1)**
Fabriekstraat 25, 2547, Lint, Antwerp, Belgium
Tel.: (32) 34601390
Web Site: https://www.silganwhitecap.be
Sales Range: $100-124.9 Million
Emp.: 500
Plastic Closure Mfr
N.A.I.C.S.: 332119

Silgan White Cap Corporation **(1)**
1701 Williamsburg Pike, Richmond, IN 47374
Tel.: (765) 983-9200
Packaging Metal Product Mfr
N.A.I.C.S.: 332439

Silgan White Cap Deutschland GmbH **(1)**
Tel.: (49) 51179050
Web Site: http://www.silganwhitecap.com
Sales Range: $100-124.9 Million
Emp.: 200
Bottle Closure Device Mfr
N.A.I.C.S.: 332119

Subsidiary (Non-US):

Silgan White Cap France S.A.S. **(2)**
Tel.: (33) 562576282
Web Site: http://plastics.silgan-closures.com
Rigid Containers Closures & Sealing Systems Mfr
N.A.I.C.S.: 332119

Silgan White Cap Holdings Spain, S.L. **(2)**
Tel.: (34) 93 859 6410
Web Site: http://www.silgan-closures.com
Container Closures & Sealing Systems Mfr
N.A.I.C.S.: 332119

Silgan White Cap Italia S.r.l. **(2)**
Tel.: (39) 0828397111
Sales Range: $100-124.9 Million
Closures & Sealing Systems for Rigid Containers
N.A.I.C.S.: 332119

Silgan White Cap Nederland N.V. **(2)**
Tel.: (31) 313478501
Web Site: http://www.silganclosures.com
Sales Range: $25-49.9 Million
Emp.: 7
Closures & Sealing Systems for Rigid Containers
N.A.I.C.S.: 332119

Silgan White Cap Polska Sp. z o.o. **(2)**
Grabska 9, 32-005, Niepolomice, Poland
Tel.: (48) 122798115
Sales Range: $100-124.9 Million
Emp.: 300
Closures & Sealing Systems for Rigid Containers
N.A.I.C.S.: 332119

Silgan White Cap UK Ltd. **(2)**
Tel.: (44) 1753832828
Web Site: http://www.silganwhitecap.com
Sales Range: $25-49.9 Million
Emp.: 5
Closures & Sealing Systems for Rigid Containers
N.A.I.C.S.: 332119

Silgan White Cap Espana S.L. **(1)**
C/ Del Mar 23-1-2A, Valencia, 46003, Spain
Tel.: (34) 963925574
Metal & Plastic Closure Distr
N.A.I.C.S.: 423840

Silgan White Cap GmbH **(1)**
Engerthstrasse 76, 1200, Vienna, Austria
Tel.: (43) 13327608
Sales Range: $10-24.9 Million
Emp.: 5
Metal & Plastic Container Mfr
N.A.I.C.S.: 332439

Silgan White Cap Holdings Spain, S.L. **(1)**
C/ Santalo 10 4 2, 08021, Barcelona, Spain
Tel.: (34) 938596410
Web Site: http://www.silganwhitecap.com
Sales Range: $25-49.9 Million
Emp.: 4
Investment Management Service
N.A.I.C.S.: 551112

Silgan White Cap LLC **(1)**
1140 31st St, Downers Grove, IL 60515
Tel.: (630) 515-8383
Web Site: http://www.silganwhitecap.com
Metal & Plastic Bottle Mfr
N.A.I.C.S.: 332431

SILICON LABORATORIES INC.

400 W Cesar Chavez, Austin, TX 78701
Tel.: (512) 416-8500 DE
Web Site: https://www.silabs.com
Year Founded: 1996
SLAB—(NASDAQ)
Rev.: $1,024,106,000
Assets: $2,169,428,000
Liabilities: $764,420,000
Net Worth: $1,405,008,000
Earnings: $91,402,000
Emp.: 1,964
Fiscal Year-end: 12/31/22
Other Communications Equipment Manufacturing
N.A.I.C.S.: 334290
Navdeep S. Sooch (Founder)
Robert J. Conrad (Sr VP-Worldwide Ops)
R. Matthew Johnson (Pres & CEO)
Dean W. Butler (CFO & Sr VP)
Sharon Hagi (Chief Security Officer)
Mark D. Mauldin (Chief Acctg Officer)

Subsidiaries:

Micrium, Inc. **(1)**
1290 Weston Rd Ste 306, Weston, FL 33326 **(100%)**
Tel.: (954) 217-2036
Web Site: http://www.micrium.com
Emp.: 50
Real Time Operating Systems for Embedded Systems
N.A.I.C.S.: 513210
Jean J. Labrosse (Founder)

Silabs India Private Limited **(1)**
Salarpuria Sattva Knowledge City Octave - 3 Parcel-4 2nd 3rd Floor, Raidurgam Village Ranga Reddy Dist, Hyderabad, 500081, Telangana, India
Tel.: (91) 4069031000
Software Development Services
N.A.I.C.S.: 541511

Silicon Laboratories Asia Pacific, Limited **(1)**

Silicon Laboratories Inc.—(Continued)

Ste 811 Tsim Sha Tsui Centre E Wing 66, Mody Rd, Tsim Sha Tsui East, Kowloon, China (Hong Kong)
Tel.: (852) 22686836
Web Site: https://www.silabs.com
Sales Range: $100-124.9 Million
Integrated Circuits Mfr
N.A.I.C.S.: 334412

Silicon Laboratories Canada ULC **(1)**
1200-1010 Rue De La Gauchetiere O, Montreal, H3B 2N2, QC, Canada
Tel.: (438) 300-6063
Wireless Connectivity Device Mfr
N.A.I.C.S.: 334220

Silicon Laboratories Denmark ApS **(1)**
Emdrupvej 28B, 2100, Copenhagen, Denmark
Tel.: (45) 39130000
Software Development Services
N.A.I.C.S.: 541511

Silicon Laboratories Finland Oy **(1)**
Alberga Business Park Bertel Jungin aukio 3, 02600, Espoo, Finland
Tel.: (358) 94355060
Computer Programming & Consultancy Services
N.A.I.C.S.: 541511

Silicon Laboratories France SAS **(1)**
318 rue de Fougeres Le Noven, 35700, Rennes, France
Tel.: (33) 299875850
Web Site: http://www.silabs.com
Sales Range: $100-124.9 Million
Integrated Circuits Sales
N.A.I.C.S.: 334412

Silicon Laboratories GmbH **(1)**
Ludwigstrasse 49, Hallbergmoos, 85399, Munich, Germany
Tel.: (49) 8119987340
Integrated Circuits Mfr
N.A.I.C.S.: 334412

Silicon Laboratories International Pte. Ltd. **(1)**
18 Tai Seng 05-01 18 Tai Seng Street, Singapore, 539775, Singapore
Tel.: (65) 65117777
Sales Range: $100-124.9 Million
Integrated Circuits Mfr
N.A.I.C.S.: 334412

Silicon Laboratories Norway AS **(1)**
Sandakerveien 118, 0484, Oslo, Norway
Tel.: (47) 23009800
Silicone Products Mfr
N.A.I.C.S.: 334413

Silicon Laboratories UK Limited **(1)**
River Court The Meadows Business Park, Camberley, GU17 9AB, Surrey, United Kingdom
Tel.: (44) 1276608550
Sales Range: $100-124.9 Million
Integrated Circuits Mfr
N.A.I.C.S.: 334412

Silicon Laboratories Y.K. **(1)**
Shiodome Building 3F 1-2-20, Kaigan Minatoku, Tokyo, 105-0022, Japan
Tel.: (81) 367218707
Web Site: https://www.silabs.com
Sales Range: $100-124.9 Million
Integrated Circuits Mfr
N.A.I.C.S.: 334412

Silicon Labs Ember, Inc. **(1)**
343 Congress St Ste 4100, Boston, MA 02210
Tel.: (617) 951-0200
Integrated Circuit Distr
N.A.I.C.S.: 423690

Telegesis (UK) Limited **(1)**
Abbey Barn Business Centre Abbey Barn Lane, High Wycombe, HP10 9QQ, United Kingdom
Tel.: (44) 1494510199
Web Site: http://www.telegesis.com
Electronic Equipment Mfr & Whslr
N.A.I.C.S.: 335999

Z-Wave Alliance, LLC **(1)**

400 W Cesar Chavez, Austin, TX 78701
Tel.: (512) 416-8500
Web Site: http://www.z-wavealliance.org
Wireless Home Control Products Mfr
N.A.I.C.S.: 334419
Mitchell Klein (Exec Dir)

Zentri, Inc. **(1)**
20 N Santa Cruz Ave, Los Gatos, CA 95030
Tel.: (408) 402-8160
Web Site: http://www.silabs.com
Semiconductor Component Mfr & Distr
N.A.I.C.S.: 334413
Jason Crawford (Founder & CTO)

SILK ROAD ENTERTAINMENT, INC.
6077 S Fort Apache Ste 140, Las Vegas, NV 89148
Tel.: (310) 277-9707 NV
Year Founded: 1998
SKRJ—(OTCIQ)
Software Development Services
N.A.I.C.S.: 541511
Philip Kramer (Pres)
Carl Philip Ranno (Gen Counsel)

SILO PHARMA INC.
560 Sylvan Ave Ste 3160, Englewood Cliffs, NJ 07632
Tel.: (718) 400-9031 NY
Web Site:
https://www.silopharma.com
Year Founded: 2010
SILO—(NASDAQ)
Rev.: $72,102
Assets: $7,746,141
Liabilities: $1,569,270
Net Worth: $6,176,871
Earnings: ($3,700,683)
Emp.: 3
Fiscal Year-end: 12/31/23
Precious Metals Buying & Recycling Services
N.A.I.C.S.: 423940
Eric Weisblum (Founder, Chm, Pres & CEO)
Daniel E. Ryweck (CFO)

SILVACO GROUP, INC.
4701 Patrick Henry Dr Bldg 23, Santa Clara, CA 95054
Tel.: (408) 567-1000
Web Site: https://www.silvaco.com
SVCO—(NASDAQ)
Emp.: 250
EDA Tools & Semiconductor IP Developer & Mfr
N.A.I.C.S.: 513210
Babak Taheri (CEO)
Farhad Hayat (VP-Global Mktg)
Greg Swyt (CFO)

Subsidiaries:

Silvaco Europe Ltd. **(1)**
Compass Point, Saint Ives, Cambridge, PE27 5JL, United Kingdom
Tel.: (44) 1480 484400
Web Site: http://www.silvaco.com
Emp.: 20
Computer Software Distr
N.A.I.C.S.: 423430
Chris Mamoth (Gen Mgr)

Silvaco Japan Co., Ltd. **(1)**
Yokohama Landmark Tower 36F 2-2-1 Minatomirai, Nishi-ku, Yokohama, 220-8136, Kanagawa, Japan
Tel.: (81) 456406188
Web Site: http://www.silvaco.com
Computer Software Distr
N.A.I.C.S.: 423430
Yoshiharu Furui (Gen Mgr)

Silvaco Korea Co. Ltd. **(1)**
5F Star-City Building 469-1 Chonho-dong, Seoul, Kangdong-gu, Korea (South)
Tel.: (82) 2 447 5421
Web Site: http://www.silvaco.co.kr
Computer Software Distr
N.A.I.C.S.: 423430

Silvaco Singapore Pte Ltd. **(1)**
International Buisness Park, Singapore, 239693, Singapore
Tel.: (65) 6872 3674
Web Site: http://www.silvaco.com
Emp.: 6
Computer Software Distr
N.A.I.C.S.: 423430
Qingda Zhao (Mng Dir)

Silvaco Taiwan Co., Ltd. **(1)**
7F No 170 Jieshou Rd, Hsin-chu, 30072, Taiwan
Tel.: (886) 3 567 9686
Computer Software Distr
N.A.I.C.S.: 423430

Silvaco, Inc. **(1)**
2811 Mission Coolge Blvd 6th Fl, Santa Clara, CA 95054
Tel.: (408) 567-1000
Electronic Design Automation & Technology CAD Software Mfr
N.A.I.C.S.: 513210
Babak Taheri (CEO)

SILVAIR, INC.
717 Market St Ste 100, San Francisco, CA 94103
Tel.: (747) 888-5978
Web Site: https://www.silvair.com
SVRS—(WAR)
Lighting Component Mfr
N.A.I.C.S.: 335139
Rafal Han (Co-Founder & CEO)
Szymon Slupik (Co-Founder & CTO)
Adam Gembala (Co-Founder & CFO)

SILVER BUCKLE MINES, INC.
Tel.: (208) 752-1131 ID
Year Founded: 1963
SBUM—(OTCIQ)
Silver Mining Services
N.A.I.C.S.: 212220
Harry James Magnuson (Pres)
Dennis M. O'Brien (Sec)

SILVER SCOTT MINES, INC.
4160 N Hwy A1A Unit 907A, Fort Pierce, FL 34949
Tel.: (908) 477-7802 NV
Web Site:
https://silverscottmines.com
Year Founded: 2004
SILS—(OTCIQ)
Mineral Exploration Services
N.A.I.C.S.: 213115
Caren D. Currier (Chm)
Stuart Fine (Pres & CEO)

SILVER SPIKE INVESTMENT CORP.
600 Madison Ave Ste 1800, New York, NY 10022
Tel.: (212) 905-4923 MD
Web Site:
https://ssic.silverspikecap.com
Year Founded: 2021
SSIC—(NASDAQ)
Rev.: $10,073
Assets: $85,031,787
Liabilities: $479,697
Net Worth: $84,552,090
Earnings: ($563,365)
Fiscal Year-end: 03/31/22
Investment Services
N.A.I.C.S.: 523999
Scott Gordon (Founder, Chm, CEO & Partner-Founding)
Umesh Mahajan (Partner, CFO & Co-Head-Credit)
William Healy (Partner & Head)
Dino Colonna (Partner & Co-Head)

SILVER VERDE MAY MINING CO.
602 Cedar St Ste 205, Wallace, ID 83873
Tel.: (208) 556-1600 ID

Year Founded: 1906
SIVE—(OTCIQ)
Mineral Mining Services
N.A.I.C.S.: 213114
Michael B. Lavigne (CEO)

SILVERCREST ASSET MANAGEMENT GROUP INC.
1330 Ave of the Americas 38th Fl, New York, NY 10019
Tel.: (212) 649-0600 DE
Web Site:
https://www.silvercrestgroup.com
Year Founded: 2011
SAMG—(NASDAQ)
Rev.: $123,217,000
Assets: $212,675,000
Liabilities: $86,843,000
Net Worth: $125,832,000
Earnings: $18,828,000
Emp.: 152
Fiscal Year-end: 12/31/22
Portfolio Management & Investment Advice
N.A.I.C.S.: 523940
Albert S. Messina (Mng Dir & Portfolio Mgr-Equity & Fixed Income Portfolios)
Van Martin (Sr VP-Equity Mgmt)
Judy B. Morrill (Mng Dir & Portfolio Mgr-Equity, Fixed Income & Balanced Portfolio)
Palmer P. Garson (Mng Dir & Portfolio Mgr)
A. Marshall Acuff Jr. (Mng Dir)
Alphonse Chan Jr. (Mng Dir)
Scott Brown Jr. (Mng Dir)
Diane Boehl (Controller)
Lorena Cardenas (Dir)
Sara Chin (Controller)
Dean H. Dewey (Mng Dir)
Matthew Fiscella (VP)
Matt Dearth (Mng Dir)
Daniel MacMillan (VP)
Richard R. Hough III (Chm, Pres & CEO)

Subsidiaries:

Silvercrest Asset Management Group LLC **(1)**
230 Ct Sq Ste 101, Charlottesville, VA 22902
Tel.: (434) 977-4420
Investment Advisory Services
N.A.I.C.S.: 523040
Evan Kwiatkowski (Sr VP-Tax)

Silvercrest L.P. **(1)**
1330 Avenue of the Americas 38th Fl, New York, NY 10019
Tel.: (212) 649-0600
Portfolio Management Services
N.A.I.C.S.: 523940

SILVERGATE CAPITAL CORPORATION
4225 Executive Sq Ste 600, La Jolla, CA 92037
Tel.: (858) 362-6300 MD
Web Site: https://silvergate.com
Year Founded: 1987
SI (NYSE)
Rev.: $175,650,000
Assets: $16,005,495,000
Liabilities: $14,396,659,000
Net Worth: $1,608,836,000
Earnings: $75,512,000
Emp.: 279
Fiscal Year-end: 12/31/21
Bank Holding Company
N.A.I.C.S.: 551111
Michael T. Lempres (Chm)

SILVERSPAC INC.
250 Greenwich St 7 World Trade Ctr 10th Fl, New York, NY 10007
Tel.: (212) 312-9265 Ky

Web Site: https://www.silverspac.com
Year Founded: 2021
SLVR—(NASDAQ)
Rev.: $10,179,060
Assets: $253,843,356
Liabilities: $265,600,194
Net Worth: ($11,756,838)
Earnings: $9,196,414
Emp.: 2
Fiscal Year-end: 12/31/22
Investment Services
N.A.I.C.S.: 523999
Tal Kerret *(Chm & CFO)*
Charles Federman *(CEO)*

SIMMONS FIRST NATIONAL CORPORATION

Simmons Bank Credit Card Center,
Pine Bluff, AR 71611
Tel.: (870) 541-1000   AR
Web Site:
  https://www.simmonsbank.com
Year Founded: 1968
SFNC—(NASDAQ)
Rev.: $1,031,801,000
Assets: $27,461,061,000
Liabilities: $24,191,699,000
Net Worth: $3,269,362,000
Earnings: $256,412,000
Emp.: 3,202
Fiscal Year-end: 12/31/22
Offices of Bank Holding Companies
N.A.I.C.S.: 551111
George A. Makris Jr. *(Exec Chm)*
Charles Daniel Hobbs *(CFO & Exec VP)*
Jennifer B. Compton *(Chief People & Corp Strategy Officer & Exec VP)*
Jay Brogdon *(Pres & CEO)*
Alex Carriles *(Chief Digital Officer)*
Tina Groves *(Chief Risk Officer)*
Rodney Hawkins *(Exec VP)*
Elizabeth Machen *(Exec VP)*
Ann Madea *(CIO)*
Chad Rawls *(Chief Credit Officer)*
Brad Yaney *(Chief Credit Risk Officer)*
George A. Makris III *(Gen Counsel, Sec & Exec VP)*

Subsidiaries:

Reliance Bancshares, Inc.   **(1)**
10401 Clayton Rd, Frontenac, MO 63131
Tel.: (314) 569-7200
Web Site:
  http://www.reliancebancshares.com
Bank Holding Company
N.A.I.C.S.: 551111
Allan D. Ivie IV *(Pres-Corp & Community Banking)*
Gaines S. Dittrich *(Vice Chm & Chief Credit Officer)*
Lisa G. Frederick *(Pres-Banking & Sls)*
Norman A. Toon *(Exec VP & Chief Lending Officer)*
Courtney Stotler *(Exec VP-HR)*
Lora Davis *(Exec Vp-Retail Banking)*
Thomas H. Brouster Sr. *(CEO)*

Subsidiary (Domestic):

Reliance Bank   **(2)**
11781 Manchester Rd, Des Peres, MO 63131
Tel.: (314) 965-5300
Web Site: http://www.reliancebankstl.com
Emp.: 4
Retail & Commercial Banking
N.A.I.C.S.: 522110
Thomas H. Brouster *(Chm)*

Simmons Bank   **(1)**
501 S Main St, Pine Bluff, AR 71601
Tel.: (870) 541-1300
Web Site: https://www.simmonsbank.com
Sales Range: $350-399.9 Million
Commericial Banking
N.A.I.C.S.: 522110
George A. Makris Jr. *(Exec Chm)*
Charles Daniel Hobbs *(CFO & Exec VP)*

Matt Reddin *(Chief Banking Officer & Exec VP)*
Jimmy Crocker *(Exec VP-Wealth Mgmt)*
Joe DiNicolantonio *(Exec VP & Head-Consumer & Bus Banking)*
Daniel Hobbs *(CFO)*

Subsidiary (Domestic):

Simmons First Finance
Company   **(2)**
100 E Reelfoot Ave, Union City, TN 38261
Tel.: (731) 885-2237
Emp.: 20
Consumer Lending Services
N.A.I.C.S.: 522291
Brian Kissel *(Pres)*

Simmons First Investment Group,
Inc.   **(2)**
11700 Cantrell Rd, Little Rock, AR 72223
Tel.: (501) 907-2290
Web Site: http://www.simmonsbank.com
Investment Banking & Advisory Services
N.A.I.C.S.: 523150

SIMON PROPERTY GROUP ACQUISITION HOLDINGS, INC.

225 W Washington St, Indianapolis,
IN 46204
Tel.: (212) 745-9649   DE
Web Site:
  http://www.simonacquisitionhold
  ings.com
Year Founded: 2020
SPGS—(NYSE)
Rev.: $8,599,852
Assets: $345,885,210
Liabilities: $369,177,678
Net Worth: ($23,292,468)
Earnings: $6,815,225
Emp.: 354
Fiscal Year-end: 12/31/21
Investment Services
N.A.I.C.S.: 523999

SIMON PROPERTY GROUP, INC.

225 W Washington St, Indianapolis,
IN 46204
Tel.: (317) 636-1600   DE
Web Site: https://www.simon.com
Year Founded: 1960
SPG—(NYSE)
Rev.: $5,658,836,000
Assets: $34,283,495,000
Liabilities: $30,791,846,000
Net Worth: $3,491,649,000
Earnings: $2,279,789,000
Emp.: 2,500
Fiscal Year-end: 12/31/23
Real Estate Investment Trust; Shopping Malls Owner & Operator
N.A.I.C.S.: 525990
Eli M. Simon *(Sr VP-Corp Investments)*
David E. Simon *(Chm, Pres & CEO)*
John Rulli *(Chief Admin Officer)*
Susan Massela *(Sr VP-HR)*
Vicki Hanor *(Mng Dir-Luxury Leasing & Sr Exec-Malls)*
Steven E. Fivel *(Gen Counsel & Sec)*
Herbert Simon *(Co-Founder)*
Stanley Shashoua *(Chief Investment Officer)*
Richard S. Sokolov *(Vice Chm)*
Adam J. Reuille *(Chief Acctg Officer & Sr VP)*
Brian J. McDade *(CFO & Exec VP)*
Pervis Bearden *(Exec VP-Leasing & Accounts-Malls-Global)*
Marla Parr *(Exec VP-Specialty Leasing-Malls)*
Russell A. Tuttle *(Chief Security Officer & Sr VP)*
Patrick E. Peterman *(Sr VP-Dev & Asset Intensification)*
Eli M. Simon *(Sr VP-Corp Investments)*

Donald G. Frey *(Treas & Exec VP)*
Matt Jackson *(Sr VP & Asst Treas)*
Kevin M. Kelly *(Gen Counsel)*
Joseph W. Chiappetta *(CTO)*
David Gorelick *(Sr VP)*
Natalie Turpin *(Exec VP)*
W. Bradford Cole *(Sr VP)*
Christine Schnauffer *(Sr VP)*
Thomas Ward *(Sr VP-IR)*
Thomas Ward *(Sr VP-IR)*

Subsidiaries:

Forever 21, Inc.   **(1)**
2001 S Alameda St, Los Angeles, CA
90058   **(37.5%)**
Tel.: (213) 741-5100
Web Site: http://www.forever21.com
Sales Range: $1-4.9 Billion
Emp.: 6,000
Women's Apparel & Accessories
N.A.I.C.S.: 458110
Don W. Chang *(Founder & Pres)*
Jin Sook Chang *(Founder)*
Daniel Kulle *(CEO)*
Winnie Y. Park *(CEO)*

Simon Capital Limited
Partnership   **(1)**
7401 Market St, Youngstown, OH 44512
Tel.: (330) 758-4511
Commercial Building Rental & Leasing Services
N.A.I.C.S.: 531120

Simon Management Associates,
LLC   **(1)**
7007 Friars Rd Ste 392, San Diego, CA
92108-1152
Tel.: (619) 297-3381
Web Site: http://www.simon.com
Sales Range: $25-49.9 Million
Emp.: 15
Real Estate Brokerage Services
N.A.I.C.S.: 531210

Simon Premium Outlets   **(1)**
60 Columbia Rd Bldg B, Morristown, NJ
07960
Tel.: (973) 228-6111
Develops, Leases, Manages & Owns Fashion Outlet Centers
N.A.I.C.S.: 531312
Matthew J. Broas *(Sr VP & Leasing Counsel)*

Subsidiary (Domestic):

Chelsea Group   **(2)**
2944 Biddle Ave, Wyandotte, MI 48192-5214
Tel.: (734) 282-7755
Web Site:
  https://www.chelseamenswear.com
Sales Range: $100-124.9 Million
Emp.: 20
Men's & Women's Clothing Stores
N.A.I.C.S.: 458110

Joint Venture (Non-US):

Chelsea Japan Co., Ltd.   **(2)**
3 2 3 Marunouchi Chiyoda Ku, Tokyo, 100
0005, Japan
Tel.: (81) 332147155
Web Site: http://www.premiumoutlets.co.jp
Sales Range: $10-24.9 Million
Emp.: 40
Leases & Manages Fashion-Oriented Outlet Centers; Joint Venture of Chelsea Property Group (40%) & Mitsubishi Estate Co., Ltd. (60%)
N.A.I.C.S.: 531190
Yoshimura Hidetoshi *(Pres)*

Simon Property Group (Illinois),
L.P.   **(1)**
288 Orland Square Dr, Orland Park, IL
60462-3211
Tel.: (708) 349-1646
Web Site: http://www.simon.com
Sales Range: $25-49.9 Million
Emp.: 55
Provider of Real Estate Investment Trust Services
N.A.I.C.S.: 525990

Simon Property Group (Texas),
L.P.   **(1)**

2350 Airport Fwy Ste 310, Bedford, TX
76022
Tel.: (817) 685-3000
Web Site: http://www.simon.com
Real Estate Investment Trust Services
N.A.I.C.S.: 525990

Simon Property Group, L.P.   **(1)**
225 W Washington St, Indianapolis, IN
46204
Tel.: (317) 636-1600
Web Site: https://www.simon.com
Rev.: $5,291,446,999
Assets: $33,011,273,999
Liabilities: $29,399,621,999
Net Worth: $3,611,651,999
Earnings: $2,444,395,000
Emp.: 2,500
Fiscal Year-end: 12/31/2022
Real Estate Investment Trust
N.A.I.C.S.: 525990

Subsidiary (Domestic):

Taubman Centers, Inc.   **(2)**
200 E Long Lake Rd Ste 300, Bloomfield
Hills, MI 48304-2324
Tel.: (248) 258-6800
Web Site: https://www.taubman.com
Real Estate Investment Trust
N.A.I.C.S.: 531390
Paul A. Wright *(Pres-Asia)*
William S. Taubman *(Pres & COO)*
Denise A. Anton *(Exec VP-Center Ops)*
Holly A. Kinnear *(Chief HR Officer & Sr VP-HR)*
Michele Walton *(Gen Counsel & Sr VP)*
Ben Meeker *(CFO, Treas & Sr VP)*

Subsidiary (Domestic):

Dolphin Mall Associates LLC   **(3)**
11401 NW 12th St, Miami, FL 33172
Tel.: (305) 365-7446
Web Site: https://www.shopdolphinmall.com
Shopping Mall Operator
N.A.I.C.S.: 531120

Unit (Domestic):

International Plaza & Bay Street   **(3)**
2223 NW Shore Blvd, Tampa, FL 33607
Tel.: (813) 342-3790
Web Site:
  https://www.shopinternationalplaza.com
Sales Range: $150-199.9 Million
Emp.: 20
Shopping Complex
N.A.I.C.S.: 459910

Subsidiary (Domestic):

MacArthur Shopping Center LLC   **(3)**
300 Monticello Ave, Norfolk, VA 23510
Tel.: (757) 627-6000
Web Site: https://www.shopmacarthur.com
Shopping Mall Operator
N.A.I.C.S.: 531120

Partridge Creek Fashion Park
LLC   **(3)**
17420 Hall Rd, Clinton Township, MI 48038
Tel.: (586) 226-0330
Web Site:
  https://www.shoppartridgecreek.com
Shopping Mall Operator
N.A.I.C.S.: 531120

Short Hills Associates, LLC   **(3)**
1200 Morris Tpke, Short Hills, NJ 07078
Tel.: (973) 376-7350
Web Site: https://www.shopshorthills.com
Shopping Mall Operator
N.A.I.C.S.: 531120

Stony Point Fashion Park Associates,
LLC   **(3)**
9200 Stony Point Pkwy, Richmond, VA
23235
Tel.: (804) 560-7467
Web Site: https://www.shopstonypoint.com
Shopping Mall Operator
N.A.I.C.S.: 531120

TJ Palm Beach Associates Limited
Partnership   **(3)**
10300 Forest Hill Blvd Ste 200, Wellington,
FL 33414
Tel.: (561) 227-6900
Web Site:
  https://www.shopwellingtongreen.com

Simon Property Group, Inc.—(Continued)

Shopping Mall Operator
N.A.I.C.S.: 531120

TRG Charlotte LLC (3)
6801 Northlake Mall Dr, Charlotte, NC
28216
Tel.: (704) 921-2000
Web Site: http://www.shopnorthlake.com
Shopping Mall Operator
N.A.I.C.S.: 531120
Adam Kamlet (Gen Mgr)
Eddie John (Dir-Security)

Subsidiary (Non-US):

Taubman (Hong Kong) Limited (3)
Suite 6311 63/F One Island East Taikoo
Place 18 Westlands Road, Quarry Bay,
Hong Kong, China (Hong Kong)
Tel.: (852) 36071333
Real Estate Manangement Services
N.A.I.C.S.: 531390

Taubman Asia Limited (3)
Suite 6311 63/F 1 Island East Taikoo Place
18 Westlands Road, Quarry Bay, Hong
Kong, China (Hong Kong) (100%)
Tel.: (852) 36071333
Web Site: https://www.taubmanasia.com
Sales Range: $300-349.9 Million
Real Estate Investment
N.A.I.C.S.: 531210
Robert S. Taubman (Chm, Co-Pres & CEO)
Paul A. Wright (Co-Pres)
Guohua Jean Zhang (Mng Dir)
Chris Wong (Gen Counsel & VP)
Winnie Tse (Chief Admin Officer, Head-Fin
& Controller)
Sam Wu (VP-Leasing)
Dean Kil (VP-Leasing & Partner Rels)
Tim Hill (VP-Grp-Ops & Asset Mgmt)

Subsidiary (Domestic):

**Taubman Cherry Creek Shopping
Center, L.L.C.** (3)
3000 E 1st Ave, Denver, CO 80206
Tel.: (303) 388-3900
Web Site: https://www.shopcherrycreek.com
Shopping Mall Operator
N.A.I.C.S.: 531120

**Taubman Prestige Outlets of Chester-
field LLC** (3)
17057 N Outer 40 Rd, Chesterfield, MO
63005
Tel.: (314) 513-1500
Web Site:
    http://www.taubmanprestigeoutlets.com
Shopping Mall Operator
N.A.I.C.S.: 531120

**Taubman Realty Group Limited
Partnership** (3)
200 E Long Lk Rd, Bloomfield Hills, MI
48304
Tel.: (248) 258-6800
Web Site: http://www.taubman.com
Sales Range: $1-4.9 Billion
Emp.: 300
Nonresidential Building Operating Services
N.A.I.C.S.: 531120
Robert S. Taubman (Chm & CEO)

The Gardens on El Paseo LLC (3)
73545 El Paseo, Palm Desert, CA 92260
Tel.: (760) 862-1990
Web Site:
    https://www.thegardensonelpaseo.com
Shopping Mall Operator
N.A.I.C.S.: 531120

The Taubman Company LLC (3)
200 E Long Lake Rd Ste 300, Bloomfield
Hills, MI 48304-2324
Tel.: (248) 258-6800
Web Site: https://www.taubman.com
Shopping Mall Operator
N.A.I.C.S.: 531120
Robert S. Taubman (Chm, Pres & CEO)
Holly A. Kinnear (Chief HR Officer & Sr VP-
HR)
William S. Taubman (Pres & COO)
Benjamin Meeker (CFO, Treas & Sr VP)
Maria Mainville (Dir-Strategic Comm)
Michele Walton (Gen Counsel & Sr VP)

Twelve Oaks Mall LLC (3)

27500 Novi Rd, Novi, MI 48377
Tel.: (248) 348-9400
Web Site: https://www.shoptwelveoaks.com
Emp.: 3
Shopping Mall Operator
N.A.I.C.S.: 531120

**Willow Bend Shopping Center Limited
Partnership** (3)
6121 W Park Blvd, Plano, TX 75093
Tel.: (972) 202-4900
Web Site: https://www.shopwillowbend.com
Shopping Mall Operator
N.A.I.C.S.: 531120

The Mills Properties (1)
5425 Wisconsin Ave Ste 300, Chevy
Chase, MD 20815
Tel.: (301) 968-6000
Sales Range: $650-699.9 Million
Emp.: 1,150
Real Estate Investment Trust; Regional Re-
tail & Entertainment Projects Owner, Devel-
oper, Manager & Marketer
N.A.I.C.S.: 525990
Paul C. Fickinger (Exec VP-Property Mgmt)

Subsidiary (Domestic):

Arizona Mills (2)
5000 S Arizona Mills Cir, Tempe, AZ 85282
Tel.: (480) 491-9700
Web Site: https://www.simon.com
Sales Range: $300-349.9 Million
Shopping & Entertainment Center Opera-
tors
N.A.I.C.S.: 531120

Arundel Mills (2)
7000 Arundel Mills Cir, Hanover, MD
21076-1282
Tel.: (410) 540-5110
Web Site: https://www.simon.com
Sales Range: $200-249.9 Million
Emp.: 200
Shopping & Entertainment Center Opera-
tors
N.A.I.C.S.: 531120

Colorado Mills LP (2)
14500 W Colfax Ave, Lakewood, CO 80401
Tel.: (303) 384-3000
Web Site: https://www.simon.com
Sales Range: $10-24.9 Million
Emp.: 30
Shopping & Entertainment Center Opera-
tors
N.A.I.C.S.: 541611

Concord Mills LP (2)
8111 Concord Mills Blvd, Concord, NC
28027
Tel.: (704) 979-5000
Sales Range: $50-74.9 Million
Emp.: 15
Shopping & Entertainment Center Opera-
tors
N.A.I.C.S.: 236117
Ray Soporowski (Gen Mgr)

Franklin Mills LLC (2)
1455 Franklin Mills Cir, Philadelphia, PA
19154
Tel.: (215) 632-1500
Web Site: http://www.franklinmills.com
Sales Range: $25-49.9 Million
Emp.: 60
Shopping & Entertainment Center Opera-
tors
N.A.I.C.S.: 237210

Grapevine Mills (2)
3000 Grapevine Mills Pkwy, Grapevine, TX
76051-2008
Tel.: (972) 724-4900
Web Site: https://www.simon.com
Sales Range: $1-9.9 Million
Emp.: 15
Shopping & Entertainment Complex Opera-
tors
N.A.I.C.S.: 531120

Katy Mills (2)
5000 Katy Mills Cir, Katy, TX 77494-4402
Tel.: (281) 644-5000
Web Site: https://www.simon.com
Sales Range: $1-9.9 Million
Emp.: 15
Shopping & Entertainment Center Opera-
tors

N.A.I.C.S.: 531120

Ontario Mills (2)
1 Mills Cir, Ontario, CA 91764-5207
Tel.: (909) 484-8301
Web Site: https://www.simon.com
Sales Range: $25-49.9 Million
Emp.: 100
Shopping & Entertainment Center Opera-
tors
N.A.I.C.S.: 722511

The Mills at Jersey Gardens (2)
651 Kapkowski Rd, Elizabeth, NJ 07201-
4901
Tel.: (908) 354-5900
Web Site: http://www.simon.com
Shopping Mall Property Management Ser-
vices
N.A.I.C.S.: 531312

SIMPLY, INC.
2001 NW 84th Ave, Miami, FL 33122
Tel.: (786) 254-6709 **MD**
Web Site: http://simplyinc.com
Year Founded: 1994
SIMP—(NASDAQ)
Rev.: $79,111,000
Assets: $30,437,000
Liabilities: $36,403,000
Net Worth: ($5,966,000)
Earnings: ($11,121,000)
Emp.: 352
Fiscal Year-end: 01/29/22
Wireless Handset & Accessory Distr
N.A.I.C.S.: 423690
Reinier Voigt (Pres & CEO)
Kevin Taylor (Chm)
Vernon A. LoForti (CFO & Sr VP)

Subsidiaries:

**InfoSonics El Salvador S.A. de
C.V.** (1)
1411 NW 84th Ave, Miami, FL 33126
Tel.: (305) 499-9222
Sales Range: $100-124.9 Million
Wireless Handset Mfr
N.A.I.C.S.: 334220

InfoSonics Latin America, Inc. (1)
4435 Eastgate Mall Ste 320, San Diego, CA
92122
Tel.: (858) 373-1600
Web Site: http://www.infosonics.com
Wireless Handset Mfr
N.A.I.C.S.: 334220

InfoSonics S.A. (1)
1411 NW 84th St, Miami, FL 33147
Tel.: (305) 499-93/1
Sales Range: $100-124.9 Million
Wireless Handset Mfr
N.A.I.C.S.: 334220

Simply Mac, Inc. (1)
1414 Foothill Dr Ste A-2, Salt Lake City, UT
84108 (100%)
Tel.: (801) 871-0221
Web Site: http://www.simplymac.com
Sales Range: $25-49.9 Million
Emp.: 200
Computer Component Distr
N.A.I.C.S.: 423430

verykool USA, Inc. (1)
3636 Nobel Dr Ste 325, San Diego, CA
92122
Tel.: (858) 373-1600
Web Site: http://www.verykool.net
Cellular Telephones Mfr
N.A.I.C.S.: 334220

**SIMPSON MANUFACTURING
COMPANY, INC.**
5956 W Las Positas Blvd, Pleasan-
ton, CA 94588
Tel.: (310) 829-5400 **DE**
Web Site:
    https://www.simpsonmfg.com
Year Founded: 1914
SSD—(NYSE)
Rev.: $2,116,087,000
Assets: $2,503,971,000
Liabilities: $1,090,592,000

Net Worth: $1,413,379,000
Earnings: $333,995,000
Emp.: 5,158
Fiscal Year-end: 12/31/22
Holding Company; Construction Con-
nectors & Venting Systems
N.A.I.C.S.: 332510
Michael Olosky (Pres & CEO)
Michael Andersen (Exec VP)
Phillip Burton (Exec VP)
Jeremy Gilstrap (Exec VP)
Jennifer Lutz (Exec VP-Human Re-
sources)
Udit Mehta (CTO)
Cassandra Payton (Gen Counsel &
Exec VP)

Subsidiaries:

**Ahorn-Gerate & Werkzeuge Vertriebs
GmbH** (1)
Schottener Strasse 8, Hungen, 35410, Ger-
many
Tel.: (49) 640252560
Sales Range: $25-49.9 Million
Emp.: 15
Building Construction Equipment Whslr
N.A.I.C.S.: 423710

Christiania Spigerverk AS (1)
Gullhaugenvej 7 Nydalen, 0402, Oslo, Nor-
way
Tel.: (47) 22021300
Construction Ventilation System Whslr
N.A.I.C.S.: 423810

**Clever Reinforcement Iberica-
Materiais de Construcao, Lda.** (1)
Rua Jose Fontana n 76 Zona Industrial de
Santa Marta de Corroios, Amora, 2845-408,
Setubal, Portugal
Tel.: (351) 212253371
Building Construction Equipment Whslr
N.A.I.C.S.: 423710

Gbo Fastening Systems AB (1)
Bruksvagen 2, 593 75, Gunnebo, Sweden
Tel.: (46) 49030000
Web Site: https://www.gunnebofastening.se
Construction Ventilation System Whslr
N.A.I.C.S.: 423810

Gbo Fastening Systems AB (1)
Bruksvagen 2, 593 75, Gunnebo, Sweden
Tel.: (46) 49030000
Web Site: https://www.gunnebofastening.se
Construction Ventilation System Whslr
N.A.I.C.S.: 423810

Gbo Fastening Systems AB (1)
Bruksvagen 2, 593 75, Gunnebo, Sweden
Tel.: (46) 49030000
Web Site: https://www.gunnebofastening.se
Construction Ventilation System Whslr
N.A.I.C.S.: 423810

Gbo Fastening Systems AB (1)
Bruksvagen 2, 593 75, Gunnebo, Sweden
Tel.: (46) 49030000
Web Site: https://www.gunnebofastening.se
Construction Ventilation System Whslr
N.A.I.C.S.: 423810

Multi Services Decoupe S.A. (1)
Rue des Fauldeurs 6, 6530, Thuin, Belgium
Tel.: (32) 7 159 7575
Web Site: https://www.msdecoupe.com
Construction Ventilation System Whslr
N.A.I.C.S.: 423810

**S&P Clever Reinforcement Company
Benelux B.V.** (1)
Aalsmeerderweg 285 J, 1432 CN, Aals-
meer, Netherlands
Tel.: (31) 297367674
Web Site: http://www.sp-reinforcement.nl
Emp.: 10
Building Reinforcement Materials Mfr
N.A.I.C.S.: 324122

**S&P Clever Reinforcement
GmbH** (1)
Hubert-Vergolst-Strasse 6, 61231, Bad
Nauheim, Germany
Tel.: (49) 6032 868 0160
Web Site: https://www.sp-reinforcement.de
Emp.: 8

Building Reinforcement System Mfr
N.A.I.C.S.: 324122
Dirk Grunewald *(Mng Dir)*

S&P Polska Sp. z o.o. **(1)**
Ul Bydgoska 9, PL82-200, Malbork, Poland
Tel.: (48) 556469700
Web Site: https://www.sp-reinforcement.pl
Carbon & Graphite Mfr
N.A.I.C.S.: 335991

S&P Reinforcement France **(1)**
173 Zone Industrielle Les Mourgues,
30350, Cardet, France
Tel.: (33) 251284477
Web Site: http://www.sp-reinforcement.fr
Carbon & Graphite Mfr
N.A.I.C.S.: 335991

S&P Reinforcement Nordic ApS **(1)**
Hedegaardsvej 11, 8300, Odder, Denmark
Tel.: (45) 8 873 7500
Web Site: https://www.sp-reinforcement.dk
Construction Ventilation System Whslr
N.A.I.C.S.: 423810

S&P Reinforcement Sp. z o.o. **(1)**
Ul Bydgoska 9, 82-200, Malbork, Poland
Tel.: (48) 556469700
Sales Range: $25-49.9 Million
Emp.: 13
Building Reinforcement Materials Mfr
N.A.I.C.S.: 324122
Marek Antoni Makarewicz *(CEO)*

S&P Reinforcement Spain, S.L. **(1)**
C/ Carlos Jimenez Diaz 17 Pol Ind La
Garena, Alcala de Henares, 28806, Madrid,
Spain
Tel.: (34) 918023114
Web Site: https://www.sp-reinforcement.es
Carbon & Graphite Mfr
N.A.I.C.S.: 335991

Sabrefix (UK) Limited **(1)**
Threxton Road Industrial Estate, Watton-at-
Stone, IP25 6NG, Norfolk, United Kingdom
Tel.: (44) 1953883919
Web Site: https://www.sabrefix.co.uk
Structural Building Product Mfr
N.A.I.C.S.: 327390
Ian Brown *(Mgr-Supply Chain)*

**Simpson Strong-Tie (Beijing) Com-
pany Limited** **(1)**
Suite 2301 Golden Tower No 1 Xibahe
Road South Chaoyang District, Beijing,
100028, China
Tel.: (86) 1064403840
Web Site: http://www.strongtie.cn
Construction Product Mfr
N.A.I.C.S.: 541330

**Simpson Strong-Tie (New Zealand)
Limited** **(1)**
52A Arrenway Drive, Albany, Auckland,
0632, New Zealand
Tel.: (64) 94774440
Web Site: https://www.strongtie.co.nz
Sales Range: $25-49.9 Million
Emp.: 3,100
Anchoring & Fastening Products Whslr
N.A.I.C.S.: 423710

Simpson Strong-Tie Asia Limited **(1)**
3/F Cambridge House Ste 301 979 King,
Taikoo Place, Quarry Bay, China (Hong
Kong)
Tel.: (852) 35111888
Web Site: http://www.strongtie.cn
Sales Range: $25-49.9 Million
Emp.: 5
Building Construction Equipment Whslr
N.A.I.C.S.: 423710
Karen Winifred Colonias *(Pres & CEO)*

**Simpson Strong-Tie Australia Pty
Limited** **(1)**
1/16 Kenoma Place, Arndell Park, 2148,
NSW, Australia
Tel.: (61) 300787664
Building Construction Whslr
N.A.I.C.S.: 423710

**Simpson Strong-Tie Canada,
Limited** **(1)**
811 - 19055 Airport Way, Pitt Meadows,
V3Y 0G4, BC, Canada
Tel.: (604) 465-0296
Sales Range: $25-49.9 Million
Emp.: 120
Building Construction Equipment Whslr

N.A.I.C.S.: 423710

**Simpson Strong-Tie Chile
Limitada** **(1)**
Roberto Simpson 1401, San Bernardo,
Santiago, Chile
Tel.: (56) 227602570
Web Site: https://www.strongtie.com
Construction Ventilation System Whslr
N.A.I.C.S.: 423810

Simpson Strong-Tie Co., Inc. **(1)**
5956 W Las Positas Blvd, Pleasanton, CA
94588
Tel.: (925) 560-9000
Web Site: https://www.strongtie.com
Sales Range: $75-99.9 Million
Emp.: 200
Steel Connectors & Adhesives Mfr For
Wood, Concrete & Masonry
N.A.I.C.S.: 332312
Mike Olosky *(COO)*

Plant (Domestic):

**Simpson Strong-Tie (Quik Drive
Factory)** **(2)**
375 N Belvedere Dr, Gallatin, TN 37066
Tel.: (615) 230-8788
Web Site: http://www.strongtie.com
Sales Range: $25-49.9 Million
Emp.: 80
Fasteners & Auto-feed Fastener Driving
Systems Mfr
N.A.I.C.S.: 339993

**Simpson Strong-Tie Europe
EURL** **(1)**
ZAC des 4 Chemins, 85400, Sainte-
Gemme-la-Plaine, France
Tel.: (33) 251284400
Web Site: https://www.simpson.fr
Emp.: 100
Building Construction Equipment Mfr
N.A.I.C.S.: 423710

Simpson Strong-Tie GmbH **(1)**
Hubert-Vergolst-Strasse 6-14, 61231, Bad
Nauheim, Germany
Tel.: (49) 603286800
Web Site: https://www.strongtie.de
Building Construction Whslr
N.A.I.C.S.: 423710

**Simpson Strong-Tie International,
Inc.** **(1)**
5956 W Las Positas Blvd, Pleasanton, CA
94588
Tel.: (925) 560-9000
Web Site: https://www.strongtie.com
Emp.: 185
Building Construction Equipment Whslr
N.A.I.C.S.: 423710

**Simpson Strong-Tie South Africa
(PTY) Ltd** **(1)**
Unit 5 Fairway Business Park Stibitz Street,
Westlake Business Park Westlake, Cape
Town, 7945, Western, South Africa
Tel.: (27) 873540629
Construction Ventilation System Whslr
N.A.I.C.S.: 423810

Simpson Strong-Tie Sp.z.o.o. **(1)**
ul Dzialkowa 115 A, 02-234, Warsaw, Po-
land
Tel.: (48) 228652200
Building Construction Whslr
N.A.I.C.S.: 423710

SIMS LIMITED
200 W Madison St Ste 3950, Chi-
cago, IL 60606
Tel.: (212) 604-0710   AU
Web Site: https://www.simsmm.com
SMSMY—(OTCIQ)
Rev.: $3,767,739,325
Assets: $2,456,481,759
Liabilities: $937,663,322
Net Worth: $1,518,818,437
Earnings: ($203,270,207)
Emp.: 4,075
Fiscal Year-end: 06/30/20
Holding Company; Metal Recycling &
Service Centers Owner & Operator
N.A.I.C.S.: 551112

Geoffrey Norman Brunsdon *(Chm)*
Warrick Ranson *(Grp CFO)*
Brad Baker *(Chief HR Officer-Grp)*
Brendan McDonnell *(CTO-Grp)*
Elise Gautier *(Chief Risk & Compli-
ance Officer-Grp)*
Gretchen Johanns *(Gen Counsel-Grp
& Sec)*
Stephen Mikkelsen *(CEO & Mng Dir)*
Ingrid Sinclair *(Pres-Global-Sims Life-
cycle Svcs)*
Ana Metelo *(Dir-IR)*
Real Hamilton-Romeo *(Head-Comm
& Mktg-Global)*

Subsidiaries:

**Sims Metal Management Limited -
Australia Head Office** **(1)**
Sir Joseph Banks Corporate Park, Level 2
32-34 Lord Street, Botany, 2019, NSW,
Australia
Tel.: (61) 281131600
Web Site: http://www.simsmm.com
Sales Range: $25-49.9 Million
Emp.: 40
Corporate Office
N.A.I.C.S.: 551114
Frank M. Moratti *(Grp Gen Counsel & Sec)*
Robert Thompson *(Chief Comml Officer-
Global)*

Subsidiary (US):

Metal Management, Inc. **(2)**
325 N LaSalle St Ste 550, Chicago, IL
60610
Tel.: (312) 645-0700
Web Site: http://www.simsmm.com
Holding Company; Metal Recycling Service
Centers Operator
N.A.I.C.S.: 551112

Subsidiary (Domestic):

**Metal Management Connecticut,
Inc.** **(3)**
Universal Dr, North Haven, CT 06473
Tel.: (203) 782-4254
Web Site: http://www.simsmm.com
Sales Range: $50-74.9 Million
Emp.: 100
Recyclable Metals Whslr
N.A.I.C.S.: 423930

Metal Management Midwest, Inc. **(3)**
2500 S Paulina St, Chicago, IL 60608-5307
Tel.: (773) 254-1200
Web Site: http://www.simm.com
Recyclable Material Whslr
N.A.I.C.S.: 423930
Lu Ross *(Pres)*

**Metal Management Northeast,
Inc.** **(3)**
Foot Hawkins St, Newark, NJ 07105
Tel.: (973) 344-4570
Web Site: http://www.simsmm.com
Sales Range: $75-99.9 Million
Emp.: 100
Metal Recycling & Service Centers
N.A.I.C.S.: 562920
Daniel Nunez *(Office Mgr)*

Unit (Domestic):

**Sims Metal Management - Jersey
City** **(4)**
1 Linden Ave E, Jersey City, NJ 07305-
4726
Tel.: (201) 577-3200
Sales Range: $25-49.9 Million
Emp.: 74
Scrap Metal Recycling
N.A.I.C.S.: 423930
Joe Payesko *(Pres-East Reg)*

Subsidiary (Domestic):

Metal Management Ohio, Inc. **(3)**
27063 State Rte 281, Defiance, OH 43512-
8963
Tel.: (419) 782-7791
Web Site: http://simsmm.com
Sales Range: $50-74.9 Million
Emp.: 100
Scrap & Recyclable Material Whslr
N.A.I.C.S.: 423930

Steve Fisher *(Mgr-Sls)*

Subsidiary (Non-US):

**Sims Group Canada Holdings
Limited** **(3)**
11760 Mitchell Rd, Richmond, V6V 1V8,
BC, Canada   **(100%)**
Tel.: (604) 324-4656
Web Site: http://www.simsmm.com
Holding Company; Metal Service Centers &
Offices
N.A.I.C.S.: 551112

Affiliate (Domestic):

**Richmond Steel Recycling
Limited** **(4)**
11760 Mitchell Road, Richmond, V6V 1V8,
BC, Canada   **(50%)**
Tel.: (604) 324-4656
Web Site: http://www.richmondsteel.ca
Emp.: 85
Metal Recycling & Service Centers Opera-
tor
N.A.I.C.S.: 562920
Doug Hallson *(CFO)*
John Rai *(VP)*

Subsidiary (US):

SA Recycling LLC **(2)**
2411 N Glassell St, Orange, CA
92865   **(50%)**
Tel.: (714) 630-5836
Web Site: http://www.sarecycling.com
Holding Company; Metal Recycling Ser-
vices
N.A.I.C.S.: 551112

Subsidiary (Domestic):

Fairway Salvage Inc. **(3)**
12428 Ctr St, South Gate, CA 90280
Tel.: (562) 630-8766
Web Site: http://www.sarecycling.com
Rev.: $13,112,737
Emp.: 36
Scrap Metal Recovery & Materials Whslr
N.A.I.C.S.: 562920
Terry Brand *(Pres)*

Golden State Metals, Inc. **(3)**
2000 E Brundage Ln, Bakersfield, CA
93307
Tel.: (661) 327-3559
Web Site: http://www.sarecycling.com
Sales Range: $1-9.9 Million
Emp.: 50
Ferrous Scrap Metal Recovery & Materials
Whslr
N.A.I.C.S.: 562920
George Adams Jr. *(Pres)*

Macoy Resource Corporation **(3)**
5815 Stockdale Rd, Paso Robles, CA
93446-9658
Tel.: (805) 227-1090
Web Site: http://www.sarecycling.com
Sales Range: $1-9.9 Million
Emp.: 5
Recyclable Materials Recovery Services &
Whslr
N.A.I.C.S.: 562920
Sean Mccormick *(Mgr-Ops)*

**Mid-City Iron & Metal
Corporation** **(3)**
2104 E 15th St, Los Angeles, CA 90021
Tel.: (213) 747-4281
Sales Range: $1-9.9 Million
Emp.: 27
Ferrous Scrap Metal Recovery & Materials
Whslr
N.A.I.C.S.: 562920

Pacific Coast Recycling, LLC **(3)**
482 Pier T Ave, Long Beach, CA 90802-
6209
Tel.: (562) 628-8100
Web Site: http://www.pacificr.com
Scrap Metal Recovery & Materials Whslr
N.A.I.C.S.: 562920

Self Serve Auto Dismantlers **(3)**
3200 E Frontera St, Anaheim, CA 92806
Tel.: (714) 630-8901
Sales Range: $10-24.9 Million
Motor Vehicle Scrap Metal Recovery & Ma-
terials Whslr
N.A.I.C.S.: 562920

Sims Limited—(Continued)

George Adams Jr. *(Pres)*
Cristi Rossi *(VP-Ops)*
Patty Flores *(Gen Mgr)*
Tammi Jones *(Gen Mgr)*
Sean McCormick *(Gen Mgr)*

Subsidiary (Domestic):

Sims Group Australia Holdings
Limited   **(2)**
Sir Joseph Banks Corporate Park Level 2,
32-34 Lord Street, Botany, 2019, NSW,
Australia   **(100%)**
Tel.: (61) 281131600
Web Site: http://www.simsmm.com.au
Emp.: 50
Holding Company; Metal Recycling & Service Centers
N.A.I.C.S.: 551112
Alice Field *(Mng Dir)*

Subsidiary (Domestic):

Sims E-Recycling Pty. Ltd.   **(3)**
82 Marple Avenue, Villawood, 2163, NSW,
Australia
Tel.: (61) 287082015
Web Site: http://apac.simsrecycling.com
Sales Range: $50-74.9 Million
Electronic Components Recycling Services
N.A.I.C.S.: 562920

Subsidiary (Non-US):

PNG Recycling Limited   **(4)**
Sect 36 Lot 9 & 10 Waigani Dr, Hohola,
3647, Port Moresby, Papua New Guinea
Tel.: (675) 3230338
Web Site: http://www.simsmm.com
Recyclable Metals Whslr
N.A.I.C.S.: 423930

Sims E-Recycling (NZ) Limited   **(4)**
69 Aintree Avenue Mangere, PO Box
107108, Airport Oaks, Auckland, 2022, New
Zealand
Tel.: (64) 92751501
Web Site:
   http://www.apac.simsrecycling.com
Sales Range: $25-49.9 Million
Emp.: 15
Recyclable Material Whslr
N.A.I.C.S.: 423930
Jay Paul Corpuz *(Mgr-Ops)*

Sims Recycling Solutions Pte
Limited   **(4)**
26 Loyang Crescent Block 302 TOPS
Street 12 03-09, Singapore, 508988, Singapore
Tel.: (65) 62140627
Web Site:
   http://www.apac.simsrecycling.com
Sales Range: $25-49.9 Million
Emp.: 4
Recyclable Material Whslr
N.A.I.C.S.: 423930
Sansan Chua *(Reg Mgr)*

Trishyiraya Recycling India Private
Ltd.   **(4)**
A-7 Phase-I Madras Exporting Zone - SEZ
Nat Hwy No 45, Tambaram, Chennai,
600045, Tamil Nadu, India
Tel.: (91) 4422628067
Web Site: http://www.simsrecycling.com
Sales Range: $25-49.9 Million
Emp.: 40
Recyclable Material Whslr
N.A.I.C.S.: 420000
Anand Narasimhan *(Mng Dir)*

Subsidiary (Domestic):

Sims Industrial Pty Limited   **(3)**
Crompton Rd, Mount Barker, 5251, SA,
Australia
Tel.: (61) 883913555
Emp.: 5
Recyclable Material Whslr
N.A.I.C.S.: 423930
Louis Baker *(Mgr)*

Sims Manufacturing Pty. Ltd.   **(3)**
17 Little Boundary Road, Laverton, 3026,
Australia
Tel.: (61) 383258700
Web Site: http://www.au.simsmm.com

Sales Range: $1-4.9 Billion
Emp.: 11
Recycled Aluminum, Plastics & Tires Processing Services
N.A.I.C.S.: 331314

Subsidiary (Domestic):

Sims Aluminum Pty. Limited   **(4)**
17 Little Boundary Rd, Laverton, 3026, VIC,
Australia
Tel.: (61) 383258700
Web Site: http://www.simsmm.com
Sales Range: $50-74.9 Million
Emp.: 10
Aluminum Recycling & Processing Services
N.A.I.C.S.: 562920

Affiliate (Non-US):

Sims Pacific Metals Limited   **(3)**
Cnr Manu and Kahu Street, Otahuhu, 1640,
New Zealand   **(50%)**
Tel.: (64) 92761809
Web Site: http://www.simspacificmetals.com
Sales Range: $75-99.9 Million
Recycling & Metal Service Centers
N.A.I.C.S.: 562920
Daniel Chapman *(Mgr-Ops)*
David Anderson *(Mgr-Ops)*

Subsidiary (Domestic):

Sims Tyrecycle Pty. Ltd.   **(3)**
30-56 Encore Avenue, Somerton, 3062,
VIC, Australia
Tel.: (61) 393052585
Web Site: http://www.simstyrecycle.com.au
Sales Range: $25-49.9 Million
Emp.: 20
Rubber Tire Recycling & Processing Services
N.A.I.C.S.: 562920
Allan Kerr *(Gen Mgr)*

Subsidiary (Non-US):

Simsmetal Industries Limited   **(3)**
Manu St, Otahuhu, Auckland, 2024, New
Zealand
Tel.: (64) 92761809
Web Site: http://www.simsmetals.co.nz
Sales Range: $50-74.9 Million
Scrap & Recyclable Material Whslr
N.A.I.C.S.: 423930
Angus Barratt *(Gen Mgr)*

Subsidiary (Domestic):

Simsmetal Services Pty Limited   **(3)**
Slr Joseph Banks Corporate Park Level 2,
32-34 Lord Street, Sydney, 2019,
Australia   **(100%)**
Tel.: (61) 299569100
Web Site: http://www.Simsmetal.com
Sales Range: $600-649.9 Million
Air & Water Resource & Waste Management Programs
N.A.I.C.S.: 924110
Darron McGree *(Mng Dir)*

Subsidiary (Non-US):

Sims Group UK Holdings Limited   **(2)**
Long Marston, Stratford-upon-Avon, CV37
8AQ, Warks, United Kingdom   **(100%)**
Tel.: (44) 1789720431
Web Site: http://uk.simsmm.com
Emp.: 80
Holding Company; Metals & Electronic
Components Recycling Services
N.A.I.C.S.: 551112

Subsidiary (Domestic):

Sims Metal Management -
Stratford-upon-Avon   **(3)**
Long Marston, Stratford-upon-Avon, CV37
8AQ, Warks, United Kingdom   **(100%)**
Tel.: (44) 1789720431
Web Site: http://www.simsmm.co.uk
Metals & Electronic Components Recycling
Services
N.A.I.C.S.: 562920

Subsidiary (Domestic):

Sims Recycling Solutions UK Holdings Ltd.   **(4)**
Long Marston, Stratford-upon-Avon, CV37
8AQ, Warks, United Kingdom   **(100%)**

Tel.: (44) 1789720431
Web Site: http://www.simsrecycling.co.uk
Sales Range: $1-4.9 Billion
Holding Company; Metals & Electronic
Components Recycling Services
N.A.I.C.S.: 551112

Subsidiary (Non-US):

Mirec B.V.   **(5)**
Hastelweg 251, NL-5652 CV, Eindhoven,
Netherlands   **(100%)**
Tel.: (31) 402508800
Web Site: http://www.mirec.nl
Sales Range: $1-4.9 Billion
Emp.: 150
Metals & Electronic Components Recycling
Services
N.A.I.C.S.: 562920
Un Geyser *(Mng Dir)*

Sims M+R GmbH   **(5)**
Rathenaustrasse 10, PO Box 1440, Bergkamen, 59192, Nordrhein-Westfalen, Germany
Tel.: (49) 2307973730
Web Site: http://www.simsrecycling.de
Sales Range: $50-74.9 Million
Emp.: 125
Recyclable Material Whslr
N.A.I.C.S.: 423930
Mark Affuepper *(Mng Dir)*

Sims Recycling Solutions AB   **(5)**
Karosserigatan 6, 641 51, Katrineholm, Sodermanland, Sweden
Tel.: (46) 150368030
Web Site: http://www.se.simsrecycling.com
Sales Range: $25-49.9 Million
Emp.: 40
Recyclable Material Whslr
N.A.I.C.S.: 423930
Hakan Scheden *(Mng Dir)*

Sims Recycling Solutions NV   **(5)**
Europark Nord 32, 9100, Saint-Niklaas,
Belgium
Tel.: (32) 37805240
Web Site: http://www.simsrecycling.com
Sales Range: $25-49.9 Million
Emp.: 10
Electronic Components Recycling Services
N.A.I.C.S.: 562920
Muir Celmens *(Gen Mgr)*

Subsidiary (Domestic):

Sims Recycling Solutions UK
Ltd.   **(5)**
Irongray Bus Pk, Lochside Industrial Estate,
Dumfries, DG2 0NR, Scotland, United
Kingdom   **(100%)**
Tel.: (44) 1387723000
Web Site: http://uk.simsrecycling.com
Sales Range: $500-549.9 Million
Emp.: 60
Electronic Components Recycling Services
N.A.I.C.S.: 562920
Martin Mitchell *(Gen Mgr)*

Subsidiary (Domestic):

United Castings Limited   **(4)**
Birchwood Ln New Birchwood, Somercotes,
Alfreton, DE55 4NH, Derbyshire, United
Kingdom
Tel.: (44) 1773528800
Web Site: http://www.unitedcastings.com
Sales Range: $10-24.9 Million
Emp.: 3
Steel Casting Mfr
N.A.I.C.S.: 331513

Subsidiary (US):

Sims Recycling Solutions Holdings
Inc.   **(2)**
1600 Harvester Rd, West Chicago, IL
60185-1618
Tel.: (630) 231-6060
Web Site: http://www.simsrecycling.com
Sales Range: $10-24.9 Million
Holding Company; Metals & Electronic
Components Recycling Services
N.A.I.C.S.: 551111
Darrell Stoecklin *(CFO)*
Steve Skurnac *(Pres)*

Subsidiary (Domestic):

Sims Recycling Solutions, Inc.   **(3)**

1600 Harvester Rd, West Chicago, IL
60185-1618
Tel.: (630) 231-6060
Web Site: http://us.simsrecycling.com
Electronic Components Recycling Services
N.A.I.C.S.: 562920
Stephen Skurnac *(Pres)*
James Glavin *(VP-Ops-North Reg)*
Marie Burke *(Dir-HR)*
Rafael Reveles *(Dir-Engrg & Technical)*
Jason Price *(Dir-Electronics Procurement)*
Darrell Stoecklin *(CFO & VP-Fin)*
Andrew Mason *(VP-Ops)*

Unit (Domestic):

Sims Recycling Solutions - Chicago
Refining   **(4)**
3700 Runge St, Franklin Park, IL 60131-
1112
Tel.: (847) 455-8800
Web Site: http://us.simsrecycling.com
Precious Metal Recycling & Refining Services
N.A.I.C.S.: 562920

SIMULATED ENVIRONMENT CONCEPTS, INC.

30 N Gould St Ste 12029, Sheridan,
WY 82801
Tel.: (615) 300-6991   **FL**
Year Founded: 2000
SMEV—(OTCIQ)
Electronic Wellness Equipment Mfr
N.A.I.C.S.: 339920
Bryan A. Wilkinson *(CEO)*
Douglass B. Vaughn *(CFO)*

SIMULATIONS PLUS, INC.

42505 10th St W STE 103, Lancaster, CA 93535
Tel.: (661) 723-7723
Web Site: https://www.simulations-
   plus.com
SLP—(NASDAQ)
Rev.: $70,013,000
Assets: $196,639,000
Liabilities: $14,208,000
Net Worth: $182,431,000
Earnings: $9,954,000
Emp.: 243
Fiscal Year-end: 08/31/24
Drug Absorption Rates Modeling Software
N.A.I.C.S.: 541512
Walter S. Woltosz *(Founder & Chm)*
John Anthony DiBella *(Pres)*
Sandra Suarez-Sharp *(Pres-
Regulatory Strategies)*
Will Frederick *(CFO & COO)*
Nguyen Nguyen *(VP-HR)*
Arlene Padron *(Dir-Mktg)*
David Miller *(VP-Cheminformatics)*
Josh Fohey *(Sr VP-Ops)*
Jill Fiedler-Kelly *(Pres)*
Dan Szot *(Chief Revenue Officer)*
Shawn M. O'Connor *(CEO)*

Subsidiaries:

Cognigen Corporation   **(1)**
1780 Wehrle Dr Ste 110, Buffalo, NY
14221   **(100%)**
Tel.: (716) 633-3463
Web Site: http://www.cognigencorp.com
Emp.: 30
Pharmaceutical Consulting Services
N.A.I.C.S.: 541690
Thaddeus Henry Grasela Jr. *(Co-Pres)*

Immunetrics Inc.   **(1)**
2403 Sidney St Ste 270, Pittsburgh, PA
15203-2163
Tel.: (412) 246-0635
Web Site: http://www.immunetrics.com
Biological Products
N.A.I.C.S.: 325414
Steve Chang *(CEO)*

Lixoft SAS   **(1)**
8 rue de la Renaissance Batiment D,
Antony, France

Tel.: (33) 972539180
Web Site: https://www.lixoft.com
Software Development Services
N.A.I.C.S.: 541511
Jerome Kalifa *(Co-Founder)*
Jonathan Chauvin *(CEO)*
Marc Lavielle *(Co-Founder)*

Prima Solutions Belgium SA   (1)
Schuttersvest 75, 2800, Mechelen, Belgium
Tel.: (32) 15434367
Software Development Services
N.A.I.C.S.: 541511

SINCLAIR, INC.

10706 Beaver Dam Rd, Hunt Valley,
MD 21030
Tel.: (410) 568-1500   MD
Web Site: https://sbgi.net
Year Founded: 2022
SBGI—(NASDAQ)
Rev.: $3,134,000,000
Assets: $6,085,000,000
Liabilities: $5,864,000,000
Net Worth: $221,000,000
Earnings: ($279,000,000)
Emp.: 7,300
Fiscal Year-end: 12/31/23
Offices of Other Holding Companies
N.A.I.C.S.: 551112
J. Duncan Smith *(Sec & VP)*
David D. Smith *(Chm)*
Frederick G. Smith *(VP)*
David R. Bochenek *(Chief Acctg Offi-cer & Sr VP)*
Lucy A. Rutishauser *(CFO & Exec VP)*
Christopher S. Ripley *(Pres & CEO)*
Delbert R. Parks III *(Pres-Tech)*

Subsidiaries:

Sinclair Broadcast Group, LLC   (1)
10706 Beaver Dam Rd, Hunt Valley, MD
21030
Tel.: (410) 568-1500
Web Site: https://www.sbgi.net
Rev.: $2,978,000,000
Assets: $4,837,000,000
Liabilities: $5,765,000,000
Net Worth: ($928,000,000)
Earnings: ($245,000,000)
Emp.: 7,299
Fiscal Year-end: 12/31/2023
Television Broadcasting Stations Owner &
Operator
N.A.I.C.S.: 516120
David D. Smith *(Exec Chm)*
David R. Bochenek *(Chief Acctg Officer &
Sr VP)*
Lucy A. Rutishauser *(CFO & Exec VP)*
Christopher S. Ripley *(Pres & CEO)*
Delbert R. Parks III *(Pres-Tech)*
Robert D. Weisbord *(COO & Pres-Brdcst)*
David Gibber *(Sr VP)*
Brian Bark *(CIO & Sr VP)*
Cory Culleton *(VP & Assoc Mgr-Grp)*
Christopher C. King *(VP-IR)*
William Bell *(Sr VP)*
Scott Livingston *(Sr VP)*
Rocky Wagonhurst *(VP/Gen Mgr-WVTV)*

Subsidiary (Domestic):

Capitol News Company, LLC   (2)
1100 Wilson Blvd Fl 6, Arlington, VA 22209-
2249
Tel.: (703) 842-1721
Web Site: http://www.politico.com
Newspaper Publishers
N.A.I.C.S.: 513110
Miki King *(Sr VP-Bus Dev)*
Robert L. Allbritton *(Founder & Chm)*
Patrick Steel *(CEO)*

Subsidiary (Domestic):

**Environment & Energy Publishing,
LLC   (3)**
122 C St NW Ste 722, Washington, DC
20001-2109
Tel.: (202) 628-6500
Web Site: http://www.eenews.net
Internet Publishing & Broadcasting & Web
Search Portals
N.A.I.C.S.: 516210

Richard Nordin *(Dir-Adv)*

Subsidiary (Domestic):

DataSphere Technologies, Inc.   (2)
3350 161st Ave SE, Bellevue, WA 98008
Tel.: (866) 912-7090
Web Site: http://www.datasphere.com
Hyperlocal Marketing Software Solution
Provider
N.A.I.C.S.: 513210
Delane Hewett *(CTO)*
Laurent Chavet *(VP & Chief Architect)*

Diamond Sports Group, LLC   (2)
616 Happy Acres Dr Ste B, Chesapeake,
VA 23323
Tel.: (757) 707-8999
Web Site:
    http://www.diamondsportsgroup.org
Sports Marketing Services
N.A.I.C.S.: 711310
Larry Kennedy *(Pres)*
Thomas Epps *(VP-Player Dev)*
Cheryl Redd *(VP)*
David DeVoe Jr. *(CFO & COO)*
David Preschlack *(CEO)*
Meredith Powers *(Chief HR Officer)*
Eric Ratchman *(Pres-Distr & Bus Dev)*

Dielectric, LLC   (2)
22 Tower Rd, Raymond, ME 04071
Tel.: (207) 655-8100
Web Site: https://www.dielectric.com
Sales Range: $25-49.9 Million
Emp.: 100
Telecommunications Equipment Mfr
N.A.I.C.S.: 334220
Jay Martin *(VP-Sales)*
Craig Gurney *(Mgr)*
John Schadler *(VP-Engineering)*
Jim Butts *(Sys Engr-Mechanical)*

Drive Auto, LLC   (2)
210 N H St, Yale, MI 74085
Tel.: (918) 387-2226
Web Site:
    http://www.driveauto.hasyourcar.com
Used Vehicle Whslr
N.A.I.C.S.: 441110

Fox Sports Net, LLC   (2)
10201 W Pico Blvd, Los Angeles, CA 90035
Tel.: (310) 584-2000
Web Site: http://www.foxsports.com
Cable Television Services
N.A.I.C.S.: 516120

KDSM, LLC   (2)
4023 Fleur Dr, Des Moines, IA 50321-2321
Tel.: (515) 287-1717
Web Site: http://www.kdsm.com
Sales Range: $200-249.9 Million
Emp.: 10
Television Broadcasting Station
N.A.I.C.S.: 516120

Sinclair Television Group, Inc.   (2)
10706 Beaver Dam Rd, Hunt Valley, MD
21030
Tel.: (410) 568-1500
Web Site: http://www.sbgi.net
Sales Range: $100-124.9 Million
Emp.: 300
Holding Company; Television Broadcasting
Stations Operator & Licensor
N.A.I.C.S.: 551112

Subsidiary (Domestic):

KABB-TV   (3)
4335 NW Loop 410, San Antonio, TX 78229
Tel.: (210) 366-1129
Web Site: https://www.foxsanantonio.com
TV Station
N.A.I.C.S.: 516120
Grace Jones *(Dir-Program)*

KAME, LLC   (3)
9711 S Eastern Ave, Las Vegas, NV 89183
Tel.: (702) 898-9190
Television Broadcasting Station
N.A.I.C.S.: 516120
Dave Slamcik *(Chief Engr)*

KBSI-TV   (3)
806 Enterprise St, Cape Girardeau, MO
63703
Tel.: (573) 334-1223
Web Site: http://www.kbsi23.com

Sales Range: $10-24.9 Million
Emp.: 40
TV Station
N.A.I.C.S.: 516120

Subsidiary (Domestic):

KBSI Licensee L.P.   (4)
806 Enterprise St, Cape Girardeau, MO
63703
Tel.: (573) 334-1223
Web Site: https://www.kbsi23.com
Emp.: 40
Television Broadcasting Stations Operator
N.A.I.C.S.: 516120

Subsidiary (Domestic):

KBTV-TV   (3)
2955 I-10 E, Beaumont, TX 77702
Tel.: (409) 892-6622
Web Site: http://www.fox4beaumont.com
Television Broadcasting Station
N.A.I.C.S.: 516120

KDNL-TV   (3)
1034 S Brentwood Ste 1910, Richmond
Heights, MO 63117
Tel.: (314) 436-3030
Web Site: https://www.abcstlouis.com
Sales Range: $75-99.9 Million
Emp.: 32
TV Station
N.A.I.C.S.: 516120

KEYE-TV   (3)
10700 Metric Blvd, Austin, TX 78758
Tel.: (512) 835-0042
Web Site: https://www.cbsaustin.com
Local Television Station
N.A.I.C.S.: 516120

KFDM-TV   (3)
1660 S 23rd St, Beaumont, TX 77707
Tel.: (409) 892-6622
Web Site: https://www.kfdm.com
Sales Range: $25-49.9 Million
Emp.: 67
Television Station
N.A.I.C.S.: 516120

KGAN-TV   (3)
600 Old Marion Rd NE, Cedar Rapids, IA
52402   (100%)
Tel.: (319) 730-3443
Web Site: https://cbs2iowa.com
Sales Range: $25-49.9 Million
Emp.: 80
Television Station
N.A.I.C.S.: 516120
Greg Stuart *(Dir-Programming)*

Subsidiary (Domestic):

KGAN Licensee, LLC   (4)
600 Old Marion Rd NE, Cedar Rapids, IA
52402-2159
Tel.: (319) 395-9060
Web Site: http://www.cbs2iowa.com
Television Broadcasting Stations Operator
N.A.I.C.S.: 516120

Unit (Domestic):

KGBT-TV   (3)
9201 W Expy 83, Harlingen, TX 78552
Tel.: (956) 366-4444
Web Site: http://www.valleycentral.com
Sales Range: $10-24.9 Million
Emp.: 75
Television Station
N.A.I.C.S.: 516120

Subsidiary (Domestic):

KMYS-TV   (3)
4335 NW Loop 410, San Antonio, TX
78229-5168
Tel.: (210) 366-1129
Web Site: http://www.kmys.com
Sales Range: $25-49.9 Million
Emp.: 260
TV Station
N.A.I.C.S.: 516120

KOCB, Inc.   (3)
1228 E Wilshire Blvd, Oklahoma City, OK
73111
Tel.: (405) 843-2525
Web Site: https://cwokc.com

Sales Range: $25-49.9 Million
Emp.: 130
TV Station
N.A.I.C.S.: 516120

Subsidiary (Domestic):

KOCB Licensee, LLC   (4)
1228 E Wilshire Blvd, Oklahoma City, OK
73111-8402
Tel.: (405) 843-2525
Web Site: https://www.okcfox.com
Sales Range: $25-49.9 Million
Emp.: 100
Television Broadcasting Stations Operator
N.A.I.C.S.: 516120

Subsidiary (Domestic):

KRXI, LLC   (3)
1790 Vassar St, Reno, NV 89502
Tel.: (775) 322-4444
Web Site: https://www.foxreno.com
Emp.: 34
Television Broadcasting Station
N.A.I.C.S.: 516120
Amie Chapman *(Gen Mgr)*

KTVL-TV   (3)
111 N Fir St, Medford, OR 97501
Tel.: (541) 773-7373
Web Site: https://www.ktvl.com
Sales Range: $100-124.9 Million
Emp.: 40
Television Station
N.A.I.C.S.: 516120

KUQI Licensee, LLC   (3)
205 W College St, Lake Charles, LA 70605-
1625
Tel.: (337) 477-2827
Television Broadcasting Services
N.A.I.C.S.: 516120

KUTV-TV   (3)
299 S Main St Ste 150, Salt Lake City, UT
84111
Tel.: (801) 839-1234
Web Site: https://kutv.com
Sales Range: $50-74.9 Million
Emp.: 250
Local Television Station
N.A.I.C.S.: 516120

KVCW, LLC   (3)
1500 Foremaster Ln, Las Vegas, NV 89101
Tel.: (702) 642-3333
Web Site: http://www.thecwlasvegas.tv
Television Broadcasting Station
N.A.I.C.S.: 516120

ONE Media, LLC   (3)
8114 Pickard Ave NE, Albuquerque, NM
87110
Tel.: (505) 506-3300
Web Site: http://www.onemediallc.com
Television Broadcasting Services
N.A.I.C.S.: 516120
Jerald Fritz *(Exec VP-Strategic & Legal Af-fairs)*
Mark A. Aitken *(Pres)*
Michael E. Bouchard *(VP-Tech Strategy)*
Sesh Simba *(VP-Advanced Tech)*

Perpetual Corporation   (3)
1000 Wilson Blvd Ste 2700, Arlington, VA
22209
Tel.: (703) 647-8700
Sales Range: $125-149.9 Million
Emp.: 15
Holding Company
N.A.I.C.S.: 551112

Subsidiary (Domestic):

Sinclair Television Stations, LLC   (4)
10706 Beaver Dam Rd, Hunt Valley, MD
21030   (100%)
Tel.: (410) 568-1500
Web Site: http://www.sbgi.net
Holding Company; Television Broadcasting
Stations
N.A.I.C.S.: 551112

Subsidiary (Domestic):

ACC Licensee, LLC   (5)
1100 Wilson Blvd, Arlington, VA 22209
Tel.: (703) 236-9552
Web Site: https://www.wjla.com

Sinclair, Inc.—(Continued)

Sales Range: $25-49.9 Million
Emp.: 150
Television Broadcasting Station; Cable Television News Services
N.A.I.C.S.: 516120

KATV, LLC (5)
401 Main St, Little Rock, AR
72201 (100%)
Tel.: (501) 324-7777
Web Site: https://katv.com
Sales Range: $25-49.9 Million
Emp.: 140
Television Broadcasting Station
N.A.I.C.S.: 516120

KTUL, LLC (5)
3333 S 29th W Ave, Tulsa, OK
74101 (100%)
Tel.: (918) 445-9398
Web Site: http://ktul.com
Sales Range: $10-24.9 Million
Emp.: 114
Television Broadcasting Station
N.A.I.C.S.: 516120
Roger Herring (Dir-Brdcst Ops)
Gregg Siegel (VP-Sls-Natl)
Jim Joly (Dir-Digital Sls-Natl)

WSET, Incorporated (5)
2320 Langhorne Rd, Lynchburg, VA
24501-1547 (100%)
Tel.: (434) 528-1313
Web Site: https://www.wset.com
Sales Range: $10-24.9 Million
Emp.: 97
Television Broadcasting Station
N.A.I.C.S.: 516120

Subsidiary (Domestic):

Sinclair Television of Nevada, Inc. (3)
10706 Beaver Dam Rd, Hunt Valley, MD
21030
Tel.: (410) 568-1500
Holding Company; Television Broadcasting Station Operator
N.A.I.C.S.: 551112

Subsidiary (Domestic):

Sinclair Television of Charleston, Inc. (4)
10706 Beaver Dam Rd, Cockeysville, MD
21030
Tel.: (410) 568-1500
Web Site: http://www.sbgi.net
Sales Range: $75-99.9 Million
Holding Company; Television Broadcasting Station Operator
N.A.I.C.S.: 551112

Subsidiary (Domestic):

WRLH-TV (5)
2001 Maywill St Ste 103, Richmond, VA
23230
Tel.: (804) 358-3535
Web Site: http://www.fox35.com
Sales Range: $10-24.9 Million
Emp.: 40
TV Station
N.A.I.C.S.: 516120

Subsidiary (Domestic):

Sinclair Television of Dayton, Inc. (4)
10706 Beaver Dam Rd, Cockeysville, MD
21030
Tel.: (410) 568-1600
Holding Company; Television Broadcasting Station Operator
N.A.I.C.S.: 551112

Sinclair Television of Tennessee, Inc. (4)
10706 Beaver Dam Rd, Cockeysville, MD
21030
Tel.: (410) 568-1500
Sales Range: $75-99.9 Million
Emp.: 50
Holding Company; Television Broadcasting Station Operator
N.A.I.C.S.: 551112

WDKY, Inc. (4)
836 Euclid Ave Ste 201, Lexington, KY
40502

Tel.: (859) 269-5656
Web Site: http://www.foxlexington.com
Sales Range: $10-24.9 Million
Emp.: 25
TV Station
N.A.I.C.S.: 516120

Subsidiary (Domestic):

KOKH-TV (5)
1228 E Wilshire Blvd, Oklahoma City, OK
73111
Tel.: (405) 843-2525
Web Site: http://www.okcfox.com
TV Station
N.A.I.C.S.: 516120

Subsidiary (Domestic):

WMYV-TV (4)
3500 Myer Lee Dr, Winston Salem, NC
27101
Tel.: (336) 722-4545
Web Site: http://www.my48.tv
Sales Range: $25-49.9 Million
Emp.: 30
Television Broadcasting Station
N.A.I.C.S.: 516120

WUTV-TV (4)
699 Hertel Ave Ste 100, Buffalo, NY 14207
Tel.: (716) 447-3200
Web Site: https://wutv29.com
Sales Range: $10-24.9 Million
Emp.: 45
TV Station
N.A.I.C.S.: 516120
Nick Magnini (Gen Mgr)

WXLV-TV (4)
3500 Myer Lee Dr, Winston Salem, NC
27101
Tel.: (336) 722-4545
Web Site: http://www.abc45.com
Sales Range: $25-49.9 Million
Emp.: 30
TV Station
N.A.I.C.S.: 516120
Angie Jordan (Sls Dir)
Thomas Caffrey (Sls Dir-Natl)

Subsidiary (Domestic):

Sinclair Television of Seattle, Inc. (3)
140 4th Ave N Ste 500, Seattle, WA 98109
Tel.: (206) 404-7000
Sales Range: $150-199.9 Million
Emp.: 776
Holding Company; Television & Radio Broadcasting Stations Operator
N.A.I.C.S.: 551112
David B. Amy (Sec)

Subsidiary (Domestic):

Sinclair Media Services Company (4)
140 4th Ave N Ste 500, Seattle, WA 98019
Tel.: (206) 404-8000
Television Broadcasting Services
N.A.I.C.S.: 516120

Sinclair Television Media, Inc. (4)
100 4th Ave N Ste 440, Seattle, WA
98109 (100%)
Tel.: (206) 404-7000
Sales Range: $50-74.9 Million
Emp.: 225
Television & Radio Broadcasting Stations Operator
N.A.I.C.S.: 516120

Subsidiary (Domestic):

KLEW-TV (5)
2626 17th St, Lewiston, ID 83501
Tel.: (208) 746-2636
Web Site: https://www.klewtv.com
Emp.: 20
Television Broadcasting Station
N.A.I.C.S.: 516120
Dan Stellmon (Gen Mgr)

KOMO-TV (5)
Ste 370 140 4th Ave N, Seattle, WA 98109
Tel.: (206) 404-4000
Web Site: https://www.komonews.com
Television Broadcasting Station
N.A.I.C.S.: 516120

Sinclair Media of Boise, LLC (5)

140 N 16th St, Boise, ID 83702
Tel.: (208) 472-2222
Web Site: http://www.kboi2.com
Sales Range: $25-49.9 Million
Emp.: 60
Television Broadcasting Station
N.A.I.C.S.: 516120

Sinclair Media of Idaho, LLC (5)
1255 E 17th St, Idaho Falls, ID 83401-6126
Tel.: (208) 522-5100
Television Broadcasting Station
N.A.I.C.S.: 516120

Sinclair Television of Bakersfield, LLC (5)
1901 Westwind Dr, Bakersfield, CA 93301
Tel.: (661) 327-7955
Web Site: https://www.bakersfieldnow.com
Sales Range: $25-49.9 Million
Emp.: 83
Television Broadcasting Station
N.A.I.C.S.: 516120

Sinclair Television of Oregon, LLC (5)
4575 Blanton Rd, Eugene, OR 97405
Tel.: (541) 342-4961
Web Site: https://kval.com
Television Broadcasting Station
N.A.I.C.S.: 516120

Unit (Domestic):

KCBY-TV (6)
3451 Broadway St, North Bend, OR 97459
Tel.: (541) 269-1111
Web Site: http://www.kcby.com
Emp.: 7
Television Broadcasting Station
N.A.I.C.S.: 516120
Daniel Corken (Gen Mgr)

Subsidiary (Domestic):

KPIC-TV (5)
655 W Umpqua St, Roseburg, OR 97471
Tel.: (541) 672-4481
Web Site: https://www.kpic.com
Emp.: 7
Television Broadcasting Station
N.A.I.C.S.: 516120

KVAL-TV (6)
4575 Blanton Rd, Eugene, OR 97405
Tel.: (541) 342-4961
Web Site: https://www.kval.com
Emp.: 50
Television Broadcasting Station
N.A.I.C.S.: 516120
Brandon Kamerman (Dir-Sports)

Subsidiary (Domestic):

Sinclair Television of Portland, LLC (5)
2153 NE Sandy Blvd, Portland, OR 97232-2819
Tel.: (503) 231-4222
Web Site: https://katu.com
Television Broadcasting Station
N.A.I.C.S.: 516120

Sinclair Television of Washington, LLC (5)
2801 Terrace Heights Dr, Yakima, WA
98901
Tel.: (509) 575-0029
Television Broadcasting Station
N.A.I.C.S.: 516120

Subsidiary (Domestic):

KEPR-TV (6)
2807 W Lewis St, Pasco, WA 99301
Tel.: (509) 547-0547
Web Site: https://www.keprtv.com
Emp.: 45
Television Broadcasting Station
N.A.I.C.S.: 516120
John Mazza (Engr)

Subsidiary (Domestic):

WABM-TV (3)
800 Concourse Pkwy Ste 200, Birmingham,
AL 35244
Tel.: (205) 403-3340
Web Site: https://www.wabm68.com

Sales Range: $10-24.9 Million
Emp.: 40
TV Station
N.A.I.C.S.: 811210

WBFF-TV (3)
2000 W 41st St, Baltimore, MD 21211
Tel.: (410) 467-4545
Web Site: https://www.foxbaltimore.com
Sales Range: $25-49.9 Million
Emp.: 50
TV Station
N.A.I.C.S.: 516120

WCGV, Inc. (3)
11520 W Calumet Rd, Milwaukee, WI
53224
Tel.: (414) 359-0659
Sales Range: $25-49.9 Million
Emp.: 40
TV Station
N.A.I.C.S.: 516120
Terry Gaughan (Gen Mgr-WCGV-TV)

WCHS-TV (3)
1301 Piedmont Rd, Charleston, WV 25301
Tel.: (304) 346-5358
Web Site: https://www.wchstv.com
Sales Range: $25-49.9 Million
Emp.: 105
Television Broadcasting Station
N.A.I.C.S.: 516120

WCIV-TV (3)
888 Allbritton Blvd, Mount Pleasant, SC
29464
Tel.: (843) 881-4444
Web Site: https://www.abcnews4.com
Emp.: 90
Television Broadcasting Station
N.A.I.C.S.: 516120
Mary Margaret Nelms (VP)
Erin Bassily (Mgr-Local Sls)
Ben Barna (Mgr-Digital Sls)
Sean Rob Mallia (Coord-NTR & Digital)

WCWN LLC (3)
1400 Balltown Rd, Schenectady, NY 12309
Tel.: (518) 381-4900
Web Site: https://www.cwalbany.com
Sales Range: $25-49.9 Million
Emp.: 50
Television Station
N.A.I.C.S.: 516120
Terry Beacham (Dir-Engrg)

WEAR-TV (3)
4990 Mobile Hwy, Pensacola, FL 32506
Tel.: (850) 456-3333
Web Site: https://www.weartv.com
Emp.: 110
Television Station
N.A.I.C.S.: 516120

Subsidiary (Domestic):

WEAR Licensee, LLC (4)
4990 Mobile Hwy, Pensacola, FL 32506-
3230
Tel.: (850) 456-3333
Web Site: http://www.weartv.com
Emp.: 100
Television Broadcasting Stations Operator
N.A.I.C.S.: 516120
Dan Shugart (Dir-Sports)

Subsidiary (Domestic):

WGME, Inc. (3)
81 Northport Dr, Portland, ME
04103-3638 (100%)
Tel.: (207) 797-1313
Web Site: https://www.wgme.com
Sales Range: $25-49.9 Million
Emp.: 85
Television Station
N.A.I.C.S.: 516120
Dave Eid (Dir-Sports)

WHAM-TV (3)
4225 W Henrietta Rd, Rochester, NY 14623
Tel.: (585) 334-8700
Web Site: https://www.13wham.com
Sales Range: $25-49.9 Million
Emp.: 105
Television Broadcasting Station
N.A.I.C.S.: 516120
Jim Joly (Dir-Digital Sls-Natl)
Danielle Turner (Dir-Admin)

WHP-TV (3)

3300 N 6th St, Harrisburg, PA 17110
Tel.: (717) 238-2100
Web Site: https://local21news.com
Sales Range: $25-49.9 Million
Emp.: 100
Television Broadcasting
N.A.I.C.S.: 516120

WICD-TV (3)
2680 E Cook St, Springfield, IL
62703 (100%)
Tel.: (217) 753-5620
Web Site: https://newschannel20.com
Sales Range: $10-24.9 Million
Emp.: 53
Television Station
N.A.I.C.S.: 516120

Subsidiary (Domestic):

WICD Licensee, LLC (4)
2680 E Cook St, Springfield, IL 62703
Tel.: (217) 753-5660
Web Site: http://www.newschannel20.com
Television Broadcasting Stations Operator
N.A.I.C.S.: 516120

Subsidiary (Domestic):

WICS-TV (3)
2680 E Cook St, Springfield, IL
62703 (100%)
Tel.: (217) 753-5620
Web Site: https://www.newschannel20.com
Sales Range: $25-49.9 Million
Emp.: 100
Television Station
N.A.I.C.S.: 516120

WJAC-TV (3)
49 Old Hickory Ln, Johnstown, PA 15905
Tel.: (814) 255-7600
Web Site: https://www.wjactv.com
Television Broadcasting Station
N.A.I.C.S.: 516120
Rob Abele (Dir-Engrg)

WJAR-TV (3)
23 Kenney Dr, Cranston, RI 02920
Tel.: (401) 455-9100
Web Site: https://www.turnto10.com
Television Broadcasting Services
N.A.I.C.S.: 516120
Jim Joly (Dir-Natl Digital Sls)
Greg Siegel (VP-Natl Digital Sls)

WKRC-TV (3)
1906 Highland Ave, Cincinnati, OH 45219
Tel.: (513) 763-5500
Web Site: https://www.local12.com
Sales Range: $50-74.9 Million
Emp.: 290
Television Broadcasting Station
N.A.I.C.S.: 516120
Tim Geraghty (Dir-News)

Unit (Domestic):

WLAJ-TV (3)
5815 S Pennsylvania Ave, Lansing, MI
48911
Tel.: (517) 394-5300
Web Site: http://www.wlaj.com
Sales Range: $10-24.9 Million
Emp.: 25
Television Station
N.A.I.C.S.: 516120

Subsidiary (Domestic):

WLFL, Inc. (3)
3012 Highwoods Blvd Ste 101, Raleigh, NC
27604
Tel.: (919) 872-2854
Web Site: https://raleighcw.com
Sales Range: $10-24.9 Million
Emp.: 60
TV Station
N.A.I.C.S.: 516120
Tom Quillen (Mgr-HR)

WLOS-TV (3)
110 Technology Dr, Asheville, NC 28803
Tel.: (828) 684-1340
Web Site: https://www.wlos.com
Sales Range: $25-49.9 Million
Emp.: 145
TV Station
N.A.I.C.S.: 516120
Courtney Youngblood (Dir-Sls)
Estee Felten (Sls Mgr-Digital)

WLUK-TV (3)
787 Lombardi Ave, Green Bay, WI 54304
Tel.: (920) 494-8711
Web Site: https://www.fox11online.com
Television Broadcasting Services
N.A.I.C.S.: 516120
Greg Bosetski (Mgr-Local Sls)
Steve Teofilo (Mgr-Digital Sls)

Unit (Domestic):

WMMP-TV (3)
888 Allbritton Blvd, Mount Pleasant, SC
29464
Tel.: (843) 881-4444
Web Site: http://www.mytvcharleston.com
Sales Range: $10-24.9 Million
Emp.: 40
Television Broadcasting Station
N.A.I.C.S.: 516120

Subsidiary (Domestic):

WMSN-TV (3)
7847 Big Sky Dr, Madison, WI 53719
Tel.: (608) 833-0047
Web Site: https://www.fox47.com
Sales Range: $10-24.9 Million
Emp.: 43
TV Station
N.A.I.C.S.: 516120

Subsidiary (Domestic):

WMSN Licensee, LLC (4)
7847 Big Sky Dr, Madison, WI 53719-4957
Tel.: (608) 833-0047
Web Site: https://www.fox47.com
Television Broadcasting Stations Operator
N.A.I.C.S.: 516120

Subsidiary (Domestic):

WNYO, Inc. (3)
699 Hertel Ave Ste 100, Buffalo, NY 14207
Tel.: (716) 447-3200
Web Site: https://www.mytvbuffalo.com
Sales Range: $25-49.9 Million
Emp.: 50
TV Station
N.A.I.C.S.: 516120
David Smith (Pres)

WOAI-TV (3)
4335 NW Loop 410, San Antonio, TX 78229
Tel.: (210) 366-1129
Web Site: https://news4sanantonio.com
Sales Range: $25-49.9 Million
Emp.: 150
Television Broadcasting Station
N.A.I.C.S.: 516120
Dean Radla (Gen Mgr)
Don Harris (Dir-Sports)

WPDE-TV (3)
10 University Blvd, Conway, SC 29526
Tel.: (843) 234-9733
Web Site: https://wpde.com
Sales Range: $10-24.9 Million
Emp.: 50
Television Broadcasting Services
N.A.I.C.S.: 516120
Billy Huggins (Pres)
Allyson Floyd (Asst Dir-News)
Victoria Spechko (Dir-News)

WPEC-TV (3)
1100 Fairfield Dr, West Palm Beach, FL
33407
Tel.: (561) 844-1212
Web Site: https://www.cbs12.com
Sales Range: $25-49.9 Million
Emp.: 100
Television Station
N.A.I.C.S.: 516120
Michael Sheffer (Dir-Engrg)

WPMI-TV (3)
661 Azalea Rd, Mobile, AL 36609
Tel.: (251) 602-1500
Web Site: https://mynbc15.com
Sales Range: $25-49.9 Million
Emp.: 105
Television Broadcasting Station
N.A.I.C.S.: 516120

WRGB-TV (3)
1400 Balltown Rd, Schenectady, NY
12309 (100%)
Tel.: (518) 346-6666
Web Site: https://www.cbs6albany.com

Sales Range: $25-49.9 Million
Emp.: 100
Television Station
N.A.I.C.S.: 516120

WSMH, Inc. (3)
G3463 W Pierson Rd, Flint, MI 48504
Tel.: (810) 785-8866
Web Site: http://www.wsmh.com
Sales Range: $10-24.9 Million
Emp.: 60
Television Broadcasting Station
N.A.I.C.S.: 516120

Unit (Domestic):

WSYT-TV (3)
1000 James St, Syracuse, NY 13203
Tel.: (315) 472-6800
Web Site: http://www.foxsyracuse.com
Sales Range: $25-49.9 Million
Emp.: 75
TV Station
N.A.I.C.S.: 516120

Subsidiary (Domestic):

WSYX-TV (3)
1261 Dublin Rd, Columbus, OH 43215
Tel.: (614) 481-6666
Web Site: https://www.abc6onyourside.com
TV Station
N.A.I.C.S.: 516120
Franco Gentile (Sls Dir)
Melody Marks (Sls Mgr-Local)
Colleen Buzza (Sls Mgr-Digital)

Subsidiary (Domestic):

WSYX Licensee, Inc. (4)
1261 Dublin Rd, Columbus, OH 43215
Tel.: (614) 816-6677
Web Site: https://abc6onyourside.com
Television Broadcasting Stations Operator
N.A.I.C.S.: 516120

Subsidiary (Domestic):

WTOV, Inc. (3)
9 Red Donley Plz, Mingo Junction, OH
43938 (100%)
Tel.: (740) 282-9999
Web Site: https://www.wtov9.com
Sales Range: $25-49.9 Million
Emp.: 75
Television Station
N.A.I.C.S.: 516120
Tom Pleva (Gen Mgr-Sls)

WTTO, Inc. (3)
800 Concourse Pkwy Ste 200, Birmingham,
AL 35244
Tel.: (205) 403-3340
Web Site: https://www.wtto21.com
Sales Range: $10-24.9 Million
Emp.: 40
TV Station
N.A.I.C.S.: 516120

Subsidiary (Domestic):

WTTO Licensee, LLC (4)
800 Concourse Pkwy Ste 200, Birmingham,
AL 35244
Tel.: (205) 403-3340
Web Site: http://www.wtto21.com
Television Broadcasting Stations Operator
N.A.I.C.S.: 516120

Subsidiary (Domestic):

WTVC-TV (3)
4279 Benton Dr, Chattanooga, TN 37406
Tel.: (423) 756-5500
Web Site: https://www.newschannel9.com
Sales Range: $25-49.9 Million
Emp.: 100
Television Station
N.A.I.C.S.: 516120
Todd Ricke (Gen Mgr)

WTVX-TV (3)
1100 Fairfield Dr, West Palm Beach, FL
33407
Tel.: (561) 681-3434
Web Site: https://cw34.com
Sales Range: $10-24.9 Million
Emp.: 30
Local Television Station
N.A.I.C.S.: 516120

Subsidiary (Domestic):

WTCN-CA (4)
1100 Fairfield Dr, West Palm Beach, FL
33407
Tel.: (561) 681-3434
Web Site: https://my15wtcn.com
Sales Range: $10-24.9 Million
Emp.: 22
Local Television Affiliate
N.A.I.C.S.: 516120
Jaime Martinez (Dir-Engrg)

WWHB-CA (4)
1100 Fairfield Dr, West Palm Beach, FL
33407
Tel.: (561) 844-1212
Web Site: https://cbs12.com
Sales Range: $10-24.9 Million
Emp.: 20
Local Television Affiliate
N.A.I.C.S.: 516120

Subsidiary (Domestic):

WTVZ, Inc. (3)
236 Clearfield Ave Ste 205, Virginia Beach,
VA 23462
Tel.: (757) 622-3333
Web Site: https://www.mytvz.com
Sales Range: $10-24.9 Million
Emp.: 20
Television Broadcasting Station
N.A.I.C.S.: 516120

WTWC-TV (3)
8440 Deerlake S, Tallahassee, FL 32312
Tel.: (850) 893-4140
Web Site: https://www.wtwc40.com
Sales Range: $25-49.9 Million
Emp.: 90
TV Broadcast Station
N.A.I.C.S.: 516120

WUCW-TV (3)
800 Hennepin Ave Ste 700, Minneapolis,
MN 55403
Tel.: (612) 594-3939
Web Site: https://www.thecwtc.com
Sales Range: $10-24.9 Million
Emp.: 25
Television Broadcasting Station
N.A.I.C.S.: 516120

WUHF-TV (3)
4225 W Henrietta Rd, Rochester, NY 14623
Tel.: (585) 334-8700
Web Site: https://foxrochester.com
Sales Range: $25-49.9 Million
Emp.: 150
TV Station
N.A.I.C.S.: 516120
Chuck Samuels (Gen Mgr)

WVTV-TV (3)
11520 W Calumet Rd, Milwaukee, WI
53224
Tel.: (414) 815-4100
Web Site: https://cw18milwaukee.com
Sales Range: $25-49.9 Million
Emp.: 40
TV Station
N.A.I.C.S.: 516120

WWHO-TV (3)
1261 Dublin Rd, Columbus, OH 43215
Tel.: (614) 485-5300
Web Site: https://www.cwcolumbus.com
Television Broadcasting Station
N.A.I.C.S.: 516120
Jim Joly (Dir-Natl Digital Sls)
Gregg Siegel (VP-Natl Digital Sls)

WWMT-TV (3)
590 W Maple St, Kalamazoo, MI 49008
Tel.: (269) 388-9339
Web Site: https://wwmt.com
Sales Range: $25-49.9 Million
Emp.: 100
Television Station
N.A.I.C.S.: 516120
George Markle (Chief Engr)

WYZZ, Inc. (3)
3131 N University, Peoria, IL 61604
Tel.: (309) 688-3131
Web Site:
　https://www.centralillinoisproud.com
Sales Range: $10-24.9 Million
Emp.: 80
TV Station

Sinclair, Inc.—(Continued)
N.A.I.C.S.: 516120

WZTV-TV (3)
631 Mainstream Dr, Nashville, TN 37228
Tel.: (615) 259-5681
Web Site: https://fox17.com
Emp.: 130
Television Broadcasting Station
N.A.I.C.S.: 516120

Subsidiary (Domestic):

The Tennis Channel, Inc. (2)
3003 Exposition Blvd, Santa Monica, CA 90404
Tel.: (310) 314-9400
Web Site: http://www.thetennischannel.com
Tennis Cable Television Network
N.A.I.C.S.: 516210

SINGLEPOINT INC.
2999 N 44th St Ste 530, Phoenix, AZ 85018   NV
Web Site: http://www.singlepoint.com
Year Founded: 2007
SING—(OTCQB)
Rev.: $21,786,149
Assets: $19,120,371
Liabilities: $23,998,245
Net Worth: ($4,877,874)
Earnings: ($8,852,677)
Emp.: 100
Fiscal Year-end: 12/31/22
Mobile Software Development Services
N.A.I.C.S.: 541511
Corey A. Lambrecht (Pres & CFO)
William Ralston (CEO)

SINGULAR GENOMICS SYSTEMS, INC.
3010 Science Park Rd, San Diego, CA 92121
Tel.: (858) 333-7830   DE
Web Site:
    https://www.singulargenomics.com
Year Founded: 2016
OMIC—(NASDAQ)
Rev.: $765,000
Assets: $327,975,000
Liabilities: $67,654,000
Net Worth: $260,321,000
Earnings: ($90,879,000)
Emp.: 275
Fiscal Year-end: 12/31/22
Computer System Design Services
N.A.I.C.S.: 541512
Sam Ropp (Chief Comml Officer)
Eli Glezer (Co-Founder & Chief Scientific Officer)
Dave Daly (Pres & COO)
Jorge Velarde (Sr VP-Corp Dev & Strategy)
Scott Thomas (Sr VP-Sls & Mktg)
Daralyn Durie (Gen Counsel)
Dalen Meeter (Head-Fin)
Vincent Brancaccio (Head-HR)
Andrew Spaventa (Co-Founder, Chm, Pres & CEO)

SINGULARITY FUTURE TECHNOLOGY LTD.
98 Cutter Mill Rd Ste 311, Great Neck, NY 11021
Tel.: (718) 888-1814   VA
Web Site: https://www.singularity.us
Year Founded: 2001
SGLY—(NASDAQ)
Rev.: $3,136,681
Assets: $18,728,039
Liabilities: $5,474,356
Net Worth: $13,253,683
Earnings: ($5,471,774)
Emp.: 15
Fiscal Year-end: 06/30/24
Shipping Consulting & Agency Services

Lei Cao (Founder, Chm & VP)
Ziyuan Liu (CEO)
Ying Cao (CFO)

Subsidiaries:

Sino-Global Shipping (HK) Ltd. (1)
20/F Hoi Kiu Commercial Building 158 Connaught Road, Central, Hong Kong, China (Hong Kong)
Tel.: (852) 37912082
Ship Management Services
N.A.I.C.S.: 488510

Sino-Global Shipping Canada Inc. (1)
201 Corot Apt 916, Verdun, H3E 1C4, QC, Canada
Tel.: (514) 967-8214
Ship Management Services
N.A.I.C.S.: 488510

Trans Pacific Shipping Limited (1)
16th Floor Tower D YeQing Plaza No 9 Wangjing North Road, Chao Yang District, Beijing, China
Tel.: (86) 1064391888
Web Site: http://ir.sino-global.com
Sales Range: $100-124.9 Million
Freight Transportation Services
N.A.I.C.S.: 488510

Subsidiary (Domestic):

Sino-Global Shipping Agency Limited (2)
903 C Buliding 4 Cross Square No 6 Fetont E Ave, Chao Yang District, Beijing, China
Tel.: (86) 1064391888
Web Site: http://www.sino-global.com
Sales Range: $100-124.9 Million
Freight Transportation Services
N.A.I.C.S.: 488510
Lei Cao (Gen Mgr)

SINO AMERICAN OIL COMPANY
2123 Pioneer Ave, Cheyenne, WY 82001
Tel.: (360) 361-8066   WY
Web Site:
    https://sinoamericanoil.com
Year Founded: 2005
OILY—(OTCEM)
Oil & Gas Exploration Services
N.A.I.C.S.: 211120

SINTX TECHNOLOGIES, INC.
1885 W 2100 S, Salt Lake City, UT 84119
Tel.: (801) 839-3500   DE
Web Site: https://www.sintx.com
Year Founded: 1996
SINT—(NASDAQ)
Rev.: $1,561,000
Assets: $15,773,000
Liabilities: $10,069,000
Net Worth: $5,704,000
Earnings: ($16,489,000)
Emp.: 41
Fiscal Year-end: 12/31/22
Orthopedic Implant Mfr & Marketer
N.A.I.C.S.: 339112
David O'Brien (COO)
Donald J. Bray (VP-Bus Dev-Industrial & Antipathogenic Mktg)
Michael Marcroft (VP-Bus Dev-Medical Tech)
Ryan Brock (VP-R&D)
Eric K. Olson (Pres & CEO)

SIPP INDUSTRIES, INC.
600 Anton Blvd Ste 1100, Costa Mesa, CA 92626
Tel.: (949) 220-0435
Web Site:
    https://www.sippindustries.com
SIPC—(OTCIQ)
Commercial & Consumer Products Importer, Exporter & Distr
N.A.I.C.S.: 425120

Syman Vong (CEO)

SITE CENTERS CORP.
3300 Enterprise Pkwy, Beachwood, OH 44122
Tel.: (216) 755-5500   OH
Web Site:
    https://www.sitecenters.com
SITC—(NYSE)
Rev.: $546,275,000
Assets: $4,061,351,000
Liabilities: $1,885,808,000
Net Worth: $2,175,543,000
Earnings: $254,547,000
Emp.: 220
Fiscal Year-end: 12/31/23
Shopping Center Real Estate Investment Trust
N.A.I.C.S.: 525990
David R. Lukes (Pres & CEO)
Conor M. Fennerty (CFO, Treas & Exec VP)
Joseph E. Chura (Sr VP-Property Ops)
Michael S. Owendoff (Deputy Gen Counsel)
Kim M. Scharf (Sr VP-IT)
Jeff Scott (Sr VP-Property Reporting)
Robert Siebenschuh (Sr VP-Property Acctg Ops)
Conor M. Fennerty (CFO, Treas & Exec VP)
John Thirkell (Sr VP)
Aaron M. Kitlowski (Gen Counsel, Sec & Exec VP)

Subsidiaries:

DDR Puerto Rico (1)
Plaza Rio Hondo Carr 167 Int Expreso De Diego, Bayamon, PR 00961
Tel.: (787) 795-6490
Web Site: http://www.ddrpuertorico.com
Emp.: 13
Commercial Property Management & Leasing Services
N.A.I.C.S.: 531312

SITEONE LANDSCAPE SUPPLY, INC.
300 Colonial Ctr Pkwy Ste 600, Roswell, GA 30076
Tel.: (470) 277-7000   DE
Web Site: https://www.siteone.com
Year Founded: 2001
SITE—(NYSE)
Rev.: $4,014,500,000
Assets: $2,533,900,000
Liabilities: $1,231,000,000
Net Worth: $1,302,900,000
Earnings: $245,400,000
Emp.: 6,570
Fiscal Year-end: 01/01/23
Holding Company; Landscape Supplies Wholesale Distr
N.A.I.C.S.: 551112
Doug Black (Chm & CEO)
John T. Guthrie (CFO, Exec VP & Asst Sec)
Briley Brisendine (Gen Counsel, Sec & Exec VP)
Scott Salmon (Exec VP Strategy & Dev)
Sean Kramer (CIO)
Allison Flynn (Dir-Integrated Mktg)
Taylor Koch (Exec VP)
Jerry Justice (Pres)
Shawn Delfausse (Sr VP)

Subsidiaries:

Across the Pond (1)
7004 Memorial Pkwy NW, Huntsville, AL 35810-1002
Tel.: (256) 852-7335
Web Site: http://www.acrossthepond.biz
Nursery, Garden Center & Farm Supply Stores
N.A.I.C.S.: 444240

Adams Wholesale Supply, Inc. (1)
1434 E Bitters Rd, San Antonio, TX 78216
Tel.: (210) 822-3141
Web Site: http://www.adamssupplyinc.com
Sales Range: $1-9.9 Million
Emp.: 12
Farm Supplies Merchant Whslr
N.A.I.C.S.: 424910
Elsie Adams (VP)

All Pro Horticulture, Inc. (1)
80 E Gates Ave, Lindenhurst, NY 11757
Tel.: (631) 789-6680
Web Site: http://www.allpro-horticulture.com
Agronomics & Erosion Control Products Distr
N.A.I.C.S.: 424910
John F. Seib Jr. (CEO)

Alpine Materials LLC (1)
1900 Brumlow Ave, Southlake, TX 76092-9733
Tel.: (817) 251-2448
Web Site: http://www.alpinematerials.com
Exterminating & Pest Control Services
N.A.I.C.S.: 561710

Atlantic Irrigation of Canada Inc. (1)
14 Canso Road, Toronto, M9W 4L8, ON, Canada
Tel.: (416) 244-5551
Farm Machinery & Equipment Distr
N.A.I.C.S.: 424930

Cape Cod Stone & Masonry Supply, Inc. (1)
300 Cranberry Hwy Route 6A, Orleans, MA 02653
Tel.: (508) 240-5700
Sales Range: $1-9.9 Million
Emp.: 9
Lumber & Building Material Whslr
N.A.I.C.S.: 444110
Bob Legge (Pres)

Daniel Stone & Landscaping Supplies, Inc. (1)
12015 W Hwy 290, Austin, TX 78737
Tel.: (512) 288-8488
Web Site: http://www.danielstoneandlandscaping.com
Landscaping Equipment & Products Distr
N.A.I.C.S.: 561730

Gateway Home & Garden Center, LLC (1)
4208 Lee Hwy, Warrenton, VA 20187
Tel.: (703) 348-9625
Web Site:
    https://www.gatewayhomeandgardencenter.com
Garden Maintenance Services
N.A.I.C.S.: 541320

J & J Materials Corp. (1)
71 Fall River Ave, Rehoboth, MA 02769-1009
Tel.: (508) 336-5363
Web Site: http://www.jjmaterials.com
Sales Range: $1-9.9 Million
Emp.: 35
Landscaping & Masonry Distr
N.A.I.C.S.: 423320

Jimstone Co of Louisiana, Inc. (1)
1823 Jefferson St, Lafayette, LA 70501
Tel.: (337) 261-5707
Web Site: http://www.jimstoneco.com
Rev.: $2,200,000
Emp.: 12
Brick, Stone & Related Construction Material Merchant Whslr
N.A.I.C.S.: 423320
Donna Gibbons (Pres)

Jmj Organics, Ltd. (1)
1006 Spanish Cove Dr, Crosby, TX 77532
Tel.: (281) 798-3056
Sales Range: $1-9.9 Million
Emp.: 25
Industrial Building Construction
N.A.I.C.S.: 236210
Carey Warren (CEO)

Kaknes Landscape Supply, Inc. (1)
31W545 Diehl Rd, Naperville, IL 60563-1077
Tel.: (630) 416-9999
Web Site: http://www.kaknes.com

Whol Farm/Garden Machinery Ret Nursery/Garden Supp
N.A.I.C.S.: 423820
David Kaknes *(Founder & Operating Partner)*

Kirkwood Material Supply, Inc. (1)
800 S Fillmore, Kirkwood, MO 63122
Tel.: (314) 822-9644
Web Site: https://www.kirkwoodmaterial.com
Construction Materials Distr
N.A.I.C.S.: 423390

L.H. Voss Materials, Inc. (1)
5965 Dougherty Rd, Dublin, CA 94568
Tel.: (925) 560-9920
Web Site: http://www.lhvoss.com
Construction Materials Distr & Landscaping Services
N.A.I.C.S.: 423390

Lucky Landscape Supply LLC (1)
4314 Katy Hockley Rd, Katy, TX 77493
Tel.: (281) 392-1007
Web Site:
    http://www.luckylandscapesupply.com
Floriculture
N.A.I.C.S.: 111422
Lee Martinez *(Mgr-Yard)*

Madison Block & Stone LLC (1)
5813 US Highway 51, Madison, WI 53704
Tel.: (608) 249-5633
Web Site:
    http://www.madisonblockandstone.com
Sales Range: $1-9.9 Million
Emp.: 30
Cut Stone & Stone Product Mfr
N.A.I.C.S.: 327991

Millican Nurseries, Inc. (1)
187 Pleasant St, Chichester, NH 03258
Tel.: (603) 435-6660
Web Site:
    http://www.millicannurseriesinc.com
Sales Range: $1-9.9 Million
Emp.: 55
Ornamental Nursery Products, Nsk
N.A.I.C.S.: 111421
John Bryant *(Co-Owner & VP)*
Ken Michael *(Co-Owner & Pres)*
Julia Cotter *(Co-Owner & Treas)*
Alan Cattabriga *(VP)*

Modern Builders Supply, Inc. (1)
825 Grand Ave, San Marcos, CA 92078
Tel.: (760) 591-4570
Web Site: http://www.modernbuilders.net
Construction & Mining (except Oil Well) Machinery & Equipment Merchant Whslr
N.A.I.C.S.: 423810

New England Silica Inc (1)
1370 John Fitch Blvd, South Windsor, CT 06074
Tel.: (860) 289-7778
Web Site: http://www.newenglandsilica.com
Rev.: $5,000,000
Emp.: 15
Brick, Stone & Related Construction Material Merchant Whslr
N.A.I.C.S.: 423320

Newsom Seed Inc. (1)
1178 Scaggsville Rd, Fulton, MD 20759
Tel.: (301) 762-2096
Web Site: http://www.newsomseed.com
Rev.: $8,000,000
Emp.: 12
Farm Supplies Merchant Whslr
N.A.I.C.S.: 424910
Bob Butterworth *(Dir-Sls)*
Perry Whaley *(Gen Mgr)*

Pioneer Sand Company Inc. (1)
5000 Northpark Dr, Colorado Springs, CO 80918-3822
Tel.: (719) 599-8100
Web Site: http://www.pioneersand.com
Lumber & Other Building Materials Distr
N.A.I.C.S.: 444180
Mike Ausburn *(VP-Ops)*
Kevin Guzior *(CEO)*

Regal Chemical Company (1)
600 Branch Dr, Alpharetta, GA 30004-3370
Tel.: (770) 521-0488
Web Site: http://www.regalchem.com
Fertilizer Mfr
N.A.I.C.S.: 325314
Will King *(VP)*

River Valley Horticultural Products, Inc. (1)
21701 Lawson Rd, Little Rock, AR 72210
Tel.: (501) 821-4770
Web Site: http://www.rivervalleyhp.com
Flower, Nursery Stock & Florists' Supplies Merchant Whslr
N.A.I.C.S.: 424930
Scott H. Smith *(Founder)*

SiteOne Landscape Supply, LLC (1)
300 Colonial Center Pkwy Ste 600, Roswell, GA 30076 **(100%)**
Tel.: (470) 277-7011
Web Site: https://www.siteone.com
Holding Company; Landscape, Irrigation & Turf Care Products Distr
N.A.I.C.S.: 423820

Subsidiary (Domestic):

Angelo's Supplies, Inc. (2)
29820 W 8 Mile Rd, Farmington Hills, MI 48336
Tel.: (248) 478-1729
Web Site: http://www.angelos-supplies.com
Brick, Stone & Related Construction Material Merchant Whslr
N.A.I.C.S.: 423320
Angelo Carlesimo *(Pres)*

Aspen Valley Landscape Supply, Inc. (2)
13148 W 159th St, Homer Glen, IL 60491
Tel.: (708) 301-0703
Web Site: http://www.aspenvalleyls.com
Landscaping Supplies Whslr
N.A.I.C.S.: 424930
Bill Hackiewicz *(COO)*

Bissett Equipment Corp. (2)
320 Long Island Ave, Holtsville, NY 11742
Tel.: (631) 289-3525
Web Site: https://www.bisettequip.com
Sales Range: $1-9.9 Million
Emp.: 13
Outdoor Equipment & Rental Services
N.A.I.C.S.: 532210
Teddy Villanueva *(Mgr-Svc)*
Gus Gomez *(Mgr-Rental Fleet)*

Bissett Nursery Corp. (2)
323 Long Island Ave, Holtsville, NY 11742-1809 **(100%)**
Tel.: (631) 289-3500
Web Site: http://www.bissettnursery.com
Flower, Nursery Stock & Florists' Supplies Merchant Whslr
N.A.I.C.S.: 424930
Nora Mahoney *(Mgr-Annuals & Perennials)*
Carlo Brucculeri *(Mgr-Bulk Materials & Mason)*
Tim Bockelmann *(Mgr-A/R Credit)*

East Haven Landscape Products (2)
182 Mill St, East Haven, CT 06512
Tel.: (203) 467-6260
Web Site: http://www.ehlp.com
Flower, Nursery Stock & Florists' Supplies Merchant Whslr
N.A.I.C.S.: 424930
Peter House *(Owner)*

Hydro-Scape Products, Inc. (2)
5805 Kearny Villa Rd, San Diego, CA 92123-1113
Tel.: (858) 560-6611
Irrigation & Landscape Supplies
N.A.I.C.S.: 221310
Skip Wallace *(Dir-Purchasing)*

Loma Vista Nursery, Inc. (2)
1107 E 23rd St, Ottawa, KS 66067
Tel.: (785) 229-7200
Web Site: https://www.lomavistanursery.com
Rev.: $6,700,000
Emp.: 80
Flower, Nursery Stock & Florists' Supplies Merchant Whslr
N.A.I.C.S.: 424930
Caitlin Hupp *(Reg Mgr-Sls)*
Mark Clear *(Owner)*
Kurt Everett *(Reg Mgr-Sls)*
Duane Huss *(Mgr-Ops)*

Marshall Stone, Inc. (2)
8605 Triad Dr, Colfax, NC 27235
Tel.: (336) 996-4918
Web Site: https://www.marshallstone.com
Architectural Stone Products Distr

N.A.I.C.S.: 423320

Pete Rose, Inc. (2)
9207 Old Staples Mill Rd, Richmond, VA 23228
Tel.: (804) 288-7436
Web Site: http://www.peteroseinc.com
Nursery Product Whslr
N.A.I.C.S.: 424930
Pete Rose Jr. *(Founder & Pres)*

Southern Landscape Supply LLC (1)
2771 Cumming Hwy, Cumming, GA 30040
Tel.: (770) 205-9393
Web Site:
    http://www.southernlandscapesupply.com
Landscaping Services
N.A.I.C.S.: 561730

Stone & Soil Depot Inc. (1)
26923 Interstate 10 Frontage Rd, Boerne, TX 78006-6507
Tel.: (210) 687-1005
Web Site: https://www.siteonestonecenter-southtexas.com
Mining
N.A.I.C.S.: 212312

Stone Center (1)
10405 Nokesville Rd, Manassas, VA 20110
Tel.: (703) 393-2828
Web Site: https://www.stonecenterofva.com
Cut Stone & Stone Product Mfr
N.A.I.C.S.: 327991
Cleil Albrite *(Co-Founder)*
Marc Salafia *(Co-Founder)*

Stone Plus, Inc. (1)
5500 Chronicle Ct, Jacksonville, FL 32256
Tel.: (904) 443-7400
Web Site: http://www.stoneplus.com
Sales Range: $1-9.9 Million
Emp.: 24
Whol Farm/Garden Mach Whol Brick/Stone Matrls Whol Cnstn Materials Ret Nursery/Garden Supp
N.A.I.C.S.: 423820

The Dirt Doctors, LLC (1)
709 Keith Ave, Pembroke, NH 03275
Tel.: (603) 229-3200
Web Site: https://www.dirtdoctorsnh.com
Landscape Product Distr
N.A.I.C.S.: 444240

Tilden Farm Nursery, LLC (1)
1008 W Central Ave, Davidsonville, MD 21035
Tel.: (410) 798-4720
Web Site: https://tildenfarm.com
Landscape Maintenance Services
N.A.I.C.S.: 541320

Trendset Concrete Products Inc. (1)
6430 240th St SE, Woodinville, WA 98072
Tel.: (425) 486-2192
Web Site: http://www.trendset.net
Concrete Block & Brick Mfr
N.A.I.C.S.: 327331

Triangle Landscape Supplies, Inc. (1)
3400 Gresham Lake Rd, Raleigh, NC 27615
Tel.: (919) 872-3632
Web Site:
    http://www.trianglelandscapesupplies.com
Rev.: $1,300,000
Emp.: 14
Nursery & Garden Centers
N.A.I.C.S.: 444240
Jeff Mangum *(Owner)*
Anthony Pruitt *(Mgr-Ops)*
Walt Webb *(Mgr-Morrisville)*

Whittlesey Landscape Supplies & Recycling, Inc. (1)
3219 S I H 35, Round Rock, TX 78664
Tel.: (512) 989-7625
Web Site: http://www.989rock.com
Sales Range: $1-9.9 Million
Emp.: 30
Ret Nursery/Garden Supp Ret Lumber/Building Mtrl Whol Brick/Stone Matrls Local Trucking Operator Whol Farm/Garden Mach
N.A.I.C.S.: 444240
Clayton Whittlesey *(Founder)*

Yard Works, LLC (1)
19001 Hull St Rd, Moseley, VA 23120-1523

Tel.: (804) 639-2030
Web Site: http://www.yardworksva.com
Recyclable Material Merchant Whslr
N.A.I.C.S.: 423930
Charles Paulette *(Mgr)*
Bill Stinson Sr. *(Co-Founder)*
Robbie Urbine *(Co-Founder)*

SITIME CORP.
5451 Patrick Henry Dr, Santa Clara, CA 95054
Tel.: (408) 328-4400
Web Site: https://www.sitime.com
Year Founded: 2004
SITM—(NASDAQ)
Rev.: $283,605,000
Assets: $750,616,000
Liabilities: $42,136,000
Net Worth: $708,480,000
Earnings: $23,254,000
Emp.: 377
Fiscal Year-end: 12/31/22
Computer Peripheral Equipment Mfr
N.A.I.C.S.: 334118
Piyush B. Sevalia *(Exec VP-Mktg)*
Rajesh Vashist *(Chm, Pres & CEO)*
Aaron Partridge *(Co-Founder)*
Vincent P. Pangrazio *(Chief Legal Officer, Sec & Exec VP)*
Fariborz Assaderaghi *(Exec VP-Tech & Engrg)*
Atul Shingal *(Exec VP-Ops)*
Elizabeth Howe *(CFO & Exec VP)*

SITIO ROYALTIES CORP.
1401 Lawrence St Ste 1750, Denver, CO 80202
Tel.: (720) 640-7620   DE
Web Site: https://www.sitio.com
Year Founded: 2016
STR—(NYSE)
Rev.: $369,612,000
Assets: $5,170,902,000
Liabilities: $1,284,307,000
Net Worth: $3,886,595,000
Earnings: $184,131,000
Emp.: 49
Fiscal Year-end: 12/31/22
Investment Management Service
N.A.I.C.S.: 523999
Jeffrey F. Brotman *(Chief Legal Officer & Sec)*
Christopher L. Conoscenti *(CEO)*
Britton James *(Exec VP-Land)*
Jarret Marcoux *(Exec VP-Operations)*
Dax McDavid *(Exec VP-Corporate Development)*
Brett Riesenfeld *(Gen Counsel, Treas, Sec & Exec VP)*
Carrie L. Osicka *(CFO)*
Dawn K. Smajstrla *(Chief Acctg Officer)*

Subsidiaries:

Brigham Minerals, Inc. (1)
5914 W Courtyard Dr Ste 200, Austin, TX 78730
Tel.: (512) 220-6350
Web Site: http://www.brighamminerals.net
Rev.: $161,217,000
Assets: $820,877,000
Liabilities: $121,203,000
Net Worth: $699,674,000
Earnings: $50,283,000
Emp.: 44
Fiscal Year-end: 12/31/2021
Mineral Exploration Services
N.A.I.C.S.: 213115
Ben M. Brigham *(Founder)*

Subsidiary (Domestic):

Brigham Resources LLC (2)
5914 W Courtyard Dr Ste 200, Austin, TX 78730
Tel.: (512) 220-1200
Web Site: http://www.brighamresources.net
Oil & Gas Product Exploration Services
N.A.I.C.S.: 213112

Sitio Royalties Corp.—(Continued)

Bud Brigham *(Co-Founder & Chm)*
Gene Shepherd *(Co-Founder & CEO)*
J. Silva *(CFO)*
Pat Medlock *(Exec VP-Exploration)*
Erik Hoover *(Exec VP-Ops)*

Rearden Minerals, LLC   **(2)**
5914 W Courtyard Dr Ste 200, Austin, TX 78730
Tel.: (512) 831-8212
Web Site: http://www.reardenminerals.net
Oil & Gas Product Services
N.A.I.C.S.: 213114
Ken Treaccar *(Exec VP)*
Robert Roosa *(Pres)*
Geoff Boyd *(VP-Mineral Acquisitions)*

SITO MOBILE LTD.
100 Town Sq Pl Ste 204, Jersey City, NJ 07310
Tel.: (201) 275-0555   **DE**
Web Site: https://ir.sitomobile.com
Year Founded: 2000
SITO—(NASDAQ)
Sales Range: $25-49.9 Million
Emp.: 65
Messaging & Voice-Based Systems Mfr
N.A.I.C.S.: 334220

SIX FLAGS ENTERTAINMENT CORP.
1000 Ballpark Way Ste 400, Arlington, TX 76011
Tel.: (972) 595-5000   **DE**
Web Site: https://www.sixflags.com
Year Founded: 1961
SIX—(NYSE)
Rev.: $1,358,236,000
Assets: $2,665,825,000
Liabilities: $3,616,390,000
Net Worth: ($950,565,000)
Earnings: $108,928,000
Emp.: 1,450
Fiscal Year-end: 01/01/23
Theme Parks Owner & Operator
N.A.I.C.S.: 713110
Selim A. Bassoul *(Exec Chm, Pres & CEO)*
Gary Mick *(CFO, Interim Principal Acctg Officer, Chief Integration Officer & Interim Controller)*
Brian Nurse *(Chief Legal Officer, Chief Compliance Officer & Sec)*
Christian Dieckmann *(Chief Strategy Officer)*
Dave Hoffman *(Chief Acctg Officer)*
Ty Tastepe *(CTO)*
Seenu Sarma *(Chief Procurement Officer)*
Bob White *(Chief Comml Officer)*
Monica Sauls *(Chief HR Officer, Chief People Officer & Chief Culture Officer)*

Subsidiaries:

Hurricane Harbor GP LLC   **(1)**
1800 E Lamar Blvd, Arlington, TX 76006
Tel.: (817) 640-8900
Amusement & Theme Park Operator
N.A.I.C.S.: 713110

Six Flags America LP   **(1)**
13710 Central Ave, Bowie, MD 20721
Tel.: (301) 249-1500
Web Site: https://www.sixflags.com
Theme Park Operator
N.A.I.C.S.: 713110
Rick Howarth *(VP-Procurement)*

Six Flags Mexico S.A. de C.V.   **(1)**
Carretera al Picacho Ajusco Km 1.5, Colonia Heroes de Padierna Alcaldia Tlalpan, 14200, Mexico, Federal District, Mexico
Tel.: (52) 53393600
Web Site: https://www.sixflags.com.mx
Amusement Park Operating Services
N.A.I.C.S.: 713110

Six Flags Theme Parks Inc.   **(1)**

924 E Ave J, Grand Prairie, TX 75050-2622
Tel.: (972) 595-5000
Web Site: http://www.sixflags.com
Sales Range: $25-49.9 Million
Operator of Amusement Parks & Water Parks
N.A.I.C.S.: 713110

Subsidiary (Domestic):

Fiesta Texas, Inc.   **(2)**
17000 IH-10 W, San Antonio, TX 78257
Tel.: (210) 697-5050
Web Site: https://www.sixflags.com
Sales Range: $50-74.9 Million
Owner & Operator of Theme Parks
N.A.I.C.S.: 713110

Six Flags Discovery Kingdom   **(2)**
1001 Fairgrounds Dr, Vallejo, CA 94589
Tel.: (707) 644-4000
Web Site: https://www.sixflags.com
Theme Park Operator
N.A.I.C.S.: 713110

Six Flags Great Adventure LLC   **(2)**
1 Six Flags Blvd, Jackson, NJ 08527
Tel.: (732) 928-2000
Web Site: https://www.sixflags.com
Theme Park
N.A.I.C.S.: 713110
John Winkler *(Pres)*

Six Flags Great America, Inc.   **(2)**
1 Great America Pkwy, Gurnee, IL 60031
Tel.: (847) 249-4636
Web Site: https://www.sixflags.com
Sales Range: $50-74.9 Million
Amusement Theme Park
N.A.I.C.S.: 713110

Six Flags Hurricane Harbor   **(2)**
1800 E Lamar Blvd, Arlington, TX 76006
Tel.: (817) 265-3356
Web Site: https://www.sixflags.com
Sales Range: $10-24.9 Million
Emp.: 50
Owner & Operator of Theme Parks
N.A.I.C.S.: 713110

Six Flags Magic Mountain & Hurricane Harbor   **(2)**
26101 Magic Mountain Pkwy, Valencia, CA 91355-1052
Tel.: (661) 255-4100
Web Site: http://www.sixflags.com
Family Theme Park
N.A.I.C.S.: 713110

Six Flags Over Georgia, Inc.   **(2)**
275 Riverside Pkwy, Austell, GA 30168
Tel.: (770) 948-9290
Web Site: https://www.sixflags.com
Theme Park
N.A.I.C.S.: 713110
Dale Kaetzel *(Pres)*

Six Flags Over Texas & Hurricane Harbor   **(2)**
1800 E Lamar Blvd, Arlington, TX 76006
Tel.: (817) 265-3356   **(100%)**
Web Site: https://www.sixflags.com
Owner & Operator of Theme Parks
N.A.I.C.S.: 713110

Six Flags Over Texas, Inc.   **(2)**
PO Box 90191, Arlington, TX 76004-0191
Tel.: (817) 640-8900
Web Site: https://www.sixflags.com
Theme Park
N.A.I.C.S.: 713110

Six Flags St. Louis LLC   **(2)**
PO Box 60, Eureka, MO 63025
Tel.: (636) 938-5300
Web Site: https://www.sixflags.com
Family Entertainment Theme Park
N.A.I.C.S.: 713110
Phil Liggett *(Pres)*

SIX FLAGS ENTERTAINMENT CORPORATION
1 Cedar Point Dr, Sandusky, OH 44870-5259
Tel.: (419) 626-0830   **DE**
Web Site:
  https://www.ir.cedarfair.com
Year Founded: 1987

FUN—(NYSE)
Rev.: $1,798,668,000
Assets: $2,240,533,000
Liabilities: $2,823,495,000
Net Worth: ($582,962,000)
Earnings: $124,559,000
Emp.: 3,350
Fiscal Year-end: 12/31/23
Owner & Operator of Amusement Parks & Resorts
N.A.I.C.S.: 711320
Brian C. Witherow *(CFO & Exec VP)*
Richard A. Zimmerman *(Pres & CEO)*
David R. Hoffman *(Chief Acctg Officer & Sr VP)*
Daniel J. Hanrahan *(Chm)*
Tim Fisher *(COO)*
Monica Sauls *(Chief HR Officer & Sr VP)*
Brian Nurse *(Chief Legal Officer, Sec & Exec VP)*
Kelley Ford *(CMO)*

Subsidiaries:

Canada's Wonderland Company   **(1)**
9580 Jane Street, Vaughan, L6A 1S6, ON, Canada
Tel.: (905) 832-8131
Web Site:
  https://www.canadaswonderland.com
Sales Range: $25-49.9 Million
Emp.: 160
Amusement Park Services
N.A.I.C.S.: 713110

Carowinds   **(1)**
14523 Carowinds Blvd, Charlotte, NC 28277
Tel.: (704) 588-2600
Web Site: https://www.carowinds.com
Sales Range: $25-49.9 Million
Amusement Park Services
N.A.I.C.S.: 713110
Pat Jones *(VP & Gen Mgr)*

Cedar Fair, L.P.   **(1)**
1 Cedar Point Dr, Sandusky, OH 44870   **(100%)**
Tel.: (419) 627-2350
Web Site: http://www.cedarpoint.com
Sales Range: $75-99.9 Million
Emp.: 260
Ferry Service
N.A.I.C.S.: 488490

Cedar Point   **(1)**
1 Cedar Point Dr, Sandusky, OH 44870   **(100%)**
Tel.: (419) 627-2350
Web Site: https://www.cedarpoint.com
Sales Range: $75-99.9 Million
Emp.: 300
Amusement Park
N.A.I.C.S.: 713110

Cedar Point Park LLC   **(1)**
1 Cedar Point Dr, Sandusky, OH 44870
Tel.: (419) 627-2350
Amusement Park Operator
N.A.I.C.S.: 713110

Dorney Park & Wildwater Kingdom   **(1)**
3830 Dorney Pk Rd, Allentown, PA 18104-5803   **(100%)**
Tel.: (610) 395-3724
Web Site: https://www.dorneypark.com
Sales Range: $400-449.9 Million
Amusement Park & Water Ride Attraction
N.A.I.C.S.: 713110

Geauga Lake & Wildwater Kingdom   **(1)**
1100 Squires Rd, Aurora, OH 44202-8706
Tel.: (330) 562-8303
Web Site: http://www.wildwaterfun.com
Sales Range: $50-74.9 Million
Emp.: 300
Amusement Park, Arcade & Attractions
N.A.I.C.S.: 713110

Great America   **(1)**
4701 Great America Pkwy, Santa Clara, CA 95054-1201
Tel.: (408) 986-5846
Web Site: https://www.cagreatamerica.com

Sales Range: $25-49.9 Million
Emp.: 150
Amusement Park Services
N.A.I.C.S.: 713110
Raul Rehnborg *(VP & Gen Mgr)*

Kings Dominion LLC   **(1)**
16000 Theme Park Way, Doswell, VA 23047
Tel.: (804) 876-5000
Web Site: https://www.kingsdominion.com
Amusement Park Operator
N.A.I.C.S.: 713110

Kings Island Company   **(1)**
6300 Kings Island Dr, Kings Mills, OH 45034
Tel.: (513) 754-5700
Web Site: https://www.visitkingsisland.com
Amusement Park Operating Services
N.A.I.C.S.: 713110
Chad Showalter *(Dir-Comm)*

Kings Island Park LLC   **(1)**
6300 Kings Island Dr Kings Island, Mason, OH 45034
Tel.: (513) 754-5700
Web Site: http://www.visitkingsisland.com
Amusement Park Operator713110
N.A.I.C.S.: 713110
Mike Koontz *(Pres)*

Knott's Berry Farm LLC   **(1)**
8039 Beach Blvd, Buena Park, CA 90620
Tel.: (714) 220-5200
Web Site: https://www.knotts.com
Amusement Park Operator
N.A.I.C.S.: 713110

Michigan's Adventure   **(1)**
4750 Whitehall Rd, Muskegon, MI 49445   **(100%)**
Tel.: (231) 766-3377
Web Site: http://www.miadventure.com
Sales Range: $10-24.9 Million
Emp.: 20
Operators of Amusement Parks
N.A.I.C.S.: 713110
Camille Jorden-Mark *(VP & Gen Mgr)*

Sawmill Creek Resort, Ltd.   **(1)**
400 Sawmill Creek Dr W, Huron, OH 44839
Tel.: (419) 433-3800
Web Site:
  https://www.sawmillcreekresort.com
Hotels (except Casino Hotels) & Motels
N.A.I.C.S.: 721110

Valleyfair   **(1)**
1 Valleyfair Dr, Shakopee, MN 55379   **(100%)**
Tel.: (952) 445-7600
Web Site: https://www.valleyfair.com
Sales Range: $25-49.9 Million
Emp.: 2,000
Amusement Park
N.A.I.C.S.: 713110
Raul Rehnborg *(Gen Mgr)*

Worlds of Fun   **(1)**
4545 Worlds of Fun Ave, Kansas City, MO 64161   **(100%)**
Tel.: (816) 303-5125
Web Site: http://www.worldsoffun.com
Sales Range: $450-499.9 Million
Amusement Park
N.A.I.C.S.: 713110

SIXTH STREET SPECIALTY LENDING, INC.
2100 McKinney Ave Ste 1500, Dallas, TX 75201
Tel.: (469) 621-3001   **DE**
Web Site:
  https://www.sixthstreetspecialtylending.com
TSLX—(NYSE)
Rev.: $309,305,000
Assets: $2,836,947,000
Liabilities: $1,495,378,000
Net Worth: $1,341,569,000
Earnings: $166,327,000
Emp.: 44
Fiscal Year-end: 12/31/22
Financial Lending
N.A.I.C.S.: 522310
Michael E. Fishman *(Co-VP)*
Joshua Easterly *(Co-Founder, Chm & CEO)*

David Stiepleman (Co-VP)
Alan Waxman (VP)
Jennifer Gordon (Co-VP)
Ian T. Simmonds (Mng Dir & CFO)
Robert Stanley (Pres)
Craig Hamrah (VP)
Steven Pluss (VP)
A. Michael Muscolino (Co-Founder & Partner)
Anton Brett (Chief Compliance Officer, Sec & VP)
Cami VanHorn (Head)

Subsidiaries:

Sixth Street Advisers, LLC   (1)
2100 Mckinney Ave Ste 1500, Dallas, TX 75201-1803
Tel.: (469) 621-3001
Web Site: http://sixthstreet.com
Investment Advisory Services
N.A.I.C.S.: 523940

Subsidiary (Domestic):

Talcott Resolution Life Insurance
Company   (2)
1 Griffin Rd N, Windsor, CT 06095
Tel.: (860) 547-5000
Web Site: http://www.talcottresolution.com
Holding Company
N.A.I.C.S.: 551112
Peter Sannizzaro (Pres & CEO)

Subsidiary (Domestic):

Hartford Life & Accident Insurance
Company   (3)
1 Hartford Plz T-14, Hartford, CT 06155
Tel.: (860) 547-5000
Holding Company; Life Insurance, Reinsurance & Investment Products & Services
N.A.I.C.S.: 551112
Peter Sannizzaro (Pres & CEO)
Ellen Below (Chief Comm Officer & Head-Implementation)
Matthew Bjorkman (Chief Auditor)
Christopher Cramer (HEad-Tax & Deputy Gen Counsel)
George Eknaian (Chief Risk Officer)
Diane Krajewski (Chief Human Resources & Head-Ops)
Matthew Poznar (CIO)
Lisa Proch (Gen Counsel & Chief Compliance Officer)
Robert Siracusa (CFO)
Samir Srivastava (CIO)

Subsidiary (Domestic):

Talcott Resolution Life Insurance
Company   (4)
1 Griffin Rd N, Windsor, CT 06095
Web Site: http://www.talcottresolution.com
Life Insurance & Investment Products & Services
N.A.I.C.S.: 524113
Peter Sannizzaro (Pres & CEO)
Ellen T. Below (Chief Comm Officer & Head-Implementation)
Matthew C. Bjorkman (Chief Auditor)
John B. Brady (Chief Actuary)
Christopher B. Cramer (Head-Tax & Gen Counsel)
George E. Eknaian (Chief Risk Officer)
Diane Krajewski (Chief HR Officer & Head-Ops)
Matthew J. Poznar (Chief Investment Officer)
Lisa M. Proch (Gen Counsel & Chief Compliance Officer)
Robert Siracusa (CFO)
Samir Srivastava (CIO)

SJW GROUP

110 W Taylor St, San Jose, CA 95110
Tel.: (408) 279-7800   DE
Web Site: https://www.sjwgroup.com
Year Founded: 1985
SJW—(NYSE)
Rev.: $620,698,000
Assets: $3,632,624,000
Liabilities: $1,029,791,000
Net Worth: $2,602,833,000
Earnings: $73,828,000
Emp.: 757

Fiscal Year-end: 12/31/22
Holding Company; Water Distr
N.A.I.C.S.: 551112
Eric W. Thornburg (Chm, Pres & CEO)
Andrew F. Walters (CFO, Principal Acctg Officer & Treas)
Bruce A. Hauk (COO)
Stephanie Orosco (Chief HR Officer)
Kristen A. Johnson (Chief Admin Officer & Sr VP)
Willie Brown (Gen Counsel, Sec & VP)
Marisa Joss (Deputy Gen Counsel & Asst Sec)
Thomas A. Hodge (VP-Bus Dev)
Wendy Avila-Walker (VP)

Subsidiaries:

Connecticut Water Service, Inc.   (1)
93 W Main St, Clinton, CT 06413
Tel.: (860) 669-8636
Web Site: http://www.ctwater.com
Rev.: $116,665,000
Assets: $951,869,000
Liabilities: $400,222,000
Net Worth: $551,647,000
Earnings: $16,695,000
Emp.: 297
Fiscal Year-end: 12/31/2018
Water Supplier
N.A.I.C.S.: 551112
Bruce A. Hauk (COO)
Maureen P. Westbrook (Pres)
Kristen A. Johnson (Sr VP-Admin)
Jay Fusco (VP-Information Sys)
Karen Maines (VP-HR)
Arthur O'Neil (VP-Customer Svc)

Subsidiary (Domestic):

New England Water Utility Services,
Inc.   (2)
93 W Main St, Clinton, CT 06413-1645
Tel.: (860) 669-8636
Web Site: http://www.ctwater.com
Emp.: 200
Water Supplier
N.A.I.C.S.: 221310

The Connecticut Water
Company   (2)
93 W Main St, Clinton, CT 06413   (100%)
Tel.: (860) 669-8630
Web Site: https://www.ctwater.com
Sales Range: $50-74.9 Million
Emp.: 168
Water Utility
N.A.I.C.S.: 221310

The Maine Water Company   (2)
855 Rockland St, Rockport, ME
04856-6307   (100%)
Tel.: (207) 236-8428
Web Site: http://www.mainewater.com
Sales Range: $10-24.9 Million
Emp.: 40
Water Utility
N.A.I.C.S.: 221310
Richard L. Knowlton (Pres)

Unit (Domestic):

The Maine Water Co. - Biddeford &
Saco   (3)
93 Industrial Park Rd, Saco, ME 04072
Tel.: (207) 282-1543
Web Site: http://www.mainewater.com
Sales Range: $1-9.9 Million
Emp.: 100
Water Supply & Irrigation Systems
N.A.I.C.S.: 221310
Richard Knowlton (Pres)

The Maine Water Co. -
Bucksport   (3)
191 School St, Bucksport, ME 04416
Tel.: (207) 469-0021
Sales Range: $10-24.9 Million
Emp.: 2
Water Utility
N.A.I.C.S.: 221310
David Bishop (Gen Mgr)

The Maine Water Co. -
Greenville   (3)

9 Norris St, Greenville, ME 04441
Tel.: (207) 695-2193
Water Utility Services
N.A.I.C.S.: 221310

The Maine Water Co. - Kezar
Falls   (3)
93 Industrial Park Rd, Saco, ME 04072
Tel.: (207) 282-1543
Web Site: http://www.mainewater.com
Water Utility Services
N.A.I.C.S.: 221310

The Maine Water Co. -
Millinocket   (3)
Route 11, Millinocket, ME 04462
Tel.: (207) 723-8731
Water Utilities
N.A.I.C.S.: 221310

The Maine Water Co. -
Skowhegan   (3)
27 Water works Dr, Skowhegan, ME 04976
Tel.: (207) 474-3521
Web Site: http://www.aquaamerica.com
Water Utilities
N.A.I.C.S.: 221310

San Jose Water Company   (1)
110 W Taylor St, San Jose, CA
95110-2131   (100%)
Tel.: (408) 279-7900
Web Site: https://www.sjwater.com
Sales Range: $75-99.9 Million
Emp.: 270
Provides Public Utility
N.A.I.C.S.: 221310
Andrew F. Walters (CFO & Treas)
Eric W. Thornburg (Chm & CEO)
Bruce A. Hauk (COO)
Wendy Avia-Walker (VP, Controller & Asst Treas)
Stephanie Orosco (Dir-HR)
John B. Tang (VP-Regulatory Affairs & Govt Rels)
Wille Brown (Sec & Asst Gen Counsel)
Jeff Hobbs (VP-Tech)
Bill Tuttle (VP-Engrg)
Tricia Zacharisen (VP-Customer Svc)
Curtis A. Rayer Jr. (VP-Ops)

Subsidiary (Domestic):

SJW Land Company   (2)
110 W Taylor St, San Jose, CA
95110-2131   (100%)
Tel.: (408) 279-7900
Web Site: http://www.sjwater.com
Sales Range: $100-124.9 Million
Emp.: 300
Land Company
N.A.I.C.S.: 221310
Andrew F. Walters (CFO & Treas)
Eric W. Thornburg (Chm, Pres & CEO)

SK GROWTH OPPORTUNITIES CORPORATION

228 Park Ave S Ste 96693, New York, NY 10003
Tel.: (917) 599-1622   Ky
Web Site:
  https://skgrowthopportunities.com
Year Founded: 2021
SKGR—(NASDAQ)
Rev.: $2,826,612
Assets: $218,781,844
Liabilities: $230,424,630
Net Worth: ($11,642,786)
Earnings: $2,109,347
Emp.: 2
Fiscal Year-end: 12/31/22
Investment Services
N.A.I.C.S.: 523999
Richard Chin (CEO & Dir)
Derek Jensen (CFO & Dir)

SKECHERS U.S.A., INC.

228 Manhattan Beach Blvd, Manhattan Beach, CA 90266
Tel.: (310) 318-3100   DE
Web Site: https://www.skechers.com
Year Founded: 1992
SKX—(NYSE)
Rev.: $8,000,342,000
Assets: $7,547,351,000

Liabilities: $3,147,309,000
Net Worth: $4,400,042,000
Earnings: $545,799,000
Emp.: 9,200
Fiscal Year-end: 12/31/23
Designs & Markets Branded Contemporary Casual, Active, Rugged & Lifestyle Footwear for Men, Women & Children
N.A.I.C.S.: 424340
Michael Greenberg (Founder & Pres)
David Weinberg (COO & Exec VP)
Robert Greenberg (Chm & CEO)
John M. Vandemore (CFO)

Subsidiaries:

Skechers Colombia, S.A.S.   (1)
Calle 82 Parque La Colina Centro Mayor Mallplaza NQS, Santafe Multiplaza Fontanar and Outlets Toberin and Las Americas, Bogota, Colombia
Tel.: (57) 14325880
Web Site: https://www.co.skechers.com
Shoe Store Operator
N.A.I.C.S.: 458210

Skechers EDC S.P.R.L.   (1)
Ave du Parc Industrial 159 Zone 3, 4041, Milmort, Belgium
Tel.: (32) 42286211
Web Site: http://www.skechers.com
Shoe Retailer
N.A.I.C.S.: 458210
Houtneyess Sobhie (Mng Dir)

Skechers Guangzhou Co., Ltd.   (1)
Guangdong Foreign Trade Plaza 66 Jianji Road, Haizhu District, Guangzhou, 510230, China
Tel.: (86) 2089160222
Footwear Distr
N.A.I.C.S.: 424340

Skechers Peru, S.R.L.   (1)
Av Paseo De La Republica 5895 Oficina 901, Miraflores, Lima, Peru
Tel.: (51) 7158282
Web Site: https://www.pe.skechers.com
Shoe Store Operator
N.A.I.C.S.: 458210

Skechers Poland Sp. z o.o.   (1)
Ul Wybrzeze Gdynskie 6 A, 01-531, Warsaw, Poland
Tel.: (48) 496074407220
Footwear Mfr
N.A.I.C.S.: 316210
Ewelina Grzelak (Mgr)

Skechers Retail India Private
Limited   (1)
Lotus Corporate Park A-1602 Goregaon East, Mumbai, 400063, India
Tel.: (91) 26) 158 9000
Emp.: 30
Footwear Distr
N.A.I.C.S.: 424340
Rahul Vira (CEO)

Skechers S.a.r.l.   (1)
Rue Mercerie 12, 1003, Lausanne, Switzerland
Tel.: (41) 564183540
Web Site: http://www.ch.skechers.com
Sales Range: $100-124.9 Million
Emp.: 3
Shoe Retailer
N.A.I.C.S.: 458210
Marvin Bernstein (Mng Dir)

Subsidiary (Non-US):

Skechers USA Portugal Unipessoal
Limitada   (2)
Comp Nassica Av Fonte Cova 400 Loja 125, Modivas, 4485-592, Vila do Conde, Portugal
Tel.: (351) 800210372
Web Site: https://www.skechers.pt
Sales Range: $25-49.9 Million
Footwear Mfr & Distr
N.A.I.C.S.: 316210

Skechers U.S.A., Inc.—(Continued)

Alexandra Mendes (Mgr-Store)

Skechers Slovakia S.R.O. (1)
Revesz Str 27, 1138, Budapest, Hungary
Tel.: (36) 15008400
Web Site: https://www.sk.skechers.com
Footwear Mfr
N.A.I.C.S.: 316210

Skechers USA Benelux B.V. (1)
Cartografenweg 16, 5141 MT, Waalwijk,
Netherlands
Tel.: (31) 416673160
Web Site: https://www.nl.skechers.com
Sales Range: $100-124.9 Million
Emp.: 16
Shoe Retailer
N.A.I.C.S.: 458210

**Skechers USA Deutschland
GmbH** (1)
Waldstr 66, 63128, Dietzenbach, Germany
Tel.: (49) 1806407220
Web Site: https://www.skechers.de
Sales Range: $100-124.9 Million
Emp.: 37
Shoe Retailer
N.A.I.C.S.: 458210

Skechers USA France SAS (1)
20 bis rue des Capucines, 75002, Paris,
France
Tel.: (33) 144553131
Web Site: http://www.fr.skechers.com
Sales Range: $100-124.9 Million
Emp.: 50
Shoe Retailer
N.A.I.C.S.: 458210

Skechers USA Iberia, S.L. (1)
Calle Serrano 40, 28001, Madrid, Spain
Tel.: (34) 900927924
Web Site: https://www.skechers.com
Shoe Retailer
N.A.I.C.S.: 458210

Skechers USA Italia S.r.l. (1)
Via Energy Park 6, 20871, Vimercate, MB,
Italy
Tel.: (39) 0399633700
Web Site: https://www.skechers.it
Shoe Retailer
N.A.I.C.S.: 458210

Skechers USA Ltd. (1)
CT3 Centrium Griffiths Way, Saint Albans,
AL1 2RD, Hertfordshire, United Kingdom
Tel.: (44) 170 765 5955
Web Site: https://www.skechers.co.uk
Shoe Retailer
N.A.I.C.S.: 458210
Pete Youell (Mng Dir)

Skechers Vietnam Co. Ltd. (1)
Room 1704-1705 17th Floor Saigon Trade
Center Building, 37 Ton Duc Thang Street
Ben Nghe Ward District 1, Ho Chi Minh
City, Vietnam
Tel.: (84) 839242705
Web Site: https://www.skechersvn.vn
Shoe Store Operator
N.A.I.C.S.: 458210

SKILLZ INC.
PO Box 445, San Francisco, CA
94104
Tel.: (415) 762-0511   DE
Web Site: https://www.skillz.com
Year Founded: 2020
SKLZ—(NYSE)
Rev.: $152,079,000
Assets: $395,826,000
Liabilities: $185,337,000
Net Worth: $210,489,000
Earnings: ($101,360,000)
Emp.: 225
Fiscal Year-end: 12/31/23
Investment Services
N.A.I.C.S.: 523999
Andrew Paradise (Co-Founder, Chm
& CEO)
Casey Chafkin (Co-Founder & Chief
Strategy Officer)
Gaetano Franceschi (CFO)
Nik Patel (Gen Counsel)

Subsidiaries:

Aarki, LLC (1)
485 N Whisman Rd Ste 200, Mountain
View, CA 94043
Tel.: (408) 382-1180
Web Site: http://www.aarki.com
Media Representatives
N.A.I.C.S.: 541840
Levon Budagyan (Co-Founder & CTO)

SKINVISIBLE, INC.
6320 S Sandhill Rd Ste 10, Las Ve-
gas, NV 89120
Tel.: (702) 433-7154   NV
Web Site:
   https://www.skinvisible.com
Year Founded: 1998
SKVI—(OTCQB)
Rev.: $20,000
Assets: $162,869
Liabilities: $9,185,912
Net Worth: ($9,023,043)
Earnings: ($2,382,440)
Emp.: 2
Fiscal Year-end: 12/31/23
Pharmaceutical & Personal Care
Product Mfr
N.A.I.C.S.: 325412
Terry H. Howlett (Founder, Pres,
CEO, CFO & Principal Acctg Officer)
Doreen McMorran (VP-Bus Dev)

SKY HARBOUR GROUP COR-
PORATION
136 Tower Rd Ste 205 Westchester
County Airport, White Plains, NY
10604
Tel.: (212) 554-5990   DE
Web Site: https://skyharbour.group
Year Founded: 2020
SKYH—(NYSEAMEX)
Rev.: $1,845,000
Assets: $331,204,000
Liabilities: $232,829,000
Net Worth: $98,375,000
Earnings: ($13,678,000)
Fiscal Year-end: 12/31/22
Other Support Activities for Air Trans-
portation
N.A.I.C.S.: 488190
Francisco Gonzalez (CFO)
Joshua P. Weisenburger (CFO, Treas
& Sec)
Michael Schmitt (Chief Acctg Officer)
Tim Herr (Treas & VP-Fin)
Willard Whitesell (COO)
Eric Stolpman (VP-Real Estate)
Neil Szymczak (VP-Real Estate)
Douglas Bush (VP-Dev)
John Bridi (VP-Airfield Ops)
Millie Hernandez-Becker (Dir-Sls &
Mktg)
Andre Sigourney (VP-Leasing)
Tal Keinan (Chm & CEO)

SKY PETROLEUM, INC.
5605 FM 423 Ste 500, Frisco, TX
75056
Tel.: (469) 319-1300   NV
Web Site: https://skypetroleum.com
Year Founded: 2002
SKPI—(OTCEM)
Investment Holding Company; Oil &
Gas Exploration Services
N.A.I.C.S.: 551112

SKY440, INC.
300 Spectrum Center Dr Ste 400,
Irvine, CA 92618
Tel.: (949) 831-3784   NV
Year Founded: 1997
SKYF—(OTCIQ)
Networking Hardware & Computer
Related Component Distr
N.A.I.C.S.: 423430
Robert Atwell (Chm)

SKYDECK ACQUISITION
CORP.
225 Dyer St 2nd Fl, Providence, RI
02903
Tel.: (401) 854-4567   Ky
Year Founded: 2021
SKYA—(NASDAQ)
Rev.: $13,022,676
Assets: $225,222,756
Liabilities: $232,710,405
Net Worth: ($7,487,649)
Earnings: $12,190,177
Emp.: 3
Fiscal Year-end: 12/31/22
Investment Services
N.A.I.C.S.: 523999
Paul J. Salem (Chm)
Martin J. Mannion (CEO)
Christopher S. Satti (CFO)
Fredric A. Flaxman (COO)

SKYE BIOSCIENCE, INC.
5910 Pacific Center Blvd Ste 320,
San Diego, CA 92121
Tel.: (949) 480-9051   NV
Web Site: http://skyebioscience.com
Year Founded: 2011
SKYE—(OTCQB)
Assets: $11,940,411
Liabilities: $14,072,229
Net Worth: ($2,131,818)
Earnings: ($37,644,784)
Emp.: 11
Fiscal Year-end: 12/31/23
Pharmaceuticals Mfr
N.A.I.C.S.: 325412
Punit S. Dhillon (Chm, Pres, CEO &
Sec)
Tu Diep (Chief Dev Officer)
Kaitlyn Arsenault (CFO)

Subsidiaries:

**Emerald Health Therapeutics,
Inc.** (1)
Suite 210-800 West Pender Street, Vancou-
ver, V6C 1J8, BC, Canada
Tel.: (250) 818-9838
Web Site: http://www.emeraldhealth.com
Rev.: $11,156,095
Assets: $76,877,785
Liabilities: $20,470,703
Net Worth: $56,407,082
Earnings: ($34,059,689)
Emp.: 110
Fiscal Year-end: 12/31/2020
Licensed Producer of Medical Cannabis
N.A.I.C.S.: 325412
Avtar Dhillon (Chm)
Rebecca Wong (VP-Quality & Regulatory
Affairs)
Allan Rewak (VP-Comm & Stakeholder
Rels)
Riaz Bandali (Pres & CEO)
Thierry Schmidt (Chief Comml Officer)
Jenn Hepburn (CFO)

Subsidiary (Domestic):

Emerald Health Botanicals, Inc. (2)
1066 W Hastings St, Vancouver, V6E 3K1,
BC, Canada (100%)
Tel.: (250) 818-9838
Web Site: http://www.emerald.care
Emp.: 20
Licensed Producer of Canadian Medical
Cannabis
N.A.I.C.S.: 325412

SKYE PETROLEUM, INC.
4771 Sweetwater Blvd Ste 213,
Sugar Land, TX 77479
Tel.: (281) 265-1199
Web Site:
   https://www.skyepetroleum.com
SKPO—(OTCIQ)
Rev.: $146,000
Assets: $581,000
Liabilities: $4,000
Net Worth: $577,000
Earnings: ($65,000)

Emp.: 2
Fiscal Year-end: 12/31/19
Gasoline Stations with Convenience
Stores
N.A.I.C.S.: 457110
Gerald Weber (Chm & CEO)

SKYLINE BANKSHARES, INC.
Tel.: (540) 745-4191   VA
Web Site:
   https://www.skylinenationalbank.com
Year Founded: 2015
PKKW—(OTCQX)
Rev.: $42,824,000
Assets: $997,734,000
Liabilities: $924,798,000
Net Worth: $72,936,000
Earnings: $10,281,000
Emp.: 223
Fiscal Year-end: 12/31/22
Bank Holding Company
N.A.I.C.S.: 551111
Blake M. Edwards Jr. (Pres & CEO)
Rodney R. Halsey (COO & Exec VP-
Skyline National Bank)
Jonathan L. Kruckow (Pres-Virginia &
Exec VP-Skyline National Bank)
Milo L. Cockerham (Chief Retail
Banking Officer & Exec VP-Skyline
National Bank)
W. David McNeill (Vice Chm)
C. Greg Edwards (Pres-North Caro-
lina & Exec VP-Skyline National
Bank)
Lori C. Vaught (CFO & Exec VP)
Beth R. Worrell (Chief Risk Officer &
Exec VP-Skyline National Bank)

Subsidiaries:

Johnson County Bank (1)
241 W Main St, Mountain City, TN 37683
Tel.: (423) 727-7701
Web Site:
   http://www.johnsoncountybank.com
Rev.: $3,400,000
Emp.: 22
Commercial Banking
N.A.I.C.S.: 522110
Christopher Reece (CEO)
Sandy Snyder (Asst VP)

Skyline National Bank (1)
113 W Main St, Independence, VA 24348
Tel.: (276) 773-2811
Web Site:
   http://www.skylinenationalbank.com
Sales Range: $25-49.9 Million
Commericial Banking
N.A.I.C.S.: 522110
Blake M. Edwards Jr. (Pres & CEO)
Rodney R. Halsey (COO & Exec VP)
Mary D. Tabor (Chief Credit Officer & Exec
VP)
Lynn T. Murray (CMO, Chief HR Officer &
Exec VP)
Jonathan L. Kruckow (Reg Pres-VA & Exec
VP)

SKYSHOP LOGISTICS, INC.
7805 NW 15th St, Miami, FL 33126
Tel.: (305) 599-1812   NV
Web Site:
   http://www.skyshoplogistics.com
Year Founded: 1998
SKPN—(OTCIQ)
Air Courier Services
N.A.I.C.S.: 492110
Albert P. Hernandez (Chm & CEO)
Christian J. Weber (Dir-Europe)
Juan Pablo Rodriguez Moll (Dir-
Digital Mktg)
Rohan M. Sivanathan (Mng Dir)
Claudia Feldman (Controller)

SKYTOP LODGE
1 Skytop Lodge Rd, Skytop, PA
18357-1099
Tel.: (570) 595-7401
Web Site: https://www.skytop.com

Year Founded: 1928
SKTP—(NASDAQ)
Golf Courses & Country Clubs
N.A.I.C.S.: 713910
Jeffrey Rudder (Gen Mgr)

SKYTOP LODGE CORP.

1 Skytop Lodge Rd, Skytop, PA
18357　　　　　　　　　　　　PA
Web Site: https://www.skytop.com
Year Founded: 1928
SKTP—(OTCIQ)
Hotels (except Casino Hotels) & Motels
N.A.I.C.S.: 721110
Gonzalo Bustos (Mktg Mgr)

SKYWARD SPECIALTY INSURANCE GROUP, INC.

800 Gessner Rd Ste 600, Houston,
TX 77024
Tel.: (713) 935-4800
Web Site:
　　https://skywardinsurance.com
Year Founded: 2006
SKWD—(NASDAQ)
Rev.: $885,969,000
Assets: $2,953,435,000
Liabilities: $2,292,404,000
Net Worth: $661,031,000
Earnings: $84,307,000
Emp.: 515
Fiscal Year-end: 12/31/23
Insurance Holding Company
N.A.I.C.S.: 551112
Andrew S. Robinson (Chm & CEO)
Andrew Robinson (CEO)
Kirby A. Hill (Pres-Captives, Programs, and Alternative Risks & Exec VP-Property & Casualty Ops)
Doug C. Davies (Pres-Global Property Division & Sr VP-Houston Specialty Insurance Co)
Dan Bodnar (CIO & CTO)
Mark Boland (Pres-E & S Wholesale Brokerage)
Ryan Burke (VP-Specialty Programs)
Rick Childs (Pres-Construction & Energy)
Chase Clark (Chief Risk Officer & Sr VP-Corp Underwriting & Ceded Reinsurance)
Sean Duffy (Chief Claims Officer & Exec VP)
Mark Haushill (CFO & Exec VP)
Sandip Kapadia (Chief Actuary Officer, Chief Analytics Officer & Exec VP)
Sarah Logue (Sr VP-Healthcare Solutions)
Jim Mormile (Pres-Professional Lines)
Rob Roberts (Pres-Energy Division)
Tom Schmitt (Chief People Officer & Acct Admin Dir)
Matt Semeraro (Pres-Surety Division)
Leslie Shaunty (Gen Counsel)
Havis Wright (Sr VP-Inland Marine)

Subsidiaries:

Imperium Insurance Company　　(1)
120 W 45th St 36th Fl, New York, NY
10036
Tel.: (212) 702-3700
Web Site:
　　http://www.imperiuminsurance.com
Sales Range: $10-24.9 Million
Emp.: 50
Insurance Services
N.A.I.C.S.: 524298

SKYWATER TECHNOLOGY, INC.

2401 E 86th St, Bloomington, MN
55425
Tel.: (952) 851-5200　　　　　DE

Web Site:
　　https://www.skywatertechnology.com
Year Founded: 2016
SKYT—(NASDAQ)
Rev.: $162,848,000
Assets: $263,598,000
Liabilities: $203,671,000
Net Worth: $59,927,000
Earnings: ($50,696,000)
Emp.: 590
Fiscal Year-end: 01/02/22
Semiconductor Mfr
N.A.I.C.S.: 334413
John C. Sakamoto (Pres & COO)
Thomas J. Sonderman (CEO)
Steve Manko (CFO)
Amanda Daniel (Chief HR Officer)
Jason Stokes (Chief Legal Officer, Gen Counsel & Sec)
Mark Litecky (Chief Revenue Officer)
Steven Kosier (CTO)
John Kent (Exec VP-Tech Dev & Design Enablement)
John Spicer (Exec VP-Ops)
Srila LaRochelle (VP-Strategic Bus Dev)
Gary J. Obermiller (Chm)

SKYWEST INC.

444 S River Rd, Saint George, UT
84790-2085
Tel.: (435) 634-3000　　　　　UT
Web Site: https://inc.skywest.com
Year Founded: 1972
SKYW—(NASDAQ)
Rev.: $3,004,925,000
Assets: $7,414,553,000
Liabilities: $5,066,922,000
Net Worth: $2,347,631,000
Earnings: $72,953,000
Emp.: 11,852
Fiscal Year-end: 12/31/22
Airline Holding Company
N.A.I.C.S.: 561599
Russell A. Childs (Pres & CEO)
Wade J. Steel (Chief Comml Officer)
Eric J. Woodward (Chief Acctg Officer)
Robert J. Simmons (CFO)
Greg Wooley (Exec VP-Ops)
Justin Esplin (VP-IT)

Subsidiaries:

Skywest Airlines, Inc.　　　　　(1)
444 S River Rd, Saint George, UT
84790-2085　　　　　　　　　(100%)
Tel.: (435) 634-3000
Web Site: https://www.skywest.com
Sales Range: $1-4.9 Billion
Emp.: 14,072
Scheduled Airline
N.A.I.C.S.: 481111
Lori Hunt (VP-Airport Ops)
Bill Dykes (Sr VP-Maintenance)
Tracy Gallo (Sr VP-Flight Ops)
Greg Wooley (Exec VP-Ops)
Sonya Wolford (Sr VP-InFlight)
Chip Childs (Pres & CEO)
Brad Blake (VP-Operations)

Branch (Domestic):

Skywest Airlines, Inc. - Idaho　　(2)
2140 N Skyline Dr, Idaho Falls, ID 83402
Tel.: (208) 529-8001
Web Site: http://www.skywest.com
Air Courier Services
N.A.I.C.S.: 492110

SKYWORKS SOLUTIONS, INC.

5260 California Ave, Irvine, CA 92617
Tel.: (949) 231-3000　　　　　DE
Web Site:
　　https://www.skyworksinc.com
Year Founded: 1962
SWKS—(NASDAQ)
Rev.: $4,178,000,000
Assets: $8,283,300,000

Liabilities: $1,946,600,000
Net Worth: $6,336,700,000
Earnings: $596,000,000
Emp.: 10,100
Fiscal Year-end: 09/27/24
Electronic & Microwave Components Mfr
N.A.I.C.S.: 334413
Kris Sennesael (CFO & Sr VP)
Robert J. Terry (Gen Counsel, Sec & Sr VP)
Carlos S. Bori (Sr VP-Sls & Mktg)
Joel R. King (Sr VP & Gen Mgr)
Reza Kasnavi (Sr VP-Tech & Mfg)
Kari A. Durham (Sr VP-HR)
Liam K. Griffin (Chm, Pres & CEO)
Yusuf Jamal (Sr VP & Gen Mgr)
Mark Thompson (Sr VP & Gen Mgr)
Philip Carter (Principal Acctg Officer)

Subsidiaries:

Avnera Corporation　　　　　　(1)
1600 NW Compton Dr Ste 300, Beaverton, OR 97006
Tel.: (503) 718-4100
Web Site: http://www.avnera.com
Sales Range: $1-9.9 Million
Other Miscellaneous Durable Goods Merchant Whslr
N.A.I.C.S.: 423990

Isolink, Inc.　　　　　　　　　(1)
880 Yosemite Way, Milpitas, CA 95035
Tel.: (408) 946-1968
Web Site: http://www.isolink.com
Optoelectronic Component Distr
N.A.I.C.S.: 334413

SiGe Semiconductor (Europe) Limited　　　　　　　　　　(1)
South Building Walden Court, Parsonage Lane, Bishop's Stortford, CM23 5DB, Herts, United Kingdom
Tel.: (44) 1279464200
Semiconductor Equipment Mfr
N.A.I.C.S.: 334413

SiGe Semiconductor (U.S.), Corp.　　　　　　　　　　　(1)
200 Brickstone Sq Ste 203, Andover, MA 01810
Tel.: (978) 327-6850
Sales Range: $100-124.9 Million
Emp.: 500
Radio Frequency Semiconductor Mfr
N.A.I.C.S.: 334413

Skyworks Global Pte Ltd　　　　(1)
10 Ang Mo Kio Street 65 Techpoint 04-07, Singapore, 569059, Singapore　(100%)
Tel.: (65) 64031971
Web Site: http://www.skyworksinc.com
Sales Range: $100-124.9 Million
Electronic & Microwave Component Sales
N.A.I.C.S.: 334419

Skyworks Semiconductor　　　　(1)
34 Ave Franklin Roosevelt, 92150, Suresnes, France　　　　　　(100%)
Tel.: (33) 0141443660
Web Site: http://www.skyworksinc.com
Sales Range: $1-9.9 Million
Emp.: 4
Electronic & Microwave Components
N.A.I.C.S.: 334419

Skyworks Solutions Company, Limited　　　　　　　　　　(1)
Shinjuku Nomura Bldg 33 Floor 1-26-2 Nishi-Shinjuku, Shinjuku-ku, Tokyo, 163-0533, Japan　　　　　　　(100%)
Tel.: (81) 368945180
Web Site: http://www.skyworksinc.com
Electronic & Microwave Component Sales
N.A.I.C.S.: 334419

Skyworks Solutions Korea Limited　　　　　　　　　　(1)
POSCO Center West Wing 12F 440 Taeheran-ro, Seoul, 06194, Korea (South)
Tel.: (82) 234903800
Web Site: http://www.skyworksinc.com
Electronic & Microwave Component Sales
N.A.I.C.S.: 334419

Skyworks Solutions Limited　　　(1)

Thremhall Park Start Hill, Parsonage Lane, Bishop's Stortford, CM22 7WE, Hertfordshire, United Kingdom　　　　(100%)
Tel.: (44) 7920838883
Web Site: http://www.skyworksinc.com
Sales Range: $100-124.9 Million
Electronic & Microwave Components
N.A.I.C.S.: 334419

Skyworks Solutions Oy　　　　　(1)
Keilaranta 16, PO Box 3, 02150, Espoo, Finland　　　　　　　　　(100%)
Tel.: (358) 925107131
Web Site: http://www.skyworksinc.com
Sales Range: $25-49.9 Million
Emp.: 10
Electronic & Microwave Components
N.A.I.C.S.: 334220

Skyworks Solutions Worldwide, Inc.　　　　　　　　　　　(1)
Suite 1316 13F COFCO Plaza No 8 Jianguomennei Avenue, Dongcheng District, Beijing, 100005, China
Tel.: (86) 1065261358
Web Site: http://www.skyworksinc.com
Electronic & Microwave Component Sales
N.A.I.C.S.: 334419

Skyworks Solutions Worldwide, Inc.　　　　　　　　　　　(1)
4F Ste198 Section 2, Tun Hwa S Road, Taipei, 106, Taiwan
Tel.: (886) 255598990
Web Site: http://www.skyworksinc.com
Sales Range: $100-124.9 Million
Emp.: 30
Electronic & Microwave Component Sales
N.A.I.C.S.: 423690

Skyworks Solutions de Mexico, S. de R.L. de C.V.　　　　　　　(1)
Calzada Gomez Morin 1690, Col Rivera, 21259, Mexicali, Baja California, Mexico
Tel.: (52) 9492313550
Sales Range: $500-549.9 Million
Emp.: 2,000
Semiconductor Mfr
N.A.I.C.S.: 334413

Trans-Tech, Inc.　　　　　　　(1)
5520 Adamstown Rd, Adamstown, MD 21710-9619　　　　　　　(100%)
Tel.: (301) 695-9400
Web Site: http://www.trans-techinc.com
Sales Range: $125-149.9 Million
Emp.: 200
Mfr of Microwave Ceramic & Ferrite Materials
N.A.I.C.S.: 334220

SKYX PLATFORMS CORP.

2855 W McNab Rd, Pompano Beach, FL 33069
Tel.: (770) 754-4711　　　　　FL
Web Site:
　　https://www.skyxplatforms.com
Year Founded: 2004
SKYX—(NASDAQ)
Rev.: $58,785,762
Assets: $76,341,203
Liabilities: $60,119,193
Net Worth: $16,222,010
Earnings: ($39,732,656)
Emp.: 60
Fiscal Year-end: 12/31/23
Electrical Lighting Fixture & Fan Power Plugs Mfr
N.A.I.C.S.: 335999
Leonard Jay Sokolow (Co-CEO)
John P. Campi (Co-CEO)
Rani R. Kohen (Founder & Chm)
Steven M. Schmidt (Pres)
Jonathan Globerson (VP-Design & Marketing)
Amy Cronin (Exec Dir-Codes & Standards)
Eliran Ben-Zikri (CTO)
Rob Powell (Chief Compliance Officer & Gen Counsel)
Marc-Andre Boisseau (CFO)

SL GREEN REALTY CORP.

Tel.: (212) 594-2700　　　　　MD
Web Site: https://www.slgreen.com

SL Green Realty Corp.—(Continued)

Year Founded: 1980
SLG—(NYSE)
Rev.: $826,739,000
Assets: $12,355,794,000
Liabilities: $7,708,872,000
Net Worth: $4,646,922,000
Earnings: ($78,074,000)
Emp.: 1,137
Fiscal Year-end: 12/31/22
Real Estate Investment Trust
N.A.I.C.S.: 525990
Marc Holliday *(Chm, Interim Pres & CEO)*
Andrew S. Levine *(Chief Legal Officer)*
Steven M. Durels *(Exec VP & Dir-Leasing & Real Property)*
Edward V. Piccinich *(COO)*
Neil H. Kessner *(Gen Counsel-Real Property & Exec VP)*
Matthew J. DiLiberto *(CFO)*
Harrison Sitomer *(Chief Investment Officer)*
Maggie Hui *(Chief Acctg Officer)*

Subsidiaries:

Green 711 Third Avenue LLC **(1)**
711 Third Ave, New York, NY 10017
Tel.: (212) 216-1687
Web Site: http://711third.slgreen.com
Sales Range: $75-99.9 Million
Property Leasing & Management Services
N.A.I.C.S.: 531210

Reckson Operating Partnership, L.P. **(1)**
420 Lexington Ave, New York, NY 10170
Tel.: (212) 594-2700
Web Site: http://www.slgreen.com
Rev.: $816,103,000
Assets: $7,009,297,000
Liabilities: $928,189,000
Net Worth: $6,081,108,000
Earnings: $194,945,000
Fiscal Year-end: 12/31/2018
Real Estate Investment Trust
N.A.I.C.S.: 525990

SL Green Funding LLC **(1)**
875 Avenue of the Americas, New York, NY 10001
Tel.: (212) 246-6749
Web Site: http://www.slgreen.com
Emp.: 23
Investment Management Service
N.A.I.C.S.: 523940

SL Green Management LLC **(1)**
420 Lexington Ave 19th Fl, New York, NY 10170
Tel.: (212) 594-2700
Real Estate Brokerage Services
N.A.I.C.S.: 531210

SL Green Operating Partnership, L.P. **(1)**
1 Vanderbilt Ave, New York, NY 10017
Tel.: (212) 594-2700
Web Site: https://www.slgreen.com
Rev.: $826,738,999
Assets: $12,355,793,999
Liabilities: $7,708,871,999
Net Worth: $4,646,921,999
Earnings: ($83,868,000)
Emp.: 1,136
Fiscal Year-end: 12/31/2022
Real Estate Investment Services
N.A.I.C.S.: 531210
Marc Holliday *(Chm & CEO)*

SLG 16 Court Street LLC **(1)**
444 S River Rd, Saint George, UT 84790-2085
Tel.: (435) 634-3000
Web Site: https://www.skywest.com
Sales Range: $25-49.9 Million
Emp.: 2
Property Leasing & Management Services
N.A.I.C.S.: 541611
Lawrence Swiger *(Sr VP-Leasing)*

SLG 609 Fifth LLC **(1)**
609 5th Ave, New York, NY 10017
Tel.: (212) 755-6393

Commercial Building Rental & Leasing Services
N.A.I.C.S.: 531120

SLG 625 Lessee LLC **(1)**
20 Lexington Ave, New York, NY 10010
Tel.: (212) 594-2700
Real Estate Brokerage Services
N.A.I.C.S.: 531210

SLG 711 Third LLC **(1)**
711 3rd Ave, New York, NY 10017
Tel.: (212) 682-3934
Sales Range: $10-24.9 Million
Emp.: 20
Property Leasing & Management Services
N.A.I.C.S.: 541611
Mike Wilder *(Mgr-Property)*

SLG IRP Realty LLC **(1)**
111 8th Ave, New York, NY 10011-5201
Tel.: (212) 982-9649
Apartment Building Rental & Leasing Services
N.A.I.C.S.: 531110

eEmerge, Inc. **(1)**
125 Park Ave, New York, NY 10017
Tel.: (212) 404-2000
Web Site: https://www.emerge212.com
Sales Range: Less than $1 Million
Emp.: 6
Real Estate & Office Infrastructure Management Services
N.A.I.C.S.: 531190
Alex Bogen *(Mng Dir)*

SLAM CORP.

55 Hudson Yards 47th Fl Ste C, New York, NY 10001
Tel.: (646) 762-8580   Ky
Web Site: https://www.slamcorp.com
Year Founded: 2020
SLAM—(NASDAQ)
Rev.: $8,428,328
Assets: $583,885,078
Liabilities: $608,383,384
Net Worth: ($24,498,306)
Earnings: $18,686,195
Emp.: 5
Fiscal Year-end: 12/31/22
Investment Services
N.A.I.C.S.: 523999
Chetan Bansal *(Chief Dev Officer)*
Himanshu Gulati *(Chm)*
Kelly Laferriere *(Pres)*
Alex Rodriguez *(CEO)*
Ryan Bright *(CFO)*

SLEEP NUMBER CORPORATION

1001 3rd Ave S, Minneapolis, MN 55404
Tel.: (763) 551-7000   MN
Web Site:
   https://www.sleepnumber.com
Year Founded: 1987
SNBR—(NASDAQ)
Rev.: $2,184,949,000
Assets: $919,540,000
Liabilities: $1,344,493,000
Net Worth: ($424,953,000)
Earnings: $153,746,000
Emp.: 5,515
Fiscal Year-end: 01/01/22
Air Mattresses, Pillows & Bedding Mfr & Retailer
N.A.I.C.S.: 337910
Shelly R. Ibach *(Chm, Pres & CEO)*
Andrea Lee Bloomquist *(Chief Innovation Officer & Exec VP)*
Melissa Barra *(Chief Sls Officer, Chief Services Officer & Exec VP)*
Christopher Krusmark *(Chief HR Officer & Exec VP)*
Francis K. Lee *(CFO & Exec VP)*
Kevin Kennedy Brown *(CMO & Exec VP)*
Joel Laing *(Chief Acctg Officer & Treas)*

Joseph Hunter Saklad *(Chief Supply Chain Officer & Exec VP)*
Samuel R. Hellfeld *(Chief Legal & Risk Officer, Sec & Sr VP)*
Julie Elepano *(Board of Directors & Sr Dir-PR)*

Subsidiaries:

Comfortaire Corporation **(1)**
103 Shaw St, Greenville, SC 29609
Tel.: (864) 277-7269
Web Site: http://www.comfortaire.com
Sales Range: $10-24.9 Million
Emp.: 24
Mattress Mfr
N.A.I.C.S.: 337910
David Karr *(Pres)*

Select Comfort Retail Corporation **(1)**
9800 59th Ave N, Minneapolis, MN 55442
Tel.: (763) 551-7000
Furniture Store Operator
N.A.I.C.S.: 449110

SleepIQ LABS Inc. **(1)**
111 W Saint John St Ste 1200, San Jose, CA 95113
Tel.: (408) 335-5020
Web Site: http://www.bamlabs.com
Healthcare Equipment Distr
N.A.I.C.S.: 423490
Richard Rifredi *(Co-Founder)*
Steve Young *(Co-Founder)*

selectcomfort.com corporation **(1)**
6105 Trenton Ln N, Minneapolis, MN 55442-3274
Tel.: (736) 551-7000
Sales Range: $150-199.9 Million
Online Bedding Retailer
N.A.I.C.S.: 423620

SLM CORPORATION

300 Continental Dr, Newark, DE 19713
Tel.: (302) 451-0200   DE
Web Site: https://www.salliemae.com
Year Founded: 1973
SLM—(NASDAQ)
Rev.: $2,839,419,000
Assets: $29,169,468,000
Liabilities: $27,288,671,000
Net Worth: $1,880,797,000
Earnings: $563,686,000
Emp.: 1,740
Fiscal Year-end: 12/31/23
Funding & Servicing Support for Higher Education Loans
N.A.I.C.S.: 522310
Donna F. Vieira *(Chief Comml Officer & Exec VP)*
Kerri Palmer *(COO)*
Steven J. McGarry *(Exec VP)*
Carter Warren Franke *(Chm)*
Peter M. Graham *(CFO, Principal Acctg Officer & Exec VP)*
Nicolas Jafarieh *(Chief Legal, Govt Affairs & Comm Officer & Sr VP)*
Jonathan W. Witter *(CEO)*
William Wolf *(Exec VP)*
Jeremy Brandon *(Chief Audit Officer)*
Munish Pahwa *(Chief Risk Officer & Exec VP)*

Subsidiaries:

Arrow Financial Services LLC **(1)**
5996 W Touhy Ave, Niles, IL 60714-4610
Tel.: (847) 557-1100
Sales Range: $400-449.9 Million
Debt Services
N.A.I.C.S.: 561440

HICA Education Loan Corporation **(1)**
2421 E Stanton Dr, Sioux Falls, SD 57103
Tel.: (605) 361-5051
Education Loan Services
N.A.I.C.S.: 611710

Nellie Mae Corporation **(1)**
50 Braintree Hill Park Ste 300, Braintree, MA 02184-8724   **(100%)**

Tel.: (781) 849-1325
Web Site: http://www.nelliemae.com
Sales Range: $75-99.9 Million
Emp.: 170
Educational Loans
N.A.I.C.S.: 522310

Pioneer Credit Recovery, Inc. **(1)**
26 Edward St, Arcade, NY 14009 **(100%)**
Tel.: (585) 492-1234
Web Site:
   https://www.pioneercreditrecovery.com
Sales Range: $350-399.9 Million
Collection Agency
N.A.I.C.S.: 561440
Caryn Benton *(Sec)*

SLM Financial Corp. **(1)**
300 Continental Dr 1 S, Newark, DE 19713   **(100%)**
Tel.: (302) 283-8000
Web Site: http://www.slmfinancial.com
Sales Range: $125-149.9 Million
Emp.: 30
Loan Broker
N.A.I.C.S.: 522299

Sallie Mae Bank **(1)**
5217 S State St Ste 210, Murray, UT 84107
Tel.: (801) 281-1423
Web Site: http://www.salliemae.com
Education Loan Services
N.A.I.C.S.: 611710
Raymond J. Quinlan *(Chm & Chm)*
Donna F. Vieira *(Exec VP)*
Jon Witter *(CEO)*
Pete Graham *(Exec VP)*
Donna Vieira *(Exec VP)*
William Wolf *(Exec VP)*
Nicolas Jafarieh *(Chief Govt Affairs Officer)*
Jeremy Brandon *(Chief Audit Officer)*
Munish Pahwa *(Exec VP)*

Southwest Student Services Corp. **(1)**
12061 Bluemont Way, Reston, VA 20190
Tel.: (703) 810-3000
Sales Range: $75-99.9 Million
Emp.: 280
Student Loan Marketing Association
N.A.I.C.S.: 522299

SLR INVESTMENT CORP.

500 Park Ave 3rd Fl, New York, NY 10022
Tel.: (212) 993-1670   MD
Web Site:
   https://slrinvestmentcorp.com
Year Founded: 2007
SLRC—(NASDAQ)
Rev.: $177,505,000
Assets: $2,537,695,000
Liabilities: $1,537,964,000
Net Worth: $999,731,000
Earnings: $76,366,000
Fiscal Year-end: 12/31/22
Investment Holding Company
N.A.I.C.S.: 551112
Bruce John Spohler *(Co-Founder, Co-CEO & COO)*
Michael S. Gross *(Co-Founder, Chm, Pres & Co-CEO)*
Guy F. Talarico *(Chief Compliance Officer)*
Shiraz Y. Kajee *(CFO, Treas & Sec)*
Ingrid Kiefer *(Partner & Chief Bus Dev Officer)*

Subsidiaries:

Crystal Financial LLC **(1)**
2 International Pl 17th Fl, Boston, MA 02110
Tel.: (617) 428-8700
Web Site: https://crystalfinco.com
Emp.: 20
Corporate Debt Investment Fund Origination, Underwriting & Management Services
N.A.I.C.S.: 523940
Robert Brown *(Dir-Treasury Ops)*
Joshua Franklin *(CFO & COO)*
Matthew J. Governali *(Mng Dir)*
Michael Pizette *(Co-CEO)*
Christopher Arnold *(Sr Mng Dir)*
Cheryl Carner *(Sr Mng Dir & Co-Head-Originations)*

Tyler Harrington *(Mng Dir)*
Kenny Smith *(Mng Dir)*
Rebecca Tarby *(Sr Mng Dir)*
Mirko Andric *(Sr Mng Dir)*
Julie Monahan *(VP-Fin & Controller)*
Michael Russell *(Dir)*
Case Fedor *(Dir)*
Jared Grigg *(Mng Dir)*

SLR Senior Investment Corp. (1)
500 Park Ave, New York, NY 10022
Tel.: (212) 993-1670
Web Site: http://www.solarseniorcap.com
Rev.: $29,319,000
Assets: $572,887,000
Liabilities: $325,204,000
Net Worth: $247,683,000
Earnings: $14,320,000
Fiscal Year-end: 12/31/2021
Investment Services
N.A.I.C.S.: 523999
Richard L. Peteka *(CFO, Treas & Sec)*

Subsidiary (Domestic):

North Mill Capital LLC (2)
821 Alexander Rd Ste 130, Princeton, NJ
08540
Tel.: (609) 917-6200
Web Site: https://slrbusinesscredit.com
Commercial Asset-Based Lending Services
N.A.I.C.S.: 522180
Jeffrey K. Goldrich *(Pres & CEO)*
Stephen Carroll *(CFO & Exec VP)*
Daniel F. Tortoriello *(COO & Exec VP)*
Patti Kotusky *(Sr VP & Ops Mgr)*
Betty Hernandez *(Chief Credit Officer &
Exec VP)*
Heidi Ames *(Sr VP)*
Tessa Brend *(VP)*
Licia Jacques *(Sr VP & Controller)*
Jennifer Borg *(Sr VP & Sr Portfolio Mgr)*
Kristin Erickson *(Mng Dir & Sr VP)*
Rochelle Hilson *(COO-IBF & Sr VP)*
Tracy Nelson *(Sr VP & Acct Exec)*
Stephanie Koveleski *(Asst VP & Acct Exec)*
Trina Garner *(Mgr-HR)*
Tammy L. Bowling *(VP-IBF & Dir-East Cost)*
David R. McFarland *(Sr VP & Acct Exec)*
Jennifer Boss *(Sr VP & Mgr-Relationship)*
Nico LaStella *(Asst VP)*

SM ENERGY COMPANY
1700 Lincoln St Ste 3200, Denver,
CO 80203
Tel.: (303) 861-8140   DE
Web Site: https://www.sm-
energy.com
Year Founded: 1908
SM—(NYSE)
Rev.: $2,373,886,000
Assets: $6,379,985,000
Liabilities: $2,764,135,000
Net Worth: $3,615,850,000
Earnings: $817,880,000
Emp.: 544
Fiscal Year-end: 12/31/23
Natural Gas & Crude Oil Explorer,
Developer, Acquirer & Producer
N.A.I.C.S.: 211120
David J. Whitcomb *(VP-Mktg)*
A. Wade Pursell *(CFO & Exec VP)*
Kenneth Knott *(Sr VP-Bus Dev &
Land)*
Herbert S. Vogel *(Pres & CEO)*
Mary Ellen Lutey *(Sr VP- Exploration,
Dev & EHS)*
Tom Morrow *(VP-Ops Support)*
Richard Jenkins *(VP-Ops)*
Susie Piehl *(VP-IR)*
James B. Lebeck *(Gen Counsel &
Exec VP)*
Andrew Urie *(VP)*

Subsidiaries:

SM Energy Company - Houston (1)
777 N Eldridge Pkwy Ste 1000, Houston,
TX 77079
Tel.: (281) 677-2800
Web Site: http://www.sm-energy.com
Oil & Gas Exploration Services
N.A.I.C.S.: 213112

**St. Mary Land & Exploration Co. -
Shreveport** (1)

330 Marshall St 1200, Shreveport, LA
71101
Tel.: (318) 424-0804
Web Site: http://www.stmaryland.com
Sales Range: $25-49.9 Million
Emp.: 30
Explorer of Gas & Oil
N.A.I.C.S.: 211120

SMA ALLIANCE, INC.
1830 Burlington Ave Ste 401, Casper,
WY 82601
Tel.: (307) 265-4698
Year Founded: 1969
SMAA—(NASDAQ)
Emp.: 79
Software Application Services
N.A.I.C.S.: 541511
Robertt A. Wharf *(Chm)*

**SMALL BUSINESS DEVELOP-
MENT GROUP, INC.**
136 4th St N, Saint Petersburg, FL
33701
Tel.: (727) 503-7104   TX
Web Site:
https://www.smallbizdevgroup.com
SBDG—(OTCIQ)
Holding Company
N.A.I.C.S.: 551112
Roy Y. Salisbury *(CEO)*
James E. Jenkins *(CFO)*

SMART CANNABIS CORP.
25422 Trabuco Rd Ste 105-297, Lake
Forest, CA 92630
Tel.: (949) 689-0612   OK
Year Founded: 2009
SCNA—(OTCIQ)
Agricultural Product Mfr & Distr
N.A.I.C.S.: 325311
Mark Cheung *(Pres)*

**SMART CARD MARKETING
SYSTEMS, INC.**
20c Trolley Sq, Wilmington, DE
19806
Tel.: (718) 717-8657   DE
Web Site:
https://www.smartcardmarketing
systems.com
Year Founded: 2006
SMKG—(OTCIQ)
Marketing Consulting Services
N.A.I.C.S.: 541613
Massimo Barone *(Founder, Chm &
CEO)*

SMART DECISION, INC.
1825 Corporate Blvd NW Ste 110,
Boca Raton, FL 33431   WY
Web Site:
https://www.smartdecisioninc.com
SDEC—(OTCIQ)
Miscellaneous Financial Investment
Activities
N.A.I.C.S.: 523999
Adam Green *(Pres & CEO)*

SMART FOR LIFE, INC.
990 Biscayne Blvd Ste 503, Miami,
FL 33132
Tel.: (786) 749-1221
Web Site: https://smartforlifecorp.com
Year Founded: 2002
SMFL—(NASDAQ)
Rev.: $8,225,792
Assets: $19,659,227
Liabilities: $26,046,681
Net Worth: ($6,387,454)
Earnings: ($22,675,741)
Emp.: 12
Fiscal Year-end: 12/31/23
Health & Wellness Nutritional Food &
Supplements Mfr
N.A.I.C.S.: 456191

Alfonso J. Cervantes Jr. *(Founder &
Chm)*
A.J. Darren Minton *(CEO)*
Alan Bergman *(CFO)*

Subsidiaries:

Ceautamed Worldwide LLC (1)
1289 Clint Moore Rd, Boca Raton, FL
33487-2718
Web Site: http://www.ceautamed.com
Pharmaceutical Preparation Mfr
N.A.I.C.S.: 325412

SMART SAND, INC.
1000 Floral Vale Blvd Ste 225, Yard-
ley, PA 19067
Tel.: (281) 231-2660   DE
Web Site:
https://www.smartsand.com
Year Founded: 2011
SND—(NASDAQ)
Rev.: $255,740,000
Assets: $360,003,000
Liabilities: $116,532,000
Net Worth: $243,471,000
Earnings: ($703,000)
Emp.: 328
Fiscal Year-end: 12/31/22
Fracturing Sand Mining & Logistics
Services
N.A.I.C.S.: 212390
Andrew Speaker *(CEO)*
Lee E. Beckelman *(CFO & Principal
Acctg Officer)*
Robert Kiszka *(Exec VP-Ops)*
William John Young *(COO)*
Ronald P. Whelan *(Exec VP-Sls)*
Jose E. Feliciano *(Chm)*
James D. Young *(Gen Counsel, Sec
& Exec VP)*
Christopher Green *(Principal Acctg
Officer & VP-Acctg)*
Rick Shearer *(Pres)*
Charles E. Young *(Founder)*

**SMARTAG INTERNATIONAL,
INC.**
3651 Lindell Rd Ste D269, Las Ve-
gas, NV 94102
Tel.: (310) 499-6730   NV
Web Site: http://www.smrntl.com
SMRN—(OTCIQ)
Investment Services
N.A.I.C.S.: 523999
Lock Sen Yow *(CEO)*
S. H. Lau *(COO)*
Winsen Tan *(CTO)*
Sunder Lama *(Gen Mgr-Mktg-UK &
Nepal)*

SMARTFINANCIAL, INC.
5401 Kingston Pike Ste 600, Knox-
ville, TN 37919
Tel.: (865) 453-2650   TN
Web Site:
https://www.smartfinancialinc.com
SMBK—(NYSE)
Rev.: $152,405,000
Assets: $4,829,387,000
Liabilities: $4,369,501,000
Net Worth: $459,886,000
Earnings: $28,593,000
Emp.: 570
Fiscal Year-end: 12/31/23
Bank Holding Company
N.A.I.C.S.: 551111
William Young Carroll Jr. *(Pres &
CEO)*
William Young Carroll Sr. *(Vice Chm)*
Ronald J. Gorczynski *(CFO & Exec
VP)*

Subsidiaries:

SmartBank (1)
2430 Teaster Ln Ste 205, Pigeon Forge, TN
37863
Tel.: (865) 868-0618

Web Site: https://www.smartbank.com
Commercial Banking
N.A.I.C.S.: 522110
William Young Carroll Jr. *(Pres & CEO)*
William Young Carroll Sr. *(Vice Chm)*
Becca Boyd *(Chief People Officer & Exec
VP)*
Miller Welborn *(Chm)*
Beverly Atchley *(Sr VP & Sr Dir-Ops)*
Travis Lytle *(Officer-Community Reinvest-
ment Act, Sr VP & Dir-Community Dev)*
Anthony Price *(Pres)*
Bobby Castle *(Pres, Pres-Sevier County &
Sr VP)*
Cheryl Sandlin *(Pres, Pres-Market-
Cookeville & Sr VP)*
David Conner *(Pres, Pres-Market-Blount
County & Sr VP)*
David Scott *(Reg Pres)*
Gary Petty *(Chief Risk Officer)*
James Fuller *(Pres, Pres-Market-Coffee
County & VP)*
John Davis *(Pres, Pres-Market-Wartburg &
VP)*
Karen Cole *(Pres, Pres-Market-Cumberland
Plateau & VP)*
Matt Jenne *(Pres, Pres-Market-Cleveland &
Sr VP)*
Mike Honeycutt *(Reg Pres)*
Nate Strall *(VP)*
Rhett Jordan *(Chief Credit Officer)*
Ron Gorczynski *(CFO, Chief HR Officer &
Exec VP)*
Tanner Harris *(Pres, Pres-Market-Knox
County & Sr VP)*
Bill Carroll *(Vice Chm)*
Billy Carroll *(CEO)*
Cathy Ackermann *(CEO-Marketing & Public
Relations)*
Brad Place *(Sr VP)*
Martin Schrodt *(Exec VP)*
Robbie Washington *(Sr VP)*
Brian Groeschell *(Reg Pres)*
Lee Smith *(Chm-Alabama)*
Jeff Williams *(Reg Pres)*
Johnnie Wright *(Reg Pres)*

Subsidiary (Domestic):

Fountain Leasing LLC (2)
5100 Poplar Ave Ste 813, Memphis, TN
38137-0800
Tel.: (901) 683-5366
Web Site: http://www.fountainleasingllc.com
General Rental Centers
N.A.I.C.S.: 532310
Wade West *(VP)*

SMARTMETRIC, INC.
3960 Howard Hughes Pkwy Ste 500,
Las Vegas, NV 89109
Tel.: (702) 990-3687   NV
Web Site:
https://www.smartmetric.com
Year Founded: 2002
SMME—(OTCIQ)
Assets: $53,223
Liabilities: $3,076,049
Net Worth: ($3,022,826)
Earnings: ($681,441)
Emp.: 1
Fiscal Year-end: 06/30/24
Biometric Card Mfr
N.A.I.C.S.: 325414
Jay M. Needelman *(CFO)*
Elizabeth Ryba *(VP-Mktg)*
Chaya Hendrick *(Founder, Chm, Pres
& CEO)*
Peter Sleep *(VP-Mktg-Asia Pacific)*

SMARTRENT, INC.
8665 E Hartford Dr, Scottsdale, AZ
85255
Tel.: (480) 371-2828   DE
Web Site: https://www.smartrent.com
SMRT—(NYSE)
Rev.: $167,821,000
Assets: $560,845,000
Liabilities: $196,645,000
Net Worth: $364,200,000
Earnings: ($96,322,000)
Emp.: 701

SmartRent, Inc.—(Continued)
Fiscal Year-end: 12/31/22
Software Publisher
N.A.I.C.S.: 513210
Daryl Stemm (CFO & Interim Principal Executive Officer)
Lucas Haldeman (CEO)
Lucas Haldeman (Founder)

Subsidiaries:

SightPlan, Inc. (1)
PO Box 4308, Orlando, FL 32802-4308
Tel.: (407) 459-7866
Web Site: http://www.sightplan.com
Sales Range: $1-9.9 Million
Emp.: 200
Software Development Services
N.A.I.C.S.: 541511
Terry Danner (CEO)
Joseph Westlake (Pres)
Daniel Polfer (CTO)

SmartRent Technologies, Inc. (1)
8665 E Hartford Dr Ste 200, Scottsdale, AZ 85255
Tel.: (844) 479-1555
Web Site: https://smartrent.com
Emp.: 100
Software Publisher
N.A.I.C.S.: 513210

TRI PLUS GRUPA d.o.o (1)
Banjavciceva 11, 10000, Zagreb, Croatia
Tel.: (385) 14004404
Information Technology Services
N.A.I.C.S.: 541511

SMARTSHEET INC.
500 108th Ave NE Ste 200, Bellevue, WA 98004　　**WA**
Web Site:
　https://www.smartsheet.com
Year Founded: 2005
SMAR—(NYSE)
Rev.: $958,338,000
Assets: $1,337,479,000
Liabilities: $731,624,000
Net Worth: $605,855,000
Earnings: ($104,631,000)
Emp.: 3,330
Fiscal Year-end: 01/31/24
Software Publisher
N.A.I.C.S.: 513210
Mark P. Mader (Pres & CEO)
Brent R. Frei (Co-Founder)
Praerit Garg (Pres-Product & Innovation)
Max Long (Pres-Go-to-Market)
Praerit Garg (Chief Product Officer & Exec VP-Engrg)
Michael P. Gregoire (Chm)
Pete Godbole (CFO)
Megan Hansen (Chief People & Culture Officer)
Jolene Marshall (Chief Legal Officer)
Geoffrey T. Barker (Executives)

Subsidiaries:

Smartsheet Australia Pty. Ltd. (1)
Level 33 60 Margaret Street, Sydney, 2000, NSW, Australia
Tel.: (61) 290558255
Software Publisher
N.A.I.C.S.: 513210
Lee O'Sullivan (Mgr-Client Dev)

TernPro Inc. (1)
321 3rd Ave S Ste 304, Seattle, WA 98104
Web Site: http://www.ternpro.com
Software Development Services
N.A.I.C.S.: 513210

SMG INDUSTRIES INC.
20475 State Hwy 249 Ste 450, Houston, TX 77070
Tel.: (713) 955-3497　　**DE**
Web Site:
　http://www.smgindustries.com
Year Founded: 2008

SMGI—(OTCQB)
Rev.: $71,021,862
Assets: $22,181,687
Liabilities: $48,703,825
Net Worth: ($26,522,138)
Earnings: ($11,610,240)
Emp.: 269
Fiscal Year-end: 12/31/22
Metal Indium Stockpiling & Purchasing Services
N.A.I.C.S.: 423510
Matthew C. Flemming (Chm)
Steven H. Madden (CTO)

Subsidiaries:

5J Oilfield Services, LLC (1)
4090 N Hwy 79, Palestine, TX 75801
Tel.: (903) 729-0969
Web Site: http://www.5joilfield.net
Oil & Gas Operations
N.A.I.C.S.: 213112

MG Cleaners LLC (1)
422 E Sabine St, Carthage, TX 75633-2720
Tel.: (903) 693-9392
Web Site: https://www.mgcleanersllc.com
Oilfield Support Services
N.A.I.C.S.: 213112
Kris Boen (VP & Gen Mgr-West Texas)

SMILEDIRECTCLUB, INC.
414 Union St, Nashville, TN 37219　DE
Web Site:
　https://www.smiledirectclub.com
Year Founded: 2019
SDC—(NASDAQ)
Rev.: $470,743,000
Assets: $597,063,000
Liabilities: $982,261,000
Net Worth: ($385,198,000)
Earnings: ($86,404,000)
Emp.: 2,700
Fiscal Year-end: 12/31/22
Holding Company
N.A.I.C.S.: 551112
Troy W. Crawford (CFO)
David Katzman (Chm & CEO)
Steven Katzman (COO)
Jordan Katzman (Founder)
Susan Greenspon Rammelt (Chief Legal Officer, Chief Legal Officer, Gen Counsel, Gen Counsel, Sec, Sec & Exec VP/Exec VP-Bus Affairs)

Subsidiaries:

SDC Canada Inc. (1)
79 Wellington St W 3000, Toronto, M5K 1N2, ON, Canada
Web Site: http://www.smiledirectclub.ca
Dental Equipment Mfr
N.A.I.C.S.: 339114

SMITH & WESSON BRANDS, INC.
2100 Roosevelt Ave, Springfield, MA 01104
Tel.: (413) 781-8300　　**NV**
Web Site: https://www.smith-wesson.com
Year Founded: 1998
SWBI—(NASDAQ)
Rev.: $479,242,000
Assets: $541,294,000
Liabilities: $156,671,000
Net Worth: $384,623,000
Earnings: $36,876,000
Emp.: 1,682
Fiscal Year-end: 04/30/23
Holding Company; Small Arms, Law Enforcement Equipment & Sporting Goods Mfr
N.A.I.C.S.: 551112
Robert L. Scott (Chm)
Deana L. McPherson (CFO, Treas, Exec VP & Asst Sec)
Susan J. Cupero (VP-Sls)
Kevin A. Maxwell (Chief Compliance Officer, Gen Counsel, Sec & Sr VP)

Subsidiaries:

Battenfeld Technologies, Inc. (1)
1800 N Rt Z, Columbia, MO 65202
Tel.: (573) 445-9200
Web Site: https://www.btibrands.com
Sales Range: $1-9.9 Million
Emp.: 45
Non-Mfr of Shooting & Hunting Brands & Accessories for Gun Enthusiasts
N.A.I.C.S.: 339920

Crimson Trace Corporation (1)
9780 SW Freeman Dr, Wilsonville, OR 97070
Tel.: (503) 783-5333
Web Site: https://www.crimsontrace.com
Small Arms Mfr
N.A.I.C.S.: 332994

Deep River Plastics, LLC (1)
12 Bridge St, Deep River, CT 06417
Tel.: (860) 526-3200
Web Site: http://www.swpc.com
Sales Range: $10-24.9 Million
Emp.: 112
Injection Molding & Contract Manufacturing Services
N.A.I.C.S.: 326199

Smith & Wesson Corp. (1)
2100 Roosevelt Ave, Springfield, MA 01104-1606
Tel.: (413) 781-8300
Web Site: https://www.smith-wesson.com
Sales Range: $150-199.9 Million
Emp.: 800
Hand Guns, Law Enforcement Equipment & Sporting Goods Mfr
N.A.I.C.S.: 332994

SMITH DOUGLAS HOMES CORP.
110 Village Trl Ste 215, Woodstock, GA 30188
Tel.: (770) 213-8067　　**DE**
Web Site:
　https://www.smithdouglas.com
Year Founded: 2008
SDHC—(NYSE)
Emp.: 364
Construction Services
N.A.I.C.S.: 236210

SMITH MICRO SOFTWARE, INC.
5800 Corporate Dr, Pittsburgh, PA 15237
Tel.: (412) 837-5300　　**DE**
Web Site:
　https://www.smithmicro.com
Year Founded: 1982
SMSI—(NASDAQ)
Rev.: $48,513,000
Assets: $103,581,000
Liabilities: $27,202,000
Net Worth: $76,379,000
Earnings: ($29,279,000)
Emp.: 315
Fiscal Year-end: 12/31/22
Wireless Communication, Internet & eBusiness Software Products Developer & Marketer
N.A.I.C.S.: 334610
David P. Sperling (CTO)
Ken Shebek (CIO)
David Blakeney (Sr VP-Engrg)
Charles Messman (VP-IR & Corp Dev)
James M. Kempton (CFO, Treas & VP)
Eytan Urbas (VP-Corp Strategy)
James M. Kempton (CFO)
Anup Kaneri (VP)
Jennifer Reinke (Gen Counsel)
William W. Smith Jr. (Pres & CEO)

Subsidiaries:

Smith Micro Software - Wireless & Broadband Division (1)
51 Columbia, Aliso Viejo, CA 92656

Tel.: (949) 362-5800
Web Site: http://www.smithmicro.com
Sales Range: $100-124.9 Million
Provider of Wireless Telephony, Video & Audio Internet Communication & Core Fax & Data Telephony Technology
N.A.I.C.S.: 513210

Smith Micro Software UK Limited (1)
8 Lincolns Inn Fields, Camden Town, London, WC2A 3BP, Greater London, United Kingdom
Tel.: (44) 1252302369
Applications Software Programming Services
N.A.I.C.S.: 541511

Smith Micro Software, Inc. (1)
185 Westridge Dr, Watsonville, CA 95076-4168　　(100%)
Tel.: (831) 761-6200
Web Site: http://www.smithmicro.com
Sales Range: $10-24.9 Million
Emp.: 65
Software Products Designer & Developer
N.A.I.C.S.: 513210

SMITH-MIDLAND CORPORATION
5119 Catlett Rd, Midland, VA 22728
Tel.: (540) 439-3266　　**DE**
Web Site:
　https://www.smithmidland.com
Year Founded: 1960
SMID—(NASDAQ)
Rev.: $59,580,000
Assets: $61,348,000
Liabilities: $27,187,000
Net Worth: $34,161,000
Earnings: $795,000
Emp.: 172
Fiscal Year-end: 12/31/23
Precast Concrete Products For Construction, Utilities & Farming Industries Develops, Mfr, Marketer, Leasor, Licenser, Seller & Installer
N.A.I.C.S.: 327390
Ashley B. Smith (Pres & CEO)
Kevin Corbett (VP-Ops)
Ali Shahid (VP-Engrg)
Roderick Smith (Gen Mgr)
Scott Hicks (Gen Mgr)

SMS ALTERNATIVES INC.
8000 Regency Pkwy Ste 542, Cary, NC 27518
Tel.: (919) 380-5000　　**DE**
Web Site: http://www.oiooroino.com
Year Founded: 1988
CICN—(OTCEM)
Rev.: $1,536,000
Assets: $360,000
Liabilities: $5,144,000
Net Worth: ($4,784,000)
Earnings: ($1,609,000)
Emp.: 14
Fiscal Year-end: 12/31/19
Application Integration Products & Services
N.A.I.C.S.: 541511
John P. Broderick (CEO & CFO)

Subsidiaries:

Level 8 Technologies, Inc. (1)
1615 Jefferson Hwy Ste 120, Fishersville, VA 22939
Tel.: (540) 416-9380
Web Site: http://www.level8tech.net
Information Technology Consulting Services
N.A.I.C.S.: 541512

SMSA CRANE ACQUISITION CORP.
4 Orinda Way Ste 180-C, Orinda, CA 94563
Tel.: (925) 791-1440　　**NV**
Year Founded: 2008
SSCR—(OTCIQ)
Assets: $1,824
Liabilities: $108,890

Net Worth: ($107,066)
Earnings: ($30,665)
Fiscal Year-end: 12/31/20
Investment Services
N.A.I.C.S.: 523999
Irwin Eskanos *(Pres, CEO, CFO, Treas & Sec)*

SNAIL, INC.
12049 Jefferson Blvd, Culver City, CA 90230
Tel.: (310) 988-0643   DE
Web Site: https://www.snail.com
Year Founded: 2022
SNAL—(NASDAQ)
Rev.: $74,444,141
Assets: $72,772,571
Liabilities: $63,407,887
Net Worth: $9,364,684
Earnings: $947,807
Emp.: 86
Fiscal Year-end: 12/31/22
Holding Company; Software Development Services
N.A.I.C.S.: 551112
Heidy Chow *(CFO & CFO-Snail Games USA)*
Tony Xuedong Tian *(Co-CEO & Co-CEO-Snail Games USA)*
Heidy Chow *(CFO)*
Hai Shi *(Founder, Chm, Co-CEO & Co-CEO-Snail Games USA)*
Peter Kang *(VP & Dir-Bus Dev & Ops)*

SNAP INC.
3000 31st St, Santa Monica, CA 90405
Tel.: (310) 399-3339   DE
Web Site: https://www.snap.com
Year Founded: 2011
SNAP—(NYSE)
Rev.: $4,606,115,000
Assets: $7,967,758,000
Liabilities: $5,553,646,000
Net Worth: $2,414,112,000
Earnings: ($1,322,485,000)
Emp.: 5,289
Fiscal Year-end: 12/31/23
Photo-Sharing Application Developer
N.A.I.C.S.: 513210
Michael M. Lynton *(Chm)*
Robert Murphy *(Co-Founder & CTO)*
Michael O'Sullivan *(Gen Counsel)*
Derek Andersen *(CFO)*
Julie Henderson *(Chief Comm Officer)*
Panayoti Haritatos *(Head)*
Jessica Shetty *(Head-North America)*
Brittany Brown *(Mgr-Marketing-Snap Games)*
Jacob Andreou *(VP-Product)*
Betsy Kenny Lack *(Head-Brand Strategy-Global)*
Eitan Pilipski *(Sr VP-Camera Platform)*
Jacqueline Beauchere *(Head-Global)*
Andy McKeon *(Dir-Asia Pacific)*
Ronan Harris *(Pres-Europe, Middle East & Africa)*
Eric Young *(Sr VP-Engrg)*
Kenneth Mitchell Jr. *(CMO)*
Evan Spiegel *(Co-Founder & CEO)*

SNAP-ON INCORPORATED
2801 80th St, Kenosha, WI 53143
Tel.: (262) 656-5200   DE
Web Site: https://www.snapon.com
Year Founded: 1920
SNA—(NYSE)
Rev.: $4,730,200,000
Assets: $7,544,900,000
Liabilities: $2,451,500,000
Net Worth: $5,093,400,000
Earnings: $1,011,100,000
Emp.: 13,200

Fiscal Year-end: 12/30/23
Hand & Power Tools, Diagnostics & Shop Equipment & Tool Storage Units Mfr, Developer & Whslr
N.A.I.C.S.: 423710
Timothy L. Chambers *(Pres-Tools Grp & Sr VP)*
Michael G. Gentile *(Pres-Ops & Product Mgmt-Tools Grp)*
Aldo J. Pagliari *(CFO)*
Iain Boyd *(VP-Ops Dev)*
Bennett L. Brenton *(VP-Innovation)*
Eugenio Amador *(Pres-Equipment)*
Joseph J. Burger *(Pres-Credit)*
James Ng *(Pres-Asia-Pacific)*
Benny Oh *(Chm-Asia-Pacific)*
Samuel E. Bottum *(CMO & VP)*
Jeffrey F. Kostrzewa *(Treas & VP)*
June C. Lemerand *(CIO & VP)*
Jesus M. Arregui *(Pres-Comml Grp & Sr VP)*
Marian T. Wells *(Pres-SNA Europe)*
John A. Wolf *(Pres-OEM Solutions)*
Marty V. Ozolins *(Principal Acctg Officer, VP & Controller)*
Raul Colon *(VP-Environment)*
Nicholas T. Pinchuk *(Chm, Pres & CEO)*

Subsidiaries:

AutoCrib EMEA GmBH   (1)
Am Guterbahnhof 7a, 21035, Hamburg, Germany
Tel.: (49) 4071 665 5900
Web Site: https://autocrib-emea.com
Inventory Vending Machine Distr
N.A.I.C.S.: 445132

Autocrib, Inc.   (1)
2882 Dow Ave, Tustin, CA 92780
Tel.: (714) 274-0400
Web Site: http://www.autocrib.com
Sales Range: $1-9.9 Million
Emp.: 25
Business Services, Nec, Nsk
N.A.I.C.S.: 561499
Stephen Pixley *(Founder)*

BTC Solutions Limited   (1)
2 Mallard Court Mallard Way, Crewe, CW1 6ZQ, Cheshire, United Kingdom
Tel.: (44) 1270539880
Web Site: http://www.b-t-c.co.uk
Automotive Software Development Services
N.A.I.C.S.: 541511

Blackhawk S.A.S.   (1)
15 rue de la Guivernone, PO Box 5, 95310, Saint-Ouen-l'Aumone, France
Tel.: (33) 134485878
Web Site: https://blackhawkcollision.com
General Automotive Repair Services
N.A.I.C.S.: 811111

Car-O-Liner (Beijing) Co., Ltd.   (1)
Building A1 Dixing Industrial Park Shuangyang Rd No 15 East Area, Beijing, 100023, China
Tel.: (86) 1067892123
Web Site: http://www.car-o-liner.com
Wheel Alignment System Distr
N.A.I.C.S.: 423120
Martin Altas *(Mng Dir)*

Car-O-Liner (Thailand) Co., Ltd.   (1)
4 Kanchanapisek Road, Prawet, Bangkok, 10250, Thailand
Tel.: (66) 21072593
Web Site: http://www.car-o-liner.com
Wheel Alignment System Distr
N.A.I.C.S.: 423120
Stefan Jonasson *(CFO)*

Car-O-Liner (UK) Limited   (1)
Great Central Way Butlers Leap, Rugby, CV21 3XH, United Kingdom
Tel.: (44) 1788574157
Web Site: http://car-o-liner.com
Wheel Alignment System Distr
N.A.I.C.S.: 423120
Stuart Alexander *(Mng Dir)*

Car-O-Liner Commercial AB   (1)
Mejerigatan 12, 641 39, Katrineholm, Sweden

Tel.: (46) 150662540
Web Site: http://www.truckcam.com
Wheel Alignment System Mfr & Distr
N.A.I.C.S.: 333310

Car-O-Liner Deutschland GmBH   (1)
Hinter Der Altdorfer Kirche 18, 64832, Babenhausen, Germany
Tel.: (49) 6073744870
Web Site: http://www.car-o-liner.com
Automotive Wheel Alignment Services
N.A.I.C.S.: 811114

Car-O-Liner Group AB   (1)
Hulda Mellgrens gata 1, 421 32, Vastra Frolunda, Sweden
Tel.: (46) 317211050
Web Site: http://www.car-o-liner.com
Collision Repair Equipment Mfr
N.A.I.C.S.: 811198

Subsidiary (US):

Car-O-Liner Company USA   (2)
29900 Anthony Dr, Wixom, MI 48393-3609
Tel.: (248) 624-5900
Web Site: http://www.car-o-liner.com
Sales Range: $1-9.9 Million
All Other Motor Vehicle Parts Mfr
N.A.I.C.S.: 336390

Car-O-Liner Holding AB   (1)
Hulda Mellgrens gata 1, 421 32, Vastra Frolunda, Sweden
Tel.: (46) 31 721 1050
Web Site: https://car-o-liner.com
Wheel Alignment System Mfr
N.A.I.C.S.: 333310

Car-O-Liner India Private Limited   (1)
804 3rd Floor Arjun Nagar Bhishma Pitamah Marg, New Delhi, 110003, India
Tel.: (91) 9910103588
Web Site: http://www.car-o-liner.com
Wheel Alignment System Distr
N.A.I.C.S.: 423120

Car-O-Liner MEA (FZE)   (1)
A2-031 Sharjah Airport International Free Zone, PO Box 123431, Sharjah, United Arab Emirates
Tel.: (971) 65668702
Wheel Alignment System Distr
N.A.I.C.S.: 423120
Adib Ketuly *(Mng Dir)*
Gulsha Rajavan *(Sls Mgr-Area)*

Car-O-Liner Norge AS   (1)
Andebu Naeringspark, Andebu, 3158, Norway
Tel.: (47) 33430270
Web Site: http://www.car-o-liner.com
Wheel Alignment System Distr
N.A.I.C.S.: 423120

Car-O-Liner S.R.L.   (1)
Via Vignolese 1132/A, 41126, Modena, Italy
Tel.: (39) 059468310
Web Site: http://www.car-o-liner.com
Wheel Alignment System Distr
N.A.I.C.S.: 423120

Car-O-Liner SAS   (1)
555 Avenue Marguerite Perey, 77127, Lieusaint, France
Tel.: (33) 169527750
Web Site: http://www.car-o-liner.com
Wheel Alignment System Distr
N.A.I.C.S.: 423120

Challenger Lifts, Inc.   (1)
2311 S Park Rd, Louisville, KY 40219
Tel.: (502) 625-0700
Web Site: http://www.challengerlifts.com
Industrial Machinery Mfr & Distr
N.A.I.C.S.: 333248

Cognitran Inc.   (1)
Ste 540 1000 Republic Dr, Allen Park, MI 48101
Tel.: (313) 202-4152
Software Development Services
N.A.I.C.S.: 541512

Cognitran Limited   (1)
Binley Business Park Harry Weston Park, Coventry, CV3 2TX, United Kingdom
Tel.: (44) 2476932066
Software Development Services
N.A.I.C.S.: 541512

Cognitran Sp. z o.o.   (1)

ul Tylne Chwaliszewo 25, 61-103, Poznan, Poland
Tel.: (48) 612256326
Software Development Services
N.A.I.C.S.: 541512

Dealer-FX Group   (1)
80 Tiverton Court 5th Floor, Markham, L3R 0G4, ON, Canada
Web Site: https://www.dealer-fx.com
Automotive Software Programming Services
N.A.I.C.S.: 541511

Dealer-FX North America Group Inc.   (1)
150 Commerce Valley Drive West Suite 900, Markham, L3T 7Z3, ON, Canada
Web Site: https://www.dealer-fx.com
Automobile Maintenance Services
N.A.I.C.S.: 811111

Edsbyns Industri AB   (1)
Bruggevagen 3, Edsbyn, 828 32, Sweden
Tel.: (46) 27127100
Hand Tool Mfr
N.A.I.C.S.: 332216
Jan Ronnqvist *(Mgr-Production)*

J.H. Williams Tool Group   (1)
19 Keystone Industrial Pk, Throop, PA 18512-1516   (100%)
Tel.: (570) 341-9500
Web Site: http://www.jhwilliamstoolgroup.com
Sales Range: $1-9.9 Million
Emp.: 20
Hand & Edge Tools Nec
N.A.I.C.S.: 423840
Mike Lamber *(Gen Mgr)*

JCSC SNA Europe Industries Bisov   (1)
Selitskogo St 21/5, PO Box 46, Minsk, 220075, Belarus
Tel.: (375) 172996822
Hand Tool Mfr
N.A.I.C.S.: 332216

John Bean   (1)
309 Exchange Ave, Conway, AR 72032
Tel.: (501) 450-1500
Web Site: http://www.johnbean.com
Sales Range: $75-99.9 Million
Emp.: 200
Automotive Wheel Aligners & Wheel Balancers, Brake Service, Tire Changing & Truing Equipment, Engine Diagnostic Analyzers, Tools & Accessories for Auto & Truck Service
N.A.I.C.S.: 333248

Josam Richttecknik GmBH   (1)
Siebenstucken 9, 24558, Henstedt-Ulzburg, Germany
Tel.: (49) 4193 502 9970
Web Site: https://nfz-werkstattausruestung.de
Wheel Alignment System Distr
N.A.I.C.S.: 423120
Bernd Kuhling *(Mng Dir)*
Rainer Schutt *(Mng Dir)*

Mitchell One   (1)
16067 Babcock St, San Diego, CA 92127   (85%)
Tel.: (858) 391-5000
Web Site: http://www.mitchell1.com
Sales Range: $75-99.9 Million
Emp.: 300
Provides Vehicle Repair Information & Business Management Systems
N.A.I.C.S.: 541511

Mitchell Repair Information Company, LLC   (1)
16067 Babcock St, San Diego, CA 92127
Tel.: (858) 391-5000
Web Site: https://www.mitchell1.com
Automotive Repair & Estimating Information Provider
N.A.I.C.S.: 513199

Mountz Torque Limited   (1)
Pier Copse Courtyard, Hants, Liphook, GU307JN, United Kingdom
Tel.: (44) 1428741756
Torque Sensor Mfr & Distr
N.A.I.C.S.: 335312

Mountz, Inc.   (1)

Snap-on Incorporated—(Continued)

1080 N 11th St, San Jose, CA 95112
Tel.: (408) 292-2214
Web Site: http://www.mountztorque.com
Sales Range: $1-9.9 Million
Emp.: 80
Industrial Equipment & Supplies Mfr
N.A.I.C.S.: 334513

**Norbar Torque Tools (Australia) Pty.
Ltd.** (1)
45-47 Ragian Avenue, Edwardstown, 5039,
SA, Australia
Tel.: (61) 882929777
Web Site: https://norbaraustralia.com.au
Measuring Equipment Mfr & Distr
N.A.I.C.S.: 334519

**Norbar Torque Tools (NZ)
Limited** (1)
B3/269A Mt Smart Rd, Onehunga, Auck-
land, 1061, New Zealand
Tel.: (64) 95798653
Machine Tools Mfr
N.A.I.C.S.: 333515

**Norbar Torque Tools (Shanghai)
Ltd** (1)
7 / F Building 91 No 1122 Qinzhou North
Road, Xuhui District, Shanghai, 201103,
China
Tel.: (86) 2161450368
Web Site: http://www.norbar.com
Torque Tool Distr
N.A.I.C.S.: 423710

**Norbar Torque Tools India Private
Limited** (1)
Plot No A-168 Khairne Industrial Area
Thane Belapur Road, Mahape, Navi Mum-
bai, 400 709, India
Tel.: (91) 2227788480
Web Site: http://www.norbar.in
Torque Tool Repair Services
N.A.I.C.S.: 811310
Narendra Borse *(Mng Dir)*

Norbar Torque Tools Limited (1)
Wildmere Road, Banbury, OX16 3JU, Ox-
fordshire, United Kingdom
Tel.: (44) 1295270333
Web Site: http://www.norbar.com
Torque Tool Mfr
N.A.I.C.S.: 332216
Catherine Rohll *(Comml Dir)*

**Norbar Torque Tools Private
Limited** (1)
194 Pandan Loop 07-20 Pantech Business
Hub, Singapore, 128383, Singapore
Tel.: (65) 68411371
Web Site: http://www.norbar.com
Torque Tool Distr
N.A.I.C.S.: 423710
Craig Brodey *(Mng Dir)*

Norbar Torque Tools, Inc. (1)
36400 Biltmore Pl, Willoughby, OH 44094
Torque Tool Mfr
N.A.I.C.S.: 332216

Power Hawk Technologies, Inc. (1)
300 Forge Way Ste 2, Rockaway, NJ 07866
Tel.: (973) 627-4646
Web Site: https://www.powerhawk.com
Hand & Edge Tool Mfr
N.A.I.C.S.: 332216

Pro-Cut International LLC (1)
10 Technology Dr, West Lebanon, NH
03784
Tel.: (603) 298-5200
Web Site: http://www.procutusa.com
Sales Range: $10-24.9 Million
Motor Vehicle Parts Whslr
N.A.I.C.S.: 423120
Jeff Hastings *(Pres)*

Ryeson Corporation (1)
555 Kimberly Dr, Carol Stream, IL 60188
Tel.: (847) 957-9907
Web Site: https://www.srtorque.com
Torque Tool Mfr
N.A.I.C.S.: 332216

SNA Europe (1)
ZAC de I Hoirie 20 Rue Charles Lacretelle,
49070, Beaucouze, France
Tel.: (33) 241229840

Automotive Tool & Equipment Mfr
N.A.I.C.S.: 336320

**SNA Europe (Czech Republic)
S.r.o.** (1)
Holadnška 2/4, Brno, 639 00, Czech Re-
public
Tel.: (420) 537022520
Automotive Repair & Maintenance Services
N.A.I.C.S.: 811198

SNA Europe (France) SARL (1)
Zac De I Hoirie 20 Rue Charles Lacretelle,
49070, Beaucouze, France
Tel.: (33) 241229840
Web Site: http://www.bahco.com
Emp.: 80
Power Driven Handtools & Tool Storage
Units Mfr
N.A.I.C.S.: 333991

SNA Europe (Spain) (1)
C/Hilanderas 1 CP, Apdo de Correos No 5,
20303, Irun, Gipuzkoa, Spain **(100%)**
Tel.: (34) 945269744
Web Site: http://www.snaeurope.com
Sales Range: $300-349.9 Million
Emp.: 1,000
Mfr of Automotive & Industrial Hand Tools
N.A.I.C.S.: 333991

SNA Germany GmbH (1)
Gewerbering 1, Hohenstein-Ernstthal,
09337, Hohenstein-Ernstthal, Germany
Tel.: (49) 3723 668 2012
Web Site: https://www.snapon.de
Power Driven Handtools & Equipment Mfr
N.A.I.C.S.: 333991

SNA Tools Belgium BVBA (1)
Chaussee de Louvain 1188 Bruxelles Capi-
tale, 1200, Woluwe-Saint-Lambert, Belgium
Tel.: (32) 27260303
Industrial Machinery Distr
N.A.I.C.S.: 423830

**Snap-on Business Solutions India
Private Limited** (1)
First Floor Tower C Logix Techno Park Plot
No 05 Noida Greater, Noida Express Way
Sector 127, Noida, 201301, Uttar Pradesh,
India
Tel.: (91) 1204268509
Web Site: http://www.snaponindia.in
Electronic Part Catalogs Publisher
N.A.I.C.S.: 513199

Snap-on Business Solutions S.L. (1)
C / Sagasta 20, 28004, Madrid, Spain
Tel.: (34) 807464381
Web Site: http://www.snapon.com
Electronic Part Catalogs Publisher
N.A.I.C.S.: 513199

Snap-on Business Solutions, Inc. (1)
4025 Kinross Lakes Pkwy, Richfield, OH
44286-9381
Tel.: (330) 659-1600
Web Site: http://www.sbs.snapon.com
Sales Range: $150-199.9 Million
Emp.: 800
Automotive, Power Equipment & Power-
sport Market Data Software & Services
N.A.I.C.S.: 513210

Subsidiary (Non-US):

**Snap-on Business Solutions
GmbH** (2)
Strabheimer Str 33, 61169, Friedberg, Ger-
many
Tel.: (49) 603187600
Web Site:
http://www.snaponbusinesssolutions.com
Sales Range: $25-49.9 Million
Emp.: 19
Automotive, Power Equipment & Power-
sport Market Data Software & Services
N.A.I.C.S.: 519290

**Snap-on Business Solutions
Limited** (2)
Imperial Way, 300 Kings Road, Reading,
RG2 0TD, Berkshire, United Kingdom
Tel.: (44) 1189357777
Web Site:
http://www.snaponbusinesssolutions.com
Sales Range: $75-99.9 Million
Emp.: 100

Automotive, Power Equipment & Powersport Market Data Software & Services
N.A.I.C.S.: 519290

**Snap-on Business Solutions,
S.A.** (2)
Paseo Pintor Rosales 16 1 dcha, 28008,
Madrid, Spain
Tel.: (34) 915912951
Web Site:
http://www.snaponbusinesssolutions.com
Sales Range: $25-49.9 Million
Emp.: 30
Automotive, Power Equipment & Power-
sport Market Data Software & Services
N.A.I.C.S.: 519290
Pedro Jimenez *(Mng Dir)*

**Snap-on Business Solutions,
SARL** (2)
54 rte Sartrouville, 78230, Le Pecq, France
Tel.: (33) 134807799
Web Site:
http://www.snaponbusinesssolutions.com
Sales Range: $50-74.9 Million
Emp.: 30
Automotive, Power Equipment & Power-
sport Market Data Software & Services
N.A.I.C.S.: 513210

**Snap-on Business Solutions,
SRL** (2)
Corso Ferrucci 77/9, Turin, 10138, Italy
Tel.: (39) 0115217798
Web Site: http://www.snapon.com
Sales Range: $25-49.9 Million
Emp.: 28
Automotive, Power Equipment & Power-
sport Market Data Software & Services
N.A.I.C.S.: 519290

Snap-on Climate Solutions S.r.l. (1)
Via L Longo 21-23, Sesto Fiorentino,
50019, Florence, Italy
Tel.: (39) 055 420 7372
Web Site: https://www.ecotechnics.com
Automatic Controlling Device Mfr
N.A.I.C.S.: 334519

Snap-on Credit LLC (1)
950 Technology Way Ste 301, Libertyville,
IL 60048
Tel.: (847) 782-7713
Web Site: http://www.snaponcredit.com
Sales Range: $75-99.9 Million
Provider of Short-Term Business Credit
Services
N.A.I.C.S.: 522299

Snap-on Diagnostics (1)
420 Barclay Blvd, Lincolnshire, IL 60069
Tel.: (847) 478-0700
Web Site: http://www.cnapondiag.com
Sales Range: $75-99.9 Million
Emp.: 150
Hand & Power Tools, Diagnostics & Shop
Equipment Developer, Mfr & Sales
N.A.I.C.S.: 332216

**Snap-on Equipment Austria
GmbH** (1)
Nr 24 Top 14, 2880, Sankt Corona am
Wechsel, Austria
Tel.: (43) 18659784
Automotive Diagnostic Equipment Distr
N.A.I.C.S.: 423120

Snap-on Equipment GmbH (1)
Konrad-Zuse-Strasse 1, 84579, Un-
terneukirchen, Germany
Tel.: (49) 86346220
Web Site: http://www.snapon-equipment.de
Vehicle Part & Power Sport Equipment Mfr
N.A.I.C.S.: 336999

Snap-on Equipment Hungary Kft. (1)
Somfalvi U 13, Sopron, 9400, Hungary
Tel.: (36) 99311206
Garage Equipment Mfr
N.A.I.C.S.: 333248

Snap-on Equipment Inc. (1)
309 Exchange Ave, Conway, AR 72032
Tel.: (501) 450-1500
Vehicle Part & Power Sport Equipment Mfr
N.A.I.C.S.: 336999

Snap-on Equipment Ltd. (1)
Unit 17 Denney Road King's Lynn, Norfolk,
PE30 4HG, United Kingdom

Tel.: (44) 1553697233
Web Site: http://www.snapon-
equipment.co.uk
Automotive Mechanical & Electrical Repair
& Services
N.A.I.C.S.: 811114

Snap-on Equipment S.r.l. (1)
Via Prov Carpi 33, 42015, Correggio, RE,
Italy
Tel.: (39) 052 273 3411
Web Site:
http://www.ofmann.snaponequipment.eu
Sales Range: $50-74.9 Million
Power Driven Handtools & Lifting Equip-
ment Mfr
N.A.I.C.S.: 333991

Snap-on Industrial (1)
2801 80th St, Kenosha, WI 53143-5656
Tel.: (262) 656-5200
Web Site:
http://www.snaponindustrialbrands.com
Sales Range: $1-4.9 Billion
Hand & Power Tool Solutions for Industrial
Accounts
N.A.I.C.S.: 332216

Snap-on Power Tools Inc. (1)
250 Snap-on Dr, Murphy, NC 28906-9033
Tel.: (828) 835-9765
Web Site: https://www.siouxtools.com
Sales Range: $50-74.9 Million
Emp.: 250
Electric Motors & Edge Tool Mfr
N.A.I.C.S.: 332216

**Snap-on Tools Hong Kong
Limited** (1)
Unit 2010 20/F Laford Centre 838 Lai Chi
Kok Road, Cheung Sha Wan, Kowloon,
China (Hong Kong)
Tel.: (852) 23703700
Web Site: http://www.snapon.com
Sales Range: $10-24.9 Million
Power Driven Handtools & Equipment Mfr
N.A.I.C.S.: 333991

Snap-on Tools International, Ltd. (1)
2801 80th St, Kenosha, WI 53143 **(100%)**
Tel.: (262) 656-5200
Web Site: http://www.snapon.com
Sales Range: $200-249.9 Million
Emp.: 500
Holding Company
N.A.I.C.S.: 551112

Subsidiary (Non-US):

**Snap-on Tools (Australia) Pty.
Ltd.** (2)
Unit 6/110 Station Road, PO Box 663,
Seven Hills, 1730, NSW, Australia **(100%)**
Tel.: (61) 298379100
Web Site: http://www.snapon.com
Sales Range: $25-49.9 Million
Developer, Manufacturer & Distributor of
Hand & Power Tools, Diagnostics & Shop
Equipment & Tool Storage Units for Profes-
sional Tool Users Worldwide
N.A.I.C.S.: 332216

Snap-on Tools Japan K.K. (2)
2-1-6 Shinkiba, Koto Ku, Tokyo, 136-0082,
Japan **(100%)**
Tel.: (81) 355341280
Web Site: http://www.snapon.co.jp
Sales Range: $50-74.9 Million
Developer, Manufacturer & Distributor of
Hand & Power Tools, Diagnostics & Shop
Equipment & Tool Storage Units for Profes-
sional Tool Users Worldwide
N.A.I.C.S.: 332216

Snap-on Tools Limited (2)
Telford Way Ind Estate, Kettering, NN16
8SN, Northants, United Kingdom **(100%)**
Tel.: (44) 1536413904
Web Site: http://www.snapon.com
Rev.: $24,000,000
Emp.: 150
Automotive Parts & Tools
N.A.I.C.S.: 441330

Snap-on Tools Italia S.r.l. (1)
Via Bizet 13 15, Cinisello Balsamo, 20092,
Milan, Italy
Tel.: (39) 0266045370
Web Site: http://www.snapon.it
Sales Range: $10-24.9 Million
Power Driven Hand Tool Distr & Mfr
N.A.I.C.S.: 333991

Snap-on Tools Korea Ltd. (1)
505 Bldg 301 Technopark 365 Samjung-dong, Ohjung-gu, Bucheon, 421-809, Gyeonggi-Do, Korea (South)
Tel.: (82) 323267310
Sales Range: $10-24.9 Million
Emp.: 8
Power Driven Handtools & Equipment Mfr
N.A.I.C.S.: 333993

Snap-on Tools Private Limited (1)
6/2 Begumpur Khatola Behind Toyota Showroom NH-8 Delhi-Jaipur Highway, Gurgaon, 122 004, Haryana, India
Tel.: (91) 1244599700
Web Site: http://www.snaponindia.in
Emp.: 50
Power Driven Handtools & Equipment Mfr
N.A.I.C.S.: 333993

Snap-on Tools Singapore Pte Ltd (1)
25 Tagore Lane 01-02, Singapore, 787602, Singapore
Tel.: (65) 6 451 5570
Web Site: https://www.snapon.com.sg
Power Driven Handtools & Equipment Mfr
N.A.I.C.S.: 333993

Sun-Electric Austria Gesellschaft m.b.H (1)
Nr 24 Top 14 Sankt Corona Am Wechsel, 2880, Neunkirchen, Austria
Tel.: (43) 186597840
Web Site:
http://www.sun.snaponequipment.eu
General Automotive Repair Services
N.A.I.C.S.: 811111
Klaus Kirstatter *(VP-Sls & Mktg)*

Torque Control Specialists Pty Ltd (1)
45-47 Raglan Ave, Edwardstown, 5039, SA, Australia
Tel.: (61) 882929777
Web Site: http://www.norbaraustralia.com.au
Torque Tool Distr
N.A.I.C.S.: 423710

Wheeltronic Ltd. (1)
6500 Mill Creek Dr, Mississauga, L5N 2W6, ON, Canada (100%)
Tel.: (905) 826-8600
Web Site: http://www.wheeltronic.com
Sales Range: $75-99.9 Million
Emp.: 10
Mfr & Designer of Hoists & Lifts for Vehicle Service Shops
N.A.I.C.S.: 333923
Michelle Van Mechelen *(Mgr-Ops)*

SNM GLOBAL HOLDINGS
7950 NW 53rd St Ste 337, Miami, FL 33166
Tel.: (410) 733-6551   NV
Year Founded: 2006
SNMN—(OTCIQ)
Holding Company
N.A.I.C.S.: 551112
Kenneth Troy Lowman *(Pres)*
Michael Gallagher *(Sec)*
Brian Campbell Hale *(VP-Operations)*

SNOWFLAKE INC.
Ste 3A 106 E Babcock St, Bozeman, MT 59715
Tel.: (844) 766-9355   DE
Web Site: https://www.snowflake.com
Year Founded: 2012
SNOW—(NYSE)
Rev.: $2,806,489,000
Assets: $8,223,383,000
Liabilities: $3,032,789,000
Net Worth: $5,190,594,000
Earnings: ($836,097,000)
Emp.: 7,004
Fiscal Year-end: 01/31/24
Software Development Services
N.A.I.C.S.: 541511
Benoit Dageville *(Co-Founder & Pres-Products)*
Denise Persson *(CMO)*
Thierry Cruanes *(Co-Founder & Chief Technical Officer)*
Derk Lupinek *(Gen Counsel)*
Sridhar Ramaswamy *(CEO)*

Subsidiaries:

Snowflake Computing Pty. Ltd. (1)
International Towers Sydney 100 Barangaroo Avenue Tower One, Suite 23 02, Barangaroo, 2000, NSW, Australia
Tel.: (61) 251040194
Software Services
N.A.I.C.S.: 541511

SOAR TECHNOLOGY ACQUISITION CORP.
405 Lexington Ave 48th Fl, New York, NY 10174
Tel.: (212) 503-2855   Ky
Year Founded: 2021
FLYA—(NYSE)
Investment Services
N.A.I.C.S.: 523999
Jonathan Poulin *(Chm & CEO)*
Vicky Bathija *(CFO & Exec VP)*
Mark J. Coleman *(Gen Counsel & Exec VP)*

SOBR SAFE, INC.
6400 S Fiddlers Green Cir Ste 1400, Greenwood Village, CO 80111
Tel.: (303) 443-4430   DE
Web Site: https://www.sobrsafe.com
Year Founded: 2007
SOBR—(NASDAQ)
Rev.: $35,322
Assets: $11,912,037
Liabilities: $2,821,684
Net Worth: $9,090,353
Earnings: ($12,354,913)
Emp.: 15
Fiscal Year-end: 12/31/22
Alcohol Detection Device for Drivers
N.A.I.C.S.: 339112
Kevin Moore *(CEO)*
David J. Gandini *(Chm)*

SOCIAL DETENTION, INC.
3000 F Danville Blvd Ste 145, Alamo, CA 94507
Tel.: (925) 575-4433   CO
Web Site: https://sodetention.com
Year Founded: 2017
SODE—(OTCIQ)
Business Management Consulting Services
N.A.I.C.S.: 541611
Robert P. Legg *(Pres)*

SOCIALPLAY USA, INC.
8275 S Eastern Ave Ste 200, Las Vegas, NV 89123
Tel.: (702) 724-2640   NV
Web Site:
http://www.socialplayusa.com
Year Founded: 2013
SPLY—(OTCIQ)
Cloud-Based Game Hosting & Management System; Software Designer & Developer
N.A.I.C.S.: 518210
Robert Rosner *(Pres, CEO & CFO)*

SOCIETY PASS INCORPORATED
701 S Carson St Ste 200, Carson City, NV 89701
Tel.: (656) 518-9382   NV
Web Site:
https://www.thesocietypass.com
Year Founded: 2018
SOPA—(NASDAQ)
Rev.: $5,635,553
Assets: $32,698,742
Liabilities: $12,687,425
Net Worth: $20,011,317
Earnings: ($33,786,107)
Fiscal Year-end: 12/31/22
Information Technology Services
N.A.I.C.S.: 541512

Arbie Pagdaganan *(VP-Product Dev)*
Doan Chu *(VP-Mktg)*
Alexandre Dubois *(VP-Tech)*
Yuki Phan *(Mktg Mgr)*
Dubois Nguyen *(Mgr-Customer Care)*
Neeraj Dharam Upadhyay *(Mgr-Tech)*
Shashi Kant Mishra *(Mgr-IT Security & Analytics)*
Patrick Soetanto *(COO)*
Dennis Nguyen *(Founder, Chm & CEO)*
Rokas Sidlauskas *(CMO)*
Howie Tg *(CTO)*
Cham NGO *(Gen Mgr-Vietnam)*
Peter Dichiara *(Gen Counsel & Sec)*
Heng Yan Rong *(Gen Mgr-Thailand)*
Yee Siong *(CFO)*

SOCKET MOBILE, INC.
40675 Encyclopedia Cir, Fremont, CA 94538
Tel.: (510) 933-3000   DE
Web Site:
https://www.socketmobile.com
Year Founded: 1992
SCKT—(NASDAQ)
Rev.: $21,237,768
Assets: $28,597,988
Liabilities: $8,276,231
Net Worth: $20,321,757
Earnings: $86,931
Emp.: 56
Fiscal Year-end: 12/31/22
Connection Solutions Developer & Retailer for Handheld Mobile Devices
N.A.I.C.S.: 334111
Charlie Bass *(Chm)*
Kevin J. Mills *(Pres & CEO)*
Leonard L. Ott *(CTO & Exec VP-Engrg)*
Lynn Zhao *(CFO, Sec & VP-Fin & Admin)*
Dave Holmes *(Chief Bus Officer)*

SOFI TECHNOLOGIES, INC.
234 1st St, San Francisco, CA 94105
Tel.: (855) 456-7634   DE
Web Site: https://www.sofi.com
Year Founded: 2020
SOFI—(NASDAQ)
Rev.: $2,912,116,000
Assets: $30,074,858,000
Liabilities: $24,840,246,000
Net Worth: $5,234,612,000
Earnings: ($300,742,000)
Emp.: 4,400
Fiscal Year-end: 12/31/23
Holding Company; Financial Services
N.A.I.C.S.: 551111
Steven Jay Freiberg *(Vice Chm)*
Anthony J. Noto *(CEO)*
Christopher Lapointe *(CFO)*
Jeremy Rishel *(CTO)*

Subsidiaries:

Social Finance, Inc. (1)
234 1st St, San Francisco, CA 94105
Tel.: (855) 456-7634
Web Site: http://www.sofi.com
Community Financial Support Services
N.A.I.C.S.: 541611
Steven Jay Freiberg *(Vice Chm)*
Anna Avalos *(Chief HR Officer)*
Chad Borton *(Pres)*
Chris Lapointe *(CFO)*
Derek White *(CEO)*
Jeremy Rishel *(CTO)*
Katie Wells *(Sr VP)*
Lauren Stafford Webb *(Chief Mktg Officer)*
Rob Lavet *(Corp Counsel)*
William Tanona *(Sr VP)*

Wyndham Capital Mortgage, Inc. (1)
6115 Park South Dr Ste 200, Charlotte, NC 28210
Tel.: (704) 525-9911
Web Site: http://www.wyndhamcapital.com
Sales Range: $25-49.9 Million
Emp.: 225
Mortgage & Nonmortgage Loan Brokers

N.A.I.C.S.: 522310
Jeffrey W. Douglas *(Founder & CEO)*
Ajay Boyd *(Mgr-Sls Div)*
Josh Hankins *(Mgr-Sls Div)*
Rob Zinger *(COO)*
Jeremy Abig *(CFO)*
Matthew Harris *(Dir-Comm)*
Melissa Smith *(Sr VP-Risk & Compliance)*
Trey Rigdon *(Sr VP-Mktg)*

SOFTECH, INC.
650 Suffolk St Ste 415, Lowell, MA 01854
Tel.: (978) 513-2700   MA
Web Site: http://www.softech.com
Year Founded: 1969
SOFT—(OTCIQ)
Sales Range: $1-9.9 Million
Emp.: 25
CAD & CAM Solutions
N.A.I.C.S.: 513210
Robert B. Anthonyson *(VP-Bus Dev)*

Subsidiaries:

SofTech S.r.l. (1)
Via Ciro Menotti 45, Legnano, 20025, Italy
Tel.: (39) 0331455499
Web Site: http://www.softech.com
Sales Range: $100-124.9 Million
Emp.: 5
Software Developer
N.A.I.C.S.: 513210
Dante Cislaghi *(Gen Mgr)*

SOHM, INC.
4195 Chino Hills Pkwy Ste 675, Chino Hills, CA 91709
Tel.: (714) 522-6700   CA
Web Site: https://www.sohm.com
Year Founded: 1998
SHMN—(OTCIQ)
Pharmaceutical Preparation Manufacturing
N.A.I.C.S.: 325412
Shailesh Shah *(Pres & CEO)*

SOLANBRIDGE GROUP INC.
Tel.: (720) 442-9960   MD
Web Site:
http://www.solanbridgegroup.com
Year Founded: 2000
SLNX—(OTCIQ)
Holding Company
N.A.I.C.S.: 551112
David J. Cutler *(CEO & CFO)*

SOLAR GOLD LTD.
73200 El Paseo Ste 2H, Palm Desert, CA 92260
Tel.: (650) 638-1975   DE
Year Founded: 1998
PLKT—(OTCIQ)
Health Care Srvices
N.A.I.C.S.: 621999
Pamela Alexander *(CFO, Treas & Sec)*
Michael James Gobuty *(CEO & CFO)*

SOLAR INTEGRATED ROOFING CORPORATION
2831 St Rose Pkwy Ste 200, Henderson, NV 89052
Tel.: (702) 762-1813   NV
Web Site:
https://www.solarintegratedroofing.com
Year Founded: 2007
SIRC—(OTCIQ)
Holding Company; Roofing & Solar Panel Installation Contractor
N.A.I.C.S.: 551112
Brad Rinehart *(CEO)*

Subsidiaries:

Mckay Roofing Company, Inc. (1)
10622 Kenney St, Santee, CA 92071
Tel.: (619) 258-7888
Web Site: https://www.mckayroofingsd.com

Solar Integrated Roofing
Corporation—(Continued)

Roofing Contractors
N.A.I.C.S.: 238160

Milholland Electric, Inc. **(1)**
1475 Cuyamaca St El Cajon, San Diego,
CA 92020
Tel.: (858) 541-1097
Web Site: http://www.milhollandelectric.com
Electrical Work, Nsk
N.A.I.C.S.: 238210
Brian Milholland (Pres)

Secure Roofing & Solar, Inc. **(1)**
999 Rancheros Dr Ste B, San Marcos, CA
92069-3099
Tel.: (760) 546-0254
Web Site:
http://www.secureroofingandsolar.com
Roofing & Solar Panel Installation Contractor
N.A.I.C.S.: 238160
David Massey (Owner)

SOLAR QUARTZ TECHNOLOGIES, INC.
5851 San Felipe Ste 455, Houston,
TX 89074-7739
Tel.: (713) 598-0938 NV
SQTI—(OTCIQ)
Semiconductor & Solar Panel Mfr
N.A.I.C.S.: 334413
Jeffrey Freedman (Pres & CFO)

SOLARIS OILFIELD INFRA-STRUCTURE, INC.
9651 Katy Fwy Ste 300, Houston, TX
77024
Tel.: (281) 501-3070 DE
Web Site:
https://www.solarisoilfield.com
Year Founded: 2017
SOI—(NYSE)
Rev.: $320,005,000
Assets: $462,576,000
Liabilities: $145,447,000
Net Worth: $317,129,000
Earnings: $21,158,000
Emp.: 344
Fiscal Year-end: 12/31/22
Proppant Management System Mfr
N.A.I.C.S.: 333132
William A. Zartler (Founder, Chm &
CEO)
Kyle S. Ramachandran (Pres & CFO)
Yvonne L. Fletcher (Sr VP-Fin & IR)
Christopher Powell (Chief Legal Officer)
Cynthia M. Durrett (Chief Admin Officer)
Greg Garcia (Exec VP-Sls & Mktg)
Christopher P. Wirtz (Chief Acctg Officer)
Brendan Gilbert (Sr VP-Service &
Quality)
Kelly Price (COO)

Subsidiaries:

Solaris Oilfield Site Services Operating, LLC **(1)**
100 Ross Dr, Early, TX 76802
Tel.: (325) 643-1785
Oil & Gas Industrial Equipment Mfr
N.A.I.C.S.: 333132

SOLARMAX TECHNOLOGY, INC.
3080 12th St, Riverside, CA 92507
Tel.: (951) 221-8172 NV
Web Site:
https://www.solarmaxtech.com
Year Founded: 2008
SMXT—(NASDAQ)
Sales Range: $75-99.9 Million
Emp.: 79
Solar Panel Mfr
N.A.I.C.S.: 333414

David Hsu (Co-Founder & CEO)
Ching Liu (Co-Founder, Chief Strategy Officer, Treas & Exec VP)
Simon Yuan (Co-Founder)
Stephen Brown (CFO)

SOLARWINDOW TECHNOLOGIES, INC.
Tel.: (301) 298-3335 NV
Web Site:
https://www.solarwindow.com
Year Founded: 1998
WNDW—(OTCIQ)
Rev.: $242,371
Assets: $5,003,628
Liabilities: $321,512
Net Worth: $4,682,116
Earnings: ($3,047,466)
Emp.: 2
Fiscal Year-end: 08/31/24
Electric Power Generation; Electricity
Generating Windows & Products
N.A.I.C.S.: 221118
Jatinder Singh Bhogal (Chm & CEO)
Joseph Sierchio (Gen Counsel)
Justin Frere (CFO, Treas, Sec &
Controller)
Patrick T. Sargent (VP-Product Engrg)
Joseph Song (VP-Ops)
Alexandra Musk (VP-Bus Dev)
In Jae Chung (Dir-Tech & Product
Innovation-Global)
Amit Singh (Pres & CEO)
Grant Trevathan (Dir-Creative)
James B. Whitaker (VP-Tech Dev)
Je Haeng Lee (Sr Engr)
Harmel S. Rayat (Founder)

SOLARWINDS CORPORATION
7171 SW Pkwy Bldg 400, Austin, TX
78735
Tel.: (512) 682-9300 DE
Web Site:
https://www.solarwinds.com
Year Founded: 2015
SWI—(NYSE)
Rev.: $758,740,000
Assets: $3,250,915,000
Liabilities: $1,808,871,000
Net Worth: $1,442,044,000
Earnings: ($9,109,000)
Emp.: 2,103
Fiscal Year-end: 12/31/23
Offices of Other Holding Companies
N.A.I.C.S.: 551112
Jason Bliss (Chief Admin Officer &
Exec VP)
Darren Beck (CMO & Exec VP)
David Owens (Sr VP-Fin & Ops-
EMEA)
Sudhakar Ramakrishna (Pres &
CEO)
Kathleen Pai (Chief People Officer)
Tiffany Nels (Chief Comm Officer &
Sr VP)
Jeff McCullough (VP-Partner Sls-
Worldwide)
Lewis Black (CFO, Principal Acctg
Officer, Treas & Exec VP)

Subsidiaries:

SQL Sentry, LLC **(1)**
4001 Yancey Rd, Charlotte, NC 28217
Tel.: (704) 895-6241
Web Site: http://www.sentryone.com
Computer Softwares Mfr
N.A.I.C.S.: 513210
Bob Potter (CEO)
Scott Brooks (VP-Customer Success)
Jason Hall (VP-Client Svcs)
Mike Lambert (Pres-Field Ops)
John Welch (CTO)
Douglas McDowell (Chief Strategy Officer)
Jennifer Miller (VP-HR)
Nick Harshbarger (Sr VP-Cloud Alliances)
Sheri Villers (VP-Product Engrg)
Scott Allison (VP-Sls)

SpamExperts B.V. **(1)**
Rokin 113-115, 1012 KP, Amsterdam, Netherlands
Tel.: (31) 208200004
Web Site: http://www.spamexperts.com
Software Development Services
N.A.I.C.S.: 513210

SOLENO THERAPEUTICS, INC.
100 Marine Pkwy Ste 400, Redwood
City, CA 94065
Tel.: (650) 213-8444 DE
Web Site: https://www.soleno.life
Year Founded: 1999
SLNO—(NASDAQ)
Rev.: $330,000
Assets: $26,497,000
Liabilities: $16,149,000
Net Worth: $10,348,000
Earnings: ($24,067,000)
Emp.: 25
Fiscal Year-end: 12/31/22
Medical Diagnostic & Therapeutic
Products Mfr
N.A.I.C.S.: 334510
Scott Madsen (VP)
Charles Horn (VP-Quality)
James H. Mackaness (CFO)
Neil M. Cowen (Sr VP-Drug Dev)
Kristen Yen (Sr VP/VP-Clinical Ops)
Patricia C. Hirano (Sr VP/VP-
Regulatory Affairs)
Lauren Budesheim (VP-People)
Dairine Dempsey (VP-Europe)
Meredith Manning (Chief Comml Officer)
Raymond Urbanski (Chief Dev Officer)
Anish Bhatnagar (Pres & CEO)

Subsidiaries:

Capnia, Inc. **(1)**
1101 Chess Dr, Foster City, CA 94404
Tel.: (650) 670-6252
Web Site: https://www.capnia.com
Medical Device Mfr
N.A.I.C.S.: 334517

Neoforce Group Inc. **(1)**
35 Commerce Dr, Ivyland, PA 18976
Tel.: (215) 672-6800
Web Site: http://www.neoforcegroup.com
Sales Range: $1-9.9 Million
Emp.: 6
Medical Devices Mfr & Supplier
N.A.I.C.S.: 423450
Mike Ragan (VP-Ops)
Louise Bucciarelli (VP-Customer Care)

SOLERA NATIONAL BANCORP, INC.
319 S Sheridan Blvd, Lakewood, CO
80226
Tel.: (303) 209-8600 DE
Web Site:
https://www.solerabank.com
Year Founded: 2006
SLRK—(OTCIQ)
Rev.: $16,641,000
Assets: $435,792,000
Liabilities: $387,762,000
Net Worth: $48,030,000
Earnings: $5,934,000
Emp.: 84
Fiscal Year-end: 12/31/20
Bank Holding Company
N.A.I.C.S.: 551111
Melissa K. Larkin (CFO & Exec VP)
Michael Drew Quagliano (Chm)

Subsidiaries:

Solera National Bank **(1)**
319 S Sheridan Blvd, Lakewood, CO 80226
Tel.: (303) 209-8600
Web Site: http://www.solerabank.com
Emp.: 20
Commericial Banking
N.A.I.C.S.: 522110

Robert J. Fenton (Pres & CEO)
Melissa K. Larkin (CFO, Sec & Sr VP)

SOLID BIOSCIENCES, INC
500 Rutherford Ave 3rd Fl, Charlestown, MA 02129
Tel.: (617) 337-4680 DE
Web Site: https://www.solidbio.com
Year Founded: 2013
SLDB—(NASDAQ)
Rev.: $8,094,000
Assets: $260,252,000
Liabilities: $48,586,000
Net Worth: $211,666,000
Earnings: ($85,981,000)
Emp.: 87
Fiscal Year-end: 12/31/22
Biotechnology Research & Development Services
N.A.I.C.S.: 541714
Kevin Tan (CFO & Principal Acctg
Officer)
Alexander Bo Cumbo (Pres & CEO)
Jessie Hanrahan (Chief Regulatory
Officer)
Paul Herzich (CTO)
Gabriel Brooks (Chief Medical Officer)
Leah Monteiro (VP-IR & Corp Comm)
Ilan Ganot (Co-Founder)
Annie Ganot (Co-Founder & Head-
Patient Advocacy)
Ty Howton (COO & Chief Admin Officer)
Shuli Kulak (Head-Corporate Strategy
& Business Development)
Ian F. Smith (Chm)

SOLID POWER, INC.
486 S Pierce Ave Ste E, Louisville,
CO 80027
Tel.: (303) 219-0720 CA
Web Site:
https://www.solidpowerbattery.com
Rev.: $11,789,000
Assets: $594,446,000
Liabilities: $39,074,000
Net Worth: $555,372,000
Earnings: ($9,555,000)
Emp.: 236
Fiscal Year-end: 12/31/22
Blank Check Company
N.A.I.C.S.: 525990
John C. Van Scoter (Pres & CEO)
John Stephens (Chm)
Linda Heller (CFO & Treas)
Joshua Buettner-Garrett (CTO)
Derek Johnson (COO)
James Liebscher (Chief Legal Officer
& Sec)
Pu Zhang (VP-Research & Development)
Jack Al Ferzly (Mng Dir-Solid Power
Korea)
Hyungrak Kim (Exec VP-Electrolyte
Technologies)
Berislav Blizanac (Exec VP-Cell
Technologies)
Stacy Morse (VP-Human Resources)
Ramelle Gilliland (Exec VP-Strategic
Supply Chain Mgmt)
Lauren McCabe (VP-Cell Technologies)

Subsidiaries:

Solid Power Operating, Inc. **(1)**
686 S Taylor Ave Ste 108, Louisville, CO
80027-3000
Tel.: (303) 993-5520

Web Site: http://www.solidpowerbattery.com
Research & Development in the Physical, Engineering & Life Sciences
N.A.I.C.S.: 541715
Douglas Campbell *(Founder & CEO)*
Will McKenna *(Dir-Mktg Comm)*

SOLIDION TECHNOLOGY INC.
13355 Noel Rd Ste 1100, Dallas, TX 75240
Tel.: (972) 918-5120   DE
Web Site:
   https://www.solidiontech.com
Year Founded: 2021
STI—(NASDAQ)
Assets: $71,345,291
Liabilities: $75,535,798
Net Worth: $28,533,250
Earnings: $19,775,602
Emp.: 32
Fiscal Year-end: 12/31/23
Battery Mfr
N.A.I.C.S.: 335910
Jaymes Winters *(CEO)*
Vlad Prantsevich *(CFO)*
Bor Jang *(Chief Science Officer)*
Songhai Chai *(CTO)*

SOLIGEN TECHNOLOGIES, INC.
700 Milam St Ste 1300, Houston, TX 77002
Tel.: (832) 871-5107   WY
Web Site:
   https://www.soligentechnologies.com
SGTN—(OTCIQ)
Computer System Design Services
N.A.I.C.S.: 541512
Gary Grimshaw *(Chm & Pres)*

SOLIGENIX, INC.
29 Emmons Dr Ste B-10, Princeton, NJ 08540
Tel.: (609) 538-8200   DE
Web Site: https://www.soligenix.com
Year Founded: 1987
SNGX—(NASDAQ)
Rev.: $948,911
Assets: $14,279,717
Liabilities: $16,750,543
Net Worth: ($2,470,826)
Earnings: ($13,798,339)
Emp.: 13
Fiscal Year-end: 12/31/22
Pharmaceutical Preparation Manufacturing
N.A.I.C.S.: 325412
Oreola Donini *(Chief Scientific Officer & Sr VP)*
Richard C. Straube *(Chief Medical Officer & Sr VP)*
Adam T. Rumage *(VP-Project Mgmt & Regulatory Affairs)*
Jonathan Guarino *(CFO, Sec & Sr VP)*

SOLITARIO ZINC CORP.
4251 Kipling St Ste 390, Wheat Ridge, CO 80033
Tel.: (303) 534-1030   CO
Web Site: https://www.solitarioxr.com
Year Founded: 1984
XPL—(NYSEAMEX)
Rev.: $131,000
Assets: $22,034,000
Liabilities: $388,000
Net Worth: $21,646,000
Earnings: ($3,928,000)
Emp.: 3
Fiscal Year-end: 12/31/22
Gold, Silver, Zinc & Platinum Mining & Exploration Services
N.A.I.C.S.: 212220
Christopher Engle Herald *(CEO)*
James R. Maronick *(CFO)*
Brian M. Labadie *(Chm)*

Subsidiaries:

Minera Solitario Peru, S.A.   **(1)**
Jiron El Bucare, Camacho La Molina, Lima, 573, Peru
Tel.: (51) 12223177
Gold Ore Mining Services
N.A.I.C.S.: 212220

SOLITRON DEVICES, INC.
901 Sansburys Way, West Palm Beach, FL 33411
Tel.: (561) 848-4311   DE
Web Site:
   https://www.solitrondevices.com
Year Founded: 1959
SODI—(OTCIQ)
Rev.: $12,757,000
Assets: $24,740,000
Liabilities: $7,672,000
Net Worth: $17,068,000
Earnings: $5,801,000
Emp.: 41
Fiscal Year-end: 02/29/24
Power Transistors, Thick Film Hybrids, Field Effect Transistors, Integrated Circuits, Power Mosfet Modules, Power MOS Devices, Bipolar Power Thin Film Resistor Products Mfr
N.A.I.C.S.: 334413
David W. Pointer *(Chm)*
Howard Timothy Eriksen *(CEO & Interim CFO)*
Mark W. Matson *(Pres & COO)*

Subsidiaries:

Micro Engineering, Inc.   **(1)**
1428 E Semoran Blvd, Apopka, FL 32703
Tel.: (407) 886-4849
Web Site: http://www.microeng.com
Sales Range: $1-9.9 Million
Emp.: 36
Semiconductor & Related Device Mfr
N.A.I.C.S.: 334413
Larry A. La Forest *(Pres)*

SOLLENSYS CORP.
1470 Treeland Blvd SE, Palm Bay, FL 32909
Tel.: (408) 273-4583   NV
Web Site: https://www.sollensys.com
Year Founded: 2010
SOLS—(OTCIQ)
Rev.: $344,467
Assets: $3,284,608
Liabilities: $5,758,391
Net Worth: ($2,473,783)
Earnings: ($16,768,111)
Emp.: 3
Fiscal Year-end: 12/31/22
Investment Services
N.A.I.C.S.: 523999
Donald Beavers *(Chm, CEO & Sec)*

SOLO BRANDS, INC.
1001 Mustang Dr, Grapevine, TX 76051
Tel.: (817) 900-2664   DE
Web Site: https://solobrands.com
Year Founded: 2021
DTC—(NYSE)
Rev.: $517,627,000
Assets: $862,347,000
Liabilities: $287,350,000
Net Worth: $574,997,000
Earnings: ($4,945,000)
Emp.: 350
Fiscal Year-end: 12/31/22
Online Shopping Services
N.A.I.C.S.: 459110
Laura A. Coffey *(CFO)*
Christopher T. Metz *(Pres & CEO)*
Michael McGoohan *(Chief Growth Officer & Exec VP)*
Matthew Webb *(COO)*
Matthew Guy-Hamilton *(Chm)*
Kent Christensen *(Gen Counsel)*
Mike Murray *(CIO)*

Subsidiaries:

Icybreeze Cooling LLC   **(1)**
14989 S Grant St, Bixby, OK 74008
Tel.: (325) 933-6518
Web Site: http://www.icybreeze.com
All Other Miscellaneous Mfr
N.A.I.C.S.: 339999

SOLUCORP INDUSTRIES LTD.
2850 N Andrews Ave, Fort Lauderdale, FL 33311
Tel.: (954) 568-7018   BC
Year Founded: 1987
SLUP—(OTCIQ)
Industrial Waste Management Services
N.A.I.C.S.: 562998
Richard Runco *(Pres)*
Bernadette Anderton *(Sec)*

SOLUNA HOLDINGS, INC.
325 Washington Ave Ext, Albany, NY 12205
Tel.: (518) 218-2500   NY
Web Site: http://www.mechtech.com
Year Founded: 1961
SLNH—(NASDAQ)
Rev.: $28,547,000
Assets: $84,961,000
Liabilities: $38,689,000
Net Worth: $46,272,000
Earnings: ($98,715,000)
Emp.: 30
Fiscal Year-end: 12/31/22
Direct Methanol Micro Fuel Cell Power Systems Developer & Commercializer; Test & Measurement Instruments & Systems Designer, Mfr & Retailer
N.A.I.C.S.: 334519
John Tunison *(CFO)*
Jessica L. Thomas *(Treas & Sec)*
Michael Toporek *(Chm)*
John Belizaire *(CEO)*

Subsidiaries:

MTI MicroFuel Cells Inc.   **(1)**
431 New Karner Rd, Albany, NY 12205
Tel.: (518) 533-2222
Web Site: http://www.mtimicrofuelcells.com
Sales Range: $25-49.9 Million
Developer & Marketer of Proprietary Direct Methanol Fuel Cells Systems as Future Power Sources for Wireless Electronic Devices
N.A.I.C.S.: 335910

SOLVAY BANK CORP.
1537 Milton Ave, Syracuse, NY 13209
Tel.: (315) 468-1661
Web Site:
   https://www.solvaybank.com
Year Founded: 1917
SOBS—(OTCIQ)
Sales Range: $10-24.9 Million
Emp.: 163
Bank Holding Company
N.A.I.C.S.: 551111
Paul P. Mello *(Pres & CEO)*
Dennis Coon *(VP)*
Jeffrey Culver *(Asst VP)*

SOLVENTUM CORPORATION
3M Ctr Bldg 275 6W 2510 Conway Ave E, Maplewood, MN 55144
Tel.: (612) 842-1263   DE
Web Site:
   https://www.solventum.com
Year Founded: 2023
SOLV—(NYSE)
Medical & Oral Care Products; Drug Delivery & Health Information Systems
N.A.I.C.S.: 339112

Wayde McMillan *(CFO)*
Marcela A. Kirberger *(Chief Legal Affairs Officer)*
Tammy L. Gomez *(Chief HR Officer)*
Paul Harrington *(Chief Supply Chain Officer)*
Bryan C. Hanson *(CEO)*

Subsidiaries:

3M Health Care   **(1)**
3M Center Bldg 275-4W-02, Saint Paul, MN 55144-1000
Tel.: (651) 733-1110
Web Site: http://www.3m.com
Sales Range: $25-49.9 Million
Emp.: 100
Medical & Oral Care Products; Drug Delivery & Health Information Systems
N.A.I.C.S.: 339112

Subsidiary (Domestic):

3M ESPE   **(2)**
3M Ctr 275 2SE 03, Saint Paul, MN 55144
Tel.: (651) 575-5144
Web Site: http://www.3m.com
Sales Range: $25-49.9 Million
Emp.: 100
Mfr of Composite Restorative & Filling Materials, Finishing & Polishing Systems, Crown & Bridge Materials & Cements
N.A.I.C.S.: 339114

Subsidiary (Domestic):

3M IMTEC Corporation   **(3)**
IMTEC Plz 2401 N Commerce St, Ardmore, OK 73401   **(100%)**
Tel.: (580) 223-4456
Sales Range: $75-99.9 Million
Dental Implant & Cone Beam Computed Tomography Scanning Equipment Mfr
N.A.I.C.S.: 339114

Subsidiary (Non-US):

3M Health Care Limited   **(2)**
6-7-29 Kitashinagawa Shinagawa-ku, Tokyo, 158-8583, Japan
Tel.: (81) 364093800
Web Site: http://www.3mcompany.jp
Medical Product Distr
N.A.I.C.S.: 423450

3M Health Care Ltd.   **(2)**
1 Morley Street, Loughborough, LE11 1EP, Leicestershire, United Kingdom
Tel.: (44) 1509611611
Web Site: http://www.mmm.com
Emp.: 30
Pharmaceutical Preparation Mfr
N.A.I.C.S.: 325412

Subsidiary (Domestic):

3M Health Information Systems   **(2)**
575 W Murray Blvd, Salt Lake City, UT 84123
Tel.: (801) 265-4200
Web Site: http://www.3mhis.com
Sales Range: $25-49.9 Million
Computer Systems & Software Development for Medical Records Coding & Patient Record Products & Services
N.A.I.C.S.: 541512
JaeLynn Williams *(Pres)*

Unit (Domestic):

3M Health Info Systems Consulting Services   **(3)**
100 Ashford Ctr N Ste 200, Atlanta, GA 30338-4862
Tel.: (770) 394-8800
Web Site: http://www.mmm.com
Rev.: $13,772,653
Emp.: 100
Hospital & Health Services Consulting
N.A.I.C.S.: 541618

Subsidiary (Domestic):

3M Unitek Corporation   **(2)**
2724 S Peck Rd, Monrovia, CA 91016   **(100%)**
Tel.: (626) 574-4000
Web Site: http://www.3munitek.com

Solventum Corporation—(Continued)

Sales Range: $75-99.9 Million
Develops, Manufactures & Markets Products for Orthodontic Treatment for Dental Professionals
N.A.I.C.S.: 339114

Subsidiary (Domestic):

Lingualcare, Inc.   **(3)**
2724 S Peck Rd, Monrovia, CA 91016
Tel.: (469) 374-9233
Web Site: http://www.lingualcare.com
Lingual Orthodontics Solutions
N.A.I.C.S.: 423450

Subsidiary (Non-US):

TOP-Service fur Lingualtechnik GmbH   **(3)**
Schledehauser Strasse 81, 49152, Essen, Germany
Tel.: (49) 547294910
Web Site: http://www.lingualtechnik.de
Sales Range: $50-74.9 Million
Emp.: 170
Orthodontic Technology & Services
N.A.I.C.S.: 423450
Gunter Gressler (Mng Dir)

Subsidiary (Domestic):

MModal Inc.   **(2)**
5000 Meridian Blvd Ste 200, Franklin, TN 37067
Tel.: (919) 867-3526
Web Site: http://www.mmodal.com
Sales Range: $400-449.9 Million
Emp.: 12,000
Clinical & Hospital Management Software
N.A.I.C.S.: 513210
G. Scott MacKenzie (CEO)

Subsidiary (Non-US):

MModal Global Services Pvt. Ltd.   **(3)**
3rd Fl Bldg No 3 Mindspace-Airoli Plot No 3, Thane Belapur Rd Airoli, Navi Mumbai, 400 708, Maharashtra, India
Tel.: (91) 22 3307 7000
Web Site: http://www.mmodal.com
Emp.: 400
Medical Practice & Hospital Management Software
N.A.I.C.S.: 513210
Agnelo John Rodrigues (Chief Compliance Officer & Sec)

Subsidiary (Domestic):

Multimodal Technologies, LLC   **(3)**
1710 Murray Ave, Pittsburgh, PA 15217
Tel.: (412) 422-2002
Sales Range: $25-49.9 Million
Emp.: 40
Custom Computer Programming Services
N.A.I.C.S.: 541511

Subsidiary (Non-US):

Suyash Software Pvt. Ltd.   **(3)**
99 East High Court Road, Ramdaspeth, Nagpur, 440010, India
Tel.: (91) 7122521028
Sales Range: $25-49.9 Million
Emp.: 200
Data Transcription & Information Management Software Publisher
N.A.I.C.S.: 513210

SOMERO ENTERPRISES INC.
14530 Global Pkwy, Fort Myers, FL 33913
Tel.: (906) 359-8506
Web Site: https://www.somero.com
SOM—(LSE)
Rev.: $88,572,000
Assets: $78,849,000
Liabilities: $15,319,000
Net Worth: $63,530,000
Earnings: $18,773,000
Emp.: 190
Fiscal Year-end: 12/31/20
Automated Construction Machinery Mfr
N.A.I.C.S.: 333120

John T. Cooney (CEO)
Howard Hohmann (Exec VP)
Lance Holbrook (VP-North America & Latin America)
Dave Raasakka (VP & Mgr-Customer Support-Global)
John Yuncza (CFO)
Dennis Mors (Sls Dir-Innovative Products & Dealer Dev)

SONAR RADIO CORP.
761-6 Coco Plum Cir, Plantation, FL 33324-3744
Tel.: (954) 981-8800
Year Founded: 1946
SONR—(OTCIQ)
Radio Communication Distribution Services
N.A.I.C.S.: 517112
Bernard A. Klein (Pres)

SONDER HOLDINGS, INC.
447 Sutter St Ste 405 Ste 542, San Francisco, CA 94108
Tel.: (617) 300-0956   DE
Year Founded: 2020
SOND—(NASDAQ)
Rev.: $602,066,000
Assets: $1,521,267,000
Liabilities: $1,897,968,000
Net Worth: ($376,701,000)
Earnings: ($295,668,000)
Emp.: 905
Fiscal Year-end: 12/31/23
Holding Company
N.A.I.C.S.: 551112
Adam K. Bowen (Chief Acctg Officer)
Dominique Bourgault (CFO)
Francis Lam Davidson (Co-Founder & CEO)
Arthur Chang (VP-Strategic Initiatives)
Bonnie Samuels (VP-Human Resources)
Mac Golonka (Sr VP-Technology)
Katherine Potter (Chief Legal Officer & Chief Admin Officer)
Martin Picard (Co-Founder & Chief Real Estate Officer)

SONENDO, INC.
26061 Merit Cir Ste 102, Laguna Hills, CA 92653
Tel.: (949) 766-3636
Web Site: https://www.sonendo.com
Year Founded: 2006
SONX—(NYSE)
Rev.: $41,656,000
Assets: $137,285,000
Liabilities: $55,330,000
Net Worth: $81,955,000
Earnings: ($57,050,000)
Emp.: 244
Fiscal Year-end: 12/31/22
Health Software Development Services
N.A.I.C.S.: 541511
John J. Bostjancic (CFO)
Bjarne Bergheim (Pres & CEO)
Bob Anthony (VP-Ops)
Alma Salazar (Assoc VP-Pro & Consumer Mktg)

SONIC AUTOMOTIVE, INC.
4401 Colwick Rd Directions, Charlotte, NC 28211
Tel.: (704) 566-2400   DE
Web Site:
https://www.sonicautomotive.com
Year Founded: 1997
SAH—(NYSE)
Rev.: $14,001,100,000
Assets: $4,978,300,000
Liabilities: $4,083,100,000
Net Worth: $895,200,000
Earnings: $88,500,000

Emp.: 10,300
Fiscal Year-end: 12/31/22
Automotive Retailer
N.A.I.C.S.: 441110
Heath R. Byrd (CFO & Exec VP)
David Bruton Smith (Chm & CEO)
Jeff Dyke (Pres)
B. Scott Smith (Co-Founder)

Subsidiaries:

Arngar, Inc.   **(1)**
10725 Pineville Rd, Pineville, NC 28134-8495
Tel.: (704) 900-2252
Web Site:
https://www.cadillacofsouthcharlotte.com
Automobile Dealership
N.A.I.C.S.: 441110
Wanda McCombs (Controller)
Bruce Dunehew (Mgr-Collison Center)

Bobby Ford Inc.   **(1)**
1200 N Highway 288-B, Richwood, TX 77531
Tel.: (979) 265-3707
Web Site: http://bobbyford.net
Sales Range: $25-49.9 Million
Emp.: 40
Car Dealer
N.A.I.C.S.: 441110
Marty Emfinger (Gen Mgr)

Don Massey Cadillac Lone Tree   **(1)**
8201 Pkwy Dr, Lone Tree, CO 80124-2754   **(100%)**
Tel.: (303) 799-1110
Web Site: http://www.donmassey.com
Sales Range: $75-99.9 Million
Emp.: 100
Automobile Dealership
N.A.I.C.S.: 441110
Dan Keenoy (Pres)

EchoPark AL, LLC   **(1)**
2001 Tom Williams Way, Birmingham, AL 35210
Tel.: (205) 670-2462
Car Dealing Services
N.A.I.C.S.: 441110

EchoPark GA, LLC   **(1)**
3296 Commerce Ave NW, Duluth, GA 30096
Tel.: (678) 671-4244
Car Dealing Services
N.A.I.C.S.: 441110

Echopark Automotive, Inc.   **(1)**
500 E 104th Ave, Thornton, CO 80229
Web Site: https://www.echopark.com
Automotive Retailer
N.A.I.C.S.: 441110

FAA Concord H, Inc.   **(1)**
1461 Concord Ave, Concord, CA 94520
Tel.: (925) 825-8000
Web Site: https://www.concordhonda.com
Emp.: 60
New & Used Car Dealer
N.A.I.C.S.: 441110

FAA Poway H, Inc.   **(1)**
13747 Poway Rd, Poway, CA 92064
Tel.: (858) 486-4300
Web Site: https://www.powayhonda.com
New Car Dealers
N.A.I.C.S.: 441110

FAA Serramonte H, Inc.   **(1)**
485 Serramonte Blvd, Colma, CA 94014
Web Site:
https://www.hondaofserramonte.com
New Car Dealers
N.A.I.C.S.: 441110

Fort Mill Ford, Inc.   **(1)**
801 Gold Hill Rd, Fort Mill, SC 29708
Tel.: (803) 547-5454
Web Site: https://www.fortmillford.com
New Car Dealers
N.A.I.C.S.: 441110

Massey Cadillac, Inc.   **(1)**
11675 Lyndon B Johnson Fwy, Garland, TX 75041   **(100%)**
Tel.: (972) 468-0817
Web Site: https://www.dallascadillac.com
Sales Range: $50-74.9 Million
Emp.: 60
Automobile Dealership

N.A.I.C.S.: 441110

Philpott Motors, LLC   **(1)**
2289 N Hwy 69, Nederland, TX 77627
Web Site: https://www.philpottmotors.net
New & Used Car Distr
N.A.I.C.S.: 441120

Philpott Motors, Ltd.   **(1)**
1400 US Hwy 69, Nederland, TX 77627
Web Site: http://www.philpottmotors.com
New Car Dealers
N.A.I.C.S.: 441110
Robert Thewman (Gen Mgr)
Kevin Speight (Mgr-Sls)
Darron Stotts (Mgr-Hyundai Parts)
Cory Lunceford (Mgr-Fin)

SAI Chamblee V, LLC   **(1)**
4401 Colwick Rd, Charlotte, NC 28211-2311
Tel.: (704) 566-2400
Automobile Dealers
N.A.I.C.S.: 441330

SAI Clearwater T, LLC   **(1)**
21799 US Highway 19 N, Clearwater, FL 33765
Web Site: https://www.clearwatertoyota.com
New Car Dealers
N.A.I.C.S.: 441110

SAI Denver B, Inc.   **(1)**
2201 S Wabash St, Denver, CO 80231-3313
Tel.: (303) 243-3001
Automobile Dealers
N.A.I.C.S.: 441330

SAI Fort Myers H, LLC   **(1)**
15421 S Tamiami Trail, Fort Myers, FL 33912
Tel.: (800) 640-9073
New Car Dealers
N.A.I.C.S.: 441110

Sonic - Lone Tree Cadillac, Inc.   **(1)**
8201 Pkwy Dr, Lone Tree, CO 80124
Tel.: (303) 799-1110
Web Site: http://www.sonicautomotive.com
New Car Dealers
N.A.I.C.S.: 441110

Sonic - Lute Riley, LP   **(1)**
13561 Goldmark Dr, Dallas, TX 75240
Tel.: (214) 357-2700
Web Site:
https://www.luterileycollisioncenter.com
New Car Dealers
N.A.I.C.S.: 441110

Sonic - University Park A, LP   **(1)**
5033 Lemmon Ave, Dallas, TX 75209
Tel.: (800) 378 9703
New Car Dealers
N.A.I.C.S.: 441110

Sonic Automotive F&I, LLC   **(1)**
4236 Las Vegas Blvd N, Las Vegas, NV 89115-1564
Tel.: (702) 632-3315
New Car Dealers
N.A.I.C.S.: 441110

Sonic Development, LLC   **(1)**
1221 Saxon BVLd, Orange City, FL 32763
Tel.: (386) 774-0963
Automotive Retailer
N.A.I.C.S.: 441110

Sonic Momentum VWA, LP   **(1)**
2405 Richmond Ave, Houston, TX 77098
New Car Dealers
N.A.I.C.S.: 441110

Sonic-Crest Cadillac, LLC   **(1)**
2121 Rosa L Parks Blvd, Nashville, TN 37228
Tel.: (615) 242-4242
Web Site: http://www.nashvillecadillac.com
Sales Range: $125-149.9 Million
Emp.: 250
Automobile Dealership
N.A.I.C.S.: 441110
Scott Webster (Controller)
Brandon Mosley (Gen Mgr)
James Jones (Dir-Fixed Ops & Svc Center)
Ryan Kimpton (Mgr-Svc)
Steve Parker (Mgr-Pre-Owned)

Sonic-North Cadillac, Inc.   **(1)**

4241 N John Young Pkwy, Orlando, FL
32804-1928
Tel.: (407) 299-6161
Web Site:
    https://www.masseycadillacnorth.com
Sales Range: $100-124.9 Million
Emp.: 100
Automobile Dealership
N.A.I.C.S.: 441110
Robert Moore *(Gen Mgr)*
Billy Dhaliwal *(Mgr-New Car)*
Eric Kriechbaum *(Mgr-Used Car)*
Brian Kowlessar *(Controller)*
Becky Williams *(Office Mgr)*
Billy Waddle *(Mgr-Svc)*
Robert Peterson *(Mgr-Parts)*
Melinda Canter *(Bus Mgr)*

Suburban Cadillac Of Lansing,
LLC   (1)
5901 S Pennsylvania Ave, Lansing, MI
48911   (100%)
Tel.: (517) 507-4921
Web Site: http://www.shaheencadillac.com
Automobile Dealership
N.A.I.C.S.: 441110
Karl Hasenwinkle *(Mgr-Used Car Sls)*
Ralph Shaheen *(Pres)*
Jason Cords *(Gen Mgr)*
Matt Platko *(Gen Mgr-Sls)*
Hayden Wiegel *(Mgr-New Car Sls)*
Duane Soulliere *(Mgr-Svc)*
Trae Townsend *(Bus Mgr)*
Kyle Humphry *(Sls Mgr-Internet)*
Ashley Dery *(Asst Mgr-Internet Sls)*

SONIC FOUNDRY, INC.

222 W Washington Ave, Madison, WI
53703
Tel.: (608) 443-1600   MD
Web Site:
    https://www.sonicfoundry.com
Year Founded: 1991
SOFO—(OTCIQ)
Rev.: $22,109,000
Assets: $12,263,000
Liabilities: $26,002,000
Net Worth: ($13,739,000)
Earnings: ($19,348,000)
Emp.: 153
Fiscal Year-end: 09/30/23
Digital Media & Internet Software
Tools Services
N.A.I.C.S.: 334220
Michael Snavely *(Gen Mgr)*
Shelley Raaths *(VP-HR)*
Joseph P. Mozden Jr. *(CEO)*
Sarah Wilde *(Mktg Dir)*
Donny Neufuss *(Dir-Bus Dev & Strategic Partnerships)*
C. J. Tao *(VP & Controller)*
Steve McKee *(Sr VP-Product & Tech)*
Duane Glader *(Sr VP-Sls)*
Ken Minor *(CFO)*
Toshihide Muneyuki *(CEO)*
Mike Snavely *(Gen Mgr)*

Subsidiaries:

International Image Services Inc. (1)
23 Prince Andrew Place, Toronto, M3C
2H2, ON, Canada
Tel.: (416) 449-3033
Sales Range: $100-124.9 Million
Media Technology Services
N.A.I.C.S.: 513199

Sonic Foundry Media Systems,
Inc.   (1)
222 W Washington Ave, Madison, WI
53703
Tel.: (608) 443-1600
Web Site: https://www.sonicfoundry.com
Sales Range: $25-49.9 Million
Emp.: 125
Internet Media Services
N.A.I.C.S.: 513199

SONIDA SENIOR LIVING, INC.

14755 Preston Rd Ste 810, Dallas,
TX 75254
Tel.: (972) 770-5600   DE

Web Site:
    https://www.sonidaseniorliving.com
Year Founded: 1988
SNDA—(NYSE)
Rev.: $238,433,000
Assets: $661,268,000
Liabilities: $762,982,000
Net Worth: ($101,714,000)
Earnings: ($58,970,000)
Emp.: 2,420
Fiscal Year-end: 12/31/22
Owner, Manager & Developer of Senior Living Communities
N.A.I.C.S.: 623110
David R. Brickman *(Gen Counsel, Sec & Sr VP)*
Michael C. Fryar *(Chief Revenue Officer)*
Carole J. Burnell *(VP-Ops-Southwest Div)*
Jay Reed *(VP-Information Technology)*
Kevin Detz *(CFO & Exec VP)*
Timothy Cober *(Chief Acctg Officer & VP)*
Tabitha Obenour *(Chief Clinical Officer)*
Reanae Clark *(VP-Business Development & Acquisitions)*
Donna Brown *(VP-Operations)*
Dawn Mount *(VP-Operations)*
Brandon M. Ribar *(Pres & CEO)*

Subsidiaries:

CGI Management, Inc.   (1)
651 Washington St Ste 200, Brookline, MA
02446-4579
Tel.: (617) 734-1900
Web Site:
    https://www.cgimanagementinc.com
Nursing Care Facilities
N.A.I.C.S.: 623110

CSL Batesville, LLC   (1)
44 Chateau Blvd, Batesville, IN 47006-5744
Tel.: (812) 393-2534
Web Site:
    http://www.chateauofbatesville.com
Emp.: 35
Women Healthcare Services
N.A.I.C.S.: 621610
Dan Kenyon *(Sec & VP)*

CSL CE Corpus, LLC   (1)
5813 Esplanade Dr, Corpus Christi, TX
78414-4113
Tel.: (361) 991-9600
Emp.: 25
Women Healthcare Services
N.A.I.C.S.: 621610
Carole J. Burnell *(VP)*

CSL CE Stephenville, LLC   (1)
2010 Good Tree St, Stephenville, TX 76401
Tel.: (254) 965-9897
Women Healthcare Services
N.A.I.C.S.: 621610

CSL Charlestown, LLC   (1)
2400 Market St, Charlestown, IN 47111
Tel.: (812) 289-6370
Web Site: http://www.capitalsenior.com
Emp.: 55
Women Healthcare Services
N.A.I.C.S.: 621610

CSL Columbus, LLC   (1)
5380 E Broad St, Columbus, OH 43213-
1391
Tel.: (614) 756-3209
Women Healthcare Services
N.A.I.C.S.: 621610

CSL Fitchburg Management,
LLC   (1)
7100 S Wilkinson Way, Perrysburg, OH
43551
Tel.: (419) 874-2564
Women Healthcare Services
N.A.I.C.S.: 621610

CSL Green Bay, LLC   (1)
1740 Condor Ln Ste A, Green Bay, WI
54313-7776
Tel.: (920) 228-8868

Residential Care Services
N.A.I.C.S.: 623990

CSL Keystone Woods, LLC   (1)
2335 N Madison Ave, Anderson, IN 46011-
9591
Tel.: (765) 246-8196
Web Site: http://www.capitalseniorliving.com
Nursing Care Facilities
N.A.I.C.S.: 623110

CSL Laurelhurst NC, LLC   (1)
1064 W Mills St, Columbus, NC 28722-
8635
Tel.: (828) 481-9149
Web Site: http://www.capitalseniorliving.net
Emp.: 30
Nursing Care Facilities
N.A.I.C.S.: 623110

CSL Miracle Hills, LLC   (1)
14160 Dallas Pkwy Ste 300, Dallas, TX
75254
Tel.: (972) 770-5600
Sales Range: $10-24.9 Million
Emp.: 55
Nursing Care Facilities
N.A.I.C.S.: 623110

CSL Riverbend IN, LLC   (1)
2715 Charlestown Pike, Jeffersonville, IN
47130
Tel.: (812) 289-6761
Web Site: http://www.capitalsenior.com
Emp.: 10
Residential Care Services & Assisted Living
Facility
N.A.I.C.S.: 623312

CSL Summit, LLC   (1)
14160 Dallas Pkwy Ste 300, Dallas, TX
75254
Tel.: (972) 770-5600
Web Site: http://www.capitalsenior.com
Women Healthcare Services
N.A.I.C.S.: 621610

CSL Towne Centre, LLC   (1)
7250 Arthur Blvd, Merrillville, IN 46410
Tel.: (219) 736-2900
Web Site: http://www.capitalsenior.com
Assisted Living Facility & Home Health
Care Services
N.A.I.C.S.: 623312

CSL Van Dorn, LLC   (1)
7208 Van Dorn St, Lincoln, NE 68506
Tel.: (402) 486-0011
Nursing Care Facilities
N.A.I.C.S.: 623110
Kylee Graham *(Office Mgr)*

CSL Virginia Beach, LLC   (1)
5417 Wesleyan Dr, Virginia Beach, VA
23455
Tel.: (757) 530-5946
Residential Care Services
N.A.I.C.S.: 623990

CSL Whispering Pines, LLC   (1)
937 E Park Ave, Columbiana, OH 44408
Tel.: (330) 846-5059
Residential Care Services
N.A.I.C.S.: 623990

CSL Whitcomb House, LLC   (1)
245 West St, Milford, MA 01757-2201
Tel.: (508) 306-8303
Web Site: http://www.capitalsenior.com
Emp.: 50
Assisted Living Facility
N.A.I.C.S.: 623312

Capital Senior Living Corporation (1)
14160 Dallas Pkwy Ste 300, Dallas, TX
75254-4383   (100%)
Tel.: (972) 770-5600
Web Site: http://www.capitalsenior.com
Sales Range: $100-124.9 Million
Emp.: 48
Investment Services
N.A.I.C.S.: 523999

Capital Senior Living ILM-B, Inc. (1)
4515 22nd St NW, Canton, OH 44708
Tel.: (330) 477-7664
Web Site: http://www.captialsenior.com
Nursing Care Facilities
N.A.I.C.S.: 623110

SONIM TECHNOLOGIES, INC.

4445 Eastgate Mall Ste 200, San Diego, CA 92121
Tel.: (650) 378-8100   DE
Web Site:
    https://www.sonimtech.com
Year Founded: 1999
SONM—(NASDAQ)
Rev.: $69,828,000
Assets: $53,686,000
Liabilities: $33,641,000
Net Worth: $20,045,000
Earnings: ($14,087,000)
Emp.: 54
Fiscal Year-end: 12/31/22
Mobile Phone Mfr
N.A.I.C.S.: 334220
Peter Liu *(CEO)*
Jeffrey Wang *(Chm)*
Clay Crolius *(CFO)*
Mike Coad *(Sr VP-Product)*
Dyan Kaplan *(Sr VP-Sales & Customer Experience)*
Zhide Wang *(Sr VP-Global Ops)*
Chris Yeatts *(Sr VP-Connected Solutions)*
Chuck Becher *(Chief Comml Officer)*
Simon Rayne *(Sr VP & Gen Mgr-UK, EMEA, and APAC)*
Alain Hon *(Sr VP-Global Engrg)*
Ian Han *(VP-Program Mgmt)*
Anette Gaven *(VP-Marketing)*

Subsidiaries:

Sonim Technologies (India) Private
Limited   (1)
Sri Gandha Arcade 564/564-1 9th Cross J
P Nagar III Phase, Bengaluru, 560 078,
India
Tel.: (91) 8040302010
Wireless Communication Equipment Mfr
N.A.I.C.S.: 334220
Geethanjali R. *(Mgr-Technical)*

Sonim Technologies (Shenzhen)
Limited   (1)
208 Building 2 Phase 2 Liu Xian 1st Road,
Gaoxinqi Strategic Emerging Industrial Park
Baoan District, Shenzhen, China
Tel.: (86) 75532998780
Wireless Communication Equipment Mfr
N.A.I.C.S.: 334220
Loco Liu *(Engr-Product)*

SONNET BIOTHERAPEUTICS HOLDINGS, INC.

100 Overlook Ctr Ste 102, Princeton,
NJ 08540
Tel.: (609) 375-2227   DE
Web Site: https://www.sonnetbio.com
Year Founded: 2005
SONN—(NASDAQ)
Rev.: $4,327,946
Assets: $2,771,030
Liabilities: $3,256,769
Net Worth: ($485,739)
Earnings: ($7,437,232)
Emp.: 13
Fiscal Year-end: 09/30/24
Holding Company; Restaurant Franchise Owner & Operator
N.A.I.C.S.: 551112
Pankaj Mohan *(Co-Founder, Chm, Pres & CEO)*
John H. Cross *(CFO)*
John K. Cini *(Co-Founder & Chief Scientific Officer)*
Terence Rugg *(Chief Medical Officer)*
Susan Dexter *(Chief Technical Officer)*

Subsidiaries:

American Roadside Burgers Smithtown, Inc.   (1)
80 E Main St, Smithtown, NY 11787
Tel.: (631) 382-9500
Web Site: http://www.americanburgerco.com
Restaurant Services
N.A.I.C.S.: 722511

Sonnet BioTherapeutics Holdings, Inc.—(Continued)

BGR Operations, LLC (1)
4621 Little Ave Ste 414, Charlotte, NC 28226
Tel.: (704) 366-5122
Web Site: http://www.bgrtheburgerjoint.com
Restaurant Operators
N.A.I.C.S.: 561110

Subsidiary (Domestic):

BGR Annapolis, LLC (2)
2101 Somerville Rd, Annapolis, MD 21401
Tel.: (667) 225-4186
Restaurant Services
N.A.I.C.S.: 722511

BGR Columbia, LLC (2)
6250 Columbia Crossing Cir Ste D, Columbia, MD 21045
Tel.: (443) 319-5542
Restaurant Services
N.A.I.C.S.: 722511

BGR Mosaic, LLC (2)
19309 Winmeade Dr Ste 333, Lansdowne, VA 20176
Tel.: (571) 223-5946
Web Site: http://www.bgrtheburgerjoint.com
Restaurant Services
N.A.I.C.S.: 722511

BGR Tysons, LLC (2)
8056 Tysons Corner Ctr, McLean, VA 22102
Tel.: (703) 790-3437
Web Site: http://www.bgrtheburgerjoint.com
Restaurant Operators
N.A.I.C.S.: 722511

BGR Tysons, LLC (2)
8056 Tysons Corner Ctr, Mclean, VA 22102
Tel.: (703) 790-3437
Restaurant Operators
N.A.I.C.S.: 722511

BGR Washingtonian, LLC (2)
RIO Washingtonian Ctr 229 Boardwalk Pl, Gaithersburg, MD 20878
Tel.: (301) 569-7086
Web Site: http://www.bgrtheburgerjoint.com
Emp.: 8
Restaurant Operators
N.A.I.C.S.: 722511

Capitol Burger, LLC (1)
1005 7th St NW, Washington, DC 20001
Tel.: (202) 638-0414
Web Site: http://www.thecapitalburger.com
Restaurant Services
N.A.I.C.S.: 722511

Hoot Australia Pty Ltd (1)
C69 24-32 Lexington Drive, Bella Vista, 2153, NSW, Australia
Tel.: (61) 296726423
Restaurant Operators
N.A.I.C.S.: 722511

Subsidiary (Domestic):

Hoot Parramatta Pty Ltd (2)
132 James Ruse Drive, Rosehill, Sydney, 2142, Australia
Tel.: (61) 296335160
Emp.: 30
Restaurant Operators
N.A.I.C.S.: 722511
Jay Ager (Gen Mgr)

Subsidiary (Non-US):

Hooters Brazil (2)
Alameda Joaquim Eugenio de Lima 612
Jardim Paulista, Sao Paulo, 01403-000, Sao Paulo, Brazil
Tel.: (55) 1135866357
Web Site: http://www.hootersbrasil.com.br
Restaurant Services
N.A.I.C.S.: 722511

SONNET BioTherapeutics, Inc. (1)
100 Overlook Ctr, Princeton, NJ 08540
Tel.: (609) 375-2227
Web Site: https://sonnetbio.com
Biotechnology Preparation, Research & Development
N.A.I.C.S.: 541714
Pankaj Mohan (Chm & CEO)

Subsidiary (Non-US):

Relief Therapeutics SA (2)
Avenue de Secheron 15, 1202, Geneva, Switzerland
Tel.: (41) 44 723 5959
Web Site: http://www.relieftherapeutics.com
Biopharmaceutical Developer
N.A.I.C.S.: 325414

SONO-TEK CORPORATION
2012 Route 9W, Milton, NY 12547
Tel.: (845) 795-2020   **NY**
Web Site: https://www.sono-tek.com
Year Founded: 1975
SOTK—(NASDAQ)
Rev.: $17,132,710
Assets: $17,625,534
Liabilities: $3,884,221
Net Worth: $13,741,313
Earnings: $2,542,573
Emp.: 67
Fiscal Year-end: 02/28/22
Ultrasonic Liquid Atomizing Nozzles Mfr & Sales
N.A.I.C.S.: 333995
Christopher L. Coccio (Exec Chm)
Robb W. Engle (Exec VP)
Stephen J. Bagley (CFO)
R. Stephen Harshbarger (Pres & CEO)
Christopher C. Cichetti (VP-Application Engrg)

Subsidiaries:

Sono-Tek Cleaning Systems, Inc. (1)
2012 Route 9W, Milton, NY 12547
Tel.: (845) 795-2020
Ultrasonic Spraying System Mfr
N.A.I.C.S.: 335999

SONOCO PRODUCTS COMPANY
1 N 2nd St, Hartsville, SC 29550
Tel.: (843) 383-7000   **SC**
Web Site: https://www.sonoco.com
Year Founded: 1899
SON—(NYSE)
Rev.: $6,781,292,000
Assets: $7,191,957,000
Liabilities: $4,760,122,000
Net Worth: $2,431,835,000
Earnings: $475,901,000
Emp.: 23,000
Fiscal Year-end: 12/31/23
Industrial & Consumer Packaging Products & Services
N.A.I.C.S.: 322130
Robert Howard Coker (Pres & CEO)
Robert R. Dillard (CFO)
John M. Florence Jr. (Gen Counsel)
Scott Byrne (Dir)
Laura Buen Abad (Sr Dir)
Ed Harrington (Dir)
Peter Gorlitz (Mgr)
Glenn Jordan (Dir)
Palace Stepps (VP)
Roger P. Schrum (VP-IR & Corp Affairs)

Subsidiaries:

Clear Lam Packaging, Inc. (1)
1950 Pratt Blvd, Elk Grove Village, IL 60007   (100%)
Tel.: (847) 439-8570
Web Site: http://www.clearlam.com
Packaging Materials Mfr
N.A.I.C.S.: 326199
Roman Forowycz (CMO)

Clear Pack Company (1)
11610 Copenhagen Ct, Franklin Park, IL 60131
Tel.: (847) 957-6282
Plastics Product Mfr
N.A.I.C.S.: 326199

Conitex Sonoco Hellas S.A. (1)
11th km PEO Thessaloniki-Kilkis, 57008, Thessaloniki, Greece

Tel.: (30) 2310781996
Web Site: https://www.conitex.gr
Paper Cone & Roller Mfr
N.A.I.C.S.: 322299

Conitex Sonoco India Pvt. Ltd. (1)
Survey No 26/1 Pimple Nilakh Jagtap Dairy
Vishal Nagar, Pune, 411027, India
Tel.: (91) 2027271019
Paper Cone & Roller Mfr
N.A.I.C.S.: 322299
Yogesh Khadke (Mgr-HR & Admin)

Conitex Sonoco Taiwan Ltd. (1)
No 5 Guangfu North Road Hsinchu Industrial Park, Hukou Township, Hsinchu, 30351, Taiwan
Tel.: (886) 35983521
Paper Cone & Roller Mfr
N.A.I.C.S.: 322299
Nancy Kung (Controller)

Conitex Sonoco UK Limited (1)
Black Dyke Mills Business Park Office 26FF
Brighouse Road Queensbury, Bradford, BD13 1QA, United Kingdom
Tel.: (44) 274884579
Paper Cone & Roller Mfr
N.A.I.C.S.: 322299

Conitex Sonoco USA, Inc. (1)
1302 Industrial Pike, Gastonia, NC 28052
Tel.: (704) 864-5406
Paper Cone & Roller Mfr
N.A.I.C.S.: 322299
Derrick Canipe (Mgr-IT)

Corenso North America LLC (1)
310 3rd Ave N, Wisconsin Rapids, WI 54495-2792
Tel.: (715) 422-7800
Paperboard Mfr
N.A.I.C.S.: 322130
Tammy Barstow (CFO)

Corenso Wisconsin Board, LLC (1)
310 3rd Ave N, Wisconsin Rapids, WI 54495
Tel.: (715) 422-7800
Core Board & Chipboard Product Mfr
N.A.I.C.S.: 321219

D & W Paper Tube, Inc. (1)
245 Duvall Rd, Chatsworth, GA 30705
Tel.: (706) 517-4033
Web Site: http://www.dwpapertube.com
Sales Range: $1-9.9 Million
Emp.: 31
Home Furnishing Whslr
N.A.I.C.S.: 423220
Robert Winkler (VP)
Darryl Davis (VP)
Herman Davis (Pres)
Seth Davis (Treas)

Graffo Paranaense De Embalagens, S.A. (1)
Rua Tomazina 254-Condominio Portal da Serra, Pinhais, 83325-040, Parana, Brazil
Tel.: (55) 4121028000
Web Site: https://www.graffo.ind.br
Emp.: 6
Packaging Services
N.A.I.C.S.: 561910

Highland Packaging Solutions, LLC (1)
1420 Gordon Food Service Dr, Plant City, FL 33563
Tel.: (863) 425-5757
Web Site: https://www.highcor.com
Packaging & Labeling Products Mfr
N.A.I.C.S.: 326199
John Baird (Pres)
Steve Maxwell (CEO)
Roger Hanna (Sr VP-Ops)
Bill Clark (Sr VP-Sls)
Scott Lindley (VP-Comml Sls)
Lisa Giesel (VP-Customer Rels)
Steve Blackwelder (VP-HR)
Chris Jastemski (VP-Fin)
Jo Ann Brockman (Mgr-Quality Sys)
Nicole Nolte (Mgr-Art Dept)

Hockenheim RIGID PAPER (1)
1 Industriestr 26, 68766, Hockenheim, Germany
Tel.: (49) 62052030
Web Site: http://www.sonocoeurope.com
Can Mfr

N.A.I.C.S.: 332431

Inapel Embalagens Ltda. (1)
Est Pres Juscelino Kubitschek de Oliveira 2783, Guarulhos, 07272-480, Sao Paulo, Brazil
Tel.: (55) 1124628800
Web Site: https://www.inapel.com.br
Packaging Material Mfr & Distr
N.A.I.C.S.: 326112

Italtubetti, SpA (1)
Via Provinciale 61, Alzano Lombardo, 24022, Bergamo, Italy
Tel.: (39) 035520333
Paper Cone & Roller Mfr
N.A.I.C.S.: 322299
Rossano Giannettoni (Mgr-Sls)

Manufacturas Sonoco, S.A. de C.V. (1)
Avenida Ignaclo Zaragoza Numero 15 Ciudad Adolfo Lopez Mateos Centro, Municipio Atizapan de Zaragoza, 52900, Mexico, Mexico   (100%)
Tel.: (52) 8444309862
Web Site: http://www.sonoco.com.mx
Packaging Paper Products Mfr
N.A.I.C.S.: 322220

Mechelen RIGID PAPER (1)
Egide Walschaertsstraat 7, 2800, Mechelen, Belgium
Tel.: (32) 15448910
Web Site: http://www.sonocoeurope.com
Packaging & Supply Chain Services
N.A.I.C.S.: 561910

Neuvibox SAS (1)
194 Allee de la Croix des Horm BP 8, Montanay, 69250, Lyon, France
Tel.: (33) 472083232
Paperboard Mfr
N.A.I.C.S.: 322219

OOO Sonoco Alcore (1)
Ave Bogatyrsky 18 Bldg 3, 197348, Saint Petersburg, Russia
Tel.: (7) 8123298833
Web Site: http://www.sonoco-alcore.all.biz
Paper Yarn Mfr
N.A.I.C.S.: 313110

Papertech SL (1)
Ctra Pamplona 2 Apartado 18 Tudela, 31500, Navarra, 31500, Spain
Tel.: (34) 948823400
Web Site: https://papertech.com
Industrial & Consumer Packaging Product Mfr
N.A.I.C.S.: 322219

Peninsula Packaging, LLC (1)
1030 N Anderson Rd, Exeter, CA 93221   (100%)
Tel.: (559) 594-6813
Web Site: http://www.sonoco.com
Plastics Product Mfr
N.A.I.C.S.: 326199

Plastique Holdings Limited (1)
Walkern Road, Stevenage, SG1 3QP, Herts, United Kingdom
Tel.: (44) 115 964 6990
Web Site: http://www.plastique.eu
Holding Company
N.A.I.C.S.: 551112

Subsidiary (Domestic):

Plastique Limited (2)
Units 17/18 Decimus Park Kingstanding Way, Tunbridge Wells, TN2 3GP, United Kingdom
Tel.: (44) 1892543211
Web Site: http://www.plastique.eu
Roof Equipment Mfr
N.A.I.C.S.: 332322

Subsidiary (Non-US):

Plastique Sp. z o.o. (2)
ul Bukowska 12, Dabrowa, 77743, Poznan, Poland
Tel.: (48) 618941500
Web Site: http://www.plastique.pl
Roof Equipment Mfr
N.A.I.C.S.: 332322

RTS Packaging, LLC (1)

1200 Abernathy Rd NE Bldg 600 Ste 1600,
Atlanta, GA 30328
Tel.: (770) 448-2244
Web Site: https://www.rtspackaging.com
Sales Range: $75-99.9 Million
Emp.: 30
Solid Fiber & Corrugated Partitions, Folding
Cartons & Paperboard Components Mfr
N.A.I.C.S.: 322219

Subsidiary (Non-US):

RTS Embalajes De Chile (2)
Limitada
Camino Santa Margarita #01160 Interior
(Calle Nueva) Lote 7, San Bernardo, San-
tiago, Chile
Tel.: (56) 2 3263 0200
Web Site: http://www.rts.cl
Emp.: 20
Protective Packaging & Paperboard Parti-
tions Mfr
N.A.I.C.S.: 322212

RTS Embalajes de Argentina SA (2)
Independencia 400 Godoy Cruz, Maipu,
Mendoza, 5501, Argentina
Tel.: (54) 2 614 315758
Web Site: http://www.rtsargentina.com.ar
Protective Packaging & Paperboard Parti-
tions Mfr
N.A.I.C.S.: 322130

RTS Empaques, S. De R.L. de (2)
CV
Bronce No 9351 Entre Omicron y Cobre,
Cuidad Industrial Mitras, Villa de Garcia,
66000, Nuevo Leon, Mexico
Tel.: (52) 8183810197
Web Site: http://www.rtspackaging.com
Sales Range: $25-49.9 Million
Emp.: 50
Protective Packaging & Paperboard Parti-
tions Mfr
N.A.I.C.S.: 322130

Branch (Domestic):

RTS Packaging - Orange (2)
14103 Borate St, Santa Fe Springs, CA
90670
Tel.: (714) 978-3150
Sales Range: $10-24.9 Million
Emp.: 50
Protective Packaging & Chipboard Parti-
tions Mfr
N.A.I.C.S.: 322130

SPC Management, Inc. (1)
1 N Second St, Hartsville, SC
29550 (100%)
Tel.: (314) 218-6049
Sales Range: $750-799.9 Million
Emp.: 2,500
Holding Company
N.A.I.C.S.: 322130
Harris E. Deloach Jr. *(Pres)*

Subsidiary (Domestic):

Sonoco International, Inc. (2)
1 N Second St, Hartsville, SC
29550 (100%)
Tel.: (843) 383-7000
Web Site: http://www.sonoco.com
Holding Company
N.A.I.C.S.: 322130

Subsidiary (Non-US):

Inversiones Sonoco do Chile do
Ltda. (3)
Alvarez de Toledo 851, Santiago,
Chile (100%)
Tel.: (56) 25558837
Web Site: http://www.sonoco.com
Sales Range: $125-149.9 Million
Industrial Products & Composite Cans Mfr
N.A.I.C.S.: 333248

SPC Resources, Inc. (1)
125 W Home Ave, Hartsville, SC
29550 (100%)
Tel.: (843) 383-7303
Web Site: http://www.sonoco.com
Temperature Control Products, Concrete
Forming Mold & Packaging Materials Devel-
oper & Mfr
N.A.I.C.S.: 326150

Subsidiary (Domestic):

SPC Capital Management, Inc. (2)
125 W Home Ave, Hartsville, SC
29550 (100%)
Tel.: (843) 383-7303
Sales Range: $750-799.9 Million
Emp.: 2,500
Holding Company
N.A.I.C.S.: 322130
Harris E. Deloach Jr. *(CEO)*

Subsidiary (Domestic):

Sonoco Machinery Inc. (3)
1 N 2nd St, Hartsville, SC
29550-3300 (100%)
Tel.: (843) 383-7000
Web Site: http://www.sonoco.com
Sales Range: $750-799.9 Million
Emp.: 2,500
Packaging Machinery Mfr
N.A.I.C.S.: 322130

Subsidiary (Domestic):

Tegrant Alloyd Brands, Inc. (2)
1401 Pleasant St, Dekalb, IL 60115
Tel.: (815) 787-5222
Web Site: http://www.alloyd.com
Emp.: 260
Packaging Products Mfr
N.A.I.C.S.: 326112

Subsidiary (Domestic):

Alloyd Brands Consumer
Packaging (3)
1401 Pleasant St, Dekalb, IL 60115-2644
Tel.: (815) 756-8451
Web Site: http://www.alloyd.com
Sales Range: $100-124.9 Million
Specialty Packaging Material Mfr
N.A.I.C.S.: 326199
William Kelly *(Pres)*

Subsidiary (Domestic):

Sonoco Alloyd-Batavia (4)
1500 Paramount Pkwy, Batavia, IL 60510
Tel.: (630) 879-0121
Web Site: http://www.alloyd.com
Sales Range: $50-74.9 Million
Emp.: 200
Box & Packaging Mfr
N.A.I.C.S.: 322212

Unit (Domestic):

Protexic (3)
800 5th Ave, New Brighton, PA 15066
Tel.: (724) 843-8200
Web Site: http://www.protexic.com
Specialty Packaging Material Mfr
N.A.I.C.S.: 326150

Subsidiary (Domestic):

ThermoSafe Brands (3)
3930 N Ventura Dr Ste 450, Arlington
Heights, IL 60004
Tel.: (847) 398-0110
Web Site: http://www.thermosafe.com
Sales Range: $25-49.9 Million
Emp.: 100
Packaging Materials Mfr
N.A.I.C.S.: 326199

Sonoco Alcore GmbH (1)
Mathias-von-den-Driesch-Str 2, Girbelsrath,
52399, Merzenich, Germany
Tel.: (49) 24217040
Packaging Products Mfr
N.A.I.C.S.: 326112
Viktor Stoeck *(Dir-HR-Central & Eastern*
Europe)

Sonoco Asia L.L.C. (1)
458 Fushon Rd Rm 815-816, Pudong,
Shanghai, 200122, China (76%)
Tel.: (86) 2158317188
Web Site: http://www.sonoco.com
Sales Range: $300-349.9 Million
Holding Company
N.A.I.C.S.: 322219

Subsidiary (Non-US):

PT Sonoco Indonesia (2)
Jl Raya Cicadas KM-9 Gunung Putri, Bogor, 16964, Jawa Barat, Indonesia (100%)

Tel.: (62) 218670417
Web Site: https://www.sonoco.com
Sales Range: $25-49.9 Million
Emp.: 140
Engineered Carriers Mfr
N.A.I.C.S.: 322219

Sonoco Australia Pty. Ltd. (2)
17 Templestowe Road, Bulleen, 3105, VIC,
Australia (100%)
Tel.: (61) 398512200
Web Site: http://www.sonoco.com
Sales Range: $25-49.9 Million
Emp.: 75
Tubes, Cores & Packaging Products Mfr &
Sales
N.A.I.C.S.: 322219

Subsidiary (Domestic):

Sonoco Australia Pty. Ltd. (3)
19 Pritchard Road, Brisbane, Virginia, 4014,
QLD, Australia (100%)
Tel.: (61) 730255500
Web Site: http://www.sonoco.com.au
Sales Range: $10-24.9 Million
Emp.: 35
Cores, Tubes & Packaging Products Mfr
N.A.I.C.S.: 322219

Sonoco Australia Pty. Ltd. -
Wodonga (3)
36 Moloney Drive, Wodonga, 3690, VIC,
Australia (100%)
Tel.: (61) 287964200
Web Site: http://www.sonoco.com.au
Sales Range: $1-9.9 Million
Emp.: 8
Tubes, Cores & Packaging Products Mfr
N.A.I.C.S.: 331210

Subsidiary (Non-US):

Sonoco New Zealand Ltd. (2)
21 Corban Ave, Henderson, Auckland,
0612, New Zealand (100%)
Tel.: (64) 98361651
Web Site: http://www.sonoco.com
Sales Range: $10-24.9 Million
Emp.: 100
Tubes, Cores & Packaging Products Mfr &
Sales
N.A.I.C.S.: 322219

Subsidiary (Domestic):

Sonoco New Zealand Ltd. (3)
1 Spencer Avenue, Kawerau, 3127, New
Zealand (100%)
Tel.: (64) 73238649
Web Site: http://www.sonoco.com
Sales Range: $10-24.9 Million
Emp.: 13
Engineered Carriers
N.A.I.C.S.: 333993

Subsidiary (Non-US):

Sonoco Products Malaysia Sdn
Bhd (2)
Lot 46 Jalan BRP 9/2, Putra Industrial Park
Bukit Rahman Putra, 47000, Sungai Buloh,
Selangor, Malaysia (100%)
Tel.: (60) 129067961
Web Site: http://www.sonoco.com.my
Sales Range: $50-74.9 Million
Emp.: 110
Engineered Carriers Mfr
N.A.I.C.S.: 333993

Sonoco Singapore Pte. Ltd. (2)
28 Pandan Road, Singapore, 609276,
Singapore (100%)
Tel.: (65) 62614479
Web Site: http://www.sonoco.com.sg
Sales Range: $25-49.9 Million
Emp.: 130
Tubes, Cores & Packaging Products Mfr &
Sales
N.A.I.C.S.: 322219
Brad Weller *(Mng Dir-Asia & Div VP)*

Sonoco Taiwan Limited (2)
20-9 Nan Shi Vlg, Yung-ho, 36057,
Taiwan (100%)
Tel.: (886) 37368128
Web Site: http://www.sonoco.com
Sales Range: $25-49.9 Million
Emp.: 106
Engineered Carriers Mfr

N.A.I.C.S.: 322219

Sonoco Thailand Limited (2)
68/13 Moo 5 Ban Bueng-Klaeng Road, Map
Phai Subdistrict Ban Bueng District, Chon
Buri, 20170, Thailand (70%)
Tel.: (66) 38444908
Web Site: https://www.sonoco.yellowpages.co.th
Sales Range: $50-74.9 Million
Emp.: 150
Tubes & Cores Mfr
N.A.I.C.S.: 322219

Sonoco Canada Corporation (1)
33 Park Ave East, Brantford, N3T 5T5, ON,
Canada (100%)
Tel.: (519) 752-6591
Engineered Carriers Mfr & Sales
N.A.I.C.S.: 322211

Division (Domestic):

Sonoco Canada Corporation (2)
530 Rue des Erables, Cap de la Madeleine,
G8T 8N6, QC, Canada (100%)
Tel.: (819) 374-5222
Web Site: http://www.sonoco.com
Sales Range: $25-49.9 Million
Emp.: 70
Engineered Carriers Mfr
N.A.I.C.S.: 322130

Sonoco Canada Corporation (2)
674 Richmond Street, Chatham, N7M 5K4,
ON, Canada
Tel.: (519) 352-8201
Web Site: http://www.sonoco.com
Sales Range: $10-24.9 Million
Emp.: 40
Rigid Paper Containers
N.A.I.C.S.: 322130

Sonoco Canada Corporation (2)
877 Cliveden Ave, Delta, V3M 5R6, BC,
Canada
Tel.: (604) 526-7888
Web Site: http://www.sonoco.com
Sales Range: $10-24.9 Million
Emp.: 15
Engineered Carriers Mfr
N.A.I.C.S.: 322130

Sonoco Canada Corporation (2)
195 Deveault Street Rue Porte 201, Hull,
Gatineau, J8Z 1S7, QC, Canada (100%)
Tel.: (819) 595-8722
Web Site: http://www.sonoco.com
Sales Range: $1-9.9 Million
Emp.: 70
Engineered Carriers Mfr
N.A.I.C.S.: 322130

Sonoco Canada Corporation (2)
7420 Bramalea Road, Mississauga, L5S
1W9, ON, Canada (100%)
Tel.: (905) 673-7373
Web Site: http://www.sonoco.com
Sales Range: $10-24.9 Million
Emp.: 40
Engineered Carriers Mfr & Sales
N.A.I.C.S.: 322130

Sonoco Canada Corporation (2)
295 Superior Blvd Unit 2, Mississauga, L5T
2L6, ON, Canada
Tel.: (905) 564-4844
Web Site: http://www.sonoco.com
Sales Range: $10-24.9 Million
Emp.: 30
Consumer Products Mfr & Sales
N.A.I.C.S.: 322130

Sonoco Canada Corporation (2)
33 Park Avenue East, Brantford, N3T 5T5,
ON, Canada (100%)
Tel.: (519) 752-6591
Web Site: http://www.sonoco.com
Paperboard Mfr & Sales
N.A.I.C.S.: 322130

Sonoco Canada Corporation (2)
2350 Dorman Rd, Nanaimo, V9S 5G2, BC,
Canada (100%)
Tel.: (250) 756-0466
Web Site: http://www.sonoco.com
Sales Range: $10-24.9 Million
Emp.: 12
Engineered Carriers Mfr
N.A.I.C.S.: 333993

Sonoco Canada Corporation (2)

Sonoco Products Company—(Continued)

799 Bayside Dr, Saint John, E2R 1A3, NB, Canada
Tel.: (506) 648-9354
Web Site: http://www.sonoco.com
Sales Range: $10-24.9 Million
Emp.: 7
Engineered Carriers Mfr
N.A.I.C.S.: 333993

Sonoco Flexible Packaging (2)
1691 Matheson Blvd, Mississauga, L4W 1S1, ON, Canada (100%)
Tel.: (905) 624-1701
Web Site: http://www.sonoco.com
Sales Range: $50-74.9 Million
Emp.: 150
Flexible Packaging Products Mfr
N.A.I.C.S.: 333993

Sonoco Flexible Packaging Limited (2)
1664 Seel Ave, Winnipeg, R3T 4X5, MB, Canada
Tel.: (204) 284-6611
Web Site: http://www.sonoco.com
Flexible Packaging Mfr
N.A.I.C.S.: 322130

Sonoco Clear Pack (1)
11610 Copenhagen Ct, Franklin Park, IL 60131-1302
Tel.: (847) 957-6282
Web Site: http://www.sonoco.com
Sales Range: $50-74.9 Million
Emp.: 140
Thermoformed & Extruded Plastic Materials
N.A.I.C.S.: 326199

Sonoco Comercial S. de R.L. de C.V. (1)
Avenida Ignacio Zaragoza Numero 15 Ciudad Adolfo Lopez Mateos Centro, Municipio Atizapan de Zaragoza, 52900, Mexico, Mexico
Tel.: (52) 5520006477
Paperboard Container Mfr
N.A.I.C.S.: 322219

Sonoco Consumer Products (1)
4633 Dues Dr, Cincinnati, OH 45246-1008
Tel.: (513) 874-7655
Web Site: http://www.sonoco.com
Sales Range: $25-49.9 Million
Emp.: 61
Rigid Paper Containers Mfr & Sales
N.A.I.C.S.: 322219

Sonoco Consumer Products Dordrecht B.V. (1)
Bunsenstraat 38, 3316 GC, Dordrecht, Netherlands
Tel.: (31) 786177666
Industrial & Consumer Packaging Product Services
N.A.I.C.S.: 322130

Sonoco Consumer Products Europe GmbH (1)
1 Industriestr 26, 68766, Hockenheim, Germany
Tel.: (49) 62052030
Industrial & Consumer Packaging Product Services
N.A.I.C.S.: 322130

Sonoco Consumer Products Mechelen BVBA (1)
Egide Walschaertsstraat 7, 2800, Mechelen, Belgium
Tel.: (32) 15448910
Industrial & Consumer Packaging Product Services
N.A.I.C.S.: 322130

Sonoco Consumer Products Montanay SAS (1)
194 Allee de la Croix des Hormes, Montanay, 69250, Lyon, 69250, France
Tel.: (33) 472083232
Industrial & Consumer Packaging Product Services
N.A.I.C.S.: 322130

Sonoco Contract Services S. de R.L. de C.V. (1)
Carr Fed Irapuato Abasolo Km 10 6 Guanajuato Col La Soled, Irapuato, 36827, Guanajuato, Mexico

Tel.: (52) 4621660300
Packaging Products Mfr & Supplier
N.A.I.C.S.: 423840

Sonoco Display and Packaging, LLC (1)
555 Aureole St, Winston Salem, NC 27107
Tel.: (336) 784-0445
Packaging Products Mfr
N.A.I.C.S.: 326112
Philippe Erhart (Div VP & Gen Mgr)

Subsidiary (Domestic):

Sebro Plastics, Inc. (2)
29200 Wall St, Wixom, MI 48393-3526 (100%)
Tel.: (248) 348-4121
Sales Range: $75-99.9 Million
Emp.: 51
Molded Plastics Mfr
N.A.I.C.S.: 326199
Jack Sanders (Pres)

Subsidiary (Domestic):

Convex Mold, Inc. (3)
35360 Beattie Dr, Sterling Heights, MI 48312-2610 (100%)
Tel.: (586) 978-0808
Web Site: http://www.sonoco.com
Sales Range: $10-24.9 Million
Emp.: 7
Molded Plastics Mfr
N.A.I.C.S.: 333514

Sonoco Do Brasil Participacoes Ltda (1)
Av Brasil 471, Jardim America, 01431-000, Brazil
Tel.: (55) 35438137
Paperboard Container Mfr
N.A.I.C.S.: 322219

Sonoco Flexible Packaging (1)
5701 Superior Dr, Morristown, TN 37814-1075
Tel.: (423) 585-5850
Web Site: http://www.sonoco.com
Sales Range: $50-74.9 Million
Emp.: 140
Flexible Packaging Mfr
N.A.I.C.S.: 322130

Sonoco Flexible Packaging Canada Corporation (1)
33 Park Ave E, Brantford, N3S 7R9, ON, Canada
Tel.: (843) 383-7000
Plastics Product Mfr
N.A.I.C.S.: 326199

Sonoco For Plas do Brazil Ltda (1)
Av Otto Barreto 1585 Dist Ind II, Araras, 13602-060, Brazil (51%)
Tel.: (55) 1935432500
Web Site:
https://www.forplasembalagens.com.br
Emp.: 208
Plastic Packaging Products Mfr
N.A.I.C.S.: 326112
Naim Bayeh (CEO)

Sonoco Hayes, Inc. (1)
1200 Independence Dr, Neenah, WI 54956-1648 (100%)
Tel.: (920) 725-7056
Web Site: http://www.sonoco.com
Sales Range: $75-99.9 Million
Emp.: 250
Engineered Carriers Mfr
N.A.I.C.S.: 322219

Sonoco Hickory, Inc. (1)
1246 Main Ave SE, Hickory, NC 28602 (100%)
Tel.: (828) 328-2466
Web Site: http://www.sonoco.com
Industrial & Consumer Packaging Products & Services
N.A.I.C.S.: 326199

Sonoco Hutchinson, LLC (1)
100 N Halstead St, Hutchinson, KS 67501-1800
Tel.: (620) 662-2331
Sales Range: $25-49.9 Million
Emp.: 120
Paperboard Mills
N.A.I.C.S.: 322130

Sonoco Luxembourg S.a.r.l. (1)
7b rue de Bettlange, Harlange, 9657, Derenbach, Luxembourg (100%)
Tel.: (352) 26953047
Holding Company
N.A.I.C.S.: 551112

Subsidiary (Non-US):

Sonoco Alcore AB (2)
Lindovagen 77, 600 06, Norrkoping, 600 06, Sweden (100%)
Tel.: (46) 11282200
Core Boards Mfr
N.A.I.C.S.: 332999

Sonoco Alcore NV (2)
Park Hill Mommaertslaan 18A, 1831, Diegem, Belgium (100%)
Tel.: (32) 27110900
Web Site: http://www.sonocoalcore.com
Sales Range: $10-24.9 Million
Tubes & Paper Products Mfr
N.A.I.C.S.: 322219

Subsidiary (Non-US):

Conitex-Sonoco (3)
Compositub/ Texpack Holding Crta C-16 Km 70, Colonia Soldevila Balsareny, 08660, Barcelona, Spain
Tel.: (34) 938391919
Web Site: http://www.sonoco.com
Industrial Products Mfr
N.A.I.C.S.: 322130

Subsidiary (Domestic):

Sonoco Consumer Products N.V. (3)
Neringstraat 17, 1840, Londerzeel, Belgium (100%)
Tel.: (32) 52310049
Web Site: http://www.sonoco.com
Sales Range: $10-24.9 Million
Paperboard & Rigid Paper Containers Mfr
N.A.I.C.S.: 322219

Subsidiary (Non-US):

Sonoco IPD France S.A. (3)
5 rue de la Gare, 67590, Schweighouse, France (100%)
Tel.: (33) 389397379
Web Site: http://www.sonoco.com
Industrial Products Mfr
N.A.I.C.S.: 322130

Sonoco Pina S.A. (3)
Poligono Industrial Pina de Ebro Calle B, Pina de Ebro, 50570, Zaragoza, Spain (100%)
Tel.: (34) 976169330
Web Site: http://www.sonoco.com
Sales Range: $10-24.9 Million
Emp.: 49
Engineered Carriers, Film Cores & Paper Mill Cores
N.A.I.C.S.: 322130

ZAO Sonoco Alcore (3)
Bogatirski pr 18/3, 197348, Saint Petersburg, Russia (100%)
Tel.: (7) 8123298833
Web Site: http://www.sonocoalcore.com
Sales Range: $10-24.9 Million
Emp.: 40
Tube & Paper Mill Cores Mfr
N.A.I.C.S.: 322211
Mariya Kyaume (Mng Dir)

Subsidiary (Non-US):

Sonoco Ambalaj Sanayi Ve Ticaret A.S. (2)
Fethiye osb Mah Gri Cad No 5, Nilufer, 16065, Bursa, Turkiye (100%)
Tel.: (90) 2242700800
Web Site: http://www.sonoco.com
Sales Range: $25-49.9 Million
Engineered Carriers & Paperboard Products Mfr
N.A.I.C.S.: 322219

Sonoco Deutschland Holdings GmbH (2)
(100%)
Tel.: (49) 592188310
Web Site: http://www.sonoco.com
Holding Company
N.A.I.C.S.: 551112

Subsidiary (Non-US):

Sonoco Alcore GmbH (3)
Tel.: (49) 934362660
Web Site: http://www.sonoco.com
Sales Range: $25-49.9 Million
Emp.: 25
Engineered Tubes & Cores Mfr
N.A.I.C.S.: 331210

Sonoco Caprex AG (3)
Tel.: (41) 417572170
Web Site: http://www.sonocoalcore.ch
Sales Range: $300-349.9 Million
Emp.: 13
Tubes, Cores & Packaging Products Mfr
N.A.I.C.S.: 322219

Sonoco Deutschland GmbH (3)
(100%)
Tel.: (49) 24217040
Web Site: http://www.sonoco.com
Packaging Mfr & Supply Chain Services
N.A.I.C.S.: 561910

Sonoco OPV Huelsen GmbH (3)
(100%)
Tel.: (49) 7807990
Web Site: http://www.sonoco.com
Sales Range: $25-49.9 Million
Emp.: 100
Engineered Carriers & Construction Cores Mfr
N.A.I.C.S.: 322299

Sonoco Plastics Germany GmbH (3)
(100%)
Tel.: (49) 224148000
Web Site: http://www.sonocoeurope.com
Sales Range: $25-49.9 Million
Emp.: 150
Molded & Extruded Plastics Mfr
N.A.I.C.S.: 326199

Sonoco Plastics Germany GmbH (3)
(100%)
Tel.: (49) 224148000
Web Site: http://www.sonoco.com
Molded & Extruded Plastic Products Mfr
N.A.I.C.S.: 326199

Subsidiary (Non-US):

Sonoco Holdings (UK) Ltd. (2)
Station Road, Rochdale, OL16 4HG, Lancashire, United Kingdom (100%)
Tel.: (44) 1706641661
Web Site: http://www.sonoco.com
Holding Company
N.A.I.C.S.: 551112

Subsidiary (Domestic):

Sonoco Board Mills Limited (3)
Holywell Green Stainland, Halifax, HX4 9PY, West Yorkshire, United Kingdom
Tel.: (44) 1422377791
Web Site: http://www.sonoco.com
Soybean Oil Mills
N.A.I.C.S.: 311224

Sonoco Consumer Products Ltd. (3)
Stokes St, Clayton, M11 4QX, United Kingdom (100%)
Tel.: (44) 1612307000
Web Site: http://www.sonoco.com
Sales Range: $25-49.9 Million
Emp.: 120
Rigid Paper Containers Mfr
N.A.I.C.S.: 322130

Sonoco Lurgan (3)
No 4 Factory Wenlock Road Portadown Road, Lurgan, BT66 8QW, Craigavon, United Kingdom (100%)
Tel.: (44) 2838323501
Web Site: http://www.sonoco.com
Sales Range: $25-49.9 Million
Emp.: 20
Film, Paper, Textile Cores & Engineered Carriers Mfr
N.A.I.C.S.: 333993

Sonoco Milnrow (3)
Station Road, Milnrow, Rochdale, OL16 4HG, Lancashire, United Kingdom (100%)
Tel.: (44) 1706641661
Web Site: http://www.sonoco.com
Sales Range: $25-49.9 Million
Emp.: 60
Cardboard Mfr

N.A.I.C.S.: 322211

Subsidiary (Domestic):

Sonoco Products Co. UK Unlimited **(4)**
Station Rd, Rochdale, OL16 4HQ, Lancashire, United Kingdom **(100%)**
Tel.: (44) 1706641661
Web Site: http://www.sonoco.com
Sales Range: $25-49.9 Million
Cardboard Mfr
N.A.I.C.S.: 322211

Subsidiary (Domestic):

Sonoco Ltd. **(5)**
Station Rd, Milnrow, Rochdale, BT60 8QW, Lancashire, United Kingdom **(100%)**
Tel.: (44) 1706641661
Web Site: http://www.sonoco.com
Sales Range: $25-49.9 Million
Emp.: 50
Cardboard Mfr
N.A.I.C.S.: 322211

Subsidiary (Domestic):

Sonoco Recycling **(3)**
Stainland Board Mill Holywell Green, Halifax, HX4 9PY, West Yorkshire, United Kingdom **(100%)**
Tel.: (44) 8000730062
Web Site: https://sonocorecycling.co.uk
Sales Range: $10-24.9 Million
Emp.: 20
Paperboard Mills
N.A.I.C.S.: 322130

Subsidiary (Non-US):

Sonoco Netherlands B.V. **(2)**
PO Box 19 Vierde Broekdijk 2, 7120 AA, Aalten, Netherlands **(100%)**
Tel.: (31) 543495495
Web Site: http://www.sonoco.com
Holding Company
N.A.I.C.S.: 551112

Sonoco Norge A/S **(2)**
Parkveien 36, Rorestrand, 3186, Horten, Norway **(100%)**
Tel.: (47) 33020500
Web Site: http://www.sonoco-alcore.net
Sales Range: $1-9.9 Million
Emp.: 21
Engineered Carriers, Film Cores, Papermill Cores & Construction Cores
N.A.I.C.S.: 322130

Sonoco Metal Packaging, LLC **(1)**
8001 Arista Pl Ste 200, Broomfield, CO 80021
Tel.: (720) 899-4900
Metal Packaging Material Mfr & Distr
N.A.I.C.S.: 332431

Sonoco Packaging Services **(1)**
18 Independence Dr, Devens, MA 01432-5294
Tel.: (978) 784-3000
Web Site: http://www.sonoco.com
Sales Range: $300-349.9 Million
Packaging Services
N.A.I.C.S.: 322220

Sonoco Paper **(1)**
1 N 2nd St, Hartsville, SC 29550-3300 **(100%)**
Tel.: (843) 383-7000
Web Site: http://www.sonoco.com
Sales Range: $25-49.9 Million
Emp.: 70
Paperboard Mfr
N.A.I.C.S.: 322130

Sonoco Paper Mill & IPD Hellas Sa **(1)**
10 5 Km Kilkis-Doirani National Road, PO Box 85, Stravohori, 61100, Kilkis, 61100, Greece
Tel.: (30) 2341051558
Web Site: http://www.sonoco.com
Emp.: 50
Packaging Paper Products Mfr
N.A.I.C.S.: 322220

Sonoco Paperboard Specialties **(1)**
3150 Clinton Ct, Norcross, GA 30071
Tel.: (770) 476-9088
Web Site: http://www.sonoco.com

Sales Range: $10-24.9 Million
Emp.: 35
Paper Mills
N.A.I.C.S.: 322130

Sonoco Paperboard Specialties **(1)**
10 Quinter St, Pottstown, PA 19464 **(100%)**
Tel.: (610) 323-9221
Web Site: http://www.sonoco.com
Sales Range: $10-24.9 Million
Emp.: 10
Paperboard & Paper Products Mfr
N.A.I.C.S.: 322211
Jeff Burgner *(Gen Mgr)*
Gus Copeletti *(Controller-Fin Segment)*

Sonoco Plastics B.V. **(1)**
Veilingweg 24, PO Box 143, 2651 BE, Berkel en Rodenrijs, Netherlands **(100%)**
Tel.: (31) 104554344
Web Site: http://www.sonoco-plastics.nl
Sales Range: $10-24.9 Million
Emp.: 80
Molded Plastics Mfr
N.A.I.C.S.: 326199
Michael Muller *(Mng Dir)*

Sonoco Products Company **(1)**
100 N Halstead St, Hutchinson, KS 67541 **(100%)**
Tel.: (620) 662-2331
Web Site: http://www.sonoco.com
Sales Range: $25-49.9 Million
Emp.: 114
Paperboard Mfr
N.A.I.C.S.: 322130

Sonoco Products Company **(1)**
3114 Kendall Dr, Florence, AL 35630-6378
Tel.: (256) 767-2429
Web Site: http://www.sonoco.com
Sales Range: $25-49.9 Million
Emp.: 39
Fiber Cores Mfr
N.A.I.C.S.: 322130

Sonoco Products Company **(1)**
309 Kinston Hwy, Opp, AL 36467 **(100%)**
Tel.: (334) 493-3567
Web Site: http://www.sonoco.com
Sales Range: $25-49.9 Million
Emp.: 43
Engineered Carriers Mfr
N.A.I.C.S.: 322130

Sonoco Products Company **(1)**
166 N Baldwin Park Blvd Industrial Carriers Division, City of Industry, CA 91746
Tel.: (626) 369-6927
Web Site: http://www.sonoco.com
Sales Range: $25-49.9 Million
Emp.: 120
Engineered Carriers & Paperboard Mfr
N.A.I.C.S.: 322130

Sonoco Products Company **(1)**
12851 Leyva St, Norwalk, CA 90650
Tel.: (562) 921-0881
Web Site: http://www.sonoco.com
Sales Range: $25-49.9 Million
Emp.: 50
Rigid Paper Containers Mfr
N.A.I.C.S.: 322130

Sonoco Products Company **(1)**
290 Mtn Ave, Berthoud, CO 80521 **(100%)**
Tel.: (970) 532-3737
Web Site: http://www.sonoco.com
Sales Range: $10-24.9 Million
Emp.: 25
Engineered Carriers Mfr
N.A.I.C.S.: 322130

Sonoco Products Company **(1)**
2580 Abutment Rd, Dalton, GA 30721-4900
Tel.: (706) 277-3033
Web Site: http://www.sonoco.com
Sales Range: $10-24.9 Million
Emp.: 20
Engineered Carriers Mfr
N.A.I.C.S.: 322130

Sonoco Products Company **(1)**
4858 Old Dixie Rd, Forest Park, GA 30297
Tel.: (404) 361-4800
Web Site: http://www.sonoco.com
Sales Range: $25-49.9 Million
Emp.: 50
Rigid Paper Containers Mfr
N.A.I.C.S.: 322219

Sonoco Products Company **(1)**
3150 Clinton Ct, Norcross, GA 30071
Tel.: (770) 476-9088
Web Site: http://www.sonoco.com
Sales Range: $25-49.9 Million
Emp.: 60
Coasters & Glass Covers Mfr
N.A.I.C.S.: 322220

Sonoco Products Company **(1)**
0123 1st St, Lewiston, ID 83501
Tel.: (208) 746-6317
Web Site: http://www.sonoco.com
Sales Range: $1-9.9 Million
Emp.: 11
Engineered Carriers Mfr
N.A.I.C.S.: 322219

Sonoco Products Company **(1)**
1 N 2nd St, Hartsville, SC 29550-3300 **(100%)**
Tel.: (843) 383-7000
Web Site: http://www.sonoco.com
Sales Range: $10-24.9 Million
Emp.: 44
Recycled Paper & Paperboard Mfr
N.A.I.C.S.: 322130

Sonoco Products Company **(1)**
1500 Powis Rd, West Chicago, IL 60185 **(100%)**
Tel.: (630) 231-8100
Web Site: http://www.sonoco.com
Sales Range: $10-24.9 Million
Rigid Paper Containers Mfr & Sales
N.A.I.C.S.: 322219

Sonoco Products Company **(1)**
1535 State Hwy 19 S, Akron, IN 46910 **(100%)**
Tel.: (574) 598-2731
Web Site: http://www.sonoco.com
Sales Range: $25-49.9 Million
Emp.: 60
Adhesive Mfr
N.A.I.C.S.: 322219

Sonoco Products Company **(1)**
912 E 24th St, Marion, IN 46953-3321 **(100%)**
Tel.: (765) 664-0135
Web Site: http://www.sonoco.com
Sales Range: $10-24.9 Million
Emp.: 50
Designed Interior Packaging & Protective Packaging Mfr
N.A.I.C.S.: 322220

Sonoco Products Company **(1)**
705 Pillsbury Ln 275, New Albany, IN 47150
Tel.: (812) 945-0224
Web Site: http://www.sonoco.com
Sales Range: $25-49.9 Million
Emp.: 100
Rigid Paper Containers Mfr
N.A.I.C.S.: 322219

Sonoco Products Company **(1)**
2105 Industrial Park Rd, Boone, IA 50036
Tel.: (515) 432-8241
Web Site: http://www.sonoco.com
Sales Range: $300-349.9 Million
Industrial Products Mfr
N.A.I.C.S.: 322219

Sonoco Products Company **(1)**
3100 Ohio St, Henderson, KY 42420
Tel.: (270) 827-5637
Web Site: http://www.sonoco.com
Sales Range: $25-49.9 Million
Emp.: 120
Metal Ends & Closures Mfr
N.A.I.C.S.: 322130

Sonoco Products Company **(1)**
3996 US Hwy 60 E, Morganfield, KY 42437
Tel.: (270) 389-2501
Web Site: http://www.sonoco.com
Sales Range: $10-24.9 Million
Emp.: 40
Industrial Products Mfr
N.A.I.C.S.: 322219

Sonoco Products Company **(1)**
1330 Enterprise Dr, Winchester, KY 40391-9668
Tel.: (859) 745-0400
Web Site: http://www.sonoco.com
Sales Range: $25-49.9 Million
Emp.: 80
Plastic Caulk Cartridges Mfr

N.A.I.C.S.: 322219

Sonoco Products Company **(1)**
2920 Rosenwald Rd, Baton Rouge, LA 70807
Tel.: (225) 355-5673
Web Site: http://www.sonoco.com
Sales Range: $10-24.9 Million
Emp.: 14
Industrial Products Mfr
N.A.I.C.S.: 322219

Sonoco Products Company **(1)**
259 Industrial Park Rd, Pittsfield, ME 04967-0486
Tel.: (207) 487-3206
Web Site: http://www.sonoco.com
Sales Range: $10-24.9 Million
Emp.: 40
Industrial Products Mfr
N.A.I.C.S.: 322130

Sonoco Products Company **(1)**
111 Mosher St, Holyoke, MA 01040
Tel.: (413) 493-1500
Web Site: http://www.sonoco.com
Sales Range: $10-24.9 Million
Emp.: 40
Industrial Products Mfr
N.A.I.C.S.: 322130

Sonoco Products Company **(1)**
200 S Water St, Holyoke, MA 01040 **(100%)**
Tel.: (413) 536-4546
Web Site: http://www.sonoco.com
Sales Range: $25-49.9 Million
Emp.: 63
Paperboard & Recycled Paper Mfr
N.A.I.C.S.: 322130

Sonoco Products Company **(1)**
13300 Interstate Dr, Maryland Heights, MO 63043
Tel.: (314) 344-2200
Web Site: http://www.sonoco.com
Sales Range: $25-49.9 Million
Emp.: 100
Rigid Paper Containers Mfr & Sales
N.A.I.C.S.: 322130

Sonoco Products Company **(1)**
5 Stults Rd, Dayton, NJ 08810 **(100%)**
Tel.: (609) 655-0300
Web Site: http://www.sonoco.com
Sales Range: $25-49.9 Million
Emp.: 50
Rigid Paper Containers Mfr
N.A.I.C.S.: 322219

Sonoco Products Company **(1)**
212 Cook Rd, Elon, NC 27244
Tel.: (336) 449-7731
Web Site: http://www.sonoco.com
Sales Range: $25-49.9 Million
Emp.: 120
Industrial Products Mfr
N.A.I.C.S.: 322219

Sonoco Products Company **(1)**
1214 Highland Ave NE, Hickory, NC 28601 **(100%)**
Tel.: (828) 322-8844
Web Site: http://www.sonoco.com
Sales Range: $10-24.9 Million
Emp.: 20
Industrial Products Mfr
N.A.I.C.S.: 322219

Sonoco Products Company **(1)**
1779 Morratock Rd, Plymouth, NC 27962-9700
Tel.: (252) 793-0351
Web Site: http://www.sonoco.com
Sales Range: $300-349.9 Million
Industrial Products Mfr
N.A.I.C.S.: 322220

Sonoco Products Company **(1)**
761 Space Dr, Beavercreek, OH 45434
Tel.: (937) 429-0040
Web Site: http://www.sonoco.com
Sales Range: $10-24.9 Million
Emp.: 75
Caulk Cartridges Mfr
N.A.I.C.S.: 322219

Sonoco Products Company **(1)**
1 N 2nd St, Hartsville, SC 29550-3300
Tel.: (740) 653-6442
Web Site: http://www.sonoco.com

Sonoco Products Company—(Continued)
Sales Range: $10-24.9 Million
Emp.: 56
Recycled Paper & Paperboard Mfr
N.A.I.C.S.: 322130

Sonoco Products Company (1)
60 Heritage Dr, Tiffin, OH 44883
Tel.: (419) 448-4428
Web Site: http://www.sonoco.com
Sales Range: $1-4.9 Billion
Emp.: 100
Designed Interior & Protective Packaging
Mfr
N.A.I.C.S.: 322219

Sonoco Products Company (1)
310 Pine St, Hanover, PA 17331
Tel.: (717) 637-2121
Web Site: http://www.sonoco.com
Plastic Caulk Cartridges Mfr
N.A.I.C.S.: 326199

Sonoco Products Company (1)
30 W Meadow Ave, Robesonia, PA 19551
Tel.: (610) 693-5804
Web Site: http://www.sonoco.com
Sales Range: $25-49.9 Million
Emp.: 95
Industrial Products Mfr
N.A.I.C.S.: 322219

Sonoco Products Company (1)
1132 Idlewilde Blvd, Columbia, SC 29201
Tel.: (803) 779-0500
Web Site: http://www.sonoco.com
Sales Range: $150-199.9 Million
Industrial Products Mfr
N.A.I.C.S.: 441330

Sonoco Products Company (1)
1900 Daisy St, Chattanooga, TN 37406
Tel.: (423) 698-6985
Web Site: http://www.sonoco.com
Sales Range: $10-24.9 Million
Emp.: 30
Rigid Paper Containers Mfr
N.A.I.C.S.: 322219

Sonoco Products Company (1)
2629 Stephenson Dr, Murfreesboro, TN
37127 (100%)
Tel.: (615) 904-7200
Web Site: http://www.sunoco.com
Sales Range: $10-24.9 Million
Emp.: 40
Rigid Paper Containers Mfr
N.A.I.C.S.: 322130

Sonoco Products Company (1)
510 Brick Church Park Dr, Nashville, TN
37207
Tel.: (615) 262-3837
Web Site: http://www.sonoco.com
Sales Range: $25-49.9 Million
Emp.: 60
Designed Interior Packaging & Protective
Packaging Products Mfr
N.A.I.C.S.: 322130

Sonoco Products Company (1)
766 Industrial Rd, Newport, TN
37821 (100%)
Tel.: (423) 623-8611
Web Site: http://www.sonoco.com
Sales Range: $75-99.9 Million
Emp.: 250
Paper & Industrial Products Mfr
N.A.I.C.S.: 322130

Sonoco Products Company (1)
2000 Exchange Dr, Arlington, TX 76011-
7822
Tel.: (817) 461-5616
Web Site: http://www.sonoco.com
Sales Range: $25-49.9 Million
Emp.: 22
Industrial Products Mfr
N.A.I.C.S.: 322219

Sonoco Products Company (1)
1925 Country Club Dr, Carrollton, TX
75006-5851
Tel.: (972) 416-2595
Web Site: http://www.sonoco.com
Sales Range: $10-24.9 Million
Emp.: 60
Rigid Paper Containers Mfr & Sales
N.A.I.C.S.: 322219

Sonoco Products Company (1)
9312 Winterberry Ave, Covington, VA 24426
Tel.: (540) 862-4134
Web Site: http://www.sonoco.com
Sales Range: $10-24.9 Million
Emp.: 29
Industrial Products
N.A.I.C.S.: 322219

Sonoco Products Company (1)
1850 Commerce Rd, Richmond, VA
23224 (100%)
Tel.: (804) 233-5411
Web Site: http://www.sonoco.com
Sales Range: $25-49.9 Million
Emp.: 85
Recycled Paperboard & Paper Mfr
N.A.I.C.S.: 322130

Sonoco Products Company (1)
326 Moore Ave, Suffolk, VA 23434
Tel.: (757) 539-8349
Web Site: http://www.sonoco.com
Sales Range: $10-24.9 Million
Emp.: 35
Rigid Paper Containers Mfr
N.A.I.C.S.: 322219

Sonoco Products Company (1)
1802 Steele Ave, Sumner, WA
98390 (100%)
Tel.: (253) 863-6366
Web Site: http://www.sonoco.com
Sales Range: $10-24.9 Million
Emp.: 60
Recycled Paperboard & Paper Mfr
N.A.I.C.S.: 322130

Sonoco Products Company (1)
31 Industrial Park Rd, Wapato, WA 98951
Tel.: (509) 877-6105
Web Site: http://www.sonoco.com
Sales Range: $300-349.9 Million
Rigid Paper Containers Mfr
N.A.I.C.S.: 322219

Sonoco Products Company (1)
1620 Downriver Dr, Woodland, WA
98674 (100%)
Tel.: (360) 225-1500
Web Site: http://www.sonoco.com
Sales Range: $25-49.9 Million
Emp.: 40
Industrial Products Mfr
N.A.I.C.S.: 322130

Sonoco Products Company (1)
11269 Waxler Rd, Keyser, WV
26726 (100%)
Tel.: (304) 726-7009
Web Site: http://www.sonoco.com
Sales Range: $10-24.9 Million
Emp.: 15
Mfr of Engineered Carriers & other Indus-
trial Products
N.A.I.C.S.: 322130

Sonoco Products Company (1)
455 Science Dr Ste 150, Madison, WI
53711
Tel.: (608) 231-3060
Web Site: http://www.sonoco.com
Sales Range: $300-349.9 Million
Emp.: 4
Research & Development Services
N.A.I.C.S.: 322220

Sonoco Products Company (1)
2225-B Bohm Dr, Little Chute, WI 54140
Tel.: (920) 757-4747
Web Site: http://www.sonoco.com
Sales Range: $10-24.9 Million
Emp.: 25
Engineered Carriers Mfr
N.A.I.C.S.: 322219

Sonoco Products Company (1)
W6385 Quality Dr, Greenville, WI
54942 (100%)
Tel.: (920) 757-7227
Web Site: http://www.sonoco.com
Sales Range: $10-24.9 Million
Emp.: 60
Rigid Paper Containers Mfr
N.A.I.C.S.: 322219

**Sonoco Products Company - Baker
Division** (1)
1901 John D Long Dr, Hartselle, AL 35640
Tel.: (256) 773-6581

Web Site: http://www.sonoco.com
Sales Range: $10-24.9 Million
Emp.: 17
Industrial, Consumer & Innovative Packag-
ing Solutions
N.A.I.C.S.: 561910

Subsidiary (Domestic):

Sonoco Baker (2)
109 Stewart Pkwy, Greensboro, GA 30642
Tel.: (706) 453-7552
Web Site: http://www.sonoco.com
Poly-Fiber Reels Mfr
N.A.I.C.S.: 326199

Sonoco Baker (2)
4608 Helton Rd, Granite Falls, NC
28630 (100%)
Tel.: (828) 396-3196
Web Site: http://www.sonoco.com
Sales Range: $10-24.9 Million
Emp.: 16
Steel & Wooden Reels for Wire & Cable
Services
N.A.I.C.S.: 322130

Sonoco Baker (2)
1609 S US Hwy 59, Jefferson, TX 75657
Tel.: (903) 665-3966
Web Site: http://www.sonoco.com
Reels for Wire & Cable Mfr
N.A.I.C.S.: 812990

**Sonoco Products Company - I.P.D.
Division** (1)
59 N Main St, Munroe Falls, OH 44262
Tel.: (330) 688-7421
Web Site: http://www.sonoco.com
Sales Range: $25-49.9 Million
Emp.: 60
Engineered Carriers & Paperboard Mfr
N.A.I.C.S.: 322130

**Sonoco Products Company -
Jackson** (1)
1682 Dr F E Wright Dr, Jackson, TN 38301
Tel.: (731) 988-5858
Web Site: http://www.sonoco.com
Rigid Paper Containers Mfr
N.A.I.C.S.: 322219

**Sonoco Products Company -
Orlando** (1)
1854 Central Florida Pkwy, Orlando, FL
32837
Tel.: (407) 851-5800
Web Site: http://www.sonoco.com
Rigid Paper Containers, Metal Ends & Clo-
sures Mfr
N.A.I.C.S.: 322219

Sonoco Recycling, Inc. (1)
1 N 2nd St, Hartsville, SC 29550 (100%)
Tel.: (843) 383-7000
Web Site: http://www.sonoco.com
Sales Range: $25-49.9 Million
Emp.: 2,500
Recycled Paper & Paperboard Mfr
N.A.I.C.S.: 425120

Sonoco Rigid Plastics (1)
833 S 60th Ave, Wausau, WI 54401
Tel.: (715) 845-7311
Web Site: http://www.sonoco.com
Sales Range: $300-349.9 Million
Emp.: 16
Rigid Paper Containers Mfr
N.A.I.C.S.: 322219

Sonoco Venezolana C.A. (1)
Calle 1 Galpon 46-47, Zona Industrial San
Vicente II, Maracay, Estado Aragua,
Venezuela (51%)
Tel.: (58) 2435516547
Web Site: http://www.sonoco.com
Sales Range: $10-24.9 Million
Emp.: 66
Paper Products, Tubes, Cores, Cones &
Composite Cans Mfr
N.A.I.C.S.: 322211

Sonoco at Whirlpool (1)
303 Upton Dr Ste MD-0216, Saint Joseph,
MI 49085
Tel.: (269) 923-6917
Web Site: http://www.sonoco.com
Sales Range: $50-74.9 Million
Interior & Protective Packaging Mfr
N.A.I.C.S.: 541330

Sonoco de Colombia Ltda. (1)
Carrera 7 No 34 - 120, Cali, Valle,
Colombia (100%)
Tel.: (57) 26818600
Web Site: http://www.sonoco.com
Sales Range: $75-99.9 Million
Emp.: 250
Mfr of Paperboard, Cones & Tubes
N.A.I.C.S.: 322211

Sonoco de Mexico, S.A. de C.V. (1)
Ignacio Zaragoza No 15, Atizapan, 52900,
Mexico, DF, Mexico (100%)
Tel.: (52) 5558255648
Web Site: http://www.sonoco.com
Sales Range: $50-74.9 Million
Emp.: 160
Paperboard Mfr
N.A.I.C.S.: 322211

Sonoco de Mexico, S.A. de C.V. (1)
Omicron Y Cto Humberto Lobo 9401
Complejo Industrial Mitras, 66000, Villa de
Garcia, 66000, NL, Mexico (100%)
Tel.: (52) 8188654050
Web Site: http://www.sonoco.com.mx
Sales Range: $25-49.9 Million
Emp.: 100
Engineered Carriers Mfr
N.A.I.C.S.: 322130

Sonoco de Mexico, S.A. de C.V. (1)
Hidalgo 175, 55540, Santa Clara, 55540,
Mexico (100%)
Tel.: (52) 5591710101
Web Site: http://www.sonoco.com
Sales Range: $100-124.9 Million
Emp.: 300
Paperboard & Related Products Mfr
N.A.I.C.S.: 322130
Jose Billeanasana (Pres)

Sonoco do Brazil Ltda. (1)
Rua Joao Sierra 246 Distrito Industrial II,
Sao Paulo, 04029-200, Brazil (100%)
Tel.: (55) 1933518100
Web Site: http://www.sonoco.com
Sales Range: $50-74.9 Million
Emp.: 190
Engineered Carriers Mfr
N.A.I.C.S.: 322130

Sonoco do Brazil Ltda. (1)
Rua Noitibo 157 - Villa Yara, Londrina,
Brazil (100%)
Tel.: (55) 4333777700
Web Site: http://www.sonoco.com
Sales Range: $400-449.9 Million
Emp.: 140
Engineered Carriers & Paperboard Mfr
N.A.I.C.S.: 322130

Sonoco do Chile S.A. (1)
Alvarez de Toledo 851, Santiago,
Chile (70%)
Tel.: (56) 25558837
Web Site: http://www.sonoco.com
Engineered Carriers & Rigid Paper Contain-
ers Mfr
N.A.I.C.S.: 322219

Sonoco of Puerto Rico, Inc. (1)
Rd 900 Int 182 KM 0 6, Yabucoa, PR
00767
Tel.: (787) 893-2889
Web Site: http://www.sonoco.com
Sales Range: $10-24.9 Million
Emp.: 18
Rigid Paper Containers Mfr
N.A.I.C.S.: 322219

Sonoco, Inc. (1)
2755 Harbor Ave, Memphis, TN
38113 (100%)
Tel.: (901) 774-6321
Web Site: http://www.sonoco.com
Sales Range: $75-99.9 Million
Emp.: 200
Metal Ends & Closures Mfr
N.A.I.C.S.: 332119

Sonoco, S.A. de C.V. (1)
Avenida 3a Norte 901, Ciudad Delicias,
33000, Chihuahua, Mexico
Tel.: (52) 6394727998
Rigid Papers & Composite Containers Mfr
N.A.I.C.S.: 322130

Sonoco-Alcore Ou (1)
Rannamoisa tee 14, Tabasalu, Harju,

76901, Estonia
Tel.: (372) 6051866
Emp.: 50
Packaging Paper Products Mfr
N.A.I.C.S.: 322220

Sonoco-Alcore Oy   (1)
Karhulantie 160, 48720, Kotka, Finland
Tel.: (358) 102342300
Industrial & Consumer Packaging Product
Services
N.A.I.C.S.: 322130
Riikka Vierula (Controller)

Sonoco-Alcore Sp. Z.O.O.   (1)
Feliksow 46A, 96-503, Sochaczew, Mazow-
ieckie, Poland
Tel.: (48) 468642040
Industrial & Consumer Packaging Product
Services
N.A.I.C.S.: 322130

Sonoco-CorrFlex   (1)
555 Aureole St, Winston Salem, NC 27107-
3201
Tel.: (336) 784-0445
Sales Range: $75-99.9 Million
Emp.: 150
Point-of-Sale Displays Mfr
N.A.I.C.S.: 326150

Branch (Domestic):

Sonoco-CorrFlex   (2)
701 Rickert St, Statesville, NC 28677-6766
Tel.: (704) 872-7777
Sales Range: $50-74.9 Million
Emp.: 100
Point of Purchase Displays Mfr
N.A.I.C.S.: 326150

ThermoSafe Brands Europe Ltd.   (1)
Quartertown Ind Estate, Mallow, P51
HWV8, Cork, Ireland
Tel.: (353) 2255112
Web Site: http://www.thermosafe.com
Sales Range: $25-49.9 Million
Emp.: 25
Temperature Controlled Packaging Product
Mfr
N.A.I.C.S.: 326150

Thermoform Engineered Quality
LLC   (1)
11320 E Main St, Huntley, IL 60142
Tel.: (847) 669-5291
Web Site: http://www.teqnow.com
Thermoformed Plastics Mfr
N.A.I.C.S.: 325211
Randall Loga (Pres)
Todd McDonald (Dir-Sls & Mktg)
Paul Sepe (VP-Fin)
Dan Williams (Mgr-Engrg)
Dale Keilman (Mgr-Technical Svc)
Tammy Brimie (Mgr-Customer Satisfaction)

Trident Graphics Canada
Corporation   (1)
4085 Sladeview Crescent Unit 5&6, Missis-
sauga, L5L 5X3, ON, Canada
Tel.: (905) 828-4647
Web Site: http://www.sonoco-trident.com
Emp.: 10
Packaging Paper Products Mfr
N.A.I.C.S.: 322220

Trident Graphics NA LLC   (1)
12000 Vance Davis Dr, Charlotte, NC
28269-7696
Tel.: (704) 875-2685
Web Site: http://www.sonoco-trident.com
Emp.: 50
Gravure Rollers Mfr
N.A.I.C.S.: 333248

Tubetex NV   (1)
Jolainstraat 45A East Flanders, Sint-Denijs,
8554, Zwevegem, Belgium
Tel.: (32) 56461131
Web Site: http://www.sonoco.com
Emp.: 14
Packaging Paper Products Mfr
N.A.I.C.S.: 322220

Tubo-Tec Nordeste Industria   (1)
Rua Prefeito Remo Rodrigues Chaves S/N
Lote 05/06 Centro, Pedras de Fogo,
Paraiba, Brazil
Tel.: (55) 8136351029
Web Site: https://www.tubotec-ne.com.br

Carton Paperboard Mfr
N.A.I.C.S.: 322219

U.S. Paper Mills Corp.   (1)
824 Fort Howard Ave, De Pere, WI
54115   (100%)
Tel.: (920) 336-4229
Web Site: http://www.sonoco.com
Sales Range: $10-24.9 Million
Emp.: 60
Mfr of Paperboard Products
N.A.I.C.S.: 322130

Weidenhammer Chile Ltda.   (1)
El Arroyo 890, Lampa, Santiago, Chile
Tel.: (56) 223536001
Packaging Products Mfr
N.A.I.C.S.: 326112
Yanett Pedraza (Mgr-Customer Svc)

Weidenhammer Hellas S.A.   (1)
Thesi Kamini, PO Box 63, Oinofita, 32011,
Greece
Tel.: (30) 2262056440
Web Site: http://www.weidenhammer.gr
Paperboard Container Mfr
N.A.I.C.S.: 322219

SONOMA PHARMACEUTI-
CALS, INC.

5445 Conestoga Ct Ste 150, Boulder,
CO 80301
Tel.: (707) 559-7380   DE
Web Site:
   https://www.sonomapharma.com
Year Founded: 1999
SNOA—(NASDAQ)
Rev.: $12,735,000
Assets: $14,740,000
Liabilities: $8,603,000
Net Worth: $6,137,000
Earnings: ($4,835,000)
Emp.: 172
Fiscal Year-end: 03/31/24
Dermatological Condition & Tissue
Care Pharmaceutical Mfr & Whslr
N.A.I.C.S.: 325412
John Dal Poggetto (Controller)
Amy Trombly (Pres & CEO)
Bruce Thornton (COO)
Jerry Dvonch (CFO)

Subsidiaries:

Oculus Innovative Sciences Nether-
lands B.V.   (1)
Boven de Wolfskuil 3A22, 6049 LX, Herten,
Netherlands
Tel.: (31) 475318666
Web Site: http://www.oculusiseu.com
Dermatological Condition & Tissue Care
Pharmaceutical Whslr
N.A.I.C.S.: 424210

Oculus Technologies of Mexico, S.A.
de C.V.   (1)
Industria Vidriera No 81 Industrial Fraccio-
namiento Zapopan Norte, Zapopan, 45130,
Jalisco, Mexico
Tel.: (52) 3338336722
Web Site: https://oculus.com.mx
Dermatological Condition & Tissue Care
Pharmaceutical Mfr & Whslr
N.A.I.C.S.: 325412

Sonoma Pharmaceuticals Nether-
lands B.V.   (1)
Boven de Wolfskuil 3 C30-C32, Herten,
6049 LX, Roermond, Netherlands
Tel.: (31) 475318666
Web Site: https://sonomapharma.eu
Pharmaceuticals Distr
N.A.I.C.S.: 423450

SONOS, INC.

301 Coromar Dr, Goleta, CA 93117
Tel.: (805) 965-3001   DE
Web Site: https://www.sonos.com
Year Founded: 2002
SONO—(NASDAQ)
Rev.: $1,518,056,000
Assets: $916,312,000
Liabilities: $487,692,000
Net Worth: $428,620,000

Earnings: ($38,146,000)
Emp.: 1,708
Fiscal Year-end: 09/28/24
Audio Equipment Mfr & Distr
N.A.I.C.S.: 334310
Patrick Spence (Pres & CEO)
Maxime Bouvat-Merlin (Chief Product
Officer)
Nicholas Millington (Chief Innovation
Officer)
Anna Fraser (Chief People Officer)
Eddie Lazarus (Chief Legal Officer,
Chief Strategy Officer & Sec)
Maxime Bouvat-Merlin (Sr VP-
Hardware & Ops)
Shamayne Braman (Chief Diversity,
Equity & Inclusion Officer)
Ruth Sleeter (CIO)
Rebecca Zavin (Sr VP)
Chris Mason (Chief Acctg Officer)
Deirdre Findlay (Chief Comml Officer)

SORTIS HOLDINGS, INC.

240 SE 2nd Ace, Portland, OR 97214
Web Site: https://www.sortis.com
SOHI—(OTCIQ)
Rev.: $2,296,000
Assets: $1,248,000
Liabilities: $212,000
Net Worth: $1,036,000
Earnings: ($4,957,000)
Emp.: 10
Fiscal Year-end: 12/31/19
Financial Management Services
N.A.I.C.S.: 523940
Jefry A. Baker (Pres & CEO)

SOTERA HEALTH COMPANY

9100 S Hills Blvd Ste 300, Broadview
Heights, OH 44147
Tel.: (440) 262-1410   DE
Web Site:
   https://www.soterahealth.com
Year Founded: 2017
SHC—(NASDAQ)
Rev.: $1,049,288,000
Assets: $3,130,420,000
Liabilities: $2,686,686,000
Net Worth: $443,734,000
Earnings: $51,376,000
Emp.: 3,000
Fiscal Year-end: 12/31/23
Health Care Srvices
N.A.I.C.S.: 621610
Alex Dimitrief (Gen Counsel & Sr VP)
Michael B. Petras Jr. (Chm & CEO)
Kristin A. Gibbs (CMO)
Robert G. Hauzie (CIO)
kathleen A. Hoffman (Sr VP-Global
Environmental, Health & Safety)
Matthew J. Klaben (Gen Counsel,
Sec & Sr VP)
Kurt M. Roth (Sr VP-Corp Dev &
Strategy)
Sally R. Turner (Chief HR Officer)
Jonathan M. Lyons (CFO & Sr VP)
Jason Peterson (Treas & VP)

Subsidiaries:

Nelson Laboratories, LLC   (1)
6280 S Redwood Rd, Salt Lake City, UT
84123
Tel.: (801) 290-7500
Web Site: https://www.nelsonlabs.com
Global Lab Testing & Expert Consulting
Services
N.A.I.C.S.: 541380
Jeffery Nelson (Chm)

Subsidiary (Domestic):

Nelson Laboratories Fairfield,
Inc.   (2)
122 Fairfield Rd, Fairfield, NJ 07004-2405
Tel.: (877) 315-5847
Web Site: https://www.nelsonlabs.com
Research & Development in the Physical,
Engineering & Life Sciences
N.A.I.C.S.: 541715

Nelson Labs NV   (1)
Romeinsestraat 12, 3001, Leuven, Belgium
Tel.: (32) 16400484
Laboratory Testing Services
N.A.I.C.S.: 541380

SOTHEBY'S

1334 York Ave, New York, NY 10021
Tel.: (212) 606-7528   MI
Web Site: https://www.sothebys.com
Year Founded: 1744
BID—(NYSE)
Rev.: $1,035,740,000
Assets: $2,689,088,000
Liabilities: $2,247,594,000
Net Worth: $441,494,000
Earnings: $108,634,000
Emp.: 1,713
Fiscal Year-end: 12/31/18
Fine Arts, Antiques & Collectibles,
Paintings, Jewelry, Decorative Arts &
Books Auction Services
N.A.I.C.S.: 551112
Kevin Ching (CEO-Asia & Hong
Kong)
Jan Prasens (Exec VP & Mng Dir-Fin
Svcs)
Helena Newman (Chm-Impressionist
& Modern Art-Europe & Head-
Worldwide)
Simon Shaw (Vice Chm-Fine Arts
Div-New York)
Mary Bartow (Sr VP & Head-Prints
Department)
David Bennett (Chm-Jewelry-Intl &
Switzerland-Worldwide)
Jennifer Biederbeck (Sr VP & Head-
San Francisco)
Gregoire Billault (Sr VP & Head-
Contemporary Art-New York)
Justin Caldwell (VP)
Nicolas Chow (Chm-Chinese Works
of Art-Asia & Head-Intl)
Cyrille Cohen (VP-Bus Getter- France
& Paris)
Lisa Dennison (Chm-Americas & New
York & Exec VP)
Thomas Denzler (Sr VP & Head-
Department-New York)
Carol Elkins (Sr VP-Jewellery)
Jean Fritts (Chm-Intl-London)
Edward Gibbs (Chm/Head-Middle
East & India)
Lauren Gioia (Exec VP & Dir-Comm-
Worldwide)
Franka Haiderer (Chm-Valuations-
Europe)
Anne Heilbronn (VP-France & Head-
Specialist, Books & Manuscripts)
Florent Heintz (Head-Department-
Worldwide)
Yasuaki Ishizaka (Chm/Mng Dir-
Japan)
Selby Kiffer (Sr VP-Intl)
Mohamoud Abdalla Mohamed
(Officer-PR)
Rivka Saker (Chm-Israel)
Gary H. Schuler (Chm-North & South
America-New York)
Katharine Thomas (Sr VP & Head-
Watches Department)
Heinrich Graf Von Spreti (Interim Mng
Dir-Germany)
George Wachter (Chm-North America
& South & Co-Chm-Old Master
Paintings-Worldwide)
John D. Ward (Sr VP & Head-Silver
Department)
Robin Wright (Sr VP)
Rongde Zhang (Sr VP)
Charles F. Stewart (Pres & CEO)
Allan Schwartzman (Chm-Fine Art &
Exec VP)

Sotheby's—(Continued)

Amy Cappellazzo (Chm-Fine Art & Exec VP-New York)
David Schrader (Sr VP & Head-Private Sls-Contemporary Art)
Laurence Nicolas (Mng Dir-Jewelry & Watches-Global & Exec VP)
Valentino D. Carlotti (Exec VP & Head-Bus Dev-Global)
Jane Levine (Exec VP & Head-Govt & Regulatory Affairs)
Jonathan A. Olsoff (Gen Counsel-Worldwide & Exec VP)
Dan Abernethy (VP-IR & Corp Comm)
Thomas Bompard (Chm-West Coast)
John Cahill (Chief Comml Officer & Exec VP)
Ken Citron (Chief Transformation Officer & Exec VP-Ops)
Charlie Adamski Caulkins (VP & Head-Office-Dallas/Fort Worth)
Fatima Ali (Asst VP-New York)
Michael Fenton Goss (CFO & Exec VP)
Christopher Apostle (Sr VP & Head-Old Master Paintings Department)
Richard Austin (Sr VP & Head-Books & Manuscripts Department-New York)

Subsidiaries:

Sotheby's   (1)
34 35 New Bond Street, London, W1A 2AA, United Kingdom   (100%)
Tel.: (44) 2072935000
Web Site: http://www.sothebys.com
Sales Range: $125-149.9 Million
Emp.: 500
Provider of Fine Art Auction Services
N.A.I.C.S.: 455219
Robin G. Woodhead (CEO)
George Bailey (Chm-Bus Dev-Europe)
Harry Dalmeny (Chm)
Jan Prasens (Mng Dir-Europe)

Sotheby's A.G.   (1)
Talstrasse 83, Zurich, 8021, Switzerland
Tel.: (41) 442262200
Web Site: http://www.sothebys.com
Emp.: 13
General Auction Houses Services
N.A.I.C.S.: 459999

Sotheby's Amsterdam BV   (1)
Emmalaan 23, Amsterdam, 1075 AT, Netherlands
Tel.: (31) 205502200
Web Site: http://www.sothebys.com
Emp.: 6
General Auction Houses Services
N.A.I.C.S.: 459999
Annite Schuiten (Gen Mgr)

Sotheby's France S.A.S.   (1)
76 Rue Du Faubour Saint Honoreway, 75384, Paris, France
Tel.: (33) 153055305
Web Site: http://www.sothebys.com
General Auction Houses Services
N.A.I.C.S.: 459999
Cecile Bernard (Mng Dir)
Mario Tavella (Pres & Dir Gen)
Pierre Mothes (VP)
Stefano Moreni (VP)
Magali Teisseire (Dir-Jewellery & Watches)

Sotheby's Global Trading   (1)
Talstrasse 83, 8001, Zurich, Switzerland
Tel.: (41) 442221595
Web Site: http://www.sothebys.com
Sales Range: $25-49.9 Million
Emp.: 2
General Auction Houses Services
N.A.I.C.S.: 459999

Sotheby's Hong Kong Ltd.   (1)
3101 3106 1 Pacific Pl 88 Queens Way 5 Fl, Hong Kong, China (Hong Kong)   (100%)
Tel.: (852) 25248121
Web Site: http://www.sothebys.com
Rev.: $49,454,000
Emp.: 140
Fine Art Auctioneers

N.A.I.C.S.: 561990
Kevin Ching (CEO-Asia)
Jonathan Wong (Dir-Gallery)

Sotheby's Italia S.r.L.   (1)
Palazzo Serbelloni Corso Venezia 16, Milan, 20121, Italy
Tel.: (39) 02295001
Web Site: http://www.sothebys.com
General Auction Houses Services
N.A.I.C.S.: 459999

SOTHERLY HOTELS INC.
306 S Henry St Ste 100, Williamsburg, VA 23185
Tel.: (757) 229-5648   MD
Web Site:
    https://www.sotherlyhotels.com
SOHO—(NASDAQ)
Rev.: $173,838,057
Assets: $393,443,480
Liabilities: $345,544,821
Net Worth: $47,898,659
Earnings: $3,941,421
Emp.: 9
Fiscal Year-end: 12/31/23
Hotel Real Estate Investment Trust
N.A.I.C.S.: 531390
David R. Folsom (Pres & CEO)
Anthony E. Domalski (CFO & Sec)
Scott M. Kucinski (COO & Exec VP)
Robert E. Kirkland IV (Gen Counsel)

Subsidiaries:

Houston Hotel Associates L.P., L.L.P   (1)
1700 Smith St, Houston, TX 77002
Tel.: (713) 739-9800
Home Management Services
N.A.I.C.S.: 721110

MHI Hospitality TRS Holding, Inc.   (1)
6411 Ivy Ln Ste 510, Greenbelt, MD 20770
Tel.: (301) 474-3307
Web Site:
    https://www.chesapeakehospitality.com
Emp.: 30
Real Estate Investment Services
N.A.I.C.S.: 525990

Sotherly Hotels LP   (1)
306 S Henry St Ste 100, Williamsburg, VA 23185
Tel.: (757) 229-5648
Web Site: https://www.sotherlyhotels.com
Rev.: $173,838,056
Assets: $395,188,012
Liabilities: $345,544,821
Net Worth: $49,643,191
Earnings: ($4,167,539)
Emp.: 8
Fiscal Year-end: 12/31/2023
Hotel Investment & Management Services
N.A.I.C.S.: 721110
Andrew M. Sims (Chm)
Herschel J. Walker (Gen Partner)
George Scott Gibson IV (Gen Partner)

SOU 300 GROUP HOLDING CO.
1645 Vlg Ctr Cir Ste 170, Las Vegas, NV 89134
Year Founded: 2010
SOUG—(OTCIQ)
Information Technology Services
N.A.I.C.S.: 541511
Ame Enriquez (CEO)

SOUND FINANCIAL BANCORP, INC.
2400 3rd Ave Ste 150, Seattle, WA 98121
Tel.: (206) 448-0884   MD
Web Site: https://www.soundcb.com
SFBC—(NASDAQ)
Rev.: $44,377,000
Assets: $976,351,000
Liabilities: $878,646,000
Net Worth: $97,705,000
Earnings: $8,804,000
Emp.: 130

Fiscal Year-end: 12/31/22
Bank Holding Company
N.A.I.C.S.: 551111
Laura Lee Stewart (Pres & CEO)
Heidi J. Sexton (COO & Exec VP)
Wes Ochs (CFO, Chief Strategy Officer & Exec VP)
David A. Raney (Chief Banking Officer & Exec VP)
Jennifer L. Mallon (Chief Acctg Officer & Sr VP)
David S. Haddad Jr. (Vice Chm)

Subsidiaries:

Sound Community Bank   (1)
2400 3rd Ave Ste 100, Seattle, WA 98121
Tel.: (206) 436-3150
Web Site: https://www.soundcb.com
Commercial Banking
N.A.I.C.S.: 522110
Laura Lee Stewart (Pres & CEO)
Heidi J. Sexton (COO & Exec VP)
Wes Ochs (CFO, Chief Strategy Officer & Exec VP)
David A. Raney (Chief Banking Officer & Exec VP)
Erin Nicolaus (Exec VP-HR)
Diana Everett (Sr VP & Mgr-Technical Svcs)
Laurie Szczepczynski (Sr VP & Mgr-Retail)
Meghan Dort (Asst VP)
Mike Ralph (VP & Mgr-Comml Banking)
Daniel Petzoldt (Officer-Comml Loan-II & Asst VP)
Scott Higgins (Officer-Comml Loan & Asst VP)
Cody Brunker (Officer-Comml Loan-II & Asst VP)

SOUNDHOUND AI, INC.
5400 Betsy Ross Dr, Santa Clara, CA 95054
Tel.: (408) 441-3200   DE
Web Site:
    https://www.soundhound.com
Year Founded: 2020
SOUN—(NASDAQ)
Rev.: $33,376
Assets: $133,343,944
Liabilities: $133,507,781
Net Worth: ($163,837)
Earnings: ($981,884)
Emp.: 3
Fiscal Year-end: 12/31/21
Miscellaneous Financial Investment Activities
N.A.I.C.S.: 523999
Keyvan Mohajer (CEO)
James Hom (VP-Production)
Tim Stonehocker (CTO)
Michael Zagorsek (COO)
Nitesh Sharan (CFO)

SOUNDTHINKING, INC.
39300 Civic Ctr Dr Ste 300, Fremont, CA 94538
Tel.: (510) 794-3100   CA
Web Site:
    https://www.soundthinking.com
Year Founded: 2001
SSTI—(NASDAQ)
Rev.: $81,003,000
Assets: $122,748,000
Liabilities: $61,803,000
Net Worth: $60,945,000
Earnings: $6,385,000
Emp.: 213
Fiscal Year-end: 12/31/22
Developer of Gunshot & Explosion Location Detection System
N.A.I.C.S.: 541511
Robert L. Showen (Co-Founder)
Ralph A. Clark (Pres & CEO)
Paul Ames (Sr VP-Products & Tech)
Marc Haydel Morial (Chm)
Alan R. Stewart (CFO)
Sam Klepper (Sr VP-Mktg & Mktg)
Nasim Golzadeh (Exec VP-Investigative Solutions, Sr VP-Customer Support & Professional Svcs & Mng Dir-Techno Logic)

Pascal N. Levensohn (Chm)
Erin Edwards (Sr VP-Sales)
Tom Chittum (Sr VP-Forensic Svcs)
Gregg Makuch (Sr VP-Marketing)
Anne Mueller (Sr VP-Human Resources)
Mark Page (Sr VP-Field Engrg, Customer Support, and Training)
Greg Holifield (Mng Dir-SafePoint)
Adan K. Pope (Sr VP-AI & Data Science)

Subsidiaries:

Forensic Logic Inc.   (1)
1255 Treat Boulevard, Suite #610, Walnut Creek, CA 94597
Tel.: (833) 267-5465
Web Site: http://www.forensiclogic.com
Electronics Stores
N.A.I.C.S.: 449210

SOUPMAN, INC.
1110 S Ave Ste 100, Staten Island, NY 10314
Tel.: (212) 768-7687   NV
Web Site:
    http://www.originalsoupman.com
Year Founded: 2008
SOUPQ—(OTCIQ)
Sales Range: $1-9.9 Million
Emp.: 7
Soup Mfr & Whslr
N.A.I.C.S.: 424490
Daniel A. Rubano (Sr VP-Franchise Dev & Ops)
Sebastian Rametta (Founder & Head-Sls)
Thomas Scipione (Interim Pres)
Jamieson A. Karson (CEO)
Barbara Axelson (VP-Tetra Pak Sls)

SOUTH AMERICAN GOLD CORP.
8275 S Eastern Ave Ste 200, Las Vegas, NV 89123   NV
Web Site:
    http://www.sativagrowth.com
SAGD—(OTCIQ)
Metal Mining & Exploration Services
N.A.I.C.S.: 213114
Gary Austin Jr. (Chm)

SOUTH ATLANTIC BANCSHARES, INC.
630 29th Ave N, Myrtle Beach, SC 29577
Tel.: (843) 839-0100
Web Site:
    https://www.southatlanticbank.com
SABK—(OTCIQ)
Rev.: $41,566,307
Assets: $946,540,599
Liabilities: $848,718,869
Net Worth: $97,821,730
Earnings: $7,196,051
Emp.: 146
Fiscal Year-end: 12/31/20
Bank Holding Company
N.A.I.C.S.: 551111
R. Scott Plyler (Pres)
K. Wayne Wicker (Chm & CEO)
Richard N. Burch (CFO & Exec VP)
Melissa K. Downs-High (Sr VP-Acctg & Controller)
Candace L. Cherry (Sr VP)
Jennifer L. Peters (Sr VP-Compliance & Dir-Internal Audit & Compliance)
Derick R. Powers (Officer-Credit Risk & Sr VP-Credit Risk)
Tifany P. Suggs (Sr VP-Deposit Ops & Dir-Deposit Ops)
Carrie S. Harris (Sr VP-HR & Dir-HR)
Kimberly D. West (Asst VP-Information Sys & Project Mgr)
Anne B. Cote (Sr VP-Loan Ops & Dir-Loan Ops)

Karen M. Atwood *(VP & Mgr-Construction Loan)*
Beth W. Branham *(VP-Mktg & Dir-Mktg)*
Donald G. Kyzer *(Sr VP-Corp Svcs & Dir-Corp Svcs)*
Peter M. Insabella *(Sr VP-Mortgage Svcs & Mgr-Mortgage Sls)*
Michelle A. Coletta *(Sr VP-Retail Sls & Sls Mgr-Retail)*
Paul E. Peeples *(Sr VP)*
Leah M. Birge *(Asst VP & Branch Mgr)*
Travis A. Minter *(COO)*
Charles W. Fisher III *(Sr VP & Mgr-Comml Relationship)*

Subsidiaries:

South Atlantic Bank   **(1)**
630 29th Ave N, Myrtle Beach, SC 29577
Tel.: (843) 839-0100
Web Site: http://www.southatlanticbank.com
Banking Services
N.A.I.C.S.: 522110
R. Scott Plyler *(Pres)*
K. Wayne Wicker *(Chm & CEO)*
R. Scott Plyler *(Pres)*
Carrie Harris *(Sr VP & Dir-HR)*

SOUTH BEACH SPIRITS, INC.
224 Datura St, West Palm Beach, FL 33401
Tel.: (561) 570-4301   NV
Web Site: http://www.thesbes.com
Year Founded: 2012
SBES—(OTCIQ)
Sales Range: Less than $1 Million
Emp.: 3
Holding Company; Distillery Operator & Beverage Marketer
N.A.I.C.S.: 551112

SOUTH DAKOTA SOYBEAN PROCESSORS LLC
Tel.: (605) 627-9240   SD
Web Site: https://sdsbp.com
Year Founded: 1993
SDSYA—(OTC)
Agriculture Product Distr
N.A.I.C.S.: 424910

SOUTH PLAINS FINANCIAL, INC.
5219 City Bank Pkwy, Lubbock, TX 79408
Tel.: (806) 792-7101   TX
Web Site: https://www.spfi.bank
SPFI—(NASDAQ)
Rev.: $237,313,000
Assets: $3,944,063,000
Liabilities: $3,587,049,000
Net Worth: $357,014,000
Earnings: $58,240,000
Emp.: 600
Fiscal Year-end: 12/31/22
Bank Holding Company
N.A.I.C.S.: 551111
Cory T. Newsom *(Pres)*
Curtis C. Griffith *(Chm & CEO)*
Steven B. Crockett *(CFO & Treas)*
Mikella D. Newsom *(Chief Risk Officer & Sec)*

Subsidiaries:

City Bank   **(1)**
5219 City Bank Pkwy, Lubbock, TX 79407
Tel.: (806) 792-7101
Web Site: https://www.city.bank
Commericial Banking
N.A.I.C.S.: 522110
Curtis C. Griffith *(Chm & CEO)*

SOUTHEASTERN BANKING CORP.
1010 North Way, Darien, GA 31305
Tel.: (912) 437-4141   GA

Web Site:
https://www.southeasternbank.com
Year Founded: 1980
SEBC—(OTCIQ)
Bank Holding Company
N.A.I.C.S.: 522110
Alyson G. Beasley *(Exec VP & COO-Southeastern Bank)*
Donald Jay Torbert Jr. *(Pres, CEO & Treas)*
Donald Jay Torbert Jr. *(Pres, CEO & Treas)*
Wanda D. Pitts *(Sec)*
Robert M. Eidson Jr. *(Treas)*
Cornelius P. Holland III *(Pres, CEO & Chief Credit Officer)*

Subsidiaries:

Southeastern Bank Inc.   **(1)**
1010 Northway St, Darien, GA 31305
Tel.: (912) 437-4141
Web Site: http://www.southeasternbank.com
Sales Range: $400-449.9 Million
Emp.: 170
State Commercial Banks
N.A.I.C.S.: 522110
Alyson G. Beasley *(COO)*
Donald Jay Torbert Jr. *(CFO & Exec VP)*
Cornelius P. Holland *(Pres & CEO)*

SOUTHERN BANCSHARES (N.C.), INC.
116 E Main St, Mount Olive, NC 28365
Tel.: (919) 658-7000   DE
Web Site:
http://www.southernbank.com
Year Founded: 1983
SBNC—(OTCIQ)
Rev.: $159,240,000
Assets: $3,835,865,000
Liabilities: $3,442,700,000
Net Worth: $393,165,000
Earnings: $44,636,000
Emp.: 575
Fiscal Year-end: 12/31/20
Bank Holding Company
N.A.I.C.S.: 551111
Taylor L. Harrell *(Pres)*
David L. Sauls Jr. *(CFO, Sec & Exec VP)*
Sondra F. McCorquoda *(Exec VP)*
W. Trent Dudley *(Exec VP)*
John H. Gray *(Chief Acctg Officer & Sr VP)*
Robert E. Wood *(Chief Comml Officer)*

Subsidiaries:

Southern Bank & Trust Co.   **(1)**
100 N Center St, Mount Olive, NC 28365
Tel.: (919) 658-7000
Web Site: http://www.southernbank.com
Commericial Banking
N.A.I.C.S.: 522110
Drew M. Covert *(Pres)*
Michael T. Bryant *(Exec VP-West Reg)*
L. Taylor Harrell *(Exec VP-Hampton Roads Reg)*
J. Grey Morgan *(Chm & CEO)*
Jerry C. Alexander *(Exec VP-Northeast Reg)*
Greg Shackelford *(Sr VP-South Reg)*
Ashley M. Bagby *(Asst VP)*
Judy Lynn *(Chief Credit Officer & Exec VP)*

SOUTHERN COMMUNITY BANCSHARES, INC.
420 2nd Ave SW, Cullman, AL 35055
Tel.: (256) 734-4863   AL
Year Founded: 1996
SCBS—(OTCIQ)
Bank Holding Company
N.A.I.C.S.: 551111
Allison Maltz *(CFO)*
St John E. Finis IV *(Chm)*
William R. Faulk *(Pres & CEO)*

SOUTHERN CONCEPTS RESTAURANT GROUP, INC.
3001 PGA Blvd Ste 305, Palm Beach Gardens, FL 33410
Tel.: (609) 433-6711   CO
Year Founded: 2008
RIBS—(OTCIQ)
Sales Range: $1-9.9 Million
Restaurant Operators
N.A.I.C.S.: 722511
James J. Fenlason *(Interim CEO)*
Ross DiMaggio *(CEO, CFO, Treas & Sec)*

SOUTHERN FIRST BANCSHARES, INC.
6 Verdae Blvd, Greenville, SC 29607
Tel.: (864) 679-9000   SC
Web Site:
https://www.southernfirst.com
SFST—(NASDAQ)
Rev.: $127,242,000
Assets: $3,691,981,000
Liabilities: $3,397,469,000
Net Worth: $294,512,000
Earnings: $29,115,000
Emp.: 293
Fiscal Year-end: 12/31/22
Bank Holding Company
N.A.I.C.S.: 551111
R. Arthur Seaver Jr. *(CEO)*
Christian Zych *(CFO & Exec VP)*
Silvia T. King *(Chief HR Officer)*
William M. Aiken III *(Chief Risk Officer)*

Subsidiaries:

Southern First Bank   **(1)**
6 Verdae Blvd, Greenville, SC 29607
Tel.: (864) 679-9000
Web Site: https://www.southernfirst.com
Commericial Banking
N.A.I.C.S.: 522110
R. Arthur Seaver Jr. *(CEO)*
Calvin C. Hurst *(Pres)*
Christian Zych *(CFO & Exec VP)*
Lindsay McCloskey *(Officer-Client Experience)*
Will Aiken *(Chief Risk Officer)*
Chris Blue *(Officer-Virtual Experience)*
Erica Brown *(Officer-Client Experience)*
Hunter Chamness *(Sr VP)*
Ken Cummings *(Sr VP)*
Tiffany Duck *(Officer-Virtual Experience)*
Dave Favela *(Chief Innovation Officer)*
Stacy Fetterman *(Chief Compliance Officer)*
Fred Gilmer III *(Chief Lending Officer)*
Derek Horton *(Sr VP)*
William Johnston *(Sr VP)*
Jimmy Kimbell III *(Sr VP)*
Silvia King *(Chief HR Officer)*
Don Kiser *(Sr VP)*
Matt Kneeland *(Sr VP)*
Kim Macklanburg *(Sr VP)*
Mark Miller *(Sr VP)*
Matthew Newton *(Sr VP)*
Nelson Poe *(Chief Mortgage Officer)*
Rob Reeves *(Sr VP)*
Phillip Siebels *(Sr VP)*
Marisa Stephens *(Dir-Marketing)*
Jordan Sztanyo *(Sr VP)*
Robert Thompson III *(Reg Pres)*
Debbie Tucker *(VP)*
Michelle Williams *(Sr VP)*
Paris Wright *(Coord-Voice)*

SOUTHERN MICHIGAN BANCORP INC.
51 W Pearl St, Coldwater, MI 49036
Tel.: (517) 279-5500   MI
Web Site: https://www.smb-t.com
Year Founded: 1871
SOMC—(OTCIQ)
Rev.: $51,514,000
Assets: $1,276,523,000
Liabilities: $1,190,359,000
Net Worth: $86,164,000
Earnings: $13,491,000
Emp.: 80
Fiscal Year-end: 12/31/22

Bank Holding Company
N.A.I.C.S.: 551111
John H. Castle *(Chm & CEO)*
Kurt G. Miller *(Pres & Chief Credit Officer)*
Danice L. Chartrand *(CFO, Treas, Sec & Sr VP)*
Nicholas M. Grabowski *(Exec VP & Head-Lending)*
Eric M. Anglin *(Chief Strategy Officer, Exec VP & Head-Bus Dev)*
Quinn White *(VP & Head-Mktg)*

Subsidiaries:

Southern Michigan Bank & Trust   **(1)**
51 W Pearl St, Coldwater, MI 49036
Tel.: (517) 279-5500
Web Site: http://www.smb-t.com
Commercial Banking
N.A.I.C.S.: 522110
John H. Castle *(Chm & CEO)*
Abby Austin *(Asst VP & Branch Mgr)*
Kurt Miller *(Pres)*
Jamie Smoker *(Sr VP-Retail Lending)*
Jean Winans *(VP)*
Nick Grabowski *(VP)*
Cammy Fleckenstein *(Mgr-Portage)*
Laurel Walkup *(Asst VP)*
Dave McKinley *(First VP & Head-Ops)*
Timothy Kilmartin *(Pres-Kalamazoo)*
Eric Anglin *(Chief Deposit Officer & Sr VP-Retail Banking Svcs)*
Matt Moses *(Sr VP & Head-Wealth Mgmt)*
Derek Naylor *(First VP & Head-Retail Lending)*
Shari Kline *(VP)*
DeAnne Hawley *(VP)*

SOUTHERN MISSOURI BANCORP, INC.
Tel.: (573) 778-1800   DE
Web Site:
https://www.bankwithsouthern.com
Year Founded: 1966
SMBC—(NASDAQ)
Rev.: $273,219,000
Assets: $4,604,316,000
Liabilities: $4,115,568,000
Net Worth: $488,748,000
Earnings: $50,182,000
Emp.: 693
Fiscal Year-end: 06/30/24
Bank Holding Company
N.A.I.C.S.: 551111
Greg A. Steffens *(Chm & CEO)*
L. Douglas Bagby *(Vice Chm)*
Kimberly A. Capps *(COO)*
Matthew T. Funke *(Pres, Chief Admin Officer & Principal Fin Officer)*
Lance K. Greunke *(Chief Risk Officer & Exec VP)*
Charles R. Love *(Sec)*
Mark E. Hecker *(Chief Credit Officer)*
Rick A. Windes *(Chief Lending Officer)*
Brett A. Dorton *(Chief Strategies Officer)*
Martin J. Weishaar *(Chief Legal Officer)*

Subsidiaries:

Citizens Bancshares Co.   **(1)**
7280 NW 87th Ter Ste 300, Kansas City, MO 64153
Tel.: (816) 459-4000
Web Site: http://www.gocitizens.bank
Rev.: $44,105,000
Assets: $897,600,000
Liabilities: $803,828,000
Net Worth: $93,772,000
Earnings: $6,213,000
Emp.: 204
Fiscal Year-end: 12/31/2019
Bank Holding Company
N.A.I.C.S.: 551111

Southern Missouri Bancorp, Inc.—(Continued)

William E. Young (Pres)
Roger M. Arwood (CEO)

Subsidiary (Domestic):

Citizens Bank & Trust Company (2)
7280 NW 87th Ter Ste 300, Kansas City, MO 64153
Tel.: (816) 459-4000
Web Site: http://www.gocitizens.bank
Sales Range: $25-49.9 Million
Commercial Banking
N.A.I.C.S.: 522110
William E. Young (Pres)
Roger Arwood (CEO)
Jon Appleby (CFO & Exec VP)
Bill Dippel (Chief Credit Officer & Exec VP)
Joe Christifano (Treas & Exec VP)
Jim Conley (Exec VP & Dir-Comml Real Estate)
Larry Taft (Exec VP & Dir-Retail Banking & Ops)
Bob Wright (Exec VP & Dir-Enterprise Risk Mgmt)
Mark Eagleton (Exec VP-Comml Banking & Wealth Mgmt)
Rick Viar (Exec VP)

Southern Bank (1)
2991 Oak Grove Rd, Poplar Bluff, MO 63901 (100%)
Tel.: (573) 778-1800
Web Site: http://www.bankwithsouthern.com
Sales Range: $100-124.9 Million
Commercial Banking
N.A.I.C.S.: 522110
Greg A. Steffens (Chm)
Sammy A. Schalk (Vice Chm)
Kimberly A. Capps (COO & Exec VP)
Matthew T. Funke (Pres, Chief Admin Officer & Principal Fin Officer)
Lance K. Greunke (Chief Risk Officer & Exec VP)
Aaron Decker (VP)
Alison Davis (Officer-HR)
Amanda Porter (Officer-Acctg Ops & VP)
Brett Dorton (Chief Strategies Officer & Exec VP)
Brook Daniels (Officer-Retail-South Reg & VP)
Courtney Littrell (Officer-Retail Ops & VP)
Jackie Bonner (Officer-Retail-West Reg & VP)
Joshua Joiner (Mgr-Market Retail)
Justin Cox (Reg Pres & Exec VP)
Kathy Brittingham (Officer-Facilities Mgmt)
Lorna Brannum (Sec)
Mark Hecker (Chief Credit Officer & VP)
Matt Bedell (Officer-Mktg)
Rebecca Mitchell (Mgr Market Retail)
Richard Windes (Chief Lending Officer & Exec VP)
Steve McAnelly (Officer-Retail-East Reg & VP)
Suzy Hills (Officer-IT & VP)
Tiffany Williams (Officer-Retail Products & VP)
Jane Butler (Officer-Fin Reporting & VP)
Laura Payne (Officer-Loan)
Collin Jones (Officer-Loan)
Larry Hafford (Officer-Loan)
Lucas Moe (Officer-Loan)
Ryan Adams (Officer-Loan)
Ben Brumitt (Pres-Community Bank)
Mel Jackson (Pres-Market)
Will Spargo (Officer-Loan)

SOUTHERN PLAINS OIL CORP.
PO Box 191767, Atlanta, GA 31119
Tel.: (404) 816-9220
Web Site:
http://www.southernplainsoil.com
SPLN—(OTCIQ)
Petroleum Mfr
N.A.I.C.S.: 324191
Erik S. Nelson (CEO)

SOUTHERN REALTY CO.
2124 Via Don Benito, La Jolla, CA 92037
Tel.: (619) 813-2833 CA
Year Founded: 1949

SRLY—(OTCIQ)
Oil & Natural Gas Exploration Services
N.A.I.C.S.: 211130
Roger L. MnNitt (Pres & Treas)
Veronika Reinelt (Sec)
Joseph Munsey (VP & Asst Sec)
Michael McNitt (VP & Asst Sec)

SOUTHERN STAR ENERGY CORP.
1218 Autrey St Ste 2, Houston, TX 77006
Tel.: (713) 522-2205 TX
SSER—(OTCIQ)
Oil & Gas Exploration Services
N.A.I.C.S.: 213112
Donald E. West (Pres)

SOUTHERN STATES BANCSHARES, INC.
615 Quintard Ave, Anniston, AL 36201
Tel.: (256) 241-1092 AL
Web Site:
https://www.southernstatesbank.net
Year Founded: 2008
SSBK—(NASDAQ)
Rev.: $91,527,000
Assets: $2,045,204,000
Liabilities: $1,863,485,000
Net Worth: $181,719,000
Earnings: $27,071,000
Emp.: 187
Fiscal Year-end: 12/31/22
Bank Holding Company
N.A.I.C.S.: 551111
Mark A. Chambers (Pres & CEO)
Lynn Joyce (CFO & Sr Exec VP)
J. Henry Smith IV (Chm, Chief Risk Officer & Sr Exec VP)
Greg Smith (Chief Risk Officer & Sr Exec VP)

Subsidiaries:

Southern States Bank (1)
615 Quintard Ave, Anniston, AL 36201-5755
Tel.: (256) 241-1092
Web Site:
https://www.southernstatesbank.net
Sales Range: $10-24.9 Million
Commercial Banking
N.A.I.C.S.: 522110
Mark A. Chambers (Pres)
Stephen Woods Whatley (CFO)
Lynn Joyce (CFO & Sr Exec VP)
Mark Chambers (Pres- & Sr Exec VP)
David Ridgeway (Pres-Metro Atlanta)
Brett Johnston (Pres-Coweta & Fayette)
Mark Thomsen (Pres-Cobb)

SOUTHLAND HOLDINGS, INC.
1100 Kubota Dr, Grapevine, TX 76051
Tel.: (817) 293-4263 DE
Web Site:
https://www.southlandholdings.com
Year Founded: 2006
SLND—(NYSE)
Rev.: $4,013,841
Assets: $283,751,241
Liabilities: $203,078,477
Net Worth: ($9,327,236)
Earnings: $1,931,302
Emp.: 2,500
Fiscal Year-end: 12/31/22
Offices of Other Holding Companies
N.A.I.C.S.: 551112
Frank Renda (Pres & CEO)
Cody Gallarda (CFO)
Walter Timothy Winn (COO & Exec VP)

SOUTHPOINT BANCSHARES, INC.
3501 Grandview Pkwy, Birmingham, AL 35243

Tel.: (205) 503-5000 AL
Year Founded: 2005
SOUB—(OTCIQ)
Rev.: $99,636,674
Assets: $1,658,996,610
Liabilities: $1,555,794,830
Net Worth: $103,201,780
Earnings: $15,589,069
Emp.: 150
Fiscal Year-end: 12/31/23
Bank Holding Company
N.A.I.C.S.: 551111
J. Stephen Smith (Chm, Pres & CEO)

SOUTHPORT ACQUISITION CORPORATION
1745 Grand Ave, Del Mar, CA 92014
Tel.: (917) 503-9722 DE
Web Site:
https://www.southportone.com
Year Founded: 2021
PORT—(NYSE)
Investment Services
N.A.I.C.S.: 523999
Jared Stone (Chm)
Jeb Spencer (CEO)

SOUTHSIDE BANCSHARES, INC.
Tel.: (903) 531-7111 TX
Web Site: https://www.southside.com
Year Founded: 1983
SBSI—(NASDAQ)
Rev.: $293,838,000
Assets: $7,558,636,000
Liabilities: $6,812,639,000
Net Worth: $745,997,000
Earnings: $105,020,000
Emp.: 813
Fiscal Year-end: 12/31/22
Bank Holding Company
N.A.I.C.S.: 551111
Lee R. Gibson III (CEO)
Julie N. Shamburger (CFO)
Keith Donahoe (Pres)
Brian K. McCabe (COO)
Curtis Burchard (Chief Lending Officer)
Suni Davis (Chief Risk Officer & Chief Treasury Officer)
Donald W. Thedford (Vice Chm)

Subsidiaries:

Southside Bank (1)
1201 S Beckham Ave, Tyler, TX 75701 (100%)
Tel.: (903) 531-7111
Web Site: https://www.southside.com
Sales Range: $150-199.9 Million
Commercial Banking
N.A.I.C.S.: 522110
Lee R. Gibson III (CEO)
Keith Donahoe (Reg Pres-Central Texas)
Curtis Burchard (Chief Lending Officer & Dir-Advisory)
Suni Davis (Chief Risk Officer & Chief Treasury Officer)
Joel Adams (Exec VP-East Texas)
Peter M. Boyd (Sr Exec VP)
Timothy F. Alexander (Chief Lending Officer)
Kim Borrelli (Officer-Mortgage Loan & Asst VP)
Steve Brittain (Officer-Mortgage Loan & Sr VP)
Ryan Drennan (Officer-Mortgage Loan)
Johnna Hutchins (Officer-Mortgage Loan)
Reagan Rains (Officer-Mortgage Loan)
Jonathan Ferrell (Sr VP-Capital Markets CRE)
Patrick Ramsier (Pres-Capital Markets CRE)
Lonny R. Uzzell (Pres-East Texas)
Jared Green (Pres-East Texas)
Lupita Salinas (Asst VP & Branch Mgr)
T. L. Arnold Jr. (Chief Credit Officer)

Southside Bank is a State Bank (1)
PO Box 1079, Tyler, TX 75710-1079
Tel.: (903) 531-7111
Commercial Banking Services

N.A.I.C.S.: 522110
Daniel Sitton (Dir-IT)

SOUTHSTATE CORPORATION
1101 1st St S Ste 202, Winter Haven, FL 33880
Tel.: (863) 293-4710 SC
Web Site:
https://www.southstatebank.com
Year Founded: 1985
SSB—(NASDAQ)
Rev.: $2,231,312,000
Assets: $44,902,024,000
Liabilities: $39,368,926,000
Net Worth: $5,533,098,000
Earnings: $494,308,000
Emp.: 5,070
Fiscal Year-end: 12/31/23
Bank Holding Company
N.A.I.C.S.: 551111
Renee R. Brooks (COO)
John C. Corbett (CEO)
Stephen D. Young (Chief Strategy Officer)
William E. Matthews V (CFO & Sr Exec VP)
Richard Murray IV (Pres-South State Corp)
John C. Pollok (Executives)
Sara G. Arana (Principal Acctg Officer & Exec VP)

Subsidiaries:

Atlantic Capital Bancshares, Inc. (1)
945 E Paces Ferry Rd NE Ste 1600, Atlanta, GA 30326
Tel.: (404) 995-6050
Web Site:
http://www.atlanticcapitalbank.com
Rev.: $109,281,000
Assets: $3,615,617,000
Liabilities: $3,277,031,000
Net Worth: $338,586,000
Earnings: $22,540,000
Emp.: 201
Fiscal Year-end: 12/31/2020
Bank Holding Company
N.A.I.C.S.: 551111
Richard A. Oglesby Jr. (Pres)
Patrick T. Oakes (CFO, Treas, Sec & Exec VP)
Kurt A. Shreiner (Pres-Corp Fin Svcs Div)
Annette F. Rollins (Chief HR Officer & Exec VP)
Mark Robertson (COO & Exec VP)
Robert R. Bugbee II (Chief Credit Officer & Exec VP)
Gary G. Fleming Jr. (Chief Risk Officer & Exec VP)

Subsidiary (Domestic):

Atlantic Capital Bank, N.A. (2)
945 E Paces Ferry Rd NE Ste 1600, Atlanta, GA 30326
Tel.: (404) 995-6050
Web Site:
http://www.atlanticcapitalbank.com
Federal Savings Bank
N.A.I.C.S.: 522180
Richard A. Oglesby Jr. (Pres-Atlanta Div)
Douglas L. Williams (Pres & CEO)
Patrick T. Oakes (CFO, Sec & Exec VP)
Mark Robertson (COO & Exec VP-Tech & Ops)
Annette Rollins (Chief HR Officer)
Kurt A. Shreiner (Founder & Pres-Corp Fin Svcs Div)
John May (Exec VP-Comml Banking-Buckhead)
Brian Harper (Mgr-SBA Div)
Alex Simmer (Sr VP & Mgr-Relationship)
Nancy Lewis (Sr VP-Bus & Not for Profit Banking & Mgr-Relationship)
Thomas Rockwood (VP-SBA Lending)
Gosa McKenna (Asst VP-SBA Lending)
Jason Robinson (Sr VP & Mgr-Relationship)
Chad Ebert (Sr VP & Mgr-Relationship)
Allen Phinney (Sr VP & Mgr-Relationship)
Katie Brenner (Sr VP & Mgr-Relationship)

Brian Whelan *(Sr VP & Mgr-Relationship)*
Cindy Taylor *(Mgr-Relationship-Comml Banking)*
Chuck Schwartz *(Sr VP & Mgr-Relationship)*
Ed Jenkins *(Sr VP & Mgr-Relationship)*
Tyler Talley *(Mgr-Relationship-Comml Banking)*
Donyale Getz *(Officer-Treasury Svcs & Sr VP)*
Glenna Reeves *(Officer-Treasury Svcs & Sr VP)*
Amily Hanson *(Officer-Treasury Svcs & Sr VP)*
Cheryl Hollingsworth *(VP & Head-Retail Banking)*
Michael Davis *(Acct Mgr-Private Banking)*
Elisabeth Cassidy *(Sr VP & Mgr-Relationship)*
Lora Fishman *(Sr VP & Mgr-Relationship)*
Adrienne White *(VP-Bus Banking & Not-for-Profit Banking)*
Robert R. Bugbee II *(Chief Credit Officer & Exec VP)*
Gary G. Fleming Jr. *(Chief Risk Officer & Exec VP)*

South State Bank, N.A.   (1)
1101 1st St S, Winter Haven, FL 33880
Tel.: (863) 419-0833
Web Site: https://www.southstatebank.com
Savings Bank
N.A.I.C.S.: 522180
Renee R. Brooks *(COO)*
John C. Corbett *(Pres & CEO)*
Stephen D. Young *(Chief Strategy Officer)*
William E. Matthews V *(CFO)*
Richard Murray IV *(Pres)*
Bryan F. Kennedy III *(Pres)*

Subsidiary (Domestic):

Corporate Billing, LLC   (2)
239 Johnston St SE, Decatur, AL 35601
Tel.: (256) 584-3600
Web Site: https://www.corpbill.com
Corporate Billing & Factoring Services
N.A.I.C.S.: 522299
Leif Founds *(CEO)*

SSB Insurance Corp.   (2)
151 Meeting St Ste 301, Charleston, SC 29401
Tel.: (843) 577-1030
Insurance Related Services
N.A.I.C.S.: 524210

SOUTHWEST AIRLINES CO.
PO Box 36611, Dallas, TX 75235-1611
Tel.: (214) 792-4000   TX
Web Site: https://www.southwest.com
Year Founded: 1971
LUV—(NYSE)
Rev.: $26,091,000,000
Assets: $36,487,000,000
Liabilities: $25,972,000,000
Net Worth: $10,515,000,000
Earnings: $465,000,000
Emp.: 74,806
Fiscal Year-end: 12/31/23
Oil Transportation Services
N.A.I.C.S.: 481111
Ron Ricks *(Vice Chm)*
Tammy Romo *(CFO & Exec VP)*
Whitney Eichinger *(Mng Dir)*
Linda B. Rutherford *(Executives)*
Linda B. Rutherford *(Chief Comm Officer & Exec VP-People & Comm)*
Scott Halfmann *(VP-Safety-Security)*
Kay Weatherford *(VP)*
Leah Koontz *(VP & Controller)*
Julie Weber *(Chief HR Officer & VP)*
Elizabeth Bryant *(VP)*
Steve Goldberg *(Sr VP-Operations)*
Landon Nitschke *(Sr VP)*
Andrew M. Watterson *(COO)*
Jason Van Eaton *(Chief Corp Affairs Officer, Chief Regulatory Officer & Exec VP)*
Alan Kasher *(Exec VP)*
Sonya Lacore *(VP)*
Dave Harvey *(VP)*
Justin Jones *(VP)*

Paul Cullen *(VP-Real Estate)*
Ryan C. Green *(CMO & Sr VP)*
Reid Grandle *(VP-Strategy-Planning)*
Bill Tierney *(VP-Marketing)*
Russell McCrady *(VP-Labor Relations)*
Thomas Merritt *(CTO & VP-Technology-Infrastructure,Svcs)*
Anthony Gregory *(VP)*
Marilyn Post *(Mng Dir & Sec)*
Sam Ford *(VP)*
Wally Devereaux *(Mng Dir)*
Ray Schuster *(Mng Dir-Accounting)*
James Ashworth *(VP-Customer Support)*
Jim Dayton *(VP-Technology-Air,Technical Ops)*
Kurt Kinder *(VP)*
Mark Wibben *(VP)*
Nan Barry *(Mng Dir)*
Jonathan Clarkson *(Mng Dir)*
Danny Collins *(Mng Dir-People)*
Ken Guckian *(Mng Dir-Tax & Controller-Operations)*
Chris Johnson *(VP)*
Jeff Jones *(VP-Technology-Comml,Customer)*
Angela Marano *(Mng Dir)*
Colleen Russell *(Mng Dir-Internal Audit)*
Michael Simmons *(Chief Information Security Officer & Chief Information Security Officer-Technology)*
Steve Sisneros *(Mng Dir)*
Juan Suarez *(Mng Dir & Deputy Gen Counsel)*
Lauren Woods *(Mng Dir-Technology-Tech Platforms)*
Stacy Malphurs *(VP-Supply Chain Management)*
John J. Herlihy *(Mng Dir-Technology)*
Scott Seymour *(Mng Dir-Technology-Enterprise Mgmt)*
Bob Waltz *(VP)*
Julia Landrum *(Mng Dir)*
Dean Jenkins *(Treas & VP)*
Robert E. Jordan *(Pres & CEO)*

Subsidiaries:

AirTran Airways, Inc.   (1)
1800 Phoenix Blvd Ste 104, Atlanta, GA 30349   (100%)
Tel.: (407) 318-5100
Web Site: http://www.airtranairways.com
Sales Range: $1-4.9 Billion
Emp.: 8,000
Domestic Commercial Airline
N.A.I.C.S.: 481111

SOUTHWEST GAS HOLDINGS, INC.
8360 S Durango Dr, Las Vegas, NV 89193-8510
Tel.: (702) 876-7237   CA
Web Site: https://www.swgasholdings.com
Year Founded: 1931
SWX—(NYSE)
Rev.: $5,433,972,000
Assets: $11,869,896,000
Liabilities: $3,845,355,000
Net Worth: $8,024,541,000
Earnings: $150,889,000
Emp.: 14,943
Fiscal Year-end: 12/31/23
Holding Company; Natural Gas Distr & Utility Infrastructure Construction Services
N.A.I.C.S.: 551112
Kenneth J. Kenny *(Treas & VP-Fin)*
Karen S. Haller *(Pres & CEO)*
Justin S. Forsberg *(VP-IR)*
Sean Corbett *(Mgr-Corp Comm)*
Robert J. Stefani *(CFO & Sr VP)*
Lori L. Colvin *(Chief Acctg Officer, VP & Controller)*

Subsidiaries:

Centuri Group, Inc.   (1)
19820 N 7th Ave Ste 120, Phoenix, AZ 85027
Tel.: (623) 582-1235
Web Site: https://www.nextcenturi.com
Holding Company; Construction Services
N.A.I.C.S.: 551112
William J. Fehrman *(Pres & CEO)*

Subsidiary (Domestic):

Canyon Pipeline Construction Inc.   (2)
1148 Legacy Crossing Blvd Ste 250, Centerville, UT 84014
Tel.: (801) 268-0058
Web Site: https://www.canyonpipeline.com
Emp.: 180
Pipeline Construction Services
N.A.I.C.S.: 237120

Enterprise Trenchless Technologies, Inc   (2)
42 Capital Ave, Lisbon Falls, ME 04252-1105
Tel.: (207) 353-5000
Web Site: http://www.hdd-etti.com
Sales Range: $1-9.9 Million
Emp.: 50
Wood Container & Pallet Mfr
N.A.I.C.S.: 321920

Linetec Services, LLC   (2)
6411 Masonic Dr, Alexandria, LA 71301
Tel.: (318) 704-6135
Web Site: https://linetecservices.com
Industrial Electrical Product Distr
N.A.I.C.S.: 423610

Subsidiary (Non-US):

NPL Canada Ltd.   (2)
1 Royal Gate Boulevard Suite E, Vaughan, L4L 8Z7, ON, Canada
Tel.: (905) 222-9224
Web Site: https://nplcanada.com
Natural Gas Distr
N.A.I.C.S.: 221210

Subsidiary (Domestic):

NPL Construction Co.   (2)
5080 S Cameron St, Las Vegas, NV 89118
Tel.: (702) 222-9224
Web Site: https://gonpl.com
Oil & Gas Pipeline Construction Services
N.A.I.C.S.: 237120

National Powerline LLC   (2)
19820 N 7th Ave Ste 120, Phoenix, AZ 85027
Tel.: (623) 879-7959
Web Site: https://nationalpowerline.com
Electronic Services
N.A.I.C.S.: 237130

New England Utility Constructors, Inc.   (2)
94 Glenn St, Lawrence, MA 01843
Tel.: (617) 389-5500
Web Site: https://www.neuco-inc.com
Natural Gas Transportation Services
N.A.I.C.S.: 211130
Craig T. Campbell *(VP-Operations)*

Riggs Distler & Company Inc.   (2)
4 Esterbrook Ln, Cherry Hill, NJ 08003
Tel.: (856) 433-6000
Web Site: https://www.riggsdistler.com
Sales Range: $100-124.9 Million
Emp.: 200
Mechanical Contractor
N.A.I.C.S.: 238220
Stephen M. Zemaitatis Jr. *(Pres & CEO)*

Subsidiary (Domestic):

HT Sweeney & Son Inc.   (3)
308 East Dutton Mill Rd, Brookhaven, PA 19015
Tel.: (610) 872-8896
Web Site: https://www.htsweeney.com
Rev.: $3,000,000
Emp.: 15
Site Preparation Contractor
N.A.I.C.S.: 238910
Kevin Sauler *(Mgr-Equipment)*

Dominion Energy Questar Pipeline, LLC   (1)
333 S State St, Salt Lake City, UT 84145-0360
Tel.: (801) 324-4400
Web Site: http://www.questarpipeline.com
Biomass Electric Power Generation Services
N.A.I.C.S.: 221117

Northern Pipeline Construction Co.   (1)
19820 N 7th Ave Ste 120, Phoenix, AZ 85027   (100%)
Tel.: (623) 582-1235
Web Site: https://www.gonpl.com
Sales Range: $1-9.9 Million
Emp.: 60
Construction of Underground Pipelines
N.A.I.C.S.: 237120
Jim Garner *(Dir-Ops)*

Paiute Pipeline Company   (1)
5241 Spring Mountain Rd, Las Vegas, NV 89150
Tel.: (702) 876-7178
Web Site: http://www.paiutepipeline.com
Natural Gas Transmission Company
N.A.I.C.S.: 221210
Mark Litwin *(VP & Gen Mgr)*
Chris Anderson *(Dir-Gas Ops)*
Carol Vogel *(Supvr-Gas Scheduling)*
Thomas McCune *(Supvr-Centralized Ops)*

Southwest Gas Corporation   (1)
8360 S Durango Dr, Las Vegas, NV 89193-8510
Tel.: (702) 876-7237
Web Site: https://www.swgas.com
Rev.: $1,935,069,000
Assets: $8,803,681,000
Liabilities: $2,983,210,000
Net Worth: $5,820,471,000
Earnings: $154,380,000
Emp.: 2,351
Fiscal Year-end: 12/31/2022
Natural Gas Distr
N.A.I.C.S.: 221210
Karen S. Haller *(Pres & CEO)*
Julie M. Williams *(Sr VP-Continuous Improvement & Optimization)*
Robert J. Stefani *(CFO & Sr VP)*
Lori L. Colvin *(Chief Acctg Officer, VP & Controller)*
Karen S. Haller *(Chief Legal & Admin Officer & Exec VP)*
Kenneth J. Kenny *(VP)*
Thomas E. Moran *(Gen Counsel)*

Southwest Gas Corporation   (1)
PO Box 24531, Oakland, CA 94623-1531
Web Site: https://www.swgas.com
Emp.: 2,300
Natural Gas Distribution Services
N.A.I.C.S.: 221210
H. G. Laub *(Founder)*

Southwest Gas Transmission Company   (1)
5241 Spring Mountain Rd, Las Vegas, NV 89150-0002   (99%)
Tel.: (702) 876-7011
Web Site: https://www.swgas.com
Sales Range: Less than $1 Million
Transportation of Natural Gas; 1% Owned by Utility Financial Corporation
N.A.I.C.S.: 221210

Utility Financial Corp.   (1)
5241 Spring Mountain Rd, Las Vegas, NV 89150   (100%)
Tel.: (702) 876-7081
Web Site: https://www.swgas.com
Sales Range: $200-249.9 Million
Financial & Investments Group
N.A.I.C.S.: 525990

W.S. Nicholls Construction Inc.   (1)
48 Cowansview Road, Cambridge, N1R 7N3, ON, Canada
Tel.: (519) 740-3757
Web Site: https://www.wsnconstruction.com
Emp.: 15
Construction Engineering Services
N.A.I.C.S.: 237990

Southwest Gas Holdings, Inc.—(Continued)

Michael Fournier *(Sr VP)*

W.S. Nicholls Industries Inc. (1)
270 Southgate Drive, Guelph, N1G 4P5,
ON, Canada
Tel.: (519) 763-2292
Web Site: http://www.wsnicholls.com
Emp.: 20
Construction Engineering Services
N.A.I.C.S.: 237990

SOW GOOD INC.
1440 N Union Bower Rd, Irving, TX
75061
Tel.: (214) 623-6055   **DE**
Web Site:
https://www.thisissowgood.com
Year Founded: 2010
SOWG—(OTCQB)
Rev.: $16,070,924
Assets: $21,488,558
Liabilities: $14,208,109
Net Worth: $7,280,449
Earnings: ($3,060,433)
Emp.: 225
Fiscal Year-end: 12/31/23
Oil & Gas Exploration Services
N.A.I.C.S.: 211120
Ira Goldfarb *(Co-Founder & Exec
Chm)*
Claudia Goldfarb *(Co-Founder &
CEO)*

SPANISH BROADCASTING
SYSTEM INC.
7007 NW 77th Ave, Miami, FL 33166
Tel.: (305) 441-6901   **DE**
Web Site:
https://www.spanishbroadcast
ing.com
Year Founded: 1983
SBSAA—(OTCIQ)
Rev.: $147,330,000
Assets: $391,536,000
Liabilities: $413,887,000
Net Worth: ($22,351,000)
Earnings: ($40,699,000)
Emp.: 465
Fiscal Year-end: 12/31/23
Radio Broadcasting Stations Owner &
Operator
N.A.I.C.S.: 516210
Albert Rodriguez *(COO)*
Donny Hudson *(VP-Sls & Gen Mgr)*
Elisa Torres *(Exec VP-Network-Natl)*
Richard D. Lara *(Gen Counsel &
Exec VP)*
Geraldo Arriaga *(VP-Digital Media Sls
& Mgr-Digital Sls & Local Sls)*
David Bailin *(Sr VP-Network Sls Dev-
Natl)*
Jose I. Molina *(CFO)*
James Lyke *(Sr VP-Sls-Network)*
Mario Taboada *(Mgr-Sls-Natl)*
Jimmy Boloix *(Specialist-Event)*
Patty Valdes *(Mgr-Local Sls)*
Carolina Patino *(Mgr-Gen Sls)*
Raul Alarcon Jr. *(Chm, Pres & CEO)*

Subsidiaries:

93.3 La Raza KRZZ FM (1)
1420 Koll Cir, San Jose, CA 95112
Tel.: (408) 546-4000
Web Site: http://www.yosoyraza.com
Sales Range: $200-249.9 Million
Emp.: 35
Radio Station Operator
N.A.I.C.S.: 516110

AIRE Radio Network LLC (1)
105 Madison Ave 2nd Fl, New York, NY
10016
Tel.: (212) 541-9200
Web Site: http://www.aireradionetworks.com
Radio Broadcasting Services
N.A.I.C.S.: 516210
Elisa Torres *(Exec VP)*
Erika Marrero *(VP-Network Sls)*

Blanca Navas *(VP-Affiliate Sls)*
Jason Corelli *(Sr VP-Network Sls)*
Jennifer Castro *(Sls Mgr-Network)*

KLAX Licensing, Inc. (1)
3191 Coral Way Ste 805, Coral Gables, FL
33145-3222
Tel.: (310) 203-0900
Radio Station Services
N.A.I.C.S.: 516110

**Spanish Broadcasting System of Cali-
fornia Inc.** (1)
5055 Wilshire Blvd 7th Fl, Los Angeles, CA
90036
Tel.: (310) 229-3200
Web Site: https://www.lamusica.com
Sales Range: $10-24.9 Million
Emp.: 40
Radio Broadcasting Stations Owner & Op-
erator
N.A.I.C.S.: 516110

WXDJ Licensing, Inc. (1)
3191 Coral Way Ste 805, Miami, FL 33145
Tel.: (305) 444-9292
Radio Station Services
N.A.I.C.S.: 516110

SPAR GROUP, INC.
1910 Opdyke Ct, Auburn Hills, MI
48326
Tel.: (248) 364-7727   **DE**
Web Site: https://www.sparinc.com
SGRP—(NASDAQ)
Rev.: $261,268,000
Assets: $94,598,000
Liabilities: $56,537,000
Net Worth: $38,061,000
Earnings: ($732,000)
Emp.: 1,437
Fiscal Year-end: 12/31/22
Merchandising & Marketing Services
Supplier
N.A.I.C.S.: 561499
Kori G. Belzer *(COO-Global)*
William H. Bartels *(Vice Chm)*
James R. Gillis *(Chm)*
Mike Matacunas *(Pres & CEO)*
Ron Lutz *(Chief Comml Officer-
Global)*

Subsidiaries:

**Resource Plus of North Florida,
Inc.** (1)
9636 Heckscher Dr, Jacksonville, FL
32226-2429   **(100%)**
Web Site: https://resourcep.com
Emp.: 850
Retail Merchandising Consulting & Support
Services
N.A.I.C.S.: 561499

SGRP Meridian (1)
16 Ennisdale Drive Durban North, Kwa Zulu
Natal, Durban, 4051, South Africa **(100%)**
Tel.: (27) 315636965
Web Site: http://www.sgrpmeridian.com
Sales Range: $25-49.9 Million
Emp.: 100
International Supplier of Retail & Marketing
Services
N.A.I.C.S.: 541613
Brian Mason *(Mng Dir)*

SGRP Meridian (Pty), Ltd. (1)
16 Ennisdale Drive, Durban, 4051, South
Africa
Tel.: (27) 315636965
Web Site: https://www.sgrpmeridian.com
Retail Merchandising Services
N.A.I.C.S.: 561499

**SPAR (Shanghai) Marketing Manage-
ment Company Ltd.** (1)
Room 2601-02 Haiseng International Build-
ing 849 Wanhangdu Road, JinAn District,
Shanghai, 200042, China
Tel.: (86) 2162310156
Web Site: http://www.sparchina.com
International Supplier of Retail & Marketing
Services
N.A.I.C.S.: 541613

SPAR Canada Company (1)
10 Planchet Road Unit 21, Vaughan, L4K

2C8, ON, Canada
Tel.: (416) 783-2676
Web Site: https://www.sparcanada.ca
Merchandising & Marketing Services
N.A.I.C.S.: 455219

SPAR China Ltd. (1)
Room 1501 Jinhang Bldg No 83 Wan-
hangdu Rd, Jing'an District, Shanghai,
200040, China
Tel.: (86) 2162886016
Web Site: https://www.spar.cn
Merchandising & Marketing Services
N.A.I.C.S.: 455219

SPAR FM Japan (1)
2-4-16 Uchihonmachi, Chuo-ku, Osaka,
540-0026, Japan   **(100%)**
Tel.: (81) 669493610
Web Site: https://sparfmjapan.co.jp
International Supplier of Retail & Marketing
Services
N.A.I.C.S.: 541613

SPAR Greece (1)
128-130 Alexandras Avenue 4th floor, PO
Box 903, Drafi Rafina, 11471, Athens,
Greece   **(100%)**
Tel.: (30) 2106443981
Sales Range: $1-9.9 Million
Emp.: 1
International Supplier of Retail & Marketing
Services
N.A.I.C.S.: 541613

**SPAR KROGNOS Marketing Private
Limited** (1)
G 6 / B 1 Ground Fl Exevo Bldg, Mohan
Cooperative Industrial Estate Mathura
Road, New Delhi, 110 044, India
Tel.: (91) 1130821755
Web Site: https://www.spar-krognos.com
Marketing Consulting Services
N.A.I.C.S.: 541613
Sandeep Verma *(CEO)*

SPAR Marketing Force, Inc. (1)
1910 Opdyke Ct, Auburn Hills, MI 48326
Tel.: (248) 364-7727
Web Site: http://www.sparinc.com
Sales Range: $25-49.9 Million
Emp.: 100
Marketing & Retail Services
N.A.I.C.S.: 541613

**SPAR TODOPROMO, SAPI, de
CV** (1)
Jose Maria Velasco No 101 PB, Colonia
San Jose Insurgentes Benito Juarez,
03900, Mexico, Mexico
Tel.: (52) 5553370800
Web Site: https://spar-todopromo.mx
Marketing Consulting Services
N.A.I.C.S.: 541613

SPAR, Inc. (1)
333 Westchester Ave S Bldg Ste 204,
White Plains, NY 10604
Tel.: (914) 332-4100
Web Site: http://sparinc.com
Merchandise Management Services
N.A.I.C.S.: 561499

SPARFACTS Australia Pty Ltd. (1)
Level 1 - 4 Prohasky Street, Port Mel-
bourne, 3207, VIC, Australia   **(100%)**
Tel.: (61) 393762255
Web Site: https://www.sparfacts.com.au
Sales Range: $75-99.9 Million
Emp.: 400
Retail Merchandising Services to Wholesal-
ers, Marketers & Retailers
N.A.I.C.S.: 541613

SPARTA COMMERCIAL SER-
VICES, INC.
555 5th Ave 14th Fl, New York, NY
10017
Tel.: (212) 239-2666   **NV**
Web Site:
https://www.spartacommercial.com
SRCO—(OTCIQ)
Rev.: $192,040
Assets: $119,681
Liabilities: $9,756,278
Net Worth: ($9,636,597)
Earnings: ($607,251)
Emp.: 4

Fiscal Year-end: 04/30/24
Power Sports Financing & Leasing
Services
N.A.I.C.S.: 532120
Anthony L. Havens *(Founder, Chm,
Pres, CEO & CFO)*
Sandra L. Ahman *(Sec & VP)*

Subsidiaries:

Agoge Global USA, Inc. (1)
6 Landmark Sq 4th Fl, Stamford, CT 06901
Web Site: https://agogeglobalusa.com
Business Intermediary Services
N.A.I.C.S.: 523910

New World Health Brands, Inc. (1)
555 5th Ave 14th Fl, New York, NY 10017
Web Site:
https://newworldhealthbrands.com
Healthcare Services
N.A.I.C.S.: 621999

iMobile Solutions, Inc. (1)
555 5th Ave 14th Fl, New York, NY 10017
Web Site:
https://www.imobilesolutionsinc.com
Vehicle Insurance Services
N.A.I.C.S.: 524126
Tyler Thornhill *(Mgr-Client Relationship)*

SPARTA HEALTHCARE AC-
QUISITION CORP.
2537 Research Blvd Ste 201, Fort
Collins, CO 80526
Tel.: (925) 400-3123   **DE**
Year Founded: 2021
SPTAU—(NASDAQ)
Investment Services
N.A.I.C.S.: 523999
Michael K. Handley *(Chm, Pres &
CEO)*
David Mehalick *(Chief Bus Officer)*
Nicholas H. Hemmerly *(CFO, Treas &
Sec)*
Cozette M. McAvoy *(Chief Legal Offi-
cer)*
Philip E. Gaucher Jr. *(COO)*

SPARTAN ACQUISITION
CORP.
9 W 57th St 43rd Fl, New York, NY
10019
Tel.: (212) 515-3200
Web Site:
http://www.spartanenergyspac.com
VDKA.P—(TSXV)
Assets: $165,208
Liabilities: $29,783
Net Worth: $135,425
Earnings: ($3,826)
Energy Consulting Services
N.A.I.C.S.: 541690
Geoffrey Strong *(Chm & CEO)*
James Crossen *(CFO & Chief Acctg
Officer)*

SPARX HOLDINGS GROUP,
INC.
780 Reservoir Ave No 123, Cranston,
RI 02910
Tel.: (774) 250-2456   **NV**
Web Site: https://www.sparx-fire.com
Year Founded: 2021
SHGI—(OTCIQ)
Assets: $100,219
Liabilities: $600
Net Worth: $99,619
Earnings: ($47,685)
Fiscal Year-end: 06/30/23
Holding Company
N.A.I.C.S.: 551112

SPECIAL OPPORTUNITIES
FUND, INC.
615 E Michigan St Fl 3, Milwaukee,
WI 53202-5207
Web Site:
https://www.specialopportunities
fundinc.com

SPE—(NYSE)
Rev.: $5,218,795
Assets: $194,847,887
Liabilities: $2,744,119
Net Worth: $192,103,768
Earnings: $2,627,371
Fiscal Year-end: 12/31/19
Other Financial Vehicles
N.A.I.C.S.: 525990
Andrew Dakos (Pres)
Phillip Franklin Goldstein (Chm &
Sec)

SPECIFICITY INC.
410 Ware Blvd Ste 508, Tampa, FL
33619
Tel.: (813) 364-4744   NV
Web Site:
    https://www.specificityinc.com
Year Founded: 2020
SPTY—(OTCQB)
Rev.: $1,148,246
Assets: $401,729
Liabilities: $1,390,066
Net Worth: ($988,337)
Earnings: ($4,344,532)
Emp.: 20
Fiscal Year-end: 12/31/22
Advertising Material Distribution Ser-
vices
N.A.I.C.S.: 541870
Jason Wood (Chm, Pres, CEO, CFO,
Treas & Sec)
Bill Anderson (COO)

SPECTACULAR SOLAR, INC.
50 Cragwood Rd Ste 101, South
Plainfield, NJ 07080
Web Site:
    https://www.spectacularsolar.com
SPSO—(OTCIQ)
Solar Electric Power Generation
N.A.I.C.S.: 221114
Douglas F. Heck (Founder, Chm &
CEO)

SPECTAIRE HOLDINGS INC.
155 Arlington St, Watertown, MA
02472
Tel.: (508) 213-8991   DE
Web Site: https://www.spectaire.com
Year Founded: 2021
SPEC—(NASDAQ)
Holding Company; Air Quality Mea-
surement Equipment Mfr
N.A.I.C.S.: 551111
Brian Semkiw (Chm & CEO)
Chris Grossman (Chief Comml Offi-
cer)
Rui Mendes (CIO)

Subsidiaries:

Spectaire Inc.   (1)
155 Arlington St, Watertown, MA 02472
Tel.: (508) 213-8991
Web Site: https://www.spectaire.com
Air Quality Measuring Equipment Mfr
N.A.I.C.S.: 334519
Brian Semkiw (CEO)

SPECTRA SYSTEMS CORPO-
RATION
40 Wminster St 2 nd Fl, Providence,
RI 02903
Tel.: (401) 274-4700
Web Site: https://www.spsy.com
SPSY—(LSE)
Rev.: $13,233,789
Assets: $31,328,681
Liabilities: $4,217,685
Net Worth: $27,110,996
Earnings: $4,335,233
Emp.: 31
Fiscal Year-end: 12/31/19
Software Development Services
N.A.I.C.S.: 541511

Nabil M. Lawandy (Founder, Pres &
CEO)
William Goltsos (VP-Engrg)
Edward Spies (CFO)

SPECTRA7 MICROSYSTEMS
INC.
2550 N 1st St Ste 500, San Jose, CA
95131
Tel.: (408) 770-2915   Ca
Web Site: http://www.spectra7.com
Year Founded: 2010
SEV—(OTCIQ)
Rev.: $1,031,933
Assets: $949,415
Liabilities: $15,226,037
Net Worth: ($14,276,622)
Earnings: ($6,157,634)
Emp.: 40
Fiscal Year-end: 12/31/20
Analog Semiconductor Mfr
N.A.I.C.S.: 334413
Andrew Kim (CTO & VP-Engrg)
John Mitchell (CMO)
Ronald J. Pasek (Chm)
Raouf Halim (CEO)
Bonnie Tomei (CFO)

SPECTRAL AI, INC.
2515 McKinney Ave Ste 1000, Dallas,
TX 75201
Tel.: (972) 499-4934   DE
Web Site: https://www.spectral-
ai.com
Year Founded: 2020
MDAI—(NASDAQ)
Rev.: $18,056,000
Assets: $10,692,000
Liabilities: $12,401,000
Net Worth: ($1,709,000)
Earnings: ($20,854,000)
Emp.: 80
Fiscal Year-end: 12/31/23
Software Development Services
N.A.I.C.S.: 541511
Stan Micek (Interim COO)
Peter M. Carlson (CEO)

SPECTRAL CAPITAL CORPO-
RATION
701 5th Ave, Seattle, WA 98104 5119
Tel.: (206) 385-6490   NV
Web Site:
    https://www.spectralcapital.com
FCCN—(OTCIQ)
Rev.: $98,323
Assets: $35,672
Liabilities: $227,674
Net Worth: ($192,002)
Earnings: ($240,988)
Emp.: 1
Fiscal Year-end: 12/31/22
Gold Mining Services
N.A.I.C.S.: 212220
Jenifer Osterwalder (Pres, CEO,
Chief Acctg Officer, Treas & Sec)
Stephen Spalding (Interim CFO &
Interim Chief Acctg Officer)

SPECTRALCAST, INC.
1850 Diamond St Ste 101, San Mar-
cos, CA 92078
Tel.: (619) 717-2315   FL
Web Site:
    http://www.spectralcast.com
Year Founded: 2006
SPEC—(OTCIQ)
Electronic Components Mfr
N.A.I.C.S.: 334419
Robert N. Meyer (CEO)
Dustin Yohner (Dir-Bus Dev)
Sreenath Reddy (Exec VP)
Elwood Sprenger (Dir-IR)
David Severson (CFO)

SPECTRUM BRANDS HOLD-
INGS, INC.
3001 Deming Way, Middleton, WI
53562
Tel.: (608) 275-3340   DE
Web Site:
    http://www.spectrumbrands.com
Year Founded: 1954
SPB—(NYSE)
Rev.: $2,918,800,000
Assets: $5,258,400,000
Liabilities: $2,740,100,000
Net Worth: $2,518,300,000
Earnings: $1,801,900,000
Emp.: 3,100
Fiscal Year-end: 09/30/23
Holding Company
N.A.I.C.S.: 551112
David M. Maura (Chm & CEO)
Ehsan Zargar (Gen Counsel, Sec &
Exec VP)
Randal D. Lewis (COO & Exec VP)
Jeremy W. Smeltser (CFO & Exec
VP)
Rebeckah Long (Sr VP-Global HR)
David Albert (Pres-Home & Personal
Care Appliances)
John Pailthorp (Pres-Global Pet
Care)
Troy Duecker (Pres-Home & Garden)
Tim Goff (Pres-Hardware & Home
Improvement)
Javier Andrade-Marin (Pres)

Subsidiaries:

Armitage Pet Care Limited   (1)
Armitage House, Colwick, Nottingham, NG4
2BA, United Kingdom
Pet Care Services
N.A.I.C.S.: 812910

Compass Production Partners,
LP   (1)
204 N Robinson Ste 1300, Oklahoma City,
OK 73102
Tel.: (405) 594-4141
Web Site:
    http://www.compassproductionlp.com
Oil & Gas Production
N.A.I.C.S.: 211120
Matthew K. Grubb (Pres & CEO)

For Life Products, LLC   (1)
2301 SW 145th Ave, Miramar, FL 33027
Web Site:
    https://www.rejuvenateproducts.com
Home Improvement Product Mfr
N.A.I.C.S.: 335220

LightSquared Company   (1)
10802 Parkridge Blvd, Reston, VA 20191-
4334
Tel.: (703) 390-2700
Web Site: http://www.lightsquared.com
Sales Range: $25-49.9 Million
Emp.: 110
Satellite Mobile Digital Voice & Data Com-
munications Services
N.A.I.C.S.: 517410

Subsidiary (Non-US):

LightSquared Company -
Canada   (2)
1601 Telesat Court, Ottawa, K1B 1B9, ON,
Canada
Tel.: (613) 742-0000
Web Site: http://www.lightsquared.com
Sales Range: $25-49.9 Million
Mobile Satellite Communications Services
N.A.I.C.S.: 517112

NZCH Corporation   (1)
450 Park Ave 29th Fl, New York, NY
10022   (99.5%)
Tel.: (212) 906-8555
Emp.: 3
Website Publisher
N.A.I.C.S.: 513199
Omar Marwan Asali (Pres)
George C. Nicholson (Acting Chief Acctg
Officer, CFO & Sr VP)

Salus Capital Partners LLC   (1)

197 First Ave Ste 250, Needham Heights,
MA 02494-2816
Tel.: (617) 420-2670
Web Site: http://www.saluscapital.com
Emp.: 12
Commercial Finance & Asset Management
Services
N.A.I.C.S.: 525990
Jacqueline M. Bamman (Sr VP-HR)
Ann M. O'Keefe (Sr VP-Collateral Over-
sight)
Alex E. Bourdony (VP & Controller)
Eric D. Campion (VP-Collateral Oversight)
Megan E. Flaherty (VP-Loan & Credit Ops)
Craig L. McGrail (VP-Capital Allocation &
Fin Analysis)
Aaron S. Miller (VP-Special Assets)

Spectrum Brands Legacy, Inc.   (1)
3001 Deming Way, Middleton, WI
53562   (100%)
Tel.: (608) 275-3340
Web Site: http://www.spectrumbrands.com
Rev.: $5,007,400,000
Assets: $7,419,700,000
Liabilities: $5,573,000,000
Net Worth: $1,846,700,000
Earnings: $295,800,000
Emp.: 16,800
Fiscal Year-end: 09/30/2017
Holding Company; Electric Appliances De-
signer, Mfr & Whslr
N.A.I.C.S.: 551112

Subsidiary (Domestic):

Armored AutoGroup Parent, Inc.   (2)
44 Old Ridgebury Rd Ste 300, Danbury, CT
06810-5107
Tel.: (203) 205-2900
Automobile Parts Mfr
N.A.I.C.S.: 336110

Subsidiary (Non-US):

Cannines Supplies de Mexico S. de
R.L. de C.V.   (2)
Tannery Street No 102, Leon, 37490, Gua-
najuato, Mexico
Tel.: (52) 4777635828
Emp.: 30
Dog & Cat Food Mfr
N.A.I.C.S.: 311111
Elizabeth Sanchez Hernandez (Coord-
Health, Safety & Environmental Supplies)

Compania Agroindustrial Agrocueros
S.A.   (2)
Panamericana Norte Km 6 1/2 El Pisque
S/N-Izamba, Ambato, Ecuador
Tel.: (593) 32854949
Electrical Appliance Whslr
N.A.I.C.S.: 423610

Subsidiary (Domestic):

IDQ Holdings, Inc.   (2)
2901 W Kingsley Rd, Garland, TX 75041
Tel.: (214) 778-4600
Holding Company
N.A.I.C.S.: 551112

Subsidiary (Non-US):

Kent Chamois Company Ltd   (2)
PO Box 16, Tunbridge Wells, TN3 0JZ,
United Kingdom
Tel.: (44) 1892837070
Automotive Parts & Accessory Store Opera-
tor
N.A.I.C.S.: 441330
Jerry Salaman (Mng Dir)

Rayovac Europe Limited   (2)
2 Stephenson Road, Washington, NE37
3HW, United Kingdom
Tel.: (44) 1914196000
Battery Distr
N.A.I.C.S.: 423610

Subsidiary (Domestic):

Salix Animal Health, LLC   (2)
198 Lock Rd, Deerfield Beach, FL 33442
Tel.: (954) 425-0001
Emp.: 25
Animal Production Services
N.A.I.C.S.: 115210

Subsidiary (Non-US):

Spectrum Brands Austria Gmbh   (2)

Spectrum Brands Holdings, Inc.—(Continued)

Europaring A04 501, 2345, Brunn am Ge-
birge, Austria
Tel.: (43) 1863390
Electrical Appliance Mfr
N.A.I.C.S.: 335220

Spectrum Brands Benelux B.V. (2)
Computerweg 8, 3542 DR, Utrecht, Nether-
lands
Web Site: http://www.spectrumbrands.com
Electrical Appliance Mfr
N.A.I.C.S.: 335220

**Spectrum Brands Brasil Industria e
Comercio de Bens de Consumo
Ltda** (2)
Rod Br 232 KM 9 3-Hall A, Jaboatao dos
Guararapes, 54240-450, Brazil
Tel.: (55) 1121472001
Battery Mfr
N.A.I.C.S.: 335910

Spectrum Brands Denmark A/S (2)
Kirkebjerg Parkvej 11A, 2605, Brondby,
Denmark
Tel.: (45) 47193333
Household Equipment Mfr
N.A.I.C.S.: 423620

**Spectrum Brands HHI (Shenzhen)
Co., Ltd** (2)
1/F Building E Area A Hongfa Technology
Industrial Park, Shenzhen, 518108, Guang-
dong, China
Tel.: (86) 75529833111
Household Equipment Mfr
N.A.I.C.S.: 423620

**Spectrum Brands HHI (Zhongshan)
Co., Ltd** (2)
No 248 Minan N Rd, Fuxing Village Xi-
aolan, Zhongshan, China
Tel.: (86) 76022252115
Emp.: 1,000
Household Equipment Mfr
N.A.I.C.S.: 423620

**Spectrum Brands HHI Mexico, S de
RL de C.V.** (2)
Circuito Siglo Xxi 2000 Colonia Rivera,
21259, Mexicali, Baja California, Mexico
Tel.: (52) 6865642000
Web Site: http://www.spectrumhhimx.com
Household Equipment Mfr
N.A.I.C.S.: 423620

Spectrum Brands Hrvatska d.o.o. (2)
Tratinska 13, Zagreb, Croatia
Tel.: (385) 12341653
Electrical Equipment Merchant Whslr
N.A.I.C.S.: 423610

Spectrum Brands Norway AS (2)
Queen Eufemias gate 16, 1414, Trollasen,
Norway
Tel.: (47) 66808400
Household Equipment Mfr
N.A.I.C.S.: 423620

**Spectrum Brands Singapore Private
Limited** (2)
410 North Bridge Road, Singapore, 188726,
Singapore
Tel.: (65) 63375381
Household Equipment Mfr
N.A.I.C.S.: 423620
Howard Lien (Gen Mgr)

Subsidiary (Domestic):

Spectrum Brands, Inc. (2)
3001 Deming Way, Middleton, WI 53562-
1431
Tel.: (608) 275-3340
Web Site: https://www.spectrumbrands.com
Holding Company; Batteries, Lighting
Equipment & Personal Care Products Mfr &
Whslr
N.A.I.C.S.: 551112

Subsidiary (Non-US):

8 in 1 Pet Products GmbH (3)
An der Schwanemuhle 2, 49324, Melle,
Germany
Tel.: (49) 54221050
Web Site: https://www.8in1.eu
Animal Food Product Mfr
N.A.I.C.S.: 311119

Subsidiary (Domestic):

HPG LLC (3)
18421 Newport Dr, Arlington, WA 98223-
5026
Tel.: (360) 631-0638
Billing Services
N.A.I.C.S.: 541219

Subsidiary (Non-US):

Iams Europe B.V. (3)
Vosmatenweg 4, Coevorden, 7742 PB,
Netherlands
Tel.: (31) 524593100
Web Site: http://www.iams.nl
Emp.: 220
Animal Feed Mfr
N.A.I.C.S.: 311111
Anja Kruger (Mng Dir)

Pifco Ltd. (3)
3rd Fl Sisson Street, Manchester, M350HS,
Lancashire, United Kingdom
Tel.: (44) 1619473000
Electrical & Electronic Appliance Whslr
N.A.I.C.S.: 423620

Subsidiary (Domestic):

**Remington Licensing
Corporation** (3)
601 Rayovac Dr, Madison, WI 53711-2497
Tel.: (608) 275-3340
Sales Range: $400-449.9 Million
Personal Care Products Licensing & Distr
N.A.I.C.S.: 533110

Subsidiary (Non-US):

Remington Consumer Products (4)
Watermans House Kingsbury Cresent, The
Causeway, Staines-upon-Thames, TW18
3BA, United Kingdom
Tel.: (44) 1784411411
Web Site: http://www.remington.co.uk
Sales Range: $10-24.9 Million
Emp.: 50
Personal Care Product Distr
N.A.I.C.S.: 423620

**Remington Consumer Products (Ire-
land) Ltd.** (4)
B12 Ballymount Corporate Park, Dublin, 12,
Ballymount, Ireland (100%)
Tel.: (353) 142 951 40
Web Site: http://www.spectrumbrands.co.uk
Sales Range: $200-249.9 Million
Emp.: 6
Personal Care Product Distr
N.A.I.C.S.: 423620

**Remington Products New Zealand
Ltd.** (4)
Level No 8 HUgo Johnston Drive, Penrose,
1061, Auckland, New Zealand (100%)
Tel.: (64) 800 736 776
Web Site: http://www.remington-
products.com
Sales Range: $150-199.9 Million
Emp.: 13
Battery & Personal Grooming Distr
N.A.I.C.S.: 423620

Subsidiary (Domestic):

Russell Hobbs, Inc. (3)
3633 S Flamingo Rd, Miramar, FL
33027 (100%)
Tel.: (954) 883-1000
Web Site: http://www.russellhobbsinc.com
Sales Range: $650-699.9 Million
Emp.: 575
Holding Company; Small Household Appli-
ance Licensing, Marketing & Distr
N.A.I.C.S.: 551112

Subsidiary (Non-US):

Applica Canada Corporation (4)
131 Saramia Crescent 2, Concord, L4K
4P7, ON, Canada
Tel.: (905) 660-3335
Electrical & Electronic Appliance Whslr
N.A.I.C.S.: 423620

Subsidiary (Domestic):

Applica Consumer Products, Inc. (4)
3633 Flamingo Rd, Miramar, FL 33027
Tel.: (954) 883-1000

Web Site: http://www.applicainc.com
Sales Range: $50-74.9 Million
Emp.: 500
Small Household Appliance Licensing, Mar-
keting & Distr
N.A.I.C.S.: 423620

Subsidiary (Non-US):

**Applica Servicios de Mexico, S. De
R.L. de C.V.** (4)
Avenida Presidente Masaryk 61 Chaplte-
pec Morales, Miguel Hidalgo, 11570,
Mexico, Mexico
Tel.: (52) 5552639918
Consumer Battery Whslr
N.A.I.C.S.: 423120

**Russell Hobbs Deutschland
GmbH** (4)
Am Unisys-Park 1, 65843, Sulzbach, Ger-
many
Tel.: (49) 61967719200
Web Site: https://www.de.russellhobbs.com
Battery Mfr & Distr
N.A.I.C.S.: 335910
Thomas Markus (Mgr-HR)

Russell Hobbs Limited (4)
Regent Mill Fir Street, Failsworth, Man-
chester, M35 0HS, United Kingdom
Tel.: (44) 161 947 3000
Web Site: http://www.spectrumbrands.co.uk
Emp.: 160
Home Appliances
N.A.I.C.S.: 335210
Timothy J. Wright (Chm-Supervisory Bd)

Salton Australia Pty. Ltd. (4)
1 Chifley Drive Chifley Business Park, Men-
tone, 3194, VIC, Australia
Tel.: (61) 385860100
Web Site:
http://www.spectrumbrands.com.au
Emp.: 25
Home Appliance Distr
N.A.I.C.S.: 335210

Subsidiary (Non-US):

SPB Sweden AB (3)
Gustavslundsvagen 133 Plan 10, 167 51,
Bromma, Sweden
Tel.: (46) 858713000
Grooming & Styling Products & Battery
Sales
N.A.I.C.S.: 423990

Subsidiary (Domestic):

Schultz Company (3)
13260 Corporate Exchange Dr, Bridgeton,
MO 63044
Tel.: (014) 290-0270
Lawn & Garden Retailer
N.A.I.C.S.: 444240

Subsidiary (Non-US):

Spectrum Brands (UK) Limited (3)
Regent Mill Fir Street, Failsworth, Man-
chester, M35 0HS, United Kingdom
Tel.: (44) 1619473000
Web Site:
https://www.spectrumbrands.co.uk
Electrical & Electronic Appliance Whslr
N.A.I.C.S.: 423620

**Spectrum Brands Australia Pty.
Ltd.** (3)
11 Chifley Dr, Mentone, 3194, VIC, Austra-
lia
Tel.: (61) 385616000
Web Site: http://www.remington-
products.com.au
Electrical & Electronic Appliance Whslr
N.A.I.C.S.: 423620

**Spectrum Brands Bulgaria
EOOD** (3)
161 Iztichna Tangenta Blvd, 1592, Sofia,
Bulgaria
Tel.: (359) 29790401
Durable Products Whslr
N.A.I.C.S.: 423990

Spectrum Brands Canada, Inc. (3)
101-255 Longside Drive, Mississauga, L5W
0G7, ON, Canada (100%)
Tel.: (905) 361-7324
Consumer Product Mfr

N.A.I.C.S.: 337126

Spectrum Brands Colombia S.A. (3)
Kra 17 No 89-40, Bogota, Colombia
Tel.: (57) 16444848
Emp.: 97
Durable Goods Whslr
N.A.I.C.S.: 423990
Sandra Baila (Mgr)

Spectrum Brands Europe GmbH (3)
Otto-Volger-Strasse 7c, 65843, Sulzbach,
Germany
Tel.: (49) 61969024000
Electrical & Electronic Appliance Whslr
N.A.I.C.S.: 423620

Spectrum Brands Hrvatska d.o.o. (3)
Petrova 120, 10 000, Zagreb, Croatia
Tel.: (385) 12341653
Durable Goods Whslr
N.A.I.C.S.: 423990

Spectrum Brands Italia S.r.L. (3)
Palazzo Pacinotti Via Ludovico il Moro n 6,
20080, Basiglio, Italy
Tel.: (39) 0821700821
Electrical & Electronic Appliance Whslr
N.A.I.C.S.: 423620

**Spectrum Brands New Zealand
Ltd.** (3)
Level 1 No 8 Hugo, PO Box 9817, Newmar-
ket, Auckland, New Zealand
Tel.: (64) 95717700
Web Site: http://www.spectrumbrands.co.nz
Emp.: 14
Battery Mfr & Distr
N.A.I.C.S.: 335910

Spectrum Brands Norway AS (3)
Trollasveien 8, PB 7, 01414, Trollasen, Nor-
way
Tel.: (47) 66808400
Emp.: 2
Grooming & Styling Products & Battery
Sales
N.A.I.C.S.: 423990

**Spectrum Brands Poland Sp.
Z.o.o.** (3)
Ul Bitwy Warszawskiej 1920r 7a, 02-366,
Warsaw, Poland
Tel.: (48) 225980700
Web Site: http://www.varta-consumer.pl
Battery Mfr & Distr
N.A.I.C.S.: 335910

Spectrum Brands Romania S.r.L. (3)
Str Ardealului Nr 7, 075100, Otopeni, Ro-
mania
Tel.: (40) 213522949
Durable Goods Whslr
N.A.I.C.S.: 423990

Spectrum Brands Spain S.L. (3)
Ballars 193 9th Floor, 08005, Barcelona,
Spain
Tel.: (34) 932070166
Grooming & Styling Products & Battery
Sales
N.A.I.C.S.: 423990

**Spectrum Brands Trgovina,
d.o.o.** (3)
Trzaska cesta 132, 1000, Ljubljana, Slove-
nia
Tel.: (386) 1 564 72 47
Emp.: 4
Grooming & Styling Products & Battery
Sales
N.A.I.C.S.: 423990
Ducan Cooo (Mng Dir)

Plant (Domestic):

**Spectrum Brands, Inc. - Fennimore
Plant** (3)
100 Rayovac Ct, Fennimore, WI 53809-
0128
Tel.: (608) 822-3272
Sales Range: $50-74.9 Million
Emp.: 180
Dry Cell Batteries & Flashlight Products Mfr
N.A.I.C.S.: 335910

Division (Domestic):

**Spectrum Brands, Inc. - Hardware &
Home Improvement** (3)
19701 DaVinci, Lake Forest, CA 92610

Tel.: (949) 672-4003
Web Site: http://www.spectrumbrands.com
Sales Range: $900-999.9 Million
Holding Company; Hardware & Home Improvement Products Mfr & Whslr
N.A.I.C.S.: 551112
Philip S. Szuba (Pres)

Subsidiary (Domestic):

Baldwin Hardware Corporation   (4)
841 E Wyomissing Blvd, Reading, PA 19611-1759
Tel.: (610) 777-7811
Web Site: http://www.baldwinhardware.com
Sales Range: $100-124.9 Million
Emp.: 200
Decorative Brass Accessories, Bath Accessories & Lighting Mfr
N.A.I.C.S.: 332510

Kwikset Corporation   (4)
19701 Da Vinci, Lake Forest, CA 92610
Tel.: (949) 672-4000
Web Site: http://www.kwikset.com
Sales Range: $450-499.9 Million
Emp.: 2,000
Locksets & Security Products Mfr
N.A.I.C.S.: 332510
Brent A. Flaharty (Pres)

Price Pfister, Inc.   (4)
19701 Da Vinci, Foothill Ranch, CA 92610-2622
Tel.: (949) 672-4000
Web Site: http://www.pricepfister.com
Sales Range: $100-124.9 Million
Emp.: 500
Decorative Faucets Mfr
N.A.I.C.S.: 332913

Tell Manufacturing, Inc.   (4)
18 Richard Dr, Lititz, PA 17543
Tel.: (717) 625-2990
Web Site: http://www.tellmfg.com
Sales Range: $25-49.9 Million
Commercial Door Locks & Hardware Mfr & Distr
N.A.I.C.S.: 332510
Mark Wooditch (Controller)

Subsidiary (Non-US):

Tetra (UK) Limited   (3)
The Clock House Mansbridge Road, Southampton, SO18 3HW, Hampshire, United Kingdom
Tel.: (44) 8700554020
Aquarium & Pond Supplier
N.A.I.C.S.: 712130

Tetra GmbH   (3)
Herrenteich 78, 49324, Melle, Germany
Tel.: (49) 54221050
Web Site: https://www.tetra.net
Emp.: 465
Aquaristic & Pond Product Mfr
N.A.I.C.S.: 311119

Tetra Japan K.K.   (3)
1-6-21 Mita Meguro-ku alto Ito Building, Meguro, 153-0062, Tokyo, Japan
Tel.: (81) 337949909
Web Site: http://www.tetra-jp.com
Aquaristic & Pond Product Mfr
N.A.I.C.S.: 311119

The Fair Manufacturing Co. Ltd.   (3)
8851 Street 598 Sangkat Chreang Chamreas, Russei Keo, Phnom Penh, Cambodia
Tel.: (855) 23864237
Web Site: http://www.fmc.com.kh
Animal Food Product Mfr
N.A.I.C.S.: 311119

Subsidiary (Domestic):

United Industries Corporation   (3)
2500 Northwinds Pkwy Ste 375, Alpharetta, GA 30004
Tel.: (770) 360-5200
Web Site: http://www.spectrumbrands.com
Sales Range: $500-549.9 Million
Insecticides, Herbicides & Chemical Plant Food Products Mfr & Whslr
N.A.I.C.S.: 325320

Subsidiary (Domestic):

Liquid Fence Co., Inc.   (4)
5683 Rte 115, Blakeslee, PA 18610

Tel.: (570) 722-8120
Web Site: http://www.liquidfence.com
Animal & Insect Repellents & Fertilizers Mfr
N.A.I.C.S.: 325998

Branch (Domestic):

United Industries Corp. -
Bridgeton   (4)
13260 Corporate Exchange Dr, Bridgeton, MO 63044-3720
Tel.: (314) 427-0780
Web Site: http://www.spectrumbrands.com
Insecticides, Herbicides & Chemical Plant Food Products Mfr & Whslr
N.A.I.C.S.: 325320

Subsidiary (Domestic):

United Pet Group, Inc.   (3)
7794 5 Mile Rd Ste 190, Cincinnati, OH 45230
Tel.: (513) 337-0600
Web Site: http://www.unitedpetgroup.com
Animal Food Product Mfr & Distr
N.A.I.C.S.: 311119

Subsidiary (Non-US):

United Pet Polska Sp. Z.o.o.   (4)
Al Jana Pawa II 15, 00-828, Warsaw, Poland
Tel.: (48) 226976699
Animal Food Product Mfr & Distr
N.A.I.C.S.: 311119

Subsidiary (Non-US):

ZAO "Spectrum Brands" Russia   (3)
Varshavskoe Shosse 9 Bldg 1B, 117105, Moscow, Russia
Tel.: (7) 4959333177
Accumulator & Battery Mfr
N.A.I.C.S.: 335910

Subsidiary (Non-US):

Toastmaster de Mexico S.A.   (2)
Centeotl No 223, Mexico, Mexico
Tel.: (52) 53972848
Emp.: 7
Bakery Products Mfr
N.A.I.C.S.: 311812

Tong Lung Philippines Metal Industry
Co., Inc.   (2)
Subic Bay Industrial Park Subic Bay Freeport Zone, Olongapo, 2200, Sambales, Philippines
Tel.: (63) 472526228
Metal Products Mfr
N.A.I.C.S.: 332999

Subsidiary (Domestic):

United Industries Corporation   (2)
1 Rider Trail Plaza Dr Ste 300, Earth City, MO 63045
Tel.: (314) 683-2400
Web Site:
    http://www.unitedindustriescorporation.com
Emp.: 900
Household Appliance Store Operator
N.A.I.C.S.: 449210

Subsidiary (Non-US):

Viking Acquisitions, S. de RL de
CV   (2)
Calle Fernando Montes de Oca 22, 54035, Tlalnepantla, Mexico
Tel.: (52) 57296561
Electrical Equipment Merchant Whslr
N.A.I.C.S.: 423610

Subsidiary (Domestic):

Weiser Lock Corporation   (2)
19701 Da Vinci, Lake Forest, CA 92610
Tel.: (520) 741-6200
Web Site: http://www.weiserlock.com
Door Locks Mfr
N.A.I.C.S.: 332510

Spectrum Brands Pet LLC   (1)
3001 Commerce St, Blacksburg, VA 24060-6671
Pet Grooming Services
N.A.I.C.S.: 812910

SPECTRUM GROUP INTERNATIONAL, INC.
1063 McGaw Ave Ste 250, Irvine, CA 92614
Tel.: (949) 955-1250   DE
SPGZ—(OTCEM)
Holding Company
N.A.I.C.S.: 551112
Greg Roberts (Pres & CEO)

Subsidiaries:

Spectrum Numismatics International,
Inc.   (1)
1231 E Dyer Rd Ste 100, Santa Ana, CA 92705
Tel.: (949) 955-1250
Web Site: http://www.stacksbowers.com
Sales Range: $150-199.9 Million
Emp.: 40
Rare Coins, Currency & Fine Wines Whslr
N.A.I.C.S.: 423940
Andrew Glassman (Pres)
Peter Treglia (Dir-Currency)

Spectrum Wine Auctions, LLC   (1)
1063 McGaw Ave, Irvine, CA 92614
Tel.: (949) 748-4845
Web Site: http://www.spectrumwine.com
Emp.: 10
Fine Wine Auction Services
N.A.I.C.S.: 561990
Gregory N. Roberts (CEO)
Amanda Keston (Dir-PR)
Kris Briggs (Mgr-Mktg)

Stack's-Bowers Numismatics,
LLC   (1)
1231 E Dyer Rd Ste 100, Santa Ana, CA 92705
Tel.: (949) 253-0916
Web Site: http://www.stacksbowers.com
Rare Coin & Currency Auction Services
N.A.I.C.S.: 561990
Brian Kendrella (Pres)
Chris Napolitano (Exec VP)
Richard Ponterio (Exec VP)
Andrew Glassman (Exec VP)
Christine Karstedt (Exec VP-Consignments)

Subsidiary (Non-US):

Stack's-Bowers & Ponterio, Ltd.   (2)
Unit 1603 Miramall, Tsim Tsa Tsui, China (Hong Kong)
Tel.: (852) 2117 1191
Web Site: http://www.stacksbowers.com
Emp.: 4
Rare Coin & Currency Auction Services
N.A.I.C.S.: 561990
Nirat Lertchitvikul (Dir-Ops-Asia)

SPEED COMMERCE, INC.
1301 E Arapaho Rd Ste 200, Richardson, TX 75081
Tel.: (214) 258-0100   MN
Web Site:
    https://www.speedcommerce.com
Year Founded: 1983
SPDC—(OTCIQ)
Emp.: 1,609
E-Commerce Services for Retailers & Manufacturers
N.A.I.C.S.: 561499
Cary Samourkachian (Pres & CEO)
Michael Manzione (COO)
Gregg Beall (VP-Information Technology)
Jason Chan (VP-Sales & Marketing)
Tim Avant (Sr Dir-Operations)
Rob Tillman (Sr Dir-Operations)
Lauren Groh (Dir-Finance)
Derek Ingram (Dir-Contact Centers)
Laura Martin (Dir-Client Success)
Amanda Perkins (Dir-Human Resources)

Subsidiaries:

Fifth Gear, Inc.   (1)
818 A1a N, Ponte Vedra Beach, FL 32082
Tel.: (904) 285-3400
Rev.: $4,000,000
Emp.: 12
Fulfillment & Customer Contact Centers

N.A.I.C.S.: 561499
Al Langsenkamp (CEO)
Jeff Dahltorp (VP-Plng & Assessment)
Don Van der Weil (CFO)
Rick Hall (VP-Client Success)
Rob McIvaine (VP-Tech)
Blake Vaughn (VP-Sls & Mktg)

Branch (Domestic):

Fifth Gear, Inc.-Missouri   (2)
3016 Georgia St, Louisiana, MO 63353
Tel.: (573) 754-5511
Post Purchase Fulfillment, Call Center & Frieght Management
N.A.I.C.S.: 493110

Fifth Gear, Inc.-Pennsylvania   (2)
1 Maplewood Dr, Hazleton, PA 18202
Tel.: (800) 383-4421
Post Purchase Fulfillment & Frieght Management
N.A.I.C.S.: 493190

Speed Commerce, Inc. - Canada   (1)
450 Export Blvd Unit A, Mississauga, L5S 2A4, ON, Canada
Tel.: (905) 672-0399
Web Site: http://www.speedcommerce.com
Sales Range: $1-9.9 Million
Emp.: 3
Distr of Home Entertainment & Multimedia Software Products
N.A.I.C.S.: 512120

SPEEDEMISSIONS, INC.
2144 Buford Hwy Ste 212, Buford, GA 30518
Tel.: (678) 765-0796
Web Site:
    https://www.speedemissions.com
SPMI—(OTCIQ)
Sales Range: $1-9.9 Million
Emp.: 43
Vehicle Emission Testing Services
N.A.I.C.S.: 811198
Richard A. Parlontieri (Pres & CEO)

SPEEDUS CORP.
1 Dag Hammarskjold Blvd, Freehold, NJ 07728   DE
Year Founded: 1995
SPDE—(OTCIQ)
Cardiac Diagnostic Product Mfr
N.A.I.C.S.: 334510
Shant A. Hovnanian (Pres & CEO)
Thomas A. Finn (CFO & Sec)

SPERO THERAPEUTICS, INC.
675 Massachusetts Ave 14th Fl, Cambridge, MA 02139
Tel.: (857) 242-1600   DE
Web Site:
    https://www.sperotherapeutics.com
Year Founded: 2013
SPRO—(NASDAQ)
Rev.: $53,509,000
Assets: $124,802,000
Liabilities: $48,868,000
Net Worth: $75,934,000
Earnings: ($46,415,000)
Emp.: 35
Fiscal Year-end: 12/31/22
Biotechnology Research & Development Services
N.A.I.C.S.: 541714
Ankit Mahadevia (Co-Founder)
Timothy Keutzer (COO)
Melissa Stundick (VP-Bus Dev)
Michael Pucci (Exec Dir-Early Drug Discovery)
Sharon Klahre (VP-IR & Strategic Fin)
Ian A. Critchley (VP-Clinical Microbiology)
Jay Blackington (VP-People, Strategy & Culture)
Angela Talley (VP-Clinical Dev)
Terese Hoekstra (VP-Market Access)
Jennifer Reese (VP-Medical Affairs)
Satyavrat Shukla (Pres & CEO)

Spero Therapeutics, Inc.—(Continued)

Sath Shukla (CFO)
Esther Rajavelu (Chief Bus Officer)
Thomas R. Parr Jr. (Chief Scientific Officer)

SPHERE ENTERTAINMENT CO.

2 Pennsylvania Plz, New York, NY 10121
Tel.: (725) 258-0001   DE
Web Site:
https://www.sphereentertainment co.com
SPHR—(NYSE)
Rev.: $1,026,889,000
Assets: $4,787,892,000
Liabilities: $2,372,340,000
Net Worth: $2,415,552,000
Earnings: ($200,649,000)
Emp.: 970
Fiscal Year-end: 06/30/24
Holding Company; Promoters of Performing Arts, Sports & Similar Events with Facilities
N.A.I.C.S.: 551112
James L. Dolan (Chm & CEO)
Rich Claffey (COO & Exec VP)
David F. Byrnes (CFO, Treas & Exec VP)
David Granville-Smith (Exec VP)
Andrea Greenberg (Pres)
Gregory Brunner (Principal Acctg Officer, Sr VP & Controller)

Subsidiaries:

MSG Networks Inc.   (1)
11 Pennsylvania Plz 3rd Fl, New York, NY 10001
Tel.: (212) 465-6400
Web Site: https://www.msgnetworks.com
Rev.: $685,797,000
Assets: $850,803,000
Liabilities: $1,403,652,000
Net Worth: ($552,849,000)
Earnings: $185,221,000
Emp.: 180
Fiscal Year-end: 06/30/2020
Sports Franchise, Live Entertainment Venue & Cable Television Network Operator
N.A.I.C.S.: 711211
Lawrence J. Burian (Gen Counsel & Exec VP)
Ari Danes (Sr VP-IR)
Dawn Darino-Gorski (Principal Acctg Officer, Sr VP & Controller)

Subsidiary (Domestic):

ALA Hospitality LLC   (2)
384 Forest Ave Ste 12, Laguna Beach, CA 92651
Tel.: (949) 497-1827
Architecture Consultant Services
N.A.I.C.S.: 541310

MSG Ventures, LLC   (2)
423 Chimney Hill Dr, College Station, TX 77840
Tel.: (979) 703-6586
Entertainment Services
N.A.I.C.S.: 713940

Subsidiary (Domestic):

Obscura Digital, Inc.   (3)
14 Louisiana St Historic Pier 70, San Francisco, CA 94107
Tel.: (415) 227-9979
Media Production Services
N.A.I.C.S.: 561990
Travis Threlkel (Founder & Chief Creative Officer)

Subsidiary (Domestic):

MSGN Holdings, L.P.   (2)
4 Pennsylvania Plaza, New York, NY 10001
Tel.: (212) 465-6034
Web Site: http://www.thegarden.com
Holding Company
N.A.I.C.S.: 551112

Unit (Domestic):

Madison Square Garden Network   (3)
2 Pennsylvania Plz 14th Fl, New York, NY 10121
Tel.: (212) 465-6000
Web Site: http://www.msgnetwork.com
Sales Range: $50-74.9 Million
Emp.: 150
Sports & Entertainment Broadcasting
N.A.I.C.S.: 516120
Andrea Greenberg (Pres & CEO)

Sake No Hana Ltd.   (1)
23 St James's Street, London, SW1A 1HA, United Kingdom
Tel.: (44) 2079258988
Restaurant Operators
N.A.I.C.S.: 722511

Venue Driver, LLC   (1)
6385 S Rainbow Blvd Ste 800, Las Vegas, NV 89118
Tel.: (702) 212-8804
Web Site: https://venuedriver.com
Club Event Services
N.A.I.C.S.: 713990

SPINDLETOP HEALTH ACQUISITION CORP.

7000 N Mopac Ste 315, Austin, TX 78731
Tel.: (512) 961-4633   DE
Year Founded: 2021
SHCAU—(NASDAQ)
Investment Services
N.A.I.C.S.: 523999
Evan S. Melrose (CEO & CFO)
James H. Henry (Chm)
Steve Whitlock (Sec)
JD Moore (Sr VP-Corp Dev)
Kelly Huang (COO)

SPINDLETOP OIL & GAS CO.

12850 Spurling Rd Ste 200, Dallas, TX 75230-1279
Tel.: (972) 644-2581   TX
Web Site:
https://www.spindletopoil.com
Year Founded: 1971
SPND—(OTCIQ)
Rev.: $8,354,000
Assets: $27,807,000
Liabilities: $10,594,000
Net Worth: $17,213,000
Earnings: $669,000
Emp.: 13
Fiscal Year-end: 12/31/22
Crude Petroleum Extraction Services
N.A.I.C.S.: 211120
Chris G. Mazzini (Chm, Pres & CEO)
Michelle H. Mazzini (Gen Counsel, Treas, Sec & VP)
Robert E. Corbin (CFO, Controller & Mgr-Acctg)

Subsidiaries:

Spindletop Drilling Company   (1)
One Spindletop Centre 12850 Spurling Rd Ste 200, Dallas, TX 75230
Tel.: (972) 644-2581
Web Site: http://www.spindletopdrilling.com
Oil & Gas Operation Services
N.A.I.C.S.: 213112

SPIRE GLOBAL, INC.

8000 Towers Crescent Dr Ste 1100, Vienna, VA 22182
Tel.: (202) 301-5127   DE
Web Site: https://www.spire.com
Year Founded: 2020
SPIR—(NYSE)
Rev.: $80,268,000
Assets: $256,512,000
Liabilities: $146,389,000
Net Worth: $110,123,000
Earnings: ($89,411,000)
Emp.: 411
Fiscal Year-end: 12/31/22

Miscellaneous Financial Investment Activities
N.A.I.C.S.: 523999
Boyd C. Johnson (Chief Legal Officer)
Jack Pearlstein (Founder)
Kamal Arafeh (Sr VP-Sls-Global)
Elizabeth Wylie (Head-Bus Dev-Australia & New Zealand)
Hillary Yaffe (Head-Comm)
Seyed Miri (Dir-Space Svcs-Australia & New Zealand)
Benjamin Hackman (Head-IR)
Leonardo Basola (CFO)
Theresa Condor (COO)
Peter Platzer (Pres & CEO)

Subsidiaries:

Spire Global Canada Subsidiary Corp.   (1)
260 Holiday Inn Dr Unit 30 Bldg B, Cambridge, N3C4E8, ON, Canada
Tel.: (519) 622-4445
Software Development Services
N.A.I.C.S.: 541511

Spire Global Luxembourg S.a.r.l.   (1)
33 Rue Sainte Zithe, 2763, Luxembourg, Luxembourg
Tel.: (352) 2855031
Software Development Services
N.A.I.C.S.: 541511

Spire Global Singapore Pte Ltd   (1)
61 Robinson Road 08-02, Singapore, 068893, Singapore
Tel.: (65) 64381630
Software Development Services
N.A.I.C.S.: 541511

Spire Global Subsidiary, Inc.   (1)
8000 Towers Crescent Dr Ste 1100, Vienna, VA 22182
Software Development Services
N.A.I.C.S.: 541511

Spire Global UK Ltd.   (1)
Skypark 6 64 Finnieston Square, Glasgow, G3 8ET, United Kingdom
Tel.: (44) 1413438260
Software Development Services
N.A.I.C.S.: 541511

exactEarth Ltd.   (1)
260 Holiday Inn Drive, Cambridge, N3C 4E8, ON, Canada
Tel.: (519) 622-4445
Web Site: http://www.exactearth.com
Data Services
N.A.I.C.S.: 518210
Sean Maybee (CFO)
Peter Mabson (CEO)

SPIRE, INC

700 Market St, Saint Louis, MO 63101
Tel.: (314) 342-0500   MO
Web Site:
https://www.spireenergy.com
Year Founded: 2001
SR—(NYSE)
Rev.: $2,235,500,000
Assets: $9,356,400,000
Liabilities: $3,749,300,000
Net Worth: $5,607,100,000
Earnings: $271,700,000
Emp.: 3,710
Fiscal Year-end: 09/30/21
Holding Company; Natural Gas Distr
N.A.I.C.S.: 551112
Suzanne Sitherwood (Pres & CEO)
Scott E. Doyle (COO & Exec VP)
Steven P. Rasche (CFO & Exec VP)
Courtney Vomund (Chief Admin Officer & Sec)
Gery Gorla (Chief HR Officer)
Adam Woodard (CFO-Gas Utility & Treas)
Matt Aplington (Chief Legal Officer & VP)

Subsidiaries:

Laclede Development Company   (1)

720 Olive St, Saint Louis, MO 63101   (100%)
Tel.: (314) 342-0500
Web Site: http://www.thelacledegroup.com
Real Estate Development Services
N.A.I.C.S.: 531390
Suzanne Sitherwood (Pres & CEO)

Subsidiary (Domestic):

Laclede Venture Corp.   (2)
720 Olive St, Saint Louis, MO 63101-2338
Tel.: (314) 342-0500
Web Site: http://www.thelacledegroup.com
Sales Range: $350-399.9 Million
Emp.: 1,000
Sales & Services for the Compression of Natural Gas to Third Parties
N.A.I.C.S.: 221210

Laclede Insurance Risk Services, Inc.   (1)
Po Box 22556, Charleston, SC 29413
Tel.: (843) 884-5902
Insurance Management Services
N.A.I.C.S.: 524298

Laclede Investment LLC   (1)
720 Olive St, Saint Louis, MO 63101   (100%)
Tel.: (314) 342-0500
Web Site: http://www.lacledegas.com
Investment Services
N.A.I.C.S.: 523999
Suzanne Sitherwood (Chm, Pres & CEO)

Subsidiary (Domestic):

Laclede Energy Resources, Inc.   (2)
720 Olive St, Saint Louis, MO 63101-2338   (100%)
Tel.: (314) 342-0500
Web Site: http://www.lacledegas.com
Sales Range: $150-199.9 Million
Natural Gas Marketing Services
N.A.I.C.S.: 213112

Subsidiary (Domestic):

Laclede Gas Family Services, Inc.   (3)
720 Olive St, Saint Louis, MO 63101   (100%)
Tel.: (314) 342-0500
Web Site: http://www.lacledegas.com
Sales Range: $75-99.9 Million
Emp.: 1,700
Insurance Services
N.A.I.C.S.: 524298
Suzanne Sitherwood (Pres)

Laclede Pipeline Company   (1)
720 Olive St, Saint Louis, MO 63101-2338   (100%)
Tel.: (314) 342-0500
Web Site: http://www.lacledegas.com
Sales Range: $1-4.9 Billion
Emp.: 1,000
Propane Pipeline Operator
N.A.I.C.S.: 486910
Suzanne Sitherwood (Pres)

Missouri Gas Energy Inc.   (1)
3420 Broadway St, Kansas City, MO 64111-7516   (100%)
Tel.: (816) 756-5261
Web Site:
http://www.missourigasenergy.com
Sales Range: $50-74.9 Million
Emp.: 200
Natural Gas Distribution
N.A.I.C.C.: 221210

MoGas Pipeline, LLC   (1)
329 Josephville Rd, Wentzville, MO 63385-3615
Tel.: (636) 856-8035
Web Site: https://www.mogaspipe.com
Natural Gas Transportation Services
N.A.I.C.S.: 486910

Omega Pipeline Company, LLC   (1)
299 Ordinance Rd Bldg 2570, Fort Leonard Wood, MO 65473
Tel.: (816) 863-0005
Web Site: https://www.omegapipeline.com
Natural Gas Distribution System
N.A.I.C.S.: 486210

Spire Alabama Inc.   (1)

605 Richard Arrington Blvd N, Birmingham,
AL 35203   **(100%)**
Tel.: (205) 326-8100
Web Site: https://www.spireenergy.com
Rev.: $494,000,000
Assets: $2,170,500,000
Liabilities: $717,800,000
Net Worth: $1,452,700,000
Earnings: $73,800,000
Emp.: 993
Fiscal Year-end: 09/30/2021
Natural Gas Distr
N.A.I.C.S.: 221210
Suzanne Sitherwood (Chm)
Steven L. Lindsey (CEO)
Adam W. Woodard (CFO & Treas)
Timothy W. Krick (Chief Acctg Officer)
Joseph B. Hampton (Pres)

Spire Missouri Inc.   **(1)**
700 Market St, Saint Louis, MO
63101   **(100%)**
Tel.: (314) 342-0500
Web Site: https://www.spireenergy.com
Rev.: $1,516,600,000
Assets: $5,058,100,000
Liabilities: $2,141,800,000
Net Worth: $2,916,300,000
Earnings: $144,100,000
Emp.: 2,489
Fiscal Year-end: 09/30/2021
Natural Gas Distr
N.A.I.C.S.: 221210
Suzanne Sitherwood (Chm)
Steven L. Lindsey (CEO)
Scott B. Carter (Pres)
Adam W. Woodard (CFO & Treas)
Timothy W. Krick (Chief Acctg Officer &
Controller)

SPIRIT AIRLINES, INC.
2800 Executive Way, Miramar, FL
33025
Tel.: (954) 447-7920   DE
Web Site: https://www.spirit.com
Year Founded: 1964
SAVE—(NYSE)
Rev.: $5,362,549,000
Assets: $9,417,237,000
Liabilities: $8,282,895,000
Net Worth: $1,134,342,000
Earnings: ($447,464,000)
Emp.: 13,167
Fiscal Year-end: 12/31/23
Passenger Airline Operator
N.A.I.C.S.: 481111
Edward M. Christie III (Pres & CEO)
Brian J. McMenamy (Interim CFO &
VP)
Brian J. McMenamy (VP & Controller)
H. McIntyre Gardner (Chm)

SPIRIT REALTY CAPITAL, INC.
2727 N Harwood St Ste 300, Dallas,
TX 75201
Tel.: (972) 476-1900   MD
Web Site: https://www.spiritrealty.com
Year Founded: 2004
SRC—(NYSE)
Rev.: $709,629,000
Assets: $8,472,866,000
Liabilities: $3,911,550,000
Net Worth: $4,561,316,000
Earnings: $275,166,000
Emp.: 89
Fiscal Year-end: 12/31/22
Real Estate Investment Trust
N.A.I.C.S.: 525990
Jay A. Young (Chief Admin Officer,
Chief Legal Officer & Exec VP)
Prakash J. Parag (Chief Acctg Officer
& Sr VP)
Michael Hughes (CFO & Exec VP)

Subsidiaries:

Spirit Management Company II   **(1)**
16767 N Perimeter Dr 210, Scottsdale, AZ
85260
Tel.: (480) 606-0820
Real Estate Investment Services
N.A.I.C.S.: 531210

Spirit Realty, L.P.   **(1)**
2727 N Harwood St Ste 300, Dallas, TX
75201
Tel.: (972) 476-1900
Rev.: $483,616,999
Assets: $6,396,785,999
Liabilities: $2,795,665,999
Net Worth: $3,601,119,999
Earnings: $26,583,000
Emp.: 81
Fiscal Year-end: 12/31/2020
Real Estate Investment Services
N.A.I.C.S.: 531210
Jackson Hsieh (Pres & CEO)

Spirit SPE Portfolio 2012-1, LLC   **(1)**
14631 N Scottsdale Rd, Scottsdale, AZ
85254
Tel.: (480) 315-6592
Emp.: 5
Investment Consulting Services
N.A.I.C.S.: 523910

SPIRITS TIME INTERNA-
TIONAL, INC.
1661 Lakeview Cir, Ogden, UT 84403
Tel.: (801) 399-3632   NV
Year Founded: 2005
SRSG—(OTCIQ)
Assets: $275,707
Liabilities: $1,262,121
Net Worth: ($986,414)
Earnings: ($286,628)
Fiscal Year-end: 12/31/22
Alcoholic Beverages Mfr
N.A.I.C.S.: 424820
Mark A. Scharmann (Chm, Pres,
CEO, CFO, COO, Treas & Sec)

SPLASH BEVERAGE GROUP,
INC.
1314 E Las Olas Blvd Ste 221, Fort
Lauderdale, FL 33301
Tel.: (941) 554-8381   CO
Web Site:
    https://splashbeveragegroup.com
Year Founded: 1992
SBEV—(NYSEAMEX)
Rev.: $18,087,486
Assets: $17,304,703
Liabilities: $7,982,569
Net Worth: $9,322,134
Earnings: ($21,690,469)
Emp.: 40
Fiscal Year-end: 12/31/22
Non-alcoholic Beverage Mfr & Distr
N.A.I.C.S.: 722515
Robert Nistico (Chm, CEO & Pres)
Justin Yorke (Sec)
Sanjeev Javia (VP-Product Dev)
Aida Aragon (Sr VP-Natl Accounts)
Julius Ivancsits (CFO)

SPOK HOLDINGS, INC.
5911 Kingstowne Village Pkwy 6th Fl,
Alexandria, VA 22315
Tel.: (703) 269-6850   DE
Web Site: https://www.spok.com
Year Founded: 2004
SPOK—(NASDAQ)
Rev.: $139,025,000
Assets: $227,684,000
Liabilities: $63,913,000
Net Worth: $163,771,000
Earnings: $15,666,000
Emp.: 384
Fiscal Year-end: 12/31/23
Wireless Messaging Services
N.A.I.C.S.: 517121
Michael W. Wallace (COO)
Vincent D. Kelly (Pres, CEO & CEO-
Spok, Inc.)
Royce G. Yudkoff (Chm)
Sharon Woods-Keisling (Treas)
Timothy E. Tindle (CIO)
Calvin C. Rice (CFO, Chief Acctg Of-
ficer & Controller)

Renee Hall (Chief Compliance Officer)
Jonathan Wax (Exec VP)

SPORTS ENTERTAINMENT
ACQUISITION CORP.
11760 US Hway 1 Golden Bear Plz
Ste W506, North Palm Beach, FL
33408
Tel.: (561) 402-0741   DE
Year Founded: 2020
SEAHU—(NYSE)
Investment Services
N.A.I.C.S.: 523999
Eric Grubman (Chm & CFO)
John Collins (CEO)

SPORTS VENTURES ACQUISI-
TION CORP.
9705 Collins Ave 1901N, Bal Har-
bour, FL 33154
Tel.: (786) 650-0074   Ky
Web Site:
    http://www.sportsventuresacq.com
Year Founded: 2020
AKIC—(NASDAQ)
Rev.: $6,467,470
Assets: $230,849,726
Liabilities: $13,632,732
Net Worth: $217,216,994
Earnings: $4,935,531
Emp.: 3
Fiscal Year-end: 12/31/21
Investment Services
N.A.I.C.S.: 523999
Alan Kestenbaum (Chm & CEO)
Robert Tilliss (Pres & CFO)
Daniel Strauss (COO)

SPORTSMAN'S WAREHOUSE
HOLDINGS, INC.
1475 W 9000 S Ste A, West Jordan,
UT 84088
Tel.: (801) 566-6681   DE
Web Site:
    https://www.sportsmans.com
SPWH—(NASDAQ)
Rev.: $1,399,515,000
Assets: $858,960,000
Liabilities: $565,847,000
Net Worth: $293,113,000
Earnings: $40,518,000
Emp.: 3,000
Fiscal Year-end: 01/28/23
Holding Company; Sporting Goods
Stores Operator
N.A.I.C.S.: 551112
Richard D. McBee (Chm)
Riley Timmer (VP-IR)
Paul E. Stone (Pres & CEO)
Jeffrey R. White (Interim CFO, Chief
Acctg Officer, Sec & VP-Fin)

Subsidiaries:

Sportsman's Warehouse, Inc.   **(1)**
10462 S River Heights Dr, South Jordan,
UT 84047
Tel.: (801) 567-1000
Sales Range: $300-349.9 Million
Hunting & Sporting Goods Stores Operator
N.A.I.C.S.: 459110
Jeremy Williams (Dir-Ops)

SPORTSMAP TECH ACQUISI-
TION CORP.
5353 W Alabama Ste 415, Houston,
TX 77056
Tel.: (713) 479-5302   DE
Year Founded: 2021
SMAP—(NASDAQ)
Rev.: $1,739,145
Assets: $119,128,173
Liabilities: $119,007,790
Net Worth: $120,383
Earnings: $36,861
Emp.: 3

Fiscal Year-end: 12/31/22
Investment Services
N.A.I.C.S.: 523999
David Gow (CEO)
Jacob Swain (CFO)
Lawson Gow (Chief Strategy Officer)

SPORTSTEK ACQUISITION
CORP.
2200 S Utica Pl Ste 450, Tulsa, OK
74114
Tel.: (918) 957-1086   DE
Year Founded: 2020
SPTK—(NASDAQ)
Rev.: $6,711,994
Assets: $173,243,487
Liabilities: $188,202,205
Net Worth: ($14,958,718)
Earnings: $4,866,198
Emp.: 3
Fiscal Year-end: 12/31/21
Investment Services
N.A.I.C.S.: 523999
Timothy W. Clark (CFO & COO)
C. Tavo Hellmund (Co-CEO)
Jeffrey Luhnow (Chm & Co-CEO)

SPOTLIGHT CAPITAL HOLD-
INGS, INC.
5904 Rainbow Blvd, Las Vegas, NV
89118
Tel.: (725) 224-5133   CO
Web Site: https://spotlightcapital.ai
Year Founded: 1997
SLCH—(OTCIQ)
Transportation & Charter Flight Ser-
vices
N.A.I.C.S.: 481211
Aaron Johnson (CEO)
Bob Morales (CTO)
Christine Kelly (CMO)

SPRINGBIG HOLDINGS, INC.
621 NW 53rd St Ste 500, Boca Ra-
ton, FL 33487
Tel.: (917) 460-7522   Ky
Web Site: https://www.springbig.com
Year Founded: 2020
SBIG—(NASDAQ)
Rev.: $26,629,000
Assets: $9,657,000
Liabilities: $13,285,000
Net Worth: ($3,628,000)
Earnings: ($13,076,000)
Emp.: 126
Fiscal Year-end: 12/31/22
Investment Services
N.A.I.C.S.: 523999
Albert Foreman (CEO)
Mark Zittman (COO)
Sergey Sherman (CFO)
Richard Taney (Chm)

Subsidiaries:

Springbig, Inc.   **(1)**
621 NW 53rd St Ste 260, Boca Raton, FL
33487
Web Site: http://www.springbig.com
Sales Range: $1-9.9 Million
Loyalty Marketing Services
N.A.I.C.S.: 541613
Jeffrey Harris (Co-Founder & CEO)
Mark Horbal (Co-Founder & Sr VP-Digital
Communication)
Sam Harris (Co-Founder-Product Dev &
Strategy & VP-Product Dev)
Sarah Bukantz (Dir-Client Success)

SPRINGWORKS THERAPEU-
TICS, INC.
100 Washington Blvd, Stamford, CT
06902
Tel.: (203) 883-9490   DE

SpringWorks Therapeutics, Inc.—(Continued)

Web Site:
https://www.springworkstx.com
Year Founded: 2017
SWTX—(NASDAQ)
Rev.: $6,147,000
Assets: $630,242,000
Liabilities: $72,050,000
Net Worth: $558,192,000
Earnings: ($277,417,000)
Emp.: 227
Fiscal Year-end: 12/31/22
Biotechnology Research & Development Services
N.A.I.C.S.: 541714
Saqib Islam *(CEO)*
Jens Renstrup *(Chief Medical Officer)*
Badreddin Edris *(COO)*
Michael P. Nofi *(Chief Acctg Officer)*
Herschel S. Weinstein *(Gen Counsel & Sec)*
Daniel Pichl *(Chief People Officer)*
Stephen Squinto *(Acting Head-R&D)*
Francis I. Perier Jr. *(CFO)*

SPRINKLR, INC.

441 9th Ave 12th Fl, New York, NY 10001
Tel.: (917) 933-7800　　　　DE
Web Site: https://www.sprinklr.com
Year Founded: 2011
CXM—(NYSE)
Rev.: $732,360,000
Assets: $1,223,110,000
Liabilities: $543,406,000
Net Worth: $679,704,000
Earnings: $51,403,000
Emp.: 3,869
Fiscal Year-end: 01/31/24
Software Development Services
N.A.I.C.S.: 541511
Ragy Thomas *(Founder, Chm & Co-CEO)*
Trac Pham *(Co-CEO)*
Diane Adams *(Chief Culture & Talent Officer)*
Manish Sarin *(CFO & Principal Acctg Officer)*
Jacob Scott *(Gen Counsel & Sec)*

Subsidiaries:

newBrandAnalytics Inc.　　　　　(1)
1250 23rd St NW Ste 450, Washington, DC 20037
Tel.: (202) 800-7850
Web Site:
http://www.newbrandanalytics.com
Social Media Intelligence & Other Online Marketing Consulting Services
N.A.I.C.S.: 541613
Bhavin Desai *(VP-Product)*
Kristen Kavalier *(VP-Customer Rels)*

SPRIZA, INC.

111 Pen St, El Segundo, CA 90245
Tel.: (403) 614-4441　　　　NV
Web Site: http://www.spriza.com
SPRZ—(OTCIQ)
Advertising & Marketing Services
N.A.I.C.S.: 541810
Robert Danard *(CEO)*
Jason Cowles *(COO)*
Christopher Robbins *(CFO, Treas & Sec)*

SPROUT SOCIAL, INC.

131 S Dearborn St Ste 700, Chicago, IL 60603　　　　DE
Web Site:
https://www.sproutsocial.com
Year Founded: 2010
SPT—(NASDAQ)
Rev.: $333,643,000
Assets: $396,585,000
Liabilities: $252,393,000
Net Worth: $144,192,000
Earnings: ($66,427,000)

Emp.: 1,383
Fiscal Year-end: 12/31/23
Software Development Services
N.A.I.C.S.: 541511
Aaron Rankin *(Co-Founder)*
Joe Del Preto *(CFO & Treas)*
Rachael Pfenning *(Sr VP-Ops)*
Heidi Jonas *(Gen Counsel)*
Alan Boyce *(Sr VP-Engrg)*
John Schoenstein *(Chief Revenue Officer)*
Scott Morris *(CMO)*
Justyn Howard *(Co-Founder & Exec Chm)*
Ryan Barretto *(Pres & CEO)*

Subsidiaries:

Simply Measured Inc.　　　　　(1)
2211 Elliott Ave Ste 310, Seattle, WA 98121
Social Media Measurement & Analytics Software
N.A.I.C.S.: 513210

SPROUT TINY HOMES, INC.

6855 Starry Night Ln, Colorado Springs, CO 80923
Tel.: (719) 247-6195　　　　CO
Web Site:
https://www.sprouttinyhomes.com
STHI—(OTCIQ)
Assets: $7,966,000
Liabilities: $12,288,000
Net Worth: ($4,322,000)
Earnings: ($1,368,000)
Fiscal Year-end: 12/31/20
New Single-Family Housing Construction (except For-Sale Builders)
N.A.I.C.S.: 236115
Rod Stambaugh *(Founder & Pres)*

SPROUTS FARMERS MARKETS, INC.

5455 E High St Ste 111, Phoenix, AZ 85054
Tel.: (480) 814-8016　　　　DE
Web Site: https://www.sprouts.com
Year Founded: 2002
SFM—(NASDAQ)
Rev.: $6,404,223,000
Assets: $3,070,380,000
Liabilities: $2,023,918,000
Net Worth: $1,046,462,000
Earnings: $261,164,000
Emp.: 31,000
Fiscal Year-end: 01/01/23
Supermarkets & Other Grocery Retailers (except Convenience Retailers)
N.A.I.C.S.: 445110
Stacy W. Hilgendorf *(Principal Acctg Officer, VP & Controller)*
Brandon F. Lombardi *(Chief Legal Officer)*
Jack L. Sinclair *(CEO)*
Hunter Bennett *(Sr VP-IT)*
Nicholas Konat *(Pres & COO)*
Alisa Gmelich *(CMO & Sr VP)*

Subsidiaries:

SFM, LLC　　　　　(1)
575 Front St, Manchester, NH 03102
Tel.: (603) 625-8400
Web Site: https://www.sfmllc.net
Financial Management Services
N.A.I.C.S.: 541611
David K. Snyder *(Partner)*

SH Markets, Inc.　　　　　(1)
6100 N Mesa St Ste A, El Paso, TX 79912
Tel.: (915) 833-3380
Crop Farming Services
N.A.I.C.S.: 111998

SPRUCE BIOSCIENCES, INC.

611 Gateway Blvd Ste 740, South San Francisco, CA 94080
Tel.: (415) 655-4168　　　　DE
Web Site: https://sprucebio.com

Year Founded: 2016
SPRB—(NASDAQ)
Rev.: $1,523,000
Assets: $85,648,000
Liabilities: $17,162,000
Net Worth: $68,486,000
Earnings: ($46,180,000)
Emp.: 27
Fiscal Year-end: 12/31/22
Research & Development in Biotechnology (except Nanobiotechnology)
N.A.I.C.S.: 541714
Samir Gharib *(Pres & CFO)*
Rosh Dias *(Chief Medical Officer)*
Chris Barnes *(VP-Biometrics & Project Leadership)*
David Moriarty *(VP-Dev & Ops)*
Dasharatha Reddy *(VP-Pharmaceutical Dev & Mfg)*
Pamela Wedel *(VP-Dev Ops)*
Javier Szwarcberg *(CEO)*

SPRUCE POWER HOLDING CORPORATION

820 Gessner Rd Ste 500, Houston, TX 77024
Tel.: (617) 718-0329　　　　DE
Web Site:
https://www.sprucepower.com
Year Founded: 2019
SPRU—(NYSE)
Rev.: $23,194,000
Assets: $826,552,000
Liabilities: $537,661,000
Net Worth: $288,891,000
Earnings: ($93,931,000)
Emp.: 318
Fiscal Year-end: 12/31/22
Investment Services
N.A.I.C.S.: 523999
Eric Tech *(Executives)*
Christopher Hayes *(Chm, Pres & CEO)*
Sarah Weber Wells *(CFO & Head-Sustainability)*

SPS COMMERCE, INC.

333 S 7th St Ste 1000, Minneapolis, MN 55402
Tel.: (612) 435-9400　　　　DE
Web Site:
https://www.spscommerce.com
Year Founded: 1987
SPSC—(NASDAQ)
Rev.: $450,875,000
Assets: $672,914,000
Liabilities: $135,841,000
Net Worth: $537,073,000
Earnings: $55,134,000
Emp.: 2,215
Fiscal Year-end: 12/31/22
On-Demand Supply Chain Management Solutions, Integration, Collaboration, Connectivity, Visibility & Data Analytics
N.A.I.C.S.: 541512
Chad Collins *(CEO)*
Kimberly K. Nelson *(CFO & Exec VP)*
James J. Frome *(Pres & COO)*
Mark O'Leary *(CMO & Sr VP)*
Jamie Thingelstad *(CTO & Sr VP)*
Erica Koenig *(Chief HR Officer & Sr VP)*
Dan Juckniess *(Chief Revenue Officer, Exec VP & Sr VP)*
Karin Lucas *(Chief Customer Success Officer & Sr VP)*

Subsidiaries:

D Masons Software, LLC　　　　　(1)
1605 Main St Ste 610, Sarasota, FL 34236
Web Site: http://www.datamasons.com
Cloud Management Services
N.A.I.C.S.: 518210

Direct EDI, Inc.　　　　　(1)

4669 Murphy Canyon Rd Ste 108, San Diego, CA 92123
Tel.: (858) 751-2626
Web Site: http://www.directedi.com
Sales Range: $25-49.9 Million
Emp.: 25
Computer Integration Services
N.A.I.C.S.: 541519

SPS Commerce Canada, Ltd.　　　(1)
44 Peel Centre Drive Suite 300, Brampton, L6T 4B5, ON, Canada
Tel.: (905) 458-9262
International Standardization Certification Services
N.A.I.C.S.: 541611
Tayyab Shaikh *(Dir-Category Svcs)*

TIE Kinetix DACH GmbH　　　　(1)
St-Georg-Str 11, 82284, Grafrath, Germany
Tel.: (49) 89990164111
Digital Supply Chain Management Services
N.A.I.C.S.: 541614

SPUTNIK ENTERPRISES INC.

10781 Satellite Blvd, Orlando, FL 34786
Tel.: (407) 377-5880　　　　NV
Web Site: http://www.sputnik.com
Year Founded: 2001
SPNI—(OTCIQ)
Sales Range: Less than $1 Million
Investment Services
N.A.I.C.S.: 523999
Anthony Gebbia *(Pres, CEO, CFO & Sec)*

SPX TECHNOLOGIES, INC.

6325 Ardrey Kell Rd Ste 400, Charlotte, NC 28277
Tel.: (980) 474-3700　　　　DE
Web Site: https://www.spx.com
Year Founded: 1912
SPXC—(NYSE)
Rev.: $1,460,900,000
Assets: $1,930,900,000
Liabilities: $851,700,000
Net Worth: $1,079,200,000
Earnings: $200,000
Emp.: 3,300
Fiscal Year-end: 12/31/22
Air-Conditioning & Warm Air Heating Equipment & Commercial & Industrial Refrigeration Equipment Manufacturing
N.A.I.C.S.: 333415
John W. Nurkin *(Gen Counsel, Sec & VP)*
NaTausha H. White *(Chief HR Officer & VP)*
Paul R. Clegg *(VP-Comm & IR)*
Eugene Joseph Lowe III *(Pres & CEO)*
Garrett Roelofs *(Asst Mgr-IR)*
Michael Daly *(VP & Head-Strategy & Bus Dev-Global)*

Subsidiaries:

Bran & Luebbe GmbH　　　　　(1)
Werkstrasse 4, 22844, Norderstedt, Germany　　　　　(100%)
Tel.: (49) 40522020
Web Site: http://www.branluebbe.com
Sales Range: $250-299.9 Million
Emp.: 250
Pumps & Metering Equipment
N.A.I.C.S.: 333914

Copes-Vulcan　　　　　(1)
Road Two Industrial Estate, Winsford, CW7 3QL, Cheshire, United Kingdom　(100%)
Tel.: (44) 1606552041
Web Site: http://www.copesvulcan.com
Sales Range: $100-124.9 Million
Emp.: 25
Mfr of Valves
N.A.I.C.S.: 332911
Mark Wheat *(Mgr-Bus Unit)*
David Edwards *(Sls Mgr-Aftermarket)*
Donna Jennings *(Mgr-Sls)*
Andrew Adam *(Mgr-Engrg)*
Carl McGilbert Jr. *(Coord-Field Svc)*

Elxsi Corporation (1)
Tel.: (800) 327-7791
Holding Company; Restaurant Owner &
Operator
N.A.I.C.S.: 551112

Subsidiary (Non-US):

CUES, Inc. (2)
Web Site: http://www.cuesinc.com
Pipeline Inspection Products Mfr & Rehabili-
tation Services; CCTV Mfr
N.A.I.C.S.: 334515

Flash Technology, LLC (1)
332 Nichol Mill Ln, Franklin, TN 37067
Tel.: (615) 637-3445
Web Site: https://www.flashtechnology.com
Lighting Equipment Mfr
N.A.I.C.S.: 335115
Marc Snoblen (Dir-Ops & Svc)
Scott Fulton (Dir-Engrg)
Scott Goldsby (Sr Mgr-Technical Field Svcs)

**Gerstenberg Schroder Brasil
Ltda.** (1)
Rua Turi 70 - Vila Madalena, Sao Paulo,
05443-050, Brazil
Tel.: (55) 1138193100
Food Product Machinery Mfr
N.A.I.C.S.: 333241
Luiz Felipe Leme (Mgr-Sls)

LAGTA Group Training Limited (1)
Lagta House Woodside Eurocentral, Moth-
erwell, ML1 4UY, Lanarkshire, United King-
dom
Tel.: (44) 1698835420
Web Site: http://www.lagta.co.uk
Automotive Technicians Training Services
N.A.I.C.S.: 488999

**Mann+Hummel Vokes Air Treatment
Holdings Limited** (1)
Farrington Road, Burnley, BB11 5SY, Lan-
cashire, United Kingdom
Tel.: (44) 1282413131
Web Site: http://www.vokesair.com
Sales Range: $450-499.9 Million
Emp.: 1,100
Holding Company; Air Filtration Products
Mfr
N.A.I.C.S.: 551112

Subsidiary (Domestic):

Volkes Air Limited (2)
Farrington Road, Burnley, BB11 5SY, Lan-
cashire, United Kingdom
Tel.: (44) 1282413131
Web Site: http://www.airsiltrations.spx.com
Sales Range: $25-49.9 Million
Emp.: 80
Air Filtration
N.A.I.C.S.: 333413
David Connolly (Plant Mgr)

Marley Canadian Inc (1)
4141 Sladeview Cres Unit 19, Mississauga,
L5L 5T1, ON, Canada
Tel.: (905) 607-6446
Emp.: 4
Industrial Machinery & Equipment Mfr
N.A.I.C.S.: 333248

Marley Mexicana S.A. de C.V. (1)
Haracio 124-1003, Col Polanco, 11560,
Mexico, Mexico
Tel.: (52) 5552507082
Web Site: https://www.spxcooling.com
Sales Range: $10-24.9 Million
Emp.: 6
Air Conditioner Mfr
N.A.I.C.S.: 333415

Pearpoint, Inc. (1)
39-740 Garand Ln Unit B, Palm Desert, CA
92211
Tel.: (760) 343-7350
Web Site: https://www.pearpoint.com
Sales Range: $1-9.9 Million
Emp.: 12
Video Pipeline Inspection Solutions
N.A.I.C.S.: 334515

Pneumatic Products Corp. (1)
4647 SW 40th Ave, Ocala, FL
34474-5788   (100%)
Tel.: (724) 745-1555

Web Site:
  https://www.pneumaticproducts.com
Sales Range: $125-149.9 Million
Filters for Air, Gases & Liquids Mfr
N.A.I.C.S.: 333413
James Doherty (Sr VP-Sls & Mktg)

Premier Mill Corp. (1)
611 Sugar Creek Rd, Delavan, WI 53115-
1337
Tel.: (610) 779-9500
Web Site: http://www.premiermill.com
Sales Range: $25-49.9 Million
Emp.: 9
Dispersing & Milling Equipment for the
Paint, Ink & Coatings Industries
N.A.I.C.S.: 333248

Radiodetection Corp. (1)
28 Tower Rd, Raymond, ME 04071
Tel.: (304) 725-1050
Web Site: http://www.radiodetection.com
Sales Range: $25-49.9 Million
Emp.: 56
Mfr & Designer of Time Domain Reflecto-
meters
N.A.I.C.S.: 423830

Subsidiary (Non-US):

Radiodetection B.V. (2)
Industriestraat 11, 7041 GD, 's-Heerenberg,
Netherlands
Tel.: (31) 314664700
Web Site: http://www.radiodetection.com
Sales Range: $10-24.9 Million
Emp.: 18
Electronic Components Mfr
N.A.I.C.S.: 334419

Radiodetection Canada Ltd. (2)
Unit 34 34-344 Edgeley Blvd, Concord, L4K
4B7, ON, Canada
Tel.: (905) 660-9995
Web Site: https://www.radiodetection.com
Sales Range: $100-124.9 Million
Emp.: 4
Testing Equipment
N.A.I.C.S.: 334515

SPX Cooling Technologies (1)
7401 W 129th St, Overland Park, KS 66213
Tel.: (913) 664-7400
Web Site: http://spxcooling.com
Sales Range: $400-449.9 Million
Emp.: 1,500
Cooling Technologies & Services
N.A.I.C.S.: 333415
Drews Ladau (Pres)

Subsidiary (Non-US):

Balcke-Duerr Italiana, S.r.l. (2)
Via Pievaiola 307, Fontignano, 06070, Pe-
rugia, Italy
Tel.: (39) 075529091
Web Site: http://www.balcke-duerr.de
Sales Range: $125-149.9 Million
Emp.: 98
Cooling & Heating Systems
N.A.I.C.S.: 333415
Paolo Gandin (Pres)

Division (Domestic):

Marley Engineered Products (2)
470 Beauty Spot Rd E, Bennettsville, SC
29512-2700
Tel.: (843) 479-4006
Web Site: https://www.marleymep.com
Sales Range: $150-199.9 Million
Emp.: 330
Residential, Commercial & Light Industrial
Heating & Ventilating Solutions
N.A.I.C.S.: 423730

Subsidiary (Non-US):

**SPX Cooling Technologies (Zhangjia-
kou) Co. Ltd** (2)
No 19 Baishan Street, Qiaoxi District,
Zhangjiakou, China
Tel.: (86) 3135985555
Web Site: http://www.spxcooling.com
Emp.: 680
Air Conditioner Mfr
N.A.I.C.S.: 333415

**SPX Cooling Technologies France
SA** (2)

10 Rue des Beaux Soleils, Osny, 95520,
France
Tel.: (33) 134359779
Sales Range: $125-149.9 Million
Cooling Systems
N.A.I.C.S.: 333415

SPX Cooling Technologies Inc. (2)
2425 Matheson Blvd E Suite 800, Missis-
sauga, L4W 5K4, ON, Canada
Tel.: (905) 607-6446
Web Site: https://www.spxcooling.com
Sales Range: $10-24.9 Million
Emp.: 4
Cooling Systems
N.A.I.C.S.: 333415

**SPX Cooling Technologies UK
Ltd.** (2)
3 Knightsbridge Park Wainwright Road,
Worcester, WR4 9FA, United Kingdom
Tel.: (44) 1905750270
Sales Range: $25-49.9 Million
Emp.: 60
Refrigerated Display Cabinets Mfr
N.A.I.C.S.: 333415
Stephen Andrew (Mgr-Parts & Svc)

Division (Domestic):

XCEL Erectors, Inc. (2)
7401 W 129th St, Overland Park, KS
66213-2634
Tel.: (913) 664-7400
Sales Range: $100-124.9 Million
Emp.: 300
Cooling Tower Solutions
N.A.I.C.S.: 333415

**SPX Cooling Technologies Trading
DMCC** (1)
14h Floor-Unit AG-14L Cluster I Jumeirah
Lake Towers, PO Box 212568, Downtown
Jebel Ali, Dubai, United Arab Emirates
Tel.: (971) 507177562
Air Conditioning & Heating Equipment Mfr
N.A.I.C.S.: 333415

SPX Dry Cooling USA, LLC (1)
7450 W 130th St Ste 310, Overland Park,
KS 66213
Tel.: (913) 685-0009
Air Conditioning & Heating Equipment Mfr
N.A.I.C.S.: 333415

SPX Genfare (1)
800 Arthur Ave, Elk Grove Village, IL
60007   (100%)
Tel.: (847) 871-1231
Web Site: http://www.spx.com
Sales Range: $50-74.9 Million
Emp.: 110
Automated Fare-Collection Systems for
Mass Transit
N.A.I.C.S.: 333310
Phil Gamperl (Sls Mgr-Aftermarket)
Brandon Reisdorf (Sls Mgr-Aftermarket)
Eric Kaled (Pres)
Daniel Gorey (Mgr-Sls)
Brittany Seagren (Mgr-Contracts)
Michael Horbrook (Engr-Technical Svc)
Christopher Skeggs (Engr-Technical Sup-
port)
Mark Mahon (Dir-Sls-Natl)

SPX Germany Holding GmbH (1)
Konigsallee 53, 40212, Dusseldorf, Ger-
many
Tel.: (49) 211586710
Holding Company
N.A.I.C.S.: 551112

SPX Heat Transfer Inc. (1)
2121 N 161st East Ave, Tulsa, OK 74116-
4802
Tel.: (918) 234-6000
Web Site: http://www.spxheattransfer.com
Sales Range: $75-99.9 Million
Emp.: 200
Heavy Pressure Vessel Mfr
N.A.I.C.S.: 332410

Branch (Domestic):

SPX Heat Transfer (2)
95 Highland Ave Ste 210, Bethlehem, PA
18017
Tel.: (610) 250-1000
Web Site: http://www.spxheattransfer.com

Sales Range: $25-49.9 Million
Emp.: 30
Mfr of Condensers, Air Removal Equipment,
Steam Dump Systems & Turbine Isolation
Dampers
N.A.I.C.S.: 332410

SPX Hydraulic Technologies (1)
5885 11th St, Rockford, IL 61109
Tel.: (815) 874-5556
Web Site: https://www.hydraulictechnologies.com
Sales Range: $125-149.9 Million
Mfr & Distr of Hydraulic & General Industrial
Equipment
N.A.I.C.S.: 333995

SPX Process Equipment (1)
5620 W Rd, McKean, PA 16426
Tel.: (814) 476-5800
Web Site: http://www.spx.com
Control Valves
N.A.I.C.S.: 332911

SPX Process Equipment (1)
611 Sugar Creek Rd, Delavan, WI 53115
Tel.: (262) 728-1900
Web Site:
  http://www.spxprocessequipment.com
Sales Range: $125-149.9 Million
Emp.: 400
Fluid Process Solutions
N.A.I.C.S.: 333414
Ryan Stalewski (Engr-Application)

SPX Process Equipment (1)
135 Mt Read Blvd, Rochester, NY
14611   (100%)
Tel.: (585) 436-5550
Web Site: http://www.spx.com
Sales Range: $200-249.9 Million
Emp.: 300
Mfr of Industrial Mixers & Aerators
N.A.I.C.S.: 425120

SPX Technologies (Pty) Ltd. (1)
1st Floor Building 32 The Woodlands Office
Park Woodlands Drive, Woodmead, 2191,
South Africa
Tel.: (27) 112366300
Air Conditioning Equipment Distr
N.A.I.C.S.: 423730

SPX Transformer Solutions, Inc. (1)
400 S Prairie Ave, Waukesha, WI
53186-5969   (100%)
Tel.: (262) 547-0121
Web Site:
  http://www.spxtransformersolutions.com
Sales Range: $125-149.9 Million
Emp.: 1,000
Power Transformers Mfr & Distr
N.A.I.C.S.: 335311

Branch (Domestic):

**SPX Transformer Solutions, Inc. -
Goldsboro** (2)
2701 US Hwy 117 S, Goldsboro, NC 27530
Tel.: (919) 734-8900
Web Site:
  http://www.spxtransformersolutions.com
Sales Range: $100-124.9 Million
Emp.: 300
Power Transformers
N.A.I.C.S.: 335311

**SPX Valley Forge Technical Informa-
tion Services, Inc.** (1)
7121 N Haggerty Rd, Canton, MI
48187-2452   (100%)
Tel.: (313) 768-2000
Sales Range: $125-149.9 Million
Emp.: 600
Service Solutions
N.A.I.C.S.: 541611

Sabik Ltd. (1)
Beacon Innovation Centre Beacon Park,
Gorleston, Great Yarmouth, NR31 7RA,
Norfolk, United Kingdom
Tel.: (44) 1493446525
Lighting Equipment Mfr
N.A.I.C.S.: 335139
Nick Sims (Reg Sls Mgr)

Sabik Ou (1)
Maealuse 2/1, 12618, Tallinn, Estonia
Tel.: (372) 6397906
Lighting Equipment Mfr
N.A.I.C.S.: 335139

SPX Technologies, Inc.—(Continued)

Sven Neeme *(Mgr-VNS R&D)*
Gerli Kulm *(Mgr-Quality)*

Sabik Oy (1)
Hoylanlastu 2 A, 06150, Porvoo, Finland
Tel.: (358) 195601100
Web Site: http://www.marine.sabik.com
Lighting Equipment Mfr
N.A.I.C.S.: 335139
Lars Mansner *(Mng Dir)*

Sabik Private Limited (1)
7500A Beach Road 07-309 The Plaza, Sin-
gapore, 199591, Singapore
Tel.: (65) 62934348
Lighting Equipment Mfr
N.A.I.C.S.: 335139
David Koh *(Reg Dir-Sls)*

Schonstedt Instrument, Co. (1)
100 Edmond Rd, Kearneysville, WV 25430
Web Site: https://www.schonstedt.com
Search And Navigation Equipment, Nsk
N.A.I.C.S.: 334511
Erick O. Schonstedt *(Founder)*

Sensors & Software Inc. (1)
1040 Stacey Court, Mississauga, L4W 2X8,
ON, Canada
Tel.: (905) 624-8909
Web Site: https://www.sensoft.ca
Navigation Equipment Mfr
N.A.I.C.S.: 334511
Troy De Souza *(Mgr-Trng)*
Greg Johnston *(Mgr-Market)*

TCI International, Inc. (1)
3541 Gateway Blvd, Fremont, CA 94538
Tel.: (510) 687-6100
Web Site: https://www.tcibr.com
Sales Range: $25-49.9 Million
Emp.: 80
Broadcasting & Communication Antenna
Systems, Radio Frequency Signal Intelli-
gence & Spectrum Monitoring Equipment
Mfr
N.A.I.C.S.: 334220

ULC Robotics, Inc. (1)
88 Arkay Dr, Hauppauge, NY 11788
Tel.: (631) 667-9200
Web Site: http://www.ulcrobotics.com
Emp.: 160
Electrical Equipment & Component Mfr
N.A.I.C.S.: 335999
Gregory Penza *(Pres)*

Weil-McLain (1)
500 Blaine St, Michigan City, IN 46300
Tel.: (219) 879-6561
Web Site: https://www.weil-mclain.com
Sales Range: $200-249.9 Million
Emp.: 600
Residential & Commercial Heating Boilers
Mfr
N.A.I.C.S.: 333414

Division (Domestic):

Williamson-Thermoflo (2)
8201 W Calumet Rd, Milwaukee, WI 53223
Tel.: (414) 354-2935
Web Site: https://www.williamson-
thermoflo.com
Hydronic Comfort Heating Systems Mfr
N.A.I.C.S.: 423730

SPYR, INC.
Tel.: (303) 991-8000   NV
Web Site:
    https://www.otcmarkets.com
Year Founded: 1992
SPYR—(OTCIQ)
Rev.: $2,000
Assets: $159,000
Liabilities: $8,863,000
Net Worth: ($8,704,000)
Earnings: ($5,534,000)
Emp.: 3
Fiscal Year-end: 12/31/21
Computer Peripheral Equipment &
Encrypted USB Flash Drives
N.A.I.C.S.: 334118
Tom Dickens *(COO)*
Trang Grace Nguyen *(Principal Fin
Officer)*

SPYRE THERAPEUTICS, INC.
221 Crescent St Ste 105, Waltham,
MA 02453
Tel.: (617) 651-5940   DE
Web Site: https://spyre.com
Year Founded: 2013
SYRE—(NASDAQ)
Rev.: $2,329,000
Assets: $71,144,000
Liabilities: $20,839,000
Net Worth: $50,305,000
Earnings: ($83,815,000)
Emp.: 69
Fiscal Year-end: 12/31/22
Biopharmaceutical Mfr
N.A.I.C.S.: 325412
Cameron Turtle *(COO)*
Heidy Abreu King-Jones *(Chief Legal
Officer & Sec)*
Jim Kastenmayer *(Gen Counsel)*
Cameron Turtle *(COO)*

**SQZ BIOTECHNOLOGIES
COMPANY**
Tel.: (617) 758-8672   DE
Web Site:
    https://www.sqzbiotech.com
Year Founded: 2013
SQZ—(NYSE)
Rev.: $21,478,000
Assets: $99,900,000
Liabilities: $42,752,000
Net Worth: $57,148,000
Earnings: ($79,464,000)
Emp.: 53
Fiscal Year-end: 12/31/22
Biotechnology Research & Develop-
ment Services
N.A.I.C.S.: 541714
Amy W. Schulman *(Chm)*
Armon Sharei *(Founder)*
Howard Bernstein *(Interim CEO)*
David First *(Chief People Officer)*
Lawrence Knopf *(Gen Counsel)*
Amy W. Schulman *(Chm)*
Hassan Javanbakht *(VP-Infectious
Disease)*
Ipsita Roymoulik *(VP-CMC & Quality)*
Jonathan Gilbert *(VP-Exploratory)*
Ricardo Zwirtes *(VP-Clinical Dev)*
Richard Capasso *(Chief Acctg Officer
& Principal Fin Officer)*

SR BANCORP, INC.
220 W Union Ave, Bound Brook, NJ
08805
Tel.: (732) 560-1700   MD
Web Site:
    https://ir.somersetsavings.com
Year Founded: 1887
SRBK—(NASDAQ)
Rev.: $40,866,000
Assets: $1,020,844,000
Liabilities: $821,361,000
Net Worth: $199,483,000
Earnings: ($10,860,000)
Emp.: 116
Fiscal Year-end: 06/30/24
Commercial Banking Services
N.A.I.C.S.: 551111
Christopher J. Pribula *(Pres & COO)*
David M. Orbach *(Chm)*
Harris M. Faqueri *(VP)*
William P. Taylor *(Vice Chm & CEO)*

SRAX, INC.
2629 Townsgate Rd Ste 215, West-
lake Village, CA 91361
Tel.: (323) 694-9800   DE
Web Site: http://www.srax.com
Year Founded: 2009
SRAX—(OTCEM)
Rev.: $27,859,000
Assets: $18,070,000
Liabilities: $27,319,000
Net Worth: ($9,249,000)

Earnings: ($31,638,000)
Emp.: 122
Fiscal Year-end: 12/31/22
Social Media Advertising Applications
& Software
N.A.I.C.S.: 513210
Christopher Miglino *(Chm & CEO)*

Subsidiaries:

Steel Media Inc. (1)
The Empire State Bldg 350 5th Ave 59th Fl.
New York, NY 10118
Tel.: (212) 601-2840
Web Site: http://www.steelmediainc.com
Digital Advertising Vendor
N.A.I.C.S.: 541890

SRM ENTERTAINMENT, INC.
1061 E Indiantown Rd Ste 110, Jupi-
ter, FL 33477
Tel.: (407) 230-8100   NV
Web Site:
    https://www.srmentertainment.com
Year Founded: 2022
SRM—(NASDAQ)
Emp.: 7
Doll, Toy & Game Manufacturing
N.A.I.C.S.: 339930
Douglas O. McKinnon *(CFO)*
Richard Miller *(Chm & CEO)*
Brian John *(Sec)*
Taft Flittner *(Pres)*

**SS INNOVATIONS INTERNA-
TIONAL, INC.**
1600 SE 15th St 512, Fort Lauder-
dale, FL 33316
Tel.: (954) 478-1410   FL
Web Site: https://ssinnovations.com
Year Founded: 2015
SSII—(OTCIQ)
Rev.: $713,447
Assets: $25,479,086
Liabilities: $11,181,102
Net Worth: $14,297,984
Earnings: $20,941,972
Emp.: 239
Fiscal Year-end: 12/31/23
Medical Equipment Mfr & Distr
N.A.I.C.S.: 334510
Barry F. Cohen *(COO-Americas)*
Sudhir Srivastava *(Founder, Chm &
CEO)*
Vishwa Srivastava *(COO & Pres-
South Asia)*
Frederic H. Moll *(Vice Chm)*

**SS&C TECHNOLOGIES HOLD-
INGS, INC.**
80 Lamberton Rd, Windsor, CT
06095
Tel.: (860) 298-4500   DE
Web Site: https://www.ssctech.com
Year Founded: 1986
SSNC—(NASDAQ)
Rev.: $5,502,800,000
Assets: $18,102,500,000
Liabilities: $11,704,800,000
Net Worth: $6,397,700,000
Earnings: $607,100,000
Emp.: 26,600
Fiscal Year-end: 12/31/23
Holding Company
N.A.I.C.S.: 551112
Normand A. Boulanger *(Vice Chm)*
Rob Stone *(Co-Head)*
William C. Stone *(Chm & CEO)*
Brian N. Schell *(CFO & Exec VP)*

Subsidiaries:

Advent Software, Inc. (1)
600 Townsend St 4 Fl, San Francisco, CA
94103
Tel.: (415) 543-7696
Web Site: http://www.advent.com
Sales Range: $350-399.9 Million
Emp.: 1,209

Stand Alone & Client/Server Software Prod-
ucts, Data Interfaces & Related Services
that Automate Securities Trade Orders &
Integrate Certain Mission-Critical Functions
Services
N.A.I.C.S.: 541511

Subsidiary (Non-US):

**Advent Software (Middle East)
Limited** (2)
412 Level 4 Gate Village 10, PO Box
506643, DIFC, Dubai, 506643, United Arab
Emirates
Tel.: (971) 4 371 1200
Web Site: http://www.advent.com
Cloud-Based Portfolio Management Plat-
form Services
N.A.I.C.S.: 518210

**Advent Software (Singapore) Pte.
Ltd** (2)
1 Raffles Quay 29-01 North Tower, Singa-
pore, 048583, Singapore
Tel.: (65) 31580311
Web Site: http://www.advent.com
Cloud-Based Portfolio Management Plat-
form Services
N.A.I.C.S.: 513210

Advent Software ApS (2)
Bredgade 23B 3rd Floor, 1260, Copenha-
gen, Denmark
Tel.: (45) 3 329 9000
Web Site: http://www.advent.com
Investment Management Software Services
N.A.I.C.S.: 513210

Advent Switzerland AG (2)
Europaallee 41, 8004, Zurich, Switzerland
Tel.: (41) 442146917
Web Site: http://www.advent.com
Cloud-Based Portfolio Management Plat-
form Services
N.A.I.C.S.: 513210

Subsidiary (Domestic):

**Black Diamond Performance Report-
ing, LLC** (2)
9000 Southside Blvd Ste 7500 Bldg 7000,
Jacksonville, FL 32256
Tel.: (904) 241-2444
Web Site: http://blackdiamond.advent.com
Cloud-Based Portfolio Management Plat-
form Services
N.A.I.C.S.: 518210

Second Street Securities, Inc. (2)
21860 Burbank Blvd Ste 150, Woodland
Hills, CA 91367   (100%)
Tel.: (010) 057-0200
Web Site: https://www.secondstr.com
Securities Brokerage & Independent Re-
search Services
N.A.I.C.S.: 523150
David Banerjee *(Principal-Gen Securities-
Fin & Ops)*

**Battea - Class Action Services,
LLC** (1)
46 Southfield Ave Ste 450, Stamford, CT
06902
Tel.: (203) 987-4949
Web Site: http://www.battea.com
Investment Claim Recovery Services
N.A.I.C.S.: 523150
Tim Dillon *(VP-Sls)*
Christie Cellini *(VP-Ops)*
Jennifer P. Carberry *(VP & Dir-Mktg)*
Keith McComb *(VP-Ops)*
Bob Williamson *(VP-Sls)*
Robert McMillen *(Chief Security Officer)*
Vincent Curran *(CFO)*
Michael J. McCreesh *(Pres)*
Peter K. Hansen *(Chm)*

Blue Prism Group plc (1)
2 Cinnamon Park Crab Lane, Warrington,
WA2 0XP, United Kingdom
Tel.: (44) 8708793000
Web Site: http://www.blueprism.com
Software Development Services
N.A.I.C.S.: 541511
Jason Kingdon *(Chm & CEO)*
Alastair Bathgate *(Co-Founder)*
Ijoma Maluza *(CFO)*
David Moss *(Co-Founder)*

Chip Coyle *(CMO)*
Ian Horobin *(Chief Product Officer)*
Jon Theuerkauf *(Chief Customer Strategy & Transformation Officer)*
Linda Dotts *(Chief Partner Strategy Officer)*
Peter O'Neill *(Chief Sls Officer)*
John Warrick *(Gen Counsel & Sec)*

Subsidiary (Non-US):

Blue Prism AB   (2)
Kistagangen 20b, Kista, 164 40, Stockholm, Sweden
Tel.: (46) 851711777
Computer Software Development Services
N.A.I.C.S.: 541511

Blue Prism GmbH   (2)
Theatinerstrasse 11, 80333, Munich, Germany
Tel.: (49) 8926207586
Computer Software Development Services
N.A.I.C.S.: 541511

Blue Prism India Pvt. Ltd.   (2)
1425 Level 14 Concorde Tower UB City 1 Vittal Mallya Road, Bengaluru, 560001, India
Tel.: (91) 8067590400
Computer Software Development Services
N.A.I.C.S.: 541511

Blue Prism K.K.   (2)
Kamiyacho MT Bldg 14th Floor 4-3-20, Toranomon Minato-ku, Tokyo, 105 0001, Japan
Tel.: (81) 363327648
Computer Software Development Services
N.A.I.C.S.: 541511

Subsidiary (Domestic):

Blue Prism Limited   (2)
2 Cinnamon Park Crab Lane, Warrington, WA2 0XP, United Kingdom
Tel.: (44) 3708793000
Computer Software Development Services
N.A.I.C.S.: 541511

Subsidiary (Non-US):

Blue Prism Pte. Ltd.   (2)
168 Robinson Road 24-01, Singapore, 068912, Singapore
Tel.: (65) 68132800
Computer Software Development Services
N.A.I.C.S.: 541511

Blue Prism Pty. Ltd.   (2)
Level 21 Tower 2 Darling Park 201 Sussex Street, Sydney, 2000, NSW, Australia
Tel.: (61) 280735822
Computer Software Development Services
N.A.I.C.S.: 541511

Blue Prism SARL   (2)
40 Rue du Colisee, 75008, Paris, France
Tel.: (33) 187393800
Computer Software Development Services
N.A.I.C.S.: 541511

Subsidiary (US):

Blue Prism Software Inc.   (2)
1688 Meridian Ave Ste 700, Miami Beach, FL 33139
Computer Software Development Services
N.A.I.C.S.: 541511

DST Global Solutions LLC   (1)
2000 Crown Colony Dr, Quincy, MA 02169
Tel.: (617) 482-8800
Emp.: 10
Software Publishing Services
N.A.I.C.S.: 513210

DST Global Solutions S.A. (Proprietary) Ltd   (1)
12 Sherborne Road Parktown, Johannesburg, 2193, South Africa
Tel.: (27) 117155600
Information Technology Consulting Services
N.A.I.C.S.: 541512

DST Global Solutions Shanghai Limited   (1)
Rm 15 Unit 111 No7 Lujiazui Rd, Shanghai, 200120, China
Tel.: (86) 2120623200
Web Site: http://www.sscinc.com
Emp.: 10

Information Technology Consulting Services
N.A.I.C.S.: 541512

DST Systems, Inc.   (1)
333 W 11th St, Kansas City, MO 64105
Tel.: (816) 435-1000
Sales Range: $1-4.9 Billion
Information Processing & Software Services & Products
N.A.I.C.S.: 513210
Blair S. Williams *(Chief Risk Officer & VP)*

Subsidiary (Domestic):

ALPS Holdings Inc   (2)
1290 Broadway Ste 1100, Denver, CO 80203
Tel.: (303) 623-2577
Holding Company
N.A.I.C.S.: 551114

Argus Health Systems, Inc.   (2)
1300 Washington St, Kansas City, MO 64105-1433   **(100%)**
Tel.: (816) 435-7498
Pharmacy Benefits Management Information Processing
N.A.I.C.S.: 541519

DST Health Solutions, Inc.   (2)
2500 Corporate Dr, Birmingham, AL 35242   **(100%)**
Tel.: (205) 437-6000
Healthcare IT Solutions
N.A.I.C.S.: 541611

Subsidiary (Non-US):

Paragon Customer Communications Limited   (2)
Park House Lower Ground Floor 16-18 Finsbury Circus, London, EC2M 7EB, United Kingdom
Tel.: (44) 2076016270
Web Site: http://www.paragon-cc.com
Integrated Print & Communications Services
N.A.I.C.S.: 561499
Jeremy Walters *(CEO)*

Paragon Data Analytics Limited   (2)
Unit 1 Alexandria Court Alexandria Drive, Ashton under Lyne, OL7 0QN, United Kingdom
Tel.: (44) 2076016270
Data Science Analytics & Consulting Services
N.A.I.C.S.: 561499

Eze Software Group, LLC   (1)
12 Farnsworth St, Boston, MA 02210
Tel.: (617) 316-1000
Web Site: https://www.ezesoft.com
Technology Solutions for Investment Management
N.A.I.C.S.: 541511
Chad Yohn *(Gen Counsel)*
Azmi Jafarey *(Sr Mng Dir-IT)*

Financial Models Company Ltd.   (1)
477 Madison Ave, New York, NY 10022-5802
Tel.: (646) 282-3360
Emp.: 3
Computer Programming Services
N.A.I.C.S.: 541511

GlobeOp Financial Services (Cayman) Limited   (1)
45 Market Street Suite 3205 2nd Floor Gardenia Court, Camana Bay, 9003, Grand Cayman, Cayman Islands
Tel.: (345) 3459433330
Information Technology Consulting Services
N.A.I.C.S.: 541512
Martin J. Veilleux *(CFO)*
Alison Gregory *(Head-Enterprise Risk Mgmt)*

IFDS Luxembourg S.A.   (1)
47 Avenue J F Kennedy, 1855, Luxembourg, Luxembourg
Tel.: (352) 4640101
Web Site: https://ifdsgroup.com
Software Development Services
N.A.I.C.S.: 513210

Innovest Systems, LLC   (1)
110 Leroy St Fifth Fl, New York, NY 10014
Tel.: (212) 266-6677
Web Site: http://www.innovestsystems.com

Sales Range: $1-9.9 Million
Emp.: 42
Custom Computer Programming Services
N.A.I.C.S.: 541511
Maryanne Campbell *(Chief Revenue Officer)*
Greg McCloskey *(Sr VP-Corp Dev)*
Warren Hadley *(CFO)*
Joanne Smith *(COO)*
Michele Hardesty *(Exec VP-Managed Svcs)*

International Financial Data Services (Canada) Limited   (1)
30 Adelaide Street East Suite 1, Toronto, M5C 3G9, ON, Canada
Tel.: (416) 506-8000
Web Site: https://www.ifdsgroup.com
Software Development Services
N.A.I.C.S.: 541511
Roy Kapoor *(CIO)*
Noelle Sargeant *(Exec VP-HR)*

International Financial Data Services (Ireland) Limited   (1)
Bishops Square Redmond's Hill, D02 TD99, Dublin, 2, Ireland
Tel.: (353) 12425499
Web Site: https://ifdsgroup.com
Software Development Services
N.A.I.C.S.: 513210

IntraLinks SRL   (1)
28-30 Academiei Street 1st District 7th Floor, Bucharest, Romania
Tel.: (40) 726034034
Software Development Services
N.A.I.C.S.: 513210

Intralinks Holdings, Inc.   (1)
622 3rd Ave 10th Fl, New York, NY 10017
Tel.: (212) 543-7700
Web Site: https://www.intralinks.com
Holding Company; Software Publisher
N.A.I.C.S.: 551112

Subsidiary (Non-US):

IntraLinks EMEA Holdings B.V.   (2)
Naritaweg 215, 1043 CB, Amsterdam, Netherlands
Tel.: (31) 202404518
Web Site: http://www.intralinks.com
Holding Company
N.A.I.C.S.: 551112

IntraLinks Pty Limited   (2)
15 Castlereagh St 7th floor, Sydney, 2000, NSW, Australia
Tel.: (61) 292275600
Web Site: http://www.intralinks.com
Cloud Management Services
N.A.I.C.S.: 518210

IntraLinks Servicos de Informatica Ltda.   (2)
Rua Ministro Jesuino Cardoso 454 - Conj 81 - 8 Andar, Itaim Bibi, Sao Paulo, 04544-051, Brazil
Tel.: (55) 1149497700
Web Site: http://www.intralinks.com
Cloud Management Services
N.A.I.C.S.: 518210

Intralinks Asia Pacific Pte. Ltd.   (2)
1 Raffles Quay North Tower 29-01, Singapore, 048583, Singapore
Tel.: (65) 69086990
Web Site: http://www.intralinks.com
Cloud Management Services
N.A.I.C.S.: 518210

Subsidiary (Domestic):

Intralinks Inc.   (2)
622 3rd Ave 10th Fl, New York, NY 10017
Tel.: (212) 543-7700
Web Site: https://www.intralinks.com
Data Communication Services
N.A.I.C.S.: 517810
Shay Gonen *(CFO)*
Daren Glenister *(CTO)*
Ken Bisconti *(Head-SS&C)*
Bob Petrocchi *(Pres-Bus)*

Intralinks India Solutions Pvt. Limited   (1)
13th Floor B Wing C-20 G Block Bandra Kurla Complex, Mumbai, 400051, India
Tel.: (91) 9820792333
Software Development Services

N.A.I.C.S.: 513210

Intralinks Servicos de Tecnologia de Mexico, S de R.L. de C.V.   (1)
Torrey Virreyes Pedregal 24 Piso 3, Molino del Rey, Mexico, Mexico
Tel.: (52) 5580007586
Software Development Services
N.A.I.C.S.: 513210

MobliCo Solutions, LLC   (1)
300 E 39th St, Kansas City, MO 64110
Web Site: https://www.moblicosolutions.com
Software Development Services
N.A.I.C.S.: 541511
Pierre Barbeau *(Co-Founder & CEO)*
Jim Barnes *(Co-Founder & CTO)*
Dan Hapke *(VP-Client Svcs)*

PT DST Global Solutions Indonesia   (1)
Sampoerna Strategic Square South Tower 18th Floor Jl Jend, Sudirman kav 45-46, Jakarta, 12930, Indonesia
Tel.: (62) 215750927
Information Technology Consulting Services
N.A.I.C.S.: 541512

Primatics Financial LLC   (1)
8401 Greensboro Dr Ste 300, McLean, VA 22102
Tel.: (703) 342-0040
Web Site: http://www.primaticsfinancial.com
Emp.: 100
Financial Management Consulting Services
N.A.I.C.S.: 541611
Michael Therrien *(Founder & Exec VP-Client Svcs)*

Prime Management Limited   (1)
12 Church Street Mechanics Building, Hamilton, HM 11, Bermuda
Tel.: (441) 4412950329
Financial Services
N.A.I.C.S.: 541611
Dan Fronchak *(Dir-IT-Canada)*
Marty Brandt *(Dir-Canada)*

SS & C Financial Services LLC   (1)
1 S Rd, Harrison, NY 10528-3309
Tel.: (914) 670-3600
Investment & Financial Management Software Services
N.A.I.C.S.: 523999

SS&C Fund Services (UK) Limited   (1)
Munro House Portsmouth Road, Cobham, KT11 1TF, Surrey, United Kingdom
Tel.: (44) 1932586300
Investment & Financial Management Software Services
N.A.I.C.S.: 523999

SS&C GlobeOp S.A.R.L.   (1)
2 Rue Jean Monnet, 2180, Luxembourg, Luxembourg
Tel.: (352) 26757000
Web Site: http://www.globeop.com
Financial Management & Investment Advisory Services
N.A.I.C.S.: 523999

Subsidiary (Non-US):

GlobeOp Financial Services (India) Private Limited   (2)
Unit 2 2nd Floor Office Level Building 3 Mindspace Thane Belapur Road, Airoli, Mumbai, 400 708, India
Tel.: (91) 2266428000
Financial Support Services
N.A.I.C.S.: 522320

Subsidiary (US):

GlobeOp Financial Services LLC   (2)
1 South Rd, Harrison, NY 10528-3309
Tel.: (914) 670-3600
Web Site: http://www.globeop.com
Sales Range: $50-74.9 Million
Emp.: 180
Business Process Outsourcing Services
N.A.I.C.S.: 561499

Subsidiary (Non-US):

GlobeOp Financial Services Limited   (2)
s 1 St Martin's Le Grand, London, EC1A

SS&C Technologies Holdings, Inc.—(Continued)

4AS, United Kingdom
Tel.: (44) 2071906600
Emp.: 140
Investment Management Service
N.A.I.C.S.: 523940

SS&C Hedge Fund Services North America, Inc. (1)
80 Lamberton Rd, Windsor, CT 06095
Tel.: (860) 298-4500
Hedge Fund Administration Services
N.A.I.C.S.: 523940

SS&C Private Equity Services, Inc. (1)
80 Lamberton Rd, Windsor, CT 06095
Tel.: (860) 298-4500
Private Equity Investment Management Services
N.A.I.C.S.: 523940

SS&C Solutions Pty Limited (1)
Level 17 469 LaTrobe Street, Melbourne, 3000, VIC, Australia
Tel.: (61) 399036700
Computer Programming Services
N.A.I.C.S.: 541511
April Hahne (Fin Mgr)

SS&C Technologies (s) Pte Ltd. (1)
1 Raffles Quay 29-01 North Tower One Raffles Quay, Singapore, 048583, Singapore
Tel.: (65) 67689711
Software Publishing Services
N.A.I.C.S.: 513210

SS&C Technologies Australia Pty Ltd. (1)
Levels 7 and 15 15 Castlereagh Street, Sydney, 2000, NSW, Australia
Tel.: (61) 280735822
Software Development Services
N.A.I.C.S.: 541511

Subsidiary (Non-US):

GlobeOp Financial Services Technologies (India) Private Limited (2)
Units 2 & 3 4th Floor Office Level Bldg 5 & 6 Mindspace, Thane Belapur Road Airoli, Navi Mumbai, 400 708, India
Tel.: (91) 22 4117 5000
Web Site: http://www.globeop.com
Financial Support Services
N.A.I.C.S.: 522320

SS&C Technologies BV (1)
Naritaweg 215, 1043 CB, Amsterdam, Netherlands **(100%)**
Tel.: (31) 20 620 6921
Web Site: http://www.ssctech.com
Sales Range: $25-49.9 Million
Emp.: 12
Provider of Software, Services & Consulting for Asset Management
N.A.I.C.S.: 541511

SS&C Technologies Canada Corp. (1)
5255 Orbitor Drive, Mississauga, L4W 5M6, ON, Canada **(99.9%)**
Tel.: (905) 629-8000
Web Site: http://www.ssctech.com
Sales Range: $150-199.9 Million
Emp.: 500
Financial Technology Products & Services
N.A.I.C.S.: 522320

SS&C Technologies Holdings, Inc.- Hong Kong
Suite 2702-4 Central Plaza 18 Harbour Road, Wanchai, China (Hong Kong)
Tel.: (852) 25341100
Web Site: http://www.ssctech.com
Software Publishing Services
N.A.I.C.S.: 513210

SS&C Technologies Hong Kong Limited (1)
Suite 2702-4 Central Plaza 18 Harbour Road, Wanchai, China (Hong Kong)
Tel.: (852) 25341100
Software Publishing Services
N.A.I.C.S.: 513210

SS&C Technologies India Private Limited (1)

5th Floor Building 16 Interface New Link Road, Mumbai, 400 064, India
Tel.: (91) 2267539000
Software Publishing Services
N.A.I.C.S.: 513210

SS&C Technologies Ireland Limited (1)
La Touche House Custom House Dock, Dublin, D01 R5P3, Ireland
Tel.: (353) 1 514 9600
Emp.: 130
Financial Services
N.A.I.C.S.: 541611

SS&C Technologies Ltd. (1)
12 Arthur Street, London, EC4R 9AB, United Kingdom **(100%)**
Tel.: (44) 2030366800
Web Site: http://www.ssctech.com
Sales Range: $25-49.9 Million
Emp.: 60
Software & Consulting Services
N.A.I.C.S.: 541511

SS&C Technologies Sdn. Bhd. (1)
V03A-07-01 Level 7 Menara Sunway Visio Lingkaran SV Sunway Velocity, 55100, Kuala Lumpur, Jalan Desa Bahagia, Malaysia **(100%)**
Tel.: (60) 32 716 7400
Web Site: http://www.sscpach.com
Sales Range: $25-49.9 Million
Emp.: 30
Financial Software Developer
N.A.I.C.S.: 541511

SS&C Technologies, Inc. (1)
80 Lamberton Rd, Windsor, CT 06095
Tel.: (212) 367-4705
Web Site: https://www.ssctech.com
Business Support Services
N.A.I.C.S.: 561499
William C. Stone (Chm & CEO)

Branch (Domestic):

SS&C Technologies, Inc. (2)
33 W Monroe Ste 420, Chicago, IL 60603 **(100%)**
Tel.: (312) 443-7501
Web Site: http://www.ssctech.com
Rev.: $79,000
Emp.: 40
Custom Computer Programming Services
N.A.I.C.S.: 541618

Subsidiary (Domestic):

SS&C Technologies, Inc. (2)
151 W 42nd St 6th Fl, New York, NY 10036 **(100%)**
Tol.: (014) 670 3800
Web Site: http://www.ssctech.com
Software, Services & Consulting Services
N.A.I.C.S.: 513210
Rahul Kanwar (Pres & COO)

SS&C Technologies, Inc. (2)
4 Times Sq, New York, NY 10036 **(100%)**
Tel.: (646) 971-5000
Web Site: http://www.ssctech.com
Sales Range: $25-49.9 Million
Emp.: 25
Financial Software Developer
N.A.I.C.S.: 236220
William C. Stone (Chm & CEO)

SSB BANCORP, INC.
8700 Perry Hwy, Pittsburgh, PA 15237
Tel.: (412) 837-6955 MD
Web Site: https://www.ssbpgh.com
Year Founded: 2017
SSBP—(OTCQX)
Rev.: $16,268,435
Assets: $295,823,969
Liabilities: $268,626,216
Net Worth: $27,197,753
Earnings: $1,900,505
Fiscal Year-end: 12/31/23
Bank Holding Company
N.A.I.C.S.: 551111
J. Daniel Moon IV (Pres & CEO)
Bernie M. Simons (Chm)
Benjamin A. Contrucci (CFO)

Subsidiaries:

SSB Bank (1)
8700 Perry Hwy, Pittsburgh, PA 15237
Tel.: (412) 837-6955
Web Site: http://www.ssbpgh.com
Banking Services
N.A.I.C.S.: 522110
J. Daniel Moon IV (Pres & CEO)
Ben Contrucci (CFO)
Margie Glassbrenner (Branch Mgr)
Josh Wynkoop (Mgr-Consumer Loan)

STAAR SURGICAL CO.
25510 Commercentre Dr, Lake Forest, CA 92630
Tel.: (626) 303-7902 DE
Web Site: https://www.staar.com
Year Founded: 1982
STAA—(NASDAQ)
Rev.: $163,460,000
Assets: $257,416,000
Liabilities: $60,194,000
Net Worth: $197,222,000
Earnings: $5,913,000
Emp.: 575
Fiscal Year-end: 01/01/21
Ophthalmic Devices & Vision Implants Mfr
N.A.I.C.S.: 339113
Patrick F. Williams (CFO & VP)
Samuel J. Gesten (Chief Legal Officer, Sec & VP-Bus Dev)
Scott D. Barnes (Chief Medical Officer)
Warren Foust (COO)
Keith Holliday (CTO)
Magda Michna (Chief Clinical Regulatory Officer & Chief Medical Affairs Officer)
Nancy Sabin (CMO)
Nathaniel Sisitsky (Gen Counsel, Sec & Sr VP)
Thomas G. Frinzi (Chm, Pres & CEO)

Subsidiaries:

Circuit Tree Medical, Inc. (1)
23322 Madero Ste F, Mission Viejo, CA 92691
Tel.: (949) 454-2208
Electric Equipment Mfr
N.A.I.C.S.: 334419

STAAR Japan Inc (1)
1-5-2 Irifune Prime Tower Shin-Urayasu 5th floor, Urayasu, 279-0012, Chiba, Japan
Tel.: (81) 47 390 7301
Web Site: https://www.staar.co.jp
Surgical & Medical Instrument Mfr
N.A.I.C.S.: 339112

STAAR Surgical AG Niederlassung Germany (1)
Harksheider Str 3, 22399, Hamburg, Germany
Tel.: (49) 323328888
Optical Instrument & Lens Mfr
N.A.I.C.S.: 333310

STAAR Surgical Company AG (1)
Hauptstrasse 104, 2560, Nidau, Switzerland
Tel.: (41) 323328888
Mfr of Visual Implants
N.A.I.C.S.: 333310
Patrick F. Williams (CFO)
Hans Blickensdoerfer (Sr VP-Comml Ops)

STAAR Surgical PTE. LTD. (1)
9 Tampines Grande Asia Green 02-11, Singapore, 528735, Singapore
Tel.: (65) 97661547
Ophthalmic Goods Mfr
N.A.I.C.S.: 339115
John Santos (VP-Quality Assurance, Regulatory & Clinical-Global)

Staar Surgical China Co., Ltd. (1)
Dr Qizhi Linna Fu Room 2801 T2, Raffles Center No 1189 Changning Road, Shanghai, 200051, China
Tel.: (86) 2152650538
Medical Equipment & Device Mfr
N.A.I.C.S.: 339112

STABILIS SOLUTIONS, INC.
11750 Katy Frwy Ste 900, Houston, TX 77079
Tel.: (832) 456-6500 FL
Web Site: https://www.stabilis-solutions.com
SLNG—(NASDAQ)
Rev.: $98,823,000
Assets: $96,580,000
Liabilities: $36,713,000
Net Worth: $59,867,000
Earnings: ($3,186,000)
Emp.: 99
Fiscal Year-end: 12/31/22
Telecommunications Network Infrastructure Solutions
N.A.I.C.S.: 333414
Casey J. Crenshaw (Chm)
James C. Reddinger (CEO)
Koby Knight (Sr VP-Ops, Engrg & Construction)
Westervelt T. Ballard Jr. (Pres)
Andrew L. Puhala (CFO)

Subsidiaries:

BOMAY Electric Industries Co. (1)
Room 403, Building H, Yihong Science and Technology Park,, 142 Tian Lin Road, Shanghai, China
Tel.: (86) 2164325985
Web Site: http://www.aeti.com
Sales Range: $100-124.9 Million
Telecommunications Network Infrastructure Solutions
N.A.I.C.S.: 335311

M&I Electric Far East Pte Ltd (1)
16 Arumugam Road LTC Building D 07-01A, Singapore, 409961, Singapore
Tel.: (65) 67412788
Web Site: https://mielectric.sg
Sales Range: $100-124.9 Million
Emp.: 10
Telecommunications Network Infrastructure Solutions
N.A.I.C.S.: 332312

M&I Electric Industries, Inc. (1)
4775 M L King Pkwy, Beaumont, TX 77705-5651
Tel.: (713) 644-8182
Web Site: https://www.mielectric.com
Sales Range: $25-49.9 Million
Emp.: 150
Provider of Switchgear & Switchboard Apparatus
N.A.I.C.S.: 335313

Omega Metals (1)
6689 Shands Rd, Keystone Heights, FL 32656
Tel.: (352) 473-4984
Web Site: http://www.aatk.com
Sales Range: $150-199.9 Million
Emp.: 72
Sheet Metal Fabrication
N.A.I.C.S.: 332322

Stabilis Energy, LLC (1)
470 Orleans St 7th Fl, Beaumont, TX 77701-3000
Tel.: (866) 564-3835
Web Site: http://www.stabilisenergy.com
Liquified Natural Gas Distr
N.A.I.C.S.: 211130

STAFFING 360 SOLUTIONS, INC.
27th Fl 757 3rd Ave, New York, NY 10017
Tel.: (646) 507-5710 NV
Web Site: https://www.staffing360solutions.com
Year Founded: 2009
STAF—(NASDAQ)
Rev.: $190,876,000
Assets: $70,725,000
Liabilities: $78,535,000
Net Worth: ($7,810,000)
Earnings: ($26,041,000)
Emp.: 150
Fiscal Year-end: 12/30/23

Professional Leasing & Employment Placement Services
N.A.I.C.S.: 561311
Brendan Flood *(Pres, CEO & Chm)*
Alicia Barker *(COO & Exec VP)*

Subsidiaries:

CBS Butler Limited (1)
Kings Mill Kings Mill Lane South Nutfield, Redhill, RH1 5NB, Surrey, United Kingdom
Tel.: (44) 1737822000
Web Site: http://www.cbsbutler.com
Employee Placement Services
N.A.I.C.S.: 561311
Phil Johnson *(Acct Dir)*
David Rowe *(Acct Mgr-Strategic)*
Alicia Barker *(COO)*
Brendan Flood *(Pres)*
Robert Harper *(CEO)*
Simon Girven *(Sr VP)*

Clement May Limited (1)
3rd Floor 3 London Wall Buildings, London, EC2M 5SY, United Kingdom
Tel.: (44) 2072517315
Web Site: http://www.clementmay.com
Employee Placement Services
N.A.I.C.S.: 561311
Nicholas Hodson *(Acct Mgr)*
Alicia Barker *(COO)*
Brendan Flood *(Pres)*
Robert Harper *(CEO)*
Simon Girven *(Sr VP)*

Cyber 360 Solutions (1)
1600 Providence Hwy, Walpole, MA 02081
Tel.: (781) 438-4380
Web Site:
  https://www.cyber360solutions.com
Sales Range: $1-9.9 Million
Cybersecurity Professional Leasing & Employment Placement Services
N.A.I.C.S.: 561330
Heather Aiello *(CEO)*

FirstPRO, Inc. (1)
1117 Perimeter Ctr W Ste N503, Atlanta, GA 30338
Tel.: (404) 495-1442
Web Site: http://www.firstproinc.com
Full Service, Independent Staffing & Recruitment Firm
N.A.I.C.S.: 541612
April Fawcett Nagel *(Co-Founder & CEO)*
Michelle Kennedy *(Dir-Corp Ops)*
Philip Nagel *(Co-Founder & Exec VP)*
Jared Kennedy *(Mng Partner)*

Headway Workforce Solutions, Inc. (1)
3100 Smoketree Ct Ste 900, Raleigh, NC 27604
Web Site: https://headwaywfs.com
Human Resource Consulting Services
N.A.I.C.S.: 541612

Lighthouse Placement Services, Inc. (1)
1600 Osgood St Ste 2082, North Andover, MA 01845
Tel.: (978) 373-2095
Web Site:
  http://www.lighthouseplacement.com
Rev.: $2,000,000
Emp.: 47
Employment Placement Services
N.A.I.C.S.: 561311
Lissa Jerez *(Mgr-Lead Acct)*
Dan Dubay *(Acct Mgr)*
Jackie Fedor *(Acct Mgr)*
Tonya Lwowski *(Coord-Client Rels)*
Bill Hurynowicz *(Mgr-Market)*
Bob Giusti *(VP-Ops)*
Liz Cummings *(Dir-Professional Svcs)*
Ed Simpson *(Sr VP)*

Monroe Staffing Services, LLC (1)
6 Research Dr Ste 440, Shelton, CT 06484
Tel.: (203) 502-8701
Web Site: http://www.monroestaffing.com
Temporary Help Service
N.A.I.C.S.: 561320
Amy Innarelli *(Sr VP-Regional Operations-North)*
Jenni Guarino *(Sr VP-Regional Operations-Northeast & HUB)*
Alicia Cintron *(Coord-Compliance & Safety)*
Carlos Asian *(Supvr-Branch Ops)*
Leo Budnick *(Specialist-Bus Dev)*
Angela Vasquez *(Mgr-Vendor Program)*

Subsidiary (Domestic):

Key Resources, Inc. (2)
3703 A W Market St, Greensboro, NC 27403
Tel.: (336) 297-1700
Web Site: http://www.keyresourcesinc.com
Employment Placement Agencies
N.A.I.C.S.: 561311
Angela Jones *(Sr VP-Ops-Southeast)*
Elizabeth Toribio *(Branch Mgr)*
Miranda Castelan *(Specialist-Staffing)*
Gabriel Pesqueira *(Specialist-Staffing)*
Ricardo Rivas *(Specialist-Staffing)*

PeopleSERVE, Inc. (1)
643 Veterans of Foreign Wars Pkwy, Chestnut Hill, MA 02467
Tel.: (617) 469-9779
Web Site: http://www.peopleserveinc.com
Information Technology Professional Leasing & Employment Placement Services
N.A.I.C.S.: 561330
Erik Schwartz *(Pres)*
Brianna Marin *(Mgr-HR & Workforce Intelligence)*
Brendan Farrand *(VP)*

The JM Group (IT Recruitment) Limited (1)
3rd Floor 3 London Wall Buildings, London, EC2M 5SY, United Kingdom
Tel.: (44) 2072517300
Web Site: http://www.thejmgroup.com
Employee Placement Services
N.A.I.C.S.: 561311
Simon Girven *(Mng Dir-Permanent Sls)*
Fiona Eddy *(Dir-Contract Sls)*

STAG INDUSTRIAL, INC.
1 Federal St 23rd Fl, Boston, MA 02110
Tel.: (617) 574-4777   MD
Web Site:
  https://www.stagindustrial.com
STAG—(NYSE)
Rev.: $707,835,000
Assets: $6,283,458,000
Liabilities: $2,837,647,000
Net Worth: $3,445,811,000
Earnings: $192,845,000
Emp.: 95
Fiscal Year-end: 12/31/23
Real Estate Investment Trust
N.A.I.C.S.: 525990
Benjamin S. Butcher *(Founder)*
Bradford F. Sweeney *(Sr VP-Acquisitions)*
Michael C. Chase *(Chief Investment Officer & Exec VP)*
William R. Crooker *(Pres & CEO)*
Jeffrey M. Sullivan *(Gen Counsel, Sec & Exec VP)*
David A. Barker *(Sr VP & Mgr-Portfolio)*
Alan H. Simmons *(Sr VP & Asst Gen Counsel)*
Kurt N. Flionis *(Sr VP-Credit)*
Andrea M. Gillespie *(Dir-HR)*
Seth A. Malamut *(Sr VP & Assoc Gen Counsel)*
Rowan McFeely *(Sr VP-Underwriting & Analyst Pool)*
Matts S. Pinard *(CFO, Treas & Exec VP)*
Steven T. Kimball *(Exec VP-Real Estate Ops)*

Subsidiaries:

STAG Mebane 1, LLC (1)
1 Federal St 23rd Fl, Boston, MA 02110
Tel.: (617) 574-4777
Real Estate Investment Services
N.A.I.C.S.: 531110

STAG Reading, LLC (1)
173 Tuckerton Rd, Reading, PA 19605-1135
Tel.: (610) 916-3200
Real Estate Investment Services
N.A.I.C.S.: 531110

STAGE STORES, INC.

2425 W Loop S, Houston, TX 77027
Web Site:
  http://www.stagestoresinc.com
Year Founded: 1988
SSI—(NYSE)
Rev.: $1,580,149,000
Assets: $744,161,000
Liabilities: $489,636,000
Net Worth: $254,525,000
Earnings: ($87,714,000)
Emp.: 13,600
Fiscal Year-end: 02/02/19
Family Clothing & Department Stores Owner & Operator
N.A.I.C.S.: 551112
Thorsten I. Weber *(Chief Mdsg Officer & Exec VP)*
Amy B. Gray *(Chief HR Officer & Exec VP)*
Jennifer Costa *(Gen Counsel, Sec & Sr VP)*
Gina R. Lampman *(Chief Acctg Officer)*
Russell A. Lundy II *(Chief Stores Officer & Exec VP)*
Steven R. Williams Jr. *(CIO & Exec VP)*

Subsidiaries:

Specialty Retailers, Inc. (1)
2425 W Loop Freeway S, Houston, TX 77027
Tel.: (713) 667-5601
Web Site: http://www.corporate.stage.com
Emp.: 9,946
Apparel Retail
N.A.I.C.S.: 458110

STAGWELL, INC.
1 World Trade Ctr Fl 65, New York, NY 10007
Tel.: (646) 429-1800   DE
Web Site: https://stagwellgroup.com
STGW—(NASDAQ)
Holding Company
N.A.I.C.S.: 551112
Mark Penn *(Chm)*
Frank Lanuto *(CFO)*
Vincenzo DiMaggio *(Chief Acctg Officer)*

Subsidiaries:

Midas OpCo Holdings LLC (1)
1 World Trade Ctr F 65, New York, NY 10007
Tel.: (646) 429-1800
Rev.: $1,244,768,000
Assets: $1,511,314,000
Liabilities: $1,920,224,000
Net Worth: ($408,910,000)
Earnings: ($228,971,000)
Emp.: 4,866
Fiscal Year-end: 12/31/2020
Holding Company; Advertising & Public Relations Agencies
N.A.I.C.S.: 551112
Rodney Earl Slater *(Sec)*
Mark J. Penn *(Chm & CEO)*
Vincenzo DiMaggio *(Chief Acctg Officer & Sr VP)*
Deirdre McGlashan *(Chief Media Officer)*
Kerry Robinson *(Sr VP-Internal Audit)*
David Kwon *(Sr VP-Corp Dev & Strategy)*
Sandy Roberts *(Sr VP-Tax-Global)*
Rodney Slater *(Sec)*
Jason Reid *(Chief Investment Officer)*
Julia Hammond *(Pres)*
Peter McElligott *(Gen Counsel)*
Stephanie Howley *(Chief People Officer)*
Merrill Raman *(CTO)*
Alexis Williams *(Chief Brand Officer)*
Ray Day *(Vice Chm)*
Unai Ortega *(VP)*
Keisha Brescia *(Sr VP)*
Michael Jacobson *(VP)*
Anas Ghazi *(Chief Affiliates Officer)*
Edmund Graff *(Sr VP)*
Rich Wulwick *(Sr VP)*
Amy Mayurnik *(Sr VP)*
Elspeth Rollert *(CMO)*
Abe Geiger *(Chief Product Officer)*
Matthew Lochner *(Mng Dir)*

Subsidiary (Non-US):

6degrees Integrated Communications Corp. (2)
1210 Sheppard Ave E Ste 700, Toronto, M2K 1E3, ON, Canada
Tel.: (416) 446-7758
Web Site: http://www.6deg.ca
Sales Range: $25-49.9 Million
Emp.: 40
Advertising Agencies
N.A.I.C.S.: 541890
Troy Yung *(Partner)*

Subsidiary (Domestic):

72andSunny Partners LLC (2)
12101 Bluff Creek Dr, Los Angeles, CA 90094
Tel.: (310) 215-9009
Web Site: http://www.72andsunny.com
Sales Range: $50-74.9 Million
Emp.: 400
Full Service
N.A.I.C.S.: 541810
Chris Kay *(CEO-Asia Pacific)*
Emma Conway *(Head-Design-Sydney)*
Luke Martin *(Head-Product-Sydney)*

Subsidiary (Non-US):

72andSunny (3)
Westerhuis 1st Fl Westerstraat 187, 1015 MA, Amsterdam, Netherlands
Tel.: (31) 202182400
Web Site: http://www.72andsunny.com
Advetising Agency
N.A.I.C.S.: 541810
Laura Visco *(Deputy Exec Creative Dir)*
John Boiler *(Co-Founder)*
Glenn Cole *(Co-Founder)*
Ida Siow *(Exec Dir-Strategy-Singapore)*
Chris Kay *(Pres/Partner-APAC)*
Johnny Tan *(Exec Creative Dir-APAC)*

Subsidiary (Non-US):

Accumark Communications, Inc. (2)
1210 Sheperd Ave E Ste 700, Toronto, M2K 1E3, ON, Canada
Tel.: (416) 446-7758
Web Site: http://www.accumark.ca
Sales Range: $25-49.9 Million
Emp.: 65
Advertising Agencies
N.A.I.C.S.: 541810

Accumark Partners Inc (2)
1210 Sheppard Ave E Ste 700, Toronto, M2K 1E3, ON, Canada
Tel.: (416) 446-7758
Web Site: http://www.6deg.ca
Marketing Consulting Services
N.A.I.C.S.: 541613

Subsidiary (Domestic):

Alveo LLC (2)
700 W Pete Rose Way Ste 426, Cincinnati, OH 45203
Tel.: (513) 557-3504
Web Site: http://www.alveohealth.com
Data Processing Services
N.A.I.C.S.: 518210
Joe Sunderman *(CEO)*
Brett Stover *(Pres-Bus Dev)*
Brigott Dawn *(VP-Client Engagement)*

Subsidiary (Non-US):

Anomaly B.V (2)
Herengracht 551, 1017 BW, Amsterdam, Netherlands
Tel.: (31) 203080380
Web Site: http://www.anomaly.com
Sales Range: $25-49.9 Million
Emp.: 1
Marketing Consulting Services
N.A.I.C.S.: 541613

Anomaly Inc. (2)
46 Spadina Ave Suite 200, Toronto, M5V 2H8, ON, Canada
Tel.: (647) 547-3440
Web Site: http://anomaly.com
Sales Range: $25-49.9 Million
Emp.: 110
Advertising Agencies
N.A.I.C.S.: 541810

Stagwell, Inc.—(Continued)

Franke Rodriguez (CEO & Partner)
Karina Wilsher (Partner & CEO-Global)
Paula Daly (CFO-Global)
Allie Sabol (Mng Partner)
Kristi Henderson (Head-Diversity-Global)

Anomaly London LLP (2)
25 Charterhouse Square, London, EC1M
6AE, United Kingdom
Tel.: (44) 2078430600
Web Site: http://www.anomaly.com
Emp.: 3
Marketing Consulting Services
N.A.I.C.S.: 541613
Camilla Harrisson (CEO & Partner)

Subsidiary (Domestic):

Anomaly Partners LLC (2)
536 Broadway 11th Fl, New York, NY 10012
Tel.: (917) 595-2200
Web Site: http://anomaly.com
Sales Range: $25-49.9 Million
Emp.: 100
Marketing Consulting Services
N.A.I.C.S.: 541613
Aisea Laungaue (Chief Strategy Officer)
Allie Sabol (Mng Partner)
Camilla Harrisson (CEO)
Candace Borland (Pres)
Damien Reid (Mng Partner)
Dave Douglass (Chief Creative Officer)
Elvis Chau (Chief Creative Officer)
Eric Lee (CEO)
Franke Rodriguez (CEO)
Josh Fell (Chief Creative Officer)
Khara Wagner (Pres)
Laura Rowan (Mng Partner)
Paula Daly (CFO)
Richard Summers (Chief Strategy Officer)
Shannon Green (Corp Counsel)
Simon Owen (CEO)
Stuart Smith (Chief Strategy Officer)
Will De Lannoy (Mng Partner)

Assembly (2)
1 World Trade Ctr 67th Fl, New York, NY
10007
Tel.: (212) 500-6900
Web Site: http://www.media-assembly.com
Sales Range: $600-649.9 Million
Emp.: 490
Advertising Agencies
N.A.I.C.S.: 541810
Kendra Mazey (Mng Partner-Detroit)
Chantal Pittman (Exec VP-Digital Ops)
Matt Speiser (Gen Counsel)

Subsidiary (Non-US):

Boom Marketing Inc (2)
1210 Sheppard Ave East Suite 700, Toronto, M2K 1E3, ON, Canada
Tel.: (416) 446-7720
Web Site: http://www.boommarketing.ca
Sales Range: $25-49.9 Million
Emp.: 4
Social Media Marketing Services
N.A.I.C.S.: 541890

Bruce Mau Design Inc. (2)
340 King Street East Suite 500, Toronto,
M5A 1K8, ON, Canada
Tel.: (416) 306-6401
Web Site: http://www.brucemaudesign.com
Sales Range: $25-49.9 Million
Emp.: 4
Graphic Design Services
N.A.I.C.S.: 541430
Diane Mahony (Partner & VP-Client Devs)
Tom Keogh (Partner & VP-Growth)
Rosanna Vitiello (Creative Dir-Consulting)
Marla Garderis (Acct Dir)
Patricia Marcucci (Acct Dir)
Kar Yan Cheung (Dir-Design Strategy)
Chris Allen (Creative Dir)

Bruce Mau Holdings Ltd. (2)
340 King Street East Suite 402, Toronto,
M5A 1K8, ON, Canada
Tel.: (416) 306-6401
Web Site: http://www.brucemaudesign.com
Design Services
N.A.I.C.S.: 541430

Bryan Mills Iradesso Corp. (2)
1129 Leslie St, Toronto, M3C 2K5, ON,
Canada

Tel.: (416) 447-4740
Web Site: http://www.bmir.com
Sales Range: $25-49.9 Million
Emp.: 25
Advertising Agencies
N.A.I.C.S.: 541810

Subsidiary (Domestic):

CP+B (2)
3390 Mary St Ste 300, Coconut Grove, FL
33133
Tel.: (305) 859-2070
Web Site: http://www.cpbgroup.com
Rev.: $1,200,000,000
Emp.: 1,000
Advertising Services
N.A.I.C.S.: 541810
Ryan Skubic (Mng Dir)

Subsidiary (Non-US):

CP+B (3)
The Brassworks 32 York Way Kings Cross,
2 Greenhill Rents, London, N1 9AB, United
Kingdom
Tel.: (44) 2035517701
Emp.: 11
N.A.I.C.S.: 541810

Branch (Domestic):

CP+B Boulder (3)
6450 Gunpark Dr, Boulder, CO 80301
Tel.: (303) 628-5100
Web Site: http://www.cpbgroup.com
Emp.: 500
N.A.I.C.S.: 541810
Tom Adams (Exec Creative Dir)
Danielle Aldrich (Pres)
Maggie Allman (Head-People & Culture)
Jen Bollman (Dir-Comm Strategy)
Tony Calcao (Creative Dir)
Dan Corken (Head-Production)
Joe Corr (Exec Creative Dir-Tech)
Jen Hruska (Co-Head-Strategy)
Courtney Loveman (Co-Head-Strategy)
Dusty Nelson (CFO-Global)
Chuck Porter (Chm & Partner)
Chris Shewmake (Dir-Comm Strategy)
Ryan Skubic (COO)

Branch (Non-US):

CP+B Canada (3)
296 Richmond St W Ste 500, Toronto, M5V
1X2, ON, Canada
Tel.: (416) 598-4944
Web Site: http://www.cpbgroup.com
Sales Range: $10-24.9 Million
Emp.: 120
N.A.I.C.S.: 541810

Subsidiary (Non-US):

Capital C Partners LP (2)
340 King Street East Suite 500, Toronto,
M5A 1K8, ON, Canada
Tel.: (416) 777-1124
Web Site: http://www.capitalc.ca
Advertising Agencies
N.A.I.C.S.: 541810

Subsidiary (Domestic):

Clifford/Bratskeir Public Relations
LLC (2)
152 Madison Ave Ste 500, New York, NY
10016
Tel.: (212) 679-2233
Web Site: http://www.bratskeir.com
Sales Range: $25-49.9 Million
Emp.: 20
Public Relations Agencies
N.A.I.C.S.: 541820

Colle & McVoy LLC (2)
400 1st Ave N Ste 700, Minneapolis, MN
55401-1954
Tel.: (612) 305-6000
Web Site: https://www.collemcvoy.com
Sales Range: $50-74.9 Million
Emp.: 200
Advertising Agencies
N.A.I.C.S.: 541810
Christine Fruechte (CEO)
Lisa Miller (CFO)
John Doyle (Exec Dir-Brand Experience)
Jessica Henrichs (Pres)
Ciro Sarmiento (Chief Creative Officer)

Subsidiary (Domestic):

Exponent (3)
400 1st Ave N Ste 700, Minneapolis, MN
55401
Tel.: (612) 305-6003
Web Site: https://www.exponentpr.com
Emp.: 25
N.A.I.C.S.: 541810
Tom Lindell (Mng Dir)
Ed Bennett (Exec Dir-Design)

Branch (Domestic):

Mobium (3)
360 N Michigan Ave 12th Fl, Chicago, IL
60604
Tel.: (312) 422-8960
Web Site: http://www.mobium.com
Rev.: $17,500,000
Emp.: 35
Agency Services
N.A.I.C.S.: 541810

Subsidiary (Domestic):

Communifx Partners LLC (2)
1253 Freedom Rd Ste 500, Cranberry
Township, PA 16066
Tel.: (724) 935-8655
Advertising Agency Services
N.A.I.C.S.: 541810

Subsidiary (Non-US):

Computer Composition of Canada
LP (2)
12 Stanley Court Unit 4A, Whitby, L1N 8P9,
ON, Canada
Tel.: (905) 430-3400
Web Site:
http://www.computercomposition.ca
Emp.: 1
Typesetting & Graphic Design Services
N.A.I.C.S.: 323120

Concentric Health Experience
Limited (2)
60 Charlotte St, London, W1T 2NU, United
Kingdom
Tel.: (44) 2076327685
Web Site: http://www.concentrichx.com
Health Care Srvices
N.A.I.C.S.: 621999
Ken Begasse (Co-Founder & CEO)
Michael Sanzen (Co-Founder & Chief Creative Officer)

Subsidiary (Domestic):

Crispin Porter & Bogusky (2)
1 World Trade Ctr 62nd Fl, New York, NY
10007
Tel.: (003) 628-5100
Web Site: http://www.cpbgroup.com
Advertising Services
N.A.I.C.S.: 541810
Chuck Porter (Chm & Partner)

Subsidiary (Non-US):

Crispin Porter & Bogusky Europe
AB (2)
Norraallegatan 5, 411 09, Gothenburg,
Sweden
Tel.: (46) 313396060
Web Site: http://www.ctbgroup.se
Emp.: 50
Advertising Agencies
N.A.I.C.S.: 541810

Crispin Porter & Bogusky Limited (2)
The Brassworks 32 York Way, London, N1
9AB, United Kingdom
Tel.: (44) 2039714242
Web Site: https://www.cpblondon.com
Emp.: 50
Advertising Agencies
N.A.I.C.S.: 541810

Subsidiary (Domestic):

Doner Partners LLC (2)
400 Galleria Officentre Ste 410, Southfield,
MI 48034
Tel.: (248) 354-9700
Advertising Services
N.A.I.C.S.: 541810
Craig Conrad (Pres)

Dotbox LLC (2)

853 Broadway, New York, NY 10003
Tel.: (212) 937-4177
Web Site: http://www.dotboxideas.com
Business Management Services
N.A.I.C.S.: 561110

Expecting Productions, LLC (2)
200 Varick St Ste 611, New York, NY 10014
Tel.: (646) 429-1800
Video Production Services
N.A.I.C.S.: 512110

Subsidiary (Non-US):

Forsman & Bodenfors AB (2)
Stora Badhusgatan 37 5th floor, 411 21,
Gothenburg, Sweden
Tel.: (46) 31176730
Web Site: https://www.forsman.com
Emp.: 150
Advetising Agency
N.A.I.C.S.: 541810
Anna Qvennerstedt (Partner & Copywriter)

Subsidiary (Non-US):

Forsman & Bodenfors - Toronto (3)
340 King St E 5th Floor, Toronto, M5A 1K8,
ON, Canada
Tel.: (416) 260-7000
Web Site: http://forsman.co
Emp.: 40
Advetising Agency
N.A.I.C.S.: 541810

Subsidiary (Non-US):

Forsman & Bodenfors Factory
AB (2)
Stora Badhusgatan 37 5th floor, 411 21,
Gothenburg, Sweden
Tel.: (46) 31176730
Web Site: http://www.forsman.com
Emp.: 150
Advertising Services
N.A.I.C.S.: 541810
Kitty Olson (Acct Dir)
Therese Kaiser (Copywriter)
Emelie Westman (Copywriter)
Fredrik Rosvall (Copywriter)
Hanna Karlsson (Copywriter)
Jesper Eronn (Copywriter)
Johanna Sjostedt (Copywriter)
Thomas Bennett (Copywriter)
Jens Wickelgren (Art Dir)
Emelie Bang (Art Dir)
Evelina Elo (Art Dir)
Linda Lundgren (Art Dir)
Pernilla Berndtsdotter (Art Dir)
Sunniva Hovensjo (Art Dir)
Aida Stalnacke (Acct Mgr)
Emma Svardstrom (Acct Mgr)
Hanna Wensheim (Acct Mgr)
Jenny Goransson (Acct Mgr)
Lina Roos (Acct Mgr)
Linda Marteus (Acct Mgr)
Martina Claesson (Acct Mgr)
Siri Nyborg (Acct Mgr)
Stefan Haggkvist (Acct Mgr)
Stina Enestig (Acct Mgr)

Forsman & Bodenfors Inhouse
AB (2)
Kungsgatan 48A, 411 15, Gothenburg,
Sweden
Tel.: (46) 31176730
Web Site: https://www.inhouse.fb.se
Advertising Services
N.A.I.C.S.: 541810
Anders Bjorkqvist (CEO)
Elias Brovik (Art Dir)
Markus Anderberg (Art Dir)

Gale Creative Agency Private
Limited (2)
Millers Road Vasanth Nagar 3/1 JP Techno
Park, Bengaluru, 560 052, Karnataka, India
Tel.: (91) 8061828500
Web Site: http://www.gale.agency
Advertising Services
N.A.I.C.S.: 541810
Pat Frend (Mng Dir)

Gale Partners Inc. (2)
171 E Liberty Street Unit 360, Toronto, M6K
3P6, ON, Canada
Tel.: (416) 306-8000
Advertising Services
N.A.I.C.S.: 541810
Sanjeev Gosain (Acct Dir)

Subsidiary (Domestic):

Gale Partners LLC (2)
1 World Trade Ctr Fl 62, New York, NY
10007
Tel.: (646) 862-3555
Web Site: https://www.gale.agency
Advertising Services
N.A.I.C.S.: 541810
Brad Simms (Pres & CEO)
Geoff Edwards (Exec Creative Dir)

Subsidiary (Non-US):

Happy Forsman & Bodenfors AB (2)
Stora Badhusgatan 37, 411 21, Gothen-
burg, Sweden
Tel.: (46) 313396200
Web Site: https://www.happy.fb.se
Design Services
N.A.I.C.S.: 541430
Catarina Akerblom (Acct Dir)
Anders Kornestedt (Creative Dir)
Camilla Smids (Mgr-Acct)
Cecilia Holmstrom (Mgr-Acct)

Subsidiary (Domestic):

Hecho Studios LLC (2)
12101 W Bluff Creek Dr, Playa Vista, CA
90094
Tel.: (310) 215-9009
Web Site: https://www.hechostudios.com
Advertising Services
N.A.I.C.S.: 541810
Adam Milano (Head-Dev)

Hello Design, LLC (2)
8522 National Blvd Ste 109, Culver City,
CA 90232
Tel.: (503) 928-3188
Web Site: https://www.hellodesign.com
Emp.: 30
Graphic Design Services
N.A.I.C.S.: 541810
David Lai (CEO & Creative Dir)

Hudson and Sunset Media LLC (2)
200 Varick St Ste 611, New York, NY 10014
Tel.: (646) 582-8630
Web Site: http://www.hudsunmedia.com
Emp.: 4
Television Shows Production Services
N.A.I.C.S.: 512191
Michael Rourke (Founder & CEO)

Hunter Public Relations, LLC (2)
1 World Trade Ctr FL 68, New York, NY
10010
Tel.: (212) 679-6600
Web Site: https://www.hunterpr.com
Emp.: 55
Public Relations Agency
N.A.I.C.S.: 541820

Subsidiary (Non-US):

Integrated Healthcare Communica-
tions, Inc. (2)
370 King St W Ste 800, PO Box 46, To-
ronto, M5V 1J9, ON, Canada
Tel.: (416) 504-8733
Web Site: http://www.ihcinc.com
Sales Range: $50-74.9 Million
Emp.: 70
N.A.I.C.S.: 522299
Krista Webster (Pres)

Subsidiary (Domestic):

Integrated Media Solutions, LCC. (2)
650 5th Ave 35th Fl, New York, NY 10019
Tel.: (212) 373-9500
Sales Range: $25-49.9 Million
Emp.: 85
Direct Response Media & Analytic Services
N.A.I.C.S.: 541840

Subsidiary (Non-US):

KWT Global LP (2)
33 Draper Street, Toronto, M5V 2M3, ON,
Canada
Tel.: (647) 374-0400
Public Relation & Communication Services
N.A.I.C.S.: 541820
Tran Nguyen (Mng Dir)

KWT Global Ltd. (2)
100 Leman Street, London, E1 8EU, United
Kingdom

Tel.: (44) 2039253410
Public Relation & Communication Services
N.A.I.C.S.: 541820
Sarah Moloney (Mng Dir)

Subsidiary (Domestic):

KWT Global, LLC (2)
1 World Trade Ctr FL 69, New York, NY
10007
Tel.: (646) 460-8910
Web Site: https://www.kwtglobal.com
Public Relation Agency Services
N.A.I.C.S.: 541820
Aaron R. Kwittken (Co-Founder & Chm)
Gabrielle Zucker (Co-Founder, Pres & CEO)
Dara Cothran (Exec VP-Global Strategy &
Insights)
Jeremy Page (Exec VP & Dir-Creative-
Global)
Dan Brady (Exec VP-Corp)
Seth Rockers (CFO)
Jessica Foster (Chief Ops Officer)
Sarah Moloney (Mng Dir)
Matthew Levison (Sr VP)
Jess Spar (Sr VP)
Emily Ganz (VP)

Subsidiary (Non-US):

Kbs+p Canada LP (2)
3510 Blvd Laurent Office 410, Montreal,
H2Z 2B2, QC, Canada
Tel.: (514) 875-7430
Web Site: http://www.kbsp.ca
Sales Range: $25-49.9 Million
Emp.: 63
Advertising Agencies
N.A.I.C.S.: 541810

Kenna Communications LP (2)
90 Burnhamthorpe Road West 5th Floor,
Mississauga, L5B 3C3, ON, Canada
Tel.: (905) 277-2900
Web Site: http://kenna.ca
Sales Range: $25-49.9 Million
Emp.: 15
Marketing Consulting Services
N.A.I.C.S.: 541613
Stephen Shaw (Chief Strategy Officer)
Raul De Sousa (CFO)
Colin Devereaux (Exec VP)
Colin Ireland (CTO)
Ken Morgan (Creative Dir)
Werner Anders (Dir-Application Dev)
Steve Turner (Dir-Insights & Analytics)

Kingsdale Partners LP (2)
The Exchange Tower, Toronto, M5X 1E2,
ON, Canada
Tel.: (416) 644-4031
Web Site:
https://www.kingsdaleadvisors.com
Advertising Services
N.A.I.C.S.: 541810
Wes Hall (Founder & Chm)
Kamika McLean (Gen Counsel)

Kwittken & Company Limited (2)
25 Charterhouse Square, London, EC1M
6AH, United Kingdom
Tel.: (44) 2076327687
Public Relation Agency Services
N.A.I.C.S.: 541820

Kwittken LP (2)
60 Charlotte Street, London, W1T 2NU,
United Kingdom
Tel.: (44) 2076327687
Advertising Services
N.A.I.C.S.: 541810
Aaron Kwittken (Chm & CEO)

Subsidiary (Domestic):

Laird + Partners New York LLC (2)
475 Tenth Ave 7th Fl, New York, NY
10018 (65%)
Tel.: (212) 474-3211
Web Site: https://lairdandpartners.com
Sales Range: $25-49.9 Million
Emp.: 75
Advertising Services
N.A.I.C.S.: 541810
Trey Laird (Founder, Chm & Chief Creative
Officer)

Left Field Labs, LLC (2)
510 Victoria Ave, Venice, CA 90291
Tel.: (424) 500-2045

Web Site: http://www.leftfieldlabs.com
Sales Range: $1-9.9 Million
Emp.: 8
Advertising Services
N.A.I.C.S.: 541810
Eric Lee (Partner)

MDC Corporate (US) Inc. (2)
The Mdc Innovation Ctr 745 5th Ave 19th
Fl, New York, NY 10151
Tel.: (646) 429-1800
Web Site: http://www.mdc-partners.com
Investment Management Service
N.A.I.C.S.: 523999

Subsidiary (Non-US):

MDC Partners Inc. (2)
33 Draper Street, Toronto, M5V 2M3, ON,
Canada
Tel.: (416) 960-9000
Advertising Services
N.A.I.C.S.: 541810

Subsidiary (Domestic):

MMI Agency, LLC (2)
1712 Pease St, Houston, TX 77003
Tel.: (917) 438-4993
Web Site: https://www.mmiagency.com
Advertising Agency Services
N.A.I.C.S.: 541810
Maggie Malek (CEO)
Brandi Lalanne (VP)
Jay Hickman (Dir-Public Relations)
Caroline Thomas (Creative Dir)
Adrienne Adair (Sr VP-Creative)

MediaCurrent Interactive Solutions
LLC (2)
5815 Windward Pkwy Ste 302, Alpharetta,
GA 30005
Tel.: (678) 580-1690
Web Site: https://www.mediacurrent.com
Software Development Services
N.A.I.C.S.: 541511

Mono Advertising LLC (2)
1350 Lagoon Ave 10th FL, Minneapolis, MN
55408
Tel.: (612) 454-4900
Web Site: https://www.mono-1.com
Emp.: 90
Advertising Agencies
N.A.I.C.S.: 541810
Michael Hart (Co-Founder & Co-Chief Cre-
ative Officer)
Chris Lange (Co-Founder & Co-Chief Cre-
ative Officer)
Jim Scott (Co-Founder & Mng Partner)
Becca Tlustosch (CFO)

New Team LLC (2)
110 E Broward Blvd Ste 2450, Fort Lauder-
dale, FL 33301
Tel.: (954) 862-2400
Advertising Consulting Services
N.A.I.C.S.: 541810

No Sleep Productions LLC (2)
PO Box 1465, Cincinnati, OH 45250
Tel.: (513) 310-9396
Web Site:
https://www.nosleepproductionson
line.com
Audio Recording Services
N.A.I.C.S.: 512240
Jerry Sanders (Owner)

Subsidiary (Non-US):

Northstar Research Holdings Canada
Inc. (2)
18 King Street East Suite 1500, Toronto,
M5C 1C4, ON, Canada
Tel.: (416) 907-7100
Web Site: https://www.northstarhub.com
Advertising Services
N.A.I.C.S.: 541810
Matthew Denomme (Mng Dir & Sr VP)
Mark Clipsham (VP-Data Science & Analyt-
ics)

Subsidiary (Domestic):

Northstar Research Holdings USA
LP (2)
160 Varick St 5th Fl, New York, NY 10013
Tel.: (646) 651-1612
Web Site: http://www.northstarhub.com

Advertising Services
N.A.I.C.S.: 541810

Subsidiary (Non-US):

Northstar Research Partners (UK)
Limited (2)
Unit B3 City Cloisters 196 Old Street, Lon-
don, EC1V 9FR, United Kingdom
Tel.: (44) 2078249870
Advertising Services
N.A.I.C.S.: 541810
Matthew Sell (COO)
Alex Wilman (Dir-Res)

Subsidiary (Domestic):

Northstar Research Partners (USA)
LLC (2)
1 World Trade Ctr Fl 67, New York, NY
10007
Tel.: (646) 651-1612
Sales Range: $25-49.9 Million
Emp.: 8
Marketing Research & Consulting Services
N.A.I.C.S.: 541910

Subsidiary (Non-US):

Northstar Research Partners Inc. (2)
18 King Street East Suite 1500, Toronto,
M5C 1C4, ON, Canada
Tel.: (416) 907-7100
Web Site: http://www.northstarhub.com
Sales Range: $25-49.9 Million
Emp.: 40
N.A.I.C.S.: 522299
Matthew Sell (COO)
Vladimir Levkov (VP-Data Support)
Jack Miles (Sr Dir-Res)
James Vaughan-Smith (Dir-Ops)
Alex Wilman (Dir-Res)
Jeffrey Johns (Sr Dir-Res)
Jessica Fennell (Assoc Dir)
Nichola Beale (Dir-Res)
Shamvir Singh (Assoc Dir-Innovation &
Analytics)
Matthew Denomme (Mng Dir & Sr VP)
Dritan Nesho (CEO)
Jennifer Yellin (Mng Dir)

Onbrand (2)
43 Davies Ave, Toronto, M4M 2A9, ON,
Canada (100%)
Tel.: (416) 366-8883
Web Site: http://www.onbranddesign.com
Sales Range: $25-49.9 Million
Emp.: 15
N.A.I.C.S.: 522299

Subsidiary (Domestic):

Redscout LLC (2)
55 Water St 6th Fl, Brooklyn, NY 11201
Tel.: (646) 336-6028
Web Site: https://www.redscout.com
Sales Range: $25-49.9 Million
Emp.: 50
Brand Development & Integration
N.A.I.C.S.: 541810
Ivan Kayser (CEO & Partner)
Dan Pratt (Dir-Strategy)
Claudia Puerta (Controller)

Branch (Domestic):

Redscout LLC - San Francisco (3)
99 Osgood Pl 3rd Fl, San Francisco, CA
94133
Tel.: (415) 651-4209
N.A.I.C.S.: 541810
Jonah Disend (Chm)

Subsidiary (Domestic):

Relevent Partners LLC (2)
475 10th Ave 9th Fl, New York, NY 10018
Tel.: (212) 206-0600
Web Site: http://www.relevent.com
Emp.: 20
Marketing Consulting Services
N.A.I.C.S.: 541613
Claire Annas Keaveney (Pres)
H. Tony Berger (Founder & CEO)
Ian Cleary (VP-Innovation & Ideation)
Andrew Levy (Head-Experiential Design)
Sutherland Jones (Sr Mgr-Production)

Sloane & Company LLC (2)
285 Fulton St 69th Fl, New York, NY 10007
Tel.: (212) 486-9500

Stagwell, Inc.—(Continued)

Web Site: http://www.sloanepr.com
Rev.: $5,000,000
Emp.: 25
N.A.I.C.S.: 541820
Darren Brandt (Co-CEO)
Whit Clay (Co-CEO)
John Hartz (Pres-Corp Comm)
Nevin Reilly (Sr Mng Dir)
Ariel Kouvaras (Mng Dir)
Erica Bartsch (Sr Mng Dir)
Mike Boccio (Sr Mng Dir)
TJ White (Mng Dir & Head-Special Situations)
Amanda Wells (Sr VP)
Elyse Petroni (VP)
Emily Mohr (VP)
Gary R. Koops (Sr Mng Dir)
Isaac Sheinkopf (VP)
Mike Adamo (VP)
Neal Nagarajan (Sr VP)
Sarah Lyons (Sr VP)

Source Marketing LLC (2)
761 Main Ave, Norwalk, CT 06851
Tel.: (203) 291-4000
Web Site: http://www.source-marketing.com
Rev.: $20,000,000
Emp.: 50
Advertising Services
N.A.I.C.S.: 541810

Subsidiary (Domestic):

Humongo (3)
155 Main St 4th Fl, Danbury, CT 06810
Tel.: (203) 730-6300
Web Site: http://www.humongoagency.com
Sales Range: $10-24.9 Million
Emp.: 7
Direct Response Marketing, Graphic Design, T.V.
N.A.I.C.S.: 541810

Subsidiary (Domestic):

Storyline Strategies LLC (2)
14950 Washington St Ste 202, Haymarket, VA 20169
Tel.: (202) 871-7934
Web Site: http://www.storylinestrategies.com
Public Relation & Communication Services
N.A.I.C.S.: 541820
Alyssa Salvo (CEO)
Josh Burris (Partner)
Shepherd Pittman (Partner)
Suzanne Conte (VP)
Andrew Grimes (VP)

Team Enterprises, Inc. (2)
1 W Las Olas Blvd, Fort Lauderdale, FL 33301
Tel.: (054) 862 2400
Web Site: https://www.teamenterprises.com
Sales Range: $1-9.9 Million
Emp.: 105
Management Consulting Services
N.A.I.C.S.: 541613

The Stagwell Group LLC (2)
1700 K St NW Ste 750, Washington, DC 20006
Tel.: (202) 524-4364
Web Site: http://www.stagwellgroup.com
Investment Services
N.A.I.C.S.: 523940
Mark J. Penn (Chm & CEO)
Jay Leveton (Partner)
Jason Reid (VP)
Ryan Greene (CFO)
Stephanie Howley (Chief People Officer)

Subsidiary (Domestic):

ForwardPMX Group LLC (3)
1 World Trade Ctr Fl 63, New York, NY 10007
Tel.: (212) 387-0300
Marketing & Advertising Services
N.A.I.C.S.: 541810
Martin McNulty (CEO)

Subsidiary (Domestic):

The Search Agency (4)
801 N Brand Blvd Ste 1020, Los Angeles, CA 91203
Tel.: (310) 873-5738
Web Site: http://www.thesearchagency.com
Search Engine Optimization

N.A.I.C.S.: 541810
David M. Hughes (CEO)
Peter Celeste (Pres)
Jason Sikora (Mng Dir-Canada)
Raashid Siddique (VP-Bus Process/Dir-India,Southeast Asia & Middle East)
Brett Shearing (VP-Bus Dev)

Holding (Domestic):

Multiview Inc. (3)
7701 Las Colinas Rdg Ste 800, Irving, TX 75063
Tel.: (972) 402-7070
Web Site: https://www.multiview.com
Sales Range: $1-9.9 Million
Emp.: 400
Prepackaged Software Services
N.A.I.C.S.: 513210
Brandon Webb (COO)
Andy Keith (CEO)
Stacy Tanner (CFO)

Subsidiary (Domestic):

Nielsen National Research Group, Inc. (3)
6255 Sunset Blvd 19th Fl, Hollywood, CA 90028
Tel.: (323) 817-2000
Market Analysis & Research Services
N.A.I.C.S.: 541910

Holding (Domestic):

Scout Marketing, Inc. (3)
3391 Peachtree Rd NE Ste 105, Atlanta, GA 30326
Tel.: (404) 917-2688
Web Site: http://www.findscout.com
Marketing Communications Firm
N.A.I.C.S.: 541613
Jennifer Brekke (CEO & Partner)

Subsidiary (Domestic):

Trade X Partners LLC (2)
711 3rd Ave 2nd Fl, New York, NY 10017
Tel.: (212) 506-0695
Web Site: http://www.tradex-partners.com
Sales Range: $50-74.9 Million
Emp.: 65
Financial Investment Services
N.A.I.C.S.: 523999
Vincent Laraia (Pres & CEO)
Gail Silberberg (VP-Procurement)
Leonard Okoskin (VP-Remarketing)
Jerry Siano (Gen Mgr)
Matt Chesler (VP-Fin & Strategy)

Subsidiary (Non-US):

Union Advertising Canada LP (2)
340 King Street East Suite 402, Toronto, M5A 1K8, ON, Canada
Tel.: (416) 598-4944
Web Site: http://www.unioncreative.com
Sales Range: $50-74.9 Million
Emp.: 87
Advertising & Marketing Services
N.A.I.C.S.: 541810

Subsidiary (Domestic):

VITRO Partners LLC (2)
2305 Historic Decatur Rd Ste 205, San Diego, CA 92106
Tel.: (619) 234-0408
Web Site: http://www.vitroagency.com
Emp.: 80
Advetising Agency
N.A.I.C.S.: 541810
John Vitro (Partner-Creative)
Michael Berberick (Dir-Studio)
Tom Sullivan (CEO & Partner)
Michael Catanzaro (Dir-Bus Partnerships)
Rachel Carrieri (Dir-Project Ops)
Guy Gouldavis (Dir-Strategy)
Patrick Rust (Dir-Media Strategy)

Subsidiary (Non-US):

Veritas Communications, Inc. (2)
340 King Street East Suite 402, Box 46, Toronto, M5V 1K8, ON, Canada (100%)
Tel.: (416) 482-2248
Web Site: http://www.veritasinc.com
Sales Range: $25-49.9 Million
Emp.: 30
N.A.I.C.S.: 522299

Subsidiary (Domestic):

VitroRobertson LLC (2)
160 Varick St 5th Fl, New York, NY 10013
Tel.: (212) 561-6005
Web Site: http://www.vitroagency.com
Sales Range: $25-49.9 Million
Emp.: 100
Advertising Agencies
N.A.I.C.S.: 541810

Yamamoto Moss Mackenzie (2)
219 2nd St N Ste 200, Minneapolis, MN 55401-1453
Tel.: (612) 573-6255
Web Site: http://www.go-yamamoto.com
Rev.: $2,800,000
Emp.: 30
Sales Promotion
N.A.I.C.S.: 541820
Lori Sharbono (Dir-Bus Dev)
Kathy McCuskey (CEO)
Grant Smith (Chief Creative Officer)
Chris Rahill (Exec Dir-Insights & Innovation)
Seth Rockers (CFO)
Dave Morrisette (Dir-Client Svcs)
Shawan Pals (Dir-Creative)
Andy Ross (Acct Dir)
Amber Graves (Acct Dir)
Patrick Clifford (Dir-Creative)

Subsidiary (Non-US):

henderson bas partnership (2)
479 Wellington Street West, Toronto, M5V 1E7, ON, Canada
Tel.: (416) 977-6660
Emp.: 100
Advetising Agency
N.A.I.C.S.: 541810

Subsidiary (Domestic):

kirshenbaum bond senecal + partners (2)
160 Varick St 4th Fl, New York, NY 10013
Tel.: (212) 633-0080
Web Site: http://www.kbsagency.com
Sales Range: $75-99.9 Million
Emp.: 300
Advertising Agency
N.A.I.C.S.: 541810

Subsidiary (Domestic):

Ramona (3)
411 Lafayette St 6th Fl, New York, NY 10003
Tel.: (212) 924-2981
Web Site: http://www.kbsp.com
Sales Range: $10-24.9 Million
Emp.: 50
Advetising Agency
N.A.I.C.S.: 541810

Branch (Non-US):

kirshenbaum bond senecal + partners - Montreal (3)
3510 Saint-Laurent Blvd Suite 410, Montreal, H2X2V2, QC, Canada
Tel.: (514) 875-7400
Web Site: http://www.kbs.ca
Sales Range: $25-49.9 Million
Emp.: 45
Advertising Services
N.A.I.C.S.: 541810

Team Epiphany (1)
195 Broadway 14th Fl, New York, NY 10007
Tel.: (212) 378-1414
Web Site: http://www.teamepiphany.com
Sales Range: $1-9.9 Million
Emp.: 22
Advetising Agency
N.A.I.C.S.: 541810
Nia Tran (Acct Mgr)
Kamaria Gboro (Mgr-Community)

STANDARD BIOTOOLS INC.
2 Tower Pl Ste 2000, South San Francisco, CA 94080
Tel.: (650) 266-6000　　　　　DE
Web Site:
　https://www.standardbio.com
Year Founded: 1999

LAB—(NASDAQ)
Rev.: $97,948,000
Assets: $390,310,000
Liabilities: $160,524,000
Net Worth: $229,786,000
Earnings: ($190,098,000)
Emp.: 523
Fiscal Year-end: 12/31/22
Integrated Fluidic Circuit Systems Developer, Mfr & Marketer
N.A.I.C.S.: 333995
Carlos V. Paya (Chm)
Michael Egholm (Pres & CEO)
Alex Kim (COO)
Jeff Black (CFO)
Jeremy Davis (Chief Comml Officer)
Betsy Jensen (Chief HR Officer)
Mona Abou-Sayed (Sr VP)
Anders Davas (Sr VP)
Agnieszka Gallagher (Chief Legal Officer)
Alex Kim (Co-Founder, Interim CFO & COO)
Sean Mackay (Chief Bus Officer)

Subsidiaries:

Fluidigm (Shanghai) Instrument Technology Company Limited (1)
Room 2907 B Building Far East International Plaza, No 317 XianXia Road, 200235, Shanghai, China
Tel.: (86) 2132558368
Web Site: http://www.fluidigm.com
Sales Range: $10-24.9 Million
Emp.: 13
Instruments & Related Products Distr
N.A.I.C.S.: 334513

Fluidigm Europe, B.V. (1)
Van Heuven Goedhartlaan 13D, 1181 LE, Amsterdam, Netherlands
Tel.: (31) 160924240
Analytical Laboratory Instrument Mfr
N.A.I.C.S.: 334516

Subsidiary (Non-US):

Fluidigm France SARL (2)
Les Conquerants - Bat Kilimandjaro 1 avenue de l Atlantique, 91940, Les Ulis, France
Tel.: (33) 16 092 4240
Web Site: http://www.fluidigm.com
Emp.: 9
Analytical Laboratory Instrument Mfr
N.A.I.C.S.: 334516

Fluidigm GmbH (2)
Zielstattstrasse 40, 81379, Munich, Germany
Tel.: (49) 160924240
Biotechnology Research & Development Services
N.A.I.C.S.: 541714

Fluidigm Sciences Inc. (1)
7000 Shoreline Ct Ste 100, South San Francisco, CA 94080
Tel.: (650) 266-6000
Web Site: http://www.fluidigm.com
Biotechnology Research & Development Services
N.A.I.C.S.: 541714

Subsidiary (Non-US):

Fluidigm Canada Inc. (2)
70 Esna Park Drive Unit 12, Markham, L3R 6E7, ON, Canada
Tel.: (905) 513-1704
Biotechnology Research & Development Services
N.A.I.C.S.: 541714

SomaLogic, Inc. (1)
2945 Wilderness Pl, Boulder, CO 80301
Tel.: (303) 625-9000
Web Site: https://somalogic.com
Rev.: $97,666,000
Assets: $647,374,000
Liabilities: $84,816,000
Net Worth: $562,558,000
Earnings: ($109,157,000)
Emp.: 451
Fiscal Year-end: 12/31/2022
Analytical Laboratory Instrument Mfr

N.A.I.C.S.: 334516
Roy Smythe *(CEO)*
Shaun Blakeman *(CFO)*

Subsidiary (Domestic):

SomaLogic Operating Co., Inc. **(2)**
2945 Wilderness Pl, Boulder, CO 80301
Tel.: (303) 625-9000
Web Site: http://www.somalogic.com
Rev.: $97,666,000
Assets: $647,374,000
Liabilities: $84,816,000
Net Worth: $562,558,000
Earnings: ($109,157,000)
Emp.: 451
Fiscal Year-end: 12/31/2022
Analytical Laboratory Instrument Mfr
N.A.I.C.S.: 334516
Eliot M. Lurier *(Interim CFO & Principal Acctg Officer)*
David McGovern *(Sr VP-Mktg)*
Angela Bakker Lee *(Exec VP-Healthcare Markets)*
Steve Mermelstein *(Sr VP-Corp Strategy, Dev, and M&A)*
Troy Cox *(Chm)*

STANDARD ENERGY CORP.

447 Bearcat Dr, Salt Lake City, UT 84115-2517
Tel.: (801) 364-9000   UT
Year Founded: 1978
STDE—(OTCIQ)
Crude Petroleum Extraction Services
N.A.I.C.S.: 211120
Dean A. Rowell *(Pres, CEO & CFO)*
Pamela A. Nelson *(Sec)*

STANDARD MOTOR PRODUCTS, INC.

37 18 Nern Blvd, Long Island City, NY 11101
Tel.: (972) 316-8107   NY
Web Site: https://www.smpcorp.com
Year Founded: 1919
SMP—(NYSE)
Rev.: $1,371,815,000
Assets: $1,254,929,000
Liabilities: $633,891,000
Net Worth: $621,038,000
Earnings: $55,351,000
Emp.: 4,900
Fiscal Year-end: 12/31/22
Automotive Replacement Parts Mfr & Marketer
N.A.I.C.S.: 336390
James J. Burke *(COO)*
Dale Burks *(Chief Comml Officer & Exec VP)*
Eric P. Sills *(Chm, Pres & CEO)*
Ray Nicholas *(CIO & VP-IT)*
William J. Fazio *(Chief Acctg Officer)*
Erin Pawlish *(Treas)*
Nathan R. Iles *(CFO)*

Subsidiaries:

Blue Streak-Hygrade Motor Products Ltd. **(1)**
7680 Tranmere Dr, Mississauga, L5S 1K4, ON, Canada   **(100%)**
Tel.: (905) 612-0222
Web Site: https://www.bluestreak.ca
Sales Range: $25-49.9 Million
Emp.: 55
Distr of Automotive Replacement Parts
N.A.I.C.S.: 441330

Four Seasons - A Division of Standard Motor Products, Inc. **(1)**
1801 Waters Rdg Dr, Lewisville, TX 75057   **(100%)**
Tel.: (972) 316-8100
Web Site: http://www.4s.com
Sales Range: $150-199.9 Million
Emp.: 387
Mfr of Air Conditioning Parts
N.A.I.C.S.: 336390

Hayden Automotive **(1)**
1801 Waters Ridge Dr, Lewisville, TX 75057-6027
Tel.: (909) 736-2665

Web Site: http://www.haydenauto.com
Sales Range: $250-299.9 Million
Mfr of Automotive Replacement Parts
N.A.I.C.S.: 336390

KADE Trading GmbH **(1)**
Wilhelm-Bergner-Str 11a, 21509, Glinde, Germany
Tel.: (49) 4055501690
Temperature Control Device Distr
N.A.I.C.S.: 423730

Motortronics, Inc. **(1)**
1600 Sunshine Dr, Clearwater, FL 33765
Tel.: (727) 573-1819
Web Site: https://www.motortronics.com
Motor Control & Electric Control Product Mfr
N.A.I.C.S.: 335314

Nissens A/S **(1)**
Ormhojgardvej 9, 8700, Horsens, Denmark
Tel.: (45) 76262626
Web Site: http://www.nissens.com
Sales Range: $250-299.9 Million
Emp.: 1,350
Cooling System Mfr
N.A.I.C.S.: 333415
Klavs Thulstrup Pedersen *(Sr VP-Automotive)*
Hans Erik Obling *(VP-Cooling Solutions)*
Mikkel Krogslund Andersen *(CEO)*
Jakob Backs *(CFO & Sr VP)*
Knud Kragpoth *(COO & Sr VP)*
Rikke Kroer Hoberg *(VP-Global HR & Grp Svcs)*

Subsidiary (Non-US):

Chlodnice Nissens Polska sp.zo.o. **(2)**
Ul Syrenia 4, 61-017, Poznan, Poland
Tel.: (48) 61 653 5207
Web Site: http://www.nissens.com.pl
Automobile Component Distr
N.A.I.C.S.: 423120
Jarosaw Tunkiel *(Branch Dir)*

Nissen France **(2)**
37 Rue du Bois Chaland Batiment 5, 91029, Lisses, France
Tel.: (33) 1 6086 0436
Automobile Component Distr
N.A.I.C.S.: 423120

Nissens (Shanghai) Auto Parts Trading Co., Ltd. **(2)**
Room 1C26 Bldg 14 No 528 Yanggao North Rd, Pudong, Shanghai, China
Tel.: (86) 2164 0905 96
Automobile Component Distr
N.A.I.C.S.: 423120

Nissens (UK) Ltd. **(2)**
14 Binns Close Tile Hill, Coventry, CV4 9TB, United Kingdom
Tel.: (44) 2476 470 340
Web Site: http://www.nissens.com
Automobile Component Distr
N.A.I.C.S.: 423120

Nissens Benelux S.A. **(2)**
ZI Hauts-Sarts Quatrieme Avenue 66, 4040, Herstal, Belgium
Tel.: (32) 4264 9822
Web Site: http://www.nissens.com
Automobile Component Distr
N.A.I.C.S.: 423120

Nissens Deutschland GmbH **(2)**
Spannstiftstr 37, 58119, Hagen, Germany
Tel.: (49) 2334504180
Automobile Component Distr
N.A.I.C.S.: 423120

Nissens Finland Oy **(2)**
Orikedonkatu 13, 20380, Turku, Finland
Tel.: (358) 2 518 6800
Automobile Component Distr
N.A.I.C.S.: 423120

Nissens Hungaria Kft. **(2)**
Cegledi ut 19, 1107, Budapest, Hungary
Tel.: (36) 1 43 1 7741
Web Site: http://www.nissens.com
Automobile Component Distr
N.A.I.C.S.: 423120

Nissens Italia SRL **(2)**
Piazza Sauro Testoni 15, 40018, San Pietro in Casale, Italy
Tel.: (39) 051 864023

Web Site: http://www.nissens.com
Automobile Component Distr
N.A.I.C.S.: 423120

Subsidiary (US):

Nissens North America, Inc. **(2)**
1125 S Ball St Ste 100, Grapevine, TX 76051
Tel.: (817) 329-5114
Web Site: http://www.nissens.com
Automobile Component Distr
N.A.I.C.S.: 423120
Jesse Cabrera *(Reg Sls Mgr)*

Subsidiary (Non-US):

Nissens Osterreich G.m.b.H **(2)**
Wienerstrasse 241, 8051, Graz, Austria
Tel.: (43) 316 24 2000
Automobile Component Distr
N.A.I.C.S.: 423120

Nissens Schweiz AG **(2)**
Rohrerstrasse 102, 5000, Aarau, Switzerland
Tel.: (41) 62 823 55 44
Automobile Component Distr
N.A.I.C.S.: 423120

Nissens Slovakia s.r.o. **(2)**
Malinovskeho 1275, 916 21, Cachtice, Slovakia
Tel.: (421) 327708500
Automobile Component Distr
N.A.I.C.S.: 423120

Nissens Sverige AB **(2)**
Importgatan 2-4, Hisings Backa, 422 46, Gothenburg, Sweden
Tel.: (46) 31 52 87 62
Automobile Component Distr
N.A.I.C.S.: 423120

Nissens Ukraine Ltd. **(2)**
Street V Hvoyki 18/14 Building 7 Office 703, Kiev, 04080, Ukraine
Tel.: (380) 44 1556
Automobile Component Distr
N.A.I.C.S.: 423120

Radiadores Nissen, S.A. **(2)**
Avenida La Prensa 33, 41007, Sevilla, Spain
Tel.: (34) 902 181 038
Automobile Component Distr
N.A.I.C.S.: 423120

SMP Automotive de Mexico, S.A. de C.V. **(1)**
Av Tlaxcala 480, 72700, Cuautlancingo, Mexico
Tel.: (52) 2222739300
Web Site: http://www.smp-automotive.com
Automotive Distr
N.A.I.C.S.: 423110

SMP Four Seasons de Mexico, S. de R.L. de C.V. **(1)**
Carr Riberena Km105 Lotes 4 Y 5 Parque Industrial Maquilpar, 88614, Reynosa, Mexico
Tel.: (52) 8999219705
Automotive Replacement Parts Mfr & Marketer
N.A.I.C.S.: 336390

SMP Poland sp. z o.o. **(1)**
ul Magazynowa 2, 15-399, Bialystok, Poland
Tel.: (48) 856644000
Web Site: https://smpkariera.pl
Emp.: 700
Automotive Parts Mfr & Distr
N.A.I.C.S.: 336390

Stabil Produkt Elektrotechnikai Kft. **(1)**
Pesti ut 78, 2119, Pecel, Hungary
Tel.: (36) 28548200
Web Site: https://stabil-produkt.com
Electronic Components Mfr
N.A.I.C.S.: 334419

Standard Motor Products (Hong Kong) Ltd **(1)**
San Miguel IndustrialBuilding 6th Floor 9 11 Shing Wan Rd, Sha Tin, N T, China (Hong Kong)   **(100%)**
Tel.: (852) 26055311
Web Site: http://www.smpcorp.com

Sales Range: $10-24.9 Million
Emp.: 50
Mfr & Marketer of Automotive Replacement Parts
N.A.I.C.S.: 336320

Standard Motor Products Greenville Div **(1)**
5150 Pelham Rd, Greenville, SC 29615   **(100%)**
Tel.: (864) 297-1700
Web Site: http://www.standardmotors.com
Sales Range: $25-49.9 Million
Emp.: 200
Marketing & Distribution of Electronic Products
N.A.I.C.S.: 336390

Standard Motor Products-Independence **(1)**
1300 W Oak St, Independence, KS 67301
Tel.: (620) 331-1000
Web Site: http://www.smpoe.com
Sales Range: $125-149.9 Million
Emp.: 400
Mfr of Automotive Control Parts
N.A.I.C.S.: 333248

Standard Motor Products-Mishawaka **(1)**
1718 N Home St, Mishawaka, IN 46545
Tel.: (574) 259-6253
Web Site: http://www.standardmotorproducts.com
Sales Range: $50-74.9 Million
Emp.: 151
Ignition Apparatus Internal Combustion Engines
N.A.I.C.S.: 336320

Stoneridge Control Devices, Inc. **(1)**
300 Dan Rd, Canton, MA 02021
Tel.: (781) 830-0340
Web Site: http://www.pollakaftermarket.com
Rev.: $200,000,000
Emp.: 36
Automotive Electrical Connector & Sensor Mfr
N.A.I.C.S.: 336320

STANDARD PREMIUM FINANCE HOLDINGS, INC.

13590 SW 134 Ave Ste 214, Miami, FL 33186
Tel.: (305) 232-7040   FL
Web Site: https://www.standardpremium.com
Year Founded: 1991
SPFX—(OTCQX)
Rev.: $8,156,537
Assets: $51,488,807
Liabilities: $45,536,365
Net Worth: $5,952,442
Earnings: $716,940
Emp.: 21
Fiscal Year-end: 12/31/22
Offices of Other Holding Companies
N.A.I.C.S.: 551112
William Koppelmann *(Chm, Pres & CEO)*
Margaret Ruiz *(Sec & Mgr-Ops)*
Brian Krogol *(CFO)*
Victor Galliano *(VP-Mktg)*
Robert Mattucci *(VP-Sls)*

STANDARD VAPE CORPORATION

480 Forest Ave Ste 507, Locust Valley, NY 11560
Tel.: (201) 220-8734   NV
Web Site: http://www.standard-vape.com
SVAP—(OTCIQ)
Tobacco Product Distr
N.A.I.C.S.: 459991
John Fruhmann *(Pres)*
Mel Ehrlich *(Founder & Chm)*
Jyothishree T. Jayadeva *(Dir-Laboratory)*

STANDEX INTERNATIONAL

STANDEX INTERNATIONAL —(CONTINUED)

CORPORATION
23 Keewaydin Dr, Salem, NH 03079
Tel.: (603) 893-9701   **DE**
Web Site: https://www.standex.com
Year Founded: 1955
SXI—(NYSE)
Rev.: $720,635,000
Assets: $1,005,057,000
Liabilities: $383,554,000
Net Worth: $621,503,000
Earnings: $73,074,000
Emp.: 3,700
Fiscal Year-end: 06/30/24
Food Service Equipment, Air Distribution Products, Engineered Products, Hydraulics Products & Engraving Equipment Mfr
N.A.I.C.S.: 333241
David A. Dunbar *(Chm, Pres & CEO)*
Alan J. Glass *(Chief Legal Officer, Sec & VP)*
Annemarie Bell *(Chief HR Officer & VP)*
Ademir Sarcevic *(CFO, Treas & VP)*
James Hooven *(Pres-Engraving)*
Timo Goodloe *(VP-Tax-Global)*

Subsidiaries:

Agile Magnetics, Inc.   **(1)**
24 Chenell Dr, Concord, NH 03301
Web Site: https://www.agilemagco.com
Electronic Components Mfr
N.A.I.C.S.: 334419

Associated American Industries, Inc.   **(1)**
265 Hobson Ste, Smithville, TN 37166
Web Site: https://www.apwwyott.com
Foodservice Equipment Mfr
N.A.I.C.S.: 333241

Custom Biogenic Systems, Inc.   **(1)**
74100 Van Dyke, Bruce Crossing, MI 48065-8065
Tel.: (586) 331-2600
Web Site: http://www.custombiogenics.com
Metal Tank Mfr
N.A.I.C.S.: 332420

Custom Hoists, Inc.   **(1)**
771 County Rd 30A W, Ashland, OH 44805   **(100%)**
Tel.: (419) 368-4721
Web Site: https://www.customhoists.com
Sales Range: $50-74.9 Million
Emp.: 173
Mfr Single & Double Acting Telescopic & Piston Rod Hydraulic Cylinders
N.A.I.C.S.: 333995

Enginetics Aerospace Corporation   **(1)**
7700 New Carlisle Pike, Huber Heights, OH 45424
Tel.: (937) 878-3800
Web Site: http://www.enginetics.com
Fabricated Structural Metal Mfr
N.A.I.C.S.: 332312

Genius Solutions Engineering Corporation   **(1)**
6421 Monclova Rd, Maumee, OH 43537
Tel.: (419) 794-9914
Web Site: http://www.gsengineering.net
Automotive Interiors Mfr
N.A.I.C.S.: 336360

Horizon Scientific, Inc.   **(1)**
125 Varnfield Dr, Summerville, SC 29483
Web Site: https://www.horizonscientific.com
Industrial Equipment Mfr
N.A.I.C.S.: 333415

IR Engraving LLC   **(1)**
5901 Lewis Rd, Sandston, VA 23150-2413
Tel.: (804) 222-2821
Web Site: http://irengraving.com
Platemaking Services
N.A.I.C.S.: 323120

Division (Domestic):

Innovent   **(2)**

107 Audubon Rd Bldg 1 Unit 20, Wakefield, MA 01880
Tel.: (781) 587-3397
Web Site: http://www.innovent.com
Aerospace, Non-Woven & Medical Device Designer & Mfr
N.A.I.C.S.: 336412

Mullen Testers   **(2)**
939 Chicopee St, Chicopee, MA 01013-2797   **(100%)**
Tel.: (413) 536-1311
Web Site: https://www.mullentesters.com
Sales Range: $10-24.9 Million
Emp.: 4
Mfr Of Mullen Burst Testers
N.A.I.C.S.: 334514

Roehlen Engraving BF Perkins   **(2)**
5901 Lewis Rd, Sandston, VA 23150-2413   **(100%)**
Tel.: (804) 222-2821
Web Site: http://www.bfperkins.com
Emp.: 100
Produces Engraved Steel & Metal Embossing Rolls & Plates
N.A.I.C.S.: 333248
Matt Pursel *(Mng Dir)*

Division (Non-US):

Standex International S.r.l. - International Engraving Division   **(2)**
Via 1 Maggio 20, Gorgonzola, Milan, I 20064, Italy
Tel.: (39) 0295740951
Web Site: http://www.standexengraving.com
Emp.: 50
Platemaking Services
N.A.I.C.S.: 323120
Flavis Maschera *(Mng Dir)*

Minntronix, Inc.   **(1)**
1600 9th Ave SW, Watertown, SD 57201
Tel.: (605) 884-0195
Web Site: http://www.minntronix.com
Sales Range: $1-9.9 Million
Emp.: 35
Power Distr & Specialty Transformer Mfr
N.A.I.C.S.: 335311
Lew Tollefson *(Pres & CEO)*
Lisa Borkhuis *(Acct Mgr)*

Mold-Tech (Dongguan) Co. Ltd.   **(1)**
Eastern 2nd Lane Keji Road, Qingxi Town, Dongguan, 523655, Guangdong, China
Tel.: (86) 76987322088
Automotive Parts & Component Mfr
N.A.I.C.S.: 334290

Mold-Tech (Suzhou) Co. Ltd.   **(1)**
Yongfeng Science and Technology Park No 17 East Suhong Road SIP, Suzhou, 215026, Jiangsu, China
Tel.: (86) 51262716388
Molded Plastic Product Mfr & Distr
N.A.I.C.S.: 326291

Mold-Tech Portugal Lda.   **(1)**
Rua Vasconcelos Costa 416, Moreira da Maia, 4470-640, Maia, Portugal   **(100%)**
Tel.: (351) 229437710
Web Site: http://www.mold-tech.com
Sales Range: $25-49.9 Million
Emp.: 100
Produces Engraved Steel Embossing Rolls & Plates for Textured Designs
N.A.I.C.S.: 331110

Mold-Tech S.A.R.L.   **(1)**
ZA Les Longues Raies, 77310, Pringy, France   **(100%)**
Tel.: (00) 100057010
Web Site: http://www.mold-tech.com
Sales Range: $25-49.9 Million
Emp.: 18
Engravers of Textured Patterns on Inside Molds & Dies to Achieve Decorative Effects on Molded Products
N.A.I.C.S.: 332812

Mold-Tech Singapore Pte. Ltd.   **(1)**
159 Kampong Ampat 01-01 KA Place, Singapore, 368328, Singapore
Tel.: (65) 62802088
Emp.: 10
Molding Rolling & Texturing Process Solution Provider
N.A.I.C.S.: 333511

Northlake Engineering, Inc.   **(1)**

8320 193rd Ave, Bristol, WI 51304
Tel.: (262) 857-9600
Web Site: https://standexelectronics.com
Electronics, Magnetics, Power Supplies & Transformers Mfr
N.A.I.C.S.: 335311
Debbie Hardt *(VP-Sls)*

Piazzo Rosa S.r.l.   **(1)**
Via G Bortolan 6 Z I Vascon, Carbonera, 31050, Treviso, Italy
Tel.: (39) 0422446686
Foodservice Equipment Mfr
N.A.I.C.S.: 332313

Renco Electronics Inc.   **(1)**
595 International Pl, Rockledge, FL 32955-4200
Tel.: (321) 637-1000
Web Site: https://www.rencousa.com
Sales Range: $25-49.9 Million
Emp.: 118
Electronic Coils & Transformers
N.A.I.C.S.: 334416
Edward Rensing *(Pres & CEO)*
John P. Rensing *(VP)*
Gary A. Jones *(Dir-Bus Dev)*
Joseph Long *(Chief Engr)*
Kevin Enser *(Mgr-Engrg)*
Mike Amick *(Mgr-Bus Dev)*
Ian Rensing *(Engr-Field Applications)*
Don Ensign *(Mgr-Bus Dev)*
Andy Wang *(Engr-Field Applications)*
Dan Kinnick *(Mgr-Bus Dev)*
Matt Miller *(Engr-Field Applications)*
Christopher Rensing *(Dir-Pur)*
Michel Augustin *(Engr-Design)*
Olga Lloreda *(Mgr-Quality Control)*
Hank Wang *(Engr-Design)*
Aundrey Strong *(Engr-Design)*

Subsidiary (Domestic):

Coils Unlimited   **(2)**
595 International Pl, Rockledge, FL 32955
Tel.: (321) 637-1000
Web Site: https://www.rencousa.com
Emp.: 15
Magnetic Components Mfr
N.A.I.C.S.: 423610

Roehlen Industries Pty. Limited   **(1)**
1 46 Dehavilland Rd, Mordialloc, 3195, VIC, Australia   **(50%)**
Tel.: (61) 395804155
Web Site: http://www.moldtech.com
Sales Range: $10-24.9 Million
Emp.: 30
Produces Engraved Steel Embossing Rolls for Textured Designs
N.A.I.C.S.: 331110

S.I. de Mexico S.A. de C.V.   **(1)**
Parque Industrial El Rio Calle Del Rio y Avenida OJO De Agua 20, Colonia Parque Industrial El Rio, 84279, Agua Prieta, Sonora, Mexico   **(100%)**
Tel.: (52) 6333389406
Web Site:
   http://www.standexelectronics.com
Sales Range: Less than $1 Million
Emp.: 500
Mfr of Electronic Components
N.A.I.C.S.: 334419

Sensor Solutions Inc.   **(1)**
3767 Forest Ln, Dallas, TX 75244-7100
Tel.: (972) 241-1193
Web Site: http://www.sensorso.com
Electronics Stores
N.A.I.C.S.: 449210
J. B. Handlin *(Pres)*

Spincraft Wisconsin   **(1)**
2455 Commerce Dr, New Berlin, WI 53151   **(100%)**
Tel.: (262) 784-8440
Web Site: http://www.spincraft.net
Sales Range: $50-74.9 Million
Emp.: 90
Spinner of Heavy & Exotic Metal Products for Aerospace, Electronic Nuclear & General Industry
N.A.I.C.S.: 332119
Sara Esser *(Gen Mgr)*

Unit (Domestic):

Spincraft   **(2)**

500 Iron Horse Park, North Billerica, MA 01862-1617
Tel.: (978) 667-2771
Web Site: http://www.spincraft.net
Sales Range: $25-49.9 Million
Emp.: 55
Metal Forming, Spinning Fabricating, Welding, Machining Assembly for Industrial Purposes
N.A.I.C.S.: 332710

Standex Electronics Japan Corporation   **(1)**
1088-7 Otsucho, Kofu, 400-0055, Yamanashi, Japan
Tel.: (81) 552081770
Web Site: https://www.standex.co.jp
Emp.: 100
Electronic Components Mfr
N.A.I.C.S.: 334419
Makoto Fukutome *(Pres & CEO)*

Standex Electronics, Inc.   **(1)**
4150 Thunderbird Ln, Fairfield, OH 45014   **(100%)**
Tel.: (513) 871-3777
Web Site:
   http://www.standexelectronics.com
Sales Range: $25-49.9 Million
Emp.: 100
Mfr of Components & Assemblies for Telecommunications, Computers Communication Equipment & Color T.V. Industry
N.A.I.C.S.: 334416
John Meeks *(Pres)*
Tom Gould *(VP-Sls-North America)*
Bob Ruff *(Dir-Quality)*
Ken Hay *(CFO)*
Kristen Richards *(VP-HR)*
Mark Faulhaber *(Dir-Engrg)*
Travis Lane *(Dir-Bus Dev-Global)*
Vineet Kshirsagar *(Gen Mgr-North America)*

Standex Food Service Equipment Group   **(1)**
11 Keewaydin Dr Swt 300, Salem, NH 03079
Tel.: (603) 893-9701
Web Site: http://www.standex.com
Sales Range: $25-49.9 Million
Emp.: 37
Commercial Food Service Equipment Mfr
N.A.I.C.S.: 333241

Subsidiary (Domestic):

BKI   **(2)**
42 Allen Martin Dr, Essex Junction, VT 05452   **(100%)**
Tel.: (802) 658 6600
Web Site: https://www.bkideas.com
Sales Range: $75-99.9 Million
Emp.: 150
Commercial Ovens, Warmers, Fryers Filters & Refrigerated Cases Mfr
N.A.I.C.S.: 311423

Unit (Domestic):

Federal Industries   **(2)**
215 Federal Ave, Belleville, WI 53508-0290
Tel.: (608) 424-3331
Web Site: https://federalind.com
Sales Range: $50-74.9 Million
Food Service Equipment
N.A.I.C.S.: 333241

Red Goat Disposers - United Service Equipment   **(2)**
914 Ridgely Rd, Murfreesboro, TN 37129
Tel.: (615) 893-8432
Web Site: http://www.redgoat.com
Sales Range: $10-24.9 Million
Emp.: 6
Mfr of Commercial Food Processors, Choppers, Grinders, Food Waste Disposers, Food Mixers & Slicers
N.A.I.C.S.: 423330

Subsidiary (Domestic):

Standex Cooking Solutions Group   **(2)**
6 Manor Pkwy 1307 N Watters Rd Ste 180, Allen, TX 75013
Tel.: (214) 421-7366
Web Site: http://www.standex.com
Sales Range: $100-124.9 Million
Emp.: 35
Commercial Food Service Equipment Mfr

N.A.I.C.S.: 333241

Subsidiary (Domestic):

APW Wyott Food Service Equipment, Inc. (3)
1307 N Watters Rd Ste180, Allen, TX 75013
Tel.: (214) 421-7366
Web Site: http://www.apwwyott.com
Sales Range: $50-74.9 Million
Emp.: 50
Foodservice Equipment Mfr
N.A.I.C.S.: 333241

Subsidiary (Domestic):

APW Wyott Food Service Equipment, Inc. (4)
1938 Wyott Dr, Cheyenne, WY 82007-2102
Tel.: (307) 634-5801
Web Site: http://www.apwwyott.com
Sales Range: $50-74.9 Million
Food Service Equipment
N.A.I.C.S.: 333241

Subsidiary (Domestic):

Bakers Pride Oven Company (3)
265 Hobson St, Smithville, TN 37166
Tel.: (914) 576-0200
Web Site: https://www.bakerspride.com
Sales Range: $50-74.9 Million
Emp.: 10
Commercial Baking, Cooking & Pizza Equipment
N.A.I.C.S.: 333310

Subsidiary (Domestic):

United Service Equipment Company (2)
735 Florence Rd, Savannah, TN 38372 (100%)
Tel.: (615) 893-8432
Web Site: https://www.useco.com
Sales Range: $10-24.9 Million
Emp.: 2
Mfr of Patient-Feeding Systems & Food Service Equipment for Hospitals, Institutions & Commercial Use
N.A.I.C.S.: 333310

Standex Holdings Limited (1)
40 Morley Road, Tonbridge, TN9 1RA, Kent, United Kingdom (100%)
Tel.: (44) 1732771023
Web Site:
    http://www.standexelectronics.com
Sales Range: $25-49.9 Million
Emp.: 75
Custom Electronic Components
N.A.I.C.S.: 334419

Subsidiary (Domestic):

Standex Electronics (UK) Limited (2)
40 Morley Road, Tonbridge, TN9 1RA, Kent, United Kingdom (100%)
Tel.: (44) 1732771023
Web Site:
    http://www.standexelectronics.com
Sales Range: $10-24.9 Million
Emp.: 50
Mfr of Reed & Electrical Surge Protection Devices
N.A.I.C.S.: 335999

Standex International Limited (2)
Unit 6 Cromwell Road Trading Estate off Cromwell Road, Bredbury, Stockport, SK6 2RF, Cheshire, United Kingdom (100%)
Tel.: (44) 1614064300
Web Site: http://www.mold-tech.com
Sales Range: $25-49.9 Million
Emp.: 30
Engraves Textured Patterns on Moulds & Dies for Decorative Effects
N.A.I.C.S.: 332812

Standex International GmbH (1)
Kolner Strasse 352-354, 47807, Krefeld, Germany (100%)
Tel.: (49) 2151371239
Web Site: http://www.standex-gmbh.de
Sales Range: $10-24.9 Million
Emp.: 20
Produces Engraved Steel Embossing Rolls Used to Produce Textured Designs on Plastic, Paper, Metal Wallpaper& Rubber

N.A.I.C.S.: 323120

Division (Domestic):

Standex International GmbH, Mold-Tech Division South (2)
Zeilbaumweg 35, 74613, Ohringen, Germany
Tel.: (49) 794191700
Web Site: http://www.standex-gmbh.de
Metal Coating & Mold Texturing
N.A.I.C.S.: 332812

Standex International GmbH, Mold-Tech North (Germany) (2)
Kolner Strasse 352-354, 47807, Krefeld, Germany (100%)
Tel.: (49) 2151371239
Web Site: http://www.standex-gmbh.de
Engraves Extured Patterns on Inside of Molds & Dies to Achieve Decorative Effects on Molded Products
N.A.I.C.S.: 332812

Standex International S.A. (100%)
Ave de los alpes 48 C-2 Oficina 13, Cornella De Llobregat, 08940, Barcelona, Spain
Tel.: (34) 933367062
Web Site: http://www.standex-gmbh.de
Sales Range: $25-49.9 Million
Emp.: 17
Produces Engraved Steel Embossing Rolls Used to Produce Textured Designs on Plastic, Paper, Metal, Wallpaper, Rubber Etc.
N.A.I.C.S.: 332812

Standex International S.A./Mold-Tech Division (1)
C/Miguel Hernandez 35-37, L'Hospitalet de Llobregat, 08908, Barcelona, Spain
Tel.: (34) 933367062
Web Site: http://www.mold-tech.com
Engraving Services
N.A.I.C.S.: 332812

Standex International S.r.l. (1)
Via 1 Maggio 20, 20064, Gorgonzola, Milano, Italy (100%)
Tel.: (39) 0295740951
Web Site: http://www.mold-tech.com
Sales Range: $25-49.9 Million
Emp.: 50
Distributions & Repairs Pumps for Carbonation of Soft Drinks; Espresso Coffee Machines, Water Booster Systems & Other Applications
N.A.I.C.S.: 423830

Division (Domestic):

Standex International S.r.L. - Mold-Tech Division (2)
Via 1 Maggio 20, 20064, Gorgonzola, Italy (100%)
Tel.: (39) 0295740951
Sales Range: $25-49.9 Million
Emp.: 50
Engraves Textured Patterns on the Inside of Molds & Dies to Achieve Decorative Effects on Molded Products
N.A.I.C.S.: 332812

Standex International S.r.L. - Procon Division (2)
Via 1 Maggio 20, Gorgonzola, 20064, Italy (100%)
Tel.: (39) 0295740951
Web Site: http://www.proconpumps.com
Sales Range: $25-49.9 Million
Emp.: 40
Distributes & Repairs Pumps for the Carbonation of Soft Drinks, for Espresso Coffee Machines, Water Booster Systems & Other Applications
N.A.I.C.S.: 333914

Standex Ireland Ltd. (1)
Acragar Rd, Mountmellick, Co Laois, Ireland (100%)
Tel.: (353) 50279114
Web Site: http://www.standex.ie
Sales Range: $25-49.9 Million
Emp.: 70
Mfr of Rotary Vane Pumps for Coffee & Soda Machines
N.A.I.C.S.: 333914

Standex Meder Electronics GmbH (1)

Ilmenauer Strasse 7i, 98701, Grossbeeren, Germany
Tel.: (49) 367812730
Electro Magnetic Component Mfr
N.A.I.C.S.: 334510

Standex de Mexico S.A. de C.V. (1)
Calle Primera 2550 Colonia Centro, Agua Prieta, 84200, Sonora, Mexico
Tel.: (52) 6333384708
Wood Products Whslr
N.A.I.C.S.: 423310

Standex-Meder Electronics (Shanghai) Co., Ltd. (1)
Building No 2 No 2960 Shengang Road, Songjiang District, Shanghai, 201612, China
Tel.: (86) 2137606000
Electro Magnetic Component Mfr
N.A.I.C.S.: 334510

Ultrafryer Systems, Inc. (1)
553 Route 3A, Bow, NH 03304
Tel.: (603) 225-6684
Web Site: https://ultrafryer.com
Industry Machinery Mfr
N.A.I.C.S.: 333310
Edward Odmark (CEO)

STANDING STONE BANK
137 W Wheeling St, Lancaster, OH 43130
Tel.: (740) 653-5115
Year Founded: 1989
SDGB—(OTCIQ)
Commercial Banking Services
N.A.I.C.S.: 522110
Galen Kelch (Chief Lending Officer)

STANLEY BLACK & DECKER, INC.
1000 Stanley Dr, New Britain, CT 06053
Tel.: (860) 225-5111   CT
Web Site:
    https://www.stanleyblackanddecker.com
Year Founded: 1843
SWK—(NYSE)
Rev.: $15,781,100,000
Assets: $23,663,800,000
Liabilities: $14,607,700,000
Net Worth: $9,056,100,000
Earnings: ($310,500,000)
Emp.: 50,500
Fiscal Year-end: 12/30/23
Hardware Tools Mfr
N.A.I.C.S.: 238120
Donald Allan Jr. (Pres & CEO)
Rhonda O. Gass (CIO-Global & VP)
Patrick D. Hallinan (CFO & Exec VP)
Janet M. Link (Gen Counsel, Sec & Sr VP)
Frank A. Mannarino (Pres-Power Tools Grp-Global Tools & Storage Div)
Allison A. Nicolaidis (Pres-Hand Tools & Storage Grp-Global Tools & Storage)
James P. O'Sullivan (Pres-Sls-North America-Global Tools & Storage)
Corbin B. Walburger (VP-Corp Bus Dev)
Sandra L. Kowaleski (VP-Ops)
Graham N. Robinson (Pres-Indus & Sr VP)
Adriana G. Mendizabal (Pres-North America)
Scot Greulach (Chief Acctg Officer)
Allison Lawrence (Pres-Global eCommerce Bus)
Tamer Abuaita (Sr VP)
K. Amir (Dir)
K. Lisa (Sr Dir)
W. Qadira (Sr Mgr)
D. Nick (Sls Mgr)
W. Eric (Mgr)
D. Nathan (Dir)
G. Michael (Dir)

K. Elyse (Dir)
M. Jason (Engr)
S. Urvashi (Program Mgr)

Subsidiaries:

3-V Fastener Co, Inc. (1)
320 Reed Cir, Corona, CA 92879
Tel.: (951) 734-4391
Bolt & Screw Mfr
N.A.I.C.S.: 332722

3xLogic Florida, LLC (1)
8350 Sunlight Dr, Fishers, IN 46037
Tel.: (407) 438-4445
Integrated Security Services
N.A.I.C.S.: 561621

3xLogic Indiana, LLC (1)
9882 E 121ST St, Fishers, IN 46037
Tel.: (303) 430-1969
Integrated Security Services
N.A.I.C.S.: 561621

3xLogic, Inc. (1)
12000 Pecos St Ste 290, Westminster, CO 80234
Tel.: (303) 430-1969
Web Site: http://www.3xlogic.com
Integrated Security Services
N.A.I.C.S.: 561621
Abell Suzi (Sr Dir-Global Mktg)
Bill Hobbs (VP-Sls-Global)
Jason Bryan (Sls Dir)
Andrew Griffith (Dir-Sls Engrg-Global)
Erron Spalsbury (Mgr-Sls Support-Global)
Cesar Gonzalez (Mgr-Key Account)

A & E SECURITY NV (1)
Saffierstraat 5 - Unit 4A/ 1, 2200, Herentals, Belgium
Tel.: (32) 37661135
Security Consulting Services
N.A.I.C.S.: 541690

AA Alarms, Inc. (1)
215 N 5th Ave, Ann Arbor, MI 48104
Tel.: (734) 665-5225
Communication Service
N.A.I.C.S.: 517810

Advanced Turf Technologies Ltd. (1)
3 Redwood Court, Campbell Way Dinnington, Sheffield, S25 3NQ, United Kingdom
Tel.: (44) 114 212 2200
Web Site: https://infinicut.com
Golf Field Maintenance Services
N.A.I.C.S.: 713910

AeroScout Japan, Co., Ltd. (1)
Ichibancho KK Bldg 7F 13-8 Ichibancho, Chiyoda-Ku, Tokyo, 102-0082, Japan
Tel.: (81) 335569003
Software Development Services
N.A.I.C.S.: 541511

AeroScout LLC (1)
2121 Monument Village Cir, Grand Junction, CO 81507
Tel.: (970) 319-8025
Web Site: http://www.aeroscout.io
Hand Tool Accessory & Equipment Distr
N.A.I.C.S.: 423710

AeroScout Ltd. (1)
3 Perkeris St Einstein Entrance 4/Fl, 76702, Rehovot, Israel
Tel.: (972) 893693000
Web Site: http://www.aeroscout.com
Software Development Services
N.A.I.C.S.: 541511

Aeroscout (Singapore) Pte. Ltd. (1)
30 Robinson Road Robinson Towers 08-03, Singapore, 048546, Singapore
Tel.: (65) 63232335
Software Development Services
N.A.I.C.S.: 541511

Avdel France SAS (1)
Bat Le Monet Paris Nord 2 9 Allee des Impressionnistes, 59328, Villepinte, France
Tel.: (33) 149909500
Hardware Distr
N.A.I.C.S.: 444140

Avdel Italia S.r.l. (1)
Viale Lombardia 51/53, 20861, Brugherio, Monza & Brianza, Italy
Tel.: (39) 039289911
Industrial Tools Mfr
N.A.I.C.S.: 333517

Avdel Spain SA (1)
Avda Castilla 1 Edificio Best Point Oficina

Stanley Black & Decker, Inc.—(Continued)

18, San Fernando de Henares, 28830, Madrid, Spain
Tel.: (34) 919490015
Industrial Tools Mfr
N.A.I.C.S.: 333517

Avfast (India) Pvt. Ltd. (1)
Ramon House 6th floor 169 Backbay Reclamation, Mumbai, 400 020, India
Tel.: (91) 2266345611
Web Site: http://www.avdel.com
Nuts, Screws & Rivets Mfr
N.A.I.C.S.: 332722

Black & Decker (U.S.) Inc. (1)
5999 Crawfordsville Rd, Indianapolis, IN 46224
Tel.: (317) 241-1200
Web Site: http://www.dewalt.com
Emp.: 8
Power-Driven Handtool Mfr
N.A.I.C.S.: 333991

Black & Decker Europe (1)
270 Bath Road, Slough, SL1 4DX, Berkshire, United Kingdom
Tel.: (44) 1753260090
Web Site: https://www.blackanddecker.co.uk
Cutlery & Hand Tool Mfr
N.A.I.C.S.: 332216

Black & Decker Polska Sp.z.o.o. (1)
ul Prosta 68, 00-838, Poznan, Poland
Tel.: (48) 221049594
Web Site: https://www.blackanddecker.pl
Sales Range: $25-49.9 Million
Emp.: 350
Power-Driven Handtool Mfr
N.A.I.C.S.: 333991

Black & Decker SSC CO., LTD. (1)
Export Processing Zone No 200 Mid, Suzhou, 215021, China
Tel.: (86) 51262581818
Industrial Tools Mfr
N.A.I.C.S.: 333517

CAMACC Systems Inc. (1)
Block B Suite 200 - 2261 Keating X Rd, Saanichton, V8M 2A5, BC, Canada
Tel.: (250) 652-3406
Web Site: http://www.camacc.com
Security Control System Services
N.A.I.C.S.: 517111
Geoff O'leary (Pres & CEO)
Steve Comber (Acct Mgr)
Dan Cromack (CFO)
Hartley Woloshuk (Natl Mgr-Svc, Installation & Support)
Jen Mayer (Ops Mgr)
Terry Franco (Natl Mgr-Safety)
Colin Owens (Mgr IT)
Mike Craft (Natl Mgr-Production)
Joe Thomas (Sls Mgr-Western)

CONNEXCENTER SA (1)
Rue Jean Burgers Straat 5a, 7850, Enghien, Belgium
Tel.: (32) 2 398 0120
Web Site: https://www.connexcenter.be
Hand Tool Accessory & Equipment Distr
N.A.I.C.S.: 423710

CRC-Evans Offshore Limited (1)
3 Abercrombie Court Arnhall Business Park, Aberdeenshire, Westhill, AB32 6FE, Aberdeenshire, United Kingdom
Tel.: (44) 1224766660
Offshore Pipeline Construction Services
N.A.I.C.S.: 237990

CRC-Evans Offshore Ltd. (1)
3 Abercrombie Court Arnhall Business Park Westhill, Aberdeen, AB32 6FE, Scotland, United Kingdom
Tel.: (44) 1224766660
Sales Range: $10-24.9 Million
Emp.: 1
Offshore Construction Services
N.A.I.C.S.: 336611
Stefan Engstrom (Mng Dir)

CRC-Evans PIH Servios De Tubulao do Brasil Ltda (1)
Alameda Santos 1940 13 Flr, Sao Paulo, 01418-200, Brazil
Tel.: (55) 71999810708
Onshore & Offshore Pipeline Construction Services

N.A.I.C.S.: 237120

CRC-Evans Weighting Systems, Inc. (1)
10700 E Independence St, Tulsa, OK 74116
Tel.: (918) 438-2100
Concrete Foundation & Contractor Services
N.A.I.C.S.: 238110

Christie Intruder Alarms Limited (1)
Security House 212-218 London Road, Waterlooville, PO7 7AJ, United Kingdom
Tel.: (44) 2392265111
Web Site: http://www.ciaalarms.co.uk
Security Consulting Services
N.A.I.C.S.: 541690
David Rayner (Fin Dir)

Clarke Security Services Incorporated (1)
1275 W Roosevelt Rd Ste 123, West Chicago, IL 60185
Tel.: (630) 293-4497
Web Site: http://www.sonitrolwc.com
Electronic Security Services
N.A.I.C.S.: 561621
Steve Hanzelin (VP & Gen Mgr)

Connex Group SA (1)
Internationalelaan 9, 1070, Brussels, Belgium
Tel.: (32) 27331144
Web Site: http://www.connexgroup.be
Emp.: 245
Security Solution Services
N.A.I.C.S.: 561621

Contract Fire Systems Ltd. (1)
CFS Business Park Coleshill Road, West Midlands, Sutton Coldfield, B75 7FS, United Kingdom
Tel.: (44) 8448012700
Web Site: http://www.cfs-group.co.uk
Security Control System Services
N.A.I.C.S.: 561621

Cooperheat of Africa Pty. Ltd. (1)
10B Angus Crescent, Longmeadow East, Modderfontein, 1609, Gauteng, South Africa
Tel.: (27) 114534115
Web Site: https://www.duicoa.co.za
Emp.: 7
Power Generation Services
N.A.I.C.S.: 221112

DADO, Inc. (1)
248 3rd St Ste 938, Oakland, CA 94607
Web Site: https://www.projectdado.com
Software Development Services
N.A.I.C.S.: 541511
Jake Olsen (CEO)

DeWALT Industrial Tool Company (1)
1646 Sulphur Spring Rd, Baltimore, MD 21227
Tel.: (410) 716-3900
Web Site: http://www.dewalt.com
Sales Range: $10-24.9 Million
Emp.: 10
Industrial Power Tools Mfr
N.A.I.C.S.: 333912

DeWalt Industrial Tools S.p.A. (1)
Via G Verdi 13, 23847, Molteno, Italy
Tel.: (39) 07551891
Web Site: http://www.dewalt.it
Industrial Tools Mfr
N.A.I.C.S.: 333517

Delta Porter-Cable (1)
4825 US Hwy 45 N, Jackson, TN 38305-7900
Tel.: (731) 668-8600
Web Site: http://www.deltaportercable.com
Sales Range: $250-299.9 Million
Emp.: 800
General-Purpose Woodworking Machinery, Including Table & Band Saws, Planers, Jointers, Grinders, Drill Presses, Shapers & Lathes Mfr
N.A.I.C.S.: 333243

Dubuis et Cie S.A.S. (1)
17-19 rue Jules Berthonneau ZI de, PO Box 3406, Villebarou, 41000, Blois, France
Tel.: (33) 254524000
Web Site: http://www.dubuis.com
Emp.: 70
Industrial Tools Mfr

N.A.I.C.S.: 333517

E.A. Patten Co., LLC (1)
303 Wetherell St, Manchester, CT 06040
Tel.: (860) 649-2851
Web Site: https://www.camaerospace.com
Tube Mfr
N.A.I.C.S.: 331210

EMIRIAN S.A.I.C.F.I.R. (1)
Calle 49 N-5144-Villa Ballester, Buenos Aires, B1653AOL, Argentina
Tel.: (54) 1147386000
Web Site: http://www.emirian.com.ar
Abrasives Distr
N.A.I.C.S.: 423840

ETAC ALARME SERVICES SECURITY SA (1)
Rue Colonel Bourg 122, Evere, 1140, Belgium
Tel.: (32) 27261142
Hand Tool Accessory & Equipment Distr
N.A.I.C.S.: 423710

Emhart Teknologies B.V. (1)
Distripark Sittard Holtum Noordweg 35, 6121 RE, Born, Netherlands
Tel.: (31) 433508492
Web Site: http://www.masterfix.com
Industrial Tools Mfr
N.A.I.C.S.: 333517

Emhart Teknologies LLC (1)
7345 N 400 E, Montpelier, IN 47359
Tel.: (586) 949-0440
Industrial Tools Mfr
N.A.I.C.S.: 333517

Excel Industries, Inc. (1)
200 S Ridge Rd, Hesston, KS 67062
Tel.: (620) 327-4911
Web Site: http://www.hustlerturfequipment.com
Sales Range: $25-49.9 Million
Emp.: 220
Mfr of Commercial Turf & Grounds Equipment
N.A.I.C.S.: 333111
Shelley Lujono (Mgr-Advertising)
Ben Houghton (Sys Engr)
Martin Tibbets (Mgr-Facility)
Jonathan Thyng (Mgr)
Joseph C. Wright (CEO)
Bobby Kindle (Dir-Quality)

Facom S.A. (1)
6/8 rue Gustave Eiffel - BP 99, 91423, Morangis, Cedex, France
Tel.: (33) 164544545
Web Site: http://www.facom.fr
Sales Range: $75-99.9 Million
Emp.: 500
Hand Tool Mfr
N.A.I.C.S.: 332216

Subsidiary (Non-US):

Facom Belgie BVBA (2)
Egide Walschaertsstraat 16, 2800, Mechelen, Belgium
Tel.: (32) 15473930
Web Site: http://www.facom.be
Sales Range: $25-49.9 Million
Tool Mfr
N.A.I.C.S.: 333517
Massimo Grassi (Pres & Dir Gen)

Facom UK Ltd. (2)
3 Europa Court-Europa Link, Sheffield Business Park, Sheffield, S9 1XZ, Staffordshire, United Kingdom
Tel.: (44) 3308080719
Web Site: http://www.facom.com
Sales Range: $75-99.9 Million
Emp.: 50
Hand Tool Mfr
N.A.I.C.S.: 332216

Fastener Jamher Taiwan Inc. (1)
No 239 Linding St, Rende Dist, T'ainan, 71742, Taiwan
Tel.: (886) 62494699
Emp.: 90
Nuts, Screws & Rivets Mfr
N.A.I.C.S.: 332722
Steve Wu (Gen Mgr)

First National AlarmCap LP/Premiere Societe en Commandite Nationale Alarmcap (1)

4780 Saint-Felix Street, Saint-Augustin-de-Desmaures, G3A 2J9, QC, Canada
Tel.: (403) 299-2299
Web Site: http://www.alarmcap.com
Security Systems Integration Services
N.A.I.C.S.: 561621

Guangzhou Emhart Fastening System Co., LTD. (1)
Bldg J15 Rand F International Airport Comprehensive Logistics Park, North Road Huadong Town Huadu District, Guangzhou, 510890, Guangdong, China
Tel.: (86) 2029156060
Office Equipment Mfr & Distr
N.A.I.C.S.: 339940

Horst Sprenger GmbH Recycling-tools (1)
Spezialwerkzeuge Pferdsweide 41, 47441, Moers, Germany
Tel.: (49) 284190580
Web Site: https://horst-sprenger.com
Emp.: 25
Industrial Tools Mfr
N.A.I.C.S.: 333517

Infastech (Guangzhou) Limited (1)
Rm 1010 Metro Plaza No 183 Tianh, Guangzhou, 510075, China
Tel.: (86) 2082211821
Office Equipment Distr
N.A.I.C.S.: 423420

Infastech (Korea) Limited (1)
355-9 Gobul-ro, Gwangju, 12769, Gyeonggi-Do, Korea (South)
Tel.: (82) 317986340
Web Site:
http://www.stanleyengineeredfastening.com
Industrial Tools Mfr
N.A.I.C.S.: 333517

Infastech (Malaysia) Sdn Bhd (1)
Lot 63 Persiaran Bunga Tanjung 1, Senawang Industrial Park, 70400, Seremban, Negeri Sembilan, Malaysia
Tel.: (60) 66767000
Nuts, Screws & Rivets Mfr
N.A.I.C.S.: 332722

Infastech (Shenzhen) Limited (1)
RM1708 17/F Nanyang Plaza 57 Hung To Rd, Kwun Tong, China (Hong Kong)
Tel.: (852) 29500665
Web Site:
http://www.stanleyengineeredfastening.com
Industrial Supply Whslr
N.A.I.C.S.: 423830

Infastech Camcar Malaysia Sbd. Bhd (1)
Lot 63 Persiaran Bunga Tanjung 1 Senawang Industrial Park, 70400, Seremban, Sembilan, Malaysia
Tel.: (60) 66767000
Web Site: http://www.349155-a.m9.com.my
Emp.: 220
Nuts, Screws & Rivets Mfr
N.A.I.C.S.: 332722

Infastech Decorah, LLC (1)
1304 Kerr Dr, Decorah, IA 52101
Tel.: (563) 382-4216
Web Site: http://www.infastech.com
Nuts, Screws & Rivets Mfr
N.A.I.C.S.: 332722

Infastech Fastening Systems (Wuxi) Limited (1)
No 9 Xi Xia Road Mechanical and Electrical Industry Park, Wuxi National High Tech Industrial Development Zone, Wuxi, 214028, Jiangsu, China
Tel.: (86) 5108 520 0026
Web Site:
http://www.stanleyengineeredfastening.com
Emp.: 270
Office Equipment Mfr & Distr
N.A.I.C.S.: 339940

Infastech Kabushiki Kaisha (1)
Center Minami Sky 3-1 Chigasaki-chuo, Tsuzuki-ku, Yokohama, 224-0032, Kanagawa, Japan
Tel.: (81) 459471200
Web Site: http://www.infastech.co.jp
Industrial Tools Mfr
N.A.I.C.S.: 333517

Infastech Thai Company Limited (1)
64/132 Moo 4 Tambon Pluakdaeng, Amphur
Pluakdaeng, Rayong, 21140, Thailand
Tel.: (66) 38656360
Security Systems Integration Services
N.A.I.C.S.: 561621

Infastehc (Singapore) Pte. Ltd. (1)
67 Ubi Avenue 1 02-08 Starhub Green
South Wing, Singapore, 408942, Singapore
Tel.: (65) 63725656
Engineering Fastener Product Mfr
N.A.I.C.S.: 332722

JMD SECURITE SA (1)
Rue De L Hydrion 113, Arlon, 6700, Bel-
gium
Tel.: (32) 63220464
Hand Tool Accessory & Equipment Distr
N.A.I.C.S.: 423710

Jiangsu Guoqiang Tools Co.,
Ltd. (1)
Tianfen Technology Hardware Industrial
Park, Lusigang Town, Qidong, 226244, Ji-
angsu, China
Tel.: (86) 51383290860
Web Site: http://www.guoqiangtools.com
Industrial Tools Mfr
N.A.I.C.S.: 333517

Lenox (1)
301 Chestnut St, East Longmeadow, MA
01028-5601
Tel.: (800) 628-3030
Web Site: https://www.cutwithlenox.com
Mfr of Band Saw Blades, Power Tool Ac-
cessories, Hand Tools & Related Products
N.A.I.C.S.: 332216

M.HART do Brasil Ltda. (1)
Rua Ricardo Cavatton 226, Sao Paulo,
05038, Brazil
Tel.: (55) 1138716460
Industrial Tools Mfr
N.A.I.C.S.: 333517

M.T.D. France SAS (1)
Impasse du Quesnet, BP 453, 76806, Saint
Etienne-du-Rouvray, France
Tel.: (33) 232919432
Web Site: https://www.mtdfrance.fr
Cutlery & Hand Tool Mfr
N.A.I.C.S.: 332216

MTD Austria Handelsgesellschaft
m.b.H. (1)
Schulleiten 7, Gschwandt, 4816, Gmunden,
Austria
Tel.: (43) 720816087
Web Site: https://mtd-at.com
Cutlery & Hand Tool Mfr
N.A.I.C.S.: 332216

MTD Hungaria Kft. (1)
Dozsa Gy u 1, 8248, Nemesvamos, Hun-
gary
Tel.: (36) 17016720
Web Site: https://mtd-hu.com
Cutlery & Hand Tool Mfr
N.A.I.C.S.: 332216

MTD Products Benelux B.V. (1)
Graafsebaan 111A, 5248 NL, Rosmalen,
Netherlands
Tel.: (31) 73 808 0374
Web Site: https://www.mtd-benelux.nl
Consumer Goods Product Distr
N.A.I.C.S.: 423990

MTD Products Denmark ApS (1)
Englsholmvej 39, 8940, Randers, Denmark
Tel.: (45) 8 711 9100
Web Site: https://www.mtd.dk
Agriculture Equipment Mfr & Distr
N.A.I.C.S.: 333111
Blair A. Cook (Co-Chm)
Ulrich Schnelle (Co-Chm)

MTD Products India Private India
Limited (1)
Gut No 53/01 Near Vijay Logistics Pune-
Nashik Highway, Kuruli, Pune, 410501, Ma-
harashtra, India
Tel.: (91) 803 591 8349
Web Site: https://www.mtdproducts.in
Emp.: 2,600
Agriculture Equipment Mfr & Distr
N.A.I.C.S.: 333111

MTD Products, Inc. (1)

5903 Grafton Rd, Valley City, OH
44280 (20%)
Tel.: (330) 225-2600
Web Site: http://www.mtdproducts.com
Sales Range: $550-599.9 Million
Emp.: 6,600
Outdoor Power Equipment Designer & Mfr
N.A.I.C.S.: 423820
Brian Blouch (Mgr)
Catherine Mattson (Dir)
Dave Hein (Chief Engr)
George Flinner (Mgr)
Kelly Sullivan (Mgr-Marketing)
Maynard Guadiz (Sys Engr)
Ralph Heysek (Mgr)
Rita Puljer (Office Mgr)
Tina Abraham (Dir)
Maelae Barney (Coord-Sales)
Paul Crawford (Mgr-Engineering-Drive Sys)
Ernie Didea (Dir-Accounting)
Roy Keating (VP-Sales & Gen Mgr)
Jason Mattern (Sr Dir-Sales)
Randall Meyer (Mgr)
Florio Nicole (Dir-Tax)
Walter Opperman (VP)
Jeff Salamon (Dir-Marketing)
Kim Weaver (Mgr-Sales-Post Sls Support)
Allen Baird (Mgr-Mktg)
Tom Rossman (VP-Sales)
Amit Saha (Dir-Business Development &
Chief Engr)
Geoff Huffman (Sys Engr)
Jason Belsito (Mgr-Operations)
James Hodkey (Mgr-Sales-Natl)
Steve Pulig (Mgr)
Scott Schlueter (Acct Mgr)
Chris Hlavna (Acct Mgr)
Joe Jocke (Chief Engr)
Micah Wolf (Sys Engr)
Jerry Shepherd (Gen Mgr)
Marc Pesetsky (Mgr)
Rich Bublitz (Mgr)
Stephanie Jurkovich (Mgr)
Michele Dorow (Sr VP & Controller)
Phil Clouse (Exec VP-Operations)
Robert T. Moll (Pres, CEO & Chm)
Rory Bringhurst (Exec VP-Product Develop-
ment)
Blair Cook (Pres-International)
Jeff Deuch (CFO & Exec VP)
Craig Dukes (Sr VP-Human Resources)

Subsidiary (Non-US):

Amgazit F.K. Ltd. (2)
Kibbutz Gezer, DN Shimshon, Rehovot,
99786, Israel
Tel.: (972) 29935285
Lawn & Garden Equipment Mfr
N.A.I.C.S.: 333112

Subsidiary (Domestic):

MTD Aircap (2)
5484 Hwy 145 S, Verona, MS 38879
Tel.: (662) 566-2332
Web Site: http://www.mtd.com
Sales Range: $75-99.9 Million
Emp.: 1,000
Outdoor Power Equipment
N.A.I.C.S.: 333112

Subsidiary (Non-US):

MTD Products Limited (2)
97 Kent Ave, Kitchener, N2G 4J1, ON,
Canada (100%)
Tel.: (519) 579-5500
Web Site: http://www.mtdcanada.com
Sales Range: $10-24.9 Million
Emp.: 100
Outdoor Power Equipment Mfr
N.A.I.C.S.: 333112
Bud Norman (Pres)
Ed Henderson (VP-Finance)

Subsidiary (Domestic):

MTD Southwest Inc. (2)
8825 N 23rd Ave Ste 100, Phoenix, AZ
85021
Tel.: (480) 961-1002
Sales Range: $25-49.9 Million
Emp.: 250
Lawn & Garden Equipment Mfr
N.A.I.C.S.: 333112

MTD Schweiz AG (1)
Hauptstrasse 8, 5506, Magenwil, Switzerland

Tel.: (41) 43 588 1362
Web Site: https://www.mtd.ch
Garden Maintenance Services
N.A.I.C.S.: 561730

Mac Tools (1)
5195 Blazer Paky, Dublin, OH 43017
Tel.: (614) 755-7000
Web Site: https://www.mactools.com
Rev.: $267,100
Emp.: 100
Automotive Tools & Equipment Distr
N.A.I.C.S.: 441330

Masterfix Products U.K. Ltd. (1)
Pacific House 2 Swiftfields, Welwyn Garden
City, AL7 1LY, Hertfordshire, United King-
dom
Tel.: (44) 1707292123
Web Site: http://www.masterfix.com
Mfr of High-Quality Blind Rivets, Blind Rivet
Nuts & Bolts & Hand & Power Tools
N.A.I.C.S.: 333991

Meta Vision Systems Limited (1)
Oakfield House Oakfield Industrial Estate,
Eynsham, OX29 4TH, Oxfordshire, United
Kingdom
Tel.: (44) 1415523513
Web Site: http://www.meta-va.com
Welding Equipment Mfr
N.A.I.C.S.: 333992
Nick Pearce (Mgr-Svc)

Microalloying International, Inc. (1)
9977 W Sam Houston Pkwy N Ste 140,
Houston, TX 77064
Tel.: (281) 664-0150
Web Site: https://www.microalloying.com
Consulting Services
N.A.I.C.S.: 541611
Robin Gordon (Sr VP)

Niscayah Holding Spain, S.L. (1)
Calle Barbadillo 7, 28042, Madrid, Spain
Tel.: (34) 913127777
Web Site:
   http://www.stanleyblackanddecker.com
Emp.: 200
Holding Company
N.A.I.C.S.: 551112

Niscayah Teknik AB (1)
Lindhagensplan 70, Box 12231, 102 26,
Stockholm, Sweden
Tel.: (46) 84445000
Electrical Contracting Services
N.A.I.C.S.: 238210
Jonas Ahl (CEO)

PIH Ltd. (1)
Farrington Road Rossendale Road Indus-
trial Estate, Burnley, BB11 5SW, United
Kingdom
Tel.: (44) 1282415323
Web Site: http://www.pih.co.uk
Emp.: 100
Offshore Construction Services
N.A.I.C.S.: 336611

PIH Services ME LLC (1)
PO Box 289, Madinat Qaboos, 115, Muscat,
Oman
Tel.: (968) 24595766
Cutlery & Hand Tool Mfr
N.A.I.C.S.: 332216

PIH Services ME Ltd. (1)
406 - 407 Sobha Ivory 1 Business Bay, PO
Box 62574, Dubai, United Arab Emirates
Tel.: (971) 48180500
Web Site: http://www.cic-evans.com
Sales Range: $50-74.9 Million
Heat Treatment Svcs
N.A.I.C.S.: 336611

PIH Services ME Ltd. (1)
PO Box 14975, Doha, Qatar
Tel.: (974) 44501921
Cutlery & Hand Tool Mfr
N.A.I.C.S.: 332216

Pacom Group AB (1)
Kistagangen 26, 164 40, Kista, Sweden
Tel.: (46) 812139800
Security Systems Integration Services
N.A.I.C.S.: 561621

Pacom Systems (North America)
Inc. (1)
339 Interstate Blvd, Sarasota, FL 34240

Tel.: (941) 378-2523
Web Site: https://www.pacom.com
Emp.: 13
Software Development Services
N.A.I.C.S.: 541511

Pacom Systems Espana SL (1)
Avenida Aragon 402, Planta Baja Oficinas
24/25/27 Pozuelo de Alarcon, 28022, Ma-
drid, Spain
Tel.: (34) 902052377
Security Systems Integration Services
N.A.I.C.S.: 561621

Pacom Systems Pty Limited (1)
Level 2 5 Eden Park Drive, Macquarie Park,
2113, NSW, Australia
Tel.: (61) 29 889 5670
Web Site: https://www.pacom.com
Security Systems Integration Services
N.A.I.C.S.: 561621

Paladin Brands, LLC (1)
2800 N Zeeb Road, Dexter, MI 48130
Tel.: (800) 456-7100
Web Site: http://www.paladinbrands.com
Construction Vehicle Attachment Tools Mfr
N.A.I.C.S.: 423810

Subsidiary (Domestic):

JRB Attachments, LLC (2)
820 Glaser Pkwy, Akron, OH 44306
Tel.: (330) 734-3000
Web Site: http://www.paladinbrands.com
Sales Range: $25-49.9 Million
Emp.: 150
Construction Machinery Attachments Mfr
N.A.I.C.S.: 333120

Jewell Attachments, LLC (2)
18135 SW Boones Ferry Rd, Portland, OR
97224
Tel.: (877) 237-3392
Web Site: http://www.jewellattachments.com
Emp.: 80
Construction Machinery Mfr
N.A.I.C.S.: 333120
Shawn Hegerberg (Mgr-Production)

Panalok Limited (1)
Gort Road Industrial Estate, Clare County,
Ennis, Clare, Ireland
Tel.: (353) 65 682 4134
Web Site: https://www.panalok.ie
Bolt & Screw Mfr
N.A.I.C.S.: 332722

Pengo Attachments, Inc. (1)
500 E Hwy 10, Laurens, IA 50554
Tel.: (800) 599-0211
Web Site:
   http://www.pengoattachments.com
Industrial Machinery Mfr
N.A.I.C.S.: 333248
Brian Rickards (VP)
Dawn Jamison (Mgr-OEM & Sls Admin)
Jon Schendel (Dir-Ops)
George Chaney (Dir-New Bus Dev)
Amy Swanson (Mgr-HR-Divisional)

Unit (Domestic):

Pengo Attachments, Inc. -
Cokato (2)
13369 60th St SW, Cokato, MN
55321-4210 (100%)
Tel.: (320) 286-5581
Construction Machinery Mfr
N.A.I.C.S.: 333120

Powers Fasteners (NZ) Limited &
Co. (1)
229 Bush Road North Shore City Auckland,
Albany, New Zealand
Tel.: (64) 94152425
Nuts, Screws & Rivets Mfr
N.A.I.C.S.: 332722

Powers Fasteners Australasia Pty
Limited (1)
810 Whitehorse Road, Box Hill, 3128, VIC,
Australia
Tel.: (61) 386695200
Web Site: http://www.powers-guide.com
Emp.: 70
Nuts, Screws & Rivets Mfr
N.A.I.C.S.: 332722

Powers Fasteners Inc. (1)
2 Powers Ln, Brewster, NY 10509

Stanley Black & Decker, Inc.—(Continued)
Tel.: (914) 235-6300
Web Site: http://www.powers.com
Sales Range: $50-74.9 Million
Emp.: 300
Anchoring Systems Mfr
N.A.I.C.S.: 333515

Subsidiary (Non-US):

Power Industries Ltd. (2)
6950 Edwards Boulevard, Mississauga,
L5T- 2W2, ON, Canada (100%)
Tel.: (905) 673-7295
Web Site: http://www.powers.com
Sales Range: $10-24.9 Million
Emp.: 15
Concrete Fasteners Mfr
N.A.I.C.S.: 339993

QRP, Inc. (1)
2307 Mercantile Dr NE, Leland, NC 28451
Tel.: (910) 371-0700
Bolt & Screw Mfr
N.A.I.C.S.: 332722

Rawl Australasia Pty. Ltd. (1)
Philip Street 10, Melbourne, 3192, VIC,
Australia
Tel.: (61) 395845800
Industrial Tools Mfr
N.A.I.C.S.: 333517

Scan Modul Byrum ApS (1)
Jegstrupvej 2 B, 7800, Skive, Denmark
Tel.: (45) 48228877
Web Site: http://www.scanmodul.com
Medical Equipment Whslr
N.A.I.C.S.: 423450

Scan Modul Orgasystem GmbH (1)
Ludwig-Erhard-Str 51, 04103, Leipzig, Germany
Tel.: (49) 34121208500
Web Site: http://www.stanleyhealthcare.com
Sales Range: $25-49.9 Million
Emp.: 8
Healthcare Equipment Services
N.A.I.C.S.: 456199

Scan Modul System AG (1)
Sihleggstr 23, 8832, Wollerau, Switzerland
Tel.: (41) 613016301
Web Site: http://www.stanleyhealthcare.com
Sales Range: $25-49.9 Million
Emp.: 5
Healthcare Equipment Services
N.A.I.C.S.: 456199

Sonitrol Distribution Canada, Inc. (1)
5875 Kennedy Rd, Mississauga, L4Z 2G3,
ON, Canada
Web Site: https://www.sonitrolcanada.com
Electronic Security Services
N.A.I.C.S.: 561612

**Sonitrol Security Systems of Buffalo,
Inc.** (1)
195 Elm St, Buffalo, NY 14203
Tel.: (716) 847-0900
Web Site: https://www.sonitrol.com
Electronic Security Services
N.A.I.C.S.: 561612
David Jones (Co-Founder & Pres)
Lisa Schieber (Controller)

Spiralock Corporation (1)
25235 Dequindre Rd, Madison Heights, MI
48071
Tel.: (248) 543-7800
Web Site: http://www.spiralock.com
Cutting Tool Mfr
N.A.I.C.S.: 333515

Stanley Assembly Technologies (1)
5335 Avion Park Dr, Cleveland, OH
44143-2328 (100%)
Tel.: (440) 461-5500
Web Site: http://www.stanleyassembly.com
Sales Range: $75-99.9 Million
Emp.: 150
Industrial Assembly & Tools & Material Handling Systems Mfr
N.A.I.C.S.: 332216

**Stanley Black & Decker (Hellas)
EPE** (1)
Strabo 7, 16674, Glyfada, Athens, Greece
Tel.: (30) 2108981616
Web Site: http://www.stanleyworks.gr

Electronic Equipment Distr
N.A.I.C.S.: 423690

**Stanley Black & Decker Austria
GmbH** (1)
Oberlaaerstrasse 248, 1230, Vienna, Austria
Tel.: (43) 1661160
Web Site: https://www.blackanddecker.at
Industrial Tools Mfr
N.A.I.C.S.: 333517

**Stanley Black & Decker Belgium
BVBA** (1)
Egide Walschaertsstraat 16, 2800,
Mechelen, Belgium
Tel.: (32) 15473765
Web Site: http://www.stanleyworks.be
Industrial Tools Mfr
N.A.I.C.S.: 333517

Stanley Black & Decker Czech Republic s.r.o. (1)
Trmice 873, 400 04, Trmice, Czech Republic
Tel.: (420) 47 531 9111
Web Site: https://www.blackanddecker-usti.cz
Industrial Tools Mfr
N.A.I.C.S.: 333517

**Stanley Black & Decker Deutschland
GmbH** (1)
Black- and Decker-Strasse 40, 65510, Idstein, Germany
Tel.: (49) 6126210
Web Site: https://www.stanleyworks.de
Emp.: 200
Industrial Tools Mfr
N.A.I.C.S.: 333517

**Stanley Black & Decker Finland
Oy** (1)
PL 47 Kumpulantie 13 B, 00520, Helsinki,
Finland
Tel.: (358) 104004333
Web Site: http://www.stanleyworks.fi
Industrial Machinery Mfr
N.A.I.C.S.: 333248

**Stanley Black & Decker France
S.A.S.** (1)
6/8 rue Gustave Eiffel, BP 99, 91423, Morangis, Cedex, France
Tel.: (33) 164544545
Web Site: http://www.stanleyoutillage.fr
Industrial Tools Mfr
N.A.I.C.S.: 333517

**Stanley Black & Decker Iberica,
S.L.** (1)
C/ Bergueda 1 Edf Muntadas Ofc 6 Parc
Negooio Mas Blau, 08820, El Prat de Llobregat, Spain
Tel.: (34) 934797400
Web Site: http://www.blackanddecker.es
Industrial Tools Mfr
N.A.I.C.S.: 333517

Stanley Black & Decker Ireland (1)
45 Eastgate Drive Little Island, Cork, Ireland
Tel.: (353) 214524468
Web Site: http://www.stanleysecurity.ie
Industrial Tools Mfr
N.A.I.C.S.: 333517

Stanley Black & Decker Limited (1)
Crispin Catherwood 210 Bath Road,
Slough, SL1 3YD, United Kingdom
Tel.: (44) 1753500604
Hand Tool Accessory & Equipment Distr
N.A.I.C.S.: 423710

**Stanley Black & Decker Logistics
BVBA** (1)
Industriezone Ravenshout Noord 3 Kanaalweg 13, 3980, Tessenderlo, Belgium
Tel.: (32) 13500400
Web Site:
　http://www.stanleyblackdecker.com
Emp.: 600
Logistics Consulting Servies
N.A.I.C.S.: 541614

**Stanley Black & Decker Netherlands
B.V.** (1)
Postbus 83, 6120 AB, Born, Netherlands
Tel.: (31) 164283065
Web Site: http://www.stanleyworks.nl

Industrial Tools Mfr
N.A.I.C.S.: 333517

**Stanley Black & Decker Norway
AS** (1)
Nydalsvelen 28, 0484, Oslo, Norway
Tel.: (47) 22909910
Web Site: http://www.stanleyworks.no
Industrial Tools Mfr
N.A.I.C.S.: 333517

**Stanley Black & Decker Polska Sp. z
o.o.** (1)
ul Prosta 68, 00-838, Warsaw, Poland
Tel.: (48) 224642700
Web Site: http://www.stanleyworks.pl
Emp.: 300
Industrial Tools Mfr
N.A.I.C.S.: 333517

**Stanley Black & Decker Sweden
AB** (1)
Flojelbergsgatan 1c, 431 35, Molndal, Sweden
Tel.: (46) 31686000
Web Site: http://www.stanleyworks.se
Security Systems Integration Services
N.A.I.C.S.: 561621

**Stanley Black & Decker UK
Limited** (1)
210 Bath Road, Slough, SL1 4DX, Berkshire, United Kingdom
Tel.: (44) 1753511234
Web Site: http://www.stanleytools.co.uk
Sales Range: $50-74.9 Million
Tools Whslr
N.A.I.C.S.: 423710
John Cowley (Pres)

Stanley Convergent Security Solutions, Inc. (1)
2150 Western Ct Ste 300, Lisle, IL 60532
Tel.: (630) 724-3600
Web Site: http://www.stanleysecurity.com
Sales Range: $25-49.9 Million
Integrated Systems & Products Mfr
N.A.I.C.S.: 334290

Subsidiary (Domestic):

**Sonitrol Franchise Company,
L.L.C.** (2)
8100 Springwood Dr, Irving, TX 75063-3119
Tel.: (630) 245-2500
Web Site: http://www.sonitrol.com
Sales Range: $100-124.9 Million
Commercial Security Solutions
N.A.I.C.S.: 561621

Stanley Engineered Fastening (1)
4 Shelter Rock Ln, Danbury, CT 06810
Tel.: (203) 837-3600
Web Site:
　http://www.stanleyengineeredfastening.com
Sales Range: $10-24.9 Million
Emp.: 5,000
Industrial Fasteners & Assembly Products
Mfr
N.A.I.C.S.: 332722

Subsidiary (Non-US):

Avdel UK Ltd. (2)
Stanley House Works Road, Letchworth,
SG6 1JY, Hertfordshire, United Kingdom
Tel.: (44) 1582900000
Web Site: http://www.avdel-global.com
Fastening & Assembly Systems Mfr
N.A.I.C.S.: 332722

Subsidiary (Domestic):

Avdel USA LLC (2)
614 NC Hwy 200 S, Stanfield, NC 28163
Tel.: (704) 888-7100
Sales Range: $10-24.9 Million
Emp.: 90
Fasteners
N.A.I.C.S.: 332722
Myron Clark (Mgr-Engrg & Quality)

Subsidiary (Non-US):

Emhart Harttung A/S (2)
Roskildevej 22, DK-2620, Albertslund, Denmark
Tel.: (45) 44841100

Web Site: The Company Headqu...
　http://www.stanleyengineeredfasten
ing.com
Emp.: 3
Fastening & Assembly Products Whslr
N.A.I.C.S.: 423840

**Emhart Teknologies (India) Private
Limited** (2)
No 54 APEX Towers 6th Floor 2nd Main
Road Raja Annamalai Puram, Chennai,
600028, Tamil Nadu, India
Tel.: (91) 4443060639
Web Site:
　http://www.stanleyengineeredfastening.com
Emp.: 13
Fastening Equipment Mfr
N.A.I.C.S.: 423710
Hemant Sharma (Mng Dir)

Emhart Teknologies GmbH (2)
Max Eyth Str 1, PO Box 111329, Giessen,
39394, Germany
Tel.: (49) 6414050
Web Site: http://www.stanley.com
Industrial Fasteners & Assembly Products
Mfr
N.A.I.C.S.: 332722

Guangzhou Emhart Fastening Systems Co., Ltd. (2)
B7 Guaguang Industrial Park No 8, Jinghu
Road Xinhua St Huadu District, Guangzhou,
510800, China
Tel.: (86) 2036902526
Industrial Fasteners & Assembly Products
Mfr
N.A.I.C.S.: 332722

Infastech (Australia) Pty Limited (2)
891 Wellington Road, Rowville, 3178, VIC,
Australia
Tel.: (61) 397656401
Web Site:
　http://www.stanleyengineeredfastening.com
Sales Range: $10-24.9 Million
Emp.: 25
Fasteners & Fastening Systems Distr
N.A.I.C.S.: 423840

Infastech (China) Limited (2)
Unit 903-904 9/F 9 Chong Yip Street, Kwun
Tong, Kowloon, China (Hong Kong)
Tel.: (852) 2 993 5138
Web Site: http://www.infastech.com
Fastening Equipment Mfr
N.A.I.C.S.: 332722

Infastech (Singapore) Pte Ltd (2)
67 Ubi Avenue 1 02-07 Starhub Green
South Wing, Singapore, 408942, Singapore
Tel.: (65) 6 372 5656
Web Site:
　https://www.stanleyengineeredfastening.com
Emp.: 22
Fastener Mfr
N.A.I.C.S.: 332722
Kevin Fernando (Pres)

Masterfix Poland Ltd. Sp.z.o.o (2)
ul Daleka 16, 60-124, Poznan, Poland
Tel.: (48) 221857752
Web Site: http://www.masterfix.com
Sales Range: $10-24.9 Million
Emp.: 11
Power-Driven Handtool Mfr
N.A.I.C.S.: 333991

**Nippon Pop Rivets & Fasteners
Ltd.** (2)
3-6 Kinicho, Chiyoda-Ku, Tokyo, 102-0094,
Japan
Tel.: (81) 332657291
Web Site: https://www.popnpr.co.jp
Emp.: 272
Pop Rivets & Fasteners Mfr
N.A.I.C.S.: 339993

**Shanghai Emhart Fastening Systems
Ltd.** (2)
9-11 Lane 615 Fengdeng Road Bldg 9, Jiading District 31, Shanghai, 201818, Malu
Town, China
Tel.: (86) 2162367600
Web Site:
　http://www.asia.stanleyengineeredfastening.com
Industrial Fasteners & Assembly Products
Mfr

N.A.I.C.S.: 339993

Spiralock do Brasil Ltda (2)
1425 Av Brigadeiro Jose Vincente Faria
Lima, Atibaia, 12942-655, Atibaia/SP, Brazil
Tel.: (55) 11 4411 1188
Web Site: http://www.spiralock.com
Hardware Marketing Services
N.A.I.C.S.: 444140

Tucker GmbH (2)
Max-Eyth-Str 1, 35394, Giessen, Germany
Tel.: (49) 641 4050
Web Site: http://www.emhart.eu
Automotive Fastening Products Mfr
N.A.I.C.S.: 425120

Stanley Engineered Fastening Benelux B.V. (1)
Holtum Noordweg 35 RE, Born, Netherlands
Tel.: (31) 437502000
Fastening Product Mfr & Distr
N.A.I.C.S.: 331110

Stanley Engineered Fastening Eastern Europe Sp. z o.o. (1)
ul Daleka 16, 60-124, Poznan, Poland
Tel.: (48) 221857752
Fastening Product Mfr & Distr
N.A.I.C.S.: 331110

Stanley Engineered Fastening France SAS (1)
6-8 Rue Gustave Eiffel, 91423, Morangis, France
Tel.: (33) 481682239
Fastening Product Mfr & Distr
N.A.I.C.S.: 331110
John Wyatt *(Pres)*

Stanley Engineered Fastening Industrial Deutschland GmbH (1)
Flurstrasse 7-19, Gevelsberg, Germany
Tel.: (49) 2332661125
Fastening Product Mfr & Distr
N.A.I.C.S.: 331110

Stanley Engineered Fastening Italy S.r.l. (1)
Via Miraflores 20, 10042, Nichelino, Italy
Tel.: (39) 0694500949
Fastening Product Mfr & Distr
N.A.I.C.S.: 331110

Stanley Engineered Fastening Spain, S.L.U. (1)
Avda Castilla 1 Best Point Building Office 18, San Fernando de Henares, 28830, Madrid, Spain
Tel.: (34) 919490015
Fastening Product Mfr & Distr
N.A.I.C.S.: 331110

Stanley Fastening Systems Poland Sp. z o.o. (1)
Ul Jerzmanowska 4, Wroclaw, 54-519, Poland
Tel.: (48) 713545501
Web Site: http://www.bostitch.pl
Sales Range: $75-99.9 Million
Emp.: 30
Fastening Equipment Mfr
N.A.I.C.S.: 423710

Stanley Fastening Systems, L.P. (1)
1000 Stanley Dr, New Britain, CT 06053
Tel.: (860) 225-5111
Industrial Fastener & Fastening Tools Mfr
N.A.I.C.S.: 333248

Stanley Grundstucksverwaltungs GmbH (1)
Max-Eyth-Str 1, 35394, Giessen, Germany
Tel.: (49) 8969381680
Real Estate Development Services
N.A.I.C.S.: 531390
Thomas Ehrhardt *(Gen Mgr)*

Stanley Grundstuecksverwaltungs GmbH (1)
Max-eyth Str 1, Giessen, 35394, Germany
Tel.: (49) 6414050
Hand Tool Accessory & Equipment Distr
N.A.I.C.S.: 423710

Stanley Healthcare Solutions France Sarl (1)
45 / 47 Boulevard Paul Vaillant Couturier, 94200, Ivry-sur-Seine, France

---

Tel.: (33) 42 619 0235
Web Site:
      https://www.stanleyhealthcare.com
Electronic Equipment Distr
N.A.I.C.S.: 423690

Stanley Hydraulic Tools (1)
3810 SE Naef Rd, Milwaukie, OR 97267
Tel.: (503) 659-5660
Web Site: http://www.stanleyhydraulic.com
Hydraulic Tools Mfr
N.A.I.C.S.: 333991

Stanley Inspection South Africa (Pty) Limited (1)
27 Brunton Circle Foundersview, Modderfontein, 1609, South Africa
Tel.: (27) 114534115
Building Inspection Services
N.A.I.C.S.: 541350
Damie Mahendranath *(Fin Dir)*

Stanley Inspection US, L.L.C. (1)
10700 E Independence, Tulsa, OK 74116-5601
Tel.: (918) 439-1300
Web Site:
      https://www.stanleyinspection.com
Non-Destructive Testing Services
N.A.I.C.S.: 541380

Stanley Inspection, L. L. C. (1)
7011 High Life Dr, Houston, TX 77066
Tel.: (832) 249-3100
Web Site: http://www.stanleyinspection.com
Non-Destructive Testing Services
N.A.I.C.S.: 541380

Stanley Pipeline Inspection, L.L.C. (1)
10700 E Independence St, Tulsa, OK 74116-5601
Tel.: (918) 439-1303
Non-Destructive Testing Services
N.A.I.C.S.: 541380
Jeremy Guretzki *(Pres)*

Stanley Security AS (1)
Nydalsveien 28, 0484, Oslo, Norway
Tel.: (47) 9 870 5010
Web Site: https://www.stanleysecurity.com
Security Systems Integration Services
N.A.I.C.S.: 561621
Espen W. Knudsen *(CEO)*
Niclas Skogstad *(Dir-Svcs)*
Bjorn A. Braathen-Hals *(Dir-Comml & KAM)*

Stanley Security Alarmcentrale B.V. (1)
Keienbergweg 50, Amsterdam Zuidoost, 1101 GC, Amsterdam, Netherlands
Tel.: (31) 88 050 6666
Web Site:
      https://www.stanleyalarmcentrale.nl
Security Systems Integration Services
N.A.I.C.S.: 561621

Stanley Security B.V. (1)
Keienbergweg 50, 1101 GC, Amsterdam, Netherlands
Tel.: (31) 880506600
Web Site: http://www.stanleysecurity.com
Security Control System Services
N.A.I.C.S.: 561621

Stanley Security Denmark ApS (1)
Smedeland 15, 2600, Glostrup, Denmark
Tel.: (45) 70234949
Web Site: http://www.stanleysecurity.dk
Security Systems Integration Services
N.A.I.C.S.: 561621

Stanley Security Deutschland Administration GmbH (1)
Kanzlerstrasse 8, 40472, Dusseldorf, Germany
Tel.: (49) 2111799604018
Security Systems Integration Services
N.A.I.C.S.: 561621

Stanley Security Deutschland GmbH (1)
Kanzlerstrasse 8, 40472, Dusseldorf, Germany
Tel.: (49) 8007826539
Web Site: http://www.stanleysecurity.de
Security Systems Integration Services
N.A.I.C.S.: 561621
Robert de Bodt *(Mng Dir)*

Stanley Security Espana, S. L. (1)
C / Barbadillo 7, Madrid, 28042, Spain
Tel.: (34) 913127777
Web Site: http://www.stanleysecurity.es
Security Systems Integration Services
N.A.I.C.S.: 561621

Stanley Security Europe BVBA (1)
Egide Walschaertsstraat 16, 2800, Mechelen, Belgium
Tel.: (32) 27331144
Web Site: http://www.stanleysecurity.com
Security Systems Integration Services
N.A.I.C.S.: 561621

Stanley Security Italia S.r.l. (1)
Via Luisa Battisotti Sassi 11, 20133, Milan, Italy
Tel.: (39) 02319641
Web Site: http://www.stanleysecurity.it
Information Technology Consulting Services
N.A.I.C.S.: 541512

Stanley Security Nederland B.V. (1)
Keienbergweg 50, 1101 GC, Amsterdam, Netherlands
Tel.: (31) 334535000
Web Site: http://www.stanleysecurity.nl
Security Systems Integration Services
N.A.I.C.S.: 561621

Stanley Security Oy (1)
PO Box 47, 00521, Helsinki, Finland
Tel.: (358) 20302001
Web Site: http://www.stanleysecurity.fi
Emp.: 200
Electronic Appliance Whslr
N.A.I.C.S.: 423620

Stanley Security Portugal, Unipessoal, Lda (1)
Rua Rodrigues Lobo 2-piso 0, 2795-174, Linda-a-Velha, Portugal
Tel.: (351) 214152700
Web Site: http://www.stanleysecurity.pt
Security Systems Integration Services
N.A.I.C.S.: 561621

Stanley Security Singapore Pte Ltd (1)
67 Ubi Avenue 1 No 02-13 Starhub Green, Singapore, 408942, Singapore
Tel.: (65) 67428618
Security System Services
N.A.I.C.S.: 561621

Stanley Security Solutions (NI) Limited (1)
Unit 6 Locksley Business Park Montgomery Road, Belfast, BT6 9UP, United Kingdom
Tel.: (44) 289 079 9988
Web Site: https://www.stanleysecurity.com
Security Systems Integration Services
N.A.I.C.S.: 561621

Stanley Security Solutions Australia Pty. Ltd. (1)
Unit 17 Riverside Centre 148 James Ruse Drive, Parramatta, 2150, NSW, Australia
Tel.: (61) 296331653
Emp.: 15
Security Systems Integration Services
N.A.I.C.S.: 561621
David Gilligin *(Gen Mgr)*

Stanley Security Solutions Taiwan Ltd. (1)
No 62 Zhongxiao 1st Street, Hou-Hu-Li, Chiayi, 600, Taiwan
Tel.: (886) 52770688
Web Site: https://www.tlhmco.com
Security Systems Integration Services
N.A.I.C.S.: 561621

Stanley Security Solutions, Inc. (1)
6161 E 75th St, Indianapolis, IN 46250
Tel.: (317) 849-2250
Web Site:
      http://www.stanleysecuritysolutions.com
Sales Range: $150-199.9 Million
Emp.: 2,500
Locks Mfr & Security Products & Services
N.A.I.C.S.: 332510
Kara Pelecky *(CIO)*
Emily Malott *(Mgr-Content)*

Subsidiary (Non-US):

Instantel Inc. (2)

---

309 Legget Drive, Ottawa, K2K 3A3, ON, Canada
Tel.: (613) 592-4642
Web Site: https://www.instantel.com
Sales Range: $25-49.9 Million
Emp.: 100
Vibration Monitoring Equipment Mfr
N.A.I.C.S.: 334419

Microtec Enterprises, Inc. (2)
2800 Avenue St-Jean-Baptiste Local 170, Quebec, G2E 6J5, QC, Canada
Tel.: (418) 874-1980
Web Site: http://www.microtec.ca
Sales Range: $10-24.9 Million
Emp.: 230
Security System Services
N.A.I.C.S.: 561621

Niscayah AB (2)
Lindhagensplan 70, PO Box 12545, Stockholm, 112 43, Sweden
Tel.: (46) 104587000
Web Site:
      http://www.stanleysecuritysolutions.se
Sales Range: $1-4.9 Billion
Security Systems Integrator
N.A.I.C.S.: 561621
Bruce Ginnever *(Chm)*

Subsidiary (US):

Niscayah, Inc. (3)
6353 El Camino Real Ste E, Carlsbad, CA 92009
Tel.: (858) 495-0200
Web Site:
      https://www.hamiltonpacificinc.com
Sales Range: $25-49.9 Million
Emp.: 50
Security Systems
N.A.I.C.S.: 561612

Unit (Non-US):

Stanley Mechanical Solutions (2)
2495 Meadowpine Blvd, Mississauga, L5N 6C3, ON, Canada
Tel.: (289) 290-7100
Web Site:
      http://www.stanleysecuritysolutions.com
Sales Range: $10-24.9 Million
Emp.: 35
Security Processes & Solutions
N.A.I.C.S.: 561621

Subsidiary (Non-US):

Stanley Security Solutions Europe Ltd. (2)
Stanley House Bramble Road, Swindon, SN2 8ER, United Kingdom
Tel.: (44) 8453016192
Web Site: http://www.stanleysecurity.co.uk
Sales Range: $250-299.9 Million
Emp.: 1,000
Security, Time Management & Communication Products & Services
N.A.I.C.S.: 811210

Stanley Security Sverige AB (1)
Lindhagensgatan 76, 112 18, Stockholm, Sweden
Tel.: (46) 104587000
Web Site: http://www.stanleysecurity.se
Security Systems Integration Services
N.A.I.C.S.: 561621

Stanley Security Switzerland Sarl (1)
Chemin des Aulx 18, 1228, Plan-les-Ouates, Switzerland
Tel.: (41) 227035600
Web Site: http://www.stanleysecurity.ch
Emp.: 18
Security Systems Integration Services
N.A.I.C.S.: 561621

Stanley Storage & Workspace Systems (1)
11 Grammes Rd, Allentown, PA 18103
Tel.: (610) 797-6600
Web Site: https://www.vidmar.com
Sales Range: $75-99.9 Million
Emp.: 225
Mfr of Modular Storage Systems for Tools & Supplies
N.A.I.C.S.: 332999

Division (Domestic):

Lista International Corporation (2)

Stanley Black & Decker, Inc.—(Continued)

106 Lowland St, Holliston, MA
01746   **(100%)**
Tel.: (508) 429-1350
Web Site: http://www.listaintl.com
Sales Range: $50-74.9 Million
Emp.: 250
Storage System & Workbenches Mfr
N.A.I.C.S.: 337127

Stanley Supply & Services, Inc.   **(1)**
335 Willow St, North Andover, MA 01845
Tel.: (978) 682-9844
Web Site:
    http://www.stanleysupplyservices.com
Sales Range: $75-99.9 Million
Emp.: 200
High Tech Tools, Test Instruments & Personal Protection & Safety Products Mfr &
Distr
N.A.I.C.S.: 423840

Stanley Svenska AB   **(1)**
Datavagen 51, 436 32, Gothenburg, Sweden
Tel.: (46) 31289770
Construction Materials Distr
N.A.I.C.S.: 423320

Stanley UK Sales Limited   **(1)**
Gowerton Road, Brackmills, Sheffield, S9
1XZ, South Yorkshire, United Kingdom
Tel.: (44) 1142768888
Web Site: http://www.stanleytools.co.uk
Emp.: 3
Machinery Equipment Whslr
N.A.I.C.S.: 423830

Stanley Works (Europe) AG   **(1)**
Ringstrasse 14 Floor 34, Dubendorf, 8600,
Switzerland
Tel.: (41) 448028093
Web Site:
    http://www.stanleyblackanddecker.com
Emp.: 20
Power-Driven Handtool Mfr
N.A.I.C.S.: 333991

Stanley Works (Europe) GmbH   **(1)**
In Luberzen 42, 8902, Urdorf, Switzerland
Tel.: (41) 447556070
Web Site: http://www.stanleyworks.ch
Emp.: 20
Security Systems Integration Services
N.A.I.C.S.: 561621

SureHand, Inc.   **(1)**
17500 Depot St Ste 170, Morgan Hill, CA
95037
Tel.: (408) 465-0315
Web Site: http://www.surehand.com
Career Development Services
N.A.I.C.S.: 611430
Christopher Brenchly *(Co-Founder & CEO)*

The Black & Decker Corporation   **(1)**
701 E Joppa Rd, Towson, MD 21286
Tel.: (410) 716-3900
Web Site: http://www.blackanddecker.com
Sales Range: $1-4.9 Billion
Emp.: 19,900
Power Tools, Household Products, Security
Hardware, Accessories & Attachments For
Power Tools, Outdoor Products, Plumbing
Products & Fastening Systems Mfr
N.A.I.C.S.: 332216
Donna Patnode *(Mgr-Video Sys)*

Subsidiary (Non-US):

Black & Decker (Belgium) N.V.   **(2)**
Egide Walschaertsstraat 16, 2800,
Mechelen, Belgium
Tel.: (32) 70225587
Web Site: https://www.blackanddecker.be
Sales Range: $125-149.9 Million
Sales & Marketing of Hardware
N.A.I.C.S.: 444140

Black & Decker (Hellas) SA   **(2)**
Stravonos 7 Leof Vouliagmenis 159, 16674,
Glyfada, Greece
Tel.: (30) 2111995530
Web Site: https://www.blackanddecker.gr
Sales Range: $25-49.9 Million
Emp.: 25
Sales & Marketing of Tools
N.A.I.C.S.: 444140
Marielle Thomas *(Mng Dir)*

Black & Decker (Ireland)   **(2)**
210 Bath Road, Slough, SL1 3YD, Berkshire, United Kingdom
Tel.: (44) 1753511234
Web Site:
    http://www.stanleyblackanddecker.com.uk
Sales Range: $25-49.9 Million
Emp.: 400
Industrial Machinery & Tools Sales & Services
N.A.I.C.S.: 425120

Black & Decker (Nederland) B.V.   **(2)**
Postbus 83, 6120 AB, Born, Netherlands
Tel.: (31) 852087766
Web Site: https://www.blackanddecker.nl
Sales Range: $25-49.9 Million
Emp.: 40
Marketing & Sales of Tools
N.A.I.C.S.: 444140

Subsidiary (Non-US):

Black & Decker Czech SRO   **(3)**
Trmice 873, 400 04, Trmice, Czech Republic
Tel.: (420) 47 531 9111
Web Site: https://www.blackanddecker-usti.cz
Sales & Marketing of Tools
N.A.I.C.S.: 444140

Subsidiary (Non-US):

Black & Decker (Overseas) AG   **(2)**
Staedtle 36, Postfach 34709, 9490, Vaduz,
Liechtenstein
Tel.: (423) 2391010
Web Site: http://www.blackanddecker.ae
Sales Range: $125-149.9 Million
Sales & Marketing of Tools
N.A.I.C.S.: 444140

Black & Decker (Thailand)
Limited   **(2)**
No 29 Building Bangkok Business Center
28th Floor Unit 2802, Sukhumvit 63 Road
Khlong Tan Nuea Wattana, Bangkok,
10110, Thailand
Tel.: (66) 25088765
Sales Range: $900-999.9 Million
Industrial Equipment Whlsr
N.A.I.C.S.: 333414

Black & Decker AG   **(2)**
Sarverland 1 B, 2600, Glostrup, Denmark
Tel.: (45) 70201530
Web Site: http://www.blackanddecker.com
Sales Range: $25-49.9 Million
Emp.: 21
Marketing of Hardware
N.A.I.C.S.: 444140

Black & Decker Aktiebolag   **(2)**
Flojelbergsgatam 1C, Molndal, 431 35,
Sweden
Tel.: (46) 31686000
Web Site: http://www.sbdinc.com
Sales Range: $50-74.9 Million
Emp.: 50
Sale & Marketing of Tools
N.A.I.C.S.: 444140
Steen Lindbo *(Mng Dir)*

Black & Decker Argentina S.A.   **(2)**
Marcos Sastre 1998 Ricardo Rojas, Partido
de Tigre, Buenos Aires, B1610CRJ, Argentina
Tel.: (54) 114 726 4400
Web Site: https://ar.blackanddecker.global
Construction & DIY Tools & Equipment;
Home Cleaning & Small Appliances;Industrial Services
N.A.I.C.S.: 425120

Black & Decker Asia Pacific Pte.
Ltd.   **(2)**
Woodlands East Industrial Estate 25 Senoko South Road, Singapore, 758081, Singapore
Tel.: (65) 67522001
Web Site:
    http://www.stanleyblackanddecker.com
Sales Range: $25-49.9 Million
Emp.: 15
Sales & Marketing of Tools
N.A.I.C.S.: 444140

Subsidiary (Non-US):

Black & Decker GmbH   **(2)**
Black And Decker Strasse 40, 65510, Id-

stein, Germany
Tel.: (49) 6126210
Web Site: https://www.blackanddecker.de
Sales Range: $50-74.9 Million
Emp.: 120
Mfr of Tools
N.A.I.C.S.: 332216

Black & Decker Iberica S.Com por
A.   **(2)**
Ctra M-300, Alcala de Henares, Alcala de
Henares, 28802, Spain
Tel.: (34) 918835730
Web Site: http://www.emhart.com
Sales Range: $50-74.9 Million
Emp.: 25
Industrial Equipment Mfr
N.A.I.C.S.: 333413

Black & Decker International   **(2)**
210 Bath Rd, Slough, SL1 3YD, Berkshire,
United Kingdom
Tel.: (44) 1753511234
Web Site:
    http://www.stanleyblackanddecker.com
Sales Range: $150-199.9 Million
Emp.: 350
Service & Repairs; Plant at Spennymoor
N.A.I.C.S.: 551112

Black & Decker Italy S.p.A.   **(2)**
Via Burno Buozzi 1, 6073, Corciano, Ellera,
Italy
Tel.: (39) 07551891
Web Site: http://www.blackanddecker.com
Sales Range: $100-124.9 Million
Emp.: 250
Mfr of Tools
N.A.I.C.S.: 332216

Black & Decker Macao   **(2)**
Macao Chamber of Commerce, 175 Rua
Sangia, Macau, China (Macau)
Tel.: (853) 780633
Sales Range: $1-4.9 Billion
Electronic Parts Mfr
N.A.I.C.S.: 334220

Subsidiary (Domestic):

Black & Decker Puerto Rico   **(2)**
PO Box 574, Caguas, PR 00726
Tel.: (507) 360-5700
Web Site:
    http://www.stanleyblackdecker.com
Sales Range: $10-24.9 Million
Emp.: 22
Tool Mfr
N.A.I.C.S.: 333991

Subsidiary (Non-US):

Black & Decker Suzhou Power Tools
Co. Ltd.   **(2)**
200 Suzhou Middle Road, Suzhou Industrial
Park, Suzhou, 215021, China
Tel.: (86) 51262581818
Web Site:
    http://www.stanleyblackanddecker.com
Sales Range: $125-149.9 Million
Emp.: 5,000
Sales & Marketing of Tools
N.A.I.C.S.: 444140

Black & Decker de Colombia
S.A.   **(2)**
Carrera 85 D No 46A-65 BG 23, San Cayetano, Bogota, Distrito Capital, Colombia
Tel.: (57) 13288976
Web Site:
    http://www.co.blackanddecker.global
Sales Range: $50-74.9 Million
Sales & Marketing of Tools
N.A.I.C.S.: 444140

Black & Decker de Espana S.A.   **(2)**
C Bergueda number 1 - Edificio Muntadas,
office 6 - Parc de Negocis Mas Blau,
08820, El Prat de Llobregat, Barcelona,
Spain
Tel.: (34) 932201806
Web Site: https://www.blackanddecker.es
Sales Range: $50-74.9 Million
Emp.: 60
Mfr of Tools
N.A.I.C.S.: 332216

Black & Decker do Brasil Ltda.   **(2)**
Rod BR 050 S N Km 167 Lote 5 Parte
Quadra 1, Uberaba, 38064-750, MG, Brazil

Tel.: (55) 3433183018
Web Site:
    http://www.blackanddecker.com.br
Sales Range: $500-549.9 Million
Emp.: 1,200
Mfr of Household Products
N.A.I.C.S.: 314120

Black and Decker, S.A. de C.V.   **(2)**
Antonio Dovali Jaime No 70 Torre B Piso 9,
Santa Fe Alvaro Obregon, 01210, Mexico,
Mexico
Tel.: (52) 5553267100
Hand Tool Accessory & Equipment Distr
N.A.I.C.S.: 423710

Maquinas y Herramientas Black &
Decker de Chile S.A.   **(2)**
Avenida Presidente Eduardo Frei Montalva
6001 Edificio 67 Conchali, Santiago, Chile
Tel.: (56) 226871700
Web Site: http://www.blackanddecker.cl
Sales Range: $125-149.9 Million
Tools Marketing
N.A.I.C.S.: 444140

The Farmington River Power
Company   **(1)**
347 Rainbow Rd, Windsor, CT 06095
Tel.: (860) 688-2156
Sales Range: $25-49.9 Million
Emp.: 2
Electric Power Distribution Services
N.A.I.C.S.: 221122
Kraig Moran *(Gen Mgr)*

The Stanley Works Pty. Ltd.   **(1)**
810 Whitehorse Road, Box Hill, 3128, VIC,
Australia
Tel.: (61) 800338002
Web Site: http://www.stanleytools.com.au
Hand Tools, Power Tools & Related Accessories
N.A.I.C.S.: 333991

Tong Lung Metal Industry Co.,
Ltd.   **(1)**
No 82 Zhonghua Rd Minxiong Township,
Chiayi, 621, Taiwan
Tel.: (886) 52918168
Web Site: https://www.ezset.com.tw
Sales Range: $150-199.9 Million
Emp.: 800
Door Locksets Mfr
N.A.I.C.S.: 337215

Troy-Bilt LLC   **(1)**
PO Box 368022, Cleveland, OH 44136
Web Site: https://www.troybilt.com
Agriculture Equipment Mfr & Distr
N.A.I.C.S.: 333111

Visiocom International Pte Ltd   **(1)**
61 Kaki Bukit Ave 1 04-09 Shun Li Industrial Park, Singapore, 417943, Singapore
Tel.: (65) 67484862
Web Site: http://www.visiocom-intl.com
Security Systems Integration Services
N.A.I.C.S.: 561621

ZAG USA, Inc.   **(1)**
110 W 53rd St, Brooklyn, NY 11232
Tel.: (718) 906-5633
Emp.: 25
Medical Equipment Whslr
N.A.I.C.S.: 423450
Abe Gluck *(Gen Mgr)*

STAR ALLIANCE INTERNATIONAL CORP.
2900 W Sahara Ave Ste 800, Las
Vegas, NV 89102   **NV**
Tel.: (310) 571-0020
Web Site:
    https://staralliancemines.com
Year Founded: 2014
STAL—(OTCIQ)
Assets: $994,423
Liabilities: $2,196,808
Net Worth: ($1,202,385)
Earnings: ($10,489,394)
Emp.: 3
Fiscal Year-end: 06/30/23
Decorative Products & Services &
Travel & Tourism Services
N.A.I.C.S.: 541490

Richard Carey *(Founder & Chm)*
Themis Glatman *(Treas & Asst Sec)*
Fernando Godina *(Exec VP)*
Anthony L. Anish *(CEO, CFO & Sec)*

STAR BUFFET, INC.
2501 N Hayden Rd Ste 103, Scottsdale, AZ 85257
Tel.: (480) 425-0454   DE
Web Site: http://www.starbuffet.com
Year Founded: 1997
STRZ—(OTCIQ)
Rev.: $26,036,000
Assets: $6,425,000
Liabilities: $9,878,000
Net Worth: ($3,453,000)
Earnings: ($541,000)
Emp.: 815
Fiscal Year-end: 01/28/19
Restaurant Owner & Operator
N.A.I.C.S.: 722511
Robert E. Wheaton *(Chm, Pres & CEO)*
Ronald E. Dowdy *(Treas, Sec & Controller)*

STAR EQUITY HOLDINGS, INC.
53 Forest Ave Ste 101, Old Greenwich, CT 06870
Tel.: (203) 489-9500   DE
Web Site: https://www.starequity.com
Year Founded: 1985
STRR—(NASDAQ)
Rev.: $112,151,000
Assets: $73,302,000
Liabilities: $31,547,000
Net Worth: $41,755,000
Earnings: ($7,168,000)
Emp.: 413
Fiscal Year-end: 12/31/22
Nuclear Medicine Imaging Equipment Mfr
N.A.I.C.S.: 334510
Jeffrey E. Eberwein *(Chm)*
Richard Kenneth Coleman Jr. *(CEO)*
David James Noble *(CFO)*
Shawn Miles *(Sr VP-Finance & Strategy)*
Hannah Bible *(Chief Legal Officer & Sec)*

Subsidiaries:

ATRM Holdings, Inc.   **(1)**
5215 Gershwin Avenue N, Oakdale, MN 55128
Tel.: (651) 704-1800
Web Site: http://www.atrmholdings.com
Rev.: $34,477,000
Assets: $11,578,000
Liabilities: $21,297,000
Net Worth: ($9,719,000)
Earnings: ($5,232,000)
Emp.: 144
Fiscal Year-end: 12/31/2018
Electromechanical Handlers & Testers for Semiconductor Industry
N.A.I.C.S.: 334514
Daniel M. Koch *(Pres & CEO)*

Subsidiary (Domestic):

EdgeBuilder, Inc.   **(2)**
5215 Gershwin Ave N, Oakdale, MN 55128
Tel.: (651) 770-9071
Web Site:
   http://www.edgebuilderwallpanels.com
Wood Panel Mfr & Whslr
N.A.I.C.S.: 321999

Glenbrook Building Supply, Inc.   **(2)**
5215 Gershwin Ave N, Oakdale, MN 55128
Tel.: (651) 770-9071
Web Site: https://www.glenbrooklumber.com
Lumber & Other Building Products Whslr
N.A.I.C.S.: 423310

KBS Builders, Inc.   **(2)**
300 Park St, South Paris, ME 04281
Tel.: (207) 739-2400
Web Site: https://www.kbsbuildersinc.com

Emp.: 170
Commercial & Institutional Building Construction Services
N.A.I.C.S.: 236220

Digirad Imaging Solutions, Inc.   **(1)**
13100 Gregg St Ste A, Poway, CA 92064
Web Site: https://www.digirad.com
Sales Range: $25-49.9 Million
Emp.: 130
Electromedical & Electrotherapeutic Apparatus Mfr
N.A.I.C.S.: 334510

Project Rendezvous Holding Corporation   **(1)**
1048 Industrial Ct, Suwanee, GA 30024
Tel.: (858) 726-1600
Holding Company
N.A.I.C.S.: 551112

STAR FINANCIAL GROUP INC.
215 W Main St, Fort Wayne, IN 46802
Tel.: (260) 467-5630
Web Site:
   https://www.starfinancial.com
Year Founded: 1943
SFIGA—(OTCIQ)
Rev.: $116,625,000
Assets: $2,104,773,000
Liabilities: $1,868,074,000
Net Worth: $236,699,000
Earnings: $24,770,000
Fiscal Year-end: 12/31/19
Bank Holding Company
N.A.I.C.S.: 551111
James C. Marcuccilli *(Chm-STAR Financial Bank)*

Subsidiaries:

STAR Financial Bank   **(1)**
735 Main St, Anderson, IN 46015
Tel.: (765) 622-4100
Web Site: http://www.starfinancial.com
Sales Range: $50-74.9 Million
Emp.: 100
State Commercial Banks
N.A.I.C.S.: 522110
Brett Carey *(Pres-Marion)*
Trent Dowling *(Reg Pres-Comml Banking)*

STAR Wealth Management Inc **(1)**
6240 Bluffton Rd, Fort Wayne, IN 46809
Tel.: (260) 479-2670
Web Site: http://www.starfinancial.com
Emp.: 175
Trusts, Nec
N.A.I.C.S.: 523991

STAR GOLD CORP.
1875 N Lakewood Dr Ste 200, Coeur D'Alene, ID 83814
Tel.: (208) 664-5066   NV
Web Site:
   https://www.stargoldcorp.com
Year Founded: 2006
SRGZ—(OTCQB)
Rev.: $3
Assets: $686,541
Liabilities: $743,910
Net Worth: ($57,369)
Earnings: ($237,711)
Fiscal Year-end: 04/30/24
Mineral Exploration Services
N.A.I.C.S.: 213114
Lindsay Edward Gorrill *(Chm)*
Kelly J. Stopher *(CFO, Treas & Sec)*
David Segelov *(Pres)*

STAR GROUP, L.P.
9 W Broad St Ste 310, Stamford, CT 06902
Tel.: (203) 328-7310   DE
Web Site:
   https://www.stargrouplp.com
SGU—(NYSE)
Rev.: $1,766,099,000
Assets: $939,611,000
Liabilities: $675,718,000
Net Worth: $263,893,000

Earnings: $35,223,000
Emp.: 3,039
Fiscal Year-end: 09/30/24
Home Heating Fuel Distr
N.A.I.C.S.: 457210
Jeffrey M. Woosnam *(Pres & CEO)*

Subsidiaries:

A.P. Woodson Co.   **(1)**
2187 Atlantic St, Stamford, CT 06902   **(100%)**
Tel.: (203) 328-7300
Sales Range: $75-99.9 Million
Emp.: 120
Home Energy Distribution & Services
N.A.I.C.S.: 457210
Daniel P. Donovan *(Pres)*

Griffith Energy Services, Inc.   **(1)**
6996 Columbia Gateway Dr Ste 202, Columbia, MD 21046   **(100%)**
Tel.: (443) 430-8882
Web Site:
   https://www.griffithenergyservices.com
Sales Range: $75-99.9 Million
Emp.: 1,500
Fuel Distribution & Installation & Maintenance of Heating, Ventilating & Air Conditioning Equipment
N.A.I.C.S.: 457210

Subsidiary (Domestic):

Carl King Inc.   **(2)**
1400 E Lebanon Rd, Dover, DE 19901-5833   **(100%)**
Tel.: (302) 697-3251
Web Site: http://www.griffithoil.com
Sales Range: $10-24.9 Million
Emp.: 50
Petroleum Product Whslr
N.A.I.C.S.: 457210
Randy Groft *(Pres)*

Hoffman Fuel Company of Stamford   **(1)**
56 Quarry Rd Ste 2, Trumbull, CT 06611
Tel.: (203) 324-6148
Web Site: http://www.hoffmanfue.com
Fuel Transportation Services
N.A.I.C.S.: 486910
Steve Goldman *(Pres & CEO)*

Meenan Holdings of New York, Inc.   **(1)**
520 Broadhollow Rd, Melville, NY 11747   **(100%)**
Tel.: (516) 809-2100
Web Site: http://www.meenan.com
Sales Range: $350-399.9 Million
Emp.: 800
Petroleum Product Whslr
N.A.I.C.S.: 457210

Subsidiary (Domestic):

Burke Fuel & Heating Co.   **(2)**
475 Commerce St, Hawthorne, NY 10532-1345   **(100%)**
Tel.: (914) 769-5050
Web Site: http://www.meenanlp.com
Sales Range: $100-124.9 Million
Emp.: 130
Home Heating Oil And Service
N.A.I.C.S.: 457210

Division (Domestic):

Christy-Halsey Meenan   **(2)**
65 Maple Ave, Chester, NJ 07930   **(100%)**
Tel.: (908) 879-5411
Web Site: http://meenanlp.com
Sales Range: $50-74.9 Million
Emp.: 14
Home Heating Oil & Service
N.A.I.C.S.: 457210

Meenan Holdings Love-Effron Division   **(2)**
47 Patrick Ln, Poughkeepsie, NY 12603
Tel.: (845) 452-2600
Web Site: http://www.loveeffron.com
Sales Range: $50-74.9 Million
Emp.: 75
Home Heating Oil & Service
N.A.I.C.S.: 457210
Erick Pope *(Gen Mgr)*
Ron Mustello *(Gen Mgr)*

Subsidiary (Domestic):

Meenan Oil Co., LP   **(2)**
3020 Burns Ave, Wantagh, NY 11793   **(100%)**
Tel.: (516) 783-1000
Web Site: https://www.meenan.com
Sales Range: $75-99.9 Million
Emp.: 100
Home Fuel Oil Distribution & Security Services
N.A.I.C.S.: 213112

Division (Domestic):

Meenan Oil Pennsylvania Division   **(3)**
8301 Landsdowne Ave, Upper Darby, PA 19082   **(100%)**
Tel.: (610) 789-4200
Web Site: http://www.meenanoil.com
Sales Range: $75-99.9 Million
Home Heating Oil & Service
N.A.I.C.S.: 457210

Ortep of Pennsylvania Inc.   **(1)**
6330 Farm Bureau Rd, Allentown, PA 18106
Tel.: (215) 942-5075
Web Site: http://www.petro.com
Heating Oil, Propane, Plumbing & Air Conditioning Services & Repairs
N.A.I.C.S.: 457210

Petro   **(1)**
48 Harbor Park Dr, Port Washington, NY 11050   **(100%)**
Tel.: (516) 686-2000
Sales Range: $75-99.9 Million
Emp.: 100
Fuel Oil Dealers
N.A.I.C.S.: 457210

Petro Fuel Co. Inc.   **(1)**
4025 Pottsville Pike, Reading, PA 19605-1201   **(100%)**
Tel.: (610) 929-4781
Web Site: http://www.petro.com
Sales Range: $50-74.9 Million
Emp.: 70
Fuel Oil Dealers
N.A.I.C.S.: 457210

Petro Holdings, Inc.   **(1)**
2187 Atlantic St, Stamford, CT 06902   **(100%)**
Tel.: (203) 325-5400
Web Site: http://www.stargas.com
Sales Range: $75-99.9 Million
Emp.: 40
Home Energy Distr & Services
N.A.I.C.S.: 457210

Subsidiary (Domestic):

Champion Energy Corporation   **(2)**
1 Radissin Plz Ste 801, New Rochelle, NY 10801
Tel.: (914) 576-6190
Web Site: http://www.championenergy.com
Heating Fuel Distr; Heating, Cooling & Plumbing Equipment Installation Services
N.A.I.C.S.: 457210

Subsidiary (Domestic):

C. Hoffberger Company Inc.   **(3)**
1400 Seadock St, Baltimore, MD 21226
Tel.: (410) 355-0665
Web Site: http://www.choffbergerfuel.com
Sales Range: $10-24.9 Million
Emp.: 60
Fuel Oil Distr
N.A.I.C.S.: 457210

Champion Oil Company Inc.   **(3)**
9 W Broad st 10, Stamford, NY 06902
Tel.: (914) 576-6190
Web Site: http://www.championenergy.com
Sales Range: $10-24.9 Million
Emp.: 12
Petroleum Products
N.A.I.C.S.: 424720

Hoffman Fuel Company of Bridgeport Inc.   **(3)**
56 Quarry Rd, Trumbull, CT 06611-4816   **(100%)**
Tel.: (203) 373-5999
Web Site: http://www.hoffmanfuel.com

Star Group, L.P.—(Continued)
Sales Range: $10-24.9 Million
Emp.: 110
Provider of Fuel Oil
N.A.I.C.S.: 457210
Peter J. Carini (Chm)

Hoffman Fuel Company of Danbury Inc. (3)
170 White St, Danbury, CT 06810-6812 **(100%)**
Tel.: (203) 744-1010
Web Site: https://www.hoffmanfuel.com
Sales Range: $10-24.9 Million
Emp.: 45
Provider of Fuel Oil
N.A.I.C.S.: 457210

J.J. Skelton Oil Company Inc. (3)
40 W Manoa Rd, Havertown, PA 19083-3617
Tel.: (610) 525-3604
Sales Range: $10-24.9 Million
Emp.: 15
Provider Of Fuel Oil
N.A.I.C.S.: 457210
Peter Carini (Chm)

Rye Fuel Company Inc. (3)
225 Greenleaf Ave, Portsmouth, NH 03840
Tel.: (603) 964-8900
Web Site: http://www.ryefuel.com
Sales Range: $10-24.9 Million
Emp.: 20
Provider of Fuel Oil
N.A.I.C.S.: 457210

Subsidiary (Domestic):

Meenan Oil Co., Inc. (2)
3020 Burns Ave, Wantagh, NY 11793
Tel.: (516) 783-1000
Web Site: http://www.meenan.com
Emp.: 40
Heating Oil & Emergency Service Provider
N.A.I.C.S.: 457210

Petroleum Heat & Power Co. Inc. (2)
9 W Broas St 3rd fl, Stamford, CT 06902 **(100%)**
Tel.: (203) 325-5400
Web Site: https://www.petro.com
Sales Range: $50-74.9 Million
Fuel Oil Dealers
N.A.I.C.S.: 457210

Subsidiary (Domestic):

Richland Partners LLC (3)
669 E Ross St, Lancaster, PA 17602
Tel.: (717) 653-1411
Web Site: https://www.lefflerenergy.com
Petroleum Products Retailer & Distr; Heat Pumps, Air Conditioning & Hot Water Heaters Installation & Service
N.A.I.C.S.: 457210

Petro Oil (1)
8900 Citation Rd, Essex, MD 21221
Tel.: (301) 735-4028
Web Site: http://www.petro.com
Sales Range: $50-74.9 Million
Emp.: 50
Fuel Oil Dealers
N.A.I.C.S.: 457210

Petro Oil Inc. (1)
520 Broadhollow Rd Ste 200, Melville, NY 11747 **(100%)**
Tel.: (516) 686-1600
Web Site: http://www.petrooil.com
Sales Range: $25-49.9 Million
Emp.: 20
Fuel Oil Dealers
N.A.I.C.S.: 457210
David Dates (Gen Mgr)

Petroleum Heat & Power Co. (1)
2187 Atlantic St, Stamford, CT 06902 **(100%)**
Tel.: (203) 328-7300
Web Site: http://www.petro.com
Sales Range: $50-74.9 Million
Emp.: 40
Provider of Home Heating Oil
N.A.I.C.S.: 457210

RegionOil Plumbing, Heating & Cooling Co., Inc. (1)

15 Rich Poline, Dover, NJ 07801 **(100%)**
Tel.: (973) 366-3100
Web Site: http://www.meenanoil.com
Sales Range: $50-74.9 Million
Emp.: 50
Home Energy Distributor & Services Provider
N.A.I.C.S.: 457210

Subsidiaries:

Star Gas Corporation (1)
2187 Atlantic St, Stamford, CT 06902-6880
Tel.: (203) 328-7300
Sales Range: $50-74.9 Million
Emp.: 35
Management Services
N.A.I.C.S.: 457210
Daniel Donovan (Pres & CEO)

Star/Petro, Inc. (1)
2187 Atlantic St, Stamford, CT 06902 **(100%)**
Tel.: (203) 328-7300
Sales Range: $75-99.9 Million
Home Energy Distributor & Services Provider
N.A.I.C.S.: 457210
Daniel Donovan (Pres)

STAR HOLDINGS, INC.
1114 Avenue of the Americas 39th Fl, New York, NY 10036
Tel.: (212) 930-9400   MD
Web Site:
  https://www.starholdingsco.com
Year Founded: 2022
STHO—(NASDAQ)
Holding Company
N.A.I.C.S.: 551112
Jay Sugarman (CEO)
Brett Asnas (CFO)

STAR JETS INTERNATIONAL, INC.
135 E 57th St 16th Fl, New York, NY 10022
Tel.: (917) 331-5152   FL
Web Site: https://private-jet-charter-flight.com
Year Founded: 1998
JETR—(OTCIQ)
Oil Transportation Services
N.A.I.C.S.: 481111
Richard Sitomer (Founder & CEO)

STAR MOUNTAIN RESOURCES, INC.
605 W Knox Rd Ste 202, Tempe, AZ 85284
Tel.: (844) 443-7677   NV
Web Site:
  http://www.starmountainresources.com
Year Founded: 2009
SMRS—(OTCIQ)
Metal Mining
N.A.I.C.S.: 212290
Joseph Hamilton Marchal (Chm & CEO)
Mark Osterberg (Pres & COO)
John Heinzig (Mgr-Ops)

STAR NUTRITION, INC.
3120 Thorntree Dr, Chico, CA 92973
Tel.: (530) 345-5808   DE
STAU—(OTCIQ)
Financial Investment Services
N.A.I.C.S.: 523999
Jackson Corley (Founder & CEO)

STARBUCKS CORPORATION
2401 Utah Ave S Ste, Seattle, WA 98134
Tel.: (206) 318-7100   WA
Web Site: https://www.starbucks.com
Year Founded: 1971
SBUX—(NASDAQ)
Rev.: $36,176,200,000
Assets: $31,339,300,000
Liabilities: $38,780,900,000
Net Worth: ($7,441,600,000)

Earnings: $3,760,900,000
Emp.: 361,000
Fiscal Year-end: 09/29/24
Specialty Coffee Roaster & Retailer
N.A.I.C.S.: 311920
Howard D. Schultz (Founder)
Andy Adams (Sr VP-Store Dev)
Michelle Burns (Exec VP-Global Coffee, Tea & Cocoa)
George Dowdie (Exec VP-Supply Chain-Global)
Scott Keller (Sr VP-Store Dev & Design)
Janet Landers (Sr VP-Bus Tech)
Denise Nelsen (Sr VP-Ops)
Rachel Ruggeri (CFO, Principal Acctg Officer & Exec VP)
Kelly Bengston (Chief Procurement Officer-Sourcing-Global & Sr VP)
Jen Frisch (Sr VP-Partner Resources, Retail, Licensed Stores & Ops Svcs)
Mark Ring (Sr VP-Licensed Stores-Latin America)
Gina Woods (Exec VP-Pub Affairs & Social Impact)
Brady Brewer (CMO & Exec VP)
Takafumi Minaguchi (CEO-Japan)
Belinda Wong (Chm-China)
Jill L. Walker (Sr VP-Corp Financial Svcs)
Shannon Garcia (Sr VP-Ops)
Duncan Moir (Pres-Europe, Middle East & Africa)
Tyson Avery (Chief Ethics & Compliance Officer, Sr VP & Deputy Gen Counsel)
Lori Digulla (Sr VP & Gen Mgr-Canada)
Kyndra Russell (Sr VP-Mktg)
Chris Tarrant (Sr VP-Retail Store Dev & Design)
Katie Young (Sr VP-Dev & Growth-Global)
Ted Adams (Sr VP-Govt Affairs, Pub Policy & Community Impact)
Dennis Brockman (Chief Inclusion & Diversity Officer & Sr VP)
Lisa Erdely (Sr VP-Fin-Americas)
Jennifer Kraft (Sec, Sr VP & Deputy Gen Counsel)
Anju Rao (Sr VP-Global Food Safety, Quality & Regulatory)
Debbie Stroud (Sr VP-Ops)
Zabrina M. Jenkins (CEO)
Natarajan Venkatakrishnan (Sr VP)
Brooke O'Berry (Sr VP)
Jon Liechty (Sr VP)
Deb Hall Lefevre (CTO)
Aswin Krishnan (Sr VP)
Sara Kelly (Chief Partner Officer)
Emmy Kan (Pres)
Aranthan Jones II (Sr VP-Global Comm & Public Affairs)
Brian R. Niccol (Chm & CEO)

Subsidiaries:

Bay Bread LLC (1)
241 E Harris Ave, South San Francisco, CA 94080
Tel.: (650) 866-4262
Web Site: http://www.laboulangebakery.com
Sales Range: $10-24.9 Million
Cafe & Retail Bakeries Operator
N.A.I.C.S.: 311811
Pascal Rigo (Gen Mgr)

Princi UK Limited (1)
135 Wardour Street, London, W1F 0UT, United Kingdom
Tel.: (44) 2074788888
Web Site: http://www.princi.com
Specialty Foods Distr
N.A.I.C.S.: 445298

Qingdao American Starbucks Coffee Company Limited (1)
1F Sunshine Plaza 38 XianGang Middle Road, Shinan Fushan Bay Area, Qingdao, Shandong, China

Tel.: (86) 53286678766
Web Site:
  https://www.qingdaochinaguide.com
Beverage & Snacks Operator
N.A.I.C.S.: 722515

SCI Europe I, Inc. (1)
2401 Utah Ave S, Seattle, WA 98134-1436
Tel.: (206) 447-1575
Beverage Shops
N.A.I.C.S.: 722515

Seattle's Best Coffee LLC (1)
PO Box 3717, Seattle, WA 98124-8891
Tel.: (206) 624-8858
Web Site: http://www.seattlesbest.com
Beverage & Cafeteria Services
N.A.I.C.S.: 722515

Starbucks Coffee International, Inc. (1)
2401 Utah Ave S Stop S-LA1, Seattle, WA 98134-1436
Tel.: (206) 467-2766
Web Site: http://www.starbucks.com
Sales Range: $150-199.9 Million
Coffee Shops
N.A.I.C.S.: 722515

Subsidiary (Non-US):

Starbucks Brasil Comercio de Cafes Ltda. (2)
Av Roque Petroni Junior 1.089, Sao Paulo, 4707970, Brazil
Tel.: (55) 1151812108
Web Site: http://www.starbucks.com.br
Cafeteria Operator
N.A.I.C.S.: 722515

Starbucks Coffee Asia Pacific Limited (2)
12 A Floor Sun Hung Kai Center 30 Harbour Road, 30 Harbour Road, Wanchai, China (Hong Kong)
Tel.: (852) 22831111
Web Site: http://www.starbucks.com
Sales Range: $50-74.9 Million
Emp.: 140
Coffee Shops; Coffee & Tea Retail
N.A.I.C.S.: 722515
Jeffery J. Hansberry (Pres-China & Asia Pacific)

Subsidiary (Non-US):

Beijing Starbucks Coffee Company Ltd. (3)
1/F Kerry Center No 1 Guanghua Rd Chaoyang Dist, Beijing, 100020, China
Tel.: (86) 1065880503
Coffe & Tea Retailer
N.A.I.C.S.: 311920

Joint Venture (Non-US):

Berjaya Starbucks Coffee Company Sdn. Bhd. (3)
Lot 10-04 Level 10 West Wing Berjaya Times Square No 1 Jalan Imbi, Federal Territory, 55100, Kuala Lumpur, Malaysia **(50%)**
Tel.: (60) 300808989
Web Site: http://www.starbucks.com.my
Cafeteria Operator
N.A.I.C.S.: 722515

Subsidiary (Non-US):

Starbucks (China) Company Limited (3)
24th Floor Xinyan Building B 65 Guiqing Road, Shanghai, 200233, China
Tel.: (86) 2160556988
Web Site: http://www.starbucks.com.cn
Cafeteria Operator
N.A.I.C.S.: 722515

Starbucks Coffee (Thailand) Co., Ltd. (3)
12th Floor Exchange Tower, 388 Sukhumvit Road Klongtoey, Bangkok, 10110, Thailand
Tel.: (66) 26636688
Coffee Shops; Coffee & Tea Retail
N.A.I.C.S.: 722515

Starbucks Coffee Company Australia Pty. Ltd. (3)
Unit 1 14 Rodborough Road, French's For-

est, 2086, NSW, Australia
Tel.: (61) 289778500
Web Site: http://www.starbucks.com.au
Coffee Shops
N.A.I.C.S.: 722515

Starbucks Coffee Japan, Ltd. (3)
Shin-Meguro Tokyu Building 2-25-2 Kamio-
saki, Shinagawa-ku, Tokyo, 141-0021,
Japan (79%)
Tel.: (81) 357455510
Web Site: http://www.starbucks.co.jp
Emp.: 4,786
Coffeeshop Operator
N.A.I.C.S.: 722515

Starbucks Coffee Singapore Pte.
Ltd. (3)
401 Commonwealth Drive #01, 04-05, Haw
Par Technocentre, Singapore, 149598, Sin-
gapore
Tel.: (65) 65137500
Web Site: http://www.starbucks.com.sg
Coffee Shops; Coffee & Tea Retail
N.A.I.C.S.: 722515

Subsidiary (Non-US):

Starbucks Coffee Canada, Inc. (2)
5140 Yonge St, Toronto, M2N 6L7, ON,
Canada
Tel.: (416) 223-9903
Web Site: http://www.starbucks.ca
Sales Range: $50-74.9 Million
Emp.: 200
Coffee Shops
N.A.I.C.S.: 722515

Starbucks Coffee EMEA BV (2)
Accraweg 19, PO Box 58081, 1047 HJ, Am-
sterdam, Netherlands
Tel.: (31) 204076400
Sales Range: $50-74.9 Million
Emp.: 150
Coffee Roaster & Sales
N.A.I.C.S.: 445298

Subsidiary (Non-US):

AmRest Coffee Sp. z o. o. (3)
Pl Grunwaldzki 25-27, Wroclaw, 50365,
Silesia, Poland
Tel.: (48) 713861000
Restaurant Operators
N.A.I.C.S.: 722511

AmRest Coffee s.r.o. (3)
Evropska 33/E, 160 00, Prague, Czech
Republic
Tel.: (420) 235013311
Web Site: http://www.starbuckscoffee.cz
Restaurant Operators
N.A.I.C.S.: 722511

Starbucks Coffee Austria GmbH (3)
Theobaldgasse 20, 1060, Vienna, Austria
Tel.: (43) 1336633
Web Site: http://www.starbucks.at
Cafeteria Operator
N.A.I.C.S.: 722515
Frank Wubben (Mng Dir)

Starbucks Coffee France S.A.S. (3)
38 rue des Jeuneurs, Paris, 75002, France
Tel.: (33) 144767300
Web Site: http://www.starbucks.fr
Cafeteria Operator
N.A.I.C.S.: 722515

Starbucks Coffee Holdings (UK)
Limited (3)
Building 4 Chiswick Park 566 Chiswick High
Road, London, W4 5YE, United Kingdom
Tel.: (44) 2088345050
Web Site: http://www.starbucks.co.uk
Holding Company; Coffee & Tea Wholesale
N.A.I.C.S.: 551112

Subsidiary (Domestic):

Starbucks Card Europe Limited (4)
Building 4 Chiswick Park 566 Chiswick High
Road, London, W45YEA , United Kingdom
Tel.: (44) 2088345000
Web Site: http://www.starbucks.co.uk
Cafeteria Operator
N.A.I.C.S.: 722515

Starbucks Coffee Company UK
Ltd. (4)
Building 4 Chiswick Park 566 Chiswick High

Road, London, W4 5YE, United Kingdom
Tel.: (44) 8452703310
Web Site: http://www.starbucks.co.uk
Coffee Roasting & Sales
N.A.I.C.S.: 311920

Subsidiary (Non-US):

Starbucks Coffee Switzerland
A.G. (3)
Industriestrasse 27, 8604, Volketswil, Swit-
zerland
Tel.: (41) 800220066
Web Site: https://www.starbucks.ch
Cafeteria Operator
N.A.I.C.S.: 722511

Starbucks Coffee Trading Company
S.A.R.L. (3)
Rue Du Grand-Chene 1, 1003, Lausanne,
Switzerland
Tel.: (41) 213212524
Web Site: http://www.starbucks.com
Purchase of Green Coffee
N.A.I.C.S.: 445298

Subsidiary (Domestic):

Starbucks Manufacturing EMEA
B.V. (3)
Acoraweg 19, 1047 HB, Amsterdam, Neth-
erlands
Tel.: (31) 204076500
Web Site: http://www.starbucks.com
Roasted Coffee Mfr
N.A.I.C.S.: 311920

Starbucks Coffee Switzerland
GmbH (1)
Industriestrasse 27, 8604, Volketswil, Swit-
zerland
Tel.: (41) 449471818
Specialty Foods Distr
N.A.I.C.S.: 445298

Starbucks EMEA Holdings Ltd (1)
Chiswick Park 566 Chiswick High Road,
London, W4 5YE, United Kingdom
Tel.: (44) 8452703310
Web Site: http://www.starbucks.co.uk
Holding Company
N.A.I.C.S.: 551112

Tata Starbucks Private Limited (1)
4th Floor New Excelsior Building Amrit Kes-
hav Nayak Marg, Fort, Mumbai, 400 001,
India
Tel.: (91) 2266113939
Web Site: https://www.starbucks.in
Beverage & Snacks Operator
N.A.I.C.S.: 722515

Teavana Holdings, Inc. (1)
3630 Peachtree Rd NE Ste 1480, Atlanta,
GA 30326
Tel.: (404) 995-8200
Web Site: http://www.teavana.com
Sales Range: $150-199.9 Million
Emp.: 473
Premium Loose-Leaf Teas, Authentic Artisa-
nal Teawares & Other Tea-Related Mer-
chandise Retailer
N.A.I.C.S.: 445298

Subsidiary (Non-US):

Teavana Canada, Inc. (2)
160-6455 MacLeod Trail SW, Calgary, T2H
0K8, AB, Canada
Tel.: (403) 251-0021
Web Site: http://www.teavana.com
Emp.: 10
Food Product Whslr
N.A.I.C.S.: 445298

Subsidiary (Domestic):

Teavana Corporation (2)
3630 Peachtree Rd NE Ste 1480, Atlanta,
GA 30326-1543
Tel.: (404) 995-8200
Web Site: http://www.teavana.com
Cafeteria Operator
N.A.I.C.S.: 722515

The New French Bakery, Inc. (1)
828 Kasota Ave SE, Minneapolis, MN
55414
Tel.: (612) 455-7500
Web Site: http://www.newfrenchbakery.com

Sales Range: $1-9.9 Million
Emp.: 37
Bakery Operator
N.A.I.C.S.: 311812

Torrefazione Italia LLC (1)
2401 Utah Ave S Ste 800, Seattle, WA
98134-1435
Tel.: (206) 447-1575
Tea & Coffee Beverage Shops
N.A.I.C.S.: 722515

STARCO BRANDS, INC.
250 26th St Ste 200, Santa Monica,
CA 90402
Tel.: (323) 266-7111   NV
Web Site:
   https://www.starcobrands.com
Year Founded: 2010
STCB—(OTCQB)
Rev.: $65,211,238
Assets: $83,345,528
Liabilities: $57,672,403
Net Worth: $25,673,125
Earnings: ($46,402,121)
Emp.: 36
Fiscal Year-end: 12/31/23
Direct Response Marketing
N.A.I.C.S.: 541890
Sanford Lang (Co-Founder)
Ross Sklar (Pres, CEO, Co-Founder
& Chm)
Darin Brown (COO & Sec)
Kevin Zaccardi (CFO-Soylent Nutri-
tion & Treas)

STARGAZE ENTERTAINMENT
GROUP, INC.
334 Cornilia St Ste 279, New York,
NY 12901
Tel.: (514) 862-7541
Web Site:
   http://www.stargazeentertainment
   group.com
Year Founded: 2015
STGZ—(OTCIQ)
Film & Video Production Services
N.A.I.C.S.: 512110
Tony Green (Pres & CEO)
Antonio Dutra (CEO & CFO)

STARLIGHT ENERGY CORP.
11757 W Ken Caryl Ave F-303, Little-
ton, CO 80127
Tel.: (303) 892-8830
Web Site:
   https://www.starlightenergy.us
SAEC—(OTCIQ)
Crude Petroleum Extraction Services
N.A.I.C.S.: 211120
Brian Bentley (Chm, CEO & CFO)
John DiNardo (Pres & Sec)

STARRY GROUP HOLDINGS,
INC.
38 Chauncy St Ste 200, Boston, MA
02111
Tel.: (617) 861-8300   DE
Web Site: https://investors.starry.com
Year Founded: 2021
STRY—(NYSE)
Emp.: 736
Holding Company
N.A.I.C.S.: 551112
Alex Moulle-Berteaux (COO)
Joseph Lipowski (CTO)
Virginia Lam Abrams (Exec VP)
William Lundregan (Chief Legal Offi-
cer)
Chaitanya Kanojia (CEO)

STARTECH LABS, INC.
244 Madison Ave, New York, NY
10016-2817
Tel.: (802) 255-4212   NV
Year Founded: 2013
LAAB—(OTCIQ)

Liabilities: $373,713
Net Worth: ($373,713)
Earnings: ($65,101)
Emp.: 1
Fiscal Year-end: 05/31/24
Mobile Apps
N.A.I.C.S.: 513210
Mark Kevin So (Pres, CEO & Sec)

STARWOOD PROPERTY
TRUST, INC.
591 W Putnam Ave, Greenwich, CT
06830
Tel.: (203) 422-7700   MD
Web Site:
   https://www.starwoodproperty
   trust.com
Year Founded: 2009
STWD—(NYSE)
Rev.: $2,049,908,000
Assets: $69,504,196,000
Liabilities: $62,481,214,000
Net Worth: $7,022,982,000
Earnings: $339,213,000
Emp.: 293
Fiscal Year-end: 12/31/23
Real Estate Investment Trust
N.A.I.C.S.: 525990
Rina Paniry (CFO, Chief Acctg Officer
& Treas)
Jeffrey G. Dishner (Pres & COO)
Jeffrey F. DiModica (Mng Dir)
Barry Stuart Sternlicht (Chm & CEO)
Denise Persau Tait (Co-Pres)
Sean Murdock (Co-Pres)
Zach Tanenbaum (Mng Dir)
Andrew Kail (Mng Dir)

Subsidiaries:

16th Street Partners, LLC (1)
1601 Washington Ave, Miami Beach, FL
33139
Tel.: (305) 672-9602
Real Estate Investment Services
N.A.I.C.S.: 525990

Diesel Ltd. (1)
Clarendon House 2 Church Street, Hamil-
ton, Bermuda
Tel.: (441) 4412951422
Real Estate Investment Services
N.A.I.C.S.: 525990

Hatfield Philips Deutschland
GmbH (1)
Wilhelm-Leuschner Strasse 78, 60329,
Frankfurt, Germany
Tel.: (49) 6971046300
Web Site: http://www.lnrpartnersalt.com
Emp.: 30
Investment Advisory Services
N.A.I.C.S.: 523940

Hatfield Spain, S.L. (1)
Calle De Alcala 61 3rd Floor, 28014, Ma-
drid, Spain
Tel.: (34) 917944668
Real Estate Debt Investment Services
N.A.I.C.S.: 522292

IMC Retail, LLC (1)
4602 Innovation Dr, Bloomington, IN 47402
Tel.: (812) 336-2362
Web Site: https://www.imc-retail.com
Metal Craft Product Retailer
N.A.I.C.S.: 459510
Ronald Davis (Founder)

LNR Partners, LLC (1)
2340 Collins Ave, Miami Beach, FL 33139
Tel.: (305) 695-5500
Web Site: https://www.lnrpartners.com
Emp.: 200
Real Estate Investment & Management
Services
N.A.I.C.S.: 531390
Job Warshaw (Mng Dir & Head-Special Ser-
vicing)

LNR Property LLC (1)
1601 Washington Ave Ste 800, Miami
Beach, FL 33139
Tel.: (305) 695-5500
Web Site: https://www.lnrproperty.com
Emp.: 300

Starwood Property Trust, Inc.—(Continued)

Real Estate Investment
N.A.I.C.S.: 531390

LNR Scotts Valley Hotel LLC (1)
6001 La Madrona Dr, Santa Cruz, CA
95060
Tel.: (831) 440-1000
Real Estate Investment Services
N.A.I.C.S.: 525990

**Novare National Settlement Service,
LLC** (1)
4400 Macarthur Blvd Ste 801, Irvine, CA
92602
Tel.: (714) 352-4088
Web Site: https://www.novarenss.com
Real Estate Services
N.A.I.C.S.: 531390

SPT WAH Wellington LLC (1)
2900 Drew St, Clearwater, FL 33759
Tel.: (727) 726-6888
Residential Building Operator
N.A.I.C.S.: 531110

Starwood Mortgage Capital LLC (1)
2340 Collins Ave, Miami Beach, FL 33139
Tel.: (305) 695-5800
Web Site:
   https://www.starwoodmortgagecapital.com
Commercial Real Estate Services
N.A.I.C.S.: 531210
Jeremy Beard (Sr VP-Capital Markets)
Gerry Santos (Sr VP-Loan Origination)
Matthew Cox (Sr VP-Credit Underwriting)
Leslie Fairbanks (Exec VP-Contract Fin)
Steve DeRose (Sr VP-Loan Origination)
Jaime Leonti (Sr VP-Credit Underwriting)
Jonathan Rosen (Chief Credit Officer)
Jamie Ruggiero (Sr VP-Loan Origination)
Michael Stone (Sr VP-Loan Origination)
Keith Thompson (Sr VP-Loan Origination)
Yorke Pharr (Sr VP-Credit Underwriting)
Steve Bartlett (Sr VP-Loan Origination)
Joe Duarte (Sr VP-)
Geoff Mucha (Sr VP-)

STATE STREET CORPORATION
1 Congress St, Boston, MA 02114-
2016
Tel.: (617) 786-3000   **MA**
Web Site:
   https://www.statestreet.com
Year Founded: 1792
STT—(NYSE)
Rev.: $11,945,000,000
Assets: $297,258,000,000
Liabilities: $273,459,000,000
Net Worth: $23,799,000,000
Earnings: $1,821,000,000
Emp.: 46,000
Fiscal Year-end: 12/31/23
Financial Holding Company
N.A.I.C.S.: 551111
Eric W. Aboaf (Vice Chm & CFO)
John Plansky (Exec VP & Head-
Alpha)
Elizabeth M. Schaefer (Chief Acctg
Officer, Sr VP & Deputy Controller)
Ilene Fiszel Bieler (COO-Global Mar-
kets & Global Credit Fin, Exec VP &
Head-IR-Global)
Andrew J. Erickson (Chief Productiv-
ity Officer, Exec VP & Head-Intl Bus)
Kathryn M. Horgan (Chief HR & Citi-
zenship Officer & Exec VP)
Donna M. Milrod (Chief Product Offi-
cer & Exec VP)
Aunoy Banerjee (Exec VP & Head-
Corp Svcs & Investments)
Todd M. Gershkowitz (Exec VP &
Head-Global Total Rewards & HR
Shared Svcs)
Spiros Giannaros (Exec VP)
Francisco Aristeguieta (CEO-
Institutional Svcs & Exec VP)
Paul Fleming (Exec VP & Head-
Alternatives Segment-Global)
Michael Goonan (Exec VP)

Michael L. Richards (Chief Admin
Officer & Exec VP)
Jessica Donohue (Head-Global In-
vestment Insights, Sustainability, and
Impact)
Dan Farley (CIO-Investment Solu-
tions Grp & Exec VP)
Lori Heinel (Exec VP)
Elizabeth Joyce (Chief Information
Security Officer & Exec VP)
Mark R. Keating (CFO-Investment
Svcs & Exec VP)
Julia McCarthy (Exec VP & Head-
Client Experience)
Yvette Hollingsworth Clark (Chief
Compliance Officer-Global & Exec
VP)
Christian Bongiovanni (Head-
Insurance-Europe, Middle East & Af-
rica)
Brenda Tsai (CMO & Exec VP)
Brenda K. Tsai (CMO)
Yvette Hollingsworth Clark (Chief
Compliance Officer)
Matt Daly (Exec VP)
Kem Danner (Head)
Kimberly DeTrask (Treas)
Michael Knowling (Exec VP)
Marcia Rothschild (Head)
Paul J. Selian (Head)
John Slyconish (Exec VP)
Mostapha Tahiri (COO)
Sarah Timby (CIO)
Gino L. Timperio (Head)
Clair Williams (Head)
K. Bradford Hu (Chief Risk Officer)
Mahi Dontamsetti (Chief Tech Risk
Officer)
Ann Fogarty (Exec VP)
Tadhg Young (Head)
Joerg Ambrosius (Chief Comml Offi-
cer & Exec VP)
Mark Shelton (Gen Counsel & Exec
VP)
Ronald Philip O'Hanley (Chm, Pres &
CEO)

Subsidiaries:

CF Global Trading, LLC (1)
527 Madison Ave 18th Fl, New York, NY
10022
Tel.: (212) 888-4711
Web Site: http://www.cfglobal.com
Secondary Market Financing
N.A.I.C.S.: 522299
Scott W. Chace (Co-Founder & CEO)

Charles River Systems, Inc. (1)
700 District Ave, Burlington, MA 01803
Tel.: (781) 238-0099
Web Site: https://www.crd.com
Emp.: 1,000
Investment Management Service
N.A.I.C.S.: 523940
Spiros Giannaros (Pres & CEO)
Randy Bullard (Dir-Wealth Mgmt-Global)
Matt Daly (Chief Revenue Officer)
Andre Bouchard (Gen Counsel & Sr VP)
Cem Er (Product Dir-)
Dmitriy Ilyin (Mng Dir)
Dean Landis (Head-Global)
Erica McGillicuddy (VP-Human Resources)
Steven Milanowycz (Product Dir-)
Chris Russo (COO)
Nidhi Singh (Chief Product Officer)

Currenex, Inc. (1)
1230 Ave Of The Americas 18th Fl, New
York, NY 10020
Tel.: (212) 340-1780
Web Site: http://www.currenex.com
Sales Range: $100-124.9 Million
Emp.: 50
Online Foreign Exchange Trading Platform
Services
N.A.I.C.S.: 523150

FX Connect, LLC (1)
1 Congress St Ste 1, Boston, MA 02114-
2016
Web Site: https://www.fxconnect.com

Fund Management Services
N.A.I.C.S.: 523940

**International Fund Services (N.A.),
L.L.C.** (1)
1290 Avenue of the Americas Fl 10, New
York, NY 10104
Tel.: (212) 339-2700
Web Site: http://www.ifs.statestreet.com
Fund Management Services
N.A.I.C.S.: 523940

**Princeton Financial Systems,
LLC** (1)
600 College Rd E, Princeton, NJ 08540
Tel.: (609) 987-2400
Web Site: http://www.statestreet.com
Financial Software
N.A.I.C.S.: 513210

Pulse Trading, Inc. (1)
2 Liberty Sq 2nd Fl, Boston, MA 02109
Tel.: (617) 316-5620
Web Site: http://www.pulsetrading.com
Sales Range: $25-49.9 Million
Emp.: 40
Electronic Brokerage Services
N.A.I.C.S.: 523150

State Street Australia Ltd. (1)
120 Collins Street Level 5, Melbourne,
3000, VIC, Australia   **(100%)**
Tel.: (61) 282491100
Web Site: http://www.statestreet.com
Sales Range: $1-4.9 Billion
Investment Administration
N.A.I.C.S.: 523940

**State Street Bank & Trust
Company** (1)
Josiah Quincy Bldg 200 Newport Ave, North
Quincy, MA 02171
Tel.: (617) 786-3000
Web Site: http://www.statestreet.com
Sales Range: $650-699.9 Million
Investment
N.A.I.C.S.: 523940

Subsidiary (Domestic):

SSB Investments, Inc. (2)
225 Franklin St, Boston, MA 02116
Tel.: (617) 786-3000
Web Site: http://www.statestreet.com
Emp.: 4
Investment Management
N.A.I.C.S.: 523940

Representative Office (Non-US):

**State Street Bank & Trust Company -
Hong Kong** (2)
68/F Two International Finance Center 8
Finance Center, Central, China (Hong
Kong)
Tel.: (852) 28405388
Web Site: http://www.statestreet.com
Sales Range: $125-149.9 Million
Emp.: 300
Banking Services & Investment Administra-
tion
N.A.I.C.S.: 523991

**State Street Bank & Trust Company -
London** (2)
20 Churchill Place, London, E14 5HJ,
United Kingdom
Tel.: (44) 2033958000
Web Site: http://www.statestreet.com
Banking Services & Investment Administra-
tion
N.A.I.C.S.: 523991

**State Street Bank & Trust Company -
Seoul** (2)
Centre 1 67 Sooha-dong, Jung-gu, Seoul,
05439, Korea (South)
Tel.: (82) 237064500
Web Site: http://www.statestreetbank.com
Sales Range: $75-99.9 Million
Emp.: 30
Banking & Investment Services
N.A.I.C.S.: 523940

**State Street Bank & Trust Company -
Singapore** (2)
168 Robinson Road 33-01 Capital Tower,
Singapore, 068912, Singapore **(100%)**
Tel.: (65) 68267100
Web Site: http://www.statestreet.com

Sales Range: $75-99.9 Million
Emp.: 30
Banking & Investment Services
N.A.I.C.S.: 523940

**State Street Bank & Trust Company -
Taipei** (2)
207 Tun Hwa South Road Sect 2 19th
Floor, Taipei, 10675, Taiwan
Tel.: (886) 227351200
Web Site: http://www.statestreet.com
Investment Advisor
N.A.I.C.S.: 523940

**State Street Bank & Trust Company -
Tokyo** (2)
Toranomon Hills Mori Tower 25F Tora-
nomon 1-23-1, Minato-Ku, Tokyo, 105-6325,
Japan
Tel.: (81) 345307600
Web Site: http://www.statestreet.com
Sales Range: $25-49.9 Million
Emp.: 30
Foreign Exchange Services & Investment
Administration
N.A.I.C.S.: 523991

Subsidiary (Non-US):

**State Street Bank Europe
Limited** (2)
1 Royal Exchange Steps Royal Exchange,
London, EC3V 3LE, Canary Wharf, United
Kingdom   **(100%)**
Tel.: (44) 2033953530
Sales Range: $550-599.9 Million
Emp.: 1,000
Bank Holding Company
N.A.I.C.S.: 551111

Subsidiary (Non-US):

State Street Bank GmbH (3)
Brienner Strasse 59, 80333, Munich,
Germany   **(100%)**
Tel.: (49) 8955878100
Web Site: http://www.statestreet.de
Sales Range: $100-124.9 Million
Emp.: 250
Banking & Investment Services
N.A.I.C.S.: 522110

Branch (Non-US):

**State Street Bank GmbH - Brussels
Branch** (4)
Avenue Reine Astrid 92 4th Fl, La Hulpe,
B-1310, Belgium
Tel.: (32) 2 663 2036
Web Site: http://www.statestreet.com
Sales Range: $10-24.9 Million
Emp.: 50
Banking Services
N.A.I.C.S.: 522110

**State Street Bank GmbH - Zurich
Branch** (4)
Beethovenstrasse 19, 8027, Zurich, Swit-
zerland
Tel.: (41) 445605000
Web Site: http://www.statestreet.ch
Sales Range: $150-199.9 Million
Emp.: 120
Banking & Investment Services
N.A.I.C.S.: 523940

Subsidiary (Non-US):

**State Street Bank Luxembourg
S.A.** (3)
47-49 Avenue J F Kennedy, 1855, Luxem-
bourg, Luxembourg   **(100%)**
Tel.: (352) 4640101
Web Site: http://www.statestreet.lu
Sales Range: $450-499.9 Million
Emp.: 900
Banking Services & Investment Administra-
tion
N.A.I.C.S.: 523991

State Street Bank S.p.A. (3)
Via Ferrante Aporti 10, 20125, Milan, Italy
Tel.: (39) 0232117001
Portfolio Management Services
N.A.I.C.S.: 523940

State Street California, Inc. (1)
1001 Marina Vlg Pkwy 30rd Fl, Alameda,
CA 94501
Tel.: (510) 521-7111

Investments & Financial Services
N.A.I.C.S.: 522320

State Street Europe Limited (1)
20 Churchill Place Canary Wharf, London,
E14 5HJ, United Kingdom
Tel.: (44) 2033952500
Portfolio Management Services
N.A.I.C.S.: 523940
Rajen Shah *(Head-Global Markets EMEA)*

State Street Financial Services (1)
200 Clarendon St, Boston, MA 02116
Tel.: (617) 937-6700
Sales Range: $1-4.9 Billion
Emp.: 4,265
Bank Holding Company
N.A.I.C.S.: 551111

**State Street Fund Services Toronto,
Inc.** (1)
30 Adelaide Street East Suite 1100, To-
ronto, M5C 3G6, ON, Canada
Tel.: (416) 362-1100
Web Site: http://www.statestreet.ca
Sales Range: $1-4.9 Billion
Emp.: 700
Funds & Investment Services
N.A.I.C.S.: 523940

State Street Global Advisors, Inc. (1)
1 Iron St, Boston, MA 02210-1641
Tel.: (617) 786-3000
Web Site: https://www.ssga.com
Sales Range: $650-699.9 Million
Emp.: 2,300
Investment Advisor
N.A.I.C.S.: 523940

Subsidiary (Non-US):

State Street Global Advisors (2)
World Trade Center Torre Sur Avda Nueva
Tajamar 481 of 2102, Las Condes, San-
tiago, Chile (100%)
Tel.: (56) 23504200
Sales Range: $650-699.9 Million
Investment Services
N.A.I.C.S.: 523940

State Street Global Advisors AG (2)
Beethovenstrasse 19, 8027, Zurich,
Switzerland (100%)
Tel.: (41) 445605000
Web Site: http://www.ssga.com
Sales Range: $650-699.9 Million
Emp.: 8
Investment Services
N.A.I.C.S.: 523940

**State Street Global Advisors Asia
Limited** (2)
68/F Two International Finance Centre 8
Finance Street, Hong Kong, China (Hong
Kong)
Tel.: (852) 21030288
Web Site: http://www.ssga.com
Sales Range: $125-149.9 Million
Emp.: 100
Investment Advisor
N.A.I.C.S.: 523940

**State Street Global Advisors Australia
Ltd.** (2)
Level 15 420 George Street, Sydney, 2000,
NSW, Australia (100%)
Tel.: (61) 292407600
Web Site: http://www.ssga.com
Sales Range: $125-149.9 Million
Emp.: 85
Investment Advice
N.A.I.C.S.: 523940

**State Street Global Advisors
GmbH** (2)
Brienner Strasse 59, 80333, Munich,
Germany (100%)
Tel.: (49) 8955878100
Web Site: http://www.statestreet.de
Sales Range: $75-99.9 Million
Emp.: 15
Investment Services
N.A.I.C.S.: 523940

**State Street Global Advisors Ireland
Limited** (2)
78 Sir John Rogerson's Quay, Upper Hatch
Street, Dublin, 2, Ireland (100%)
Tel.: (353) 17763000

Web Site:
http://www.statestreetglobaladvisors.com
Asset Management Services
N.A.I.C.S.: 523999
Ann Prendergast *(Mng Dir)*

**State Street Global Advisors
Limited** (2)
20 Churchill Place, Canary Wharf, London,
E14 5HJ, United Kingdom (100%)
Tel.: (44) 2033957000
Investment Administration
N.A.I.C.S.: 523991
Steve Muzzlewhite *(Sr Mgr-Sls)*
Elliot Hentov *(Head-Policy & Res-Official
Institutions Grp)*
Altaf Kassam *(Head-Investment Strategy &
Res-Investment Solutions Grp-EMEA)*
Miles O'Connor *(Head-Institutional-EMEA)*
Cuan Coulter *(Head-EMEA)*
Cyrus Taraporavela *(Pres & CEO)*
Andrew Benton *(Sr Mng Dir & Head-
Institutional Bus)*
Amlan Roy *(Sr Mng Dir)*

**State Street Global Advisors
SA/NV** (2)
chaussee de 120 Terhulpensesteenweg, La
Hulpe, 1000, Belgium (100%)
Tel.: (32) 26632036
Web Site: http://www.ssga.statestr.com
Sales Range: $75-99.9 Million
Emp.: 30
Asset Management
N.A.I.C.S.: 523940

**State Street Global Advisors Singa-
pore Limited** (2)
168 Robinson Road, 33-01 Capital Tower,
Singapore, 68912, Singapore
Tel.: (65) 68267555
Web Site: http://www.ssga.com
Sales Range: $650-699.9 Million
Investment Services
N.A.I.C.S.: 523940

State Street Global Markets, LLC (1)
1 Lincoln St, Boston, MA 02111
Tel.: (617) 786-3000
Web Site: http://www.statestreet.com
Investment Advisory Services
N.A.I.C.S.: 523940

Subsidiary (Non-US):

SSGM International UK (2)
525 Ferry Road, Edinburgh, EH5 2AW,
United Kingdom
Tel.: (44) 1314792500
Financial Investment Services
N.A.I.C.S.: 523940

**State Street International Ireland
Limited** (1)
78 Sir John Rogerson's Quay, Dublin, Ire-
land
Tel.: (353) 17768000
Investment Management Service
N.A.I.C.S.: 523940
Tadhg Young *(CEO-Svcs Bus-Global)*

Subsidiary (Domestic):

**International Fund Services (Ireland)
Limited** (2)
78 Sir John Rogerson's Quay, Dublin, 2,
Ireland
Tel.: (353) 17768000
Emp.: 150
Investment Consulting Services
N.A.I.C.S.: 523999

**State Street Fund Services Ireland
LTD** (2)
78 Sir John Rogersons Quay, Dublin, Ire-
land
Tel.: (353) 17768000
Financial Services
N.A.I.C.S.: 523940

**State Street Massachusetts Securi-
ties Corporation** (1)
1 Lincoln St, Boston, MA 02111
Tel.: (617) 786-3000
Web Site: http://www.statestreet.com
Sales Range: $1-4.9 Billion
Security Brokers
N.A.I.C.S.: 523910

**State Street Trust Company
Canada** (1)

30 Adelaide Street East Suite 1100, To-
ronto, M5C 3G6, ON, Canada
Tel.: (416) 362-1100
Investment Management Service
N.A.I.C.S.: 523940

STATERA BIOPHARMA, INC.
2580 E Harmony Rd Ste 316, Fort
Collins, CO 80528 DE
Web Site:
https://www.staterabiopharma.com
Year Founded: 2003
CBLI—(NASDAQ)
Rev.: $1,487,036
Assets: $21,169,685
Liabilities: $22,676,453
Net Worth: ($1,506,768)
Earnings: ($101,850,818)
Emp.: 46
Fiscal Year-end: 12/31/21
Drug Discovery & Development Ser-
vices
N.A.I.C.S.: 541715
Christopher Zosh *(Exec VP-Fin)*
Michael K. Handley *(Chm, Pres &
CEO)*
Bob Buckheit *(CTO)*

STATSURE DIAGNOSTIC SYS-
TEMS, INC.
1333 E 9 St, Brooklyn, NY 11230
Tel.: (917) 417-4489
Web Site:
http://www.statsurediagnostics.com
Year Founded: 1991
SSUR—(OTCEM)
Surgical & Medical Instrument Mfr
N.A.I.C.S.: 339112
Mo Bodner *(CEO)*

STEEL CONNECT, INC.
590 Madison Ave 32nd Fl, New York,
NY 10022
Tel.: (914) 461-1276 DE
Web Site:
https://www.steelconnectinc.com
Year Founded: 1986
STCN—(NASDAQ)
Rev.: $174,109,000
Assets: $485,628,000
Liabilities: $93,708,000
Net Worth: $391,920,000
Earnings: $87,980,000
Emp.: 939
Fiscal Year-end: 07/31/24
Supply Chain Management & Market-
ing Distribution Solutions
N.A.I.C.S.: 541614
Glen M. Kassan *(Vice Chm)*
Ryan O'Herrin *(CFO)*
Gary W. Tankard *(Chief Acctg Officer)*

Subsidiaries:

@Ventures (1)
187 Ballardvale St, Wilmington, MA 01887
Tel.: (978) 658-8980
Web Site: http://www.ventures.com
Sales Range: $25-49.9 Million
Emp.: 2
Venture Capital
N.A.I.C.S.: 523910

ModusLink (Shanghai) Co. Ltd. (1)
Building New 2 No 52 FaSai Road,
Waigaoqiao Free Trade Zone, Shanghai,
200131, China
Tel.: (86) 2150485758
Supply Chain Management Solutions
N.A.I.C.S.: 541614

ModusLink Australia Pty Limited (1)
Unit 4 202/214 Milperra Rd, Milperra, 2214,
NSW, Australia
Tel.: (61) 292669001
Web Site: http://www.ocs.au.com
Sales Range: $10-24.9 Million
Emp.: 10
Software License Management Services
N.A.I.C.S.: 561499

ModusLink B.V. (1)

Laan Van De Leeuw 4, PO Box 501, 7324
BD, Apeldoorn, Netherlands
Tel.: (31) 555434422
Supply Chain Management & Marketing
Services
N.A.I.C.S.: 541613

ModusLink Corp. (1)
1601 Trapelo Rd Ste 170, Waltham, MA
02451
Tel.: (781) 663-5000
Web Site: http://www.moduslink.com
Sales Range: $650-699.9 Million
Computer Related Services
N.A.I.C.S.: 541519
Fawaz Khalil *(Pres & CEO)*
Cathy Venable *(CFO)*
John Heffernan *(COO)*
Krishna Kundur *(CIO)*
John Perry *(Sr VP)*
A. J. Wesseler *(Sr VP)*

Subsidiary (Non-US):

**ModusLink De Mexico, S.R.L. De
C.V.** (2)
Calle 1 No 1375 Nave 8, Zona Industrial,
Guadalajara, Jalisco, Mexico
Tel.: (52) 3333431500
Web Site: http://www.moduslink.com
Sales Range: $125-149.9 Million
Supply Chain Management
N.A.I.C.S.: 334112

ModusLink International (2)
11 Avenue Buffon, PO Box 6509, 45065,
Orleans, Cedex 2, France (100%)
Tel.: (33) 238494200
Web Site: http://www.moduslink.com
Sales Range: $25-49.9 Million
Emp.: 100
Supply Chain Management
N.A.I.C.S.: 334610

ModusLink International B.V. (2)
Wapenrustlaan 11-31, 7321 DL, Apeldoorn,
Netherlands (100%)
Tel.: (31) 555434422
Web Site: http://www.moduslink.com
Digital & Supply Chain Solutions
N.A.I.C.S.: 541519

**ModusLink International B.V. Apel-
doorn Solution Center** (2)
Laan Van De Leeuw 4, 7324 BD, Apel-
doorn, Netherlands (100%)
Tel.: (31) 555434422
Web Site: http://www.moduslink.com
Sales Range: $150-199.9 Million
Emp.: 200
Supply Chain Management
N.A.I.C.S.: 541330

ModusLink Kildare (1)
Monasterevin Road, Kildare, Ireland
Tel.: (353) 45527100
Web Site: http://www.moduslink.com
Supply Chain Management & Marketing
Distribution Solutions
N.A.I.C.S.: 541614

ModusLink PTS, Inc. (1)
2000 S Liberty Dr, Bloomington, IN 47403-
5137
Tel.: (812) 824-9331
Web Site:
http://www.moduslinkptstvboards.com
Supply Chain Management & Repair Services
N.A.I.C.S.: 541614

ModusLink Recovery LLC (1)
1610 Garden of the Gods Rd Ste 100,
Colorado Springs, CO 80907
Tel.: (719) 886-8000
Electronic Product Distr
N.A.I.C.S.: 423690

**ModusLink Securities
Corporation** (1)
1601 Trapelo Rd Ste 170, Waltham, MA
02451
Tel.: (781) 663-5000
Electronic Product Distr
N.A.I.C.S.: 423690

ModusLink Services Europe (1)
Monasterevin Road, Kildare Town, Kildare,
Ireland
Tel.: (353) 45 527 100

Steel Connect, Inc.—(Continued)

Supply Chain Management Services
N.A.I.C.S.: 541614

**ModusLink Solutions Service Pte.
Ltd.** (1)
51 Ubi Avenue 3, Singapore, 408858, Singapore
Tel.: (65) 68859000
Sales Range: $75-99.9 Million
Emp.: 300
Supply Chain Management Solutions
N.A.I.C.S.: 541614

Open Channel Solutions (1)
2 28 7 Kami Ochiai, Shinjuku-ku, Tokyo,
161-0034, Japan
Tel.: (81) 353318871
Software License Management Services
N.A.I.C.S.: 561499

Open Channel Solutions B.V. (1)
Laan van de Leeuw 4, 7324 BD, Apeldoorn,
Netherlands
Tel.: (31) 555 434 423
Web Site: http://www.moduslink.com
Software License Management Services
N.A.I.C.S.: 561499

STEEL DYNAMICS, INC.
7575 W Jefferson Blvd, Fort Wayne,
IN 46804
Tel.: (260) 969-3500   IN
Web Site:
  https://www.steeldynamics.com
Year Founded: 1993
STLD—(NASDAQ)
Rev.: $22,260,774,000
Assets: $14,159,984,000
Liabilities: $6,245,682,000
Net Worth: $7,914,302,000
Earnings: $3,862,674,000
Emp.: 12,060
Fiscal Year-end: 12/31/22
Steel Products Mfr
N.A.I.C.S.: 331110
Mark D. Millett *(Co-Founder, Chm &
CEO)*
Christopher A. Graham *(Sr VP-Long
Products Steel Grp)*
James S. Anderson *(Sr VP-Steel
Fabrication)*
Theresa E. Wagler *(CFO, Principal
Acctg Officer, Sec & Exec VP)*
Barry T. Schneider *(Pres & COO)*
Richard P. Teets Jr. *(Co-Founder)*

Subsidiaries:

Iron Dynamics (1)
4500 County Rd 59, Butler, IN
46721-9747   (100%)
Tel.: (260) 888-8000
Web Site: http://www.stld.com
Sales Range: $150-199.9 Million
Emp.: 800
Steel Mills
N.A.I.C.S.: 331110

KES Acquisition Company (1)
2704 S Big Run Rd W, Ashland, KY 41102
Tel.: (606) 929-1200
Web Site:
  http://www.kentuckyelectricsteel.com
Flat, Square & Round Steel Products Mfr
N.A.I.C.S.: 332111
John Scheel *(Plant Mgr)*
Brian Tipton *(Sls Mgr)*
Ron Witzig *(Gen Mgr)*

Mesabi Nugget Delaware, LLC (1)
1330 Jersey Ave S, Minneapolis, MN 55426
Tel.: (218) 225-6000
Iron Product Mfr
N.A.I.C.S.: 331110

**New Millennium Building Systems,
LLC** (1)
1690 Broadway St Bldg 19 Ste 160, Fort
Wayne, IN 46802   (100%)
Tel.: (260) 969-3500
Web Site: https://www.newmill.com
Sales Range: $50-74.9 Million
Emp.: 35
Mfr of Steel Joists

N.A.I.C.S.: 332111

Plant (Domestic):

**New Millennium Building
Systems** (2)
100 Diuguids Ln, Salem, VA 24153-2272
Tel.: (540) 389-0211
Web Site: http://www.newmill.com
Sales Range: $75-99.9 Million
Mfr of Steel Joists
N.A.I.C.S.: 332312
Rich Madden *(Mgr-Mktg)*
Richard Butler *(Mgr-IT)*
Doug Rees-Evans *(Mgr-Quality Assurance)*
Alex Therien *(Mgr-Market Dev)*
Joe Buntyn *(Mgr-Bus Dev)*
Sean Smith *(Mgr-Market Dev)*
Justin Hoover *(Mgr-Environmental)*
Rob Allen *(Controller-Div)*
Seamus Robins *(Sls Mgr-Natl Accounts)*

OmniSource Corporation (1)
7575 W Jefferson Blvd, Fort Wayne, IN
46804
Tel.: (260) 422-5541
Web Site: http://www.omnisource.com
Sales Range: $1-4.9 Billion
Emp.: 2,000
Ferrous & Non-Ferrous Scrap Metal Collection, Processing & Whslr
N.A.I.C.S.: 423930
Theresa E. Wagler *(CFO & Exec VP)*

Subsidiary (Domestic):

OmniSource Southeast, LLC (2)
2061 Nazareth Church Rd, Spartanburg,
SC 29301
Tel.: (864) 439-7039
Web Site: http://www.omnisource.com
Emp.: 150
Holding Company; Regional Managing Office
N.A.I.C.S.: 551112

OmniSource, LLC (1)
7575 W Jefferson Blvd, Fort Wayne, IN
46804
Tel.: (260) 422-5541
Web Site: https://www.omnisource.com
Metal Recycling Services
N.A.I.C.S.: 423510

Steel Dynamics Columbus, LLC (1)
7575 W Jefferson Blvd, Fort Wayne, IN
46804
Tel.: (260) 969-3500
Steel Products Mfr
N.A.I.C.S.: 331110
Mark D. Millett *(VP & Gen Mgr)*
Madhu Ranade *(VP & Gen Mgr)*
Mark Millett *(VP & Gen Mgr)*

Steel Dynamics Heartland, LLC (1)
455 W Industrial Dr, Terre Haute, IN
47802   (100%)
Tel.: (812) 299-4157
Web Site: http://www.steeldynamics.com
Steel Mfrs
N.A.I.C.S.: 331110

**Steel Dynamics Roanoke Bar
Division** (1)
102 Westside Blvd NW, Roanoke, VA
24017-6757
Tel.: (540) 342-1831
Web Site: http://www.roanokesteel.com
Sales Range: $500-549.9 Million
Emp.: 420
Mfr, Processor & Marketer of Merchant
Steel Products & Billets
N.A.I.C.S.: 331110

Steel of West Virginia, Inc. (1)
17th St & 2nd Ave, Huntington, WV
25703   (100%)
Tel.: (304) 696-8200
Web Site: https://www.swvainc.com
Sales Range: $150-199.9 Million
Emp.: 400
Steel Milling & Steel Fabrication Services
N.A.I.C.S.: 331110

Plant (Domestic):

Marshall Steel, Inc. (2)
1555 Harbor, Memphis, TN 38113
Tel.: (901) 946-1124

Web Site: http://www.swvainc.com
Rev.: $15,000,000
Emp.: 21
Steel Fabrication Services
N.A.I.C.S.: 332312

United Steel Supply, LLC (1)
248 Addie Roy Rd Ste C200, Austin, TX
78746   (75%)
Tel.: (512) 263-0954
Web Site: https://unitedsteelsupply.com
Metal Service Centers & Other Metal Merchant Whslr
N.A.I.C.S.: 423510
Bret Curtis *(Founder)*

Vulcan Threaded Products, Inc. (1)
10 Crosscreek Trl, Pelham, AL
35124   (100%)
Tel.: (205) 620-5100
Web Site: https://www.vulc.com
Emp.: 225
Machine Shops
N.A.I.C.S.: 332710

STEEL PARTNERS HOLDINGS
L.P.
590 Madison Ave 32nd FlNew, York,
NY 10022
Tel.: (212) 520-2300   DE
Web Site:
  https://www.steelpartners.com
Year Founded: 1992
SPLP—(NYSE)
Rev.: $1,695,441,000
Assets: $3,235,849,000
Liabilities: $2,434,389,000
Net Worth: $801,460,000
Earnings: $205,972,000
Emp.: 4,100
Fiscal Year-end: 12/31/22
Holding Company; Investment Services
N.A.I.C.S.: 551112
Jack L. Howard *(Pres)*
Warren G. Lichtenstein *(Exec Chm)*
Gary W. Tankard *(Chief Acctg Officer)*
Joseph Martin *(Chief Admin Officer &
Chief Legal Officer)*
Maria Reda *(Corp Counsel)*

Subsidiaries:

API Group plc (1)
Second Avenue Poynton Industrial Estate
Poynton, Stockport, SK12 1ND, Cheshire,
United Kingdom   (100%)
Tel.: (44) 1625858700
Web Site: http://www.apigroup.com
Sales Range: $150-199.9 Million
Emp.: 495
Holding Company; Paper Coating & Packaging; Security Systems; Foil Printing
N.A.I.C.S.: 551112

Subsidiary (US):

API (USA) Holdings Limited (2)
329 New Brunswick Ave, Rahway, NJ
07065
Tel.: (732) 382-6800
Packaging Materials Mfr
N.A.I.C.S.: 322220

Subsidiary (Domestic):

API Laminates Limited (2)
2nd Avenue Poynton Industrial Estate,
Poynton, SK12 1ND, Cheshire, United
Kingdom   (100%)
Tel.: (44) 1625650500
Web Site: http://www.apigroup.com
Emp.: 85
Metallized Packaging & Tape Mfr
N.A.I.C.S.: 322220

BASEBALL HEAVEN INC. (1)
350 Sills Rd, Yaphank, NY 11980
Tel.: (631) 205-5109
Web Site:
  https://www.lasordalegacypark.com
Baseball Club Operator
N.A.I.C.S.: 711211
Frank Zitaglio *(Gen Mgr)*
Chris Zitaglio *(Asst Gen Mgr)*
Nick Attardi *(Dir-Steel Sports Academy)*

Dunmore Corporation (1)
145 Wharton Rd, Bristol, PA 19007
Tel.: (215) 781-8895
Web Site: https://www.dunmore.com
Coated, Laminated & Metallized Films Mfr
N.A.I.C.S.: 326113
Matthew Sullivan *(CEO)*
Thomas S. Rimel Jr. *(Pres)*

Division (Domestic):

Dunmore Corporation/Brewster (2)
3633 Danbury Rd Route 6, Brewster, NY
10509
Tel.: (845) 279-5061
Web Site: http://www.dunmore.com
Metallizing, Coatings, Laminating, Printing
of Plastics Films, Papers & Fabrics
N.A.I.C.S.: 322120

Subsidiary (Non-US):

Dunmore Europe GmbH (2)
Hausener Weg 1, 79111, Freiburg, Germany
Tel.: (49) 761490460
Web Site: http://www.dunmore.de
Laminated Plastic Film Mfr
N.A.I.C.S.: 424610

Handy & Harman Ltd. (1)
590 Madison Ave 32nd Fl, New York, NY
10022   (100%)
Tel.: (212) 520-2300
Web Site: http://www.handyharman.com
Rev.: $828,343,000
Assets: $836,520,000
Liabilities: $669,925,000
Net Worth: $166,595,000
Earnings: ($10,944,000)
Fiscal Year-end: 12/31/2016
Engineered Industrial Products Mfr
N.A.I.C.S.: 332812
Jack L. Howard *(Vice Chm & CEO)*
Warren G. Lichtenstein *(Chm)*
Douglas B. Woodworth *(CFO & Sr VP)*
Leonard J. McGill *(Chief Legal Officer & Sr
VP)*

Subsidiary (Domestic):

Handy & Harman Group, Ltd. (2)
1133 Westchester Ave, White Plains, NY
10604
Tel.: (914) 461-1300
Engineered Industrial Product Mfr
N.A.I.C.S.: 331110
Jeffrey A. Svoboda *(Co-Pres & Co-CEO)*

Subsidiary (Domestic):

Handy & Harman Inc. (3)
1133 Westchester Ave, White Plains, NY
10604
Tel.: (914) 461-1300
Engineered Industrial Product Mfr
N.A.I.C.S.: 331491

Subsidiary (Domestic):

East 74th Street Holdings, Inc. (4)
4102 S 74th East Ave, Tulsa, OK 74145-
4700
Tel.: (918) 627-5210
Web Site: http://www.conind.com
Gas & Water Distribution Systems
N.A.I.C.S.: 326122

H&H LTD. (4)
1133 Westchester Ave, White Plains, NY
10604
Tel.: (914) 461-1300
Law firm
N.A.I.C.S.: 541199

Affiliate (Non-US):

Handy & Harman Manufacturing (Singapore) Pte. Ltd. (4)
No 20 Tuas Ave 5, Jurong, 639343, Singapore
Tel.: (65) 68611766
Web Site: https://www.hhpms.com
Emp.: 50
Precision Metal Refining
N.A.I.C.S.: 331410

Subsidiary (Domestic):

Handy & Harman Tube Co., Inc. (4)

701 W Township Ln Rd, Norristown, PA 19403
Tel.: (610) 539-3900
Web Site: http://www.handytube.com
Small Diameter Precision Drawn Stainless Steel, Carbon Steel & Nickel Alloy Tubing Mfr
N.A.I.C.S.: 331210

Handytube Corporation (4)
124 Vepco Blvd, Camden-Wyoming, DE 19934
Tel.: (302) 697-9521
Web Site: https://www.handytube.com
Sales Range: $25-49.9 Million
Emp.: 150
Stainless Steel Tubing
N.A.I.C.S.: 331210

Indiana Tube Corp. (4)
2100 Lexington Ave, Evansville, IN 47720
Tel.: (812) 424-9028
Web Site: https://www.indianatube.com
Sales Range: $25-49.9 Million
Emp.: 142
Small Diameter Refrigeration Grade Carbon Steel Tubing
N.A.I.C.S.: 331210

Subsidiary (Non-US):

LUCAS MILHAUPT RIBERAC SA (4)
ZAE Les Chaumes, BP 27, 24600, Riberac, France
Tel.: (33) 55 392 5300
Web Site: http://www.lucasmilhaupt.com
Emp.: 37
Soldering Equipment Mfr
N.A.I.C.S.: 333992

LUCAS-MILHAUPT BRAZING MATE-RIALS (SUZHOU) CO. LTD. (4)
8-B No 428 Xing Long Street, SuChun Industrial Square Suzhou Industrial Park, Suzhou, 215122, Jiangsu, China
Tel.: (86) 5126 289 1510
Web Site: http://www.lucasmilhaupt.com
Emp.: 30
Brazing Metal Distr
N.A.I.C.S.: 332811

Subsidiary (Domestic):

LUCAS-MILHAUPT WARWICK LLC. (4)
235 Kilvert St, Warwick, RI 02886
Tel.: (401) 739-9550
Machine Tool Accessory Mfr
N.A.I.C.S.: 333515
George Cullen *(Mgr-IT)*

Lucas-Milhaupt, Inc. (4)
5656 S Pennsylvania Ave, Cudahy, WI 53110
Tel.: (414) 769-6000
Web Site: https://www.lucasmilhaupt.com
Sales Range: $25-49.9 Million
Emp.: 130
Preformed Rings & Shapes for Brazing & Soldering; Automated Brazing Equipment
N.A.I.C.S.: 331491

Micro-Tube Fabricators Inc. (4)
250 Lackland Dr, Middlesex, NJ 08846
Tel.: (732) 469-7420
Web Site: http://www.handytube.com
Sales Range: $25-49.9 Million
Emp.: 50
Steel Tube Mfr
N.A.I.C.S.: 331210

OMG, Inc. (4)
153 Bowles Rd, Agawam, MA 01001-2900
Tel.: (413) 789-0252
Web Site: https://www.omgroofing.com
Sales Range: $50-74.9 Million
Emp.: 600
Die & Tool Mfr
N.A.I.C.S.: 333514
Hubert McGovern *(Pres & CEO)*

PAM FASTENING TECHNOLOGY, INC. (4)
2120 Gateway Blvd, Charlotte, NC 28208-2733
Tel.: (704) 394-3141
Fastener Mfr
N.A.I.C.S.: 339993

SL Industries, Inc. (4)
520 Fellowship Rd Ste A114, Mount Laurel, NJ 08054 **(100%)**
Tel.: (856) 727-1500
Machine Tool Accessory Mfr
N.A.I.C.S.: 333515
Louis J. Belardi *(CFO)*

Subsidiary (Domestic):

Cedar Corporation (5)
604 Wilson Ave, Menomonie, WI 54751
Tel.: (715) 235-9081
Web Site: https://www.cedarcorp.com
Emp.: 200
Engineeering Services
N.A.I.C.S.: 541330
Dean Zanon *(Pres)*
Troy Peterson *(Dir-Transportation)*

Subsidiary (Domestic):

MTE Corporation (3)
N83 W13330 Leon Rd, Menomonee Falls, WI 53051
Tel.: (262) 253-8200
Web Site: http://www.mtecorp.com
Electromagnetic Products Mfr
N.A.I.C.S.: 335311
Todd Shudarek *(Dir-Engrg)*

SL Montevideo Technology, Inc. (3)
8201 109th St Ste 500, Montevideo, MN 56265
Tel.: (320) 269-6562
Web Site: http://www.slmti.com
Electric Motor Products, Motor Controllers & Components Mfr
N.A.I.C.S.: 334511
Adam Behlman *(Pres)*
Aimee Foreman *(VP)*
Bill Irby *(Pres)*
Chris Cook *(VP)*
Daryl Barry *(VP)*
Ken Azzollini *(VP)*
Larry Brown *(Founder)*
Mindy Rapp *(VP)*
Seth Liubakka *(Mng Dir)*

Subsidiary (Domestic):

JPS Composite Materials Corporation (2)
2200 S Murray Ave, Anderson, SC 29624
Tel.: (864) 260-3326
Web Site: https://www.jpscm.com
Fiberglass & Synthetic Fabrics Mfr
N.A.I.C.S.: 313210

ROGUE PRESSURE SERVICES LTD. (1)
8601 Derrick Ave, Williston, ND 58801
Tel.: (701) 609-5242
Web Site:
    http://www.roguepressureservices.com
Oilfield Support Services
N.A.I.C.S.: 213112

SP Asset Management LLC (1)
20380 Town Center Ln Ste 205, Cupertino, CA 95014
Tel.: (408) 257-7711
Web Site:
    https://www.spassetmanagement.net
Asset Management Services
N.A.I.C.S.: 531390

Subsidiary (Non-US):

VILLA IMMOBILIARE SRL (2)
via Marco D'Oggiono 27, 23848, Oggiono, LC, Italy
Tel.: (39) 0341577131
Web Site: https://www.villaimmobiliare.it
Real Estate Investment Services
N.A.I.C.S.: 531210

Steel Excel Inc. (1)
1133 Westchester Ave Ste N222, White Plains, NY 10604 **(100%)**
Tel.: (914) 461-1300
Web Site: http://www.steelexcel.com
Sales Range: $125-149.9 Million
Emp.: 658
Investment Services
N.A.I.C.S.: 523999
Warren G. Lichtenstein *(Chm)*

Subsidiary (Domestic):

BASIN WELL LOGGING WIRELINE SERVICES, INC., (2)

PO Box 1156, Farmington, NM 87499
Tel.: (505) 327-5244
Financial Investment Services
N.A.I.C.S.: 523999

Basin Well Logging Wireline Services, Inc. (2)
2345 E Main St, Farmington, NM 87401-7719
Tel.: (505) 327-5244
Oil & Gas Operations Wireline Services
N.A.I.C.S.: 213112

Black Hawk Energy Services, Inc. (2)
118 84th St, Williston, ND 58801
Tel.: (701) 774-3001
Web Site:
    http://www.blackhawkenergyservices.com
Oil Field Equipment Distr
N.A.I.C.S.: 423830

Steel Sports Inc. (2)
845 Palm Dr, Hermosa Beach, CA 90254-4176
Tel.: (408) 957-2250
Web Site: http://www.steel-sports.com
Financial Support Services
N.A.I.C.S.: 522320
Nathan Clinkenbeard *(Mgr-Comm)*
Nanette Yang *(VP-Strategy & Growth)*
Joe Santilli *(Dir-Baseball)*
Mark Cole *(Pres & COO)*

Sun Well Service, Inc. (2)
118 84th St W, Williston, ND 58801
Tel.: (701) 774-3001
Web Site: http://sunwellservice.com
Emp.: 100
Equipment Rental Services
N.A.I.C.S.: 532412

iGo, Inc. (2)
61 E Main St Ste B, Los Gatos, CA 95030 **(80.2%)**
Tel.: (480) 596-0061
Web Site: http://www.igo.com
Portable & Handheld Computers Docking Stations & Power Products
N.A.I.C.S.: 334118
Jack L. Howard *(Chm)*
Douglas B. Woodworth *(CFO)*
Gordon Walker *(Pres)*

Subsidiary (Domestic):

Kasco LLC (3)
1569 Tower Grove Ave, Saint Louis, MO 63110
Tel.: (314) 771-1550
Web Site: http://www.kasco.com
Sales Range: $25-49.9 Million
Emp.: 55
Butcher Supplies, Cutlery for Retail Butchers, Meat Packers & Other Food Processors Mfr
N.A.I.C.S.: 332215
Thomas Orelup *(CFO)*

Holding (Non-US):

Atlantic Service Co. Ltd. (4)
929 Rue Michelin, Laval, H7L 5B6, QC, Canada
Tel.: (514) 722-3438
Web Site: https://www.kascocanada.ca
Emp.: 20
Engineered Industrial Product Mfr
N.A.I.C.S.: 331110

Subsidiary (Non-US):

Atlantic Service Co. (U.K.) Ltd. (5)
Willow Road, Pen-Y-Fan Industrial Estate, Crumlin, NP11 4EG, United Kingdom
Tel.: (44) 1495246012
Web Site: http://www.atlantic-service.co.uk
Sales Range: $25-49.9 Million
Emp.: 43
Butcher's Equipment Manufacturing
N.A.I.C.S.: 332215
Huw James *(Mng Dir)*
Martin Hughes *(CFO)*
Mark Owen *(Mgr-Production & Engrg)*
David Hunt *(Mgr-Quality)*
Jacquie Hughes *(Office Mgr)*
Elena Harries *(Sls Mgr-Intl)*

Holding (Non-US):

Bertram & Graf GmbH (4)

Bahnhofstr 7, 23689, Pansdorf, Germany
Tel.: (49) 4504707310
Web Site: https://www.bgraf.de
Sales Range: $10-24.9 Million
Emp.: 20
Mfr of Cutting Tools
N.A.I.C.S.: 333515
Frank Timmermann *(Mng Dir)*

Steel Partners Holdings GP Inc. (1)
590 Madison Ave 32nd Fl, New York, NY 10022
Tel.: (212) 520-2300
Holding Company
N.A.I.C.S.: 551112
William T. Fejes Jr. *(COO & Pres-Steel Services Ltd)*
Gordon Walker *(Sr VP)*

Steel Partners LLC (1)
590 Madison Ave 32nd Fl, New York, NY 10022
Tel.: (212) 520-2300
Web Site: https://www.steelpartners.com
Sales Range: $10-24.9 Million
Emp.: 30
Mutual Fund Manager
N.A.I.C.S.: 523999
Warren G. Lichtenstein *(Chm)*

UK ELITE SOCCER INC. (1)
210 Malapardis Rd Ste 101, Cedar Knolls, NJ 07927
Web Site: https://www.ukelite.com
Soccer Club Operator
N.A.I.C.S.: 711211
Mark Cole *(Pres)*

WebBank (1)
215 S State St Ste 1000, Salt Lake City, UT 84111
Tel.: (801) 993-5025
Web Site: http://www.webbank.com
Sales Range: $50-74.9 Million
Emp.: 67
Financial Advisory Services & Products
N.A.I.C.S.: 522220
Jason Lloyd *(Pres & CEO)*
Jeff Berkson *(Chief Risk Officer & Exec VP)*
Erik Cannon *(Sr VP-Due Diligence & Implementation)*
Jim Jackson *(Sr VP-Strategic Partner Oversight)*
James Peterson *(Chief Credit Officer & Sr VP)*
Steve Stanford *(CFO & Sr VP)*
Jack Howard *(Chm)*
Alicia Perry *(Sr VP-Tech Enablement)*
Parris Sanz *(Gen Counsel & Exec VP)*
Aaron Blankenstein *(Chief Compliance Officer & Sr VP)*

Subsidiary (Domestic):

National Partners PFco, LLC (2)
1600 Stout Street Suite 900, Denver, CO 80202
Tel.: (800) 506-8901
Web Site: https://www.nationalpartners.com
Insurance Brokerage
N.A.I.C.S.: 524210

Subsidiary (Domestic):

Security Premium Finance Co. (3)
5959 Blue Lagoon Dr, Miami, FL 33126
Tel.: (305) 269-1975
Web Site: http://www.securitypremium.com
Rev.: $3,168,000
Emp.: 8
Consumer Lending
N.A.I.C.S.: 522291

STEELCASE INC.
901 44th St SE, Grand Rapids, MI 49508-7594
Tel.: (616) 247-2710 MI
Web Site: https://www.steelcase.com
Year Founded: 1912
SCS—(NYSE)
Rev.: $3,232,600,000
Assets: $2,202,800,000
Liabilities: $1,376,600,000
Net Worth: $826,200,000
Earnings: $35,300,000
Emp.: 11,600
Fiscal Year-end: 02/24/23

Steelcase Inc.—(Continued)

Office Furnishings Mfr & Office Design Services
N.A.I.C.S.: 337214
Gale Moutrey *(VP-Innovation & Brand Mgmt)*
David C. Sylvester *(CFO, Principal Acctg Officer & Sr VP)*
Lizbeth S. O'Shaughnessy *(Chief Admin Officer, Gen Counsel, Sec & Sr VP)*
Sara E. Armbruster *(Pres & CEO)*
Donna K. Flynn *(VP-Talent Mgmt-Global)*
Mike O'Meara *(Dir-IR & Financial Plng & Analysis)*
Thomas Cook *(Dir-Strategy & Corp Dev)*
Terry Lenhardt *(VP-Product Mgmt-Global)*
Nicole C. McGrath *(Chief Acctg Officer, VP & Controller)*
Allan W. Smith Jr. *(Chief Revenue Officer)*
Robert C. Pew III *(Chm)*

Subsidiaries:

AMQ Solutions   (1)
764 Walsh Ave, Santa Clara, CA 95050
Web Site: https://www.amqsolutions.com
Office Furnishing Installation Contractor Services
N.A.I.C.S.: 238390

Coalesse   (1)
901 44th St SE, Grand Rapids, MI 49508
Web Site: http://www.steelcase.com
Sales Range: $10-24.9 Million
Office Furniture Mfr
N.A.I.C.S.: 337214

Branch (Domestic):

Coalesse   (2)
901 44th St SE, Grand Rapids, MI
49508   (100%)
Tel.: (336) 434-4151
Web Site: http://www.coalesse.com
Office Furniture Mfr
N.A.I.C.S.: 337211

Designtex Group Inc.   (1)
200 Varick St 8th, Fl, New York, NY 10014-7433
Tel.: (212) 886-8100
Web Site: https://www.designtex.com
Sales Range: $10-24.9 Million
Emp.: 70
Textile Design & Sales
N.A.I.C.S.: 424310

Unit (Domestic):

Designtex - Portland   (2)
14 Industrial Way, Portland, ME 04103
Tel.: (207) 774-2689
Web Site: http://www.designtex.com
Sales Range: $1-9.9 Million
Emp.: 25
Commercial Flexographic Printing
N.A.I.C.S.: 323111

Hedberg Data Systems Inc.   (1)
1699 King St, Enfield, CT 06082
Tel.: (860) 758-9000
Web Site:
    https://www.hedbergdatasystems.com
Sales Range: $10-24.9 Million
Emp.: 30
Integrated Business Systems for Contract Office Furniture Industry
N.A.I.C.S.: 541512
Bryan Walch *(Dir-IT)*
Melissa Walsh *(Product Mgr)*

PolyVision NV   (1)
Zuiderring 56, 3600, Genk, Belgium
Tel.: (32) 89323130
Web Site: https://polyvision.com
Office Furnishing Services
N.A.I.C.S.: 532420

Smith System Manufacturing Company   (1)

1150 Luna Rd, Carrollton, TX 75006
Tel.: (972) 398-4050
Web Site: https://www.smithsystem.com
Office, Library & School Furniture Mfr
N.A.I.C.S.: 337127

Steelcase AG   (1)
Brienner Strasse 42, Munich, 80333, Germany
Tel.: (49) 892488146
Furniture Product Mfr
N.A.I.C.S.: 337121
Jean Jacques Hausknecht *(Dir-Ops)*

Steelcase Australia Pty. Ltd.   (1)
Suite G 06/54 Market St Southbank, Melbourne, 3006, VIC, Australia   (100%)
Tel.: (61) 296605511
Web Site: http://www.steelcase.com
Sales Range: $10-24.9 Million
Emp.: 12
Office Furniture Sales
N.A.I.C.S.: 423210

Steelcase Canada Limited   (1)
200 King Street West Suite 2400, Toronto, M5H 3T4, ON, Canada   (100%)
Tel.: (416) 542-7700
Sales Range: $100-124.9 Million
Emp.: 100
Office Furniture Mfr & Sales
N.A.I.C.S.: 337214

Steelcase Czech Republic s.r.o.   (1)
Ostrov u Stribra 18, Kostelec, 349 01, Tachov, Czech Republic
Tel.: (420) 377012626
Furniture Product Mfr
N.A.I.C.S.: 337211

Steelcase Financial Services, Inc.   (1)
901 44th St SE, Grand Rapids, MI 49508-7594
Tel.: (616) 247-2710
Web Site: http://www.steelcase.com
Sales Range: $25-49.9 Million
Emp.: 2,000
Dealer Financing Services
N.A.I.C.S.: 522220

Steelcase Furniture (Dongguan) Company Limited   (1)
No 6 Langzhou Village, Changping Town, Dongguan, 523560, China
Tel.: (86) 76982826288
Furniture Product Mfr
N.A.I.C.S.: 337121
Beck Zheng *(Engr-Operating)*

Steelcase Health   (1)
SLC 3 PO Box 1967, Grand Rapids, MI 49501
Tel.: (616) 248-7038
Web Site: http://nurture.steelcase.com
Sales Range: $100-124.9 Million
Furniture Mfr for Healthcare Environments
N.A.I.C.S.: 337127

Steelcase Hong Kong Ltd.   (1)
15th Floor Kinwick Centre, 32 Hollywood Road, Central, China (Hong Kong) (100%)
Tel.: (852) 25200160
Web Site: http://www.steelcase.com
Sales Range: $10-24.9 Million
Emp.: 50
Furniture Sales
N.A.I.C.S.: 449110

Steelcase Inc.   (1)
901 44th St SE, Grand Rapids, MI
49508-7594   (100%)
Tel.: (010) 247-2710
Web Site: https://www.steelcase.com
Sales Range: $100-124.9 Million
Emp.: 20
Office Furniture Mfr
N.A.I.C.S.: 337214

Steelcase Japan, K.K.   (1)
Kowa Hiroo Building 4F 5-2-32 Minami-Azabu, Minato-ku, Tokyo, 106-0047, Japan
Tel.: (81) 5031965275
Web Site: https://jp.steelcase.com
Sales Range: $10-24.9 Million
Emp.: 10
Office Furniture & Equipment Sales
N.A.I.C.S.: 337214
Guinner Uli *(Pres)*

Steelcase S.A.   (1)

Espace Europeen de l'Entreprise1 Allee d'Oslo, BP 40033, Schiltigheim, 67012, Strasbourg, Cedex, France
Tel.: (33) 388133030
Furniture Product Mfr
N.A.I.C.S.: 337121
Florence Lambla *(Mgr-Pricing)*

Steelcase SAS   (1)
Espace Europeen de l'Entreprise 1 Allee d'Oslo, BP 40033, Schiltigheim, 67300, Strasbourg, Cedex, France   (100%)
Tel.: (33) 388133030
Web Site: https://www.steelcase.fr
Sales Range: $350-399.9 Million
Emp.: 1,500
Office Furniture & Equipment Mfr
N.A.I.C.S.: 337214

Subsidiary (Non-US):

AF Steelcase S.A.   (2)
C/ Antonio Lopez 243, 28041, Madrid, Spain
Tel.: (34) 914759000
Web Site: http://www.af-steelcase.com
Office Furniture Mfr
N.A.I.C.S.: 337211

Steelcase Werndl AG   (1)
Georg-Aicher Strasse 7, Rosenheim, 83026, Germany
Tel.: (49) 80314050
Web Site: http://www.steelcase.de
Sales Range: $150-199.9 Million
Emp.: 500
Office Furniture Mfr
N.A.I.C.S.: 337211

Steelcase de Mexico, S. de R.L. de C.V.,
Pedregal 24 Interior 1601 Molino del Rey Miguel Hidalgo, 11040, Ciudad Delicias, Mexico
Tel.: (52) 5555409916
Furniture Product Mfr
N.A.I.C.S.: 337211

Steelcase plc   (1)
77-79 Farringdon Road, London, EC1M 3JU, United Kingdom
Tel.: (44) 2074219000
Web Site: http://www.steelcase.com
Sales Range: $10-24.9 Million
Emp.: 40
Furniture Sales
N.A.I.C.S.: 449110

Turnstone   (1)
PO Box 1967, Grand Rapids, MI 49501
Tel.: (616) 554-8102
Web Site: http://www.turnstonefurniture.com
Sales Range: $25-49.9 Million
Emp.: 100
Office Furniture Mfr
N.A.I.C.S.: 337214
Rena Burden *(Chief Dev Officer)*

Vecta   (1)
901 44th St SE, Grand Rapids, MI
49508-7594   (100%)
Tel.: (616) 247-2710
Web Site: https://www.steelcase.com
Sales Range: $100-124.9 Million
Emp.: 290
Office Furniture, Tables & Area Seating Designer & Mfr
N.A.I.C.S.: 337214

STEELE OCEANIC CORP
2658 Del Mar Hts Rd #520, Del Mar, CA 92014
Tel.: (888) 847-9090   OK
SELR—(OTCIQ)
Sales Range: Less than $1 Million
Holding Company
N.A.I.C.S.: 551112
Scott D. Landow *(Chm, CEO & CFO)*

STELLAR BANCORP, INC.
9 Greenway Plz Ste 110, Houston, TX 77046
Tel.: (713) 210-7600   TX
Web Site: https://www.stellar.bank
Year Founded: 2007
STEL—(NASDAQ)
Rev.: $343,348,000

Assets: $10,900,437,000
Liabilities: $9,517,261,000
Net Worth: $1,383,176,000
Earnings: $51,432,000
Emp.: 1,025
Fiscal Year-end: 12/31/22
Bank Holding Company
N.A.I.C.S.: 551111
J. Pat Parsons *(Vice Chm)*
Robert R. Franklin Jr. *(Chm, Pres & CEO)*
Steve Retzloff *(Exec Chm)*
Paul P. Egge *(CFO)*
Ramon A. Vitulli III *(Pres)*

Subsidiaries:

Allegiance Bancshares, Inc.   (1)
8847 W Sam Houston Pkwy N Ste 200, Houston, TX 77040
Tel.: (281) 894-3200
Web Site: http://www.allegiancebank.com
Rev.: $261,746,000
Assets: $7,104,954,000
Liabilities: $6,288,486,000
Net Worth: $816,468,000
Earnings: $81,553,000
Emp.: 594
Fiscal Year-end: 12/31/2021
Bank Holding Company
N.A.I.C.S.: 551111

Subsidiary (Domestic):

Allegiance Bank   (2)
8727 W Sam Houston Pkwy N, Houston, TX 77040-5191
Tel.: (281) 894-3200
Web Site: https://www.allegiancebank.com
Sales Range: $100-124.9 Million
Commercial Banking
N.A.I.C.S.: 522110
Steven F. Retzloff *(Chm)*
Okan I. Akin *(Pres & Chief Risk Officer)*
Paul P. Egge *(CFO & Exec VP)*
Daryl D. Bohls *(Vice Chm-Asset Quality)*
Romi L. Sandel *(Chief Credit Officer & Exec VP)*
Stacy J. Tiger *(Chief HR Officer & Exec VP)*
Doug Skiba *(CIO & Exec VP)*
Ramon A. Vitulli III *(CEO)*
Ignacio Pujol Jr. *(Dir)*
Amber J. Welchel *(Sr VP)*
Carson T. Hughes *(Sr VP)*
Danny R. Hudson *(Sr VP)*
Glenda K. Roesner *(Sr VP)*
Michelle S. Droubi *(Pres)*

Subsidiary (Domestic):

American Prudential Capital, Inc.   (3)
10216 Fairbanks N Houston Rd, Houston, TX 77064-3406
Tel.: (713) 352-7088
Web Site:
    https://www.americanprudentialcapital.com
Sales Range: $1-9.9 Million
Emp.: 15
Financial Services
N.A.I.C.S.: 523999
Brenda Standlee Wetherbe *(Pres)*
Gloria Rodriguez *(Gen Mgr & Dir-Ops)*
Barbara Dyar *(Chief Credit Officer)*
Eric Standlee *(VP-Mktg & Broker Dev)*

CommunityBank of Texas, N.A.   (1)
5999 Delaware St, Beaumont, TX 77706
Tel.: (409) 861-7200
Web Site:
    http://www.communitybankoftx.com
Federal Savings Bank
N.A.I.C.S.: 522180

STEM CELL AUTHORITY, LTD.
123 S Miller Rd, Fairlawn, OH 44333
Tel.: (330) 835-0200   NV
SCAL—(OTCIQ)
Healtcare Services
N.A.I.C.S.: 621610
C. Bernard Cardwell *(Pres, CEO & Treas)*

STEM HOLDINGS, INC.
2201 NW Corporate Blvd Ste 205, Boca Raton, FL 33431

Tel.: (561) 237-2931 NV
Web Site:
  https://www.stemholdings.com
Year Founded: 2016
STEM—(CNSX)
Rev.: $35,769,000
Assets: $57,188,000
Liabilities: $22,954,000
Net Worth: $34,234,000
Earnings: ($64,364,000)
Emp.: 450
Fiscal Year-end: 09/30/21
Real Estate Manangement Services
N.A.I.C.S.: 531210
Matthew J. Cohen (Co-Founder, CEO & CFO)

Subsidiaries:

Driven Deliveries, Inc. (1)
134 Penn St, El Segundo, CA 90245
Tel.: (833) 378-6420
Web Site: http://www.drvd.com
Rev.: $2,822,575
Assets: $7,250,727
Liabilities: $5,628,314
Net Worth: $1,622,413
Earnings: ($12,560,570)
Emp.: 150
Fiscal Year-end: 12/31/2019
Cannabis Industry Logistics & Delivery Solutions
N.A.I.C.S.: 492110
Jerrin James (COO)
Sal Villanueva (Pres)
Lisa Chow (Dir-Ops)
Jason Gloria (Dir-E-commerce)
Maddie Halvorson (Mktg Dir)
Jeanette Villanueva (Dir-HR)

STEM, INC.
4 Embarcadero Ctr Ste 710, San
Francisco, CA 94111
Tel.: (415) 937-7836 DE
Web Site: https://www.stem.com
Year Founded: 2018
STEM—(NYSE)
Rev.: $362,980,000
Assets: $1,421,893,000
Liabilities: $869,726,000
Net Worth: $552,167,000
Earnings: ($124,054,000)
Emp.: 660
Fiscal Year-end: 12/31/22
Investment Services
N.A.I.C.S.: 523999
Michael D. Wilds (CFO & Chief Acctg Officer)
John Carrington (CEO)
Rahul Shukla (Chief Acctg Officer)
Michael Carlson (COO)
David Buzby (Chm)
Spencer Doran Hole (CFO & Exec VP)
David S. Buzby (Exec Chm & Interim CEO)

Subsidiaries:

Stem, Inc. (1)
100 Rollins Rd, Millbrae, CA 94030
Tel.: (415) 378-3823
Web Site: http://www.stem.com
Professional, Scientific & Technical Services
N.A.I.C.S.: 541990
John Carrington (CEO)
Benjamin Kearns (VP-Tech)
Larsh Johnson (CTO)
Polly Shaw (VP-Regulatory Affairs & Comm)
Bill Bush (CFO)
John Carrington (CEO)
Mark Triplett (COO)
Alan Russo (Sr VP-Sls-Global)
Matt Tappin (VP-Dev)

STEMSATION USA, INC.
7777 Glades Rd Ste 203, Boca Raton, FL 33434 FL
Web Site:
  http://www.stemsation.global
STSN—(OTCIQ)

Natural Product Distr
N.A.I.C.S.: 424490
David Casanova (Sr VP)
Nick Panza (VP-Ops)
Ray C. Carter Jr. (Founder, Pres & CEO)

STEPAN COMPANY
1101 Skokie Blvd Ste 500, Northbrook, IL 60062
Tel.: (847) 446-7500 DE
Web Site: https://www.stepan.com
Year Founded: 1932
SCL—(NYSE)
Rev.: $2,773,270,000
Assets: $2,433,172,000
Liabilities: $1,267,107,000
Net Worth: $1,166,065,000
Earnings: $147,153,000
Emp.: 2,453
Fiscal Year-end: 12/31/22
All Other Miscellaneous Chemical
Product & Preparation Manufacturing
N.A.I.C.S.: 325998
F. Quinn Stepan Jr. (Chm)
Scott R. Behrens (Pres & CEO)
Sean T. Moriarty (VP & Gen Mgr-Surfactants)
Janet A. Catlett (Chief HR Officer & VP)
Richard F. Stepan (VP & Gen Mgr-Polymers)
David G. Kabbes (Gen Counsel, Sec & VP)
Jason S. Keiper (Chief Tech & Sustainability Officer & VP)
Robert Haire (Exec VP-Supply Chain)

Subsidiaries:

Stepan Asia Pte. Ltd. (1)
2 International Business Park 06-24/32 The
Strategy Tower 2, Singapore, 609930, Singapore
Tel.: (65) 63799599
Specialty Chemicals Mfr
N.A.I.C.S.: 325998
John Hall (VP)

Stepan Canada, Inc. (1)
3800 Longford Mills Road, Longford Mills,
L0K 1L0, ON, Canada
Tel.: (705) 330-3367
Web Site: http://www.stepan.com
Sales Range: $1-9.9 Million
Emp.: 2
Chemical Mfr & Technical Services
N.A.I.C.S.: 325199

Stepan Colombia S.A.S. (1)
Edificio Siracusa Calle 98 No 9 A-21 Piso 6,
Bogota, DC, Colombia
Tel.: (57) 16362808
Intermediate Chemical Mfr
N.A.I.C.S.: 325998

Stepan Company - Elwood Polymer & Surfactant Plant (1)
22500 W Millsdale Rd, Elwood, IL 60421-9646
Tel.: (815) 727-4991
Web Site: http://www.stepan.com
Sales Range: $150-199.9 Million
Emp.: 346
Mfr of Organic Chemicals
N.A.I.C.S.: 325199

Stepan Deutschland GmbH (1)
Rodenkirchner Strasse, D-50389, Wesseling, Germany
Tel.: (49) 2232210021
Basic Organic Chemical Mfr
N.A.I.C.S.: 325199

Stepan Europe S.A. (1)
Chemin Jongkind, BP 127, F-38343,
Voreppe, Cedex, France (100%)
Tel.: (33) 476505100
Web Site:
  https://extranet.stepaneurope.com
Sales Range: $25-49.9 Million
Emp.: 140
Chemical Products Mfr
N.A.I.C.S.: 325998

Stepan Mexico, S.A. de C.V. (1)
Av Insurgentes Sur 662 - Piso 9 Col del
Valle Nte, Benito Juarez, 3103, Mexico,
Mexico
Tel.: (52) 5583112700
Sales Range: $10-24.9 Million
Emp.: 10
Chemicals Manufacturer
N.A.I.C.S.: 325199

Stepan Polska Sp. z o.o. (1)
ul Urazka 8 a b c, 56-120, Brzeg Dolny,
Poland
Tel.: (48) 716666012
Sales Range: $25-49.9 Million
Emp.: 50
Intermediate Chemical Mfr
N.A.I.C.S.: 325998

Stepan Quimica Ltda. (1)
Rua Tangara 170, Vila Mariana, Sao Paulo,
04019-030, Brazil
Tel.: (55) 1150892200
Web Site: www.stepan.com
Chemical Sales
N.A.I.C.S.: 325199

Stepan UK Limited (1)
Bridge House Bridge Street, Stalybridge,
SK15 1PH, United Kingdom (100%)
Tel.: (44) 1613389000
Web Site: https://www.stepan.com
Sales Range: $25-49.9 Million
Emp.: 120
Chemicals
N.A.I.C.S.: 325199

STEPSTONE GROUP INC.
450 Lexington Ave 31st Fl, New York,
NY 10017
Tel.: (212) 351-6100 DE
Web Site:
  https://www.stepstonegroup.com
Year Founded: 2019
STEP—(NASDAQ)
Rev.: $1,365,525,000
Assets: $4,188,125,000
Liabilities: $2,363,795,000
Net Worth: $1,824,330,000
Earnings: $193,885,000
Emp.: 790
Fiscal Year-end: 03/31/22
Investment Management Service
N.A.I.C.S.: 523940
David Y. Park (Chief Acctg Officer)
Matthew Jansen (Sr Mng Dir)
Jose Fernandez (Co-Founder, Partner & Co-COO)
Monte M. Brem (Chm)
Scott W. Hart (CEO)
Michael I. McCabe (Bd of Dirs & Head-Strategy)
Anthony Keathley (Chief Acctg Officer)
David Y. Park (Partner & CFO)

Subsidiaries:

Greenspring Associates Limited
Partnership (1)
100 Painters Mill Rd Ste 700, Owings Mills,
MD 21117
Tel.: (410) 363-2725
Web Site:
  http://www.greenspringassociates.com
Portfolio Management Services
N.A.I.C.S.: 523940
Eric Thompson (COO)
Lindsay Redfield (Gen Partner)
Hunter Somerville (Gen Partner)
Adair Newhall (Partner)
John Avirett (Gen Partner)
Seyonne Kang (Partner)
Stephen West (VP)
Anthony Giambrone (VP)
Jason Stall (Dir-Tax)
Julieanna Wiley (Controller)
Laura Antonelli (Controller)
Sarah Knox (Dir-Mktg & Comm)
Michael Classen (Exec Officer)
Huff Millard (VP-Portfolio Impact)
Erik Peterson (Dir-IT)
Melissa Beccio (Controller)
Jeannette Torres (Dir-Events)
Brian Kiernan (Mgr-Acctg)

Jennifer Spalding (Mgr-Admin)
David DiPietro (Dir-Portfolio)
Chris Ancona (Chief Compliance Officer)
Bill Baird (Exec Officer)
Jennifer Berg (Dir-Fund Mgmt)
Katelyn Bottner (Mgr-Fin Reporting)
Yoshi Maisami (CTO)
Joan Callaghan (Dir-Bus Intelligence)
Sydney McCormick (Coord-IR)
Phil Cummins (Partner-Venture)
Madaleine Dukes (Coord-Event)
Carrie McIntyre (CFO)
Deric Emry (Partner-Venture)
A. J. Frey (Gen Counsel)
Brett Garner (Mgr-Performance)
Todd Ruppert (Partner-Venture)
Robyn Schuerholz (Mgr-HR)
J. D. Hall (VP)
Amy Schartner (Chief HR Officer)
Mike Hoover (Chief People Officer)
Dale Irby (Partner-Venture)
Andy Jones (Partner-Venture)
Matt Sedney (Mktg Mgr)
Becky Spezzano (Mgr-Acctg)
Grace Uniacke (VP)
Ashton Newhall (Founder & Managing Gen Partner)
Jim Lim (Managing Gen Partner)

StepStone Gestao de Recursos
Ltda. (1)
Av Brigadeiro Faria Lima 3355 8th Floor,
Itaim Bibi, Sao Paulo, 04538-133, Brazil
Tel.: (55) 1151051515
Investment Management Service
N.A.I.C.S.: 523940

StepStone Group (China)
Limited (1)
Kerry Centre South Tower 2117 -2130 21st
Floor 1 Guang Hua Road, Chaoyang District, Beijing, 100020, China
Tel.: (86) 1085298784
Investment Management Service
N.A.I.C.S.: 523940

StepStone Group (HK) Limited (1)
Level 15 Nexxus Building 41 Connaught
Road, Central, China (Hong Kong)
Tel.: (852) 37579898
Investment Management Service
N.A.I.C.S.: 523940

StepStone Group Europe Alternative
Investments Limited (1)
Newmount House 22-24 Lower Mount
Street, Dublin, 2, Ireland
Tel.: (353) 15361400
Investment Management Service
N.A.I.C.S.: 523940

STEREO VISION ENTERTAINMENT, INC.
601 E Charleston Blvd Studio 100,
Las Vegas, NV 89104
Tel.: (818) 326-6018
Web Site:
  https://www.stereovision.com
SVSN—(OTCIQ)
Audio & Video Equipment Manufacturing
N.A.I.C.S.: 334310
Eric Honour (Chm)
Danna Paige (VP)
Jack Honour (Pres & CEO)
Stephen Curran (Vice Chm)
Gregory Previch (VP-Investor Relations)

STEREOTAXIS, INC.
710 N Tucker Blvd Ste 110, Saint
Louis, MO 63101
Tel.: (314) 678-6100 DE
Web Site:
  https://www.stereotaxis.com
Year Founded: 1990
STXS—(NYSEAMEX)
Rev.: $28,147,000
Assets: $53,413,000
Liabilities: $27,067,000
Net Worth: $26,346,000
Earnings: ($19,635,000)
Emp.: 130
Fiscal Year-end: 12/31/22

Stereotaxis, Inc.—(Continued)

Cardiology Instrument Control System Designer, Mfr & Marketer
N.A.I.C.S.: 334510
David Leo Fischel (Chm & CEO)
Michael Tropea (VP-Sls-North American)
Casey Payne (VP-Sls-APAC & Trng-Global)
Kimberly R. Peery (CFO)
Frank Van Hyfte (VP)
Keith Galloway (VP)
Laura Spencer Garth (Gen Counsel)

STERLING BANCORP

2 Blue Hill Plz 2 Fl, Pearl River, NY 10965
Tel.: (845) 369-8040   DE
Web Site:
    http://www.sterlingbancorp.com
Year Founded: 1998
STL—(NYSE)
Rev.: $1,149,583,000
Assets: $29,820,138,000
Liabilities: $25,229,624,000
Net Worth: $4,590,514,000
Earnings: $225,769,000
Emp.: 1,460
Fiscal Year-end: 12/31/20
Bank Holding Company
N.A.I.C.S.: 551111
Rodney C. Whitwell (Chief Admin Officer & Sr Exec VP)
Michael E. Finn (Chief Risk Officer & Sr Exec VP)
James P. Blose (Chief Legal Officer, Gen Counsel & Exec VP)
Javier L. Evans (Chief Bus Ops Officer & Exec VP)
Beatrice Ordonez (CFO & Exec VP)

Subsidiaries:

Sterling National Bank   (1)
400 Rella Blvd Ste 308, Montebello, NY 10901
Tel.: (845) 369-8040
Web Site: http://www.snb.com
Commercial Banking
N.A.I.C.S.: 522110
Vincent L. DeLucia (Pres-Community Dev Banking-Hudson Valley)
Mark Long (Sr Portfolio Mgr-Asset-Based Lending)
Michael Haddad (Pres-Capital Fin)
Terry O'Grady (Mng Dir-Asset-Based Lending)
Patricia Robins (Sr Mng Dir-Mortgage Warehouse Lending)
Joe Giamartino (Sr Mng Dir-Comml Banking)
Troy Grasinger (Mng Dir)
Jan Hanssen (Mng Dir-Asset-Based Lending)
Mark Cargo (Mng Dir)
Robert Mocerino (Mng Dir-Comml Svcs)
Ed Blaskey (Pres-Makrket)
Harold Peterson (Sr Mng Dir-Municipal & Not-For-Profit)
Luis Rivera (Sr Mng Dir)
Elvis Grgurovic (Mng Dir)
Kurt Fuoti (Mng Dir-Comml Banking)
Juan Acosta (Mng Dir)
Lindy Baldwin (Mng Dir-Franchise Financing)
Sharon Bender (Mng Dir-Asset-Based Lending)
Arlene Bhoorasingh (Mng Dir)
John Bierwirth (Mng Dir)
James Bodie (Sr Mgr-Portfolio-Comml Svcs)
Adam Brenner (Sr Mng Dir-Comml Banking)
Tania Broschart (Mng Dir)
David Carballeira (Mng Dir)
Michael Carbonaro (Mng Dir-Comml Banking)
Patty Carrotta (Mng Dir)
Kenneth Cohen (Sr Mng Dir-Comml Banking)
Deborah Connelly (Mng Dir)
Elizabeth DeJesus (Mng Dir)
Oralene Davis (Mng Dir)

Marissa Weidner (Chief HR Officer & Exec VP)
James Griffin (Exec VP & Head-Consumer & Bus Banking)
Kevin Henry (Mng Dir-Comml Svcs-Originations)

Subsidiary (Domestic):

Advantage Funding Management Co., Inc.   (2)
1 Marcus Ave, Lake Success, NY 11042
Tel.: (888) 246-4091
Web Site: http://www.advantagefund.com
Financial Lending Services
N.A.I.C.S.: 522220

Sterling Factors Corporation   (2)
500 7th Ave, New York, NY 10018 (100%)
Tel.: (212) 575-4415
Web Site: http://www.sterlingfactors.com
Sales Range: $250-299.9 Million
Factoring Services
N.A.I.C.S.: 522390

Unit (Domestic):

Sterling Trade Capital   (3)
500 Seventh Ave 10th Fl, New York, NY 10018
Tel.: (212) 273-5800
Web Site:
    http://www.sterlingtradecapital.com
Investment Advisory Services
N.A.I.C.S.: 523940

Subsidiary (Domestic):

Sterling National Mortgage Company, Inc.   (2)
98 Cuttermill Rd Ste 200 N, Great Neck, NY 11021-3006   (100%)
Tel.: (516) 487-0018
Web Site: http://www.sterlingnational.com
Sales Range: $50-74.9 Million
Emp.: 100
Residential Motgage Loan Services
N.A.I.C.S.: 522292

Sterling Resource Funding Corp.   (2)
177 Crossways Park Dr, Woodbury, NY 11797
Tel.: (516) 682-1400
Web Site:
    http://www.sterlingresourcefunding.com
Sales Range: $1-9.9 Million
Emp.: 100
Payroll Funding & Management Services
N.A.I.C.S.: 522390

STERLING BANCORP, INC.

1 Towne Sq Ste 1900, Southfield, MI 48076
Tel.: (248) 355-2400   MI
Web Site:
    https://www.sterlingbank.com
Year Founded: 1948
SBT—(NASDAQ)
Rev.: $101,279,000
Assets: $2,444,735,000
Liabilities: $2,132,108,000
Net Worth: $312,627,000
Earnings: $(14,194,000)
Emp.: 270
Fiscal Year-end: 12/31/22
Banking Services
N.A.I.C.S.: 522110
Christine Meredith (COO & Sr Exec VP)
Karen Knott (CFO & Exec VP)
Thomas M. O'Brien (Chm, Pres & CEO)
Scott J. Seligman (Founder)
Elizabeth M. Keogh (Chief Legal Officer & Sec)

Subsidiaries:

Sterling Bank & Trust, FSB   (1)
1 Towne Sq Fl 19, Southfield, MI 48076-3729
Tel.: (248) 355-2400
Web Site: http://www.sterlingbank.com
Rev.: $71,731,500
Emp.: 100
Federal Savings Bank

N.A.I.C.S.: 522180
Christine Meredith (COO & Sr Exec VP)
Karen Knott (CFO & Exec VP)
Scott Seligma (Chm & COO)
John Frelich (Asst VP-Residential Lending)
Dan Brown (Asst VP-Strategic Initiatives)

STERLING CHECK CORP.

6150 Oak Tree Blvd Ste 490, Independence, OH 44131   DE
Web Site:
    https://www.sterlingcheck.com
Year Founded: 2015
STER—(NASDAQ)
Rev.: $766,782,000
Assets: $1,407,254,000
Liabilities: $670,608,000
Net Worth: $736,646,000
Earnings: $19,410,000
Emp.: 6,000
Fiscal Year-end: 12/31/22
Identity Verification Services
N.A.I.C.S.: 561611
Richard S. Dziadzio (Interim CFO & Exec VP)
Joshua Peirez (CEO)
Lou Paglia (Pres & COO)
Steven Barnett (Chief Legal & Risk Officer, Sec & Exec VP)
Angela Stelle (CMO & Head-Client Experience)
Danielle Korins (Chief People Officer)
Peter Lehmann (Chief Strategy Officer)
Michael Grebe (Chm)

Subsidiaries:

A-Check America Inc.   (1)
1501 Research Park Dr, Riverside, CA 92507-2114
Tel.: (951) 750-1501
Web Site: http://www.acheckamerica.com
Financial Transactions Processing, Reserve & Clearinghouse Activities
N.A.I.C.S.: 522320
Sheree Warner (Mgr-Client Rels)
Michael Hoyal (Pres)

STERLING CONSOLIDATED CORP.

1105 Green Grove Rd, Neptune, NJ 07753
Tel.: (732) 918-8004   NV
Web Site:
    http://www.sterlingseal.com
Year Founded: 2011
STCC—(OTCIQ)
Rev.: $10,444,631
Assets: $6,763,242
Liabilities: $4,424,863
Net Worth: $2,338,379
Earnings: $807,851
Emp.: 23
Fiscal Year-end: 12/31/21
Holding Company; Industrial Sealing Components Distr
N.A.I.C.S.: 551112
Darren DeRosa (CEO)
Angelo DeRosa (Chm)
Scott R. Chichester (CFO)

Subsidiaries:

Sterling Seal & Supply, Inc.   (1)
1105 Green Grove Rd, Neptune, NJ 07753
Tel.: (732) 918-8004
Web Site: http://www.sterlingseal.com
Industrial Sealing Components Distr
N.A.I.C.S.: 423840
Darren DeRosa (CEO)

STERLING ENERGY RESOURCES INC.

39502 N 98th Way Ste 108, Scottsdale, AZ 85262
Tel.: (913) 451-2771   NV
Year Founded: 1999
SGER—(OTCIQ)
Oil & Gas Exploration Services

N.A.I.C.S.: 213112
Reid Scofield (Chm & CEO)
Dennis Beeby (Treas & Sec)

STERLING INFRASTRUCTURE, INC.

1800 Hughes Landing Blvd Ste 250, The Woodlands, TX 77380
Tel.: (281) 214-0800   DE
Web Site: https://www.strlco.com
Year Founded: 1955
STRL—(NASDAQ)
Rev.: $1,769,436,000
Assets: $1,441,620,000
Liabilities: $963,821,000
Net Worth: $477,799,000
Earnings: $106,461,000
Emp.: 600
Fiscal Year-end: 12/31/22
Heavy Civil Construction Services; Transportation & Water Infrastructure Building & Reconstruction Services
N.A.I.C.S.: 237310
Ronald A. Ballschmiede (Exec VP)
Joseph A. Cutillo (CEO)
Thomas M. White (Chm)
Sharon R. Villaverde (CFO & Chief Acctg Officer)
Mark D. Wolf (Chief Compliance Officer, Gen Counsel & Sec)
Noelle Dilts (VP-IR & Corp Strategy)

Subsidiaries:

DeWitt Excavation, LLC   (1)
14463 W Colonial Dr, Winter Garden, FL 34787
Tel.: (407) 656-1799
Web Site: http://www.dewittexc.com
Emp.: 195
Excavation Contractor Services
N.A.I.C.S.: 238910
Greg Rogers (Pres & CEO)
Brad Carroll (COO & Exec VP)
Ernie Scoggins (VP-Construction)
Earl McCoy (Project Mgr)
Peter Nunes (Project Mgr)

J. Banicki Construction, Inc.   (1)
4720 E Cotton Gin Loop Ste 240, Phoenix, AZ 85040
Tel.: (480) 921-8016
Web Site: https://www.banicki.com
Heavy Civil Construction Services
N.A.I.C.S.: 237990
Mike Abraham (Pres)
Don Davis (Mgr-APDM)
Eric Rotner (Mgr-Ops)
George Lane-Roberts (Mgr-Alternative Delivery & Preconstruction)
Chris Rodriquez (Mgr-Safety)

Myers & Sons Construction, L.P.   (1)
45 Morrison Ave, Sacramento, CA 95838
Tel.: (916) 283-9950
Web Site: https://www.myers-sons.com
Heavy Civil Construction Services
N.A.I.C.S.: 237990
Jenna Carlson (Dir-HR)

Myers & Sons Construction, LLC   (1)
5200 W Century Blvd Ste 350, Los Angeles, CA 90045
Tel.: (424) 227-3285
Heavy Construction Services
N.A.I.C.S.: 237310
David Staats (Project Mgr)

Petillo, Inc.   (1)
167 Flanders Netcong Rd, Flanders, NJ 07836
Tel.: (973) 347-6166
Web Site: https://www.petillo.com
Site Preparation Contractor
N.A.I.C.S.: 238910

Plateau Excavation, Inc.   (1)
375 Lee Industrial Blvd, Austell, GA 30168
Tel.: (770) 948-2600
Web Site:
    https://www.plateauexcavation.com
Site Infrastructure Improvements Contractor
N.A.I.C.S.: 238910

Greg Rogers *(Pres & CEO)*
Brad Carroll *(COO & Exec VP)*
David Shewchuk *(VP-Preconstruction)*
Ryan Duke *(VP-Construction)*
Greg Farr *(VP-Equipment)*
John Osterland *(VP)*
Joe Davis *(Project Mgr)*
Joseph Dudley *(Dir-Corp Safety)*
Nate Hrinsin *(CFO)*

Professional Plumbers Group, Inc. (1)
1322 Century Way, Wylie, TX 75098
Tel.: (972) 429-5575
Sales Range: $1-9.9 Million
Emp.: 50
Plumbing, Heating & Air-Conditioning Contractors
N.A.I.C.S.: 238220
R. Ottwell *(Pres)*

Road & Highway Builders LLC (1)
950 E Mustang Rd, Sparks, NV 89434
Tel.: (775) 852-7283
Web Site:
  https://www.roadandhighwaybuilders.com
Sales Range: $25-49.9 Million
Emp.: 250
Concrete Construction Services
N.A.I.C.S.: 237310
Steve Blakely *(VP)*
Kelly Schafer *(Safety Dir)*

Steel City Products, Inc. (1)
200 Center St, McKeesport, PA 15132
Tel.: (412) 896-7271
Sales Range: $10-24.9 Million
Emp.: 50
Automotive Accessories, Non-food Pet Supplies & Lawn & Garden Products
N.A.I.C.S.: 334610
Mark O'Hara *(Dir-Garden)*

Sterling Hawaii Asphalt, LLC (1)
1800 Hughes Landing Blvd Ste 250, The Woodlands, TX 77380
Tel.: (808) 691-9401
Heavy Civil Construction Services
N.A.I.C.S.: 237990

Tealstone Commercial, Inc. (1)
3201 Teasley Ln Ste 801, Denton, TX 76210
Tel.: (940) 383-2887
Heavy Construction Services
N.A.I.C.S.: 237310
James Wyner *(Project Mgr)*

Texas Sterling Construction Co. (1)
20810 Fernbush Dr, Houston, TX 77073
Tel.: (281) 821-9091
Web Site: https://www.texassterling.com
Heavy Civil Construction Services
N.A.I.C.S.: 237990
Adolph Pavlicek *(Dir-Corp Equipment)*
Tim Creson *(Pres)*
Clint Warren *(Mgr-Construction)*
Justin Wild *(Mgr-North Texas Area)*
Chris Compton *(Mgr-South Texas Area)*
Ronnie Wine *(Mgr-Div RDI Foundation)*

STEVEN MADDEN, LTD.
52 16 Barnett Ave, Long Island City, NY 11104
Tel.: (718) 446-1800   DE
Web Site:
  https://www.stevemadden.com
Year Founded: 1990
SHOO—(NASDAQ)
Rev.: $2,122,009,000
Assets: $1,257,988,000
Liabilities: $414,125,000
Net Worth: $843,863,000
Earnings: $216,061,000
Emp.: 2,800
Fiscal Year-end: 12/31/22
Shoes Designer, Whslr & Retailer
N.A.I.C.S.: 316210
Awadhesh Sinha *(COO)*
Amelia Newton Varela *(Pres)*
Edward R. Rosenfeld *(Chm & CEO)*
Lisa Keith *(Gen Counsel & Sec)*
Zine Mazouzi *(CFO)*

Subsidiaries:

B.B. Dakota Inc. (1)

275 B Mccormick Ave, Costa Mesa, CA 92626
Tel.: (949) 515-2200
Web Site: http://www.dakotacollective.com
Sales Range: $10-24.9 Million
Emp.: 36
Clothing Designer & Mfr
N.A.I.C.S.: 424350

BJ Acquisition LLC (1)
52-16 Barnett Ave, Long Island City, NY 11104
Tel.: (703) 637-6374
Web Site: https://betseyjohnson.com
Clothing Apparel Retailer
N.A.I.C.S.: 424350

Big Buddha, Inc. (1)
52-16 Barnett Ave, Long Island City, NY 11104-1018
Tel.: (212) 857-9580
Web Site: http://www.ebigbuddha.com
Fashion Apparels Retailer
N.A.I.C.S.: 458110

Cejon Accessories, Inc. (1)
Tel.: (212) 967-4663
Web Site: https://www.cejon.com
Sales Range: $50-74.9 Million
Emp.: 30
Women's & Children's Accessories Designer & Whslr
N.A.I.C.S.: 424350
David Seeherman *(Pres & CEO)*

Daniel M. Friedman & Associates, Inc. (1)
52-16 Barnett Ave, Long Island City, NY 11104
Tel.: (212) 695-5545
Apparel Accessories Mfr & Distr
N.A.I.C.S.: 315990

Subsidiary (Domestic):

Turn-On Products Inc. (2)
270 W 38th St 19th Fl, New York, NY 10018
Tel.: (212) 764-2121
Web Site: http://www.youniqueclothing.com
Rev.: $38,432,281
Emp.: 60
Provider of Women's Sportswear
N.A.I.C.S.: 315250

Diva Acquisition Corp. (1)
52-16 Barnett Ave, Long Island City, NY 11104-1018
Tel.: (718) 446-1800
Footwear Whslr
N.A.I.C.S.: 424340

Dolce Vita Holdings, Inc. (1)
111 S Jackson St, Seattle, WA 98104
Tel.: (206) 257-6052
Web Site: http://www.dolcevita.com
Footwear Distr
N.A.I.C.S.: 424340

Madden International Ltd. (1)
Rm 1102-05 11/f9 Wing Hong St Cheung Sha Wan, Hong Kong, China (Hong Kong)
Tel.: (852) 39637000
Footwear Distr
N.A.I.C.S.: 424340

SML Canada Acquisition Corp. (1)
3625 Shaganappi Trail NW, Calgary, T3A 0E2, AB, Canada
Tel.: (403) 247-7449
Web Site: https://www.stevemadden.ca
Emp.: 12
Shoe Retailer
N.A.I.C.S.: 423850

Schwartz & Benjamin, Inc. (1)
52-16 Barnett Ave, Long Island City, NY 11104
Tel.: (212) 541-9092
Shoes Distr & Whslr
N.A.I.C.S.: 316210

Trendy Imports S.A. de C.V. (1)
Tel.: (52) 8008804503
Web Site:
  https://www.stevemadden.com.mx
Foot Wear & Accessories Distr
N.A.I.C.S.: 424340

STEVIA CORP.

72 Adelhaide Ln, East Islip, NY 11730
Tel.: (917) 670-9541   NV
Web Site: http://www.stevia.co
Year Founded: 2007
STEV—(OTCIQ)
Assets: $6,000
Liabilities: $2,439,000
Net Worth: ($2,433,000)
Earnings: ($81,000)
Emp.: 1
Fiscal Year-end: 03/31/23
Web-Based Management Software
N.A.I.C.S.: 513210
Kenneth Maciora *(Chm, Pres, Treas & Sec)*

STEWART INFORMATION SERVICES CORPORATION
1360 Post Oak Blvd Ste 100, Houston, TX 77056
Tel.: (800) 729-1900   DE
Web Site: https://www.stewart.com
Year Founded: 1893
STC—(NYSE)
Rev.: $3,048,351,000
Assets: $2,737,879,000
Liabilities: $1,367,614,000
Net Worth: $1,370,265,000
Earnings: $162,305,000
Emp.: 7,100
Fiscal Year-end: 12/31/22
Holding Company; Title Insurance Products & Services
N.A.I.C.S.: 551112
Emily A. Kain *(Chief HR Officer)*
Frederick H. Eppinger *(CEO)*
Thomas G. Apel *(Chm)*
Elizabeth Giddens *(Chief Legal Officer & Sec)*
David Hisey *(CFO)*
Brad Rable *(Pres-Technology & Operations)*
Iain Bryant *(Grp Pres)*

Subsidiaries:

Advantage Title of Ft. Bend, LC (1)
14100 SW Freeway Ste 201, Sugar Land, TX 77478
Tel.: (281) 491-7050
Title Abstract Services
N.A.I.C.S.: 541191

All New York Title Agency, Inc. (1)
222 Bloomingdale Rd Ste - 306, White Plains, NY 10605
Tel.: (914) 686-5600
Web Site: http://www.allnewyorktitle.com
Title Insurance Agency Services
N.A.I.C.S.: 524127
John M. Martin *(Gen Counsel & VP)*
Augustine Arena *(VP)*
Edward V. Vicinanza *(VP-Bus Dev)*
Joseph S. Petrillo *(Pres)*
Steven Peikes *(VP-Sls)*
Barbara Diana *(Asst Controller)*
Liz Pulcini *(Controller)*

AmSac Rivers Escrow, Inc. (1)
5252 Sunrise Blvd Ste 5, Fair Oaks, CA 95628
Tel.: (916) 880-1130
Web Site:
  http://www.amsacriversescrow.com
Sales Range: $25-49.9 Million
Emp.: 10
Real Estate Escrow Services
N.A.I.C.S.: 531390

Asset Preservation, Inc. (1)
1420 Rocky Ridge Dr Ste 270, Roseville, CA 95661
Tel.: (916) 791-5991
Web Site: https://www.apiexchange.com
Tax Intermediary Services
N.A.I.C.S.: 523910

Bedrock Title Company, LLC (1)
8240 N Mopac Expy Ste 200, Austin, TX 78759
Tel.: (512) 372-6015
Emp.: 40

General Insurance Services
N.A.I.C.S.: 524210

Brokers Title, LLC (1)
602 Delaware Str, Leavenworth, KS 66048
Tel.: (816) 988-9262
Emp.: 4
Title Insurance Carrier Services
N.A.I.C.S.: 524127

CTO 24/7 (Private) Limited (1)
Metro Model Town Building G-Block, Link Road Model Town, Lahore, Pakistan
Tel.: (92) 4235926462
Software Development Services
N.A.I.C.S.: 541511
Amin Ansari *(Pres)*

F.A.S.B., Inc. (1)
801 Main Ave, Norwalk, CT 06856-5116
Tel.: (203) 847-0700
Web Site: https://www.fasb.org
Financial Accounting Services
N.A.I.C.S.: 541219
James L. Kroeker *(Vice Chm)*
Russell G. Golden *(Chm)*
Jeffrey D. Mechanick *(Asst Dir-Nonpub Entities)*
Melissa Maroney *(Asst Dir)*
Mary Mazzella *(Asst Dir)*
Alex Casas *(Asst Dir)*
Richard R. Jones *(Co-Chm)*
Hillary H. Salo *(Dir-Tech)*
Elena Kirillova *(Asst Mgr-Project)*

First Ohio Title Insurance Agency, Ltd. (1)
4183 Pkwy Centre Dr, Grove City, OH 43123
Tel.: (614) 273-6270
Title Insurance Carrier Services
N.A.I.C.S.: 524127

Graystone Title Company, LLC (1)
8240 N MoPac Expy Ste 200, Austin, TX 78759
Tel.: (512) 615-9698
Web Site: https://www.graystonetitle.com
Direct Title Insurance Services
N.A.I.C.S.: 524127

Heart of America Title & Escrow, LLC (1)
1583 NE Rice Rd, Lees Summit, MO 64086
Tel.: (816) 988-9650
Web Site: http://www.stewart.com
Emp.: 2
Title Abstract Services
N.A.I.C.S.: 541191

I & S Holdings, LLC (1)
775 NE Midway Blvd, Oak Harbor, WA 98277
Tel.: (360) 240-9610
Title Search & Insurance Services
N.A.I.C.S.: 541191

Landon Title Company, LLC (1)
3575 Lone Star Cir Ste 309, Fort Worth, TX 76177
Tel.: (817) 491-7201
Title Search & Insurance Services
N.A.I.C.S.: 541191

Millennium Title of Houston, LC (1)
10720 W Sam Houston Pkwy N, Houston, TX 77041
Tel.: (713) 625-2888
Web Site: http://www.stewart.com
Title Abstract Services
N.A.I.C.S.: 541191

Monroe-Gorman Title Agency, LLC (1)
34 William St, Lyons, NY 14489
Tel.: (315) 946-5125
Emp.: 6
Title Abstract Services
N.A.I.C.S.: 541191

National Transfer Services, LLC (1)
1980 Post Oak Blvd, Houston, TX 77056
Tel.: (713) 625-8122
Emp.: 6
All Professional Services
N.A.I.C.S.: 541990

Oklahoma Land Title Services, LLC (1)
301 W Broadway, Ardmore, OK 73041
Tel.: (580) 220-2950

Stewart Information Services
Corporation—(Continued)

Web Site: https://www.olts.net
Title Abstract Services
N.A.I.C.S.: 541191
Amanda Roberts (Office Mgr-Title Insurance Dept)

Pro-Teck Services Ltd. (1)
465 Waverley Oaks Rd Ste 320, Waltham, MA 02452
Tel.: (781) 899-4949
Web Site: https://www.proteckservices.com
Offices Real Estate Appraisers
N.A.I.C.S.: 531320

PropertyInfo Corporation (1)
1360 Post Oak Blvd Ste 100, Houston, TX 77056
Tel.: (855) 330-2800
Web Site: https://www.propertyinfo.com
Real Estate Transaction Software Publisher & Technology Services
N.A.I.C.S.: 513210

Red River Title Services, Inc. (1)
35 4th St N Ste 101, Fargo, ND 58102
Tel.: (701) 232-3341
Web Site: https://www.rrtitle.com
Title Abstract Services
N.A.I.C.S.: 541191
Jessica Miller (Pres-Div)

San Juan Abstract Company, Inc. (1)
Royal Bank Ctr 255 Ponce de Leon Ave Ste 809, Hato Rey, PR 00917
Tel.: (787) 753-1200
Real Estate Escrow Services
N.A.I.C.S.: 531390
Maritza Brimeyer Quezada (VP & Gen Mgr)

Signature Closers, LLC (1)
3136 Kingsdale Ctr Ste 117, Upper Arlington, OH 43221
Tel.: (888) 677-7462
Web Site: http://www.signatureclosers.com
Sales Range: $1-9.9 Million
Notary Closing Services
N.A.I.C.S.: 541199
Stacie Cordle (Coord-Closing)
Mark Fleming Jr. (Founder)
Stacie Cordle Wilkens (Mgr)
Mark Fleming (Sr VP)

Stewart Financial Services, Inc. (1)
7375 Executive Pl Ste 300, Lanham, MD 20706
Tel.: (301) 794-4290
Web Site: https://www.sfsinc.co
Investment Advisory Services
N.A.I.C.S.: 523940
Anthony Stewart (Pres & CEO)
Linda Macklin (District Mgr & Office Mgr)
Maurice Bailey (Sr Dir-Agency Mktg)
Alan Stewart (Mgr)
Tony L. Brown Sr. (Sr Dir)
Yvondra Caprese Hayes (District Mgr)
Saran T. Baker (Mgr)

Stewart Pakistan (Private) Limited
Metro Model Town Building G-Block Link Road, Model Town, Lahore, Pakistan
Tel.: (92) 4235926462
Web Site: https://www.stewart.com
Information Technology Consulting Services
N.A.I.C.S.: 541613
Amin Ansari (Sr Dir-IT)
Brad Rable (Pres-Grp-Ops and Tech)
John Hamm (CIO-Tech and Bus Svcs)
Ahmed Azmat (Head-Stewart Enterprise Fulfillment Svcs)
Jawad Bashir (Head-Quality Assurance)
Habib Rehman (Head-Application Support)
Sohail Saleem (Head-Bus Solutions Svcs)
Shahzad Anjum (Head-Finance)
Bilal Shahzad (CTO)
Kamran Butt (Head-Development)

Stewart Title & Trust of Tucson (1)
3939 E Broadway Blvd, Tucson, AZ 85711
Tel.: (520) 327-7373
Web Site: http://www.tucson.stewartaz.com
Title Search & Insurance Services
N.A.I.C.S.: 541191
Bob Dytko (Officer-Bus Dev)
Johanna Simental (Officer-Bus Dev)
Lauren Smith Klase (Officer-Bus Dev)

Michael Bock (Officer-Bus Dev)
Eva Hendrix (Officer-Bus Dev)
Shawna Ruboyianes (Pres-Div)
Michelle Jolly (Officer-Escrow-Comml & Branch Mgr)
Brenda Whitney (Officer-Escrow)
Lee Ann Watterson (Officer-Escrow)
Shelley Lamoureux (Officer-Escrow)
Yvonne Lopez (Officer-Escrow)
Darlene Snyder (Officer-Escrow, Asst VP & Branch Mgr)
Lori Ruboyianes (Officer-Escrow)

Stewart Title Company (1)
1360 Post Oak Blvd Ste 100, Houston, TX 77056
Tel.: (713) 625-8100
Web Site: http://www.stewart.com
Title Insurance Products & Services
N.A.I.C.S.: 524127

Subsidiary (Domestic):

Stewart Title Company - Kissimmee (2)
1201 W Emmett St, Kissimmee, FL 34741
Tel.: (407) 846-7477
Web Site: http://www.stewart.com
Real Estate Title Insurance Services
N.A.I.C.S.: 524127

Stewart Title Group, LLC (1)
11 Dupont Cir NW Ste 750, Washington, DC 20036
Tel.: (202) 349-0220
Web Site: http://www.stewarttitlegroup.com
Sales Range: $25-49.9 Million
Emp.: 8
Title Search & Insurance Services
N.A.I.C.S.: 541191
Ferky Azib (Gen Counsel)

Stewart Title Guaranty Company (1)
360 Post Oak Blvd Ste 100, Houston, TX 77056
Tel.: (713) 625-8225
Web Site: https://www.stewart.com
Sales Range: $100-124.9 Million
Personnel & Underwriting Support Services
N.A.I.C.S.: 524298
John A. Frates (Sr VP & District Mgr-Northeast States)
Thomas G. Apel (Chm)
Elizabeth Giddens (Chief Legal Officer)
David Hisey (CFO)
Brad Rable (Pres-Technology & Operations)
Emily Kain (Chief HR Officer)
Iain Bryant (Grp Pres)
Steve M. Lessack (Grp Pres)

Subsidiary (Domestic):

Stewart Title Insurance Company (2)
140 E 45th St Ste 3300, New York, NY 10017
Tel.: (212) 922-0050
Web Site: https://www.stewart.com
Title Insurance Underwriting Services
N.A.I.C.S.: 524127
John A. Frates (Pres & Gen Counsel)
Alayne Plevrites (Asst VP & Ops Mgr)
James F. Shannon (VP, VP & Sr Mgr-New York Agency)
Paul F. Bugoni (VP)
Yeidy Rodriguez (Asst VP)

Co-Headquarters (Domestic):

Stewart Title Insurance Corp. - Upstate Corporate Office (3)
47 W Main St, Rochester, NY 14614
Tel.: (585) 232-2070
Web Site: http://www.stewartnewyork.com
Sales Range: $25-49.9 Million
Emp.: 50
Corporate Office; Title Insurance Underwriting Services
N.A.I.C.S.: 551114

Subsidiary (Domestic):

Stewart Title of California, Inc. (2)
525 N Brand Blvd 2nd Fl, Glendale, CA 91203
Tel.: (818) 502-2700
Title Insurance Underwriting Services
N.A.I.C.S.: 524127
Julie Lloyd (Officer-Escrow)
Kelvin Ly (Officer-Escrow)

Judy Arrington (Mgr-Escrow Ops-LA/Ventura County)
Chris Ocampo (Officer-Title)
Rudy Baiza (Officer-Title)
Aaron Rigney (Mgr-Customer Service)

Stewart Title Insurance Agency of Utah, Inc. (1)
727 N 1550 E Ste 150, Orem, UT 84097
Tel.: (801) 375-3600
Title Insurance Carrier Services
N.A.I.C.S.: 524127

Stewart Title Ltd. (1)
11 Haymarket, London, SW1Y 4BP, United Kingdom
Tel.: (44) 207 010 7820
Web Site: https://www.stewartuk.com
Emp.: 9
Title Search & Insurance Services
N.A.I.C.S.: 541191
Jonathan Woodcraft (Head-Sls & Mktg)
Larry Thompson (CFO)
Sacha Mitrakos (VP-HR)
Stephen Smith (Country Mgr)
Robert Kelly (Mgr-Comml Bus Dev)
Mark Davies (Dir-Underwriting)

Stewart Title Puerto Rico, Inc. (1)
MCS Plz Ste 1207 255 Ponce De Leon Ave, Hato Rey, PR 00917
Tel.: (787) 753-1200
Direct Title Insurance Services
N.A.I.C.S.: 524127

Stewart Title of Alabama, LLC (1)
24190 US Highway 98, Fairhope, AL 36532
Tel.: (251) 990-6797
General Insurance Services
N.A.I.C.S.: 524210

Stewart Title of Albuquerque, LLC (1)
7801 Academy Rd NE Ste 101, Albuquerque, NM 87109
Tel.: (505) 828-1700
Web Site: http://www.stewarttitle.com
Emp.: 60
Title Search & Insurance Services
N.A.I.C.S.: 541191
Amber Killian (Officer-Escrow)

Stewart Title of Arkansas, LLC (1)
10310 W Markham St, Little Rock, AR 72205
Tel.: (501) 228-0493
Title Abstract Services
N.A.I.C.S.: 541191

Stewart Title of Cameron County, Inc. (1)
700 FM 802 Bldg A, Brownsville, TX 78520
Tel.: (956) 986-2700
Emp.: 35
Real Estate Escrow Services
N.A.I.C.S.: 531390
Belinda Bernal (Pres)
Diana Delgado (Office Mgr)

Stewart Title of Lubbock, Inc. (1)
11005 Quaker Ave, Lubbock, TX 79424-8317
Tel.: (806) 793-1389
Title Abstract Services
N.A.I.C.S.: 541191

Stewart Title of Minnesota, Inc. (1)
1700 W 82nd St Ste 100, Bloomington, MN 55431
Tel.: (952) 888-6353
Web Site: http://www.stewart.com
Emp.: 30
Title Abstract Services
N.A.I.C.S.: 541191

Stewart Title of Nevada Holdings, Inc. (1)
376 E Warm Springs Rd Ste 190, Las Vegas, NV 89119
Tel.: (702) 791-7000
Title Search & Insurance Services
N.A.I.C.S.: 541191

Stewart Title of Oklahoma, Inc. (1)
1620 SW 122nd St Ste 100, Oklahoma City, OK 73170
Tel.: (405) 691-9284
Title Insurance Carrier Services
N.A.I.C.S.: 524127

Stewart Title s.r.o. (1)

Bozdechova 7, 150 00, Prague, Czech Republic
Tel.: (420) 225275300
Web Site: http://www.stewart.com
Title Search & Insurance Services
N.A.I.C.S.: 541191

Thomas Title & Escrow, LLC (1)
4800 N Scottsdale Rd Ste 4300, Scottsdale, AZ 85251
Tel.: (480) 222-1116
Web Site: https://www.thomastitle.com
Sales Range: $1-9.9 Million
Emp.: 18
Title Insurance, Real Estate Settlement & Escrow Services
N.A.I.C.S.: 531390
Sheila Hunter (Officer-Comml Escrow & VP)
Bryan Selna (Officer, Officer-Escrow & VP)
Dustin Gaskey (Pres)
Hannah Schest (VP)
Eric Stewart (Dir-Natl Title Ops)
Joel Montemayor (Officer-Commercial-Escrow)

United States Appraisals LLC (1)
7500 W 110th St Ste 420, Overland Park, KS 66210
Web Site: http://www.unitedstatesappraisals.com
Offices of Real Estate Appraisers
N.A.I.C.S.: 531320
Aaron Fowler (Pres)

United Title Guaranty Agency, LLC (1)
3350 Midtown Place Ste 102, Anchorage, AK 99503
Tel.: (907) 261-7550
Emp.: 3
Title Search & Insurance Services
N.A.I.C.S.: 541191

ValuGuard Solutions, LLC (1)
7500 W 110th St Ste 420, Overland Park, KS 66210
Tel.: (913) 951-3692
Web Site: https://www.valuguardsolutions.com
Software Development Services
N.A.I.C.S.: 541511
Aaron Fowler (CEO)
Chris Purcell (CFO)
James Webster (CTO)

Yankton Title Company, Inc. (1)
202 W 3rd St, Yankton, SD 57078
Tel.: (605) 665-5775
Web Site: https://www.yanktontitle.com
Title Abstract Services
N.A.I.C.S.: 541191

Yukon Title Company, Inc. (1)
714 Gaffney Rd, Fairbanks, AK 99701
Tel.: (907) 456-3476
Web Site: http://www.yukontitle.com
Activities Related to Real Estate
N.A.I.C.S.: 531390
Beverly Floerchinger (CEO)
Andrew Dains (Officer-Escrow & Mgr-Escrow)
Jennifer Nachtrieb (Officer-Escrow)
Ciarra Neumeister (Officer-Escrow)
Shelby French (Officer-Escrow)
Jamie Nosko (Officer-Escrow)
Bobbi Hamilton (Chief Title Officer & Mgr-Title)
Denise Goss (Officer-Title)
Krystle Bryan (Officer-Title)
Terry Bryan (Branch Mgr-Ops)
Kara Watson (Office Mgr)
Sara Smith (Officer-Title)
Anne Castle (Mgr-Acctg)
Rena Cantil (Ops Mgr)

STG GROUP, INC.
11091 Sunset Hills Rd Ste 200, Reston, VA 20190
Tel.: (703) 691-2480　　　　DE
Web Site: http://www.stginc.com
Year Founded: 2013
STGG—(OTCIQ)
Sales Range: $150-199.9 Million
Emp.: 940
Cyber, Software & Intelligence Solutions for Government
N.A.I.C.S.: 541519

Simon S. Lee *(Chm)*
Joseph P. Nicholas *(Sr VP-Cyber Security & Secure Info Sys)*
Paul Rempfer *(Sr VP-Bus Dev)*
Keith Lynch *(VP-Fin & Acctg)*

Subsidiaries:

STG, Inc. (1)
110191 Sunset Hills Rd Ste 200, Reston, VA 20190
Tel.: (703) 691-2480
Web Site: http://www.stginc.com
Emp.: 1,500
Government Support Services Contractor
N.A.I.C.S.: 541990
Simon S. Lee *(Chm & CEO)*
Paul A. Fernandes *(Co-Pres & Co-COO)*
Paul Fernandez *(Exec VP)*
Bill Perlowitz *(CTO & Sr VP)*
Charles Cosgrove *(CFO)*
Dale Davis *(Chief Integration Officer)*
Cheryl Garrison *(Chief People Officer & VP-Human Capital)*
Maurice Guyant *(VP-Intelligence Support Sector)*

STI GROUP
3127 Texas Ave, Bridge City, TX 77611
Tel.: (409) 994-3570
Web Site: https://setxind.com
Year Founded: 1978
STUO—(OTCIQ)
Information Technology Services
N.A.I.C.S.: 541512

STIFEL FINANCIAL CORP.
1 Financial Plz 501 N Broadway, Saint Louis, MO 63102-2188
Tel.: (314) 342-2255   DE
Web Site: https://www.stifel.com
Year Founded: 1983
SF—(NYSE)
Rev.: $5,159,280,000
Assets: $37,727,460,000
Liabilities: $32,433,029,000
Net Worth: $5,294,431,000
Earnings: $485,255,000
Emp.: 9,000
Fiscal Year-end: 12/31/23
Holding Company; Securities Brokerage, Dealing & Investment Advisory Services
N.A.I.C.S.: 551112
James Mark Zemlyak *(Co-Pres)*
David D. Sliney *(COO)*
Victor J. Nesi *(Co-Pres & Dir-Institutional Grp)*
James M. Marischen *(CFO & Sr VP)*
Eric Needleman *(Head-Fixed Income Capital Markets-Global)*
Brad Raymond *(Head-Investment Banking-Global)*
Mark P. Fisher *(Gen Counsel)*
Hugo J. Warns III *(Head-Equities-Global)*
Ronald J. Kruszewski *(Chm & CEO)*
Thomas Wilson Weisel *(Sr Mng Dir)*

Subsidiaries:

1919 Investment Counsel, LLC (1)
1 South St 25th Floor Ste 2500, Baltimore, MD 21202
Tel.: (844) 200-1919
Web Site: http://www.1919ic.com
Investment Advisory & Asset Management Services
N.A.I.C.S.: 523940
Aimee M. Eudy *(Mng Dir & Portfolio Mgr)*
Harry O'Mealia *(Pres & CEO)*
Margaret M. Pasquarella *(CFO & Dir-HR)*
Christopher Delpi *(Mng Dir)*
Robert J. Fisher *(Principal)*
Brian P. Gallagher *(Mng Dir & Chief Admin Officer)*
Thomas W. Krygowski *(Mng Dir)*
Dessie Locher *(Mng Dir & Portfolio Mgr)*
Meredith A. Mowen *(Mng Dir & Portfolio Mgr)*

R. Scott Pierce *(Mng Dir, Head-Fixed Income & Portfolio Mgr)*
Matthew P. Robinson *(Principal)*
Eric G. Thompson *(Mng Dir)*
Philip J. Yakim *(Mng Dir & Head-Trading)*
Lauren Webb *(Principal & Portfolio Mgr)*
Michael McAndrew *(VP & Portfolio Mgr)*

Subsidiary (Domestic):

Rand Wealth, LLC (2)
49 Stevenson St Ste 1075, San Francisco, CA 94105
Tel.: (415) 500-6700
Web Site: https://1919ic.com
Investment Management Service
N.A.I.C.S.: 523150
Andrew Rand *(Mng Dir)*

B&F Capital Markets, Inc. (1)
635 W Lakeside Ave Ste 201, Cleveland, OH 44113
Tel.: (216) 472-2701
Web Site: https://www.bfcmi.com
Commercial Banking Services
N.A.I.C.S.: 522110
Alistair Fyfe *(Principal)*
Derek Beitzel *(Principal)*
Dolf Roell *(Exec Dir)*

B&F Capital Markets, LLC (1)
635 W Lakeside Ave Ste 201, Cleveland, OH 44113
Tel.: (216) 472-2701
Web Site: https://bfcmi.com
Interest Rate Risk Management Services
N.A.I.C.S.: 541611

Century Securities Associates, Incorporated (1)
501 N Broadway, Saint Louis, MO 63102   (100%)
Tel.: (314) 342-2000
Web Site: http://www.centurysecurities.com
Sales Range: $1-4.9 Billion
Emp.: 400
Independent Securities Brokerage & Dealing Services
N.A.I.C.S.: 523150

East Shore Aircraft LLC (1)
701 Lake St E 300, Wayzata, MN 55391
Tel.: (952) 345-0700
Aircraft Leasing & Consulting Services
N.A.I.C.S.: 532411

Eaton Partners, LLC (1)
677 Washington Blvd 9th Fl, Stamford, CT 06901   (100%)
Tel.: (203) 831-2970
Web Site: http://www.eatonpartnersllc.com
Investment Advisory Services
N.A.I.C.S.: 523940

Subsidiary (Non-US):

Eaton Partners (UK) LLP (2)
150 Cheapside 4th Fl, London, EC2V 6ET, United Kingdom
Tel.: (44) 2072922100
Web Site: http://www.eatonpartnersllc.com
Financial Services
N.A.I.C.S.: 523940

Subsidiary (Domestic):

Eaton Partners, LLC - San Diego (2)
4660 La Jolla Vlg Dr Ste 1040, San Diego, CA 92122
Tel.: (858) 200-3060
Web Site: http://www.eatonpartnersllc.com
Emp.: 75
Investment Advisory Services
N.A.I.C.S.: 523940

Finance 500, Inc. (1)
19762 MacArthur Blvd, Irvine, CA 92612
Tel.: (949) 253-4000
Web Site: http://www.finance500.com
Sales Range: $1-9.9 Million
Emp.: 22
Security Brokerage Services
N.A.I.C.S.: 523150
Lance Hicks *(Pres)*
Paul Savage *(VP)*

George K. Baum & Company (1)
4801 Main St Ste 500, Kansas City, MO 64112
Tel.: (816) 474-1100
Web Site: http://www.gkbaum.com

Sales Range: $50-74.9 Million
Emp.: 65
Investment Banking
N.A.I.C.S.: 523150
Julia Donnelly *(Mgr & Sr VP)*

KBW, Inc. (1)
The Equitable Bldg 787 7th Ave Fl 4, New York, NY 10019
Tel.: (212) 887-7777
Web Site: https://www.kbw.com
Sales Range: $250-299.9 Million
Emp.: 537
Investment Banking Services
N.A.I.C.S.: 523999
Thomas B. Michaud *(Pres & CEO)*
Frederick L. Cannon *(Dir-Global,Res & Exec VP)*
Peter J. Wirth *(Chm-Investment Banking Grp)*
Scott R. Anderson *(Head-Investment Banking-Global)*
Joseph S. Berry *(Mng Dir & Head-Investment Banking)*
Paul McCaffery *(Mng Dir & Co-Head-Equity Sls)*
George Karamanos *(Head-Res-Europe)*
Seth Bair *(Mng Dir & Head-Insurance)*
R. J. Grant *(Mng Dir & Head)*
Scott Jaffe *(Mng Dir)*
Robert Lee *(Mng Dir-Res)*
Victor Sack *(Mng Dir & Head-Equity Capital Markets)*
Sanjay Sakhrani *(Mng Dir-Res)*
Meyer Shields *(Mng Dir-Res)*
Deron Wolfe *(Mng Dir & Co-Head-Equity Sls)*
Garth Hackshall *(Mng Dir)*
Robin Mann *(Mng Dir & Head-Investment Banking-Europe)*
Richard Wynne-Griffith *(Mng Dir & Co-Head-Sls)*
Michael Garea *(Mng Dir-Capital Markets)*
Katherine Baken *(Mng Dir & Co-COO)*
Christopher McGratty *(Head-Bank Res-US)*
Richard Smith *(Mng Dir & CFO)*
Caroline Cameron *(Co-Dir & Co-COO)*
David Konrad *(Mng Dir)*
Erickson Davis *(Mng Dir & Head-European Equities)*
William Hawkins *(Mng Dir & Dir-Res)*
Andrew Stimpson *(Mng Dir & Head-European Banks Res)*
Aaron Axton *(Mng Dir)*
Simon Barrass *(Mng Dir)*
Jim Chester *(Mng Dir)*
Wesley Fox *(Mng Dir)*
Paul Friday *(Mng Dir)*
Joseph Gulash *(Mng Dir)*
James Harasimowicz *(Mng Dir)*
Jonathan Hemmert *(Mng Dir)*
Gareth Hunt *(Mng Dir)*
Michael Jones *(Mng Dir)*
Patrick Koster *(Mng Dir)*
Allen Laufenberg *(Mng Dir)*
David Lazar *(Mng Dir)*
Patrick Long *(Mng Dir)*
Pat McJoynt *(Mng Dir)*
Craig McMahen *(Mng Dir)*
Joseph H. Moeller *(Mng Dir)*
Ben Plotkin *(Mng Dir)*
Matthew Kelley *(Dir & Mng Dir)*
Keith Meyers *(Mng Dir & Head)*
Matthew Kelley *(Dir & Mng Dir)*
Keith Meyers *(Mng Dir & Head)*
John Guzzo *(Mng Dir)*
Manabu Sasaki *(Mng Dir)*
Murat Tastan *(Mng Dir)*
Rick Wassmundt *(Mng Dir)*
Jason White *(Mng Dir)*
Brian Foley *(VP)*
Graham Hixon *(VP)*
Claudia Katten *(VP)*
Paras Kaushal *(VP)*
Connor Schaible *(VP)*
Richard Gallagher *(Mng Dir)*
Michael Brown *(Mng Dir)*
Bose George *(Mng Dir)*
Vasundhara Govil *(Mng Dir)*
Steven Kwok *(Mng Dir)*
Kelly Motta *(Mng Dir)*
Michael Perito *(Mng Dir)*
Jade Rahmani *(Mng Dir)*
Melissa Roberts *(Mng Dir)*
Ryan Tomasello *(Mng Dir)*
Kyle Voigt *(Mng Dir)*

Subsidiary (Domestic):

Keefe, Bruyette & Woods Inc. (2)
The Equitable Bldg 787 7th Ave 4th Fl, New York, NY 10019
Tel.: (212) 887-7777
Web Site: https://www.kbw.com
Sales Range: $300-349.9 Million
Emp.: 67
Security Brokers & Dealers
N.A.I.C.S.: 523150
Keith Meyers *(Mng Dir & Head-FinTech & Fin Svcs Investment Banking)*
Katherine Baken *(Mng Dir & Co-COO)*
Christopher McGratty *(Mng Dir & Head)*
Peter J. Wirth *(Chm)*
Erickson Davis *(Mng Dir & Head-Europe)*
R. J. Grant *(Mng Dir & Head-Equity Trading Desk)*
Victor Sack *(Mng Dir & Head-Equity Capital Markets)*
Richard Wynne-Griffith *(Mng Dir & Co-Head-Sales)*
Seth Bair *(Mng Dir & Head-Insurance)*
George Karamanos *(Dir, Mng Dir & Co-Head-Sales)*
William Hawkins *(Dir & Mng Dir)*
Paul McCaffery *(Mng Dir & Head)*
Deron Wolfe *(Mng Dir & Head)*
Scott Anderson *(Head-Global)*
Joseph S. Berry *(Mng Dir & Head)*
Richard Smith *(Mng Dir & CFO)*
Rob Mann *(Mng Dir & Head-Europe)*
Caroline Cameron *(Co-Dir & Co-COO)*
Michael Garea *(Mng Dir)*
Andrew Fenwick *(Dir & Mng Dir)*
Frank Cicero *(Mng Dir)*
Wesley Fox *(Mng Dir)*
Paul Friday *(Mng Dir)*
John Guzzo *(Mng Dir)*
James Harasimowicz *(Mng Dir)*
Jonathan Hemmert *(Mng Dir)*
Joseph H. Moeller *(Mng Dir)*
Ben Plotkin *(Mng Dir & Exec VP)*
Manabu Sasaki *(Mng Dir)*
Murat Tastan *(Mng Dir)*
Rick Wassmundt *(Mng Dir)*
Jason White *(Mng Dir)*
Jordan Banov *(Dir)*
Ashwan Bimbhet *(Dir)*
Igor Borodulin *(Dir)*
Peter Houston *(Dir)*
Matthew Dinneen *(Dir)*
Louis DeRose *(Dir)*
Stephen Pollock *(Dir)*
Brian Foley *(VP)*
Jeffrey Hann *(VP)*
Graham Hixon *(VP)*
Michael Garea *(Mng Dir)*
Andrew Fenwick *(Dir & Mng Dir)*
Frank Cicero *(Mng Dir)*
Wesley Fox *(Mng Dir)*
Paul Friday *(Mng Dir)*
John Guzzo *(Mng Dir)*
James Harasimowicz *(Mng Dir)*
Jonathan Hemmert *(Mng Dir)*
Joseph H. Moeller *(Mng Dir)*
Ben Plotkin *(Mng Dir & Exec VP)*
Manabu Sasaki *(Mng Dir)*
Murat Tastan *(Mng Dir)*
Rick Wassmundt *(Mng Dir)*
Jason White *(Mng Dir)*
Jordan Banov *(Dir)*
Ashwan Bimbhet *(Dir)*
Igor Borodulin *(Dir)*
Peter Houston *(Dir)*
Matthew Dinneen *(Dir)*
Louis DeRose *(Dir)*
Stephen Pollock *(Dir)*
Brian Foley *(VP)*
Jeffrey Hann *(VP)*
Graham Hixon *(VP)*
Alex Smith *(Mng Dir)*
Gonzalo Smolders *(Mng Dir)*
Claudia Katten *(VP)*
Paras Kaushal *(VP)*
Connor Schaible *(VP)*
Scott Jaffe *(Mng Dir)*
Matthew Kelley *(Mng Dir)*
Richard Gallagher *(Mng Dir)*
Michael Brown *(Mng Dir)*
Bose George *(Mng Dir)*
Vasundhara Govil *(Mng Dir)*
David Konrad *(Mng Dir)*
Steven Kwok *(Mng Dir)*
Kelly Motta *(Mng Dir)*
Michael Perito *(Mng Dir)*
Jade Rahmani *(Mng Dir)*

Stifel Financial Corp.—(Continued)

Melissa Roberts *(Mng Dir)*
Ryan Tomasello *(Mng Dir)*
Kyle Voigt *(Mng Dir)*
Sanjay Sakhrani *(Mng Dir)*

Subsidiary (Domestic):

Keefe, Bruyette & Woods Inc. -San Francisco (3)
1 Montgomery St Ste 3700, San Francisco, CA 94104
Tel.: (415) 591-5020
Web Site: http://www.kbw.com
Sales Range: $150-199.9 Million
Brokerage Firm
N.A.I.C.S.: 523150

Subsidiary (Non-US):

Keefe, Bruyette & Woods Limited (2)
150 Cheapside 4th Fl, London, EC2V 6ET, United Kingdom
Tel.: (44) 2076635400
Investment Banking Services
N.A.I.C.S.: 523150

Mooreland Partners LLC (1)
950 Tower Ln Ste 1950, Foster City, CA 94404-2195
Tel.: (650) 330-3790
Investment Advice
N.A.I.C.S.: 523940

Oriel Asset Management LLP (1)
150 Cheapside, London, EC2V 6ET, United Kingdom
Tel.: (44) 2077107470
Asset Management Services
N.A.I.C.S.: 531390
Richard Scrope *(Mgr-Fund)*
Patrick Barton *(Mgr-Fund)*
Jamie Ward *(Mgr-Fund)*

Stifel Bank (1)
501 N Broadway, Saint Louis, MO 63102
Tel.: (314) 721-8003
Web Site: https://www.bankwithstifel.com
Sales Range: $10-24.9 Million
Emp.: 61
Commercial Banking
N.A.I.C.S.: 522110
Christopher K. Reichert *(Executives)*
Andrew Weissler *(Sr VP)*
Aaron Sestrich *(VP)*
Paul Lakamp *(Sr VP)*
Katrina Russell *(VP-Private Banking & Branch Mgr-Clayton)*
Kathleen Tallis *(VP)*
Kelly Bender *(VP)*
George Krioghaucor *(VP Comml Lending)*
Patrick Shuff *(Sr VP)*
Melissa Wilson *(Mgr & Sr VP)*
Dan Weber *(Officer)*
Brad Ellis *(Mng Dir)*
Chris Frein *(Chief Lending Officer & Sr VP)*
Terri Mills *(Asst VP)*
Kelly O'Brien *(Asst VP)*
Andy Szczuka *(Asst VP)*
John P. Dubinsky *(Chm)*
Kelli Gilliam *(Sr VP-)*
Rodney Malone *(VP)*

Stifel Bank & Trust (1)
1 Financial Plz 501 N Broadway, Saint Louis, MO 63102
Tel.: (314) 342-2251
Web Site: https://www.stifel.com
Commercial Banking
N.A.I.C.S.: 522110

Stifel Europe Advisory GmbH (1)
Bockenheimer Landstrasse 24, 60323, Frankfurt am Main, Germany
Tel.: (49) 692474140
Strategic Advice & Investment Banking Services
N.A.I.C.S.: 523150

Stifel Europe Bank AG (1)
Maffeistrasse 4, 80333, Munich, Germany
Tel.: (49) 899 992 9820
Banking Services
N.A.I.C.S.: 522110

Stifel Independent Advisors, LLC (1)
501 N Broadway, Saint Louis, MO 63102
Tel.: (314) 342-4051

Web Site:
https://www.stifelindependence.com
Financial Consulting Services
N.A.I.C.S.: 541611

Stifel Schweiz AG (1)
Tessinerplatz 7, 8002, Zurich, Switzerland
Tel.: (41) 43 888 6100
Financial Investment Services
N.A.I.C.S.: 523999

Stifel Trust Company, National Association (1)
1 Financial Plz 501 N Broadway, Saint Louis, MO 63102
Tel.: (314) 342-4450
Web Site: https://www.stifeltrust.com
Financial Advisory Services
N.A.I.C.S.: 523150
Kurt D. Longworth *(COO & Pres)*

Stifel Venture Corp. (1)
501 N Broadway, Saint Louis, MO 63102
Tel.: (314) 342-2000
Asset Management Services
N.A.I.C.S.: 531390

Stifel, Nicolaus & Company, Incorporated (1)
501 N Bdwy, Saint Louis, MO 63102
Tel.: (314) 342-2000
Web Site: http://www.stifel.com
Regional Securities Brokerage & Dealing Services
N.A.I.C.S.: 523150

Subsidiary (Non-US):

Stifel Nicolaus Europe Limited (2)
150 Cheapside, London, EC2V 6ET, United Kingdom
Tel.: (44) 2077107600
General Marketing Services
N.A.I.C.S.: 541613

Subsidiary (Non-US):

MainFirst Bank AG (3)
Kennedyallee 76, 60596, Frankfurt am Main, Germany
Tel.: (49) 69244374400
Web Site: http://www.mainfirst.com
Emp.: 160
Investment Banking Services
N.A.I.C.S.: 523150
Ebrahim Attarzadeh *(CEO)*
Bjoern Kirchner *(CFO)*

Subsidiary (Domestic):

Stifel Nicolaus Insurance Agency, Incorporated (2)
501 N Broadway, Saint Louis, MO 63102-2131
Tel.: (314) 342-2000
Web Site: http://www.stifel.com
Insurance Brokerage Services
N.A.I.C.S.: 524210

Stone & Youngberg LLC (1)
1 Ferry Bldg, San Francisco, CA 94111
Tel.: (415) 445-2300
Sales Range: $50-74.9 Million
Emp.: 95
Bond Dealers & Brokers
N.A.I.C.S.: 523150
Ronald J. Kruszewski *(Chm & CEO)*

Thomas Weisel Partners Group, Inc. (1)
1 Montgomery St, San Francisco, CA 94104
Tel.: (415) 364-2500
Web Site: http://www.tweisel.com
Sales Range: $150-199.9 Million
Emp.: 461
Holding Company; Investment Banking, Brokerage, Research & Asset Management Services
N.A.I.C.S.: 551112
Thomas Wilson Weisel *(Founder)*
Blake J. Jorgensen *(Co-Founder)*

Subsidiary (Domestic):

Thomas Weisel Capital Management LLC (2)
1 Montgomery St, San Francisco, CA 94104
Tel.: (415) 364-2500
Financial Services
N.A.I.C.S.: 523940

McGibben Baiba *(Dir-Ops)*

Thomas Weisel Partners LLC (2)
1 Montgomery St Ste 3700, San Francisco, CA 94104
Tel.: (415) 364-2500
Web Site: http://www.tweisel.com
Sales Range: $125-149.9 Million
Emp.: 300
Investment Banking, Brokerage, Research & Asset Management Services
N.A.I.C.S.: 523150

Ziegler Capital Management, LLC (2)
30 S Wacker Dr Ste 2800, Chicago, IL 60606
Tel.: (312) 368-1442
Web Site: https://www.zcm.com
Asset Management Services
N.A.I.C.S.: 531390
Scott Roberts *(Pres & CEO)*
John K. Brinckerhoff *(CMO)*
Devansh Patel *(Sr Mng Dir-Strategy)*
Craig Vanucci *(Sr Mng Dir-Mktg & Client Svcs)*
Matthew Kowieski *(Dir-Ops)*
Paula Horn *(Sr Portfolio Mgr & Chief Investment Officer)*
Monika Singh *(Chief Compliance Officer)*
Renee Ansbro *(CFO)*
William Fitzgerald *(CEO)*
Evans Papanikolaou *(Chief Admin Officer)*
Jack O'Callahan *(Sr Mng Dir)*
William Fitzgerald *(CEO)*
Evans Papanikolaou *(Chief Admin Officer)*
Jack O'Callahan *(Sr Mng Dir)*

Subsidiary (Domestic):

Sagewood Asset Management LLC (3)
100 Park Ave 22nd Fl, New York, NY 10017
Tel.: (212) 231-8770
Web Site: https://www.sagewoodam.com
Financial Services
N.A.I.C.S.: 523940
Defina Maluki *(Co-Founder & Chief Investment Officer)*
David Travis *(CFO & COO)*
William J. Belleville Jr. *(Co-Founder)*

Torreya Partners LLC (1)
555 Madison Ave Ste 1201, New York, NY 10022
Tel.: (212) 331-7843
Web Site: http://www.torreyapartners.com
Investment Banking & Security Brokerage Services
N.A.I.C.S.: 523150

Washington Crossing Advisors, LLC (1)
18 Columbia Tpke, Florham Park, NJ 07932-2289
Tel.: (973) 549-4051
Web Site:
http://www.washingtoncrossingadvisors.com
Financial Services
N.A.I.C.S.: 523999
Kevin R. Caron *(Co-Founder & Sr Portfolio Mgr)*
Chad A. Morganlander *(Co-Founder & Sr Portfolio Mgr)*
Matthew J. Battipaglia *(Portfolio Mgr)*
Suzanne Ashley *(Mgr-)*

STITCH FIX, INC.
1 Montgomery St Ste 1100, San Francisco, CA 94104
Tel.: (415) 882-7765   DE
Web Site: https://www.stitchfix.com
Year Founded: 2011
SFIX—(NASDAQ)
Rev.: $1,337,468,000
Assets: $486,864,000
Liabilities: $299,842,000
Net Worth: $187,022,000
Earnings: ($128,840,000)
Emp.: 4,570
Fiscal Year-end: 08/03/24
Online Shopping Services
N.A.I.C.S.: 458110
Katrina Lake *(Founder & Exec Chm)*
Debbie Rose Woloshin *(CMO)*

Casey O'Connor *(Chief Legal Officer)*
Tony Bacos *(Chief Product & Tech Officer)*
Debbie Rose Woloshin *(CMO)*
Matt Baer *(CEO)*
Lillian Reaume *(Chief People Officer)*
David Aufderhaar *(CFO & Principal Acctg Officer)*

STOCK PLUS AD
Tel.: (359) 896819001
Web Site: https://www.stockplus.org
Year Founded: 2005
STKP-—(BUL)
Sales Range: Less than $1 Million
Real Estate Services
N.A.I.C.S.: 531390
Yavor Panev *(Dir-IR)*

STOCK YARDS BANCORP, INC.
1040 E Main St, Louisville, KY 40232-2890
Tel.: (502) 582-2571   KY
Web Site: https://www.syb.com
Year Founded: 1988
SYBT—(NASDAQ)
Rev.: $340,801,000
Assets: $7,496,261,000
Liabilities: $6,735,829,000
Net Worth: $760,432,000
Earnings: $93,294,000
Emp.: 1,040
Fiscal Year-end: 12/31/22
Bank Holding Company
N.A.I.C.S.: 551111
James A. Hillebrand *(Chm & CEO)*
Philip S. Poindexter *(Pres)*
T. Clay Stinnett *(CFO, Treas & Exec VP)*
Michael B. Newton *(Chief Acctg Officer & Sr VP)*
Michael J. Croce *(Exec VP-Retail Banking Grp)*
Michael V. Rehm *(Chief Lending Officer & Exec VP)*
William M. Dishman III *(Chief Risk Officer & Exec VP)*

Subsidiaries:

Commonwealth Bancshares, Inc. (1)
4912 US Hwy 42, Louisville, KY 40222
Tel.: (502) 259-2000
Web Site: http://www.cbandt.com
Sales Range: $25-49.9 Million
Emp.: 266
Bank Holding Company
N.A.I.C.S.: 551111

Subsidiary (Domestic):

Commonwealth Bank & Trust Company (2)
4350 Brownsboro Rd Ste 310, Louisville, KY 40207
Tel.: (502) 259-2000
Web Site: http://www.cbandt.com
Sales Range: $10-24.9 Million
Commercial Banking
N.A.I.C.S.: 522110
Ann C. Wells *(Chm & CEO)*
Darrell R. Wells *(Vice Chm & Sr Exec VP)*
Michael E. Dugle *(CFO & Exec VP)*
Dave Ising *(Chief Retail Banking Officer & Sr VP)*
Courtney Giesel *(Exec VP & Head-Corp Banking)*
John Bollman *(Exec VP-Mortgage)*
Mark J. Kennedy *(Exec VP)*
Carla Cooper *(Sr VP & Dir-HR)*
Robert R. Hawkins *(CIO & Sr VP)*
Brian S. Stivers *(Sr VP & Portfolio Mgr)*
John Michael Fidler *(Sr VP & Dir-Alternative Investments)*
Erik N. Evans *(Sr VP & Portfolio Mgr)*
Stephen L. McCool *(Sr VP & Portfolio Mgr)*
Christopher A. Nunnelley *(Sr VP & Mgr-Trust Svcs)*
Michael R. Motsinger *(Sr VP)*
Stephen L. Zeitz *(Sr VP & Mgr-Trust Ops)*
Toby Nutt *(Sr VP)*
Jack M. Combs Jr. *(Sr VP)*

Kentucky Bancshares, Inc. (1)
339 Main St, Paris, KY 40361
Tel.: (859) 987-1795
Web Site: http://www.kybank.com
Rev.: $42,685,000
Assets: $1,239,505,000
Liabilities: $1,111,163,000
Net Worth: $128,342,000
Earnings: $11,697,000
Emp.: 236
Fiscal Year-end: 12/31/2020
Bank Holding Company
N.A.I.C.S.: 551111

Subsidiary (Domestic):

KBI Insurance Company, Inc. (2)
18660 SW Boones Ferry Rd, Tualatin, OR 97062
Tel.: (503) 564-1039
Insurance Agency & Brokerage Services
N.A.I.C.S.: 524210

Kentucky Bank (2)
400 Main St, Paris, KY 40361
Tel.: (859) 987-8663
Web Site: http://www.kybank.com
Sales Range: $25-49.9 Million
Commericial Banking
N.A.I.C.S.: 522110
Louis Prichard (Pres & CEO)
Shane Foley (Exec VP & Dir-Retail Banking)
Quin Broadbent (VP & Sr Portfolio Mgr)
Selina Shepherd (VP-Mgr-Trust Admin)
Melissa Ritchie (Officer-Trust Ops & VP)

Stock Yards Bank & Trust Company (1)
1040 E Main St, Louisville, KY 40206 (100%)
Tel.: (502) 582-2571
Web Site: https://www.syb.com
Sales Range: $125-149.9 Million
Emp.: 500
Commercial Banking Services
N.A.I.C.S.: 522110
James A. Hillebrand (Chm & CEO)
Philip S. Poindexter (Pres)
T. Clay Stinnett (CFO, Treas & Exec VP)

STOKE THERAPEUTICS, INC.
45 Wiggins Ave, Bedford, MA 01730
Tel.: (781) 430-8200 DE
Web Site:
https://www.stoketherapeutics.com
Year Founded: 2014
STOK—(NASDAQ)
Rev.: $12,405,000
Assets: $256,067,000
Liabilities: $71,218,000
Net Worth: $184,849,000
Earnings: ($101,067,000)
Emp.: 117
Fiscal Year-end: 12/31/22
Biotechnology Research & Development Services
N.A.I.C.S.: 541714
Thomas Leggett (CFO & Principal Acctg Officer)
Barry S. Ticho (Chief Medical Officer)
Dawn Kalmar (Chief Comm Officer)
Isabel Aznarez (Co-Founder & Sr VP/Grp VP-Discovery Res)
Huw M. Nash (COO & Chief Bus Officer)
Joan Wood (Chief HR Officer)
Shamim Ruff (Chief Regulatory Officer)
Jonathan Allan (Gen Counsel & Deputy Gen Counsel)
Jason Hoitt (Chief Comml Officer)
Adrian R. Krainer (Co-Founder)
Edward M. Kaye (CEO)
Huw M. Nash (Chief Bus Officer)

STONE HARBOR EMERGING MARKETS INCOME FUND
31 W 52nd St 16th FL, New York, NY 10019 MA
Web Site: https://www.shiplpcef.com
Year Founded: 2010
EDF—(NYSE)

Sales Range: $25-49.9 Million
Investment Services
N.A.I.C.S.: 523999
Peter J. Wilby (Pres & CEO)
Thomas K. Flanagan (Chm)
Pablo Cisilino (Exec VP)
James E. Craige (Exec VP)
David Griffiths (Exec VP)
Angus Halkett (Exec VP)
David A. Oliver (Exec VP)
William Perry (Exec VP)
David Scott (Exec VP)
Adam J. Shapiro (Chief Legal Officer & Sec)
Jeffrey S. Scott (Chief Compliance Officer & Asst Sec)
Gina Meyer (Asst Treas)
Amanda Suss (Treas)

STONE HARBOR EMG MKTS TOTAL INCOME FUND
LP 31 W 52nd St, New York, NY 10019
Tel.: (212) 548-1200
EDI—(NYSE)
Rev.: $11,206,709
Assets: $105,710,132
Liabilities: $7,155,555
Net Worth: $98,554,577
Earnings: $9,033,288
Fiscal Year-end: 11/30/19
Investment Management Service
N.A.I.C.S.: 525990
Jim Craige (Mgr-Fund)

STONERIDGE, INC.
39675 MacKenzie Dr Ste 400, Novi, MI 48377
Tel.: (248) 489-9300 OH
Web Site:
https://www.stoneridge.com
Year Founded: 1965
SRI—(NYSE)
Rev.: $899,923,000
Assets: $652,105,000
Liabilities: $371,163,000
Net Worth: $280,942,000
Earnings: ($14,056,000)
Emp.: 5,250
Fiscal Year-end: 12/31/22
Electrical & Electronic Components Mfr for Cars, Trucks & Other Motor Vehicles
N.A.I.C.S.: 336320
Theresa G. Mitchell (CIO)
Matthew R. Horvath (CFO & Treas)
Susan C. Benedict (Chief HR Officer & Asst Gen Counsel-Labor & Employment)
Caetano Ferraiolo (Pres-Stoneridge Brazil Div)
James Zizelman (Pres-Control Devices Div)
Salvatore Orsini (Chief Procurement Officer)
Archie Nimmer (VP-Ops)
James Zizelman (Pres & CEO)
Rajaey Kased (Pres)
Peter Osterberg (Pres)
Robert J. Hartman Jr. (Chief Acctg Officer)

Subsidiaries:

Bolton Conductive Systems, LLC (1)
28001 Cabot Dr Ste 100, Novi, MI 48377
Tel.: (248) 669-7080
Web Site:
http://boltonconductivesystems.com
Wire Harnesses & Control Panels & Automotive Electrical Systems Mfr
N.A.I.C.S.: 336320

Minda Stoneridge Instruments Limited (1)
Gut No 287-295 298 Nanekarwadi Chakan Tal Khed, Pune, 410501, Maharashtra, India
Tel.: (91) 2135662000

Web Site: https://www.sparkminda.com
Electronics Instrument Mfr
N.A.I.C.S.: 335313
Nitin Saxena (COO)
Ajay Kumar Choudhary (CFO)
Rajeev Khanna (Asst VP-Mktg)

Orlaco GmbH (1)
Alte Landstrasse 21, Bei Munchen, 85521, Ottobrunn, Germany
Tel.: (49) 8963879260
Web Site: https://www.orlaco.de
Camera Mfr & Distr
N.A.I.C.S.: 333310

Orlaco Inc. (1)
33 Confederate Ave, Jasper, GA 30143
Tel.: (706) 301-9227
Web Site: http://www.orlaco.com
Emp.: 225
Camera Mfr & Distr
N.A.I.C.S.: 333310

Orlaco Products B.V. (1)
Albert Plesmanstraat 42, 3772 MN, Barneveld, Netherlands
Tel.: (31) 342404555
Web Site: https://www.orlaco.nl
Camera Monitoring Services
N.A.I.C.S.: 561621
Erik van der Burg (Mgr-Procurement)

Stoneridge Asia Pacific Electronics (Suzhou) Co. Ltd. (1)
1 RuiCi Lane, Suzhou Industrial Park Loufeng North District SIP, Suzhou, 215001, Jiangsu, China
Tel.: (86) 51262558190
Web Site: https://www.stoneridge.com
Sales Range: $100-124.9 Million
Emp.: 180
Electronic Components Mfr
N.A.I.C.S.: 334419

Stoneridge Electronics AB (1)
Gustav III s Boulevard 26, 169 73, Solna, Sweden
Tel.: (46) 8154400
Sales Range: $25-49.9 Million
Emp.: 160
Automotive Electronic Equipment Mfr
N.A.I.C.S.: 336320

Stoneridge Electronics AB (1)
Gustav III s Boulevard 26, 169 73, Solna, Sweden
Tel.: (46) 8154400
Sales Range: $25-49.9 Million
Emp.: 160
Automotive Electronic Equipment Mfr
N.A.I.C.S.: 336320

Stoneridge Electronics AB (1)
Gustav III s Boulevard 26, 169 73, Solna, Sweden
Tel.: (46) 8154400
Sales Range: $25-49.9 Million
Emp.: 160
Automotive Electronic Equipment Mfr
N.A.I.C.S.: 336320

Stoneridge Electronics AB (1)
Gustav III s Boulevard 26, 169 73, Solna, Sweden
Tel.: (46) 8154400
Sales Range: $25-49.9 Million
Emp.: 160
Automotive Electronic Equipment Mfr
N.A.I.C.S.: 336320

Stoneridge Electronics Ltd. (1)
Charles Bowman Avenue, Claverhouse Industrial Park, Dundee, DD4 9UB, Scotland, United Kingdom
Tel.: (44) 1382866400
Web Site: http://www.stoneridge-electronics.com
Electronic Components Mfr
N.A.I.C.S.: 334419

Stoneridge Electronics, Inc. (1)
8640 East Market St, Warren, OH 44484
Tel.: (330) 856-2443
Rev.: $200,000,000
Emp.: 100
Electronic Components Mfr
N.A.I.C.S.: 334419

Stoneridge Nordic AB (1)
Gustav III s Boulevard 26, 169 73, Solna, Sweden

Tel.: (46) 8154400
Web Site: https://stoneridgetruckshop.com
Electronic Products Mfr
N.A.I.C.S.: 335313

TED de Mexico S.A. de C.V. (1)
Parque Industrial A J Bermudez No 950, Ciudad Juarez, 32470, Mexico
Tel.: (52) 6566880650
Sales Range: $150-199.9 Million
Emp.: 800
Automotive Electronic Equipment Mfr
N.A.I.C.S.: 336320
Nick Di Nardo (Plant Mgr)

STONEX GROUP INC.
230 Park Ave 10th Fl, New York, NY 10169
Tel.: (212) 485-3500 DE
Web Site: https://www.stonex.com
Year Founded: 1987
SNEX—(NASDAQ)
Rev.: $99,887,800,000
Assets: $27,466,300,000
Liabilities: $25,757,200,000
Net Worth: $1,709,100,000
Earnings: $260,800,000
Emp.: 4,500
Fiscal Year-end: 09/30/24
Holding Company; International Securities & Commodities Markets Investment Services
N.A.I.C.S.: 551112
David Bolte (Sec & Deputy Gen Counsel)
William J. Dunaway (CFO)
Aaron M. Schroeder (Chief Acctg Officer)
John Stanislas Albert Radziwill (Chm)
Sean Michael O'Connor (Pres & CEO)
Philip A. Smith (CEO-Europe, Middle East & Africa & Asia Ops)
Kent R. Coughlin (Dir-PR)
Kevin Murphy (Treas)
Mark Maurer (Chief Risk Officer)
Abbey Perkins (CIO)
Diego A. Rotsztain (Chief Governance & Legal Officer)
Glenn Stevens (Head-Retail & Foreign Exchange)

Subsidiaries:

CDI - Societe Cotonniere de Distribution S.A. (1)
Chemin de Contigny 5, Case Postal 1001, Lausanne, Switzerland
Tel.: (41) 216126565
Web Site: https://cdi.stonex.com
Apparel Cotton Distr
N.A.I.C.S.: 424990

Carl Kliem S.A. (1)
251 Route d'Arlon, Luxembourg, 1150, Luxembourg
Tel.: (352) 458484
Web Site: http://www.carlkliem.lu
Interbank & Securities Brokerage Services
N.A.I.C.S.: 523150

CoinInvest GmbH (1)
Taunusanlage 8, 60329, Frankfurt am Main, Germany
Tel.: (49) 6934877570
Web Site: http://www.coininvest.com
Gold Retailer
N.A.I.C.S.: 423940

European Precious Metal Trading GmbH (1)
Taunusanlage 8, 60329, Frankfurt am Main, Germany
Tel.: (49) 6934877570
Web Site: http://www.silver-to-go.com
Silver Coin Retailer
N.A.I.C.S.: 423940

FCStone Group, Inc. (1)
1251 NW Briarcliff Pkwy Ste 800, Kansas City, MO 64116 (100%)
Tel.: (816) 410-5636
Web Site: http://www.fcstone.com

StoneX Group Inc.—(Continued)

Holding Company; Commodity Risk Management Consulting & Trading Services
N.A.I.C.S.: 551112

Subsidiary (Non-US):

FCStone Canada ULC (2)
90 Garry St Ste 103, Winnipeg, R3C4HI, MB, Canada
Tel.: (866) 634-7392
Risk Management
N.A.I.C.S.: 523160

Subsidiary (Domestic):

FCStone Merchant Services, LLC (2)
1075 Jordan Creek Pkwy Ste 300, West Des Moines, IA 50266
Tel.: (515) 223-3728
Web Site: http://www.intlfcstone.com
Commodities Financing & Trade Facilitation Services
N.A.I.C.S.: 523160

FCStone Trading, LLC (2)
2829 Westown Pkwy Ste 100, West Des Moines, IA 50266
Tel.: (515) 223-3788
Web Site: http://www.fcstone.com
Financial Services
N.A.I.C.S.: 523999

Subsidiary (Non-US):

FCStone do Brasil Ltda. (2)
Av Jose Bonifacio Coutinho Nogueira 103, 2 Andar - Jardim Madalena, Campinas, 13091-611, SP, Brazil
Tel.: (55) 1921021300
Web Site: http://www.intlfcstone.com.br
Emp.: 80
All Other Business Support Services
N.A.I.C.S.: 561499

GAIN Capital Holdings, Inc. (1)
135 US Highway 202 206 Ste 11, Bedminster, NJ 07921
Tel.: (908) 731-0700
Web Site: http://www.gaincapital.com
Sales Range: $200-249.9 Million
Emp.: 800
Investment Banking & Securities Dealing & Internet Publishing & Trading Services
N.A.I.C.S.: 523150
Diego A. Rotsztain (Gen Counsel, Sec & Head-Corp Dev)
Timothy O'Sullivan (Chief Risk Officer)
Nigel Rose (CFO)
Alastair Hine (COO)

Subsidiary (Non US):

City Index (Holdings) Ltd. (2)
16 Finsbury Circus Park House, London, EC2M 7EB, United Kingdom
Tel.: (44) 2071077371
Holding Company
N.A.I.C.S.: 551112

Faraday Research LLP (2)
CMA House Newham Road, Truro, TR1 2SU, Cornwall, United Kingdom
Tel.: (44) 872265333
Web Site: http://www.faradayresearch.co.uk
Market Research Services
N.A.I.C.S.: 541613

GAIN Capital Japan Co., Ltd. (2)
4-4-10 Nihombashimuromachi, Chuo-Ku, Tokyo, 100-0022, Japan
Tel.: (81) 352056161
Web Site: http://www.gaincapital.com
Online Trading Services
N.A.I.C.S.: 522299

GAIN Capital Singapore Pte. Ltd. (2)
168 Robinson Road Capital Tower 20-01, Singapore, 068912, Singapore
Tel.: (65) 68269988
Web Site: http://www.cityindex.com.sg
Financial Investment Services
N.A.I.C.S.: 523999

GAIN Capital UK Limited (2)
Devon House 58 St Katharine's Way, London, E1W 1JP, United Kingdom
Tel.: (44) 2031941801
Web Site: http://www.cityindex.co.uk

Contracts for Difference Trading, Foreign Currency Exchange Trading & Sports Betting Services
N.A.I.C.S.: 523999

GAIN Capital-Forex.com U.K., Ltd. (2)
Park House 16 Finsbury Circus, London, EC2M 7EB, United Kingdom
Tel.: (44) 2031941801
Web Site: http://www.gaincapital.com
Securities Brokerage Services
N.A.I.C.S.: 523150

GFT Global Markets Asia PTE, Ltd. (2)
6 Battery Road 20-01, Singapore, 049909, Singapore
Tel.: (65) 62275519
Web Site: http://www.gftasia.com
Online Trading Services
N.A.I.C.S.: 522320

Subsidiary (Domestic):

GTX SEF, LLC (2)
135 US Hwy 202/206 Ste 11, Bedminster, NJ 07921
Tel.: (908) 212-3939
Web Site: http://www.gaingtx.com
Software Development Services
N.A.I.C.S.: 541511

Gain Capital Group LLC (2)
Bedminster One 135 US Highway 202/206 Ste 11, Bedminster, NJ 07921
Tel.: (908) 731-0700
Web Site: http://www.forex.com
Sales Range: $50-74.9 Million
Emp.: 175
Foreign Currency Exchange Services
N.A.I.C.S.: 523160

Subsidiary (Non-US):

Galvan Research & Trading, Ltd. (2)
CMA House Newham Road, Truro, TR1 2SU, Cornwall, United Kingdom
Tel.: (44) 1872262622
Web Site: http://www.galvan.co.uk
Financial Advisory Services
N.A.I.C.S.: 523940

Subsidiary (Domestic):

Global Asset Advisors, LLC (2)
100 S Wacker Dr Ste 1225, Chicago, IL 60606
Tel.: (312) 706-7600
Web Site: http://www.danielstrading.com
Security Services
N.A.I.C.S.: 561612
Ken Packard (CMO & Chief Sls Officer)
Andrew Daniels (Founder & CEO)
Glenn A. Swanson (Pres)
Heather Krakora (Dir-Compliance)
Adam M. Nicholson (VP-Mktg)

Global Forex Trading (2)
618 Kenmoor Ave SE Ste 201, Grand Rapids, MI 49546
Tel.: (616) 956-9273
Web Site: http://www.gftforex.com
Rev.: $60,800,000
Emp.: 300
Online Currency Traders
N.A.I.C.S.: 523999

Global Futures & Forex, Ltd. (2)
618 Kenmoor Ave SE, Grand Rapids, MI 49546
Tel.: (616) 956-9273
Online Trading Services
N.A.I.C.S.: 523999

GMP Securities, LLC (1)
530 5th Ave 15th Fl, New York, NY 10036 **(100%)**
Tel.: (212) 692-5100
Web Site: http://www.gmpsecuritiesllc.com
Sales Range: $50-74.9 Million
Emp.: 100
Securities Brokerage Services
N.A.I.C.S.: 523150
Robert Schoenthal (Pres)

Gainvest Uruguay Asset Management S.A. (1)
World Trade Center, Luis A de Herrera 1902 19 Fl, 11300, Montevideo, Uruguay
Tel.: (598) 26283047

Asset Management Services
N.A.I.C.S.: 523940

INTL Advisory Consultants Inc. (1)
800 Shades Creek Pkwy Suite 700, Birmingham, AL 35209
Tel.: (205) 414-3332
Investment Advisory & Asset Management Services
N.A.I.C.S.: 523940

INTL Asia Pte. Ltd (1)
1 Raffles Place 52-00 OUB Centre Downtown, Singapore, 48616, Singapore
Tel.: (65) 63091000
Web Site: http://www.intlfcstone.com
Securities & Commodity Services
N.A.I.C.S.: 523160

INTL CIBSA S.A. (1)
Sarmiento 459 9 piso, 1182, Buenos Aires, Argentina
Tel.: (54) 1143907500
Web Site: http://www.intlfcstone.com.ar
Commodity Contracts Brokerage Services
N.A.I.C.S.: 523160

INTL Capital Limited (1)
Level 1 Gate Village 05, PO Box 506645 DIFC, Dubai, United Arab Emirates
Tel.: (971) 43653110
Sales Range: $650-699.9 Million
Asset Management & Trade Finance Services
N.A.I.C.S.: 523999

INTL Capital S.A. (1)
Sarmiento 459 9 no piso, Capital Federal, Buenos Aires, 1041, Argentina
Tel.: (54) 1143907595
Commodity Futures Investment Services
N.A.I.C.S.: 523999

INTL Custody & Clearing Solutions Inc. (1)
2600 N Military Trl Ste 290, Boca Raton, FL 33431
Tel.: (561) 544-7611
Web Site: http://www6.intlfcstone.com
Securities Trade Clearing Services
N.A.I.C.S.: 522320
Steven zum Tobel (Mng Dir)

INTL FCStone (HK) Ltd. (1)
Unit 701 7th Floor 100 Queen's Road Central, Hong Kong, China (Hong Kong)
Tel.: (852) 34691900
Commodity Contracts Dealing Services
N.A.I.C.S.: 523160
Lawronce Huang (Gen Mgr)

INTL FCStone (Shanghai) Trading Co., Ltd (1)
Room 416 Wangfu Century 55 Dong An Men Avenue, Shanghai, China
Tel.: (86) 1065130855
Commodity Contracts Dealing Services
N.A.I.C.S.: 523160

INTL FCStone Banco de Cambio S.A. (1)
Rua Joaquim Floriano 413 14th Floor, Itaim Bibi, Sao Paulo, SP, Brazil
Tel.: (55) 11 3509 5467
Foreign Exchange Banking
N.A.I.C.S.: 523160
Joao Vilhena (Coord-Ops-FX)

INTL FCStone Capital Assessoria Financeira Ltda. (1)
Rua Joaquim Floriano 413 14th andar, SP 01310 200, Sao Paulo, Brazil
Tel.: (55) 11 3509 5400
Asset Management Services
N.A.I.C.S.: 523999

INTL FCStone Commodities DMCC (1)
Office 48D Al Mas Tower Jumeirah Lakes Towers, PO Box 125942, Dubai, United Arab Emirates
Tel.: (971) 44478500
Commodity Contracts Dealing Services
N.A.I.C.S.: 523160
Simon Walsh (CEO)

INTL FCStone DTVM Ltda. (1)
Rua Joaquim Floriano 133 14o Andar, Sao Paulo, 1451, Brazil
Tel.: (55) 1135095400

Web Site: http://www.intlfcstone.com
Emp.: 50
Commodity Brokerage Services
N.A.I.C.S.: 523160

INTL FCStone Europe S.A. (1)
251 Route Darlon, 1150, Luxembourg, Luxembourg
Tel.: (352) 4584841
Financial Services
N.A.I.C.S.: 541611
Mika Valanki (Mng Dir)

INTL FCStone Financial (Canada) Inc. (1)
20 Adelaide Street East Suite 1001, Toronto, M5C 2T6, ON, Canada
Tel.: (647) 475-0451
Web Site: https://www.stonex.com
Commodity Contracts Dealing
N.A.I.C.S.: 523160
Rambaldini Ernesto (CEO)

INTL FCStone Financial Inc. (1)
329 N Park Ave, Winter Park, FL 32789 **(100%)**
Tel.: (407) 741-5399
Web Site: http://www.intlmarketmaking.com
Sales Range: $100-124.9 Million
Emp.: 45
Securities Brokerage
N.A.I.C.S.: 523150
Robert LaForte (Head-Fixed Income)
Grant Garcia (Dir-Structured Product Sls)
George Brickfield (Mng Dir-Distressed Debt & Loan Sls)
Anthony Diciollo (Head-Fixed Income Div)

INTL FCStone Pte. Ltd. (1)
ONE Raffles Place 12-62 Tower 2, Singapore, 048616, Singapore
Tel.: (65) 63091000
Commodity Contracts Dealing Services
N.A.I.C.S.: 523160
Malcolm Wilde (Exec Chm & CEO)

INTL FCStone Pty. Ltd. (1)
Suite 7 03 Level 7 25 Bligh Street, Sydney, 2000, NSW, Australia
Tel.: (61) 280942000
Financial Services
N.A.I.C.S.: 541611
Brett Cooper (Sr Mgr-Trading)
David Skelly (Sr Mgr-Metals)
Sandra Matthews (Mgr-Compliance)
Merren Carnegie (Mgr-Ops)
Sophie Chao (CFO)

INTL FCStone de Mexico, S. de R.L. de C.V. (1)
Av Paseo de la Reforma 350 Piso 11, Col Juarez CDMX, Mexico, DF 06600, Mexico
Tel.: (52) 5591711526
Commodity Contracts Dealing
N.A.I.C.S.: 523160
Luis Garcia (Mng Dir-Comml)

INTL Gainvest S.A. (1)
Sarmiento 459 9 piso, CP 1041 CABA, Buenos Aires, Argentina
Tel.: (54) 11 4390 7595
Web Site: http://www.gainvest.net
Commodity Investment Fund Management Services
N.A.I.C.S.: 523940

INTL Global Currencies Limited (1)
Phoenix House 3rd Floor 18 King William St, London, EC4N 7BP, United Kingdom
Tel.: (44) 2072206060
Foreign Exchange & Treasury Services
N.A.I.C.S.: 523999

INTL Korea Limited (1)
903 Invest Korea Plaza 7 Heolleungno, Seochu-gu, Seoul, 137-170, Korea (South)
Tel.: (82) 234971989
Financial Advisory Services
N.A.I.C.S.: 523940

INTL Netherlands B.V. (1)
Rietlandpark 125, Amsterdam, 1019 DT, Noord-Holland, Netherlands
Tel.: (31) 206704455
Stock Exchange Services
N.A.I.C.S.: 523160
Doron Shamir (Mng Dir)

Incomm S.A.S. (1)
Calle 19 Norte No 2N- 29 Oficina 3002-A, Edificio Torre de, Cali, Colombia

Tel.: (57) 25249444
Web Site: https://incomm.com.co
Logistics Consulting Servies
N.A.I.C.S.: 541614

SA Stone Wealth Management Inc. (1)
2 Perimeter Park S Ste 500W, Birmingham, AL 35243
Web Site: https://www.saswealth.com
Securities Broker & Dealer
N.A.I.C.S.: 523150
Jay W. Carter *(Pres & CEO)*
Marcus Richardson *(COO)*
Brian Parker *(Chief Compliance Officer)*
Stephanie Bova *(Sr VP-Admin)*
Maribeth Williams *(Sr VP-Client Rels)*
Stephen O'Neill *(Dir-Bus Dev)*
Matt C. Kelley *(Head-Bus Dev)*
Matthew Hill *(Dir-Fiduciary Svcs)*
Mark Hugo *(Assoc Dir-Supervision)*

StoneX (Shanghai) Trading Co., Ltd. (1)
Azia Center Room 302 1233 Lujiazui Ring Road, Shanghai, 200120, China
Tel.: (86) 2151081234
Futures Brokerage Services
N.A.I.C.S.: 524210

StoneX Banco de Cambio S.A. (1)
Rua Joaquim Floriano 413 - 6th floor, Itaim Bibi, Sao Paulo, 04534-011, Brazil
Tel.: (55) 1135095492
Web Site: https://banco.stonex.com
Comprehensive Range Financial Support Services
N.A.I.C.S.: 523999

StoneX Colombia S.A. (1)
Carrera 9 N 115 - 06/30 Of 902 - Ed Torre Tierra Firme, Bogota, Colombia
Tel.: (57) 6017451351
Web Site: https://www.stonexcolombia.com
Electronic Deposit & Payment Services
N.A.I.C.S.: 522320

StoneX Commodities DMCC (1)
Office 48D Almas Tower Jumeirah Lakes Towers, PO Box 125942, Dubai, United Arab Emirates
Tel.: (971) 44478500
Futures Brokerage Services
N.A.I.C.S.: 524210

StoneX DTVM Ltda. (1)
Rua Joaquim Floriano 413-14 andar, Itaim Bibi, Sao Paulo, 04534-011, Brazil
Tel.: (55) 1135095400
Web Site: https://dtvm.stonex.com
Futures Brokerage Services
N.A.I.C.S.: 524210

StoneX Digital International Limited (1)
3rd Floor Portview House Thorncastle Street, Dublin, 4, Ireland
Tel.: (353) 316349140
Futures Brokerage Services
N.A.I.C.S.: 524210

StoneX Europe Ltd. (1)
PO Box 23378, 1682, Nicosia, Cyprus
Tel.: (357) 22818456
Foreign Exchange & Financial Services
N.A.I.C.S.: 523999

StoneX Financial Europe S.A. (1)
251 Route D arlon, 1150, Luxembourg, Luxembourg
Tel.: (352) 458484200
Financial Services
N.A.I.C.S.: 523999
Valank Mika *(Mng Dir)*
Hedlund Larissa *(Sr VP-Precious Metal Sls)*

StoneX Financial GmbH (1)
Taunusturm Taunustor 1, 60310, Frankfurt am Main, Germany
Tel.: (49) 69222294650
Web Site: https://payments.stonex.com
Foreign Exchange & Financial Services
N.A.I.C.S.: 523999

StoneX Investimentos Ltda. (1)
Rua Joaquim Floriano 413 - 14 andar, Itaim Bibi, Sao Paulo, 04534-011, Brazil
Tel.: (55) 1130143257
Web Site: https://asset.stonex.com
Foreign Exchange & Financial Services

N.A.I.C.S.: 523999

StoneX Poland sp. z o.o. (1)
Ul Szlak 49, 31-153, Krakow, Poland
Tel.: (48) 539534658
Futures Brokerage Services
N.A.I.C.S.: 524210

StoneX Securities S.A. (1)
Sarmiento 459 9 piso, Buenos Aires, Argentina
Tel.: (54) 1143907500
Web Site: https://stonex.com.ar
Foreign Exchange & Financial Services
N.A.I.C.S.: 523999

STR HOLDINGS, INC.
10 Water St, Enfield, CT 06082
Tel.: (860) 272-4235 DE
Web Site: http://www.strsolar.com
Year Founded: 1944
STRI—(OTCIQ)
Rev.: $10,879,000
Assets: $27,149,000
Liabilities: $5,146,000
Net Worth: $22,003,000
Earnings: ($5,760,000)
Emp.: 63
Fiscal Year-end: 12/31/18
Holding Company; Solar Power Module Encapsulant Mfr
N.A.I.C.S.: 551112
Robert S. Yorgensen *(Chm, Pres & CEO)*
Thomas D. Vitro *(CFO, Chief Acctg Officer & VP)*

Subsidiaries:

Specialized Technology Resources (Connecticut), LLC (1)
1699 King St Ste 400, Enfield, CT 06082
Tel.: (860) 758-7300
Solar Electric Power Generation Services
N.A.I.C.S.: 221114

Specialized Technology Resources (Malaysia) Sdn. Bhd. (1)
Plot 20 Jalan Tanjung A/3 Port of Tanjung Pelepas, 81560, Gelang Patah, Johor, Malaysia
Tel.: (60) 7507318586
Solar Electric Power Generation Services
N.A.I.C.S.: 221114

Specialized Technology Resources Espana S.A. (1)
Parque Tecnologico de, Parcela 36, Llanera, 33428, Asturias, Spain
Tel.: (34) 985732333
Solar Electric Power Generation Services
N.A.I.C.S.: 221114
Florez Nava Susana *(Dir-Mktg & Sls)*

Specialized Technology Resources Solar (Suzhou) Co. Limited (1)
Chang Kun Industrial Park No 26 Nanxin Road, Shajiabang Changshu, Suzhou, Jiangsu, China
Tel.: (86) 51252139202
Solar Electric Power Generation Services
N.A.I.C.S.: 221114

Specialized Technology Resources, Inc. (1)
18 Craftsman Rd, East Windsor, CT 06088
Tel.: (860) 758-7400
Sales Range: $25-49.9 Million
Research & Development Services
N.A.I.C.S.: 541715
Luke Strzegowski *(Dir-Global Sls & Tech)*

Subsidiary (Domestic):

STR Inc. (2)
85 John Rd, Canton, MA 02021-2816
Tel.: (781) 821-2200
Web Site: http://www.ul.com
Sales Range: $10-24.9 Million
Emp.: 75
Research Laboratory
N.A.I.C.S.: 541380

Subsidiary (Non-US):

STR Laboratuar Hizmetleri A.S. (2)
Gursel Mahallesi Yesiltepe Sokak No:22/3,

ERG Is Merk Kagithane 6, 80260, Istanbul, Kagithane, Turkiye
Tel.: (90) 2123211960
Web Site: http://www.str-turkiye.com
Sales Range: $10-24.9 Million
Emp.: 30
Laboratory Testing & Inspection Services
N.A.I.C.S.: 541380
Aron Pickering *(Gen Mgr)*

STR Testing & Inspection AG (2)
Amperestrasse 5, PO Box 46, 9323, Steinach, Switzerland
Tel.: (41) 714478585
Web Site: http://www.strtest.ch
Sales Range: $10-24.9 Million
Emp.: 30
Testing, Analysis & Quality Control Laboratory for Textiles, Polymers, Toys, Household Supply, Electrical & Electronic Products; European Headquarters
N.A.I.C.S.: 541380
Matthias Rosenthal *(Gen Mgr)*

STRAINSFORPAINS, INC.
244 5th Ave Ste S242, New York, NY 10001
Tel.: (347) 218-0844 NV
Web Site:
   https://www.strainsforpains.com
Year Founded: 1990
EBYH—(OTCIQ)
Rev.: $9,450
Assets: $6,990
Liabilities: $1,855,732
Net Worth: ($1,848,742)
Earnings: ($89,286)
Fiscal Year-end: 12/31/19
Medical Cannabis Product Distr
N.A.I.C.S.: 459999
Yeshua Shainberg *(Founder & CEO)*

STRAN & COMPANY, INC.
2 Heritage Dr Ste 600, Quincy, MA 02171
Tel.: (617) 822-6950 NV
Web Site: https://www.stran.com
Year Founded: 1995
SWAG—(NASDAQ)
Rev.: $58,953,467
Assets: $56,626,108
Liabilities: $17,261,556
Net Worth: $39,364,552
Earnings: ($778,441)
Emp.: 98
Fiscal Year-end: 12/31/22
Marketing Services
N.A.I.C.S.: 541613
Andrew Stranberg *(Founder, Chm, Treas & Sec)*
David Browner *(CFO)*
Howie Turkenkopf *(VP-Marketing)*
Nick Kiefer *(Exec VP-Sales)*
Stacy Miller *(VP-Sales)*
Michele Pytlinski *(Sr VP-Client Strategy)*
Laura Woodward *(Dir-Human Resources)*
Mike Krauser *(VP-Sales)*
Jack Audibert *(VP-Growth & Strategic Initiatives)*
Ian Thomas Wall *(CIO)*
Randy Birney *(VP-Sales)*

Subsidiaries:

Stran Loyalty Solutions, LLC (1)
2 Heritage Dr Ste 600, Quincy, MA 02171
Tel.: (617) 822-6950
Marketing Services
N.A.I.C.S.: 541613

Subsidiary (Domestic):

Bangarang Enterprises, LLC (2)
2183 Fairview Rd Ste 212, Costa Mesa, CA 92627
Tel.: (949) 791-6500
Web Site: http://www.gandergroup.com
Sales Range: $1-9.9 Million
Emp.: 50
Advertising Agency Services

N.A.I.C.S.: 541810
Josh Blake *(CEO)*

T.R. Miller Co., Inc. (1)
290 S St, Walpole, MA 02081
Tel.: (508) 660-0915
Web Site: http://www.trmiller.com
Durable Goods Merchant Wholesalers
N.A.I.C.S.: 423990
Thomas R. Miller *(Founder & CEO)*

STRATA SKIN SCIENCES, INC.
5 Walnut Grove Dr Ste 140, Horsham, PA 19044
Tel.: (215) 619-3200 DE
Web Site:
   https://www.strataskinsciences.com
Year Founded: 1989
SSKN—(NASDAQ)
Rev.: $36,161,000
Assets: $52,272,000
Liabilities: $30,441,000
Net Worth: $21,831,000
Earnings: ($5,549,000)
Emp.: 114
Fiscal Year-end: 12/31/22
Hand-Held Medical Devices Mfr
N.A.I.C.S.: 339112
Dolev Rafaeli *(Vice Chm, Pres & CEO)*
Uri Geiger *(Chm)*
Brent Cowgill *(VP-Mktg)*
Christopher Lesovitz *(CFO)*

STRATEGIC ACQUISITIONS, INC.
401 8th Ave, Brooklyn, NY 11215
Tel.: (401) 751-0120 NV
Web Site: https://strategic-
   acquisitions.com
Year Founded: 1989
STQN—(OTCIQ)
Rev.: $58,938
Assets: $5,672,340
Liabilities: $5,629,653
Net Worth: $42,687
Earnings: ($162,260)
Fiscal Year-end: 12/31/23
Investment Services
N.A.I.C.S.: 523999
John P. O'Shea *(Pres & CFO)*
Yuanyuan Huang *(Treas & Sec)*

STRATEGIC EDUCATION, INC.
2303 Dulles Station Blvd Stop 6C, Herndon, VA 20171
Tel.: (703) 561-1600 MD
Web Site:
   https://www.strategiceducation.com
Year Founded: 1892
STRA—(NASDAQ)
Rev.: $1,065,480,000
Assets: $2,161,747,000
Liabilities: $525,957,000
Net Worth: $1,635,790,000
Earnings: $46,670,000
Emp.: 3,907
Fiscal Year-end: 12/31/22
Holding Company; Educational Services
N.A.I.C.S.: 611310
Daniel W. Jackson *(CFO & Exec VP)*
Karl McDonnell *(CEO)*
Robert S. Silberman *(Exec Chm)*
Lizette B. Herraiz *(Gen Counsel & Sr VP)*
Tal Darmon *(Chief Acctg Officer)*

Subsidiaries:

Capella Education Company (1)
Capella Tower 225 S 6th St 9th Fl, Minneapolis, MN 55402
Web Site: http://www.capellaeducation.com
Rev.: $440,411,000
Assets: $279,021,000
Liabilities: $63,630,000
Net Worth: $215,391,000
Earnings: $23,505,000
Emp.: 2,954

Strategic Education, Inc.—(Continued)

Fiscal Year-end: 12/31/2017
Online Post-Secondary Education Services
N.A.I.C.S.: 611310

Subsidiary (Domestic):

Capella University, Inc.   (2)
225 S 6th St 9th Fl, Minneapolis, MN 55402
Tel.: (612) 339-8650
Web Site: http://www.capella.edu
Sales Range: $50-74.9 Million
Emp.: 2,500
Degree Granting Online University
N.A.I.C.S.: 611310
Richard Senese (Pres)
Constance St. Germain (Sr VP-Academic
Affairs)
Eric Jolly (Chm)
Charlyn Hilliman (VP-Academic Enrichment
& Learner Support)
Constance Saint Germain (Sr VP)

DevMountain, LLC   (1)
1550 W Digital Dr Ste 400, Lehi, UT 84043
Tel.: (801) 851-5466
Web Site: https://www.devmountain.com
Education Services
N.A.I.C.S.: 611710

Hackbright Academy, Inc.   (1)
683 Sutter St, San Francisco, CA 94102
Tel.: (415) 862-0595
Web Site:
     https://www.hackbrightacademy.com
School Operator
N.A.I.C.S.: 611110

Media Design School Limited   (1)
10 Madden St, Central Auckland, Auckland,
1010, New Zealand
Tel.: (64) 93030402
Web Site:
     https://www.mediadesignschool.com
Higher Education Services
N.A.I.C.S.: 611710
Mike Hughes (Sr Mgr-Mktg)
Hugo Contente (VP-People & Talent)
Sophie-Anne Hawke (Mgr-Student Recruit-
ment)
Kyle Glass (Mgr-Brand & Digital Mktg)

Sophia Learning, LLC   (1)
Capella Tower 225 S 6th St Ste 900, Min-
neapolis, MN 55402
Web Site: https://www.sophia.org
Online Teaching Services
N.A.I.C.S.: 611691

Strayer University   (1)
2303 Dulles Station Blvd, Herndon, VA
20171
Tel.: (703) 561-1710
Web Site: http://www.strayer.edu
Colleges & Universities
N.A.I.C.S.: 611310
Andrea Backman (Pres)

Think: Colleges Pty Ltd   (1)
Level 24 680 George Street, Sydney, 2000,
NSW, Australia
Tel.: (61) 285884733
Web Site: http://www.think.edu.au
Higher Education Services
N.A.I.C.S.: 611710
Linda Brown (CEO)
Alwyn Louw (Dir-Academic)
Hugo Contente (VP-People & Talent)
Julie Craig (VP-Governance, Strategy &
Student Admin)
Bryce Ives (VP-Comm & Pub Affairs)

**STRATEGIC ENVIRONMENTAL
& ENERGY RESOURCES, INC.**
370 Interlocken Blvd Ste 680, Broom-
field, CO 80021
Tel.: (720) 460-3522
Web Site: https://www.seer-corp.com
SENR—(OTCQB)
Rev.: $2,899,600
Assets: $851,000
Liabilities: $14,139,500
Net Worth: ($13,288,500)
Earnings: ($2,380,500)
Emp.: 12
Fiscal Year-end: 12/31/23
Industrial & Environmental Services

N.A.I.C.S.: 561499
Goerge Smith III (Interim CFO)
Joseph John Combs III (Pres, CEO,
Founder, Chm, Sec & Gen Counsel)

Subsidiaries:

Resource Environmental Group Ser-
vices, LLC   (1)
7130 Dahlia St, Commerce City, CO 80022
Tel.: (303) 295-6297
Web Site: https://www.regs-llc.com
Sales Range: $1-9.9 Million
Emp.: 15
Remediation Services
N.A.I.C.S.: 562910
Michael Cardillo (Founder & Pres)

**STRATEGIC MANAGEMENT &
OPPORTUNITY CORP.**
404 Gardenwood Pl, Valrico, FL
33594
Tel.: (941) 720-1920   NV
Year Founded: 1999
SMPP—(OTCIQ)
Financial Consulting Services
N.A.I.C.S.: 541611
James Sinkes (Accountant)
Steven W. Swank (Pres, CEO & Sec)

**STRATIM CLOUD ACQUISI-
TION CORP.**
100 W Liberty St Ste 100, Reno, NV
89501
Tel.: (775) 318-3629   DE
Web Site:
     https://www.stratimcloud.com
Year Founded: 2020
SCAQ—(NASDAQ)
Rev.: $10,840,979
Assets: $253,440,543
Liabilities: $262,299,932
Net Worth: ($8,859,389)
Earnings: $9,217,598
Emp.: 2
Fiscal Year-end: 12/31/22
Investment Services
N.A.I.C.S.: 523999
Sreekanth Ravi (Chm & CEO)
Zachary Abrams (CFO, Chief Strat-
egy Officer & Sec)

**STRATTEC SECURITY COR-
PORATION**
3333 W Good Hope Rd, Milwaukee,
WI 53209
Tel.: (414) 247-3333   WI
Web Site: https://www.strattec.com
STRT—(NASDAQ)
Rev.: $452,265,000
Assets: $318,680,000
Liabilities: $98,267,000
Net Worth: $220,413,000
Earnings: $7,032,000
Emp.: 3,373
Fiscal Year-end: 07/03/22
Other Motor Vehicle Parts Manufac-
turing
N.A.I.C.S.: 336390
Rolando J. Guillot (Interim Pres, In-
terim CEO, COO & Sr VP-Ops)
Richard P. Messina (VP-Pur & Engrg-
Global)
Dennis Bowe (CFO, Principal Acctg
Officer & VP)

Subsidiaries:

Strattec Power Access LLC   (1)
2998 Dutton Rd, Auburn Hills, MI 48326-
1864
Tel.: (248) 824-7580
Web Site:
     http://www.strattecpoweraccess.com
Automobile Parts Mfr & Distr
N.A.I.C.S.: 332510

Strattec de Mexico S.A. de C.V.   (1)
C Auxiliar No 1 - No 512, Parque Industrial

Gema, 32640, Ciudad Juarez, Chihuahua,
Mexico
Tel.: (52) 6566398900
Sales Range: $300-349.9 Million
Automotive Lock & Key Mfr
N.A.I.C.S.: 336110

STRATUS CAPITAL CORP.
8480 E Orchard Rd Ste 1100, Green-
wood Village, CO 80111
Tel.: (720) 214-5000   DE
Web Site: https://stratuscap.com
Year Founded: 2004
SRUS—(OTCIQ)
Assets: $3,105
Liabilities: $471,385
Net Worth: ($468,280)
Earnings: ($142,292)
Emp.: 1
Fiscal Year-end: 12/31/21
Real Estate Investment Services
N.A.I.C.S.: 531190
Pedro C. Gonzalez (Chm, Pres,
CEO, CFO & Sec)
Chris Garcia (Dir-Operations)
Christopher Furman (Dir-Dev Moun-
tain West)
Carlos Pena (Dir-Development)
Gina Madrid (Sec-Investor Relations)
Richard Dean (Dir)

STRATUS PROPERTIES, INC.
212 Lavaca St Ste 300, Austin, TX
78701
Tel.: (512) 478-5788   DE
Web Site:
     https://www.stratusproperties.com
STRS—(NASDAQ)
Rev.: $37,498,000
Assets: $445,140,000
Liabilities: $173,067,000
Net Worth: $272,073,000
Earnings: $89,743,000
Emp.: 31
Fiscal Year-end: 12/31/22
Land Subdivision
N.A.I.C.S.: 237210
William H. Armstrong III (Chm, Pres
& CEO)
Erin D. Pickens (CFO & Sr VP)

Subsidiaries:

Stratus Investments, LLC   (1)
550 Sw 12th Ave Ste 550, Deerfield Beach,
FL 33442
Tel.: (954) 418-0208
Real Estate Development Services
N.A.I.C.S.: 237210

**STRAWBERRY FIELDS REIT,
INC.**
6101 Nimtz Pkwy, South Bend, IN
46628
Tel.: (574) 807-0800   MD
Web Site:
     https://www.strawberryfieldsreit.com
Year Founded: 2019
STRW—(NYSEAMEX)
Rev.: $92,543,000
Assets: $547,000,000
Liabilities: $497,616,000
Net Worth: $49,384,000
Earnings: $1,852,000
Emp.: 8
Fiscal Year-end: 12/31/22
Real Estate Investment Services
N.A.I.C.S.: 531210
Moishe Gubin (Founder, Chm &
CEO)
Nahman Eingal (CFO)

Subsidiaries:

Momence Meadows Realty, LLC   (1)
500 S Walnut St, Momence, IL 60954
Tel.: (815) 472-2423
Nursing Centre Services
N.A.I.C.S.: 623110

**STREAMLINE HEALTH SOLU-
TIONS, INC.**
2400 Old Milton Pkwy Ste 1353, Al-
pharetta, GA 30009   DE
Web Site:
     https://www.streamlinehealth.net
Year Founded: 1989
STRM—(NASDAQ)
Rev.: $24,889,000
Assets: $61,521,000
Liabilities: $26,010,000
Net Worth: $35,511,000
Earnings: ($11,379,000)
Emp.: 112
Fiscal Year-end: 01/31/23
Document Imaging & Workflow Appli-
cations for Healthcare Professionals
N.A.I.C.S.: 541512
Jawad Shaikh (Chief Strategy Officer)
Wyche Tee Green III (Chm)
Benjamin L. Stilwill (CEO)
Andrew Brodnik (VP-Client Success)
Wendy Lovvorn (Chief People Officer)
Bryant Reeves (CFO)

Subsidiaries:

Avelead Consulting, LLC   (1)
1172 Satellite Blvd Ste 100, Suwanee, GA
30024
Web Site: http://www.avelead.com
Sales Range: $1-9.9 Million
Emp.: 40
Information Technology Development Ser-
vices
N.A.I.C.S.: 541512

Meta Health Technology, Inc.   (1)
330 7th Ave, New York, NY 10001
Tel.: (212) 695-5870
Web Site: http://www.metahealth.com
Sales Range: $10-24.9 Million
Emp.: 30
Prepackaged Software Mfr
N.A.I.C.S.: 513210

STRIDE, INC.
11720 Plz Dr 9th Fl, Reston, VA
20190
Tel.: (703) 483-7000   DE
Web Site:
     https://www.stridelearning.com
Year Founded: 1999
LRN—(NYSE)
Rev.: $2,040,069,000
Assets: $1,920,465,000
Liabilities: $744,440,000
Net Worth: $1,176,025,000
Earnings: $204,183,000
Emp.: 7,800
Fiscal Year-end: 06/30/24
Online Curriculum, Software & Edu-
cational Services
N.A.I.C.S.: 611710
Bryan W. Flood (Sr VP-Pub Affairs)
Peter G. Stewart (Sr VP-School Dev)
James J. Rhyu (CEO)
Valerie Maddy (Sr VP-HR)
Kevin P. Chavous (Pres)
Mike Kraft (Sr VP-Corp Comm)
Doug McCollum (Sr VP-Products)
Vincent Mathis (Gen Counsel, Sec &
Exec VP)
Todd Goldthwaite (CMO & Sr VP)
Todd Thorpe (Sr VP-School Svcs-
Central Reg)
Darren Reed (Sr VP-School Svcs-
Northern Reg)
Jodi Marshall (Sr VP-K12 Learning
Solutions)
Karen Ghidotti (Sr VP-Customer Ex-
perience)
Megan Sandoval (Sr VP-School
Svcs-Western Reg)

Charles A. Bennett (Sr VP-School Mgmt)
Mike Lawson (VP-IR)
Tim Casey (Sr Dir-IR)
Arjun Sreekumar (Dir-IR & Fin)
Donna Blackman (CFO)
Dana Still (Dir-Comm)

Subsidiaries:

Capital Education LLC   (1)
1750 Tysons Blvd 13th Fl, McLean, VA 22102
Web Site: https://www.capitaleducation.com
Educational Support Services
N.A.I.C.S.: 611699

Galvanize Inc.   (1)
1644 Platte St, Denver, CO 80202
Tel.: (720) 640-6022
Web Site: https://www.galvanize.com
Educational Institution Services
N.A.I.C.S.: 611710
Bill Blackstone (Gen Mgr)

Subsidiary (Domestic):

Tech Elevator Inc.   (2)
7100 Euclid Ave, Cleveland, OH 44103
Web Site: https://www.techelevator.com
Educational Support Services
N.A.I.C.S.: 611710

International School of Berne AG (1)
Allmendingenweg 9, Gumligen, 3073, Bern, Switzerland
Tel.: (41) 319591000
Web Site: https://www.isberne.ch
Sales Range: $25-49.9 Million
Emp.: 60
Educational Support Services
N.A.I.C.S.: 611710
Brette Book (Coord-IB DP)
Dom Thomas (Head-Ops & Comm)
Maria Szalay (Chm)
Kirsty DeWilde (Principal-Middle School)

Middlebury Interactive Languages LLC   (1)
23 Pond Ln, Middlebury, VT 05753
Tel.: (802) 458-9400
Web Site:
    http://www.middleburyinteractive.com
Educational Support Services
N.A.I.C.S.: 611710
Jonathan Weible (Mgr-Enrollment)

Stride Online Tutoring, Inc.   (1)
11720 Plaza America Dr 9th Fl, Reston, VA 20190
Web Site: https://stridetutoring.com
Online Tutoring Services
N.A.I.C.S.: 561320

Tallo LLC   (1)
11720 Plaza America Dr 9th Fl, Reston, VA 20190
Web Site: https://www.tallo.com
Emp.: 9,000
Career Guidance Services
N.A.I.C.S.: 561320

STRONG SOLUTIONS, INC.
102 N Curry St, Carson City, NV 89703
Tel.: (775) 434-4451   NV
Year Founded: 2014
SGOU—(OTCIQ)
Liabilities: $284,231
Net Worth: ($284,231)
Earnings: ($649,402)
Fiscal Year-end: 12/31/21
Real Estate Services
N.A.I.C.S.: 531390
Andrii Guzii (Founder, CEO & CFO)

STRONGHOLD DIGITAL MINING, INC.
2151 Lisbon Rd, Kennerdell, PA 16374
Tel.: (845) 579-5992   DE
Web Site:
    https://www.strongholddigitalmining.com
Year Founded: 2021

SDIG—(NASDAQ)
Rev.: $106,033,102
Assets: $216,955,981
Liabilities: $133,930,837
Net Worth: $83,025,144
Earnings: ($89,261,230)
Emp.: 168
Fiscal Year-end: 12/31/22
Mining Services
N.A.I.C.S.: 212115
Gregory A. Beard (Co-Chm & CEO)
William B. Spence (Co-Chm)
Richard J. Shaffer (Sr VP-Asset Mgr & Environmental Lead)
Charles D. Talcott (Dir-Fin & Ops)
Thomas B. Tyree III (VP-Fin)

STRUCTURE THERAPEUTICS INC.
601 Gateway Blvd Ste 900, South San Francisco, CA 94080
Tel.: (628) 229-9277   Ky
Web Site: https://structuretx.com
Year Founded: 2016
GPCR—(NASDAQ)
Rev.: $1,257,000
Assets: $97,845,000
Liabilities: $212,985,000
Net Worth: ($115,140,000)
Earnings: ($52,836,000)
Emp.: 68
Fiscal Year-end: 12/31/22
Biotechnology Research & Development Services
N.A.I.C.S.: 541714
Yingli Ma (CTO)
Jun Yoon (CFO)
Belen Carrillo-Rivas (Sr VP-Regulatory Affairs)
Bob Gatmaitan (Sr VP-People)
Lani Ibarra (Sr VP-Clinical Dev Ops)
Xinglong Jiang (Sr VP-Preclinical Dev)
Hui Lei (Sr VP-Chemistry)
Tony Peng (Sr VP-Legal)
Karen S. Wright (Sr VP-Finance & Controller)
Xichen Lin (Chief Scientific Officer & Gen Mgr)
Fang Zhang (Exec VP & Head)
Marc Navre (Sr VP & Head)
Raymond C. Stevens (Co-Founder & CEO)
Ashley F. Hall (Chief Dev Officer)

STRYKER CORPORATION
1941 Stryker Way, Portage, MI 49002
Tel.: (269) 385-2600   MI
Web Site: https://www.stryker.com
Year Founded: 1941
SYK—(NYSE)
Rev.: $20,498,000,000
Assets: $39,912,000,000
Liabilities: $21,319,000,000
Net Worth: $18,593,000,000
Earnings: $3,165,000,000
Emp.: 52,000
Fiscal Year-end: 12/31/23
Specialty Surgical & Medical Products Developer, Mfr & Marketer
N.A.I.C.S.: 339112
Jeanne M. Blondia (Treas & VP-Fin)
Irene B. Corbe (VP-Internal Audit)
David G. Furgason (VP-Tax)
M. Kathryn Fink (Chief HR Officer & VP)
Spencer S. Stiles (Pres-Orthopaedics & Spine Grp)
J. Andrew Pierce (Pres-MedSurg-Neurotechnology Grp)
Robert Fletcher (Chief Legal Officer & VP)
Jody Powell (VP-Regulatory Affairs & Quality Assurance)
Dana McMahon (Chief Compliance Officer & VP)

Alan Douville (CIO, Chief Information Security Officer & VP)
Robert Cummings (VP-Tax)
Kevin A. Lobo (Chm & CEO)
William B. Berry (Chief Acctg Officer, VP & Controller)

Subsidiaries:

Berchtold Asia SDN BHD   (1)
35 Jalan Sumazau 3C/KU5 Bandar Bukit Raja, 41200, Klang, Selangor, Malaysia
Tel.: (60) 361502242
Hospital Equipments Mfr
N.A.I.C.S.: 339113

Berchtold China Ltd   (1)
Unit 3301 Hong Kong New World Tower 300 Middle Huai Hai Road, Shanghai, 200020, China
Tel.: (86) 2163916887
Hospital Equipments Mfr
N.A.I.C.S.: 339113

Berchtold Consulting GmbH   (1)
Rheinweg 5, 8200, Schaffhausen, Switzerland
Tel.: (41) 526330906
Web Site: http://www.berchtold.biz
Hospital Equipments Mfr
N.A.I.C.S.: 339113

Berchtold Espana S.L.   (1)
Calle Jose Ortega Y Gasset 6 - 3 LEFT, 28006, Madrid, Spain
Tel.: (34) 917283500
Hospital Equipments Mfr
N.A.I.C.S.: 339113

Berchtold GmbH & Co KG   (1)
Ludwigstaler Str 25, 78532, Tuttlingen, Germany
Tel.: (49) 74611810
Health Care Srvices
N.A.I.C.S.: 621610

Berchtold Italia Srl   (1)
Largo Donegani 2, 20121, Milan, Italy
Tel.: (39) 03455800380
Hospital Equipments Mfr
N.A.I.C.S.: 339113

Berchtold Japan KK   (1)
Tokyo Sogo Accounting & Co Yaesuguchi Kaikan 8F 7-20 Yaesu 1-Chome, Chuo-ku, Tokyo, Japan
Tel.: (81) 335107562
Hospital Equipments Mfr
N.A.I.C.S.: 339113

Berchtold Pacific Pty   (1)
5 Orion Rd, Lane Cove, 2066, NSW, Australia
Tel.: (61) 1300651368
Emp.: 50
Hospital Equipments Mfr
N.A.I.C.S.: 339113

Berchtold UK Limited   (1)
First Floor the Barn, Newbury, RG14 6AL, Berkshire, United Kingdom
Tel.: (44) 1635521541
Hospital Equipments Mfr
N.A.I.C.S.: 339113

Concentric Medical, Inc.   (1)
301 E Evelyn Ave, Mountain View, CA 94041-1530
Tel.: (650) 938-2100
Web Site: http://www.concentric-medical.com
Sales Range: $10-24.9 Million
Emp.: 81
Blood Flow Restoration Device Designer, Developer & Marketer
N.A.I.C.S.: 334510

HeartSine Technologies Limited   (1)
207 Airport Road West, Belfast, BT3 9ED, Northern Ireland, United Kingdom
Tel.: (44) 2890939400
Web Site: http://uk.heartsine.com
Medical & Surgical Equipment Distr
N.A.I.C.S.: 423450
Uel McChesney (CEO)

HeartSine Technologies, LLC   (1)
121 Friends Ln Ste 400, Newtown, PA 18940
Tel.: (215) 860-8100

Web Site: http://uk.heartsine.com
Medical Equipment Mfr
N.A.I.C.S.: 339112

Howmedica Osteonics Corp.   (1)
325 Corporate Dr, Mahwah, NJ 07430   (100%)
Tel.: (269) 831-5000
Web Site: http://www.stryker.com
Sales Range: $450-499.9 Million
Emp.: 1,500
Orthopedic Implants, Trauma Products & Bone Cement Mfr
N.A.I.C.S.: 339113
David K. Floyd (Pres)

HyperBranch Medical Technology, Inc.   (1)
800-12 Capitola Dr, Durham, NC 27713-4410
Tel.: (919) 433-3325
Web Site: http://www.hyperbranch.com
Professional Equipment & Supplies Merchant Whslr
N.A.I.C.S.: 423490

Instrumedics, LLC   (1)
4177 Varsity Dr Ste B, Ann Arbor, MI 48108
Tel.: (734) 662-2488
Emp.: 8
Hospital Equipments Mfr
N.A.I.C.S.: 339113

Invuity, Inc.   (1)
444 De Haro St, San Francisco, CA 94107
Tel.: (415) 655-2100
Web Site: http://www.invuity.com
Rev.: $39,619,000
Assets: $45,495,000
Liabilities: $46,357,000
Net Worth: ($862,000)
Earnings: ($39,918,000)
Emp.: 161
Fiscal Year-end: 12/31/2017
Medical Device Mfr
N.A.I.C.S.: 339112
Scott D. Flora (Interim Pres & CEO)
Doug Heigel (Sr VP-Ops)
Steven Annen (VP-Product Mgmt & Strategy)
Sham Shiblaq (VP-Comml Ops)
Lauren Budesheim (Sr Dir-HR)

Ivy Sports Medicine GmbH   (1)
Lochhamer Schlag 17, 82166, Grafelfing, Germany
Tel.: (49) 8955054590
Web Site: http://www.ivysportsmed.com
Emp.: 8
Medical Equipment Distr
N.A.I.C.S.: 423450

K2M Germany GmbH   (1)
Mangfallstrasse 37, 83026, Rosenheim, Germany
Tel.: (49) 80313519980
Spine Product Distr
N.A.I.C.S.: 423450
Felix Krehl (Acct Mgr)

K2M Group Holdings, Inc.   (1)
600 Hope Pkwy SE, Leesburg, VA 20175
Tel.: (703) 777-3155
Web Site: http://www.k2m.com
Holding Company; Medical Device Mfr
N.A.I.C.S.: 551112
John P. Kostuik (Founder & Chief Medical Officer)

Subsidiary (Domestic):

K2M, Inc.   (2)
600 Hope Pkwy SE, Leesburg, VA 20175
Tel.: (866) 526-4171
Web Site: http://www.k2m.com
Medical Research & Development Services
N.A.I.C.S.: 541715

K2M UK Limited   (1)
Ground Floor 1 Roundwood Avenue Stockley Park, Uxbridge, UB11 1FG, United Kingdom
Tel.: (44) 2033265670
Spine Product Distr
N.A.I.C.S.: 423450

MAKO Surgical Corp.   (1)
2555 Davie Rd, Fort Lauderdale, FL 33317
Tel.: (954) 927-2044
Web Site: http://www.makosurgicalcorp.com

Stryker Corporation—(Continued)

Sales Range: $100-124.9 Million
Emp.: 436
Medical Devices Focusing on Orthopedic
Knee Advanced Robotic Solutions & Implants
N.A.I.C.S.: 339113
David K. Floyd (Pres)
Samantha C. Brodsky (Dir-HR)
Robert C. Cohen (VP & Gen Mgr)

Memometal UK Limited (1)
14 Brewery Court, Theale, Reading, RG7
5AJ, United Kingdom
Tel.: (44) 1189033280
Web Site: http://uk.memometal.com
Hospital Equipments Mfr
N.A.I.C.S.: 339113

Mobius Imaging, LLC (1)
2 Shaker Rd F-100, Shirley, MA 01464
Tel.: (978) 386-9619
Web Site: http://www.mobiusimaging.com
Medical Device Mfr
N.A.I.C.S.: 339112
Eugene A. Gregerson (Founder, Pres & CEO)
Marc R. Buntaine (VP-Sls & Mktg)
John Marrazzo (VP-Svcs)
Kevin Provencher (VP-Mfg)
Michael Flynn (VP-Quality)

Muka Metal Ticaret ve Sanayi Anonim Sirketi (1)
Kayseri Serbest Bolgesi 2 Cad No 17,
38070, Kayseri, Turkiye
Tel.: (90) 3523214300
Web Site: https://www.stryker.com
Medical Equipment Distr
N.A.I.C.S.: 423450

N.V. Stryker SA (1)
Airport Plaza-Kyoto Building Leonardo da
Vincilaan 19/C, Ikaroslaan 12, 1831, Diegem, Belgium
Tel.: (32) 27179210
Medical & Surgical Hospitals
N.A.I.C.S.: 622110

OrthoSensor, Inc. (1)
1855 Griffin Rd Ste A-310, Dania Beach, FL
33004-2200
Tel.: (954) 577-7770
Web Site: https://www.orthosensor.com
Medical Sensor Product Mfr
N.A.I.C.S.: 334510
Ivan Delevic (Pres & CEO)
Martin Roche (Founder & Chief Medical Officer)
Roman Bensen (CFO)
Steve Seger (Chief Comml Officer)
Jack Leo (Gen Counsel)
Jonathan Trousdale (CTO)
Michael Conditt (VP-Clinical Dev)
Michael Stansky (Chm)

OrthoSpace, Ltd. (1)
Halamish 7, Caesarea, Israel
Tel.: (972) 46667330
Web Site: http://www.orthospace.co.il
Medical Device Mfr
N.A.I.C.S.: 339112
Ilana Melamed (Mgr-Production)

Orthovita, Inc. (1)
77 Great Valley Pkwy, Malvern, PA 19355-1302
Tel.: (610) 640-1775
Sales Range: $75-99.9 Million
Emp.: 150
Mfr, Developer & Marketer of Bone Regeneration Products & Devices
N.A.I.C.S.: 339112

Unit (Non-US):

Orthovita (2)
Interleuvenlaan 5, 3001, Leuven, Belgium
Tel.: (32) 16392890
Web Site: http://www.orthovita.com
Sales Range: $100-124.9 Million
Emp.: 8
Bone Regeneration Products & Devices
Developer, Mfr & Marketer
N.A.I.C.S.: 339112

Physio-Control Canada Sales Ltd. (1)
7111 Syntex Drive 3rd Floor, Mississauga,

L5N 8C3, ON, Canada
Spine Product Distr
N.A.I.C.S.: 423450
Kenneth Stubbs (Mgr-Territory)

Physio-Control Singapore Pte. Ltd. (1)
Blk 108 Pasir Panjang Road 03-04, Singapore, 118535, Singapore
Tel.: (65) 67182080
Medical Instrument Distr
N.A.I.C.S.: 423450

Physio-Control UK Sales Ltd. (1)
Hambridge Road, Newbury, RG14 5AW,
Berkshire, United Kingdom
Tel.: (44) 1635500665
Medical Instrument Distr
N.A.I.C.S.: 423450

Physio-Control, Inc. (1)
11811 Willows Rd NE, Redmond, WA
98052
Tel.: (425) 867-4000
Web Site: https://www.physio-control.com
Medical Electronics Products Mfr
N.A.I.C.S.: 334510

Subsidiary (Non-US):

Jolife AB (2)
Scheelevagen 17, Ideon Science Park, SE-223 70, Lund, Sweden
Tel.: (46) 462865000
Web Site: https://www.lucas-cpr.com
Emergency Response Medical Products Mfr
N.A.I.C.S.: 339112

Subsidiary (Domestic):

Physio-Control Manufacturing, Inc. (2)
11811 Willows Rd NE, Redmond, WA
98052
Tel.: (425) 867-4000
Web Site: http://www.physio-control.com
Electromedical & Electrotherapeutic Apparatus Mfr
N.A.I.C.S.: 334510

Subsidiary (Non-US):

Physio-Control Operations Netherlands B.V. (2)
Herikerbergweg 145, 1101 CN, Amsterdam,
Netherlands
Tel.: (31) 20 7070560
Web Site: http://www.physio-control.com
Electromedical Equipment Mfr
N.A.I.C.S.: 334510

Pivot Medical, Inc. (1)
247 Humboldt Courtyard, Sunnyvale, CA
94009
Tel.: (408) 774-1452
Web Site: http://www.pivotmedical.com
Surgical Appliance & Supply Mfr
N.A.I.C.S.: 339113

SafeAir AG (1)
Platz 3 D4, 6039, Root, Switzerland
Tel.: (41) 788280419
Web Site: http://www.safeair.ch
Medical Device Mfr
N.A.I.C.S.: 339112

Sage Products, LLC (1)
3909 3 Oaks Rd, Cary, IL 60013
Tel.: (815) 455-4700
Web Site: https://www.sageproducts.com
Hospital Equipments Mfr
N.A.I.C.S.: 339113
Jim Layer (VP Dus Dev)

Scopis GmbH (1)
Heinrich-Heine-Platz 10, 10555, Berlin, Germany
Tel.: (49) 3020169380
Medical Instrument Distr
N.A.I.C.S.: 423450
B. Kosmecki (CEO)

Small Bone Innovations, Inc. (1)
1380 S Pennsylvania Ave, Morrisville, PA
19067
Tel.: (215) 428-1791
Web Site: http://www.totalsmallbone.com
Sales Range: $1-9.9 Million
Emp.: 40
Surgical & Medical Instrument Mfr
N.A.I.C.S.: 339112

Stryker (Shanghai) Healthcare Products Co., Ltd. (1)
Unit 3601 HK New World Tower, No 300
Middle Huaihai Road, Shanghai, 200020,
China
Tel.: (86) 2123210000
Web Site: http://www.stryker.com
Hospital Equipments Mfr
N.A.I.C.S.: 339113

Stryker (Suzhou) Medical Technology Co Ltd. (1)
No 18 Wuxiang EPZ Zone A 200 Suhong
Rd SIP, Export Processing Zone No 200,
Suzhou, 215021, Jiangsu, China
Tel.: (86) 51282273388
Web Site: https://www.stryker.com
Medical Equipment Mfr
N.A.I.C.S.: 334510

Stryker (Thailand) Limited (1)
Rasa Tower II 11th Floor 555 Phaholyothin
Road, Chatuchak, Bangkok, 10900, Thailand
Tel.: (66) 29371189
Web Site: https://www.stryker.com
Hospital Equipments Mfr
N.A.I.C.S.: 339113

Stryker AB (1)
Langhusgatan 5B, Box 50425, 215 86,
Malmo, Sweden (100%)
Tel.: (46) 406918100
Web Site: https://www.stryker.com
Sales Range: $50-74.9 Million
Developer of Medical Instruments & Other
Products
N.A.I.C.S.: 339112

Stryker Australia Pty. Ltd. (1)
8 Herbert Street, Saint Leonards, 2065,
NSW, Australia (100%)
Tel.: (61) 294671000
Web Site: https://www.stryker.com
Sales Range: $75-99.9 Million
Sales of Specialy Medical & Surgical Equipment
N.A.I.C.S.: 423450

Stryker B.V. (1)
Herikerbergweg 110, 1101 CM, Amsterdam,
Netherlands
Tel.: (31) 202192600
Medical Device Mfr
N.A.I.C.S.: 339112

Stryker Benelux (1)
Koeweistraat 8, Waardenburg, 4181 CD,
Netherlands (100%)
Tel.: (31) 418 569 800
Web Site: http://www.benelux.stryker.com
Sales Range: $25-49.9 Million
Emp.: 80
Sales of Specialty Surgical & Medical Products
N.A.I.C.S.: 423450

Stryker Biotech LLC (1)
35 S St, Hopkinton, MA 01748
Tel.: (508) 416-5200
Web Site: http://www.stryker.com
Sales Range: $25-49.9 Million
Emp.: 150
Developer of Biotechnology Products
N.A.I.C.S.: 541720

Stryker Canada Holding Company (1)
45 Innovation Dr, Dundas, L9H 7L8, ON,
Canada
Tel.: (905) 690-5700
Emp.: 0
Medical & Surgical Equipment Whslr
N.A.I.C.S.: 423450

Subsidiary (Domestic):

Stryker Canada Inc. (1)
2 Medicorum Place, Waterdown, L8B 1W2,
ON, Canada
Tel.: (905) 690-5700
Web Site: http://www.stryker.com
Sales Range: $50-74.9 Million
Developer of Medical Instruments & Other
Products
N.A.I.C.S.: 339112

Stryker China Limited (1)
9th Floor 12 Taikoo Wan Road, Taikoo
Shing, China (Hong Kong)

Tel.: (852) 39691330
Web Site: https://www.stryker.com
Health Care Srvices
N.A.I.C.S.: 621610

Stryker Colombia SAS (1)
Calle 116 No 7-15 Piso 10 Oficina 1001,
Bogota, Colombia
Tel.: (57) 17438200
Web Site: https://www.stryker.com
Health Care Srvices
N.A.I.C.S.: 621610

Stryker Endoscopy (1)
5900 Optical Ct, San Jose, CA 95138
Tel.: (408) 754-2000
Web Site: http://www.stryker.com
Sales Range: $75-99.9 Million
Emp.: 300
Medical Device Mfr
N.A.I.C.S.: 339113

Subsidiary (Domestic):

Ivy Sports Medicine, LLC (2)
102 Chestnut Ridge Rd Ste 204, Montvale,
NJ 07645
Tel.: (201) 573-5423
Web Site: http://www.ivysportsmed.com
Surgical Implants Mfr
N.A.I.C.S.: 339112

Stryker France SAS (1)
ZAC avenue Satolas Green, 69330, Pusignan, France (100%)
Tel.: (33) 472453600
Web Site: https://www.stryker.com
Sales Range: $50-74.9 Million
Provider of Specialty Surgical & Medical
Products
N.A.I.C.S.: 339112

Division (Domestic):

Stryker France S.A.-Leibinger Med-Surg Division (2)
ZAC Avenue de Satolas Green, 69330, Pusignan, France (100%)
Tel.: (33) 472453600
Web Site: http://www.stryker.com
Sales Range: $10-24.9 Million
Emp.: 70
Mfr of Products for Craniomaxillofacial,
Hand & Foot Surgery
N.A.I.C.S.: 339112
Lionel Ulrich (Mng Dir)

Stryker GmbH (1)
Euro Plaza Gebaude G Am Euro Platz 2,
Vienna, 1120, Austria
Tel.: (43) 18132000
Medical Equipment Mfr
N.A.I.C.S.: 334510

Stryker GmbH (1)
Bohnackerweg 1, Selzach, 2545, Solothurn,
Switzerland (100%)
Tel.: (41) 326416666
Web Site: http://www.stryker.com
Specialized Medical & Surgical Supplies Mfr
N.A.I.C.S.: 339112

Stryker GmbH & Co. KG (1)
Botzinger Str 39-41, 79111, Freiburg im
Breisgau, Germany
Tel.: (49) 76145120
Web Site: https://www.stryker.com
Emp.: 750
Health Care Srvices
N.A.I.C.S.: 621610

Stryker GmbH & Co. KG (1)
Dr-Homer- Stryker- Platz 1, 47228, Duisburg, Germany (100%)
Tel.: (49) 20658370
Web Site: http://www.stryker.com
Sales Range: $50-74.9 Million
Emp.: 750
Mfr of Spinal Implants
N.A.I.C.S.: 339112
Markus Wiegmann (Mng Dir)

Stryker Grundstucks GmbH & Co KG (1)
Botzinger 41, D-79111, Freiburg, Germany
Tel.: (49) 76145120
Emp.: 500
Hospital Equipments Mfr
N.A.I.C.S.: 339113
Mr Gerver (Gen Mgr)

Stryker Holdings BV **(1)**
Koeweistraat 8, 4181 CD, Waardenburg,
Netherlands **(100%)**
Tel.: (31) 418569800
Sales Range: $10-24.9 Million
Emp.: 30
Developer of Medical Products
N.A.I.C.S.: 339112

Subsidiary (Domestic):

**Stryker EMEA Supply Chain Services
BV** **(2)**
Herikerbergweg 110 Luna Arena 4th Floor,
1101 CM, Amsterdam, Netherlands
General Warehousing Services
N.A.I.C.S.: 493110

Stryker Japan Holdings BV **(2)**
Koeweistraat 8, 4181 CD, Waardenburg,
Netherlands
Tel.: (31) 418569700
Property Development Services
N.A.I.C.S.: 525920

Stryker Netherlands BV **(2)**
Herikerbergweg 110 Luna Arena 4th Floor,
1101 CM, Amsterdam,
Netherlands **(100%)**
Tel.: (31) 202415984
Web Site: https://www.stryker.com
Developer of Medical Products
N.A.I.C.S.: 339112

Stryker Iberia, S.L. **(1)**
Calle Sepulveda 17, Alcobendas, 28108,
Madrid, Spain **(100%)**
Tel.: (34) 917283500
Web Site: https://www.stryker.com
Sales Range: $25-49.9 Million
Mfr of Specialty Medical & Sugical Equip-
ment
N.A.I.C.S.: 339112

Stryker India Private Limited **(1)**
6 floor Unit no 0602 Block 1-Phase 1 Inter-
national Tech Park, Sector 59 Behrampur
Village, Gurgaon, 122101, Haryana, India
Tel.: (91) 8001038030
Web Site: https://www.stryker.com
Emp.: 1,000
Medical Machinery, Equipment & Supply
Whslr
N.A.I.C.S.: 423450
Mohit Malhotra *(Mng Dir)*

**Stryker Instruments Ireland
Limited** **(1)**
Ida Indus Est, Carrigtohill, Ireland **(100%)**
Tel.: (353) 214532900
Web Site: http://www.stryker.com
Sales Range: $75-99.9 Million
Emp.: 280
Developer of Medical Instruments & Other
Products
N.A.I.C.S.: 339112
Aitan Oshea *(Mng Dir)*

Stryker Italia SRL **(1)**
Viale Alexandre Gustave Eiffel 13/15,
00148, Rome, Italy
Tel.: (39) 0694500800
Web Site: https://www.stryker.com
Health Care Srvices
N.A.I.C.S.: 621610

Stryker Japan Holding KK **(1)**
Sumitomo Fudosan Iidabashi First Tower
29F/30F 2-6-1 Koraku, Bunkyo-ku, Tokyo,
112-0004, Japan
Tel.: (81) 368940000
Investment Services
N.A.I.C.S.: 523150

Subsidiary (Domestic):

Stryker Japan K.K. **(2)**
30th floor Iidabashi First Tower 2-6-1 Kor-
aku, Bunkyo-Ku, Tokyo, 112-0004,
Japan **(100%)**
Tel.: (81) 368940000
Web Site: https://www.stryker.com
Emp.: 1,045
Medical & Surgical Instruments Mfr
N.A.I.C.S.: 339112

Stryker Korea Ltd. **(1)**
6th Fl ASEM Tower 517 Yeongdong-daero,
Gangnam-gu, Seoul, 06164, Korea
(South) **(100%)**

Tel.: (82) 25657303
Web Site: https://www.stryker.com
Sales Range: $25-49.9 Million
Developer of Medical Instruments & Other
Products
N.A.I.C.S.: 339112

**Stryker Leibinger GmbH & Co.
KG** **(1)**
Botzinger Str 39-41, 79111, Freiburg im
Breisgau, Germany **(100%)**
Tel.: (49) 76145120
Web Site: http://www.stryker.com
Sales Range: $10-24.9 Million
Craniomaxillofacial Products Mfr, Hand &
Foot Surgery
N.A.I.C.S.: 339112
Markus Wiegmann *(Mng Dir)*

Stryker Leibinger Inc. **(1)**
750 Trade Centre Way Ste 200, Portage,
MI 49002-1747
Tel.: (269) 324-5346
Web Site: http://www.stryker.com
Sales Range: $25-49.9 Million
Emp.: 40
Mfr of Products for Craniomaxillofacial,
Hand & Foot Surgery
N.A.I.C.S.: 423450

Stryker Mexico, S.A. de C.V. **(1)**
Mariano Escobedo No 476 Piso 4 Of 406
Col Nueva Anzures, Delegacion Miguel Hi-
dalgo, 11590, Mexico, Mexico **(100%)**
Tel.: (52) 5591830961
Web Site: https://www.stryker.com
Sales Range: $10-24.9 Million
Developer of Medical Instruments & Other
Products
N.A.I.C.S.: 339112

Stryker Nederland BV **(1)**
Herikerbergweg 110 Luna Arena 4th Floor,
1101 CM, Amsterdam, Netherlands
Tel.: (31) 202415984
Web Site: https://www.stryker.com
Health Care Srvices
N.A.I.C.S.: 621610

Stryker New Zealand Limited **(1)**
511 Mount Wellington Highway, PO Box
17136, Mt Wellington, Auckland, 1060, New
Zealand **(100%)**
Tel.: (64) 95731890
Web Site: http://www.stryker.com
Sales Range: $10-24.9 Million
Developer of Medical Instruments & Other
Products
N.A.I.C.S.: 339112

Stryker Osteonics AG **(1)**
Burgunderstrasse 13, 4562, Biberist, Swit-
zerland
Tel.: (41) 326416950
Web Site: https://www.stryker.com
Emp.: 50
Health Care Srvices
N.A.I.C.S.: 621610

**Stryker Osteonics Romania
S.R.L.** **(1)**
7 Iuliu Maniu Boulevard Building A 2nd
Floor, Bucharest, 061072,
Romania **(100%)**
Tel.: (40) 215299100
Web Site: https://www.stryker.com
Sales Range: $10-24.9 Million
Emp.: 25
Developer of Medical Instruments & Other
Products
N.A.I.C.S.: 339112

Stryker Pacific Limited **(1)**
9th Floor 12 Taikoo Wan Road, Quarry Bay,
Taikoo Shing, China (Hong Kong) **(100%)**
Tel.: (852) 39691200
Web Site: http://www.stryker.com
Sales Range: $10-24.9 Million
Provider of Specialized Medical & Surgical
Products
N.A.I.C.S.: 339112

Stryker Polska Sp. zo.o. **(1)**
Ul Poleczki 35, 02-822, Warsaw, Poland
Tel.: (48) 22 429 5550
Web Site: https://www.stryker.com
Developer of Medical Instruments & Other
Products
N.A.I.C.S.: 339112

**Stryker Portugal - Produtos Medicos
Unipessoal, Lda.** **(1)**

Palacio Sottomayor Rua Sousa Martins n 1
- 1 Esq, 1069-316, Lisbon, Portugal
Tel.: (351) 34917283500
Web Site: https://www.stryker.com
Health Care Srvices
N.A.I.C.S.: 621610

**Stryker Portugal Produtos Medicos,
Lda** **(1)**
Amoreiras Torre 2 15th A Floor, 1070274,
Lisbon, Portugal **(100%)**
Tel.: (351) 218394910
Web Site: http://www.stryker.com
Emp.: 17
Developer of Medical Instruments & Other
Products
N.A.I.C.S.: 339112

Stryker Puerto Rico, Ltd **(1)**
Hwy 3 Km 131 2, Arroyo, PR
00714 **(100%)**
Tel.: (939) 307-2500
Web Site: http://www.stryker.com
Sales Range: $1-9.9 Million
Emp.: 15
Specialized Sugical & Medical Products
N.A.I.C.S.: 339112

Stryker Romania SRL **(1)**
7 Iuliu Maniu Boulevard Building A 2nd
Floor, 061072, Bucharest, Romania
Tel.: (40) 215299100
Web Site: https://www.stryker.com
Health Care Srvices
N.A.I.C.S.: 621610

**Stryker S.A.-European
Headquarters** **(1)**
Cite Centre Grand Rue 92, PO Box 1568,
1820, Montreux, Switzerland **(100%)**
Tel.: (41) 219661201
Web Site: http://www.strykereurope.com
Sales Range: $25-49.9 Million
Emp.: 70
Distr of Orthopedic Implants & Surgical
Medical Equipment
N.A.I.C.S.: 423450

Stryker Sales Corporation **(1)**
2825 Airview Blvd, Portage, MI 49002-1803
Tel.: (269) 385-2600
Web Site: http://www.stryker.com
Medical Equipment Mfr
N.A.I.C.S.: 334510

**Stryker Singapore Private
Limited** **(1)**
438B Alexandra Technopark Block B 06-11,
Singapore, 119968, Singapore **(100%)**
Tel.: (65) 65009500
Web Site: https://www.stryker.com
Medical & Surgical Equipment Distr
N.A.I.C.S.: 423450

**Stryker South Africa (Proprietary)
Limited** **(1)**
Stryker Building Waterfall Industrial Park,
Cnr Pretoria Main Road Bridal Veil Rd Mid-
rand, Johannesburg, South Africa
Tel.: (27) 117914644
Web Site: https://www.stryker.com
Medical Equipment Mfr
N.A.I.C.S.: 334510

Stryker Spine **(1)**
2 Pearl Ct, Allendale, NJ 07401
Tel.: (201) 749-8000
Web Site: http://www.strykerspine.com
Sales Range: $100-124.9 Million
Emp.: 180
Spinal Implant Products Mfr & Whslr
N.A.I.C.S.: 339113
Brad Caddock *(Pres)*

Stryker Spine SA **(1)**
Le Cret-du-Locle 10a, La Chaux-De-Fonds,
2301, La Chaux-de-Fonds, Switzerland
Tel.: (41) 329246000
Web Site: http://www.stryker.com
Medical Equipment Mfr
N.A.I.C.S.: 334510

Stryker Spine SAS **(1)**
Zone Industrielle de Marticot, 33610, Ces-
tas, France
Tel.: (33) 557970630
Medical Equipment Mfr
N.A.I.C.S.: 334510

**Stryker Sustainability Solutions,
Inc.** **(1)**
1810 W Drake Dr, Tempe, AZ 85283
Tel.: (480) 763-5300
Web Site: http://sustainability.stryker.com
Sales Range: $100-124.9 Million
Medical Device Reprocessing & Remanu-
facturing
N.A.I.C.S.: 339112
Brian J. White *(Pres)*

Stryker Trauma GmbH **(1)**
Professor-Kuntscher-Strasse 1, 24232,
Schonkirchen, Germany **(100%)**
Tel.: (49) 43487020
Web Site: http://www.stryker.com
Sales Range: $200-249.9 Million
Emp.: 660
Mfr of Implantable Orthopedic Devices &
Hospital Products
N.A.I.C.S.: 339999

Stryker UK Ltd. **(1)**
Stryker House Hambridge Road, Newbury,
RG14 5AW, Berkshire, United
Kingdom **(100%)**
Tel.: (44) 1635262400
Web Site: https://www.stryker.com
Sales Range: $50-74.9 Million
Mfr of Specialized Medical & Surgical Sup-
plies
N.A.I.C.S.: 339112

Stryker-Osteonics SA **(1)**
Burgunderstrasse 13, 4562, Biberist, Vaud,
Switzerland
Tel.: (41) 326416950
Medical Equipment Mfr
N.A.I.C.S.: 334510

TMJ Solutions, LLC **(1)**
6059 King Dr, Ventura, CA 93003
Tel.: (805) 650-3391
Web Site: http://www.tmjconcepts.com
Sales Range: $1-9.9 Million
Emp.: 15
Medical Device Mfr
N.A.I.C.S.: 339112
Craig Rose *(Dir)*

TSO3 Inc. **(1)**
2505 avenue Dalton, Quebec, G1P 3S5,
QC, Canada
Tel.: (418) 651-0003
Web Site: http://www.tso3.com
Rev.: $2,532,000
Assets: $22,183,000
Liabilities: $20,315,000
Net Worth: $1,868,000
Earnings: ($13,244,000)
Emp.: 57
Fiscal Year-end: 12/31/2018
Ozone Sterilization
N.A.I.C.S.: 423450

Subsidiary (US):

TSO3 Corporation **(2)**
1636 American Way, Myrtle Beach, SC
29577
Tel.: (843) 839-0403
Sterilization Equipment Distr
N.A.I.C.S.: 423450

Thermedx LLC **(1)**
31200 Solon Rd 1, Solon, OH 44139
Tel.: (440) 542-0883
Fluid Management System Mfr
N.A.I.C.S.: 333996
Michael A. Haritakis *(Exec VP)*

**Trauson Holdings Company
Limited** **(1)**
No 9 Longmen Road, Wujin Hi-Tech Indus-
trial Zone, Changzhou, 213163, Jiangsu,
China
Tel.: (86) 519 8166 5318
Web Site: http://www.trauson.com
Holding Company; Medical Products Mfr
N.A.I.C.S.: 551112

Subsidiary (Domestic):

**Trauson (China) Medical Instrument
Company Limited** **(2)**
Longmen Rd9, Wujin Hi-Tech Industrial
Zone, Changzhou, 213164, Jiangsu, China
Tel.: (86) 51981665318
Web Site: http://www.trauson.com
Emp.: 1,000

Stryker Corporation—(Continued)

Orthopaedic Product Mfr
N.A.I.C.S.: 339112
Aiguo Wang *(Chm & Gen Mgr)*

Vertos Medical Inc. (1)
101 Enterprise Ste 100, Aliso Viejo, CA
92656-2604
Web Site: http://www.vertosmed.com
Medical, Dental & Hospital Equipment &
Supplies Merchant Whslr
N.A.I.C.S.: 423450
Stephen E. Paul *(Chief Comml Officer)*
Eric Wichems *(Pres & CEO)*
Mehrzad Khakpour *(CTO)*

Vexim Italia Srl (1)
Viale Matteotti 1, 20121, Milan, Italy
Tel.: (39) 0283422576
Spine Product Distr
N.A.I.C.S.: 423450

Vexim SA (1)
8 Rue de Vidailhan Hills Plaza Bat B 1er
Etage, 31130, Balma, France
Tel.: (33) 561488663
Web Site: http://en.vexim.com
Emp.: 65
Spine Pain Medical Device Mfr
N.A.I.C.S.: 339112

Vexim Spine SL (1)
Paseo de Recoletos 7-9 5, 28004, Madrid,
Spain
Tel.: (34) 935952454
Spine Product Distr
N.A.I.C.S.: 423450

Vocera Communications, Inc. (1)
525 Race St, San Jose, CA 95126
Tel.: (408) 882-5100
Web Site: http://www.vocera.com
Rev.: $198,420,000
Assets: $406,821,000
Liabilities: $225,805,000
Net Worth: $181,016,000
Earnings: ($9,656,000)
Emp.: 688
Fiscal Year-end: 12/31/2020
Wireless Voice Communications Systems
Mfr, Sales & Distr
N.A.I.C.S.: 334220
James Blastos *(VP-Ops)*
Rob Born *(VP-Bus & Corp Dev)*
Paul T. Johnson *(Exec VP-Sls & Svcs)*
Rhonda Collins *(Chief Nursing Officer)*
Lori Stahl *(VP-People)*
Kathy Doub English *(CMO)*
Benjamin Kanter *(Chief Medical Info Officer)*
Mary Bridget Duffy *(Chief Medical Officer)*
Douglas A. Carlen *(Gen Counsel)*
Dave Lively *(VP-Product Mgmt)*
Steve Anheier *(CFO)*

Subsidiary (Non-US):

Vocera Canada, Ltd. (2)
8 Market Street Suite 300, Toronto, M5E
1M6, ON, Canada
Tel.: (416) 323-4400
Telecommunication Servicesb
N.A.I.C.S.: 541618
Maria Scozzaro *(Acct Mgr)*

**Vocera Communications Australia Pty
Ltd.** (2)
8 Herbert St, Saint Leonards, 2065, NSW,
Australia
Tel.: (61) 300862372
Web Site: http://www.vocera.com
Wireless Voice Communications System
Sales & Distr
N.A.I.C.S.: 517112

Vocera Communications UK Ltd. (2)
100 Longwater Avenue Green Park, Read-
ing, RG2 6GP, Berkshire, United Kingdom
Tel.: (44) 8443351237
Web Site: http://www.vocera.com
Sales Range: $10-24.9 Million
Emp.: 10
Wireless Voice Communications System
Sales & Distr
N.A.I.C.S.: 517112

WM Netherlands C.V. (1)
Valeriusstraat 5, 3122 AM, Schiedam, Neth-
erlands
Tel.: (31) 104718888
Medical Device Mfr

N.A.I.C.S.: 339112

STRYVE FOODS, INC.
5801 Tennyson Pkwy, Ste 275,
Plano, TX 75024
Tel.: (972) 987-5130   DE
Year Founded: 2016
SNAX—(NASDAQ)
Food Mfr
N.A.I.C.S.: 311919
Christopher James Boever *(CEO)*
Alex Hawkins *(CFO)*
Katie Grady *(Chief Customer Officer)*
Eric Fleming *(Chief Supply Chain Of-
ficer)*
Kevin Vivian *(Chm)*
Norma L. Garcia *(Chief HR Officer,
Gen Counsel & Sec)*

STS EVERMEDIA CORP.
60 State St 7th Fl, Boston, MA 02109
Tel.: (617) 955-0302
SEVM—(OTCIQ)
Information Technology Management
Services
N.A.I.C.S.: 541512
Jonathan Sym *(Pres & CEO)*

STURGIS BANCORP, INC.
113-125 E Chicago Rd, Sturgis, MI
49091
Tel.: (269) 651-9345   MI
Web Site: https://www.sturgis.bank
Year Founded: 2001
STBI—(OTCIQ)
Rev.: $30,753,000
Assets: $643,606,000
Liabilities: $596,494,000
Net Worth: $47,112,000
Earnings: $6,006,000
Emp.: 146
Fiscal Year-end: 12/31/20
Bank Holding Company
N.A.I.C.S.: 551111
Ronald W. Scheske *(COO & Exec
VP-Sturgis Bank)*
Jason Hyska *(Sr VP & Head-Retail
Banking-Sturgis Bank)*
Steve Merchant *(Asst VP-Sturgis
Bank)*
Elizabeth Mayer *(Officer-Loss Mitiga-
tion & VP-Sturgis Bank)*
Camille Wilson *(Officer-Comml Loan
& VP-Sturgis Bank)*
Matthew Scheske *(Sr VP & Head-
Comml Lending-Sturgis Bank)*

Subsidiaries:

Sturgis Bank & Trust Company (1)
113-125 E Chicago Rd, Sturgis, MI 49091
Tel.: (269) 651-9345
Web Site: http://www.sturgisbank.com
Sales Range: $10-24.9 Million
Commerical Banking
N.A.I.C.S.: 522110
Eric L. Eishen *(Pres & CEO)*
Ronald W. Scheske *(COO & Exec VP)*
Brian P. Hoggatt *(CFO, Treas & Sr VP)*
Jose D. Albarran *(VP)*
Steven G. Gage *(Sr VP-Comml Lending)*
Debora L. Capman *(VP & Trust Officer)*
Tracey L. Parker *(Chief Credit Officer & Sr
VP)*
Trudy R. Gloy *(Asst VP)*
Jason J. Hyska *(VP-Retail Lending)*
Christine M. Moline *(First VP-Private Bank-
ing)*
Camille M. Wilson *(VP)*
Elizabeth M. Weinberg *(VP)*
John D. Johnson *(VP-Bus Dev)*

**STURM, RUGER & COMPANY,
INC.**
1 Lacey Pl, Southport, CT 06890
Tel.: (203) 259-7843   DE
Web Site: https://www.ruger.com
Year Founded: 1949

RGR—(NYSE)
Rev.: $595,842,000
Assets: $484,763,000
Liabilities: $168,025,000
Net Worth: $316,738,000
Earnings: $88,332,000
Emp.: 1,880
Fiscal Year-end: 12/31/22
Pistols, Revolvers, Shotguns & Rifles
Mfr & Sales; Golf Equipment
N.A.I.C.S.: 332994
Christopher J. Killoy *(Pres & CEO)*
John A. Cosentino Jr. *(Vice Chm)*
Michael O. Fifer *(Vice Chm)*
Thomas A. Dineen *(CFO, Principal
Acctg Officer, Treas & Sr VP-Fin)*
Shawn C. Leska *(VP-Sls)*
Sarah F. Colbert *(VP-Admin)*
Michael W. Wilson *(VP-Mayodan
Ops)*
Timothy M. Lowney *(VP-Prescott
Ops)*
Randall S. Wheeler *(VP-Newport &
Ruger Engineered Component Ops)*
Kevin B. Reid Sr. *(Gen Counsel, Sec
& VP)*
Robert J. Werkmeister Jr. *(VP-Mktg)*

Subsidiaries:

Sturm, Ruger & Co., Inc. (1)
200 Ruger Rd, Prescott, AZ 86301
Tel.: (336) 949-5200
Web Site: http://www.ruger.com
Sales Range: $1-4.9 Billion
Mfr of Small Arms
N.A.I.C.S.: 331529

Division (Domestic):

**Sturm, Ruger & Co., Inc.-Prescott
Firearms Division** (2)
200 Ruger Rd, Prescott, AZ 86301
Tel.: (928) 541-8892
Web Site: http://www.ruger.com
Sales Range: $25-49.9 Million
Emp.: 100
Titanium, Aluminum & Steel Castings Mfr
N.A.I.C.S.: 331529

Sturm, Ruger-Newport Plant (1)
411 Sunapee St, Newport, NH 03773
Tel.: (336) 949-5200
Web Site: http://www.ruger.com
Sales Range: $150-199.9 Million
Emp.: 1,000
Small Arms Manufacturing
N.A.I.C.S.: 332994

STWC HOLDINGS, INC.
1350 Independence St Ste 300,
Lakewood, CO 80215
Tel.: (303) 736-2442   UT
Year Founded: 2007
STWC—(OTCIQ)
Assets: $573,813
Liabilities: $1,775,222
Net Worth: ($1,201,409)
Earnings: ($2,275,276)
Emp.: 5
Fiscal Year-end: 01/31/19
Marijuana Producer
N.A.I.C.S.: 111998
Elizabeth Illa *(Accountant)*

**SUBURBAN PROPANE PART-
NERS, L.P.**
240 Rte 10 W, Whippany, NJ 07981-
0206
Tel.: (973) 887-5300   DE
Web Site:
https://www.suburbanpropane.com
Year Founded: 1996
SPH—(NYSE)
Rev.: $1,288,755,000
Assets: $2,051,730,000
Liabilities: $1,626,309,000
Net Worth: $425,421,000
Earnings: $122,793,000
Emp.: 3,131

Fiscal Year-end: 09/25/21
Liquefied Petroleum Gas Dealers
N.A.I.C.S.: 457210
Michael A. Stivala *(Pres & CEO)*
A. Davin D'Ambrosio *(Treas & VP)*
Douglas T. Brinkworth *(Sr VP-Product
Supply, Pur, and Logistics)*
Michael A. Kuglin *(CFO)*
Neil E. Scanlon *(Sr VP-Information
Svcs)*
Daniel S. Bloomstein *(Chief Acctg
Officer & Controller)*
Michael A. Schueler *(VP-Product
Supply)*
Keith P. Onderdonk *(VP-Operational
Support)*
Bryon L. Koepke *(Gen Counsel, Sec
& VP)*
Daniel W. Boyd *(VP-Area Ops)*
Gregory L. Boyd *(VP-Area Ops)*
Francesca Cleffi *(VP-HR)*
M. Douglas Dagan *(VP-Strategic
Initiatives-Renewable Energy)*
Robert T. Ross *(VP-Area Ops)*
Nandini Sankara *(VP-Mktg & Brand
Strategy)*
Dee Arthur Tate *(VP-Area Ops)*
Tom Ross *(VP)*
Art Tate *(VP)*

Subsidiaries:

Agway Energy Services, LLC (1)
PO Box 4819, Syracuse, NY 13221-4819
Tel.: (315) 449-7061
Web Site: https://www.agwayenergy.com
Sales Range: $1-4.9 Billion
Natural Gas & Electricity Supplier
N.A.I.C.S.: 221210

Gas Connection, LLC (1)
18150 SE Division St, Portland, OR 97236
Tel.: (503) 661-4821
Web Site:
http://www.hometownhearthandgrill.com
Sales Range: $25-49.9 Million
Emp.: 5
Gas Appliances Whslr
N.A.I.C.S.: 449210

Independent Propane Company (1)
4209 State Hwy 64 W, Henderson, TX
75652
Tel.: (972) 712-8877
Web Site:
http://www.independentpropane.com
Sales Range: $25-49.9 Million
Emp.: 100
Liquefied Petroleum Gas Delivery
N.A.I.C.S.: 457210
Robert Blackwell *(Pres & CEO)*
Sheryl Davison *(Mgr-Pine Junction Cus-
tomer Svc)*
Randy Milfs *(Mgr-Pine Junction Field)*
Bill Hansen *(Mgr-Granby Plant)*

Ira Wyman, Inc. (1)
366 Clinton St, Penn Yan, NY 14527
Tel.: (315) 536-2378
Web Site: http://www.irawymanfuels.com
Sales Range: $25-49.9 Million
Emp.: 8
Propane Gas Dealer
N.A.I.C.S.: 457210
Christo Miller *(Gen Mgr)*

Jenkins Gas & Oil Co., Inc. (1)
221 Main St, Pollocksville, NC 28573
Tel.: (252) 224-8911
Web Site: http://www.jenkinsgas.com
Sales Range: $25-49.9 Million
Liquefied Petroleum Gas Dealers
N.A.I.C.S.: 457210

Live Oak Gas Co. (1)
1717 W Howard St PO Drawer A, Live Oak,
FL 32064
Tel.: (386) 362-2424
Web Site: http://www.liveoakgas.com
Rev.: $15,913,944
Emp.: 4
Propane Gas Dealer
N.A.I.C.S.: 457210
John Firmon *(Gen Mgr)*

Suburban Franchising, LLC (1)

240 Route 10 W, Whippany, NJ 07981
Tel.: (973) 503-9252
Web Site: http://www.suburbanpropane.com
Liquefied Petroleum Gas Distr
N.A.I.C.S.: 221210

Suburban Propane Group, Inc.   (1)
240 SR 10 W, Whippany, NJ 07981
Tel.: (803) 775-2334
Web Site: http://www.suburbanpropane.com
Sales Range: $25-49.9 Million
Emp.: 15
Purchase, Delivery & Retail Propane
N.A.I.C.S.: 457210

Suburban Propane, L.P.   (1)
8 Hitchiner Way, Milford, NH 03055
Tel.: (603) 679-3366
Web Site: http://www.suburbanpropane.com
Sales Range: $10-24.9 Million
Emp.: 25
Fuel Oil Dealers
N.A.I.C.S.: 457210

Suburban Propane, L.P.   (1)
5793 Widewaters Pkwy, De Witt, NY 13214
Tel.: (315) 385-4484
Petroleum Product Distr
N.A.I.C.S.: 424720

Suburban Propane, L.P.   (1)
9586 River Rd, Marcy, NY 13403
Tel.: (315) 724-7187
Web Site: http://www.suburbanpropane.com
Oil & Gas Field Operating Services
N.A.I.C.S.: 213112

United Propane   (1)
205 Najoles Rd, Millersville, MD 21108
Tel.: (410) 987-9000
Web Site: http://www.suburbanpropane.com
Rev.: $30,242,209
Emp.: 60
Propane Gas, Bottled
N.A.I.C.S.: 457210

SUGARMADE, INC.

750 Royal Oaks Dr Ste 108, Monrovia, CA 91016   DE
Web Site: http://www.sugarmade.com
Year Founded: 1986
SGMD—(OTCIQ)
Rev.: $3,979,049
Assets: $19,432,951
Liabilities: $14,662,733
Net Worth: $4,770,218
Earnings: ($5,926,134)
Emp.: 7
Fiscal Year-end: 06/30/21
Tree-Free Copy Paper Mfr
N.A.I.C.S.: 322299
Jimmy Chan (Chm, CEO & CFO)

SUIC WORLDWIDE HOLDINGS LTD.

136-20 38th Ave Unit 3G, Flushing, NY 11354
Tel.: (929) 391-2550   NV
Web Site: https://sinounitedco.com
Year Founded: 2006
SUIC—(OTCIQ)
Rev.: $150,000
Assets: $384,279
Liabilities: $427,040
Net Worth: ($42,761)
Earnings: $7,825
Emp.: 6
Fiscal Year-end: 12/31/23
Blockchain Technology & Services
N.A.I.C.S.: 551112
Yanru Zhou (Chm, CEO & CFO)
Bill Tan Yee Wei (CTO)

SUMMER ENERGY HOLDINGS, INC.

5847 San Felipe St Ste 3700, Houston, TX 77057
Tel.: (713) 375-2790   NV
Web Site:
  http://www.summerenergy.com
Year Founded: 2005
SUME—(OTCQB)
Rev.: $166,315,793

Assets: $51,497,772
Liabilities: $46,463,553
Net Worth: $5,034,219
Earnings: ($10,733,089)
Emp.: 90
Fiscal Year-end: 12/31/19
Electric Power Distribution Services
N.A.I.C.S.: 221122
Jaleea Pyle George (CFO, Treas & Sec)
Neil M. Leibman (CEO)
Stuart C. Gaylor (Chm)
Steve Madden (Pres)

SUMMIT FINANCIAL GROUP, INC.

300 N Main St, Moorefield, WV 26836
Tel.: (304) 530-1000   WV
Web Site: https://www.summitfgi.com
Year Founded: 1996
SMMF—(NASDAQ)
Rev.: $176,900,000
Assets: $3,916,692,000
Liabilities: $3,562,162,000
Net Worth: $354,530,000
Earnings: $53,216,000
Emp.: 432
Fiscal Year-end: 12/31/22
Financial Holding Company
N.A.I.C.S.: 551111
H. Charles Maddy III (Vice Chm, Pres & CEO)
Patrick N. Frye (Exec VP)
Robert S. Tissue (CFO & Exec VP)
Oscar M. Bean (Chm)
Scott C. Jennings (COO & Exec VP)
Bradford E. Ritchie (Exec VP)
Danyl R. Freeman (Chief HR Officer)
Joseph Hager (Chief Risk Officer)
Angela Zirk (Chief Experience Officer)

Subsidiaries:

PSB Holding Corp.   (1)
PO Box 219, Preston, MD 21655
Tel.: (410) 673-2401
Rev.: $19,231,078
Assets: $462,707,823
Liabilities: $419,624,645
Net Worth: $43,083,178
Earnings: $3,522,859
Fiscal Year-end: 12/31/2019
Bank Holding Company
N.A.I.C.S.: 551111
David H. Wilson (Chm)
Melissa Quirk (Pres & CEO)

Summit Community Bank, Inc.   (1)
310 N Main St, Moorefield, WV 26836   (100%)
Tel.: (304) 530-1000
Web Site: https://www.mysummit.bank
Sales Range: $75-99.9 Million
Commericial Banking
N.A.I.C.S.: 522110

SUMMIT HOTEL PROPERTIES, INC.

13215 Bee Cave Pkwy Ste B-300, Austin, TX 78738
Tel.: (512) 538-2300   MD
Web Site: https://www.shpreit.com
Year Founded: 2004
INN—(NYSE)
Rev.: $675,695,000
Assets: $3,022,270,000
Liabilities: $1,614,320,000
Net Worth: $1,407,950,000
Earnings: ($16,929,000)
Emp.: 74
Fiscal Year-end: 12/31/22
Hotel Real Estate Investment Trust
N.A.I.C.S.: 525990
Christopher R. Eng (Chief Risk Officer, Gen Counsel, Sec & Exec VP)
Paul Ruiz (Chief Acctg Officer & Sr VP)

Jonathan P. Stanner (Pres & CEO)
William H. Conkling (CFO & Exec VP)

Subsidiaries:

Carnegie Hotels, LLC   (1)
1216 W State of Franklin Rd, Johnson City, TN 37604
Tel.: (423) 979-6400
Web Site: https://www.carnegiehotel.com
Hotel & Resort Management Services
N.A.I.C.S.: 721110

SUMMIT MATERIALS, INC.

1801 California St Ste 3500, Denver, CO 80202
Tel.: (303) 893-0012   DE
Web Site: https://www.summit-materials.com
Year Founded: 2014
SUM—(NYSE)
Rev.: $2,409,669,000
Assets: $4,239,125,000
Liabilities: $2,415,913,000
Net Worth: $1,823,212,000
Earnings: $152,184,000
Emp.: 5,500
Fiscal Year-end: 01/01/22
Holding Company; Construction Materials Mfr & Whslr
N.A.I.C.S.: 551112
Scott Anderson (CFO & Exec VP)
Anne P. Noonan (Pres & CEO)
Karli S. Anderson (Chief People & ESG Officer, Exec VP & Head-Comm)
Christopher B. Gaskill (Chief Legal Officer, Sec & Exec VP)
Andy Larkin (VP-IR)
Thomas A. Beck (Exec VP)
David Loomes (Sr VP)

Subsidiaries:

Alleyton Resource Company, LLC   (1)
7555 FM 762 Rd, Richmond, TX 77469
Tel.: (281) 238-1010
Web Site: http://www.alleytonresource.net
Quality Construction Material Whslr
N.A.I.C.S.: 423320
Erin Anderson (Dir-HR)
Norma Yanez (Mgr-HR)
Stephen Gardner (Dir-Safety)
Lisa Thomas (Coord-Safety & Claims)
Alyssa Veit (Mgr-Aggregate Safety)
Emily Schnitzer (Supvr-Payroll)

Buildex, LLC   (1)
832 Pennsylvania, Lawrence, KS 66044
Tel.: (785) 242-2177
Web Site: https://www.buildex.com
Other Concrete Product Mfr
N.A.I.C.S.: 327390
Cheryl Conner (VP)

Carolina Sand - Johnsonville   (1)
541 Macks Lk Rd, Johnsonville, SC 29555
Tel.: (843) 386-2021
Brick, Stone & Related Construction Material Merchant Whslr
N.A.I.C.S.: 423320

Con-Agg Companies, LLC   (1)
2604 N Stadium Blvd, Columbia, MO 65202
Tel.: (573) 446-0905
Web Site: https://conagg-mo.com
Emp.: 500
Land Construction Services
N.A.I.C.S.: 236220

Concrete Supply of Topeka, LLC   (1)
2500 SW 3rd St, Topeka, KS 66606
Tel.: (785) 235-1585
Web Site: https://cst-bc.com
Building Materials Mfr
N.A.I.C.S.: 327120

Glasscock Company Inc.   (1)
5378 Broad St, Sumter, SC 29154
Tel.: (803) 494-2694
Trucking Business & Ready Mix Concrete Supplier
N.A.I.C.S.: 484121

Green America Recycling, LLC   (1)
16401 Swingley Ridge Rd Ste 610, Chesterfield, MO 63017
Tel.: (636) 532-7440
Web Site:
  https://www.greenamericarecycling.com
Reuse Waste Material Services
N.A.I.C.S.: 562920

Jefferson Quarry, LLC   (1)
369 Quarry Rd, Jefferson, GA 30549
Tel.: (706) 693-2433
Building Materials Whslr
N.A.I.C.S.: 423390

Lewis & Lewis, Inc.   (1)
370 Blairtown Rd, Rock Springs, WY 82902
Tel.: (307) 362-7948
Web Site: https://www.lewisandlewisinc.com
Ready Mix Concrete & Aggregate Whslr
N.A.I.C.S.: 423320

Mainland Construction Materials ULC   (1)
9525 - 201 Street Unit 317, Langley, V1M 4A5, BC, Canada
Tel.: (604) 882-5650
Web Site: https://www.mainlandcm.com
Construction Material & Concrete Distr
N.A.I.C.S.: 423320

Mid-Missouri Limestone, LLC   (1)
1803 Old US Hwy 54, Auxvasse, MO 65231
Tel.: (573) 386-5666
Web Site:
  http://www.mertensconstruction.com
Construction Material Mfr & Whslr
N.A.I.C.S.: 551112

Peak Materials, LLC   (1)
28755 Hwy ste 9, Silverthorne, CO 80497
Tel.: (970) 468-2521
Web Site: http://www.peakmaterials.com
Asphalt & Concrete Whslr
N.A.I.C.S.: 423320

R.D. Johnson Excavating Company, LLC   (1)
1451 N 1823 Rd, Lawrence, KS 66044
Tel.: (785) 842-9100
Web Site: https://www.rdje.com
Heavy Civil Construction Services
N.A.I.C.S.: 238910
Jason Dahl (Dir-Ops)
Kyle Frank (Mgr-Utility)
Kelly Thomas (Mgr-Project)
Matt Bowlin (Mgr-Equipment)
Benjamin Bryant (Engr-Project)
Mike Brown (Mgr-Survey)

Summit Finance Group, LLC   (1)
2000 Crow Canyon Pl Ste 450, San Ramon, CA 94583
Tel.: (925) 866-7800
Web Site: https://www.summitadvisors.com
Management Firm Services
N.A.I.C.S.: 541611
Steven M. Wilcox (Partner)
Nathan Bennett (Partner)
Jay Gilson (Sr Dir)
Angela King (Mgr-Mktg)
Erin Haubner (Dir-Ops)
Breanne Powers (Mgr-Bus Ops)
Teresa Hookey (Controller)
Jeffrey Lee (Mgr-Practice)
Cristina Holloway (Coord-New Bus)
Monika Orrey (Mgr-Practice)
Cindy Loeffler (Mgr-Practice)
Laurie Murthy (Mgr-Practice)
Wanda Ladrillono (Mgr-Practice)
Keith Campbell (Mgr-Compliance & Trading)
Rachael Kepke (Mgr-Fin Plng & Professional Svcs)

Summit Materials Finance Corp.   (1)
8200 E 34st N Bldg 1600 Ste 1607, Wichita, KS 67226
Tel.: (316) 220-6152
Construction Material Mfr & Whslr
N.A.I.C.S.: 327320

Summit Materials, LLC   (1)
1550 Wynkoop, Denver, CO 80202   (100%)
Tel.: (303) 893-0012
Web Site: http://www.summit-materials.com
Rev.: $2,412,521,999
Assets: $4,255,691,999
Liabilities: $2,243,701,999
Net Worth: $2,011,989,999

Summit Materials, Inc.—(Continued)

Earnings: $272,144,999
Emp.: 4,799
Fiscal Year-end: 12/31/2022
Aggregates, Ready-Mix Concrete, Cement
& Asphalt Facilities Operator
N.A.I.C.S.: 561110
Karli S. Anderson *(Chief People Officer)*
Anne P. Noonan *(Pres & CEO)*
Scott Anderson *(CFO)*
Karli S. Anderson *(Chief People Officer)*
Christopher B. Gaskill *(Chief Legal Officer)*
Kekin M. Ghelani *(Chief Strategy Officer)*

Subsidiary (Domestic):

Altaview Concrete, LLC (2)
9547 S 500 W, Sandy, UT 84070
Tel.: (801) 255-3580
Web Site: http://www.altaviewconcrete.com
Rev.: $12,900,000
Emp.: 25
Concrete Mixture Mfr
N.A.I.C.S.: 423320
R. Scott Reynolds *(COO)*
Lee Anderson *(Gen Mgr)*
Jamie Rentmeister *(Coord-Sls)*
Mark Hanyon *(Mgr-Dispatch)*
Kelli Boutwell *(Supvr-Customer Relation-ship)*
Scott Bushnell *(Mgr-Ops-North)*
Kelly Chatterton *(Dir-Sls)*
Jeremy Kirkham *(Mgr-Ops-South)*
Dave Palmer *(Mgr-Sls)*
Misty Crawford *(Mgr-Acctg)*
Rich Kauss *(Mgr-Sls)*
Darin Davis *(Mgr-Quality Assurance-Southern Div)*
Ryan Skidmore *(Mgr-Quality Assurance-Northern)*
Christopher Pali *(Mgr-Quality Control-Northern Div)*
Marshall Lay *(Mgr-Credit)*
Evan Cope *(Mgr-Quality Control-Southern Div)*

American Materials Company, LLC (2)
1410 Commonwealth Dr Ste 201, Wilming-ton, NC 28403
Tel.: (910) 799-1411
Web Site:
    https://www.americanmaterialsco.com
Construction Sand & Gravel Mining
N.A.I.C.S.: 212321

Austin Materials, LLC (2)
9020 N Capital of TX Hwy Bldg II St 250,
Austin, TX 78759
Tel.: (512) 251-3713
Web Site: http://www.austinmaterials.com
Sales Range: $10-24.9 Million
Aggregate & Asphalt Supplier; Paving Con-tractor
N.A.I.C.S.: 324121

Subsidiary (Domestic):

Asphalt Paving Company of Austin, LLC (3)
14701 S I H 35, Buda, TX 78610
Tel.: (512) 275-1900
Sales Range: $1-9.9 Million
Emp.: 35
Asphalt Paving Services
N.A.I.C.S.: 237310

Subsidiary (Domestic):

Boxley Materials Company (2)
15418 W Lynchburg Salem Tpke, Blue
Ridge, VA 24064
Tel.: (540) 777-7600
Web Site: https://www.boxley.com
Crushed & Broken Limestone
N.A.I.C.S.: 423320
Abney S. Boxley III *(Chm)*

Con-Agg of MO, LLC (2)
2604 N Stadium Blvd, Columbia, MO 65202
Tel.: (573) 446-0905
Web Site: https://www.conagg.com
Sales Range: $10-24.9 Million
Emp.: 500
Ready-Mixed Concrete Mfr, Crushed Lime-stone & Other Stone Products Quarrying
N.A.I.C.S.: 327320
Alan Barnes *(Pres)*
Bob Cathey *(Dir-Safety)*

Ronnie Simms *(Gen Mgr-Aggregates)*
Troy Dawkins *(Mgr-Ready Mix Ops)*
Ryan Sutherland *(Mgr-Sls)*
Greg Black *(Mgr-Equipment)*
Kyle Wyatt *(Mgr-Fin)*
Natalie Timmerman *(Mgr-HR)*
Doug Mertens *(Dir-Bus Dev)*

Concrete Supply of Topeka, Inc. (2)
2500 SW 3rd St, Topeka, KS 66606
Tel.: (785) 235-1585
Web Site: https://www.cst-bc.com
Sales Range: $1-9.9 Million
Emp.: 7
Ready-Mix Concrete & Aggregates Supplier
N.A.I.C.S.: 327320
Jerry Marney *(COO)*
Gerad Hale *(Mgr-Safety)*
Cathy Deters *(Mgr-Fin)*

Continental Cement Company, LLC (2)
16401 Swingley Ridge Rd Ste 610, Ches-terfield, MO 63017
Tel.: (636) 532-7440
Web Site:
    https://www.continentalcement.com
Sales Range: $100-124.9 Million
Emp.: 20
Cement Mfr
N.A.I.C.S.: 327310
Carrie Jenks *(VP)*
Chris Cason *(VP)*
Joey Biasatti *(VP)*
Tim Noud *(VP)*

Cornejo & Sons, LLC (2)
2060 E Tulsa St, Wichita, KS 67216
Tel.: (316) 522-5100
Web Site: https://www.cornejocorp.com
Sales Range: $25-49.9 Million
Emp.: 575
Construction Materials & Paving Services
N.A.I.C.S.: 212319

Elam Construction, Inc. (2)
556 Struthers Ave, Grand Junction, CO
81501
Tel.: (970) 242-5370
Web Site: https://www.elamconstruction.com
Sales Range: $10-24.9 Million
Emp.: 150
Asphalt Mfr, Aggregate Sales & Paving Ser-vices
N.A.I.C.S.: 237310

Hamm, Inc. (2)
609 Perry Pl, Perry, KS 66073
Tel.: (785) 597-5111
Web Site: https://www.nirhamm.com
Sales Range: $150-199.9 Million
Emp.: 500
Building Materials Distr
N.A.I.C.S.: 212312
Charlie Sedlock *(VP-Waste Svcs Div)*
Jeff Hamm *(VP-Asphalt & Transportation)*
Ryan Blosser *(Pres)*
Ramon Gonzalez *(Mgr-Aggregate Sls)*
Jeremy Hamm *(Gen Mgr-Waste Svcs Div)*
Brad Hern *(Dir-HR & Safety Kansas Ops)*
Travis Morris *(Dir)*
Josh Moore *(Dir-Construction)*
Mike Curry *(Dir-Bus Dev & Mktg)*

Hinkle Contracting Company, LLC (2)
395 N Middletown Rd, Paris, KY 40361-2138
Tel.: (859) 987-3670
Web Site: https://www.hinklecontracting.com
Sales Range: $50-74.9 Million
Emp.: 050
Transportation & Waterway Infrastructure
Construction Contractor, Limestone Mining,
Asphalt & Concrete Block Mfr
N.A.I.C.S.: 237990
Tracey Bubnick *(Dir-Safety)*
Greg Howard *(VP-Property & Dev)*
Jeff Mingus *(VP-Equipment)*
J. Gregory Gillum *(Dir-HR)*

Unit (Domestic):

Hinkle Block & Masonry (3)
39 Garner School Rd, Somerset, KY 42501
Tel.: (606) 451-8898
Web Site: https://www.hinkleblock.com
Sales Range: $1-9.9 Million
Emp.: 35
Concrete Block & Brick Mfr

N.A.I.C.S.: 327331
James Saylor *(Gen Mgr)*

Hinkle Contracting Co., LLC -Jackson (3)
Kentucky Hwy 15, Jackson, KY 41339
Tel.: (606) 666-5462
Web Site: http://www.hinklecontracting.com
Asphalt Mfr & Paving Services
N.A.I.C.S.: 324121

Hinkle Contracting Co., LLC -Lexington (3)
605 Blue Sky Pkwy, Lexington, KY 40509
Tel.: (859) 263-7558
Web Site: http://www.hinklecontracting.com
Civil, Environmental & Rail Construction
Services & Concrete Mfr
N.A.I.C.S.: 237990

Hinkle Contracting Co., LLC -Somerset (3)
2530 Monticello St, Somerset, KY 42501
Tel.: (606) 678-4316
Web Site: http://www.hinklecontracting.com
Sales Range: $1-9.9 Million
Asphalt Mfr & Paving Services
N.A.I.C.S.: 324121
Greg Howard *(VP-Property & Dev)*
Warren Hawkridge *(Sr VP-Ops)*
Jamie King *(VP-Asphalt Plants & Logistics)*
Steven Lee *(CFO)*
Jeff Mingus *(VP-Equipment)*
Tom Ralston *(VP-Asphalt Paving)*
Larry Winkleman *(Pres & CEO)*

Subsidiary (Domestic):

Kentucky Hauling, Inc. (3)
395 N Middletown Rd, Paris, KY 40361-2138
Tel.: (859) 987-3670
Sales Range: $25-49.9 Million
Emp.: 50
Stone & Paving Mixture Local Trucking Ser-vices
N.A.I.C.S.: 484220
Henry Hinkle *(Pres)*

Nally & Gibson Georgetown, LLC (3)
1267 E Main St, Georgetown, KY 40324
Tel.: (502) 863-1771
Web Site: http://www.hinklecontracting.com
Limestone & Other Crushed Stone Mining
N.A.I.C.S.: 212312

Ohio Valley Asphalt, LLC (3)
3508 Hwy 227, Carrollton, KY 41008
Tel.: (502) 732-6606
Web Site: http://www.hinklecontracting.com
Sales Range: $1-9.9 Million
Emp.: 47
Asphalt Mfr & Paving Services
N.A.I.C.S.: 324121

Subsidiary (Domestic):

Industrial Asphalt, LLC (2)
1114 Lost Creek Blvd Ste 410, Austin, TX
78746
Tel.: (512) 275-0303
Web Site: http://www.industrialasphalt.com
Sales Range: $1-9.9 Million
Emp.: 55
Asphalt Mfr & Rock Mining
N.A.I.C.S.: 324121

Kilgore Companies, LLC (2)
7057 W 2100 S, Salt Lake City, UT 84128
Tel.: (801) 250-0132
Web Site: http://www.kilgorecompanies.com
Sales Range: $25-49.9 Million
Emp.: 40
Asphalt Production & Paving Services
N.A.I.C.S.: 324121

LeGrand Johnson Construction Co. (2)
1000 S Main St, Logan, UT 84321
Tel.: (435) 752-2001
Web Site: https://www.legrandjohnson.com
Asphalt & Concrete Whslr
N.A.I.C.S.: 423320

Sierra Ready Mix, LLC (2)
4150 Smiley Rd, North Las Vegas, NV
89081
Tel.: (702) 644-8700
Web Site: https://www.sierrareadymix.com

Sales Range: $1-9.9 Million
Emp.: 61
Lumber And Other Building Materials, Nsk
N.A.I.C.S.: 444180

Troy Vines, Inc. (2)
2817 Rankin Hwy, Midland, TX 79706
Tel.: (432) 682-7031
Web Site: http://www.troyvinesconcrete.com
Sales Range: $1-9.9 Million
Ready Mix Concrete Mfr 7 Distr
N.A.I.C.S.: 327320

Westroc, Inc. (2)
7057 W 2100 S, Salt Lake City, UT 84128
Tel.: (801) 785-5600
Web Site: http://www.westrocinc.com
Sales Range: $10-24.9 Million
Emp.: 100
Ready-Mix Concrete & Aggregate Products
Mfr
N.A.I.C.S.: 327320

Wind River Materials, LLC (2)
120 E Elk St, Kemmerer, WY 83101
Tel.: (307) 877-3400
Sales Range: $1-9.9 Million
Emp.: 75
Aggregate Products & Ready-Mix Concrete
Mfr
N.A.I.C.S.: 327320

Walker Sand & Gravel Ltd. Co. (1)
100 Walker Dr, Bellevue, ID 83313
Tel.: (208) 788-4525
Web Site: http://www.walker-sand-gravel.business.site
Sand & Gravel Whslr
N.A.I.C.S.: 423320

SUMMIT MIDSTREAM PART-NERS, LP
910 Louisiana St Ste 4200, Houston,
TX 77002
Tel.: (832) 413-4770   DE
Web Site:
    https://www.summitmidstream.com
Year Founded: 2009
SMLP—(NYSE)
Rev.: $369,594,000
Assets: $2,559,964,000
Liabilities: $1,795,146,000
Net Worth: $764,818,000
Earnings: ($140,605,000)
Emp.: 252
Fiscal Year-end: 12/31/22
Midstream Energy Infrastructure
Owner & Operator
N.A.I.C.S.: 211120
J. Heath Deneke *(Chm, Pres & CEO)*
Matthew B. Sicinski *(Chief Acctg Offi-cer)*
Hugo Guerrero *(Sr VP)*
James Johnston *(Chief Compliance
Officer)*

Subsidiaries:

Epping Transmission Company, LLC (1)
1790 Hughes Landing Blvd Ste 500, The
Woodlands, TX 77380
Tel.: (720) 441-0244
Midstream Energy Infrastructure Operator
N.A.I.C.S.: 213112
Michael C. Smith *(Sr VP-Corp Dev)*
Megan Davis *(VP)*

Grand River Gathering, LLC (1)
999 18th St Ste 3400 S, Denver, CO 80202
Tel.: (720) 452-6220
Oil & Gas Field Support Services
N.A.I.C.S.: 213112

Summit Midstream Finance Corp. (1)
2100 Mckinney Ave Ste 1250, Dallas, TX
75201
Tel.: (214) 242-1955
Oil & Gas Field Support Services
N.A.I.C.S.: 213112

SUMMIT STATE BANK

500 Bicentennial Way, Santa Rosa,
CA 95403
Tel.: (707) 568-6000
Web Site:
https://www.summitstatebank.com
SSBI—(NASDAQ)
Rev.: $32,663,000
Assets: $695,978,000
Liabilities: $628,634,000
Net Worth: $67,344,000
Earnings: $6,477,000
Emp.: 93
Fiscal Year-end: 12/31/19
Banking Services
N.A.I.C.S.: 522180
James E. Brush *(Chm)*
Brandy A. Lee Seppi *(Chief Lending Officer & Exec VP)*
Brian Reed *(Pres & CEO)*
Michael Castilo *(Chief Credit Officer & Sr VP)*
Camille D. Kazarian *(CFO & Exec VP)*
Genie M. Del Secco *(COO & Exec VP)*

Subsidiaries:

Summit State Bank **(1)**
10 Raley's Towne Ctr, Rohnert Park, CA
94928
Tel.: (707) 568-4955
Web Site: http://www.summitstatebank.com
Rev.: $5,400,000
Emp.: 60
National Commercial Banks
N.A.I.C.S.: 522110
Peggy Wyman *(VP & Mgr)*

SUMMIT THERAPEUTICS INC.
2882 Sand Hill Rd Ste 106, Menlo
Park, CA 94025
Tel.: (650) 460-8308
Web Site: https://www.smmttx.com
SMMT—(NASDAQ)
Rev.: $1,001,000
Assets: $202,949,000
Liabilities: $125,257,000
Net Worth: $77,692,000
Earnings: ($614,928,000)
Emp.: 105
Fiscal Year-end: 12/31/23
Antibiotic Product Distr
N.A.I.C.S.: 424210
Robert W. Duggan *(Chm & Co-CEO)*
Manmeet Singh Soni *(COO)*
Mahkam Zanganeh *(Pres & Co-CEO)*
Fong Clow *(Chief Biometrics Officer)*
Urte Gayko *(Chief Regulatory, Quality & Pharmacovigilance Officer)*
Allen S. Yang *(Chief Medical Officer)*
Robert W. Duggan *(Chm & Co-CEO)*
Dave Gancarz *(Chief Bus & Strategy Officer)*
Fong Clow *(Chief Biometrics Officer)*
Allen S. Yang *(Chief Medical Officer)*
Shelley D. Spray *(Head-Mktg)*

Subsidiaries:

Summit Therapeutics Limited **(1)**
136a Eastern Avenue Milton Park, Abingdon, OX14 4SB, Oxfordshire, United Kingdom
Tel.: (44) 1235443939
Web Site: https://www.summittxinc.com
Rev.: $20,652,454
Assets: $95,908,127
Liabilities: $18,228,617
Net Worth: $77,679,510
Earnings: ($28,897,171)
Emp.: 70
Fiscal Year-end: 12/31/2019
Pharmaceutical Product Developer
N.A.I.C.S.: 325412
Mahkam Zanganeh *(COO)*
David Powell *(Chief Scientific Officer)*
Melissa Strange *(VP-Fin)*
Ventzislav Stefanov *(Exec VP)*
Divya Chari *(Head-Clinical Ops-Global)*

Subsidiary (Domestic):

Summit (Oxford) Limited **(2)**

136a Eastern Avenue, Abingdon, OX14
4SB, Oxfordshire, United Kingdom
Tel.: (44) 1235443939
Pharmaceuticals Product Mfr
N.A.I.C.S.: 325412

SUN COMMUNITIES, INC.
27777 Franklin Rd Ste 300, Southfield, MI 48034
Tel.: (248) 208-2500   MD
Web Site: https://www.suninc.com
Year Founded: 1975
SUI—(NYSE)
Rev.: $3,224,600,000
Assets: $16,940,700,000
Liabilities: $9,767,700,000
Net Worth: $7,173,000,000
Earnings: ($213,300,000)
Emp.: 6,780
Fiscal Year-end: 12/31/23
Real Estate Investment Trust
N.A.I.C.S.: 525990
Karen J. Dearing *(Exec VP-Special Projects)*
Baxter R. Underwood *(CEO-Safe Harbor)*
Fernando Castro-Caratini *(CFO)*
Gary A. Shiffman *(Chm & CEO)*

Subsidiaries:

Apple Carr Village Mobile Home
Park, LLC **(1)**
516 Courtland, Muskegon, MI 49442
Tel.: (231) 788-2222
Web Site: http://www.applecarr.com
Sales Range: $25-49.9 Million
Emp.: 4
Real Estate Lending Services
N.A.I.C.S.: 531190

Bright Insurance Agency, Inc. **(1)**
27777 Franklin Rd Ste 200, Southfield, MI
48034
Tel.: (248) 208-2515
Web Site: http://www.brightins.com
Emp.: 2
Insurance Agencies & Brokerage Services
N.A.I.C.S.: 524210

Brookside Village Mobile Home Park,
LLC **(1)**
3130 Slater Ave, Kentwood, MI 49512
Tel.: (616) 942-0550
Real Estate Lending Services
N.A.I.C.S.: 531190

CC RP LLC **(1)**
251 Post St Ste 520, San Francisco, CA
94108
Tel.: (415) 655-7000
Web Site: https://www.ccrpllc.com
Commercial Real Estate Investment Services
N.A.I.C.S.: 531312
Mark G. Stefan *(Co-Founder & Pres)*
Sigurd J. Anderson *(Co-Founder & CEO)*
Eric J. Anderson *(Exec VP)*
Peter Staver *(VP)*
Jana Chapital *(Ops Mgr)*
Jessica LeGare *(Sr Mgr)*
Kassandra Kappelos *(Gen Mgr)*
Jordan Stefan *(Mgr-Property)*
Krysina Grussing *(Sr Mgr)*
Roman Sousa *(Dir)*
Celena Spychalla *(Mgr)*

Carriage Cove, LLC **(1)**
500 Carriage Cove Way, Sanford, FL 32773
Tel.: (407) 323-8160
Web Site: https://www.suncommunities.com
Emp.: 4
Real Estate Asset Management Services
N.A.I.C.S.: 531390

Dutton Mill Village, LLC **(1)**
6720 W Mill Run, Caledonia, MI 49316
Tel.: (616) 698-8610
Web Site: https://www.suncommunities.com
Sales Range: $25-49.9 Million
Emp.: 3
Real Estate Lending Services
N.A.I.C.S.: 531190

Egelcraft, LLC **(1)**
2129 Arrowhead Dr, Muskegon, MI 49442
Tel.: (231) 777-5555

Web Site: https://www.suncommunities.com
Real Estate Investment Services
N.A.I.C.S.: 531210

FC Meadowbrook LLC **(1)**
9859 Spring Rdg Ln, Charlotte, NC 28215
Tel.: (704) 545-2163
Web Site: https://www.suncommunities.com
Real Estate Brokerage Services
N.A.I.C.S.: 531210

FC Pebble Creek LLC **(1)**
225 Pebblecreek Dr, Greenwood, IN 46143-
7590
Tel.: (317) 885-3910
Web Site: http://www.suncommunities.com
Sales Range: $25-49.9 Million
Emp.: 4
Real Estate Brokerage Services
N.A.I.C.S.: 531210

Fox Creek Reserve, L.L.C. **(1)**
2350 Adobe Rd, Bullhead City, AZ 86442
Tel.: (928) 763-1149
Web Site: https://www.suncommunities.com
Property Investment Services
N.A.I.C.S.: 531311

GCP Lamplighter, LLC **(1)**
3202 S Nova Rd, Port Orange, FL 32129
Tel.: (386) 761-2481
Web Site: https://www.suncommunities.com
Mobile Home Dealing Distr
N.A.I.C.S.: 459930

Hickory Hills Village, LLC **(1)**
10450 6 Mile Rd Ste 131, Battle Creek, MI
49014
Web Site: http://www.suncommunities.com
Emp.: 4
Real Estate Lending Services
N.A.I.C.S.: 531190

Hidden Ridge An RV Community,
LLC **(1)**
2306 12th St, Hopkins, MI 49328
Tel.: (269) 672-9196
Real Estate Lending Services
N.A.I.C.S.: 531190
Janie Linscott *(Office Mgr)*

Jensen's Inc. **(1)**
246 Redstone St, Southington, CT 06489
Tel.: (860) 793-0281
Web Site:
http://www.jensencommunities.com
Mobile Home Site Operators
N.A.I.C.S.: 531190
Kristian Jensen III *(Pres & CEO)*

Kerrville Camp-Resort, LLC **(1)**
2605 Jct Hwy 27, Kerrville, TX 78028
Tel.: (830) 460-3262
Web Site:
http://www.jellystoneguadalupe.com
Amusement Park Services
N.A.I.C.S.: 713110

Lakeshore Landings, LLC **(1)**
2000 W 33rd St, Orlando, FL 32839
Tel.: (407) 843-6827
Mobile Home Dealing Distr
N.A.I.C.S.: 459930

Maple Brook, L.L.C. **(1)**
21635 Ridgeland Dr, Matteson, IL 60443
Tel.: (708) 720-5410
Real Estate Investment Services
N.A.I.C.S.: 531210

Palm Creek Holdings LLC **(1)**
1110 N Hennes Rd, Casa Grande, AZ
85222
Tel.: (520) 421-7000
Holding Company
N.A.I.C.S.: 551112

Port Milford LLC **(1)**
164 Rogers Ave, Milford, CT 06460
Tel.: (203) 877-7802
Rev.: $1,022,000
Emp.: 7
Marinas
N.A.I.C.S.: 713930

SHM Anacapa Isle, LLC **(1)**
3001 Peninsula Rd, Oxnard, CA 93035
Tel.: (805) 985-6035
Boat Operating Services
N.A.I.C.S.: 487210

SHM Annapolis, LLC **(1)**

519 Chester Ave, Annapolis, MD 21403
Tel.: (410) 268-8282
Boat Operating Services
N.A.I.C.S.: 487210

SHM Aqua Yacht, LLC **(1)**
3832 Hwy 25, Iuka, MS 38852
Tel.: (662) 423-2222
Boat Operating Services
N.A.I.C.S.: 487210

SHM Aqualand, LLC **(1)**
6800 Lights Ferry Rd, Flowery Branch, GA
30542
Tel.: (770) 967-6811
Boat Operating Services
N.A.I.C.S.: 487210

SHM Bahia Bleu, LLC **(1)**
2812 River Dr Thunderbolt, Savannah, GA
31404
Tel.: (912) 354-2283
Boat Operating Services
N.A.I.C.S.: 487210

SHM Ballena Isle, LLC **(1)**
1150 Ballena Blvd, Alameda, CA 94501
Tel.: (510) 523-5528
Boat Operating Services
N.A.I.C.S.: 487210

SHM Beaufort, LLC **(1)**
1006 Bay St, Beaufort, SC 29902
Tel.: (843) 524-4422
Boat Operating Services
N.A.I.C.S.: 487210

SHM Beaver Creek, LLC **(1)**
8929 E Hwy 92, Monticello, KY 42633
Tel.: (606) 348-7280
Boat Operating Services
N.A.I.C.S.: 487210

SHM Belle Maer, LLC **(1)**
41700 Conger Bay Dr, Harrison Township,
MI 48045
Tel.: (586) 465-4534
Boat Operating Services
N.A.I.C.S.: 487210

SHM Bohemia Vista, LLC **(1)**
140 Vista Marina Rd, Chesapeake City, MD
21915
Tel.: (410) 885-2056
Boat Operating Services
N.A.I.C.S.: 487210

SHM Brady Mountain, LLC **(1)**
4120 Brady Mountain Rd, Royal, AR 71968
Tel.: (501) 767-3422
Boat Operating Services
N.A.I.C.S.: 487210

SHM Bruce & Johnson, LLC **(1)**
145 S Montowese St, Branford, CT 06405
Tel.: (203) 488-8329
Boat Operating Services
N.A.I.C.S.: 487210

SHM Burnside, LLC **(1)**
680 W Lakeshore Dr, Burnside, KY 42519
Tel.: (606) 561-4223
Boat Operating Services
N.A.I.C.S.: 487210

SHM Cabrillo Isle, LLC **(1)**
1450 Harbor Island Dr, San Diego, CA
92101
Tel.: (619) 297-6222
Boat Operating Services
N.A.I.C.S.: 487210

SHM Cape Harbour, LLC **(1)**
5828 Cape Harbour Dr Ste 200, Cape
Coral, FL 33914
Tel.: (239) 945-4330
Boat Operating Services
N.A.I.C.S.: 487210

SHM Capri, LLC **(1)**
15 Orchard Beach Blvd, Port Washington,
NY 11050
Tel.: (516) 883-7800
Boat Operating Services
N.A.I.C.S.: 487210

SHM Carroll Island, LLC **(1)**
114 Carroll Island Rd, Baltimore, MD 21220
Tel.: (410) 335-4900
Boat Operating Services
N.A.I.C.S.: 487210

Sun Communities, Inc.—(Continued)

SHM Charleston Boatyard, LLC (1)
130 Wando Creek Ln, Charleston, SC
29492
Tel,: (843) 884-3000
Boat Operating Services
N.A.I.C.S.: 487210

**SHM Charleston City Marina,
LLC** (1)
7 Lockwood Dr, Charleston, SC 29401
Tel.: (843) 723-5098
Boat Operating Services
N.A.I.C.S.: 487210

SHM Cove Haven, LLC (1)
101 Narragansett Ave, Barrington, RI 02806
Tell: (401) 246-1600
Boat Operating Services
N.A.I.C.S.: 487210

SHM Cowesett, LLC (1)
1 Masthead Dr, Warwick, RI 02886
Tel.: (401) 884-0544
Boat Operating Services
N.A.I.C.S.: 487210

SHM Crystal Point, LLC (1)
4000 River Rd, Point Pleasant, NJ 08742
Tel.: (732) 892-2300
Boat Operating Services
N.A.I.C.S.: 487210

SHM Dauntless, LLC (1)
37 Pratt St, Essex, CT 06426
Tel.: (860) 767-8267
Boat Operating Services
N.A.I.C.S.: 487210

SHM Deep River, LLC (1)
50 River Ln, Deep River, CT 06417
Tel.: (860) 526-5560
Boat Operating Services
N.A.I.C.S.: 487210

SHM Detroit River, LLC (1)
100 Meadowbrook St, Detroit, MI 48214
Tel.: (313) 822-4500
Boat Operating Services
N.A.I.C.S.: 487210

SHM Eagle Cove, LLC (1)
5899 Eagles Cove Rd, Byrdstown, TN
38549
Tel.: (931) 864-3456
Boat Operating Services
N.A.I.C.S.: 487210

SHM Emerald Coast, LLC (1)
115 W John Sims Pkwy, Niceville, FL 32578
Tel.: (850) 389-8318
Boat Operating Services
N.A.I.C.S.: 487210

SHM Emerald Point, LLC (1)
5973 Hiline Rd, Austin, TX 78734
Tel.: (512) 266-1535
Boat Operating Services
N.A.I.C.S.: 487210

SHM Emeryville, LLC (1)
3310 Powell St, Emeryville, CA 94608
Tel.: (510) 654-3716
Boat Operating Services
N.A.I.C.S.: 487210

SHM Ferry Point, LLC (1)
29 Essex Rd, Old Saybrook, CT 06475
Tel.: (860) 388-3260
Boat Operating Services
N.A.I.C.S.: 487210

SHM Fiddler's Cove, LLC (1)
42 Fiddler's Cove Rd, North Falmouth, MA
02556
Tel.: (508) 564-6327
Boat Operating Services
N.A.I.C.S.: 487210

SHM Gaines, LLC (1)
141 Lake St, Rouses Point, NY 12979
Tel.: (518) 297-7000
Boat Operating Services
N.A.I.C.S.: 487210

SHM Glen Cove, LLC (1)
128 Shore Rd, Glen Cove, NY 11542
Tel.: (516) 671-5563
Boat Operating Services
N.A.I.C.S.: 487210

SHM Grand Isle, LLC (1)
1 Grand Isle Dr, Grand Haven, MI 49417
Tel.: (616) 842-9330
Boat Operating Services
N.A.I.C.S.: 487210

SHM Great Island, LLC (1)
419 Harpswell Islands Rd, Harpswell, ME
04079
Tel.: (207) 729-1639
Boat Operating Services
N.A.I.C.S.: 487210

SHM Great Lakes, LLC (1)
1920 Lakeshore Dr, Muskegon, MI 49441
Tel.: (231) 759-8230
Boat Operating Services
N.A.I.C.S.: 487210

SHM Great Oak Landing, LLC (1)
22170 Great Oak Landing Rd, Chestertown,
MD 21620
Tel.: (410) 778-5007
Boat Operating Services
N.A.I.C.S.: 487210

SHM Green Harbor, LLC (1)
239 Dyke Rd, Marshfield, MA 02050
Tel.: (781) 837-1181
Boat Operating Services
N.A.I.C.S.: 487210

SHM Greenport, LLC (1)
500 Beach Rd, Greenport, NY 11944
Tel.: (631) 477-9594
Boat Operating Services
N.A.I.C.S.: 487210

SHM Greenwich Bay, LLC (1)
252 2nd Point Rd, Warwick, RI 02889
Tel.: (401) 884-1810
Boat Operating Services
N.A.I.C.S.: 487210

SHM Grider Hill, LLC (1)
115 Grider Hill Dock Rd, Albany, KY 42602
Tel.: (606) 387-5501
Boat Operating Services
N.A.I.C.S.: 487210

SHM Hacks Point, LLC (1)
1645 Glebe Rd, Earleville, MD 21919
Tel.: (410) 275-9151
Boat Operating Services
N.A.I.C.S.: 487210

SHM Harborage YC, LLC (1)
955 N W Flagler Ave, Stuart, FL 34994
Tel.: (772) 692-4000
Boat Operating Services
N.A.I.C.S.: 487210

SHM Harbors View, LLC (1)
451107 E 320 Rd, Afton, OK 74331
Tel.: (918) 782-0445
Boat Operating Services
N.A.I.C.S.: 487210

SHM Harbortown, LLC (1)
1936 Harbortown Dr, Fort Pierce, FL 34946
Tel.: (772) 466-7300
Boat Operating Services
N.A.I.C.S.: 487210

SHM Haverstraw, LLC (1)
600 Beach Rd, West Haverstraw, NY 10993
Tel.: (845) 429-2001
Boat Operating Services
N.A.I.C.S.: 487210

SHM Hawthorne Cove, LLC (1)
10 White St, Salem, MA 01970
Tel.: (978) 740-9890
Boat Operating Services
N.A.I.C.S.: 487210

SHM Hideaway Bay, LLC (1)
6334 Mitchell St, Flowery Branch, GA
30542
Tel.: (770) 967-5500
Boat Operating Services
N.A.I.C.S.: 487210

SHM Holly Creek, LLC (1)
7855 Holly Creek Rd, Celina, TN 38551
Tel.: (931) 243-2116
Boat Operating Services
N.A.I.C.S.: 487210

SHM Islamorada, LLC (1)
80461 Overseas Hwy, Islamorada, FL
33036

Tel.: (305) 664-8884
Boat Operating Services
N.A.I.C.S.: 487210

SHM Island Park, LLC (1)
109 Point Rd, Portsmouth, RI 02871
Tel.: (401) 683-3030
Boat Operating Services
N.A.I.C.S.: 487210

SHM Jamestown Boatyard, LLC (1)
60 Racquet Rd, Jamestown, RI 02835
Tel.: (401) 423-0600
Boat Operating Services
N.A.I.C.S.: 487210

SHM Jamestown, LLC (1)
3677 S Hwy 92 E, Jamestown, KY 42629
Tel.: (270) 285-0444
Boat Operating Services
N.A.I.C.S.: 487210

SHM Jefferson Beach, LLC (1)
24400 Jefferson Ave, Saint Clair Shores, MI
48080
Tel.: (586) 778-7600
Boat Operating Services
N.A.I.C.S.: 487210

SHM King's Point, LLC (1)
18020 Kings Point Dr, Cornelius, NC 28031
Tel.: (704) 892-3223
Boat Operating Services
N.A.I.C.S.: 487210

SHM Lakefront, LLC (1)
1805 W Lakeshore Dr, Port Clinton, OH
43452
Tel.: (419) 734-5576
Boat Operating Services
N.A.I.C.S.: 487210

SHM Loch Lomond, LLC (1)
110 Loch Lomond Dr, San Rafael, CA
94901
Tel.: (415) 454-7228
Boat Operating Services
N.A.I.C.S.: 487210

SHM Manasquan, LLC (1)
217 Riverside Dr N, Brick, NJ 08724
Tel.: (732) 840-0300
Boat Operating Services
N.A.I.C.S.: 487210

SHM Marina Bay, LLC (1)
333 Victory Rd, Quincy, MA 02171
Tel.: (617) 847-1800
Boat Operating Services
N.A.I.C.S.: 487210

SHM Mystic, LLC (1)
56 Roseleah Dr, Mystic, CT 06355
Tel.: (860) 536-2293
Boat Operating Services
N.A.I.C.S.: 487210

SHM Narrows Point, LLC (1)
428 Kent Narrow Way N, Grasonville, MD
21638
Tel.: (410) 827-8888
Boat Operating Services
N.A.I.C.S.: 487210

SHM New Port Cove, LLC (1)
255 E 22nd Ct, Riviera Beach, FL 33404
Tel.: (561) 844-2504
Boat Operating Services
N.A.I.C.S.: 487210

SHM North Palm Beach, LLC (1)
1037 Marina Dr, North Palm Beach, FL
33408
Tel.: (501) 020-4919
Boat Operating Services
N.A.I.C.S.: 487210

SHM Old Port Cove, LLC (1)
116 Lakeshore Dr, North Palm Beach, FL
33408
Tel.: (561) 626-1760
Boat Operating Services
N.A.I.C.S.: 487210

SHM Onset Bay, LLC (1)
3 Green St, Buzzards Bay, MA 02532
Tel.: (508) 295-0338
Boat Operating Services
N.A.I.C.S.: 487210

SHM Pier 121, LLC (1)
1481 E Hill Park Rd, Lewisville, TX 75056

Tel.: (972) 625-2233
Boat Operating Services
N.A.I.C.S.: 487210

SHM Pilots Point, LLC (1)
63 Pilots Point Dr, Westbrook, CT 06498
Tel.: (860) 399-7906
Boat Operating Services
N.A.I.C.S.: 487210

SHM Pineland, LLC (1)
13921 Waterfront Dr, Bokeelia, FL 33922
Tel.: (239) 283-3593
Boat Operating Services
N.A.I.C.S.: 487210

SHM Plymouth, LLC (1)
14 Union St, Plymouth, MA 02360
Tel.: (508) 746-4500
Boat Operating Services
N.A.I.C.S.: 487210

SHM Port Royal, LLC (1)
502 London Ave, Port Royal, SC 29935
Tel.: (843) 379-9444
Boat Operating Services
N.A.I.C.S.: 487210

SHM Post Road, LLC (1)
155 E Boston Post Rd, Mamaroneck, NY
10543
Tel.: (914) 698-0295
Boat Operating Services
N.A.I.C.S.: 487210

SHM Puerto Del Rey, LLC (1)
4900 State Rd 3 Km 51 4, Fajardo, PR
00738
Tel.: (787) 860-1000
Boat Operating Services
N.A.I.C.S.: 487210

SHM Regatta Pointe, LLC (1)
1005 Riverside Dr, Palmetto, FL 34221
Tel.: (941) 729-6021
Boat Operating Services
N.A.I.C.S.: 487210

SHM Reserve Harbor, LLC (1)
2040 Willbrook Blvd, Pawleys Island, SC
29585
Tel.: (843) 314-5100
Boat Operating Services
N.A.I.C.S.: 487210

SHM Rockland, LLC (1)
60 Ocean St, Rockland, ME 04841
Tel.: (207) 596-0082
Boat Operating Services
N.A.I.C.S.: 487210

SHM Rybovich WPB TRS, LLC (1)
4200 N Flagler Dr, West Palm Beach, FL
33407
Tel.: (561) 840-8190
Boat Operating Services
N.A.I.C.S.: 487210

SHM Sakonnet, LLC (1)
222 Narragansett Blvd, Portsmouth, RI
02871
Tel.: (401) 683-3551
Boat Operating Services
N.A.I.C.S.: 487210

SHM Sandusky, LLC (1)
1 Huron St, Sandusky, OH 44870
Tel.: (419) 627-1201
Boat Operating Services
N.A.I.C.S.: 487210

SHM Shelburne, LLC (1)
4584 Harbor Rd, Shelburne, VT 05482
Tel.: (802) 985-3326
Boat Operating Services
N.A.I.C.S.: 487210

SHM Shelter Island, LLC (1)
2330 Shelter Island Dr Ste 1, San Diego,
CA 92106
Tel.: (619) 222-0481
Boat Operating Services
N.A.I.C.S.: 487210

SHM Siesta Key, LLC (1)
1265 Old Stickney Point Rd, Sarasota, FL
34242
Tel.: (941) 349-1970
Web Site: https://www.skmarina.com
Shipyard Services
N.A.I.C.S.: 336611

SHM Silver Spring, LLC (1)
362 Pond St Wakefield-Peacedale, South Kingstown, RI 02879
Tel.: (401) 783-0783
Boat Operating Services
N.A.I.C.S.: 487210

SHM Skippers Landing, LLC (1)
1152 Perth Rd, Troutman, NC 28166
Tel.: (704) 528-3328
Boat Operating Services
N.A.I.C.S.: 487210

SHM Skull Creek, LLC (1)
1 Waterway Ln, Hilton Head Island, SC 29926
Tel.: (843) 681-8436
Boat Operating Services
N.A.I.C.S.: 487210

SHM South Bay, LLC (1)
640 Marina Pkwy, Chula Vista, CA 91910
Tel.: (619) 422-2595
Boat Operating Services
N.A.I.C.S.: 487210

SHM Sportsman, LLC (1)
27844 Canal Rd, Orange Beach, AL 36561
Tel.: (251) 981-6247
Boat Operating Services
N.A.I.C.S.: 487210

SHM Stratford, LLC (1)
605 Broad St, Stratford, CT 06615
Tel.: (203) 377-4477
Boat Operating Services
N.A.I.C.S.: 487210

SHM Sunroad, LLC (1)
955 Harbor Island Dr, San Diego, CA 92101
Tel.: (619) 574-0736
Boat Operating Services
N.A.I.C.S.: 487210

SHM Sunset Bay, LLC (1)
2 A St, Hull, MA 02045
Tel.: (781) 925-2828
Boat Operating Services
N.A.I.C.S.: 487210

SHM Toledo Beach, LLC (1)
11840 Toledo Beach Rd, La Salle, MI 48145
Tel.: (734) 243-3800
Boat Operating Services
N.A.I.C.S.: 487210

SHM Trade Winds, LLC (1)
5577 Marina Pkwy, Appling, GA 30802
Tel.: (706) 541-1380
Boat Operating Services
N.A.I.C.S.: 487210

SHM Ventura Isle, LLC (1)
1363 Spinnaker Dr, Ventura, CA 93001
Tel.: (805) 644-5858
Boat Operating Services
N.A.I.C.S.: 487210

SHM Vineyard Haven, LLC (1)
100 Lagoon Pond Rd, Vineyard Haven, MA 02568
Tel.: (508) 693-4174
Boat Operating Services
N.A.I.C.S.: 487210

SHM Walden, LLC (1)
12050 Melville Dr, Montgomery, TX 77356
Tel.: (936) 582-1060
Boat Operating Services
N.A.I.C.S.: 487210

SHM Wentworth, LLC (1)
116 Morgans Way, New Castle, NH 03854
Tel.: (603) 433-5050
Boat Operating Services
N.A.I.C.S.: 487210

SHM Westport, LLC (1)
7879 Water Oaks Dr, Denver, NC 28037
Tel.: (704) 483-5172
Boat Operating Services
N.A.I.C.S.: 487210

SHM Wickford Cove, LLC (1)
65 Reynolds St, North Kingstown, RI 02852
Tel.: (401) 884-7014
Boat Operating Services
N.A.I.C.S.: 487210

SHM Wisdom Dock, LLC (1)
7613 Wisdom Dock Rd, Albany, KY 42602

Tel.: (606) 387-5821
Boat Operating Services
N.A.I.C.S.: 487210

SHM Yacht Haven, LLC (1)
181 Harbor Dr, Stamford, CT 06902
Tel.: (203) 359-4500
Boat Operating Services
N.A.I.C.S.: 487210

SHM Zahnisers, LLC (1)
245 C St, Solomons, MD 20688
Tel.: (410) 326-2166
Boat Operating Services
N.A.I.C.S.: 487210

Safe Harbor Marinas LLC (1)
14785 Preston Rd Ste 975, Dallas, TX 75254
Tel.: (972) 488-1314
Web Site: http://shmarinas.com
Emp.: 1,109
Marina Operation
N.A.I.C.S.: 713930
Katheryn Burchett *(COO)*
Baxter Underwood *(CEO)*
Gavin McClintock *(CFO)*
Brad Alesi *(CMO)*
John Ray *(Chief Transaction Officer)*
Peter Clark *(Chief Dev Officer)*
Meagan Thompson *(Chief Acctg Officer)*

Subsidiary (Domestic):

American Shipyard Co., LLC (2)
1 Washington St, Newport, RI 02840
Tel.: (401) 846-6000
Web Site: http://www.newportshipyard.com
Marinas
N.A.I.C.S.: 713930
Mindy Campbell *(Mgr-Marina)*
Isabella Ridall *(VP-Hospitality-Marinas)*
Susan Grindell *(Bus Mgr)*
John Post *(Project Mgr)*
Veronica Brown *(Dir-Experiences-Marinas)*
Samantha Pattavina *(Mgr-Mdsg-Marinas)*

Chula Vista Marina/Rv Park, Ltd. (2)
550 Marina Pkwy, Chula Vista, CA 91910
Tel.: (619) 691-1384
Web Site: http://www.chulavistarv.com
Marinas, Nsk
N.A.I.C.S.: 713930
William M. Chance *(Gen Partner)*

Hideaway Bay Marina, Inc. (2)
6334 Mitchell St, Flowery Branch, GA 30542-5674
Tel.: (770) 967-5500
Web Site: https://shmarinas.com
Lessors of Residential Buildings & Dwellings
N.A.I.C.S.: 531110

Rybovich Boat Company LLC (2)
4200 N Flagler Dr, West Palm Beach, FL 33407
Tel.: (561) 301-3660
Web Site: http://www.rybovich.com
Shipbuilding & Repairing
N.A.I.C.S.: 336611

Southwood Village Mobile Home Park, LLC (1)
440 60th St SE, Grand Rapids, MI 49548
Tel.: (616) 455-9660
Web Site: https://www.suncommunities.com
Sales Range: $25-49.9 Million
Emp.: 4
Real Estate Lending Services
N.A.I.C.S.: 531190
Camen Buntjer *(Office Mgr)*

Stockton Delta Resort, LLC (1)
14900 Hwy 12, Lodi, CA 95242
Tel.: (209) 369-1041
Web Site: https://www.towerparkresort.com
Amusement Park Services
N.A.I.C.S.: 713110

Sun Blazing Star LLC (1)
1120 W Loop 1604 N, San Antonio, TX 78251
Tel.: (210) 680-2443
Real Estate Investment Services
N.A.I.C.S.: 531210

Sun Camelot Villa LLC (1)
17111 Hall Rd, Macomb, MI 48044
Tel.: (586) 286-0618
Web Site: https://www.suncommunities.com

Real Estate Investment Services
N.A.I.C.S.: 531210

Sycamore Village Mobile Home Park, LLC (1)
900 W Columbia St, Mason, MI 48854
Tel.: (517) 676-5575
Web Site: http://www.4sycamore.com
Emp.: 7
Real Estate Lending Services
N.A.I.C.S.: 531190

Thunderhill Estates, L.L.C. (1)
417 N 14th Pl, Sturgeon Bay, WI 54235
Tel.: (920) 743-8050
Web Site: https://www.suncommunities.com
Real Estate Investment Services
N.A.I.C.S.: 531210

Vizcaya Lakes Communities, LLC (1)
3939 Hollis Ave, Port Charlotte, FL 33953
Tel.: (941) 625-1006
Web Site: https://www.suncommunities.com
Real Estate Investment Services
N.A.I.C.S.: 531210

Wildwood L.P. (1)
1 Birch Dr, Sandwich, IL 60548
Tel.: (815) 498-3000
Web Site: https://www.suncommunities.com
Real Estate Investment Services
N.A.I.C.S.: 531210

SUN COUNTRY AIRLINES HOLDINGS, INC.
2005 Cargo Rd, Minneapolis, MN 55450
Tel.: (651) 905-2737   DE
Web Site:
https://www.suncountry.com
SNCY—(NASDAQ)
Rev.: $894,444,000
Assets: $1,524,412,000
Liabilities: $1,031,700,000
Net Worth: $492,712,000
Earnings: $17,676,000
Emp.: 2,510
Fiscal Year-end: 12/31/22
Holding Company; Passenger & Cargo Airline Operator
N.A.I.C.S.: 551112
Dave Davis *(Pres & CFO)*
Jude I. Bricker *(CEO)*
Jim Stathopoulos *(CIO & Sr VP)*
Colton Snow *(CMO & Sr VP)*
Jennifer Vogel *(Chm)*

Subsidiaries:

Sun Country, Inc. (1)
2005 Cargo Rd, Minneapolis, MN 55450
Tel.: (651) 905-2737
Passenger & Cargo Air Transportation Services
N.A.I.C.S.: 481112
Dave Davis *(Pres & CFO)*
Jude I. Bricker *(CEO)*
Greg Mays *(COO)*
Eric Levenhagen *(Chief Admin Officer & Gen Counsel)*
Jeff Mader *(CIO)*
Brian Davis *(CMO)*

SUN PACIFIC HOLDING CORP
345 Hwy 9 S Ste 388, Manalapan, NJ 07726
Tel.: (732) 845-0906   NJ
Web Site:
https://www.sunpacificholding.com
Year Founded: 2005
SNPW—(OTCIQ)
Rev.: $265,573
Assets: $177,390
Liabilities: $3,273,948
Net Worth: ($3,096,558)
Earnings: ($278,610)
Emp.: 2
Fiscal Year-end: 12/31/22
Environmental Technology Equipment Mfr
N.A.I.C.S.: 423830

Nicholas B. Campanella *(Founder, Chm, Pres, CEO & CFO)*

Subsidiaries:

Street Smart Outdoor Corp. (1)
345 US Hwy 9 Ste 388, Manalapan, NJ 07726
Web Site:
https://www.streetsmartoutdoor.com
Outdoor Advertising Services
N.A.I.C.S.: 541850

Sun Pacific Power Corp. (1)
345 Hwy 9 S Ste 388, Manalapan, NJ 07726
Tel.: (732) 845-0946
Web Site: https://www.sunpacificpower.com
Solar Panels & Lighting Mfr, Installer & Contractor
N.A.I.C.S.: 334419
Nicholas Campanella *(Chm & CEO)*

SUN TZU CORP.
37 Prospect St, Amsterdam, NY 12010
Tel.: (518) 842-3453   WA
Year Founded: 1974
STZU—(OTCIQ)
Beverage Distr
N.A.I.C.S.: 424810
Bretton McCarthy *(Pres)*
Terry Barker *(Chm)*

SUNCAST SOLAR ENERGY, INC.
1550 Larimer St Ste 306, Denver, CO 80202
SUNC—(OTCEM)
Testing Laboratory Services
N.A.I.C.S.: 541380
Winston Buzz Willis *(Pres & CEO)*

SUNCOKE ENERGY, INC.
1011 Warrenville Rd Ste 600, Lisle, IL 60532
Tel.: (630) 824-1000   DE
Web Site: https://www.suncoke.com
Year Founded: 1962
SXC—(NYSE)
Rev.: $2,063,200,000
Assets: $1,660,400,000
Liabilities: $1,014,900,000
Net Worth: $645,500,000
Earnings: $57,500,000
Emp.: 871
Fiscal Year-end: 12/31/23
Blast-Furnace Coke Mfr
N.A.I.C.S.: 324199
Katherine T. Gates *(Pres & CEO)*
Mark W. Marinko *(CFO & Sr VP)*
John F. Quanci *(CTO & VP)*
P. Michael Hardesty *(Sr VP-Comml Ops, Business Development, Terminals, and Intl Coke)*

Subsidiaries:

Haverhill North Coke Company (1)
2446 Gallia Pke, Franklin Furnace, OH 45629
Tel.: (740) 355-9800
Sales Range: $50-74.9 Million
Emp.: 125
Coal Producer
N.A.I.C.S.: 324199

Jewell Resources Corporation (1)
15498 Riverside Dr, Oakwood, VA 24631
Tel.: (276) 935-8810
Sales Range: $200-249.9 Million
Emp.: 250
Coal Producer
N.A.I.C.S.: 324199
Tim Thompson *(Mgr-Health & Safety)*

Subsidiary (Domestic):

Dominion Coal Corporation (2)
RR 460, Vansant, VA 24656
Tel.: (276) 935-8810

SunCoke Energy, Inc.—(Continued)
Sales Range: $100-124.9 Million
Emp.: 200
Coal Producer
N.A.I.C.S.: 212115

Jewell Coal & Coke Company, Inc. (2)
RR 460, Vansant, VA 24656
Tel.: (276) 935-8810
Coal Producer
N.A.I.C.S.: 324199

Jewell Smokeless Coal Corporation (2)
RR 460, Vansant, VA 24656
Tel.: (276) 935-8810
Sales Range: $25-49.9 Million
Emp.: 50
Coal Producer
N.A.I.C.S.: 212114
Rick Waddell *(Pres)*

SunCoke Energy Partners, L.P. (1)
1011 Warrenville Rd 6th Fl, Lisle, IL
60532 (100%)
Tel.: (630) 824-1000
Web Site: https://www.suncoke.com
Sales Range: $800-899.9 Million
Soft Drinks Mfr
N.A.I.C.S.: 312111

Subsidiary (Domestic):

Kanawha River Terminals LLC (2)
100 Main & Riv Stre 4226, Ceredo, WV
25507
Tel.: (304) 526-0759
Coal Product Mfr
N.A.I.C.S.: 423520

SunCoke Logistics LLC (2)
1011 Warrenville Rd Fl 6, Lisle, IL 60532
Tel.: (630) 824-1000
Emp.: 236
Bricks Mfr
N.A.I.C.S.: 327331

SUNDANCE ENERGY AUSTRALIA LIMITED

1050 17th St Ste 700, Denver, CO
80265
Tel.: (303) 543-5700 AU
Web Site:
http://www.sundanceenergy.net
SNDE—(NASDAQ)
Rev.: $203,580,000
Assets: $813,914,000
Liabilities: $460,517,000
Not Worth: $363,307,000
Earnings: ($39,590,000)
Emp.: 79
Fiscal Year-end: 12/31/19
Energy Exploration Services
N.A.I.C.S.: 211120
Stephen J. McDaniel *(Chm)*
Cathy L. Anderson *(CFO)*
Mike Wolfe *(VP-Land-Sundance Energy Inc)*
Keith D. Kress *(VP-Ops-Sundance Energy Inc)*
John Roberts *(VP-Fin & IR)*
Eric P. McCrady *(CEO & Mng Dir)*

SUNDANCE STRATEGIES, INC.

4626 N 300 W Ste No 365, Provo,
UT 84604
Tel.: (801) 717-3935 NV
Web Site:
https://www.sundancestrategies.com
SUND—(OTCQB)
Assets: $338,935
Liabilities: $6,278,860
Net Worth: ($5,939,925)
Earnings: ($1,834,991)
Emp.: 1
Fiscal Year-end: 03/31/24
Financial Services
N.A.I.C.S.: 523999

Lisa L. Fuller *(Gen Counsel)*
Kraig T. Higginson *(Exec Chm, Chm & Dir)*
Randall F. Pearson *(Pres, CEO, CFO & Dir)*

SUNFIRE ACQUISITION CORP LIMITED

1800 Avenue of the Stars Ste 1475,
Los Angeles, CA 90067
Tel.: (213) 616-0011 Ky
Year Founded: 2021
SUNFU—(NASDAQ)
Investment Services
N.A.I.C.S.: 523999
Barry M. Kostiner *(CFO)*
Thomas W. Neukranz *(CEO)*
Barry Kostiner *(CFO)*
Jiayin Liu *(VP-Business Development)*

SUNHYDROGEN, INC.

BioVentures Ctr 2500 Crosspark Rd,
Coralville, IA 52241
Tel.: (805) 966-6566 NV
Web Site:
https://www.sunhydrogen.com
Year Founded: 2009
HYSR—(OTCQB)
Rev.: $2,013,974
Assets: $43,367,816
Liabilities: $759,514
Net Worth: $42,608,302
Earnings: ($9,881,203)
Emp.: 7
Fiscal Year-end: 06/30/24
Solar Concentrator Developer & Mfr
N.A.I.C.S.: 335311
Timothy Young *(Chm, Pres, CEO & Acting CFO)*
Sylvia Joun Lee *(Dir-Tech)*
Syed Mubeen Jawahar Hussaini *(Chief Scientific Officer)*
Woosuk Kim *(COO)*
Odessa Stork *(Dir-Comm)*

SUNLIGHT FINANCIAL HOLDINGS INC.

101 N Tyron St Ste 1000, Charlotte,
NC 28246
Web Site:
https://www.sunlightfinancial.com
SUNL—(NYSE)
Rev.: $98,506,000
Assets: $452,195,000
Liabilities: $83,868,000
Net Worth: $368,327,000
Earnings: ($511,936,000)
Emp.: 232
Fiscal Year-end: 12/31/22
Investment Services
N.A.I.C.S.: 523999
Matthew Potere *(CEO)*
Rodney Yoder *(CFO)*

Subsidiaries:

Sunlight Financial LLC (1)
101 N Tryon St Ste 1000, Charlotte, NC
28246
Web Site: https://www.sunlightfinancial.com
Sales Range: $1-9.9 Million
Emp.: 200
Financial Services
N.A.I.C.S.: 523999
Matt Potere *(CEO)*
Tim Parsons *(COO)*
Scott Mulloy *(CIO)*
Rodney Yoder *(CFO)*

SUNLINK HEALTH SYSTEMS, INC.

900 Cir 75 Pkwy Ste 690, Atlanta, GA
30339
Tel.: (770) 933-7000 OH
Web Site:
https://www.sunlinkhealth.com
Year Founded: 1959

SSY—(NYSEAMEX)
Rev.: $32,440,000
Assets: $20,612,000
Liabilities: $4,639,000
Net Worth: $15,973,000
Earnings: ($1,527,000)
Fiscal Year-end: 06/30/24
Hospital Management Services
N.A.I.C.S.: 622110
Robert M. Thornton Jr. *(Chm, Pres & CEO)*
Sheila G. Brockman *(VP)*

Subsidiaries:

Carmichael's Nutritional Distributor, Inc. (1)
1002 N Parkerson Ave, Crowley, LA 70526-3613
Tel.: (337) 783-7263
Health Food Supplement Stores
N.A.I.C.S.: 456191

SunLink Healthcare LLC (1)
900 Circle 75 Pkwy Ste 1120, Atlanta, GA
30339 (100%)
Tel.: (770) 933-7000
Web Site: http://www.sunlinkhealth.com
Sales Range: $10-24.9 Million
Manager of Hospitals & Nursing Homes
N.A.I.C.S.: 622110

Subsidiary (Domestic):

Southern Health Corporation of Dahlongea, Inc. (2)
227 Mtn Dr, Dahlonega, GA 30533
Tel.: (706) 864-6136
Operator of Hospital
N.A.I.C.S.: 622110
Neil Miller *(Dir-IT)*

Southern Health Corporation of Ellijay, Inc. (100%)
1362 S Main St, Ellijay, GA 30540
Tel.: (706) 276-4741
Web Site:
http://www.northgeorgiamedicalcenter.com
Operator of Hospital & Nursing Home
N.A.I.C.S.: 622110
Earl Whiteley *(CEO)*

Southern Health Corporation of Houston, Inc. (2)
Hwy 8 E, Houston, MS 38851 (100%)
Tel.: (662) 456-3701
Operator of Hospital & Nursing Home
N.A.I.C.S.: 622110
Gary Staton *(CEO)*

SunLink Healthcare Professional Property, LLC (1)
900 Cir 75 Pkwy Se Ste 1120, Atlanta, GA
30339
Tel.: (770) 933-7000
Emp.: 3
Property Management Services
N.A.I.C.S.: 531312

SUNNOVA ENERGY INTERNATIONAL INC.

20 E Greenway Plz Ste 540, Houston, TX 77046
Tel.: (281) 892-1588 DE
Web Site: https://www.sunnova.com
Year Founded: 2019
NOVA—(NYSE)
Rev.: $720,653,000
Assets: $1,677,350,000
Liabilities: $1,161,218,000
Net Worth: $516,132,000
Earnings: ($417,961,000)
Emp.: 2,047
Fiscal Year-end: 12/31/23
Holding Company
N.A.I.C.S.: 551112
William J. Berger *(Chm, Pres & CEO)*
Stuart D. Allen *(Exec VP-HR)*
Michael P. Grasso *(CMO & Exec VP)*
Kris H. Hillstrand *(Exec VP-Tech & Svc Ops)*
Meghan Nutting *(Exec VP-Policy & Comm)*

Rodney McMahan *(VP-IR)*
Eric M. Williams *(CFO & Exec VP)*
Robert L. Lane *(Sr VP-Fin)*

SUNOCO LP

8111 Wchester Dr, Dallas, TX 75225
Tel.: (214) 981-0700 DE
Web Site: https://www.sunocolp.com
SUN—(NYSE)
Rev.: $23,068,000,000
Assets: $6,826,000,000
Liabilities: $5,848,000,000
Net Worth: $978,000,000
Earnings: $394,000,000
Emp.: 2,389
Fiscal Year-end: 12/31/23
Gasoline & Diesel Supplier
N.A.I.C.S.: 424720
Christopher R. Curia *(Exec VP-HR)*
Matthew S. Ramsey *(Chm)*
Joseph Kim *(Pres & CEO)*
Brian A. Hand *(Chief Sls Officer)*
Alison Gladwin *(Chief Mktg & Admin Officer)*
Dylan A. Bramhall *(CFO)*
Rick J. Raymer *(Principal Acctg Officer)*

Subsidiaries:

Aloha Petroleum, Ltd. (1)
1132 Bishop St Ste 1700, Honolulu, HI
96813
Tel.: (808) 522-9700
Web Site: http://www.alohagas.com
Sales Range: $250-299.9 Million
Petrol & Gasoline Operator & Retail Stores
N.A.I.C.S.: 424720

NuStar Energy L.P. (1)
19003 IH 10 W, San Antonio, TX 78257
Tel.: (210) 918-2000
Web Site: https://www.nustarenergy.com
Rev.: $1,683,223,000
Assets: $4,973,686,000
Liabilities: $4,071,370,000
Net Worth: $902,316,000
Earnings: $222,747,000
Emp.: 1,167
Fiscal Year-end: 12/31/2022
Oil & Pipeline Production Services
N.A.I.C.S.: 486910
Bradley C. Barron *(Chm, Pres & CEO)*
Amy Perry *(Gen Counsel & Exec VP-Strategic Dev)*

Subsidiary (Domestic):

NuStar Energy L.P. - Wichita (2)
7340 W 21st St N Ste 200, Wichita, KS
67205
Tel.: (316) 721-7010
Sales Range: $10-24.9 Million
Emp.: 35
Transportation of Petroleum Pipeline Products
N.A.I.C.S.: 486910
Gary Koegeboehn *(Mgr-Ops)*

NuStar GP Holdings, LLC (2)
19003 IH-10 W, San Antonio, TX 78257
Tel.: (210) 918-2000
Holding Company; Pipeline Operator
N.A.I.C.S.: 551112
Robert A. Coleman *(Founder, Chm & CEO)*

Subsidiary (Domestic):

Riverwalk Holdings, Ltd. (3)
1132 Glade Rd, Colleyville, TX 76034
Tel.: (817) 251-7000
Debt Collection Agency
N.A.I.C.S.: 561440

Subsidiary (Domestic):

NuStar Marketing LLC (2)
7811 S Presa St, San Antonio, TX 78223
Tel.: (210) 532-5300
Web Site: http://www.nustarenergy.com
Crude Petroleum & Natural Gas Extraction
Services
N.A.I.C.S.: 211120

NuStar Pipeline Company, LLC (2)
2608 E Hwy 50, Yankton, SD 57078-6417
Tel.: (605) 665-7477

Sales Range: $25-49.9 Million
Emp.: 2
Pipeline Transportation Services
N.A.I.C.S.: 486910
Curt Grafting (Mgr)

Subsidiary (Non-US):

NuStar Terminals Marine Services
N.V.   (2)
Tumbledown Dick Bay, PO Box 70, Sint Eu-
statius, Netherlands
Tel.: (31) 3182300
Web Site: http://www.nustarenergy.com
Sales Range: $250-299.9 Million
Emp.: 250
Oil & Gas Pipelines & Storage
N.A.I.C.S.: 237120

Subsidiary (Non-US):

NuStar Terminals Canada
Partnership   (3)
4090 Port Malcolm Road, Point Tupper,
B9A 1Z5, NS, Canada
Tel.: (902) 625-1711
Web Site: http://www.nustarenergy.com
Sales Range: $25-49.9 Million
Emp.: 75
Petroleum Storage Facility
N.A.I.C.S.: 493190
Blaise MacDonnell (Pres)

Subsidiary (US):

Statia Terminals, Inc.   (3)
2345 N Central Expy, Richardson, TX
75080
Tel.: (972) 699-6170
Sales Range: $25-49.9 Million
Emp.: 35
Storage of Petroleum
N.A.I.C.S.: 551112

Subsidiary (Domestic):

Shore Terminals LLC   (2)
841 Paloma, Wilmington, CA 90744
Tel.: (310) 816-1200
Liquefied Petroleum Gas Storage Services
N.A.I.C.S.: 424710

Subsidiary (Non-US):

Terminals Pty. Ltd   (2)
70-78 MacKenzie Rd, Melbourne, 3000,
VIC, Australia
Tel.: (61) 383871900
Web Site: http://www.terminalspl.com.au
Sales Range: $25-49.9 Million
Emp.: 60
Storage & Transportation Services
N.A.I.C.S.: 493110
Ross Napier (Mgr-Comml)

Sandford Petroleum, Inc.   (1)
206 US Hwy 380, Bridgeport, TX 76426
Tel.: (940) 683-2501
Fuel Distr
N.A.I.C.S.: 457210

Susser Holdings Corporation   (1)
4525 Ayers St, Corpus Christi, TX 78415-
1401
Tel.: (361) 884-2463
Rev.: $6,213,815,000
Assets: $1,374,605,000
Liabilities: $749,095,000
Net Worth: $625,510,000
Earnings: $32,804,000
Emp.: 6,454
Fiscal Year-end: 12/29/2013
Holding Company; Convenience Store &
Gas Station Owner, Operator & Franchisor;
Fuel Distr
N.A.I.C.S.: 551112

Subsidiary (Domestic):

Stripes LLC   (2)
4525 Ayers St, Corpus Christi, TX 78415
Tel.: (361) 853-0691
Web Site: http://www.stripesstores.com
Sales Range: $200-249.9 Million
Emp.: 250
Convenience Store Operator
N.A.I.C.S.: 445131

Subsidiary (Domestic):

Sac-N-Pac Stores, Inc.   (3)

1405 United Dr Ste 115, San Marcos, TX
78666
Tel.: (512) 392-6484
Sales Range: $10-24.9 Million
Emp.: 8
Convenience Store
N.A.I.C.S.: 445131
Natalie Longoria (Gen Mgr)

Susser Petroleum Company LLC   (3)
555 E Airtex Dr, Houston, TX 77073
Tel.: (832) 234-3600
Sales Range: $50-74.9 Million
Emp.: 28
Petroleum Product Whslr
N.A.I.C.S.: 424720

Subsidiary (Domestic):

GoPetro Transport LLC   (4)
555 E Airtex Dr, Houston, TX 77073
Tel.: (832) 234-3608
Web Site: http://www.sunocolp.com
Emp.: 8
Freight Transportation Services
N.A.I.C.S.: 484121

Susser Petroleum Operating Com-
pany LLC   (1)
555 E Airtex Dr, Houston, TX 77073
Tel.: (832) 234-3600
Web Site: http://www.susser.com
Emp.: 466
Motor Fuel Whslr
N.A.I.C.S.: 424720

Subsidiary (Domestic):

Direct Fuels LLC   (2)
1112 E Copeland Rd, Arlington, TX 76011
Tel.: (817) 354-2700
Web Site: http://www.dfuels.com
Petroleum Product Whslr
N.A.I.C.S.: 424720
Brock McIntire (Mgr-Terminal)

Mid-Atlantic Convenience Stores,
LLC   (2)
1011 Boulder Springs Dr, Richmond, VA
23225
Tel.: (804) 706-4702
Convenience Stores & Fuel Whslr
N.A.I.C.S.: 457110
Ruth Ann Lilly (Mgr-Tobacco Category)
Robert Owens (CEO)

Subsidiary (Domestic):

Uppy's Convenience Stores Inc.   (3)
1011 Boulders Spring Dr, Richmond, VA
23225
Tel.: (804) 706-4702
Web Site: http://www.uppys.com
Sales Range: $25-49.9 Million
Emp.: 55
Convenience Store
N.A.I.C.S.: 445131

Subsidiary (Domestic):

Southside Oil LLC   (2)
1011 Boulders Spring Dr 100, Richmond,
VA 23225
Tel.: (804) 706-4702
Rev.: $14,904,902
Emp.: 9
Liquefied Petroleum Gas Whslr
N.A.I.C.S.: 457210

T&C Wholesale LLC   (2)
118 N Broadway, Mertzon, TX 76941
Tel.: (325) 632-2106
Petroleum Product Distr
N.A.I.C.S.: 424710

SUNPOWER CORPORATION

880 Harbour Way S Ste 600, Rich-
mond, CA 94804
Tel.: (408) 240-5500   DE
Web Site: https://us.sunpower.com
Year Founded: 1985
SPWR—(NASDAQ)
Rev.: $1,741,072,000
Assets: $1,780,007,000
Liabilities: $1,204,353,000
Net Worth: $575,654,000
Earnings: $56,037,000
Emp.: 4,710

Fiscal Year-end: 01/01/23
Solar Electric Power Products De-
signer, Mfr & Whslr
N.A.I.C.S.: 221118
Thomas H. Werner (Exec Chm &
Principal Exec Officer)
Elizabeth Eby (CFO, Principal Acctg
Officer & Exec VP)
Josh Koppelman (CTO)
Eileen Evans (Chief Legal Officer)
Douglas J. Richards (Chief People
Officer & Exec VP-Admin)
Julie Blunden (Executives)
Julie Blunden (Executives)

Subsidiaries:

Blue Raven Solar, LLC   (1)
1403 N Research Way, Orem, UT 84097
Tel.: (855) 927-0275
Web Site: http://www.blueravensolar.com
Solar Electric Power Generation Services
N.A.I.C.S.: 221114
Ben Peterson (CEO)

SunPower Corporation, Systems   (1)
1414 Harbour Way S, Richmond, CA 94804
Tel.: (510) 540-0550
Sales Range: $75-99.9 Million
Emp.: 85
Solar Power Systems
N.A.I.C.S.: 221118
Thomas H. Werner (Chm, Pres & CEO)
Jack Peurach (Exec VP-Products)
Bill Kelly (VP & Mng Dir)
Thomas Leyden (Sr Dir-Sls)
Diana Ama (VP-Mfg)
Richard M. Swanson (Founder)
Elizabeth Eby (CFO)
Peter Faricy (CEO)

SunPower Corporation-East Coast
Regional Office   (1)
700 S Clinton Ave, Trenton, NJ 08611
Tel.: (609) 964-8901
Sales Range: $50-74.9 Million
Emp.: 20
Solar Power Systems
N.A.I.C.S.: 221118

SunPower Energy Systems Spain,
S.L.   (1)
Paseo de la Castellana 141, 28046, Madrid,
Spain
Tel.: (34) 80085581111
Web Site: http://us.sunpowercorp.com
Sales Range: $50-74.9 Million
Emp.: 65
Solar Power Systems Developer & Mfr
N.A.I.C.S.: 221118

SunPower Energy
Systems-Korea   (1)
30 Fl Asem Tower Qwer 159-1 Samsung
Dong Gangnam, Gangam-gu, Seoul, 135
875, Korea (South)
Tel.: (82) 234530941
Web Site: http://www.us.sunpowercorp.com
Sales Range: $50-74.9 Million
Emp.: 5
Solar Power Systems
N.A.I.C.S.: 221118

SunPower Malaysia Manufacturing
Sdn. Bhd.   (1)
Melaka World Solar Valley Alor Gajah,
78000, Melaka, Malaysia
Tel.: (60) 63308800
Solar Panel Mfr
N.A.I.C.S.: 423720
Edz Valenciano (Mgr-Engrg)

SunPower Systems Sarl   (1)
Route de Pre-Bois 14 15 Airport, 1215, Ge-
neva, Switzerland
Tel.: (41) 80078635
Web Site: http://www.sunpower.com
Solar Power Systems
N.A.I.C.S.: 221118

Woongjin Energy Co., Ltd.   (1)
Daedeok Techno Vally 1316 Beonji
Kwanpyung-Dong, Yuseong-Gu, Daejeon,
Korea (South)
Tel.: (82) 429398114
Web Site: http://www.woongjinenergy.com
Rev.: $149,254,111
Assets: $213,069,912

Liabilities: $175,989,132
Net Worth: $37,080,780
Earnings: ($100,585,055)
Emp.: 306
Fiscal Year-end: 12/31/2018
Solar Cell Ingots & Wafers Mfr
N.A.I.C.S.: 339999

SUNRIDGE INTERNATIONAL,
INC.

16857 E Saguaro Blvd, Fountain
Hills, AZ 85268
Tel.: (480) 837-6165   NV
Web Site: http://www.oi-pnt.com
Year Founded: 2001
SNDZ—(OTCEM)
Sales Range: Less than $1 Million
Ophthalmic Product Mfr
N.A.I.C.S.: 339115
G. Richard Smith (Pres & CEO)

SUNRUN INC.

225 Bush St Ste 1400, San Fran-
cisco, CA 94104
Tel.: (415) 580-6900   DE
Web Site: https://www.sunrun.com
RUN—(NASDAQ)
Rev.: $2,259,813,000
Assets: $20,450,237,000
Liabilities: $14,212,401,000
Net Worth: $6,237,836,000
Earnings: ($1,604,497,000)
Emp.: 10,833
Fiscal Year-end: 12/31/23
Solar Panel Systems Designer, Whslr
& Installation Services
N.A.I.C.S.: 423730
Paul S. Dickson (Pres & Chief Rev-
enue Officer)
Lynn Jurich (Co-Chm)
Edward Fenster (Co-Chm)
Patrick Jobin (Sr VP-Fin & IR)
Mary G. Powell (CEO)
Danny Abajian (CFO & Principal
Acctg Officer)
Paul Dickson (Chief Revenue Officer)
Chance Allred (Chief Experience Offi-
cer)
Chris McClellan (Chief Field Ops Offi-
cer)
Sandy Anuras (CTO)

Subsidiaries:

AEE Solar, Inc.   (1)
775 Fiero Ln Ste 200, San Luis Obispo, CA
93401
Tel.: (707) 923-2277
Web Site: https://www.aeesolar.com
Sales Range: $25-49.9 Million
Solar Power Products Distr
N.A.I.C.S.: 423690
Antonio Cintra (Pres)
Melissa Haupt (Dir-Customer Fulfillment &
Sls Support)
Josh Brister (Sr Mgr-Product Mgmt & Tech-
nical Sls)
Thomas Madison (Mgr-Credit Risk)

Vivint Solar, Inc.   (1)
1800 Ashton Blvd, Lehi, UT 84043 (100%)
Tel.: (801) 762-6270
Web Site: http://www.vivintsolar.com
Rev.: $341,041,000
Assets: $2,799,390,000
Liabilities: $2,522,174,000
Net Worth: $277,216,000
Earnings: ($102,175,000)
Emp.: 2,998
Fiscal Year-end: 12/31/2019
Holding Company; Solar Panel Systems
Sales & Installation Services
N.A.I.C.S.: 551112
Dana C. Russell (CFO & Exec VP)
L. Chance Allred (Chief Sls Officer)
Paul S. Dickson (Chief Revenue Officer)
Thomas G. Plagemann (Chief Comml Offi-
cer)
Bryan Christiansen (COO)
Erica Dahl (VP-Pub Policy & Govt Affairs)
Rob Kain (VP-Investor Relations)
Dan Black (Chief Legal Officer, Sec & Exec
VP)

Sunrun Inc.—(Continued)

Miranda Barnard (VP-Mktg)
Jeremy Sabin (VP-Human Resources)
Heather Hurst (Dir-Public Relations)

Subsidiary (Domestic):

Vivint Solar Operations, LLC   (2)
3301 N Thanksgiving Way, Lehi, UT 84043
Tel.: (801) 377-9111
Web Site: https://www.vivintsolar.com
Solar Panel Systems Sales & Installation
Services
N.A.I.C.S.: 238160

SUNSET ISLAND GROUP, INC.
20420 Spence Rd, Salinas, CA
93908
Tel.: (424) 239-6230   CO
Web Site:
    http://www.sunsetislandgroup.com
Year Founded: 2005
SIGO—(OTCIQ)
Emp.: 6
Drug Mfr
N.A.I.C.S.: 325412
Lori Livacich (Pres & CEO)

SUNSTOCK, INC.
111 Vista Creek Cir, Sacramento, CA
95835
Tel.: (916) 860-9622   DE
Web Site:
    https://www.sunstockinc.com
Year Founded: 2012
SSOK—(NASDAQ)
Rev.: $12,397,189
Assets: $2,148,013
Liabilities: $777,734
Net Worth: $1,370,279
Earnings: $5,886
Emp.: 3
Fiscal Year-end: 12/31/23
Investment Services
N.A.I.C.S.: 523999
Jason C. Chang (Pres, CEO,
    Founder, , Officer-Investor Relations,
    Chm & Sec)
Ramnik S. Clair (VP)

**SUNSTONE HOTEL INVES-
TORS, INC.**
15 Enterprise Ste 200, Aliso Viejo,
CA 92656
Tel.: (949) 330-4000   MD
Web Site:
    https://www.sunstonehotels.com
Year Founded: 1994
SHO—(NYSE)
Rev.: $912,053,000
Assets: $3,082,817,000
Liabilities: $997,856,000
Net Worth: $2,084,961,000
Earnings: $73,042,000
Emp.: 40
Fiscal Year-end: 12/31/22
Real Estate Investment Trust
N.A.I.C.S.: 525990
Bryan Albert Giglia (CEO)
Robert C. Springer (Pres & Chief In-
    vestment Officer)
Chris Ostapovicz (COO & Sr VP)
Aaron R. Reyes (CFO, Exec VP & Sr
    VP)
David M. Klein (Gen Counsel & Exec
    VP)

Subsidiaries:

Buy Efficient, LLC   (1)
120 Vantis Ste 405, Aliso Viejo, CA 92656-
2678
Tel.: (949) 382-3000
Real Estate Investment Services
N.A.I.C.S.: 531210

Sunstone Saint Clair Lessee,
Inc.   (1)
633 N Saint Clair St, Chicago, IL 60611
Tel.: (312) 787-1234

Web Site: https://www.hyatt.com
Real Estate Investment Services
N.A.I.C.S.: 531210

Sunstone Saint Clair, LLC   (1)
120 Vantis Dr Ste 350, Aliso Viejo, CA
92656
Tel.: (949) 382-3096
Web Site: https://www.sunstonehotels.com
Emp.: 24
Real Estate Investment Services
N.A.I.C.S.: 531210

SUNVALLEY SOLAR, INC.
398 Lemon Creek Dr Ste A, Walnut,
CA 91789
Tel.: (909) 598-0618   NV
Web Site:
    http://www.sunvalleysolarinc.com
Year Founded: 2007
SSOL—(OTCIQ)
Sales Range: $1-9.9 Million
Emp.: 23
Solar Power Technology & System
Integration
N.A.I.C.S.: 335311
James Zhang (Pres & CEO)
Mandy Chung (CFO, Chief Acctg Of-
    ficer, Treas & Sec)
Fang Xu (CTO)
Shirley Liao (Dir-Admin)
William Hsien (Exec VP)
Mehmet Cercioglu (VP)

SUNWORKS, INC.
1030 Winding Creek Rd Ste 100, Ro-
seville, CA 95678
Tel.: (916) 409-6900   DE
Web Site:
    https://www.sunworksusa.com
Year Founded: 2002
SUNW—(NASDAQ)
Rev.: $161,935,000
Assets: $119,940,000
Liabilities: $56,003,000
Net Worth: $63,937,000
Earnings: ($28,211,000)
Emp.: 622
Fiscal Year-end: 12/31/22
Solar Panel Mfr
N.A.I.C.S.: 335311

**SUPER LEAGUE ENTER-
PRISE, INC.**
2912 Colorado Ave Ste 203, Santa
Monica, CA 90404
Tel.: (802) 294-2754   DE
Web Site:
    https://www.superleague.com
Year Founded: 2014
SLE—(NASDAQ)
Rev.: $19,677,000
Assets: $30,210,000
Liabilities: $11,006,000
Net Worth: $19,204,000
Earnings: ($85,451,000)
Emp.: 101
Fiscal Year-end: 12/31/22
Indoor Games & Recreational Ser-
vices
N.A.I.C.S.: 713990
Anne Hand (Chm, Pres & CFO)
David Steigelfest (Co-Founder)
Clayton Haynes (CFO)
Matthew Edelman (Pres & Chief
    Comml Officer)
Andy Babb (Chief Games Officer)
Anne Gailliot (VP-Special Projects)
John Miller (Co-Founder)
John Boyden (Sr VP & Gen Mgr-
    Consumer Properties)
Stephen Dao (Exec VP-Engrg)

**SUPER MICRO COMPUTER,
INC.**
980 Rock Ave, San Jose, CA 95131
Tel.: (408) 503-8000   DE

Web Site:
    https://www.supermicro.com
SMCI—(NASDAQ)
Rev.: $7,123,482,000
Assets: $3,674,729,000
Liabilities: $1,702,559,000
Net Worth: $1,972,170,000
Earnings: $639,998,000
Emp.: 5,126
Fiscal Year-end: 06/30/23
Computer Hardware Mfr
N.A.I.C.S.: 334118
Charles Liang (Co-Founder, Chm,
    Pres & CEO)
Don Clegg (Sr VP-Worldwide Sls)
Sara Liu (Co-Founder & Sr VP)
George Kao (Sr VP-Ops)
David Weigand (CFO, Chief Compli-
    ance Officer & Sr VP)

Subsidiaries:

Gemini Open Cloud Computing,
Inc.   (1)
11F-3 No 158 Sec 2 Gongdao 5th Rd, Hsin-
chu, Taiwan
Tel.: (886) 36590698
Web Site: https://www.geminiopencloud.com
Industrial Research & Development Ser-
vices
N.A.I.C.S.: 541713

Super Micro Computer B.V.   (1)
Het Sterrenbeeld 28, 5215 ML, 's-
Hertogenbosch, Netherlands
Tel.: (31) 736400390
Computer Hardware Sales & Service
N.A.I.C.S.: 423430

Super Micro Computer Taiwan
Inc.   (1)
3F No 150 Jian 1st Rd, Zhonghe Dist, New
Taipei City, 235, Taiwan
Tel.: (886) 282263990
Computer Hardware Design, Sales & Ser-
vice
N.A.I.C.S.: 334118

Supermicro KK   (1)
S-7F NES Bldg 22-14 Sakuragaoka-cho,
Shibuya-ku, Tokyo, 150-0031, Japan
Tel.: (81) 3 5728 5196
Web Site: http://www.supermicro.com
Emp.: 10
Computer Hardware Design, Sales & Ser-
vice
N.A.I.C.S.: 423430

Supermicro Technology (Beijing) Co.,
Ltd.   (1)
Tel.: (86) 1062969165
Computer Hardware Design, Sales & Ser-
vice
N.A.I.C.S.: 334118

**SUPERIOR GROUP OF COM-
PANIES, INC.**
200 Central Ave Ste 2000, Saint Pe-
tersburg, FL 33701
Tel.: (727) 397-9611   FL
Web Site:
    https://www.superiorgroupofcom
    panies.com
Year Founded: 1920
SGC—(NASDAQ)
Rev.: $578,831,000
Assets: $456,941,000
Liabilities: $264,342,000
Net Worth: $192,599,000
Earnings: ($31,970,000)
Emp.: 10,900
Fiscal Year-end: 12/31/22
Cut & Sew Apparel Manufacturing
(except Contractors)
N.A.I.C.S.: 315250
Michael Benstock (Chm, Pres &
    CEO)
Andrew D. Demott Jr. (Exec VP)
Michael Koempel (CFO & Principal
    Acctg Officer)
Catherine Beldotti Donlan (Pres)

Jake Himelstein (Pres)
Dominic Leide (Pres)
Soo-Jin Behrstock (CIO)

Subsidiaries:

BAMKO, LLC   (1)
11620 Wilshire Blvd Ste 610, Los Angeles,
CA 90025
Tel.: (310) 470-5859
Web Site: http://www.bamko.net
Sales Range: $25-49.9 Million
Merchandise Sourcing & Promotional Prod-
ucts Agency
N.A.I.C.S.: 339999
Philip Koosed (Founder)
Jake Himelstein (Pres)

Subsidiary (Domestic):

Gifts By Design, Inc.   (2)
151 Western Ave W Ste 350, Seattle, WA
98119
Tel.: (206) 286-6688
Web Site: http://www.giftsbydesign.net
Sales Range: $1-9.9 Million
Emp.: 17
Gift, Novelty, And Souvenir Shop, Nsk
N.A.I.C.S.: 459420
Ali Dewing (Acct Exec)
Bailey Hurston (Acct Coord)
Dani Millen (Acct Mgr)
Heidi Kristofferson (Controller & Mgr)
Jamie Stone (Pres)

CID Resources, Inc.   (1)
601 S Royal Ln Ste 100, Coppell, TX 75019
Tel.: (972) 584-1550
Web Site:
    https://www.b2b.cidresources.com
Medical Uniform Distr
N.A.I.C.S.: 458110
Alex Ahn (VP)

Superior Uniform Group, Inc. - Mar-
tin's Uniforms Division   (1)
10055 Seminole Blvd, Seminole, FL 33772
Tel.: (727) 397-9611
Web Site:
    http://www.superioruniformgroup.com
Sales Range: $75-99.9 Million
Emp.: 100
Public Safety Transportation & Industrial
Uniform Mfr
N.A.I.C.S.: 424350

Superior Uniform Group, Inc. - Shane
Uniforms Division   (1)
10055 Seminole Blvd, Seminole, FL 33772-
2564
Tel.: (727) 397-9611
Web Site:
    http://www.superioruniformgroup.com
Sales Range: $75-99.9 Million
Emp.: 100
Mfr of Uniforms for Industrial, Public Safety
& Transportation Purposes
N.A.I.C.S.: 315250

Superior Uniform Group, Inc. - Work-
lon Division   (1)
10055 Seminole Blvd, Seminole, FL 33772
Tel.: (727) 397-9611
Sales Range: $50-74.9 Million
Emp.: 32
Mfr & Marketer of Special Purpose Apparel
for Industrial Purposes
N.A.I.C.S.: 315250
Andrew Zemott (Pres)

The Office Gurus, Ltd.   (1)
18 Joseph Andrews Drive, El Cayo, San
Ignacio, Belize
Tel.: (501) 824 3144
Web Site: http://theofficegurus.com
Call Center Services
N.A.I.C.S.: 561421

**SUPERIOR INDUSTRIES IN-
TERNATIONAL INC**
26600 Telegraph Rd Ste 400, South-
field, MI 48033
Tel.: (248) 352-7300   CA
Web Site: https://www.supind.com
Year Founded: 1957
SUP—(NYSE)
Rev.: $1,639,902,000
Assets: $1,133,739,000

Liabilities: $935,200,000
Net Worth: $198,539,000
Earnings: $37,034,000
Emp.: 7,700
Fiscal Year-end: 12/31/22
Other Motor Vehicle Parts Manufacturing
N.A.I.C.S.: 336390
Parveen Kakar (Sr VP-Sls, Mktg & Product Dev)
Majdi B. Abulaban (Pres & CEO)
Kevin Burke (Chief HR Officer & Sr VP)
Michael Dorah (COO & Exec VP)
Sven Damm (Pres)
David M. Sherbin (Chief Compliance Officer)

Subsidiaries:

Superior Industries Automotive Germany GmbH (1)
Altenaer Strasse 170a, 58513, Ludenscheid, Germany
Tel.: (49) 2392806390
Motor Vehicle Parts Distr
N.A.I.C.S.: 423140

Superior Industries Europe AG (1)
Gustav-Kirchhoff-Strasse 10, 67098, Bad Durkheim, Germany
Tel.: (49) 632298996400
Motor Vehicle Parts Distr
N.A.I.C.S.: 423140

Superior Industries International Kansas, LLC (1)
1621 E Sosa Dr, Fayetteville, AR 72701
Tel.: (479) 443-7870
Web Site: http://www.supind.com
Sales Range: $1-4.9 Billion
Automotive Alloy Wheels Mfr
N.A.I.C.S.: 336390

Superior Industries International Michigan, LLC (1)
26600 Telegraph Rd Ste 400, Southfield, MI 48033-7492
Tel.: (248) 352-7300
Web Site: http://www.supind.com
Motor Vehicle Parts Mfr
N.A.I.C.S.: 336390

Superior Industries Leichtmetallrader Germany GmbH (1)
Gustav-Kirchhoff-Strasse 10, 67098, Bad Durkheim, Germany
Tel.: (49) 632298996000
Motor Vehicle Parts Distr
N.A.I.C.S.: 423140

Superior Industries Production Germany GmbH (1)
In der Lacke 7-9, 58791, Werdohl, Germany
Tel.: (49) 2392806390
Motor Vehicle Parts Distr
N.A.I.C.S.: 423140

Superior Industries de Mexico, S.A. de C.V. (1)
Juan Ruiz De Alarcon 306, 31136, Chihuahua, Mexico
Tel.: (52) 6144 290 9700
Web Site: http://www.superior.com
Sales Range: $500-549.9 Million
Emp.: 2,000
Automotive Parts & Accessories Mfg.
N.A.I.C.S.: 336390

Superior Industries-Fayetteville (1)
1621 E Sosa Dr, Fayetteville, AR 72701
Tel.: (479) 443-7870
Web Site: http://www.supind.com
Sales Range: $750-799.9 Million
Emp.: 1,200
Mfr of Custom Auto Accessories
N.A.I.C.S.: 331524

Superior Industries-Southfield (1)
26600 Telegraph Rd Ste 400, Southfield, MI 48033
Tel.: (248) 352-7300
Sales Range: $25-49.9 Million
Emp.: 15
Aluminum Foundries & Automotive Parts
N.A.I.C.S.: 423130

Uniwheels AG (1)

Gustav-kirchhoff-strasse 10, 67098, Bad Durkheim, Germany
Tel.: (49) 632298996400
Emp.: 3,302
Cast & Forged Aluminum Wheel Distr
N.A.I.C.S.: 423120
Wolfgang Hiller (CEO)

SUPERNUS PHARMACEUTICALS, INC.
9715 Key W Ave, Rockville, MD 20850
Tel.: (301) 838-2500   DE
Web Site: https://www.supernus.com
SUPN—(NASDAQ)
Rev.: $667,238,000
Assets: $1,702,508,000
Liabilities: $816,304,000
Net Worth: $886,204,000
Earnings: $60,711,000
Emp.: 612
Fiscal Year-end: 12/31/22
Pharmaceutical Mfr, Researcher & Developer
N.A.I.C.S.: 325412
Jack A. Khattar (Founder, Pres, CEO & Sec)
Timothy C. Dec (CFO & Sr VP)
Jonathan Rubin (Chief Medical Officer & Sr VP-R&D)
Charles W. Newhall III (Chm)

Subsidiaries:

Adamas Pharmaceuticals, Inc. (1)
1900 Powell St Ste 1000, Emeryville, CA 94608
Tel.: (510) 450-3500
Web Site: http://www.adamaspharma.com
Rev.: $74,461,000
Assets: $120,029,000
Liabilities: $170,005,000
Net Worth: ($49,976,000)
Earnings: ($57,403,000)
Emp.: 138
Fiscal Year-end: 12/31/2020
Pharmaceuticals Mfr
N.A.I.C.S.: 325412
David L. Mahoney (Chm)
Sarah Mathieson (Head-Corp Comm, Patient Advocacy & Engagement)
Vijay Shreedhar (Chief Comml Officer)
Jill Jene (Head-Corp Dev, Strategy, Portfolio Plng & Alliance Mgmt)

SUREPURE, INC.
405 Lexington Ave 26th Fl, New York, NY 10174
Tel.: (917) 368-8480   NV
Year Founded: 2008
SURP—(OTCIQ)
Sales Range: $1-9.9 Million
Emp.: 6
Liquid Photo-Purification Technology for Beverages & Other Liquids
N.A.I.C.S.: 541715
Guy E. Kebble (Pres & CEO)
Stephen M. Robinson (CFO, Chief Acctg Officer, Treas & Sec)

SURETY HOLDINGS CORP.
PO Box 409, Blackshear, GA 31516
Tel.: (912) 816-2428   DE
SHDC—(OTCIQ)
Real Estate Manangement Services
N.A.I.C.S.: 531390
Howard A. Knapp (Pres & CEO)

SURF AIR MOBILITY INC.
12111 S Crenshaw Blvd, Hawthorne, CA 90250
Tel.: (424) 332-5480   DE
Web Site: https://www.surfair.com
Year Founded: 2021
SRFM—(NYSE)
Holding Company; Chartered Air Travel & Travel Arrangement Services
N.A.I.C.S.: 551112

Stan Little (Founder-Southern Airways)
Stan Little (CEO)

Subsidiaries:

Southern Airways Express, LLC (1)
2875 S Ocean Blvd Ste 256, Palm Beach, FL 33480
Tel.: (901) 672-7820
Web Site: https://iflysouthern.com
Emp.: 100
Airline Operator
N.A.I.C.S.: 481211

Subsidiary (Domestic):

Multi-Aero, Inc. (2)
1436 Perrine Rd Bldg E, Farmington, MO 63640
Tel.: (800) 795-7192
Web Site: http://www.multiaero.com
Rev.: $1,010,000
Emp.: 100
Other Airport Operations
N.A.I.C.S.: 488119
Shane Storz (Owner)

Surf Air Inc. (1)
12111 S Crenshaw Blvd, Hawthorne, CA 90250
Tel.: (424) 332-5480
Web Site: https://www.surfair.com
Chartered Air Travel Arrangement Services
N.A.I.C.S.: 561599

SURGALIGN HOLDINGS, INC.
520 Lake Cook Rd Ste 315, Deerfield, IL 60015
Tel.: (224) 303-4651   DE
Web Site: https://www.surgalign.com
Year Founded: 1998
SRGA—(NASDAQ)
Rev.: $81,979,000
Assets: $70,242,000
Liabilities: $85,965,000
Net Worth: ($15,723,000)
Earnings: ($54,605,000)
Emp.: 217
Fiscal Year-end: 12/31/22
Holding Company
N.A.I.C.S.: 551112
Sheryl L. Conley (Chm)
Terry M. Rich (Pres, CEO & Pres-Global Spine)
Paolo Amoruso (Chief Legal Officer, Gen Counsel & Sec)

Subsidiaries:

Paradigm Spine, LLC (1)
505 Park Ave 14th Fl, New York, NY 10022
Tel.: (212) 367-7274
Offices of Physicians (except Mental Health Specialists)
N.A.I.C.S.: 621111

SURGE COMPONENTS, INC.
95 E Jefryn Blvd, Deer Park, NY 11729
Tel.: (631) 595-1818   NV
Web Site:
https://www.surgecomponents.com
Year Founded: 1981
SPRS—(OTCIQ)
Rev.: $39,828,257
Assets: $21,751,740
Liabilities: $8,569,055
Net Worth: $13,182,685
Earnings: $2,510,761
Emp.: 43
Fiscal Year-end: 09/30/21
Electronic Components Distr
N.A.I.C.S.: 423690
Ira Levy (Pres, CEO, CFO & Chm)
Steven J. Lubman (Treas, Sec & VP)

SURGEPAYS INC.
3124 Brother Blvd Ste 104, Bartlett, TN 38133
Tel.: (901) 302-9587

Web Site:
https://www.surgepays.com
Year Founded: 2006
SURG—(NASDAQ)
Rev.: $121,544,190
Assets: $34,003,506
Liabilities: $28,885,253
Net Worth: $5,118,253
Earnings: ($680,763)
Fiscal Year-end: 12/31/22
All Other Telecommunications
N.A.I.C.S.: 517810
Anthony Evers (CFO)
Kevin Brian Cox (Chm & CEO)

SURMODICS, INC.
9924 W 74th St, Eden Prairie, MN 55344-3523
Tel.: (952) 500-7000   MN
Web Site:
https://www.surmodics.com
Year Founded: 1979
SRDX—(NASDAQ)
Rev.: $126,078,000
Assets: $178,562,000
Liabilities: $59,665,000
Net Worth: $118,897,000
Earnings: ($11,542,000)
Emp.: 389
Fiscal Year-end: 09/30/24
Surface Modification Solutions to the Medical Device Industry
N.A.I.C.S.: 325414
Joseph J. Stich (Sr VP & Gen Mgr-HR & In Vitro Diagnostics)
Susan E. Knight (Chm)
Timothy J. Arens (CFO & Sr VP-Fin & IT)
Gary R. Maharaj (Pres & CEO)
John D. Manders (Controller)
Teryl L. W. Sides (CMO & Sr VP-Product Dev)
Nusrath Sultana (VP-Clinical Affairs)
Gordon S. Weber (Gen Counsel, Sec & Sr VP-Legal)

Subsidiaries:

Creagh Medical Limited (1)
IDA Business Park, Ballinasloe, Galway, Ireland
Tel.: (353) 909646300
Surgical Product Mfr
N.A.I.C.S.: 339113

Normedix, LLC (1)
3050 Ranchview Ln N, Plymouth, MN 55447-1459
Tel.: (763) 557-4929
Web Site: http://www.normedix.com
Medical Device Mfr
N.A.I.C.S.: 339113

SurModics IVD, Inc. (1)
9924 W 74th St, Eden Prairie, MN 55344
Tel.: (952) 500-7200
Web Site: http://shop.surmodics.com
In Vitro Diagnostics
N.A.I.C.S.: 541715
Joseph J. Stich (VP & Gen Mgr)

SurModics MD, LLC (1)
9700 W 76th St Ste 123, Eden Prairie, MN 55344-4201
Tel.: (952) 500-7000
Medical Device Mfr
N.A.I.C.S.: 339112

SURO CAPITAL CORP.
640 5th Ave 12th Fl, New York, NY 10019
Tel.: (212) 931-6331
Web Site: https://www.surocap.com
Year Founded: 2010
SSSS—(NASDAQ)
Rev.: $3,456,193
Assets: $284,412,858
Liabilities: $74,320,156
Net Worth: $210,020,702
Earnings: ($14,708,008)
Emp.: 10

SuRo Capital Corp.—(Continued)

Fiscal Year-end: 12/31/22
Investment Services
N.A.I.C.S.: 523999
Keri Findley (Sr Mng Dir)
Maulik Sardhara (Controller)
Allison Green (CFO, Chief Compliance Officer, Treas & Sec)
Mark David Klein (Chm, Pres & CEO)

SURROZEN, INC.

171 Oyster Point Blvd Ste 400, South San Francisco, CA 94080
Tel.: (650) 489-9000   DE
Web Site: https://www.surrozen.com
Year Founded: 2020
SRZN—(NASDAQ)
Rev.: $12,500,000
Assets: $89,435,000
Liabilities: $13,434,000
Net Worth: $76,001,000
Earnings: ($36,004,000)
Emp.: 74
Fiscal Year-end: 12/31/22
Investment Services
N.A.I.C.S.: 523999
Craig Parker (CEO)
Yang Li (Exec VP-Research)
Charles Williams (CFO & COO)
Craig C. Parker (Pres & CEO)

SUSQUEHANNA COMMUNITY FINANCIAL, INC.

940 High St, West Milton, PA 17886
Tel.: (570) 568-6851   PA
Web Site: https://scb.bank
Year Founded: 1920
SQCF—(OTCIQ)
Rev.: $5,390,600
Emp.: 44
Financial Investment Services
N.A.I.C.S.: 523999
David Runk (Pres & CEO)
Michael Morrison (Mgr-Comml Relationship)
Rexford Hilton (Mgr-Comml Relationship)
Ariana Allen (Specialist-Treasury Mgmt)
Chris Romig (VP & Mgr-Comml Relationship)
Eugene Morrison (VP & Mgr-Comml Relationship)
Jack Emery (VP & Mgr-Comml Relationship)
Jeffrey Hollenbach (COO & Exec VP)
Michael Loeh (VP & Mgr-Comml Relationship & Comml Svcs)
Stephen Stanko (VP & Mgr-Comml Relationship)
Jehna Clymer (Officer & Asst VP)

SUSTAINABLE GREEN TEAM LTD.

24200 County Rd 561, Astatula, FL 34705
Tel.: (407) 886-8733   DE
Web Site: https://thesustainablegreenteam.com
SGTM—(OTCIQ)
Landscaping Services
N.A.I.C.S.: 561730
Victor Spangler (CMO)
Anthony Raynor (Founder & CEO)
Brian Rivera (Sr VP-Dev & Strategy & VP)
Barry Papenfuss (CFO)
Josh Ganganna (COO)
Minera Myers (VP-Continuous Bus Improvement)
Wayne Jones (Dir-Liaison)
Alesia Hopkins (VP-Bus Strategy & Sales)
John Schultz (Dir-Revenue & Operations)
Rebecca Mahoney (VP-Logistics)

SUSTAINABLE PROJECTS GROUP INC.

2316 Pine Ridge Rd Ste 383, Naples, FL 34109
Tel.: (305) 814-2915   NV
Web Site: https://www.spgroupe.com
Year Founded: 2009
SPGX—(OTCIQ)
Assets: $3,069,604
Liabilities: $3,010,712
Net Worth: $58,892
Earnings: ($2,747,952)
Emp.: 14
Fiscal Year-end: 12/31/23
Natural Resources Holding & Development Company
N.A.I.C.S.: 211130
Stefan Muehlbauer (Pres, CEO, CFO, Chief Comm Officer & Principal Acctg Officer)
Tiffany Muehlbauer (COO)

SUTRO BIOPHARMA, INC.

111 Oyster Pt Blvd, South San Francisco, CA 94080
Tel.: (650) 881-6500   DE
Web Site: https://www.sutrobio.com
Year Founded: 2003
STRO—(NASDAQ)
Rev.: $153,731,000
Assets: $470,736,000
Liabilities: $321,087,000
Net Worth: $149,649,000
Earnings: ($106,793,000)
Emp.: 302
Fiscal Year-end: 12/31/23
Biotechnology Research & Development Services
N.A.I.C.S.: 541714
Edward C. Albini (CFO & Sec)
William J. Newell (CEO)
Shabbir T. Anik (Chief Technical Ops Officer)
Linda Fitzpatrick (Chief People & Comm Officer)
Robert Kiss (Sr VP-Process & Analytical Dev)
Nicki Vasquez (Chief Portfolio Strategy & Alliance Officer)
Andreas Maderna (VP-Chemistry)
Kristin Bedard (VP-Discovery)
Craig Berman (VP-Clinical)
Regina Cheng (VP-Fin & Controller)
Jane Chung (Pres & COO)
Annie J. Chang (Head-IR)
Carlos Lugo (VP-Quality & CMC Regulatory Ops)
Devendra Luhar (VP-Mfg & Plant Ops)
David Pauling (Gen Counsel)
Jane Chung (Chief Comml Officer)
Hans-Peter Gerber (Chief Scientific Officer)

SUTTER GOLD MINING, INC.

2414 Garland St, Lakewood, CO 80215
Tel.: (303) 238-1438   BC
Web Site:
http://www.suttergoldmining.com
SGMNF—(OTCIQ)
Sales Range: Less than $1 Million
Gold Mining
N.A.I.C.S.: 212220
Mark Thomas Brown (Chm)
David A. Cochrane (VP-Environmental Health & Safety)
Richard A. Winters (Bd of Dirs, Pres & CEO)
Amanda Miller (CFO, CFO-Investor Relations & Sec)

SVB FINANCIAL GROUP

3003 Tasman Dr, Santa Clara, CA 95054
Tel.: (408) 654-7400   DE

Web Site: https://www.svb.com
Year Founded: 1999
SIVB—(NASDAQ)
Rev.: $7,401,000,000
Assets: $211,793,000,000
Liabilities: $195,498,000,000
Net Worth: $16,295,000,000
Earnings: $1,609,000,000
Emp.: 8,553
Fiscal Year-end: 12/31/22
Financial Services Holding Company
N.A.I.C.S.: 551111
Eric A. Benhamou (Chm)
William Kosturos (Chief Restructuring Officer)
Nicholas Grossi (Interim CFO)

Subsidiaries:

Growth Partners, L.P.   (1)
5023 Parkway Calabasas, Calabasas, CA 91302
Tel.: (818) 713-8000
Web Site: http://www.growthpartners.net
Investment Advisory Services
N.A.I.C.S.: 523940
Jeffrey R. Knakal (Mng Partner)

Qualified Investors Fund III, LLC   (1)
2770 Sand Hill Rd, Menlo Park, CA 94025
Tel.: (650) 926-0440
Commercial Banking Services
N.A.I.C.S.: 522110

SVB Analytics, Inc.   (1)
3003 Tasman Dr, Santa Clara, CA 95054
Tel.: (408) 654-7400
Web Site: http://www.svb.com
Sales Range: $650-699.9 Million
Corporate Equity Management Services
N.A.I.C.S.: 523999

SVB Business Partners (Beijing) Co. Ltd.   (1)
Unit 2315 China World Office 1 No 1 Jian Guo Men Wai Avenue, Beijing, 100004, China
Tel.: (86) 1057328500
Emp.: 10
Investment Management Service
N.A.I.C.S.: 523940
Daniel Quon (Mng Dir)

SVB Global Financial, Inc.   (1)
2 Palo Alto Sq Ste 110, Palo Alto, CA 94306
Tel.: (650) 812-0682
Financial Banking Services
N.A.I.C.S.: 522320

SVB Israel Advisors, Ltd.   (1)
28 Harbaa Street North Tower 25th Floor, PO Box 12104, Tel Aviv, 6473925, Israel
Tel.: (972) 9 972 2100
Web Site: https://www.svb.com
Investment Management Service
N.A.I.C.S.: 523940
David Cohen (Gen Mgr)
Gadi Moshe (Mng Dir)
Alon Oz (Mng Dir-Global Markets)

SVB Wealth Advisory, Inc.   (1)
505 Howard St Fl 3, San Francisco, CA 94105
Tel.: (415) 764-3100
Commercial Banking Services
N.A.I.C.S.: 522110

Strategic Investors Fund V-B, L.P.   (1)
2400 Hanover St, Palo Alto, CA 94304
Tel.: (650) 855-3033
Commercial Banking Services
N.A.I.C.S.: 522110

Strategic Investors Fund VII, L.P.   (1)
2770 Sand Hill Rd, Menlo Park, CA 94025
Tel.: (650) 926-0440
Commercial Banking Services
N.A.I.C.S.: 522110

SVF INVESTMENT CORP.

1 Cir Star Way, San Carlos, CA 94070
Tel.: (345) 949-0100   Ky
Web Site:
http://www.svfinvestmentcorp.com

Year Founded: 2020
SVFA—(NASDAQ)
Investment Services
N.A.I.C.S.: 523999
Navneet Govil (CEO)

SWEEGEN, INC.

25892 Twn Ctr Dr N, Foothill Ranch, CA 92610
Tel.: (949) 709-0583   NV
Web Site: https://sweegen.com
Year Founded: 2013
SWEE—(NYSE)
Sales Range: Less than $1 Million
Electronic Equipment Distr
N.A.I.C.S.: 423620
Steven Chen (CEO, CFO, Treas & Sec)
Luca Giannone (Head & Global Sls)
Karen Dominique Pierik (Head-Digital Mktg)
Hadi Omrani (VP-Regulatory Affairs)
John Zhang (Gen Counsel)

SWEETGREEN, INC.

3102 W 36th St, Los Angeles, CA 90018
Tel.: (323) 990-7040   DE
Year Founded: 2006
SG—(NYSE)
Rev.: $470,105,000
Assets: $908,935,000
Liabilities: $367,709,000
Net Worth: $541,226,000
Earnings: ($190,441,000)
Emp.: 5,952
Fiscal Year-end: 12/25/22
Restaurant Operators
N.A.I.C.S.: 722511
Rossann Williams (COO)
Mitch Reback (CFO)
Chris Carr (COO)
John Curry (Dir-Flight Ops)
Rich Kube (Dir-Production)
Mark Mikolajczyk (Dir-Operations)
John Roy (Dir-Human Resources)
Wouleta Ayele (CTO)
Adrienne Gemperle (Chief People Officer)
Nicolas Jammet (Co-Founder, Chief Concept Officer & Sec)
Jonathan Neman (Co-Founder, Pres & CEO)
Nathaniel Ru (Co-Founder, Chief Brand Officer & Treas)

SWIFTY GLOBAL

26 Broadway Ste 934, New York, NY 10004
Tel.: (917) 970-1433   NV
Web Site: https://www.swifty.global
Year Founded: 2010
DRCR—(OTCIQ)
Farming Equipment Rental Services
N.A.I.C.S.: 532490
James Gibbons (CEO)
Nick Link (Chm)

SWISS HELVETIA FUND, INC.

615 E Michigan St, Milwaukee, WI 53202
SWZ—(NYSE)   DE
Rev.: $2,661,629
Assets: $129,271,230
Liabilities: $407,397
Net Worth: $128,863,833
Earnings: $122,416
Fiscal Year-end: 12/31/19
Investment Management Service
N.A.I.C.S.: 525990

SYBLEU INC.

109 E 17th St Ste 460, Cheyenne, WY 82001   WY
Web Site: https://www.sybleu.com
Year Founded: 2020

SYBE—(OTCIQ)
Rev.: $11,696
Assets: $330,468
Liabilities: $681,413
Net Worth: ($350,945)
Earnings: ($180,304)
Fiscal Year-end: 06/30/23
Biotechnology Research & Development Services
N.A.I.C.S.: 541714
Joseph G. Vaini *(Chm, CEO, CFO & Chief Acctg Officer)*
Harry Lander *(Chief Scientific Officer)*

SYLIOS CORP.
244 2nd Ave N Ste 9, Saint Petersburg, FL 33701
Tel.: (727) 482-1505   FL
Web Site: http://www.sylios.com
Year Founded: 2008
UNGS—(OTCIQ)
Oil & Natural Gas Exploration, Development & Production Services; Real Estate Services
N.A.I.C.S.: 211120
Wayne Anderson *(Pres, Tres & Sec)*

SYLVAMO CORPORATION
6077 Primacy Pkwy, Memphis, TN 38119
Tel.: (901) 519-8000   DE
Web Site: https://www.sylvamo.com
Year Founded: 1898
SLVM—(NYSE)
Rev.: $3,628,000,000
Assets: $2,710,000,000
Liabilities: $2,032,000,000
Net Worth: $678,000,000
Earnings: $118,000,000
Emp.: 6,500
Fiscal Year-end: 12/31/22
Paper Mfr & Distr
N.A.I.C.S.: 322120
Jean-Michel Ribieras *(Chm & CEO)*
John V. Sims *(CFO & Sr VP)*
Peggy Maes *(Chief People Officer & Sr VP)*
Matthew Barron *(Chm, Gen Counsel & Sr VP)*
Thomas A. Cleves *(Sr VP-)*
Rodrigo Davoli *(Sr VP & Gen Mgr-North America)*
Patrick Wilczynski *(Sr VP-Operational Excellence)*
Tatiana Kalman *(Sr VP & Gen Mgr)*
Oliver Taudien *(Sr VP & Gen Mgr)*
Marcie Vargas *(Chief People Officer & Sr VP)*

Subsidiaries:

Sylvamo Sweden AB   (1)
Nymollavagen, 29573, Nymolla, Sweden
Tel.: (46) 104644000
Web Site: https://www.sylvamo.com
Paper Products Mfr
N.A.I.C.S.: 322220

SYMBOTIC, INC.
200 Research Dr, Wilmington, MA 01887
Tel.: (978) 284-2800
Web Site: https://www.symbotic.com
SYM—(NASDAQ)
Rev.: $1,176,891,000
Assets: $1,050,710,000
Liabilities: $1,053,426,000
Net Worth: ($2,716,000)
Earnings: ($23,866,000)
Emp.: 1,300
Fiscal Year-end: 09/30/23
Miscellaneous Financial Investment Activities
N.A.I.C.S.: 523999
Maria G. Freve *(Chief Acctg Officer, VP & Controller)*

Richard B. Cohen *(Chm, Pres, CEO & Chief Product Officer)*
Carol J. Hibbard *(CFO & Treas)*

Subsidiaries:

Symbotic LLC   (1)
200 Research Dr, Wilmington, MA 01887
Tel.: (978) 284-2800
Web Site: http://www.symbotic.com
Professional, Scientific & Technical Services
N.A.I.C.S.: 541990
Richard B. Cohen *(Pres)*
Jeff Paranay *(Sr Engr-Electrical)*

SYNAPTICS INCORPORATED
1109 McKay Dr, San Jose, CA 95131
Tel.: (408) 904-1100   DE
Web Site: https://www.synaptics.com
Year Founded: 1986
SYNA—(NASDAQ)
Rev.: $959,400,000
Assets: $2,825,000,000
Liabilities: $1,358,200,000
Net Worth: $1,466,800,000
Earnings: $125,600,000
Emp.: 1,716
Fiscal Year-end: 06/29/24
Human Interface Hardware & Software Solutions
N.A.I.C.S.: 334118
Nelson C. Chan *(Chm)*
Michael E. Hurlston *(Pres & CEO)*
Nicole Singer *(Sr VP-HR)*
Alex Chou *(Sr VP & Gen Mgr-Wireless Connectivity Div)*
Satish Ganesan *(Chief Strategy Officer)*
Venkat Kodavati *(Chief Product Officer & Sr VP)*
Janice Mori *(Sr VP-Bus Dev)*
Divyesh Shah *(Sr VP-Ops)*
Ken Rizvi *(CFO & Sr VP)*
Michael Brooker *(CIO & Sr VP-IT)*
Todd Lepinski *(Sr VP-Worldwide Sls)*

Subsidiaries:

DSP Group, Inc.   (1)
2055 Gtwy Pl Ste 480, San Jose, CA 95110
Tel.: (408) 986-4300
Web Site: http://www.dspg.com
Rev.: $114,480,000
Assets: $216,473,000
Liabilities: $60,235,000
Net Worth: $156,238,000
Earnings: ($6,790,000)
Emp.: 352
Fiscal Year-end: 12/31/2020
Semiconductor Components Mfr
N.A.I.C.S.: 334413
Dror Levy *(CFO, Sec & VP-Fin)*
Ofer Elyakim *(CEO)*
Dima Friedman *(VP-Ops)*
Tali Chen *(Chief Bus Officer & VP)*
Alex Sin *(VP-Sls)*
Ran Klier *(Gen Mgr-Unified Comm & Hearables Bus Lines)*
Hila Manoach *(VP-HR)*
Avi Keren *(CTO & VP)*
Yosi Brosh *(VP-SmartVoice Product Line)*
Dotan Sokolov *(VP & Head-R&D)*
Fredy Rabih *(VP-Product Mgmt)*

Joint Venture (Non-US):

DSP BlackRock Investment Managers Private Limited   (2)
302 Natraj, Plot no 194, MB Rd Junction, Western Express Highway, Andheri east, Mumbai, 400069, India   (60%)
Tel.: (91) 2267178000
Web Site: http://www.dspblackrock.com
Investment Management Service
N.A.I.C.S.: 541611
Kalpen Parekh *(Pres)*

Subsidiary (Non-US):

DSP Group (Shenzhen) Limited   (2)
Unit 802 8/F Building A Zhuoyue Bozhong Times Square First Stage, Baohua Road Xin'an Block Baoan District, Shenzhen, 518001, China
Tel.: (86) 75523226313

Semiconductor & Related Device Distr
N.A.I.C.S.: 423690

DSP Group HK Limited   (2)
Units 1903-04 of 19/F AIA Financial Centre 712 Prince Edward Road East, Kowloon, China (Hong Kong)
Tel.: (852) 39655888
Consumer Electronics Mfr
N.A.I.C.S.: 334413

DSP Group Ltd.   (2)
3 Arik Einstein Street, Herzliya Pituach, Israel
Tel.: (972) 99529696
Wireless Chipset Mfr
N.A.I.C.S.: 334413

DSP Technology   (2)
Myungsin Bldg 3rd Fl 840 12 0 Yeoksan 1 Dong, Kangnam Ku, Seoul, 135 280, Korea (South)   (100%)
Tel.: (82) 25547494
Web Site: http://www.widermax.com
Sales Range: $150-199.9 Million
Provider of Telecommunications Equipment
N.A.I.C.S.: 238210

DSP Technology Indian Private Limited   (2)
4th Floor MFAR Green Heart Building, Manyata Embassy Business Park Nagawara, Bengaluru, 560 045, Karnataka, India
Tel.: (91) 8049558010
Consumer Electronics Mfr
N.A.I.C.S.: 334413

DSPG Edinburgh Ltd.   (2)
Geddes House Kirkton North, Livingston, EH54 6GU, West Lothian, United Kingdom
Tel.: (44) 1223772200
Web Site: https://www.dspg.com
Emp.: 3
Semiconductor & Related Device Mfr
N.A.I.C.S.: 334413

SoundChip SA   (2)
Rue Champ-de-l'Essert 32, Aran-Villette, 1091, Lausanne, Switzerland
Tel.: (41) 215520848
Web Site: http://www.soundchip.ch
Audio Equipment Mfr
N.A.I.C.S.: 334310
Mark Weldon *(Chm)*
Mark Donaldson *(CEO)*
Paul Darlington *(CTO)*
Ben Skelton *(COO)*

DisplayLink (UK) Limited   (1)
22 Cambridge Science Park Milton Road, Cambridge, CB4 0GH, United Kingdom
Tel.: (44) 1223443920
Computer Peripheral Equipment Mfr
N.A.I.C.S.: 334118

Displaylink Corp.   (1)
480 S California Ave, Palo Alto, CA 94306-1623
Tel.: (650) 485-9030
Web Site: http://www.displaylink.com
Relay & Industrial Control Mfr
N.A.I.C.S.: 335314

Emza Visual Sense Ltd.   (1)
Floor 30 HaShachar Tower Ariel Sharon St 4, Box 52, Givatayim, Israel
Tel.: (972) 36830855
Web Site: https://www.emza-vs.com
Miniature Machine Vision Device Mfr
N.A.I.C.S.: 334519
Yoram Zylberberg *(CEO)*
Elad Baram *(VP)*
Tomer Kimhi *(VP-Research & Development)*
Tal Hendel *(Head)*

Synaptics Europe Sarl   (1)
Avenue de la Gare 33, Gratta Paille 2, 1003, Lausanne, Switzerland
Tel.: (41) 218112100
Computer Peripheral Equipment Mfr
N.A.I.C.S.: 334118

Synaptics Hong Kong Ltd.   (1)
Units 1601-1603 16th Floor Two Harbourfront 22 Tak Fung Street, Hung Hom, Kowloon, China (Hong Kong)   (100%)
Tel.: (852) 36582288
Sales Range: $10-24.9 Million
Emp.: 60
Computer Systems Mfr
N.A.I.C.S.: 541512

Synaptics International Inc.   (1)
1251 Mckay Dr, San Jose, CA 95131   (100%)
Tel.: (408) 454-5100
Web Site: http://www.synaptics.com
Sales Range: $75-99.9 Million
Emp.: 350
Computer Systems Mfr
N.A.I.C.S.: 541511

Synaptics Japan (K.K.) Limited   (1)
Front Tower Shiba Park 20F 2-6-3 Shibakoen Minato, Tokyo, 105-0011, Japan
Tel.: (81) 354084401
Sales Range: $25-49.9 Million
Emp.: 30
Electronic Computer Mfr
N.A.I.C.S.: 334111

Synaptics Japan GK   (1)
Nakano Central Park South Building 4-10-2, Nakano-ku, Tokyo, 164-0001, Japan
Tel.: (81) 359135720
Semiconductor & Related Product Mfr
N.A.I.C.S.: 334413
Yoshinori Goto *(Country Mgr)*

SYNAPTOGENIX, INC.
1185 Ave of the Americas 3rd Fl, New York, NY 10036
Tel.: (973) 242-0005   FL
Web Site:
https://www.synaptogen.com
Year Founded: 2011
NTRP—(NASDAQ)
Rev.: $378,707
Assets: $17,897,821
Liabilities: $479,056
Net Worth: $17,418,765
Earnings: ($15,134,750)
Emp.: 5
Fiscal Year-end: 12/31/19
Pharmaceutical & Medical Products Mfr
N.A.I.C.S.: 325412
Daniel L. Alkon *(Pres & Chief Science Officer)*
Robert Weinstein *(Treas, Sec & Exec VP)*
William S. Singer *(Vice Chm)*
Alan Tuchman *(Acting Chief Medical Officer)*
Elaine Grenier *(Exec Dir-Clinical Ops)*

SYNAPTOGENIX, INC.
1185 Avenue of the Americas 3rd Fl, New York, NY 10036
Tel.: (973) 242-0005   DE
Web Site:
https://www.synaptogen.com
Year Founded: 2012
SNPX—(NASDAQ)
Rev.: $10,561,039
Assets: $38,607,806
Liabilities: $5,914,833
Net Worth: $32,692,973
Earnings: ($5,573,957)
Emp.: 1
Fiscal Year-end: 12/31/22
Biotechnology Research & Development Services
N.A.I.C.S.: 541714

SYNCHRONOSS TECHNOLOGIES, INC.
200 Crossing Blvd, Bridgewater, NJ 08807   DE
Web Site:
https://www.synchronoss.com
Year Founded: 2000
SNCR—(NASDAQ)
Rev.: $252,628,000
Assets: $398,072,000
Liabilities: $329,975,000
Net Worth: $68,097,000
Earnings: ($17,468,000)
Emp.: 1,391
Fiscal Year-end: 12/31/22

Synchronoss Technologies, Inc.—(Continued)

Cloud, Digital, Messaging & Internet of Things (IoT) Platforms, Products & Solutions
N.A.I.C.S.: 518210
Patrick J. Doran (CTO)
Louis W. Ferraro Jr. (CFO)
Mina Lackner (Chief HR Officer)
Christina Gabrys (Chief Legal Officer)
Jeffrey G. Miller (Pres & CEO)
Stephen G. Waldis (Founder & Exec Chm)

Subsidiaries:

Voxmobili S.A.　　　　(1)
36 rue Brunel, 75017, Paris, France　　　　(100%)
Tel.: (33) 1 40 26 23 34
Emp.: 35
Develops & Markets Software Applications for Mobile Operators
N.A.I.C.S.: 513210
Martin Nappert (Gen Mgr)

SYNCHRONY FINANCIAL

777 Long Ridge Rd, Stamford, CT 06902
Tel.: (866) 419-4096　　　　**DE**
Web Site: https://www.synchrony.com
SYF—(NYSE)
Rev.: $20,710,000,000
Assets: $117,479,000,000
Liabilities: $103,576,000,000
Net Worth: $13,903,000,000
Earnings: $2,196,000,000
Emp.: 20,000
Fiscal Year-end: 12/31/23
Consumer Financial & Banking Services
N.A.I.C.S.: 525990
Brian D. Doubles (Pres & CEO)
Jonathan S. Mothner (Gen Counsel, Sec & Exec VP)
Alberto Casellas (CEO-Health & Wellness & Exec VP)
Kurt Grossheim (COO & Exec VP)
Carol D. Juel (CTO & Exec VP)
Mark Martinelli (Exec VP-Chief Audit Executive)
Bart Schaller (CEO-Digital & Exec VP)
Paul Whynott (Chief Risk Officer & Exec VP)
Trish Mosconi (Chief Strategy Officer-Corp Dev & Exec VP)
Curtis Howse (CEO-Home & Auto)
David P. Melito (Sr VP & Controller)
Dana Randell (Exec VP)

Subsidiaries:

CareCredit LLC　　　　(1)
Web Site: http://www.carecredit.com
Healthcare Credit Card Issuing Services
N.A.I.C.S.: 522210

CareCredit LLC　　　　(1)
Web Site: http://www.carecredit.com
Healthcare Credit Card Issuing Services
N.A.I.C.S.: 522210

CareCredit LLC　　　　(1)
Web Site: http://www.carecredit.com
Healthcare Credit Card Issuing Services
N.A.I.C.S.: 522210

CareCredit LLC　　　　(1)
Web Site: http://www.carecredit.com
Healthcare Credit Card Issuing Services
N.A.I.C.S.: 522210

GPShopper LLC　　　　(1)
50 W 23rd St Ste 1400, New York, NY 10010
Tel.: (212) 488-2222
Web Site: http://www.gpshopper.com
Software Publisher
N.A.I.C.S.: 513210
Alex Muller (Co-Founder)
Maya Mikhailov (Co-Founder)

Synchrony Bank　　　　(1)

170 Election Rd Ste 125, Draper, UT 84020
Web Site: http://www.synchronybank.com.
Federal Savings & Credit Card Issuing Bank
N.A.I.C.S.: 522180

Synchrony Financial Canada　　　　(1)
PO Box 940, STN Agincourt, Toronto, M1S 0G2, ON, Canada
Tel.: (203) 750-3441
Credit Card Issuing Services
N.A.I.C.S.: 522210

SYNDAX PHARMACEUTICALS, INC.

35 Gatehouse Dr Bldg D Fl 3, Waltham, MA 02451
Tel.: (781) 419-1400　　　　**DE**
Web Site: https://www.syndax.com
Year Founded: 2005
SNDX—(NASDAQ)
Rev.: $21,163,000
Assets: $612,880,000
Liabilities: $58,684,000
Net Worth: $554,196,000
Earnings: ($209,360,000)
Emp.: 184
Fiscal Year-end: 12/31/23
Pharmaceuticals Mfr
N.A.I.C.S.: 325412
Kate Madigan (Chief Medical Officer)
Neil Gallagher (Pres & Head-R&D)
Luke Albrecht (Gen Counsel)
Anjali Ganguli (Chief Bus Officer)
Kevin McManus (Chief People Officer)
Michael A. Metzger (CEO)
Keith A. Goldan (CFO, Principal Acctg Officer & Treas)
Steve Closter (Chief Comml Officer)

SYNERGY CHC CORP.

865 Spring St, Westbrook, ME 04092
Tel.: (615) 939-9004　　　　**NV**
Web Site: https://www.synergychc.com
Year Founded: 2010
SNYR—(OTCIQ)
Rev.: $29,357,546
Assets: $5,190,629
Liabilities: $10,393,980
Net Worth: ($5,203,351)
Earnings: ($9,207,447)
Emp.: 36
Fiscal Year-end: 12/31/19
Medical Products Marketer & Distr
N.A.I.C.S.: 424210
Jack Ross (Chm, Pres, CEO & CFO)
Jaime Fickett (Sr VP-Fin & Ops)
Al Baumeler (Exec VP-Sls & Mktg Retail)

SYNLOGIC, INC

PO Box 30, Winchester, MA 01890
Tel.: (617) 401-9975　　　　**DE**
Web Site: https://www.synlogictx.com
Year Founded: 2007
SYBX—(NASDAQ)
Rev.: $1,180,000
Assets: $110,865,000
Liabilities: $28,255,000
Net Worth: $82,610,000
Earnings: ($66,147,000)
Emp.: 72
Fiscal Year-end: 12/31/22
Pharmaceuticals Mfr
N.A.I.C.S.: 325412
Timothy Lu (Founder)
Peter Barrett (Chm)
Adam Thomas (Chief People Officer & Sec)
Michael Slater (Head-Regulatory Affairs)
Caroline B. Kurtz (Chief Dev Officer)
David Hava (Chief Scientific Officer)
Daniel Rosan (VP-Fin & Head-Corp Fin & IR)
Michael Conlon (VP-Corp Dev)

Jamie Austin (Head-Regulatory Affairs)
Molly Harper (Chief Bus Officer)

SYNOPSYS, INC.

675 Almanor Ave, Sunnyvale, CA 94085
Tel.: (650) 584-5000　　　　**DE**
Web Site: https://www.synopsys.com
Year Founded: 1986
SNPS—(NASDAQ)
Rev.: $6,127,436,000
Assets: $13,073,561,000
Liabilities: $4,050,355,000
Net Worth: $9,023,206,000
Earnings: $2,235,810,000
Emp.: 20,000
Fiscal Year-end: 10/31/24
Semiconductor Design & Verification Software Developer
N.A.I.C.S.: 541512
Vivie Lee (Executives, Bd of Dirs)
Lisa L. Ewbank (VP-IR)
Aart J. de Geus (Founder & Exec Chm)
Erika Varga McEnroe (Chief Ethics & Compliance Officer & Deputy Gen Counsel)
Sudhindra Kankanwadi (Chief Acctg Officer & Sr VP-Fin)
Deirdre R. Hanford (Chief Security Officer)
Sassine Ghazi (Pres & CEO)
Sriram Sitaraman (CIO)
Shankar Krishnamoorthy (Gen Mgr-Silicon Realization Grp)
Jason Schmitt (Gen Mgr-Software Integrity Grp)
Raja Tabet (Sr VP-Custom Design & Mfg Grp)
Antonio Varas (Chief Strategy Officer)
Alessandra Costa (Sr VP-Customer Success Grp)
Michael Sanie (VP-Enterprise Mktg & Comm)
Jacob Avidan (Sr VP-Engrg)
Shelagh Glaser (CFO)
Rick Mahoney (Chief Revenue Officer)
Rick Runkel (Corp Counsel)
Ravi Subramanian (Gen Mgr)
Kimio Fujii (Pres-Japan & Reg VP-Sls)
Qun Go (Proa China & Rog VP Sls)
Robert Li (VP)
Kevin Maguire (VP)
Steve McDonald (VP)
John F. Runkel Jr. (Gen Counsel & Sec)

Subsidiaries:

Atrenta Inc.　　　　(1)
2077 Gateway Pl, San Jose, CA 95110
Tel.: (408) 453-3333
Web Site: http://www.atrenta.com
Rev.: $5,000,000
Emp.: 43
Custom Computer Programming Services
N.A.I.C.S.: 541511

Black Duck Software, Inc.　　　　(1)
800 District Ave Ste 201, Burlington, MA 01803
Tel.: (781) 891-5100
Software Compliance Management Solutions Developer
N.A.I.C.S.: 541519

Codenomicon Oy　　　　(1)
Tutkijantie 4E, FIN-90590, Oulu, Finland
Tel.: (358) 424 7431
Web Site: http://www.synopsys.com
Emp.: 11,000
Software Publisher
N.A.I.C.S.: 513210

Subsidiary (US):

Codenomicon Ltd.　　　　(2)

185 Berry St Ste 6500, San Francisco, CA 94107
Tel.: (415) 321-5237
Web Site: http://www.codenomicon.com
Software Publisher
N.A.I.C.S.: 513210
Steve Hayes (VP)

Coverity, Inc.　　　　(1)
185 Berry St Ste 6500, San Francisco, CA 94107
Tel.: (415) 321-5200
Web Site: http://www.coverity.com
Sales Range: $10-24.9 Million
Emp.: 140
Computer Application Software
N.A.I.C.S.: 541519

EVE Design Automation Pvt. Ltd.　　　　(1)
J K Ashwath Lakshmi Heritage 1st Floor No 777, 80 Feet Road 4th Block, Bengaluru, 560034, Karnataka, India
Tel.: (91) 8041460680
Applications Software Programming Services
N.A.I.C.S.: 541511

NTT Security AppSec Solutions Inc.　　　　(1)
741 Technology Dr Ste 300, Santa Clara, CA 95110
Tel.: (408) 343-8300
Web Site: http://www.whitehatsec.com
Security Software Development Services
N.A.I.C.S.: 541511
Craig Hinkley (CEO)

Nihon Synopsys G.K.　　　　(1)
2-21-1 Tamagawa Futako Tamagawa Rise Office, Setagaya-ku, Tokyo, 158-0094, Japan
Tel.: (81) 367463500
Software Publishing Services
N.A.I.C.S.: 513210
Masahiro Kurihara (Sr Mgr)

Optical Solutions Group　　　　(1)
3280 E Foothill Blvd Ste 300, Pasadena, CA 91107
Tel.: (626) 795-9101
Web Site: http://www.opticalres.com
Sales Range: $25-49.9 Million
Emp.: 85
Imaging & Illumination Design & Analysis Software Mfr
N.A.I.C.S.: 513210

PikeTec GmbH　　　　(1)
Waldenserstrasse 2-4, 10551, Berlin, Germany
Tel.: (49) 30394096830
Web Site: https://piketec.com
Software Development & Testing Services
N.A.I.C.S.: 541519

RSoft Design Group, Inc.　　　　(1)
400 Executive Blvd Ste 100, Ossining, NY 10562
Tel.: (914) 923-2164
Web Site: http://www.rsoftdesign.com
Applications Software Programming Services
N.A.I.C.S.: 541511

RSoft, Inc.　　　　(1)
400 Executive Blvd Ste 100, Ossining, NY 10562
Tel.: (914) 923-2164
Photonics Design & Simulation Software Publisher
N.A.I.C.S.: 513210
Robert Scarmozzino (CEO & CTO)

Synopsys (India) Private Limited　　　　(1)
7th Floor Blocks B and C DivyaSree Omega Survey No 13 EE 13/U, Kondapur Village, Hyderabad, 500032, Andhra Pradesh, India
Tel.: (91) 4040331000
Applications Software Programming Services
N.A.I.C.S.: 541511

Synopsys (Singapore) Pte. Ltd.　　　　(1)
300 Beach Road 31 02, The Concourse, Singapore, 199555, Singapore
Tel.: (65) 62967433
Web Site: http://www.synopsys.com
Semiconductor Design & Verification Software Developer

N.A.I.C.S.: 513210

Subsidiary (Non-US):

Nihon Synopsys GK (2)
2-21-1 Tamagawa, Setagaya-ku, Tokyo,
158-0094, Japan
Tel.: (81) 36 746 3500
Web Site: https://www.synopsys.com
Software Development Services
N.A.I.C.S.: 513210

Synopsys Korea Inc. (2)
12th Floor Star Tower 737 Yeoksam dong,
Kangnam gu, Seoul, 135 984, Korea
(South)
Tel.: (82) 234042700
Sales Range: $10-24.9 Million
Emp.: 20
Semiconductor Design & Verification Soft-
ware Developer
N.A.I.C.S.: 513210

Synopsys Taiwan Co., Ltd. (2)
4F 1 28 Tai Yuan Street, Chupei City, Hsin-
chu, 302, Taiwan
Tel.: (886) 35525880
Web Site: http://www.synopsys.com
Software Publisher
N.A.I.C.S.: 513210

Synopsys Armenia CJSC (2)
41 Arshakunyats Avenue ViaSphere Tech-
nopark Bldg 1, Yerevan, 0026, Armenia
Tel.: (374) 10492100
Web Site: http://www.synopsys.am
Sales Range: $125-149.9 Million
Emp.: 600
Applications Software Programming Ser-
vices
N.A.I.C.S.: 541511

**Synopsys Emulation and Verification
S.A.S.** (1)
Batiment le Cormoran, 3 Avenue Jeanne
Garnerin Air Park Paris Sud, 91320, Wis-
sous, France
Tel.: (33) 164532730
Software Publishing Services
N.A.I.C.S.: 513210
Gerald Couaillier (Sr Mgr-R&D)

Synopsys Global Kft. (1)
Kalman Imre Utca 1, Budapest, 1054, Hun-
gary
Tel.: (36) 14751387
Applications Software Programming Ser-
vices
N.A.I.C.S.: 541511

**Synopsys Hardware Platforms Group
AB** (1)
Kalkstensvagen 3, 224 78, Lund, Sweden
Tel.: (46) 46162900
Web Site: http://www.synopsys.com
Sales Range: $25-49.9 Million
Emp.: 20
Applications Software Programming Ser-
vices
N.A.I.C.S.: 541511

Synopsys International Limited (1)
Blanchardstown Corp Park Block 1, Dublin,
15, Ireland
Tel.: (353) 14368800
Web Site: http://www.synopsys.com
Semiconductor Design & Verification Soft-
ware Developer
N.A.I.C.S.: 513210

Subsidiary (Non-US):

Synopsys (Northern Europe) Ltd. (2)
100 Brook Dr Greenpark, Reading, RG2
6UJ, United Kingdom
Tel.: (44) 1189313822
Web Site: http://www.europe.synopsys.com
Sales Range: $10-24.9 Million
Emp.: 59
Semiconductor & System Design Creation,
Simulation & Verification Software & Ser-
vices
N.A.I.C.S.: 513210

Synopsys Denmark ApS (2)
Vester Farimagsgade 3 3rd Floor, 1606,
Copenhagen, Denmark
Tel.: (45) 70212222
Web Site: http://www.synopsys.com
Semiconductor Design & Verification Soft-
ware Developer

N.A.I.C.S.: 513210

Synopsys Switzerland LLC (2)
Affolternstrasse 52, 8050, Zurich, Switzer-
land
Tel.: (41) 445671600
Web Site: http://europe.synopsys.com
Semiconductor Design & Verification Soft-
ware Developer
N.A.I.C.S.: 513210

Synopsys Italia S.R.L. (1)
Viale Colleoni 11 - Palazzo Sirio 3 Centro
Direzionale Colleoni, Palazzo Sirio 3,
20864, Agrate Brianza, Italy
Tel.: (39) 0396846700
Sales Range: $10-24.9 Million
Emp.: 25
Semiconductor Design & Verification Soft-
ware Developer
N.A.I.C.S.: 513210

Synopsys LLC (1)
Smolensky Passage Regus Center Office
621 Smolenskaya Square 3, 121099, Mos-
cow, Russia
Tel.: (7) 4959331015
Applications Software Programming Ser-
vices
N.A.I.C.S.: 541511
Elena Ivanova (Mng Dir)

Synopsys SARL (2)
Immeuble Amsterdam 54 56 rue d'Arcueil
Silic 137, Rungis, Rungis, France
Tel.: (33) 145120606
Applications Software Programming Ser-
vices
N.A.I.C.S.: 541511

**Synopsys Software Science and
Technology (Shanghai) Co., Ltd.** (1)
5F Tower 1 EBA Center 387 Huimin Road
Lot 10, Yangpu District, Shanghai, 200433,
China
Tel.: (86) 2135874500
Software Security & Quality Testing Ser-
vices
N.A.I.C.S.: 541519

Synopsys Spb LLC (1)
Prof Popova Str 23-D, 197376, Saint Pe-
tersburg, Russia
Tel.: (7) 8124087400
Web Site: http://www.synopsys.com
Applications Software Programming Ser-
vices
N.A.I.C.S.: 541511

Synopsys Taiwan Co., Ltd. (1)
No 25 Industry East Road IV Science-
Based Industrial Park, Hsinchu, 300, Taiwan
Tel.: (886) 35794567
Software Services
N.A.I.C.S.: 541519
Robbins Yeh (Chm)

Synplicity, LLC (1)
600 W California Ave, Sunnyvale, CA 94086
Tel.: (408) 215-6000
Sales Range: $50-74.9 Million
Emp.: 328
Semiconductor Design & Verification Soft-
ware Developer
N.A.I.C.S.: 334610

Subsidiary (Non-US):

S.N.P.S. Israel Ltd (2)
Herzelia Business Park 4 Maskit St Building
C 2nd Floor, PO Box 12323, Herzliyya,
46733, Israel
Tel.: (972) 9971 9600
Web Site: http://www.synopsys.com
Semiconductor Design & Verification Soft-
ware Developer
N.A.I.C.S.: 513210

Synopsys GmbH (2)
Next-Building Karl Hammerschmidt Strasse
34, Aschheim, D-85609, Dornach, Germany
Tel.: (49) 89993200
Web Site: http://www.synopsys.com
Sales Range: $100-124.9 Million
Semiconductor Design & Verification Soft-
ware Developer
N.A.I.C.S.: 513210
Willi Ahnen (Mng Dir)

SYNOVUS FINANCIAL CORP.

1111 Bay Ave Ste 500, Columbus,
GA 31901
Tel.: (706) 641-6500 GA
Web Site: https://www.synovus.com
Year Founded: 1888
SNV—(NYSE)
Rev.: $3,050,358,000
Assets: $59,809,534,000
Liabilities: $54,665,386,000
Net Worth: $5,144,148,000
Earnings: $507,755,000
Emp.: 4,663
Fiscal Year-end: 12/31/23
Commercial Banking Services
N.A.I.C.S.: 551111
Alison W. Dowe (Chief Comm & Corp
Responsibility Officer & Exec VP)
Kevin S. Blair (Chm, Pres & CEO)
Gloria C. Banks (Chief Ethics & Com-
pliance Officer & Exec VP)
Elizabeth Dukes Wolverton (Chief
Strategy & Customer Experience Offi-
cer & Exec VP)
Shellie R. Creson (Chief Risk Officer)
Jonathan Edwards (Pres)
Chris Layeux (Sr VP)
Roman Mazo (Mng Dir)
Jayan Krishnan (Mng Dir)
Katherine M. Weislogel (Head)
Tom Dierdorff (Head)
Jennifer Demba (Dir-IR)
Andrew Jamie Gregory Jr. (CFO &
Exec VP)

Subsidiaries:

**Broadway Asset Management,
Inc.** (1)
1111 Bay Ave, Columbus, GA 31901
Tel.: (706) 649-2311
Asset Management Services
N.A.I.C.S.: 523940

Synovus Bank (1)
1111 Bay Ave Ste 500, Columbus, GA
31901
Web Site: http://www.synovus.com
Commercial Banking
N.A.I.C.S.: 522110
Kessel D. Stelling Jr. (Chm & CEO)
Wayne Akins (Chief Community Banking
Officer)
Allen Barker (CEO-North Georgia)
Tom Dierdorff (Head-Corp & Investment
Banking)
Ken Ho (Chief Analytics Officer)
Liz Wolverton (Exec VP & Head-Consumer
Banking & Brand Experience)

Synovus Bank (1)
1111 Bay Ave Ste 500, Columbus, GA
31901
Web Site: http://www.synovus.com
Commericial Banking
N.A.I.C.S.: 522110
Kessel D. Stelling Jr. (Chm & CEO)
Wayne Akins (Chief Community Banking
Officer)
Allen Barker (CEO-North Georgia)
Tom Dierdorff (Head-Corp & Investment
Banking)
Ken Ho (Chief Analytics Officer)
Liz Wolverton (Exec VP & Head-Consumer
Banking & Brand Experience)

Subsidiary (Domestic):

**Aspenwood Square Apartments,
LP** (2)
3235 Innsbrock Ln, Memphis, TN 38115
Tel.: (901) 542-9700
Web Site: https://aspenwood-square-
apartments.business.site
Residential Building Rental & Leasing Ser-
vices
N.A.I.C.S.: 531110

Burger Phillips Building, LLC (2)
1914 3rd Ave N, Birmingham, AL 35203
Tel.: (205) 790-2374
Web Site: http://www.burgerphillips.com
Real Estate Manangement Services
N.A.I.C.S.: 531390

**Commercial Bank & Trust
Company** (2)

200 N Greenwood St, LaGrange, GA 30240
Tel.: (706) 880-2200
Web Site: http://combanktrust.synovus.com
Sales Range: $25-49.9 Million
Emp.: 37
Commericial Banking
N.A.I.C.S.: 522110

First Bank of Jasper (2)
200 18th St W, Jasper, AL 35501
Tel.: (205) 221-3121
Web Site: http://www.synovus.com
Sales Range: $75-99.9 Million
Emp.: 175
Commericial Banking
N.A.I.C.S.: 522110
Shawn Morgan (Pres-Market)

First State Bank and Trust Co. (2)
3650 Inner Perimeter Rd, Valdosta, GA
31602
Tel.: (229) 242-5725
Web Site: http://fsbtc.synovus.com
Sales Range: $25-49.9 Million
Emp.: 91
Commericial Banking
N.A.I.C.S.: 522110

Synovus Mortgage Corp. (2)
800 Shades Creek Pkwy MS 100, Birming-
ham, AL 35209
Tel.: (205) 868-9111
Investment Management Service
N.A.I.C.S.: 523940
Mary Beth Balzli (Pres & CEO)

**Synovus Trust Company, National
Association** (2)
1137 1st Ave 1st Fl, Columbus, GA 31901
Tel.: (706) 644-3496
Financial Investment Services
N.A.I.C.S.: 523999

Tallahassee State Bank (2)
601 N Monroe St, Tallahassee, FL 32301
Tel.: (850) 576-1182
Web Site: http://www.talstatebank.com
Sales Range: $10-24.9 Million
Emp.: 60
Banking
N.A.I.C.S.: 522110
Bill Moore (Pres-Market)

Union Hill Apartments, L.P. (2)
235 Union Hill Dr 18a, Forsyth, GA 31029
Tel.: (478) 994-2255
Web Site:
http://www.unionhillapartments.com
Residential Building Rental & Leasing Ser-
vices
N.A.I.C.S.: 531110

Synovus Bank (1)
1111 Bay Ave Ste 500, Columbus, GA
31901
Web Site: http://www.synovus.com
Commericial Banking
N.A.I.C.S.: 522110
Kessel D. Stelling Jr. (Chm & CEO)
Wayne Akins (Chief Community Banking
Officer)
Allen Barker (CEO-North Georgia)
Tom Dierdorff (Head-Corp & Investment
Banking)
Ken Ho (Chief Analytics Officer)
Liz Wolverton (Exec VP & Head-Consumer
Banking & Brand Experience)

Synovus Bank (1)
1111 Bay Ave Ste 500, Columbus, GA
31901
Web Site: http://www.synovus.com
Commericial Banking
N.A.I.C.S.: 522110
Kessel D. Stelling Jr. (Chm & CEO)
Wayne Akins (Chief Community Banking
Officer)
Allen Barker (CEO-North Georgia)
Tom Dierdorff (Head-Corp & Investment
Banking)
Ken Ho (Chief Analytics Officer)
Liz Wolverton (Exec VP & Head-Consumer
Banking & Brand Experience)

Subsidiary (Domestic):

**Aspenwood Square Apartments,
LP** (2)
3235 Innsbrock Ln, Memphis, TN 38115
Tel.: (901) 542-9700

Synovus Financial Corp.—(Continued)

Web Site: https://aspenwood-square-
apartments.business.site
Residential Building Rental & Leasing Services
N.A.I.C.S.: 531110

Burger Phillips Building, LLC **(2)**
1914 3rd Ave N, Birmingham, AL 35203
Tel.: (205) 790-2374
Web Site: http://www.burgerphillips.com
Real Estate Manangement Services
N.A.I.C.S.: 531390

**Commercial Bank & Trust
Company** **(2)**
200 N Greenwood St, LaGrange, GA 30240
Tel.: (706) 880-2200
Web Site: http://combanktrust.synovus.com
Sales Range: $25-49.9 Million
Emp.: 37
Commericial Banking
N.A.I.C.S.: 522110

First Bank of Jasper **(2)**
200 18th St W, Jasper, AL 35501
Tel.: (205) 221-3121
Web Site: http://www.synovus.com
Sales Range: $75-99.9 Million
Emp.: 175
Commericial Banking
N.A.I.C.S.: 522110
Shawn Morgan *(Pres-Market)*

First State Bank and Trust Co. **(2)**
3650 Inner Perimeter Rd, Valdosta, GA
31602
Tel.: (229) 242-5725
Web Site: http://fsbtc.synovus.com
Sales Range: $25-49.9 Million
Emp.: 91
Commericial Banking
N.A.I.C.S.: 522110

Synovus Mortgage Corp. **(2)**
800 Shades Creek Pkwy MS 100, Birming-
ham, AL 35209
Tel.: (205) 868-9111
Investment Management Service
N.A.I.C.S.: 523940
Mary Beth Balzli *(Pres & CEO)*

**Synovus Trust Company, National
Association** **(2)**
1137 1st Ave 1st Fl, Columbus, GA 31901
Tel.: (706) 644-3496
Financial Investment Services
N.A.I.C.S.: 523999

Tallahassee State Bank **(2)**
601 N Monroe St, Tallahassee, FL 32301
Tel.: (850) 576-1182
Web Site: http://www.talstatebank.com
Sales Range: $10-24.9 Million
Emp.: 60
Banking
N.A.I.C.S.: 522110
Bill Moore *(Pres-Market)*

Union Hill Apartments, L.P. **(2)**
235 Union Hill Dr 18a, Forsyth, GA 31029
Tel.: (478) 994-2255
Web Site:
  http://www.unionhillapartments.com
Residential Building Rental & Leasing Ser-
vices
N.A.I.C.S.: 531110

Synovus Securities, Inc. **(1)**
1137 1st Ave, Columbus, GA
31901 **(100%)**
Tel.: (706) 649-2327
Web Site: http://www.synovus.com
Sales Range: $150-199.9 Million
Emp.: 153
Management of Fixed Income Portfolios &
Execution of Securities Transactions
N.A.I.C.S.: 523150
Kessel D. Stelling Jr. *(Chm & CEO)*
Shellie Creson *(Chief Risk Officer)*
Bob Derrick *(Chief Credit Officer)*
Sharon Goodwine *(Chief HR Officer)*
Jamie Gregory *(CFO)*
Kevin J. Howard *(Chief Wholesale Banking
Officer)*

**SYNTEC OPTICS HOLDING,
INC.**

515 Lee Rd, Rochester, NY 14606
Tel.: (585) 768-2513   DE
Web Site: https://syntecoptics.com
Year Founded: 2021
OPTX—(NASDAQ)
Rev.: $29,441,180
Assets: $26,547,913
Liabilities: $13,484,171
Net Worth: $13,063,742
Earnings: $1,976,433
Emp.: 148
Fiscal Year-end: 12/31/23
Holding Company
N.A.I.C.S.: 551112
Al Kapoor *(Chm & CEO)*
Al Kapoor *(Chm)*
Robert O. Nelson II *(CFO)*
Joseph Mohr *(Chief Mfg Officer)*
Donna Berke *(Sec & Corp Mgr-Fin)*

Subsidiaries:

Syntec Optics, Inc. **(1)**
7100 Junction Rd, Pavilion, NY 14525
Tel.: (585) 768-2513
Web Site: http://www.syntecoptics.com
Sales Range: $1-9.9 Million
Emp.: 47
Plastics Product Mfr
N.A.I.C.S.: 326199
Al Kapoor *(Pres)*

**SYNTHESIS ENERGY SYS-
TEMS, INC.**
1029 State Hwy 6 Ste 650 No 183,
Houston, TX 77079
Tel.: (713) 579-0600   DE
Web Site:
  http://www.synthesisenergy.com
SYNE—(OTCEM)
Rev.: $51,000
Assets: $2,656,000
Liabilities: $7,726,000
Net Worth: ($5,070,000)
Earnings: ($10,716,000)
Emp.: 6
Fiscal Year-end: 06/30/19
Coal Producer
N.A.I.C.S.: 324199
Lorenzo C. Lamadrid *(Chm)*
Robert W. Rigdon *(Vice Chm, Pres,
CEO & CFO)*
David Hiscocks *(Chief Acctg Officer,
Sec & Controller)*
Charles B. Runnels *(Pres & CEO)*

Subsidiaries:

SES New Energy Technologies,
(Shanghai) Co., Ltd. **(1)**
516 Pine City Ctr 777 Zhaojiabang Rd,
Shanghai, 200032, China
Tel.: (86) 2154962299
Fuel & Chemical Industry Support Services
N.A.I.C.S.: 213112

Synthesis Energy Systems, Inc. -
Shanghai **(1)**
Room 910, 9th Floor, No. 2 Building,
No.711 Yishan Road, Xuhui, Shanghai,
200233, China **(100%)**
Tel.: (86) 2154962299
Web Site: http://www.synthesisenergy.com
Sales Range: $150-199.9 Million
Emp.: 50
Coal Gasification Operations
N.A.I.C.S.: 213112

Synthesis Energy Systems, Inc. -
Zaozhuang **(1)**
No 2 Tangshan Rd, Zaozhuang, 277000,
Shandong Province, China **(100%)**
Tel.: (86) 6324161799
Sales Range: $75-99.9 Million
Emp.: 60
Alternative Energy Production
N.A.I.C.S.: 213113

SYNTROL CORP.
2120 March Rd, Roseville, CA 95747
Tel.: (916) 350-1992   FL
Year Founded: 2001

SNLP—(OTCIQ)
Engineering & Construction Services
N.A.I.C.S.: 541330

SYPRIS SOLUTIONS, INC.
101 Bullitt Ln Ste 450, Louisville, KY
40222
Tel.: (502) 329-2000   DE
Web Site: https://www.sypris.com
Year Founded: 1998
SYPR—(NASDAQ)
Rev.: $110,121,000
Assets: $104,144,000
Liabilities: $84,569,000
Net Worth: $19,575,000
Earnings: ($2,494,000)
Emp.: 719
Fiscal Year-end: 12/31/22
Mfr of Integrated Data Storage & Re-
trieval Systems, Magnetic Instru-
ments, Current Measuring Devices;
Specialized Contract Manufacturing,
Testing & Calibration for Electronics &
Industrial Customers
N.A.I.C.S.: 334419
Jeffrey T. Gill *(Chm, Pres & CEO)*
Rebecca R. Eckert *(Chief Acctg Offi-
cer, Principal Financial Officer, VP &
Controller)*
Richard L. Davis *(Treas, Sr VP &
Asst Sec)*

Subsidiaries:

Sypris Electronics, LLC **(1)**
10421 University Center Dr, Tampa, FL
33612
Tel.: (813) 972-6000
Web Site: https://www.sypriselectronics.com
Sales Range: $150-199.9 Million
Emp.: 250
Electronics Manufacturing And Engineering
Services For Government Agencies
N.A.I.C.S.: 334412

Sypris Technologies Toluca, S.A. de
C.V. **(1)**
Indutrias Quimicas 200 Zona Industrial,
50071, Toluca, Estado de Mexico, Mexico
Tel.: (52) 7222623300
Web Site:
  https://www.sypristechnologies.com
Motor Vehicle Parts Mfr; Forged & Ma-
chined Axle Shafts Supplier
N.A.I.C.S.: 336390

Sypris Technologies, Inc. **(1)**
101 Bullitt Ln Ste 450, Louisville, KY 40222
Tel.: (502) 420-1222
Web Site:
  https://www.sypristechnologies.com
Forged Auto Parts Mfr
N.A.I.C.S.: 336390

Plant (Domestic):

Sypris Technologies, Inc. - Tube
Turns Facility **(2)**
2612 Howard St, Louisville, KY 40211
Tel.: (502) 774-6011
Web Site: https://www.tubeturns.com
Sales Range: $75-99.9 Million
Emp.: 145
Mfr of Process Piping Components & Upset
Forgings
N.A.I.C.S.: 332111

SYRA HEALTH CORP.
1119 Keystone Way N Ste 201, Car-
mel, IN 46032
Tel.: (463) 345-8950   DE
Web Site:
  https://www.syrahealth.com
Year Founded: 2020
SYRA—(NASDAQ)
Rev.: $5,617,706
Assets: $2,319,642
Liabilities: $1,609,544
Net Worth: $710,098
Earnings: ($2,118,165)
Emp.: 64
Fiscal Year-end: 12/31/22

Custom Computer Programming Ser-
vices
N.A.I.C.S.: 541511
Sandeep Allam *(Chm & Pres)*
Priya Prasad *(CFO & COO)*

**SYROS PHARMACEUTICALS,
INC.**
35 CambridgePark Dr 4th Fl, Cam-
bridge, MA 02140
Tel.: (617) 744-1340   DE
Web Site: https://www.syros.com
SYRS—(NASDAQ)
Rev.: $14,880,000
Assets: $244,486,000
Liabilities: $116,750,000
Net Worth: $127,736,000
Earnings: ($94,654,000)
Emp.: 117
Fiscal Year-end: 12/31/22
Pharmaceutical Preparation Manufac-
turing
N.A.I.C.S.: 325412
David A. Roth *(Chief Medical Officer)*
Gerald E. Quirk *(Chief Legal & Admin
Officer)*
Nathanael S. Gray *(Co-Founder)*
Kristin Stephens *(Chief Dev Officer)*
Jason Haas *(CFO)*
Lisa Roberts *(VP)*
Richard A. Young *(Co-Founder)*
Conley Chee *(Pres & CEO)*
James E. Bradner *(Co-Founder)*
Jason R. Haas *(CFO)*

Subsidiaries:

Tyme Technologies, Inc. **(1)**
1 Pluckemin Way Ste 103, Bedminster, NJ
07921
Tel.: (212) 461-2315
Web Site: http://www.tymeinc.com
Rev.: $1,887,536
Assets: $88,015,185
Liabilities: $7,931,753
Net Worth: $80,083,432
Earnings: ($23,626,047)
Emp.: 13
Fiscal Year-end: 03/31/2022
Clinical-stage Biotechnology Company
N.A.I.C.S.: 541714
Jonathan M. Eckard *(Chief Bus Officer)*
Michael S. Demurjian *(Co-Founder)*
Barbara C. Galaini *(Principal Acctg Officer
& Controller)*

SYSCO CORPORATION
1390 Enclave Pkwy, Houston, TX
77077-2099
Tel.: (281) 584-1390   DE
Web Site: https://www.sysco.com
Year Founded: 1969
SYY—(NYSE)
Rev.: $78,844,000,000
Assets: $24,917,000,000
Liabilities: $23,057,000,000
Net Worth: $1,860,000,000
Earnings: $1,955,000,000
Emp.: 76,000
Fiscal Year-end: 06/29/24
Food Service Related Equipment
Distr
N.A.I.C.S.: 551112
Neil A. Russell *(Chief Admin Officer &
Sr VP)*
Thomas R. Peck Jr. *(Chief Informa-
tion & Digital Officer & Exec VP)*
Joel T. Grade *(Exec VP-Corp Dev)*
Greg Keller *(Sr VP-Sls-Natl)*
Greg D. Bertrand *(COO-Global &
Exec VP)*
Eve M. McFadden *(Gen Counsel,
Sec & Sr VP-Legal)*
Scott B. Stone *(VP-Fin Reporting)*
Anita A. Zielinski *(CFO-Foodservice
Operations-US & Sr VP)*
C. Marie Robinson *(Chief Supply
Chain Officer & Exec VP)*

Chris Jasper *(Pres-Broadline Food-service Ops-US & Sr VP)*
Elizabeth Ubell *(Sr VP-Local Sls & Customer Support)*
Kenny K. Cheung *(CFO & Exec VP)*
Tom Peck *(CIO, Chief Digital Officer & Exec VP)*
Ron Phillips *(Chief HR Officer & Exec VP)*
Sandy Romoser *(Pres-Guest World-wide)*
Jennifer L. Johnson *(Chief Acctg Officer & Sr VP)*
Paulo Peereboom *(Pres-Foodsvc Ops-Intl & Exec VP)*

Subsidiaries:

A.M. Briggs, Inc.   (1)
2130 Queens Chapel Rd Ne, Washington, DC 20018
Tel.: (202) 832-2600
Web Site: http://www.ambriggs.com
Emp.: 25
Seafood Distr
N.A.I.C.S.: 424460
Harvey Burton *(Pres)*
Brad Harris *(Gen Mgr)*

Arnotts (Fruit) Limited   (1)
16-20 Dunbar Street, Belfast, BT1 2LH, Northern Ireland, United Kingdom
Tel.: (44) 2890324236
Web Site: http://www.arnottsfruit.com
Emp.: 30
Fresh Fruit & Vegetable Distr
N.A.I.C.S.: 424480

Bahamas Food Services, Ltd.   (1)
Gladstone Road, PO Box N-4401, Nassau, NP, Bahamas
Tel.: (242) 361 2000
Web Site: http://www.bahamafood.com
Emp.: 400
Food Products & Restaurant Equipment Distr
N.A.I.C.S.: 424480
Karen Casey *(Pres)*
Ron Hepburn *(CFO & VP-Fin)*
Nikia Forbes *(Dir-HR)*
Richard Flint *(VP-Sls)*
Phil Duncombe *(VP-Ops)*
Tiffani Evans *(Dir-Mdsg)*

Brake Bros Limited   (1)
Tower House 2nd Floor, 10 Southampton St, London, WC2E 7HA, United Kingdom
Tel.: (44) 207 599 5600
Web Site: http://www.brakesgroup.com
Holding Company; Food Service Industry Supply & Support Services
N.A.I.C.S.: 551112
Michael Ball *(CFO)*

Subsidiary (Domestic):

Brake Bros Foodservice Limited   (2)
Swan House New Mill Road, St Pauls Cray, Orpington, BR5 3QD, Kent, United Kingdom
Tel.: (44) 1689 301 201
Web Site: http://www.countrychoice.co.uk
Frozen Food Supplier
N.A.I.C.S.: 424420

Branch (Domestic):

Brake Bros Ltd. - Ashford Head Office   (2)
Enterprise House, Eureka Business Park, Ashford, TN25 4AG, Kent, United Kingdom
Tel.: (44) 1233 206 000
Web Site: http://www.brake.co.uk
Food Service Industry Supply & Support Services
N.A.I.C.S.: 424410

Unit (Domestic):

Brake Bros Ltd. - Thorpe Depot   (2)
Alpha Way Thorpe Industrial Park, Thorpe, TW20 8RZ, Surrey, United Kingdom
Tel.: (44) 1784 485 050
Food Service Industry Supply & Support Services
N.A.I.C.S.: 722310

Subsidiary (Domestic):

Brakes Catering Equipment   (2)

Maybrook Industrial Park, Armley, Leeds, LS12 2EL, United Kingdom
Tel.: (44) 844 725 9494
Web Site: http://www.brakesce.co.uk
Catering Equipment Supplier
N.A.I.C.S.: 423440

Unit (Domestic):

Brakes Foodservice NI Limited   (2)
221 Hillhall Road, Lisburn, BT27 5JQ, County Antrim, United Kingdom
Tel.: (44) 2892 664 231
Web Site: http://www.brake.eu
Food Service Industry Supply & Support Services
N.A.I.C.S.: 722310

Subsidiary (Domestic):

Cucina Acquisition (UK) Limited   (2)
Enterprise House Eureka Business Park, Ashford, TN25 4AG, Kent, United Kingdom
Tel.: (44) 1233 206 000
Investment Management Service
N.A.I.C.S.: 523940

Subsidiary (Non-US):

Davigel SAS   (2)
Zone Louis Delaporte, 76370, Rouxmesnil-Bouteilles, Cedex, France
Tel.: (33) 2 35 04 88 25
Web Site: http://www.davigel.fr
Emp.: 3,000
Frozen & Chilled Products Mfr
N.A.I.C.S.: 311412
Christophe Romefort *(Dir-Intl)*

Subsidiary (Domestic):

Freshfayre Limited   (2)
Enterprise House Eureka Business Park, Ashford, TN25 4AG, Kent, United Kingdom
Tel.: (44) 113 277 3001
Web Site: http://www.freshfayre.co.uk
Grocery Product Distr
N.A.I.C.S.: 424490
Eddie Hagan *(Sls Mgr-Depot)*

M&J Seafood Limited   (2)
Charbridge Way, Bicester, OX26 4SW, Oxfordshire, United Kingdom
Tel.: (44) 344 873 0868
Web Site: https://www.mjseafood.com
Fresh & Frozen Seafood Whslr
N.A.I.C.S.: 424460

Subsidiary (Non-US):

Menigo Foodservice AB   (2)
Arenavagen 61, 121 77, Johanneshov, Sweden
Tel.: (46) 87221400
Web Site: http://www.menigo.se
Food Service Product & Equipment Distr
N.A.I.C.S.: 424410
Jonas Kohler *(CEO)*
Helena Matson *(Dir-HR)*
Jenny Pranting *(Dir-Category & Pur)*
Martin Sagne *(Dir-Logistics)*
Pontus Lindqvist *(Dir-IT)*

Subsidiary (Domestic):

Isacsson Frukt & Gront AB   (3)
Partihandlarvagen 50, Arsta, 120 44, Stockholm, Sweden
Tel.: (46) 8 4490940
Fruit & Vegetable Supplier
N.A.I.C.S.: 424480

Subsidiary (Domestic):

Wild Harvest Limited   (2)
Units B61-64 New Covent Garden Market, London, SW8 5HH, United Kingdom
Tel.: (44) 20 7498 5397
Web Site: http://www.wildharvestuk.com
Food Ingredient Supplier
N.A.I.C.S.: 424490

Brakes Foodservice NI Limited   (1)
221 Hillhall Road, Antrim, Lisburn, BT27 5JQ, United Kingdom
Tel.: (44) 2892664231
Web Site: http://www.brake.eu
Food Product Whslr
N.A.I.C.S.: 424490

Buckhead Beef Company   (1)

4500 Wickersham Dr College Park, Atlanta, GA 30337
Tel.: (404) 355-4400
Web Site: http://www.buckheadbeef.com
Sales Range: $300-349.9 Million
Emp.: 400
Fresh, Precision-Cut Steaks & Other Specialty Meats & Protein Products Distr
N.A.I.C.S.: 424470

Division (Domestic):

Buckhead Beef Northeast   (2)
220 Raritan Center Pkwy, Edison, NJ 08837
Tel.: (908) 222-1004
Web Site: http://www.buckheadbeef.com
Sales Range: $50-74.9 Million
Emp.: 52
Beef Products Wholesale Distr
N.A.I.C.S.: 424470

Buckhead Meat & Seafood of Houston, Inc.   (1)
10310 Greens Crossing Blvd, Houston, TX 77038
Tel.: (281) 405-3200
Food Products Distr
N.A.I.C.S.: 424430
Robert Turbow *(Exec VP)*

Buckhead Meat Company   (1)
51 Graystone St, Warwick, RI 02886
Tel.: (401) 734-8200
Food Products Distr
N.A.I.C.S.: 424430

Buckhead Meat Midwest, Inc.   (1)
200 Flannigan Rd, Hampshire, IL 60140
Tel.: (847) 683-2009
Food Products Distr
N.A.I.C.S.: 424430

Buckhead Meat of Dallas, Inc.   (1)
4216 Mint Way, Dallas, TX 75237
Tel.: (214) 331-8711
Food Products Distr
N.A.I.C.S.: 424430

Buckhead Meat of Denver, Inc.   (1)
2351 E 70th Ave, Denver, CO 80229
Tel.: (303) 298-0997
Food Products Distr
N.A.I.C.S.: 424430
Mike Vargason *(Pres)*

Buckhead Meat of San Antonio, LP   (1)
4241 Director Dr, San Antonio, TX 78219
Tel.: (210) 337-1011
Food Products Distr
N.A.I.C.S.: 424430

Crossgar Pallas Ltd   (1)
Down Business Park 46 Belfast Road, Downpatrick Co Down, Newcastle, BT30 9UP, United Kingdom
Tel.: (44) 2844811500
Web Site: http://www.pallasfoods.com
Food Products Distr
N.A.I.C.S.: 424490

Crown I Enterprises Inc.   (1)
85 Saxon Ave, Bay Shore, NY 11706
Tel.: (631) 206-2620
Web Site: http://www.crown1enterprises.com
Food Product Mfr & Distr
N.A.I.C.S.: 311999
Andrew Murphy *(Dir-Mfg)*

Curleys Quality Foods Limited   (1)
Carrowbrowne, Castlegar, Galway, Ireland
Tel.: (353) 91753064
Web Site: http://www.curleysqualityfoods.com
Food & Catering Product Distr
N.A.I.C.S.: 424490

Davigel Beligum S.A.   (1)
Rijksweg 19, 2880, Bornem, Belgium
Tel.: (32) 38979340
Web Site: http://www.davigel.be
Food Product Whslr
N.A.I.C.S.: 424490

Doerle Food Services, LLC   (1)
113 Kol Dr, Broussard, LA 70518
Tel.: (337) 252-8551
Web Site: http://www.sysco.com
Producer of Packaged Frozen Goods

N.A.I.C.S.: 424420
Carolyn Doerle *(CEO & Mng Dir)*

Economy Foods, Inc.   (1)
48811 Warm Springs Blvd, Fremont, CA 94539
Tel.: (510) 438-8600
Sales Range: $75-99.9 Million
Emp.: 99
Producer of Packaged Frozen Goods
N.A.I.C.S.: 424420

Edward Don & Company   (1)
9801 Adam Don Pkwy, Woodridge, IL 60517
Tel.: (708) 442-9400
Web Site: http://www.don.com
Food Service Equipment, Furnishings & Supplies Distr
N.A.I.C.S.: 423440

Division (Domestic):

Atlanta Fixture & Sales Company Inc.   (2)
3185 NE Expy, Atlanta, GA 30341
Tel.: (770) 455-8844
Restaurant Equipment & Supplies Distr
N.A.I.C.S.: 423850

Eko Fagel Fisk o mittemellan AB   (1)
Hallmastarvagen 10, 121 62, Johanneshov, Sweden
Tel.: (46) 855613180
Web Site: http://www.ekofisk.se
Fish & Seafood Whslr
N.A.I.C.S.: 424490

European Imports, Ltd.   (1)
600 E Brook Dr, Arlington Heights, IL 60005
Tel.: (847) 631-6000
Web Site: http://www.eiltd.com
Sales Range: $50-74.9 Million
Emp.: 150
Grocery Imports
N.A.I.C.S.: 424410

Focus Foodservice, LLC   (1)
300 Knightsbridge Parkway Ste 500, Lincolnshire, IL 60069
Tel.: (847) 968-3881
Web Site: http://www.focusfoodservice.com
Grocery Retailer
N.A.I.C.S.: 424490

Freedman Food Service, Inc.   (1)
2901 Polk St, Houston, TX 77003
Tel.: (713) 229-8000
Meat Transactions Service
N.A.I.C.S.: 424490

Subsidiary (Domestic):

Freedman Food Service of Dallas, Inc.   (2)
4216 Mint Way, Dallas, TX 75237
Tel.: (214) 331-8711
Web Site: http://www.freedmanfoods.com
Meat & Meat Products Distr
N.A.I.C.S.: 424470

Freedman Food Service of Denver, Inc.   (2)
2351 E 70th Ave, Denver, CO 80229
Tel.: (303) 298-0997
Web Site: http://www.freedmanfoods.com
Grocery Retailer
N.A.I.C.S.: 424490

Freedman Food Service of San Antonio, LP   (2)
4241 Director Dr, San Antonio, TX 78219
Tel.: (210) 337-1011
Emp.: 150
Meat Product Distr
N.A.I.C.S.: 424470
Burton Chase *(Gen Mgr)*

Fresh Direct (UK) Limited   (1)
Charbridge Way, Bicester, OX26 4SW, Oxfordshire, United Kingdom
Tel.: (44) 3448730868
Web Site: https://www.freshdirect.co.uk
Food Products Distr
N.A.I.C.S.: 492110

Fresh Direct Limited   (1)
Charbridge Way, Bicester, OX26 4SW, Oxfordshire, United Kingdom
Tel.: (44) 1869365700
Web Site: http://www.freshdirect.co.uk

Sysco Corporation—(Continued)

Fruit & Vegetable Distr
N.A.I.C.S.: 424480
Jamie Hiscock *(Comm Mgr)*

FreshPoint Vancouver, Ltd. (1)
1020 Malkin Ave, Vancouver, V6A 3S9, BC,
Canada
Tel.: (604) 253-1551
Web Site: http://www.freshpointcanada.com
Emp.: 315
Fresh Fruit & Vegetable Distr
N.A.I.C.S.: 424480

FreshPoint, Inc. (1)
10710 Greens Crossing Blvd, Houston, TX
77038
Tel.: (713) 679-5222
Web Site: http://www.freshpoint.com
Sales Range: $150-199.9 Million
Fresh Produce Distr
N.A.I.C.S.: 424480
Robert Gordon *(Pres & CEO)*
Ted Beall *(VP-Sls)*
Bryan Uyesugi *(Reg VP)*
Greg Musselwhite *(VP-Ops)*
Steve Pressman *(VP-Field Sls)*
Jon Haynie *(VP-Mdsg)*
Kate Kerg *(Reg VP)*

Subsidiary (Domestic):

Armstrong Produce Ltd. (2)
802 Mapunapuna St, Honolulu, HI 96819-
2037
Tel.: (808) 538-7051
Web Site:
   http://www.armstrongproduce.com
Sales Range: $100-124.9 Million
Emp.: 200
Distr of Fresh Fruits & Vegetables
N.A.I.C.S.: 424480
Mark Teruya *(Chm & CEO)*

Subsidiary (Domestic):

Kula Produce Co, Ltd (3)
217 Hoohana St, Kahului, HI 96732
Tel.: (808) 871-6232
Rev.: $7,500,000
Emp.: 31
Fruit & Vegetable Markets
N.A.I.C.S.: 445230

Subsidiary (Domestic):

FreshPoint Arizona, Inc. (2)
611 S 80th Ave, Tolleson, AZ 85353
Tel.: (480) 785-4808
Web Site: http://www.freshpoint.com
Fruit & Vegetable Distr
N.A.I.C.S.: 424480

FreshPoint Atlanta, Inc. (2)
1200 Oakley Indurtrial Blvd Ste B, Fairburn,
GA 30213   **(100%)**
Tel.: (770) 305-8500
Sales Range: $100-124.9 Million
Emp.: 160
Fresh Fruits & Vegetables Whslr
N.A.I.C.S.: 424480
Joe Lafiosca *(VP-Sls-Reg)*

FreshPoint California, Inc. (2)
5900 N Golden State Blvd, Turlock, CA
95382-9671
Tel.: (209) 216-0200
Web Site: http://www.freshpoint.com
Emp.: 240
Holding Company; Fruit & Vegetable Distr
N.A.I.C.S.: 551112
Trudy Palmer *(Reg VP-Sls)*

Subsidiary (Domestic):

**FreshPoint Central California,
Inc.** (3)
5900 N Golden State Blvd, Turlock, CA
95382-9671
Tel.: (209) 216-0200
Web Site: http://www.freshpoint.com
Emp.: 240
Grocery Related Products Merchant Whslr
N.A.I.C.S.: 424490
Pamela Bava *(Reg Pres)*
Robert Sereno *(Reg Mgr-Food Safety)*
Jason Pineda *(VP-HR-Area)*
Javier Vasquez *(Reg VP-Mdsg)*

Scott Savage *(Reg Mgr-Safety)*
Sean Gaffaney *(VP-Ops)*
Trudy Palmer *(Reg VP-Sls)*
Joshua Cole *(VP-Sls)*

FreshPoint San Francisco, Inc. (3)
30340 Whipple Rd, Union City, CA
94587   **(100%)**
Tel.: (510) 476-5900
Web Site: http://sanfrancisco.freshpoint.com
Sales Range: $50-74.9 Million
Emp.: 135
Fresh Fruits & Vegetables Whslr
N.A.I.C.S.: 445230

**FreshPoint Southern California,
Inc.** (3)
155 N Orange Ave, City of Industry, CA
91744-3432
Tel.: (626) 855-1400
Web Site: http://www.freshpoint.com
Emp.: 300
Grocery Retailer
N.A.I.C.S.: 424490
Jeff Ronk *(VP-Mdsg)*
Luis Garcia *(VP-Sls)*
John Collie *(VP-Ops)*
Karen Beverlin *(VP-Specialty Produce)*
Preston Fletcher *(Pres)*
Jamie Holveck *(VP-Fin)*

Subsidiary (Domestic):

FreshPoint Central Florida, Inc. (2)
8801 Exchange Dr, Orlando, FL
32809-7970   **(100%)**
Tel.: (407) 857-3930
Web Site: http://www.freshpoint.com
Sales Range: $50-74.9 Million
Emp.: 250
Fresh Fruits & Vegetables Wholesale Distr
N.A.I.C.S.: 424480
Greg Musselwhite *(VP-Ops)*
John Kovalik *(Reg Pres)*
David Yelenosky *(VP-Fin)*
Josh MacNaughton *(Reg VP-Pur)*
Kelly Kerney *(Sls Mgr-District)*
Laura Parkins *(Reg VP-Sls)*
Bill Oehmler *(VP-Ops)*

FreshPoint Connecticut, LLC (2)
105 Reserve Rd, Hartford, CT 06114
Tel.: (860) 522-2226
Web Site: http://www.freshpoint.com
Emp.: 200
Grocery Retailer
N.A.I.C.S.: 424490

FreshPoint Dallas, Inc. (2)
4721 Simonton Rd, Dallas, TX
75244-5316   **(100%)**
Tel.: (972) 385-5800
Web Site: http://www.freshpoint.com
Sales Range: $100-124.9 Million
Emp.: 200
Fresh Fruits & Vegetables Wholesale Distr
N.A.I.C.S.: 424480
Pedro Del Busto *(VP-Ops)*

FreshPoint Denver, Inc. (2)
5151 N Bannock St, Denver, CO 80216-
1846
Tel.: (303) 382-1700
Web Site: http://www.freshpoint.com
Emp.: 200
Grocery Related Products Merchant Whslr
N.A.I.C.S.: 424490
Jenny Frese *(Mgr-Pur)*
Paul Savage *(VP-Ops)*
Robert Crespo *(VP-Value Added)*

FreshPoint Il Paese, Inc. (2)
4721 Simonton Rd, Dallas, TX 75244-5316
Tel.: (972) 385-5810
Web Site: http://www.freshpoint.com
Emp.: 350
Food Products Services
N.A.I.C.S.: 445298

FreshPoint Nashville, Inc. (2)
740 Massman Dr, Nashville, TN 37210
Tel.: (615) 256-0614
Web Site: http://www.freshpoint.com
Sales Range: $125-149.9 Million
Emp.: 250
Sales of Fresh Fruits & Vegetables
N.A.I.C.S.: 424480

FreshPoint North Florida, Inc. (2)
3100 Hilton St, Jacksonville, FL 32209-2703

Tel.: (904) 764-7681
Web Site: http://www.freshpoint.com
Sales Range: $100-124.9 Million
Emp.: 200
Fresh Fruits & Vegetables Wholesale Distr
N.A.I.C.S.: 445230

FreshPoint Oklahoma City, LLC (2)
3100 N I-35 Service Rd, Oklahoma City,
OK 73099
Tel.: (405) 879-0400
Emp.: 80
Grocery Related Products Merchant Whslr
N.A.I.C.S.: 424490
Tal Harris *(VP-Procurement)*

FreshPoint Puerto Rico, LLC (2)
Carr 848 St 2 Ste 110 Ind Zone St Just,
Trujillo Alto, PR 00976
Tel.: (787) 748-9047
Web Site: http://www.freshpoint.com
Grocery Product Whslr
N.A.I.C.S.: 424490
Jon Lasko *(Pres)*

FreshPoint South Florida, Inc. (2)
2300 NW 19th St, Pompano Beach, FL
33069   **(100%)**
Tel.: (954) 917-7272
Web Site: http://www.freshpoint.com
Sales Range: $75-99.9 Million
Emp.: 125
Fresh Fruits & Vegetables Wholesaler
N.A.I.C.S.: 424480

FreshPoint South Texas, LP (2)
4651 Greatland Dr, San Antonio, TX 78218
Tel.: (210) 699-9391
Web Site: http://www.freshpoint.com
Emp.: 90
Fresh Fruit & Vegetable Distr
N.A.I.C.S.: 424480

FreshPoint Tomato, LLC (2)
740 Massman Dr, Nashville, TN 37210
Tel.: (615) 226-2305
Web Site: http://www.freshpoint.com
Emp.: 95
Grocery Distr
N.A.I.C.S.: 424490

Fulton Provision Company (1)
16123 NE Airport Way, Portland, OR 97294
Tel.: (503) 254-3000
Web Site: http://www.sysco.com
Sales Range: $75-99.9 Million
Emp.: 100
Food Products Wholesale Distr
N.A.I.C.S.: 424490

G&S Real Estate, Inc. (1)
24333 S Field Rd 111, Southfield, MI 48075
Tel.: (248) 809-9386
Web Site: http://www.gsincrealestate.com
Real Estate Services
N.A.I.C.S.: 531210

GHS Classic Drinks Limited (1)
Classic Drinks Courtstown Industrial Estate,
Little Island, T45 A029, Ireland
Tel.: (353) 214510066
Food Products Distr
N.A.I.C.S.: 492110

**Gilchrist & Soames Holdings
Corporation** (1)
2425 E Perry Rd Ste 150, Plainfield, IN
46168
Tel.: (888) 227-9845
Cosmetic Preparation Mfr
N.A.I.C.S.: 325620

Gilchrist & Soames UK Limited (1)
4 Venus House Calleva Park, Werrington,
Aldermaston, RG7 8DA, Berkshire, United
Kingdom
Tel.: (44) 1733384100
Web Site: https://uk.gilchristsoames.com
Cosmetic Preparation Mfr
N.A.I.C.S.: 325620

Goldberg and Solovy Foods, Inc. (1)
5925 S Alcoa Ave, Vernon, CA 90058
Tel.: (323) 581-6161
Web Site: http://www.gsfoods.com
Food Service & Grocery Related Products
Merchant Whslr
N.A.I.C.S.: 424490
Paul Paget *(Pres)*

Guest Packaging, LLC (1)

414 E Inman Ave, Rahway, NJ 07065-4705
Tel.: (732) 382-7270
Personal Care Products Mfr & Packaging &
Labeling Services
N.A.I.C.S.: 561499

**J. King's Food Service Professionals
Inc.** (1)
700 Furrows Rd, Holtsville, NY 11742
Tel.: (631) 289-8401
Web Site: http://www.jkings.com
Emp.: 300
Groceries & Related Products,
N.A.I.C.S.: 424490
John King *(Founder, CEO & Chief Cus-
tomer Officer)*

Subsidiary (Domestic):

Cookies & More, Inc. (2)
145 Price Pkwy, Farmingdale, NY 11735
Tel.: (631) 501-9141
Web Site: http://cookiesandmoreinc.com
Rev.: $3,000,000
Emp.: 20
Fiscal Year-end: 12/31/2006
Specialty Food Products Distr
N.A.I.C.S.: 424490
Mark Abruscato *(CEO)*

Kent Frozen Foods (1)
Kent House Priory Park Mills Road, Ayles-
ford, ME20 7PP, Kent, United Kingdom
Tel.: (44) 8085829798
Web Site: http://www.kff.co.uk
Food Product Whslr
N.A.I.C.S.: 424490

Les Ateliers Du Gout (1)
1 rue Melusine, 85240, Foussais-Payre,
France
Tel.: (33) 251000326
Web Site: http://www.ateliers-du-gout.com
Chocolate Product Mfr
N.A.I.C.S.: 311351

M&J Seafood Holdings Limited (1)
Charbridge Way Bicester Distribution Park,
Bicester, OX26 4SW, United Kingdom
Tel.: (44) 1296610600
Web Site: http://www.mjseafood.com
Fish & Seafood Whslr
N.A.I.C.S.: 424460

Malcolm Meats Company (1)
2657 Tracy Rd, Northwood, OH 43619-
1006
Tel.: (419) 666-0702
Web Site: http://www.sysco.com
Sales Range: $75-99.9 Million
Emp.: 100
Meat & Meat Products Wholesale Distr
N.A.I.C.S.: 424470

Manchester Mills, LLC (1)
300 Davidson Ave, Somerset, NJ 08873
Web Site:
   https://healthcare.manchestermills.com
Food Products Distr
N.A.I.C.S.: 492110

**Newport Meat Northern California,
Inc.** (1)
48811 Warm Springs Blvd, Fremont, CA
94539
Food Products Distr
N.A.I.C.S.: 424430

**Newport Meat Pacific Northwest,
Inc.** (1)
16123 NE Airport Way, Portland, OR 97230
Tel.: (503) 254-3000
Food Products Distr
N.A.I.C.S.: 424430
Charlie Benton *(Pres)*

**Newport Meat Southern California,
Inc.** (1)
16691 Hale Ave, Irvine, CA 92606
Tel.: (949) 474-4040
Food Products Distr
N.A.I.C.S.: 424430

Newport Meat of Nevada, Inc. (1)
5420 S Valley View Blvd, Las Vegas, NV
89118
Tel.: (702) 364-5533
Web Site: http://www.newportmeatnv.com
Food Products Distr
N.A.I.C.S.: 424430

John Foster *(Pres)*
Raymond Morehouse *(VP-Sls & Mktg)*
Marty McDougall *(VP-Pur)*
Jocelyn Magno *(Dir-Bus Dev)*
Scott Marshall *(Dir-Production)*

North Star Seafood, LLC (1)
2213 NW 30th Place Ste 7A, Pompano
Beach, FL 33069-1026 **(100%)**
Tel.: (954) 984-0006
Web Site: http://www.northstarseafood.com
Sales Range: $125-149.9 Million
Emp.: 50
Fresh Fish & Seafood Supplier
N.A.I.C.S.: 445250
Rick Burman *(Founder)*

Palisades Ranch, Inc. (1)
5925 S Alcoa Ave, Vernon, CA 90058
Tel.: (323) 581-6161
Food Products Distr
N.A.I.C.S.: 424420

Pallas Foods (1)
Newcastle West, Limerick, Ireland
Tel.: (353) 6920200
Web Site: http://www.pallasfoods.eu
Food Products Distr
N.A.I.C.S.: 445298

**Pallas Foods Farm Fresh Unlimited
Company** (1)
Foodservice Centre, Killamonan The Ward,
Dublin, D11 VP3F, Ireland
Tel.: (353) 14566550
Food Products Distr
N.A.I.C.S.: 424420

**Pallas Foods Unlimited
Company** (1)
Pallas Foods Newcastle West, Limerick,
Ireland
Tel.: (353) 6920200
Food Products Distr
N.A.I.C.S.: 424420

Paragon Wholesale Foods Corp. (1)
173 Thorn Hill Rd, Warrendale, PA 15086
Tel.: (724) 741-9100
Web Site: https://paragonfresh.com
Food Retailer
N.A.I.C.S.: 445110

Restaurangakdemien AB (1)
Rokerigatan 4, 121 62, Johanneshov, Swe-
den
Tel.: (46) 81 286 0360
Web Site:
   https://www.restaurangakademien.se
Education Services
N.A.I.C.S.: 611710
Hanna Halpern *(CEO & Officer-Data Protec-
tion)*
Jenny Hagberg *(Mktg Dir & Sls Mgr)*
Morgan Kjellstrom *(Head-Education)*

**Robert Orr-Sysco Food Services,
LLC** (1)
1 Hermitage Plz, Nashville, TN
37209-1002 **(100%)**
Tel.: (281) 584-1390
Web Site: http://www.sysco.com
Sales Range: $350-399.9 Million
Emp.: 450
Food Products Wholesale Distr
N.A.I.C.S.: 424490

Roots of Oxford Limited (1)
Unit 6 Ferry Mills Osney Mead, Oxford,
OX2 0ES, United Kingdom
Tel.: (44) 1865792060
Web Site: http://www.rootsofoxford.com
Fruit & Vegetable Merchant Whslr
N.A.I.C.S.: 424480

SYY Netherlands C.V. (1)
Naritaweg 165, 1043 BW, Amsterdam,
Netherlands
Tel.: (31) 205722300
Food Products Distr
N.A.I.C.S.: 424420

Stockholms Fiskauktion AB (1)
Hallvagen 9, 12162, Johanneshov, Sweden
Tel.: (46) 841014350
Web Site:
   http://www.stockholmsfiskauktion.se
Fish & Seafood Whslr
N.A.I.C.S.: 424460
Henrik Johansson *(CEO)*

Sysco Albany, LLC (1)
1 Liebich Ln, Halfmoon, NY
12065-1421 **(100%)**
Tel.: (518) 877-3200
Web Site: http://www.syscoalb.com
Sales Range: $400-449.9 Million
Emp.: 400
Food Products Wholesale Distr
N.A.I.C.S.: 424490

Sysco Arizona Leasing, Inc. (1)
611 S 80th Ave, Phoenix, AZ 85353
Tel.: (623) 936-9920
Emp.: 400
Food Products Distr
N.A.I.C.S.: 532490

Sysco Arizona, Inc. (1)
611 S 80th Ave, Tolleson, AZ 85353-4025
Tel.: (623) 936-9920
Web Site: http://www.ag.sysco.com
Sales Range: $400-449.9 Million
Emp.: 550
Food Products Wholesale Distr
N.A.I.C.S.: 424490

Sysco Arkansas (1)
5700 W 65th St, Little Rock, AR 72209
Tel.: (501) 562-4111
Web Site: http://www.arkansas.sysco.com
Sales Range: $300-349.9 Million
Emp.: 350
Food Products Wholesale Distr
N.A.I.C.S.: 424490

Sysco Asian Foods, Inc. (1)
1300 LOrient St, Saint Paul, MN
55117 **(100%)**
Tel.: (651) 558-2400
Web Site: http://www.asianfoods.com
Sales Range: $50-74.9 Million
Emp.: 230
Whslr of Asian Food Services for Restau-
rants
N.A.I.C.S.: 424410

Sysco Atlanta, LLC (1)
2225 Riverdale Rd, College Park, GA
30337 **(100%)**
Tel.: (404) 765-9900
Web Site: http://www.syscoatlanta.com
Sales Range: $500-549.9 Million
Emp.: 800
Food Products Wholesale Distr
N.A.I.C.S.: 424490

Sysco Austin, Inc. (1)
101 S Chisholm Trl, Round Rock, TX
78681-5044
Tel.: (512) 388-8000
Web Site: http://www.syscocentraltexas.com
Sales Range: $300-349.9 Million
Emp.: 320
Food Products Wholesale Distr
N.A.I.C.S.: 424490

Sysco Baltimore, LLC (1)
8000 Dorsey Run Rd, Jessup, MD 20794-
9482
Tel.: (410) 799-7000
Web Site: http://www.syscobalt.com
Sales Range: $400-449.9 Million
Emp.: 600
Food Service Wholesale Distr
N.A.I.C.S.: 424490

Sysco Baraboo, LLC (1)
910 S Blvd, Baraboo, WI
53913-2793 **(100%)**
Tel.: (608) 356-5711
Web Site: http://www.baraboosysco.com
Sales Range: $400-449.9 Million
Emp.: 650
Food Products Wholesale Distr
N.A.I.C.S.: 424490

Sysco Boston LLC (1)
99 Spring St, Plympton, MA 02367 **(100%)**
Tel.: (781) 422-2300
Web Site: http://www.syscobostonllc.com
Sales Range: $550-599.9 Million
Emp.: 50
Food Products Wholesale Distr
N.A.I.C.S.: 424410
Chuck Fraser *(Pres)*

Sysco Canada, Inc. (1)
7055 Kennedy Rd, Mississauga, L5S 1Y7,
ON, Canada **(100%)**
Tel.: (905) 670-8605

Web Site: http://www.sysco.ca
Sales Range: $50-74.9 Million
Emp.: 80
Food Products Wholesale Distr
N.A.I.C.S.: 424490
Randy J. White *(Pres)*
Sarah Anseeuw *(VP-Sls & Mktg)*
Bart Dawdy *(VP-Mdsg)*
Jason Welter *(VP-Field HR)*
Andrew Wentzell *(CFO & Sr VP-Fin)*

Unit (Domestic):

Sysco Atlantic Canada (2)
1 Duck Pond Road, Lakeside, B3T 1M5,
NS, Canada
Tel.: (902) 876-2311
Web Site: http://www.syscoatlantic.ca
Sales Range: $25-49.9 Million
Emp.: 250
Packaged Food Distr
N.A.I.C.S.: 722310
Joe Flinn *(VP-Fin & Ops)*
Jim McGuire *(Pres)*

Sysco Calgary (2)
4639 - 72nd Avenue SE, Calgary, T2C 4H7,
AB, Canada
Tel.: (403) 720-1300
Web Site: http://www.syscocalgary.ca
Emp.: 425
Food Products Wholesale Distr
N.A.I.C.S.: 424490
Dave Desormeaux *(Pres)*

Subsidiary (Domestic):

Sysco Central Ontario, Inc. (2)
65 Elmdale Road, Cavan Monaghan, Peter-
borough, K9J 7B1, ON, Canada **(100%)**
Tel.: (705) 748-6701
Web Site: https://www.sysco.ca
Emp.: 450
Food Products Wholesale Distr
N.A.I.C.S.: 424490
Ray Lee *(Pres)*

Sysco Kelowna, Ltd. (2)
9385 Jim Bailey Road, Kelowna, V4V 1S4,
BC, Canada
Tel.: (250) 766-0011
Web Site: https://www.sysco.ca
Grocery Related Products Merchant Whslr
N.A.I.C.S.: 424490

Unit (Domestic):

Sysco Quebec (2)
11625 55 Ave, Montreal, H1E 2K2, QC,
Canada
Tel.: (514) 494-5200
Web Site: http://www.syscoquebec.ca
Sales Range: $125-149.9 Million
Food Products Wholesale Distr
N.A.I.C.S.: 424490

Sysco Toronto (2)
7055 Kennedy Rd, Mississauga, L5S 1Y7,
ON, Canada
Tel.: (905) 670-8605
Web Site: http://www.syscotoronto.ca
Food Products Wholesale Distr
N.A.I.C.S.: 424490

Sysco Vancouver (2)
1346 Kingsway Avenue, Port Coquitlam,
V3C 6G4, BC, Canada
Tel.: (604) 944-4410
Web Site: http://www.syscovancouver.com
Emp.: 250
Food Products Wholesale Distr
N.A.I.C.S.: 424490
Rob Cinkant *(Pres)*

Sysco Central Alabama, Inc. (1)
1000 Sysco Dr, Calera, AL 35040
Tel.: (205) 668-0001
Web Site: http://www.sysco.com
Sales Range: $350-399.9 Million
Emp.: 403
Food Products Wholesale Distr
N.A.I.C.S.: 424410

Sysco Central California, Inc. (1)
136 S Mariposa Rd, Modesto, CA
95354-4122 **(100%)**
Tel.: (209) 527-7700
Web Site:
   http://www.syscocentralcalifornia.com

Sales Range: $300-349.9 Million
Emp.: 400
Food Products Wholesale Distr
N.A.I.C.S.: 424490
Patrick Kissee *(Pres & CEO)*

Sysco Central Florida, Inc. (1)
200 Story Rd, Ocoee, FL
34761-3004 **(100%)**
Tel.: (407) 877-8500
Web Site: http://www.sysco.com
Sales Range: $350-399.9 Million
Emp.: 500
Food Products Wholesale Distr
N.A.I.C.S.: 424490

Sysco Central Illinois, Inc. (1)
1 Sysco Dr, Lincoln, IL 62656-0620
Tel.: (217) 735-6100
Web Site: http://www.sysco.com
Sales Range: $25-49.9 Million
Emp.: 85
Packaged Frozen Goods, Groceries & Re-
lated Products Distr
N.A.I.C.S.: 424410

**Sysco Central Pennsylvania,
LLC** (1)
3905 Corey Rd, Harrisburg, PA 17109
Tel.: (717) 561-4000
Web Site: http://www.syscocentralpa.com
Sales Range: $350-399.9 Million
Emp.: 500
Food Products Wholesale Distr
N.A.I.C.S.: 424490

Sysco Central Texas, Inc. (1)
1260 Schwab Rd, New Braunfels, TX
78132-5155 **(100%)**
Tel.: (830) 730-1000
Web Site: http://www.syscocentraltexas.com
Sales Range: $300-349.9 Million
Emp.: 350
Food Products Wholesale Distr
N.A.I.C.S.: 424490

Sysco Charlotte, LLC (1)
4500 Corporate Dr NW, Concord, NC
28027
Tel.: (704) 786-4500
Web Site: http://www.sysco.com
Sales Range: $350-399.9 Million
Emp.: 400
Food Products Wholesale Distr
N.A.I.C.S.: 424490

Sysco Chicago, Inc. (1)
250 Wieboldt Dr, Des Plaines, IL 60016-
3192
Tel.: (847) 699-5400
Web Site: http://www.sysco.com
Sales Range: $450-499.9 Million
Emp.: 400
Food Products Wholesale Distr
N.A.I.C.S.: 445298
Garry Silvestrini *(CEO)*

Sysco Cincinnati, LLC (1)
10510 Evendale Dr, Cincinnati, OH
45241-2516 **(100%)**
Tel.: (513) 563-6300
Web Site: http://www.syscocincinnati.com
Sales Range: $150-199.9 Million
Emp.: 307
Food Products Wholesale Distr
N.A.I.C.S.: 424490

Sysco Cleveland, Inc. (1)
4747 Grayton Rd, Cleveland, OH
44135 **(100%)**
Tel.: (216) 201-3000
Web Site: http://www.syscocleveland.com
Sales Range: $450-499.9 Million
Emp.: 700
Food Products Wholesale Distr
N.A.I.C.S.: 424490

Sysco Columbia, LLC (1)
131 Sysco Ct, Columbia, SC
29209 **(100%)**
Tel.: (803) 239-4000
Web Site: http://www.sysco.com
Sales Range: $350-399.9 Million
Emp.: 500
Food Products Wholesale Distr
N.A.I.C.S.: 424490

Sysco Connecticut, LLC (1)
100 Inwood Rd, Rocky Hill, CT 06067-3412
Tel.: (860) 571-5600

Sysco Corporation—(Continued)

Web Site: http://www.sysco.com
Sales Range: $400-449.9 Million
Emp.: 300
Food Products Wholesale Distr
N.A.I.C.S.: 424490

Sysco Dallas, Inc. (1)
800 Trinity Dr, Lewisville, TX
75056 **(100%)**
Tel.: (469) 384-6000
Web Site: http://www.syscodallas.com
Sales Range: $400-449.9 Million
Emp.: 650
Food Products Wholesale Distr
N.A.I.C.S.: 424490
Don Tarwater (Pres)

Sysco Denver, Inc. (1)
5000 Beeler St, Denver, CO 80238
Tel.: (303) 585-2000
Web Site: http://www.syscodenver.com
Rev.: $350,000,000
Emp.: 600
Food Products Wholesale Distr
N.A.I.C.S.: 424490
Bill Mikulka (Pres)

Sysco Detroit, LLC (1)
41600 Van Born Rd, Canton, MI
48188-2797 **(100%)**
Tel.: (734) 397-7990
Web Site: http://www.sysco.com
Sales Range: $450-499.9 Million
Emp.: 450
Food Products Wholesale Distr
N.A.I.C.S.: 424490
Sean McCausland (Pres)

Sysco East Texas, LLC (1)
4577 Estes Pkwy, Longview, TX 75603
Tel.: (903) 252-6100
Web Site: http://www.syscoeasttexas.com
Food & Beverage Services
N.A.I.C.S.: 311999
Don Connell (Pres)

Sysco Eastern Maryland, LLC (1)
33300 Peach Orchard Rd, Pocomoke City,
MD 21851-3909 **(100%)**
Tel.: (410) 677-5555
Web Site: http://www.syscoeasternmd.com
Sales Range: $450-499.9 Million
Emp.: 450
Food Products Wholesale Distr
N.A.I.C.S.: 424490
Mike Gershenfeld (Pres)

Sysco Eastern Wisconsin, LLC (1)
1 Sysco Dr, Jackson, WI 53037-9226
Tel.: (262) 677-1100
Web Site: http://www.syscoeast.com
Sales Range: $400-449.9 Million
Emp.: 580
Food Products Wholesale Distr
N.A.I.C.S.: 424490

Sysco France SAS (1)
14 rue Gerty Archimede, 75012, Paris,
France
Tel.: (33) 478663800
Food Products Distr
N.A.I.C.S.: 492110

Sysco Grand Rapids, LLC (1)
3700 Sysco Ct SE, Grand Rapids, MI
49512-2083 **(100%)**
Tel.: (616) 949-3700
Web Site: http://www.syscogr.com
Sales Range: $350-399.9 Million
Emp.: 375
Food Products Wholesale Distr
N.A.I.C.S.: 424490

Sysco Guest Supply, LLC (1)
300 Davidson Ave, Somerset, NJ 08873
Tel.: (732) 868-2200
Web Site: http://www.guestsupply.com
Sales Range: $75-99.9 Million
Emp.: 1,000
Toiletries, Personal Care Products, House-
keeping, Hotel Amenities & Supplies Mfr &
Distr
N.A.I.C.S.: 325620

Subsidiary (Domestic):

Gilchrist & Soames, Inc. (2)
300 Davidson Ave, Somerset, NJ 08873
Tel.: (317) 786-8286

Web Site:
https://contractmanufacturing.gilchristso
ames.com
Soap, Hair Products & Toiletries Mfr
N.A.I.C.S.: 325620

Subsidiary (Non-US):

Guest Supply Asia, Limited (2)
30/F 3 Lockhart Road, Wanchai, China
(Hong Kong)
Tel.: (852) 28084133
Web Site: http://www.guestsupply.com.hk
Emp.: 23
Grocery Retailer
N.A.I.C.S.: 424490

Sysco Guest Supply Canada Inc. (2)
570 Matheson Blvd East Unit 5, Missis-
sauga, L4Z 4G3, ON, Canada **(100%)**
Tel.: (905) 896-1060
Web Site: http://www.guestsupply.ca
Sales Range: $25-49.9 Million
Emp.: 50
Personal Care Products, Toiletries, House-
keeping & Accessories Mfr & Distr
N.A.I.C.S.: 325612

**Sysco Guest Supply Europe
Limited** (2)
4 Venus House, Calleva Park, Aldermaston,
RG7 8DA, Berkshire, United
Kingdom **(100%)**
Tel.: (44) 118 981 7377
Web Site: http://www.guestsupply.co.uk
Emp.: 26
Toiletries, Personal Care Products, House-
keeping & Accessories Mfr & Distr
N.A.I.C.S.: 325612
Andrew Keating (Mng Dir)

Unit (Domestic):

**Sysco Guest Supply, LLC - Hawaii
Distribution Center** (2)
300 E Parkridge Ave, Corona, CA 92879
Tel.: (951) 520-2540
Web Site: http://www.guestsupply.com
Sales Range: $25-49.9 Million
Emp.: 4
Food Products Wholesale Distr
N.A.I.C.S.: 424490

Sysco Gulf Coast, Inc. (1)
2001 W Magnolia, Geneva, AL 36430
Tel.: (334) 684-4000
Web Site: http://www.sysco.com
Emp.: 300
Packaged Frozen Food Merchant Whslr
N.A.I.C.S.: 424420

Sysco Hampton Roads, Inc. (1)
7000 Harbour View Blvd, Suffolk, VA 23436-
2756
Tel.: (757) 673-4000
Web Site: http://www.sysco.com
Sales Range: $300-349.9 Million
Emp.: 400
Food Products Wholesale Distr
N.A.I.C.S.: 424490
Scott Thibodeau (CEO)

Sysco Hawaii, Inc. (1)
716 Umi St, Honolulu, HI 96819
Tel.: (808) 843-3200
Web Site: http://www.hfmfoodservice.com
Food Products Distr
N.A.I.C.S.: 424490

Sysco Houston, Inc. (1)
10710 Greens Crossing Blvd, Houston, TX
77000 1002 **(100%)**
Tel.: (713) 672-8080
Sales Range: $400-449.9 Million
Emp.: 600
Food Products Wholesale Distr
N.A.I.C.S.: 424490
Theodore R. Murray (Exec VP)

Sysco Idaho, Inc. (1)
5710 Pan Am Ave, Boise, ID
83716-9612 **(100%)**
Tel.: (208) 345-9500
Web Site: http://www.sysco.com
Sales Range: $125-149.9 Million
Emp.: 225
Food Products Wholesale Distr
N.A.I.C.S.: 424490

Sysco Indianapolis, LLC (1)

4000 W 62nd St, Indianapolis, IN 46268-
2518
Tel.: (317) 291-2020
Web Site: http://www.sysco.com
Sales Range: $300-349.9 Million
Emp.: 400
Food Products Wholesale Distr
N.A.I.C.S.: 424490

Sysco Intermountain, Inc. (1)
9494 S Prosperity Rd, West Jordan, UT
84081
Tel.: (801) 563-6300
Web Site:
http://www.syscointermountain.com
Sales Range: $350-399.9 Million
Emp.: 450
Food Products Wholesale Distr
N.A.I.C.S.: 424490
Lisa C. Gough (Exec VP)

**Sysco International Food Group,
Inc.** (1)
2401 Police Center Dr Ste 240, Plant City,
FL 33566
Tel.: (813) 707-6161
Emp.: 250
Food Products Services
N.A.I.C.S.: 445298

Sysco Iowa, Inc. (1)
1 Sysco Pl, Ankeny, IA
50021-3998 **(100%)**
Tel.: (515) 289-5300
Web Site: http://www.sysco.com
Sales Range: $125-149.9 Million
Emp.: 270
Food Products Wholesale Distr
N.A.I.C.S.: 424490

Sysco Jackson, LLC (1)
4400 Milwaukee St, Jackson, MS
39209-2636 **(100%)**
Tel.: (601) 354-1701
Web Site: http://www.sysco.com
Sales Range: $500-549.9 Million
Emp.: 425
Food Products Wholesale Distr
N.A.I.C.S.: 445298

Sysco Jacksonville, Inc. (1)
1501 Lewis Industrial Dr, Jacksonville, FL
32254-1660 **(100%)**
Tel.: (904) 786-2600
Web Site: http://www.sysco-jax.com
Sales Range: $350-399.9 Million
Emp.: 350
Food Products Wholesale Distr
N.A.I.C.S.: 424490
Rick Rawald (Pres)

Sysco Kansas City, Inc. (1)
1915 E Kansas City Rd, Olathe, KS
66061-5858 **(100%)**
Tel.: (913) 829-5555
Web Site: http://www.kc.sysco.com
Sales Range: $400-449.9 Million
Emp.: 563
Food Products Wholesale Distr
N.A.I.C.S.: 424490

Sysco Knoxville, LLC (1)
900 Tennessee Ave, Knoxville, TN 37921-
2630
Tel.: (865) 545-5600
Web Site: http://www.syscoknoxville.com
Sales Range: $150-199.9 Million
Emp.: 215
Food Distr
N.A.I.C.S.: 722310

Sysco Labs Pvt. Ltd. (1)
55A Srimath Anagarika Dharmapala Ma-
watha, 00300, Colombo, Sri Lanka
Tel.: (94) 112024500
Web Site: https://syscolabs.lk
Food Products Distr
N.A.I.C.S.: 492110

**Sysco Labs Technologies (Private)
Limited** (1)
55A Srimath Anagarika Dharmapala Ma-
watha, Colombo, Sri Lanka
Tel.: (94) 112024500
Web Site: http://www.syscolabs.lk
IT Services
N.A.I.C.S.: 541519
Shanil Fernando (Mng Dir & Sr VP-Engng)
Rohana Kumara (VP-Engrg & Architecture)
Nilupa Kiringoda (Sr Dir-Delivery)

Sysco Las Vegas, Inc. (1)
6201 E Centennial Pkwy, Las Vegas, NV
89115 **(100%)**
Tel.: (702) 632-1800
Web Site: http://www.lbsysco.com
Sales Range: $300-349.9 Million
Emp.: 350
Food Products Wholesale Distr
N.A.I.C.S.: 424490

**Sysco Lincoln Transportation Com-
pany, Inc.** (1)
900 Kingbird Rd, Lincoln, NE 68521-1230
Tel.: (402) 423-1031
Web Site: http://www.sysco.com
Grocery Retailer
N.A.I.C.S.: 424490

Sysco Lincoln, Inc. (1)
900 Kingbird Rd, Lincoln, NE 68521
Tel.: (402) 423-1031
Web Site: http://www.syscolincoln.com
Sales Range: $600-649.9 Million
Emp.: 540
Food Products Marketer & Wholesale Distr
N.A.I.C.S.: 445110

Sysco Los Angeles, Inc. (1)
20701 E Currier Rd, Walnut, CA 91789-
2904
Tel.: (909) 595-9595
Web Site: http://www.syscola.com
Sales Range: $1-4.9 Billion
Emp.: 1,252
Food Products Distr
N.A.I.C.S.: 424410
Bryan Allred (Pres)

Sysco Louisville, Inc. (1)
7705 National Tpke, Louisville, KY
40214-4803 **(100%)**
Tel.: (502) 364-4300
Web Site: http://www.sysco.com
Sales Range: $400-449.9 Million
Emp.: 300
Food Products Wholesale Distr
N.A.I.C.S.: 424490

Sysco Memphis, LLC (1)
4359 BF Goodrich Blvd, Memphis, TN
38118-7306 **(100%)**
Tel.: (901) 795-2300
Web Site: http://www.sysco.com
Sales Range: $400-449.9 Million
Emp.: 600
Food Products Wholesale Distr
N.A.I.C.S.: 424490

Sysco Metro New York, LLC (1)
20 Theodore Conrad Dr, Jersey City, NJ
07305
Tel.: (201) 433-2000
Web Site: http://metrony.sysco.com
Sales Range: $400-449.9 Million
Emp.: 600
Food Products Marketer & Wholesale Distr
N.A.I.C.S.: 424490
Michael Schonberg (Pres)

Sysco Minnesota, Inc. (1)
2400 County Rd J, Saint Paul, MN
55112-4503 **(100%)**
Tel.: (763) 785-9000
Web Site: http://www.syscomn.com
Sales Range: $450-499.9 Million
Emp.: 550
Food Products Wholesale Distr
N.A.I.C.S.: 424490

Sysco Montana, Inc. (1)
1509 Monad Rd, Billings, MT 59107
Tel.: (406) 247-1100
Web Site: http://www.sysco.com
Sales Range: $100-124.9 Million
Emp.: 376
Food Products Wholesale Distr
N.A.I.C.S.: 424490

Sysco Nashville, LLC (1)
1 Hermitage Plz, Nashville, TN 37209
Tel.: (615) 350-7100
Web Site: http://www.sysco.com
Emp.: 350
Food Products Distr
N.A.I.C.S.: 424420

Sysco New Mexico, LLC (1)
601 Comanche Rd NE, Albuquerque, NM
87107-4103
Tel.: (505) 761-1200
Web Site: http://www.sysconm.com

Sales Range: $125-149.9 Million
Emp.: 500
Food Products Wholesale Distr
N.A.I.C.S.: 424490

Sysco New Orleans, LLC (1)
1451 River Oaks W, Harahan, LA
70123-2176 **(100%)**
Tel.: (504) 731-1015
Web Site: http://www.sysconola.com
Sales Range: $125-149.9 Million
Emp.: 250
Food Products Wholesale Distr
N.A.I.C.S.: 424490

Sysco Newport Meat Company (1)
16691 Hale Ave, Irvine, CA 92606-5025
Tel.: (949) 474-4040
Web Site: http://www.newportmeat.com
Sales Range: $100-124.9 Million
Emp.: 140
Meat Wholesale Distr
N.A.I.C.S.: 424470

Sysco North Dakota, Inc. (1)
3225 12th Ave N, Fargo, ND 58102-3029
Tel.: (701) 293-8900
Web Site: http://www.syscond.com
Emp.: 180
Food Service Distr
N.A.I.C.S.: 424420

Sysco Northern New England, Inc. (1)
36 Thomas Dr, Westbrook, ME 04092-3825
Tel.: (207) 871-0700
Web Site: http://www.sysconne.com
Sales Range: $200-249.9 Million
Emp.: 300
Food Products Wholesale Distr
N.A.I.C.S.: 424490
Jane Brett (Pres)

Sysco Oklahoma (1)
1350 W Tecumseh Rd, Norman, OK 73069-8512
Tel.: (405) 717-2700
Web Site: http://oklahoma.sysco.com
Sales Range: $100-124.9 Million
Emp.: 320
Food Products Wholesale Distr
N.A.I.C.S.: 424490

Sysco Philadelphia, LLC (1)
600 Packer Ave, Philadelphia, PA 19148-5304
Tel.: (215) 463-8200
Web Site: http://www.syscophilly.com
Sales Range: $350-399.9 Million
Emp.: 500
Food Products Wholesale Distr
N.A.I.C.S.: 424490

Sysco Pittsburgh, LLC (1)
1 Whitney Dr, Harmony, PA 16037
Tel.: (724) 452-2100
Web Site: http://www.sysco.com
Sales Range: $100-124.9 Million
Emp.: 200
Food Products Wholesale Distr
N.A.I.C.S.: 424490
Kate Kerg (Pres)

Sysco Portland, Inc. (1)
26250 SW Pkwy Ctr Dr, Wilsonville, OR 97070-9606
Tel.: (503) 682-8700
Web Site: http://www.syscoportland.com
Sales Range: $400-449.9 Million
Emp.: 600
Food Products Wholesale Distr
N.A.I.C.S.: 424490
Liz Aspray (Pres)

Sysco Produce Marketing & Merchandising Services (1)
1622 Moffett St, Salinas, CA 93905-3354 **(100%)**
Tel.: (831) 771-5000
Sales Range: $350-399.9 Million
Emp.: 55
Fresh Fruits & Vegetables Whslr
N.A.I.C.S.: 424480

Sysco Raleigh, LLC (1)
1032 Baugh Rd, Selma, NC 27576-9105
Tel.: (919) 755-2455
Web Site: http://www.syscoraleigh.com
Food Products Distr
N.A.I.C.S.: 424490

Sysco Sacramento, Inc. (1)
7062 Pacific Ave, Pleasant Grove, CA 95668
Tel.: (916) 569-7000
Web Site: http://www.syscosac.com
Sales Range: $300-349.9 Million
Emp.: 412
Food Products Wholesale Distr
N.A.I.C.S.: 424490
John Rispler (Pres)

Sysco San Diego, Inc. (1)
12180 Kirkham Rd, Poway, CA 92064-6879
Tel.: (858) 513-7300
Web Site: http://www.sysco.com
Sales Range: $350-399.9 Million
Emp.: 400
Food Products Wholesale Distr
N.A.I.C.S.: 424410
Kevin Mangan (Pres)

Sysco San Francisco, Inc. (1)
5900 Stewart Ave, Fremont, CA 94538-3134 **(100%)**
Tel.: (510) 226-3000
Web Site: http://www.syscosf.com
Sales Range: $550-599.9 Million
Emp.: 500
Food Products Wholesale Distr
N.A.I.C.S.: 445110
Patrick Kissee (Pres)

Sysco Seattle, Inc. (1)
22820 54th Ave S, Kent, WA 98032-1813
Tel.: (206) 622-2261
Web Site: http://www.syscoseattle.com
Sales Range: $400-449.9 Million
Emp.: 500
Food Products Wholesale Distr
N.A.I.C.S.: 424410

Sysco South Florida, Inc. (1)
12500 NW 112th Ave, Medley, FL 33178 **(100%)**
Tel.: (305) 651-5421
Web Site: http://www.sysco.com
Sales Range: $450-499.9 Million
Emp.: 700
Food Products Wholesale Distr
N.A.I.C.S.: 424490
Thomas C. Crytser (Exec VP)

Sysco Southeast Florida, LLC (1)
1999 Dr Martin Luther King Jr Blvd, Riviera Beach, FL 33404-6639 **(100%)**
Tel.: (561) 842-1999
Web Site: http://www.sysco.com
Sales Range: $300-349.9 Million
Emp.: 300
Fresh Fruits & Vegetables Wholesale Distr
N.A.I.C.S.: 424490
Nathen Sams (Reg VP-Fin)

Sysco Spokane, Inc. (1)
300 N Baugh Way, Post Falls, ID 83854-5224
Tel.: (208) 777-9511
Web Site: http://www.syscospokane.com
Grocery Related Products Merchant Whslr
N.A.I.C.S.: 424490

Sysco St. Louis, LLC (1)
3850 Mueller Rd, Saint Charles, MO 63301-8042
Tel.: (636) 940-9230
Web Site: http://www.sysco.com
Sales Range: $150-199.9 Million
Food Products Wholesale Distr
N.A.I.C.S.: 424490

Sysco Syracuse, LLC (1)
2508 Warners Rd, Warners, NY 13164 **(100%)**
Tel.: (315) 672-7000
Web Site: http://www.syscosyracuse.com
Sales Range: $350-399.9 Million
Emp.: 500
Food Products Wholesale Distr
N.A.I.C.S.: 424490

Sysco Ventura, Inc. (1)
3100 Sturgis Rd, Oxnard, CA 93030
Tel.: (805) 205-7000
Emp.: 300
Grocery Related Products Whslr
N.A.I.C.S.: 424490
Rob Resnick (Mgr)

Sysco Victoria, Inc. (1)
2881 Amy Road, Victoria, V9B 0B2, BC, Canada

Tel.: (250) 475-3333
Web Site: https://www.sysco.ca
Emp.: 300
Food Products Distr
N.A.I.C.S.: 424420

Sysco Virginia, LLC (1)
5081 South Valley Pike, Harrisonburg, VA 22801-7520 **(100%)**
Tel.: (540) 434-0761
Web Site: http://www.sysco.com
Sales Range: $300-349.9 Million
Emp.: 450
Food Products Wholesale Distr
N.A.I.C.S.: 424490
Dave Kraft (Pres & CEO)

Sysco West Coast Florida, Inc. (1)
3000 69th St E, Palmetto, FL 34221-8440 **(100%)**
Tel.: (941) 721-1450
Web Site: http://sysco.com
Sales Range: $550-599.9 Million
Emp.: 625
Food Products Wholesale Distr
N.A.I.C.S.: 445298
Don Wilson (Pres)

Sysco Western Minnesota (1)
900 S Hwy 10, Saint Cloud, MN 56304
Tel.: (320) 251-3200
Web Site: http://www.sysco.com
Food Wholesale Distr
N.A.I.C.S.: 425120

Sysco Western Minnesota, Inc. (1)
900 Highway 10 S, Saint Cloud, MN 56304
Tel.: (320) 251-3200
Food Products Distr
N.A.I.C.S.: 424420

The Sygma Network, Inc. (1)
4895 Geneva St, Denver, CO 80238
Tel.: (720) 374-9400
Web Site: http://www.sygmanetwork.com
Sales Range: $1-4.9 Billion
Emp.: 4,200
Food Products Wholesale Distr
N.A.I.C.S.: 424410
Amy Humenay (VP-Pur)
David Myers (Pres)
Dawn Rezkalla (CFO)
Ellen Jones (VP-HR)
Gary Toth (VP-Ops-South)
John Rivers (VP-Ops-West)
Mike Bain (VP-Bus Tech & Admin)
Tasha Swartwout (VP-Sls & Customer Svcs)
Lucas Jackson (VP-Ops)

Division (Domestic):

The Sygma Network of Pennsylvania (2)
4000 Industrial Rd, Harrisburg, PA 17110-2947
Tel.: (717) 221-6700
Web Site: http://www.sygmanetwork.com
Sales Range: $150-199.9 Million
Food & Related Products Wholesale Distr
N.A.I.C.S.: 424490

The Sygma Network, Inc. (2)
5550 Blazer Pkwy Ste 300, Dublin, OH 43017
Tel.: (614) 734-2500
Web Site: http://www.sygmanetwork.com
Sales Range: $100-124.9 Million
Emp.: 400
Food Products Distr
N.A.I.C.S.: 425120
Lucas Jackson (VP-Ops-North)
David Myers (Pres)
Dawn Rezkalla (CFO)
Mike Bain (VP-Bus Tech & Admin)
Amy Humenay (VP-Pur & Logistics)
Ellen Jones (VP-HR & Compliance)
Tasha Swartwout (VP-Sls & Customer Svcs)
John Rivers (VP-Ops-West)
Gary Toth (VP-Ops-South)

Watson Sysco Food Services, Inc. (1)
714 2nd Pl, Lubbock, TX 79401
Tel.: (806) 747-2678
Web Site: http://www.sysco.com
Sales Range: $100-124.9 Million
Emp.: 200
Food Service Wholesale Distr

N.A.I.C.S.: 424490

SYSOREX, INC.
13880 Dulles Corner Ln Ste 120, Herndon, VA 20171
Tel.: (703) 961-1125 NV
SYSX—(OTCIQ)
Rev.: $17,313,000
Assets: $13,240,000
Liabilities: $29,121,000
Net Worth: ($15,881,000)
Earnings: ($12,193,000)
Emp.: 14
Fiscal Year-end: 12/31/22
Wireless Telecommunication Services
N.A.I.C.S.: 517112
Zaman Khan (CEO-Sysorex Government Services, Inc.)
Vincent Loiacono (CFO & Sec)
Wayne Wasserberg (CEO & Pres-TTM Digital Assets & Technologies, Inc.)

SYSTEM1, INC.
4235 Redwood Ave, Los Angeles, CA 90066
Tel.: (310) 924-6037 DE
Web Site: https://system1.com
Year Founded: 2020
SST—(NYSE)
Computing Infrastructure Providers, Data Processing, Web Hosting & Related Services
N.A.I.C.S.: 518210
Michael L. Blend (Founder, Chm & CEO)
Beth Sestanovich (Chief People Officer)
Brian Coppola (Chief Product Officer)
Tridivesh Kidambi (CFO)
Daniel J. Weinrot (Gen Counsel)
Jen Robinson (CTO)

Subsidiaries:

CyberSecurity Service LLC (1)
752 N State St 172, Westerville, OH 43082
Web Site: https://www.cybersecurityservices.com
Cyber Security Services
N.A.I.C.S.: 561311

T STAMP, INC.
3017 Bolling Way NE Fl 2, Atlanta, GA 30305
Tel.: (404) 806-9906 DE
Web Site: https://www.truststamp.ai
Year Founded: 2016
IDAI—(NASDAQ)
Rev.: $5,385,077
Assets: $6,411,918
Liabilities: $5,786,774
Net Worth: $625,144
Earnings: ($12,091,540)
Emp.: 78
Fiscal Year-end: 12/31/22
Custom Computer Programming Services
N.A.I.C.S.: 541511
Gareth Genner (CEO)
Andrew Gowasack (Pres)
Scott Francis (CTO)
Alex Valdes (CFO & Exec VP)
Norman Poh (Chief Science Officer)
David Story (Chm)

T-REX ACQUISITION CORP.
151 N Nob Hill Rd Ste 402, Plantation, FL 33324
Tel.: (954) 960-7100 NV
Web Site: https://trex-acq.com
Year Founded: 2008
TRXA—(OTCIQ)
Rev.: $15,824
Assets: $152,249
Liabilities: $1,259,444
Net Worth: ($1,107,195)
Earnings: ($1,007,654)

T-REX Acquisition Corp.—(Continued)

Emp.: 1
Fiscal Year-end: 06/30/24
Management Consulting Services
N.A.I.C.S.: 541618
Frank James Horkey (Pres)
John Bennett (CFO)
Michael Nelson Christiansen (Treas & Sec)

Subsidiaries:

Raptor Mining LLC (1)
7553 NW 50th St, Miami, FL 33166
Tel.: (786) 801-9012
Mining Engineering Services
N.A.I.C.S.: 541330

T. ROWE PRICE GROUP INC.

100 E Pratt St, Baltimore, MD 21202
Tel.: (410) 345-2000   MD
Web Site:
  https://www.troweprice.com
Year Founded: 2000
TROW—(NASDAQ)
Rev.: $6,460,500,000
Assets: $12,278,800,000
Liabilities: $2,581,700,000
Net Worth: $9,697,100,000
Earnings: $1,788,700,000
Emp.: 7,906
Fiscal Year-end: 12/31/23
Investment & Financial Services
N.A.I.C.S.: 523160
Kimberly H. Johnson (COO & VP)
Cynthia L. Egan (Founder)
Robert W. Sharps (Chm, Pres & CEO)
Michelle Swanenburg (VP & Head-HR)
Steph Jackson (Head-Investment Mgmt)
Glenn R. August (Exec VP)
Kelly Shen (Chief Data Officer)
Eric L. Veiel (Co-Chief Investment Officer)
Andrew C. McCormick (Co-Chief Investment Officer)
Josh Nelson (VP)
Glenn Russell August (VP)

Subsidiaries:

Oak Hill Advisors (Australia) Pty. Ltd. (1)
Governor Phillip Tower Level 28 1 Farrer Place, Sydney, 2000, NSW, Australia
Tel.: (61) 286675731
Alternative Credit Investment Services
N.A.I.C.S.: 523150

Oak Hill Advisors (Europe), LLP (1)
45 Pall Mall 4th Floor, London, SW1Y 5JG, United Kingdom
Tel.: (44) 2079683670
Investment Management Service
N.A.I.C.S.: 523940

Oak Hill Advisors (Hong Kong) Limited (1)
7/F Chater House 8 Connaught Road, Central, Hong Kong, China (Hong Kong)
Tel.: (852) 25367378
Alternative Credit Investment Services
N.A.I.C.S.: 523150

Oak Hill Advisors Sarl (1)
51 Boulevard Grande Duchesse Charlotte, L-1331, Luxembourg, Luxembourg
Tel.: (352) 28269687
Finance Investment Services
N.A.I.C.S.: 523999

T. Rowe Price Advisory Services, Inc. (1)
100 E Pratt St Fl 4, Baltimore, MD 21202-1081
Tel.: (410) 345-2000
Web Site: http://www.troweprice.com
Investment Advisory Services
N.A.I.C.S.: 523940

T. Rowe Price Associates, Inc. (1)

100 E Pratt St, Baltimore, MD 21202
Tel.: (410) 345-2000
Web Site: http://www.troweprice.com
Sales Range: $1-4.9 Billion
Emp.: 4,000
Investment Management Firm
N.A.I.C.S.: 525910

Subsidiary (Non-US):

T. Rowe Price Funds SICAV (2)
35 Boulevard Prince Henri 3rd Floor, L-1724, Luxembourg, Luxembourg
Tel.: (352) 2747251
Asset Management Services
N.A.I.C.S.: 523940

T. Rowe Price International Ltd (2)
60 Queen Victoria Street, London, EC4N 4TZ, United Kingdom
Tel.: (44) 2076518200
Web Site: http://www.troweprice.com
Sales Range: $100-124.9 Million
Investment Management Service
N.A.I.C.S.: 523940
Robert C. T. Higginbotham (Chm & CEO)

Subsidiary (Non-US):

T. Rowe Price (Switzerland) GmbH (3)
Talstrasse 65 6th Floor, 8001, Zurich, Switzerland
Tel.: (41) 442271550
Asset Management Services
N.A.I.C.S.: 523940

Subsidiary (Domestic):

T. Rowe Price International, Inc. (2)
100 E Pratt St, Baltimore, MD 21202
Tel.: (410) 345-2000
Web Site: http://www.troweprice.com
Sales Range: $650-699.9 Million
Emp.: 55
Investment Management Firm
N.A.I.C.S.: 523940

T. Rowe Price Investment Services Inc. (2)
100 E Pratt St, Baltimore, MD 21202
Tel.: (410) 345-2000
Sales Range: $125-149.9 Million
Emp.: 100
Investment Services
N.A.I.C.S.: 523940
James Aloysius Charles Kennedy (VP)

T. Rowe Price Retirement Plan Services, Inc. (2)
4515 Painters Mill Rd, Owings Mills, MD 21117-4903
Investment Advisory Services
N.A.I.C.S.: 523940
Diana Awed (Head-Retirement Product & Mktg)

T. Rowe Price Australia, Ltd. (1)
Level 28 Governor Phillip Tower 1 Farrer Place, Sydney, 2000, NSW, Australia
Tel.: (61) 286675700
Investment & Financial Services
N.A.I.C.S.: 523160
Darren Hall (Head-Distr-Australia & New Zealand)
Amie Boscacci (Mgr-Relationship-Victoria & Tasmania)

T. Rowe Price Japan, Inc. (1)
GranTokyo South Tower 10F 1-9-2 Marunouchi, Chiyoda-ku, Tokyo, 100-6610, Japan
Tel.: (81) 367583800
Investment & Financial Services
N.A.I.C.S.: 523160

T.J.T., INC.

843 N Washington Ave, Emmett, ID 83617-9560
Tel.: (208) 472-2500   WA
Web Site: http://www.tjtusa.com
Year Founded: 1977
AXLE—(OTCIQ)
Axles & Tires Reconditions & Sales; Vinyl Siding Distr
N.A.I.C.S.: 423140
Terrence J. Sheldon (Founder & CEO)

Vicki Morrow (Pres)
Paul G. Smith (Chief Compliance Officer)
Teri Howard (Sec)

T2 BIOSYSTEMS, INC.

101 Hartwell Ave, Lexington, MA 02421
Tel.: (781) 457-1200   DE
Web Site:
  https://www.t2biosystems.com
Year Founded: 2006
TTOO—(NASDAQ)
Rev.: $22,305,000
Assets: $34,327,000
Liabilities: $73,982,000
Net Worth: ($39,655,000)
Earnings: ($62,333,000)
Emp.: 158
Fiscal Year-end: 12/31/22
In-Vitro Diagnostics Mfr, Researcher & Developer
N.A.I.C.S.: 325413
John M. Sprague (CFO)
Kelley Morgan (Chief People Officer)
John J. Sperzel III (Chm, Pres & CEO)

TABLE TRAC, INC.

6101 Baker Rd Ste 206, Minnetonka, MN 55345
Tel.: (952) 548-8877   NV
Web Site:
  https://www.casinotrac.com
Year Founded: 1995
TBTC—(OTCQX)
Rev.: $11,056,587
Assets: $10,674,250
Liabilities: $2,398,558
Net Worth: $8,275,692
Earnings: $1,624,453
Emp.: 35
Fiscal Year-end: 12/31/22
Casino Gaming Software Development Services
N.A.I.C.S.: 541511
Chad B. Hoehne (Founder, Chm, Pres & CTO)
Randy W. Gilbert (CFO)

TABOOLA.COM LTD.

16 Madison Sq W 7th Fl, New York, NY 10010
Tel.: (212) 206-7633
Web Site: https://www.taboola.com
Year Founded: 2007
TBLA—(NASDAQ)
Rev.: $1,401,150,000
Assets: $1,529,623,000
Liabilities: $695,088,000
Net Worth: $834,535,000
Earnings: ($11,975,000)
Emp.: 1,815
Fiscal Year-end: 12/31/22
Online Content Recommendation Software Developer
N.A.I.C.S.: 513210
Eldad Maniv (Pres & COO)
Lior Golan (CTO)
Ariel Pisetzky (VP-IT)
Kristy Sundjaja (Chief People Officer)
Stephen Walker (CFO)
Ran Buck (Sr VP)
Blythe Holden (Gen Counsel)
Ehud Furman (Sr VP)
Bill Glass (CEO)
Gil Chamiel (VP)
Ning Ning Yu (VP)
Ran Gishri (VP)
Harel Uliel (VP)
Jon Westnedge (VP)
Nadav Perry (VP)
Paul Harraghy (VP)
Jonny Harvey (Mng Dir)
Tom Inbal (VP)
Fernando Tassinari (VP)

Eric Lee (VP)
Chanan Fogel (VP)
James Arthur (VP)
John Rusconi (VP)
Tal Sliwowicz (VP)
Mosh Salomon (VP)
Yochai Salomon (VP)
Eyal Pincu (VP)
Ido Azriel (VP)
Liat Nahum (VP)
Adam Singolda (Founder & CEO)

Subsidiaries:

ION Acquisition Corp 1 Ltd. (1)
89 Medinat Hayehudim Street, Herzliya, L3 4676672, Israel
Tel.: (972) 9970 3620
Financial Investment
N.A.I.C.S.: 523999
Gilad Shany (CEO)

TACTILE SYSTEMS TECHNOLOGY, INC.

3701 Wayzata Blvd Ste 300, Minneapolis, MN 55416
Tel.: (612) 355-5100
Web Site:
  https://www.tactilemedical.com
Year Founded: 2004
TCMD—(NASDAQ)
Rev.: $274,423,000
Assets: $281,438,000
Liabilities: $87,796,000
Net Worth: $193,642,000
Earnings: $28,515,000
Emp.: 992
Fiscal Year-end: 12/31/23
Medical Device Mfr & Distr
N.A.I.C.S.: 423450
Elaine M. Birkemeyer (CFO)
Sunday J. Hoy (Officer-Compliance & VP)
Brett L. Demchuk (VP-Quality & Regulatory Affairs)
Sheri Louise Dodd (CEO)
Sherri L. Ferstler (Sr VP-Sls)
David J. Kaercher (CIO)
Janelle M. Strop (Chief HR Officer)
Kristie T. Burns (Sr VP)
Rachel L. Gustad (Sr VP)
Jerry A. Sauber (Sr VP)
Antonios P. Gasparis (Chief Medical Officer)

TAIHE GROUP, INC.

4870 Haygood Rd Ste 107, Virginia Beach, VA 23455
Tel.: (757) 554-0926   FL
TIHE—(OTCIQ)
Liabilities: $43,967
Net Worth: ($43,967)
Earnings: ($43,967)
Emp.: 1
Fiscal Year-end: 12/31/22
Healtcare Services
N.A.I.C.S.: 621610
Phillip Enlow (Chm)

TAILORED BRANDS, INC.

6380 Rogerdale Rd, Houston, TX 77072-1624
Tel.: (281) 776-7000   TX
Web Site:
  http://www.tailoredbrands.com
Year Founded: 1973
TLRD—(NYSE)
Rev.: $2,881,261,000
Assets: $2,418,959,000
Liabilities: $2,517,265,000
Net Worth: ($98,306,000)
Earnings: ($82,276,000)
Emp.: 13,700
Fiscal Year-end: 02/01/20

Men's Clothing Store Owner & Operator
N.A.I.C.S.: 458110
Mark Neutze (Exec VP-Stores Ops)
Jamie Bragg (Chief Supply Chain Officer & Exec VP)
A. Alexander Rhodes (Chief Compliance Officer, Gen Counsel & Exec VP)
Dinesh S. Lathi (Pres)
Richard Hansen (Exec VP-Strategy & Analytics)
Steve Ricci (Pres-Brand-K&G)
Carrie Ann Ask (Chief Customer Officer)
Michael Stefanov (Mgr-PR)
Michael Shane Smith (Chief HR Officer & Exec VP)
John Vazquez (Principal Fin Officer, Chief Acctg Officer & Treas)
Bob Hull (Co-CEO)
Peter Sachse (Co-CEO)
Scott Vifquain (CTO & Exec VP)
Brandy Richardson (CFO)
Yen D. Chu (Chief Legal Officer, Sec & Exec VP)

Subsidiaries:

Jos. A. Bank Clothiers, Inc.   (1)
6380 Rogerdale Rd, Houston, TX 77072
Tel.: (346) 201-4596
Web Site: http://www.josbank.com
Men's Clothing Stores
N.A.I.C.S.: 458110
Frank Barbarino (VP & Gen Mgr-Mdse)

Joseph Abboud Manufacturing
Corp.   (1)
689 Belleville Ave, New Bedford, MA 02745
Tel.: (508) 999-1301
Men's Clothing Store Operator
N.A.I.C.S.: 458110
Richard Motta (VP-Ops)

K&G Men's Center, Inc.   (1)
1225 Chattahoochee Ave, Atlanta, GA 30318
Tel.: (404) 351-7987
Web Site: http://www.kgmens.com
Sales Range: $150-199.9 Million
Emp.: 100
Discounted Mens Clothing Retailer
N.A.I.C.S.: 458110

K&G Men's Company Inc.   (1)
4009 W Airport Fwy, Irving, TX 75062
Tel.: (972) 870-9618
Web Site: http://www.kgstores.com
Men's Clothing Store Operator
N.A.I.C.S.: 458110

Moores Clothing For Men   (1)
129 Carlingview Dr, Etobicoke, M9W 5E7,
ON, Canada   (100%)
Tel.: (416) 798-8082
Web Site: http://www.mooresclothing.com
Sales Range: $100-124.9 Million
Emp.: 50
Men's Clothing Retailer
N.A.I.C.S.: 458110

Subsidiary (Domestic):

Golden Brand Clothing (Canada)
Ltd.   (2)
Bureau 900 5800 rue Saint Denis, Montreal,
H2S 3L5, QC, Canada
Tel.: (514) 274-3694
Men's Clothing Mfr
N.A.I.C.S.: 458110

Moores Clothing For Men   (2)
129 Carlingview Drive, Etobicoke, M9W
5E7, ON, Canada   (100%)
Tel.: (416) 798-8082
Web Site: http://www.mooresclothing.com
Sales Range: $50-74.9 Million
Emp.: 50
Men's & Boys' Clothing
N.A.I.C.S.: 315210

TMW Marketing Company, Inc.   (1)
6100 Stevenson Blvd, Fremont, CA 94538
                                    (100%)
Tel.: (510) 723-8200

Web Site: http://www.menswearhouse.com
Sales Range: $10-24.9 Million
Emp.: 9
Business Services
N.A.I.C.S.: 541910

TMW Merchants LLC   (1)
6380 Rogerdale Rd, Houston, TX 77072-1624
Tel.: (281) 776-7111
Web Site: http://www.menswearhouse.com
Business Services
N.A.I.C.S.: 561499

Subsidiary (Domestic):

TMW Purchasing LLC   (2)
6380 Rogerdale Rd, Houston, TX 77072
                                    (100%)
Tel.: (281) 776-7000
Sales Range: $10-24.9 Million
Business Services
N.A.I.C.S.: 561499

The Mens Wearhouse, Inc   (1)
6380 Rogerdale Rd, Houston, TX 77072
Web Site: http://www.menswearhouse.com
Men Clothing & Accessorie Retailer
N.A.I.C.S.: 458110

TAITRON COMPONENTS INCORPORATED
28040 W Harrison Pkwy, Valencia, CA 91355
Tel.: (661) 257-6060   CA
Web Site:
  https://www.taitroncomponents.com
Year Founded: 1989
TAIT—(NASDAQ)
Rev.: $8,423,000
Assets: $17,137,000
Liabilities: $1,001,000
Net Worth: $16,136,000
Earnings: $3,208,000
Emp.: 15
Fiscal Year-end: 12/31/22
Contract Electronic Mfr & Distr of
Transistors, Diodes & other Discrete
Semiconductors, Optoelectronic Devices & Passive Components
N.A.I.C.S.: 423690
Tzu Sheng Ku (Co-Founder & Chm)
Stewart Wang (Co-Founder, Pres & CEO)
David Vanderhorst (CFO & Sec)

Subsidiaries:

Taitron Components Incorporated
Taiwan   (1)
6F No 190 Sec 2 Zhongxing Rd, Xindian
Dist, Taipei, Taiwan
Tel.: (886) 229136238
Sales Range: $100-124.9 Million
Semiconductor & Other Electrical Devices
Mfr
N.A.I.C.S.: 334413

Taitron Components Incorporated e
Representacoes do Brasil LTDA (1)
Rua Ferraz De Vasconcelos 55, 04035-000,
Guarulhos, Brazil
Tel.: (55) 1155747949
Web Site:
  http://www.taitroncomponents.com
Sales Range: $1-9.9 Million
Emp.: 2
Semiconductor & Other Electrical Devices
Mfr
N.A.I.C.S.: 334413

Taitron Components Mexico, S.A. de
C.V.   (1)
Blvd Central No 5000-5, Parque Industrial
Atitalaquia, Naucalpan, 42970, Hidalgo,
Mexico
Tel.: (52) 5555601519
Web Site:
  http://www.taitroncomponents.com
Sales Range: $100-124.9 Million
Emp.: 3
Semiconductor & Other Electrical Devices
Mfr
N.A.I.C.S.: 334413

TAKE-TWO INTERACTIVE SOFTWARE, INC.
110 W 44th St, New York, NY 10036
Tel.: (646) 536-2842   DE
Web Site:
  https://www.take2games.com
Year Founded: 1993
TTWO—(NASDAQ)
Rev.: $5,349,600,000
Assets: $12,216,900,000
Liabilities: $6,549,000,000
Net Worth: $5,667,900,000
Earnings: ($3,744,200,000)
Emp.: 12,371
Fiscal Year-end: 03/31/24
Software Development Services
N.A.I.C.S.: 541511
Strauss H. Zelnick (Chm & CEO)
Daniel P. Emerson (Gen Counsel & Exec VP)
Lainie J. Goldstein (CFO)
Karl Slatoff (Pres)

Subsidiaries:

2K Czech, s.r.o.   (1)
Turanka 115, 627 00, Brno, Czech Republic
Tel.: (420) 532199311
Web Site: http://www.2kczech.com
Video Game Developer & Publisher
N.A.I.C.S.: 513210

2K Games, Inc.   (1)
10 Hamilton Landing, Novato, CA 94949
Tel.: (415) 479-3634
Web Site: https://2k.com
Software & Games Publishers
N.A.I.C.S.: 513210

2K Play, Inc.   (1)
622 Broadway, New York, NY 10012
Tel.: (646) 536-2842
Emp.: 4
Software & Games Publishers
N.A.I.C.S.: 513210
Steve Lux (VP-Bus Dev)

2K Vegas, Inc.   (1)
302 E Carson Ave Ste 900, Las Vegas, NV 89101-5905
Tel.: (213) 999-2049
Web Site: https://www.2kvegas.com
Video Game Developer & Publisher
N.A.I.C.S.: 513210

2k Games West   (1)
4373 Park Ter Dr, Westlake Village, CA 91361
Tel.: (818) 707-7063
Developer, Publisher & Marketer of Interactive Computer Software Primarily Based on
Well Recognized Intellectual Content
N.A.I.C.S.: 513210

Double Take LLC   (1)
568 Memory Ln, Carmel, IN 46032
Tel.: (317) 796-7705
Web Site: https://www.doubletakellc.com
Brand Consulting Services
N.A.I.C.S.: 541320

Ghost Story Games, LLC   (1)
PO Box 803, Westwood, MA 02090
Web Site: http://www.ghoststorygames.com
Software & Games Publishers
N.A.I.C.S.: 513210

Joytech Europe Limited   (1)
Saxon House 2-4 Victoria Street, Windsor,
SL4 1EN, United Kingdom
Tel.: (44) 1753496700
Video Game Peripheral Mfr & Distr
N.A.I.C.S.: 339930

Rockstar International Limited   (1)
555 Kings Road 1st Floor, London, SW6 2EB, United Kingdom
Tel.: (44) 2077512555
Video Game Developer & Publisher
N.A.I.C.S.: 513210

Rockstar London, Ltd.   (1)
555 Kings Road, London, SW6 2EB, United Kingdom
Tel.: (44) 2077512555
Web Site: http://www.rockstarlondon.com
Sales Range: $25-49.9 Million
Emp.: 23
Software & Games Publishers

N.A.I.C.S.: 513210

Rockstar North Ltd.   (1)
Barclay House 108 Holyrood Road, Edinburgh, EH8 8AS, United Kingdom
Tel.: (44) 8009536962
Web Site: http://www.rockstarnorth.com
Software & Games Publishers
N.A.I.C.S.: 513210

Rockstar San Diego, Inc.   (1)
5966 La Pl Ct Ste 170, Carlsbad, CA 92008-8830
Tel.: (760) 929-0700
Software & Games Publishers
N.A.I.C.S.: 513210

Social Point, S.L.   (1)
Carrer de Llacuna 166 - 10th Floor, 08018,
Barcelona, Spain
Tel.: (34) 931814098
Web Site: https://www.socialpoint.es
Online Game Development Services
N.A.I.C.S.: 513210
Horacio Martos (Co-Founder)
Andres Bou (Co-Founder)

Take-Two Interactive Benelux
B.V.   (1)
Tel.: (31) 765481350
Software & Games Publishers
N.A.I.C.S.: 513210

Take-Two Interactive Software Europe Limited   (1)
Saxon House 2-4 Victoria Street, Windsor,
SL4 1EN, United Kingdom
Tel.: (44) 1753496600
Video Game Developer & Publisher
N.A.I.C.S.: 513210
Seb Belcher (Gen Counsel & Sr VP)

Zynga Israel Ltd.   (1)
7 Rival St, Tel Aviv, 67778, Israel
Tel.: (972) 516285491
Software Publishing Services
N.A.I.C.S.: 541511

TALIS BIOMEDICAL CORPORATION
1375 W Fulton Market Ste 700, Chicago, IL 60607
Tel.: (650) 433-3000   DE
Web Site: https://www.talis.bio
Year Founded: 2013
TLIS—(NASDAQ)
Rev.: $4,812,000
Assets: $169,290,000
Liabilities: $42,551,000
Net Worth: $126,739,000
Earnings: ($113,012,000)
Emp.: 102
Fiscal Year-end: 12/31/22
Biotechnology Research & Development Services
N.A.I.C.S.: 541714
Brian Coe (Co-Founder)
Karen E. Flick (Sr VP-Legal)
Robert Kelley (CEO)
Ramesh Ramakrishnan (Sr VP-R&D)
Rustem F. Ismagilov (Co-Founder)
Rebecca Markovich (Interim CFO)

TALKSPACE, INC.
Tel.: (212) 284-7206   DE
Web Site: https://www.talkspace.com
Year Founded: 2012
TALK—(NASDAQ)
Rev.: $119,567,000
Assets: $156,254,000
Liabilities: $28,718,000
Net Worth: $127,536,000
Earnings: ($79,672,000)
Emp.: 339
Fiscal Year-end: 12/31/22
Health Care Srvices
N.A.I.C.S.: 621610
Ian Harris (CFO)
Douglas Braunstein (Chm)
Gil Margolin (CTO)
Jon R. Cohen (CEO)

TALON INTERNATIONAL, INC.

Talon International, Inc.—(Continued)

21900 Burbank Blvd Ste 101, Woodland Hills, CA 91367
Tel.: (818) 444-4100 DE
Web Site:
https://taloninternational.com
Year Founded: 1893
TALN—(OTCIQ)
Sales Range: $25-49.9 Million
Emp.: 201
Curtain & Linen Mills
N.A.I.C.S.: 314120
Mark Dyne (Chm)
Chris Roberts (VP-Sls-Trim Div)
Larry Dyne (CEO & Interim CFO)
Gary Dyne (VP-Sls-Fastener Div)
Herman Roup (VP-Ops-Tekfit)
Jamey Johns (Chief Acctg Officer, VP & Controller)
Daniel Ryu (Chief Strategy Officer & Sec)

Subsidiaries:

Tag-It Pacific (HK) Ltd (1)
Unit 101 1 Fl Sunbeam Ctr 27 Shing Yip St Kwun Tong, Hong Kong, Kowloon, China (Hong Kong)
Tel.: (852) 29470888
Web Site: http://www.talonzippers.com
Sales Range: $25-49.9 Million
Emp.: 100
Zipper, Fastener & Other Apparel Components Mfr
N.A.I.C.S.: 339993
Margaret Chen (CFO)

Talon Zipper (Shenzhen) Co. Ltd. (1)
16 Floor Block C Renmin South Road Tian An International Building, Luohu District, Shenzhen, 518001, Guangdong, China
Tel.: (86) 75589630288
Apparel Distr
N.A.I.C.S.: 458110

TALON REAL ESTATE HOLDING CORP.

100 S 1st St 583357, Minneapolis, MN 55458
Tel.: (612) 604-4600 UT
Web Site: http://www.talonreit.com
Year Founded: 2007
TALR—(OTCIQ)
Real Estate Investment Services
N.A.I.C.S.: 523999
Matthew G. Kaminski (Chm & CEO)

Subsidiaries:

Talon First Trust, LLC (1)
180 5th St E, Saint Paul, MN 55101-2672
Tel.: (651) 291-3599
Real Estate Investment Services
N.A.I.C.S.: 525990

Talon OP, L.P. (1)
5500 Wayzata Blvd Ste 1070, Minneapolis, MN 55416-1263
Tel.: (952) 449-3633
Real Estate Manangement Services
N.A.I.C.S.: 531210

TALOS ENERGY INC.

333 Clay St Ste 3300, Houston, TX 77002
Tel.: (713) 328-3000 DE
Web Site:
https://www.talosenergy.com
Year Founded: 2017
TALO—(NYSE)
Rev.: $1,651,980,000
Assets: $3,058,626,000
Liabilities: $1,893,050,000
Net Worth: $1,165,576,000
Earnings: $381,915,000
Emp.: 436
Fiscal Year-end: 12/31/22
Holding Company; Petroleum & Natural Gas Extraction
N.A.I.C.S.: 551112

John B. Spath (Principal Operating Officer, Exec VP & Head-Ops)
Timothy S. Duncan (Co-Founder)
John A. Parker (Co-Founder)
John B. Spath (Exec VP & Head-Ops)
Deborah Huston (VP & Deputy Gen Counsel)
C. Gordon Lindsey (VP-Corp Dev)
Sergio L. Maiworm Jr. (CFO & Exec VP)
Jim Brysch (VP-Mktg)
Robin H. Fielder (Chief Sustainability Officer & Exec VP-Low Carbon Strategy)
Megan Dick (VP-Human Resources)
Joe Sauvageau (VP-Asset Dev)
Joel Plauche (VP-HSE, Regulatory, and Compliance)
Francisco Noyola (VP-Mexico)
Truitt Smith (VP-Geoscience)
William S. Moss III (Gen Counsel & Exec VP)
Joseph A. Mills (Interim Pres & Interim CEO)

Subsidiaries:

EnVen Energy Corporation (1)
609 Main St, Ste 3200, Houston, TX 77002
Tel.: (713) 335-7000
Web Site: http://www.enven.com
Sales Range: $400-449.9 Million
Emp.: 140
Oil & Natural Gas Exploration Services
N.A.I.C.S.: 211130
Steve Weyel (Chm & CEO)
John P. Wilkirson (CFO & Exec VP)
David Carmony (COO)
Jeffrey A. Starzec (Gen Counsel, Sec & Exec VP)
David Williams (VP-Exploration & Dev)
Nick Gibbens (VP-Land & Bus Dev)
Andrew Schaefer (CTO & VP)
David Rogers (VP-Mktg & Risk Mgmt)
Kendall Meyers (VP-Engrg)
David M. Dunwoody Jr. (Pres)
Larry Willis Jr. (Treas & VP-Fin & IR)

Talos Energy LLC (1)
333 Clay St Ste 3300, Houston, TX 77002
Tel.: (713) 328-3000
Web Site: https://www.talosenergy.com
Oil & Gas Exploration, Development & Production
N.A.I.C.S.: 213112
John B. Spath (Sr VP-Production Ops)
Timothy S. Duncan (Founder)
Stephen E. Heitzman (Co-Founder, COO & Exec VP)
John A. Parker (Co-Founder & Exec VP-Exploration)
William S. Moss III (Gen Counsel & Exec VP)

TALPHERA, INC.

1850 Gateway Dr Ste 175, San Mateo, CA 94404
Tel.: (650) 216-3500 DE
Web Site: https://talphera.com
Year Founded: 2005
TLPH—(NASDAQ)
Rev.: $1,771,000
Assets: $47,487,000
Liabilities: $25,673,000
Net Worth: $21,814,000
Earnings: $42,329,000
Emp.: 19
Fiscal Year-end: 12/31/22
Pharmaceutical Preparation Manufacturing
N.A.I.C.S.: 325412
Badri N. Dasu (Chief Engrg Officer)
Vincent J. Angotti (CEO)
Raffi M. Asadorian (CFO)
Adrian Adams (Chm)

TANDEM DIABETES CARE, INC.

11075 Roselle St, San Diego, CA 92121

Tel.: (858) 366-6900 DE
Web Site:
https://www.tandemdiabetes.com
Year Founded: 2006
TNDM—(NASDAQ)
Rev.: $747,718,000
Assets: $952,658,000
Liabilities: $639,026,000
Net Worth: $313,632,000
Earnings: ($222,611,000)
Emp.: 2,400
Fiscal Year-end: 12/31/23
Diabetes-Related Medical Products Mfr
N.A.I.C.S.: 339112
John F. Sheridan (Pres & CEO)
Paul M. DiPerna (Founder)
Susan M. Morrison (Chief Admin Officer & Exec VP)
Leigh A. Vosseller (CFO, Treas & Exec VP)
Jim Leal (Sr VP-Ops)
Rick Carpenter (Chief Technical Officer)
Libba Sapitsky (Sr VP-Customer Care)
Rizwan Pervez (Sr VP-Quality & Regulatory)
Shannon Hansen (Chief Compliance Officer)
Huzefa Neemuchwala (Sr VP)
Jordan Pinsker (Dir)
Jean-Claude Kyrillos (COO & Exec VP)
Tom Fox (Sr VP-HR & Organizational Dev)

Subsidiaries:

Tandem Diabetes Canada (1)
675 Cochrane Drive East Tower 6th Floor Room 611, Markham, L3R 0B8, ON, Canada
Insulin Pump Mfr
N.A.I.C.S.: 339112

TANDY LEATHER FACTORY, INC.

1900 SE Loop 820 Bldg B, Fort Worth, TX 76140
Tel.: (817) 872-3200 DE
Web Site:
https://www.tandyleather.com
Year Founded: 1980
TLF—(NASDAQ)
Rev.: $80,935,000
Assets: $68,579,000
Liabilities: $17,116,000
Net Worth: $51,463,000
Earnings: $1,227,000
Emp.: 494
Fiscal Year-end: 12/31/22
Leather Products Mfr & Distr
N.A.I.C.S.: 316990
Jefferson Gramm (Chm)

Subsidiaries:

The Leather Factory of Canada Ltd. (1)
5562 Tomken Rd, Mississauga, L4W 1P4, ON, Canada
Leather Goods Store Operator
N.A.I.C.S.: 458320
Brad Trauzzi (Gen Mgr)

TANGER INC.

3200 Nline Ave Ste 360, Greensboro, NC 27408
Tel.: (336) 856-6100 NC
Web Site: https://www.tanger.com
Year Founded: 1993
SKT—(NYSE)
Rev.: $464,407,000
Assets: $2,324,119,000
Liabilities: $1,732,806,000
Net Worth: $591,313,000
Earnings: $99,151,000
Emp.: 364

Fiscal Year-end: 12/31/23
Real Estate Investment Trust
N.A.I.C.S.: 531210
Leslie Swanson (COO & Exec VP)
Stephen J. Yalof (Pres & CEO)
Virginia R. Summerell (Sr VP-Fin)
Carrie A. Warren (CMO & Exec VP-Mktg)
Leslie Swanson (Exec VP-Ops)
Michael Bilerman (CFO, Chief Investment Officer & Exec VP)
Andrew Wingrove (Chief Comml Officer)
Justin Stein (Exec VP)
Thomas J. Guerrieri Jr. (Chief Acctg Officer & Sr VP)

Subsidiaries:

COROC/Myrtle Beach L.L.C. (1)
10835 Kings Rd, Myrtle Beach, SC 29572
Tel.: (843) 449-0491
Web Site: http://www.coroc.com
Shopping Center Rental & Leasing Services
N.A.I.C.S.: 531120

COROC/Park City L.L.C. (1)
6699 N Landmark Dr, Park City, UT 84098
Tel.: (435) 645-7078
Web Site: http://www.tangeroutlet.com
Shopping Center Rental & Leasing Services
N.A.I.C.S.: 531120

Charlotte Outlets, LLC (1)
5410 New Fashion Way Ste 210, Charlotte, NC 28278
Tel.: (704) 583-0222
Apparel Retail Store
N.A.I.C.S.: 459999

Outlet Mall of Savannah, LLC (1)
300 Park Ave, Pooler, GA 31322
Tel.: (912) 348-3125
Apparel Retail Store
N.A.I.C.S.: 459999

Outlets at Westgate, LLC (1)
3200 Northline Ave Ste 360, Greensboro, NC 27408-7612
Tel.: (623) 877-9500
Retailers Stores
N.A.I.C.S.: 459999

TWMB Associates, LLC (1)
3200 Northline Ave Ste 360, Greensboro, NC 27408-7612
Tel.: (336) 292-3010
Sales Range: $50-74.9 Million
Emp.: 93
Property Management Services
N.A.I.C.S.: 531312

Tanger Branson, LLC (1)
300 Tanger Blvd, Branson, MO 65616
Tel.: (417) 337-9328
Web Site: https://www.tanger.com
Shopping Services
N.A.I.C.S.: 812990

Tanger Charleston, LLC (1)
4840 Tanger Outlet Blvd N, Charleston, SC 29418
Tel.: (843) 529-3095
Web Site: https://www.tanger.com
Shopping Services
N.A.I.C.S.: 812990

Tanger Daytona, LLC (1)
1100 Cornerstone Blvd, Daytona Beach, FL 32117
Tel.: (386) 843-7459
Shopping Services
N.A.I.C.S.: 812990
Sarah Rasheid (Gen Mgr)

Tanger Fort Worth, LLC (1)
15853 N Fwy, Fort Worth, TX 76177
Tel.: (817) 464-5400
Web Site: https://www.tanger.com
Shopping Services
N.A.I.C.S.: 812990
Melissa Garcia (Gen Mgr)

Tanger Grand Rapids, LLC (1)
350 84th St SW, Byron Center, MI 49315
Tel.: (616) 277-1133
Web Site: https://www.tanger.com

Apparel Retail Store
N.A.I.C.S.: 459999

Tanger Jeffersonville, LLC (1)
8000 Factory Shops Blvd, Jeffersonville, OH 43128
Tel.: (740) 948-9091
Shopping Services
N.A.I.C.S.: 812990

Tanger Outlets Deer Park, LLC (1)
152 The Arches Cir, Deer Park, NY 11729
Tel.: (631) 667-0600
Web Site: https://www.tanger.com
Apparel Retail Store
N.A.I.C.S.: 459999
Eileen Rupnick (Asst Gen Mgr)

Tanger Properties Limited Partnership (1)
3200 Northline Ave Ste 360, Greensboro, NC 27408
Tel.: (336) 292-3010
Web Site: https://www.tangeroutlet.com
Rev.: $442,612,999
Assets: $2,217,011,000
Liabilities: $1,703,077,000
Net Worth: $513,933,999
Earnings: $85,831,000
Emp.: 340
Fiscal Year-end: 12/31/2022
Property Management Services
N.A.I.C.S.: 525990
Steven B. Tanger (CEO)

Tanger Riverhead, LLC (1)
200 Tanger Mall Dr, Riverhead, NY 11901
Tel.: (631) 369-2732
Women Outlet Distr
N.A.I.C.S.: 458110

Tanger Terrell, LLC (1)
301 Tanger Dr, Terrell, TX 75160
Tel.: (972) 524-6034
Shopping Services
N.A.I.C.S.: 812990

Tanger Wisconsin Dells, LLC (1)
210 N Gasser Rd Ste 105, Wisconsin Dells, WI 53913
Tel.: (608) 253-5380
Shopping Center Rental & Leasing Services
N.A.I.C.S.: 531120

TANGO THERAPEUTICS, INC.
201 Brookline Ave Ste 901, Boston, MA 02215
Tel.: (857) 320-4900   DE
Web Site: https://www.tangotx.com
Year Founded: 2020
TNGX—(NASDAQ)
Rev.: $24,860,000
Assets: $436,470,000
Liabilities: $186,994,000
Net Worth: $249,476,000
Earnings: ($108,176,000)
Emp.: 110
Fiscal Year-end: 12/31/22
Investment Services
N.A.I.C.S.: 523999
Timothy Lu (Co-Founder)
Adam S. Crystal (Pres-R&D)
Barbara Weber (Pres & CEO)
Amanda Galgay (Sr VP-Corp Comm)
Barbara Weber (Pres & CEO)

TANKE, INC.
606 S 9th St, Las Vegas, NV 89101
Tel.: (702) 418-0581   NV
Year Founded: 1984
TNKE—(OTCIQ)
Financial Consulting Services
N.A.I.C.S.: 541611
Nick Balomenos (COO)
Xiaoying Zhang (CEO)

TANXIA SYSTEM, INC.
321 E Floral Ave, Arcadia, CA 91006
Tel.: (408) 649-7045   CA
TASY—(OTCIQ)
Data Processing Services
N.A.I.C.S.: 518210
Hanyang Xu (CEO)

TAPESTRY, INC.
10 Hudson Yards, New York, NY 10001
Tel.: (212) 946-8400   MD
Web Site: https://www.tapestry.com
Year Founded: 1941
TPR—(NYSE)
Rev.: $6,671,200,000
Assets: $13,396,300,000
Liabilities: $10,499,400,000
Net Worth: $2,896,900,000
Earnings: $816,000,000
Emp.: 18,600
Fiscal Year-end: 06/29/24
Leather Handbags & Accessories Mfr; Retail Store Operator
N.A.I.C.S.: 316990
Todd Kahn (Pres-Coach Brand)
Andrea Shaw Resnick (Chief Comm Officer)
David L. Casey (Chief Inclusion &Social Impact Officer)
Christina Colone (Head-IR-Global)
Manesh B. Dadlani (Controller)
Scott A. Roe (CFO & COO)
Ashish Parmar (CIO & Sr VP)
David Howard (Gen Counsel & Sec)
Logan Duran (VP-ESG & Sustainability)
Kelsey Mueller (Dir-IR)
Noam Paransky (Chief Digital Officer)
Joanne C. Crevoiserat (Pres & CEO)
Anne T. Gates (Chm)

Subsidiaries:

Coach Hong Kong Limited (1)
Unit 1508-1516 C-Bons International Center 108 Wai Yip Street, Kwun Tong, Kowloon, China (Hong Kong)
Tel.: (852) 800960698
Web Site: https://hongkong.coach.com
Women's Handbag & Purse Mfr
N.A.I.C.S.: 316990

Coach International Limited (1)
Rm 3613 36/F The Gateway Tower, 6 Canton Road Tsim Sha Tsui, Hong Kong, China (Hong Kong)
Tel.: (852) 27097763
Leather Goods Mfr
N.A.I.C.S.: 316990

Coach Services, Inc. (1)
10 Hudson Yards, New York, NY 10001-1311
Tel.: (212) 594-1850
Web Site: https://www.coach.com
Womens Handbag & Purse Mfr
N.A.I.C.S.: 316990

Coach Stores Belgium (1)
Zetellaan 139, Maasmechelen, 3630, Limburg, Belgium
Tel.: (32) 89773570
Carriage Designer
N.A.I.C.S.: 316990
Jing Xie (Supvr-Store)

Kate Spade & Company LLC (1)
2 Park Ave, New York, NY 10016
Web Site: http://www.katespade.com
Branded Women's & Men's Apparel, Accessories & Fragrance Products Designer & Marketer
N.A.I.C.S.: 315990
Michele Parsons (Sr VP)
Roy Chan (Pres-Intl)

Subsidiary (Domestic):

Kate Spade LLC (2)
2 Park Ave, New York, NY 10016
Tel.: (212) 739-6550
Web Site: http://www.katespade.com
Women's Handbag Designer, Distr & Retailer
N.A.I.C.S.: 424350
Nicola Glass (Creative Dir)

Subsidiary (Non-US):

Kate Spade Japan Co., Ltd. (3)
6F Harajuku Piazza Bldg 4-26-18 Jingumae, Shibuya-ku, Tokyo, 150-0001, Japan   (100%)

Tel.: (81) 05055789152
Web Site: http://www.katespade.jp
Women's Handbag Distr & Retailer
N.A.I.C.S.: 424350
Kiyo Kogai (Sec)

Stuart Weitzman, LLC (1)
10 Hudson Yards 18th Fl, New York, NY 10001
Tel.: (212) 750-2555
Web Site: http://www.stuartweitzman.com
Women's Footwear & Handbag Designer, Whslr & Retailer
N.A.I.C.S.: 424340
Jackie Giusti Seaman (Sr VP-Global Mktg & Comm)
Kaisy Mae O'Reilly (Sr VP-Digital, Strategy & Customer Innovation)

TAPINATOR, INC.
1776 Broadway Ste 2002, New York, NY 10019
Tel.: (914) 930-6232
Web Site: https://www.tapinator.com
TAPM—(OTCIQ)
Rev.: $4,454,000
Assets: $1,273,000
Liabilities: $1,238,000
Net Worth: $35,000
Earnings: ($547,000)
Emp.: 6
Fiscal Year-end: 12/31/20
Mobile Game Publisher
N.A.I.C.S.: 513210
Ilya Nikolayev (Chm & CEO)

TARGA RESOURCES CORP.
811 Louisiana St Ste 2100, Houston, TX 77002
Tel.: (713) 584-1000   DE
Web Site:
https://www.targaresources.com
Year Founded: 2003
TRGP—(NYSE)
Rev.: $16,060,300,000
Assets: $20,671,800,000
Liabilities: $16,061,800,000
Net Worth: $4,610,000,000
Earnings: $1,345,900,000
Emp.: 3,182
Fiscal Year-end: 12/31/23
Holding Company
N.A.I.C.S.: 551112
Matthew J. Meloy (CEO)
Robert M. Muraro (Chief Comml Officer & Gen Partner)
D. Scott Pryor (Pres-Logistics & Transportation & Gen Partner)
Patrick J. McDonie (Pres-Gathering & Processing & Gen Partner)
G. Clark White (Exec VP-Ops & Gen Partner)
Julie H. Boushka (Chief Acctg Officer, Sr VP & Gen Partner)
Jennifer R. Kneale (Gen Partner & Pres-Fin & Admin)
Sanjay Lad (VP-Fin & IR)
Regina L. Gregory (Gen Counsel, Sec, Exec VP & Gen Partner)
Denny Latham (Exec VP)

Subsidiaries:

Floridian Natural Gas Storage Company, LLC (1)
811 Louisiana St Ste 2100, Houston, TX 77002
Web Site:
http://www.floridiangasstorage.com
Natural Gas Storage Services
N.A.I.C.S.: 424710
Bradley Williams (Principal)
David W. Sharp (Principal)

Lucid Energy Group II, LLC (1)
3100 McKinnon St Ste 800, Dallas, TX 75201
Tel.: (214) 420-4950
Web Site: http://www.lucid-energy.com
Crude Oil & Natural Gas Pipeline Transportation & Other Midstream Services
N.A.I.C.S.: 213112

Southcross Energy Operating, LLC (1)
2103 City West Blvd, Suite 900, Houston, TX 77042
Tel.: (703) 580-0265
Web Site:
https://www.southcrossenergy.com
Natural Gas Distribution Industry.
N.A.I.C.S.: 221210

TPL Arkoma Midstream LLC (1)
37791 State Hwy 3, Coalgate, OK 74538
Tel.: (580) 927-9133
Natural Gas Distribution Services
N.A.I.C.S.: 221210

Targa Energy LP (1)
1000 Louisiana St Ste 4300, Houston, TX 77002
Tel.: (713) 584-1080
Sales Range: $1-4.9 Billion
Natural Gas Distribution Services
N.A.I.C.S.: 221210
Jeffrey J. McParland (Pres-Fin & Admin)

Targa Resources LLC (1)
811 Louisiana Ste 2100, Houston, TX 77002   (100%)
Tel.: (713) 584-1000
Web Site: https://www.targaresources.com
Sales Range: $5-14.9 Billion
Emp.: 950
Holding Company; Natural Gas Upstream, Midstream & Downstream Services
N.A.I.C.S.: 551112
Joe Bob Perkins (CEO)

Subsidiary (Domestic):

Targa Resources Finance Corp. (2)
1000 Louisiana Ste 4300, Houston, TX 77002
Tel.: (713) 584-1000
Web Site: http://www.targresources.com
Sales Range: $350-399.9 Million
Financial Management Services
N.A.I.C.S.: 523999

Targa Resources GP LLC (2)
1000 Louisiana Ste 4300, Houston, TX 77002
Tel.: (713) 584-1000
Web Site: http://www.targaresources.com
Sales Range: $125-149.9 Million
Emp.: 400
Corporate Management Services
N.A.I.C.S.: 561110
Matthew J. Meloy (Co-CEO & Gen Partner)
Robert M. Muraro (Chief Comml Officer)
D. Scott Pryor (Pres-Logistics & Mktg)
Patrick J. McDonie (Pres-Gathering & Processing)
Jennifer R. Kneale (CFO)

Subsidiary (Domestic):

Targa Resources Partners LP (3)
811 Louisiana St Ste 2100, Houston, TX 77002   (100%)
Tel.: (713) 584-1000
Web Site: http://www.targaresources.com
Rev.: $8,260,299,999
Assets: $15,828,500,000
Liabilities: $9,076,400,000
Net Worth: $6,752,100,000
Earnings: ($1,758,800,000)
Fiscal Year-end: 12/31/2020
Natural Gas & Natural Gas Liquids Supplier
N.A.I.C.S.: 486210
Paul W. Chung (Chm)

Subsidiary (Domestic):

SeaPort Sound Terminal LLC (4)
2628 Marine View Dr, Tacoma, WA 98422
Tel.: (253) 272-9348
Fuel Terminal Operator
N.A.I.C.S.: 424710
Troy Goodman (VP)

Subsidiary (Non-US):

Targa Canada Liquids Inc. (4)
150 6 Ave SW Suite 3000, Calgary, T2P 3Y7, AB, Canada
Tel.: (403) 213-6414
Web Site: http://www.targaresources.com
Emp.: 1
Oil & Gas Exploration Services
N.A.I.C.S.: 213112

Targa Resources Corp.—(Continued)

Subsidiary (Domestic):

Targa Downstream LLC (4)
1000 Louisiana St Ste 4300, Houston, TX 77002
Tel.: (713) 584-1053
Natural Gas Transmission Services
N.A.I.C.S.: 486210

Targa Gas Marketing LLC (4)
1000 Louisiana Ste 4300, Houston, TX 77002
Tel.: (713) 584-1000
Web Site: http://www.targaresources.com
Midstream Natural Gas & Natural Gas Liquids Supplier
N.A.I.C.S.: 486210
Joe Bob Perkins (CEO)

Targa Intrastate Pipeline LLC (4)
1000 Louisiana Ste 4300, Houston, TX 77002
Tel.: (713) 584-1000
Sales Range: $25-49.9 Million
Emp.: 100
Midstream Natural Gas & Natural Gas Liquids Supplier
N.A.I.C.S.: 486210

Targa Liquids Marketing & Trade LLC (4)
1000 Louisiana Ste 4300, Houston, TX 77002
Tel.: (713) 584-1000
Web Site: http://www.targaresources.com
Gas Products Marketing Services
N.A.I.C.S.: 541613

Targa Louisiana Intrastate LLC (4)
1399 Davison Rd, Sulphur, LA 70665
Tel.: (337) 583-4642
Pipeline System Distr Services
N.A.I.C.S.: 486210

Targa Midstream Services LLC (4)
1000 Louisiana Ste 4300, Houston, TX 77002
Tel.: (713) 584-1422
Web Site: http://www.targaresources.com
Natural Gas Pipeline Transportation & Processing
N.A.I.C.S.: 486210

Branch (Domestic):

Targa Midstream Services LLC - Cameron (5)
5022 Gulf Beach Highway, Cameron, LA 70631
Tel.: (337) 569-2307
Web Site: http://www.targaresources.com
Emp.: 14
Industrial Gas Mfr
N.A.I.C.S.: 325120

Subsidiary (Domestic):

Targa Pipeline Partners GP LLC (4)
811 Louisiana St Ste 2100, Houston, TX 77002-5036 (100%)
Tel.: (713) 584-1000
Natural Gas Processing & Pipeline Distribution Asset Management Services
N.A.I.C.S.: 523940
Joe Bob Perkins (CEO)

Affiliate (Domestic):

Targa Pipeline Partners LP (5)
1000 Louisiana Ste 4300, Houston, TX 77002
Tel.: (713) 584-1000
Rev.: $2,975,120,000
Assets: $4,824,733,000
Liabilities: $2,306,266,000
Net Worth: $2,518,467,000
Earnings: $229,644,000
Emp.: 450
Fiscal Year-end: 12/31/2014
Holding Company; Natural Gas Processing & Pipeline Distribution Services
N.A.I.C.S.: 551112
Jeffrey J. McParland (Pres-Fin & Admin)
Gerald R. Shrader (Chief Legal Officer)
Robert W. Karlovich III (CFO)

Subsidiary (Domestic):

Atlas Pipeline Mid-Continent West-Tex, LLC (6)

110 W 7th St Ste 2300, Tulsa, OK 74119-1017
Tel.: (918) 574-3500
Support Activities for Oil & Gas Operations
N.A.I.C.S.: 213112

Targa Pipeline Mid-Continent LLC (6)
110 W 7th St Ste 2300, Tulsa, OK 74119
Tel.: (918) 574-3500
Pipeline Transportation of Natural Gas
N.A.I.C.S.: 486210

Subsidiary (Domestic):

Targa Resources Operating LLC (4)
1000 Louisiana Ste 4300, Houston, TX 77002
Tel.: (713) 584-1000
Web Site: http://www.targaresources.com
Emp.: 2,000
Midstream Natural Gas & Natural Gas Liquids Supplier
N.A.I.C.S.: 486210
Joe Bob Perkins (Chm)
Regina L. Gregory (Gen Counsel, Sec & Exec VP)

Venice Energy Services Company, L.L.C. (4)
1565 Tidewater Rd, Venice, LA 70091
Tel.: (985) 534-4050
Web Site: http://www.targaresources.com
Emp.: 45
Oil & Gas Exploration Services
N.A.I.C.S.: 213112

TARGET CORPORATION
1000 Nicollet Mall, Minneapolis, MN 55403
Tel.: (612) 304-6073   MN
Web Site: https://www.target.com
Year Founded: 1902
TGT—(NYSE)
Rev.: $107,412,000,000
Assets: $55,356,000,000
Liabilities: $41,924,000,000
Net Worth: $13,432,000,000
Earnings: $4,138,000,000
Emp.: 415,000
Fiscal Year-end: 02/03/24
Department Store Retailer
N.A.I.C.S.: 551112
Mark J. Schindele (Chief Stores Officer & Exec VP)
Laysha L. Ward (Chief External Engagement Officer & Exec VP)
Jill K. Sando (Chief Mdsg Officer & Exec VP)
A. Christina Hennington (Chief Growth Officer & Exec VP)
Don H. Liu (Chief Legal Officer, Chief Compliance Officer, Sec & Exec VP)
Michael J. Fiddelke (CFO, COO & Exec VP)
Katie Boylan (Chief Comm Officer & Exec VP)
Melissa K. Kremer (Chief HR Officer & Exec VP)
Cara Sylvester (Chief Guest Experience Officer & Exec VP)
Richard H. Gomez (Chief Food & Beverage Officer & Exec VP)
Prat Vemana (Chief Digital & Product Officer & Exec VP)
Rick Gomez (Chief Food & Beverage Officer)
Wesley S. McDonald (Dir-IT Financial Analysis)
Arthur L. Valdez Jr. (Chief Supply Chain & Logistics Officer & Exec VP)
Brian C. Cornell (Chm & CEO)

Subsidiaries:

TCDC, Inc. (1)
1070 33rd Ave SE, Minneapolis, MN 55414-2707
Tel.: (651) 645-3611
Web Site: https://tcdcinc.com
Emp.: 200
Aluminum & Magnesium Die Casting Mfr
N.A.I.C.S.: 331523

Target Corporation India Private Limited (1)
Embassy Manyata Tech Park No C-2 Manyata Embassy Business Park, Outer Ring Road MS Ramaiah North City Nagavara, Bengaluru, 560045, Karnataka, India
Tel.: (91) 8046734000
Web Site: https://india.target.com
Business Support Services
N.A.I.C.S.: 541611

Target Stores, Inc. (1)
1000 Nicollet Mall, Minneapolis, MN 55403
Tel.: (612) 304-6073
Web Site: http://www.target.com
Sales Range: $50-74.9 Billion
General Merchandise & Food Store Operator
N.A.I.C.S.: 455110

TARGETED MEDICAL PHARMA, INC.
2980 Beverly Glen Cir, Los Angeles, CA 90077
Tel.: (310) 474-9809   DE
Web Site:
http://www.tmedpharma.com
Year Founded: 1999
TRGM—(OTCEM)
Sales Range: $1-9.9 Million
Emp.: 15
Pharmaceuticals Mfr
N.A.I.C.S.: 325412
David Samuel Silver (Chief Medical Officer)

Subsidiaries:

Complete Claims Processing, Inc. (1)
2980 N Beverly Glen Cir Ste 100, Los Angeles, CA 90077
Tel.: (310) 943-4180
Web Site: http://www.ccpicentral.com
Insurance Claims Processing Services
N.A.I.C.S.: 524292
William Shell (Pres)

TARSIER LTD.
750 Lexington Ave 9th Fl, New York, NY 10022
Tel.: (212) 986-8229   DE
Web Site: http://www.tsmartcity.com
Year Founded: 2005
TAER—(OTCIQ)
Sales Range: $10-24.9 Million
High Frequency Induction & LED Lighting Products Mfr
N.A.I.C.S.: 335139
Isaac H. Sutton (Chm & CEO)
William May (Head-Innovation)
Jason Rappaport (CTO)

Subsidiaries:

1-800 NY Bulbs, Limited (1)
620 Fayette Ave, Mamaroneck, NY 10543
Tel.: (800) 692-8527
Web Site: http://www.nybulbs.com
Lighting Product Distr
N.A.I.C.S.: 423610
Randall Satin (Co-Founder & Pres)
Lawrence Merson (Co-Founder & VP)

TARSIN MOBILE, INC.
5045 Kietzke Ln Ste 100, Reno, NV 89511
Tel.: (408) 898-6191   FL
Web Site:
http://www.tarsinmobile.com
TMIX—(OTCIQ)
Software Development Services
N.A.I.C.S.: 541511
Joseph R. Cellura (Chm & CEO)
Michael F. Ghiselli (CFO, Treas & Sec)

TARSUS PHARMACEUTICALS, INC.
15440 Laguna Canyon Rd Ste 160, Irvine, CA 92618

Tel.: (949) 409-9820   DE
Web Site: https://www.tarsusrx.com
Year Founded: 2016
TARS—(NASDAQ)
Rev.: $25,816,000
Assets: $227,863,000
Liabilities: $34,963,000
Net Worth: $192,900,000
Earnings: ($62,091,000)
Emp.: 87
Fiscal Year-end: 12/31/22
Biotechnology Research & Development Services
N.A.I.C.S.: 541714
Jeffrey S. Farrow (CFO & Chief Strategy Officer)
D. Michael Ackermann (Chm)
Bobak Azamian (Founder, Pres & CEO)
Aziz Mottiwala (Chief Comml Officer)
Sesha Neervannan (COO)
Mark Holdbrook (VP-Clinical Affairs)
Kim Norman (Sr Dir-Fin)
Stephanie Baba (Dir-Clinical Affairs)
Maaza Martin (Dir-Mktg)
Steven Reyes (Dir-Project Mgmt)
Bryan Wahl (Gen Counsel)
Dianne Whitfield (Chief HR Officer)
Arthur Chan (VP-Medical Affairs)
Mai Sirimanne (VP-Clinical Affairs)
Matt Gay (Sr Dir-Quality Assurance)

TASKUS, INC.
1650 Independence Dr Ste 100, New Braunfels, TX 78132   DE
Web Site: https://www.taskus.com
Year Founded: 2018
TASK—(NASDAQ)
Rev.: $960,489,000
Assets: $902,015,000
Liabilities: $446,402,000
Net Worth: $455,613,000
Earnings: $40,422,000
Emp.: 49,500
Fiscal Year-end: 12/31/22
Business Process Outsourcing Services
N.A.I.C.S.: 541611
Bryce Maddock (Co-Founder, Chm & CEO)
Jaspar Weir (Co-Founder & Pres)
Balaji Sekar (CFO)
Jarrod Johnson (Chief Customer Officer)
Aleks Bogdanovski (VP-Div & Business Development)
Bailey Boyd (VP-Div & Business Development)
Brett Ransom (VP Bus Dev)
Charley LeMaster (Sr VP-Sales)
Cindy Castellanos Zavala (VP-Payroll)
Chris O'Bryant (Dir-Operations)
Gretchen Barker (Head-Staff)
Isaac Puno (VP-Sales & Enablement)
Jackie Lineberger Henrikson (VP-Business Development)
Jewel Bowers (Sr Mgr-Operations)
Jon Wouters (VP-Div Global, Growth Facilities, and Sustainability)
Lysandra Castaneda (Dir-Client Services)
Manish Pandya (VP-Div Digital)
Mark Sterling (VP-Div)
Mike Serpan (Sr VP-Client Services)
Rachel Lutz Guevara (VP-Trust & Safety)
Phil Tomlinson (Sr VP-Global Offerings)
Ricky Girson (VP-Business Development)
Sally Rittenhouse (VP-Business Development)
Stephan Daoust (COO)
Shawn Stoner (Dir-Client Services)
Vinay Sharma (VP-Div, Learning, and Development)

TASTY FRIES, INC.
190 N Canon Dr Ste 420, Beverly Hills, CA 90210
Tel.: (818) 744-8490   NV
TFRY—(OTCIQ)
Prepared Food Mfr
N.A.I.C.S.: 311991

TATTOOED CHEF, INC.
6305 Alondra Blvd, Paramount, CA 90723
Tel.: (562) 602-0822   DE
Web Site:
   https://www.ittellafoods.com
TTCF—(NASDAQ)
Rev.: $213,430,000
Assets: $267,201,000
Liabilities: $49,898,000
Net Worth: $217,303,000
Earnings: ($87,404,000)
Emp.: 800
Fiscal Year-end: 12/31/21
Plant-Based Food Mfr
N.A.I.C.S.: 311999

Subsidiaries:

New Mexico Food Distributors, Inc.   (1)
3041 University Blvd SE, Albuquerque, NM 87106
Tel.: (505) 888-0104
Web Site:
   https://www.foodsofnewmexico.com
Sales Range: $10-24.9 Million
Emp.: 85
Canned Food Services
N.A.I.C.S.: 311422
Dj Valles *(Mgr-Plant & Quality Assurance)*

TAURIGA SCIENCES, INC.
4 Nancy Court Ste 4, Wappingers Falls, NY 12590
Tel.: (917) 796-9926   FL
Web Site: http://www.tauriga.com
Year Founded: 2001
TAUG—(OTCIQ)
Rev.: $354,667
Assets: $2,488,703
Liabilities: $1,217,456
Net Worth: $1,271,247
Earnings: ($3,626,446)
Emp.: 2
Fiscal Year-end: 03/31/21
Immunotherapy Developer
N.A.I.C.S.: 541715
Kevin P. Lacey *(CFO & Principal Acctg Officer)*
Keith A. Aqua *(Chief Medical Officer)*
Adina Miles *(CMO)*

TAUTACHROME INC.
1846 E Innovation Park Dr, Oro Valley, AZ 85755
Tel.: (520) 318-5578   DE
Web Site:
   https://www.tautachrome.com
Year Founded: 2006
TTCM—(OTCIQ)
Rev.: $262
Assets: $144,810
Liabilities: $4,779,104
Net Worth: ($4,634,294)
Earnings: ($5,080,191)
Fiscal Year-end: 12/31/21
Investment Services
N.A.I.C.S.: 523999

Subsidiaries:

Polybia Studios Pty, Ltd   (1)
Unit B/5 Glenelg Avenue Mermaid Waters, Gold Coast, Australia
Tel.: (61) 755545883
Web Site: http://www.polybiastudios.com
Software Development Services
N.A.I.C.S.: 513210

TAYLOR CONSULTING INC.
1773 Westborough Dr, Katy, TX 77449
Tel.: (832) 487-7760   DE
Web Site:
   https://taylorconsultingservices.com
Year Founded: 2012
TAYO—(OTCIQ)
Consulting Services
N.A.I.C.S.: 541618
Zane D. Russell *(CEO)*
Amzy E. Hibler *(CFO)*
Thomas Craig Takacs *(Sec)*
Robert Sonfield *(Corp Counsel)*

TAYLOR DEVICES, INC.
90 Taylor Dr, North Tonawanda, NY 14120
Tel.: (716) 694-0800   NY
Web Site:
   https://www.taylordevices.com
Year Founded: 1955
TAYD—(NASDAQ)
Rev.: $44,582,807
Assets: $63,077,418
Liabilities: $11,830,732
Net Worth: $51,246,686
Earnings: $8,998,762
Emp.: 125
Fiscal Year-end: 05/31/24
Manufacture & Sales of Products Used to Absorb Shock, Control Vibrations & Store Energy
N.A.I.C.S.: 333248
Mark V. McDonough *(Sec)*
John Burgess *(Chm)*
Alan R. Klembczyk *(Pres & VP-Sales-Engineering)*
Timothy J. Sopko *(CEO)*
Paul Heary *(CFO)*

TAYSHA GENE THERAPIES, INC.
3000 Pegasus Park Dr Ste 1430, Dallas, TX 75247
Tel.: (214) 612-0000   DE
Web Site: https://www.tayshagtx.com
Year Founded: 2019
TSHA—(NASDAQ)
Rev.: $2,502,000
Assets: $126,276,000
Liabilities: $125,327,000
Net Worth: $949,000
Earnings: ($166,014,000)
Emp.: 65
Fiscal Year-end: 12/31/22
Research & Development in Biotechnology (except Nanobiotechnology)
N.A.I.C.S.: 541714
Sukumar Nagendran *(Pres & Head-R&D)*
Sean P. Nolan *(Chm & CEO)*
R. A. Session II *(Founder)*
Kamran Alam *(CFO)*
Fred Porter *(Chief Technical Officer)*
Emily McGinnis *(Chief Patient Officer & Head-Govt Affairs)*
Sean McAuliffe *(Chief Comml Officer)*
Jim Rouse *(CIO)*
Niren Shah *(VP-Bus Ops)*
Sean P. Nolan *(Chm & CEO)*
Sukumar Nagendran *(Pres & Head-R&D)*
Greg Gara *(Sr VP-Mfg)*
Kimberly Lee *(Chief Corp Affairs Officer)*
Mary Newman *(Chief Dev Officer)*
Timothy J. Douros *(Chief Legal Officer & Sec)*
Tracy M. Porter *(Chief People Officer)*

TC BANCSHARES, INC.
131 S Dawson St, Thomasville, GA 31799
Tel.: (229) 226-3221   GA
Web Site: https://www.tcfederal.com
Year Founded: 2021

TCBC—(NASDAQ)
Rev.: $15,456,873
Assets: $429,617,526
Liabilities: $344,339,692
Net Worth: $85,277,834
Earnings: $1,760,413
Emp.: 59
Fiscal Year-end: 12/31/22
Offices of Bank Holding Companies
N.A.I.C.S.: 551111
Scott C. McLean *(CFO)*
Gregory H. Eiford *(Pres & CEO)*
Jefferson L. Johnson *(Vice Chm)*

TCG GROWTH OPPORTUNITIES CORP.
12180 Millennium Dr Ste 500, Playa Vista, CA 90094
Tel.: (310) 633-2900   DE
Year Founded: 2020
TCGGU—(NASDAQ)
Investment Services
N.A.I.C.S.: 523999
Jesse Jacobs *(Co-CEO)*
Mike Kerns *(Co-CEO)*
Jennifer Randle *(CFO)*
Michael Kerns *(Co-CEO)*

TCR2 THERAPEUTICS, INC.
100 Binney St Ste 710, Cambridge, MA 02142
Tel.: (617) 949-5200   DE
Web Site: https://www.tcr2.com
Year Founded: 2015
TCRR—(NASDAQ)
Rev.: $1,938,000
Assets: $208,236,000
Liabilities: $67,377,000
Net Worth: $140,859,000
Earnings: ($151,822,000)
Emp.: 66
Fiscal Year-end: 12/31/22
Biotechnology Research & Development Services
N.A.I.C.S.: 541714
Garry E. Menzel *(Pres & CEO)*
Eric M. Sullivan *(CFO & Principal Acctg Officer)*
Alfonso Quintas Cardama *(Chief Medical Officer)*
Andrew Cornforth *(VP-Process Dev)*
Stephen Turkowiak *(VP-Fin)*
Patrick A. Baeuerle *(Founder)*
Robert Tighe *(VP-Translational Res)*
Dario Gutierrez *(VP-Discovery & Innovation)*
Nigel Williams *(VP-Mfg)*
Angela Justice *(Chief People Officer)*
Margaret Siegel *(Sec, VP & Head-Legal)*
Peter Olagunju *(COO)*
Gregg McConnell *(Head-Bus Dev)*
Viera Muzithras *(VP-Regulatory Affairs)*

TCV ACQUISITION CORP.
250 Middlefield Rd, Menlo Park, CA 94025
Tel.: (659) 614-8200   Ky
Web Site:
   http://www.tcvacquisition.com
Year Founded: 2021
TCVA—(NYSE)
Investment Services
N.A.I.C.S.: 523999
Jay C. Hoag *(Chm)*
Christopher Marshall *(Co-CEO)*
Frederic Fenton *(Pres)*
Erez Elisha *(CFO)*
Jon Reynolds Jr. *(Co-CEO)*

TCW SPECIAL PURPOSE ACQUISITION CORP.
865 S Figueroa St Ste 1800, Los Angeles, CA 90017
Tel.: (213) 244-0000   DE

Web Site: http://www.tcwspac.com
Year Founded: 2020
TSPQ—(NYSE)
Emp.: 3
Investment Services
N.A.I.C.S.: 523999
Joseph R. Shaposhnik *(Chm & CEO)*
Richard M. Villa *(CFO)*
Leo L. Chan *(Exec VP)*
Meredith Jackson *(Dir-Mgmt)*

TCW STRATEGIC INCOME FUND, INC.
865 S Figueroa St Ste 1800, Los Angeles, CA 90017
Tel.: (213) 244-0000   MD
TSI—(NYSE)
Rev.: $17,975,668
Assets: $280,520,051
Liabilities: $7,227,066
Net Worth: $273,292,985
Earnings: $15,564,068
Fiscal Year-end: 12/31/19
Investment Management Service
N.A.I.C.S.: 525990

TD SYNNEX CORP
44201 Nobel Dr, Fremont, CA 94538
Tel.: (510) 656-3333   DE
Web Site: https://www.tdsynnex.com
Year Founded: 1980
SNX—(NYSE)
Rev.: $57,555,416,000
Assets: $29,412,814,000
Liabilities: $21,229,632,000
Net Worth: $8,183,182,000
Earnings: $626,911,000
Emp.: 23,000
Fiscal Year-end: 11/30/23
Computer Hardware, Peripheral & Software Distr
N.A.I.C.S.: 541519
Marshall W. Witt *(CFO)*
Ann F. Vezina *(Chm)*
Liz Morali *(Sr Mgr-IR)*
Patrick Zammit *(COO)*
David Vetter *(Chief Legal Officer)*
Bonnie K. Smith *(CIO)*
Beth Simonett *(Chief HR Officer)*
Sergio Farache *(Chief Strategy Officer)*
Patrick Zammit *(Pres & CEO)*
Bonnie K. Smith *(CIO & Exec VP)*
Simon Leung *(Chief Bus Officer)*

Subsidiaries:

BPO Holdco Cooperatief U.A.   (1)
Strawinskylaan 3501 Route, 1077 ZX, Amsterdam, Netherlands
Tel.: (31) 205214777
Business Management Consulting Services
N.A.I.C.S.: 561110

Concentrix (Canada) Limited   (1)
4011 14th Avenue, Markham, L3R 0Z9, ON, Canada
Tel.: (905) 944-3449
Computer Peripheral Equipment & Software Whslr
N.A.I.C.S.: 423430
Marianne Pileggi *(Coord-HR)*

Concentrix CRM Services Germany GmbH   (1)
Im Eichsfeld 6, Russelsheim, 65428, Germany
Tel.: (49) 61426030
Emp.: 9
Computer Peripheral Equipment Distr
N.A.I.C.S.: 423430

Concentrix Duisburg GmbH   (1)
Neudorfer Strasse 43, 47057, Duisburg, Germany
Tel.: (49) 203545480
Computer Peripheral Equipment & Software Distr
N.A.I.C.S.: 423430

Concentrix Dusseldorf GmbH   (1)
Schiessstr 76, 40549, Dusseldorf, Germany

TD Synnex Corp—(Continued)
Tel.: (49) 2115421500
Computer Peripheral Equipment & Software Distr
N.A.I.C.S.: 423430

Concentrix Europe Limited (1)
9 Lanyon Place, Belfast, BT1 3LP, United Kingdom
Tel.: (44) 2890227777
Business Consulting Services
N.A.I.C.S.: 541611
Stephanie McVea *(Project Mgr-IT)*

Concentrix Frankfurt a. M. GmbH (1)
Ben Gurion Ring 174, 60437, Frankfurt, Germany
Tel.: (49) 693660110
Computer Peripheral Equipment & Software Distr
N.A.I.C.S.: 423430

Concentrix Gera GmbH (1)
Greizer Strasse 44, 07545, Gera, Germany
Tel.: (49) 365205030
Computer Peripheral Equipment & Software Distr
N.A.I.C.S.: 423430

Concentrix Halle GmbH (1)
Grenzstrasse 21, 06112, Halle, Germany
Tel.: (49) 34523950
Computer Peripheral Equipment & Software Distr
N.A.I.C.S.: 423430
Lucienne Karnbach *(Ops Mgr)*

Concentrix Leipzig GmbH (1)
Torgauer Platz 1, 04315, Leipzig, Germany
Tel.: (49) 34159410
Computer Peripheral Equipment & Software Distr
N.A.I.C.S.: 423430
Frank Meichsner *(Ops Mgr)*

Concentrix Management Holding GmbH & Co. KG (1)
Rheiner Landstrasse 195, 49078, Osnabruck, Germany
Tel.: (49) 54194620
Computer Peripheral Equipment & Software Distr
N.A.I.C.S.: 423430
Bernd Rehder *(Mng Dir)*

Concentrix Munster GmbH (1)
An den Loddenbuschen 95, 48155, Munster, Germany
Tel.: (49) 25160670
Computer Peripheral Equipment & Software Distr
N.A.I.C.S.: 423430
Mihail Manouras *(VP-Acct Mgmt)*

Concentrix Osnabruck GmbH (1)
Rheiner Landstrasse 195, 49078, Osnabruck, Germany
Tel.: (49) 54194620
Computer Peripheral Equipment & Software Distr
N.A.I.C.S.: 423430

Concentrix Schwerin GmbH (1)
Hopfenbruch Weg 6, 19059, Schwerin, Germany
Tel.: (49) 385202700
Computer Peripheral Equipment & Software Distr
N.A.I.C.S.: 423430

Concentrix Service Hungary Kft (1)
Rakoczi ut 60, 7621, Pecs, Hungary
Tel.: (36) 72536700
Telecommunication Servicesb
N.A.I.C.S.: 517810
Zoltan Lengyel *(Mgr-Facilities)*

Concentrix Services (Netherlands) B.V (1)
Van Heuven Goedhartlaan 11 A Parktoren, 1181 LE, Amstelveen, Netherlands
Tel.: (31) 207105000
Financial Trust Management Services
N.A.I.C.S.: 522110

Concentrix Services (Poland) spollka z o.o. (1)
Mokotowska 49, 00-542, Warsaw, Mazowieckie, Poland

Tel.: (48) 223788900
Business Consulting Services
N.A.I.C.S.: 541611

Concentrix Services Portugal, Sociedade Unipessoal, LDA (1)
Largo Da Estacao Edificio Estacao Ro, Maximinos, 4700-223, Braga, Portugal
Tel.: (351) 253199026
Business Consulting Services
N.A.I.C.S.: 541611

Concentrix Services Pty Ltd (1)
Grnd Flr 146 Arthur Street, North Sydney, 2060, NSW, Australia
Tel.: (61) 1300288808
Business Consulting Services
N.A.I.C.S.: 541611
Evangeline Maylad *(Mgr-Bus Ops)*

Concentrix Wismar GmbH (1)
Altwismarstrasse 7-17, 23966, Wismar, Germany
Tel.: (49) 38416440
Computer Peripheral Equipment & Software Distr
N.A.I.C.S.: 423430

Concentrix Wuppertal GmbH (1)
Friedrichstrasse 51, 42105, Wuppertal, Germany
Tel.: (49) 202693850
Computer Peripheral Equipment & Software Distr
N.A.I.C.S.: 423430

Corporate Mobile Recycling Espana S.L. (1)
Calle Alfareria 18, Mostoles, 28933, Madrid, Spain
Tel.: (34) 913717959
Mobile Phone & Microsoft Surface Services
N.A.I.C.S.: 541519

Corporate Mobile Recycling Ltd. (1)
3 Long Yard, Holborn England, London, WC1N 3LS, United Kingdom
Tel.: (44) 2074046440
Web Site: https://www.cmrecycling.co.uk
Mobile Phone & Microsoft Surface Services
N.A.I.C.S.: 541519

CyberLogistics Corporation (1)
Tokyo East 21 Business Center 2F 6-3-1 Toyo, Koto-ku, Tokyo, 135-0016, Japan
Tel.: (81) 356658738
Web Site: https://www.cyberlogistics.co.jp
Business Consulting Services
N.A.I.C.S.: 541611

Hyve Solutions Corporation (1)
44201 Nobel Dr, Fremont, CA 94538
Tel.: (510) 668-3877
Web Site: https://hyvesolutions.com
Electronic Parts Whslr
N.A.I.C.S.: 423690

Japan Concentrix K.K (1)
2F Kinshicho Prime Tower 1-5-7 Kameido, Koto-ku, Tokyo, 136-0071, Japan
Tel.: (81) 344131515
Web Site: https://www.japan.concentrix.com
Business Consulting Services
N.A.I.C.S.: 541611

License Online, Inc. (1)
44201 Nobel Dr, Fremont, CA 94538-3178
Tel.: (510) 656-3333
Web Site: https://www.licenseonline.com
Electric Component Whslr
N.A.I.C.S.: 423430

New Age Electronics, Inc. (1)
21950 Arnold Ctr Rd Ste 100, Carson, CA 90810
Tel.: (310) 549-0000
Web Site: http://www.newageinc.com
Sales Range: $900-999.9 Million
Emp.: 175
Consumer Electronics, Office Equipment & Photography Equipment Distr
N.A.I.C.S.: 423420
Fred Towns *(Pres)*
Randy Mora *(Sr Dir-Sls)*
Eric Kirkendall *(Sr VP-Sls)*
Matthew Dyenson *(Sr Dir-Product Mgmt)*
Julie Coughlin *(Sr Dir-Product Mgmt)*
Adam Del Vecchio *(Dir-Product Mgmt)*
Morgan Milosevich *(Supvr-Retail Mktg)*
Jason Michaels *(VP-Sls)*

Subsidiary (Domestic):

Jack of All Games, Inc. (2)
9271 Meridian Way, West Chester, OH 45069
Tel.: (513) 326-3020
Web Site: http://www.jackofallgames.com
Sales Range: $25-49.9 Million
Emp.: 35
Video Games Distr
N.A.I.C.S.: 423430

PC Wholesale Canada (1)
200 Ronson Dr, Toronto, M9W 5Z9, ON, Canada
Tel.: (416) 240-1901
Web Site: http://www.synnex.ca
Emp.: 15
Computer & Computer Peripheral Equipment & Software Merchant Whslr
N.A.I.C.S.: 423430

SYNNEX Canada Ltd. (1)
200 Ronson Dr, Toronto, M9W 5Z9, ON, Canada
Tel.: (416) 240-7012
Web Site: http://www.synnex.ca
Computer Products Distr & Whslr
N.A.I.C.S.: 449210
Mitchell P. Martin *(Co-Pres)*
Michael Dunne *(VP-Ops)*
Mark Hardy *(VP-Product Mgmt)*
Jim Kapogianis *(VP-Consumer Sls & Office Products)*
Pierre D. Montminy *(VP-Product Mgmt Consumer Products & Components)*
Russ Brown *(VP-Comml Sls)*
Alan Buttery *(Sr VP-Fin Ops)*
Debra LaTourette *(Sr VP-HR-North America)*
Robert Stegner *(Sr VP-Mktg-North America)*
Emily Ignoto *(VP-Fin Ops)*

SYNNEX Co., Ltd. (1)
3 2 5 Ueno, Taito Ku, Tokyo, 100-0050, Japan
Tel.: (81) 356882340
Web Site: http://www.synnex.co.jp
Sales Range: $25-49.9 Million
Emp.: 58
Mfr of Computer Peripherals & Software
N.A.I.C.S.: 334118

SYNNEX Information Technologies (Beijing) Ltd. (1)
6/F B Block International Science And Technology Exhibition Cent, Beijing, 100029, China
Tel.: (86) 10820125882236
Electronic Components Distr
N.A.I.C.S.: 423430

SYNNEX Infotec Corporation (1)
2nd Floor Tokyo East 21 Business Center 3-1 Toyo 6-chome, Koto-ku, Tokyo, 135-8559, Japan
Tel.: (81) 356658511
Web Site: http://www.synnex.co.jp
Emp.: 599
Computer Equipment Whslr
N.A.I.C.S.: 423430

SYNNEX de Mexico, S.A. de C.V. (1)
Av Ceylan No 709 Colonia Industrial Vallejo, Mexico, 2300, Mexico
Tel.: (52) 15521227800
Web Site: http://www.synnex.com.mx
Sales Range: $25-49.9 Million
Emp.: 5
Electronic Equipment Distr
N.A.I.C.S.: 423430

Shyft Global Services, Inc. (1)
5300 CenterPoint Pkwy, Groveport, OH 43125
Tel.: (614) 669-6600
Web Site: https://www.shyftservices.com
Supply Chain Management, IT & Other Technical Services
N.A.I.C.S.: 541990
Ron Brinckerhoff *(Sr VP)*

Subsidiary (Domestic):

Cokeva, Inc. (2)
9000 Foothills Blvd Ste 150, Roseville, CA 95747
Tel.: (916) 462-6000
Web Site: http://www.cokeva.com

Computer Related Services
N.A.I.C.S.: 541519
Dominick Derosa *(CFO)*

TD SYNNEX AS Czech s.r.o. (1)
Libalova 2348/1, Prague 11, 149 00, Chodova Plana, Czech Republic
Tel.: (420) 225299111
Web Site: https://cz.tdsynnex.com
Information Technology Services
N.A.I.C.S.: 541512

TD SYNNEX Austria GmbH (1)
Kranichberggasse 6 / Europlaza K, 1120, Vienna, Austria
Tel.: (43) 1488010
Web Site: https://at.tdsynnex.com
Information Technology Services
N.A.I.C.S.: 541512

TD SYNNEX Canada ULC (1)
107 Woodlawn Road West, Guelph, N1H 1B4, ON, Canada
Tel.: (519) 837-2444
Information Technology Services
N.A.I.C.S.: 541512

TD SYNNEX Croatia d.o.o. (1)
Lastovka 23, 10000, Zagreb, Croatia
Tel.: (385) 16184831
Information Technology Services
N.A.I.C.S.: 541512

TD SYNNEX Czech s.r.o. (1)
Libalova 1/2348, 14900, Prague, Czech Republic
Tel.: (420) 737264386
Information Technology Services
N.A.I.C.S.: 541512

TD SYNNEX Europe GmbH (1)
Kistlerhofstr 75, 81379, Munich, Germany
Tel.: (49) 8947000
Information Technology Services
N.A.I.C.S.: 541512

TD SYNNEX Finland OY (1)
Sokerilinnantie 11 C, 02660, Espoo, Finland
Tel.: (358) 201553636
Web Site: https://fi.tdsynnex.com
Information Technology Services
N.A.I.C.S.: 541512

TD SYNNEX France S.A.S. (1)
5 Avenue de l Europe, Marne la vallee, 77600, Bussy-Saint-Georges, Cedex 03, France
Tel.: (33) 825328000
Web Site: https://fr.tdsynnex.com
Information Technology Services
N.A.I.C.S.: 541512

TD SYNNEX Germany GmbH & Co. OHG (1)
Kistlerhofstrasse 75, 81379, Munich, Germany
Tel.: (49) 8947000
Information Technology Services
N.A.I.C.S.: 541512

TD SYNNEX Hungary Kft (1)
Budafoki Ut 91-93, 1117, Budapest, Hungary
Tel.: (36) 305114279
Information Technology Services
N.A.I.C.S.: 541512

TD SYNNEX Ireland Limited (1)
Unit 1i 1st Floor Block 71C The Plaza Parkwest Business Park, Dublin, D12 WDN2, Ireland
Tel.: (353) 18055680
Web Site: https://ie.tdsynnex.com
Information Technology Services
N.A.I.C.S.: 541512

TD SYNNEX Italy s.r.l. (1)
Via Tolstoj 65, San Giuliano Milanese, 20098, Milan, Italy
Tel.: (39) 02984951
Web Site: https://it.tdsynnex.com
Information Technology Services
N.A.I.C.S.: 541512

TD SYNNEX Kft (1)
Budafoki Ut 91-93, 1117, Budapest, Hungary
Tel.: (36) 305114279
Information Technology Services
N.A.I.C.S.: 541512

TD SYNNEX Netherlands B.V. (1)

Tolnasingel 2, 2411 PV, Bodegraven, Netherlands
Tel.: (31) 881334000
Web Site: https://nl.tdsynnex.com
Information Technology Services
N.A.I.C.S.: 541512

TD SYNNEX Norway AS (1)
Innspurten 1A, 0663, Oslo, Norway
Tel.: (47) 22897000
Web Site: https://no.tdsynnex.com
Information Technology Services
N.A.I.C.S.: 541512

TD SYNNEX Poland sp. z o.o. (1)
Batory Office Building II Al Jerozolimskie 212, 02-486, Warsaw, Poland
Tel.: (48) 225479200
Information Technology Services
N.A.I.C.S.: 541512

TD SYNNEX Portugal, Lda (1)
Avenida da Boavista 265 Piso 7, 4100-137, Porto, Portugal
Tel.: (351) 229390800
Web Site: https://pt.tdsynnex.com
Information Technology Services
N.A.I.C.S.: 541512

TD SYNNEX Spain, S.L.U. (1)
Acer 30-32, 08038, Barcelona, Spain
Tel.: (34) 932970000
Web Site: https://www.holatdsynnex.com
Information Technology Services
N.A.I.C.S.: 541512

TD SYNNEX Sweden AB (1)
Gustav III s Boulevard 32, Solna, 169 73, Stockholm, Sweden
Tel.: (46) 87952000
Web Site: https://se.tdsynnex.com
Information Technology Services
N.A.I.C.S.: 541512

TD SYNNEX Switzerland GmbH (1)
Birkenstrasse 47, 6343, Rotkreuz, Switzerland
Tel.: (41) 417991000
Web Site: https://ch.tdsynnex.com
Information Technology Services
N.A.I.C.S.: 541512

TD SYNNEX UK Limited (1)
Maplewood Crockford Lane Chineham Park, Basingstoke, RG24 8YB, Hampshire, United Kingdom
Tel.: (44) 1256788000
Web Site: https://uk.tdsynnex.com
Information Technology Services
N.A.I.C.S.: 541512

Td Synnex K.K. (1)
2nd Floor Tokyo East 21 Business Center 3-1 Toyo 6chome, Koto-ku, Tokyo, 135-8559, Japan
Tel.: (81) 356658511
Web Site: https://www.synnex.co.jp
Emp.: 791
Computer Hardware Product Whslr
N.A.I.C.S.: 423430

Tec D Distribution (Malaysia) Sdn. Bhd. (1)
6th Floor Wisma Prosper No 3 Jalan SS 7/19, Kelana Jaya, 47301, Petaling Jaya, Selangor, Malaysia
Tel.: (60) 376641800
Web Site: https://mytecd.com
Information Technology Services
N.A.I.C.S.: 541512

Tech Data Advanced Private Limited (1)
A-301 Supreme Business Park Behind lake Castle Hiranandani Gardens, Powai, Mumbai, 400076, Maharashtra, India
Tel.: (91) 2269410200
Logistics Management Services
N.A.I.C.S.: 541614

Tech Data Corporation (1)
5350 Tech Data Dr, Clearwater, FL 33760
Tel.: (727) 539-7429
Web Site: http://www.techdata.com
Sales Range: $25-49.9 Billion
Emp.: 14,000
Information Technology Hardware & Software Mfr & Distr
N.A.I.C.S.: 423430
Charles V. Dannewitz *(CFO & Exec VP)*
Beth E. Simonetti *(Chief HR Officer & Exec VP)*

Jaideep Malhotra *(Pres-Asia Pacific)*
Bonnie Smith *(CIO & Exec VP)*
Al Morales *(Chief Transformation Officer & Exec VP)*

Subsidiary (Non-US):

AKL Telecommunications GmbH (2)
Wehlistrabe 27-29 Stg 1/3 Stock, Vienna, 1200, Austria
Tel.: (43) 174379750
Web Site: http://www.aklt.at
Telecommunications Resellers
N.A.I.C.S.: 517121

Group (Domestic):

Avnet Technology Solutions (2)
2211 S 47th St, Phoenix, AZ 85034
Tel.: (480) 643-2000
Sales Range: $1-4.9 Billion
Computer Products, Software, Networking & Enterprise Solutions Distr
N.A.I.C.S.: 449210
William Joseph Amelio *(CEO)*
Ken Arnold *(Chief People Officer)*
Tom Liguori *(CFO)*
MaryAnn Miller *(Chief Admin Officer)*
Michael McCoy *(Gen Counsel & Chief Legal Officer)*

Subsidiary (Non-US):

Avnet Abacus Herlev (3)
Lyskaer 9, DK-2730, Herlev, Denmark
Tel.: (45) 86 84 84 84
Computer & Computer Peripheral Device Distr
N.A.I.C.S.: 423430

Avnet Abacus Madrid (3)
C/Chile 10 2a Plta Oficina 229, Las Matas, 28290, Madrid, Spain
Tel.: (34) 913727200
Custom Computer Programming Services
N.A.I.C.S.: 541511

Avnet Technology (Thailand) Ltd. (3)
Unit A3005 Tower A Floor 30th Cyber World Tower, 90 Ratchadaphisek Rd Huai Khwang, Bangkok, 10310, Thailand
Tel.: (66) 2645367880
Electronic Components Distr
N.A.I.C.S.: 423690

Avnet Technology Solutions (China) Ltd (3)
Unit 175 Building No 12 Taiyanggong, Middle Road Chaoyang District, Beijing, 100028, China
Tel.: (86) 10 5632 3666
Web Site: http://www.avenet.net
Electronic Product Distr
N.A.I.C.S.: 423690

Avnet Technology Solutions (Tianjin) Ltd (3)
Level 1 2 Block D17 Eastern Area No 2 Xue Fu West Road, Xue Fu Industrial Area Xi Qing District, Tianjin, 300382, China
Tel.: (86) 2223696825
Electronic Components Distr
N.A.I.C.S.: 423690

Subsidiary (Domestic):

Prosys Information Systems Inc. (3)
6025 The Corners Pkwy Ste 120, Norcross, GA 30092
Tel.: (678) 268-1300
Web Site: http://www.prosysis.com
Computers, Peripherals & Software Mfr
N.A.I.C.S.: 541690

Subsidiary (Non-US):

Tech Data Advanced Solutions (ANZ) Limited (3)
Level 2 67 Epping Rd Macquarie Park, Macquarie, 2113, NSW, Australia
Tel.: (61) 288750500
Web Site: http://www.asia.techdata.com
IT Products Distr
N.A.I.C.S.: 423430

Tech Data Advanced Solutions (India) Private Limited (3)
A301 3rd floor Floor Supreme Business Park, Behind Lake Castle Hiranandani Business Par Powai, Mumbai, 400076, India
Tel.: (91) 2244200200

Web Site: http://www.asia.techdata.com
Electronic Components Distr
N.A.I.C.S.: 423690

Tech Data Advanced Solutions (Malaysia) Sdn. Bhd. (3)
Unit 3-01 Level 3 Menara Uac 12 Jalan PJU 7/5, Petaling Jaya, 47800, Selangor Darul Ehsan, Malaysia
Tel.: (60) 377221980
Web Site: http://www.mytecd.com
Electronic Components Distr
N.A.I.C.S.: 423690

Tech Data Advanced Solutions (Singapore) Pte. Ltd. (3)
10 Ang Mo Kio Street 65, Singapore, 569059, Singapore
Tel.: (65) 62951788
Web Site: http://www.asia.techdata.com
Electronic Components Distr
N.A.I.C.S.: 423690

Tech Data Bilgisayar Sistemleri A.S. (3)
Saray Mahallesi Site Yolu Sokak Anel is Merkezi No 5 Kat 8, Istanbul, 34768, Istanbul, Turkiye
Tel.: (90) 216999 53 00
Web Site: http://www.tr.techdata.com
Information Technology Consulting Services
N.A.I.C.S.: 541512
Behcet Yumrukcalli *(Gen Mgr)*

Tech Data Distribution Ireland (3)
14 Joyce Way Nangor Road Park West Business Park, Dublin, D12 F9X8, Ireland
Tel.: (353) 18055600
Web Site: http://www.ie.techdata.com
Electronic Components Distr
N.A.I.C.S.: 423690

Tech Data GmbH & Co. OHG (3)
Lotscher Weg 100, 41334, Nettetal, 41334, Germany
Tel.: (49) 21537330
Web Site: http://www.de.techdata.com
Electronic Components Distr
N.A.I.C.S.: 449210

Subsidiary (Non-US):

Client Solutions Ltd. (4)
14 Joyce Way Park West Business Park, Dublin, D12 F9X8, Ireland **(100%)**
Tel.: (353) 19631860
Web Site: http://www.clientsolutions.ie
Software Development & Consultancy Services
N.A.I.C.S.: 541690
James Shemas Eivers *(Co-Founder & Chm)*
Teddy McCarthy *(Co-Founder & Mng Dir)*
Mary Gaughan *(Mgr-HR)*
Ciaran Doherty *(Mgr-Sls)*
Thibault Dartevelle *(Mgr-SAP Solutions Div)*
Declan Ballantyne *(Dir-Digital Transformation)*
Brian Kelly *(Mgr-IT)*
Damian Maloney *(Dir-BI & Analytics)*
Leo Murphy *(Sls Dir)*
Patricia O'Herlihy *(Fin Dir)*
David Reilly *(Mgr-Svc Mgmt Div)*

Tech Data AS Czech s.r.o. (4)
Libalova 1 2348, Prague, 149 00, Czech Republic
Tel.: (420) 225 299 111
Web Site: http://www.cz.techdata.com
Computer & Electronic Equipment Sales & Marketer
N.A.I.C.S.: 541519

Tech Data AS Kft (4)
Budafoki ut 91-93, IP West Irodahaz, H-1117, Budapest, Hungary
Tel.: (36) 18882333
Computer & Electronic Equipment Sales & Distr
N.A.I.C.S.: 423430
Szegvari Janos *(Sls Mgr)*

Tech Data Advanced Solutions NV (4)
Kouterveldstraat 20, 1831, Diegem, Belgium
Tel.: (32) 2 583 83 11
Web Site: http://www.be.techdata.com
Computer & Electronic Equipment Sales & Distr
N.A.I.C.S.: 423430

Tech Data Ltd. (4)
Redwood 2 Crockord Lane Chineham Park, Basingstoke, RG24 8WQ, United Kingdom
Tel.: (44) 01256 864 244
Web Site: http://www.uk.techdata.com
Computer & Electronic Equipment Sales & Distr
N.A.I.C.S.: 423430
Andy Gass *(Sr VP-UK, Ireland & Digital Europe)*
David Watts *(Mng Dir-UK & Ireland)*
Simon Coldwell *(Dir-Logistics)*
Phil Auld *(Dir-Legal)*

Tech Data Nederland B.V. (4)
Beatrix de Rijkweg 8, 5657 EG, Eindhoven, Netherlands
Tel.: (31) 402502602
Web Site: http://www.as.techdata.eu
Computer & Electronic Sales & Distr
N.A.I.C.S.: 423430

Tech Data Osterreich GmbH (4)
Kranichberggasse 6 Europlaza K, Vienna, 1120, Austria
Tel.: (43) 1 48801 0
Web Site: http://www.at.techdata.com
Computer & Electronic Equipment Sales & Distr
N.A.I.C.S.: 423430

WBT Systems Ltd. (4)
Block 2 Harcourt Centre, Harcourt Street, Dublin, Ireland **(100%)**
Tel.: (353) 14170100
Web Site: http://www.wbtsystems.com
Business Intelligence & Management Learning Solutions
N.A.I.C.S.: 561499
Paul Dooley *(CEO)*
Linda Bowers *(CTO)*
Michelle Brien *(VP-Mktg & Product Strategy)*
Mike Bourassa *(Dir-Bus Dev)*
Rachel Corrigan *(Mgr-Program)*

Subsidiary (Non-US):

Azlan Logistics Limited (2)
Lion House 4 Pioneer Business Park, York, YO30 4GH, United Kingdom
Tel.: (44) 1904695000
Web Site: http://www.azlan.com
Emp.: 100
Micro Computer Related Products Distr
N.A.I.C.S.: 423430

Azlan Scandinavia AB (2)
Fagerstagatan 18 B, Lund, 163 91, Sweden
Tel.: (46) 87952000
Web Site: http://www.azlan.se
Sales Range: $75-99.9 Million
Emp.: 25
Software Services
N.A.I.C.S.: 423450

Subsidiary (Domestic):

DLT Solutions, LLC (2)
2411 Dulles Corner Park Ste 800, Herndon, VA 20171
Tel.: (703) 709-7172
Web Site: http://www.dlt.com
Sales Range: $800-899.9 Million
Emp.: 250
Government Information Technology Services & Products Whslr
N.A.I.C.S.: 541512
Julie Bintzler *(VP-Acctg & Controller)*
Steve McDaneld *(VP-Fin Plng & Analysis)*
Dennis Kappeler *(VP-Sls Ops)*
David Blankenhorn *(CTO)*
Jim Propps *(Sr Dir-Platforms & Data Mgmt)*
Ron Tucker *(VP-IT)*
Scott Needleman *(Gen Counsel & VP)*
Chris Wilkinson *(Pres)*
Skip Liesegang *(VP-Channels)*
James Soliday *(Dir-Engrg)*
Kirk Fisher *(VP-Digital Design)*
Tom Mahoney *(Sr Dir-Mktg)*
Lloyd McCoy *(Dir-Market Intelligence)*

Subsidiary (Non-US):

EKM Global Limited (2)
Office 4 Crusader House, Roman Way Crusader Business Park, Warminster, BA12 8SP, Wiltshire, United Kingdom
Tel.: (44) 1985217920
Web Site: https://www.ekmglobal.com

TD Synnex Corp—(Continued)

Software Management Services
N.A.I.C.S.: 541511
Ian McRae (Mng Dir)

Hakro-Oosterberg-Nijkerk B.V. (2)
Londenstraat 11, Deventer, 7418 EE, Netherlands
Tel.: (31) 570680500
Web Site: http://www.hon.nl
Computer & Computer Peripheral Equipment & Software Whslr
N.A.I.C.S.: 423430

IQBlade Limited (2)
Liverpool Science Park 131 Mount Pleasant, Liverpool, L3 5TF, United Kingdom
Tel.: (44) 1514829700
Web Site: https://www.iqblade.com
Software Development Services
N.A.I.C.S.: 541511

PT Tech Data Advanced Solutions Indonesia (2)
Prudential Centre Level 10 Unit D - H JI Casablanca Kav 88, Jakarta Selatan, 12870, Indonesia
Tel.: (62) 2150882399
Web Site: https://asia.techdata.com
Electronic Parts Whslr
N.A.I.C.S.: 423690

Quote Components B.V. (2)
Marconistraat 1, Oldenzaal, 7575 AR, Netherlands
Tel.: (31) 541573737
Web Site: http://www.quote.nl
Computer & Computer Peripheral Equipment & Software Whslr
N.A.I.C.S.: 423430

Subsidiary (Domestic):

Signature Technology Group, Inc. (2)
2424 W Desert Cove, Phoenix, AZ 85029
Tel.: (602) 427-4500
Web Site:
http://www.signaturetechnology.com
Sales Range: $1-9.9 Million
Emp.: 55
Computer Maintenance & Repair
N.A.I.C.S.: 811210

Subsidiary (Non-US):

Specialist Distribution Group (SDG) Limited (2)
James House Warwick Road, Birmingham, B11 2LE, United Kingdom
Tel.: (44) 8451557766
Software Publishing Services
N.A.I.C.S.: 513210

TD Tech Data AB (2)
Box 56, Spanga, 163 91, Stockholm, Sweden
Tel.: (46) 856473057
Electronic Parts Whslr
N.A.I.C.S.: 423690

TD Tech Data Portugal Lda (2)
Av D Joao II Lote 1 07 21 Floor 1 Wing A, 1998-014, Lisbon, Portugal
Tel.: (351) 214728400
Web Site: http://pt.techdata.com
Computer & Software Whslr
N.A.I.C.S.: 423430

Tech Data (Schweiz) GmbH (2)
Birkenstrasse 47, Rotkreuz, 6343, Zug, Switzerland
Tel.: (41) 417991000
Web Site: http://ch.techdata.com
Sales Range: $25-49.9 Million
Emp.: 120
Computer & Computer Peripheral Equipment & Software Whslr
N.A.I.C.S.: 423430

Tech Data (Singapore) Pte. Ltd. (2)
APAC City Center Office 10 Ang Mo Kio Street 65 05-17/20, Singapore, 569059, Singapore
Tel.: (65) 62951788
Electronic Parts Whslr
N.A.I.C.S.: 423690

Tech Data Advanced Solutions (ANZ) Limited (2)
Level 2 67 Epping Rd, Macquarie Park, 2113, NSW, Australia
Tel.: (61) 1300362525
Web Site: https://www.techdata.com
Electronic Parts Whslr
N.A.I.C.S.: 423690

Tech Data Advanced Solutions (Singapore) Pte. Ltd. (2)
Information Technology Hardware & Software Distr
N.A.I.C.S.: 423430
Keivin Nye (Sls Mgr-Channel)

Tech Data Advanced Solutions (Thailand) Limited (2)
AIA Sathorn Tower Room no S9021 S9022 No 11/1 South Sathon Road, 9th Floor Yannawa Sathon, Bangkok, 10120, Thailand
Tel.: (66) 20558600
Web Site: https://www.techdata.com
Electronic Parts Whslr
N.A.I.C.S.: 423690

Tech Data Advanced Solutions (Vietnam) Company Limited (2)
Tuoi Tre Newspaper Building No 60AHoang Van Thu Street, Ward 09 Phu Nhuan District, Ho Chi Minh City, Vietnam
Tel.: (84) 2838478000
Web Site: https://www.techdata.com
Information Technology Hardware & Software Distr
N.A.I.C.S.: 423430

Tech Data Austria GmbH (2)
Wienerbergstrabe 41/F, Wiener Neudorf, 1120, Wien, Austria
Tel.: (43) 1488010
Web Site: http://www.techdata.at
Computer Realated Equipment & Software Whslr
N.A.I.C.S.: 423430

Tech Data Brasil, Ltda (2)
Rua Doutor Rafael de Barros 209 - 11 andar Paraiso, Sao Paulo, 4003-041, Brazil
Tel.: (55) 8007241115
Electronic Parts Whslr
N.A.I.C.S.: 423690

Holding (Non-US):

Tech Data Canada Corporation (2)
6911 Creditview Road, Mississauga, L5N 8G1, ON, Canada **(100%)**
Tel.: (905) 286-6800
Web Site: http://www.techdata.ca
Sales Range: $75-99.9 Million
Emp.: 400
Software Service & Solutions
N.A.I.C.S.: 541511

Subsidiary (Non-US):

Tech Data Colombia S.A.S. (2)
Km 1 8 Autopista Medellin Edificio B piso 2, Parque Industrial Soko Cota, Cundinamarca, Colombia
Tel.: (57) 17437760
Electronic Parts Whslr
N.A.I.C.S.: 423430

Tech Data Computer Service (Hong Kong) Limited (2)
Unit 1 20/F Tower 2 Enterprise Square Five 38 Wang Chiu Road, Kowloon Bay, China (Hong Kong)
Tel.: (852) 21972888
Information Technology Hardware & Software Distr
N.A.I.C.S.: 423430

Tech Data Computer Service (Macau) Limited (2)
Avenida Comercial de Macau No 251A-301 AIA Tower 20 andar, Macau, China (Macau)
Tel.: (853) 82946259
Electronic Parts Whslr
N.A.I.C.S.: 423690

Tech Data Croatia d.o.o. (2)
Korzo 11 Primorsko-goranska, Rijeka, Croatia
Tel.: (385) 51320200
Information Technology Hardware & Software Distr
N.A.I.C.S.: 423430

Subsidiary (Domestic):

Tech Data Delaware, Inc. (2)

2424 W Desert Cove Ave, Phoenix, AZ 85029-4713
Tel.: (602) 427-4503
Emp.: 50
Computer Maintenance & Repair Services
N.A.I.C.S.: 811210

Subsidiary (Non-US):

Tech Data Denmark ApS (2)
Banevaenget 13, 3460, Birkerod, Denmark
Tel.: (45) 44887575
Web Site: http://dk.techdata.com
Emp.: 30
Computer & Software Whslr
N.A.I.C.S.: 423430

Tech Data Deutschland GmbH (2)
Kistlerhofstrasse 75, 81379, Munich, Germany
Tel.: (49) 8947000
Information Technology Hardware & Software Distr
N.A.I.C.S.: 423430

Tech Data Distribution Croatia d.o.o. (2)
Radnicka cesta 80/5, 10000, Zagreb, Croatia
Tel.: (385) 15625740
Software Development Services
N.A.I.C.S.: 541511

Tech Data Distribution s.r.o. (2)
Libalova 1/2348, 149 00, Prague, Czech Republic
Tel.: (420) 225299111
Web Site: http://cz.techdata.com
Computer & Computer Peripheral Equipment & Software Whslr
N.A.I.C.S.: 423430
Petr Pavlícek (Sls Dir-Endpoint Solutions)

Tech Data Espana S.L.U. (2)
Acer 30-32, 08038, Barcelona, Spain
Tel.: (34) 902519251
Web Site: http://www.holatechdata.com
Information Technology Services
N.A.I.C.S.: 423430

Tech Data Europe GmbH (2)
Kistlerhofstrasse 75, 81379, Munich, Germany
Tel.: (49) 8947000
Web Site: http://eu.techdata.com
Emp.: 3,483
Computer Related Equipment & Software Whslr
N.A.I.C.S.: 423430
Stephen Nolan (Sr VP-Endpoint Solutions)
Miriam Murphy (Sr VP-Advanced & Specialised Solutions)

Tech Data European Management GmbH (2)
Kistlerhofstrasse 75, 81379, Munich, Germany
Tel.: (49) 8947000
Web Site: http://eu.techdata.com
Emp.: 50
Computer & Software Whslr
N.A.I.C.S.: 423430

Holding (Non-US):

Tech Data France SAS (2)
5 Avenue de l'Europe, Bussy saint Georges, 77611, Marne-la-Vallee, Cedex 3, France
Tel.: (33) 811640198
Web Site: http://fr.techdata.com
Computer Hardware & Software Distr
N.A.I.C.S.: 449210

Tech Data GMBH & Co OHG (2)
Kistlerhofstrasse 75, 81379, Munich, Germany **(100%)**
Tel.: (49) 8947000
Web Site: http://www.techdata.de
Sales Range: $300-349.9 Million
Emp.: 1,200
Computer Hardware & Software Distr
N.A.I.C.S.: 449210
Michael Dressen (Mng Dir)

Subsidiary (Non-US):

Azlan Group PLC (3)
Hampshire House, Wade Road, Basingstoke, RG24 8NE, Hants, United Kingdom **(100%)**

Tel.: (44) 8700603344
Web Site: http://www.azlan.com
Computer Networking & Communications Technology Distr
N.A.I.C.S.: 541513
Gareth Hansford (Mng Dir)

Tech Data Limited (3)
Redwood 2 Crockford Lane Chineham Park, Basingstoke, RG24 8WQ, Hants, United Kingdom
Tel.: (44) 1256 788 000
Web Site: http://www.techdata.co.uk
Computer Hardware & Software Distr
N.A.I.C.S.: 513210
Howard Tuffnail (Dir-Fin-Reg)
David Watts (Sr VP)
Martin Boyce (Dir-Sls-Grp)
Julian Klein (Dir-Ops)
Simon Coldwell (Dir-Logistics)
Jodie Carroll (Dir-HR)
Matt Child (Mng Dir-Advanced Solutions)
Linda Patterson (Dir-Mktg-Grp)
James Reed (Mng Dir-Endpoint Solutions)
Phil Auld (Dir-Legal)

Subsidiary (Non-US):

Tech Data GmbH & Co. oHG (2)
Kistlerhofstrasse 75, 81379, Munich, Germany
Tel.: (49) 8947000
Web Site: http://www.techdata.de
Computer Peripheral Equipment & Software Whslr
N.A.I.C.S.: 423430

Tech Data GmbH & Co. oHG (2)
Kistlerhofstrasse 75, 81379, Munich, Germany
Tel.: (49) 8947000
Web Site: http://www.techdata.de
Computer Peripheral Equipment & Software Whslr
N.A.I.C.S.: 423430

Tech Data Hungary kft. (2)
Budafoki ut 91-93, 1117, Budapest, Hungary
Tel.: (36) 18882333
Web Site: http://hu.techdata.com
Electronics Merchant Whslr
N.A.I.C.S.: 423620

Subsidiary (Domestic):

Tech Data Latin America, Inc. (2)
2200 NW 112 Ave, Miami, FL 33172
Tel.: (305) 593-5000
Web Site: http://www.techdata.com
Sales Range: $25-49.9 Million
Emp.: 100
Information Technology Products
N.A.I.C.S.: 541519

Subsidiary (Non-US):

Tech Data Mexico S. de R. L. de C. V. (2)
Insurgentes Sur No 859 Piso 4, Colonia Napoles, Mexico, 03810, Mexico
Tel.: (52) 5580003000
Web Site: http://americas.as.techdata.com
Computer & Computer Peripheral Equipment & Software Whslr
N.A.I.C.S.: 423430
Raffaelo Piccolo (Mng Dir)

Tech Data Mobile Acquisition Limited (2)
Redwood 2 Crockford Lane, Chineham, Basingstoke, RG24 8WQ, United Kingdom
Tel.: (44) 8718803533
Web Site: http://www.techdatamobile.co.uk
Transportation & Logistics Management Services
N.A.I.C.S.: 541614

Tech Data Mobile Belgium, BVBA (2)
Assesteenweg 117/1, 1740, Ternat, Belgium
Tel.: (32) 25838311
Web Site:
http://www.techdatamobilebelgium.be
Electronic Product Whslr
N.A.I.C.S.: 423620

Tech Data Mobile Limited (2)
Redwood 2 Crockford Lane, Chineham

Park, Basingstoke, RG24 8WQ, United Kingdom
Tel.: (44) 1256864699
Web Site: http://www.techdatamobile.co.uk
Emp.: 40
Mobile & Accessories Distr
N.A.I.C.S.: 449210

Tech Data Mobile Netherlands B.V. (2)
Rijksweg 79, Naarden, 1411 GE, Netherlands
Tel.: (31) 356954755
Web Site: http://www.techdatamobile.nl
Online Mobile & Accessories Retailer
N.A.I.C.S.: 423690

Tech Data Norge AS (2)
Innspurten 1A, 0663, Oslo, Norway
Tel.: (47) 22897000
Web Site: http://no.techdata.com
Software Services
N.A.I.C.S.: 423430

Tech Data Osterreich GmbH (2)
Kranichberggasse 6 / Europlaza K, 1120, Vienna, Austria
Tel.: (43) 1488010
Web Site: http://www.techdata.at
Emp.: 7
Computer Realated Equipment & Software Whslr
N.A.I.C.S.: 423430

Tech Data Polska Sp. z.o.o. (2)
Batory Office Building II Al Jerozolimskie 212, 02-486, Warsaw, Poland
Tel.: (48) 225479200
Web Site: http://www.pl.techdata.com
Emp.: 150
Computer Software Whslr
N.A.I.C.S.: 423430

Tech Data bvba/sprl (2)
Assesteenweg 117/1, 1740, Ternat, Belgium
Tel.: (32) 25838311
Web Site: http://be.techdata.com
Sales Range: $150-199.9 Million
Emp.: 400
Computer & Computer Peripheral Equipment & Software Whslr
N.A.I.C.S.: 423430
Els Demeester (Mng Dir)

Tech Data Distribution (Hong Kong) Limited (1)
21/F Tower One Millennium City 1 388 Kwun Tong Road, Kowloon, China (Hong Kong)
Tel.: (852) 25651682
Logistics Management Services
N.A.I.C.S.: 541614

Tech Data Distribution (Singapore) Pte. Ltd. (1)
No 2 Serangoon North Ave 5 05-03, Singapore, 554911, Singapore
Tel.: (65) 63610100
Logistics Management Services
N.A.I.C.S.: 541614

Tigerspike FZ-LLC (1)
1906 Marina Plaza - Dubai Marina, PO Box 393929, Dubai, United Arab Emirates
Tel.: (971) 43499882
Software Development Services
N.A.I.C.S.: 541511
Michal Hicks (Head-Experience Design)

Tigerspike KK (1)
The Park Rex Nihonbashi Bakurocho 4th Floor, 2-7-15 Nihonbashi Bakurocho Chuo-ku, Tokyo, 103-0002, Japan
Tel.: (81) 368045576
Software Development Services
N.A.I.C.S.: 541511

Tigerspike Ltd (1)
Level 4 Kings Court 2-16 Goodge St, London, W1T 2QA, United Kingdom
Tel.: (44) 2071486600
Software Development Services
N.A.I.C.S.: 541511

Tigerspike Pte. Ltd. (1)
38 Maxwell Rd 04-01, Singapore, 069116, Singapore
Tel.: (65) 62223683
Software Development Services
N.A.I.C.S.: 541511

Steven Zhang (Sr Engr-Software)

Tigerspike Pty Ltd (1)
Level 1 115 Cooper St, Surry Hills, 2010, NSW, Australia
Tel.: (61) 293615132
Web Site: http://tigerspike.com
Software Development Services
N.A.I.C.S.: 541511
Luke Janssen (Co-Founder)
Oliver Palmer (Co-Founder)
Dean Jezard (Co-Founder)
Josephine Bale (Project Mgr)

Tigerspike, Inc. (1)
235 Park Ave S Fl 12, New York, NY 10003
Tel.: (646) 330-4636
Software Development Services
N.A.I.C.S.: 541511
Steve Weiss (Sr Project Mgr)

Westcon Group, Inc. (1)
520 White Plains Rd, Tarrytown, NY 10591
Tel.: (914) 829-7000
Web Site: http://www.westconcomstor.com
Networking Equipment Resale Services
N.A.I.C.S.: 423430
Rakesh Parbhoo (CEO-Sub Saharan Africa)
Ivan Dittrich (CFO)
Dwight Pitter (CIO)
Donna Bain (Sr VP-HR-Intl)
Kevin Brzezinski (Sr VP-Ops)

Subsidiary (Domestic):

Comstor Corporation (2)
14840 Conference Ctr Dr Ste 200, Chantilly, VA 20151
Tel.: (703) 345-5100
Web Site: http://www.westconcomstor.com
Computer Networking Resale Services
N.A.I.C.S.: 423430
Clive Hailstone (Mng Dir-UK & Ireland)

Subsidiary (Non-US):

Westcon Brasil, Ltda. (2)
Av Alfredo Egidio de Souza Aranha 100 Bloco B-9 Andar, Sao Paulo, 04726-170, Brazil
Tel.: (55) 11 5525 7300
Web Site: http://www.westconcomstor.com
Security Management Software Distr
N.A.I.C.S.: 423430

Subsidiary (Domestic):

Westcon Cala, Inc. (2)
3350 SW 148th Ave Ste 401, Miramar, FL 33027
Tel.: (954) 308-0570
Web Site: http://www.westconcomstor.com
Software Consulting Services
N.A.I.C.S.: 541512

Subsidiary (Non-US):

Westcon Canada Systems (WCSI) Inc. (2)
1383 Joshuas Creek Drive, Oakville, L6H 7G4, ON, Canada
Tel.: (514) 420-5400
Web Site: http://www.westcongroup.com
Networking Components Distr
N.A.I.C.S.: 423430

Westcon Group Africa Operations Limited (2)
Chandlers House Wilkinson Road, Cirencester, GL7 1YT, Glos, United Kingdom
Tel.: (44) 1285 647 000
Web Site: http://www.westcongroup.com
Information Technology Consulting Services
N.A.I.C.S.: 541512

Westcon Group European Operations Limited (2)
210 Bath Road, Slough, SL1 3XE, Berks, United Kingdom
Tel.: (44) 1753797800
Web Site: http://www.westconcomstor.com
Telecommunication Equipment Distr
N.A.I.C.S.: 423690

Subsidiary (Domestic):

Westcon Convergence UK (3)
Astral Towers Betts Way, Crawley, RH10 9UY, W Sussex, United Kingdom
Tel.: (44) 1293 806 000

Web Site: http://uk.ucc.westcon.com
Telecommunication Servicesb
N.A.I.C.S.: 517810

Subsidiary (Non-US):

Westcon Group Limited (2)
32 Canaveral Drive, Albany North Shore, Auckland, 0632, New Zealand
Tel.: (64) 94156220
Web Site: http://www.westconcomstor.com
Software Publishing Services
N.A.I.C.S.: 513210

Subsidiary (Domestic):

Westcon Group North America, Inc. (2)
660 White Plains Rd, Tarrytown, NY 10591
Tel.: (914) 460-4800
Web Site: http://www.westcongroup.com
Computer Peripheral Equipment Distr
N.A.I.C.S.: 423430

Subsidiary (Non-US):

Westcon Group Pty Limited (2)
Unit 4 39 Herbert Street, Saint Leonards, Sydney, 2065, NSW, Australia
Tel.: (61) 294321000
Web Site: http://www.westconcomstor.com
Information Technology & Consulting Services
N.A.I.C.S.: 541512

Westcon Mexico S.A. de C.V. (2)
Torre Vistral Av Insurgentes Sur 730 Piso 11, Col Del Valle Benito Juarez, Mexico, DF 03100, Mexico
Tel.: (52) 55 5001 4950
Web Site: http://www.westconcomstor.com
Information Technology Consulting Services
N.A.I.C.S.: 541512

Westcon SA (Pty) Limited (2)
1 Tugela Lane Westcon Building Waterfall Logistics Precinct, Corner of Bridal Veil Road & R101 Jukskei View, 2090, Johannesburg, South Africa
Tel.: (27) 11 848 9000
Web Site: http://za.westcon.com
Software Consulting Services
N.A.I.C.S.: 541512

TDMY TECHNOLOGY GROUP, INC.
1180 N Town Center Dr Ste 100, Las Vegas, NV 89144
Tel.: (702) 781-4313   DE
Web Site:
http://www.dmytechnology.com
Year Founded: 2021
TDMY.U—(NYSE)
Investment Services
N.A.I.C.S.: 523999
Niccolo de Masi (CEO)
Harry L. You (Chm)

TEAM, INC.
13131 Dairy Ashford Rd, Sugar Land, TX 77478
Tel.: (281) 331-6154   TX
Web Site: https://www.teaminc.com
Year Founded: 1973
TISI—(NYSE)
Rev.: $840,208,000
Assets: $616,645,000
Liabilities: $498,885,000
Net Worth: $117,760,000
Earnings: $70,079,000
Emp.: 5,200
Fiscal Year-end: 12/31/22
Industrial Services
N.A.I.C.S.: 541990
Michael J. Caliel (Chm)
Michael R. Wood (Sr VP-Health, Safety & Environment)
Nelson M. Haight (CFO, CFO, Exec VP & Exec VP)
Keith D. Tucker (CEO)
Matthew E. Acosta (Chief Acctg Officer & VP)

Subsidiaries:

Cooperheat-MQS Inc. (1)
200 Hermann Dr, Alvin, TX 77511-6592
Tel.: (713) 735-6900
Web Site:
http://www.teamindustrialservices.com
Sales Range: $200-249.9 Million
Emp.: 1,400
Provider of Laboratory Services
N.A.I.C.S.: 541715

Furmanite Corporation (1)
10370 Richmond Ave Ste 600, Houston, TX 77042
Tel.: (713) 634-7777
Web Site: http://www.furmanite.com
Specialized Technical Services
N.A.I.C.S.: 323113

Subsidiary (Non-US):

Furmanite (Malaysia) Sdn. Bhd. (2)
Lot 1013 Jln Tg Kidurong, Kidurong Light Estate, 97007, Bintulu, Bintulu Sarawak, Malaysia
Tel.: (60) 86252482
Web Site: http://www.furmanite.com
Plant & Pipeline Maintenance Services
N.A.I.C.S.: 541330

Furmanite A/S (2)
Isefjordsvej 3, 6701, Esbjerg, Denmark
Tel.: (45) 35346080
Web Site: http://www.furmanite.com
Emp.: 3
Plant & Pipeline Maintenance Services
N.A.I.C.S.: 811310

Furmanite AB (2)
Verkstadsv gen 5, 441 31, Stenungsund, Sweden
Tel.: (46) 30365680
Web Site: http://www.furmanite.com
Plant & Pipeline Maintenance Services
N.A.I.C.S.: 541330

Furmanite AS (2)
Versvikvegen 6B, 3937, Porsgrunn, Norway
Tel.: (47) 35922001
Web Site: http://www.furmanite.com
Plant & Pipeline Maintenance Services
N.A.I.C.S.: 541330

Furmanite BV (2)
Driemanssteeweg 150, 3084 CB, Rotterdam, Netherlands
Tel.: (31) 107420940
Web Site: http://www.furmanite.com
Plant & Pipeline Maintenance Services
N.A.I.C.S.: 541330

Furmanite Canada Corp (2)
Unit #2 1373 Confederation Street, Sarnia, N7S 5P1, ON, Canada
Tel.: (519) 344-9292
Web Site: http://www.furmanite.com
Plant & Pipeline Maintenance Services
N.A.I.C.S.: 541330

Furmanite International Ltd. - IPSCO (2)
Sunningdale House Sunningdale Rd, South Park Industrial Estate, Scunthorpe, DN172ty, Lincolnshire, United Kingdom (100%)
Tel.: (44) 1724849904
Web Site: http://www.furmanite.com
Plant & Pipeline Maintenance
N.A.I.C.S.: 333914

Furmanite SAS (2)
158 rue Jean Perrin Z I De Dorignies, PO Box 308, Douai, 59351, France
Tel.: (33) 327998979
Web Site: http://www.furmanite.com
Plant & Pipeline Maintenance Services
N.A.I.C.S.: 541330

Furmanite Singapore PTE Ltd. (2)
42D Penjuru Road 05M-01C, Singapore, 609162, Singapore
Tel.: (65) 63209570
Web Site: http://www.furmanite.com
Plant & Pipeline Maintenance Services
N.A.I.C.S.: 541330

Subsidiary (Domestic):

Furmanite Worldwide, Inc. (2)

Team, Inc.—(Continued)

10370 Richmond Ave Ste 600, Houston, TX 77042
Tel.: (713) 634-7777
Web Site: http://www.furmanite.com
Specialized Industrial Services
N.A.I.C.S.: 811210

Self Leveling Machines, Inc. (2)
25123 Harper Rd, The Woodlands, TX 77380
Tel.: (281) 364-0007
Web Site: http://www.furmanite.com
On Site Machining Service
N.A.I.C.S.: 811310

Furmanite GmbH (1)
Technologiepark West Zum Frenser Feld 1, 50127, Bergheim, Germany
Tel.: (49) 2271989460
Industrial Engineering Services
N.A.I.C.S.: 541330

Global Ascent, Inc. (1)
Raymer Industrial Ctr 2003 Raymer Ave Ste G, Fullerton, CA 92833
Tel.: (714) 879-1350
Web Site: http://www.global-ascent.com
Industrial Rope Mfr
N.A.I.C.S.: 332618

P3 Pullen Polyurethane Products B.V. (1)
Bedrijvenstraat 4-2, 4283 JH, Giessen, Netherlands
Tel.: (31) 183678066
Web Site: http://www.p3products.nl
Plastics Product Mfr
N.A.I.C.S.: 326111

QualSpec, Inc. (1)
224 Deerwood Glen Dr, Deer Park, TX 77536
Tel.: (281) 479-3300
Web Site: http://www.qualspecgroup.com
Emp.: 1,000
Industrial Inspection Services
N.A.I.C.S.: 541350
Declan Rushe (Pres & CEO)

Quality Inspection Services B.V. (1)
Kuisel 11, 4703 RL, Roosendaal, Netherlands
Tel.: (31) 165554849
Non-Destructive Testing Services
N.A.I.C.S.: 541380

Quality Inspection Services BVBA (1)
16 Michigan Street, 2030, Antwerp, Belgium
Tel.: (32) 38084594
Web Site: https://qis-ndt.be
Non-Destructive Testing Services
N.A.I.C.S.: 541380

Quest Integrity CAN Ltd. (1)
1339 40 Avenue N Bay 27, Calgary, T2E 8N6, AB, Canada
Tel.: (403) 273-0051
Administrative & Management Consulting Services
N.A.I.C.S.: 541611
Todd Ring (Branch Mgr)

Quest Integrity Deutschland GmbH (1)
Zeppelinstrasse 2, 76185, Karlsruhe, Germany
Tel.: (49) 7219595757
Application Software Development Services
N.A.I.C.S.: 541511

Quest Integrity Middle East FZ-LLC (1)
Thuraya Tower 1 Floor 22 office 2207, PO Box 502776, Dubai, United Arab Emirates
Tel.: (971) 42772015
Asset Management Services
N.A.I.C.S.: 523940

Quest Integrity NLD B.V. (1)
Kamerlingh Onnesweg 3, 4131 PK, Vianen, Netherlands
Tel.: (31) 347320140
Web Site: http://www.questintegrity.com
Sales Range: $25-49.9 Million
Emp.: 3
Industrial Engineering Services
N.A.I.C.S.: 541330

TCI Services, Inc. (1)
4333 W 21st St, Tulsa, OK 74107
Tel.: (918) 583-3968
Web Site: http://www.tank-consultants.com
Inspection Services
N.A.I.C.S.: 541990

Team Industrial Services (UK) Limited (1)
Unit 2 Westside Business Park Estate Road No 2, South Humberside Ind Estate, Grimsby, DN31 2TG, United Kingdom
Tel.: (44) 1472263600
Web Site: http://www.teaminc.com
Industrial Engineering Services
N.A.I.C.S.: 541330

Team Industrial Services Asia Private Ltd. (1)
42D Penjuru Road 05M - 01C, Singapore, Singapore
Tel.: (65) 62613566
Web Site: http://www.teamindustrialservices.com
Sales Range: $25-49.9 Million
Emp.: 20
Industrial Engineering Services
N.A.I.C.S.: 541330

Team Industrial Services Belgium (1)
Michiganstraat 16 bus3, 2030, Antwerp, Belgium
Tel.: (32) 38205250
Web Site: https://www.leak-repairs-specam.nl
Sales Range: $25-49.9 Million
Emp.: 20
Industrial Mechanical Repair Services
N.A.I.C.S.: 238990

Team Industrial Services Malaysia Sdn Bhd (1)
Lot 1013 K4 Jalan Tg Kidurong Light Industrial Estate, Kidurong, 97000, Bintulu, Malaysia
Tel.: (60) 86252781
Inspection Services
N.A.I.C.S.: 541990
Quah Keat (Gen Mgr)

Team Industrial Services, Inc. (1)
200 Hermann Dr, Alvin, TX 77511-3425 **(100%)**
Tel.: (281) 388-5659
Web Site: http://www.teamindustrialservices.com
Sales Range: $10-24.9 Million
Emp.: 135
Environmental Monitoring & Industrial Pipe Repairs
N.A.I.C.S.: 811210
Phillp J. Hawk (Chm & CEO)

Branch (Domestic):

Team Industrial Services (2)
1145 N University Ave, Lafayette, LA 70506-1005 **(100%)**
Tel.: (337) 233-7676
Sales Range: $10-24.9 Million
Emp.: 50
Environmental Monitoring & Industrial Pipe Repairs
N.A.I.C.S.: 811210
Anthony Landry (Mgr-Ops)

Team Technical School, LLC (1)
200 Hermann Dr, Alvin, TX 77511
Tel.: (281) 388-5535
Web Site: https://www.teaminc.com
Industrial Engineering Services
N.A.I.C.S.: 541330

Team Valve and Rotating Services Limited (1)
1 Hudson Quay, Middlesbrough, TS3 6RT, United Kingdom
Tel.: (44) 1642467652
Industrial Machinery Repair & Maintenance Services
N.A.I.C.S.: 811310

Turbinate International, B.V. (1)
Kamerlingh Onnesweg 3, 4131 PK, Vianen, Netherlands
Tel.: (31) 347320140
Web Site: https://turbinate.com
Oil & Gas Pipeline Construction Services
N.A.I.C.S.: 237120

TEB BANCORP, INC.
2290 N Mayfair Rd, Wauwatosa, WI 53226
Tel.: (414) 476-6434 MD
Web Site: http://www.tebbancorp.com
TBBA—(OTCIQ)
Rev.: $23,716,602
Assets: $315,701,802
Liabilities: $282,577,935
Net Worth: $33,123,867
Earnings: $6,385,987
Emp.: 91
Fiscal Year-end: 06/30/21
Bank Holding Company
N.A.I.C.S.: 551111
John P. Matter (Chm)
William A. Behm (Chief Credit Officer & VP)
John Udvare (CFO)
Jennifer L. Provancher (Pres & CEO)
Thomas Sattler (Sr VP-Sls & Mktg)
Erin K. Arneson (Sec)
Jason Jesberger (VP)
Lauren Poppen (Treas, Controller & Asst VP)

TECH & ENERGY TRANSITION CORPORATION
125 W 55th St, New York, NY 10019
Tel.: (212) 231-1000 DE
Year Founded: 2017
TETC—(NASDAQ)
Rev.: $13,463,837
Assets: $385,828,806
Liabilities: $405,685,687
Net Worth: ($19,856,881)
Earnings: $10,607,556
Emp.: 4
Fiscal Year-end: 03/31/22
Investment Services
N.A.I.C.S.: 523999
John Spirtos (Pres & CEO)
Greg Callman (Chief Investment Officer)
Gautham Srinivas (Chief Legal Officer & Sec)
Andrew Ancone (CFO)

TECH CENTRAL INC.
Abundance Bldg 43537 Ridge Park Dr, Temecula, CA 92590 WY
Web Site:
http://www.techcentralinc.com
Year Founded: 2014
TCHC—(OTCIQ)
Sales Range: Less than $1 Million
Mobile Software Development Services
N.A.I.C.S.: 513210
Joseph Lewis (CEO, Treas & Sec)

TECHNICAL COMMUNICATIONS CORPORATION
100 Domino Dr, Concord, MA 01742-2892
Tel.: (978) 287-5100 MA
Web Site: https://www.tccsecure.com
Year Founded: 1961
TCCO—(OTCQB)
Rev.: $1,303,935
Assets: $1,950,843
Liabilities: $3,885,822
Net Worth: ($1,934,979)
Earnings: ($2,331,139)
Emp.: 19
Fiscal Year-end: 09/24/22
Communications Security Devices & Receivers Mfr
N.A.I.C.S.: 334220
Carl H. Guild Jr. (Chm, Pres, CEO, Acting CFO, Treas & Asst Sec)
Thomas J. Conte (Sr Dir, Pres, CEO, Corp Counsel, Exec VP & Sr VP)

Subsidiaries:

TCC Investment Corp. (1)

100 Domino Dr, Concord, MA 01742-2892
Tel.: (978) 287-5100
Web Site: http://www.tccsecure.com
Sales Range: $650-699.9 Million
Investment Services
N.A.I.C.S.: 523999
Carl H. Guild Jr. (Chm, Pres & CEO)

TECHNOLOGY GENERAL CORP.
12 Cork Hill Rd, Franklin, NJ 07416
Tel.: (973) 827-4143 NJ
TCGN—(OTCIQ)
Metal Products Mfr
N.A.I.C.S.: 331491
Helen A. Fletcher (Sec)

TECHPOINT, INC.
2550 N 1st St Ste 550, San Jose, CA 95131
Tel.: (408) 324-0588
Web Site: https://www.techpoint.co.jp
Year Founded: 2012
6697—(TKS)
Rev.: $66,007,900
Assets: $95,700,820
Liabilities: $13,144,860
Net Worth: $82,555,960
Earnings: $17,902,250
Emp.: 83
Fiscal Year-end: 12/31/23
Integrated Circuit Mfr & Distr
N.A.I.C.S.: 334413
Darron Ma (COO)
Darron Ma (VP-Sls & Mktg-Worldwide & Gen Mgr)
Fan Kung (VP-Ops)
Hiroshi Kondo (VP-Corp Mktg)
Fumihiro Kozato (Founder, Chm, Pres & CEO)
Feng Kuo (CTO)

TECHPRECISION CORPORATION
1 Bella Dr, Westminster, MA 01473
Tel.: (978) 874-0591 DE
Web Site:
https://www.techprecision.com
TPCS—(NASDAQ)
Rev.: $31,591,059
Assets: $34,746,695
Liabilities: $26,943,804
Net Worth: $7,802,891
Earnings: ($7,042,172)
Emp.: 162
Fiscal Year-end: 03/31/24
Large Metal Fabrications Mfr & Precision Machining Services
N.A.I.C.S.: 332312
Richard S. McGowan (Chm)
Alexander Shen (CEO)

Subsidiaries:

Ranor, Inc. (1)
1 Bella Dr, Westminster, MA 01473
Tel.: (978) 874-0591
Web Site: https://www.ranor.com
Fabricated Structural Metal Mfr
N.A.I.C.S.: 332312
Barbara M. Lilley (Controller)
Alexander Shen (Pres)

Wuxi Critical Mechanical Components (1)
No 9 Yanyu Middle Rd, Qianzhou Town Huishan District, Wuxi, 214181, Jiangsu, China
Tel.: (86) 51083390148
Web Site: http://www.wcmcsolutions.com
Power Generating Equipment Mfr
N.A.I.C.S.: 334519
Christopher L. Poplaski (Pres)

TECHTARGET, INC.
275 Grove St, Newton, MA 02466
Tel.: (617) 431-9200 DE
Web Site: https://www.techtarget.com

Year Founded: 1999
TTGT—(NASDAQ)
Rev.: $297,488,000
Assets: $764,717,000
Liabilities: $547,243,000
Net Worth: $217,474,000
Earnings: $41,609,000
Emp.: 1,000
Fiscal Year-end: 12/31/22
Information Services & Solutions for IT Industry
N.A.I.C.S.: 425120
Don Hawk (Co-Founder & Exec Dir-Product Innovation)
Gregory Strakosch (Exec Chm)
Michael Cotoia (CEO)
Daniel T. Noreck (CFO & Treas)
Stephen A. Duplessie (Co-Founder)
Rebecca Kitchens (Pres)
Steve Niemiec (COO & Chief Revenue Officer)
Garrett Mann (Sr Dir-Corp Comm)
Paul Healey (VP-AI Strategy)
Kelley Damore (Chief Content Officer)
Jennifer Labelle (Exec VP)
John Steinert (CMO)
Michelle Wilcon (Sr VP)

Subsidiaries:

Bitpipe, Inc.   (1)
275 Grove St, Newton, MA 02466
Tel.: (617) 431-9200
Web Site: http://www.techtarget.com
Sales Range: $25-49.9 Million
Emp.: 40
Online Network of Information Technology & Business Web Sites for Information Technology Marketers
N.A.I.C.S.: 513199

BrightTALK Limited   (1)
4 Christopher Street, London, EC2A 2BS, United Kingdom
Tel.: (44) 2039000000
Web Site: http://www.brighttalk.com
Sales Range: $10-24.9 Million
Emp.: 50
Marketing Software Development Services
N.A.I.C.S.: 513210
Paul Heald (Co-Founder & CEO)
Dorian Logan (Co-Founder & CTO)
Jeff Wheeler (CFO)
Ryan Ashburn (Pres & Chief Revenue Officer)
David Pitta (CMO)
Peter Rance (Chief Product Officer)
Kathrine Nachtwey (Exec VP-Customer Success)
Jenny Swisher (Exec VP-People Ops)
Vasu Ramachandra (Exec VP-Engrg)
Paul Holden (VP-Ops & Security)

Subsidiary (US):

BrightTALK Inc.   (2)
501 Folsom St 2nd Fl, San Francisco, CA 94105
Tel.: (415) 625-1500
Web Site: http://www.brighttalk.com
Online Event Solutions
N.A.I.C.S.: 513210
Paul Heald (Co-Founder & CEO)
Dorian Logan (Co-Founder & CTO)
Ryan Ashburn (Pres)
Jeff Wheeler (CFO)
David Pitta (CMO)
Simon Lees (Chief Bus Officer)
Peter Rance (Chief Product Officer)
Katherine Nachtwey (Exec VP-Customer Success)
Jenny Swisher (Exec VP-People Ops)
Vasu Ramachandra (Exec VP-Engrg)
Paul Holden (Exec VP-Ops & Security)

TechTarget (Singapore) PTE. Ltd.   (1)
133 Cecil Street 16-01 Keck Seng Tower, Singapore, 069535, Singapore
Tel.: (65) 60222455
Commercial Gravure Printing Services
N.A.I.C.S.: 323111

TechTarget Germany GmbH   (1)

Landwehrstrasse 61, 80336, Munich, Germany
Tel.: (49) 8921551840
Commercial Gravure Printing Services
N.A.I.C.S.: 323111

TechTarget Limited   (1)
TechTarget 10 Exchange Square Level 9 West, London, EC2A 2BR, United Kingdom
Tel.: (44) 2071861400
Sales Range: $25-49.9 Million
Emp.: 45
Online Technical Content Provider
N.A.I.C.S.: 518210

The Enterprise Strategy Group, Inc.   (1)
20 Asylum St, Milford, MA 01757
Tel.: (508) 482-0188
Web Site:
   http://www.enterprisestrategygroup.com
Rev.: $2,300,000
Emp.: 26
Information Technology Consulting Services
N.A.I.C.S.: 541618
Stephen A. Duplessie (Founder)
Walter Mason (CFO & Exec VP)
John McKnight (Exec VP-Res & Analyst Svcs)
Tony Prigmore (Mng Partner)
Mike Beaudet (Exec VP-Client Rels)
Brian Garrett (Exec VP-Validation Svcs)
Noëlle Marzullo (Dir-Bus Ops)
Doug Cahill (VP & Grp Dir-Cybersecurity)

TECOGEN INC.

76 Treble Cove Rd Bldg 1, North Billerica, MA 01862
Tel.: (781) 466-6400   DE
Web Site: https://www.tecogen.com
Year Founded: 2000
TGEN—(OTCQX)
Rev.: $25,002,614
Assets: $28,252,857
Liabilities: $9,265,107
Net Worth: $18,987,750
Earnings: ($2,447,927)
Emp.: 85
Fiscal Year-end: 12/31/22
Other Engine Equipment Manufacturing
N.A.I.C.S.: 333618
John N. Hatsopoulos (Founder)
Jeffrey Glick (VP-Sls)
William Martini (VP-Sls)
Joseph E. Gehret (VP-Ops)
Joseph Gehret (CTO)
Roger Deschenes (Chief Acctg Officer & Treas)
Stephen Lafaille (VP-Bus Dev)
Abinand Rangesh (CEO, CFO & Treas)

Subsidiaries:

American DG Energy Inc.   (1)
45 1st Ave, Waltham, MA 02451   (100%)
Tel.: (877) 292-2343
Emp.: 12
Energy Saving Device Distr & Operator
N.A.I.C.S.: 221122

Subsidiary (Domestic):

EuroSite Power Inc.   (2)
45 1st Ave, Waltham, MA 02451
Tel.: (781) 622-1120
Web Site: http://www.eurositepower.co.uk
Sales Range: $1-9.9 Million
Clean On-Site Energy Systems Distr, Owner & Operator
N.A.I.C.S.: 221122

TECTONIC FINANCIAL, INC.

16200 Dallas Pkwy Ste 190, Dallas, TX 75248
Tel.: (713) 250-4200   TX
Web Site: https://www.t.financial
Year Founded: 2016
TECTP—(NASDAQ)
Rev.: $73,425,000
Assets: $612,536,000
Liabilities: $516,038,000
Net Worth: $96,498,000

Earnings: $17,030,000
Emp.: 182
Fiscal Year-end: 12/31/22
Holding Company
N.A.I.C.S.: 551112
Patrick Howard (Pres)
George L. Ball (Chm)
Patrick Howard (Pres)
Ken Bramlage (CFO, Principal Acctg Officer & Exec VP)
David Clifford (COO)
Michelle Baird (Exec VP)
Thad Hutcheson (CIO)
Arthur Haag Sherman (Founder & CEO)

Subsidiaries:

T Bancshares, Inc.   (1)
16200 Dallas Pkwy Ste 190, Dallas, TX 75248
Tel.: (972) 720-9000
Web Site: http://www.tbank.com
Bank Holding Company
N.A.I.C.S.: 551111

Subsidiary (Domestic):

T Bank, N.A.   (2)
16200 Dallas Pkwy Ste 190, Dallas, TX 75248
Tel.: (972) 720-9000
Web Site: https://t.bank
Banking Services
N.A.I.C.S.: 522110
Patrick Howard (Pres & CEO)
D. Craig Barnes (Chief Credit Officer & Exec VP)
Ken Bramlage (CFO & Exec VP)
Thad Hutcheson (CTO)
Steve M. Jones (Pres-Plano Market)
Charles Holmes (Chief Trust Officer)
Beth Parsons (Sr VP)
Shari S. Jensen (VP)

Tectonic Advisors, LLC   (1)
600 Travis St 59th Fl, Houston, TX 77002
Tel.: (713) 250-4200
Web Site: https://www.tectonicadvisors.com
Asset Management Services
N.A.I.C.S.: 523940
Susan Bailey (Sec)
Michelle Baird (CFO)
David Clifford (Chief Strategy Officer)
Paul Lyons (Sr Mng Dir)
A. Haag Sherman (CEO)

TECTONIC THERAPEUTIC, INC.

490 Arsenal Way Ste 210, Watertown, MA 02472
Tel.: (339) 666-3320   DE
Web Site: https://tectonictx.com
Year Founded: 2015
AVRO—(NASDAQ)
Assets: $103,949,000
Liabilities: $28,579,000
Net Worth: $75,370,000
Earnings: ($105,890,000)
Emp.: 78
Fiscal Year-end: 12/31/22
Research & Development in Biotechnology (except Nanobiotechnology)
N.A.I.C.S.: 541714
Deanna Petersen (Chief Bus Officer)
Steven Avruch (Chief Legal Officer)
Erik Ostrowski (Interim CEO & CFO)
Georgette Verdin (Chief HR Officer)
Holly May (Chief Comml Officer)
Jose F. Gomez (Sr VP-Market Access & Value-Global)
Monique da Silva (Sr VP-Corp Comm)
Matthew Arnold (Head-Ops)
Christopher Mason (Founder)
Diana M. Escolar (Chief Medical Officer)
Kim Raineri (Chief Mfg & Tech Officer)
Azadeh Golipour (Sr VP-CMC & Mfg)
Andreas Kouri (Sr VP-Supply Chain & External Mfg-Global)

Bruce Booth (Chm)
Bruce L. Booth (Chm)
Alise S. Reicin (Pres & CEO)

TEGNA INC.

8350 Broad St Ste 2000, Tysons, VA 22102
Tel.: (703) 873-6600   DE
Web Site: https://www.tegna.com
Year Founded: 1906
TGNA—(NYSE)
Rev.: $3,279,245,000
Assets: $7,328,896,000
Liabilities: $4,257,174,000
Net Worth: $3,071,722,000
Earnings: $630,469,000
Emp.: 6,300
Fiscal Year-end: 12/31/22
Holding Company; Television Stations Operator & Digital Media Publishing Services
N.A.I.C.S.: 551112
Lynn Beall (COO-Media Ops & Exec VP)
Jeffery Newman (Chief HR Officer & Sr VP)
W. Edmond Busby (Chief Strategy Officer & Sr VP)
Julie Heskett (CFO & Sr VP)
Grady Tripp (Chief Diversity Officer & VP)
Kurt Rao (CTO & Sr VP)
Robert Dwyer (Pres-KCEN KAGS & Gen Mgr-KCEN KAGS)
Kristie Gonzales (VP-Media Ops)
Julie Heskett (Sr VP-Fin Plng & Analysis)
Anne Bentley (VP-Corp Comm)
Michael F. Steib (Pres & CEO)

Subsidiaries:

101, INC.   (1)
745 Fort St Tower Lobby, Honolulu, HI 96813
Tel.: (808) 951-6790
Web Site: http://www.101thingstodo.com
Advertising Agencies
N.A.I.C.S.: 541810
Dennis E. Francis (CEO)
J. David Kennedy (Chief Revenue Officer)
Jay Higa (VP-Bus Dev & Reg Sls)
Linda Woo (Publr)
Gina Lambert (Creative Dir)

Belo Corp.   (1)
400 S Record St, Dallas, TX 75202-4841
Tel.: (214) 977-6606
Sales Range: $75-99.9 Million
Emp.: 2,500
Holding Company; Newspaper Publishing, Television Broadcasting, Cable News & Electronic Media
N.A.I.C.S.: 551112
Gracia C. Martore (Pres)
Katy Murray (CFO & Exec VP)

Subsidiary (Domestic):

KENS-TV   (2)
5400 Fredericksburg Rd, San Antonio, TX 78229   (100%)
Tel.: (210) 366-5000
Web Site: https://www.kens5.com
Sales Range: $50-74.9 Million
Emp.: 200
Television Broadcasting
N.A.I.C.S.: 516120
Jack Acosta (Dir-News)
James Keith (Asst Dir-News)
Gregory Matthews (Dir-Digital Media)
Joe Reinagel (Dir-Sports)
Luke Simons (Mgr-Discovery Desk)
Frank Peterman (Dir-Tech)

KHOU Holdings, Inc.   (2)
1945 Allen Pkwy, Houston, TX 77019-2506
Tel.: (713) 526-1111
Web Site: http://www.khou.com
Sales Range: $50-74.9 Million
Emp.: 200
Television Broadcasting
N.A.I.C.S.: 516120

TEGNA Inc.—(Continued)

Subsidiary (Domestic):

KHOU-TV, Inc. (3)
5718 Westheimer Rd, Houston, TX
77057   **(100%)**
Tel.: (713) 526-1111
Web Site: https://www.khou.com
Sales Range: $50-74.9 Million
Emp.: 200
Television Broadcasting
N.A.I.C.S.: 516120
Sally Ramirez (Exec Dir-News)

Subsidiary (Domestic):

KMSB-TV, Inc. (2)
7831 N Business Park Dr, Tucson, AZ
85743
Tel.: (520) 744-1313
Web Site: https://www.kold.com
Sales Range: $1-9.9 Million
Emp.: 50
Television Broadcasting Station
N.A.I.C.S.: 516120

KONG-TV, Inc. (2)
1501 1st Ave S Ste 300, Seattle, WA 98134
Tel.: (206) 448-5555
Web Site: https://www.king5.com
Sales Range: $200-249.9 Million
Emp.: 350
Television Broadcasting
N.A.I.C.S.: 516120
Susannah Frame (Head-Journalism Dev)

KSKN Television, Inc. (2)
4103 S Regal St, Spokane, WA 99223
Tel.: (509) 838-7393
Web Site: https://www.krem.com
Sales Range: $25-49.9 Million
Emp.: 20
Television Broadcasting
N.A.I.C.S.: 516120
Laura Papetti (Dir-Community Mktg)

KTTU-TV, Inc. (2)
3800 N Central Ave Ste 460, Phoenix, AZ
85012
Tel.: (520) 624-0180
Sales Range: $200-249.9 Million
Emp.: 15
Television Broadcasting
N.A.I.C.S.: 516120
Brad Hargrove (Pres & Gen Mgr)

KVUE-TV (2)
3201 Steck Ave, Austin, TX 78757 **(100%)**
Tel.: (512) 459-6521
Web Site: https://www.kvue.com
Sales Range: $50-74.9 Million
Emp.: 200
Television Broadcasting
N.A.I.C.S.: 516120
Jeff Jones (Dir-Sports)
Saige Villanueva (Editor-Digital Assignments)
Kristie Gonzales (Pres & Gen Mgr)
Rick Grinstead (Dir-Tech)
John Gusky (Ops Mgr-News)
Andrew McKibbin (Asst Dir-News)
Byron Wilkinson (Sls Dir)

WCNC-TV, Inc. (2)
1001 Wood Ridge Center Dr, Charlotte, NC
28217-1901
Tel.: (704) 329-3636
Web Site: https://www.wcnc.com
Sales Range: $25-49.9 Million
Emp.: 100
Television Broadcasting
N.A.I.C.S.: 516120
Jodi Winterton (Dir-Technology)

WVEC-Television, Inc. (2)
613 Woodis Ave, Norfolk, VA
23510-1017   **(100%)**
Tel.: (757) 625-1313
Web Site: https://www.13newsnow.com
Sales Range: $50-74.9 Million
Emp.: 160
Television Broadcasting
N.A.I.C.S.: 516120
Keith O'Malley (Dir-Tech)
Doug Wieder (Pres & Gen Mgr)
Chris Gregg (Dir-News)
Brian Farrell (Dir-Digital, Mobile & Social
Media Content)
Michel J. Pelletier (Dir-Mktg, Programming
& Community Rels)
Angela New (Sls Mgr-Major Accounts)
Mike Topping (Sls Mgr-Local)

WWL-TV, Inc. (2)
1024 N Rampart St, New Orleans, LA
70116
Tel.: (504) 529-6298
Web Site: https://www.wwltv.com
Sales Range: $50-74.9 Million
Emp.: 156
Television Broadcasting Station
N.A.I.C.S.: 516120
Tom Planchet (Dir-Digital)
Doug Mouton (Dir-Sports)

CAPE PUBLICATIONS, INC. (1)
1 Gannett Plz, Melbourne, FL 32940
Tel.: (321) 242-3500
Web Site: http://www.floridatoday.com
Sales Range: $25-49.9 Million
Emp.: 150
Newspaper Publishers
N.A.I.C.S.: 513110
Mara Bellaby (Exec Editor)
John McCarthy (Editor-Special Projects &
Space)
Christina LaFortune (Editor-Entertainment &
TgIF)
Dave Berman (Editor-Govt)

**COMBINED COMMUNICATIONS
CORPORATION OF OKLAHOMA,
LLC** (1)
645 3 Mile Rd NW, Grand Rapids, MI
49544
Tel.: (616) 785-1313
Web Site: http://www.wzzm13.com
Sales Range: $25-49.9 Million
Emp.: 150
Television Broadcasting Services
N.A.I.C.S.: 516120

FRANKLINS HOLDINGS, LLC (1)
PO Box 10638, Eugene, OR 97440
Tel.: (541) 683-0771
Holding Company
N.A.I.C.S.: 551114
Richard J. Bell (Controller)

G/O DIGITAL MARKETING, LLC (1)
3800 N Central Ave Ste 460, Phoenix, AZ
85012
Tel.: (855) 389-3059
Advertise Agency Services
N.A.I.C.S.: 541810

**Gannett Direct Marketing
Services** (1)
3400 Robards Ct, Louisville, KY 40218-
4544
Tel.: (502) 454-6660
Web Site: http://www.gdms.com
Sales Range: $200-249.9 Million
Emp.: 100
Direct Marketing
N.A.I.C.S.: 541810

KVUE TELEVISION, INC. (1)
3201 Steck Ave, Austin, TX 78757
Tel.: (512) 533-2231
Web Site: https://www.kvue.com
Television Broadcasting Services
N.A.I.C.S.: 516120
Byron Wilkinson (Pres)

**MULTIMEDIA HOLDINGS
CORPORATION** (1)
1070 E Adams St, Jacksonville, FL 32202
Tel.: (904) 354-1212
Web Site: https://www.firstcoastnews.com
Newspaper Publishers
N.A.I.C.S.: 513110

MULTIMEDIA KSDK, INC. (1)
1000 Market Ct, Saint Louis, MO 63101
Tel.: (314) 421-5055
Web Site: https://www.ksdk.com
Television Broadcasting Services
N.A.I.C.S.: 516120

NEWSQUEST PLC (1)
58 Church Street, Weybridge, KT13 8DP,
Surrey, United Kingdom
Tel.: (44) 1932821212
Web Site: http://www.newsquest.co.uk
Sales Range: $10-24.9 Million
Emp.: 15
Newspaper Publishers
N.A.I.C.S.: 513110

NUTRITION DIMENSION, INC. (1)
2609 Fancy Farm Rd, Bedford, VA 24523-
3363

Tel.: (800) 866-0919
Newspaper Publishers
N.A.I.C.S.: 513110

Point Roll, Inc. (1)
7950 Jones Branch Dr, McLean, VA 22102
Tel.: (267) 558-1300
Advetising Agency
N.A.I.C.S.: 541810

Branch (Domestic):

Point Roll, Inc. - Chicago (1)
225 N Michigan Ave Ste 1600, Chicago, IL
60601
Tel.: (312) 616-5800
N.A.I.C.S.: 541810

Point Roll, Inc. - Detroit (2)
340 E Big Beaver Rd Ste 150, Troy, MI
48083
Tel.: (248) 680-7111
Sales Range: $25-49.9 Million
Emp.: 1
N.A.I.C.S.: 541810

ROVION, LLC (1)
7950 Jones Branch Dr, Mclean, VA 22107
Tel.: (703) 854-6000
Emp.: 13
Telecommunication Servicesb
N.A.I.C.S.: 517111

RadiOhio, Inc. (1)
605 S Front St Ste 300, Columbus, OH
43215
Tel.: (614) 460-3850
Web Site: https://www.radiohio.com
Sales Range: $1-9.9 Million
Emp.: 75
Radio Broadcast Station
N.A.I.C.S.: 516110
Michael J. Fiorile (Chm)

SCHEDULE STAR, LLC (1)
1145 Market St, Wheeling, WV 26003
Tel.: (800) 258-8550
Web Site: http://www.schedulestar.com
Software Publisher
N.A.I.C.S.: 513210

SCREENSHOT DIGITAL, INC. (1)
400 S Record St Ste 950, Dallas, TX 75202
Tel.: (214) 977-4700
Emp.: 9
Advertising Services
N.A.I.C.S.: 541810

SISTER CIRCLE LLC (1)
PO Box 84, Timonium, MD 21094
Tel.: (410) 227-4836
Web Site: https://www.sisterscircle.org
Education Services
N.A.I.C.S.: 611110
Heather Harvison (Founder & Exec Dir)
Stephanie Radday (Dir-Mentor Recruitment
& Support)

TEGNA Broadcasting Group (1)
8350 Broad St Ste 2000, Tysons, VA 22102
Tel.: (703) 873-6600
Web Site: https://www.tegna.com
Television Broadcasting Stations Operator
N.A.I.C.S.: 516120

Subsidiary (Domestic):

**ARKANSAS TELEVISION
COMPANY** (2)
720 S Izard St, Little Rock, AR 72201
Tel.: (501) 376-9935
Advertising Agencies
N.A.I.C.S.: 541810

Unit (Domestic):

First Coast News (2)
1070 E Adams St, Jacksonville, FL
32202   **(100%)**
Tel.: (904) 354-1212
Web Site: https://www.firstcoastnews.com
Television Broadcasting Services
N.A.I.C.S.: 516120
Chris Porter (Dir-Sports)

KARE-TV (2)
8811 Olson Memorial Hwy, Minneapolis,
MN 55427
Tel.: (763) 546-1111
Web Site: https://www.kare11.com
Emp.: 170

Television Broadcasting Services
N.A.I.C.S.: 516120
Eric Perkins (Dir-Sports)
Stacey Nogy (Dir-News Content)
Jeremiah Jacobsen (Mgr-Digital Video)

Subsidiary (Domestic):

KBMT Operating Company, LLC (2)
525 Interstate Hwy 10 S, Beaumont, TX
77701
Tel.: (409) 833-7512
Web Site: http://www.12newsnow.com
Emp.: 20
Television Broadcasting Station
N.A.I.C.S.: 516120
Don Hawn (Producer-Weekend)
Gregory Snyder (Producer)
Michael T. Morris (Dir-News)
Daniel T. Goforth (Producer-Evening)
Stephanie A. Dugosh (Reporter)
Rebecca Alvidrez (Reporter)
Steve Harmon (Dir-Sales & Mktg)
David Ingram (Editor-Assignments)

**KIDY/KXVA Operating Company,
LLC** (2)
5 S Chadbourne St, San Angelo, TX 76903
Tel.: (325) 655-6006
Web Site: https://www.myfoxzone.com
Emp.: 44
Television Broadcasting Station
N.A.I.C.S.: 516120

Unit (Domestic):

KPNX-TV (2)
200 E Van Buren St, Phoenix, AZ 85004
Tel.: (602) 257-1212
Web Site: https://www.12news.com
Television Broadcasting Services
N.A.I.C.S.: 516120

KSDK-TV (2)
1000 Market St, Saint Louis, MO
63101   **(100%)**
Tel.: (314) 444-5231
Web Site: https://www.ksdk.com
Emp.: 200
Television Broadcasting Services
N.A.I.C.S.: 516120

KTHV-TV (2)
720 S Izard St, Little Rock, AR
72201-4026   **(100%)**
Tel.: (501) 376-1111
Web Site: https://www.thv11.com
Television Broadcasting Station
N.A.I.C.S.: 516120

KUSA-TV (2)
500 Speer Blvd, Denver, CO
80203   **(100%)**
Tel.: (303) 871-9999
Web Site: https://www.9news.com
Television Broadcasting Services
N.A.I.C.S.: 516120
Rod Mackey (Dir-Sports)

Subsidiary (Domestic):

KXTV Inc. (2)
400 Broadway, Sacramento, CA
95818-2098   **(100%)**
Tel.: (916) 441-2345
Web Site: https://www.abc10.com
Television Broadcasting Services
N.A.I.C.S.: 516120

KYTX Operating Company, LLC (2)
2211 ESE Loop 323, Tyler, TX 75701
Tel.: (903) 581-2211
Web Site: https://www.cbs19.tv
Television Broadcasting Station
N.A.I.C.S.: 516120
Kevin Meyer (Mgr-Comml Production)

Pacific & Southern, LLC (2)
7950 Jones Branch Dr, McLean, VA 22102
Tel.: (703) 854-6899
Emp.: 99
Television Broadcasting Services
N.A.I.C.S.: 516120

Unit (Domestic):

WATL-TV (3)
One Monroe Pl, Atlanta, GA 30324
Tel.: (404) 892-1611
Web Site: http://www.myatltv.com
Television Broadcasting Services
N.A.I.C.S.: 516120

WCSH-TV (3)
1 Congress Sq, Portland, ME 04101
Tel.: (207) 828-6666
Web Site: http://www.newscentermaine.com
Sales Range: $25-49.9 Million
Emp.: 100
Television Broadcasting Services
N.A.I.C.S.: 516120

Subsidiary (Domestic):

WLBZ-TV (3)
329 Mt Hope Ave, Bangor, ME 04401
Tel.: (207) 942-4821
Web Site: http://www.wlbz2.com
Emp.: 30
Television Broadcasting Services
N.A.I.C.S.: 516120

Unit (Domestic):

WMAZ-TV (3)
1314 Gray Hwy, Macon, GA 31211
Tel.: (478) 752-1313
Web Site: https://www.13wmaz.com
Sales Range: $25-49.9 Million
Emp.: 100
Television Broadcasting Services
N.A.I.C.S.: 516120

WXIA-TV (3)
1 Monroe Pl NE, Atlanta, GA
30324 (100%)
Tel.: (404) 733-2203
Web Site: https://www.11alive.com
Sales Range: $50-74.9 Million
Emp.: 250
Television Broadcasting Services
N.A.I.C.S.: 516120
Kristie Anderson (Mng Editor-Daily Content)

Subsidiary (Domestic):

WBIR, Inc. (2)
1513 Bill Williams Ave, Knoxville, TN
37917-3851 (100%)
Tel.: (865) 637-1010
Web Site: https://www.wbir.com
Emp.: 140
Television Station
N.A.I.C.S.: 516120
David Hunt (Gen Mgr)
Beth Weissfeld (Sls Dir)

WFAA-TV, Inc. (2)
606 Young St, Dallas, TX 75202 (100%)
Tel.: (214) 748-9631
Web Site: https://www.wfaa.com
Emp.: 250
Television Broadcasting
N.A.I.C.S.: 516120

Unit (Domestic):

Texas Cable News (3)
606 Young St, Dallas, TX 75202 (100%)
Tel.: (214) 977-4500
Web Site: http://www.txcn.com
Sales Range: $1-9.9 Million
Emp.: 15
Television Broadcasting
N.A.I.C.S.: 516120

Subsidiary (Domestic):

WFMY Television, LLC (2)
1615 Phillips Ave, Greensboro, NC 27405
Tel.: (336) 379-9369
Web Site: https://www.wfmynews2.com
Television Broadcasting Services
N.A.I.C.S.: 516120

Unit (Domestic):

WGRZ-TV (2)
259 Delaware Ave, Buffalo, NY 14202
Tel.: (716) 849-2222
Web Site: https://www.wgrz.com
Television Broadcasting Station
N.A.I.C.S.: 516120
Julie Mecklenburg (Sls Mgr-Local)

WKYC-TV (2)
1333 Lakeside Ave, Cleveland, OH
44114 (51%)
Tel.: (216) 344-3333
Web Site: http://www.wkyc.com
Emp.: 150
Television Broadcasting Services
N.A.I.C.S.: 516120
Micki Byrnes (Pres & Gen Mgr)

WLTX-TV (2)
6027 Garners Ferry Rd, Columbia, SC
29209 (100%)
Tel.: (803) 776-3600
Web Site: https://www.wltx.com
Emp.: 80
Television Broadcasting Services
N.A.I.C.S.: 516120

WOI-DT (2)
3903 Westown Pkwy, West Des Moines, IA
50266-1009
Tel.: (515) 457-9645
Web Site: https://www.weareiowa.com
Television Broadcasting Station
N.A.I.C.S.: 516120
Amber Sexton (Mgr-Digital Sls)

WTSP-TV (2)
11450 Gandy Blvd, Saint Petersburg, FL
33702-1908 (100%)
Tel.: (727) 577-1010
Web Site: https://www.wtsp.com
Television Broadcasting Services
N.A.I.C.S.: 516120

WUSA-TV (2)
4100 Wisconsin Ave NW, Washington, DC
20016-2810 (100%)
Tel.: (202) 895-5999
Web Site: https://www.wusa9.com
Television Broadcasting
N.A.I.C.S.: 811210

WZZM-TV (2)
645 3 Mile Rd NW, Grand Rapids, MI
49544 (100%)
Tel.: (616) 559-1416
Web Site: https://www.wzzm13.com
Television Broadcasting Services
N.A.I.C.S.: 516120
Jay Andel (Founder)

**VERTICORE COMMUNICATIONS
LTD.** (1)
11 King Street West 6th Floor, Toronto,
M5H 4C7, ON, Canada
Tel.: (416) 861-1177
Online News Publishing Services
N.A.I.C.S.: 513110

WBIR-TV, LLC (1)
1513 Bill Williams Ave, Knoxville, TN
37917-3851
Tel.: (865) 637-1010
Web Site: https://www.wbir.com
Television Broadcasting Services
N.A.I.C.S.: 516120
Corey Presley (Dir-News)

WBNS TV, Inc. (1)
770 Twin Rivers Dr, Columbus, OH 43215-
1127
Tel.: (614) 460-3950
Web Site: https://www.10tv.com
Sales Range: $50-74.9 Million
Emp.: 100
Television & Radio Broadcasting Services
N.A.I.C.S.: 516120

WTHR-TV (1)
1000 N Meridian St, Indianapolis, IN 46204-
1015
Tel.: (317) 636-1313
Web Site: http://www.wthr.com
Sales Range: $50-74.9 Million
Emp.: 300
Television Broadcasting Station
N.A.I.C.S.: 516120

WTOL, LLC (1)
730 N Summit St, Toledo, OH 43604-1808
Tel.: (419) 248-1111
Web Site: https://www.wtol.com
Television Broadcasting Station
N.A.I.C.S.: 516120
Kyle Omlor (Dir-Mktg Art)
Russ Slee (Sls Mgr-Local)
Sabrina Mccue-Haskell (Sls Mgr-Digital)
Mary Gerken (Gen Sls Mgr)
Jerry Fairchild (Sls Dir)
Lauren Weppler (Dir-News)
Paul Kwapich (Ops Mgr-News)
Erin Sifuentes (Mktg Dir)
Mike Fay (Dir-Res)
Jordan Strack (Dir-Sports)

TEGO CYBER INC.

8565 S Eern Ave Ste 150, Las Ve-
gas, NV 89123 NV
Web Site: https://www.tegocyber.com
Year Founded: 2019
TGCB—(OTCQB)
Assets: $236,472
Liabilities: $1,020,967
Net Worth: ($784,495)
Earnings: ($10,738,393)
Emp.: 5
Fiscal Year-end: 06/30/23
Software Development Services
N.A.I.C.S.: 541511
Alissa Valentina Knight (CMO)
Robert E. Mikkelsen (CEO & CFO)
Shannon Wilkinson (Co-Founder)
Stephen Seminew (Co-Founder)
Brent Watkins (Dir)
Didem Mize (Sr Portfolio Mgr)

TEJON RANCH COMPANY
4436 Lebec Rd, Lebec, CA 93243
Tel.: (661) 248-3000 DE
Web Site:
https://www.tejonranch.com
Year Founded: 1843
TRC—(NYSE)
Rev.: $79,217,000
Assets: $566,791,000
Liabilities: $89,197,000
Net Worth: $477,594,000
Earnings: $15,808,000
Emp.: 78
Fiscal Year-end: 12/31/22
Real Estate Developers
N.A.I.C.S.: 531120
Allen E. Lyda (COO & Exec VP)
Barry Zoeller (Sr VP-Corp Comm &
IR)
Brett A. Brown (CFO & Exec VP)
Robert D. Velasquez (Chief Acctg
Officer & Sr VP-Fin)
Michael R.W. Houston (Gen Counsel,
Sec & Sr VP)
Hugh F. McMahon IV (Exec VP-Real
Estate)

Subsidiaries:

High Desert Hunt Club LLC. (1)
30830 Lancaster Rd, Los Angeles, CA
93243
Tel.: (661) 724-1218
Web Site: http://www.highdeserthunt.com
Hunting Club Operator
N.A.I.C.S.: 713990

Tejon Agricultural Corp. (1)
4436 Lebec Rd, Lebec, CA 93243-1000
Tel.: (661) 327-8481
Web Site: http://www.tejonranch.com
Sales Range: $10-24.9 Million
Emp.: 100
General Farming
N.A.I.C.S.: 111335

Tejon Hounds, LLC. (1)
1401 Crane Canyon Rd, Lebec, CA 93243
Tel.: (661) 248-5181
Web Site: http://www.tejonhounds.com
Hunting Club Operator
N.A.I.C.S.: 713990

Tejon Mountain Village, LLC. (1)
4436 Lebec Rd, Lebec, CA 93243
Tel.: (661) 248-3000
Web Site:
https://www.tejonmountainvillage.com
Real Estate Development Services
N.A.I.C.S.: 531210

TEKEGLDMPIRE, INC.
39120 Argonaut Way 126, Fremont,
CA 94538
Tel.: (628) 243-2002
Year Founded: 2004
TKGL—(OTCIQ)
Telecommunication Application Inte-
gration Services
N.A.I.C.S.: 517810
Govindarajan Venkatasesha (Pres)

**TEKKORP DIGITAL ACQUISI-
TION CORP.**
1980 Festival Plz Dr Ste 300, Las
Vegas, NV 89135
Tel.: (702) 879-9687 Ky
Web Site: http://tekkorpdigital.com
Year Founded: 2020
TEKK—(NASDAQ)
Rev.: $37,760,758
Assets: $250,555,225
Liabilities: $275,875,018
Net Worth: ($25,319,793)
Earnings: $31,504,114
Emp.: 3
Fiscal Year-end: 12/31/21
Investment Services
N.A.I.C.S.: 523999
Matthew Davey (CEO)
Morris Bailey (Chm)
Eric Matejevich (CFO)
Robin Chhabra (Pres)

**TEL-INSTRUMENT ELEC-
TRONICS CORP.**
Tel.: (201) 933-1600 NJ
Web Site:
https://www.telinstrument.com
Year Founded: 1947
TIKK—(OTCQB)
Rev.: $8,809,087
Assets: $10,751,790
Liabilities: $3,898,163
Net Worth: $6,853,627
Earnings: $341,891
Emp.: 38
Fiscal Year-end: 03/31/24
Avionics Test & Measurement Solu-
tions Designer & Mfr
N.A.I.C.S.: 334515
Jeffrey C. O'Hara (Pres & CEO)
Robert H. Walker (Chm)
Pauline X. Romeo (Chief Acctg Offi-
cer)

TELA BIO, INC.
1 Great Valley Pkwy Ste 24, Malvern,
PA 19355
Tel.: (484) 320-2930 DE
Web Site: https://www.telabio.com
Year Founded: 2012
TELA—(NASDAQ)
Rev.: $41,418,000
Assets: $67,855,000
Liabilities: $53,550,000
Net Worth: $14,305,000
Earnings: ($44,296,000)
Emp.: 173
Fiscal Year-end: 12/31/22
Biotechnology Research & Develop-
ment Services
N.A.I.C.S.: 541714
Antony Koblish (Pres & CEO)
Roberto Cuca (CFO & COO)
E. Skott Greenhalgh (CTO)
Peter Murphy (Chief Comml Officer)
Megan Smeykal (Chief Acctg Officer
& Controller)
Jennifer Armstrong (Sr VP)
Marissa Conrad (VP)

TELADOC HEALTH, INC.
2 Manhattanville Rd Ste 203, Pur-
chase, NY 10577
Tel.: (203) 635-2002 DE
Web Site:
https://www.teladochealth.com
Year Founded: 2002
TDOC—(NYSE)
Rev.: $2,602,415,000
Assets: $4,392,369,000
Liabilities: $2,066,296,000
Net Worth: $2,326,073,000
Earnings: ($220,368,000)
Emp.: 5,600
Fiscal Year-end: 12/31/23
Healtcare Services

Teladoc Health, Inc.—(Continued)

N.A.I.C.S.: 621999
Adam C. Vandervoort (Chief Legal Officer)
Stephany Verstraete (CMO & Chief Engagement Officer)
Kelly M. Bliss (Pres-Health-Grp-U.S.)
Mala Murthy (CFO)
Carlos Nueno (Pres-Intl)
Alan Matas (Pres-Betterhelp)
Michael Waters (COO)
Andy Puterbaugh (Pres)
Vidya Raman-Tangella (Chief Medical Officer)
Charles Divita III (CEO)
Joseph R. Catapano (Chief Acctg Officer & Sr VP)

Subsidiaries:

AcuteCare Telemedicine, LLC **(1)**
993-F Johnson Ferry Rd NE Ste 120, Atlanta, GA 30342
Tel.: (770) 441-6077
Web Site: http://www.acutecaretelemed.com
Telemedicine Services
N.A.I.C.S.: 621999
Michael Woodcock (Exec Dir-Sls)

Advance Medical Health Care Management Services Chile S.A. **(1)**
Avda Lota 2267 Of 402, Santiago, Chile
Tel.: (56) 223455042
Health Care Srvices
N.A.I.C.S.: 622110

Advance Medical Health-Care Management Services, S.A. **(1)**
Via Augusta 252, 08017, Barcelona, Spain
Tel.: (34) 932540010
Health Care Srvices
N.A.I.C.S.: 622110

Advance Medical, Inc. **(1)**
1250 Hancock St Ste 201N, Quincy, MA 02169
Web Site: http://www.advance-medical.net
Health Care Srvices
N.A.I.C.S.: 622110

Best Doctors Portugal Ltd. **(1)**
Rua Tierno Galvan Amoreiras Torre 3 - 8 Andar, 1070-274, Lisbon, Portugal
Tel.: (351) 213592070
Web Site: http://bestdoctors.com
Health Care Srvices
N.A.I.C.S.: 622110

Best Doctors, Inc. **(1)**
100 Federal St 21 St, Boston, MA 02110
Tel.: (617) 426-3666
Web Site: http://www.bestdoctors.com
Management Consulting Services
N.A.I.C.S.: 541611
Jason N. Gorevic (CEO)

Subsidiary (Non-US):

Best Doctors Canada Inc. **(2)**
214 King Street West Suite 300, Toronto, M5H 3S6, ON, Canada
Tel.: (416) 504-8555
Web Site: https://bestdoctors.com
Health Care Srvices
N.A.I.C.S.: 622110
Steven Solomon (VP-Acct Mgmt)

Subsidiary (Domestic):

Rise Health, Inc. **(2)**
1111 W 22nd St Ste 270, Oak Brook, IL 60523
Tel.: (630) 873-2230
Web Site: http://www.risehealth.com
Health Care Srvices
N.A.I.C.S.: 622110

Compile, Inc. **(1)**
405 El Camino Real Ste 608, Menlo Park, CA 94025-4312
Web Site: https://www.compile.com
Software Development Services
N.A.I.C.S.: 513210

Consultant Connect Limited **(1)**
One St Aldates, Oxford, OX1 1DE, United Kingdom
Tel.: (44) 1865261467

Web Site: https://www.consultantconnect.org.uk
Telephone Advice & Guidance Services
N.A.I.C.S.: 624190
Jonathan Patrick (CEO)
Scott Welpton (CFO & COO)
Roger Tweedale (Chief Clinical Engagement Officer)
Roger Ahn (Chief Product Officer)

Livongo Health, Inc. **(1)**
150 W Evelyn Ave Ste 150, Mountain View, CA 94041
Web Site: http://www.livongo.com
Healthcare Software Development Services
N.A.I.C.S.: 541511
Stacey DeWeerdt (VP-Strategic Client Relationships)

Medecin Direct **(1)**
18 rue de Londres, 75009, Paris, France
Tel.: (33) 974488846
Web Site: http://www.medecindirect.fr
Online Medical Consultation Services
N.A.I.C.S.: 621999

Stat Health, LLC **(1)**
1850 Sunrise Hwy, Bay Shore, NY 11706
Tel.: (631) 581-5900
Web Site: http://www.stathealthny.com
Health Care Srvices
N.A.I.C.S.: 622110

Teladoc Health Brasil - Servicos de Consultoria em Saude Ltda **(1)**
Av Engineer Luis Carlos Berrini 716 - Conj 11 and 12, Itaim Bibi, Sao Paulo, 04571-010, Brazil
Tel.: (55) 1135044900
Behavioral Healthcare Services
N.A.I.C.S.: 621330

Teladoc Health Portugal, S.A. **(1)**
Avenida Duque de Avila 46 5C, 1050-083, Lisbon, Portugal
Tel.: (351) 210990939
Behavioral Healthcare Services
N.A.I.C.S.: 621330

myStrength, Inc. **(1)**
1875 Lawrence St Ste 550, Denver, CO 80202
Tel.: (720) 593-8200
Web Site: http://www.mystrength.com
Behavioral Healthcare Services
N.A.I.C.S.: 621330

TELCO CUBA, INC.

454 S Yonge St Ste 7C, Ormond Beach, FL 32174
Tel.: (305) 747-7647   NV
Web Site: http://www.telcocuba.com
QBAN—(OTCIQ)
Rev.: $235,088
Assets: $776,508
Liabilities: $899,527
Net Worth: ($123,019)
Earnings: $15,001
Fiscal Year-end: 11/30/19
Telecommunication Servicesb
N.A.I.C.S.: 517810
William J. Sanchez (Chm, Pres & CEO)

Subsidiaries:

Amgentech Inc. **(1)**
454 S Yonge St Ste 7C, Ormond Beach, FL 32174
Web Site: http://www.amgentech.com
Web Development Services
N.A.I.C.S.: 541511

Naked Papers Brands, Inc. **(1)**
454 S Yonge St Ste 7C, Ormond Beach, FL 32174
Web Site: http://www.nakedpapers.com
Rolling Paper Mfr & Distr
N.A.I.C.S.: 322299

TELE GROUP CORP.

530 5th Ave 9th Fl, New York, NY 10036
Tel.: (212) 202-0026   NV
Year Founded: 2007
TMLL—(OTCIQ)
Investment Holding Company

N.A.I.C.S.: 551112
Zhilong Liao (CEO)
Rosemary Wang (Accountant)

TELEDYNE TECHNOLOGIES INCORPORATED

1049 Camino Dos Rios, Thousand Oaks, CA 91360-2362
Tel.: (805) 373-4545   DE
Web Site: https://www.teledyne.com
Year Founded: 1960
TDY—(NYSE)
Rev.: $5,635,500,000
Assets: $14,527,900,000
Liabilities: $5,302,100,000
Net Worth: $9,225,800,000
Earnings: $885,700,000
Emp.: 14,900
Fiscal Year-end: 12/31/23
Electronic & Communication Products, Systems Engineering Solutions & Aerospace Engines & Components Mfr
N.A.I.C.S.: 541330
Cynthia Y. Belak (VP & Controller)
Robert Mehrabian (Exec Chm)
Jason Vanwees (Vice Chm)
Melanie S. Cibik (Chief Compliance Officer, Gen Counsel, Sec & Exec VP)
Edwin Roks (CEO)
George C. Bobb III (Pres & COO)
Stephen F. Blackwood (CFO & Sr VP)
Carl Adams (VP-Bus Risk Assurance)
Jason W. Connell (VP-HR & Assoc Gen Counsel)
Scott Hudson (CIO & VP)
Sean B. O'Connor (CFO-Environmental & Electronic Measurement Instrumentation)
Kevin Prusso (VP-Grp & Gen Mgr-Teledyne Test & Measurement)
Paul DeLaRose (Chief Procurement Officer)
Duncan Forsythe (VP)
Chanh N. Nguyen (CTO)
George C. Bobb III (Pres-Aerospace & Defense Electronics Segment & Exec VP)

Subsidiaries:

ChartWorld Americas Maritime Services Ltd. **(1)**
906-1112 West Pender Street, Vancouver, V6E 2S1, BC, Canada
Tel.: (604) 294-3944
Digital Maritime Data Services
N.A.I.C.S.: 518210

ChartWorld Asia Pacific Pte. Ltd. **(1)**
15 Jalan Kilang Barat Frontech Centre 07-05, Singapore, 159357, Singapore
Tel.: (65) 65133500
Digital Maritime Data Services
N.A.I.C.S.: 518210

ChartWorld GmbH **(1)**
Atlantic Haus Zirkusweg 1, 20359, Hamburg, Germany
Tel.: (49) 40853586940
Digital Maritime Data Services
N.A.I.C.S.: 518210

Chartworld International Limited **(1)**
Iris House 3rd Floor - Unit 340A 8 John F Kennedy, 3106, Limassol, Cyprus
Tel.: (357) 25248930
Digital Maritime Data Services
N.A.I.C.S.: 518210

FLIR Systems Company Ltd. **(1)**
Unit 505 Building 20E Phase 3 Hong Kong Science Park, Pak Shek Kok N T, Sha Tin, China (Hong Kong)
Tel.: (852) 93856275
Thermal Imaging System Mfr & Distr
N.A.I.C.S.: 334513

FLIR Unmanned Aerial Systems AS **(1)**

Nye Vakas Vei 56, 1395, Hvalstad, Norway
Tel.: (47) 66779100
Thermal Imaging System Mfr & Distr
N.A.I.C.S.: 334513

Gas Measurement Instruments Limited **(1)**
Inchinnan Business Park, Renfrew, PA4 9RG, United Kingdom
Tel.: (44) 1418123211
Portable Detectors Mfr
N.A.I.C.S.: 334290

Lumenera Corporation **(1)**
7 Capella Crt, Ottawa, K2E 8A7, ON, Canada
Tel.: (613) 736-4077
Web Site: http://www.lumenera.com
Digital Camera Mfr
N.A.I.C.S.: 333310
Dany Longval (VP-Sls-Worldwide)
Rob Sample (VP-Mfg)
Doug Sanderson (VP-Engrg)
Stephen Shaw (VP-Fin)

Noiseless Accoustics OY **(1)**
Hiomotie 3 2nd Floor, 00380, Helsinki, Finland
Tel.: (358) 105833240
Web Site: https://www.nlacoustics.com
Electric Device Mfr
N.A.I.C.S.: 335999

Oceanscience Group, Ltd. **(1)**
14020 Stowe Dr, Poway, CA 92064
Tel.: (760) 754-2400
Web Site: http://www.oceanscience.com
Sales Range: $1-9.9 Million
Emp.: 20
Marine Sensor Platforms & Unmanned Surface Vehicles Designer & Mfr
N.A.I.C.S.: 334511

Oldham SAS **(1)**
Rue Orfila-ZI Est CS 20417, 62027, Arras, France
Tel.: (33) 321608080
Web Site: http://www.oldhamgas.com
Gas Leak Detectors Mfr
N.A.I.C.S.: 334519

Oldham Winter GmbH **(1)**
Gernotstrasse 19, 44319, Dortmund, Germany
Tel.: (49) 23192410
Web Site: http://www.oldhamgas.com
Gas Leak Detectors Mfr
N.A.I.C.S.: 334519

Roper Scientific, Inc. **(1)**
3660 Quakerbridge Rd, Trenton, NJ 08619
Tel.: (609) 587-9797
Web Site: http://www.princetoninstruments.com
Mfr of Instruments for Digital Imaging & Spectroscopy
N.A.I.C.S.: 333310

Subsidiary (Domestic):

Photometrics **(2)**
3440 East Britannia Dr Ste 100, Tucson, AZ 85706
Tel.: (520) 889-9933
Web Site: http://www.photomet.com
High Resolution & Special Use Camera Mfr
N.A.I.C.S.: 333310

Princeton Instruments Inc. **(2)**
3660 Quakerbridge Rd, Trenton, NJ 08619
Tel.: (609) 587-9797
Web Site: https://www.princetoninstruments.com
High Resolution & Specialty Use Camera Mfr
N.A.I.C.S.: 333310

SevenCs GmbH **(1)**
Zirkusweg 1, 20359, Hamburg, Germany
Tel.: (49) 408517240
Web Site: https://www.sevencs.com
Maritime Navigation Software Mfr & Distr
N.A.I.C.S.: 334511

Teledyne Benthos, Inc. **(1)**
49 Edgerton Dr, North Falmouth, MA 02556
Tel.: (508) 563-1000
Web Site: https://www.teledynemarine.com
Sales Range: $10-24.9 Million
Emp.: 112

Underwater, Environmental & Oceanographic Products Mfr; Food & Beverage Container Inspection Systems
N.A.I.C.S.: 334511

Division (Domestic):

Teledyne TapTone (2)
49 Edgerton Dr, North Falmouth, MA 02556-2821
Tel.: (508) 563-1000
Web Site: https://www.taptone.com
Food & Beverage Processors Inspection Systems
N.A.I.C.S.: 334511

Teledyne BlueView, Inc. (1)
2151 N Northlake Way Ste 214, Seattle, WA 98103
Tel.: (206) 545-7260
Web Site: http://www.blueview.com
High-Resolution Underwater Acoustic Imaging & Measuring Equipment Mfr
N.A.I.C.S.: 334511

Teledyne Brown Engineering, Inc. (1)
300 Sparkman Dr, Huntsville, AL 35805
Tel.: (256) 726-1000
Web Site: https://www.tbe.com
Sales Range: $250-299.9 Million
Emp.: 1,750
Systems Engineering & Technology Solutions to Defense, Space, Environmental & Information Problems
N.A.I.C.S.: 541715
Janice L. Hess (Pres)
Anna Curenton (Sr VP-Contracts)
Jonathan S. Hall (Sr VP-Maritime Sys & Hardware Ops)
Debbie K. McGriff (Sr VP)
Mitch Icard (VP-)
Chuck Herbert (VP-)
Jeff Holley (VP-Manufacturing &)

Teledyne CARIS USA, Inc. (1)
415 North Alfred St 1, Alexandria, VA 22314
Tel.: (703) 299-9712
Emp.: 3
Electric & Environmental Engineering Services
N.A.I.C.S.: 541330
Josh Mode (Acct Mgr)

Teledyne CARIS, Inc. (1)
115 Waggoners Lane, Fredericton, E3B 2L4, NB, Canada
Tel.: (506) 458-8533
Web Site: https://www.teledynecaris.com
Software Services
N.A.I.C.S.: 513210

Teledyne CDL, Inc. (1)
10661 Shadow Wood Dr, Houston, TX 77043
Tel.: (281) 710-7276
Emp.: 3
Sensor Mfr
N.A.I.C.S.: 334511
Neil Manning (Pres)

Teledyne CollaborX, Inc. (1)
1755 Telstar Dr Ste 120, Colorado Springs, CO 80920
Tel.: (719) 487-1530
Space Defense Programming Services
N.A.I.C.S.: 541511

Teledyne Controls (1)
1365 Corporate Ctr Curve Ste 100, Eagan, MN 55121
Tel.: (651) 994-1000
Web Site: https://www.teledynecontrols.com
Sales Range: $75-99.9 Million
Marketing of Aircraft Instrumentation, Monitoring & Recording Products
N.A.I.C.S.: 541330

Teledyne Cougar (1)
1274 Terra Bella Ave, Mountain View, CA 94043
Tel.: (650) 691-9800
Web Site: http://www.teledynemicrowave.com
Sales Range: $10-24.9 Million
Emp.: 150
Microwave Components
N.A.I.C.S.: 334419
Daniel Cheadle (CTO)

Teledyne DALSA, Inc. (1)

605 McMurray Road, Waterloo, N2V 2E9, ON, Canada
Tel.: (519) 886-6000
Web Site: http://www.teledynedalsa.com
Sales Range: $200-249.9 Million
Emp.: 1,012
Digital Imaging Equipment & Semiconductor Wafer Mfr
N.A.I.C.S.: 334413
Keith Reuben (Pres-Asia Pacific, Exec VP & Gen Mgr-Digital Imaging-Montreal)
Claude Jean (Exec VP & Gen Mgr-Foundry Ops-Semiconductor)
Gareth Ingram (Exec VP & Gen Mgr-Digital Imaging-Waterloo)
Guido Aelbers (Exec VP & Gen Mgr-Professional Imaging)

Subsidiary (Domestic):

Optech Inc. (2)
300 Interchange Way, Vaughan, L4K 5Z8, ON, Canada (100%)
Tel.: (905) 660-0808
Web Site: http://www.optech.ca
Sales Range: $50-74.9 Million
Emp.: 250
Survey Instrument Mfr
N.A.I.C.S.: 334511

Unit (Domestic):

Teledyne DALSA, Inc. (2)
880 Rue Mccaffrey, Saint Laurent, H4T 2C7, QC, Canada
Tel.: (514) 333-1301
Web Site: http://www.teledynedalsa.com
Sales Range: $25-49.9 Million
Emp.: 100
Video Imaging Software
N.A.I.C.S.: 541512
Silvio Favrin (Exec VP-Fin)
Gareth Ingram (Exec VP & Gen Mgr-Digital Imaging-Waterloo)
Claude Jean (Exec VP & Gen Mgr-Foundry Operation & Semiconductor)
Guido Aelbers (Exec VP & Gen Mgr-Professional Imaging)

Teledyne Defense Electronics, LLC (1)
11361 Sunrise Park Dr, Rancho Cordova, CA 95742
Tel.: (916) 638-3344
Web Site: http://www.teledynedefenseelectronics.com
Electronic Parts & Equipment Whslr
N.A.I.C.S.: 423690

Teledyne FLIR, LLC (1)
27700 SW Pkwy Ave, Wilsonville, OR 97070
Tel.: (503) 498-3547
Web Site: http://www.flir.com
Rev.: $1,923,689,000
Assets: $3,252,348,000
Liabilities: $1,368,974,000
Net Worth: $1,883,374,000
Earnings: $212,584,000
Emp.: 4,179
Fiscal Year-end: 12/31/2020
Thermal Imaging & Camera Systems Mfr
N.A.I.C.S.: 334511
Robert Mehrabian (Exec Chm)
Melanie S. Cibik (Chief Compliance Officer, Gen Counsel & Sec)
Edwin Roks (Pres & CEO)
Susan L. Main (Sr VP)
David Ray (Pres-Govt & Defence Bus Unit)
Frank Pennisi (Pres-Industrial Bus Unit)
Mark Stock (VP & Gen Mgr-Sensors Line of Business)
Paul Clayton (VP & Gen Mgr-Components Line of Bus)
Rickard Lindvall (VP & Gen Mgr-Solutions Line of Bus)
Edwin Roks (Pres & CEO)
Melanie Cibik (Chief Compliance Officer, Gen Counsel & Sec)
Jason VanWees (Exec VP)
Todd Booth (CFO & Sr VP)
JihFen Lei (VP/Gen Mgr-Surveillance Bus)
Cherie Buntyn (Controller)
John Bergeron (VP-Global Svcs-Surveillance)

Subsidiary (Domestic):

Acyclica Inc. (2)

1610 Wynkoop St Ste 200, Denver, CO 80202
Tel.: (888) 404-2213
Web Site: http://www.acyclica.com
Intersection-level Integration & High Resolution Data Help Agencies
N.A.I.C.S.: 518210
Daniel Benhammou (Owner)

FLIR Commercial Systems, Inc. (2)
70 Castilian Dr, Goleta, CA 93111
Tel.: (805) 964-9797
Electronic Systems & Equipment Mfr
N.A.I.C.S.: 334511

FLIR Government Systems, Inc. (2)
27700 SW Pkwy Ave, Wilsonville, OR 97070
Tel.: (503) 498-3547
Web Site: http://www.flir.com
Sales Range: $150-199.9 Million
Emp.: 380
Thermal Imaging Infrared Camera Mfr & Marketer
N.A.I.C.S.: 423410

Subsidiary (Non-US):

FLIR Integrated Imaging Solutions (2)
12051 Riverside Way, Richmond, V6W 1K7, BC, Canada
Tel.: (604) 242-9937
Web Site: https://www.flir.ca
Digital Camera Mfr
N.A.I.C.S.: 333310

Subsidiary (Domestic):

FLIR Outdoor & Tactical Systems (2)
3150 Commercial Ave, Northbrook, IL 60062 (100%)
Tel.: (650) 492-7755
Web Site: https://www.armasight.com
Manufactures a Broad Variety of Image Intensified Night Vision, Long-Wave Thermal Imaging, Laser Aiming & Illumination & Day Optical Systems
N.A.I.C.S.: 333310

Subsidiary (Non-US):

FLIR Systems AB (2)
Antennvagen 6, PO Box 7376, SE-187 15, Taby, Sweden (100%)
Tel.: (46) 87532500
Web Site: https://www.flir.eu
Sales Range: $50-74.9 Million
Emp.: 400
Infrared Measurement Instrument Developer & Mfr
N.A.I.C.S.: 334513

FLIR Systems CV (2)
Charles Petitweg 2, Breda, 4847, Netherlands
Tel.: (31) 765794194
Web Site: http://www.flir.com
Sales Range: $10-24.9 Million
Emp.: 10
Thermal Imaging & Camera Systems Mfr
N.A.I.C.S.: 334511

FLIR Systems Holding AB (2)
Rinkebyvagen 19, Danderyd, 182 36, Stockholm, Sweden
Tel.: (46) 87532500
Camera Distr
N.A.I.C.S.: 423410

FLIR Systems Ltd. (2)
2 Kings Hill Avenue, Kings Hill, West Malling, ME19 4AQ, Kent, United Kingdom (100%)
Tel.: (44) 1732220011
Web Site: https://www.flir.co.uk
Sales Range: $100-124.9 Million
Emp.: 30
Producer of Infrared Systems
N.A.I.C.S.: 334511

Lorex Technology Inc. (2)
250 Royal crest Court, Markham, L3R 3S1, ON, Canada
Web Site: https://www.lorex.com
Emp.: 75
Video Surveillance System Distr
N.A.I.C.S.: 423690

Subsidiary (Domestic):

Digimerge Technologies Inc. (3)
300 Alden Road, Markham, L3R 4C1, ON, Canada
Tel.: (905) 946-8477
Web Site: http://www.digimerge.com
Sales Range: $25-49.9 Million
Emp.: 60
Video Surveillance System Distr
N.A.I.C.S.: 423690

Subsidiary (US):

Lorex Corporation (3)
999 Corporate Blvd Ste 110, Linthicum, MD 21090
Tel.: (410) 525-1905
Web Site: http://lorexstore.lorextechnology.com
Video Surveillance System Distr
N.A.I.C.S.: 423690

Subsidiary (Domestic):

Raymarine Inc. (2)
110 Lowell Rd, Hudson, NH 03051
Tel.: (603) 324-7900
Web Site: https://www.raymarine.com
Sales Range: $50-74.9 Million
Emp.: 270
Marine Electronics Mfr
N.A.I.C.S.: 334511

Subsidiary (Non-US):

Raymarine UK Ltd. (3)
Marine House Cartwright Drive, Fareham, PO15 5RJ, United Kingdom
Tel.: (44) 1329246700
Web Site: https://www.raymarine.com
Sales Range: $150-199.9 Million
Emp.: 556
Marine Electronics Mfr
N.A.I.C.S.: 334511

Teledyne France SAS (1)
Les Nertieres 5 Avenue Hector Pintus, La Gaude, 06610, France
Tel.: (33) 492110930
Web Site: http://www.teledynemarine.com
Current Measuring Device Mfr
N.A.I.C.S.: 334511

Teledyne Gavia ehf. (1)
Vesturvor 29, 200, Kopavogur, Iceland
Tel.: (354) 5112990
Web Site: https://www.teledynemarine.com
Sales Range: $10-24.9 Million
Emp.: 20
Autonomous Underwater Vehicles Mfr & Distr
N.A.I.C.S.: 334511

Teledyne Germany GmbH (1)
Kopfchenstrasse 1, 57223, Kreuztal, Germany
Tel.: (49) 27324020
Electronic & Communication Products Mfr
N.A.I.C.S.: 334220

Teledyne Impulse- PDM Ltd. (1)
4-6 Alton Business Centre Omega Park, Alton, GU34 2YU, Hampshire, United Kingdom
Tel.: (44) 1420552200
Web Site: https://www.teledynemarine.com
Connector Mfr
N.A.I.C.S.: 334417
Paul Anthony (Mgr-European Bus Dev)

Teledyne Instruments, Inc. (1)
16830 Chestnut St, City of Industry, CA 91748
Tel.: (626) 934-1500
Web Site: https://www.teledyneinstruments.com
Sales Range: $25-49.9 Million
Emp.: 200
Monitoring & Process Control Instrument Mfr
N.A.I.C.S.: 334519

Subsidiary (Domestic):

Hanson Research Corp. (2)
9810 Variel Ave, Chatsworth, CA 91311
Tel.: (818) 882-7266
Web Site: http://www.hansonresearch.com
Rev.: $7,333,333
Emp.: 25

Teledyne Technologies Incorporated—(Continued)

Instruments & Related Products Manufacturing for Measuring, Displaying & Controlling Industrial Process Variables
N.A.I.C.S.: 334513
William A. Hanson (Founder)

Scientific Systems Inc. (2)
349 Science Park Rd, State College, PA 16803-2215
Tel.: (814) 234-7311
Web Site: http://www.ssihplc.com
Analytical Laboratory Instrument Mfr
N.A.I.C.S.: 334516

Unit (Domestic):

Teledyne CETAC Technologies (2)
14306 Industrial Rd, Omaha, NE 68144
Tel.: (402) 733-2829
Web Site: https://www.teledynecetac.com
Sales Range: $25-49.9 Million
Emp.: 100
Analytical Laboratory Instrument Mfr
N.A.I.C.S.: 334516

Teledyne Isco (1)
4700 Superior St, Lincoln, NE 68504-1398
Tel.: (402) 464-0231
Web Site: https://www.teledyneisco.com
Sales Range: $50-74.9 Million
Emp.: 430
Water Pollution Monitoring Equipment, Wastewater Samplers & Chemical Separation Instruments Mfr, Designer & Marketer
N.A.I.C.S.: 334513

Teledyne LeCroy India Trading Private Ltd. (1)
154/63 1st Main Road Dr Rajkumar Road 1st Block, Rajajinagar, Bengaluru, 560010, India
Tel.: (91) 8067722888
Web Site: http://teledynelecroy.com
Electronic Components Mfr
N.A.I.C.S.: 334419

Teledyne LeCroy Singapore Pte. Ltd. (1)
Blk 750C Chai Chee Road 02-08, Singapore, 469003, Singapore
Tel.: (65) 64424880
Electronic Components Mfr
N.A.I.C.S.: 334419

Teledyne LeCroy Xena ApS. (1)
Gammel Lundtoftevej 1B 2nd floor, 2800, Lyngby, Denmark
Tel.: (45) 70200823
Web Site: https://www.xenanetworks.com
Computer Networking Product Mfr
N.A.I.C.S.: 334111

Teledyne LeCroy, Inc. (1)
700 Chestnut Ridge Rd, Chestnut Ridge, NY 10977-6499
Tel.: (845) 425-2000
Web Site: https://www.teledynelecroy.com
Emp.: 494
Electronic Signal Measurement Equipment Developer, Mfr & Distr
N.A.I.C.S.: 334515

Subsidiary (Domestic):

Frontline Test Equipment, Inc. (2)
337 W Rio Rd, Charlottesville, VA 22901
Tel.: (434) 984-4500
Web Site: http://www.fte.com
Rev.: $1,600,000
Emp.: 20
Custom Computer Programming Services
N.A.I.C.S.: 541511
Eric Kaplan (Founder)

LeCroy Lightspeed Corporation (2)
700 Chestnut Rdg Rd, Chestnut Ridge, NY 10977 (100%)
Tel.: (845) 425-2000
Web Site:
  http://www.teledynetechnologies.com
Sales Range: $75-99.9 Million
Emp.: 250
Electronics Mfr
N.A.I.C.S.: 334515

Quantum Data Inc. (2)
2111 Big Timber Rd, Elgin, IL 60123-1100
Tel.: (847) 888-0450

Web Site: http://www.quantumdata.com
Rev.: $9,000,000
Emp.: 15
Totalizing Fluid Meter & Counting Device Mfr
N.A.I.C.S.: 334514

Subsidiary (Non-US):

Teledyne LeCroy (Beijing) Trading Co., Ltd. (2)
Unit A Horizon Plaza No 6 Zhichun Road Rm 2001 Office, Rm 2002 Service Center Haidian District, Beijing, 100088, China
Tel.: (86) 108 280 0318
Web Site: http://www.teledynelecroy.com
Sales Range: $10-24.9 Million
Emp.: 18
Testing & Measurement Equipment Distr
N.A.I.C.S.: 334515

Teledyne LeCroy GmbH (2)
Im Breitspiel 11c, 69126, Heidelberg, Germany (100%)
Tel.: (49) 622182700
Web Site: http://www.lecroy.de
Sales Range: $10-24.9 Million
Emp.: 30
Electronic Components
N.A.I.C.S.: 334419

Teledyne LeCroy Japan Corporation (2)
TSC Building 4F 1-14-33 Esaka-cyo Suitashi, Yodogawa Ku, Osaka, 564-0063, Japan (100%)
Tel.: (81) 663960961
Web Site: http://www.lecroy.com
Sales Range: $1-9.9 Million
Emp.: 4
Electronic Components Mfr
N.A.I.C.S.: 334419

Teledyne LeCroy Korea, Ltd. (2)
10th Floor 333 Young Tong Tae Ro Gang Nangu, Seoul, 135 280, Korea (South) (100%)
Tel.: (82) 234520400
Web Site: http://www.teledynelecroy.co.kr
Sales Range: $10-24.9 Million
Emp.: 16
Electronic Components Mfr
N.A.I.C.S.: 334419

Unit (Domestic):

Teledyne LeCroy, Inc. - Protocol Solutions Group (2)
765 Sycamore Dr, Milpitas, CA 95035
Tel.: (408) 727-6600
Web Site: http://www.teledynelecroy.com
Sales Range: $10-24.9 Million
Emp.: 72
Oscilloscopes, Protocol Analyzers & Related Test & Measurement Solutions
N.A.I.C.S.: 334519

Subsidiary (Non-US):

Teledyne LeCroy, S.A. (2)
2 Route de Peney, Case postale 830, Vernier, 1215, Geneva, Switzerland (100%)
Tel.: (41) 225911900
Web Site: https://www.lecroy.com
Sales Range: $10-24.9 Million
Emp.: 50
Electronic Components
N.A.I.C.S.: 334419

Teledyne LeCroy, S.A.R.L (2)
19 Avenue de Norvege Immeuble Narvik ZA de Courtaboeuf 1, 01053, Courtaboeuf, Codex, France (100%)
Tel.: (33) 169188820
Web Site: https://www.teledyne.com
Sales Range: $100-124.9 Million
Emp.: 15
Electronic Components Distr
N.A.I.C.S.: 423690

Teledyne LeCroy, S.R.L. (2)
Centro Direzionale Valecenter Office, Via E Mattei 1 102 Marcon, 30020, Venice, Italy (100%)
Tel.: (39) 0415997011
Web Site: https://teledynelecroy.com
Electronic Components Mfr
N.A.I.C.S.: 334419

Teledyne Leeman Labs (1)

4736 Socialville Foster Rd, Mason, OH 45040
Tel.: (603) 886-8400
Web Site:
  https://www.teledyneleemanlabs.com
Sales Range: $10-24.9 Million
Emp.: 100
Analytical Laboratory Instrument Mfr
N.A.I.C.S.: 334516
Tom Grondine (VP & Opers Dir)

Teledyne Ltd. (1)
9-13 Napier Road, Cumbernauld, Glasgow, G68 0EF, United Kingdom
Tel.: (44) 7884002600
Web Site: https://www.teledynecontrol.com
Sales Range: $10-24.9 Million
Emp.: 20
Replay & Analyst Tools Mfr
N.A.I.C.S.: 333515

Subsidiary (Domestic):

Intelek Limited (2)
106 Waterhouse Lane, Chelmsford, CM1 2QU, Essex, United Kingdom
Tel.: (44) 1793827000
Holding Company; Global Communications, Avionics & Aerospace Products Mfr
N.A.I.C.S.: 551112

Subsidiary (Domestic):

CML Group Ltd (3)
Price St, Birkenhead, CH41 3PT, United Kingdom
Tel.: (44) 1516475531
Web Site: http://www.cml-group.com
Sales Range: $25-49.9 Million
Emp.: 110
Aerostructure Components Mfr
N.A.I.C.S.: 334511

Subsidiary (US):

Paradise Datacom LLC (3)
328 Innovation Blvd, State College, PA 16803
Tel.: (814) 238-3450
Web Site: http://www.paradisedata.com
Sales Range: $25-49.9 Million
Emp.: 70
Satellite Communication Equipment Mfr
N.A.I.C.S.: 334220

Subsidiary (Domestic):

Paradise Datacom Ltd (3)
106 Waterhouse Lane, Essex, Chelmsford, CM1 2QU, United Kingdom
Tel.: (44) 1245847520
Web Site: http://www.paradisedata.com
Sales Range: $10-24.9 Million
Emp.: 22
Satellite Communication Equipment Mfr
N.A.I.C.S.: 334220

Subsidiary (Domestic):

Teledyne Labtech Limited (2)
Unit 1 Brodaxe Business Park, Presteigne, Powys, LD8 2UK, United Kingdom
Tel.: (44) 1544260093
Web Site: https://www.teledynelabtech.com
Microwave Circuit Solutions Mfr
N.A.I.C.S.: 334418

Plant (Domestic):

Teledyne Labtech Ltd. - Milton Keynes Plant (3)
8 Vincent Avenue, Crownhill, Milton Keynes, MK8 0AB, United Kingdom (100%)
Tel.: (44) 1908261755
Web Site: http://www.teledynelabtech.com
Sales Range: $25-49.9 Million
Emp.: 25
Microwave Circuit Solutions Mfr
N.A.I.C.S.: 334418

Teledyne Micralyne, Inc. (1)
1911 - 94 Street, Edmonton, T6N 1E6, AB, Canada
Tel.: (780) 431-4400
Web Site: https://www.micralyne.com
Nano Technology Services
N.A.I.C.S.: 541713
Stephen Bonham (Plant Mgr)
Collin Twanow (Dir-Tech)

Dean Spicer (Dir-Engrg)
Dan Djukich (Sls Dir-Global)
Khalid Aman (Project Mgr)

Teledyne Microelectronic Technologies (1)
12964 Panama St, Los Angeles, CA 90066
Tel.: (310) 822-8229
Web Site: http://www.teledynemicro.com
Sales Range: $75-99.9 Million
Emp.: 300
Traveling Wave Tubes, Microwave Subsystems, EW Systems, Solid State Amplifiers, High Power Amplifiers, Active Integrated Modules
N.A.I.C.S.: 334413

Teledyne Monitor Labs, Inc. (1)
35 Inverness Dr E, Englewood, CO 80112
Tel.: (303) 792-3300
Web Site: https://www.teledyne-ml.com
Sales Range: $25-49.9 Million
Emp.: 82
Mfr & Marketer of Environmental Monitoring Instruments
N.A.I.C.S.: 334519

Teledyne Oil & Gas (1)
1026 N Williamson Blvd, Daytona Beach, FL 32114
Tel.: (386) 236-0780
Web Site: http://www.teledyneoilandgas.com
Sales Range: $50-74.9 Million
Emp.: 500
Mfr of Subsea Electrical & Fiber Optic Interconnect Systems
N.A.I.C.S.: 334417

Teledyne Oldham Simtronics SAS (1)
ZI Est-rue Orfila, BP 417, 62027, Arras, France
Tel.: (33) 321608080
Flame Gas Detection Services
N.A.I.C.S.: 238220

Teledyne Optech Incorporated (1)
300 Interchange Way, Vaughan, L4K 5Z8, ON, Canada
Tel.: (905) 660-0808
Electric & Environmental Engineering Services
N.A.I.C.S.: 541330

Teledyne Paradise Datacom Limited (1)
106 Waterhouse Lane, Essex, Chelmsford, CM1 2QU, United Kingdom
Tel.: (44) 1245847520
Web Site: http://www.paradisedata.com
Emp.: 20
Satellite Communication Product Mfr & Distr
N.A.I.C.S.: 334220
John Restivo (CEO)

Teledyne Paradise Datacom, LLC (1)
11361 Sunrise Park Dr, Rancho Cordova, CA 95742
Tel.: (814) 238-3450
Web Site: http://www.paradisedata.com
Satellite Communication Products Mfr & Distr
N.A.I.C.S.: 334220

Teledyne RD Instruments, Inc. (1)
14020 Stowe Dr, Poway, CA 92064
Tel.: (858) 842-2600
Web Site: http://www.teledynemarine.com
Sales Range: $25-49.9 Million
Emp.: 150
Acoustic Doppler Products Mfr
N.A.I.C.S.: 334511
William Kikendall (Pres)

Teledyne RD Technologies (Shanghai) Co., Ltd. (1)
1311 Holiday Inn Business Building 899 Dongfang Road, Pu Dong, Shanghai, 020122, China
Tel.: (86) 2158306939
Sales Range: $25-49.9 Million
Emp.: 10
Research & Development Services
N.A.I.C.S.: 541715

Teledyne RESON A/S (1)
Fabriksvangen 13, 3550, Slangerup, Denmark
Tel.: (45) 47380022

Web Site: https://www.teledyne-reson.com
Navigational Instrument Mfr
N.A.I.C.S.: 334511

Teledyne RESON B.V. (1)
Stuttgartstraat 42-44, 3047 AS, Rotterdam,
Netherlands
Tel.: (31) 10 245 1500
Web Site: http://www.teledyne-pds.com
Electronic Components Mfr
N.A.I.C.S.: 334419

Teledyne RESON GmbH (1)
Flughafenallee 28, 28199, Bremen, Germany
Tel.: (49) 42137709600
Electronic Components Mfr
N.A.I.C.S.: 334419
Daniel Rosenboom (Dir-Sls)

Teledyne RESON, Inc. (1)
1026 N Williamsons Blvd, Daytona Beach,
FL 32114
Tel.: (805) 964-6260
Emp.: 30
Electronic Components Mfr
N.A.I.C.S.: 334419
Jon Marcus (Gen Mgr)

Teledyne RISI, Inc. (1)
PO Box 359, Tracy, CA 95378
Tel.: (925) 456-9700
Web Site: http://www.teledynerisi.com
Emp.: 19
Precision Secondary Explosive Component
Mfr
N.A.I.C.S.: 325920

**Teledyne Rad-icon Imaging
Corp.** (1)
888 E Arques Ave, Sunnyvale, CA 94085
Tel.: (408) 736-6000
Web Site: http://www.rad-icon.com
Image Sensor Distr
N.A.I.C.S.: 423690

**Teledyne Real Time Systems
Inc.** (1)
103 Industrial Loop Ste 1100, Fredericksburg, TX 78624
Tel.: (830) 990-2340
Web Site: http://www.real-time-sys.com
Emp.: 20
Electronic Parts & Equipment Mfr
N.A.I.C.S.: 334419

Teledyne Reynolds Inc. (1)
1001 Knox St, Torrance, CA 90502
Tel.: (310) 823-5491
Web Site: http://www.teledynereynolds.com
Rev.: $29,283,831
Emp.: 150
Electronic Connectors
N.A.I.C.S.: 334417

Teledyne Reynolds UK (1)
Navigation House Canal View Road,
Newbury, RG14 5UR, Berkshire, United
Kingdom
Tel.: (44) 1635262200
Web Site:
https://www.teledynereynolds.co.uk
Sales Range: $25-49.9 Million
Emp.: 60
Cable & Wire Equipment Mfr
N.A.I.C.S.: 335921

**Teledyne Scientific & Imaging,
LLC** (1)
1049 Camino Dos Rios, Thousand Oaks,
CA 91360
Tel.: (805) 373-4545
Web Site: https://www.teledyne-si.com
Sales Range: $125-149.9 Million
Emp.: 400
Imaging Sensors & Optics Developer & Mfr
N.A.I.C.S.: 333310

Subsidiary (Domestic):

Teledyne Judson Technologies (2)
221 Commerce Dr, Montgomeryville, PA
18936-9641
Tel.: (215) 368-6900
Web Site: https://www.teledynejudson.com
Sales Range: $10-24.9 Million
Emp.: 70
Infrared Detector Mfr
N.A.I.C.S.: 334511

Teledyne SeaBotix Inc. (1)

49 Edgerton Dr, North Falmouth, MA 02556
Tel.: (508) 563-1000
Web Site: https://www.teledynemarine.com
Sales Range: $25-49.9 Million
Emp.: 50
Metalworking Machines Mfr
N.A.I.C.S.: 333519

**Teledyne Signal Processing Devices
Sweden AB** (1)
Teknikringen 8D, 583 30, Linkoping, Sweden
Tel.: (46) 134650600
Web Site: https://www.spdevices.com
Electric & Environmental Engineering Services
N.A.I.C.S.: 541330

Teledyne Storm Cable (1)
9215 Premier Row, Dallas, TX 75247
Tel.: (214) 637-1381
Web Site: http://www.teledynemarine.com
Sales Range: $75-99.9 Million
Emp.: 115
Cable & Wire Mfr
N.A.I.C.S.: 332618

Teledyne TSS Limited (1)
1 Blackmoor Lane, Croxley Green Business
Park, Watford, WD18 8GA, Hertfordshire,
United Kingdom
Tel.: (44) 1923216020
Web Site: http://www.tss-international.com
Emp.: 55
Marine Navigation Equipment Mfr
N.A.I.C.S.: 334511

Teledyne Tekmar (1)
4736 Socialville Foster Rd, Mason, OH
45040-8265
Tel.: (513) 229-7000
Web Site: https://www.teledynetekmar.com
Sales Range: $25-49.9 Million
Emp.: 125
Mfr & Wholesaler of Laboratory Analytical
Instruments & Equipment
N.A.I.C.S.: 334516
Tom Hartlein (Mgr-SVOC Product Line)

Teledyne VariSystems, Inc. (1)
5304 Hubalta Road SE, Calgary, T2B 1T6,
AB, Canada
Tel.: (403) 272-0318
Web Site: http://www.varisystems.com
Electrical & Fiber Optic Interconnect Systems Mfr
N.A.I.C.S.: 423610

Teledyne e2v Limited (1)
106 Waterhouse Lane, Chelmsford, CM1
2QU, Essex, United Kingdom
Tel.: (44) 1245493493
Web Site: https://www.teledyne-e2v.com
Sales Range: $300-349.9 Million
RF, Microwave & Sensing Component &
Sub-Systems Mfr
N.A.I.C.S.: 334290

Subsidiary (Domestic):

Teledyne e2v (UK) Limited (2)
106 Waterhouse Lane, Chelmsford, CM1
2QU, Essex, United Kingdom
Tel.: (44) 1245493493
Web Site: http://www.teledyne-e2v.com
Electronic Capacitor Mfr
N.A.I.C.S.: 334416

Subsidiary (Non-US):

**Teledyne e2v Semiconductors
SAS** (2)
4 Rue De Rochepleine, BP 123, 38120,
Saint Egreve, Cedex, France
Tel.: (33) 476583000
Web Site: https://semiconductors.teledyne-e2v.com
Electrical Equipment & Component Mfr
N.A.I.C.S.: 335999

Subsidiary (US):

Teledyne e2v, Inc. (2)
765 Sycamore Dr, Milpitas, CA 95035
Tel.: (408) 737-0992
Web Site: http://www.e2v.com
Electron Tube Mfr
N.A.I.C.S.: 334419

Subsidiary (Domestic):

Teledyne e2v US, Inc. (3)

700 Chestnut Ridge Rd, Chestnut Ridge,
NY 10977
Tel.: (845) 425-2000
Web Site: https://www.teledyne-e2v.com
Electronic Components Sales & Distr
N.A.I.C.S.: 423690

TELEFLEX INCORPORATED

550 E Swedesford Rd Ste 400,
Wayne, PA 19087
Tel.: (610) 225-6800   DE
Web Site: https://www.teleflex.com
Year Founded: 1943
TFX—(NYSE)
Rev.: $2,974,489,000
Assets: $7,532,546,000
Liabilities: $3,091,558,000
Net Worth: $4,440,988,000
Earnings: $356,328,000
Emp.: 14,500
Fiscal Year-end: 12/31/23
Medical Technology Products Distr
N.A.I.C.S.: 339113
Liam J. Kelly (Chm, Pres & CEO)
John R. Deren (Chief Acctg Officer &
VP)
Timothy F. Duffy (CIO & VP)
Cameron P. Hicks (Chief HR Officer
& VP)
Karen T. Boylan (VP-Strategic Projects)
Petro Barchuk (VP-Fin Plng & Analysis)
Marie Hendrixson (VP-Internal Audit)
Bert Lane (VP-Logistics & Distr-Global)
Justin McMurray (VP-Strategic R&D-Global)
Daniel Price (VP-Comml Fin)
Jay White (Pres-Comml-Global & VP)
James Winters (VP-Mfg & Supply
Chain)
Daniel V. Logue (Gen Counsel, Sec
& VP)
Matthew James (Pres-Urology-EMEA
& Global)
Howard Cyr (Chief Compliance Officer)
Lawrence Keusch (VP)
Michael Kryukov (VP)
Dominik Reterski (VP)
Whitney Reynolds (VP)
Matt Tomkin (VP)
Mark Singleton (VP-Fin-Americas
Strategic Bus Units)
Thomas E. Powell (CFO & Exec VP)

Subsidiaries:

Arrow Interventional, Inc. (1)
155 S Limerick Rd, Limerick, PA 19468
Tel.: (610) 948-5100
Medical Equipment Mfr
N.A.I.C.S.: 339113

Hotspur Technologies, Inc. (1)
880 Maude Ave Ste A, Mountain View, CA
94043
Tel.: (650) 969-3150
Web Site: http://www.hotspur-inc.com
Sales Range: $25-49.9 Million
Emp.: 28
Blood Flow Apparatus & Medical Device Mfr
& Distr
N.A.I.C.S.: 334510

Human Medics Co., Ltd. (1)
71-5 Bangbae-Ro 26-Gil, Seocho-gu,
Seoul, 137-836, Korea (South)
Tel.: (82) 25367550
Surgical Equipment Distr
N.A.I.C.S.: 423450

ICOR AB (1)
Centralvagen 1, 194 76, Upplands Vasby,
Stockholm, Sweden
Tel.: (46) 87920582
Medical Devices & Surgery Product Mfr &
Distr
N.A.I.C.S.: 339113

NeoTract, Inc. (1)

4155 Hopyard Rd, Pleasanton, CA 94588-8570
Tel.: (925) 401-0700
Web Site: http://www.neotract.com
Surgical & Medical Instrument Mfr
N.A.I.C.S.: 339112
Justin Hall (VP & Gen Mgr-EMEA)

Productos Aereos, S.A. de C.V. (1)
Angel Flores Y Altamirano 100 Fracc Soler,
22100, Tijuana, Baja California, Mexico
Tel.: (52) 6646804335
Medical Devices & Surgery Product Mfr &
Distr
N.A.I.C.S.: 339112

Rusch Austria GmbH (1)
Lazarettgasse 24, 1090, Vienna, Austria
Tel.: (43) 1 402 4772
Web Site: http://www.teleflex.com
Surgical Appliance Mfr
N.A.I.C.S.: 339113

T.K India Private Limited (1)
346&347 Phase 2 Industrial Area, Chandigarh, 160002, India
Tel.: (91) 1725075440
Medical Equipment Mfr
N.A.I.C.S.: 339113

TFX Group Limited (1)
The Broadway, Amersham, HP7 0UT, Buckinghamshire, United Kingdom
Tel.: (44) 1494532761
Web Site: http://www.teleflex.com
Sales Range: $10-24.9 Million
Emp.: 4
Medical Devices & Surgery Product Mfr &
Distr
N.A.I.C.S.: 339112

Teleflex Funding Corporation (1)
2751 Centerville Rd Ste 3208, Wilmington,
DE 19808
Tel.: (302) 225-5049
Investment Management Service
N.A.I.C.S.: 522291

**Teleflex Grundstucks GmbH & Co.
KG** (1)
Willy-Rusch-str 4-10, 71394, Kernen, Germany
Tel.: (49) 71514060
Surgical Appliance Mfr
N.A.I.C.S.: 339113

Teleflex Incorporated - Limerick (1)
155 S Limerick Rd, Limerick, PA 19468
Tel.: (610) 948-5100
Medical Devices & Surgery Product Mfr &
Distr
N.A.I.C.S.: 339113

Teleflex Medical Australia Pty Ltd (1)
Level 4 197 Coward St, Mascot, Sydney,
2020, NSW, Australia
Tel.: (61) 300360226
Surgical Appliance Distr
N.A.I.C.S.: 423450

Teleflex Medical Colombia SAS (1)
Carrera 11 No 79 - 66 Piso 4 Edificio
Spaces, 110731, Bogota, Colombia
Tel.: (57) 16533135
Surgical Appliance Distr
N.A.I.C.S.: 423450

Teleflex Medical GmbH (1)
IDA Business and Technology Park Dublin
Road, Athlone, Co Westmeath, Ireland
Tel.: (353) 906460800
Surgical & Medical Instrument Distr
N.A.I.C.S.: 423450

Teleflex Medical Group (1)
4024 Stirrup Creek, Research Triangle
Park, NC 27703
Tel.: (919) 544-8000
Web Site: http://www.teleflexmedical.com
Sales Range: $800-899.9 Million
Emp.: 11,000
Medical Devices, Surgical Instruments &
Disposable Medical Products Mfr & Distr
N.A.I.C.S.: 339112

Teleflex Incorporated—(Continued)

Plant (Domestic):

CarTika Medical (2)
6550 Wedgwood Rd N Ste 300, Maple Grove, MN 55311
Tel.: (763) 545-5188
Web Site: http://www.cartikamedical.com
Sales Range: $1-9.9 Million
Emp.: 50
Catheters & Medical Devices Mfr
N.A.I.C.S.: 339113

Subsidiary (Non-US):

LMA Urology B.V. (2)
Tel.: (31) 206717452
Medical Devices & Surgery Product Mfr & Distr
N.A.I.C.S.: 339112

Subsidiary (Non-US):

LMA Urology Suisse SA (3)
Tel.: (41) 223548900
Medical Devices & Surgery Product Mfr & Distr
N.A.I.C.S.: 339112

Subsidiary (Non-US):

Medical Service GmbH (2)
Luisenstrasse 8, Bad Liebenzell, 75378, Germany
Tel.: (49) 7052403100
Web Site: http://www.medical-service.de
Sales Range: $25-49.9 Million
Emp.: 180
Medical Devices & Surgery Product Mfr & Distr
N.A.I.C.S.: 339112

Rusch Uruguay Ltda. (2)
Cno Carrasco 7365, Montevideo, 12100, Uruguay
Tel.: (598) 26019835
Medical Devices & Surgery Product Mfr & Distr
N.A.I.C.S.: 339112

Subsidiary (Domestic):

Specialized Medical Devices, LLC (2)
300 Running Pump Rd, Lancaster, PA 17603
Tel.: (717) 392-8570
Web Site: http://www.specializedmedical.com
Sales Range: $10-24.9 Million
Emp.: 140
Holding Company; Medical & Surgical Instruments Mfr
N.A.I.C.S.: 551112

Plant (Domestic):

TFX Medical OEM (2)
50 Plantation Dr, Jaffrey, NH 03452 **(100%)**
Tel.: (603) 532-7706
Web Site: http://www.teleflexmedicaloem.com
Sales Range: $75-99.9 Million
Emp.: 300
Medical Device Mfr
N.A.I.C.S.: 339112

Subsidiary (Domestic):

TFX Medical Wire Products, Inc. (2)
3750 Annapolis Ln N Ste 160, Minneapolis, MN 55447-5438
Tel.: (763) 559-6414
Medical Devices & Surgery Product Mfr & Distr
N.A.I.C.S.: 339112

Subsidiary (Non-US):

Teleflex Medical (Proprietary) Limited (2)
PO Box 1716, Paulshof Extension 45, Kelvin, 2054, South Africa
Tel.: (27) 118074887
Web Site: http://www.teleflex.com
Disposable Catheters, Heart Assist Devices & Other Critical & Cardiac Care Related Products Distr
N.A.I.C.S.: 423450

Teleflex Medical Asia Pte Ltd. (2)
6 Battery Road 07-02, Singapore, 049909, Singapore
Tel.: (65) 64393000
Web Site: http://www.teleflex.com
Medical Devices & Surgery Product Mfr & Distr
N.A.I.C.S.: 339112

Teleflex Medical BV (2)
Lange Dreef 11J, 4131 NJ, Vianen, Netherlands
Tel.: (31) 880021500
Medical Devices & Surgery Product Mfr & Distr
N.A.I.C.S.: 339112

Teleflex Medical Canada Inc. (2)
500 Hood Road Suite 310, Markham, L3R 9Z3, ON, Canada
Web Site: http://www.teleflex.com
Surgical Instruments Marketer & Distr
N.A.I.C.S.: 423450

Subsidiary (Domestic):

Pyng Medical Corp. (3)
Unit 210 13480 Crestwood Place, Richmond, V6V 2J9, BC, Canada
Tel.: (604) 303-7964
Web Site: http://www.pyng.com
Medical Device Mfr & Sales
N.A.I.C.S.: 334510

Subsidiary (Non-US):

Teleflex Medical EDC BVBA (2)
Heerstersweg Veldweg 11, Tongeren, 3700, Belgium
Tel.: (32) 12459070
Web Site: http://www.telefex.com
Emp.: 130
Medical Devices & Surgery Product Mfr & Distr
N.A.I.C.S.: 339112

Teleflex Medical Europe Limited (2)
IDA Business and Technology Park Dublin Road, Co Westmeath, Athlone, Ireland
Tel.: (353) 906460800
Medical Devices & Surgery Product Mfr & Distr
N.A.I.C.S.: 339112

Teleflex Medical Hellas A.E.E. (2)
Chalandri, 15231, Halandri, Athens, Greece
Tel.: (30) 2106777717
Web Site: http://www.teleflex.com
Sales Range: $25-49.9 Million
Emp.: 10
Disposable Catheters, Heart Assist Devices & Other Critical & Cardiac Care Related Products Distr
N.A.I.C.S.: 423450

Teleflex Medical Iberia S.A. (2)
Calle Quito s/n - nave 1-5 Poligono Industrial de Camporroso, 28806, Alcala de Henares, Madrid, Spain
Tel.: (34) 91 830 0451
Web Site: http://www.teleflex.com
Emp.: 55
Medical Devices & Surgery Product Mfr & Distr
N.A.I.C.S.: 339113

Teleflex Medical Japan, Ltd. (2)
Shinjuku NS Bldg 5F 2-4-1, Nishi-Shinjuku, Tokyo, 163-0805, Japan
Tel.: (81) 57 005 5160
Web Site: http://www.arrowjapan.co.jp
Sales Range: $25-49.9 Million
Emp.: 60
Disposable Catheters, Heart Assist Devices & Other Critical & Cardiac Care Related Products Distr
N.A.I.C.S.: 423450

Teleflex Medical Private Limited (2)
1st Floor Embassy Vogue Municipal No 2/1, Bengaluru, 560 052, India
Tel.: (91) 80 4093 4790
Web Site: http://www.teleflex.com
Medical Devices & Surgery Product Mfr & Distr
N.A.I.C.S.: 339113

Teleflex Medical SAS (2)
La Pousaraque, 31460, Le Faget, France
Tel.: (33) 562187940
Web Site: http://www.teleflex.com

Emp.; 100
Medical Devices & Surgery Product Mfr & Distr
N.A.I.C.S.: 339113
Dominique Baric *(Pres)*

Teleflex Medical Tuttlingen GmbH (2)
Kaufgasse 1, Wurmlingen, 78573, Tuttlingen, Germany
Tel.: (49) 7461770970
Medical Devices & Surgery Product Mfr & Distr
N.A.I.C.S.: 339113

Teleflex Medical de Mexico, S. de R.L. de C.V. (2)
Ave Industrias No 5954, Parque Industrial Finsa, 88275, Nuevo Laredo, Tamaulipas, Mexico
Tel.: (52) 8677113750
Medical Devices & Surgery Product Mfr & Distr
N.A.I.C.S.: 339112

Subsidiary (Domestic):

Hudson Respiratory Care Tecate, S. de R.L. de C.V. (3)
Prolongacion Eusebio Quino No 1316 Rancho El Descanso, Tecate, 21478, Mexico
Tel.: (52) 6655211168
Medical Devices & Surgery Product Mfr & Distr
N.A.I.C.S.: 339113

Subsidiary (Non-US):

Teleflex Medical s.r.l. (2)
Via Torino 5, 20814, Varedo, MB, Italy
Tel.: (39) 03 625 8911
Web Site: http://www.teleflex.com
Medical Devices & Surgery Product Mfr & Distr
N.A.I.C.S.: 339113

Teleflex Medical, s.r.o. (2)
Valova 49, 92101, Piestany, Slovakia
Tel.: (421) 337725428
Web Site: http://www.teleflex.com
Sales Range: $150-199.9 Million
Emp.: 1
Disposable Catheters, Heart Assist Devices & Other Critical & Cardiac Care Related Products Distr
N.A.I.C.S.: 423450

Teleflex Medical, s.r.o. (2)
Prazska trida 209/182, 500 04, Hradec Kralove, Czech Republic
Tel.: (420) 49 575 9118
Web Site: http://www.teleflex.com
Medical Devices & Surgery Product Mfr & Distr
N.A.I.C.S.: 339113

WIRUTEC Rusch Medical Vertriebs GmbH (2)
Fichtenweg 3, 66280, Sulzbach, Germany
Tel.: (49) 689 792 4920
Web Site: https://www.wirutec.de
Medical Device & Surgery Product Mfr & Distr
N.A.I.C.S.: 339112

Subsidiary (Domestic):

Wolfe-Tory Medical, Inc. (2)
79 W 4500 S Ste 18, Salt Lake City, UT 84107-2647
Tel.: (801) 281-3000
Sales Range: $25-49.9 Million
Emp.: 35
Disposable Medical Device Mfr & Distr
N.A.I.C.S.: 339112

Teleflex Medical Incorporated (1)
2917 Weck Dr Research Triangle Park, Durham, NC 27709-0186
Tel.: (919) 544-8000
Emp.: 2,174
Surgical Applicance Mfr & Distr
N.A.I.C.S.: 339112

Teleflex Swiss Holding GmbH (1)
Industriestrasse 47, 6304, Zug, Switzerland
Tel.: (41) 318184090
Web Site: http://www.teleflex.com
Medical Devices & Surgery Product Mfr & Distr

N.A.I.C.S.: 339113

Truphatek (Beijing) Trading Co., Ltd. (1)
Fortune Street 1-4-503 Chaoyang Road, Chaoyang District, Beijing, 100123, China
Tel.: (86) 1085758552
Medical Equipment Whslr
N.A.I.C.S.: 423450

Truphatek International Limited (1)
14 Beni Gaon Street Building B2, PO Box 8051, Netanya, 4250443, Israel
Tel.: (972) 98851155
Web Site: http://www.truphatek.com
Medical Equipment Whslr
N.A.I.C.S.: 423450
Ravit Levy *(CFO)*

Truphatek Product Resources India Private Limited (1)
Plot No A246 Road No 30 B Opposite Wagle Police Station, Wagle Industrial Estate, Thane, 400 604, India
Tel.: (91) 2225831634
Medical Equipment Whslr
N.A.I.C.S.: 423450

Vascular Solutions, Inc. (1)
6464 Sycamore Ct N, Minneapolis, MN 55369
Tel.: (763) 656-4300
Web Site: http://www.vasc.com
Medical Device Mfr
N.A.I.C.S.: 339112
James Hennen *(CFO & Sr VP-Fin)*

VasoNova, Inc. (1)
155 Jefferson Dr, Menlo Park, CA 94025
Tel.: (877) 236-6869
Web Site: http://www.teleflex.com
Biopharmaceutical & Vascular Navigation System Mfr
N.A.I.C.S.: 325412

Vidacare Corp. (1)
4350 Lockhill Selma Rd Ste 150, Shavano Park, TX 78249
Tel.: (210) 375-8500
Web Site: http://www.vidacare.com
Sales Range: $1-9.9 Million
Emp.: 39
Intraosseous Medicine Delivery Developer
N.A.I.C.S.: 334510

Z-Medica, LLC (1)
4 Fairfield Blvd, Wallingford, CT 06492
Tel.: (203) 294-0000
Web Site: http://www.z-medica.com
Rev.: $5,400,000
Emp.: 27
Medical, Dental & Hospital Equipment & Supplies Merchant Whslr
N.A.I.C.S.: 423450
Ernest Waaser *(Chm)*

TELEPHONE & DATA SYSTEMS, INC.
30 N LaSalle St Ste 4000, Chicago, IL 60602
Tel.: (312) 592-5379 DE
Web Site: https://www.tdsinc.com
Year Founded: 1969
TDS—(NYSE)
Rev.: $5,160,000,000
Assets: $13,921,000,000
Liabilities: $7,925,000,000
Net Worth: $5,996,000,000
Earnings: ($569,000,000)
Emp.: 4,300
Fiscal Year-end: 12/31/23
Telecommunications Resellers
N.A.I.C.S.: 517111
Vicki L. Villacrez *(CFO & Exec VP)*
Julie D. Mathews *(Dir-IR)*
Kenneth M. Kotylo *(VP-Acquisitions & Corp Dev)*
Theodore E. Wiessing *(Chief Security & Privacy Officer & VP-IT Operational Svcs)*
Laurie A. Ruchti *(CIO & VP)*
David D. Gillman *(VP-Tax)*
John M. Toomey *(Treas & VP)*
Daniel J. DeWitt *(Sr VP-HR)*
Peter D. Taft *(VP-Strategy)*

Michelle Brukwicki *(VP-Fin Analysis & Strategic Plng)*
Colleen Thompson *(VP-Corp Rels)*
Vicki L. Villacrez *(CFO)*
John N. Greene *(VP)*
Anita J. Kroll *(Chief Acctg Officer, VP & Controller)*
LeRoy T. Carlson Jr. *(Pres & CEO)*

Subsidiaries:

Bend Cable Communications
LLC   **(1)**
63090 Sherman Rd, Bend, OR
97703   **(100%)**
Tel.: (541) 382-5551
Web Site: http://bendbroadband.com
Emp.: 300
High Speed Internet, Cable Television &
Telephone Services
N.A.I.C.S.: 516210

COMMUNICATIONS CORPORATION
OF INDIANA   **(1)**
127 N Meridian St, Roachdale, IN 46172-
9261
Tel.: (765) 522-1111
Voice & Data Communications Services
N.A.I.C.S.: 517112

Oneneck IT Services
Corporation   **(1)**
5301 N Pima Rd Ste 100, Scottsdale, AZ
85250
Tel.: (480) 315-3000
Web Site: http://www.oneneck.com
Sales Range: $50-74.9 Million
Emp.: 230
Information Technology Outsourcing Ser-
vices
N.A.I.C.S.: 541519

Suttle-Straus Inc.   **(1)**
1000 Uniek Dr, Waunakee, WI
53597   **(80%)**
Tel.: (608) 849-1000
Web Site: https://www.suttle-straus.com
Sales Range: $25-49.9 Million
Emp.: 200
Printing Distribution Services
N.A.I.C.S.: 323111
Ted Norman *(Dir-Mfg)*
Ted Straus *(Pres & CEO)*
Brett Keene *(VP-Ops)*
Steve Harold *(VP-Bus Dev)*
Susan Pschorr *(Dir-HR)*
Phil Salvatore *(Dir-Client Svcs)*
Jim Twieg *(VP-Tech)*

TDS BAJA BROADBAND LLC   **(1)**
901 N Florida Ave, Alamogordo, NM 88310
Tel.: (575) 437-3101
Web Site: http://www.hellotds.com
Telecommunication Servicesb
N.A.I.C.S.: 517810

TDS Metrocom   **(1)**
525 Junction Rd, Madison, WI 53717
Tel.: (608) 664-4000
Web Site: http://www.tdstelecom.com
Telephone, DSL & Long Distance Services
N.A.I.C.S.: 812990

Subsidiary (Domestic):

TDS Metro-Com   **(2)**
30925 2nd St, Pequot Lakes, MN 56472
Tel.: (218) 568-4000
Web Site: http://www.tdstelecom.com
Telephone Communications
N.A.I.C.S.: 517810

TDS Telecom   **(1)**
127 N Meridian St, Roachdale, IN
46172   **(100%)**
Tel.: (765) 522-1111
Web Site: http://www.tdstelecom.com
Sales Range: $10-24.9 Million
Emp.: 65
Telephone Company
N.A.I.C.S.: 517810

TDS Telecom   **(1)**
108 N Mulberry St, Waldron, IN
46182   **(100%)**
Tel.: (765) 525-4301
Web Site: http://www.tdstelecom.com
Sales Range: $1-9.9 Million
Emp.: 5
Telephone Company

N.A.I.C.S.: 517121

TDS Telecom   **(1)**
102 W Fremont St, Arcadia, OH 44804-
0157
Tel.: (419) 894-6411
Web Site: http://www.tdstelecom.com
Sales Range: $1-9.9 Million
Emp.: 6
Telephone Company
N.A.I.C.S.: 517121

TDS Telecom   **(1)**
PO Box 22610, Knoxville, TN
37933   **(100%)**
Tel.: (865) 966-5828
Web Site: http://www.tdstelecom.com
Sales Range: $10-24.9 Million
Emp.: 35
Telephone Company
N.A.I.C.S.: 813410

TDS Telecom   **(1)**
30502 Broad St, Bruceton, TN
38317   **(100%)**
Tel.: (731) 586-2222
Web Site: http://www.tdstelecom.com
Sales Range: $200-249.9 Million
Telephone Company
N.A.I.C.S.: 517121

TDS Telecom   **(1)**
702 E Main, Kendrick, ID 83537   **(100%)**
Tel.: (208) 289-5701
Web Site: http://www.tdstelecom.com
Sales Range: $10-24.9 Million
Emp.: 7
Telephone Company
N.A.I.C.S.: 517121

TDS Telecom   **(1)**
2495 Main St, Choctaw, OK
73020-0220   **(100%)**
Tel.: (405) 390-2291
Web Site: http://www.tdstelecom.com
Sales Range: $10-24.9 Million
Emp.: 25
Telephone Company
N.A.I.C.S.: 517121

TDS Telecom   **(1)**
119 W Gilliam, Condon, OR 97823   **(100%)**
Tel.: (541) 384-2211
Web Site: http://www.tdstelecom.com
Sales Range: $200-249.9 Million
Telephone Company
N.A.I.C.S.: 517121

TDS Telecom   **(1)**
525 Junction Rd, Madison, WI
53717   **(100%)**
Tel.: (218) 568-2529
Web Site: http://www.tdstelecom.com
Sales Range: $900-999.9 Million
Emp.: 2,500
Telephone Company
N.A.I.C.S.: 517121

TDS Telecom   **(1)**
20 Stetson Rd, Corinna, ME
04928   **(100%)**
Tel.: (207) 278-3283
Web Site: http://www.tdstelecom.com
Sales Range: $1-9.9 Million
Emp.: 5
Telephone Company
N.A.I.C.S.: 517121

TDS Telecom   **(1)**
229 E Green Bay St, Bonduel, WI 54107
Tel.: (715) 758-2192
Sales Range: $1-9.9 Million
Emp.: 5
Telephone Paging System
N.A.I.C.S.: 517111

TDS Telecom   **(1)**
N 287 Military Rd, Sherwood, WI
54169   **(100%)**
Tel.: (920) 776-1700
Web Site: http://www.tdstelecom.com
Sales Range: $200-249.9 Million
Telephone Company
N.A.I.C.S.: 517121

TDS Telecom   **(1)**
525 Jct Rd, Madison, WI 53717   **(100%)**
Tel.: (608) 664-4000
Web Site: http://www.tdstelecom.com
Sales Range: $1-9.9 Million
Emp.: 2,000
Telephone Company

N.A.I.C.S.: 517121
Vicki L. Villacrez *(CFO & Sr VP-Fin)*
Ken Paker *(CTO & Sr VP-Information & Network Technologies)*
Andrew Petersen *(Sr VP-Corp Affairs)*
Shane West *(Sr VP-Mktg, Sls & Customer Ops)*
Mark Barber *(Sr VP-Network Ops)*
Kathy Cefalu *(Chief HR Officer & VP)*
Karl Betz *(VP-Information Technologies)*
Andrew Buchert *(VP-Field Svcs)*
David Dudsak *(VP-Svc Assurance & Sup-port)*
Michael Gasser *(VP & Controller)*
Benjamin C. Goth *(VP-Network Svcs)*
Julie Maiers *(VP-Mktg & Product Dev)*
Joe Read *(VP-Supply Chain Svcs)*
John Sango *(VP-Customer Contact Ops)*
Michael Zalewski *(VP-Bus Dev)*

TDS Telecom   **(1)**
15 W St, Williston, SC 29853-0100   **(100%)**
Tel.: (803) 266-7411
Web Site: http://www.tdstelecom.com
Sales Range: $10-24.9 Million
Emp.: 11
Telephone Company
N.A.I.C.S.: 449210

TDS Telecom   **(1)**
16400 Court St, Amelia Court House, VA
23002   **(100%)**
Tel.: (804) 561-2111
Web Site: http://www.tdstelecom.com
Emp.: 5
Telephone Company
N.A.I.C.S.: 517810

TDS Telecom   **(1)**
4712 Main St, Millington, MI 48746   **(100%)**
Tel.: (608) 831-1000
Sales Range: $200-249.9 Million
Emp.: 27
Telephone Company
N.A.I.C.S.: 517121

TDS Telecom   **(1)**
102 Spence St, Tellico Plains, TN
37385-0009   **(100%)**
Tel.: (423) 253-2101
Web Site: http://www.tdstelecom.com
Sales Range: $10-24.9 Million
Emp.: 14
Telephone Company
N.A.I.C.S.: 517121

TDS Telecom   **(1)**
PO Box 366, Rison, AR 71665   **(100%)**
Tel.: (870) 325-6266
Sales Range: $1-9.9 Million
Emp.: 10
Telephone Company
N.A.I.C.S.: 924110

TDS Telecom   **(1)**
120 S Main St, Alma, WI 54610   **(100%)**
Tel.: (608) 685-3000
Sales Range: $1-9.9 Million
Emp.: 3
Telephone Company
N.A.I.C.S.: 517111
Brian E. Gardner *(Mgr)*

TDS Telecom   **(1)**
203 S Academy Ave, Butler, AL
36904   **(100%)**
Tel.: (205) 459-3766
Web Site: http://www.tdstelecom.com
Sales Range: $10-24.9 Million
Emp.: 25
Telephone Company
N.A.I.C.S.: 517121
Vicki L. Villacrez *(Exec VP)*
Jim Butman *(Pres & CEO)*
Ken Paker *(CTO & Sr VP-Information & Network Technologies)*
Andrew Petersen *(Sr VP-Corp Affairs)*
Shane West *(Sr VP-Mktg, Sls & Customer Ops)*
Mark Barber *(Sr VP-Network Ops)*
Kathy Cefalu *(Chief HR Officer & VP)*
Cheryl McCollum *(Assoc Mgr-Comm)*
Andrew Buchert *(VP-Field Svcs)*
David Dudsak *(VP-Svc Assurance & Sup-port)*
Michael Gasser *(VP & Controller)*
Benjamin C. Goth *(VP-Network Svcs)*
Julie Maiers *(VP-Mktg & Product Dev)*
Joe Read *(VP-Supply Chain Svcs)*
John Sango *(VP-Customer Contact Ops)*

Michael Zalewski *(VP-Bus Dev)*
Karl Betz *(VP-IT)*
Kit Beyer *(Dir-External Affairs & Comm)*
Missy Kellor *(Assoc Mgr-Comm)*

TDS Telecom   **(1)**
121 S Church St, Grove Hill, AL
36451   **(100%)**
Tel.: (251) 275-3011
Web Site: http://www.tdstelecom.com
Sales Range: $200-249.9 Million
Telephone Company
N.A.I.C.S.: 517121

TDS Telecom   **(1)**
PO Box 7, Cornersville, TN 37047-0007
Tel.: (931) 293-2222
Web Site: http://www.tdstelecom.com
Sales Range: $1-9.9 Million
Emp.: 1
Telephone Company
N.A.I.C.S.: 517121

TDS Telecom   **(1)**
5265 Murfreesboro Rd, La Vergne, TN
37086
Tel.: (615) 280-3050
Sales Range: $200-249.9 Million
Telephone Company
N.A.I.C.S.: 517121

TDS Telecom   **(1)**
4112 N Mount Juliet Rd, Mount Juliet, TN
37122
Web Site: http://www.tdstelecom.com
Sales Range: $200-249.9 Million
Telephone Services
N.A.I.C.S.: 517121

TDS Telecom   **(1)**
215 S Main St, Waynesboro, TN 38485
Tel.: (931) 722-3691
Web Site: http://www.tdstelecom.com
Sales Range: $200-249.9 Million
Telephone Company
N.A.I.C.S.: 517121

TDS Telecom   **(1)**
107 W Franklin St, Quincy, FL 32351
Tel.: (850) 875-2111
Web Site: http://www.tdstelecom.com
Sales Range: $10-24.9 Million
Emp.: 26
Telephone Company
N.A.I.C.S.: 517121

TDS Telecom   **(1)**
22076 Main St, Hyden, KY 41749
Tel.: (606) 672-2303
Web Site: http://www.tdstelecom.com
Sales Range: $10-24.9 Million
Emp.: 20
Telephone Company
N.A.I.C.S.: 517121

TDS Telecom   **(1)**
132 Grand Ave, Paonia, CO
81428-9905   **(100%)**
Tel.: (970) 872-2122
Web Site: http://www.tdstelecom.com
Sales Range: $10-24.9 Million
Emp.: 20
Telephone Company
N.A.I.C.S.: 517121

TDS Telecom   **(1)**
1912 Parmenter St, Middleton, WI 53562-
3139
Tel.: (608) 831-1000
Web Site: http://www.tdstelecom.com
Sales Range: $25-49.9 Million
Emp.: 115
Telephone Company
N.A.I.C.S.: 517121

TDS Telecom   **(1)**
1125 Lincoln Ave, Fennimore, WI 53809
Tel.: (608) 822-3733
Sales Range: $10-24.9 Million
Emp.: 11
Wireless Communications
N.A.I.C.S.: 334220

TDS Telecom   **(1)**
221 E Main St, Salem, KY 42078-8071
Tel.: (270) 988-3112
Sales Range: Less than $1 Million
Emp.: 6
Telephone Communications
N.A.I.C.S.: 517810

Telephone & Data Systems, Inc.—(Continued)

TDS Telecom (1)
110 W 5th St, Stonewall, OK
74871 (100%)
Tel.: (580) 265-4211
Web Site: http://www.tdstelecom.com
Sales Range: $1-9.9 Million
Emp.: 4
Telephone Company
N.A.I.C.S.: 517121

**TDS Telecommunications
Corporation** (1)
525 Junction Rd, Madison, WI
53717 (100%)
Tel.: (608) 664-4000
Web Site: https://www.tdstelecom.com
Sales Range: $800-899.9 Million
Telecommunications Company
N.A.I.C.S.: 517121
James W. Butman (Pres & CEO)

Subsidiary (Domestic):

Black Earth Telephone Co. (2)
1125 Mills St, Black Earth, WI 53515-9454
Tel.: (608) 767-2591
Web Site: http://www.tds.net
Sales Range: $200-249.9 Million
Telephone Communications
N.A.I.C.S.: 517810

Blue Ridge Telephone Co. (2)
3233 E 1st St, Blue Ridge, GA 30513-0607
Tel.: (706) 632-2211
Sales Range: $200-249.9 Million
Telephone Communication Services
N.A.I.C.S.: 517810

**Camden Telephone & Telegraph
Company, Inc.** (2)
103 Martha Dr, Saint Marys, GA 31558-8938
Tel.: (912) 882-1400
Web Site: http://tdstelecom.com
Telephone Communications
N.A.I.C.S.: 517810

Cobbosseecontee Telephone Co. (2)
250 Collins Mills Rd, Gardiner, ME 04345
Tel.: (207) 724-9911
Telephone Communications
N.A.I.C.S.: 812990

Delta County Tele-Comm Inc. (2)
132 Grand Ave, Paonia, CO 81428
Tel.: (866) 571-6662
Web Site: http://tdstelecom.com
Telephone Company
N.A.I.C.S.: 517111

Deposit Telephone Co. Inc. (2)
87 Front St, Deposit, NY 13754
Tel.: (607) 467-2111
Web Site: http://www.tdstelecom.com
Sales Range: $10-24.9 Million
Emp.: 50
Telephone Company
N.A.I.C.S.: 517111

Dickeyville Telephone, LLC (2)
525 Junction Rd, Madison, WI 53717
Tel.: (608) 831-1000
Web Site: http://tdstelecom.com
Telephone Company
N.A.I.C.S.: 517111

Kearsarge Telephone Co. (2)
173 Main St, New London, NH 03257
Tel.: (603) 526-9911
Web Site: http://www.tdstelecom.com
Sales Range: $200-249.9 Million
Emp.: 45
Telephone Communications
N.A.I.C.S.: 517810

**Lewisport Telephone Company
Inc.** (2)
30 Pell St, Lewisport, KY 42351-2531
Tel.: (866) 571-6662
Web Site: http://tdstelecom.com
Telephone Communications & Cable Services
N.A.I.C.S.: 517810

Merrimack County Telephone Company, Inc. (2)
11 Kearsarge Ave, Merrimack, NH 03229
Tel.: (603) 746-9911

Sales Range: $200-249.9 Million
Telephone Communications
N.A.I.C.S.: 517810

Mid-State Telephone Co. (2)
2345 Rice St Ste 230, Roseville, MN 55113
Tel.: (320) 354-7700
Web Site: http://www.tdstelecom.com
Telephone Communications
N.A.I.C.S.: 517810

New Castle Telephone Company (2)
320 Salem Ave, New Castle, VA 24127
Tel.: (608) 664-5629
Rev.: $1,668,000
Emp.: 7
Wired Telecommunications Carriers
N.A.I.C.S.: 517111

Northfield Telephone Company (2)
24 Depot Sq, Northfield, VT 05663-6721
Tel.: (802) 485-9911
Web Site: http://www.tdstelecom.com
Emp.: 8
Telecommunication Servicesb
N.A.I.C.S.: 517810

Norway Telephone Co. Inc. (2)
8432 Savannah Hwy, Norway, SC 29113
Web Site: http://tdstelecom.com
Telephone Communications
N.A.I.C.S.: 517810

**Oakman Telephone Company,
Inc.** (2)
8233 Market St, Oakman, AL 35579
Tel.: (866) 571-6662
Web Site: http://tdstelecom.com
Telephone Communications
N.A.I.C.S.: 517810

**Oriskany Falls Telephone Corp,
Inc.** (2)
PO Box 900, Vernon, NY 13475
Tel.: (315) 821-7211
Web Site: http://www.tdstelecom.com
Sales Range: $200-249.9 Million
Telephone Communications
N.A.I.C.S.: 517810

Shiawassee Telephone Co. Inc. (2)
129 S Main St, Perry, MI 48872
Tel.: (517) 625-3930
Sales Range: $1-9.9 Million
Emp.: 10
Telephone Communications
N.A.I.C.S.: 517810

**Southwestern Telephone
Company** (2)
150 W Sunset Ave, Quartzsite, AZ 85359
Tel.: (928) 927-6346
Web Site: http://tdstelecom.com
Telephone Communications
N.A.I.C.S.: 517810

TDS Telecom (2)
1599 Barnardsville Hwy, Barnardsville, NC 28709
Tel.: (828) 749-9090
Sales Range: $200-249.9 Million
Telephone Communications
N.A.I.C.S.: 517810

Tenney Telephone Company (2)
120 S Main St, Alma, WI 54610
Tel.: (608) 685-4609
Web Site: http://www.tdstelecom.com
Sales Range: $200-249.9 Million
Telephone Communications
N.A.I.C.S.: 517810

**Tri-County Communications
Corp.** (2)
23669 Washington St, Independence, WI 54747
Tel.: (715) 695-2691
Sales Range: $10-24.9 Million
Emp.: 17
Cable & Pay Television Service
N.A.I.C.S.: 517111

Vernon Telephone Co. (2)
103 N Main St, Westby, WI 54667-1105
Tel.: (608) 634-3136
Web Site: http://www.vernontel.com
Sales Range: $1-9.9 Million
Telephone Communications
N.A.I.C.S.: 812990

**TEAM DES MOINES PARTNERS,
LLC** (1)

390 Alices Rd, Waukee, IA 50263
Tel.: (515) 987-1191
Telecommunication Servicesb
N.A.I.C.S.: 517810

THE FARMERS TELEPHONE COMPANY, LLC (1)
140 N Monroe St, Lancaster, WI 53813
Tel.: (608) 723-3633
Communication Equipment Installation Services
N.A.I.C.S.: 238210

**UNION TELEPHONE
COMPANY** (1)
850 N Highway 414, Mountain View, WY 82939
Tel.: (307) 782-6131
Web Site: https://www.unionwireless.com
Emp.: 300
Telecommunication Servicesb
N.A.I.C.S.: 517810

USCC SERVICES, LLC (1)
8410 W Bryn Mawr Ave Ste 700, Chicago, IL 60631
Tel.: (773) 399-7918
Management Consulting Services
N.A.I.C.S.: 541611

**United States Cellular
Corporation** (1)
8410 W Bryn Mawr Ave, Chicago, IL
60631-3486 (96%)
Tel.: (773) 399-8900
Web Site: http://www.uscellular.com
Rev.: $4,169,000,000
Assets: $11,119,000,000
Liabilities: $6,549,000,000
Net Worth: $4,570,000,000
Earnings: $30,000,000
Emp.: 4,900
Fiscal Year-end: 12/31/2022
Cellular Telephone Service
N.A.I.C.S.: 517112
Douglas W. Chambers (CFO, Treas & Exec VP)
Laurent C. Therivel (Pres & CEO)
Sheila Crisostomo (VP-Retail Sls & Operations)
Renae Grob (VP-Supply Chain)
Denise Lintz (VP-Enterprise Portfolio Mgmt & Tech Shared Svcs)
Rebecca Murphy Thompson (VP-Government Affairs)
Kevin R. Lowell (Chief People Officer, Exec VP & Head-Comm)
Kimberly Green-Kerr (Sr VP-Enterprise Sls & Operations)
Jeffrey S. Hoersch (VP & Controller)
Nancy Fratzke (VP-Customer Support)
Frederick Lubeley (VP-Financial Plng & Analysis)
Verchele W. Roberts (VP-Brand Mgmt)
Mike Sweeney (VP-Enterprise Infrastructure & Security)
Adriana Rios Welton (Gen Counsel & Head)

Subsidiary (Domestic):

**MCDANIEL CELLULAR TELEPHONE
COMPANY** (2)
1640 S Gold St, Centralia, WA 98531-8950
Tel.: (312) 630-1900
Telecommunications Resellers
N.A.I.C.S.: 517121

(1)

TELESIS BIO, INC.
10431 Wateridge Cir Ste 150, San
Diego, CA 92121-2993
Tel.: (858) 228-4115 DE
Web Site: https://www.telesisbio.com
Year Founded: 2011
TBIO—(NASDAQ)
Rev.: $27,435,000
Assets: $81,362,000
Liabilities: $34,797,000
Net Worth: $46,565,000
Earnings: ($48,471,000)
Emp.: 223
Fiscal Year-end: 12/31/22
Research & Development in Biotechnology (except Nanobiotechnology)
N.A.I.C.S.: 541714
William J. Kullback (CFO)
Todd R. Nelson (Founder & CEO)

Daniel G. Gibson (CTO)
Anissa Agadir (VP-Manufacturing & Quality System)
Laurence Warden (VP-Engrg & Instrumentation)
Laura B. Puga (VP-People & Culture)
Justin O. Emory (VP-IT)
Madoo Varma (VP-Corp Bus Dev)
Decky Goodrich (VP-Global Sls)
Jen Carroll (VP-IR)
Todd R. Nelson (Founder)
Eric E. Esser (Chm, Pres & CEO)

Subsidiaries:

Eton Bioscience Inc. (1)
10179 Huennekens St Ste 201, San Diego, CA 92121
Web Site: http://www.etonbio.com
Testing Laboratories
N.A.I.C.S.: 541380
Angelica Lavallee (Dir-Sls & Mktg)
Tony Chen (CEO)

TELIDYNE INC.
338 Jericho Turnpike Ste 345, Syosset, NY 11791
Tel.: (516) 531-4069 DE
Web Site: http://www.telidyne.com
TLDN—(OTCIQ)
Rev.: $16,752
Assets: $66,173
Liabilities: $139,956
Net Worth: ($73,783)
Earnings: ($33,942)
Fiscal Year-end: 01/31/20
Transmission Towers & Related Products Mfr
N.A.I.C.S.: 237130
Aron K. Govil (Chm, Pres, CEO, CFO, Principal Acctg Officer, Treas & Sec)

Subsidiaries:

Anhui TEC Tower Co., Ltd. (1)
Xinqiao Industrial Zone, Shenzhen, 242600, Anhui, China
Tel.: (86) 563 8023488
Sales Range: $100-124.9 Million
Emp.: 300
Mobile Communication Tower Mfr
N.A.I.C.S.: 332312

Ducon Infratechnologies Limited (1)
Ducon House A/4, MIDC Wagle Industrial Estate Road No.1, Thane, 400 604, India (56%)
Tel.: (91) 2241122114
Web Site: https://www.duconinfra.co.in
Rev.: $47,495,450
Assets: $33,066,795
Liabilities: $18,394,725
Net Worth: $14,672,070
Earnings: $491,397
Emp.: 61
Fiscal Year-end: 03/31/2023
Diversified Technology Services
N.A.I.C.S.: 561499
Darshit Parikh (Compliance Officer & Compliance Officer)
Arun Govil (Mng Dir)
Harish Shetty (CFO)
Chandrasekhar Ganesan (Exec Dir)

TELIGENT, INC.
105 Lincoln Ave, Buena, NJ 08310
Tel.: (856) 697-1441 DE
Web Site: https://www.teligent.com
Year Founded: 1977
TLGT—(NASDAQ)
Rev.: $45,309,000
Assets: $87,788,000
Liabilities: $197,940,000
Net Worth: ($110,152,000)
Earnings: ($122,022,000)
Emp.: 142
Fiscal Year-end: 12/31/20
Pharmaceutical Product Mfr & Distr
N.A.I.C.S.: 325412
Ernest Robert De Paolantonio (CFO)
Mark Mantel (VP-Sls & Mktg & Gen Mgr-Canada)

Eric Muse (VP-Bus Dev)
Anneli Simm (Gen Mgr-Estonia)
Timothy B. Sawyer (Pres & CEO)
Antonio Di Nicola (VP-Ops & Gen Mgr)
Ken Bonnell (VP-Quality)
Philip K. Yachmetz (Chief Legal Officer & Corp Sec)

TELKONET, INC.
20800 Swenson Dr Ste 175, Waukesha, WI 53186
Tel.: (414) 302-2299　　　　　　UT
Web Site: https://www.telkonet.com
Year Founded: 1999
TKOI—(OTCQB)
Rev.: $8,448,019
Assets: $7,878,817
Liabilities: $3,282,119
Net Worth: $4,596,698
Earnings: ($1,285,237)
Emp.: 29
Fiscal Year-end: 12/31/22
Powerline Communications Technology Systems Application Developer
N.A.I.C.S.: 517810
Arthur E. Byrnes (Chm)
Piercarlo Gramaglia (CEO)

Subsidiaries:

Telkonet Communications, Inc.　　(1)
10200 W Innovation Dr Ste 300, Milwaukee, WI 53226-4826　　　　(100%)
Tel.: (240) 912-1800
Web Site: http://www.telkonet.com
Sales Range: $10-24.9 Million
Emp.: 15
Communication Equipment Mfr
N.A.I.C.S.: 334290
Jason L. Tienor (CEO)

TELLZA INC.
1250 E Hlallandale Beach Blvd Ste Ph 1, Hallandale Beach, FL 33009
Tel.: (954) 456-3191　　　　　　ON
Web Site: http://www.tellza.com
Year Founded: 1984
TEL—(TSX)
Sales Range: $500-549.9 Million
Long Distance Telecommunications Reseller
N.A.I.C.S.: 517121
Michael Vazquez (CEO)
Anuj Sethi (Pres)
Luciano Garavaglia (CEO-Matchcom)

Subsidiaries:

Phonetime Networks, Inc.　　　　(1)
1250 E Hallandale Beach Blvd Ste 703, Hallandale Beach, FL 33009-4641
Tel.: (954) 456-3191
Web Site: http://www.phonetime.com
Sales Range: $25-49.9 Million
Emp.: 15
Long Distance Telecommunications Reseller
N.A.I.C.S.: 517121
Mike Vazquez (Gen Mgr)

TELOMIR PHARMACEUTICALS, INC.
855 N Wolfe St Ste 601, Baltimore, MD 21205
Tel.: (813) 864-2558　　　　　　FL
Web Site:
　https://www.telomirpharma.com
Year Founded: 2021
TELO—(NASDAQ)
Assets: $4,773,768
Liabilities: $1,335,564
Net Worth: $3,438,204
Earnings: ($13,071,864)
Emp.: 1
Fiscal Year-end: 12/31/23
Pharmaceutical Product Mfr & Distr
N.A.I.C.S.: 325412
Michelle Yanez (CFO)

TELOS CORPORATION
19886 Ashburn Rd, Ashburn, VA 20147
Tel.: (703) 724-3800　　　　　　MD
Web Site: https://www.telos.com
Year Founded: 1967
TLS—(NASDAQ)
Rev.: $216,887,000
Assets: $237,397,000
Liabilities: $65,043,000
Net Worth: $172,354,000
Earnings: ($53,428,000)
Emp.: 738
Fiscal Year-end: 12/31/22
IT Solutions
N.A.I.C.S.: 541512
John B. Wood (Chm, Pres & CEO)
Rinaldi Pisani (Sr VP-Strategic Bus Dev)
Mark Bendza (CFO & Exec VP)
Malcolm Cooke (Chief Information Tech Officer)
Donna Hill (VP)
Victoria Harding (Chief Acctg Officer)
E. Hutchinson Robbins Jr. (Gen Counsel & Exec VP)

TEMPEST THERAPEUTICS, INC.
2000 Sierra Point Pkwy Ste 400, Brisbane, CA 94005
Tel.: (415) 798-8589　　　　　　DE
Web Site: https://www.tempesttx.com
Year Founded: 2011
TPST—(NASDAQ)
Rev.: $549,000
Assets: $46,089,000
Liabilities: $27,978,000
Net Worth: $18,111,000
Earnings: ($35,709,000)
Emp.: 19
Fiscal Year-end: 12/31/22
In-Vitro Female Fertility Research & Development Services
N.A.I.C.S.: 325413
Stephen Brady (CEO)
Sharon Sakai (Head-Regulatory & Quality)
Darrin Bomba (VP-Clinical Ops)
Henry Johnson (VP-Chemistry)
Sam Whiting (Chief Medical Officer & Head-Research & Development)
Nicholas Maestas (Sec & VP-Strategy & Strategy)
Lindsay Young (Head-Human Resources)
Stephen R. Brady (Pres & CEO)

TEMPLETON DRAGON FUND, INC.
300 SE 2nd St, Fort Lauderdale, FL 33301-1923
Tel.: (954) 527-7500　　　　　　FL
TDF—(NYSE)
Rev.: $15,996,055
Assets: $738,623,077
Liabilities: $1,195,609
Net Worth: $737,427,468
Earnings: $6,343,302
Fiscal Year-end: 12/31/19
Investment Management Service
N.A.I.C.S.: 525990
Gregory Eugene Johnson (VP)

TEMPLETON GLOBAL INCOME FUND
1 Franklin Pkwy, San Mateo, CA 94403
Tel.: (650) 312-2000
GIM—(NYSE)
Rev.: $57,575,182
Assets: $929,625,595
Liabilities: $24,247,336
Net Worth: $905,378,259
Earnings: $51,339,288
Fiscal Year-end: 12/31/19
Investment Management Service

N.A.I.C.S.: 525990
Rupert Harris Johnson Jr. (Chm & VP)
Sonal Desai (Mgr-Fund)

TEMPO AUTOMATION HOLDINGS, INC.
2460 Alameda St, San Francisco, CA 94103
Tel.: (415) 320-1261　　　　　　DE
Year Founded: 2013
TMPO—(NASDAQ)
Rev.: $12,049,000
Assets: $20,589,000
Liabilities: $46,612,000
Net Worth: ($26,023,000)
Earnings: ($144,851,000)
Emp.: 74
Fiscal Year-end: 12/31/22
Electronics Mfr
N.A.I.C.S.: 334419

TEMPUR SEALY INTERNATIONAL, INC.
1000 Tempur Way, Lexington, KY 40511
Tel.: (859) 259-0754　　　　　　DE
Web Site:
　https://www.tempursealy.com
Year Founded: 1992
TPX—(NYSE)
Rev.: $4,925,400,000
Assets: $4,553,900,000
Liabilities: $4,230,500,000
Net Worth: $323,400,000
Earnings: $368,100,000
Emp.: 12,000
Fiscal Year-end: 12/31/23
Mattresses & Pillows Sales
N.A.I.C.S.: 337910
David Montgomery (Exec VP-Global Bus Strategy & Dev)
Bhaskar Rao (CFO & Exec VP)
Scott L. Thompson (Chm, Pres & CEO)
Scott Vollet (Exec VP-Ops-Global)
Cliff Buster (CEO-North America)
Steve Rusing (Pres-Sls & Exec VP)
Hansbart Wijnand (Exec VP)

Subsidiaries:

Burlington Mattress Co. LLC　　(1)
1228 N Roselle Rd, Schaumburg, IL 60195
Tel.: (847) 416-6130
Web Site: http://www.bmcmattress.com
Mattress Mfr
N.A.I.C.S.: 337910

Comfort Revolution, LLC　　　　(1)
442 Route 35 S Bldg A, Eatontown, NJ 07724
Tel.: (732) 272-9111
Web Site: http://www.comfortrevolution.com
Household Textile Product Mfr & Distr
N.A.I.C.S.: 423210

Dan-Foam ApS　　　　　　　　(1)
Holmelund 43, Arup, 5560, Denmark
Tel.: (45) 63434343
Web Site: https://www.dan-foam.dk
Sales Range: $50-74.9 Million
Mattresses & Pillows Mfr & Distr
N.A.I.C.S.: 337910
Kasper Soerensen (Mng Dir)

Dreams Ltd.　　　　　　　　　(1)
Knaves Beech Industrial Estate, Loudwater, High Wycombe, HP10 9YU, Bucks, United Kingdom
Tel.: (44) 1628 535 353
Web Site: http://www.dreams.co.uk
Furniture Store Operator
N.A.I.C.S.: 449110
Jonathan Hirst (CEO)
Jo Martin (CMO)
Linda Meade (Chief Customer Officer)
Kal Singh (COO)
Kim Zaheer (CFO)
Petra Kasperova (CTO)
Dan West (CIO)

Innovative Mattress Solutions, LLC　　　　　　　　　　　(1)
1721 Jaggie Fox Way, Lexington, KY 40511
Tel.: (859) 455-8546
Web Site: http://www.innovativemattresssolutions.com
Emp.: 400
Bedding & Mattresses Mfr
N.A.I.C.S.: 337910
Kim Knopf (Pres & CEO)
Steve Kyger (Exec VP-Sls)
Karen Keck (CMO)

Subsidiary (Domestic):

Mattress King, Inc.　　　　　　(2)
7095 University Dr Hwy 72, Huntsville, AL 35806
Tel.: (256) 722-0252
Web Site: http://www.mattressking.net
Furniture Retailer
N.A.I.C.S.: 449110
Kay Koswoski (Co-Founder)
Wayne Koswoski (Co-Founder)

Sealy Corporation　　　　　　　(1)
Sealy Dr One Office Pkwy, Trinity, NC 27370
Tel.: (336) 861-3500
Web Site: http://www.sealy.com
Sales Range: $1-4.9 Billion
Emp.: 4,267
Mattresses, Foundations, Box Springs, Wood Bedroom Furniture, Convertible Sleep Sofas Mfr
N.A.I.C.S.: 337910

Subsidiary (Non-US):

Mattress Holdings International B.V.　　　　　　　　　　(2)
Keplerstraat 34, 1171CD, Badhoevedorp, Noord-Holland, Netherlands
Tel.: (31) 203055700
Investment Management Service
N.A.I.C.S.: 523940

Plant (Domestic):

Ohio-Sealy Mattress Manufacturing - Fort Worth　　　　　　　(2)
6550 Wuliger Way, North Richland Hills, TX 76180-6020
Tel.: (817) 485-8052
Sales Range: $25-49.9 Million
Emp.: 145
Mattresses & Box Springs Mfr
N.A.I.C.S.: 337910

Subsidiary (Non-US):

Sealy Argentina SRL　　　　　　(2)
Marcos Sastre 2300 CP 1617, General Pacheco, Buenos Aires, Argentina
Tel.: (54) 11 4846 7600
Web Site: http://www.sealy.com.ar
Mattresses Distr
N.A.I.C.S.: 423210

Joint Venture (Non-US):

Sealy Asia (Hong Kong) Ltd　　(2)
Room 1503 15/F Park Commercial Centre, 180 Tung Lo Wan Road, Causeway Bay, China (Hong Kong)　　　　(50%)
Tel.: (852) 2578 8989
Web Site: http://www.sealy.com.hk
Mattresses & Box Springs Mfr
N.A.I.C.S.: 337910

Sealy Asia (Singapore) Pte, Ltd.　(2)
SIS Bldg 4 Leng Kee Rd Suite 05-06/07, Singapore, 68898, Singapore　　(50%)
Tel.: (65) 64756166
Web Site: http://www.sealy.com.sg
Mattresses & Bedding Products Distr
N.A.I.C.S.: 423210

Subsidiary (Non-US):

Sealy Canada, Ltd.　　　　　　(2)
145 Milner Ave, Scarborough, M1S 3R1, ON, Canada　　　　　　(100%)
Web Site: https://www.sealy.ca
Sales Range: $25-49.9 Million
Mattresses Mfr & Marketer
N.A.I.C.S.: 337910

Plant (Domestic):

Sealy Components Group - Colorado Springs　　　　　　　　　(2)

Tempur Sealy International, Inc.—(Continued)

6275 Lake Shore Ct, Colorado Springs, CO 80915
Tel.: (719) 574-6945
Web Site: http://www.sealy.com
Sales Range: $25-49.9 Million
Emp.: 100
Mfr of Spring Units for Mattresses
N.A.I.C.S.: 337910

Sealy Components Group - Delano   (2)
9 Schultz Dr, Delano, PA 18220
Tel.: (570) 467-2721
Web Site: http://www.sealy.com
Sales Range: $25-49.9 Million
Emp.: 120
Mfr of Spring Units for Mattresses
N.A.I.C.S.: 337910

Subsidiary (Domestic):

Sealy Mattress Company   (2)
1070 Lake Rd, Medina, OH 44256
Tel.: (330) 725-4146
Web Site: http://www.sealy.com
Sales Range: $25-49.9 Million
Emp.: 175
Mattresses, Foundations & Box Springs Mfr
N.A.I.C.S.: 337910

Sealy Mattress Company of Albany, Inc.   (2)
Railroad Ave & Brown Rd, Albany, NY 12205
Tel.: (518) 459-1651
Sales Range: $50-74.9 Million
Emp.: 300
Mattresses & Box Springs Mfr & Marketer
N.A.I.C.S.: 337910
Tony Vivenzio (Dir-Mfg)

Sealy Mattress Company of Illinois   (2)
1030 E Fabyan Pkwy, Batavia, IL 60510
Tel.: (630) 879-8011
Sales Range: $50-74.9 Million
Emp.: 250
Mattresses & Box Springs Mfr
N.A.I.C.S.: 337910

Sealy Mattress Company of Kansas City, Inc.   (2)
435 River Park Dr, Kansas City, KS 66105
Tel.: (913) 321-3677
Sales Range: $25-49.9 Million
Emp.: 100
Mattresses & Box Springs Mfr
N.A.I.C.S.: 337910

Sealy Mattress Company of Puerto Rico   (2)
El Commandante Industrial Ctr No 1 San Marcos, Carolina, PR 00982
Tel.: (809) 769-0295
Web Site: http://www.sealy.com
Emp.: 25
Foundation & Box Spring Mfr
N.A.I.C.S.: 337910

Sealy Mattress Corporation   (2)
Sealy Dr 1 Office Pkwy, Trinity, NC 27370
Tel.: (336) 861-3500
Sales Range: $25-49.9 Million
Mattresses & Box Springs Mfr, Distr & Marketer
N.A.I.C.S.: 337910

Sealy Real Estate, Inc.   (2)
10681 Haddington Dr Ste 190, Houston, TX 77043
Tel.: (713) 688-6300
Web Site: http://www.sealynet.com
Emp.: 6
Real Estate Brokerage Services
N.A.I.C.S.: 531210

Plant (Domestic):

Sealy Stearns & Foster Manufacturing - Atlanta   (2)
1705 Rockdale Industrial Blvd NW, Conyers, GA 30012
Tel.: (770) 483-3810
Sales Range: $25-49.9 Million
Emp.: 200
Mattresses, Foundations & Box Springs Mfr
N.A.I.C.S.: 337910

Sealy Stearns & Foster Manufacturing - Houston   (2)
1201 Hwy 290 W, Brenham, TX 77833-5232
Tel.: (979) 836-6644
Mattresses & Box Springs Mfr
N.A.I.C.S.: 337910

Sealy Stearns & Foster Manufacturing - Orlando   (2)
850 Jetstream Dr, Orlando, FL 32824
Tel.: (407) 855-8523
Sales Range: $50-74.9 Million
Emp.: 250
Mattresses, Foundations & Box Springs Mfr
N.A.I.C.S.: 337910

Subsidiary (Domestic):

Sealy Technology LLC   (2)
1 Office Pkwy, Trinity, NC 27370
Tel.: (336) 861-3588
Emp.: 50
Mattress & Bedsprings Mfr
N.A.I.C.S.: 337910
Larry Rogers (Pres)

Sealy of Maryland and Virginia, Inc.   (2)
11835 Newgate Blvd, Hagerstown, MD 21740
Tel.: (301) 223-9700
Emp.: 130
Mattress & Bedspring Mfr
N.A.I.C.S.: 337910

Sealy of Minnesota, Inc.   (2)
825 Transfer Rd, Saint Paul, MN 55114
Tel.: (651) 645-8143
Web Site: http://www.sealy.com
Sales Range: $25-49.9 Million
Emp.: 125
Mfr of Mattresses & Box Springs
N.A.I.C.S.: 337910

Tempur Australia Pty. Ltd.   (1)
118 Colemans Road, Carrum Downs, 3201, VIC, Australia
Tel.: (61) 39 785 4900
Web Site: https://au.tempur.com
Emp.: 40
Mattress Mfr & Distr
N.A.I.C.S.: 337910

Tempur Benelux B.V.   (1)
Traverse 2, PO Box 493, 3905 NL, Veenendaal, Netherlands
Tel.: (31) 8699200
Web Site: https://www.nl.tempur.com
Sales Range: $10-24.9 Million
Emp.: 23
Mattresses & Pillows Mfr & Distr
N.A.I.C.S.: 337910

Tempur Danmark A/S   (1)
Holmelund 43, 5560, Arup, Denmark
Tel.: (45) 63434369
Web Site: http://www.tempur.com
Sales Range: $10-24.9 Million
Emp.: 300
Mattress & Pillow Mfr
N.A.I.C.S.: 337910

Tempur Deutschland GmbH   (1)
Carl-Benz-Strasse 8, 33803, Steinhagen, Germany
Tel.: (49) 5204100050
Web Site: http://de.tempur.com
Sales Range: $25-49.9 Million
Mattress & Pillow Mfr
N.A.I.C.S.: 337910
Thomas Bauer (Mng Dir)

Tempur France SARL   (1)
176 rue des Chardonnerets Paris Nord 2 Roissy CDG, PO Box 62988, 95973, Roissy-en-France, France
Tel.: (33) 148149400
Web Site: http://www.tempur.fr
Mattress & Pillow Mfr
N.A.I.C.S.: 337910

Tempur Norge AS   (1)
Radhsugt 26, 0151, Oslo, Norway
Tel.: (47) 22427000
Web Site: https://no.tempur.com
Sales Range: $10-24.9 Million
Emp.: 10
Mattress & Pillow Mfr
N.A.I.C.S.: 337910

Tempur Production USA, LLC   (1)
203 Tempur Pedic Dr Ste 102, Duffield, VA 24244-5321
Tel.: (276) 431-7150
Web Site: http://www.tempurpedic.com
Mattress & Pillow Mfr
N.A.I.C.S.: 337910

Tempur Schweiz AG   (1)
Rossliweg 29 B, 4852, Rothrist, Switzerland
Tel.: (41) 6238786686
Web Site: https://www.tempur.com
Sales Range: $10-24.9 Million
Emp.: 15
Mattress & Pillow Mfr
N.A.I.C.S.: 337910
Patrick Nef (Mng Dir)

Tempur Sealy Benelux B.V.   (1)
Maxwellstraat 47, Ede, 6716, Netherlands
Tel.: (31) 8699200
Mattresses & Pillows Whslr
N.A.I.C.S.: 423210

Tempur Sealy DACH GmbH   (1)
Carl-Benz-Strasse 8, 33803, Steinhagen, Germany
Tel.: (49) 5204100050
Web Site: https://de.tempur.com
Bedding Product Supplier
N.A.I.C.S.: 423210

Tempur Sealy Deutschland GmbH   (1)
Carl-Benz - Str 8, 33803, Steinhagen, Germany
Tel.: (49) 5204100050
Mattress Mfr
N.A.I.C.S.: 337910
Timo Hoffmann (Dir-Sls)

Tempur Sealy Espana S.A.   (1)
Calle Norias No 92 Nucleo a Planta 0 Majahonda, 28221, Madrid, Spain
Tel.: (34) 915219333
Web Site: https://es.tempur.com
Mattress & Pillow Mfr
N.A.I.C.S.: 337910

Tempur Sealy France SAS   (1)
Zac Des Tulipes 8 Avenue Du Xxi Siecle, CS 50098, 95505, Gonesse, France
Tel.: (33) 134290900
Web Site: http://fr.tempur.com
Mattress Mfr
N.A.I.C.S.: 337910

Tempur Sealy Japan Yugen Kaisha, Ltd.   (1)
13F Taiki Life Kobe Sannomiya Building 119 Ito-cho, Chuo-ku, Kobe, 650 0032, Hyogo, Japan
Tel.: (81) 783352277
Web Site: http://jp.tempur.com
Bedding Product Supplier
N.A.I.C.S.: 423210

Tempur Singapore Pte Ltd.   (1)
20 Martin Road 01 01 Seng Kee Building, Singapore, 239070, Singapore
Tel.: (65) 69337667
Web Site: https://sg.tempur.com
Sales Range: $100-124.9 Million
Mattress & Pillow Mfr
N.A.I.C.S.: 337910

Tempur Suomi OY   (1)
Asematie 4-10, 01300, Vantaa, Finland
Tel.: (358) 445316694
Web Site: http://www.tempur.fi
Sales Range: $100-124.9 Million
Emp.: 19
Mattress & Pillow Mfr
N.A.I.C.S.: 337910

Tempur Sverige AB   (1)
Torsgatan 4, PO Box 1055, 101 39, Stockholm, Sweden
Tel.: (46) 20452222
Web Site: http://se.tempur.com
Sales Range: $100-124.9 Million
Emp.: 17
Mattress & Pillow Mfr
N.A.I.C.S.: 337910

Tempur UK Limited   (1)
Tempur House Caxton Point Printing House Lane, Hayes, UB3 1AP, United Kingdom
Tel.: (44) 8000111083
Web Site: http://www.tempur.co.uk
Mattress & Pillow Mfr

N.A.I.C.S.: 337910

Tempur-Pedic America, LLC   (1)
7875 Montgomery Rd, Cincinnati, OH 45236-4344
Tel.: (513) 984-9200
Web Site: http://www.tempurpedic.com
Emp.: 8
Mattress Mfr
N.A.I.C.S.: 337910

TEMPUS AI, INC.
600 W Chicago Ave Ste 510, Chicago, IL 60654
Tel.: (833) 514-4187
Web Site: http://www.tempus.com
Year Founded: 2015
TEM—(NASDAQ)
Biotechnology Research & Development Services
N.A.I.C.S.: 541714
Eric Lefkofsky (Founder & CEO)
Terron Bruner (Chief Comml Officer)
Shane Colley (CTO)
Ryan Fukushima (COO)
Andy Polovin (Gen Counsel)

Subsidiaries:

AKESOgen, Inc.   (1)
3155 Northwoods Pl NW, Norcross, GA 30071
Tel.: (770) 542-0890
Biotechnology Research & Development Services
N.A.I.C.S.: 541714

TEMPUS APPLIED SOLUTIONS HOLDINGS, INC.
471 McLaws Cir Ste A, Williamsburg, VA 23185
Tel.: (757) 875-7779   DE
TMPS—(OTCIQ)
Sales Range: $10-24.9 Million
Emp.: 22
Holding Company; Transportation Solutions
N.A.I.C.S.: 551112
Benjamin Scott Terry (CEO)
Johan Aksel Bergendorff (CFO)
R. Lee Priest Jr. (Sec)

Subsidiaries:

Tempus Applied Solutions, LLC   (1)
471 McLaws Circle, Williamsburg, VA 23185
Tel.: (757) 875-7779
Government & Defense Aircraft Modification & Engineering Services
N.A.I.C.S.: 541990
Benjamin Scott Terry (Founder & CEO)

Subsidiary (Domestic):

Tempus Jets Inc.   (2)
Denvers Centennial Airport 12260 E Control Tower Rd, Englewood, CO 80112
Tel.: (303) 799-9999
Web Site: http://www.tempusaircraft.com
Oil Transportation Services
N.A.I.C.S.: 481219
Monica Lucas (Dir-Client Rels)

Tempus Training Solutions LLC   (2)
Redbird Skyport San Marcos Airport-KHYI 2080 Airport Dr, San Marcos, TX 78666
Tel.: (512) 878-6670
Web Site: http://www.tempusflight.com
Flight Training Services
N.A.I.C.S.: 611512

TENABLE HOLDINGS, INC.
6100 Merriweather Dr 12th Fl, Columbia, MD 21044
Tel.: (410) 872-0555   DE
Web Site: https://www.tenable.com
Year Founded: 2002
TENB—(NASDAQ)
Rev.: $683,191,000
Assets: $1,439,530,000
Liabilities: $1,168,664,000
Net Worth: $270,866,000
Earnings: ($92,222,000)

Emp.: 1,900
Fiscal Year-end: 12/31/22
Holding Company
N.A.I.C.S.: 551112
Amit Y. Yoran *(Chm, Pres & CEO)*
John C. Huffard Jr. *(Founder)*
Stephen A. Vintz *(CFO)*
Mark Thurmond *(COO)*
Terry Dolce *(Sr VP-Ops, Bus Dev-Global & Channels)*
Matt Olton *(Sr VP-Corp Dev & Strategy)*
Robert Huber *(Chief Security Officer)*
Michela Stribling *(Chief Comm Officer)*
Nico Popp *(Chief Product Officer)*
David Bartholomew *(Acting Gen Counsel & Asst Sec)*
Glen Pendley *(CTO)*
Brian Goldfarb *(CMO)*
Michelle VonderHaar *(Chief Legal Officer)*
Patricia Grant *(CIO)*
James Hayes *(Sr VP)*

TENAX THERAPEUTICS, INC.

101 Glen Lennox Dr Ste 300, Chapel Hill, NC 27517
Tel.: (919) 855-2100   DE
Web Site:
https://www.tenaxthera.com
TENX—(NASDAQ)
Assets: $11,684,627
Liabilities: $3,586,520
Net Worth: $8,098,107
Earnings: ($7,710,673)
Emp.: 5
Fiscal Year-end: 12/31/23
Pharmaceutical Preparation Manufacturing
N.A.I.C.S.: 325412
Nancy Hecox *(Gen Counsel, Sec & Exec VP-Legal Affairs)*
Doug Randall *(Exec VP-Bus & Comml Ops)*
Douglas Hay *(Sr VP-Regulatory Affairs)*
Christopher T. Giordano *(Pres & CEO)*
Stuart Rich *(Chief Medical Officer)*

TENAYA THERAPEUTICS, INC.

171 Oyster Point Blvd Ste 500, South San Francisco, CA 94080
Tel.: (650) 825-6990   DE
Web Site:
https://www.tenayatherapeutics.com
Year Founded: 2016
TNYA—(NASDAQ)
Rev.: $1,956,000
Assets: $278,945,000
Liabilities: $35,569,000
Net Worth: $243,376,000
Earnings: ($123,665,000)
Emp.: 141
Fiscal Year-end: 12/31/22
Biotechnology Research & Development Services
N.A.I.C.S.: 541714
Faraz Ali *(CEO)*
David V. Goeddel *(Chm)*
Timothy Hoey *(Board of Directors & Chief Scientific Officer)*
Kee-Hong Kim *(CTO & Sr VP-Mfr & Technical Ops)*
Matthew Pollman *(Sr VP-Clinical Dev)*
Jay Vora *(Sr VP-Portfolio & Program Mgmt)*
Joanna Auch *(Sr VP-People & Culture)*
Kathy Ivey *(Sr VP-Res)*
Jennifer Drimmer *(Gen Counsel)*
Chihiro Saito *(Sr VP-Accounting & Fin Ops)*
Naymisha Patel *(Sr VP-Quality)*
Whedy Wang *(Sr VP-Biometrics)*

TENET HEALTHCARE CORPORATION

14201 Dallas Pkwy, Dallas, TX 75254
Tel.: (469) 893-2000   CA
Web Site:
https://www.tenethealth.com
Year Founded: 1969
THC—(NYSE)
Rev.: $20,548,000,000
Assets: $28,312,000,000
Liabilities: $25,195,000,000
Net Worth: $3,117,000,000
Earnings: $611,000,000
Emp.: 106,500
Fiscal Year-end: 12/31/23
General Hospitals & Related Healthcare Facilities Owner & Operator
N.A.I.C.S.: 622110
Paola M. Arbour *(CIO & Exec VP)*
Sun Park *(CFO & Exec VP)*
R. Scott Ramsey *(Chief Acctg Officer, Sr VP & Controller)*
Michael T. Maloney *(Exec VP-Corp Dev)*
Saumya Sutaria *(Chm & CEO)*
Maggie Gill *(Grp Pres-East)*
Matthew Stone *(Grp Pres-Central Grp)*
Brett Brodnax *(Pres/CEO-USPI)*
Nicholas Tejeda *(Grp Pres-Western Grp)*
Tom Arnst *(Chief Admin Officer)*
Judy Chabot *(VP)*
Roger Davis *(Pres)*
Jana Durfee *(Chief Compliance Officer)*
Lisa Foo *(Exec VP)*

Subsidiaries:

Advanced Center for Surgery - Vero Beach, LLC   **(1)**
1155 35th Ln Ste 100, Vero Beach, FL 32960
Tel.: (772) 569-2330
Web Site: http://www.veroortho.com
Hospital Health Care Services
N.A.I.C.S.: 622110

Advanced Regional Surgery Center, LLC   **(1)**
360 Missouri Ave Ste 102, Jeffersonville, IN 47130
Tel.: (812) 722-1480
Web Site:
https://www.advancedregionalsc.com
Surgical Care Services
N.A.I.C.S.: 621493

Advanced Spine Center of Wisconsin, LLC   **(1)**
1380 Tullar Rd, Neenah, WI 54956
Tel.: (920) 215-3603
Web Site: https://www.ascofwi.com
Surgical Center Services
N.A.I.C.S.: 622110

Advanced Surgery Center of Bethesda, LLC   **(1)**
6430 Rockledge Dr Ste 160, Bethesda, MD 20817
Tel.: (301) 312-6144
Web Site: https://www.ascbethesda.com
Surgical Care Services
N.A.I.C.S.: 621493

Advanced Surgery Center of Metairie, LLC   **(1)**
720 Veterans Blvd, Metairie, LA 70005
Tel.: (504) 293-4955
Hospital Services
N.A.I.C.S.: 622110

Advanced Surgery Center of Northern Louisiana, LLC   **(1)**
1601 Louisville Ave, Monroe, LA 71201
Tel.: (318) 998-5555
General Medical & Surgical Services
N.A.I.C.S.: 622110

Advanced Surgery Center of Sarasota, LLC   **(1)**
2621 Cattleman Rd Ste 100, Sarasota, FL 34232

Tel.: (941) 444-5510
Web Site: https://www.ascsarasota.com
Surgical Care Services
N.A.I.C.S.: 621493

Advanced Surgery Center of Tampa, LLC   **(1)**
1881 W Kennedy Blvd Ste C, Tampa, FL 33606
Tel.: (813) 693-5000
Web Site: https://www.asctampa.com
Surgical Care Services
N.A.I.C.S.: 621493

Advanced Surgical Care of Clearwater, LLC   **(1)**
93 Park Pl Blvd Ste 102, Clearwater, FL 33759
Tel.: (727) 240-2088
Web Site: https://www.ascclearwater.com
Surgical Center Services
N.A.I.C.S.: 622110

Advanced Surgical Care of St Louis, LLC   **(1)**
232 Mayfair Plz, Florissant, MO 63033
Tel.: (314) 736-4344
Web Site: https://www.ascstlouis.com
Surgical Care Services
N.A.I.C.S.: 621493

AdventHealth Surgery Center Davenport, LLC   **(1)**
107 Park Pl Blvd, Davenport, FL 33837
Tel.: (863) 419-2812
Web Site: https://davenportsurgery.com
Outpatient Surgical Services
N.A.I.C.S.: 621498

AdventHealth Surgery Center Mills Park, LLC   **(1)**
1812 N Mills Ave Ste 210, Orlando, FL 32803
Tel.: (407) 420-0100
Web Site: https://millsparkasc.com
General Medical & Surgical Services
N.A.I.C.S.: 622110

AdventHealth Surgery Center Wellswood, LLC   **(1)**
5013 N Armenia Ave, Tampa, FL 33603
Tel.: (813) 875-0562
Web Site: https://www.ahsurgerycenterwellswood.com
General Medical & Surgical Services
N.A.I.C.S.: 622110

Arizona Care Network - Next, LLC.   **(1)**
4222 E Thomas Rd Ste 400, Phoenix, AZ 85018
Tel.: (602) 406-7226
Web Site: https://www.azcarenetwork.org
Emp.: 5,500
Health Care Srvices
N.A.I.C.S.: 621999
Todd Ricotta *(COO)*
Conley Cervantes *(CEO)*
Dan LeClair *(CFO)*

Ascension Saint Thomas Lebanon Surgery Center, LLC   **(1)**
100 Physician's Way Ste 300, Lebanon, TN 37090
Tel.: (615) 449-6868
Health Care Srvices
N.A.I.C.S.: 621111

Atlantic Coast Surgical Suites, LLC   **(1)**
325 Lafayette Rd, Seabrook, NH 03874-4539
Tel.: (603) 218-1793
Web Site: https://www.atlanticcoastss.com
Surgical Care Services
N.A.I.C.S.: 621493

BBH PBMC, LLC   **(1)**
701 Princeton Ave Sw, Birmingham, AL 35211
Tel.: (205) 783-3000
Web Site:
https://www.princetonbaptistmedicalcenter.com
Speciality Health Care Services
N.A.I.C.S.: 621420
Sarah Nunnelly *(CEO)*

BBH SBMC, LLC   **(1)**
1000 1st St N, Alabaster, AL 35007

Tel.: (205) 620-8100
Web Site:
https://www.shelbybaptistmedicalcenter.com
Speciality Health Care Services
N.A.I.C.S.: 621420

BBH WBMC, LLC   **(1)**
3400 Hwy 78 E, Jasper, AL 35501
Tel.: (205) 387-4000
Speciality Health Care Services
N.A.I.C.S.: 621420

BW Sports Practice, LLC   **(1)**
200 Montgomery Hwy Ste 200, Vestavia Hills, AL 35216-1842
Tel.: (205) 877-2663
Medical Equipment Distr
N.A.I.C.S.: 423450

Bear Creek Surgery Center, LLC   **(1)**
100 Bourland Rd Ste 110, Keller, TX 76248
Tel.: (817) 518-9130
Web Site:
https://www.bearcreeksurgerycenter.com
Surgical Care Services
N.A.I.C.S.: 621493

Bethesda Chevy Chase Surgery Center, LLC   **(1)**
6931 Arlington Rd Ste E, Bethesda, MD 20814
Tel.: (301) 968-3184
Web Site: https://www.bethesdaccsc.com
Outpatient Surgical Services
N.A.I.C.S.: 621498

Braselton Endoscopy Center, LLC   **(1)**
2334 Sparta Way Ste 200, Buford, GA 30519
Tel.: (678) 997-2151
Gastroenterology Care Services
N.A.I.C.S.: 621111

Brookwood Baptist Imaging, LLC   **(1)**
513 Brookwood Blvd, Birmingham, AL 35209
Tel.: (205) 802-6900
Diagnostic Imaging Center Operator
N.A.I.C.S.: 621512

Brookwood Primary Care - Grand River, L.L.C.   **(1)**
1115 Payton Way Ste 111, Leeds, AL 35094
Tel.: (205) 352-1175
Health Care Srvices
N.A.I.C.S.: 622110

Cancer Centre London LLP   **(1)**
49 Parkside, Wimbledon, London, SW19 5NB, United Kingdom
Tel.: (44) 2082473351
Web Site:
http://www.cancercentrelondon.co.uk
Cancer Treatment Services
N.A.I.C.S.: 622310

Captive Insurance Services, Inc.   **(1)**
1300 Sawgrass Corporate Pkwy Ste 220, Sunrise, FL 33323
Tel.: (561) 912-0222
Insurance Management Services
N.A.I.C.S.: 524298

CareSpot of Orlando/HSI Urgent Care, LLC   **(1)**
115 E Park Dr Ste 300, Brentwood, TN 37027
Tel.: (407) 890-1890
Health Care Srvices
N.A.I.C.S.: 622110

Carmel Specialty Surgery Center, LLC   **(1)**
11590 N Meridian St Ste 130, Carmel, IN 46032
Tel.: (317) 660-0260
Web Site: https://www.carmelspecialty.com
Surgical Care Services
N.A.I.C.S.: 621493

Carondelet St. Mary's-Northwest, L.L.C.   **(1)**
2220 W Orange Grove Rd, Tucson, AZ 85741
Tel.: (520) 877-5660
Health Care Srvices

Tenet Healthcare Corporation—(Continued)

N.A.I.C.S.: 622110

Centennial ASC, L.P. (1)
4401 Coit Rd Ste 100, Frisco, TX 75035
Tel.: (214) 619-0120
Web Site:
http://www.centennialsurgerycenter.net
Medical Devices
N.A.I.C.S.: 622110

Charlotte Endoscopic Surgery Center, LLC (1)
23970 Suncoast Blvd, Port Charlotte, FL 33980
Tel.: (941) 625-3636
Health Care Srvices
N.A.I.C.S.: 622110

Claremont Hospital LLP (1)
401 Sandygate Road, Sheffield, S10 5UB, United Kingdom
Tel.: (44) 1142630330
Web Site: http://www.claremont-hospital.co.uk
Health Care Srvices
N.A.I.C.S.: 622110
Carol Jones (Dir-Nursing & Clinical Svcs)
Richard Lee (Dir-Admin & Fin Projects)
Dora Eko (Mgr-Pharmacy)
Andrew Thornton (Dir-Hospital)
Nicola Manton (Dir-Facilities)
Nicola Ashworth (Mgr-Guest Rels)
Will Banyard (Mgr-Building Svcs)
David Bell (Mgr-Ward)
Ron Davis (Mgr-Theatre)
Paula Lee (Head-Publications & Mgr-Bus Dev)
Heather MacPherson (Mgr-Outpatients)
Amy Irlam (Mgr-Physiotherapy)
Louise Pindar (Mgr-Radiology)
Leon Coppinger (Mgr-Materials)

Colorado Urologic Surgery Center, LLC (1)
3 Superior Dr Ste 301, Superior, CO 80027
Tel.: (720) 544-6140
Web Site: https://www.unitedurology.com
Urologic Surgery Services
N.A.I.C.S.: 622110

Columbus Specialty Surgery Center LLC (1)
2425 NorthPark Dr Ste 20, Columbus, IN 47203
Tel.: (812) 657-7800
Web Site: https://columbusspecialty.com
Outpatient Surgical Services
N.A.I.C.S.: 621498

Conifer Health Solutions, LLC (1)
7624 Warren Pkwy, Frisco, TX 75034
Tel.: (469) 803-3000
Web Site: https://www.coniferhealth.com
Emp.: 1,000
Health Care Srvices
N.A.I.C.S.: 621999
Bryan Forry (CFO)
Deborah Cornett (VP-Clinical Revenue Integrity)
Mary Bacaj (VP-Value-Based Care)
Tim Galloway (Chief Ops Restructuring Officer & Chief Ops Restructuring Officer)
Deepali Narula (COO)
Aaron Epstein (Sr VP)
Scott Fiscus (VP-)
Matt Rakes (VP-)
Daniel Thomas (VP-)
Mike McMann (VP)

Subsidiary (Domestic):

Conifer Physician Services, Inc. (2)
8151 W 183rd St Ste B, Tinley Park, IL 60487
Tel.: (708) 864-2177
Web Site: https://www.coniferhealth.com
Billing & Revenue Cycle Management Services
N.A.I.C.S.: 541219
Ken Christensen (COO)
Scott Fiscus (VP)

Conifer Revenue Cycle Solutions, LLC (2)
2401 Internet Blvd Ste 201, Frisco, TX 75034
Tel.: (877) 266-4337
Medical Devices

N.A.I.C.S.: 622110

Conifer Value-Based Care, LLC (2)
15821 Ventura Blvd Ste 600, Encino, CA 91436
Tel.: (818) 461-5000
Health Care Srvices
N.A.I.C.S.: 621999

Subsidiary (Domestic):

Conifer Care Continuum Solutions, LLC (3)
1596 Whitehall Rd, Annapolis, MD 21409
Tel.: (410) 972-2025
Web Site: http://www.coniferhealth.com
Medical Management Services
N.A.I.C.S.: 541611

Conifer Holdings, Inc. (1)
3001 W Big Beaver Rd Ste 200, Troy, MI 48084
Web Site: https://www.cnfrh.com
General Medical & Surgical Services
N.A.I.C.S.: 622110

Delray Beach ASC, LLC (1)
4800 Linton Blvd Bldg B, Delray Beach, FL 33445
Tel.: (561) 495-9111
Web Site: https://www.delraybeachasc.com
Surgical Care Services
N.A.I.C.S.: 621493

Doctors Outpatient Center for Surgery, LLC (1)
8436 W 3rd St Ste 700, Los Angeles, CA 90048
Tel.: (310) 274-8228
Web Site: http://doctorsoutpatientcenter.com
Outpatient Care Services
N.A.I.C.S.: 621498

Edinburgh Medical Services Limited (1)
40 Colinton Road, Edinburgh, EH10 5BT, United Kingdom
Tel.: (44) 1314472340
Web Site: http://www.edinburghclinic.com
Health Care Srvices
N.A.I.C.S.: 622110
Hazel Monteith (Mgr-Interim-Clinic)

El Paso Center for Gastrointestinal Endoscopy, LLC (1)
1620 N Mesa St, El Paso, TX 79902
Tel.: (915) 545-5300
Web Site: http://www.elpasogi.com
Health Care Srvices
N.A.I.C.S.: 622110

Endoscopy ASC of Middle Georgia, LLC (1)
610 3rd St, Macon, GA 31201
Tel.: (478) 309-1082
Web Site: https://endomiddlega.com
Surgical Center Services
N.A.I.C.S.: 622110

Endoscopy Center of Lake County LLC (1)
9614 Old Johnnycake Ridge Rd, Mentor, OH 44060
Tel.: (440) 205-1225
Endoscopy Treatment Services
N.A.I.C.S.: 621493

Endoscopy Center of South Sacramento, LLC (1)
8120 Timberlake Way Ste 103, Sacramento, CA 95823
Tel.: (916) 681-2350
Web Site: https://southsacendo.com
General Medical & Surgical Services
N.A.I.C.S.: 622110

Florida Springs Surgery Center, LLC (1)
366 Beverly Ct, Spring Hill, FL 34606
Tel.: (352) 600-0220
Web Site: https://www.fsscsurgery.com
Surgical Center Services
N.A.I.C.S.: 622110

Gainesville Endoscopy Center, LLC (1)
2324 Limestone Overlook, Gainesville, GA 30501
Tel.: (770) 297-5324
General Medical & Surgical Services

N.A.I.C.S.: 622110

Gardendale Surgical Associates, LLC (1)
1 Chase Corporate Dr, Birmingham, AL 35244-1026
Tel.: (205) 824-6250
Health Care Srvices
N.A.I.C.S.: 622110
Lee Stubbs (Mgr)

Geneva Surgical Suites, LLC (1)
119 Elizabeth Ln, Genoa City, WI 53128
Tel.: (262) 295-1213
Web Site:
https://www.genevasurgicalsuites.com
Surgical Care Services
N.A.I.C.S.: 621493

Georgia Northside Ear, Nose and Throat, L.L.C. (1)
1360 Upper Hembree Rd Ste 201, Roswell, GA 30076-1171
Tel.: (770) 475-3361
Health Care Srvices
N.A.I.C.S.: 622110

Georgia Spine Surgery Center, LLC (1)
1061 Dowdy Rd Ste 103, Athens, GA 30606
Tel.: (706) 543-9222
General Medical & Surgical Services
N.A.I.C.S.: 622110

Glen Echo Surgery Center, LLC (1)
5550 Friendship Blvd Ste 100, Chevy Chase, MD 20815
Tel.: (240) 534-2972
Web Site: https://www.glenechosc.com
Surgical Care Services
N.A.I.C.S.: 621493

Grand Rapids Surgical Suites, LLC (1)
2505 E Paris Ave SE Ste 105, Grand Rapids, MI 49546
Tel.: (616) 551-3149
Web Site: https://grandrapidsasc.com
Outpatient Surgical Services
N.A.I.C.S.: 621498

Great Lakes Surgical Suites, LLC (1)
9200 Calumet Ave Ste N500, Munster, IN 46321
Tel.: (219) 513-9955
Web Site: https://www.greatlakessurg.com
Surgical Care Services
N.A.I.C.S.: 621493

Gulfshore Endoscopy Center, LLC (1)
1084 Goodlette Rd, Naples, FL 34102
Tel.: (239) 435-9330
Web Site:
https://gulfshoreendoscopycenter.com
Surgical Center Services
N.A.I.C.S.: 622110

HNMC, Inc. (1)
710 Cypress Creek Pkwy, Houston, TX 77090
Tel.: (281) 440-1000
Web Site: http://www.hnmc.com
Sales Range: $50-74.9 Million
Emp.: 600
General Medical Services
N.A.I.C.S.: 622110

Hagerstown Surgery Center, LLC (1)
11236 Robinwood Dr Ste 201, Hagerstown, MD 21742
Tel.: (240) 347-4836
Web Site:
https://www.hagerstownsurgerycenter.com
Surgical Care Services
N.A.I.C.S.: 621493

Harbor Heights Surgery Center, LLC (1)
6710 Oxon Hill Rd Ste 500, Oxon Hill, MD 20745
Tel.: (240) 493-7533
Web Site: https://www.harborheightssc.com
Surgical Care Services
N.A.I.C.S.: 621493

Haymarket Surgery Center, LLC (1)

15195 Heathcote Blvd Ste 210, Haymarket, VA 20169
Tel.: (571) 445-3800
Web Site:
https://haymarketsurgerycenter.com
Surgical Center Services
N.A.I.C.S.: 621493

Health Services Network Hospitals, Inc. (1)
1445 Ross Ave Ste 1400, Dallas, TX 75240
Tel.: (469) 893-2200
Hospital
N.A.I.C.S.: 622110

Subsidiary (Domestic):

Alabama Hand and Sports Medicine, L.L.C. (2)
200 Montgomery Hwy Ste 125, Vestavia Hills, AL 35216-1842
Tel.: (205) 822-9595
Health Care Srvices
N.A.I.C.S.: 621999
Ann Syx (Gen Mgr)

Brookwood - Maternal Fetal Medicine, L.L.C. (2)
2006 Brookwood Medical Ctr Dr Ste 604, Birmingham, AL 35209
Tel.: (205) 877-5113
Web Site:
http://www.wrookwoodcarenetwork.com
Medical Devices
N.A.I.C.S.: 622110

Brookwood Medical Partners - ENT, L.L.C. (2)
2018 Brookwood Medical Ctr Dr Ste 314, Birmingham, AL 35209
Tel.: (205) 877-2950
Health Care Srvices
N.A.I.C.S.: 621999

Brookwood Primary Care - Inverness, L.L.C. (2)
4902 Valleydale Rd, Birmingham, AL 35242-4613
Tel.: (205) 980-8099
Web Site: http://bbhcarenetwork.com
Health Care Srvices
N.A.I.C.S.: 621999

Brookwood Primary Care - Mountain Brook, L.L.C. (2)
4500 Montevallo Rd Ste E101, Irondale, AL 35210-3129
Tel.: (205) 940-4690
Health Care Srvices
N.A.I.C.S.: 621999

Brookwood Primary Care - Oak Mountain, L.L.C. (2)
2705 Pelham Pkwy Ste 100, Pelham, AL 35124-1185
Tel.: (205) 733-1130
Web Site: http://bbhcarenetwork.com
Emp.: 14
Health Care Srvices
N.A.I.C.S.: 621999

Brookwood Primary Care Cahaba Heights, L.L.C. (2)
4274 Cahaba Heights Ct Ste 130, Birmingham, AL 35243-5712
Tel.: (205) 977-8484
Web Site: http://bbhcarenetwork.com
Health Care Srvices
N.A.I.C.S.: 621610

Brookwood Primary Care Hoover, L.L.C. (2)
5295 Preserve Pkwy Ste 210, Hoover, AL 35244
Tel.: (205) 682-6077
Health Care Srvices
N.A.I.C.S.: 621999

Brookwood Primary Care The Narrows, L.L.C. (2)
13521 Old Highway 280 Ste 201, Birmingham, AL 35242
Tel.: (205) 408-4349
Health Care Srvices
N.A.I.C.S.: 621999

Brookwood Specialty Care - Endocrinology, L.L.C. (2)

513 Brookwood Blvd Ste 400, Birmingham,
AL 35209-6862
Tel.: (205) 802-6722
Health Care Srvices
N.A.I.C.S.: 621111

**Brookwood Sports and Orthopedics,
L.L.C.** (2)
13521 Old Hwy 280 Ste 201b, Birmingham,
AL 35242-1405
Tel.: (205) 877-2663
Orthopaedic Services
N.A.I.C.S.: 621111

**Brookwood Women's Care,
L.L.C.** (2)
2006 Brookwood Medical Ctr Dr Ste 202,
Birmingham, AL 35209
Tel.: (205) 397-8850
Web Site:
 http://brookwoodwomenshealth.com
Medical Devices
N.A.I.C.S.: 622110

**Cardiology Physicians Associates,
L.L.C.** (2)
602 Morganton Blvd SW, Lenoir, NC 28645
Tel.: (828) 754-1919
Health Care Srvices
N.A.I.C.S.: 621999
Mike Thomas *(Office Mgr)*

**Cardiology Physicians Corporation,
L.L.C.** (2)
1771 Tate Blvd Southeast Ste 201, Hickory,
NC 28602-4250
Tel.: (828) 324-4804
Web Site: http://www.wphc.com
Medical Devices
N.A.I.C.S.: 622110

**Cardiovascular Associates of the
Southeast, L.L.C.** (2)
3980 Colonnade Pkwy, Birmingham, AL
35243
Tel.: (205) 510-5000
Web Site: http://www.cvapc.com
Radiological Services
N.A.I.C.S.: 621111

Cedar Hill Primary Care, L.L.C. (2)
6420 The Cedars Ct, Cedar Hill, MO 63016
Tel.: (636) 274-2700
Web Site: https://cedarhillprimarycare.com
Health Care Srvices
N.A.I.C.S.: 621999

**Coast Healthcare Management,
LLC** (2)
4909 Lakewood Blvd Ste 200, Lakewood,
CA 90712
Tel.: (562) 602-1563
Web Site: http://www.coasthealthcare.com
Senior Care Services
N.A.I.C.S.: 624120

Delray Medical Center, Inc. (2)
5352 Linton Blvd, Delray Beach, FL 33484
Tel.: (561) 498-4440
Web Site: https://www.delraymedicalctr.com
Hospital
N.A.I.C.S.: 622110
Shannon Wills *(Chief HR Officer-)*
Maggie Gill *(CEO)*
Libby Flippo *(Chief Nursing Officer-Palm
Beach)*
Daniel Listi *(CEO)*
Michelle Cartwright *(CFO-)*
Heather Havericak *(COO)*
Jennifer Shoemaker *(Chief Nursing Officer)*

Subsidiary (Domestic):

DMC Imaging, L.L.C. (3)
5130 Linton Blvd Ste I-1, Delray Beach, FL
33484
Tel.: (561) 637-5300
Health Care Srvices
N.A.I.C.S.: 621999

Subsidiary (Domestic):

**Desert Regional Medical Center,
Inc.** (2)
1150 N Indian Canyon Dr, Palm Springs,
CA 92262
Tel.: (760) 323-6511
Web Site: http://www.desertregional.com
Health Care & Emergency Care Services
N.A.I.C.S.: 621999

Michele Finney *(CEO)*
Scott White *(Sec)*

**Doctors Hospital of Manteca,
Inc.** (2)
1205 E N St, Manteca, CA 95336
Tel.: (209) 823-3111
Web Site: https://www.doctorsmanteca.com
Sales Range: $50-74.9 Million
Emp.: 500
Hospital
N.A.I.C.S.: 622110

**Doctors Medical Center of Modesto,
Inc.** (2)
1441 Florida Ave, Modesto, CA 95350
Tel.: (209) 578-1211
Web Site: https://www.dmc-modesto.com
Emp.: 2,600
Hospital
N.A.I.C.S.: 622110

Subsidiary (Domestic):

**Health & Wellness Surgery Center,
L.P.** (3)
1801 Colorado Ave, Turlock, CA 95382
Tel.: (209) 216-3400
Web Site: http://www.tower-health.com
General Hospital Services
N.A.I.C.S.: 622110

Modesto Radiology Imaging, Inc. (3)
1524 McHenry Ave Ste 100, Modesto, CA
95350
Tel.: (209) 577-4444
Web Site:
 http://modestoradiologyimaging.com
Diagnostic Imaging Services
N.A.I.C.S.: 621512

Turlock Imaging Services, LLC (3)
3900 Geer Rd, Turlock, CA 95382
Tel.: (209) 669-0600
Web Site:
 http://www.turlockimagingservices.com
Medical Laboratory Operator
N.A.I.C.S.: 621511

Subsidiary (Domestic):

**East Cooper Coastal Family Physi-
cians, L.L.C.** (2)
851 Leonard Fulghum Blvd Ste 100, Mount
Pleasant, SC 29464
Tel.: (843) 849-1300
Web Site: http://coastalfamilyphysicians.com
Sales Range: $10-24.9 Million
Health Care Srvices
N.A.I.C.S.: 621610

East Cooper Hyperbarics, L.L.C. (2)
2 Office Park Ct Ste 103, Columbia, SC
29223
Tel.: (843) 856-1771
Health Care Srvices
N.A.I.C.S.: 621999

East Cooper OBGYN, L.L.C. (2)
851 Leonard Fulghum Blvd Ste 200, Mount
Pleasant, SC 29464-3787
Tel.: (843) 654-0461
Web Site:
 https://www.eastcooperobgyn.com
Health Care Srvices
N.A.I.C.S.: 621999

**East Cooper Primary Care Physi-
cians, L.L.C.** (2)
2 Office Park Ct Ste 103, Columbia, SC
29223
Tel.: (843) 883-3176
Health Care Srvices
N.A.I.C.S.: 621999

FryeCare Physicians, L.L.C. (2)
415 N Ctr St Ste 203, Hickory, NC 28601-
5036
Tel.: (828) 323-8281
Medical Devices
N.A.I.C.S.: 622110

FryeCare Valdese, L.L.C. (2)
721-B Malcolm Blvd, Connelly Springs, NC
28612
Tel.: (828) 893-0097
Web Site: http://www.piedmontcardio.com
Health Care Srvices
N.A.I.C.S.: 621999

FryeCare Watauga, L.L.C. (2)

245 Winklers Creek Rd Ste C, Boone, NC
28607-7838
Tel.: (828) 262-1800
Health Care Srvices
N.A.I.C.S.: 621999

**Greater Northwest Houston
Enterprises** (2)
11302 Fallbrook Dr Ste 201, Houston, TX
77065-4235
Tel.: (281) 746-3070
Web Site: http://www.healthcare.com
Emp.: 9
Health Care Srvices
N.A.I.C.S.: 621999

**Greystone Internal Medicine - Brook-
wood, L.L.C.** (2)
101 Missionary Rdg Ste 200, Birmingham,
AL 35242-5202
Tel.: (205) 995-2260
Web Site:
 http://bpcgreystone.portalforpatients.com
Health Care Srvices
N.A.I.C.S.: 621999

**Healthpoint of North Carolina,
L.L.C.** (2)
1333 2nd NE Ste 200, Hickory, NC 28601
Tel.: (828) 485-4333
Health Care Srvices
N.A.I.C.S.: 621610

Hialeah Hospital, Inc. (2)
651 E 25th St, Hialeah, FL 33013
Tel.: (305) 693-6100
Web Site: https://www.hialeahhosp.org
Emp.: 900
Medical Devices
N.A.I.C.S.: 622110
Michael J. Bell *(CEO)*

JFK Memorial Hospital, Inc. (2)
47111 Monroe St, Indio, CA 92201
Tel.: (760) 347-6191
Web Site: http://www.jfkmemorialhosp.com
Sales Range: $1-9.9 Million
Emp.: 600
Hospital
N.A.I.C.S.: 622110
Gary Honts *(CEO)*
Richard Twiss *(Chm)*
M. Elizabeth Sassano *(Sec)*
Bev Blessing *(Treas)*

Jackson Medical Center, L.L.C. (2)
220 Port Saint, Jackson, AL 36545
Tel.: (251) 246-9021
Web Site: https://www.jmc.org
Emp.: 115
Health Care Srvices
N.A.I.C.S.: 621999
Jennifer Ryland *(CEO)*
Teresa Napper *(Chief Nursing Officer)*
B. J. Garrick *(Dir-IT)*
Jennifer Butts *(Office Mgr)*

**Modesto On-Call Services,
L.L.C.** (2)
1441 Florida Ave, Modesto, CA 95350
Tel.: (209) 342-3124
Health Care Srvices
N.A.I.C.S.: 621999

**Premier Medical Specialists,
L.L.C.** (2)
8790 Watson Rd Ste 103, Saint Louis, MO
63119
Tel.: (314) 729-1725
Web Site:
 http://www.premiermedicalspecialists.com
Health Care Srvices
N.A.I.C.S.: 621999

**Rock Bridge Surgical Institute,
L.L.C.** (2)
2500 Hospital Blvd Ste 410, Roswell, GA
30076-4907
Tel.: (770) 667-4991
Medical Devices
N.A.I.C.S.: 622110

**Saint Francis Center for Surgical
Weight Loss, L.L.C.** (2)
6005 Park Ave Ste 1010 B, Memphis, TN
38119
Tel.: (901) 881-0602
Web Site: https://www.saintfrancishosp.com
Medical Devices
N.A.I.C.S.: 622110

Robert Wegner *(Dir-Medical)*

**Saint Francis Hospital Inpatient Phy-
sicians, L.L.C.** (2)
5959 Park Ave, Memphis, TN 38119
Tel.: (901) 765-1000
Web Site: http://www.saintfrancishosp.com
Medical Devices
N.A.I.C.S.: 622110

**Saint Francis Hospital Pro Fee Bill-
ing, L.L.C.** (2)
14201 Dallas Pkwy, Dallas, TX 75254-2916
Tel.: (901) 765-2057
Health Care Srvices
N.A.I.C.S.: 621999

**Saint Francis Medical Partners, East,
L.L.C.** (2)
2018 S Germantown Rd, Germantown, TN
38138
Tel.: (901) 754-8880
Web Site: https://sfmp.com
Sales Range: $10-24.9 Million
Medical Devices
N.A.I.C.S.: 622110

**Saint Francis Surgical Associates,
L.L.C.** (2)
14201 Dallas Pkwy, Dallas, TX 75254-2916
Tel.: (617) 750-0850
Health Care Srvices
N.A.I.C.S.: 621999

**San Ramon Regional Medical Center,
Inc.** (2)
6001 Norris Canyon Rd, San Ramon, CA
94583
Tel.: (925) 275-9200
Web Site: https://www.sanramonmedctr.com
Sales Range: $50-74.9 Million
Hospital
N.A.I.C.S.: 622110
Pam Yoo *(Chief Strategy Officer)*
Beenu Chadha *(CFO)*
Dennis Mills *(Chief HR Officer)*
A. Eric Ramos *(Chief Medical Officer)*
Wendy Sirivar *(Chief Nursing Officer)*

Subsidiary (Domestic):

**Pleasanton Diagnostic Imaging,
Inc.** (3)
5860 Owens Dr, Pleasanton, CA 94588
Tel.: (925) 467-1400
Web Site:
 http://www.pleasantonimaging.com
Diagnostic Imaging Services
N.A.I.C.S.: 621512

Subsidiary (Domestic):

San Ramon Surgery Center, LLC (2)
100 Park Place Ste 110, San Ramon, CA
94583
Tel.: (925) 838-6880
Fiscal Year-end: 12/31/2006
Ambulatory & Other Health Care Services
N.A.I.C.S.: 621999

**Sierra Providence Health Network,
Inc.** (2)
1625 Medical Ctr Dr, El Paso, TX 79902
Tel.: (915) 577-7746
Web Site: http://www.sphn.com
Health Care Srvices
N.A.I.C.S.: 621999

**South Carolina SeWee Family Medi-
cine, L.L.C.** (2)
570 Long Point Rd Ste 130, Mount Pleasant, SC 29464
Tel.: (843) 884-2133
Web Site:
 http://www.seweefamilymedicine.com
Health Care Srvices
N.A.I.C.S.: 621999

**Southern Orthopedics and Sports
Medicine, L.L.C.** (2)
851 Leonard Fulghum Blvd Ste 101, Mount
Pleasant, SC 29464
Tel.: (843) 936-0715
Web Site:
 https://www.southernorthosports.com
Sales Range: $10-24.9 Million
Medical Devices
N.A.I.C.S.: 622110

Tenet Healthcare Corporation—(Continued)

Sun View Imaging, L.L.C. (2)
2525 S Telshor Blvd, Las Cruces, NM 88011
Tel.: (575) 522-6236
Web Site: http://www.sunviewlascruces.com
Emp.: 35
Medical Related Services
N.A.I.C.S.: 622110

Tenet Florida, Inc. (2)
5810 Coral Rdg Dr Ste 300, Coral Springs, FL 33076
Tel.: (954) 509-3600
Web Site: http://www.tenetflorida.com
Health Care Srvices
N.A.I.C.S.: 621999

Subsidiary (Domestic):

Tenet Florida Physician Services, L.L.C. (3)
1411 N Flagler Dr Ste 4900, West Palm Beach, FL 33401
Tel.: (561) 357-6277
Web Site: http://www.tenetfloridaphysicianservices.com
Health Care Srvices
N.A.I.C.S.: 621999
Michael S. Davis (CEO)

Subsidiary (Domestic):

Sunrise Medical Group I, L.L.C. (4)
3540 N. Pine Island Road, Sunrise, FL 33351
Tel.: (954) 321-1776
Web Site: http://www.sunrisepractices.com
Health Care Srvices
N.A.I.C.S.: 621999

Sunrise Medical Group II, L.L.C. (4)
7369 Sheridan St Ste 101, Hollywood, FL 33024
Tel.: (954) 981-3850
Web Site: http://www.sunrisepractices.com
Emp.: 15
Pulmonary Clinical Services
N.A.I.C.S.: 621111

Tenet Florida Physician Services III, L.L.C. (4)
14201 Dallas Pkwy, Dallas, TX 75254
Tel.: (561) 288-5530
Allopathic & Osteopathic Clinical Services
N.A.I.C.S.: 621111

Subsidiary (Domestic):

West Boca Medical Center, Inc. (3)
21644 State Rd 7, Boca Raton, FL 33428
Tel.: (561) 488-8000
Web Site: https://www.westbocamedctr.com
Sales Range: $10-24.9 Million
Hospital
N.A.I.C.S.: 622110
Stephanie Sherman (Chief HR Officer)
Stewart Newman (Chm)
Randy Nobles (Vice Chm)
Austin R. Wratchford (COO)
Ricardo J. Ramirez (Chief Nursing Officer)
Kim Cole (CFO)
Jerad Hanlon (CEO)

Subsidiary (Domestic):

Tenet Frisco, Ltd (2)
12505 Lebanon Rd, Frisco, TX 75035-8298
Tel.: (972) 963-3333
Emp.: 500
Health Care Srvices
N.A.I.C.S.: 621999
Joe Thomason (CEO)

Tenet Unifour Urgent Care Center, L.L.C. (2)
1105 Fairgrove Church Rd SE, Conover, NC 28613
Tel.: (828) 267-0551
Web Site: https://www.fryecarephysicians.com
Medical Devices
N.A.I.C.S.: 622110

Healthcare Network Hospitals, Inc. (1)
1445 Ross Ave Ste 14000, Dallas, TX 75202

Tel.: (469) 893-2200
Hospital
N.A.I.C.S.: 622110
Doug Rabe (Pres)

Highgate Hospital LLP (1)
17-19 View Road, Highgate, London, N6 4DJ, United Kingdom
Tel.: (44) 2083414182
Web Site: http://www.highgatehospital.co.uk
Health Care Services
N.A.I.C.S.: 622110

Hill Country Surgery Center, LLC (1)
1411 Medical Pkwy Ste 100, Cedar Park, TX 78613
Tel.: (512) 528-2000
Web Site: https://www.hillcountry-sc.com
Health Care Srvices
N.A.I.C.S.: 622110

Hilton Head Regional Physician Network - Georgia, LLC (1)
4 Dunmore Ct Bldg C Ste 301, Hilton Head Island, SC 29926
Tel.: (843) 686-2448
Web Site: https://www.hiltonheadregionalphysiciannetwork.com
General Medical & Surgical Services
N.A.I.C.S.: 622110

Holston Valley Ambulatory Surgery Center, LLC (1)
103 W Stone Dr, Kingsport, TN 37660
Tel.: (423) 224-4910
General Medical & Surgical Services
N.A.I.C.S.: 622110

Horizon Ridge Surgery Center, LLC (1)
10561 Jeffreys St Ste 130, Henderson, NV 89052
Tel.: (702) 724-8900
Web Site: https://horizonridgesurgerycenter.com
General Medical & Surgical Services
N.A.I.C.S.: 622110

Hospital Underwriting Group, Inc. (1)
1445 Ross Ave Ste 1400, Dallas, TX 75202-2703
Tel.: (469) 893-6545
Insurance Management Services
N.A.I.C.S.: 524298

Howard County Gastrointestinal Diagnostic Center, LLC (1)
10710 Charter Dr Ste 120, Columbia, MD 21044
Tel.: (410) 772-7345
Web Site: https://howardcountygi.com
Gastrointestinal Diagnostic Services
N.A.I.C.S.: 621111

Intracoastal Surgery Center, LLC (1)
2200 W Eau Gallie Blvd Ste 100, Melbourne, FL 32935
Tel.: (321) 610-3460
Web Site: https://www.intracoastalsurg.com
Surgical Care Services
N.A.I.C.S.: 621493

Jacksonville Endoscopy Centers, LLC (1)
1610 Barrs St, Jacksonville, FL 32204-4569
Tel.: (904) 387-6750
Web Site: https://www.jacksonvilleendoscopy.com
Health Care Srvices
N.A.I.C.S.: 622110

Lake Endoscopy Center, LLC (1)
17355 SE 109th Terrace Rd, Summerfield, FL 34491
Tel.: (352) 245-0846
Web Site: http://www.gaocala.com
Health Care Srvices
N.A.I.C.S.: 622110

Lancaster Specialty Surgery Center, LLC (1)
3056 Columbus Lancaster Rd NW, Lancaster, OH 43130
Tel.: (740) 785-9350
Web Site: https://www.lancastersurg.com
Surgical Care Services
N.A.I.C.S.: 621493

Landmark Surgical Suites, LLC (1)

2990 Gottbrath Pkwy, Jeffersonville, IN 47130
Tel.: (812) 671-0990
Web Site: https://landmarksurgicalsuites.com
Outpatient Surgical Services
N.A.I.C.S.: 621498

Leonardtown Surgery Center, LLC (1)
40900 Merchants Ln Ste 200, Leonardtown, MD 20650
Tel.: (301) 690-2203
Web Site: https://www.leonardtownsc.com
Surgical Care Services
N.A.I.C.S.: 621493

Longleaf Surgery Center, LLC (1)
3010 Starkey Blvd, New Port Richey, FL 34655
Tel.: (727) 372-0600
Web Site: https://www.longleafsc.com
Surgical Care Services
N.A.I.C.S.: 621493

Maple Lawn Surgery Center, LLC (1)
7625 Maple Lawn Blvd Ste 110, Fulton, MD 20759
Tel.: (301) 490-5025
Web Site: https://www.maplelawnsc.com
Surgical Care Services
N.A.I.C.S.: 621493

Marion Surgery Center, LLC (1)
2207 SW 1st Ave, Ocala, FL 34471
Tel.: (352) 732-4020
Web Site: https://www.marionsurg.com
Surgical Care Services
N.A.I.C.S.: 621493

Mayfield Spine Surgery Center, LLC (1)
4020 Smith Rd, Cincinnati, OH 45209
Tel.: (513) 619-5899
Web Site: https://www.mayfieldsurgerycenter.com
Health Care Srvices
N.A.I.C.S.: 622110

Medical Center of Garden Grove, Inc. (1)
12601 Garden Grove Blvd, Garden Grove, CA 92843
Tel.: (714) 537-5160
Web Site: https://www.gardengrovehospital.com
Sales Range: $25-49.9 Million
Emp.: 500
Medical Devices
N.A.I.C.S.: 622110

Memorial Hermann Surgery Center Texas Medical Center, LLP (1)
6400 Fannin St Ste 1500, Houston, TX 77030
Tel.: (713) 790-7700
Web Site: https://www.mhsc-tmc.com
Health Care Srvices
N.A.I.C.S.: 622110

Merced Ambulatory Surgery Center, LLC (1)
1390 E Yosemite Ave Ste B, Merced, CA 95340
Tel.: (209) 580-3400
Web Site: https://www.universitysurgerycenter.com
Health Care Srvices
N.A.I.C.S.: 622110

Metro Specialty Surgery Center, LLC (1)
200 Missouri Ave Bldg 18 Ste A, Jeffersonville, IN 47130
Tel.: (812) 920-0055
Web Site: https://www.metrospecialty.com
Surgical Care Services
N.A.I.C.S.: 621493

MetroWest HomeCare & Hospice, LLC (1)
200 Nickerson Rd Ste 110, Marlborough, MA 01752
Tel.: (508) 383-7000
Web Site: https://locations.amedisys.com
Home & Hospice Care Services
N.A.I.C.S.: 621610

Miami Surgical Suites, LLC (1)

9035 Sunset Dr Ste 200, Miami, FL 33173
Tel.: (786) 615-6210
Web Site: https://www.miamisurgsuites.com
Surgical Care Services
N.A.I.C.S.: 621493

Michigan Outpatient Surgical Solutions, LLC (1)
46325 W 12 Mile Rd Ste 100, Novi, MI 48377
Tel.: (248) 618-2121
Web Site: https://michiganopss.com
Outpatient Surgical Services
N.A.I.C.S.: 621498

Midwest Specialty Surgery Center, LLC (1)
6920 Gatwick Dr, Indianapolis, IN 46241
Tel.: (317) 821-0000
Web Site: https://www.midwestspecialtysurgery.com
Hospital Services
N.A.I.C.S.: 622110

Minimally Invasive Surgery Center of NE, LLC (1)
4 Hawthorne Dr, Bedford, NH 03110
Tel.: (603) 218-1912
Web Site: https://miscne.com
Surgical Center Services
N.A.I.C.S.: 622110

Minimally Invasive Surgicenter LLC (1)
6646 W Atlantic Ave, Delray Beach, FL 33446
Tel.: (561) 774-2647
Web Site: https://www.minimallyinvasivesc.com
Invasive Surgery Center Services
N.A.I.C.S.: 621111

Minimally Invasive Surgicenter of Delray, LLC (1)
6646 W Atlantic Ave, Delray Beach, FL 33446
Tel.: (561) 774-2647
Web Site: https://www.minimallyinvasivesc.com
General Medical & Surgical Services
N.A.I.C.S.: 622110

Monocacy Surgery Center, LLC (1)
4991 New Design Rd Ste 103, Frederick, MD 21703
Tel.: (301) 363-5858
Web Site: https://www.monocacysc.com
Surgical Care Services
N.A.I.C.S.: 621493

Mount Pleasant Outpatient Surgery Center, LLC (1)
1439 Stuart Engals Blvd Ste 100, Mount Pleasant, SC 29464
Tel.: (843) 531-0015
Web Site: https://mountpleasantosc.com
Outpatient Surgical Services
N.A.I.C.S.: 621498

Munster Specialty Surgery Center, LLC (1)
9200 Calumet Ave, Munster, IN 46321
Tel.: (219) 595-0789
Web Site: https://www.munsterspecialty.com
Surgical Care Services
N.A.I.C.S.: 621493

NME Rehabilitation Properties, Inc. (1)
1445 Ross Ave, Dallas, TX 75202
Tel.: (469) 893-2200
Web Site: http://www.tenethealthcare.com
Sales Range: $50-74.9 Million
Emp.: 600
Hospital
N.A.I.C.S.: 622110

Nassau Crossing Endoscopy Center, LLC (1)
73675 Harper Chapel Rd Ste 300, Yulee, FL 32097
Tel.: (904) 398-7205
Gastroenterology Healthcare Services
N.A.I.C.S.: 621111

National Diagnostic Imaging Centers, Inc. (1)
25700 Science Park Ste 180, Beachwood, OH 44122
Tel.: (216) 514-1199
Web Site: https://www.ndximaging.com
Emp.: 4

Health Care Srvices
N.A.I.C.S.: 621999
David H. Berns *(Founder, Pres & CEO)*
Howard Rothman *(Chief Technical Officer)*
Teagan Cummins *(Specialist-IT)*
Bill Cech *(Dir-IT)*

National Surgery Center Holdings, Inc. (1)
1445 Ross Ave Ste 1400, Dallas, TX 75202
Tel.: (469) 893-2000
Holding Company
N.A.I.C.S.: 551112
Kristina A. Mack *(Sec)*

Subsidiary (Domestic):

Bluffton Okatie Surgery Center, L.L.C. (2)
40 Okatie Center Blvd S Ste 125, Okatie, SC 29909
Tel.: (843) 705-8804
Web Site:
https://www.blufftonokatiesurgerycen
ter.com
Health Care Srvices
N.A.I.C.S.: 621999

Coral Ridge Outpatient Center, LLC (2)
5301 N Dixie Hwy Ste 100, Oakland Park, FL 33334
Tel.: (954) 832-3300
Web Site:
https://www.coralridgeoutpatient.com
Health Care Srvices
N.A.I.C.S.: 621999

El Mirador Surgery Center, L.L.C. (2)
1180 N Indian Canyon Dr Ste W-110, Palm Springs, CA 92262
Tel.: (760) 416-4600
Web Site:
https://www.elmiradorsurgerycenter.com
Health Care Srvices
N.A.I.C.S.: 621999

El Paso Day Surgery, LLC (2)
1300 Murchison Dr Ste 200, El Paso, TX 79902
Tel.: (915) 577-8467
Web Site:
https://www.thehospitalsofprovidence.com
Health Care Srvices
N.A.I.C.S.: 621999

Fountain Valley Surgery Center, LLC (2)
11190 Warner Ave Ste 212, Fountain Valley, CA 92708
Tel.: (714) 338-1650
Web Site:
https://www.fountainvalleyhospital.com
Surgical Hospital Services
N.A.I.C.S.: 622110

GCSA Ambulatory Surgery Center, LLC (2)
1445 Ross Ave Ste 1400, Dallas, TX 75202-2703
Tel.: (469) 893-2000
Health Care Srvices
N.A.I.C.S.: 621999

Hyde Park Surgery Center, LLC (2)
4611 Guadalupe St Ste 100, Austin, TX 78751
Tel.: (512) 420-2303
Web Site: https://www.hydeparksc.com
Outpatient Care Center Operator
N.A.I.C.S.: 621498

Murdock Ambulatory Surgical Center, LLC (2)
1400 Education Way, Port Charlotte, FL 33948
Tel.: (941) 625-9800
Web Site:
https://www.murdocksurgerycenter.com
Health Care Srvices
N.A.I.C.S.: 621999

North Anaheim Surgery Center, LLC (2)
1154 N Euclid, Anaheim, CA 92801
Tel.: (714) 635-6272
Web Site:
http://www.northanaheimsurgerycen
ter.com

Surgical Hospital Services
N.A.I.C.S.: 622110

Pacific Endoscopy & Surgery Center, LLC (2)
17815 Newhope St Ste R, Fountain Valley, CA 92708
Tel.: (714) 432-8881
Web Site:
https://www.pacificendoscopy.com
Fiscal Year-end: 12/31/2006
Health Care Srvices
N.A.I.C.S.: 621999
Jennifer Holloway *(Mgr-Bus Office)*
Rachel Harris *(Dir-Clinical)*

Pediatric Surgery Center - Odessa, LLC (2)
14111 State Rd 54, Odessa, FL 33556
Tel.: (813) 343-5690
Web Site:
https://www.surgerycenterforkids.com
Health Care Srvices
N.A.I.C.S.: 621999

Pediatric Surgery Centers, LLC (2)
10080 Balaye Run Dr, Tampa, FL 33619
Tel.: (813) 490-6100
Web Site:
https://www.surgerycenterforkids.com
Health Care Srvices
N.A.I.C.S.: 621999

South Florida Ambulatory Surgical Center, LLC (2)
6110 SW 70th St, South Miami, FL 33413
Tel.: (305) 662-3100
Web Site:
https://www.southfloridasurgerycenter.com
Emp.: 40
Fiscal Year-end: 12/31/2006
Health Care Srvices
N.A.I.C.S.: 621999

Surgery Center of Okeechobee, LLC (2)
14201 Dallas Pkwy, Dallas, TX 75254
Tel.: (863) 357-6220
Health Care Srvices
N.A.I.C.S.: 621999

Surgery Center of Pembroke Pines, L.L.C. (2)
7261 Sheridan St Ste 100 A, Hollywood, FL 33024
Tel.: (781) 820-6134
Health Care Srvices
N.A.I.C.S.: 621999

Surgical Elite of Avondale, L.L.C. (2)
10815 W Mcdowell Rd Ste 101, Avondale, AZ 85392
Tel.: (623) 433-0110
Web Site: http://www.surgicalelite.com
Emp.: 15
Physician Office Services
N.A.I.C.S.: 621111

The Tresanti Surgical Center, LLC (2)
5201 Norris Canyon Rd Ste 100, San Ramon, CA 94583
Tel.: (925) 973-0605
Web Site: https://www.tresantisurgery.com
Surgical Hospital Services
N.A.I.C.S.: 622110

Theda Oaks Gastroenterology & Endoscopy Center, LLC (2)
19226 Stonehue Ste 103, San Antonio, TX 78258-3480
Tel.: (210) 268-0100
Health Care Srvices
N.A.I.C.S.: 621999

Winter Haven Ambulatory Surgical Center, L.L.C. (2)
325 Ave B NW, Winter Haven, FL 33881
Tel.: (863) 291-4000
Web Site: https://www.winterhavenasc.com
Health Care Srvices
N.A.I.C.S.: 621999

Worcester Center, L.P. (2)
300 Grove St, Worcester, MA 01605
Tel.: (508) 754-0700
Web Site:
https://www.worcestersurgicalcenter.com
Emp.: 75
Outpatient Surgery Services

N.A.I.C.S.: 621999

National Urgent Care Holdings, Inc. (1)
1751 Earl Core Rd, Morgantown, WV 26505
Tel.: (304) 225-2500
Holding Company
N.A.I.C.S.: 551112

Subsidiary (Domestic):

AMC/North Fulton Urgent Care #1, L.L.C. (2)
1230 S Hairston Rd Ste 30, Stone Mountain, GA 30088-2761
Tel.: (404) 292-9034
Web Site: http://www.carespot.com
Health Care Srvices
N.A.I.C.S.: 621999

AMC/North Fulton Urgent Care #5, L.L.C. (2)
3576 Highway 38 SE, Stockbridge, GA 30281
Tel.: (770) 474-7448
Web Site: http://www.medpost.com
Emp.: 7
Health Care Srvices
N.A.I.C.S.: 621999

Memphis Urgent Care #2, L.L.C. (2)
14201 Dallas Pkwy, Dallas, TX 75254-2916
Tel.: (469) 893-6273
Health Care Srvices
N.A.I.C.S.: 621999

NUCH of Texas (2)
9100 Viscount Blvd, El Paso, TX 79925
Tel.: (915) 594-4475
Health Care Srvices
N.A.I.C.S.: 621999

Selma Carlson, Inc. (2)
77 Casa St Ste 102, San Luis Obispo, CA 93405
Tel.: (805) 546-7733
Web Site: https://www.selmacarlson.com
Health Care Srvices
N.A.I.C.S.: 621999

Spalding Regional Urgent Care Center at Heron Bay, L.L.C. (2)
3334 Hwy 155 S, Locust Grove, GA 30248
Tel.: (678) 583-0241
Health Care Srvices
N.A.I.C.S.: 621999

St. Louis Urgent Care #2, L.L.C. (2)
15420 Manchester Rd, Ellisville, MO 63011-3029
Tel.: (636) 220-9727
Health Care Srvices
N.A.I.C.S.: 621999
Angie Soltysiak *(Gen Mgr)*

Urgent Care Centers of Arizona, LLC (2)
3800 N Central Ave Ste 460, Phoenix, AZ 85012
Tel.: (602) 273-7373
Emp.: 5
Ambulatory Health Care Services
N.A.I.C.S.: 621999

Walker Street Imaging Care, Inc. (2)
10601 WaLakeer St Ste 150, Cypress, CA 90630
Tel.: (714) 656-2130
Web Site:
http://www.walkerstreetimagingcare.com
Health Care Srvices
N.A.I.C.S.: 621999

North Atlantic Surgical Suites, LLC (1)
23 Keewaydin Dr Ste 100, Salem, NH 03079
Tel.: (603) 386-0272
Web Site: https://www.northatlanticss.com
Surgical Care Services
N.A.I.C.S.: 621493

North Campus Surgery Center, LLC (1)
8040 Clearvista Pkwy Ste 150, Indianapolis, IN 46256
Tel.: (855) 621-0300
Health Care Srvices
N.A.I.C.S.: 622110

North Central Surgical Center, L.L.P. (1)
9301 N Central Expy Ste 100, Dallas, TX 75231
Tel.: (214) 265-2810
Web Site:
https://www.northcentralsurgical.com
Health Care Srvices
N.A.I.C.S.: 622110
Mike Quaglieri *(CFO)*

North Shore Medical Center, Inc. (1)
1100 NW 95th St, Miami, FL 33150
Tel.: (305) 835-6000
Web Site: https://www.northshoremc.org
General Medical & Surgical Services
N.A.I.C.S.: 622110

North Shore Surgical Suites, LLC (1)
8400 Lakeview Pkwy Ste 800, Pleasant Prairie, WI 53158
Tel.: (262) 455-7548
Web Site:
https://www.northshoresurgicalsuites.com
Surgical Care Services
N.A.I.C.S.: 621493

NorthPointe Surgical Suites, LLC (1)
3250 Northpointe Dr, Zanesville, OH 43701
Tel.: (740) 487-1823
Web Site: https://www.northpointess.com
Surgical Care Services
N.A.I.C.S.: 621493

Northern Michigan Surgical Suites, LLC (1)
825 Moll Dr, Boyne City, MI 49712
Tel.: (231) 497-1031
Web Site: https://northmichiganss.com
Outpatient Surgical Services
N.A.I.C.S.: 621498

Northwest Regional Surgery Center, LLC (1)
8900 Broadway Ste 110W, Merrillville, IN 46410
Tel.: (219) 576-6260
Web Site: https://www.nwregionalsc.com
Surgical Care Services
N.A.I.C.S.: 621493

Northwest Surgery Center, Ltd (1)
11111 Research Blvd Ste LL3, Austin, TX 78759
Tel.: (512) 349-4004
Web Site: https://northwestsc.com
General Medical & Surgical Services
N.A.I.C.S.: 622110

Oklahoma Center for Orthopedic and Multi-Specialty Surgery, LLC (1)
8100 S Walker Ave Bldg C, Oklahoma City, OK 73139
Tel.: (405) 602-6500
Web Site: https://ocomhospital.com
General Medical & Surgical Services
N.A.I.C.S.: 622110

Onyx & Pearl Surgical Suites, LLC (1)
465 N Cleveland Ave Ste 150, Westerville, OH 43082
Tel.: (614) 918-0030
Web Site: https://onyxandpearlss.com
Surgical Center Services
N.A.I.C.S.: 622110

Ophthalmology Surgery Center of Orlando, LLC (1)
105 Bonnie Loch Ct, Orlando, FL 32806
Tel.: (407) 428-0040
Web Site: https://orlandosc.com
General Medical & Surgical Services
N.A.I.C.S.: 622110

Optimum Spine Center, LLC (1)
5555 Peachtree Dunwoody Rd Ste G-99, Atlanta, GA 30342
Tel.: (678) 539-6575
Web Site: https://optimumspinecenter.com
General Medical & Surgical Services
N.A.I.C.S.: 622110

OrNda Hospital Corporation (1)
1445 Ross Ave, Dallas, TX 75202
Tel.: (469) 893-2200
Web Site: http://www.tenethealth.com
Sales Range: $50-74.9 Million
Emp.: 800
Hospital
N.A.I.C.S.: 622110

Tenet Healthcare Corporation—(Continued)

Subsidiary (Domestic):

Coral Gables Hospital, Inc. (2)
3100 Douglas Rd, Coral Gables, FL 33134
Tel.: (305) 445-8461
Web Site:
  http://www.coralgableshospital.com
Hospital
N.A.I.C.S.: 622110
Jonathan Fraginals (Dir)
Cristina Jimenez (CEO)
Denise Hernandez-Figueroa (Chief Nursing Officer)
Pedro Iriarte (Dir)
David Araya (Dir-Strategy)
Christina Garcia (Compliance Officer)
Sergio Alvarez (Dir)
Junior Maldonado (Dir)
Carlos J. Rodriguez (Supvr)

Subsidiary (Domestic):

CGH Hospital, Ltd. (3)
3100 Douglas Rd, Coral Gables, FL 33134-6914
Tel.: (305) 445-8461
Health Care Srvices
N.A.I.C.S.: 621999

Subsidiary (Domestic):

Lake Pointe Partners, Ltd. (2)
6800 Science Dr, Rowlett, TX 75088
Tel.: (972) 412-2273
Web Site:
  http://www.lakepointemedicalpartners.com
Medical Devices
N.A.I.C.S.: 622110

Subsidiary (Domestic):

Lake Pointe Operating Company, L.L.C. (3)
301 N Washinton Ave, Dallas, TX 75246
Tel.: (972) 412-2273
Web Site: https://www.bswhealth.com
Medical Devices
N.A.I.C.S.: 622110
Brett Lee (CEO)

Subsidiary (Domestic):

Billing Center Lake Pointe Medical, L.L.C. (4)
6800 Scenic Dr, Rowlett, TX 75088-4552
Tel.: (972) 412-2273
Health Care Srvices
N.A.I.C.S.: 621999

Subsidiary (Domestic):

Newhope Imaging Center, Inc. (2)
11190 Warner Ave Ste 110, Fountain Valley, CA 92708
Tel.: (714) 431-0303
Web Site: http://www.newhopeimaging.net
Radiological Services
N.A.I.C.S.: 621111

Saint Vincent Hospital, L.L.C. (2)
123 Summer St, Worcester, MA 01608
Tel.: (508) 363-5000
Web Site: https://www.stvincenthospital.com
Sales Range: $100-124.9 Million
Emp.: 2,200
Hospital
N.A.I.C.S.: 622110
Peter C. Lindblad (Chm)
Peter Beaulieu (Dir-Mission Integration & Pastoral Care)
Carolyn Jackson (CEO)
Bogdan Nedelescu (Pres)
George Abraham (Treas)
John Whitlock (CFO)
Darrin Cook (COO)
Jay Prosser (Chief Nursing Officer)
Christian Bartholomew (Chief HR Officer)

Orange Park Endoscopy Center, LLC (1)
805 Wells Rd 1st Fl, Orange Park, FL 32073
Tel.: (904) 643-3326
Web Site:
  https://orangeparkendoscopycenter.com
Surgical Center Services
N.A.I.C.S.: 622110

Orlando Outpatient Center for Surgery, LLC (1)
1736 33rd St, Orlando, FL 32839
Tel.: (407) 385-1555
Web Site: https://orlandooutpatientasc.com
Outpatient Surgical Services
N.A.I.C.S.: 621498

Oro Valley Surgical Suites, LLC (1)
8500 N Oracle Rd Ste 150, Oro Valley, AZ 85704
Tel.: (520) 462-0220
Web Site: https://orovalleyss.com
Outpatient Surgical Services
N.A.I.C.S.: 621498

OrthoArizona Surgery Center Gilbert, LLC (1)
1675 E Melrose St Ste 201, Gilbert, AZ 85297
Tel.: (602) 772-3800
General Medical & Surgical Services
N.A.I.C.S.: 622110

Palm Beach International Surgery Center, LLC (1)
5325 Greenwood Ave Ste 301, West Palm Beach, FL 33407
Tel.: (561) 273-4333
Web Site:
  https://palmbeachinternationalsurgery center.com
General Medical & Surgical Services
N.A.I.C.S.: 622110

Palos Health Surgery Center, LLC (1)
15300 W Ave Ste 260 Main Entrance 1 Elevator A, Orland Park, IL 60462
Tel.: (708) 981-3660
Web Site:
  https://www.paloshealthsurgerycenter.com
Surgical Center Services
N.A.I.C.S.: 621493

ParkCreek ASC, LLC (1)
6806 N State Rd 7, Coconut Creek, FL 33073
Tel.: (954) 312-3500
Web Site: http://parkcreeksurgery.com
Surgical Center Services
N.A.I.C.S.: 621493

Parkway Recovery Care Center, LLC (1)
100 N Green Valley Pkwy Ste 330, Henderson, NV 89074
Tel.: (702) 826-5801
Web Site:
  https://parkwayrecoverycarecenter.com
General Medical & Surgical Services
N.A.I.C.S.: 622110

Physician's Surgery Center of Chattanooga, L.L.C. (1)
924 Spring Creek Rd, Chattanooga, TN 37412
Tel.: (423) 899-1600
Web Site: https://www.psc-chattanooga.com
Emp.: 33
Health Care Srvices
N.A.I.C.S.: 622110

Physicians Surgery Center of Tempe, LLC (1)
1940 E Southern Ave, Tempe, AZ 85282
Tel.: (480) 820-7101
Web Site: http://www.tempesc.com
Health Care Srvices
N.A.I.C.S.: 621493
Harriet McFadden (Dir-Medical)
Blue Haught (Dir-Clinical)
Suzanne Rayl (Office Mgr-Bus)

Piccard Surgery Center, LLC (1)
1330 Piccard Dr Ste 102, Rockville, MD 20850
Tel.: (301) 208-7350
Web Site:
  https://www.piccardsurgcenter.com
Surgery Services
N.A.I.C.S.: 621493

Piedmont Physician Network, LLC (1)
200 S Herlong Ave Ste C, Rock Hill, SC 29732
Tel.: (803) 323-5795
Web Site: https://www.piedmontphysiciannet work.com

General Medical & Surgical Services
N.A.I.C.S.: 622110

Piedmont/Carolinas Radiation Therapy, LLC (1)
228 S Herlong Ave, Rock Hill, SC 29732-1158
Tel.: (803) 366-5186
Health Care Srvices
N.A.I.C.S.: 622110

Potomac View Surgery Center, LLC (1)
6710 Oxon Hill Rd Ste 150, Oxon Hill, MD 20745
Tel.: (240) 766-2734
Web Site: https://www.potomacviewsc.com
Surgical Care Services
N.A.I.C.S.: 621493

Premier ACO Physicians Network, LLC (1)
10833 Valley View St Ste 300, Cypress, CA 90630
Tel.: (832) 353-7777
Web Site: http://www.premieraco.com
Health Care Srvices
N.A.I.C.S.: 622110
Khalid Saeed (Dir-Medical)
Lisa Crutchfield (Compliance Officer)
Rodney Farrar (Officer-Quality Assurance & Improvement)

Premier Endoscopy ASC, LLC (1)
2563 S Val Vista Dr Ste 101, Gilbert, AZ 85295
Tel.: (480) 786-6655
Health Care Srvices
N.A.I.C.S.: 622110

Premier at Exton Surgery Center LLC (1)
491 John Young Way Ste 100, Exton, PA 19341
Tel.: (484) 872-8408
Web Site: https://premierexton.com
Outpatient Surgical Services
N.A.I.C.S.: 621498

Prince Frederick Surgery Center, LLC (1)
70 Sherry Ln Ste 101, Prince Frederick, MD 20678
Tel.: (443) 486-4230
Web Site: https://princefredericksc.com
Outpatient Surgical Services
N.A.I.C.S.: 621498

Prince William Ambulatory Surgery Center, LLC (1)
8644 Sudley Rd Ste 201, Manassas, VA 20110
Tel.: (703) 369-8525
Web Site: http://pwasc.org
Medical Clinic Services
N.A.I.C.S.: 621111

Radsource, LLC (1)
750 Old Hickory Blvd Ste 1-260, Brentwood, TN 37027
Tel.: (615) 376-7502
Web Site: https://www.radsource.us
Health Care Srvices
N.A.I.C.S.: 622110
Mark H. Awh (Pres)
Jeffrey W. Carden (COO)
Michelle Whitlock (Dir-Ops)
Melanie Meadows (Mktg Dir)
Leon R. Toye (Dir-Medical)
Michael E. Stadnick (Dir-Medical)
Michael Bragg (Dir-Sys-Technology)
Marc Potvin (Chief Dev Officer)
Christopher D. Logue (Sr Engr)

Reagan Street Surgery Center, L.L.C. (1)
10904 Reagan St, Los Alamitos, CA 90720
Tel.: (562) 596-3140
Web Site:
  https://reaganstreetsurgerycenter.com
General Medical & Surgical Services
N.A.I.C.S.: 622110

Red Cedar Surgery Center, LLC (1)
5668 Okemos Rd, Haslett, MI 48840
Tel.: (517) 481-2883
Web Site: https://www.redcedarsc.com
Surgical Care Services
N.A.I.C.S.: 621493

Renaissance Surgery Center, LLC (1)
2365 E Fir Ave, Fresno, CA 93720
Tel.: (559) 797-9100
Web Site: https://www.rscfresno.com
Health Care Services
N.A.I.C.S.: 621999

Resurgens East Surgery Center, LLC (1)
3241 Iris Dr, Covington, GA 30016
Tel.: (678) 712-7624
Web Site: https://www.resurgenseast.com
Health Care Srvices
N.A.I.C.S.: 622110
Randy Newman (Dir-Medical)

Resurgens Fayette Surgery Center, LLC (1)
1336 Hwy 54 W Bldg 400 Ste A, Fayetteville, GA 30214
Tel.: (678) 251-0200
Web Site: https://resurgens-fayette.com
General Medical & Surgical Services
N.A.I.C.S.: 622110

Riva Road Surgery Center, LLC (1)
2635 Riva Rd Ste 118, Annapolis, MD 21401
Tel.: (410) 571-9595
Web Site: https://www.rivaroadsc.com
Surgical Care Services
N.A.I.C.S.: 621493

Riva Road Surgical Center, L.L.C. (1)
2635 Riva Rd Ste 118, Annapolis, MD 21401
Tel.: (410) 571-9595
Web Site: https://rivaroadsc.com
Orthopaedic Surgical Services
N.A.I.C.S.: 621498

Rockville Surgical Suites, LLC (1)
3200 Tower Oaks Blvd Ste 100, Rockville, MD 20852
Tel.: (240) 623-0033
Web Site: https://www.rockvillesc.com
Surgical Care Services
N.A.I.C.S.: 621493

SFMPE - Crittenden, L.L.C. (1)
1445 Ross Ave Ste 1400, Dallas, TX 75202
Tel.: (870) 400-0433
Health Care Srvices
N.A.I.C.S.: 622110

SLH Vista, Inc. (1)
3635 Vista Ave, Saint Louis, MO 63110
Tel.: (314) 577-8000
Medical Healthcare Services
N.A.I.C.S.: 622110

Subsidiary (Domestic):

SLH Physicians, L.L.C. (2)
3635 Vista Ave, Saint Louis, MO 63110
Tel.: (314) 577-8007
Health Care Srvices
N.A.I.C.S.: 621999

SLUH Anesthesia Physicians, L.L.C. (2)
3635 Vista Ave, Saint Louis, MO 63110
Tel.: (314) 577-8000
Health Care Srvices
N.A.I.C.S.: 621999

SMSJ Tucson Holdings, LLC (1)
350 N Wilmot Rd, Tucson, AZ 85711
Tel.: (520) 872-3000
Holding Company
N.A.I.C.S.: 551112

Saint Francis Hospital Medicare ACO, LLC (1)
6005 Park Ave, Memphis, TN 38119
Tel.: (901) 765-2391
Web Site: https://www.saintfrancisaco.com
Health Care Srvices
N.A.I.C.S.: 621999
Staci Taylor (Chief HR Officer)
Cheryl Garth (Officer-Compliance)
David Schwartz (Chief Medical Officer-)
Ryan Nelson (CFO-)
Cameron Murphy (Chief Nursing Officer)
Mose Franck (COO)
Scott Smith (CEO)

Salmon Surgery Center, LLC (1)

2200 NW Myhre Rd Ste 102, Silverdale,
WA 98383
Tel.: (360) 340-9993
Web Site: https://salmonsurgerycenter.com
General Medical & Surgical Services
N.A.I.C.S.: 622110

Same Day SC of Central NJ,
LLC **(1)**
225 May St Unit C, Edison, NJ 08837
Tel.: (732) 661-0570
Web Site:
    https://samedaysurgerycentraljersey.com
General Medical & Surgical Services
N.A.I.C.S.: 622110

San Fernando Valley Surgery Center,
L.P. **(1)**
11550 Indian Hills Rd, Mission Hills, CA
91345
Tel.: (818) 256-2100
Web Site: https://www.providence.org
Health Care Srvices
N.A.I.C.S.: 622110

Santa Barbara Outpatient Surgery
Center, LLC **(1)**
3045 De La Vina St, Santa Barbara, CA
93105-3351
Tel.: (805) 569-3226
Web Site:
    https://www.santabarbarasurgerycen
    ter.com
Health Care Srvices
N.A.I.C.S.: 622110

Scottsdale Endoscopy ASC, LLC **(1)**
9787 N 91st St Ste 103, Scottsdale, AZ
85258
Tel.: (480) 657-0889
Web Site:
    https://www.scottsdaleendoscopycen
    ter.com
Endoscopy Care Services
N.A.I.C.S.: 621111

Seaside Surgery Center, LLC **(1)**
1879 Veterans Park Dr Ste 1101, Naples,
FL 34109
Tel.: (239) 592-4955
Web Site:
    https://www.seasidesurgerycenter.com
Surgical Care Services
N.A.I.C.S.: 621493
Robert J. Zehr (CEO & Dir-Medical)
H. Kurtis Biggs (Treas)
Steven S. Goldberg (COO)

Select Physicians Surgery Center,
LLC **(1)**
3440 W Dr Martin Luther King Jr Blvd Ste
103, Tampa, FL 33607
Tel.: (813) 321-1618
Web Site:
    https://selectphysicianssurgerycenter.com
Outpatient Surgical Services
N.A.I.C.S.: 621498

Shelby Baptist Ambulatory Surgery
Center, LLC **(1)**
1010 1st St Ste 140, Alabaster, AL 35007
Tel.: (205) 620-8400
Web Site: https://www.shelbyasc.com
Ambulatory Health Care Services
N.A.I.C.S.: 621493

Silver Cross Ambulatory Surgery
Center, LLC **(1)**
1003 Pawlak Pkwy, New Lenox, IL 60451
Tel.: (815) 717-1740
Web Site:
    https://www.silvercrosssurgerycenter.com
Health Care Srvices
N.A.I.C.S.: 622110

Silver Cross/USP Surgery Center,
LLC **(1)**
1003 Pawlak Pkwy, New Lenox, IL 60451
Tel.: (815) 717-1740
Web Site:
    https://silvercrosssurgerycenter.com
Outpatient Surgical Services
N.A.I.C.S.: 621498

South Plains Endoscopy Associates,
LLC **(1)**
3610 24th St, Lubbock, TX 79410
Tel.: (806) 454-7302
Health Care Srvices

N.A.I.C.S.: 621111

South Suburban Surgical Suites,
LLC **(1)**
9200 Calumet Ave Ste E100, Munster, IN
46321
Tel.: (219) 595-0601
Web Site:
    https://southsuburbansurgicalsuites.com
Health Care Srvices
N.A.I.C.S.: 621999

Southeast Ohio Surgical Suites,
LLC **(1)**
20 University Estates Blvd Ste 110, Athens,
OH 45701
Tel.: (740) 589-7710
Web Site:
    https://southeastohiosurgicalsuites.com
General Medical & Surgical Services
N.A.I.C.S.: 622110

Southwest Endoscopy, LLC **(1)**
2223 E Baseline Rd Ste B, Gilbert, AZ
85234
Tel.: (480) 289-5266
Web Site: https://swendoscopy.com
General Medical & Surgical Services
N.A.I.C.S.: 622110

Spicewood Surgery Center LLC **(1)**
13617 Caldwell Dr Ste 200, Austin, TX
78750
Tel.: (512) 637-5563
Web Site: https://spicewoodsurgery.com
Outpatient Surgical Services
N.A.I.C.S.: 621498

St. Augustine Endoscopy Center,
LLC **(1)**
40 Groover Loop Ste 100, Saint Augustine,
FL 32086
Tel.: (904) 824-6108
Web Site:
    https://staugustineendoscopycenter.com
General Medical & Surgical Services
N.A.I.C.S.: 622110

Stark Ambulatory Surgery Center,
LLC **(1)**
4360 Fulton Dr NW Ste C Lower Level,
Canton, OH 44718
Tel.: (330) 305-2020
Surgical Center Services
N.A.I.C.S.: 622110

Summit Ambulatory Surgical Center,
L.L.C. **(1)**
810 Bestgate Rd Ste 200, Annapolis, MD
21401
Tel.: (443) 231-1500
Outpatient Surgical Services
N.A.I.C.S.: 622110

SurgCenter Camelback, LLC **(1)**
6245 N 24th Pkwy, Phoenix, AZ 85016
Tel.: (602) 682-7005
Web Site:
    http://www.surgcentercamelback.com
Surgical Care Services
N.A.I.C.S.: 621493

SurgCenter Northeast, LLC **(1)**
2438 Dr Martin Luther King Jr St N Ste C,
Saint Petersburg, FL 33704
Tel.: (727) 565-0740
Web Site: https://www.scnortheast.com
Surgical Care Services
N.A.I.C.S.: 621493

SurgCenter Pinellas, LLC **(1)**
12416 66th St N, Largo, FL 33733
Tel.: (727) 408-5310
Web Site: https://scpinellas.com
Surgical Care Services
N.A.I.C.S.: 621493

SurgCenter Tucson, LLC **(1)**
3945 E Fort Lowell, Tucson, AZ 85712
Tel.: (520) 396-4420
Hospital Services
N.A.I.C.S.: 621111

SurgCenter at Paradise Valley,
LLC **(1)**
8415 N Pima Rd Ste 190, Scottsdale, AZ
85258
Tel.: (480) 800-3200
Web Site: https://www.scpimacrossing.com
Surgical Care Services

N.A.I.C.S.: 621493

SurgCenter of Glen Burnie, LLC **(1)**
308 Hospital Dr Ste 102, Glen Burnie, MD
21061
Tel.: (410) 760-8100
Web Site: https://scglenburnie.com
Surgical Center Services
N.A.I.C.S.: 622110

SurgCenter of Greater Jacksonville,
LLC **(1)**
9143 Philips Hwy Ste 500, Jacksonville, FL
32256
Tel.: (904) 586-8540
Web Site: https://www.scgjacksonville.com
Surgical Care Services
N.A.I.C.S.: 621493

SurgCenter of Northern Baltimore,
LLC **(1)**
215 Schilling Cir Ste 110-112, Hunt Valley,
MD 21031
Tel.: (410) 657-8008
Web Site: https://www.scnorthbaltimore.com
Surgical Care Services
N.A.I.C.S.: 621493

SurgCenter of Palm Beach Gardens,
LLC **(1)**
900 Village Square Crossing Ste 100, Palm
Beach Gardens, FL 33410
Tel.: (561) 429-6880
Web Site: https://www.surgpalmbeach.com
Surgical Care Services
N.A.I.C.S.: 621493

SurgCenter of Plano, LLC **(1)**
6101 Windhaven Pkwy Ste 195, Plano, TX
75093
Tel.: (469) 209-7054
Web Site: https://surgcenterofplano.net
General Medical & Surgical Services
N.A.I.C.S.: 622110

SurgCenter of Silver Spring, LLC **(1)**
8710 Cameron St Ste 100, Silver Spring,
MD 20910
Tel.: (301) 326-2921
Web Site: https://www.scsilverspring.com
Surgical Care Services
N.A.I.C.S.: 621493

SurgCenter of Southern Maryland,
LLC **(1)**
9001 Woodyard Rd Ste B, Clinton, MD
20735
Tel.: (301) 868-4950
Web Site: https://www.scsouthmd.com
Surgical Care Services
N.A.I.C.S.: 621493

SurgCenter of St. Lucie, LLC **(1)**
10521 SW Village Center Dr Ste 104, Port
Saint Lucie, FL 34987
Tel.: (772) 345-8600
Web Site: https://www.scstlucie.com
Surgical Care Services
N.A.I.C.S.: 621493

SurgCenter of White Marsh, LLC **(1)**
11605 Crossroads Cir Ste A, Baltimore, MD
21220
Tel.: (410) 344-0003
Web Site: https://www.whitemarshsc.com
Surgical Care Services
N.A.I.C.S.: 621493

SurgCenter of the Potomac, LLC **(1)**
Bedford Bldg 6500 Rock Spring Dr Ste 100,
Bethesda, MD 20817
Tel.: (240) 483-0282
Web Site: https://scpotomac.com
General Medical & Surgical Services
N.A.I.C.S.: 622110

Surge Center of Glen Burnie
LLC **(1)**
308 Hospital Dr Ste 102, Glen Burnie, MD
21061
Tel.: (410) 760-8100
Web Site: https://www.scglenburnie.com
Surgical Care Services
N.A.I.C.S.: 621493

Surgery Centre of SW Florida,
LLC **(1)**
12631 Whitehall Dr, Fort Myers, FL 33907
Tel.: (239) 337-7874

Web Site:
    http://www.surgerycenterofswfl.com
Health Care Srvices
N.A.I.C.S.: 622110

Surgical Specialty Center of Mid-
Atlantic, LLC **(1)**
6430 Rockledge Dr Ste 110, Bethesda, MD
20817
Tel.: (240) 630-8241
Web Site: https://www.ssmidatlantic.com
Surgical Center Services
N.A.I.C.S.: 622110

Tampa Bay Joint & Spine, LLC **(1)**
26034 US Hwy 19 N, Clearwater, FL 33763
Tel.: (727) 371-2500
Web Site: https://www.tampa-bay.steadfa.st
Surgical Care Services
N.A.I.C.S.: 621493

Tenet HealthSystem Medical,
Inc. **(1)**
14201 Dallas Pkwy, Dallas, TX
75254 **(100%)**
Tel.: (469) 893-2000
Web Site: http://www.tenthealth.com
Hospitals & Related Healthcare Facilities
N.A.I.C.S.: 622110

Subsidiary (Domestic):

Amisub (SFH), Inc. **(2)**
5959 Park Ave, Memphis, TN 38119
Tel.: (901) 765-1000
Web Site: http://www.saintfransis.com
Healtcare Services
N.A.I.C.S.: 621610

Subsidiary (Domestic):

Saint Francis Hospital Billing Center,
L.L.C. **(3)**
5959 Park Ave, Memphis, TN 38119
Tel.: (901) 765-1000
Health Care Srvices
N.A.I.C.S.: 621999
Trevor Fetter (Pres)

Saint Francis Surgery Center,
L.L.C. **(3)**
5999 Park Ave, Memphis, TN 38119-5200
Tel.: (901) 818-1080
Web Site:
    https://www.saintfrancissurgerycenter.com
Medical Devices
N.A.I.C.S.: 622110

Subsidiary (Domestic):

Bluffton Okatie Primary Care,
L.L.C. **(2)**
40 Okatie Center Blvd S Ste 100, Okatie,
SC 29909
Tel.: (843) 256-3634
Web Site:
    https://www.blufftonokatieprimarycare.com
Sales Range: $10-24.9 Million
Medical Devices
N.A.I.C.S.: 622110

Broad River Primary Care, L.L.C. **(2)**
35 Bill Fries Dr Island Medical Plz Bldg A,
Hilton Head Island, SC 29926-2730
Tel.: (843) 682-7470
Medical Devices
N.A.I.C.S.: 622110

Brookwood Center Development
Corporation **(2)**
2010 Brookwood Medical Ctr Dr, Birming-
ham, AL 35209
Tel.: (205) 877-1000
Web Site:
    http://www.brookwoodbaptisthealth.com
Emp.: 9
General Medical Services
N.A.I.C.S.: 622110
Greg Johnston (CFO)

Subsidiary (Domestic):

Alabama Digestive Health Endoscopy
Center, L.L.C. **(3)**
2010 Brookwood Medical Center Dr Ste G
100, Birmingham, AL 35209
Tel.: (205) 877-1187
Web Site: http://www.adhec.net
Health Care Srvices
N.A.I.C.S.: 621999

Tenet Healthcare Corporation—(Continued)

BWP Associates, Ltd. (3)
872 S Milwaukee Ave Ste 221, Libertyville, IL 60048
Tel.: (708) 361-4997
Web Site: https://www.bwpassociates.com
Health Care Srvices
N.A.I.C.S.: 621999
Mark Friedman (Pres)
Debra A. Hill (Mng Dir)

Brookwood Home Health, LLC (3)
2010 Brookwood Medical Ctr Dr, Birmingham, AL 35209
Tel.: (205) 877-1000
Web Site: http://www.bwmc.com
Health Care Srvices
N.A.I.C.S.: 621999

Medplex Outpatient Surgery Center, Ltd. (3)
4511 Southlake Pkwy, Birmingham, AL 35244
Tel.: (205) 985-4398
Health Care Srvices
N.A.I.C.S.: 621999

Subsidiary (Domestic):

Brookwood Health Services, Inc. (2)
2010 Brookwood Medical Ctr Dr, Birmingham, AL 35209
Tel.: (205) 877-1000
Web Site: http://www.bwmc.com
Sales Range: $250-299.9 Million
Emp.: 2,500
Healtcare Services
N.A.I.C.S.: 622110
Jeremy Clark (CEO-)
Colin Weaver (COO)
Jackie Martinek (Chief Nursing Officer)
David Roebuck (CFO)

Burnt Church Primary & Urgent Care, L.L.C. (2)
1 Burnt Church Rd, Bluffton, SC 29910-6405
Tel.: (843) 757-9229
Health Care Srvices
N.A.I.C.S.: 621999

Catawba-Piedmont Cardiothoracic Surgery, L.L.C. (2)
197 Piedmont Blvd Ste 100, Rock Hill, SC 29732
Tel.: (803) 324-1950
Web Site: http://piedmontcardiovascularsurgery.com
Medical Devices
N.A.I.C.S.: 622110

Coastal Carolina Medical Center, Inc. (2)
1000 Medical Ctr Dr, Hardeeville, SC 29927
Tel.: (843) 784-8000
Web Site: http://www.coastalhospital.com
Health Care Srvices
N.A.I.C.S.: 621999

East Cooper Community Hospital, Inc. (2)
2000 Hospital Dr, Mount Pleasant, SC 29464
Tel.: (843) 881-0100
Web Site: http://www.eastcoopermedctr.com
Emp.: 500
Health Care Srvices
N.A.I.C.S.: 621999
Rodly Millet (Chm)

Subsidiary (Domestic):

The Southeastern Spine Institute Surgery Center, L.L.C. (3)
1625 Hospital Dr, Mount Pleasant, SC 29464
Tel.: (843) 849-1551
Web Site: https://www.southeasternspine.com
Emp.: 200
Health Care Srvices
N.A.I.C.S.: 621999
R. N. Karen Blakely (Dir-Clinical Ops)

Subsidiary (Domestic):

Good Samaritan Medical Center, Inc. (2)

1309 N Flagler Dr, West Palm Beach, FL 33401
Tel.: (561) 655-5511
Web Site: https://www.goodsamaritanmc.com
Emp.: 1,200
Medical Devices
N.A.I.C.S.: 622110
Sheri Montgomery (CEO)
Kevin Caracciolo (Chief HR Officer)
Taylor Guittap (CFO)
Michele Thoman (COO)
Colleen Thielk (Chief Nursing Officer)
Libby Flippo (Chief Nursing Officer--Palm Beach Health Network)

Heritage Medical Group of Hilton Head, L.L.C. (2)
460 William Hilton Pkwy, Hilton Head Island, SC 29926
Tel.: (843) 681-5305
Health Care Srvices
N.A.I.C.S.: 621999

Hilton Head Health System, L.P. (2)
25 Hospital Center Blvd, Hilton Head Island, SC 29926
Tel.: (843) 681-6122
Web Site: https://www.hiltonheadregional.com
Health Care Srvices
N.A.I.C.S.: 621610

Hilton Head Regional OB/GYN Partners, L.L.C. (2)
25 Hospital Center Blvd Ste 305, Hilton Head Island, SC 29926
Tel.: (843) 580-3608
Web Site: http://hiltonheadobgyn.com
Emp.: 12
Medical Devices
N.A.I.C.S.: 622110

Houston Specialty Hospital, Inc. (2)
1313 Hermann Dr, Houston, TX 77004
Tel.: (713) 285-1000
Web Site: http://www.hcahoustonhealthcare.com
Health Care Srvices
N.A.I.C.S.: 621999

Imaging Center at Baxter Village, L.L.C. (2)
509 6th Baxter Crossing, Fort Mill, SC 29708
Tel.: (803) 802-4949
Web Site: https://www.piedmontmedicalcenter.com
Medical Devices
N.A.I.C.S.: 622110

Irvine Regional Hospital & Medical Center (2)
16200 Sand Canyon Rd, Irvine, CA 92618
Tel.: (949) 753-2000
Web Site: http://www.irvineregionalhospital.com
Sales Range: $50-74.9 Million
Hospital
N.A.I.C.S.: 622110

Magnetic Resonance Imaging of San Luis Obispo, Inc. (2)
77 Casa St Ste 102 Selma A Carlson Diagnostic Ctr, San Luis Obispo, CA 93405
Tel.: (805) 546-7733
Medical Imaging Services
N.A.I.C.S.: 621512

Mid-Island Primary & Urgent Care, L.L.C. (2)
50 Shelter Cove Ln Ste L, Hilton Head Island, SC 29928-3571
Tel.: (843) 681-2074
Health Care Srvices
N.A.I.C.S.: 621999

Okatie Surgical Partners, L.L.C. (2)
75 Baylor Dr Ste 290, Bluffton, SC 29910
Tel.: (843) 558-8428
Web Site: https://www.okatiesurgical.com
Sales Range: $10-24.9 Million
Emp.: 12
Healtcare Services
N.A.I.C.S.: 622110

Orthopedic Associates of the Lowcountry, L.L.C. (2)
22 Bethea Dr, Hilton Head Island, SC 29926

Tel.: (843) 547-0183
Web Site: https://hhiorthopedics.com
Sales Range: $10-24.9 Million
Medical Devices
N.A.I.C.S.: 622110

PMC Physician Network, L.L.C. (2)
1190 Filbert Hwy Ste 110, York, SC 29745
Tel.: (803) 994-9272
Web Site: https://piedmontwesturgentcare.com
Sales Range: $10-24.9 Million
Emp.: 2
Healtcare Services
N.A.I.C.S.: 622110

Palm Beach Gardens Community Hospital, Inc. (2)
3360 Burns Rd, Palm Beach Gardens, FL 33410
Tel.: (561) 622-1411
Web Site: http://www.pbgmc.com
Sales Range: $50-74.9 Million
Hospital
N.A.I.C.S.: 622110
Marian Jones (Chief HR Officer)
Tiffany Berry (CFO)
Naomi Seymour (Chief Nursing Officer)
Libby Flippo (CEO)

Physician Performance Network of Georgia, L.L.C. (2)
340 Blvd NE Ste 101, Atlanta, GA 30312-1278
Tel.: (404) 265-4346
Web Site: http://www.ppnga.com
Health Care Srvices
N.A.I.C.S.: 621999

Piedmont Behavioral Medicine Associates, L.L.C. (2)
200 S Herlong Ave Ste C, Rock Hill, SC 29732
Tel.: (803) 324-3500
Web Site: http://www.pmcphysiciannetwork.com
Healtcare Services
N.A.I.C.S.: 622110

Piedmont Carolina OB/GYN of York County, L.L.C. (2)
360 S Herlong Ave, Rock Hill, SC 29732
Tel.: (803) 399-7430
Web Site: https://www.carolinaobgynrockhill.com
Sales Range: $10-24.9 Million
Medical Devices
N.A.I.C.S.: 622110

Piedmont East Urgent Care Center, L.L.C. (2)
760 Addison Ave, Rock Hill, SC 29730
Tel.: (803) 329-1930
Web Site: http://www.piedmonteasturgentcare.com
Sales Range: $10-24.9 Million
Emp.: 10
Medical Devices
N.A.I.C.S.: 622110
Louis Glynn (Mgr)

Piedmont Family Practice at Rock Hill, L.L.C. (2)
2633 Celanese Rd, Rock Hill, SC 29732
Tel.: (803) 258-0948
Web Site: https://www.piedmontfpatrockhill.com
Sales Range: $10-24.9 Million
Medical Devices
N.A.I.C.S.: 622110

Piedmont Family Practice at Tega Cay, L.L.C. (2)
773 Stockbridge Dr, Fort Mill, SC 29708
Tel.: (803) 339-9279
Web Site: https://www.piedmontfpategacay.com
Sales Range: $10-24.9 Million
Emp.: 10
Medical Devices
N.A.I.C.S.: 622110

Piedmont Urgent Care Center at Baxter Village, L.L.C. (2)
502 6th Baxter Crossing, Fort Mill, SC 29708
Tel.: (803) 339-9359
Web Site: https://www.piedmonturgentcarebaxter.com
Surgical Care Services

Piedmont West Urgent Care Center LLC (2)
1190 Filbert Hwy Ste 110, York, SC 29745
Tel.: (803) 628-0004
Web Site: https://www.piedmontphysiciannetwork.com
Emp.: 15
Medical Devices
N.A.I.C.S.: 622110

Piedmont/Carolina (2)
228 S Herlong Ave, Rock Hill, SC 29732-1158
Tel.: (803) 366-5186
Medical Devices
N.A.I.C.S.: 622110

Saint Francis Hospital-Bartlett, Inc. (2)
2986 Kate Bond Rd, Bartlett, TN 38133
Tel.: (901) 820-7000
Web Site: http://www.saintfrancisbartlett.com
Hospital
N.A.I.C.S.: 622110
Tina Kovacs (CFO-Market)
Chris Jenkins (COO)
Jacquelyn Whobrey (Co-Chief Nursing Officer)
David Schwartz (Chief Medical Officer-Market)
Cheryl Garth (Compliance Officer)
Scott Smith (CEO)
Ryan Nelson (CFO-)

St. Mary's Medical Center, Inc. (2)
2900 1st Ave, Huntington, WV 25702
Tel.: (304) 526-1234
Web Site: https://www.st-marys.org
Emp.: 2,600
Medical Devices
N.A.I.C.S.: 622110
Denver Hopkins (Chief HR Officer)
Michelle Cartwright (CFO)
Libby Flippo (Chief Nurse Officer)

Subsidiary (Domestic):

The Heart and Vascular Clinic, L.L.C. (3)
927 45th St Ste 204, West Palm Beach, FL 33407-2450
Tel.: (561) 844-6300
Health Care Srvices
N.A.I.C.S.: 621999

Subsidiary (Domestic):

Surgicare of Miramar, L.L.C. (2)
14601 SW 29th St Ste 301, Miramar, FL 33027
Tel.: (954) 266-3801
Web Site: https://www.surgicaremiramar.com
Emp.: 20
Health Care Srvices
N.A.I.C.S.: 621999

Tenet Hilton Head Heart, L.L.C. (2)
25 Hospital Ctr Blvd Ste 300, Hilton Head Island, SC 29926
Tel.: (843) 682-2800
Web Site: http://hhheart.com
Health Care Srvices
N.A.I.C.S.: 621999

Tenet South Carolina Island Medical, L.L.C. (2)
880 Island Park Dr Ste 200 Daniel Island, Charleston, SC 29492-8500
Tel.: (843) 856-1771
Web Site: http://islandmedicalspamd.com
Healtcare Services
N.A.I.C.S.: 622110

Tenet South Carolina Lowcountry OB/GYN, L.L.C. (2)
851 Leonard Fulghum Blvd Ste 101, Mount Pleasant, SC 29464-3261
Tel.: (843) 884-5133
Web Site: http://lcobgyn.com
Sales Range: $10-24.9 Million
Medical Devices
N.A.I.C.S.: 622110

Texas Endoscopy Centers, LLC (1)

8080 Independence Pkwy Ste 160, Plano,
TX 75025
Tel.: (972) 908-3000
Web Site: https://texasendo.com
General Medical & Surgical Services
N.A.I.C.S.: 622110

Texas Spine and Joint Hospital,
LLC   (1)
1814 Roseland Blvd Ste 100, Tyler, TX
75701
Tel.: (903) 525-3300
Web Site: https://www.tsjh.org
Health Care Srvices
N.A.I.C.S.: 622110
Greg Cummings (CFO)

The Healthcare Underwriting Com-
pany, a Risk Retention Group   (1)
100 Bank St Ste 610, Burlington, VT 05401
Tel.: (802) 864-5599
Insurance Management Services
N.A.I.C.S.: 524298

The Surgery Center at Jensen
Beach, LLC   (1)
3995 NW Goldenrod Rd, Jensen Beach, FL
34957
Tel.: (772) 497-0020
Web Site: https://thesurgerycenteratjensen
beach.com
General Medical & Surgical Services
N.A.I.C.S.: 622110

Timonium Surgery Center, LLC   (1)
1954 Greenspring Dr LL18, Timonium, MD
21093
Tel.: (410) 560-3301
Web Site: https://www.timoniumsurg.com
Surgical Care Services
N.A.I.C.S.: 621493

Total Joint Center of the Northland,
LLC   (1)
200 NE 54th St Ste 200, Kansas City, MO
64118
Tel.: (816) 499-8500
Web Site:
https://www.totaljointcenternorthland.com
Health Care Srvices
N.A.I.C.S.: 622110

Trinity Health of New England/USP
Surgery Centers, L.L.C.   (1)
1000 Asylum St, Hartford, CT 06105
Tel.: (860) 714-4425
Web Site: https://www.trinityhealthofne.org
Healtcare Services
N.A.I.C.S.: 621111
Haris Athar (Mng Dir)
James C. Smith (Chm)
JoAnn H. Price (Vice Chm)

U.S. Center for Sports Medicine,
L.L.C.   (1)
333 S Kirkwood Rd Ste 205, Saint Louis,
MO 63122
Tel.: (314) 909-1666
Web Site:
https://www.uscenterforsportsmedi
cine.com
General Medical & Surgical Services
N.A.I.C.S.: 622110

USPI Holding Company, Inc.   (1)
15305 Dallas Pkwy, Addison, TX 75001
Tel.: (972) 713-3500
Holding Company
N.A.I.C.S.: 551112

Subsidiary (Domestic):

AIG Holdings, LLC   (2)
17000 Jeanette St, Southfield, MI 48075
Tel.: (248) 495-4520
Holding Company
N.A.I.C.S.: 551112

ARC Worcester Center L.P.   (2)
300 Grove St, Worcester, MA 01605
Tel.: (508) 754-0700
Web Site:
https://www.worcestersurgicalcenter.com
Health Care Srvices
N.A.I.C.S.: 622110

Advanced Ambulatory Surgical Care,
L.P.   (2)
10448 Old Olive St Rd Ste 100, Creve Coeur, MO 63141

Tel.: (314) 743-8091
Web Site: https://www.advanced-sc.com
Ambulatory Health Care Services
N.A.I.C.S.: 621493

Advanced Surgical Concepts,
LLC   (2)
9118 Bluebonnet Centre Blvd, Baton
Rouge, LA 70809
Tel.: (225) 368-2330
Web Site:
https://www.advancedsurgicalbaton
rouge.com
Ambulatory Health Care Services
N.A.I.C.S.: 621493
Glennis Blade (Office Mgr-Bus)
Kelly Boussert (Dir-Medical)
Christopher Boothe (Dir-Clinical)

AdventHealth Surgery Center Cel-
ebration, LLC   (2)
400 Celebration Pl, Celebration, FL 34747
Tel.: (407) 303-4005
Health Care Srvices
N.A.I.C.S.: 621491

Alamo Heights Surgicare, L.P.   (2)
5307 Broadway Ste 100, San Antonio, TX
78209-5724
Tel.: (210) 826-7366
Health Care Srvices
N.A.I.C.S.: 622110

Ambulatory Surgical Associates,
LLC   (2)
725 Kings Ln, Tullahoma, TN 37388
Tel.: (931) 455-1976
Web Site: https://www.tullahomasc.com
Ambulatory Health Care Services
N.A.I.C.S.: 621493

Ambulatory Surgical Center of
Somerville, LLC   (2)
1 US-206, Somerville, NJ 08876
Tel.: (908) 393-8360
Web Site: https://www.sasctr.com
Ambulatory Health Care Services
N.A.I.C.S.: 621493

Arlington Orthopedic and Spine Hos-
pital, LLC   (2)
707 Highlander Blvd, Arlington, TX 76015
Tel.: (817) 583-7100
Web Site: http://www.baylorarlington.com
Health Care Srvices
N.A.I.C.S.: 622110
Tabitha Lee (CFO)

Arrowhead Endoscopy and Pain
Management Center, LLC   (2)
18699 N 67th Ave Ste 140, Glendale, AZ
85308-7144
Tel.: (623) 376-8600
Web Site: http://www.aepmc.org
Health Care Srvices
N.A.I.C.S.: 622110

Baptist Plaza Surgicare, L.P.   (2)
2004 Hayes St Ste 450, Nashville, TN
37203
Tel.: (615) 515-4000
Web Site: https://stsc-midtown.com
Health Care Srvices
N.A.I.C.S.: 622110

Baptist Surgery Center, L.P.   (2)
312 21st Ave N, Nashville, TN 37203-1846
Tel.: (615) 321-7330
Web Site: https://www.baptistasc.com
Ambulatory Health Care Services
N.A.I.C.S.: 621493

Baylor Surgicare at Ennis, LLC   (2)
2200 Physicians Blvd Ste A, Ennis, TX
75119
Tel.: (972) 875-5538
Health Care Srvices
N.A.I.C.S.: 622110

Baylor Surgicare at Granbury,
LLC   (2)
1717 Paluxy Rd, Granbury, TX 76048
Tel.: (817) 579-8863
Web Site: http://granbury-surgicalplaza.com
Health Care Srvices
N.A.I.C.S.: 622110
Carol Fleck (Office Mgr-Bus)
Sancy Joyce (Dir-Nursing)
Christopher Buchanan (Dir-Medical)

Baylor Surgicare at Mansfield,
LLC   (2)
280 Regency Pkwy, Mansfield, TX 76063
Tel.: (817) 453-2744
Web Site:
https://mansfieldsurgerycenter.com
Health Care Srvices
N.A.I.C.S.: 622110
Jessica Eubanks (Dir-Nursing)
Sam Moffett (Office Mgr-Bus)

Baylor Surgicare at North Dallas,
LLC   (2)
12230 Coit Rd Ste 200, Dallas, TX 75251
Tel.: (469) 374-6400
Web Site:
http://baylorsurgicareatnorthdallas.com
Health Care Srvices
N.A.I.C.S.: 622110
Chanda Thompson (Office Mgr-Bus)

Baylor Surgicare at Plano Parkway,
LLC   (2)
4031 W Plano Pkwy Ste 100, Plano, TX
75093
Tel.: (469) 326-0202
Web Site:
http://www.baylorsurgicareatplanopark
way.com
Health Care Srvices
N.A.I.C.S.: 622110
Alexander I. Glogau (Dir-Medical)
Ana Benavides (Coord-Bus Office)
Katie Huchingson (Dir-Clinical)

Beaumont Surgical Affiliates, Ltd. (2)
3560 College St, Beaumont, TX 77701
Tel.: (409) 835-7070
Web Site: https://www.baptistbsa.com
Emp.: 19
Health Care Srvices
N.A.I.C.S.: 622110

Bellaire Outpatient Surgery Center,
L.L.P.   (2)
7200 Oakmont Blvd, Fort Worth, TX 76132
Tel.: (817) 732-3300
Web Site: https://www.baylorsurgicare-
oakmont.com
Health Care Srvices
N.A.I.C.S.: 622110
Phi Lubrano (Dir-Medical)
Katherine Lawson (Dir-Clinical)
Brandie Senn (Office Mgr-Bus)
Dianna Nguyen (Mgr-Materials)

Bon Secours Surgery Center at Har-
bour View, LLC   (2)
5818 Harbour View Blvd Ste 102, Suffolk,
VA 23435
Tel.: (757) 673-5832
Web Site: https://www.bshv-sc.com
Ambulatory Health Care Services
N.A.I.C.S.: 621493
Lisa Mason (Office Mgr-Bus)

Bon Secours Surgery Center at Vir-
ginia Beach, LLC   (2)
828 Healthy Way Ste 115, Virginia Beach,
VA 23462
Tel.: (757) 495-8070
Web Site:
https://www.bonsecoursambulatory-
sc.com
Ambulatory Health Care Services
N.A.I.C.S.: 621493
Lataya Keene (Dir-Medical)
Terri Farley (Office Mgr-Bus)

Briarcliff Ambulatory Surgery Center,
L.P.   (2)
4150 N Mulberry Dr Ste 100, Kansas City,
MO 64154
Tel.: (816) 214-4364
Web Site: https://www.briarcliff-sc.com
Health Care Srvices
N.A.I.C.S.: 622110

Brookwood Women's Diagnostic Cen-
ter, LLC   (2)
2006 Brookwood Medical Ctr Dr Women's
Medical Ctr Ste 112, Birmingham, AL 35209
Tel.: (205) 802-6900
Web Site:
https://www.brookwoodbaptisthealth.com
Diagnostic Imaging Center Operator
N.A.I.C.S.: 621512

CHRISTUS Cabrini Surgery Center,
L.L.C.   (2)

3436 Masonic Dr, Alexandria, LA 71301
Tel.: (318) 427-6500
Web Site: https://www.christuscabrini-
sc.com
Ambulatory Health Care Services
N.A.I.C.S.: 621493
Denise Bolden (Office Mgr-Bus)
Chrystal Jones (Mgr-Materials)
Gabriel Gregory (Dir-Clinical)

Camp Lowell Surgery Center,
L.L.C.   (2)
4620 E Camp Lowell, Tucson, AZ 85712
Tel.: (520) 618-6058
Web Site:
https://www.camplowellsurgerycenter.com
Ambulatory Health Care Services
N.A.I.C.S.: 621493

Cascade Spine Center, LLC   (2)
6464 Borland Rd Ste A-3, Tualatin, OR
97062
Tel.: (971) 404-3366
Web Site:
https://www.cascadespinecenter.com
Ambulatory Health Care Services
N.A.I.C.S.: 621493
Debbie Snook (Mgr-Bus Office)

Castle Rock Surgery Center,
LLC   (2)
4700 Castleton Way Ste 101, Castle Rock,
CO 80109
Tel.: (720) 519-1418
Web Site: http://castlerocksurgicenter.com
Health Care Srvices
N.A.I.C.S.: 622110

Cedar Park Surgery Center,
L.L.P.   (2)
351 Cypress Creek Rd Ste 102, Cedar
Park, TX 78613
Tel.: (512) 498-9006
Web Site:
https://www.cedarparksurgerycenter.com
Ambulatory Health Care Services
N.A.I.C.S.: 621493

Central Jersey Surgery Center,
LLC   (2)
97 Corbett Way, Eatontown, NJ 07724
Tel.: (732) 460-2777
Web Site: https://www.centraljersey-sc.com
Ambulatory Health Care Services
N.A.I.C.S.: 621493

Central Virginia Surgi-Center,
L.P.   (2)
1500 Dixon St Ste 101, Fredericksburg, VA
22401
Tel.: (540) 371-5349
Web Site: https://www.sccva.com
Ambulatory Health Care Services
N.A.I.C.S.: 621493

Chandler Endoscopy Ambulatory Sur-
gery Center, LLC   (2)
2095 W Pecos Rd Ste 1, Chandler, AZ
85224
Tel.: (480) 292-9795
Web Site: https://www.chandler-endoscopy-
center.com
Diagnostic Imaging Center Operator
N.A.I.C.S.: 621512

Chattanooga Pain Management Cen-
ter, LLC   (2)
1016 Executive Dr, Hixson, TN 37343
Tel.: (423) 648-4525
Web Site: http://chattpainsurg.com
Pain Therapy Center Operator
N.A.I.C.S.: 621498

Chesterfield Ambulatory Surgery Cen-
ter, L.P.   (2)
17050 Baxter Rd Ste 110, Chesterfield, MO
63005
Tel.: (636) 537-0122
Web Site:
https://www.chesterfieldsurgerycenter.com
Ambulatory Health Care Services
N.A.I.C.S.: 621493

Chico Surgery Center, L.P.   (2)
615 W E Ave, Chico, CA 95926
Tel.: (530) 895-1800
Web Site: http://www.chicosc.com
Ambulatory Health Care Services
N.A.I.C.S.: 621493
Anne Breuker (Office Mgr-Bus)
Daniel Thomas (Dir-Medical)

Tenet Healthcare Corporation—(Continued)

Clarkston ASC Partners, LLC (2)
5701 Bow Pointe Dr Ste 145, Clarkston, MI 48346
Tel.: (248) 922-4800
Web Site:
https://www.clarkstonsurgerycenter.com
Ambulatory Health Care Services
N.A.I.C.S.: 621493
Beth Brown (Dir-Clinical)

Clarksville Surgery Center, LLC (2)
793 Weatherly Dr, Clarksville, TN 37043
Tel.: (931) 645-1373
Ambulatory Health Care Services
N.A.I.C.S.: 621493
Kristy Davis-Zimmerman (Office Mgr)

Coast Surgery Center, L.P. (2)
3445 Pacific Coast Hwy Ste 110, Torrance, CA 90505
Tel.: (310) 325-4555
Web Site:
https://www.coastsurgerycenter.com
Ambulatory Health Care Services
N.A.I.C.S.: 621493

Corpus Christi Surgicare, Ltd. (2)
3636 S Alameda St Ste A, Corpus Christi, TX 78411
Tel.: (361) 853-2200
Web Site: http://ccos-tx.com
Health Care Srvices
N.A.I.C.S.: 622110

Creekwood Surgery Center, L.P. (2)
211 NE 54th St Ste 100, Kansas City, MO 64118
Tel.: (816) 455-4214
Web Site: https://www.creekwood-sc.com
Ambulatory Health Care Services
N.A.I.C.S.: 621493

Crown Point Surgery Center, LLC (2)
9397 Crown Crest Blvd Ste 110, Parker, CO 80138
Tel.: (720) 974-6499
Web Site: https://www.crownpoint-sc.com
Ambulatory Health Care Services
N.A.I.C.S.: 621493

Denton Surgicare Partners, Ltd. (2)
350 S Interstate 35 E, Denton, TX 76205
Tel.: (940) 323-1393
Web Site: https://www.denton-surgicare.com
Sales Range: $1-9.9 Million
Emp.: 20
Health Care Srvices
N.A.I.C.S.: 622110
Kay Streater (Office Mgr)

Denville Surgery Center, LLC (2)
3130 Route 10 W Ste 220, Denville, NJ 07834
Tel.: (973) 328-3475
Web Site:
https://www.denvillesurgerycenter.com
Emp.: 242
Ambulatory Health Care Services
N.A.I.C.S.: 621493
Vicki Christopher (Dir-Nursing)

Desert Ridge Outpatient Surgery, LLC (2)
20940 N Tatum Blvd Ste 100, Phoenix, AZ 85050
Tel.: (480) 502-4000
Web Site: http://desertridgeoutpatient-sc.com
Ambulatory Health Care Services
N.A.I.C.S.: 621493

Desoto Surgicare Partners, Ltd. (2)
7992 W Virginia Dr, Dallas, TX 75237
Tel.: (972) 283-2400
Web Site: https://www.northtexas-sc.com
Health Care Srvices
N.A.I.C.S.: 622110

Destin Surgery Center, LLC (2)
1225 Airport Rd, Destin, FL 32541
Tel.: (850) 650-7606
Web Site: https://www.destin-surgery.com
Ambulatory Health Care Center Operator
N.A.I.C.S.: 621493

Doctors Outpatient Surgicenter, Ltd. (2)
3534 Vista Blvd, Pasadena, TX 77504

Tel.: (713) 947-0330
Web Site: http://www.doctors-osc.com
Health Care Srvices
N.A.I.C.S.: 622110
Avette Mathis (Dir-Nursing)
Steven Fein (Dir-Medical)
Vanessa Galvan (Office Mgr-Bus)
Keith Schauder (Dir-Medical)

East El Paso Physicians' Medical Center, LLC (2)
1416 George Dieter Dr, El Paso, TX 79936
Tel.: (915) 598-4240
Web Site: http://www.fshelpaso.com
Emp.: 312
Health Care Srvices
N.A.I.C.S.: 622110
Alfredo Ontiveros (CEO)
Mark Defreitas (Dir-Matls Mgmt)

East Portland Surgery Center, LLC (2)
9200 SE 91st Ave Ste 100, Portland, OR 97086
Tel.: (503) 772-6160
Web Site: https://www.eastportlandsc.com
Ambulatory Health Care Services
N.A.I.C.S.: 621493
Trudy Pratt (Office Mgr-Bus)
Joel Schmitt (Dir-Clinical)

East West Surgery Center, L.P. (2)
2041 Mesa Valley Way Ste 125, Austell, GA 30106
Tel.: (678) 309-8100
Web Site: http://www.eastwestsc.com
Ambulatory Health Care Services
N.A.I.C.S.: 621493

Effingham Surgical Partners, LLC (2)
904 W Temple, Effingham, IL 62401
Tel.: (217) 342-1234
Web Site:
https://www.effinghamsurgerycenter.com
Emp.: 20
Ambulatory Health Care Services
N.A.I.C.S.: 621493

Einstein Montgomery Surgery Center, LLC (2)
609 W Germantown Pike Ste 100, East Norriton, PA 19403-4243
Tel.: (610) 239-2600
Health Care Srvices
N.A.I.C.S.: 622110

Encinitas Endoscopy Center, LLC (2)
700 Garden View Ct Ste 101, Encinitas, CA 92024
Tel.: (760) 274-2700
Web Site: https://www.theendocenter.net
Ambulatory Health Care Services
N.A.I.C.S.: 621493

Endoscopy Center of Hackensack, LLC (2)
170 Prospect Ave Ste 10, Hackensack, NJ 07601
Tel.: (201) 498-0030
Web Site: https://hackensackendo.com
Ambulatory Health Care Services
N.A.I.C.S.: 621493
Michael Tenned (Dir-Clinical)

Eye Surgery Center of Nashville, LLC (2)
310 25th Ave N Ste 105, Nashville, TN 37203
Tel.: (615) 329-9023
Web Site:
https://www.eyesurgerycenterofnashville.com
Eye Surgery Center Operator
N.A.I.C.S.: 621493

Flatirons Surgery Center, LLC (2)
70 Health Park Dr, Louisville, CO 80027
Tel.: (720) 890-2721
Web Site: https://www.flatirons-surgery.com
Ambulatory Health Care Services
N.A.I.C.S.: 621493

Folsom Outpatient Surgery Center, L.P. (2)
1651 Creekside Dr Ste 100, Folsom, CA 95630
Tel.: (916) 673-1990

Web Site: https://www.folsom-sc.com
Health Care Srvices
N.A.I.C.S.: 622110
Mary Horn (Mgr-Bus Office)

Fort Worth Surgicare Partners, Ltd. (2)
1800 Park Plc Ave, Fort Worth, TX 76110
Tel.: (682) 703-5600
Web Site: https://www.bshfw.com
Emp.: 130
Health Care Srvices
N.A.I.C.S.: 622110
Ved Aggarwal (Dir-Medical-Outpatient Center)
Laura Sittler (COO & Chief Nursing Officer)
Daud Ashai (Dir-Medical)
Jeff Brooks (CFO)

Franklin Endoscopy Center, LLC (2)
9160 Carothers Pkwy Ste 100, Franklin, TN 37067-6300
Tel.: (615) 550-6066
Web Site:
https://www.franklinsurgerycenter.com
Health Care Srvices
N.A.I.C.S.: 621498

Frisco Medical Center, L.L.P. (2)
5601 Warren Pkwy, Frisco, TX 75034
Tel.: (214) 407-5000
Web Site: https://baylorfrisco.com
Health Care Srvices
N.A.I.C.S.: 622110
Kevin Coats (CFO)
Jimmy Laferney (Chief Medical Officer)
Mickey Morgan (Chm)
Trevor Castaneda (CEO)

Frontenac Ambulatory Surgery & Spine Care Center, L.P. (2)
10435 Clayton Rd Ste 110, Frontenac, MO 63131
Tel.: (314) 995-3990
Web Site:
https://www.frontenacspineandsc.com
Ambulatory Health Care Services
N.A.I.C.S.: 621493

Gamma Surgery Center, LLC (2)
107 Gamma Dr Ste 200, Pittsburgh, PA 15238
Tel.: (412) 963-7917
Web Site: http://gammasurgerycenter.com
Health Care Srvices
N.A.I.C.S.: 622110

Garland Surgicare Partners, Ltd. (2)
530 Clara Barton Blvd Ste 100, Garland, TX 75042-5703
Tel.: (972) 494-2400
Web Site: https://www.pas-garland.com
Health Care Srvices
N.A.I.C.S.: 622110
William Nicholson (Dir-Medical)

Gateway Endoscopy Center, L.P. (2)
12855 N 40 Dr Ste 150 S Tower, Saint Louis, MO 63141
Tel.: (314) 336-1130
Diagnostic Imaging Center Operator
N.A.I.C.S.: 621512
Brian McMorrow (Dir-Medical)

Genesis ASC Partners, LLC (2)
46000 Ann Arbor Rd E Ste 201, Plymouth, MI 48170
Tel.: (517) 708-3200
Surgical Center Operator
N.A.I.C.S.: 621493
Sandy Goldman (Office Mgr)

Georgia Endoscopy Center, LLC (2)
3330 Preston Ridge Rd Ste 200, Alpharetta, GA 30005
Tel.: (770) 821-6800
Web Site:
https://www.georgiaendoscopycenter.com
Diagnostic Imaging Center Operator
N.A.I.C.S.: 621512

Grapevine Surgicare Partners, Ltd. (2)
2040 W State Hwy 114, Grapevine, TX 76051
Tel.: (817) 410-4300
Web Site: http://www.grapevine-sc.com
Health Care Srvices
N.A.I.C.S.: 622110
David Ackerman (Dir-Medical)

Grass Valley Outpatient Surgery Center, L.P. (2)
408 Sierra College Dr, Grass Valley, CA 95945
Tel.: (530) 271-2282
Web Site:
https://www.grassvalleysurgery.com
Health Care Srvices
N.A.I.C.S.: 622110
D. Joseph Lloyd (Dir-Medical)

Greenwood ASC, LLC (2)
7447 E Berry Ave Ste 100, Greenwood Village, CO 80111
Tel.: (720) 493-4100
Web Site: https://coloradopremier-greenwood.com
Ambulatory Health Care Services
N.A.I.C.S.: 621493

Hacienda Outpatient Surgery Center, LLC (2)
4626 Willow Rd Ste 100, Pleasanton, CA 94588
Tel.: (925) 734-6744
Web Site: https://haciendasurgery.com
Ambulatory Health Care Services
N.A.I.C.S.: 621493

Harvard Park Surgery Center, LLC (2)
1000 E Harvard Ave, Denver, CO 80210
Tel.: (720) 738-3910
Web Site: https://www.harvardpark-sc.com
Ambulatory Health Care Services
N.A.I.C.S.: 621493

Heritage Park Surgical Hospital, LLC (2)
3601 N Calais St, Sherman, TX 75090
Tel.: (903) 870-0999
Web Site: https://baylorsherman.com
Health Care Srvices
N.A.I.C.S.: 622110
Marc Devorsetz (CEO)

Hershey Outpatient Surgery Center, L.P. (2)
15 Hope Dr, Hershey, PA 17033
Tel.: (717) 520-8200
Web Site:
https://www.hersheyoutpatientsurgerycenter.com
Ambulatory Health Care Services
N.A.I.C.S.: 621493
Niraja Rajan (Dir-Medical)

Hinsdale Surgical Center, LLC (2)
10 Salt Creek Ln, Hinsdale, IL 60521
Tel.: (630) 325-5035
Web Site:
https://www.hinsdalesurgerycenter.com
Health Care Srvices
N.A.I.C.S.: 622110
Craig Gardner (Dir-Medical)

Houston Ambulatory Surgical Associates, L.P. (2)
970 Campbell Rd, Houston, TX 77024
Tel.: (713) 461-3547
Web Site:
https://www.westhoustonsurgicare.com
Ambulatory Health Care Services
N.A.I.C.S.: 621493

Implant Solutions, LLC (2)
1000 Corporate Dr, Marshfield, WI 54449
Tel.: (715) 486-0626
Web Site:
https://www.solutionsforimplants.com
Medical Equipment Distr
N.A.I.C.S.: 423450

Jackson Surgical Center, LLC (2)
27 S Cooks Bridge Rd Ste L2 Lower Level, Jackson, NJ 08527-2524
Tel.: (732) 928-1099
Web Site:
https://www.jacksonsurgicalcenter.com
Health Care Srvices
N.A.I.C.S.: 621610
Francis Lonigro (Mgr)

KHS Ambulatory Surgery Center LLC (2)
405 Hurffville Crosskeys Rd Ste 210, Sewell, NJ 08080
Tel.: (856) 582-2072
Web Site:
http://www.selectsurgicalcenter.com
Ambulatory Health Care Services
N.A.I.C.S.: 621493

Lake Lansing ASC Partners, LLC (2)
1707 Lake Lansing Rd, Lansing, MI 48912
Tel.: (517) 997-8211
Web Site: https://michigangastro.com
Health Care Srvices
N.A.I.C.S.: 622110

Lakewood Surgery Center, LLC (2)
1215 Route 70 Ste 2000, Lakewood, NJ 08701
Tel.: (732) 719-1800
Web Site: https://www.lakewoodsurgery.com
Health Care Srvices
N.A.I.C.S.: 622110
Cynthia Shashaty *(Dir-Clinical)*

Lawrenceville Surgery Center, L.L.C. (2)
758 Old Norcross Rd Ste 125, Lawrenceville, GA 30046
Tel.: (678) 987-0820
Web Site: https://www.lawrenceville-sc.com
Ambulatory Health Care Services
N.A.I.C.S.: 621493
Scott Quisling *(Dir-Medical)*

Lebanon Endoscopy Center, LLC (2)
100 Physicians Way Ste 340, Lebanon, TN 37090
Tel.: (615) 466-9532
Web Site:
https://www.lebanonendoscopycenter.com
Health Care Srvices
N.A.I.C.S.: 622110

Liberty Ambulatory Surgery Center, L.P. (2)
834 W Kansas Ste B, Liberty, MO 64068
Tel.: (816) 883-2004
Web Site: http://www.libertysurg.com
Health Care Srvices
N.A.I.C.S.: 622110
Gregory Mulcahy *(Dir-Medical)*
Michelle Bramble *(Office Mgr)*

Liberty Ambulatory Surgery Center, LLC (2)
377 Jersey Ave Ste 510, Jersey City, NJ 07302
Tel.: (201) 878-3200
Health Care Srvices
N.A.I.C.S.: 622110

Lone Star Endoscopy Center, LLC (2)
180 Bear Creek Pkwy, Keller, TX 76248
Tel.: (817) 337-3671
Web Site: http://lonestartx.com
Endoscopy Imaging Center Operator
N.A.I.C.S.: 621512

Manchester Ambulatory Surgery Center, LP (2)
1040 Old Des Peres Rd, Des Peres, MO 63131
Tel.: (314) 775-2264
Web Site: http://manchester-sc.com
Ambulatory Health Care Services
N.A.I.C.S.: 621493
Shonna Taylor *(Office Mgr-Bus)*
Michael Nogalski *(Dir-Medical)*
Trevor Vaughn *(Dir-Medical)*

Mary Immaculate Ambulatory Surgery Center, LLC (2)
12720 McManus Blvd Ste 103, Newport News, VA 23602
Tel.: (757) 369-7000
Web Site: https://mi-asc.com
Health Care Srvices
N.A.I.C.S.: 622110
Jonathan Snyder *(Dir-Medical)*

Medical Park Tower Surgery Center, LLC (2)
1301 W 38th St Ste 109, Austin, TX 78705-1010
Tel.: (512) 354-3000
Web Site: https://www.medicalparksc.com
Health Care Srvices
N.A.I.C.S.: 622110
Morgan Meadors *(Office Mgr-Bus)*

Memorial Hermann Bay Area Endoscopy Center, LLC (2)
444 FM 1959 Ste B, Houston, TX 77034-5416
Tel.: (281) 892-2420
Web Site:
https://www.memorialhermann.org

Ambulatory Health Care Services
N.A.I.C.S.: 621493
Amy Chenoweth *(Mgr-Nurse)*

Memorial Hermann Endoscopy & Surgery Center North Houston, L.L.C. (2)
275 Lantern Bend Ste 400, Houston, TX 77090
Tel.: (281) 440-5797
Web Site:
https://www.memorialhermann.org
Health Care Srvices
N.A.I.C.S.: 621498

Memorial Hermann Endoscopy Center North Freeway, LLC (2)
1900 N Loop W Ste 550, Houston, TX 77018
Tel.: (713) 457-2750
Web Site:
https://www.memorialhermann.org
Physician Health Care Services
N.A.I.C.S.: 621111

Memorial Hermann Specialty Hospital Kingwood, L.L.C. (2)
300 Kingwood Medical Dr, Kingwood, TX 77339
Tel.: (281) 312-4000
Web Site:
https://www.memorialhermannking
wood.com
Health Care Srvices
N.A.I.C.S.: 622110

Memorial Hermann Surgery Center - The Woodlands, LLP (2)
9200 Pinecroft Dr Ste 200 Medical Plz 3, The Woodlands, TX 77380
Tel.: (281) 297-9500
Web Site: https://www.mhsc-tw.com
Health Care Srvices
N.A.I.C.S.: 622110
William Varner *(Dir-Medical)*

Memorial Hermann Surgery Center Katy, LLP (2)
23920 Katy Fwy Ste 200, Katy, TX 77494
Tel.: (281) 644-3200
Web Site: https://www.mhsckaty.com
Health Care Srvices
N.A.I.C.S.: 622110
Terri Shemka *(Mgr-OR)*

Memorial Hermann Surgery Center Kingsland, LLC (2)
21720 Kingsland Blvd Ste 101, Katy, TX 77450
Tel.: (281) 492-1234
Web Site: https://www.kingsland-sc.com
Physician Health Care Services
N.A.I.C.S.: 621111
Mark Hancock *(Dir-Medical)*
Austin Tony *(Mgr-Materials)*

Memorial Hermann Surgery Center Memorial City, L.L.C. (2)
1120 Busiiness Ctr Dr Ste 110, Houston, TX 77043
Tel.: (713) 337-1111
Web Site: https://memorialhermann.org
Health Care Srvices
N.A.I.C.S.: 621498
David L. Callender *(Pres & CEO)*

Memorial Hermann Surgery Center Pinecroft, LLC (2)
9305 Pinecroft Dr Ste 200, The Woodlands, TX 77380
Tel.: (832) 823-5156
Web Site: http://www.memorialhermann.org
Physician Health Care Services
N.A.I.C.S.: 621111

Memorial Hermann Surgery Center Richmond, LLC (2)
21155 SW Fwy, Richmond, TX 77469
Tel.: (281) 344-5444
Web Site:
https://www.memorialhermann.org
Health Care Srvices
N.A.I.C.S.: 621498

Memorial Hermann Surgery Center Southwest, LLP (2)
7600 Beechnut St, Houston, TX 77074
Tel.: (713) 456-5000

Web Site:
https://www.memorialhermann.org
Physician Health Care Services
N.A.I.C.S.: 621111

Memorial Hermann Surgery Center Sugar Land, LLP (2)
17510 W Grand Pkwy Ste 200, Sugar Land, TX 77479
Tel.: (281) 238-1600
Web Site: https://www.mhsc-sugarland.com
Health Care Srvices
N.A.I.C.S.: 622110
Sheila Wallen *(Dir-Nursing)*

Memorial Hermann Surgery Center Woodlands Parkway, LLC (2)
1441 Woodstead Ct Ste 100, The Woodlands, TX 77380
Tel.: (281) 363-0058
Web Site: http://www.memorialhermann.org
Physician Health Care Services
N.A.I.C.S.: 621111

Memorial Hermann Texas International Endoscopy Center, LLC (2)
6620 Main St Ste 1500, Houston, TX 77030
Tel.: (713) 520-8432
Web Site: https://www.texasendoscopy.com
Health Care Srvices
N.A.I.C.S.: 622110

Memorial Surgery Center, LLC (2)
8131 S Memorial Dr Ste 107, Tulsa, OK 74133
Tel.: (918) 252-5114
Web Site: https://www.memorial-sc.com
Ambulatory Health Care Services
N.A.I.C.S.: 621493

Metro Surgery Center, LLC (2)
6790 W Thunderbird Rd, Peoria, AZ 85381
Tel.: (623) 979-1717
Web Site: https://www.phoenixmetrosc.com
Ambulatory Health Care Services
N.A.I.C.S.: 621493

Metrocrest Surgery Center, L.P. (2)
4780 N Josey Ln, Carrollton, TX 75010
Tel.: (972) 395-0440
Web Site:
https://www.baylorsurgicareofcarroll
ton.com
Health Care Srvices
N.A.I.C.S.: 622110
James Guess *(Dir-Medical)*

Metroplex Surgicare Partners, Ltd. (2)
1600 Central Dr Ste 180, Bedford, TX 76022
Tel.: (817) 571-1999
Web Site: http://www.metroplex-surgicare.com
Health Care Srvices
N.A.I.C.S.: 622110
Kay Streater *(Office Mgr)*
M. Stanton *(Dir-Medical)*

Metropolitan New Jersey, LLC (2)
433 Hackensack Ave LL01, Hackensack, NJ 07601
Tel.: (201) 527-6800
Web Site:
https://www.metrosurgerycenter.com
Ambulatory Health Care Services
N.A.I.C.S.: 621493
Lisa Van Buskirk *(Office Mgr-Bus)*

Mid Rivers Ambulatory Surgery Center, L.P. (2)
5401 Veterans Memorial Pkwy Ste 100, Saint Peters, MO 63376
Tel.: (636) 441-0906
Web Site: https://www.midrivers-sc.com
Ambulatory Health Care Services
N.A.I.C.S.: 621493

Mid-State Endoscopy Center, LLC (2)
1115 Dow St Ste A, Murfreesboro, TN 37130-2443
Tel.: (615) 848-9234
Web Site: https://www.midstateendoscopy-sc.com
Health Care Srvices
N.A.I.C.S.: 622110

Middle Tennessee Ambulatory Surgery Center, L.P. (2)

1800 Medical Center Pkwy Ste 120, Murfreesboro, TN 37129
Tel.: (615) 849-7500
Web Site:
https://www.middletennesseeasc.com
Health Care Srvices
N.A.I.C.S.: 622110

Midland Texas Surgical Center, LLC (2)
5609 Deauville, Midland, TX 79706
Tel.: (432) 699-4224
Web Site:
https://www.texassurgicalcenter.com
Ambulatory Health Care Services
N.A.I.C.S.: 621493
Donald Floyd *(Partner & Dir-Medical)*

Midwest Digestive Health Center, LLC (2)
3601 NE Ralph Powell Rd, Lees Summit, MO 64064
Tel.: (816) 525-4440
Web Site: https://www.midwestphysicians-sc.com
Health Care Srvices
N.A.I.C.S.: 622110
Marc K. Taormina *(Dir-Medical)*
Michelle Bramble *(Office Mgr-Bus)*

Millennium Surgical Center, LLC (2)
2090 Springdale Rd Ste A, Cherry Hill, NJ 08003-2024
Tel.: (856) 751-4555
Web Site: https://www.mscsurgery.com
Ambulatory Health Care Services
N.A.I.C.S.: 621493

Mountain Empire Surgery Center, L.P. (2)
601 Med Tech Pkwy, Johnson City, TN 37604
Tel.: (423) 610-1020
Web Site:
https://www.mountainempiresc.com
Health Care Srvices
N.A.I.C.S.: 622110

New Horizons Surgery Center, LLC (2)
1167 Independence Ave, Marion, OH 43302
Tel.: (740) 375-5854
Web Site: http://www.newhorizonsc.com
Ambulatory Health Care Services
N.A.I.C.S.: 621493
Peter Schuler *(Dir-Medical)*
Connie Stone *(Office Mgr-Bus)*

New Mexico Orthopaedic Surgery Center, L.P. (2)
8300 Constitution Ave NE, Albuquerque, NM 87110
Tel.: (505) 291-2300
Web Site: https://www.nmscortho.com
Health Care Srvices
N.A.I.C.S.: 622110
Anthony Pachelli *(Dir-Medical)*

North Garland Surgery Center, L.L.P. (2)
7150 N President George Bush Hwy Ste 101, Garland, TX 75044
Tel.: (214) 703-1800
Web Site: https://www.northgarland-sc.com
Health Care Srvices
N.A.I.C.S.: 622110

North Haven Surgery Center, LLC (2)
52 Washington Ave Ste 1, North Haven, CT 06473
Tel.: (203) 234-7727
Web Site:
https://www.northhavensurgeryctr.com
Health Care Srvices
N.A.I.C.S.: 622110

North Shore Same Day Surgery, L.L.C. (2)
3725 W Touhy Ave, Lincolnwood, IL 60712
Tel.: (847) 324-7770
Web Site: https://www.northshore-sc.com
Health Care Srvices
N.A.I.C.S.: 622110

Northern Monmouth Regional Surgery Center, L.L.C. (2)
195 US Hwy 9 Ste 210, Manalapan, NJ 07726-8294
Tel.: (732) 358-6500
Web Site: https://www.nmrsc.com
Ambulatory Health Care Services

Tenet Healthcare Corporation—(Continued)

N.A.I.C.S.: 621493
Peter Rienzo *(Dir-Medical)*
Elisa Luciano *(Mgr-Pre-Op & PACU)*

Northridge Surgery Center, L.P. **(2)**
647 Myatt Dr, Madison, TN 37115
Tel.: (615) 868-8942
Web Site: https://www.northridgesc.com
Health Care Srvices
N.A.I.C.S.: 622110

Northwest Ambulatory Surgery Center, LLC **(2)**
1515 NW 18th Ave Ste 200, Portland, OR 97209
Tel.: (503) 542-4888
Web Site: https://www.northwest-asc.com
Ambulatory Health Care Services
N.A.I.C.S.: 621493
Melissa Gibbons *(Office Mgr-Bus)*

Northwest Georgia Orthopaedic Surgery Center, LLC
2550 Windy Hill Rd Ste 218, Marietta, GA 30067
Tel.: (770) 953-8058
Web Site: https://www.nwga-sc.com
Ambulatory Health Care Services
N.A.I.C.S.: 621493
Irma Cumba *(Office Mgr-Bus)*
Gary Simon *(Dir-Medical)*

Northwest Regional ASC, LLC **(2)**
10170 Church Ranch Way Ste 110, Westminster, CO 80021
Tel.: (303) 328-3400
Web Site: https://www.nwrasc.com
Ambulatory Health Care Services
N.A.I.C.S.: 621493
Margo Smith *(Office Mgr-Bus)*
John Schultz *(Dir-Medical)*
Jami Follett *(Dir-Clinical)*

Northwest Surgery Center, LLP **(2)**
11111 Research Blvd Ste LL3, Austin, TX 78759
Tel.: (512) 349-4004
Web Site: https://www.northwestsc.com
Health Care Srvices
N.A.I.C.S.: 622110
Burton Lee *(Dir-Nursing)*
Barbara Sebastian *(Dir-Medical)*
Candice Stacks *(Office Mgr-Bus)*

OLOL Pontchartrain Surgery Center, LLC **(2)**
4407 Highway 190 E Service Rd Ste 200, Covington, LA 70433-4957
Tel.: (985) 234-9700
Ambulatory Health Care Services
N.A.I.C.S.: 621493
Jenny Greco *(Office Mgr)*

Old Tesson Surgery Center, L.P. **(2)**
12639 Old Tesson Rd Ste 130, Saint Louis, MO 63128
Tel.: (314) 748-4225
Web Site: https://www.oldtessonsc.com
Ambulatory Health Care Services
N.A.I.C.S.: 621493

Orthopedic South Surgical Partners, LLC **(2)**
156 Foster Dr Ste A, McDonough, GA 30253
Tel.: (678) 422-4280
Web Site: https://www.ortho-south.com
Orthopedic Health Care Services
N.A.I.C.S.: 622310
Yvette Thomas *(Coord-Bus Office)*

Orthopedic and Surgical Specialty Company, LLC **(2)**
2905 W Warner Rd Ste 1, Chandler, AZ 85224
Tel.: (480) 603-9000
Web Site:
https://www.dignityhealthazsh.com
Orthopedic Health Care Services
N.A.I.C.S.: 622310

Pacific Endo-Surgical Center, L.P. **(2)**
3445 Pacific Coast Hwy Ste 120, Torrance, CA 90505
Tel.: (310) 326-1666
Web Site: https://www.pac-endo.com
Ambulatory Health Care Services

N.A.I.C.S.: 621493
Pain Diagnostic and Treatment Center, L.P. **(2)**
2805 J St Ste 200, Sacramento, CA 95816
Tel.: (916) 231-8755
Web Site: https://www.paindiagnostic.com
Health Care Srvices
N.A.I.C.S.: 622110
Stephen Parkinson *(Dir-Medical)*

Pain Treatment Centers of Michigan, LLC **(2)**
4450 Fashion Sq Blvd Ste 200, Saginaw, MI 48603-1251
Tel.: (989) 790-7950
Web Site:
https://www.matrixsurgerycenter.com
Health Care Srvices
N.A.I.C.S.: 622110

Paramus Endoscopy, LLC **(2)**
80 Eisenhower Dr, Paramus, NJ 07652
Tel.: (201) 336-1100
Web Site: https://www.endobergenco.com
Health Care Srvices
N.A.I.C.S.: 622110
Juliana Brickner *(Dir-Clinical)*

Park Cities Surgery Center, LLC **(2)**
6901 Snider Plz Ste 300, University Park, TX 75205
Tel.: (214) 706-6901
Web Site: https://www.parkcitiessurgery.com
Health Care Srvices
N.A.I.C.S.: 622110
Billy Farrington *(Dir-Clinical)*

Parkway Surgery Center, LLC **(2)**
100 N Green Valley Pkwy Ste 125, Henderson, NV 89074-6392
Tel.: (702) 616-4954
Web Site: https://www.parkway-sc.com
Ambulatory Health Care Services
N.A.I.C.S.: 621493
Greg Linderer *(Dir-Medical)*

Parkwest Surgery Center, L.P. **(2)**
9430 ParkW Blvd Ste 210, Knoxville, TN 37923-4204
Tel.: (865) 531-0494
Web Site: https://www.parkwest-sc.com
Emp.: 50
Ambulatory Health Care Services
N.A.I.C.S.: 621493
Melissa Mcteer *(Coord-Accts Receivable)*

Patient Partners, LLC **(2)**
890 N Blue Jay Way, Gallatin, TN 37066
Tel.: (615) 575-9000
Web Site:
https://www.patientpartnerssurgerycenter.com
Ambulatory Health Care Services
N.A.I.C.S.: 621493

Pearland Ambulatory Surgery Center, LP **(2)**
15015 Kirby Dr Ste 100, Pearland, TX 77047-2573
Tel.: (832) 255-7500
Web Site:
https://www.pearlandsurgerycenter.net
Ambulatory Health Care Services
N.A.I.C.S.: 621493

Physician's Surgery Center of Knoxville, LLC **(2)**
1819 Clinch Ave Ste 206, Knoxville, TN 37916-2435
Tel.: (865) 522-2949
Web Site: https://www.pscofknoxville.com
Ambulatory Health Care Services
N.A.I.C.S.: 621493
Betty Marshall *(Dir-Clinical)*
Greg King *(Dir-Medical)*
Beth Rulon *(Office Mgr-Bus)*
Nicholas Doiron *(Dir-Medical)*

Physicians Pavilion, L.P. **(2)**
100 Winners Cir Ste 220, Brentwood, TN 37027
Tel.: (615) 220-3720
Health Care Srvices
N.A.I.C.S.: 622110

Physicians Surgery Center at Good Samaritan, LLC **(2)**
2 Good Samaritan Way Ste 200, Mount Vernon, IL 62864-2476

Tel.: (618) 899-5703
Web Site: https://www.goodsamaritan-sc.com
Ambulatory Health Care Services
N.A.I.C.S.: 621493
Terri Gowler *(Office Mgr-Bus)*
Kay Anne Wagner *(Dir-Clinical)*

Resurgens Surgery Center, LLC **(2)**
5671 Peachtree Dunwoody Rd NE Ste 800, Atlanta, GA 30342
Tel.: (404) 531-8532
Web Site: https://www.resurgens-sc.com
Ambulatory Health Care Services
N.A.I.C.S.: 621493

River North Same Day Surgery, L.L.C. **(2)**
1 E Erie Ste 300, Chicago, IL 60611
Tel.: (312) 649-3939
Web Site: https://www.rivernorth-sc.com
Health Care Srvices
N.A.I.C.S.: 622110

Riverside Ambulatory Surgery Center, LLC **(2)**
100 Village Square Shopping Ctr, Hazelwood, MO 63042
Tel.: (314) 373-8931
Web Site: https://www.riverside-asc.com
Ambulatory Health Care Services
N.A.I.C.S.: 621493

Rockwall Ambulatory Surgery Center, L.L.P. **(2)**
825 W Yellowjacket Ln, Rockwall, TX 75087
Tel.: (972) 772-6166
Web Site: https://www.rockwallsurgery.com
Health Care Srvices
N.A.I.C.S.: 622110
Tom Sudela *(Dir-Medical)*
Richard Gammill *(Mgr-OR)*
Yvonne Huff *(Office Mgr-Bus)*
Lacy Eves *(Dir-Clinical)*
Stephanie Gammill *(Mgr-Pre-Op & PACU)*

Rockwall/Heath Surgery Center, L.L.P. **(2)**
6435 S FM 549 Ste 101, Rockwall, TX 75032
Tel.: (972) 722-9003
Web Site:
http://www.baylorsurgicareheath.com
Health Care Srvices
N.A.I.C.S.: 622110
Susan Hodgson *(Dir-Clinical)*

Roseville Surgery Center, L.P. **(2)**
1420 E Roseville Pkwy Ste 100, Roseville, CA 95661-3080
Tel.: (916) 677-2488
Web Site: https://www.roseville-sc.com
Health Care Srvices
N.A.I.C.S.: 622110
Cherri Huff *(Dir-Clinical)*

Roswell Surgery Center, L.L.C. **(2)**
1285 Hembree Rd Ste 200-C, Roswell, GA 30076-5720
Tel.: (770) 772-5520
Web Site: https://www.roswell-sc.com
Ambulatory Health Care Services
N.A.I.C.S.: 621493

SSM St. Clare Surgical Center, L.L.C. **(2)**
1055 Bowles Ave Ste 100, Fenton, MO 63026
Tel.: (636) 203-9700
Web Site: https://www.stclare-sc.com
Health Care Srvices
N.A.I.C.S.: 622110
Tina Schaaf *(Dir-RN)*
Jillian Kennon *(Mgr-Bus Office)*

Sacramento Midtown Endoscopy Center, LLC **(2)**
3941 J St Ste 460, Sacramento, CA 95819-3633
Tel.: (916) 733-6940
Web Site:
https://sacramentomidtownendoscopy.com
Endoscopy Center Operator
N.A.I.C.S.: 621112

Saint Thomas Campus Surgicare, L.P. **(2)**
4230 Harding Pike Rd Medical Plz E Ste 300, Nashville, TN 37205

Tel.: (615) 783-1260
Web Site: https://www.stthomas-sc.com
Health Care Srvices
N.A.I.C.S.: 622110

San Antonio Endoscopy, L.P. **(2)**
8550 Datapoint Dr Ste 100, San Antonio, TX 78229
Tel.: (210) 615-7232
Web Site: https://www.sa-endo.com
Health Care Srvices
N.A.I.C.S.: 622110

San Gabriel Valley Surgical Center, L.P. **(2)**
1250 S Sunset Ave Ste 100, West Covina, CA 91790
Tel.: (626) 960-6623
Web Site: https://www.sangabrielvalley-sc.com
Ambulatory Health Care Services
N.A.I.C.S.: 621493

San Martin Surgery Center, LLC **(2)**
8530 W Sunset Rd Ste 100, Las Vegas, NV 89113-2244
Tel.: (702) 789-5700
Web Site: https://www.durangooutpatient-sc.com
Health Care Srvices
N.A.I.C.S.: 622110
Gregory Linderer *(Dir-Medical)*

Santa Clarita Surgery Center, L.P. **(2)**
26357 McBean Pkwy Ste 100, Santa Clarita, CA 91355
Tel.: (661) 799-8300
Web Site: https://www.summit-asc.com
Ambulatory Health Care Services
N.A.I.C.S.: 621493

Scripps Encinitas Surgery Center, LLC **(2)**
320 Santa Fe Dr Ste LL2, Encinitas, CA 92024
Tel.: (760) 632-3900
Web Site: https://www.scrippsencinitas-sc.com
Health Care Srvices
N.A.I.C.S.: 622110
Brian Pazevic *(Dir-Medical)*

Shore Outpatient Surgicenter, L.L.C. **(2)**
360 Route 70, Lakewood, NJ 08701
Tel.: (732) 942-9835
Web Site: https://www.shoreoutpatient-sc.com
Ambulatory Health Care Services
N.A.I.C.S.: 621493
Daniel Burzon *(Dir-Medical)*
Barbara Mace *(Mgr-Materials)*
Nicole Mace *(Dir-Clinical)*

Shoreline Surgery Center, LLP **(2)**
718 Elizabeth St, Corpus Christi, TX 78404
Tel.: (361) 882-3204
Web Site: https://www.corpuschristi-sc.com
Health Care Srvices
N.A.I.C.S.: 622110
Jacqueline Shew *(Mgr-Bus Office)*

Shrewsbury Surgery Center, LLC **(2)**
655 Shrewsbury Ave, Shrewsbury, NJ 07702
Tel.: (732) 450-6000
Web Site: https://www.shrewsbury-sc.com
Health Care Srvices
N.A.I.C.S.: 622110
Ted Kutzin *(Dir-Medical)*
Valerie McDermott *(Mgr-Bus Office)*

South County Outpatient Endoscopy Services, L.P. **(2)**
5139 Mattis Rd Ste 100, Saint Louis, MO 63128
Tel.: (314) 729-9780
Web Site: https://www.scopes-stlouis.com
Ambulatory Health Care Services
N.A.I.C.S.: 621493
Polly Schwab *(Mgr-Bus Office)*
Kim Graves *(Dir-Clinical)*

Southwestern Ambulatory Surgery Center, LLC **(2)**
500 N Lewis Run Rd Ste 202, Pittsburgh, PA 15122
Tel.: (412) 469-6964
Web Site: https://www.southwesternasc.com
Ambulatory Health Care Services
N.A.I.C.S.: 621493

Melissa Cervone *(Office Mgr)*

Spinal Diagnostics and Treatment Centers, L.L.C. **(2)**
901 Campus Dr Ste 310, Daly City, CA
94015
Tel.: (650) 755-0733
Web Site: http://www.spinaldiagnostics.com
Ambulatory Health Care Services
N.A.I.C.S.: 621493
Richard Derby *(Dir-Medical)*

St. Joseph's Outpatient Surgery Center, LLC **(2)**
240 W Thomas Rd, Phoenix, AZ 85013
Tel.: (602) 406-3552
Web Site: https://www.sjosc.com
Health Care Srvices
N.A.I.C.S.: 622110
Toni Olguin *(Mgr-Bus Office)*

St. Joseph's Surgery Center, L.P. **(2)**
1800 N California St Ste 1, Stockton, CA
95204
Tel.: (209) 467-6316
Web Site: https://www.stjosephs-sc.com
Health Care Srvices
N.A.I.C.S.: 622110
Natalie Lee *(Dir-Medical)*

St. Louis Surgical Center, LC **(2)**
760 Office Pkwy, Creve Coeur, MO 63141-7105
Tel.: (314) 995-4700
Web Site: http://saintlouissurgicalcenter.com
Ambulatory Health Care Services
N.A.I.C.S.: 621493

St. Mary's Ambulatory Surgery Center, LLC **(2)**
1501 MaPle Ave Ste 300, Richmond, VA
23226
Tel.: (804) 287-7878
Web Site: https://www.stmarys-asc.com
Ambulatory Health Care Services
N.A.I.C.S.: 621493

St. Mary's Surgical Center, LLC **(2)**
203 NW R D Mize Rd Ste 218, Blue
Springs, MO 64014
Tel.: (816) 874-4181
Web Site: https://www.stmarys-sc.com
Health Care Srvices
N.A.I.C.S.: 621493
Tamsen Robinson *(Mgr-Nurse)*

Stockton Outpatient Surgery Center, LLC **(2)**
2388 N California St, Stockton, CA 95204
Tel.: (209) 944-9100
Web Site: https://www.ascstockton.com
Ambulatory Health Care Services
N.A.I.C.S.: 621493
Gary Bry *(Mgr-Materials)*
Gary Alegre *(Dir-Medical)*
Karen Sapinozo *(Dir-Nursing)*

Suburban Endoscopy Center, LLC **(2)**
799 Bloomfield Ave Ste 101, Verona, NJ
07044
Tel.: (973) 571-1600
Web Site: https://www.suburbansc.com
Ambulatory Health Care Services
N.A.I.C.S.: 621493

Summit View Surgery Center, LLC **(2)**
7730 S Broadway, Littleton, CO 80122
Tel.: (303) 730-2376
Web Site: https://www.summitview-sc.com
Ambulatory Health Care Services
N.A.I.C.S.: 621493

Surgery Center at University Park, LLC **(2)**
983 S Beneva Rd, Sarasota, FL 34232
Tel.: (941) 365-5355
Web Site: https://www.sarasotasc.com
Health Care Srvices
N.A.I.C.S.: 622310

Surgery Center of Atlanta, LLC **(2)**
4200 Northside Pkwy NW Bldg 8 100, Atlanta, GA 30327
Tel.: (404) 233-3833
Health Care Srvices
N.A.I.C.S.: 622110

Surgery Center of Canfield, LLC **(2)**

4147 Westford Dr, Canfield, OH 44406
Tel.: (330) 702-1489
Web Site: http://www.canfieldsc.com
Ambulatory Health Care Services
N.A.I.C.S.: 621493
John Jakubek *(Dir-Medical)*
Tom Pitko *(Office Mgr)*

Surgery Center of Columbia, L.P. **(2)**
305 N Keene St Ste 107, Columbia, MO
65201
Tel.: (573) 256-6272
Web Site:
  https://www.columbiasurgerycenter.com
Ambulatory Health Care Services
N.A.I.C.S.: 621493
Brandi Chick *(Coord-Bus Office)*
Wendy Faulkner *(Mgr-Clinical)*
Steve Dalbec *(Dir-Medical)*
William Kinney *(Dir-Medical)*

Surgery Center of Gilbert, L.L.C. **(2)**
6003 E Baseline Rd, Mesa, AZ 85206
Tel.: (480) 641-6500
Web Site: https://www.gilbert-sc.com
Ambulatory Health Care Services
N.A.I.C.S.: 621493
John Meernik *(Dir-Medical)*

Surgery Center of Peoria, L.L.C. **(2)**
13260 N 94th Dr Ste 200, Peoria, AZ 85381
Tel.: (623) 933-2900
Web Site: https://www.peoriasc.com
Ambulatory Health Care Services
N.A.I.C.S.: 621493

Surgery Center of Scottsdale, LLC **(2)**
8962 E Desert Cove, Scottsdale, AZ 85260
Tel.: (480) 661-5232
Web Site: http://www.scottsdale-sc.com
Ambulatory Health Care Services
N.A.I.C.S.: 621493
Dawn Barnes *(Dir-Bus Ops)*
Julie Lentz *(Mgr-Bus Office)*
Amber Bruns *(Dir-Clinical Ops)*
Tory McJunkin *(Dir-Medical)*

Surgery Center of Tempe, LLC **(2)**
1940 E Southern Ave, Tempe, AZ 85282
Tel.: (480) 820-7101
Web Site: http://www.tempesc.com
Ambulatory Health Care Services
N.A.I.C.S.: 621493
Suzanne Rayl *(Mgr-Bus Office)*

SurgiCenter of Baltimore, LLP **(2)**
23 Crossroads Dr Ste 100, Owings Mills,
MD 21117
Tel.: (410) 356-0300
Web Site: https://lifebridgehealth.org
Ambulatory Health Care Services
N.A.I.C.S.: 621493
Aniqa Alam *(Dir-Medical)*
Tina Farrell *(Coord-Clinical)*
Jennifer Grue Gongon *(Mgr-Bus Office)*

Surgical Institute of Reading, LLC **(2)**
2752 Century Blvd, Wyomissing, PA 19610
Tel.: (610) 378-8800
Web Site: https://www.sireading.com
Health Care Srvices
N.A.I.C.S.: 622110

Surgical Specialists at Princeton, LLC **(2)**
136 Stanhope St, Princeton, NJ 08540
Tel.: (609) 799-1130
Web Site:
  https://www.surgicalspecialistsatprince
  ton.com
Health Care Srvices
N.A.I.C.S.: 622110
Alexander Vukasin *(Dir-Medical)*

TOPS Specialty Hospital, Ltd. **(2)**
17080 Red Oak Dr, Houston, TX 77090
Tel.: (281) 957-8688
Web Site: https://www.tops-hospital.com
Ambulatory Health Care Services
N.A.I.C.S.: 621493
Grant Magness *(CEO)*

Tamarac Surgery Center, LLC **(2)**
4485 N State Rd 7, Lauderdale Lakes, FL
33319
Tel.: (954) 735-0096
Web Site: https://www.sc-fortlauderdale.com
Health Care Srvices

N.A.I.C.S.: 622110

Terre Haute Surgical Center, LLC **(2)**
227 E McCallister Dr, Terre Haute, IN
47802
Tel.: (812) 234-4315
Web Site:
  https://www.terrehautesurgicalcenter.com
Ambulatory Health Care Services
N.A.I.C.S.: 621493
Robin Turner *(Dir-Clinical)*

Teton Outpatient Services, LLC **(2)**
150 Buffalo Way, Jackson, WY 83001
Tel.: (307) 733-8677
Web Site: https://www.tetonops.com
Health Care Srvices
N.A.I.C.S.: 622110
Matthew Zeleznik *(Dir-Medical)*
Lindsay Emerson *(Dir-Clinic)*
Kelly Hargis *(Mgr-Materials)*

Texan Ambulatory Surgery Center, L.P. **(2)**
7000 N MoPac Expy Ste 120, Austin, TX
78731-3030
Tel.: (512) 342-0900
Web Site: https://www.texansurgery.com
Health Care Srvices
N.A.I.C.S.: 622110

Texas Orthopedics Surgery Center, LLC **(2)**
4700 Seton Center Pkwy Ste 100, Austin,
TX 78759
Tel.: (512) 439-1006
Web Site:
  https://www.texasorthopedicssurgerycen
  ter.com
Orthopedic Health Care Services
N.A.I.C.S.: 622310

The Center for Ambulatory Surgical Treatment, L.P. **(2)**
1090 Glendon Ave, Los Angeles, CA 90024
Tel.: (310) 209-6500
Ambulatory Health Care Services
N.A.I.C.S.: 621493

The Christ Hospital Spine Surgery Center, LLC **(2)**
4020 Smith Rd, Cincinnati, OH 45209
Tel.: (513) 619-5899
Web Site: http://mayfieldsurgerycenter.com
Ambulatory Health Care Services
N.A.I.C.S.: 621493

The Physicians' Center, L.P. **(2)**
3131 University Dr E, Bryan, TX 77802
Tel.: (979) 731-3100
Web Site:
  https://www.thephysicianscentre.com
Health Care Srvices
N.A.I.C.S.: 622110
Suzy Hoyle *(Chief Nursing Officer)*
Beverly Hutchinson *(Dir-Bus Ops)*
Courtney Coats *(Dir-Med Surg, Bariatrics, and Quality)*
Jonathan Shirley *(Dir-HR)*
Rita Cooper *(Coord-Bus Office)*
Ian Andersen *(Dir-Mktg & PR)*
Carlee Supak *(Dir-Athletic Trng)*
Megan Moonjian *(Dir-Pharmacy)*
Harold Engle *(CEO)*
Pat Solis *(CFO)*

The Surgery Center at Williamson, LLC **(2)**
301 Seton Pkwy Ste 200, Round Rock, TX
78665
Tel.: (512) 861-4200
Web Site: https://www.williamson-sc.com
Health Care Srvices
N.A.I.C.S.: 622110
Heather Haferkamp *(Mgr-Bus Office)*
Jeffrey Brand *(Dir-Medical)*
Patricia Rosado *(Mgr-Materials)*

Titusville Center for Surgical Excellence, LLC **(2)**
814 S Washington Ave, Titusville, FL 32780
Tel.: (321) 567-6300
Web Site:
  https://www.titusvillesurgicalexcellence.net
Health Care Srvices
N.A.I.C.S.: 622110

Toms River Surgery Center, L.L.C. **(2)**

1430 Hooper Ave Ste 301, Toms River, NJ
08753
Tel.: (732) 240-2277
Web Site: https://tomsriver-sc.com
Health Care Srvices
N.A.I.C.S.: 622110
Robert Mako *(Dir-Medical)*
Lisa Gagliano *(Mgr-Bus Office)*

Trophy Club Medical Center, L.P. **(2)**
2850 E State Hwy 114, Trophy Club, TX
76262
Tel.: (817) 837-4600
Web Site: https://baylortrophyclub.com
Health Care Srvices
N.A.I.C.S.: 622110
Jonathan Saunders *(CEO)*
Austin Stovall *(Mgr-Ops)*
Ron Shields *(Dir-IT)*
Rish Desai *(Dir-Pharmacy)*
Mary Skinner *(Dir-Laboratory)*
Marshall Johnson *(Dir-Plant Ops)*
Starla Holt *(Mgr-Materials)*
Tiffney Watson *(Dir-Radiology)*
Karen Priddy *(Mgr-Case)*
Jeff Hinkel *(Chief Quality Officer)*
Melissa Wright *(Dir-Bus Office)*
Jeff Ailshie *(Dir-Surgery)*
Melinda Hudson *(Dir-PAT, Pre-Op & PACU-Post Surgical Unit)*
Julie Camp *(Chief Nursing Officer)*

Tuscan Surgery Center at Las Colinas, LLC **(2)**
701 Tuscan Dr Ste 100, Irving, TX 75039
Tel.: (214) 442-1900
Web Site:
  https://www.tuscansurgerycenteratlasco
  linas.com
Ambulatory Health Care Services
N.A.I.C.S.: 621493
Neville Fernandes *(Dir-Medical)*
Breda Smithson *(Mgr-Bus Office)*

Twin Cities Ambulatory Surgery Center, L.P. **(2)**
1101 W Gannon Dr, Festus, MO 63028
Tel.: (636) 931-5997
Web Site: https://www.twincities-sc.com
Ambulatory Health Care Services
N.A.I.C.S.: 621493

USP Maryland, Inc. **(2)**
23 Crossroads Dr Ste 200, Owings Mills,
MD 21117
Tel.: (410) 356-2626
Hospital & Clinic Operator
N.A.I.C.S.: 621111

USPI Holdings, Inc. **(2)**
320 Park Ave Ste 2500, New York, NY
10022
Tel.: (212) 848-2750
Holding Company
N.A.I.C.S.: 551112
Jason Cagle *(CFO)*

United Surgical Partners International, Inc. **(2)**
14201 Dallas Pkwy, Dallas, TX
75254 **(95%)**
Tel.: (972) 713-3500
Web Site: https://www.uspi.com
Sales Range: $600-649.9 Million
Emp.: 18,500
Surgical Hospitals & Centers Owner, Manager & Operator
N.A.I.C.S.: 622110
Brett P. Brodnax *(Pres & CEO)*
Mark C. Garvin *(COO)*
Owen Morris *(CFO)*
Stuart Simon *(Dir-Medical)*
Andy McCawley *(Chief Dev Officer)*
Jana Durfee *(Chief Compliance Officer & VP)*
Andy Johnston *(Chief Admin Officer)*
Tamala Norris *(Chief Nursing Officer)*
Jonathan Bailey *(Pres)*
Sara Bressman *(Pres)*
Nick Crafts *(Pres)*
Donita Fleming *(Pres)*

Subsidiary (Domestic):

CareSpot **(3)**
2001 Glen Echo Rd, Nashville, TN 37215
Tel.: (615) 348-7346
Web Site: http://www.carespot.com

Tenet Healthcare Corporation—(Continued)

General Medical Services
N.A.I.C.S.: 621999
Eric Enderle (*Pres & CEO*)
Fran J. Coyne (*VP-Sls & Occupational Health Svcs*)
Susie Hardin (*VP-HR*)
Matthew Kitchin (*VP-Information Svcs*)
Dan Murphy (*CFO*)
Stephen Marley (*Chief Dev Officer*)
Shannone Raybon (*Sec*)
Kevin F. Fox (*VP-Procurement & Supply Chain*)
Ben Goodman (*VP-Mktg*)
Linda Mattson (*VP-Western Div*)
Richard Walsh (*VP-Eastern Div*)

Subsidiary (Domestic):

Solantic Corporation (4)
115 E Park Dr Ste 300, Brentwood, TN 37027
Tel.: (904) 223-2320
Urgent Care Facilities
N.A.I.C.S.: 621111

Affiliate (Domestic):

Dallas Surgical Partners, L.L.P. (3)
3920 Worth St, Dallas, TX 75246
Tel.: (972) 961-1685
Web Site: http://www.baylor-surgicare.com
Sales Range: $50-74.9 Million
Multi-specialty Surgery Outpatient Center
N.A.I.C.S.: 622110

Subsidiary (Domestic):

University Surgery Center, Ltd. (2)
7251 University Blvd Ste 100, Winter Park, FL 32792
Tel.: (407) 677-0066
Web Site: https://www.university-sc.com
Health Care Srvices
N.A.I.C.S.: 622110

Upper Cumberland Physicians' Surgery Center, LLC (2)
467 N Whitney Ave, Cookeville, TN 38501
Tel.: (931) 528-5007
Web Site: http://uppercumberlandphysicianssurgerycenter.com
Health Care Srvices
N.A.I.C.S.: 622110
Leslie Johnson (*Mgr-Bus Office*)
Scott Copeland (*Dir-Medical*)

Utica ASC Partners, LLC (2)
14201 Dallas Pkwy, Dallas, TX 75254
Tel.: (586) 254-2280
Ambulatory Health Care Services
N.A.I.C.E.: 621403

Victoria Ambulatory Surgery Center, L.P. (2)
6404 Nursery Dr Ste 300, Victoria, TX 77904
Tel.: (361) 570-8311
Web Site: https://www.victoriasc.com
Emp.: 5
Health Care Srvices
N.A.I.C.S.: 622110

Warner Park Surgery Center, L.P. (2)
604 W Warner Rd, Chandler, AZ 85225
Tel.: (480) 899-2571
Web Site: http://www.warnerparksurgerycenter.com
Ambulatory Health Care Services
N.A.I.C.S.: 621493
Khoa Le (*Dir-Medical*)
Tracy Sherman (*Mgr-Bus Office*)
Karin Brown (*Dir-Clinical*)

Underwood Surgery Center, LLC (1)
110 Underwood St Ste B, Orlando, FL 32806
Tel.: (407) 648-9151
Web Site: https://www.underwoodsurgerycenter.com
Surgical Care Services
N.A.I.C.S.: 621493

Upper Bay Surgery Center, LLC (1)
360 E Pulaski Hwy Ste 2A, Elkton, MD 21921
Tel.: (410) 620-3348
Web Site: https://www.upperbaysurgery.com

Surgical Care Services
N.A.I.C.S.: 621493

Vanguard Health Systems, Inc. (1)
20 Burton Hills Blvd Ste 100, Nashville, TN 37215
Tel.: (615) 665-6000
Web Site: http://www.vanguardhealth.com
Rev.: $5,999,400,000
Assets: $5,042,600,000
Liabilities: $4,636,600,000
Net Worth: $406,000,000
Earnings: $69,100,000
Emp.: 33,700
Fiscal Year-end: 06/30/2013
Hospital Owner & Operator
N.A.I.C.S.: 622110

Subsidiary (Domestic):

Allegian Insurance Company (2)
4801 NW Loop 410 Ste 380, San Antonio, TX 78220
Tel.: (956) 389-2273
Web Site: http://www.valleyhealthplans.com
General Insurance Services
N.A.I.C.S.: 524210

CML-Chicago Market Labs, Inc. (2)
3231 S Euclid Ave 1st Fl MacNeal Professional Service Bldg, Berwyn, IL 60402
Tel.: (708) 783-5117
Web Site: http://www.weisshospital.com
General Medical Services
N.A.I.C.S.: 622110

Harlingen Physician Network, Inc. (2)
2121 Pease St Ste 1g, Harlingen, TX 78550
Tel.: (956) 389-6565
Web Site: http://www.physicians.harlingen.com
Health Care Srvices
N.A.I.C.S.: 621999

Heart & Vascular Institute of Texas, Inc. (2)
Greenspoint Bldg 1933 NE Loop 410, San Antonio, TX 78217
Tel.: (210) 804-6000
Web Site: http://havit.com
General Medical & Surgical Care Services
N.A.I.C.S.: 622110
Nancy Raines (*COO*)

Hospital Development of West Phoenix, Inc. (2)
13677 W McDowell Rd, Goodyear, AZ 85395
Tel.: (623) 882-1500
Web Site: https://www.abrazohealth.com
General Medical Services
N.A.I.C.S.: 622110
Brian Elisco (*CEO*)

Journey Home Healthcare of San Antonio, LLC (2)
1715 Aaron Brenner Dr Ste701, Cordova, TN 38120
Tel.: (901) 937-3030
Health Care Srvices
N.A.I.C.S.: 621999

Lakefront Medical Associates, LLC (2)
4700 N Marine Dr Ste 315, Chicago, IL 60640
Tel.: (773) 564-5030
Web Site: http://www.chicagohealthmedicalgroup.com
General Medical Services
N.A.I.C.S.: 622110

MacNeal Health Providers, Inc. (2)
750 Pasquinelli Dr Ste 216, Westmont, IL 60559
Tel.: (708) 783-7100
Web Site: http://www.chicagohealthsystem.com
General Medical Services
N.A.I.C.S.: 622110

Magnolia Surgery Center Limited Partnership (2)
14571 Magnolia St Ste 107, Westminster, CA 92683
Tel.: (714) 903-9039
Web Site: https://www.surgeryatmagnolia.com
General Medical Services

N.A.I.C.S.: 622110

Midwest Pharmacies, Inc. (2)
1 Erie Ct, Oak Park, IL 60302
Tel.: (708) 524-2250
Emp.: 3
Pharmacy Services
N.A.I.C.S.: 622110
Aann Montgomery (*Dir-Pharmacy*)

North Anaheim Surgicenter, Ltd. (2)
1154 N Euclid St, Anaheim, CA 92801
Tel.: (714) 635-6272
General Medical Services
N.A.I.C.S.: 622110

Primary Care Physicians Center, LLC (2)
5197 Roswell Rd NE, Atlanta, GA 30342
Tel.: (404) 252-1230
Web Site: http://www.primarycarephysiciancenter.com
General Medical Services
N.A.I.C.S.: 622110

Resolute Health Family Urgent Care, Inc. (2)
555 Creekside Xing, New Braunfels, TX 78130
Tel.: (830) 500-6900
Web Site: http://www.resolutehealth.com
Emp.: 35
General Medical Services
N.A.I.C.S.: 622110

Resolute Health Physicians Network, Inc. (2)
66 Gruene Park Dr Ste 210, New Braunfels, TX 78130-2460
Tel.: (615) 665-6000
Health Care Srvices
N.A.I.C.S.: 621999

VHS Acquisition Corporation (2)
5102 W Campbell Ave, Phoenix, AZ 85031
Tel.: (623) 848-5000
Web Site: http://www.abrazohealth.com
Holding Company; General Medical Services
N.A.I.C.S.: 551112

Subsidiary (Domestic):

Arizona Heart Hospital, LLC (3)
1930 E Thomas Rd, Phoenix, AZ 85016 (70.6%)
Tel.: (602) 532-1000
Web Site: http://www.azhearthospital.com
Sales Range: $50-74.9 Million
Cardiovascular Services
N.A.I.C.S.: 622310

VHS Acquisition Subsidiary Number 1, Inc. (3)
3929 E Bell Rd, Phoenix, AZ 85032
Tel.: (602) 923-5000
Web Site: https://www.abrazohealth.com
General Hospital Services
N.A.I.C.S.: 622110
Sue Rainey (*Chief Nursing Officer*)
Naman Mahajan (*CEO*)
Keslie Blackwell (*CFO*)
Erin Gonzalez (*Chief HR Officer*)

VHS Arizona Heart Institute, Inc. (3)
2632 N 20th St, Phoenix, AZ 85006
Tel.: (602) 266-2200
Web Site: http://www.azheart.com
Emp.: 50
General Medical Services
N.A.I.C.S.: 622110

VHS Outpatient Clinics, Inc. (3)
3800 N Central Ave Ste 460, Phoenix, AZ 85012
Tel.: (602) 674-6501
General Medical Services
N.A.I.C.S.: 622110

Subsidiary (Domestic):

Abrazo Medical Group Urgent Care, LLC (4)
6565 E Greenway Pkwy Ste 102, Scottsdale, AZ 85254-2073
Web Site: http://abrazomedicalgroup.com
General Medical Services
N.A.I.C.S.: 622110

Subsidiary (Domestic):

VHS of Phoenix, Inc. (3)
2000 W Bethany Home Rd, Phoenix, AZ 85015-2443
Tel.: (602) 249-0212
Web Site: https://www.abrazohealth.com
General Medical Services
N.A.I.C.S.: 622110
Tami Biggs (*Chief Nursing Officer-Administration-Nursing,Arizona Heart Hospital*)
Edgar Staren (*Chief Admin Officer*)
Robbie Shappley (*COO*)
Kyle Bennion (*Chief Strategy Officer*)
Michelle Henderson (*Chief Nursing Officer*)
Greg Pearson (*CEO*)
Tim Howard (*Chief HR Officer*)

VHS of South Phoenix, Inc. (3)
3800 N Central Ave Ste 460, Phoenix, AZ 85012
Tel.: (602) 258-5111
Emp.: 23
General Medical Services
N.A.I.C.S.: 622110

Subsidiary (Domestic):

Arizona Health Partners, LLC (4)
3800 N Central Ave Ste 460, Phoenix, AZ 85012
Tel.: (623) 215-9432
Web Site: http://
General Medical Services
N.A.I.C.S.: 622110

Phoenix Health Plans, Inc. (4)
3800 N Central Ave Ste 460, Phoenix, AZ 85012
Tel.: (602) 824-3700
Web Site: http://www.phoenixhealthplan.com
Health Care Srvices
N.A.I.C.S.: 621999

Subsidiary (Domestic):

VHS Acquisition Partnership Number 2, L.P. (2)
7901 Walker St, La Palma, CA 90623-1722
Tel.: (714) 670-6025
Health Care Srvices
N.A.I.C.S.: 621999

VHS Acquisition Subsidiary Number 3, Inc. (2)
4646 N Marine Dr, Chicago, IL 60640
Tel.: (773) 878-8700
General Medical Services
N.A.I.C.S.: 622110

VHS Acquisition Subsidiary Number 4, Inc. (2)
420 William St 2nd Fl, River Forest, IL 60305-1920
Tel.: (708) 488-2300
Web Site: http://www.westsubmc.com
Emp.: 40
General Medical Services
N.A.I.C.S.: 622110

VHS Acquisition Subsidiary Number 7, Inc. (2)
14201 Dallas Pkwy, Dallas, TX 75254
Tel.: (508) 383-1000
Emp.: 1
General Medical Services
N.A.I.C.S.: 622110

Subsidiary (Domestic):

Saint Vincent Physician Services, Inc. (3)
155 Federal St Ste 700, Boston, MA 02110
Tel.: (508) 363-9421
Health Care Srvices
N.A.I.C.S.: 621999

Subsidiary (Domestic):

VHS Acquisition Subsidiary Number 9, Inc. (2)
435 King St, Franklin, MA 02038
Tel.: (508) 553-3275
Web Site: https://www.mwmc.com
General Medical Services
N.A.I.C.S.: 622110

VHS San Antonio Imaging Partners, L.P. (2)

1763 Medical Way, New Braunfels, TX 78132
Tel.: (830) 327-1878
Web Site:
https://www.baptistmsimaging.com
Diagnostic Imaging Services
N.A.I.C.S.: 621512

VHS Valley Health System, LLC (2)
2075 E Flamingo Rd, Las Vegas, NV 89119
Tel.: (702) 388-4888
Web Site:
https://www.valleyhealthsystemlv.com
General Hospital & Medical Center Operator
N.A.I.C.S.: 622110

Subsidiary (Domestic):

VBOA ASC Partners, L.P. (3)
5700 N Expressway 77/83, Brownsville, TX 78526
Tel.: (956) 698-4870
General Medical Services
N.A.I.C.S.: 622110

VHS Brownsville Hospital Company, LLC (3)
1040 W Jefferson St, Brownsville, TX 78520
Tel.: (956) 698-5400
Web Site: https://www.valleybaptist.net
Sales Range: $50-74.9 Million
Emp.: 600
General Medical Services
N.A.I.C.S.: 622110

VHS Harlingen Hospital Company, LLC (3)
2101 Pease St, Harlingen, TX 78550
Tel.: (956) 389-1100
Web Site: https://www.valleybaptist.net
Sales Range: $100-124.9 Million
Emp.: 2,000
General Medical Services
N.A.I.C.S.: 622110

Valley Baptist Lab Services, LLC (3)
2121 Pease St Ste 102, Harlingen, TX 78550
Tel.: (956) 389-3800
Web Site: https://www.valleybaptist.net
General Medical Services
N.A.I.C.S.: 622110

Subsidiary (Domestic):

VHS Westlake Hospital, Inc. (2)
1225 W Lake St, Melrose Park, IL 60160-4000
Tel.: (708) 681-3000
Web Site: http://www.westlakehosp.com
General Medical Services
N.A.I.C.S.: 622110
Pat Shehorn (CEO)

VHS of Michigan, Inc. (2)
40600 Ann Arbor Rd E Ste 201, Plymouth, MI 48170
Tel.: (313) 745-5004
General Medical Services
N.A.I.C.S.: 622110

Subsidiary (Domestic):

DMC Education & Research (3)
40600 Ann Arbor Rd E Ste 201, Plymouth, MI 48170
Tel.: (615) 665-6006
Health Care Srvices
N.A.I.C.S.: 621999

Unit (Domestic):

Detroit Medical Center (3)
3663 Woodward Ave Orchestra Pl 4th Fl, Detroit, MI 48201
Tel.: (313) 745-5111
Web Site: http://www.dmc.org
Sales Range: $1-4.9 Billion
Emp.: 12,500
Hospital & Medical Center Operator
N.A.I.C.S.: 622110
Rudolph P. Valentini (Chief Medical Officer)
Gennie Snow (Chief Strategy Officer)
Brittany Lavis (CEO)
Quadiru Kent (Chief HR Officer)
Faye Griffin (Chief Compliance Officer)
John Levy (Chm)
Kathy Donovan (COO)

Tonita R. Cheatham (Chief Community Engagement Officer)
Brian Taylor (Dir-Communications)
Lela Hickonbottom (Chief Nursing Officer)

Unit (Domestic):

DMC Cardiovascular Institute (4)
3990 John R St, Detroit, MI 48201
Tel.: (313) 745-2700
Web Site: http://www.dmccvi.org
Cardiovascular Medical Center Operator
N.A.I.C.S.: 621999

Subsidiary (Domestic):

Heart & Vascular Institute of Michigan (3)
2340 Stonebridge Dr Bldg H, Flint, MI 48532
Tel.: (810) 422-9840
Web Site: https://www.hvimi.com
Health Care Srvices
N.A.I.C.S.: 621999

Michigan Pioneer ACO, LLC (3)
28411 Northwestern Hwy Ste 750, Southfield, MI 48034
Tel.: (248) 595-8819
Web Site:
http://www.michiganpioneeraco.com
Emp.: 30
General Medical Services
N.A.I.C.S.: 622110

VHS Children's Hospital of Michigan, Inc. (3)
3901 Beaubien Blvd, Detroit, MI 48201
Tel.: (313) 745-5437
Web Site: https://www.dmc.org
Sales Range: $150-199.9 Million
Emp.: 2,341
Children's Hospital & Specialty Medical Center Operator
N.A.I.C.S.: 622110
Kathy Donovan (CEO)

VHS Detroit Receiving Hospital, Inc. (3)
4201 St Antoine Blvd, Detroit, MI 48201
Tel.: (313) 745-3000
Web Site: https://www.dmc.org
Hospital
N.A.I.C.S.: 622110
Audrey Gregory (CEO)
Gary Purushotham (CEO--Grace Hospital)
Archie Drake (CEO-, , and)
Patty Jobbitt (CEO-)
Amy Hamilton (Chief Nursing Officer-)
Daniel Lee (Chief Strategy Officer-)
Allison DeMarais (Chief HR Officer-)
Lance Beus (CEO--Sinai Hospital)
Josh Hester (COO-)
Tommy Tran (COO-)
Ron Sagritalo (Chief Compliance Officer)

VHS Harper-Hutzel Hospital, Inc. (3)
3990 John R St, Detroit, MI 48201
Tel.: (313) 745-8040
Web Site: https://www.dmc.org
Hospitals & Medical Centers Operator
N.A.I.C.S.: 622110

Unit (Domestic):

DMC Surgery Hospital (4)
30671 Stephenson Hwy, Madison Heights, MI 48071
Tel.: (248) 733-2200
Hospital Operator
N.A.I.C.S.: 622110

Hutzel Women's Hospital (4)
3990 John R St, Detroit, MI 48201
Tel.: (313) 745-8040
Web Site: https://www.dmc.org
Women's Hospital Operator
N.A.I.C.S.: 622110
Thomas A. Malone (Pres)

Subsidiary (Domestic):

VHS Huron Valley-Sinai Hospital, Inc. (3)
1 William Carls Dr, Commerce Township, MI 48382
Tel.: (248) 937-3300
Web Site: http://www.dmc.org
Hospital Operator
N.A.I.C.S.: 622110

VHS Rehabilitation Institute of Michigan, Inc. (3)
261 Mack Blvd, Detroit, MI 48201
Tel.: (313) 745-1203
Web Site: https://www.rimrehab.org
Medical Rehabilitation Hospital & Health Centers Operator
N.A.I.C.S.: 622310

VHS Sinai-Grace Hospital, Inc. (3)
6071 W Outer Dr, Detroit, MI 48235
Tel.: (313) 966-3300
Web Site: https://www.dmc.org
Hospital & Specialty Care Medical Centers Operator
N.A.I.C.S.: 622110
Gary Purushotham (CEO)

VHS University Laboratories, Inc. (3)
4201 St Antoine Ste 3E 1, Detroit, MI 48201
Tel.: (313) 745-4100
Web Site: https://www.dmc.org
Medical Laboratory Services
N.A.I.C.S.: 621511

Subsidiary (Domestic):

Valley Health Care Network (2)
2101 Pease St, Harlingen, TX 78550
Tel.: (956) 389-1633
Web Site: http://www.valleybaptist.net
Emp.: 10
Health Care Srvices
N.A.I.C.S.: 621999

Vanguard Home Care, LLC (1)
2315 Enterprise Dr Ste 110, Westchester, IL 60154
Tel.: (708) 447-3555
Web Site:
http://www.vanguardhomecare.net
Women Healthcare Services
N.A.I.C.S.: 621610

Ventana Surgical Center, LLC (1)
18133 Ventura Blvd Ste 400, Tarzana, CA 91356-3645
Tel.: (818) 462-0280
Health Care Srvices
N.A.I.C.S.: 622110

Ventura Endoscopy Center Partners, LLC (1)
5810 Ralston St, Ventura, CA 93003
Tel.: (805) 650-5500
Ambulatory Health Care Services
N.A.I.C.S.: 621498

Wellington Endo, LLC (1)
1157 S State Rd 7, Wellington, FL 33414
Tel.: (561) 214-6094
Web Site:
http://wellingtonendoscopycenter.com
Surgical Center Services
N.A.I.C.S.: 621493

West Chester Surgical Suites, LLC (1)
8742-8744 Union Ctr Blvd, West Chester, OH 45069
Tel.: (513) 881-9270
Web Site:
https://westchestersurgicalsuites.com
Orthopaedic Surgical Services
N.A.I.C.S.: 621498

Westgate Surgery Center, LLC (1)
7330 N 99th Ave Ste 100, Glendale, AZ 85307
Tel.: (623) 888-5500
Web Site: http://westgatesurgerycenter.com
Surgical Center Services
N.A.I.C.S.: 621493

Westminster Surgery Center, LLC (1)
826 Washington Rd Ste 131, Westminster, MD 21157
Tel.: (410) 871-9440
Web Site: https://westminstersurg.com
Orthopaedic Surgical Services
N.A.I.C.S.: 621498

White Fence Surgical Suites, LLC (1)
7277 Smiths Mill Rd Ste 300, New Albany, OH 43054
Tel.: (614) 289-6282
Web Site: https://whitefencesurg.com

General Medical & Surgical Services
N.A.I.C.S.: 622110

Windsor Mill Surgery Center, LLC (1)
2373 Rolling Rd, Windsor Mill, MD 21244
Tel.: (443) 200-5600
Web Site:
https://windsormillsurgerycenter.com
General Medical & Surgical Services
N.A.I.C.S.: 622110

Wisconsin Specialty Surgery Center, LLC (1)
7401 104th Ave Ste 100, Kenosha, WI 53142
Tel.: (262) 697-1006
Web Site:
https://www.wisconsinspecialty.com
Surgical Care Services
N.A.I.C.S.: 621493

Yuma Advanced Surgical Suites, LLC (1)
1030 W 24th St Ste H, Yuma, AZ 85364
Tel.: (928) 259-7522
Web Site: https://yumasurgicalsuites.com
Surgical Center Services
N.A.I.C.S.: 622110

TENGJUN BIOTECHNOLOGY CORP.
527 Siltstone Pl, Cary, NC 27519
Tel.: (919) 869-0279   NV
Year Founded: 2010
TJBH—(OTCQB)
Rev.: $150,136,738
Assets: $58,629,500
Liabilities: $43,656,963
Net Worth: $14,972,537
Earnings: $11,346,841
Emp.: 27
Fiscal Year-end: 12/31/22
Holding Company
N.A.I.C.S.: 551112
Caihong Qu (Sec)
Qingbao Wang (CEO & CFO)

Subsidiaries:

Shandong Tengjunxiang Biotechnology Ltd. (1)
South Side Of Huimin Road East Side Of Jinze Road, Jinxiang Food Industry Economic and Technological Development Zone, Jining, China
Tel.: (86) 5378711599
Web Site: https://www.sdtjxsw.com
Tea Powder Mfr
N.A.I.C.S.: 311920

TENNANT COMPANY
10400 Clean St, Eden Prairie, MN 55344-2650
Tel.: (763) 540-1200   MN
Web Site: https://www.tennantco.com
Year Founded: 1870
TNC—(NYSE)
Rev.: $1,092,200,000
Assets: $1,085,100,000
Liabilities: $613,000,000
Net Worth: $472,100,000
Earnings: $66,300,000
Emp.: 4,299
Fiscal Year-end: 12/31/22
Non-Residential Floor Maintenance Equipment & Related Products Mfr, Designer & Retailer
N.A.I.C.S.: 333998
Fay West (CFO & Sr VP)
Rusty H. Zay (Chief Comml Officer & Sr VP)
David W. Huml (Pres & CEO)
Barb Balinski (Sr VP-Innovation & Tech)
Brock Christianson (Chief HR Officer & Sr VP)
Lorenzo Bassi (VP-Fin & IR)
Kristin Erickson (Gen Counsel, Sec & Sr VP)

Tennant Company—(Continued)

Subsidiaries:

Anhui Rongen Environmental Protection Technology Co., Ltd. (1)
Building 2 No 503 Xiangpu Road, High-tech Zone, Hefei, Anhui, China
Tel.: (86) 55165992060
Web Site: https://www.rongenclean.com
Emp.: 300
Cleaning Equipment Mfr
N.A.I.C.S.: 333310

Crawford Laboratories, Inc. (1)
1120 W Exchange Ave, Chicago, IL 60609-2699 (100%)
Tel.: (773) 376-7132
Web Site: http://www.florock.net
Sales Range: $1-9.9 Million
Emp.: 200
Polymer Flooring Services
N.A.I.C.S.: 423310

Eagle International LLC (1)
825 Main St, Lyons, NE 68038
Tel.: (605) 242-5213
Web Site: http://www.eagle-equipment.com
Tiles Mfr
N.A.I.C.S.: 333310

Foma Norge AS (1)
Regnbueveien 6, 1405, Langhus, Norway
Tel.: (47) 64917000
Web Site: https://foma.no
Non-residential Floor Maintenance Equipment Retailer
N.A.I.C.S.: 423850

IP Cleaning S.r.l. (1)
Viale Treviso 63, Summaga di Portogruar, 30026, Venice, VE, Italy
Tel.: (39) 0421205511
Web Site: https://www.ipcworldwide.com
Non-residential Floor Maintenance Equipment Retailer
N.A.I.C.S.: 423850

IP Gansow GmbH (1)
Dreherstrasse 9, 59425, Unna, Germany
Tel.: (49) 23 032 5800
Web Site: https://www.ipcworldwide.com
Vaccum Cleaner Whslr
N.A.I.C.S.: 423620

IPC Eagle Corporation (1)
12450 Oliver Ave S Ste 300, Burnsville, MN 55337
Tel.: (651) 686-5399
Web Site: https://www.ipcworldwide.com
Non-residential Floor Maintenance Equipment Retailer
N.A.I.C.S.: 423850

Interclean Assistance ICA S.A. (1)
346 avenue de la Couronne des Pres ZI, 78680, Epone, France
Tel.: (33) 13 095 0606
Web Site: https://www.ica.eu.com
Non-residential Floor Maintenance Equipment Retailer
N.A.I.C.S.: 423850

Tennant Australia (1)
Unit 11/4 Southridge Street, Eastern Creek, 2766, NSW, Australia
Tel.: (61) 29 839 9700
Web Site: https://au.tennantco.com
Sales Range: $50-74.9 Million
Emp.: 100
Floor Maintenance Machinery Mfr
N.A.I.C.S.: 333998

Tennant CEE GmbH (1)
Sommerfeld 1, 5202, Neumarkt, Am Wallersee, Austria
Tel.: (43) 6216452412
Web Site: http://www.tennantco.com
Sales Range: $75-99.9 Million
Emp.: 18
Floor Maintenance Equipment Mfr
N.A.I.C.S.: 333414

Tennant Cleaning System & Equipment Co. Ltd. (1)
Room 608 Building 5 Hongqiao Jiahui Lane 928 Shenhong Road, Minhang District, Shanghai, 201700, China
Tel.: (86) 2167008000
Web Site: https://www.tennantco.com.cn

Sales Range: $900-999.9 Million
Emp.: 100
Floor Maintenance Equipment Mfr
N.A.I.C.S.: 333414

Tennant Company Commercial, USA (1)
12875 Ransom St, Holland, MI 49424
Tel.: (616) 994-4000
Web Site: https://www.tennantco.com
Emp.: 200
Carpet Cleaning Equipment & Carpet Maintenance Mfr
N.A.I.C.S.: 333310

Tennant Europe B.V. (1)
Industrielaan 6, 5405 AB, Uden, Netherlands
Tel.: (31) 413241241
Web Site: https://nl.tennantco.com
Cleaning Equipment Mfr & Distr
N.A.I.C.S.: 423850

Tennant Europe N.V. (1)
Berchemstadionstraat 78, 2600, Antwerp, Belgium
Tel.: (32) 32179411
Sales Range: $25-49.9 Million
Emp.: 60
Floor Maintenance Machinery Mfr
N.A.I.C.S.: 333998

Tennant GmbH & Co. KG (1)
Dreherstrasse 9, D-59425, Unna, Germany
Tel.: (49) 230325800
Web Site: https://de.tennantco.com
Emp.: 60
Floor Maintenance Equipment Mfr
N.A.I.C.S.: 333998

Tennant Holding B.V. (1)
Industrielaan 6, 5405 AB, Uden, Netherlands (100%)
Tel.: (31) 413241241
Sales Range: $75-99.9 Million
Emp.: 200
Service Industry Machines
N.A.I.C.S.: 333310

Tennant N.V. (1)
Industrielaan 6, 5405 AB, Uden, Netherlands
Tel.: (31) 413241111
Emp.: 250
Cleaning Machinery & Equipment Mfr
N.A.I.C.S.: 333998

Tennant S.A. (1)
Tour Baikal 22 rue de Rome, Tremblay en France, 93 290, Villepinte, France
Tel.: (33) 149905000
Web Site: https://www.tennantco.com
Indoor & Outdoor Floor Cleaning & Maintenance Equipment Designer & Mfr
N.A.I.C.S.: 333998

Tennant Sales & Service Spain S.A. (1)
Avenida de las dos Castillas 33 Edificio Atica 3 planta 1 modulo A, Pozuelo de Alarcon, 28223, Madrid, Spain
Tel.: (34) 900900150
Web Site: https://www.tennantco.com
Floor Maintenance & Cleaning Equipment Mfr
N.A.I.C.S.: 333414

Tennant Sales and Service Company (1)
701 N Lilac Dr, Minneapolis, MN 55440
Tel.: (763) 540-1200
Web Site: https://www.tennantco.com
Floor Maintenance Equipment Sales & Repair Services
N.A.I.C.S.: 423850

Water Star, Inc. (1)
12369 Kinsman Rd Unit K, Parkman, OH 44080
Tel.: (440) 996-0800
Web Site: http://www.waterstarinc.com
Emp.: 15
Electrodes Mfr
N.A.I.C.S.: 335991

TENNESSEE VALLEY AUTHORITY
400 W Summit Hill Dr, Knoxville, TN 37902

Tel.: (865) 632-2101
Web Site: http://www.tva.com
Year Founded: 1933
TVE—(NYSE)
Rev.: $10,503,000,000
Assets: $52,456,000,000
Liabilities: $37,991,000,000
Net Worth: $14,465,000,000
Earnings: $1,512,000,000
Emp.: 10,192
Fiscal Year-end: 09/30/21
Electric Power Generation & Distr
N.A.I.C.S.: 221111
Jeannette Mills *(Chief External Rels Officer & Exec VP)*
Heidi T. Smith *(Dir-Global Bus)*
Diane T. Wear *(VP & Controller)*
Susan E. Collins *(Chief Comm Officer, Chief People Officer & Exec VP)*
Jeffrey J. Lyash *(Pres & CEO)*
Timothy S. Rausch *(Chief Nuclear Officer & Exec VP)*
David B. Fountain *(Gen Counsel & Exec VP)*
Donald A. Moul *(COO & Exec VP)*
Stephen Surles *(Dir-Economic Dev Incentive Programs)*
Lee Johnson *(Sr Mgr-Field Ops)*
Harry Schmidt *(Mgr, Corp Counsel, Sec, Exec VP, Sr VP & Sr VP)*
Bess Hubbard *(Mgr, Mgr, Corp Counsel, Sec, Exec VP, Sr VP & Sr VP)*
John M. Thomas III *(CFO, Chief Strategy Officer & Exec VP)*

TENNESSEE VALLEY FINANCIAL HOLDINGS, INC.
401 S Illinois Ave, Oak Ridge, TN 37830

Tel.: (865) 483-9444   TN
Year Founded: 1995
TVLF—(OTCIQ)
Bank Holding Company
N.A.I.C.S.: 551111
Thomas E. Tuck *(Chm, Pres & CEO)*
Debbie Lindsey *(Sr VP)*
Sarah Robinson *(CFO & Sr VP)*

TENON MEDICAL, INC.
104 Cooper Ct, Los Gatos, CA 95032

Tel.: (408) 649-5760   DE
Web Site: https://www.tenonmed.com
Year Founded: 2012
TNON—(NASDAQ)
Rev.: $691,000
Assets: $11,089,000
Liabilities: $4,837,000
Net Worth: $6,252,000
Earnings: ($18,917,000)
Emp.: 22
Fiscal Year-end: 12/31/22
Medical Device Mfr
N.A.I.C.S.: 339112
Richard M. Ferrari *(Chm)*
Steven M. Foster *(Co-Chm, Pres, CEO & Sec)*
Richard Ginn *(Co-Founder & CTO)*
Richard Ferrari *(Chm)*

TERADATA CORPORATION
17095 Via del Campo, San Diego, CA 92127   DE

Web Site: https://www.teradata.com
Year Founded: 1979
TDC—(NYSE)
Rev.: $1,833,000,000
Assets: $1,873,000,000
Liabilities: $1,738,000,000
Net Worth: $135,000,000
Earnings: $62,000,000
Emp.: 6,500
Fiscal Year-end: 12/31/23
Holding Company; Data Warehousing & Analytic Technology Products & Services
N.A.I.C.S.: 551112

Stephen Brobst *(CTO)*
Hillary Ashton *(Chief Product Officer)*
Stephen McMillan *(Pres & CEO)*
Nicolas Chapman *(Chief Strategy Officer)*
Molly Treese *(Chief Legal Officer)*
Claire Bramley *(CFO & Principal Acctg Officer)*
Jacqueline Woods *(CMO)*
Michael Hutchinson *(Chief Customer Officer)*

Subsidiaries:

PT. TData Indonesia (1)
Indonesia Stock Exchange Tower 2 17th Floor Suite 4 5, Jl Jendral Sudirman Kav 52-53, Jakarta, 12190, Indonesia
Tel.: (62) 2152917417
Data Warehousing & Analytic Technology Products & Services
N.A.I.C.S.: 518210

TDATA Corporation (Malaysia) Sdn. Bhd. (1)
Level 7 Menara Pernas Tower 7 Avenue 7 The Horizon Phase 2, Bangsar South No 8 Jalan Kerinchi, 59200, Kuala Lumpur, Malaysia
Tel.: (60) 322813600
Web Site: https://
Data Warehousing & Analytic Technology Products & Services
N.A.I.C.S.: 518210

TDC Colombia Limitada (1)
Transversal 23 No 97-73 Oficina 204, Bogota, Colombia
Tel.: (57) 14322610
Sales Range: $10-24.9 Million
Emp.: 24
Data Warehousing & Analytic Technology Products & Services
N.A.I.C.S.: 518210

TRDT Brasil Tecnologia Ltda. (1)
JK Iguatemi Avenida Presidente Juscelino Kubitschek 2041, Sao Paulo, 04543-011, Brazil
Tel.: (55) 91158066766
Sales Range: $25-49.9 Million
Emp.: 60
Data Warehousing & Analytic Technology Products & Services
N.A.I.C.S.: 518210

TeraWarehouse Korea Co., Ltd. (1)
7/F S7001-7002 431 Teheran-ro, Gangnam-gu, Seoul, 06164, Korea (South)
Tel.: (82) 220714300
Web Site: http://www.teradata.kr
Sales Range: $25-49.9 Million
Emp.: 50
Data Warehousing & Analytic Technology Products & Services
N.A.I.C.S.: 518210

Teradata (NZ) Corporation (1)
Level 26 PwC Tower 188 Quay Street, Auckland, New Zealand
Tel.: (64) 21435423
Data Warehousing & Analytic Technology Products & Services
N.A.I.C.S.: 518210

Teradata (Singapore) Pte. Ltd. (1)
6 Temasek Boulevard 15-01/02 Suntec Tower Four, Singapore, 038986, Singapore
Tel.: (65) 63983200
Data Warehousing & Analytic Technology Products & Services
N.A.I.C.S.: 518210
Attif Khattari *(Gen Mgr)*

Teradata (Thailand) Co Ltd (1)
63 Athenee Tower 15th Floor Unit 1507/1 Wireless Road, Lumpini Pathumwan, Bangkok, 10330, Thailand
Tel.: (66) 21688161
Web Site: http://www.teradata.com
Sales Range: $10-24.9 Million
Emp.: 40
Data Warehousing & Analytic Technology Products & Services
N.A.I.C.S.: 518210
Jeerapa Kongswangwongsa *(Mng Dir)*

Teradata Australia Pty. Ltd. (1)
Tel.: (61) 261221211

Sales Range: $25-49.9 Million
Emp.: 100
Data Warehousing & Analytic Technology
Products & Services
N.A.I.C.S.: 518210

Teradata Austria GmbH (1)
Parkring 2, 1010, Vienna, Austria
Tel.: (43) 1227150
Web Site: http://www.teradata.com
Data Warehousing & Analytic Technology
Products & Services
N.A.I.C.S.: 518210

Teradata Belgium SNC (1)
Avenue Louise 489, 1050, Brussels, Belgium
Tel.: (32) 205128180
Web Site: https://www.teradataemea.com
Sales Range: $10-24.9 Million
Emp.: 20
Data Warehousing & Analytic Technology
Products & Services
N.A.I.C.S.: 518210

Teradata Bilisim Sistemleri Ltd. Sti. (1)
Barbaros Mah Agaoglu My Prestije, No 1 K 1 146/A Atasehir, Istanbul, 34746, Turkiye
Tel.: (90) 2165594000
Web Site: http://www.teradata.com
Business Analytics, Hybrid Cloud, Data Warehousing & Analytic Technology Products & Services
N.A.I.C.S.: 518210

Teradata Canada ULC (1)
6303 Airport Road Suite 300, Mississauga, L4V 1R8, ON, Canada
Tel.: (905) 364-4649
Web Site: http://www.teradata.com
Data Warehousing & Analytic Technology
Products & Services
N.A.I.C.S.: 518210

Teradata Ceska republika spol. s r.o. (1)
Na Strzi 1702/65, 140 00, Prague, 4, Czech Republic
Tel.: (420) 261384326
Software Application Services
N.A.I.C.S.: 541511

Teradata Chile Tecnologias de Informacion Limitada (1)
Cerro Colorado 5240 Torre del Parque II Piso 16, Las Condes, 7560995, Santiago, Chile
Tel.: (56) 228629800
Data Warehousing & Analytic Technology
Products & Services
N.A.I.C.S.: 518210

Teradata Czech Republic, spol. s r.o. (1)
Na Strzi 1702/65, 140 00, Prague, Czech Republic
Tel.: (420) 261384111
Web Site: http://www.teradata.com
Sales Range: $25-49.9 Million
Emp.: 200
Data Warehousing & Analytic Technology
Products & Services
N.A.I.C.S.: 518210

Teradata Danmark ApS (1)
Tuborg Boulevard 12 Suites 410 434 436, Hellerup, 2900, Copenhagen, Denmark
Tel.: (45) 38143000
Sales Range: $10-24.9 Million
Emp.: 60
Data Warehousing & Analytic Technology
Products & Services
N.A.I.C.S.: 518210

Teradata Egypt WLL (1)
5th Settlement 90th Street Downtown Mall Building S2 2A 2nd Floor, 11835, New Cairo, Egypt
Tel.: (20) 235703266
Data Warehousing & Analytic Technology
Product & Services
N.A.I.C.S.: 493190

Teradata Finland Oy (1)
Metsanneidonkuja 10, 02130, Espoo, Finland
Tel.: (358) 104218700
Data Warehousing & Analytic Technology
Products & Services

N.A.I.C.S.: 518210

Teradata France SAS (1)
Antony Parc I 2-6 place du General de Gaulle, 92184, Antony, Cedex, France
Tel.: (33) 178953400
Sales Range: $25-49.9 Million
Emp.: 110
Data Warehousing & Analytic Technology
Products & Services
N.A.I.C.S.: 518210

Teradata GmbH (1)
Tel.: (49) 89444451500
Web Site: http://www.teradata.com
Data Warehousing & Analytic Technology
Products & Services
N.A.I.C.S.: 518210

Teradata Iberia SLU (1)
Tel.: (34) 910765500
Sales Range: $25-49.9 Million
Emp.: 95
Data Warehousing & Analytic Technology
Products & Services
N.A.I.C.S.: 518210
Jose Andres Garcia *(Mng Dir)*

Teradata India Private Limited (1)
5th floor Building No 5 Plot No 3 Mindspace, Serene Properties pvt Ltd SEZ Thane Belapur Road Airoli Navi, Mumbai, 400708, India
Tel.: (91) 2261050100
Data Warehousing & Analytic Technology
Products & Services
N.A.I.C.S.: 518210

Teradata Information Systems (Beijing) Limited (1)
9th Floor Block A Gemdale Plaza No 91 Jianguo Road, Chaoyang District, Beijing, 100022, China
Tel.: (86) 1059055099
Data Warehousing & Analytic Technology
Products & Services
N.A.I.C.S.: 518210

Teradata Ireland Limited (1)
Block B The Crescent Building, Northwood Santry, Dublin, D09 C6X8, Ireland
Tel.: (353) 18934126
Data Warehousing & Analytic Technology
Products & Services
N.A.I.C.S.: 518210

Teradata Italia S.r.l. (1)
Via Cusago 150/4, 20153, Milan, Italy
Tel.: (39) 0245339001
Data Warehousing & Analytic Technology
Products & Services
N.A.I.C.S.: 518210

Teradata Japan Ltd. (1)
2-23-1 Akasaka, Minato-ku, Tokyo, 107-0052, Japan
Tel.: (81) 367596161
Web Site: https://www.teradata.jp
Emp.: 500
Data Warehousing & Analytic Technology
Products & Services
N.A.I.C.S.: 518210

Teradata LLC (1)
Denisovskliy pereulok 26 5th floor, 105005, Moscow, Russia
Tel.: (7) 4957818226
Web Site: http://www.teradata.com
Sales Range: $25-49.9 Million
Emp.: 130
Data Warehousing & Analytic Technology
Product & Services
N.A.I.C.S.: 493190

Teradata Magyarorszag Kft (1)
Hermina ut 17, Budapest, 1146, Hungary
Tel.: (36) 14719700
Web Site: http://www.teradata.com
Data Warehousing & Analytic Technology
Products & Services
N.A.I.C.S.: 518210

Teradata Netherlands B.V. (1)
Barbara Strozzilaan 201, 1083 HN, Amsterdam, Netherlands
Tel.: (31) 205128180
Web Site: http://in.teradata.com
Emp.: 75
Data Processing & Hosting Services
N.A.I.C.S.: 518210

Teradata Norge AS (1)
Nydalsveien 33, Oslo, 0484, Norway
Tel.: (47) 21520259
Sales Range: $10-24.9 Million
Emp.: 15
Data Warehousing & Analytic Technology
Products & Services
N.A.I.C.S.: 518210

Teradata Operations, Inc. (1)
17095 Via Del Campo, San Diego, CA 92127
Tel.: (937) 242-4030
Data Warehousing & Analytic Technology
Product & Services
N.A.I.C.S.: 334111
Laura Jividen *(Dir)*
Angie Snavely *(Dir)*
Bruce Teeters *(Pres)*
Brian Pierson *(Treas)*

Subsidiary (Domestic):

Claraview, Inc. (2)
11400 Commerce Park Dr Ste 500, Reston, VA 20191
Tel.: (703) 269-1500
Web Site: http://www.claraview.com
Emp.: 175
Data Warehousing & Business Intelligence Services
N.A.I.C.S.: 518210

Hadapt Inc. (2)
614 Massachusetts Ave 4th Fl, Cambridge, MA 02139
Tel.: (617) 539-6110
Web Site: http://www.hadapt.com
Sales Range: $1-9.9 Million
Big Data Analytics Software
N.A.I.C.S.: 513210

Division (Domestic):

Teradata Aster Data (2)
999 Skyway Rd Ste 100, San Carlos, CA 94070
Tel.: (650) 232-4400
Web Site: http://www.asterdata.com
Data Management & Analysis Solutions
N.A.I.C.S.: 513210

Subsidiary (Domestic):

Teradata Government Systems LLC (1)
181 Harry S Truman Pkwy Ste 100, Annapolis Junction, MD 21401
Tel.: (410) 379-9200
Data Warehousing & Analytic Technology
Product & Services
N.A.I.C.S.: 493190

Think Big Analytics, Inc. (2)
520 San Antonio Rd Ste 210, Mountain View, CA 94040
Tel.: (650) 949-2350
Web Site: http://www.thinkbiganalytics.com
Sales Range: $1-9.9 Million
Information Technology Services
N.A.I.C.S.: 541511

Teradata Pakistan Limited (1)
1st Floor Nic Building 63 Jinnah Avenue, Blue Area, Islamabad, Pakistan
Tel.: (92) 512871400
Data Warehousing & Analytic Technology
Products & Services
N.A.I.C.S.: 518210

Teradata Philippines LLC, Manila Branch (1)
3rd Floor Midway Court 241 EDSA Wack-Wack Greenhills, Mandaluyong, 1555, Philippines
Tel.: (63) 27558890
Sales Range: $10-24.9 Million
Emp.: 10
Data Warehousing & Analytic Technology
Products & Services
N.A.I.C.S.: 518210
Ella Mae Ortega *(Country Mgr)*

Teradata Polska Sp. z o.o (1)
Tel.: (48) 224389700
Web Site: http://www.teradata.pl
Data Warehousing & Analytic Technology
Products & Services
N.A.I.C.S.: 518210

Teradata Saudi Arabia LLC (1)

Centria Center 5th floor Olaya Street, PO Box 9820, Riyadh, 11423, Saudi Arabia
Tel.: (966) 112246723
Electronic Computer Mfr
N.A.I.C.S.: 334111

Teradata Schweiz GmbH (1)
Tel.: (41) 445679308
Web Site: https://www.teradata.com
Sales Range: $25-49.9 Million
Emp.: 50
Data Warehousing & Analytic Technology
Products & Services
N.A.I.C.S.: 518210

Teradata Sweden AB (1)
Kronborgsgrand 5, 164 87, Kista, Stockholm, Sweden
Tel.: (46) 86338900
Sales Range: $10-24.9 Million
Emp.: 20
Data Warehousing & Analytic Technology
Products & Services
N.A.I.C.S.: 518210
Magnus Palmaer *(Mng Dir)*

Teradata Taiwan LLC (1)
34/F Unit 3761 Taipei Nanshan Plaza 100 Songren Road, Xinyi District, Taipei, 110, Taiwan
Tel.: (886) 221754501
Data Warehousing & Analytic Technology
Product & Services
N.A.I.C.S.: 493190

Teradata UK Limited (1)
3 London Bridge Street 4th Floor, London, SE1 9SG, United Kingdom
Tel.: (44) 2081649000
Web Site: https://www.teradata.com
Sales Range: $25-49.9 Million
Emp.: 120
Data Warehousing & Analytic Technology
Products & Services
N.A.I.C.S.: 518210

Teradata de Argentina S.R.L. (1)
Juan Diaz de Solis 1270- Piso 1 1638, Vincente Lopez, Buenos Aires, Argentina
Tel.: (54) 1148371500
Data Warehousing & Analytic Technology
Products & Services
N.A.I.C.S.: 518210
Juan Pablo do Carmo *(Country Mgr)*

Teradata de Mexico, S. de R.L. de C.V. (1)
Mariano Escobedo 476-103 Nueva Anzures, Miguel Hidalgo, 11590, Mexico, Mexico
Tel.: (52) 5541518000
Web Site: http://www.teradata.com
Data Warehousing & Analytic Technology
Products & Services
N.A.I.C.S.: 518210

TERADYNE, INC.
600 Riverpark Dr, North Reading, MA 01864
Tel.: (978) 370-2700   MA
Web Site: https://www.teradyne.com
Year Founded: 1960
TER—(NASDAQ)
Rev.: $2,676,298,000
Assets: $3,486,824,000
Liabilities: $960,927,000
Net Worth: $2,525,897,000
Earnings: $448,752,000
Emp.: 6,500
Fiscal Year-end: 12/31/23
Automatic Test Equipment Designer & Mfr
N.A.I.C.S.: 334515
Paul G. Igoe *(Asst Sec & Assoc Gen Counsel)*
Michal Kimeldorfer Rabinowitz *(VP-HR)*
Brad Robbins *(Pres-LitePoint)*
Andrew Blanchard *(VP-Corp Rels)*
Gregory S. Smith *(Pres & CEO)*
Sanjay Mehta *(CFO, Treas & VP)*
John Wood *(VP & Gen Mgr-Sys Test Grp)*
Richard Burns *(Pres-Semiconductor Test Div)*
Kim Povlsen *(Pres-Universal Robots)*

Teradyne, Inc.—(Continued)

Subsidiaries:

Eagle Test Systems, Inc. (1)
2200 Millbrook Dr, Buffalo Grove, IL 60089
Tel.: (847) 478-0331
Web Site: https://www.teradyne.com
Automated Test Equipment Mfr
N.A.I.C.S.: 333242

Lemsys SA (1)
18 chemin des Aulx, 1228, Geneva, Switzerland
Tel.: (41) 227061050
Web Site: https://www.lemsys.com
Electronic Components Mfr
N.A.I.C.S.: 334419
Giuseppe Santandrea (CEO)

LitePoint Corp. (1)
180 Rose Orchard Way, San Jose, CA 95134
Tel.: (408) 456-5000
Web Site: https://www.litepoint.com
Sales Range: $75-99.9 Million
Wireless Device Testing Solutions
N.A.I.C.S.: 541330
Benny Madsen (Co-Founder)
Christian Olgaard (Co-Founder & CTO)
Faruq Palla (Sr VP-Ops)
Niels Vinggaard (Sr VP-Engrg)
James Chang (VP-Fin)
David Yin (VP-)

Subsidiary (Domestic):

Ztec Instruments, Inc. (2)
7715 Tiburon St NE, Albuquerque, NM 87109
Tel.: (505) 342-0132
Web Site: http://www.ztecinstruments.com
Sales Range: $1-9.9 Million
Emp.: 25
Modular RF & Baseband Test Equipment Mfr
N.A.I.C.S.: 334513

LitePoint Europe A/S (1)
Alfred Nobels Vej 27 3, 9220, Aalborg, Denmark
Tel.: (45) 4 810 7070
Web Site: https://www.litepoint.com
Emp.: 100
Automatic Test Equipment Mfr
N.A.I.C.S.: 334515

LitePoint Japan K.K. (1)
7F MM park Building 3-6-3 Minatomirai, Nishi-ku, Yokohama, 220-0012, Japan
Tel.: (81) 454143641
Web Site: http://www.litepoint.com
Sales Range: $25-49.9 Million
Emp.: 6
Automated Test Equipment Distr
N.A.I.C.S.: 423830

LitePoint Technology (Shanghai) Company Ltd. (1)
Room G-I 6F K-Building No 28 Keji South Road 12th, Nanshan District, Shenzhen, 518057, China
Tel.: (86) 7553 391 0588
Web Site: https://www.litepoint.com
Automated Test Equipment Distr
N.A.I.C.S.: 423830

Mobile Industrial Robots A/S (1)
Emil Neckelmanns Vej 15F, 5220, Odense, Denmark
Tel.: (45) 20377577
Web Site: https://www.mobile-industrial-robots.com
Mobile Robot Mfr
N.A.I.C.S.: 336110

Mobile Industrial Robots GmbH (1)
Frankfurter Str 27, Eschborn, 65760, Frankfurt am Main, Germany
Tel.: (49) 61967754751
Mobile Robot Mfr
N.A.I.C.S.: 336110

Mobile Industrial Robots Pte. Ltd. (1)
51 Science Park Road 02-01 The Aries Singapore Science Park 2, Singapore, 117586, Singapore
Tel.: (65) 67700822
Mobile Robot Mfr

Teradata Norge AS
N.A.I.C.S.: 336110

Mobile Industrial Robots, Inc. (1)
1340-2 Lincoln Ave, Holbrook, NY 11741
Tel.: (631) 675-1838
Mobile Robot Mfr
N.A.I.C.S.: 336110

Teradyne (Shanghai) Co., Ltd (1)
Building 10 2nd Fl 1201 Gui Qiao Rd, Jin Qiao Export Processing Zone Pudong, Shanghai, 201206, China
Tel.: (86) 213 842 4668
Web Site: https://www.teradyne.com
Emp.: 200
Automatic Test Equipment Mfr
N.A.I.C.S.: 334515

Teradyne GmbH (1)
Inselkammerstrase 14, 82008, Unterhaching, Germany
Tel.: (49) 8 941 8610
Web Site: https://www.teradyne.com
Emp.: 50
Automatic Test Equipment Mfr
N.A.I.C.S.: 334515

Teradyne Korea Ltd. (1)
Hi-Brand Bldg Rm 1012-1022 10th Fl 215 Yangjae-dong, Seocho-ku, Seoul, 006-771, Korea (South)
Tel.: (82) 221552888
Automatic Test Equipment Mfr & Distr
N.A.I.C.S.: 334515

Teradyne Robots (Germany) GmbH (1)
Inselkammerstrase 14, 82008, Unterhaching, Germany
Tel.: (49) 89418610
Temperature Control Device Distr
N.A.I.C.S.: 423730

Teradyne Taiwan Ltd. (1)
Tai Yuen Hi-Tech Industrial Park 3F No 20 Tai Yuen St, Jubei City, Hsin-chu, 302, Taiwan
Tel.: (886) 35530808
Automatic Test Equipment Mfr
N.A.I.C.S.: 334515

Teradyne, Inc.-Assembly Test Division (1)
700 Riverpark Dr, North Reading, MA 01864
Tel.: (978) 370-2700
Web Site: http://www.teradyne.com
Sales Range: $100-124.9 Million
Emp.: 1,000
Circuit Board Test Systems
N.A.I.C.S.: 334515

Teradyne, Inc.-Integra Test Division (1)
500 Riverpark Dr, North Reading, MA 01864-2615
Tel.: (781) 275-1817
Web Site: http://www.teradyne.com
Sales Range: $25-49.9 Million
Emp.: 100
Semiconductor Test Equipment
N.A.I.C.S.: 334413

Teradyne, Inc.-Memory Test Division (1)
30701 Agoura Rd, Agoura Hills, CA 91301
Tel.: (818) 991-2900
Web Site: http://www.teradyne.com
Sales Range: $1-4.9 Billion
VLSI Logic Test Systems, Memory Test Systems
N.A.I.C.S.: 334220

Teradyne, K.K. (1)
MM Park Building 7F 3-6-3 Minatomirai, Nishi-ku, Yokohama, 220-0012, Kanagawa, Japan
Tel.: (81) 962921300
Web Site: https://www.teradyne.co.jp
Sales Range: $75-99.9 Million
Emp.: 192
Sales of Electronic Test Systems
N.A.I.C.S.: 541380
Andrew Blanchard (Pres)

Universal Robots (India) Pte. Ltd. (1)
Regus Centre Level 9 Raheja Towers 26-27 Mahatma Gandhi Road, E1 Manyata Embassy Business Park Nagawara, Bengaluru,

560001, KA, India
Tel.: (91) 9172289666
Industrial Robot Development Services
N.A.I.C.S.: 541380

Universal Robots (Shanghai) Co. Ltd. (1)
19th Floor Building B Jing'An International Center No 88 Puji Road, Jingan District, Shanghai, 200070, China
Tel.: (86) 2161326418
Industrial Robot Development Services
N.A.I.C.S.: 541380

Universal Robots (Singapore) Pte. Ltd. (1)
51 Science Park Road The Aries Science Park II 02-19, Singapore, 117586, Singapore
Tel.: (65) 67700821
Industrial Robot Development Services
N.A.I.C.S.: 541380

Universal Robots (Spain) S.L. (1)
c/Agricultura 106, 08019, Barcelona, Spain
Tel.: (34) 933158076
Industrial Robot Development Services
N.A.I.C.S.: 541380

Universal Robots (USA), Inc. (1)
909 Lk Carolyn Pkwy Ste 1850, Irving, TX 75039
Tel.: (469) 284-8520
Industrial Robot Development Services
N.A.I.C.S.: 541380

Universal Robots A/S (1)
Energivej 25, 5260, Odense, Denmark
Tel.: (45) 89938989
Web Site: https://www.universal-robots.com
Industrial Robot Development Services
N.A.I.C.S.: 541380
Peter Hern (Mgr-Australia & New Zealand)
Kim Povlsen (Pres)

Universal Robots GmbH (1)
Zielstattstr 36, 81379, Munich, Germany
Tel.: (49) 8912189720
Industrial Robot Development Services
N.A.I.C.S.: 541380

TERAWULF INC.
9 Federal St, Easton, MD 21601
Tel.: (410) 770-9500   DE
Web Site: https://www.terawulf.com
WULF—(NASDAQ)
Rev.: $15,033,000
Assets: $317,687,000
Liabilities: $199,933,000
Net Worth: $117,754,000
Earnings: ($91,574,000)
Emp.: 8
Fiscal Year-end: 12/31/22
Investment Services
N.A.I.C.S.: 523999
Paul Prager (Co-Founder, Chm & CEO)

Subsidiaries:

Ikonics Corporation (1)
4832 Grand Ave, Duluth, MN 55807
Tel.: (218) 628-2217
Web Site: http://www.ikonics.com
Rev.: $13,432,220
Assets: $15,435,399
Liabilities: $3,596,053
Net Worth: $11,839,346
Earnings: ($439,320)
Emp.: 50
Fiscal Year-end: 12/31/2020
Mfr, Developer & Marketer of Petrochemical Imaging Products
N.A.I.C.S.: 325992
Kenneth Hegman (COO)

Division (Domestic):

Chromaline Screen Print Products (2)
4832 Grand Ave, Duluth, MN 55807
Tel.: (218) 628-2217
Web Site: https://www.chromaline.com
Sales Range: $100-124.9 Million
Imaging Products Mfr
N.A.I.C.S.: 323111

IKONSIGN Etch (2)

4832 Grand Ave, Duluth, MN 55807
Tel.: (218) 628-2217
Sales Range: $75-99.9 Million
Sign Mfr
N.A.I.C.S.: 339950
William C. Ulland (Chm, Pres & CEO)

TERAX ENERGY, INC.
13355 Noel Rd Ste 124 PMB-415, Dallas, TX 75244
Tel.: (214) 386-7350   NV
TEXG—(OTCIQ)
Oil & Gas Exploration Services
N.A.I.C.S.: 213112
Charles Stidham (Pres & CEO)

TEREX CORPORATION
45 Glover Ave, Norwalk, CT 06850
Tel.: (203) 222-7170   DE
Web Site: https://www.terex.com
Year Founded: 1986
TEX—(NYSE)
Rev.: $4,417,700,000
Assets: $3,118,100,000
Liabilities: $1,936,900,000
Net Worth: $1,181,200,000
Earnings: $300,000,000
Emp.: 9,300
Fiscal Year-end: 12/31/22
Heavy-Duty Earthmoving & Lifting Equipment for the Infrastructure, Construction & Mining Industries
N.A.I.C.S.: 423830
Stacey B. Babson-Smith (Chief Ethics & Compliance Officer & VP)
Amy J. George (Chief HR Officer & Sr VP-HR)
Andrew Campbell (CIO & VP)
Simon A. Meester (Pres & CEO)
Julie A. Beck (CFO & Sr VP)
Scott J. Posner (Gen Counsel, Sec & Sr VP)
Randy S. Williamson (Chief Strategy Officer & VP-Corp Dev)
Simon A. Meester (Pres-Genie)
Stacey Babson Kaplan (VP)
Paretosh Misra (Head-IR)
Kieran Hegarty (Pres-Matls Processing)

Subsidiaries:

CBI Europe B.V. (1)
Fuulweg 0, 7442 CL, Nijverdal, Netherlands
Tel.: (31) 548374906
Industrial Machinery & Equipment Distr
N.A.I.C.S.: 423830
Ulf Osterroos (Sls Mgr)

CMI Terex Corporation (1)
9528 W I40 Service Rd, Oklahoma City, OK 73128
Tel.: (405) 787-6020
Web Site: http://www.terex.com
Sales Range: $800-899.9 Million
Emp.: 2,000
Road Paving & Construction Equipment Mfr
N.A.I.C.S.: 333120

Subsidiary (Non-US):

CMI International (2)
Shepherd's Grove Indus. Est., Stanton, Bury Saint Edmunds, IP31 2AR, Suffolk, United Kingdom
Sales Range: $900-999.9 Million
Management Training
N.A.I.C.S.: 611430

Subsidiary (Domestic):

Terex Advance Mixer, Inc. (2)
7727 Freedom Way, Fort Wayne, IN 46818
Tel.: (260) 497-0728
Web Site: https://www.terex.com
Sales Range: $100-124.9 Million
Emp.: 110
Mixers
N.A.I.C.S.: 333120
Keith Brown (Mgr-Parts)

Environmental Solutions Group (1)
201 W Main St Ste 300, Chattanooga, TN 37408
Web Site: https://www.doveresg.com
Holding Company; Solid Waste Collection Vehicles & Equipment Mfr
N.A.I.C.S.: 551112

Subsidiary (Domestic):

Alliance Wireless Technologies, Inc. (2)
9940 W Sam Houston Pkwy, Houston, TX 77099 (100%)
Tel.: (713) 690-4100
Web Site: http://www.awti.com
Sales Range: $1-9.9 Million
Emp.: 23
Mobile & Facility Vision Technology Solutions
N.A.I.C.S.: 423690
Darrick Reed (Pres)

Bayne Machine Works, Inc. (2)
910 Fork Schoals Rd, Greenville, SC 29605 (100%)
Tel.: (864) 288-3877
Web Site: http://www.baynethinline.com
Waste Handling Machine Mfr
N.A.I.C.S.: 333248

Marathon Equipment Company (2)
Hwy 9 S, Vernon, AL 35592-1798
Tel.: (205) 695-9105
Web Site:
    https://www.marathonequipment.com
Waste Compaction Equipment Mfr
N.A.I.C.S.: 333310

The Heil Co. (2)
201 W Main St Ste 300, Chattanooga, TN 37408
Web Site: https://www.heil.com
Dump Body & Hoist Mfr
N.A.I.C.S.: 333924

Subsidiary (Non-US):

Heil Asia Limited (3)
168 Moo 16 Udomsorayut Road Bang Grasan, Bang Pa-in, Ayutthaya, 13160, Thailand
Tel.: (66) 35221090
Web Site: http://www.heilasia.com
Dry Bulk Tanks & Trailer Mfr
N.A.I.C.S.: 332420

Heil Farid European Company Limited (3)
Taxi Way Hillend Industrial Estate, Dunfermline, KY11 9ES, Fife, United Kingdom
Tel.: (44) 1383823625
Web Site: http://www.hillendeng.com
Waste Management Vehicle Bodies Mfr
N.A.I.C.S.: 336110

Unit (Domestic):

The Heil Co. - Alabama (3)
106 45th St NE, Fort Payne, AL 35967
Tel.: (256) 845-4912
Web Site: http://www.heil.com
Sales Range: $200-249.9 Million
Emp.: 27,000
Truck & Bus Bodies Mfr
N.A.I.C.S.: 336211

The Heil Co. - Mississippi (3)
1425 Hwy 25, Tishomingo, MS 38873-9770
Tel.: (662) 438-7800
Web Site: http://www.duraclass.com
Sales Range: $50-74.9 Million
Emp.: 150
Truck & Bus Bodies Mfr
N.A.I.C.S.: 336211

Genie Scandinavia AB (1)
Arods Industrivag 34, 422 43, Hisings Backa, Sweden
Tel.: (46) 31575100
Software Services
N.A.I.C.S.: 541511

Horsky Hotel TATRA, spol. s.r.o. (1)
Na Mikulçove 505, 756 06, Velke Karlovice, Czech Republic
Tel.: (420) 571444323
Web Site: http://www.hoteltatra.cz
Sales Range: $125-149.9 Million
Emp.: 15
Hotel

N.A.I.C.S.: 721110

Platform Service and Repair Limited (1)
Shropshire House Hortonwood 1, Telford, TF1 7GN, Shropshire, United Kingdom
Tel.: (44) 8081694984
Web Site:
    http://www.platformservicerepair.co.uk
Industrial Machinery Repair & Maintenance Services
N.A.I.C.S.: 811310

TBA Romania S.R.L. (1)
Str Ady Endre nr 2, Satu-Mare, Romania
Tel.: (40) 747033263
Construction Machinery Equipment Mfr
N.A.I.C.S.: 333120

Terex Aerial Work Platforms (1)
20021 120th Ave NE, Bothell, WA 98011
Tel.: (425) 881-1800
Web Site: http://www.terex.com
Sales Range: $150-199.9 Million
Emp.: 280
Aerial Work Platform, Lift & Boom Developer & Mfr
N.A.I.C.S.: 423830
Simon A. Meester (COO)

Subsidiary (Domestic):

Genie Industries, Inc. (2)
6464 185th Ave NE, Redmond, WA 98052
Tel.: (425) 881-1800
Web Site: http://www.genielift.com
Machinery & Equipment Leasing Services
N.A.I.C.S.: 333923

Subsidiary (Non-US):

Genie Australia Pty. Ltd. (3)
591 Bourdary Rd, Darra, 4076, QLD, Australia
Tel.: (61) 733751660
Web Site:
    http://www.genieindustries.com.au
Sales Range: $25-49.9 Million
Emp.: 60
Scissor & Boom Lifts & Aerial Work Platforms
N.A.I.C.S.: 333923

Genie Brasil LTDA (3)
Avenida Tambore 290 Tambore Barueri, Sao Paulo, 06460-000, Brazil
Tel.: (55) 1140825600
Web Site: http://www.terexla.com
Sales Range: $125-149.9 Million
Emp.: 60
Scissor & Boom Lifts & Aerial Work Platforms
N.A.I.C.S.: 333923
Jacob Thomas (Pres-Latin America)

Genie France S.A.R.L. (3)
ZAC Parc d'Archevilliers 1 rue Joseph Fourier CS 50284, 28008, Chartres, Cedex, France
Tel.: (33) 237260999
Web Site: http://www.genielift.fr
Sales Range: $25-49.9 Million
Scissor & Boom Lifts & Aerial Work Platforms
N.A.I.C.S.: 333923
Rousseau Christoph (Dir-Sls-Southern Europe & North Africa)

Genie Germany GmbH (3)
Stedinger Str 324, Oldenburg, Delmenhorst, 27751, Germany
Tel.: (49) 4221491810
Sales Range: $10-24.9 Million
Emp.: 20
Construction Machinery Mfr
N.A.I.C.S.: 333120

Genie Industries Iberica, S.L. (3)
Pol Ind Pla D'en Coll - C/Gaia 31, 08110, Montcada I Reixac, Barcelona, Spain
Tel.: (34) 935725090
Web Site: http://www.genielift.es
Sales Range: $25-49.9 Million
Scissor & Boom Lifts & Aerial Work Platforms
N.A.I.C.S.: 333923

Subsidiary (Domestic):

Genie Manufacturing, Inc. (3)
6464 185th Ave NE, Redmond, WA 98052

Tel.: (425) 881-1800
Web Site: http://www.genielift.com
Industrial Machinery Mfr
N.A.I.C.S.: 333923

Subsidiary (Non-US):

Genie UK Limited (3)
The Maltings Wharf Road, Grantham, NG31 6BH, Nottinghamshire, United Kingdom
Tel.: (44) 1476584333
Web Site: http://genielift.it
Emp.: 50
Industry Equipment Mfr
N.A.I.C.S.: 333310

Subsidiary (Domestic):

Hydra Platforms Mfg. Inc. (2)
1205 Galleria Blvd, Rock Hill, SC 29730
Tel.: (803) 366-8195
Web Site: http://www.inspectabridge.com
Emp.: 8
Construction Equipment Mfr
N.A.I.C.S.: 333120

Subsidiary (Non-US):

Terex Lifting Australia Pty. Ltd. (2)
585 Curtin Avenue East, PO Box 1396, Eagle Farm, 4009, QLD, Australia
Tel.: (61) 738689600
Web Site: http://www.terex.com.au
Sales Range: $25-49.9 Million
Emp.: 100
Mobile Telescopic & Lattice Boom Cranes
N.A.I.C.S.: 333923

Terex Lifting U.K. Limited (2)
Centrl Blvd Pro Logis Park, Coventry, CV6 4BX, West Midlands, United Kingdom
Tel.: 24 76339400
Sales Range: $100-124.9 Million
Emp.: 500
Construction Machinery Mfr
N.A.I.C.S.: 333120

TerexLift S.r.l. (2)
Zona Industriale Buzzacchero, Umbertide, 06019, PG, Italy
Tel.: (39) 0075941811
Web Site: http://www.terexlift.com
Sales Range: $50-74.9 Million
Emp.: 175
Telescopic Material Handlers
N.A.I.C.S.: 332999

Terex Betim Equipamento Ltda (1)
Rod BR 381 km 488, Betim, 32681-200, Minas Gerais, Brazil
Tel.: (55) 3121254000
Web Site: http://www.terexritz.com.br
Industrial Machinery & Equipment Distr
N.A.I.C.S.: 423830

Terex Construction (1)
200 Nyala Farm Rd, Westport, CT 06880
Tel.: (203) 222-7170
Web Site: http://www.terex.com
Sales Range: $50-74.9 Million
Emp.: 100
Construction Vehicle Developer & Mfr
N.A.I.C.S.: 423810

Subsidiary (Non-US):

Terex Compact Equipment (2)
Central Boulevard Prologis Pk, Keresley End, Coventry, CV6 4BX, United Kingdom
Tel.: (44) 2476339400
Web Site: http://www.terex.com
Designer, Mfr & Marketer of Heavy-Duty, Off-Highway, Earthmoving & Lifting Equipment for the Infrastructure, Construction & Mining Industries
N.A.I.C.S.: 333120

Subsidiary (Domestic):

Terex Construction Americas (2)
8800 Rostin Rd, Southaven, MS 38671
Tel.: (662) 393-1800
Web Site: http://www.terexamericas.com
Sales Range: $75-99.9 Million
Construction Vehicle Developer & Mfr
N.A.I.C.S.: 423810

Terex Light Construction (2)
590 Huey Rd, Rock Hill, SC 29730-3377
Tel.: (803) 324-3011
Web Site: http://www.terex.com

Sales Range: $25-49.9 Million
Emp.: 115
Construction Related Equipment Mfr
N.A.I.C.S.: 335312

Terex Cranes, Inc. (1)
106 12th St SE, Waverly, IA 50677
Tel.: (319) 352-3920
Web Site: http://www.terexcranes.com
Sales Range: $100-124.9 Million
Emp.: 100
Crane Developer & Mfr
N.A.I.C.S.: 333923

Subsidiary (Non-US):

Atlas Maschinen GmbH (2)
Atlasstrasse 6, 27777, Ganderkesee, Germany
Tel.: (49) 42229540
Web Site: https://www.atlasgmbh.com
Sales Range: $25-49.9 Million
Emp.: 550
Excavators & Truck Mounted Cranes
N.A.I.C.S.: 333120
Fil Filipov (Owner & Chm)

Gru Comedil S.r.l. (2)
Via delle Innovazioni 17, Fontanafredda, 33074, Pordenone, Italy
Tel.: (39) 0434989111
Construction Equipment Mfr & Distr
N.A.I.C.S.: 333120

Sichuan Changjiang Engineering Crane Co., Ltd. (2)
Qiancaoba Industrial Park, Jiangyang, Luzhou, 646006, China
Tel.: (86) 3580202
Web Site: http://www.cj-crane.com
Sales Range: $300-349.9 Million
Emp.: 190
Truck Crane Mfr
N.A.I.C.S.: 333923

Terex Cranes Hungary Kft. (2)
Nagyarpadi ut 11, Pecs, 7631, Hungary
Tel.: (36) 72550150
Web Site: http://www.terex.com
Construction Machinery Equipment Mfr
N.A.I.C.S.: 333120

Terex Cranes Korea Co., Ltd. (2)
3F 620 Sasang-ro Buk-gu, Busan, Korea (South)
Tel.: (82) 513311806
Construction Machinery Equipment Mfr
N.A.I.C.S.: 333120

Terex Cranes Pty. Ltd. (2)
195 Osborne Ave, Clayton South, Melbourne, 3169, VIC, Australia
Tel.: (61) 3 9551 8644
Emp.: 5
Construction Machinery Mfr
N.A.I.C.S.: 333120

Subsidiary (Domestic):

Terex Cranes Wilmington, Inc. (2)
3147 S 17th St Ste 100, Wilmington, NC 28412
Tel.: (910) 395-8500
Web Site: http://www.terex.com
Construction Equipment Mfr
N.A.I.C.S.: 333120

Subsidiary (Non-US):

Terex Italia S.r.l. (2)
Via Cassoletta 76, 40056, Crespellano, BO, Italy
Tel.: (39) 051 650 1011
Web Site: http://www.terex.it
Sales Range: $125-149.9 Million
Terrain Cranes
N.A.I.C.S.: 333923

Terex Deutschland Bau-Beteiligungen GmbH (1)
Industriestr 3, 76669, Bad Schonborn, Germany
Tel.: (49) 7253840
Construction Machinery Equipment Mfr
N.A.I.C.S.: 333120

Terex GB Limited (1)
Coalisland Road, Dungannon, BT71 4DR, United Kingdom
Tel.: (44) 2887718500
Emp.: 550

Terex Corporation—(Continued)

Conveyor Equipment Mfr
N.A.I.C.S.: 333922

Subsidiary (Domestic):

Powerscreen International (U.K.) Limited (2)
200 Coalisland Rd, Dungannon, BT71 4DP, Co Tyrone, United Kingdom
Tel.: (44) 2887718500
Sales Range: $100-124.9 Million
Emp.: 500
Engineering Services
N.A.I.C.S.: 541330
Damian Power (Gen Mgr)

Powerscreen International Limited (2)
200 Coalisland, Dungannon, BT71 4DR, Tyrone, United Kingdom
Tel.: (44) 2887718500
Web Site: https://www.powerscreen.com
Recycling Equipment Mfr
N.A.I.C.S.: 333310

Terex Distribution Limited (2)
Station Road, Watford, NN6 7XN, Northants, United Kingdom
Tel.: (44) 8444994499
Web Site: http://www.terex.co.uk
Construction Machinery Mfr
N.A.I.C.S.: 333120

Terex Germany GmbH & Co. K.G. (1)
Tel.: (49) 21159884410
Web Site: http://www.terex.de
Material Processing Machinery, Lifting & Height Access Technology Mfr
N.A.I.C.S.: 333998
Lutz Henschen (Mng Dir)

Terex India Private Limited (1)
5th Floor West Wing E City Tower 2 94/2 95/2, Electronic City Phase 1, Bengaluru, 560 100, Karnataka, India
Tel.: (91) 8033151000
Web Site: https://www.terex.com
Construction Machinery Mfr
N.A.I.C.S.: 333120

Terex Latin America Equipamentos Ltda. (1)
Alameda Rio Negro 161 - 10 Andar Alphaville Empresarial, Bairro Portao, Barueri, 06454-000, SP, Brazil
Tel.: (55) 1140825600
Web Site: http://www.terex.com
Construction Machinery Equipment Mfr
N.A.I.C.S.: 333120

Terex Malaysia Sdn Bhd (1)
Lot 53674 Persiaran Subang Indah Sungai Penaga Industrial Estate, Subang Jaya, 47610, Selangor Darul Ehsan, Malaysia
Tel.: (60) 356226103
Overhead Traveling Crane, Hoist & Monorail System Mfr
N.A.I.C.S.: 333923
Joleen Leng (Mgr-Fin)

Terex Material Handling A/S (1)
Mileparken 9 A, 2740, Skovlunde, Denmark
Tel.: (45) 44828400
Overhead Traveling Crane, Hoist & Monorail System Mfr
N.A.I.C.S.: 333923
Jann Rene Hansen (Mng Dir)

Terex Material Handling AG (1)
Bahnhofstrasse 3, 8305, Dietlikon, Switzerland
Tel.: (41) 448351111
Web Site: http://www.demagcranes.ch
Overhead Traveling Crane, Hoist & Monorail System Mfr
N.A.I.C.S.: 333923

Terex Material Handling GmbH (1)
Vilniusstrasse 5, 5020, Salzburg, Austria
Tel.: (43) 662889060
Web Site: http://www.demagcranes.at
Overhead Traveling Crane, Hoist & Monorail System Mfr
N.A.I.C.S.: 333923

Terex Material Handling Sp. z o.o. (1)
ul Minska 63 A, 03-828, Warsaw, Poland

Tel.: (48) 223308400
Web Site: http://www.demagcranes.pl
Overhead Traveling Crane, Hoist & Monorail System Mfr
N.A.I.C.S.: 333923

Terex Material Handling spol. s.r.o. (1)
Bienerova 1536, Slany, 274 01, Central Bohemia, Czech Republic
Tel.: (420) 312514101
Overhead Traveling Crane, Hoist & Monorail System Mfr
N.A.I.C.S.: 333923
Petra Cerna (Mgr-Mktg)

Terex Materials Processing & Mining (1)
200 Nyala Farm Rd, Westport, CT 06880
Tel.: (203) 222-7170
Web Site: http://www.terex.com
Sales Range: $100-124.9 Million
Mining, Crushing & Grinding Machinery Developer & Mfr
N.A.I.C.S.: 333131

Subsidiary (Non-US):

BL - Pegson Limited (2)
Mammoth Street, Coalville, LE67 3GN, Leicestershire, United Kingdom
Tel.: (44) 530518600
Mobile & Jaw Crushers
N.A.I.C.S.: 333998

Jaques International Holdings Pty. Ltd. (2)
187 Osborne Ave, PO Box 1525, Clayton, 3169, VIC, Australia
Tel.: (61) 396479300
Web Site: https://www.terexjaques.com
Sales Range: $25-49.9 Million
Emp.: 38
Heavy-Duty Crushers & Feeders
N.A.I.C.S.: 333998

Subsidiary (Non-US):

Jaques (Thailand) Limited (3)
Sermsrap Building Floor 4 169/98 Ratchadapisek Road, Din Daeng, Bangkok, 10320, Thailand
Tel.: (66) 2 692 6666
Web Site: http://www.terexjaques.com
Sales Range: $125-149.9 Million
Heavy-Duty Crushers & Feeders
N.A.I.C.S.: 333998

Subsidiary (Non-US):

Powerscreen International Distribution Limited (2)
200 Coalisland Road, Dungannon, BT71 4DR, County Tyrone, United Kingdom
Tel.: (44) 2887718500
Web Site: http://www.terex.com
Sales Range: $50-74.9 Million
Emp.: 450
Mfr of Material Handling Machines
N.A.I.C.S.: 811310

Subsidiary (US):

Powerscreen USA LLC (3)
11001 Electron Dr, Louisville, KY 40299
Tel.: (502) 736-5233
Web Site: http://www.powerscreenusa.com
Sales Range: $125-149.9 Million
Dry Screening, Washing & Recycling Equipment
N.A.I.C.S.: 333922

Subsidiary (Domestic):

Simplicity Engineering, Inc. (2)
212 S Oak St, Durand, MI 48429-1621 (100%)
Tel.: (989) 288-3121
Web Site: http://www.simplicityengineering.com
Sales Range: $50-74.9 Million
Emp.: 120
Mfr of Heavy Duty Vibrating Screens, Conveyors & Feeders; Foundry Shakeouts
N.A.I.C.S.: 333922
Michelle Fox (Controller)

Terex Minerals Processing Systems (2)

3900 Fountains Blvd NE Ste 101, Cedar Rapids, IA 52411
Tel.: (319) 363-3511
Web Site: https://www.terex.com
Sales Range: $25-49.9 Million
Emp.: 100
Crushing & Screening Pavers & Hot Mix Asphalt Mfr
N.A.I.C.S.: 333120

Terex Redrill (2)
3501 S Fm Hwy 1417, Denison, TX 75020-8904
Tel.: (903) 786-2981
Rev.: $73,000,000
Emp.: 350
Mining & Construction Equipment Mfr
N.A.I.C.S.: 333131

Terex NFLG (Quanzhou) Mobile Processing Equipment Co Ltd (1)
Sports St High-tech Industrial Park District 700, Quanzhou, 362 021, Fujian, China
Tel.: (86) 595 28672030
Construction Machinery Mfr
N.A.I.C.S.: 333120
John Zhu (Gen Mgr)

Terex South Dakota, Inc. (1)
600 Oakwood Rd, Watertown, SD 57201-4140
Tel.: (605) 882-4000
Overhead Traveling Crane, Hoist & Monorail System Mfr
N.A.I.C.S.: 333923

Terex Utilities, Inc. (1)
3140-15th Ave SE, Watertown, SD 57201-6150 (100%)
Tel.: (605) 882-4000
Web Site: http://www.terex.com
Sales Range: $100-124.9 Million
Emp.: 475
Digger Derricks & Insulated Truck Mounted Platforms Mfr
N.A.I.C.S.: 333120
Clint Weber (VP & Gen Mgr)

Division (Domestic):

Terex Utilities South (2)
200 EdenWay Dr, White House, TN 37188-8146
Tel.: (615) 672-4911
Web Site: http://www.terexutilities.com
Sales Range: $125-149.9 Million
Digger Derricks & Insulated Truck Mounted Platforms Mfr
N.A.I.C.S.: 333120

Terex Utilities West (2)
12805 SW 77th Pl, Portland, OR 97223
Tel.: (503) 620-0611
Web Site: http://www.terex.com
Sales Range: $125-149.9 Million
Emp.: 30
Digger Derricks & Insulated Truck Mounted Platforms Mfr
N.A.I.C.S.: 333120

Terex Verwaltungs GmbH (1)
Schonbrunner Strasse 222, 1120, Vienna, Austria
Tel.: (43) 496332831601
Web Site: http://www.terex.com
Construction Machinery Mfr
N.A.I.C.S.: 333120

Terex-Telelect, Inc. (1)
500 Oakwood Rd, Watertown, SD 57201-4140
Tel.: (605) 882-4000
Construction Machinery Mfr
N.A.I.C.S.: 333120

TERME BANCORP, INC.
15 Salt Creek Ln Ste 210 Unit 6, Hinsdale, IL 60521
Tel.: (312) 268-2424 MD
Year Founded: 1986
TMEB—(OTCIQ)
Bank Holding Company
N.A.I.C.S.: 551111
John G. Yedinak (CEO)
Edward Brooks III (Sec)

TERMINUS ENERGY, INC.

2214 Torrance Blvd Ste 101, Torrance, CA 90501
Tel.: (310) 328-3588 DE
Year Founded: 1993
TMGY—(OTCIQ)
Energy Generation Platform Distr
N.A.I.C.S.: 221118
Dan B. Pratte (Pres & CEO)

TERNS PHARMACEUTICALS, INC.
1065 E Hillsdale Blvd Ste 100, Foster City, CA 94404
Tel.: (650) 525-5535 DE
Web Site:
https://www.ternspharma.com
Year Founded: 2016
TERN—(NASDAQ)
Rev.: $2,042,000
Assets: $287,026,000
Liabilities: $10,083,000
Net Worth: $276,943,000
Earnings: ($60,345,000)
Emp.: 46
Fiscal Year-end: 12/31/22
Biotechnology Research & Development Services
N.A.I.C.S.: 541714
Amy Burroughs (CEO)
Erin Quirk (Pres & Head-R&D)
Mark Vignola (CFO)
Bryan Yoon (COO & Gen Counsel)
David Fellows (Chm)
Jeffrey R. Jasper (Sr VP & Head-Res)
Diana Chung (Chief Dev Officer & Sr VP)
Kerry Russell (Chief Medical Officer-Metabolic)
Emil Kuriakose (Chief Medical Officer-Oncology)
Weidong Zhong (Founder)

TERRA ENERGY & RESOURCE TECHNOLOGIES, INC.
2405 Essington Rd B109, Joliet, IL 60435
Tel.: (312) 613-4564 DE
Web Site: http://www.terrainsight.com
Year Founded: 2005
TEGR—(OTCEM)
Sales Range: Less than $1 Million
Emp.: 7
Mapping & Analytic Services
N.A.I.C.S.: 541360
Alexandre Agaian (Pres)

TERRA PROPERTY TRUST, INC.
205 W 28th St 12th Fl, New York, NY 10001
Tel.: (212) 753-5100 MD
Web Site:
https://www.terrapropertytrust.com
Year Founded: 2015
TPTA—(NYSE)
Rev.: $56,614,446
Assets: $813,336,892
Liabilities: $491,454,718
Net Worth: $321,882,174
Earnings: ($6,951,693)
Emp.: 61
Fiscal Year-end: 12/31/22
Real Estate Investment Services
N.A.I.C.S.: 531210
Sarah Schwarzschild (CTO)
Gregory M. Pinkus (CFO, COO, Treas & Sec)
Vikram S. Uppal (Chm, CEO & Chief Investment Officer)

TERRENO REALTY CORPORATION

10500 NE 8th St Ste 1910, Bellevue,
WA 98004
Tel.: (415) 655-4580   MD
Web Site: https://www.terreno.com
Year Founded: 2009
TRNO—(NYSE)
Rev.: $323,590,000
Assets: $3,904,677,000
Liabilities: $990,050,000
Net Worth: $2,914,627,000
Earnings: $150,745,000
Emp.: 42
Fiscal Year-end: 12/31/23
Real Estate Investment Services
N.A.I.C.S.: 525990
W. Blake Baird (Co-Founder, Chm &
CEO)
John T. Meyer (COO & Exec VP)
Michael A. Coke (Co-Founder &
Pres)
Jaime Jackson Cannon (CFO, Princi-
pal Acctg Officer, Sec & Exec VP)
John T. Meyer (Exec VP)

Subsidiaries:

Terreno 3601 Pennsy LLC   (1)
101 Montgomery St 200, San Francisco,
CA 94104
Tel.: (415) 655-4586
Emp.: 4
Motor Vehicle Financial Leasing Services
N.A.I.C.S.: 525990

Terreno Airgate LLC   (1)
101 Montgomery St Ste 200, San Fran-
cisco, CA 94104
Tel.: (415) 655-4584
Real Estate Investment Services
N.A.I.C.S.: 525990

TERRITORIAL BANCORP INC.

1132 Bishop St Pauahi Tower Ste
500, Honolulu, HI 96813
Tel.: (808) 946-1400   MD
Web Site:
      https://www.territorialsavings.net
TBNK—(NASDAQ)
Rev.: $66,911,000
Assets: $2,169,592,000
Liabilities: $1,913,042,000
Net Worth: $256,550,000
Earnings: $16,156,000
Emp.: 253
Fiscal Year-end: 12/31/22
Bank Holding Company
N.A.I.C.S.: 551111
Allan S. Kitagawa (Chm, Pres &
CEO)
Karen J. Cox (Sr VP-Admin-Territorial
Savings Bank)
Richard K. C. Lau (Chief Lending Of-
ficer & Sr VP-Territorial Savings
Bank)
Melvin M. Miyamoto (CFO & Sr VP)

Subsidiaries:

Territorial Savings Bank   (1)
1132 Bishop St Ste 2200, Honolulu, HI
96813
Tel.: (808) 949-5989
Web Site: http://www.territorialsavings.net
Sales Range: $75-99.9 Million
Emp.: 240
Federal Savings & Loan Associations
N.A.I.C.S.: 522180
Allan S. Kitagawa (Chm, Pres & CEO)
Karen J. Cox (Sr VP-Admin)
Richard K. C. Lau (Chief Lending Officer &
Sr VP)
Dennis Hironaka (Sr VP-Internal Audit)

TESLA, INC.

1 Tesla Rd, Austin, TX 78725
Tel.: (512) 516-8177   DE
Web Site: https://www.tesla.com
Year Founded: 2003
TSLA—(NASDAQ)
Rev.: $96,773,000,000
Assets: $106,618,000,000

Liabilities: $43,251,000,000
Net Worth: $63,367,000,000
Earnings: $14,997,000,000
Emp.: 140,473
Fiscal Year-end: 12/31/23
Electric-Powered Automobile Mfr
N.A.I.C.S.: 336110
Jeffrey B. Straubel (Co-Founder)
Robyn M. Denholm (Chm)
Laurie J. Yoler (Co-Founder)
Vaibhav Taneja (CFO)
Tom Zhu (Sr VP-Automotive)
Elon Reeve Musk (Co-Founder &
CEO)

Subsidiaries:

Grohmann Engineering Trading
(Shanghai) Co. Ltd.   (1)
1F Tomson Industrial Park 358 Fu Te Road
North, Wagaoqiao Free Trade Zone
Gaoqiao, Shanghai, 200131, China
Tel.: (86) 2161940525
Automotive Distr
N.A.I.C.S.: 423110

Grohmann USA, Inc.   (1)
5550 W Chandler Blvd, Chandler, AZ 85226
Tel.: (480) 525-8592
Electric Powered Automobile Mfr
N.A.I.C.S.: 336110

Hibar China Co. Ltd.   (1)
Room 1215-1218 Building C4 No 8 Lane
299 Guanghua Road, Hi-tech Zone,
Ningbo, China
Tel.: (86) 57487900782
Dispensing Pump Mfr
N.A.I.C.S.: 333914

Hibar Systems Europe GmbH   (1)
Neumuhleweg 34, 73660, Urbach, Germany
Tel.: (49) 71819944201
Dispensing Pump Mfr
N.A.I.C.S.: 333914

Hibar Systems Limited   (1)
35 Pollard Street, Richmond Hill, L4B 1A8,
ON, Canada
Tel.: (905) 731-2400
Web Site: http://www.hibar.com
Dispensing Pump Mfr
N.A.I.C.S.: 333914
Steve Mark (VP)

Maxwell Technologies, Inc.   (1)
3888 Calle Fortunada, San Diego, CA
92123
Tel.: (858) 503-3300
Web Site: http://www.maxwell.com
Rev.: $90,459,000
Assets: $163,731,000
Liabilities: $73,140,000
Net Worth: $90,591,000
Earnings: ($36,548,000)
Emp.: 367
Fiscal Year-end: 12/31/2018
Ultracapacitor Cells, High-Voltage Capaci-
tors & Radiation-Hardened Microelectronics
Products Mfr
N.A.I.C.S.: 551112

Subsidiary (Non-US):

Maxwell Technologies GmbH   (2)
Leopoldstrasse 244, 80807, Munich, Ger-
many
Tel.: (49) 8941614030
Web Site: http://www.maxwell.com
Sales Range: $10-24.9 Million
Emp.: 10
Automotive Business
N.A.I.C.S.: 336110

Maxwell Technologies Korea Co.,
Ltd   (2)
17 Dongtangiheung-ro 681Beon-gil,
Giheung-gu, Yongin, 17102, Gyeonggi-do,
Korea (South)
Tel.: (82) 312890700
Electronic Components Mfr
N.A.I.C.S.: 334419

Nesscap Korea Co., Ltd   (2)
17 Dongtangiheung-ro 681Beon-gil
Giheung-gu, Yongin, 017-102, Gyeonggi-do,
Korea (South)
Tel.: (82) 312890700
Web Site: http://www.nesscap.com

Capacitor Mfr & Distr
N.A.I.C.S.: 334416

Orange Vehicle Sales LLC   (1)
7421 NW 54th St, Miami, FL 33166
Tel.: (786) 444-8436
Web Site:
      https://www.orangeautosalesmiami.com
Automobile Maintenance Services
N.A.I.C.S.: 811111

Perbix Machine Company, Inc.   (1)
6305 Sandburg Rd, Golden Valley, MN
55427
Tel.: (763) 546-7122
Industrial Machinery Mfr
N.A.I.C.S.: 333998

Shoreline Vehicle Sales LLC   (1)
10621 Ocean Gtwy, Berlin, MD 21811
Tel.: (410) 883-5355
Web Site: https://www.shorelineautosale.net
New Car Dealers
N.A.I.C.S.: 441110

SolarCity Corp.   (1)
3055 Clearview Way, San Mateo, CA 94402
Tel.: (650) 638-1028
Web Site: http://www.solarcity.com
Rev.: $730,342,000
Assets: $9,130,756,000
Liabilities: $7,199,326,000
Net Worth: $1,931,430,000
Earnings: ($820,347,000)
Emp.: 12,243
Fiscal Year-end: 12/31/2016
Solar Power System Installation Services
N.A.I.C.S.: 238990
Neil Cowie (CEO)

Tesla Automation GmbH   (1)
Rudolf-Diesel-Strasse 14, 54595, Prum,
Germany
Tel.: (49) 6551680
Web Site: https://teslaautomation.de
Automobile Mfr
N.A.I.C.S.: 336110

Tesla Canada LP   (1)
6702 Fairmount Dr SE, Calgary, T2H 0X3,
AB, Canada
Tel.: (403) 910-0521
Automobile Mfr
N.A.I.C.S.: 336110

Tesla Czech Republic s.r.o.   (1)
727 V Oblouku, 252 43, Pruhonice, Czech
Republic
Tel.: (420) 228882612
Automobile Mfr
N.A.I.C.S.: 336110

Tesla France S.a r.l.   (1)
1030 Rue Jean Rene Guilibert Gauthier de
la Lauzie, 13100, Aix-en-Provence, France
Tel.: (33) 442290414
Automobile Mfr
N.A.I.C.S.: 336110

Tesla Grohmann Automation
GmbH   (1)
Rudolf-Diesel-Strasse 14, 54595, Prum,
Germany
Tel.: (49) 6551680
Engineering Consulting Services
N.A.I.C.S.: 541330

Tesla Hungary Kft.   (1)
20 Vaci ut, 1044, Budapest, Hungary
Tel.: (36) 19876737
Automobile Mfr
N.A.I.C.S.: 336110

Tesla Italy S.r.l.   (1)
7 Via Campi Spini, 24127, Bergamo, Italy
Tel.: (39) 0356306675
Automobile Mfr
N.A.I.C.S.: 336110

Tesla Motors Australia, Pty Ltd   (1)
33 Herbert Street St Leonards, Sydney,
2065, NSW, Australia
Tel.: (61) 284249500
Electric Vehicle Mfr & Distr
N.A.I.C.S.: 336211
Grace Petre (Mgr-HR & Recruitment)

Tesla Motors Austria GmbH   (1)
Triester Strasse 207-209, 1230, Vienna,
Austria
Tel.: (43) 12535967

Web Site: https://www.tesla.com
Automobile Mfr
N.A.I.C.S.: 336110

Tesla Motors Belgium SPRL   (1)
Avenue De La Toison D or 49, 1000, Brus-
sels, Belgium
Tel.: (32) 25034561
Electric Vehicle Distr
N.A.I.C.S.: 423140
Jean-Pierre Vander Elst (Mgr-Store)

Tesla Motors Iceland ehf.   (1)
Vatnagaroar 24, 104, Reykjavik, Iceland
Tel.: (354) 6202191260
Web Site: https://www.tesla.com
Automobile Mfr
N.A.I.C.S.: 336110

Tesla Motors Luxembourg S.a r.l.   (1)
194 Route De Thionville, L-2610, Luxem-
bourg, Luxembourg
Tel.: (352) 27860572
Electric Vehicle Distr
N.A.I.C.S.: 423140
Bastian Hosmar (Mgr-Store)

Tesla Motors UT, Inc.   (1)
2312 S State St, Salt Lake City, UT 84115-
2755
Tel.: (801) 596-4620
Electric Vehicle Mfr & Distr
N.A.I.C.S.: 336110
Carlos Romano (Coord-Delivery Experi-
ence)

Tesla Norway AS   (1)
Bekkenstenveien 15, 0976, Oslo, Norway
Tel.: (47) 21514010
Electric Car Distr
N.A.I.C.S.: 423110

Tesla Poland Sp. z o.o.   (1)
229 Tadeusza Kosciuszki, 40-600, Kato-
wice, Poland
Tel.: (48) 323235004
Automobile Mfr
N.A.I.C.S.: 336110

Tesla Switzerland GmbH   (1)
7 Gewerbepark Bata, 4313, Mohlin, Swit-
zerland
Tel.: (41) 618553020
Automobile Mfr
N.A.I.C.S.: 336110

TETON ADVISORS, INC.

189 Mason St, Greenwich, CT 06830
Tel.: (914) 457-1070
Web Site: https://www.tetonadv.com
TETAA—(OTCIQ)
Investment Management Service
N.A.I.C.S.: 523999
Michael L. Corbat (Founder)
Manjit Kalha (VP)
Nicholas Francis Galluccio (Pres &
CEO)
Michael J. Mancuso (CFO)
Deanna B. Marotz (Chief Compliance
Officer)

Subsidiaries:

Keeley-Teton Advisors, LLC   (1)
141 West Jackson Ste 2150, Chicago, IL
60604
Tel.: (312) 786-5050
Web Site: http://www.keeleyteton.com
Financial Investment Services
N.A.I.C.S.: 523940
Kevin M. Chin (Portfolio Mgr & CIO)
Nicholas F. Galluccio (Pres, Mng Dir & Port-
folio Mgr)
Scott R. Butler (Sr VP & Portfolio Mgr)
Brian R. Keeley (Portfolio Mgr)
Kevin M. Keeley (Chm)
Deanna B. Marotz (Chief Compliance Offi-
cer)
Thomas E. Browne. Jr. (Portfolio Mgr)

TETRA TECH, INC.

3475 E Foothill Blvd, Pasadena, CA
91107
Tel.: (626) 351-4664   DE

Tetra Tech, Inc.—(Continued)

Web Site: https://www.tetratech.com
Year Founded: 1966
TTEK—(NASDAQ)
Rev.: $4,522,550,000
Assets: $3,820,477,000
Liabilities: $2,416,971,000
Net Worth: $1,403,506,000
Earnings: $273,420,000
Emp.: 27,000
Fiscal Year-end: 10/01/23
Environmental Engineering & Consulting Services; Client-Sponsored Research & Development & Environmental Assessment
N.A.I.C.S.: 541330
Dan L. Batrack (Chm & CEO)
Preston Hopson (Gen Counsel, Sec & Sr VP)
Brendan O'Rourke (Sr VP-Enterprise Risk Mgmt)
Keith Brown (Pres-Global Dev Svcs Div)
Stuart W. Fowler (Pres-High Performance Buildings Div)
Leslie L. Shoemaker (Chief Sustainability and Leadership Development)
Richard A. Lemmon (Sr VP-Corp Admin)
Craig L. Christensen (CIO & Sr VP)
Brian N. Carter (Chief Acctg Officer, Sr VP & Controller)
Steven M. Burdick (Exec VP)

Subsidiaries:

AEG West, Inc. (1)
11501 Dublin Blvd, Dublin, CA 94568
Tel.: (925) 452-8256
Engineeering Services
N.A.I.C.S.: 541330

Advanced Management Technology, Inc. (1)
1515 Wilson Blvd Ste 1100, Arlington, VA 22209
Tel.: (703) 841-2684
Web Site: http://www.amti.com
Information Technology & Aerospace Management Services
N.A.I.C.S.: 541618
Mary McMillan (Sr VP-Aerospace Safety & Environ)

America's Schoolhouse Council, LLC (1)
12010 Carmel Park Ln, Austin, TX 78727
Tel.: (630) 645-1920
Web Site:
    http://www.americasschoolhouse.com
Educational Planning & Support Services
N.A.I.C.S.: 611710
Patrick Brosnan (Pres)

American Environmental Group Ltd. (1)
3600 Brecksville Rd Ste 100, Richfield, OH 44286
Tel.: (330) 659-5930
Web Site: http://www.aegl.net
Sales Range: $75-99.9 Million
Emp.: 500
Waste Management & Environmental Services
N.A.I.C.S.: 541620

Subsidiary (Domestic):

Power Management, Inc. (2)
5770 Thornwood Dr Ste B, Goleta, CA 93117
Tel.: (805) 692-8904
Web Site: http://www.powrmgt.com
Sales Range: $1-9.9 Million
Emp.: 14
Administrative Management & General Management Consulting Service
N.A.I.C.S.: 541611

Ardaman & Associates, Inc. (1)
8008 S Orange Ave, Orlando, FL 32809
Tel.: (407) 855-3860
Web Site: https://www.ardaman.com
Sales Range: $25-49.9 Million
Emp.: 400
Engineeering Services

N.A.I.C.S.: 541330
Mohamad Al-Hawaree (Pres)
Ernie Cox (Sr VP)
Jim Jamwant (Comptroller)
Donna Reubelt (Dir-HR)
Brett Buxbaum (Dir-Safety)

BIOCNG, LLC (1)
8413 Excelsior Dr Ste 160, Madison, WI 53717
Tel.: (630) 410-7202
Web Site: http://www.biocng.us
Oil & Gas Related Services
N.A.I.C.S.: 213112
Michael S. Michels (Exec VP-Technical)
Kay Turgeson (Mgr-Sls & Bus)
Paul J. Stout (Project Mgr)
Tom Bilgri (Engr-Lead)
Steve Wittmann (Sr Mgr-Client)
Bill Bloomenkranz (Engr-Project)
Toby Hahn (Engr-Process)
Daryl O'Dell (Mgr-Client)
Kyle Kneser (Engr-Start-up)
Doug Tholo (Mgr-Client)

BNG Specialized Engineering Services Ltd (1)
Millbourne Professional Centre Suite 300
Tower 1 38 Avenue, Millwoods Road, Edmonton, T6K 3L6, AB, Canada
Tel.: (780) 463-5542
Engineeering Services
N.A.I.C.S.: 541330

BPR CSO Solutions Inc. (1)
2003 Mill Creek Dr, Arlington, TX 76010-5618
Tel.: (817) 719-4038
Engineeering Services
N.A.I.C.S.: 541330

BPR Groupe-Conseil, S.E.N.C. (1)
464 Boul Saint-Germain, Rimouski, G5L 3P1, QC, Canada
Tel.: (418) 723-8151
Emp.: 50
Engineeering Services
N.A.I.C.S.: 541330
Siederec Mcween (Gen Mgr)

BPR-Batiment Inc. (1)
4655 Wilfrid-Hamel Blvd, Quebec, G1P 2J7, QC, Canada
Tel.: (418) 871-8151
Web Site: http://www.bpr.ca
Engineering & Consulting Services
N.A.I.C.S.: 541330

BPR-Energie Inc. (1)
2100 rue King Ouest Ste 110, Sherbrooke, J1J 2E8, QC, Canada
Tel.: (819) 562-7266
Engineeering Services
N.A.I.C.S.: 541330

BPR-Infrastructure Inc. (1)
1925 Rue Girouard Ouest, Saint-Hyacinthe, J2S 3A5, QC, Canada
Tel.: (450) 773-5942
Engineeering Services
N.A.I.C.S.: 541330

BPR-Triax Inc. (1)
300-4650 Boul Des Laurentides, Laval, H7K 2J4, QC, Canada
Tel.: (450) 622-4252
Engineeering Services
N.A.I.C.S.: 541330

Bluewater Federal Solutions, Inc. (1)
14420 Albemarle Point Pl Ste 200, Chantilly, VA 20151-1690
Tel.: (703) 773 6477
Web Site: http://www.bwfed.com
Process, Physical Distribution & Logistics Consulting Services
N.A.I.C.S.: 541614
Laura Price (CFO)

Bridgenet International (1)
20201 SW Birch St Ste 250, Newport Beach, CA 92660-1773
Tel.: (949) 250-1222
Web Site: http://www.airportnetwork.com
Engineeering Services
N.A.I.C.S.: 541330

Clancy Environmental Consultants, Inc. (1)
20 Mapleville Depot, Saint Albans, VT 05478-1857

Tel.: (802) 527-2460
Environmental Consulting Services
N.A.I.C.S.: 541690

Clear Creek Holdings, LLC (1)
7690 Silver Spur Loop, Idaho Falls, ID 83406
Tel.: (208) 357-4256
Holding Company
N.A.I.C.S.: 551112

Coffey International Limited (1)
Level 19 Tower B Citadel Tower, 799 Pacific Highway, Chatswood, 2067, NSW, Australia
Tel.: (61) 2 9406 1000
Web Site: http://www.coffey.com
Sales Range: $350-399.9 Million
Holding Company; Infrastructure Consultancy Services
N.A.I.C.S.: 551112
Urs Meyerhans (CEO)
Stewart Phillis (Gen Mgr-Engrg)
Andrew Mailer (Gen Mgr-NSW, ACT & QLD)
Dawn Watt (CEO-Testing)
Matthew Hill (Gen Mgr-South)
Michael Norman (Ops Mgr-Geotechnics)

Subsidiary (Non-US):

Coffey International Development Holdings Limited (2)
The Malthouse 1 Northfield Rd, Reading, RG1 8AH, Berkshire, United Kingdom
Tel.: (44) 1189566066
Web Site: http://www.coffey.com
Emp.: 80
Holding Company; Geotechnical Construction & Consultancy Services
N.A.I.C.S.: 551112
Ben Ward (Mng Dir)

Subsidiary (Domestic):

Coffey International Development Limited (3)
The Malthouse 1 Northfield Road, Reading, RG1 8AH, United Kingdom
Tel.: (44) 1189566066
Web Site: http://www.coffey.com
Business Management Consulting Services
N.A.I.C.S.: 541611

Subsidiary (Domestic):

Coffey International Development Pty. Ltd. (2)
Worldpark Level 1 33 Richmond Road, Keswick, 5035, SA, Australia
Tel.: (61) 883754400
Web Site: http://www.coffey.com
Professional Consulting Services
N.A.I.C.S.: 541618

Subsidiary (Non-US):

Coffey International Development Sp. z.o.o. (2)
ul Krucza 16 22, 00 526, Warsaw, Poland
Tel.: (48) 225782280
Web Site: http://www.coffey.com
Emp.: 10
Business Consulting Services
N.A.I.C.S.: 541611

Coffey Mining (South Africa) Pty. Ltd. (2)
Block D Somerset Ofc Estate 604 Kudu St, Allens Nek, Roodepoort, 1709, Gauteng, South Africa
Tel.: (27) 116793331
Web Site: http://www.coffey.com
Sales Range: $50-74.9 Million
Emp.: 15
Mining Consultancy Services
N.A.I.C.S.: 213114

Subsidiary (Domestic):

Coffey Mining Pty. Ltd. (2)
Lev 3 15 Astor Terr, Springhill, 4000, QLD, Australia
Tel.: (61) 736082500
Web Site: http://www.coffey.com.au
Sales Range: $50-74.9 Million
Emp.: 9
Mining Consultancy Services
N.A.I.C.S.: 213114

Coffey Projects (Australia) Pty. Ltd. (2)
47 Doggett Street, Newstead, 4006, Queensland, Australia
Tel.: (61) 736082500
Web Site: http://www.coffey.com
Business Management Consulting Services
N.A.I.C.S.: 541611

Subsidiary (Non-US):

Coffey Projects (New Zealand) Limited (2)
Level 11 7 City Road Grafton, Newmarket, Auckland, 1010, New Zealand
Tel.: (64) 93799463
Web Site: http://www.coffey.com
Business Management Services
N.A.I.C.S.: 561499

Cornerstone Environmental Group, LLC (1)
100 Crystal Run Rd Ste 101, Middletown, NY 10941
Tel.: (845) 695-0200
Web Site: http://www.cornerstoneeg.com
Environmental Engineering & Consulting Services
N.A.I.C.S.: 541620
David Damon (CFO)
Christopher C. Peters (Dir-Ops-Central & Project Mgr-Landfill Engrg & Design)
Kenneth J. Karl (Pres & COO)
Michael S. Michels (Exec VP-Bus Dev & Project Mgr-Biogas & Landfill Gas)
Gary DiPippo (Project Mgr-Environmental Plng)
Paul Stout (Reg VP-West)
Mark Torresani (VP & Project Mgr-Biogas & Landfill Gas)
Garth Bowers (Sr Dir-Ops-West)
Robert Holmes (Dir-Ops-East & Project Mgr-Solar Energy, Site & Civil Design)
John Oswald (Dir-Ops-Central & Project Mgr-Solar Energy)
Prentiss Shaw (Project Mgr-Organics Mgmt)
Steve Wittmann (Project Mgr-Biogas & Landfill Gas)
Carl Beuter (Project Mgr-Site & Civil Design)
Tiffany L. Medley (Project Mgr-Air Quality)
Scott Miller (Project Mgr-Air Quality)
Timothy Roeper (Project Mgr-Remediation)
Leslie Sparrow (Project Mgr-Remediation)
Edwin Valis (Project Mgr-Air Quality)
Matt Beebe (Project Mgr-Biogas & Landfill Gas)
Tom Bilgri (Project Mgr-Biogas & Landfill Gas)
Matthew Boudreau (Project Mgr-Air Quality)
Jennifer Bowyer (Project Mgr-Landfill Engrg & Design)
Edwin Calvache (Project Mgr-Ops & Maintenance)
Michael Contestabile (Project Mgr)
Jennifer Deal (Project Mgr-Environmental & Engrg)
Maura Dougherty (Project Mgr-Biogas & Landfill Gas)
Carl Eller (Project Mgr-Site & Civil Design)
Tyler Field (Project Mgr)
Donald Hullings (Mgr-Client)
Arie P. Kremen (Project Mgr-Landfill Engrg & Design)
Khaled Mahmood (Project Mgr-Air Quality)
Scott McCallister (Mgr-Client)
Jerry McGraner (Mgr-Client)
Magdalena Mendola (Project Mgr)
Suzan Pankenier (Project Mgr-Air Quality)
Ray Ramos (Project Mgr-Air Quality)
Tami Sands (Project Mgr-Air Quality)
Andrew Schellberg (Project Mgr-Transfer, Recycling & Processing Facilities)
Michael Schumaci (Project Mgr-Ops & Maintenance)
David Sonne (Project Mgr-Site & Civil Design)
Doug Tholo (Project Mgr-Alternative Energy)
Rich Calogero (Project Mgr-Environmental Plng)
Paul Mutch (Project Mgr-Site & Civil Design)

Joseph Nemesh *(Project Mgr-Remediation)*
William Soukup *(Project Mgr-Hydrogeology)*
Bodhi Piedmont-Fleischmann *(Project Mgr)*
Eric Anderson *(Project Mgr)*
Gavin Casson *(Project Mgr)*
Lee Daigle *(Sr Project Mgr)*
David Knapp *(Mgr-Client)*
Mark Krieski *(Project Mgr)*
Daniel Roche *(Project Mgr)*
Mark Swyka *(Project Mgr-Landfill Engrg & Design)*
Chris Ulrich *(Project Mgr)*
James Walker *(Project Mgr-Landfill Engrg & Design)*
Kay Turgeson *(Mgr-Mktg)*
Kristen Thordahl *(Project Mgr-Site & Civil Design)*

Cosentini Associates, Inc. (1)
498 7th Ave, New York, NY 10018
Tel.: (212) 615-3600
Web Site: https://www.cosentini.com
Sales Range: $50-74.9 Million
Emp.: 300
Engineering Services
N.A.I.C.S.: 541330
Marvin A. Mass *(Chm)*
Douglas C. Mass *(Pres)*
Edward Barbieri *(Exec VP)*
Michael W. Maybaum *(Exec VP)*
Scott R. Ceasar *(Sr VP & Dir-Sustainable Design)*
Dominick DeRobertis *(Sr VP & Dir-Healthcare)*
Robert M. Leber *(Sr VP & Dir-Cambridge Office)*
Bruno J. Spiewak *(Sr VP & Dir-Chicago Office)*
Onorius Vaidean *(Sr VP & Dir-IT)*
Vladimir Yarmarkovich *(Sr VP)*
Roman Kuzmicki *(VP & Dir-Quality Control)*
Jordan Fox *(VP & Dir-Interiors)*
Rockwood J. Edwards *(Dir-Code Consulting)*
Whitney Smith *(Dir-Sustainable Svcs)*
Adrian Enache *(VP & Dir-Plumbing & Fire Protection Engrg)*
Lenore LeDonne *(Dir-HR)*

DCK-TTEC LLC (1)
6 PPG PL ste 700, Pittsburgh, PA 15222
Tel.: (412) 384-1000
Web Site: http://www.dckww.com
Construction Engineering Services
N.A.I.C.S.: 236220

Delaney Crushed Stone Products, Inc. (1)
410 State Highway 30, Northville, NY 12134
Tel.: (518) 661-5304
Concrete Mfr
N.A.I.C.S.: 327320
Brian Manzer *(Gen Mgr)*

Evergreen Utility Contractors, Inc. (1)
22823 State Rte 9 SE, Woodinville, WA 98072
Tel.: (425) 481-1155
Sales Range: $250-299.9 Million
Utility Contractor
N.A.I.C.S.: 237110

Fort Point Associates, Inc. (1)
31 State St 3rd Fl, Boston, MA 02109
Tel.: (617) 357-7044
Web Site: http://www.fpa-inc.com
Urban Planning & Environmental Consulting Services
N.A.I.C.S.: 541690
Jamie M. Fay *(Founder & Pres)*
Judith T. Kohn *(VP)*
Kenneth Fields *(Sr Project Mgr)*
Katie T. Moniz *(Sr Project Mgr)*

Global Tech, Inc. (1)
1900 Gallows Rd Ste 800, Vienna, VA 22182
Tel.: (703) 652-0991
Web Site: http://www.eglobaltech.com
IT Services, Cybersecurity & Management-consulting Firm
N.A.I.C.S.: 541611
Sanjiv Jain *(CEO)*

Hagler Bailly Pakistan (Private) Limited (1)
39 Street 3 E7, Islamabad, 44000, Pakistan
Tel.: (92) 5126102007

Web Site: http://www.haglerbailly.com.pk
Environmental Engineering & Consulting Services
N.A.I.C.S.: 541330

Indus Corporation (1)
1951 Kidwell Dr 8th Fl, Vienna, VA 22182
Tel.: (703) 506-6700
Web Site: http://www.induscorp.com
Custom Computer Programming Services
N.A.I.C.S.: 541511
Shivram Krishnan *(Chm & CEO)*
Hari Sury *(CIO)*
Elizabeth Bolak *(VP-Federal Civilian Programs)*
Ted Milone *(VP-Ops-Defense Programs & Mgr-Program-Alliant)*

LDIS, LLC (1)
5620 Ward Rd Unit 200, Arvada, CO 80002-1347
Tel.: (303) 953-5333
Web Site: http://www.ldisllc.com
Engineering Layout Design & Installation Services
N.A.I.C.S.: 541330
Ben Schwenk *(Owner)*

LS Technologies, LLC. (1)
2750 Prosperity Ave, Fairfax, VA 22031
Tel.: (703) 205-9146
Web Site: http://www.lstechllc.com
Rev.: $1,500,000
Emp.: 21
Other Scientific & Technical Consulting Services
N.A.I.C.S.: 541690
Derek Bigelow *(CFO)*

Management Systems International Inc. (1)
200 12th St S Ste 1200, Arlington, VA 22202
Tel.: (703) 979-7100
Web Site: http://www.msiworldwide.com
Economic Consulting Services
N.A.I.C.S.: 541618
Keith Brown *(Pres)*
Andrew Griminger *(Exec VP)*
Sandra Amis *(VP)*
Ellen Yount *(VP)*
Jeff Davis *(Dir-Tech)*
Chip Temm *(CTO & VP)*
Joseph Christoff *(Sr VP)*
Bobby Herman *(Sr VP)*
Rodeina AbdelFattah *(VP)*
Erin Stone *(Controller)*
Kathy Shelton *(Dir-Ops)*

Municipal Design Group, LLC (1)
360 Bay St, Augusta, GA 30901-1546
Tel.: (706) 736-4868
Engineeering Services
N.A.I.C.S.: 541330

Nehtruh-EBA Consulting Ltd. (1)
PO Box 110, Aklavik, Inuvik, X0E 0A0, NT, Canada
Tel.: (867) 978-2053
Web Site: http://www.eba.ca
Engineering & Consulting Services
N.A.I.C.S.: 541330

PRO-telligent, LLC (1)
1225 S Clark St Crystal Gateway II Ste 1475, Arlington, VA 22202
Tel.: (703) 414-5520
Web Site: http://www.pro-telligent.com
Emp.: 25
Business Management Consulting Services
N.A.I.C.S.: 541611
Patrick Haun *(Pres)*

Parkland Pipeline Contractors Ltd (1)
5710 - 48th Avenue, Olds, T4H 1V1, AB, Canada
Tel.: (403) 507-2774
Web Site: http://www.parklandpipeline.com
Oil & Gas Pipeline Installation Services
N.A.I.C.S.: 237120

Subsidiary (Domestic):

Park L Projects Ltd. (2)
44 Collins Road, PO Box 60, Dawson Creek, V1G 4E9, BC, Canada
Tel.: (250) 719-0056
Oil & Gas Field Operating Services
N.A.I.C.S.: 213112

Parkland Projects Ltd. (1)
1127 West 14th Street, North Vancouver, V7P 1J9, BC, Canada
Tel.: (604) 988-1999
Web Site: http://www.parklandprojects.com
Business Support Services
N.A.I.C.S.: 561499

Proteus Engineers Pty Ltd. (1)
370 Murray Street, Perth, 6000, WA, Australia
Tel.: (61) 863133200
Web Site: http://www.proteuseng.com.au
Construction Engineering Services
N.A.I.C.S.: 541330

Rooney Engineering, Inc. (1)
115 Inverness Dr E Ste 300, Englewood, CO 80112
Tel.: (303) 792-5911
Web Site: http://www.rooney-eng.com
Sales Range: $10-24.9 Million
Emp.: 50
Pipeline Engineering Firm
N.A.I.C.S.: 237120
Mark B. Johnke *(VP-Engrg)*

SCM Consultants, Inc. (1)
7601 W Clearwater Ave Ste 301, Kennewick, WA 99336-1677
Tel.: (509) 783-1625
Web Site: http://www.scm-ae.com
Sales Range: $25-49.9 Million
Emp.: 60
Consulting & Engineering Firm; Designing of Irrigation, Water & Wastewater Systems, Facility & Infra
N.A.I.C.S.: 541330

Segue Technologies, Inc. (1)
1515 Wilson Blvd Ste 1100, Arlington, VA 22209
Tel.: (703) 549-8033
Web Site: https://www.seguetech.com
Sales Range: $1-9.9 Million
Custom Computer Programming Services
N.A.I.C.S.: 541511
Brian Callahan *(Pres & CEO)*
Mark Shapiro *(CTO)*

Tetra Tech BAS, Inc. (1)
1360 Vly Vista Dr, Diamond Bar, CA 91765
Tel.: (909) 860-7777
Engineeering Services
N.A.I.C.S.: 541330

Tetra Tech Canada Inc. (1)
25 Milvan Dr, North York, M9L 1Y8, ON, Canada
Tel.: (416) 749-7400
Web Site: http://www.sentrexco.com
Construction Engineering Services
N.A.I.C.S.: 541330

Tetra Tech Cape Canaveral, LLC (1)
11 Riverside Dr Ste 204, Cocoa, FL 32922
Tel.: (321) 636-6470
Sales Range: $25-49.9 Million
Emp.: 5
Environmental Engineering & Consulting Services
N.A.I.C.S.: 541330
Matthew Shelton *(Gen Mgr)*

Tetra Tech Coffey Pty. Ltd. (1)
Level 19 Tower B Citadel Tower 799 Pacific Highway, Chatswood, 2067, NSW, Australia
Tel.: (61) 294061000
Engineeering Services
N.A.I.C.S.: 541330

Tetra Tech Consultoria Ltda (1)
R Fidalga 711, Vila Madalena, Sao Paulo, Brazil
Tel.: (55) 1130377131
Emp.: 38
Engineeering Services
N.A.I.C.S.: 541330

Tetra Tech Contingency Constructors, LLC (1)
5250 Challedon Dr, Virginia Beach, VA 23462-6304
Tel.: (757) 502-8610
Commercial & Institutional Building Construction Services
N.A.I.C.S.: 236220

Tetra Tech EC, Inc. (1)
1000 The American Rd, Morris Plains, NJ 07950-2446

Tel.: (973) 630-8000
Web Site: http://www.tteci.com
Sales Range: $250-299.9 Million
Emp.: 1,600
Environmental Consulting, Engineering & Remediation Services
N.A.I.C.S.: 541618

Tetra Tech EM Inc. (1)
Fl 37 1 S Wacker Dr, Chicago, IL 60606-4651
Tel.: (312) 201-7700
Sales Range: $25-49.9 Million
Emp.: 85
Enviromental Consulting Engineering Firmncy
N.A.I.C.S.: 541611
Anjli Patel *(Engr-Environmental)*

Tetra Tech EM Inc. (1)
4940 Pearl E Cir Ste 100, Boulder, CO 80301
Tel.: (303) 441-7900
Sales Range: $1-9.9 Million
Emp.: 30
Water & Sewer Utility Construction; Telephone Apparatus Mfr
N.A.I.C.S.: 237130
Darrell Longwell *(Office Mgr)*
Dan Pastor *(Office Mgr)*

Tetra Tech EMC, Inc. (1)
100 Camino Ruiz, Camarillo, CA 93012
Tel.: (805) 484-9082
Web Site: http://www.emc-inc.com
Sales Range: $75-99.9 Million
Emp.: 30
Engineering Consulting
N.A.I.C.S.: 541330
Patrick Haun *(Pres)*
James E. Bailey *(VP & Dir-Contracts)*
Jerry McMahan *(VP-Aviation & Weapon Sys Support)*
Amy Galan *(VP-Fin & Gen Admin)*
Craig Hendrickson *(VP-Bus Dev)*
Stephen Beal *(VP-Engrg Svcs)*

Tetra Tech Engineering & Architecture Services (1)
1420 5th Ave Ste 600, Seattle, WA 98101-1010
Tel.: (206) 883-9300
Sales Range: $10-24.9 Million
Emp.: 80
Engineering Services Firm Specializing in Areas of Water Quality, Water & Wastewater Systems, Surface Water Management, Fisheries & Facilities
N.A.I.C.S.: 541330

Tetra Tech FHC, Inc. (1)
7645 E 63rd St Ste 301, Tulsa, OK 74133
Tel.: (918) 249-3909
Civil Engineering Services
N.A.I.C.S.: 541330

Tetra Tech HEI, Inc. (1)
1009 Commerce Park Dr Ste 300 A, Oak Ridge, TN 37830
Tel.: (865) 483-9900
Engineering Consulting Services
N.A.I.C.S.: 541330

Tetra Tech India Limited (1)
951 9th Floor Aggarwal Metro Heights Netaji Subhash Place, Pitampura, New Delhi, 110034, India
Tel.: (91) 1145007500
Web Site: http://www.tetratechindia.com
Environmental Engineering & Consulting Services
N.A.I.C.S.: 541330

Tetra Tech NUS, Inc. (1)
661 Andersen Dr Foster Plz 7, Pittsburgh, PA 15220
Tel.: (412) 921-7090
Web Site: http://www.ttnus.com
Sales Range: $50-74.9 Million
Emp.: 150
Environmental Consulting, Engineering, Remediation/Construction & Information Technology
N.A.I.C.S.: 541690

Tetra Tech Nuclear (1)
24 Frank Lloyd Wright Dr, Ann Arbor, MI 48105-9484
Tel.: (734) 930-7500
Web Site: http://www.tetratechnuclear.com

Tetra Tech, Inc.—(Continued)

Nuclear Consulting & Engineering Services
N.A.I.C.S.: 541330

Tetra Tech OGD Inc. (1)
10851 Shellbridge Way Ste 100, Richmond,
V6X 2W8, BC, Canada
Tel.: (604) 270-7728
Construction Engineering Services
N.A.I.C.S.: 541330

Tetra Tech RMC, Inc. (1)
1900 S Sunset St Ste 1E, Longmont, CO
80501
Tel.: (303) 772-5282
Emp.: 30
Engineering Services
N.A.I.C.S.: 541330
Tom Hesemann (VP)
Gayle Meining (Controller)

Tetra Tech Tesoro, Inc. (1)
5250 Challedon Dr, Virginia Beach, VA
23462
Tel.: (757) 518-8491
Web Site: http://www.tesorocorp.com
Sales Range: $50-74.9 Million
Emp.: 161
Commercial & Office Building Contractors
N.A.I.C.S.: 236210

Tetra Tech, Inc. - Ann Arbor (1)
710 Avis Dr, Ann Arbor, MI 48108-9649
Tel.: (734) 930-7500
Environmental Engineering & Consulting
Services
N.A.I.C.S.: 541330
Lesli L. Shoemaker (Exec VP-Ops)

Tetra Tech, Inc. - Breckenridge (1)
130 Ski Hill Rd Ste 130, Breckenridge, CO
80424
Tel.: (970) 453-6394
Sales Range: $10-24.9 Million
Emp.: 8
Consulting & Engineering Firm Specializing
in Water Resource Engineering
N.A.I.C.S.: 541330

Tetra Tech, Inc. - Burlington (1)
159 Bank St Ste 300, Burlington, VT 05401
Tel.: (802) 495-0282
Business Management Consulting Services
N.A.I.C.S.: 541611

Tetra Tech, Inc. - Framingham (1)
1 Grant St, Framingham, MA 01702-6708
Tel.: (508) 903-2000
Sales Range: $25-49.9 Million
Emp.: 170
Civil Engineering, Transportation Planning &
Design, Assessment, Remediation, Compli-
ance & Natural Resource Services
N.A.I.C.S.: 541330

Tetra Tech, Inc. - Lexington (1)
424 Lewis Hargett Cir Ste 110, Lexington,
KY 40503
Tel.: (859) 223-8000
Sales Range: $25-49.9 Million
Emp.: 25
Water Treatment Facility Management
N.A.I.C.S.: 221320

Tetra Tech, Inc. - Madison (1)
6410 Enterprise Ln Ste 300, Madison, WI
53719
Tel.: (608) 316-3700
Environmental Engineering & Consulting
Services
N.A.I.C.S.: 541330

Tetra Tech/KCM, Inc. (1)
1420 5th Ave Ste 600 , Seattle, WA 98101-
2357
Tel.: (206) 443-5300
Sales Range: $10-24.9 Million
Emp.: 80
Engineering Services
N.A.I.C.S.: 541330
Tony Melone (VP)

The Kaizen Company, LLC. (1)
1604 7th St NW Ste B, Washington, DC
20001-3219
Tel.: (202) 299-9801
Web Site:
http://www.thekaizencompany.com
General Management Consulting Services
N.A.I.C.S.: 541611

Kevin Wheeler (CEO)

Topo Planification Inc. (1)
4655 Wilfrid-Hamel Blvd, Quebec, G1P 2J7,
QC, Canada
Tel.: (418) 683-8676
Web Site: http://www.topo-planification.ca
Engineering Services
N.A.I.C.S.: 541330

WYG Plc (1)
Arndale Court Otley Road Headingley,
Leeds, LS6 2UJ, United Kingdom
Tel.: (44) 1132787111
Web Site: http://www.wyg.com
Rev.: $208,238,021
Assets: $113,899,456
Liabilities: $79,414,600
Net Worth: $34,484,856
Earnings: ($6,761,789)
Emp.: 1,641
Fiscal Year-end: 03/31/2018
Civil, Electrical, Environmental, Mechanical
& Structural Engineering Consulting Ser-
vices
N.A.I.C.S.: 541330
Dave Corbin (Head-Project Mgmt & Dir)

Subsidiary (Domestic):

AKT II Limited (2)
100 Saint John Street, London, EC1M 4EH,
United Kingdom (100%)
Tel.: (44) 2072507777
Web Site: http://www.akt-uk.com
Sales Range: $10-24.9 Million
Emp.: 250
Structural & Civil Engineering Consulting
N.A.I.C.S.: 541330
Hanif Kara (Founder & Dir-Design)
Albert Williamson-Taylor (Dir)

Tweeds Limited (2)
Cavern Ct 8 Mathew St, L26RE, Liverpool,
United Kingdom (100%)
Tel.: (44) 1512364502
Web Site: http://www.tweeds.co.uk
Emp.: 40
Engineering Services
N.A.I.C.S.: 541330

WYG Consulting Limited (2)
Craigievar House 77, Craigmount Brae,
EH128XF, Edinburgh, United
Kingdom (100%)
Tel.: (44) 1313695494
Management Consulting Services
N.A.I.C.S.: 541618

**WYG Environment Planning Trans-
port Limited** (2)
Longcross Court 47 Newport Road, Cardiff,
CF24 0AD, South Glamorgan, United King-
dom
Tel.: (44) 2920829200
Web Site: http://www.wyg.com
Emp.: 70
Environmental Consulting Services
N.A.I.C.S.: 541620

Subsidiary (Non-US):

**WYG Environmental (Ireland)
Limited** (2)
Unit 2 University Technology Centre, Curra-
heen Road, Cork, Ireland (100%)
Tel.: (353) 214933200
Emp.: 20
Engineering Services
N.A.I.C.S.: 541330

Subsidiary (Domestic):

WYG Environmental Limited (2)
Arndale Court Otley Road Headingley,
LS62UJ, Leeds, United Kingdom (100%)
Tel.: (44) 1132787111
Web Site: http://www.wyg.com
Emp.: 260
Environmental Consulting Services
N.A.I.C.S.: 541620

WYG International Limited (2)
Geneva Bldg Lakeview Dr, Sherwood Busi-
ness Park, Annesley, NG15 0ED, Notting-
ham, United Kingdom (100%)
Tel.: (44) 1623684500
Web Site: http://www.wyg.com
Emp.: 100
Heavy & Civil Engineering Construction
N.A.I.C.S.: 237990

Subsidiary (Non-US):

WYG Ireland Limited (2)
PH McCarthy House Nutgrove Office Park,
Nutgrove Avenue Rathfarnham, Dublin,
Ireland (100%)
Tel.: (353) 12914800
Web Site: http://www.wyg.com
Engineering Services
N.A.I.C.S.: 541330

Subsidiary (Domestic):

**WYG Management Services
Limited** (2)
5th Floor Horton House, Liverpool, L2 3PF,
United Kingdom
Tel.: (44) 1512364502
Web Site: http://www.wyg.com
Emp.: 30
Chartered Quantity Surveyor
N.A.I.C.S.: 541990

Subsidiary (Non-US):

**WYG Nolan Ryan Tweeds
Limited** (2)
Ph Mccarthy House Nutgrove Office park
Nutgrove Ave, Dublin, Ireland
Tel.: (353) 16624011
Engineering Services
N.A.I.C.S.: 541330

TETRA TECHNOLOGIES, INC.

24955 Interstate 45 N, The Wood-
lands, TX 77380
Tel.: (281) 367-1983   DE
Web Site: https://onetetra.com
Year Founded: 1981
TTI—(NYSE)
Rev.: $553,213,000
Assets: $434,366,000
Liabilities: $327,969,000
Net Worth: $106,397,000
Earnings: $7,839,000
Emp.: 1,300
Fiscal Year-end: 12/31/22
Specialty Organic Chemical Products,
Services & Process Technologies
N.A.I.C.S.: 325130
Matthew J. Sanderson (Chief Comml
Officer & Exec VP)
Brady M. Murphy (Pres & CEO)
Roy E. McNiven (Sr VP-Energy Svcs
Ops)
Tim Moeller (Sr VP-Global Supply
Chain & Chemicals)
Jacek Mucha (Treas & VP-Fin)
Alicia P. Boston (Chief Compliance
Officer)
Elijio V. Serrano (CFO, Principal
Acctg Officer & Sr VP)

Subsidiaries:

**Ahmad Albinali & TETRA Arabia
Company Ltd.** (1)
PO Box 2925, Dammam, 31461, Saudi
Arabia
Tel.: (966) 138574190
Inorganic Chemical Mfr
N.A.I.C.S.: 325180

Compressco, Inc. (1)
5300 S Rockwell Ave, Oklahoma City, OK
73179
Tel.: (405) 745-4274
Web Site: http://www.compressco.com
Emp.: 109
Petroleum & Natural Gas Production En-
hancement Equipment Mfr
N.A.I.C.S.: 213112

Greywolf Energy Services Ltd. (1)
42 McCool Crescent, PO Box 1381, Cross-
field, T0M 0S0, AB, Canada
Tel.: (403) 946-4445
Web Site: http://www.greywolfsystems.ca
Oil & Gas Field Machinery Mfr
N.A.I.C.S.: 333132

Optima Solutions U.K. Limited (1)
Altens Industrial Estate, Aberdeen, AB12
3LE, United Kingdom
Tel.: (44) 1224537300

Web Site: https://www.optimauk.com
Oil & Gas Field Machinery Mfr
N.A.I.C.S.: 333132
Andy Christie (Mgr-Bus Dev)
Craig Oliver (Ops Mgr)

T-Production Testing LLC (1)
24955 Interstate 45 N, The Woodlands, TX
77380
Tel.: (281) 367-1983
Web Site: http://www.tetratec.com
Sales Range: $650-699.9 Million
Emp.: 1,001
Specialty Organic Chemical Products, Ser-
vices & Process Technologies
N.A.I.C.S.: 213112

**TETRA Applied Holding
Company** (1)
24955 Interstate 45 N, The Woodlands, TX
77380-3063
Tel.: (281) 367-1983
Web Site: http://www.tetratec.com
Sales Range: $100-124.9 Million
Emp.: 400
Offices of Other Holding Companies
N.A.I.C.S.: 551112

TETRA Chemicals Europe AB (1)
Box 901, 251 09, Helsingborg, Sweden
Tel.: (46) 424532700
Sales Range: $25-49.9 Million
Emp.: 17
Calcium Chloride Mfr & Marketer
N.A.I.C.S.: 325180

TETRA Chemicals Europe OY (1)
Kemirantie 1, PO Box 551, 67701, Kokkola,
Finland
Tel.: (358) 207212500
Web Site: https://tetrachemicals.fi
Calcium Chloride Mfr & Marketer
N.A.I.C.S.: 325180

TETRA Technologies UK Limited (1)
Tel.: (44) 1224537200
Sales Range: $10-24.9 Million
Emp.: 15
Specialty Organic Chemical Products, Ser-
vices & Process Technologies
N.A.I.C.S.: 325199

**TETRA Technologies de Mexico, S.A.
de C.V.** (1)
Calle Hierro No 7 Colonia Ciudad Industrial,
86010, Villahermosa, Tabasco, Mexico
Tel.: (52) 933531055
Web Site: http://www.tetra.
Specialty Organic Chemical Products Mfr
N.A.I.C.S.: 325130

**TETRA Technologies do Brasil,
Limitada** (1)
Av Republica do Chile 330 Edificio Ventura
- Sala 424, Centro Rio das Ostras RJ, Rio
de Janeiro, 28890-000, Brazil
Tel.: (55) 2227966600
Web Site: http://www.tetratec.com.br
Sales Range: $1-9.9 Million
Emp.: 20
Specialty Organic Chemical Products, Ser-
vices & Process Technologies
N.A.I.C.S.: 325199

Tetra Financial Services, Inc. (1)
6995 S Union Park Ctr Ste 400, Cotton-
wood Heights, UT 84047
Tel.: (801) 748-2200
Web Site: http://www.tetrafinancial.com
Equipment Leasing Services
N.A.I.C.S.: 532490

TETRALOGIC PHARMACEUTI-
CALS CORPORATION

343 Phoenixville Pike, Malvern, PA
19355
Tel.: (610) 889-9900   DE
Web Site: http://www.tlog.com
Year Founded: 2001
TLOG—(OTCIQ)
Sales Range: Less than $1 Million
Emp.: 29
Biopharmaceutical Mfr
N.A.I.C.S.: 325412
Stephen Condon (VP-Chemistry)
Andrew L. Pecora (Chm)

Richard L. Sherman (Gen Counsel & Sec)

Tony Meehan (VP-Alliance Mgmt & Ops)

Subsidiaries:

Shape Pharmaceuticals Pty Ltd   (1)
17 Smith Street, Bedfordview, Johannesburg, South Africa
Tel.: (27) 116228649
Web Site: http://www.shapehealth.co.za
Pharmaceuticals Product Mfr
N.A.I.C.S.: 325412

TETRAPHASE PHARMACEUTICALS, INC.

480 Arsenal Way, Watertown, MA 02472
Tel.: (617) 715-3600   DE
Web Site: http://www.tphase.com
Year Founded: 2006
TTPH—(NASDAQ)
Rev.: $7,376,000
Assets: $36,385,000
Liabilities: $13,218,000
Net Worth: $23,167,000
Earnings: ($70,085,000)
Emp.: 67
Fiscal Year-end: 12/31/19
Biopharmaceutical Mfr
N.A.I.C.S.: 325412
Leonard Patrick Gage (Chm)
Maria D. Stahl (Chief Bus Officer)

TEUCRIUM AGRICULTURAL FUND

c/o Teucrium Trading, LLC 232 Hidden Lake Rd Bldg A, Brattleboro, VT 05301
Tel.: (802) 257-1617
Web Site:
   http://www.teucriumtagsfund.com
TAGS—(NYSA)
Investment Services
N.A.I.C.S.: 523999
Barbara Riker (CFO, Chief Compliance Officer & Chief Acctg Officer)

TEUCRIUM CORN FUND

c/o Teucrium Trading LLC 232 Hidden Lake Rd Bldg A, Brattleboro, VT 05301
Tel.: (802) 257-1617   DE
Web Site:
   http://www.teucriumcornfund.com
Year Founded: 2009
CORN—(NYSA)
Sales Range: Less than $1 Million
Investment Services
N.A.I.C.S.: 523999
Sal Gilbertie (Pres)
Barbara Riker (CFO)

TEUCRIUM SOYBEAN FUND

232 Hidden Lake Rd, Brattleboro, VT 05301
Tel.: (802) 257-1617   DE
Web Site:
   http://www.teucriumsoybfund.com
SOYB—(NYSA)
Sales Range: Less than $1 Million
Investment Services
N.A.I.C.S.: 523999
Barbara Riker (CFO)

TEUCRIUM SUGAR FUND

c/o Teucrium Trading LLC 232 Hidden Lake Rd Bldg A, Brattleboro, VT 05301
Tel.: (802) 257-1617   DE
Web Site:
   http://www.teucriumcanefund.com
CANE—(NYSA)
Sales Range: Less than $1 Million
Investment Services
N.A.I.C.S.: 523999
Barbara Riker (CFO)

TEUCRIUM WHEAT FUND

c/o Teucrium Trading LLC 232 Hidden Lake Rd Bldg A, Brattleboro, VT 05301
Tel.: (802) 257-1617   DE
Web Site:
   http://www.teucriumweatfund.com
WEAT—(NYSA)
Sales Range: Less than $1 Million
Investment Services
N.A.I.C.S.: 523999
Barbara Riker (CFO)

TEXAS CAPITAL BANCSHARES, INC.

5800 Granite Pkwy Ste 150, Plano, TX 75024
Tel.: (214) 932-6600   DE
Web Site:
   https://www.texascapitalbank.com
Year Founded: 1998
TCBI—(NASDAQ)
Rev.: $1,493,766,000
Assets: $28,414,642,000
Liabilities: $25,359,291,000
Net Worth: $3,055,351,000
Earnings: $332,478,000
Emp.: 2,198
Fiscal Year-end: 12/31/22
Bank Holding Company
N.A.I.C.S.: 551111
Rob C. Holmes (Pres & CEO)
John W. Cummings (Chief Admin Officer & Exec VP)
Ellen Detrich (Chief Acctg Officer & Controller)
Julia Harman (Head-Corporate Banking & Exec VP--Corporate Banking)
Anna M. Alvarado (Chief Legal Officer & Sec)
M. Anna Alvarado (Chief Legal Officer)

Subsidiaries:

Texas Capital Bank, N.A.   (1)
2000 Mckinney Ave Ste 190, Dallas, TX 75201-1985
Tel.: (214) 932-6700
Web Site: http://www.texascapitalbank.com
Sales Range: $1-4.9 Billion
Emp.: 1,600
Commercial Bank
N.A.I.C.S.: 522110
Russell Hartsfield (Pres-Sponsored Lending)
Rob C. Holmes (Pres & CEO)
John W. Cummings (Chief Admin Officer & Exec VP)
Nelson Henry (Exec VP)
William Wilson (Exec Mng Dir-SBA & Bus Banking)
John C. Sarvadi (Exec Mng Dir-Middle Market Banking)
Matt Love (Sr VP)
Chris Capriotti (Exec VP-Asset Based Lending)
J. J. Ponce (Officer-Comm Dev)
Effie Dennison (Exec VP-Community Dev & Corp Responsibility)
Charles Adams (VP)
Ana Chandler (VP-Treasury & Liquidity)
Philip Toscano (Sr VP)
Peter Stringer (Exec VP-Line Bus & Mgr-Fin Svcs)
Jeff Wagner (Exec VP & Mgr-Sls)
J. Russell Guess (Sr VP)
Brook Silvestri (Sr VP)
Curtis Anderson (Exec VP)
Shannon Woods (Exec VP & Dir-Internal Audit)
Nancy McDonnell (Exec VP & Head-Treasury Svcs)
Matthew Quale (Exec VP & Head-Consumer Banking)
Brian Frank (Exec VP & Mgr-Grp)
Brat McCain (Sr VP)
Byron Terwege (Sr VP)
Julia Harman (Head-Corp Banking)
Beth Martin (Sr VP)
Julie Woidneck (Sr VP & Sr Mgr-Relationship-Corp Banking)

Austin Tabor (VP & Mgr-Relationship-Corp Banking)
Paul Forthman (Sr VP)
Chris Beard (Asst VP)
Joe Valenzuela (Sr Mgr-Diversity, Equity & Inclusion)
Don Goin (CIO)
Greg Yokum (Sr VP)
Anna Sanchez (Sr VP)
Rick Rodman (Head-Bus Banking)
Matt Scurlock (CFO & Exec VP)
Dave Monaghan (Sr VP-Bus Banking)
Madison Simm (Pres-Mortgage Fin)
Jon M. Larson (Head-Homebuilder & Community Fin)
Vivek Misra (Chief Compliance Officer & Exec VP)
Bryan Kucholtz (Exec VP & Head-Private Wealth)
David A. Youngberg Jr. (Mng Dir & Chief Credit Officer)

Division (Domestic):

BankDirect   (2)
2350 Lakeside Blvd Ste 800, Richardson, TX 75082
Tel.: (214) 932-6600
Web Site: http://www.bankdirect.com
Sales Range: $25-49.9 Million
Emp.: 90
Internet Based Banking & Financial Services
N.A.I.C.S.: 522110

TEXAS COMMUNITY BANCSHARES, INC.

Tel.: (903) 569-2602   MD
Web Site:
   https://investors.broadstreet.bank
Year Founded: 1934
TCBS—(NASDAQ)
Rev.: $14,434,000
Assets: $417,346,000
Liabilities: $361,476,000
Net Worth: $55,870,000
Earnings: $1,754,000
Emp.: 61
Fiscal Year-end: 12/31/22
Bank Holding Company
N.A.I.C.S.: 551111
James H. Herlocker III (Chm, Pres & CEO)

Subsidiaries:

Mineola Community Bank SSB   (1)
215 W Broad St, Mineola, TX 75773
Tel.: (903) 569-2602
Web Site: https://www.mineolacb.com
Rev.: $1,505,000
Emp.: 5
Banking Services
N.A.I.C.S.: 522180
Robin Averett (VP)
Sheree Mize (Sec)
Becky Champion (Branch Mgr)
Ammie Saucier (Branch Mgr)
Michelle Henry (Branch Mgr)
Sherrie Lynn Kitchens (Officer-Loan)
Rocio Maritnez (Officer-Loan)
Duncan McAdoo (VP & Officer-Bus Dev)
Martrice Parish (Officer-Loan)
Mitzi Pearce (Officer-Loan)
Keith Riley (Officer-Loan)
Julie Yarbrough (CFO)

TEXAS GULF ENERGY, INCORPORATED

1602 Old Underwood Rd, La Porte, TX 77571
Tel.: (281) 867-8400   NV
Web Site: http://www.tgnrg.com
Year Founded: 2007
TXGE—(OTCEM)
Sales Range: $1-9.9 Million
Emp.: 32
Investment Services
N.A.I.C.S.: 523999
Karim Ayed (Chm, Interim Pres & CEO)

TEXAS INSTRUMENTS INCORPORATED

12500 TI Blvd, Dallas, TX 75243
Tel.: (972) 995-2011   DE
Web Site: https://www.ti.com
Year Founded: 1930
TXN—(NASDAQ)
Rev.: $17,519,000,000
Assets: $32,348,000,000
Liabilities: $15,451,000,000
Net Worth: $16,897,000,000
Earnings: $6,510,000,000
Emp.: 34,000
Fiscal Year-end: 12/31/23
Electronics, Semiconductors, Software Productivity Tools & Electrical Controls Mfr & Sales
N.A.I.C.S.: 334413
Richard K. Templeton (Chm)
Dave Pahl (VP-Investor Relations)
Haviv Ilan (Pres & CEO)
Julie M. Van Haren (Sr VP-Communications-Investor Relations)
Hagop H. Kozanian (Sr VP-Analog Signal Chain)
Ahmad S. Bahai (CTO & Sr VP)
Mark S. Gary (Sr VP-Analog Power Products)
Julie Knecht (Chief Acctg Officer)
Krunali Patel (CIO & Sr VP)

Subsidiaries:

ActSolar, Inc.   (1)
3350 Thomas Rd, Santa Clara, CA 95054
Tel.: (408) 694-3940
Semiconductor & Electronic Component Mfr
N.A.I.C.S.: 334413

Algorex Inc.   (1)
447 Battery St Ste 3, San Francisco, CA 94111
Tel.: (415) 616-9676
Software Development Services
N.A.I.C.S.: 541511

Benchmarq Microelectronics Corporation of South Korea   (1)
17919 Waterview Pkwy, Dallas, TX 75252
Tel.: (972) 437-9195
Semiconductor & Electronic Component Mfr & Distr
N.A.I.C.S.: 334413

Electronica NSC de Mexico, S.A. de C.V.   (1)
Avenida de las Naciones No 1 Piso 33 Oficina 38 Edificio WTC, Col Napoles, Mexico, 03810, Mexico
Tel.: (52) 54880135
Electronic Component Mfr & Distr
N.A.I.C.S.: 334419

Energy Recommerce Inc.   (1)
116 Oliva Ct, Novato, CA 94947
Tel.: (415) 493-5402
Emp.: 7
Measuring & Controlling Device Mfr
N.A.I.C.S.: 334519

Mediamatics, Inc.   (1)
PO BOX 655474, Dallas, TX 75265
Tel.: (408) 721-3635
Electronic Component Mfr & Distr
N.A.I.C.S.: 334419

National Semiconductor (Maine), Inc.   (1)
5 Foden Rd, South Portland, ME 04106
Tel.: (207) 541-8100
Emp.: 4
Semiconductor & Electronic Component Mfr
N.A.I.C.S.: 334413

National Semiconductor (Pte) Limited   (1)
United Square 30-01 101 Thomson Rd, Singapore, 307591, Singapore
Tel.: (65) 65116699
Holding Company
N.A.I.C.S.: 551112

National Semiconductor Corporation   (1)
2900 Semiconductor Dr, Santa Clara, CA 95051-0606
Tel.: (408) 721-5000
Web Site: http://www.national.com

Texas Instruments Incorporated—(Continued)

Sales Range: $1-4.9 Billion
Emp.: 5,700
Integrated Circuits & Microprocessors Mfr
N.A.I.C.S.: 334413

National Semiconductor International B.V. (1)
Delftechpark 19, 2628 XJ, Delft, Netherlands
Tel.: (31) 157890050
Business Management Consulting Services
N.A.I.C.S.: 541611

National Semicondutores da America do Sul Ltda. (1)
World Trade Center Av das Nacoes Unidas 12551-18 andar-cj 1801, Brooklin, Sao Paulo, 04578-903, Brazil
Tel.: (55) 1130437450
Semiconductor & Electronic Component Mfr
N.A.I.C.S.: 334413

National Semicondutores do Brasil Ltda. (1)
Rua Dep Lacerda Franco 120 Pinheiros, Sao Paulo, 03258-000, Brazil
Tel.: (55) 1138121181
Semiconductor & Electronic Component Mfr & Distr
N.A.I.C.S.: 334413

TI (Philippines), Inc. (1)
19F Regus Center Marco Polo Ortigas Manila Sapphire Road, Ortigas Center, Pasig, 1600, Philippines
Tel.: (63) 288835200
Semiconductors & Related Devices Mfr
N.A.I.C.S.: 334413

Telogy Networks, Inc. (1)
20450 Century Blvd, Germantown, MD 20874-1174
Tel.: (301) 515-8580
Communication Equipment Mfr
N.A.I.C.S.: 334290

Texas Instruments (India) Private Limited (1)
Bagmane Tech Park No 66/3 Adjacent to LRDE Byrasandra, C V Raman Nagar Post, Bengaluru, 560 093, Karnataka, India
Tel.: (91) 8066831000
Semiconductor & Electronic Component Mfr
N.A.I.C.S.: 334413

Texas Instruments Austin Incorporated (1)
108 Wild Basin Rd 350, West Lake Hills, TX 78746-3326
Tel.: (512) 279-8800
Emp.: 60
Semiconductor & Electronic Component Mfr
N.A.I.C.S.: 334413

Texas Instruments Australia Pty Limited (1)
195 Wellington Rd, Clayton, 3168, VIC, Australia
Tel.: (61) 1300 138 140
Web Site: http://www.ti.com
Semiconductors & Related Devices Mfr
N.A.I.C.S.: 334413

Texas Instruments Belgium SA (1)
Avenue Jules Bordetlaan 11, Brussels, 1140, Belgium (100%)
Tel.: (32) 2 242 3080
Electronic Components Sales & Distr
N.A.I.C.S.: 423690

Texas Instruments Broadband Communications Group (1)
165 Gibraltar Ct, Sunnyvale, CA 94089-1301
Tel.: (972) 644-5580
Web Site: http://www.ti.com
Sales Range: $25-49.9 Million
Emp.: 100
Micro-to-Mainframe Communications Products Distr
N.A.I.C.S.: 513210

Texas Instruments Business Expansion GmbH (1)
Haggertystr 1, 85356, Freising, Germany
Tel.: (49) 8161800
Web Site: http://www.ti.com
Semiconductors & Related Devices Mfr

Texas Instruments Canada Limited (1)
505 March Road Suite 200, Kanata, K2K 2M5, ON, Canada
Tel.: (613) 271-8649
Web Site: http://focus.ti.com
Sales Range: $100-124.9 Million
Semiconductor Mfr
N.A.I.C.S.: 334413

Texas Instruments China Trading Limited (1)
Rm 1508 15/f Grand Century Place Tw 193 Prince Edward Rd W, Mong Kok, Hong Kong, China (Hong Kong)
Tel.: (852) 29567288
Professional Equipment Whslr
N.A.I.C.S.: 423490

Texas Instruments Denmark A/S (1)
Sofiendalsvej 93, Ayngeyhovepgade 4, 2800, Lyngby, Denmark
Tel.: (45) 96346868
Web Site: http://www.ti.com
Sales Range: $25-49.9 Million
Emp.: 132
Mobile Phone Design; Digital Audio Power Amplifiers & Calculators Mfr & Distr
N.A.I.C.S.: 334419

Texas Instruments Deutschland GmbH (1)
Haggertystrasse 1, 85356, Freising, Germany (100%)
Tel.: (49) 3091589890
Web Site: http://www.ti.com
Sales Range: $400-449.9 Million
Electronic Components Mfr
N.A.I.C.S.: 334419

Texas Instruments Espana, S.A. (1)
C/ Enrique Granados 6 Edificio B Planta 1 Mod, 28224, Pozuelo de Alarcon, Spain
Tel.: (34) 917102910
Industrial Equipment Whsr
N.A.I.C.S.: 423830

Texas Instruments Finland Oy (1)
Porkkalankatu 22, 00180, Helsinki, Finland (100%)
Tel.: (358) 941333400
Web Site: http://www.ti.com
Sales Range: $10-24.9 Million
Emp.: 30
Integrated Circuits & Microprocessors Mfr
N.A.I.C.S.: 334413

Texas Instruments France SA (1)
Noda Building 185-187 Qual de la Bataille de Stalingrad, 92130, Issy-les-Moulineaux, France (100%)
Tel.: (33) 185149829
Web Site: http://www.ti.com
Sales Range: $300-349.9 Million
Electronic Components Distr
N.A.I.C.S.: 423690

Texas Instruments Hong Kong Ltd. (1)
Unit 912 9/F Tower 1 Kowloon Commerce Centre 51 Kwai Cheong Road, Kwai Chung, Kowloon, New Territories, China (Hong Kong) (100%)
Tel.: (852) 29567288
Sales Range: $150-199.9 Million
Emp.: 35
Electronic Components Distr
N.A.I.C.S.: 423690
Richard K. Templeton (Chm, Pres & CEO)

Texas Instruments Incorporated - Plug & Power (1)
27715 Diehl Rd, Warrenville, IL 60555-3998
Tel.: (630) 393-6901
Web Site: http://www.ti.com
Sales Range: $50-74.9 Million
Emp.: 175
Switch Mfr
N.A.I.C.S.: 335313

Texas Instruments International Trade Corporation (1)
Halsingegatan 40, 113 43, Stockholm, Sweden (100%)
Tel.: (46) 858755500
Web Site: http://www.ti.com
Sales Range: $25-49.9 Million
Emp.: 32
Electronics Sales & Distr

Texas Instruments Israel Ltd. (1)
26 Zarhin Street 43, PO Box 2329, 66250, Ra'anana, Israel
Tel.: (972) 97906333
Web Site: http://www.ti.com
Sales Range: $100-124.9 Million
Emp.: 400
Electronic Components Mfr
N.A.I.C.S.: 334419

Texas Instruments Italia S.p.A. (1)
Via Paracelso 14, 20041, Agrate Brianza, Italy (100%)
Tel.: (39) 03965681
Sales Range: $25-49.9 Million
Emp.: 25
Electronic Components Sales & Distr
N.A.I.C.S.: 423690

Texas Instruments Italia S.r.l. (1)
Quartiere Torri Bianche Via Torri Bianche 6, Vimercate MB, 20871, Palazzo Tiepolo, Italy
Tel.: (39) 0699748075
Electronic System Mfr & Distr
N.A.I.C.S.: 334111

Texas Instruments Japan Ltd. (1)
Shinagawa Season Terrace 1-2-70 Konan, Minato-ku, Tokyo, 108-0075, Japan (100%)
Tel.: (81) 366344911
Web Site: http://www.tij.co.jp
Sales Range: $1-4.9 Billion
Electronics Sales & Distr
N.A.I.C.S.: 423690
Tomoaki Taguchi (Pres)

Texas Instruments Japan Semiconductor Limited (1)
6-24-1 Nishishinjuku Nishishinjukumitsui Bldg, Shinjuku-Ku, Tokyo, 160-0023, Japan
Tel.: (81) 343313100
Web Site: http://www.ti.com
Semiconductor & Related Devices Mfr
N.A.I.C.S.: 334413

Texas Instruments Limited (1)
Northumberland Buildings, Queen Square, Bath, BA1 2JB, United Kingdom
Tel.: (44) 604663000
Web Site: http://www.ti.com
Electronics Sales & Distr
N.A.I.C.S.: 423690

Texas Instruments Malaysia Sdn. Bhd. (1)
No 1 Lorong Enggang 33 Ulu Kelang Free Trade Z, Ampang, 54200, Malaysia
Tel.: (60) 342643333
Semiconductor & Electronic Component Mfr
N.A.I.C.S.: 334413

Texas Instruments Marketing & Finance GmbH & Co. KG (1)
Haggertystr 1, Freising, 85356, Bayern, Germany
Tel.: (49) 8161800
Web Site: http://www.ti.com
Emp.: 1,200
Semiconductors & Related Devices Mfr
N.A.I.C.S.: 334413

Texas Instruments Melbourne Incorporated (1)
3900 Sarno Rd, Melbourne, FL 32934
Tel.: (321) 409-7225
Microprocessor Mfr
N.A.I.C.S.: 334413

Texas Instruments Norway AS (1)
Hoffsveien 70 C, 0377, Oslo, Norway
Tel.: (47) 23369800
Web Site: http://www.ti.com
Circuits for Short Range Wireless Devices
N.A.I.C.S.: 334412

Texas Instruments Palo Alto Incorporated (1)
2185 Park Blvd, Palo Alto, CA 94306
Tel.: (650) 323-2955
Electronic Component Mfr & Distr
N.A.I.C.S.: 334419

Texas Instruments Russia Sales OOO (1)
White Stone Business Centre 4th Lesnoy Pereulok 4, 125047, Moscow, Russia

Tel.: (7) 4959167154
Semiconductor Mfr
N.A.I.C.S.: 334413

Texas Instruments Semiconductor Group (1)
13532 N Central Expy, Dallas, TX 75243-1108 (100%)
Tel.: (972) 644-5580
Web Site: http://www.ti.com
Sales Range: $75-99.9 Million
Emp.: 250
Semiconductors, Defense Electronics Systems, Software Productivity Tools, Mobile Computing Products & Consumer Electronics Products, Electrical Controls & Metallurgical Materials Mfr
N.A.I.C.S.: 334413
Richard K. Templeton (Chm, Pres & CEO)

Texas Instruments Semiconductor Manufacturing (Chengdu) Co., Ltd. (1)
10F E2 Tower 1268 Tianfu Avenue, Tianfu Software Park, Chengdu, 610015, Sichuan Province, China
Tel.: (86) 2862350811
Semiconductors & Related Devices Mfr
N.A.I.C.S.: 334413
Jim Lee (Gen Mgr)

Texas Instruments Semiconductor Technologies (Shanghai) Co., Ltd. (1)
10th Floor New Bund Center No 555 Haiyang Xi Road, Pudong New Area, Shanghai, 200126, China
Tel.: (86) 4008198694
Web Site: http://www.ti.com
Emp.: 300
Semiconductor & Electronic Component Mfr & Distr
N.A.I.C.S.: 334413

Texas Instruments Singapore (Pte.) Ltd. (1)
83 Clemenceau Ave 07-05, Shell House, Singapore, 239920, Singapore (100%)
Tel.: (65) 68336000
Web Site: http://focus.ti.com
Sales Range: $10-24.9 Million
Emp.: 70
Integrated Circuits Sales & Distr
N.A.I.C.S.: 334413

Texas Instruments Southeast Asia Pte. Ltd. (1)
83 Clemenceau Avenue 07 05/08 UE Square, Singapore, 239920, Singapore
Tel.: (65) 63894658
Electronic Parts & Equipment Distr
N.A.I.C.S.: 423690

Texas Instruments Sunnyvale Incorporated (1)
165 Gibraltar Ct, Sunnyvale, CA 94089
Tel.: (408) 541-9900
Semiconductors & Related Devices Mfr
N.A.I.C.S.: 334413

Texas Instruments Tucson Corporation (1)
5411 E Williams Blvd, Tucson, AZ 85711
Tel.: (520) 750-2000
Web Site: http://www.myti.com
Emp.: 256
Semiconductors & Related Devices Mfr
N.A.I.C.S.: 334413

TEXAS MINERAL RESOURCES CORP.
539 El Paso St, Sierra Blanca, TX 79851
Tel.: (915) 369-2133   **DE**
Web Site: https://tmrcorp.com
Year Founded: 1970
TMRC—(OTCQB)
Rev.: $120,594
Assets: $906,493
Liabilities: $42,664
Net Worth: $863,829
Earnings: ($833,009)
Emp.: 2
Fiscal Year-end: 08/31/24
Mineral Exploration & Mining Services

N.A.I.C.S.: 213115
Daniel E. Gorski *(CEO)*
Anthony Gabriel Marchese *(Chm)*

TEXAS OIL & MINERALS, INC.
900 N E Loop Ste D214, San Antonio, TX 78209
Tel.: (210) 824-5957   TX
TOMI—(OTCIQ)
Oil & Gas Exploration Services
N.A.I.C.S.: 213112
Stuart S. Seim *(CEO)*

TEXAS PACIFIC LAND CORP.
1700 Pacific Ave Ste 2900, Dallas, TX 75201
Tel.: (214) 969-5530   TX
Web Site:
  https://www.texaspacific.com
Year Founded: 1888
TPL—(NYSE)
Rev.: $631,595,000
Assets: $1,156,398,000
Liabilities: $113,202,000
Net Worth: $1,043,196,000
Earnings: $405,645,000
Emp.: 100
Fiscal Year-end: 12/31/23
Land Trust Company
N.A.I.C.S.: 531210
Chris Steddum *(CFO)*
John R. Norris III *(Chm)*
David E. Barry *(Vice Chm)*
Tyler Glover *(Pres, CEO & Sec)*
Micheal W. Dobbs *(Gen Counsel, Sec & Sr VP)*
Katie Keenan *(VP & Asst Gen Counsel)*
Stephanie Buffington *(Chief Acctg Officer)*
Jeremy Smith *(VP)*

TEXAS ROADHOUSE, INC.
6040 Dutchmans Ln, Louisville, KY 40205
Tel.: (502) 426-9984   DE
Web Site:
  https://www.texasroadhouse.com
Year Founded: 1993
TXRH—(NASDAQ)
Rev.: $4,631,672,000
Assets: $2,793,376,000
Liabilities: $1,635,865,000
Net Worth: $1,157,511,000
Earnings: $304,876,000
Emp.: 91,000
Fiscal Year-end: 12/26/23
Steak Restaurant Chain Owner & Operator
N.A.I.C.S.: 722511
David Christopher Monroe *(CFO)*
Gregory N. Moore *(Chm)*
Cortney Terry *(Coord-IR)*
Gerald L. Morgan *(CEO)*
Regina A. Tobin *(Pres)*
Keith V. Humpich *(Principal Acctg Officer)*

Subsidiaries:

Texas Roadhouse Delaware LLC **(1)**
4568 S Dupont Hwy, Camden-Wyoming, DE 19934
Tel.: (302) 698-4268
Emp.: 200
Restaurant Operating Services
N.A.I.C.S.: 722511

Texas Roadhouse Holdings LLC **(1)**
6040 Dutchmans Ln Ste 200, Louisville, KY 40205
Tel.: (502) 426-9984
Sales Range: $25-49.9 Million
Emp.: 280
Restaurant Operating Services
N.A.I.C.S.: 722511

Subsidiary (Domestic):

Texas Roadhouse of Jacksonville, NC, LLC   **(2)**

4578 Tropea Way, Jacksonville, FL 32246
Tel.: (904) 641-6350
Emp.: 40
Restaurant Operating Services
N.A.I.C.S.: 722511

Texas Roadhouse of Warwick, LLC   **(2)**
1200 Quaker Ln Bldg 1, East Greenwich, RI 02818
Tel.: (401) 884-4185
Restaurant Operating Services
N.A.I.C.S.: 722511

Texas Roadhouse of Austin, Ltd.   **(1)**
9300 S I-35 Service Rd Bldg F, Austin, TX 78748
Tel.: (512) 282-7427
Restaurant Operating Services
N.A.I.C.S.: 722511

Texas Roadhouse of Austin-North, Ltd.   **(1)**
13435 N US 183 SVRD NB Bldg 7, Austin, TX 78750
Tel.: (512) 336-7427
Sales Range: $10-24.9 Million
Emp.: 80
Restaurant Operating Services
N.A.I.C.S.: 722511
Kyle Costa *(Mng Partner)*

Texas Roadhouse of Bakersfield, LLC   **(1)**
3203 Ming Ave, Bakersfield, CA 93304
Tel.: (661) 397-0422
Restaurant Services
N.A.I.C.S.: 722511

Texas Roadhouse of Baytown, TX, LLC   **(1)**
6615 Garth Rd, Baytown, TX 77521
Tel.: (281) 421-3060
Sales Range: $25-49.9 Million
Emp.: 180
Restaurant Operating Services
N.A.I.C.S.: 722511

Texas Roadhouse of Cedar Falls, LLC   **(1)**
5715 University Ave, Cedar Falls, IA 50613
Tel.: (319) 266-3200
Web Site: http://www.texasroadhouse.com
Restaurant Operating Services
N.A.I.C.S.: 722511

Texas Roadhouse of Cheyenne, LLC   **(1)**
1931 Bluegrass Cir, Cheyenne, WY 82009
Tel.: (307) 638-1234
Web Site: http://www.texasroadhouse.com
Sales Range: $25-49.9 Million
Emp.: 150
Restaurant Operating Services
N.A.I.C.S.: 722511
Jimmy Dolan *(Mng Partner)*

Texas Roadhouse of Conway, Inc.   **(1)**
650 S Amity Rd, Conway, AR 72032
Tel.: (501) 585-7720
Restaurant Services
N.A.I.C.S.: 722511

Texas Roadhouse of Corona, CA LLC   **(1)**
6040 Dutchmans Ln, Louisville, KY 40205
Tel.: (502) 426-9984
Full Service Restaurant Operator
N.A.I.C.S.: 722511

Texas Roadhouse of Elyria, LLC   **(1)**
245 Market Dr, Elyria, OH 44035
Tel.: (440) 324-2002
Web Site: http://www.texasroadhouse.com
Emp.: 100
Restaurant Operating Services
N.A.I.C.S.: 722511

Texas Roadhouse of Fort Wayne, LLC   **(1)**
710 W Washington Ctr Rd, Fort Wayne, IN 46825
Tel.: (260) 416-0919
Emp.: 100
Restaurant Operating Services
N.A.I.C.S.: 722511
Natt Cobb *(Mng Partner)*
Douglas Giltrap *(Mng Partner)*

Texas Roadhouse of Grand Junction, LLC   **(1)**
2870 N Ave, Grand Junction, CO 81501
Tel.: (970) 243-5700
Restaurant Operating Services
N.A.I.C.S.: 722511

Texas Roadhouse of Hendersonville, de Novo, LLC   **(1)**
309 Indian Lk Blvd, Hendersonville, TN 37075-1231
Tel.: (615) 826-4207
Sales Range: $10-24.9 Million
Emp.: 75
Restaurant Operating Services
N.A.I.C.S.: 722511

Texas Roadhouse of Huber Heights, LLC   **(1)**
5611 Merily Way, Huber Heights, OH 45424
Tel.: (937) 233-7427
Sales Range: $25-49.9 Million
Emp.: 150
Restaurant Operating Services
N.A.I.C.S.: 722511

Texas Roadhouse of Kansas, LLC   **(1)**
2329 Iowa St Ste T, Lawrence, KS 66046
Tel.: (785) 312-7427
Restaurant Operating Services
N.A.I.C.S.: 722511

Texas Roadhouse of Lancaster OH, LLC   **(1)**
2890 Columbus-Lancaster Rd NW, Lancaster, OH 43130
Tel.: (740) 687-5021
Restaurant Operating Services
N.A.I.C.S.: 722511

Texas Roadhouse of Lancaster, LLC   **(1)**
2317 Lincoln Hwy E, Lancaster, PA 17602
Tel.: (717) 394-6161
Web Site: http://www.texasroadhouse.com
Restaurant Operating Services
N.A.I.C.S.: 722511
Matt Lowman *(Mng Partner)*

Texas Roadhouse of Lansing, LLC   **(1)**
208 E Edgewood Blvd, Lansing, MI 48911
Tel.: (517) 887-8181
Web Site: http://www.texasroadhouse.com
Restaurant Operating Services
N.A.I.C.S.: 722511

Texas Roadhouse of Lynchburg, LLC   **(1)**
3816 Wards Rd, Lynchburg, VA 24502
Tel.: (434) 237-1516
Web Site: http://www.texasroadhouse.com
Emp.: 90
Restaurant Operating Services
N.A.I.C.S.: 722511
Travis McCauley *(Mng Partner)*

Texas Roadhouse of Mansfield, Ltd.   **(1)**
940 N Highway 287, Mansfield, TX 76063
Tel.: (682) 518-6725
Sales Range: $25-49.9 Million
Emp.: 100
Restaurant Operating Services
N.A.I.C.S.: 722511

Texas Roadhouse of Menifee, CA, LLC   **(1)**
29860 Haun Rd, Menifee, CA 92586
Tel.: (951) 244-0600
Restaurant Operating Services
N.A.I.C.S.: 722511

Texas Roadhouse of Parker, LLC   **(1)**
11205 S Parker Rd, Parker, CO 80134
Tel.: (303) 805-5848
Restaurant Operating Services
N.A.I.C.S.: 722511

Texas Roadhouse of Reno, NV, LLC   **(1)**
150 Damonte Ranch Pkwy, Reno, NV 89521
Tel.: (775) 852-6333
Web Site: http://www.texasroadhouse.com
Restaurant Operating Services
N.A.I.C.S.: 722511

Texas Roadhouse of Richmond, LLC   **(1)**
4807 Waterview Meadow Dr, Richmond, TX 77407
Tel.: (346) 762-2040
Restaurant Operating Services
N.A.I.C.S.: 722511

Texas Roadhouse of Roseville, LLC   **(1)**
20201 13 Mile Rd, Roseville, MI 48066
Tel.: (586) 294-0838
Restaurant Operating Services
N.A.I.C.S.: 722511

Texas Roadhouse of Stillwater, OK, LLC   **(1)**
2000 N Perkins Rd, Stillwater, OK 74075-3080
Tel.: (405) 707-7427
Restaurant Operating Services
N.A.I.C.S.: 722511

TEXCOM, INC.
3600 S Gessner Ste 200, Houston, TX 77063
Tel.: (713) 914-9193   NV
Web Site:
  http://www.texcomresources.com
TEXC—(OTCIQ)
Environmental Consulting Services
N.A.I.C.S.: 541620
Robert S. May *(Pres & CEO)*
Stephen J. Barth *(Sec)*

Subsidiaries:

Eagle Ford Environmental Services, LLC   **(1)**
15963 S State Hwy 16, Jourdanton, TX 78026
Tel.: (830) 784-3600
Environmental Services
N.A.I.C.S.: 541620

Texcom Bennett Environmental Services, LLC   **(1)**
7452 Hwy 65 S, Clinton, AR 72031
Tel.: (501) 745-5118
Environmental Services
N.A.I.C.S.: 541620

Texcom Environmental Services, LLC   **(1)**
3600 S Gessner Ste 200, Houston, TX 77063
Tel.: (713) 914-9193
Environmental Services
N.A.I.C.S.: 541620

Texcom Peak Environmental Services, LLC   **(1)**
9268 Hwy 65 S, Bee Branch, AR 72013
Tel.: (501) 745-7101
Environmental Services
N.A.I.C.S.: 541620

TEXTRON INC.
40 Westminster St, Providence, RI 02903
Tel.: (401) 421-2800   DE
Web Site: https://www.textron.com
Year Founded: 1923
TXT—(NYSE)
Rev.: $13,683,000,000
Assets: $16,856,000,000
Liabilities: $9,869,000,000
Net Worth: $6,987,000,000
Earnings: $921,000,000
Emp.: 35,000
Fiscal Year-end: 12/30/23
Holding Company; Commercial & Military Aviation Vehicles, Components & Related Equipment Mfr
N.A.I.C.S.: 551112
Scott C. Donnelly *(Chm, Pres & CEO)*
Mark S. Bamford *(VP & Controller)*
Thomas N. Nichipor *(VP-Audit Svcs)*
Eric Salander *(Treas & VP-IR)*
Dana L. Goldberg *(VP-Tax)*
Scott P. Hegstrom *(VP-Mergers & Acquisitions & Strategy)*

Textron Inc.—(Continued)

Lawrence J. La Sala *(VP & Deputy Gen Counsel-Litigation)*
Kimberly A. Mackenroth *(CIO & VP)*
Janet S. Fogarty *(VP & Deputy Gen Counsel)*
Shannon Hines *(Sr VP)*
Shannon H. Hines *(Sr VP)*
Frank T. Connor *(CFO & Exec VP)*
E. Robert Lupone *(Gen Counsel, Sec & Exec VP)*
E. Robert Lupone *(Gen Counsel, Sec & Exec VP)*

Subsidiaries:

Able Aerospace Services, Inc. (1)
7706 E Velocity Way, Mesa, AZ 85212
Tel.: (602) 304-1227
Web Site: https://www.ableengineering.com
Emp.: 450
Aircraft Part & Auxiliary Equipment Mfr
N.A.I.C.S.: 336413
Lee Benson *(CEO)*

Airborne Tactical Advantage Company, LLC (1)
1001 Providence Blvd, Newport News, VA 23602
Tel.: (757) 874-8100
Web Site: https://www.atacusa.com
Aircraft Training Services
N.A.I.C.S.: 611512
Jeffrey Parker *(CEO & Founder)*
Scott Stacy *(Gen Mgr)*
Mark Hubbard *(VP-Navy Ops)*
Dennis Rieke *(VP-Excellence)*
John Zentner *(Dir-Business Development)*
Greg Guilfoyle *(Dir)*
Ronald Waltman *(Dir-Quality Control)*
Lemar Graham *(Dir-Finance)*
Richard Zins *(VP-Bus Ops)*

Arctic Cat Inc. (1)
600 Brooks Ave, Thief River Falls, MN 56701
Tel.: (218) 681-8558
Web Site: https://arcticcat.txsv.com
Snowmobiles, All-Terrain Vehicles, Garments & Accessories Mfr & Sales
N.A.I.C.S.: 336999

Subsidiary (Non-US):

Arctic Cat GmbH (2)
Industriestrasse 43, A-5600, Saint Johann im Pongau, Austria
Tel.: (43) 6412 2014 0
Web Site: http://www.arcticcat.eu
Emp.: 40
Snowmobiles & All-Terrain Vehicles Distr
N.A.I.C.S.: 441227

Subsidiary (Non-US):

Arctic Cat Espana S.L. (3)
Centro de Negocios Cristina, Paseo de las Delicias No 1, 41001, Seville, Spain
Tel.: (34) 954562907
Web Site: http://www.arcticcat.eu
All Terrain Vehicles Mfr
N.A.I.C.S.: 336999

Arctic Cat UK Ltd (3)
Monometer House Rectory Grove, Leigh-on-Sea, Southend-on-Sea, SS9 2HN, Essex, United Kingdom
Tel.: (44) 1702 603364
Web Site: http://www.arcticcat.eu
Snowmobiles & ATV's Distr
N.A.I.C.S.: 441227

Avco Corporation (1)
40 Westminster St, Providence, RI, 02903 (100%)
Tel.: (401) 421-2800
Aircraft Maintenance & Heavy Transport Mfr
N.A.I.C.S.: 336411

Aviation Service servis letal, doo, Ljubljana (1)
Begunjska Cesta 10, 4248, Lesce, Slovenia
Tel.: (386) 45307330
Web Site: http://www.aviationservice.si
Aviation Support Services
N.A.I.C.S.: 488119

Beechcraft Corporation (1)

PO Box 85, Wichita, KS 67201-0085
Tel.: (316) 676-5034
Web Site: http://www.beechcraft.com
Sales Range: $1-4.9 Billion
Emp.: 4,000
Aircraft Designer & Mfr
N.A.I.C.S.: 336411

Subsidiary (Domestic):

Textron Aviation Defense LLC (2)
9709 E Central Ave Building 91 B01, Wichita, KS 67206-2507
Tel.: (316) 515-4731
Web Site: http://www.defense.txtav.com
Artists Agent Services
N.A.I.C.S.: 711410

Bell Helicopter Textron, Inc. (1)
600 E Hurst Blvd, Hurst, TX 76053 (100%)
Tel.: (817) 280-2011
Web Site:
   http://www.bellhelicopter.textron.com
Sales Range: $1-4.9 Billion
Emp.: 8,000
Helicopter Mfr
N.A.I.C.S.: 336411
Lisa Atherton *(Pres & CEO)*

Subsidiary (Non-US):

Bell Helicopter Asia (Pte) Ltd. (2)
6 Seletar Aerospace Heights, Singapore, 797545, Singapore (100%)
Tel.: (65) 422422
Web Site: http://www.bellhelicopter.com
Sales Range: $10-24.9 Million
Emp.: 30
Helicopters & Helicopter Parts Sales
N.A.I.C.S.: 336413

Bell Helicopter India Inc. (2)
3rd Floor Corporate One District Centre Jasola, New Delhi, 110 025, India
Tel.: (91) 1149343100
Aircraft Mfr
N.A.I.C.S.: 336411

Subsidiary (Domestic):

Bell Helicopter Miami Inc. (2)
2011 S Perimeter Rd Ste L, Fort Lauderdale, FL 33309
Aircraft Maintenance & Heavy Transport Mfr
N.A.I.C.S.: 336411

Subsidiary (Non-US):

Bell Helicopter Supply Center N.V. (2)
Schipholweg 303, 1171 PL, Badhoevedorp, Netherlands
Tel.: (31) 204496500
Web Site: http://www.bellhelicopter.com
Sales Range: $10-24.9 Million
Emp.: 18
Helicopter Equipment Distr
N.A.I.C.S.: 336413
Mike Griesa *(Mng Dir)*

Bell Helicopter Textron Canada Limited (2)
12800 Rue de lAvenir, Mirabel, J7J 1R4, QC, Canada
Tel.: (450) 437-3400
Web Site:
   http://www.bellhelicopter.textron.com
Sales Range: $400-449.9 Million
Emp.: 1,200
Helicopter Mfr
N.A.I.C.S.: 336411

Subsidiary (Domestic):

Bell Technical Services Inc. (2)
600 E Hurst Blvd, Fort Worth, TX 76053
Tel.: (817) 280-2011
Web Site:
   http://www.bellhelicopter.textron.com
Sales Range: $75-99.9 Million
Helicopter Inspection & Testing Services
N.A.I.C.S.: 541350

Bell Textron Asia (Pte) Ltd. (1)
No 6 Seletar Aerospace Heights, Singapore, 797545, Singapore
Tel.: (65) 69339600
Emp.: 90
Aircraft Services
N.A.I.C.S.: 488190
Yih Han Yeoh *(Mgr-Quality)*

Bell Textron Prague, A.S. (1)
Vaclav Havel Airport Prague K Letisti 1063/27, 161 00, Prague, Czech Republic
Tel.: (420) 234624111
Aircraft Services
N.A.I.C.S.: 488190
Vlastimil Cepicka *(Gen Mgr)*

Cessna Aircraft Company (1)
1 Cessna Blvd, Wichita, KS 67215-1400 (100%)
Tel.: (316) 517-6000
Web Site: http://www.cessna.com
Sales Range: $1-4.9 Billion
Emp.: 10,000
Mfr of General Aviation Aircraft
N.A.I.C.S.: 336411

Unit (Domestic):

McCauley Propeller Systems (2)
3 Cessna Blvd, Wichita, KS 67215
Tel.: (316) 831-4021
Web Site: https://www.mccauley.txtav.com
Sales Range: $10-24.9 Million
Emp.: 25
Airplane Propeller Designer & Mfr
N.A.I.C.S.: 541330

Cessna Zurich Citation Service Center GmbH (1)
Bimenzaltenstrasse, 8302, Kloten, Switzerland
Tel.: (41) 438158111
Web Site: http://www.textron.com
Aviation Support Services
N.A.I.C.S.: 488119

Doncaster Citation Service Centre Limited (2)
Hangar 2 Fourth Avenue Robin Hood Airport, Doncaster, DN9 3GE, United Kingdom
Tel.: (44) 1302511047
Aircraft Maintenance Services
N.A.I.C.S.: 488190

E-Z-GO Textron (1)
1451 Marvin Griffin Rd, Augusta, GA 30906-3852 (100%)
Tel.: (706) 798-4311
Web Site: https://www.ezgo.txtsv.com
Sales Range: $400-449.9 Million
Emp.: 1,100
Golf Cart & Utility Vehicle Mfr
N.A.I.C.S.: 336999

Subsidiary (Non-US):

E-Z-GO Canada Limited (2)
21 Carmichael Dr, Whitby, L1N 9A4, ON, Canada
Tel.: (905) 217-0021
General Automotive Repair & Services
N.A.I.C.S.: 811111

Edwards Rotorcraft Solutions Inc (1)
1750 SW 34th St, Fort Lauderdale, FL 33315
Tel.: (954) 491-5071
Web Site: http://www.rotorcraftsolutions.com
Helicopter Community Support Service
N.A.I.C.S.: 487990

Hawker Beechcraft Global Customer Support, LLC (1)
1980 Airport Rd, Wichita, KS 67209
Tel.: (316) 676-4503
Aircraft Mfr
N.A.I.C.S.: 336411

Jacobsen Professional Lawn Care Inc. (1)
2540 E County Rd 50S, Fillmore, IN 46128
Tel.: (765) 246-7737
Web Site: https://www.dixiechopper.com
Emp.: 200
Lawn Maintenance Services
N.A.I.C.S.: 561730

Jacobsen Textron (1)
11108 Quality Dr, Charlotte, NC 28273 (100%)
Tel.: (704) 504-6600
Web Site: http://www.jacobsen.com
Sales Range: $800-899.9 Million
Turf Maintenance Equipment & Industrial Vehicles Mfr
N.A.I.C.S.: 333112

Opto-Electronics Inc. (1)
70 Frid St Ste 4, Hamilton, L8P 4M4, ON, Canada
Tel.: (905) 645-1702
Web Site: http://www.greenlee.com
Sales Range: $10-24.9 Million
Emp.: 4
Aircraft Mfr
N.A.I.C.S.: 336411

Overwatch Systems, Ltd. (1)
5301 SW Pkwy, Austin, TX 78735
Tel.: (512) 358-2600
Web Site: http://www.overwatch.com
Software Services
N.A.I.C.S.: 513210

Subsidiary (Domestic):

Medical Numerics, Inc. (2)
20410 Observation Dr Ste 210, Germantown, MD 20876
Tel.: (240) 686-3460
Web Site: http://www.medicalnumerics.com
Sales Range: $1-9.9 Million
Emp.: 12
Software Publishing Services
N.A.I.C.S.: 513210

Subsidiary (Non-US):

Textron Atlantic Holding GmbH (3)
(100%)
Tel.: (49) 2284880
Holding Company
N.A.I.C.S.: 551112

Subsidiary (Non-US):

Kautex Textron GmbH & Co. KG (4)
Tel.: (49) 2284480
Web Site: https://www.kautex.com
Sales Range: $200-249.9 Million
Emp.: 700
Automotive Fuel Tank Mfr
N.A.I.C.S.: 336110

Textron Acquisition Limited (4)
(100%)
Tel.: (44) 2077667110
Sales Range: $50-74.9 Million
Emp.: 6
Investment Services
N.A.I.C.S.: 523999

Textron Germany Holding GmbH (4)
Tel.: (49) 2284880
Web Site: http://www.kautex.de
Emp.: 70
Investment Consulting Services
N.A.I.C.S.: 523940

Textron Verwaltungs-GmbH (4)
Tel.: (49) 2284880
Web Site: http://www.kautex.de
Automotive Products Mfr
N.A.I.C.S.: 336390

Premiair Aviation Maintenance Pty Ltd (1)
24 Compass Road Airport, Jandakot, 6164, WA, Australia
Tel.: (61) 894141105
Web Site:
   https://www.premiairaviation.com.au
Aviation Services
N.A.I.C.S.: 488190
Brad Mortimer *(Gen Mgr)*
Andrew Ross *(Mgr-Engrg)*
Laurie Catalano *(Mgr-Quality Maintenance)*

Ransomes Jacobsen France S.A.S (1)
3 Chemin Des Silos -ZI Du, Chapitre, 31100, Toulouse, France
Tel.: (33) 534478640
Web Site: https://www.ransomesjacobsen.fr
Aircraft Mfr
N.A.I.C.S.: 336411

Rotor Blades Limited (1)
Unit 5B Crusader Park, Warminster, BA12 8BT, Wiltshire, United Kingdom
Tel.: (44) 1985847040
Web Site: http://www.bellhelicopter.com
Emp.: 9
Aircraft Maintenance Services
N.A.I.C.S.: 488190

TRU Simulation + Training Inc. (1)
5 Alliance Dr, Goose Creek, SC 29445

Tel.: (843) 574-5200
Web Site: https://www.trusimulation.com
Commercial & Military Aviation Simulation Products & Technical Support Services
N.A.I.C.S.: 333310

Subsidiary (Non-US):

Mechtronix Textron Canada Inc.   **(2)**
6767 Cote de Liesse, Saint Laurent, H4T 1E5, QC, Canada
Tel.: (514) 342-0800
Web Site: http://www.mechtronix.com
Aviation Simulation Equipment & Technical Support Services
N.A.I.C.S.: 333310

Subsidiary (Domestic):

OPINICUS Textron Inc.   **(2)**
1827 NorthPointe Pkwy, Lutz, FL 33558
Tel.: (813) 792-9300
Web Site: http://www.trusimulation.com
Emp.: 175
Flight Simulation Systems Developer
N.A.I.C.S.: 333310

TRU Simulation + Training LLC   **(1)**
6144 Innovation Way, Carlsbad, CA 92009
Tel.: (843) 574-5330
Pilot Training Services
N.A.I.C.S.: 488190

TUG Technologies Corporation   **(1)**
PO Box 3028, Kennesaw, GA 30156
Tel.: (770) 422-7230
Web Site: http://tectron.com
Emp.: 300
Ground Support Equipment Mfr
N.A.I.C.S.: 332994

Textron Aviation Defense LLC   **(1)**
9709 E Central Ave Bldg 91 B01, Wichita, KS 67206-2507
Tel.: (316) 515-4731
Web Site: http://www.defense.txtav.com
Aircraft Maintenance & Heavy Transport Mfr
N.A.I.C.S.: 336411
Chuck Gummow (Reg Dir-New Aircraft & Aftermarket Sls-Africa & Europe)
Tom Webster (Reg Dir-New Aircraft & After-market Sls-Asia Pacific)
Fouad Kasri (Reg Dir-New Aircraft & After-market Sls-Middle East)
Brett Pierson (Pres, CEO & Sr VP-Defense & Special Missions)

Textron Financial Corporation   **(1)**
2 Cessna Blvd Ste 100, Wichita, KS 67215   **(100%)**
Web Site: http://www.textronfinancial.com
Sales Range: $150-199.9 Million
Emp.: 467
Aircraft Leasing Service
N.A.I.C.S.: 532490

Subsidiary (Domestic):

Cessna Finance Corporation   **(2)**
2 Cessna Blvd Ste 100, Wichita, KS 67215   **(100%)**
Tel.: (316) 660-1200
Web Site: http://www.cessnafinance.com
Sales Range: $50-74.9 Million
Emp.: 60
Financing of Aircraft Sales
N.A.I.C.S.: 522220

Systran Financial Services Corp.   **(2)**
4949 SW Meadows Rd Ste 500, Lake Oswego, OR 97035-4285
Web Site: http://www.textronfinancial.com
Sales Range: $10-24.9 Million
Emp.: 50
Financial Management Services
N.A.I.C.S.: 561110

Subsidiary (Non-US):

Textron Capital B.V.   **(2)**
Schipholweg 303, 1171 PL, Badhoevedorp, Netherlands
Tel.: (31) 204496500
Aircraft Mfr
N.A.I.C.S.: 336411

Subsidiary (Domestic):

Textron Financial Investment Corporation   **(2)**
40 Westminster St, Providence, RI 02903

Tel.: (401) 421-2800
Sales Range: $1-4.9 Billion
Provider of Financial Services
N.A.I.C.S.: 522210
David Azzolina (Dir-Pension Investments)

Textron International Mexico, S de RL de CV   **(1)**
Ave Cristobal Colon Fontarrosa No 22101, 31170, Chihuahua, Mexico
Tel.: (52) 6142387006
Aircraft Engine & Part Mfr
N.A.I.C.S.: 336412

Textron Lycoming   **(1)**
652 Oliver St, Williamsport, PA 17701
Tel.: (570) 323-6181
Web Site: https://www.lycoming.com
Sales Range: $200-249.9 Million
Emp.: 400
Piston Aircraft Engines & Replacement Parts
N.A.I.C.S.: 336412
Micheal Kraft (Sr VP & Gen Mgr)
Shannon Massey (Sr VP & Gen Mgr)
Kelvin Hart (VP-Quality-Lycoming Engines)
Aaron Spotts (VP-Engineering)
Valerie Berube (Dir-Supply Chain-Lycoming Engines)
Brian Hudson (Fin Dir)
Elesha Riebe (Sr Mgr-Human Resources)
James Wright (Sr Mgr-Operations)
Thad Temple (Sr Mgr)
Hannah Peachey (Sr Mgr-Logistics)
Matt Joiner (Mgr-Marketing-Communications)

Textron Marine & Land Systems   **(1)**
1010 Gause Blvd, Slidell, LA 70458
Tel.: (985) 661-3690
Web Site: http://www.textronsystems.com
Marine Products such as Air Cushion Vehicles, Surface Effect Ships & Conventional Marine Vessels Developer & Mfr; Military & Commercial Application
N.A.I.C.S.: 336612

Textron Systems Canada Inc.   **(1)**
350 Sparks Street Suite 706, Ottawa, K1R 7S8, ON, Canada
Tel.: (613) 907-8098
Web Site: http://www.textronsystems.com
Engineeering Services
N.A.I.C.S.: 541330
Michael Kraft (Sr VP)

Textron Systems Corporation   **(1)**
201 Lowell St, Wilmington, MA 01887-4113   **(100%)**
Tel.: (978) 657-5111
Web Site: https://www.textronsystems.com
Sales Range: $500-549.9 Million
Emp.: 1,000
Weapons Systems, Aircraft Control Component, Surveillance System, Intelligence Software & Military Vehicle Mfr
N.A.I.C.S.: 334511
Ryan Hazlett (Sr VP-Global Military Sls & Strategy)
Michael P. Kieran (Sr VP-Integrated Supply Chain)
Dennis Kim (Gen Counsel & Sr VP)
Steve Mensh (Sr VP-Electronic Sys)
Wayne Prender (Sr VP-Air Sys)
David A. Phillips (Sr VP-Land Sys)
Scott Allen (Sr VP-Sea Sys)
Henry Finneral (Sr VP-Weapon Sys)
Sara Flower (Sr VP-HR)
Nathan Harwood (CIO & VP)
Jennifer W. Williamson (Gen Counsel & Sr VP)
Michael Kraft (Sr VP)
Shannon Massey (Sr VP & Mgr-Lycoming Engines)
Scott Stacy (Sr VP & Gen Mgr)
Jeff Stewart (CFO & Sr VP)

Subsidiary (Domestic):

AAI Corporation   **(2)**
124 Industry Ln, Hunt Valley, MD 21030   **(100%)**
Tel.: (410) 666-1400
Web Site: http://www.aai.textron.com
Sales Range: $550-599.9 Million
Training & Simulation Systems, Unmanned Air Vehicles, Automated Aircraft Test & Maintenance Equipment, Combat Vehicles & Ordinance Systems & Ground Transportation Components Mfr

N.A.I.C.S.: 336413
Frederick M. Strader (Pres)
Bill Irby (Sr VP & Gen Mgr-Unmanned Aircraft Sys)

Subsidiary (Non-US):

AAI Aerosonde Pty Ltd.   **(3)**
Unit 1 585 Blackburn Road, Notting Hill, 3168, VIC, Australia
Tel.: (61) 395187300
Web Site: http://www.aerosonde.com
Aircraft Systems Mfr
N.A.I.C.S.: 336411

Subsidiary (Domestic):

AAI Corp. - Automated Test Equipment   **(3)**
4401 Freidrich Ln Bldg 2 Ste 200, Austin, TX 78744
Tel.: (512) 328-7799
Web Site: http://www.aaicorp.com
Sales Range: $10-24.9 Million
Emp.: 61
High-Performance Functional Test Solutions for Commercial, Space & Defence Applications
N.A.I.C.S.: 334515

AAI Services Corporation   **(3)**
318 Clubhouse Rd, Hunt Valley, MD 21031
Tel.: (410) 667-7170
Sales Range: $75-99.9 Million
Commercial & Government Engineering & Operations Consulting Services
N.A.I.C.S.: 541618

Subsidiary (Domestic):

McTurbine, Inc.   **(4)**
401 Junior Beck Dr, Corpus Christi, TX 78405
Tel.: (361) 851-1290
Web Site: http://www.mcturbine.com
Sales Range: $25-49.9 Million
Emp.: 35
Helicopter Repair & Maintenance Services
N.A.I.C.S.: 336412

Subsidiary (Non-US):

ESL Defence Ltd   **(3)**
16 Compass Point Ensign Way, Hamble, Southampton, S031 4RA, Hampshire, United Kingdom
Tel.: (44) 2380455110
Web Site: http://www.esldefence.co.uk
Sales Range: $10-24.9 Million
Emp.: 50
Military Optical Device Mfr
N.A.I.C.S.: 333310

Subsidiary (Domestic):

Howe & Howe Technologies, Inc.   **(3)**
661 Main St, Waterboro, ME 04087
Tel.: (207) 247-2777
Web Site: https://www.howeandhowe.com
Armored Wheeled Vehicle Mfr
N.A.I.C.S.: 336992

Subsidiary (Non-US):

Textron Systems Australia Pty Ltd.   **(3)**
585 Blackburn Road, Notting Hill, 3168, VIC, Australia
Tel.: (61) 39 518 7300
Web Site: https://www.textronsystems.com
Unmanned Aircraft Mfr
N.A.I.C.S.: 336411

Textron Systems Electronic Systems UK (Holdings) Limited   **(3)**
16 Compass Point Ensign Way, Hamble, Southampton, SO31 4RA, Hampshire, United Kingdom
Tel.: (44) 2380455110
Web Site: http://www.esldefence.co.uk
Holding Company
N.A.I.C.S.: 551112

Subsidiary (Domestic):

Millenworks   **(2)**
1361 Valencia Ave, Tustin, CA 92780
Tel.: (714) 426-5500
Web Site: http://www.millenworks.com

Sales Range: $25-49.9 Million
Emp.: 65
Vehicle Design & Engineering
N.A.I.C.S.: 336320

United Industrial Corporation   **(1)**
124 Industry Ln, Hunt Valley, MD 21030
Tel.: (410) 628-3500
Emp.: 2,316
Engineeering Services
N.A.I.C.S.: 541330

Wuxi Textron Specialized Vehicles Co., Ltd.   **(1)**
No 30 Wanquan Road, Xishan District, Wuxi, Jiangsu, China
Tel.: (86) 51083896033
All Terrain Vehicle & Wheeled Mfr
N.A.I.C.S.: 336999

Zhenjiang Bell Textron Aviation Services Limited   **(1)**
No 33 Block 1 Yangzijiang Road, Zhenjiang, Jiangsu, China
Tel.: (86) 51183126776
Aviation Services
N.A.I.C.S.: 488190

TFF PHARMACEUTICALS, INC.
1751 River Run Ste 400, Fort Worth, TX 76107
Tel.: (817) 438-6168   DE
Web Site: https://www.tffpharma.com
Year Founded: 2018
TFFP—(NASDAQ)
Rev.: $495,805
Assets: $24,120,215
Liabilities: $1,240,756
Net Worth: $22,879,459
Earnings: ($31,770,062)
Emp.: 15
Fiscal Year-end: 12/31/22
Research & Development in Biotechnology (except Nanobiotechnology)
N.A.I.C.S.: 541714
Kirk Coleman (CFO)
Harlan F. Weisman (Pres & CEO)

TFS FINANCIAL CORPORATION
7007 Broadway Ave, Cleveland, OH 44105
Tel.: (216) 441-6000
Web Site: https://www.thirdfederal.com
TFSL—(NASDAQ)
Rev.: $633,348,000
Assets: $16,917,979,000
Liabilities: $14,990,618,000
Net Worth: $1,927,361,000
Earnings: $75,250,000
Emp.: 995
Fiscal Year-end: 09/30/23
Financial Services
N.A.I.C.S.: 523999
Marc A. Stefanski (Chm, Pres & CEO)
Meredith S. Weil (CFO, COO & Sec)
Cathy W. Zbanek (Chief Synergy Officer)
Timothy W. Mulhern (CFO & VP)
Ashley H. Williams (Vice Chm)
Susanne N. Miller (Chief Acctg Officer)
Andrew J. Rubino (CIO)
Russell C. Holmes (Chief Retail Officer)
Bradley T. Stefanski (Chief Strategy Officer)
Gavin B. Stefanski (Chief Lending Officer)

Subsidiaries:

Third Federal Savings & Loan Association of Cleveland   **(1)**
7007 Broadway Ave, Cleveland, OH 44105
Tel.: (216) 441-6000
Web Site: http://www.thirdfederal.com

TFS Financial Corporation—(Continued)

Sales Range: $550-599.9 Million
Federal Savings Institutions
N.A.I.C.S.: 522180
Ralph M. Betters (CIO)
Marc A. Stefanski (Chm, Pres & CEO)
Meredith S. Weil (CFO)
Timothy W. Mulhern (Chief Innovation Officer)

TG THERAPEUTICS, INC.
3020 Carrington Mill Blvd Ste 475,
Morrisville, NC 27560-5435
Tel.: (212) 554-4484　　DE
Web Site:
　https://www.tgtherapeutics.com
Year Founded: 1993
TGTX—(NASDAQ)
Rev.: $2,785,000
Assets: $193,572,000
Liabilities: $134,985,000
Net Worth: $58,587,000
Earnings: ($198,335,000)
Emp.: 226
Fiscal Year-end: 12/31/22
Pharmaceutical Mfr, Developer &
Marketer
N.A.I.C.S.: 325412
Donald W. Landry (Co-Founder)
Michael S. Weiss (Chm)

TG VENTURE ACQUISITION CORP.
1390 Market St Ste 200, San Francisco, CA 94102
Tel.: (628) 251-1369　　DE
Web Site:
　https://www.tgventureacquisition.com
Year Founded: 2021
TGVC—(NASDAQ)
Rev.: $1,648,827
Assets: $119,244,269
Liabilities: $120,139,110
Net Worth: ($894,841)
Earnings: ($857,534)
Emp.: 2
Fiscal Year-end: 12/31/22
Investment Services
N.A.I.C.S.: 523999
Patrick Pui Lan Tsang (Chm & CEO)
Philip Rettger (CFO)

TGI SOLAR POWER GROUP INC.
525 Milltown Rd Ste 103, North
Brunswick, NJ 08902
Tel.: (917) 353-5099　　DE
Web Site: https://www.tgipower.com
Year Founded: 1967
TSPG—(OTCIQ)
Sales Range: Less than $1 Million
Emp.: 1
Business Consulting Services
N.A.I.C.S.: 541613

THARIMMUNE, INC.
1200 Route 22 E Ste 2000, Bridgewater, NJ 08807
Tel.: (908) 955-3140　　DE
Web Site: https://tharimmune.com
Year Founded: 2017
THAR—(NASDAQ)
Assets: $6,688,628
Liabilities: $1,144,973
Net Worth: $5,543,655
Earnings: ($8,473,182)
Emp.: 1
Fiscal Year-end: 12/31/22
Pharmaceuticals Product Mfr
N.A.I.C.S.: 325412
Randy Milby (Chm & CEO)
Thomas Hess (CFO)
Sireesh Appajosyula (COO)

THC FARMACEUTICALS, INC.

1000 Newbury Rd Ste 138 B, Thousand Oaks, CA 91320
Tel.: (805) 978-5609　　UT
Year Founded: 2005
CBDG—(OTCIQ)
Sales Range: Less than $1 Million
Holding Company; Automated Teller
Machines Owner & Operator
N.A.I.C.S.: 551112

THC THERAPEUTICS, INC.
2831 St Rose Pkwy Ste 200, Henderson, NV 89052
Tel.: (702) 217-9518　　NV
Web Site: https://www.thct.io
Year Founded: 2007
THCT—(OTCIQ)
Assets: $480,068
Liabilities: $2,957,394
Net Worth: ($2,477,326)
Earnings: ($1,885,445)
Emp.: 1
Fiscal Year-end: 07/31/21
Oil & Gas Exploration Services
N.A.I.C.S.: 211120
Scott A. Cox (Interim CEO)
Brandon Romanek (Pres, CFO &
Sec)
Victor Nacif (Head-Design)
John J. Pierce (Dir-Medical)

THE ADIRONDACK TRUST COMPANY
473 Broadway, Saratoga Springs, NY
12866-5607
Tel.: (518) 584-5844　　NY
Web Site:
　https://www.adirondacktrust.com
Year Founded: 1901
ADKT—(OTCIQ)
Rev.: $64,330,868
Assets: $1,495,890,772
Liabilities: $1,355,562,256
Net Worth: $140,328,515
Earnings: $8,314,211
Emp.: 250
Fiscal Year-end: 12/31/20
Banking Services
N.A.I.C.S.: 522110
Alicia Butler (Asst Treas)
Jenifer Riggi (Asst VP-Residential
Lending & Consumer Lending)
Ellen Brodie (Officer-Comml Loan &
Asst VP)
Brian D. Charbonneau (VP)
Michael Brodt (Sr VP & Dir-Wealth
Mgmt)
Caroline Putman (Asst Treas)
Michael O'Connell (Exec VP-Lending
& Retail Banking)
Edward Hart (Sr VP & Mgr-Comml
Loan)
John W. Murphy (Officer-Comml Loan
& Sr VP)
Andrew Ferrara (Officer-Comml Loan
& VP)
Christine Hart Mesick (Officer-Comml
Loan & VP)
Michael Murray (Officer-Comml Loan,
Exec VP & VP)
Kelley Peluso (Officer-Comml Loan &
VP)
Susanne Rogan (Officer-Comml Loan
& VP)
Christopher Rose (VP)
Saad Junaid (Asst Treas)
Matthew C. Harrison (VP & Mgr-
Residential Lending)
Jack Arnold (CFO, Chief Admin Officer, Treas & Exec VP)
Edward M. Connell (VP)
Dean A. Kolligian (VP)
Meredith L. Rumpf (VP)
Angela M. Kedik (VP)
Patrick B. Reilly (Sr VP)
Robert F. Loughran (Sr VP)

Matthew P. D'Abate (Sr VP)
Natalie I. Wait (VP-Regulatory Affairs)
Richard F. Carman (VP-Audit)
Charles V. Wait Jr. (Chm, Pres &
CEO)

THE AES CORPORATION
4300 Wilson Blvd, Arlington, VA
22203
Tel.: (703) 522-1315　　DE
Web Site: https://www.aes.com
Year Founded: 1981
AES—(NYSE)
Rev.: $12,668,000,000
Assets: $44,799,000,000
Liabilities: $38,814,000,000
Net Worth: $5,985,000,000
Earnings: $249,000,000
Emp.: 9,600
Fiscal Year-end: 12/31/23
Electricity Distribution Services
N.A.I.C.S.: 221111
Andres R. Gluski (Pres & CEO)
Ricardo Manuel Falu (COO, Pres-
New Energy Technologies & Sr VP)
Kenneth Joseph Zagzebski (Pres-
Utilities Strategic Bus Unit & Sr VP)
Joel Abramson (Sr VP-Mergers & Acquisitions)
Bernerd Da Santos (Chief Operating
& Infrastructure Officer & Exec VP)
Paul L. Freedman (Gen Counsel, Sec
& Exec VP)
Tish D. Mendoza (Chief HR Officer &
Exec VP)
Sherry Kohan (Chief Acctg Officer &
Sr VP)
Lorraine Paskett (VP)
John Christopher Shelton (Chief
Product Officer, Pres-AES Next & Sr
VP)
Stephen Coughlin (CFO & Exec VP)
Ricardo Manuel Falu (Exec VP)
Tish Mendoza (Chief HR Officer)
Susan Harcourt (VP)
Max Trask (Sr Mgr)

Subsidiaries:

ACWA Power Barka S.A.O.G.　**(1)**
Al Batinah, PO BOX 572, Barka, 320,
Oman　　　　　　　　　　　　**(58%)**
Tel.: (968) 26894382
Sales Range: $10-24.9 Million
Emp.: 60
Power Generation
N.A.I.C.S.: 221112
Nadeem Rizvi (CEO)

AES Andes, Inc.　　　　　　**(1)**
Callao 410 4 Fl, C 1107 AAF, Buenos Aires,
Argentina　　　　　　　　　**(100%)**
Tel.: (54) 1140002300
Web Site: http://www.aes.com
Sales Range: $100-124.9 Million
Emp.: 100
Producer of Electricity for Argentina, Chile &
Uruguay
N.A.I.C.S.: 221122

Subsidiary (Non-US):

AES Andes SA　　　　　　　**(2)**
Rosario Norte 532 19th floor, Box No 3514,
Las Condes, Santiago, Chile　**(100%)**
Tel.: (56) 26868900
Web Site: http://www.gener.cl
Rev.: $2,411,773,000
Assets: $8,442,560,000
Liabilities: $5,895,164,000
Net Worth: $2,547,396,000
Earnings: $124,441,000
Emp.: 1,313
Fiscal Year-end: 12/31/2019
Electricity Generator & Distr
N.A.I.C.S.: 221111
Ricardo Manuel Falu (Executives, Bd of
Dirs)

AES Ballylumford　　　　　**(1)**
Ballylumford Ferris Bay Road Islandmagee
Larne Co, Antrim, BT40 3RS, United
Kingdom　　　　　　　　　　**(100%)**

Tel.: (44) 2893381100
Sales Range: $250-299.9 Million
Emp.: 120
Power Generation
N.A.I.C.S.: 221118
Davy Watson (Mgr-Maintenance)
Janice Hagan (Safety & Security)
Denis McBride (Mgr-Production)

AES Ballylumford Limited　　**(1)**
Ballylumford Islandmagee, Larne, BT40
3RS, United Kingdom
Tel.: (44) 2893381100
Web Site: http://www.aesglobal.com
Emp.: 120
Electric Power Distribution Services
N.A.I.C.S.: 221122

AES Bulgaria Trading EOOD　**(1)**
Office Building Aries, 1407, Sofia, Yugozapaden, Bulgaria
Tel.: (359) 29881275
Electrical Installation Services
N.A.I.C.S.: 238210

AES Chengdu　　　　　　　**(1)**
San ZhongJin Tang, Yuan District,
Chengdu, 610400, China　　**(100%)**
Tel.: (86) 2884936575
Web Site: http://www.aesconsultant.com
Sales Range: $350-399.9 Million
Producer & Distributor of Electricity for Australia, Hawaii & India
N.A.I.C.S.: 221122

AES Chivor & Cia S.C.A. E.S.P.　**(1)**
Calle 100 N 19 - 54 Of 901 Edificio Prime
Tower, Bogota, Colombia
Tel.: (57) 1 594 1400
Web Site: https://www.aescol.com
Emp.: 25,000
Electric Power Generation Distr
N.A.I.C.S.: 221122

AES DPL Holdings, LLC　　**(1)**
4300 Wilson Blvd, Arlington, VA 22203
Tel.: (703) 522-1315
Holding Company
N.A.I.C.S.: 551112

AES Distributed Energy, Inc.　**(1)**
4875 Pearl East Cir Ste 200, Boulder, CO
80301
Tel.: (303) 444-3020
Web Site: http://aesdistributedenergy.com
Solar Energy Equipment Distr
N.A.I.C.S.: 423720

**AES Drax Power Finance Holdings
Limited**　　　　　　　　　　**(1)**
18 Parkshot, Richmond, London, TW9 2RG,
United Kingdom
Tel.: (44) 2083345300
Holding Company
N.A.I.C.S.: 551112

AES Elsta BV　　　　　　　**(1)**
Herbert H Dowweg 5d Haven 193, 4542
NM, Hoek, Netherlands
Tel.: (31) 0115641400
Web Site: http://www.elstacogen.nl
Sales Range: $25-49.9 Million
Emp.: 50
Power Generation
N.A.I.C.S.: 221112

AES Enerji Limited Sirketi　　**(1)**
Buyukdere Cad Metro City MDS Merkezi
No 171 A Blok Kat, Esentepe, Turkiye
Tel.: (90) 2123166201
Sales Range: $25-49.9 Million
Emp.: 10
Electric Power Generation Distr
N.A.I.C.S.: 221122

AES Global Insurance Company　**(1)**
76 Saint Paul St Ste 500, Burlington, VT
05401
Tel.: (802) 862-4400
Insurance Agency Services
N.A.I.C.S.: 524210

AES Hames LLC　　　　　　**(1)**
141 Depot Rd, Uncasville, CT
06382-2441　　　　　　　　**(100%)**
Tel.: (860) 848-9223
Web Site: http://www.aes.com

Sales Range: $50-74.9 Million
Emp.: 57
Coal Generation for Electricity
N.A.I.C.S.: 221122

AES Huntington Beach, L.L.C. (1)
21730 Newland St, Huntington Beach, CA
92646
Tel.: (310) 870-9101
Web Site: http://aescalifornia.com
Sales Range: $25-49.9 Million
Emp.: 24
Electric Power Generation Distr
N.A.I.C.S.: 221122

AES Kalaeloa Venture, L.L.C. (1)
91-650 Malakole St, Kapolei, HI 96707
Tel.: (808) 682-4113
Marine Cargo Handling Services
N.A.I.C.S.: 488320

AES Kilroot Power Limited (1)
Larne Rd, Carrickfergus, BT38 7LX, United
Kingdom
Tel.: (44) 2893356300
Web Site: http://www.aes.com
Sales Range: $50-74.9 Million
Emp.: 100
Power Generation
N.A.I.C.S.: 221112
Mark Miller *(Mng Dir)*

AES Lal Pir (Pvt) Ltd. (1)
PO Box 89, Muzaffargarh, Multan, 34200,
Punjab, Pakistan
Tel.: (92) 661422967
Sales Range: $200-249.9 Million
Power Generation
N.A.I.C.S.: 221112

**AES Merida Management Services,
S. de R.L. de C.V.** (1)
Km 2 Anillo Periferico Entre Carr, Merida
Uman, Merida, 97288, Yuc, Mexico
Tel.: (52) 9999300224
Electric Power Generation Distr
N.A.I.C.S.: 221122

**AES Merida Operaciones SRL de
CV** (1)
Carretera Km 2 S/N, 97288, Merida, Yu-
catan, Mexico
Tel.: (52) 9999300220
Management Consulting Services
N.A.I.C.S.: 541611

**AES Pacific Ocean Holdings
B.V.** (1)
Parklaan 32, Rotterdam, 3016 BC, Nether-
lands
Tel.: (31) 102229020
Sales Range: $25-49.9 Million
Emp.: 1
Electric Power Generation Distr
N.A.I.C.S.: 221122

AES Panama S.A. (1)
Business Park II Torre V Piso 1 Ave La Ro-
tonda, Costa del Este, Panama, Panama
Tel.: (507) 2062600
Web Site: http://www.aespanama.com
Sales Range: $250-299.9 Million
Emp.: 172
Electricity Generation Services
N.A.I.C.S.: 221112
Manuel Perez Dubuc *(Pres)*
Adviel Centeno Mayta *(Gen Mgr)*

AES Panama, S.R.L. (1)
Business Park II Torre V piso 11 Ave La
Rotonda Costa del Este, Panama, Panama
Tel.: (507) 2062600
Web Site: https://www.aespanama.com
Power Generation Services
N.A.I.C.S.: 221122
Miguel Bolinaga *(Country Mgr)*

AES Poland Wind Sp.z o.o. (1)
Hryniewickiego kod pocztowy, 81340, Gdy-
nia, Poland
Tel.: (48) 587176000
Sales Range: $25-49.9 Million
Emp.: 5
Electric Power Generation Distr
N.A.I.C.S.: 221122

AES Puerto Rico, L.P. (1)
Carretera 3 KM 142 0 - B Pte Jobos,
Guayama, PR 00784
Tel.: (787) 866-8117

Web Site: http://www.aespuertorico.com
Electric Power Generation Distr
N.A.I.C.S.: 221122

AES Red Oak, L.L.C. (1)
832 Red Oak Ln, Sayreville, NJ 08872
Tel.: (732) 238-1462
Web Site: http://www.aes.com
Sales Range: $10-24.9 Million
Emp.: 6
Provider of Electric Power Generation Ser-
vices
N.A.I.C.S.: 221118

AES Services, Inc. (1)
111 S Wacker Dr, Chicago, IL 60606
Tel.: (312) 235-6783
Web Site: http://www.aesser.com
Electric Power Generation Distr
N.A.I.C.S.: 221122

AES Servicios America S.R. L. (1)
Av Callao 410 piso 1, 1022, Buenos Aires,
Argentina
Tel.: (54) 1140002300
Web Site: https://www1.aesservicios.com.ar
Business Management Services
N.A.I.C.S.: 561110

AES Solar Alcudia, S.L. (1)
Calle Golfo De Salonica 27 - Apartment 6
A, 28033, Madrid, Spain
Tel.: (34) 913108574
Eletric Power Generation Services
N.A.I.C.S.: 221118

AES Southland, LLC (1)
690 N Studebaker Rd, Long Beach, CA
90803-2221
Tel.: (310) 870-9101
Web Site: http://www.aescalifornia.com
Eletric Power Generation Services
N.A.I.C.S.: 221114
Eric Pendergraft *(VP-Bus Dev-US)*

**AES TEG Operations, S. de R.L. de
C.V.** (1)
Carret Camino A Estacion Tamuin K M 8,
Tamuin, 79200, Mexico
Tel.: (52) 4893881151
Emp.: 100
Eletric Power Generation Mexico
N.A.I.C.S.: 221111

**AES Uruguaiana Empreendimentos
S.A.** (1)
Br 472 Km 576, Uruguaiana, 97510-431,
Brazil
Tel.: (55) 1121951000
Emp.: 70
Electric Power Generation & Distribution
Services
N.A.I.C.S.: 221111

AES Warrior Run, Inc. (1)
11600 Mexico Farm Rd SE, Cumberland,
MD 21502
Tel.: (301) 777-0055
Web Site: http://www.aes.com
Sales Range: $25-49.9 Million
Emp.: 65
Electric Power Generation
N.A.I.C.S.: 221118

AES-Tisza Eromu Kft (1)
Verebely Lutca 2, 3580, Tiszaujvaros, Hun-
gary
Tel.: (36) 49547333
Web Site: http://www.tiszapower.eu
Sales Range: $50-74.9 Million
Emp.: 200
Power Generation
N.A.I.C.S.: 221112

Andes Solar SpA (1)
Av Del Parque 4160 Torre A Oficina 701,
Ciudad Empresarial, Huechuraba, Santiago,
Chile
Tel.: (56) 226235500
Web Site: https://www.andes-solar.com
Solar Electric Power Generation Services
N.A.I.C.S.: 221114

**CMS Generation San Nicolas
Company** (1)
One Energy Plz, Jackson, MI 49201
Tel.: (517) 788-0550
Web Site: http://www.cmsenergy.com
Electric Power Generation & Distribution
Services

N.A.I.C.S.: 221111

**Central Electricity Supply Company of
Orissa Limited** (1)
2nd Floor Idco Tower Janpath, Bhubane-
swar, 751 022, India
Tel.: (91) 6742541575
Web Site: http://www.cescoorissa.com
Electric Power Distribution Services
N.A.I.C.S.: 221122
Hemant Sharma *(Chm)*

**Companhia Brasiliana de
Energia** (1)
Rua Lourenco Marques 158 1 Andar Sala
C, Sao Paulo, 04547-100, Brazil
Web Site:
   http://www.companhiabrasiliana.com.br
Electric Power Generation & Distribution
Services
N.A.I.C.S.: 221111

DPL Inc. (1)
1065 Woodman Dr, Dayton, OH 45432
Tel.: (937) 259-7215
Web Site: http://www.dplinc.com
Rev.: $869,000,000
Assets: $2,422,400,000
Liabilities: $2,546,100,000
Net Worth: ($123,700,000)
Earnings: ($4,700,000)
Emp.: 547
Fiscal Year-end: 12/31/2022
Holding Company; Electric Power Genera-
tion Services
N.A.I.C.S.: 221122
Kenneth Joseph Zagzebski *(Chm, Pres &
CEO)*
Gustavo Garavaglia *(CFO & VP)*
Lisa Krueger *(Chm)*
Sherry Kohan *(Interim CFO & VP)*
Kristina Lund *(Pres & CEO)*
Karin M. Nyhuis *(Controller)*
Ahmed Pasha *(CFO)*
Jon S. Byers *(Controller)*

Subsidiary (Domestic):

Miami Valley Lighting, LLC (2)
1065 Woodman Dr, Dayton, OH 45432
Tel.: (937) 259-7192
Web Site: https://www.lightingsimplified.com
Operator of Street Lighting Systems
N.A.I.C.S.: 221122

**The Dayton Power and Light
Company** (2)
1065 Woodman Dr, Dayton, OH
45432 **(100%)**
Tel.: (937) 259-7215
Web Site: https://www.aes-ohio.com
Rev.: $860,100,000
Assets: $2,405,900,000
Liabilities: $1,664,100,000
Net Worth: $741,800,000
Earnings: $18,900,000
Emp.: 546
Fiscal Year-end: 12/31/2022
Electric Power Transmission & Distribution
Services
N.A.I.C.S.: 221122
Kenneth Joseph Zagzebski *(Chm, Pres &
CEO)*
Barry Joe Bentley *(Sr VP-Utility Ops)*
Gustavo Garavaglia *(CFO & VP)*
Lisa Krueger *(Chm)*
Kristina Lund *(Pres & CEO)*
Karin M. Nyhuis *(Controller)*
Thomas A. Raga *(VP-External Rels)*
Karin M. Nyhuis *(Controller)*
Ahmed Pasha *(CFO)*
Jon S. Byers *(Controller)*
Brian Hylander *(Gen Counsel)*
Aaron Cooper *(Chief Comml Officer)*
Kathy Storm *(VP)*

Don Humberto SpA (1)
Lib B O'Higgins 560, Coquimbo, La Serena,
Chile
Tel.: (56) 512216419
Web Site:
   https://www.restaurantedonhumberto.cl
Restaurant Operators
N.A.I.C.S.: 722511

Eloy ESD Solar Holdings, LLC (1)
15344 N 83rd Way, Scottsdale, AZ 85260
Tel.: (480) 398-2740
Holding Company

N.A.I.C.S.: 551112

Elsta BV & Co. CV (1)
Herbert H Dowweg 5 D, Hoek, 4542 NM,
Terneuzen, Netherlands
Tel.: (31) 115627765
Web Site: https://www.elstacogen.nl
Sales Range: $25-49.9 Million
Emp.: 45
Electric Power Generation Distr
N.A.I.C.S.: 221122

**Empresa Electrica Campiche
S.A.** (1)
Alonso de Cordova 5151 Las Condes, San-
tiago, Chile
Tel.: (56) 25979300
Electric Power Generation Distr
N.A.I.C.S.: 221122

Empresa Electrica Santiago SpA (1)
Jorge Hirmas, 2964, Renca, Santiago, Chile
Tel.: (56) 26804760
Web Site: http://www.electricasantiago.cl
Eletric Power Generation Services
N.A.I.C.S.: 221118

**Empresa Electrica de Oriente, S.A.
de C.V.** (1)
Cl A Cdad Pacifica Col Garcia Fnl 8 Cl Pte,
San Salvador, El Salvador
Tel.: (503) 25069000
Electric Power Distribution Services
N.A.I.C.S.: 221122

Eviva-Lebork Sp.z o.o. (1)
Borchardta 79, 76-200, Slupsk, Pomorskie,
Poland
Tel.: (48) 598483523
Electric Power Generation Distr
N.A.I.C.S.: 221122

Fundacion AES Gener (1)
Jorge Hirmas 2960, Renca, Santiago, Chile
Tel.: (56) 226804710
Web Site: http://www.fundacionaesgener.cl
Educational Support Services
N.A.I.C.S.: 611710

GHGS Coal Mine Methane, LLC (1)
4300 Wilson Blvd Ste 11, Arlington, VA
22203
Tel.: (703) 682-6353
Bituminous Coal Surface Mining Services
N.A.I.C.S.: 212114

Gasoducto GasAndes S.A. (1)
Av Chena 11650 Parque Industrial Puerta
Sur, San Bernardo, Santiago, Chile
Tel.: (56) 223665960
Web Site: https://www.gasandes.com
Natural Gas Pipeline Transportation Ser-
vices
N.A.I.C.S.: 486210

Global Atreo S.L. (1)
C/ Golfo De Salonica 27 6 A, Madrid, Spain
Tel.: (34) 913451027
Eletric Power Generation Services
N.A.I.C.S.: 221118

IC Ictas Elektrik Uretim A.S. (1)
Mevlana Bulvari Ege Plz Kat 23, 06520,
Ankara, Turkiye
Tel.: (90) 3124192950
Web Site: http://www.ictasenerji.com.tr
Emp.: 50
Electric Power Generation Distr
N.A.I.C.S.: 221122

IPALCO Enterprises, Inc. (1)
1 Monument Cir, Indianapolis, IN 46204
Tel.: (317) 261-8261
Web Site: https://www.iplpower.com
Rev.: $1,791,710,999
Assets: $1,979,957,000
Liabilities: $889,439,000
Net Worth: $1,090,518,000
Earnings: $96,626,000
Emp.: 1,086
Fiscal Year-end: 12/31/2022
Holding Company; Electric Power Genera-
tion & Distribution Services
N.A.I.C.S.: 551112
Kenneth Joseph Zagzebski *(Chm, Pres &
CEO)*
Gustavo Garavaglia *(CFO & VP)*
Lisa Krueger *(Executives, Bd of Dirs)*

Subsidiary (Domestic):

**Indianapolis Power & Light
Company** (2)

The AES Corporation—(Continued)

1 Monument Cir, Indianapolis, IN 46206-1595
Tel.: (317) 261-8111
Web Site: https://www.aesindiana.com
Sales Range: $1-4.9 Billion
Electric Power Generation & Distribution Services
N.A.I.C.S.: 221112
Kenneth Joseph Zagzebski *(Chm, Pres & CEO)*
Barry Joe Bentley *(VP-Power Delivery)*
Gustavo Garavaglia *(CFO & VP)*
Joe Bentley *(Sr VP-Utility Ops)*
Judi Sobecki *(Gen Counsel, Sec & VP)*
Mike Schruba *(Sr Dir-T&D Ops)*
Tom Tatham *(Dir-Strategic Accounts & Customer Programs)*

Mid-America Capital Resources, Inc.   **(2)**
1 Monument Cir, Indianapolis, IN 46206   **(100%)**
Tel.: (317) 261-8261
Sales Range: $1-9.9 Million
Emp.: 17
Holding Company for Nonutility Operations
N.A.I.C.S.: 541715

JBSolar Malagon, S.L.   **(1)**
Calle Golfo de Salonica 27 - Piso 6 A, 28033, Madrid, Spain
Tel.: (34) 917026412
Eletric Power Generation Services
N.A.I.C.S.: 221118

MacGregor Park, Inc.   **(1)**
1065 Woodman Dr, Dayton, OH 45432
Tel.: (937) 224-6000
Real Estate Services
N.A.I.C.S.: 531210

Motor EV, LLC   **(1)**
4300 Wilson Blvd, Arlington, VA 22203
Web Site: http://www.motorev.net
Vehicle Charging Product Distr
N.A.I.C.S.: 457120

Orissa Power Generation Corporation Limited   **(1)**
Zone A 7th Floor Fortune Towers, Chandrasekharpur, Bhubaneswar, 751023, Odisha, India
Tel.: (91) 6742303765
Web Site: https://www.opgc.co.in
Sales Range: $500-549.9 Million
Emp.: 672
Eletric Power Generation Services
N.A.I.C.S.: 221122
Indranil Dutta *(Mng Dir)*
Alok Mukherjee *(Dir-Ops)*
Pravakar Mohanty *(Dir-Fin)*
Bishnupada Sethi *(Co-Chm)*
Nikunja Bihari Dhal *(Co-Chm)*
Prasant Kumar Mohapatra *(Mng Dir)*

Remittance Processing Services, LLC   **(1)**
2955 N Meridian St Ste 100, Indianapolis, IN 46208
Tel.: (517) 913-8954
Web Site: https://www.remitprocess.com
Payment Processing & Accounting Services
N.A.I.C.S.: 541219

Scituate Solar I, LLC   **(1)**
2711 Centerville Rd Ste 400, Wilmington, DE 19808
Tel.: (212) 419-4843
Emp.: 8
Eletric Power Generation Services
N.A.I.C.S.: 221118

SeaWest Properties, LLC   **(1)**
30092 Ivy Glenn Dr Ste 100, Laguna Niguel, CA 92677-5027
Tel.: (949) 495-1685
Electric Power Generation Distr
N.A.I.C.S.: 221122

Selen Elektrik Uretim A.S.   **(1)**
Ehlibeyt Mah. 1259. Sk. No: 7/1 Balgat, 65 Sokak, Ankara, Turkiye
Tel.: (90) 3122858363
Sales Range: $25-49.9 Million
Emp.: 40
Electric Power Generation Distr
N.A.I.C.S.: 221122
Kris Larson *(Gen Mgr)*

Sociedad Electrica Santiago S.A.   **(1)**
Jorge Hirmas 2964, Renca, Santiago, Chile
Tel.: (56) 26804760
Web Site: http://www.electricasantiago.cl
Electricity Generation Services
N.A.I.C.S.: 221113

Somerset Railroad Corporation   **(1)**
7725 Lk Rd, Barker, NY 14012
Tel.: (716) 795-9501
Sales Range: $1-9.9 Million
Emp.: 8
Railroad
N.A.I.C.S.: 482111

Sugar Maple Solar, LLC   **(1)**
195 Montague St 14th Fl Ste 1461, Brooklyn, NY 11201
Renewable Energy Services
N.A.I.C.S.: 221114

Sycarpha Bolton, LLC   **(1)**
645 Madison Ave, New York, NY 10022
Tel.: (212) 419-4844
Eletric Power Generation Services
N.A.I.C.S.: 221118

Thermo Fuels Company, Inc.   **(1)**
1100 Melody Ln Ste 206 Placer, Roseville, CA 95678-5206
Tel.: (916) 677-1717
Fuels Whslr
N.A.I.C.S.: 423520

ThinkAES, Inc.   **(1)**
4300 Wilsons Blvd Ste 1100, Arlington, VA 22203   **(100%)**
Tel.: (703) 522-1315
Web Site: http://www.aes.com
Sales Range: $400-449.9 Million
Emp.: 250
Retail Energy, eCommerce & Telecommunication Services
N.A.I.C.S.: 221118

Uplight, Inc.   **(1)**
2560 55th St, Boulder, CO 80301
Web Site: http://uplight.com
Software Development Services
N.A.I.C.S.: 541511
Thomas R. McDaniel *(Chm)*
Adrian Tuck *(CEO)*
David Tuohy *(Sr VP & Gen Mgr-Europe)*
Paul Dick *(VP-Utility Solutions & Strategy)*
Jess Melanson *(VP-Utility Solutions & Strategy)*
Bob Davis *(Dir-Customer Ops)*
Collin Mariner *(Dir-Technical Ops)*
Hunter Albright *(Sr VP-New Markets)*

Subsidiary (Domestic):

Simple Energy, Inc.   **(2)**
1215 Spruce St Ste 301, Boulder, CO 80302
Tel.: (303) 953-4735
Web Site: http://www.simpleenergy.com
Software Development Services
N.A.I.C.S.: 513100
Yoav Lurie *(Co-Founder & CEO)*
Justin Segall *(Co-Founder & Pres)*
Derek Derek *(CFO)*
Jennifer Kinney *(CTO)*
Judd Moritz *(Sr VP-Solutions)*

THE ALKALINE WATER COMPANY INC.
4400 N Scottsdale Rd Ste 308, Scottsdale, AZ 85251
Tel.: (480) 656-2423   **NV**
Web Site: https://www.thealkalinewaterco.com
Year Founded: 2012
WTER—(NASDAQ)
Rev.: $63,777,289
Assets: $18,030,103
Liabilities: $23,366,831
Net Worth: ($5,336,728)
Earnings: ($27,405,193)
Emp.: 31
Fiscal Year-end: 03/31/23
Bottled Water Manufacturing
N.A.I.C.S.: 312112
Aaron Keay *(Chm)*
David A. Guarino *(Interim Pres, Interim CEO, CFO, Treas & Sec)*
Jeff Wright *(Dir-IR)*
Tom Hutchison *(CMO)*

THE ALLSTATE CORPORATION
3100 Sanders Rd, Northbrook, IL 60062
Tel.: (847) 402-5000   **DE**
Web Site: https://www.allstate.com
Year Founded: 1931
ALL—(NYSE)
Rev.: $57,094,000,000
Assets: $103,362,000,000
Liabilities: $85,732,000,000
Net Worth: $17,630,000,000
Earnings: ($316,000,000)
Emp.: 53,000
Fiscal Year-end: 12/31/23
Auto, Fire, Personal Liability, Homeowners, Life & Business Insurance; Financial Services
N.A.I.C.S.: 524126
Thomas Joseph Wilson II *(Chm, Pres & CEO)*
Eric K. Ferren *(Chief Acctg Officer, Sr VP & Controller)*
Mario Rizzo *(Pres-Property-Liability)*
Jesse E. Merten *(CFO & Exec VP)*
Christine M. DeBiase *(Chief Legal Officer, Gen Counsel, Sec & Exec VP)*
Elizabeth Brady *(Chief Mktg , Customer & Comm Officer-Allstate Insurance Company)*
W. Guy Hill Jr. *(Exec VP)*
Troy Hawkes *(Exec VP)*
Mark Prindiville *(Chief Risk Officer)*
Bob Toohey *(Chief HR Officer)*

Subsidiaries:

Allstate India Private Limited   **(1)**
RMZ Ecoworld Building No 1 7th Floor, Devarabeesanahali Village Varthur Hobli, Bengaluru, 560103, India
Tel.: (91) 8040873300
Web Site: https://www.allstateindia.com
Software Development Services
N.A.I.C.S.: 541511

Allstate Insurance Company   **(1)**
2775 Sanders Rd, Northbrook, IL 60062
Tel.: (847) 402-5000
Web Site: http://www.allstate.com
Sales Range: $125-149.9 Million
Insurance Services
N.A.I.C.S.: 524126
Thomas Joseph Wilson II *(Chm, Pres & CEO)*
John E. Dugenske *(Pres-Investments & Corp Strategy)*
Mario Rizzo *(Pres-Property-Liability)*
Jesse E. Merten *(CFO & Exec VP)*
Carrie Blair *(Chief HR Officer & Exec VP)*
Eric Brandt *(Chief Claims Officer & Exec VP)*
Jess Merten *(Exec VP)*
John O'Donnell *(Pres)*
Mark Prindiville *(Chief Risk Officer & Exec VP)*
Terrance Williams *(Exec VP & Gen Mgr-Allstate Agency Distr)*

Allstate Insurance Company of Canada   **(1)**
27 Allstate Parkway Suite 100, Markham, L3R 5P8, ON, Canada   **(100%)**
Tel.: (905) 477-6900
Web Site: https://www.allstate.ca
Emp.: 2,400
Fire, Marine & Casualty Insurance Services
N.A.I.C.S.: 524126

Allstate Investments, LLC   **(1)**
3075 Sanders Rd Ste G5, Northbrook, IL 60062
Tel.: (847) 402-5600
Web Site: http://www.allstateinvestments.com
Emp.: 300
Investment Management Service
N.A.I.C.S.: 523940
John E. Dugenske *(Pres)*
Peter Keehn *(Sr Mng Dir-Alternative Assets & Private)*
Mike Moran *(Mng Dir-Real Estate)*
Mark Pittman *(Sr Mng Dir-Global Res & Pub Markets)*
Mick Solimene *(Mng Dir-Opportunistic Investments)*
Elliot Stultz *(Sr VP, Asst Sec & Deputy Gen Counsel)*
Philip Brides *(Sr Mng Dir-Multi-Asset Grp)*
Natalie Burkart *(Mng Dir-Strategy & Global Res)*
Mario Imbarrato *(CFO & Sec)*
Sumeena Jairaj *(CIO-Investments Tech Div)*
Hiren Parikh *(Chief Investment & Risk Analytics Officer)*
Michael Barzyk *(Mng Dir-)*
Janelie Woodward *(Sr Mng Dir--Asset Grp)*

Allstate Life Insurance Company   **(1)**
3075 Sanders Rd, Northbrook, IL 60062
Tel.: (847) 402-5000
Web Site: http://www.allstate.com
Rev.: $3,153,000,000
Assets: $41,129,000,000
Liabilities: $33,320,000,000
Net Worth: $7,809,000,000
Earnings: $580,000,000
Fiscal Year-end: 12/31/2019
Fire Insurance Services
N.A.I.C.S.: 524130
Steven E. Shebik *(Bd of Dirs, Executives)*
John C. Pintozzi *(Sr VP & Controller)*
Mario Rizzo *(CFO)*

Allstate Motor Club, Inc.   **(1)**
3100 Sanders Rd Ste 201, Northbrook, IL 60062-7155
Tel.: (847) 402-5000
Web Site: https://www.allstatemotorclub.com
Membership Based Roadside Assistance Services, Travel Planning Assistance
N.A.I.C.S.: 488490

Allstate New Jersey Insurance Company   **(1)**
3075 Sanders Rd Ste H2D, Northbrook, IL 60062-0307
Tel.: (908) 252-5000
Direct Property & Casualty Insurance Services
N.A.I.C.S.: 524126

Allstate Non-Insurance Holdings, Inc.   **(1)**
2775 Sanders Rd, Northbrook, IL 60062
Tel.: (847) 402-5000
Web Site: https://www.allstatecorporation.com
Sales Range: $550-599.9 Million
Emp.: 1,000
Holding Company
N.A.I.C.S.: 551112

Subsidiary (Domestic):

SquareTrade, Inc.   **(2)**
2000 Siorra Point Pkwy, Brisbane, CA 94005
Tel.: (877) 927-7268
Web Site: https://www.squaretrade.com
Management Consulting Services
N.A.I.C.S.: 541611
Mark Etnyre *(CFO)*
Kevin Gillan *(Mng Dir-Europe)*
Karl Wiley *(Pres & CEO)*
Wini Hebalkar *(Chief Services Officer)*
Zuqair Ali *(CIO)*
Margaret Reeves *(Sr VP-Product & Program Mgmt)*
Mike Zmugg *(Chief Revenue Officer)*
Brad Snyder *(VP-Revenue & Ops)*
Jim Schinella *(VP-New Bus Dev)*
Micheal Costanza *(VP-Bus Dev)*
Jason Siciliano *(VP & Creative Dir)*
Debbi Holmgren *(Gen Counsel & VP)*
John Whelan *(VP-Customer Experience)*
John Hiestand *(VP & Controller)*
Vince Marchi *(VP-Fin & Analytics)*

Subsidiary (Domestic):

PlumChoice, Inc.   **(3)**
Cross Point 900 Chelmsford St, Lowell, MA 01851-8100
Tel.: (781) 275-1114
Web Site: http://www.plumchoice.com
Online Computer Support Services
N.A.I.C.S.: 541519
Wynn Grubbs *(Partner-Development & Sr VP)*
David L. Temlak *(Sr VP-Technology)*
James E. Carr *(CFO)*
Michael Prendergast *(VP)*

Karen McPhillips *(Chief Acctg Officer & VP-Finance)*
Christine Phaneuf *(VP-Human Resources)*
David Shimoni *(CEO)*
Dave Hauser *(VP)*
Bing He *(VP)*
Dave Blahnik *(VP-Finance)*
Rich MacKeen *(VP)*
Robert P. Schechter *(Chm)*

Subsidiary (Domestic):

Everon Technology Services, LLC **(4)**
100 High St Ste 1104, Boston, MA 02110
Tel.: (617) 737-3800
Web Site: https://www.everonit.com
Rev.: $4,000,000
Emp.: 34
Administrative & General Management Consulting Services
N.A.I.C.S.: 541611
Josh Clifford *(CTO)*

Allstate Northbrook Indemnity Company **(1)**
3075 Sanders Rd Ste H1E, Northbrook, IL 60062
Tel.: (847) 402-5000
Insurance Management Services
N.A.I.C.S.: 524298

Allstate Northern Ireland Limited **(1)**
10 Mays Meadow, Belfast, BT1 3PH, Northern Ireland, United Kingdom
Tel.: (44) 2890678000
Web Site: https://www.allstateni.com
Emp.: 2,400
Insurance Services
N.A.I.C.S.: 524128

Allstate Solutions Private Limited **(1)**
RMZ Ecoworld 7th Floor Building No 1, Devarabeesanahali Village Varthur Hobli, Bengaluru, 560 103, India
Tel.: (91) 804 087 3300
Web Site: https://www.allstateindia.com
Investment Management Service
N.A.I.C.S.: 523940
Chetan Garga *(Mng Dir)*
Irshan Mohamed *(Dir-Strategy)*
Sabu Thomas *(Chief HR Officer)*
K. V. Gopinath *(Dir-Administration)*
Hemlata Nevetia *(CFO)*
Mona Nandedkar *(Chief Transformation Officer & Chief Information Officer)*
Manoj Kumar *(Dir-Information Technology)*
Manjula Nanjappa *(Dir-Delivery-Risk Management)*
Subhobroto Ghosh *(Head)*
Sarish Paul *(Dir-Risk-Compliance)*
Tanay Kediyal *(COO)*
Milind Patil *(Dir-Operations)*
Shibu Mathew *(Dir)*
Monarch Limaye *(Dir & Chief HR Officer)*

American Heritage Life Insurance Company **(1)**
1776 American Heritage Life Dr, Jacksonville, FL 32224-6688 **(100%)**
Tel.: (904) 992-1776
Web Site: https://www.allstate.com
Sales Range: $400-449.9 Million
Emp.: 875
Life & Health Insurance Services
N.A.I.C.S.: 524210
Don Civgin *(Pres & CEO-Allstate Financial)*

Subsidiary (Domestic):

E.R.J. Insurance Group, Inc. **(2)**
9675 Montgomery Rd Ste 101, Montgomery, OH 45242 **(100%)**
Tel.: (513) 984-5255
Web Site: https://americanheritageins.com
Sales Range: $10-24.9 Million
Emp.: 25
Sales Training Services
N.A.I.C.S.: 611430

American Heritage Life Investment Corporation **(1)**
1776 American Heritage Life Dr, Jacksonville, FL 32224
Tel.: (904) 992-1776
Insurance Management Services
N.A.I.C.S.: 524298

Answer Financial, Inc. **(1)**

15910 Ventura Blvd 6th Fl, Encino, CA 91436
Tel.: (818) 644-4000
Web Site: http://www.answerfinancial.com
Online Insurance Retailing Services
N.A.I.C.S.: 524298
Jennifer Sherry *(Sr VP-Agency Compliance, Trng & HR)*
Shelby Fogelman *(Compliance Officer, Corp Counsel & VP)*
Sangram Reddy *(Dir-Design & Customer Experience)*

Charter National Life Insurance Company **(1)**
3075 Sanders Rd Ste H1A, Northbrook, IL 60062
Tel.: (847) 402-5000
Insurance Management Services
N.A.I.C.S.: 524298

Deerbrook Insurance Company **(1)**
2775 Sanders Rd, Northbrook, IL 60062
Tel.: (800) 349-7284
Web Site: http://www.deerbrook.com
Sales Range: $10-24.9 Million
Emp.: 10,000
Automobile Insurance Services
N.A.I.C.S.: 524298
Casey J. Sylla *(Chief Investment Officer & Sr VP)*
Casey J. Sylla *(Chief Investment Officer & Sr VP)*

Encompass Insurance Company **(1)**
2775 Sanders Rd Ste C1, Northbrook, IL 60062-6127
Web Site:
   http://www.encompassinsurance.com
Direct Property & Casualty Insurance Carriers
N.A.I.C.S.: 524126
Patrick Macellaro *(Pres)*
Marisela Brum *(CIO)*
Lauren Brokaw *(Dir-Finance)*
Jason Heiger *(Dir)*
Mark Hord *(Dir)*
Ken Koehler *(VP-Sales-Marketing)*
Brian Savage *(VP)*
Mary Zagorski *(Dir-Operations)*

Esurance Insurance Services, Inc. **(1)**
650 Davis St, San Francisco, CA 94111
Tel.: (415) 875-4500
Web Site: https://www.esurance.com
Sales Range: $10-24.9 Million
Emp.: 26
Internet-Based Personal Lines Insurance Supplier
N.A.I.C.S.: 524210

Esurance Property & Casualty Insurance Company **(1)**
650 Davis St, San Francisco, CA 94111
Tel.: (415) 875-4500
Web Site: https://www.esurance.com
Emp.: 4
Insurance Management Services
N.A.I.C.S.: 524298

First Colonial Insurance Company **(1)**
1776 American Heritage Life Dr Bldg B, Jacksonville, FL 32224-6688
Tel.: (904) 992-1776
Web Site:
   https://www.allstatedealerservices.com
Insurance Management Services
N.A.I.C.S.: 524298

InfoArmor, Inc. **(1)**
7001 N Scottsdale Rd Ste 2020, Scottsdale, AZ 85253
Tel.: (480) 302-6701
Web Site: http://www.infoarmor.com
Privacy Management Services
N.A.I.C.S.: 541618
Drew Germain *(Chief Quality Officer)*
Anila Joy *(CTO)*
Dustin Hofstein *(Exec VP-Ops)*
Meghann Carroll *(Exec VP-Sls)*
Jason Park *(Chief Growth Officer)*
David Harris *(Chief Comml Officer)*
Robert Neel *(Chief Information Security Officer)*
Cynthia Bowers *(Chief HR Officer)*
Chris Suarez *(CFO)*
Kevin Goulet *(Exec VP-Product & Category Mgmt)*

Insurance Answer Center, LLC **(1)**
15910 Ventura Blvd 6th Fl, Encino, CA 91436-2802
Tel.: (818) 644-4476
Insurance Management Services
N.A.I.C.S.: 524298

Intramerica Life Insurance Company **(1)**
878 Veterans Memorial Hwy Ste 400, Hauppauge, NY 11788
Tel.: (631) 357-8923
Web Site:
   http://www.insuranceproviders.com
Direct Property & Casualty Insurance Carriers
N.A.I.C.S.: 524126

Ivantage Insurance Brokers Inc. **(1)**
27 Allstate Parkway Suite 100, Markham, L3R 5P8, ON, Canada
Tel.: (905) 946-7735
Web Site: https://www.ivantageinsurance.ca
Insurance Management Services
N.A.I.C.S.: 524298

National General Holdings Corp. **(1)**
59 Maiden Ln 38th Fl, New York, NY 10038
Tel.: (212) 380-9500
Web Site: http://www.nationalgeneral.com
Rev.: $5,552,285,000
Assets: $10,127,894,000
Liabilities: $6,911,896,000
Net Worth: $3,215,998,000
Earnings: $513,331,000
Emp.: 9,700
Fiscal Year-end: 12/31/2020
Holding Company; Property & Casualty Insurance Products & Services
N.A.I.C.S.: 551112
Jeffrey Weissmann *(Gen Counsel, Sec & Exec VP)*
Peter A. Rendall *(COO & Exec VP)*
Lawrence J. Moloney *(Chief Acctg Officer, Sr VP & Controller)*
Thomas J. Wilson *(Chm)*
Barry Karfunkel *(CEO)*

Subsidiary (Domestic):

ABC Agency Network of Texas, LLC **(2)**
2010 Gilmer Rd, Longview, TX 75604
Tel.: (903) 297-4570
Insurance Related Services
N.A.I.C.S.: 524298

ABC Agency Network, Inc. **(2)**
4670 I-49 N Service Rd, Opelousas, LA 70570
Tel.: (337) 942-5691
Insurance Related Services
N.A.I.C.S.: 524298

Agent Alliance Insurance Company **(2)**
1231 I St Ste 201, Sacramento, CA 95814
Tel.: (916) 283-9473
Insurance Related Services
N.A.I.C.S.: 524298

AgentCubed, LLC **(2)**
7950 N Horseshoe Bend Rd Ste 104, Boise, ID 83714
Tel.: (877) 424-5888
Property & Casualty Insurance Services
N.A.I.C.S.: 524126
Lucas Sheehan *(Dir-Ops)*

Assigned Risk Solutions Ltd. **(2)**
200 N Grand Ave, Lansing, MI 48901-7985
Tel.: (201) 368-8055
Assigned Risk Auto, Private Passenger Auto & Investigative & Cost Containment Services
N.A.I.C.S.: 524298

Care Financial of Texas, LLC **(2)**
2044 N State Hwy 360, Grand Prairie, TX 75050
Tel.: (972) 660-4713
Health Care Srvices
N.A.I.C.S.: 621610

Century-National Insurance Company **(2)**
16650 Sherman Way, Van Nuys, CA 91406-3782
Tel.: (818) 760-0880
Web Site: https://www.centurynational.com

Property & Casualty Insurance Products & Services
N.A.I.C.S.: 524126

Direct General Corporation **(2)**
1281 Murfreesboro Rd, Nashville, TN 37217
Tel.: (615) 399-4700
Emp.: 2,426
Personal Auto, Life, Hospital Indemnity & Travel Insurance Services
N.A.I.C.S.: 524126
John W. Mullen *(CEO)*
Julia Park *(Dir-Sls Trng)*
Adarsh Raveendran *(Project Mgr-IT & Portfolio)*

Subsidiary (Non-US):

Euro Accident Livforsakring AB **(2)**
Svardvagen 3 a, 182 33, Danderyd, Sweden
Tel.: (46) 87878000
Web Site: https://euroaccident.com
Emp.: 350
Insurance Services
N.A.I.C.S.: 524128

Subsidiary (Domestic):

Health Network Group, LLC **(2)**
301 Clematis Str Ste 3000, West Palm Beach, FL 33401
Web Site: https://www.healthnetwork.com
Health Insurance Services
N.A.I.C.S.: 524114
Sean Sullivan *(Founder)*
Jeremy Kayne *(CEO)*
Erika Sullivan *(COO & Gen Counsel)*
Janna Gilleland *(Creative Dir)*

HealthCompare Insurance Services, Inc. **(2)**
1100 NW Compton Dr Ste 200, Hillsboro, OR 97006
Web Site: https://www.healthcompare.com
Life & Health Insurance Services
N.A.I.C.S.: 524210

Healthcare Solutions Team, LLC **(2)**
1900 S Highland Ave 203, Lombard, IL 60148
Tel.: (630) 261-3000
Web Site: https://www.myhst.com
Emp.: 12
Health Care Srvices
N.A.I.C.S.: 621999
Joe Eichman *(Pres)*

Imperial Insurance Managers, LLC **(2)**
14800 Quorum Dr Ste 250, Dallas, TX 75254
Tel.: (337) 942-5691
Insurance Related Services
N.A.I.C.S.: 524298

Imperial Marketing Corporation **(2)**
38150 Plymouth Rd, Livonia, MI 48150
Tel.: (248) 353-0950
Web Site: http://www.imperialmarketing.com
Marketing Consulting Services
N.A.I.C.S.: 541613

Integon Indemnity Corporation **(2)**
PO Box 3199, Winston Salem, NC 27102-3199
Tel.: (336) 435-2000
Insurance Related Services
N.A.I.C.S.: 524298

Integon National Insurance Company **(2)**
500 W 5th St, Winston Salem, NC 27101-2728
Tel.: (336) 435-2612
Insurance Related Services
N.A.I.C.S.: 524298

Subsidiary (Non-US):

Integon Service Co, S.A. de C.V. **(2)**
Paseo de los Heroes No 9539-PB, Zona Urbana Rio, 22010, Tijuana, BC, Mexico
Tel.: (52) 6646346190
Web Site: https://integonserviceco.mx
Emp.: 500
Insurance Services
N.A.I.C.S.: 524128

Subsidiary (Domestic):

LeadCloud, LLC **(2)**

The Allstate Corporation—(Continued)

15310 Leondina Dr, Glenwood, MD 21738
Web Site: https://www.leadcloud.us
Marketing Services
N.A.I.C.S.: 541613
Brian Ocheltree (CEO)

National Automotive Insurance
Company (2)
111 Veterans Blvd Ste 1420, Metairie, LA
70005
Tel.: (504) 828-6855
Insurance Related Services
N.A.I.C.S.: 524298

National Farmers Union Property &
Casualty Company (2)
5619 DTC Pkwy Ste 300, Greenwood Village, CO 80111-3013
Tel.: (303) 337-5500
Insurance And Reinsurance Services
N.A.I.C.S.: 524126

National General Management
Corp. (2)
2626 Glenwood Ave Ste 550, Raleigh, NC
27608
Web Site: https://nationalgeneral.com
Property & Casualty Insurance Products &
Services
N.A.I.C.S.: 524126
Jodi M. Swartz (CMo & Exec VP)

Subsidiary (Domestic):

National General Insurance
Company (3)
13736 Riverport Dr Ste 700, Maryland
Heights, MO 63043
Tel.: (314) 493-8000
Web Site: https://www.gmacinsurance.com
Sales Range: $100-124.9 Million
Emp.: 150
Property & Casualty Insurance Underwriter
N.A.I.C.S.: 524126

Subsidiary (Domestic):

National General Motor Club,
Inc. (2)
PO Box 3199, Winston Salem, NC 27102-
3199
Web Site:
https://www.nationalgeneralmotorclub.com
Insurance Services
N.A.I.C.S.: 524128

Quotit Corporation (2)
3333 Michelson Dr Ste 500, Irvine, CA
92612
Web Site: https://www.quotit.com
Online Insurance Quote Application Developer & Services
N.A.I.C.S.: 541511
Chad Hogan (Pres)
David Freeman (Dir-Prodcut & Plng)
Steve Trattner (VP-Bus Dev)
Eric Carlson (Dir-Application Dev)
Jessica Grover (Mktg Dir)
Rebecca Fowler (Dir-Customer Success)
Lori White (Dir-Carrier Rels)
Rick Newman (Dir-Carrier Ops)

Rac Insurance Partners, LLC (2)
6101 Blue Lagoon Dr, Miami, FL 33126
Tel.: (305) 260-3600
Insurance Related Services
N.A.I.C.S.: 524298
Henri Cuadra (VP)

Standard Property & Casualty Insurance Company
1028 S Grand Ave W, Springfield, IL 62704
Tel.: (217) 546-2894
Web Site: https://www.standardmutual.com
Provider of Insurance Services
N.A.I.C.S.: 524126

Subsidiary (Domestic):

North Light Specialty Insurance
Company (1)
2775 Sanders Rd, Northbrook, IL 60062
Web Site:
https://www.northlightspecialty.com
Insurance Agencies & Brokerages
N.A.I.C.S.: 524210

Northeast Agencies Inc. (1)
2495 Main St Ste 209, Buffalo, NY 14214
Tel.: (716) 837-8804

Web Site: http://www.neagencies.com
Sales Range: $50-74.9 Million
Emp.: 100
Whslr of Commercial & Personal Insurance
N.A.I.C.S.: 524210

Pafco Insurance Company (1)
27 Allstate Parkway Suite 100, Markham,
L3R 5P8, ON, Canada
Tel.: (905) 513-4000
Web Site: https://www.pafco.ca
Direct Property & Casualty Insurance Carriers Services
N.A.I.C.S.: 524126

Pembridge Insurance Company (1)
27 Allstate Parkway Suite 100, Markham,
L3R 5P8, ON, Canada
Tel.: (905) 513-4013
Web Site: https://www.pembridge.com
Sales Range: $25-49.9 Million
Emp.: 800
Property & Casualty Insurance Carrier
N.A.I.C.S.: 524126

Right Answer Insurance Agency,
LLC (1)
15910 Ventura Blvd 6th Fl, Encino, CA
91436
Tel.: (818) 644-4000
Web Site:
https://www.rightanswerinsurance.com
Insurance Management Services
N.A.I.C.S.: 524126
Joseph Guillory (Officer-Information)
Jennifer Sherry (Sr VP- & Human Resources)
Shelby Fogelman (Officer-Compliance)

Signature Agency, Inc. (1)
1784 Heritage Center Dr Ste 204, Wake
Forest, NC 27587-3949
Tel.: (919) 878-8989
Web Site: https://signatureagency.com
Emp.: 19
Financial Transaction Processing Services
N.A.I.C.S.: 522320

Signature Motor Club, Inc. (1)
2775 Sanders Rd Ste E2E, Northbrook, IL
60062
Tel.: (847) 402-5000
Web Site: https://www.sigmotorclub.com
Insurance Management Services
N.A.I.C.S.: 524298

SquareTrade Holding Company,
Inc. (1)
4216 Center Key Rd, Winter Park, FL
32792
Tel.: (321) 591-2055
Product Warranty Insurance Services
N.A.I.C.S.: 524128

SquareTrade Limited (1)
2nd Floor 5 Golden Square, London, W1F
9BS, United Kingdom
Tel.: (44) 2035142354
Web Site: https://www.squaretrade.co.uk
Product Warranty Insurance Services
N.A.I.C.S.: 524128
Brad Snyder (VP-Operations)
Kevin Gillan (Mng Dir)
Masha Zolotokrylina (VP-Business Development)
Aditya Hindocha (VP-)
Alastair Douglas (Sr VP)
Amelia Lowe (VP-Operations)

Tech-Cor, LLC (1)
110 E Palatine Rd, Wheeling, IL
60090 (100%)
Tel.: (847) 667-2330
Web Site: http://www.tech-cor.com
Sales Range: $10-24.9 Million
Emp.: 100
Automotive Damage Resistant Research
Services
N.A.I.C.S.: 524298

THE AMERICAN ENERGY GROUP, LTD.
1 Gorham Island Ste 303, Westport,
CT 06880
Tel.: (203) 222-7315 NV
Web Site: http://www.aegg.net
AEGG—(OTCIQ)
Sales Range: Less than $1 Million

Emp.: 2
Oil & Gas Exploration Services
N.A.I.C.S.: 213112
R. Pierce Onthank (Pres, CEO, Treas
& Sec)

THE ANDERSONS INCORPORATED
1947 Briarfield Blvd, Maumee, OH
43537
Tel.: (419) 893-5050 OH
Web Site:
https://www.andersonsinc.com
Year Founded: 1947
ANDE—(NASDAQ)
Rev.: $14,750,112,000
Assets: $3,855,007,000
Liabilities: $2,338,620,000
Net Worth: $1,516,387,000
Earnings: $101,190,000
Emp.: 2,334
Fiscal Year-end: 12/31/23
Grain Merchandising, Handling & Related Products; Retail Stores; Agricultural & Lawn Fertilizer Products; Corn
Cob Milling
N.A.I.C.S.: 111191
Brian K. Walz (Treas & VP-Fin)
William E. Krueger (Pres & CEO)
Joseph E. McNeely (Pres-Nutrient &
Industrial)
Brian A. Valentine (CFO & Exec VP)
Christine M. Castellano (Gen Counsel, Sec & Exec VP)
Patrick E. Bowe (Chm)

Subsidiaries:

Bridge Agri Partners, Inc. (1)
495 WT Hill Blvd South Suites 21 And 22,
Lethbridge, T1J 1Y6, AB, Canada
Tel.: (403) 942-1200
Web Site:
https://www.bridgeagripartners.com
Agricultural Product Logistics Services
N.A.I.C.S.: 541614

Capstone Commodities, LLC (1)
PO Box 2363, Round Rock, TX 78681
Tel.: (512) 671-6626
Web Site:
https://www.capstonecommodities.com
Animal Feed Ingredient Distr
N.A.I.C.S.: 423820

Kay Flo Industries, Inc. (1)
1919 Grand Ave, Sioux City, IA 51106-5708
Tel.: (712) 277-2011
Animal Nutrients Mfr & Distr
N.A.I.C.S.: 311119
Alexander Uhl (Mgr-Maintenance & Facilities)

Lansing Trade Group LLC (1)
10975 Benson Dr Ste 400, Overland Park,
KS 66210
Tel.: (913) 748-3000
Web Site: http://www.lansingtradegroup.com
Commodity Wholesale Trading & Marketing
Services
N.A.I.C.S.: 523160
Tom Carew (Gen Counsel & Exec VP)

Subsidiary (Domestic):

Lansing Ethanol Services, LLC (2)
10975 Benson Dr, Overland Park, KS
66210
Tel.: (913) 748-3000
Trading & Transportation of Physical Ethanol
N.A.I.C.S.: 523160

Lansing Louisiana, LLC (2)
10975 Benson Dr Ste 400, Overland Park,
KS 66210
Tel.: (318) 724-6696
Commodity Wholesale Trading & Marketing
Services
N.A.I.C.S.: 523160

Affiliate (Non-US):

Thompsons Limited (2)

2 Hyland Drive, Blenheim, N0P 1A0, ON,
Canada (50%)
Tel.: (519) 676-5411
Web Site: http://www.thompsonslimited.com
Sales Range: $400-449.9 Million
Corn, Soybeans, Wheat & Dry Beans Distr,
Farm Supplies Retailer & Edible Bean Processor
N.A.I.C.S.: 424510

Plant Nutrient Group (1)
1947 Briarfield Blvd, Maumee, OH 43537
Tel.: (419) 893-5050
Web Site:
http://www.andersonsplantnutrient.com
Sales Range: $10-24.9 Million
Emp.: 50
Operating Group; Dry & Liquid Agricultural
Products Mfr, Distr & Whslr
N.A.I.C.S.: 325320

Subsidiary (Domestic):

Mineral Processing Company (2)
1855 County Hwy 99, Carey, OH
43316 (100%)
Tel.: (419) 396-3501
Web Site:
https://www.andersonsmineralprocessing.com
Emp.: 20
Lime & Gypsum Products Mfr
N.A.I.C.S.: 327410

New Eezy-Gro Inc. (2)
218 Toledo St, Carey, OH 43316
Tel.: (419) 396-3586
Agricultural Nutrients & Industrial Products
Mfr & Whslr
N.A.I.C.S.: 325311

Division (Domestic):

The Andersons, Southern
Region (2)
800 Trafalgar Ct Ste 320, Maitland, FL
32751
Tel.: (407) 682-6100
Web Site:
http://www.andersonssouthernregion.com
Sales Range: $25-49.9 Million
Emp.: 20
Fertilizers, Mixing Only
N.A.I.C.S.: 325314

Skyland Grain, LLC (1)
202 S Main St, Johnson, KS
67855 (65%)
Tel.: (620) 492-6210
Web Site: http://www.skylandgrain.com
Sales Range: $25-49.9 Million
Emp.: 130
Grain Elevators; Joint Venture of Johnson
Cooperative Grain Co. (50%) & ADM Grain
Co. (50%)
N.A.I.C.S.: 493130
David Cron (CEO & Sec)
Guy Martin (COO & Exec VP)
Wade Tucker (Pres)
David Rodriguez (Dir-Credit & PR)
Chris Roberts (CFO-Cunningham)
Matt Overturf (Exec VP-Grain Mktg)
Justin Ochs (Exec VP-Crop Nutrients)
Teresa Hammond (Dir-HR)
Scott Deweese (Exec VP-Strategy)
David Malone (Reg Mgr-6)
Bobbie Smith (Mgr-Grain-Northern Area)
Paige German (Controller)
Cindy Williamson (Mgr-Credit)
Aaron Murphy (Mgr-Relationship-
Cunningham)
Gragg Allen (Exec VP)
Bret Brown (CFO & Exec VP)
Bryce Ackerman (Exec VP-HR)
Dennis Flowers (Exec VP-Cotton)
Brian Martin (Exec VP-Energy)
Ryan Riddle (Exec VP-Crop Protection
Products & Seed)
Clifford Alexander (VP)

The Andersons Canada Limited (1)
712 Richmond Street, Chatham, N7M 5J5,
ON, Canada
Tel.: (519) 676-5411
Web Site: https://andersonscanada.com
Grocery & Food Services
N.A.I.C.S.: 624210

The Andersons Clymers Ethanol
LLC (1)

3389 W County Rd 300 S, Logansport, IN 46947
Tel.: (574) 722-2627
Web Site: http://www.andersonsinc.com
Natural Gas & Oil Exploration Service
N.A.I.C.S.: 213112

The Andersons Denison Ethanol LLC (1)
2404 W Hwy 30, Denison, IA 51442
Tel.: (712) 263-2676
Web Site: http://www.andersonsinc.com
Emp.: 35
Chemical Products Mfr
N.A.I.C.S.: 325998

The Andersons Lawn Fertilizer Division, Inc. (1)
480 W Dussel Dr Ste A, Maumee, OH 43537
Tel.: (419) 893-5050
Web Site: http://www.andersonsinc.com
Farm Supplies Whslr
N.A.I.C.S.: 424910

The Andersons Marathon Ethanol LLC (1)
5728 Sebring Warner Rd, Greenville, OH 45331-9800
Tel.: (937) 316-3700
Crude Petroleum Natural Gas Extraction
N.A.I.C.S.: 211120
Neill Mkinstray (Pres)

The Andersons, Inc. - Auburn Grain (1)
315 N Auburn Rd, Auburn, MI 48611
Tel.: (989) 662-4423
Web Site: http://www.andersonsgrain.com
Sales Range: $50-74.9 Million
Beans & Grain Whslr
N.A.I.C.S.: 424510
Mark Hintz (Supvr-Ops)

Thompsons USA Limited (1)
41703 US Hwy 2 SW, East Grand Forks, MN 56721
Tel.: (218) 773-9821
Grain Farming Services
N.A.I.C.S.: 111199
Jim Vrolyk (Mgr)
Bud Vance (Asst Mgr)

Titan Lansing, LLC (1)
3802 MLK Jr Blvd, Lubbock, TX 79404
Tel.: (806) 993-0554
Web Site: https://www.titanlansing.com
Rail & Truck Logistics Services
N.A.I.C.S.: 488510

THE ARENA GROUP HOLDINGS, INC

200 Vesey St 24th Fl, New York, NY 10281
Tel.: (775) 600-2765   DE
Web Site: https://thearenagroup.net
Year Founded: 1990
AREN—(NYSEAMEX)
Rev.: $220,935,000
Assets: $203,719,000
Liabilities: $255,865,000
Net Worth: ($52,146,000)
Earnings: ($70,858,000)
Emp.: 391
Fiscal Year-end: 12/31/22
Investment Services
N.A.I.C.S.: 523999
Manoj Bhargava (Pres)
Douglas B. Smith (Principal Acctg Officer & Sec)
Paul Edmondson (Pres-Platform)
Jill Marchisotto (CMO)
Ben Trott (Chief Product Officer)
Indraneel Mukherjee (CTO)
Eric Aledort (Sr VP-Bus Dev & Partnerships)
Stephanie Mazzamaro (VP-Data Strategy & Ops, Adv, Partnerships & Revenue)
Jeremy Fass (Sr VP-Digital Ad Revenue)
Rachael Fink (Mgr-PR)
Grady Tripp (Sr VP-People)
Katie Kulik (Chief Revenue Officer)

Subsidiaries:

Say Media, Inc. (1)
442 Post St Ste 901, San Francisco, CA 94102
Tel.: (415) 738-5100
Web Site: http://www.saymedia.com
Web Advertising & Publishing Services
N.A.I.C.S.: 541890
Matt Sanchez (Founder)

TheStreet, Inc. (1)
14 Wall St 15th Fl, New York, NY 10005
Tel.: (212) 321-5000
Web Site:
    http://www.corporate.thestreet.com
Rev.: $53,089,452
Assets: $85,741,692
Liabilities: $30,173,235
Net Worth: $55,568,457
Earnings: $18,214,574
Emp.: 556
Fiscal Year-end: 12/31/2018
Financial News, Commentary & Investment Information Internet-Related Sources, Mobile Devices & Online TV Channels Publisher
N.A.I.C.S.: 513199
Jim Cramer (Founder)

Subsidiary (Non-US):

Management Diagnostics Limited (2)
Elizabeth House 5th Floor York Road, London, SE1 7NQ, United Kingdom
Tel.: (44) 2071609600
Web Site: http://www.boardex.com
Management Consulting Services
N.A.I.C.S.: 541618

Subsidiary (Domestic):

TheStreet.com Ratings, Inc. (2)
1430 Endeavour Dr, Jupiter, FL 33478
Tel.: (561) 627-3300
Sales Range: $75-99.9 Million
Emp.: 6
Corporate & Investment Financial Rating Services
N.A.I.C.S.: 525990

Themaven Network, Inc. (1)
5048 Roosevelt Way NE, Seattle, WA 98105
Tel.: (775) 600-2765
Emp.: 15
Software Development Services
N.A.I.C.S.: 541511

THE AZEK COMPANY INC.
1330 W Fulton St Ste 350, Chicago, IL 60607
Web Site: https://www.azekco.com
Year Founded: 2013
AZEK—(NYSE)
Rev.: $1,441,448,000
Assets: $2,167,711,000
Liabilities: $810,846,000
Net Worth: $1,356,865,000
Earnings: $153,379,000
Emp.: 2,276
Fiscal Year-end: 09/30/24
Holding Company
N.A.I.C.S.: 551112
Jesse G. Singh (Pres & CEO)
Scott Van Winter (Pres-Comml Segment)
Bobby Gentile (Sr VP-Ops)
Jonathan Skelly (Pres-Residential & Comml)
Michelle Kasson (CIO)
Peter G. Clifford (CFO, COO & Sr VP)
Amanda Cimaglia (VP-ESG)
Sandra Lamartine (Chief HR Officer & Sr VP)
Morgan Fox Walbridge (Chief Legal Officer, Sec & Sr VP)
Samara Toole (CMO & Sr VP)
Daniel Boss (Sr VP-R&D)
Chris Latkovic (Sr VP)

Subsidiaries:

Return Polymers, Inc. (1)

400 Westlake Dr, Ashland, OH 44805
Tel.: (419) 289-1998
Web Site: https://www.returnpolymers.com
Recycled Plastic Material Mfr
N.A.I.C.S.: 325991

The AZEK Group LLC (1)
1330 W Fulton St Ste 350, Chicago, IL 60607
Tel.: (312) 809-1093
Web Site: https://azekco.com
Sales Range: $500-549.9 Million
Emp.: 2,000
Building Materials Mfr & Distr
N.A.I.C.S.: 326199
Gary E. Hendrickson (Chm)
Peter Clifford (Sr VP)
Samara Toole (Sr VP)
Jonathan Skelly (Pres)
Scott Van Winter (Pres)
Morgan Walbridge (Sr VP)
Sandra Lamartine (Sr VP)
Chris Latkovic (Sr VP)
Michelle Kasson (CIO)
Amanda Cimaglia (VP)

Subsidiary (Domestic):

Scranton Products Inc. (2)
801 E Corey St, Scranton, PA 18505
Tel.: (570) 558-8000
Web Site:
    https://www.scrantonproducts.com
Sales Range: $25-49.9 Million
Emp.: 300
Plastic Partition & Locker Mfr
N.A.I.C.S.: 337215
Scott Van Winter (Pres)

UltraLox Technology, LLC (1)
2737 W Service Rd, Eagan, MN 55121
Web Site: https://ultralox.com
Architectural Railing Mfr
N.A.I.C.S.: 332323

Versatex Building Products, LLC (1)
400 Steel St, Aliquippa, PA 15001
Tel.: (724) 857-1111
Web Site: https://versatex.com
Building Design Services
N.A.I.C.S.: 541310

Vycom Plastics (1)
801 E Corey St, Scranton, PA 18505
Tel.: (570) 346-8254
Web Site: https://www.vycomplastics.com
Emp.: 100
Plastics Product Mfr
N.A.I.C.S.: 326130
Kevin Duffy (VP & Gen Mgr)

THE BALDWIN INSURANCE GROUP, INC.
4211 W Boy Scout Blvd Ste 800, Tampa, FL 33607
Tel.: (813) 259-8032   DE
Web Site: https://baldwin.com
Year Founded: 2019
BWIN—(NASDAQ)
Rev.: $980,720,000
Assets: $3,462,182,000
Liabilities: $2,322,630,000
Net Worth: $1,139,552,000
Earnings: ($41,772,000)
Emp.: 3,800
Fiscal Year-end: 12/31/22
Holding Company
N.A.I.C.S.: 551112
Daniel Galbraith (Pres & CEO-Retail Brokerage Ops)
Lowry Baldwin (Co-Founder & Chm)
Elizabeth Krystyn (Co-Founder)
Laura Sherman (Co-Founder)
Trevor L. Baldwin (CEO)
Kris Wiebeck (Chief Strategy Officer)
Dan Galbraith (COO)
John Valentine (Chief Partnership Officer)
Bradford Hale (CFO)
Christopher Stephens (Gen Counsel)
Corbyn Galloway (Chief Acctg Officer)
Rachel Carr (Dir-Mktg)
Chase Bedsole (Pres-Guided Medicare Solutions)

Joe Finney (Pres-Guided Solutions)
Erin King (Chief Colleague Officer)
Bonnie Bishop (Exec Dir-IR)
Rajasekhar Kalahasthi (Chief Digital & Info Officer)

Subsidiaries:

Armfield, Harrison & Thomas, Inc. (1)
20 S King St, Leesburg, VA 20175
Tel.: (703) 777-2341
Web Site: http://www.ahtins.com
Sales Range: $10-24.9 Million
Emp.: 100
Insurance Agents
N.A.I.C.S.: 524210
David Schaefer (Pres & CEO)
Kate Armfield (Mng Dir)
George Forrester (Partner)
Mark Ganley (Partner)
Ned Sander (Mng Partner)
Lynne Sorrentino (Dir-Acctg)

Subsidiary (Domestic):

Mason & Mason Insurance Agency, Inc. (2)
458 S Ave, Whitman, MA 02382
Tel.: (781) 447-5531
Insurance Brokerage Services
N.A.I.C.S.: 524298
Philip W. Mason (Founder & Pres)

Subsidiary (Domestic):

Mason & Mason Technology Insurance Services, Inc. (3)
458 S Ave, Whitman, MA 02382
Tel.: (781) 447-5531
Web Site: http://www.masoninsure.com
Insurance Brokerage Services
N.A.I.C.S.: 524210
Philip W. Mason (Founder & Pres)

Baldwin Krystyn Sherman Partners, LLC (1)
4211 W Boy Scout Blvd Ste 800, Tampa, FL 33607
Tel.: (813) 984-3200
Web Site: https://www.bks-partners.com
Sales Range: $1-9.9 Million
Emp.: 80
Designs Holistic Insurance & Employee Benefit Programs for Businesses & Individuals
N.A.I.C.S.: 524298
Lowry Baldwin (Partner)
Trevor L. Baldwin (CEO)
Andrew Mann (Mng Partner)
Austin Jett (Partner)
Bill Furie (Partner)
Brent Wick (Mng Partner)
Chris Huber (Mng Dir)
Chris Poynter (Mng Partner)
Chriss Spires Jr. (Partner)
Daniel Weinkauf (Partner)
Edward Litke (Partner)
Frank Baker (Partner)
Garrett Gardi (Partner)
Gregg Schieffelbein (Partner)
Gregory Rosenthal (Partner)
Jackson Vaughan (Partner)
Jeff Hughes (Pres)
Jennifer Berry (Partner)
Josh Helmuth (Partner)
Karyl Foray (Partner)
Lori Bassano (Partner)
Mark R. Webb (Partner)
Matthew Felman (Partner)
Michael Ballew (Mng Partner)
Michael DeGeorge (Partner)
Michael Minsky (Mng Partner)
Michael Ortoll (Partner)
Nicholas Aronson (Partner)
Rick Russo (Partner)
Ricky Metzelder (Partner)
Russ Blakely (Partner)
Steve Maloof (Mng Partner)
Steven Zisook (Partner)
Taylor Reilly (Mng Dir)
Todd Fredella (Partner)
Tom G. Panos (Partner)
Trevor Harkness (Partner)
Will Montoya (Partner)
William Taulbee (Mng Partner)
Amy DeForeest (Dir-Business Development & Private Risk Mgmt)

The Baldwin Insurance Group, Inc.—(Continued)

Tom Krystyn *(Partner)*
Shane Wingo *(Partner)*
Rich Thompson *(Partner)*
Matthew Hammer *(Partner)*
Kathryn Koch *(Partner)*
Joey Masters *(Partner)*
Joe Malzacher *(Partner)*
Joe Harris *(Partner)*
Jim Martinelli *(Partner)*
Jason Lunsford *(Partner)*
Janette L'Heureux *(Partner)*
Garrett Jones *(Partner)*
Fritz Archerd *(Partner)*
Florence Conlan *(Partner)*
Brian Caputo *(Partner)*
Brad Tamulski *(Partner)*
Kristy Desmarais *(Mng Dir-Employee Benefits Grp)*
Carrie Farnum *(Sr Dir-Bus Dev Employee Benefits Grp)*

Subsidiary (Domestic):

Construction Risk Partners LLC (2)
1250 Route 28 Ste 201, Branchburg, NJ 08876
Tel.: (908) 566-1010
Web Site:
https://www.constructionriskpartners.com
Sales Range: $10-24.9 Million
Property Insurance Services
N.A.I.C.S.: 524126
Al Marquis *(Partner)*
Pete Forenza *(Partner)*
Rob Pitts *(Partner)*
Bill Linney *(Partner)*
Rob Rapp *(Partner)*
Fred Nicholson *(Partner)*
Joe Kent *(Partner)*
Frank Mason *(Partner)*
Bill Harrison *(Partner)*
Frank Baxter *(Dir)*
Andy Obrien *(Partner)*
Dave Glasser *(Partner)*
Joe Charczenko *(Partner)*
Mary Bishop *(Assoc Partner)*
Sarah Shepard McGuinness *(Partner)*

Insgroup, Inc. (2)
5151 San Felipe St Ste 2400, Houston, TX 77056
Tel.: (713) 541-7272
Web Site: https://www.insgroup.net
Emp.: 200
Insurance Advisory Services
N.A.I.C.S.: 524210
Andrew Bean *(Partner)*
Jay Gerstenhaber *(Partner)*
Brian J. Kapiloff *(Reg Pres)*
Greg Scheinman *(Partner)*
J. Mace Meeks *(Mng Partner)*
Ken Collier *(Mng Dir-Private Client)*
Philip B. Wise *(Mng Partner-Property & Casualty)*
Tommy Harris *(Mng Partner-Employee Benefits)*
Jill King *(Dir-Client Experience Claims & Risk Mgmt)*
Jenifer Moss *(Dir-Private Risk)*
Stacy Figg *(Dir-HR)*
Ryan Shinkle *(Mng Dir)*
Adeel Rashid *(Dir-Acctg)*
Kyle Lanigan *(Dir-Client Experience Comml Brokerage)*
Peter Schidlowski *(Mgr-Partnership)*
Jacob Crawford *(Dir-Bus Dev Property & Casualty)*
Bill Bray *(Dir-Bus Dev Employee Benefits)*
Butch Novy *(Partner)*

Subsidiary (Domestic):

The Fawcett Group, Inc. (3)
5625 Cypress Creek Pkwy Ste 400, Houston, TX 77069
Tel.: (281) 587-8167
Web Site: http://www.thefawcettgroup.com
General Insurance Management Services
N.A.I.C.S.: 524298
Jan Fawcett-Heilman *(Pres)*

Subsidiary (Domestic):

Russ Blakely & Associates, LLC (2)
246 E 11th St Ste 302, Chattanooga, TN 37402
Tel.: (423) 266-8306
Web Site: http://www.rbabenefits.com

Advisory Services
N.A.I.C.S.: 541618

Southern Protective Group, LLC (2)
4595 Towne Lk Pkwy Ste 300-210, Woodstock, GA 30189-5518
Tel.: (770) 591-6353
Web Site:
http://www.southernprotectivegroup.com
Insurance Agencies & Brokerages
N.A.I.C.S.: 524210
Gregg Schieffelbein *(Pres)*

Trinity Benefit Advisors, Inc. (2)
4823 Old Kingston Pike Ste 205, Knoxville, TN 37919
Tel.: (865) 531-9898
Web Site: http://www.trinityben.com
Insurance Advisory Services
N.A.I.C.S.: 524210
Drew Mann *(Mng Partner)*
Chris Poynter *(Mng Partner)*
Katie Burkhardt *(Mgr-Client)*
Robert Peace *(Partner)*
Sandy Wright *(Sr Mgr-Client)*
Rick Metzelder *(Partner)*
Stephanie Hall *(Assoc Dir-Benefit Compliance)*

Baldwin Risk Partner's LLC (1)
4211 W Boy Scout Blvd Ste 800, Tampa, FL 33607-5757
Business Insurance Services
N.A.I.C.S.: 541618
Trevor L. Baldwin *(CEO)*
Brian Kapiloff *(Reg Pres)*
David Robinson *(Reg Pres)*
David Schaefer *(Reg Pres)*
Joe Finney *(Reg Pres)*
Kris Allison *(Reg Pres)*
Michael Robinson *(Reg Pres)*
Ryan Shinkle *(Pres)*

Guided Insurance Solutions, LLC (1)
4211 W Boy Scout Blvd Ste 800, Tampa, FL 33607
Tel.: (813) 782-1777
Web Site: http://www.guidedsolutions.com
Insurance Agency Services
N.A.I.C.S.: 524210

Laureate Insurance Partners, LLC (1)
13630 Sachs Ave Ste 100, Orlando, FL 32827-7698
Tel.: (407) 675-3880
Web Site:
https://www.laureateinsurance.com
Insurance Claims Services
N.A.I.C.S.: 524291

RogersGray Inc. (1)
434 Route 104, South Dennis, MA 02660
Tel.: (508) 398-7980
Web Site: http://www.rogersgray.com
Claim Adjusting Services
N.A.I.C.S.: 524291
Lynn Mason-Small *(Sr VP)*
David T. Robinson *(Pres & CEO)*
Erin Viehl *(Sr VP-HR)*
Jim Lopes *(CFO & Sr VP)*
Allison McEachern *(Sr VP & Dir-HR)*
Peter Cullivan *(CIO)*
Erin Schaaf *(COO)*
John Gaynier *(Partner/Exec VP-Kingston)*
Michael C. Robinson Jr. *(Chm)*

The Villages Insurance Partners, LLC (1)
2619 W Torch Lk Dr, The Villages, FL 32163
Tel.: (352) 751-6622
Web Site:
https://www.thevillagesinsurance.com
Property Insurance Services
N.A.I.C.S.: 524126
Kelly Burrows *(Sr Mgr-Comml & Acct)*

Westwood Insurance Agency, Inc. (1)
Web Site:
https://www.westwoodinsurance.com
Sales Range: $50-74.9 Million
Emp.: 70
General Insurance Services
N.A.I.C.S.: 524210
Alan Umaly *(Pres)*
Tom Kriby *(VP-Client Dev & Partnerships)*
Ben Sokoll *(VP-Customer Support)*

THE BANCORP, INC.
409 Silverside Rd Ste 105, Wilmington, DE 19809
Tel.: (302) 385-5000   DE
Web Site:
https://www.thebancorp.com
TBBK—(NASDAQ)
Rev.: $413,978,000
Assets: $7,903,000,000
Liabilities: $7,208,969,000
Net Worth: $694,031,000
Earnings: $130,213,000
Emp.: 717
Fiscal Year-end: 12/31/22
Offices of Bank Holding Companies
N.A.I.C.S.: 551111
Damian M. Kozlowski *(Pres & CEO)*
Paul Frenkiel *(CFO, Sec & Exec VP-Strategy)*
Thomas G. Pareigat *(Gen Counsel & Exec VP)*
Jeff Nager *(Exec VP & Head-Comml Lending)*
Mark Leo Connolly *(Exec VP & Head-Credit Markets)*
John N. Leto *(Exec VP & Head-Institutional Banking)*
Jennifer F. Terry *(Chief HR Officer & Exec VP)*
Erika Caesar *(Mng Dir, Chief Diversity Officer & Asst Gen Counsel)*
Gregor J. Garry *(COO & Exec VP)*
Ryan Harris *(Exec VP & Head-Fintech Solutions)*
Maria Wainwright *(CMO & Exec VP)*
Matt Wallace *(CIO & Exec VP)*
Rachel Weiss *(VP & Comm Mgr)*
Olek DeRowe *(Exec VP)*

Subsidiaries:

The Bancorp Bank (1)
409 Silverside Rd Ste 105, Wilmington, DE 19809
Tel.: (302) 385-5000
Web Site: http://www.thebancorp.com
Retail & Commercial Banking
N.A.I.C.S.: 522110
Damian M. Kozlowski *(Pres)*

THE BANK OF NEW YORK MELLON CORPORATION
240 Greenwich St, New York, NY 10286
Tel.: (212) 495-1784   NY
Web Site: https://www.bny.com
Year Founded: 1784
BK—(NYSE)
Rev.: $17,502,000,000
Assets: $409,953,000,000
Liabilities: $369,029,000,000
Net Worth: $40,924,000,000
Earnings: $3,051,000,000
Emp.: 53,400
Fiscal Year-end: 12/31/23
Financial Investment Services
N.A.I.C.S.: 551111
Jane Kevin McCarthy *(Gen Counsel & Sr Exec VP)*
Hani A. Kablawi *(Chm-Intl)*
Senthil Kumar *(Chief Risk Officer & Sr Exec VP)*
Robin A. Vince *(Pres & CEO)*
Alejandro Perez *(Chief Admin Officer)*
Leigh-Ann Russell *(CIO & Head-Engrg-Global)*
Dermot McDonogh *(CFO)*
James T. Crowley *(Head-BNY Pershing)*
Shannon Hobbs *(Chief People Officer)*
Jose Minaya *(Head-BNY Investments & Wealth)*
Emily Portney *(Head-Asset Servicing)*
Cathinka Wahlstrom *(Chief Comml Officer)*

Subsidiaries:

Alcentra Limited (1)

160 Queen Victoria Street, London, EC4V 4LA, United Kingdom
Tel.: (44) 2071636000
Web Site: https://www.alcentra.com
Asset Management Services
N.A.I.C.S.: 523940
Greg Brisk *(Chm)*
Chris Barris *(CIO-Liquid Credit-Acting)*
Vinay Patel *(Head-Fin)*
Brandon Chao *(Mng Dir & Portfolio Mgr)*
Hiram Hamilton *(Co-Head-Structured Credit & Portfolio Mgr)*
Eric Larsson *(Mng Dir & Portfolio Mgr-Special Situations)*
Laurence Raven *(Mng Dir & Portfolio Mgr-Special Situations Funds)*
Adriana Rodgers *(VP)*
Alan Dixon *(VP)*
Alex Naylor *(VP)*
Alex Walker *(Mng Dir)*
Amelia Carleton *(VP)*
Amy Lattimore *(Mng Dir)*
Ashley Maguire *(VP)*
Bastian Stange *(VP)*
Cameron McKenzie *(VP)*
Carson Lau *(VP)*
Chris Schubert *(VP)*
Claire Herrenschmidt *(VP)*
Daire Wheeler *(Mng Dir)*
Emma Blakey *(Mng Dir)*
Felicity Rivett-Carnac *(Mng Dir)*
Florence Manley *(VP)*
Franky Lee *(Mng Dir)*
Frederic Mereau *(Mng Dir)*
Hasnain Haideri *(VP)*
Heather Smilgys *(VP)*
Howard Sharp *(Mng Dir)*
Jay Bains *(VP)*
Jennifer Laurie *(VP)*
Joanna Layton *(Mng Dir)*
Julia Leung *(VP)*
Ke Xin Chen *(VP)*
Michael McClean *(VP)*
Natalie Rocks *(Mng Dir)*
Naveed Aslam *(VP)*
Nicole Corazza *(VP)*
Paul Hollis *(VP)*
Paul Ramier *(VP)*
Premil Bhadeshia *(VP)*
Richard Carmoody *(VP)*
Richard Pope *(VP)*
Roshani Shah *(VP)*
Rupert McNeil *(VP)*
Ruth Davis *(Mng Dir)*
Samantha Kerr *(VP)*
Simon Perry *(Mng Dir)*
Stuart Medlen *(Mng Dir)*
Tapiwa Mashingaidze *(VP)*
William Moorhouse *(VP)*

BNY Fund Services (Ireland) Ltd. (1)
One Dockland Central Guild Street, Dublin, Ireland
Tel.: (353) 19008500
Web Site: http://www.bnymellon.com
Sales Range: $200-249.9 Million
Emp.: 600
Banking Services
N.A.I.C.S.: 522110
Michael Buttanshaw *(Mng Dir)*

BNY International Financing Corporation (1)
1 Wall St 9th Fl, New York, NY 10286
Tel.: (212) 495-1784
Banking & Financial Services
N.A.I.C.S.: 522299

BNY Mellon (Poland) sp. z o.o. (1)
Ul Swobodna 3, 50-088, Wroclaw, Poland
Tel.: (48) 713798200
Web Site: https://www.bnymellon.com
Commercial Banking Services
N.A.I.C.S.: 522110

BNY Mellon ARX Investimentos Ltda. (1)
Av Borges de Medeiros 633/4th Floor Leblon, 22430-041, Rio de Janeiro, Brazil
Tel.: (55) 2132652000
Web Site: http://www.bnymellonarx.com.br
Commercial Banking Services
N.A.I.C.S.: 522110

BNY Mellon Asset Management Japan Limited (1)
Marunouchi Trust Tower Main 1-8-3, Marunouchi Chiyoda-ku, Tokyo, 100-0005, Japan

Tel.: (81) 3 6756 4600
Web Site: http://www.bnymellon.com
Commercial Banking Services
N.A.I.C.S.: 522110

BNY Mellon Asset Servicing B.V. (1)
WTC building Podium office B Tower
Strawinskylaan 337, Amsterdam, 1077,
Netherlands (100%)
Tel.: (31) 202035600
Web Site: http://www.bny.com
Sales Range: $25-49.9 Million
Emp.: 56
Investment Processing Services
N.A.I.C.S.: 522320

**BNY Mellon Capital Markets,
LLC** (1)
1 Wall St 18th Fl, New York, NY 10286
Tel.: (212) 635-1027
Web Site: http://www.bankofny.com
Sales Range: $200-249.9 Million
Emp.: 150
Investment Banking
N.A.I.C.S.: 523150
Robert Chiuch (Mng Dir & Head-Equity Fin-
Global)

**BNY Mellon Fund Management (Lux-
embourg) SA** (1)
2-4 rue Eugene Ruppert Vertigo Building-
Polaris, L-2453, Luxembourg, Luxembourg
Tel.: (352) 245241
Financial Investment Services
N.A.I.C.S.: 523999
Ben Goldsbrough (Officer-Conducting)

**BNY Mellon Fund Managers
Limited** (1)
BNY Mellon Centre 160 Queen Victoria
Street, London, EC4V 4LA, United Kingdom
Tel.: (44) 2033224806
Capital Market Investment Services
N.A.I.C.S.: 523940
Helena Louise Morrissey (CEO)

**BNY Mellon International Asset Man-
agement Group Limited** (1)
B N Y Mellon House Ingrave Rd, Brent-
wood, CM15 8TG, Essex, United Kingdom
Tel.: (44) 2071635566
Web Site: http://www.bnymellon.com
Financial Services
N.A.I.C.S.: 522320

**BNY Mellon International Operations
(India) Private Limited** (1)
CommerZone Survey Nos 144 and 145 Yer-
wada Samrat Ashok Path, Off Airport Road,
Pune, 411 006, India
Tel.: (91) 2030125100
Web Site: https://www.bnymellon.com
Emp.: 7,000
Banking & Investment Services
N.A.I.C.S.: 523940

**BNY Mellon Investment Management
EMEA Limited** (1)
BNY Mellon Centre 160 Queen Victoria
Street, London, EC4V 4LA, United Kingdom
Tel.: (44) 20 7163 5566
Web Site: http://www.mellon.com
Financial Assets Management Services
N.A.I.C.S.: 523999

**BNY Mellon Investment Servicing (In-
ternational) Limited** (1)
Riverside Two Sir John Rogersons Quay,
Grand Canal Dock, Dublin, Ireland (100%)
Tel.: (353) 19003500
Web Site: http://www.bnymellon.com
Sales Range: $125-149.9 Million
Emp.: 30
Financial Processing, Trust & Custodial
Services
N.A.I.C.S.: 523991

**BNY Mellon Investment Servicing
(US) Inc.** (1)
301 Bellevue Pkwy, Wilmington, DE
19809-3701 (100%)
Tel.: (302) 791-1700
Web Site: http://www.bnymellon.com
Sales Range: $900-999.9 Million
Emp.: 4,450
Financial Processing & Information Technol-
ogy Services
N.A.I.C.S.: 522320

**BNY Mellon Securities Services (Ire-
land) Limited** (1)

Guild House Guild Street IFSC, Dublin,
Ireland
Tel.: (353) 16428225
Securities Brokerage Services
N.A.I.C.S.: 523150

BNY Mellon Singapore (1)
One Temasek Avenue 02-01 Millenia Tower,
Singapore, 039192, Singapore (100%)
Tel.: (65) 64320222
Web Site: http://www.bnymellon.com
Sales Range: $10-24.9 Million
Emp.: 400
Commericial Banking
N.A.I.C.S.: 522110
David Cruikshank (Chm-Asia Pacific & Exec
VP)

**BNY Mellon Trust Company of
Illinois** (1)
2 N La Salle St Ste 700, Chicago, IL 60602
Tel.: (312) 827-8500
Banking & Investment Services
N.A.I.C.S.: 523991

BNY Mellon Trust of Delaware (1)
301 Bellevue Pkwy Ste 19A-0307, Wilming-
ton, DE 19809
Tel.: (302) 791-3600
Web Site: http://www.bnymellon.com
Commericial Banking
N.A.I.C.S.: 522110

**BNY Mellon Wealth
Management** (1)
1 N Franklin St Ste 900, Chicago, IL 60606-
3461
Tel.: (312) 647-2484
Web Site: http://www.bnymellonwealth.com
Emp.: 30
Wealth Management Services
N.A.I.C.S.: 523940
Lawrence Hughes (Executives)

Branch (Domestic):

**BNY Mellon Wealth Management -
Menlo Park** (2)
3000 Sand Hill Rd Ste 3-290, Menlo Park,
CA 94025
Tel.: (650) 233-1200
Web Site: http://www.bnymellonwealth.com
Wealth Management Services
N.A.I.C.S.: 523940
Eunice Kim (Pres)

Subsidiary (Domestic):

Lifespan Brands, LLC (2)
1200 Thorndale Ave, Elk Grove Village, IL
60007
Web Site: http://www.lifespanbrandsco.com
Motion Lamps Mfr
N.A.I.C.S.: 335131
Joseph Kostelc (CFO)
Patrick McCartin (VP-Sls)
Jim Thiele (Controller)
Sharon Carl (Dir-Pur)
Tami Craig (Mgr-Social Media Mktg)
David Seguin (Sls Mgr-Natl)

**BNY Mellon, National
Association** (1)
1 Mellon Ctr 500 Grant St 47th Fl, Pitts-
burgh, PA 15258-0001
Tel.: (412) 234-5000
Capital Market Investment Services
N.A.I.C.S.: 523940
Mike Keslar (Pres)
Eric Boughner (Chm)

BNY Mellon-Hong Kong (1)
Level 24 3 Pacific Place, 1 Queen's Road
East, Hong Kong, China (Hong
Kong) (100%)
Tel.: (852) 28409888
Web Site: http://www.bnymellon.com
Sales Range: $25-49.9 Million
Emp.: 100
Commercial Bank
N.A.I.C.S.: 522110

CIBC Mellon (1)
320 Bay Street, Toronto, M5H 4A6, ON,
Canada (50%)
Tel.: (416) 643-5000
Web Site: http://www.cibcmellon.com
Emp.: 1,000
Investment Processing Services
N.A.I.C.S.: 523991

Kelly Hastings (Chief Risk Officer)
Rob Ferguson (Chief Capital Markets Offi-
cer)
Shane Kuros (Chief Bus Dev & Product Of-
ficer)
Richard Anton (COO & Sr VP)
Steven R. Wolff (CEO)
Bill Graves (CTO & Chief Data Officer)
Karen Rowe (CFO)
Paul Cunliffe (CMO & Chief Comm Officer)
Tedford Mason (Chief Legal Officer)
Ash Tahbazian (Chief Relationship & Rev-
enue Officer)
Maple Tam (Chief HR Officer)
Catherine Thrasher (VP-Strategic Client So-
lutions)
Mary Ann MacKenzie (VP-Relationship
Mgmt)
Mike Garneau (VP-Relationship Mgmt-
Eastern Canada)
David Planden (VP-Relationship Mgmt-
Western Canada)
Ronald C. Landry (Head-Product Mgmt &
ETF Svcs)
Michelle Spencer (Dir-BDRM Ops)
Alistair Almeida (Exec Dir-Relationship Dev)
Gordon Kosokowsky (Exec Dir-Relationship
Dev)
Lisa Tomada (VP-Global Securities Lend-
ing)
Sarah Markus (Sec)
Brent Merriman (Asst VP-Corp Comm &
Mktg)

**Cutwater Asset Management
Corp.** (1)
113 King St, Armonk, NY 10504
Tel.: (914) 273-4545
Web Site: http://www.cutwater.com
Sales Range: $125-149.9 Million
Emp.: 400
Investment Management Service
N.A.I.C.S.: 523940

DPM Mellon LLC (1)
400 Atrium Dr, Somerset, NJ 08873
Tel.: (732) 667-1122
Financial Management Services
N.A.I.C.S.: 523999

EACM Advisors LLC (1)
200 Connecticut Ave 6th Fl, Norwalk, CT
06854
Tel.: (203) 854-7000
Web Site: http://www.eacm.com
Sales Range: $75-99.9 Million
Emp.: 43
Investment Advisory Services
N.A.I.C.S.: 523940
Keith L. Stransky (Chief Investment Officer-
Traditional & Sr Portfolio Mgr)

Eagles Investment Systems LLC (1)
65 LaSalle Rd Ste 305, West Hartford, CT
06107
Tel.: (860) 561-4602
Web Site: http://www.eagleinvsys.com
Sales Range: $10-24.9 Million
Emp.: 20
Financial Software Developer & Mfr
N.A.I.C.S.: 513210
Steve Taylor (CTO)

**Insight Investment Funds Manage-
ment Limited** (1)
33 Old Broad St Tower Hill, London, EC2N
1HZ, United Kingdom
Tel.: (44) 8457772233
Web Site: http://www.bnymellon.com
Miscellaneous Financial Investment Activities
N.A.I.C.S.: 523999

**Insight Investment Management (Eu-
rope) Limited** (1)
Riverside 2 Sir John Rogerson's Quay,
Dublin, D02 KV60, Ireland
Tel.: (353) 19003500
Banking & Investment Services
N.A.I.C.S.: 523940

**Insight Investment Management
(Global) Limited** (1)
160 Queen Victoria Street, London, EC4V
4LA, United Kingdom
Tel.: (44) 207 163 4000
Web Site:
  https://www.insightinvestment.com
Commercial Banking Services

N.A.I.C.S.: 522110
Abdallah Habib Nauphal (CEO)
Bruce Murphy (Dir-Australia & New Zea-
land)

**Insight Investment Management
Limited** (1)
160 Queen Victoria Street, London, EC4V
4LA, United Kingdom
Tel.: (44) 2071634000
Web Site: http://www.insightinvestment.com
Investment Management Service
N.A.I.C.S.: 523999

Lockwood Advisors, Inc. (1)
760 Moore Rd, King of Prussia, PA 19406
Web Site: http://www.lockwoodadvisors.com
Commercial Banking Services
N.A.I.C.S.: 522110

Mellon Bank, N.A. (1)
500 Grant St, Pittsburgh, PA 15258-0001
Tel.: (412) 234-5530
Web Site: http://www.bnymellon.com
Sales Range: $100-124.9 Million
National Commercial Banks
N.A.I.C.S.: 522110

Mellon Funding Corporation (1)
500 Grant St One Mellon Ctr, Pittsburgh,
PA 15258
Tel.: (412) 234-5000
Web Site: http://www.bnymellon.com
Banking Services
N.A.I.C.S.: 522110

Mellon Investments Corporation (1)
50 Fremont St Ste 3900, San Francisco,
CA 94105
Tel.: (415) 546-6056
Web Site: http://www.mellon.com
Investment Management Service
N.A.I.C.S.: 523940
Linda Lillard (Chief Transformation Officer)
Stephanie Pierce (CEO-ETF, Index & Cash
Investment Strategies)
David Leduc (Co-CIO & Head-Fixed In-
come)
Jennifer Cassedy (Chief Compliance Offi-
cer)
Gerald Cosgrove (Head-Consultant Rels &
US Institutional Sls)
Amy Koch Flynn (Head-Trading)
Michael Germano (COO & CEO-Active
Mgmt)
Partick Lyn (Head-Product & Relationship
Mgmt)
George Passaro (Head-Bus Strategy)
Dimitri Curtil (Co-CIO & Head-Multi-Asset)
Marissa Murray (CMO)
Martin Stephan (Head-Quantitative Res)
Deepak Agrawal (Head-Fixed Income
Quantitative Res)
John C. Bailer (Sr Portfolio Mgr)
Joseph M. Corrado (Sr Portfolio Mgr)
Brian Ferguson (Sr Portfolio Mgr)
Peter D. Goslin (Sr Portfolio Mgr)
Patrick Kent (Sr Portfolio Mgr)
James A. Lydotes (Sr Portfolio Mgr)
Julianne McHugh (Sr Portfolio Mgr)
Leigh N. Todd (Sr Portfolio Mgr)
Eric Baumhoff (Head-Stable Value)
Robert M. Bayston (Head-Rates & Securi-
tized)
Federico Garcia Zamora (Head-Emerging
Markets Debt)
Matt Fontaine (Head-Global Credit)
Paul L. Benson (Head-Fixed Income Effi-
cient Beta)
Brendan J. Murphy (Head-Global & Multi-
Sector Fixed Income)
Daniel A. Rabasco (Head-Municipal Bonds)
Roberto M. Croce (Head-Risk Parity & Liq-
uid Alts)
Vassilis Dagioglu (Head-Asset Allocation
Portfolio Mgmt)
Stephanie Hill (Head-Index)
Karen Fernandes (Mgr-Consultant Rels)
Kristen A. Fontaine (Mgr-Consultant Rels)
Michael R. Houle (Head-Relationship Mgmt)
John R. Porter III (Co-CIO & Head-Equity)

**Newton Capital Management
Limited** (1)
160 Queen Victoria Street, London, EC4V
4LA, United Kingdom
Tel.: (44) 2071635566
Web Site: http://www.newton.co.uk
Sales Range: $1-4.9 Billion
Emp.: 319
Financial Investment Services

The Bank of New York Mellon
Corporation—(Continued)

N.A.I.C.S.: 523999

**Pareto Investment Management
Limited** (1)
160 Queen Victoria St, London, EC4V 4LA,
United Kingdom
Tel.: (44) 02071631000
Web Site: http://www.paretopartners.com
Sales Range: $150-199.9 Million
Emp.: 35
Investment & Risk Management Services
N.A.I.C.S.: 523940

Pershing Group LLC (1)
1 Pershing Plz, Jersey City, NJ 07399
Tel.: (201) 413-2000
Web Site: http://www.pershing.com
Emp.: 2,800
Securities Brokerage Services
N.A.I.C.S.: 523150
Jim Crowley (CEO)
Emily Schlosser (COO)

Subsidiary (Domestic):

Pershing LLC (2)
1 Pershing Plz, Jersey City, NJ 07399
Tel.: (800) 445-4467
Web Site: http://www.pershing.com
Sales Range: $10-24.9 Million
Investment Management Firm Services
N.A.I.C.S.: 522320
James T. Crowley (Co-CEO)
David Hopkins (Mng Dir & Head-Institutional
Solutions)
Claire Santaniello (Mng Dir)
Joan Schwartz (Chief Legal Officer)
Maura Creekmore (Mng Dir)
Ramaswamy Nagappan (CIO)
Michael Row (Chief Relationship Officer)
Mark Swenarton (Mng Dir)
Geoffrey Towers (CEO)
Ben Harrison (Mng Dir & Head-Advisor So-
lutions)
Thomas Sholes (Mng Dir & Chief Strategy
Officer)
Tonia Bottoms (Mng Dir)
Jason Lofting (CFO)
Emily Schlosser (COO)
Margreet Van Dijk (Mng Dir & Sr Dir-HR)
James Kearney III (Chief Risk Officer-
Global)

Subsidiary (Domestic):

Albridge Solutions, Inc. (3)
1009 Lenox Dr Bldg 4, Lawrenceville, NJ
08648
Tel.: (609) 620-5800
Web Site: http://www.albridge.com
Portfolio Accounting & Enterprise Wealth
Management Services
N.A.I.C.S.: 921130
Natasha Horn (Dir)
Peter Antonucci (Mng Dir)
Andre Carrier (Dir)
Trevor Davies (Dir)
Jennifer Feinerman (Dir)
Sravan Nerella (Dir)
Charles Granito Jr. (CEO & Mng Dir)

Lockwood Financial Group, Inc. (3)
760 Moore Rd, King of Prussia, PA 19406
Tel.: (484) 801-8048
Web Site: http://www.lockwoodadvisors.com
Sales Range: $150-199.9 Million
Emp.: 100
Security Brokers & Dealers
N.A.I.C.S.: 523910

Subsidiary (Non-US):

Pershing Limited (3)
Royal Liver Building Pier Head, Liverpool,
L3 1LL, United Kingdom
Tel.: (44) 20 7163 8000
Web Site: http://www.pershing.com
Execution, Clearing, Settlement & Custody
Services for Investment Management Firms
N.A.I.C.S.: 522320
Geoff Towers (CEO)
Elizabeth Canning (COO)
Steve Chaney (Mng Dir & Head-Client Svc
Delivery)
Niall Harrington (Dir & Country Mgr-Ireland)
Maarten Heukshorst (Chief Comml Officer)
Peter Norman (Mng Dir-Client Svc Delivery)
Alpesh Patel (CIO)
Lee Dobson (CFO)

**Promontory Interfinancial Network,
LLC** (1)
1300 N 17th St Ste 1800, Arlington, VA
22209
Tel.: (703) 292-3400
Web Site: https://www.intrafi.com
Emp.: 178
Commercial Banking Services
N.A.I.C.S.: 522110
Art Certosimo (Vice Chm)
Mark P. Jacobsen (Co-Founder & CEO)
Eugene A. Ludwig (Co-Founder & Chm)
Alan S. Blinder (Co-Founder & Vice Chm)
Dan Henson (Co-Chm)
Rob Blackwell (Chief Content Officer &
Head-External Affairs)

**Standish Mellon Asset Management
Company LLC** (1)
1 Boston Pl, Boston, MA 02108
Tel.: (617) 248-6000
Web Site: http://www.standishmellon.com
Sales Range: $25-49.9 Million
Emp.: 150
Asset Management & Investment Services
N.A.I.C.S.: 523940

The Bank of New York (1)
23rd Floor Young-Poong Bldg 33 Seolin-
Dong Chongro-ku, PO Box 4906, Seoul,
110-752, Korea (South) (100%)
Tel.: (82) 239900016
Web Site: http://www.bankofnymellon.com
Sales Range: $10-24.9 Million
Emp.: 60
Commercial Bank
N.A.I.C.S.: 522110

The Bank of New York (1)
Rue Montoyer 46, Brussels, 1000,
Belgium (100%)
Tel.: (32) 25458111
Web Site: http://www.bnymellon.com
Sales Range: $450-499.9 Million
Emp.: 950
Commercial Bank
N.A.I.C.S.: 522110

The Bank of New York (1)
1 Canada Sq, London, E14 5AL, United
Kingdom (100%)
Tel.: (44) 2075701784
Web Site: http://www.bankofnewyork.com
Sales Range: $900-999.9 Million
Emp.: 3,000
Commercial Bank
N.A.I.C.S.: 522110

**The Bank of New York Capital Mar-
kets, Limited** (1)
1 Canada Square, London, E14 5AL,
United Kingdom (100%)
Tel.: (44) 2079646274
Web Site: http://www.bankofnewyork.com
Sales Range: $650-699.9 Million
Investment Counseling
N.A.I.C.S.: 523940

**The Bank of New York Mellon
SA/NV** (1)
46 Rue Montoyerstraat, 1000, Brussels,
Belgium
Tel.: (32) 2 545 8111
Web Site: http://www.bnymellon.com
Sales Range: $200-249.9 Million
Emp.: 700
Commercial Banking Services
N.A.I.C.S.: 522110

**The Bank of New York Mellon Trust
Company, N.A.** (1)
700 S Flower St Ste 500, Los Angeles, CA
90017-4100
Tel.: (213) 630-6400
Web Site: http://www.bnymellon.com
Sales Range: $250-299.9 Million
Emp.: 200
Investment Management & Banking Ser-
vices
N.A.I.C.S.: 523150

The Dreyfus Corporation (1)
200 Park Ave, New York, NY 10166
Tel.: (212) 922-7045
Web Site: http://www.dreyfus.com
Sales Range: $900-999.9 Million
Emp.: 2,000
Mutual Funds, Investment & Management
N.A.I.C.S.: 523910

Mark Santero (CEO)

Walter Scott & Partners Limited (1)
One Charlotte Square, Edinburgh, EH2
4DR, Midlothian, United Kingdom
Tel.: (44) 131 225 1357
Web Site: https://www.walterscott.com
Emp.: 100
Asset Management Services
N.A.I.C.S.: 541618
Jane Henderson (Mng Dir)
Roy Leckie (Dir-Investment & Client Svcs)
Charlie Macquaker (Dir-Investment)
Jimmy Smith (Dir-Investment Ops)
Alan Edington (Co-Head-Res)
Alex Torrens (Co-Head-Res)
Des Armstrong (Mgr-Investment)
Alistair Ceurvorst (Mgr-Investment)
Yuanli Chen (Mgr-Investment)
Fraser Fox (Mgr-Investment)
Matthew Gerlach (Mgr-Investment)
Alan Lander (Mgr-Investment)
Paul Loudon (Mgr-Investment)
Fiona MacRae (Mgr-Investment)
Francis Sempill (Head-Client Svc)
Tom Duff (Head-Consultants & Distr Part-
ners)
Justin Atkinson (Mgr-Client Investment)
Kiersten Christensen (Mgr-Client Invest-
ment)
George Dent (Mgr-Client Investment)
Margaret Foley (Mgr-Client Investment)
Murdo Maclean (Mgr-Client Investment)
Dennis Wyles (Mgr-Client Investment)

THE BEACHBODY COMPANY,
INC.
400 Continental Blvd Ste 400, El Se-
gundo, CA 90245
Tel.: (310) 883-9003   DE
Web Site:
https://www.thebeachbodycom
pany.com
Year Founded: 2020
BODI—(NYSE)
Rev.: $692,199,000
Assets: $443,395,000
Liabilities: $231,853,000
Net Worth: $211,542,000
Earnings: ($194,192,000)
Emp.: 737
Fiscal Year-end: 12/31/22
Miscellaneous Financial Investment
Activities
N.A.I.C.S.: 523999
Kathy P. Vrabeck (COO)
Idan Shani (CTO)
Carl Daikeler (CEO)
Mark Goldston (Chm)
Bradley Ramberg (CFO)

THE BEAUTY HEALTH COM-
PANY
2165 Spring St, Long Beach, CA
90806   DE
Web Site:
https://www.beautyhealth.com
Year Founded: 2020
SKIN—(NASDAQ)
Rev.: $365,876,000
Assets: $1,008,907,000
Liabilities: $837,431,000
Net Worth: $171,476,000
Earnings: $44,384,000
Emp.: 1,034
Fiscal Year-end: 12/31/22
Holding Company; Beauty Products
Mfr
N.A.I.C.S.: 551112
Daniel Watson (Chief Revenue Offi-
cer)
Brenton L. Saunders (Chm)
Michael P. Monahan (CFO)
Mingo Ku (Pres-APAC)
Jon Arnold (Pres-Europe, Middle East
& Africa)
Sheri Lewis (Chief Supply Chain Offi-
cer & Chief Ops Officer)
Celeste Ortiz (Chief HR Officer)
Paul Bokota (Gen Counsel & VP)
Marla Malcolm Beck (Pres & CEO)

Subsidiaries:

Edge Systems Intermediate, LLC (1)
2165 E Spring St, Long Beach, CA 92708
Web Site: https://hydrafacial.com
Skin Care Services
N.A.I.C.S.: 812112

Edge Systems, LLC (1)
2277 Redondo Ave, Long Beach, CA 90755
Tel.: (562) 597-0102
Web Site: http://www.hydrafacial.com
Medical And Hospital Equipment, Nsk
N.A.I.C.S.: 423450
Bill Cohen (Sec & VP)

HydraFacial UK Limited (1)
Unit 40 Sir Frank Whittle Business Centre
Great Central Way, Butlers Leap, Rugby,
CV21 3XH, United Kingdom
Tel.: (44) 1788572007
Web Site: https://hydrafacial.co.uk
Skin Care Services
N.A.I.C.S.: 812112

**The HydraFacial Company Iberia,
S.L.U.** (1)
Calle Claudio Coello 75 1st Floor A, 28001,
Madrid, Spain
Tel.: (34) 910579908
Web Site: https://www.hydrafacial.es
Skin Care Services
N.A.I.C.S.: 812112

**The HydraFacial Company Japan
K.K.** (1)
Vort Ginza Miyuki St 6F 6-8-19 Ginza,
Chuo-ku, Tokyo, 104-0061, Japan
Tel.: (81) 362806453
Web Site: https://hydrafacial.co.jp
Skin Care Services
N.A.I.C.S.: 812112

**The HydraFacial Company MX, S. de
R.L. de C.V.** (1)
Calle 14 Entre Ruiz y Obregon 318 Zona
Centro, 22800, Ensenada, Baja California,
Mexico
Tel.: (52) 16461205855
Web Site: https://hydrafacial.com.mx
Skin Care Services
N.A.I.C.S.: 812112

THE BETTER BEING CO.
222 Main St Ste 1600, Salt Lake City,
UT 84101
Tel.: (435) 655-6000   DE
Year Founded: 1993
BBCO—(NYSE)
Rev.: $319,310,000
Assets: $504,323,000
Liabilities: $464,779,000
Net Worth: $39,544,000
Earnings: ($32,651,000)
Emp.: 974
Fiscal Year-end: 09/30/20
Vitamin Product Mfr & Distr
N.A.I.C.S.: 325412
Monty Sharma (CEO)
Ankit Dhawan (CFO)
Bob Gandert (Chief Revenue Officer)
Peter Noverr (COO)
Jeff Burchfield (Chief Legal Officer &
Sec)
Brian L. Slobodow (CEO)

THE BOEING COMPANY
100 N Riverside, Chicago, IL 60606-
1596
Tel.: (425) 237-7389   DE
Web Site: https://www.boeing.com
Year Founded: 1916
BA—(NYSE)
Rev.: $77,794,000,000
Assets: $137,012,000,000
Liabilities: $154,240,000,000
Net Worth: ($17,228,000,000)
Earnings: ($2,222,000,000)
Emp.: 171,000
Fiscal Year-end: 12/31/23
Commercial & Military Aircraft, Mis-
siles, Space Exploration Equipment,

Defense Electronic Systems, Computer Services & Large-Scale Information Networks Developer
N.A.I.C.S.: 336412
Brett C. Gerry (Chief Legal Officer & Exec VP-Compliance-Global)
Stephanie Pope (CFO & VP)
Brendan Curran (VP-Comml Svcs-Global Svcs)
Susan Doniz (CIO & Sr VP-IT & Data Analytics)
William A. Ampofo II (VP-Supply Chain-Global Svcs)
William H. Osborne (Sr VP-Total Quality, Ops, and Security-Boeing Defense,Space)
Stephanie F. Pope (COO & Exec VP)
Susan Doniz (CIO, Chief Data Analytics Officer & Sr VP-IT & Data Analytics)
Michael P. Delaney (Chief Aerospace Safety Officer & Sr VP-Global Aerospace Safety)
Christopher Raymond (Chief Sustainability Officer & Exec VP)
Ziad S. Ojakli (Exec VP-Govt Ops)
Brian West (CFO & Exec VP-Finance)
Stephen E. Biegun (Sr VP-Global Public Policy)
Todd Citron (CTO)
Darrin A. Hostetler (Chief Compliance Officer & VP-Global Compliance)
Howard McKenzie (Exec VP-Engrg Test & Technology)
Brian Moran (Chief Sustainability Officer)
Robert Kelly Ortberg (Pres & CEO)

Subsidiaries:

Aurora Flight Sciences Corporation (1)
9950 Wakeman Dr, Manassas, VA 20110
Tel.: (703) 369-3633
Web Site: http://www.aurora.aero
Designs, Manufactures & Operates Unmanned Aerial Vehicles (UAVs) for Federal Agencies & Aerospace Contractors
N.A.I.C.S.: 336411
Tom Clancy (CTO)
John Tylko (Chief Innovation Officer)
Matthew G. Hutchison (Sr VP-Ops)
Fariba Hogge (CFO & VP-Fin)
Brian Yutko (Sr VP-Programs)
Blythe Jameson (VP-Comm & Mktg)
Jeanine Boyle (VP-HR)
Per Beith (Pres & CEO)

Boeing Aerospace Operations, Inc. (1)
2601 Liberty Pkwy, Midwest City, OK 73110-2856
Tel.: (210) 932-6990
Engineeering Services
N.A.I.C.S.: 541330

Boeing Capital Corporation (1)
500 Naches Ave SW 3rd Fl, Renton, WA 98057 (100%)
Tel.: (206) 655-2121
Web Site: http://www.boeing.com
Rev.: $436,000,000
Assets: $4,422,000,000
Liabilities: $3,925,000,000
Net Worth: $497,000,000
Earnings: $48,000,000
Emp.: 146
Fiscal Year-end: 12/31/2012
Financial Services
N.A.I.C.S.: 531110
Timothy Myers (Pres)

Boeing Capital Loan Corporation (1)
2215 Renaissance Dr, Las Vegas, NV 89119
Tel.: (702) 740-4244
Commercial & Personal Lending Services
N.A.I.C.S.: 522310

Boeing Commercial Airplane Group (1)
1901 Oakesvale Ave SW, Renton, WA 98055 (100%)

Tel.: (425) 237-2121
Sales Range: $300-349.9 Million
Commercial Airplane Mfr
N.A.I.C.S.: 336411
Kevin Schemm (VP & CFO)
Kevin G. McAllister (Pres)
Conrad Chun (VP-Comm)
Stan Deal (CEO)
Ihssane Mounir (Sr VP-Global Supply Chain)
Brad McMullen (Sr VP-Comml Sls & Mktg)

Unit (Domestic):

Boeing Commercial Airplane Group - Everett (2)
3003 W Casino Rd, Everett, WA 98204
Tel.: (425) 237-2019
Sales Range: $10-24.9 Million
Emp.: 10
Design & Production of 747 & 767 Aircraft
N.A.I.C.S.: 336411

Unit (Domestic):

The Boeing Co. - 777 Program (3)
3303 W Casino Rd, Everett, WA 98204
Tel.: (206) 655-2121
Design & Development of the 777 Jetliner
N.A.I.C.S.: 336411
Elizabeth Lund (VP & Gen Mgr)

Unit (Domestic):

Boeing Commercial Airplane Group - Seattle (2)
PO Box 3707, Seattle, WA 98124
Tel.: (206) 655-1131
Web Site: http://www.boeing.com
Sales Range: $300-349.9 Million
Design & Production of the 737 & 757 Aircraft
N.A.I.C.S.: 336411

Division (Domestic):

Boeing Commercial Aviation Services (2)
PO Box 3707, Seattle, WA 98124
Tel.: (206) 655-1131
Web Site: http://www.boeing.com
Aviation Support Services
N.A.I.C.S.: 488190

Subsidiary (Domestic):

Boeing Distribution, Inc. (3)
2750 Regent Blvd DFW Airport, Dallas, TX 75261-9048
Tel.: (972) 586-1982
Sales Range: $1-4.9 Billion
Emp.: 1,009
New Aviation Parts, Supply-Chain Management & Other Aerospace Aftermarket Related Services
N.A.I.C.S.: 336413

Subsidiary (Non-US):

Aviall Australia Pty. Ltd. (4)
Level 10 Exchange House 10 Bridge St, PO Box 771, Sydney, 2000, NSW, Australia
Tel.: (61) 290863300
Web Site: https://www.boeing.com.au
Sales Range: $10-24.9 Million
Emp.: 6
Commercial & General Aftermarket Aviation Parts Distr
N.A.I.C.S.: 336413

Aviall New Zealand (4)
Unit 2/17 Airpark Dr Airport Oaks, Auckland, 2022, New Zealand
Tel.: (64) 92750571
Aircraft Mfr
N.A.I.C.S.: 336411

Aviall PTE LTD (4)
331 North Bridge Road 06-06 Odeon Towers, Singapore, 188720, Singapore
Tel.: (65) 65425420
Emp.: 70
Aircraft Mfr
N.A.I.C.S.: 336411

Subsidiary (Domestic):

Boeing Training & Flight Services (3)
1301 SW 16th St, Renton, WA 98055
Tel.: (206) 662-4088

Web Site: http://www.boeing.com
Sales Range: $750-799.9 Million
Airline Training Services
N.A.I.C.S.: 611512

Jeppesen Sanderson, Inc. (3)
55 Inverness Dr E, Englewood, CO 80112
Tel.: (303) 799-9090
Web Site: http://www.jeppesen.com
Rev.: $235,000,000
Emp.: 1,300
General & Commercial Aviation Flight Information
N.A.I.C.S.: 611699

Subsidiary (Non-US):

Jeppesen (Canada) Ltd. (4)
999 De Maisonneuve W 9th Fl, Montreal, H3A 3L4, QC, Canada
Tel.: (514) 282-1800
Web Site: http://www.jeppesen.com
Sales Range: $25-49.9 Million
Emp.: 40
Aircraft Mfr
N.A.I.C.S.: 336411

Jeppesen Asia/Pacific Pte. Ltd. (4)
331 North Bridge Road Odeon Towers No 06-01, Singapore, 118720, Singapore
Tel.: (65) 63091500
Web Site: http://ww1.jeppesen.com
Emp.: 30
Transportation Information Services
N.A.I.C.S.: 519290

Subsidiary (Domestic):

Jeppesen DataPlan, Inc. (4)
225 W Santa Clara St Ste 1600, San Jose, CA 95113
Tel.: (408) 963-2000
Web Site: http://ww1.jeppesen.com
Aircraft Mfr
N.A.I.C.S.: 336411

Subsidiary (Non-US):

Jeppesen GmbH (4)
Frankfurter Strasse 233, 63263, Neu-Isenburg, Germany
Tel.: (49) 61025070
Web Site: http://www.jeppesen.com
Sales Range: $25-49.9 Million
Emp.: 400
Data Collection & Analysis, Chart Production & Distribution
N.A.I.C.S.: 518210

Jeppesen Poland Spolka z ogranic-zona odpowiedzialnoscia (4)
Arkonska 6 Budynek A5, 80-387, Gdansk, Poland
Tel.: (48) 587606100
Web Site: http://www.jeppesen.com
Sales Range: $25-49.9 Million
Emp.: 170
Aircraft Mfr
N.A.I.C.S.: 336411
Rafal Stepnowski (Mng Dir)

Jeppesen Systems AB (4)
Odinsgatan 9, 411 03, Gothenburg, Sweden
Tel.: (46) 317208100
Web Site: http://www.jeppesen.com
Sales Range: $50-74.9 Million
Emp.: 380
Aircraft Mfr
N.A.I.C.S.: 336411
Peter Andersson (CEO)

Boeing Defense, Space & Security Group (1)
325 James S McDonnell Blvd, Hazelwood, MO 63042
Tel.: (314) 232-0232
Web Site: http://www.boeing.com
Sales Range: $25-49.9 Billion
Emp.: 63,000
Military Aircraft, Space Systems & Other Military Applications Mfr
N.A.I.C.S.: 336411
Theodore Colbert III (Pres & CEO)
Kay N. Sears (VP)
Jeff Shockey (VP-Sls & Mktg-Global)
James H. Chilton (Sr VP-Space & Launch)
Scott G. Drach (VP-HR)
Denise Russell Fleming (VP-IT Bus Partners)
Rik Geiersbach (VP-Strategy)

Shelley K. Lavender (Sr VP-Strike, Surveillance & Mobility)
Timothy Peters (VP & Gen Mgr-Comml Derivative Aircraft)
Kristin A. Robertson (VP & Gen Mgr-Autonomous Sys)
Norm E. Tew (VP & Gen Mgr-Missile & Weapon Sys)
Todd Citron (VP-Engrg)
Torbjorn Sjogren (VP-Intl Govt & Defence)
Tony Martin (VP-Total Quality)
Steve Parker (VP & Gen Mgr-Vertical Lift)
Darrin A. Hostetler (VP)
Marti Powers (VP-Comm)
Penny White (VP-Supply Chain)

Subsidiary (Domestic):

Argon ST, Inc. (2)
12701 Fair Lakes Cir Ste 800, Fairfax, VA 22033
Tel.: (703) 322-0881
Web Site: http://www.argonst.com
Sales Range: $350-399.9 Million
Emp.: 1,063
Developer of Command, Control, Communications, Computers, Combat Systems, Intelligence, Surveillance & Reconnaissance (C5ISR) Systems
N.A.I.C.S.: 334511
Troy A. Stoner (CEO)

Boeing Advanced Information Systems-Maryland Operations (2)
131 National Bus Pkwy Ste 120, Annapolis Junction, MD 20701 (100%)
Tel.: (301) 497-2800
Web Site: http://www.conquestnet.com
Large-Scale Systems & Software Technology Solutions
N.A.I.C.S.: 541511

Boeing Intelligence & Analytics, Inc. (2)
131 National Business Pkwy Ste 120, Annapolis Junction, MD 20701
Tel.: (443) 661-4800
Web Site: http://www.bia-boeing.com
Software & Hardware Engineering Services & Solutions
N.A.I.C.S.: 541512
Chad Scott (Dir-Bus Dev & Corp Strategy)

Division (Domestic):

Boeing Military Aircraft Division (2)
9725 E Marginal Way S, Seattle, WA 98108-4040
Tel.: (206) 655-2121
Web Site: http://www.boeing.com
Sales Range: $15-24.9 Billion
Emp.: 23,000
Military Aircraft Mfr
N.A.I.C.S.: 336411

Division (Domestic):

The Boeing Co. - Helicopter Division (3)
5000 E McDowell Rd, Mesa, AZ 85215
Tel.: (480) 891-3000
Web Site: http://www.boeing.com
Sales Range: $450-499.9 Million
Emp.: 4,200
Helicopter Mfr, Research & Development, Systems Integration, Aerospace Support
N.A.I.C.S.: 336411

Subsidiary (Domestic):

Boeing Satellite Systems International, Inc. (2)
2260 E Imperial Hwy, El Segundo, CA 90245
Tel.: (310) 364-4000
Sales Range: $600-649.9 Million
Emp.: 7,500
Communications, Meteorological, Military & Research Satellite Mfr
N.A.I.C.S.: 517410

Digital Receiver Technology Inc. (2)
12409 Milestone Center Dr, Germantown, MD 20876
Tel.: (301) 916-5554
Web Site: http://www.drti.com
Sales Range: $100-124.9 Million
Emp.: 470
Wireless Surveillance & Tracking Equipment Mfr

The Boeing Company—(Continued)

N.A.I.C.S.: 334290

Insitu, Inc.   (2)
118 E Columbia River Way, Bingen, WA
98605
Tel.: (509) 493-8600
Web Site: http://www.insitu.com
Sales Range: $125-149.9 Million
Emp.: 700
Unmanned Air Surveillance System Designer, Developer & Mfr
N.A.I.C.S.: 336411
Mark Bauman (VP-Global Growth)
Donald Williamson (VP & Gen Mgr-Defense)
Andrew Duggan (VP)
Matthew Bartow (CTO)
Rita McMullen (CFO)
Megan Davies (CEO)

Miro Technologies, Inc.   (2)
Regents Sq 4250 Executive Sq Ste 300, La
Jolla, CA 92037
Tel.: (858) 677-2100
Web Site: http://www.mirotechnologies.com
Sales Range: $1-9.9 Million
Emp.: 120
Aftermarket Logistics Support & Maintenance Services Software Developer
N.A.I.C.S.: 513210

Tapestry Solutions, Inc.   (2)
6910 Carroll Rd, San Diego, CA
92121-2211   (100%)
Tel.: (858) 503-1990
Web Site: http://www.tapestrysolutions.com
Custom Software Development, Training,
Consulting & Support Services
N.A.I.C.S.: 513210
Robin Wright (Pres & CEO)

Division (Domestic):

Tapestry Solutions   (3)
5643 Copley Dr, San Diego, CA 92111
Tel.: (858) 503-1990
Web Site: http://www.tapestrysolutions.com
Sales Range: $25-49.9 Million
Emp.: 100
Software Publisher
N.A.I.C.S.: 513210

Unit (Domestic):

The Boeing Co. - Anaheim   (2)
3370 E Miraloma Ave, Anaheim, CA 92806-1911
Tel.: (714) 762-7775
Web Site: http://www.boeing.com
Sales Range: $100-124.9 Million
Electronic Systems & Missile Defense Systems
N.A.I.C.S.: 336415

The Boeing Co. - El Paso   (2)
9566 RailRd Dr, El Paso, TX 79924
Tel.: (915) 834-1000
Sales Range: $50-74.9 Million
Emp.: 220
Computer Aviation Software & Circuitry Mfr
N.A.I.C.S.: 334412
Debbie Coch (Mgr-HR)

**The Boeing Co. - Electronic
Systems**   (2)
20403 68th Ave S, Kent, WA 98032-2316
Tel.: (206) 655-2121
Sales Range: $1-4.9 Billion
Defense Systems, Including the E-3
AWACS, 767 AWACS, Maritime Avionics, as
well as Design & Manufacture of Electronics
for all Boeing Divisions
N.A.I.C.S.: 488119

The Boeing Co. - Huntsville   (2)
499 Boeing Blvd SW, Huntsville, AL 35824-3001
Tel.: (256) 461-2121
Web Site: http://www.boeing.com
Sales Range: $550-599.9 Million
Emp.: 3,000
Airplane & Software Mfr
N.A.I.C.S.: 334511

The Boeing Co. - Oak Ridge   (2)
767 Boeing Rd, Oak Ridge, TN 37830-9100
Tel.: (312) 544-2000
Web Site: http://www.boeing.com

Sales Range: $150-199.9 Million
Emp.: 415
Mfr of Missile Support Systems for Minuteman Missile
N.A.I.C.S.: 336413

Boeing Distribution Services Inc.   (1)
1300 Corporate Ctr Way, Wellington, FL
33414
Tel.: (561) 383-5100
Web Site: http://investor.klx.com
Rev.: $1,740,800,000
Assets: $3,790,000,000
Liabilities: $1,520,100,000
Net Worth: $2,269,900,000
Emp.: 3,000
Fiscal Year-end: 01/31/2018
Aerospace Fasteners, Consumables & Logistics Services
N.A.I.C.S.: 336413
Michael F. Senft (CFO, Treas & VP)

Subsidiary (Domestic):

AAA Aircraft Supply, LLC   (2)
68 Shaker Rd, Enfield, CT 06082-3106
Tel.: (860) 749-5192
Airframe Fasteners Engine Mfr
N.A.I.C.S.: 336412

Subsidiary (Non-US):

B/E Aerospace Fischer GmbH   (2)
Muller-Armack-Str 4, 84034, Landshut, Germany
Tel.: (49) 871932480
Web Site: http://www.fischer-seats.com
Aircraft Seat Mfr
N.A.I.C.S.: 316990

Subsidiary (Domestic):

Boeing Distribution Services   (2)
3760 W. 108th St, Miami, FL
33018   (100%)
Tel.: (305) 925-2600
Aerospace Supply Chain
N.A.I.C.S.: 488119

Subsidiary (Non-US):

**Boeing Distribution Services II
GmbH**   (2)
Nordportbogen 6, Norderstedt, 22848, Germany
Tel.: (49) 408222850
Web Site: http://www.boeingdistribution.com
Aircraft Hardware Product Distr
N.A.I.C.S.: 423710

Subsidiary (Domestic):

**Boeing Distribution Services
GmbH**   (3)
Nordportbogen 6, 22848, Norderstedt, Germany
Tel.: (49) 408222850
Web Site: http://www.boeingdistribution.com
Commercial Aircraft Designer & Mfr
N.A.I.C.S.: 336413

Subsidiary (Non-US):

**Boeing Distribution Services II
Limited**   (2)
7 & 8 Grove Court Grove Park, Enderby,
LE19 1SA, Leicestershire, United Kingdom
Tel.: (44) 1162823558
Web Site: http://www.boeingdistribution.com
Aircraft Mfr & Distr
N.A.I.C.S.: 336413

Subsidiary (Domestic):

Boeing Distribution Services Inc.   (3)
3760 W 108th St, Miami, FL 33018
Tel.: (305) 925-2600
Web Site: http://www.boeingdistribution.com
Aircraft Hardware Distr
N.A.I.C.S.: 336413

Plant (Domestic):

**Boeing Distribution Services,
Inc.-Paramus**   (3)
650 From Rd Ste 120, Paramus, NJ 07652
Tel.: (201) 265-8770
Web Site: http://www.boeingdistribution.com
Fasteners, Industrial Nuts, Bolts & Screws
N.A.I.C.S.: 423840

Subsidiary (Non-US):

**Boeing Distribution Services
SAS**   (2)
27 Av Etienne Audibert, BP 30169, 60305,
Senlis, Cedex, France
Tel.: (33) 344216868
Web Site: http://www.boeingdistribution.com
Aircraft Parts Distr
N.A.I.C.S.: 423860

Branch (Domestic):

**Boeing Distribution Services -
Toulouse**   (3)
Aeroparc Saint Martin BAT C01 -12 rue de
Caulet, 31300, Toulouse, France
Tel.: (33) 534551152
Web Site: http://www.boeingdistribution.com
Commercial & General Aviation Aircraft Mfr
& Distr
N.A.I.C.S.: 336413

Subsidiary (Domestic):

KLX Energy Services   (2)
3040 Post Oak Blvd 15th Fl, Houston, TX
77056
Tel.: (832) 844-1015
Web Site: http://www.klxenergy.com
Emp.: 1,000
Oil & Energy Drilling Solutions
N.A.I.C.S.: 213112
Thomas P. McCaffrey (CFO)
Gary Roberts (VP & Gen Mgr)
Douglas Barnette (VP-HSE)
Tim Cooksley (VP-Sls)
Jay Survant (VP-HR)
Wesley D. Heiskell (VP-Products & Svcs)

**Boeing Intellectual Property Licensing
Company**   (1)
700 SO Renton Vlg Pl MC 6M7-65, Renton,
WA 98055-3235
Tel.: (206) 662-6628
Web Site: http://www.boeingimages.com
Aircraft Mfr
N.A.I.C.S.: 336411

Boeing International Corporation   (1)
100 N Riverside, Chicago, IL 60606-1501
Tel.: (312) 544-2000
Web Site: http://www.boeing.com
Sales Range: $1-4.9 Billion
Holding Company
N.A.I.C.S.: 551112

Subsidiary (Non-US):

AeroInfo Systems, Inc.   (2)
13575 Commerce Pkwy Ste 200, Richmond, V6V 2I1, BC, Canada   (100%)
Tel.: (604) 232-4200
Web Site: http://www.aeroinfo.com
Sales Range: $25-49.9 Million
Emp.: 170
Custom Computer Programming Services
N.A.I.C.S.: 541511

Subsidiary (Non-US):

Boeing International B.V. & Co. Holding KGaA   (3)
Lennestrasse 9, 10785, Berlin,
Germany   (100%)
Tel.: (49) 30773770
Web Site: http://www.boeing.de
Sales Office
N.A.I.C.S.: 522220

Subsidiary (Non-US):

**Boeing Australia Holdings Proprietary
Limited**   (2)
Level 10 Exchange House 10 Bridge St,
Sydney, 2000, NSW, Australia
Tel.: (61) 290863300
Web Site: http://www.boeing.com.au
Investment Management Service
N.A.I.C.S.: 551112

Subsidiary (Domestic):

**Boeing Aerostructures Australia Pty
Ltd.**   (3)
226 Lorimer St, Port Melbourne, 3207, VIC,
Australia
Tel.: (61) 396473111
Emp.: 800
Aircraft Components Mfr

N.A.I.C.S.: 336413

Boeing Defence Australia LTD   (3)
150 Charlotte Street, Brisbane, 4000, QLD,
Australia
Tel.: (61) 73 306 3000
Web Site: https://www.boeing.com.au
Aircraft Mfr
N.A.I.C.S.: 336411

Subsidiary (Non-US):

Boeing Canada Operations Ltd.   (2)
99 Murray Park Rd, Winnipeg, R3J 3M6,
MB, Canada
Tel.: (204) 888-2300
Web Site: http://www.boeing.ca
Aircraft Mfr
N.A.I.C.S.: 336411

Boeing Deutschland GmbH   (2)
Lennestrasse 9, 10785, Berlin, Germany
Tel.: (49) 30773770
Web Site: http://www.boeing.de
Aircraft Equipment Mfr
N.A.I.C.S.: 336411

Branch (Non-US):

**Boeing International Corp. -
Australia**   (2)
GPO Box 48, Sydney, 2001, NSW, Australia
Tel.: (61) 293174767
Sales Range: $25-49.9 Million
Emp.: 7
Sales Office
N.A.I.C.S.: 423860
Maureen Dougherty (Pres-Australia, New
Zealand & South Pacific)

**Boeing International Corp. -
France**   (2)
75 rue du Faubourg Saint Honore, 75008,
Paris, France
Tel.: (33) 170370747
Web Site: http://www.boeing.fr
Sales Range: $25-49.9 Million,
Emp.: 10
Sales Office
N.A.I.C.S.: 423860

Subsidiary (Non-US):

Boeing Japan Co., Ltd.   (2)
1-6-6 Nippon Life Insurance Marunouchi
Building, Marunouchi Chiyoda Ku, Tokyo,
100-0005, Japan
Tel.: (81) 352231234
Web Site: https://www.boeing.jp
Aircraft Equipment Mfr & Maintenance Services
N.A.I.C.S.: 336413
Brett C. Gerry (Pres)

Boeing Netherlands B.V.   (2)
Hoogoorddreef 15, Amsterdam, 1101 BA,
Netherlands
Tel.: (31) 205407700
Web Site: http://www.boeing.com
Emp.: 50
Jetliners & Military Aircraft Mfr
N.A.I.C.S.: 336411

**Boeing Singapore Training and Flight
Services Pte. Ltd.**   (2)
30 Changi North Rise, Singapore, 498780,
Singapore
Tel.: (65) 63091500
Aircraft Mfr
N.A.I.C.S.: 336411
Patrick Curtin (Sr Gen Mgr)

**Boeing Training & Flight Services
Australia Pty Ltd**   (2)
3 Melia St Brisbane Airport, Brisbane, 4009,
Qld, Australia
Tel.: (61) 733079300
Web Site: http://www.boeing.com.au
Emp.: 30
Flight Training Services
N.A.I.C.S.: 611512

Boeing United Kingdom Limited   (2)
25 Victoria Street, London, SW1H 0EX,
United Kingdom   (100%)
Tel.: (44) 2073401900
Web Site: http://www.boeing.co.uk
Sales Range: $10-24.9 Million
Emp.: 40
Aircraft Sales & Service

N.A.I.C.S.: 423860

Subsidiary (Domestic):

Boeing Defence UK Limited (3)
25 VICTORIA ST, London, SW1H 0EX,
United Kingdom
Tel.: (44) 2073401900
Web Site: http://www.boeing.co.uk
Aircraft Manufacturing
N.A.I.C.S.: 336411

Branch (Domestic):

Boeing UK Ltd. - Hounslow (3)
Heathrow House 6th Fl Bath Road, Houn-
slow, TW5 9QQ, Mddx, United Kingdom
Tel.: (44) 2082355600
Web Site: http://www.boeing.co.uk
Sales Range: $10-24.9 Million
Emp.: 60
Sales Office
N.A.I.C.S.: 423860

Subsidiary (Non-US):

Boeing Winnipeg (2)
99 Murray Park Rd, Winnipeg, R3J 3M6,
MB, Canada   (100%)
Tel.: (204) 888-2300
Web Site: https://www.boeing.ca
Emp.: 1,000
Mfr of Plane Parts
N.A.I.C.S.: 336412

Boeing Launch Services, Inc. (1)
5301 Bolsa Ave, Huntington Beach, CA
92647
Tel.: (714) 896-5195
Emp.: 1
Guided Missiles & Space Vehicles Mfr
N.A.I.C.S.: 336414

Boeing Nevada, Inc. (1)
2215 Renaissance Dr, Las Vegas, NV
89119
Tel.: (702) 940-2580
Aircraft Mfr
N.A.I.C.S.: 336411

**Boeing North American Services
Inc.** (1)
3373 Breckinridge Blvd, Richardson, TX
75082-3511   (100%)
Tel.: (972) 705-8000
Web Site: http://www.boeing.com
Sales Range: $25-49.9 Million
Emp.: 100
Industrial Management Services
N.A.I.C.S.: 561110

Boeing Realty Corporation (1)
15480 Laguna Canyon Rd Ste 200, Irvine,
CA 92618-2114   (100%)
Tel.: (562) 797-2020
Sales Range: Less than $1 Million
Emp.: 11
Real Estate Development
N.A.I.C.S.: 531390

C-Map/Commercial, Ltd. (1)
133 Falmouth Rd, Mashpee, MA 02649
Tel.: (508) 539-4350
Web Site: http://commercialmarine.c-
map.com
Aircraft Mfr
N.A.I.C.S.: 336411

Continental DataGraphics (1)
6141 Katella Ave, Cypress, CA 90630
Tel.: (714) 503-4200
Web Site: http://www.cdgnow.com
Sales Range: $150-199.9 Million
Emp.: 1,000
Engineering Services
N.A.I.C.S.: 541330
David Malmo *(Pres & CEO)*

Subsidiary (Non-US):

Continental DataGraphics Ltd. (2)
Building 1 First Floor Albany Place Hyde-
way, Welwyn Garden City, AL7 3BG, Hert-
fordshire, United Kingdom
Tel.: (44) 1707367700
Web Site: http://www.cdgl.com
Sales Range: $25-49.9 Million
Emp.: 120
Engineeering Services
N.A.I.C.S.: 541330
Andrew Masson *(Mng Dir)*

ForeFlight LLC (1)
2323 S Shepherd Dr Ste 912, Houston, TX
77019-7028
Tel.: (817) 203-8683
Web Site: http://www.foreflight.com
Aviation Services; Mobile & Web-based
Aviation Applications
N.A.I.C.S.: 513210
Tyson Weihs *(Co-Founder & CEO)*
Jason Miller *(Co-Founder & CTO)*
Gregg Goldstein *(Gen Counsel)*
Tim Schuetze *(Exec VP-Strategy & Bus
Dev)*
Stephen Newman *(Exec VP-Sls & Mktg)*
Malcolm Toon *(Exec VP-Mapping, Naviga-
tion & Military Technologies)*
Adam Houghton *(COO & Exec VP-Engrg)*

Subsidiary (Domestic):

Aviation Logistics Corp. (2)
635 Camino De Los Mares Ste 312, San
Clemente, CA 92673   (100%)
Tel.: (949) 424-7100
Web Site: http://www.jetfuelx.com
Rev.: $4,530,000
Emp.: 6
Aviation Services
N.A.I.C.S.: 488119
Jason Talley *(Pres)*

HRL Laboratories, LLC (1)
3011 Malibu Canyon Rd, Malibu, CA 90265-
4797
Tel.: (310) 317-5000
Web Site: http://www.hrl.com
Sales Range: $100-124.9 Million
Emp.: 300
Research & Development Labs
N.A.I.C.S.: 541330
Paul G. Kaminski *(Chm)*
P. C. Albright *(Pres & CEO)*

Inventory Locator Service, LLC (1)
8001 Centerview Pkwy Ste 400, Cordova,
TN 38018
Tel.: (901) 794-5000
Web Site: http://www.ilsmart.com
Emp.: 1,400
Aircraft Mfr
N.A.I.C.S.: 336411
Bert Seaton *(Pres)*

Liquid Robotics, Inc. (1)
1329 Moffett Park Dr, Sunnyvale, CA
94089   (100%)
Tel.: (408) 636-4200
Web Site: http://www.liquid-robotics.com
Robot Design Services
N.A.I.C.S.: 541330
Roger Hine *(Co-Founder)*
Jerome Pereira *(VP-Mfg)*
Graham Hine *(Co-Founder & CEO)*
Jeff Fiedorowicz *(CTO)*

Millennium Space Systems, Inc. (1)
2265 E El Segundo Blvd, El Segundo, CA
90245-4608
Tel.: (310) 683-5850
Web Site: http://www.millennium-space.com
Guided Missile & Space Vehicle Manufac-
turing
N.A.I.C.S.: 336414

**Montana Aviation Research
Company** (1)
Facility 921 Ave D, Saint Marie, MT 59231
Tel.: (406) 524-3777
Emp.: 8
Aircraft Mfr
N.A.I.C.S.: 336411
Stacy Sukut *(Office Mgr)*

Spectrolab Inc. (1)
12500 Gladstone Ave, Sylmar, CA
91342-5322   (100%)
Tel.: (818) 365-4611
Web Site: http://www.spectrolab.com
Sales Range: $150-199.9 Million
Emp.: 300
Mfr of Solar Cells & Panels
N.A.I.C.S.: 334413
Anthony Muller *(Pres)*

The Boeing Co. - Long Beach (1)
3855 N Lakewood Blvd, Long Beach, CA
90846-0003
Tel.: (562) 593-5511
Web Site: http://www.boeing.com

Sales Range: $75-99.9 Million
Personal Service Agents Brokers & Bureaus
N.A.I.C.S.: 541690

The Boeing Co. - Ridley Park (1)
Stewart Ave & Industrial Hwy, Ridley Park,
PA 19078
Tel.: (610) 591-7097
Sales Range: $150-199.9 Million
Emp.: 450
Helicopter Mfr
N.A.I.C.S.: 336411

The Boeing Co. - Seattle (1)
7755 E Marginal Way S, Seattle, WA
98108-4002
Tel.: (206) 544-2406
Web Site: http://www.boeing.com
Sales Range: $300-349.9 Million
Commercial & Military Airplane Mfr; Soft-
ware Design
N.A.I.C.S.: 336411

THE BON TON STORES, INC.
2801 E Market St, York, PA 17402
Tel.: (717) 757-7660   PA
Web Site: https://www.bonton.com
Year Founded: 1898
BONTQ—(NASDAQ)
Sales Range: $1-4.9 Billion
Emp.: 23,300
Departmental Store Operator
N.A.I.C.S.: 455110
Christopher Hoffman *(VP-Loss Pre-
vention)*

Subsidiaries:

Carson Pirie Scott & Co. (1)
2801 E Market St, York, PA 17402
Tel.: (717) 757-7660
Web Site: http://www.carsons.com
Emp.: 62,000
Department Stores
N.A.I.C.S.: 455110

Subsidiary (Domestic):

Herberger's, Inc. (2)
600 W St Germain, Saint Cloud, MN 56301
Tel.: (320) 251-5202
Web Site: http://www.herbergers.com
Sales Range: $25-49.9 Million
Emp.: 125
Retail Department Stores
N.A.I.C.S.: 455110

Carson Pirie Scott II, Inc. (1)
331 W Wisconsin Ave, Milwaukee, WI
53203
Tel.: (414) 347-4141
Departmental Store Operator
N.A.I.C.S.: 445110

**The Bon-Ton Department Stores,
Inc.** (1)
2801 East Market St, York, PA 17402-2406
Tel.: (717) 757-7660
Web Site: http://www.bonton.com
Sales Range: $300-349.9 Million
Emp.: 1,000
Provider of Retail Services
N.A.I.C.S.: 455110

The Bon-Ton Giftco, Inc. (1)
2801 E Market St, York, PA 17402-2406
Tel.: (717) 757-7660
Sales of Consumer Goods
N.A.I.C.S.: 455110

The Elder-Beerman Stores Corp. (1)
2801 E Market St, York, PA 17402
Tel.: (717) 757-7660
Web Site: http://www.elder-beerman.com
Sales Range: $1-4.9 Billion
Emp.: 15,000
Department & Furniture Store Distr
N.A.I.C.S.: 449110

THE BOSTON BEER COM-
PANY, INC.
1 Design Ctr Pl Ste 850, Boston, MA
02210
Tel.: (617) 368-5000   MA
Web Site:
    https://www.bostonbeer.com
Year Founded: 1985

SAM—(NYSE)
Rev.: $2,133,292,000
Assets: $1,429,993,000
Liabilities: $352,064,000
Net Worth: $1,077,929,000
Earnings: $76,250,000
Emp.: 2,793
Fiscal Year-end: 12/30/23
Beer Brewery
N.A.I.C.S.: 312120
Samuel A. Calagione III *(Co-Founder)*
Michael Spillane *(Pres & CEO)*
C. James Koch *(Founder)*
Philip A. Hodges *(Chief Supply Chain
Officer)*
Matthew D. Murphy *(Interim CFO,
Chief Acctg Officer & Interim Treas)*
Michael G. Andrews *(Sec & Assoc
Gen Counsel)*
Lesya Lysyj *(CMO)*
Carolyn L. OBoyle *(Chief People Offi-
cer)*
Annette A. Fritsch *(VP)*
Quincy B. Troupe *(Sr VP-Supply
Chain)*

Subsidiaries:

Boston Brewing Company, Inc. (1)
30 Germania St, Boston, MA 02130
Tel.: (617) 368-5080
Web Site: http://www.sammueladam.com
Sales Range: $25-49.9 Million
Emp.: 35
Nonalcoholic Beer Brewing Mfr
N.A.I.C.S.: 312120
Jennifer Glanville *(Program Dir)*

Dogfish Head Craft Brewery, Inc. (1)
6 Cannery Village Ctr, Milton, DE 19968
Tel.: (302) 684-1000
Web Site: http://www.dogfish.com
Brewery & Restaurant
N.A.I.C.S.: 312120
Samuel A. Calagione III *(Co-Founder)*
Sam Calagione *(Founder)*
Mariah Calagione *(Co-Founder)*

THE BRINK'S COMPANY
1801 Bayberry Ct, Richmond, VA
23226-8100
Tel.: (804) 289-9600   VA
Web Site: https://us.brinks.com
Year Founded: 1984
BCO—(NYSE)
Rev.: $4,874,600,000
Assets: $6,601,800,000
Liabilities: $6,081,600,000
Net Worth: $520,200,000
Earnings: $96,600,000
Emp.: 66,000
Fiscal Year-end: 12/31/23
Holding Company; Security Guard &
Armored Car Services
N.A.I.C.S.: 551112
Laurent P. Borne *(Chief Experience
Officer & Exec VP)*
Dominik Bossart *(Pres-Svcs-Global,
MEA & Asia & Sr VP)*
Simon Davis *(Chief HR Officer & Sr
VP)*
Raphael J. Shemanski *(Pres-Canada
& Sr VP)*
Michael Sweeney *(VP & Controller)*
Chris Parks *(Pres-Europe & Sr VP)*
Kurt B. McMaken *(CFO & Exec VP)*
Mark Eubanks *(Pres & CEO)*

Subsidiaries:

A.G.S. Groep B.V. (1)
Haringbuisweg 31 A, 3133 KP, Vlaardingen,
Netherlands
Tel.: (31) 105927863
Web Site: http://www.agsgroep.nl
Security System Services
N.A.I.C.S.: 561621

**Brink's Cash & Valuable Services
S.A.** (1)
52 Koritsas St, Votanikos, 104 47, Athens,
Greece

The Brink's Company—(Continued)

Tel.: (30) 2103484000
Security Guard & Patrol Services
N.A.I.C.S.: 561612

Brink's Cash Services (Ireland) Limited (1)
Bluebell Avenue, Bluebell Industrial Estate, Dublin, D12 DR4R, Ireland
Tel.: (353) 1890474000
Web Site: http://ie.brinks.com
Security Guard & Patrol Services
N.A.I.C.S.: 561612

Brink's Chile, S.A. (1)
Olivos 778 Recoleta, Santiago, Chile
Tel.: (56) 26800700
Logistic Services
N.A.I.C.S.: 484110
Laetitia Laudanski (Ops Mgr)

Brink's Cyprus (Private Security Services) Limited (1)
17 Diianiras Street, Strovolos, 2045, Nicosia, Cyprus
Tel.: (357) 22745300
Web Site: https://www.cy.brinks.com
Emp.: 700
Security Guard & Patrol Services
N.A.I.C.S.: 561612

Brink's Global Holdings B.V. (1)
Prins Bernhard Plein 200, 1097 JB, Amsterdam, Netherlands
Tel.: (31) 306395959
Security System Services
N.A.I.C.S.: 561621

Subsidiary (Domestic):

AGS-SecuTrans B.V. (2)
Haringbuisweg 31, 3133KP, Vlaardingen, Netherlands
Tel.: (31) 105927863
Logistic & Secure Transportation Consulting Services
N.A.I.C.S.: 541614

Brink's India Private Limited (1)
Pankaj Building 1st Floor Unit No 102, Behind ICE Factory Raheja Vihar Chandivali Andheri E, Mumbai, 400072, Maharashtra, India
Tel.: (91) 2261484900
Web Site: http://www.brinks.com
Security Services
N.A.I.C.S.: 561612

Brink's Worldbridge Secure Logistics Co., Ltd. (1)
No 694 NR No 2 Sangkat Chak Angre Krom, Khan Meanchey, Phnom Penh, Cambodia
Tel.: (855) 235555330
Security Guard & Patrol Services
N.A.I.C.S.: 561612

Brink's, Incorporated (1)
1801 Bayberry Ct, Richmond, VA 23226-8100 (100%)
Tel.: (804) 289-9600
Web Site: http://www.brinks.com
Sales Range: $100-124.9 Million
Emp.: 100
Security Guard, Armored Transportation & Specialty Logistics Services
N.A.I.C.S.: 561612

Subsidiary (Domestic):

Brink's Global Services International, Inc. (2)
580 5th Ave Ste 400, New York, NY 10036
Tel.: (212) 704-9500
Web Site: http://www.brinksinc.com
Risk Management & Secure Logistic Services
N.A.I.C.S.: 541614

Subsidiary (Non-US):

Brink's Global Services (BGS) Botswana (Proprietary) Limited (3)
Diamond Technology Park Plot 67782 Block B Atrium Suite 102, PO Box 404215, Gaborone, Botswana
Tel.: (267) 3160478
Web Site: http://www.bricksglobal.com
Emp.: 15
Freight Transportation Services

N.A.I.C.S.: 484121

Brink's Global Services Antwerp BVBA (3)
Höveniersstraat 2, PO Box 408, 2018, Antwerp, Belgium
Tel.: (32) 32342151
Sales Range: $25-49.9 Million
Emp.: 23
Security Guard & Armored Car Services
N.A.I.C.S.: 561612
Silvie Grundland (Gen Mgr)

Brink's Global Services Deutschland GmbH (3)
Cargo City NorthGate 26Building 458 2nd Floor, 60549, Frankfurt, Germany
Tel.: (49) 6969711160
Logistic Services
N.A.I.C.S.: 541614
Peter Lenzen-Schroeder (Mgr-Acctg)

Brink's Global Services FZE (3)
Dubai Airport Freezone, PO Box 85079, Dubai, 85079, United Arab Emirates
Tel.: (971) 4 425 5876
Web Site: https://ae.brinks.com
Emp.: 55
Security Guard & Armored Car Services
N.A.I.C.S.: 561612

Brink's Global Services Korea Limited - Yunan Hoesa Brink's Global (3)
Rm 1122 Changgang Bldg 86 Mapo-Daero, Mapo-gu, Seoul, 121-763, Korea (South)
Tel.: (82) 704 1138
Web Site: http://www.brinksglobal.com
Sales Range: $25-49.9 Million
Emp.: 17
Freight Transportation Services
N.A.I.C.S.: 484121

Brink's Global Services Poland Sp.zo.o. (3)
Ul Bokserska 64, 02-690, Warsaw, Poland
Tel.: (48) 228535344
Security Services
N.A.I.C.S.: 561612

Brink's Global Services S.r.l. (3)
Via Edison 33/a-37, 52100, Arezzo, Italy
Tel.: (39) 057 598 4434
Web Site: http://www.brinksglobal.com
Emp.: 6
Security Guard & Armored Car Services
N.A.I.C.S.: 561612

Subsidiary (Domestic):

Brink's Puerto Rico, Inc. (2)
Paris St Ste 249 Floral Park, San Juan, PR 00917-3622
Tel.: (787) 754-8024
Web Site: http://www.brinks.com
Emp.: 50
Security Guard & Armored Car Services
N.A.I.C.S.: 561612

Brink's Security International, Inc. (2)
1801 Bayberry Ct, Richmond, VA 23226
Tel.: (804) 289-9600
Web Site: http://www.brinks.com
Holding Company; Security Guard & Armored Car Services
N.A.I.C.S.: 551112

Subsidiary (Non-US):

Brink's (Israel) Limited (3)
Diamond Exchange Maccabi Building 1 Jabotinsky St, Ramat Gan, 52520, Israel
Tel.: (972) 35750111
Web Site: http://www.brinks.co.il
Security Guard & Armored Car Services
N.A.I.C.S.: 561612

Brink's (UK) Limited (3)
Unit 1 Radius Park Faggs Road, Feltham, TW14 0NG, Middlesex, United Kingdom
Tel.: (44) 208 818 0601
Web Site: http://www.brinksglobal.com
Sales Range: $75-99.9 Million
Security Guard & Armored Car Services
N.A.I.C.S.: 561612

Brink's Argentina S.A. (3)
Av Int Francisco Rabanal 3120, Buenos Aires, C1437FQS, Argentina
Tel.: (54) 114 016 4400

Web Site: http://www.brinks.com.ar
Emp.: 2,400
Security Guard & Armored Car Services
N.A.I.C.S.: 561612

Brink's Australia Pty. Ltd (3)
Unit 6 4 Huntley Street, Alexandria, 2015, NSW, Australia
Tel.: (61) 28 396 8888
Web Site: http://www.brinks.com.au
Security Guard & Armored Car Services
N.A.I.C.S.: 561612
Douglas Allen Pertz (Pres & CEO)
Michael F. Beech (Pres-Latin America & Global Security & Exec VP)

Brink's Beteiligungsgesellschaft mbH (3)
Insterburger Str 7, 60487, Frankfurt, Germany
Tel.: (49) 692477500
Investment Management Service
N.A.I.C.S.: 523940

Subsidiary (Non-US):

Brink's Global Services (4)
Av Insurgentes Sur 60 Col Napoles Del Benito Juarez, 03810, Mexico, Mexico
Tel.: (52) 555 627 3289
Web Site: http://www.brinksglobal.com
Logistics Consulting Servies
N.A.I.C.S.: 541614

Subsidiary (Non-US):

Brink's Bolivia S.A. (3)
Av Mutualista No 2400, Santa Cruz, Bolivia
Tel.: (591) 3 312 8400
Web Site: http://www.brinksglobal.com
Security Guard & Armored Car Services
N.A.I.C.S.: 561612

Brink's C.L. Hungaria Limited (3)
Hauszmann Alajos street 9-11, 1119, Budapest, Hungary
Tel.: (36) 012040200
Web Site: http://www.brinks.com
Sales Range: $100-124.9 Million
Security Guard & Armored Car Services
N.A.I.C.S.: 561612

Brink's Canada Limited (3)
2233 Argentia Road Suite 400, Mississauga, L5N 2X7, ON, Canada (100%)
Tel.: (905) 306-9600
Web Site: https://www.brinks.ca
Sales Range: $10-24.9 Million
Emp.: 50
Security Guard & Armored Car Services
N.A.I.C.S.: 561612

Brink's Diamond & Jewellery Services (International) Ltd (3)
Diamond Exchange Maccabi Building 1a, Jabotinsky St, Ramat Gan, 52520, Israel
Tel.: (972) 35750111
Business Support Services
N.A.I.C.S.: 561499
Raz Zvi (CEO)
Tomer Agasi (Mgr)

Brink's EMEA SAS (3)
58 Rue De La Victoire, Paris, 75009, France
Tel.: (33) 155079920
Emp.: 18
Security Guard & Armored Car Services
N.A.I.C.S.: 561612
Michael Beech (CEO)

Brink's Far East Limited (3)
Room 606 ShangZhiYuan Plaza No 10 WangJiaYuan, Dong Cheng District, Beijing, 100027, China
Tel.: (86) 1065510536
Security Guard & Armored Car Services
N.A.I.C.S.: 561612

Brink's Guvenlik Hizmetleri Anonim Sirketi (3)
Leylak Sokak No 1 Nursanlar Is Merkezi 4 Kat No 17, Sisli Kustepe Sisli, Istanbul, Turkiye
Tel.: (90) 212 250 6700
Web Site: https://www.brinks.com.tr
Security Guard & Armored Car Services
N.A.I.C.S.: 561612

Brink's Hong Kong Limited (3)
10/F Kailey Tower 16 Stanley Street, Cen-

tral, China (Hong Kong)
Tel.: (852) 2 877 9717
Web Site: https://hk.brinks.com
Security Guard & Armored Car Services
N.A.I.C.S.: 561612

Brink's International Holdings AG (3)
Baarerstrasse 95, Zug, 6300, Switzerland
Tel.: (41) 417120770
Holding Company
N.A.I.C.S.: 551112

Subsidiary (Non-US):

Brink's Diamond & Jewelry Services BVBA (4)
Hoveniersstraat 2 Box 408, 2018, Antwerp, Belgium
Tel.: (32) 32342151
Web Site: http://www.brinksglobal.com
Sales Range: $10-24.9 Million
Emp.: 25
Diamond & Jewelry Secure Transportation Services
N.A.I.C.S.: 561613

Brink's Global Services Korea Limited (4)
Rm 1122 Chang Kang bldg 22 Dohwadong, Mapo-gu, Seoul, Korea (South)
Tel.: (82) 27041138
Logistic Services
N.A.I.C.S.: 484110
Young Seuck Kim (Country Mgr)

Brink's Nederland B.V. (4)
Hogehilweg 12, Amsterdam, 101 CD, Netherlands
Tel.: (31) 20 430 7500
Web Site: http://www.nl.brinks.com
Security Guard & Armored Car Services
N.A.I.C.S.: 561612

Brink's Singapore Pte Ltd. (4)
1 Kaki Bukit Road 1 02-33 Enterprise One, Enterprise One, Singapore, 415934, Singapore
Tel.: (65) 6 591 7799
Web Site: https://www.brinkssingapore.com.sg
Emp.: 60
Security Guard & Armored Car Services
N.A.I.C.S.: 561612

Subsidiary (Non-US):

Brink's Ireland Limited (3)
Unit G5 Calmount Business Park, Ballymount, Dublin, D12 T651, Ireland
Tel.: (353) 189 047 4000
Web Site: https://www.ie.brinks.com
Security Guard & Armored Car Services
N.A.I.C.S.: 561612

Brink's Japan Limited (3)
5-13-1-2F Shinbashi, Minato-ku, Tokyo, 105-0004, Japan
Tel.: (81) 36 435 7830
Web Site: https://www.brinks.co.jp
Sales Range: $10-24.9 Million
Emp.: 63
Security Guard & Armored Car Services
N.A.I.C.S.: 561612

Brink's Limited (Bahrain) EC (3)
11 Cargo Agents Building Bahrain International Aiprort, PO Box 24255, Muharraq, Bahrain
Tel.: (973) 17217040
Sales Range: $25-49.9 Million
Emp.: 2
Security Guard & Armored Car Services
N.A.I.C.S.: 561612
Ebrahim Balooshi (Gen Mgr)

Brink's Luxembourg S.A. (3)
8 Rue de Bitburg, Hamm, 1273, Luxembourg, Luxembourg
Tel.: (352) 42 515 1267
Web Site: https://www.brinks.lu
Sales Range: $10-24.9 Million
Emp.: 70
Security Guard & Armored Car Services
N.A.I.C.S.: 561612

Brink's Security Services, B.V. (3)
Meidoornkade 3, 3992 AG, Houten, Netherlands
Tel.: (31) 205214777
Web Site: http://www.brinks.nl
Investigation & Security Services

N.A.I.C.S.: 561612

Brink's Security Transportation (Shanghai) Company Limited (3)
Room A 619-620 No 1701 Century Avenue, Pudong, Shanghai, 200121, China
Tel.: (86) 2151698686
Sales Range: $25-49.9 Million
Emp.: 100
Security Guard & Armored Car Services
N.A.I.C.S.: 561612
Reagan Kong (Gen Mgr)

Brink's Southern Africa Pty Ltd. (3)
9 Derrick Road, Spartan Kempton Park, Johannesburg, Gauteng, South Africa
Tel.: (27) 11 392 2006
Web Site: http://www.brinksglobal.com
Freight Transportation Services
N.A.I.C.S.: 484121

Brink's Taiwan Security Limited (3)
Room 222 2F-1 No 144 Min Chuan East Road Section 3, Taipei, 105, Taiwan
Tel.: (886) 2 545 3288
Web Site: https://www.brinks.com.tw
Secure Transportation & Logistics Services
N.A.I.C.S.: 484121

Brink's Vietnam, Incorporated (3)
Room 407A 4/F SCSC Cargo Terminal 30 Phan Thuc Duyen Street, Ward 4 Tan Binh District, Ho Chi Minh City, Vietnam
Tel.: (84) 83 844 4681
Web Site: http://www.brinksglobal.com
Secure Transportation & Logistics Services
N.A.I.C.S.: 484121

Division (Domestic):

Brink's U.S. (2)
555 Dividend Dr Ste 100, Coppell, TX 75019
Tel.: (469) 549-6000
Web Site: http://www.us.brinksinc.com
Security Guard & Armored Car Services
N.A.I.C.S.: 561612

Brinks Mongolia LLC (1)
Building 32 16th Micro District, Bayanzurkh District, Ulaanbaatar, Mongolia
Tel.: (976) 70159979
Emp.: 11
Security Services
N.A.I.C.S.: 561612
Gary Freedman (Exec Dir)

Dunbar Armored Inc. (1)
50 Schilling Rd, Hunt Valley, MD 21031-1105
Tel.: (410) 584-9800
Web Site: http://www.dunbararmored.com
Sales Range: $250-299.9 Million
Emp.: 4,600
Detective & Armored Car Services
N.A.I.C.S.: 561613

Ets Pierre Kess et Fils S.A. (1)
Zare Est n7, 4385, Ehlerange, Luxembourg
Tel.: (352) 491155
Web Site: http://www.pierrekess.lu
Security Services
N.A.I.C.S.: 561612

ICD Americas, Inc. (1)
555 Dividend Dr Ste 100, Coppell, TX 75019
Tel.: (561) 340-9167
Security Guard & Armored Car Services
N.A.I.C.S.: 561612

ICD Engineering (Beijing) Co., Ltd. (1)
Suite 1201-1203 A Tower Ocean International Center, No 56 East 4th Ring Middle Road Chaoyang, Beijing, 100025, China
Tel.: (86) 1059081188
Web Site: http://www.icdsecurity.com
Sales Range: $25-49.9 Million
Emp.: 100
Security Guard & Armored Car Services
N.A.I.C.S.: 561612

ICD Security Solutions (HK) Limited (1)
Unit 2501-2503 25/F Aitken Vanson Centre, No 61 Hoi Yuen Road Kwun Tong, Kowloon, China (Hong Kong)
Tel.: (852) 28938899
Web Site: http://www.icdsecurity.com

Security System Integrator & Service Provider
N.A.I.C.S.: 561612

ICD Security Solutions (India) Private Ltd. (1)
No 21 Ground Flr Brigade Square Cambridge Road Ulsoor Road, Bengaluru, 560008, Karnataka, India
Tel.: (91) 8042898000
Web Site: http://www.icdsecurity.com
Sales Range: $25-49.9 Million
Emp.: 70
Security System Integrator & Service Provider
N.A.I.C.S.: 561612

ICD Security Solutions Pte. Ltd. (1)
CT Hub 2Lobby 206-83 114 Lavender Street, Singapore, 338729, Singapore
Tel.: (65) 65703973
Web Site: http://www.icdsecurity.com
Security System Integrator & Service Provider
N.A.I.C.S.: 561612

Limited Liability Company Brink's (1)
12 Smolnaya Str Almazny Mir office, Moscow, 125493, Russia
Tel.: (7) 74952235780
Logistics Consulting Servies
N.A.I.C.S.: 541614

Maco Litoral S.A. (1)
Catamarca 2319, S2000JRC, Rosario, Santa Fe, Argentina
Tel.: (54) 3414353355
Security System Services
N.A.I.C.S.: 561612

Maxxim Rebuild Company, Inc. (1)
12003 Virginia Blvd, Ashland, KY 41102
Tel.: (606) 928-7911
Used Equipment Contractor
N.A.I.C.S.: 811310

NoteMachine Limited (1)
Russell House Elvicta Business Park, Powys, Crickhowell, NP8 1DF, United Kingdom
Tel.: (44) 1873811634
Web Site: http://www.notemachine.com
Sales Range: $100-124.9 Million
Emp.: 220
Automated Teller Machine Installation & Monitoring Services
N.A.I.C.S.: 238290
Peter D. McNamara (Founder & CEO)
Mike Kingston (CFO)
Nigel Constable (COO)
Charlie Evans (Sls Dir)

PT Brinks Solutions Indonesia (1)
Jl Ciputat Raya No 18 Pondok Pinang, Kebayoran Lama, Jakarta, 12310, Indonesia
Tel.: (62) 2129544880
Web Site: http://www.id.brinks.com
Security Guard & Patrol Services
N.A.I.C.S.: 561612

Pittston Coal Company (1)
16016 Porterfield Hwy, Abingdon, VA 24210
Tel.: (276) 739-3420
Sales Range: $75-99.9 Million
Emp.: 244
Coal Mining Services
N.A.I.C.S.: 212115

Subsidiary (Domestic):

Pittston Coal Management Company (2)
16016 Porterfield Hwy, Abingdon, VA 24210
Tel.: (276) 739-3420
Emp.: 244
Investment Management Service
N.A.I.C.S.: 523940
William Ledger (Mgr)

Rodoban Seguranca e Tranpsorte de Valores Ltda (1)
Rua dos Pampas 780 - Bairro Prado, Belo Horizonte, 30411-030, Minas Gerais, Brazil
Tel.: (55) 3121042222
Web Site: https://www.rodoban.com.br
Logistic Services
N.A.I.C.S.: 484110

Servicio Panamericano de Vigilancia Curacao, N.V. (1)

Kaya Jose Jo Pinedoe, Willemstad, Curacao
Tel.: (599) 98696382
Sales Range: $25-49.9 Million
Emp.: 60
Security Guard Services
N.A.I.C.S.: 561612
Carlos Monasterios (Gen Mgr)

Temis Conseil & Formation (1)
46 rue Marcel Grosmesnil, Villejuif, 94800, France
Tel.: (33) 142111920
Web Site: http://www.temis.fr
Fiduciary Agency Services
N.A.I.C.S.: 523991

Worldbridge Secure Logistics Co., Ltd. (1)
No 99 Preah Norodom Blvd 41 corner of St 214 WorldBridge Building, 12211, Phnom Penh, Cambodia
Tel.: (855) 235555330
Web Site: http://www.kh51746.yp.com.kh
Marine Shipping & Custom Broker Services
N.A.I.C.S.: 488510

THE BUCKLE, INC.
2407 W 24th St, Kearney, NE 68845-4915
Tel.: (308) 236-8491   NE
Web Site: https://www.buckle.com
Year Founded: 1948
BKE—(NYSE)
Rev.: $1,345,187,000
Assets: $837,579,000
Liabilities: $461,265,000
Net Worth: $376,314,000
Earnings: $254,626,000
Emp.: 3,100
Fiscal Year-end: 01/28/23
Casual Apparel, Footwear & Accessories Retailer
N.A.I.C.S.: 458110
Robert M. Carlberg (Sr VP-Men's Mdsg)
Brady M. Fritz (Gen Counsel, Sec & Sr VP)
Jennifer L. Morrow (VP-Men's Mdsg)
Carissa N. Crocker (VP-Men's Mdsg)
Brett P. Milkie (Sr VP-Leasing)
Michelle M. Hoffman (Sr VP-Sls)
Adam J. Akerson (VP-Fin, Controller-Corp & Asst Treas)
Daniel J. Hirschfeld (Chm)
Dennis H. Nelson (Pres & CEO)
Thomas B. Heacock (CFO, Treas & Sr VP-Fin)
Kari G. Smith (Exec VP-Stores)

THE CARLYLE GROUP INC.
1001 Pennsylvania Ave NW, Washington, DC 20004-2505
Tel.: (202) 729-5626   DE
Web Site: https://www.carlyle.com
Year Founded: 1987
CG—(NASDAQ)
Rev.: $2,963,900,000
Assets: $21,176,000,000
Liabilities: $15,391,500,000
Net Worth: $5,784,500,000
Earnings: ($608,400,000)
Emp.: 2,200
Fiscal Year-end: 12/31/23
Holding Company; Private Equity & Investment Management Firm
N.A.I.C.S.: 551112
Harvey M. Schwartz (CEO)
Barclay G. Jones III (Mng Dir)
Claudius E. Watts IV (Founder-Tech Buyout Bus)
Bruce E. Rosenblum (Head-Risk Mgmt)
John C. Redett (CFO & Head-Corp Strategy)
Mark Jenkins (Mng Dir & Head-Global Credit-New York, NY)
Michael Haas (CIO)
Scott H. Hughes (COO-Corp Private Equity-Americas)

Norma Kuntz (COO-Private Equity-Global & CFO-Private Equity-Global)
Kara Helander (Chief Diversity , Equity & Inclusion Officer)
Ashley Evans (Mng Dir-Media, Tech, and Telecom Group)
Ashley Evans (Mng Dir-Media, Tech, and Telecom Group)
Patrick R. McCarter (Partner & Head-Tech, Media, and Telecommunications Sector-Global)
Catherine Ziobro (Chief Compliance Officer)
Reginald Van Lee (Chief Transformation Officer)
James Stavridis (Vice Chm-Global Affairs & Mng Dir-Washington, DC)
Macky Tall (Chm-Infrastructure Grp)
Megan Foster Starr (Head-Impact-Global)
Jeffrey W. Ferguson (Gen Counsel)
Joe Bress (Mng Dir)
Geoff Hutchinson (Mng Dir & Head-Private Equity-Australia & New Zealand)
William McMullan (Mng Dir)
Jeff Bronaugh (CTO)
Bethany De Lude (Chief Information Security Officer)
David M. Garofalo (COO)
David S. McCann (Head)
Eleena Melamed (Head)
Robert Rosen (Head)
Daniel A. D'Aniello (Co-Founder)
David M. Rubenstein (Co-Founder & Co-Chm)
William E. Conway Jr. (Co-Founder & Co-Chm)
Charles E. Andrews Jr. (Chief Acctg Officer)
James G. Stavridis (Vice Chm & Mng Dir)

Subsidiaries:

ADB Safegate bvba (1)
Leuvensesteenweg 585, 1930, Zaventem, Belgium
Tel.: (32) 27221711
Web Site: http://adbsafegate.com
Emp.: 1,000
Airfield Guidance Solutions
N.A.I.C.S.: 488119
Christian Onselaere (CEO)
Sebastien Dreyer (CFO)
Henrik Linderberth (VP-Sls & Mktg)
Steve Rutland (COO)
Joe Pokoj (CEO-Americas)
Jean-Francois Delbar (VP-HR)
Jean Luc Devisscher (Dir-Mktg)

Subsidiary (US):

ADB Airfield Solutions (2)
720 Hopmeadow St, Simsbury, CT 06070
Tel.: (614) 864-2069
Web Site: http://www.adb-air.com
Airport Operations
N.A.I.C.S.: 488119
Glenn Anderson (Acct Mgr-Strategic)

ADB Safegate Americas, LLC (2)
977 Gahanna Pkwy, Columbus, OH 43230-6610
Tel.: (614) 861-1304
Web Site: http://adbsafegate.com
Airfield Lighting Solutions & Services
N.A.I.C.S.: 488119
Joe Pokoj (CEO-Americas)

Accolade Wines Holdings Australia Pty Limited (1)
Reynell Road, Reynella, Adelaide, 5161, SA, Australia
Tel.: (61) 883922222
Web Site: http://www.accoladewines.com
Holding Company; Wine Production & Whslr
N.A.I.C.S.: 551112
Lydia Freeman (Mktg Mgr)
Martin MacKinnon (Gen Mgr-Travel Retail-Global)

The Carlyle Group Inc.—(Continued)

Subsidiary (Domestic):

Accolade Wines Australia Limited (2)
Level 10 10 Franklin Street, Reynella, Adelaide, 5000, SA, Australia
Tel.: (61) 883922222
Web Site: http://www.accoladewines.com
Producer, Marketer & Exporter of Wines
N.A.I.C.S.: 312130
Michael East (Gen Mgr-Comml-Australia & New Zealand)
Tim Matz (Mng Dir-North America)
Freddie Choong (Gen Mgr-Comml-Asia Pacific)
David Cunningham (CMO)

Branch (Domestic):

Accolade Wines Australia Ltd. - Botany (3)
Level 2 Building E 40 Lord Street, Botany, 2019, NSW, Australia
Tel.: (61) 131 492
Web Site: http://www.accoladewines.com
Wine Producer
N.A.I.C.S.: 312130

Accolade Wines Australia Ltd. - Mount Waverley (3)
Unit 11 270 Ferntree Gully Road, Notting Hill, 3168, VIC, Australia
Tel.: (61) 395588322
Winery
N.A.I.C.S.: 312130

Unit (Domestic):

Hardy's Tintara Winery (3)
202 Main Road, McLaren Vale, 5171, SA, Australia
Tel.: (61) 61883294124
Web Site: http://www.hardyswines.com
Winery
N.A.I.C.S.: 312130

Houghton Wines (3)
4070 Caves Road, Wilyabrup, Busselton, 6280, WA, Australia
Tel.: (61) 897556042
Web Site: http://www.houghton-wines.com.au
Wine Mfr & Seller
N.A.I.C.S.: 312130

Subsidiary (Non-US):

Accolade Wines Holdings Europe Limited (2)
Thomas Hardy House 2 Heath Road, Weybridge, KT13 8TB, Surrey, United Kingdom
Tel.: (44) 1932428600
Web Site: http://www.accoladewines.com
Holding Company; Wine Whslr
N.A.I.C.S.: 551112

Subsidiary (Domestic):

Accolade Wines Limited (3)
Thomas Hardy House 2 Heath Road, Weybridge, GU3.1LR, Surrey, United Kingdom
Tel.: (44) 1932428600
Web Site: http://www.accoladewines.com
Winery Production
N.A.I.C.S.: 312130
Caroline Thompson-Hill (Mng Dir-Europe)
Martin McGowan (Sls Dir-UK & Ireland)

Subsidiary (Non-US):

Accolade Wines Japan K.K. (2)
2-10-2 Shirokanedai, Minato-ku, Tokyo, 108-0071, Japan
Tel.: (81) 357913337
Web Site: http://www.accoladewines.com
Alcoholic Beverage Distr
N.A.I.C.S.: 424820
Jun Imai (Pres)

Accolade Wines New Zealand Limited (2)
22 Liverpool Street Riverlands Estate RD4, Blenheim, 7274, New Zealand
Tel.: (64) 35206011
Wine Producer
N.A.I.C.S.: 312130

Unit (Domestic):

Mud House Wine (3)
22 Liverpool Street Riverlands Estate, Blenheim, New Zealand
Tel.: (64) 3 520 6011
Web Site: http://www.mudhouse.co.nz
Wine Producer
N.A.I.C.S.: 312130
Tom Bullen (Mgr-Central Otogo Vineyard)
Jean-Luc Dufour (Mgr-Waipara Valley Vineyard)
Nev Gane (Mgr-Vineyard-Marlborough)

Waipara Hills Wine (3)
780 Glasnevin Rd SH1, North Canterbury, Waipara, New Zealand
Tel.: (64) 33146900
Web Site: http://waiparahills.co.nz
Wine Producer
N.A.I.C.S.: 312130
Nev Gane (Mgr-Vineyard-Marlborough)
Jean-Luc Dufour (Mgr-Vineyard-Waipara Valley)
Tom Bullen (Mgr-Vineyard-Central Otago)
Ben Roiri (Asst Mgr-Vineyard-Waipara Valley)

Subsidiary (Non-US):

Accolade Wines South Africa (Pty) Ltd. (2)
Flagstone Winery WR Quinan Boulevard Paardevlei, Somerset West, 7600, South Africa
Tel.: (27) 218525052
Web Site: http://www.accoladewines.com
Wine Distr
N.A.I.C.S.: 424820
Ari Mervis (Chm)
Mike Walsh (CFO)
Anton Van Heerden (Dir-Supply Chain & Ops)
Anjanette Murfet (Dir-People, Comm & Govt Rels)
Sandy Mayo (Dir-Mktg & Global Brands)

Accudyne Industries, LLC (1)
2728 N Harwood St Ste 200, Dallas, TX 75201-1579
Tel.: (469) 518-4777
Sales Range: $1-4.9 Billion
Emp.: 3,000
Holding Company; Industrial Pumps & Compressors Mfr
N.A.I.C.S.: 551112
Donna Peruta (CIO)
Steve Murphy (VP-Bus Dev)
Erin Paisan (Mgr-Corp Comm)
Kevin McGlinchey (Gen Counsel)
Tom Stubbins (VP-HR)
Chris Krieps (Pres-Precision Flow Sys)

Subsidiary (Non-US):

Accudyne Industries Asia Pte. Ltd. (2)
501 510 Thomson Rd 13-01, Singapore, 298135, Singapore
Tel.: (65) 64557559
Emp.: 20
High-Pressure Pumps, Gas Boosters & Valves Distr
N.A.I.C.S.: 423830
Danny Yue (Reg Mgr)

Subsidiary (Domestic):

Haskel International, LLC (2)
100 E Graham Pl, Burbank, CA 91502-2027
Tel.: (818) 843-4000
Web Site: http://www.haskel.com
Sales Range: $100-124.9 Million
Emp.: 1,300
High-Pressure Pumps, Gas Boosters & Valves Mfr & Distr
N.A.I.C.S.: 333914
Pat Kealey (Pres)

Subsidiary (Non-US):

Haskel Europe Ltd. (3)
North Hylton Road, Sunderland, SR5 3JD, Tyne & Wear, United Kingdom
Tel.: (44) 1915491212
Web Site: http://www.haskel-europe.com
High-Pressure Pumps, Gas Boosters & Valves Mfr & Distr
N.A.I.C.S.: 333914

Stephen Learney (Mng Dir)
Dave Angus (Mgr-Quality)
Nicola Miller (Mgr-HR)
Graham Fox (Mgr-Svc)

Plant (Domestic):

Haskel Europe Ltd. - Aberdeen (4)
Unit 14 Airways Industrial Estate, Pitmedden Road, Dyce, AB21 0DT, Scotland, United Kingdom
Tel.: (44) 1224771784
Web Site: http://www.haskel-europe.com
High-Pressure Pumps, Gas Boosters & Valves Mfr
N.A.I.C.S.: 333914

Subsidiary (Non-US):

Haskel France SAS (4)
34 Rue Des Chateaux, 59290, Wasquehal, France
Tel.: (33) 320046600
Web Site: http://www.haskel.fr
High-Pressure Pumps, Gas Boosters & Valves Distr
N.A.I.C.S.: 423830
Alexandre Clay (Mng Dir)

Haskel Sistemas de Fluidos Espana, S.R.L. (4)
Paseo Ubarburu No 81 Edificio 5 Planta 1 Locales 1 y 2, Poligono 27 Martutene, 20115, Astigarraga, Gipuzkoa, Spain
Tel.: (34) 943474566
Web Site: http://www.haskel-es.com
Emp.: 6
High-Pressure Pumps, Gas Boosters & Valves Mfr & Distr
N.A.I.C.S.: 333914

Subsidiary (Non-US):

M2S Middle East FZE (2)
LOB 16 Suite 16614, PO Box 262384, Jebel Ali, Dubai, United Arab Emirates
Tel.: (971) 48875646
Emp.: 25
High-Pressure Pumps, Gas Boosters & Valves Distr
N.A.I.C.S.: 423830
Robert Roy (Dir-Sls)

Subsidiary (Domestic):

Milton Roy, LLC (2)
201 Ivyland Rd, Ivyland, PA 18974-1706
Tel.: (215) 441-0800
Web Site: http://www.miltonroy.com
Sales Range: $75-99.9 Million
Controlled Volume (Metering) Pumps & Related Equipment Mfr
N.A.I.C.S.: 333914
Kris Kimmel (Product Mgr YZ Sys)
Tom Humphreys (Area Mgr-Western)
Jeff Ives (Area Mgr-Eastern)
Kenny Louque (Area Mgr-Southern)
David Urena (Area Mgr-Latin America)
David Pressler (Area Mgr-Central)
Patti McDonald (Mgr-Customer Svc & Application Engr)

Division (Domestic):

Milton Roy - Hartell Division (3)
201 Ivyland Rd, Ivyland, PA 18974
Tel.: (215) 441-0800
Web Site: http://www.hartell.com
Sales Range: $50-74.9 Million
Pumps Mfr
N.A.I.C.S.: 333914
Lisa Haines (Mgr-Sls-Western Reg)
Steve Wolfe (Product Mgr)

Subsidiary (Non-US):

Milton Roy Europe (3)
10 Grande Rue, Pont-Saint-Pierre, 27360, France
Tel.: (33) 232683000
Web Site: http://www.miltonroy-europe.com
Sales Range: $100-124.9 Million
Emp.: 250
Pumps & Compressors Mfr
N.A.I.C.S.: 333914

Subsidiary (Domestic):

Milton Roy Liquid Metronics Incorporated (3)
8th Post Office Sq, Acton, MA 01720-3948

Tel.: (978) 635-4999
Web Site: http://www.lmipumps.com
Sales Range: $25-49.9 Million
Measuring & Dispensing Pumps
N.A.I.C.S.: 333914

Williams Instrument Company (3)
201 Ivyland Rd, Warminster, PA 18974-1706
Tel.: (215) 441-0800
Web Site: http://www.williamspumps.com
Sales Range: $1-9.9 Million
Pneumatic Metering Pumps & Chemical Injection Systems Mfr
N.A.I.C.S.: 333914

Y-Z Systems Inc. (3)
8875 North Sam Houston Pkwy West, Houston, TX 77064
Tel.: (281) 362-6500
Web Site: http://www.yzsystems.com
Sales Range: $25-49.9 Million
Emp.: 12
Odorization Systems Mfr
N.A.I.C.S.: 334516
Kris Kimmel (Mgr-Sls)

Subsidiary (Domestic):

Sundyne, LLC (2)
14845 W 64th Ave, Arvada, CO 80007-7523
Tel.: (303) 425-0800
Web Site: http://www.sundyne.com
Sales Range: $125-149.9 Million
Emp.: 400
Pumps & Pumping Equipment Mfr
N.A.I.C.S.: 333914
Daryl Lamy (Dir-Sls-Tactical,Worldwide)
Marie Weiss-Rich (Dir-HR-Worldwide)
Colin Guppy (VP-Chemical & Indus-Global)
Shawn Olson (Gen Mgr-Americas)
Jeffrey Wiemelt (Pres)
Tom Helmreich (Dir-Product Dev)
Steve Rose (Gen Mgr-UK & Spain)
Pat Hicks (Dir-Fin-Worldwide)
Scott Allen (Dir-Ops)
Alan Brown (Sls Mgr-Americas)
Cameron Freiboth (Mgr-Continuous Improvement, Quality, and EH&S)
Tim Humiston (Mgr-Aftermarket Svcs)
Breanne Taylor (Mgr-HR)
Mary S. Zappone (CEO)
Mark Sefcik (COO)
Andrew Matsuyama (CFO)
Mary S. Zappone (CEO)
Rodney Vinegar (Chief HR Officer & VP-Environmental, Health, and Safety)
Alton Smith (Reg Sls Mgr-North & Latin America)
Aaron Bridges (Chief Comml Officer)
Michael O'Neil (VP-Hydrogen & PPI Compressor Sls)
Victoria Moshashvili (Dir-Corp Dev & Strategic Analysis)
Kevin Lance (Gen Mgr)

AlpInvest Partners Limited (1)
701 Champion Tower 3 Garden Road, Hong Kong, China (Hong Kong)
Tel.: (852) 28787099
Investment Management Service
N.A.I.C.S.: 523940
Sander van Maanen (Mng Dir)
Wendy Zhu (Mng Dir)
Alex Forster (VP)
Joe Ma (VP)
Digvijay Lamba (VP)
Aquila Chu (Principal)
John Kim (Principal)

Joint Venture (US):

RSA Security LLC (2)
174 Middlesex Tpke, Bedford, MA 01730
Tel.: (781) 515-5000
Web Site: http://www.rsa.com
Security Management Services
N.A.I.C.S.: 561621
Zulfikar Ramzan (CTO)
Holly Rollo (CMO & Sr VP)
Doug Howard (VP-Global Svcs)
Rohit Ghai (CEO)
William Chrisholm (Chm)
Bill Diaz (CEO-RSA Archer)

Subsidiary (Non-US):

RSA Security GmbH (3)
Osterfeldstrasse 84, 85737, Ismaning, Germany

Tel.: (49) 89930910
Web Site: http://www.rsa.com
Network Security Systems & Risk Solutions
N.A.I.C.S.: 541512

RSA Security UK Limited (3)
Rsa House Western Road, Bracknell, RG12
1RT, Berkshire, United Kingdom
Tel.: (44) 1344781000
Web Site: http://www.rsa.com
Network Security Systems
N.A.I.C.S.: 541512

**Amalgamated Electronic Corporation
Limited** (1)
Amecor House 14 Richard Road Industria
North, Roodepoort, 1706, South Africa
Tel.: (27) 114772600
Web Site: http://www.amecor.com
Electric Equipment Mfr
N.A.I.C.S.: 334515
Keith Vieira (CEO)
Guy Williamson (Chief Dev Officer-FSK
Grp)
Duran Vieira (Mng Dir-FSK Grp)

Subsidiary (Domestic):

FSK Electronics SA (Pty) Ltd (2)
Amecor House 14 Richard Rd Industria
North, Johannesburg, South Africa
Tel.: (27) 114772600
Web Site: https://www.amecor.com
Wireless Communication Mfr
N.A.I.C.S.: 334220
Duran Vieira (Mng Dir)
Natasha Loubser (Mgr-Natl Sls)
Gary Stanley (Branch Mgr)
Kevin Medcalf (Branch Mgr)
Guy Williamson (Chief Dev Officer)
Keith Vieira (CEO)

**Sabre Radio Networks SA (Pty)
Ltd** (2)
14 Richard Rd Industria N, Johannesburg,
1709, Gauteng, South Africa
Tel.: (27) 114772600
Web Site:
    http://www.sabreradionetworks.co.za
Radio Networks Management & Mainte-
nance Services
N.A.I.C.S.: 516210

**Asia Satellite Telecommunications
Holdings Limited** (1)
12/F Harbour Centre 25 Harbour Road,
Wanchai, China (Hong Kong)
Tel.: (852) 25000888
Web Site: http://www.asiasat.com
Rev.: $184,072,286
Assets: $921,704,344
Liabilities: $457,659,986
Net Worth: $464,044,358
Earnings: $54,814,891
Emp.: 133
Fiscal Year-end: 12/31/2018
Satellite Telecommunication Services
N.A.I.C.S.: 517410
Sue Chiu Yeung (CFO & Sec)
Roger Tong (CEO)
Catherine Chang (Gen Counsel)
Barrie Woolston (Chief Comml Officer)
Yan Zhang (VP-China)
Fred Ho (VP-Technical Ops)
Saphina Ho (Gen Counsel)
Ina Lui (Sr VP-Comml, Bus Dev & Strategy)
Fred Vong (VP-Engrg)
Raymond Chow (VP-Bus Dev & Strategy)
Tony Chung (VP-Data Svcs)

Subsidiary (Domestic):

**Asia Satellite Telecommunications
Co., Ltd.** (2)
15 Dai Kwai Street, Tai Po Industrial Estate,
Hong Kong, New Territories, China (Hong
Kong)
Tel.: (852) 25000888
Web Site: http://www.asiasat.com
Sales Range: $25-49.9 Million
Emp.: 50
Satellite Telecommunication Services
N.A.I.C.S.: 517410
Sabrina Cubbon (Gen Mgr-Mktg)

BTI Studios AB (1)
Kungsbro Strand 15a, 112 26, Stockholm,
Sweden
Tel.: (46) 8 458 00 55
Web Site: http://www.btistudios.com

Emp.: 300
Video Postproduction Services
N.A.I.C.S.: 512191
Lennart Lof (Mng Dir-Nordic Subtitling)
Henrik Wikren (CFO)
Robert Holmstrom (CTO)
Maria D'Alessandro (Sr Dir-Broadcast Svcs)
Carlo DeCianti (Sr VP-Sls & Bus Dev-
Global)
Joe Kahle (Sr VP-Sls-Americas)
Niclas Ekstedt (Mgr-Studio-Dubbing)
Mathias Henning (Head-Multimedia Local-
ization)
Chris Carey (Mng Dir/Chief Revenue
Officer-Americas)
Shaun Gregory (CEO)

Subsidiary (Non-US):

BTI Studios - Romania (2)
Bv Dacia 34-36, Oradea, 410339, Romania
Tel.: (40) 259 452911
Video Postproduction Services
N.A.I.C.S.: 512191
Sandor Barany (Dir-Studio)

BTI Studios Sp. z o.o (2)
Chocimska 6, 00-791, Warsaw, Poland
Tel.: (48) 225470260
Video Postproduction Services
N.A.I.C.S.: 512191

Iyuno UK III Ltd. (2)
3rd Floor 578-586 Chiswick High Road,
London, W4 5RP, United Kingdom
Tel.: (44) 2074405407
Emp.: 50
Video Postproduction Services
N.A.I.C.S.: 512191
Mark Kirkpatrick (Sr VP-Sls-Europe, Middle
East & Africa)

Banker'S Toolbox, Inc. (1)
12331-B Riata Trace Pkwy Bldg 4 Ste 200,
Austin, TX 78741
Tel.: (888) 201-2231
Web Site: http://www.abrigo.com
Software Developer
N.A.I.C.S.: 513210

Subsidiary (Domestic):

DI Com Software Corp. (2)
2301 Lucien Way Ste 450, Maitland, FL
32751
Tel.: (407) 246-8060
Web Site: http://www.dicomsoftware.com
Rev.: $2,000,000
Emp.: 15
Software Publisher
N.A.I.C.S.: 513210
Josie Harmacek (VP)
Steve Wert (Pres & CEO)

TPG Software, Inc. (2)
5858 Westheimer Rd, Houston, TX 77057
Tel.: (713) 974-1375
Web Site: http://www.tpgsoftware.com
Sales Range: $1-9.9 Million
Emp.: 28
Accounting Software Publisher
N.A.I.C.S.: 513210
Ursula H. Felmet (CEO & CFO)
Cory Sokoloski (VP-Sls & Mktg)
Rick Schnitger (VP-Product Mgmt)
Slavek R. Rotkiewicz (Pres & CTO)

Barbon Insurance Group Limited (1)
Hestia House Unit 2 Edgewest Road, Lin-
coln, LN6 7EL, United Kingdom
Tel.: (44) 8000358258
Web Site: http://homelet.co.uk
Emp.: 300
Residential & Commercial Property Insur-
ance Products & Services
N.A.I.C.S.: 524126
Nigel Robbins (Mgr-Broker Network Dev)
Andy Glynne (Dir-Comml)
Andy Webb (COO & Mng Dir)
Nigel Archer (Chief Risk Officer)
Sharon Phillips (Dir-HR)

Bodegas Bilbainas, S.A. (1)
Estacion s/n, 26200, Haro, Spain
Tel.: (34) 941310147
Web Site: https://www.15bodegas.com
Wine Mfr
N.A.I.C.S.: 312130
Mayte Calvo (Dir)

**CARLYLE SINGAPORE INVEST-
MENT ADVISORS PTE LTD** (1)

1 Temasek Avenue, Millenia Tower, Singa-
pore, 039192, Singapore
Tel.: (65) 62129600
Investment Advisory Services
N.A.I.C.S.: 523940

**CECP Investment Advisors France
S.A.R.L.** (1)
112 avenue Kleber, 75116, Paris, France
Tel.: (33) 153703520
Investment Advisory Services
N.A.I.C.S.: 523940

CFGI, LLC (1)
1 Lincoln St Ste 1301, Boston, MA 02111
Tel.: (617) 531-8270
Web Site: https://www.cfgi.com
Accounting Services
N.A.I.C.S.: 541219
Nick Hart (Partner)
Nick Nardone (Co-Founder & Co-CEO)
Shane Caiazzo (Co-Founder & Co-CEO)
Angela Barcelos (Partner)
Robert Keep (Partner)
Matt Pantera (Partner)
Michael Muccio (Partner)
Chris Nyers (Partner)
Joachim Bader (Mng Dir)
Robert Carrino (Mng Dir)
Catherine Thorpe (Mng Partner-Stamford
Office)

Subsidiary (Domestic):

Pine Hill Group LLC (2)
1835 Market St Ste 2400, Philadelphia, PA
19103
Tel.: (215) 558-2860
Investment Advisory Services
N.A.I.C.S.: 524298

CICF L.L.C. (1)
English Foundation Building 615 N Alabama
St Ste 300, Indianapolis, IN 46204-1498
Tel.: (317) 634-2423
Web Site: https://www.cicf.org
Welfare Trust Services
N.A.I.C.S.: 523991

CREA Germany GmbH (1)
Promenadenplatz 8, 80333, Munich, Ger-
many
Tel.: (49) 892444600
Investment Advisory Services
N.A.I.C.S.: 523940

**Carlyle Asia Investment Advisors
Limited** (1)
Two Pacific Place 88 Queensway 28th
Floor Suite 2801, Hong Kong, China (Hong
Kong)
Tel.: (852) 28787000
Investment Management Service
N.A.I.C.S.: 523940

Carlyle Aviation Partners LLC (1)
848 Brickell Ave Ste 500, Miami, FL 33131
Tel.: (305) 579-2340
Web Site: https://carlyle.aero
Emp.: 115
Aircraft Parts Mfr & Distr
N.A.I.C.S.: 336413

**Carlyle Aviation Securities Partners,
LLC** (1)
848 Brickell Ave Ste 700, Miami, FL 33131
Tel.: (305) 504-8777
Web Site: https://casp.aero
Investment Management Service
N.A.I.C.S.: 523940

Subsidiary (Domestic):

Carlyle Aviation Group, LLC (2)
848 Brickell Ave Ste 500, Miami, FL 33131
Tel.: (305) 579-2340
Web Site: https://www.carlyle.aero
Commercial Jet Aircraft, Engines & Equip-
ment Acquisition, Refurbishment, Marketing
& Leasing Services
N.A.I.C.S.: 532411
Robert Korn (Co-Founder & Pres)
William Hoffman (Co-Founder, Chm & Prin-
cipal)
Robert Taylor (Chief Technical Officer)
Javier Meireles (CFO & COO)
Alexander Rasnavad (Mng Dir & Chief
Comml Officer)
Z. Clifton Dameron (Chief Legal Officer)
Jason Avdenko (Chief Compliance Officer)

Churchill Financial LLC (1)
400 Park Ave Ste 1510, New York, NY
10022
Tel.: (212) 763-4600
Web Site: http://www.churchillnet.com
Sales Range: $50-74.9 Million
Emp.: 72
Corporate Financing & Venture Capital Firm
N.A.I.C.S.: 523999

**Claren Road Asset Management
LLC** (1)
51 Astor 12th Fl, New York, NY
10003 (55%)
Tel.: (212) 888-1433
Web Site: http://www.clarenroad.com
Sales Range: $25-49.9 Million
Emp.: 12
Investment Consulting Services
N.A.I.C.S.: 523940
Albert Marino (Principal)

Claritas LLC (1)
8044 Montgomery Rd Ste 455, Cincinnati,
OH 45236
Tel.: (800) 866-6511
Web Site: http://www.claritas.com
Sociological & Educational Research Ser-
vices
N.A.I.C.S.: 541910
Mike Nazzaro (CEO)
Karthik Iyer (COO)
Jay Stockwell (Chief Revenue Officer)
R. Chase Miller (Exec VP-Strategy & Corp
Dev)
Angie Hemmelgarn (Chief HR Officer)
Jim Schuster (CFO)

Client Network Services Inc. (1)
2277 Research Blvd, Rockville, MD 20850
Tel.: (301) 634-4600
Web Site: http://www.cns-inc.com
Information Technology & Business Process
Outsourcing Services
N.A.I.C.S.: 541513
Arnold Morse (Chief Compliance Officer &
Gen Counsel)
C. K. Kumar (Mng Dir & Sr VP-Chennai)
Todd Stottlemyer (CEO)
Harish Nanda (CTO & Exec VP)
Carl Rosenblatt (Chief Bus Dev Officer &
Exec VP)
David Adams (CFO & Exec VP)
Bob McCord (Pres & COO)
Mike Jin (CIO & Chief Info Security Officer)
Patricia Scott (Chief HR Officer & Exec VP)
Kevin McFarling (Chief Delivery Officer &
Exec VP)
Kelly Schlageter (CMO & Sr VP)
Gaurav Maini (Sr VP/Mng Dir-Chennai)
Verlon Johnson (Sr VP-Corp Strategy)

**Cogentrix Energy Power Manage-
ment, LLC** (1)
13860 Ballantyne Corporate Pl Ste 300,
Charlotte, NC 28277
Tel.: (704) 525-3800
Web Site: http://www.cogentrix.com
Asset Management, Engineering & Corpo-
rate Support Services
N.A.I.C.S.: 523940
John Gasbarro (Sr VP-M&A, Asset Mgmt &
Fuels)
Linda A. Okowita (Sr VP-HR)
Jacob A. Pollack (Gen Counsel, Sec & Sr
VP)
William L. Felts (Exec VP-Portfolio Mgmt)
Robert B. Howard (COO & Exec VP)
John Ragan (CEO)
Jay Crawford (Sr VP-Asset Mgmt)
Jeff Ingraham (Sr VP-Generation Svcs)
Jason Solimini (CFO & Sr VP)
Olaf Honerkamp (VP-Risk Mgmt)
Ernie Schism (VP-IT)

Comdata SpA (1)
via Sebastiano Caboto, Corsico, 20094,
Milan, Italy
Tel.: (39) 024149931
Web Site: http://www.comdatagroup.com
Call Center, Help Desk & Document Man-
agement Outsourcing Services
N.A.I.C.S.: 561422
Massimo Canturi (CEO)
Maxime Didier (CEO-France)
Ulrike Becker (CFO)
Alessandro Zunino (CEO-Comdata Grp &
CEO-Comdata Italy)
Angel Parra (CEO-Comdata Spain &
Latam)

The Carlyle Group Inc.—(Continued)

Andrea Tonoli (CEO-Comdata UK, Czech Republic & Germany)
Ronen Melnik (Head-Comdata Digital)
Adriano Mureddu (Chief HR Officer)
Frederic Donati (Chief Comml Officer)
Antonio Salvo (Dir-Merger & Acq & Corp Dev)
Patrice Mazoyer (Chief Transformation & Integration Officer & Head-Comm)

Subsidiary (Non-US):

Comdata Holding SA　　　　(2)
1 Avenue du General de Gaulle, 92230, Gennevilliers, France
Tel.: (33) 820892000
Web Site: http://france.comdatagroup.com
Business Support Services
N.A.I.C.S.: 561499
Sebastien Litou (CFO)
Frederic Donati (Gen Mgr-Bus Dev)
Didier Manzari (Gen Mgr-Morroco & Barcelona)
Gaelle Bonnefond (Chief HR Officer)
Guillaume Joinau-Dumail (COO)
Sebastien Nicolas (CTO)

Counter Brands LLC　　　　(1)
1733 Ocean Ave, Santa Monica, CA 90401
Tel.: (310) 828-0111
Web Site: http://www.beautycounter.com
Cosmetics Products Mfr
N.A.I.C.S.: 456120
Mia Davis (VP-Health & Safety)
Gregg Renfrew (Founder, Chm & Chief Brand Officer)
Nital Scott (CFO)
Marc Rey (CEO)

Curia, Inc.　　　　(1)
26 Corporate Cir, Albany, NY 12212
Tel.: (518) 512-2000
Web Site: http://curiaglobal.com
Contract Chemistry Research & Development Services
N.A.I.C.S.: 541715
Christopher Conway (Pres-Res & Dev)
Dawn Von Rohr (Sr VP-Strategy)
Joseph D. Sangregorio (Chief HR Officer)
Diane M. Beno (Sr VP-Quality)
John Ratliff (Chm)
Mike Kleppinger (Chief Comml Officer)
Jason Knoblauch (CFO)
Prakash Pandian (CIO)
Stacei Phillips (Sec & Gen Counsel)
Hua Tu (CTO)
Scott Wagner (Sr VP-Global Ops)
Scott Waldman (Sr VP-Corp Dev)
Niall Condon (Pres-Mfg-Div)
Philip Macnabb (CEO)
Gerald Auer (CFO)

Subsidiary (Domestic):

CURIA INDIANA, LLC　　　　(2)
3065 Kent Ave, West Lafayette, IN 47906-1076
Tel.: (765) 463-0112
Life Science, Physical, Engineering Research & Development Services
N.A.I.C.S.: 541715

Subsidiary (Non-US):

Curia France SAS　　　　(2)
Zone Industrielle de Laville, 47240, Bon Encontre, France
Tel.: (33) 553691300
Fine Chemicals Mfr
N.A.I.C.S.: 325998

Curia Germany GmbH　　　　(2)
Industriepark Hochst, 65926, Frankfurt, Germany
Tel.: (49) 6930522055
Pharmaceutical Ingredient Mfr
N.A.I.C.S.: 325199

Curia Holdings (UK) Limited　　　　(2)
Todd Campus West of Scotland Science Park, Glasgow, G20 0XA, Lanarkshire, United Kingdom
Tel.: (44) 1419458400
Drug Research & Development Services
N.A.I.C.S.: 541715

Subsidiary (Domestic):

Curia (Scotland) Limited　　　　(3)

Todd Campus West of Scotland Science Park, Glasgow, G20 0XA, Lanarkshire, United Kingdom
Tel.: (44) 1419458400
Aseptic Formulation Development & Drug Product Mfr
N.A.I.C.S.: 325412

Subsidiary (Non-US):

Curia India Private Limited　　　　(2)
Plot 9 MN Park Turkapally Shameerpet Genome Valley, RR District, Hyderabad, 500 078, India
Tel.: (91) 4066876666
Chemical & Pharmaceutical Research
N.A.I.C.S.: 541715

Subsidiary (Domestic):

Curia Massachusetts, Inc.　　　　(2)
99 S Bedford St, Burlington, MA 01803
Tel.: (781) 270-7900
Pharmaceutical Preparation Mfr
N.A.I.C.S.: 325412

Curia Missouri, Inc.　　　　(2)
2460 W Bennett St, Springfield, MO 65807-1229
Tel.: (417) 868-3458
Pharmaceutical Ingredient Mfr
N.A.I.C.S.: 325199

Curia New Mexico, LLC　　　　(2)
4401 Alexander Blvd NE, Albuquerque, NM 87107
Tel.: (505) 923-1500
Surgical & Medical Instrument Mfr
N.A.I.C.S.: 339112

Curia New York, Inc.　　　　(2)
33 Riverside Ave, Rensselaer, NY 12144
Tel.: (518) 433-7700
Pharmaceuticals Mfr
N.A.I.C.S.: 325412

Curia Services, Inc.　　　　(2)
26 Corporate Cir, Albany, NY 12203
Tel.: (518) 512-2000
Pharmaceuticals Product Mfr
N.A.I.C.S.: 325412

Curia Washington, Inc.　　　　(2)
26 Corporate Cir, Albany, NY 12203
Tel.: (518) 512-2000
Natural Products Drug Discovery & In Vitro Biology Research
N.A.I.C.S.: 541714

Dynamic Precision Group　　　　(1)
3651 SE Commerce Ave, Stuart, FL 34997
Tel.: (772) 287-7770
Web Site: http://www.gotodpg.com
Gas Turbine Engine Parts Mfr
N.A.I.C.S.: 336412

Holding (Domestic):

Paradigm Precision Holdings, LLC　　　　(2)
404 W Guadalupe Rd, Tempe, AZ 85283
Tel.: (480) 839-0501
Web Site: http://www.paradigmprecision.com
Holding Company; Aerospace & Industrial Gas Turbine Engine Complex Machined Components Mfr
N.A.I.C.S.: 551112
Ronojoy Ghosh (VP-Bus Dev-Manchester)
Steve Croke (Pres & CEO)

Plant (Domestic):

Paradigm Precision - Berlin　　　　(3)
134 Commerce St, East Berlin, CT 06023
Tel.: (860) 828-0344
Web Site: http://www.paradigmprecision.com
Sales Range: $1-9.9 Million
Emp.: 75
Machine Shops
N.A.I.C.S.: 332710
Don Balducci (VP-Ops)

Paradigm Precision - Malden　　　　(3)
243 Medford St, Malden, MA 02148-7301
Tel.: (781) 321-0480
Web Site: http://www.paradigmprecision.com

Sales Range: $25-49.9 Million
Emp.: 185
Aircraft Engine Components Mfr
N.A.I.C.S.: 336412
Tom Mitchell (VP)

Paradigm Precision - Tempe　　　　(3)
404 W Guadalupe Rd, Tempe, AZ 85283
Tel.: (480) 839-0501
Web Site: http://www.paradigmprecision.com
Sales Range: $25-49.9 Million
Emp.: 100
Aircraft Engines & Engine Parts Mfr
N.A.I.C.S.: 336412
Eric Hall (Dir-IT)

Plant (Non-US):

Paradigm Precision - Tunis　　　　(3)
Route De Sousse GP 1 KM7, 2033, Megrine, Tunisia
Tel.: (216) 71 429 605
Web Site: http://www.paradigmprecision.com
Sales Range: $25-49.9 Million
Emp.: 300
Aerospace & Aircraft Engine Parts Mfr
N.A.I.C.S.: 336412

Holding (Domestic):

TurboCombustor Technology, Inc.　　　　(2)
3651 SE Commerce Ave, Stuart, FL 34997
Tel.: (772) 287-7770
Web Site: http://www.tct-inc.com
Sales Range: $100-124.9 Million
Emp.: 490
Turbo Combustor Mfr
N.A.I.C.S.: 336412
Steve Croke (Pres & CEO)
Ray Grochowski (Gen Counsel & VP)
Brenda M. Thulen (VP-HR)
Rita Lei (CFO)
Alec Searle (COO)

Subsidiary (Non-US):

TurboCombustor Kft.　　　　(3)
Grassalkovich ut 294, 1239, Budapest, Hungary
Tel.: (36) 12878270
Turbo Combustor Mfr
N.A.I.C.S.: 336412

Envea Global SAS　　　　(1)
111 Boulevard Robespierre, CS 80004, 78300, Poissy, Cedex 4, France
Tel.: (33) 139223800
Web Site: http://www.envea.global
Sales Range: $75-99.9 Million
Environment Monitoring Instrument Mfr & Whslr
N.A.I.C.S.: 334513
Stephane Kempenar (CFO)
Pompilia Sopco (Mgr-Grp Mktg & Comm)

Subsidiary (US):

California Analytical Instruments, Inc.　　　　(2)
1312 W Grove Ave, Orange, CA 92865
Tel.: (714) 974-5560
Web Site: http://www.gasanalyzers.com
Rev.: $9,405,000
Emp.: 45
Instruments & Related Products Manufacturing for Measuring, Displaying & Controlling Industrial Process Variables
N.A.I.C.S.: 334513
Frank Smith (Sr VP-Sls & Mktg)
Loren Mathews (Sr VP)
Murty Neti (VP-R&D)
Doug Omer (CFO)
Hal Peper (Sr VP)

Subsidiary (Non-US):

Envea China Ltd.　　　　(2)
Creative Industrial Base A207 No 5 Guangshun North Street, Chaoyang District, Beijing, 100102, China
Tel.: (86) 1084967875
Monitoring Instrument Mfr
N.A.I.C.S.: 334513

Envea GmbH　　　　(2)
Liebigstrasse 5, 85757, Karlsfeld, Germany
Tel.: (49) 8131505720
Monitoring Instrument Mfr

N.A.I.C.S.: 334513

Subsidiary (US):

Envea Inc.　　　　(2)
2623 Kaneville Ct, Geneva, IL 60134
Tel.: (630) 262-4400
Monitoring Instrument Mfr
N.A.I.C.S.: 334513
Malek Hattar (Gen Mgr)

Subsidiary (Non-US):

Envea India Pvt Ltd　　　　(2)
D/ 16 3 and 4 TTC Industrial Area MIDC, Turbhe, Navi Mumbai, 400705, India
Tel.: (91) 2245020000
Monitoring Instrument Mfr
N.A.I.C.S.: 334513

Envea Process GmbH　　　　(2)
Gutedelstrasse 31, Schliengen, 79418, Lorrach, Germany
Tel.: (49) 76358272480
Monitoring Instrument Mfr
N.A.I.C.S.: 334513

Envea UK Ltd.　　　　(2)
ENVEA House Rose and Crown Road, Swavesey, Cambridge, CB24 4RB, United Kingdom
Tel.: (44) 1480468200
Monitoring Instrument Mfr
N.A.I.C.S.: 334513
Chris Shelley (Mng Dir)
Linda Furnell (Mgr-MarComs)
Mark Hayman (Mgr-Engrg)

PCME Ltd.　　　　(2)
Clearview Building 60 Edison Road, Saint Ives, PE27 3GH, Cambs, United Kingdom
Tel.: (44) 1480468200
Web Site: http://www.pcme.com
Emp.: 60
Industrial Continuous Emission Monitor Developer, Mfr & Whslr
N.A.I.C.S.: 334513
William Averdieck (Founder & Mng Dir)
Jon Malins (Head-R&D)

Flender GmbH　　　　(1)
Alfred-Flender-Strasse 77, 46395, Bocholt, Germany
Tel.: (49) 2871920
Web Site: http://www.flender.com
Sales Range: $1-4.9 Billion
Emp.: 8,600
Mfr of Mechanical & Electrical Drive Equipment & Industrial Gears
N.A.I.C.S.: 333612
Ulrich Stock (CFO)
Andreas Evertz (CEO)
Horst Kayser (Chm-Supervisory Bd)

Subsidiary (Non-US):

Bruinhof BV　　　　(2)
Boterdiep 37, 3077 AW, Rotterdam, Netherlands
Tel.: (31) 0104970808
Web Site: http://www.bruinhof.nl
Sales Range: $25-49.9 Million
Emp.: 30
Marine Gears, Bearings, Clutches & Couplings Sales & Service
N.A.I.C.S.: 333612

Subsidiary (US):

Enlighted, Inc.　　　　(2)
3979 Freedom Cir Ste 210, Santa Clara, CA 95054
Tel.: (650) 964-1094
Web Site: http://www.enlightedinc.com
Sensor Software Development Services
N.A.I.C.S.: 541512
Bret Neely (Exec VP)

Flender Corporation　　　　(2)
950 Tollgate Rd, Elgin, IL 60123
Tel.: (847) 931-1990
Sales Range: $25-49.9 Million
Emp.: 60
Drive Train & Gear Mfr
N.A.I.C.S.: 333612

Subsidiary (Non-US):

Flender Ges.m.b.H.　　　　(2)
Industriezentrum No Sud Strasse 4 Objekt

14, PO Box 132, 2355, Wiener Neudorf, Austria
Tel.: (43) 223664570
Web Site: http://www.flender.at
Sales Range: $25-49.9 Million
Emp.: 16
Drive Train & Gear Mfr
N.A.I.C.S.: 333612

Flender Graffenstaden S.A.   **(2)**
1 rue du Vieux Moulin, 67400, Illkirch-Graffenstaden, France
Tel.: (33) 388676000
Web Site: http://www.flender-graff.com
Sales Range: $150-199.9 Million
Emp.: 320
Mfr of High Speed Gear Units, Journal Bearings & Chemical Processing Pumps
N.A.I.C.S.: 333612
Uwe Bierwirth *(Pres & Editorial Dir)*

Flender Iberica S.A.   **(2)**
Poligono Industrial San Marcos Calle Morse 31 Parcela D15, Getafe, E 28906, Madrid, Spain
Tel.: (34) 916836186
Web Site: http://www.flender.es
Sales Range: $25-49.9 Million
Emp.: 25
Drive Train & Gear Mfr
N.A.I.C.S.: 333612

Flender Limited   **(2)**
2 St Georges Gate Road, 5th Fl Hastings, Kolkata, 700022, India
Tel.: (91) 3322230545
Sales Range: $25-49.9 Million
Emp.: 30
Gear Mfr
N.A.I.C.S.: 333612

Flender Power Transmission (Pty.) Ltd.   **(2)**
Corner Furnace & Quality Rd, PO Box 131, Kempton Park, 1600, Isando, South Africa
Tel.: (27) 115712000
Web Site: http://www.seimens.com
Sales Range: $50-74.9 Million
Emp.: 200
Gear Mfr
N.A.I.C.S.: 333613

Flender de Mexico, S.A. de C.V.   **(2)**
17 Poniente 713 Col Centro, Puebla, 72000, Mexico
Tel.: (52) 2222371900
Web Site: http://www.flendermexico.com
Sales Range: $25-49.9 Million
Emp.: 1
Gear Mfr
N.A.I.C.S.: 333612

Subsidiary (Domestic):

Sachsen Guss GmbH   **(2)**
Obere Hauptstrasse 228-230, 09228, Chemnitz, Germany
Tel.: (49) 3722640
Web Site: https://www.sachsenguss.de
Sales Range: $150-199.9 Million
Emp.: 751
Grey Cast Iron & Spheroidal Cast Iron Foundries
N.A.I.C.S.: 331511

Subsidiary (Non-US):

Siemens AB   **(2)**
Evenemangsgatan 21, 169 79, Solna, Sweden
Tel.: (46) 200116621
Web Site: https://www.siemens.com
Sales Range: $1-4.9 Billion
Gear Mfr
N.A.I.C.S.: 333612

Subsidiary (Domestic):

Siemens Geared Motors GmbH   **(2)**
Bahnhofstrasse 40-44, 72072, Tubingen, Germany
Tel.: (49) 70717070
Sales Range: $150-199.9 Million
Emp.: 650
Geared Motor Mfr
N.A.I.C.S.: 333612

Subsidiary (Non-US):

Siemens Ltd.   **(2)**
885 Mountain Highway, Bayswater, 3153,

VIC, Australia
Tel.: (61) 397223000
Web Site: http://new.siemens.com
Gear Mfr
N.A.I.C.S.: 333612

Fly Leasing Limited   **(1)**
West Pier Business Campus, Dun Laoghaire, A96 N6T7, County Dublin, Ireland
Tel.: (353) 12311900
Web Site: http://www.flyleasing.com
Rev.: $334,355,000
Assets: $3,167,585,000
Liabilities: $2,378,589,000
Net Worth: $788,996,000
Earnings: ($67,425,000)
Fiscal Year-end: 12/31/2020
Aircraft Leasing Services
N.A.I.C.S.: 488190
Joseph M. Donovan *(Chm)*

Fortitude Group Holdings, LLC   **(1)**
Chesney House 96 Pits Bay Road 3rd Floor, Pembroke, HM 08, Bermuda   **(71.5%)**
Web Site: http://www.fortitude-re.com
Holding Company
N.A.I.C.S.: 551111
James Bracken *(CEO)*

Subsidiary (US):

Prudential Annuities Life Assurance Corporation   **(2)**
1 Corporate Dr, Shelton, CT 06484
Tel.: (203) 926-1888
Web Site: http://www.prudential.com
Rev.: $7,488,807,000
Assets: $58,578,130,000
Liabilities: $56,896,403,000
Net Worth: $1,681,727,000
Earnings: $4,965,361,000
Emp.: 12,500
Fiscal Year-end: 12/31/2021
Insurance Annuities Investment Services
N.A.I.C.S.: 523999
Dylan J. Tyson *(Pres & Co-CEO)*
Susan M. Mann *(CFO, Chief Acctg Officer & Exec VP)*

Freeport Retail Limited   **(1)**
7 Bell Yard, London, WC2A 2JR, United Kingdom
Tel.: (44) 2036420914
Web Site: http://www.freeportretail.com
Retail Outlet Centers Developer & Property Manager
N.A.I.C.S.: 531312
Iestyn Roberts *(CEO)*
Chris Milliken *(Comml Dir)*

Grupo Empresarial Palacios Alimentacion SA   **(1)**
Ctra de Logrono s/n 26120, Albelda de Iregua, La Rioja, Spain
Tel.: (34) 902443032
Web Site: https://www.palacios-en.com
Food Production
N.A.I.C.S.: 424420
Pedro Dominguez *(Gen Mgr)*

Subsidiary (US):

Elore Enterprises LLC   **(2)**
1055 NW 159th Dr, Miami, FL 33169
Tel.: (305) 477-1650
Web Site: http://www.palacios.us
Meat Processing Services
N.A.I.C.S.: 311612
Sergio Pires *(Dir-Sls)*

H.C. Starck GmbH & Co. KG   **(1)**
Im Schleeke 78 91, 38642, Goslar, Germany
Tel.: (49) 53217510
Web Site: http://www.hcstarck.com
Sales Range: $1-4.9 Billion
Ceramics & Refractory Metals Mfr
N.A.I.C.S.: 325180
Jan Losch *(Member-Exec Bd)*
Jens Knoll *(Member-Exec Bd)*

Subsidiary (US):

H.C. Starck Inc   **(2)**
45 Industrial Pl, Newton, MA 02461-1951
Tel.: (617) 630-5800
Web Site: http://www.hcstarck.com

Sales Range: $25-49.9 Million
Emp.: 175
Mfr of Capacitor Grade Tantalum Powder, Tantalum & Niobium Mill Products for Electronic, Chemical Processing, Aerospace & Nuclear Industries
N.A.I.C.S.: 331410
Jacques Gagnon *(Mgr-Facility Maintenance & Ops Support)*

Branch (Domestic):

H.C. Starck Inc   **(3)**
21801 Tungsten Rd, Euclid, OH 44117
Tel.: (216) 692-3990
Web Site: http://www.hcstarck.com
Sales Range: $50-74.9 Million
Mfr of Alloys & Molybdenum Products
N.A.I.C.S.: 541330
Craig W. Butchello *(Coord-EDM)*

H.C. Starck, Inc.   **(3)**
1250 E 222 St, Euclid, OH 44117
Tel.: (201) 438-9000
Web Site: http://www.hcstarck.com
Sales Range: $25-49.9 Million
Emp.: 110
Mfr of Nonferrous Rolling & Drawing
N.A.I.C.S.: 331491
Craig W. Butchello *(Coord-EDM)*
Chip Urban *(Engr-Inside Sls)*
Gerald Stavlas *(Mgr-Maintenance & Facilities)*
Ray Blasko *(Supvr-Machine Shop)*
Melody Randolph *(Supvr-Outside Svcs)*

Subsidiary (Non-US):

H.C. Starck, Inc.   **(2)**
Portemarsh Industrial Estate 1 Harris Road, Calne, SN11 9PT, Wiltshire, United Kingdom
Tel.: (44) 1249823832
Web Site: http://www.hcstarck.com
Sales Range: $25-49.9 Million
Emp.: 44
Production & Distribution of Metallurgical Product Mfr
N.A.I.C.S.: 332812

Harwood Wealth Management Group plc   **(1)**
5 Lancer House Hussar Court Westside View, Waterlooville, PO7 7SE, Hampshire, United Kingdom
Tel.: (44) 2393552004
Web Site: http://www.harwoodwealth.co.uk
Sales Range: $25-49.9 Million
Emp.: 136
Financial Management Services
N.A.I.C.S.: 541611
Alan Durrant *(CEO)*
Mark Howard *(Chief Comml Officer)*
Gillian Davies *(CFO)*

HireVue, Inc.   **(1)**
10876 S River Frnt Pkwy Ste 500, South Jordan, UT 84095
Tel.: (801) 316-2910
Web Site: http://www.hirevue.com
Computer Software Services
N.A.I.C.S.: 541511
Anthony A. Reynolds *(CEO)*
Kevin Coombs *(CFO)*
Ilene Landon *(Sr VP-Professional Services & Delivery)*
Ricky Simmons *(Sr VP-Product)*
Tara Ault *(Sr VP-Engrg)*
Geoff Camplin *(Sr VP-Customer Success)*
Naziol S. Nazarinia Scott *(Gen Counsel)*

Homair Vacances SA   **(1)**
570 avenue du Club Hippique, The Derby, 13097, Aix-en-Provence, Cedex, France
Tel.: (33) 484390860
Web Site: http://www.homair.com
Sales Range: $50-74.9 Million
Emp.: 123
Mobile Home Camping Park Owner & Operator
N.A.I.C.S.: 721211
Quentin Schaepelynck *(Deputy Mng Dir)*

Subsidiary (Non-US):

Greenbank Holidays Limited   **(2)**
Chelford House, Gadbrook Park, Northwich, CW9 7LN, Cheshire, United Kingdom   **(100%)**
Tel.: (44) 1606787190

Web Site: https://beta.eurocamp.co.uk
Ferry & Campsite Booking Services for Self-Drive Camping & Motorhome Holidays in Europe
N.A.I.C.S.: 561599

InnoVista Sensors   **(1)**
2945 Townsgate Rd, Westlake Village, CA 91361
Tel.: (805) 716-0322
Web Site: http://www.innovistasensors.com
Sales Range: $600-649.9 Million
Sensors & Engineered Subsystems Mfr
N.A.I.C.S.: 334419
Rosie Franco *(Mgr-Mktg)*
Eric Pilaud *(Pres & CEO)*
Albert Vazquez *(VP-Mktg & Strategy)*
Marianne Carton *(Sr VP-HR, Comm & Transformation)*
Claude Maison *(VP-Ops-Global)*
Ben Watt *(CFO)*

Jagex Ltd.   **(1)**
220 Science Park, Cambridge, CB4 0WA, United Kingdom
Tel.: (44) 8445886690
Web Site: http://www.jagex.com
Emp.: 700
Online & Mobile Device Game Developer
N.A.I.C.S.: 513210
Phil Mansell *(CEO)*
Cassia Curran *(Head-Bus Dev)*
John Burns *(Sr VP-Publ)*
Neil McClarty *(VP-Product Mgmt)*

JenCap Holdings LLC   **(1)**
1350 Broadway Ste 602, New York, NY 10018
Tel.: (347) 338-3416
Web Site: http://www.jencapholdings.com
Holding Company; Insurance Brokerage, Underwriting & Management Services
N.A.I.C.S.: 551112
Mark P. Maher *(Pres)*
Paul Orlando *(Mng Dir-Sls)*
John LaCava *(COO)*
John F. Jennings *(CEO)*
Les Hoss *(Exec VP)*
David Nielsen *(CFO)*
Peter Byrne *(CIO)*
Maria Hurley *(Sr VP-HR)*
Kathryn Smith *(Mng Dir-Mktg)*
Denise Walsh *(Gen Counsel)*
Ben Beazley *(Exec VP-National Accounts-Property)*

Subsidiary (Domestic):

Jencap Insurance Services Inc.   **(2)**
1343A E Kingsley, Springfield, MO 65804
Tel.: (417) 883-2688
Web Site: https://www.mjkelly.com
Insurance Brokerage & Services
N.A.I.C.S.: 524210

NIF Group, Inc.   **(2)**
30 Park Ave, Manhasset, NY 11030
Tel.: (516) 365-7440
Web Site: http://www.nifgroup.com
Insurance Underwriting, Wholesale Brokerage & Program Administration Services
N.A.I.C.S.: 524298
Mark P. Maher *(Pres & COO)*
Paul Orlando *(VP-Mktg & Sls)*
Michael A. Orlando *(Chm & CEO)*
David L. Vicari *(Pres-NIF Pro & Exec VP)*
Daphne Alvarado *(VP-Exec Admin & HR)*
John A. Buckley *(Pres-NIF Svcs of NY & Exec VP)*
Joann Parrotta *(VP-Corp Acctg & Fin)*

Subsidiary (Domestic):

Agency Intermediaries, Inc.   **(3)**
1575 Boston Post Rd, Guilford, CT 06437
Tel.: (203) 453-2859
Insurance Related Activities
N.A.I.C.S.: 524298

Subsidiary (Domestic):

Quaker Agency, Inc.   **(2)**
12 Christopher Way Ste 201, Eatontown, NJ 07724
Tel.: (732) 223-6666
Web Site: http://www.qsr-insurance.com
Insurance Agencies & Brokerages
N.A.I.C.S.: 524210
Frank Walsh *(Pres)*
Michael Walsh *(VP)*
Tom Murphy *(VP)*

The Carlyle Group Inc.—(Continued)

Wholesale Trading Insurance Services, LLC (2)
135 Main St Ste 1875, San Francisco, CA 94105
Web Site: http://www.wtisllc.com
Wholesale Insurance Brokerage & Services
N.A.I.C.S.: 524210
Kristopher Bauer (Pres-Casualty)
David Bamford (VP-Casualty)
Sheryl Smith (Dir-Casualty)
Sean P. Burke (Dir-Fin Svcs)
Stephanie Lymore (VP-Fin Svcs)
Julie Sylim-Uang (VP-Program)
Sean Shannon (VP-Property)
Chris Kiley (Mng Dir-Property)
William Reyes (Dir-Casualty)
Alex Megenis (VP-Casualty)
Ryan Sims (VP-Casualty)
Brian Manassero (Asst VP-Casualty)
Joseph K. Hayes (Mng Dir-Casualty)
Mark McInnis (Asst VP-Casualty)
David Duran (VP-Casualty)
Laura Farley (VP-Casualty)
Ashley Ward (VP-Casualty)
Erika Alexandre (Asst VP-Casualty)
Danielle Maggio (Mgr-Client Svcs-Casualty)
Josh Ream (Mng Dir-Property)
Ben Robinson (VP-Property)
Bruce F. Norris (Dir-Property)
Ofelia Padilla (Mgr-Client Svcs-Property)

KFC Holdings Japan Ltd. (1)
okohama iMark Place 5F and 6F 4-4-5 Minatomirai, Nishi-ku, Yokohama, 220-8586, Kanagawa, Japan (51.2%)
Tel.: (81) 453070700
Web Site: https://www.japan.kfc.co.jp
Rev.: $943,993,600
Assets: $462,326,480
Liabilities: $203,386,480
Net Worth: $258,940,000
Earnings: $44,111,760
Emp.: 1,049
Fiscal Year-end: 03/31/2022
Holding Company
N.A.I.C.S.: 551112
Takayuki Hanji (Pres)

Kyoden Co., Ltd. (1)
482-1 Mikka-machi Oaza Minowa-cho, Kamiina-gun, Nagano, 399-4603, Japan
Tel.: (81) 265790012
Web Site: http://www.kyoden.co.jp
Rev.: $260,705,080
Assets: $128,467,880
Liabilities: $74,403,640
Net Worth: $54,064,240
Earnings: $13,229,940
Fiscal Year-end: 07/31/2024
Circuit Board Mfr & Whslr
N.A.I.C.S.: 334412

Subsidiary (Domestic):

Showa KDE Co., Ltd. (2)
Shirakiji Bldg6F 1-2-33, higashigotanda shinagawa-ku, Tokyo, 141-0012, Japan
Tel.: (81) 354229525
Web Site: https://www.showa-hp.co.jp
Emp.: 212
Glass Fiber Raw Material Mfr
N.A.I.C.S.: 327212
Motohiro Tanaka (Pres)

Liberty Tire Services, LLC (1)
600 River Ave 3rd Fl, Pittsburgh, PA 15212
Tel.: (412) 562-0148
Web Site: http://www.libertytire.com
Sales Range: $25-49.9 Million
Emp.: 22
Used Tire Collection, Processing & Recycling Services
N.A.I.C.S.: 562998
C. Andrew Russell (VP)
Thomas Womble (CEO)

Subsidiary (Domestic):

Lakin Tire West Inc. (2)
15305 Spring Ave, Santa Fe Springs, CA 90670
Tel.: (562) 802-7584
Web Site: http://www.lakintire.com
Nondurable Goods Merchant Wholesalers
N.A.I.C.S.: 424990
Sean Lakin (Mgr)

Liberty Tire Recycling (2)

12498 Wyoming Ave, Savage, MN 55378
Tel.: (952) 894-5280
Web Site: http://www.libertytire.com
Sales Range: $25-49.9 Million
Tire Recycling Services
N.A.I.C.S.: 562211
Thomas Womble (CIO)
Mark Vescovi (CIO)
Frank J. Decarlo (Gen Counsel & Sec)
Dale B. Mikus (CFO & Sr VP)
Scott Fowler (Sr VP-Reg Ops)
Barry Mathis (Sr VP-HR & Operational Excellence)
Steve Bigelow (Sr VP-Sls & Mktg)
Leigh Eastman (Sr VP-Support Svcs)

Liberty Tire Recycling, LLC (2)
1914 E Euclid Ave Bldg A, Des Moines, IA 50313
Tel.: (515) 262-4900
Web Site: http://www.libertytire.com
Tire Recycling Services
N.A.I.C.S.: 326211
Nils E. Larsen (Chm)
Thomas Womble (CEO)
Barry Mathis (Sr VP-HR & Operational Excellence)
Dale B. Mikus (CFO & Sr VP)
Frank J. Decarlo (Gen Counsel & Sec)
Leigh Eastman (Sr VP-Support Svcs)
Mark Vescovi (CIO)
Scott Fowler (Sr VP-Reg Ops)
Steve Bigelow (Sr VP-Sls & Mktg)

LifeCare Holdings, Inc. (1)
5340 Legacy Dr Bldg 4 Ste 150, Plano, TX 75024-3131
Tel.: (469) 241-2100
Web Site: http://www.lifecare-hospitals.com
Sales Range: $350-399.9 Million
Emp.: 4,500
Hospital Owner & Operator
N.A.I.C.S.: 622310

Linens 'n Things, Inc. (1)
210 N State Rt 17, Paramus, NJ 07652
Tel.: (201) 225-9026
Web Site: http://www.lnt.com
Linens & Domestic Household Items Retailer
N.A.I.C.S.: 449129

Logoplaste Investimento, S.G.P.S., S.A. (1)
Edificio Logoplaste Estrada da Malveira 900, 2750-834, Cascais, Portugal (60%)
Tel.: (351) 214 858 500
Web Site: http://www.logoplaste.com
Emp.: 2,000
Holding Company; Rigid Plastic Packaging Products Mfr & Whslr
N.A.I.C.S.: 551112
Filipe de Botton (Co-CEO)
Alexandre Relvas (Co-CEO)
Roberto Villaquiran (CFO)

Subsidiary (Non-US):

Logoplaste (M) Kuantan Sdn Bhd (2)
Lot 3831 Kuantan Port Industrial Area, 26080, Kuantan, Pahang Darul Makmur, Malaysia
Tel.: (60) 95835505
Plastic Packaging Distr
N.A.I.C.S.: 423840
Bakri Alias (Plant Mgr)

Logoplaste Canada Inc. (2)
846 Churchill Ave, Ottawa, K1Z 5G8, ON, Canada
Tel.: (613) 762-7218
Plastic Packaging Distr
N.A.I.C.S.: 423840

Logoplaste Czech, s.r.o. (2)
Na Pankraci 1062 / 58, 140 00, Prague, Czech Republic
Tel.: (420) 222511140
Plastic Packaging Distr
N.A.I.C.S.: 423840

Logoplaste Do Brasil Ltda (2)
Alameda Santos 787 - 5 andar, Bairro - Cerqueira Cesar, Sao Paulo, 01419-001, Brazil
Tel.: (55) 1121320400
Plastic Packaging Distr
N.A.I.C.S.: 423840

Logoplaste Elst B.V. (2)
Manege 15, 6662 WC, Elst, Netherlands
Tel.: (31) 481351946
Plastic Packaging Distr
N.A.I.C.S.: 423840
Andrew Skelson (Plant Mgr)

Logoplaste Mexico S de R.L. De C.V. (2)
Blvd Manuel Avila Camacho 76 piso 1, Col Lomas de Capultepec, 11000, Mexico, Mexico
Tel.: (52) 7222621622
Plastic Packaging Distr
N.A.I.C.S.: 423840
Gabriel Leal (Dir Gen)

Logoplaste Russia LLC (2)
4-a Centralnaya, Otradnoe, 187330, Leningradskaya, Russia
Tel.: (7) 8124935051
Plastic Packaging Distr
N.A.I.C.S.: 423840
Vasiliy Mazov (Gen Mgr)

Subsidiary (US):

Logoplaste USA, Inc. (2)
14420 Van Dyke Rd, Plainfield, IL 60544
Tel.: (815) 230-6961
Plastic Packaging Distr
N.A.I.C.S.: 423840
Lumie Emini (Controller-Fin & Acctg)

Subsidiary (Non-US):

Logoplaste Ukraine LLC (2)
19B Moskovskiy Prospekt, 4073, Kiev, Ukraine
Tel.: (380) 445850026
Plastic Packaging Distr
N.A.I.C.S.: 423840
Vasiliy Mazov (Gen Mgr)

ManTech International Corporation (1)
2251 Corporate Park Dr, Herndon, VA 20171
Tel.: (703) 218-6000
Web Site: http://www.mantech.com
Rev.: $2,553,956,000
Assets: $2,639,565,000
Liabilities: $964,145,000
Net Worth: $1,675,420,000
Earnings: $137,017,000
Emp.: 9,800
Fiscal Year-end: 12/31/2021
Systems Engineering Technologies & Solutions
N.A.I.C.S.: 541511
Kevin M. Phillips (Chm)
Jeffrey S. Brown (Gen Counsel, Sec & Exec VP)
Brian McHugh (Sr VP-External Affairs)
Bonnie J. Cook (Exec VP-Bus Svcs)
Mike Uster (CIO & Sr VP)
Matthew A. Tait (Pres & CEO)
Daniel Payne (Chief Security Officer & Sr VP)
Troy Walter (Dir-Bus Dev)
Richard Smith (VP-Dept-Homeland Security Portfolio)
Joseph Cubba (Chief Growth Officer)
Franc Wertheimer (Co-Founder)
Julie Anna Barker (Chief HR Officer-Interim)
Sheila Blackwell (VP-Mktg & Comm)
Russell Smith (Program Dir-Cybersecurity)
JoAnne Dukeshire (VP-Contracts)
Stephen Deitz (Exec VP-Federal Civilian & Gen Mgr-Federal Civilian)
Mark Bortfeld (Sr VP-Navy)
David I lathaway (Exec VP-Defense & Gen Mgr-Defense)

Subsidiary (Domestic):

7Delta, Inc. (2)
10490 Little Patuxent Pkwy Ste 300, Columbia, MD 21044
Tel.: (443) 552-0661
Web Site: http://www.7delta.com
Sales Range: $25-49.9 Million
Emp.: 82
Information Technology Services
N.A.I.C.S.: 541512

Allied Technology Group Inc. (2)
1803 Research Blvd, Rockville, MD 20850
Tel.: (301) 309-1234
Web Site: http://www.alliedtech.com

Sales Range: $10-24.9 Million
Emp.: 30
Information Technology & Engineering
N.A.I.C.S.: 541512

Definitive Logic Corporation (2)
4121 Wilson Blvd Ste 300, Arlington, VA 22203
Tel.: (703) 955-4186
Web Site: http://www.definitivelogic.com
Custom Computer Programming Services
N.A.I.C.S.: 541511
Paul Burke (CEO)

Edaptive Systems, LLC (2)
400 Red Brook Blvd Ste 120, Owings Mills, MD 21117
Tel.: (410) 327-3366
Web Site: https://www.edaptivesys.com
Emp.: 300
Custom Computer Programming Services
N.A.I.C.S.: 541511

InfoZen, LLC (2)
6700A Rocklidge Dr 300, Rockville, MD 20817 (100%)
Tel.: (301) 605-8000
Web Site: http://www.infozen.com
IT Services, Government & Cloud Broker
N.A.I.C.S.: 541511
Stephen C. Penyak (Sr VP)

Kforce Government Solutions, Inc. (2)
2677 Prosperity Ave Ste 100, Fairfax, VA 22031
Tel.: (703) 245-7350
Web Site: http://www.kforcegov.com
Computer Consulting Services
N.A.I.C.S.: 541512
Maureen Coyle (CEO)

ManTech Advanced Systems International Inc. (2)
12015 Lee Jackson Hwy, Fairfax, VA 22033-3300
Tel.: (703) 218-6000
Web Site: http://www.mantech.com
Sales Range: $700-749.9 Million
Provider of Engineering Services
N.A.I.C.S.: 541330

ManTech Environmental Research Services Corp. (2)
12015 Lee Jackson Highway, Fairfax, VA 22033-3300
Tel.: (703) 218-6000
Web Site: http://www.mantech.com
Sales Range: $25-49.9 Million
Emp.: 100
Business Consulting Services
N.A.I.C.S.: 541715
George J. Pedersen (Chm & CEO-ManTech Intl)

ManTech Europe Systems Corporation (2)
2251 Corporate Park Dr, Herndon, VA 20171-4839
Tel.: (703) 218-6000
Web Site: http://www.mantech.com
Sales Range: $10-24.9 Million
Emp.: 200
Engineeering Services
N.A.I.C.S.: 541330
George J. Pedersen (Chm & CEO)

ManTech SRS Technologies, Inc. (2)
440 Stevens Ave, Solana Beach, CA 92075
Tel.: (858) 345-1952
Web Site: http://www.srs.com
Sales Range: $150-199.9 Million
Emp.: 800
Defense Electronics Research & Development; Systems Engineering & Technical Support; Software Development
N.A.I.C.S.: 541512

ManTech Security & Mission Assurance (2)
7799 Leesburg Pike Ste 700 S, Falls Church, VA 22043
Tel.: (703) 847-6070
Web Site: http://www.mantech.com
Sales Range: $150-199.9 Million
Emp.: 600
Computer Design Services
N.A.I.C.S.: 541512

ManTech Sensor Technologies, Inc. (2)

200 Schultz Dr Ste 6, Red Bank, NJ 07701-6776
Tel.: (703) 814-8370
Web Site: http://www.mantech.com
Sales Range: $300-349.9 Million
Corporate & Government IT Development Services
N.A.I.C.S.: 541330

ManTech Technical Services Inc. (2)
12015 Lee Jackson Hwy, Fairfax, VA 22033-3300
Tel.: (703) 218-6000
Web Site: http://www.mantech.com
Sales Range: $25-49.9 Million
Computer Integrated Systems Design
N.A.I.C.S.: 541512

ManTech Telecommunications (2)
2250 Corporate Park Dr, Herndon, VA 20171
Tel.: (703) 814-8370
Web Site: http://www.mantech.com
Sales Range: $25-49.9 Million
Emp.: 120
Telephone Communication, Except Radio
N.A.I.C.S.: 541330
Margo Mentus *(Sr VP-HR)*

ManTech Telecommunications & Information Systems Corporation (2)
14119 Sullyfield Cir A, Chantilly, VA 20151
Tel.: (703) 814-4200
Web Site: http://www.mantech.com
Sales Range: $25-49.9 Million
Emp.: 100
Provider of Computer Integrated Systems Design
N.A.I.C.S.: 541330

Tapestry Technologies, Inc. (2)
5000 Letterkenny Rd Ste 250, Chambersburg, PA 17201-8384
Tel.: (717) 264-6777
Web Site: http://www.tapestrytech.com
Cybersecurity Defense
N.A.I.C.S.: 561621

Technology Management Corp. (2)
12015 Lee Jackson Memorial Hwy, Fairfax, VA 22033-3300
Tel.: (703) 218-6000
Web Site: http://www.mantech.com
Sales Range: $125-149.9 Million
Emp.: 600
Technology Consulting Services
N.A.I.C.S.: 541618

Welkin Associates, Ltd (2)
4801 Stonecroft Blvd Ste 210, Chantilly, VA 20151
Tel.: (703) 633-8100
Web Site: http://www.welkin.com
Information Service Management Provider
N.A.I.C.S.: 519290

Manna Pro Products, LLC (1)
707 Spirit 40 Park Dr Ste 150, Chesterfield, MO 63005-1137
Tel.: (636) 681-1700
Web Site: http://www.mannapro.com
Sales Range: $100-124.9 Million
Emp.: 175
Animal Feeds Mfr & Distr
N.A.I.C.S.: 311119
Robert McCoy *(VP-Nutrition)*
John Howe *(Pres)*

Subsidiary (Domestic):

Dinovite Inc. (2)
101 Miller Dr, Crittenden, KY 41030
Tel.: (859) 428-1000
Web Site: http://www.dinovite.com
Nondurable Goods Merchant Whslr
N.A.I.C.S.: 424990
Dan Turner *(Dir-Ops)*
J. B. Kropp *(Pres)*

Marelli Motori S.p.A. (1)
Via Sabbionara 1, 36071, Arzignano, Italy
Tel.: (39) 0444479711
Web Site: http://www.marellimotori.com
Sales Range: $200-249.9 Million
Emp.: 600
Electric Motor & Generator Mfr
N.A.I.C.S.: 335312
Michela Mattiello *(Dir-Corp Comm)*
Giordano Prandelli *(COO)*
Marco Rondelli *(CFO)*

Roberto Andresani *(Mgr-Supply Chain)*
Christian Sanson *(Dir-Pur)*
Luca Parolari *(CEO)*
Luciano Anzolin *(Dir-Svc & Product Quality)*
Nicola Battistin *(Dir-Ops)*
Paolo Bedin *(Chief Comml Officer)*
Paolo Buratto *(Chief HR & Change Officer)*
Andrea Casella *(CTO)*
Mario Longo *(CIO)*

Subsidiary (Non-US):

Marelli Asia Pacific Sdn Bhd (2)
Lot PT 5038-5041 Jalan Teluk Datuk 28/40, Off Persiaran Sepang Seksyen 28, 40400, Shah Alam, Malaysia
Tel.: (60) 3 5192 7213
Web Site: http://www.marellimotori.com
Electric Motor & Generator Mfr
N.A.I.C.S.: 335312

Marelli Central Europe GmbH (2)
Heilswannenweg 50, Hildesheim, 31008, Elze, Germany
Tel.: (49) 5068462400
Web Site: http://www.marellimotori.com
Sales Range: $25-49.9 Million
Emp.: 25
Electric Motor & Generator Mfr
N.A.I.C.S.: 335312
Franco Amadore *(Gen Mgr)*

Marelli Electrical Machines South Africa (Pty) Ltd. (2)
Unit 2 Corner Director And Megawatt Road Spartan Ext 23, Kempton Park, 1619, South Africa
Tel.: (27) 11 392 1920
Web Site: http://www.marellimotori.com
Emp.: 10
Electric Motor & Generator Mfr
N.A.I.C.S.: 335312

Marelli UK Ltd. (2)
Main Street The Old Rectory Glenfield, Leicester, LE3 8DG, United Kingdom
Tel.: (44) 1162325167
Electric Motor & Generator Mfr
N.A.I.C.S.: 335312
Anthony Cooling *(Mgr-Accts)*

Subsidiary (US):

Marelli USA, Inc. (2)
2200 Norcross Pkwy Ste 290, Norcross, GA 30071
Tel.: (859) 734-2588
Web Site: http://www.marellimotori.com
Sales Range: $25-49.9 Million
Emp.: 8
Electric Motor & Generator Mfr
N.A.I.C.S.: 335312
Stephen Waite *(Gen Mgr)*

MedRisk, LLC (1)
2701 Renaissance Blvd Ste 200, King of Prussia, PA 19406
Tel.: (610) 768-5812
Web Site: http://www.medrisknet.com
Physical Medicine & Diagnostic Imaging Services
N.A.I.C.S.: 621512
Thomas Weir *(CFO)*
Shelley L. Boyce *(Founder)*
Michael Ryan *(Exec Chm)*
Jennifer Tronc *(Exec VP-Acct Mgmt)*
Jamie Davis *(Exec VP-Sls Mgmt)*
Chris Neil *(Exec VP-Client Strategy & Solutions)*
Michelle Buckman *(Chief Strategy Officer)*
Mary O'Donoghue *(Chief Clinical Officer & Chief Product Officer)*
Rommy Blum *(Exec VP-Mktg)*
John Jakovcic *(CTO)*
Sri Sridharan *(CEO)*

Subsidiary (Domestic):

Medata Inc. (2)
2741 Walnut Ave, Tustin, CA 92780
Tel.: (714) 918-1310
Web Site: http://www.medata.com
Rev.: $5,000,000
Emp.: 30
Software Publisher
N.A.I.C.S.: 513210
Tori Henson *(VP-Mktg)*
Bryan A. Lowe *(CFO)*
Don T. Theis *(Sr VP)*
Eric Fritz *(CIO & Sr VP)*
Tom Herndon *(Pres & COO)*

NEP Group, Inc. (1)
2 Beta Dr, Pittsburgh, PA 15238
Tel.: (800) 444-0054
Web Site: http://www.nepinc.com
Rev.: $442,752,000
Assets: $1,117,091,000
Liabilities: $981,277,000
Net Worth: $135,814,000
Earnings: ($41,215,000)
Emp.: 1,512
Fiscal Year-end: 12/31/2014
Live & Broadcast Production Solutions
N.A.I.C.S.: 713990
Dean Naccarato *(Chief Legal Officer)*
Mike Werteen *(Pres-Broadcast Svcs-Global)*
Glen Levine *(Pres-Broadcast Svcs-US)*
Carrie Galvin *(Chief Strategy Officer)*
John Gierl *(CIO)*
Scott Rothenberg *(Sr VP-Plng & Program)*
Jeff Hughes *(COO)*
Julie Bellani *(Chief HR Officer)*
Martin Stewart *(CEO)*
Doug Kovach *(CFO)*
Susan Matis *(VP-Global Mktg)*
Jordan Conigliaro *(Mgr-PR)*

Subsidiary (Domestic):

Bexel Corporation (2)
2701 N Ontario St, Burbank, CA 91504
Tel.: (818) 841-5051
Web Site: http://www.bexel.com
Video Equipment & Ancillary Support Gear
N.A.I.C.S.: 449210
Oyette Auary *(Controller)*

Broadcast Sports International, LLC (2)
7455 Race Rd, Hanover, MD 21076
Tel.: (410) 564-2600
Web Site: http://www.broadcastsportsinc.com
Emp.: 150
Television Broadcasting Services
N.A.I.C.S.: 516120
Peter Larsson *(Co-Founder & Pres)*
Jeremy Pink *(CEO)*
Lisa Jacques *(CFO)*
Dean Coughlan *(Dir-Engrg & Technical Ops)*

Subsidiary (Non-US):

Creative Technology Ltd. (2)
Units 2-4 Manor Gate Manor Royal, Gatwick Rd, Crawley, RH10 9SX, United Kingdom (100%)
Tel.: (44) 1293582000
Web Site: https://www.ct-group.com
Sales Range: $25-49.9 Million
Emp.: 130
Specialist Services Provider to the Corporate, Presentation, Entertainment & Broadcast Markets
N.A.I.C.S.: 561110
Mark Boden *(Dir-Audio)*
Scott Burges *(Dir-Special Projects)*
Jonathan Sheard *(Dir-LED)*
Dave Crump *(CEO)*
Nick Askew *(Mgr-Acct)*
Mark Brinkhurst *(Mgr-Transport)*
Tom Burford *(Head-Technical Svcs)*
Dan Burgess *(Mgr-Acct)*
Marc Butterworth *(Dir-Ops)*
Rachel Cox *(Coord-Mktg & Sls)*
Rob Day *(Sr Mgr-Project)*
Pat Dore *(Project Mgr)*
Philip Eeles *(Mgr-Hire Ops)*
Chris Ellis *(Mgr-Project)*
Matthew Eve *(Head-Corp Events)*
Mark Gent *(Sr Mgr-Project)*
Matt Hartfree *(Mgr-Project)*
Andy Head *(Mgr-Project)*
Dominic Hill *(Mgr-Project)*
Mick Jones *(Mgr-Acct)*
Chris Jordan *(Sr Mgr-Project)*
Nick Knowles *(Mgr-Project)*
Sid Lobb *(Head-Vision & Integrated Networks)*
Ben Tompsett *(Head-Brdcst)*
Leigh Reeve *(Mgr-Project)*
Emma Rossi *(Mgr-Project)*

Subsidiary (Non-US):

Creative Technology GmbH Co. KG (3)
Kelterstrasse 69, Teck, 73265, Dettingen an der Erms, Germany (100%)

Tel.: (49) 70222530
Web Site: https://www.ct-group.com
Sales Range: $1-9.9 Million
Emp.: 5
Specialist Services Provider to the Corporate, Presentation, Entertainment & Broadcast Markets
N.A.I.C.S.: 561990

Subsidiary (US):

Creative Technology Group, Inc (3)
2200 S Mount Prospect Rd Unit A, Des Plaines, IL 60018
Tel.: (847) 671-9670
Web Site: https://www.ct-group.com
Sales Range: $25-49.9 Million
Audio & Video Equipment Rental Services
N.A.I.C.S.: 532490
Sim Elwood *(Gen Mgr)*
Kristi Ventura *(Dir-Natl Sls)*
Mendy Medlin *(Coord-Labour)*
Herb Brandt *(Gen Mgr-Las Vegas)*
Jean Armstrong *(Mgr-Sls-Las Vegas)*
Dan Hajek *(Dir-Ops-Las Vegas)*
Carl Hampton *(Coord-Labour-Las Vegas)*
Graham Andrews *(CEO-Los Angeles)*
Stephen Gray *(COO-Los Angeles)*
Jason O'Donnell *(Dir-Ops)*
Chai Abdennabi *(Coord-Labor)*

Branch (Domestic):

Creative Technology Chicago (4)
2200 S Mount Prospect Rd Unit A, Des Plaines, IL 60018
Tel.: (847) 671-9670
Web Site: http://www.ctus.com
Sales Range: $25-49.9 Million
Emp.: 55
Specialist Audio & Video Staging Services
N.A.I.C.S.: 561499
Mendy Medlin *(Coord-Labour)*
Dominic Tosterud *(Dir-Ops)*

Creative Technology Los Angeles (4)
14000 Arminta St, Panorama City, CA 91402 (100%)
Tel.: (818) 779-2400
Web Site: http://www.ctus.com
Sales Range: $25-49.9 Million
Specialist Services Provider to the Corporate, Presentation, Entertainment & Broadcast Markets
N.A.I.C.S.: 532289
Graham Andrews *(CEO)*

Creative Technology San Francisco (4)
14072 Catalina St, San Leandro, CA 94577-5037
Tel.: (510) 217-2700
Web Site: http://www.ctus.com
Sales Range: $25-49.9 Million
Emp.: 100
Specialist Services Provider to the Corporate, Presentation, Entertainment & Broadcast Markets
N.A.I.C.S.: 561499

Subsidiary (Domestic):

Screenworks LLC (4)
1900 Compton Ave Ste 101, Corona, CA 92881
Tel.: (951) 279-8877
Web Site: http://www.screenworksnep.com
Sales Range: $100-124.9 Million
Emp.: 1
Large Scale Video Screen Provider
N.A.I.C.S.: 532210

Unit (Domestic):

Screenworks LLC - Operations & Technical Support (5)
1580 Magnolia Ave, Corona, CA 92879-1350
Tel.: (951) 279-8877
Web Site: http://www.screenworksnep.com
Sales Range: $25-49.9 Million
Large Scale Video Screen Provider
N.A.I.C.S.: 512110

Subsidiary (Domestic):

NEP Broadcasting, LLC (2)
2 Beta Dr, Pittsburgh, PA 15238
Tel.: (412) 826-1414

The Carlyle Group Inc.—(Continued)

Web Site: http://www.nepinc.com
Sales Range: $75-99.9 Million
Emp.: 150
Television Film Production
N.A.I.C.S.: 512110
Kevin M. Rabbitt (CEO)
Debra Honkus (Founder & Chm)
Joe Scionti (Sr Acct Mgr)
George Hoover (CTO)
Glen Levine (VP-Mobile Engrg & Ops)
Gerry Delon (CFO)
Scott Rothenberg (VP-Tech & Asset Mgmt)
Dean Naccarato (Gen Counsel)
Lynda Wilkes (VP-HR)
Barry Katz (Sr VP & Gen Mgr-Studios)
Carrie Galvin (Chief Strategy Officer)
John Gierl (Sr VP-IT)

Division (Domestic):

Corplex, Inc.   (3)
915 Sherwood Dr, Lake Bluff, IL 60044
Tel.: (847) 582-8800
Sales Range: $10-24.9 Million
Emp.: 25
Mobile Broadcasting & Production Services
N.A.I.C.S.: 512110
Carter Ruehrdanz (CEO)
Joe Scionti (VP-Sls)
Robert Danko (CFO)
David Greany (VP-Ops & Engrg)

New Century Productions, Inc.   (3)
1501 Lehigh St Ste 101, Allentown, PA
18103
Tel.: (610) 798-4072
Emp.: 15
Mobile Broadcasting & Production Services
N.A.I.C.S.: 512110

Subsidiary (Non-US):

NEP New Zealand Holdings Ltd.   (2)
60 Stanley Street Parnell, PO Box 137058,
Auckland, 0930, New Zealand
Tel.: (64) 96005990
Web Site: http://www.nepgroup.co.nz
Broadcasting Services
N.A.I.C.S.: 516120
Oliver Pitkin (Gen Mgr)
Wendy Bremner (Mgr-Ops)
Sam Scally (Mgr-Tech)
Kerry McLaughlan (Mgr-Office)

Subsidiary (Domestic):

Vitec Broadcast Services Inc.   (2)
2701 N Ontario St, Burbank, CA 91504
Tel.: (818) 565-4322
Web Site: http://www.bexel.com
Broadcasting Equipments Rental & Sales
N.A.I.C.S.: 423690
Scott Nardelli (VP & Gen Mgr-Bexel ESS)
Craig Schiller (VP-Ops)
Lee Estroff (VP-Sls)
Edd Bonner (Dir-Engrg & Ops)
Joe Wire (VP-Bus Dev)
John Mills (Mgr-Bus Dev)
Johnny Pastor (VP-Tech Svcs)
Julia Rodgers (Mgr-Strategic Accts)
Kirsten Ballard (VP-Svcs Fulfillment)
Rod Allen (Sr Project Mgr)
Tom Dickinson (CTO)
Howard Rosenthal (VP-Strategic Accts &
Global Resources)
Mike King (Mgr-Strategic Accts)
Monique Rowland (Mgr-Mktg)
Sandy Colonna (Mgr-Strategic Accts)
Meri Guyumdzhyan (Coord-Labor & Travel)
Robert Hughbanks (Engr Audio)
Bryan Kirby (Mgr-Project)
Michael Lai (Mgr-Strategic Accts)
Steven Lopez (Engr-Audio)
Ted Marvin (Mgr-Audio)
Christina McCrae (Coord-Sls)
David Paucar (Engr-Sys)
Jose Serrano (Coord-Sls)
Dale Storz (VP)
Marcus Talamantez (Mgr-Ops)
Jim Turner (Engr-Sys)
Miguel Vargas (Engr-Audio)
Lane Robbins (Engr-Sys)
Gerald Rojo (Engr-Sys)
Chris Chang (Asst Mgr-Engrg)
Angela S. Davila (Coord-E-Commerce)
Andy Berry (Engr-Fiber)

NSM Insurance Group, LLC   (1)

555 N Ln Ste 6060, Conshohocken, PA
19428
Tel.: (800) 970-9778
Web Site: http://www.nsminc.com
Holding Company; Commercial Property &
Casualty Insurance Products & Services
N.A.I.C.S.: 551112
Jonathan Costello (CFO)
Bill McKernan (Pres)
Geof McKernan (CEO)
Marc Castellucci (COO)

Subsidiary (Domestic):

American Collectors Insurance,
Inc.   (2)
951 Haddonfield Rd Ste 2A, Cherry Hill, NJ
08002
Tel.: (856) 779-7212
Web Site:
http://www.americancollectors.com
Collector Vehicle Insurance Services
N.A.I.C.S.: 524210
Regina Buckley (Ops Mgr)

Embrace Pet Insurance Agency,
LLC   (2)
4530 Richmond Rd, Cleveland, OH 44128
Tel.: (800) 511-9172
Web Site:
http://www.embracepetinsurance.com
Pet Health Insurance Services
N.A.I.C.S.: 524210
Brian Macias (Pres)
Will Lazzaro (VP-Tech)
David Rodgers (VP-Mktg)
Chris Hagesfeld (Sr Dir-Ops)
Melissa Ing (Sr Dir-Bus Process)
Maggie Acklin (Sls Dir)
Jenna Mahan (Dir-Claims)
Kelly Coffey (Dir-Bus Dev)

KBK Insurance Group, Inc.   (2)
1425 Sams Ave Ste 201, Harahan, LA
70123
Tel.: (504) 736-0690
Web Site: http://www.kbkinsgroup.com
Other Health & Personal Care Stores
N.A.I.C.S.: 456199
Kyle Murray (VP)
Ken Murray (Pres)

NSM Insurance Group, Inc.   (2)
555 North Ln Ste 6060, Conshohocken, PA
19428
Tel.: (610) 941-9877
Web Site: http://www.nsminc.com
Commercial Property & Casualty Insurance
Products & Services
N.A.I.C.S.: 524126

Nationwide Accident Repair Services
Ltd   (1)
17a Thorney Leys Park, Witney, OX28
4GE, Oxfordshire, United Kingdom
Tel.: (44) 1993701720
Web Site:
http://www.nationwiderepairs.co.uk
Sales Range: $250-299.9 Million
Emp.: 60
Automotive Crash Repair & Accident Admin-
istration Services
N.A.I.C.S.: 811111
Michael Wilmshurst (CEO)

Subsidiary (Domestic):

Just Car Clinics   (2)
Rawcliffe Road, Goole, DN14 6XL, East
Yorkshire, United Kingdom
Tel.: (44) 904609099
Web Site: http://www.justcarclinics.co.uk
Sales Range: $50-74.9 Million
Collision Repair Services
N.A.I.C.S.: 811111
Dawn Swales (Mgr-HR & Trng)
Paul Waites (Mgr-Grp Ops-Northern)
Mike Crow (Controller-Fin)
Andrew Firbank (Mgr-Grp Compliance)
John Pattinson (Mgr-Grp Ops)

Nationwide Network Services Ltd   (2)
Greystone House Rudheath Way Gadbrook
Park, Northwich, CW9 7LL, United Kingdom
Tel.: (44) 1606562233
Web Site:
http://www.nationwiderepairs.co.uk
Accident Management & Repair Solutions
Provider
N.A.I.C.S.: 811111

Stephen Thompson (Mng Dir)
Janice Kennaway (Head-Ops)
Sara Wilcox (Mgr-Natl Acct)

Net Health Systems, Inc.   (1)
40 24th St 1st Fl, Pittsburgh, PA 15222
Web Site: http://www.nethealth.com
Custom Computer Programming Services
N.A.I.C.S.: 541511
Patrick Colletti (Chief Innovation Officer)
Anthony Sanzo (Exec Chm)
Patrick Rooney (CFO)
Christopher Hayes (CTO)
Jason Baim (Chief Strategy Officer & Chief
Corp Dev Officer)
James J. Quagliaroli (Chm)
Josh Pickus (CEO)
Christine Jones (Chief Client Officer)
Jason James (CIO)
Aaron Brandwein (Chief Revenue Officer)
Linda Kricher (Chief HR Officer)

Subsidiary (Domestic):

Casamba, LLC   (2)
5210 Lewis Rd Ste 10, Agoura Hills, CA
91301
Tel.: (818) 991-9111
Web Site: http://www.casamba.net
Sales Range: $1-9.9 Million
Emp.: 16
Software Developer for Healthcare Industry
N.A.I.C.S.: 513210
Jane Moffett (Chief Product Officer)
Ronnie Amrany (Founder & Chm)
Doron Hetz (VP-Ops)
Don Moore (VP-IT Ops)
Veronica Ornelas (VP-Fin)
Will Jacobus (Sr Project Mgr)
Brian Dwyer (Chief Revenue Officer)
Billie Nutter (CEO)

Optima Healthcare Solutions,
LLC   (2)
4229 SW High Meadows Ave, Palm City,
FL 34990
Tel.: (772) 403-1301
Web Site: http://www.optimahcs.com
Sales Range: $1-9.9 Million
Emp.: 90
Physical Therapy Software Publisher
N.A.I.C.S.: 513210
Steve Mackie (Co-Founder)
Michael Katri (Co-Founder & COO)
Ryan Katri (Co-Founder)
Aaron Brandwein (Chief Revenue Officer)
Pat Clark (Co-CFO)
Josh Pickus (CEO)
Randy Wallin (Chief Security Officer)
Jason James (CIO)
Dinesh Senanayake (Co-CFO & Gen Mgr-
RCM)
Christine Jones (Chief Customer Officer)
Jeff Browning (Chief Product & Engrg Offi-
cer)

Subsidiary (Domestic):

Vantage Clinical Solutions, LLC   (3)
1567 SW Chandler Ave, Bend, OR 97702
Tel.: (541) 550-7291
Revenue Cycle Management, Digital Mar-
keting & Consulting Services
N.A.I.C.S.: 541613

Subsidiary (Domestic):

PointRight, Inc.   (2)
150 CambridgePark Dr Ste 301, Cam-
bridge, MA 02140
Tel.: (781) 457-5900
Web Site: http://www.pointright.com
Software Publisher
N.A.I.C.S.: 513210
Dean Staley (VP-Fin & Admin)
Steven Scott (CEO)
Alan Dahl (Chm)
Steven Littlehale (Chief Clinical Officer &
Exec VP)
Michael Laureno (CFO)
Cesar Goulart (CIO)

Nouryon Chemicals Holding B.V.   (1)
Tel.: (31) 889841000
Web Site: https://www.nouryon.com
Emp.: 78,000
Holding Company; Chemicals Mfr & Whslr
N.A.I.C.S.: 551112
Charlie Shaver (Chm & CEO)
Vivi Hollertt (Chief Comm Officer & Chief
Sustainability Officer)

Tift Shepherd (Chief HR Officer & Sr VP)
Suzanne M. Carroll (Sr VP-Consumer &
Life Sciences)
Sobers Sethi (Sr VP-Emerging Markets &
China)
Sandeep Singh (CIO, Chief Digital Officer &
Sr VP)
Sean Lannon (CFO & Exec VP)
Rajeev Rao (Sr VP-Corporate Develop-
ment)
Paresh Bhakta (Chief Integrated Supply
Chain Officer & Sr VP)
Michael Finn (Gen Counsel, Sec & Exec
VP-Bus Affairs)
Larry Ryan (Pres)
Joppe Smit (Sr VP-Resource Solutions)
Johan Landfors (CTO, Pres-Europe & VP-
Strategy & Asset Plng)
Egbert Henstra (Pres-Netherlands & Sr VP-
Global Transformation)
Alain Rynwalt (Sr VP-Performance Materi-
als)

Subsidiary (Domestic):

Nobian Chemicals B.V.   (2)
Van Asch van Wijckstraat, 53 3811 LP,
Amersfoort, Netherlands   (100%)
Tel.: (31) 850006000
Web Site: https://www.nobian.com
Specialty Chemicals Mfr
N.A.I.C.S.: 325998

Joint Venture (Domestic):

Delamine B.V.   (3)
Stationsplein 121 Argonaut, 3818 LE,
Amersfoort, Netherlands
Tel.: (31) 334224600
Web Site: http://www.delamine.com
Ethylene Amines Mfr
N.A.I.C.S.: 325199

Subsidiary (Domestic):

Nobian Industrial Chemicals B.V.   (3)
Van Asch v. Wijckstraat, 53 3811 LP,
Amersfoort, Netherlands
Tel.: (31) 850006000
Web Site: https://www.nobian.com
Industrial Chemicals Mfr
N.A.I.C.S.: 325998
Michael Koenig (CEO)

Subsidiary (Domestic):

Nouryon Chemicals International
B.V.   (2)
Haaksbergweg 88, De Oliphant Building
Floor 14 and 15, 1101 BZ, Amsterdam,
Netherlands
Tel.: (31) 889841000
Holding Company
N.A.I.C.S.: 551112

Subsidiary (Non-US):

Akzo Nobel Chemical Ltd.   (3)
1 City Ctr Dr Ste 318, Mississauga, L5B
1M2, ON, Canada   (100%)
Tel.: (905) 273-5959
Web Site: http://www.akzonobel.com
Industrial Inorganic Chemicals
N.A.I.C.S.: 325998

Subsidiary (US):

Akzo Nobel Chemicals LLC   (3)
525 W Van Buren St, Chicago, IL 60607
Tel.: (312) 544-7000
Mfr Specialty Chemicals & Industrial Prod-
ucts
N.A.I.C.S.: 325199

Subsidiary (Domestic):

Akzo Nobel Surface Chemistry
LLC   (4)
525 W Van Buren St, Chicago, IL 60607
Tel.: (312) 544-7159
Surface Active Agent Mfr
N.A.I.C.S.: 325613

Subsidiary (Non-US):

Akzo Nobel Chemicals Pty Ltd   (3)
8 Kellaway Pl, Wetherill Park, 2164, NSW,
Australia
Tel.: (61) 2 9616 6900

Sales Range: $25-49.9 Million
Emp.: 3
Chemical Products Mfr
N.A.I.C.S.: 325199
Brian Patten (Country Mgr)

Akzo Nobel Chemicals S.A. (3)
Autovia de Castelldefels Km 4 65, El Prat
de Llobregat, 8820, Barcelona, Spain
Tel.: (34) 93 4784411
Chemical Products Mfr
N.A.I.C.S.: 325998

Akzo Nobel Chemicals Sa de CV (3)
Av Morelos 49 Col Tecamachalco, 56500,
Los Reyes, La Paz, Mexico   (100%)
Tel.: (52) 5558580700
Organic Peroxides & Other Specialty
Chemicals
N.A.I.C.S.: 325199

**Akzo Nobel Functional Chemicals
AB** (3)
Horneborgvagen 11, 89126, Ornskoldsvik,
Sweden
Tel.: (46) 303 850 00
Emp.: 110
Cellulose Derivative Mfr
N.A.I.C.S.: 325998

**Akzo Nobel Functional Chemicals
Verwaltungs-GmbH** (3)
Liebigstrasse 7, 07973, Greiz, Germany
Tel.: (49) 3661780
Chemical Products Mfr
N.A.I.C.S.: 325998

**Akzo Nobel Industrial Chemicals
AB** (3)
Marieholmsgatan 70, Gothenburg, 41502,
Sweden
Tel.: (46) 31 733 1880
Sales Range: $50-74.9 Million
Emp.: 6
Industrial Chemical Mfr & Distr
N.A.I.C.S.: 325998

**Akzo Nobel Pulp and Performance
Chemicals AB** (3)
Farjevagen 1, SE 445 34, Bohus,
Sweden   (100%)
Tel.: (46) 31587000
Miscellaneous Chemical Product Mfr
N.A.I.C.S.: 325998

**Akzo Nobel Pulp and Performance
Chemicals Norway AS** (3)
Svaddeveien 119, 3660, Rjukan, Norway
Tel.: (47) 35080880
Web Site: http://www.nouryon.com
Specialty Chemicals Mfr
N.A.I.C.S.: 325998

Akzo Nobel Salt A/S (3)
Hadsundvej 17, 9550, Mariager,
Denmark   (50%)
Tel.: (45) 96687888
Specialty Chemicals Mfr
N.A.I.C.S.: 212390

Akzo Nobel UK Limited (3)
The Akzonobel Building, Wexham Road,
Slough, SL2 5DS, United Kingdom
Tel.: (44) 1928511521
Research & Development Technologies
N.A.I.C.S.: 325998

AkzoNobel (3)
Sutton Fields Industrial Estate, Rotterdam
Rd, Hull, HU7 OXX, United Kingdom
Tel.: (44) 1482825101
Coatings Marketing, Production & Research
N.A.I.C.S.: 325910

**Carbosulf Chemische Werke
GmbH** (3)
Geestemunderstasse 26, Cologne, 50735,
Germany   (67%)
Tel.: (49) 22174960
Web Site: https://www.nouryon.com
Specialty Chemicals Mfr
N.A.I.C.S.: 325998

Celanese Switzerland AG (3)
Industriestrasse 17A, Sempach Station,
6203, Lucerne, Switzerland
Tel.: (41) 414696969
Web Site: http://www.elotex.com
Building Material Additives Mfr & Distr
N.A.I.C.S.: 541715

Nicolas Ruiz (Key Acct Mgr)

Subsidiary (Domestic):

Claviag AG (4)
Neumattstrasse 196, Moosleerau, 5054,
Aargau, Switzerland
Tel.: (41) 627388888
Web Site: http://www.elotex.ch
Synthetic Polymers Mfr
N.A.I.C.S.: 325998

Subsidiary (Non-US):

**Eka Chemicals (Australia) Pty
Ltd** (3)
15 Conquest Way, Hallam, VIC, Australia
Tel.: (61) 397023422
Chemical Product Mfr & Distr
N.A.I.C.S.: 325998

**Eka Chemicals (Guangzhou) Co.,
Ltd.** (3)
61 Hong Jing Rd East Section, Guangzhou
Economic & Technolog, Guangzhou,
510760, China
Tel.: (86) 2083969688
Chemical Product Mfr & Distr
N.A.I.C.S.: 325998

Eka Chemicals Canada, Inc. (3)
1900 Rue St Patrice E, Magog, J1X4X6,
QC, Canada   (100%)
Tel.: (819) 843-8772
Web Site: https://www.nouryon.com
Bleaching Chemical Preparations
N.A.I.C.S.: 325998

Eka Chemicals do Brasil S.A. (3)
Rod Dom Gabriel Paulino Bueno Couto Km
65 2, PO Box 151, 13200-970, Jundiai, Sao
Paulo, Brazil
Tel.: (55) 1145894800
Chemical Products Mfr
N.A.I.C.S.: 325998

Joint Venture (Non-US):

Lion Akzo Co., Ltd. (3)
3 17 3-chome Obata, Yokkaichi, 510-0875,
Mie, Japan
Tel.: (81) 593468218
Web Site: http://www.lion.co.jp
Nitriles, Amines, Quarternary Ammonium
Salts, Amine Oxides, Monoamides &
Alkoxylated Amines Mfr; Joint Venture of
Lion Corporation (50%) & Akzo Nobel N.V.
(50%)
N.A.I.C.S.: 325998

Subsidiary (Non-US):

**Nouryon Chemicals Argentina
SAU** (3)
Ruta 11 Km 25, S2200MEC, San Lorenzo,
Santa Fe, Argentina
Tel.: (54) 3476422005
Sulfuric Acid Mfr
N.A.I.C.S.: 325180

**Nouryon Chemicals Argentina
SAU** (3)
Ruta 11 Km 25, S2200FQB, San Lorenzo,
Argentina
Tel.: (54) 3476422005
Web Site: https://www.nouryon.com
Sulfuric Acid, Sulphur Derivatives, Polyeth-
ylene & Phthalic Anhydride Mfr
N.A.I.C.S.: 325180

**Nouryon Chemicals Argentina
SAU** (3)
Avenida Paseo Colon 221 5 Piso, Buenos
Aires, C1063ACC, Argentina
Tel.: (54) 1143432011
Web Site: https://www.nouryon.com
Mfr of Wine Chemicals, Tartaric Acid, Vinic
Alcohol & Grape Seed Oil
N.A.I.C.S.: 325199
Mario Mariuzzi (Pres)

Nouryon Chemicals GmbH (3)
Am Coloneum 2,, 50829, Köln,
Germany   (100%)
Tel.: (49) 22174960
Production of Thiocyanites, Amonium Sul-
fide, Sodium, Hydrosulfide
N.A.I.C.S.: 325998

Nouryon Chemicals GmbH (3)
Amtsgericht Hauptniederlassung, Düren,

HRB 63, Germany
Tel.: (49) 2822976900
Polymer Chemicals Marketing, Sales & Mfr
N.A.I.C.S.: 325998

Nouryon Chemicals Limited (3)
Suite 1, 7th Floor 50 Broadway, London,
SW1H 0BL, United Kingdom
Tel.: (44) 1932247891
Production of Specialty Chemicals
N.A.I.C.S.: 325998

**Nouryon Chemicals MCA (Taixing)
Co. Ltd** (3)
Bin Jiang Bei Road 2-8 Jiangsu Province,
Taixing, 225404, Greater, China
Tel.: (86) 52387676001
Web Site: https://www.nouryon.com
Polymer Chemical Product Mfr
N.A.I.C.S.: 325998

**Nouryon Functional Chemicals
AB** (3)
Stenunge Allé 3 Stenungsund, Västra Göta-
land, 44430, Sweden   (100%)
Tel.: (46) 0317242197
Marketing & Sales of Salt & Basic Chemi-
cals
N.A.I.C.S.: 424690

**Nouryon Functional Chemicals
GmbH** (3)
Liebigstrasse 7, Greiz, 7973, Germany
Tel.: (49) 3661780
Web Site: https://www.nouryon.com
Chemical Products Mfr
N.A.I.C.S.: 325998

**Nouryon Pulp and Performance
Chemicals (Taiwan) Co. Ltd** (3)
6th Fl No 51 Sec 2 Gongyi Road, Nantun
District, Taichung, 408, Taiwan
Tel.: (886) 423270520
Web Site: https://www.nouryon.com
Chemical Product Mfr & Distr
N.A.I.C.S.: 325998
Steve Wang (Gen Mgr)

Joint Venture (Non-US):

Perla Greek Salt Ltd. (3)
22 Fleming Street, 182 33, Agios Ioannis
Rentis, Greece
Tel.: (30) 2104832466
Salt Producer
N.A.I.C.S.: 325998

Subsidiary (Domestic):

**Nouryon Functional Chemicals
B.V.** (2)
Haaksbergweg 88, De Oliphant Building
Floor 14 and 15, 1101 BZ, Amsterdam,
Netherlands
Tel.: (31) 889841000
Web Site: https://www.nouryon.com
Chemical Intermediates & Performance
Chemicals Mfr
N.A.I.C.S.: 325998

**Nouryon Pulp and Paper Chemicals
B.V.** (2)
Haaksbergweg 88, De Oliphant Building
Floor 14 and 15, 1101 BZ, Amsterdam,
Netherlands
Tel.: (31) 889841000
Web Site: https://www.nouryon.com
Chemical Products Mfr
N.A.I.C.S.: 325998

Novetta Solutions, LLC (1)
7921 Jones Branch Dr 5th Fl, McLean, VA
22102
Tel.: (571) 282-3000
Web Site: http://www.novetta.com
Holding Company; Data Analytics, Cyber
Security, Cloud Computing & Custom Solu-
tions Software & Services
N.A.I.C.S.: 551112
Richard P. Sawchak (CFO)
Chris Hagner (Sr VP-Products & Tech)
Tiffany Gates (Pres & CEO)
Bryan Rich (Sr VP-Open Source Intelli-
gence Tech)
Brian Hobbs (Sr VP-Bus Dev & Strategy)
Thomas W. Rabaut (Chm)
Ryan Fairchild (VP-Enterprise Solutions-Info
Exploitation)
Todd Massengill (VP-Emerging
Technologies-Info Exploitation)
Kevin Heald (Sr VP-Info Exploitation)

PA Consulting Holdings Limited (1)
10 Bressenden Place, London, SW1E 5DN,
United Kingdom   (100%)
Tel.: (44) 2077309000
Web Site: http://www.paconsulting.com
Sales Range: $550-599.9 Million
Emp.: 2,545
Management Consulting Services
N.A.I.C.S.: 541611
Andrew Hooke (Head-Consulting Sectors)
Alan Middleton (CEO)
Marcus Agius (Deputy Chm)
Kully Janjuah (Sec)
Hamish Maule (Head-Ops)
Jo Scarlett (CMO)
John Alexander (Chm)
Ruairidh Cameron (CFO)
Anita Chandraker (Head-Innovation)
Adam Hughes (Head-Transformation)
Conrad Thompson (Head-Bus Transforma-
tion)
Michel Vaja (Partner)

Subsidiary (Domestic):

7Safe Limited (2)
30 Crown Place, London, EC2A 4EB,
United Kingdom
Tel.: (44) 870 600 1667
Web Site: http://www.7safe.com
Computer Forensic & Information Security
Services
N.A.I.C.S.: 541512

Subsidiary (US):

Astro Studios, Inc. (2)
348 6th St, San Francisco, CA 94103
Tel.: (415) 487-6787
Web Site: http://www.astrostudios.com
Sales Range: $1-9.9 Million
Emp.: 17
Administrative Management & General
Management Consulting Service
N.A.I.C.S.: 541611
Brett Lovelady (Founder & CEO)

Cooper Perkins, Inc. (2)
10 Maguire Rd Bldg 4, Lexington, MA
02421-3110
Tel.: (781) 538-5536
Web Site: http://www.cooperperkins.com
Engineeering Services
N.A.I.C.S.: 541330
Gerhard Pawelka (CEO)

Subsidiary (Non-US):

PA Consulting Group A/S (2)
Tel.: (45) 39255000
Web Site: http://www.paconsulting.com
Emp.: 150
Information Technology Consulting Services
N.A.I.C.S.: 541512

PA Consulting Group AB (2)
Jakobsbergsgatan 17, 111 44, Stockholm,
Sweden
Tel.: (46) 84541900
Web Site: http://www.paconsulting.com
Information Technology Consulting Services
N.A.I.C.S.: 541512
Magnus Krusberg (Head-PA)

PA Consulting Group AS (2)
Verkstedveien 1, PO Box 150, Skoyen,
0212, Oslo, Norway
Tel.: (47) 67586758
Web Site: http://www.paconsulting.com
Information Technology Consulting Services
N.A.I.C.S.: 541512
Monica Odegaard (Head-PA)

PA Consulting Group GmbH (2)
An der Welle 3, 60322, Frankfurt, Germany
Tel.: (49) 6971702363
Web Site: http://www.paconsulting.com
Emp.: 60
Information Technology Consulting Services
N.A.I.C.S.: 541512
Jost Kamenik (Head-PA)

Subsidiary (US):

PA Consulting Group Inc (2)
1611 N Kent St Ste 301, Arlington, VA
22209
Tel.: (571) 227-9000
Web Site: http://www.paconsulting.com
Emp.: 10

The Carlyle Group Inc.—(Continued)

Information Technology Consulting Services
N.A.I.C.S.: 541512

Subsidiary (Non-US):

PA Consulting Services (India) Private Limited (2)
3A & 3B Nitesh Broadway 9/3 M G Road,
Bengaluru, 560 001, India
Tel.: (91) 80 25318855
Web Site: http://www.paconsulting.com
Emp.: 100
Information Technology Consulting Services
N.A.I.C.S.: 541512

Subsidiary (Domestic):

PA Consulting Services Limited (2)
10 Bressenden Place, London, SW1E 5DN,
United Kingdom
Tel.: (44) 1763285285
Web Site: http://www.paconsulting.com
Information Technology Consulting Services
N.A.I.C.S.: 541512

PQ Holdings Inc. (1)
300 Lindenwood Dr, Malvern, PA 19355-
1740
Tel.: (610) 651-4200
Rev.: $1,084,782,000
Assets: $2,333,480,000
Liabilities: $2,214,761,000
Net Worth: $118,719,000
Earnings: $6,972,000
Emp.: 2,418
Fiscal Year-end: 12/31/2012
Holding Company; Specialty Inorganic Performance Chemicals, Specialty Catalysts &
Specialty Glass Materials Mfr
N.A.I.C.S.: 551112
William J. Sichko Jr. (Chief Admin Officer &
Sr VP)

Subsidiary (Domestic):

PQ Corporation (2)
300 Lincolnwood Dr, Berwyn, PA 19355-
1740
Tel.: (610) 651-4200
Web Site: https://www.pqcorp.com
Sales Range: $500-549.9 Million
Sodium Silicate Mfr
N.A.I.C.S.: 325180

Subsidiary (Non-US):

**PQ (Tianjin) Silicates Technology Co.
Ltd.** (3)
Room 1106it Binjian International Hotel No
105 Jianshe Road, 300042, Tianjin, Heping,
China
Tel.: (00) 22 5066 0705
Hollow Microspheres & Sodium Silicate Mfr
N.A.I.C.S.: 325180

PQ Australia Pty. Ltd. (3)
9-13 Ruhr St, PO Box 4389, Dandenong,
3175, VIC, Australia
Tel.: (61) 397089200
Sales Range: $25-49.9 Million
Emp.: 32
Hollow Microspheres & Sodium Silicate Mfr
N.A.I.C.S.: 325180
David Rice (Gen Mgr)
John Marsden (Gen Mgr)

PQ Chemicals (Thailand) Ltd. (3)
246 Sukhumvit Road, Times Square Bldg
26th floor Between Soi 12-14, Bangkok,
10110, Thailand
Tel.: (00) 22294094
Web Site: http://www.pqcorporation.com
Hollow Microspheres & Sodium Silicate Mfr
N.A.I.C.S.: 325180

PQ Corporation (3)
4 Liverpool Rd, Warrington, WA5 1AB,
United Kingdom
Tel.: (44) 1925416100
Sales Range: $75-99.9 Million
Emp.: 250
Silica & Alumina Mfr; 60% Owned by The
Carlyle Group, 40% by INEOS Group Limited
N.A.I.C.S.: 327999

PQ Europe GmbH (3)
Werk Worms Mainzer Strasse 184, 67547,
Worms, Germany

Tel.: (49) 6241413563
Web Site: http://www.tqcorp.com
Emp.: 8
Hollow Microspheres & Sodium Silicate Mfr
N.A.I.C.S.: 325180

PQ Finland Oy (3)
Satamatie 2, 21100, Naantali, Finland
Tel.: (358) 24356099
Sales Range: $25-49.9 Million
Emp.: 5
Hollow Microspheres & Sodium Silicate Mfr
N.A.I.C.S.: 325180
Mika Raittila (Plant Mgr)

PQ France S.A.S. (3)
Usine De Lamotte, PO Box 30, 60350,
Trosly-Breuil, France
Tel.: (33) 344854760
Sales Range: $25-49.9 Million
Emp.: 44
Hollow Microspheres & Sodium Silicate Mfr
N.A.I.C.S.: 325180
Leguillerme Silva (Gen Mgr)

PQ Italy S.r.l. (3)
Via Giacomo Leopardi 31, 57121, Livorno,
Italy
Tel.: (39) 0586444151
Sales Range: $25-49.9 Million
Emp.: 2
Hollow Microspheres & Sodium Silicate Mfr
N.A.I.C.S.: 325180

PQ Nederland B.V. (3)
De Brand 24, 3800, Amersfoort, Netherlands
Tel.: (31) 334509030
Emp.: 14
Hollow Microspheres & Sodium Silicate Mfr
N.A.I.C.S.: 325180
S. Rendellth (Mng Dir)

PQ Silicates Ltd. (3)
9th Floor 10 Heng Yang Road, Taipei,
00100, Taiwan
Tel.: (886) 223830515
Hollow Microspheres & Sodium Silicate Mfr
N.A.I.C.S.: 325180

PQ Sweden AB (3)
Tegelbruksgatan 5, 656 72, Karlstad, Sweden
Tel.: (46) 547764460
Web Site: http://www.pqcorporation.com
Sales Range: $25-49.9 Million
Emp.: 8
Hollow Microspheres & Sodium Silicate Mfr
N.A.I.C.S.: 325180
Berndt Jackstat (Gen Mgr)

**Silicatos y Derivados S.A. de
C.V.** (3)
Fracc Ind San Nicolas, Rio Lerma 55, Tlalnepantla, Mexico
Tel.: (52) 55 227 6800
Hollow Microspheres & Sodium Silicate Mfr
N.A.I.C.S.: 325180

Joint Venture (Domestic):

Zeolyst International (3)
PO Box 830, Valley Forge, PA 19482
Tel.: (610) 651-4621
Web Site: http://www.zeolyst.com
Sales Range: $25-49.9 Million
Catalysts & Adsorbents Mfr
N.A.I.C.S.: 325180

PartyLite, Inc. (1)
600 Cordwainer Dr, Norwell, MA 02061
Tel.: (781) 347-9549
Web Site: http://www.partylite.com
Sales Range: $450-499.9 Million
Candles, Candle Accessories & Home Fragrance Products Mfr
N.A.I.C.S.: 339999

Subsidiary (Non-US):

Nordlicht GmbH (2)
Max-Planck-Strasse 26, 61381, Friedrichsdorf, Germany
Tel.: (49) 6172996260
Web Site: http://www.nordlicht.de
Candles & Decorative Items Mfr
N.A.I.C.S.: 339999
Kerstin Daudert (Mng Dir)
Peter Barsch (Head-Sls)

Subsidiary (Domestic):

PartyLite Gifts, Inc. (2)

600 Cordwainer Dr, Norwell, MA 02061
Web Site: http://www.partylite.com
Candle Mfr & Distr
N.A.I.C.S.: 424990

Subsidiary (Non-US):

PartyLite Gifts, Ltd. (3)
100 York Boulevard Suite 402, Richmond
Hill, L4B 1J8, ON, Canada
Web Site: http://www.partylite.ca
Residential Electric Lighting Fixture Mfr
N.A.I.C.S.: 335131
Tracie Graham (Country Mgr, VP-Sls & VP-
Admin)

PartyLite GmbH (3)
Im Breitspiel 7, 69126, Heidelberg, Germany
Tel.: (49) 622131360
Web Site: http://www.partylite.de
Candles & Decorative Items Mfr
N.A.I.C.S.: 339999
Axel Flecken (Area Mng Dir-PartyLite
D-A-CH & BeNeLux)

**PartyLite Handelsgesellschaft
m.b.H.** (3)
Wehlistr 27 b, 1200, Vienna, Austria
Tel.: (43) 19126240
Web Site: http://www.partylite.at
Candles & Decorative Objects Mfr
N.A.I.C.S.: 339999
Axel Patches (Mng Dir-PartyLite DA-CH &
BeNeLux)

PartyLite Oy (3)
Itsehallintokuja 6, 02600, Espoo, Finland
Tel.: (358) 984964199
Web Site: http://www.partylite.fi
Residential Electric Lighting Fixture Mfr
N.A.I.C.S.: 335131
Marko Saarenkanta (CEO)
Riitta Rutanen (Sls Dir-PartyLite Finland)

PartyLite Trading S.A. (3)
Rte d Agy 14/16, Granges Paccot, 1763,
Fribourg, Switzerland
Tel.: (41) 264603636
Web Site: http://www.partylite.ch
Candles & Decorative Objects Mfr
N.A.I.C.S.: 339999
Axel Flecken (Area Managing Dir-PartyLite
D-A-CH & BeNeLux)

PartyLite UK Ltd (3)
Building 3 Unit 1a Hatters Lane, Croxley
Park, Watford, WD18 8YG, Herts, United
Kingdom
Tel.: (44) 1923477500
Web Site: http://www.partylite.co.uk
Residential Electric Lighting Fixture Mfr
N.A.I.C.S.: 335131
Sandra Whittle (Mng Dir-UK & Ireland)
Claire Hacking (Mktg Dir)

Subsidiary (Domestic):

Walter Drake Inc. (2)
2155 S Oakwood Rd, Oshkosh, WI 54906
Web Site: https://www.wdrake.com
Mail Order Services
N.A.I.C.S.: 425120
Joseph Feigen (Owner)

Subsidiary (Non-US):

Wax Lyrical Limited (2)
London Road Lindal-in-Furness, Ulverston,
LA12 0LD, Cumbria, United Kingdom
Tel.: (44) 1229461140
Web Site: http://www.wax-lyrical.co.uk
Candles & Decorative Objects Mfr
N.A.I.C.S.: 339999
Joanne Barber (Mng Dir)
Liz Kerr (Controller-Fin)
Lyn Place (Mgr-MIS)
Emma Stevenson (Mgr-HR)

Plateno Group Co. Ltd. (1)
Plateno Group Plaza No 300 Xin Jiao Xi
Road, Haizhu District, Guangzhou, Guangdong, China
Tel.: (86) 20 8911 5109
Web Site: http://www.plateno-group.com
Hotel Owner & Operator
N.A.I.C.S.: 721110
Lynn Meng (Pres & CEO-Plateno Internet
Company)

**PrimeFlight Aviation Services,
Inc.** (1)
3 Sugar Creek Center Blvd Ste 450, Sugar
Land, TX 77478
Tel.: (281) 942-6800
Web Site: http://www.primeflight.com
Emp.: 8,000
Air Transportation Support Services
N.A.I.C.S.: 488190
Edward Zwirn (Exec VP)
Dan Bucaro (Pres & CEO)
Rob Hiegel (CFO & Exec VP)
Matt Barry (Sr VP-Ops)
Greg Sutphin (Sr VP-Ops)

Subsidiary (Domestic):

Global Aviation Services, LLC (2)
920 Aldrin Dr Ste 250, Eagan, MN 55121
Tel.: (763) 259-0200
Web Site:
http://www.globalaviationservicesllc.com
Emp.: 250
Aviation Equipment Repair & Maintenance
Services
N.A.I.C.S.: 488190
Brad Osborn (CEO)
Barb Severson (VP-Fin)
Dan Miling (VP-Ops)
Gina Coleal (VP-HR & Org Dev)
Allan Ramirez (Mgr-Natl-Southeast)
Brent Hauge (Mgr-Health, Safety & Environmental)
Brian Heiskary (Mgr-Natl-South)
Bruce Teeple (Mgr-Natl-West)
Chris Van Den Heuvel (Dir-Support Svcs)
Jason Adams (Head-IT)
Jeff Ebsen (Dir-Facilities Maintenance)
Jeff Tincher (Dir-Continuous Improvements
& Quality Sys)
John Bryant (Dir-Strategic Accounts)
Luis Martinez (Dir-Maintenance)
Randy Bammert-Mueller (Mgr-Inventory
Control)
Scott Brau (Mgr-Facilities Maintenance
Ops)
Tom Kor (Mgr-Natl Trng-Organizational Dev)
Tyler Franklin (Mgr-Natl-Northeast)

RAC Ltd. (1)
RAC House, Brockhurst Crescent, Walsall,
WS5 4AW, United Kingdom
Tel.: (44) 1922437000
Web Site: http://www.rac.co.uk
Sales Range: $125-149.9 Million
Emp.: 4,000
Vehicle Services & Repairs
N.A.I.C.S.: 811114

SENQCIA Corporation (1)
Momento Shiodome Bldg 2-3-17 Higashi-
Shimbashi, Minato-ku, Tokyo, 105-8319,
Japan
Tel.: (81) 342141972
Web Site: http://www.senqcia.com
Emp.: 287
Floor Systems, Building Components,
Chains & Sprockets Mfr
N.A.I.C.S.: 332311
Nobuyasu Kasahara (Pres & CEO)
Kouji Masuoka (Exec Officer)
Hiroaki Sorano (Exec Officer)
Tomotaka Hoshiai (CFO)
Kazunobu Tsuneyoshi (Exec Officer)
Masahiro Sorimachi (Exec Officer)
Yuichi Mochida (Exec Officer)
Koichiro Katsuyama (Exec Officer)
Masahiro Hori (Exec Officer)

Schaltbau Holding AG (1)
Hollerithstrasse 5, 81829, Munich, (78%)
Germany
Tel.: (49) 89930050
Web Site: http://www.schaltbaugroup.com
Rev.: $632,765,911
Assets: $505,833,449
Liabilities: $394,389,092
Net Worth: $111,444,356
Earnings: $6,955,523
Emp.: 2,916
Fiscal Year-end: 12/31/2020
Holding Company
N.A.I.C.S.: 551112
Volker Kregelin (Member-Exec Bd)
Jurgen Brandes (CEO & Member-Exec Bd)
Steffen Munz (CFO & Member-Exec Bd)
Stephane Rambaud-Measson (Chm-
Supervisory Bd)

Subsidiary (Non-US):

Bode Korea Co. Ltd. (2)
160-3 Dayoon Bldg Garak-Dong, Songpa-gu, 138-809, Seoul, Korea (South)
Tel.: (82) 230120560
Electric Equipment Mfr
N.A.I.C.S.: 335311

Subsidiary (US):

Bode North America Inc. (2)
660 John Dodd Rd, Spartanburg, SC 29303
Tel.: (864) 578-9683
Web Site: http://www.bodenorthamerica.com
Door Mfr
N.A.I.C.S.: 321911
Keith Frazier *(Pres & CEO)*

Subsidiary (Domestic):

Gebr. Bode GmbH & Co. KG (2)
Ochshauser Str 14, 34123, Kassel, Germany
Tel.: (49) 56150090
Electric & Pneumatic Vehicle Door System Mfr
N.A.I.C.S.: 336320

Subsidiary (Non-US):

Pintsch B.V. (2)
Krommewetering 91, 3543 AN, Utrecht, Netherlands
Tel.: (31) 346583958
Railway Infrastructure Product Mfr
N.A.I.C.S.: 336510

Subsidiary (Domestic):

Pintsch GmbH (2)
Hunxer Strasse 149, 46537, Dinslaken, Germany
Tel.: (49) 20646020
Web Site: http://pintsch.net
Railway Infrastructure Product Mfr
N.A.I.C.S.: 336510

Subsidiary (US):

Pintsch Tiefenbach US Inc. (2)
810 Skyline Dr, Marion, IL 62959
Tel.: (618) 993-8513
Web Site: http://pintschtiefenbach.us.com
Railway Equipment Mfr
N.A.I.C.S.: 336510
Bennie Manion *(Pres)*

Subsidiary (Non-US):

Rawicka Fabryka Wyposazenia Wagonow Sp.z.o.o. (2)
Tysiaclecia 5, Rawicz, 63-900, Leszno, Poland
Tel.: (48) 655462424
Web Site: https://www.rawag.pl
Electric & Pneumatic Vehicle Door System Mfr
N.A.I.C.S.: 336320

SPII S.p.A. (2)
Via don Volpi 37 Angolo Via Montoli, 21047, Saronno, VA, Italy
Tel.: (39) 029622921
Railway Equipment Mfr
N.A.I.C.S.: 336510

Schaltbau Asia Pacific Ltd. (2)
31C Billion Plaza 2 10 Cheung Yue Street, Lai Chi Kok, Kowloon, China (Hong Kong)
Tel.: (852) 37695627
DC Contactor Mfr & Retailer
N.A.I.C.S.: 335999

Schaltbau Austria GmbH (2)
Ignaz-Kock-Strasse 10 Top 3 6, 1210, Vienna, Austria
Tel.: (43) 13833333
Railway Equipment Mfr
N.A.I.C.S.: 336510

Schaltbau France S.A.S. (2)
10 rue Desire Granet, 95104, Argenteuil, Cedex, France
Tel.: (33) 139984949
Railway Equipment Mfr
N.A.I.C.S.: 336510

Schaltbau India Pvt. Ltd. (2)
116-118 Ansal Classique Tower Plot No1 J Block Community Centre, Rajouri Garden, New Delhi, 110027, India

Tel.: (91) 1125104342
DC Contactor Mfr & Retailer
N.A.I.C.S.: 335999

Schaltbau Machine Electrics Ltd. (2)
335-336 Woodside Way, Springvale Industrial Estate, Cwmbran, NP44 5BR, United Kingdom
Tel.: (44) 1633877555
Web Site: http://www.schaltbau.com
Mechanical Handling Equipment Mfr
N.A.I.C.S.: 333998

Subsidiary (US):

Schaltbau North America Inc. (2)
225 Oser Ave, Hauppauge, NY 11788
Tel.: (631) 351-6993
Railway Equipment Mfr
N.A.I.C.S.: 336510

Subsidiary (Non-US):

Schaltbau Transportation UK Ltd. (2)
Unit 2 Patriot Drive Rooksley, Milton Keynes, MK13 8PU, United Kingdom
Tel.: (44) 1908224140
Electric & Pneumatic Vehicle Door System Mfr
N.A.I.C.S.: 336320

Shenyang Schaltbau Electrical Corporation Ltd. (2)
No 3 12 Jia The 13th Street, Shenyang Economy Technology Development District, Shenyang, 110027, China
Tel.: (86) 2428312000
DC Contactor Mfr & Retailer
N.A.I.C.S.: 335999

Sciens Building Solutions, LLC (1)
5925 Stonebridge Dr, Pleasanton, CA 94588
Tel.: (925) 249-7700
Web Site: http://sciensbuildingsolutions.com
Fire Protection Services
N.A.I.C.S.: 922160
Terry Heath *(CEO)*
Michael Dawid *(CFO)*
Kurt Schoonover *(COO)*
Frank LoPresti *(VP-Ops)*
Sarah DeCuir *(VP-People & Culture)*

Subsidiary (Domestic):

Absolute Protective Systems, Inc. (2)
3 Kellogg Ct Ste 13, Edison, NJ 08817
Tel.: (732) 287-4500
Web Site: http://www.absps.com
Sales Range: $1-9.9 Million
Emp.: 30
Plumbing, Heating & Air-Conditioning Contractors
N.A.I.C.S.: 238220
Paul Smoley *(Pres)*

Anchor Fire Protection Co. (2)
270 Renninger Rd, Perkiomenville, PA 18074
Tel.: (610) 754-7836
Rev.: $2,400,000
Emp.: 25
Commercial & Institutional Building Construction
N.A.I.C.S.: 236220
Theodore C. Wills *(Pres)*
Anthony Ferrugio *(Mgr-Life Safety Sys & Fire Alarm)*

Bass-United Fire & Security Systems, Inc. (2)
1480 SW 3rd St Ste 9, Pompano Beach, FL 33069
Tel.: (954) 785-7800
Web Site: http://www.bassunited.com
Sales Range: $1-9.9 Million
Emp.: 39
Electrical Apparatus & Equipment, Wiring Supplies & Related Equipment Merchant Whslr
N.A.I.C.S.: 423610
Brad Higdon *(Pres & CEO)*

Cen-Cal Fire Systems Inc. (2)
PO Box 1284, Lodi, CA 95240-5240
Tel.: (209) 334-9119
Web Site: http://www.cen-calfire.com
Plumbing, Heating & Air-Conditioning Contractors

N.A.I.C.S.: 238220
Wayne Weisz *(Owner & VP)*

Empire Electric Maintenance & Service, Inc. (2)
2200 SW 67TH Avenue, Miami, FL 33155
Tel.: (305) 264-9982
Electrical Contractor
N.A.I.C.S.: 238210

Fire Alarm Control Systems, Inc. (2)
12961 Park Central, San Antonio, TX 78216
Tel.: (210) 344-2901
Web Site: http://www.facssa.com
Sales Range: $1-9.9 Million
Emp.: 12
Electrical Apparatus & Equipment, Wiring Supplies & Related Equipment Merchant Whslr
N.A.I.C.S.: 423610
Benton Terry *(Mgr-Ops)*

Low Voltage Integrated Systems Inc. (2)
1930 Watson Way, Vista, CA 92081
Tel.: (760) 598-4110
Web Site: http://www.sdlvis.com
Electrical Contractor
N.A.I.C.S.: 238210
Michael Arguijo *(Pres)*

Open Systems Integrators, Inc. (2)
211 Yardville Hamilton Sq Rd, Hamilton, NJ 08620
Tel.: (732) 792-2112
Web Site: https://www.osicorp.net
Sales Range: $1-9.9 Million
Emp.: 24
Custom Computer Programming Services
N.A.I.C.S.: 541511
Bill Baroska *(Pres)*

Smartwatch Security & Sound, LLC (2)
742 S Rossiter St, Mount Dora, FL 32757
Tel.: (352) 383-2479
Security, Fire Alarm & Sound System Integration Services
N.A.I.C.S.: 561621

West Fire Systems, Inc. (2)
53 Pixley Industrial Pky, Rochester, NY 14624
Tel.: (585) 663-8530
Web Site: http://www.westfiresystems.com
Electrical Apparatus & Equipment, Wiring Supplies & Related Equipment Whslr
N.A.I.C.S.: 423610

Sedgwick Claims Management Services, Inc. (1)
8215 Sedgwick Way, Memphis, TN 38125
Tel.: (901) 415-7400
Web Site: http://www.sedgwick.com
Claims, Title Insurance & Specialty Insurance Services
N.A.I.C.S.: 524291
David A. North *(Chm & CEO)*
Robert Peterson *(Pres)*
Henry Lyons *(CFO)*
Scott Rogers *(Chief Client Officer)*
Ian V. Muress *(CEO-Intl)*
Paul White *(Deputy CEO-UK)*
Stewart Steel *(CEO-UK)*
Jessica Reimers *(COO-Europe)*
Stephen Raper *(Dir-Fin-Europe, Middle East & Africa)*
Jim Ryan *(COO-Americas)*
John Stanzi *(Pres-Casualty Ops-Americas)*
Adam R. Fisher *(Chief Data Officer)*
Elizabeth Demaret *(Pres-Specialty Solutions)*

Subsidiary (Domestic):

Absentys, LLC (2)
1206 Pointe Centre Dr Ste 220, Chattanooga, TN 37421
Tel.: (423) 893-5310
Web Site: http://www.absentys.com
Emp.: 12
Software Publisher
N.A.I.C.S.: 513210
Dana Jackson *(VP)*
Leah Cooper *(VP-Application Dev)*

Subsidiary (Non-US):

EFI Global Canada (2)
50 Burnhamthorpe Road West Suite 1102,

Mississauga, L5B 3C2, ON, Canada
Tel.: (905) 896-8181
Web Site: http://www.efiglobal.ca
Forensic Engineering Services
N.A.I.C.S.: 561611
Richard Nellis *(Asst VP-Natl Lead Forensic Svcs)*
Kevin Burgher *(VP)*

Subsidiary (Domestic):

EFI Global, Inc. (2)
8811 FM 1960 Byp Rd W Ste 400, Humble, TX 77338
Tel.: (281) 358-4441
Web Site: http://www.efiglobal.com
Forensic Engineering Services
N.A.I.C.S.: 561611
E. Metts Hardy *(VP-Fire Investigations)*
Ted M. Cleveland *(VP-Ops)*
Keith Pokorny *(VP-North)*
Jock Marshall *(VP-Central)*
Jeremy J. Mele *(Pres)*
Donald Peak *(VP-West)*
Timothy R. Jonas *(VP-South)*
Ron Maggard *(VP-Geo Svcs Div)*
David P. Amori *(VP-Engrg)*
Alan Anderson *(VP-Sls)*

Managed Care Advisors, Inc. (2)
7700 Old Georgetown Rd Ste 750, Bethesda, MD 20814-6100
Tel.: (301) 469-1660
Web Site:
    http://www.managedcareadvisors.com
General Management Consulting Services
N.A.I.C.S.: 541611
Marianne Cloeren *(Dir-Medical)*
Lisa Firestone *(Pres & CEO)*

Metro Appraisal, Inc. (2)
3109 Lithia Pinecrest Rd, Valrico, FL 33594
Tel.: (813) 286-7440
Web Site: http://www.metfl.com
Sales Range: $1-9.9 Million
Emp.: 20
Business Support Services
N.A.I.C.S.: 561499
Scott Eskine *(Owner)*

Nautilus Investigations, Inc. (2)
9245 SW 157th St Ste 208, Miami, FL 38157-1975
Tel.: (305) 232-9555
Web Site:
    http://www.nautilusinvestigations.com
Investigation Services
N.A.I.C.S.: 561611
Glenn Kutner *(Founder & Pres)*

Subsidiary (Non-US):

Sedgwick Belgium SA (2)
Noorderlaan 133, 2030, Antwerp, Belgium
Tel.: (32) 35414539
Web Site: http://www.sedgwick.com
Insurance Risk, Claims & Loss Management Services
N.A.I.C.S.: 524298
Bob Vermeiren *(Gen Mgr)*
Peter Dehaemers *(Head-Intl Desk)*

Subsidiary (Domestic):

Sedgwick Factual Photo, Inc. (2)
1230 E Diehl Rd Ste 300, Naperville, IL 60563
Tel.: (630) 416-9020
Web Site:
    http://www.sedgwickfactualphoto.com
Sales Range: $10-24.9 Million
Emp.: 100
Investigation Services
N.A.I.C.S.: 561611
George S. Oliver *(Pres)*

Subsidiary (Non-US):

Sedgwick France S.A. (2)
5-6 Esplanade Charles de Gaulle 5eme etage, Immeuble Le Carillon, 92000, Nanterre, France
Tel.: (33) 140228080
Web Site: http://www.sedgwick.com
Emp.: 800
Insurance Risk, Claims & Loss Management Services
N.A.I.C.S.: 524298
Eric Alessandrini *(Mgr-Liability Hub)*

Sedgwick Nederland B.V. (2)

The Carlyle Group Inc.—(Continued)

Westerstraat 21, PO Box 23212, 3001 KE, Rotterdam, Netherlands
Tel.: (31) 882866464
Web Site: http://www.sedgwick.com
Insurance Risk, Claims & Loss Management Services
N.A.I.C.S.: 524298
Jeroen Frohlich (*CEO-Netherlands & Head-Continental Europe*)
Rens Kramer (*Gen Mgr*)
Isabel Bann (*Asst Coord-Intl Program-Amstelveen*)
Marius Bakker (*Mgr-Marine*)
Jack de Klerk (*Mgr-Ops & Bus Dev*)
Johannes Marinus (*Gen Mgr*)
Sarah Niekerk (*Mgr-HR*)

Sedgwick Risk Services Limited   (2)
60 Fenchurch Street, London, EC3M 4AD, United Kingdom
Tel.: (44) 2075300600
Web Site: http://www.sedgwick.com
Insurance Risk, Claims & Loss Management Services
N.A.I.C.S.: 524298

Subsidiary (Domestic):

Sedgwick International UK   (3)
60 Fenchurch Street, London, EC3M 4AD, United Kingdom
Tel.: (44) 2075300600
Web Site: http://www.sedgwick.com
Insurance Risk, Claims & Loss Management Services
N.A.I.C.S.: 524298
Steve Abrahams (*Dir-Engrg*)
Terri Adams (*Dir-Forensic Advisory Svcs Div*)
David Aiston (*Dir-Strategic Bus Dev*)
Leigh Allen (*Relationship Mgr*)
Rob Allum (*Assoc Dir-Comml Claims*)
Christian Aplin (*Deputy Head-Retail Markets-Manchester*)
Paul White (*CEO*)
Stewart Steel (*CEO-EMEA*)
Wayne Manning (*Head-Client Svcs-Intl*)

Subsidiary (Domestic):

T&H Global Holdings, LLC   (2)
1833 Ctr Point Cir Ste 139, Naperville, IL 60563-1484
Tel.: (630) 245-7000
Web Site: http://www.vericlaiminc.com
Holding Company; Loss Adjusting, Claims Management Forensic Engineering & Investigation Services
N.A.I.C.S.: 551112

Subsidiary (Domestic):

BPO Technical Services LLC   (3)
PO Box 905, Hempstead, TX 77445
Tel.: (281) 371-3022
Web Site: http://www.bpotechnical.com
Emp.: 100
Large Commercial & Residential Property Loss Adjusters & Appraisal Services
N.A.I.C.S.: 524291
Thomas L. Powell (*Pres*)
Daniel T. Powell (*VP-Claims*)

Farrell & Associates Insurance Services   (3)
15800 Boones Ferry Rd, Lake Oswego, OR 97035
Tel.: (503) 697-5870
Web Site: http://www.farrell-associates.com
Insurance Related Activities
N.A.I.C.S.: 524298
Mike Farrell (*Owner*)

Unified Investigations & Sciences, Inc.   (3)
2150 Northmont Pkwy Ste F, Duluth, GA 30096
Tel.: (770) 246-0026
Web Site: http://www.uis-usa.com
Sales Range: $25-49.9 Million
Emp.: 200
Forensic Engineering & Investigation Services
N.A.I.C.S.: 561611
Steven T. Powell (*Pres*)
Timothy R. Jonas (*VP-East Area*)
Don Peak (*VP-West Area*)

David L. Rivers (*District Mgr-East Svc Center*)
James Swain (*District Mgr-West Svc Center*)

Subsidiary (Domestic):

O'Connor Engineering   (4)
1172 National Dr Ste 100, Sacramento, CA 95834
Tel.: (916) 640-0640
Web Site: http://www.oconnor-engineering.com
Engineering Services
N.A.I.C.S.: 541330
Michael J. O'Connor (*Engr*)
Kathryn Burns (*Coord-Engrg*)

Subsidiary (Non-US):

VeriClaim UK Limited   (3)
1 Alie Street, London, E1 8DE, United Kingdom
Tel.: (44) 2077094040
Web Site: http://www.vrsvericlaim.co.uk
Loss Adjusting & Claims Management Services
N.A.I.C.S.: 524291
Alistair Halley (*Head-Complex & Major Loss*)
Ian Huckstep (*Dir-Comml Div*)
Mike Weatherhead (*Head-Technical Best Practice*)
Trevor Day (*Assoc Dir*)
James Henry (*Assoc Dir*)

Subsidiary (Domestic):

Temporary Accommodations, Inc.   (2)
6 Piedmont Ctr NE, Atlanta, GA 30305
Tel.: (404) 874-3321
Web Site:
   http://www.temporaryaccommodations.net
Rev.: $2,400,000
Emp.: 30
All Other Travel Arrangement & Reservation Services
N.A.I.C.S.: 561599
Aaron Wilson (*Pres & CEO*)
Tommy Chapman (*VP*)
Chris Baldwin (*CFO*)
Mike Leslie (*VP-Sls & Mktg*)
Joseph Tate (*VP-Ops & Fin*)

Vale National Training Center Inc.   (2)
2424 E Randol Mill Rd, Arlington, TX 76011
Tel.: (817) 633-4800
Web Site:
   http://www.valetrainingsolutions.com
Training of Appraisers for Auto & Property Physical Damage
N.A.I.C.S.: 611519

York Risk Services Group, Inc.   (2)
101 Hudson St Ste 3500, Jersey City, NJ 07302
Tel.: (866) 391-9675
Web Site: http://www.yorkrisk.com
Holding Company; Insurance, Risk Management & Claims Management Services
N.A.I.C.S.: 551112
Michael Krawitz (*Gen Counsel & Exec VP*)
Patrick J. Walsh (*Chief Claims Officer & Exec VP*)
Louis E. Keyes (*Chief Sls Officer*)
Maria Conry (*CMO & Sr VP*)
Mark Bilger (*CIO & Exec VP*)
Dennis Duchene (*Exec VP-Managed Care*)
Sas Mukherjee (*CFO & Exec VP*)
Jody Moses (*Exec VP & Gen Mgr-Public Entity*)
Thomas W. Warsop III (*Chm & CEO*)

Subsidiary (Domestic):

Northeast Association Management, Inc.   (3)
Airport Park 9 Cornell Rd, Latham, NY 12110
Tel.: (518) 220-1111
Web Site: http://www.neami.com
Management Services
N.A.I.C.S.: 541611
Ann Gergen (*Sr VP*)
Jeff van Dyk (*Exec VP*)

StandardAero Business Aviation Services LLC   (1)

6710 N Scottsdale Rd Ste 250, Scottsdale, AZ 85253
Tel.: (480) 377-3100
Web Site: http://www.standardaero.com
Aviation Maintenance, Repair & Overhaul (MRO) Services
N.A.I.C.S.: 488119
Russell Ford (*Chm & CEO*)
Scott Starrett (*Pres-Military & Energy*)
Rick Stine (*Pres-Components, Helicopters & Accessories*)
Tony Brancato (*Sr VP-Business Integration & Pres-Associated Air Center*)
Marc Drobny (*Pres-Bus Aviation*)
Dan Satterfield (*CFO*)

Subsidiary (Domestic):

PAS Technologies Inc.   (2)
1234 Atlantic St N, Kansas City, MO 64116-4142
Tel.: (816) 556-5113
Web Site: http://www.pas-technologies.com
Aviation Component Repair & Maintenance Services; Welding, Brazing, Coating & Heat Treating
N.A.I.C.S.: 336413
Thomas C. Hutton (*CEO*)
Timothy J. Puglielli (*CFO*)
Dragos Grigorescu (*Gen Mgr & VP*)

Subsidiary (Non-US):

Asian Surface Technologies Pte. Ltd.   (3)
55 Loyang Drive, Singapore, 508967, Singapore   (80%)
Tel.: (65) 65458255
Fan Blade Overhaul & Plasma Coating Services for Aerospace & Industrial Engineering Products
N.A.I.C.S.: 336412

Subsidiary (Domestic):

Bolton Aerospace, Inc.   (3)
321 Progress Dr, Manchester, CT 06042-2296
Tel.: (860) 649-2727
Aerospace Industry Repair & Overhaul Services
N.A.I.C.S.: 332710

Subsidiary (Non-US):

StandardAero   (2)
2 Allen Dyne Rd, Winnipeg, R3H 0T7, MB, Canada
Tel.: (204) 318-7544
Web Site: http://www.standardaero.com
Aircraft Engine Repair & Overhaul Services
N.A.I.C.S.: 336412
Dan Satterfield (*CFO*)
Russell Ford (*Chm & CEO*)

Turbine Repair Services Global Ireland Ltd   (2)
Carrigtwohill Industrial Est, Carrigtwohill, Co Cork, Ireland
Tel.: (353) 214287300
Web Site: http://www.trsglobal.com
Sales Range: $25-49.9 Million
Aircraft Turbine Component Remanufacturing Services
N.A.I.C.S.: 336412
Declan O'Leary (*Gen Mgr*)
Phil Letman (*Sr VP-Bus Dev*)

Vector Aerospace France   (2)
1 Boulevard du 19 Mars 1962, BP 50064, 95503, Gonesse, France
Tel.: (33) 130185444
Aircraft Part Mfr
N.A.I.C.S.: 336413

Syniverse Holdings, Inc.   (1)
8125 Highwoods Palm Way, Tampa, FL 33647-1765
Tel.: (813) 637-5000
Web Site: http://www.syniverse.com
Rev.: $793,512,000
Assets: $3,147,926,000
Liabilities: $2,187,519,000
Net Worth: $960,407,000
Earnings: ($24,594,000)
Emp.: 2,179
Fiscal Year-end: 12/31/2017
Holding Company; Wireless Telecommunications Technology Solutions, Transaction Processing & Clearinghouse Services

N.A.I.C.S.: 551112
Dean C. J. Douglas (*Pres & CEO*)
James A. Attwood Jr. (*Chm*)
Laura E. Binion (*Gen Counsel & Sr VP*)
Chris Rivera (*CTO*)
Norris Powell (*Chief HR Officer*)
Bill Corbin (*Sr VP-Indirect Markets & Strategic Partnerships*)
Jeff Bak (*VP-Product Mgmt-Cloud Messaging Svcs*)
John P. Wick Jr. (*Sr VP-Network*)
Tony G. Holcombe (*Vice Chm*)

Subsidiary (Non-US):

Syniverse Technologies Limited   (2)
18 Mansell Street, London, E1 8AA, United Kingdom
Tel.: (44) 27756280
Web Site: http://www.syniverse.com
Sales Range: $25-49.9 Million
Emp.: 80
Wireless Telecommunications Technology Solutions, Transaction Processing & Clearinghouse Services
N.A.I.C.S.: 517810
Jeff Gordon (*Mng Dir*)

Subsidiary (Domestic):

Syniverse Technologies, LLC   (2)
8125 Highwoods Palm Way, Tampa, FL 33647-1765
Tel.: (813) 637-5000
Web Site: http://www.syniverse.com
Wireless Telecommunications Technology Solutions, Transaction Processing & Clearinghouse Services
N.A.I.C.S.: 517810
Dean Douglas (*Pres*)
Andrew Davies (*CEO*)
Bill Sansalone (*CFO*)

TC Group, LLC   (1)
1001 Pennsylvania Ave NW Ste 220, Washington, DC 20004   (100%)
Tel.: (202) 729-5626
Web Site: https://www.carlyle.com
Emp.: 2,000
Private Equity Investment Services
N.A.I.C.S.: 523999
Martin W. Sumner (*Principal*)
Ian I. Fujiyama (*Mng Dir*)
Adam Joseph Palmer (*Mng Dir & Head-Global Aerospace, Defense, and Govt Svcs*)

Subsidiary (Non-US):

AlpInvest Partners B.V.   (2)
Jachthavenweg 118, 1081 KJ, Amsterdam, Netherlands   (60%)
Tel.: (31) 205407575
Web Site: https://www.alpinvest.com
Sales Range: $50-74.9 Million
Emp.: 75
Private Equity Firm
N.A.I.C.S.: 523999
Erica Herberg (*CFO*)

Subsidiary (US):

AlpInvest Partners Inc.   (3)
299 Park Ave 35th Fl, New York, NY 10171
Tel.: (212) 332-6240
Web Site: http://www.alpinvest.com
Sales Range: $25-49.9 Million
Emp.: 60
Private Equity Investment Firm
N.A.I.C.S.: 523999
Richard Dunne (*Principal*)

Subsidiary (Non-US):

Carlyle Japan Asset Management YK   (2)
Shin-Marunouchi Building 1-5-1
Marunouchi, Chiyoda-ku, Tokyo, 100-6535, Japan
Tel.: (81) 352084350
Web Site: http://www.carlyle.jp
Private Equity Investment & Portfolio Management Services
N.A.I.C.S.: 523999
Tamotsu Adachi (*Mng Dir*)

Holding (Domestic):

KITO Corporation   (3)
2000 Tsuijiarai Showa-Cho, Nakakoma-gun,

Yamanashi, 409-3853, Japan **(74.1%)**
Tel.: (81) 552757521
Web Site: http://www.kito.com
Rev.: $501,472,400
Assets: $629,848,560
Liabilities: $333,960,000
Net Worth: $295,888,560
Earnings: $22,689,920
Emp.: 2,262
Fiscal Year-end: 03/31/2021
Material Handling Equipment Mfr, Sales, Repair & Maintenance
N.A.I.C.S.: 811310
Yoshio Kito (Pres, CEO & Exec Officer)
Tsuneo Yuzurihara (Mng Dir, Chief Quality & Mfg Officer & Sr Exec Officer)
Toshio Kono (Exec Officer & Gen Mgr-Procurement Div)
Edward W. Hunter (Co-CMO, Exec Officer & Exec VP)
Shigeki Osozawa (Mng Dir, CFO, Sr Exec Officer & Gen Mgr-Fin Mgmt Div)
Mamoru Horiuchi (Sr Exec Officer & Gen Mgr-Bus Div-Asia)
Hiroshi Yamada (Exec Officer & Gen Mgr-Chain Mfg Div)
Longlin Huang (Co-CMO, Sr Exec Officer & Gen Mgr-Bus Div-China)
Kimiaki Hayakawa (Exec Officer & Gen Mgr-Hoist Mfg Div)
Kiyohito Hamada (Auditor)
Scott D. Miller (Exec Officer & Head-Powered Chain Hoists)
Yoshio Morita (Exec Officer & Head-Reg Bus Admin)
Carlo Lonardi (Exec Officer & Gen Mgr-Bus Div-Americas)
Marc Premont (Exec Officer & Deputy Gen Mgr-Bus Div-Americas)
Kentaro Yoneyama (Auditor)
Martin Rothe (Exec Officer, Mng Dir-Kito Europe & Gen Mgr-Bus Div-EMEA)
Kazumitsu Ishikawa (Exec Officer & Gen Mgr-Dev & Tech Div)
Eiko Hakoda (Auditor)

Subsidiary (US):

KITO Americas, Inc. **(4)**
401 W End Ave, Manheim, PA 17545
Tel.: (717) 665-2000
Web Site: https://www.kitoamericas.com
Material Handling Equipment Mfr & Sales
N.A.I.C.S.: 333248
Carlo Lonardi (Pres & CEO)
Marc Premont (COO)
Chris Hess (VP-Quality & Product Dev Engrg)
Jason Said (Dir-Bus Dev)

Subsidiary (Domestic):

Harrington Hoists, Inc. **(5)**
401 W End Ave, Manheim, PA 17545 **(100%)**
Tel.: (717) 665-2000
Web Site: http://www.harringtonhoists.com
Sales Range: $50-74.9 Million
Emp.: 85
Manual & Electric Chain Hoists & Overhead Traveling Bridge Cranes Mfr
N.A.I.C.S.: 333923
Carlo Lonardi (CEO)
Drew Schoenberger (Mgr-Engrg & Quality)
Guy Haney (Plant Mgr)

Peerless Industrial Group, Inc. **(5)**
1416 E Sanborn St, Winona, MN 55987
Web Site: http://www.peerlesschain.com
Sales Range: $100-124.9 Million
Chain, Fittings, Overhead Lifting Products & Traction Products Mfr & Distr
N.A.I.C.S.: 333248

Subsidiary (Domestic):

Peerless Chain Company **(6)**
1416 E Sanborn St, Winona, MN 55987
Tel.: (507) 457-9100
Web Site: http://www.peerlesschain.com
Sales Range: $100-124.9 Million
Emp.: 300
Tire Chains Mfr
N.A.I.C.S.: 332618
Jed Ranzenberger (Mgr-Natl Sls)
Kevin O'Reilly (Mgr-Pur)
George Kosidowski (Pres)

Subsidiary (Domestic):

Security Chain Company **(7)**

PO Box 949, Clackamas, OR 97015-0949
Tel.: (503) 656-5400
Web Site: http://www.scc-chain.com
Emp.: 20
Automobile Traction Product Mfr
N.A.I.C.S.: 336390

Subsidiary (Non-US):

KITO Canada Inc. **(4)**
309-3815 1st Ave, Burnaby, V5C 3V6, BC, Canada
Web Site: https://www.kito.ca
Emp.: 30
Manual & Electric Hoists & Crane Components Distr
N.A.I.C.S.: 423830
Marc Premont (Pres)

Kito Europe GmbH **(4)**
Heerdter Lohweg 93, 40549, Dusseldorf, Germany
Tel.: (49) 2115280090
Web Site: http://www.kito.net
Manual & Electric Chain Hoists, Crane Systems, Trolleys & Spares Distr
N.A.I.C.S.: 423830
Martin Rothe (Mng Dir)

Subsidiary (Domestic):

Kokusai Kogyo Co., Ltd. **(3)**
2 Rokubancho Chiyoda-ku, Tokyo, 102-0085, Japan
Tel.: (81) 423077200
Web Site: http://www.kkc.co.jp
Sales Range: $250-299.9 Million
Emp.: 2,032
Engineering & Technical Consulting Services
N.A.I.C.S.: 541330
Satoshi Hijikata (Pres)
Shunji Ueno (Exec VP)
Sandra Wu (Chm & CEO)
Kuniharu Kajita (Sr Corp Exec Officer)
Toshiyuki Kaneko (Sr Exec Officer)
Moritaka Ike (Sr Exec Officer)
Takeo Nakajima (Sr Exec Officer)
satoshi Kato (Exec Officer)
Jumpei Inoue (Exec Officer)
Akira Doi (Exec Officer)
Kiyoaki Ssugiyama (Exec Officer)
Masayuki Fukui (Exec Officer)
Nobuo Fujita (Exec Officer)
Yuji Moriyama (Exec Officer)

Affiliate (Domestic):

Simplex Inc.
19F Toranomon Hills Mori Tower 1-23-1 Toranomon, Minato-ku, Tokyo, 105-6319, Japan
Tel.: (81) 332786750
Web Site: https://www.simplex.inc
Emp.: 1,047
Financial Industry Technology Consulting & Technical Support Services
N.A.I.C.S.: 541690
Hideki Kaneko (CEO)
Mitsuru Igarashi (Sr Mng Dir)
Kenichi Tanaka (Sr Mng Dir)
Yasuhito Fukui (Sr Mng Dir)
Yoshihiro Kuji (Sr Mng Dir)
Kozo Sukema (Sr Mng Dir)
Hajime Yamamoto (Sr Mng Dir)
Shinichi Okabe (Mng Dir)
Hidekazu Sugiura (Mng Dir)
Masataka Soda (Mng Dir)
Seiji Hattori (Mng Dir)
Masaki Hayashibe (Mng Dir)
Keigo Fukuyama (Mng Dir)
Taiyo Matsuzaki (Mng Dir)
Noriyuki Mizutani (Mng Dir)

Subsidiary (Domestic):

Virtualex Consulting, Inc. **(4)**
Hulic Kamiyacho Building 8F 4-3-13 Toranomon, Minato-ku, Tokyo, 105-0001, Japan **(51%)**
Tel.: (81) 335785300
Web Site: http://www.virtualex.co.jp
Emp.: 748
Computer Consulting Services
N.A.I.C.S.: 541690
Eiki Maruyama (Chm)
Hayato Maruyama (CEO)
Shotaro Okumura (Officer-Operating)

Virtualex Holdings, Inc. **(4)**

Hulic Kamiyacho Building 8F 4-3-13 Toranomon Minato-ku, Tokyo, 105-0001, Japan
Tel.: (81) 335785300
Web Site: http://www.vx-holdings.com
Rev.: $44,234,120
Assets: $23,293,640
Liabilities: $11,712,920
Net Worth: $11,580,720
Earnings: $1,335,220
Emp.: 1,010
Fiscal Year-end: 03/31/2024
Business Management Services
N.A.I.C.S.: 561110
Eiki Maruyama (CEO)
Hideo Furukawa (Auditor)
Kunio Suzuki (Auditor)
Tomomi Kobayashi (Auditor)

Holding (Domestic):

Totoku Electric Co., Ltd. **(3)**
8-3 Nishi-Shinbashi 3-Chome, Minato-ku, Tokyo, 105-0003, Japan **(93.1%)**
Tel.: (81) 368602126
Web Site: http://www.totoku.com
Rev.: $202,515,280
Assets: $268,494,160
Liabilities: $90,159,520
Net Worth: $178,334,640
Earnings: $22,602,800
Emp.: 271
Fiscal Year-end: 03/31/2022
Electrical Wire Product Mfr
N.A.I.C.S.: 332618
Hiroshi Kawaguchi (Pres)

Subsidiary (Non-US):

TTI LAGUNA PHILIPPINES INC. **(4)**
Bldg 5 Panorama Compound 5 Laguna Technopark Annex, Binan, 4024, Laguna, Philippines
Tel.: (63) 495762722
Electrical Wire Distr
N.A.I.C.S.: 423510
Alan Medrano (Plant Mgr)

Holding (Domestic):

Tsubaki Nakashima Co., Ltd. **(3)**
19 Shakudo, Katsuragi, 639-2162, Nara, Japan **(96.6%)**
Tel.: (81) 745482891
Web Site:
https://www.tsubaki-nakashima.com
Rev.: $569,589,330
Assets: $1,177,493,020
Liabilities: $793,626,240
Net Worth: $383,866,780
Earnings: ($9,124,830)
Emp.: 3,066
Fiscal Year-end: 12/31/2023
Ball Bearing Mfr
N.A.I.C.S.: 332991
Shakil Ohara (CFO, Exec Officer & Sr Exec VP)
Koji Hirota (Co-Pres & CEO)
Kazuaki Kayahara (Exec Officer & VP-Engrg, Intellectual Property & CAPEX)
Zhang Li (Exec Officer, Pres-China & VP)
Yasuo Yoshida (Exec Officer, Pres-Europe & VP)
Tomofumi Gotsubo (COO)
Mike Hand (Exec Officer & VP-Sls & Mktg)
Franco Dutto (Exec Officer & Sr VP-Compliance & HR Sustainability)
Satoshi Aimi (Exec Officer & VP-Pur)
Cosimo Colasanti (Exec Officer & VP-Mfg)
Hidekazu Mukai (Co-Pres, Exec Officer & VP)
Hisashi Tate (Exec Officer & VP-Bus Plng & Strategy)

Branch (Domestic):

TC Group, LLC - Los Angeles **(2)**
11100 Santa Monica Blvd, Los Angeles, CA 90025
Tel.: (310) 575-1700
Web Site: http://www.carlyle.com
Private Equity Investment Services
N.A.I.C.S.: 523999
Kunal M. Soni (Mng Dir)

TC Group, LLC - New York **(2)**
2100 Smithtown Ave, New York, NY 11779
Tel.: (631) 200-2000
Web Site: http://www.carlyle.com
Sales Range: $50-74.9 Million
Emp.: 150
Private Equity Investment Services

N.A.I.C.S.: 523999
James A. Attwood Jr. (Mng Dir)
Sandra J. Horbach (Mng Dir-Consumer & Retail)
Alex Popov (Mng Dir & Head-Carlyle Credit Opportunities Fund)
Inoki Suarez (Mng Dir-Global Credit)
Lauren Dillard (Mng Dir & Head-Investment Solutions Grp)
Mark Jenkins (Mng Dir & Head-Global Credit)
Timothy Broadbent (Mng Dir-Capital Solutions Grp)
James F. Burr (Mng Dir-Global Fin Svcs Grp)
William H. Allen (Mng Dir-Global Fin Svcs Buyout)
Jeremy Bailys (VP-Direct Lending Grp)
Akhil Bansal (Mng Dir & Head-Credit Bus Dev-Global Credit)
Nadim Barakat (Mng Dir-Corp Private Equity)
David Basto (Mng Dir-Carlyle Equity Opportunity Fund)
Wael O. Bayazid (Mng Dir-IR)
Andrew Curry (Mng Dir & Deputy COO-Global Credit)
Rahul Culas (Mng Dir & Co-Head-Energy Credit Grp)
Mandy Cheuk (VP-Global Credit Mgmt)
Michael D. Gershenson (Mng Dir-Real Estate Opportunities)
Erica Frontiero (Mng Dir-Carlyle Global Credit & Head-Capital Markets)
Christopher Freeze (Mng Dir-IR Mgmt Grp)
Paul J. Ferraro (Mng Dir & Head-Private Client Grp)
Anthony Ecock (Mng Dir-Carlyle Equity Opportunity Fund)
Jitij Dwivedi (Principal-Global Fin Svcs Buyout)
Anh Do (VP-Global Credit)
Patrick Delay (VP-IR Mgmt Grp)
Jason P. Hart (Mng Dir-Real Estate Opportunities)

TC Group, LLC - San Francisco **(2)**
555 California St, San Francisco, CA 20004-2505
Tel.: (202) 729-5626
Web Site: http://www.carlyle.com
Private Equity Investment Services
N.A.I.C.S.: 523999

Tempo Participacoes S.A. **(1)**
Rua Bonnard N 980 Edificio 19, Condominio Green Valley-Av Andromeda 2000 Alphaville, 06465-134, Barueri, Sao Paulo, Brazil
Tel.: (55) 11 4208 8000
Web Site: http://www.tempoassist.com.br
Specialized Assistance & Call Center Services
N.A.I.C.S.: 561499
Gibran Vega Marona (CEO)

The Carlyle Group (Luxembourg) S.a.r.l. **(1)**
2 Avenue Charles de Gaulle, L-1653, Luxembourg, Luxembourg
Tel.: (352) 26102747
Investment Management Service
N.A.I.C.S.: 523940

The TCW Group, Inc. **(1)**
865 S Figueroa St Ste 1800, Los Angeles, CA 90017
Tel.: (213) 244-0000
Web Site: http://www.tcw.com
Sales Range: $150-199.9 Million
Emp.: 500
Financial Advisors
N.A.I.C.S.: 523999
David B. Lippman (Pres & CEO)
Marc Irwin Stern (Chm)
Eric Arentsen (Mng Dir-Fixed Income)
Penelope D. Foley (Head-Emerging Markets & Intl Equities Grp & Portfolio Mgr)
David I. Robbins (Mng Dir-Emerging Markets Grp & Intl Equities)
Tad Rivelle (Mng Dir & Chief Investment Officer-Fixed Income)
Meredith S. Jackson (Gen Counsel & Exec VP)
Joseph C. Carieri (Mng Dir & Head-Mktg)

The Carlyle Group Inc.—(Continued)

Cheryl L. Marzano *(Mng Dir & Head-HR)*
Richard M. Villa *(CFO)*
Mark Gertzof *(Mng Dir-Direct Lending Grp)*
Andrea Almeida Mack *(Mng Dir)*
Doug O. Morris *(Head-Comm)*
Michael D. Wright *(Sr VP-Institutional Mktg)*
Jeffrey Engelsman *(Mng Dir & Chief Compliance Officer-Global)*
Ray S. Prasad *(Mng Dir & Portfolio Mgr-Emerging Markets & Intl Equities)*
William T. Lloyd *(Mng Dir-Alternative Products)*
Yuri Khalif *(Mng Dir-Private Client)*
Alex B. McCulloch *(Mng Dir & Head-Retail Mktg)*
Jamie Farnham *(Mng Dir & Dir-Credit Res)*
Jerry Cudzil *(Mng Dir & Head-Credit Trading)*
Melinda Newman *(Sr VP-Fixed Income)*
Drew Sweeney *(Sr VP-Fixed Income)*
Diane E. Jaffee *(Mng Dir-Relative Value)*
Jae H. Lee *(Mng Dir-Emerging Markets)*
Jeffrey Nuruki *(Sr VP-Emerging Markets)*
Javier Segovia *(Mng Dir-Emerging Markets)*
Patrick Moore *(Grp Mng Dir & Head-Client Svcs)*
Cal Rivelle *(Mng Dir & Head-Investment Tech)*
Daniel J. Kale *(Mng Dir & Dir-IT)*
Bibi H. Khan *(Mng Dir & Dir-Investment Ops)*
Richard T. Miller *(Mng Dir-Direct Lending)*
Laird R. Landmann *(Mng Dir & Dir-Fixed Income)*
Liz Kraninger *(COO)*
Manish Ghayalod *(CTO)*
Olivia Albrecht *(Head-Environmental, Social & Governance-Global)*

Subsidiary (Domestic):

TCW Asset Management Co., Inc. (2)
865 S Figueroa St Ste 1800, Los Angeles, CA 90017
Tel.: (213) 244-0000
Web Site: http://www.tcw.com
Sales Range: $125-149.9 Million
Emp.: 400
Investment Advice
N.A.I.C.S.: 523940
Robert Addison Day *(Chm)*
Robert Addison Day *(Chm)*

TCW Capital Investment Corporation (2)
865 S Figueroa St, Los Angeles, CA 90017-2543
Tel.: (213) 244-0000
Web Site: http://www.tcm.com
Sales Range: $150-199.9 Million
Emp.: 500
Investment Office
N.A.I.C.S.: 525990

TCW Funds Management, Inc. (2)
865 S Figueroa St, Los Angeles, CA 90017-2543
Tel.: (213) 244-0000
Web Site: http://www.tcw.com
Sales Range: $150-199.9 Million
Security Brokers & Dealers
N.A.I.C.S.: 523150

Trust Company of the West (2)
865 S Figueroa St Ste 1800, Los Angeles, CA 90017
Tel.: (213) 244-0000
Web Site: http://www.tcw.com
Investment Advice Services
N.A.I.C.S.: 523999

Tok & Stok Ltda. (1)
Avenida Tucunare 500 Tambore, Barueri, 06460-020, SP, Brazil
Tel.: (55) 1121868600
Web Site: http://www.tokstok.com.br
Sales Range: $450-499.9 Million
Emp.: 3,300
Furniture & Home Furnishings Retailer
N.A.I.C.S.: 449110

Traxys S.A. (1)
19-21 Route D Arlon Immeuble Serenity Batiments C-D 2nd Floor, 8009, Strassen, Luxembourg
Tel.: (352) 4599991
Web Site: http://www.traxys.com

Sales Range: $1-4.9 Billion
Emp.: 100
Financial & Logistics Consulting Services
N.A.I.C.S.: 541614

Subsidiary (Non-US):

Traxys Africa Pty. Ltd. (2)
25 Culross Road, Johannesburg, Bryanston, 2191, South Africa
Tel.: (27) 115910500
Sales Range: $150-199.9 Million
Emp.: 171
Commodities Trading & Financial Services
N.A.I.C.S.: 522320
Molleen Fiona de Wet *(CFO-Trading)*
Anila C. Swart *(Sec)*
Michael S. Golding *(COO-Investments & Resources)*

Traxys North America LLC (2)
Tel.: (212) 918-8000
Web Site: http://www.traxys.com
Sales Range: $25-49.9 Million
Emp.: 50
Financial & Logistics Consulting Services
N.A.I.C.S.: 541614

Subsidiary (Domestic):

Traxys Cometals USA LLC (3)
2050 Ctr Ave Ste 250, Fort Lee, NJ 07024
Tel.: (201) 302-0888
Web Site: http://www.traxys.com
Metal Marketing & Distribution
N.A.I.C.S.: 425120

Two Six Technologies, Inc. (1)
901 N Stuart St Ste 1000, Arlington, VA 22203
Tel.: (703) 543-9662
Web Site: https://twosixtech.com
Software Publisher
N.A.I.C.S.: 513210
Joe Logue *(CEO)*
Bob Kwaja *(CFO)*
Larry Prior *(Chm)*

Subsidiary (Domestic):

IST Research Corp. (2)
3006 Lafayette Blvd, Fredericksburg, VA 22408-4121
Tel.: (540) 845-7355
Web Site: http://www.istresearch.com
Professional, Scientific & Technical Services
N.A.I.C.S.: 541990
Ryan Paterson *(Founder & CEO)*
Amy Dalton *(COO)*
Michael Paley *(Pres)*
Madison Bahmer *(CTO)*
Greg Lee *(Exec VP-Product Dev)*

Unison Software, Inc. (1)
21251 Ridgetop Cir Ste 100, Dulles, VA 20166-6501
Tel.: (571) 449-4000
Web Site: http://www.unisonglobal.com
Government Agency Acquisition & Program Management Software Publisher
N.A.I.C.S.: 513210
Reid Jackson *(Pres & CEO)*
Brock Lending *(CTO)*
Dan Ilisevich *(Chief Fin & Admin Officer)*

Subsidiary (Domestic):

PRICE Systems, LLC (2)
17000 Commerce Pkwy Ste A, Mount Laurel, NJ 08054
Tel.: (856) 608-7200
Web Site: http://www.pricesystems.com
Sales Range: $10-24.9 Million
Emp.: 33
Provider of Computer Rental & Leasing Services
N.A.I.C.S.: 532420
Anthony A. DeMarco *(Pres)*
Bruce Fad *(VP)*
Georges-Toussaint Teologlou *(Sr VP-Intl)*
Robert Becker *(VP-Bus Dev-Americas)*
Zachary Jasnoff *(VP-Pro Svcs-Americas)*

Subsidiary (Non-US):

PRICE Systems Ltd. (3)
Price House Meridian Off Pk, Osborn Way, Hook, RG27 9HY, United Kingdom (100%)
Tel.: (44) 1256760012
Web Site: http://www.pricesystems.com

Sales Range: $1-9.9 Million
Emp.: 6
Provider of Computer Rental & Leasing Services
N.A.I.C.S.: 532420
Anthony Denicola *(Mng Dir)*
Georges-Toussaint Teologlou *(Sr VP-Intl)*

Unit (Non-US):

PRICE Systems Deutschland GmbH (4)
Eisenstrasse 49, 65428, Russelsheim, Germany
Tel.: (49) 6142966080
Software Development Services
N.A.I.C.S.: 513210

Subsidiary (Domestic):

Unison Marketplace, Inc. (2)
8500 Leesburg Pike 6th Floor, Tysons, VA 22182
Web Site: http://www.unisonglobal.com
Full-service Online Marketplace
N.A.I.C.S.: 425120
Reid Jackson *(Pres & CEO)*

United Road Services, Inc. (1)
41100 Plymouth Rd 4th Fl, Plymouth, MI 48170
Tel.: (734) 947-7900
Web Site: http://www.unitedroad.com
Emp.: 1,800
Vehicle Towing, Storage & Impounding Services
N.A.I.C.S.: 484230
Patrick M. Riley *(Sr VP-Pur & Asset Mgmt)*
Charles E. Baxter *(Sr VP-Risk Mgmt)*
Matthew A. Cartwright *(CIO)*
Michael R. Martin *(VP-Ops-Western)*
Vickey Patterson *(VP-Admin)*
Kathleen McCann *(Chm)*
Dave Koster *(Sr VP-Logistics)*
Mark Anderson *(Pres & CEO)*
Eric Madison *(VP-HR)*
Dave Gann *(CFO)*
Anita Felcher *(VP-Fin & Controller)*
Ryan Kraft *(Chief Digital Officer)*
Nicholas Cole *(Sr VP-Sls & Mktg)*

Subsidiary (Domestic):

Team Drive-Away, Inc. (2)
401 W Frontier Ln Ste 100, Olathe, KS 66061
Tel.: (913) 825-4776
Web Site: http://www.teamdriveaway.com
Emp.: 45
Freight Transportation Arrangement
N.A.I.C.S.: 488510
Scott Shacklett *(COO)*

Veritas Technologies LLC (1)
2625 Augustine Dr, Santa Clara, CA 95054
Tel.: (866) 837-4827
Web Site: http://www.veritas.com
Data Management Software Services
N.A.I.C.S.: 518210
Gregory Hughes *(CEO)*
Edward F. Malysz *(Gen Counsel & Sr VP)*
Mark Dentinger *(Exec VP & CFO)*
Lenny Alugas *(Exec VP-Customer Success)*
Deepak Mohan *(Exec VP-Products Org)*
Brian Hamel *(Exec VP-Field Ops-Worldwide)*
Lawrence Wong *(Chief Strategy Officer & Sr VP)*
Jane Zhu *(Sr VP-Corp Ops)*
David Staffanson *(Chief HR Officer & VP)*
Lissa Hollinger *(CMO & Sr VP)*
Karthik Ramamurthy *(Sr VP-Subscription Transformation Office)*

Subsidiary (Domestic):

Globanet Consulting Services, Inc. (2)
15233 Ventura Blvd Ste PH16, Sherman Oaks, CA 91403
Tel.: (310) 202-0757
Web Site: http://www.globanet.com
Computer System Design Services
N.A.I.C.S.: 541512
Jacklin Vitullo *(Sec)*
Sam Elbeck *(VP-Bus Dev)*
Sevag Ajemian *(Pres & CEO)*

Vigor Industrial LLC (1)
5555 N Channel Ave, Portland, OR 97217

Tel.: (503) 247-1777
Web Site: http://www.vigor.net
Sales Range: $25-49.9 Million
Emp.: 350
Holding Company; Ship Building & Repairing Services
N.A.I.C.S.: 551112
Greg Lind *(Dir-Estimating)*
Thomas Hickman *(VP-Sls & Mktg-Complex Fabrication)*

Subsidiary (Domestic):

Cascade General Inc. (2)
5555 N Channel Ave, Portland, OR 97217-7655
Tel.: (503) 247-1777
Web Site: http://www.vigor.net
Sales Range: $25-49.9 Million
Emp.: 250
Shipbuilding & Repairing
N.A.I.C.S.: 336611
Frank J. Foti *(CEO)*

Everett Shipyard, Inc. (2)
2730 Federal Ave, Everett, WA 98201
Tel.: (425) 259-0137
Web Site: http://www.everettship.com
Sales Range: $10-24.9 Million
Emp.: 40
Shipyard
N.A.I.C.S.: 336611

Marine Hydraulics International, Inc. (2)
543 E Indian River Rd, Norfolk, VA 23523
Tel.: (757) 545-6400
Web Site: http://www.mhi-shiprepair.com
Emp.: 500
Military Ship Repair, Overhaul & Conversion Services
N.A.I.C.S.: 336611
Thomas Epley *(Pres & CEO)*
Rolland Long *(Dir-Estimating)*
Chris Ceglio *(Dir-Comml Mktg)*

Marine Industries Northwest, Inc. (2)
313 East F St, Tacoma, WA 98421
Tel.: (253) 627-9136
Web Site: http://vigorindustrial.com
Sales Range: $10-24.9 Million
Emp.: 50
Shipbuilding & Repairing
N.A.I.C.S.: 336611
Mark Donahue *(Gen Mgr)*

Vigor Alaska Ship & Drydock Inc. (2)
3801 Tongass Ave, Ketchikan, AK 99901
Tel.: (907) 225-7199
Emp.: 200
Ship Building & Repair Services
N.A.I.C.S.: 336611
Mike Tearson *(Gen Mgr)*

Vigor Machine LLC (2)
5926 N Basin Ave, Portland, OR 97217
Tel.: (503) 283-2795
Ship Building & Repair Services
N.A.I.C.S.: 336611

Vigor Marine LLC (2)
3410 Terminal Ave, Everett, WA 98201
Tel.: (425) 259-1230
Marine Engineering Services
N.A.I.C.S.: 541330
Dave Byers *(Dir-Project Mgmt)*

Vigor Shipyards (2)
1801 16th Ave SW Harbor Island, Seattle, WA 98134-1017
Tel.: (206) 623-1635
Web Site: http://www.vigor.net
Ship Building & Repairing
N.A.I.C.S.: 336611
Frank J. Foti *(CEO)*
Bruce A. Dummer *(CFO)*
Spiro Risvas *(Dir-Special Projects-Ship Repair Facilities)*
John Lockwood *(Dir-Mktg & Bus Dev)*
David A. Whitcomb *(COO)*

Subsidiary (Non-US):

Vigor Works LLC (2)
5555 N Channel Ave., Portland, 97217, OR, Afghanistan
Tel.: (503) 247-1777
Web Site: https://vigor.net
Sales Range: $10-24.9 Million
Emp.: 200
Fiscal Year-end: 12/31/2014

Steel Fabrication & Manufacturing Services
N.A.I.C.S.: 332312
Tae Rhee *(Gen Counsel & Sec)*
Frank Collins *(Sr VP-Govt & Pub Affairs)*
Dawn Cartwright *(VP-HR Svcs & Risk Mgmt)*
Chris Palmer *(VP-Fabrication)*
Adam L. Beck *(Pres-Alaska & Exec VP-Ship Repair)*
Steve Zogas *(CFO)*
Jim Marcotuli *(CEO)*

WU Holdco, Inc. (1)
705 Tri State Pkwy, Gurnee, IL 60031
Tel.: (847) 263-3500
Web Site: http://www.weiman.com
Surface Care Mfr
N.A.I.C.S.: 325612
Carl DeMasi *(Chm)*
John Brennan *(Sr VP-Sls)*
Brandon Alvarez *(Coord-Shipping)*
Greg Weeg *(Dir-Facilities)*
James Sommerfield *(Coord-Warehouse)*
Melanie Loomis *(Dir-Sls Dev)*
Minerva Alday *(Dir-Acctg)*
Rhonda Fonk *(Dir-Art)*
Tania Camacho *(Acct Coord)*
Wendy Burr *(Acct Mgr)*
Edward Duffy *(VP-Weiman Healthcare)*
Billy Vanderploeg *(Mgr-Supply Chain)*
Coleen Smith *(Mgr-Logistics)*
Sylwia Aldrin *(Dir-R&D)*
Chris Bauder *(CEO)*
Dexter Reid Jr. *(Coord-Medical Accts)*

Division (Domestic):

Burnishine Products (2)
755 Tri State Pkwy, Gurnee, IL 60031
Tel.: (847) 263-3500
Web Site: http://www.weiman.com
Sales Range: $10-24.9 Million
Chemical Products Mfr
N.A.I.C.S.: 325998
Patty Vick *(Mgr-Natl Sls)*
Carl DeMasi *(Pres & CEO)*

J.A. Wright & Co. (2)
755 Tri State Pkwy, Gurnee, IL 60031
Tel.: (847) 263-3500
Web Site: http://www.jawright.com
Metal Care Products Mfr
N.A.I.C.S.: 325612

WellDyneRx, LLC (1)
500 Eagles Landing Dr, Lakeland, FL 33810
Tel.: (303) 793-9954
Web Site: https://www.welldynerx.com
Drugs & Druggists' Sundries Merchant Whslr
N.A.I.C.S.: 424210
Zach Johnson *(Pres)*
David King *(CIO)*
Stephen Saft *(CFO & Chief Admin Officer)*
Mark SantaCroce *(Chief Comml Officer)*
Philip Stafford *(Sr VP-Ops)*
Denise Cabrera *(Sr VP-Client Svcs)*
Nick Page *(Chief Pharmacy Officer)*
Damien Lamendola *(Executives, Bd of Dirs)*

WingArc1st Inc. (1)
Roppongi Grand Tower 3-2-1, Roppongi Minato - ku, Tokyo, 106-0032, Japan
Tel.: (81) 359627400
Web Site: http://www.wingarc.com
Sales Range: $100-149.9 Billion
Emp.: 482
Holding Company; Software Developer
N.A.I.C.S.: 551112
Hiroyuki Uchino *(Chm)*
Jun Tanaka *(Pres)*
Satoshi Okuda *(Exec Officer)*
Kenji Haga *(Auditor)*
Taisuke Fujimoto *(CFO & Exec Officer)*
Ko Shimazawa *(CTO & Exec Officer)*
Nagako Oe *(Auditor)*
Kotaro Yamazawa *(Auditor)*
Masaki Moriwaki *(Exec Officer)*
Steven Hulse *(Exec Officer)*
Yoshiyuki Yoshida *(Exec Officer)*

Subsidiary (Non-US):

WingArc Dalian Inc. (2)
20F Senmao Building No 147 Zhongshan Road, Xigang District, Dalian, 116011, China (100%)
Tel.: (86) 41139893301
Web Site: http://dalian.wingarc.com

Software Development Services
N.A.I.C.S.: 541511

WingArc Shanghai Inc. (2)
Room 707 7F Building D Sun Moon Light Center No 33 Caobao Road, Xuhui District, Shanghai, 200235, China
Tel.: (86) 2134197890
Web Site: http://www.wingarc.com
Software Development Services
N.A.I.C.S.: 541511

WingArc Singapore Pte. Ltd. (2)
20 Collyer Quay 23-01, Singapore, 049319, Singapore
Tel.: (65) 66538391
Web Site: http://www.wingarc.com
Software Development Services
N.A.I.C.S.: 541511

Worldpac, Inc. (1)
37137 Hickory St,, Newark, CA 94560
Tel.: (800) 888-9982
Web Site: https://www.worldpac.com
Automotive Parts Wholesaler & Distr.
N.A.I.C.S.: 423110
John Hamilton *(Pres & CEO)*

Zodiac Marine & Pool (1)
1 Quai de Grenelle, Paris, 75015, France (96%)
Tel.: (33) 145780188
Web Site: http://www.zodiac-marine-pool.com
Holding Company; Pools, Pool Care Products, Inflatable Boats & Environmental Products Mfr & Whslr
N.A.I.C.S.: 551112

Subsidiary (Non-US):

Europool Italia S.r.l. (2)
Via Mazzini 28 Z, 46043, Castiglione della Stiviere, MN, Italy (100%)
Tel.: (39) 0376861611
Web Site: http://www.europoolitalia.it
Inflatable & Modular Swimming Pools & Filtering Systems Mfr & Distr
N.A.I.C.S.: 339920

Subsidiary (Domestic):

Zodiac European Pools (2)
32 Bis Bd Haussmann, 75009, Paris, France (100%)
Tel.: (33) 176767100
Web Site: http://www.zodiacpools.com
Holding Company; Swimming Pools Mfr, Marketer & Distr
N.A.I.C.S.: 551112

Zodiac International (2)
1 Quai de Grenelle, Paris, 75015, France (100%)
Tel.: (33) 176767100
Web Site: http://www.zodiacmarine.com
Holding Company; Recreational & Military Inflatable Boat, Raft & Rescue Products Mfr
N.A.I.C.S.: 551112

Subsidiary (Non-US):

Avon Inflatables Ltd. (3)
Dafen, Llanelli, SA14 8NA, Carmarthenshire, United Kingdom (100%)
Tel.: (44) 1554882000
Web Site: http://www.zodiacmilpro.com
Sales Range: $25-49.9 Million
Emp.: 68
Inflatable Recreational Boats Mfr & Whslr
N.A.I.C.S.: 339920

Zodiac Espanola S.A. (3)
Via Layetana 47 2e, PO Box 138, Figueras, Barcelona, 08003, Spain (100%)
Tel.: (34) 933179408
Web Site: http://www.zodiacmilpro.com
Sales Range: $25-49.9 Million
Emp.: 10
Inflatable Boat Distr
N.A.I.C.S.: 441222

Zodiac Group Australia Pty. Ltd. (3)
219 Woodpark Road, Smithfield, 2164, NSW, Australia (100%)
Tel.: (61) 1300784423
Web Site: https://www.baracuda.com.au
Sales Range: $50-74.9 Million
Emp.: 80
Swimming Pools, Pool Care Supplies, Inflatable Boats & Rafts Distr

N.A.I.C.S.: 423910

Zodiac Hurricane Technologies Inc. (3)
7830 Vantage Way, Delta, V4G 1A7, BC, Canada (100%)
Tel.: (604) 940-2999
Web Site: http://www.zodiacmilpro.com
Sales Range: $25-49.9 Million
Emp.: 125
Rigid Hull Inflatable Boats Mfr & Distr
N.A.I.C.S.: 336612

Zodiac Italia Srl (3)
Via Pascoli 8/B, 20090, Novegro di Segrate, Italy (100%)
Tel.: (39) 0270200341
Web Site: http://www.zodiac.it
Sales Range: $25-49.9 Million
Emp.: 6
Inflatable Recreational Boat Distr
N.A.I.C.S.: 423910

Subsidiary (Non-US):

Zodiac Pool Care South Africa Pty. Ltd. (2)
4 Slaet Avenue N1 Business Park Kosmosdal, Randjespark, Centurion, South Africa (100%)
Tel.: (27) 11 237 3900
Web Site: http://www.zodiac.co.za
Sales Range: $25-49.9 Million
Emp.: 80
Swimming Pool Equipment Mfr & Distr
N.A.I.C.S.: 339920

Zodiac Pool Deutschland GmbH (2)
Bauhofstr 18D, 63762, Grossostheim, Germany (100%)
Tel.: (49) 602697950
Sales Range: $25-49.9 Million
Emp.: 100
Inflatable & Modular Pools Mfr & Pool Equipment Distr
N.A.I.C.S.: 339920

Branch (Domestic):

Zodiac Pool Deutschland GmbH - Mombris (3)
Bauhofstrasse 18 D, 63762, Grossostheim, Germany
Tel.: (49) 602697950
Sales Range: $25-49.9 Million
Emp.: 70
Inflatable Recreational Boats & Pool Care Products Distr
N.A.I.C.S.: 423910

Subsidiary (Non-US):

Zodiac Pool Iberica S.L.U. (2)
Pol In Palou Nord-c/mollet 15, Barcelona, 08401, Granollers, Spain (100%)
Tel.: (34) 938794752
Web Site: http://www.zodiac-poolcare.com
Sales Range: $25-49.9 Million
Emp.: 50
Pool Care Equipment Distr
N.A.I.C.S.: 423910

Zodiac Pool Systems Canada, Inc. (2)
2115 South Service Road West Unit 3, Oakville, L6L 5W2, ON, Canada (100%)
Tel.: (800) 822-7933
Web Site: http://www.zodiacpoolsystems.ca
Sales Range: $25-49.9 Million
Emp.: 10
Swimming Pool Equipments Distr
N.A.I.C.S.: 423910
Steven Barcley *(Gen Mgr)*

Subsidiary (US):

Zodiac Pool Systems, Inc. (2)
6000 Condor Dr, Moorpark, CA 93021 (100%)
Tel.: (707) 776-8200
Web Site: http://www.zodiacpoolsystems.com
Sales Range: $50-74.9 Million
Emp.: 200
Swimming Pool Pumps, Filters, Heaters & Other Equipment Mfr
N.A.I.C.S.: 333310
Troy Franzen *(Mng Dir)*
Scott Frost *(Sec & Treas)*

Subsidiary (Domestic):

Grand Effects, Inc. (3)
23121 Arroyo Vista Ste B, Rancho Santa Margarita, CA 92688
Tel.: (949) 697-5270
Web Site: http://www.grandeffects.com
Outdoor Decorative Water & Fire Products Mfr
N.A.I.C.S.: 337212

Unit (Domestic):

Zodiac Pool Systems, Inc. - Polaris Products (3)
2620 Commerce Way, Vista, CA 92081-8438
Tel.: (760) 599-9600
Web Site: http://www.polarispoolsystems.com
Sales Range: $25-49.9 Million
Emp.: 100
Swimming Pool Cleaners & Spa Products Mfr
N.A.I.C.S.: 333310

Subsidiary (US):

Zodiac of North America, Inc. (2)
540 Thompson Creek Rd, Stevensville, MD 21666
Tel.: (410) 643-4141
Sales Range: $25-49.9 Million
Emp.: 50
Consumer, Military & Commercial Rigid-Hull Inflatable Boat Mfr & Distr
N.A.I.C.S.: 336612
Lionel Boudeau *(Pres & CEO)*

Division (Domestic):

Zodiac of North America, Inc. - Recreational Marine Division (3)
124 Spaniel Ln, Summerville, SC 29483
Tel.: (843) 285-7263
Web Site: http://www.zodiacmarineusa.com
Inflatable Recreational Boat & Raft Mfr & Distr
N.A.I.C.S.: 339920

iNova Pharmaceuticals (Australia) Pty Limited (1)
Level 10 12 Help Street, Chatswood, 2067, NSW, Australia
Tel.: (61) 289186322
Web Site: http://www.inovapharma.com
Pharmaceuticals Product Mfr
N.A.I.C.S.: 325412
Dan Spira *(CEO)*
Sancha Ernst *(Pres-Asia)*
Joe Basile *(CFO)*
Geoff Rudland *(COO)*
Kate Messiter *(Gen Counsel & Head-Legal & Compliance)*
Andrew Davis *(Chief Bus Dev Officer & Chief M&A Officer)*
Blane Coulcher *(Exec Dir-Strategy, People & Tech)*
Filomena Maiese *(Exec Dir-Portfolio Strategy & Innovation)*

Subsidiary (Non-US):

iNova Pharmaceuticals (Pty) Limited (2)
15e Riley Road, PO Box 3115, Bedfordview, 2008, South Africa
Tel.: (27) 110870000
Web Site: http://www.inovapharma.co.za
Pharmaceuticals Product Mfr
N.A.I.C.S.: 325412
Kym Hampton *(Country Mgr)*
Victoria Taylor *(Head-Fin)*

THE CATO CORPORATION
8100 Denmark Rd, Charlotte, NC 28273-5975
Tel.: (704) 554-8510 DE
Web Site: https://www.catofashions.com
Year Founded: 1946
CATO—(NYSE)
Rev.: $708,059,000
Assets: $486,817,000
Liabilities: $294,496,000
Net Worth: $192,321,000
Earnings: ($23,941,000)

The Cato Corporation—(Continued)

Emp.: 7,300
Fiscal Year-end: 02/03/24
Women's Clothing Retailer
N.A.I.C.S.: 458110
John P. Derham Cato (Chm, Pres & CEO)
Jeffrey R. Shock (Sr VP & Controller)
Gordon D. Smith (Chief Real Estate & Store Dev Officer & Exec VP)
Chuck Knight (CFO & Exec VP)
Charles D. Knight (CTO)

Subsidiaries:

CHW LLC   (1)
8100 Denmark Rd, Charlotte, NC 28273
Tel.: (704) 554-8510
Web Site: http://www.catofashions.com
Sales Range: $150-199.9 Million
Emp.: 800
Retailer of Women's Clothing
N.A.I.C.S.: 458110

Cato Southwest, Inc.   (1)
8100 Denmark Rd, Charlotte, NC 28273
Tel.: (704) 554-8510
Web Site: http://www.catofashions.com
Sales Range: $100-124.9 Million
Women's Clothing Retailer
N.A.I.C.S.: 458110

Cato of Texas L.P.   (1)
8100 Denmark Rd, Charlotte, NC 28273
Tel.: (704) 554-8510
Web Site: http://www.catofashions.com
Sales Range: $100-124.9 Million
Emp.: 600
Retailer of Women's Clothing
N.A.I.C.S.: 458110

catocorp.com, LLC   (1)
8100 Denmark Rd, Charlotte, NC 28273
Tel.: (704) 554-8510
Web Site: http://www.catofashions.com
Rev.: $2,100,000
Emp.: 800
Online Retailer of Women's Clothing
N.A.I.C.S.: 458110

THE CHARLES SCHWAB CORPORATION

3000 Schwab Way, Westlake, TX 76262
Tel.: (817) 859-5000   CA
Web Site:
https://www.aboutschwab.com
Year Founded: 1986
SCHW—(NYSE)
Rev.: $18,837,000,000
Assets: $493,178,000,000
Liabilities: $452,220,000,000
Net Worth: $40,958,000,000
Earnings: $4,649,000,000
Emp.: 33,000
Fiscal Year-end: 12/31/23
Holding Company; Financial Investment Services
N.A.I.C.S.: 551112
Joseph R. Martin (COO & Sr Exec VP)
Charles Robert Schwab Jr. (Founder)
Neesha Hathi (Exec VP & Head-Wealth & Advice Solutions)
Walter W. Bettinger II (Chm & CEO)
Richard A. Wurster (Pres)
Carolyn Schwab-Pomerantz (Mng Dir)
Peter J. Morgan III (Mng Dir)
Brian Bender (Mng Dir)
Stacy Hammond (CMO)
James Kostulias (Head)

Subsidiaries:

Charles Schwab & Company, Inc.   (1)
211 Main St, San Francisco, CA 94105-4122   (100%)
Tel.: (415) 636-7000
Web Site: http://www.schwab.com
Emp.: 23,000

Financial Services, Discount Stock Broker, Electronic Brokerage, Mutual Funds
N.A.I.C.S.: 523150
Charles Robert Schwab Jr. (Founder)
Carolyn Schwab-Pomerantz (Mng Dir-Consumer Education)

Charles Schwab Bank   (1)
5190 Neil Rd, Reno, NV 89502
Tel.: (775) 689-6800
Web Site: http://www.schwabbank.com
Sales Range: $25-49.9 Million
Emp.: 42
Banking Services
N.A.I.C.S.: 522110
Charles Robert Schwab Jr. (Chm)
Walter W. Bettinger II (Co-Chm)
Richard F. Kenny (Founder)

Charles Schwab Investment Management, Inc.   (1)
211 Main St, San Francisco, CA 94105
Tel.: (415) 667-9200
Web Site:
https://www.schwabassetmanagement.com
Sales Range: $1-4.9 Billion
Equity Investment Services
N.A.I.C.S.: 523940
Richard A. Wurster (CEO)
Jonathan de St. Paer (Pres & COO)

Family Wealth Alliance, LLC   (1)
333 N Michigan Ave 32nd Fl, Chicago, IL 60601
Tel.: (312) 248-8820
Web Site: http://www.fwalliance.com
Rev.: $1,530,000
Emp.: 9
Administrative & General Management Consulting Services
N.A.I.C.S.: 541611
Christine Markevicius (Mng Dir)

Schwab Performance Technologies Inc.   (1)
434 Fayetteville St 13th Fl, Raleigh, NC 27601-1701
Tel.: (919) 743-5000
Web Site: http://www.schwabpt.com
Rev.: $1,400,000
Emp.: 70
Computer Software Development
N.A.I.C.S.: 541511

TD Ameritrade Holding Corporation   (1)
200 S 108th Ave, Omaha, NE 68154
Web Site: https://www.amtd.com
Holding Company; Online Securities Brokerage, Trading, Market Research & Financial Services
N.A.I.C.S.: 551112
J. J. Kinahan (Mng Dir-Trading & Education)

Subsidiary (Non-US):

TD Ameritrade Asia Pte. Ltd.   (2)
Tel.: (65) 68232250
Securities Brokerage Services
N.A.I.C.S.: 523150

TD Ameritrade Hong Kong Limited   (2)
Suite 1211-13 Two Pacific Place 88 Queensway, Hong Kong, China (Hong Kong)
Tel.: (852) 23747888
Web Site: http://www.tdameritrade.com.hk
Software Development Services
N.A.I.C.S.: 513210

TD Ameritrade Singapore Pte. Ltd.   (2)
1 Temasek Avenue 15-02 Millenia Tower, Singapore, 039192, Singapore
Tel.: (65) 68232250
Web Site: https://www.tdameritrade.com.sg
Software Development Services
N.A.I.C.S.: 513210

Subsidiary (Domestic):

TD Ameritrade, Inc.   (2)
200 S 108th Ave, Omaha, NE 68154-2631   (100%)
Tel.: (402) 331-7856
Web Site: http://www.tdameritrade.com
Sales Range: $650-699.9 Million
Online Stock Brokerage Services
N.A.I.C.S.: 523150

Subsidiary (Domestic):

TD Ameritrade Clearing, Inc.   (3)
200 S 108th Ave, Omaha, NE 68154-2631
Tel.: (402) 331-2744
Web Site: http://www.tdameritrade.com
Securities Brokerage Services
N.A.I.C.S.: 523150

TD Ameritrade Futures & Forex LLC   (3)
600 W Chicago Ave Ste 100, Chicago, IL 60654-2597
Tel.: (773) 435-3210
Financial Management Services
N.A.I.C.S.: 541611

TD Ameritrade Services Company, Inc.   (3)
1600 7th Ave Ste 115, Seattle, WA 98101
Tel.: (206) 389-8080
Web Site: http://www.tdameritrade.com
Investment Management Service
N.A.I.C.S.: 523940

TD Ameritrade Trust Company   (3)
717 17th St Ste 1800, Denver, CO 80202   (100%)
Tel.: (443) 766-7142
Web Site: http://www.tdameritradetrust.com
Sales Range: $650-699.9 Million
Trust & Asset Custody Services
N.A.I.C.S.: 523991

Division (Domestic):

thinkorswim   (3)
600 W Chicago Ave Ste 800, Chicago, IL 60654-2597
Tel.: (773) 435-3210
Web Site: http://www.thinkorswim.com
Sales Range: $1-9.9 Million
Emp.: 120
Online Brokerage Services
N.A.I.C.S.: 523160

Subsidiary (Domestic):

ThinkTech, Inc.   (2)
1 Plz Four A, Jersey City, NJ 07311
Tel.: (201) 369-5700
Web Site: http://www.tdameritrade.com
Online Security Brokerage Services
N.A.I.C.S.: 523150

TradeWise Advisors, Inc.   (2)
600 W Chicago Ave Ste 100, Chicago, IL 60654-2597   (100%)
Tel.: (773) 244-7736
Web Site: http://www.tradewise.com
Emp.: 5
Investment Advisory Services
N.A.I.C.S.: 523940
Chris Wright (Mgr-Ops)

myTrade, Inc.   (2)
2527 Nelson Miller Pkwy, Louisville, KY 40223
Tel.: (502) 572-4535
Web Site: http://www.mytrade.com
Asset Management Services
N.A.I.C.S.: 531390

The Charles Schwab Corporation - Austin   (1)
11601 Alterra Pkwy Ste 150, Austin, TX 78758
Tel.: (512) 684-3590
Web Site: https://www.schwab.com
Rev.: $18,837,000,000
Assets: $493,178,000,000
Liabilities: $452,220,000,000
Net Worth: $40,958,000,000
Earnings: $5,067,000,000
Emp.: 33,000
Fiscal Year-end: 12/31/2023
Electronic Trading Technology & Brokerage Services
N.A.I.C.S.: 523150

USAA Investment Management Co.   (1)
9800 Fredericksburg Rd, San Antonio, TX 78240   (100%)
Tel.: (210) 498-2211
Web Site: http://www.usaa.com
Sales Range: $1-4.9 Billion
Emp.: 8,000
Mutual Funds & Investment Strategy
N.A.I.C.S.: 523150

Wasmer, Schroeder & Company, LLC   (1)
600 5th Ave S Ste 210, Naples, FL 34102
Tel.: (239) 263-6877
Web Site:
https://www.wasmerschroeder.com
Investment Advisory & Portfolio Management Services
N.A.I.C.S.: 523940

optionsXpress Holdings, Inc.   (1)
150 S Wacker 12th Fl, Chicago, IL 60606-4663
Tel.: (312) 630-3300
Web Site: http://www.optionsxpress.com
Sales Range: $200-249.9 Million
Emp.: 408
Online Brokerage Services
N.A.I.C.S.: 523150
James A. Gray (Co-Founder)

Subsidiary (Domestic):

brokersXpress, LLC   (2)
311 W Monroe St Ste 1000, Chicago, IL 60606   (100%)
Tel.: (312) 680-3300
Sales Range: $50-74.9 Million
Online Business Management Services for Investment Professionals & Brokers
N.A.I.C.S.: 541611

Subsidiary (Non-US):

optionsXpress Singapore Pte Ltd.   (2)
1 George St07-01A, Singapore, 49145, Singapore   (100%)
Tel.: (65) 65363922
Web Site: http://www.optionsxpress.com.sg
Sales Range: $150-199.9 Million
Emp.: 6
Online Options & Stock Trading Services
N.A.I.C.S.: 523150

THE CHEFS' WAREHOUSE, INC.

100 E Ridge Rd, Ridgefield, CT 06877
Tel.: (203) 894-1345   DE
Web Site:
https://www.chefswarehouse.com
Year Founded: 1985
CHEF—(NASDAQ)
Rev.: $1,745,757,000
Assets: $1,073,795,000
Liabilities: $723,584,000
Net Worth: $350,211,000
Earnings: ($4,923,000)
Emp.: 2,712
Fiscal Year-end: 12/24/21
Specialty Food Products Distr
N.A.I.C.S.: 424490
Christopher Pappas (Co-Founder, Chm, Pres & CEO)
John Pappas (Co-Founder, Vice Chm & COO)
Christina Polychroni (Chief HR Officer)
James E. Leddy (CFO)
Timothy McCauley (Chief Acctg Officer)

Subsidiaries:

Bassian Farms, Inc.   (1)
1865 S 10th St, San Jose, CA 95112
Tel.: (408) 286-6262
Food Service Contractors
N.A.I.C.S.: 722310

Cambridge Packing Co., Inc.   (1)
41 Food Mart Rd, Boston, MA 02118-2801
Tel.: (617) 269-6700
Web Site:
http://www.cambridgepacking.com
Animal Slaughtering
N.A.I.C.S.: 311611

Chef Middle East LLC   (1)
ADPF, PO Box 26747, Dubai Investment

Park 2, Dubai, United Arab Emirates
Tel.: (971) 48159888
Web Site: https://www.chefmiddleeast.com
Gourmet Food Distr
N.A.I.C.S.: 424490

Dairyland Produce, LLC (1)
2301 Purchase St, New Bedford, MA 02746
Tel.: (718) 842-8700
Food Ingredient Distr
N.A.I.C.S.: 424490

Dairyland USA Corporation (1)
1300 Viele Ave, Bronx, NY 10474
Tel.: (718) 842-8700
Rev.: $38,600,000
Emp.: 200
Distr & Whslr of Dairy Products & Groceries
N.A.I.C.S.: 424490
Christopher Pappas (Chm, Pres & CEO)
John Pappas (Vice Chm)
John Pathos (VP)

Subsidiary (Domestic):

BelCanto Foods, LLC (2)
240 Sunset Dr, Bronx, NY 10474-7134
Tel.: (718) 497-3888
Sales Range: $25-49.9 Million
Emp.: 35
Importer & Distr of Specialty Food Products
N.A.I.C.S.: 445298

Fells Point Wholesale Meats, Inc. (1)
2730 Wilmarco Ave, Baltimore, MD 21223
Tel.: (410) 539-5600
Web Site: http://www.fpwmeats.com
Meat & Poultry Products Mfr & Distr
N.A.I.C.S.: 311612
Erik Oosterwijk (Co-Founder)
Leo Pruissen (Co-Founder)

Hardie's Fruit & Vegetable Co., LP (1)
1005 N Cockrell Hill Rd, Dallas, TX 75211
Tel.: (214) 426-5666
Web Site: http://www.hardies.com
Grain & Field Bean Merchant Whslr
N.A.I.C.S.: 424510
Michelle Weech (VP-Marketing)

Michael's Finer Meats, LLC (1)
3775 Zane Trace Dr, Columbus, OH 43228
Tel.: (614) 527-4900
Web Site: http://www.michaelsmeats.com
Food Products Mfr
N.A.I.C.S.: 311412

Oakville Produce Partners, LLC (1)
1955 Jerrold Ave, San Francisco, CA 94124
Tel.: (415) 647-2991
Rev.: $7,500,000
Emp.: 31
Fruit & Vegetable Markets
N.A.I.C.S.: 445230
John Lysdahl (Mgr-Credit)
Dale VanMatre (Mgr-Sls)
Francisco Ochoa (Mgr-HR)

Qzina Specialty Foods, Inc. (1)
1726 W Atlantic Blvd, Pompano Beach, FL 33069
Tel.: (954) 590-4000
Web Site: http://www.qzina.com
Food Products Mfr
N.A.I.C.S.: 311412

The Chefs' Warehouse West Coast LLC (1)
16633 E Gale Ave, City of Industry, CA 91745
Tel.: (626) 465-4200
Web Site: http://www.chefswarehouse.com
Rev.: $37,210,989
Emp.: 65
Specialty Food Items Distr
N.A.I.C.S.: 424490

THE CHEMOURS COMPANY
1007 Market St, Wilmington, DE 19801
Tel.: (302) 773-1000   DE
Web Site: https://www.chemours.com
CC—(NYSE)
Rev.: $6,027,000,000
Assets: $8,251,000,000
Liabilities: $7,512,000,000
Net Worth: $739,000,000

Earnings: ($238,000,000)
Emp.: 6,200
Fiscal Year-end: 12/31/23
Chemical Products Mfr
N.A.I.C.S.: 325998
Curtis V. Anastasio (Founder)
Shane W. Hostetter (CFO & Principal Acctg Officer)
Alvenia Scarborough (Chief Brand Officer & Sr VP-Corp Comm)
Susan M. Kelliher (Sr VP-HR & Health Svcs)
Matthew S. Abbott (Chief Enterprise Transformation Officer & Sr VP)
Denise M. Dignam (Pres & CEO)
Kristine Wellman (Gen Counsel, Sec & Sr VP)
Amber Wellman (Chief Sustainability Officer)
Jonathan Lock (Chief Dev Officer, Chief Dev Officer & Sr VP)
Kurt Bonner (Mgr-IR)
Thom Sueta (Dir-Comm)
Gerardo Familiar Calderon (Pres-Advanced Performance Matls)
Jonathan S. Lock (Chief Dev Officer)
Joseph T. Martinko (Pres-Thermal & Specialized Solutions)
Cassie Olszewski (Mgr-Media Rels & Fin Comm)
Brandon Ontjes (VP-Fin Plng & Analysis & IR)
David A. Will (Chief Acctg Officer & Controller)

Subsidiaries:

Chemours Deutschland GmbH (1)
Frankfurter Str 229, 63263, Neu-Isenburg, Germany
Tel.: (49) 6102822330
Chemical Products Distr
N.A.I.C.S.: 424690

Chemours International Operations Sarl (1)
2 Chemin Du Pavillon Le Grand-Saconnex, 1218, Geneva, Switzerland
Tel.: (41) 227191500
Chemical Products Distr
N.A.I.C.S.: 424690

Chemours Kabushiki Kaisha (1)
Kamiyacho Prime Place 7F 4-1-17 Tora-nomon, Minato-ku, Tokyo, 105-0001, Japan
Tel.: (81) 5038230513
Chemical Products Distr
N.A.I.C.S.: 424690

Chemours Korea Inc. (1)
12FL Majestarcity Tower 1 12 Seocho-daero 38-gil, Seocho-gu, Seoul, 06655, Korea (South)
Tel.: (82) 222225207
Chemical Products Distr
N.A.I.C.S.: 424690

Chemours Netherlands BV (1)
Baanhoekweg 22, 3313 LA, Dordrecht, Netherlands
Tel.: (31) 786310111
Chemical Products Distr
N.A.I.C.S.: 424690
Nils Hofman (Coord-Environmental)

Noluma International, LLC (1)
1007 Market St 10th Fl, Wilmington, DE 19899
Web Site: http://www.noluma.com
Chemical Products Mfr
N.A.I.C.S.: 325998
Divya Chopra (Pres)
Georgia Kollias (VP-Global Brand Comm & Press)
Chris O'Grady (Bus Dir)

The Chemours (Taiwan) Company Limited (1)
7th Floor 167 Tun Hwa North Road, Taipei, 10549, Taiwan
Tel.: (886) 34838800
Chemical Products Distr
N.A.I.C.S.: 424690

The Chemours (Thailand) Company Limited (1)

Unit 1502 15th Floor GPF Witthayu Tower A 93/1 Wireless Road, Lumpini Pathumwan, Bangkok, 10330, Thailand
Tel.: (66) 26594000
Chemical Products Distr
N.A.I.C.S.: 424690

The Chemours Canada Company (1)
151 Bloor Street West - 12th Floor, Toronto, M5S 1S4, ON, Canada
Tel.: (905) 816-2310
Chemical Products Distr
N.A.I.C.S.: 424690

The Chemours Chemical (Shanghai) Company Limited (1)
9F SCG Parkside Building 868 Ying Hua Road, Pudong New District, Shanghai, 201204, China
Tel.: (86) 4008056528
Chemical Products Distr
N.A.I.C.S.: 424690

The Chemours China Holding Co., Ltd. (1)
Bldg 11 399 Ke Yuan Road Zhangjiang Hi-Tech Park Pudong New District, Shanghai, 201203, China
Tel.: (86) 2138622888
Chemical Products Distr
N.A.I.C.S.: 424690

The Chemours Company FC, LLC (1)
12501 Strang Rd, La Porte, TX 77571-8704
Tel.: (281) 471-2771
Web Site: http://www.chemours.com
Chemical Labrortary Mfr
N.A.I.C.S.: 334516

Subsidiary (Domestic):

First Chemical Corp. (2)
1001 Industrial Rd, Pascagoula, MS 39581   (100%)
Tel.: (228) 762-0870
Sales Range: $50-74.9 Million
Production & Marketing of Industrial & Specialty Chemicals; Aniline, Nitrobenzene & Nitrotoluenes
N.A.I.C.S.: 325199

First Chemical Texas, L.P. (2)
PO Box 1607, Baytown, TX 77522-1607   (100%)
Tel.: (281) 383-1400
Sales Range: $1-9.9 Million
Emp.: 36
Chemicals Mfr
N.A.I.C.S.: 325110

The Chemours Company Singapore Pte. Ltd. (1)
1 Harbourfront Place 16-01 Harbourfront Tower One, Singapore, 098633, Singapore
Tel.: (65) 67158688
Chemical Products Distr
N.A.I.C.S.: 424690

The Chemours India Private Limited (1)
Gala Impecca 1st Floor Andheri Kurla Road Chakala, Andheri East, Mumbai, 400069, Maharashtra, India
Tel.: (91) 2262273300
Chemical Products Distr
N.A.I.C.S.: 424690

The Chemours Malaysia Sdn. Bhd. (1)
Suite 20-01 & 20-02B Level 20 The Pinnacle Persiaran Lagoon, Subang Jaya, 47500, Bandar Sunway, Selangor, Malaysia
Tel.: (60) 356244300
Chemical Products Distr
N.A.I.C.S.: 424690

THE CHILDREN'S PLACE, INC.
500 Plaza Dr, Secaucus, NJ 07094
Tel.: (204) 272-8312   DE
Web Site:
    https://www.childrensplace.com
Year Founded: 1969
PLCE—(NASDAQ)
Rev.: $1,708,482,000
Assets: $986,281,000
Liabilities: $827,803,000

Net Worth: $158,478,000
Earnings: ($1,138,000)
Emp.: 1,400
Fiscal Year-end: 01/28/23
Children's Clothing & Accessories Retailer
N.A.I.C.S.: 458110
Sheamus Toal (CFO & COO)
Mary Beth Sheridan (Chief Mdsg Officer)
Jennifer Groves (Sr VP-Design & Brand Creative)
Rajat Jain (CTO)
Sheamus Toal (CFO & Sr VP)
Jared E. Shure (Gen Counsel & Sr VP)
Muhammad Umair (Pres)
Muhammad Asif Seemab (Vice Chm)
Claudia Lima-Guinehut (Pres-Brand)

Subsidiaries:

The Children's Place (Canada), LP (1)
6040 Cantay Rd, Mississauga, L5R 4J2, ON, Canada
Tel.: (201) 558-2400
Childrens & Infants Clothing Retailer
N.A.I.C.S.: 458110

The Children's Place (Hong Kong) Limited (1)
30/F 1st Hung To Rd, Kwun Tong, China (Hong Kong)
Tel.: (852) 34712286
Web Site: http://www.thechildrensplace.com
Childrens & Infants Clothing Retailer
N.A.I.C.S.: 458110

The Children's Place (Virginia), LLC (1)
4802 Vly View Blvd Nw, Roanoke, VA 24012-2001
Tel.: (540) 362-4888
Childrens & Infants Clothing Retailer
N.A.I.C.S.: 458110

The Childrens Place (Canada), LP (1)
2525 36th Street Ne, Calgary, T1Y 5T4, AB, Canada
Tel.: (403) 293-1410
Children's Apparel Store
N.A.I.C.S.: 458110

THE CIGNA GROUP
900 Cottage Grove Rd, Bloomfield, CT 06002
Tel.: (860) 226-6000   DE
Web Site:
    https://www.thecignagroup.com
Year Founded: 1792
CI—(NYSE)
Rev.: $195,265,000,000
Assets: $152,761,000,000
Liabilities: $106,517,000,000
Net Worth: $46,244,000,000
Earnings: $5,164,000,000
Emp.: 72,500
Fiscal Year-end: 12/31/23
Financial Investment Services
N.A.I.C.S.: 551112
David M. Cordani (Chm, Pres & CEO)
John M. Murabito (Exec VP-HR & Svcs)
Eric P. Palmer (Pres/CEO-Evernorth Health Svcs & Exec VP-Enterprise Strategy)
Brian C. Evanko (CFO & Exec VP)
David J. Brailer (Chief Health Officer & Exec VP)
Everett Neville (Exec VP-Corp Dev, Strategy & Solutions)
Jason D. Sadler (Pres-Intl Markets)
Michael W. Triplett (Pres-Comml)
Jeffrey Young (VP-Sls-Ohio & West Virginia)
Bryan Holgerson (Chief Underwriting Officer-Comml-US)

The Cigna Group—(Continued)

Ralph Giacobbe *(Sr VP & Head-IR)*
Paul Sanford *(Exec VP-Ops)*
Brian Evanko *(CFO & Exec VP)*

Subsidiaries:

Cigna Holding Company   **(1)**
900 Cottage Grove Rd, Bloomfield, CT
06002
Tel.: (860) 226-6000
Web Site: http://www.cigna.com
Holding Company; Insurance, Investment
Management, Health Care & Financial Ser-
vices
N.A.I.C.S.: 551101
David M. Cordani *(Pres & CEO)*
John M. Murabito *(Chief HR Officer & Exec
VP)*
Eric P. Palmer *(CFO & Exec VP)*
Tim Wentworth *(Pres-Express Scripts &
Svcs)*
Mary T. Hoeltzel *(Chief Acctg Officer & Sr
VP-Tax)*
Nicole S. Jones *(Gen Counsel & Exec VP)*
Mark L. Boxer *(CIO & Exec VP)*
Ralph Holmes *(Sr VP-Comml-Southwest)*
Michael Triplett *(Pres-Comml)*
Jim Hickey *(Pres-South Texas)*
Steve Miller *(Chief Clinical Officer)*
Kristen Lauria *(CMO-Global)*
Glen D. Stettin *(Chief Innovation Officer-
Express Scripts & Cigna Svcs & Sr VP)*
John J. Webb *(Pres-West Tennessee, Ar-
kansas & Mississippi)*
Keith Barnes *(Pres-Comml Health Care &
Related Benefits Plans-North Texas)*

Subsidiary (Non-US):

**Cigna & CMB Life Insurance Com-
pany Limited**   **(2)**
Unit 7A Mirae Asset Tower No 166 Lu Jia
Zui Ring Road, Pudong New Area, Shang-
hai, 200120, China
Tel.: (86) 4008303633
Web Site: http://www.cignacmb.com
Insurance Management Services
N.A.I.C.S.: 524298

**Cigna Finans Emeklilik ve Hayat
A.S.**   **(2)**
Barbaros Mah Kardelen Sok Palladium
Tower No 2 Floor 28-29, Atasehir, 34746,
Istanbul, Turkiye
Tel.: (90) 2164680300
Web Site: https://www.cignafinans.com.tr
Life Insurance Management Services
N.A.I.C.S.: 524298

Subsidiary (Domestic):

Cigna Holdings, Inc.   **(2)**
590 Naamans Rd, Claymont, DE
19703-2308   **(100%)**
Tel.: (302) 797-3469
Web Site: http://www.cigna.com
Sales Range: $25-49.9 Million
Emp.: 12
Holding Company
N.A.I.C.S.: 551112

Subsidiary (Domestic):

**Benefits Management
Corporation**   **(3)**
2640 Cordova Ln Ste 101, Rancho Cor-
dova, CA 95670-5018
Tel.: (916) 340-7000
Web Site: https://www.webpayee.com
Health Insurance Services
N.A.I.C.S.: 524114

Bravo Health, LLC   **(3)**
3601 O Donnell St, Baltimore, MD 21224
Tel.: (410) 864-4400
Health Care Srvices
N.A.I.C.S.: 621111

Subsidiary (Domestic):

**Bravo Health of Pennsylvania,
Inc.**   **(4)**
340 N 12th St Ste 202, Philadelphia, PA
19107
Tel.: (215) 606-6400
Health Care Srvices
N.A.I.C.S.: 621491

Subsidiary (Non-US):

**CIGNA Life Insurance Company of
Canada**   **(3)**
100 Consilium Place Suite 301, Scarbor-
ough, M1H 3E3, ON, Canada   **(100%)**
Tel.: (416) 290-6666
Fire Insurance Services
N.A.I.C.S.: 524113

Subsidiary (Domestic):

Cigna Benefits Financing, Inc.   **(3)**
900 Cottage Grove Rd Wilde Bldg-A4Col,
Bloomfield, CT 06002
Tel.: (860) 226-9018
Emp.: 17
Investment Advisory Services
N.A.I.C.S.: 523940

Cigna Corporate Services, LLC   **(3)**
2 Liberty Plc 1601 Chestnut St, Philadel-
phia, PA 19192
Tel.: (215) 761-1000
Insurance & Health Services
N.A.I.C.S.: 524210

Cigna Dental Health, Inc.   **(3)**
300 NW 82nd Ave Ste 700, Plantation, FL
33324   **(100%)**
Tel.: (954) 514-6600
Dental Health Insurance Services
N.A.I.C.S.: 524114

Subsidiary (Domestic):

**Cigna Dental Health of Kansas,
Inc.**   **(4)**
7400 W 110th St Ste 400, Overland Park,
KS 66210
Tel.: (913) 339-4700
Health Insurance Services
N.A.I.C.S.: 524114

Subsidiary (Domestic):

Cigna Global Holdings, Inc.   **(3)**
590 Naamans Rd, Claymont, DE 19850
Tel.: (302) 797-3469
Web Site: http://www.cigna.com
Sales Range: $250-299.9 Million
Holding Company; Insurance & Financial
Services
N.A.I.C.S.: 551112

Subsidiary (Non-US):

**Cigna Europe Insurance Company
S.A.-N.V.**   **(4)**
Avenue de Cortenbergh 52, 1000, Brussels,
Belgium
Tel.: (32) 27402750
Web Site: http://www.cigna.be
Sales Range: $25-49.9 Million
Emp.: 12
Health Insurance Services
N.A.I.C.S.: 524114

**Cigna European Services (UK)
Limited**   **(4)**
13th Floor 5 Aldermanbury Square,
Greenock, EC2V 7HR, Inverclyde, United
Kingdom
Tel.: (44) 1475492222
Web Site: http://www.cigna.co.uk
Health Insurance Services
N.A.I.C.S.: 524114

**Cigna Insurance Public Company
Limited**   **(4)**
7th and 10th Floor Q House Ploenchit
Building 598 Ploenchit Road, Lumpini Pa-
thumwan, Bangkok, 10330, Thailand
Tel.: (66) 2 651 5995
Web Site: https://www.cigna.co.th
Health Insurance Services
N.A.I.C.S.: 524114

Subsidiary (Domestic):

Cigna International Corporation   **(4)**
1601 Chestnut St, Philadelphia, PA
19192   **(100%)**
Tel.: (215) 761-1000
Sales Range: $75-99.9 Million
Emp.: 70
Holding Company; Owner of International
Insurance & Financial Service Providers
N.A.I.C.S.: 524113

Subsidiary (Non-US):

**Cigna Life Insurance Company of
Europe S.A.- N.V.**   **(4)**
Kortenberglaan 52 Avenue de Cortenbergh
52, 1000, Brussels, Belgium
Tel.: (32) 477970675
Web Site: http://www.cignaeurope.com
Life Insurance Management Services
N.A.I.C.S.: 524298

**Cigna Worldwide General Insurance
Company Limited**   **(4)**
16/F 348 Kwun Tong Road, Kwun Tong,
Kowloon, China (Hong Kong)
Tel.: (852) 25399222
Web Site: https://www.cigna.com.hk
Health Care Srvices
N.A.I.C.S.: 621610

Subsidiary (Domestic):

**Cigna Worldwide Insurance
Company**   **(4)**
1601 Chestnut St, Philadelphia, PA
19192   **(100%)**
Tel.: (215) 761-1000
Web Site: http://www.cigna.com.hk
Sales Range: $150-199.9 Million
Holding Company; International Insurance &
Financial Services
N.A.I.C.S.: 524114
David M. Cordani *(Chm & CEO)*

Subsidiary (Domestic):

Cigna Health Corporation   **(3)**
1601 Chestnut St 2 Liberty Pl, Philadelphia,
PA 19192-0001   **(100%)**
Tel.: (215) 761-1000
Web Site: http://www.cigna.com
Sales Range: $10-24.9 Million
Holding Company; Managed Healthcare &
Insurance Services
N.A.I.C.S.: 524114

Subsidiary (Domestic):

Cigna Healthcare of Arizona, Inc.   **(4)**
25500 N Norterra Dr Bldg B, Phoenix, AZ
85085
Tel.: (623) 277-1000
Web Site: http://www.cigna.com
Health Maintenance Organization
N.A.I.C.S.: 524113

**Cigna Healthcare of California,
Inc.**   **(4)**
400 N Brand Blvd Fourth Fl, Glendale, CA
91203-2357
Tel.: (818) 500-6262
Web Site: http://www.cigna.com
Healtcare Services
N.A.I.C.S.: 524114

**Cigna Healthcare of Colorado,
Inc.**   **(4)**
3900 E Mexico Ave Ste 1100, Denver, CO
80210-3946
Tel.: (303) 782-1500
Health Maintenance Organization
N.A.I.C.S.: 524113

**Cigna Healthcare of Connecticut,
Inc.**   **(4)**
900 Cottage Grove Rd C8NAS, Hartford,
CT 06152-7314
Tel.: (860) 226-6000
Web Site: http://www.cigna.com
Health Insurance Services
N.A.I.C.S.: 524114

Cigna Healthcare of Florida, Inc.   **(4)**
2701 N Rocky Point Dr Ste 800, Tampa, FL
33607
Tel.: (813) 637-1200
Web Site: http://www.cigna.com
Health Maintenance Organization
N.A.I.C.S.: 524114

**Cigna Healthcare of Georgia,
Inc.**   **(4)**
Two Securities Centre 3500 Piedmont RD
Ste 200, Atlanta, GA 30305
Tel.: (404) 443-8800
Web Site: http://www.cigna.com
Health Maintenance Organization
N.A.I.C.S.: 524114
William M. Pastore *(Pres)*

Cigna Healthcare of Illinois, Inc.   **(4)**
525 W Monroe St Ste 300, Chicago, IL
60661
Tel.: (312) 648-2460
Web Site: http://www.cigna.com
Sales Range: $75-99.9 Million
Emp.: 150
Health Maintenance Organization
N.A.I.C.S.: 524114

Cigna Healthcare of Indiana, Inc.   **(4)**
1 Penn Mark Plz 11595 N Meridian St Ste
500, Carmel, IN 46032
Tel.: (317) 208-3230
Sales Range: $10-24.9 Million
Emp.: 17
Healtcare Services
N.A.I.C.S.: 524114

**Cigna Healthcare of Massachusetts,
Inc.**   **(4)**
2223 Washington St, Newton, MA 02462
Tel.: (617) 630-4300
Health & Medical Insurance Services
N.A.I.C.S.: 524114
Donald M. Curry *(Pres/Gen Mgr-New Eng-
land)*

**Cigna Healthcare of New Hampshire,
Inc.**   **(4)**
2 College Park Dr, Hooksett, NH 03106
Tel.: (603) 268-7000
Web Site: http://www.hlthsrc.com
Managed Health Care Services
N.A.I.C.S.: 524114

**Cigna Healthcare of New Jersey,
Inc.**   **(4)**
44 Whippany Rd, Morristown, NJ 07960
Tel.: (862) 242-2600
Health Insurance Services
N.A.I.C.S.: 524114

**Cigna Healthcare of North Carolina,
Inc.**   **(4)**
701 Corporate Center Dr, Raleigh, NC
27607
Tel.: (919) 854-7000
Web Site: http://www.cigna.com
Sales Range: $100-124.9 Million
Emp.: 300
Health Insurance Services
N.A.I.C.S.: 524210
Brian Evanko *(Pres & CEO)*

Cigna Healthcare of Ohio, Inc.   **(4)**
3 Summit Pk Dr Ste 250, Independence,
OH 44131
Tel.: (216) 642-1700
Web Site: http://www.cigna.com
Health Maintenance Organization
N.A.I.C.S.: 524114

**Cigna Healthcare of South Carolina,
Inc.**   **(4)**
4000 Faber Pl Ste 220, North Charleston,
SC 29405
Tel.: (843) 566-7400
Sales Range: $10-24.9 Million
Emp.: 65
Health Insurance Services
N.A.I.C.S.: 621410

**Cigna Healthcare of St. Louis,
Inc.**   **(4)**
231 S Bemiston Ave Ste 500, Saint Louis,
MO 63105-1914
Tel.: (314) 290-7300
Web Site: http://www.cigna.com
Sales Range: $50-74.9 Million
Emp.: 100
Health Maintenance Organization
N.A.I.C.S.: 524114

**Cigna Healthcare of Tennessee,
Inc.**   **(4)**
1000 Corporate Centre Dr Ste 500, Frank-
lin, TN 37067
Tel.: (615) 595-3377
Web Site: http://www.cigna.com
Health Maintenance Organization
N.A.I.C.S.: 524114

Cigna Healthcare of Texas, Inc.   **(4)**
2700 Post Oak Ste 700, Houston, TX
77056
Tel.: (713) 576-4300
Web Site: http://www.cigna.com

Sales Range: $100-124.9 Million
Emp.: 200
Health Maintenance Organization
N.A.I.C.S.: 524114

Cigna Healthcare of Virginia, Inc. (4)
One James Ctr 901 E Cary St Ste 2000, Richmond, VA 23219
Tel.: (804) 344-3030
Sales Range: $25-49.9 Million
Emp.: 80
Health Maintenance Organization
N.A.I.C.S.: 524114

Tel Drug, Inc. (4)
4901 N 4th St, Sioux Falls, SD 57104-0444
Tel.: (605) 373-0100
Web Site: http://www.teldrug.com
Mail-Order Pharmaceutical Services
N.A.I.C.S.: 456110

Subsidiary (Domestic):

Tel Drug of Pennsylvania, LLC (5)
206 Welsh Rd, Horsham, PA 19044-2208
Tel.: (215) 706-5100
Web Site: http://www.teldrug.com
Rev.: $29,700,000
Emp.: 350
Mail Order Pharmaceuticals Distr
N.A.I.C.S.: 456110

Subsidiary (Domestic):

Cigna Integratedcare, Inc. (3)
1601 Chestnut St, Philadelphia, PA 19192-0003
Tel.: (215) 761-1000
Health Insurance & Employee Benefits
N.A.I.C.S.: 524114

Evernorth Behavioral Health, Inc. (3)
11095 Viking Dr Ste 350, Eden Prairie, MN 55344
Tel.: (952) 996-2000
Web Site: http://www.cignabehavioral.com
Inpatient, Outpatient & Partial Hospitalization Services for Substance Abuse & Mental Health Clients
N.A.I.C.S.: 524114

Subsidiary (Domestic):

Evernorth Behavioral Health of California, Inc. (4)
450 N Brand Blvd Ste 500, Glendale, CA 91203-2349 **(100%)**
Tel.: (818) 551-2200
Web Site: http://www.cigna.com
Sales Range: $150-199.9 Million
Managed Mental Health & Substance Abuse Services
N.A.I.C.S.: 524114

Subsidiary (Domestic):

HealthSpring, Inc. (3)
9009 Carothers Pkwy Ste 501, Franklin, TN 37067
Tel.: (615) 291-7000
Web Site: http://www.healthspring.com
Sales Range: $1-4.9 Billion
Holding Company; Managed Care Services
N.A.I.C.S.: 551112

Subsidiary (Domestic):

HealthSpring of Florida, Inc. (4)
11401 SW 40th St, Miami, FL 33165
Tel.: (305) 559-5366
Web Site: http://www.lmchealthplans.com
Health Care Srvices
N.A.I.C.S.: 621999
Henry Hernandez (Pres & CEO)

Subsidiary (Domestic):

Life Insurance Company of North America (3)
1601 Chestnut St, Philadelphia, PA 19192
Tel.: (215) 761-1000
Web Site: http://www.cigna.com
Life Insurance Management Services
N.A.I.C.S.: 524298

NewQuest, LLC (3)
44 Vantage Way Ste 300, Nashville, TN 37228
Tel.: (615) 291-7000
Health Care Srvices
N.A.I.C.S.: 621111

QualCare Alliance Networks, Inc. (3)
30 Knightsbridge Rd, Piscataway, NJ 08854
Tel.: (732) 562-0833
Web Site: http://www.qualcareinc.com
Health Care Srvices
N.A.I.C.S.: 524114
Susan Grodsky (Mgr-Experience)
Alice Herron Lihou (Pres)

Subsidiary (Domestic):

QualCare, Inc. (4)
30 Knightsbridge Rd, Piscataway, NJ 08854
Tel.: (732) 562-0833
Web Site: https://www.qualcareinc.com
Health Insurance Services
N.A.I.C.S.: 524114
Annette Catino (CEO)
Jennifer Lagasca (VP-Network & Delivery Sys)

Scibal Associates, Inc. (4)
100 Decadon Dr, Egg Harbor Township, NJ 08234
Tel.: (609) 653-8400
Web Site: http://www.qual-lynx.com
Property, Casualty & Workers' Compensation Claims Services
N.A.I.C.S.: 524291
Ann Noble (Pres & CEO)

Subsidiary (Domestic):

Vanbreda International LLC (3)
1571 Sawgrass Corporate Pkwy Ste300, Sunrise, FL 33323
Tel.: (202) 623-3137
Health Insurance Services
N.A.I.C.S.: 524114

Subsidiary (Non-US):

Vanbreda International N.V. (4)
Plantin en Moretuslei 299, 2140, Antwerp, Belgium
Tel.: (32) 32175730
Web Site: http://www.vanbreda-international.com
Insurance Agency Services
N.A.I.C.S.: 524210

Subsidiary (Non-US):

Cigna Insurance Services (Europe) Limited (2)
1 Drake Circus, Plymouth, PL1 1QH, United Kingdom
Tel.: (44) 3301026558
Web Site: http://www.cignainsurance.co.uk
Insurance Management Services
N.A.I.C.S.: 524298

Cigna International Health Services BVBA (2)
Plantin en Moretuslei 299, 2140, Antwerp, Belgium
Tel.: (32) 32175730
Web Site: http://www.cignahealthbenefits.com
Health Insurance Services
N.A.I.C.S.: 524114

Cigna International Services Australia Pty. Ltd. (2)
Level 20 Tower 2 Darling Park 201 Sussex Street, Sydney, 2000, NSW, Australia
Tel.: (61) 290061788
Business Support Services
N.A.I.C.S.: 561499
Brock Judiesch (Dir-Bus Dev)

Cigna Life Insurance New Zealand Limited (2)
12-14 Northcroft Street, Takapuna, Auckland, 0622, New Zealand
Tel.: (64) 44707737
Web Site: http://www.cigna.co.nz
Life Insurance Management Services
N.A.I.C.S.: 524298
Gail Costa (CEO)
Craig Musker (CIO)
Debbie Eye (COO)
Mark Schollum (CFO)
Tony Lane (Chief Risk Officer)

CignaTTK Health Insurance Company Limited (2)
401/402 Raheja Titanium Off Western Express Highway Goregaon East, Mumbai, 400063, India

Tel.: (91) 2249854100
Health Insurance Services
N.A.I.C.S.: 524114

Subsidiary (Domestic):

Health-Lynx, Inc. (2)
30 Knightsbridge Rd, Piscataway, NJ 08854
Tel.: (732) 529-8676
Web Site: http://www.health-lynx.com
Health Care Srvices
N.A.I.C.S.: 621999
Annette Catino (Pres & CEO)
Tim Ford (Exec VP)

Loyal American Life Insurance Company (2)
11200 Lakeline Blvd Ste 100, Austin, TX 78755
Tel.: (512) 451-2224
Sales Range: $150-199.9 Million
Emp.: 300
Disability & Life Insurance
N.A.I.C.S.: 524113
Beth McDade (Dir-Ops)

The Cigna Group Foundation (2)
1601 Chestnut St 26th Fl, Philadelphia, PA 19192-0001 **(100%)**
Tel.: (215) 761-4880
Web Site: http://www.cigna.com
Charitable & Community Contribution Services
N.A.I.C.S.: 813211

Verity Solutions Group, Inc. (2)
12131 113th Ave NE Ste 200, Kirkland, WA 98034
Tel.: (425) 947-1922
Web Site: https://www.verity340b.com
Software Development Services
N.A.I.C.S.: 541511
George Puckett (Pres & CEO)
Jon Sortland (CFO)
Scott LaChute (VP-Ops)

Subsidiary (Non-US):

Vielife Limited (2)
24 Southwark Bridge Road, London, SE1 9HF, United Kingdom
Tel.: (44) 2071832289
Web Site: http://www.vielife.com
Medical Care Equipment Distr
N.A.I.C.S.: 456199

Cigna Insurance Middle East S.A.L. (1)
Holcom Building Corniche Al Nahr Bloc B 3rd floor, Beirut, Lebanon
Tel.: (961) 1999654
Health Insurance Services
N.A.I.C.S.: 524114

Evernorth Health, Inc. (1)
1 Express Way, Saint Louis, MO 63121
Web Site: https://www.evernorth.com
Health Insurance Services
N.A.I.C.S.: 524114

Express Scripts Holding Company (1)
1 Express Way, Saint Louis, MO 63121
Tel.: (800) 282-2881
Web Site: http://www.express-scripts.com
Holding Company; Pharmacy Benefit Management Services
N.A.I.C.S.: 551112
Timothy C. Wentworth (CEO-Evernorth)
Brian Seiz (Pres-Pharmacy)
John Arlotta (CEO-Evicore & Health Care)

Subsidiary (Domestic):

ESI Mail Order Processing, Inc. (2)
1 Express Way, Saint Louis, MO 63121
Tel.: (817) 850-5000
Pharmaceuticals Product Mfr
N.A.I.C.S.: 325412

Express Scripts Administrators, LLC (2)
1 Express Way, Saint Louis, MO 63121
Tel.: (314) 996-0900
Prescription Drug Distr
N.A.I.C.S.: 456110

Express Scripts, Inc. (2)
8931 Springdale Ave, Saint Louis, MO 63134
Tel.: (314) 587-4000

Web Site: http://www.express-scripts.com
Pharmacy Benefit Management Services
N.A.I.C.S.: 456110

Subsidiary (Domestic):

CuraScript, Inc. (3)
6272 Lee Vista Blvd, Orlando, FL 32822
Tel.: (407) 852-4903
Web Site: http://www.curascript.com
Sales Range: $1-4.9 Billion
Emp.: 2,500
Pharmaceuticals Product Mfr
N.A.I.C.S.: 325412

Subsidiary (Non-US):

ESI Canada (3)
5770 Hurontario Street 10th Floor, Mississauga, L5R 3G5, ON, Canada
Tel.: (905) 712-8615
Web Site: http://www.express-scripts.ca
Sales Range: $75-99.9 Million
Emp.: 250
Pharmacy Benefit Management Services
N.A.I.C.S.: 456110
Dorian Lo (Pres)
Stephanie Myner-Nham (Chief Admin Officer)
Vigna Vivekanand (CFO)

Branch (Domestic):

ESI Canada (4)
625 President Kennedy Avenue 16th Floor, Montreal, H3A 1K2, QC, Canada **(100%)**
Tel.: (514) 844-4420
Web Site: http://www.express-scripts.ca
Sales Range: $10-24.9 Million
Emp.: 35
Pharmaceutical Products Distr
N.A.I.C.S.: 424210
Dorian Lo (Pres)
Michael Roszak (COO)
Stephanie Myner-Nham (Chief Admin Officer)
Vigna Vivekanand (CFO)
Michael Simpson (CIO)

Subsidiary (Domestic):

Express Scripts (3)
6301 Cecilia Cir Ste 200, Bloomington, MN 55439-2604 **(100%)**
Tel.: (952) 820-7000
Sales Range: $750-799.9 Million
Emp.: 1,500
Pharmacy Management Programs
N.A.I.C.S.: 456110
Chris Gould (Corp Treas & VP-Fin)
Dennis Lee (Sr Mgr-Midrange Dev)

Subsidiary (Non-US):

Express Scripts Canada Co. (3)
5770 Hurontario Street 10th Floor, Mississauga, L5R 3G5, ON, Canada
Tel.: (905) 712-8615
Web Site: https://www.express-scripts.ca
Health Care Srvices
N.A.I.C.S.: 621610

Subsidiary (Domestic):

MAH Pharmacy, LLC (2)
100 Parsons Pond Dr, Franklin Lakes, NJ 07417-2604
Tel.: (201) 269-2368
Pharmaceutical Products Distr
N.A.I.C.S.: 325412

Matrix Healthcare Services, Inc. (2)
3111 W Martin Luther King Jr Blvd Ste 800, Tampa, FL 33607
Tel.: (813) 247-2077
Web Site: https://www.mymatrixx.com
Pharmacy Benefits Services
N.A.I.C.S.: 524114
Michael Geis (CIO)
Phil Walls (Chief Clinical Officer)
Ronda Clement-Woble (VP-Mktg)
Mike Cirillo (Pres)

Medco Health Solutions, Inc. (2)
100 Parsons Pond Dr, Franklin Lakes, NJ 07417
Tel.: (201) 269-3400
Web Site: http://www.medcohealth.com
Sales Range: $50-74.9 Billion
Emp.: 22,100

The Cigna Group—(Continued)

Holding Company; Pharmaceutical Products & Services
N.A.I.C.S.: 551112

Subsidiary (Domestic):

Accredo Health, Incorporated (3)
1620 Century Center Pkwy, Memphis, TN 38134 (100%)
Tel.: (901) 385-3600
Web Site: https://www.accredo.com
Sales Range: $1-4.9 Billion
Emp.: 1,980
Pharmaceuticals Product Mfr
N.A.I.C.S.: 325412

Subsidiary (Domestic):

Accredo Care Network, Inc. (4)
7420 Goodlet Farm Pkwy Ste 110, Cordova, TN 38016
Tel.: (877) 943-7712
Health Care Srvices
N.A.I.C.S.: 621610

Accredo Health Group, Inc. (4)
1640 Century Center Pkwy Ste 110, Memphis, TN 38134
Tel.: (901) 385-3707
Web Site: http://www.accredo.com
Sales Range: $150-199.9 Million
Emp.: 900
Specialty Pharmacy Care & Related Services
N.A.I.C.S.: 456110

Subsidiary (Domestic):

AHG of New York, Inc. (5)
500 Executive Blvd, Elmsford, NY 10523
Tel.: (914) 592-0333
Emp.: 11
Pharmaceuticals Product Mfr
N.A.I.C.S.: 325412
Joe Kraemer (Acct Mgr)
Elizabeth Lakis (Acct Mgr)

Subsidiary (Domestic):

Critical Care Systems of New York, Inc. (4)
15 Technology Pl 2, East Syracuse, NY 13057
Tel.: (315) 434-1980
Web Site: http://www.optioncare.com
Emp.: 15
Health Care Srvices
N.A.I.C.S.: 621610

Subsidiary (Domestic):

DNA Direct, Inc. (3)
Pier 9 Ste 105, San Francisco, CA 94111
Tel.: (415) 646-0222
Web Site: http://www.dnadirect.com
Medical Laboratories
N.A.I.C.S.: 621511
John J. Arlotta (Pres)
David Smith (Pres-Medical Benefits Mgmt)
Andy Eilert (Pres-Growth & Innovation)
Timothy Cook (CFO)
Kathleen Mercier (Chief People & Talent Officer & Exec VP)
Laurie Johnson (Chief Legal & Compliance Officer, Sec & Exec VP)
Ellen Clarke (CIO)
Elias G. Wahesh (Exec VP-Corp Ops)

Subsidiary (Non-US):

Manipal Cigna Health Insurance Company Limited (3)
401/402 Raheja Titanium Western Express Highway, Goregaon East, Mumbai, 400 063, India
Tel.: (91) 2249854100
Web Site: https://www.manipalcigna.com
Health Care Srvices
N.A.I.C.S.: 621610

Subsidiary (Domestic):

Medco Health Solutions of Las Vegas, LLC (3)
6225 Annie Oakley Dr, Las Vegas, NV 89120
Tel.: (702) 436-8800
Pharmaceuticals Mail Order Houses
N.A.I.C.S.: 456110

Medco Health Solutions of Richmond, LLC (3)
9210 Forest Hill Ave Ste B, Richmond, VA 23235-6880
Tel.: (804) 330-0070
Sales Range: $25-49.9 Million
Emp.: 27
Home Delivery Pharmacy Services
N.A.I.C.S.: 456110

Medco Health Solutions of Texas, LLC (3)
8111 Royal Rdg Pkwy, Irving, TX 75063
Tel.: (972) 915-2737
Sales Range: $200-249.9 Million
Emp.: 800
Mail Order Prescription Drugs
N.A.I.C.S.: 456110

UBC Late Stage, Inc. (3)
3822 Summit, Kansas City, MO 64111
Tel.: (816) 421-6400
Health Care Srvices
N.A.I.C.S.: 621610
Patrick Lindsay (CEO)

Subsidiary (Non-US):

UBC Scientific Solutions, Limited (3)
Envision House 5 North Street, Horsham, RH12 1XQ, West Sussex, United Kingdom
Tel.: (44) 1403322000
Health Care Srvices
N.A.I.C.S.: 621610
Brian Hepburn (CEO)

Subsidiary (Domestic):

United BioSource Patient Solutions, Inc. (2)
4445 Willard Ave 12th Fl, Chevy Chase, MD 20815
Tel.: (201) 269-2368
Business Support Services
N.A.I.C.S.: 541611

eviCore healthcare MSI, LLC (2)
400 Buckwalter Place Blvd, Bluffton, SC 29910
Web Site: http://www.evicore.com
Healtcare Services
N.A.I.C.S.: 621999
Andy Eilert (Pres-Growth & Innovation)
John J. Arlotta (Pres)
David Smith (Pres-Medical Benefits Mgmt)
Laurie Johnson (Chief Compliance Officer, Chief Legal Officer, Sec & Exec VP)
Elias G. Wahesh (Exec VP-Corp Ops)

THE CLOROX COMPANY

1221 Broadway, Oakland, CA 94612-1888
Tel.: (510) 271-7000 CA
Web Site:
https://www.thecloroxcompany.com
Year Founded: 1913
CLX—(NYSE)
Rev.: $7,093,000,000
Assets: $5,751,000,000
Liabilities: $5,259,000,000
Net Worth: $492,000,000
Earnings: $292,000,000
Emp.: 8,000
Fiscal Year-end: 06/30/24
Polish & Other Sanitation Good Manufacturing
N.A.I.C.S.: 325612
Chau Banks (CIO, Chief Data Officer & Sr VP)
Denise A. Garner (Chief Innovation Officer & Sr VP)
Eric Reynolds (COO & Exec VP)
Kevin B. Jacobsen (CFO & Exec VP)
Kirsten M. Marriner (Chief People & Corp Affairs Officer & Exec VP)
Diego J. Barral (Sr VP/Gen Mgr-Intl Div)
Stacey Harris Grier (Exec VP & Chief Growth & Strategy Officer)
Lisah Burhan (VP-Investor Relations)
Chau Banks (Chief Information & Enterprise Analytics Officer & Sr VP)
Angela Hilt (Chief Legal Officer & Sr VP)

L. Peck (Chief Acctg Officer, VP & Controller)
Rick McDonald (Chief Product Supply Officer & Sr VP)
Rhonda Ramlo (Gen Mgr-Strategy & Acq-New Bus Dev)
Patricia Paola Gonzalez (VP-Global FP&A)
Matthew John Shattock (Chm)

Subsidiaries:

Aplicare Inc. (1)
550 Research Pkwy, Meriden, CT 06450-7172
Tel.: (203) 630-0500
Web Site: http://www.aplicare.com
Sales Range: $25-49.9 Million
Emp.: 90
Antiseptic & Personal Care Products Mfr
N.A.I.C.S.: 325412

Brita (USA), Inc. (1)
1221 Broadway, Oakland, CA 94612-1888
Tel.: (510) 271-7000
Web Site: http://www.brita.com
Sales Range: $800-899.9 Million
Emp.: 1,700
Mfr of Water Filter Systems
N.A.I.C.S.: 423720

Burt's Bees Inc. (1)
Tel.: (919) 998-5200
Web Site: https://www.burtsbees.com
Sales Range: $150-199.9 Million
Emp.: 350
Skin Care, Makeup & Fragrance Products Mfr & Distr
N.A.I.C.S.: 456120
Doug Haensel (CEO-Interim)

Clorox Argentina S.A. (1)
Cazadores de Coquimbo 2860 4to Piso, Vicente Lopez, B1605DXP, Munro, Buenos Aires, Argentina
Tel.: (54) 1152308200
Web Site: http://www.clorox.com.ar
Sales Range: $200-249.9 Million
Emp.: 400
Cleaning Product Mfr & Distr
N.A.I.C.S.: 325612

Clorox Dominicana S.R.L. (1)
Calle I 35 Zona Industrial De Herrera, Santo Domingo, Dominican Republic
Tel.: (809) 8095307667
Polishes & Sanitation Goods Mfr
N.A.I.C.S.: 325612
Luisa Duran (Mgr-Cost)

Clorox Products Manufacturing Company (1)
5822 Armour Dr, Houston, TX 77020
Tel.: (713) 672-1768
Web Site: http://www.cloroxweb.com
Sales Range: $25-49.9 Million
Emp.: 60
Unsupported Plastics Film & Sheet
N.A.I.C.S.: 325612

Clorox Professional Products Company (1)
1221 Broadway, Oakland, CA 94612-1837 (100%)
Tel.: (510) 271-7000
Sales Range: $800-899.9 Million
Emp.: 1,000
Distr of Food & Non-Food Products to the Commercial & Institutional Food Service Markets
N.A.I.C.S.: 325612

Clorox Services Company (1)
1221 Broadway, Oakland, CA 94612-1829
Tel.: (510) 271-7000
Web Site: http://www.clorox.com
Polish & Other Sanitation Good Mfr
N.A.I.C.S.: 325612

Glad Manufacturing Co. (1)
317 Zane Snead Dr, Amherst, VA 24521
Tel.: (434) 946-3100
Sales Range: $250-299.9 Million
Emp.: 328
Mfr of Plastic Laminated & Coated Bags
N.A.I.C.S.: 326111

Plant (Domestic):

Glad Manufacturing (2)

1700 N 13th St, Rogers, AR 72756-2308
Tel.: (479) 636-2845
Sales Range: $750-799.9 Million
Plastic Laminated & Coated Bags Mfr
N.A.I.C.S.: 326111

Division (Domestic):

Paulsboro Packaging Co. (2)
477 Lexington Ave, Painesville, OH 44077-3001
Tel.: (856) 423-5090
Web Site: http://www.clorox.com
Sales Range: $25-49.9 Million
Emp.: 125
Mfr Auto Products
N.A.I.C.S.: 325612

HV Food Products Company (1)
1221 Broadway, Oakland, CA 94612
Tel.: (510) 271-7000
Web Site: http://www.thecloroxcompany.com
Salad Dressing Mixes Mfr
N.A.I.C.S.: 561110

HV Manufacturing Company (1)
2950 N Wood Dr, Okmulgee, OK 74447
Tel.: (918) 756-9620
Polish & Other Sanitation Good Mfr
N.A.I.C.S.: 325612

Mohamed Ali Abudawood for Industry and Partners for Industry Company Ltd. (1)
6449 Fayd As Samaa, AR Ruwais District 3756, Jeddah, 23213-3756, Saudi Arabia
Tel.: (966) 126502525
Web Site:
https://www.cloroxabudawoodjvs.com
Household Chemical Mfr
N.A.I.C.S.: 325998

Nutranext, LLC (1)
1301 Sawgrass Corporate Pkwy, Sunrise, FL 33323
Tel.: (800) 752-7873
Web Site: http://www.nutranext.net
Pharmaceuticals Product Mfr
N.A.I.C.S.: 325412

ReNew Life Canada Inc. (1)
1273 North Service Rd E Unit 8, Oakville, L6H 1A7, ON, Canada
Tel.: (905) 842-9130
Web Site: http://www.renewlife.ca
Emp.: 22
Health Supplement Product Mfr
N.A.I.C.S.: 325412

Renew Life Formulas, LLC (1)
1221 Broadway, Oakland, CA 94612
Web Site: https://www.betteryourhealth.com
Health Supplements & Therapeutic Products Mfr
N.A.I.C.S.: 456191

Subsidiary (Domestic):

Nature's Products, Inc. (2)
1301 Sawgrass Corporate Pkwy, Sunrise, FL 33323
Tel.: (954) 233-3300
Pharmaceutical Preparation Mfr
N.A.I.C.S.: 325412

Subsidiary (Domestic):

Stop Aging Now, LLC (3)
7250 Woodmont Ave Ste 300, Bethesda, MD 20814
Tel.: (240) 479-2500
Web Site: http://www.stopagingnow.com
Vitamins, Food Supplements, Skin Care & Pet Care Products Whslr
N.A.I.C.S.: 456191

Soy Vay Enterprises, Inc. (1)
5969 Hillside Dr, Felton, CA 95018
Tel.: (831) 335-3824
Web Site: http://www.soyvay.com
Sauce Marinade & Dressing Mfr
N.A.I.C.S.: 311942

The Clorox Company - Kennesaw Plant (1)
3900 Kennesaw 75 Pkwy NW, Kennesaw, GA 30144-6431
Tel.: (770) 794-2400
Web Site: http://www.thecloroxcompany.com

Sales Range: $150-199.9 Million
Emp.: 100
Engineeering Services
N.A.I.C.S.: 541330

**The Clorox International
Company** (1)
1221 Broadway, Oakland, CA
94612-1888 **(100%)**
Tel.: (510) 271-7000
Web Site: https://www.clorox.com
Holding Company
N.A.I.C.S.: 551112

Subsidiary (Non-US):

**Clorox Africa Holdings (Proprietary)
Ltd.** (2)
20 Georgian Crescent Hampton Park East-
bury House, Bryanston, 2194, South Africa
Tel.: (27) 118755912
Web Site: https://www.glad.co.za
Sales Range: $25-49.9 Million
Emp.: 13
Polish & Other Sanitation Good Manufactur-
ing
N.A.I.C.S.: 325612

Clorox Australia Pty. Ltd. (2)
Level 3 10 Herb Elliott Avenue, Sydney
Olympic Park, Sydney, 2127, NSW, Austra-
lia
Tel.: (61) 287372400
Web Site: http://www.clorox.com.au
Sales Range: $50-74.9 Million
Emp.: 65
Polish & Other Sanitation Good Mfr
N.A.I.C.S.: 325612

Subsidiary (Domestic):

**Clorox Manufacturing Company of
Puerto Rico, Inc.** (2)
HC-05 Caguas, Caguas, PR 00725
Tel.: (787) 641-5000
Web Site: https://puerto-rico.clorox.com
Sales Range: $25-49.9 Million
Emp.: 75
Mfr of Household Bleaches
N.A.I.C.S.: 325612
Maria Luisa De Boyrie (Dir-Sls)

Plant (Domestic):

**Clorox Manufacturing Company of
Puerto Rico, Inc.** (3)
Rte 1 Sector Lachanga Caguas Puerto Rico
00725, Bayamon, PR 00959
Tel.: (787) 641-4951
Web Site: http://www.clorox.com
Sales Range: $25-49.9 Million
Mfr of Household Bleaches
N.A.I.C.S.: 325612

**Clorox Manufacturing Company of
Puerto Rico, Inc.** (3)
Rd 798 Km 09 Bo Rio Canas, Caguas, PR
00725
Tel.: (787) 641-2500
Mfr of Cleaning Compounds
N.A.I.C.S.: 325612

Subsidiary (Non-US):

**Clorox Mexicana S. de R.L. de
C.V.** (2)
Av Henry Ford No 31 Fracc Ind San Nico-
las, Tlalnepantla De Baz, Mexico, 54030,
Mexico
Tel.: (52) 5557296500
Web Site: http://www.clorox.com.mx
Emp.: 300
Polish & Other Sanitation Good Mfr
N.A.I.C.S.: 325612
Roberto Manjarres (CEO)

Clorox New Zealand Limited (2)
Level 8 Building 5 Central Park 666 Great
South Road Penrose, Auckland, 1061, New
Zealand
Tel.: (64) 800108858
Web Site: https://www.betterliving.co.nz
Emp.: 2
Polish & Other Sanitation Good Mfr
N.A.I.C.S.: 325612

Clorox de Mexico S.A. de C.V. (2)
Avenida De Henry Ford No 31, Fracciona-
miento Tlalyepant Edo, 54030, Mexico,
Mexico **(100%)**

Tel.: (52) 18002888368
Web Site: https://mexico.clorox.com
Sales Range: $75-99.9 Million
Emp.: 230
Mfr of Liquid Bleach
N.A.I.C.S.: 325612

National Cleaning Products Ltd. (2)
2nd Industrial City, PO Box 5952, Dam-
mam, 31432, Saudi Arabia **(30%)**
Tel.: (966) 138122191
Web Site: http://www.clorox.com
Sales Range: $150-199.9 Million
Emp.: 50
Mfr of Liquid Bleach
N.A.I.C.S.: 325612

**The Clorox Company of Canada
Ltd.** (2)
150 Biscayne Crescent, Brampton, L6W
4V3, ON, Canada **(100%)**
Tel.: (519) 941-0720
Web Site: http://www.clorox.com
Sales Range: $100-124.9 Million
Emp.: 300
Mfr of Paper Bags
N.A.I.C.S.: 322220

Branch (Domestic):

**The Clorox International Company -
Miami Office** (2)
9500 S Dadeland Blvd Ste 800, Miami, FL
33156
Tel.: (305) 260-4300
Web Site: http://www.clorox.com
Emp.: 12
Regional Managing Office
N.A.I.C.S.: 551114

The Glad Products Company (1)
317 Zane Snead Dr, Amherst, VA 24521
Tel.: (434) 946-3100
Polish & Other Sanitation Good Mfr
N.A.I.C.S.: 325612
Matt Roeser (Mgr)

**The Kingsford Products
Company** (1)
1221 Broadway, Oakland, CA
94612-1837 **(100%)**
Tel.: (510) 271-7000
Web Site: http://www.kingsford.com
Sales Range: $1-4.9 Billion
Emp.: 2,000
Charcoal Briquets, Barbecue Products &
Food Products Mfr
N.A.I.C.S.: 325194
Jon Balousek (CEO)

Plant (Domestic):

**Kingsford Manufacturing
Company** (2)
Rte 46 Beryl, Keyser, WV 26726
Tel.: (304) 355-2311
Web Site: http://www.kingsford.com
Polish & Other Sanitation Good Mfr
N.A.I.C.S.: 325612

THE COCA-COLA COMPANY
1 Coca Cola Plz, Atlanta, GA 30313
Tel.: (404) 676-2121 DE
Web Site: https://www.coca-
colacompany.com
Year Founded: 1886
KO—(NYSE)
Rev.: $45,754,000,000
Assets: $97,703,000,000
Liabilities: $70,223,000,000
Net Worth: $27,480,000,000
Earnings: $10,714,000,000
Emp.: 79,100
Fiscal Year-end: 12/31/23
Soft Drinks, Noncarbonated Beverage
Concentrates & Syrups, Waters,
Juices & Juice Drinks, Teas, Coffees,
Energy & Sports Drinks Producer,
Marketer & Distr
N.A.I.C.S.: 312111
Stacy Apter (Treas, Sr VP, VP &
Head-Corp Fin)
Marie D. Quintero-Johnson (VP-
Merger & Acq-Insights & Corp Real
Estate & Head-Corp Dev)
John Murphy (Pres & CFO)

Lawrence R. Cowart (VP & Dir-Bus
Devel)
Juan D. Johnson (VP & Dir-Diversity
Strategies)
Carl Presley (Dir-Compensation &
Benefits)
Carlton L. Curtis (VP)
Nancy W. Quan (Chief Technical &
Innovation Officer & Sr VP)
Manuel Arroyo (CMO-Global & Exec
VP)
Mark Randazza (Chief Acctg Officer,
Sr VP, VP & Asst Controller)
Beatriz R. Perez (Chief Comm Offi-
cer, Chief Sustainability Officer, Chief
Strategic Partnerships Officer & Exec
VP)
James Quincey (Chm & CEO)
Barry Ballow (VP-Internal Audit)
Lisa V. Chang (Chief People Officer-
Global & Sr VP)
Monica Howard Douglas (Gen Coun-
sel & Sr VP)
Kathy Loveless (VP & Controller)
Jeffrey Gilbert (Chief Security Officer
& VP)
Lucy Reid (VP-Strategic Ingredient
Supply)
Lori George Billingsley (Chief Diver-
sity , Equity & Inclusion Officer-
Global)
Pamela Stewart (Chief Customer Offi-
cer)
Devyani i Rajya Laxm Rana (VP-Pub
Affairs, Comm & Sustainability-India
& Southwest Asia)
Felix Poh (VP-Strategy & Corp Dev-
Global)
Neeraj Tolmare (CIO-Global & VP)
Pamela Stewart (Chief Customer
Officer-Retail North America)
Robert J. Jordan Jr. (Gen Counsel-
Tax & VP)

Subsidiaries:

C.H.I. Limited (1)
14 Chivita Avenue Ajao Estate, PO Box
2978, Ikeja, Lagos, Nigeria
Tel.: (234) 128067709
Web Site: https://www.chilimited.com
Beverage & Snacks Mfr
N.A.I.C.S.: 311421

Caribbean Refrescos Inc. (1)
172 Industrial Ave Km 13 Hm 4, Cidra, PR
00739 **(100%)**
Tel.: (787) 739-8452
Web Site: http://www.cocacola.com
Sales Range: $150-199.9 Million
Emp.: 406
Beverage Bases & Concentrates Mfr
N.A.I.C.S.: 311930

Coca Cola de Chile, S.A. (1)
Av Kennedy 5757 Piso 12 Torre Oriente,
Las Condes, Santiago, Chile **(100%)**
Tel.: (56) 800219999
Web Site: https://www.cocacoladechile.cl
Importation of Soft-Drink Syrup Bases; Bot-
tling, Marketing & Distribution of Soft Drinks
in Chile
N.A.I.C.S.: 424490

**Coca-Cola (China) Beverages
Ltd.** (1)
Unit 1702 Full Link Plaza, 18 Chaoyang-
menwai Dajie, Beijing, China
Tel.: (86) 1065881698
Web Site: http://www.coca-cola.com.cn
Sales Range: $250-299.9 Million
Emp.: 72
Soft Drink Mfr & Distr
N.A.I.C.S.: 312111

Coca-Cola (Japan) Co., Ltd. (1)
4-6-3 Shibuya, Shibuya-ku, Tokyo, 150-
0002, Japan
Tel.: (81) 354668000
Web Site: http://www.cocacola.co.jp
Emp.: 538
Soft Drinks Mfr
N.A.I.C.S.: 312111

Jorge Garduno (Pres & CEO)

**Coca-Cola Africa (Proprietary)
Limited** (1)
116 Oxford Drive Houghton Estate, Johan-
nesburg, 2196, South Africa
Tel.: (27) 860112526
Web Site: https://www.coca-cola.com
Soft Drinks Mfr
N.A.I.C.S.: 312111
Patricia Obozuwa (VP-Communications-
Africa)

Subsidiary (Domestic):

Appletiser SA (Pty) Ltd. (2)
9 Junction Avenue Parktown, Parktown,
2193, South Africa
Tel.: (27) 11 644 0666
Web Site: http://www.appletiser.co.za
Branded Fruit, Natural Drinks, Spring Water
& Fruit Concentrate Mfr & Distr
N.A.I.C.S.: 311411

**Coca-Cola Beverages (Shanghai)
Company Limited** (1)
No 1188 Ziyue Road, Zizhu Science Park
Minhang District, Shanghai, 200241, China
Tel.: (86) 2131301000
Web Site: https://www.coca-cola.com.cn
Soft Drinks Mfr
N.A.I.C.S.: 312111

**Coca-Cola Bottling Co. UNITED
Inc** (1)
174 Refreshment Ln SW, Cleveland, TN
37311 **(100%)**
Tel.: (424) 476-1131
Web Site: http://cocacolaunited.com
Refreshing Beverages Mfr & Dist
N.A.I.C.S.: 312111

Coca-Cola Financial Corporation (1)
1 Coca Cola Plz NW, Atlanta, GA
30313-2420 **(100%)**
Tel.: (404) 676-2121
Web Site: http://www.cocacola.com
Sales Range: $125-149.9 Million
Loans & Other Forms of Financing to Coca-
Cola Bottlers & Customers for Purchase of
Sales-Related Equipment & Other Business
Purposes
N.A.I.C.S.: 522220

Coca-Cola Fountain Inc. (1)
Three Park Plz Ste 600, Irvine, CA
92614-2575 **(100%)**
Tel.: (949) 250-5961
Web Site: http://www.cocacola.com
Sales Range: $50-74.9 Million
Emp.: 160
Beverage & Soft Drink Sales
N.A.I.C.S.: 532490

Coca-Cola GmbH (1)
Stralauer Allee 4, 10245, Berlin,
Germany **(100%)**
Tel.: (49) 30226069000
Web Site: https://www.coca-cola-
deutschland.de
Sales Range: $1-4.9 Billion
Emp.: 8,000
Importation of Soft-Drink Syrup Bases; Bot-
tling, Marketing & Distr of Soft Drinks
Throughout Eastern Europe
N.A.I.C.S.: 424490
Hendrik Steckhan (Mng Dir)

Coca-Cola Great Britain (1)
1A Wimpole Street, London, W1G 0EA,
United Kingdom
Tel.: (44) 2082373000
Web Site: https://www.coca-cola.co.uk
Sales Range: $350-399.9 Million
Emp.: 200
Soft Drink Syrup Bases Importer; Soft
Drinks Distr, Bottling & Marketing Through-
out the United Kingdom & Northwestern
Europe
N.A.I.C.S.: 424490

**Coca-Cola Holdings (United King-
dom) Limited** (1)
1A Wimpole Street, London, W1G 0EA,
United Kingdom
Tel.: (44) 208 237 3000
Web Site: https://www.coca-cola.co.uk
Softdrink Mfr & Distr
N.A.I.C.S.: 312111

The Coca-Cola Company—(Continued)

Coca-Cola Holdings Overseas Ltd. **(1)**
1 Coca Cola Plz NW, Atlanta, GA
30313-2420 **(100%)**
Tel.: (404) 676-2121
Web Site: http://www.cocacola.com
Sales Range: $1-4.9 Billion
Emp.: 10,400
Mfr of Flavoring Extracts & Syrups
N.A.I.C.S.: 311930

Coca-Cola India Limited **(1)**
Enkay Towers Udyog Vihar, Gurgaon, 122
016, Haryana, India
Tel.: (91) 18002082653
Web Site: https://www.coca-cola.com
Sales Range: $50-74.9 Million
Emp.: 100
Soft Drink Mfr & Distr
N.A.I.C.S.: 312111

Coca-Cola Interamerican Corp. **(1)**
1 Coca-Cola Plz, Atlanta, GA
30313-2420 **(100%)**
Tel.: (404) 676-2121
Web Site: http://www.cocacola.com
Sales Range: $250-299.9 Million
Flavored Syrup Mfr
N.A.I.C.S.: 312111

Coca-Cola Interamerican Corporation **(1)**
La Uruca Aptdo 2749-1000, San Jose,
Costa Rica **(100%)**
Tel.: (506) 22472000
Sales Range: $75-99.9 Million
Emp.: 120
Importation of Soft-Drink Syrup Bases; Bot-
tling, Marketing & Distribution of Soft Drinks
in the Caribbean
N.A.I.C.S.: 424490

Coca-Cola Italia SRL **(1)**
Viale T Edison 110/B, Sixth San Giovanni,
20099, Milan, Italy
Tel.: (39) 0800836000
Web Site: https://www.coca-colaitalia.it
Beverage Company
N.A.I.C.S.: 312111

Coca-Cola Latin America **(1)**
Ruben Dario 115 Col Chapultepec Forest,
11580, Mexico, Mexico **(100%)**
Tel.: (52) 8007044400
Web Site: https://www.coca-
colamexico.com.mx
Sales Range: $100-124.9 Million
Emp.: 200
Importation of Soft-Drink Syrup Bases; Bot-
tling, Marketing & Sales of Soft Drinks in
Northern Latin America
N.A.I.C.S.: 424490

Coca-Cola North America **(1)**
121 Baker St NW, Atlanta, GA
30313-2499 **(100%)**
Tel.: (404) 676-5151
Web Site: https://us.coca-cola.com
Orange Juice & Other Juices; Processing of
Citrus Products; Dairy Products; Flavoring
Extracts & Syrups Mfr
N.A.I.C.S.: 311411

Subsidiary (Non-US):

Coca-Cola Ltd. **(2)**
335 King Street East, Toronto, M5A 1L1,
ON, Canada **(100%)**
Tel.: (416) 756-8100
Web Site: https://www.coca-cola.ca
Bottled & Canned Soft Drinks
N.A.I.C.S.: 312111

Subsidiary (Domestic):

Coca-Cola Refreshments Canada Company **(3)**
335 King Street East, Toronto, M5A 1L1,
ON, Canada
Tel.: (647) 256-7200
Web Site: http://www.coca-cola.ca
Emp.: 300
Soft Drinks Mfr
N.A.I.C.S.: 312111

Minute Maid Company Canada Inc. **(3)**
781 Lansdowne St W, Peterborough, K9J

1Z2, ON, Canada **(100%)**
Tel.: (705) 742-8011
Web Site: http://www.minutemaid.ca
Sales Range: $50-74.9 Million
Emp.: 150
Juice Products Mfr & Distr
N.A.I.C.S.: 311411
John Hackett (Pres)

Unit (Domestic):

Coca-Cola North America **(2)**
427 San Christopher Dr, Dunedin, FL
34698 **(100%)**
Tel.: (727) 733-2121
Web Site: http://www.coca-cola.com
Sales Range: $100-124.9 Million
Emp.: 200
Mfr Of Frozen Fruit Juice Concentrates
N.A.I.C.S.: 311411
Allison Lewis (Sr VP-Marketing)

Subsidiary (Domestic):

Coca-Cola North America **(2)**
7551 Schantz Rd, Allentown, PA
18106-9009 **(100%)**
Tel.: (610) 530-3900
Web Site: https://us.coca-cola.com
Sales Range: $100-124.9 Million
Emp.: 120
Syrup Concentrate Mfr
N.A.I.C.S.: 311930

Coca-Cola USA Ontario Syrup **(2)**
1650 S Vintage Ave, Ontario, CA
91761 **(100%)**
Tel.: (909) 975-5200
Web Site: http://www.cocacola.com
Sales Range: $50-74.9 Million
Soft Drink Syrup Mfr
N.A.I.C.S.: 311930

Energy Brands, Inc. **(2)**
17-20 Whitestone Expwy, Whitestone, NY,
11357-3000
Tel.: (718) 746-0087
Web Site: https://www.glaceau.com
Sales Range: $350-399.9 Million
Bottled Water Mfr & Distr
N.A.I.C.S.: 312112

Coca-Cola Refreshments USA, Inc. **(1)**
1 Coca-Cola Plz, Atlanta, GA 30313
Tel.: (404) 676-2121
Sales Range: $15-24.9 Billion
Emp.: 70,000
Holding Company; Soft Drink Bottler & Distr
N.A.I.C.S.: 551112
William W. Douglas III (Exec VP)

Subsidiary (Domestic):

Austin Coca-Cola Bottling Company **(2)**
9600 Burnet Rd, Austin, TX 78758
Tel.: (512) 836-7272
Sales Range: $750-799.9 Million
Emp.: 2,000
Bottled & Canned Soft Drink Mfr
N.A.I.C.S.: 312111

Bluegrass Coca Cola Bottling Company **(2)**
10653 N Hwy 27, Eubank, KY
42567-7705 **(100%)**
Tel.: (606) 379-5000
Emp.: 400
Soft Drinks
N.A.I.C.S.: 424490

Central States Coca-Cola Bottling Company **(2)**
3800 Mueller Rd, Saint Charles, MO 63301
Tel.: (636) 443-6154
Sales Range: $250-299.9 Million
Soft Drink Bottler
N.A.I.C.S.: 312112

Coca Cola Bottling of Memphis **(2)**
499 South Hollywood St, Memphis, TN
38111-1521
Tel.: (901) 454-8700
Sales Range: $150-199.9 Million
Emp.: 400
Bottling & Water Mfr
N.A.I.C.S.: 312112

Coca-Cola Bottling Co **(2)**
5601 Citrus Blvd, New Orleans, LA 70123
Tel.: (504) 818-7000
Web Site: http://cocacolaunited.com
Sales Range: $300-349.9 Million
Emp.: 800
Mfr of Bottled & Canned Soft Drinks
N.A.I.C.S.: 312111

Coca-Cola Bottling Co. **(2)**
1 Coca Cola Pl, San Antonio, TX 78219-
3712
Tel.: (210) 225-2601
Sales Range: $550-599.9 Million
Emp.: 1,200
Soft Drink Bottler
N.A.I.C.S.: 312111

Coca-Cola Bottling Co. **(2)**
1300 Martin Luther King Jr Dr, Monroe, LA
71202-3738
Tel.: (318) 388-4900
Web Site: https://cocacolaunited.com
Sales Range: $100-124.9 Million
Emp.: 185
Soft Drink Bottler
N.A.I.C.S.: 312111
Henry W. Flint (Pres & COO)

Coca-Cola Bottling Co. of New England **(2)**
9 B St, Needham Heights, MA
02494-2701 **(100%)**
Tel.: (781) 449-4300
Web Site: http://www.ccnne.com
Sales Range: $350-399.9 Million
Emp.: 3,500
Soft Drink Bottler
N.A.I.C.S.: 312111

Coca-Cola Bottling Co. of Shreveport **(2)**
5405 Campus Dr, Shreveport, LA
71129-2676 **(100%)**
Tel.: (318) 603-8440
Web Site: https://cocacolaunited.com
Sales Range: $250-299.9 Million
Soft Drink Bottler
N.A.I.C.S.: 312111

Coca-Cola Bottling Co. of Texarkana **(2)**
1930 New Boston Rd And Reading Ave,
Texarkana, TX 75501-3506 **(100%)**
Tel.: (903) 794-5135
Sales Range: $25-49.9 Million
Emp.: 75
Selling Beverages
N.A.I.C.S.: 312111

Unit (Non-US):

Coca-Cola Bottling Company **(2)**
42 Overlea Blvd, Toronto, M4H 1B6, ON,
Canada **(100%)**
Tel.: (416) 424-6000
Web Site: http://www.cocacola.com
Sales Range: $200-249.9 Million
Emp.: 450
Bottled & Canned Soft Drinks
N.A.I.C.S.: 312111

Coca-Cola Bottling Company **(2)**
2450 United Blvd, Coquitlam, V3K 6H1, BC,
Canada **(100%)**
Tel.: (604) 524-1118
Web Site: http://www.coca-cola.ca
Sales Range: $50-74.9 Million
Emp.: 100
Bottling Division For Coco Cola
N.A.I.C.S.: 312111

Coca-Cola Bottling Company **(2)**
940 Rue Andre Line, Granby, J2J 1E2, QC,
Canada **(100%)**
Tel.: (450) 375-2429
Web Site: http://www.cocacola.com
Sales Range: $50-74.9 Million
Emp.: 50
Bottled & Canned Soft Drinks
N.A.I.C.S.: 312111

Subsidiary (Domestic):

Coca-Cola Bottling Company of India- napolis, Inc. **(2)**
5000 W 25th St, Indianapolis, IN 46224
Tel.: (317) 243-7701
Sales Range: $25-49.9 Million
Emp.: 5
Bottled & Canned Soft Drinks

N.A.I.C.S.: 312111
Kady Slavin (VP)

Coca-Cola Bottling of Los Angeles **(2)**
1334 S Central Ave, Los Angeles, CA
90021-2210
Tel.: (213) 746-5555
Web Site: http://www.cokecce.com
Rev.: $100,000,000
Emp.: 300
Mfr of Bottled & Canned Soft Drinks
N.A.I.C.S.: 312111

Coca-Cola Bottling of North Texas **(2)**
3400 Fossil Creek Blvd, Fort Worth, TX
76137 **(100%)**
Tel.: (817) 847-3000
Sales Range: $125-149.9 Million
Emp.: 800
Beverage Bottling
N.A.I.C.S.: 312111

Coca-Cola Refreshments USA, Inc. - Bellevue **(2)**
1150 124th Ave NE, Bellevue, WA 98005-
2102
Tel.: (425) 455-2000
Sales Range: $150-199.9 Million
Emp.: 350
Mfr of Bottled & Canned Soft Drinks
N.A.I.C.S.: 312111
Richard Maloney (Mgr-Market Dev)

Coca-Cola Refreshments USA, Inc. - Kansas **(2)**
10001 Industrial Blvd, Lenexa, KS 66215-
1209
Tel.: (913) 492-8100
Web Site: http://www.ccr.com
Sales Range: $100-124.9 Million
Emp.: 104
Mfr of Soft Drinks
N.A.I.C.S.: 512110

Coca-Cola Refreshments USA, Inc. - Niles **(2)**
7400 N Oak Park Ave, Niles, IL 60714-3818
Tel.: (847) 647-0200
Sales Range: $750-799.9 Million
Emp.: 600
Soft Drink Bottling
N.A.I.C.S.: 312111
Sandy Day (Office Mgr)

Coca-Cola of Tucson Inc. **(2)**
5551 W Coca Cola Pl, Tucson, AZ
85743-8920 **(100%)**
Tel.: (520) 744-1333
Web Site: https://www.swirecc.com
Sales Range: $100-124.9 Million
Emp.: 200
Mfr of Bottled & Canned Soft Drinks
N.A.I.C.S.: 312111

Coca-Cola-Atlanta **(2)**
121 Baker St NW, Atlanta, GA 30313
Tel.: (404) 676-5151
Web Site: https://us.coca-cola.com
Sales Range: $1-4.9 Billion
Emp.: 15,000
Marketer, Producer & Distributor of Coca-
Cola Products
N.A.I.C.S.: 312111
Polly Howes (Media Rels Coord)

Delaware Coca-Cola Bottling Com- pany, Inc. **(2)**
10330 Old Columbia Rd, Columbia, MD
21046-1526 **(100%)**
Tel.: (410) 381-7800
Sales Range: $75-99.9 Million
Emp.: 160
Bottling & Water Mfr
N.A.I.C.S.: 312112

Erie Coca-Cola Bottling Company **(2)**
2209 W 50th St, Erie, PA 16506-4927
Tel.: (814) 833-0101
Web Site: http://www.cocacola.com
Sales Range: $50-74.9 Million
Emp.: 100
Bottling & Water Mfr
N.A.I.C.S.: 312112

Florida Coca-Cola Bottling Company **(2)**

3350 Pembroke Rd, Hollywood, FL 33021-
8320
Tel.: (954) 985-5000
Sales Range: $50-74.9 Million
Emp.: 150
Bottling & Water Mfr
N.A.I.C.S.: 312112

Glenbrook Coca-Cola (2)
5800 Surrey Square St, Houston, TX
77017-5908
Tel.: (713) 943-3318
Web Site: http://www.thecoca-
colacompany.com
Sales Range: $250-299.9 Million
Sales & Distribution of Coca-Cola Products
N.A.I.C.S.: 312111

**Johnston Coca-Cola Bottling Group,
Inc.** (2)
Hwy 64 Bypass, Cleveland, TN 37311
Tel.: (423) 476-1131
Sales Range: $125-149.9 Million
Emp.: 300
Bottling & Water Mfr
N.A.I.C.S.: 312112
Tony Leath (Mgr-Ops)

Mid-Atlantic Coca-Cola Co. (2)
5401 Seminary Rd, Alexandria, VA 22311-
1213
Tel.: (703) 933-1390
Web Site: http://www.coca-cola.com
Sales Range: $50-74.9 Million
Emp.: 200
Soft Drink Bottling
N.A.I.C.S.: 312111
John Franklin Brock (Chm & CEO)

**Montgomery Coca Cola Bottling
Co.** (2)
300 Coca Cola Rd, Montgomery, AL 36105
Tel.: (334) 323-2100
Web Site: https://cocacolaunited.com
Sales Range: $125-149.9 Million
Emp.: 310
Soft Drink Bottling
N.A.I.C.S.: 312111

Natchez Coca-Cola Bottling Co. (2)
191 Devereaux Dr, Natchez, MS 39120-
3754
Tel.: (601) 442-1641
Web Site: http://www.coca-cola.com
Sales Range: $50-74.9 Million
Emp.: 40
Soft Drink Distr
N.A.I.C.S.: 424490

**Philadelphia Coca-Cola Bottling
Co.** (2)
725 E Erie Ave, Philadelphia, PA 19134
Tel.: (215) 427-4500
Sales Range: $400-449.9 Million
Emp.: 1,200
Soft Drinks Mfr & Distr
N.A.I.C.S.: 312111
Francis McGorry (Pres & CEO)

**Phoenix Coca-Cola Bottling
Company** (2)
1850 W Elliot Rd, Tempe, AZ 85284
Tel.: (480) 345-3000
Web Site: http://www.coca-cola.com
Marketer, Bottler & Distrbutor of Beverages
N.A.I.C.S.: 523999

**The Akron Coca-Cola Bottling
Company** (2)
1560 Triplett Blvd, Akron, OH 44306
Tel.: (330) 784-2653
Sales Range: $150-199.9 Million
Emp.: 300
Bottled & Canned Soft Drinks
N.A.I.C.S.: 312111
Matt Cartaglia (Gen Mgr)

**The Coca-Cola Bottling Co. of Mem-
phis, Tennessee** (2)
499 S Hollywood St, Memphis, TN 38111-
1521
Tel.: (901) 454-8700
Sales Range: $250-299.9 Million
Bottler
N.A.I.C.S.: 312112

**The Coca-Cola Bottling Co. of New
York, Inc.** (2)
3 Skyline Dr, Hawthorne, NY 10532-2174
Tel.: (914) 345-3900

Sales Range: $75-99.9 Million
Emp.: 200
Soft Drinks Distr & Bottler
N.A.I.C.S.: 312111

**The Laredo Coca-Cola Bottling Com-
pany, Inc.** (2)
1402 Industrial Blvd, Laredo, TX 78041-
2508
Tel.: (956) 726-2672
Sales Range: $50-74.9 Million
Emp.: 100
Bottling & Water Mfr
N.A.I.C.S.: 312111
Anissa Gonzales (Office Mgr)

**Valley Coca-Cola Bottling Company,
Inc.** (2)
2400 Expwy 83 W, McAllen, TX 78501
Tel.: (956) 632-3700
Sales Range: $50-74.9 Million
Emp.: 100
Bottling & Water Mfr
N.A.I.C.S.: 312112

Western Container Corporation (2)
2277 Plaza Dr Ste 270, Sugar Land, TX
77479
Tel.: (346) 309-3238
Web Site:
    https://www.westerncontainercoke.com
Sales Range: $50-74.9 Million
Emp.: 300
Plastics Bottle Mfr
N.A.I.C.S.: 326160

**Coca-Cola Reinsurance Services
Limited** (1)
Industrial Est Donore Rd, Louth, Drogheda,
Ireland
Tel.: (353) 419836471
Insurance Agency & Brokerage Services
N.A.I.C.S.: 524210

**Coca-Cola Servicios de Venezuela,
C.A.** (1)
Av Principal de Los Ruices Edif Siemens
Torre Norte Piso 2 Los Ruices, Caracas,
Venezuela
Tel.: (58) 2122038000
Soft Drink Distr
N.A.I.C.S.: 424490

**Coca-Cola South Asia Holdings,
Inc.** (1)
1 Coca-Cola Plz, Atlanta, GA 30313
Tel.: (404) 676-3731
Investment Services
N.A.I.C.S.: 523999

**Coca-Cola South Pacific Pty
Limited** (1)
Level 9 40 Mount Street, North Sydney,
2060, NSW, Australia
Tel.: (61) 294368818
Web Site: https://www.coca-cola.com.au
Soft Drinks Mfr
N.A.I.C.S.: 312111
Claudia Lorenzo (Pres-Asia & South Pa-
cific)

**Coca-Cola Southern Africa (Pty)
Ltd.** (1)
9 Junction Ave, Johannesburg, Parktown,
2193, South Africa
Tel.: (27) 116440666
Web Site: http://www.coca-cola.co.za
Sales Range: $125-149.9 Million
Emp.: 260
Importation of Soft-Drink Syrup Bases; Bot-
tling, Marketing & Distribution of Soft Drinks
in Africa
N.A.I.C.S.: 424490

Coca-Cola Trading Company (1)
1 Coca Cola Plz NW, Atlanta, GA 30313-
2420
Tel.: (404) 676-2121
Web Site: http://www.cococolacompany.com
Sales Range: $75-99.9 Million
Emp.: 250
Tourist Attraction Services
N.A.I.C.S.: 712190
Albert Cahen (Pres)

Coca-Cola de Espana (1)
C/Ribera del Loira 20-22, 28042, Madrid,
Spain (100%)
Tel.: (34) 900199202
Web Site: https://www.cocacola.es

Sales Range: $100-124.9 Million
Emp.: 200
Importation of Soft-Drink Syrup Bases; Bot-
tling, Distribution & Marketing of Soft Drinks
in Spain
N.A.I.C.S.: 312111

Costa Ltd. (1)
Whitbread Court Houghton Hall Business
Park, Dunstable, LU5 5XE, Beds, United
Kingdom
Tel.: (44) 582424200
Web Site: http://www.costa.co.uk
Coffee Processor, Whslr & Retailer
N.A.I.C.S.: 311920
Jill McDonald (CEO)

Subsidiary (Non-US):

CHI Polska S.A. (2)
Atrium Centrum al Jana Pawla II 27, 00-
867, Warsaw, Poland
Tel.: (48) 223327900
Web Site: http://www.coffeeheaven.pl
Sales Range: $10-24.9 Million
Emp.: 70
Coffeeshop Operator
N.A.I.C.S.: 722513

Honest Tea (1)
4827 Bethesda Ave, Bethesda, MD 20814
Tel.: (301) 652-3556
Web Site: http://www.honesttea.com
Sales Range: $25-49.9 Million
Emp.: 35
Beverages Mfr
N.A.I.C.S.: 312111
Seth Goldman (Co-Founder)

Innocent Ltd. (1)
Fruit Towers 342 Ladbroke Grove, London,
W10 5BU, United Kingdom
Tel.: (44) 2079933311
Web Site: https://www.innocentdrinks.co.uk
Sales Range: $25-49.9 Million
Emp.: 200
Specialty Drinks Mfr & Distr
N.A.I.C.S.: 312111

**Refreshment Product Services,
Inc.** (1)
1 Coca Cola Plz NW, Atlanta, GA 30313-
2420
Tel.: (404) 676-2121
Grocery Product Distr
N.A.I.C.S.: 424490

Soft Drink Services Company (1)
1 Coca-Cola Plz NW, Atlanta, GA 30313-
2420
Tel.: (404) 676-2121
Web Site: http://www.cocacola.com
Sales Range: $50-74.9 Million
Emp.: 90
Flavoring Extracts & Syrups Mfr
N.A.I.C.S.: 311930

The Coca-Cola Company (1)
680 N Gonzales Blvd, Huachuca City, AZ
85616-9659 (100%)
Tel.: (520) 456-1805
Web Site: http://www.cocacola.com
Sales Range: $25-49.9 Million
Emp.: 21
Mfr of Bottled & Canned Carbonated Soft
Drinks
N.A.I.C.S.: 312111

The Coca-Cola Company (1)
6445 Lemmon Ave, Dallas, TX 75209
Tel.: (214) 654-4100
Web Site: http://www.cocacola.com
Sales Range: $75-99.9 Million
Emp.: 130
Soft Drink Syrup Mfr
N.A.I.C.S.: 312111

The Coca-Cola Company (1)
9300 Ctr Pt Dr, Houston, TX
77054-3704 (100%)
Tel.: (713) 799-7295
Web Site: http://www.cocacola.com
Sales Range: $150-199.9 Million
Emp.: 500
Mfr of Bottled & Canned Carbonated Soft
Drinks
N.A.I.C.S.: 312111

The Coca-Cola Company (1)
2455 Watkins Rd, Columbus, OH
43207 (100%)

Tel.: (614) 491-9740
Web Site: http://www.cocacola.com
Sales Range: $50-74.9 Million
Emp.: 130
Beverage Syrup Mfr
N.A.I.C.S.: 311930
Terrance McGann (Opers Mgr)

The Coca-Cola Company (1)
880 Rado Dr, Naugatuck, CT
06770-2211 (100%)
Tel.: (203) 723-6555
Web Site: http://www.cocacola.com
Sales Range: $150-199.9 Million
Emp.: 300
Bottling Company
N.A.I.C.S.: 311930

**The Coca-Cola Company - Aviation
Department** (1)
4000 Fulton Industrial Blvd SW, Atlanta, GA
30336
Tel.: (404) 676-8255
Web Site: http://www.cocacola.com
Sales Range: $25-49.9 Million
Emp.: 40
Corporate Aviation Department
N.A.I.C.S.: 311999

**The Coca-Cola Export
Corporation** (1)
One Coca Cola Plz NW, Atlanta, GA 30313-
2420
Tel.: (404) 676-2121
Web Site: https://www.coca-cola.com
Soft Drink Products Export Marketing
N.A.I.C.S.: 312111

Division (Non-US):

Coca-Cola Ltd. (2)
101 McGregor Ave, Stellarton, B0K 1S0,
NS, Canada (100%)
Tel.: (902) 752-8505
Web Site: https://www.cocacola.com
Sales Range: $10-24.9 Million
Emp.: 12
Coca Cola Bottling Services
N.A.I.C.S.: 312112

Coca-Cola Ltd. (2)
355 King Street East, Toronto, M5A 1L1,
ON, Canada (100%)
Tel.: (647) 256-7200
Web Site: http://www.cokecce.com
Emp.: 450
Bottling of Beverages
N.A.I.C.S.: 312111

Coca-Cola Ltd. (2)
Lakeside Park Dr 20, PO Box 8150, Halifax,
B0J 1Z3, NS, Canada (100%)
Tel.: (902) 876-8661
Sales Range: $50-74.9 Million
Emp.: 100
Bottled & Canned Soft Drinks
N.A.I.C.S.: 312111

Division (Domestic):

Inmex Corporation (2)
1 Coca Cola Plz NW PO Box 1734, Atlanta,
GA 30303-2420
Tel.: (404) 676-2121
Web Site: http://www.thecoca-cola.com
Sales Range: $250-299.9 Million
Mfr of Flavoring Extracts & Syrups
N.A.I.C.S.: 312112
Douglas Daft (CEO)

The Minute Maid Company (1)
38279 W Red Arrow Hwy, Paw Paw, MI
49079-9384 (100%)
Tel.: (616) 657-3171
Web Site: http://www.minutemaid.com
Sales Range: $200-249.9 Million
Emp.: 500
Fruit Juices
N.A.I.C.S.: 311421

Voltic (GH) Limited (1)
Medie Kotoku Road, Accra, 00233, Ghana
Tel.: (233) 302774248
Web Site: https://www.volticghana.com
Mineral & Bottled Water Mfr
N.A.I.C.S.: 312112

**THE COOPER COMPANIES,
INC.**

The Cooper Companies, Inc.—(Continued)

6101 Bollinger Canyon Rd Ste 500,
San Ramon, CA 94583
Tel.: (925) 460-3600   DE
Web Site:
  https://www.coopercos.com
Year Founded: 1980
COO—(NYSE)
Rev.: $3,593,200,000
Assets: $11,658,900,000
Liabilities: $4,107,900,000
Net Worth: $7,551,000,000
Earnings: $294,200,000
Emp.: 15,000
Fiscal Year-end: 10/31/23
Medical Device Mfr
N.A.I.C.S.: 551112
Albert G. White III *(Pres & CEO)*
Daniel G. McBride *(COO & Exec VP)*
Kim Duncan *(VP-IR & Risk Mgmt)*
Brian G. Andrews *(CFO, Treas & Exec VP)*
William A. Kozy *(Vice Chm)*
Agostino Ricupati *(Chief Acctg Officer & Sr VP-Fin & Tax)*
Mark J. Drury *(Gen Counsel, Sec & VP)*
Nicholas S. Khadder *(Corp Counsel)*

Subsidiaries:

Cell Care Australia Pty. Ltd.   (1)
PO Box 833, Moorabbin, 03189, VIC, Australia
Tel.: (61) 1800071075
Web Site: https://cellcare.com.au
Stem Cell Storing & Collecting Services
N.A.I.C.S.: 621991

CooperSurgical, Inc.   (1)
75 Corporate Dr, Trumbull, CT
06611-1350   (100%)
Tel.: (203) 601-5200
Sales Range: $150-199.9 Million
Emp.: 350
Mfr of Opthalmological & Gynecological Products
N.A.I.C.S.: 325412
Holly R. Sheffield *(Pres)*
Kerry Blair *(COO)*
John Calcagno *(Exec VP-Fin)*
Val Choumitsky *(Sr VP-Customer Experience)*
David T. Hansen *(Pres-Global Fertility & Genomics)*
Russell S. Heinrich *(Exec VP-R&D)*
Dhiresh Jethwa *(VP-IT)*
Kurt R. Karcher *(Exec VP & Architect)*
Claudia Navarro *(Sr VP-Regulatory Affairs & Quality Assurance)*
Graceann A. Pisano *(Corp Counsel)*
Kerry Tehan *(VP-HR)*
Matthew J. Topliff *(Exec VP-Bus Dev & Strategy)*
Mark P. Valentine *(Pres-Global Medical Devices)*
Marc Gelnett *(Exec VP)*
Charles Smith *(Sr VP)*

Subsidiary (Domestic):

AEGEA Medical Inc.   (2)
4055 A Campbell Ave, Menlo Park, CA 94025
Tel.: (650) 701-1125
Web Site: http://www.aegeamedical.com
Surgical & Medical Instrument Mfr
N.A.I.C.S.: 339112
Maria Sainz *(Pres)*
Paul Goeld *(Chm)*

CooperGenomics Inc.   (2)
3 Regent St Ste 301, Livingston, NJ 07039
Web Site: https://www.coopergenomics.com
Testing Laboratory Services
N.A.I.C.S.: 541380

LifeGlobal Group LLC   (2)
393 Soundview Rd, Guilford, CT 06437
Web Site: http://www.lifeglobalgroup.com
Surgical & Medical Instrument Mfr
N.A.I.C.S.: 339112
Monica Mezezi *(Pres)*

Milex Puerto Rico   (2)

Colley Toste 329 Baldrich, Hato Rey, PR 00918
Tel.: (787) 767-7358
Sales Range: $50-74.9 Million
Emp.: 3
Obstetrical & Gynecological Products
N.A.I.C.S.: 424210

Reprogenetics, LLC   (2)
3 Regent St Ste 301, Livingston, NJ 07039
Tel.: (973) 436-5000
Web Site: http://www.reprogenetics.com
Preimplantation Genetic Diagnostic Laboratory Operator
N.A.I.C.S.: 541380

CooperVision Iberia SL   (1)
Ronda De Poniente, 12-Plt 1 Ala Iz Oficina C Tres Cantos, Madrid, 28760, Spain
Tel.: (34) 918070000
Drugs & Druggist Sundries Merchant Whslr
N.A.I.C.S.: 424210
Alberto Martin Ares *(Mgr-Key Acct)*

CooperVision Iberia SL   (1)
Avenida de Labradores 1 3rd floor, 28760, Tres Cantos, Spain
Pharmaceutical Products Distr
N.A.I.C.S.: 424210

CooperVision Nordic AB   (1)
Johan Willins gata 8, 416 64, Gothenburg, Sweden
Tel.: (46) 317067670
Web Site: http://www.coopervision.se
Ophthalmic Goods Mfr
N.A.I.C.S.: 339115
Jonas Eisenhardt *(Mng Dir & Country Mgr)*

CooperVision RUS LLC   (1)
7071/1 Room Building 2 Presnenskaya Nab 6 Tower Empire, Moscow, Russia
Tel.: (7) 4959958015
Lens Mfr
N.A.I.C.S.: 333310

CooperVision do Brasil Ltda   (1)
Avenida Antartica 62-an 5, Sao Paulo, Brazil
Tel.: (55) 1136110715
Web Site: http://www.coopervision.com.br
General Warehousing & Storage Services
N.A.I.C.S.: 493110

CooperVision, Inc.   (1)
209 High Point Dr Ste 100, Victor, NY 14564
Tel.: (585) 385-6810
Web Site: https://www.coopervision.com
Contact Lenses Mfr & Sales
N.A.I.C.S.: 333310
Jerry Warner *(Pres)*
Simon Seshadri *(VP-Mktg)*
Mary Rothormol *(VP-Sls-East)*
James Gardner *(VP-Sls-West)*
Mary Petromallo *(Dir-Customer Svc)*

Subsidiary (Non-US):

CooperVision Canada Corp.   (2)
Tel.: (905) 475-8555
Web Site: http://www.coopervision.ca
Optical Instrument & Lens Mfr
N.A.I.C.S.: 333310

CooperVision GmbH   (2)
West Park 45 Siemensstrasse 3, 64859, Eppertshausen, Germany
Tel.: (49) 60713050
Optical Instrument & Lens Mfr
N.A.I.C.S.: 333310
Johannes Zupfer *(Head-Sls-DACH)*
Petra Zapsky *(Head-Professional Svc-DACH)*
Andreas Sudrow *(Mgr-Customer Svc-DACH)*
Jerome Kuzio *(Head-Mktg-DACH)*
Toni Muller *(Head-Fin & Controlling)*
Alexandra Helmerich *(Mgr-HR-DA-CH & BeNeLux)*
Dan McBride *(Pres)*

CooperVision Limited   (2)
Delta Park Concorde Way, Segensworth North, Fareham, PO15 5RL, United Kingdom
Tel.: (44) 8709000055
Web Site: http://www.coopervision.co.uk
Contact Lens & Ophthalmic Surgery Product Mfr
N.A.I.C.S.: 333310

A. Thomas Bender *(CEO)*
Debbie Olive *(Country Mgr-Ireland)*

CooperVision Nederland BV   (2)
Avelingen-West 40, 4202 MS, Gorinchem, Netherlands
Tel.: (31) 183406080
Web Site: http://www.coopervision.nl
Soft Contact Lens Mfr
N.A.I.C.S.: 333310
Rienk Keuning *(Mgr-Benelux)*

Subsidiary (Domestic):

Procornea Nederland B.V.   (3)
Kollergang 9, 6961 LZ, Eerbeek, Netherlands
Tel.: (31) 313677677
Web Site: http://www.procornea.nl
Ophthalmic Goods Distr
N.A.I.C.S.: 423460
Alex Lamse *(Mng Dir)*

Subsidiary (Non-US):

CooperVision S.A.S.   (2)
Les 2 Arcs 1800 Route des Cretes, PO Box 273, 06905, Sophia-Antipolis, France
Soft Contact Lens Mfr
N.A.I.C.S.: 333310

Origio A/S   (2)
Knardrupvej 2, 2760, Malov, Denmark
Tel.: (45) 46790202
Web Site: http://www.origio.com
Sales Range: $50-74.9 Million
Emp.: 255
Fertility Drug Research, Services & Development
N.A.I.C.S.: 621512
Jeannett Hvidkjaer *(CFO)*

Subsidiary (Non-US):

Origio France Sarl   (3)
Parc Gvio Batiment 1 1 rue des Vergers, 69760, Limonest, France   (100%)
Tel.: (33) 472564800
Web Site: http://www.origio.com
Sales Range: $10-24.9 Million
Emp.: 6
Fertility Services & Solutions
N.A.I.C.S.: 621512

Origio Ltd.   (3)
7 Castlefield Road, Reigate, RH2 0SA, Surrey, United Kingdom   (100%)
Tel.: (44) 1737 243869
Web Site: http://www.origio.com
N.A.I.C.S.: 621512

Subsidiary (Domestic):

Paragon Vision Sciences, Inc.   (2)
2120 W Guadalupe Rd Ste 112, Gilbert, AZ 85233
Tel.: (480) 892-7602
Web Site: http://www.paragonvision.com
Ophthalmic Goods Mfr
N.A.I.C.S.: 339115
Lisa Nicolai *(Mgr-Customer Svc)*
Natalie Stevens *(CFO & VP-Fin & Ops)*
J. P. Wei *(VP-Science & Tech)*

Coopervision S.A. (Pty) Limited   (1)
137 Sivewright Ave, Johannesburg, 2094, South Africa
Tel.: (27) 115380600
Food Store Operator
N.A.I.C.S.: 445298
Liezel Kotze *(Mgr-South Africa)*

Coopervision S A (Pty) Limited   (1)
108 Tramway Rd Park Hill, Kwazulu-Natal, Durban, South Africa
Tel.: (27) 315636726
Optical Goods Retail Distr
N.A.I.C.S.: 456130

Generate Life Sciences, Inc.   (1)
11915 La Grange Ave, Los Angeles, CA 90025
Web Site: https://www.generate.com
Emp.: 500
Sperm & Egg Donation Services
N.A.I.C.S.: 621991

Origio, Inc.   (1)
2400 Hunters Way, Charlottesville, VA 22911
Tel.: (434) 979-4000

Health Care Srvices
N.A.I.C.S.: 621610
Margaret Sheehan *(Gen Mgr)*

Sauflon CL Ltd   (1)
49-53 York Street, Twickenham, TW1 3LP, United Kingdom
Tel.: (44) 2083224200
Web Site: http://www.saufloncl.co.uk
Health Care Srvices
N.A.I.C.S.: 621610

Subsidiary (Non-US):

CooperVision CL Kft   (2)
Ophthalmic Goods Mfr
N.A.I.C.S.: 339115

SynergEyes UK Ltd.   (1)
Swallow House Theaklen Drive, East Sussex, Saint Leonards, TN38 9AZ, United Kingdom
Tel.: (44) 8446698099
Web Site: https://www.synergeyes.co.uk
Hybrid Contact Lens Mfr & Distr
N.A.I.C.S.: 339115

THE CORETEC GROUP INC.
333 Jackson Plz, Ann Arbor, MI 48103
Tel.: (918) 494-0505   OK
Web Site:
  https://www.thecoretecgroup.com
Year Founded: 1995
CRTG—(OTCQB)
Rev.: $8,260
Assets: $3,621,536
Liabilities: $1,793,216
Net Worth: $1,828,320
Earnings: ($2,863,324)
Emp.: 7
Fiscal Year-end: 12/31/22
Volumetric, Three-Dimension Projection & Display Technology
N.A.I.C.S.: 541990
Victor F. Keen *(Co-Chm)*
Simon Calton *(Co-Chm)*
Lindsay McCarthy *(Dir-Ops)*
Matthew J. Kappers *(CEO)*

THE CRYPTO COMPANY
23823 Malibu Rd Ste 50477, Malibu, CA 90265
Tel.: (424) 228-9955   UT
Web Site:
  https://www.thecryptocompany.com
Year Founded: 2013
CRCW—(OTCIQ)
Rev.: $619,538
Assets: $1,556,561
Liabilities: $4,616,001
Net Worth: ($3,059,440)
Earnings: ($5,662,918)
Emp.: 8
Fiscal Year-end: 12/31/22
Women Fitness Clothing Whslr
N.A.I.C.S.: 458110
Ron Levy *(Founder, Chm, CEO, COO, CFO & Sec)*

THE DEWEY ELECTRONICS CORPORATION
27 Muller Rd, Oakland, NJ 07436
Tel.: (201) 337-4700   NY
Web Site:
  https://www.deweyelectronics.com
Year Founded: 1955
DEWY—(OTCIQ)
Sales Range: $1-9.9 Million
Emp.: 23
Small Arms, Ordnance & Ordnance Accessories Manufacturing
N.A.I.C.S.: 332994
John H. D. Dewey *(Chm, Pres, CEO & Sec)*
Edward L. Proskey *(Sr VP)*
Donna Marie Medica *(CFO, Chief Acctg Officer & Controller)*

Subsidiaries:

Hedco Div. (1)
27 Muller Rd, Oakland, NJ
07436-1313 **(100%)**
Tel.: (201) 337-4700
Web Site: http://www.deweyelectronics.com
Sales Range: $50-74.9 Million
Emp.: 30
Designs, Manufacturing & Marketing of
Snow-Making Machinery
N.A.I.C.S.: 332993
Edward Proskey (Sr VP)

INI Power Systems, Inc. (1)
137 Trans air Dr, Morrisville, NC 27560
Tel.: (919) 677-7112
Electrical Equipment & Component Mfr
N.A.I.C.S.: 335999

Pitometer Log Div. (1)
27 Muller Rd, Oakland, NJ 07436 **(100%)**
Tel.: (201) 337-4700
Web Site: http://www.deweyelectronics.com
Sales Range: $50-74.9 Million
Emp.: 24
Mfr of Ship Speed & Distance Measuring
Instrumentation
N.A.I.C.S.: 332993

THE DIXIE GROUP, INC.
PO Box 2007, Dalton, GA 30722
Tel.: (706) 876-5814 TN
Web Site:
  https://www.thedixiegroup.com
Year Founded: 1920
DXYN—(NASDAQ)
Rev.: $303,570,000
Assets: $202,946,000
Liabilities: $171,432,000
Net Worth: $31,514,000
Earnings: ($35,079,000)
Emp.: 1,000
Fiscal Year-end: 12/31/22
Floorcovering Products, Carpet
Yarns, High-End Residential & Con-
tract Commercial Carpet & Designer
Rugs Mfr & Sale
N.A.I.C.S.: 314110
D. Kennedy Frierson Jr. (COO)
Thomas M. Nuckols (Pres-Residential
& VP)
Thomas M. Nuckols Jr. (Pres-)

Subsidiaries:

Fabrica International, Inc. (1)
3201 S Susan St, Santa Ana, CA 92704
Tel.: (949) 261-7181
Web Site: http://www.fabrica.com
Carpet & Rug Mfr
N.A.I.C.S.: 314110

TDG Operations, LLC (1)
716 Bill Myles Dr, Saraland, AL 36571
Tel.: (706) 629-9234
Web Site: http://www.maslandcontract.com
Carpet & Rug Mill Operator
N.A.I.C.S.: 314110

Division (Domestic):

Masland Carpets (2)
716 Bill Myles Dr, Saraland, AL
36571-3302 **(100%)**
Tel.: (251) 675-9080
Web Site: http://www.maslandcarpets.com
Mfr & Marketer of Carpet Yarns &
Floorcovering Products for Specialty Mar-
kets
N.A.I.C.S.: 314110

THE DUCKHORN PORTFOLIO, INC.
1201 Dowdell Ln, Saint Helena, CA
94574
Tel.: (707) 302-2658 DE
Web Site:
  https://www.duckhornportfolio.com
Year Founded: 2016
NAPA—(NYSE)
Rev.: $402,996,000
Assets: $1,347,682,000
Liabilities: $405,274,000

Net Worth: $942,408,000
Earnings: $69,298,000
Emp.: 470
Fiscal Year-end: 07/31/23
Wine Mfr
N.A.I.C.S.: 312130
Deirdre A. Mahlan (Chm, Interim Pres
& Interim CEO)
Jennifer Fall Jung (CFO & Exec VP)
Sean Sullivan (Chief Strategy Officer,
Chief Legal Officer & Exec VP)
Sean Sullivan (Chief Admin Officer,
Gen Counsel & Exec VP)
Pete Przybylinski (Chief Sls Officer &
Exec VP)
Zachary Rasmuson (COO & Exec
VP)
Carol Reber (CMO, Chief DTC Offi-
cer & Exec VP)
Dan Duckhotn (Co-Founder)
Margaret Duckhorn (Co-Founder)

Subsidiaries:

Sonoma-Cutrer Vineyards, Inc. (1)
4401 Slusser Rd, Windsor, CA 95492-7601
Tel.: (707) 237-3489
Web Site: http://www.sonomacutrer.com
Sales Range: $1-9.9 Million
Emp.: 150
Wine Producer
N.A.I.C.S.: 111332

THE E.W. SCRIPPS COMPANY
312 Walnut St Ste 2800, Cincinnati,
OH 45202
Tel.: (513) 977-3000 OH
Web Site: https://www.scripps.com
Year Founded: 1878
SSP—(NASDAQ)
Rev.: $2,453,215,000
Assets: $6,431,005,000
Liabilities: $4,300,180,000
Net Worth: $2,130,825,000
Earnings: $145,597,000
Emp.: 5,700
Fiscal Year-end: 12/31/22
Diversified Media Company
N.A.I.C.S.: 513110
Lisa Ann Knutson (COO)
William Appleton (Gen Counsel &
Exec VP)
Mark L. Koors (VP-Audit & Compli-
ance)
Brian G. Lawlor (Pres-Scripps Sports)
Julie L. McGehee (Sec & VP-
Environmental & Social Governance)
Adam P. Symson (Pres & CEO)
Carolyn Pione Micheli (Sr VP-Corp
Comm & IR)
Kate O'Brian (Pres-Scripps News)
Jason Combs (CFO)
Keisha Taylor (CMO)
Laura Tomlin (Chief Admin Officer)
Brian Norris (Chief Revenue Officer)
Jonathan Katz (Head-Entertainment-
Networks)
Rebecca Riegelsberger (Treas & VP-
Tax)
Daniel W. Perschke (Principal Acctg
Officer, VP & Controller)

Subsidiaries:

ION Media Networks, Inc. (1)
14901 NE 20th Ave, Miami, FL 33181
Tel.: (561) 659-4122
Web Site: http://www.ionmedia.com
Sales Range: $200-249.9 Million
Emp.: 453
Holding Company; Network Television
Broadcasting Services
N.A.I.C.S.: 551112
Stephen P. Appel (Pres-Adv Sls)
R. Brandon Burgess (Chm & CEO)
Chris Addeo (Sr VP-Mktg & Promos)
Tim Clyne (CFO)
Cara Conte (Sr VP-MVPD Rels)
Michele Corrente (Sr VP-HR)
J. Matthew Hijuelos (VP-Bus Dev)
Martie Kretchmar (VP-Network Ops)
Damian Riordan (Sr VP-Brdcst Rels)

Subsidiary (Domestic):

ION Media Hits, Inc. (2)
601 Clearwater Park Rd, West Palm Beach,
FL 33401
Tel.: (561) 659-4122
Web Site: http://www.ionmedia.com
Broadcasting Services
N.A.I.C.S.: 516120

ION Media Songs, Inc. (2)
601 Clearwater Park, West Palm Beach, FL
33401
Tel.: (561) 659-4122
Web Site: http://www.iontelevision.com
Sales Range: $10-24.9 Million
Emp.: 75
Broadcasting Services
N.A.I.C.S.: 334220

ION Media of Albany, Inc. (2)
1 Charles Blvd, Guilderland, NY 12084
Tel.: (518) 464-0143
Web Site: http://www.ionmedia.com
Sales Range: $10-24.9 Million
Emp.: 2
Television Broadcasting Station
N.A.I.C.S.: 516120
Laura Dubossarsky (Bus Mgr)

ION Media of Atlanta, Inc. (2)
200 Cobb Pkwy N Ste 114, Marietta, GA
30062
Tel.: (770) 919-0575
Sales Range: $10-24.9 Million
Emp.: 5
Television Broadcasting Station
N.A.I.C.S.: 516120

ION Media of Battle Creek, Inc. (2)
2610 Horizon Dr SE 135 Ste E, Grand Rap-
ids, MI 49546
Tel.: (616) 222-6443
Web Site: http://www.ionmedia.com
Sales Range: $10-24.9 Million
Emp.: 2
Television Broadcasting Station
N.A.I.C.S.: 516120
Bradon Burgess (CEO)

ION Media of Birmingham, Inc. (2)
2085 Golden Crest Dr, Birmingham, AL
35209
Tel.: (205) 870-4404
Sales Range: $10-24.9 Million
Emp.: 5
Television Broadcasting Station
N.A.I.C.S.: 516120

ION Media of Boston, Inc. (2)
1120 Soldiers Field Rd, Boston, MA 02134
Tel.: (617) 787-6868
Web Site: http://www.iontelevision.com
Sales Range: $10-24.9 Million
Emp.: 5
Television Broadcasting Station
N.A.I.C.S.: 516120
Robert Gilbert (Gen Sls Mgr)

ION Media of Brunswick, Inc. (2)
7434 Blythe Is Hwy, Brunswick, GA 31523
Tel.: (912) 267-0021
Web Site: http://www.ionmedia.tv
Television Broadcasting Station
N.A.I.C.S.: 516120

ION Media of Buffalo, Inc. (2)
726 Exchange St Ste 819, Buffalo, NY
14210
Tel.: (716) 852-1818
Web Site: http://www.ionmedia.com
Sales Range: $10-24.9 Million
Emp.: 7
Television Broadcasting Station
N.A.I.C.S.: 516120

ION Media of Cedar Rapids, Inc. (2)
1957 Blairs Ferry Rd NE, Cedar Rapids, IA
52402
Tel.: (319) 378-1260
Web Site: http://www.ionmedia.com
Sales Range: $10-24.9 Million
Emp.: 5
Television Broadcasting Station
N.A.I.C.S.: 516120

ION Media of Chicago, Inc. (2)
333 S Desplaines St Ste 101, Chicago, IL
60661
Tel.: (312) 376-8520
Television Broadcasting Station

N.A.I.C.S.: 516120
Patty Golden (Gen Sls Mgr)

ION Media of Dallas, Inc. (2)
600 6 Flags Dr Ste 652, Arlington, TX
76011-6353
Tel.: (817) 633-6843
Web Site: http://www.ionmedia.com
Sales Range: $50-74.9 Million
Emp.: 5
Television Broadcasting Station
N.A.I.C.S.: 516120

ION Media of Denver, Inc. (2)
3001 S Jamaica Ct Ste 200, Aurora, CO
80014
Tel.: (303) 751-5959
Sales Range: $10-24.9 Million
Emp.: 22
Television Broadcasting Station
N.A.I.C.S.: 516120

ION Media of Des Moines, Inc. (2)
4570 114th St, Urbandale, IA 50322
Tel.: (515) 331-3939
Web Site: http://www.ionmedia.com
Sales Range: $10-24.9 Million
Emp.: 5
Television Broadcasting Station
N.A.I.C.S.: 516120
Dan Olson (Gen Sls Mgr)

ION Media of Detroit, Inc. (2)
3975 Varsity Dr, Ann Arbor, MI 48108-2225
Tel.: (734) 973-7900
Web Site: http://www.irmedia.com
Sales Range: $10-24.9 Million
Emp.: 5
Television Broadcasting Station
N.A.I.C.S.: 516120

ION Media of Fayetteville, Inc. (2)
19234 NC 71 Hwy N, Lumber Bridge, NC
28357
Tel.: (910) 843-3884
Web Site: http://www.ionmedia.com
Sales Range: $10-24.9 Million
Emp.: 2
Television Broadcasting Station
N.A.I.C.S.: 516120

ION Media of Greensboro, Inc. (2)
1114 N O'Henry Blvd, Greensboro, NC
27405
Tel.: (336) 272-9227
Web Site: http://www.ionmedia.tv
Sales Range: $10-24.9 Million
Emp.: 3
Television Broadcasting Station
N.A.I.C.S.: 516120
Glenn Haygood (Gen Sls Mgr)

ION Media of Greenville, Inc. (2)
1301 South Glenburnie Rd, New Bern, NC
28561
Tel.: (252) 636-2550
Sales Range: $10-24.9 Million
Emp.: 7
Television Broadcasting Station
N.A.I.C.S.: 516120

ION Media of Honolulu, Inc. (2)
875 Waimanu St Ste 630, Honolulu, HI
96813
Tel.: (808) 591-1275
Web Site: http://www.iontelevision.com
Sales Range: $10-24.9 Million
Emp.: 2
Television Broadcasting Station
N.A.I.C.S.: 516120
Brandon Burgess (Pres)

ION Media of Indianapolis, Inc. (2)
2441 Production Dr Ste 104, Indianapolis,
IN 46241
Tel.: (317) 486-0633
Web Site: http://www.ionmedia.com
Sales Range: $10-24.9 Million
Emp.: 2
Television Broadcasting Station
N.A.I.C.S.: 516120

ION Media of Kansas City, Inc. (2)
4720 Oak St, Kansas City, MO 64112
Tel.: (816) 924-5050
Television Broadcasting Station
N.A.I.C.S.: 516120

The E.W. Scripps Company—(Continued)

Alan Fuchsman (Gen Sls Mgr)

ION Media of Knoxville, Inc. (2)
9000 Executive Park Dr Bldg D Ste 210,
Knoxville, TN 37923
Tel.: (865) 531-4037
Web Site: http://www.ion.com
Sales Range: $10-24.9 Million
Emp.: 6
Television Broadcasting Station
N.A.I.C.S.: 516120

ION Media of Lexington, Inc. (2)
2166 McCausey Ridge Rd, Frenchburg, KY
40322
Tel.: (606) 768-9282
Web Site: http://www.ionmedia.com
Sales Range: $10-24.9 Million
Emp.: 4
Television Broadcasting Station
N.A.I.C.S.: 516120
Carol Wright-Holzhauer (Gen Sls Mgr)

ION Media of Los Angeles, Inc. (2)
2600 Olive Ave Ste 900, Burbank, CA
91505
Tel.: (818) 563-1005
Web Site: http://www.ionmedia.com
Sales Range: $10-24.9 Million
Emp.: 9
Television Broadcasting Station
N.A.I.C.S.: 516120

ION Media of Memphis, Inc. (2)
Brihtehrehr, Bartlett, TN 38133
Tel.: (901) 384-9324
Web Site: http://www.rubydavis.com
Television Broadcasting Station
N.A.I.C.S.: 516120
Vance Collins (Local Sls Mgr)

ION Media of Milwaukee, Inc. (2)
6161 N Flint Rd Ste F, Milwaukee, WI
53209
Tel.: (414) 247-0117
Web Site: http://www.ionmedia.com
Sales Range: $10-24.9 Million
Emp.: 2
Television Broadcasting Station
N.A.I.C.S.: 516120

ION Media of Minneapolis, Inc. (2)
22601 176th St NW, Big Lake, MN 55309
Tel.: (763) 263-8666
Web Site: http://www.ionmedia.tv
Sales Range: $10-24.9 Million
Emp.: 8
Television Broadcasting Station
N.A.I.C.S.: 516120

ION Media of Nashville, Inc. (2)
1281 N Mt Juliet Rd, Mount Juliet, TN
37122
Tel.: (615) 773-6100
Web Site: http://www.iontelevision.com
Sales Range: $10-24.9 Million
Emp.: 7
Television Broadcasting Station
N.A.I.C.S.: 516120
Dan Barber (Gen Sls Mgr)

ION Media of New Orleans, Inc. (2)
3900 Veterans Memorial Blvd Ste 202,
Metairie, LA 70002
Tel.: (504) 887-9795
Web Site: http://www.ionmedia.tv
Sales Range: $10-24.9 Million
Emp.: 4
Television Broadcasting Station
N.A.I.C.S.: 516120

ION Media of New York, Inc. (2)
810 7th Ave 33th Fl, New York, NY 10019
Tel.: (212) 757-3100
Web Site: http://www.ionmedia.com
Sales Range: $10-24.9 Million
Emp.: 40
Television Broadcasting Station
N.A.I.C.S.: 516120

ION Media of Norfolk, Inc. (2)
230 Clearfield Ave, Virginia Beach, VA
23462
Tel.: (757) 499-1261
Web Site: http://www.ionmedia.com
Sales Range: $10-24.9 Million
Emp.: 6
Television Broadcasting Station
N.A.I.C.S.: 516120

David Rogers (VP-Sls)

ION Media of Oklahoma City, Inc. (2)
13424 Railway Dr, Oklahoma City, OK
73114
Tel.: (405) 751-6800
Web Site: http://www.ionmedia.tv
Sales Range: $10-24.9 Million
Emp.: 6
Television Broadcasting Station
N.A.I.C.S.: 516120
Wes Milbourn (Gen Sls Mgr)

ION Media of Orlando, Inc. (2)
7091 Grand NAtional Dr Ste 100, Orlando,
FL 32819
Tel.: (407) 370-5600
Web Site: http://www.ionmedia.tv
Sales Range: $10-24.9 Million
Emp.: 5
Television Broadcasting Station
N.A.I.C.S.: 516120

ION Media of Philadelphia, Inc. (2)
3901 B Main St Ste 301, Philadelphia, PA
19127
Tel.: (215) 482-4770
Sales Range: $10-24.9 Million
Emp.: 5
Television Broadcasting Station
N.A.I.C.S.: 516120
Joe Collins (Gen Sls Mgr)
Dan Borowicz (Reg Dir-Engrg)

ION Media of Phoenix, Inc. (2)
2777 E Camelback Rd Ste 220, Phoenix,
AZ 85016
Tel.: (602) 340-1466
Television Broadcasting Station
N.A.I.C.S.: 516120
Alison Findlay (Continuity Dir)

ION Media of Portland, Inc. (2)
811 SW Naito Pkwy Ste 100, Portland, OR
97204
Tel.: (503) 222-2221
Web Site: http://www.ionmedia.com
Sales Range: $10-24.9 Million
Emp.: 6
Television Broadcasting Station
N.A.I.C.S.: 516120

ION Media of Providence, Inc. (2)
3 Shaws Cove Ste 226, New London, CT
06320
Tel.: (860) 444-2626
Web Site: http://www.ionmedia.com
Sales Range: $10-24.9 Million
Emp.: 6
Television Broadcasting Station
N.A.I.C.S.: 516120

ION Media of Raleigh, Inc. (2)
3209 Gresham Lk Rd Ste 151, Raleigh, NC
27615
Tel.: (919) 827-4801
Sales Range: $10-24.9 Million
Emp.: 5
Television Broadcasting Station
N.A.I.C.S.: 516120
Michelle Barnhill (Mgr-Ops)

ION Media of Roanoke, Inc. (2)
401 3rd St SW, Roanoke, VA 24011
Tel.: (540) 857-0038
Web Site: http://www.ionmedia.tv
Sales Range: $10-24.9 Million
Emp.: 2
Television Broadcasting Station
N.A.I.C.S.: 516120

ION Media of Sacramento, Inc. (2)
3352 Mather Field Rd, Sacramento, CA
95670
Tel.: (916) 368-2929
Sales Range: $10-24.9 Million
Emp.: 7
Television Broadcasting Station
N.A.I.C.S.: 516120

ION Media of San Antonio, Inc. (2)
6100 Bandera Rd Ste 304, San Antonio, TX
78238
Tel.: (210) 682-2626
Web Site: http://www.ionline.tv
Sales Range: $10-24.9 Million
Emp.: 6
Television Broadcasting Station
N.A.I.C.S.: 516120

Brandon Burgess (Pres)

ION Media of San Jose, Inc. (2)
660 Price Avenue Suite B, Redwood City,
CA 94063
Tel.: (650) 261-1370
Television Broadcasting Station
N.A.I.C.S.: 516120

ION Media of Scranton, Inc. (2)
409 Lackawanna Ave Ste 700, Scranton,
PA 18503
Tel.: (570) 344-6400
Web Site: http://www.ionmedia.com
Sales Range: $10-24.9 Million
Emp.: 2
Television Broadcasting Station
N.A.I.C.S.: 516120

ION Media of Seattle, Inc. (2)
8112-C 304th Ave SE, Preston, WA 98050
Tel.: (425) 222-6010
Web Site: http://www.ionmedia.com
Sales Range: $10-24.9 Million
Emp.: 2
Television Broadcasting Station
N.A.I.C.S.: 516120

ION Media of Spokane, Inc. (2)
1201 W Sprague Ave, Spokane, WA 99201
Tel.: (509) 340-3405
Web Site: http://www.ionmedia.tv
Sales Range: $10-24.9 Million
Emp.: 2
Television Broadcasting Station
N.A.I.C.S.: 516120
Bill Storms (Gen Sls Mgr)

ION Media of Syracuse, Inc. (2)
6508 B Basile Rowe, East Syracuse, NY
13057
Tel.: (315) 414-0178
Web Site: http://www.ionmedia.com
Sales Range: $10-24.9 Million
Emp.: 2
Television Broadcasting Station
N.A.I.C.S.: 516120
Brandon Burgess (CEO)

ION Media of Tulsa, Inc. (2)
Ste 101 5800 E Skelly Dr, Tulsa, OK
74135-6419
Tel.: (918) 664-1044
Web Site: http://www.paxson.com
Sales Range: $10-24.9 Million
Emp.: 5
Television Broadcasting Station
N.A.I.C.S.: 516120

ION Media of Washington, Inc. (2)
6199 Old Arrington Lane, Fairfax Station,
VA 22039
Tel.: (703) 503-7966
Web Site: http://www.ionmedia.com
Emp.: 4
Television Broadcasting Station
N.A.I.C.S.: 516120
Amanda Sheehan (Gen Sls Mgr)

ION Media of West Palm Beach, Inc. (2)
13801 NW 14th St, Sunrise, FL 33323
Tel.: (954) 703-1921
Web Site: http://www.iontelevision.com
Sales Range: $10-24.9 Million
Emp.: 4
Television Broadcasting Station
N.A.I.C.S.: 516120
Donna Lane (Gen Sls Mgr)

KASW-TV (1)
645 E Missouri Ave Ste 100, Phoenix, AZ
85012
Tel.: (480) 661-6161
Web Site: http://www.yourphx.com
Television Broadcasting Station
N.A.I.C.S.: 516120

KERO-TV (1)
321 21st St, Bakersfield, CA
93301 (100%)
Tel.: (661) 637-2300
Web Site: https://www.turnto23.com
Sales Range: $10-24.9 Million
Emp.: 75
Television Broadcasting
N.A.I.C.S.: 516120

KGTV (1)
4600 Air Way, San Diego, CA
92102 (100%)

Tel.: (619) 237-1010
Web Site: https://www.10news.com
Sales Range: $50-74.9 Million
Emp.: 200
Television Broadcasting
N.A.I.C.S.: 516120

KGUN-TV (1)
7280 E Rosewood St, Tucson, AZ 85710
Tel.: (520) 722-5486
Web Site: https://www.kgun9.com
Emp.: 125
Television Broadcasting Operations
N.A.I.C.S.: 516120
Leeza Glazier Starks (Dir-News)

KIVI-TV (1)
1866 E Chisholm Dr, Nampa, ID 83687
Tel.: (208) 336-0500
Web Site: https://www.kivitv.com
Emp.: 80
Television Broadcasting Station
N.A.I.C.S.: 516120

KJRH (1)
3701 S Peoria, Tulsa, OK 74105 (100%)
Tel.: (918) 743-2222
Web Site: https://www.kjrh.com
Sales Range: $25-49.9 Million
Emp.: 107
Television Broadcasting Station
N.A.I.C.S.: 516120

KMGH-TV (1)
123 E Speer Blvd, Denver, CO
80203-3417 (100%)
Tel.: (303) 832-7777
Web Site: https://www.denver7.com
Sales Range: $25-49.9 Million
Emp.: 150
Television Broadcasting
N.A.I.C.S.: 516120

KMTV-TV (1)
10714 Mockingbird Dr, Omaha, NE 68127
Tel.: (402) 592-3333
Web Site: https://www.3newsnow.com
Television Broadcasting Station
N.A.I.C.S.: 516120
Geoffrey Roth (Dir-News)
Joe Borgwardt (Natl Sls Mgr)

KNXV-TV (1)
515 N 44th St, Phoenix, AZ 85008
Tel.: (602) 273-1500
Web Site: https://www.abc15.com
Sales Range: $50-74.9 Million
Emp.: 162
Television Station
N.A.I.C.S.: 516120
Trish Greening (Dir-Res)

KSHB-TV (1)
4720 Oak St, Kansas City, MO
64112 (100%)
Tel.: (816) 753-4141
Web Site: https://www.kshb.com
Sales Range: $50-74.9 Million
Emp.: 180
Television Station
N.A.I.C.S.: 516120
Mick Shaffer (Dir-Sports)
Matthew Waggoner (Dir-News)

KTNV-TV (1)
3355 S Vly View Blvd, Las Vegas, NV
89102
Tel.: (702) 876-1313
Web Site: https://www.ktnv.com
Television Broadcasting
N.A.I.C.S.: 516120
Greg Rogers (Dir-Ops & Engrg)

NewsChannel 5 Network (1)
474 James Robertson Pkwy, Nashville, TN
37219
Tel.: (615) 244-5000
Web Site: https://www.newschannel5.com
Television Broadcasting Station
N.A.I.C.S.: 516120

Queen City Broadcasting of New York, Inc. (1)
7 BRdcast Plz, Buffalo, NY 14202-2699
Tel.: (716) 845-6100
Web Site: http://www.wkbw.com
Television Broadcasting Station
N.A.I.C.S.: 516120

Scripps Media, Inc. (1)

1330 N Meridian St, Indianapolis, IN 46202-2364
Tel.: (317) 635-9788
News Syndicates Services
N.A.I.C.S.: 516210

Subsidiary (Domestic):

United Media, Inc. (2)
200 Madison Ave 4th Fl, New York, NY
10016-3905 **(100%)**
Tel.: (212) 293-8500
Licensing & News Feature Syndication
N.A.I.C.S.: 533110

Triton Digital Canada, Inc. (1)
1440 Ste-Catherine W Suite 1200, Montreal, H3G 1R8, QC, Canada
Tel.: (514) 448-4037
Web Site: https://tritondigital.com
Newspaper Publisher Services
N.A.I.C.S.: 513110

WCPO-TV (1)
1720 Gilbert Ave, Cincinnati, OH
45202 **(100%)**
Tel.: (513) 721-9900
Web Site: https://www.wcpo.com
Sales Range: $50-74.9 Million
Emp.: 180
Television Broadcasting Station
N.A.I.C.S.: 516120
Mike Canan (Sr Dir-Local)

WEWS-TV (1)
3001 Euclid Ave, Cleveland, OH 44115
Tel.: (216) 431-5555
Web Site: https://www.news5cleveland.com
Sales Range: $50-74.9 Million
Emp.: 100
Television Broadcasting
N.A.I.C.S.: 516120
Peter Gunn (Dir-Sls)
Nicole Nichols (Mgr-Sls-Local & Natl)
Tara Washburn (Mgr-Sls-Local & Natl)
Joe Donatelli (Dir-Digital)
Jodie Heisner (Dir-News)

WFTS-TV (1)
4045 N Himes Ave, Tampa, FL
33607 **(100%)**
Tel.: (813) 354-2828
Web Site: https://www.abcactionnews.com
Sales Range: $50-74.9 Million
Emp.: 150
Television Station
N.A.I.C.S.: 516120

WMAR-TV (1)
6400 York Rd, Baltimore, MD
21212 **(100%)**
Tel.: (410) 377-2222
Web Site: https://www.wmar2news.com
Sales Range: $25-49.9 Million
Emp.: 149
Television Broadcasting
N.A.I.C.S.: 516120

WMYD-TV (1)
20777 W Ten Mile Rd, Southfield, MI 48075
Tel.: (248) 827-9289
Web Site: https://www.tv20detroit.com
Sales Range: $25-49.9 Million
Emp.: 67
Television Station
N.A.I.C.S.: 516120

WPTV (1)
1100 Banyon Blvd, West Palm Beach, FL
33401 **(100%)**
Tel.: (561) 655-5455
Web Site: https://www.wptv.com
Sales Range: $25-49.9 Million
Emp.: 140
Television Broadcasting Station
N.A.I.C.S.: 516120

WRTV (1)
1330 N Meridian St, Indianapolis, IN
46202-2364 **(100%)**
Tel.: (317) 635-9788
Web Site: https://www.wrtv.com
Sales Range: $25-49.9 Million
Emp.: 145
Television Broadcasting
N.A.I.C.S.: 516120

WSYM-TV Fox 47 (1)
600 W Saint Joseph St Ste 47, Lansing, MI
48933
Tel.: (517) 484-7747

Web Site: https://www.fox47news.com
Emp.: 27
Television Broadcasting Station
N.A.I.C.S.: 516120
Lynn Dziedzic (Gen Mgr-Sls & Adv)
Dana Kromer (Sr Acct Exec)
Dan Lomas (Acct Exec-Integrated)
Don Garchow (Sr Acct Exec)
Adam Purdue (Acct Exec-Integrated)
Chris Lewis (Dir-Digital)
Joel Riebow (Dir-Creative Svcs)
Christine Mitchell (Acct Exec-Integrated)
Kristi Tabor (Acct Exec-Integrated & Adv)
Matthew Volz (Acct Exec-Integrated)
Kristine Melser (Acct Mgr)
Laura Torongeau (Editor-Copy)

WXYZ-TV (1)
20777 W 10 Mile Rd, Southfield, MI
48037 **(100%)**
Tel.: (248) 827-7777
Web Site: http://www.wxyz.com
Sales Range: $75-99.9 Million
Emp.: 250
Television Station
N.A.I.C.S.: 516120
Mike Murri (Gen Mgr)
Chuck Stokes (Dir-Editorial)
Rhonda LaVelle (Dir-News)
Lyle Cifuentes (Dir-Digital)
Phil Wrobel (Dir-Creative Svcs)
Tamika Heslip (Partner-HR Bus)
Tony Lamerato (Sls Dir)
Donn Bousquet (Ops Mgr)
Kirk Allen (Dir-Engrg)
Greg Flash (Fin Dir)
Steve Kopicki (Natl Sls Mgr)
Dan Clark (Sls Mgr-Local)
Greg Smith (Sls Mgr-Local)
Dan Buemi (Dir-Res)
Mike Talik (Sls Mgr-Digital)

THE EASTERN COMPANY
1518 Walnut St No 1308, Philadelphia, PA 19102
Tel.: (215) 255-6955   CT
Web Site:
    https://www.easterncompany.com
Year Founded: 1858
EML—(NASDAQ)
Rev.: $246,522,823
Assets: $266,328,935
Liabilities: $151,726,671
Net Worth: $114,602,264
Earnings: $9,349,171
Emp.: 1,191
Fiscal Year-end: 01/01/22
Locks & Industrial Hardware Mfr
N.A.I.C.S.: 561621
Peter O'Hara (CFO)
Mark A. Hernandez (Pres & CEO)
Nicholas Vlahos (CFO)
Jeffrey Fleming (Mng Dir)
Dan McGrew (Pres)

Subsidiaries:

Argo Transdata Corporation (1)
1 Heritage Park Rd, Clinton, CT 06413
Tel.: (860) 669-2233
Web Site: https://www.argoems.com
Rev.: $6,000,000
Emp.: 30
Other Electronic Component Mfr
N.A.I.C.S.: 334419

Associated Toolmakers Ltd. (1)
15-16 Bridgeway Centre, Wrexham Industrial Estate, Wrexham, LL13 9PS, United Kingdom
Tel.: (44) 1978660380
Web Site: http://www.atm-limited.co.uk
Plastic Injection Mould Tool Design & Mfr
N.A.I.C.S.: 333511
David Chiddy (Mng Dir)

Big 3 Precision Products, Inc. (1)
2923 S Wabash Ave, Centralia, IL 62801
Tel.: (618) 533-3251
Web Site: https://www.big3precision.com
Sales Range: $10-24.9 Million
Emp.: 150
Injection Blow Mold, Tooling & Fabrication Products Mfr
N.A.I.C.S.: 333514

Subsidiary (Domestic):

Big 3 Precision Mold Services, LLC (2)
2923 S Wabash Ave, Centralia, IL 62801
Tel.: (856) 293-1400
Web Site: http://www.big3precision.com
Sales Range: $1-9.9 Million
Blow Mold Tooling Mfr
N.A.I.C.S.: 333511

CCL Security Products (1)
301 W Hintz Rd, Wheeling, IL 60090
Tel.: (847) 537-1800
Web Site: http://www.cclsecurity.com
Sales Range: $50-74.9 Million
Emp.: 50
Mfr of Safety & Security Products Locks
N.A.I.C.S.: 332510

Division (Domestic):

The Illinois Lock Company (2)
301 W Hintz Rd, Wheeling, IL 60090-5754
Tel.: (847) 537-1800
Web Site: http://www.illinoislock.com
Sales Range: $50-74.9 Million
Mfr DUO High Security Locks
N.A.I.C.S.: 332510

Canadian Commercial Vehicles Corporation (1)
8775 C Jim Bailey Crescent, Kelowna, V4V 2L7, BC, Canada
Tel.: (250) 766-2282
Web Site: http://www.ccvbc.com
Sales Range: $10-24.9 Million
Emp.: 40
Lightweight Structure Mfr for Transportation Industry
N.A.I.C.S.: 488999

Eastern Industrial Ltd., Shanghai (1)
20 Lane 2248 Liuxiang Road, Shanghai,
201801, China
Tel.: (86) 2169152508
Web Site:
    https://www.easternindustrialchina.com.cn
Sales Range: $150-199.9 Million
Metal Stampings & Fabrications
N.A.I.C.S.: 423510

Eberhard Manufacturing Division (1)
21944 Drake Rd, Strongsville, OH 44149-9712
Tel.: (440) 238-9720
Web Site: https://www.eberhard.com
Sales Range: $75-99.9 Million
Emp.: 150
Industrial Truck Body Trailer & Custom Hardware Mfr
N.A.I.C.S.: 332510
Tim Kramer (Mgr-Sls-Natl)
Patrick O'Reilly (Mgr-Customer Svc)
Bob Dinallo (Reg Sls Mgr)
Logan Cerny (Mgr-Technical & Mktg)

Subsidiary (Non-US):

Eberhard Hardware Manufacturing Ltd. (2)
1523 Bell Mill SideRoad, Tillsonburg, N4G OC9, ON, Canada **(100%)**
Tel.: (519) 842-8457
Web Site: http://www.eberhard.com
Sales Range: $25-49.9 Million
Emp.: 50
Mfr of Locking & Closing Devices for the Transportation & Computer Industries
N.A.I.C.S.: 332510

Frazer & Jones Division (1)
3000 Milton Ave, Syracuse, NY 13221
Tel.: (315) 468-6251
Web Site: https://www.frazerandjones.com
Sales Range: $25-49.9 Million
Emp.: 140
Mfr of Mine Roof Supports
N.A.I.C.S.: 331511
James Murray (Sls Dir-Intl)

Greenwald Industries Division (1)
212 Middlesex Ave, Chester, CT 06412
Tel.: (860) 526-0800
Web Site:
    https://www.greenwaldindustries.com
Sales Range: $125-149.9 Million
Coin-Operated Machines & Custom-Designed OEM Subassemblies; Mechanical, Electromechanical &/or Electronic

N.A.I.C.S.: 333310
Jim Costeines (Sls Mgr-Global)
Anthony J. DeRusso (Controller-Div)
Bob Gifford (Mgr-Engrg & Product)
Nancy Kelly (Mgr-Materials)
Bob Triggs (Sr Engr-Mechanical)

Hallink Moulds, Inc. (1)
284 Pinebush Road, Cambridge, N1T 1Z6, ON, Canada
Tel.: (519) 624-9720
Web Site: http://www.hallink.com
Blow Mold Machinery Mfr & Distr
N.A.I.C.S.: 326199

Sesamee Mexicana, S.A. de C.V. (1)
Lot 103 and 105 Warehouse 13 14 and 15 La Bomba, 52044, Lerma, Mexico
Tel.: (52) 7282822887
Web Site: https://www.sesamee.com.mx
Sales Range: $25-49.9 Million
Emp.: 55
Metal Products Mfr
N.A.I.C.S.: 423510

Velvac Incorporated (1)
2405 S Calhoun Rd, New Berlin, WI 53151-2709
Tel.: (262) 786-0700
Web Site: https://www.velvac.com
Specialty Vehicle Components Mfr
N.A.I.C.S.: 336390

Subsidiary (Domestic):

Sureflex, Inc. (2)
1122 NW Valley Ridge Dr, Grain Valley, MO 64029
Tel.: (816) 847-6333
Sales Range: $1-9.9 Million
Emp.: 18
Electronic Coil, Transformer & Other Inductor Mfr
N.A.I.C.S.: 334416
Gary Calvert (VP)

World Lock Co. Ltd. (1)
17F No 908 Jingguo Rd, Luzhu Dist, Taoyuan, 338, Taiwan **(100%)**
Tel.: (886) 33524308
Web Site: https://www.worldlock.com.tw
Sales Range: $25-49.9 Million
Emp.: 30
Mfr of Custom Locks
N.A.I.C.S.: 332510
Roger Chang (Mng Dir)

THE ENSIGN GROUP, INC.
29222 Rancho Viejo Rd Ste 127, San Juan Capistrano, CA 92675
Tel.: (949) 487-9500   DE
Web Site:
    https://www.ensigngroup.net
Year Founded: 1999
ENSG—(NASDAQ)
Rev.: $3,729,355,000
Assets: $4,177,541,000
Liabilities: $2,680,224,000
Net Worth: $1,497,317,000
Earnings: $209,399,000
Emp.: 35,300
Fiscal Year-end: 12/31/23
Skilled Nursing & Rehabilitation Facility Owner & Operator
N.A.I.C.S.: 623110
Christopher R. Christensen (Co-Founder & Chm)
Suzanne D. Snapper (CFO & Exec VP)
Chad A. Keetch (Chief Investment Officer, Sec & Exec VP)
Gregory K. Stapley (Co-Founder)
Barry R. Port (CEO)
Spencer Burton (Pres & COO)

Subsidiaries:

Allen Creek Healthcare, Inc. (1)
5925 47th Ave NE, Marysville, WA 98270
Tel.: (360) 659-1259
Web Site:
    http://www.mountainviewrehab.net
Healtcare Services
N.A.I.C.S.: 621498

The Ensign Group, Inc.—(Continued)

Alpowa Healthcare, Inc. (1)
1370 Bridge St, Clarkston, WA 99403
Tel.: (509) 758-2568
Web Site: http://www.elitehhh.com
Healtcare Services
N.A.I.C.S.: 621498
Sherri Osburn *(Dir-Nursing)*

Angeles Home Health Care, Inc. (1)
6345 Balboa Blvd Ste 140, Encino, CA 91316
Tel.: (213) 487-5131
Web Site:
http://www.angeleshomehealthcare.com
Emp.: 30
Women Healthcare Services
N.A.I.C.S.: 621610
Rita Doll *(Pres)*
Doug Jena *(Pres)*

Anza Healthcare, Inc. (1)
654 S Anza St, El Cajon, CA 92020-6602
Tel.: (619) 440-5005
Web Site: https://www.victoriapostacute.com
Healtcare Services
N.A.I.C.S.: 621498

Apismellis Homecare LLC (1)
149350 Ukiah Trl, Earp, CA 92242
Tel.: (760) 665-5255
Web Site: http://www.apismellis.com
Women Healthcare Services
N.A.I.C.S.: 621610
Heidi Pawlowicz *(Mgr)*

Arvada Care & Rehabilitation Center (1)
6121 W 60th Ave, Arvada, CO 80003
Tel.: (303) 420-4550
Web Site: http://arvadacare.com
Nursing Care Facilities Services
N.A.I.C.S.: 623110

Atlantic Memorial Healthcare Associates, Inc. (1)
2750 Atlantic Ave, Long Beach, CA 90806
Tel.: (562) 424-8101
Web Site: https://atlanticmemorial.com
Nursing Care Facilities Services
N.A.I.C.S.: 623110

Avalanche Healthcare, Inc. (1)
220-05 Jamaica Ave 2nd Fl, Queens Village, NY 11428
Tel.: (718) 454-2038
Web Site: http://www.avalanchecare.com
Women Healthcare Services
N.A.I.C.S.: 621610

Avenues Healthcare, Inc. (1)
105 E 1000, Salt Lake City, UT 81402
Tel.: (801) 322-5521
Web Site: https://citycreekpostacute.com
Health Care Srvices
N.A.I.C.S.: 621999
April Cundall *(Gen Mgr)*

Aztec Healthcare, Inc. (1)
8008 S Jesse Owens Pkwy, Phoenix, AZ 85042-6516
Tel.: (602) 243-2780
Nursing Care Facility Operator
N.A.I.C.S.: 623110

Bakorp L.L.C. (1)
826 E 78th Ave, Denver, CO 80229
Tel.: (303) 296-1900
Web Site: http://www.pmdxray.com
Radiology Services
N.A.I.C.S.: 621512

Baseline Healthcare, Inc. (1)
1101 Stewart Ave Ste 104, Garden City, NY 11530
Tel.: (516) 778-5488
Web Site: http://www.baselinehealthny.com
Health Care Srvices
N.A.I.C.S.: 621999
Todd Halper *(Mng Dir)*

Bayside Healthcare, Inc. (1)
553 F St, Chula Vista, CA 91910
Tel.: (619) 426-8611
Web Site: https://southbaypostacute.com
Healtcare Services
N.A.I.C.S.: 621498

Beacon Hill Healthcare, Inc. (1)

128 Beacon Hill Dr, Longview, WA 98632-5854
Tel.: (360) 423-4060
Web Site:
http://www.beaconhillrehabilitation.com
Healtcare Services
N.A.I.C.S.: 621498

Bridgestone Living LLC (1)
1600 W Broadway Rd Ste 100, Tempe, AZ 85282
Tel.: (602) 313-4599
Web Site: http://pinnaciesi.com
Nursing Care Services
N.A.I.C.S.: 623110

Subsidiary (Domestic):

Brenwood Park Senior Living, Inc. (2)
9535 W Loomis Rd, Franklin, WI 53132
Tel.: (414) 501-7224
Web Site: http://brenwoodparkliving.com
Residential Care Services
N.A.I.C.S.: 623312

Denmark Senior Living, Inc. (2)
346 Scandinavian Ct, Denmark, WI 54208-8908
Tel.: (920) 210-0088
Residential Care Services
N.A.I.C.S.: 623312

Kenosha Senior Living, Inc. (2)
3109 30th Ave, Kenosha, WI 53140
Tel.: (262) 300-4242
Web Site:
http://www.kenoshaseniorliving.com
Residential Care Services
N.A.I.C.S.: 623312

Madison Senior Living, Inc. (2)
351 Keny Blvd, London, OH 43140
Tel.: (740) 845-1100
Residential Care Services
N.A.I.C.S.: 623312
Deborah Cassel *(Mgr-Residence)*

Manitowoc Senior Living, Inc. (2)
2115 Cappaert Rd, Manitowoc, WI 54220-1065
Tel.: (920) 360-3904
Residential Care Services
N.A.I.C.S.: 623312

Mountain Vista Senior Living, Inc. (2)
4800 Tabor St, Wheat Ridge, CO 80033
Tel.: (303) 421-4161
Web Site: http://www.mountainvista.net
Residential Care Services
N.A.I.C.S.: 623312
Peggy Manweiler *(Coord-Community Rels)*
Raenell Simmons *(Dir-Nursing)*

Riverview Village Senior Living, Inc. (2)
W176 N9430 River Crest Dr, Menomonee Falls, WI 53051
Tel.: (262) 946-5226
Web Site:
http://www.riverviewvillageliving.com
Residential Care Services
N.A.I.C.S.: 623312

Sandstone Senior Living, Inc. (2)
2010 Windmill Dr, Spearfish, SD 57783
Tel.: (605) 642-4910
Web Site:
http://www.sandstoneseniorliving.com
Senior Resident Care Services
N.A.I.C.S.: 023990

Stevens Point Senior Living, Inc. (2)
1800 Bluebell Ln, Stevens Point, WI 54482-8983
Tel.: (715) 340-4357
Residential Care Services
N.A.I.C.S.: 623312

Stoughton Senior Living, Inc. (2)
2321 Jackson St, Stoughton, WI 53589-5405
Tel.: (608) 228-4966
Residential Care Services
N.A.I.C.S.: 623312

Terrace Court Senior Living, Inc. (2)
3312 Terrace Ct, Wausau, WI 54401-4914
Tel.: (715) 848-6257

Web Site:
http://www.mountainterraceliving.com
Residential Care Services
N.A.I.C.S.: 623312

Willow Creek Senior Living, Inc. (2)
500 Willow Creek Dr, Henning, MN 56551
Tel.: (218) 548-6683
Web Site:
http://www.willowcreekseniorliving.com
Residential Care Services
N.A.I.C.S.: 623312

Wisconsin Rapids Senior Living, Inc. (2)
2230 14th St S, Wisconsin Rapids, WI 54494-6408
Tel.: (715) 340-4356
Residential Care Services
N.A.I.C.S.: 623312

Brown Road Senior Housing LLC (1)
262 E Brown Rd, Mesa, AZ 85201
Tel.: (480) 844-7336
Emp.: 10
Nursing & Residential Care Services
N.A.I.C.S.: 623312
Nathan Bascom *(Mng Dir)*

Brownsville Care Associates, Inc. (1)
510 Paredes Line Rd, Brownsville, TX 78521
Tel.: (956) 546-5358
Web Site: https://altavistarehab.net
Sales Range: $25-49.9 Million
Emp.: 100
Skilled Nursing & Rehabilitative Care Services
N.A.I.C.S.: 623110

Bruno Dialysis, LLC (1)
972 W Town & Country Rd, Orange, CA 92868-4714
Tel.: (253) 382-1869
Health Care Srvices
N.A.I.C.S.: 621492

Buena Vista Hospice Care, Inc. (1)
143 Triunfo Canyon Rd Ste 103, Westlake Village, CA 91361
Tel.: (805) 777-1133
Web Site:
http://www.buenavistahospicecare.com
Hospice Care Facilities
N.A.I.C.S.: 623110
Andrea Doctor *(Exec Dir)*
Helen Audish *(Dir-Patient Care Svcs)*
Razmig Krumian *(Dir-Medical)*

C Street Health Associates LLC (1)
1300 N C St, Oxnard, CA 93030-4006
Tel.: (805) 983-0305
Web Site: http://www.ensigngroup.net
Sales Range: $25-49.9 Million
Emp.: 120
Women Healthcare Services
N.A.I.C.S.: 621610
Trent Clagg *(Mng Dir)*

Camarillo Community Care, Inc. (1)
205 Granada St, Camarillo, CA 93010-7715
Tel.: (805) 482-9805
Web Site: http://camarillohealthcare.com
Nursing Care Facilities Services
N.A.I.C.S.: 623110

Carmel Mountain Rehabilitation and Healthcare Center (1)
11895 Avenue of Industry, San Diego, CA 92128
Tel.: (858) 673-0101
Web Site: http://www.carmelmountain.net
Nursing & Rehabilitation Services
N.A.I.C.S.: 622310

Carrollton Heights Healthcare, Inc. (1)
1618 Kirby Rd, Carrollton, TX 75006
Tel.: (972) 245-1573
Web Site: https://carrolltonhealth.com
Nursing Care Facilities Services
N.A.I.C.S.: 623110

Chateau Julia Healthcare, Inc. (1)
3401 S Lafayette St, Englewood, CO 80113-2926
Tel.: (303) 761-0075
Web Site: http://juliatemple.com
Ambulatory Health Care Services

N.A.I.C.S.: 621999
Eddie Boyle *(Pres)*

Claydelle Healthcare, Inc. (1)
151 Claydelle Ave, El Cajon, CA 92020-4505
Tel.: (619) 442-0245
Web Site:
http://www.somersetsubacute.com
Healtcare Services
N.A.I.C.S.: 621498

Connected Healthcare, Inc. (1)
7515 NE Ambassador Pl Ste C, Portland, OR 97220
Tel.: (503) 261-8599
Web Site: http://www.connectedhh.com
Sales Range: $10-24.9 Million
Emp.: 18
Nursing Care Facilities Services
N.A.I.C.S.: 623110

Costa Victoria Healthcare LLC (1)
340 Victoria St, Costa Mesa, CA 92627
Tel.: (949) 642-0387
Web Site: https://victoriacares.com
Sales Range: $25-49.9 Million
Nursing & Residential Care Services
N.A.I.C.S.: 623312
Michael Yuhas *(Gen Mgr)*

Cypress Creek Healthcare, Inc. (1)
13600 Birdcall Ln, Cypress, TX 77429
Tel.: (281) 477-7771
Web Site:
http://www.cypresscreekrehab.com
Health Care Srvices
N.A.I.C.S.: 621999

Da Vinci Healthcare, Inc. (1)
1313 W Magee Rd, Tucson, AZ 85704-3326
Tel.: (520) 797-2600
Nursing Care Facility Operator
N.A.I.C.S.: 623110

Downey Care Center Corp. (1)
13007 Paramount Blvd, Downey, CA 90242
Tel.: (562) 923-9301
Web Site:
http://www.downeycarecenter.com
Nursing Care Services
N.A.I.C.S.: 623110

Eagle Harbor Healthcare, Inc. (1)
911 Hildebrand Ln Ne Ste 102, Bainbridge Island, WA 98110
Tel.: (206) 842-2690
Web Site:
http://www.eagleharborhealthandchiropractic.com
Healtcare Services
N.A.I.C.S.: 621498

Emblem Healthcare, Inc. (1)
88 S San Marcos Pl, Chandler, AZ 85225
Tel.: (480) 821-8338
Web Site: http://www.emblemhospice.com
Emp.: 60
Healtcare Services
N.A.I.C.S.: 621498

Emerald Healthcare, Inc. (1)
655 SE Walton Rd, Port Saint Lucie, FL 34952
Tel.: (772) 337-1333
Web Site: http://www.emeraldhc.com
Health Care Srvices
N.A.I.C.S.: 621610

Empirecare Health Associates, Inc. (1)
3401 Lemon St, Riverside, CA 92501-2861
Tel.: (951) 686-8202
Web Site: http://www.thegrovecare.com
Healtcare Services
N.A.I.C.S.: 621498

Ensign Cloverdale LLC (1)
300 Cherry Creek Rd, Cloverdale, CA 95425
Tel.: (707) 894-5201
Web Site: https://cloverdalehealthcare.com
Nursing Care Facilities Services
N.A.I.C.S.: 623110

Ensign Montgomery LLC (1)
3751 Montgomery Dr, Santa Rosa, CA 95405
Tel.: (707) 525-1250
Nursing Care Facilities Services
N.A.I.C.S.: 623110

Ensign Panorama LLC (1)
9541 Van Nuys Blvd, Panorama City, CA 91402
Tel.: (818) 893-6385
Nursing & Residential Care Services
N.A.I.C.S.: 623312

Ensign Pleasanton LLC (1)
1349 S Dora St, Ukiah, CA 95482-6512
Tel.: (707) 462-8864
Web Site: https://ukiahpostacute.com
Nursing Care Facilities Services
N.A.I.C.S.: 623110

Ensign Santa Rosa LLC (1)
1280 Summerfield Rd, Santa Rosa, CA 95405
Tel.: (707) 539-1515
Nursing Care Facilities for Seniors
N.A.I.C.S.: 623110
Janet Weinberger *(Dir-Rehabilitation)*

Ensign Sonoma LLC (1)
1250 Broadway, Sonoma, CA 95476
Tel.: (707) 938-8406
Web Site:
  https://broadwayvillapostacute.com
Nursing Care Facilities Services
N.A.I.C.S.: 623110

Ensign Whittier West LLC (1)
12385 Washington Blvd, Whittier, CA 90606
Tel.: (562) 693-7701
Emp.: 200
Nursing Care Facilities Services
N.A.I.C.S.: 623110

Ensign Willits LLC (1)
64 Northbrook Way, Willits, CA 95490
Tel.: (707) 459-5592
Nursing Care Facilities Services
N.A.I.C.S.: 623110

Founders RX LLC (1)
4162 E Bijou St, Colorado Springs, CO 80909
Tel.: (719) 247-1108
Web Site: https://foundersrx.net
Healtcare Services
N.A.I.C.S.: 622110

Gate Three Healthcare LLC (1)
24962 Calle Aragon, Laguna Woods, CA 92637
Tel.: (949) 587-9000
Nursing Care Facilities Services
N.A.I.C.S.: 623110
Jackson Skousen *(Dir-Admin)*

Gateway Healthcare, Inc. (1)
249 Roosevelt Ave Ste 205, Pawtucket, RI 02860
Tel.: (401) 724-8400
Web Site: http://www.gatewayhealth.org
Management of Nursing & Assisted Living Facilities
N.A.I.C.S.: 531312

Subsidiary (Domestic):

Cherokee Healthcare, Inc. (2)
725 N 2nd St, Cherokee, IA 51012
Tel.: (712) 225-2561
Sales Range: $10-24.9 Million
Emp.: 40
Nursing Care Facilities Services
N.A.I.C.S.: 623110
Penny Moellers *(Mng Dir)*

Great Plains Healthcare, Inc. (2)
212 W Bluff St, Cherokee, IA 51012-1817
Tel.: (712) 225-5129
Web Site: http://www.caragehomecare.org
Emp.: 13
Women Healthcare Services
N.A.I.C.S.: 621610
Kim Rupp *(Mgr)*

Gypsum Creek Healthcare, Inc. (2)
728 14Th Ave N, Fort Dodge, IA 50501
Tel.: (515) 576-7226
Nursing Care Facilities Services
N.A.I.C.S.: 623110

Monroe Healthcare, Inc. (2)
1800 Irving St, Beatrice, NE 68310-2236
Tel.: (402) 223-2311
Web Site:
  http://www.beatricehealthandrehab.com
Sales Range: $25-49.9 Million
Nursing Care Facilities Services
N.A.I.C.S.: 623110

Spencer Morris *(Mng Dir)*

Stanton Lake Healthcare, Inc. (2)
1720 Burton Dr, Falls City, NE 68355-2438
Tel.: (402) 245-4466
Web Site: http://fallscityrehab.com
Sales Range: $10-24.9 Million
Nursing Care Facilities
N.A.I.C.S.: 623110

Gold Standard Resources, Inc. (1)
433 Carlisle Dr, Herndon, VA 20170
Tel.: (703) 787-9894
Management Consulting Services
N.A.I.C.S.: 541618

Graceland Senior Living, Inc. (1)
7350 Graceland Dr, Omaha, NE 68134-4328
Tel.: (402) 572-5750
Web Site: https://keystonevillasliving.com
Emp.: 200
Senior Living Facility Services
N.A.I.C.S.: 624120

Grand Villa PHX, Inc. (1)
169 Lake Park Rd, Lewisville, TX 75057-2303
Tel.: (972) 436-7571
Web Site: https://lakevillagenursing.com
Emp.: 90
Nursing Care Facilities Services
N.A.I.C.S.: 623110

Grassland Healthcare and Rehabilitation, Inc. (1)
2900 Stillhouse Rd, Paris, TX 75462-2029
Tel.: (903) 785-1601
Web Site: http://www.stillhouserehab.com
Healtcare Services
N.A.I.C.S.: 621498

Greenfields Assisted Living LLC (1)
723 E 2nd Ave, Mesa, AZ 85204
Tel.: (480) 649-3911
Web Site:
  http://www.greenfieldsassistedliving.com
Nursing Care Facilities
N.A.I.C.S.: 623110
Chrissy Hall *(Exec Dir)*

Harlingen Healthcare, Inc. (1)
4301 S Expy 83, Harlingen, TX 78550
Tel.: (956) 423-4959
Web Site: http://www.verandarehab.com
Nursing Care Facilities Services
N.A.I.C.S.: 623110

Hartwell Health Holdings LLC (1)
94 Cade St, Hartwell, GA 30643
Tel.: (706) 376-3185
Web Site: https://www.hartwellhealth.org
Medical Care Services
N.A.I.C.S.: 621610

Healthlift Medical Transportation, Inc. (1)
12921 Misty Willow Dr, Houston, TX 77070
Tel.: (713) 391-8839
Web Site: http://www.healthliftmtc.com
Medical Transportation Services
N.A.I.C.S.: 621910

Highland Healthcare LLC (1)
4635 N 14th St, Phoenix, AZ 85014-4016
Tel.: (602) 264-9039
Web Site: https://camelbackrehab.com
Nursing Care Facilities
N.A.I.C.S.: 623110
Bret King *(CEO)*

Higley Healthcare, Inc. (1)
5121 E Broadway Rd, Mesa, AZ 85206-1308
Tel.: (480) 832-5555
Nursing Care Facility Operator
N.A.I.C.S.: 623110

Homedale Healthcare, Inc. (1)
108 W Owyhee Ave, Homedale, ID 83628-3206
Tel.: (208) 337-3168
Web Site: http://owyheehealth.com
Healtcare Services
N.A.I.C.S.: 621498

Hopewell Healthcare, Inc. (1)
41865 Pomeroy Pike, Pomeroy, OH 45769-9473
Tel.: (740) 992-0540
Web Site: http://www.hopewellhealth.org

Health Care Srvices
N.A.I.C.S.: 621610

Subsidiary (Domestic):

Rock Hill Healthcare, Inc. (2)
159 Segwood Dr, Rock Hill, SC 29732-1159
Tel.: (803) 329-6565
Web Site: https://rockhillcarecenter.com
Nursing Care Services
N.A.I.C.S.: 623110

Southern Charm Healthcare, Inc. (2)
300 Agape Dr, West Columbia, SC 29169-3307
Tel.: (803) 739-5282
Health Care Srvices
N.A.I.C.S.: 621610

Stoney Hill Healthcare, Inc. (2)
2416 Sunset Blvd, West Columbia, SC 29169-4718
Tel.: (803) 796-8024
Nursing Care Facility Operator
N.A.I.C.S.: 623110

Hoquiam Healthcare, Inc. (1)
3035 Cherry St, Hoquiam, WA 98550-3007
Tel.: (360) 532-7882
Web Site: http://www.pacificcarecenter.com
Sales Range: $25-49.9 Million
Nursing Care Facility Services
N.A.I.C.S.: 623110

Hueneme Healthcare, Inc. (1)
575 E 1400 S, Orem, UT 84097
Tel.: (801) 225-4741
Web Site: https://www.oremrehab.com
Nursing Care Facilities Services
N.A.I.C.S.: 623110

JRT Healthcare, Inc. (1)
2303 Park Ave, Burley, ID 83318-0106
Tel.: (208) 677-3073
Web Site: http://parkeviewrehab.com
Emp.: 64
Nursing Care Facility Services
N.A.I.C.S.: 623110

Jefferson Health Care, Inc. (1)
834 Sheridan St, Port Townsend, WA 98368
Tel.: (360) 385-2200
Web Site: http://jeffersonhealthcare.org
Sales Range: $1-9.9 Million
Emp.: 145
Healtcare Services
N.A.I.C.S.: 621498

La Jolla Skilled, Inc. (1)
3884 Nobel Dr, La Jolla, CA 92122-5700
Tel.: (858) 625-8700
Web Site: http://www.sprlj.com
Nursing & Rehabilitative Care Services
N.A.I.C.S.: 623110
Adam Willits *(CEO)*

Lightning Healthcare, Inc. (1)
5701 E Hillsborough Ave Ste 1202, Tampa, FL 33610
Tel.: (813) 955-4567
Web Site:
  https://www.lightninghealthcare.com
Health Insurance Services
N.A.I.C.S.: 524114

Lindahl Healthcare, Inc. (1)
811 E 14th St, Wayne, NE 68787-1216
Tel.: (402) 375-1922
Nursing Care Facilities Services
N.A.I.C.S.: 623110

Livingston Care Associates, Inc. (1)
4001 Highway 59 N, Livingston, TX 77351-4663
Tel.: (936) 327-4446
Web Site: https://timberwoodrehab.com
Emp.: 130
Nursing Care Facilities Services
N.A.I.C.S.: 623110

Lynnwood Health Services, Inc. (1)
5821 188th St SW, Lynnwood, WA 98037
Tel.: (425) 776-5512
Web Site: https://lynnwoodparc.com
Emp.: 3
Nursing Care Facilities Services
N.A.I.C.S.: 623110

Manor Park Healthcare LLC (1)
1710 Plz Way, Walla Walla, WA 99362-4362
Tel.: (509) 529-4218

Web Site:
  https://parkmanorrehabilitation.com
Nursing Care Facilities Services
N.A.I.C.S.: 623110

Market Bayou Healthcare, Inc. (1)
12350 Wood Bayou Dr, Houston, TX 77013
Tel.: (713) 453-0446
Web Site:
  http://www.montebellowellness.com
Healtcare Services
N.A.I.C.S.: 621498
Guillermo Rojas *(Exec Dir)*

Mission Trails Healthcare, Inc. (1)
8787 Center Dr, La Mesa, CA 91942-3034
Tel.: (619) 460-4444
Web Site:
  http://www.grossmontpostacute.com
Healtcare Services
N.A.I.C.S.: 621498

Mohave Healthcare, Inc. (1)
2755 Silver Creek Rd Ste D127, Bullhead City, AZ 86442
Tel.: (928) 763-6979
Web Site: http://www.mohavehomecare.com
Residential Care Services
N.A.I.C.S.: 623312

Montebello Wellness Center (1)
Jackson Street Hospital Campus 1705 Jackson St, Richmond, TX 77469
Tel.: (281) 341-3000
Web Site:
  https://www.oakbendmedcenter.org
Sales Range: $25-49.9 Million
Emp.: 100
Nursing Care Facilities Services
N.A.I.C.S.: 623110

Morning Glory Healthcare, Inc. (1)
1075 Hadley Ave N Ste 110, Saint Paul, MN 55128
Tel.: (651) 493-1251
Web Site: https://mghome.care
Women Healthcare Services
N.A.I.C.S.: 621610

Nautilus Healthcare, Inc. (1)
7160 Fay Ave, La Jolla, CA 92037-5511
Tel.: (858) 459-4361
Web Site: https://thecoveatlajolla.com
Emp.: 75
Healtcare Services
N.A.I.C.S.: 621498

New England Medical Transportation, Inc. (1)
1111 Elm St Ste 5, West Springfield, MA 01089
Tel.: (413) 241-3375
Web Site: http://www.newenglandmtc.com
Medical Transportation Services
N.A.I.C.S.: 621910

Northern Oaks Healthcare, Inc. (1)
2722 Old Anson Rd, Abilene, TX 79603
Tel.: (325) 676-1677
Web Site: http://northernoaksliving.com
Sales Range: $10-24.9 Million
Nursing Care Facilities Services
N.A.I.C.S.: 623110

Oceanview Healthcare, Inc. (1)
519 Ninth Ave N, Texas City, TX 77590
Tel.: (409) 949-9499
Emp.: 111
Nursing Care Facilities
N.A.I.C.S.: 623110

PMDCA, LLC (1)
1810 Gillespie Way Ste 104, El Cajon, CA 92020-0917
Tel.: (602) 249-4790
Health Care Srvices
N.A.I.C.S.: 621610

Palomar Vista Healthcare Center (1)
201 N Fig St, Escondido, CA 92025-3416
Tel.: (760) 746-0303
Web Site: http://www.palomarvista.com
Nursing Care Facilities Services
N.A.I.C.S.: 623110

Park Waverly Healthcare LLC (1)
2001 N Park Ave, Tucson, AZ 85719-3558
Tel.: (520) 882-6151
Web Site: http://parkavenuehealthcare.com
Nursing Care Facilities Services
N.A.I.C.S.: 623110

The Ensign Group, Inc.—(Continued)

Parkside Healthcare, Inc. (1)
444 W Lexington Ave, El Cajon, CA 92020-4416
Tel.: (619) 442-7744
Web Site: http://www.parksidehealth.net
Healtcare Services
N.A.I.C.S.: 621498

Peak Construction, Inc. (1)
PO Box 33515, Juneau, AK 99803
Tel.: (907) 321-7792
Web Site: http://www.peakconstruction-inc.com
Residential &Commercial Construction Services
N.A.I.C.S.: 236220

Piney Lufkin Healthcare, Inc. (1)
501 N Medford Dr, Lufkin, TX 75901
Tel.: (936) 639-1252
Nursing Care Facilities Services
N.A.I.C.S.: 623110
Becky Jerky (Office Mgr)

Portside Healthcare, Inc. (1)
3680 Reynard Way, San Diego, CA 92103-3847
Tel.: (619) 297-4484
Web Site:
http://www.missionhillspostacute.com
Healtcare Services
N.A.I.C.S.: 621498

Presidio Health Associates LLC (1)
2611 N Warren Ave, Tucson, AZ 85719-3160
Tel.: (520) 795-9574
Web Site: https://catalinacare.com
Nursing Care Facilities Services
N.A.I.C.S.: 623110

Price Healthcare, Inc. (1)
1340 E 300 N, Price, UT 84501-2707
Tel.: (435) 637-9213
Web Site: https://pinnaclenursing.com
Emp.: 70
Nursing Care Facilities Services
N.A.I.C.S.: 623110

Quorum Services, Inc. (1)
203 N Armenia Ave Ste 102, Tampa, FL 33609
Tel.: (813) 514-6222
Web Site: http://www.quorumservices.com
Residential & Commercial Property Management Services
N.A.I.C.S.: 531311

Radiant Hills Health Associates LLC (1)
9155 N 3rd St, Phoenix, AZ 85020-2410
Tel.: (602) 218-9483
Nursing Care Facilities Services
N.A.I.C.S.: 623110
Jason Postl (Mng Dir)

Red Cliffs Healthcare, Inc. (1)
1745 E 280 N, Saint George, UT 84770
Tel.: (435) 628-7770
Web Site: http://redcliffsrehab.com
Healtcare Services
N.A.I.C.S.: 621498

Red Rock Healthcare, Inc. (1)
1664 S Dixie Dr Ste E-102, Saint George, UT 84770
Tel.: (435) 688-0648
Web Site: http://www.zions-way.squarespace.com
Emp.: 100
Healtcare Services
N.A.I.C.S.: 621498
Justin Hofer (Dir-Bus Dev)
Sonya Weston (Dir-Home Health-Clinical Ops)
Jason Olsen (Dir-Compliance)
Kameron Magnuson (Dir-Rehabilitation)
Kirsta Olsen (Dir-Social Svcs)
Lynsey Doms (Mgr-Billing)
Marisa Moses (Coord-Admissions)
Cortney Mathews (Exec Dir)

Redmond Care & Rehabilitation Center (1)
7900 Willows Rd NE, Redmond, WA 98052
Tel.: (425) 885-0808
Web Site:
https://redmondcareandrehab.com

Redmond Heights Senior Living (1)
7950 Willows Rd NE, Redmond, WA 98052-6813
Tel.: (425) 885-4157
Web Site:
http://redmondheightsseniorliving.com
Senior Living Facility Services
N.A.I.C.S.: 624120

Richmond Senior Services, Inc. (1)
500 Jewett Ave, Staten Island, NY 10302
Tel.: (718) 816-1811
Nursing Care Facilities Services
N.A.I.C.S.: 623110

River's Edge Rehabilitation & Living Center (1)
714 N Butte Ave, Emmett, ID 83617-2725
Tel.: (208) 365-4425
Web Site: http://www.riversedgerehab.com
Emp.: 60
Nursing Care Facilities Services
N.A.I.C.S.: 623110

Riverwalk Healthcare, Inc. (1)
2468 FM 1101, New Braunfels, TX 78130
Tel.: (830) 420-6500
Health Care Srvices
N.A.I.C.S.: 621610

Rose Park Healthcare Associates, Inc. (1)
4029 E Anaheim St, Long Beach, CA 90804-4110
Tel.: (562) 494-4421
Web Site: https://shorelinehealthcare.com
Nursing Care Facilities Services
N.A.I.C.S.: 623110

Sagebrush Healthcare, Inc. (1)
8379 W Sunset Rd Ste 210, Las Vegas, NV 89113
Tel.: (702) 851-1600
Web Site: https://sagebrushhealth.com
Medical Care Services
N.A.I.C.S.: 621610

Salado Creek Senior Care, Inc. (1)
603 Corrine, San Antonio, TX 78218
Tel.: (210) 824-7331
Web Site: http://www.northeastiehab.net
Sales Range: $25-49.9 Million
Emp.: 84
Nursing Care Facilities Services
N.A.I.C.S.: 623110

Sand Hollow Healthcare, Inc. (1)
1032 East 100 S, Saint George, UT 84770-3005
Tel.: (435) 628-0488
Nursing Care Facility Operator
N.A.I.C.S.: 623110

Sand Lily Healthcare, Inc. (1)
4631 N May Ave, Oklahoma City, OK 73112
Tel.: (405) 639-3939
Web Site: http://www.excellcares.com
Healtcare Services
N.A.I.C.S.: 621610

Savoy Healthcare, Inc. (1)
2135 N Denton Dr, Carrollton, TX 75006-3103
Tel.: (972) 242-0666
Sales Range: $25-49.9 Million
Emp.: 100
Nursing Care Facilities Services
N.A.I.C.S.: 623110

Sequoia Home Health (1)
830 Hillview Ctr Ste 225, Milpitas, CA 95035-4563
Tel.: (510) 739-1992
Web Site: http://www.sequoiahh.com
Women Healthcare Services
N.A.I.C.S.: 621610

Silver Lake Healthcare, Inc. (1)
308 E 4500 S Ste 100, Murray, UT 84107
Tel.: (801) 433-0344
Web Site: http://www.symbiihealth.com
Emp.: 30
Women Healthcare Services
N.A.I.C.S.: 621610

South Valley Healthcare, Inc. (1)

12702 S Fort St, Draper, UT 84020-9755
Tel.: (801) 571-2704
Nursing Care Facilities Services
N.A.I.C.S.: 623110
Marianne Osborne (Mgr-HR)

Southern Oaks Healthcare, Inc. (1)
3202 S Willis St Bldg B, Abilene, TX 79605-6650
Tel.: (325) 692-6145
Web Site: http://wisteriaplaceliving.com
Nursing Care Facilities Services
N.A.I.C.S.: 623110

Southland Management LLC (1)
11701 Studebaker Rd, Norwalk, CA 90650
Tel.: (562) 868-9761
Web Site: http://southlandliving.com
Investment Management Service
N.A.I.C.S.: 523940
Tyler Albrechtsen (Exec Dir)
Victoria Tran (Dir-Bus Dev)

Southside Healthcare, Inc. (1)
4835 S 49th St, Omaha, NE 68117
Tel.: (402) 733-7200
Web Site:
https://omahanursingandrehab.com
Emp.: 35
Healtcare Services
N.A.I.C.S.: 621498

Stonebridge Healthcare, Inc (1)
100 Hollinshead Spring Rd, Skillman, NJ 08558
Tel.: (609) 683-8355
Web Site:
http://www.stonebridgeatmontgomery.org
Retirement Community Services
N.A.I.C.S.: 623311

Summit Healthcare, Inc. (1)
3018 E Lk St, Minneapolis, MN 55406
Tel.: (612) 721-7776
Emp.: 3
Women Healthcare Services
N.A.I.C.S.: 621610
Maxwell Aforo (Gen Mgr)

Symbol Healthcare, Inc. (1)
4002 Tacoma Mall Blvd Ste 204, Tacoma, WA 98409
Tel.: (253) 581-9410
Web Site: http://www.pugetsoundhh.com
Women Healthcare Services
N.A.I.C.S.: 621610

Teton Healthcare, Inc. (1)
420 S Orchard St, Boise, ID 83705
Tel.: (208) 344-6500
Web Site: http://www.lifesdoors.com
Women Healthcare Services
N.A.I.C.S.: 621610
Mary L. Langenfeld (CEO)

Thomas Road Senior Housing, Inc. (1)
2935 N 18th Pl, Phoenix, AZ 85016
Tel.: (602) 265-9813
Emp.: 4
Health Care Services
N.A.I.C.S.: 621610

Thompson Peak Healthcare LLC (1)
16300 E Keith McMahan Dr, Fountain Hills, AZ 85268
Tel.: (480) 836-4800
Web Site: https://fountainhillspa.com
Skilled Nursing & Rehabilitation Services
N.A.I.C.S.: 623110

Thunder Healthcare, Inc. (1)
1354 E 15th St, Edmond, OK 73013
Tel.: (405) 861-0224
Web Site: https://thunderhealthcare.com
Healtcare Services
N.A.I.C.S.: 621999

Tortolita Healthcare, Inc (1)
7970 N La Canada Dr, Tucson, AZ 85704-2007
Tel.: (520) 797-1191
Nursing Care Facility Operator
N.A.I.C.S.: 623110

Town East Healthcare, Inc. (1)
2231 Hwy 80 E, Mesquite, TX 75150
Tel.: (972) 279-3601
Nursing Care Facilities
N.A.I.C.S.: 623110

Union Hill Healthcare, Inc. (1)
7900 Willows Rd NE, Redmond, WA 98052-6813
Tel.: (425) 885-0808
Web Site:
http://www.redmondcareandrehab.com
Healtcare Services
N.A.I.C.S.: 621498

Upland Community Care, Inc. (1)
1221 E Arrow Hwy, Upland, CA 91786
Tel.: (909) 985-1903
Web Site: http://uplandcare.com
Nursing Care Facilities Services
N.A.I.C.S.: 623110

Valley View Health Services, Inc. (1)
1071 Renee Ave, Pocatello, ID 83201
Tel.: (208) 233-1411
Web Site: https://montevistahills.com
Emp.: 60
Women Healthcare Services
N.A.I.C.S.: 621610

Vesper Healthcare, Inc. (1)
6345 Balboa Blvd Ste 210, Encino, CA 91316
Tel.: (818) 881-9855
Web Site: http://www.vesperhospice.com
Emp.: 100
Healtcare Services
N.A.I.C.S.: 621498
Brenton L. Saunders (Chm & CEO)
Manisha Narasimhan (CFO)

Victoria Ventura Healthcare LLC (1)
5445 Everglades St, Ventura, CA 93003-6523
Tel.: (805) 642-1736
Emp.: 200
Nursing Care Facilities Services
N.A.I.C.S.: 623110

Viewpoint Healthcare, Inc. (1)
4704 W Diana Ave, Glendale, AZ 85302
Tel.: (623) 247-3949
Web Site: https://www.horizonglendale.com
Healtcare Services
N.A.I.C.S.: 621498

Villa Maria Healthcare Center, LLC (1)
425 Barcellus Ave, Santa Maria, CA 93454-6941
Tel.: (805) 922-3558
Nursing Care Services
N.A.I.C.S.: 623110

Virgin River Healthcare, Inc. (1)
1664 S Dixie Dr Ste C105, Saint George, UT 84770-7327
Tel.: (435) 674-3640
Residential Care Services
N.A.I.C.S.: 623312

Vista Woods Health Associates LLC (1)
2000 Westwood Rd, Vista, CA 92083
Tel.: (760) 630-2273
Web Site: https://vistaknoll.com
Emp.: 150
Nursing Care Facilities Services
N.A.I.C.S.: 623110

Watson Woods Healthcare, Inc. (1)
1045 Scott Dr, Prescott, AZ 86301-1731
Tel.: (928) 778-9603
Nursing Care Facility Operator
N.A.I.C.S.: 623110

Wellington Healthcare, Inc. (1)
1802 S 31st St, Temple, TX 76504-6712
Tel.: (254) 778-4231
Web Site: https://wellingtonplaceliving.com
Emp.: 40
Nursing Care Facilities Services
N.A.I.C.S.: 623110

Wildcreek Healthcare, Inc. (1)
2045 Silverada Blvd, Reno, NV 89512-2051
Tel.: (775) 359-3161
Web Site: https://rosewoodreno.com
Nursing Care Facilities Services
N.A.I.C.S.: 623110

Woodard Creek Healthcare, Inc. (1)
520 Lilly Rd NE Bldg 3, Olympia, WA 98506
Tel.: (360) 455-4500
Web Site: http://woodardcreekfh.com
Nursing Care Services
N.A.I.C.S.: 623110

Sales Range: $10-24.9 Million
Emp.: 150
Senior Nursing Care Facility
N.A.I.C.S.: 623110

Youngtown Health, Inc. (1)
12207 N 113th Ave, Youngtown, AZ 85363-1208
Tel.: (623) 977-6532
Nursing Care Facility Services
N.A.I.C.S.: 623110
Sean Hill (CEO)

THE ESTEE LAUDER COMPANIES INC.
767 5th Ave, New York, NY 10153
Tel.: (212) 572-4200   DE
Web Site:
    https://www.elcompanies.com
Year Founded: 1946
EL—(NYSE)
Rev.: $15,608,000,000
Assets: $21,677,000,000
Liabilities: $16,363,000,000
Net Worth: $5,314,000,000
Earnings: $409,000,000
Emp.: 62,000
Fiscal Year-end: 06/30/24
Personal care Product Mfr
N.A.I.C.S.: 325620
William P. Lauder (Chm)
Jane Hertzmark Hudis (Pres-Brand)
Quentin Roach (Chief Procurement Officer & Sr VP)
Carl Haney (Officer-Innovation & Exec VP-Res Product-Global)
Michael O'Hare (Exec VP-HR-Global)
Deirdre Stanley (Gen Counsel & Exec VP)
Laraine Mancini (Sr VP-IR)
Deirdre Stanley (Gen Counsel & Exec VP)
Nicole Monson (Sr VP-Equity & Engagement)
Meridith Webster (Exec VP-Pub Affairs & Comm-Global)
Emily Corstorphan (Mgr-Digital & Social Media-Smashbox Cosmetics & Glamglow)
Roberto Canevari (Exec VP-Supply Chain-Global)
Kate Gildea (Dir-Enterprise Mktg & Data-Australia & New Zealand)
Emmerentia Wilding (Mng Dir-Australia & New Zealand)
Bart Dubbeld (VP-Travel Retail-South-East Asia & Gen Mgr-Travel Retail-South-East Asia)
Karen Housman (Sr VP-Travel Retail-Asia Pacific & Gen Mgr-Travel Retail-Asia Pacific)
Jane Lauder (Chief Data Officer & Exec VP-Enterprise Mktg)

Subsidiaries:

Aveda Corporation (1)
4000 Pheasant Rdg Dr, Blaine, MN 55449
Tel.: (763) 783-4000
Web Site: https://www.aveda.com
Sales Range: $900-999.9 Million
Emp.: 1,500
Cosmetics Mfr
N.A.I.C.S.: 325620

Aveda Services Inc. (1)
4000 Pheasant Ridge Dr, Blaine, MN 55449-7106
Tel.: (763) 783-4000
Web Site: http://www.aveda.com
Sales Range: $200-249.9 Million
Provider of Business Services
N.A.I.C.S.: 325620

Bobbi Brown Professional
Cosmetics (1)
575 Broadway, New York, NY 10012 (100%)
Tel.: (646) 613-6500
Web Site:
    http://www.bobbibrowncosmetics.com
Rev.: $1,700,000
Emp.: 70
Perfumes & Cosmetics
N.A.I.C.S.: 456120

Clinique Laboratories, Inc. (1)

767 5th Ave, New York, NY 10153
Tel.: (212) 572-3800
Web Site: http://www.clinique.com
Sales Range: $150-199.9 Million
Skin Care, Makeup & Fragrance Products Mfr & Distr
N.A.I.C.S.: 325620
Ronald S. Lauder (Chm)
Michelle Freyre (Sr VP & Gen Mgr-Global)

ELC Management LLC (1)
125 Pinelawn Rd, Melville, NY 11747
Tel.: (631) 454-7000
Administrative Management Services
N.A.I.C.S.: 561110
Kenny Cianchette (Project Mgr)

Estee Lauder (1)
350 S Service Rd, Melville, NY 11747-3233
Tel.: (631) 454-7000
Sales Range: $150-199.9 Million
Mfr of Cosmetics
N.A.I.C.S.: 325620
William Rotor (CEO)

Estee Lauder AG Lachen (1)
Hardtumstrasse 11, CH-8031, Zurich, Switzerland
Tel.: (41) 442839393
Cosmetic Product Distr
N.A.I.C.S.: 456120

Estee Lauder Clinique & Aramis (1)
48 Rue Cambon, 75001, Paris, France
Tel.: (33) 140068900
Web Site: http://www.esteelauder.com
Emp.: 200
Perfumes
N.A.I.C.S.: 325620

Estee Lauder Coordination Center BVBA (1)
Nijverheidsstraat 15, 2260, Westerlo, Belgium
Tel.: (32) 14258611
Cosmetic Research Services
N.A.I.C.S.: 424210
Bart Taeymans (Gen Mgr)

Estee Lauder Cosmetics Limited (1)
One Fitzroy 6 Mortimer Street, London, W1T 3JJ, United Kingdom
Tel.: (44) 8000542444
Cosmetic Product Distr
N.A.I.C.S.: 456120

Estee Lauder Cosmetics Ltd. (1)
130 Bloor Street West Suite 801, Toronto, M5S 1N5, ON, Canada (100%)
Tel.: (416) 413-5250
Web Site: http://www.esteelauder.com
Sales Range: $10-24.9 Million
Emp.: 300
Perfumes & Cosmetics Mfr
N.A.I.C.S.: 325620

Estee Lauder Inc. (1)
767 5th Ave, New York, NY 10153
Tel.: (212) 572-4200
Web Site: https://www.esteelauder.in
Personal Care Products Whslr
N.A.I.C.S.: 456120

Estee Lauder S.R.L. (1)
Via Turati 3, Milan, 20121, Italy
Tel.: (39) 0263771
Web Site: https://www.esteelauder.it
Sales Range: $50-74.9 Million
Emp.: 200
Cosmetics, Toiletries & Fragrances
N.A.I.C.S.: 325620

M.A.C. Cosmetics (1)
100 Alden Rd, Markham, L3R 4C1, ON, Canada
Tel.: (905) 470-7877
Web Site: http://www.maccosmetics.com
Sales Range: $200-249.9 Million
Emp.: 400
Cosmetics Mfr
N.A.I.C.S.: 325620
Philippe Pinatel (Sr VP & Gen Mgr)

Northtec LLC (1)
411 Sinclair St, Bristol, PA 19007-1525
Tel.: (215) 781-7500
Web Site: http://www.esteelauder.com
Rev.: $30,000,000
Emp.: 200
Cosmetic Preparations
N.A.I.C.S.: 325620

Prescriptives Inc. (1)
767 5th Ave, New York, NY 10153-0023
Tel.: (212) 572-4400
Web Site: http://www.prescriptives.com
Rev.: $1,500,000
Emp.: 7
Cosmetics
N.A.I.C.S.: 424210

Tom Ford International, LLC (1)
845 Madison Ave, New York, NY 10021-4908
Tel.: (212) 359-0300
Web Site: http://www.tomford.com
New Car Dealers
N.A.I.C.S.: 441110
Guillaume Jesel (Pres & CEO)
Peter Hawkings (Creative Dir)
Rebecca Mason (Sr VP-Intl Brand Image)
Paolo Cigognini (Sr VP-Intl Comm & Media)

Too Faced Cosmetics, LLC (1)
18231 W McDurmott, Irvine, CA 92614
Web Site: https://www.toofaced.com
Cosmetic Products Mfr & Whslr
N.A.I.C.S.: 325620
Jeremy Johnson (Co-Founder)

Whitman Packaging Corp. (1)
1516 Motor Pkwy, Hauppauge, NY 11749
Tel.: (631) 232-5200
Rev.: $37,900,000
Emp.: 300
Provider of Packaging & Labeling Services
N.A.I.C.S.: 326199

THE EUROPEAN EQUITY FUND, INC.
345 Park Ave, New York, NY 10154
G1E—(BER)
Fund Management Services
N.A.I.C.S.: 523940
Gerd Kirsten (Mgr-Fund)
Christian H. Strenger (Chm)
Hepsen Uzcan (Pres & CEO)

THE EVERMEDIA GROUP, INC.
60 State St 7th Fl, Boston, MA 02109
Tel.: (813) 438-5225
Web Site:
    http://www.theevermediagroup.com
EVRM—(OTCIQ)
Sales Range: $50-74.9 Million
Biometric-Based Authentication, Verification & Identity Theft Protection Systems
N.A.I.C.S.: 561621
Jonathan Sym (Chm & CEO)
Robert Skinnion (Mgr-Ops)
Lawrence Cardinal (Program Mgr-Sys Tech Solutions)

THE FARMERS BANK OF APPOMATTOX
223 Main St, Appomattox, VA 24522
Tel.: (434) 352-7171   VA
Web Site:
    https://www.thefarmersbankva.com
FBPA—(OTCQB)
Rev.: $12,472,000
Assets: $316,208,000
Liabilities: $288,410,000
Net Worth: $27,798,000
Earnings: $3,208,000
Emp.: 72
Fiscal Year-end: 12/31/22
Commercial Banking Services
N.A.I.C.S.: 522110
John R. Caldwell (Pres & CEO)
Cassandra R. Mullins (VP & Head-Compliance)
Thomas L. Rasey Jr. (COO & Sr VP)
Brian D. Wilkerson (Chief Retail Lending Officer & First VP)
Kenneth A. Shorter (Chief Information Technology Officer & First VP)
J. Christian Pemberton (VP & Controller)

THE FIRST BANCORP, INC.
Tel.: (207) 563-3195   ME

Web Site: https://www.thefirst.com
Year Founded: 1985
FNLC—(NASDAQ)
Rev.: $109,909,000
Assets: $232,684,000
Liabilities: $3,761,000
Net Worth: $228,923,000
Earnings: $38,990,000
Emp.: 273
Fiscal Year-end: 12/31/22
Bank Holding Company
N.A.I.C.S.: 551111
F. Stephen Ward (Bd of Dirs, Executives)
Richard M. Elder (CFO & Treas)
Tony C. McKim (Pres & CEO)
Robert B. Gregory (Bd of Dirs & Atty)

Subsidiaries:

The First, N.A. (1)
223 Main St, Damariscotta, ME 04543
Tel.: (207) 563-3195
Web Site: https://www.thefirst.com
Sales Range: $125-149.9 Million
Emp.: 50
Commericial Banking
N.A.I.C.S.: 522110
Richard M. Elder (CFO & Exec VP)
Tony C. McKim (Pres & CEO)
James Strout (Officer-Comml Loan)
Jon Dolloff (Portfolio Mgr-Wealth Mgmt)
Parker Sanderson (Asst Portfolio Mgr-Wealth Mgmt)

THE FIRST BANCSHARES, INC.
6480 US Hwy 98 W Ste A, Hattiesburg, MS 39402
Tel.: (601) 268-8998   MS
Web Site:
    https://www.thefirstbank.com
Year Founded: 1996
FBMS—(NASDAQ)
Rev.: $237,354,000
Assets: $6,461,717,000
Liabilities: $5,815,054,000
Net Worth: $646,663,000
Earnings: $62,919,000
Emp.: 870
Fiscal Year-end: 12/31/22
Bank Holding Company
N.A.I.C.S.: 551111
Milton Ray Cole Jr. (Vice Chm, Pres & CEO)
E. Ricky Gibson (Chm)

Subsidiaries:

Heritage Southeast Bancorporation, Inc. (1)
101 N Main St, Jonesboro, GA 30236
Tel.: (770) 824-9934
Web Site: http://myhsbi.q4ir.com
Rev.: $38,084,000
Assets: $1,336,051,000
Liabilities: $1,200,116,000
Net Worth: $135,935,000
Earnings: $876,000
Emp.: 300
Fiscal Year-end: 12/31/2019
Bank Holding Company
N.A.I.C.S.: 551111
Katherine S. Zovlonsky (Chief Admin Officer & Exec VP)
Bradley Serff (Pres & Chief Banking Officer)
Lon Langston (Chief People Officer & Exec VP)
Philip Resch (CFO & Exec VP)
Paul Hoerig (Chief Credit & Risk Officer & Exec VP)

The First, A National Banking Association (1)
6480 Hwy 98 W, Hattiesburg, MS 39404 (100%)
Tel.: (601) 268-8998
Web Site: http://www.thefirstbank.com
Sales Range: $125-149.9 Million
Savings Bank
N.A.I.C.S.: 522180
Milton Ray Cole Jr. (Pres & CEO)
Donna T. Lowery (CFO & Exec VP)

The First Bancshares, Inc.—(Continued)

THE FIRST OF LONG ISLAND CORPORATION

275 Broad Hollow Rd.Ste 200, Melville, NY 11747
Tel.: (516) 671-4900 NY
Web Site: https://www.fnbli.com
Year Founded: 1984
FLIC—(NASDAQ)
Rev.: $146,626,000
Assets: $4,281,511,000
Liabilities: $3,916,975,000
Net Worth: $364,536,000
Earnings: $46,932,000
Emp.: 303
Fiscal Year-end: 12/31/22
Offices of Bank Holding Companies
N.A.I.C.S.: 551111
Christopher Becker (Pres & CEO)
Jay P. McConie (CFO, Treas & Exec VP)
Richard P. Perro (Chief Retail Officer-Bank & Exec VP)
Christopher Hilton (Exec VP)
Susanne Pheffer (Exec VP)
Michael J. Spolarich (Exec VP)
Janet T. Verneuille (Chief Risk Officer & Exec VP)
Tanweer S. Ansari (Chief Compliance Officer)

Subsidiaries:

The First National Bank of Long Island (1)
10 Glen Head Rd, Glen Head, NY 11545 (100%)
Tel.: (516) 674-6650
Web Site: https://www.fnbli.com
Sales Range: $25-49.9 Million
Emp.: 100
Commericial Banking
N.A.I.C.S.: 522110
Donald L. Manfredonia (Officer-Bus Dev & Exec VP)
Christopher Becker (Pres & CEO)
Jay P. McConie (Chief Investment Officer & Sr VP)
Richard P. Perro (Exec VP)
Christopher J. Hilton (Exec VP)
Janet T. Verneuille (Chief Risk Officer & Exec VP)
Michael J. Spolarich (Chief Credit Officer & Exec VP)

Subsidiary (Domestic):

FNY Service Corp. (2)
10 Glen Head Rd, Glen Head, NY 11545
Tel.: (516) 671-4900
Sales Range: $650-699.9 Million
Investment Services
N.A.I.C.S.: 523999
Jane Carmody (VP)

Subsidiary (Domestic):

The First of Long Island REIT, Inc. (3)
10 Glen Head Rd, Glen Head, NY 11545
Tel.: (516) 671-4900
Sales Range: $250-299.9 Million
Real Estate Investment Trust
N.A.I.C.S.: 525990

THE FIRST REPUBLIC CORPORATION OF AMERICA

302 5th Ave, New York, NY 10001-3604
Tel.: (212) 279-6100 DE
Year Founded: 1961
FRPC—(OTCEM)
Diversified Holding Company Engaged in Real Estate, Hotel, Seafood & Textiles Businesses
N.A.I.C.S.: 313210
Jonathan A. Rosen (CEO & COO)

Subsidiaries:

First Republic Corp., Real Estate Div. (1)

302 5th Ave, New York, NY 10001-3604
Tel.: (212) 279-6100
Sales Range: $10-24.9 Million
Owns & Operates Commercial Real Estate
N.A.I.C.S.: 114112

Hanora Spinning (1)
159 Singleton St, Woonsocket, RI 02895-1852 (100%)
Tel.: (401) 767-3360
Web Site: http://www.alliantenergyisco.com
Sales Range: $25-49.9 Million
Textile Spinning
N.A.I.C.S.: 313110

The First Republic Building Corp. (1)
302 5th Ave, New York, NY 10001-3604
Tel.: (212) 279-6100
Sales Range: $10-24.9 Million
Real Estate
N.A.I.C.S.: 114112

THE FREEDOM BANK OF VIRGINIA

10555 Main St Ste 100, Fairfax, VA 22030
Tel.: (703) 667-4167 VA
Web Site: https://www.freedom.bank
Year Founded: 2001
FDVA—(OTCIQ)
Rev.: $22,875,049
Assets: $500,392,674
Liabilities: $436,366,259
Net Worth: $64,026,415
Earnings: $2,705,217
Fiscal Year-end: 12/31/19
Commericial Banking
N.A.I.C.S.: 522110
Kathleen S. Croson (Exec VP)
Joseph J. Thomas (Pres & CEO)
Shaun E. Murphy (COO, Chief Credit Officer & Exec VP)
Raj Mehra (CFO & Exec VP)
Richard A. Hutchison (Exec VP)
Kerry Borosh (VP)
Dhruva Patel (VP)
Dawn Giorgi-Nethercott (Asst VP)
Kevin Ferryman (Sr VP & Head-SBA Div)

THE FRESH MARKET HOLDINGS, INC.

300 N Greene St Ste 1100, Greensboro, NC 27401
Tel.: (336) 389-5795 DE
Year Founded: 2016
TFM—(NASDAQ)
Rev.: $1,887,452,000
Assets: $1,495,401,000
Liabilities: $1,360,912,000
Net Worth: $134,489,000
Earnings: $26,914,000
Emp.: 10,000
Fiscal Year-end: 01/31/21
Holding Company
N.A.I.C.S.: 551112
Jason Potter (Pres & CEO)
Brian Johnson (Sr VP-Store Ops)
Carlos Clark (Sec, Sr VP & Gen Counsel)
Chris Himebauch (Chief HR Officer & Sr VP)
Kevin Miller (CMO & Sr VP)
Dan Portnoy (Chief Mdsg Officer & Sr VP)
Andrew Jhawar (Chm)
Adrian Bartella (CFO)
Peter Mayes (Grp VP-Mdsg)
Wade Yenny (VP-Center Store)

THE GABELLI GLOBAL SMALL & MID CAP VALUE TRUST

1 Corporate Center, Rye, NY 10580-1422
Tel.: (914) 921-5070 DE
Year Founded: 2014

GGZ—(NYSE)
Rev.: $3,299,429
Assets: $164,925,797
Liabilities: $3,936,590
Net Worth: $160,989,207
Earnings: $1,067,266
Fiscal Year-end: 12/31/19
Investment Management Service
N.A.I.C.S.: 525990
Christopher J. Marangi (Mgr-Fund)
Richard J. Walz (Chief Compliance Officer)
Daniel Hughes (VP-Ombudsman)
Bethany A. Uhlein (VP-Ombudsman)
Laurissa M. Martire (VP)
John C. Ball (Pres, Principal Acctg Officer & Treas)
Peter Goldstein (Pres & Sec)
Mario J. Gabelli (Chm & Chief Investment Officer)

THE GABELLI GO ANYWHERE TRUST

1 Corporate Center, Rye, NY 10580-1434
Tel.: (914) 921-5070 NY
GGO—(NYSEAMEX)
Investment Management Service
N.A.I.C.S.: 525990
Gian Maria Magrini (Mgr-Fund)

THE GAP, INC.

2 Folsom St, San Francisco, CA 94105
Tel.: (415) 427-0100 DE
Web Site: https://www.gapinc.com
Year Founded: 1969
GPS—(NYSE)
Rev.: $14,889,000,000
Assets: $11,044,000,000
Liabilities: $8,449,000,000
Net Worth: $2,595,000,000
Earnings: $502,000,000
Emp.: 85,000
Fiscal Year-end: 02/03/24
Clothing Accessories Retailer
N.A.I.C.S.: 458110
Richard Dickson (Pres & CEO)
Katrina O'Connell (CFO)
Julie Gruber (Chief Legal & Compliance Officer & Sec)
Sally Gilligan (Chief Growth Transformation Officer)
Mark Breitbard (Pres & CEO-Gap Brand)
Sandra Stangl (Pres & CEO-Banana Republic)
John F. Strain (Head-ECommerce & Tech)
Eric K. Chan (Chief Bus & Strategy Officer)
John F. Strain (Founder)

Subsidiaries:

Athleta (1)
6007 Green Pointe Dr, Groveport, OH 43125
Tel.: (614) 744-3913
Web Site: http://www.athleta.gap.com
Sales Range: $10-24.9 Million
Emp.: 120
Women's Sportswear Mfr & Retailer
N.A.I.C.S.: 315250
Tom Herbst (Interim CMO)

Athleta (ITM) Inc. (1)
2 Folsom St, San Francisco, CA 94105
Tel.: (415) 427-3190
Sporting Clothes & Goods Distr
N.A.I.C.S.: 459110

Banana Republic (1)
2 Folsom St, San Francisco, CA 94105
Tel.: (415) 427-5575
Web Site: http://www.bananarepublic.com
Sales Range: $100-124.9 Million
Specialty Apparel Retailer
N.A.I.C.S.: 458110
Mark Breitbard (Pres & CEO)

GPS Services, Inc. (1)
14846 State Hwy 56 W, Adams, MN 55909
Tel.: (507) 582-7725
Web Site: https://www.farmtech.com
Clothing Accessories Distr
N.A.I.C.S.: 423990

Gap (Italy) Srl. (1)
Via della Natura 13, 28069, Trecate, NO, Italy
Tel.: (39) 03 215 3479
Web Site: https://www.gapitaly.com
Clothing Accessories Distr
N.A.I.C.S.: 423990

Gap (UK Holdings) Limited (1)
Next Plc Desford Road, Enderby, Leicester, LE19 4AT, United Kingdom
Tel.: (44) 3337774578
Family Clothing Stores
N.A.I.C.S.: 458110

Gap Canada, Inc. (1)
60 Bloor St W Ste 1501, Toronto, M4W 3B8, ON, Canada (100%)
Tel.: (416) 921-2711
Web Site: https://www.gapcanada.ca
Family Clothing Stores
N.A.I.C.S.: 458110

Subsidiary (Domestic):

Banana Republic (2)
220 Yonge Street, Toronto, M5B 2H1, ON, Canada (100%)
Tel.: (416) 595-6336
Web Site: http://www.bananarepublic.ca
Emp.: 180
Womens Clothing
N.A.I.C.S.: 458110

Gap International Sourcing Limited (1)
20-22/f Millennium City 5 Bea Twr 418 Kwun Tong Rd, Kwun Tong, China (Hong Kong)
Tel.: (852) 27309883
Web Site: http://www.gp.hk
Emp.: 500
Family Clothing Stores
N.A.I.C.S.: 458110

Janie & Jack LLC (1)
4995 Industrial Way, Benicia, CA 94510
Web Site: http://www.janieandjack.com
Apparel Mfr & Distr
N.A.I.C.S.: 315250
Linda Heasley (Pres & CEO)

Old Navy (1)
801 Market St, San Francisco, CA 94103-1901
Tel.: (415) 344-0375
Web Site: http://www.oldnavy.com
Sales Range: $400-449.9 Million
Emp.: 1,000
Specialty Apparel Retailer
N.A.I.C.S.: 458110
Jennifer J. Ming (Executives)
Nancy Green (Pres & Chief Creative Officer)
Horacio Barbeito (Pres)

Old Navy (Apparel), LLC (1)
45215 Worth Ave, California, MD 20619-2422
Tel.: (301) 866-0396
Web Site: https://www.oldnavy.gap.com
Clothing Accessories Distr
N.A.I.C.S.: 423990

Old Navy (Canada) Inc. (1)
9500 Mclaughlin Road North, Brampton, L6X 0B8, ON, Canada
Web Site: https://oldnavy.gapcanada.ca
Fashion Apparels Retailer
N.A.I.C.S.: 458110

The Gap (1)
1 Harrison St, San Francisco, CA 94105-1602 (100%)
Tel.: (650) 952-4400
Web Site: http://www.gap.com
Sales Range: $100-124.9 Million
Specialty Apparel Retailer
N.A.I.C.S.: 458110
Alegra O'Hare (CMO & Sr VP)

THE GARDEN CITY COMPANY

1905 W Fulton, Garden City, KS 67846
Tel.: (620) 276-3246   CO
Year Founded: 1930
GCCO—(OTCIQ)
Holding Company
N.A.I.C.S.: 551112
Chris Sohn *(Sec)*
Kyle H. Hybl *(VP)*
Jessica Heckel *(Asst Sec)*
David J. Palenchar *(Asst Treas)*
Elaine Martinez *(Treas)*
William J. Hybl *(Chm)*
R. Thayer Tutt Jr. *(Pres & CEO)*
Troy J. Dumler *(Sr VP & Gen Mgr)*

THE GEO GROUP, INC.

4955 Technology Way, Boca Raton, FL 33431
Tel.: (561) 893-0101   FL
Web Site: https://www.geogroup.com
Year Founded: 1984
GEO—(NYSE)
Rev.: $2,376,727,000
Assets: $3,760,383,000
Liabilities: $2,595,295,000
Net Worth: $1,165,088,000
Earnings: $171,813,000
Emp.: 15,800
Fiscal Year-end: 12/31/22
Juvenile & Adult Correction & Detention Center Operator
N.A.I.C.S.: 922140
George C. Zoley *(Founder & Chm)*
Wayne H. Calabrese *(Pres, COO & Sr VP)*
Brian R. Evans *(CEO & Sr VP)*
Ronald A. Brack *(Chief Acctg Officer, Exec VP & Controller)*
Richard Kent Long *(Sr VP-Project Dev)*
Joe Negron *(Gen Counsel, Sec & Sr VP)*
Matthew T. Albence *(Sr VP-Client Rels)*
James H. Black *(CTO)*
Christopher D. Ryan *(Sr VP)*
Mark J. Suchinski *(CFO & Sr VP)*

Subsidiaries:

B.I. Incorporated (CO)   (1)
6265 Gunbarrel Ave Ste B, Boulder, CO 80301
Tel.: (303) 218-1000
Web Site: http://www.bi.com
Software Development Services
N.A.I.C.S.: 541511

BI Incorporated   (1)
6265 Gunbarrel Ave Ste B, Boulder, CO 80301
Tel.: (303) 218-1000
Web Site: https://bi.com
Sales Range: $100-124.9 Million
Electronic Monitoring Equipment Technology & Services & Community Correctional Services
N.A.I.C.S.: 561621
Jock Waldo *(Pres)*

Cornell Interventions, Inc.   (1)
2221 W 64th St, Woodridge, IL 60515
Tel.: (630) 968-6477
Sales Range: $25-49.9 Million
Emp.: 100
Substance Abuse Treatment Centers
N.A.I.C.S.: 621420

Correctional Properties, LLC   (1)
1300 E Hwy 107, La Villa, TX 78562
Tel.: (956) 262-4511
Health Care Srvices
N.A.I.C.S.: 621420

Fulham Correctional Centre   (1)
110 Hopkins Road, Fulham, Victoria, 3851, VIC, Australia
Tel.: (61) 351423800
Web Site: https://www.geogroup.com
Management of Correctional & Health Care Services
N.A.I.C.S.: 922140

GEO Amey PECS, Ltd.   (1)
Unit A Redwing Centre Mosley Road Trafford Park, Manchester, M17 1RJ, United Kingdom
Tel.: (44) 1454288560
Web Site: https://www.geoamey.co.uk
Health Care Srvices
N.A.I.C.S.: 621420

GEO Australia Management Services Pty, Ltd.   (1)
44 Market Street, Sydney, 2000, NSW, Australia
Tel.: (61) 1300302348
Health Care Srvices
N.A.I.C.S.: 621420

GEO Care of South Carolina, Inc.   (1)
6650 Rivers Ave, North Charleston, SC 29406
Tel.: (803) 935-0505
Correctional Health Care Services
N.A.I.C.S.: 621420
Bruce McClease *(Dir-Securuty)*

GEO Care, Inc.   (1)
800 E Cypress Dr, Pembroke Pines, FL 33025-4543
Tel.: (954) 392-3080
Web Site: http://www.geocarellc.com
Correctional Health Care Services
N.A.I.C.S.: 621420
Jon Swatsburg *(VP-Youth Svcs)*
Ann M. Schlarb *(Pres & Sr VP)*
David O. Meehan *(Exec VP-Partnership Dev)*
David S. Burch *(VP-Continuum of Care)*
Derrick D. Schofield *(Exec VP-Continuum of Care & Reentry Svcs)*
Larry Sherman *(VP-Fin)*

GEO Corrections and Detention, LLC   (1)
4955 Technology Way, Boca Raton, FL 33431
Tel.: (561) 893-0101
Health Care Srvices
N.A.I.C.S.: 621420

Great Plains Correctional Facility   (1)
700 Sugar Creek Rd, Hinton, OK 73047
Tel.: (405) 542-3711
Sales Range: $50-74.9 Million
Privatized Correctional, Detention & Pre-release Services to Governmental Agencies
N.A.I.C.S.: 922140
Richard Barger *(Mgr)*

Highpoint Investments, LLC   (1)
7724 Girard Ave Ste 300, La Jolla, CA 92037
Tel.: (858) 622-4900
Real Estate Investment Services
N.A.I.C.S.: 531210

Junee Correctional Centre   (1)
Park Lane, PO Box 197, Junee, Wagga Wagga, 2663, NSW, Australia
Tel.: (61) 269243222
Web Site: https://www.geogroup.com
Emp.: 150
Management of Correctional Institutions
N.A.I.C.S.: 922140
Scott Brideoake *(Gen Mgr)*

Kutama Sinthumule Correctional Centre   (1)
Sparrow Road, Louis Trichardt, 0920, Limpopo, South Africa
Tel.: (27) 155194500
Web Site: https://www.geogroup.com
Emp.: 500
Correctional Institution
N.A.I.C.S.: 922140

Parklea Correctional Centre   (1)
66 Sentry Drive, Parklea, Blacktown, 2768, NSW, Australia
Tel.: (61) 2 9678 4888
Web Site: http://www.geogroup.com.au
Management of Correctional Institutions
N.A.I.C.S.: 922140

South Africa Custodial Management Inc.   (1)
Oak Place Woodmead Office Park 145 Western Service Road, Woodmead, Sandton, 2191, South Africa

Tel.: (27) 118024440
Web Site: http://www.sacms.com
Sales Range: $25-49.9 Million
Emp.: 10
Construction & Operation of Juvenile & Adult Correction & Detention Centers
N.A.I.C.S.: 922140

South African Custodial Management Pty, Ltd.   (1)
Oak Place Woodmead Office Park 145 Western Service Road, PO Box 835, Woodmead, Sandton, 2191, South Africa
Tel.: (27) 118024440
Web Site: http://www.sacms.com
Health Care Srvices
N.A.I.C.S.: 621420
Lazarus Ncongwane *(Mng Dir)*

The GEO Group Australia Pty, Ltd.   (1)
Level 18 44 Market Street, Sydney, 2000, NSW, Australia
Tel.: (61) 29 262 6100
Web Site: https://www.geogroup.com.au
Management of Correctional Institutions & Correctional Health Services
N.A.I.C.S.: 922140
Pieter Bezuidenhout *(Mng Dir)*
Frank Thorn *(Dir-Comml)*
Sarah Gray *(Dir-Rehabilitation & Reintegration-Natl)*
Dom Karauria *(Dir-Correctional Svcs)*
Kim Blinkhorn *(Dir-Governance & Continuous Improvement)*

The GEO Group Ltd.   (1)
10 Suttons Business Park Sutton Park Avenue, Earley, Reading, RG6 1AZ, Berkshire, United Kingdom
Tel.: (44) 1189359460
Private Custodial & Related Services
N.A.I.C.S.: 922140

The GEO Group UK Ltd   (1)
Second Fl Horizon Bldg Honey Ln, Suttons Park Avenue, Hurley, SL6 6RJ, Berks, United Kingdom   (100%)
Tel.: (44) 1189359460
Web Site: http://www.thegeogroupinc.co.uk
Sales Range: $300-349.9 Million
Management of Prisons, Immigration Removal Centres & Escorting Services
N.A.I.C.S.: 922140
George C. Zoley *(Chm)*

THE GLIMPSE GROUP, INC.

15 W 38th St Fl 12, New York, NY 10018
Tel.: (609) 256-6622   NV
Web Site:
   https://www.theglimpsegroup.com
Year Founded: 2016
VRAR—(NASDAQ)
Rev.: $8,804,199
Assets: $15,558,603
Liabilities: $4,020,118
Net Worth: $11,538,485
Earnings: ($6,394,295)
Emp.: 112
Fiscal Year-end: 06/30/24
Custom Computer Programming Services
N.A.I.C.S.: 541511
Lyron Live Bentovim *(Pres, CEO, Co-Founder & Chm)*
Lyron Bentovim *(Pres, CEO & Chm)*
David J. Smith *(Co-Founder & Chief Creative Officer)*
Maydan Rothblum *(CFO, COO, Treas & Sec)*

Subsidiaries:

Sector 5 Digital, LLC   (1)
4300 Amon Carter Blvd, Fort Worth, TX 76155
Tel.: (682) 348-1785
Web Site: https://www.sector5digital.com
Marketing Consulting Services
N.A.I.C.S.: 541613

THE GNS GROUP, INC.

4017 Colby Ave, Everett, WA 98201
Tel.: (855) 387-7383   WA

Web Site:
   http://www.thegnsgroup.com
Year Founded: 2006
GNSG—(OTCIQ)
Furniture Distr
N.A.I.C.S.: 423210
Roula Jarjour *(Pres)*

Subsidiaries:

Naples Soap Company, Inc.   (1)
17041 Alico Commerce Ct Ste 1, Fort Myers, FL 33967
Tel.: (239) 325-8263
Web Site: http://www.naplessoap.com
Sales Range: $1-9.9 Million
Emp.: 40
Soap Retailer
N.A.I.C.S.: 456120
Deanna Wallin *(Founder & CEO)*
Patrick Renda *(COO & Exec VP-Bus Dev)*

THE GOLDFIELD CORPORATION

1684 W Hibiscus Blvd, Melbourne, FL 32901
Tel.: (321) 724-1700   DE
Web Site:
   http://www.goldfieldcorp.com
Year Founded: 1968
GV—(NYSEAMEX)
Rev.: $180,645,718
Assets: $129,367,178
Liabilities: $63,196,424
Net Worth: $66,170,754
Earnings: $6,726,607
Emp.: 529
Fiscal Year-end: 12/31/19
Mining & Milling of Copper, Zinc & Silver; Electrical Construction
N.A.I.C.S.: 237110
Stephen R. Wherry *(Acting Co-CEO, CFO, Treas, Sr VP & Asst Sec)*
Jason M. Spivey *(Acting Co-CEO)*

Subsidiaries:

Bayswater Development Corporation   (1)
1684 W Hibiscus Blvd, Melbourne, FL 32901
Tel.: (321) 795-4200
Sales Range: $25-49.9 Million
Real Estate Development Services
N.A.I.C.S.: 238210

Subsidiary (Domestic):

Cape Club of Brevard   (2)
1684 W Hibiscus Blvd, Melbourne, FL 32901-2631
Tel.: (321) 724-1700
Web Site: http://www.bayswater.cc
Sales Range: $1-9.9 Million
Emp.: 12
Real Estate Development Services
N.A.I.C.S.: 713940

Florida Coastal Homes Inc.   (2)
1684 W Hibiscus Blvd, Melbourne, FL 32901-2631   (100%)
Tel.: (321) 795-4200
Web Site: http://www.bayswater.cc
Real Estate Development Services
N.A.I.C.S.: 236115

Pineapple House of Brevard, Inc.   (2)
1684 W Hibiscus Blvd, Melbourne, FL 32901
Tel.: (321) 795-4200
Web Site:
   http://www.pineapplehousecondo.com
Sales Range: $25-49.9 Million
Emp.: 13
Real Estate Development Services
N.A.I.C.S.: 811210

Power Corporation of America   (1)
4647 Clyde Morris Blvd Unit 501, Port Orange, FL 32129
Tel.: (386) 333-6441
Web Site: http://www.pcapower.com
Power Line Construction Services
N.A.I.C.S.: 237130

The Goldfield Corporation—(Continued)

Jason M. Spivey *(Pres)*
Jennifer Cunningham *(Coord-People & Culture)*
Mike Fisher *(Mgr-Fleet, Logistics, DOT & Compliance)*
Dan Gadacz *(VP-Safety-CUSP)*

Subsidiary (Domestic):

C. & C. Power Line, Inc.   **(2)**
12035 Palm Lake Dr, Jacksonville, FL
32218
Tel.: (904) 751-6020
Web Site: http://www.ccpowerline.com
Emp.: 30
Electrical Contractor
N.A.I.C.S.: 237130
Jesse B. Colley *(Pres)*
Michael E. Sprenger *(VP)*

Precision Foundations, Inc.   **(2)**
1684 W Hibiscus Blvd, Melbourne, FL
32901
Tel.: (321) 360-5274
Web Site:
   http://www.precisionfoundationsinc.com
Foundation Drilling Contractor Services
N.A.I.C.S.: 238910
Jason M. Spivey *(Pres)*
Jason Johnston *(VP)*

Southeast Power Corporation   **(2)**
1805 Hammock Rd, Titusville, FL
32796   **(100%)**
Tel.: (321) 268-0540
Web Site: http://www.southeastpower.com
Electrical Construction
N.A.I.C.S.: 237130
Jason M. Spivey *(Pres)*
Jack Brady *(Exec VP)*
Brian Tilton *(VP-Carolina)*
Zane E. Taylor *(Exec VP-Florida)*
Todd Davis *(VP-Texas Reg)*

THE GOLDMAN SACHS GROUP, INC.

200 W St 29th Fl, New York, NY
10282
Tel.: (212) 902-1000   **DE**
Web Site:
   https://www.goldmansachs.com
Year Founded: 1869
GS—(NYSE)
Rev.: $47,365,000,000
Assets: $1,441,799,000,000
Liabilities: $1,324,610,000,000
Net Worth: $117,189,000,000
Earnings: $11,261,000,000
Emp.: 48,500
Fiscal Year-end: 12/31/22
Financial Investment Services
N.A.I.C.S.: 551111
David M. Solomon *(Chm & CEO)*
Denis P. Coleman III *(CFO)*
John E. Waldron *(Pres & COO)*
Brian J. Lee *(Chief Risk Officer)*
Sheara J. Fredman *(Chief Acctg Officer)*
Kathryn H. Ruemmler *(Chief Legal Officer & Gen Counsel)*
John F. W. Rogers *(Sec & Exec VP)*
Carey Halio *(Treas-Global)*

Subsidiaries:

Archon Group, L.P.   **(1)**
6011 Connection Dr, Irving, TX 75039
Tel.: (972) 368-2200
Financial Management For Business
N.A.I.C.S.: 561110

Subsidiary (Non-US):

Archon Group Europe GMBH   **(2)**
Sendlinger Str 12, 95030, Neuhof, Germany
Tel.: (49) 9281140150
Web Site: http://www.delmora-bank.de
Emp.: 154
Investment Banking Services
N.A.I.C.S.: 523150

GSTM LLC   **(1)**
1620 Michigan Ave Ste 127, Detroit, MI
48216

Web Site: https://gstm.us
Investment Banking Services
N.A.I.C.S.: 523150

Goldman Sachs & Co. LLC   **(1)**
200 W St, New York, NY 10282
Tel.: (212) 902-1000
Web Site: https://www.goldmansachs.com
Sales Range: $25-49.9 Billion
Investment Banking, Asset Management &
Brokerage Services
N.A.I.C.S.: 523150
Lloyd C. Blankfein *(Chm & CEO)*
Maria S. Jelescu Dreyfus *(Executives)*
David T. Hamamoto *(Partner & Co-Head-Real Estate Principal Investment Area)*
Thomas R. Knott *(Mng Dir)*

Subsidiary (Non-US):

Goldman Sachs Canada Inc.   **(2)**
TD North Tower 77 King Street West Suite
3400, PO Box 38, Toronto, M5K 1B7, ON,
Canada   **(100%)**
Tel.: (416) 343-8900
Web Site: http://www.gs.com
Sales Range: $100-124.9 Million
Emp.: 50
Full-Service International Investment Banking & Brokerage Firm
N.A.I.C.S.: 523150

Goldman Sachs Canada Inc.   **(2)**
3835 855 2nd St SW, Bankers Hall E
Tower, Calgary, T2P 4J8, AB,
Canada   **(100%)**
Tel.: (403) 233-9293
Web Site: http://www.gs.com
Sales Range: $10-24.9 Million
Emp.: 65
Institutional Broker
N.A.I.C.S.: 425120

**Goldman Sachs Do Brasil Banco
Multiplo S/A**   **(2)**
Leopoldo Couto Magalhaes Jr 700,16 and
Itaim Bibi, Sao Paulo, 04542-000, Brazil
Tel.: (55) 1133710700
Web Site: https://www.goldmansachs.com
Leasing & Financial Services
N.A.I.C.S.: 523999
Bruno Amorim *(VP-Equity Res)*

Division (Domestic):

**Goldman Sachs Merchant Banking
Division**   **(2)**
200 W St, New York, NY 10282
Tel.: (212) 902-1000
Web Site: http://www.gs.com
Corporate, Real Estate & Infrastructure Investments
N.A.I.C.S.: 523999

Subsidiary (Domestic):

GS Capital Partners L.P.   **(3)**
85 Broad Street, New York, NY 10004
Tel.: (212) 902-8890
Web Site: http://www.goldmansachs.com
Privater Equity Firm
N.A.I.C.S.: 523999
Carl A. Grimstad *(Mng Partner)*

Joint Venture (Non-US):

**Associated British Ports Holdings
Ltd.**   **(4)**
25 Bedford Street, London, WC2E 9ES,
United Kingdom   **(23.34%)**
Tel.: (44) 2074301177
Web Site: https://www.abports.co.uk
Holding Company; Marine Ports Operator &
Cargo Handling Activities
N.A.I.C.S.: 551112
Harm van Weezel *(CIO)*
Julian Walker *(Chief Comml Officer)*
Alison Rumsey *(Chief HR Officer)*
Angela Morgan *(Corp Counsel)*
Marina Wyatt *(CFO)*

Unit (Domestic):

ABP Ayr   **(5)**
Port Office North Harbour Street, Ayr, KA8
8AH, United Kingdom
Tel.: (44) 1292281687
Sales Range: $100-124.9 Million
Emp.: 30
Marine Cargo Handling

N.A.I.C.S.: 488320

ABP Barrow   **(5)**
Port Office Ramsey Way, Barrow-in-Furness, LA14 2GR, Cumbria, United Kingdom
Tel.: (44) 1229822911
Sales Range: $25-49.9 Million
Emp.: 30
Marine Cargo Handling Distr
N.A.I.C.S.: 488320
Paul Jervis *(Mgr-Port)*

ABP Cardiff   **(5)**
QA House Cargo Road, Cardiff, CF10 4LY,
United Kingdom
Tel.: (44) 8706096699
Sales Range: $25-49.9 Million
Emp.: 100
Marine Cargo Handling
N.A.I.C.S.: 488320
Matthew Kennerley *(Dir-Ports-South Wales)*

ABP Fleetwood   **(5)**
Dock Office, Fleetwood, FY7 6PP, Lancs,
United Kingdom
Tel.: (44) 1253872323
Sales Range: $100-124.9 Million
Emp.: 15
Marine Cargo Handling
N.A.I.C.S.: 488320
Nick Ridehalgh *(Dir-Short-Sea Ports)*

ABP Garston   **(5)**
Port Office Garston, Liverpool, L19 2JW,
United Kingdom
Tel.: (44) 1514275971
Sales Range: $25-49.9 Million
Emp.: 20
Marine Cargo Handling
N.A.I.C.S.: 488320
Paul Jervis *(Mgr-Port)*

ABP Goole   **(5)**
Port Office East Parade, Goole, DN14 5RB,
East Yorkshire, United Kingdom
Tel.: (44) 1482327171
Web Site: http://www.abport.co.uk
Sales Range: $50-74.9 Million
Emp.: 250
Marine Cargo Handling
N.A.I.C.S.: 488320
Phil Coombes *(Mgr-Comml)*

ABP Hull   **(5)**
Port House Northern Gateway, PO Box 1,
Hull, HU9 5PQ, Yorkshire, United Kingdom
Tel.: (44) 1482327171
Sales Range: $25-49.9 Million
Emp.: 125
Port & Harbor Operations
N.A.I.C.S.: 488310

ABP Ipswich   **(5)**
Old Custom House Key Street, Ipswich, IP4
1BY, United Kingdom
Tel.: (44) 1473231010
Sales Range: $25-49.9 Million
Emp.: 23
Marine Cargo Handling
N.A.I.C.S.: 488320
Alastair MacFarlane *(Mgr-Port)*

ABP Plymouth   **(5)**
Port Office Millbay Docks, Plymouth, PL1
3EF, Devon, United Kingdom
Tel.: (44) 1752662191
Sales Range: $25-49.9 Million
Emp.: 22
Passenger Ferry & Marine Cargo Handling
Services
N.A.I.C.S.: 488320

Subsidiary (Non-US):

**BPL Medical Technologies Private
Ltd.**   **(4)**
11th KM Arakere Bannerghatta Road, Bengaluru, 560 076, India
Tel.: (91) 8026484350
Web Site:
   https://www.bplmedicaltechnologies.com
Medical Device Mfr
N.A.I.C.S.: 339112
Sunil Khurana *(CEO)*

Subsidiary (Non-US):

Penlon Limited   **(5)**
Abingdon Science Park, Barton Lane,

Abingdon, OX14 3NB, Oxfordshire, United
Kingdom
Tel.: (44) 1235547000
Web Site: https://www.penlon.com
Hospital Equipments Mfr
N.A.I.C.S.: 339112
Linda Moss *(Dir-HR)*
Mary Ryan *(Dir-Quality Assurance & Regulatory Affairs)*

Joint Venture (Non-US):

Continental Bakeries B.V.   **(4)**
Pieter Zeemanweg 17, 3316 GZ, Dordrecht,
Netherlands
Tel.: (31) 786537653
Web Site:
   https://www.continentalbakeries.com
Sales Range: $350-399.9 Million
Emp.: 1,550
Bread, Cookie & Biscuit Mfr
N.A.I.C.S.: 311821
Ruud van Henten *(CEO)*

Joint Venture (Domestic):

EPC Power Corp.   **(4)**
13100 Kirkham Way Ste 209, Poway, CA
92064-7128
Web Site: http://www.epcpower.com
Electronic Components Mfr
N.A.I.C.S.: 334419
Allan Abela *(Pres)*
Devin Dilley *(Co-Founder & CEO)*

Joint Venture (Non-US):

Flint Group SA   **(4)**
26b Boulevard Royal, 2449, Luxembourg,
Luxembourg
Web Site: http://www.flintgrp.com
Sales Range: $1-4.9 Billion
Emp.: 6,800
Holding Company; Printing Inks & Colourants Mfr & Distr
N.A.I.C.S.: 551112
William B. Miller *(Pres-Print Media-Transatlantic & Japan)*
Doug Aldred *(Pres-Packaging & Narrow Web-EMEA & North America)*
Jan Paul van der Velde *(Sr VP-Procurement, Sustainability, Regulatory & IT)*
Adhemur Pilar *(Pres-Flint Grp-Latin America)*
Rico Hagedorn *(Sr Mgr-Technical Svcs Plates-Flexographic Products)*
Benoit Chatelard *(Pres/CEO-Digital Solutions)*
Dagmar Schmidt *(Pres-Flexographic)*

Subsidiary (Non-US):

Flint Group GmbH   **(5)**
Siegle Strasse 25, 70469, Stuttgart, Germany
Tel.: (49) 71198160
Web Site: https://www.flintgrp.com
Sales Range: $1-4.9 Billion
Emp.: 1,040
Printing Ink, Plate & Colorant Mfr
N.A.I.C.S.: 551114

Subsidiary (US):

Flint Group, Inc.   **(6)**
4550 Main St Ste 220, Kansas City, MO
64111
Tel.: (816) 226-6924
Web Site: http://www.flintgrp.com
Sales Range: $1-4.9 Billion
Emp.: 150
Ink & Coating Mfr
N.A.I.C.S.: 325910
Adhemur Pilar *(Pres)*
Benoit Chatelard *(Pres-Digital Solutions)*
Pierre-Marie De Leener *(Chm)*
Michael Fien *(Chief Digitalisation Officer)*

Subsidiary (Domestic):

Cranney Companies, Inc.   **(7)**
24 Water St, Danvers, MA 01923
Tel.: (978) 716-5698
Web Site:
   http://www.cranneyhomeservices.com
Electrical Contractor
N.A.I.C.S.: 238210
Joe Ciampa *(Gen Mgr)*
Brian Cranney *(Owner)*

Southwest Plumbing & Water Heaters, Inc. (7)
2401 SW Alaska St, Seattle, WA 98106
Tel.: (206) 932-1777
Web Site: http://www.southwestplumbing.biz
Plumbing, Heating & Air-Conditioning Contractors
N.A.I.C.S.: 238220

Subsidiary (Non-US):

Xeikon NV (6)
Brieversstraat 70, 4529 GZ, Ede, Netherlands
Tel.: (31) 117 37 50 20
Web Site: http://www.xeikon.com
Digital Printing Machinery Mfr & Marketer
N.A.I.C.S.: 333248
Benoit Chatelard (Pres & CEO)
Vlad Sljapic (VP-Sls-Global)
Robert Welford (VP-R&D)

Subsidiary (US):

Xeikon America, Inc. (7)
1375 E Irving Park Rd, Itasca, IL 60143
Tel.: (630) 438-7900
Web Site: https://www.xeikon.com
Developer, Mfr & Distr of High Quality Digital Printing Systems
N.A.I.C.S.: 333248

Subsidiary (Non-US):

Xeikon Japan Co., Ltd. (7)
3-1-3 Yushima, Bunkyo-Ku, Tokyo, 113-0034, Japan
Tel.: (81) 358070210
Web Site: http://www.xeikon.jp
Digital Color Printing Solutions
N.A.I.C.S.: 323111

Xeikon Manufacturing and R&D Center (7)
Duwijckstraat 17, 2500, Lier, Belgium
Tel.: (32) 34431311
Web Site: http://www.xeikon.com
Provider of Digital Color Printing Solutions
N.A.I.C.S.: 323111

Joint Venture (Non-US):

HRA Pharma, SA (4)
15 rue Beranger, 75 003, Paris, France
Tel.: (33) 1 40 33 11 30
Web Site: http://www.hra-pharma.com
Pharmaceutical Product Mfr & Distr
N.A.I.C.S.: 325412
Geoff Allan (CFO)
Martyn Hilton (CEO)
Paul Carter (Chief Scientific Officer)

Subsidiary (Non-US):

HRA Pharma Deutschland, GmbH (5)
Massenbergstrasse 9-13, 44787, Bochum, Germany
Tel.: (49) 234 51 65 92 0
Web Site: http://www.hra-pharma.com
Pharmaceutical Products Distr
N.A.I.C.S.: 424210

HRA Pharma Iberia S.L. (5)
Paseo de la Castellana 1436B, 28046, Madrid, Spain
Tel.: (34) 902107428
Web Site: http://www.hra-pharma.com
Pharmaceutical Products Distr
N.A.I.C.S.: 424210

HRA Pharma Italia S.r.l. (5)
Via Cristoforo Colombo 436, 00145, Rome, Italy
Tel.: (39) 06 59600987
Web Site: http://www.hra-pharma.com
Pharmaceutical Products Distr
N.A.I.C.S.: 424210

HRA Pharma UK & Ireland Ltd (5)
Haines House 21 John Street, London, WC1N 2BF, Bloomsbury, United Kingdom
Tel.: (44) 2037501720
Web Site: http://www.hra-pharma.com
Pharmaceutical Products Distr
N.A.I.C.S.: 424210
Tony Fraser (Dir-European Affiliates)

Joint Venture (Non-US):

ISS Holding A/S (4)

Bredgade 30, DK-1260, Copenhagen, Denmark (44%)
Tel.: (45) 38170000
Web Site: http://www.issworld.com
Sales Range: $5-14.9 Billion
Emp.: 520,000
Holding Company
N.A.I.C.S.: 551112
Charles L. Allen (Chm-ISS World Services A/S)
Jeff Olsen Gravenhorst (CEO)

Subsidiary (Domestic):

ISS A/S (5)
Buddingevej 197, 2860, Soborg, Denmark
Tel.: (45) 38170000
Web Site: https://www.issworld.com
Rev.: $11,650,403,463
Assets: $7,061,967,849
Liabilities: $5,503,960,894
Net Worth: $1,558,006,955
Earnings: $48,123,195
Emp.: 352,749
Fiscal Year-end: 12/31/2023
Holding Company; Commercial Facility Maintenance & Business Support Services
N.A.I.C.S.: 551112
Bjorn Raasteen (Gen Counsel-Grp)
Charles L. Allen (Chm)
Joseph Nazareth (VP & Head-Health, Safety, Environment & Quality)
Jacob Gotzsche (CEO-Europe)
Troels Bjerg (COO-Grp)
Thomas Berglund (Deputy Chm)
Henrik Poulsen (Deputy Chm)
Corinna Refsgaard (Chief People & Culture Officer-Grp)
Jacob Aarup-Andersen (CEO-Grp)
Kasper Fangel (Deputy CFO-Grp)
Sam Hockman (CEO)
Kristoffer Lykke-Olesen (CEO & Head)
Jacob Schmidt Johansen (CEO, Head & Head)
Kristian Tankred (Sr Mgr, CEO, Head & Head)
Niels Smedegaard (Sr Mgr, CEO, Chm, Head & Head)
Lars Petersson (Sr Mgr, CEO, Chm, Head, Head & Deputy Chm)
Celia Liu (CEO)
Liz Benison (CEO)
Carl-Fredrik Langard-Bjor (CEO)
Susanne Jorgensen (CEO)
Agostino Renna (Chief Comml Officer)
Scott Davies (CEO)

Subsidiary (Domestic):

ISS Global A/S (6)
Buddingevej 197, Soborg, 2860, Denmark
Tel.: (45) 38170000
Web Site: http://www.issworld.com
Sales Range: $50-74.9 Million
Emp.: 160
Holding Company
N.A.I.C.S.: 551112
Bjorn Raasteen (Grp Gen Counsel & Sr VP)
Henrik Andersen (COO-EMEA & Grp)
Jeff Olsen Gravenhorst (COO)

Subsidiary (Non-US):

ISS Facility Services A.E. (7)
14 Thrasimachou Str, GR-104 42, Athens, Greece
Tel.: (30) 2102705600
Web Site: http://www.gr.issworld.com
Sales Range: $75-99.9 Million
Emp.: 100
Commercial Facility Maintenance & Business Support Services
N.A.I.C.S.: 561210

ISS Facility Services A/S (7)
PO Box 132 OKern, 0509, Oslo, Norway
Tel.: (47) 22885000
Web Site: http://www.no.issworld.com
Commercial Facility Maintenance & Business Support Services
N.A.I.C.S.: 561210
Bjorn Nilsen (Mng Dir)

Subsidiary (Domestic):

ISS Facility Services A/S (7)
Gyngemose Parkvej 50, 2860, Soborg, Denmark
Tel.: (45) 38171717
Web Site: http://www.dk.issworld.com

Emp.: 11,000
Commercial Facility Maintenance & Business Support Services
N.A.I.C.S.: 561210
Maarten van Engeland (Mng Dir)

Subsidiary (Non-US):

ISS Facility Services AB (7)
Arstaangsvagen 11, Stockholm, 11743, Sweden
Tel.: (46) 86816000
Web Site: http://www.se.issworld.com
Emp.: 300
Commercial Facility Maintenance & Business Support Services
N.A.I.C.S.: 561210
Majken Daugaard Larsen (CFO)
Nina Junehed (CIO)

ISS Facility Services Australia Limited (7)
Units 1 & 2 12 Mars Road, Lane Cove, 2066, NSW, Australia
Tel.: (61) 286449700
Web Site: http://www.au.issworld.com
Emp.: 21,000
Commercial Facility Maintenance & Business Support Services
N.A.I.C.S.: 561210
Ian Scanlon (CFO)
Stuart Rose (CEO)
Elizabeth Turner (COO)

ISS Facility Services GmbH (7)
Brunner Strasse 85, 1210, Vienna, Austria
Tel.: (43) 57400
Web Site: http://www.at.issworld.com
Sales Range: $75-99.9 Million
Emp.: 300
Commercial Facility Maintenance & Business Support Services
N.A.I.C.S.: 561210

ISS Facility Services GmbH (7)
Wanheimer Strasse 92, Dusseldorf, 40468, Germany
Tel.: (49) 211302780
Web Site: http://www.de.issworld.com
Commercial Facility Maintenance & Business Support Services
N.A.I.C.S.: 561210
Frank Merry (Gen Mgr-HR)
Martin Gieser (Country Mgr)

ISS Facility Services Lda. (7)
Rua Moinho da Barrunchada 4 1st Dt, Carnaxide, 2790-109, Portugal
Tel.: (351) 214246760
Web Site: http://www.pt.issworld.com
Commercial Facility Maintenance & Business Support Services
N.A.I.C.S.: 561210

ISS Facility Services Limited (7)
6F Dorset House Taikoo Place 979 Kings Road, Quarry Bay, China (Hong Kong)
Tel.: (852) 2826 9166
Web Site: http://www.hk.issworld.com
Commercial Facility Maintenance & Business Support Services
N.A.I.C.S.: 561210
William Fung (CFO & Exec Dir)

Subsidiary (Domestic):

ISS EastPoint Facility Services Limited (8)
18/F Warwick House West Taikoo Place 979 King's Road, Quarry Bay, China (Hong Kong)
Tel.: (852) 28269166
Web Site: http://www.hk.issworld.com
Sales Range: $50-74.9 Million
Commercial Facility Maintenance & Support Services
N.A.I.C.S.: 561210
Keith Futcher (CEO)

Subsidiary (Non-US):

ISS Facility Services S.A. (7)
Rue Christophe Plantin 5, 2339, Gasperich, Luxembourg
Tel.: (352) 4246201
Web Site: http://www.lu.issworld.com
Sales Range: $75-99.9 Million
Commercial Facility Maintenance & Business Support Services
N.A.I.C.S.: 561210

Kris Cloots (Country Mgr)

ISS Facility Services s.r.o. (7)
Antala Staska 38/510, Prague, 14000, Czech Republic
Tel.: (420) 261392311
Web Site: http://www.cz.issworld.com
Sales Range: $50-74.9 Million
Commercial Facility Maintenance & Business Support Services
N.A.I.C.S.: 561210

ISS Facility Services spol. s r.o. (7)
Dubraska Cesta 14, 841 04, Bratislava, Slovakia
Tel.: (421) 232630111
Web Site: http://www.sk.issworld.com
Sales Range: $75-99.9 Million
Emp.: 60
Commercial Facility Maintenance & Business Support Services
N.A.I.C.S.: 561210
Peter Szavo (Mng Dir)

Subsidiary (US):

ISS Facility Services, Inc. (7)
1017 Central Pkwy N Ste 100, San Antonio, TX 78232-5027
Tel.: (210) 495-6021
Web Site: http://www.us.issworld.com
Sales Range: $300-349.9 Million
Emp.: 10,000
Commercial Facility Maintenance & Support Services
N.A.I.C.S.: 561210

Subsidiary (Domestic):

Guckenheimer Enterprise, Inc. (8)
1850 Gateway Dr Ste 500, San Mateo, CA 94404
Tel.: (650) 592-3800
Web Site: http://www.guckenheimer.com
Emp.: 3,200
Holding Company; Corporate Food Service Contracting Services
N.A.I.C.S.: 551112
Randall Boyd (CEO & COO)
Steve Selcer (CFO)
Helene Kennan (Chief Innovation Officer)
Karla Lacey (CMO)
Amelia Ekus (Gen Mgr-New York)
Charlie Frisco (Dir-Ops & Chef Mgr)

Branch (Domestic):

ISS Facility Services, Inc. - Austin Regional Office (8)
10435 Burnet Rd Ste 102, Austin, TX 78758-3818
Tel.: (512) 836-9516
Web Site: http://www.us.issworld.com
Sales Range: $50-74.9 Million
Emp.: 170
Commercial Facility Maintenance & Support Services
N.A.I.C.S.: 561210
Trent Harr (Gen Mgr)

ISS Facility Services, Inc. - Dallas Regional Office (8)
1620 N I 35 E Ste 311, Carrollton, TX 75006
Tel.: (972) 446-1223
Web Site: http://www.us.issworld.com
Sales Range: $125-149.9 Million
Emp.: 500
Commercial Facility Maintenance & Support Services
N.A.I.C.S.: 561210
Amy Vaughan (Gen Mgr)

ISS Facility Services, Inc. - Greensboro Regional Office (8)
18-A Oak Branch Dr, Greensboro, NC 27407
Tel.: (336) 855-8480
Web Site: http://www.us.issworld.com
Sales Range: $75-99.9 Million
Emp.: 218
Commercial Facility Maintenance & Support Services
N.A.I.C.S.: 561210
Randy Jordan (Gen Mgr)

ISS Facility Services, Inc. - Houston Regional Office (8)
320 Garden Oaks Blvd, Houston, TX 77018
Tel.: (713) 956-2277

The Goldman Sachs Group, Inc.—(Continued)

Web Site: http://www.us.issworld.com
Sales Range: $25-49.9 Million
Emp.: 14
Commercial Facility Maintenance & Support Services
N.A.I.C.S.: 561210
Jim Roll *(Gen Mgr)*

ISS Facility Services, Inc. - Kansas City Regional Office **(8)**
1225 E 18th St, Kansas City, MO 64108
Tel.: (816) 421-8088
Web Site: http://www.us.issworld.com
Emp.: 600
Commercial Facility Maintenance & Support Services
N.A.I.C.S.: 561210
John Combs *(Mgr-Bus Dev)*

ISS Facility Services, Inc. - Las Vegas Regional Office **(8)**
2700 E Patrick Ln Ste 3, Las Vegas, NV 89120
Tel.: (702) 822-2133
Web Site: http://www.us.issworld.com
Sales Range: $75-99.9 Million
Commercial Facility Maintenance & Support Services
N.A.I.C.S.: 561210

ISS Facility Services, Inc. - Memphis Regional Office **(8)**
3043 Broad Ave, Memphis, TN 38112-3003
Tel.: (901) 452-3770
Sales Range: $25-49.9 Million
Emp.: 10
Commercial Facility Maintenance & Support Services
N.A.I.C.S.: 561210
Remiro Alvarev *(Gen Mgr)*

ISS Facility Services, Inc. - Phoenix Regional Office **(8)**
3800 N Central Ave Ste 460, Phoenix, AZ 85012
Tel.: (602) 222-2555
Web Site: http://www.us.issworld.com
Commercial Facility Maintenance & Support Services
N.A.I.C.S.: 561210

ISS Facility Services, Inc. - San Antonio Regional Office **(8)**
8506 Speedway Dr, San Antonio, TX 78230-5331
Tel.: (210) 349-4647
Web Site: http://www.us.issworld.com
Sales Range: $250-299.9 Million
Emp.: 800
Commercial Facility Maintenance & Support Services
N.A.I.C.S.: 561210

Subsidiary (Domestic):

ISS TMC Services, Inc. **(8)**
81 Dorsa Ave, Livingston, NJ 07039
Tel.: (973) 740-0032
Web Site: http://www.us.issworld.com
Emp.: 1,500
Commercial Facility Maintenance & Support Services
N.A.I.C.S.: 561210
Lisa Ostermann *(Gen Mgr)*

Subsidiary (Non-US):

ISS Ireland Ltd. **(7)**
4 6 Rivorwalk Citywest Business Campus, Dublin, Ireland
Tel.: (353) 1 468 2900
Web Site: http://www.ie.issworld.com
Emp.: 3,700
Commercial Facility Maintenance & Business Support Services
N.A.I.C.S.: 561210
Eric Doyle *(Mng Dir)*

ISS Island ehf. **(7)**
Austurhrauni 7, 210, Gardabaer, Iceland
Tel.: (354) 5800600
Web Site: http://www.is.issworld.com
Emp.: 50
Commercial Facility Maintenance & Business Support Services
N.A.I.C.S.: 561210
Gudmundur Gudmundsson *(Country Mgr)*

ISS N.V. **(7)**
Leuvensesteenweg 248C, 1800, Vilvoorde, Belgium
Tel.: (32) 22636611
Web Site: https://www.be.issworld.com
Sales Range: $75-99.9 Million
Emp.: 500
Commercial Facility Maintenance & Business Support Services
N.A.I.C.S.: 561210

ISS Nederland B.V. **(7)**
Rijnzathe 8, 3454 PV, De Meern, Netherlands
Tel.: (31) 302424344
Web Site: http://www.nl.issworld.com
Emp.: 110
Commercial Facility Maintenance & Business Support Services
N.A.I.C.S.: 561210

Subsidiary (Domestic):

De Loge Schoonmaakdiensten B.V. **(8)**
Van Deventerlaan 30-40, NL-3528 AE, Utrecht, Netherlands
Tel.: (31) 30 242 4344
Web Site: http://www.nl.issworld.com
Sales Range: $75-99.9 Million
Facility Janitorial & Specialty Cleaning Services
N.A.I.C.S.: 561720

Subsidiary (Domestic):

ISS Facility Services **(9)**
Rijnzathe 8, 3454 PV, De Meern, Netherlands
Tel.: (31) 302424344
Web Site: https://www.nl.issworld.com
Sales Range: $50-74.9 Million
Emp.: 200
Food Industry Facility Sanitizing & Maintenance Services
N.A.I.C.S.: 561210
Peter Vorm *(Gen Mgr)*

Subsidiary (Domestic):

ISS Integrated Facility Services B.V. **(8)**
Rijnzathe 8, NL-3528, De Meern, Netherlands
Tel.: (31) 302424344
Web Site: http://www.nl.issworld.com
Sales Range: $50-74.9 Million
Integrated Facility Support Management Services
N.A.I.C.S.: 541611

Subsidiary (Domestic):

ISS Hospital Services B.V. **(9)**
Rijnzathe 8, 3454 PV, De Meern, Netherlands
Tel.: (31) 302424800
Web Site: http://www.nl.issworld.com
Sales Range: $50-74.9 Million
Emp.: 200
Management of Integrated Hospital Support Services
N.A.I.C.S.: 541611

Subsidiary (Non-US):

ISS Palvelut Oy **(7)**
Karvaamokuja 2 A, PO Box 100, 01055, Helsinki, Finland
Tel.: (358) 205155
Web Site: https://www.fi.issworld.com
Emp.: 12,000
Commercial Facility Maintenance & Business Support Services
N.A.I.C.S.: 561210

ISS Schweiz AG **(7)**
Vulkanplatz 3, PO Box 8010, 8010, Zurich, Switzerland
Tel.: (41) 587878000
Web Site: https://www.ch.issworld.com
Holding Company; Facility Support Services
N.A.I.C.S.: 551112
David Macherel *(Mng Dir)*
John Ruf *(Mng Dir)*
Martin Zubler *(Mng Dir)*
Christophe Favier-Bosson *(Mng Dir)*

Subsidiary (Domestic):

ISS Facility Services AG **(8)**

Buckhauserstrasse 22, CH-8010, Zurich, Switzerland
Tel.: (41) 587878000
Web Site: http://www.iss.ch
Sales Range: $75-99.9 Million
Emp.: 500
Commercial Facility Support Services
N.A.I.C.S.: 561210
Andre Nauer *(CEO)*

Subsidiary (Non-US):

ISS Servisystem Kft. **(7)**
Peterdy utca 15, Budapest, 1071, Hungary
Tel.: (36) 1 413 3140
Web Site: http://www.hu.issworld.com
Sales Range: $75-99.9 Million
Commercial Facility Maintenance & Business Support Services
N.A.I.C.S.: 561210
Peter Szabo *(Country Mgr)*

ISS Servisystem d.o.o. **(7)**
Ptujska Cesta 95, SI-2000, Maribor, Slovenia
Tel.: (386) 24503300
Web Site: http://www.si.issworld.com
Sales Range: $10-24.9 Million
Commercial Facility Maintenance & Business Support Services
N.A.I.C.S.: 561210
Rudi Zupan *(Mng Dir)*

ISS Servisystem do Brasil Ltda. **(7)**
Estrada Kaiko 8 Embu, 06843-195, Sao Paulo, Brazil
Tel.: (55) 1121353700
Web Site: http://www.br.issworld.com
Sales Range: $25-49.9 Million
Commercial Facility Maintenance & Business Support Services
N.A.I.C.S.: 561210

ISS UK Limited **(7)**
Velocity 1 Brooklands Drive Brooklands, Weybridge, KT13 0SL, Surrey, United Kingdom
Tel.: (44) 8450576500
Web Site: https://www.uk.issworld.com
Emp.: 200
Holding Company; Commercial Facility Maintenance & Business Support Services
N.A.I.C.S.: 551112
David Openshaw *(Middle East & South Africa)*
Liz Benison *(CEO)*
Sam Hockman *(CEO)*

Subsidiary (Domestic):

ISS Facility Services Limited **(8)**
Velocity 1 Brooklands Brooklands Drive, Weybridge, KT13 0SL, Surrey, United Kingdom
Tel.: (44) 8450576400
Web Site: http://www.uk.issworld.com
Sales Range: $750-799.9 Million
Commercial Facility Maintenance & Business Support Services
N.A.I.C.S.: 561210
Phil Jones *(Mng Dir)*

Branch (Domestic):

ISS Facility Services Ltd. - London **(9)**
9- 10- 11th Fl South Keuy Plz, London, E14 9FH, United Kingdom
Tel.: (44) 8449361030
Web Site: http://www.uk.issworld.com
Sales Range: $50-74.9 Million
Commercial Facility Maintenance & Support Services
N.A.I.C.S.: 561210

Joint Venture (Non-US):

KION Group AG **(4)**
Thea-Rasche-Strasse 8, 60549, Frankfurt am Main, Germany
Tel.: (49) 69201100
Web Site: https://www.kiongroup.com
Rev.: $12,339,412,907
Assets: $18,765,810,490
Liabilities: $12,535,829,916
Net Worth: $6,229,980,574
Earnings: $330,023,743
Emp.: 41,552
Fiscal Year-end: 12/31/2023
Industrial Equipment Mfr

N.A.I.C.S.: 551112
Pong Quek Ching *(Chief Asia Pacific & Americas Officer & Member-Exec Bd)*
Ozcan Pancarci *(Deputy Chm-Supervisory Bd)*
Michael Macht *(Chm-Supervisory Bd)*
Hasan Dandashly *(Pres)*
Andreas Krinninger *(Pres)*
Henry Puhl *(CTO)*
Marcus A. Wassenberg *(CFO)*

Subsidiary (US):

Dematic Corp. **(5)**
507 Plymouth Ave NE, Grand Rapids, MI 49505
Tel.: (877) 725-7500
Web Site: http://www.dematic.com
Materials Handling Equipment & Logistics Systems Mfr & Distr
N.A.I.C.S.: 333922
Hasan Dandashly *(Pres & CEO)*
Michele Longo *(Sr VP-HR)*
Michael Larsson *(Exec VP)*
Michael Jerogin *(Sr VP)*
Meraj Anas *(Sr VP)*
Shibu Sasidharan *(Sr VP)*
Deidre Cusack *(Exec VP)*
David Dechavassine *(Sr VP)*
Howard Yntema *(CFO)*
Erin Dillard *(Sr VP)*
Eric Sharon *(Sr VP)*
Chris Petitt *(Sr VP)*
Chris Steiner *(Sr VP)*

Subsidiary (Non-US):

Dematic GmbH **(6)**
Martinseestrasse 1, D-63150, Heusenstamm, Germany
Tel.: (49) 69 58 30 25 0
Web Site: http://www.dematic.com
Holding Company; Regional Managing Office
N.A.I.C.S.: 551112
Jens Hardenacke *(Mng Dir)*

Subsidiary (Domestic):

Dematic GmbH **(7)**
Carl-Legien-Strasse 15, Offenbach, D-63073, Germany
Tel.: (49) 6989030
Web Site: http://www.dematic.com
Materials Handling Equipment & Electronics Assembly Systems Mfr
N.A.I.C.S.: 333922

Subsidiary (Non-US):

Dematic GmbH **(7)**
Industriestrasse 50, 8112, Otelfingen, Switzerland
Tel.: (41) 434556065
Web Site: https://www.dematic.com
Materials Handling Equipment & Electronics Assembly Systems Mfr
N.A.I.C.S.: 333922

Subsidiary (Domestic):

Dematic Logistics GmbH **(7)**
Marie-Curie-Strasse 3a, 48599, Gronau, Germany
Tel.: (49) 2562 70108 0
Web Site: http://www.dematic.com
Automated Material Handling Systems & Solutions
N.A.I.C.S.: 541614

Dematic Logistics GmbH **(7)**
Schelpmilser Weg 20, 33609, Bielefeld, Germany
Tel.: (49) 521 92277 100
Web Site: http://www.dematic.com
Material Handling Equipment Solutions & Electronics Assembly Systems Mfr
N.A.I.C.S.: 541614

Subsidiary (Non-US):

Dematic Ltd. **(7)**
Banbury Business Park Trinity Way, Adderbury, Banbury, OX17 3SN, Oxon, United Kingdom
Tel.: (44) 1295 274 600
Web Site: http://www.dematic.com
Automated Logistics Solutions
N.A.I.C.S.: 541614

Subsidiary (Non-US):

Dematic Holdings Pty. Ltd. (6)
24 Narabang Way, Belrose, 2085, NSW, Australia
Tel.: (61) 294865555
Web Site: http://www.dematic.com
Emp.: 4,000
Holding Company
N.A.I.C.S.: 551112
Hasan Dandashly *(Pres & CEO)*
Michael Jerogin *(Sr VP-APAC Reg)*
Deidre Cusack *(Sr VP-Global Products & Solutions)*
Michele Longo *(Sr VP-HR)*
Michael Larsson *(Exec VP)*
Bernard Biolchini *(Exec VP)*
Meraj Anas *(Sr VP)*
Shibu Sasidharan *(Sr VP)*
David Dechavassine *(Pres)*
Howard Yntema *(CFO)*
Erin Dillard *(VP)*
Eric Sharon *(Sr VP)*
Chris Petitt *(Sr VP)*
Chris Steiner *(Sr VP)*

Subsidiary (Domestic):

Dematic Pty. Ltd. (7)
24 Narabang Way, Belrose, 2085, NSW, Australia
Tel.: (61) 294865555
Web Site: http://www.dematic.com.au
Emp.: 500
Materials Handling Equipment & Logistics Systems Mfr & Distr
N.A.I.C.S.: 333922

Subsidiary (Domestic):

Dematic Reddwerks (6)
1122 S Capital of Texas Hwy Ste 150, Austin, TX 78746
Tel.: (512) 597-6810
Web Site: http://www.dematicreddwerks.com
Emp.: 200
Warehouse Management System Software
N.A.I.C.S.: 513210
Francisco Arzu *(CTO)*

Subsidiary (Domestic):

Linde Material Handling GmbH (5)
Schweinheimer Strasse 34, PO Box 62, 63743, Aschaffenburg, Germany
Tel.: (49) 6021990
Web Site: http://www.linde-mh.de
Sales Range: $1-4.9 Billion
Emp.: 12,531
Forklifts, Industrial Trucks & Hydraulic Engineering Equipment Mfr
N.A.I.C.S.: 333924

Subsidiary (Non-US):

A.G. Pruden & Cia. S.A. (6)
Av Hipolito Yrigoyen 2441/2465 Martinez, B1640HFW, Buenos Aires, Argentina
Tel.: (54) 1147332500
Web Site: https://www.agpruden.com
Sales Range: $25-49.9 Million
Emp.: 120
Forklifts, Industrial Trucks & Hydraulics Equipment Distr
N.A.I.C.S.: 333924

EDNIL d.o.o. Sarajevo (6)
Izeta Delica Br 1A, 71320, Sarajevo, Bosnia & Herzegovina
Tel.: (387) 33 425 200
Web Site: http://www.toyota-viljuskari.ba
Sales Range: $25-49.9 Million
Emp.: 30
Forklifts & Industrial Trucks Sales & Maintenance
N.A.I.C.S.: 333924
Mesud Rizvo *(Mng Dir)*

Fenwick-Linde S.A.R.L. (6)
1 RUE Du Marechal De Lattre De Tassigny, Saint-Quentin-en-Yvelines, 78854, France
Tel.: (33) 130684412
Web Site: http://www.fenwick-linde.com
Sales Range: $300-349.9 Million
Emp.: 350
Forklifts & Industrial Trucks Mfr
N.A.I.C.S.: 333924

Division (Domestic):

Fenwick-Linde Hydraulics (7)

1 rue du Marechal de Lattre de Tassigny, 78854, Saint-Quentin-en-Yvelines, Cedex, France
Tel.: (33) 130684647
Web Site: http://www.fl-hydraulics.fr
Sales Range: $100-124.9 Million
Emp.: 300
Hydraulic Pumps & Motors Mfr
N.A.I.C.S.: 333996

Subsidiary (US):

KION North America Corporation (6)
2450 W 5th N St, Summerville, SC 29483
Tel.: (843) 875-8000
Web Site: http://www.kion-na.com
Forklifts & Industrial Trucks Mfr
N.A.I.C.S.: 333924
Max Heller *(Pres, CEO & CFO)*
Michael Gore *(VP-Sls)*
Daniel Schlegel *(VP-Ops)*
Paul Antor *(VP-Product Support)*
David Brown *(Dir-HR)*
Ben Lee *(Dir-Key Acct Sls)*
Jeff Peterson *(Dir-Mfg)*
Christian Loew *(VP-Product Dev)*
Julie Richardson *(Dir-Inside Sls)*
Rick Schiel *(Dir-Dealer Sls)*

Subsidiary (Non-US):

Linde (China) Forklift Truck Corp., Ltd. (6)
No 89 Jinshang Rd, PO Box 0956, Xiamen, 361009, China
Tel.: (86) 5925533800
Web Site: http://www.linde-china.com
Sales Range: $125-149.9 Million
Forklifts & Industrial Trucks Mfr
N.A.I.C.S.: 333924

Linde Fordertechnik GmbH (6)
Franzosenhausweg 35, 4030, Linz, Austria
Tel.: (43) 50389510
Web Site: https://www.linde-mh.at
Sales Range: $75-99.9 Million
Emp.: 160
Forklifts, Industrial Trucks & Hydraulic Equipment Mfr
N.A.I.C.S.: 333924

Linde Heavy Truck Division Ltd. (6)
Linde Industrial Park, Merthyr Tydfil, CF48 4LA, United Kingdom
Tel.: (44) 1443624200
Web Site: http://www.linde-htd.com
Sales Range: $125-149.9 Million
Large Forklifts & Industrial Trucks Mfr
N.A.I.C.S.: 333924

Linde High Lift Chile S.A. (6)
Avenida El Retiro 1251 Centro Industrial El Montijo, Complejo Megacentro, Renca, 8640000, Chile
Tel.: (56) 24398100
Web Site: http://www.lindehighlift.cl
Sales Range: $50-74.9 Million
Emp.: 150
Forklifts & Industrial Trucks Mfr
N.A.I.C.S.: 333924

Linde Lansing Fordertechnik AG (6)
Alte Dubendorferstrasse 20, 8305, Dietlikon, Switzerland
Tel.: (41) 448352300
Web Site: https://www.linde-mh.ch
Sales Range: $50-74.9 Million
Emp.: 170
Forklifts & Industrial Trucks Mfr
N.A.I.C.S.: 333924

Linde Material Handling (Australia) Pty. Ltd. (6)
3 Healey Circuit, Huntingwood, 2148, Australia
Tel.: (61) 1300 454 633
Web Site: http://www.lindemh.com.au
Sales Range: $75-99.9 Million
Emp.: 220
Forklifts & Industrial Trucks Mfr
N.A.I.C.S.: 333924

Linde Material Handling (Pty) Ltd. (6)
Milkway & Newton Road Linbro Park, PO Box 1101, Cnr Milkyway & Neutron Ave, 2001, Johannesburg, South Africa
Tel.: (27) 0117237000
Web Site: http://www.linde.co.za

Sales Range: $75-99.9 Million
Emp.: 185
Forklifts & Industrial Trucks Mfr
N.A.I.C.S.: 333924
Branton Alexander *(Mng Dir)*

Linde Material Handling (UK) Ltd. (6)
Kingsclere Road, Basingstoke, RG21 6XJ, Hampshire, United Kingdom
Tel.: (44) 1256 342 000
Web Site: http://www.linde-mh.co.uk
Sales Range: $200-249.9 Million
Emp.: 300
Fork Lifts & Industrial Trucks Mfr
N.A.I.C.S.: 333924
Ulrike Just *(Mng Dir)*

Linde Material Handling Ceska republica s.r.o. (6)
Polygraficka 622/2, Prague, 108 00, Czech Republic
Tel.: (420) 271078111
Web Site: http://www.linde-mh.cz
Sales Range: $75-99.9 Million
Emp.: 200
Forklifts & Industrial Trucks Mfr
N.A.I.C.S.: 333924

Linde Material Handling Iberica S.A. (6)
Avenida Prat de la Riba 181, Palleja, 08780, Spain
Tel.: (34) 936633232
Web Site: http://www.linde-mh.es
Sales Range: $75-99.9 Million
Emp.: 400
Forklifts & Industrial Trucks Mfr
N.A.I.C.S.: 333924
Paul F. Drumm *(Mng Dir)*

Linde Material Handling Italia S.p.A. (6)
Via Luguzzone Zona Industriale, Brunello, Buguggiate, 21020, Varese, Italy
Tel.: (39) 0332877111
Web Site: http://www.linde-mh.it
Sales Range: $25-49.9 Million
Emp.: 96
Forklifts & Industrial Trucks Mfr
N.A.I.C.S.: 333924

Linde Material Handling do Brasil Ltda. (6)
Rua Victorino 134, Barueri, 06230-110, SP, Brazil
Tel.: (55) 1136044755
Web Site: http://www.linde-mh.com.br
Sales Range: $25-49.9 Million
Emp.: 80
Forklifts & Industrial Trucks Distr, Sales & Service
N.A.I.C.S.: 333924

Linde Vilicari Hrvatska d.o.o. (6)
Novoselska 25, 10040, Zagreb, Croatia
Tel.: (385) 12991111
Web Site: http://www.linde.hr
Sales Range: $25-49.9 Million
Emp.: 100
Forklifts & Industrial Trucks Mfr
N.A.I.C.S.: 333924

Motocar Service Company (MSC) (6)
Komatevsko shouse Str 26, 4007, Plovdiv, Bulgaria
Tel.: (359) 32625051
Web Site: http://www.motocarservice.com
Sales Range: $25-49.9 Million
Emp.: 94
Forklifts & Industrial Trucks Mfr
N.A.I.C.S.: 333924
George Terzeiv *(Chm & Gen Mgr-Sls)*

Motrac Handling & Cleaning n.v.-s.a. (6)
Noorderlaan 612, 2030, Antwerp, Belgium
Tel.: (32) 33601111
Web Site: http://www.motrac.be
Sales Range: $75-99.9 Million
Emp.: 150
Parts Distr & Maintenance Services for Forklifts & Industrial Trucks
N.A.I.C.S.: 811198

Subsidiary (Non-US):

OM Carrelli Elevatori S.p.A. (5)

Viale A de Gasperi 7, 20020, Lainate, Milan, Italy
Tel.: (39) 02937651
Web Site: http://www.om-still.it
Sales Range: $350-399.9 Million
Emp.: 1,232
Forklifts & Industrial Trucks Mfr
N.A.I.C.S.: 333924
Angelo Zanotti *(CEO-Sls & Svc)*

Subsidiary (Non-US):

Ibercarretillas OM Espana S.A. (6)
Pol Ind Pratense - Calle 111 s/n, 8820, El Prat de Llobregat, Spain
Tel.: (34) 934798500
Sales Range: $25-49.9 Million
Emp.: 70
Forklifts & Industrial Trucks Mfr
N.A.I.C.S.: 333924

Subsidiary (Domestic):

STILL GmbH (5)
Berzeliusstrasse 10, PO Box 740720, D-22113, Hamburg, Germany
Tel.: (49) 4073390
Web Site: http://www.still.de
Sales Range: $1-4.9 Billion
Emp.: 6,258
Forklifts & Industrial Trucks Mfr
N.A.I.C.S.: 333924
Henry Puhl *(Chm-Mgmt Bd, Pres & Mng Dir)*
Frank Muller *(Sr VP)*

Subsidiary (Non-US):

STILL AG (6)
Industrie strasse 50, 8112, Otelfingen, Switzerland
Tel.: (41) 448465111
Web Site: http://www.still.ch
Sales Range: $25-49.9 Million
Emp.: 60
Forklifts & Industrial Trucks Mfr
N.A.I.C.S.: 333924

STILL CR, spol. s r.o. (6)
Sterboholska 102 10 Hostivar, 102 19, Prague, Czech Republic
Tel.: (420) 274001411
Web Site: https://www.still.cz
Sales Range: $50-74.9 Million
Emp.: 130
Forklifts & Industrial Trucks Mfr
N.A.I.C.S.: 333924

STILL Danmark A/S (6)
Essen 1, 6000, Kolding, Denmark
Tel.: (45) 76319800
Web Site: https://www.still.dk
Sales Range: $25-49.9 Million
Emp.: 100
Forklifts & Industrial Trucks Mfr
N.A.I.C.S.: 333924

STILL Gesellschaft m.b.H. (6)
Industriezentrum No Sud Strabe 3 Objekt 6, 2351, Wiener Neudorf, Austria
Tel.: (43) 2236615010
Web Site: http://www.still.at
Sales Range: $25-49.9 Million
Emp.: 102
Forklifts & Industrial Trucks Mfr
N.A.I.C.S.: 333924

STILL Intern Transport B.V. (6)
Nijverheidsweg 5, PO Box 500, 3340 AD, Hendrik-Ido-Ambacht, Netherlands
Tel.: (31) 786845200
Web Site: https://www.still.nl
Sales Range: $75-99.9 Million
Emp.: 200
Forklifts & Industrial Trucks Mfr
N.A.I.C.S.: 333924

STILL Italia S.p.A. (6)
Corso Europa 5, 20020, Lainate, Italy
Tel.: (39) 0293 5761
Web Site: http://www.still.it
Sales Range: $25-49.9 Million
Emp.: 85
Forklifts & Industrial Trucks Mfr
N.A.I.C.S.: 333924

STILL Materials Handling Ltd. (6)
Aston Way Moss Side, Leyland, PR26 7UX, Lancashire, United Kingdom
Tel.: (44) 1772644300
Web Site: http://www.still.co.uk

The Goldman Sachs Group, Inc.—(Continued)

Sales Range: $25-49.9 Million
Emp.: 55
Forklifts & Industrial Trucks Mfr
N.A.I.C.S.: 333924
Gillian Reed (Mng Dir)

STILL N.V. (6)
Vosveld 9, 2110, Wijnegem, Belgium
Tel.: (32) 33606200
Web Site: http://www.still.be
Sales Range: $50-74.9 Million
Emp.: 125
Forklifts & Industrial Trucks Mfr
N.A.I.C.S.: 333924
Jean-Paul DuBois (Mng Dir)

STILL S.A. (6)
Calle Primer De Maig-Pg Ind Gran Via Sud
38 - 48 L hospitalet de, Llobregat, 08908,
Barcelona, Spain
Tel.: (34) 933946000
Web Site: http://www.still.es
Sales Range: $50-74.9 Million
Emp.: 150
Forklifts & Industrial Trucks Mfr
N.A.I.C.S.: 333924

STILL S.A.S. (6)
6 Bd Michael Faraday Serris, 77716,
Marne-la-Vallee, France
Tel.: (33) 164174000
Web Site: http://www.still-fr.com
Sales Range: $200-249.9 Million
Emp.: 700
Forklifts & Industrial Trucks Mfr
N.A.I.C.S.: 333924

Subsidiary (Domestic):

STILL Wagner GmbH & Co. KG (6)
Ernst Wagner Weg 1-5, PO Box 2943,
D-72766, Reutlingen, Germany
Tel.: (49) 7127815541
Web Site: http://www.kiongroup.com
Sales Range: $125-149.9 Million
Emp.: 500
Forklifts & Industrial Trucks Mfr
N.A.I.C.S.: 333924

Affiliate (Domestic):

Klemm Tank Lines, Inc. (4)
2204 Pamperin Rd, Green Bay, WI 54313
Tel.: (920) 434-6343
Bulk Hazardous Materials & Petroleum
Transportation Services
N.A.I.C.S.: 484230

Joint Venture (Non-US):

LNI Verkko Holding Oy (4)
Televiciokatu 1 A, FIN 00240, Helsingfors,
Finland (45%)
Tel.: (358) 2058611
Holding Company; Energy Solutions Services
N.A.I.C.S.: 551112

Holding (Domestic):

Lifetime Industries, Inc. (4)
5960 Inglewood Dr Ste 115, Pleasanton,
CA 94588
Tel.: (209) 491-4797
Web Site: http://www.boydcorp.com
Sealing, Thermal Management & Protection
Products Mfr
N.A.I.C.S.: 326299
Jerry Toth (Sr VP-Engrg & Tech)
Michael Sutsko (Chief Comml Officer)
Dan Lee (OOO)
David Huang (Pres-Asia & Enterprise Sector)
Doug Britt (Pres & CEO)
Jeremiah Shives (Chief Compliance Officer,
Gen Counsel & Sr VP)
Flavio Magalhaes (Chief Integration Officer)
Nikhil Sud (CIO)
Jack Monti (VP)
Jen Wall (VP)

Subsidiary (Domestic):

A.B. Boyd Co. (5)
600 S McClure Rd, Modesto, CA 95357
Tel.: (209) 236-1111
Web Site: http://www.boydcorp.com
Sealing, Thermal Management & Protection
Products Mfr

N.A.I.C.S.: 326299
Eric Struik (CFO & Sr VP)
Stan Lewis (Sr VP-Integration-Global)
Jerry Toth (Sr VP-Engrg & Tech)
Michael Sutsko (Chief Comml Officer)
Dan Lee (Sr VP-Mfg Ops-Global)
David Huang (Sr VP)
Bobby Ireland (Sr VP-HR)
Jeremiah Shives (Chief Compliance Officer,
Gen Counsel & Sr VP)
Doug Britt (Pres & CEO)

Division (Domestic):

Aavid (6)
1 Aavid Cir, Laconia, NH 03246
Tel.: (603) 528-3400
Web Site: http://www.aavid.com
Thermal Engineering & Thermal Management Solutions to Semiconductor Industry
N.A.I.C.S.: 334419

Subsidiary (Domestic):

Aavid Allcast, LLC (7)
217 Weis St, Allenton, WI 53002
Tel.: (262) 629-5566
Emp.: 75
Aluminum Die-Casting Foundries
N.A.I.C.S.: 331523
John Cleary (Plant Mgr)
Mark Magnarini (Pres & CEO)
Kevin Healy (Mgr-Sls)
Lynn Klein (Mgr-Quality)
Jay Garrison (Mgr-Ops)

Subsidiary (Non-US):

Aavid China (7)
No 1199 Xin Fei Rd, Songjiang, Shanghai,
201611, China
Tel.: (86) 21 6115 2000
Web Site: http://www.boydcorp.com
Thermal Engineering & Thermal Management Solutions to Semiconductor Industry
N.A.I.C.S.: 334419

Aavid India (7)
7 Manjusar Gidc, Savli, Vadodara, 391175,
Gujarat, India
Tel.: (91) 2667 264781
Web Site: http://www.boydcorp.com
Thermal Engineering & Thermal Management Solutions to Semiconductor Industry
N.A.I.C.S.: 334419

Subsidiary (Domestic):

Aavid Niagara LLC (7)
3315 Haseley Dr, Niagara Falls, NY 14304
Tel.: (716) 297-0652
Web Site: http://www.niagarathermal.com
Emp.: 120
Heat Exchangers & Heat Transfer Systems
Mfr & Whslr
N.A.I.C.S.: 333414

Subsidiary (Non-US):

Aavid Thermalloy S.r.l. (7)
Via Del Fonditore 4, 40138, Bologna,
Italy (100%)
Tel.: (39) 051764011
Thermal Engineering & Thermal Management Solutions to Semiconductor Industry
N.A.I.C.S.: 334419

Boyd Thermal Systems Taiwan Inc. (7)
20F-6 No 79 Sec 1 Xinthia 5th Rd, Xizhi
District, Taipei, 221, Taiwan
Tel.: (886) 226989888
Web Site: https://www.boydcorp.com
Thermal Engineering & Thermal Management Solutions to Semiconductor Industry
N.A.I.C.S.: 334419

Subsidiary (Domestic):

Lytron Incorporated (7)
55 Dragon Ct, Woburn, MA 01801
Tel.: (781) 933-7300
Web Site: http://www.lytron.com
Cold Plates, Cooling Systems & Heat Exchangers Mfr
N.A.I.C.S.: 333415

Thermacore, Inc. (7)
780 Eden Rd, Lancaster, PA 17601
Tel.: (717) 569-6551
Web Site: http://www.thermacore.com

Thermal Management Systems Designer &
Mfr
N.A.I.C.S.: 332999

Subsidiary (Domestic):

KTC Management Corporation (8)
2000 Cabot Blvd W Ste 150, Langhorne,
PA 19047-2011
Tel.: (215) 375-3035
Web Site: http://www.thermacore.com
Emp.: 17
Designer & Mfr of Thermal Management
Products for Power Electronics Cooling
N.A.I.C.S.: 334419
Adam Rosen (Sr VP & Gen Mgr)

Subsidiary (Non-US):

Thermacore Europe Ltd. (8)
12 Wansbeck Business Park, Ashington,
NE63 8QW, Northd, United Kingdom
Tel.: (44) 1670859500
Thermal Management Systems Designer &
Mfr
N.A.I.C.S.: 332999

Subsidiary (Domestic):

GM Nameplate Inc. (6)
2040 15th Ave W, Seattle, WA 98119-2728
Tel.: (206) 284-2200
Web Site: http://www.gmnameplate.com
Sales Range: $25-49.9 Million
Emp.: 887
Provider of Personalized Products
N.A.I.C.S.: 332812
Alan Elser (CFO)

Division (Domestic):

Solimide (6)
1560 Hwy 371 S, Magnolia, AR 71753-8972
Tel.: (972) 461-8026
Web Site: http://www.solimide.com
Specialty Foam Products Mfr
N.A.I.C.S.: 326150

Subsidiary (Domestic):

The Durbin Group, LLC (6)
7101 Monument Ct, Spotsylvania, VA
22553-1967
Tel.: (540) 840-0376
Web Site: http://www.durbingroup.com
Engineeering Services
N.A.I.C.S.: 541330
John Durbin (Pres)

Subsidiary (Domestic):

Action Fabricators, Inc. (5)
3760 E Paris Ave SE, Grand Rapids, MI
49512
Tel.: (616) 957-2032
Flexible Material Converted Products Mfr
N.A.I.C.S.: 339999
Matt Alferink (VP-Mfg)

Specification Seals, Inc. (5)
4990 E Hunter Ave, Anaheim, CA 92807
Tel.: (714) 777-5995
Sales Range: $1-9.9 Million
Emp.: 12
Industrial Supplies Merchant Whslr & Distr
N.A.I.C.S.: 423840
Ken Schaefer (Pres)
Paul Ess (Gen Mgr)

Joint Venture (Domestic):

Neovia Logistics Services, LLC (4)
6363 N State Hwy 161 Ste 700, Irving, TX
75038
Tel.: (469) 513-7000
Web Site: http://www.neovialogistics.com
Third Party Logistics Services
N.A.I.C.S.: 541614
Zach Green (Chief Legal Officer)
Thomas Musgrave (Chief Ops & Tech Officer)
Stephen Boone (Sr Dir-Comm)
Michael Foss (Chief HR Officer)
Christopher Synek (CEO)
Dave Moore (COO)
Carlos Rodriguez (Chm)

Subsidiary (Non-US):

Neovia Logistics Germany GmbH (5)

Tel.: (49) 71176991111
Third Party Logistics Services
N.A.I.C.S.: 541614

**Neovia Logistics Services (U.K.)
Ltd.** (5)
Peckleton Lane, Desford, LE9 9JU, United
Kingdom
Tel.: (44) 1162186000
Emp.: 1,000
Logistic Services
N.A.I.C.S.: 488999

Neovia Logistics Services International NV (5)
Steenstraat 20/2, PO Box 2, 1800, Vilvoorde, Belgium
Tel.: (32) 22 63 46 11
Web Site: http://www.neovialogistics.com
Emp.: 65
Logistic Services
N.A.I.C.S.: 488999

**Neovia Logistics Services Spain
S.A.** (5)
Guadalajara Jalisco 5, Guadalajara, 19004,
Spain
Tel.: (34) 949325010
Logistic Services
N.A.I.C.S.: 561499

Subsidiary (Domestic):

North Canton Transfer Company (5)
2515 Greensburg Rd, North Canton, OH
44720
Tanker Services
N.A.I.C.S.: 484121

Petro-Chemical Transport (5)
3440 Sojourn Dr 100, Carrollton, TX 75006
Distribution & Logistics Services
N.A.I.C.S.: 541614

Joint Venture (Domestic):

Nuxeo (4)
181 N 11th St Ste 307, New York, NY
11211
Tel.: (888) 882-0969
Web Site: http://www.nuxeo.com
Sales Range: $10-24.9 Million
Content Management Software
N.A.I.C.S.: 513210

Holding (Domestic):

Restaurant Technologies, Inc. (4)
2250 Pilot Knob Rd Ste 100, Mendota
Heights, MN 55120-1127
Tel.: (651) 796-1600
Web Site: http://www.rti-inc.com
Foodservice Fryer Oil Management Equipment Installation & Support Services
N.A.I.C.S.: 562112
Robert E. Weil (CFO)
Lisa J. Merryfield (VP-McDonalds Bus Unit)
Jason Cocco (Sr VP-Sls)
Tina Swanson (VP-Bus Dev & Partnerships)
Alissa Partee (Chief People Officer)
Diana Geseking (Gen Counsel & Sec)
David Wolf (VP-Fin)
Josh Renihan (VP-Field Sls)
Andy Dulka (CIO)

Holding (Non-US):

Robyg S.A. (4)
Aleja Rzeczypospolitej 1, 02-972, Warsaw,
Poland
Tel.: (48) 224191100
Web Site: http://www.robyg.pl
Real Estate Investment Services
N.A.I.C.S.: 531390
Zbigniew Wojciech Okonski (Chm-Mgmt Bd)
Oscar Kazanelson (Chm-Supervisory Bd)
Marta Hejak (VP)
Dariusz Pawlukowicz (VP)

Joint Venture (Domestic):

Sterling Infosystems, Inc. (4)
1 State St Plz 24th Fl, New York, NY 10004
Tel.: (212) 736-5100
Web Site: https://www.sterlingbackcheck.ca
Employment & Background Screening Services
N.A.I.C.S.: 561499
Lou Paglia (Pres & COO)
Angela Stelle (CMO)
Peter Walker (CFO)

Peter Lehmann *(Chief Strategy Officer)*
Jennifer Ketchens *(Chief Diversity & Social Responsibility Officer)*
G.V. Prasad *(CEO-India & Head-Fulfillment-Global)*
Ivneet Kaur *(Exec VP)*
Meg Wilson *(Chief Product Officer)*
Robyn Price *(Exec VP)*
Steven Smith *(Pres)*

Subsidiary (Domestic):

EmployeeScreenIQ, Inc. (5)
PO Box 22627, Cleveland, OH 44122
Tel.: (216) 514-2800
Web Site: http://www.employeescreen.com
Background Screening Services
N.A.I.C.S.: 561499
Jason B. Morris *(Founder, Pres & COO)*
Les Fishman *(Chm & CEO)*
Nick Fishman *(CMO & Exec VP)*
Kevin Bachman *(Sr VP-Ops)*
Andrew Cashman *(Gen Mgr-Ops)*
Joel Cheesman *(Dir-Strategic Alliances)*
Kelly Lucha *(Dir-Client Rels)*
Dawn Shanklin *(Dir-Applicant Mgmt)*
Lauren Skrovan *(Dir-HR)*
Angela Preston *(Gen Counsel & VP-Compliance)*
Greg Schnitter *(Dir-Sls)*

Transport Service Co. (5)
2001 Spring Rd Ste 400, Oak Brook, IL 60523
Tel.: (630) 472-5900
Web Site:
http://www.transportserviceco.com
Sales Range: $125-149.9 Million
Emp.: 40
Contract Haulers
N.A.I.C.S.: 484121

Holding (Non-US):

eKomi, Ltd. (4)
Markgrafenstrasse 11, 10969, Berlin, Germany
Tel.: (49) 30 2000 444 999
Web Site: http://www.ekomi.de
Emp.: 200
Internet Consumer Information Management Services
N.A.I.C.S.: 541519
Michael Ambros *(Co-Founder & CEO)*
Gunther Schmidt *(Co-Founder & Mng Dir)*

Subsidiary (Domestic):

Goldman Sachs Urban Investment Group (3)
200W St, New York, NY 10282
Tel.: (212) 902-1000
Web Site: http://www.gs.com
Sales Range: $250-299.9 Million
Emp.: 225
Financial Investment
N.A.I.C.S.: 523999

Joint Venture (Domestic):

H2O Plus, LLC (4)
845 W Madison St, Chicago, IL 60607
Tel.: (312) 850-9283
Sales Range: $75-99.9 Million
Water-Based Skincare Products Mfr & Distr
N.A.I.C.S.: 325620
Joy Chen *(Pres & CEO)*

Subsidiary (Non-US):

Goldman Sachs Paris Inc. Et Cie (2)
85 avenue Marceau, 75116, Paris, France
Tel.: (33) 142121000
Web Site: https://www.goldmansachs.com
Investment Banking Services
N.A.I.C.S.: 523150

Branch (Domestic):

Goldman, Sachs & Co. (2)
125 High St Ste 1700, Boston, MA 02110-2719
Tel.: (617) 204-2000
Web Site: http://www2.goldmansachs.com
Investment Banking & Brokerage Services
N.A.I.C.S.: 523150
W. Matthew Kelly *(Executives)*

Subsidiary (Non-US):

Goldman, Sachs & Co. Wertpapier GMBH (2)

Messeturm Friedrich-ebert-anlage 49, Frankfurt, 60308, Germany
Tel.: (49) 6975321111
Leasing & Financial Services
N.A.I.C.S.: 523999
Michael Schmitz *(Mng Dir)*

Goldman Sachs (Asia) LLC (1)
Cheung Kong Center 68th Floor, 2 Queen's Road, Central, China (Hong Kong)
Tel.: (852) 29781000
Investment Banking, Trading & Principal Investments, Asset Management & Brokerage Services
N.A.I.C.S.: 523150
Ian M. Smith *(Mng Dir & Head-Electronic Trading-Asia Pacific)*
Ken Hitchner *(Pres-Asia Pacific)*
Canute Dalmasse *(Head-Execution Svcs-Asia Pacific)*
Matthew Westerman *(Head-Investment Banking Div-Asia Pacific)*
Andrea Vella *(Co-Head-Fin Grp-Asia Pacific)*
Jonathan Penkin *(Co-Head-Fin Grp-Asia Pacific)*
Anthony Miller *(Head-Investment Banking Solutions-Asia Pacific)*
John Kim *(Head-Mergers & Acq)*
Richard Campbell-Breeden *(Vice Chm-Investment Banking)*

Goldman Sachs (Singapore) PTE. (1)
1 Raffles Link 07-01 South Lobby, Singapore, 039393, Singapore
Tel.: (65) 68891000
Investment Banking Services
N.A.I.C.S.: 523150
Jason Moo *(CEO)*
Frederick Towfigh *(Dir-Advisory)*

Subsidiary (Domestic):

Goldman Sachs Foreign Exchange (Singapore) PTE (2)
1 Raffles Link, Singapore, 03939-3, Singapore
Tel.: (65) 68891000
Web Site: http://www.gs.com
Investment Banking Services
N.A.I.C.S.: 523150

Goldman Sachs Asset Management, L.P. (1)
200 West St, New York, NY 10282
Tel.: (212) 902-5400
Web Site: http://www.gsam.com
Asset Management & Investment Advisory Services
N.A.I.C.S.: 523940
Gregg J. Felton *(Founder)*
Jo Naturi *(Partner)*

Subsidiary (Non-US):

Froy ASA (2)
Sirholmen 34, 7260, Froya, Norway (90.82%)
Tel.: (47) 40007260
Web Site: https://froygruppen.no
Rev.: $248,725,202
Assets: $936,594,361
Liabilities: $552,083,611
Net Worth: $384,490,749
Earnings: $26,092,934
Emp.: 722
Fiscal Year-end: 12/31/2022
Agriculture Product Distr
N.A.I.C.S.: 424910
Sondre Vevstad *(CFO)*
Svein Sivertsen *(Chm)*
Tonje Foss *(CEO)*

Goldman Sachs Asset Management Co., Ltd. (2)
Roppongi Hills Mori Tower 10-1 Roppongi 6-chome, Minato-ku, Tokyo, 106-6147, Japan
Tel.: (81) 364376000
Leasing & Financial Services
N.A.I.C.S.: 523999

Joint Venture (Domestic):

MDVIP, LLC (2)
4950 Communication Ave Ste 100, Boca Raton, FL 33431-8561
Tel.: (561) 544-4000
Web Site: http://www.mdvip.com

Operational, Technological & Managerial Support (for Physicians)
N.A.I.C.S.: 561499
Matthew Hashem *(Pres & CFO)*
Bret Jorgensen *(Chm & CEO)*
Roy R. Harris *(Gen Counsel)*
Donald F. Hankus *(CIO)*
Chris Lillich *(CMO)*
Ben Behroozi *(Exec VP-Bus Dev & Ops)*
David Barrie *(Exec VP-Physician Dev)*

Goldman Sachs Australia Group Holdings Pty Ltd (1)
Level 17 101 Collins Street, GPO Box 2050, Melbourne, 3001, VIC, Australia
Tel.: (61) 396791111
Holding Company
N.A.I.C.S.: 551112

Goldman Sachs Australia Pty Ltd (1)
Levels 22 101 Collins Street, Melbourne, 3000, VIC, Australia
Tel.: (61) 396791111
Investment Banking Services
N.A.I.C.S.: 523150

Goldman Sachs BDC, Inc. (1)
200 West St, New York, NY 10282
Tel.: (212) 902-0300
Web Site:
https://www.goldmansachsbdc.com
Rev.: $357,452,000
Assets: $3,591,311,000
Liabilities: $2,088,917,000
Net Worth: $1,502,394,000
Earnings: $228,571,000
Emp.: 141
Fiscal Year-end: 12/31/2022
Investment Services
N.A.I.C.S.: 523999
Tucker Greene *(COO)*
Jon Yoder *(COO)*
Julien Yoo *(Chief Compliance Officer)*
Alex Chi *(Co-CEO)*
Justin Betzen *(VP)*
Greg Watts *(VP)*

Goldman Sachs Bank (Europe) PLC (1)
47-49 St Stephen's Green, Dublin, D02 W634, Ireland
Tel.: (353) 14368650
Banking Services
N.A.I.C.S.: 522110
Joerg Kukies *(Head-Securities-Germany & Austria)*

Goldman Sachs Bank Europe SE (1)
Marienturm Taunusanlage 9-10, 60329, Frankfurt am Main, Germany
Tel.: (49) 6975321000
Web Site: https://www.goldmansachs.com
Investment Banking Services
N.A.I.C.S.: 523150

Goldman Sachs Bank USA (1)
200 West St, New York, NY 10282 (100%)
Tel.: (212) 902-1000
Web Site: https://www.goldmansachs.com
Commercial Banking, Lending & Derivatives Dealing Services
N.A.I.C.S.: 522110

Goldman Sachs Global Commodities (Canada) Corporation (1)
3835 855 2nd Street SW Bankers Hall-East Tower, Calgary, T2P 4J8, AB, Canada
Tel.: (403) 233-3445
Investment Banking Services
N.A.I.C.S.: 523150

Goldman Sachs International (1)
Plumtree Court 25 Shoe Lane, London, EC4A 4AU, United Kingdom
Tel.: (44) 207 774 1000
Web Site: http://www.goldmansachs.com
Sales Range: $5-14.9 Billion
Investment Banking, Trading & Principal Investments, Asset Management & Brokerage Services
N.A.I.C.S.: 523150
Richard J. Gnodde *(CEO)*

Subsidiary (Domestic):

Goldman Sachs Asset Management International (2)
Plumtree Court 25 Shoe Lane, London, EC4A 4AU, United Kingdom

Tel.: (44) 207 774 1000
Web Site: https://www.gsam.com
Asset Management Services
N.A.I.C.S.: 523940
Katherine P. Uniacke *(Chm)*

Goldman Sachs Group Holdings (U.K.) (2)
Plumtree Court 25 Shoe Lane, London, EC4A 4AU, United Kingdom
Tel.: (44) 2077741000
Holding Company
N.A.I.C.S.: 551112
Denis P. Coleman III *(Head-Leveraged Fin-Europe)*

Goldman Sachs International Bank (2)
Peterborough Court 133 Fleet Street, London, EC4A 2BB, United Kingdom
Tel.: (44) 2077741000
Security Brokerage Services
N.A.I.C.S.: 523150

Goldman Sachs Japan Co., Ltd. (1)
Roppongi Hills Mori Tower 10-1 Roppongi 6-chome, Minato-ku, Tokyo, 106-6147, Japan (100%)
Tel.: (81) 364371000
Sales Range: $1-4.9 Billion
Securities Brokerage, Investment Banking, Asset Management & Realty Services
N.A.I.C.S.: 523150

Goldman Sachs Middle Market Lending Corp. (1)
200 W St, New York, NY 10282-2198
Tel.: (212) 902-0300
Rev.: $145,743,000
Assets: $1,706,375,000
Liabilities: $761,586,000
Net Worth: $944,789,000
Earnings: $82,845,000
Fiscal Year-end: 12/31/2019
Investment Management Service
N.A.I.C.S.: 523940
Timothy J. Leach *(Chm)*
Jon Yoder *(COO)*

Goldman Sachs Mitsui Marine Derivative Products, LP (1)
85 Broad St, New York, NY 10004
Tel.: (212) 902-7510
Web Site: http://www.gs.com
Sales Range: $125-149.9 Million
International Securities Dealers
N.A.I.C.S.: 522110

Goldman Sachs Private Middle Market Credit LLC (1)
200 W St, New York, NY 10282
Tel.: (212) 902-0300
Web Site: https://www.goldmansachs.com
Rev.: $68,806,000
Assets: $602,568,000
Liabilities: $198,957,000
Net Worth: $403,611,000
Earnings: $51,148,000
Fiscal Year-end: 12/31/2022
Investment Management Service
N.A.I.C.S.: 523940
Tucker Greene *(COO, COO-Goldman Sachs Private Middle Market Credit II LLC, COO-Goldman Sachs Middle Market Lending Corp. II, COO-Phillip Street Middle Market Lending Fund LLC & COO-Goldman Sachs Private Credit Corp)*
Jaime Ardila *(Chm)*
Alex Chi *(Pres & CEO)*

Goldman Sachs Realty Japan Ltd. (1)
6-10-1 Roppongi Hills Mori Tower, Roppongi Minato-ku, Tokyo, 106-6142, Japan
Tel.: (81) 364390111
Investment Banking Services
N.A.I.C.S.: 523150

Goldman Sachs Realty Management Europe GmbH (1)
Neuer Wall Business Center Neuer Wall 63 office 311, Hamburg, 20354, Germany
Tel.: (49) 9281140150
Web Site: http://www.goldmansachs.com
Investment Banking Services
N.A.I.C.S.: 523150

J. Aron Holdings L.P. (1)
85 Broad St Fl 4, New York, NY 10004

The Goldman Sachs Group, Inc.—(Continued)

Tel.: (212) 902-1000
Sales Range: $650-699.9 Million
Emp.: 101
Holding Company; Commodity Contracts
Broker & Dealer
N.A.I.C.S.: 551112
Lloyd C. Blankfein *(CEO)*
Lloyd C. Blankfein *(CEO)*

Subsidiary (Domestic):

J. Aron & Co.   (2)
200 West St, New York, NY 10282
Tel.: (212) 902-1000
Web Site: http://www.gs.com
Sales Range: $650-699.9 Million
Emp.: 5,000
Commodity Contracts Broker & Dealer
N.A.I.C.S.: 523160

Subsidiary (Non-US):

J. Aron & Company (Singapore) PTE.   (2)
50 Raffles Place Suite 29-01 Singapore
Land Tower, Singapore, 048623, Singapore
Tel.: (65) 62288180
Petroleum Product Distr
N.A.I.C.S.: 424720

Kahoot! ASA   (1)
Fridtjof Nansens plass 7, Oslo,
Norway   (84.31%)
Tel.: (47) 92832905
Web Site: http://kahoot.com
Rev.: $145,960,000
Assets: $787,118,000
Liabilities: $178,888,000
Net Worth: $608,230,000
Earnings: $2,288,000
Emp.: 462
Fiscal Year-end: 12/31/2022
Online Educational Games
N.A.I.C.S.: 513210
Eilert Giertsen Hanoa *(CEO)*

Subsidiary (Non-US):

Actimo ApS   (2)
Fruebjergvej 3, 2100, Copenhagen, Denmark
Tel.: (45) 38414700
Web Site: https://www.actimo.com
Consulting Services
N.A.I.C.S.: 541611

Subsidiary (US):

Clever Inc.   (2)
1263 Mission St, San Francisco, CA 94103
Web Site: http://www.clever.com
Educational Platform & Software Publisher
N.A.I.C.S.: 611710
Tyler Bosmeny *(Founder & CEO)*

Subsidiary (Non-US):

DragonBox Finland Oy   (2)
Lapinlahdenkatu 16, 00180, Helsinki, Finland
Tel.: (358) 504413637
Web Site: https://www.dragonbox.fi
Educational Support Services
N.A.I.C.S.: 611710

MTGLQ Investors, L.P.   (1)
200 West St, New York, NY 10282
Tel.: (212) 902-1000
Web Site: http://www.gs.com
Sales Range: $250-299.9 Million
Investment Holding Company
N.A.I.C.S.: 551112

NN Investment Partners Holdings N.V.   (1)
Schenkkade 65, PO Box 90470, 2509 LL,
Hague, Netherlands
Tel.: (31) 70 378 1781
Web Site: http://www.nnip.com
Rev.: $227,000,000,000
Emp.: 1,100
Holding Company; Investment Management
Services
N.A.I.C.S.: 551112
Eric Verret *(Head-Corp Loans-Alternative Credit)*
Niels Bodenheim *(Head-Alternative Credit)*

Edith Siermann *(Head-Fixed Income & Responsible Investing)*
Marcin Adamczyk *(Head-Emerging Market Debt)*

Subsidiary (Non-US):

NN Investment Partners (France) S.A.   (2)
47 rue de la Victoire, 75009, Paris, France
Tel.: (33) 1 56 79 34 50
Web Site: http://www.nnip.com
Investment Management Service
N.A.I.C.S.: 523999
Anthony Guerra *(Mgr-Sls-Third Party Distr)*
Gilles Darde *(Sr Mgr-Sls-Third Party Distr)*
Philippe Fidaire *(Sr Mgr-Sls-Institutional)*
Gerard Castro *(Sr Mgr-Sls-institutional)*
Paul van Eynde *(Mng Dir-Europe)*
Florence Melix *(Mgr-Mktg)*
Christian Paris *(Gen Mgr)*

NN Investment Partners Belgium N.V.   (2)
Marnixlaan 23, B 1000, Brussels, Belgium
Tel.: (32) 2 504 47 00
Web Site: http://www.nnip.com
Sales Range: $600-649.9 Million
Investment Management
N.A.I.C.S.: 523999

NN Investment Partners Spain   (2)
C/ Genova 27 6a Planta, 28004, Madrid,
Spain
Tel.: (34) 91 769 41 01
Web Site: http://www.nnip.com
Emp.: 2
Investment Management Service
N.A.I.C.S.: 523999
Ana Gasca Elosegui *(Dir-Institutional Clients)*

OOO Goldman Sachs Bank   (1)
14th Floor Ducat III 6 Gasheka Street,
125047, Moscow, Russia
Tel.: (7) 4956454200
Investment Banking Services
N.A.I.C.S.: 523150
John E. Waldron *(Pres & COO)*

The Ayco Company, L.P.   (1)
321 Broadway, Saratoga Springs, NY
12866
Tel.: (518) 886-4000
Web Site: https://www.ayco.com
Sales Range: $75-99.9 Million
Emp.: 25
Comprehensive Financial Counseling &
Education Services
N.A.I.C.S.: 523940
David M. Quinn *(Mng Dir-Tax Policy & Res)*
Larry Restieri *(Pres & CEO)*
Greg Wilson *(Mng Dir & Head-Workplace Solutions)*
Shelley Luks *(Mng Dir & Controller)*
Angela J. Platt *(Mng Dir)*
Ashley King *(VP)*
Laura Carroll *(VP)*
Christine Ngo Isaac *(VP)*
Brian Teague *(VP)*

United Capital Financial Advisers, LLC   (1)
620 Newport Ctr Dr Ste 500, Newport
Beach, CA 92660
Tel.: (949) 999-8500
Web Site: http://www.unitedcp.com
Financial Advisory & Wealth Management
Services
N.A.I.C.S.: 523940
Joseph J. Duran *(CEO, Mng Dir & Head-Personal Fin Mgmt)*
Gary L. Roth *(Mng Dir)*
Michael Capelle *(Mng Dir)*
Jorge Bernal *(Mng Dir)*
Jason Gordo *(VP)*
Rachel Schnoll *(Mng Dir)*
Jim Rivers *(Mng Dir)*

Subsidiary (Domestic):

Harvest Group Financial Services, Corp.   (2)
1707 Langhorne-Newtown Rd Ste 1, Langhorne, PA 19047
Tel.: (215) 860-6056
Financial & Retirement Planning Services
N.A.I.C.S.: 523940

Branch (Domestic):

United Capital Financial Advisers, LLC - Silicon Valley   (2)

4300 El Camino Real Ste 205, Los Altos,
CA 94022
Tel.: (650) 964-7024
Web Site: http://www.unitedcp.com
Wealth Management Services
N.A.I.C.S.: 523940
John Han *(VP)*

Whitehall Street Real Estate L.P.   (1)
85 Broad St, New York, NY 10004-2434
Tel.: (212) 902-5652
Web Site: http://www.gs.com
Real Estate Investment Trust
N.A.I.C.S.: 525990

THE GOODHEART-WILLCOX CO., INC.

18604 W Creek Dr, Tinley Park, IL
60477-6243
Tel.: (708) 687-5000   DE
Web Site: https://www.g-w.com
Year Founded: 1921
GWOX—(OTCIQ)
Sales Range: $25-49.9 Million
Emp.: 65
Mechanical, Technical & Home Economics Textbooks Publisher
N.A.I.C.S.: 513130
John F. Flanagan *(Pres)*
Todd J. Scheffers *(VP-Sls)*

THE GOODYEAR TIRE & RUBBER COMPANY

200 Innovation Way, Akron, OH
44316-0001
Tel.: (330) 796-2121   OH
Web Site:
  https://corporate.goodyear.com
Year Founded: 1898
GT—(NASDAQ)
Rev.: $20,066,000,000
Assets: $21,582,000,000
Liabilities: $16,745,000,000
Net Worth: $4,837,000,000
Earnings: ($687,000,000)
Emp.: 71,000
Fiscal Year-end: 12/31/23
Tires & Tubes Mfr for Industrial, Auto,
Truck, Earthmover, Aviation, Industrial
& Engineered Products, Shoe &
Graphic Products, Plastics & Films,
Chemicals & Adhesives
N.A.I.C.S.: 326211
Christina L. Zamarro *(CFO & Exec VP)*
Evan M. Scocos *(VP-Finance-Americas)*
Chris Delaney *(Pres-Europe, Middle East & Africa)*
Gary Vanderlind *(Chief HR Officer & Sr VP)*
Laura Duda *(Chief Comm Officer & Sr VP)*
Mark W. Stewart *(Pres & CEO)*
David E. Phillips *(Gen Counsel & Sr VP)*
Nathanial Madarang *(Pres-Asia Pacific)*
Kate Rock-Rees *(Head-External Comm-Europe, Middle East & Africa)*
Jordan Coughlin *(Treas & VP)*
Christian Gadzinski *(Sr Dir-IR)*
Joe Burke *(VP-Comml Bus-North America)*

Subsidiaries:

Belt Concepts of America Inc.   (1)
605 N Pine St, Spring Hope, NC
27882   (100%)
Tel.: (252) 478-2200
Web Site: https://belt-concepts.com
Sales Range: $50-74.9 Million
Emp.: 85
Miscellaneous Fabricated Wire Products
N.A.I.C.S.: 332618

Companhia Goodyear do Brasil Produtos de Borracha   (1)

Avenida Paulista 854, Sao Paulo,
Brazil   (100%)
Tel.: (55) 1166187288
Sales Range: $125-149.9 Million
Mfr & Marketing of Tires, Tubes, Plastic
Hose & Industrial Products
N.A.I.C.S.: 326211

Subsidiary (Non-US):

Compania Anonima Goodyear de Venezuela   (2)
Carretera Nationale Valencia Los Guayos,
PO Box 186, Valencia, 2011, Estado Carabobo, Venezuela   (100%)
Tel.: (58) 2418393111
Web Site: http://www.goodyear.com.ve
Sales Range: $125-149.9 Million
Emp.: 600
Mfr & Marketing of Tires, Tubes & Industrial
Products
N.A.I.C.S.: 326211

Compania Goodyear Del Peru, S.A.   (2)
Av Argentina No 6037, Carmen de la Legua
Reynoso, Callao, Peru
Tel.: (51) 80019080
Web Site: https://www.goodyear.com.pe
Sales Range: $125-149.9 Million
Tires, Tubes & Industrial Products Mfr &
Marketer
N.A.I.C.S.: 326211

Goodyear de Chile S.A.I.C.   (2)
Camino Melipilla KM16, Maipu, Santiago,
Chile   (100%)
Tel.: (56) 225301353
Web Site: https://www.goodyear.cl
Tiles Mfr
N.A.I.C.S.: 326211

Goodyear de Colombia S.A.   (2)
Calle 10D 15-39, Yumbo, 76001,
Colombia   (100%)
Tel.: (57) 6026088300
Web Site: https://www.goodyear.com.co
Mfr & Marketing of Tires, Tubes & Industrial
Rubber Products
N.A.I.C.S.: 326211

Neumaticos Goodyear S.R.L.   (2)
Av Pte Gral Julio A Roca 71 O Piso 2,
C1041AAX, Buenos Aires,
Argentina   (100%)
Tel.: (54) 1128210047
Web Site: https://www.goodyear.com.ar
Tires, Tubes & Industrial Rubber Products &
Fabric Marketer & Mfr.
N.A.I.C.S.: 326211

Cooper Tire & Rubber Company   (1)
701 Lima Ave, Findlay, OH 45840
Tel.: (419) 423-1321
Web Site: http://www.coopertire.com
Rev.: $2,521,074,000
Assets: $2,971,573,000
Liabilities: $1,560,982,000
Net Worth: $1,410,591,000
Earnings: $142,789,000
Emp.: 9,839
Fiscal Year-end: 12/31/2020
Replacement Tires Mfr
N.A.I.C.S.: 326211
Phil F. Kortokrax *(Sr VP-Global Ops & Procurement)*
Mark A. Young *(Chief Acctg Officer & VP)*
Anne Roman *(VP-Comm & Pub Affairs)*
Megan James *(Mgr-Comm)*
Christopher Ball *(Pres-Americas & Sr VP)*
Alan Yang *(VP & Gen Mgr-Asia)*
Jacob Drerup *(Mgr-IR)*
John Bodart *(Sr VP-Transformation)*
Paula S. Whitesell *(Chief HR Officer & Sr VP)*
Jaap van Wessum *(Gen Mgr-Europe, Middle East & Africa)*

Subsidiary (Domestic):

CTTG Inc.   (2)
701 Lima Ave, Findlay, OH 45840
Tel.: (419) 424-4184
Web Site: http://www.coopertire.com
Emp.: 2,000
Tire Distr
N.A.I.C.S.: 423130

Subsidiary (Non-US):

Cooper Tire & Rubber Company Europe Ltd.   (2)

Bath Road, Melksham, SN12 8AA, Wiltshire, United Kingdom **(100%)**
Tel.: (44) 122 570 3101
Web Site: https://www.coopertire.co.uk
Sales Range: $250-299.9 Million
Emp.: 200
Mfr of Tires
N.A.I.C.S.: 326211
Michiel Kramer *(Dir-Marketing-Sales)*

Cooper Tire & Rubber Company de Mexico S.A. **(2)**
Km 20-25 Carretera El Salto-La Capilla Col Mezquite Redondo, Ixtlahuacan del los Membrillos, Jalisco, 45680, Mexico
Tel.: (52) 13312244513
Web Site: http://www.mx.coopertire.com
Tire Distr
N.A.I.C.S.: 441340

Cooper Tire & Rubber Company de Mexico S.A. de CV **(2)**
Km 2 0-2 5 Carretera El Salto-La Capilla Col Mezquite Redondo, Ixtlahuacan del los Membrillos, 45680, El Salto, Jalisco, Mexico
Tel.: (52) 13312244513
Web Site: https://esmx.coopertire.com
Tire & Tube Whslr
N.A.I.C.S.: 423130

Plant (Domestic):

Cooper Tire & Rubber Company, Clarksdale Plant **(2)**
PO Box 130, Clarksdale, MS 38614 **(100%)**
Tel.: (662) 624-4366
Sales Range: $25-49.9 Million
Emp.: 45
Mfr of Inner Tubes For Tires
N.A.I.C.S.: 326211
Fred Doster *(Plant Mgr)*

Cooper Tire & Rubber Company, Texarkana Plant **(2)**
3500 Washington Rd, Texarkana, AR 71854
Tel.: (870) 779-4268
Web Site: http://www.coopertire.com
Sales Range: $450-499.9 Million
Emp.: 2,000
Mfr of Tires
N.A.I.C.S.: 326211

Subsidiary (Non-US):

Cooper Tyre & Rubber Company UK Limited **(2)**
Bath Road, Melksham, SN12 8AA, Wiltshire, United Kingdom
Tel.: (44) 1225703101
Web Site: http://www.coopertire.co.uk
Emp.: 800
Tiles Mfr
N.A.I.C.S.: 326211
Alberto Benavides *(Chm, Pres & CEO)*

Subsidiary (Non-US):

Cooper Tire & Rubber Company Deutschland GmbH **(3)**
Otto-Hahn-Str 46, 63303, Dreieich, Germany
Tel.: (49) 610 396 0760
Web Site: https://www.coopertire.de
Sales Range: $25-49.9 Million
Emp.: 15
Tiles Mfr
N.A.I.C.S.: 326211

Cooper Tire & Rubber Company Espana S.L. **(3)**
Centro de Negocios Eisenhower Avenida Sur del Aeropuerto de Barajas 38, Ed 4 Bajo 3, 28042, Madrid, Spain
Tel.: (34) 91 746 2300
Web Site: https://www.coopertire.es
Emp.: 10
Tiles Mfr
N.A.I.C.S.: 326211

Cooper Tire & Rubber Holding Netherlands 1 B.V. **(3)**
Haaksbergweg 31, 1101 BP, Amsterdam, Netherlands
Tel.: (31) 206509060
Web Site: http://coopertire.com
Holding Company
N.A.I.C.S.: 551112

Cooper Tire & Rubber Holding Netherlands 2 B.V. **(3)**
Herikerbergweg 238 route, 1101 CM, Amsterdam, Netherlands
Tel.: (31) 205755600
Holding Company
N.A.I.C.S.: 551112

Subsidiary (Domestic):

Max-Trac Tire Co., Inc. **(2)**
4600 Prosper Dr, Stow, OH 44224-1038
Tel.: (330) 928-9092
Tire & Tube Whslr
N.A.I.C.S.: 423130
Dominick Wycoff *(Pres)*

Cosmoflex, Inc. **(1)**
4142 Industrial Loop, Hannibal, MO 63401
Tel.: (573) 221-0242
Web Site: http://www.goodyear.com
Sales Range: $25-49.9 Million
Emp.: 50
Mfr of Plastic Industrial Hose
N.A.I.C.S.: 326122

Deutsche Goodyear GmbH **(1)**
Xantener Str 105, 50733, Cologne, Germany **(100%)**
Tel.: (49) 221976661
Web Site: http://www.goodyear.de
Sales Range: $75-99.9 Million
Emp.: 260
Mfr & Marketing of Tires, Rubber & Industrial Products & Plastic Hose
N.A.I.C.S.: 326211

G.I.E. Goodyear Mireval **(1)**
Route Departmentale 612, Mireval, France
Tel.: (33) 467517177
Rubber Products Mfr
N.A.I.C.S.: 326299

Goodyear Australia Pty Limited **(1)**
Level 1 470 Church Street, Parramatta, 2151, Australia
Tel.: (61) 297686000
Sales Range: $25-49.9 Million
Emp.: 14
Dist Tires
N.A.I.C.S.: 441340
Julie Brogan *(Dir-Fin)*

Subsidiary (Domestic):

Goodyear & Dunlop Tyres (Australia) Pty Ltd **(2)**
Level 2 464 St Kilda Road 658 Church Street, Melbourne, 3004, VIC, Australia
Tel.: (61) 384167280
Tire Manufacturing
N.A.I.C.S.: 326211

Subsidiary (Non-US):

Goodyear & Dunlop Tyres (NZ) Limited **(3)**
415 East Tamaki Rd, East Tamaki, Auckland, New Zealand
Tel.: (64) 44392600
Web Site: https://www.goodyear.co.nz
Tire Distr
N.A.I.C.S.: 423130

Subsidiary (Domestic):

Goodyear Earthmover Pty Limited **(2)**
460 Church St Level 2, Parramatta, 2151, NSW, Australia
Tel.: (61) 297686011
Web Site: http://www.goodyear.com
Mfr & Sales of Tires & Tubes
N.A.I.C.S.: 326211

Goodyear Tyres Pty Ltd **(2)**
Unit 1/552 Church Street, Parramatta, 2151, NSW, Australia
Tel.: (61) 29 890 4222
Web Site: https://www.goodyear.com.au
Dist Tires
N.A.I.C.S.: 441340

Goodyear Belgium N.V./SA **(1)**
Prins Boudewijnlaan 5, 2550, Kontich, Belgium
Tel.: (32) 38203250
Tiles Mfr
N.A.I.C.S.: 326211

Goodyear Canada Inc. **(1)**

450 Kipling Ave, Toronto, M8Z 5E1, ON, Canada **(100%)**
Tel.: (416) 201-4300
Web Site: https://www.goodyear.ca
Sales Range: $125-149.9 Million
Tires & Rubber Products Distr
N.A.I.C.S.: 326211

Goodyear Dunlop Tires Europe B.V. **(1)**
De Boelelaan 7, Amsterdam, 1083 HJ, Netherlands
Tel.: (31) 203010101
Sales Range: $250-299.9 Million
Emp.: 200
Holding Company
N.A.I.C.S.: 551112
Xavier Fraipont *(Mng Dir-Motorsport & Motorcycle-EMEA)*
Gregory Boucharlat *(Grp Dir-Truck Tyre Retreading-EMEA)*

Subsidiary (Non-US):

Dunlop Grund und Service Verwaltungs GmbH **(2)**
Dunlopstr 2, 63450, Hanau, Germany
Tel.: (49) 61816801
Business Management Services
N.A.I.C.S.: 541611

GD Handelssysteme GmbH **(2)**
Xantener Str 105, 50733, Cologne, Germany
Tel.: (49) 221947130
Web Site: http://www.gdhs-tagungen.de
Emp.: 80
Rubber Products Mfr
N.A.I.C.S.: 326299
Goran Zubanovic *(Mng Dir)*

GD Versicherungsservice GmbH **(2)**
Dunlopstr 2, 63450, Hanau, Germany
Tel.: (49) 6181681861
Emp.: 5
Insurance Agency Services
N.A.I.C.S.: 524210

Goodyear Dunlop Sava Tires d.o.o. **(2)**
Skofjeloska cesta 6, 4000, Kranj, Slovenia
Tel.: (386) 42077000
Web Site: http://www.goodyear-slovenija.si
Automotive Tire Mfr
N.A.I.C.S.: 326211

Goodyear Dunlop Tires Austria GmbH **(2)**
Lehrbachgasse 13, Vienna, 1120, Austria
Tel.: (43) 161404
Web Site: http://www.goodyear.eu
Sales Range: $25-49.9 Million
Emp.: 60
Mfr of Tires
N.A.I.C.S.: 326211

Goodyear Dunlop Tires Baltic OU **(2)**
Jarvevana Tee 9, 11314, Tallinn, EE-113 14, Estonia
Tel.: (372) 6388600
Tire Distr
N.A.I.C.S.: 423130

Goodyear Dunlop Tires Belgium N.V. **(2)**
Prins Boudewijnlaan 5, 2550, Kontich, Belgium
Tel.: (32) 38203250
Web Site: http://www.goodyear.be
Sales Range: $75-99.9 Million
Emp.: 100
Mfr of Tires & Tubes
N.A.I.C.S.: 326211

Goodyear Dunlop Tires Czech s.r.o. **(2)**
Vyskocilova 1481/4, Michle Praha 4, Prague, 14000, Czech Republic
Tel.: (420) 234092711
Web Site: http://www.goodyear.com
Tire Mfr & Distr
N.A.I.C.S.: 326211

Goodyear Dunlop Tires Danmark A/S **(2)**
Rosenlundsgatan 50, PO Box 38181, 100 64, Stockholm, Sweden
Tel.: (46) 84662000
Tire Distr

N.A.I.C.S.: 423130

Goodyear Dunlop Tires Espana S.A. **(2)**
Calle Campezo 1 Edif 6 Plta 4, Poligono Las Mercedes, 28022, Madrid, Spain
Tel.: (34) 917461840
Web Site: http://www.goodyear.eu
Sales Range: $25-49.9 Million
Emp.: 100
Mfr & Sales of Tires
N.A.I.C.S.: 326211

Goodyear Dunlop Tires France **(2)**
8 Rue Lionel Terray, Rueil-Malmaison, 92500, France
Tel.: (33) 4 70 02 39 00
Rubber Products Mfr
N.A.I.C.S.: 326299
Camille Mounier *(Dir-Mktg)*
Mark Thys *(Mng Dir)*
Boris Stevanovic *(Dir-Comml Product Bus)*

Goodyear Dunlop Tires Hellas S.A.I.C. **(2)**
69 Ipirou & L Katsoni Anargiroi, Anargiroi, Athens, 13562, Greece
Tel.: (30) 2102640400
Web Site: http://www.goodyear.com
Emp.: 35
Tire Distr
N.A.I.C.S.: 423130

Goodyear Dunlop Tires Ireland Ltd **(2)**
Unit 20 Fonthill Ind pk Clondalkin, Dublin, Ireland
Tel.: (353) 16238500
Web Site: http://www.goodyear.com
Emp.: 16
Tire Manufacturing
N.A.I.C.S.: 326211

Goodyear Dunlop Tires Italia S.p.A. **(2)**
Strada 4 Palazzo A10, Milanofiori, 20090, Assago, MI, Italy
Tel.: (39) 0257521
Web Site: http://www.goodyear.eu
Sales Range: $25-49.9 Million
Emp.: 60
Sales & Marketing of Tires & Tubes
N.A.I.C.S.: 423130

Goodyear Dunlop Tires Operations Romania S.r.L. **(2)**
Strada Tipografilor Nr 11-15 Cladirea S Parc Parter Sector 1, Bucharest, Romania
Tel.: (40) 40 21 209 17 02
Sales Range: $25-49.9 Million
Emp.: 4
Automotive Tire Mfr
N.A.I.C.S.: 326211

Goodyear Dunlop Tires Operations S.A. **(2)**
Avenue Gordon-Smith 59, L-7750, Colmar-Berg, Luxembourg
Tel.: (352) 81991
Web Site: http://www.goodyear.eu
Tiles Mfr
N.A.I.C.S.: 326211

Goodyear Dunlop Tires Polska Sp z.o.o. **(2)**
Al Jerozolimskie 212 a, Warsaw, 02-486, Poland
Tel.: (48) 225715900
Tire Distr
N.A.I.C.S.: 423130

Goodyear Dunlop Tires Portugal Unipessoal, Ltda **(2)**
Avenida da Republica 50 - 2Edificio Mar Vermelho, 1050-196, Lisbon, Portugal
Tel.: (351) 210349000
Web Site: http://www.goodyear.pt
Sales Range: $10-24.9 Million
Emp.: 15
Mfr of Tires & Tubes
N.A.I.C.S.: 326211

Goodyear Dunlop Tires Romania S.r.L. **(2)**
Bucharest Business Park Sos Bucuresti Ploiesti Nr 1A, Cladirea C Parter Sector 1, 013681, Bucharest, Romania
Tel.: (40) 212091700
Tire Distr

The Goodyear Tire & Rubber
Company—(Continued)

N.A.I.C.S.: 423130
Cristian Rosioru *(Reg Mgr-Retail)*

Goodyear Dunlop Tires Slovakia
s.r.o. **(2)**
Ruzinovska 42, 821 03, Bratislava, Slovakia
Tel.: (421) 248207894
Tire Distr
N.A.I.C.S.: 423130

Goodyear Dunlop Tires Suisse
SA **(2)**
Industriestrasse 28, 8604, Volketswil, Switzerland
Tel.: (41) 449478600
Web Site: http://www.goodyear.eu
Sales Range: $25-49.9 Million
Emp.: 70
Tires & Tubes Marketer & Mfr
N.A.I.C.S.: 326211

Goodyear Dunlop Tires Sverige
AB **(2)**
Rosenlundsgatan 50, PO Box 38181, 100
64, Stockholm, Sweden
Tel.: (46) 84662000
Web Site: http://www.goodyear.eu
Sales Range: $10-24.9 Million
Emp.: 150
Motor Vehicle Supplies & New Parts
N.A.I.C.S.: 423120

Goodyear Dunlop Tyres UK Ltd. **(2)**
2920 Trident Court Solihull Parkway, Birmingham Business Park, Birmingham, B37
7YN, United Kingdom
Tel.: (44) 1213787000
Web Site: http://www.goodyear.eu
Sales Range: $300-349.9 Million
Emp.: 250
Mfr & Marketing of Tires
N.A.I.C.S.: 326211

Goodyear Europe B.V. **(1)**
Regus Vianen Businesspark Lange Dreef
11, 4131 NJ, Vianen, Netherlands
Tel.: (31) 3238203250
Tiles Mfr
N.A.I.C.S.: 326211

Goodyear Export Inc. **(1)**
1144 E Market St, Akron, OH 44316
Tel.: (330) 796-2121
Tire Distr
N.A.I.C.S.: 423130

Goodyear France SAS **(1)**
Tour First 1 Place des Saisons, Courbevoie
La Defense 1, Paris, 92400, France
Tel.: (33) 147165959
Automotive Tire Mfr
N.A.I.C.S.: 326211

Goodyear Germany GmbH **(1)**
Dunlopstr 2, D-63450, Hanau, Germany
Tel.: (49) 61816801
Web Site: https://www.goodyear.eu
Motor Vehicle Parts Mfr
N.A.I.C.S.: 336390

Goodyear Hellas S.A.I.C. **(1)**
Lambrou & Katsoni ie Anargiri 13562, Athens, Greece
Tel.: (30) 2102640400
Web Site: http://www.goodyear.gr
Sales Range: $125-149.9 Million
Emp.: 42
Mfr & Marketing of Tires & Tubes
N.A.I.C.S.: 326211

Goodyear Hrvatska d.o.o. **(1)**
Kovinska 4a, 10000, Zagreb, Croatia
Tel.: (385) 13498021
Tiles Mfr
N.A.I.C.S.: 326211

Goodyear International
Corporation **(1)**
200 Innovation Way, Akron, OH 44316
Tel.: (330) 796-2121
Web Site: http://www.goodyear.com
Tiles Mfr
N.A.I.C.S.: 326211
Richard J. Kramer *(Chm, Pres & CEO)*

Goodyear Japan Ltd. **(1)**
9-13 Akasaka 1- Chome Sankaido Building,

PO Box 1054, Minato-ku, Tokyo, 107-0052,
Japan
Tel.: (81) 3 5572 8235
Web Site: http://www.goodyear.co.jp
Tire Whslr
N.A.I.C.S.: 423130

Goodyear Lastikleri Turk Anonim
Sirketi **(1)**
Maslak Mahallesi Sumer Sokak MOB No 4
Sariyer, PO Box 41, 34485, Istanbul,
Turkiye **(75%)**
Tel.: (90) 2123295000
Web Site: http://www.goodyear.com.tr
Sales Range: $300-349.9 Million
Emp.: 70
Mfr & Marketing of Tires & Tubes
N.A.I.C.S.: 326211

Goodyear Luxembourg Tires SA **(1)**
Ave Gordon Smith, 7750, Colmar-Berg,
Luxembourg **(100%)**
Tel.: (352) 81993111
Web Site: http://www.goodyear.com
Sales Range: $25-49.9 Million
Emp.: 3,000
Mfr & Marketing of Tires, Fabrics, Steel Tire
Cord, Tire Molds & Machines
N.A.I.C.S.: 326211

Goodyear Marketing & Sales Sdn.
Bhd. **(1)**
Lot 51 Persiaran Selangor Seksyen 15,
40200, Shah Alam, Selangor Darul Ehsan,
Malaysia
Tel.: (60) 355203200
Emp.: 60
Tire & Tube Distr
N.A.I.C.S.: 423130

Goodyear Middle East FZE **(1)**
Dubai Silicon Oasis A-Wing 4th Floor, PO
Box 33528, Dubai, United Arab Emirates
Tel.: (971) 43724800
Tire & Tube Distr
N.A.I.C.S.: 423130
Jeanette Pass *(Mgr-HR)*

Goodyear Nederland BV **(1)**
Ledeboerstraat 21, 5048 AC, Tilburg, Netherlands
Tel.: (31) 134626555
Retreading of Aircraft Tires
N.A.I.C.S.: 326212

Goodyear Orient Company Private
Limited **(1)**
8 Shenton Way 20-01, Singapore, 068811,
Singapore
Tel.: (65) 69306888
Web Site: http://www.goodyear.com.sg
Automotive Tire Mfr & Distr
N.A.I.C.S.: 326211
Richard J. Kramer *(Chm, Pres & CEO)*

Goodyear Polska Sp. z o.o. **(1)**
Ul Krakowiakow 46, 02-255, Warsaw, Poland
Tel.: (48) 225715900
Web Site: http://www.goodyear.eu
Tiles Mfr
N.A.I.C.S.: 326211

Goodyear Portugal Unipessoal,
Ltda **(1)**
Centro Empresarial Torres de Lisboa, Rua
Tomas da Fonseca - Torre G 1 Piso, 1600-209, Lisbon, Portugal
Tel.: (351) 210349000
Tiles Mfr
N.A.I.C.S.: 326211

Goodyear S.A. **(1)**
8 rue Lionel Terray, PO Box 310, 92500,
Rueil-Malmaison, Cedex, France
Tel.: (33) 147162300
Web Site: http://www.goodyear.fr
Sales Range: $1-4.9 Billion
Emp.: 400
Mfr of Synthetic Polymers, Specialty Chemicals & Resins
N.A.I.C.S.: 325211

Goodyear Servicios Comerciales S.A.
de C.V. **(1)**
Carretera Mexico Toluca No 5631 Piso 4
Oficina 423, ColCuajimalpa Del Cuajimalpa,
Mexico, 05000, DF, Mexico **(100%)**
Tel.: (52) 5591405600
Web Site: https://www.goodyear.com.mx

Mfr & Marketing of Tires, Tubes, Industrial
Products & Films
N.A.I.C.S.: 326211

Goodyear South Africa (Pty) Ltd **(1)**
Algoa Road, Uitenhage, 6229, South Africa
Tel.: (27) 860400401
Web Site: https://www.goodyear.eu
Tiles Mfr
N.A.I.C.S.: 326211

Goodyear Suisse S.A. **(1)**
Industriestrasse 28, 8604, Volketswil, Switzerland
Tel.: (41) 449478600
Tiles Mfr
N.A.I.C.S.: 326211

Goodyear Sverige A.B. **(1)**
Magnus Ladulasgatan 63 5 tr, Box 38181,
100 64, Stockholm, Sweden
Tel.: (46) 84662000
Automotive Tire Mfr
N.A.I.C.S.: 326211

Goodyear Tire Management Company (Shanghai) Ltd. **(1)**
28 F K Wah Center No 1010 Huaiha,
Shanghai, 200131, China
Tel.: (86) 2161326000
Web Site: http://www.goodyear.com.cn
Sales Range: $125-149.9 Million
Rubber Mat & Solid Tire Mfr
N.A.I.C.S.: 326211

Subsidiary (Non-US):

Goodyear India Ltd. **(2)**
1st Floor ABW Elegance Tower, Jasola,
New Delhi, 110025, India
Tel.: (91) 1147472727
Web Site: https://www.goodyear.co.in
Emp.: 908
Tires & Inner Tubes Mfr & Distr
N.A.I.C.S.: 326211
Sandeep Mahajan *(Mng Dir)*
Mitesh Mittal *(CFO)*

Goodyear Malaysia Bhd **(2)**
Lot 51 Persiaran Selangor Seksyen 15,
40200, Shah Alam, Malaysia **(100%)**
Tel.: (60) 355203200
Web Site: https://www.goodyear.com.my
Sales Range: $75-99.9 Million
Mfr of Tires & Inner Tubes
N.A.I.C.S.: 326211

Goodyear Philippines, Inc. **(2)**
Alabang-Zapote Road, Almanza, Las Pinas
City, Philippines **(100%)**
Tel.: (63) 28429198
Web Site: http://www.goodyear.com.ph
Mfr & Marketing of Tires & Tubes
N.A.I.C.S.: 326211

Goodyear Taiwan Limited **(2)**
4F No 71 Sec 2 Nan Ching E Rd, Taipei,
104, Taiwan **(100%)**
Tel.: (886) 225514330
Web Site: http://www.goodyear.com.tw
Sales Range: $75-99.9 Million
Emp.: 200
Mfr & Marketing of Tires & Tubes
N.A.I.C.S.: 326211

Goodyear Thailand Public Co.
Ltd. **(2)**
50/9 Village No 3 Phahonyothin Road Km
36, Khlong Nueng Subdistrict, Khlong Luang, 12120, Pathum Thani,
Thailand **(67%)**
Tel.: (66) 29098080
Web Site: https://www.goodyear.co.th
Sales Range: $25-49.9 Million
Emp.: 70
Mfr of Tires & Aero Retreading Facility
N.A.I.C.S.: 326212

Goodyear Tyre & Rubber Holdings
(Pty) Ltd **(1)**
Algoa Road, Uitenhage, 6229, South Africa
Tel.: (27) 86 040 0401
Web Site: http://www.goodyear.eu
Holding Company
N.A.I.C.S.: 551112

Goodyear Tyres Ireland Ltd. **(1)**
Unit 20 Fonthill Industrial Park, Clondalkin,
Dublin, 22, Ireland
Tel.: (353) 16238500
Automotive Tire Mfr

N.A.I.C.S.: 326211

Goodyear Tyres UK Limited **(1)**
2920 Trident Court Birmingham Business
Park Solihull Pkwy, Birmingham, B37 7YN,
United Kingdom
Tel.: (44) 1213787000
Tiles Mfr
N.A.I.C.S.: 326211

Goodyear Ukraine **(1)**
Street Yaroslavskaya 58 Floor 2 BC Astarta,
04071, Kiev, Ukraine
Tel.: (380) 444962388
Web Site: http://www.goodyear.eu
Tiles Mfr
N.A.I.C.S.: 326211

Granford Manufacturing, Inc. **(1)**
127 Rang Parent, Saint Alphonse-de-Granby, J0E 2A0, QC, Canada
Tel.: (450) 375-5050
Sales Range: $100-124.9 Million
Emp.: 225
Mfr & Marketing of Hose Products
N.A.I.C.S.: 314999

Hi-Q Automotive (Pty) Ltd **(1)**
12 Forge Rd, Kempton Park, 1620, Gauteng, South Africa
Tel.: (27) 113943150
Web Site: http://www.hiq.co.za
Tire Distr
N.A.I.C.S.: 423130

Laurelwood Properties Inc. **(1)**
5750 Brookstone Walk NW, Acworth, GA
30101-8402
Tel.: (770) 424-3505
Real Estate Agency Services
N.A.I.C.S.: 531210

Luxembourg Mounting Center
S.A. **(1)**
Avenue Gordon Smith, 7740, Colmar-Berg,
Luxembourg
Tel.: (352) 81994065
Web Site: http://www.luxlmc.com
Tire & Wheel Assembly Machinery Mfr
N.A.I.C.S.: 333310

Nippon Goodyear Ltd **(1)**
9-13 Akasaka 1- Chome Sankaido Building,
CPO Box 1054, Minato-ku, Tokyo, 107-0052, Japan
Tel.: (81) 355728235
Automotive Tires Distr
N.A.I.C.S.: 423130

P.T. Goodyear Indonesia Tbk **(1)**
Jl Pemuda No 27, Bogor, 16101, Jawa Barat, Indonesia
Tel.: (62) 2518322071
Web Site: https://www.goodyear-indonesia.com
Tiles Mfr
N.A.I.C.S.: 326211

Raben Tire Co. Inc. **(1)**
2100 N New York Ave, Evansville, IN 47711
Tel.: (812) 465-5565
Web Site: https://www.rabentire.com
Automotive Tires
N.A.I.C.S.: 441340
Eric Glover *(Pres)*

Reifen Baierlacher GmbH **(1)**
Holzhofstrasse 14, 82362, Weilheim, Germany
Tel.: (49) 8819275000
Web Site: https://www.baierlacher.com
Tire Distr
N.A.I.C.S.: 423130

T&WA, Inc. **(1)**
1630 Lyndon Farm Ct, Louisville, KY 40223
Tel.: (502) 425-5999
Motor Vehicle Wheel & Parts Mfr
N.A.I.C.S.: 336390

Tire Company Debica S.A. **(1)**
ul 1 Maja 1, 39 200, Debica,
Poland **(76.4%)**
Tel.: (48) 146702831
Web Site: https://www.debica.com.pl
Rev.: $760,267,020
Assets: $617,623,474
Liabilities: $253,941,564
Net Worth: $363,681,910
Earnings: $72,244,156
Emp.: 3,007

Fiscal Year-end: 12/31/2023
Tire Manufacturing (except Retreading)
N.A.I.C.S.: 326211
Jacek Pryczek (Chm-Supervisory Bd)
Dominikus Golsong (Deputy Chm-Supervisory Bd)
Janusz Ras (Member-Mgmt Bd)
Ireneusz Maksymiuk (Member-Mgmt Bd & Dir-Fin)
Michal Medrek (Member-Mgmt Bd & Dir-Logistics)
Leszek Szafran (Chm-Mgmt Bd & Sls Dir)
Miroslaw Maziarka (Member-Mgmt Bd & Dir-Production)
Francois Colin de Verdiere (Deputy Chm-Supervisory Bd)

Tredcor Kenya Limited (1)
Mombasa Road, Nairobi, Kenya
Tel.: (254) 722730004
Web Site: https://www.tredcorkenya.com
Tiles Mfr
N.A.I.C.S.: 326211

Trentyre (Lesotho) (Pty) Ltd (1)
Kingsway Industrial Area, PO Box 4510,
Maseru, Lesotho
Tel.: (266) 22311628
Tire Distr
N.A.I.C.S.: 423130

Vulco Developpement (1)
95 Avenue De La Chataigneraie, Rueil Malmaison Cedex, 92506, Paris, France
Tel.: (33) 1 47 16 28 17
Web Site: http://www.vulco.com
Automobile Parts Mfr
N.A.I.C.S.: 336110

Vulco Truck Services (1)
BP 70158, 38504, Voiron, France
Tel.: (33) 825106262
Web Site: http://www.vulco.com
Automotive Repair & Maintenance Services
N.A.I.C.S.: 811198

Weeting Tyres Limited (1)
20B Highbury Road, Brandon, IP27 0ND,
Suffolk, United Kingdom
Tel.: (44) 184 281 0772
Web Site: https://www.weetingtyres.co.uk
Automotive Tires Distr
N.A.I.C.S.: 441340

Wingfoot Australia Partner Pty Ltd (1)
L 1 460 Church St N, Parramatta, 2151,
NSW, Australia
Tel.: (61) 297686022
Emp.: 2,087
Tiles Mfr
N.A.I.C.S.: 326211

Wingfoot Commercial Tire Systems, LLC (1)
1000 S 21st St, Fort Smith, AR 72901-4008
Tel.: (479) 788-6400
Web Site: https://www.wingfootct.com
Sales Range: $700-749.9 Million
Emp.: 4,000
Tire Distr & Retreader
N.A.I.C.S.: 326212

Wingfoot Corporation (1)
801 W Robinson Dr Ste 200, North Salt
Lake, UT 84054
Tel.: (801) 936-0111
Web Site: https://www.wingfootservices.com
Janitorial Services
N.A.I.C.S.: 561720

THE GORMAN-RUPP COMPANY

600 S Airport Rd, Mansfield, OH
44903
Tel.: (419) 755-1011   OH
Web Site:
   https://www.gormanrupp.com
Year Founded: 1933
GRC—(NYSE)
Rev.: $521,027,000
Assets: $872,830,000
Liabilities: $541,636,000
Net Worth: $331,194,000
Earnings: $11,195,000
Emp.: 620
Fiscal Year-end: 12/31/22

Pump & Pumping Equipment Mfr
N.A.I.C.S.: 333914
Jeffrey S. Gorman (Exec Chm)
Scott A. King (Pres & CEO)
Angela M. Morehead (Treas)
Barbara A. Woodman (VP)

Subsidiaries:

AMT Pump Company (1)
400 Spring St, Royersford, PA 19468
Tel.: (610) 948-3800
Web Site: https://amtpumps.com
Pumps Designer & Mfr
N.A.I.C.S.: 333914

Gorman-Rupp Belgium SA (1)
Zoning industriel de Rhisnes Rue des Metiers 11, Suarlee, 5020, Namur, Belgium
Tel.: (32) 81779977
Pump & Pumping Equipment Distr
N.A.I.C.S.: 423830

Gorman-Rupp Europe B.V. (1)
Zandweistraat 19, 4181 CG, Waardenburg,
Netherlands
Tel.: (31) 857730080
Web Site: https://www.grpumps.nl
Emp.: 10
Pump & Pumping Equipment Mfr
N.A.I.C.S.: 333914
Chris Van der Gaag (Mng Dir)

Gorman-Rupp Industries (1)
180 Hines Ave, Bellville, OH 44813
Tel.: (419) 886-3001
Web Site: https://www.gripumps.com
Sales Range: $25-49.9 Million
Emp.: 60
Dispensing Pump Mfr
N.A.I.C.S.: 333914
Chuck McKenzie (Coord-Western Territory Sls)
Tina Spearman (Sls Mgr-Intl)
Aaron Hill (Sr Mgr-Territory)
Jeremy Stapleton (Mgr-Western Territory)
Jim Fehrman (Mgr-Mktg)
Brian Morris (VP-Ops)
Melisa Elkins (Dir-Quality Assurance)
Victor Swisher (Dir-Engrg)

Gorman-Rupp Rental SPRL (1)
Zoning industriel de Rhisnes Rue des Metiers 11, Suarlee, 5020, Namur, Belgium
Tel.: (32) 81779977
Industrial Machinery & Equipment Whslr
N.A.I.C.S.: 423830

Gorman-Rupp of Canada Limited (1)
70 Burwell Road, Saint Thomas, N5P 3R7,   (100%)
ON, Canada
Tel.: (519) 631-2870
Web Site: http://www.grpumps.ca
Sales Range: $25-49.9 Million
Emp.: 30
Pumps Mfr
N.A.I.C.S.: 333914

Hydro+ SA (1)
Zoning industriel de Rhisnes 673 Route De
Gembloux, 5020, Namur, Belgium
Tel.: (32) 81779977
Web Site: http://www.hydro-plus.be
Pumping Equipment Distr
N.A.I.C.S.: 423830

National Pump Company (1)
7706 N 71st Ave, Glendale, AZ 85303-1703
Tel.: (623) 979-3560
Web Site:
   https://www.nationalpumpcompany.com
Sales Range: $25-49.9 Million
Pumps & Pumping Equipment Mfr & Distr
N.A.I.C.S.: 333914

Subsidiary (Domestic):

Bayou City Pump Company (2)
109 Richey St, Pasadena, TX 77506
Tel.: (713) 641-6818
Sales Range: $10-24.9 Million
Emp.: 25
Pumping Systems Repair Services
N.A.I.C.S.: 423830

Branch (Domestic):

National Pump Company (2)
11176 Green Valley Dr, Olive Branch, MS
38654

Tel.: (662) 895-1110
Web Site:
   https://www.nationalpumpcompany.com
Pumps & Pump Equipment Sales
N.A.I.C.S.: 423830

Subsidiary (Domestic):

**National Pump Company -
Lubbock** (2)
4229 Adrian St, Lubbock, TX 79415
Tel.: (806) 745-5396
Web Site:
   http://www.nationalpumpcompany.com
Pumps & Pump Equipment Mfr & Distr
N.A.I.C.S.: 333914

Patterson Pump Company (1)
2129 Ayersville Rd, Toccoa, GA 30577
Tel.: (706) 886-2101
Web Site: https://www.pattersonpumps.com
Sales Range: $100-124.9 Million
Emp.: 336
Mfr of Pumps
N.A.I.C.S.: 333914

Subsidiary (Non-US):

Patterson Pump Ireland Limited (2)
Unit 1 IDA Ardmore Business & Technology
Park, Marlinstown, Mullingar, N91 R762,
Westmeath, Ireland
Tel.: (353) 449347078
Web Site:
   https://www.ie.pattersonpumps.com
Emp.: 40
Assembly of Pumps
N.A.I.C.S.: 333914

Pumptron (Proprietary) Limited (1)
2 Kelly Rd, Jet Park, Boksburg, 1459,
South Africa
Tel.: (27) 113973536
Web Site: http://www.grpumps.com
Emp.: 35
Pumps & Pumping Equipment Distr
N.A.I.C.S.: 423830

The Gorman-Rupp International Company (1)
600 S Airport Rd, Mansfield, OH 44901-1217
Tel.: (419) 755-1011
Web Site: http://www.grpumps.com
Sales Range: $150-199.9 Million
Emp.: 500
Pump Equipment Distr
N.A.I.C.S.: 423830

THE GRAYSTONE COMPANY, INC.

150SPineIslandRdSte300, Plantation,
FL 33324
Tel.: (702) 289-4827   DE
Web Site:
   https://www.thegraystoneco.com
Year Founded: 2010
GYST—(OTCIQ)
Sales Range: Less than $1 Million
Emp.: 20
Investment Services
N.A.I.C.S.: 523999
Paul J. Howarth (CEO)

THE GREATER CANNABIS COMPANY, INC.

2833 Smith Ave Ste 333, Baltimore,
MD 21209
Tel.: (443) 738-4051   FL
Web Site: https://www.gcanrx.com
Year Founded: 2014
GCAN—(OTCIQ)
Assets: $280,447
Liabilities: $825,277
Net Worth: ($544,830)
Earnings: ($360,268)
Emp.: 1
Fiscal Year-end: 12/31/22
Business Management Services
N.A.I.C.S.: 561110
Aitan Zacharin (Chm, Pres, CEO,
CFO-Acting & Treas)
Motti Stenge (COO)

THE GREENBRIER COMPANIES, INC.

1 Centerpointe Dr Ste 200, Lake
Oswego, OR 97035
Tel.: (503) 684-7000   OR
Web Site: https://www.gbrx.com
Year Founded: 1981
GBX—(NYSE)
Rev.: $3,544,700,000
Assets: $4,254,500,000
Liabilities: $2,717,900,000
Net Worth: $1,536,600,000
Earnings: $172,700,000
Emp.: 14,200
Fiscal Year-end: 08/31/24
Transportation Equipment & Services
N.A.I.C.S.: 336510
Adrian J. Downes (CFO & Sr VP)
William A. Furman (Co-Founder)
William G. Glenn (Pres-Europe & Sr VP)
Jack Isselmann (Sr VP-External Affairs & Comm)
Lorie L. Tekorius (Pres & CEO)
Brian J. Comstock (Pres-The Americas & Exec VP)
William Krueger (Pres-Mfg Ops)
Rick Galvan (Sr VP-Ops Maintenance Svcs)
William Krueger (COO-The Americas & Sr VP)
Laurie Dornan (Chief HR Officer & Sr VP)
Matthew J. Meyer (Chief Acctg Officer & Sr VP-Fin)
Justin M. Roberts (Treas & VP-Corp Fin)
Michael Donfris (CFO & Sr VP)
Christian Lucky (Chief Legal Officer,
Chief Compliance Officer, Sec & Sr VP)

Subsidiaries:

Alliance Castings Company, LLC (1)
1001 E Broadway St, Alliance, OH 44601-2602
Tel.: (330) 829-5600
Steel Casting Mfr
N.A.I.C.S.: 488210

GBW Railcar Services, LLC (1)
10895 Grandview Dr Ste 350, Overland
Park, KS 66210
Tel.: (888) 968-4364
Web Site: http://www.gbwservices.com
Emp.: 2,100
Locomotive & Railcar Repair Services
N.A.I.C.S.: 811310
Ray Pericola (Pres)

Plant (Domestic):

**Watco Mechanical Services, LLC -
Cudahy** (2)
5000 S Whitnall Ave, Cudahy, WI 53110
Tel.: (414) 744-1612
Web Site: http://www.gbwservices.com
Sales Range: $10-24.9 Million
Emp.: 35
Railcar Repair & Maintenance Services
N.A.I.C.S.: 811310

**Watco Mechanical Services, LLC -
Jacksonville** (2)
7305 Old Kings Rd N, Jacksonville, FL
32219
Tel.: (904) 786-1700
Web Site: http://www.watcocompanies.com
Sales Range: $25-49.9 Million
Emp.: 80
Railcar Repair Services
N.A.I.C.S.: 811310

Greenbrier Germany GmbH (1)
Welterstrasse 57, 57072, Siegen,
Germany   (100%)
Tel.: (49) 2712507201
Web Site: http://www.gbrxeu.com
Sales Range: $300-349.9 Million
Railroad Freight Car Sales, Marketing &
Engineering
N.A.I.C.S.: 336510

The Greenbrier Companies, Inc.—(Continued)

Greenbrier Railcar LLC (1)
1 Centerpointe Dr Ste 200, Lake Oswego,
OR 97035
Tel.: (503) 684-7000
Web Site: http://www.gbrx.com
Sales Range: $10-24.9 Million
Emp.: 50
Railcar Lessor
N.A.I.C.S.: 532411
William A. Furman (Pres & CEO)

**Greenbrier-Maxion Equipamentos e
Servicos Ferroviarios S.A.** (1)
Dr Othon Barcellos St 77 Centro, Cruzeiro,
12730-010, SP, Brazil (60%)
Tel.: (55) 1221221400
Foundry & Railway Components Mfr
N.A.I.C.S.: 332999

**Gunderson - GIMSA S. A. de
C.V.** (1)
Presidente Carranza 150F City, Frontera
Township, 25680, Coahuila, Mexico
Tel.: (52) 866 649 3100
Web Site: https://www.gunderson-
gimsa.com.mx
Railroad Transportation Equipment Services
N.A.I.C.S.: 336510

Gunderson LLC (1)
4350 NW Front Ave, Portland, OR 97210
Tel.: (503) 972-5700
Sales Range: $750-799.9 Million
Emp.: 1,300
Holding Company; Railroad Freight Car &
Marine Barge Builder & Refurbisher
N.A.I.C.S.: 551112

Gunderson Rail Services, LLC (1)
4350 NW Front Ave, Portland, OR 97210
Tel.: (503) 684-7000
Web Site: http://www.gbrx.com
Sales Range: $150-199.9 Million
Railcar Parts, Wheels, Repair, Maintenance
& Refurbishment Services
N.A.I.C.S.: 336510

Unit (Domestic):

American Hydraulics (2)
2700 N Broadway, Red Oak, IA 51566
Tel.: (402) 453-8281
Web Site: http://www.ahigears.com
Sales Range: $50-74.9 Million
Emp.: 100
Railcar End Cushioning Devices Mfr & Re-
conditioning Services
N.A.I.C.S.: 336510

Subsidiary (Domestic):

**Greenbrier Rail Services Wheel
Division** (2)
1200 Corporate Dr Ste 450, Birmingham,
AL 35242
Tel.: (205) 991-0384
Web Site: http://www.meridianrail.com
Sales Range: $200-249.9 Million
Emp.: 16
Holding Company; Railcar Wheel & Axle
Components Mfr & Reconditioning Services
N.A.I.C.S.: 551112

Meridian Rail Acquisition Corp. (1)
1200 Corporate Dr Ste 450, Birmingham,
AL 35242
Tel.: (205) 991-0384
Sales Range: $10-24.9 Million
Emp.: 10
Railroad Transportation Equipment & Ser-
vices
N.A.I.C.S.: 336510
Jerry Ellison (VP-Ops)

**Rayvag Vagon Sanayi ve Ticaret
A.S.** (1)
Adana Haci Sabanci Organize Sanayi
Bolgesi, OSB Celal Bayar Bulvari No 28
Saricam, Adana, Turkiye
Tel.: (90) 322394508
Web Site: http://www.rayvag.com.tr
Motor Vehicle Parts Mfr
N.A.I.C.S.: 336510

**Southwest Steel Casting
Company** (1)
600 Foundry Dr, Longview, TX 75604
Tel.: (214) 733-1717

Web Site: http://www.swscc.com
Engineering Services
N.A.I.C.S.: 541330

WagonySwidnica S.A. (1)
Ul Strzelinska 35, 58 100, Swidnica,
Poland (100%)
Tel.: (48) 748562000
Web Site: http://www.gbrxeu.com
Sales Range: $350-399.9 Million
Emp.: 1,000
Railroad Freight Car Mfr
N.A.I.C.S.: 336510

WagonySwidnica sp. z o.o. (1)
Ul Strzelinska 35, 58-100, Swidnica, Poland
Tel.: (48) 748562000
Motor Vehicle Parts Mfr
N.A.I.C.S.: 336510

YSD Doors, S.A. de C.V (1)
Domicilio Conocido, 43930, Tlanalapa, Hi-
dalgo, Mexico
Tel.: (52) 7919138800
Transportation Equipment Distr
N.A.I.C.S.: 423860

THE HACKETT GROUP, INC.
1001 Brickell Bay Dr 30th Fl, Miami,
FL 33131
Tel.: (305) 375-8005   FL
Web Site:
  https://www.thehackettgroup.com
Year Founded: 1991
HCKT—(NASDAQ)
Rev.: $239,482,000
Assets: $192,545,000
Liabilities: $51,658,000
Net Worth: $140,887,000
Earnings: $5,473,000
Emp.: 1,047
Fiscal Year-end: 01/01/21
Administrative Management & Gen-
eral Management Consulting Ser-
vices
N.A.I.C.S.: 541611
Ted A. Fernandez (Co-Founder, Chm
& CEO)
David N. Dungan (Co-Founder, Vice
Chm & COO)
Robert A. Ramirez (CFO & Exec VP-
Fin)

Subsidiaries:

Hackett Group (India) Ltd. (1)
Plot 6 1-55/4/RP/L1/W1 W2, Raja Prasa-
dam Kondapur, Hyderabad, 500 084, India
Tel.: (01) 4044004000
Information Technology Solutions
N.A.I.C.S.: 541511

Hackett-REL Limited (1)
Martin House 5 Martin Ln, London, EC4R
0DP, United Kingdom
Tel.: (44) 2073989100
Web Site: http://www.thehackettgroup.com
Management Consulting Services
N.A.I.C.S.: 541611

**The Hackett Group Australia Pty.
Ltd.** (1)
Suite 404 45 Lime Street, Sydney, 2000,
NSW, Australia
Tel.: (61) 1300457779
Web Site: http://www.thehackettgroup.com
Emp.: 15
Operations Improvement Consulting Ser-
vices
N.A.I.C.S.: 541618

The Hackett Group BV (1)
Camerastraat 25, 1322 BB, Almere, Nether-
lands
Tel.: (31) 365350082
Web Site: http://www.thehackettgroup.com
Emp.: 13
Management Consulting Services
N.A.I.C.S.: 541618

The Hackett Group GmbH (1)
Neue Rothoffstrasse 13-19, 60313, Frank-
furt am Main, Germany
Tel.: (49) 699002170
Business Management Consulting Services
N.A.I.C.S.: 541611

**THE HAIN CELESTIAL GROUP,
INC.**
221 River St, Hoboken, NJ 07030
Tel.: (516) 587-5000   DE
Web Site: https://www.hain.com
Year Founded: 1993
HAIN—(NASDAQ)
Rev.: $1,736,286,000
Assets: $2,117,548,000
Liabilities: $1,174,635,000
Net Worth: $942,913,000
Earnings: ($75,042,000)
Emp.: 2,786
Fiscal Year-end: 06/30/24
Natural & Organic Foods & Personal
Care Products Mfr
N.A.I.C.S.: 311999
Dawn M. Zier (Chm)
Irwin David Simon (Founder)
Michael J. Ragusa (Chief Acctg Offi-
cer & Sr VP)
Kristy Rogan Meringolo (Chief Com-
pliance Officer, Gen Counsel & Sr
VP)
Wendy P. Davidson (Pres & CEO)
David J. Karch (COO & Exec VP)
Jeff George (Sr VP-Research & De-
velopment)
JoAnn Murray (Chief HR Officer)
Ari Labell (Sr VP-Customer & Chan-
nel Strategy)
Irwin D. Simon (Founder)
Amber D. Jefferson (Chief People
Officer)
Lee A. Boyce (CFO & Exec VP)
Jen Davis (Chief Comm Officer)

Subsidiaries:

Avalon Natural Products, Inc. (1)
1105 Industrial Ave, Petaluma, CA 94952
Tel.: (707) 769-5120
Web Site: http://www.avalonorganics.com
Organic Personal Care Products Mfr
N.A.I.C.S.: 325620

Celestial Seasonings, Inc. (1)
4600 Sleepytime Dr, Boulder, CO
80301-3292 (100%)
Tel.: (303) 581-1219
Web Site:
  https://www.celestialseasonings.com
Sales Range: $125-149.9 Million
Emp.: 275
Herbal & Specialty Teas Mfr
N.A.I.C.S.: 311920
Mo Siegel (Founder)

Charter Baking Company, Inc. (1)
3300 Walnut St Unit C, Boulder, CO 80301
Tel.: (303) 447-0495
Web Site: http://www.charterbaking.com
Bread Baking & Distr
N.A.I.C.S.: 311813

Clark's UK Limited (1)
Units 7 and 8 Estuary Court Queensway
Meadows Industrial Estate, Newport, NP19
4SX, United Kingdom
Tel.: (44) 8000224339
Web Site: http://www.clarksit.co.uk
Confectionery Merchant Whslr
N.A.I.C.S.: 424450

Cully & Sully Limited (1)
The Hen House First Floor Elm Court
Boreenmanna Road, Cork, Ireland
Tel.: (353) 214293584
Web Site: https://www.cullyandsully.com
Emp.: 10
Soups & Hot Pots Mfr
N.A.I.C.S.: 311999

Daniels Group Limited (1)
Unit 4 Acorn Business Park, Leeds, LS14
6UF, United Kingdom (100%)
Tel.: (44) 1132480770
Web Site: http://www.danielgroup.eu
Prepared Chilled Meal Mfr
N.A.I.C.S.: 424420

Subsidiary (Domestic):

Daniels Chilled Foods Ltd. (2)
4 Acorn Business Park, Killingbeck Dr York

Rd, Leeds, LS146UF, United
Kingdom (100%)
Tel.: (44) 1132480770
Web Site: http://www.haindaniels.com
Sales Range: $25-49.9 Million
Emp.: 50
Chilled Meal Mfr
N.A.I.C.S.: 424420

Farmhouse Fare Limited (2)
Templar House 4225 Park Approach Thorpe
Park, Lincoln Way, Leeds, LS15 8GB, Lan-
cashire, United Kingdom (100%)
Tel.: (44) 8000014403
Web Site: https://www.farmhousefare.co.uk
Sales Range: $25-49.9 Million
Emp.: 90
Frozen Specialty Food Mfr
N.A.I.C.S.: 311412

**The New Covent Garden Soup Com-
pany Limited** (2)
Westwood Farm Westwood, Peterborough,
PE3 9UW, Cambs, United Kingdom
Tel.: (44) 1733843400
Web Site: http://www.haindaniels.com
Natural & Organic Food Products Mfr
N.A.I.C.S.: 311999

DeBoles Nutritional Foods, Inc. (1)
58 S Service Rd, Melville, NY 11747
Tel.: (631) 730-2200
Sales Range: $125-149.9 Million
Emp.: 200
Mfr of Organic Pasta
N.A.I.C.S.: 424490
Irwin David Simon (Pres & CEO)

Ella's Kitchen Group Limited (1)
1 St Andrews Hill, London, EC4V 5BY,
United Kingdom
Tel.: (44) 1215546922
Holding Company
N.A.I.C.S.: 551112

Subsidiary (Domestic):

Ella's Kitchen (Brands) Limited (2)
Ellas Barn 22 Greys Green Farm, Rother-
field Greys, Henley-on-Thames, RG9 4QG,
United Kingdom
Tel.: (44) 1491629120
Web Site: https://www.ellaskitchen.co.uk
Emp.: 70
Grocery Product Distr
N.A.I.C.S.: 424410

GG UniqueFiber AS (1)
Hegdalveien 73, 3261, Larvik, Vestfold,
Norway
Tel.: (47) 40482468
Web Site: http://www.gguniquefiber.no
Natural & Organic Food Products Distr &
Mfr
N.A.I.C.S.: 311999

Hain BPC, Inc. (1)
13020 Yukon AveHawthorne, Hawthorne,
CA 90250-5346
Tel.: (212) 414-5741
Food Processing & Distr
N.A.I.C.S.: 311412

Hain Celestial Europe B.V. (1)
Groendreef 101, 9880, Aalter,
Belgium (100%)
Tel.: (32) 26097651
Web Site: http://www.hain-celestial.eu
Sales Range: $25-49.9 Million
Emp.: 50
Organic Food Products Mfr
N.A.I.C.S.: 311999

Subsidiary (Domestic):

Hain Celestial Belgium BVBA (2)
Rue de la Montagne 30-34, 1000, Brussels,
Belgium (100%)
Tel.: (32) 26097651
Web Site: http://www.hain-celestial.eu
Sales Range: $10-24.9 Million
Emp.: 4
Organic Food Products Mfr
N.A.I.C.S.: 311999

Subsidiary (Domestic):

Grains Noir (3)
Rue Joseph Schols 13 15, Molenbeek,
1080, Belgium (100%)
Tel.: (32) 50728696

Web Site: http://www.grainsnoirs.com
Mfr of Organic Prepared Appetizers, Salads, Sandwiches & Full-Plate Dishes
N.A.I.C.S.: 311423

Lima S.A./N.V. (3)
Groendreef 101, 9880, Aalter, Belgium
Tel.: (32) 50728696
Web Site: http://www.hain-celestial.eu
Mfr of Food Products
N.A.I.C.S.: 311423

Subsidiary (Non-US):

Natumi AG (2)
Gierlichsstrasse 17, 53840, Troisdorf, Germany
Tel.: (49) 224125670
Web Site: https://www.natumi.com
Natural & Organic Food Products Mfr
N.A.I.C.S.: 311999

Hain Celestial UK Limited (1)
2100 Century Way, Thorpe Parl, Leeds, LS15 8ZB, United Kingdom (100%)
Tel.: (44) 1132480770
Web Site: http://www.haindaniels.com
Organic Food Products Mfr
N.A.I.C.S.: 311999

Histon Sweet Spreads Limited (1)
4 Acorn Business Park Killingbeck Drive, Leeds, LS14 6UF, United Kingdom
Tel.: (44) 1132480770
Web Site: http://www.haindaniels.com
Emp.: 50
Food Processing & Distr
N.A.I.C.S.: 311412

Jason Natural Products Inc. (1)
8468 Warner Dr, Culver City, CA 90232
Tel.: (310) 838-7543
Web Site: http://www.jason-natural.com
Sales Range: $25-49.9 Million
Emp.: 100
All Natural Health & Beauty Products Mfr & Distr
N.A.I.C.S.: 325620

Mona Naturprodukte GmbH (1)
Schottengasse 10 2 Stock, 1010, Vienna, Austria
Tel.: (43) 18972300
Web Site: https://joya.info
Food Products Mfr
N.A.I.C.S.: 311999

Plainville Farms, LLC (1)
304 S Water St, New Oxford, PA 17350
Tel.: (717) 624-2191
Web Site: https://www.plainvillefarms.com
Food Products Distr
N.A.I.C.S.: 424470

Rudi's Organic Bakery, Inc. (1)
3300 Walnut St Unit C, Boulder, CO 80301
Tel.: (303) 447-0495
Web Site: https://www.rudisbakery.com
Sales Range: $1-9.9 Million
Emp.: 120
Bread Mfr
N.A.I.C.S.: 311812
Brian McGuire (CEO)

Spectrum Organic Products, Inc. (1)
1105 Industrial Ave, Petaluma, CA 94952-1141
Tel.: (631) 730-2200
Web Site: http://www.spectrumorganics.com
Sales Range: $25-49.9 Million
Emp.: 25
Organic & Natural Culinary & Nutritional Oils Mfr
N.A.I.C.S.: 311225

The Hain Daniels Group Limited (1)
Tel.: (44) 8000014403
Web Site: https://www.haindaniels.com
Emp.: 70
Timber Product Mfr
N.A.I.C.S.: 311421

Tilda Marketing Inc. (1)
2160 N Central Rd Ste 205, Fort Lee, NJ 07024
Tel.: (201) 461-1600
Web Site: http://www.tildausa.com
Food Processing & Distr
N.A.I.C.S.: 311412

Tilda Rice Limited (1)

Coldharbour Lane, Rainham, RM13 9YQ, United Kingdom
Tel.: (44) 1708717777
Food Products Mfr
N.A.I.C.S.: 311999

Westbrae Natural, Inc. (1)
1111 Marcus Ave, Lake Success, NY 11042
Tel.: (631) 730-2200
Web Site: http://www.westbrae.com
Sales Range: $100-124.9 Million
Emp.: 300
Marketing of Natural & Organic Food Products
N.A.I.C.S.: 424490
Irwin David Simon (Pres)

Subsidiary (Domestic):

Little Bear Organic Foods, Inc. (2)
1111 Marcus Ave, Lake Success, NY 11042 (100%)
Tel.: (631) 730-2200
Web Site: http://www.hain.com
Natural & Organic Snack Foods
N.A.I.C.S.: 311230

Westbrae Natural Foods, Inc. (2)
58 S Service Rd, Melville, NY 11747 (100%)
Tel.: (631) 730-2200
Web Site: http://www.sammonspreston.com
Sales Range: $125-149.9 Million
Emp.: 180
Natural Foods Mfr & Distr
N.A.I.C.S.: 424490

THE HANOVER INSURANCE GROUP, INC.
440 Lincoln St, Worcester, MA 01653
Tel.: (508) 855-1000   DE
Web Site: https://www.hanover.com
THG—(NYSE)
Rev.: $5,993,500,000
Assets: $14,612,600,000
Liabilities: $12,147,000,000
Net Worth: $2,465,600,000
Earnings: $35,300,000
Emp.: 4,800
Fiscal Year-end: 12/31/23
Holding Company; Property & Casualty Insurance, Reinsurance & Other Insurance Products & Services
N.A.I.C.S.: 551112
Richard W. Lavey (Pres-Agency Markets & Exec VP)
Warren E. Barnes (Chief Acctg Officer, Sr VP & Controller)
John C. Roche (Pres & CEO)
Jeffrey M. Farber (CFO & Exec VP)
Bryan J. Salvatore (Pres-Specialty & Exec VP)
Denise M. Lowsley (Chief HR Officer & Exec VP)
Willard T. Lee (Chief Info & Innovation Officer & Exec VP)
David J. Lovely (Chief Claims Officer & Exec VP)
Charles F. Cronin (Sr VP)
Catherine E. Eska (Chief Risk Officer)
Gayle Falvey (COO)
Carrie M. Farrell (Sr VP)
William M. Finn (Chief Actuary & Data Officer)
Lindsay F. Greenfield (Chief Investment Officer)
Daniel C. Halsey (Pres)
Olga C. Harris (Sr VP)
Jennifer F. Luisa (CMO)
Oksana Y. Lukasheva (Sr VP)
Basil C. Morris (Chief Strategy Officer)
Armando G. Petruzziello (Sr VP)
Stephen P. Marohn (Pres-Specialty Property & Casualty)
Bryan J. Salvatore (Pres-Specialty & Exec VP)

Subsidiaries:

Campania Holding Company, Inc. (1)

12100 Sunset Hills Rd Ste 250, Reston, VA 20190-5913
Tel.: (800) 831-9506
Holding Company
N.A.I.C.S.: 551112

Chaucer Syndicate Services Limited (1)
52 Lime Street, London, EC3M 7AF, United Kingdom
Tel.: (44) 2073979700
Web Site: https://www.chaucergroup.com
Underwriting Insurance Standard Services
N.A.I.C.S.: 524298

Educators Insurance Agency, Inc. (1)
440 Lincoln St, Worcester, MA 01653
Web Site: https://www.educatorsinsuranceagency.com
Emp.: 6
Insurance Management Services
N.A.I.C.S.: 524298

Front Street Financing LLC (1)
2417 N Frnt St, Harrisburg, PA 17110
Tel.: (717) 562-0701
Web Site: http://www.frontstreetfin.com
Insurance Investigation Services
N.A.I.C.S.: 524298

Lonham Group Limited (1)
The Maltings Princes Street, Suffolk, Ipswich, IP1 1SB, United Kingdom
Tel.: (44) 1473216116
Web Site: https://www.lonham.co.uk
Marine Transportation Services
N.A.I.C.S.: 488320
Mike Ayres (Dir-Underwriting)
Christine Midwood (Dir-Claims)

Pacific Underwriting Corporation Pty Ltd (1)
Level 15 45 Clarence Street, Sydney, 2000, NSW, Australia
Tel.: (61) 292491500
Web Site: https://prod-combined-host-gkfuhbfk.azurewebsites.net
Insurance Underwriting Services
N.A.I.C.S.: 524126

SLE Worldwide Pty Limited (1)
Level 15 45 Clarence Street, Sydney, 2000, NSW, Australia
Tel.: (61) 92494850
Web Site: https://www.sleworldwide.com.au
Underwriting Insurance Agency Services
N.A.I.C.S.: 524298
Peter McKenzie (Gen Mgr)
Peter Traynor (Mgr-Claims)
Shane Cornford (Mgr-Claims)
Tom Thoroughgood (Officer-Casualty Claims)
Carl Kilbourne (Officer-Property Claims)
Michael Bersiga (Officer-Personal Accident Claims)
Sarah Mead (Officer-Personal Accident Claims)
Olivia Parades (Officer-Personal Accident Claims)
Tanjina Satter (Officer-Personal Accident Claims)
Grace Everett (Officer-Personal Accident Claims)

The Hanover Insurance Company (1)
440 Lincoln St, Worcester, MA 01653
Tel.: (508) 855-1000
Web Site: https://www.hanover.com
Sales Range: $1-4.9 Billion
Property & Casualty Insurance Products & Services
N.A.I.C.S.: 524126

Subsidiary (Domestic):

AIX Holdings, Inc. (2)
5 Waterside Crossing Ste 201, Windsor, CT 06095
Tel.: (860) 683-4250
Web Site: http://www.aixgroup.com
Sales Range: $50-74.9 Million
Emp.: 150
Insurance Services
N.A.I.C.S.: 524298

Subsidiary (Domestic):

AIX, Inc. (3)

440 Lincoln St, Worcester, MA 01653
Tel.: (860) 683-4250
Emp.: 120
Insurance Management Services
N.A.I.C.S.: 524298
Russell Renvyle (Reg Pres)

Nova American Group, Inc. (3)
726 Exchange St Ste 1020, Buffalo, NY 14210
Tel.: (716) 842-0502
Insurance Brokers
N.A.I.C.S.: 524210

Subsidiary (Domestic):

AIX Specialty Insurance Company (4)
5 Waterside Crossing Ste 3201, Windsor, CT 06095
Tel.: (860) 683-4250
Web Site: https://www.aixspecialty.com
Insurance Management Services
N.A.I.C.S.: 524298

Subsidiary (Domestic):

Campmed Casualty & Indemnity Company, Inc. (2)
440 Lincoln St, Worcester, MA 01653-0002
Tel.: (508) 853-7200
Sales Range: $25-49.9 Million
Emp.: 35
Insurance Brokerage Services
N.A.I.C.S.: 524210
Matt Mitchell (Pres)

Citizens Insurance Company of America (2)
645 W Grand River Ave, Howell, MI 48843-2151 (100%)
Tel.: (512) 837-7100
Sales Range: $800-899.9 Million
Emp.: 192
Auto, Property & Casualty Insurance
N.A.I.C.S.: 524126

Hanover Lloyd's Insurance Company (2)
Premier Place 5910 N Central Expy #300, Dallas, TX 75206 (100%)
Tel.: (214) 615-1510
Web Site: http://www.hanover.com
Rev.: $3,317,000
Emp.: 24
Fire & Casualty Insurance
N.A.I.C.S.: 524126

Massachusetts Bay Insurance Co. (2)
440 Lincoln St, Worcester, MA 01653 (100%)
Tel.: (508) 855-1000
Web Site: https://www.hanover.com
Sales Range: $350-399.9 Million
Emp.: 3,400
Insurance; Property & Casualty
N.A.I.C.S.: 524126

THE HARTFORD FINANCIAL SERVICES GROUP, INC.
1 Hartford Plz, Hartford, CT 06155
Tel.: (860) 547-5000   DE
Web Site: https://www.thehartford.com
Year Founded: 1810
HIG—(NYSE)
Rev.: $24,527,000,000
Assets: $76,780,000,000
Liabilities: $61,453,000,000
Net Worth: $15,327,000,000
Earnings: $2,483,000,000
Emp.: 18,700
Fiscal Year-end: 12/31/23
Financial Investment Services
N.A.I.C.S.: 551111
Jonathan R. Bennett (Exec VP & Head-Grp Benefits)
Robert W. Paiano (Exec VP)
John Kinney (Head-Claims & Ops)
Lori A. Rodden (Chief HR Officer & Exec VP)
Beth A. Costello (CFO & Exec VP)
Christopher John Swift (Chm & CEO)

The Hartford Financial Services Group, Inc.—(Continued)

Subsidiaries:

HIMCO Distribution Services
Company   (1)
1 Hartford Plz, Hartford, CT 06155
Tel.: (860) 547-7675
General Insurance Services
N.A.I.C.S.: 524210

Hartford Fire Insurance Co.   (1)
690 Asylum Ave, Hartford, CT 06105
Tel.: (860) 547-5000
Web Site: http://www.thehartford.com
Commercial Property & Casualty Insurance,
Life & Health Insurance
N.A.I.C.S.: 524126

Subsidiary (Domestic):

Hartford International Insurance
Company   (2)
690 Asylum Ave, Hartford, CT 06155
Tel.: (860) 547-5000
Web Site: http://www.hfpinsurance.com
Sales Range: $1-4.9 Billion
Insurance Services
N.A.I.C.S.: 524113

Hartford Funds Management Group,
Inc.   (1)
690 Lee Rd, Wayne, PA 19807
Tel.: (610) 386-1773
Web Site: http://www.hartfordfunds.com
Mutual Fund
N.A.I.C.S.: 525910
James Davey (Pres)
Gregory Frost (CFO)
Martin Swanson (CMO)
Vernon Meyer (Chief Investment Officer)
Theodore Lucas (Head-Investment Strategies & Solutions)
Walter Garger (Gen Counsel)
Joseph Melcher (Chief Compliance Officer)
Jamie Davis (Head-HR)

Subsidiary (Domestic):

Hartford Funds Management Company, LLC   (2)
690 Lee Rd, Wayne, PA 19807
Tel.: (610) 386-4000
Web Site: http://www.hartfordfunds.com
Mutual Fund
N.A.I.C.S.: 525910
David Hescheles (Mng Dir)

Subsidiary (Domestic):

Lattice Strategies LLC   (3)
1 Embarcadero Ctr 23rd Fl Ste 2350, San
Francisco, CA 94111   (100%)
Tel.: (415) 508-4983
Life Insurance Carrier Services
N.A.I.C.S.: 524113
Mauricio F. Cevallos (Sr Partner)

Hartford Investment Management
Company   (1)
1 Hartford Plz, Hartford, CT 06155
Tel.: (860) 297-6700
Web Site: https://www.himco.com
Emp.: 289
Investment Services
N.A.I.C.S.: 523940
Amy M. Stepnowski (Pres)
Jack Maher (Mng Dir & Head-)
Tracy Eccles (Exec VP & Head)
Ira Edelblum (Exec VP & Head)
Elaine J. Nigro (Exec VP & Head)
Peter Perrotti (Exec VP & Head)
Tracy Eccles (Exec VP & Head)
Ira Edelblum (Exec VP & Head)
Elaine J. Nigro (Exec VP & Head)
Peter Perrotti (Exec VP & Head)
Tracy Eccles (Exec VP & Head)
Ira Edelblum (Exec VP & Head)
Elaine J. Nigro (Exec VP & Head)
Peter Perrotti (Exec VP & Head)
Rene Aube (Exec VP)

Horizon Management Group,
LLC   (1)
100 High St, Boston, MA 02110-1713
Tel.: (617) 526-8500
Web Site: http://www.hartford.com
Sales Range: $150-199.9 Million
Emp.: 200
Insurance Services

N.A.I.C.S.: 524113

The Navigators Group, Inc.   (1)
400 Atlantic St, Stamford, CT 06901
Tel.: (203) 905-6090
Web Site: http://www.navg.com
Rev.: $1,912,961,000
Assets: $5,603,449,000
Liabilities: $4,416,599,000
Net Worth: $1,186,850,000
Earnings: $34,239,000
Emp.: 838
Fiscal Year-end: 12/31/2018
Insurance Holding Company
N.A.I.C.S.: 551112
William H. Steinberg (Head)

Subsidiary (Non-US):

Assurances Continentales - Continentale Verzekeringen N.V.   (2)
Entrepotkaai 5, 2000, Antwerp, Belgium
Tel.: (32) 33392400
Web Site: https://premiaholdings.com
Insurance Services
N.A.I.C.S.: 524126

Bracht, Deckers & Mackelbert
N.V.   (2)
Entrepotkaai 5, 2000, Antwerp, Belgium
Tel.: (32) 32337838
Web Site: https://www.bdmantwerp.be
Insurance Services
N.A.I.C.S.: 524126

Navigators (Asia) Ltd.   (2)
AIA Central Room 2842 28th Floor 1 Connaught Road, Central, China (Hong Kong)
Tel.: (852) 36516195
Insurance Services
N.A.I.C.S.: 524126

Subsidiary (Domestic):

Navigators California Insurance Services, Inc.   (2)
433 California St Ste 300, San Francisco,
CA 94104
Tel.: (415) 399-9109
Web Site: http://www.navg.com
Sales Range: $10-24.9 Million
Emp.: 35
Insurance Agents, Brokers & Service
N.A.I.C.S.: 524126
Christopher A. Johnson (Pres-Marine Div)

Subsidiary (Non-US):

Navigators Holdings UK Ltd.   (2)
6 Bevis Marks Floors 7-8, London, EC3A
7BA, United Kingdom
Tel.: (44) 2072209314
Web Site: http://www.navigators.co.uk
Insurance Holding Company
N.A.I.C.S.: 551112

Subsidiary (Domestic):

Navigators Management UK Ltd.   (3)
6 Bevis Marks 8th Floor Bury Court, London, EC3A 7BA, United Kingdom
Tel.: (44) 2072206900
Web Site: http://www.navigators.com
Sales Range: $25-49.9 Million
Emp.: 91
Insurance Underwriting Services
N.A.I.C.S.: 524126

Navigators Underwriting Agency
Ltd.   (3)
4th Floor 2 Minster Court Mincing Lane,
London, EC3R 7BB, United Kingdom
Tel.: (44) 2072206900
Web Site: http://www.navigators.com
Sales Range: $25-49.9 Million
Emp.: 110
Marine & D&O Insurance Underwriting
N.A.I.C.S.: 524126

Subsidiary (Domestic):

Navigators Insurance Company   (2)
1 Penn Plz 50th Fl, New York, NY 10119-5500
Tel.: (212) 613-4200
Web Site: http://www.navg.com
Sales Range: $25-49.9 Million
Emp.: 75
Fire, Marine & Casualty Insurance
N.A.I.C.S.: 524126

Navigators Management Company,
Inc.   (2)
Reckson Executive Park 6 International Dr,
Rye Brook, NY 10573   (100%)
Tel.: (914) 934-8999
Web Site: http://www.navg.com
Sales Range: $1-9.9 Million
Emp.: 60
Insurance Agents, Brokers & Service
N.A.I.C.S.: 524210
Stanley A. Galanski (Chm)

Y-Risk, LLC   (1)
29 Mill St, Unionville, CT 06085
Tel.: (860) 255-7194
Web Site: https://www.yrisk.com
Insurance Services
N.A.I.C.S.: 524126
Mike Visintainer (COO & Head-Actuarial)
Kati Duff (Dir-Ops)
Iain Boyer (Chief Underwriting Officer)
Jillian Florian (Head-On-demand Svcs &
Asset Sharing)

THE HEALING COMPANY INC.
135 W 50th St 2nd Fl, New York, NY
10020
Tel.: (206) 203-4100   NV
Web Site:
https://www.healingcompany.com
Year Founded: 2008
HLCO—(OTCQB)
Rev.: $8,895,000
Assets: $12,771,000
Liabilities: $14,733,000
Net Worth: ($1,962,000)
Earnings: ($21,309,000)
Emp.: 20
Fiscal Year-end: 06/30/23
Mineral Exploration Services
N.A.I.C.S.: 213115

Subsidiaries:

NOEO, GmbH   (1)
Pestalozzistrasse 38, 80469, Munich, Germany
Tel.: (49) 89416171940
Web Site: https://www.noeo.com
Software Development Services
N.A.I.C.S.: 541511

Your Superfoods GmbH   (1)
Grunberger Strasse 44a, 10245, Berlin,
Germany
Tel.: (49) 30398202300
Web Site: https://yoursuperfoods.de
Protein Powder Mfr & Distr
N.A.I.C.S.: 325411

THE HERSHEY CO.
19 E Chocolate Ave, Hershey, PA
17033
Tel.: (717) 534-4200   DE
Web Site:
https://www.thehersheycompany.com
Year Founded: 1894
HSY—(NYSE)
Rev.: $11,164,992,000
Assets: $11,902,941,000
Liabilities: $7,803,855,000
Net Worth: $4,099,086,000
Earnings: $1,861,787,000
Emp.: 18,650
Fiscal Year-end: 12/31/23
Cocoa, Chocolate & Confectionery
Products Mfr
N.A.I.C.S.: 311351
Steven E. Voskuil (CFO & Sr VP)
Rohit Grover (Pres-Intl)
Jason Reiman (Chief Supply Chain
Officer & Sr VP)
James Turoff (Gen Counsel, Sec &
Sr VP)
Jennifer L. McCalman (Chief Acctg
Officer & VP)
Kris Meulen (Chief Dev Officer)
Michele G. Buck (Chm, Pres & CEO)

Subsidiaries:

Amplify Snack Brands, Inc.   (1)

500 W 5th St Ste 900, Austin, TX 78701
Tel.: (512) 600-9893
Web Site: https://amplifysnackbrands.com
Snack Food Mfr
N.A.I.C.S.: 311919
Héctor de la Barreda (Pres)

Subsidiary (Non-US):

Tyrrells Potato Crisps Ltd.   (2)
Tyrrells Court Farm Stretford Bridge,
Leominster, HR6 9DQ, Herefordshire,
United Kingdom
Tel.: (44) 15 6872 0244
Web Site: http://www.tyrrellscrisps.co.uk
Food Products Mfr
N.A.I.C.S.: 311919

Artisan Confections Company   (1)
1025 N Fillmore St Ste H, Arlington, VA
22201
Tel.: (703) 524-0007
Web Site: http://artisanconfections.com
Fiscal Year-end: 12/31/2006
Chocolate & Confectionery Mfr
N.A.I.C.S.: 311351

H.B. Reese Candy Co.   (1)
925 Reese Ave, Hershey, PA 17033
Tel.: (717) 534-4100
Sales Range: $550-599.9 Million
Emp.: 1,200
Mfr of Chocolate Candies
N.A.I.C.S.: 311340

Hershey Asia Pacific Pte. Ltd.   (1)
541 Orchard Rd 19-01/04 Liat Towers, 23
Singapore Orchard, Singapore, Singapore
Tel.: (65) 66035260
Chocolate Mfr
N.A.I.C.S.: 333241
Vikram Behl (Dir-HR-Supply Chain Solutions)

Hershey Canada, Inc.   (1)
400-5750 Explore Dr, Mississauga, L4W
0B1, ON, Canada
Tel.: (905) 602-9200
Mfr of Chocolate, Cocoa & Confectionery
Products
N.A.I.C.S.: 311352

Hershey Chocolate & Confectionery
Company   (1)
4860 Robb St Ste 204, Wheat Ridge, CO
80033
Tel.: (303) 463-6550
Sales Range: $250-299.9 Million
Candy Mfr
N.A.I.C.S.: 311352
William J. Morris III (Pres)

Subsidiary (Domestic):

Dagoba Organic Chocolate   (2)
1105 Benson Way, Ashland, OR 97520
Tel.: (541) 482-2001
Web Site: http://www.dagobachocolate.com
Sales Range: $25-49.9 Million
Emp.: 40
Candy Mfr
N.A.I.C.S.: 311352

Hershey Chocolate of Virginia,
Inc.   (1)
120 Harold Cook Dr, Stuarts Draft, VA
24477   (100%)
Tel.: (540) 337-4700
Web Site:
https://www.thehersheycompany.com
Sales Range: $200-249.9 Million
Emp.: 420
Chocolate Mfr
N.A.I.C.S.: 311352

Hershey Foods Corp.-Hazleton
Plant   (1)
6 Scotchpine Dr, Hazleton, PA 18202
Tel.: (570) 384-3271
Web Site: http://www.hersheys.com
Sales Range: $200-249.9 Million
Emp.: 375
Mfr of Candies & Choclates
N.A.I.C.S.: 311352

Hershey Foods International Trade
(Shanghai) Co. Ltd.   (1)
18/f Xinmei Lianhe Plaza No999, Shanghai,
200120, China
Tel.: (86) 2161656200
Food Products Mfr

N.A.I.C.S.: 424420

Hershey India Private Limited (1)
Chemtex House Hiranandani Garden,
Powai, Mumbai, 400 076, India
Tel.: (91) 800221456
Web Site: https://www.hersheyland.in
Confectionery & Beverages Mfr & Marketer
N.A.I.C.S.: 311352

Subsidiary (Domestic):

**Hershey India Confectionery Private
Limited** (2)
Chemtex House Hiranandani Gardens,
Powai, Mumbai, 400 076, India
Tel.: (91) 2225727800
Web Site: http://www.hersheyindia.com
Chocolate Mfr
N.A.I.C.S.: 333241

Hershey International Ltd. (1)
4860 Robb St, Wheat Ridge, CO 80033
Tel.: (303) 463-6550
Web Site: http://www.hersheys.com
Chocolate Mfr
N.A.I.C.S.: 311351

Hershey Japan Co., Ltd. (1)
5F Tokyu Yotsuya Building 6-6 Kojimachi,
Chiyoda-ku, Tokyo, 102-0083, Japan
Tel.: (81) 357725527
Web Site: https://www.hersheyland.jp
Chocolate Products Marketer
N.A.I.C.S.: 424450
Park Sun-young (CEO)

Hershey Mexico, S.A. de C.V. (1)
Carr Guadalajara El Castillo Km 8 05, CP
45680, El Salto, Jalisco, Mexico
Tel.: (52) 18009569964
Web Site: https://www.hersheyland.mx
Sales Range: $600-649.9 Million
Candy Mfr
N.A.I.C.S.: 311351

Hersmex S. de R.L. de C.V. (1)
Avenida Industrias Del Poniente 201Centro,
Escobedo, Mexico
Tel.: (52) 8181541300
Emp.: 2,000
Chocolate Mfr
N.A.I.C.S.: 333241
Jose Rodriguez (Gen Mgr)

Nutrine Confectionery Company Private Limited (1)
P B 38 B V Reddy Colony, Chittoor, 517
002, India
Tel.: (91) 8572229873
Chocolate Mfr
N.A.I.C.S.: 333241
G. S. Srinivas (Deputy Gen Mgr)

ONE Brands, LLC (1)
5400 W W T Harris Blvd Ste L, Charlotte,
NC 28269
Web Site: https://www.one1brands.com
Peanut Butter & Dark Chocolate Distr
N.A.I.C.S.: 445292

**The Allan Candy Company
Limited** (1)
3 Robert Speck Parkway Suite 250, Mississauga, L4Z 2G5, ON, Canada
Tel.: (905) 270-2221
Web Site: http://www.allancandy.com
Confectionery Mfr
N.A.I.C.S.: 311340

Y & S Candies (1)
400 Running Pump Rd, Lancaster, PA
17603 (100%)
Tel.: (717) 509-9795
Web Site:
   http://www.thehersheycompany.com
Sales Range: $300-349.9 Million
Emp.: 700
Mfr Candy
N.A.I.C.S.: 311340

THE HOME DEPOT, INC.
2455 Paces Ferry Rd, Atlanta, GA
30339
Tel.: (770) 433-8211　　　DE
Web Site:
   https://www.homedepot.com
Year Founded: 1978

HD—(NYSE)
Rev.: $152,669,000,000
Assets: $76,530,000,000
Liabilities: $75,486,000,000
Net Worth: $1,044,000,000
Earnings: $15,143,000,000
Emp.: 463,100
Fiscal Year-end: 01/28/24
Household Product Distr
N.A.I.C.S.: 551112
Teresa Wynn Roseborough (Gen
Counsel, Sec & Exec VP)
Ann-Marie Campbell (Sr Exec VP)
Kenneth Gerald Langone (Co-Founder)
John Deaton (Exec VP-Supply Chain
& Product Dev)
Edward P. Decker (Chm, Pres &
CEO)
Richard V. McPhail (CFO & Exec VP)
Kimberly R. Scardino (Chief Acctg
Officer, Sr VP-Fin & Controller)
Timothy A. Hourigan (Exec VP-HR)
Hector Padilla (Exec VP-Outside Sls
& Svc)
Marc Brown (Sr VP-Supply Chain)
Jim Hovis (Sr VP-Mdsg & Building
Materials)
Paul Antony (Sr VP-Tech)
Michael Rowe (Pres-Canada)
Arlette Guthrie (Sr VP-HR)
William Bastek (Exec VP-Mdsg)
Chris Berg (Pres)
Scott Bomar (Sr VP)
Angie Brown (Sr VP)
Chip Devine (Sr VP)

Subsidiaries:

Compact Power Equipment, Inc. (1)
3326 Highway 51, Fort Mill, SC 29715
Tel.: (803) 548-4348
Web Site: http://www.cpiequipment.com
Building Equipment Installation
N.A.I.C.S.: 238290
Norman Boling (CFO)

HD Supply Holdings, Inc. (1)
3400 Cumberland Blvd SE, Atlanta, GA
30339
Tel.: (770) 852-9000
Web Site: http://www.hdsupply.com
Rev.: $6,146,000,000
Assets: $4,715,000,000
Liabilities: $3,363,000,000
Net Worth: $1,352,000,000
Earnings: $452,000,000
Emp.: 11,500
Fiscal Year-end: 02/02/2020
Holding Company; Industrial Equipment &
Supplies Distr
N.A.I.C.S.: 551112
Evan J. Levitt (CFO, Chief Admin Officer &
Sr VP)
Bradley Paulsen (Pres-HD Supply Facilities
Maintenance)
Anna Stevens (Chief People & Officer/VP-
HR-HD Supply Inc)
Shane O'Kelly (CEO)
Isabel Janci (Asst Treas)

Subsidiary (Domestic):

HD Supply, Inc. (2)
3400 Cumberland Blvd SE, Atlanta, GA
30339
Tel.: (770) 852-9000
Web Site: https://www.hdsupply.com
Rev.: $6,145,999,999
Assets: $4,714,999,999
Liabilities: $3,362,999,999
Net Worth: $1,351,999,999
Earnings: $451,999,999
Emp.: 11,499
Fiscal Year-end: 02/02/2020
Construction & Maintenance-Related Products Wholesale Distr
N.A.I.C.S.: 423390
John A. Stegeman (Exec VP)
Dan S. McDevitt (Sec & Gen Counsel)
Anna Stevens (Chief People Officer & VP-
HR)
Bradley Paulsen (Pres-HD Supply Facilities
Maintenance)

Sheila Schnellenberger (Chief Sls Officer)
Tony Drew (Sr VP)
Chris Kelley (Pres)
Scott Bohrer (CFO)
Sabrina Green (Chief HR Officer)
Mike Guhl (CIO)
Chris Raabe (Sr VP)
Ted Russ (VP)
Sami Nassar (VP)

Subsidiary (Domestic):

AAP Metals, LLC (3)
1010 W 37th Pl, Tulsa, OK 74107-5716
Tel.: (918) 446-1671
Web Site: https://www.metalsinc.com
Stainless Steel Plate, Sheet, Coil, Bar &
High Nickel Alloy Products

**HD Supply Facilities Maintenance,
Ltd.** (3)
3400 Cumberland Blvd, Atlanta, GA 30339
Tel.: (877) 694-4932
Web Site: http://www.hdsupplysolutions.com
Maintenance & Repair Supplies

**ISI Design And Installation Solutions,
Inc.** (3)
10 Bunsen, Irvine, CA 92618
Flooring, Cabinets, Countertops & Window
Coverings
N.A.I.C.S.: 326199

Subsidiary (Domestic):

Redi-Carpet, Inc. (2)
10101 Fountaingate Dr, Stafford, TX 77477
Tel.: (832) 310-2000
Web Site: http://www.redicarpet.com
Home Furnishing Merchant Whslr
N.A.I.C.S.: 423220
Brian Caress (CEO)

**Home Depot Mexico, S. de R.L. de
C.V.** (1)
Ricardo Margain Zozaya 605 Col Santa Engracia, San Pedro, 66267, Garza Garcia,
Mexico (100%)
Tel.: (52) 8181556978
Web Site: http://www.homedepot.com.mx
Sales Range: $25-49.9 Million
Emp.: 25
Home Improvement Products & Services
Retailer
N.A.I.C.S.: 444110

Home Depot U.S.A., Inc. (1)
2455 Paces Ferry Rd, Atlanta, GA
30339-4024 (100%)
Tel.: (770) 433-8211
Web Site: http://www.homedepot.com
Sales Range: $125-149.9 Million
Emp.: 5,000
Home Improvement Products & Services
Retailer
N.A.I.C.S.: 444110

Subsidiary (Domestic):

Home Decorators Collection Inc. (2)
8920 Pershall Rd, Hazelwood, MO 63042-
2809
Tel.: (314) 521-6178
Web Site: http://www.homedecorators.com
Online & Catalog Retailer of Home Furnishings & Decor
N.A.I.C.S.: 449129

Division (Domestic):

Home Depot Direct (2)
2455 Paces Ferry Rd SE, Atlanta, GA
30339-1834
Tel.: (770) 433-8211
Online Home Improvement Products Retailer
N.A.I.C.S.: 444110

Home Depot of Canada Inc. (1)
400 - 1 Concorde Gate, Toronto, M3C 4H9,
ON, Canada
Tel.: (416) 386-5841
Web Site: https://www.homedepot.ca
Sales Range: $125-149.9 Million
Emp.: 500
Home Improvement Products & Services
Retailer
N.A.I.C.S.: 444110
Michael Rowe (Pres)

Interline Brands, Inc. (1)

801 W Bay St, Jacksonville, FL 32204
Tel.: (904) 421-1400
Web Site: http://www.interlinebrands.com
Sales Range: $5-14.9 Billion
Repair, Maintenance & Operations Products
Marketer & Distr
N.A.I.C.S.: 238220

Subsidiary (Domestic):

SupplyWorks (2)
701 San Marco Blvd Fl 18, Jacksonville, FL
32207
Tel.: (904) 399-4145
Web Site: http://www.supplyworks.com
Emp.: 6
Janitorial, Cleaning & Facility Maintenance
Supplies Distr
N.A.I.C.S.: 423850

Your Other Warehouse (1)
2900 Westfork Dr Ste 300, Baton Rouge,
LA 70827-0007
Tel.: (225) 215-9500
Web Site:
   http://www.yourotherwarehouse.com
Sales Range: $350-399.9 Million
Emp.: 900
Distr of Faucets, Plumbing Fixtures, Lighting, Fans & Hardware Products
N.A.I.C.S.: 423720

**THE INTERPUBLIC GROUP OF
COMPANIES, INC.**
909 3rd Ave, New York, NY 10022
Tel.: (212) 704-1200　　　DE
Web Site:
   https://www.interpublic.com
Year Founded: 1930

IPG—(NYSE)
Rev.: $10,889,300,000
Assets: $19,267,300,000
Liabilities: $15,263,500,000
Net Worth: $4,003,800,000
Earnings: $1,098,400,000
Emp.: 57,400
Fiscal Year-end: 12/31/23
Holding Company; Advertising Agencies
N.A.I.C.S.: 551112
Rick Weber (Chief Comml Officer &
Sr VP)
Alessandro Nisita (Treas & Sr VP)
Alex Leikikh (Exec VP)
Jemma Gould (Chief Sustainability
Officer)
Patricia Hinerman (CIO)
Jeriad Zoghby (Chief Commerce
Strategy Officer)
Philippe Krakowsky (CEO)
Ellen T. Johnson (CFO & Exec VP)
Christopher F. Carroll (Chief Acctg
Officer, Sr VP & Controller)
Joe Kelly (Chief Talent Officer & Sr
VP)
Simon Bond (Chief Growth Officer &
Sr VP)
Helene Yan (Chief Client Officer-
Health & Sr VP)
Jerome J. Leshne (Sr VP-IR)
Richard J. Haray (Sr VP-Corp Svcs)
Anthony G. Alexandrou (Sr VP-
Taxation-Global)
Alex Hesz (Chief Strategy Officer-
Global)
Jacki Kelley (Chief Bus Officer, Chief
Client Officer & Exec VP)
Jayna Kothary (Chief Solutions Officer)

Subsidiaries:

303 MullenLowe (1)
Level 2 Commonwealth Bank Bldg 242
Murray Street, Perth, 6000, WA, Australia
Tel.: (61) 94600303
Web Site: http://303mullenlowe.com.au
Emp.: 50
Advetising Agency

The Interpublic Group of Companies,
Inc.—(Continued)

N.A.I.C.S.: 541810
Rene Migliore (Co-Mng Dir)
Joanna Gray (Co-Mng Dir)
Bart Pawlak (Exec Creative Dir)

Subsidiary (Domestic):

303 MullenLowe - Sydney (2)
Level 2 33 Playfair Street, The Rocks, Sydney, 2000, NSW, Australia
Tel.: (61) 295522100
Web Site: http://303mullenlowe.com.au
Advetising Agency
N.A.I.C.S.: 541810
Charles Rallings (Dir-Digital & Customer Experience)
Marque Kabbaz (Exec Dir-CX & Digital)

Accentmarketing (1)
La Puerta Del Sol Ste 100 800 Douglas Rd,
Coral Gables, FL 33134-3187
Tel.: (305) 461-1112
Web Site: http://www.accentmarketing.com
Rev.: $18,000,000
Emp.: 20
Advertising Services
N.A.I.C.S.: 541810

Branch (Domestic):

Accentmarketing (2)
8687 Melrose Ave 7th Fl, West Hollywood,
CA 90069
Tel.: (310) 584-8250
Web Site: http://www.accentmarketing.com
Emp.: 15
Advertising Services
N.A.I.C.S.: 541810

Acxiom LLC (1)
301 E Dave Ward Dr, Conway, AR 72032-7114
Tel.: (888) 322-9466
Web Site: http://www.acxiom.com
Technology Products Mfr & Data Services
N.A.I.C.S.: 518210
Rick Erwin (Pres-Audience Solutions Div)

Subsidiary (Non-US):

Acxiom Australia Pty Ltd (2)
Level 24 Three International Towers, 300
Barangaroo Ave, Barangaroo, 2000, NSW,
Australia
Tel.: (61) 280678366
Web Site: http://www.acxiom.com
Sales Range: $25-49.9 Million
Emp.: 60
Marketing & Data Processing Services
N.A.I.C.S.: 541613

Subsidiary (Domestic):

Acxiom CH, Inc. (2)
601 E 3rd St, Little Rock, AR 72201
Tel.: (501) 342-1000
Emp.: 3
Technology & Marketing Services
N.A.I.C.S.: 541613

Subsidiary (Non-US):

Acxiom Deutschland GmbH (2)
Martin-Behaim Str 12, 63263, Neu-Isenburg, Germany
Tel.: (49) 61027363
Web Site: http://www.acxiom.de
Data Processing Services
N.A.I.C.S.: 518210
Carsten Diepenbrock (Mng Dir)

Acxiom France SAS (2)
25 Rue Anatole France, 92300, Levallois-Perret, France
Tel.: (33) 158177300
Web Site: https://liveramp.fr
Marketing Management Services
N.A.I.C.S.: 541613

**Acxiom Global Service Center Polska
Sp.z.o.o.** (2)
AL Grunwaldzka 472B Olivia Business Center Olivia Four, 80-309, Gdansk, Poland
Tel.: (48) 587813400
Web Site: http://www.acxiom.pl
Data Processing Services
N.A.I.C.S.: 518210

Subsidiary (Domestic):

**Acxiom Government Services,
Inc.** (2)
601 E 3rd St, Little Rock, AR 72201
Tel.: (501) 342-7799
Technology & Marketing Services
N.A.I.C.S.: 541613

Subsidiary (Non-US):

Acxiom Japan K. K. (2)
Nagatacho SR building 8F 2-12-8 Nagata-cho, Chiyoda-Ku, Tokyo, 100-0014, Japan
Tel.: (81) 362066241
Web Site: http://www.acxiom.jp
Information Technology Consulting Services
N.A.I.C.S.: 541512

Acxiom Ltd. (2)
16 Old Bailey, Farringdon, London, EC4M
7EG, United Kingdom (100%)
Tel.: (44) 2075265100
Web Site: https://www.acxiom.co.uk
Sales Range: $75-99.9 Million
Emp.: 200
Computer Marketing Systems
N.A.I.C.S.: 423430

CMGRP, Inc. (1)
909 3rd Ave, New York, NY 10022-3914
Tel.: (212) 445-8000
Web Site: https://webershandwick.com
Administrative Management Consulting Services
N.A.I.C.S.: 541611

Subsidiary (Non-US):

CMGRP UK Limited (2)
2 Waterhouse 140 Holborn, London, EC1N
2ST, United Kingdom
Tel.: (44) 2070670000
Advertising Agencies
N.A.I.C.S.: 541810

Campbell-Ewald Company (1)
2000 Brush St Ste 601, Detroit, MI 48226
Tel.: (586) 558-6256
Web Site: https://www.c-e.com
Sales Range: $200-249.9 Million
Emp.: 1,100
Advetising Agency
N.A.I.C.S.: 541810
Laura Rogers (Exec Dir-Content)
Sal Taibi (Pres)
Jamie Lewis (Mng Dir)
Jamie Rubin (Mng Dir-Media)
Chip Rich (Exec Creative Dir)
Jorge Moya (Exec Creative Dir)
Colin Padden (Dir-Acct Svc)
Chris Marchegiani (Dir)
Kyra Wilson (Media Dir)
Bill Silarski (Fin Dir)
Silmo Bonomi (Co-Chief Creative Officer)
Clarence Bradley (Co-Chief Creative Officer)
Barb Rozman-Stokes (Chief Talent Officer)
Suzanne McGee (Dir-Marketing-Public Relations)
Walter Harris (Grp Acct Dir)
Nat Resende (Exec Creative Dir)
David MacKereth (Exec Creative Dir)
Ale Ortiz (Exec Creative Dir)
Helen Giles (Grp Dir)
Kyle Smalley (Dir-Operations)
Dana Delle (Grp Dir-Media)
Tamara Gardellis (Dir)
Martha Carter (Assoc Dir)
Heather Collins (Dir)
Kayley Miah (Assoc Dir-Accounting)
Kiley Weber (Sr Dir)
Silmo Bonomi (Co-Chief Creative Officer)
Clarence Bradley (Co-Chief Creative Officer)
Barb Rozman-Stokes (Chief Talent Officer)
Suzanne McGee (Dir-Marketing-Public Relations)
Walter Harris (Grp Acct Dir)
Nat Resende (Exec Creative Dir)
David MacKereth (Exec Creative Dir)
Ale Ortiz (Exec Creative Dir)
Helen Giles (Grp Dir)
Kyle Smalley (Dir-Operations)
Dana Delle (Grp Dir-Media)
Tamara Gardellis (Dir)
Martha Carter (Assoc Dir)
Heather Collins (Dir)
Kayley Miah (Assoc Dir-Accounting)
Kiley Weber (Sr Dir)

Subsidiary (Non-US):

Campbell-Ewald (2)
AL Shatha Tower 26 Floor, PO Box 502146,
Dubai, United Arab Emirates
Tel.: (971) 43910377
Web Site: http://www.campbell-ewald.com
Sales Range: $25-49.9 Million
Emp.: 6
N.A.I.C.S.: 541810

Subsidiary (Domestic):

Campbell-Ewald Detroit (2)
2000 Brush St Ste 601, Detroit, MI 48226
Tel.: (586) 574-3400
Web Site: https://c-e.com
Emp.: 100
N.A.I.C.S.: 541810

Campbell-Ewald Los Angeles (2)
1840 Century Park E 16th Fl, Los Angeles,
CA 90067
Tel.: (310) 358-4800
Web Site: http://www.c-e.com
Advertising Agencies
N.A.I.C.S.: 541810

Unit (Domestic):

Campbell-Ewald San Antonio (2)
816 Camaron St, San Antonio, TX 78212
Tel.: (210) 242-3760
N.A.I.C.S.: 541810
Kathleen Donald (Mng Dir)

Carmichael Lynch, Inc. (1)
110 N 5th St, Minneapolis, MN 55403
Tel.: (612) 334-6000
Web Site: https://www.carmichaellynch.com
Sales Range: $50-74.9 Million
Emp.: 300
Advetising Agency
N.A.I.C.S.: 541810
Marcus Fischer (CEO)
Stacy Janicki (Dir-Acct Mgmt)
Marty Senn (Chief Creative Officer)
Neil Goodspeed (Dir-Media)
Milton Un (Dir-Design)
Lachlan Badenoch (Chief Strategy Officer)
John Green (Mng Partner & CFO)
Emily Moe (Dir-HR)
Steve Diedrich (Dir-IT)

Subsidiary (Domestic):

Carmichael Lynch Relate (2)
110 N 5th St, Minneapolis, MN 55403
Tel.: (612) 375-8500
Web Site:
https://www.carmichaellynchrelate.com
Public Relations
N.A.I.C.S.: 541820
Jill Schmidt (Chm-Corp Practice & Exec
VP)
Julie Batliner (Pres)
Marcus Fischer (CEO)
Marty Senn (Chief Creative Officer)
Grete Lavrenz (Chm-Food & Nutrition Practice & Gen Mgr)
John Green (CFO & COO)
Beth Garcia (Chm-Home & Design Practice
& Exec VP)
Lachlan Badenoch (Chief Strategy Officer)
Carol Frazer Haynesworth (Dir-Multicultural
Strategy & Inclusion)
Erika Collins (Sr Dir-New Bus)
Orlee Tatarka (Dir-Integrated Production)
Emily Moe (Dir-HR)
Regine Labossiere (Assoc Dir-Media Rels)
Megan Weber (Deputy Chm-Home & Design Practice & VP)
Jamie Tanker (Deputy Chm-Home & Design
Practice & VP)
Charlie Wolfe (Sr Mgr-Print Production
Svcs)
Charles Veit (Ops Mgr-Mac Sys)
Brenna Smithson (Dir-Brand Plng)
Milton Un (Dir-Design)
Laura Norton (Dir-Office Svcs)
Tracy Krulich (Grp Dir-Media)
Ashley Solem (Mgr-Creative)
Eden Thompson (Dir-Plng)
Ed Huerta Margotta (Dir-Recruiting)
Nellie Murray (Assoc Dir-Media)
Bob Ringer (Assoc Dir-Social)

Branch (Domestic):

Carmichael Lynch Spong (3)

100 W 33rd St 7th Fl, New York, NY 10001
Tel.: (612) 375-8500
Web Site:
http://www.carmichaellynchrelate.com
Sales Range: $25-49.9 Million
Emp.: 5
Advetising Agency
N.A.I.C.S.: 541810
Meredith Kisch (Sr Mgr-Media Rels)
Serena Tesler (Dir-Media Rels)

Carmichael Lynch Spong (3)
110 N 5th St, Minneapolis, MN 55403
Tel.: (612) 375-8500
Web Site: https://carmichaellynchrelate.com
N.A.I.C.S.: 541820

Casanova Pendrill, LLC (1)
3337 Susan St Ste 200, Costa Mesa, CA
92626
Tel.: (714) 918-8200
Web Site: https://www.casanova.com
Sales Range: $10-24.9 Million
Emp.: 80
Advertising, Bilingual Marketing, Communications, Hispanic Marketing, Media Buying
Services
N.A.I.C.S.: 541810

Creative Media Services GmbH (1)
Hongkongstrasse 8, 20457, Hamburg, Germany
Tel.: (49) 40431960
Web Site: https://www.bpnww.de
Advertising Agencies
N.A.I.C.S.: 541810

Dailey & Associates (1)
8687 Melrose Ave, West Hollywood, CA
90069
Tel.: (310) 360-3100
Web Site: http://www.daileyideas.com
Rev.: $250,000,000
Emp.: 100
Advertising Services
N.A.I.C.S.: 541810

DeVries Public Relations (1)
919 3rd Ave, New York, NY 10022
Tel.: (212) 546-8500
Web Site: http://www.devries-pr.com
Rev.: $25,000,000
Emp.: 110
Public Relations Services
N.A.I.C.S.: 541820

Deutsch, Inc. (1)
387 Park Ave S, New York, NY 10016
Tel.: (212) 981-7600
Web Site: https://deutschny.com
Sales Range: $200-249.9 Million
Emp.: 943
Advertising Services
N.A.I.C.S.: 541810

Subsidiary (Non-US):

Adcomm Limited (2)
110 Love Road Tejgaon, Dhaka, 1208, Bangladesh
Tel.: (880) 28853222
Web Site: https://www.adcommad.com
Advertising Services
N.A.I.C.S.: 541810

Branch (Non-US):

Adventa Lowe (2)
23a Voznesensky uzviz 4th floor office 23,
040531, Kiev, Ukraine
Tel.: (380) 672458875
Web Site:
https://www.adventa.mullenlowe.com
Emp.: 70
Advertising Services
N.A.I.C.S.: 541810

BB&M Lowe & Partners (2)
Calle 54 Este Ciudad De, Panama, Panama
Tel.: (507) 263 9300
Web Site: http://www.bbm-panama.com
Rev.: $22,000,000
Emp.: 70
Advertising Services
N.A.I.C.S.: 541810
Rafael E. Barcenas (Pres)
Jaime Sosa (Gen Mgr)

Subsidiary (Non-US):

Change Communications GmbH (2)

Solmstrasse 4, 60486, Frankfurt am Main,
Germany
Tel.: (49) 69975010
Web Site: http://www.change.de
Emp.: 100
Advertising Services
N.A.I.C.S.: 541810
Klaus Flettner *(Mng Dir)*

Branch (Non-US):

DLKW Lowe (2)
C-Space 37-45 City Road, London, EC1Y
1AT, United Kingdom
Tel.: (44) 2075845033
Rev.: $167,200,000
Emp.: 75
Advertising Services
N.A.I.C.S.: 541810

Subsidiary (Domestic):

Deutsch LA (2)
12901 W Jefferson Blvd, Los Angeles, CA
90066
Tel.: (310) 862-3000
Web Site: https://deutschla.com
Emp.: 450
Advertising Services
N.A.I.C.S.: 541810

Branch (Domestic):

Ergo (Ergonomic
Communications) (2)
PO Box 195006, San Juan, PR 00919-5006
Tel.: (787) 754-8888
Web Site: http://www.bblatina.com
Emp.: 100
Advertising Services
N.A.I.C.S.: 541810

Branch (Non-US):

Grape Communications (2)
31-5 6th Floor Duk-Yang bldg Jang- Chung-
Dong 1, Jung- Gu, Seoul, 100-391, Korea
(South)
Tel.: (82) 2 2260 5400
Advertising Services
N.A.I.C.S.: 541810

Subsidiary (Domestic):

Huge (2)
45 Main St 3rd Fl, Brooklyn, NY 11201
Tel.: (718) 625-4843
Web Site: https://www.hugeinc.com
Emp.: 175
Advertising Services
N.A.I.C.S.: 541810
Fura Johannesdottir *(Chief Design Officer)*
Matthew Weiss *(Pres)*

Branch (Non-US):

Lola Madrid (2)
C. Marques de Cubas, 4, Madrid, 28014,
Spain
Tel.: (34) 696 499 580
Advertising Services
N.A.I.C.S.: 541810

Lola MullenLowe (2)
Edificio Diogo Cao Doca de Alcantara
Norte, Lisbon, 1350-352, Portugal
Tel.: (351) 213406200
Web Site: http://www.lola-normajean.com
Advertising Services
N.A.I.C.S.: 541810
Rodrigo Silva Gomes *(CEO)*

Lowe (2)
Suite 12 01 Level 12 South Wing Menara
OBYU 4 Jalan PJU 8/8A, Bandar Daman-
sara Perdana, Petaling Jaya, 47820, Selan-
gor Darul Ehsan, Malaysia
Tel.: (60) 37 801 6000
Web Site: http://malaysia.mullenlowe.com
Emp.: 60
Advertising Services
N.A.I.C.S.: 541810
Adrian S'ng *(CEO)*
Sathi Anand *(Exec Creative Dir)*
Gavin Teoh *(Dir-Client Servicing)*

Lowe (2)
6/F Oxford House House tai Koo Place 979
Kings Road, Quarry Bay, China (Hong
Kong)
Tel.: (852) 2895 0669

Emp.: 50
Advertising Services
N.A.I.C.S.: 541810

Lowe (2)
Ground 4th 6th Floors Victoria Building Jl
Sultan Hasanuddin kav 47-51, Jakarta,
12160, Indonesia
Tel.: (62) 2129279279
Web Site:
     http://www.indonesia.mullenlowe.com
Advertising Services
N.A.I.C.S.: 541810

Lowe (2)
15-17th/f Rufino Pacific Towers 6784 Ayala
Avenue Makati City, Makati City, Manila,
1226, Philippines
Tel.: (63) 2 811 1111
Sales Range: $50-74.9 Million
Advertising Services
N.A.I.C.S.: 541810

Lowe (2)
11 F 2 Lane 150 Section 5 Hsin Yi Road,
Taipei, 11059, Taiwan
Tel.: (886) 227289121
Sales Range: $10-24.9 Million
Emp.: 30
Advertising Services
N.A.I.C.S.: 541810

Lowe (2)
54 Kapodistriou Ave and Eleftherias Str
Agia Filothei Marousi, Athens, 151 23,
Greece
Tel.: (30) 210 68 77 500
Web Site: http://athens.mullenlowe.com
Emp.: 50
Advertising Services
N.A.I.C.S.: 541810

Lowe (2)
Unit 1301 Floor 13 Harbour View Tower 35
Nguyen Hue Street, Ben Nghe Ward District
1, Ho Chi Minh City, Vietnam
Tel.: (84) 8 914 1765
Advertising Services
N.A.I.C.S.: 541810

Lowe (2)
Av Javier Prado Oeste 2021 San Isidro,
Lima, Peru
Tel.: (51) 14692185
Web Site: http://www.mullenlowe.pe
Advertising Services
N.A.I.C.S.: 541810

Lowe (2)
Kehrwieder 10, 20457, Hamburg, Germany
Tel.: (49) 40414410
Advertising Services
N.A.I.C.S.: 541810

Lowe (2)
1 Empire Tower 28/F Unit 2801/1 2813-4,
South Sathorn Rd, Bangkok, 10120,
Yamawa Sathorn, Thailand
Tel.: (66) 26277000
Web Site: http://thailand.mullenlowe.com
Emp.: 277
Advertising Services
N.A.I.C.S.: 541810

Lowe (2)
Amstelveensweg 404, Amsterdam, 1076
CT, Netherlands
Tel.: (31) 205731111
Rev.: $16,962,400
Emp.: 60
Advertising Services
N.A.I.C.S.: 541810

Lowe & Partners (2)
Strada Grigore Alexandrescu Nr 89-97 Inc-
inta Metropolis Bravo, Sector 1, Bucharest,
10624, Romania
Tel.: (40) 21 301 0000
Advertising Agencies
N.A.I.C.S.: 541810
Veronica Savanciuc *(Pres & CEO)*

Lowe & Partners (2)
Calle del Marques de Cubas 4, Madrid,
28014, Spain
Tel.: (34) 917893350
Emp.: 70
Advertising Services
N.A.I.C.S.: 541810
Miguel Simoes *(CEO-Western Europe)*

Lowe Adventa (2)
1st Volkonskiy pereulok 13 str 2, Moscow,
Russia
Tel.: (7) 495 739 0110
Advertising Services
N.A.I.C.S.: 541810

Lowe And Partners SA (2)
705 South Am Road V&A Waterfront, Cape
Town, 8001, South Africa
Tel.: (27) 214878900
Web Site: http://www.mullenlowe.co.za
Advertising Services
N.A.I.C.S.: 541810
Kirk Gainsford *(Chief Creative Officer)*
Joanina Pastoll *(Exec Creative Dir-Design &*
Promo)
Riska Emeran *(Head-TV & Radio Produc-*
tion)

Lowe Avanta (2)
Prule 19, Ljubljana, 1000, Slovenia
Tel.: (386) 1 200 7980
Web Site: http://www.avanta.si
Emp.: 5
Advertising Services
N.A.I.C.S.: 541810
Maja Hawlina *(Mng Dir)*

Lowe Brindfors (2)
Eriksbergsgatan 8B, PO Box 6518, Stock-
holm, 114 30, Sweden
Tel.: (46) 856625500
Advertising Services
N.A.I.C.S.: 541810

Lowe China (2)
36/F Huai Hai Plaza 1045 Huai Hai Zhong
Road, Shanghai, 200031, China
Tel.: (86) 21 2411 0888
Web Site: http://www.china.mullenlowe.com
Advertising Services
N.A.I.C.S.: 541810

Lowe FMRG (2)
Pau Claris 186 4th Floor, Barcelona, 08037,
Spain
Tel.: (34) 932 803 355
Emp.: 13
Advertising Services
N.A.I.C.S.: 541810

Lowe GGK (2)
Libusina 49/3, Prague, 128 00, Czech Re-
public
Tel.: (420) 777 716 343
Web Site: http://www.mullenlowe.cz
Advertising Services
N.A.I.C.S.: 541810

Lowe GGK (2)
16 Wesselenyi street, Budapest, H-1077,
Hungary
Tel.: (36) 18878204
Web Site: http://www.mullenlowegroup.com
Advertising Services
N.A.I.C.S.: 541810

Lowe GGK (2)
Domaniewska 39, Budynek Nefryt IV pietro,
02-672, Warsaw, Poland
Tel.: (48) 223120100
Advertising Services
N.A.I.C.S.: 541810

Lowe GGK (2)
Mlynske Luhy 86A, Bratislava, 821 05, Slo-
vakia
Tel.: (421) 2 592 07611
Web Site: http://www.mullenloweggk.sk
Emp.: 50
Advertising Services
N.A.I.C.S.: 541810
Marek Pajtas *(CEO)*
Erik Reingraber *(Exec Creative Dir)*
Robert Cyprich *(Dir-Strategy)*
Martin Albert *(Dir-Client Svc)*
Vlado Slivka *(Creative Dir)*

Subsidiary (Non-US):

Lowe GGK (2)
Mariahilfer Strasse 17, 1060, Vienna, Aus-
tria
Tel.: (43) 1910100
Web Site: http://www.ggk-mullenlowe.com
Sales Range: $25-49.9 Million
Emp.: 42
Advertising Services
N.A.I.C.S.: 541810

Lowe Ginkgo (2)
Av Tomas Giribaldi 2222, 11300, Montevi-
deo, Uruguay
Tel.: (598) 27116161
Web Site: http://www.www.ginkgo.com.uy
Advertising Services
N.A.I.C.S.: 541810

Branch (Non-US):

Lowe LDB (2)
No 42 Fife Road, 05, Colombo, Sri Lanka
Tel.: (94) 772348313
Web Site: https://srilanka.mullenlowe.com
Emp.: 60
Advertising Services
N.A.I.C.S.: 541810

Lowe MENA (2)
MCN Hive 11th/12th Floor Tecom Section
C, PO Box 500242, Dubai Media City,
Dubai, United Arab Emirates
Tel.: (971) 44454141
Web Site: http://mena.mullenlowe.com
Advertising Services
N.A.I.C.S.: 541810
Mounir Harfouche *(CEO)*
Matthew Butterworth *(Mng Dir)*
Khaled Farid *(Gen Mgr-Client Svcs-Reg)*
George Giessen *(Head-Plng-Reg)*
Paul Banham *(Exec Creative Dir-Reg)*
Chris Dormer *(Reg Dir-Fin)*
Racha El Saadaoui *(Bus Dir)*
Rami Ghanem *(Grp Acct Dir)*
Eduardo Branco *(Creative Dir)*
Hagall Muniz *(Creative Dir)*
Mounir Mohamad *(Creative Dir-Svcs)*
Fatin Baz *(Dir-Strategy)*

Lowe Pirella Fronzoni (2)
Via Riva Di Trento 11A, Milan, 20139, Italy
Tel.: (39) 02 85 721
Web Site: http://www.lowepirella.it
Sales Range: $10-24.9 Million
Emp.: 10
Advertising Services
N.A.I.C.S.: 541810
Ferdinando Galletti *(Dir-Art)*
Lorenzo Guagni *(Dir-Art)*
Angello Marino *(Dir-Art)*

Lowe Porta (2)
Avda Del Parque 4314 Cuidad Empresaria
Huechuraba, Huechuraba, Santiago, Chile
Tel.: (56) 2 750 7700
Web Site: http://www.loweporta.cl
Advertising Services
N.A.I.C.S.: 541810

Lowe Roche (2)
260 Queen St W Ste 301, Toronto, M5V
1Z8, ON, Canada
Tel.: (416) 927-9794
Web Site: http://www.loweroche.com
Rev.: $85,000,000
Emp.: 50
Advertising Services
N.A.I.C.S.: 541810

Lowe SSPM (2)
Carrera 9, 79A - 19 Piso 6, Bogota, Colom-
bia
Tel.: (57) 1 605 8000
Advertising Services
N.A.I.C.S.: 541810

Lowe Scanad (2)
PO Box 34537 5th Fl The Chancery, Valley
Road, Nairobi, Kenya
Tel.: (254) 20 271 0021
Web Site: http://www.scanad.com
Advertising Services
N.A.I.C.S.: 541810

Lowe Singapore (2)
CIDC 90 Eu Tong Sen Street Block A 04-
01/02, Creative Innovative Development
Centre, Singapore, 059811, Singapore
Tel.: (65) 68494888
Web Site: http://singapore.mullenlowe.com
Fiscal Year-end: 12/31/2003
Advertising Services
N.A.I.C.S.: 541810
Subarna Prabhakar *(Dir-Global Bus)*
Sheng Jin Ang *(Exec Creative Dir)*
Desh Balakrishnan *(Head-Media)*
Shaifali Dayal *(Reg Dir-Bus & Strategy)*
Abhishek Goyal *(Bus Dir)*
Mark Haycock *(Grp Dir-Digital)*
Daniel Kee *(Exec Creative Dir)*

The Interpublic Group of Companies, Inc.—(Continued)

Gonzalo Olivera *(Dir-Growth)*
Ateet Shroff *(Creative Dir)*
Sanjai Srivastava *(Bus Dir-Global)*
Vinay Vinayak *(Bus Dir-Global)*

Lowe Strateus (2)
80 Rue Taitbout, Paris, 75009, France
Tel.: (33) 140415600
Web Site: http://www.lola-mullenlowe.fr
Emp.: 130
Advertising Services
N.A.I.C.S.: 541810
Philippe Adenot *(Pres)*

Lowe Swing Communications (2)
92-94 Tzar Assen St, Sofia, 1463, Bulgaria
Tel.: (359) 2 954 9346
Web Site: http://www.loweswing.com
Emp.: 11
Advertising Services
N.A.I.C.S.: 541810

Subsidiary (Non-US):

Mullen Lowe Brasil (2)
Rua Frei Caneca 1355 6 Andar, Consolacao, Sao Paulo, 01307-003, SP, Brazil
Tel.: (55) 1149357800
Web Site: https://brasil.mullenlowe.com
Advertising Services
N.A.I.C.S.: 541810

Mullen Lowe Lintas Group (2)
A Wing 16th floor Parinee Crescenzo
Bandra-Kurla Complex, Bandra, Mumbai,
400 051, Maharashtra, India
Tel.: (91) 2250854000
Web Site: https://www.mullenlowelintas.in
Advertising Services
N.A.I.C.S.: 541810
Amer Jaleel *(Chm & Co-Chief Creative Officer)*
S. Subramanyeswar *(Chief Strategy Officer-Grp)*
Vivek Kamath *(CFO & COO-Grp)*
Virat Tandon *(CEO-Grp)*
Sagar Kapoor *(Co-Chief Creative Officer)*
Prateek Bhardwaj *(Co-Chief Creative Officer)*

MullenLowe Accra (2)
Ad Vantage House Klanaa Street, Box
1262, Osu Ako-Adjei Park, Accra, Ghana
Tel.: (233) 2772321
Web Site: http://www.mullenloweaccra.com
Marketing Communications Network; Advertising Services
N.A.I.C.S.: 541810
Barbara Davies *(Exec Dir)*

Ponce Buenos Aires (2)
Avenida del Libertador 14950 Acassuso,
A1641BNS, Buenos Aires, Argentina
Tel.: (54) 1147335100
Emp.: 70
Advertising Services
N.A.I.C.S.: 541810

Publicidad Comercial (2)
Edificio Comercial Avenida el Espino No 77,
Urbanizacion Madre Selva Antiguo, La Libertad, El Salvador
Tel.: (503) 2442222
Web Site: https://www.pcomercial.com
Advertising Services
N.A.I.C.S.: 541810

Branch (Non-US):

Publicidad Interamerica (2)
Avenida Abraham Lincoln 604, Santo Domingo, 10127, Dominican Republic
Tel.: (809) 567 8281
Emp.: 50
Advertising Services
N.A.I.C.S.: 541810

Quadrant Communications Ltd. (2)
Raut Sadan Ground Floor Kadeshwari
Road Near Mount Marys Steps, Bandra W,
Mumbai, 400050, Maharashtra, India
Tel.: (91) 2226451836
Advertising Services
N.A.I.C.S.: 541810

Subsidiary (Non-US):

Standard Advertising, Inc. (2)

2-8-5 Jiyugaoka, Meguro-ku, Tokyo, 152-0035, Japan
Tel.: (81) 364398550
Web Site: https://www.standard.co.jp
Advertising Services
N.A.I.C.S.: 541810
M. Akira *(Mgr-Acct)*

Branch (Domestic):

deutschMedia (2)
330 W 34th St, New York, NY 10001
Tel.: (212) 981-7600
Web Site: http://www.deutschinc.com
Advertising Services
N.A.I.C.S.: 541830

FCB Worldwide, Inc. (1)
100 W 33rd St, New York, NY 10001-2900
Tel.: (212) 885-3000
Web Site: https://fcbchi.com
Emp.: 900
Advetising Agency
N.A.I.C.S.: 541810
Vita Harris *(Chief Strategy Officer-Global)*

Subsidiary (Non-US):

360 Marketing Communications & Contacts (2)
Luis F Thomen No 620 A El Millon, Plaza
Merengue Oficina 218, Santo Domingo, Dominican Republic
Tel.: (809) 7326256
Sales Range: $25-49.9 Million
Emp.: 22
Full Service
N.A.I.C.S.: 541810

AdMedia (2)
37 Third Crescent Asylum Down, Accra,
Ghana
Tel.: (233) 21 250 123
Sales Range: $25-49.9 Million
Emp.: 30
N.A.I.C.S.: 541810

Afirma (2)
Cara Dusana 42, 11000, Belgrade, Serbia
Tel.: (381) 11 328 4620
Web Site: http://www.fcbafirma.rs
N.A.I.C.S.: 541810

Business Data Ltd. (2)
7 Gerlovo Str, 1407, Sofia, Bulgaria
Tel.: (359) 28462077
Sales Range: $25-49.9 Million
Emp.: 8
N.A.I.C.S.: 541810

CREA Publicidad (2)
Plaza Tempo, San Jose, Costa Rica
Tel.: (506) 40020733
Web Site: http://cr.fcbcrea.com
Advertising Services
N.A.I.C.S.: 541810
Borja Prado *(Mng Dir)*

CREA Publicidad (2)
Colonia Payaqui Edificio Novel Center Local
3, Tegucigalpa, Honduras
Tel.: (504) 2355052
Sales Range: $25-49.9 Million
Emp.: 10
N.A.I.C.S.: 541810

Caragas AJL/PARK (2)
Torre Multinvest Piso 4 Plaza La Castellana, PO Box 60684, Chacao, Caracas,
1060, Venezuela
Tel.: (58) 2122632355
Web Site: http://www.fcb.com
Advetising Agency
N.A.I.C.S.: 541810

Circuit (2)
F-78 Block 5 Scheme 5 Kehkashan, Clifton,
Karachi, 75600, Pakistan
Tel.: (92) 2135866201
Sales Range: $25-49.9 Million
Emp.: 70
N.A.I.C.S.: 541810

Cread (2)
Residence 5 Palmirs Route Royale Port
Louis, Port Louis District, Beau Bassin,
Mauritius
Tel.: (230) 4546414
Sales Range: $25-49.9 Million
Emp.: 25
N.A.I.C.S.: 541810

Vino Sookloll *(Mng Dir & Exec Dir-Creative)*

Direct Response (Thailand) Ltd. (2)
885 Soi Sukhumvit 62 Sukhmvit Road
Bangchak Section 3, Bangkok, 10260, Thailand
Tel.: (66) 2715 3000
Sales Range: $25-49.9 Million
Emp.: 5
N.A.I.C.S.: 541810
Phisal Prahasdangkura *(Pres)*

Branch (Domestic):

Draftfcb (2)
Metro Office Park Ste 1 St Building 8 2nd Fl
Guayanabo, San Juan, PR 00968
Tel.: (787) 793-3500
Sales Range: $25-49.9 Million
Emp.: 50
N.A.I.C.S.: 541810

Draftfcb (2)
17600 Gillette Ave, Irvine, CA 92614
Tel.: (949) 851-3050
Sales Range: $25-49.9 Million
Emp.: 80
N.A.I.C.S.: 541810

Subsidiary (Non-US):

Draftfcb (Thailand) Ltd. (2)
88 Soi Sukhumvit 62 Sukhumvit Road
Bangchak, Bangkok, 10260, Thailand
Tel.: (66) 27153000
Web Site: http://www.prakit.com
Sales Range: $25-49.9 Million
Emp.: 120
N.A.I.C.S.: 541810

Draftfcb Ad Fabrika (2)
Sobieskiego 104 Street, Warsaw, 00-764,
Poland
Tel.: (48) 22 48 08 400
Web Site: http://www.fcb.com
Sales Range: $25-49.9 Million
Emp.: 20
N.A.I.C.S.: 541810

Draftfcb Canada Inc. (2)
219 Dufferin Street 302C, Toronto, M6K
3J1, ON, Canada
Tel.: (416) 483-3600
Web Site: http://www.fcb.com
Sales Range: $50-74.9 Million
Emp.: 230
Communications, Direct Marketing,
Publicity/Promotions
N.A.I.C.S.: 541810

Branch (Domestic):

Draftfcb (3)
413 rue Saint-Jacques 10th floor, Montreal,
H2Y 1N9, QC, Canada
Tel.: (514) 938-4141
Sales Range: $25-49.9 Million
Emp.: 35
N.A.I.C.S.: 541810

Subsidiary (Non-US):

Draftfcb Cape Town (2)
5 Armadale St Woodstock, Rondesbosch,
7925, Cape Town, South Africa
Tel.: (27) 214040300
Web Site: http://www.draftfcb.com
Sales Range: $25-49.9 Million
Emp.: 115
Financial, Full Service, Health Care,
Internet/Web Design, Public Relations, Retail, Strategic Planning
N.A.I.C.S.: 541010

Draftfcb Durban (2)
17 Cranbrook Crescent La Lucia Ridge Office Estate La Lucia, 4051, Durban, South
Africa
Tel.: (27) 315667900
Web Site: http://fcbdurban.co.za
Sales Range: $25-49.9 Million
Emp.: 10
Full Service
N.A.I.C.S.: 541810

Unit (Domestic):

Draftfcb HealthCare (2)
100 W 33rd St, New York, NY 10001
Tel.: (212) 672-2336
Web Site: http://www.fcbhealthcare.com

Sales Range: $75-99.9 Million
Emp.: 600
Advetising Agency
N.A.I.C.S.: 541810
Dana Maiman *(Pres & CEO)*
Rich Levy *(Chief Creative Officer)*

Subsidiary (Non-US):

Draftfcb Johannesburg (2)
Pin Mill Farm 164 Katherine St, Sandown,
Johannesburg, 2196, South Africa
Tel.: (27) 115666000
Web Site: http://www.fcb.co.za
Sales Range: $50-74.9 Million
Emp.: 500
Full Service
N.A.I.C.S.: 541810
Thabang Skwambane *(Mng Dir)*
Ahmed Tilly *(Chief Creative Officer)*

Draftfcb MA (2)
58/10 Gaidara Str 2nd Floor, Kiev, 01033,
Ukraine
Tel.: (380) 44 201 1040
Sales Range: $25-49.9 Million
Emp.: 20
N.A.I.C.S.: 541810

Draftfcb Partners Werbeagentur Ges.m.b.H. (2)
Mariahilfer Strasse 17, 1060, Vienna, Austria
Tel.: (43) 137911
Web Site: http://www.fcb.com
Advertising Services
N.A.I.C.S.: 541810
Micheal Kapfer *(Chm)*
Dieter Pivrnec *(Exec Dir-Creative)*
Isabell Fabsich *(Mgr-HR)*

Draftfcb Russia (2)
Chaplygina Street 20/7, 105062, Moscow,
Russia
Tel.: (7) 495 669 2370
Web Site: http://www.fcb.com
Advertising Services
N.A.I.C.S.: 541810
Dora Kiralyhidi-Criveanu *(Mng Dir)*
Elena Lenkova *(Dir-HR)*

Draftfcb Shimoni Finkelstein (2)
57 Rothschild Blvd, 65785, Tel Aviv, Israel
Tel.: (972) 74 717 777
Sales Range: $25-49.9 Million
Emp.: 50
N.A.I.C.S.: 541810

Draftfcb Ulka (2)
No 1104-08 Barton Centre 11th Floor No 84
M G Road, Bengaluru, 560001, India
Tel.: (91) 8065399801
Sales Range: $25-49.9 Million
Emp.: 30
Full Service
N.A.I.C.S.: 541810

Draftfcb Ulka (2)
4th Floor Nirmal Building Nariman Point,
Mumbai, 400 021, India
Tel.: (91) 22 6670 7070
Sales Range: $50-74.9 Million
Emp.: 300
Full Service
N.A.I.C.S.: 541810
Nitin Karkare *(CEO)*

Draftfcb Ulka (2)
1/2 Lord Sinha Road, Kolkata, 700 071,
India
Tel.: (91) 33 2282 9625
Sales Range: $25-49.9 Million
Emp.: 10
Full Service
N.A.I.C.S.: 541810
Nitin Karkare *(COO)*

Draftfcb Ulka (2)
Vallamattam Estate Mahatma Gandhi Road,
Ravipuram, Cochin, 682 015, India
Tel.: (91) 484 236 7443
Sales Range: $25-49.9 Million
Emp.: 15
Full Service
N.A.I.C.S.: 541810
Bambi Diventry *(Head-New Bus Initiatives)*

Draftfcb Ulka (2)
Unitech Trade Centre 3rd Floor Sushant
Lok Phase-1 Sector 43, Sushant Lok Phase
1, Gurgaon, 122 001, Haryana, India

Tel.: (91) 124 668 1600
Sales Range: $25-49.9 Million
Emp.: 100
Full Service
N.A.I.C.S.: 541810
Swathi Batchriya *(Chief Creative Officer)*

Branch (Domestic):

Draftfcb West (2)
1425 4th Ave Ste 1000, Seattle, WA 98101
Tel.: (206) 223-6464
Sales Range: $25-49.9 Million
Emp.: 25
N.A.I.C.S.: 541810

Draftfcb West (2)
1160 Battery St Ste 250, San Francisco, CA 94111
Tel.: (415) 820-8000
Web Site: http://www.draftfcb.com
Sales Range: $25-49.9 Million
Emp.: 105
N.A.I.C.S.: 541810

Subsidiary (Non-US):

Dzuka Communications (2)
39 Scott Road, Blantyre, Malawi
Tel.: (265) 1 877 385
Sales Range: $25-49.9 Million
Emp.: 10
Full Service, Graphic Design
N.A.I.C.S.: 541810

EFPZ (2)
Wilson Ferreira Aldunate 1212, Montevideo, 11100, Uruguay
Tel.: (598) 29 032 803
Sales Range: $25-49.9 Million
Emp.: 22
N.A.I.C.S.: 541810

FCB Africa (2)
164 Katherine St Barlow Park, Sandton, Johannesburg, 2196, South Africa
Tel.: (27) 115666000
Web Site: https://www.fcb.co.za
Full Service Advertising
N.A.I.C.S.: 541810

FCB Australia Pty Ltd (2)
Street Level 1 4-14 Foster Street, Surry Hills, 2010, NSW, Australia
Tel.: (61) 295663000
Web Site: http://fcbsydney.com.au
Sales Range: $25-49.9 Million
Emp.: 10
Advetising Agency
N.A.I.C.S.: 541810

FCB CREA Publicidad (2)
5ta Calle Poniente 5348 101 Avenida Norte Colonia Escalon, San Salvador, El Salvador
Tel.: (503) 22445466
Web Site: http://www.sv.fcbcrea.com
Advetising Agency
N.A.I.C.S.: 541810
Rodrigo Argueta *(Gen Mgr)*
Alex Velasquez *(Creative Dir)*

Subsidiary (Domestic):

FCB Chicago (2)
875 N Michigan Ave 21st Fl, Chicago, IL 60611
Tel.: (312) 425-5000
Web Site: http://fcbchi.com
Emp.: 750
Advetising Agency
N.A.I.C.S.: 541810
Jennifer Rowland *(Exec VP & Dir-Grp Mgmt)*
Cary Pierce *(Exec VP & Dir-Grp Mgmt)*
Andres Ordonez *(Chief Creative Officer)*
Fernando Espejel *(CTO)*
Michelle Stoessel *(Co-CFO)*
Antoniette Wico *(Exec VP & Grp Dir-Mgmt)*
Eric Chun *(Exec VP & Mng Dir-Strategic Analytics)*

Subsidiary (Non-US):

FCB Dos Puntos CREA (2)
Km 8 6 Antigua Carretera a El Salvador Centro Corporativo Muxbal, Torre Este Nivel 9 Sta Catarina Pinula, 01051, Guatemala, Guatemala
Tel.: (502) 23263800
Web Site: https://fcb.com
Emp.: 30

Advertising Services
N.A.I.C.S.: 541810
Evelyn De Leon *(Chief Media Officer)*

Subsidiary (Domestic):

FCB Health (2)
100 W 33rd St, New York, NY 10001
Tel.: (212) 672-2300
Web Site: https://www.fcbhealthcare.com
Advetising Agency
N.A.I.C.S.: 541810
Joerg Hempelmann *(Pres-Europe)*

Subsidiary (Non-US):

FCB Kuala Lumpur (2)
Penthouse 16-1 Wisma UOA Damansara II 6 Jalan Changkat Semantan, Damansara Heights, 50490, Kuala Lumpur, Malaysia
Tel.: (60) 327792453
Web Site: http://www.fcb.co.za
Emp.: 100
Advertising Agency
N.A.I.C.S.: 541810

FCB Manila (2)
1009 Metropol Building Metropolitan Avenue, Makati, Philippines
Tel.: (63) 28120471
Web Site: https://fcbmanila.com
Emp.: 58
Advetising Agency
N.A.I.C.S.: 541810

FCBUlka Advertising (2)
1st Floor Golden Towers 262 Royapettah High Road, Chennai, 600 014, India
Tel.: (91) 9043024571
Web Site: http://www.fcb.com
Advertising Agency
N.A.I.C.S.: 541810

Faltman & Malmen AB (2)
Valhallavagen 86, PO Box 26057, 114 27, Stockholm, Sweden
Tel.: (46) 84066500
Web Site: https://www.faltman-malmen.se
Sales Range: $10-24.9 Million
Emp.: 25
Advetising Agency
N.A.I.C.S.: 541810

Gnomi + Draftfcb (2)
Iroos Matsi & Archaiou Theatrou Str, Alimos, 17456, Athens, Greece
Tel.: (30) 2109626707
Web Site: http://www.fcbgnomi.gr
Sales Range: $25-49.9 Million
Emp.: 30
Full Service
N.A.I.C.S.: 541810
Christina Hohlakidis *(Mng Dir)*

Gramma Publicidad (2)
C Ignacio Cordero N 8461 Zona Calacoto, San Miguel Calacoto, La Paz, Bolivia
Tel.: (591) 2277 2831
Sales Range: $25-49.9 Million
Emp.: 35
Advetising Agency
N.A.I.C.S.: 541810

Subsidiary (Domestic):

HackerAgency, Inc. (2)
1326 5th Ave Ste 350, Seattle, WA 98101
Tel.: (206) 805-1500
Web Site: https://www.hal2l.com
Advetising Agency
N.A.I.C.S.: 541810
Spyro Kourtis *(CEO)*
Jill Kourtis *(Partner-Client-Serum)*

Subsidiary (Non-US):

Horizon Draftfcb Dubai (2)
Office No 109 1st Floor Garhoud Atrium Building Al Garhoud, PO Box 112411, Dubai, 112411, United Arab Emirates
Tel.: (971) 42825826
Sales Range: $25-49.9 Million
Emp.: 35
N.A.I.C.S.: 541810

Horizon Draftfcb Jeddah (2)
Intl Economy Tower 3rd Floor Wali Al Ahed Street, Jeddah, 21433, Saudi Arabia
Tel.: (966) 2 650 3100

Sales Range: $25-49.9 Million
Emp.: 30
N.A.I.C.S.: 541810

Horizon Holdings (2)
City Plaza 85 Vouliagmenis Avenue, 166 74 Glyfada, Athens, 16674, Greece
Tel.: (30) 210 960 3600
Web Site: http://www.fcb.com
Sales Range: $25-49.9 Million
Emp.: 7
N.A.I.C.S.: 541810
Rafic S. Saadeh *(Chm & CEO)*

Horizon.Draftfcb Kuwait (2)
Al Arabiya Tower 11 Fl Ahmed Al Jaber St Sharq Safat, Kuwait, 13062, Kuwait
Tel.: (965) 2226 7371
Web Site: http://www.horizonfcb.com
Sales Range: $25-49.9 Million
Emp.: 25
N.A.I.C.S.: 541810

Horizon.Draftfcb Riyadh (2)
Al Mas Plaza Thahlia Street Office 205 2nd Floor, Riyadh, 11474, Saudi Arabia
Tel.: (966) 1 461 7557
Sales Range: $25-49.9 Million
Emp.: 30
N.A.I.C.S.: 541810

ICC Health Limited (2)
6 Dukes Gate Acton Lane Chiswick, London, W4 5DX, United Kingdom
Tel.: (44) 2089876700
Web Site: http://www.icc-hc.com
Emp.: 200
Advetising Agency
N.A.I.C.S.: 541810

IDEA Estonia (2)
Kompassi Maja 1st Floor Tartu Road 13, Tallinn, 10145, Estonia
Tel.: (372) 669 1000
Web Site: http://www.idea.ee
Sales Range: $25-49.9 Million
Emp.: 34
N.A.I.C.S.: 541810

Interface Communications Ltd. (2)
Phoenix House A wing 2nd Floor Senapati Bapat Marg 206 Lower Parel, Worli, Mumbai, 400 013, India
Tel.: (91) 22 6666 4550
Sales Range: $25-49.9 Million
Emp.: 132
N.A.I.C.S.: 541810
Joe Thaliath *(CEO)*
Robby Mathew *(Natl Dir-Creative)*

Lindo/FCB (2)
14 Ruthven Road, Kingston, Jamaica
Tel.: (876) 9261194
Sales Range: $25-49.9 Million
Emp.: 15
N.A.I.C.S.: 541810
Jason Lindo *(Mng Dir)*

Marcom (2)
Plot 178 Unit 3 Gaborone International Commerce, Gaborone, Botswana
Tel.: (267) 391 9365
Sales Range: $25-49.9 Million
Emp.: 13
Advetising Agency
N.A.I.C.S.: 541810

Marquez Worldwide (2)
Calle 63B Los Angeles 20, Panama, Panama
Tel.: (507) 236 0755
Web Site: http://www.fcbmarkez.com
Sales Range: $25-49.9 Million
Emp.: 35
N.A.I.C.S.: 541810
Bolivar Marquez *(Mng Dir)*

Mayo (2)
Ctro Empresarial Torre Platino Av Cra 19, No 95-31/55 Piso 7, Bogota, Colombia
Tel.: (57) 14875353
Sales Range: $25-49.9 Million
Emp.: 20
N.A.I.C.S.: 541810

Mayo Ecuador (2)
Humboldt N 27-77 y San Ignacio, Quito, Ecuador
Tel.: (593) 2 222 5496
Sales Range: $25-49.9 Million
Emp.: 25
N.A.I.C.S.: 541810

Mayo Publicidad (2)
Avenida Apoquindo 3846 Los Condes, Santiago, 7550 123, Chile
Tel.: (56) 2 377 7900
Sales Range: $25-49.9 Million
Emp.: 64
N.A.I.C.S.: 541810

Minds FCB (2)
31/1 Castle Street, Markar Mawatha, Colombo, 00400, Sri Lanka
Tel.: (94) 11 474 1700
Sales Range: $25-49.9 Million
Emp.: 10
N.A.I.C.S.: 541810

Prakit & FCB Vietnam (2)
13D Phan Chu Trinh Street P2, Binh Thanh District, Ho Chi Minh City, Vietnam
Tel.: (84) 835512202
Sales Range: $25-49.9 Million
Emp.: 50
Full Service
N.A.I.C.S.: 541810
Thanun Anurakjunyong *(Gen Mgr)*

Publicentro (2)
Bolonia Optica Vision 1/2c Al S, Managua, Nicaragua
Tel.: (505) 2666544
Sales Range: $25-49.9 Million
Emp.: 30
N.A.I.C.S.: 541810

Redline (2)
Unit 10 Kya Sand Industrial Village 22 Elsecar Street, Kya Sand, Johannesburg, South Africa
Tel.: (27) 117080465
Web Site: http://www.redlinelogistics.co.za
Sales Range: $25-49.9 Million
Emp.: 15
N.A.I.C.S.: 541820
Pauline Besseling *(Mgr-Fin & Key Accounts)*
Sean Knipe *(Ops Mgr)*
Kerzner Mkhabile *(Supvr-Warehouse)*

Segal Licensing (2)
219 Dufferin Street, Toronto, M6K 3JI, ON, Canada
Tel.: (416) 588-8727
Web Site:
http://www.segalcommunications.com
Sales Range: $25-49.9 Million
Emp.: 25
Above-the-Line, Advertising, Below-the-Line, Broadcast
N.A.I.C.S.: 541810

Sembera Vanak/FCB (2)
Hviezdna 38, Bratislava, 821 06, Slovakia
Tel.: (421) 2 4020 0810
Sales Range: $25-49.9 Million
Emp.: 12
N.A.I.C.S.: 541810

General Motors R*Works (1)
1 Woodward Ste 1200, Detroit, MI 48226
Tel.: (313) 596-9000
Media Buying Services
N.A.I.C.S.: 541830
Derek Werner *(Mgr-Promos)*

Gillespie, Inc. (1)
1911 Brookside Ln, Kingsport, TN 37660
Tel.: (423) 378-5119
Web Site: https://gillespieinc.com
Emp.: 4
Trucking Service
N.A.I.C.S.: 484110

Golin/Harris International, Inc. (1)
John Hancock Ctr 875 N Michigan Ave 26th Fl, Chicago, IL 60611
Tel.: (312) 729-4000
Web Site: https://www.golin.com
Public Relations Agency
N.A.I.C.S.: 541820
Ellen Ryan Mardiks *(Chm)*
Brian Beck *(CFO)*
Scott Farrell *(Pres-Corp Comm-Global)*
Gary Rudnick *(Pres & COO)*
Matt Neale *(CEO)*
Ginger Porter *(Pres-Midwest Reg)*
Simon Ruparelia *(Head-Growth-Asia)*
Jane Morgan *(Mng Dir-Hong Kong)*
Margenett Moore-Roberts *(Chief Inclusion & Diversity Officer)*
Matthew Lackie *(Pres-Tech Practice-Global)*

The Interpublic Group of Companies, Inc.—(Continued)

Lindsay Peterson *(Mng Dir-Canada)*
Roxana Diba *(Mng Dir-Romania)*
Cristina Butunoi *(Deputy Mng Dir)*
Tiffiny Bolden *(Head-HR-Global)*
Carrie von der Sitt *(Head-Growth-Global)*

Subsidiary (Non-US):

Action Global Communications Ltd. (2)
6 Kondilaki Street, 1090, Nicosia, Cyprus
Tel.: (357) 22818884
Web Site: https://www.actionprgroup.com
Emp.: 30
N.A.I.C.S.: 541820

Subsidiary (Non-US):

Action Hellas (3)
15A Xenofontos Str 1st Floor, Syntagma, Athens, 10557, Greece
Tel.: (30) 210 724 0160
Web Site: http://www.actionprgroup.com
Sales Range: $25-49.9 Million
Emp.: 10
N.A.I.C.S.: 541820

Subsidiary (Domestic):

Action PR Cyprus (3)
6 Kondilaki Street, PO Box 24676, 1090, Nicosia, Cyprus
Tel.: (357) 2 281 8884
Web Site: http://www.actionprgroup.com
Sales Range: $25-49.9 Million
Emp.: 40
Communications, Public Relations
N.A.I.C.S.: 541820
Tony Christodoulou *(Founder)*
Kathy Christodoulou *(CMO)*
Chris Christodoulou *(CEO)*
Dimitris Ioannides *(Gen Mgr)*
Kyriacos Michaelides *(Exec Dir-Fin & Ops)*
Rebecca Theodorou *(Head-Intl Client Hub)*

Subsidiary (Non-US):

Comunica (2)
st 5th Yamskogo polya 7 building 2, Moscow, Russia
Tel.: (7) 4959371914
Web Site: http://www.comunica.ru
Emp.: 50
Public Relation Agency Services
N.A.I.C.S.: 541820
Mikhail Umarov *(CEO)*

Unit (Domestic):

Comunicadora Nexus (2)
650 Avenida Muoz Rivera Edificio Doral
San Juan, Hato Rey, PR 00968
Tel.: (787) 764-5999
Sales Range: $25-49.9 Million
Emp.: 11
N.A.I.C.S.: 541820

Subsidiary (Domestic):

GolinHarris (2)
45 Fremont St 11th Fl, San Francisco, CA 94105
Tel.: (415) 262-5422
Web Site: https://golin.com
Sales Range: $25-49.9 Million
Emp.: 10
Communications, High Technology, Public Relations
N.A.I.C.S.: 541820

GolinHarris International (2)
909 3rd Ave 9th Fl, New York, NY 10022
Tel.: (212) 373-6000
Web Site: https://golin.com
Sales Range: $25-49.9 Million
Emp.: 60
Communications, Public Relations
N.A.I.C.S.: 541810
Mathew Neale *(CEO)*

GolinHarris (2)
1840 Century Park E 16th Fl, Los Angeles, CA 90067
Tel.: (213) 335-5500
Web Site: https://golin.com
Sales Range: $25-49.9 Million
Emp.: 80
Public Relations

Branch (Domestic):

GolinHarris (2)
2809 Boston St 8, Baltimore, MD 21224
Tel.: (410) 558-2103
Sales Range: $25-49.9 Million
Emp.: 4
N.A.I.C.S.: 541820

Subsidiary (Domestic):

GolinHarris (2)
Galleria Tower 2 13455 Noel Rd Fl 11, Dallas, TX 75240
Tel.: (972) 341-2500
Web Site: https://golin.com
Sales Range: $25-49.9 Million
Emp.: 25
N.A.I.C.S.: 541820
Ginger Porter *(Mng Dir)*
Chuck Hemann *(Exec Dir-Analytics)*
Jacqi Moore Richardson *(Dir-Consumer Practice)*

Branch (Domestic):

GolinHarris (2)
275 Mccormick Ave Ste A100, Costa Mesa, CA 92626
Tel.: (949) 260-1300
Sales Range: $25-49.9 Million
Emp.: 6
N.A.I.C.S.: 541820
Lisa Falcetti *(Exec VP)*

GolinHarris (2)
1360 Post Oak Blvd Ste 2020, Houston, TX 77056
Tel.: (713) 513-9560
Sales Range: $25-49.9 Million
Emp.: 12
N.A.I.C.S.: 541820

Subsidiary (Non-US):

GolinHarris (2)
207 Queen's Quay W Ste 400, Toronto, M5J 1A7, ON, Canada
Tel.: (416) 642-7887
Sales Range: $10-24.9 Million
Emp.: 21
N.A.I.C.S.: 541820

Branch (Domestic):

GolinHarris (2)
73310 St NW Ste 900, Washington, DC 20001
Tel.: (703) 741-7500
Web Site: http://www.golinharris.com
Rev.: $35,000,000
Emp.: 30
N.A.I.C.S.: 541820

Subsidiary (Non-US):

GolinHarris (2)
Avenue de Cortenbergh 100, 1000, Brussels, Belgium
Tel.: (32) 28949076
Web Site: http://golin.com
Sales Range: $25-49.9 Million
Emp.: 50
N.A.I.C.S.: 541820

GolinHarris (2)
Capricorn Tower 7th Floor Sheikh Zayed RD, PO Box 116462, Dubai, United Arab Emirates
Tel.: (971) 43323308
Web Site: http://www.golinharris.com
Public Relations & Markets Communications Services
N.A.I.C.S.: 541820
Yiannis Vafeas *(Mng Dir)*

GolinHarris (2)
Schutzenstrasse 21, 22761, Hamburg, Germany
Tel.: (49) 40607712800
Web Site: https://www.golin.com
Public Relations & Markets Communications Services
N.A.I.C.S.: 541820
Uta Schwaner *(Mng Dir-Germany)*

GolinHarris (2)
99 Clifton Street, 140 Holborn, London, EC2A 4LG, United Kingdom
Tel.: (44) 2070670600

Web Site: http://www.golin.com
Public Relations & Markets Communications Services
N.A.I.C.S.: 541820
Ondine Whittington *(Mng Dir)*

GolinHarris (2)
Paseo de la Castellana 135 Planta 11 Edif Cuzco III, 28046, Madrid, Spain
Tel.: (34) 917458604
Web Site: http://golin.com
Sales Range: $25-49.9 Million
Emp.: 10
N.A.I.C.S.: 541820
Natalia Sanchez *(Mng Dir)*

GolinHarris (2)
Via Spadolini 7Edificio B, 20141, Milan, Italy
Tel.: (39) 03487407372
N.A.I.C.S.: 541820

GolinHarris (2)
Square dOrleans 80 rue Taitbout, 75439, Paris, Cedex 9, France
Tel.: (33) 140415628
Web Site: http://www.golinharris.com
Emp.: 20
N.A.I.C.S.: 541820
Anne Le Brouster *(Mng Dir)*

GolinHarris (2)
1305 China Life Tower 16 Chaoyangmen Wai Da Jie, Beijing, 100020, China
Tel.: (86) 1085699898
Web Site: http://www.golin.com
Public Relations & Markets Communications Services
N.A.I.C.S.: 541820
Lydia Shen *(Mng Dir)*

GolinHarris (2)
Room 1501 the Centrepoint 374-2 Beijing Road, No 18 Zhongshan Er Road, Guangzhou, 510080, China
Tel.: (86) 2038879683
Web Site: http://www.golinharris.com
N.A.I.C.S.: 541820

GolinHarris (2)
36/F HuaiHai Plaza 1045 HuaiHai Zhong Road, Shanghai, 200031, China
Tel.: (86) 2124110088
N.A.I.C.S.: 541820

GolinHarris (2)
40A Orchard Road 07-01, The MacDonald House, Singapore, 238838, Singapore
Tel.: (65) 62353121
Web Site: https://golin.com
Sales Range: $25-49.9 Million
Emp.: 20
Public Relations
N.A.I.C.S.: 541820
Simon Ruparelia *(Head-Growth-Asia Pacific)*
Darren Burns *(Pres-Asia Pacific)*

GolinHarris (2)
Hamza Nael Street, PO Box 6308, King Abdullah Road, Jeddah, 21442, Saudi Arabia
Tel.: (966) 2 650 2741
N.A.I.C.S.: 541820
John Badenhorst *(Mng Dir)*

Subsidiary (Domestic):

GolinHarris (2)
1375 Peachtree St NE Ste 175N, Atlanta, GA 30318
Tel.: (470) 419-8634
Web Site: https://golin.com
Sales Range: $10-24.9 Million
Emp.: 25
N.A.I.C.S.: 541820

Unit (Domestic):

GolinHarris/Panache (2)
430 Pacific Ave, San Francisco, CA 94133-4607
Tel.: (415) 274-7900
Web Site: http://www.golinharris.com
Sales Range: $25-49.9 Million
Emp.: 25
Public Relations
N.A.I.C.S.: 541820

Subsidiary (Non-US):

S2Publicom Weber Shandwick (2)

Ed Sudameris Av Eng Luiz Carlos Berrini, 1297 - 3 andar, Sao Paulo, CEP 04571-010, Brazil
Tel.: (55) 11 5505 1628
Web Site: http://www.s2publicom.com.br
Public Relation Engagement Services
N.A.I.C.S.: 541820

The Brooklyn Brothers Limited (2)
11-29 Smiths Court, London, W1D 7DP, United Kingdom
Tel.: (44) 2072926200
Web Site:
http://www.thebrooklynbrothers.com
Advetising Agency
N.A.I.C.S.: 541810
Jackie Stevenson *(Partner & Mng Dir)*

Zimat Consultores (2)
Paseo de la Reforma 155 4th floor PH1 and PH2, Lomas - Viceroyes Lomas de Chapultepec, 11000, Mexico, Mexico
Tel.: (52) 5555545419
Web Site: https://www.zimat.com
Sales Range: $25-49.9 Million
Emp.: 60
N.A.I.C.S.: 541820

Gotham Incorporated (1)
622 3rd Ave 19th Fl, New York, NY 10017
Tel.: (212) 414-7000
Web Site: http://www.beautyatgotham.com
Sales Range: $125-149.9 Million
Emp.: 60
Advertising Services
N.A.I.C.S.: 541810.

Huge, LLC (1)
45 Main St 3rd Fl, Brooklyn, NY 11201
Tel.: (718) 625-4843
Web Site: https://www.hugeinc.com
Emp.: 450
Advertising Agencies
N.A.I.C.S.: 541810
Raj Singhal *(CEO-Acting, CFO & COO)*
Scott Schreiber *(Chief Legal & Admin Officer)*

ID Media (1)
100 W 33rd St, New York, NY 10001
Tel.: (212) 907-7003
Web Site: https://www.idmediaww.com
Sales Range: $50-74.9 Million
Emp.: 100
Media Buying Services
N.A.I.C.S.: 541830

Subsidiary (Domestic):

ID Media-Chicago (2)
875 N Michigan Ave 18th Fl, Chicago, IL 60611
Tel.: (312) 799-6900
Web Site: http://www.idmediaww.com
Emp.: 20
Advertising Services
N.A.I.C.S.: 541810

Branch (Domestic):

ID Media-Los Angeles (2)
8687 Melrose Ave, West Hollywood, CA 90069-5701
Tel.: (310) 360-5700
Web Site: http://www.idmediaww.com
Emp.: 75
Advertising Services
N.A.I.C.S.: 541830

IPG Mediabrands (1)
100 W 33rd St, New York, NY 10001
Tel.: (212) 883-4751
Web Site: http://www.ipgmediabrands.com
Emp.: 8,500
Media Buying Services
N.A.I.C.S.: 541830
Leigh Terry *(CEO-Asia Pacific)*
Daryl Lee *(CEO-Global)*
Mat Baxter *(CEO-Initiative-Global)*
Dimitri Maex *(CEO-Reprise-Global)*
Mark Coad *(CEO)*
Kim Lion *(Chief Culture & Comm Officer)*
Jackie Edwards *(Mng Dir-Orion)*

Subsidiary (Non-US):

Marvelous Nordic (2)
Skt Petri Passage 5 2, 1165, Copenhagen, Denmark
Tel.: (45) 31794900

Web Site: http://www.mrvls.com
Emp.: 50
Advertising Services
N.A.I.C.S.: 541810
Christian Strand (Mng Dir-Nordic)
Jesper Grubb (Creative Dir)
Rasmus Mikkelsen (Creative Dir-Digital)
Camilla Jane Bunnage (Sr Mgr-Acct)
Victor Thygesen (Coord-Digital Project)

Subsidiary (Non-US):

Marvelous Finland (3)
Peramiehenkatu 12 E, 00150, Helsinki,
Finland
Tel.: (358) 207426700
Web Site: http://www.mrvls.com
Advertising Services
N.A.I.C.S.: 541810
Janne Sirainen (Art Dir)
Samuli Salokangas (Head-Marvelous)

Marvelous Sverige (3)
Grev Turegatan 11A, 114 97, Stockholm,
Sweden
Tel.: (46) 856301400
Web Site: http://www.mrvls.com
Advertising Services
N.A.I.C.S.: 541810

Subsidiary (Non-US):

Media Experts (2)
200 Wellington St W 14th Floor, Toronto,
M5V 3C7, ON, Canada
Tel.: (416) 597-0707
Web Site: http://www.mediaexperts.com
Emp.: 150
Media Buying Services
N.A.I.C.S.: 541830
Mark Sherman (Founder & Chm)
Flavia D'Orazio (Partner-Client Bus & Sr
VP)
Robert Jenkyn (Pres)
Lisa Di Marco (COO)
Richard Ivey (Chief Procurement Officer)
Kris Davis (Partner-Client Bus & Sr VP)
Vasso Fragos (VP-Fin)
Karel Wegert (Exec VP)
Patricia Gray (VP-Digital Media)

Branch (Domestic):

Media Experts (3)
7236 rue Marconi, Montreal, H2R 2Z5, QC,
Canada
Tel.: (514) 844-5050
Web Site: http://www.mediaexperts.com
Media Buying Services
N.A.I.C.S.: 541830
Mark Sherman (Founder & CEO)
Patricia Gray (VP-Digital Media)

Initiative Worldwide (1)
100 W 33rd St 4th Fl, New York, NY 10001
Tel.: (212) 605-7000
Web Site: https://www.initiative.com
Sales Range: $550-599.9 Million
Emp.: 3,500
Media Buying Services
N.A.I.C.S.: 541830
Pele Cortizo-Burgess (Chief Strategy Offi-
cer)
Jarrod Martin (Chief Data & Transformation
Officer-Global)

Subsidiary (Non-US):

Initiative (2)
Pinmill Farm - 164 Katherine Street, Block
Strathavon - Building 2 - Sandton, Johan-
nesburg, 2191, Gauteng, South Africa
Tel.: (27) 117806117
Web Site: http://www.initiative.com
Emp.: 40
Media Buying Services
N.A.I.C.S.: 541830

Initiative (2)
Atlas Arena Asia Building Hoogoorddreef 5,
1011 BA, Amsterdam, Netherlands
Tel.: (31) 207993000
Web Site: http://www.initiative.com
Emp.: 5
Media Buying Services
N.A.I.C.S.: 541830
Leonie Koning (CEO)
Lars Vink (Grp Dir-Bus)
Eva Hollander (Grp Dir-Bus)

Branch (Domestic):

Initiative (2)
1 Dag Hammarskjold Plz 5th Fl, New York,
NY 10017
Tel.: (212) 605-7000
Web Site: http://www.initiative.com
Media Buying Services
N.A.I.C.S.: 541830
Maureen Bosetti (Chief Partnerships Offi-
cer)
Tricia Camarillo-Quiambao (Mng Dir-
Philippines)
David Stopforth (Chief Comm Design Offi-
cer)
Hallie Johnston (Chief Client Officer)
Pele Cortizo-Burgess (Chief Strategy Offi-
cer)
Sarah Robertson (Pres-Rufus)
Kym Miller (Head-Ops)
Jonathan Vu (Head-Diversity & Inclusion)
Kat So (Mng Dir)
Stacy Deriso (CEO)
Thor Peterson (CFO)
Joy Joseph (Chief Data & Analytics Officer)

Subsidiary (Non-US):

Initiative Athens (2)
Business Plaza - K2 89-91, Ethn Anti-
staseos 1-3 Tzavella strs, 15231, Halandri,
Greece
Tel.: (30) 2106798700
Web Site: http://www.initiative.com
Emp.: 23
Media Buying Services
N.A.I.C.S.: 541830
Michael Galgos (Mng Dir)
Triadafillos Karametros (Head-TV)
Artemis Tsimrikidou (Dir-Grp Acct)
Loretta Panou (Dir-Digital)
Eleni Theodorakea (Dir-Digital)

Branch (Domestic):

Initiative Atlanta (2)
5909 Peachtree Dunwoody Rd Ste 600,
Atlanta, GA 30328
Tel.: (404) 814-8711
Web Site: http://www.initiative.com
Media Buying Services
N.A.I.C.S.: 541830

Subsidiary (Non-US):

Initiative Bangkok (2)
195 Empire Tower 28/F South Sathorn
Road, Yannawa, Bangkok, 10120, Thailand
Tel.: (66) 205559946
Web Site: http://www.initiative.com
Emp.: 100
Media Buying Services
N.A.I.C.S.: 541830

Initiative Barcelona (2)
Avinguda Diagonal 613 8a planta, 8034,
Barcelona, Spain
Tel.: (34) 934921600
Web Site: http://www.initiative.com
Emp.: 10
Media Buying Services
N.A.I.C.S.: 541830
Vincente Ros (Chief Digital & Transforma-
tion Officer)
Beatriz Balaguer (Head-Rufus)
Oscar Gonzalez (Head-Clients & Transfor-
mation)

Initiative Beirut (2)
Badaro Trade Center Suite 801 Sami El
Solh Avenue, PO Box 16, 6070, Beirut,
Lebanon
Tel.: (961) 1393950
Web Site: http://www.initiative.com
Emp.: 6
Media Buying Services
N.A.I.C.S.: 541830

Initiative Bogota (2)
Avenida 19 114A-59 Piso 5, Bogota, Co-
lombia
Tel.: (57) 16585252
Web Site: http://www.initiative.com
Media Buying Services
N.A.I.C.S.: 541830

Initiative Brussels (2)
Ildefonse Vandammestraat 5-7, Hoeilaart,
11560, Brussels, Belgium
Tel.: (32) 27736800

Web Site: http://initiative.com
Media Buying Services
N.A.I.C.S.: 541830
Sophie Jadoul (COO)

Initiative Budapest (2)
Vajdahunyad utca 33-43, 1082, Budapest,
Hungary
Tel.: (36) 18025100
Media Buying Services
N.A.I.C.S.: 541830
Zsolt Zaprel (CEO)
Krisztina Palinkas (Head-Res)
Attila Eros (Head-Digital)

Initiative Buenos Aires (2)
Costa Rica 6012, CP1414BTN, Buenos Ai-
res, Argentina
Tel.: (54) 1143186500
Web Site: http://www.initiative.com
Emp.: 200
Media Buying Services
N.A.I.C.S.: 541830

Initiative Caracas (2)
Torre Multinvest Piso 4 Plaza la Castellana
Altamira, Codigo 1060 Campo Alegre, Cara-
cas, 1060, Venezuela
Tel.: (58) 2128166996
Media Buying Services
N.A.I.C.S.: 541830
Carmen Maria Gonzalez (Mng Dir)

Initiative Dubai (2)
MCN Hive 3rd Floor Barsha Heights, PO
Box 502149, Dubai Media City, Dubai,
United Arab Emirates
Tel.: (971) 44477074
Web Site: http://www.initiative.com
Emp.: 30
Media Buying Services
N.A.I.C.S.: 541830

Initiative Dublin (2)
6th Floor Iveagh Court Block E 6/8 Harcourt
Road, Dublin, Ireland
Tel.: (353) 14751895
Web Site: http://www.initiative.com
Emp.: 28
Media Buying Services
N.A.I.C.S.: 541830
Eamon Fitzpatrick (CEO)
Gary Colton (Officer-Cultural Insights &
Analytics)

Branch (Non-US):

Initiative Group B.V. (2)
Atlas ArenA Amsterdam Asia building Hoo-
goorddreef 5, 1101, Amsterdam, Nether-
lands
Tel.: (31) 207993000
Web Site: http://www.initiativegroup.nl
Emp.: 300
Advertising Services
N.A.I.C.S.: 541810
Leonie Koning (Mng Dir)

Subsidiary (Non-US):

Initiative Hamburg (2)
Hongkongstrasse 10, 20457, Hamburg,
Germany
Tel.: (49) 4043196
Web Site: http://www.hamburg-logistik.net
Emp.: 100
Media Buying Services
N.A.I.C.S.: 541830
Mathias Glatter (COO)
Bastian Schwarmer (Mng Partner-Digital &
Mng Dir)
Daniela Jessen (Mng Partner-Client Advice
Mgmt)

Initiative Hong Kong (2)
Suite 1302-4 Oxford House Taikoo Place
979 King's Road, 979 Kings Rd, Quarry
Bay, China (Hong Kong)
Tel.: (852) 24069000
Web Site: http://www.initiative.com
Emp.: 10
Advertising Agencies
N.A.I.C.S.: 541810

Initiative Jakarta (2)
Victoria Building 5th Floor Jl Sultan
Hasanuddin 47-51, Jakarta, 12160, Indone-
sia
Tel.: (62) 217254860
Web Site: http://www.initiative.com
Media Buying Services

N.A.I.C.S.: 541830

Initiative Lima (2)
Ave Salaverry No 2423 San Isidro, 27,
Lima, Peru
Tel.: (51) 7978
Web Site: http://www.initiative.com
Emp.: 50
Media Buying Services
N.A.I.C.S.: 541830

Initiative Lisbon (2)
Edificio Heron Castilho Rua Braamcamp 40
- 6th floor, 1250, Lisbon, Portugal
Tel.: (351) 217217700
Web Site: http://www.initiative.co.pt
Emp.: 40
Media Buying Services
N.A.I.C.S.: 541830
Rui Freire (Mng Dir)

Initiative London (2)
42 St John's Square, London, EC1M 4EA,
United Kingdom
Tel.: (44) 2076637000
Web Site: http://www.initiative.com
Emp.: 700
Advertising Services
N.A.I.C.S.: 541810

Subsidiary (Domestic):

Initiative Los Angeles (2)
5700 Wilshire Blvd 400, Los Angeles, CA
90036
Tel.: (323) 370-8000
Web Site: http://www.initiative.com
Emp.: 300
Media Buying Services
N.A.I.C.S.: 541830

Subsidiary (Non-US):

Initiative Madrid (2)
Paseo de la Castellana 135-10 Plaza Car-
los Trias Beltran 7 Planta 5a, 28046, Ma-
drid, Spain
Tel.: (34) 917893240
Web Site: http://www.initiative.com
Emp.: 30
Media Buying Services
N.A.I.C.S.: 541830

Initiative Media Australia Pty Ltd (2)
Ground L 10 Pirrama Rd, Pyrmont, 2009,
NSW, Australia
Tel.: (61) 285862000
Advertising Agencies
N.A.I.C.S.: 541810
Lee Leggett (CEO)
Andrew Livingston (Natl COO)

Initiative Melbourne (2)
Level 9 15 William St, Melbourne, 3000,
VIC, Australia
Tel.: (61) 388882900
Web Site: http://www.au.initiative.com
Emp.: 19
Media Buying Services
N.A.I.C.S.: 541830
Melissa Fein (CEO)
Sam Geer (Mng Dir-Natl)
Megan Davey (Gen Mgr)
Sarah James (Mng Dir)

Branch (Non-US):

Initiative Mexico City (2)
Avenida Miguel De Cervantes Saavedra
193 Piso 7, Mexico, Mexico
Tel.: (52) 53505700
Web Site: http://www.initiative.com
Media Buying Services
N.A.I.C.S.: 541830

Subsidiary (Domestic):

Initiative Miami (2)
4500 Biscayne Blvd, Miami, FL 33137
Tel.: (305) 572-2157
Emp.: 10
Media Buying Services
N.A.I.C.S.: 541830
Mauricio Sabogal (Mng Dir-Worldwide)
Richard Beaven (CEO-World Wide)

Subsidiary (Non-US):

Initiative Milan (2)
Via Giovanni Spadolini 7 Centro Leoni Palazzo B, 20141, Milan, Italy

The Interpublic Group of Companies,
Inc.—(Continued)

Tel.: (39) 02725251
Web Site: http://initiative.com
Media Buying Services
N.A.I.C.S.: 541830

Branch (Non-US):

Initiative Moscow (2)
Office 407-408 Bldg 1, 18 Malaya Pirogovs-
kaya str, Moscow, 119435, Russia
Tel.: (7) 095 77 53 601
Emp.: 25
Advertising Services
N.A.I.C.S.: 541810

Subsidiary (Non-US):

Initiative Mumbai (2)
3rd Floor Phoenix Complex Senapati Bapat
Marg, Lower Parel, Mumbai, 400 013, India
Tel.: (91) 2224935477
Web Site: http://www.initiative.com
Media Buying Services
N.A.I.C.S.: 541830

Initiative Paris (2)
La Chocolaterie 79 - 83 Rue Baudin,
92309, Paris, France
Tel.: (33) 147153500
Web Site: http://www.initiative.com
Emp.: 100
Media Buying Services
N.A.I.C.S.: 541830

Initiative Perth (2)
344 Hay Street, Perth, Subiaco, 6008, WA,
Australia
Tel.: (61) 893852300
Web Site: http://www.initiative.com
Emp.: 10
Media Buying Services
N.A.I.C.S.: 541830

Initiative Prague (2)
Palac Karlin Thamova 11, Prague, 8, Czech
Republic
Tel.: (420) 225341160
Web Site: http://www.initiative.cz
Emp.: 20
Media Buying Services
N.A.I.C.S.: 541830

Branch (Domestic):

Initiative San Diego (2)
4747 Executive Dr Ste 1080, San Diego,
CA 92121
Tel.: (858) 677-2714
Web Site: http://www.initiative.com
Emp.: 3
Media Buying Services
N.A.I.C.S.: 541830

Subsidiary (Non-US):

Initiative Santiago (2)
Avenue Isidora Goyenechea 2800 Piso 9
office 903, Las Condes, 7550611, Santiago,
Chile
Tel.: (56) 24656600
Emp.: 100
Media Buying Services
N.A.I.C.S.: 541830

Initiative Singapore (2)
3D River Valley Rd 02-01 Clarke Quay, The
MacDonald House 04-01, Singapore,
238838, Singapore
Tel.: (65) 8388
Web Site: http://www.initiative.com
Advertising Services
N.A.I.C.S.: 541830
Will Anstee (Pres-Asia Pacific)

Initiative Sydney (2)
Level 1 / 11-17 Buckingham St, Surry Hills,
2010, NSW, Australia
Tel.: (61) 285862000
Web Site: http://www.au.initiative.com
Media Buying Services
N.A.I.C.S.: 541830
Geoff Clarke (COO)

Initiative Taipei (2)
4F No 1 Nan King E Rd Sec 5, Taipei, Tai-
wan
Tel.: (886) 227603338
Web Site: http://www.initiative.com
Media Buying Services

N.A.I.C.S.: 541830
Jimmy Chu (Deputy Gen Mgr)
Anderson Wang (Head-Product)

Branch (Non-US):

Initiative Tokyo (2)
Shin Aoyama Building East 1-1-1 Minami
Aoyama, Minato-Ku, Tokyo, 107-8679, Ja-
pan
Tel.: (81) 3 3746 8111
Emp.: 100
Media Buying Services
N.A.I.C.S.: 541830
Keiji Tarada (Exec Dir-Bus)

Initiative Toronto (2)
10 Bay Street Suite 1605, Toronto, M5J
2R8, ON, Canada
Tel.: (416) 933-5800
Web Site: http://www.initiative.com
Emp.: 30
Media Buying Services
N.A.I.C.S.: 541830

Subsidiary (Non-US):

Initiative Universal Copenhagen (2)
Oestergade 26 A 4th Floor, 1100, Copenha-
gen, Denmark
Tel.: (45) 33694900
Web Site: http://www.ium.dk
Media Buying Services
N.A.I.C.S.: 541830
Peter Sevel (Mng Partner)

Initiative Universal Media (2)
Grev Turegatan 11A, 114 97, Stockholm,
Sweden
Tel.: (46) 856301400
Web Site: http://www.ium.se
Emp.: 40
Advertising Services
N.A.I.C.S.: 541810
Maria Carlsson (Head-Insight)

Initiative Universal Oslo (2)
Sandakerveien 24C Boks 4229, Nydalen,
473, Oslo, Norway
Tel.: (47) 22543880
Web Site: http://www.iumas.no
Emp.: 50
Media Buying Services
N.A.I.C.S.: 541830
Borre Sunde (Mng Dir)
Kim Thorvaldsen (Dir-Digital)

Initiative Universal Warsaw (2)
Cybernetyki 19, 02-677, Warsaw, Poland
Tel.: (48) 225723300
Web Site: http://www.initiative.pl
Media Buying Services
N.A.I.C.S.: 541830
Pawol Orkiszewski (Chief Strategy Officer)
Paulina Pawinska (Dir-Grp Acct)

Initiative Vienna (2)
Operngasse 21/9, 1040, Vienna, Austria
Tel.: (43) 158896217
Web Site: http://www.initiativemedia.com
Emp.: 30
Media Buying Services
N.A.I.C.S.: 541830
John Oakley (Mng Dir)

Initiative Zurich (2)
Heinrichstr 267 entrance C, 8005, Zurich,
Switzerland
Tel.: (41) 443963383
Web Site: http://www.initiative.com
Emp.: 20
Media Buying Services
N.A.I.C.S.: 541830

Subsidiary (Domestic):

Media Partnership Corporation (2)
800 Connecticut Ave 3rd Fl N Wing, Nor-
walk, CT 06854
Tel.: (203) 855-6711
Web Site:
  https://www.mediapartnership.com
Emp.: 14
Media Buying Services
N.A.I.C.S.: 541830
Jim Jarboe (Sr VP & Dir-Brdcst Svcs)
Matt Thornbrough (Mng Dir & Sr VP)
Adam Cohen (Acct Dir)
Alex Chik (Sr VP & Dir-Brdcst Svcs)
Donna Cataldo (VP & Acct Dir)
Amy Bytell (Assoc Dir-Media Strategy)

**Newspaper Services of America,
Inc.** (2)
2200 Cabot Dr Ste 330, Lisle, IL 60532
Tel.: (630) 729-7500
Web Site: https://www.nsamedia.com
Emp.: 350
Media Buying Services
N.A.I.C.S.: 541830

Outdoor Advertising Group (2)
3025 Highland Pkwy, Downers Grove, IL
60515
Tel.: (646) 808-1282
Web Site: http://www.rapportww.com
Outdoor Media Planning & Buying Agency
N.A.I.C.S.: 541830

Branch (Domestic):

**Outdoor Advertising Group - Detroit
Office** (3)
2000 Brush St Ste 601, Detroit, MI 48226
Tel.: (586) 753-8642
Web Site: http://www.rapportww.com
Outdoor Media Planning & Buying Agency
N.A.I.C.S.: 541830

Subsidiary (Domestic):

**Outdoor Advertising Group - Los An-
geles Office** (3)
5700 Wilshire Blvd Ste 400, Los Angeles,
CA 90036
Tel.: (323) 370-8710
Web Site: http://www.rapportww.com
Outdoor Media Planning & Buying Agency
N.A.I.C.S.: 541830

Subsidiary (Domestic):

Wahlstrom Group (2)
1290 E Main St, Stamford, CT 06902
Tel.: (203) 299-4200
Rev.: $225,000,000
Emp.: 260
Media Buying Services
N.A.I.C.S.: 541830

Subsidiary (Domestic):

Wahlstrom Group (3)
200 S Broad St, Philadelphia, PA 19102-
3803
Tel.: (215) 790-3100
Emp.: 8
Advertising Services
N.A.I.C.S.: 541810

Branch (Domestic):

Wahlstrom Group (3)
222 S 9th St Ste 2850, Minneapolis, MN
55402-3399
Tel.: (952) 346-6686
Interactive, Yellow Pages Advertising
N.A.I.C.S.: 541830

**Interpublic Group Deutschland
GmbH** (1)
Grosser Hasenpfad 44, 60598, Frankfurt,
Germany
Tel.: (49) 69605070
Web Site: http://www.mrm.de
Emp.: 300
Advertising Services
N.A.I.C.S.: 541890

Interpublic Limited (1)
135 Bishopsgate, London, EC2M 3TP,
United Kingdom
Tel.: (44) 2070820120
Holding Company
N.A.I.C.S.: 551112

Jack Morton UK Limited (1)
Foundry Building 4th Floor 77 Fulham Pal-
ace Road, London, W6 8AF, United King-
dom
Tel.: (44) 2087352000
Web Site: https://www.jackmorton.com
Marketing Communications & Service
N.A.I.C.S.: 541613

Jack Morton Worldwide (1)
33 Arch St Ste 1400 14th Fl, Boston, MA
02110
Tel.: (617) 585-7000
Web Site: http://www.jackmorton.com
Sales Range: $150-199.9 Million
Emp.: 600
Advertising Services

N.A.I.C.S.: 541810
Josh McCall (Chm & CEO)
Bill Davies (CFO & COO)
Julian Pullan (Vice Chm & Pres-Intl)
Charles Robinson (Sr VP & Mng Dir)
Melissa Rose (Chief HR Officer)
Sharon Crichton (VP & Gen Mgr)
Craig Millon (Chief Client Officer)
Edward Scott (Pres)
Natalie Ackerman (Exec VP-Talent & Inclu-
sion)
Martyn Clarkson (Exec VP & Head-
Strategy-Global)
John Howard (Exec VP)

Division (Domestic):

Genuine Interactive, LLC (2)
500 Harrison Ave 5R, Boston, MA 02118
Tel.: (617) 451-9700
Web Site: https://www.wearegenuine.com
Emp.: 50
Digital Advertising Services
N.A.I.C.S.: 541810
Stephen Potter (Sr VP & Dir-Creative)
Jen Poirer (Mng Dir & Sr VP)
Craig Millon (CEO)
Aileen Wong (Sr VP-Experience Design)
Greg Knoff (Sr VP-Acct Svcs)
Josh Hoekwater (Sr VP-Strategic Partner-
ships)
Mary-ann Dithomas (VP-Project Mgmt)

Subsidiary (Domestic):

Jack Morton Exhibits (2)
10 Applegate Dr, Robbinsville, NJ 08691
Tel.: (609) 259-0500
Web Site: http://www.jackmorton.com
Emp.: 60
Advertising Services
N.A.I.C.S.: 541810

Branch (Non-US):

Jack Morton Worldwide (2)
7/F Oxford House TaiKoo Place, Quarry
Bay, China (Hong Kong)
Tel.: (852) 28 05 1767
Web Site: http://www.jackmorton.com
Emp.: 60
Advertising Services
N.A.I.C.S.: 541820
Natalie Ackerman (Exec VP-Greater China)

Branch (Domestic):

Jack Morton Worldwide (2)
500 Harrison Ave Ste 5R, Boston, MA
02118
Tel.: (617) 585-7000
Web Site: http://www.jackmorton.com
Emp.: 50
Advertising Services
N.A.I.C.S.: 541810

Subsidiary (Non-US):

Jack Morton Worldwide (2)
Foundry Building 4th Floor 77 Fulham Pal-
ace Road, The Vale, London, W6 8AF,
United Kingdom
Tel.: (44) 2087352000
Web Site: https://jackmorton.com
Emp.: 90
Advertising Services
N.A.I.C.S.: 541810

Branch (Domestic):

Jack Morton Worldwide (2)
875 N Michigan Ave 27th fl, Chicago, IL
60611
Tel.: (312) 274-6060
Web Site: https://jackmorton.com
Emp.: 25
Advertising Services
N.A.I.C.S.: 541810
Matt Pensinger (Mng Dir & Sr VP)
Shelley Elkins (Sr VP & Grp Dir-Creative)

Jack Morton Worldwide (2)
142 Berkeley St, Boston, MA 02116
Tel.: (203) 851-7800
Advertising Services
N.A.I.C.S.: 541810

Jack Morton Worldwide (2)
8687 Melrose Ave Ste G510, West Hollywood, CA 90069
Tel.: (310) 967-2400

Advertising Services
N.A.I.C.S.: 541810
Edward Scott *(Mng Dir)*

Subsidiary (Non-US):

Jack Morton Worldwide (2)
822 George Street Chippendale, The
Rocks, Sydney, 2008, NSW, Australia
Tel.: (61) 282314500
Web Site: https://jackmorton.com
Emp.: 25
Advertising Services
N.A.I.C.S.: 541810

Jack Morton Worldwide (2)
68 Clarke Street Southbank, Melbourne,
3006, VIC, Australia
Tel.: (61) 386442100
Web Site: https://jackmorton.com
Emp.: 10
Advertising Services
N.A.I.C.S.: 541810

Subsidiary (Domestic):

Jack Morton Worldwide (2)
1921 Northwood Dr, Troy, MI 48084
Tel.: (248) 269-8300
Web Site: http://www.jackmorton.com
Emp.: 40
Advertising Services
N.A.I.C.S.: 541810

Branch (Non-US):

Jack Morton Worldwide (2)
17/F China Life Tower, 1600 Chao Wai Av-
enue, 100020, Beijing, China
Tel.: (86) 10 85699700
Web Site: http://www.jackmorton.com
Advertising Services
N.A.I.C.S.: 541810

Branch (Domestic):

Jack Morton Worldwide (2)
909 3rd Ave 8th Fl, New York, NY 10022
Tel.: (212) 401-7000
Web Site: https://jackmorton.com
Emp.: 150
Advertising Services
N.A.I.C.S.: 541810

**Jack Morton Worldwide - San
Francisco** (2)
45 Fremont Fl 3, San Francisco, CA 94105
Tel.: (415) 318-4300
Web Site: https://jackmorton.com
Advertising Services
N.A.I.C.S.: 541810

Lowe & Partners Worldwide Ltd (1)
C-Space 37-45 City Road, London, EC1Y
1AT, United Kingdom
Tel.: (44) 2075845033
Advetising Agency
N.A.I.C.S.: 541810
Tony Wright *(Chm)*

Subsidiary (Domestic):

Lowe Profero Limited (2)
C-Space 37-45 City Road, London, EC1Y
1AT, United Kingdom
Tel.: (44) 2078945800
Web Site:
http://www.mullenloweprofero.com
Advertising Agency
N.A.I.C.S.: 541810
Dean Lanzman *(Head-Data)*

Subsidiary (Non-US):

Lowe Profero (HK) Limited (3)
25/F Fook Lee Commercial Ctr, 33 Lockhart
Rd, Wanchai, China (Hong Kong)
Tel.: (852) 2524 5188
Web Site: http://www.loweprofero.com
Emp.: 10
Advetising Agency
N.A.I.C.S.: 541810
Radhe Vaswani *(Mng Dir-Southeast Asia &
Hong Kong)*

**Lowe Profero (Shanghai) Co.,
Ltd.** (3)
36/F Huai Hai Plaza 1045 Huai Hai Zhong
Road, Taikang Rd, Shanghai, 200031,
China
Tel.: (86) 2124110828

Web Site: http://www.loweprofero.com
Emp.: 40
Advertising Agency
N.A.I.C.S.: 541810

Lowe Profero Iberia S.A. (3)
Molina 47, 28029, Madrid, Spain
Tel.: (34) 91 300 5182
Web Site: http://www.loweprofero.com
Emp.: 50
Advertising Agency
N.A.I.C.S.: 541810

Lowe Profero Pty. Limited (3)
Level 2 11-17 Buckingham St, Sydney,
2010, NSW, Australia
Tel.: (61) 290268600
Web Site: http://www.loweprofero.com
Advertising Agency
N.A.I.C.S.: 541810

Plan.net (3)
Friedenstr 24, 81671, Munich, Germany
Tel.: (49) 89205030
Web Site: http://www.plan-net.de
Advetising Agency
N.A.I.C.S.: 541810
Florian Haller *(Mng Dir)*

McCann Worldgroup, LLC (1)
622 3rd Ave, New York, NY 10017
Tel.: (646) 865-3000
Web Site: http://www.mccann.com
Sales Range: $15-24.9 Billion
Emp.: 20,000
Holding Company; Advertising Agencies
N.A.I.C.S.: 551114
Rob Reilly *(Chm-Creative-Global)*
Prasoon Joshi *(Chm-Asia Pacific &
CEO/Chief Creative Officer-India)*
Alex Lopez *(Pres & Chief Creative Officer-
Global)*
John Mescall *(Pres-Creative Council)*

Subsidiary (Non-US):

A1 Outdoor (2)
Nangwenya Rd plot No 4177 Post net No
619, PBAG E891, Rhodes Park, Lusaka,
Zambia
Tel.: (260) 211254901
Web Site: https://www.a1outdoor.co.tz
Advetising Agency
N.A.I.C.S.: 541810

**Astos Dizainas McCann Erickson
Vilnius** (2)
Marironio g 11, Vilnius, 01124, Lithuania
Tel.: (370) 852124509
Web Site: http://www.mccann.com
Emp.: 30
N.A.I.C.S.: 541810
Limas Pakalhiskis *(Mng Dir)*

Subsidiary (Domestic):

Avrett Free Ginsberg (2)
192 Lexington Ave, New York, NY 10016
Tel.: (212) 832-3800
Web Site: http://www.avrettfreeginsberg.com
Rev.: $280,000,000
Emp.: 80
Advertising Services
N.A.I.C.S.: 541810
Frank Ginsberg *(Founder, Chm & CEO)*
Joe Petruccio *(Co-Chief Creative Officer)*
Yucel Erdogan *(Co-Chief Creative Officer)*
Tara DeCoursey *(Exec & Exec)*
Agostino Colotti *(CFO & COO)*
Gib Marquardt *(Co-Chief Creative Officer)*
Jonathan Schleyer *(Dir-Plng-Global)*

Subsidiary (Non-US):

Cottman McCann Advertising (2)
PO Box 835, Blantyre, Malawi
Tel.: (265) 1 67 17 20
Web Site: http://www.mccann.com
Sales Range: $25-49.9 Million
Emp.: 12
N.A.I.C.S.: 541810

De La Ma/McCann Erickson (2)
36 B Georgiou Griva Digeni, 1066, Nicosia,
Cyprus
Tel.: (357) 22660300
Web Site: https://www.delema.com
Rev.: $12,000,000
Emp.: 52
N.A.I.C.S.: 541810

Despo Lefkariti *(Mng Dir)*
Irene Kalogirou-Karaoli *(VP & Exec Dir-
Media)*
Andreas Pavlou *(Dir-Digital Svc)*
Christina Chrysostomou *(Grp Acct Dir-Client
Service-Grp)*
Elena Georgallas *(Art Dir & Mgr-Creative)*
Theano Papastavrou *(Acct Dir-Client Ser-
vice)*
George Souglides *(Asst Dir-Media)*
Chrystalla Theodoridou *(Head-
Administration)*
Stella Violari *(Dir-Public Relations)*
Julie Papamichael *(Exec Creative Dir & VP)*
Christina Rotsaka *(Controller-Traffic)*
Myrto Panayiotides *(Art Dir)*
Sophia Kanari *(Art Dir)*
Georgia Georgiadou *(Mgr-Media)*
Adamos Christodoulou *(Art Dir)*
Michael Georgiades *(Asst Mgr-Media)*
Stella Violari *(Dir-Public Relations)*
Julie Papamichael *(Exec Creative Dir & VP)*
Christina Rotsaka *(Controller-Traffic)*
Myrto Panayiotides *(Art Dir)*
Sophia Kanari *(Art Dir)*
Georgia Georgiadou *(Mgr-Media)*
Adamos Christodoulou *(Art Dir)*
Michael Georgiades *(Asst Mgr-Media)*

Subsidiary (Domestic):

Fitzgerald+CO (2)
944 Brady Ave NW, Atlanta, GA 30318
Tel.: (404) 504-6900
Web Site: https://fitzco.com
Rev.: $200,000,000
Emp.: 120
Advetising Agency
N.A.I.C.S.: 541810
David P. Fitzgerald *(Founder & CEO)*
Keri Palmer *(CFO)*
Evan Levy *(Pres)*
Lisa Galanti *(Co-Founder)*
Ryan Boblett *(Head-Creative)*
Stephanie Hanley *(Head-Acct Mgmt)*
James Lou *(Head-Strategy)*
Claire Russell *(Head-Media)*
Jeff Quick *(Head-Growth)*
Hannah Oates Williams *(Creative Dir)*
Brandi Watkins *(Dir-Digital Platforms)*
Michelle Chong *(Dir-Media Plng)*
Natalie Schofield *(Coord-Billing)*
David Brooker *(Dir-IT)*
Katie McAlister *(Sr Project Mgr)*
Becky Michaels *(Mgr-Client Acctg)*
Bryce Burton *(Editor-Content)*
Logan Frost *(Assoc Dir-Media)*
Lisa Ingraham *(Acct Coord)*
Brian Wallace *(Editor)*
Sarah Monte *(Acct Coord)*

FutureBrand (2)
622 3rd Ave 21st Fl, New York, NY 10022
Tel.: (212) 931-6300
Web Site: https://www.futurebrand.com
Advetising Agency
N.A.I.C.S.: 541810

Subsidiary (Non-US):

FutureBrand (3)
135 Bishopsgate, London, EC2M 3AN,
United Kingdom
Tel.: (44) 2070670010
Web Site: http://www.futurebrand.com
Advetising Agency
N.A.I.C.S.: 541810
Nick Sykes *(CEO-Global)*

FutureBrand (3)
40A Orchard Road 07-01 Macdonald
House, Singapore, 238838, Singapore
Tel.: (65) 63913600
Web Site: http://www.futurebrand.com
Sales Range: $10-24.9 Million
Emp.: 37
N.A.I.C.S.: 541810

Branch (Non-US):

FutureBrand (3)
8/F Oxford House Taikoo Place 979 Kings
Rd, Quarry Bay, China (Hong Kong)
Tel.: (852) 68494817
Web Site: http://www.futurebrand.com
Advetising Agency
N.A.I.C.S.: 541810
Richard Curtis *(CEO-Australia)*
Sophie Cheng *(Gen Mgr)*
Jacob Mahoney *(Dir-Design)*

Emma Waterman *(Sr Strategist)*
Victoria Berry *(Head-Strategy)*
Josh McGregor *(Creative Dir)*

Subsidiary (Non-US):

FutureBrand (3)
Level 18 1 Nicholson Street, Melbourne,
3001, VIC, Australia
Tel.: (61) 282314575
Web Site: https://www.futurebrand.com
Advetising Agency
N.A.I.C.S.: 541810
Richard Curtis *(CEO)*

FutureBrand (3)
Enrique Jardiel Poncela 6, 28016, Madrid,
Spain
Tel.: (34) 915679000
Web Site: https://www.futurebrand.es
Advetising Agency
N.A.I.C.S.: 541810

FutureBrand (3)
69 Boulevard du General, Leclerc Levallois
Perret, 92110, Clichy, Cedex, France
Tel.: (33) 155631320
Web Site: http://www.futurebrand.com
Emp.: 30
N.A.I.C.S.: 541810

FutureBrand (3)
Demaria 4659, C1425AEE, Buenos Aires,
Argentina
Tel.: (54) 1147772277
Web Site: https://www.futurebrand.com
Sales Range: $25-49.9 Million
Emp.: 40
N.A.I.C.S.: 541810
Gustavo Koniszczer *(Mng Dir-America)*

FutureBrand (3)
Avenida El Bosque Norte 0123 Oficina 301,
Las Condes, Santiago, Chile
Tel.: (56) 23742350
Web Site: https://www.futurebrand.com
Sales Range: $25-49.9 Million
Emp.: 15
N.A.I.C.S.: 541810

FutureBrand (3)
Rua Natingui 862, Sao Paulo, 05443-001,
Brazil
Tel.: (55) 1138211166
Web Site: https://www.futurebrand.com
Emp.: 120
N.A.I.C.S.: 541810
Helio Mariz de Carvalho *(CEO, Partner &
Mng Dir)*

Branch (Non-US):

FutureBrand (3)
400-207 Queens Quay W, Toronto, M5J
1A7, ON, Canada
Tel.: (416) 408-0838
Web Site: http://www.futurebrand.com
Sales Range: $25-49.9 Million
Emp.: 20
Advertising Agency
N.A.I.C.S.: 541810

Subsidiary (Non-US):

FutureBrand (3)
17/F China Life Tower, 16 Chaoyangmen
Wai Da Jie, Beijing, 100020, China
Tel.: (86) 18511596664
Web Site: https://www.futurebrand.com
N.A.I.C.S.: 541810

FutureBrand (3)
Floor 7 Aurora Tower, PO Box 512062,
Dubai, United Arab Emirates
Tel.: (971) 2070670010
Web Site: https://www.futurebrand.com
Sales Range: $75-99.9 Million
N.A.I.C.S.: 541810

FutureBrand (3)
via Vigevano 18, 20144, Milan, Italy
Tel.: (39) 022909831
Web Site: https://www.futurebrand.com
Sales Range: $25-49.9 Million
Emp.: 2
Advetising Agency
N.A.I.C.S.: 541810
Alessandra Iovinella *(Mng Dir)*

FutureBrand Gio Rossi (3)
via Vigevano 18, 20144, Milan, Italy

The Interpublic Group of Companies,
Inc.—(Continued)

Tel.: (39) 022909831
Web Site: http://www.futurebrand.com
N.A.I.C.S.: 541810

Subsidiary (Non-US):

Hasan & Partners Oy (2)
Roineentie 10, 00150, Helsinki, Finland
Tel.: (358) 4246711
Web Site: https://www.hasanpartners.fi
Emp.: 90
N.A.I.C.S.: 541810
Reino Tikkanen (Dir-Bus)
Joseph Bayne (Dir-Design)
Tobias Wacker (Exec Creative Dir)

Subsidiary (Non-US):

Perfect Fools AB (3)
Torsgatan 2, 111 23, Stockholm,
Sweden (51%)
Tel.: (46) 86788370
Web Site: https://www.perfectfools.com
Sales Range: $1-9.9 Million
Emp.: 35
Marketing Services
N.A.I.C.S.: 541810
Tony Hogqvist (Co-Founder)
Mattias Mattisson (Dir-Design)
Tony Sajdak (Co-Founder & CTO)
Petter Esbjornsson (Copywriter)
Maria Lundvall (Head-Accounts)
Karl Nord (Art Dir)
Daniel Berg (Copywriter)

Subsidiary (Non-US):

Linea 12/McCann Erickson (2)
16 Shota Rustaveli vul 9th Floor, Kiev,
03150, Ukraine
Tel.: (380) 44 205 4266
Web Site: http://www.bruciecollections.com
Sales Range: $25-49.9 Million
Emp.: 80
N.A.I.C.S.: 541810
Vadim Yatsenko (Chm & Mng Dir)

MCL McCann (2)
7 Lourdel Road Nakasero, PO Box 213,
Kampala, Uganda
Tel.: (256) 41 231212
Web Site: http://www.mccann.com
N.A.I.C.S.: 541810

Subsidiary (Domestic):

MRM//McCann (2)
622 3rd Ave, New York, NY 10017
Tel.: (646) 865-6230
Web Site: http://www.mrm-mccann.com
Rev.: $1,800,000,000
Emp.: 2,000
Advertising Services
N.A.I.C.S.: 541810
Marcy Q. Samet (CMO)
Andy Queen (CFO-Global)
Jeff Cruz (Chief Creative Officer-Detroit)
Tamy Harms (Pres-Detroit)
Ariana Stolarz (Chief Strategy Officer)
Nick Handel (Mng Dir-Asia Pacific)
Kazz Ishihara (Exec Creative Dir-Tokyo)
Caspar Ouvaroff (Pres-Japan)
Mary Anne Powers (Sr VP-Project Mgmt)
Linda Sorbera (Chief Talent Officer-Global)
Kate MacNevin (Chm, CEO & Global)
Bradley Rogers (COO-Global)
Nicole Dowswell (VP-Communications-Global)
Jayna Kothary (CTO-Global)
Chris Alberta (Sr VP & Dir-Data & Analytics)
Maggie Connors (Chief Growth Officer)
Peter Rooney (Mng Dir)
Jocelyn Weiss (Dir)
Maggie Connors (Chief Growth Officer)
Peter Rooney (Mng Dir)
Jocelyn Weiss (Dir)

Branch (Non-US):

Dittborn & Unzueta MRM (3)
Avenid Isidora Goyenechea 3477 Piso 8,
Las Condes, Santiago, Chile
Tel.: (56) 2 338 9500
Web Site: http://www.mrmworldwide.com
Emp.: 40
Advertising Services
N.A.I.C.S.: 541860

Fortune Promoseven Dubai (3)
Sheikh Zayed Road emaar Atrium Building
Block B 4th Floor, PO Box 6834, Dubai,
United Arab Emirates
Tel.: (971) 4 321 0007
Web Site: http://www.promoseven.com
Advertising Services
N.A.I.C.S.: 541810

Subsidiary (Non-US):

MRM Brazil (3)
Pereira Leite 55, Sao Paulo, 05442-000,
Brazil
Tel.: (55) 1130323339
Web Site: https://www.mrm-brasil.com
Emp.: 50
Advertising Services
N.A.I.C.S.: 541860

MRM China (3)
11/F Huaihai Plaza 1045 Huaihai Zhon
Road, Shanghai, 100031, China
Tel.: (86) 2124111110
Advertising Services
N.A.I.C.S.: 541810

Branch (Domestic):

MRM Gillespie (3)
3450 Princeton Pike, Lawrenceville, NJ
08648
Tel.: (609) 895-8230
Web Site: http://www.mrmworldwide.com
Emp.: 175
Advertising Services
N.A.I.C.S.: 541810

Subsidiary (Non-US):

MRM London (3)
14 Buckingham Street, London, WC2N
6DF, United Kingdom
Tel.: (44) 2033269900
Web Site: https://www.mrm-london.com
Emp.: 275
Advertising Services
N.A.I.C.S.: 541860
Nicky Bullard (Chm & Chief Creative Officer)

Branch (Non-US):

MRM Manchester (3)
Bonis Hall Bonis Hall Lane, Prestbury,
Cheshire, SK10 4EF, United Kingdom
Tel.: (44) 1625 822 200
Web Site:
http://www.mecommmanchester.com
Emp.: 270
Advertising Services
N.A.I.C.S.: 541810

Subsidiary (Non-US):

MRM Mexico (3)
Palo Santo 22, Col Lomas Altas Miguel Hidalgo, 11950, Mexico, Mexico
Tel.: (52) 5552585900
Web Site: http://www.mrmworldwide.com
Emp.: 45
Advertising Services
N.A.I.C.S.: 541860

Branch (Non-US):

MRM Munich (3)
Seidlstrasse 26, Munich, 80335, Germany
Tel.: (49) 89 54302 00
Advertising Services
N.A.I.C.S.: 541810

MRM Paris (3)
62 Rue d alsace, 92583, Clichy, France
Tel.: (33) 147594201
Web Site: http://www.mrmworldwide.fr
Emp.: 200
Advertising Services
N.A.I.C.S.: 541810

Subsidiary (Non-US):

MRM Partners Dialogo (3)
Via Giovanni Spadolini n 7 Centro Leoni
Building B, 20141, Milan, Italy
Tel.: (39) 0285291
Web Site: http://www.mrmworldwide.com
Emp.: 28
Advertising Services
N.A.I.C.S.: 541860

MRM Philippines (3)
Unit C 2nd Floor 1963 Taft Avenue, Malate,
Manila, 1004, Metro Manila, Philippines
Tel.: (63) 284050011
Web Site: https://www.mrm.net
Emp.: 12
Advertising Services
N.A.I.C.S.: 541810

MRM Spain (3)
Carrer de Ciutat de Granada 123, 08018,
Barcelona, Spain
Tel.: (34) 932525500
Emp.: 20
Advertising Services
N.A.I.C.S.: 541810
Marina Specht (Reg Dir-EMEA MRM Worldwide)

MRM Thailand (3)
98 Sathorn Square Office Tower 25th-26th
Floor, North Sathorn Road Silom Bangrak,
Bangkok, 10500, Thailand
Tel.: (66) 23436000
Web Site: http://mrm-mccann.com
Advertising Services
N.A.I.C.S.: 541810

Branch (Non-US):

MRM Turkey (3)
Buyukdere Caddesi Ecza Sokak No 6, Levent, Istanbul, 34330, Turkiye
Tel.: (90) 212 317 5660
Web Site: http://www.mrmworldwide.com
Emp.: 14
Advertising Services
N.A.I.C.S.: 541810

Subsidiary (Non-US):

MRM Worldwide (3)
Enrique Jardiel Poncela 6, 28016, Madrid,
Spain
Tel.: (34) 914360138
Web Site: http://www.mrmworldwide.com
Emp.: 50
Advertising Services
N.A.I.C.S.: 541860
Marina Specht (CEO)

MRM Worldwide (3)
Shin Aoyama Bldg E 21F 1-1-1 Minami-Aoyama, Minato-ku, Tokyo, 107-0062, Japan
Tel.: (81) 337468900
Web Site: https://www.mrmjapan.co.jp
Emp.: 40
Advertising Services
N.A.I.C.S.: 541810
Caspar Ouvaroff (Pres)
Rie Otsuka (Dir)
Kazz Ishihara (Exec Creative Dir)
Ryan Mizuno (Dir)
Joto Hori (Dir-Planning)
Kuniko Isoda (Dir)

Branch (Non-US):

MRM Worldwide (3)
166 William Street, Woolloomooloo, Sydney, 2011, NSW, Australia
Tel.: (61) 2 9994 4000
Emp.: 25
Advertising Services
N.A.I.C.S.: 541810

Subsidiary (Non-US):

MRM Worldwide (3)
F-Block Voltas House TB Kadam Marg,
Chinchpokli, Mumbai, 400 033, India
Tel.: (91) 9920816696
Web Site: http://www.mrmworldwide.com
Emp.: 22
Advertising Services
N.A.I.C.S.: 541860

Subsidiary (Domestic):

MRM Worldwide (3)
600 Battery St, San Francisco, CA 94111
Tel.: (415) 262-5600
Web Site: http://www.mrmworldwide.com
Emp.: 300
Advertising Services
N.A.I.C.S.: 541810

MRM Worldwide (3)
360 W Maple Rd, Birmingham, MI 48009
Tel.: (248) 203-8000

Web Site: http://www.mrmworldwide.com
Emp.: 15
Advertising Services
N.A.I.C.S.: 541810
Fred Seidelman (CTO)
Jeff Cruz (Chief Creative Officer)
Subu Desaraju (Dir & Exec VP)
Nolan Grumley (CFO)
Jennifer Kohler (Sr VP)
Mark Rebhan (Dir-Strategy & Exec VP)

Branch (Non-US):

MRM Worldwide (3)
KulturBrauerei Haus P, Schonhauser Allee
37, Berlin, 60313, Germany
Tel.: (49) 30 44030 0 0
Web Site: http://www.mrmworldwide.com
Emp.: 10
Advertising Services
N.A.I.C.S.: 541810

Subsidiary (Non-US):

MRM Worldwide Brazil (3)
Rua Visc de Ouro Preto 05 - 12th floor
Botafogo, Rio de Janeiro, 22250-180, Brazil
Tel.: (55) 2121062500
Web Site: http://www.mrmworldwide.com
Emp.: 25
Advertising Services
N.A.I.C.S.: 541810

MRM Worldwide Hong Kong (3)
15/F One Taikoo Place 979 Kings Road,
Quarry Bay, China (Hong Kong)
Tel.: (852) 28087226
Web Site: https://www.mrm.com
Emp.: 40
Advertising Services
N.A.I.C.S.: 541860

MRM Worldwide India (3)
8 Balaji Estate Guru Ravi Dass Marg, Kalkaji, New Delhi, 110019, India
Tel.: (91) 1126002600
Web Site: http://www.mrmworldwide.com
Emp.: 50
Advertising Services
N.A.I.C.S.: 541860

Subsidiary (Domestic):

MRM Worldwide New York (3)
622 3rd Ave, New York, NY 10017
Tel.: (646) 865-6230
Web Site: http://www.mrmworldwide.com
Emp.: 180
Advertising Services
N.A.I.C.S.: 541810

Branch (Non-US):

MRM Worldwide Paraguay (3)
Alejo Garcia 2589 c/ Rio de la Plata, Asuncion, Paraguay
Tel.: (595) 21 42 4735
Web Site: http://www.mrmworldwide.com
Emp.: 15
Advertising Services
N.A.I.C.S.: 541860

Subsidiary (Non-US):

MRM Worldwide Singapore (3)
40A Orchard Street 09-01 The MacDonald
House, Singapore, 238838, Singapore
Tel.: (65) 67379911
Web Site: http://www.mrmworldwide.com
Advertising Services
N.A.I.C.S.: 541810
Dante Abelarde (Exec Creative Dir)

MRM Worldwide Spain (3)
Enrique Jardiel Poncela 6, 7 Dcha, 28016,
Madrid, Spain
Tel.: (34) 914360138
Web Site: http://www.mrmworldwide.com
Emp.: 60
Advertising Services
N.A.I.C.S.: 541860
Marina Specht (CEO)
Maria Martinez (Gen Mgr)
Miguel Bemfica (Chief Creative Officer)
Elizabeth Localio (Dir-Client Service)
Francisco Gutierrez Villaverde (CTO)
Eladio Portela (Head)
Alex Bartumeus Roses (Mng Dir)

Branch (Non-US):

MRM//McCann China (3)

25th Floor Huaihai International Plaza 1045, Huaihai Road, Shanghai, 200031, China
Tel.: (86) 2124111121
Web Site: http://www.mrm-mccann.com
Advertising Services
N.A.I.C.S.: 541810

Subsidiary (Domestic):

Optaros, Inc. (3)
622 3rd Ave, New York, NY 10017
Tel.: (646) 865-6230
Web Site: http://www.optaros.com
Emp.: 170
Digital e-Commerce Services
N.A.I.C.S.: 513210

Subsidiary (Non-US):

Mayer-McCann (2)
Dunajska cesta 163, 1000, Ljubljana, Slovenia
Tel.: (386) 15636550
Web Site: http://www.mayermccann.com
Sales Range: $25-49.9 Million
Emp.: 23
N.A.I.C.S.: 541810
Marko Majer (Founder)

Mayer/McCann-Erickson s.r.o. (2)
Dubravska cesta 2, 841 05, Bratislava, Slovakia
Tel.: (421) 267267101
Web Site: https://www.mayer.sk
Sales Range: $25-49.9 Million
Emp.: 50
N.A.I.C.S.: 541810

McCann AS (2)
Bryggegata 9, 0250, Oslo, Norway
Tel.: (47) 22543600
Web Site: http://www.mccann.no
Advetising Agency
N.A.I.C.S.: 541810

McCann Erickson (2)
2A Raul Valenberg St, Tel Aviv, 69719, Israel
Tel.: (972) 3 768 6868
Web Site: http://www.mccann.co.il
Advetising Agency
N.A.I.C.S.: 541810
Ilan Shiloh (Chm & CEO)

McCann Erickson (2)
Heinzelova 33A, 10000, Zagreb, Croatia
Tel.: (385) 15555102
Web Site: https://www.mccann.hr
Emp.: 40
N.A.I.C.S.: 541810

McCann Erickson (Jamaica) Ltd. (2)
Seven Barbados Avenue St Andrew, PO Box 168, Kingston, 5, Jamaica
Tel.: (876) 9261410
Web Site: http://www.mccann.com
Sales Range: $25-49.9 Million
Emp.: 26
N.A.I.C.S.: 541810

McCann Erickson (Singapore) Private Limited (2)
40A Orchard Road 06-00 the MacDonald House, Singapore, 238838, Singapore
Tel.: (65) 67379911
Web Site: http://www.mccann.com
Emp.: 100
Full Service
N.A.I.C.S.: 541810

McCann Erickson Azerbaijan (2)
42 Zahid Khalilov Street, AZ1073, Baku, Azerbaijan
Tel.: (994) 124923535
Web Site: http://www.mccann.com
Advertising Campaigns
N.A.I.C.S.: 541810

McCann Erickson Budapest (2)
Central udvar Wesselenyi utca 16, 1077, Budapest, Hungary
Tel.: (36) 18878100
Web Site: http://www.mccann.hu
Rev.: $69,103,242
Emp.: 80
N.A.I.C.S.: 541810
Andras Kubicsko (Mng Dir)

McCann Erickson Cameroon (2)
39 Rue Kitchener Place de la Chamber de Commerce, Douala, 12516, Cameroon

Tel.: (237) 33439188
Web Site: http://www.mccann.com
Sales Range: $25-49.9 Million
Emp.: 20
N.A.I.C.S.: 541810
Annie Barla (Mng Dir)

McCann Erickson Central (2)
Mccann Erickso Communications House Highlands Road Shirley, Solihull, B90 4WE, West Midlands, United Kingdom
Tel.: (44) 1217133500
Web Site:
    http://www.mccannbirmingham.co.uk
Sales Range: $50-74.9 Million
Emp.: 300
Advertising Agencies
N.A.I.C.S.: 541810
Jonathan Jesson (Chief Growth Officer)

McCann Erickson Corp. Publicidad S.A. (2)
Av Miguel H Alcivar 0 Y Nahim Isaias Sl 29 Kennedy Norte, Frente a las Torres del Norte, Guayaquil, Ecuador
Tel.: (593) 42681245
Web Site: http://www.mccann.com
Sales Range: $25-49.9 Million
Emp.: 30
N.A.I.C.S.: 541810

McCann Erickson Deutschland GmbH (2)
Zweigniederlassung Berlin Schonhauser Allee 37, 10435, Berlin, Germany
Tel.: (49) 304403000
Web Site: http://www.mccann.de
Sales Range: $10-24.9 Million
Emp.: 10
Advetising Agency
N.A.I.C.S.: 541810

McCann Erickson Georgia (2)
71 VazhaPshavela Ave 4th floor BCV office 26, 186, Tbilisi, Georgia
Tel.: (995) 322207355
Web Site: https://www.mccann.com.ge
Advetising Agency
N.A.I.C.S.: 541810
Armen Gasparyan (Mng Dir)

McCann Erickson Group (2)
Terazije 7-9, 11000, Belgrade, Serbia
Tel.: (381) 112029100
Web Site: http://www.mccann.rs
N.A.I.C.S.: 541810

McCann Erickson Guangming Ltd. (2)
21/F Huaihai Plaza, 1045 Huaihai Zhong Rd, Shanghai, 200031, China
Tel.: (86) 21 2411 1488
N.A.I.C.S.: 541810

McCann Erickson Guangming Ltd. (2)
33/F Telecom Plaza 18 Zhong Shan Er Road, Beijing Road, Guangzhou, 510115, China
Tel.: (86) 2088888438
Web Site:
    http://www.mccannworldgroup.com
Advertising & Public Relations Agency
N.A.I.C.S.: 541810

McCann Erickson India (2)
Valencia 5th- 6th Flr Rajkamal Marg Off Dr S S Rao Road, Parel East, Mumbai, 400012, India
Tel.: (91) 22 241 76600
Web Site: http://www.mccann.com
N.A.I.C.S.: 541810

McCann Erickson India (2)
Landmark Plaza 299 Langford Road, Richmond Town, Bengaluru, 560 025, Karnataka, India
Tel.: (91) 8022990543
Web Site: http://www.mccann.com
N.A.I.C.S.: 541810

McCann Erickson India (2)
Old No 10 New No 64 Sriman Srinivasa Cross Street Alwarpet, Chennai, 600018, India
Tel.: (91) 4424323481
Web Site: http://www.mccann.com
Sales Range: $25-49.9 Million
Emp.: 25
N.A.I.C.S.: 541810

McCann Erickson Kazakhstan (2)
Zhumaliev St 157, Almaty, Kazakhstan
Tel.: (7) 272590725
Web Site: http://www.mccann.com
Sales Range: $25-49.9 Million
Emp.: 21
N.A.I.C.S.: 541810

McCann Erickson Macedonia (2)
Pirinska 23, 1000, Skopje, MKD, North Macedonia
Tel.: (389) 9203253525
Web Site: http://mccann.com.mk
N.A.I.C.S.: 541810

McCann Erickson Mexico (2)
Palo Santo No 22, Colonia Lomas Altas, 11950, Mexico, Mexico
Tel.: (52) 5552585900
Web Site: http://www.mccann.com
Rev.: $2,000,000
Emp.: 230
Full Service
N.A.I.C.S.: 541810

McCann Erickson Prague (2)
Riegrovy Sady 28, 120 00, Prague, Czech Republic
Tel.: (420) 222009101
Web Site: https://www.mccann.cz
Sales Range: $10-24.9 Million
Emp.: 60
N.A.I.C.S.: 541810
Jan Binar (CEO)
Jitka Kucharova (CFO)
Martina Hejdova (COO)
Razvan Capanescu (Chief Creative Officer)
Jan Suda (Dir-Media)
Peter Hermann (Dir-PR & Social)
Leonard Savage (Chief Creative Officer)

McCann Erickson Publicidad (2)
Calle Los Chaguaramos, Edificio Centro Denu Piso 2 La Castellana, Caracas, Venezuela
Tel.: (58) 2122633660
Web Site: http://www.mccann.com
Rev.: $37,454,000
Emp.: 55
Communications
N.A.I.C.S.: 541810

McCann Erickson Riga (2)
30 Terbatas Str, Riga, 1011, Latvia
Tel.: (371) 67503314
Web Site: http://www.mccann.lv
Sales Range: $25-49.9 Million
Emp.: 12
N.A.I.C.S.: 541810

McCann Erickson Romania (2)
18 Jules Michelet Street, 010463, Bucharest, Romania
Tel.: (40) 212323727
Web Site: http://www.mccann.ro
Advertising Services
N.A.I.C.S.: 541810

McCann Erickson Sarajevo (2)
Gabrielle Moreno Locatelli 21, Sarajevo, Bosnia & Herzegovina
Tel.: (387) 33267111
Web Site: http://www.mccann.ba
Sales Range: $25-49.9 Million
Emp.: 24
N.A.I.C.S.: 541810
Enisa Haznadarevic (Dir-Acct)
Adela Icindic (Acct Mgr)
Amra Jusovic Alihodzic (Mgr-Acct & PR)
Enisa Mandra (Mgr-Digital)
Albina Sisic (Coord)
Alis Brkic (Dir)
Alis Brkic (Dir)

McCann Erickson Sofia (2)
15 Targovska Str Kurilo Distr, 1280, Novi Iskar, Bulgaria
Tel.: (359) 29818995
Emp.: 25
N.A.I.C.S.: 541810
Ivan Kirov (Dir-Creative)

McCann Erickson Uzbekistan/Tashkent (2)
16/2 Street Glinka Mirabad Area Tashkent Region, Tashkent, 100170, Uzbekistan
Tel.: (998) 901879490
N.A.I.C.S.: 541810

McCann Erickson Vietnam (2)
429 Vo Van Tan St Ward 5 Dist 3, Ho Chi

Minh City, Vietnam
Tel.: (84) 88321848
Web Site:
    http://www.mccannworldgroup.com
Advertising Agencies
N.A.I.C.S.: 541810

McCann Erickson Worldgroup/Panama, S.A. (2)
Plaza Banco General Calle 50 y Aquilino de la Guardia piso 19, Panama, Panama
Tel.: (507) 3667000
Web Site: http://www.mccann.com
Sales Range: $25-49.9 Million
Emp.: 30
N.A.I.C.S.: 541810

Subsidiary (Domestic):

McCann Erickson Worldwide (2)
622 3rd Ave, New York, NY 10017
Tel.: (646) 865-2000
Web Site: https://www.mccann.com
Rev.: $107,000,000
Emp.: 10,300
Advertising Services
N.A.I.C.S.: 541810
Hank Summy (Pres-North America)

Branch (Non-US):

Biedermann Publicidad S.A. (3)
Alejo Garcia c/ Rio de la Plata, 2589, Asuncion, Paraguay
Tel.: (595) 21424280
Web Site: http://www.biedermann.com.py
Rev.: $12,000,000
Emp.: 65
Advertising Services
N.A.I.C.S.: 541810

Fortune Promoseven-HQ (3)
Emarat Atrium Bldg 4th Fl Wing B Sheikh Zayed Rd, Dubai, United Arab Emirates
Tel.: (971) 43210007
Web Site: http://www.promoseven.com
Emp.: 300
Advertising Services
N.A.I.C.S.: 541810

Subsidiary (Non-US):

Eshareh Advertising Agency (4)
No 2 21st Alley North Sheikh Bahaei St, Seoul Ave, 19957 75353, Tehran, Iran
Tel.: (98) 2188044244
Web Site: https://www.eshareh.com
Emp.: 60
Advertising Services
N.A.I.C.S.: 541810

Branch (Domestic):

FP7 Abu Dhabi (4)
2454 Khalifa Park Complex Pink Building No 2 Floor 2, PO Box 2454, Abu Dhabi, United Arab Emirates
Tel.: (971) 2 401 2454
Web Site: http://www.fp7.com
Advertising Services
N.A.I.C.S.: 541810
Jon Marchant (Mng Dir-Dubai)
Tarek Miknas (CEO)
Binit Shah (CFO-Reg)
Fouad Malak (Exec Creative Dir-Reg)
Olly Robinson (Exec Creative Dir-Reg)
Emad Saeed (Fin Dir-Reg)
Anis Zantout (Reg Dir-Digital)
Tahaab Rais (Head-Strategy)

Subsidiary (Non-US):

FP7 McCann Algeria (4)
31 rue Mohamed el Khoudi El Biar Alger, 16000, Algiers, Algeria
Tel.: (213) 21792242
Web Site: http://www.fp7.com
Emp.: 36
Advertising Services
N.A.I.C.S.: 541810

Branch (Non-US):

FP7 McCann-Tunisia (4)
Immeuble Astree Rue du Lac D Annecy - Le Berges Du Lac, Mutllville, 1053, Tunis, Tunisia
Tel.: (216) 97144454777
Web Site: http://www.promoseven.com

The Interpublic Group of Companies,
Inc.—(Continued)

Emp.: 25
Advertising Services
N.A.I.C.S.: 541810

Fortune Promoseven (4)
Promoseven Building 1st Floor Office 11
Building 1130 M Road 1531, PO Box 5989,
Manama, Bahrain
Tel.: (973) 17500777
Advertising Services
N.A.I.C.S.: 541810
Tarek Miknas (CEO)

Fortune Promoseven-Lebanon (4)
Ashrafieh 784 Bldg Sodeco, PO Box 116-
5288, Beirut, Lebanon
Tel.: (961) 1428428
Web Site: http://www.promoseven.com
Emp.: 70
Advertising Services
N.A.I.C.S.: 541810

Fortune Promoseven-Qatar (4)
Barwa Al Sadd Tower 1 9th Floor Suhaim
Bin Hamad Street, PO Box 13645, Doha,
Qatar
Tel.: (974) 40421777
Web Site: http://www.promoseven.com
Emp.: 30
Advertising Services
N.A.I.C.S.: 541810

HAMS (4)
PO Box 19038, Sana'a, Yemen
Tel.: (967) 1 421 642
Advertising Services
N.A.I.C.S.: 541810

Promoseven-Morocco (4)
444 Rue Mustapha El Maani 1Er Etage,
Casablanca, 20140, Morocco
Tel.: (212) 522775200
Web Site: http://www.promoseven.com
Public Relations
N.A.I.C.S.: 541810

Branch (Non-US):

**M2 Universal Communications
Management** (3)
10 Bay St 1000, Toronto, M5J 2S3, ON,
Canada
Tel.: (416) 594-6200
Web Site: http://www.maclaren.com
Advertising Services
N.A.I.C.S.: 541810

Subsidiary (Non-US):

McCann Erickson (3)
Juan Bautista Alberdi 431 Piso 11 Ollvos
Provincia, B1865XAA, Buenos Aires, Argen-
tina
Tel.: (54) 1155500500
Web Site: http://www.mccann.com
Advertising Services
N.A.I.C.S.: 541810

McCann Erickson (Kenya) Ltd. (3)
Royal Offices 4th Floor Mogotio Road Park-
lands, Nairobi, Kenya
Tel.: (254) 203743248
Advertising Services
N.A.I.C.S.: 541810

Branch (Non-US):

**McCann Erickson (Malaysia) Sdn.
Bhd.** (3)
5-01 & 5-02 Wisma Lyl No 12 Jalan
51a/223 Petaling Jaya, Selangor Darul Eh-
san, 46100, Kuala Lumpur, Malaysia
Tel.: (60) 378412898
Web Site: http://www.mccann.com
Sales Range: $25-49.9 Million
Emp.: 140
Advertising Services
N.A.I.C.S.: 541810

**McCann Erickson (Nederland)
B.V.** (3)
Wibautstraat 224, 1097 DN, Amsterdam,
Netherlands
Tel.: (31) 205731111
Web Site: https://www.fcb-amsterdam.nl
Advertising Services
N.A.I.C.S.: 541810

Subsidiary (Non-US):

**McCann Erickson (Peru) Publicidad
S.A.** (3)
Calle Tripoli 102 Miraflores, 18, Lima, Peru
Tel.: (51) 16108100
Web Site:
http://www.mccannworldgroup.com
Rev.: $400,000
Emp.: 80
Advertising Services
N.A.I.C.S.: 541810

McCann Erickson (Trinidad) Ltd. (3)
8 Rapsey Street St Clair, Port of Spain,
Trinidad & Tobago
Tel.: (868) 6289109
Web Site:
http://www.mccannportofspain.com
Rev.: $2,000,000
Emp.: 75
Advertising Services
N.A.I.C.S.: 541810

Branch (Non-US):

McCann Erickson / SP (3)
Rua Loefgreen 2527, Vila Clementino,
04040-033, Sao Paulo, Vila Clementino,
Brazil
Tel.: (55) 1137753000
Web Site: http://www.wmccann.com
Emp.: 245
Advertising Services
N.A.I.C.S.: 541810

Subsidiary (Domestic):

**McCann Erickson Publicidade
Ltda.** (4)
Rua Visconde de Ouro Preto 05 - 12th floor
Botafogo, Rio de Janeiro, 22250-180, Brazil
Tel.: (55) 1137753023
Web Site: http://www.mocann.com.br
Advertising Services
N.A.I.C.S.: 541810

Branch (Domestic):

Paim Comunicacao (4)
Av Maryland 477, 90440-191, Porto Alegre,
Brazil
Tel.: (55) 51 2102 2577
Web Site: http://www.paim.com.br
Advertising Services
N.A.I.C.S.: 541810

Subsidiary (Non-US):

**McCann Erickson Advertising
Ltd.** (3)
135 Bishopsgate, London, EC2M 3TP,
United Kingdom
Tel.: (44) 2078373737
Web Site: http://www.mccannlondon.com
Advertising Services
N.A.I.C.S.: 541810
Rob Doubal (Co-Pres & Co-Chief Creative
Officer)
Laurence Thomson (Co-Pres & Co-Chief
Creative Officer)
Sergio Lopez (Chief Prod Officer)
Karen Crum (Dir-Global Brand Strategy)
Jason McNamee (Mktg Dir)
Elizabeth Bernstein (Head-New Business)
Polly McMorrow (CEO)
Mark Young (CFO)
Cat Shingler (Dir)
Mark Young (CFO)
Cat Shingler (Dir)

Subsidiary (Domestic):

McCann Erickson Bristol (4)
5th Floor Tower Wharf Cheese Lane, Bris-
tol, BS2 0JJ, United Kingdom
Tel.: (44) 1179211764
Web Site: https://www.mccannbristol.co.uk
Advertising Services
N.A.I.C.S.: 541810
Claire Banks (Mng Partner-Development)
Andy Reid (Mng Dir)
Sue Hendry (Mng Partner-Media)
Jon Elsom (Dir-Creative)
Pat Southwell (Mng Partner-Public Rela-
tions)
Zane Radcliffe (Exec Creative Dir)
Laura Lear (Mng Partner-Public Relations)
Zane Radcliffe (Exec Creative Dir)
Laura Lear (Mng Partner-Public Relations)

McCann Manchester Ltd. (4)
Bonis Hall Lane, Prestbury, SK10 4EF,
Cheshire, United Kingdom
Tel.: (44) 1625822200
Web Site:
http://www.mccannmanchester.com
Advertising Services
N.A.I.C.S.: 541810
Richard Aldiss (Mng Dir)

Mediabrands EMEA Ltd. (4)
16 Old Bailey, London, EC4M 7EG, United
Kingdom
Tel.: (44) 20707373
Web Site: https://emea.ipgmediabrands.com
Advertising Services
N.A.I.C.S.: 541810
Christian Johansen (CEO)

Branch (Non-US):

**McCann Erickson Advertising Pty.
Ltd.** (3)
Royal Naval House 32 Grosvenor St, Syd-
ney, 2000, NSW, Australia
Tel.: (61) 299944000
Web Site: http://mccann.com.au
Advertising Services
N.A.I.C.S.: 541810
Zain Hoosen (CFO)
Robert Stone (Chief Talent Officer)
Ben Lilley (Chm)
Lauren Jennings (Head)
Tim Evans (Mng Dir)
Cinnamon Darvall (Head)
Ben Lilley (Chm)
Lauren Jennings (Head)
Tim Evans (Mng Dir)
Cinnamon Darvall (Head)

Branch (Domestic):

**McCann Erickson Advertising Pty.
Ltd. - Brisbane** (4)
Level 3 Unit 3001 200 Creek Street, Bris-
bane, 4000, QLD, Australia
Tel.: (61) 755121050
Web Site: http://mccann.com.au
Advertising Services
N.A.I.C.S.: 541810
Carla Steadman (Gen Mgr)
Jeremy Bews (Mng Partner)

**McCann Erickson Advertising Pty.
Ltd. - Melbourne** (4)
Level 7 574 Saint Kilda, South, Melbourne,
3000, VIC, Australia
Tel.: (61) 399939333
Web Site: http://www.mccann.com.au
Advertising Services
N.A.I.C.S.: 541810
Simon McCrudden (Chief Strategy Officer)

Subsidiary (Non-US):

McCann Erickson Athens (3)
2 H2 Ydras Street & 280 Kifissias Ave, Ha-
landri, 15232, Athens, Greece
Tel.: (30) 2108171100
Web Site: http://www.mccann.gr
Rev.: $55,000,000
Emp.: 23,000
Advertising Services
N.A.I.C.S.: 541810
George Tridimas (Dir-Client Svc)
Harry Parianos (CFO)
Aleka Papadia (Exec Creative Dir)
Theokritos Chatziris (CFO)
Effie Issaakidou (Mng Dir)
Veni Kleonakou (Gen Mgr)
Katerina Yiannouli (Gen Mgr)
Harry Parianos (CEO)
Aleka Papadia (Exec Creative Dir)
Theokritos Chatziris (CFO)
Effie Issaakidou (Mng Dir)
Veni Kleonakou (Gen Mgr)
Katerina Yiannouli (Gen Mgr)

**McCann Erickson Centroamericana
(Costa Rica) S.A.** (3)
Edificio Torre Del Este-2do, piso frente a
Facultad de Derecho de la UCR, 4505-
1000, San Jose, Costa Rica
Tel.: (506) 22027300
Web Site: https://www.mccann.com
Rev.: $16,000,000
Emp.: 80
Advertising Services
N.A.I.C.S.: 541810

**McCann Erickson Centroamericana
(Honduras) S. de R.L.** (3)
3er Piso Torre Santa Monica Boulevard del
Norte hacia Puerto Cortes, San Pedro Sula,
1161, Honduras
Tel.: (504) 25535300
Web Site: http://www.mccann.com
Rev.: $8,600,000
Emp.: 45
Advertising Services
N.A.I.C.S.: 541810

Branch (Non-US):

**McCann Erickson Communications
Group** (3)
11th Fl No 2 Lane 150 Section 5 Hsin Yi
Rd, Taipei, 110, Taiwan
Tel.: (886) 227585000
Web Site: http://www.mccann.com
Sales Range: $10-24.9 Million
Emp.: 100
Advertising Services
N.A.I.C.S.: 541810

Subsidiary (Non-US):

**McCann Erickson Corp. Publicidad
S.A.** (3)
Finlandia N36 41 y Suecia, Quito, Ecuador
Tel.: (593) 23966800
Web Site: http://www.mccann.com
Advertising Services
N.A.I.C.S.: 541810

McCann Erickson Corp. S.A. (3)
Calle 96 13A-33 Cundinamarca, Bogota,
Colombia
Tel.: (57) 16464141
Web Site: http://www.mccann.com
Emp.: 185
Advertising Services
N.A.I.C.S.: 541810

Branch (Non-US):

McCann Erickson Deutschland (3)
Grosser Hasenpfad 44, D-60598, Frankfurt
am Main, Germany
Tel.: (49) 69605070
Web Site: http://www.mccann.de
Advertising Services
N.A.I.C.S.: 541810

Branch (Domestic):

**McCann Erickson Brand Communica-
tions Agency** (4)
Grosser Hasenpad 44, 60598, Frankfurt am
Main, Germany
Tel.: (49) 69 60 50 70
Web Site: http://www.mccann.de
Advertising Service
N.A.I.C.S.: 541810

**McCann Erickson Communications
House M.E.C.H.** (4)
Schonhauser Allee 37, Kulturbrauerei,
10435, Berlin, Germany
Tel.: (49) 304403000
Web Site: http://www.mccann.de
Emp.: 10
Advertising Services
N.A.I.C.S.: 541810

Subsidiary (Domestic):

McCann Healthcare (4)
Grosser Hasenpfad 44, 60598, Frankfurt
am Main, Germany
Tel.: (49) 61133399330
Advertising Services
N.A.I.C.S.: 541810
Jorg Kuhler (Mng Dir)
Simon Holt (Pres-Consulting)
John Cahill (CEO-Global)
Kieran Delaney (Exec Dir-creative)
Adrian Parr (Exec Dir-EMEA)
Jamie Avallone (Mng Dir-Consulting-New
York)
Mark Archer (Mng Dir-Consulting-London)
Marcus Sigurdsson (Chief Digital Officer-
Global)
Connie Lo (Pres-Greater China)
Sam Wong (Gen Mgr-Hong Kong)
Effie Baouis (Pres-West Europe)
John Reid (Chief Creative Officer/Exec VP-
New Jersey)
Marcia Goddard (Pres-New Jersey)

Branch (Domestic):

McEmotion (4)
Neuer Wall 43/II, D-20354, Hamburg, Germany
Tel.: (49) 40 36 00 90
Emp.: 40
Advertising Services
N.A.I.C.S.: 541810

Subsidiary (Domestic):

Universal McCann GmbH (4)
Torhaus Westhafen Speicherstrasse 57 - 59, 60327, Frankfurt, Germany
Tel.: (49) 69794040
Web Site: http://www.universalmccann.de
Emp.: 100
Advertising Services
N.A.I.C.S.: 541810

Branch (Non-US):

McCann Erickson Dublin (3)
Hambleden House 19-26 Lower Pembroke Street, Dublin, 2, Ireland
Tel.: (353) 16766366
Emp.: 50
Advertising Services
N.A.I.C.S.: 541810

McCann Erickson El Salvador (3)
87 Ave Norte y Calle El Mirador - EdifTorre Futura Nivel 15 Local 3, Colonia Escalon, San Salvador, El Salvador
Tel.: (503) 2090909
Web Site: http://oyrmccann.com
Advertising Services
N.A.I.C.S.: 541810

Subsidiary (Non-US):

McCann Erickson Gesellschaft m.b.H. (3)
Mariahilfer Str 17, PO Box 57, 1060, Vienna, Austria
Tel.: (43) 136055
Web Site: https://www.mccann.at
Rev.: $46,500,000
Emp.: 10
N.A.I.C.S.: 541810
Christof Sigel (Mng Dir)

McCann Erickson Hong Kong Ltd. (3)
31/f Hysan Place 500 Hennessy Road, Causeway Bay, China (Hong Kong)
Tel.: (852) 28087888
Web Site: http://www.mccann.com
Rev.: $90,000,000
Emp.: 136
Advertising Services
N.A.I.C.S.: 541810

Branch (Non-US):

McCann Erickson Italiana S.p.A. (3)
Via Valtellena 17, 20159, Milan, Italy
Tel.: (39) 0285291
Web Site: http://www.mccann.com
Emp.: 350
Advertising Services
N.A.I.C.S.: 541810

Branch (Domestic):

McCann Erickson Italiana S.p.A. (4)
Viale Libano 68/74, 154, Rome, Italy
Tel.: (39) 06500991
Web Site: http://www.mccann.com
Sales Range: $25-49.9 Million
Emp.: 15
Advertising Services
N.A.I.C.S.: 541810

Subsidiary (Domestic):

Universal McCann (4)
Via Spadolini 7Centro Leoni B, 20141, Milan, Italy
Tel.: (39) 020066041
Sales Range: $50-74.9 Million
Emp.: 50
Advertising Services
N.A.I.C.S.: 541810

Subsidiary (Non-US):

McCann Erickson Japan Inc. (3)
Shin Aoyama Bldg E 1-1-1 Minami-aoyama,

Minato-ku Minato-ku, Tokyo, 107-8679, Japan
Tel.: (81) 337468111
Advertising Services
N.A.I.C.S.: 541810
Hiroaki Mori (Pres & CEO)

Subsidiary (Domestic):

McCann Erickson Inc. (4)
Aqua Dojima West 19th Floor 1-4-16, Dojimahama Kita-ku, Osaka, 530-0004, Japan
Tel.: (81) 663426800
Sales Range: $25-49.9 Million
Emp.: 40
Advertising Services
N.A.I.C.S.: 541810

Branch (Non-US):

McCann Erickson Paris (3)
69 Boulevard du General Leclerc, 92110, Clichy, France
Tel.: (33) 147593456
Web Site: http://www.mccann-paris.fr
Sales Range: $10-24.9 Million
Emp.: 188
Advertising Services
N.A.I.C.S.: 541810
Patrick Lorrain (COO)

Subsidiary (Non-US):

McCann Erickson S.A. (3)
Avda Diagonal 662-664, 08034, Barcelona, Spain
Tel.: (34) 932520400
Web Site: http://www.mccann.com
Emp.: 55
Advertising Services
N.A.I.C.S.: 541810

Branch (Non-US):

McCann Erickson S.A. de Publicidad (3)
Avenue Andres Bello 2711 7th Floor Las Condes, Comuna las Condes, Santiago, Chile
Tel.: (56) 23376777
Web Site: http://www.mccann.com
Emp.: 150
Advertising Services
N.A.I.C.S.: 541810

Subsidiary (Non-US):

McCann Erickson Switzerland (3)
15 passage Malbuisson, 1211, Geneva, Switzerland
Tel.: (41) 223177777
Web Site: http://www.mccann.ch
Sales Range: $10-24.9 Million
Emp.: 40
Advertising Services
N.A.I.C.S.: 541810

McCann Erickson Uruguay (3)
Cambara 1620 Ap 101, 11500, Montevideo, Uruguay
Tel.: (598) 26056757
Emp.: 30
Advertising Services
N.A.I.C.S.: 541810

Branch (Non-US):

McCann Erickson WorldGroup Turkey (3)
Buyukdere Caddesi Ecza Sokak No 6 Levent, Levent, 34330, Istanbul, Turkiye
Tel.: (90) 2123175777
Web Site: http://www.mccann.com
Emp.: 150
Advertising Services
N.A.I.C.S.: 541810

Subsidiary (Non-US):

McCann Erickson, Inc. (3)
7F 31 Bongeunsa-ro2-gil, Gangnam-gu, Seoul, 06123, Korea (South)
Tel.: (82) 221869700
Web Site: http://www.mccann.co.kr
Rev.: $45,900,000
Emp.: 90
Advertising Services
N.A.I.C.S.: 541810

Branch (Domestic):

McCann Erickson/Salt Lake City (3)

32 Exchange Pl Ste 200, Salt Lake City, UT 84111
Tel.: (801) 257-7700
Advertising Services
N.A.I.C.S.: 541810

Subsidiary (Non-US):

McCann Health Singapore (3)
435 Orchard Road 16-03 Wisma Atria Office Tower, The MacDonald House, Singapore, 238877, Singapore
Tel.: (65) 69326950
Sales Range: $10-24.9 Million
Emp.: 15
Advertising Services
N.A.I.C.S.: 541810
Michael Banner (Gen Mgr)

Branch (Non-US):

McCann Healthcare Melbourne (3)
Level 7 574 St Kilda Rd, Melbourne, 3000, VIC, Australia
Tel.: (61) 99939333
Web Site: http://www.mccann.com.au
Emp.: 15
Advertising Services
N.A.I.C.S.: 541810
Stuart Black (CEO-Grp)

Subsidiary (Non-US):

McCann Healthcare Sydney (3)
351 Crown Street, Surry Hills, Sydney, 2010, NSW, Australia
Tel.: (61) 290588500
Advertising Services
N.A.I.C.S.: 541810
June Laffey (Exec Dir-Creative-Australia & Southeast Asia)

Branch (Non-US):

McCann Helsinki (3)
Pieni Roobertinkatu 1-3, 00130, Helsinki, Finland
Tel.: (358) 4246311
Web Site: http://www.mccann.fi
Rev.: $20,000,000
Emp.: 49
Advertising Services
N.A.I.C.S.: 541810

Subsidiary (Non-US):

McCann Johannesburg (3)
Block B The Main Straight Office Park Main Road, Bryanston, Johannesburg, 2021, South Africa
Tel.: (27) 112584000
Web Site: https://mccann1886.co.za
Rev.: $7,711,600
Emp.: 102
Advertising Services
N.A.I.C.S.: 541810
Fraser Lamb (CEO)

McCann Worldgroup (Singapore) Pte Ltd (3)
40A Orchard Road 08-01 the MacDonald House, 06-01 The MacDonald House, Singapore, 238838, Singapore
Tel.: (65) 67379911
Web Site:
    http://www.mccannworldgroup.com
Advertising Services
N.A.I.C.S.: 541810
Nick Handel (CEO)

Branch (Non-US):

McCann Worldgroup Philippines, Inc. (3)
5/F Active Fun Building 9th Avenue corner 28th Street City Center, Bonifacio Global City, 1634, Taguig, Philippines
Tel.: (63) 25486200
Web Site: http://www.mccann.com
Emp.: 250
Advertising Services
N.A.I.C.S.: 541810
Joey Dy (Chief Creative Officer)

Subsidiary (Non-US):

McCann Worldgroup Thailand (3)
98 Sathorn Square Office Tower 25th-26th Floor, North Sathorn Road Silom Bangrak, Bangkok, 10500, Thailand

Tel.: (66) 23436000
Rev.: $60,000,000
Emp.: 125
Advertising Services
N.A.I.C.S.: 541810
Pishasinee Lovichit (Mng Dir)
Thamy Sakornsinthu (Mng Dir-Momentum)

Branch (Non-US):

Multi-Media Systems (3)
33 Freetown Road, Belize, Belize
Tel.: (501) 23 0528
Advertising Services
N.A.I.C.S.: 541810
Rene Villanueva (Pres)

Subsidiary (Non-US):

Publicidad McCann Erickson Centroamericana (Guatemala) S.A. (3)
7a Ave Final Universidad Galileo Edificio Publicentro, Zona 10, Guatemala, Guatemala
Tel.: (502) 22857575
Emp.: 20
Advertising Services
N.A.I.C.S.: 541810

Branch (Domestic):

Regan Campbell Ward McCann (3)
150 East 42nd St, New York, NY 10017-5636
Tel.: (646) 742-2100
Web Site: http://www.rcw.com
Advertising Services
N.A.I.C.S.: 541810

Branch (Domestic):

Regan Campbell Ward West (4)
6863 Friars Rd, San Diego, CA 92108
Tel.: (619) 209-4200
Web Site: http://www.mccannrcw.com
Emp.: 15
Advertising Services
N.A.I.C.S.: 541810

Branch (Non-US):

Universal McCann (3)
Huai Hai Plaza 15 th Floor 1045 Huaihai Road, Shanghai, 200031, China
Tel.: (86) 21 2411 1409
Media Buying Services
N.A.I.C.S.: 541830

Universal McCann (3)
23rd Floor Sunning Plaza, Hysan Ave, Causeway Bay, China (Hong Kong)
Tel.: (852) 2808 7228
Advertising Services
N.A.I.C.S.: 541810

Subsidiary (Non-US):

McCann Erickson/Hora (2)
Rua Engenheiro Canto Resende No 2, 1070-046, Lisbon, Portugal
Tel.: (351) 217517500
Web Site: http://www.mccann.com
Sales Range: $25-49.9 Million
Emp.: 40
N.A.I.C.S.: 541810

McCann Manchester Limited (2)
Bonis Hall Lane Prestbury, Macclesfield, SK10 4EF, Cheshire, United Kingdom
Tel.: (44) 1625822200
Web Site:
    http://www.mccannmanchester.com
Advertising Agencies
N.A.I.C.S.: 541810
Dave Price (Exec Creative Dir)

McCann Worldgroup (2)
135 Bishopsgate, London, EC2M 3TP, United Kingdom
Tel.: (44) 2078373737
Web Site: https://www.mccannlondon.com
Advetising Agency
N.A.I.C.S.: 541810
Cynthia H. Augustine (Chief Talent Officer-Global)
Elizabeth Bernstein (Head-New Business)
Jessica Bayat (Dir-Communications)
Mark Lund (Pres)

McCann Worldgroup Indonesia (2)
Victoria Building 5th Floor Jl Sultan

The Interpublic Group of Companies,
Inc.—(Continued)

Hasanuddin 47-51, Kav 9-11, Jakarta,
12160, Indonesia
Tel.: (62) 2152922555
Web Site: http://www.mccann.com
Advertising Agency
N.A.I.C.S.: 541810
Vishal Mehta *(Mng Dir)*

**McCann Worldgroup South Africa
(Pty) Ltd** **(2)**
22 Westbrooke Drive, Sandown Johannes-
burg, Sandton, 2196, South Africa
Tel.: (27) 112354600
Web Site: http://www.mccann.com
Emp.: 100
Advertising Agency
N.A.I.C.S.: 541810

McCann Yerevan **(2)**
1/21 Azatutyan Ave Ste 3, Yerevan, 0037,
Armenia
Tel.: (374) 10254527
Advetising Agency
N.A.I.C.S.: 541810

**McCann-Erickson Central
Limited** **(2)**
Communications House Highlands Road,
Solihull, B90 4WE, West Midlands, United
Kingdom
Tel.: (44) 1217133500
Web Site:
http://www.mccannbirmingham.co.uk
Emp.: 300
Advertising Agencies
N.A.I.C.S.: 541810
Jonathan Jesson *(Chief Growth Officer)*
Chris Davies *(Dir-Bus Dev)*

**McCann-Erickson Deutschland GmbH
& Co Management Property KG** **(2)**
Grosser Hasenpfad 44, 60598, Frankfurt
am Main, Germany
Tel.: (49) 61133399330
Web Site: http://www.mccann.de
Advertising Services
N.A.I.C.S.: 541810

Subsidiary (Domestic):

McCann-Erickson USA, Inc. **(2)**
622 3rd Ave, New York, NY 10017
Tel.: (646) 865-2000
Web Site: http://www.mccannny.com
Advertising Agencies
N.A.I.C.S.: 541810

Unit (Domestic):

McCann Erickson **(3)**
360 W Maple Rd, Birmingham, MI 48009
Tel.: (248) 203-8000
Web Site: http://www.mccannerickson.com
N.A.I.C.S.: 541810
Rita Lindholm *(CFO)*

McCann Erickson Corp. (S.A.) **(3)**
Carr 176 1 6 RG Cupey Plz 3er Piso, San
Juan, PR 00902-3389
Tel.: (787) 774-3600
Web Site: http://www.mccann.com
N.A.I.C.S.: 541810

McCann Erickson North America **(3)**
622 3rd Ave, New York, NY 10017
Tel.: (646) 865-2000
Web Site: http://www.mccann.com
Emp.: 800
N.A.I.C.S.: 541810
Eric Silver *(Chief Creative Officer)*

McCann Erickson Seattle **(3)**
1741 1st Ave S, Seattle, WA 98134
Tel.: (206) 971-4200
Advetising Agency
N.A.I.C.S.: 541810

McCann Erickson/Los Angeles **(3)**
5700 Wilshire Blvd Ste 225, Los Angeles,
CA 90036
Tel.: (323) 900-7175
Web Site: http://www.mccann.com
Advertising Agency
N.A.I.C.S.: 541810

McCann Erickson/New York **(3)**
622 3rd Ave, New York, NY 10017
Tel.: (646) 865-2000

Web Site: http://www.mccannny.com
Advertising Agency
N.A.I.C.S.: 541810
Sean Bryan *(Co-Chief Creative Officer)*

McCann Worldgroup **(3)**
600 Battery St, San Francisco, CA 94111
Tel.: (415) 262-5600
Web Site: http://www.mccann.com
N.A.I.C.S.: 541810

Subsidiary (Non-US):

Media Enterprises **(2)**
31 Shirley Park Avenue, PO Box N-9240,
Nassau, NP, Bahamas
Tel.: (242) 3258210
Web Site: https://www.bahamasmedia.com
Sales Range: $25-49.9 Million
Emp.: 8
N.A.I.C.S.: 541810

Subsidiary (Domestic):

Momentum Worldwide LLC **(2)**
300 Vesey St 15th Fl, New York, NY 10282
Tel.: (646) 638-5400
Web Site: http://www.momentumww.com
Sales Range: $350-399.9 Million
Emp.: 2,000
Entertainment, Event Planning & Marketing,
Retail, Sales Promotion, Sponsorship,
Sports Marketing
N.A.I.C.S.: 541810
Chris Weil *(Chm & CEO)*
Kevin McNulty *(Pres & CMO)*
Donnalyn Smith *(Pres-North America)*
Maria Laura Nicotero *(Pres-Brazil)*
Elena Klau *(Chief Strategy & Analytics
Officer-Global)*
Christine Shoaf *(Exec VP & Acct Dir-Global)*
Philippe Touzot *(CFO)*
Jennifer Frieman *(Chief Talent Officer)*
Gus Guthrie *(Founder)*
Imelda Hodson *(Mng Partner)*
Matt Lewis *(Pres-UK)*

Subsidiary (Domestic):

Chase Design, LLC **(2)**
1326 New Seneca Tpke, Skaneateles, NY
13152
Tel.: (315) 685-1000
Web Site: https://www.chasedesign.net
Sales Range: $10-24.9 Million
Emp.: 100
Product, Packaging & Communication De-
sign & Marketing Services
N.A.I.C.S.: 541613
Brad D. Hall *(Mng Partner)*
Melissa E. Chapman *(Mng Partner)*
Scott W. Osiecki *(Mng Partner)*
Alex Root *(Dir-HR)*
Stuart Scarr *(Mng Partner)*
Ben Watkins *(VP-Strategy)*
Eric Meier *(Dir-Design)*
Glenn N. Christoffel *(VP-Design & Imple-
mentation)*
Joel R. Masters *(Dir-IT)*
Ali Costikyan *(Acct Dir)*
Bonny Dudden *(Production Mgr)*
Cassie Buehler *(Dir-Ops)*
Dave Hine *(Dir-Design)*
Ellie Kelley *(Coord-HR)*
Kara Gjersvig *(Sr Dir-Design)*
Kyle Pienkowski *(Fin Dir)*

Branch (Domestic):

Momentum **(3)**
944 Brady Ave, Atlanta, GA 30318-5581
Tel.: (670) 627-5322
Web Site: http://www.momentumww.com
Sales Range: $10-24.9 Million
Emp.: 25
Event Marketing, Full Service, Sales Pro-
motion
N.A.I.C.S.: 541810

Momentum **(3)**
360 W Maple, Birmingham, MI 48009
Tel.: (248) 203-8000
Web Site: http://www.momentumww.com
Sales Range: $25-49.9 Million
Emp.: 2
Event Marketing, Full Service, Sales Pro-
motion
N.A.I.C.S.: 541810

Momentum **(3)**

625 Eden Park Dr Ste 775, Cincinnati, OH
45202
Tel.: (513) 621-1210
Sales Range: $25-49.9 Million
Emp.: 17
Event Marketing, Full Service, Sales Pro-
motion
N.A.I.C.S.: 541810

Momentum **(3)**
444 N Michigan Ave Ste 2700, Chicago, IL
60611
Tel.: (312) 245-3500
Sales Range: $25-49.9 Million
Emp.: 62
N.A.I.C.S.: 541810
Peter Office *(Chief People Officer)*

Momentum **(3)**
700 N San Vicente Blvd Ste G900, West
Hollywood, CA 90069-5053
Tel.: (310) 289-6200
Web Site: http://www.momentumww.com
Sales Range: $25-49.9 Million
Emp.: 70
N.A.I.C.S.: 541810

Momentum **(3)**
1831 Chestnut St 7th Fl, Saint Louis, MO
63103
Tel.: (314) 646-6200
Web Site: http://www.momentumww.com
Sales Range: $75-99.9 Million
Emp.: 270
Consulting, Entertainment, Event Marketing,
Point of Purchase, Sales Promotion, Sports
Marketing
N.A.I.C.S.: 541820

Unit (Domestic):

PMK*BNC **(3)**
622 3rd Ave 20th Fl, New York, NY 10017
Tel.: (212) 878-5501
Web Site:
http://www.rogersandcowanpmk.com
Public Relations & Communications
N.A.I.C.S.: 541820
Cindy Berger *(Co-Chm & CEO)*

PMK*BNC **(3)**
1840 Century Park E Ste 1400, Los Ange-
les, CA 90067
Tel.: (310) 289-6200
Web Site: http://www.pmkbnc.com
Sales Range: $25-49.9 Million
Emp.: 100
N.A.I.C.S.: 541820
Chris Robichaud *(CEO)*

Subsidiary (Non-US):

Orient/McCann **(2)**
2nd Floor 84-B-1 Ghalib Road-Gulberg-3,
Lahore, 54000, Pakistan
Tel.: (92) 42111666622
Web Site: https://orientm-mccann.pk
N.A.I.C.S.: 541810

Orient/McCann **(2)**
Orient House 194-1 SMCHS, Karachi,
74400, Pakistan
Tel.: (92) 21111666622
Web Site: https://orientm-mccann.pk
N.A.I.C.S.: 541810
Omer Murad *(Sr Exec Dir)*
Oswald Lucas *(Chief Creative Officer)*
Ahmad Javad *(Dir-Area)*
S. Masood Hashmi *(Pres & CEO)*
Saad Khalique *(Dir-Operations)*
Nabeel Butt *(Reg Dir)*

Publicio McCann **(2)**
6 Rue St Georges, Port Louis, Mauritius
Tel.: (230) 212 1161
Web Site: http://www.mccann.com
N.A.I.C.S.: 541810

Storakers McCann **(2)**
GrevTuregatan 11A, 102 48, Stockholm,
Sweden
Tel.: (46) 850650000
Web Site: http://www.mccann.se
Sales Range: $10-24.9 Million
Emp.: 35
N.A.I.C.S.: 541810

The Division **(2)**
Pohja pst 27A, 10415, Tallinn, Estonia
Tel.: (372) 6270070
Web Site: https://www.division.ee

N.A.I.C.S.: 541810
Madis Kimmel *(Mgr)*
Annika Saar *(Art Dir)*
Kerttu Keermaa *(Creative Dir)*

Subsidiary (Domestic):

The Martin Agency, Inc. **(2)**
1 Shockoe Plz, Richmond, VA 23219-4132
Tel.: (804) 698-8000
Web Site: http://www.martinagency.com
Sales Range: $125-149.9 Million
Emp.: 456
Advertising Agencies
N.A.I.C.S.: 541810
Danny Robinson *(Chief Creative Officer)*
Kristen Cavallo *(CEO)*
Elizabeth Paul *(Chief Strategy Officer)*

Branch (Domestic):

**Ingenuity Media Group at The Martin
Agency** **(3)**
1 Shockoe Plz, Richmond, VA 23219-4132
Tel.: (804) 698-8000
Web Site: http://www.ingenuitymedia.com
Emp.: 85
Advertising Services
N.A.I.C.S.: 541830

**The Martin Agency, Inc. - New
York** **(3)**
71 Fifth Ave 4th Fl, New York, NY 10003
Tel.: (212) 405-4800
Web Site: http://www.martinagency.com
Emp.: 31
Advertising Services
N.A.I.C.S.: 541810

Subsidiary (Domestic):

The Media Investment Group **(2)**
3060 Peachtree Rd NW Ste 500, Atlanta,
GA 30305
Tel.: (404) 262-8909
Web Site: http://www.fitzco.com
Sales Range: $75-99.9 Million
Emp.: 16
Advetising Agency
N.A.I.C.S.: 541810

**Torre Lazur Healthcare Group,
LLC** **(2)**
3 Sylvan Way 2nd Fl, Parsippany, NJ
07054
Tel.: (973) 917-6000
Web Site: http://www.mccanntorrelazur.com
Sales Range: $50-74.9 Million
Emp.: 200
Advetising Agency
N.A.I.C.S.: 541810

Unit (Domestic):

Echo Torre Lazur **(3)**
120 Eagle Rock Ave, East Hanover, NJ
07936
Tel.: (973) 884-4707
Web Site: http://www.echo-tl.com
N.A.I.C.S.: 541810

Subsidiary (Non-US):

Unitrend Ltd. **(2)**
31/A Western Road 1st Floor, DOHS Ba-
nani, Dhaka, 1206, Bangladesh
Tel.: (880) 29896660
Web Site: https://www.unitrendbd.com
N.A.I.C.S.: 541810
Muneer Ahmed Khan *(Mng Dir)*
Zulfiqar Ahmed *(Dir)*
Angshuman Chatterjee *(Exec Creative Dir)*

Subsidiary (Domestic):

**Universal McCann Worldwide,
Inc.** **(2)**
100 W 33rd St, New York, NY 10001
Tel.: (212) 883-4700
Web Site: https://www.umww.com
Emp.: 300
Advetising Agency
N.A.I.C.S.: 541810
Andrew Littlewood *(Chief Product Officer-)*
Dan Chapman *(Chief Strategy Officer-)*
Grant Ogburn *(Chief Growth Officer)*
Leith Mellors *(Chief Talent Officer-)*
Neena Koyen *(Chief Comm Officer-)*
Jennifer Wadeyka *(Chief Client Ops Officer-
)*

Erin Quintana *(CEO-)*
Chris Wilhelmi *(Chief Analytics Officer-US)*
Marcy Greenberger *(Chief Investment Officer-)*
Brendon Volpe *(Chief Intelligence Officer-)*

Subsidiary (Non-US):

Universal Communication (3)
Britselei 23, 2000, Antwerp, Belgium
Tel.: (32) 8181
Web Site: http://www.uc.be
Sales Range: $25-49.9 Million
Emp.: 15
N.A.I.C.S.: 541810

Universal Communication (3)
1 Vandammestraat 5-7D, Hoeilaart, 1560, Brussels, Belgium
Tel.: (32) 26764211
Sales Range: $25-49.9 Million
Emp.: 22
Media Buying Services, Production
N.A.I.C.S.: 541830

Universal McCann (3)
La chocolaterie 79-83 rue Baudin, 92300, Levallois-Perret, France
Tel.: (33) 141491400
Sales Range: $25-49.9 Million
Emp.: 45
N.A.I.C.S.: 541810

Universal McCann (3)
Speicherstrasse 57 - 59, 60327, Frankfurt am Main, Germany
Tel.: (49) 6979404335
Web Site: http://www.umww.de
Sales Range: $50-74.9 Million
Emp.: 200
N.A.I.C.S.: 541810
Rene Kassner *(Mng Partner-Digital)*
Andreas Rommel *(Mng Partner-Buying)*

Universal McCann (3)
Ecza Sokak Number 6 Buyukdere Caddesi, Levent, 80498, Istanbul, Turkiye
Tel.: (90) 2123175600
Web Site: http://www.mccann.com
Sales Range: $25-49.9 Million
Emp.: 40
N.A.I.C.S.: 541810

Branch (Domestic):

Universal McCann (3)
5700 Wilshire Blvd Ste 450, Los Angeles, CA 90036
Tel.: (323) 900-7400
Web Site: http://www.umww.com
Media Buying Services
N.A.I.C.S.: 541830

Subsidiary (Non-US):

Universal McCann (3)
Zhaowei Building 2/F No 14 Jiuxianqiao Road, Beijing, 100016, Chaoyang, China
Tel.: (86) 10 6438 0011
Sales Range: $25-49.9 Million
Emp.: 26
Media Buying Services
N.A.I.C.S.: 541830

Universal McCann (3)
33/F Telecom Plz, No 18 Zhong Shan Er Rd, Guangzhou, 510081, China
Tel.: (86) 20 8888 8438
Sales Range: $25-49.9 Million
Emp.: 22
Media Buying Services
N.A.I.C.S.: 541830

Universal McCann, S.A. (3)
Calle Santa Maria Magdalena 8, 28026, Madrid, Spain
Tel.: (34) 917691919
Sales Range: $50-74.9 Million
Emp.: 150
Media Buying Services
N.A.I.C.S.: 541830

Universal Media (3)
Via Giovanni Spadolini 7-Centro Leoni Building B, 20141, Milan, Italy
Tel.: (39) 039028529
Web Site: http://www.mccann.com
N.A.I.C.S.: 541810

Universal Media Hellas SA (3)
280 Kifissias Avenue Building 2, Athens,

15232, Greece
Tel.: (30) 210 8179600
Sales Range: $25-49.9 Million
Emp.: 15
N.A.I.C.S.: 541830

Subsidiary (Non-US):

Upton Fulton McCann Pvt. Ltd. (2)
40 Sandringham Drive Alex Park, PO Box 789, Mount Pleasant, Harare, Zimbabwe
Tel.: (263) 4745828
Web Site: http://www.mccann.com
Advertising Services
N.A.I.C.S.: 541810

ZK Advertising (2)
PO Box 71035, Ilala, Dar es Salaam, Tanzania
Tel.: (255) 2226688520
Web Site: http://www.zkcommunications.com
N.A.I.C.S.: 541810
Zadock Koola *(Chm)*

Mediabrands Belgium S.A. (1)
Ildefonse Vandammelaan 5-7, 1560, Hoeilaart, Vlaams Brabant, Belgium
Tel.: (32) 27736800
Web Site: https://ipgmediabrands.be
Advertising Services
N.A.I.C.S.: 541810

Mediahub Minneapolis, LLC (1)
510 S Marquette Ave, Minneapolis, MN 55402
Tel.: (617) 226-9400
Advertising & Digital Marketing Services
N.A.I.C.S.: 541810

Megameios - Publicidade E Meios, A.C.E. (1)
Av October 5 68 - 8B, 1050-059, Lisbon, Portugal
Tel.: (351) 217220500
Web Site: https://www.megameios.pt
Sales Range: $25-49.9 Million
Emp.: 6
Advertising Agencies Services
N.A.I.C.S.: 541810

Middle East Communication Networks - MCN (1)
PO Box 6834, Sheikh Zayed Rd, Dubai, United Arab Emirates
Tel.: (971) 44454008
Web Site: https://www.mcnholding.com
Sales Range: $75-99.9 Million
Emp.: 375
Advertising Services
N.A.I.C.S.: 541810

Mnet Mobile Pty. Ltd. (1)
Level 1 16 Anster Street, Adelaide, 5000, SA, Australia
Tel.: (61) 881156600
Web Site: http://www.mnetmobile.com
Emp.: 110
Mobile Engagement & Marketing Services
N.A.I.C.S.: 541870
Travis Johnson *(CEO)*

Mullen Communications, Inc. (1)
40 Broad St, Boston, MA 02109
Tel.: (617) 226-9000
Web Site: http://www.mullen.com
Sales Range: $150-199.9 Million
Emp.: 350
Advetising Agency
N.A.I.C.S.: 541810
Paul Slack *(CFO)*

Branch (Domestic):

Mullen (2)
525 Vine St Ste-340, Winston Salem, NC 27101
Tel.: (336) 765-3630
Web Site: http://ws.mullenloweus.com
Sales Range: $50-74.9 Million
Emp.: 150
Advertising Agencies
N.A.I.C.S.: 541810
Susanna Gates Rose O'Connell *(Dir-Brdcst Production & Sr VP)*

Mullen (2)
The Crane Bldg 40 24th St, Pittsburgh, PA 15222-4600
Tel.: (412) 402-0200
Web Site: http://www.mullen.com

Sales Range: $25-49.9 Million
Emp.: 50
Full Service, Outdoor
N.A.I.C.S.: 541810

Mullen (2)
1 Woodroad Ave, Detroit, MI 48226
Tel.: (313) 596-9002
Web Site: http://www.mullen.com
Sales Range: $10-24.9 Million
Emp.: 210
N.A.I.C.S.: 541810

NSA Media (1)
2200 Cabot Dr Ste 330, Lisle, IL 60532
Tel.: (630) 729-7500
Web Site: https://www.nsamedia.com
Emp.: 200
Media Planning & Buying Agency
N.A.I.C.S.: 541830
Steve Mueller *(Pres & CEO)*
Shannon Wagner *(Chief Client Officer)*
Susan Saarnio *(VP-HR)*
Karin Kasper *(VP-Media Integration)*
Jim Hagan *(Dir-Digital)*

New Honor Society, Inc. (1)
555 Washington Ave Ste 200, Saint Louis, MO 63101
Tel.: (314) 231-2400
Web Site: https://www.newhonorsociety.com
Sales Range: $50-74.9 Million
Advertising & Media Buying Agency
N.A.I.C.S.: 541810

Subsidiary (Domestic):

Rivet Markcom Midwest, Inc. - Chicago Office (2)
875 N Michigan Ave 19th Fl, Chicago, IL 60611
Tel.: (312) 799-4000
Sales Range: $25-49.9 Million
Emp.: 50
Sales Promotion
N.A.I.C.S.: 541810

Octagon (1)
290 Harbor Dr, Stamford, CT 06902
Tel.: (203) 354-7400
Web Site: http://www.octagon.com
Sales Range: $200-249.9 Million
Emp.: 800
Sports Marketing Services
N.A.I.C.S.: 711320
Lisa Murray *(Chief Mktg & Inclusive Diversity Officer & Chief Mktg & Inclusive Diversity Officer)*
Simon Wardle *(Chief Strategy Officer-Worldwide)*
John Shea *(CEO-Sports & Entertainment Network)*
Eva Conforti *(Coord)*
Alex Rozis *(VP)*
Eva Conforti *(Coord)*
Alex Rozis *(VP)*

Subsidiary (Non-US):

Octagon (2)
2 Waterhouse Square 140 Holborn, London, EC1N 2AE, United Kingdom
Tel.: (44) 2078620000
Web Site: http://www.octagon.com
Emp.: 50
Sports Marketing Services
N.A.I.C.S.: 541810

Octagon (2)
Octagon House 21 Scott Street, Waverly, Johannesburg, 2090, South Africa
Tel.: (27) 723951349
Sports Marketing Services
N.A.I.C.S.: 541810
Alroy Oliphant *(Dir-Bus)*

Octagon (2)
Speicherstr 57, Hessen, 60327, Frankfurt, Germany
Tel.: (49) 6915041210
Web Site: http://www.octagon.com
Emp.: 2
Sports Marketing Services
N.A.I.C.S.: 541810

Branch (Non-US):

Octagon (2)
237 Labrador Drive, Waterloo, N2K 4M8, ON, Canada
Tel.: (519) 749-1582

Web Site: http://www.octagon.com
Emp.: 2
Sports Marketing Services
N.A.I.C.S.: 541810

Octagon (2)
1335 Carling Avenue Suite 320, Ottawa, K1Z 8N8, ON, Canada
Tel.: (613) 238-5740
Web Site: http://www.octagonna.com
Emp.: 4
Sports Marketing Services
N.A.I.C.S.: 541810

Subsidiary (Non-US):

Octagon (2)
16 Bis Rue de Billancourt, Clichy, 92583, France
Tel.: (33) 147593237
Web Site: http://www.octagon.com
Emp.: 20
Sports Marketing Services
N.A.I.C.S.: 541810

Octagon (2)
18/F Huaihai Plaza 1045 Huai Hai Zhong Road, Shanghai, 200031, China
Tel.: (86) 2124110153
Emp.: 20
Sports Marketing Services
N.A.I.C.S.: 541810

Subsidiary (Domestic):

Octagon Access (2)
909 3rd Ave, New York, NY 10022
Tel.: (212) 308-2650
Web Site: http://www.octagonaccess.com
Emp.: 20
Advertising Agencies
N.A.I.C.S.: 541810

Subsidiary (Non-US):

Octagon EMEA (2)
100 Avenue de Cortenbergh, 1000, Brussels, Belgium
Tel.: (32) 28949080
Sports Marketing Services
N.A.I.C.S.: 541810

Octagon Sydney (2)
Royal Naval House 32 Grosvenor Street the Rocks, Woolloomooloo, Sydney, 2000, NSW, Australia
Tel.: (61) 299944405
Web Site: http://www.octagon.com
Emp.: 20
Sports Marketing Services
N.A.I.C.S.: 541810

Orion Trading (1)
622 3rd Ave 2nd Fl, New York, NY 10017
Tel.: (212) 551-4000
Web Site: http://www.oriontradingww.com
Sales Range: $10-24.9 Million
Emp.: 350
Media Buying Services
N.A.I.C.S.: 541830

Orion Trading Canada Inc. (1)
10 Bay Street, Toronto, M5J 2R8, ON, Canada
Tel.: (416) 643-4933
Web Site: https://www.orionworldwide.com
Emp.: 400
Advertising Agency Services
N.A.I.C.S.: 541810

PMK-BNC, Inc. (1)
1840 Century Park E Ste 1400, Los Angeles, CA 90067
Tel.: (310) 854-4400
Web Site: http://www.pmkbnc.com
Advertising Agency Services
N.A.I.C.S.: 541810
Michael Fein *(Sr VP-Strategy & Analytics)*
Victoria Greene *(Exec VP-Brand Growth & Experiential)*
Alan Nierob *(Chm-Entertainment)*

R/GA Media Group, Inc. (1)
450 W 33rd St 12th Fl, New York, NY 10001
Tel.: (212) 946-4000
Web Site: http://www.rga.com
Sales Range: $100-124.9 Million
Brand Development, E-Commerce, Electronic Media, Interactive Agencies, Internet/Web Design

The Interpublic Group of Companies, Inc.—(Continued)

N.A.I.C.S.: 541810
Kris Kiger (Exec Creative Dir & Exec VP)
Stephen Plumlee (Vice Chm)
Richard Ting (Chief Creative Officer, Chief Experience Officer & Exec VP)
Dave Edwards (Sr VP & Mng Dir-Business Development)
Chapin Clark (Exec Creative Dir, Exec VP & Mng Dir)
Mike Rigby (Head-Global)
Nick Coronges (CTO & Exec VP-Global)
Sean Lyons (CEO-Global)
Angela Hannam (Chief Talent Officer-Global & Exec VP)
Yosuke Suzuki (Mng Dir)
Tuomas Peltoniemi (Exec VP & Mng Dir-APAC)
Ben Williams (Chief Experience Officer-Global)
Seamus Higgins (Chief Creative Officer & VP-APAC)
Tiffany Rolfe (Chief Creative Officer-Global)
Alex Sehnaoui (Mng Dir-Growth & Dev-Global & Sr VP)
Victoria Curro (Mng Dir-Sydney)
Ben Miles (Exec Creative Dir-Asia Pacific)
Christa Balom (Exec Dir & VP)
Christopher Brown (Mng Dir & Sr VP)
Kelly Harrison (Sr Dir-Marketing-Communications)
Margo Lowry (Exec Dir-Content Studio)
Rachel Mercer (VP & Head-Strategy)
Neda Whitney (Mng Dir-Client Services & VP)
Ashish Prashar (CMO-Global)
Erin Rabasca (Sr VP & Exec Dir-Global-Talent Mgmt)
Tania Secor (CFO-Global)
Jai Tedeschi (VP & Exec Dir-Culture & Ops-Global)
Paul Turzio (Sr VP-Data & Mktg Sciences)
Melanie Mahaffey (Exec Dir-Communications-Global)
Shannon Washington (Exec Creative Dir & Sr VP)
Meghann MacKenzie (Exec Dir-Strategy & VP)
Lucien Etori (Exec Dir-Strategy & VP)
Brandon Kaplan (Exec Dir & VP)
Ethel Jones (Exec Dir)
Melanie Mahaffey (Exec Dir-Communications-Global)
Shannon Washington (Exec Creative Dir & Sr VP)
Meghann MacKenzie (Exec Dir-Strategy & VP)
Lucien Etori (Exec Dir-Strategy & VP)
Brandon Kaplan (Exec Dir & VP)
Ethel Jones (Exec Dir)

Subsidiary (Non-US):

R/GA London (2)
135 Bishopsgate 6th Floor, London, EC2M 3TP, United Kingdom
Tel.: (44) 2070713300
Web Site: https://www.rga.com
Sales Range: $25-49.9 Million
Emp.: 50
N.A.I.C.S.: 541810
Rebecca Bezzina (Mng Dir & Sr VP)
Nick Pringle (Sr VP & Exec Creative Dir)

Subsidiary (Domestic):

R/GA Los Angeles (2)
12777 W Jefferson Blvd Bldg 101 Ste A, Los Angeles, CA 90066
Tel.: (310) 882-2680
Web Site: http://www.rga.com
Sales Range: $25-49.9 Million
Emp.: 1
N.A.I.C.S.: 541810
Stephen Larkin (Exec VP-Growth & Dev & Sr VP)
Melanie Mahaffey (Sr Dir-Global Media Rels)

R/GA San Francisco (2)
35 S Park, San Francisco, CA 94107
Tel.: (415) 624-2000
Web Site: http://www.rga.com
Sales Range: $25-49.9 Million
Emp.: 80
N.A.I.C.S.: 541810
Hana Newman (Grp Dir-Production-Studios)

Subsidiary (Non-US):

R/GA Sao Paulo (2)
Rua Natingui 862 - 3 Floor, Vila Madalena, Sao Paulo, 05443-001, SP, Brazil
Tel.: (55) 1139580900
Web Site: https://www.rga.com
N.A.I.C.S.: 541810

Subsidiary (Domestic):

R/GA Ventures LLC (2)
450 W 33rd St, New York, NY 10001
Tel.: (212) 946-4000
Web Site: https://www.ventures.rga.com
Venture Capital Firm
N.A.I.C.S.: 523999
Nick Coronges (Partner)
Josh Daghir (Assoc Dir-Strategy & Portfolio Mgr)
David Isaacs (Dir-Creative)
Stephen Plumlee (Mng Partner)
Jonathan Bradley (Partner)
Liz David (Sr Dir-Comm & Events)
Craig Poplar (Exec Dir-Production)
Fielding Jamieson (Dir-Strategy)

Joint Venture (Domestic):

Macquarie Capital Venture Studio (3)
125 West 55th St, New York, NY 10019
Tel.: (212) 231-1000
Web Site: http://www.macquarie.com
Venture Capital Firm
N.A.I.C.S.: 523999

Reprise Media, Inc. (1)
100 W 33rd St 3rd Fl, New York, NY 10001
Tel.: (212) 605-4811
Web Site: https://www.reprisedigital.com
Search Engine Optimization
N.A.I.C.S.: 541810
David Mataranglo (Mng Dir-USA)

Subsidiary (Non-US):

Reprise Media Asia (2)
16/F One Taikoo Place 979 King's Road, 979 Kings Rd, Quarry Bay, China (Hong Kong)
Tel.: (852) 29018403
Web Site: http://www.reprisemedia.com
Emp.: 50
N.A.I.C.S.: 541810

Reprise Media Australia (2)
Level 2 100 Chalmers Street, Surry Hills, Sydney, 2010, NSW, Australia
Tel.: (61) 299944000
Web Site: http://www.reprise.com
N.A.I.C.S.: 541810
Jules Kilmartin (Gen Mgr)
Johan Micheelsen (Head-Paid Media-Sydney & Brisbane)

The Endeavor Agency LLC (1)
9601 Wilshire Blvd Fl, Beverly Hills, CA 90210
Tel.: (310) 285-9000
Web Site: http://www.wma.com
N.A.I.C.S.: 711410

Tierney Communications (1)
1700 Market St Ste 29, Philadelphia, PA 19103
Tel.: (215) 790-4100
Web Site: https://tierneyagency.com
Sales Range: $150-199.9 Million
Emp.: 142
Advertising & Public Relations Agency
N.A.I.C.S.: 541810
Tracey Santilli (Pres)

Translation LLC (1)
145 West 45th Str 12th Fl, New York, NY 10036
Tel.: (212) 299-5505
Web Site: http://www.translationllc.com
Sales Range: $100-124.9 Million
Emp.: 35
Advertising Services
N.A.I.C.S.: 541810
John Greene (VP-Strategy)
Jonathan Lutzky (Gen Counsel)
Alex Kaplan (Grp Dir-Creative)
Damian Garbaccio (Pres)
Angel Navedo (Dir-Context)
Edwin Sosa (Coord-Facilities)
Matthew DeSimone (Dir-Project Mgmt)

Keith Jackson (Grp Acct Dir)
Joel Rodriguez (Grp Dir-Context)
Solange Foster (Dir-Experiential)
Maria Zadorozhnaya (Mgr-Billing & A/R)
Paz Molina (Art Dir)
Hugh Pringle (Sr Dir-Context)
Dylan Simel (Art Dir)
Nora DeLigter (Copywriter)
Sam Howard (Grp Acct Dir)
Andy Ferguson (Creative Dir)
Thalia Tsouros (Dir-Bus Affairs)
Dewi Paulino (VP-Mktg)
Jason Nuttall (Art Dir)
Susanna Swartley (Head-Client Svcs)
Juli Profumo (Grp Dir-Data Strategy)
Shon Mogharabi (Dir-Strategy)
John Fulbrook (Creative Dir-Design Grp)
Sandi Preston (Chief Strategy Officer)

Universal Media Seven FZ-LLC (1)
Emarat Atrium Building Office No 420 421 & 422 Sheikh Zayed Rd, Dubai, United Arab Emirates
Tel.: (971) 43210009
Web Site: http://www.universalmena.com
Sales Range: $25-49.9 Million
Emp.: 100
Advertising Agencies
N.A.I.C.S.: 541810

Weber Shandwick (1)
909 3rd Ave, New York, NY 10022
Tel.: (212) 445-8000
Web Site: http://www.webershandwick.com
Sales Range: $25-49.9 Million
Emp.: 60
Public Relations Agency
N.A.I.C.S.: 541820
Laura Schoen (Pres-Global Healthcare Practice-Latin America)
Chris Perry (Chief Innovation Officer)
Joy Farber Kolo (Pres-North America)
Michael Wehman (Gen Mgr)
Sung Chang (Chief Impact Officer)
Brian Offutt (Chief Workforce Innovation & Ops Officer)
Deb Nichols (CFO)
Lewis T. Williams (Exec VP & Head-Brand Impact)

Affiliate (Non-US):

AC-Sanafor (2)
Kalevankatu 13, 00100, Helsinki, Finland
Tel.: (358) 408406368
Web Site: http://www.acsanafor.fi
Sales Range: $25-49.9 Million
Emp.: 10
Public Relations
N.A.I.C.S.: 541820

Subsidiary (Domestic):

Cassidy & Associates/Weber Shandwick Government Relations (2)
607 14th St NW Ste 400, Washington, DC 20005
Tel.: (202) 347-0773
Web Site: https://cassidy.com
Sales Range: $100-124.9 Million
Government/Political/Public Affairs
N.A.I.C.S.: 561110
Jordan Bernstein (COO)
Russell J. Thomasson (Exec VP)
Kai Anderson (CEO)
Barry D. Rhoads (Chm)
Jen Adler (Sr VP)
Kevin Binger (Sr VP)
Charles Brittingham (Sr VP)
Donna Jo Denison (VP)
Nicole Di Resta (Sr VP)
Julie Eddy Rokala (Sr VP)
Susann Edwards (VP)
Michelle Greene (Sr VP)
Amelia F. Jenkins (Exec VP)
Michael Johnson (Sr VP)
Arthur Mason (Exec VP)
Ryan Mulvenon (VP)
Vernon Simmons (Sr VP)
Barbara Sutton (Exec VP)
Chad Sydnor (VP)
Jed Dearborn (Sr VP)

Subsidiary (Non-US):

Corporate Voice-Weber Shandwick (2)
23 HAL Old Airport Rd HAL 2nd Stage Kodihalli, Indiranagar, Bengaluru, 560008, Kar-

nataka, India
Tel.: (91) 8042451200
Web Site: http://www.webershandwick.com
Sales Range: $25-49.9 Million
Emp.: 50
N.A.I.C.S.: 541820

Corporate Voice-Weber Shandwick (2)
15th Floor Tower B DLF Cyber Greens Phase 3 Sector 24, New Delhi, 122002, Gurugram, India
Tel.: (91) 1244153200
Web Site: http://www.webershandwick.com
Sales Range: $25-49.9 Million
Emp.: 45
N.A.I.C.S.: 541820

David Chapman Associates Ltd. (2)
Dominions House North Dominions Arcade, Brigantine Pl, Cardiff, CF10 2AR, United Kingdom
Tel.: (44) 2920345500
Web Site: http://www.webershandwick.co.uk
Sales Range: $25-49.9 Million
Emp.: 10
Public Relations
N.A.I.C.S.: 541820

Affiliate (Non-US):

Extend Comunicaciones-Weber Shandwick (2)
Rosario Norte 555 Piso 12, Edificio Neruda Las Condes, Santiago, Chile
Tel.: (56) 224377700
Web Site: http://www.extend.cl
Sales Range: $25-49.9 Million
Emp.: 70
N.A.I.C.S.: 541820
Maria De La Luz Velasco (CEO, Partner & Exec VP)
Ana Maria Velasco (Partner & Dir-New Bus)
Isabel Hohlberg (Partner & Chief Comml Officer)
Nora Van Der Schraft (Partner & Dir-Strategic)
Alejandro Bascur (Partner & Dir-Strategic)
Paula Mackenzie (Partner & Dir-Strategic)
Claudia Zamora (Partner & Dir-Proposals)
Mariana Baltierra (Partner & Dir-Strategic)
Maria Teresa Ovalle (Dir-Strategic)

Subsidiary (Non-US):

Flipside Group (2)
135 Bishopsgate, London, EC2M 3AN, United Kingdom
Tel.: (44) 2038160293
Web Site: https://flipsidegroup.com
Advertising Services
N.A.I.C.S.: 541810
Tim Drake (Mng Dir)

Gaspar & Asociados (2)
R D Ana Helena De Salles Gusmao 230, Jd Paulistano, 01457-040, Sao Paulo, Brazil
Tel.: (55) 11 3037 3220
Web Site: http://www.gaspar.com.br
Sales Range: $25-49.9 Million
Emp.: 3
Public Relations
N.A.I.C.S.: 541820
Agostinho Gaspar (Founder & Partner)
Heloisa Picos (Partner & VP)
Lais Guarizz (Pres & Partner)

Affiliate (Non-US):

Geelmuyden-Kiese (2)
Vimmelskaftet 47 1, DK-1161, Copenhagen, Denmark
Tel.: (45) 339 59697
Web Site: http://www.geelmuyden-kiese.dk
Sales Range: $25-49.9 Million
Emp.: 30
N.A.I.C.S.: 541820

Subsidiary (Non-US):

Geelmuyden-Kiese (2)
Kornhamnstorg 61, 111 27, Stockholm, Sweden
Tel.: (46) 850650000
Web Site: https://www.gknordic.com
Sales Range: $25-49.9 Million
Emp.: 5
Public Relations
N.A.I.C.S.: 541820

Gillian Gamsy International (2)
51 West Street, Houghton, 2198, South Africa
Tel.: (27) 117281363
Web Site: https://www.ggisa.com
Sales Range: $25-49.9 Million
Emp.: 12
Public Relations
N.A.I.C.S.: 541820
Gillian Gamsy (Founder & CEO)

KRC Research (2)
Fox Court 14 Gray s Inn Road, London, WC1X 8WS, United Kingdom
Tel.: (44) 2026281118
Web Site: https://www.krcresearch.com
Sales Range: $25-49.9 Million
Emp.: 5
Public Relations Agency
N.A.I.C.S.: 541820

Subsidiary (Domestic):

KRC Research (2)
733 10th St NW, Washington, DC 20001
Tel.: (202) 628-1118
Web Site: https://www.krcresearch.com
Sales Range: $25-49.9 Million
Emp.: 15
Public Relations
N.A.I.C.S.: 541820
Mark David Richards (Sr VP & Supvr-Mgmt)
Wilson Law (CFO)
Devon Delmonico (VP-HR)
Ruth Yi (Dir-Field)
Pam Jenkins (Pres-Global Pub Affairs)
Doug Baker (Sr VP)

Subsidiary (Non-US):

Nueva Comunicacion-Weber Shandwick (2)
Norte 555 piso 12 Las Condes, Santiago, Rosario, Argentina
Tel.: (54) 24377700
Web Site: http://www.webershandwick.com
Sales Range: $25-49.9 Million
Emp.: 20
Advertising Agencies, Communications, Magazines, Media Buying Services, Outdoor, Print, Public Relations, Radio, T.V.
N.A.I.C.S.: 541820

Affiliate (Non-US):

Nueva Comunicacion-Weber Shandwick (2)
Ellauri 1212, 11300, Montevideo, Uruguay
Tel.: (598) 2 707 9956
Web Site: http://www.webershandwick.com
Sales Range: $25-49.9 Million
Emp.: 12
Public Relations
N.A.I.C.S.: 541820

PRP-Public Relations & Promotion Group (2)
Floor 4 Bldg 1 22/26 Ermolaevskiy per, Moscow, Russia
Tel.: (7) 4959373170
Web Site: http://www.prp.ru
Public Relations
N.A.I.C.S.: 541820
Irina Hartmann (Mng Dir)

Subsidiary (Domestic):

Powell Tate-Weber Shandwick (2)
733 10th St NW, Washington, DC 20001
Tel.: (202) 383-9700
Web Site: http://www.powelltate.com
Sales Range: $25-49.9 Million
Government/Political/Public Affairs, Public Relations
N.A.I.C.S.: 541820
Paul Massey (Pres)
Victoria Baxter (Exec VP-Social Impact)
Mac Cullen (Sr VP-Analytics)
Ellen DeMunter (Sr VP-Bus Dev)
Michelle Giuda (Exec VP-Geopolitical Strategy & Risk)
Kristine Fitton (Exec VP-Strategy & Plng)
Maureen Golga (Exec VP-Client Experience)
Jim Meszaros (Exec VP-Pub Affairs-Intl)
Saakshi Monga (Sr VP-Paid Plng & Buying)
Tim Ryan (Exec VP-Integrated Media Strategy)

Sally Squires (Sr VP-Food & Nutrition)
James Walker (Sr VP-Integrated Media Strategy)

Subsidiary (Non-US):

Prime time (2)
Einsteinova 23 Digital Park II Blok C, 851 01, Bratislava, Slovakia
Tel.: (421) 267267340
Web Site: https://www.primetime.sk
Sales Range: $25-49.9 Million
Emp.: 15
N.A.I.C.S.: 541820

Affiliate (Non-US):

Rimon Cohen-Weber Shandwick (2)
Raul Walenberg st 2a, Tel Aviv, Israel
Tel.: (972) 3 7684 444
Web Site: http://www.webershandwick.com
Public Relations
N.A.I.C.S.: 541820

Subsidiary (Domestic):

Rogers & Cowan (2)
1840 Century Park E 18th Fl, Los Angeles, CA 90067
Tel.: (310) 854-8100
Web Site: https://www.rcpmk.com
Sales Range: $25-49.9 Million
Public Relations Agency
N.A.I.C.S.: 541820
Shirley Hughes (Pres-Brands)

Subsidiary (Domestic):

Rogers & Cowan (3)
909 3rd Ave 9th fl, New York, NY 10022
Tel.: (212) 878-5501
Web Site: http://www.rogersandcowan.com
Sales Range: $25-49.9 Million
Emp.: 22
N.A.I.C.S.: 541820
Alan Nierob (Chm-Entertainment)
Shirley Hughes (Pres-Brands)

Unit (Domestic):

Sawyer Miller Advertising (2)
870 N Michigan Ste 24, Chicago, IL 60611
Tel.: (312) 988-2400
Web Site: http://www.webershandwick.com
Sales Range: $50-74.9 Million
N.A.I.C.S.: 541820

Sawyer Miller Advertising (2)
919 3rd Ave Ste 1500, New York, NY 10022
Tel.: (212) 445-8200
Web Site: http://www.webershandwick.com
Sales Range: $50-74.9 Million
Public Relations
N.A.I.C.S.: 541820

Subsidiary (Non-US):

Sigma International (Poland) Ltd. (2)
Nowogrodzka 31, 00-511, Warsaw, Poland
Tel.: (48) 22 628 04 88
Web Site: http://www.sigma.com.pl
Sales Range: $10-24.9 Million
Emp.: 25
Public Relations
N.A.I.C.S.: 541820
Tadeusz Jacewicz (Chm-Exec Bd)
Dawid Krazynski (Acct Mgr)
Anna Rosochacz (Acct Mgr)
Karol Witowski (Acct Mgr)

Subsidiary (Domestic):

The Rhoads Group (2)
607 14th St NW Ste 400, Washington, DC 20005
Tel.: (202) 347-0773
Web Site: https://cassidy.com
Sales Range: $25-49.9 Million
Emp.: 25
N.A.I.C.S.: 541820

Affiliate (Non-US):

Total Media Ggi (2)
1st Fl Old Warehouse Black, Fir Road Observatory, Cape Town, 7700, South Africa
Tel.: (27) 21 448 2020
Sales Range: $25-49.9 Million
Emp.: 11
N.A.I.C.S.: 541820

Subsidiary (Non-US):

Weber Shandwick (2)
im Klapperhof 3-5, 50670, Cologne, Germany
Tel.: (49) 2219499180
Web Site: http://www.webershandwick.de
Sales Range: $25-49.9 Million
Emp.: 30
Public Relations Agency
N.A.I.C.S.: 541820

Weber Shandwick (2)
Kehrwieder 10, 20457, Hamburg, Germany
Tel.: (49) 40 35 74 60 0
Web Site: http://www.webershandwick.de
Sales Range: $75-99.9 Million
Emp.: 25
Communications, Government/Political/Public Affairs, Investor Relations, Public Relations
N.A.I.C.S.: 541820

Weber Shandwick (2)
Heinzelova 33a, 10 000, Zagreb, Croatia
Tel.: (385) 1 5555 100
Sales Range: $25-49.9 Million
Emp.: 6
N.A.I.C.S.: 541820

Weber Shandwick (2)
Schonhauser Allee 37 Geb 11, 10435, Berlin, Germany
Tel.: (49) 30203510
Web Site: http://www.webershandwick.de
Sales Range: $25-49.9 Million
Emp.: 12
Public Relations
N.A.I.C.S.: 541820
Ilan Schafer (CEO)

Weber Shandwick (2)
351 King St E Suite 800, Toronto, M5G 0L6, ON, Canada
Tel.: (416) 964-6444
Web Site: https://webershandwick.ca
Sales Range: $25-49.9 Million
Public Relations
N.A.I.C.S.: 541820
Greg Power (Pres & CEO)
Robyn Adelson (Exec VP)
Alicia Aleksandrowicz (VP)
Ryan Bazeley (Sr VP)
Shipra Chauhan (VP)
Michelle Connolly (VP)
Sandra D Ambrosio (Sr VP)
Melissa Graham (Sr VP)
Rachel Hlinko (VP)
Leanne James (VP)
Melissa Legaspi (VP)
Marie-Eve Noel (VP)
Jackie Power (VP)
Alex Satouri (VP)
Jeffrey Spivock (Sr VP)
Cameron Summers (Sr VP)
Jennifer Wasley (VP)
Becca Young (Sr VP)
Jen Mcleod (VP)

Weber Shandwick (2)
207 Queen s Quay W Ste 400, Toronto, M5J 1A7, ON, Canada
Tel.: (416) 964-6444
Web Site: http://www.webershandwick.com
Sales Range: $25-49.9 Million
Emp.: 60
Public Relations
N.A.I.C.S.: 541820

Weber Shandwick (2)
2015 Main Street, Vancouver, V5T 3C2, BC, Canada
Tel.: (604) 681-7557
Web Site: http://www.webershandwick.com
Sales Range: $25-49.9 Million
Emp.: 2
Public Relations
N.A.I.C.S.: 541820

Weber Shandwick (2)
28-34 Boulevard du Parc, 92521, Neuilly-sur-Seine, France
Tel.: (33) 147595600
Web Site: https://www.webershandwick.fr
Sales Range: $25-49.9 Million
Emp.: 24
Government/Political/Public Affairs, Public Relations
N.A.I.C.S.: 541820

Weber Shandwick (2)
Speicherstrasse 59, 60327, Frankfurt am Main, Germany
Tel.: (49) 6991304370
Web Site: http://www.webershandwick.de
Sales Range: $25-49.9 Million
Emp.: 9
Public Relations
N.A.I.C.S.: 541820
Torsten Rotharmmel (Mng Dir-Health)

Weber Shandwick (2)
Karlstrasse 68, 80335, Munich, Germany
Tel.: (49) 893801790
Web Site: http://www.webershandwick.de
Sales Range: $25-49.9 Million
Emp.: 30
N.A.I.C.S.: 541820
Olaf Pempel (Exec VP-Client Experience)

Weber Shandwick (2)
Montevideo utca 10, 1037, Budapest, Hungary
Tel.: (36) 18878350
Web Site: http://www.webershandwick.hu
Sales Range: $25-49.9 Million
Emp.: 13
Government/Political/Public Affairs, Public Relations
N.A.I.C.S.: 541820

Weber Shandwick (2)
Via Vigevano 18, 20144, Milan, Italy
Tel.: (39) 02573781
Web Site: https://www.webershandwick.it
Sales Range: $25-49.9 Million
Public Relations
N.A.I.C.S.: 541820
Furio Garbagnati (CEO)

Weber Shandwick (2)
Via Magazzini Generali 18, 00154, Rome, Italy
Tel.: (39) 06 8404 341
Web Site: http://www.webershandwick.it
Sales Range: $25-49.9 Million
Emp.: 12
Public Relations
N.A.I.C.S.: 541820
Furio Garbagnati (CEO)

Weber Shandwick (2)
Via Luisa del Carretto 65, 10131, Turin, Italy
Tel.: (39) 011 819 3151
Web Site: http://www.webershandwick.com
Sales Range: $25-49.9 Million
Emp.: 12
Public Relations
N.A.I.C.S.: 541820

Weber Shandwick (2)
Casuariestraat 9, 2511 VB, Hague, Netherlands
Tel.: (31) 703121070
Web Site: https://www.webershandwick.nl
Sales Range: $25-49.9 Million
Emp.: 20
Public Relations
N.A.I.C.S.: 541820
Hafida Abahai (Mng Dir)

Weber Shandwick (2)
C/ Ciutat de Granada 123, 08018, Barcelona, Spain
Tel.: (34) 932360900
Web Site: http://www.webershandwick.es
Sales Range: $25-49.9 Million
Emp.: 25
Public Relations
N.A.I.C.S.: 541820
Raquel Capellas (Dir-Practice)
Natalia Sanchez (Dir-Practice)

Weber Shandwick (2)
Calle Enrique Jardiel Poncela 6, Edificio Cuzco III, 28016, Madrid, Spain
Tel.: (34) 917458600
Web Site: https://www.webershandwick.es
Sales Range: $25-49.9 Million
Emp.: 50
Public Relations
N.A.I.C.S.: 541820

Weber Shandwick (2)
Rue Francois-Bellot 10, 1206, Geneva, Switzerland
Tel.: (41) 228798500
Web Site: https://webershandwick.ch
Sales Range: $10-24.9 Million
Emp.: 20
Public Relations

The Interpublic Group of Companies,
Inc.—(Continued)
N.A.I.C.S.: 541820

Weber Shandwick (2)
Royal Naval House 32 Grosvenor Street
The Rocks, Sydney, 2000, NSW, Australia
Tel.: (61) 299944450
Web Site: http://webershandwickindia.com
Sales Range: $25-49.9 Million
Emp.: 26
Public Relations
N.A.I.C.S.: 541820

Weber Shandwick (2)
17th Floor China Life Tower 16 Chaoyang-
men Wai Da Jie, 16 Chaoyangmen Rd
Chaoyang, Beijing, 100020, China
Tel.: (86) 1085699999
Web Site: https://www.webershandwick.cn
Sales Range: $25-49.9 Million
Public Relations
N.A.I.C.S.: 541820
David Liu (Chm)

Weber Shandwick (2)
Room 1501-1508 the Centrepoint 374-2
Beijing Road, Yuexiu District, Guangzhou,
510030, China
Tel.: (86) 2088888100
Web Site: http://www.webershandwick.com
Sales Range: $25-49.9 Million
Emp.: 10
Public Relations
N.A.I.C.S.: 541820

Weber Shandwick (2)
18/F HuaiHai Plaza 1045 HuaiHai Zhong
Road, Shanghai, 200031, China
Tel.: (86) 2124110000
Web Site: http://www.webershandwick.cn
Emp.: 120
Public Relations
N.A.I.C.S.: 541820

Weber Shandwick (2)
8/F Oxford House Taikoo Place 979 King's
Road, 979 King's Rd, Quarry Bay, China
(Hong Kong)
Tel.: (852) 28451008
Web Site: http://www.webershandwick.com
Sales Range: $25-49.9 Million
Emp.: 50
Public Relations
N.A.I.C.S.: 541820

Weber Shandwick (2)
Menara Standard Chartered Lt 10, Jl Prof
Dr Satrio No 164, Jakarta, 12930, Indone-
sia
Tel.: (62) 2129543188
Web Site: http://webershandwick.co.id
Public Relations Agency
N.A.I.C.S.: 541820
Helina Wulandari (Office Mgr)

Weber Shandwick (2)
Mita Kokusai Bldg 13th Fl 1-4-28 Mita,
Minato-ku, Tokyo, 108-0073, Japan
Tel.: (81) 354277311
Web Site: http://www.webershandwick.com
Emp.: 60
Public Relations
N.A.I.C.S.: 541820

Weber Shandwick (2)
4-01 4th Fl Wisma LYL No 12 Jalan
51A/223, 46100, Petaling Jaya, Malaysia
Tel.: (60) 3 7843 3100
Web Site: http://www.webershandwick.com
Sales Range: $25-40.0 Million
Emp.: 25
Public Relations
N.A.I.C.S.: 541820
Rozani Jainudeen (Mng Dir)

Weber Shandwick (2)
10/F Jaka Bldg 6780 Ayala Ave Makati City,
Manila, 1200, Philippines
Tel.: (63) 2 817 5670
Web Site: http://www.webershandwick.com
Sales Range: $25-49.9 Million
Emp.: 20
N.A.I.C.S.: 541820

Weber Shandwick (2)
40A Orchard Road 07-01 MacDonald
House, Singapore, 238838, Singapore
Tel.: (65) 68258000

Web Site:
https://www.webershandwick.com.sg
Sales Range: $25-49.9 Million
Emp.: 50
Public Relations
N.A.I.C.S.: 541820
Baxter Jolly (Chm-Asia Pacific)
Tyler Kim (CEO-Asia Pacific)
Albert Shu (Pres)

Weber Shandwick (2)
1900 19th Floor No 2 Lane 150 Xinyi Road
Sec 5, Taipei, 11059, Taiwan
Tel.: (886) 227225779
Web Site: http://www.webershandwick.com
Emp.: 24
Public Relations
N.A.I.C.S.: 541820

Weber Shandwick (2)
Avenue De Cortenbergh 100, 1000, Brus-
sels, Belgium
Tel.: (32) 28949000
Web Site: https://webershandwick.eu
Sales Range: $25-49.9 Million
Emp.: 45
Communications, Public Relations
N.A.I.C.S.: 541820

Weber Shandwick - Mumbai (2)
G1/B Chhibber House Ground Floor, Saki-
naka Junction, Mumbai, 400072, Kurla
West, India
Tel.: (91) 2240311200
Web Site: http://webershandwickindia.com
Emp.: 70
Public Relations Agency
N.A.I.C.S.: 541820
Valerie Pinto (CEO)
Rohan Kanchan (Mng Dir-Consulting &
Strategy)

Weber Shandwick UK (2)
135 Bishopsgate, London, EC2M 3AN,
United Kingdom
Tel.: (44) 2070670000
Web Site:
https://www.webershandwick.co.uk
Sales Range: $75-99.9 Million
Emp.: 300
Public Relations
N.A.I.C.S.: 541820

Weber Shandwick Worldwide (2)
930 - 540 5 Ave Sw, Calgary, T2P 0M2, AB,
Canada
Tel.: (403) 294-9592
Web Site: http://www.webershandwick.com
Sales Range: $25-49.9 Million
Emp.: 4
Public Relations
N.A.I.C.S.: 541820

Subsidiary (Domestic):

Weber Shandwick-Atlanta (2)
944 Brady Ave, Atlanta, GA 30318
Tel.: (404) 266-7500
Web Site: http://www.webershandwick.com
Sales Range: $25-49.9 Million
Emp.: 10
Communications, Public Relations, Strategic
Planning
N.A.I.C.S.: 541820

Unit (Domestic):

Weber Shandwick-Austin (2)
2009 S Capital of Texas Hwy Ste 300, Aus-
tin, TX 78746
Tel.: (512) 794-4700
Web Site: http://www.webershandwick.com
Sales Range: $25-49.9 Million
Emp.: 10
Public Relations
N.A.I.C.S.: 541820

Subsidiary (Domestic):

Weber Shandwick-Baltimore (2)
3600 O'Donnell St Ste 250, Baltimore, MD
21224
Tel.: (410) 558-2100
Web Site: http://www.webershandwick.com
Sales Range: $25-49.9 Million
Emp.: 35
Digital/Interactive, Public Relations
N.A.I.C.S.: 541820

Weber Shandwick-Boston (2)
33 Arch St 14th Fl, Boston, MA 02110

Tel.: (617) 661-7900
Web Site: http://www.webershandwick.com
Sales Range: $25-49.9 Million
Emp.: 140
Public Relations
N.A.I.C.S.: 541820
Micho F. Spring (Chief Reputation Officer &
Chm-Global Corp Practice)

Weber Shandwick-Chicago (2)
875 N Michigan Ave Ste 2400, Chicago, IL
60611
Tel.: (312) 988-2400
Web Site: http://www.webershandwick.com
Sales Range: $50-74.9 Million
Emp.: 315
Public Relations
N.A.I.C.S.: 541820

Weber Shandwick-Dallas (2)
13455 Noel Rd 11th Fl, Dallas, TX 75240
Tel.: (469) 917-6200
Web Site: http://www.webershandwick.com
Sales Range: $25-49.9 Million
Emp.: 60
N.A.I.C.S.: 541820

Weber Shandwick-Denver (2)
999 18th St Ste 2700, Denver, CO 80202
Tel.: (303) 357-2381
Web Site: http://www.webershandwick.com
N.A.I.C.S.: 541820

Weber Shandwick-Detroit (2)
1 Detroit Ctr 500 Woodward Ave Ste 1800,
Detroit, MI 48226
Tel.: (248) 203-8000
Web Site: http://www.webershandwick.com
Sales Range: $25-49.9 Million
Emp.: 25
Public Relations
N.A.I.C.S.: 541820

Weber Shandwick-Los Angeles (2)
1840 Century Park E 2nd Fl, Los Angeles,
CA 90067
Tel.: (310) 854-8200
Web Site: http://www.webershandwick.com
Rev.: $50,000,000
Emp.: 28
N.A.I.C.S.: 541820
Sara Gavin (Pres-North America)

Weber Shandwick-Minneapolis (2)
510 Marquette Ave 13F, Minneapolis, MN
55402
Tel.: (952) 832-5000
Web Site:
http://webershandwickminneapolis.com
Sales Range: $50-74.9 Million
N.A.I.C.S.: 541820

Weber Shandwick-Saint Louis (2)
1831 Chestnut St, Saint Louis, MO 63101
Tel.: (314) 436-6565
Web Site: http://www.webershandwick.com
Sales Range: $25-49.9 Million
Emp.: 20
Public Relations
N.A.I.C.S.: 541820

Weber Shandwick-San Francisco (2)
45 Fremont St 11th Fl, San Francisco, CA
94105
Tel.: (415) 262-5600
Web Site: http://www.webershandwick.com
Sales Range: $25-49.9 Million
Emp.: 20
N.A.I.C.S.: 541820

Weber Shandwick-Seattle (2)
The Cloud Rm 1424 11th Ave Ste 400, Se-
attle, WA 98122
Tel.: (206) 576-5500
Web Site: http://webershandwickseattle.com
Sales Range: $25-49.9 Million
Emp.: 50
Public Relations
N.A.I.C.S.: 541820
Will Ludlam (Pres-West)
Christiaan Brown (Exec VP-West)
Brooke Shepard (Exec VP-Insights Lead-
Global)
Autumn Lerner (Sr VP-Health & Social Im-
pact)
Andrea Courtney (VP-Media Rels)
Megan Taubeneck (VP-Social Impact)

Unit (Domestic):

Weber Shandwick-Sunnyvale (2)

150 Mathilda Pl, Sunnyvale, CA 94086
Tel.: (408) 530-8400
Web Site: http://www.webershandwick.com
Sales Range: $25-49.9 Million
Emp.: 20
Public Relations
N.A.I.C.S.: 541820

Affiliate (Non-US):

Zimat-Weber Shandwick (2)
Avenida Rio Churubusco 422, Col Del Car-
men, Coyoacan, 04100, Mexico
Tel.: (52) 55 5658 4114
Web Site: http://www.webershandwick.com
Sales Range: $10-24.9 Million
Public Relations
N.A.I.C.S.: 541820

agencytwofifteen (1)
215 Leidesdorff St Fl 3, San Francisco, CA
94111
Tel.: (415) 262-3500
Sales Range: $25-49.9 Million
Emp.: 45
Advertising Agencies
N.A.I.C.S.: 541810
Jeremy Diessner (Exec Dir-Creative)

THE J.M. SMUCKER COM-PANY

1 Strawberry Ln, Orrville, OH 44667-
0280
Tel.: (330) 682-3000   **OH**
Web Site:
https://www.jmsmucker.com
Year Founded: 1897
SJM—(NYSE)
Rev.: $8,529,200,000
Assets: $14,991,400,000
Liabilities: $7,700,600,000
Net Worth: $7,290,800,000
Earnings: ($91,300,000)
Emp.: 5,800
Fiscal Year-end: 04/30/23
Food Products Mfr & Marketer
N.A.I.C.S.: 311421
Julia L. Sabin (VP-Govt Rels & Corp
Sustainability)
Mark T. Smucker (Chm, Pres & CEO)
Jeannette L. Knudsen (Chief Legal &
Compliance Officer & Sec)
Tucker H. Marshall (CFO)
John P. Brase (COO)
Jill R. Penrose (Chief People & Ad-
min Officer)
James Randal Day (Sr VP-Supply
Chain & Ops)
Robert D. Ferguson (Sr VP & Gen
Mgr-Pet Food & Pet Snacks)
Joseph Stanziano (Sr VP & Gen Mgr-
Coffee)
Amy C. Held (Chief Strategy & Intl
Officer)
Lindsey A. Tomaszewski (Sr VP-HR)
Bryan Hutson (Sr VP-Information
Svcs)
Dan Nowicki (Sr VP-Procurement &
Commodities)

Subsidiaries:

Ainsworth Pet Nutrition, Inc. (1)
18746 Mill St, Meadville, PA 16335
Tel.: (814) 724-7710
Web Site: http://www.betterthanbrands.com
Dry & Semi-Moist Canned Pet Foods Mfr
N.A.I.C.S.: 311111

Division (Domestic):

**Ainsworth Pet Nutrition, Inc. - Ains-
worth Specialty Brands Division** (2)
18746 Mill St, Meadville, PA 16335
Tel.: (800) 219-2558
Animal Feed Mfr
N.A.I.C.S.: 311119

Big Heart Pet Brands (1)
1 Maritime Plz, San Francisco, CA 94111
Tel.: (415) 247-3000
Web Site: http://www.bigheartpet.com

Sales Range: $1-4.9 Billion
Emp.: 2,200
Dog & Cat Food Mfr & Distr
N.A.I.C.S.: 311111

Plant (Domestic):

Big Heart Pet Brands - Bloomsburg
Plant **(2)**
6670 Low St, Bloomsburg, PA 17815-8613
Tel.: (570) 416-0232
Dog & Cat Food Mfr & Distr
N.A.I.C.S.: 311111

Subsidiary (Domestic):

Natural Balance Pet Foods, Inc. **(2)**
100 N 1st St Ste 200, Pacoima, CA 91502
Tel.: (818) 897-2521
Web Site:
   https://www.naturalbalanceinc.com
Pet Foods Mfr & Supplier
N.A.I.C.S.: 311119

Hostess Brands, Inc. **(1)**
7905 Quivira Rd, Lenexa, KS 66215
Tel.: (816) 701-4600
Web Site: https://www.hostessbrands.com
Rev.: $1,358,207,000
Assets: $3,492,199,000
Liabilities: $1,695,115,000
Net Worth: $1,797,084,000
Earnings: $164,195,000
Emp.: 2,800
Fiscal Year-end: 12/31/2022
Snack Cakes & Cookies Mfr & Distr
N.A.I.C.S.: 311812
Jeannette L. Knudsen *(Chief Legal Officer & Sec)*
Tucker H. Marshall *(CFO)*
John P. Brase *(Pres)*
Stuart Blankenhorn *(VP)*
Tina Lambert *(VP)*
Nadeem S. Ali *(Treas & VP)*
Peter O. Farah *(VP & Asst Sec)*

Holding (Non-US):

Hostess Brands, LLC **(2)**
(100%)
Tel.: (816) 701-4600
Web Site: https://www.hostesscakes.com
Snack Cake Mfr & Distr
N.A.I.C.S.: 311812

Subsidiary (Non-US):

Voortman Cookies Limited **(2)**
4475 North Service Road Suite 600, Burlington, L7L 4X7, ON, Canada
Tel.: (905) 335-9500
Web Site: https://www.voortman.com
Cookies Mfr & Retailer
N.A.I.C.S.: 311821
Douglas MacFarlane *(CEO)*

J.M. Smucker LLC **(1)**
1050 Stanton St, Ripon, WI 54971-0345
Tel.: (920) 745-6100
Vegetable Shortening & Peanut Butter Mfr
N.A.I.C.S.: 311225

JMS Foodservice, LLC **(1)**
1368 Progress Rd, Suffolk, VA 23434
Tel.: (757) 538-5664
Packaged Foods & Grains Mfr
N.A.I.C.S.: 311991

Knudsen & Sons, Inc. **(1)**
37 Speedway Ave, Chico, CA 95927
Tel.: (530) 899-5010
Web Site: http://www.rwknudsenfamily.com
Fruit & Vegetable Juice Mfr
N.A.I.C.S.: 311411

Rowland Coffee Roasters, Inc. **(1)**
5605 NW 82 Ave, Doral, FL 33166
Tel.: (305) 594-9063
Rev.: $110,000,000
Coffee Mfr & Whlsr
N.A.I.C.S.: 445298
Luis Huelga *(Coord-Nat'l Inventory & Pur)*
Cecilia Jimenez *(Sec)*

Subsidiary (Domestic):

Bustelo Coffee Roasting Co. **(2)**
60 Page Rd, Clifton, NJ 07012
Tel.: (973) 574-2700
Web Site: http://www.cafebustelo.com

Sales Range: $25-49.9 Million
Emp.: 52
Coffee Mfr
N.A.I.C.S.: 445298

Sahale Snacks, Inc. **(1)**
3411 S 120th Pl Ste 100, Seattle, WA 98168
Tel.: (206) 624-7244
Web Site: http://www.sahalesnacks.com
Sales Range: $25-49.9 Million
Emp.: 150
Snack Food Mfr
N.A.I.C.S.: 311919

Smucker Foods of Canada Corp. **(1)**
80 Whitehall Dr, Markham, L3R 0P3, ON, Canada **(100%)**
Tel.: (905) 940-9600
Web Site:
   https://www.smuckerawayfromhome.ca
Sales Range: $75-99.9 Million
Emp.: 200
Food Products Mfr
N.A.I.C.S.: 311999

Smucker Foodservice, Inc. **(1)**
1 Strawberry Ln, Orrville, OH 44667
Tel.: (330) 682-3000
Web Site:
   https://www.smuckerawayfromhome.com
Convenience Foods Mfr & Distr
N.A.I.C.S.: 311999

Smucker Natural Foods, Inc. **(1)**
37 Speedway Ave, Chico, CA 95928
Tel.: (530) 899-5000
Web Site: http://www.smucker.com
Sales Range: $200-249.9 Million
Emp.: 400
Mfr & Distr of Fruit Juices, Fruit Bars & Juice Spritzers
N.A.I.C.S.: 312111
Richard K. Smucker *(CEO)*

Smucker Specialty Foods
Company **(1)**
1050 Stanton St, Ripon, WI 54971
Tel.: (920) 745-6100
Web Site: http://www.smucker.com
Sales Range: $50-74.9 Million
Emp.: 150
Mfr of Fruit Spreads, Fruit Sauces & other Fruit Products for Consumers & Food Services
N.A.I.C.S.: 311421

The Folgers Coffee Company **(1)**
1 Strawberry Ln, Orrville, OH 44667-0280
Tel.: (330) 682-3000
Web Site: http://www.folgerscoffee.com
Sales Range: $1-4.9 Billion
Emp.: 1,250
Coffee & Tea Products Mfr
N.A.I.C.S.: 311920

THE JOINT CORP.

16767 N Perimeter Dr Ste 110,
Scottsdale, AZ 85260
Tel.: (480) 245-5960   DE
Web Site: https://www.thejoint.com
Year Founded: 1999
JYNT—(NASDAQ)
Rev.: $117,696,356
Assets: $87,150,859
Liabilities: $62,378,977
Net Worth: $24,771,882
Earnings: ($9,752,197)
Emp.: 444
Fiscal Year-end: 12/31/23
Chiropractic Care Clinics
N.A.I.C.S.: 621310
Jake Singleton *(CFO)*
Eric Simon *(VP-Franchise Sls & Dev)*
Charles Nelles *(CTO)*
Krischelle Tennessen *(Chief HR Officer)*

THE KROGER CO.

1014 Vine St, Cincinnati, OH 45202-1100
Tel.: (513) 762-4000   OH
Web Site:
   https://www.thekrogerco.com
Year Founded: 1883

KR—(NYSE)
Rev.: $150,039,000,000
Assets: $50,505,000,000
Liabilities: $38,904,000,000
Net Worth: $11,601,000,000
Earnings: $2,164,000,000
Emp.: 414,000
Fiscal Year-end: 03/02/24
Grocery & Multi-Department Store Operator
N.A.I.C.S.: 445110
Yael Cosset *(CIO & Sr VP)*
Stuart W. Aitken *(CMO, Chief Merchant Officer & Sr VP)*
Timothy A. Massa *(Chief People Officer & Sr VP-HR & Labor Rels)*
Erin S. Sharp *(VP-Mfg-Grp)*
Mary Ellen Adcock *(Sr VP-Ops)*
Todd A. Foley *(Interim CFO, Chief Acctg Officer, Grp VP & Controller)*
Christine S. Wheatley *(Gen Counsel, Sec & Grp VP)*
Kristal Howard *(Dir-Media Rels & Corp Comm)*
Gabriel Arreaga *(Sr VP-Supply Chain)*
Dan De La Rosa *(Grp VP-Fresh Mdsg)*
Rob Quast *(Head-IR)*
W. Rodney McMullen *(Chm & CEO)*

Subsidiaries:

84.51 LLC **(1)**
100 W 5th St, Cincinnati, OH 45202
Tel.: (513) 632-1020
Web Site: https://www.8451.com
Marketing Analysis & Research Services
N.A.I.C.S.: 541910
Terron Wilson *(Mgr-Talent-Diversity & Inclusion)*
Milen Mahadevan *(Pres)*
Bob Welch *(Sr VP-Customer Comm & Media)*
Cara Pratt *(Sr VP-Media)*
Allison Unkraut *(Sr VP-Client Leadership)*

Agri Products Inc **(1)**
2012 S Grant Ave, York, NE 68467
Tel.: (402) 362-5500
Web Site: https://www.agriproductsinc.com
Agriculture Products Mfr
N.A.I.C.S.: 926140

America's Beverage Co. **(1)**
1331 E Airport Fwy, Irving, TX 75062
Tel.: (972) 438-7632
Web Site: http://www.kroger.com
Sales Range: $250-299.9 Million
Emp.: 170
Carbonated Beverages Mfr
N.A.I.C.S.: 312111

Axium Healthcare Pharmacy,
Inc. **(1)**
550 Technology Pk Ste 1000, Lake Mary, FL 32746
Tel.: (407) 865-7795
Web Site: http://www.axiumhealthcare.com
Sales Range: $150-199.9 Million
Emp.: 200
Pharmacies
N.A.I.C.S.: 456110

Axium Pharmacy Holdings, Inc. **(1)**
108 State Rd 2 Ste 302, Guaynabo, PR 00966
Tel.: (787) 780-7200
Web Site: http://www.axiumhealthcare.com
Holding Company
N.A.I.C.S.: 551112

Baker's Supermarkets, Inc. **(1)**
5222 S 136th St, Omaha, NE 68137
Tel.: (402) 397-4321
Web Site: http://www.bakersplus.com
Sales Range: $50-74.9 Million
Emp.: 15
Supermarkets & Pharmacies
N.A.I.C.S.: 456110

CB&S Advertising Agency Inc **(1)**
3800 SE 22nd Ave, Portland, OR 97202
Tel.: (503) 797-3200
Advertising Agencies Services
N.A.I.C.S.: 541810

Rhonda Clark *(Mgr-Fin)*

Cala Co. **(1)**
1100 W Artesia Blvd, Compton, CA 90220
Tel.: (310) 884-9000
Emp.: 867
Grocery Store Operator
N.A.I.C.S.: 445110

Dillon Companies, Inc. **(1)**
725 E 4Th Ave, Hutchinson, KS 67501-1981 **(100%)**
Tel.: (620) 662-3316
Web Site: http://www.dillons.com
Sales Range: $550-599.9 Million
Emp.: 600
Grocery Products Retailer
N.A.I.C.S.: 445110

Subsidiary (Domestic):

King Soopers Inc. **(2)**
65 Tejon St, Denver, CO 80223
Tel.: (303) 778-3100
Web Site: http://www.kingsoopers.com
Sales Range: $1-9.9 Million
Grocery Store Operator
N.A.I.C.S.: 445110
Joe Kelley *(Pres)*

Distribution Trucking Company **(1)**
3800 SE 22nd Ave, Portland, OR 97202
Tel.: (503) 232-8844
Emp.: 5
General Freight Trucking Services
N.A.I.C.S.: 484121

Fred Meyer, Inc. **(1)**
3800 SE 22nd Ave, Portland, OR 97202-2918
Tel.: (503) 232-8844
Web Site: http://www.fredmeyer.com
Sales Range: $25-49.9 Billion
Emp.: 90,000
Holding Company
N.A.I.C.S.: 445110

Subsidiary (Domestic):

Fred Meyer Stores, Inc. **(2)**
10116 NE 8th St, Bellevue, WA 98004
Tel.: (425) 455-0870
Web Site: http://www.fredmeyer.com
Grocery Stores
N.A.I.C.S.: 445110

Fred Meyer Stores, Inc. **(2)**
3805 Se Hawthorne Blvd, Portland, OR 97214 **(100%)**
Tel.: (503) 872-3300
Web Site: http://www.fredmeyer.com
Sales Range: $400-449.9 Million
Emp.: 1,500
Department Stores
N.A.I.C.S.: 455110
Dan De La Rosa *(Pres-Columbus)*

Subsidiary (Domestic):

FM Retail Services Inc. **(3)**
222 Maurin Rd, Chehalis, WA 98532 **(100%)**
Tel.: (360) 740-6600
Web Site: http://www.fredmeyer.com
Sales Range: $10-24.9 Million
Emp.: 400
General Warehousing & Storage
N.A.I.C.S.: 493110

Fred Meyer Jewelers, Inc. **(3)**
3800 SE 22nd Ave, Portland, OR 97202 **(100%)**
Tel.: (503) 232-8844
Web Site:
   http://www.fredmeyerjewelers.com
Sales Range: $10-24.9 Million
Emp.: 1,500
Jewelry & Watch Retailer
N.A.I.C.S.: 458310

Fred Meyer of Alaska **(3)**
1000 E Northern Lights Blvd, Anchorage, AK 99508-4218
Tel.: (907) 264-9600
Web Site: http://www.fredmeyer.com
Rev.: $81,300,000
Emp.: 200
Department Stores, Discount
N.A.I.C.S.: 455110

Subsidiary (Domestic):

Ralphs Grocery Company **(2)**

The Kroger Co.—(Continued)

1100 W Artesia Blvd, Compton, CA
90220-5108　**(100%)**
Tel.: (310) 884-9000
Web Site: http://www.ralphs.com
Sales Range: $5-14.9 Billion
Emp.: 34,600
Retail Grocery Stores
N.A.I.C.S.: 445110
Mike Murphy (Pres)

Subsidiary (Domestic):

**Food 4 Less of Southern California,
Inc.**　**(3)**
1900 W Rosecrans Ave, Compton, CA
90220
Tel.: (310) 609-3385
Web Site: http://www.food4less.com
Sales Range: $100-124.9 Million
Grocery Products Retailer
N.A.I.C.S.: 445110

Subsidiary (Domestic):

**Smith's Food & Drug Centers,
Inc.**　**(2)**
828 S 900 W, Salt Lake City, UT 84104-
5105
Tel.: (801) 364-2548
Web Site:
　http://www.smithsfoodanddrug.com
Sales Range: $25-49.9 Million
Emp.: 300
Grocery & Drug Stores Chain
N.A.I.C.S.: 445110

Fry's Food and Drug Stores　**(1)**
500 S 99th Ave, Tolleson, AZ 85353
Tel.: (623) 936-2100
Web Site: http://www.frysfoodstores.com
Sales Range: $1-4.9 Billion
Emp.: 18,000
Supermarket & Multi-Department Stores
N.A.I.C.S.: 457110

Harris Teeter Supermarkets, Inc.　**(1)**
701 Crestdale Rd, Matthews, NC 28105-
1700
Tel.: (704) 844-3904
Web Site: http://www.harristeeter.com
Rev.: $4,709,866,000
Assets: $2,013,237,000
Liabilities: $884,365,000
Net Worth: $1,128,872,000
Earnings: $107,892,000
Emp.: 600
Fiscal Year-end: 10/01/2013
Holding Company; Supermarket Operator
N.A.I.C.S.: 551112

Subsidiary (Domestic):

**American & Efird Enterprises,
Inc.**　**(2)**
22 American St, Mount Holly, NC 28120
Tel.: (704) 951-2996
Web Site: https://www.amefird.com
Thread & Yarn Mfr
N.A.I.C.S.: 313110
Wesley Locust (Mgr-HR)

Subsidiary (Non-US):

**A&E Iplik Sanayi ve Ticaret Anonim
Sirketi**　**(3)**
Tugayyolu cad No 22v, cevizli Maltepe,
34846, Istanbul, Turkiye
Tel.: (90) 2164589842
216 305 65 15
N.A.I.C.S.: 313110
Selim Deniver (Mgr-Export)

**American & Efird (A&E Europe), Su-
kanci d.o.o.**　**(3)**
Novakova Ulica 6, 2000, Maribor, Slovenia
Tel.: (386) 2 250 43 30
Web Site: http://www.amefird.si
Yarn & Straps Mfr
N.A.I.C.S.: 313110

American & Efird (G.B.) Limited　**(3)**
Bankside Mills Chapelfield Radcliffe, Bury,
M26 1JF, United Kingdom
Tel.: (44) 1617661544
Web Site: http://www.amefird.co.uk
Sales Range: $25-49.9 Million
Emp.: 7
Industrial Sewing Thread Mfr

N.A.I.C.S.: 313110

**American & Efird (Malaysia) SDN.
BHD.**　**(3)**
5 Jalan Tembaga Desa Perindustrian, Kulai,
81000, Malaysia
Tel.: (60) 7 652 3381
Web Site: http://www.amefird.com
Industrial Sewing Thread Mfr
N.A.I.C.S.: 313110

**American & Efird Canada
Incorporated**　**(3)**
8301 Ray Lawson Blvd, Ville d'Anjou, H1J
1X9, QC, Canada
Tel.: (514) 385-0880
Web Site: http://www.amefird.ca
Emp.: 35
Industrial Sewing Thread Distr
N.A.I.C.S.: 423840

**American & Efird Mills (S) Pte.
Ltd.**　**(3)**
27 Mandai Estate 06-10 Innovation Place
Tower 2, Singapore, 729931, Singapore
Tel.: (65) 63647316
Sales Range: $25-49.9 Million
Emp.: 5
Industrial Sewing Thread Mfr
N.A.I.C.S.: 313110
Kenny Hui (Owner)

**American & Efird de Mexico, S.A. de
C V**　**(3)**
Calle 21 No 93-E x 14 Col Itzimna, 97100,
Merida, Yucatan, Mexico
Tel.: (52) 9999429800
Industrial Sewing Thread Mfr
N.A.I.C.S.: 313110

Hilos A&E de Costa Rica, S.A.　**(3)**
Zona Franca Metropolitana, Heredia, 106,
Costa Rica
Tel.: (506) 2509 2200
Web Site: http://www.amefird.com
Industrial Sewing Thread Mfr
N.A.I.C.S.: 313110

**Hilos A&E de El Salvador, S.A. de
C.V.**　**(3)**
Edificio D Kilometro 36 Carretera Panameri-
cana a Santa Ana Ciudad Arce, Departa-
mento La Libertad, San Salvador, El Salva-
dor
Tel.: (503) 23309800
Thread Mfr
N.A.I.C.S.: 313110

**Hilos American & Efird de Honduras,
S.A. de C.V.**　**(3)**
Complejo Elca, Choloma, Cortes, Honduras
Tel.: (504) 6695151
Thread Mfr
N.A.I.C.S.: 313110

**Hilos American & Efird de Mexico,
S.A. de C.V.**　**(3)**
Calle 21 93E x 14 Col Itzimna, 97100,
Merida, Yucatan, Mexico
Tel.: (52) 999 942 9800
Industrial Sewing Thread Distr
N.A.I.C.S.: 423840

Subsidiary (Non-US):

**Dongguan Dongmei Thread Mfg. Co.
Ltd.**　**(2)**
South China Dyeing Finishing Plant Nange
Industrial Village, Daojiao Town, Dongguan,
523172, Guangdong, China
Tel.: (86) 76988386828
Industrial Thread Mfr
N.A.I.C.S.: 313110

Subsidiary (Domestic):

Harris Teeter, Inc.　**(2)**
701 Crestdale Rd, Matthews, NC
28105　**(100%)**
Tel.: (704) 844-3904
Web Site: https://www.harristeeter.com
Sales Range: $1-4.9 Billion
Emp.: 14,500
Supermarket
N.A.I.C.S.: 445110

Ruddick Operating Company　**(2)**
300 Delaware Ave, Wilmington, DE 19801
Tel.: (302) 421-7361
Supermarket Operating Services

N.A.I.C.S.: 445110

**Infusion Solutions of Puerto Rico,
LLC**　**(1)**
108 Carr 2 Ste 301, Guaynabo, PR 00966-
1830
Tel.: (787) 780-7200
Infusion Therapy Services
N.A.I.C.S.: 621498

Inter-American Foods, Inc.　**(1)**
1014 Vine St, Cincinnati, OH 45202
Tel.: (513) 762-4000
Web Site:
　https://www.interamericanproducts.com
Coffee & Tea Mfr
N.A.I.C.S.: 311920

Ita, Inc.　**(1)**
150 Pierce Rd Ste 550, Itasca, IL 60143
Tel.: (847) 364-1121
Web Site: https://www.itaoffice.com
Pharmacy Store Services
N.A.I.C.S.: 456110
Shin Kishioka (Pres)
Ritu Agrawal (Mktg Dir)
Sam Ohta (Sr Mgr)
Takahiro Kumagai (Mgr)
Daisuke Higashimori (Mgr)

KPF, LLC　**(1)**
2 Embarcadero Ctr Fl 8, San Francisco, CA
94111
Tel.: (415) 944-5491
Business Support Services
N.A.I.C.S.: 561499

KRGP Inc.　**(1)**
7640 Beechmont Ave, Cincinnati, OH 45255
Tel.: (513) 232-1883
Web Site: https://www.kitchen1883.com
Hotel & Restaurant Management Services
N.A.I.C.S.: 721110

Kenlake Foods　**(1)**　**(100%)**
808 N 12Th St, Murray, KY 42071
Tel.: (270) 759-3021
Dry Mixes Packaging
N.A.I.C.S.: 311911

Kiosk Medicine Kentucky, LLC　**(1)**
2620 Elm Hill Pike, Nashville, TN 37214
Tel.: (615) 425-4200
Web Site: http://www.thelittleclinic.com
Healtcare Services
N.A.I.C.S.: 621999

Kroger Delta Marketing Area　**(1)**
800 Ridge Lake Blvd, Memphis, TN 38120
Tel.: (901) 765-4100
Sales Range: $10-24.9 Million
Emp.: 85
Supermarket
N.A.I.C.S.: 561110

Kroger Limited Partnership I　**(1)**
150 Tri County Pkwy, Cincinnati, OH 45246
Tel.: (513) 782-3300
Emp.: 21,000
Grocery Store Operator
N.A.I.C.S.: 445110

Kroger Prescription Plans, Inc.　**(1)**
1014 Vine St, Cincinnati, OH 45202
Tel.: (513) 762-4968
Web Site: https://www.kpp-rx.com
Sales Range: $25-49.9 Million
Emp.: 10
Pharmacy Services
N.A.I.C.S.: 456110

**Kroger Specialty Infusion AL,
LLC**　**(1)**
2511 Ross Clark Cir, Dothan, AL 36301
Institutional Pharmacy Services
N.A.I.C.S.: 456110
Lee Jones (Acct Mgr-Specialty)

**Kroger Specialty Infusion CA,
LLC**　**(1)**
19110 Van Ness Ave, Torrance, CA 90501
Institutional Pharmacy Services
N.A.I.C.S.: 456110
Ryan Ferguson (Acct Mgr-Specialty)

**Kroger Specialty Infusion TX,
LLC**　**(1)**
1748 N Greenville Ave, Richardson, TX
75081
Institutional Pharmacy Services
N.A.I.C.S.: 456110

Sandy DiTullio (Acct Mgr-Specialty)

Kroger Specialty Pharmacy, Inc.　**(1)**
3200 Lake Emma Rd Ste 1000, Lake Mary,
FL 32746
Web Site:
　https://www.krogerspecialtypharmacy.com
Institutional Pharmacy Services
N.A.I.C.S.: 456110
Chris Anderson (Acct Mgr-Specialty)
Tom Shelly (Gen Mgr)
John King (Sr VP-Sls)
Mark Landry (Sr VP-Ops)

Subsidiary (Domestic):

**Kroger Specialty Pharmacy FL 2
LLC**　**(2)**
3200 Lake Emma Rd Ste 1000, Lake Mary,
FL 32746
Web Site:
　https://www.krogerspecialtyinfusion.com
Grocery Store Operator
N.A.I.C.S.: 445110

**Kroger Specialty Pharmacy LA,
LLC**　**(2)**
2731 Manhattan Blvd Ste B17, Harvey, LA
70058
Institutional Pharmacy Services
N.A.I.C.S.: 456110
Bright Ogbogu (Acct Mgr-Specialty)

MPearlRock LP　**(1)**
3835 PGA Blvd, Ste 901 Palm, Beach Gar-
dens, FL 33410
Tel.: (212) 497-1400
Web Site: https://www.mpearlrock.com
Food & Beverage
N.A.I.C.S.: 311999

Subsidiary (Domestic):

Green Grass Foods, Inc.　**(2)**
15900 SE Eastgate Way Bldg B Ste 125,
Bellevue, WA 98008
Web Site: http://www.nutpods.com
Sales Range: $10-24.9 Million
Emp.: 23
Dairy Products Distr
N.A.I.C.S.: 424430
Geoff Haydon (CFO)
Emi Ha (Coord-Logistics)
Andrew Prentice (Coord-Key Accts)
Natalie Esteb (Coord-Mktg)

Main & Vine LLC　**(1)**
5010 Point Fosdick Dr NW, Gig Harbor, WA
98335
Tel.: (253) 432-7116
Web Site: http://www.mainandvineshop.com
Alcoholic Beverage Distr
N.A.I.C.S.: 424820

Market6, Inc.　**(1)**
Corporate 500 Ctr 500 Lake Cook Rd Ste
150, Deerfield, IL 60015　**(100%)**
Web Site: http://www.market6.com
Emp.: 55
Personalized Shopping Services
N.A.I.C.S.: 541512

Michigan Dairy, L.L.C.　**(1)**
29601 Industrial Rd, Livonia, MI 48150
Tel.: (734) 367-5390
Grocery Retailer
N.A.I.C.S.: 445110

Mini Mart, Inc.　**(1)**
1600 Broadway, Kerrville, TX 78028
Tel.: (830) 257-6464
Web Site: https://mini-mart.com
Supermarket Store Services
N.A.I.C.S.: 445110

Murray's LIC LLC　**(1)**
264 Bleecker St, New York, NY 10014
Tel.: (646) 476-8882
Web Site:
　http://www.murrayscheesebar.com
Restaurant Services
N.A.I.C.S.: 722511
Cara Seigel (Dir-Bus Dev & Hospitality)

Murrays Cheese LLC　**(1)**
254 Bleecker St, New York, NY 10014
Tel.: (212) 243-3289
Web Site: https://www.murrayscheese.com
Cheese Merchant Whslr
N.A.I.C.S.: 424450

Pace Dairy Foods (1)
2700 Valleyhigh Dr NW, Rochester, MN
55901
Tel.: (507) 288-6315
Sales Range: $125-149.9 Million
Emp.: 300
Cheese Products Mfr
N.A.I.C.S.: 311513
Jim Lehman (Gen Mgr)

Pace Dairy Foods Company (1)
2700 Valleyhigh Dr NW, Rochester, MN
55901-7601
Tel.: (507) 288-6315
Dairy Products Mfr
N.A.I.C.S.: 311514
Tristan Torres (Mgr-HR)

Peyton's-Southeastern, Inc. (1)
153 Refreshment Ln SW, Cleveland, TN
37311
Tel.: (423) 614-1000
Emp.: 1,000
Warehouse Product Distr
N.A.I.C.S.: 424990

Pontiac Foods, Inc. (1)
813 Bookman Rd, Elgin, SC 29045-9609
Tel.: (803) 699-1600
Coffee & Tea Mfr
N.A.I.C.S.: 311920
John Masa (Gen Mgr)

Relish Labs LLC (1)
400 N Michigan Ave Ste 1400, Chicago, IL
60611
Tel.: (872) 225-2433
Web Site: http://www.homechef.com
Emp.: 700
Meal Delivery Services
N.A.I.C.S.: 492210
Pat Vihtelic (Founder)
Pat Sullivan (CFO)
Erik Jensen (CEO)
Rich DeNardis (Chief Revenue Officer)
Latasha Kempadoo (Chief People Officer)
David McCoy (VP-Fin)
Alice Thompson (COO)
Katie Bevier (CTO)

Roundys, Inc. (1)
875 E Wisconsin Ave, Milwaukee, WI 53202
Tel.: (414) 231-5000
Web Site: http://www.roundys.com
Emp.: 7,764
Grocery & Multi-department Store Operator
N.A.I.C.S.: 445110

Subsidiary (Domestic):

Roundy's Supermarkets Inc. (2)
875 E Wisconsin Ave, Milwaukee, WI 53202
Tel.: (414) 231-5000
Web Site: http://www.roundys.com
Sales Range: $1-4.9 Billion
Wholesale & Retail Food Distribution
N.A.I.C.S.: 424490
Michael Marx (Pres)

Schnuck Markets, Inc. (1)
11420 Lackland Rd, Saint Louis, MO
63146-3559
Tel.: (314) 994-9900
Web Site: https://schnucks.com
Emp.: 12,000
Supermarkets & Other Grocery Retailers
(except Convenience Retailers)
N.A.I.C.S.: 445110
Todd R. Schnuck (Chm & CEO)
Bill Bradley (Chief Mktg & Comm Officer)

Scott's Food and Pharmacy (1)
4118 N Clinton St, Fort Wayne, IN 46805-
1210
Tel.: (260) 483-9537
Web Site: http://www.scottsfood.com
Sales Range: $10-24.9 Million
Emp.: 40
Grocery Stores
N.A.I.C.S.: 445110

Second Story, Inc. (1)
1330 NW 14th Ave, Portland, OR 97209
Tel.: (503) 444-3710
Web Site: http://www.secondstory.com
Business Support Services
N.A.I.C.S.: 561990
Chris Dewan (Dir-Design)

Smith's Beverage of Wyoming (1)

2531 Foothill Blvd, Rock Springs, WY
82901
Tel.: (307) 362-1722
Sales Range: $25-49.9 Million
Emp.: 90
Drug & Proprietary Stores
N.A.I.C.S.: 456110

Smiths Food & Drugs, Inc. (1)
195 3rd Ave E N, Kalispell, MT 59901
Tel.: (406) 752-5037
Grocery Stores, Chain
N.A.I.C.S.: 445110

**Southern Ice Cream Specialties
Inc** (1)
1058 King Industrial Dr, Marietta, GA 30062
Tel.: (770) 428-0452
Snack & Nonalcoholic Beverage Bars
N.A.I.C.S.: 722515

TH Midwest, Inc. (1)
1910 Stringtown Rd, Grove City, OH 43123
Tel.: (614) 871-1289
Web Site: http://www.turkeyhillstores.com
Supermarket & Grocery Stores
N.A.I.C.S.: 445110

TLC Corporate Services LLC (1)
8 Cadillac Dr, Brentwood, TN 37027
Tel.: (615) 425-4207
Professional Scientific & Technical Services
N.A.I.C.S.: 541990

Tara Foods (1)
1900 Cowles Ln, Albany, GA 31705
Tel.: (229) 431-1330
Web Site: http://www.kroger.com
Sales Range: $50-74.9 Million
Emp.: 150
Peanut Butter Suppliers
N.A.I.C.S.: 311911

The Kroger Co. of Michigan (1)
40399 Grand River Rd Ste 110, Novi, MI
48375
Tel.: (248) 536-1500
Supermarket & Grocery Retailer
N.A.I.C.S.: 445110
Ken DeLuca (Pres)

The Little Clinic LLC (1)
375 Crossroads Blvd, Cold Spring, KY
41076
Tel.: (859) 448-1201
Web Site: http://www.thelittleclinic.com
Sales Range: $25-49.9 Million
Emp.: 2
Supermarket & Grocery Products Whslr
N.A.I.C.S.: 445110

Subsidiary (Domestic):

The Little Clinic of Arizona LLC (2)
6470 S Higley Rd, Gilbert, AZ 85298
Tel.: (480) 809-2409
Freestanding Emergency Medical Services
N.A.I.C.S.: 621493

The Little Clinic of Colorado LLC (2)
9551 S University Blvd, Littleton, CO 80126
Tel.: (303) 459-5639
Web Site: http://www.thelittleclinic.com
Emp.: 3
Health Care & Allied Services
N.A.I.C.S.: 621999

The Little Clinic of IN LLC (2)
815 Highlander Point Dr, Floyds Knobs, IN
47119
Tel.: (812) 923-7146
Web Site: http://www.thelittleclinic.com
Health Care & Allied Services
N.A.I.C.S.: 621999

The Little Clinic of Ohio LLC (2)
1745 Morse Rd, Columbus, OH 43229
Tel.: (614) 405-9415
Offices Of Health Practitioner
N.A.I.C.S.: 621399

**The Little Clinic of Tennessee
LLC** (2)
210 Franklin Rd Ste 100, Brentwood, TN
37027
Tel.: (615) 393-6550
Web Site: http://www.thelittleclinic.com
Medical Devices
N.A.I.C.S.: 622110

Vitacost.com, Inc. (1)

4700 Exchange Ct Ste 200, Boca Raton,
FL 33431
Tel.: (561) 982-4180
Web Site: https://www.vitacost.com
Vitamins & Nutraceuticals Online Retailer &
Catalog Sales
N.A.I.C.S.: 424210

THE LGL GROUP, INC.
2525 Shader Rd, Orlando, FL 32804
Tel.: (407) 298-2000   DE
Web Site: https://www.lglgroup.com
LGL—(NYSEAMEX)
Rev.: $1,655,000
Assets: $39,785,000
Liabilities: $1,295,000
Net Worth: $38,490,000
Earnings: ($2,992,000)
Emp.: 5
Fiscal Year-end: 12/31/22
Holding Company; Electronic Compo-
nent Mfr
N.A.I.C.S.: 551112
Timothy Foufas (Co-CEO)
Marc J. Gabelli (Chm & Co-CEO)

Subsidiaries:

Precise Time & Frequency, LLC (1)
50L Audubon Rd, Wakefield, MA 01880
Tel.: (781) 245-9090
Web Site: https://www.ptf-llc.com
Sales Range: $1-9.9 Million
Search, Detection, Navigation, Guidance,
Aeronautical & Nautical System & Instru-
ment Manufacturing
N.A.I.C.S.: 334511

THE LOVESAC COMPANY
2 Landmark Sq Ste 300, Stamford,
CT 06901
Tel.: (207) 273-9733   DE
Web Site: https://www.lovesac.com
Year Founded: 1995
LOVE—(NASDAQ)
Rev.: $651,545,000
Assets: $418,054,000
Liabilities: $224,794,000
Net Worth: $193,260,000
Earnings: $28,242,000
Emp.: 769
Fiscal Year-end: 01/29/23
Furniture Mfr & Retailer
N.A.I.C.S.: 337121
Mary Fox (Pres & COO)
Keith Siegner (CFO & Exec VP)
Shawn D. Nelson (CEO)

THE MACERICH COMPANY
401 Wilshire Blvd Ste 700, Santa
Monica, CA 90401
Tel.: (310) 394-6000   MD
Web Site: https://www.macerich.com
Year Founded: 1965
MAC—(NYSE)
Rev.: $859,164,000
Assets: $8,094,139,000
Liabilities: $5,144,790,000
Net Worth: $2,949,349,000
Earnings: ($66,068,000)
Emp.: 650
Fiscal Year-end: 12/31/22
Real Estate Investment Trust
N.A.I.C.S.: 525990
Jackson Hsieh (Pres & CEO)
Edward C. Coppola (Founder)
Christopher J. Zecchini (Chief Acctg
Officer & Sr VP)
Scott W. Kingsmore (CFO, Treas &
Sr Exec VP)
David M. Short (Exec VP-Asset
Mgmt)
Ken Volk (Exec VP-Bus Dev)
Michael Slavin (Sr VP-IT)
Doug Healey (Sr Exec VP-Leasing)
Olivia Bartel Leigh (Exec VP-Portfolio
Ops & People)
Jamie Bourbeau (Sr VP-Outlet Div)
F. K. Grunert (Exec VP-Leasing)

Michael Guerin (Exec VP-Leasing)
Scott Nelson (Sr VP-Real Estate
Svcs)
Ann C. Menard (Chief Legal Officer,
Sec & Sr Exec VP)
Will Voegele (Chief Dev Officer &
Exec VP)
Garrett Newland (Sr VP-Real Estate
Svcs)
Bob Beffa (Sr VP)
Tom Birdsall (Sr VP)
Eric Bunyan (Sr VP)
Kimberly Choukalas (Sr VP)
Melissa Freas (Sr VP)
David Hofmeister (Sr VP)
Jennifer Jensen (Sr VP)
Ted Kaminski (Sr VP)
Mark Klein (Sr VP)
Neal Kleinman (Sr VP)
Brad Miller (Sr VP)
Nancy S. Rendos (Sr VP)
Kathy Sherwood (Sr VP)
Alison Wais (Sr VP)
Zack Gaskell (Sr VP)
Jeanne Butz (VP)
Erin Byrne (VP)
Meghan Kaltenstein (VP)
Nikki Keiser (VP)
Aaron Keswick (VP)
John Kinsella (VP)
Michael Morlan (VP)
Hillary Muss (VP)
Hayley Rable (VP)

Subsidiaries:

Arrowhead Towne Center LLC (1)
7700 W Arrowhead Towne Ctr, Glendale,
AZ 85308-8612
Tel.: (623) 979-7777
Web Site:
  https://www.arrowheadtownecenter.com
Sales Range: $25-49.9 Million
Emp.: 10
Nonresidential Building Rental & Leasing
Services
N.A.I.C.S.: 531120
Jesse Benites (Mgr-Property)

CCP VALENCIA LLC (1)
4706 Broadway Ste 260, Kansas City, MO
64112
Tel.: (816) 561-4442
Non Residential Building Operator
N.A.I.C.S.: 531120
Bruce Crockett (Dir-Facilities)

**Camelback Colonnade Associates
Limited Partnership** (1)
11411 N Tatum Blvd, Phoenix, AZ 85028
Tel.: (602) 953-6200
Nonresidential Building Rental & Leasing
Services
N.A.I.C.S.: 531120

Corte Madera Village, LLC (1)
1618 Redwood Hwy, Corte Madera, CA
94925
Tel.: (415) 924-8588
Web Site:
  https://www.villageatcortemadera.com
Nonresidential Building Rental & Leasing
Services
N.A.I.C.S.: 531120

Desert Sky Mall LLC (1)
7611 W Thomas Rd, Phoenix, AZ 85033
Tel.: (623) 245-1400
Web Site: https://www.desertskymall.com
Nonresidential Building Rental & Leasing
Services
N.A.I.C.S.: 531120
Zeke Valenzuela (Sr Mgr-Property Mgmt)
Jose Barbosa (Mgr-Leasing Dev)

Fashion Outlets of Chicago LLC (1)
5220 Fashion Outlets Way Ste 230, Rose-
mont, IL 60018
Tel.: (847) 928-7500
Web Site:
  https://www.fashionoutletsofchicago.com
Clothing Retail Stores
N.A.I.C.S.: 458110
James Hansen (Sr Mgr-Property Mgmt)
Katie Walsh (Sr Mgr-Mktg)

The Macerich Company—(Continued)

Jennifer Devermann (Sr Mgr-Tourism)
Erica Strama (Sr Mgr-Bus Dev-Midwest)
Lee Ra Johnson (Asst VP-Outlet Leasing)

Flagstaff Mall SPE LLC (1)
4650 N US Hwy 89, Flagstaff, AZ 86004
Tel.: (928) 526-3949
Web Site: http://www.flagstaffmall.com
Emp.: 30
Nonresidential Building Rental & Leasing Services
N.A.I.C.S.: 531120

Flatiron Property Holding, LLC (1)
1 W Flatiron Crossing Dr, Broomfield, CO 80021
Tel.: (720) 887-9900
Web Site: https://www.flatironcrossing.com
Emp.: 15
Nonresidential Building Rental & Leasing Services
N.A.I.C.S.: 531120
Heather Drake (Sr Mgr-Mktg)
Kate Taggart Honea (Mgr-Property)

Green Acres Mall, L.L.C. (1)
2034 Green Acres Mall Sunrise Hwy, Valley Stream, NY 11581
Tel.: (516) 561-7360
Web Site: https://www.greenacresmallonline.com
Commercial Building Rental Services
N.A.I.C.S.: 531120
Joseph Floccari (Mgr-Property Mgr)

Green Tree Mall LLC (1)
757 E Lewis and Clark Pkwy, Clarksville, IN 47129
Tel.: (812) 283-0741
Web Site: https://www.greentreemall.com
Nonresidential Building Rental & Leasing Services
N.A.I.C.S.: 531120

MACD LLC (1)
1821 S Main St, Weatherford, TX 76086
Tel.: (817) 613-1189
Health Club
N.A.I.C.S.: 713940

MACERICH DB LLC (1)
11411 N Tatum Blvd, Phoenix, AZ 85028-2399
Tel.: (602) 953-6200
Web Site: https://www.macerich.com
Real Estate Agency Services
N.A.I.C.S.: 531210

MACERICH LAKEWOOD LP (1)
500 Lakewood Ctr Mall, Lakewood, CA 90712
Tel.: (562) 633-0437
Emp.: 3
Business Management Services
N.A.I.C.S.: 561110
Annette B. Norwood (Sr Mgr-Mktg)

Macerich Broadway Plaza LLC (1)
1275 Broadway Plz, Walnut Creek, CA 94596
Tel.: (925) 939-7601
Web Site: https://www.broadwayplaza.com
Nonresidential Building Rental & Leasing Services
N.A.I.C.S.: 531120

Macerich Deptford LLC (1)
1750 Deptford Ctr Rd, Deptford, NJ 08096
Tel.: (856) 848-8100
Web Site: http://www.doptfordmall.com
Emp.: 6
Nonresidential Building Rental & Leasing Services
N.A.I.C.S.: 531120

Macerich Lake Square Mall LLC (1)
10401 US-441, Leesburg, FL 34788
Tel.: (352) 787-1200
Web Site: https://www.lakesquaremall.com
Sales Range: $25-49.9 Million
Emp.: 5
Nonresidential Building Rental & Leasing Services
N.A.I.C.S.: 531120

Macerich Lakewood, LLC (1)
500 Lakewood Ctr, Lakewood, CA 90712
Tel.: (562) 633-0437

Web Site:
https://www.shoplakewoodcenter.com
Nonresidential Building Rental & Leasing Services
N.A.I.C.S.: 531120

Macerich Lubbock GP Corp. (1)
6002 Slide Rd, Lubbock, TX 79414-4310
Tel.: (806) 792-4654
Web Site: http://www.southplainsmall.com
Sales Range: $25-49.9 Million
Emp.: 8
Nonresidential Building Rental & Leasing Services
N.A.I.C.S.: 531120
Beth Bridges (Sr Mgr-Property Mgmt)
Ashley Knox (Sr Mgr-Mktg)
Megan Renfro (Mgr-Leasing Dev)
Meghan Guarino (Sr Mgr-Leasing)
Bryan Vesely (Coord-Tenant)

Macerich North Park Mall LLC (1)
320 W Kimberly Rd, Davenport, IA 52806
Tel.: (563) 391-4500
Web Site: https://www.north-park-mall-ia.com
Emp.: 8
Nonresidential Building Rental & Leasing Services
N.A.I.C.S.: 531120

Macerich Northridge LP (1)
796 Northridge Mall, Salinas, CA 93906
Tel.: (831) 449-7226
Web Site: https://www.shop-northridge-mall.com
Nonresidential Building Rental & Leasing Services
N.A.I.C.S.: 531120

Macerich Oaks LLC (1)
350aW Hillcrest Dr, Thousand Oaks, CA 91360
Tel.: (805) 495-2032
Web Site: http://www.shoptheoaksmall.com
Nonresidential Building Rental & Leasing Services
N.A.I.C.S.: 531120

Macerich Panorama LP (1)
8401 Van Nuys Blvd, Panorama City, CA 91402
Tel.: (818) 894-9258
Web Site: https://www.panoramamall.com
Sales Range: $25-49.9 Million
Emp.: 10
Nonresidential Building Rental & Leasing Services
N.A.I.C.S.: 531120
Aaron Luna (Mgr-Specialty Leasing)

Macerich Rimrock GP Corp. (1)
300 S 24th St W, Billings, MT 59102
Tel.: (406) 656-3206
Web Site: http://www.rimrockmall.com
Nonresidential Building Rental & Leasing Services
N.A.I.C.S.: 531120

Macerich Santa Monica LP (1)
401 Wilshire Blvd Ste 700, Santa Monica, CA 90401
Tel.: (800) 421-7237
Sales Range: $75-99.9 Million
Emp.: 350
Nonresidential Building Rental & Leasing Services
N.A.I.C.S.: 531120

Macerich Santa Monica Place Corp. (1)
315 Colorado Ave, Santa Monica, CA 90401
Tel.: (310) 260-8333
Web Site: http://www.santamonicaplace.com
Nonresidential Building Rental & Leasing Services
N.A.I.C.S.: 531120
Julia Ladd (Asst VP-Property Mgmt)
Leeta Warren (Sr Mgr-Specialty Leasing)
Stephanie Eglin (Mgr-Mktg)
Hayley Rable (VP-Leasing)
Aaron Pratt (Asst VP-Tenant Coordination)
Jessica Janes (Mgr-Restaurant Leasing)

Macerich South Park Mall LLC (1)
4500 16th St, Moline, IL 61265
Tel.: (309) 797-6142
Web Site: https://www.shopsouthparkmall-il.com

Emp.: 5
Nonresidential Building Rental & Leasing Services
N.A.I.C.S.: 531120

Macerich South Plains LP (1)
6002 Slide Rd, Lubbock, TX 79414-8208
Tel.: (806) 792-4653
Web Site: https://www.southplainsmall.com
Nonresidential Building Rental & Leasing Services
N.A.I.C.S.: 531120

Macerich Southridge Mall LLC (1)
1111 E Army Post Rd, Des Moines, IA 50315-5970
Tel.: (515) 287-3881
Web Site:
https://www.shopsouthridgemall.com
Nonresidential Building Rental & Leasing Services
N.A.I.C.S.: 531120

Macerich Stonewood, LLC (1)
251 Stonewood St, Downey, CA 90241
Tel.: (562) 904-1832
Web Site:
https://www.shopstonewoodcenter.com
Nonresidential Building Rental & Leasing Services
N.A.I.C.S.: 531120

Macerich Twenty Ninth Street LLC (1)
1710 29th St, Boulder, CO 80301
Tel.: (303) 444-0722
Web Site: http://www.twentyninthstreet.com
Sales Range: $25-49.9 Million
Emp.: 10
Nonresidential Building Rental & Leasing Services
N.A.I.C.S.: 531120

Macerich Tysons LLC (1)
1961 Chain Bridge Rd, Tysons Corner, VA 22102
Tel.: (703) 847-7300
Web Site:
https://www.tysonscornercenter.com
Nonresidential Building Rental & Leasing Services
N.A.I.C.S.: 531120

Macerich Valley River Center LLC (1)
293 Valley River Ctr, Eugene, OR 97401
Tel.: (541) 683-5513
Web Site: https://www.valleyrivercenter.com
Emp.: 15
Nonresidential Building Rental & Leasing Services
N.A.I.C.S.: 531120
Rob McOmie (Mgr-Property)

Macerich Victor Valley LLC (1)
14400 Bear Vly Rd Ste 735, Victorville, CA 92392
Tel.: (760) 241-3145
Web Site:
http://www.themallofvictorvalley.com
Nonresidential Building Rental & Leasing Services
N.A.I.C.S.: 531120
Terri Relf (Sr Mgr-Mktg)
Laura Andre (Mgr-Property)

Macerich Vintage Faire Limited Partnership (1)
3401 Dale Rd Ste 483, Modesto, CA 95356
Tel.: (209) 408-1850
Web Site:
https://www.shopvintagefairemall.com
Emp.: 100
Nonresidential Building Rental & Leasing Services
N.A.I.C.S.: 531120

Macerich Westside GP Corp. (1)
10800 W Pico Blvd Ste 312, Los Angeles, CA 90064
Tel.: (310) 474-2785
Nonresidential Building Rental & Leasing Services
N.A.I.C.S.: 531120

Macerich Westside Pavilion Property LLC (1)
10800 W Pico Blvd Ste 312, Los Angeles, CA 90064
Tel.: (310) 474-2785

Web Site: http://www.westsidepavilion.com
Sales Range: $25-49.9 Million
Emp.: 10
Nonresidential Building Rental & Leasing Services
N.A.I.C.S.: 531120

North Bridge Chicago LLC (1)
520 N Michigan Ave, Chicago, IL 60611
Tel.: (312) 222-1622
Web Site:
https://www.theshopsatnorthbridge.com
Sales Range: $25-49.9 Million
Emp.: 15
Nonresidential Building Rental & Leasing Services
N.A.I.C.S.: 531120
Erica Strama (Sr Mgr-Bus Dev-Midwest)
Katie Walsh (Sr Mgr-Mktg)

Northgate Mall Associates (1)
5800 Northgate Mall Ste 200, San Rafael, CA 94903
Tel.: (415) 479-5956
Web Site: http://www.shopatnorthgate.com
Sales Range: $25-49.9 Million
Emp.: 25
Nonresidential Building Rental & Leasing Services
N.A.I.C.S.: 531120
May Mar (Mgr-Property)

PPR Washington Square LLC (1)
9585 SW Washington Sq Rd, Portland, OR 97223-4450
Tel.: (503) 639-8860
Web Site:
https://www.shopwashingtonsquare.com
Nonresidential Building Rental & Leasing Services
N.A.I.C.S.: 531120

QUEENS CENTER REIT LLC (1)
401 Wilshire Blvd, Santa Monica, CA 90401
Tel.: (310) 394-6000
Web Site: http://www.macerich.com
Nonresidential Building Construction Services
N.A.I.C.S.: 531120

Rotterdam Square, LLC (1)
93 W Campbell Rd, Schenectady, NY 12306
Tel.: (518) 374-3713
Web Site: http://www.rotterdammall.com
Emp.: 50
Nonresidential Building Rental & Leasing Services
N.A.I.C.S.: 531120

SM Eastland Mall, LLC (1)
800 N Green River Rd, Evansville, IN 47715
Tel.: (812) 477-4848
Web Site:
https://www.shopeastlandmall.com
Sales Range: $25-49.9 Million
Emp.: 10
Nonresidential Building Rental & Leasing Services
N.A.I.C.S.: 531120
Shawn Hayden (Sr Mgr-Property)
Sean Ferguson (Sr Mgr-Specialty Leasing & Mktg)
David Hulsey (Ops Mgr)

Scottsdale Fashion Square LLC (1)
7014-590 E Camelback Rd, Scottsdale, AZ 85251
Tel.: (480) 945-5495
Web Site: http://www.fashionsquare.com
Sales Range: $25-49.9 Million
Emp.: 15
Nonresidential Building Rental & Leasing Services
N.A.I.C.S.: 531120
Christina Lanoue (Asst VP-Property Mgmt)
Melanie Sutton (Sr Mgr-Mktg)

Scottsdale Fashion Square Partnership (1)
7014 E Camelback Rd Ste 2132, Scottsdale, AZ 85251
Tel.: (480) 945-5495
Web Site: https://www.fashionsquare.com
Sales Range: $1-9.9 Million
Emp.: 70
Lessors of Nonresidential Buildings (except Miniwarehouses)
N.A.I.C.S.: 531120

Shoppingtown Mall, LLC (1)
3649 Erie Blvd E, De Witt, NY 13214
Tel.: (315) 446-9159
Web Site:
https://www.shoppingtownmall.com
Emp.: 8
Nonresidential Building Rental & Leasing
Services
N.A.I.C.S.: 531120

TWC Chandler LLC (1)
3111 W Chandler Blvd, Chandler, AZ 85226
Tel.: (480) 812-8488
Web Site:
https://www.shopchandlerfashioncen
ter.com
Emp.: 9
Nonresidential Building Rental & Leasing
Services
N.A.I.C.S.: 531120

TWC II-Prescott Mall, LLC (1)
3250 Gateway Blvd, Prescott, AZ 86303
Tel.: (928) 443-0067
Nonresidential Building Rental & Leasing
Services
N.A.I.C.S.: 531120

The Macerich Company (1)
11411 N Tatum Blvd, Phoenix, AZ 85028-2399
Tel.: (602) 953-6200
Web Site: https://www.macerich.com
Sales Range: $10-24.9 Million
Emp.: 170
Subdividers & Developers; Commercial
Property Owner & Manager
N.A.I.C.S.: 237210

The Macerich Partnership, L.P. (1)
401 Wilshire Blvd Ste 700, Santa Monica,
CA 90401
Tel.: (310) 394-6000
Real Estate Agency Services
N.A.I.C.S.: 531210

**VALLEY STREAM GREEN ACRES
LLC** (1)
2a W Midway, Valley Stream, NY 11581
Tel.: (516) 561-1157
Nonresidential Building Construction Ser-
vices
N.A.I.C.S.: 531120

West Acres Development, LLP (1)
3902 13th Ave S Ste 3717, Fargo, ND
58103
Tel.: (701) 282-2222
Web Site: https://www.westacres.com
Emp.: 35
Nonresidential Building Rental & Leasing
Services
N.A.I.C.S.: 531120
Brad Schlossman (CEO)

Wilton Mall, LLC (1)
3065 Rte 50, Saratoga Springs, NY 12866
Tel.: (518) 583-2138
Web Site: https://www.wiltonmall.com
Emp.: 4
Nonresidential Building Rental & Leasing
Services
N.A.I.C.S.: 531120
Mike Shaffer (Mgr-Property)

**THE MANITOWOC COMPANY,
INC.**
1 Park Plz 11270 W Park Pl Ste
1000, Milwaukee, WI 53224
Tel.: (414) 760-4600   WI
Web Site:
https://www.manitowoc.com
Year Founded: 1902
MTW—(NYSE)
Rev.: $2,032,500,000
Assets: $1,615,500,000
Liabilities: $1,077,700,000
Net Worth: $537,800,000
Earnings: ($123,600,000)
Emp.: 4,800
Fiscal Year-end: 12/31/22
Holding Company; Crane Equipment
Mfr & Distr
N.A.I.C.S.: 551112
Brian P. Regan (CFO & Exec VP)
David J. Antoniuk (Exec VP)

Aaron H. Ravenscroft (Pres & CEO)
Leslie L. Middleton (Exec VP-Mobile
Cranes)
Jennifer L. Peterson (Gen Counsel)
James S. Cook (Sr VP)

Subsidiaries:

Aspen Equipment Company Inc. (1)
9150 Pillsbury Ave S, Bloomington, MN
55420-3626
Tel.: (952) 888-2525
Web Site: https://www.aspenequipment.com
Sales Range: $10-24.9 Million
Emp.: 98
Truck Equipment Distr
N.A.I.C.S.: 336211
Aaron Carlson (Coord-Rentals)
Michael Hutter (Coord-Warranty)
Phil Maestas (Coord-Pur)
Becky Marini (Mgr-Marketing)

Electrogen International Ltd. (1)
Rathregan R154, Batterstown, Meath,
A86PX01, Ireland
Tel.: (353) 18251644
Web Site: https://www.electrogen.ie
Sales Range: $25-49.9 Million
Emp.: 7
Industrial Machinery & Equipment Whslr
N.A.I.C.S.: 423830
Fergal Bent (Mng Dir)

Fabristeel Private Limited (1)
Plot No 117 2nd Floor Sector-44, Gurgaon,
122003, Haryana, India
Tel.: (91) 1244780100
Web Site: http://www.manitowoc.com
Commercial Food Service Equipment Mfr
N.A.I.C.S.: 332215

Landis Holdings LLC (1)
1102 Prairie Ave, Goshen, IN 46526
Tel.: (574) 533-0106
Emp.: 2
Holding Company
N.A.I.C.S.: 551114

MGX Equipment Services, LLC (1)
1 Park Plz 11270 W Park Pl Ste 1000, Mil-
waukee, WI 53224
Tel.: (414) 760-4600
Web Site: https://mgxequipment.com
Crane Equipment Mfr & Distr
N.A.I.C.S.: 333923

**Manitowoc Crane Companies,
Inc.** (1)
1 Park Pl 11270 W Park Pl Ste 1000, Mil-
waukee, WI 53224   (100%)
Tel.: (414) 760-4600
Web Site: http://www.manitowoc.com
Sales Range: $1-4.9 Billion
Holding Company; Crane Mfr & Distr
N.A.I.C.S.: 551112
Barry L. Pennypacker (Pres & CEO)
David Hiull (Sr VP-Sls & Mktg-North
America)

Subsidiary (Domestic):

Grove U.S. LLC (2)
1565 Buchanan Trl E, Shady Grove, PA
17256
Tel.: (717) 597-8121
Web Site: http://www.manitowoccranes.com
Sales Range: $150-199.9 Million
Emp.: 2,400
Mfr of Mobile Hydraulic Cranes & Self Pro-
pelled Aerial Work Platforms
N.A.I.C.S.: 332999

Branch (Non-US):

Manitowoc Crane Care - France (2)
16 Chaussee Jules Cesar, Cergy, 95520,
Pontoise, France   (100%)
Tel.: (33) 130313150
Web Site: http://www.manitowoccranes.fr
Sales Range: $50-74.9 Million
Emp.: 100
Crane Distr & Maintenance Services
N.A.I.C.S.: 423810

Subsidiary (Non-US):

**Manitowoc Crane Group (UK)
Ltd.** (2)
Manitowoc House Network 421 Radclive

Road, Gawcott, Buckingham, MK18 4FD,
United Kingdom   (100%)
Tel.: (44) 1280818830
Sales Range: $25-49.9 Million
Crane Distr & Maintenance Services
N.A.I.C.S.: 423810
Steve Barnett (Dir-Commercial & Mng Dir)

**Manitowoc Crane Group Asia Pte.
Ltd.** (2)
42A Penjuru Road 07-00, Singapore,
609164, Singapore
Tel.: (65) 62641188
Web Site:
https://www.manitowoccranes.com
Sales Range: $50-74.9 Million
Special Industry Machinery
N.A.I.C.S.: 333310

**Manitowoc Crane Group Germany
GmbH** (2)
Industriegelaende West, Postfach 1853,
26358, Wilhelmshaven, Germany   (100%)
Tel.: (49) 44212940
Web Site: https://www.manitowoc.com
Crane Distr & Maintenance Services
N.A.I.C.S.: 423810

Subsidiary (Domestic):

Manitowoc Cranes, Inc. (2)
2401 S 30th St, Manitowoc, WI
54220   (100%)
Tel.: (920) 684-6621
Web Site: http://www.manitowoccranes.com
Sales Range: $300-349.9 Million
Emp.: 700
Crane Mfr
N.A.I.C.S.: 333923

Subsidiary (Non-US):

Potain S.A. (2)
18 Rue De Charbonnieres, PO Box 173,
69132, Ecully, France   (100%)
Tel.: (33) 472182020
Web Site: http://www.potain.fr
Sales Range: $50-74.9 Million
Emp.: 170
Mfr of Cranes, Site Lifts & Self-propelled
Platforms
N.A.I.C.S.: 333120

**Manitowoc Crane Group Australia Pty
Ltd.** (1)
51 Fourth Avenue, Blacktown, 2148, NSW,
Australia
Tel.: (61) 288224000
Web Site: http://www.manitowoccranes.com
Emp.: 60
Lifting & Handling Equipment Mfr
N.A.I.C.S.: 333998

**Manitowoc Crane Group Colombia,
S.A.S.** (1)
Carrera 15 No 98 42 Oficina 406, Bogota,
Colombia
Tel.: (57) 16386112
Crane & Heavy Equipment Mfr
N.A.I.C.S.: 333120

**Manitowoc Crane Group France
SAS** (1)
66 chemin du Moulin Carron, 69574, Dard-
illy, France
Tel.: (33) 472182020
Sales Range: $25-49.9 Million
Emp.: 200
Lifting & Handling Equipment Mfr
N.A.I.C.S.: 333998

**Manitowoc Crane Group Netherlands
B.V.** (1)
Veilingkade 15, 4815 HC, Breda, Nether-
lands
Tel.: (31) 765783999
Web Site: http://www.manitowoccranes.com
Sales Range: $10-24.9 Million
Lifting & Handling Equipment Mfr
N.A.I.C.S.: 333998

**Manitowoc Crane Group Poland
Sp** (1)
ul Racjonalizacji 6/8, 02-673, Warsaw, Po-
land
Tel.: (48) 22 843 3824
Web Site: https://www.manitowoc-crane-
group-poland-sp-z-oo.polskiefirmy.net
Lifting & Handling Equipment Mfr
N.A.I.C.S.: 333998

Manitowoc FSG Operations, LLC (1)
2400 S 44th St, Manitowoc, WI 54221-0066
Tel.: (920) 652-2222
Coolers & Refrigerator Mfr
N.A.I.C.S.: 333415

Manitowoc Group (UK) Limited (1)
Manitowoc House Network 421 Radclive
Road, Buckingham, MK18 4FD, United
Kingdom
Tel.: (44) 1280818834
Crane & Heavy Equipment Mfr
N.A.I.C.S.: 333120

**Manitowoc Re-Manufacturing,
Inc.** (1)
16013 W Sardis Rd, Bauxite, AR 72011
Tel.: (501) 557-5800
Web Site: http://www.manitowoccranes.com
Sales Range: $10-24.9 Million
Emp.: 18
Rebuild Used Manitowoc Cranes For Re-
sale & Rebuild Customer-Owned Cranes
On a Contract Basis
N.A.I.C.S.: 333923

**Manitowoc Western Company,
Inc.** (1)
16018 Adelante St, Irwindale, CA 91706
Tel.: (626) 334-2950
Sales Range: $25-49.9 Million
Emp.: 32
Mfr of Industrial Machinery & Equipment
N.A.I.C.S.: 333415

Potain India Pvt. Ltd. (1)
Gat No 244/2 256 and 257 Talegaon Cha-
kan Road, Chakan MIDC Phase II, Pune,
410 501, Maharashtra, India
Tel.: (91) 2135646700
Tower Cranes Mfr & Distr
N.A.I.C.S.: 333120
Berry Pennypacker (CEO)

Walter Payton Power Equipment (1)
930 W 138th St, Riverdale, IL
60827-1673   (100%)
Tel.: (708) 656-7700
Web Site: https://www.wppellc.com
Sales Range: $25-49.9 Million
Emp.: 30
Wholesale Distribution of Cranes & Con-
struction Equipment
N.A.I.C.S.: 423830

**Zhang Jia Gang Manitowoc Crane
Trading Co. Ltd.** (1)
No 55 Jintang Road Zhangjiagang Eco-
nomic, Development Zone, Zhangjiagang,
Jiangsu, China
Tel.: (86) 51256991200
Web Site: http://www.manitowoccrane.com
Agricultural Equipment Whslr
N.A.I.C.S.: 423820

THE MARCUS CORPORATION
100 E Wisconsin Ave, Milwaukee, WI
53202
Tel.: (414) 905-1000   WI
Web Site:
https://www.marcuscorp.com
Year Founded: 1935
MCS—(NYSE)
Rev.: $458,244,000
Assets: $1,188,361,000
Liabilities: $734,747,000
Net Worth: $453,614,000
Earnings: ($43,293,000)
Emp.: 7,500
Fiscal Year-end: 12/30/21
Owner & Operator of Hotels, Motels
& Theaters
N.A.I.C.S.: 721110
Thomas F. Kissinger (Gen Counsel,
Sec & Sr Exec VP)
Bruce J. Olson (Bd of Dirs, Execu-
tives)
Gregory S. Marcus (Chm, Pres &
CEO)
Kim M. Lueck (CIO)
Chad M. Paris (CFO & Treas)
Michael R. Evans (Pres-Marcus Ho-
tels & Resorts)
Steven V. Martin (Chief HR Officer)

The Marcus Corporation—(Continued)

Subsidiaries:

First American Finance Corporation (1)
100 E Wisconsin Ave, Milwaukee, WI 53202-4107
Tel.: (414) 905-1000
Web Site: http://www.marcuscorp.com
Financial Services
N.A.I.C.S.: 522299

Grand Geneva Resort & Spa (1)
7036 Grand Geneva Way, Lake Geneva, WI 53147
Tel.: (262) 248-8811
Web Site: https://www.grandgeneva.com
Sales Range: $50-74.9 Million
Emp.: 100
Holding Companies
N.A.I.C.S.: 551112
Steve Magnuson (Mng Dir)

Grand Geneva, LLC (1)
7036 Grand Geneva Way, Lake Geneva, WI 53147
Tel.: (262) 248-8811
Web Site: https://www.grandgeneva.com
Sales Range: $100-124.9 Million
Emp.: 900
Hotels & Lodging Services
N.A.I.C.S.: 721110

Green Lake Resort, LLC (1)
643 Illinois Ave, Green Lake, WI 54941
Tel.: (920) 294-3344
Web Site: http://www.heidelhouse.com
Resort & Spa Operator
N.A.I.C.S.: 721110

Marcus Corporation (1)
100 E Wisconsin Ave, Milwaukee, WI 53202 **(100%)**
Tel.: (414) 905-1000
Web Site: https://www.marcuscorp.com
Sales Range: $1-9.9 Million
Emp.: 150
Hotels & Resorts
N.A.I.C.S.: 721110

Marcus Hotels Associates, Inc. (1)
100 E Wisconsin Ave Ste 1950, Milwaukee, WI 53202-4113
Tel.: (414) 905-1200
Hotels & Lodging Services
N.A.I.C.S.: 721110
Thomas F. Kissinger (Chief Legal Officer)
Jim Waldvogel (Area VP)
Ed Carrella (Corp Dir-Restaurants)
Peggy Williams-Smith (Sr VP-SafeHouse Restaurants)
Eric Grimm (Gen Mgr-Mason Street Grill)
Cristina Gliatis (Asst Gen Mgr-Mason Street Grill)
Tom Mason (Area VP)
Steve Martin (VP-HR)
Thomas F. Kissinger (Interim Pres)

Marcus Madison, LLC (1)
706 John Nolen Dr, Madison, WI 53713
Tel.: (608) 251-2300
Web Site: http://www.sheratonmadison.com
Emp.: 110
Hotels & Lodging Services
N.A.I.C.S.: 721110

Marcus Management Las Vegas, LLC (1)
211 E Flamingo Rd, Las Vegas, NV 89169
Tel.: (702) 365-5000
Web Site: https://www.theplatinumhotel.com
Emp.: 20
Hotels & Lodging Services
N.A.I.C.S.: 721110

Marcus Northstar, Inc. (1)
618 2nd Ave S, Minneapolis, MN 55402-1901
Tel.: (612) 338-2288
Web Site: https://www.cpmnneapolis.com
Hotels & Lodging Services
N.A.I.C.S.: 721110

Marcus Theatres Corp. (1)
100 E Wisconsin Ave #1900, Milwaukee, WI 53202 **(100%)**
Tel.: (414) 905-1500
Web Site: http://www.marcustheatres.com
Theatres

N.A.I.C.S.: 512131
Thomas F. Kissinger (Chief Legal Officer)
Mark A. Gramz (Pres)
Steve Bunnell (Exec VP-Content Strategy)

Subsidiary (Domestic):

Movie Tavern, Inc. (2)
12400 Coit Rd Ste 800, Dallas, TX 75251-2067
Tel.: (281) 248-8396
Web Site: http://www.movietavern.com
Motion Picture & Video Production
N.A.I.C.S.: 512110
John Hersker (CEO)

Milwaukee City Center, LLC (1)
509 W Wisconsin Ave, Milwaukee, WI 53203
Tel.: (414) 271-7250
Web Site: http://www.hilton.com
Hotels & Lodging Services
N.A.I.C.S.: 721110

Pfister, LLC (1)
424 E Wisconsin Ave, Milwaukee, WI 53202
Tel.: (414) 273-8222
Web Site: https://www.thepfisterhotel.com
Theater & Hotel Operator
N.A.I.C.S.: 721110

Rush Ontario, LLC (1)
630 N Rush St, Chicago, IL 60611
Tel.: (312) 981-6600
Hotels & Lodging Services
N.A.I.C.S.: 721110

The Pfister Hotel (1)
424 E Wisconsin Ave, Milwaukee, WI 53202
Tel.: (414) 273-8222
Web Site: https://www.thepfisterhotel.com
Hotel Operator
N.A.I.C.S.: 721110

THE MARKETING ALLIANCE, INC.
1010 111 W Port Plz, Saint Louis, MO 63146-3017
Tel.: (314) 275-8713 NC
Web Site:
https://www.themarketingalliance.com
Year Founded: 1996
MAAL—(OTCIQ)
Rev.: $17,940,089
Assets: $18,586,754
Liabilities: $11,932,477
Net Worth: $6,654,277
Earnings: $574,930
Fiscal Year-end: 03/31/23
Insurance Marketing & Distribution Services
N.A.I.C.S.: 524298
Timothy M. Klusas (Pres)
Douglas J. Allenbaugh (Exec VP-Insurance Distr)
Alan Protzel (Sr VP-Insurance Mktg)
Paul Seyler (Sr VP-Bus Svc Center)
Laura Hahn (Sr VP-Admin)
Linda Thomas (Mgr-Status & New Bus)
Annette Jacks (Mgr-Case)
Brenda Leise (Mgr-Case)
Mitchell Fisher (Sr VP-Bus Svc Center)
Angela Brandt (Office Mgr)
Mary Badalucco (Mgr-Case)
Jeremy Hellman (VP)
Arthur C. Jetter Jr. (Sec)

THE MARQUIE GROUP, INC.
7901 4th St N Ste 4887, Saint Petersburg, FL 33702 FL
Web Site:
https://www.themarquiegroup.com
Year Founded: 2008
TMGI—(OTCIQ)
Rev.: $384,017
Assets: $6,247,137
Liabilities: $6,030,701
Net Worth: $216,436
Earnings: ($165,456)

Emp.: 1
Fiscal Year-end: 05/31/24
Live Radio Programming Producer
N.A.I.C.S.: 334220
Marc Angell (Chm, CEO, Chief Acctg Officer & Sec)

THE MARYGOLD COMPANIES, INC.
120 Calle Iglesia Unit B, San Clemente, CA 92672
Tel.: (949) 429-5370 NV
Web Site:
https://www.themarygoldcompanies.com
MGLD—(NYSEAMEX)
Rev.: $32,836,000
Assets: $32,899,000
Liabilities: $6,285,000
Net Worth: $26,614,000
Earnings: ($4,069,000)
Emp.: 116
Fiscal Year-end: 06/30/24
Wireless Internet Services
N.A.I.C.S.: 334220
Nicholas Daniel Gerber (Chm, Pres & CEO)
David W. Neibert (COO & Sec)
Kathryn D. Rooney (Chief Comm Officer)

Subsidiaries:

Gourmet Foods, Ltd. (1)
144 Birch Ave, Judea, Tauranga, 3110, New Zealand
Tel.: (64) 75779905
Web Site:
https://www.gourmetfoodsltd.co.nz
Meat Product Mfr & Distr
N.A.I.C.S.: 311615

Printstock Products Limited (1)
3 Turner Place, Onekawa, Napier, 4010, New Zealand
Tel.: (64) 68434952
Web Site: https://www.printstock.co.nz
Flexographic Printing Services
N.A.I.C.S.: 561990

USCF Investments, Inc. (1)
1290 Broadway Ste 1000, Denver, CO 80203
Web Site: https://www.uscfinvestments.com
Investment Management Service
N.A.I.C.S.: 523999

United States Commodity Funds, LLC (1)
1320 Harbor Bay Pkwy Ste 145, Alameda, CA 94502 **(100%)**
Tel.: (510) 522-3336
Web Site: http://www.unitedstatescommodityfunds.com
Sales Range: $25-49.9 Million
Emp.: 11
Investment Services
N.A.I.C.S.: 523999
Robert L. Nguyen (Co-Founder & Principal)
Andrew F. Ngim (Co-Founder, COO, Principal & Portfolio Mgr)
John P. Love (Pres & CEO)
Stuart P. Crumbaugh (CFO)
Ray Allen (Dir-Exchange Traded Derivatives & Portfolio Mgr)
Kevin Baum (Chief Investment Officer)
Darius Coby (Ops Mgr)
Daphne Frydman (Gen Counsel)
Ryan Katz (Natl Dir-Sls)
Maya Lowry (Head-Distr)
Carolyn M. Yu (Chief Compliance Officer)

Subsidiary (Domestic):

UNITED STATES DIESEL-HEATING OIL FUND, LP (2)
1850 Mt Diablo Blvd Ste 640, Walnut Creek, CA 94596
Tel.: (510) 522-9600
Web Site: http://www.uscfinvestments.com
Sales Range: Less than $1 Million
Heating & Oil Investment Fund Services
N.A.I.C.S.: 525910
Nicholas Daniel Gerber (Chm & VP)
Katie Rooney (CMO)

United States 12 Month Natural Gas Fund, LP (2)
1850 Mt Diablo Blvd Ste 640, Walnut Creek, CA 94596
Tel.: (510) 522-9600
Web Site: https://www.uscfinvestments.com
Rev.: $3,951,786
Assets: $25,109,987
Liabilities: $118,053
Net Worth: $24,991,934
Earnings: $3,632,266
Fiscal Year-end: 12/31/2022
Investment Fund
N.A.I.C.S.: 525910
Nicholas Daniel Gerber (VP & Dir-Mgmt)
John P. Love (Chm, Pres & CEO)
Ray W. Allen (Dir-Exchange Traded Derivatives & Portfolio Mgr)
Kevin A. Baum (Chief Investment Officer)
Daphne Frydman (Gen Counsel)
Ryan Katz (Natl Dir-Sls)
Maya Lowry (Head-Distr)
Stuart Crumbaugh (CFO)
Seth Lancaster (Portfolio Mgr)
Andrew Ngim (Pres)
Robert Nguyen (Principal)
Katie Rooney (CMO)
Ayana Stevenson (Mgr)

United States 12 Month Oil Fund, LP (2)
1850 Mt Diablo Blvd Ste 640, Walnut Creek, CA 94596
Tel.: (510) 522-9600
Web Site: https://www.uscfinvestments.com
Rev.: $39,436,827
Assets: $87,222,657
Liabilities: $3,914,325
Net Worth: $83,308,332
Earnings: $38,362,556
Fiscal Year-end: 12/31/2022
Oil Investment Fund
N.A.I.C.S.: 525910

United States Brent Oil Fund, LP (2)
1850 Mt Diablo Blvd Ste 640, Walnut Creek, CA 94596
Tel.: (510) 522-9600
Web Site: https://www.uscfinvestments.com
Rev.: $85,216,007
Assets: $235,119,050
Liabilities: $3,376,741
Net Worth: $231,742,309
Earnings: $82,570,759
Fiscal Year-end: 12/31/2022
Investment Fund Services
N.A.I.C.S.: 523999

United States Commodity Index Funds Trust (2)
1850 Mt Diablo Blvd Ste 640, Walnut Creek, CA 94596
Tel.: (510) 522-9600
Web Site: https://www.uscfinvestments.com
Rev.: $474,723
Assets: $426,156,578
Liabilities: $782,689
Net Worth: $425,373,889
Earnings: $65,691,279
Fiscal Year-end: 12/31/2022
Investment Services
N.A.I.C.S.: 523999
John P. Love (Chm, Pres & CEO)
Ray Allen (Portfolio Mgr)

United States Gasoline Fund, LP (2)
1850 Mt Diablo Blvd Ste 640, Walnut Creek, CA 94596
Tel.: (510) 522-9600
Web Site: https://www.uscfinvestments.com
Rev.: $28,415,786
Assets: $87,046,675
Liabilities: $409,495
Net Worth: $86,637,180
Earnings: $27,371,099
Fiscal Year-end: 12/31/2022
Gasoline Investment Services
N.A.I.C.S.: 523999
Nicholas Daniel Gerber (VP & Dir-Mgmt)
Stuart P. Crumbaugh (CFO)
Ray Allen (Dir)
Kevin Baum (Chief Investment Officer)
Darius Coby (Dir)
Stuart Crumbaugh (CFO)
Daphne Frydman (Gen Counsel)
Ryan Katz (Natl Dir)
Seth Lancaster (Portfolio Mgr)

Maya Lowry *(Head)*
Andrew Ngim *(COO)*
Robert Nguyen *(Principal)*
Katie Rooney *(CMO)*

United States Natural Gas Fund, LP (2)
1850 Mt Diablo Blvd Ste 640, Walnut Creek, CA 94596
Tel.: (510) 522-9600
Web Site: https://www.uscfinvestments.com
Rev.: $80,016,838
Assets: $430,675,504
Liabilities: $1,337,028
Net Worth: $429,338,476
Earnings: $75,029,489
Fiscal Year-end: 12/31/2022
Investment Fund
N.A.I.C.S.: 525910
John P. Love *(Pres & CEO)*
Ray Allen *(Dir)*
Kevin Baum *(Chief Investment Officer)*
Darius Coby *(Dir)*
Daphne Frydman *(Gen Counsel)*
Ryan Katz *(Dir)*
Seth Lancaster *(Portfolio Mgr)*
Maya Lowry *(Head)*
Katie Rooney *(CMO)*
Ayana Stevenson *(Office Mgr)*

United States Short Oil Fund, LP (2)
1850 Mt Diablo Blvd Ste 640, Walnut Creek, CA 94596
Tel.: (510) 522-9600
Web Site: http://www.uscfinvestments.com
Investment Fund Services
N.A.I.C.S.: 525910
Nicholas Daniel Gerber *(Chm & VP)*

THE MEDIA GLOBO CORPORATION
999 18th St Ste 3000, Denver, CO 80202
Web Site:
https://www.mediaglobocorp.com
MGLO—(OTCIQ)
Holding Company
N.A.I.C.S.: 551112
Michael Grandon *(Pres, CEO & Sec)*

THE MIDDLEBY CORPORATION
1400 Toastmaster Dr, Elgin, IL 60120
Tel.: (847) 741-3300   DE
Web Site: https://www.middleby.com
Year Founded: 1888
MIDD—(NASDAQ)
Rev.: $4,036,605,000
Assets: $6,906,692,000
Liabilities: $3,656,803,000
Net Worth: $3,249,889,000
Earnings: $400,882,000
Emp.: 10,722
Fiscal Year-end: 12/30/23
Commercial Foodservice Equipment Mfr & Retailer
N.A.I.C.S.: 333241
Timothy J. FitzGerald *(CEO)*
Darcy Bretz *(Dir-Corp Comm)*
Bryan E. Mittelman *(CFO)*
Steven P. Spittle *(Chief Comml Officer)*
Brittany Cerwin *(Chief Acctg Officer)*

Subsidiaries:

A/S Wodschow & Co. (1)
Industrisvinget 6, Brondby, 2605, Denmark
Tel.: (45) 43442288
Commercial Food Service Equipment Retailer
N.A.I.C.S.: 423440

AGA Rayburn Ltd (1)
AGA Rangemaster Station Road, Ketley, Telford, TF1 5AQ, Shropshire, United Kingdom
Tel.: (44) 1952643149
Web Site: http://www.agaliving.com
Household Appliance Store Operator
N.A.I.C.S.: 449210

Alkar-RapidPak, Inc. (1)
932 Development Dr, Lodi, WI 53555

Tel.: (608) 592-3211
Web Site: https://www.alkar.com
Household Appliance & Equipment Distr
N.A.I.C.S.: 449210

Subsidiary (Domestic):

Alkar-RapidPak-MP Equipment, Inc. (2)
932 Development Dr, Lodi, WI 53555
Tel.: (608) 592-3211
Web Site: http://www.rapidpak.com
Food Product Equipment Mfr
N.A.I.C.S.: 333241

Anetsberger, LLC (1)
39 Sheep Davis Rd, Pembroke, NH 03275
Tel.: (603) 225-6684
Web Site: https://www.anets.com
Food Product Equipment Mfr
N.A.I.C.S.: 333241

Armor Inox S.A. (1)
PA de Broceliande, 56430, Mauron, France
Tel.: (33) 29 722 6263
Web Site: https://www.armorinox.com
Sales Range: $25-49.9 Million
Emp.: 60
Food Product Equipment Mfr
N.A.I.C.S.: 333241

Auto-Bake Pty Ltd (1)
211 Woodpark Rd, Smithfield, 2164, NSW, Australia
Tel.: (61) 294761144
Food Product Machinery Mfr
N.A.I.C.S.: 333241
Scott McCally *(Pres-Auto-Bake Serpentine)*
Brent Grantham *(Acct Mgr-Natl)*
Dan Christie *(Acct Mgr-Natl)*
Billy Rinks *(Acct Mgr-Natl)*
Rod Gregg *(Exec VP)*

Automatic Bar Controls, Inc. (1)
2060 Cessna Dr, Vacaville, CA 95688
Tel.: (707) 448-5151
Web Site: https://www.wunderbar.com
Sales Range: $25-49.9 Million
Beverage, Sauce & Condiment Dispensing Equipment Designer, Mfr & Whslr
N.A.I.C.S.: 333310

Baker Thermal Solutions LLC (1)
8182 US 70 W, Clayton, NC 27520
Tel.: (919) 674-3750
Web Site: https://bakerthermal.com
Bakery Equipment Distr
N.A.I.C.S.: 423830

Beech Ovens Pty Ltd. (1)
26 Curtin Ave W, Eagle Farm, Hamilton, 4009, QLD, Australia
Tel.: (61) 73 397 0277
Web Site: https://www.beechovens.com.au
Food Product Equipment Mfr
N.A.I.C.S.: 333241
Stephen Trood *(Dir-Sls & Engrg-Intl)*
Janelle Dunlea *(Sls Mgr)*

Blodgett Oven Company Inc (1)
44 Lakeside Ave, Burlington, VT 05401
Tel.: (802) 658-6600
Web Site: http://www.blodgett.com
Sales Range: $200-249.9 Million
Emp.: 150
Commercial Cooking Equipment
N.A.I.C.S.: 333310

Division (Domestic):

Blodgett Combi (2)
44 Lakeside Ave, Burlington, VT 05401
Tel.: (802) 658-6600
Web Site: http://www.blodgett.com
Sales Range: $50-74.9 Million
Emp.: 200
Equipment Manufacturing Company
N.A.I.C.S.: 333310
Selim Bassoul *(CEO)*

Subsidiary (Domestic):

Magikitch'n, Inc. (2)
265 Hobson St, Smithville, TN 37166
Web Site: http://www.magikitchn.com
Kitchen Equipment Mfr
N.A.I.C.S.: 337127

Pitco Frialator Inc. (2)
553 Route 3A, Bow, NH 03304
Tel.: (603) 225-6684

Web Site: https://www.pitco.com
Sales Range: $75-99.9 Million
Commercial Frying Systems Mfr
N.A.I.C.S.: 333310

Brava Home, Inc. (1)
312 Chestnut St, Redwood City, CA 94063
Tel.: (408) 675-2569
Web Site: https://www.brava.com
Food Products Distr
N.A.I.C.S.: 424490
Thomas Cheng *(Co-Founder & CTO)*
John Pleasants *(Co-Founder & CEO)*
Dan Yue *(Co-Founder)*

Burford Bakery Solutions Limited (1)
Gresham House Pinetrees Road, Norwich, NR7 9BB, United Kingdom
Tel.: (44) 1603708370
Web Site: https://burford.com
Commercial Food Service Equipment Retailer
N.A.I.C.S.: 423440

Burford Corp. (1)
11284 OK-74, Maysville, OK 73057
Tel.: (405) 867-4467
Web Site: https://burford.com
Food Product Machinery Mfr
N.A.I.C.S.: 333241
Joyce Tate *(Mgr-IT)*
Sean Wright *(Controller)*
Josh Hughes *(Acct Mgr-Sls)*
Megan Sutton *(Mgr-HR)*

CP Packaging, LLC. (1)
2530 W Everett St, Appleton, WI 54914
Tel.: (920) 832-8528
Web Site: http://www.cppac.com
Sales Range: $1-9.9 Million
Emp.: 10
Packaging Machinery Mfr
N.A.I.C.S.: 333993
Keith J. Wietham *(VP-Sls & Mktg)*
Wayne P. Henry *(CFO, Treas & Sec)*
Raymond G. Buchko Sr. *(Founder)*
Raymond G. Buchko Jr. *(Pres & CEO)*

Carter-Hoffmann, LLC (1)
1551 McCormick Ave, Mundelein, IL 60060
Tel.: (847) 362-5500
Web Site: https://www.carter-hoffmann.com
Sales Range: $10-24.9 Million
Emp.: 150
Mobile Refrigerators & Freezers, Cafeteria Serving Lines, Food Carts & Foodservice Equipment Mfr
N.A.I.C.S.: 333241

Catering Equipment Industry srl (1)
Industrial Zone F3 Snc, 83051, Nusco, Italy
Tel.: (39) 0827607193
Web Site: http://www.catequip.net
Commercial Kitchen Equipment Whslr
N.A.I.C.S.: 423440

Char-Griller (1)
2465 Demere Rd Ste 210, Saint Simons Island, GA 31522-1630
Tel.: (912) 638-4724
Web Site: http://www.chargriller.com
Industrial Machinery & Equipment Merchant Whslr
N.A.I.C.S.: 423830

Cinoxplan, S.L. (1)
Pol Ind Mas Roger C Marconi 21, Pineda de Mar, 08397, Barcelona, Spain
Tel.: (34) 933997651
Web Site: http://www.cinoxplan.com
Industrial Machinery Parts Mfr
N.A.I.C.S.: 333120

Concordia Coffee Company, Inc. (1)
1287 120th Ave NE, Bellevue, WA 98005
Tel.: (425) 453-2800
Web Site: http://www.concordiacoffee.com
Sales Range: $10-24.9 Million
Commercial Coffee Machines Mfr & Whslr
N.A.I.C.S.: 335210
Chris Duffy *(Pres)*
Lisa Weingart *(Controller)*

CookTek LLC (1)
156 N Jefferson St Ste 300, Chicago, IL 60661
Tel.: (312) 563-9600
Web Site: http://www.cooktek.com
Sales Range: $10-24.9 Million
Emp.: 60
Commercial Foodservices Equipment Mfr

N.A.I.C.S.: 311999

Cozzini, LLC (1)
2567 Greenleaf Ave, Elk Grove Village, IL 60007
Tel.: (773) 478-9700
Web Site: https://www.cozzini.com
Sales Range: $50-74.9 Million
Emp.: 250
Food Processing Equipment Mfr
N.A.I.C.S.: 333241

Subsidiary (Non-US):

Cozzini Middleby de Mexico, S. de R.L.de C.V. (2)
Av Ignacio Sepulveda No 116 Parque Industrial Kalos La Encarnacion, 66633, Apodaca, Nuevo Leon, Mexico
Tel.: (52) 8182626000
Web Site: http://www.cozzini.com
Sales Range: $25-49.9 Million
Emp.: 25
Food Product Equipment Mfr
N.A.I.C.S.: 333241
Belinda Zamora *(CEO)*

Cozzini do Brasil Ltda (2)
R Antonio das Chagas 439 Chacara Santo Antonio, 04714-000, Sao Paulo, Brazil
Tel.: (55) 1133215858
Food Product Equipment Distr
N.A.I.C.S.: 423830

Desmon S.p.A. (1)
Industrial Zone F3, 83051, Nusco, Italy
Tel.: (39) 0827607318
Web Site: https://www.desmon.it
Refrigerator Equipment Mfr
N.A.I.C.S.: 333415
Angelo Dello Iacono *(Mgr-Sales)*

Emery Thompson Machine Supply Co. (1)
1349 Inwood Ave, Bronx, NY 10452
Tel.: (718) 588-7300
Web Site: http://www.emerythompson.com
Sales Range: $1-9.9 Million
Emp.: 11
Food Product Machinery Mfr
N.A.I.C.S.: 333241
Slade Harmon *(VP)*

Evo America, LLC (1)
20360 SW Avery Ct, Tualatin, OR 97062
Tel.: (503) 626-1802
Web Site: https://evoamerica.com
Household Cooking Appliance Mfr
N.A.I.C.S.: 335220
Bob Shingler *(Founder, Chief Innovation Officer & VP-Innovation & R&D)*
Scott Heim *(Pres)*
Dennis Francis *(VP-Sales)*
Leanne Williams *(VP-Marketing & Sales)*

F.R. Drake Company (1)
1410 Genicom Dr, Waynesboro, VA 22980
Tel.: (540) 569-4368
Web Site: https://www.drakeloader.com
Sales Range: $1-9.9 Million
Emp.: 65
Machine Shops
N.A.I.C.S.: 332710

Firex S.r.l. (1)
Zona Industriale Gresal 28, 32036, Sedico, BL, Italy
Tel.: (39) 0437852700
Web Site: https://www.firex.com
Emp.: 100
Kitchen Equipment Mfr
N.A.I.C.S.: 333241

Flavor Burst Co. LLP (1)
499 Commerce Dr, Danville, IN 46122-7848
Tel.: (317) 745-2952
Web Site: http://www.flavorburst.com
Sales Range: $1-9.9 Million
Emp.: 25
Grocery & Related Products Merchant Whslr
N.A.I.C.S.: 424490

Follett LLC (1)
801 Church Ln, Easton, PA 18040
Tel.: (610) 252-7301
Web Site: https://www.follettice.com
Food Service Equipment & Medical Grade Refrigeration
N.A.I.C.S.: 423740

The Middleby Corporation—(Continued)

Korey Kohl *(Pres)*

G.S. Blodgett Corporation (1)
42 Allen Martin Dr, Essex Junction, VT 05452
Tel.: (802) 658-6600
Web Site: https://www.blodgett.com
Emp.: 250
Foodservice Equipment Mfr & Retailer
N.A.I.C.S.: 333241

Globe Food Equipment Company (1)
2153 Dryden Rd, Dayton, OH 45439
Tel.: (937) 299-5493
Web Site: https://globefoodequip.com
Commercial Equipment Merchant Whslr
N.A.I.C.S.: 423440
Ryan Feasel *(Reg Sls Mgr)*

Goldstein Eswood Commercial Cooking Pty Ltd (1)
211-217 Woodpark Road, Smithfield, 2164, NSW, Australia
Tel.: (61) 296047333
Web Site: https://middleby.com.au
Foodservice Equipment Mfr
N.A.I.C.S.: 333415

Grange Furniture Inc. (1)
1855 Griffin Rd Ste C400, Dania, FL 33004
Tel.: (212) 685-9057
Furniture Store Operator
N.A.I.C.S.: 449110

Grange Luxembourg SARL (1)
Route de Luxembourg 87, 7240, Walferdange, Luxembourg
Tel.: (352) 515869
Furniture Store Operator
N.A.I.C.S.: 449110

Hinds-Bock Corporation (1)
2606 51st Ave E Unit Ste 113, Palmetto, FL 34221
Tel.: (425) 885-1183
Web Site: https://hinds-bock.com
Sales Range: $10-24.9 Million
Food, Bakery & Specialty Chemical Machinery Mfr
N.A.I.C.S.: 333241
Chris Armer *(Mgr-Parts)*
Rod Gregg *(Exec VP)*
Shane Smith *(Mgr-Customer Service)*
Carolynn Coiner *(Mng Dir)*

Inline Filling Systems, LLC (1)
216 Seaboard Ave, Venice, FL 34285
Tel.: (941) 486-8800
Web Site: https://www.fillers.com
Liquid Packaging Machinery Mfr
N.A.I.C.S.: 333993
Jerry Schaefer *(Mgr-Customer Svc & Parts)*

Johs. Lassen Fjellebroen A/S (1)
Norgesvej 8, 5700, Svendborg, Denmark
Tel.: (45) 62616666
Web Site: https://www.bago-line.dk
Food Product Machinery Mfr
N.A.I.C.S.: 333241

Josper, S.A. (1)
Gutenberg 11 Pol Ind Mas Roger, Pineda de Mar, 08397, Barcelona, Spain
Tel.: (34) 937671516
Web Site: https://www.jospergrill.com
Kitchen Equipment Mfr
N.A.I.C.S.: 333241

L2F Inc. (1)
48531 Warm Springs Blvd Ste 408, Fremont, CA 94539
Tel.: (510) 249-9077
Web Site: http://www.l2finc.com
Service Industry Machinery Mfr
N.A.I.C.S.: 333310
Shawn Lange *(Co-Founder & Pres)*
Li Gao *(Sr Engr-Staff-AI & ML)*

Lincat Group PLC (1)
Whisby Road, Lincoln, LN6 3QZ, United Kingdom
Tel.: (44) 1522875555
Commercial Equipment Mfr & Distr
N.A.I.C.S.: 335210

Lynx Grills, Inc. (1)
7300 Flores St, Downey, CA 90242
Tel.: (562) 299-6900

Web Site: http://www.lynxgrills.com
Gas Grills & Other Household Cooking Appliances & Accessories Mfr & Distr
N.A.I.C.S.: 335220

Lynx Holdco Inc (1)
11111 Santa Monica Blvd Ste 1650, Los Angeles, CA 90025
Tel.: (310) 575-9400
Commercial Catering Equipment Mfr & Distr
N.A.I.C.S.: 335210

MP Equipment, LLC (1)
2395 Murphy Blvd, Gainesville, GA 30504
Tel.: (770) 503-7605
Web Site: https://www.mpequipment.com
Sales Range: $10-24.9 Million
Emp.: 55
Bakery Machinery & Equipment Mfr
N.A.I.C.S.: 333241

Marsal & Sons, Inc. (1)
175 E Hoffman Ave, Lindenhurst, NY 11757
Tel.: (631) 226-6688
Web Site: http://www.marsalsons.com
Emp.: 30
Restaurant Equipment Mfr
N.A.I.C.S.: 333241

Masterbuilt Manufacturing, LLC (1)
1 Masterbuilt Ct, Columbus, GA 31907-1313
Tel.: (706) 256-3943
Web Site: https://www.masterbuilt.com
Household Cooking Appliance Mfr
N.A.I.C.S.: 335220
John McLemore *(CEO)*

Middleby Australia Pty Ltd (1)
12/210 Queensport Road North, Murarrie, 4172, QLD, Australia
Tel.: (61) 296047333
Web Site: https://www.middleby.com.au
Food Product Equipment Mfr
N.A.I.C.S.: 333241
Douglas Dunn *(Pres & Mng Dir)*

Middleby Celfrost Innovations Pvt Ltd (1)
Unit Nos 713-716 7th Floor JMD Megapolis Sohna Road Sector-48, Gurgaon, 122018, Haryana, India
Tel.: (91) 1244828500
Web Site: https://www.middlebycelfrost.com
Food Product Equipment Mfr & Distr
N.A.I.C.S.: 333241

Middleby China Corporation (1)
12F Bldg D Mapletree Business City 2337 Gu Dai Road, Minhang District, Shanghai, 201108, China
Tel.: (86) 2167690808
Food Product Equipment Mfr
N.A.I.C.S.: 333241
Jerry Koo *(Reg VP)*

Middleby Cozzini Brasil Equipamentos, Ltda (1)
Rua Antonio Das Chagas 439, Chacara Santo Antonio, Sao Paulo, 04714-000, SP, Brazil
Tel.: (55) 1133215858
Web Site: https://www.middleby.com.br
Sales Range: $25-49.9 Million
Emp.: 37
Food Product Equipment Mfr
N.A.I.C.S.: 333241

Middleby Espana SLU (1)
Edificio Elor C/ Astintze 2, 48160, Derio, Bizkaia, Spain
Tel.: (34) 944542815
Web Site: https://www.middleby.es
Food Product Equipment Mfr
N.A.I.C.S.: 333241

Middleby India Engineering Pvt Ltd (1)
45 Jigani Industrial Area Anekal Taluk, Bengaluru, 562 106, India
Tel.: (91) 8025127600
Web Site: http://www.middleby.com
Engineering Consulting Services
N.A.I.C.S.: 541330
Balaji Subramaniam *(Pres)*

Middleby Korea Corporation (1)
Samkwang Bldg 255 53 Yongdoo Dong Ste 503, 025553, Seoul, Korea (South) **(100%)**
Tel.: (82) 29290662

Web Site: http://www.middleby.com
Sales Range: $1-9.9 Million
Emp.: 8
N.A.I.C.S.: 333241

Middleby Marshall, Inc. (1)
1400 Toastmaster Dr, Elgin, IL 60120-9274
Tel.: (847) 741-3300
Web Site: https://www.middlebymarshall.com
Sales Range: $50-74.9 Million
Emp.: 220
Mfr of Commercial Cooking & Warming Equipment
N.A.I.C.S.: 333241
David Shave *(Pres)*
Andrea Coldwell *(Gen Mgr)*
Trevor Henke *(VP-Intl Sls)*
Andrew Ostrowski *(Reg VP-Sales)*

Middleby Mexico SA de CV (1)
Calle 5 de Mayo 32, Parque Industrial Naucalpan, Mexico, 53370, Mexico
Tel.: (52) 5530670200
Web Site: http://www.middleby.com.mx
Food Product Equipment Mfr
N.A.I.C.S.: 333241

Middleby Packaging Solutions, LLC (1)
440 S Mclean Blvd, Elgin, IL 60123
Tel.: (847) 741-3500
Web Site: https://www.cv-tek.com
Packaging Machinery Mfr
N.A.I.C.S.: 333993

Middleby Philippines Corporation (1)
113 Technology Avenue Laguna Technopark, Binan, 4024, Laguna, Philippines **(100%)**
Tel.: (63) 285194401
Web Site: https://www.middleby.com.ph
Commercial Foodservice Equipment Designer, Retailer & Mfr
N.A.I.C.S.: 333241

Middleby UK Ltd (1)
Middleby House Unit 15 Bridge Bank Close, Stonecross Park Golborne, Wigan, WA3 3JD, United Kingdom **(100%)**
Tel.: (44) 1925821280
Web Site: https://middlebyuk.co.uk
Sales Range: $10-24.9 Million
Emp.: 20
Commercial Food Equipment
N.A.I.C.S.: 333241
Wendy Cunningham *(Mgr-Internal Sls)*
Paul Chapple *(Mgr-Tech Svc)*
Chris Clark *(Mng Dir)*
Nathan Flemming *(Dir-Finance)*
Phil Denness *(Dir-Sales & Marketing)*
Debora Douglass *(Dir-HR European)*
Steven Edwards *(Dir-Natl Accts)*
Donna Brown *(Mgr-Group Natl Acct)*
Lindsey Nash *(Mgr-Group Natl Acct)*
Keith Shelly *(Mgr-Group Natl Acct)*
Paul York *(Mgr-UK Bus)*
Lee Stacey *(Mgr-Bus Dev SW)*
Oliver Eaglen *(Mgr-Bus Dev South)*
David Cresswell *(Mgr-Bus Dev Scotland/North)*
Paul Hickman *(Dir-Culinary)*
Lana Wynn Davies *(Mgr-European Mktg)*
Clare Gibson *(Mgr-After Sls Support)*

Subsidiary (Domestic):

AGA Rangemaster Group plc (2)
Juno Drive, Leamington Spa, CV3 3RG, Warwickshire, United Kingdom
Tel.: (44) 1926455755
Web Site: http://www.agaliving.com
Emp.: 2,500
Holding Company; Household Cooking, Heating & Refrigeration Appliance Mfr & Distr; Wood Cabinetry Mfr; Cookware, Wall & Floor Coverings Retailer
N.A.I.C.S.: 551112
Shaun Smith *(CFO)*

Subsidiary (US):

AGA Marvel (USA) (3)
1260 E Van Deinse St, Greenville, MI 48838
Web Site: http://www.agamarvel.com
Emp.: 200
Cooking Appliance Mfr
N.A.I.C.S.: 335220

Subsidiary (Domestic):

AGA Rangemaster Limited (3)
AGA Rangemaster Meadow Lane, Long Eaton, Nottingham, NG10 2GD, Warwickshire, United Kingdom
Tel.: (44) 195 264 3149
Web Site: https://www.agaliving.com
Household Cooking, Heating & Refrigeration Appliance Mfr & Distr; Cookware, Wall & Floor Coverings Retailer
N.A.I.C.S.: 335220

Subsidiary (Domestic):

Fired Earth Limited (4)
Twyford Mill nr Banbury Oxford Road, Banbury, OX17 3SX, Oxfordshire, United Kingdom
Tel.: (44) 1295814399
Web Site: http://www.firedearth.com
Wall & Floor Tiles, Paint & Other Coverings Retailer
N.A.I.C.S.: 449121

Subsidiary (Non-US):

La Cornue SAS (4)
14 Rue Du Bois Du Pont, 95310, Saint-Ouen-l'Aumone, France
Tel.: (33) 134483636
Web Site: https://www.lacornue.com
Emp.: 70
Household Cooking Appliance Mfr
N.A.I.C.S.: 335220

La Cornue SAS (4)
14 Rue Du Bois Du Pont, 95310, Saint-Ouen-l'Aumone, France
Tel.: (33) 134483636
Web Site: https://www.lacornue.com
Emp.: 70
Household Cooking Appliance Mfr
N.A.I.C.S.: 335220

La Cornue SAS (4)
14 Rue Du Bois Du Pont, 95310, Saint-Ouen-l'Aumone, France
Tel.: (33) 134483636
Web Site: https://www.lacornue.com
Emp.: 70
Household Cooking Appliance Mfr
N.A.I.C.S.: 335220

La Cornue SAS (4)
14 Rue Du Bois Du Pont, 95310, Saint-Ouen-l'Aumone, France
Tel.: (33) 134483636
Web Site: https://www.lacornue.com
Emp.: 70
Household Cooking Appliance Mfr
N.A.I.C.S.: 335220

Waterford Stanley Ltd. (4)
Unit 401-403 Waterford Industrial Estate Cork Road, Waterford, X91 DR76, Ireland
Tel.: (353) 5 130 2300
Web Site: https://www.waterfordstanley.com
Household Cooking Appliance & Wood Stove Mfr & Distr
N.A.I.C.S.: 335220

Subsidiary (Domestic):

Mercury Appliances Limited (3)
Juno Drive, Leamington Spa, CV31 3RG, Warwickshire, United Kingdom
Tel.: (44) 8707561236
Web Site: http://www.mercury-appliances.co.uk
Household Appliance Retailer
N.A.I.C.S.: 449210
Najib Maalouf *(Mng Dir)*

Subsidiary (Domestic):

Armor Inox UK Ltd. (2)
Fairways, Rhosrobin, Wrexham, LL114 PT, Denbighshire, United Kingdom
Tel.: (44) 1978263482
Sales Range: $10-24.9 Million
Emp.: 2
Food Product Equipment Mfr
N.A.I.C.S.: 333241
Jean Luc Treano *(Gen Mgr)*

IMC Ltd (2)
Unit 1 Abbey Road Wrexham Industrial Estate, Wrexham, LL13 9RF, United Kingdom
Tel.: (44) 1978661155
Web Site: http://www.imco.co.uk

Emp.: 70
Food Product Equipment Mfr
N.A.I.C.S.: 333241

Lincat Limited (2)
Whisby Road, Lincoln, LN6 3QZ, United Kingdom
Tel.: (44) 1522875500
Web Site: https://www.lincat.co.uk
Emp.: 200
Kitchen, Bar & Food Processing Equipment & Machinery Mfr & Household Appliance Mfr & Retailer
N.A.I.C.S.: 333241

Subsidiary (Domestic):

Britannia Kitchen Ventilation Limited (3)
10 Highdown Road Sydenham Industrial Estate, Southam, CV31 1XT, Warwickshire, United Kingdom
Tel.: (44) 8450760390
Web Site: http://www.kitchen-ventilation.co.uk
Sales Range: $25-49.9 Million
Emp.: 40
Commercial Kitchen Ventilation Mfr & Installer
N.A.I.C.S.: 333415

Imperial Machine Company Limited (3)
Unit 1 Abbey Road Wrexham Industrial Estate, Wrexham, LL13 9RF, Hertfordshire, United Kingdom
Tel.: (44) 1978661155
Web Site: http://www.imco.co.uk
Sales Range: $25-49.9 Million
Emp.: 80
Kitchen, Bar & Food Processing Equipment Mfr
N.A.I.C.S.: 333241
Ian Washington (Dir-Operation)
Joanna Street (Mgr-Customer Svcs)
Eddy Plumb (Mgr-Engrg)
Tony Bright (Comml Dir)

Subsidiary (Domestic):

Peak Drink Dispense Limited (2)
Unit 15 Bridge Bank Close Off Yew Tree Way, Golborne, WA3 3JD, Lancashire, United Kingdom
Tel.: (44) 1942270854
Web Site:
https://www.wunderbardispensing.co.uk
Industrial Equipment Mfr
N.A.I.C.S.: 334513

TurboChef Technologies Europe, LTD (2)
Business & Technology Centre Bessemer Drive, Stevenage, SG1 2DX, United Kingdom
Tel.: (44) 8456021544
Food Product Equipment Mfr & Distr
N.A.I.C.S.: 333241

Middleby Worldwide Mexico SA de CV (1)
Autop Mexico-Queretaro Km 26 5 S/N Lomas Boulevares, 54020, Tlalnepantla, Edo Mex, Mexico
Tel.: (52) 5530670200
Web Site: https://www.middleby.com.mx
Food Product Equipment Distr
N.A.I.C.S.: 423830

Nieco Corporation (1)
7950 Cameron Dr, Windsor, CA 95492
Tel.: (707) 284-7100
Web Site: https://nieco.com
Restaurant Operators
N.A.I.C.S.: 722511

Nu-Vu Foodservice Systems (1)
5600 13th St, Menominee, MI 49858
Tel.: (906) 863-4401
Web Site: https://www.nu-vu.com
Sales Range: $25-49.9 Million
Emp.: 70
Steel & Aluminum Food Service & Meal Delivery Equipment
N.A.I.C.S.: 333241

Packaging Progressions, Inc. (1)
261 Schoolhouse Rd Ste 7, Souderton, PA 18964
Tel.: (610) 489-8601

Web Site: http://www.pacproinc.com
Emp.: 100
Confectionery Manufacturing from Purchased Chocolate
N.A.I.C.S.: 311352
Larry Ward (Founder)
Jim Sonet (Supvr-Svc)
Melissa Steffy (Coord-Customer Svc)
Tim Govan (Mgr-Svc)
Rob Todoro (Coord-Svc)
Dante Pietrinferni (Pres)
John T. Fry (Controller & Dir-HR)
Nate Riordan (Exec VP-Sls-Global)
Mike Kozlowski (Sls Mgr-District)
Parker Reusch (Acct Mgr-Sls)
Craig Deppert (Sls Mgr-Material)
Bart Leussink (Mgr-Bus Dev)
Bob Tomko (Engr-Sls)
Tom Dougherty (Mgr-Materials)
Frank Rocchino (Dir-Safety & Mgr-Quality Assurance)

Perfect Fry Company LCC (1)
PO Box 501, Concord, NH 03302-0501
Tel.: (603) 225-6684
Web Site: http://www.perfectfry.com
Sales Range: $1-9.9 Million
Emp.: 22
Fast Food Appliance Mfr
N.A.I.C.S.: 332215

Powerhouse Dynamics Inc. (1)
1 Bridge St 2nd Fl, Newton, MA 02458
Tel.: (617) 340-6582
Web Site:
https://www.powerhousedynamics.com
Emp.: 25
Software Development Services
N.A.I.C.S.: 541511
Martin Flusberg (CEO)
Benjamin Sprachman (VP-Engrg)
Jay Fiske (VP-Strategy & Ops)
Vinny Gebhart (VP-Customer Ops)
Jason Roeder (Sr Dir-Product Mgmt)

QualServ Solutions LLC (1)
7400 S 28th Str, Fort Smith, AR 72908
Web Site: https://www.qualservcorp.com
Commercial Food Service Equipment Retailer
N.A.I.C.S.: 423440

Scanico A/S (1)
Gugvej 152 C, DK-9210, Aalborg, SO, Denmark
Tel.: (45) 96203050
Web Site: https://scanico.com
Emp.: 75
Food Processing Equipment Mfr
N.A.I.C.S.: 333241

Southbend (1)
1100 Old Honeycutt Rd, Fuquay Varina, NC 27526
Tel.: (919) 762-1000
Web Site: https://www.southbendnc.com
Sales Range: $75-99.9 Million
Emp.: 150
Mfr & Retailer of Commercial Foodservice Equipment, Designs Develops & Manufactures Equipment Used for the Cooking, Warming
N.A.I.C.S.: 333310
John Perruccio (Pres-Grp)
Mike Cervantes (VP-Sls-West Coast & North Midwest)
Bryant Woolcock (VP-Sls-Mid-Central & Gulf States)

Star Manufacturing International, Inc. (1)
10 Sunnen Dr, Saint Louis, MO 63143
Tel.: (314) 781-2777
Web Site: http://www.star-mfg.com
Sales Range: $100-124.9 Million
Commercial Cooking & Food Warming Equipment Mfr
N.A.I.C.S.: 333241

Subsidiary (Domestic):

Holman Cooking Equipment Inc. (2)
10 Sunnen Dr, Saint Louis, MO 63143
Tel.: (207) 282-1589
Rev.: $12,000,000
Commercial Cooking Equipment Mfr
N.A.I.C.S.: 333241
Steve Lombardo (Exec VP)
Bradley W. Wimpee (Dir-Sls)

Stewart Systems Baking, LLC (1)
808 Stewart Ave, Plano, TX 75074
Tel.: (972) 422-5808
Web Site: https://www.stewart-systems.com
Bakery Equipment Mfr
N.A.I.C.S.: 333241

Sveba Dahlen Rus. Ltd. (1)
197341 Kolomayzhsky Prospect 27 Liter A, Saint Petersburg, Russia
Tel.: (7) 8123400220
Commercial Food Service Equipment Retailer
N.A.I.C.S.: 423440

Sveba-Dahlen Baltic OU (1)
Nurme 5A, Viljandi, 71008, Estonia
Tel.: (372) 435 1563
Web Site: https://www.sveba-dahlen.ee
Food Product Machinery Mfr
N.A.I.C.S.: 333241
Marge Tirgo (Sls Dir)
Raul Jarve (Mgr-Factory)

Sveba-Dahlen Espana (1)
Avda Quitapesares 33 nave 4, Villaviciosa de Odon, 28670, Madrid, Spain
Tel.: (34) 916657839
Web Site: https://sveba-dahlen.es
Food Product Machinery Mfr
N.A.I.C.S.: 333241

Sveba-Dahlen Group AB (1)
Industrivagen 8, SE-513 82, Fristad, Sweden
Tel.: (46) 33151500
Web Site: https://www.sveba-dahlen.com
Bakery Equipment Mfr & Supplier
N.A.I.C.S.: 333241
Mattias Nilsson (Project Mgr-Industrial)
Asa Ericsson (Mgr-Mktg)
Robert Backman (Coord-Mktg)
Henrik Tillander (Sls Mgr-Industrial)
Johan Andersson (Mgr-After Sls)

Synesso, Inc. (1)
5610 4th Ave S, Seattle, WA 98108
Tel.: (206) 764-0600
Web Site: http://www.synesso.com
Industrial Valve Equipment Mfr
N.A.I.C.S.: 332911
Charles Gonzalez (Sls Mgr-Acct-Intl)

Taylor Company (1)
750 N Blackhawk Blvd, Rockton, IL 61072
Tel.: (815) 624-8333
Web Site: https://www.taylor-company.com
Commercial Ice Cream, Milk Shake, Frozen Confection & Slush Machinery & Cooking Utensils
N.A.I.C.S.: 333241

The Alluvian Spa, LLC (1)
325D Howard St, Greenwood, MS 38930
Tel.: (662) 451-6700
Web Site: http://www.thealluvian.com
Spa & Beautycare Services
N.A.I.C.S.: 713940

The Alluvian, LLC (1)
318 Howard St, Greenwood, MS 38930
Tel.: (662) 453-2114
Web Site: https://www.thealluvian.com
Hotel Operator
N.A.I.C.S.: 721110

The Middleby Worldwide Europe (1)
Edificio Larre Astintze 2 Bajo, 48180, Bilbao, Vizcaya, Spain (100%)
Tel.: (34) 944542815
Web Site: http://www.middleby.es
Sales Range: $10-24.9 Million
Emp.: 12
N.A.I.C.S.: 333241

Thurne-Middleby Ltd (1)
Gresham House Pinetrees Road, Norwich, NR7 9BB, United Kingdom
Tel.: (44) 1603700755
Web Site: https://www.thurne.com
Industrial Equipment Whsr
N.A.I.C.S.: 423830

TurboChef Technologies, Inc. (1)
2801 Trade Center Dr, Carrollton, TX 75007
Tel.: (214) 379-6000
Web Site: https://www.turbochef.com
Sales Range: $100-124.9 Million
Emp.: 258
Proprietary Cooking Technologies Designer & Developer

N.A.I.C.S.: 335220

Division (Non-US):

TurboChef International (2)
Business & Technology Centre, Bessemer Drive, Stevenage, SG1 2DX, Hertfordshire, United Kingdom
Tel.: (44) 8456021544
Web Site: http://www.turbochef.com
Sales Range: $100-124.9 Million
Emp.: 3
Proprietary Cooking Technologies Designer & Developer
N.A.I.C.S.: 333241

U-Line Corporation (1)
8900 N 55th St, Milwaukee, WI 53223
Tel.: (414) 354-0300
Web Site: https://www.u-line.com
Sales Range: $50-74.9 Million
Emp.: 110
Household Refrigerator & Home Freezer Mfr
N.A.I.C.S.: 335220

Varimixer A/S (1)
Elementfabrikken 9, 2605, Brondby, Denmark
Tel.: (45) 43442288
Web Site: https://www.varimixer.com
Emp.: 60
Mixer Mfr
N.A.I.C.S.: 333241
Peter M. Frederiksen (Sls Dir)
Marianne Sennenwald (Coord-Svc)
Henrik Lykke Mose (CFO)

Ve.Ma.C. Srl (1)
Via Rio Dei Gamberi 9 A/B, 41051, Castelnuovo Rangone, MO, Italy
Tel.: (39) 05 953 6683
Web Site: https://www.vemacautomazioni.it
Industrial Food Processing Machinery Mfr
N.A.I.C.S.: 333241

Viking Cooking Schools, LLC (1)
325 C Howard St, Greenwood, MS 38930
Tel.: (662) 451-6750
Web Site:
http://www.vikingcookingschool.com
Emp.: 20
Food Product Equipment Mfr
N.A.I.C.S.: 333241

Viking Range Corporation do Brasil Importacao e Comercio Ltda. (1)
Al Gabriel Monteiro Da Silva 1847, Sao Paulo, 01441-001, Brazil
Tel.: (55) 1130652580
Web Site: http://www.vikingrange.com.br
Emp.: 14
Household Appliance Distr
N.A.I.C.S.: 449210

Viking Range LLC (1)
111 Front St, Greenwood, MS 38930
Tel.: (662) 455-1200
Web Site: https://www.vikingrange.com
Commercial Gas Cooking Stoves & Other Major Appliances for the Home Mfr
N.A.I.C.S.: 335220

Wells Bloomfield LLC (1)
10 Sunnen Dr, Saint Louis, MO 63143-3800 (100%)
Tel.: (314) 678-6336
Web Site: http://www.wellsbloomfield.com
Sales Range: $50-74.9 Million
Emp.: 300
Commercial Food Service Equipment & Beverage Systems
N.A.I.C.S.: 333310

Wunder-Bar Dispensing UK Ltd. (1)
Unit 15 Bridge Bank Close Off Yew Tree Way, Golborne, WA3 3JD, Lancashire, United Kingdom
Tel.: (44) 1942270854
Web Site:
http://www.wunderbardispensing.co.uk
Beverage Dispensing Equipment Mfr
N.A.I.C.S.: 333241

Wunder-Bar International, Inc. (1)
2060 Cessna Dr, Vacaville, CA 95688
Tel.: (707) 448-5151
Web Site: https://www.wunderbar.com
Industrial Equipment Mfr
N.A.I.C.S.: 334513

The Mosaic Company—(Continued)

THE MOSAIC COMPANY
101 E Kennedy Blvd Ste 2500,
Tampa, FL 33602
Web Site: https://www.mosaicco.com
Year Founded: 2004
MOS—(NYSE)
Rev.: $13,696,100,000
Assets: $23,032,800,000
Liabilities: $10,600,000,000
Net Worth: $12,432,800,000
Earnings: $1,164,900,000
Emp.: 14,049
Fiscal Year-end: 12/31/23
Agricultural Chemical Mfr.
N.A.I.C.S.: 325320
Karen A. Swager (Sr VP-Supply
Chain)
Walter F. Precourt III (Chief Admin
Officer & Sr VP)
Russell A. Flugel (Principal Acctg Of-
ficer)
Clint C. Freeland (CFO & Sr VP)
Christopher A. Lewis (Sr VP-HR)
Bruce Bodine (Sr VP)
Corrine Ricard (Sr VP)
Walt Precourt (Sr VP)
Phil Bauer (Gen Counsel)
Bruce M. Bodine Jr. (Pres & CEO)

Subsidiaries:

Mosaic Canada ULC   (1)
1700-210 12th Ave, Regina, S4P0M3,
Canada
Tel.: (306) 523-2800
Web Site: https://www.mosaicco.com
Sales Range: $250-299.9 Million
Emp.: 500
Mining, Refining & Production of Potash
N.A.I.C.S.: 212390

Subsidiary (Domestic):

Mosaic Esterhazy Holdings ULC   (2)
Highway 80 East, Esterhazy, S0A 0X0, SK,
Canada
Tel.: (306) 745-4200
Emp.: 900
Investment Management Service
N.A.I.C.S.: 523940

Mosaic Potash Colonsay ULC   (2)
2 Miles South, Colonsay, S0K0Z0, SK,
Canada
Tel.: (306) 944-2223
Web Site: https://www.mosaicco.com
Emp.: 1,000
Potash Plant
N.A.I.C.S.: 212390

Mosaic Potash Esterhazy Limited
Partnership   (2)
Highway 80 East, Esterhazy, S0A 0X0, SK,
Canada
Tel.: (306) 745-4200
Emp.: 1,000
Potash Soda & Borate Mining Services
N.A.I.C.S.: 212390

Mosaic Crop Nutrition, LLC   (1)
8813 Highway 41 S, Riverview, FL 33578
Tel.: (813) 671-6127
Fertilizer Products Mfr
N.A.I.C.S.: 325314
Betty Kendall-Jones (Mgr-Municipal Bids &
Contracts)

Mosaic Fertilizantes P&K Ltda   (1)
Av Roque Petroni Jr 999 - 14th Floor,
Brooklin, Sao Paulo, 04707-910, Brazil
Tel.: (55) 1149502600
Web Site: https://www.mosaicco.com.br
Agricultural Chemical Mfr
N.A.I.C.S.: 325320

Subsidiary (Domestic):

Mosaic Fertilizantes P&K S.A.   (2)
Praia de Botafogo 186 Salas 501 a 1901,
Rio de Janeiro, 22250-145, Brazil
Tel.: (55) 2134855000
Web Site: http://www.mosaicco.com.br
Fertilizer Producer
N.A.I.C.S.: 325312

Mosaic Fertilizer, LLC   (1)
13830 Circa Crossing Dr, Lithia, FL 33547
Tel.: (813) 500-6523
Web Site: https://www.mosaic.co.com
Sales Range: $150-199.9 Million
Emp.: 540
Phosphatic Fertilizer Mfr
N.A.I.C.S.: 325312
John Pillard (Coord)

Mosaic Global Holdings Inc.   (1)
3033 Campus Dr Ste E490, Plymouth, MN
55441
Tel.: (763) 577-2700
Web Site: http://www.mosaicco.com
Emp.: 350
Producer & Supplier of Agricultural Products
& Services, Salt & Industrial Chemicals,
Phosphate & Potash Crop Nutrients & Ani-
mal Feed Ingredients
N.A.I.C.S.: 325312

Mosaic Potash Carlsbad Inc   (1)
1361 Potash Mines Rd, Carlsbad, NM
88220
Tel.: (575) 887-2871
Web Site: https://www.mosaicco.com
Farm Supplies Merchant Whslr
N.A.I.C.S.: 424910

PRP-GP LLC   (1)
100 S Saunders Rd Ste 300, Lake Forest,
IL 60045
Tel.: (847) 739-1200
Agricultural Chemical Mfr
N.A.I.C.S.: 325320

The Mosaic Company   (1)
5880 Manley Rd, Fort Meade, FL 33841
Tel.: (863) 375-4100
Sales Range: $50-74.9 Million
Emp.: 200
Phosphatic Fertilizer Producer
N.A.I.C.S.: 325312

The Mosaic Company   (1)
3200 State Rd 60 W, Bartow, FL 33830-
7805
Tel.: (863) 534-9626
Web Site: http://www.mosaicco.com
Sales Range: $125-149.9 Million
Emp.: 400
Phosphatic Fertilizer Mfr
N.A.I.C.S.: 325312

THE MOVIE STUDIO, INC.
2542B E Sunrise Blvd, Fort Lauder-
dale, FL 33304
Tel.: (954) 332-6600   DE
Web Site:
https://www.themoviestudio.com
Year Founded: 1961
MVES—(OTCIQ)
Assets: $1,032,000
Liabilities: $236,000
Net Worth: $796,000
Earnings: ($520,000)
Emp.: 1
Fiscal Year-end: 06/30/20
Motion Picture & Video Production
N.A.I.C.S.: 512110
Gordon Scott Venters (Pres & CEO)
Jeff Hines (VP)
Brain Breach (Dir-Social Media)

Subsidiaries:

Emerging Media Corp.   (1)
49 W 27th St 8th fl, New York, NY 10001
Tel.: (212) 245-6767
Web Site: http://www.emergingpictures.com
Motion Picture & Video Production
N.A.I.C.S.: 512110

THE MUSIC ACQUISITION
CORPORATION
9000 W Sunset Blvd Ste 1500, Holly-
wood, CA 90069
Tel.: (747) 203-7219   DE
Web Site:
http://www.musicacquisition.com
Year Founded: 2020
TMAC—(NYSE)
Rev.: $4,724,875
Assets: $230,813,881

Liabilities: $248,554,849
Net Worth: ($17,740,968)
Earnings: $3,578,969
Emp.: 2
Fiscal Year-end: 12/31/21
Investment Services
N.A.I.C.S.: 523999
Neil Jacobson (Chm & CEO)
Todd J. Lowen (CFO, COO & Sec)

THE NATIONAL SECURITY
GROUP, INC.
661 E Davis St, Elba, AL 36323
Tel.: (334) 897-2273   DE
Web Site: http://www.nationalsecurity
group.com
Year Founded: 1947
NSEC—(NASDAQ)
Rev.: $66,210,000
Assets: $151,683,000
Liabilities: $107,881,000
Net Worth: $43,802,000
Earnings: $582,000
Emp.: 72
Fiscal Year-end: 12/31/21
Holding Company; Insurance Prod-
ucts & Services
N.A.I.C.S.: 524130
William L. Brunson Jr. (Pres & CEO)
Walter P. Wilkerson (Chm)
Brian R. McLeod (CFO, Treas & VP-
Fin & Operation)

Subsidiaries:

National Security Fire and Casualty
Company   (1)
661 E Davis St, Elba, AL 36323
Tel.: (334) 897-2273
Web Site:
http://www.nationalsecuritygroup.com
Sales Range: $50-74.9 Million
Home & Automobile Casualty Insurance
N.A.I.C.S.: 524126

National Security Insurance
Company   (1)
661 E Davis St, Elba, AL 36323
Tel.: (334) 897-2273
Web Site:
http://www.nationalsecuritygroup.com
Sales Range: $50-74.9 Million
Life, Hospital, School Insurance
N.A.I.C.S.: 524126

THE NEW YORK TIMES COM-
PANY
620 8th Ave, New York, NY 10018
Tel.: (212) 556-1234   NY
Web Site: https://www.nytco.com
Year Founded: 1896
NYT—(NYSE)
Rev.: $2,426,152,000
Assets: $2,714,595,000
Liabilities: $951,376,000
Net Worth: $1,763,219,000
Earnings: $232,387,000
Emp.: 5,900
Fiscal Year-end: 12/31/23
Newspaper Publishing
N.A.I.C.S.: 513110
R. Anthony Benten (Chief Acctg Offi-
cer, Treas & Sr VP)
Stephen Dunbar-Johnson (Pres-Intl)
William Bardeen (CFO & Exec VP)
Carolyn Ryan (Mng Editor-The New
York Times)
Meredith Kopit Levien (Pres & CEO)
David S. Perpich (Founder)
David Rubin (CMO)
Joseph Kahn (Exec Editor)
Kathleen Kingsbury (Editor-Opinion)
Hannah Y. Yang (Chief Growth Officer
& Chief Customer Officer)
Theodore Kim (Dir-Newsroom Fellow-
ships & Internships)
Jordan Jacobson (Assoc Dir-Creative
& Mktg)

Julia Simon (Dir-Audience & Ops-
Audio)
Kathy Ryan (Dir-Photography-The
New York Times Magazine)
Jacqueline M. Welch (Chief HR Offi-
cer & Exec VP)
Holly Harnisch (Dir-Brand Mktg)
Kathleen Lingo (Dir-Editorial-Film &
TV)
Tara Sarath (Sr Mgr-Email Ops)
Keith McLeod (VP-Mktg Ops)
Felice Belman (Deputy Editor-Metro
Desk)
Alison Mitchell (Dir-News-Intl)
Jeremy White (Editor)
Veronica Chambers (Editor)

Subsidiaries:

Fake Love LLC   (1)
45 Main St 842, Brooklyn, NY 11201
Tel.: (212) 995-9787
Web Site: https://www.fakelove.tv
Graphic Design Services
N.A.I.C.S.: 541430
Alexander Chen (Mgr)
Grace Diggens (Sr Mgr)
Carly Blake (Bus Dir)
Rachel Czipo (Program Mgr)
Sania Rana (Mgr)
Janel McCann (Mgr-Business Development)
Kendra Schaaf (VP-Client Services)
Kate Carrington (Head)
Jessica Strode (Exec Dir-Strategy)
Taylor Hight (Mng Dir)

International Herald Tribune
S.A.S.   (1)
6 Bis Rue De Graviers, Neuilly-sur-Seine,
92521, France
Tel.: (33) 141439300
Web Site: http://www.iht.com
Sales Range: $100-124.9 Million
Emp.: 300
Newspaper Publishing
N.A.I.C.S.: 513110

Subsidiary (Non-US):

International Herald Tribune Ltd.   (2)
1 New Oxford Street, London, WC1A 1NU,
United Kingdom
Tel.: (44) 2070613500
Newspaper Publishers
N.A.I.C.S.: 513110

International New York Times   (2)
Vaartweg 127/A, 1217 SN, Hilversum, Neth-
erlands
Tel.: (31) 356220101
Web Site: http://www.nytimes.com
Emp.: 1
International Newspaper Publisher
N.A.I.C.S.: 513110

International Herald Tribune U.S.
Inc.   (1)
229 W 43rd St, New York, NY 10036
Tel.: (212) 556-7707
Newspaper Publishers
N.A.I.C.S.: 513110

NYT Capital, LLC   (1)
620 8th Ave, New York, NY 10018
Tel.: (212) 556-3906
Newspaper Publishers
N.A.I.C.S.: 513110

Subsidiary (Domestic):

Midtown Insurance Company   (2)
1519 S Salina St, Syracuse, NY 13205
Tel.: (315) 476-5374
Emp.: 4
Insurance Management Services
N.A.I.C.S.: 524298
Susan Hrynyk (Gen Mgr)

NYT Management Services, Inc.   (2)
620 8th Ave, New York, NY 10018
Tel.: (212) 556-1234
Web Site: http://www.nytimes.com
Holding Company

N.A.I.C.S.: 551112

Subsidiary (Domestic):

The New York Times **(3)**
620 8th Ave, New York, NY 10018
Tel.: (212) 556-1234
Web Site: https://www.nytimes.com
Newspapers
N.A.I.C.S.: 513110

Subsidiary (Domestic):

NYT Shared Service Center, Inc. **(2)**
229 W 43rd St, New York, NY 10036
Tel.: (212) 556-1234
Web Site: https://www.nytimes.com
Emp.: 24
N.A.I.C.S.: 513110

Subsidiary (Domestic):

International Media Concepts, Inc. **(3)**
1111 Marcus Ave Ste M21, New Hyde Park, NY 11042
Tel.: (516) 209-5800
Emp.: 85
Newspaper Publishers
N.A.I.C.S.: 513110

NYT Singapore PTE. LTD. **(1)**
1 Marina Boulevard 01 Marina, Singapore, Singapore
Tel.: (65) 63919620
Newspaper Publishers
N.A.I.C.S.: 513110

New York Times Limited **(1)**
18 Museum Street, London, WC1A 1JN, United Kingdom
Tel.: (44) 2070613501
Graphic Design Services
N.A.I.C.S.: 541430

New York Times Television **(1)**
620 8th Ave, New York, NY 10036
Tel.: (212) 556-5971
Web Site: http://www.nytimes.com
Sales Range: $200-249.9 Million
Television Broadcasting Services
N.A.I.C.S.: 516120

The New York Times Syndication Sales Corporation **(1)**
620 8th Ave Frnt 5, New York, NY 10018 **(100%)**
Tel.: (212) 556-4063
Web Site: https://www.nytsyn.com
Sales Range: $10-24.9 Million
Emp.: 25
Newspaper Publishers
N.A.I.C.S.: 513110

Subsidiary (Domestic):

The New York Times News Service **(2)**
620 8th Ave 9th Fl, New York, NY 10018 **(100%)**
Tel.: (212) 556-1927
Web Site: http://www.nytsyn.com
Sales Range: $10-24.9 Million
Markets News & Photo Services Columns Magazine & Book Excerpts Feature Packages to Newspapers & Magazines Worldwide
N.A.I.C.S.: 516210

THE NOW CORPORATION
1100 NE 45th St M195, Oakland Park, FL 33334
Tel.: (561) 318-1903 **NY**
Web Site:
https://www.thenowcorp.net
NWPN—(OTCIQ)
Research & Development in Biotechnology (except Nanobiotechnology)
N.A.I.C.S.: 541714
Ken Williams *(CEO & Mng Dir)*
Juan Salazar *(COO)*
Jeffrey B. Martin *(CTO)*
Brian Martin *(Chief Innovation Officer)*
Augustus Redmond *(Dir-Bus & Economic Dev)*

Subsidiaries:

Green Rain Solar, Inc. **(1)**

201 E 5th St, Sheridan, WY 82801
Tel.: (212) 624-9090
Web Site: https://www.greenrainsolar.com
Solar Installation Services
N.A.I.C.S.: 221114
Madeline Cammarata *(Founder)*
James C. DiPrima *(CEO)*
James Ware *(VP)*

THE O.T. MINING CORPORATION
919 Flowerree St, Helena, MT 59601
Tel.: (514) 935-2445 **MT**
Web Site: https://www.otmining.com
Year Founded: 1987
OTMN—(OTCIQ)
Metal Mining
N.A.I.C.S.: 212290
Rosemary L. Christensen *(Chm & Pres)*
Pierre-Yves Le Dilicocq *(CEO)*

THE ODP CORPORATION
6600 N Military Trl, Boca Raton, FL 33496
Tel.: (561) 438-4800 **DE**
Web Site:
https://www.officedepot.com
Year Founded: 1986
ODP—(NASDAQ)
Rev.: $8,491,000,000
Assets: $4,149,000,000
Liabilities: $2,862,000,000
Net Worth: $1,287,000,000
Earnings: $166,000,000
Emp.: 25,000
Fiscal Year-end: 12/31/22
Office Supplies, Equipment & Furniture Retailer; Copy & Printing Services
N.A.I.C.S.: 459410
David Centrella *(Pres & Exec VP)*
John W. Gannfors *(Chief Mdsg & Supply Chain Officer, Pres-Veyer & Exec VP)*
Zoe Maloney *(Chief HR Officer & Exec VP)*
Gerry P. Smith *(CEO & Principal Financial Officer)*

Subsidiaries:

4Sure.com, Inc. **(1)**
6 Cambridge Dr, Trumbull, CT 06611-4746
Tel.: (203) 615-7000
Web Site: http://www.4sure.com
Sales Range: $25-49.9 Million
Emp.: 130
Direct Marketer of Computer & Technology Products to Businesses & Consumers
N.A.I.C.S.: 449210

Division (Domestic):

Computers4Sure.com, Inc. **(2)**
55 Corporate Dr Ste 5, Trumbull, CT 06611
Tel.: (203) 615-7000
Web Site: http://www.computers4sure.com
Sales Range: $25-49.9 Million
Emp.: 75
Internet Based Computer Product Superstore
N.A.I.C.S.: 449210

TechDepot **(2)**
6 Cambridge Dr, Trumbull, CT 06611
Tel.: (203) 615-7000
Web Site: http://www.techdepot.com
Computer & Technology Products Direct Marketer
N.A.I.C.S.: 423430

Admiral Express, LLC **(1)**
3412 NW 178th St Ste A, Oklahoma City, OK 73012
Tel.: (405) 942-6060
Web Site: http://www.admiralexpress.com
Emp.: 60
Fiscal Year-end: 12/31/2011
Retail Office Product Distr
N.A.I.C.S.: 459410

Americas Office Source, Inc. **(1)**

706 Turnbull Ave Ste 305, Altamonte Springs, FL 32701
Tel.: (407) 478-0637
Web Site:
https://www.americasofficesource.com
Office Products Distr
N.A.I.C.S.: 459410

Bertelson Brothers, Inc. **(1)**
44 Northern Stacks Dr Ste 120, Minneapolis, MN 55421
Tel.: (763) 595-5300
Web Site:
https://www.bebusinessessentials.com
Fiscal Year-end: 12/31/2009
Stationery & Office Product Distr
N.A.I.C.S.: 459410
Mark R. Bertelson *(Owner)*

BuyerQuest Holdings Inc. **(1)**
343 W Bagley Rd Ste 300, Berea, OH 44017
Tel.: (866) 937-0670
Web Site: http://www.buyerquest.com
Sales Range: $1-9.9 Million
Information Technology Consulting Services
N.A.I.C.S.: 541512
Karen Bare *(VP)*
Jack Mulloy *(CEO)*
Matt McCarrick *(CMO)*
Nicholas Cron *(CTO)*
Salman Siddiqui *(COO)*
Matt Fisher *(Sr VP)*
Kyle Muskoff *(VP)*
Luke Batman *(VP-Finance)*
Brian Mohr *(VP-Engineering)*
Eric Lynch *(VP)*
Martin Kelly *(VP-Sales)*

COS Business Products & Interiors, Inc. **(1)**
1548 Riverside Dr, Chattanooga, TN 37406
Web Site: https://www.cosonline.com
Business Management Services
N.A.I.C.S.: 561110

Complete Office of Wisconsin, Inc. **(1)**
N115 W18500 Edison Dr, Germantown, WI 53022
Tel.: (262) 255-5500
Web Site: https://www.cowiweb.com
Emp.: 150
Office Products Distr
N.A.I.C.S.: 459410

Complete Office, Llc. **(1)**
11521 E Marginal Way S Ste 100, Seattle, WA 98168
Tel.: (206) 628-0059
Web Site: https://www.complete-office.com
Fiscal Year-end: 12/31/2006
Office Products Distr
N.A.I.C.S.: 327910

CompuCom Systems Holdings LLC **(1)**
7171 Forest Ln, Dallas, TX 75230
Tel.: (972) 856-3600
Furniture Product Whslr
N.A.I.C.S.: 459410

Discount Office Items, Inc. **(1)**
302 Industrial Dr, Columbus, WI 53925
Tel.: (920) 623-9528
Web Site: https://www.officesupply.com
General Office Product Distr
N.A.I.C.S.: 459410

Grand & Toy Limited **(1)**
200 Aviva Park Drive, Vaughan, L4L 9C7, ON, Canada
Tel.: (416) 401-6300
Web Site: https://www.grandandtoy.com
Office Products Distr
N.A.I.C.S.: 423420
Marla Allan *(VP-HR)*
Stan Dabic *(VP & Gen Mgr)*
Alnoor Jiwani *(VP-IT)*
Lynn Stanley *(Sr Dir-Pricing Strategy)*
John Trauzzi *(Sr Dir-Fin)*
Bal Sahjpaul *(VP-Digital Mktg & Customer Care)*
Chris Henwood *(Sr Dir-Mdsg)*

HC Land Company L.C. **(1)**
Tel.: (703) 448-8300
Office Supply & Stationery Whslr
N.A.I.C.S.: 459410

Notus Aviation, Inc. **(1)**
8215 Madison Blvd Ste 135, Madison, AL 35758
Tel.: (256) 325-4483
Web Site: http://www.notus-inc.com
Business Consulting Services
N.A.I.C.S.: 541611

OD Medical Solutions LLC **(1)**
2306 Hawksmoor Pl, Cordova, TN 38016
Tel.: (901) 388-3110
Medical Equipment Distr
N.A.I.C.S.: 423450

Office Depot Asia Holding Limited **(1)**
Suite 614 Tsim Sha Tsui Centre East Wing 66 Mody Road, Tsim Sha Tsui, Kowloon, China (Hong Kong)
Tel.: (852) 37161300
Holding Company
N.A.I.C.S.: 551112

Office Depot Business Solutions Division **(1)**
6600 N Military Trl, Boca Raton, FL 33496
Tel.: (561) 438-4800
Web Site: https://www.odpbusiness.com
Sales Range: $25-49.9 Million
Emp.: 25
Direct Distr of Office Supplies, Furniture, Computer Equipment & Janitorial Supplies to Businesses
N.A.I.C.S.: 424110

Branch (Domestic):

Office Depot Business Solutions Division-New Jersey **(2)**
4 Brighton Rd Ste 300, Clifton, NJ 07012
Tel.: (973) 594-3000
Office Products, Coffee & Refreshment Supplies, Computer Supplies, Printing Equipment, Office Furniture & Promotional Products
N.A.I.C.S.: 424120

Office Depot Overseas Limited **(1)**
6600 N Military Trial, Delray Beach, FL 33445 **(100%)**
Tel.: (561) 438-4800
Retailers of Office Products
N.A.I.C.S.: 459410
Charles E. Brown *(Pres)*

Office Depot Puerto Rico, LLC **(1)**
Rafael Cordero Ave Hwy Ste 30, Caguas, PR 00725
Tel.: (787) 744-5728
Office Supply & Stationery Product Distr
N.A.I.C.S.: 459410

OfficeMax Incorporated **(1)**
1363 Ridgeland Ave, Naperville, IL 60563
Tel.: (630) 245-1213
Web Site: https://www.officedepot.com
Sales Range: $1-4.9 Billion
Emp.: 19,000
Holding Company; Office Equipment & Supplies Commercial Whslr & Retailer
N.A.I.C.S.: 551112

Subsidiary (Non-US):

OfficeMax Canada **(2)**
33 Green Belt Drive, Toronto, M3C 1M1, ON, Canada **(100%)**
Tel.: (416) 445-7255
Web Site: http://www.officemaxcanada.com
Sales Range: $75-99.9 Million
Emp.: 250
Office Products Including Furniture Retailer & Whslr
N.A.I.C.S.: 337211

Subsidiary (Domestic):

OfficeMax North America, Inc. **(2)**
3462 Mayfield Rd, Cleveland Heights, OH 44118
Tel.: (216) 297-9789
Web Site: http://www.officedepot.com
Emp.: 5
Office Supplies & Furniture Stores & Printing Services
N.A.I.C.S.: 459410

Perimeter Office Products, Inc. **(1)**
3505 Newpoint Pl Ste 475, Lawrenceville, GA 30043

The ODP Corporation—(Continued)

Tel.: (770) 689-1900
Web Site: https://www.perimeteroffice.com
Stationery & Office Product Distr
N.A.I.C.S.: 459410

Regency Franchise Group, LLC **(1)**
8024 Glenwood Ave Ste 200, Raleigh, NC
27612
Web Site:
https://regencyfranchisegroup.com
Business Management Services
N.A.I.C.S.: 561110
Eric Beguelin *(Pres)*

Regency Office Products, LLC **(1)**
8024 Glenwood Ave Ste 200, Raleigh, NC
27612
Tel.: (919) 676-0522
Web Site: https://www.regencybusinesssolu
tions.com
Retail Office Product Distr
N.A.I.C.S.: 459410

Trio Supply Company **(1)**
45 Northern Stacks Dr Ste 100, Fridley, MN
55421-2629
Tel.: (612) 522-3822
Web Site: https://www.triosupply.com
Office Equipment Distr
N.A.I.C.S.: 423420
Steve Isakson *(Co-Founder)*
Don Larson *(Co-Founder)*
Dan Bonk *(Partner)*

Viking Office Products, Inc. **(1)**
13809 S Figueroa St, Los Angeles, CA
90061
Tel.: (213) 321-4493
Office Supply & Stationery Product Distr
N.A.I.C.S.: 459410

ZerBee, LLC **(1)**
44 Northern Stacks Dr Ste 120, Minneapo-
lis, MN 55421
Tel.: (763) 595-5333
Web Site: https://www.zerbee.com
Stationery Product Distr
N.A.I.C.S.: 459410

THE OHIO ART COMPANY, INC.

1 Toy St PO Box 111, Bryan, OH
43506-0111
Tel.: (419) 636-3141 OH
Web Site: http://www.ohioart.com
Year Founded: 1908
OART—(OTCIQ)
Sales Range: $10-24.9 Million
Emp.: 105
Toys, Games, Sporting Goods & Cre-
ativity Products Designer & Mfr
N.A.I.C.S.: 339930
John Gostkowski *(VP-Lithographic
Ops)*
Michelle Gibbs *(Mgr-HR)*
Elena West *(CEO)*
Bill Waters *(Dir-Lithographic Ops)*
Martin L. Killgallon II *(Pres)*

Subsidiaries:

Allstate Can Corporation **(1)**
1 Wood Hollow Rd, Parsippany, NJ 07054-
2821
Tel.: (973) 560-9030
Web Site: https://www.allstatecan.com
Sales Range: $50-74.9 Million
Emp.: 50
Mfr of Tin Cans
N.A.I.C.S.: 332431
Michael F. Papera *(Sr Dir)*
Leslie Wing *(Mgr-Mktg)*
Bob Cucci *(Controller)*
Dave D'Agostino *(Dir-Sls)*

THE OLB GROUP, INC.

1120 Ave of the Americas 4th Fl, New
York, NY 10036
Tel.: (212) 278-0900 DE
Web Site: https://www.olb.com
Year Founded: 1993
OLB—(NASDAQ)
Rev.: $30,368,979
Assets: $38,653,819

Liabilities: $4,016,042
Net Worth: $34,637,777
Earnings: ($8,189,172)
Emp.: 26
Fiscal Year-end: 12/31/22
Services Prepackaged Software
N.A.I.C.S.: 513210
Ronny Yakov *(Founder, Chm & CEO)*
Rachel Boulds *(CFO)*
Patrick Smith *(VP-Corp Fin)*

THE ONCOLOGY INSTITUTE, INC.

18000 Studebaker Rd Ste 800, Cerri-
tos, CA 90703
Tel.: (562) 735-3226 DE
Web Site:
https://www.theoncologyinsti
tute.com
Year Founded: 2007
TOI—(NASDAQ)
Rev.: $252,483,000
Assets: $261,665,000
Liabilities: $138,490,000
Net Worth: $123,175,000
Earnings: $152,000
Emp.: 750
Fiscal Year-end: 12/31/22
Investment Services
N.A.I.C.S.: 523999
Mihir Shah *(CFO)*
Richard Barasch *(Chm)*
Daniel Virnich *(Pres & CEO)*
Jeremy N. Castle *(COO)*
Laura Szitar *(Chief People Officer)*
Jordan McInerney *(Chief Dev Officer)*
Yale D. Podnos *(Chief Medical Officer
& Pres-Practice)*

Subsidiaries:

Broward Oncology Associates,
P.A. **(1)**
6405 N Federal Hwy Ste 201, Fort Lauder-
dale, FL 33308-1414
Tel.: (954) 771-0692
Web Site: http://www.browardoncology.com
Health Practitioners
N.A.I.C.S.: 621399
Gina Ortiz *(Sec-Medical)*

THE ONE GROUP HOSPITAL-ITY, INC.

1624 Market St Ste 311, Denver, CO
80202
Tel.: (646) 624-2400 DE
Web Site: https://www.togrp.com
Year Founded: 2006
STKS—(NASDAQ)
Rev.: $316,638,000
Assets: $291,024,000
Liabilities: $222,434,000
Net Worth: $68,590,000
Earnings: $13,534,000
Emp.: 262
Fiscal Year-end: 12/31/22
Investment Services
N.A.I.C.S.: 523999
Jonathan Segal *(Founder & Chm)*
Emanuel P. N. Hilario *(Pres & CEO)*
Tyler Loy *(CFO)*
Christi Hing *(Chief Acctg Officer)*
Caroline O'Mahony-Baker *(Sr VP)*
Daniel Cunningham *(CIO)*

Subsidiaries:

Bagatelle Little West 12th, LLC **(1)**
1 Little W 12th St, New York, NY 10014
Tel.: (212) 488-2110
Web Site: http://www.bagatellenyc.com
Restaurant Operators
N.A.I.C.S.: 722511
Aymeric Clemente *(Founder)*

Kona Grill Inc. **(1)**
7014 E Camelback Rd, Scottsdale, AZ
85251
Tel.: (480) 429-1100
Web Site: http://www.konagrill.com

Sales Range: $150-199.9 Million
Emp.: 2,968
Restaurant Operators
N.A.I.C.S.: 711110
Christi Hing *(CFO & Exec Officer)*

Subsidiary (Domestic):

Kona Sushi, Inc. **(2)**
7150 E Camelback Rd, Scottsdale, AZ
85251
Tel.: (480) 922-8100
Web Site: http://www.konasushi.com
Emp.: 7
Restaurant Operating Services
N.A.I.C.S.: 722511

Kona Texas Restaurants, Inc. **(2)**
5061 Westheimer Rd Ste 8040, Houston,
TX 77056-5775
Tel.: (713) 877-9191
Web Site: http://www.konagrill.com
Sales Range: $10-24.9 Million
Emp.: 50
Restaurant Operating Services
N.A.I.C.S.: 722511

STK Atlanta, LLC **(1)**
1075 Peachtree St NE, Atlanta, GA 30309
Tel.: (404) 793-0144
Restaurant Operators
N.A.I.C.S.: 722511
Nadia Randolph *(Mgr-Events & Mktg)*

STK Chicago, LLC **(1)**
9 W Kinzie St, Chicago, IL 60654
Tel.: (312) 340-5636
Restaurant Operators
N.A.I.C.S.: 722511
Manuel Sanchez *(Mgr)*

STK DC, LLC **(1)**
1250 Connecticut Ave NW, Washington, DC
20036
Tel.: (202) 909-1610
Restaurant Operators
N.A.I.C.S.: 722511
Jasmine Beane *(Mgr-Events & Mktg)*

STK Ibiza, LLC **(1)**
C illa Plana S/N Marina botafach, Ibiza,
Spain
Tel.: (34) 689333965
Web Site: http://www.stkibiza.com
Restaurant Operators
N.A.I.C.S.: 722511

STK Miami, LLC **(1)**
2305 Collins Ave, Miami Beach, FL 33139
Tel.: (305) 604-6988
Emp.: 16
Restaurant Operators
N.A.I.C.S.: 722511
Sarah Percy *(Gen Mgr)*

STK Midtown, LLC **(1)**
1114 Avenue of the Americas, New York,
NY 10036
Tel.: (646) 624-2455
Restaurant Operators
N.A.I.C.S.: 722511

STK Nashville, LLC **(1)**
700 12th Ave S, Nashville, TN 37203
Tel.: (615) 619-3500
Web Site: https://stksteakhouse.com
Restaurant Operators
N.A.I.C.S.: 722511

STK Orlando, LLC **(1)**
1580 E Buena Vista Dr, Orlando, FL 32830
Tel.: (407) 917-7440
Restaurant Operators
N.A.I.C.S.: 722511
Kate Naumann *(Mgr-Events & Mktg)*

STK-LA, LLC **(1)**
930 Hilgard Ave, Los Angeles, CA 90024
Tel.: (310) 659-3535
Restaurant Operators
N.A.I.C.S.: 722511

STK-Las Vegas, LLC **(1)**
3708 Las Vegas Blvd S, Las Vegas, NV
89109
Tel.: (702) 698-7990
Restaurant Operators
N.A.I.C.S.: 722511
Eunji Hong *(Mgr-Restaurant)*

THE PENNANT GROUP, INC.

1675 E Riverside Dr, Eagle, ID 83616
Tel.: (208) 401-1400
Web Site:
https://www.pennantgroup.com
Year Founded: 2019
PNTG—(NASDAQ)
Rev.: $473,241,000
Assets: $512,119,000
Liabilities: $386,462,000
Net Worth: $125,657,000
Earnings: $7,243,000
Emp.: 5,335
Fiscal Year-end: 12/31/22
Holding Company; Nursing & Health
Care Services
N.A.I.C.S.: 551112
Daniel H. Walker *(Chm)*
John J. Gochnour *(Pres & COO)*
Brent J. Guerisoli *(CEO)*
Jennifer L. Freeman *(Sr VP-Strategic
Partnerships)*
Lynette B. Walbom *(CFO)*

Subsidiaries:

Bear River Healthcare LLC **(1)**
2329 Center St, Boyne Falls, MI 49713
Tel.: (231) 535-2822
Web Site: https://www.bearriverhealth.com
Outpatient Rehabilitation Services
N.A.I.C.S.: 621420
Jason E. Sweeney *(Dir-Compliance)*
Chris Frasz *(Dir-Clinical Outreach)*
Daniel J. Hartman *(CEO)*
Jackie Guzman *(COO)*
Thomas Hartman *(CIO)*
Huston Mayer *(CFO)*

Cornerstone Healthcare, Inc. **(1)**
535 W Thomas Rd Ste 103, Phoenix, AZ
85013
Tel.: (208) 401-1400
Web Site:
https://www.cornerstonehealthcareaz.com
Healthcare Services
N.A.I.C.S.: 621610
Brian Wayment *(Pres)*

First Choice Home Health **(1)**
205 Haggerty Ln Ste 120, Bozeman, MT
59715-8804
Tel.: (406) 551-2273
Web Site:
http://www.firstchoicemontana.com
Women Healthcare Services
N.A.I.C.S.: 621610
Norm Dreyer *(Mgr)*

Pinnacle Senior Living LLC **(1)**
1600 W Broadway Rd Ste 100, Tempe, AZ
85282
Tel.: (602) 313-4599
Web Site: http://www.pinnaclesl.com
Senior Living Services
N.A.I.C.S.: 623312

Sentinel Healthcare LLC **(1)**
111 S Jackson St, Seattle, WA 98104
Web Site: http://www.alertive.com
Health & Wellness Care Services
N.A.I.C.S.: 621999
Nirav Shah *(CEO)*
Jorge Sanchez *(Chief Medical Officer)*
Noah Manders *(CTO)*
Michael Jue *(VP-Sls)*
Rama Aysola *(Head-Bus Dev)*

Southern Pines Healthcare LLC **(1)**
6140 Congress St, New Port Richey, FL
34653
Tel.: (727) 842-8402
Web Site:
http://www.southernpineshealthcare.com
Health Care Srvices
N.A.I.C.S.: 621610
Michael Keyes-Bowman *(CEO)*
Jenny Waters *(Dir-Nursing)*
Victoria Fortino *(Office Mgr-Bus)*
Michelle Hines *(Mktg Dir)*
Lorrie Jonas *(Dir-Quality of Life)*

THE PNC FINANCIAL SER-VICES GROUP, INC.

The Tower at PNC Plz 300 5th Ave,
Pittsburgh, PA 15222-2401
Tel.: (412) 762-2000 PA

THE PNC FINANCIAL SERVICES GROUP, INC.

Web Site: https://www.pnc.com
Year Founded: 1983
PNC—(NYSE)
Rev.: $31,882,000,000
Assets: $561,580,000,000
Liabilities: $510,439,000,000
Net Worth: $51,141,000,000
Earnings: $5,153,000,000
Emp.: 54,813
Fiscal Year-end: 12/31/23
Bank Holding Company
N.A.I.C.S.: 551111
Michael P. Lyons (Pres)
Alex Overstrom (Exec VP & Head-Retail Banking)
William S. Demchak (Chm & CEO)
Michael J. Hannon (Chief Credit Officer & Exec VP)
Gregory H. Kozich (Sr VP & Controller)
Gregory Baldwin Jordan (Chief Admin Officer, Gen Counsel & Exec VP-Govt Affairs)
Robert Q. Reilly (CFO & Exec VP)
Vicki C. Henn (Chief HR Officer & Exec VP)
Michael P. Lyons (Exec VP & Head-Corp & Institutional Banking)
Bryan K. Gill (Exec VP & Dir-IR)
Gregory Baldwin Jordan (Chief Admin Officer, Gen Counsel & Exec VP-Govt Affairs)
Carole Brown (Exec VP & Head-Asset Mgmt-Grp)
Richard K. Bynum (Chief Corp Responsibility Officer & Exec VP)
Keiran J. Fallon (Chief Risk Officer & Exec VP)
Ganesh Krishnan (CIO-Enterprise & Exec VP)
Alex Overstrom (Head-Retail Banking)
E. William Parsley III (COO & Exec VP)

Subsidiaries:

BBVA USA Bancshares, Inc. (1)
2200 Post Oak Blvd, Houston, TX 77056
Tel.: (205) 297-3000
Web Site: http://www.bbvacompass.com
Rev.: $4,173,700,000
Assets: $102,756,203,000
Liabilities: $91,064,841,000
Net Worth: $11,691,362,000
Earnings: ($1,863,711,000)
Emp.: 10,410
Fiscal Year-end: 12/31/2020
Bank Holding Company
N.A.I.C.S.: 551111
William C. Helms (Vice Chm)
Javier Rodriguez Soler (Pres & CEO)

Subsidiary (Domestic):

BBVA USA Bancshares, Inc. (2)
2001 Kirby Dr 661, Houston, TX 77019
Tel.: (713) 831-5525
Bank Holding Company
N.A.I.C.S.: 551111

Compass Bank (2)
15 S 20th St, Birmingham, AL 35233-2000
Tel.: (205) 297-3000
Web Site: http://www.bbvacompass.com
Savings, Loans, Commercial & Investment Banking Services
N.A.I.C.S.: 522110

Subsidiary (Domestic):

Compass Insurance Agency, Inc. (3)
280 Ann St NW, Grand Rapids, MI 49504
Tel.: (713) 968-8254
Sales Range: $50-74.9 Million
Emp.: 100
Insurance Services
N.A.I.C.S.: 524210

Harris Williams & Co. (1)
1001 Haxall Point 9th Fl, Richmond, VA 23219
Tel.: (804) 648-0072
Web Site: https://www.harriswilliams.com

Sales Range: $25-49.9 Million
Emp.: 150
Mergers & Acquisitions Advisor
N.A.I.C.S.: 561499
Turner A. M. Bredrup (Mng Dir)
Matthew G. White (Mng Dir-Energy, Power & Infrastructure)
Jershon Jones (Mng Dir-Transportation & Logistics Grp)
H. Hiter Harris III (Co-Founder, Chm & Mng Dir)
William Bain (Mng Dir-Consumer Grp-London)
Daniel Wang (Mng Dir)
Zach England (Dir-Consumer Grp)
Graham Gillam (Dir-Bus Svcs Grp)
Taylor Morris (Mng Dir)
Kelly McPhilliamy (Mng Dir-Consumer Grp)
Lane Hopkins (Mng Dir & Chief Talent Officer)
Tiff Armstrong (Mng Dir)
Taylor Will (VP)
Brent Spiller (Mng Dir-Consumer Grp)
Ryan Freeman (Mng Dir-Consumer Grp)
Paul Hepper (Mng Dir-Healthcare & Life Sciences Grp)
Drew G. Spitzer (Mng Dir)
Shinik Patel (VP)
Lucas Scholl (VP)
Andrew Hoft (VP)
Konstantin Molinari (VP)
Chuck Walter (VP)
Robert Engelhardt (VP)
Pete Morgan (VP)
Ned Valentine (Exec Mng Dir)
John Neuner (Mng Dir)
Cheairs Porter (Mng Dir)
Bill Watkins (Mng Dir)
Sean Bielawski (VP)
Charles Busch (VP)
Peter Creech (VP)
Matt Crisafi (VP)
Ben de Fiebre (VP)
Rob Devlin (VP)
Christopher Durolf (VP)
Patrick Fitzimmons (VP)
Richard Furseth (VP)
Bill Greven (VP)
Rebecca Herter (VP)
Brian Jones (VP)
Hilary King (VP)
Dominic Latino (VP)
Stefan Van de Ven (VP)
Phoebe Willis (VP)
Tyler Tripp (VP)
Dan Leonard (VP)
Michael Meyer (VP)
Maury Nolen (VP)
Krishna Patel (VP)
Alan Rodriguez-Villares (VP)
Thomas Saunders (VP)
Dan Savage (VP)
Gunnar Shaw (VP)
Trey Shehan (VP)
Cameron Thomas (VP)
John Arendale (Mng Dir)
Anthony Basmajian (Mng Dir)
Julian Feneley (Mng Dir)
John Lautemann (Mng Dir)
Andy Leed (Mng Dir)
Christopher Darlington (Mng Dir)
Jeff Kidd (Mng Dir)
J. Cheairs Porter Jr. (Mng Dir-Healthcare & Life Sciences)
Geoffrey W. Smith Jr. (Mng Dir-Healthcare & Life Sciences)

Miller Advisors Inc. (1)
11 10th Ave, Kirkland, WA 98033-5406
Tel.: (425) 822-8122
Web Site: https://www.milleradvisors.com
Administrative Management & General Management Consulting Services
N.A.I.C.S.: 541611
Nicole Miller (Mng Partner)

PNC Bancorp, Inc. (1)
300 Delaware Ave, Wilmington, DE 19899 (100%)
Tel.: (302) 427-5896
Bank Holding Company
N.A.I.C.S.: 551111
Michael Foley (Sr VP & Dir-Wealth Mgmt)
Lou Cestello (Exec VP)
Joseph G. Meterchick (Pres-Bank)

Subsidiary (Domestic):

PNC Bank, National Association (2)

300 Delaware Ave, Wilmington, DE 19801 (100%)
Tel.: (215) 585-6425
Web Site: http://www.pnc.com
Sales Range: $15-24.9 Billion
Emp.: 51,293
Savings Bank
N.A.I.C.S.: 522180
Michael P. Lyons (Pres)
David Millhouse (Sr VP)

Subsidiary (Domestic):

National City Mortgage Co. (3)
PO Box 1820, Dayton, OH 45401
Tel.: (937) 910-1200
Sales Range: $125-149.9 Million
Mortgage Banker
N.A.I.C.S.: 522310

Division (Domestic):

PNC Bank, Central Pennsylvania (3)
4242 Carlisle Pike, Camp Hill, PA 17011 (100%)
Tel.: (717) 730-2200
Web Site: http://www.pnc.com
Sales Range: $125-149.9 Million
Banking Services
N.A.I.C.S.: 522110

PNC Bank, Greater Maryland (3)
2 Hopkins Plz, Baltimore, MD 21201-2930
Tel.: (410) 237-5977
Web Site: http://www.pnc.com
Sales Range: $25-49.9 Million
Emp.: 125
Banking Services
N.A.I.C.S.: 522110

Branch (Domestic):

Mercantile Southern Maryland Bank (4)
41615 Park Ave, Leonardtown, MD 20650
Tel.: (301) 475-8081
Commericial Banking
N.A.I.C.S.: 522110

Division (Domestic):

PNC Bank, Greater Washington, D.C. Area (3)
800 17th St NW, Washington, DC 20006 (100%)
Tel.: (410) 237-5967
Web Site: http://www.pnc.com
Sales Range: $125-149.9 Million
Commercial Banking Services
N.A.I.C.S.: 522110

PNC Bank, Kentucky & Indiana (3)
101 S 5th St, Louisville, KY 40202 (100%)
Tel.: (502) 581-6424
Web Site: http://www.pnc.com
Sales Range: $125-149.9 Million
Commercial Banking Services
N.A.I.C.S.: 522110

Branch (Domestic):

PNC Bank (4)
4090 Tates Creek Rd, Lexington, KY 40517
Tel.: (859) 281-0567
Sales Range: $50-74.9 Million
Emp.: 165
State Commercial Bank & Trust
N.A.I.C.S.: 522110
Sarah Beeson (Sr VP-Real Estate Banking)

Division (Domestic):

PNC Bank, Northeast Pennsylvania (3)
201 Penn Ave, Scranton, PA 18503 (100%)
Tel.: (570) 961-7116
Web Site: http://www.pnc.com
Sales Range: $200-249.9 Million
Emp.: 10
Banking
N.A.I.C.S.: 522110

PNC Bank, Northwest Pennsylvania (3)
901 State St, Erie, PA 16501 (100%)
Tel.: (814) 871-9317
Web Site: http://www.pnc.com
Sales Range: $125-149.9 Million
Banking Services
N.A.I.C.S.: 522110

PNC Bank, Ohio & Northern Kentucky (3)
201 E 5th St, Cincinnati, OH 45202 (100%)
Tel.: (877) 762-2000
Sales Range: $550-599.9 Million
Emp.: 2,000
Bank
N.A.I.C.S.: 522110
Lacie Jakubec (Branch Mgr-Churchill)

PNC Bank, Philadelphia & Southern New Jersey (3)
1600 Market St, Philadelphia, PA 19103 (100%)
Tel.: (215) 585-6425
Web Site: http://www.pnc.com
Sales Range: $125-149.9 Million
Emp.: 10
Commercial Banking Services
N.A.I.C.S.: 522110
J. William Mills (Reg Pres)

Subsidiary (Domestic):

Sixpoint Partners, LLC (3)
909 3rd Ave 15th Fl, New York, NY 10022
Tel.: (212) 751-8690
Web Site: http://www.sixpointpartners.com
Secondary Market Financing
N.A.I.C.S.: 522299
Laurence Smith (Partner)
Matthew Mitchell (Mng Dir)
Eric Zoller (Founder & Partner)
Markus Schmalhofer (CFO)
Matthew Thornton (Partner)
Andrew Gulotta (Mng Dir)
Sean Joffe (Mng Dir)
Erin Breslawski (Dir)
Ben Newman (Dir)
Kristy Hogan (Dir)
Michael Leonardo (VP)
Alex Lorusso (VP)
Richard Siegel (VP)
Mark Swicegood (Controller)
Lea Peragallo (Head-Admin & Office Mgr)

Subsidiary (Domestic):

PNC Delaware Trust Company (2)
222 Delaware Ave, Wilmington, DE 19801
Tel.: (610) 254-5517
Web Site: https://www.pnc.com
Investment Management
N.A.I.C.S.: 523940

PNC Capital Advisors, LLC (1)
1 E Pratt St, Baltimore, MD 21202
Tel.: (412) 768-6899
Web Site: https://www.pnccapitaladvisors.com
Sales Range: $1-4.9 Billion
Investment Advisor & Fund Administrator
N.A.I.C.S.: 523940
Graham E. Fuller (Mng Dir-Alabama & Georgia)

PNC Capital Finance, LLC (1)
2 PNC Plz 620 Liberty Ave 22nd Fl, Pittsburgh, PA 15222
Tel.: (412) 768-6809
Web Site: http://www.pncmezzanine.com
Equity Investment Firm
N.A.I.C.S.: 523999

Joint Venture (Domestic):

Identity Group Holdings Corp. (2)
51 Century Blvdd Ste 100, Nashville, TN 37214
Tel.: (931) 432-4000
Web Site: http://www.identitygroup.com
Sales Range: $25-49.9 Million
Emp.: 250
Signs, Stamps & Stationery Mfr
N.A.I.C.S.: 339940
Lee Brantley (Exec VP-HR)
Paul Morgan (Mgr-Mfg Engrg)
Brad Wolf (Pres & CEO)
Brian Mogensen (CFO & Exec VP)
David Durfee (Exec VP-Ops)
Warren Soltis (Exec VP-Info Svcs)

Division (Domestic):

PNC Riverarch Capital (2)
Two PNC Plz 620 Liberty Ave 22nd Fl, Pittsburgh, PA 15222
Tel.: (412) 762-7172
Web Site: http://www.pncriverarch.com

The PNC Financial Services Group,
Inc.—(Continued)

Privater Equity Firm
N.A.I.C.S.: 523999
Michael D. Rost *(Mng Dir)*
Robert W. Dolan *(Principal)*
Andrew J. Wiechkoske *(Mng Dir)*

Holding (Domestic):

**North American Breaker Co.,
LLC**   **(3)**
2870 N Ontario St, Burbank, CA 91504
Tel.: (818) 567-7341
Web Site: http://www.nabreaker.com
Circuit Breaker Whslr
N.A.I.C.S.: 423610

Safco Dental Supply LLC   **(3)**
1111 Corporate Grove Dr, Buffalo Grove, IL
60089
Tel.: (800) 621-2178
Web Site: http://www.safcodental.com
Dental Products Supplier
N.A.I.C.S.: 339114
Lauren Bolger *(Mgr-Customer Svc)*

The Tranzonic Companies   **(3)**
26301 Curtiss Wright Pkwy Ste 200, Rich-
mond Heights, OH 44143-2123
Tel.: (216) 535-4300
Web Site: http://www.tranzonic.com
Disposable Sanitary & Safety Products Mfr
& Distr
N.A.I.C.S.: 322291

PNC Capital Markets LLC   **(1)**
225 Fifth Ave Three PNC Plz 26th Fl, Pitts-
burgh, PA 15222
Tel.: (412) 762-1754
Sales Range: $650-699.9 Million
Emp.: 30
Securities Brokerage & Bonds
N.A.I.C.S.: 523150
Nic Malas *(Mng Dir-Transportation Fin &
Municipal Utilities)*

PNC Commercial Corporation   **(1)**
Fifth Ave and Wood St, Pittsburgh, PA
15222
Tel.: (412) 762-4980
Sales Range: $25-49.9 Million
Emp.: 50
Finance Leasing of Equipment & Vehicles
N.A.I.C.S.: 522299
Barbara Bernardini *(Mgr-Corp Comm)*

**PNC Community Development
Corp.**   **(1)**
1 PNC Plz 249 5th Ave, Pittsburgh, PA
15222   **(100%)**
Tel.: (412) 762-1553
Web Site: http://www.pnccommunityinvolve
ment.com
Sales Range: $1-4.9 Billion
Community Development & Financial Lend-
ing Services
N.A.I.C.S.: 523999

PNC Investment Corp.   **(1)**
1 PNC Plaza 249 5th Ave, Pittsburgh, PA
15222
Tel.: (215) 762-2000
Sales Range: $650-699.9 Million
Financial Investment Firm
N.A.I.C.S.: 523999

PNC Leasing LLC   **(1)**
2 PNC Plz 620 Liberty Ave, Pittsburgh, PA
15222
Tel.: (412) 762-7172
Web Site: http://www.pnc.com
Sales Range: $25-49.9 Million
Emp.: 70
Equipment Leasing
N.A.I.C.S.: 522110

PNC Life Insurance Company   **(1)**
249 5th AveBldg 5th, Pittsburgh, PA 15222-
2707
Tel.: (412) 762-2000
Web Site: http://www.pnc.com
Sales Range: $125-149.9 Million
Fire Insurance Services
N.A.I.C.S.: 522110

PNC Realty Services   **(1)**
620 Liberty Ave Fl 19, Pittsburgh, PA
15222-2722
Tel.: (412) 762-2000

Web Site: http://www.realtyservices.pnc.com
Sales Range: $1-9.9 Million
Emp.: 30
Real Estate & Equipment Leasing
N.A.I.C.S.: 531120

Solebury Trout LLC   **(1)**
1010 Washington Blvd Ste 1050, Stamford,
CT 06901
Tel.: (203) 428-3250
Capital Management Services
N.A.I.C.S.: 523999
Jeff Grossman *(CEO)*

THE PROCTER & GAMBLE
COMPANY

1 P G Plz, Cincinnati, OH 45202
Tel.: (513) 983-1100   **OH**
Web Site:
   https://www.pginvestor.com
Year Founded: 1837
PG—(NYSE)
Rev.: $84,039,000,000
Assets: $122,370,000,000
Liabilities: $71,811,000,000
Net Worth: $50,559,000,000
Earnings: $14,974,000,000
Emp.: 108,000
Fiscal Year-end: 06/30/24
Household Products Mfr
N.A.I.C.S.: 325620
Monica Turner *(Pres-North America)*
Marc S. Pritchard *(Chief Brand Offi-
cer)*
Jon R. Moeller *(Chm, Pres & CEO)*
Philip J. Duncan *(Chief Design Offi-
cer)*
Kirti V. Singh *(Chief Analytics & In-
sights Officer)*
Fatima D. Francisco *(CEO-Baby &
Feminine Care)*
Henry Karamanoukian *(Pres-Digital
Commerce)*
R. Alexandra Keith *(CEO-Beauty)*
Juan Fernando Posada *(Pres-Latin
America)*
Matthew S. Price *(Pres-Greater
China)*
Magesvaran Suranjan *(Pres-Asia Pa-
cific, Middle East & Africa)*
Markus Strobel *(Pres-Skin & Per-
sonal Care)*
Loic Tassel *(Pres-Europe)*
Sundar Raman *(Pres-Home Care &
P&G Professional)*
Laura Becker *(Pres-Bus Svcs-Global)*
Jennifer L. Davis *(CEO-Health Care)*
Tracey Grabowski *(Chief HR Officer)*
Shelly McNamara *(Chief Equality &
Inclusion Officer)*
Vittorio Cretella *(CIO)*
Paul Gama *(Pres-Personal Health
Care)*
Virginie Helias *(Chief Sustainability
Officer)*
Ken Patel *(Chief Ethics & Compli-
ance Officer)*
Mindy Sherwood *(Chief Sls Officer &
Pres-Walmart-Global)*
Shailesh G. Jejurikar *(COO)*
Andre Schulten *(CFO)*
Victor Aguilar *(Chief R&D & Innova-
tion Officer)*
Guy B. Persaud *(Pres-New Bus)*
Matthew W. Janzaruk *(Chief Acctg
Officer & Sr VP)*
Damon Jones *(Chief Comm Officer)*

Subsidiaries:

Agile Pursuits Franchising, Inc.   **(1)**
1 Procter & Gamble Plz, Cincinnati, OH
45202
Tel.: (513) 983-1000
Sanitary Paper Product Mfr
N.A.I.C.S.: 322291

An-Pro Company   **(1)**
2902 Bernard Way, Russellville, AR 72802-
9647

Tel.: (479) 967-8200
Other Animal Food Mfr
N.A.I.C.S.: 311119

Arbora & Ausonia, S.L.   **(1)**
Passeig Til Lers 2 6, Barcelona, 08034,
Spain   **(50%)**
Tel.: (34) 932905600
Web Site: http://www.arbora-ausonia.com
Sales Range: $400-449.9 Million
Emp.: 2,000
Personal Hygiene Products Mfr
N.A.I.C.S.: 325611

Arborinvest, S.A.U.   **(1)**
Diagonal - Plt 10 609, Barcelona, 08028,
Spain
Tel.: (34) 932091199
Investment Management Service
N.A.I.C.S.: 523940

**Compania Procter & Gamble Mexico,
S. de R.L. de C.V.**   **(1)**
Loma Florida 32 Lomas de Vista Hermosa,
Federal District, 05100, Mexico, Mexico
Tel.: (52) 57242000
Web Site: http://www.pg.com.mx
Household Products Mfr
N.A.I.C.S.: 335220

Compania Quimica S.A.   **(1)**
Av Nestor Gambetta, 4651, Callao, Peru
Tel.: (51) 15148700
Web Site: https://www.ciaqui.com.pe
Detergents & Soap Mfr
N.A.I.C.S.: 325611

Cosmetic Suppliers Pty. Ltd.   **(1)**
L 4 1 Innovation Rd, North Ryde, 2113,
NSW, Australia
Tel.: (61) 800021085
Web Site: http://www.pg.com
Toilet Preparation Mfr
N.A.I.C.S.: 325620

Cover Girl Cosmetics   **(1)**
11050 York Rd, Hunt Valley, MD 21030-
2005
Tel.: (410) 785-7300
Web Site: http://www.covergirl.com
Sales Range: $1-4.9 Billion
Emp.: 2,000
Cosmetics Mfr
N.A.I.C.S.: 325620

FPG Oleochemicals Sdn. Bhd.,   **(1)**
Lot 3831, Kuantan Port Industrial Area,
26080, Kuantan, Malaysia
Tel.: (60) 95852233
Web Site: https://www.fpg.com.my
Sales Range: $75-99.9 Million
Emp.: 26
Chemicals Mfr
N.A.I.C.S.: 325199
Haridas Nair *(Gen Mgr)*

Fameccanica Data S.p.A.   **(1)**
Via Aterno 136, Sambuceto di, 66020, San
Giovanni Teatino, Chieti, Italy
Tel.: (39) 08545531
Web Site: https://www.fameccanica.com
Sales Range: $200-249.9 Million
Emp.: 670
Service Establishment Equipment & Sup-
plies
N.A.I.C.S.: 423850

**Fameccanica Machinery (Shanghai)
Co., Ltd.**   **(1)**
No 1951 Duhui Road Plant 10 - Xin Zhuang
Industry Park, Min Hang District, Shanghai,
201108, China
Tel.: (86) 2164422977
Web Site: http://www.fameccanica.com
Emp.: 80
Machinery Mfr
N.A.I.C.S.: 333998

Fameccanica North America, Inc.   **(1)**
8511 Trade Ctr Dr Ste 400, West Chester,
OH 45011
Tel.: (513) 645-9900
Packaging Machinery Mfr
N.A.I.C.S.: 333993
Eugenio Venturato *(Pres)*

Fater Portugal Unipessoal Lda   **(1)**
Rua Monte Dos Pipos 105, Matosinhos,
4460-865, Custoias, Portugal
Tel.: (351) 220009225
Web Site: http://www.fatergroup.com

Detergents Mfr
N.A.I.C.S.: 325611

Fater S.p.A.   **(1)**
Via Mare Adriatico 122, Spoltore, 65010,
Pescara, Italy
Tel.: (39) 0853551111
Web Site: http://www.fatergroup.com
Paper Products Mfr
N.A.I.C.S.: 322291

Frederic, LLC   **(1)**
903 3rd Ave 20th Fl, New York, NY 10022-
4756
Tel.: (212) 583-3200
Web Site: http://www.fekkai.com
Salon & Beauty Spa Operating Services
N.A.I.C.S.: 812199

Gillette Australia Pty. Ltd.   **(1)**
Eastern Suburbs Mail Centre, PO Box 619,
Sydney, 2004, NSW, Australia
Tel.: (61) 800641820
Web Site: https://gillette.com.au
Consumer Goods Mfr
N.A.I.C.S.: 339991

Gillette Dominicana, S.A.   **(1)**
Novo Centro Building Av Lope de Vega No
29, Winston Churchill, Santo Domingo, Do-
minican Republic
Tel.: (809) 8099550120
Cosmetics Mfr
N.A.I.C.S.: 325620

Gillette del Uruguay, S.A.   **(1)**
Javier de Viana 2350, Montevideo, Uruguay
Tel.: (598) 24194013
Cosmetic Product Mfr & Distr
N.A.I.C.S.: 325620

Gresham Cosmetics Pty. Ltd.   **(1)**
30 Smallwood Rw, Tingalpa, 4173, QLD,
Australia
Tel.: (61) 738903233
Cosmetics Products Mfr
N.A.I.C.S.: 325620

Hyginett KFT   **(1)**
Hatar ut 3, Csomor, 2141, Budapest, Hun-
gary
Tel.: (36) 28446810
Web Site:
   https://www.hyginettkft.kozuleti.com
N.A.I.C.S.: 322299

Intpropco S.A.   **(1)**
Malzgasse 15, 4052, Basel, Switzerland
Tel.: (41) 612069620
Toilet Preparation Mfr
N.A.I.C.S.: 325620

**Ismail Abudawood Procter & Gamble
- Dammam**   **(1)**
5th Floor 6521 King Abdullah Branch Rd, Ar
Ruwais, Jeddah, 23214, Saudi Arabia
Tel.: (966) 126572222
Web Site: https://en-ae.pg.com
Consumer Product Retailer
N.A.I.C.S.: 532210

Laboratorios Vicks, S.L.   **(1)**
Av de Bruselas 24, 28108, Alcobendas, Ma-
drid, Spain
Tel.: (34) 917222100
Cosmetics Mfr
N.A.I.C.S.: 325620

Mielle Organics, LLC   **(1)**
8707 Louisiana St, Merrillville, IN 46410
Web Site: https://www.mielleorganics.com
Personal Care Services
N.A.I.C.S.: 812199

Modern Industries Company   **(1)**
Po Box 4927, Dammam, Saudi Arabia
Tel.: (966) 38121062
Cosmetics Beauty Supplies & Perfume
Stores
N.A.I.C.S.: 456120

**Modern Products Company -
Jeddah**   **(1)**
King Abdullah Road Saudi France Building
5th Fl Ruwais, PO Box 2056, Jeddah,
21451, Saudi Arabia
Tel.: (966) 126572222
Web Site: http://www.pg.com
Cosmetics Products Mfr
N.A.I.C.S.: 325620

New Chapter, Inc. **(1)**
90 Technology Dr, Brattleboro, VT 05301
Tel.: (802) 257-0018
Web Site: https://www.newchapter.com
Pharmaceutical Preparation Mfr
N.A.I.C.S.: 325412

Noxell Corporation **(1)**
11050 York Rd, Hunt Valley, MD 21030
Tel.: (410) 785-7300
Cosmetic Product Mfr & Distr
N.A.I.C.S.: 325620
Carroll A. Bodie *(VP)*

Olay Company, Inc. **(1)**
One Procter & Gamble Plz, Cincinnati, OH
45202 **(100%)**
Tel.: (513) 983-1100
Web Site: http://www.olay.com
Sales Range: $150-199.9 Million
Health & Beauty Care Products Mfr
N.A.I.C.S.: 325620

Oral-B Laboratories, G.P. **(1)**
1832 Lower Muscatine Rd, Iowa City, IA
52240
Tel.: (319) 338-5411
Cosmetic Product Mfr & Distr
N.A.I.C.S.: 325620

**P&G Distribution East Africa
Limited** **(1)**
Westlands Road Purshottam Place 7th
Floor, PO Box 30454-00100, Nairobi, Kenya
Tel.: (254) 203601000
Chemical Product & Preparation Mfr
N.A.I.C.S.: 325998

P&G Israel M.D.O. Ltd. **(1)**
6 Hanechoshet St, Tel Aviv, 69710, Israel
Tel.: (972) 37675444
Web Site: http://www.pgisrael.co.il
Detergents & Soaps Mfr
N.A.I.C.S.: 325611

P&G Prestige Products **(1)**
909 3rd Ave 20th Fl, New York, NY 10022
Tel.: (212) 980-6400
Web Site: http://www.pandg.com
Sales Range: $25-49.9 Million
Emp.: 100
Cosmetics & Fragrances Mfr
N.A.I.C.S.: 325620

P&G Prestige Service GmbH **(1)**
Venloer Str 241, Cologne, 50823, Germany
Tel.: (49) 2215728100
Cosmetic Product Mfr & Distr
N.A.I.C.S.: 325620

**P&G South African Trading (Pty.)
Ltd.** **(1)**
12th Floor 15 Alice Lane Towers, Sandton,
2196, South Africa
Tel.: (27) 100019650
Web Site: https://africa.pg.com
Consumer Goods Mfr
N.A.I.C.S.: 339991

PGIO S.A. Agencia en Chile **(1)**
Av Pdte Riesco 5335 Piso 17 Las Condes,
Santiago, Chile
Tel.: (56) 28165000
Web Site: http://www.pg.com
Toilet Preparation Mfr
N.A.I.C.S.: 325620
Maite Del Arena *(CEO)*

Procter & Gamble (China) Ltd. **(1)**
27-33/F Centre Plaza 161 Lin He Xi Heng
Road, Guangzhou, 510620, China
Tel.: (86) 2085186688
Consumer Goods Mfr
N.A.I.C.S.: 339999

**Procter & Gamble (Egypt) Manufac-
turing Company** **(1)**
Building B1, Cairo Festival City, New Cairo,
11221, Egypt
Tel.: (20) 24617500
Web Site: http://www.pg.com
Toilet Preparation Mfr
N.A.I.C.S.: 325620

**Procter & Gamble (Ireland)
Limited** **(1)**
The Graan House Units E1 & E14, Cal-
mount Park Ballymount, Dublin, 12,
Ireland **(100%)**
Tel.: (353) 6750167

Sales Range: $300-349.9 Million
Emp.: 650
Household Products & Cosmetics Mfr
N.A.I.C.S.: 325620

**Procter & Gamble (Malaysia) Sdn.
Bhd.** **(1)**
10th Floor Surian Tower No 1 Jalan PJU
7/3, Mutiara Damansara, 47810, Petaling
Jaya, Selangor, Malaysia **(100%)**
Tel.: (60) 377243333
Household Product Distr
N.A.I.C.S.: 423620

Procter & Gamble Argentina SRL **(1)**
Suipacha 664 2nd Floor, C1008AAN, Bue-
nos Aires, Argentina
Tel.: (54) 13230600
Consumer Goods Mfr
N.A.I.C.S.: 339999

**Procter & Gamble Asia Holding
B.V.** **(1)**
Watermanweg 100, Rotterdam, 3067 GG,
Zuid-Holland, Netherlands
Tel.: (31) 102863100
Toilet Preparation Mfr
N.A.I.C.S.: 325620

**Procter & Gamble Australia Propri-
etary Limited** **(1)**
Level 4 1 Innovation Road, Macquarie Park,
2113, NSW, Australia
Tel.: (61) 1800028280
Sales Range: $150-199.9 Million
Emp.: 337
Consumer Products, Personal Products &
Pharmaceuticals
N.A.I.C.S.: 325611
Yasuhiko Iida *(Dir-Mktg)*

Procter & Gamble Austria GmbH **(1)**
Wiedner Gurtel 13, 100, Vienna,
Austria **(100%)**
Tel.: (43) 1588570
Sales Range: $25-49.9 Million
Emp.: 80
Household Cleaning Products
N.A.I.C.S.: 325611
Tobias Grase *(Gen Mgr)*

**Procter & Gamble Brazil Holdings
B.V.** **(1)**
Watermanweg 100, Rotterdam, 3067 GG,
Zuid-Holland, Netherlands
Tel.: (31) 102863100
Web Site: http://www.pg.com
Toilet Preparation Mfr
N.A.I.C.S.: 325620

**Procter & Gamble Bulgaria
EOOD** **(1)**
Bd Bulgaria nr 69, 1404, Sofia, Bulgaria
Tel.: (359) 29174600
Cosmetic Product Mfr & Distr
N.A.I.C.S.: 325620
Miroslav Nerandjich *(Gen Mgr)*

**Procter & Gamble Business Services
Canada Company** **(1)**
4711 Yonge St, Toronto, M2N 6K8, ON,
Canada
Tel.: (416) 730-4711
Web Site: http://www.pg.ca
Investment Management Service
N.A.I.C.S.: 523940

**Procter & Gamble Canada Holding
B.V.** **(1)**
Watermanweg 100, Rotterdam, 3067 GG,
Netherlands
Tel.: (31) 102863100
Beauty Salons
N.A.I.C.S.: 812112

Procter & Gamble Chile Limitada **(1)**
Presidente Riesco 5335 Piso 17, Las Con-
des, Santiago, Chile
Tel.: (56) 28165000
Toilet Preparation Mfr
N.A.I.C.S.: 325620

**Procter & Gamble Commercial
Company** **(1)**
PO Box 363187, San Juan, PR 00936
Tel.: (787) 620-7070
Web Site: http://www.pg.com
Sales Range: $200-249.9 Million
Emp.: 200
Cosmetics Mfr

N.A.I.C.S.: 325620

**Procter & Gamble Commercial
Company** **(1)**
1 Procter & Gamble Plz, Cincinnati, OH
45202 **(100%)**
Tel.: (513) 983-1100
Web Site: http://www.pg.com
Sales Range: $150-199.9 Million
Emp.: 1,000
Soap & Detergents Sales
N.A.I.C.S.: 325611

**Procter & Gamble Czech Republic
s.r.o.** **(1)**
Ottova 402, 269 01, Rakovnik, Czech Re-
public
Tel.: (420) 313512961
Household Products Mfr
N.A.I.C.S.: 325620

Procter & Gamble Danmark ApS **(1)**
Stensmosevej 15 st, 2620, Albertslund,
Denmark
Tel.: (45) 33269100
Cosmetic Product Mfr & Distr
N.A.I.C.S.: 325620

**Procter & Gamble Detergent (Beijing)
Ltd.** **(1)**
Yitai Plaza No 986 Jiefang North Road,
Guangzhou, 510040, Guangdong, China
Tel.: (86) 1058127188
Toilet Preparation Mfr
N.A.I.C.S.: 325620

**Procter & Gamble Distributing (Philip-
pines) Inc.** **(1)**
6750 Ayala Avenue Office Tower Ayala Cen-
ter, Makati, Philippines
Tel.: (63) 25588100
Web Site: http://www.pg.com
Cosmetic Product Distr
N.A.I.C.S.: 424210

**Procter & Gamble Distributing
Company** **(1)**
1 Procter & Gamble Plz, Cincinnati, OH
45202 **(100%)**
Tel.: (513) 983-1100
Web Site: http://www.pg.com
Sales Range: $900-999.9 Million
Household Cleaning Products & Pharma-
ceuticals Distr
N.A.I.C.S.: 561499

**Procter & Gamble Distributing New
Zealand** **(1)**
Unit 3 62 Paul Matthews Road, PO Box
5861, Albany, Auckland, 1001, New
Zealand **(100%)**
Tel.: (64) 94157800
Sales Range: $10-24.9 Million
Emp.: 15
Cosmetics & Household Products Distr
N.A.I.C.S.: 325620

**Procter & Gamble Distribution
S.R.L.** **(1)**
Blvd Dimitrie Pompeiu 9-9A Building 2A
Sector 2, 20335, Bucharest, Romania
Tel.: (40) 213011110
Emp.: 300
Electrical & Electronic Goods Merchant
Whslr
N.A.I.C.S.: 423610

Procter & Gamble Egypt **(1)**
Building B1 Cairo Festival City, New Cairo,
Egypt
Tel.: (20) 225298800
Web Site: https://en-eg.pg.com
Consumer Goods Mfr
N.A.I.C.S.: 339991

Procter & Gamble Espana, S.A. **(1)**
Av de Bruselas 24, Alcobendas, 28108, Ma-
drid, Spain **(100%)**
Tel.: (34) 917222100
Web Site: http://es.pg.com
Sales Range: $500-549.9 Million
Emp.: 1,250
Household Cleaning, Health & Beauty Care
Products, Pharmaceuticals, Cosmetics &
Fragrances
N.A.I.C.S.: 325611
Carlos Matos *(Mng Dir)*

Procter & Gamble Finland Oy **(1)**

Lars Sonckin Kaari 10, 02601, Espoo,
Finland **(100%)**
Tel.: (358) 9613399
Web Site: http://www.pg.com
Sales Range: $25-49.9 Million
Emp.: 10
Home & Personal Care Products
N.A.I.C.S.: 812199

Procter & Gamble France S.A.S. **(1)**
163 Quai Aulagnier, 92600, Asnieres-sur-
Seine, Cedex, France **(100%)**
Tel.: (33) 140885511
Web Site: http://fr.pg.com
Sales Range: $1-4.9 Billion
Emp.: 2,050
Mfr, Sales & Marketing of Household Clean-
ing Products
N.A.I.C.S.: 325611
Christoff Guron *(Pres)*

Subsidiary (Domestic):

Ondal France SARL **(2)**
2 Rue Denis Papin, 57200, Sarreguemines,
France
Tel.: (33) 387987474
Emp.: 3,000
Cosmetics Mfr
N.A.I.C.S.: 325620

Procter & Gamble Amiens S.A.S. **(2)**
Zone Industrielle Rue Andre Durouchez, BP
1336, Amiens, 80013, France
Tel.: (33) 322543200
Household Products Mfr
N.A.I.C.S.: 335220

Procter & Gamble Blois S.A.S. **(2)**
126 Avenue De Vendome, 41000, Blois,
France
Tel.: (33) 254522200
Web Site: http://www.pg.com
Personal Care Product Mfr
N.A.I.C.S.: 325620

Procter & Gamble Neuilly S.A.S. **(2)**
163 Quai Aulagneir, Asnieres, 92600,
France
Tel.: (33) 140885511
Health Care Srvices
N.A.I.C.S.: 621610

Procter & Gamble GmbH **(1)**
(100%)
Tel.: (49) 61968901
Web Site: http://www.procterundgamble.de
Sales Range: $900-999.9 Million
Emp.: 1,500
Household Cleaning Products
N.A.I.C.S.: 325611

Subsidiary (Domestic):

**Procter & Gamble Germany
GmbH** **(2)**
Sulzbacher Str 40-50, 65824, Schwalbach,
Germany
Tel.: (49) 61968901
Web Site: http://www.pg.com
Emp.: 150
Household Products Mfr
N.A.I.C.S.: 325620

**Procter & Gamble Germany GmbH &
Co. Operations oHG** **(2)**
Suilbacher Str 40-50, 65823, Schwalbach,
Germany **(100%)**
Tel.: (49) 61968901
Web Site: http://www.pg.com
Emp.: 2,000
Personal Care Products Mfr & Sales
N.A.I.C.S.: 325620

**Procter & Gamble Manufacturing Ber-
lin GmbH** **(2)**
Oberlandstr 75 84, 12099, Berlin, Germany
Tel.: (49) 3075640
Toilet Preparation Mfr
N.A.I.C.S.: 325620

**Procter & Gamble Manufacturing Co-
logne GmbH** **(2)**
Wilhelm Mauser Strasse 40, 50827, Co-
logne, Germany
Tel.: (49) 2215728547
Personal Products Mfr
N.A.I.C.S.: 325620

**Procter & Gamble Service
GmbH** **(2)**

The Procter & Gamble Company—(Continued)

Sulzbacher Strasse 40, Schwalbach,
65824, Germany
Tel.: (49) 61968901
Toilet Preparation Mfr
N.A.I.C.S.: 325620

Wick Pharma (2)
Sulzbacher St 40-50, 65823, Schwalbach,
Germany (100%)
Tel.: (49) 61968901
Web Site: http://www.procterandgamble.de
Sales Range: $200-249.9 Million
Emp.: 1,500
Pharmaceuticals
N.A.I.C.S.: 325412

**Procter & Gamble Grundstucks-und
Vermogensverwaltungs GmbH & Co.
KG** (1)
Sulzbacher Str 40, 65824, Schwalbach,
Hessen, Germany
Tel.: (49) 61968901
Web Site: http://www.pg.com
Cosmetic Product Mfr & Distr
N.A.I.C.S.: 325620

Procter & Gamble Gulf FZE (1)
12th Roundabout, PO Box 33060, Dubai,
United Arab Emirates
Tel.: (971) 43349993
Consumer Goods Mfr
N.A.I.C.S.: 339999

**Procter & Gamble Health & Beauty
Care Limited** (1)
The Heights, Weybridge, KT13 0XP, Surrey,
United Kingdom (100%)
Tel.: (44) 1932896000
Web Site: http://www.pg.com
Sales Range: $350-399.9 Million
Emp.: 800
Mfr of Perfumes, Cosmetics & Toiletries
N.A.I.C.S.: 325620

Subsidiary (Domestic):

**Procter & Gamble - Research &
Development** (2)
Rusham Park Whitehall Ln, Egham, TW20
9NW, Surrey, United Kingdom
Tel.: (44) 1784474900
Web Site: http://www.pgsupplier.com
Sales Range: $150-199.9 Million
Emp.: 800
Research & Development Services
N.A.I.C.S.: 541715

**Procter & Gamble Health
Products** (1)
7000 St Km 2 Hm 3 Rr 735, Cayey, PR
00736
Tel.: (787) 738-2191
Web Site: http://www.pg.com
Rev.: $37,200,000
Emp.: 300
Analgesics
N.A.I.C.S.: 325412
Alex Bergara (Acctg Mgr)
Mark Hollard (Plant Mgr)

**Procter & Gamble Hellas Single
Member Ltd.** (1)
Lofos Kirillou Attiki Odos-Exit 4, 193 00, As-
propyrgos, Greece
Tel.: (30) 2108764521
Home Care Product Mfr
N.A.I.C.S.: 325612

**Procter & Gamble Holding (HK)
Limited** (1)
6 Floor Shui On Centre 6 8 Harbour Road,
Wanchai, China (Hong Kong)
Tel.: (852) 25833583
Toilet Preparation Mfr
N.A.I.C.S.: 325620

**Procter & Gamble Holding (Thailand)
Limited** (1)
622 Sukhumvit Road, Bangkok, 10110,
Klong Toei, Thailand
Tel.: (66) 26675000
Toilet Preparation Mfr
N.A.I.C.S.: 325620
Sirinporn Vatanaparadorn (Dir-Sls)

**Procter & Gamble Holding France
S.A.S.** (1)
163 quai Aulagnier, 92600, Asnieres-sur-

Seine, France
Tel.: (33) 140885511
Web Site: https://fr.pg.com
Consumer Goods Mfr
N.A.I.C.S.: 339999

**Procter & Gamble Holding
GmbH** (1)
Sulzbacher Strasse 40, 65824, Schwal-
bach, Germany
Tel.: (49) 61968901
Web Site: http://www.pg.com
Emp.: 300
Toilet Preparation Mfr
N.A.I.C.S.: 325620

Procter & Gamble Holding S.r.l. (1)
Viale Giorgio Ribotta 11, 00144, Rome, Italy
Tel.: (39) 0650971
Toilet Preparation Mfr
N.A.I.C.S.: 325620

**Procter & Gamble Home Products
Limited** (1)
Procter & Gamble India P&G plaza Cardinal
Gracias Road Chakala, Andheri East, Mum-
bai, 400099, India
Tel.: (91) 2228266000
Cosmetic Product Mfr & Distr
N.A.I.C.S.: 325620

**Procter & Gamble Hong Kong
Limited** (1)
6/F Shui On Centre 6-8 Harbour Road,
Wanchai, China (Hong Kong)
Tel.: (852) 28959488
Web Site: https://www.pghongkong.com
Cosmetics Mfr
N.A.I.C.S.: 325620

**Procter & Gamble Hygiene and
Health Care Limited** (1)
P&G Plaza Cardinal Gracias Road, Chakala
Andheri East, Mumbai, 400099, India
Tel.: (91) 2228266000
Web Site: http://www.pg.com
Sales Range: $125-149.9 Million
Emp.: 150
Cosmetics & Household Cleaning Products
Mfr & Sales
N.A.I.C.S.: 325620
R. A. Shah (Chm)
Madhusudan Gopalan (Mng Dir)

Procter & Gamble Inc. (1)
4711 Yonge Street, Toronto, M2N 6K8, ON,
Canada
Tel.: (416) 730-4711
Web Site: http://www.pg.ca
Sales Range: $1-4.9 Billion
Emp.: 3,500
Household Products, Food Products, Toilet-
ries, Paper Products Mfr & Distr
N.A.I.C.S.: 325611
Magesvaran Suranjan (Pres-Asia Pacific,
Middle East & Africa)

**Procter & Gamble Industrial e Comer-
cial Ltda.** (1)
Regus Torre Z Av Dr Chucri Zaidan 296 -
23 andar - Vila Cordeiro, Sao Paulo, 04583-
110, Brazil
Tel.: (55) 1137480264
Web Site: https://br.pg.com
Emp.: 100
Consumer Goods Mfr
N.A.I.C.S.: 339999

**Procter & Gamble International Fund-
ing SCA** (1)
26 Boulevard Royal, Luxembourg, 2449,
Luxembourg
Tel.: (352) 2299995241
Washing Products Mfr
N.A.I.C.S.: 325611

**Procter & Gamble International Op-
erations Pte. Ltd.** (1)
11 North Buona Vista Drive 21-07 The Me-
tropolis Tower 2, Singapore, 138589, Singa-
pore
Tel.: (65) 67125000
Web Site: http://www.pg.com
Toilet Preparation Mfr
N.A.I.C.S.: 325620
Ong Yuh Hwang (CEO-Malaysia, Singapore
& Brunei)

**Procter & Gamble International Op-
erations SA-ROHQ** (1)

10th Floor Petron Megaplaza Building,
Makati, 1200, Philippines
Tel.: (63) 25583000
Management Consulting Services
N.A.I.C.S.: 561110
Paul Albano (Assoc Dir-Sls)

Procter & Gamble Italia, S.p.A. (1)
Viale Giorgio Ribotta 11, Rome, Italy
Tel.: (39) 0650971
Web Site: http://it.pg.com
Toilet Preparation Mfr
N.A.I.C.S.: 325620

Procter & Gamble Japan K.K. (1)
7-1-18 Onoe-dori, Chuo-ku, Kobe, 651-
0088, Hyogo, Japan
Tel.: (81) 783366000
Web Site: http://jp.pg.com
Holding Company; Cleaning & Personal
Care Products Developer, Mfr & Whslr
N.A.I.C.S.: 551112

Subsidiary (Domestic):

P&G Innovation Godo Kaisha (2)
7-1-18 Onoe-dori, Chuo-ku, Kobe, 651-
0088, Hyogo, Japan
Tel.: (81) 783366000
Cleaning & Personal Care Product Research & Development
N.A.I.C.S.: 541715

P&G K.K. (2)
7-1-18 Onoe-dori, Chuo-ku, Kobe, 651-
0088, Hyogo, Japan
Tel.: (81) 783366000
Web Site: http://jp.pg.com
Cleaning & Personal Care Products Mfr
N.A.I.C.S.: 325611

Procter & Gamble LLC (1)
16A Leningradskoe shosse building 2,
125171, Moscow, Russia
Tel.: (7) 4952585888
Web Site: http://www.procterandgamble.ru
Emp.: 800
Cosmetics Mfr
N.A.I.C.S.: 325620

**Procter & Gamble Manufacturing
(Thailand) Ltd.** (1)
20th-22nd floor the Emporium Tower 622
Sukhumvit Rd, Kwaeng Klongton Khet
Klongtoey, Bangkok, 10110,
Thailand (100%)
Tel.: (66) 26645000
Sales Range: $10-24.9 Million
Emp.: 24
Household Cleaning Product Mfr
N.A.I.C.S.: 325611

**Procter & Gamble Manufacturing Bel-
gium N.V.** (1)
Temselaan 100, Strombeek-Bever, 1853,
Belgium (100%)
Tel.: (32) 24564511
Web Site: http://www.eu.pg.com
Sales Range: $1-4.9 Billion
Emp.: 1,300
Household Cleaning, Washing Products &
Hygiene Products Mfr & Sales
N.A.I.C.S.: 325611

Subsidiary (Domestic):

P&G Prestige Products N.V. (2)
100 Temselaan, Strombeek-Bever, 1853,
Belgium
Tel.: (32) 24566000
Sales Range: $450-499.9 Million
Toilet Preparation Mfr
N.A.I.C.S.: 325620

**Procter & Gamble Distribution Com-
pany (Europe) BVBA** (2)
Temselaan 55, 1853, Strombeek-Bever,
Belgium
Tel.: (32) 24562111
Web Site: http://www.procterandgamble.com
Toilet Preparation Mfr
N.A.I.C.S.: 325620

**Procter & Gamble Health & Beauty
Care Belgium** (2)
Temselaan 55, 1853, Strombeek-Bever,
Belgium (100%)
Tel.: (32) 24562111
Web Site: http://www.eu.pg.com

Sales Range: $1-4.9 Billion
Emp.: 1,200
Cosmetics Mfr & Sales
N.A.I.C.S.: 325620

**Procter & Gamble Services Company
N.V.** (2)
Temselaan 100, 1853, Strombeek-Bever,
Belgium
Tel.: (32) 24562111
Web Site: http://www.pg.com
Sales Range: $550-599.9 Million
Emp.: 1,200
Service Establishment Equipment & Sup-
plies
N.A.I.C.S.: 423850

**Procter & Gamble Manufacturing
Company** (1)
1 Procter & Gamble Plz, Cincinnati, OH
45202 (100%)
Tel.: (513) 983-1100
Web Site: http://www.pg.com
Sales Range: $150-199.9 Million
Soaps & Detergents Mfr
N.A.I.C.S.: 325611

**Procter & Gamble Manufacturing
Mexico S. de R.L. de C.V.** (1)
Loma Florida 32 Lomas de Vista Hermosa,
05100, Mexico, Mexico
Tel.: (52) 57242000
Chemical Product & Preparation Mfr
N.A.I.C.S.: 325998

**Procter & Gamble Marketing Roma-
nia SRL** (1)
9-9A Dimitrie Pompei Blvd Building 2A, Dis-
trict 2, 020335, Bucharest, Romania
Tel.: (40) 213011110
Emp.: 300
Cosmetic Product Mfr & Distr
N.A.I.C.S.: 325620

**Procter & Gamble Marketing and Ser-
vices doo** (1)
Spansih Boraca 3, Belgrade, 11070, Serbia
Tel.: (381) 113016868
Web Site: http://www.pgbelkans.com
Toilet Preparation Mfr
N.A.I.C.S.: 325620

**Procter & Gamble Nederland
B.V.** (1)
Watermanweg 100, 3067 GG, Rotterdam,
Netherlands (100%)
Tel.: (31) 102863100
Web Site: http://www.nl.pg.com
Sales Range: $75-99.9 Million
Emp.: 250
Feminine Hygiene Products
N.A.I.C.S.: 325620

Subsidiary (Domestic):

**Procter & Gamble Netherlands Ser-
vices B.V.** (2)
Watermanweg 100, Rotterdam, 3067 GG,
Netherlands
Tel.: (31) 102863100
Web Site: http://www.pg.com
Toilet Preparation Mfr
N.A.I.C.S.: 325620

**Procter & Gamble Nigeria
Limited** (1)
1st Commercial Road Oluyole Industrial Es-
tate, GRA Ikeja, Ibadan, Nigeria
Tel.: (234) 22310116
Consumer Goods Mfr
N.A.I.C.S.: 325611

Procter & Gamble Nordic LLC (1)
Hangovagen 20, Stockholm, 102 54, Swe-
den
Tel.: (46) 852808100
Web Site: http://www.pg.com
Cosmetic Product Mfr & Distr
N.A.I.C.S.: 325620

Procter & Gamble Norge AS (1)
Tvetenveien 40, 666, Oslo, 666, Norway
Tel.: (47) 22632600
Sales Range: $25-49.9 Million
Emp.: 80
Toilet Preparation Mfr
N.A.I.C.S.: 325620

**Procter & Gamble Operations Polska-
Spolka z o.o.** (1)

Ul Zabraniecka 20, 03-872, Warsaw, Poland
Tel.: (48) 226708200
Web Site: https://pl.pg.com
Health Care Products Mfr
N.A.I.C.S.: 456199

Procter & Gamble Overseas India B.V. (1)
Weena 505 - floor 10B, 3013 AL, Rotterdam, Netherlands
Tel.: (31) 107105200
Web Site: https://nl-nl.pg.com
Household Products Mfr
N.A.I.C.S.: 335220

Subsidiary (Non-US):

Procter & Gamble Health Ltd. (2)
Ground Floor and First Floor P&G Plaza, Cardinal Gracious Road Chakala Andheri-E, Mumbai, 400099, India (51%)
Tel.: (91) 2262109000
Web Site: https://www.pghealthindia.com
Rev.: $153,917,400
Assets: $121,992,780
Liabilities: $37,841,895
Net Worth: $84,150,885
Earnings: $26,278,980
Emp.: 1,368
Fiscal Year-end: 06/30/2022
Pharmaceuticals & Chemicals Product Mfr
N.A.I.C.S.: 325412
Suresh Narsappa Talwar (Chm)
Amit Gupta (CFO)
Preeti Bishnoi (Compliance Officer & Sec)
Milind Thatte (Mng Dir)

Procter & Gamble Pakistan (Private) Limited (1)
12th Floor The Harbour Front Abdul Sattar Edhi Avenue HC-3 Block-4, Dolmen City Clifton, Karachi, 75600, Pakistan
Tel.: (92) 21111000764
Web Site: https://pk.pg.com
Cosmetic Product Mfr & Distr
N.A.I.C.S.: 325620

Procter & Gamble Paper Products Company (1)
1 Procter & Gamble Plz, Cincinnati, OH 45202
Tel.: (513) 983-2222
Web Site: http://www.pg.com
Sales Range: $200-249.9 Million
Emp.: 1,000
Toiletries & Diapers
N.A.I.C.S.: 325620

Procter & Gamble Peru S.R.L. (1)
Av Felipe Pardo y Aliaga 695, Apartado Postal 3848, San Isidro, 27, Lima, Peru (100%)
Tel.: (51) 12153300
Web Site: http://www.pg.com
Sales Range: $200-249.9 Million
Emp.: 200
Perfumes, Cosmetics, Toiletries & Cleaning Products Mfr
N.A.I.C.S.: 325620

Procter & Gamble Polska-Spolka z o.o (1)
Ul Zabraniecka 20, 03-872, Warsaw, Poland
Tel.: (48) 226708200
Toilet Preparation Mfr
N.A.I.C.S.: 325620

Procter & Gamble Porto - Fabricacao De Produtos De Consumo, Sociedade Unipessoal Lda (1)
R Monte Pipos 105 Guifoes, Matosinhos, 4460-059, Portugal
Tel.: (351) 214409000
Sales Range: $25-49.9 Million
Emp.: 34
Toilet Preparation Mfr
N.A.I.C.S.: 325620
Padro Ferreira (Exec Mgr)

Procter & Gamble Portugal - Produtos De Consumo, Higiene e Saude S.A. (1)
Rua da Fonte de Caspolima 6 and 6-A, Quinta da Fonte Alvares Cabral Building, 2774-527, Paco d'Arcos, Lisbon, Portugal
Tel.: (351) 214409000
Web Site: https://pt.pg.com

Pharmaceuticals Product Mfr
N.A.I.C.S.: 325412

Procter & Gamble Product Supply (U.K.) Limited (1)
Hedley Avenue West Thurrock, Grays, RM20 4AL, Essex, United Kingdom
Tel.: (44) 1375395000
Consumer Goods Mfr
N.A.I.C.S.: 325611

Procter & Gamble S.r.l. (1)
viale Giorgio Ribotta 11, 00144, Rome, Italy (100%)
Tel.: (39) 0650971
Sales Range: $300-349.9 Million
Emp.: 650
Health & Beauty Aids
N.A.I.C.S.: 325620

Procter & Gamble SA (Pty) Ltd. (1)
Alice Lane Towers 15 Alice Lane 12th Floor, Sandton, Johannesburg, 2196, South Africa
Tel.: (27) 100019650
Web Site: https://africa.pg.com
Cosmetic Products & Consumer Goods Mfr & Distr
N.A.I.C.S.: 325620
Mohamed Samir (Pres-India, Middle East & Africa Selling & Market Ops)

Procter & Gamble Satis ve Dagitim Ltd. Sti. (1)
Serin sok No 9 Kosifler Is Merkezi A Blok Icerenkoy/ Kadikoy, 34752, Istanbul, Turkiye
Tel.: (90) 2164638000
Toilet Preparation Mfr
N.A.I.C.S.: 325620

Procter & Gamble Services (Switzerland) SA (1)
47 route de St-Georges, 1213, Petit-Lancy, Geneva, Switzerland
Tel.: (41) 227096111
Toilet Preparation Mfr
N.A.I.C.S.: 325620

Procter & Gamble Services GmbH (1)
Sulzbacher Strasse 40 - 50, 65824, Schwalbach am Taunus, Germany
Tel.: (49) 61968901
Web Site: https://de.pg.com
Consumer Goods Mfr
N.A.I.C.S.: 325611

Procter & Gamble Services LT (1)
Zalgirio G 92, Vilnius, 09303, Lithuania
Tel.: (370) 52051261
Sales Range: $25-49.9 Million
Emp.: 7
Toilet Preparation Mfr
N.A.I.C.S.: 325620

Procter & Gamble Servicse EESTI OU (1)
Paldiski mnt 27/29, Tallinn, 10612, Estonia
Tel.: (372) 6675040
Sales Range: $25-49.9 Million
Emp.: 9
Drugs & Druggists Sundries Merchant Whslr
N.A.I.C.S.: 424210

Procter & Gamble Singapore Pte. Ltd. (1)
11 North Buona Vista Drive 21-07 The Metropolis Tower 2, Singapore, 138589, Singapore (100%)
Tel.: (65) 67125000
Web Site: http://www.pg.com
Sales Range: $750-799.9 Million
Emp.: 1,000
Cleaning Products Distr
N.A.I.C.S.: 325611

Procter & Gamble South America Holding B.V. (1)
Weena 505 - floor 10B, 3013 AL, Rotterdam, Netherlands
Tel.: (31) 107105200
Web Site: http://www.tmv.com
Service Establishment Equipment & Supplies
N.A.I.C.S.: 423850

Procter & Gamble Sverige AB (1)
Hangovagen 20, Box 27303, 10254, Stockholm, Sweden

Tel.: (46) 852808100
Web Site: http://www.se.pg.com
Emp.: 100
Cosmetic Product Mfr & Distr
N.A.I.C.S.: 325620

Procter & Gamble Sweden (1)
Hangovagen 20, PO Box 27303, 102 54, Stockholm, Sweden (100%)
Tel.: (46) 852808100
Web Site: http://www.se.pg.com
Sales Range: $550-599.9 Million
Emp.: 300
Detergents & Other Consumer Products Mfr
N.A.I.C.S.: 325611

Procter & Gamble Switzerland Sarl (1)
47 route de St-Georges, 1213, Petit-Lancy, Geneva, Switzerland (100%)
Tel.: (41) 227096111
Web Site: http://www.pg.com
Sales Range: $1-4.9 Billion
Emp.: 2,000
Cosmetics
N.A.I.C.S.: 325620

Procter & Gamble Taiwan Limited (1)
7th Floor No 106 Section 5 Xinyi Road, Taipei, 110, Taiwan
Tel.: (886) 287806388
Web Site: https://www.pgtaiwan.com.tw
Toilet Preparation Mfr
N.A.I.C.S.: 325620

Procter & Gamble Technical Centres Limited (1)
The Heights Brooklands, Weybridge, KT13 0XP, Surrey, United Kingdom
Tel.: (44) 1932896000
Web Site: http://www.pg.co.uk
Chemical Suppliers
N.A.I.C.S.: 424690

Procter & Gamble Technology (Beijing) Co., Ltd. (1)
27-33/F Centre Plaza 161 Lin He Xi Heng Road, Haidian District, Guangzhou, 510620, China
Tel.: (86) 2085186688
Commercial & Physical Research Services
N.A.I.C.S.: 541715

Procter & Gamble Trading (Thailand) Limited (1)
The Emporium Tower 622 Sukhumvit Road, Kwaeng Klongton Khet Klongtoey 20th-22nd floor, Bangkok, 10110, Thailand
Tel.: (66) 26645000
Toilet Preparation Mfr
N.A.I.C.S.: 325620

Procter & Gamble Tuketim Mallari Sanayii A.S. (1)
Serin sok No 9 Kosifler Is Merkezi A Blok, Kadikoy, 34752, Turkiye
Tel.: (90) 2164638000
Personal Health Care Products Mfr
N.A.I.C.S.: 339999

Procter & Gamble U.K. (1)
The Heights Brooklands, Weybridge, KT13 0XP, Surrey, United Kingdom (100%)
Tel.: (44) 1932896000
Web Site: https://www.pg.co.uk
Sales Range: $150-199.9 Million
Emp.: 800
Household Cleaning Products
N.A.I.C.S.: 325611

Procter & Gamble UK Ltd. (1)
The Heights Brooklands, Weybridge, KT13 0XP, Surrey, United Kingdom
Tel.: (44) 1932896000
Toilet Preparation Mfr
N.A.I.C.S.: 325620

Procter & Gamble UK Parent Company Ltd. (1)
Brooklands, Weybridge, KT13 0XP, Surrey, United Kingdom
Tel.: (44) 1932896000
Cosmetic Product Mfr & Distr
N.A.I.C.S.: 325620

Procter & Gamble Ukraine (1)
5/13 Naberezhno-Khreschatytska str, 04070, Kiev, Ukraine
Tel.: (380) 444900900

Web Site: http://www.pg.com.ua
Cosmetic Product Mfr & Distr
N.A.I.C.S.: 325620

Procter & Gamble d.o.o. (1)
Business Center Bani 110, 10010, Zagreb, Croatia
Tel.: (385) 16690300
Toilet Preparation Mfr
N.A.I.C.S.: 325620

Procter & Gamble do Brasil S/A (1)
Av Maria Coelho Aguiar 215, Jardim Sao Luis, Sao Paulo, 05805-000, Brazil
Tel.: (55) 1137480264
Web Site: http://www.br.pg.com
Detergents Mfr
N.A.I.C.S.: 325611
Alberto Carvalho (Pres)

Procter & Gamble do Brazil, LLC (1)
P G Plz, Cincinnati, OH 45202
Tel.: (513) 983-1100
Web Site: http://www.pg.com
Soap & Detergent Mfr
N.A.I.C.S.: 325611
Allen Lafley (Pres)

Procter & Gamble-Rakona, s.r.o. (1)
Ottova 402, 269 01, Rakovnik, Czech Republic (100%)
Tel.: (420) 313522222
Web Site: https://pg.jobs.cz
Sales Range: $100-124.9 Million
Emp.: 300
Detergents, Fabric Softeners, Dishwashing Products & Shampoos
N.A.I.C.S.: 325611

Productos Cosmeticos, S.L.U. (1)
Avda Bruselas 24, 28108, Alcobendas, Spain
Tel.: (34) 917222100
Cosmetic Product Distr
N.A.I.C.S.: 424210

Professional Care Logistics, S.L.U. (1)
Avda Bruselas 24, 28108, Alcobendas, Spain
Tel.: (34) 916560011
Logistics Consulting Servies
N.A.I.C.S.: 541614

Riverfront Music Publishing Co., Inc. (1)
1 Proctor Gamble, Cincinnati, OH 45202-3315
Tel.: (513) 983-1100
Music Publishing Services
N.A.I.C.S.: 512230

SPD Development Company Limited (1)
Clearblue Innovation Centre Stannard Way, Priory Business Park, Bedford, MK44 3UP, United Kingdom
Tel.: (44) 1234835000
Web Site: http://www.swissprecisiondiagnostics.com
Sales Range: $50-74.9 Million
Emp.: 170
Health Care Equipment & Supplies
N.A.I.C.S.: 423440

SPD Swiss Precision Diagnostics GmbH (1)
47 route de Saint-Georges, Petit-Lancy, 1213, Geneva, Switzerland
Tel.: (41) 227096300
Web Site: https://www.swissprecisiondiagnostics.com
Consumer Goods Mfr
N.A.I.C.S.: 325611

Sebastian Europe GmbH (1)
Sulzbacher Str 40, Schwalbach am Taunus, 65824, Hessen, Germany
Tel.: (49) 6151340
Cosmetic Product Distr
N.A.I.C.S.: 424210

Snowberry New Zealand Limited (1)
26 Homeward Bound Drive RD4, Wellsford, 0974, Auckland, New Zealand
Tel.: (64) 92637900
Web Site: http://www.snowberry.co.nz
Cosmetic Preparation Mfr
N.A.I.C.S.: 325620

TAOS - FL, LLC (1)

The Procter & Gamble Company—(Continued)

6100 Blue Lagoon Dr Ste 150, Miami, FL
33126
Tel.: (305) 593-0667
Web Site: http://www.theartofshaving.com
Sales Range: $25-49.9 Million
Emp.: 40
Shaving Products Mfr
N.A.I.C.S.: 339999

TULA Life, Inc. (1)
228 Park Ave S PMB 23606, New York, NY
10003-1502
Web Site: https://www.tula.com
Skin Care Product Retailer
N.A.I.C.S.: 456120

The Art of Shaving - FL, LLC (1)
1 Gillette Park, Boston, MA 02127
Tel.: (305) 593-0667
Web Site: http://theartofshaving.com
Sales Range: $25-49.9 Million
Emp.: 50
Health Care Products Mfr
N.A.I.C.S.: 339999
Eric Malka *(Founder)*

The Gillette Company (1)
1 Gillette Pk, Boston, MA 02127
Tel.: (617) 421-7000
Web Site: http://www.gillette.com
Sales Range: $5-14.9 Billion
Emp.: 28,700
Consumer Products Mfr
N.A.I.C.S.: 325620

Subsidiary (Non-US):

Braun (Shanghai) Co. Ltd. (2)
475-495 Lu Chun Road, 200245, Shanghai,
China
Tel.: (86) 2164309388
Web Site: http://www.braun.com
Sales Range: $350-399.9 Million
Emp.: 750
Small Electrical Appliances Mfr
N.A.I.C.S.: 325412

Subsidiary (Domestic):

Braun North America (2)
1 Gillette Park, Boston, MA 02127-1028
Tel.: (781) 939-8300
Web Site: http://www.braun.com
Sales Range: $1-4.9 Billion
Electric Appliances Mfr
N.A.I.C.S.: 423620

Subsidiary (Non-US):

**Braun-Gillette Immobilien GmbH &
Co. KG** (2)
Frankfurter Str 145, Hessen, 61476, Ger-
many
Tel.: (49) 6173300
Web Site: http://www.braun.com
Emp.: 1,200
Sanitary Paper Product Mfr
N.A.I.C.S.: 322291

Subsidiary (Domestic):

Gillette (2)
Prudential Tower Bldg, Boston, MA 02199-
8004
Tel.: (617) 421-7000
Web Site: http://www.gillette.com
Sales Range: $1-4.9 Billion
Dental Care Products Mfr
N.A.I.C.S.: 325620

Subsidiary (Non-US):

Gillette (Hong Kong) Limited (2)
Rm 13F Sunning Plz 10 Hysan Ave, Cause-
way Bay, China (Hong Kong)
Tel.: (852) 2539 9800
Sales Range: $150-199.9 Million
Electric Appliances Mfr
N.A.I.C.S.: 423620

Gillette Aesop Ltd. (2)
The Heights, Weybridge, KT13 0XP, United
Kingdom
Tel.: (44) 1932896000
Web Site: http://www.pgsuppliers.com
Sales Range: $150-199.9 Million
Emp.: 50
Drugs Drug Proprietaries & Druggists Sun-
dries Whslr

N.A.I.C.S.: 424210

Gillette Holding GmbH (2)
Frankfurter St 145, 61476, Kronberg, Ger-
many
Tel.: (49) 6173300
Web Site: http://www.braun.com
Sales Range: $75-99.9 Million
Emp.: 175
Holding Company
N.A.I.C.S.: 551111

Subsidiary (Domestic):

Braun GmbH (3)
Frankfurter Strasse 145, 61476, Kronberg,
61476, Germany
Tel.: (49) 18002021364
Web Site: http://www.png.com
Sales Range: $350-399.9 Million
Electric Appliances Mfr
N.A.I.C.S.: 335210

Gillette Beteiligungs GmbH (3)
Suzbacher St 40-50, 65824, Schwalbach,
Germany
Tel.: (49) 61968901
Web Site: http://www.procter.com
Sales Range: $100-124.9 Million
Business Services
N.A.I.C.S.: 561499

Subsidiary (Domestic):

**Gillette Deutschland GmbH & Co.
OHG** (4)
Oberlandstrasse 75 84, Berlin, 12099, Ger-
many
Tel.: (49) 3075640
Web Site: http://www.gillette.de
Razor Blade Mfr
N.A.I.C.S.: 332215

**Gillette Gruppe Deutschland GmbH &
Co.oHG** (4)
Frankfurter Strasse 145, 61476, Kronberg,
Germany
Tel.: (49) 6173305000
Web Site: http://www.pg.com
Oral Hygiene, Including Toothbrushes, Elec-
tric Toothbrushes, Toothpastes & Mouth-
washes Mfr
N.A.I.C.S.: 339114

Subsidiary (Non-US):

Gillette India Limited (2)
P&G Plaza Cardinal Gracias Road, Chakala
Andheri East, Mumbai, 400099, Maharash-
tra, India
Tel.: (91) 2228266000
Web Site: http://in.pg.com
Sales Range: $75-99.9 Million
Personal Grooming Products Whslr
N.A.I.C.S.: 456199
Bansidhar S. Mehta *(Chm)*

Gillette Industries Limited (2)
Rusham Park Whitehall Lane, Egham, TW7
5NP, Surrey, United Kingdom
Tel.: (44) 2085601234
Web Site: http://www.pgsupplier.com
Sales Range: $250-299.9 Million
Emp.: 1,998
Health & Beauty Aids Mfr
N.A.I.C.S.: 456199

Subsidiary (Domestic):

Gillette UK Ltd. (3)
5th Floor Voyager House Chicago Avenue,
Manchester Airport, Manchester, M90 3DQ,
Berkshire, United Kingdom
Tel.: (44) 2033676033
Web Site: https://www.gillette.co.uk
Sales Range: $500-549.9 Million
Emp.: 800
Consumer Products Mfr
N.A.I.C.S.: 335210

Subsidiary (Non-US):

N.V. Duracell Batteries, S.A. (3)
Nijverheidslaan 7, 3200, Aarschot, Belgium
Tel.: (32) 16552011
Web Site: http://www.duracell.be
Sales Range: $350-399.9 Million
Emp.: 800
Battery Mfr
N.A.I.C.S.: 335910

Subsidiary (Non-US):

Gillette International B.V. (2)
Watermanweg 100, Rotterdam, 3067 GG,
Zuid-Holland, Netherlands
Tel.: (31) 102863100
Web Site: http://www.procterandgamble.com
Emp.: 300
Sanitary Paper Product Mfr
N.A.I.C.S.: 322291

Gillette Pakistan Limited (2)
11th Floor The Harbour Front Dolmen City
HC 3 Block 4, Abdul Sattar Edhi Avenue
Clifton, Karachi, 75600, Pakistan
Tel.: (92) 21111000764
Web Site: https://www.gillettepakistan.com
Consumer Goods Mfr
N.A.I.C.S.: 339991

**Gillette Poland International sp.
z.o.o.** (2)
Nowy Jozefow 70, Lodz, 94-406, Poland
Tel.: (48) 801258825
Web Site: https://www.gillette.pl
Sales Range: $250-299.9 Million
Emp.: 100
Sanitary Paper Product Mfr
N.A.I.C.S.: 322291

Subsidiary (Domestic):

Gillette Safety Razor Company (2)
1 Gillette Park, Boston, MA 02127
Tel.: (800) 445-5388
Web Site: http://www.gillette.com
Razors, Shaving Cream, Deodorants &
Other Hygienic Products Mfr
N.A.I.C.S.: 335210

Subsidiary (Non-US):

Gillette del Peru S.C. (2)
Av Pardo y Aliaga 695, Lima, 27, Peru
Tel.: (51) 12113700
Web Site: http://www.oralb.com
Sales Range: $25-49.9 Million
Emp.: 35
Razors & Razor Blades Mfr
N.A.I.C.S.: 332215

Groupe Gillette France S.A. (2)
163 Quai Aulagnier, 92600, Asnieres-sur-
Seine, France
Tel.: (33) 140885511
Web Site: http://www.fr.pg.com
Sales Range: $150-199.9 Million
Emp.: 500
Health & Beauty Aids
N.A.I.C.S.: 456199

Productos Gillette Chile Limitada (2)
Presidente Riesco 5335 Piso 17 Las Con-
des, Santiago, Chile
Tel.: (56) 2 816 5000
Web Site: http://www.gillette.com
Sales Range: $25-49.9 Million
Earnings: $23,000,000
Emp.: 100
Men's Grooming Products Mfr & Distr
N.A.I.C.S.: 456120

**The Procter & Gamble U.S. Business
Services Company** (1)
1 P&G Plz, Cincinnati, OH 45202
Tel.: (513) 983-1100
Web Site: http://www.pg.com
Toilet Preparation Mfr
N.A.I.C.S.: 325620

VitaminHaus Pty Ltd (1)
69 Station Street, Malvern, 3144, NSW,
Australia
Tel.: (61) 386063518
Web Site: http://www.voostvitamins.com
Vitamin Product Mfr & Distr
N.A.I.C.S.: 325411
Thomas Siebel *(Founder & Mng Dir)*
Laura Riepe *(Fin Mgr)*
Samantha Hilleard *(Gen Mgr-Mktg & Bus
Dev)*
Kelly Evans *(Coord-Social Media)*

Zirh Holdings LLC (1)
900 3rd Ave Fl 9, New York, NY 10022-
4728
Tel.: (212) 813-2100
Web Site: http://www.zirh.com
Sales Range: $25-49.9 Million
Male Grooming Product Mfr
N.A.I.C.S.: 325620

Zogi SRL (1)
Via Giovanni XXIII 2, 36030, Vicenza, Italy
Tel.: (39) 0445602001
Beauty Salons
N.A.I.C.S.: 812112

THE PROGRESSIVE CORPO-
RATION

6300 Wilson Mills Rd, Mayfield Vil-
lage, OH 44143
Tel.: (440) 461-5000   **OH**
Web Site:
   https://www.progressive.com
Year Founded: 1937
PGR—(NYSE)
Rev.: $62,108,500,000
Assets: $28,324,000,000
Liabilities: $8,046,900,000
Net Worth: $20,277,100,000
Earnings: $3,864,800,000
Emp.: 61,400
Fiscal Year-end: 12/31/23
Financial Investment Services
N.A.I.C.S.: 551112
Susan Patricia Griffith *(Pres & CEO)*
John P. Sauerland *(CFO & VP)*
Daniel P. Mascaro *(Chief Legal Offi-
cer, Sec & VP)*
Steven A. Broz *(CIO)*
Patrick K. Callahan *(Pres-Personal
Lines)*
Andrew J. Quigg *(Chief Strategy Offi-
cer)*
Jonathan S. Bauer *(Chief Investment
Officer)*
Karen B. Bailo *(Pres-Comml Lines)*
Bill Clawson *(Chief HR Officer)*
Remi Kent *(CMO)*
Mariann Wojtkun Marshall *(Chief
Acctg Officer & VP)*

Subsidiaries:

ARX Holding Corp. (1)
1 Asi Way N, Saint Petersburg, FL 33702
Tel.: (727) 821-8765
Holding Company
N.A.I.C.S.: 551112

Subsidiary (Domestic):

ASI Services, Inc. (2)
2212 Verus St, San Diego, CA 92154
Tel.: (619) 474-2600
Web Site: https://asiservicesinc.com
Emp.: 4
Ship Building & Repairing Services
N.A.I.C.S.: 336611
Frank Safley *(Pres)*

Safe Harbour Underwriters, LLC (2)
805 Executive Ctr Dr W Ste 300, Saint Pe-
tersburg, FL 33702-2407
Tel.: (727) 456-2741
Web Site: http://www.shuw.org
Insurance Agency & Brokerage Services
N.A.I.C.S.: 524210

**Sunshine Security Insurance Agency,
Inc.** (2)
1 Asi Way, Saint Petersburg, FL 33702
Tel.: (727) 825-0663
Insurance Agency & Brokerage Services
N.A.I.C.S.: 524210

Drive Insurance Holdings, Inc. (1)
6300 Wilson Mills Rd, Mayfield Village, OH
44143
Tel.: (440) 461-5000
Web Site: http://www.progressive.com
Insurance Services
N.A.I.C.S.: 524298

Subsidiary (Domestic):

**Drive New Jersey Insurance
Company** (2)
820 Bear Tavern Rd Ste 305, West Trenton,
NJ 08628
Tel.: (440) 461-5000
Insurance Services
N.A.I.C.S.: 524126

**Progressive Hawaii Insurance
Corp.** (2)

6300 Wilson Mills Rd, Mayfield Village, OH 44143-2109
Tel.: (440) 461-5000
Web Site: http://www.progressive.com
Insurance Services
N.A.I.C.S.: 524298

Progressive Advanced Insurance Company (1)
6300 Wilson Mills Rd, Mayfield Village, OH 44143
Insurance Services
N.A.I.C.S.: 524126

Progressive American Insurance Company (1)
4030 Crescent Park Dr, Riverview, FL 33578 (100%)
Tel.: (855) 347-3939
Web Site: http://www.progressiveintl.com
Rev.: $98,000,000
Insurance Services
N.A.I.C.S.: 524113

Progressive Capital Management Corp. (1)
3 Parklands Dr, Darien, CT 06820-3654
Tel.: (203) 656-6000
Sales Range: $25-49.9 Million
Emp.: 10
Investment Services
N.A.I.C.S.: 523150
Bill Cody (CIO)
Tom King (Pres)

Progressive Casualty Insurance Company (1)
300 N Commons Blvd, Mayfield Village, OH 44143 (100%)
Tel.: (440) 395-1901
Web Site: http://www.progressive.com
Sales Range: $150-199.9 Million
Property & Casualty Insurance Services Supplier
N.A.I.C.S.: 524126

Subsidiary (Domestic):

Progressive Gulf Insurance Company (2)
6300 Wilson Mills Rd, Mayfield Village, OH 44143-2109
Tel.: (440) 461-5000
Web Site: http://www.progressive.com
Insurance Services
N.A.I.C.S.: 524126

Progressive Specialty Insurance Company (2)
6300 Wilson Mills Rd, Mayfield Village, OH 44143-2109
Tel.: (440) 461-5000
Web Site: http://www.progressive.com
Insurance Services
N.A.I.C.S.: 524298

Progressive Consumer Insurance (1)
6300 Wilson Mills Rd, Cleveland, OH 44143-2109 (100%)
Tel.: (440) 461-5000
Web Site:
   http://www.progressiveinsurance.com
Sales Range: $750-799.9 Million
Emp.: 3,000
Insurance Services
N.A.I.C.S.: 524126
Glenn M. Renwick (Chm, Pres & CEO)

Progressive Corp. - Agency Group (1)
6300 Wilson Mills Rd, Cleveland, OH 44143-2109
Tel.: (440) 461-5000
Sales Range: $50-74.9 Million
Emp.: 200
Private Passenger Automobile, Small Commercial Vehicle & Motorcycle Insurance Services
N.A.I.C.S.: 524210
David Todd (Mgr-IT Risk & Compliance Grp)

Progressive County Mutual Insurance Co. (1)
6300 Wilson Mills Rd, Mayfield Village, OH 44143-2109
Tel.: (440) 461-5000
Web Site: http://www.progressiveins.com

Sales Range: $700-749.9 Million
Emp.: 1,000
Fire, Marine & Casualty Insurance
N.A.I.C.S.: 524126

Progressive Halcyon Insurance Co. (1)
743 Edgewood Rd, Cleveland, OH 44143 (100%)
Tel.: (440) 461-5000
Web Site: http://www.progressive.com
Sales Range: $150-199.9 Million
Insurance Services
N.A.I.C.S.: 524126

Progressive Insurance Agency, Inc. (1)
10929 Disk Dr, Rancho Cordova, CA 95670 (100%)
Tel.: (440) 461-5000
Web Site: http://www.progressive.com
Sales Range: $1-4.9 Billion
Emp.: 10,000
Insurance Agents
N.A.I.C.S.: 524126

Progressive Investment Company, Inc. (1)
2125 Main St, Ferdinand, IN 47532-0068
Tel.: (812) 367-0616
Web Site: https://www.proinvestco.com
Investment Management Service
N.A.I.C.S.: 523940

Progressive Northern Insurance Company (1)
6300 Wilson Mills Rd, Cleveland, OH 44143-2109 (100%)
Tel.: (440) 461-5000
Web Site: http://www.progressive.com
Sales Range: $125-149.9 Million
Emp.: 3,000
Insurance Services
N.A.I.C.S.: 524128

Progressive Preferred Insurance Company (1)
6300 Wilson Mills Rd, Mayfield Village, OH 44143-2109
Tel.: (440) 461-5000
Web Site: http://www.progressive.com
Insurance Services
N.A.I.C.S.: 524126

Progressive Premier Insurance Company of Illinois (1)
6300 Wilson Mills Rd, Mayfield Village, OH 44143-2182
Tel.: (440) 461-5000
Web Site: http://www.progressive.com
Insurance Services
N.A.I.C.S.: 524298

Progressive Southeastern Insurance Company (1)
5903 Oleander, Wilmington, NC 28403
Tel.: (910) 799-1126
Web Site: http://www.progressive.com
Automobile Insurance Services
N.A.I.C.S.: 524126

Progressive West Insurance Company (1)
10929 Disk Dr, Rancho Cordova, CA 95670
Tel.: (916) 864-6000
Web Site: http://www.progressive.com
Sales Range: $500-549.9 Million
Emp.: 800
Insurance Agents
N.A.I.C.S.: 524126
Glenn M. Renwick (Chm, Pres & CEO)

Protective Insurance Corporation (1)
111 Congressional Blvd, Carmel, IN 46032
Tel.: (317) 636-9800
Web Site:
   http://www.protectiveinsurance.com
Rev.: $468,749,000
Assets: $1,722,827,000
Liabilities: $1,359,745,000
Net Worth: $363,082,000
Earnings: $4,463,000
Emp.: 490
Fiscal Year-end: 12/31/2020
Casualty Insurance Marketing & Underwriting for the Trucking Industry
N.A.I.C.S.: 524126
John R. Barnett (CFO)

Subsidiary (Domestic):

B&L Brokerage Services, Inc. (2)

111 Congressional Blvd, Carmel, IN 46032
Tel.: (800) 644-5501
Web Site: http://www.blbrokerage.com
Insurance Brokerage Services
N.A.I.C.S.: 524210

Protective Insurance Company (2)
111 Congressional Blvd Ste 500, Carmel, IN 46032 (100%)
Tel.: (317) 636-9800
Web Site:
   https://www.protectiveinsurance.com
Fiscal Year-end: 12/31/2018
Provider of Casualty Insurance for Large Trucking Fleets
N.A.I.C.S.: 524126
John D. Nichols Jr. (Chm)

Subsidiary (Domestic):

Protective Specialty Insurance Company (3)
111 Congressional Blvd Ste 500, Carmel, IN 46032
Tel.: (317) 636-9800
Web Site:
   http://www.protectivespecialty.com
Emp.: 400
Insurance Agencies & Brokerage Services
N.A.I.C.S.: 524210

Sagamore Insurance Company (3)
111 Congressional Blvd Ste 500, Carmel, IN 46032
Tel.: (317) 636-6400
Web Site:
   http://www.sagamoreinsurance.com
Insurance Brokerage Services
N.A.I.C.S.: 524210

United Financial Casualty Company (1)
6300 Wilson Mills Rd, Cleveland, OH 44143-2109
Tel.: (440) 461-5000
Web Site:
   http://www.progressivecommercial.com
Property & Casualty Insurance Company
N.A.I.C.S.: 524128

THE PULSE BEVERAGE CORPORATION
11678 N Huron St, Northglenn, CO 80234
Tel.: (720) 382-5476   NV
Web Site:
   http://www.pulsebeverage.com
PLSB—(OTCIQ)
Sales Range: $1-9.9 Million
Emp.: 14
Water-Based Beverages Mfr
N.A.I.C.S.: 312112
Parley Sheya (Sec, VP & Mgr-Natl Sls)
Adam Schneider (Mgr-Natural Foods Brand & Sls)
Robert Yates (Pres, CEO, CFO & CTO)

THE REALREAL, INC.
55 Francisco St Ste 150, San Francisco, CA 94133   DE
Web Site:
   https://www.therealreal.com
Year Founded: 2011
REAL—(NASDAQ)
Rev.: $603,493,000
Assets: $615,641,000
Liabilities: $785,733,000
Net Worth: ($170,092,000)
Earnings: ($196,445,000)
Emp.: 3,468
Fiscal Year-end: 12/31/22
Online Luxury Goods Retailer
N.A.I.C.S.: 423940
Todd A. Suko (Chief Legal Officer & Sec)
John E. Koryl (CEO)
Todd Suko (Chief Legal Officer & Sec)
Rati Sahi Levesque (Pres & COO)
Ajay Gopal (CFO)

Luke Friang (CTO, Chief Product Officer & Chief Tech Officer)
Chatelle Lynch (Chief People Officer)

THE RENEWABLE CORPORATION
1313 So Killian Dr, Lake Park, FL 33403
Tel.: (561) 328-6488   WA
RNWB—(OTCIQ)
Inorganic Chemical Mfr
N.A.I.C.S.: 325180
Gary R. Smith (Pres & CEO)

THE RESERVE PETROLEUM COMPANY
6801 Broadway Ext Ste 300, Oklahoma City, OK 73116-9037
Tel.: (405) 848-7551   DE
Web Site: http://www.reserve-petro.com
Year Founded: 1931
RSRV—(OTCIQ)
Rev.: $16,170,884
Assets: $38,727,133
Liabilities: $6,341,771
Net Worth: $32,385,362
Earnings: $4,000,751
Emp.: 6
Fiscal Year-end: 12/31/22
Crude Petroleum & Natural Gas Extraction
N.A.I.C.S.: 211120
Cameron R. McLain (Pres & CEO)
Lawrence R. Francis (CFO & First VP)

THE RMR GROUP INC.
2 Newton Pl 255 Washington St Ste 300, Newton, MA 02458-1634
Tel.: (617) 796-8230   MD
Web Site: https://www.rmrgroup.com
Year Founded: 2015
RMR—(NASDAQ)
Rev.: $962,316,000
Assets: $582,424,000
Liabilities: $158,761,000
Net Worth: $423,663,000
Earnings: $57,147,000
Emp.: 37,000
Fiscal Year-end: 09/30/23
Holding Company; Trust & Fund Management Services
N.A.I.C.S.: 551112
Adam David Portnoy (Chm, Pres, CEO & Mng Dir)
Jennifer Babbin Clark (Mng Dir, Gen Counsel, Sec & Exec VP)
Fernando Diaz (VP)
Matthew P. Jordan (CFO, Treas & Exec VP)
Thomas J. Lorenzini (Sr VP)
Christopher Bilotto (Sr VP)
Timothy Bonang (Sr VP)
Adam David Portnoy (Pres & CEO)
Jennifer Francis (Exec VP)
Jonathan Pertchik (Exec VP)
Jeffrey Leer (Sr VP)
Tamara Brown (VP-Hotel Asset Mgmt)
Fernando Diaz (VP)
Brian Donley (VP-Acctg)
Yael Duffy (Sr VP)
Christopher Ranjitkar (Sr Dir-Mktg & Comm)
Marvin Cine (VP & Asst Gen Counsel)
Carl Awalt (VP)
Jean DeFlorio (VP)
John Forester (VP)
John Murray (Exec VP)
Matthew Brown (Sr VP)

The RMR Group Inc.—(Continued)

Gregory Carey (Sr VP)
Carlos Flores (Sr VP)
Katherine Potter (Sr VP)
Jacquelyn Anderson (Sr VP)
Todd Hargreaves (Sr VP)
Andrew Fay (Sr VP)
Diane Bastianelli (VP-Acquisitions Diligence & Dispositions)
Jesse Abair (VP-Dev)
Jared Lewis (VP-Underwriting)
Dan Melia (VP)
Steve Skelley (VP-Tremont Realty Capital)
Diane Proctor (VP-HR)
Kristin Sage-Black (VP-Hotel Asset Mgmt)
Rob Lester (Sr VP)
Stefanie Bertcher (VP)
Rebecca Buchanan (VP)
Jim Driver (VP)
Noah Echols (VP)
Stephen Hendrix (VP)
Marc Krohn (VP)
Mike Martello (VP)
Tiffany Sy (VP)
Summit Walia (VP)
Sadler Walker (VP)

Subsidiaries:

Sonesta International Hotels Corporation (1)
255 Washington St, Newton, MA 02458
Tel.: (617) 421-5400
Web Site: http://www.sonesta.com
Sales Range: $50-74.9 Million
Emp.: 718
Holding Company Resorts & Hotels Operator
N.A.I.C.S.: 551112
John G. Murray (Pres & CEO)
Jennifer Babbin Clark (Sec)
Jane Colby (Dir-Acct-Global)
Jon Elliott (Sr Dir-Acct-Global)
Blair McSheffrey (VP-Hotel Sls-Global)
Vera Manoukian (COO)
Garine Ferejian-Mayo (Chief Comml Officer)
Elizabeth Harlow (Chief Mktg & Brand Officer)
Kathleen James (Sr Dir-Extended Stay Sls)
Jeff Knowlton (CIO)

Subsidiary (Domestic):

Brewster Wholesaler Company (2)
116 Huntington Ave Ste 9, Boston, MA 02116-5021 (100%)
Tel.: (617) 421-5430
Web Site: http://www.sonesta.net
Sales Range: $25-49.9 Million
Emp.: 30
Hotels & Management Services
N.A.I.C.S.: 423440

Red Lion Hotels Corp. (2)
1550 Market St 350, Denver, CO 80202
Tel.: (509) 459-6100
Web Site: http://www.redlion.com
Rev.: $114,288,000
Assets: $246,518,000
Liabilities: $99,497,000
Net Worth: $147,021,000
Earnings: ($19,029,000)
Emp.: 285
Fiscal Year-end: 12/31/2019
Owner, Manager & Franchisor of Hotels & Motels
N.A.I.C.S.: 721110
Thomas L. McKeirnan (Gen Counsel & Exec VP)
Amanda Marcello (Sr VP-Brand Strategy)
Jordan Langlois (Sr VP-Franchise Ops)
Vinod Sankar (Mng Dir-RLabs)
Paul Moerner (Chief Acctg Officer & Sr VP)
Christopher Trick (CMO & Sr VP)
Judith A. Jarvis (Gen Counsel & Exec VP)
Jennifer B. Clark (Sec)
Carlos R. Flores (Pres)
Stephen P. Miano (Treas)

Subsidiary (Domestic):

Red Lion Anaheim, LLC (3)
1850 S Harbor Blvd, Anaheim, CA 92802

Tel.: (714) 750-4833
Web Site: http://www.redlion.com
Home Management Services
N.A.I.C.S.: 721110

TicketsWest.com, Inc. (3)
201 W N River Dr Ste 100, Spokane, WA 99201-2262
Tel.: (509) 459-6100
Sales Range: $100-124.9 Million
Online Ticket Sales
N.A.I.C.S.: 541519

Unit (Domestic):

Royal Sonesta New Orleans (2)
300 Bourbon St, New Orleans, LA 70130
Tel.: (504) 586-0300
Web Site: http://www.sonesta.com
Sales Range: $25-49.9 Million
Emp.: 300
Hotel Operator
N.A.I.C.S.: 721110
Alfred L. Groos (Gen Mgr)
Kristin Crawford (Dir-Sls & Mktg)
Elizabeth Nelson (Dir-Catering & Convention Svcs)
Daneen Zeringue (Dir-Revenue)
Zachary Martin (Dir-Food & Beverage)
Jeffrey Martin (Dir-Rooms)
Zakaria Nyangoro (Dir-Engrg)
Robin Keller (Sr Mgr-PR)
Lorie Juliano (Dir-Comm)

Sonesta Bayfront Hotel Coconut Grove (2)
2889 McFarlane Rd, Coconut Grove, FL 33133
Tel.: (305) 529-2828
Web Site: http://www.sonesta.com
Emp.: 100
Hotel
N.A.I.C.S.: 721110

The RMR Group LLC (1)
2 Newton Pl 255 Washington St, Newton, MA 02458-1634 (51.7%)
Tel.: (617) 796-8390
Web Site: http://www.rmrgroup.com
Rev.: $27,600,000,000
Trust & Fund Management Services
N.A.I.C.S.: 523940
Richard W. Siedel Jr. (Sr VP)
Jennifer Babbin Clark (Gen Counsel, Sec & Exec VP)
Ethan S. Bornstein (Sr VP)
Brian E. Donley (Sr VP)
Thomas M. O'Brien (Exec VP)
Thomas M. O'Brien (Exec VP)
Peter J. Crage (Sr VP)
Fernando Diaz (Sr VP)
Tiffany R. Sy (VP)
Christopher Bilotto (VP-Asset Mgmt)
Christopher J. Bilotto (Exec VP)
George Martin (VP-Tax)
Katherine E. Potter (Sr VP-Legal)
David Campoli (Sr VP)
Steve Miano (VP-Acctg)
Jacquelyn Anderson (VP-Legal)
Matthew Brown (Sr VP)
Gregory Carey (Sr VP)
Douglas Lanois (Sr VP)
Jeffrey Leer (Sr VP)
Bill Myers (Sr VP)
Diane Proctor (VP-HR)
Diane Bastianelli (VP-Acquisitions Diligence & Dispositions)
Scott Bloomfield (VP-Acctg Info Sys)
Tamara Brown (VP-Hotel Asset Mgmt)
Jared Lewis (VP-Underwriting)
Kristin Sage-Black (VP-Hotel Asset Mgmt)
Lynn Schemmel (VP)

Affiliate (Domestic):

Office Properties Income Trust (2)
2 Newton Pl 255 Washington St Ste 300, Newton, MA 02458-1634
Tel.: (617) 219-1460
Web Site: https://www.opireit.com
Rev.: $554,275,000
Assets: $3,979,977,000
Liabilities: $2,593,642,000
Net Worth: $1,386,335,000
Earnings: ($6,109,000)
Fiscal Year-end: 12/31/2022
Real Estate Investment Trust
N.A.I.C.S.: 525990
Jennifer Babbin Clark (Sec & Mng Trustee)
Brian E. Donley (CFO & Treas)

Yael Duffy (Pres & COO)
Vern D. Larkin (Dir-Internal Audit)
Kevin Barry (Sr Dir-IR)

Subsidiary (Domestic):

Select Income REIT (3)
2 Newton Pl 255 Washington St Ste 300, Newton, MA 02458-1634
Tel.: (617) 796-8303
Sales Range: $450-499.9 Million
Real Estate Investment Trust
N.A.I.C.S.: 525990

Subsidiary (Domestic):

Industrial Logistics Properties Trust (4)
2 Newton Pl 255 Washington St Ste 300, Newton, MA 02458-1634 (69.2%)
Tel.: (617) 219-1460
Web Site: https://www.ilptreit.com
Rev.: $388,151,000
Assets: $5,676,166,000
Liabilities: $4,345,395,000
Net Worth: $1,330,771,000
Earnings: ($226,723,000)
Fiscal Year-end: 12/31/2022
Real Estate Investment Trust
N.A.I.C.S.: 525990
Jennifer Babbin Clark (Sec)
Tiffany R. Sy (CFO & Treas)
Jennifer B. Clark (Sec)
Marc Krohn (VP)

Subsidiary (Domestic):

Monmouth Real Estate Investment Corporation (5)
101 Crawfords Cor Rd Ste 1405, Holmdel, NJ 07733
Tel.: (732) 577-4054
Web Site: http://www.mreic.reit
Rev.: $183,133,000
Assets: $2,215,883,000
Liabilities: $1,121,149,000
Net Worth: $1,094,734,000
Earnings: $44,764,000
Emp.: 14
Fiscal Year-end: 09/30/2021
Real Estate Investment Trust
N.A.I.C.S.: 525990
Eugene W. Landy (Founder)
Samuel A. Landy (Executives)
Richard P. Molke (VP-Asset Mgmt)
Allison Viscardi (VP-Property Mgmt)
Ashley Tripodi (Mgr-Property)
Matthew R. Santonocito (Mgr-IT)
Katie Rytter (Controller)
Laura Teman (Asst Controller)
Becky Coleridge (VP-IR)
Michael D. Prashad (Gen Counsel)

Subsidiary (Domestic):

RMR Advisors LLC (2)
2 Newton Pl 255 Washington St Ste 300, Newton, MA 02458-2076
Tel.: (617) 332-9530
Web Site: http://www.rmrfunds.com
Investment Advisory & Fund Management Services
N.A.I.C.S.: 523940

Tremont Realty Advisors LLC (2)
2 Newton Pl 255 Washington St Ste 300, Newton, MA 02458-1634
Tel.: (617) 867-0700
Web Site: http://www.tremontcapital.com
Realty Investment Capital Funding Services
N.A.I.C.S.: 522299
Matthew P. Jordan (Pres & CEO)
David M. Blackman (Pres & CEO)
Douglas Lanois (Sr VP)

Affiliate (Domestic):

Seven Hills Realty Trust (3)
2 Newton Pl 255 Washington St Ste 300, Newton, MA 02458-1634
Tel.: (617) 332-9530
Web Site: https://www.sevnreit.com
Rev.: $38,362,000
Assets: $746,847,000
Liabilities: $475,268,000
Net Worth: $271,579,000
Earnings: $27,640,000
Fiscal Year-end: 12/31/2022
Investment Management Service
N.A.I.C.S.: 525990

Fernando Diaz (CFO & Treas)
Thomas J. Lorenzini (Pres)
Tiffany Sy (CFO)

Tremont Mortgage Trust (3)
2 Newton Pl 255 Washington St Ste 300, Newton, MA 02458-1634 (19.2%)
Tel.: (617) 796-8317
Web Site: http://www.trmtreit.com
Rev.: $18,030,000
Assets: $294,182,000
Liabilities: $205,279,000
Net Worth: $88,903,000
Earnings: $8,851,000
Fiscal Year-end: 12/31/2020
Real Estate Investment Trust
N.A.I.C.S.: 525990
Jennifer Babbin Clark (Sec)
Thomas J. Lorenzini (Pres)
G. Douglas Lanois (CFO & Treas)

THE SCOTTS MIRACLE-GRO COMPANY
14111 Scottslawn Rd, Marysville, OH 43041
Tel.: (937) 644-0011   OH
Web Site: https://www.scottsmiraclegro.com
Year Founded: 1868
SMG—(NYSE)
Rev.: $3,551,300,000
Assets: $3,413,700,000
Liabilities: $3,681,000,000
Net Worth: ($267,300,000)
Earnings: ($380,100,000)
Emp.: 5,500
Fiscal Year-end: 09/30/23
Agriculture Product Distr
N.A.I.C.S.: 551112
James S. Hagedorn (Chm, Pres & CEO)
Matthew Garth (CFO)
Nathan Baxter (COO & Exec VP)
Katherine Hagedorn Littlefield (Vice Chm)
David C. Evans (Bd of Dirs, Executives)
Ivan C. Smith (Chief Compliance Officer, Gen Counsel, Sec & Exec VP)
Nathan Baxter (COO & Exec VP)
Matthew E. Garth (CFO & Exec VP)
Christopher J. Hagedorn (Exec VP)
Dimiter Todorov (Exec VP)
Tom Matthews (Chief Comm Officer-Corp Affairs)

Subsidiaries:

Agrolux Nederland B.V. (1)
Honderdland 251, 2676 LV, Maasdijk, Netherlands
Tel.: (31) 174610820
Web Site: https://www.agrolux.nl
Horticultural Lighting Services
N.A.I.C.S.: 561730

Bonnie Plants, LLC (1)
2801 Interstate Dr, Opelika, AL 36801
Web Site: https://bonnieplants.com
Vegetable & Herb Plants Distr
N.A.I.C.S.: 424990

Gavita International B.V. (1)
Oosteinderweg 127, 1432 AH, Aalsmeer, Netherlands
Tel.: (31) 297380450
Web Site: http://www.gavita.com
Horticultural Lighting Mfr & Distr
N.A.I.C.S.: 335132
Arjan Pauw (Dir-Sls-Horticulture)

Subsidiary (Non-US):

Gavita AS (2)
Moreneveien 1, 3158, Andebu, Norway
Tel.: (47) 33438080
Commodity Trading Services
N.A.I.C.S.: 523160

HDP Trading B.V. (1)
Dwarskulk 29, 3151 ZD, Hoek van Holland, Netherlands
Tel.: (31) 174610813
Web Site: http://www.hdptrading.nl
Commodity Trading Services

N.A.I.C.S.: 523160

SMG Growing Media, Inc. (1)
14111 Scottslawn Rd, Marysville, OH 43041
Tel.: (937) 644-0011
Lawn Grass Seed & Chemical Fertilizer Mfr
N.A.I.C.S.: 325311

Subsidiary (Domestic):

AeroGrow International, Inc. (2)
5405 Spine Rd, Boulder, CO
80301 (100%)
Tel.: (303) 444-7755
Web Site: http://www.aerogarden.com
Sales Range: $25-49.9 Million
Emp.: 40
Indoor Garden Systems Mfr & Distr
N.A.I.C.S.: 811411
Michael C. Lukemire *(Pres)*

Hyponex Corporation (2)
14111 Scottslawn Rd, Marysville, OH 43041
Tel.: (937) 644-0011
Sales Range: $1-4.9 Billion
Emp.: 1,000
Natural Soils, Amendments & Mulches Mfr
N.A.I.C.S.: 212390

Rod McLellan Company (2)
914 S Claremont St, San Mateo, CA 94402
Tel.: (650) 373-3900
Lawn Grass Seed & Chemical Fertilizer Mfr
N.A.I.C.S.: 325311

Scotts Manufacturing Company (1)
25520 Ave Stanford Ste 304, Valencia, CA
91355
Tel.: (800) 544-5596
Lawn & Garden Product Mfr & Marketer
N.A.I.C.S.: 325320

Subsidiary (Domestic):

Miracle-Gro Lawn Products, Inc. (2)
14111 Scottslawn Rd, Marysville, OH 43041
Tel.: (937) 644-0011
Sales Range: $500-549.9 Million
Emp.: 2,000
Nitrogenous Fertilizer Mfr
N.A.I.C.S.: 325311

Scotts Professional Products Co. (1)
14111 Scottslawn Rd, Marysville, OH 43041
Tel.: (937) 644-7079
Web Site: http://www.scotts.com
Lawn & Garden Product Mfr & Marketer
N.A.I.C.S.: 325320

**Scotts Temecula Operations,
LLC** (1)
42375 Remington Ave, Temecula, CA
92590-2512
Tel.: (951) 719-1700
Chemical Fertilizer & Insect Control Product
Mfr
N.A.I.C.S.: 325311

**Scotts-Sierra Horticultural Products
Co.** (1)
7200 Investment Dr, North Charleston, SC
29418-8302 (100%)
Tel.: (843) 760-0679
Sales Range: $10-24.9 Million
Emp.: 22
Horticultural Products & Fertilizers Mfr
N.A.I.C.S.: 325311

Scotts-Sierra Investments, Inc. (1)
1105 N Market St 1300, Wilmington, DE
19801-1241
Tel.: (302) 622-9269
Financial Investment Services
N.A.I.C.S.: 523999

Subsidiary (Non-US):

Scotts Canada Ltd. (2)
2000 Argentia Rd Plz 5 Ste 101, Mississauga, L5N 2R7, ON, Canada (100%)
Tel.: (905) 814-7425
Web Site: http://www.scottscanada.ca
Sales Range: $25-49.9 Million
Emp.: 25
Lawn & Garden Services
N.A.I.C.S.: 333112

Swiss Farms Products, Inc. (1)
3993 Howard Hughes Pkwy, Las Vegas, NV
89169
Tel.: (702) 866-2202

Lawn Grass Seed & Chemical Fertilizer Mfr
N.A.I.C.S.: 325311

The Scotts Company LLC (1)
14111 Scottslawn Rd, Marysville, OH 43041
Tel.: (937) 644-0011
Web Site: http://www.scotts.com
Lawn Care Products Mfr & Distr
N.A.I.C.S.: 325314

Unit (Domestic):

Scotts Earthgro (2)
20 Industrial Park Rd, Lebanon, CT 06249
Tel.: (860) 642-7591
Sales Range: $25-49.9 Million
Emp.: 70
Fertilizers
N.A.I.C.S.: 325314

The Scotts Company (2)
42375 Remington Ave, Temecula, CA
92590-2512
Tel.: (951) 719-1700
Sales Range: $100-124.9 Million
Emp.: 250
Lawn Services
N.A.I.C.S.: 333112

The Scotts Company (2)
535 West Main St, Molalla, OR
97038-9200 (100%)
Tel.: (503) 829-2781
Web Site: http://www.scotts.com
Sales Range: $25-49.9 Million
Emp.: 30
Lawn Services
N.A.I.C.S.: 212390

The Scotts Company (2)
20605 State Rd 19, Goldenrod, FL
34736 (100%)
Tel.: (352) 429-0066
Sales Range: $25-49.9 Million
Emp.: 45
Lawn Services
N.A.I.C.S.: 325311

The Scotts Company (2)
W 124 N 9899 Wasaukee Rd, Germantown,
WI 53022-5400
Tel.: (262) 242-0500
Sales Range: $10-24.9 Million
Emp.: 26
Lawn Services
N.A.I.C.S.: 325314

The Scotts Company (2)
Three Assembly Ct, Fountain, CO 80817-
2710
Tel.: (719) 390-5431
Web Site: http://www.scotts.com
Lawn Services
N.A.I.C.S.: 325311

The Scotts Company (2)
332 Graham Rd, Imlay City, MI 48444-9738
Tel.: (800) 241-8110
Web Site: http://www.scott.com
Sales Range: $25-49.9 Million
Emp.: 50
Lawn Services
N.A.I.C.S.: 325311

The Scotts Company (2)
2057 Hwy 42 N, Jackson, GA 30233-3977
Tel.: (770) 775-5081
Sales Range: $25-49.9 Million
Emp.: 90
Lawn Services
N.A.I.C.S.: 325314
Daniel Keal *(Plant Mgr)*

The Scotts Company (2)
14419 N White & Parker Rd, Maricopa, AZ
85138-3915 (100%)
Tel.: (520) 568-2216
Web Site: http://www.scotts.com
Sales Range: $25-49.9 Million
Emp.: 40
Lawn Services
N.A.I.C.S.: 325311

The Scotts Company (2)
Hwy 460 W RR 614 Gen Mahone Hwy,
Waverly, VA 23890 (100%)
Tel.: (804) 834-3896
Web Site: http://www.scotts.com
Sales Range: $25-49.9 Million
Emp.: 30
Lawn Services

N.A.I.C.S.: 111920

The Scotts Company (2)
1284 Hwy 75 N, Huntsville, TX
77320 (100%)
Tel.: (936) 291-6386
Sales Range: $10-24.9 Million
Emp.: 35
Lawn Services
N.A.I.C.S.: 325311

The Scotts Company (2)
10638 Mount Moriah Rd, Vance, AL 35490
Tel.: (205) 556-9771
Sales Range: $50-74.9 Million
Emp.: 30
Mfr & Wholsale of Fertilizers Natural (Organic) Except Compost
N.A.I.C.S.: 424990

The Scotts Company (2)
1910 48th St, Fort Madison, IA 52627-3265
Tel.: (319) 376-5000
Sales Range: $75-99.9 Million
Emp.: 160
Lawn Care Services
N.A.I.C.S.: 325311
Leslie Malinski *(Plant Mgr)*

The Scotts Company (2)
1489 Beltline Rd, Chester, SC 29706
Tel.: (803) 581-4511
Sales Range: $10-24.9 Million
Emp.: 34
Lawn Services
N.A.I.C.S.: 325314
Micheal Gaineas *(Gen Mgr)*

The Scotts Company (2)
264 Nicatou Industrial Ln, Medway, ME
04460
Tel.: (207) 746-9033
Web Site: http://www.scotts.com
Sales Range: $10-24.9 Million
Emp.: 20
Lawn Services
N.A.I.C.S.: 325320

The Scotts Company (2)
6 New Venture Dr, South Dennis, MA
02660
Tel.: (508) 398-0105
Web Site: http://www.scottslawnservice.com
Sales Range: $1-9.9 Million
Emp.: 35
Lawn Services
N.A.I.C.S.: 561730

THE SHERWIN-WILLIAMS COMPANY

101 W Prospect Ave, Cleveland, OH
44115-1075
Tel.: (216) 566-2000 OH
Web Site: https://www.sherwin-
williams.com
Year Founded: 1866
SHW—(NYSE)
Rev.: $23,051,900,000
Assets: $22,954,400,000
Liabilities: $19,238,600,000
Net Worth: $3,715,800,000
Earnings: $2,388,800,000
Emp.: 64,088
Fiscal Year-end: 12/31/23
Paints & Coatings Mfr, Whslr & Retailer
N.A.I.C.S.: 325510
John G. Morikis *(Exec Chm)*
Allen J. Mistysyn *(CFO & Sr VP-Fin)*
Justin T. Binns *(Pres-The Americas
Grp)*
Mary L. Garceau *(Gen Counsel, Sec
& Sr VP)*
Karl J. Jorgenrud *(Pres-Performance
Coatings Grp)*
James R. Jaye *(Sr VP-IR & Corp
Comm)*
Eric R. Swanson *(VP-IR)*
Jane M. Cronin *(Sr VP-Enterprise
Finance)*
Todd D. Rea *(Pres-Consumer Brands
Grp)*
Gregory P. Sofish *(Sr VP)*
Heidi G. Petz *(Pres & CEO)*

Subsidiaries:

CTS National Corporation (1)
101 Prospect Ave, Cleveland, OH 44115
Tel.: (216) 566-2000
Food Transportation Services
N.A.I.C.S.: 488490

Columbia Paint & Coatings (1)
112 N Haven St, Spokane, WA 99220
Tel.: (509) 535-0954
Web Site: http://www.columbiapaint.com
Sales Range: $50-74.9 Million
Emp.: 323
Paint, Industrial Finishes & Paint Related
Supplies Mfr, Distr & Retailer
N.A.I.C.S.: 325510

**Compania Sherwin-Williams, S.A. de
C.V.** (1)
Calle Pte 140 595 Industrial Vallejo, 02300,
Mexico, CDMX, Mexico (100%)
Tel.: (52) 5553331501
Web Site: https://www.sherwin.com.mx
Sales Range: $75-99.9 Million
Emp.: 270
Mfr & Sale of Paint
N.A.I.C.S.: 325510
Pablo Garcia Casas *(Gen Mgr)*

Duckback Products (1)
2644 Hegan Ln, Chico, CA 95928-9572
Tel.: (530) 343-3261
Web Site: http://www.superdeck.com
Sales Range: $10-24.9 Million
Emp.: 36
Outdoor Wood, Concrete & Composite Material Sealant & Preservation Products Mfr
N.A.I.C.S.: 325510

Dupli-Color Products Company (1)
101 W Prospect Ave Ste 722, Cleveland,
OH 44115
Tel.: (216) 566-1882
Web Site: http://www.duplicolor.com
Sales Range: $50-74.9 Million
Emp.: 200
Mfr of Automotive Paints
N.A.I.C.S.: 325510

Duron, Inc. (1)
10406 Tucker St, Beltsville, MD 20705-2201
Tel.: (301) 902-3090
Web Site: http://www.duron.com
Sales Range: $300-349.9 Million
Emp.: 1,800
Paints & Wallcoverings Mfr
N.A.I.C.S.: 424950

EPS B.V. (1)
Neon 13, 4751 XA, Oud Gastel, Netherlands
Tel.: (31) 180442266
Web Site: https://epsbv.com
Pump Installation Services
N.A.I.C.S.: 238290
Menno de Visser *(Mgr-Strategic Acct Sls)*

Euronavy - Tintas Maritimas e Industriais S.A. (1)
aicep BlueBiz - Estrada do Vale da Rosa,
2910-845, Setubal, Portugal
Tel.: (351) 265720450
Web Site:
 https://engineering.euronavyengineer
ing.com
Paint Coatings Research & Development
Services
N.A.I.C.S.: 541715

Geocel Limited (1)
Western Wood Way Langage Science Park,
Plympton, PL7 5BG, United Kingdom
Tel.: (44) 1752334350
Web Site: http://www.geocel.co.uk
Chemical Mfr & Distr
N.A.I.C.S.: 325199

**Guangdong Huarun Paints Co.,
Ltd.** (1)
No 7 Wusha Section Shunfan Road,
Shunde District, Foshan, Guangdong,
China
Tel.: (86) 95105517
Web Site: https://www.huarun.com
Paint & Coating Mfr
N.A.I.C.S.: 325510

Guardsman Australia Pty Limited (1)
13 Columbia Way, Norwest Business Park,
Baulkham Hills, 2153, NSW, Australia

The Sherwin-Williams Company—(Continued)

Tel.: (61) 800249252
Web Site:
https://www.guardsmanaustralia.com
Furniture Care Product Mfr & Distr
N.A.I.C.S.: 325612

Guardsman Industries Limited (1)
152 Brook Drive Milton Park, Oxfordshire,
Abingdon, OX14 4SD, United Kingdom
Tel.: (44) 1235444700
Web Site: https://guardsman.co.uk
Paint & Coating Mfr
N.A.I.C.S.: 325510

ICA Deutschland Lacke GmbH (1)
Industriestrasse 52, 48629, Metelen, Germany
Tel.: (49) 25564049400
Web Site: https://www.icadeutschland.de
Paint Mfr & Distr
N.A.I.C.S.: 325510

ICA Polska Sp. z o.o. (1)
Ul Gliniana 10, 97-300, Piotrkow Trybunalski, Poland
Tel.: (48) 446453080
Web Site: https://www.icapolska.pl
Emp.: 131
Paint Mfr & Distr
N.A.I.C.S.: 325510

Inver Industrial Coatings Srl (1)
Berceni Street 96 Corp A aet 19 ap A19 03
sector 4, 041918, Bucharest, Romania
Tel.: (40) 724275636
Industrial Coatings Supplier
N.A.I.C.S.: 424950

Inver Polska Spolka Z o.o. (1)
Ul Metalowcow 49, 39-200, Debica, Poland
Tel.: (48) 146584100
Paint Mfr & Distr
N.A.I.C.S.: 325510

Invercolore Bologna Srl (1)
13 Via IV Novembre, 40061, Minerbio, Italy
Tel.: (39) 0516606191
Paint Distr
N.A.I.C.S.: 424950

Invercolor Toscana Srl (1)
Via Comunale Tiglio 279, 55012, Capannori, Italy
Tel.: (39) 0583983319
Web Site: http://www.inver.com
Paint Distr
N.A.I.C.S.: 424950

Isva Vernici Srl (1)
Circonvallazione Esterna 9 TO, 10043, Orbassano, Torino, Italy
Tel.: (39) 0119034260
Paint Distr
N.A.I.C.S.: 424950

**Jiangsu Pulanna Coating Co.,
Ltd.** (1)
No 20 Huashan Rd, Xinbei, Changzhou,
China
Tel.: (86) 51985129777
Paint & Coating Mfr
N.A.I.C.S.: 325510

Klumpp Coatings do Brasil Ltd. (1)
Rua Bom Jesus do Iguape no 4780 Boqueirao 81, Curitiba, 730-020, Brazil
Tel.: (55) 4132877007
Industrial Coatings Supplier
N.A.I.C.S.: 424950

ML Campbell & Fabulon (1)
224 Catherine St, PO Box 218, Fort Erie,
L2A 1J7, ON, Canada (100%)
Tel.: (905) 871-2724
Web Site: https://www.mlcampbell.com
Sales Range: $25-49.9 Million
Emp.: 65
Mfr of Industrial & Special Purpose Coatings & Adhesives
N.A.I.C.S.: 325510

Minwax Company (1)
101 Prospect Ave, Cleveland, OH
44115 (100%)
Tel.: (201) 818-7500
Web Site: https://www.minwax.com
Sales Range: $50-74.9 Million
Emp.: 60
Wood Care Products Mfr & Marketer

N.A.I.C.S.: 444120

Oskar Nolte GmbH (1)
Im Obrock 55-61, 32278, Kirchlengern, Germany
Tel.: (49) 522371194
Web Site: https://www.oskar-nolte.de
Paint & Coating Mfr
N.A.I.C.S.: 325510

Oy Sherwin-Williams Finland Ab (1)
Lyhtytie 17, 00750, Helsinki, Finland
Tel.: (358) 102183600
Chemical Mfr & Distr
N.A.I.C.S.: 325199
Henrik Karlsson (Controller-Bus)

**P.T. Friedrich Klumpp
Woodcoatings** (1)
Kawasan Industri Candi Jalan Gatot Subroto Blok 23B No 2B, Semarang, 50185,
Indonesia
Tel.: (62) 247627374
Industrial Coatings Supplier
N.A.I.C.S.: 424950

Pratt & Lambert Paints (1)
101 Prospect Ave, Cleveland, OH 44115-
1093
Web Site: https://www.prattandlambert.com
Sales Range: $100-124.9 Million
Emp.: 150
Paint & Varnish Mfr
N.A.I.C.S.: 561499

Ronseal Limited (1)
Thorncliffe Park, Chapeltown, Sheffield, S35
2YP, United Kingdom
Tel.: (44) 1142409469
Wall Care Services
N.A.I.C.S.: 444120

SWIMC, Inc. (1)
850 Library Ave Ste 204 H, Newark, DE
19711
Tel.: (302) 738-3548
Web Site: http://www.swimcinc.com
Sales Range: $10-24.9 Million
Emp.: 5
Holding Company; Patents & Trademarks
N.A.I.C.S.: 524210

**Sherwin Williams Colombia
S.A.S.** (1)
Autopista Medellin Kilometro 7, Funza, Colombia
Tel.: (57) 17454515
Paint & Coating Mfr
N.A.I.C.S.: 325510

**Sherwin-Williams (Shanghai)
Limited** (1)
Building 11 Shibei One Center NO 1401
JiangChang Road, Jingan District, Shanghai, 200072, China
Tel.: (86) 2160560999
Web Site: https://sherwin.com.cn
Emp.: 3,500
Paint & Coating Mfr
N.A.I.C.S.: 325510

**Sherwin-Williams (Thailand) Co.,
Ltd.** (1)
700/254 Moo 1 Amata Nakorn Industrial
Estate, Bankao, Phan Thong, 20160, Panthong, Thailand
Tel.: (66) 38465220
Paint & Coating Mfr
N.A.I.C.S.: 325510
Bent Kidmose (Application Mgr)

**Sherwin-Williams (West Indies)
Ltd.** (1)
White Marl St Catherine, PO Box 35, Kingston, Jamaica (100%)
Tel.: (876) 98427879
Web Site: https://www.sherwin-
williams.com.jm
Sales Range: $25-49.9 Million
Emp.: 70
Mfr of Paints, Varnishes, Lacquers, Enamels & Allied Products
N.A.I.C.S.: 325510

**Sherwin-Williams Argentina I.y
C.S.A.** (1)
Hipolito Yrigoyen 1579, B1702FWW, Ciudadela, Buenos Aires, Argentina
Tel.: (54) 1144699700
Web Site: https://www.sherwin.com.ar

Paint & Wallpaper Stores
N.A.I.C.S.: 444120

**Sherwin-Williams Automotive Finishes
Corporation** (1)
4440 Warrensville Ctr Rd, Warrensville
Heights, OH 44128
Tel.: (216) 332-8330
Web Site: http://www.sherwin-
automotive.com
Sales Range: $150-199.9 Million
Emp.: 2,600
Mfr of Automotive Refinish Products
N.A.I.C.S.: 441330

Sherwin-Williams Balkan S.R.L. (1)
DN 59 KM 8 550M Chisoda, PO Box 513,
Timis, 307221, Timisoara, Romania
Tel.: (40) 256420320
Web Site: http://www.sherwin-williams.com
Emp.: 20
Chemicals Mfr
N.A.I.C.S.: 325199

Sherwin-Williams Bel (1)
47 48 office 12 14 building liter A1-2/p Ozertso vill, PO Box 34, 223021, Minsk, Belarus
Tel.: (375) 175076774
Chemical Mfr & Distr
N.A.I.C.S.: 325199

Sherwin-Williams Benelux NV (1)
Ambachtsweg 9, 9820, Merelbeke, Belgium
Tel.: (32) 92524364
Web Site: http://www.sherwinwilliams.com
Emp.: 10
Chemical Mfr & Distr
N.A.I.C.S.: 325199

Sherwin-Williams Chile S.A. (1)
Av La Divisa 0689, San Bernardo, Santiago, Chile
Tel.: (56) 6002001222
Web Site: https://www.sherwin.cl
Paint & Coating Mfr
N.A.I.C.S.: 325510

**Sherwin-Williams Co. - Diversified
Brands Division** (1)
101 W Prospect Ave NW, Cleveland, OH
44115
Tel.: (216) 566-2000
Web Site: http://www.sherwinwilliams.com
Sales Range: $200-249.9 Million
Emp.: 2,800
Mfr, Distributor & Seller of Aerosol Custom
Loaders & Industrial Aerosol Specialties,
Paint Applicators
N.A.I.C.S.: 325510

**Sherwin-Williams Co. - Industrial
Coatings Division** (1)
630 E 13th St, Andover, KS 67002
Tel.: (316) 733-1361
Web Site: http://www.sherwin.com
Sales Range: $75-99.9 Million
Emp.: 149
Mfr of Industrial Specialties
N.A.I.C.S.: 332812

Sherwin-Williams Coatings India Private Limited (1)
158 1st Floor Dani Corporate Park Vidya
Nagari Marg Kalina, Santacruz East, Mumbai, 400098, Maharashtra, India
Tel.: (91) 2266113366
Emp.: 300
Paint & Coating Mfr
N.A.I.C.S.: 325510
Arun Hedge (Mng Dir)

**Sherwin-Williams Consumer
Group** (1)
101 W Prospect Ave W, Cleveland, OH
44115-1093 (100%)
Tel.: (216) 566-2000
Web Site: http://www.sherwin-williams.com
Sales Range: $25-49.9 Million
Emp.: 1,800
Mfr of Rubberset Paint Applications
N.A.I.C.S.: 325520
Christopher M. Connor (Chm)

**Sherwin-Williams Czech Republic
spol. s.r.o.** (1)
Druzstevni 56, 594-01, Velke Mezirici,
Czech Republic
Tel.: (420) 566501411
Paint & Coating Mfr

N.A.I.C.S.: 325510

Sherwin-Williams Denmark A/S (1)
Nystedvej 5, 7400, Herning, Denmark
Tel.: (45) 97216111
Emp.: 20
Chemical Distr
N.A.I.C.S.: 424690

**Sherwin-Williams Deutschland
GmbH** (1)
Paul-Gerhardt-Str 31, 42389, Wuppertal,
Germany
Tel.: (49) 20257470
Paint & Coating Mfr
N.A.I.C.S.: 325510

**Sherwin-Williams Diversified Brands
Limited** (1)
Thorncliffe Park Chapeltown, Sheffield, S35
2YP, United Kingdom
Tel.: (44) 1142467171
Paint & Coating Mfr
N.A.I.C.S.: 325510
Rhonda House (Mgr-Pur)

**Sherwin-Williams France Finishes
SAS** (1)
Rue Boileau, Z I les Pres l'Elie, 91530,
Saint-Cheron, France
Tel.: (33) 160811300
Web Site: https://www.sayerlack.fr
Emp.: 357
Paint & Coating Mfr
N.A.I.C.S.: 325510

Sherwin-Williams Ireland Ltd. (1)
Unit 644 Jordanstown Road, Aerodrome
Business Park Rathcoole CO, Dublin,
D24XK40, Ireland
Tel.: (353) 14019304
Emp.: 18
Industrial Wood Coatings Mfr
N.A.I.C.S.: 324122

Sherwin-Williams Italy S.r.l. (1)
Via del Fiffo 12, Pianoro, 40065, Bologna,
Italy
Tel.: (39) 051770511
Web Site: https://www.sherwin-williams.it
Paint & Coating Mfr
N.A.I.C.S.: 325510

Sherwin-Williams Jersey Limited (1)
748 Communipaw Ave, Jersey City, NJ
07304-1708
Tel.: (201) 946-7817
Industrial Coatings Supplier
N.A.I.C.S.: 424950

Sherwin-Williams Norway AS (1)
Marenlundveien 2, Postboks 70, 2021,
Skedsmokorset, Norway
Tel.: (47) 63871020
Paint & Coating Mfr
N.A.I.C.S.: 325510
Per Egil Salicath (Gen Mgr)

Sherwin-Williams Paint Group (1)
399 Garrisonville Rd, Stafford, VA 22554-
1578
Tel.: (540) 659-0585
Web Site: http://www.sherwinwilliams.com
Sales Range: Less than $1 Million
Emp.: 7
Paint, Glass, And Wallpaper Stores
N.A.I.C.S.: 444120

**Sherwin-Williams Paint Stores
Group** (1)
2021 W 25th St, Cleveland, OH 44113-4113
Tel.: (216) 589-9583
Web Site: http://www.sherwin-williams.com
Sales Range: $1-4.9 Billion
Emp.: 3,000
Architectural Coatings, Industrial Finishes,
Wallcoverings, Floorcoverings, Window
Treatments, Paint Sundries & Spray Equipment
N.A.I.C.S.: 424950
Allen Mistysyn (CEO & Sr VP)

Branch (Non-US):

**Sherwin-Williams Paint Stores
Group** (2)
170 Brunel Rd, Mississauga, L4Z 1T5, ON,
Canada (100%)
Tel.: (905) 507-3966
Web Site: http://www.sherwin-williams.com

Sales Range: $50-74.9 Million
Emp.: 15
Wholesale For Paints
N.A.I.C.S.: 424990

Sherwin-Williams Peru S.R.L. **(1)**
Jr Comunidad Industrial 298 - Urb La Villa,
Chorrillos, Peru
Tel.: (51) 12512929
Web Site: http://www.sherwin.com.pe
Paint & Coating Mfr
N.A.I.C.S.: 325510

Sherwin-Williams Poland Sp. z
o.o **(1)**
Gluchowo Ul Teczowa 2, 62-052, Ko-
morniki, Poland
Tel.: (48) 616244500
Emp.: 50
Paint & Coating Mfr
N.A.I.C.S.: 325510

Sherwin-Williams Protective & Marine
Coatings **(1)**
Tower Works Kestor Street, Bolton, BL2
2AL, United Kingdom
Tel.: (44) 1204521771
Web Site: http://protectiveemea.sherwin-
williams.com
Emp.: 270
Paint & Coating Mfr & Distr
N.A.I.C.S.: 325510

Sherwin-Williams Services (Malaysia)
Sdn. Bhd. **(1)**
No 32 Jalan Instri USJ 1 47600 USJ 1/4
Taman Peridunstrian, 47600, Subang Jaya,
Selangor, Malaysia
Tel.: (60) 380241834
Paint & Coating Mfr
N.A.I.C.S.: 325510
Manchulla Sre Kalamelu *(Mgr-HR & Admin)*

Sherwin-Williams Spain Coatings
S.L. **(1)**
C/Aldaya 9 - Poligono Industrial Beniparrell,
Beniparrell, Valencia, Spain
Tel.: (34) 961218980
Paint Mfr & Distr
N.A.I.C.S.: 325510

Sherwin-Williams Sweden AB **(1)**
Industrigatan 5, 195 60, Arlandastad, Swe-
den
Tel.: (46) 38126100
Web Site: http://oem.sherwin-williams.com
Wood Surface Treatment Product Mfr
N.A.I.C.S.: 325510

Subsidiary (Non-US):

Sherwin-Williams Czech spol.
s.r.o **(2)**
Druzstevni 56, 594 01, Velke Mezirici,
Czech Republic
Tel.: (420) 566501411
Web Site: http://www.sherwin-williams.eu
Emp.: 30
Paint & Varnishes Whslr
N.A.I.C.S.: 424950

Sherwin-Williams UK Coatings
Limited **(1)**
A1 Business Park, Knottingley, WF11 0BU,
United Kingdom
Tel.: (44) 1977673363
Paint & Coating Mfr
N.A.I.C.S.: 325510

Sherwin-Williams Uruguay S.A. **(1)**
Avenida Italia, 3950, Montevideo, Uruguay
Tel.: (598) 25079835
Web Site: https://www.sherwin.com.uy
Paint & Coating Mfr
N.A.I.C.S.: 325510

Sherwin-Williams do Brasil Industria e
Comercio Limitada **(1)**
Av Ibirama 480 - Sao Judas Tadeu, Taboao
da Serra, Sao Paulo, 06785-300,
Brazil **(100%)**
Tel.: (55) 1121375000
Web Site: https://www.sherwin.com.br
Mfr & Retailer of Paint
N.A.I.C.S.: 325510

Syntema I Vaggeryd AB **(1)**
Garahovsvagen, 567 32, Vaggeryd, Sweden
Tel.: (46) 39312730
Web Site: https://www.syntema.nu

Paint & Coating Mfr
N.A.I.C.S.: 325510

The Sherwin-Williams Co. - Distribu-
tion Service Center - Waco **(1)**
2700 Texas Central Pkwy, Waco, TX 76712
Tel.: (254) 666-7600
Emp.: 400
Paint & Associated Products Distr Center
for Retail Stores in South Central Region
N.A.I.C.S.: 493190
Brad Glasson *(Dir-Distr)*

The Sherwin-Williams Co. - San Di-
ego (Frazee Paint) Plant **(1)**
6625 Miramar Rd, San Diego, CA 92121-
2508
Tel.: (858) 453-6260
Web Site: https://www.sherwin-williams.com
Paint Mfr & Whslr
N.A.I.C.S.: 325510
David Jerge *(Mgr-Quality Assurance)*

The Valspar Corporation **(1)**
1101 S 3rd St, Minneapolis, MN 55415-
1211
Tel.: (612) 851-7000
Web Site: https://www.coatings.com
Paints, Coatings, Resins & Colorants Mfr
N.A.I.C.S.: 325510
John G. Morikis *(Pres)*

Subsidiary (Non-US):

Dongguan Lilly Paint Industries
Limited **(2)**
XinTang District Da Ling Shan Town, Dal-
ingshan Town, Dongguan, 523822, China
Tel.: (86) 13826994036
Web Site: http://www.valspar-asia.com
Paints Mfr
N.A.I.C.S.: 325510

Subsidiary (Domestic):

Engineered Polymer Solutions,
Inc. **(2)**
1400 N State St, Marengo, IL 60152
Tel.: (815) 568-3020
Web Site: http://www.epscca.com
Resins & Colorants Supplier
N.A.I.C.S.: 325510

Subsidiary (Domestic):

EPS/CCA **(3)**
1215 Nelson Blvd, Rockford, IL 61104
Tel.: (815) 987-3700
Web Site: http://www.epscca.com
Water-Based Colorants, Alkyd Emulsions &
Urethanes Mfr
N.A.I.C.S.: 325510

Subsidiary (Non-US):

Inver S.p.A. **(2)**
Via di Corticella 205, 40128, Bologna, Italy
Tel.: (39) 0516380411
Web Site: http://www.inver.com
Industrial Coating & Powder Mfr
N.A.I.C.S.: 325510

Subsidiary (Non-US):

Inver East Med S.A. **(3)**
Sorou 22 Maroussi, 15125, Athens, Greece
Tel.: (30) 21061099304
Web Site: https://www.inver.gr
Industrial Coating & Powder
N.A.I.C.S.: 325510

Inver Frane SAS **(3)**
2 Rue Jean Devaux, PO Box 88, 79102,
Thouars, France
Tel.: (33) 5499602500
Web Site: http://www.inverfrance.fr
Industrial Coating & Powder Mfr
N.A.I.C.S.: 325510

Inver GmbH **(3)**
Oskar-Von-Miller-Str 3A, Essenbach-
Altheim, 84051, Landshut, Germany
Tel.: (49) 8703906583
Web Site: http://www.inver.com
Industrial Coating & Powder Mfr
N.A.I.C.S.: 325510

Inver Polska Sp.z.o.o. **(3)**
UL Metalowcow 49, 39-200, Debica, Poland
Tel.: (48) 146809020
Web Site: http://www.inver.com

Industrial Coating & Powder Mfr
N.A.I.C.S.: 325510

Subsidiary (Non-US):

Lilly Industries (Shanghai)
Limited **(2)**
838 Jiaxin Highway Jiading District Malu
Town, Jiading District, Shanghai, 201818,
China
Tel.: (86) 2160865888
Web Site: http://www.valspar-asia.com
Paints Mfr
N.A.I.C.S.: 325510

Subsidiary (Domestic):

Plasti-Kote Company Inc. **(2)**
1000 Lake Rd, Medina, OH 44256
Tel.: (330) 725-4511
Web Site: http://www.plasti-kote.com
Aerosol Paint & Enamel Products Mfr
N.A.I.C.S.: 325510

Subsidiary (Non-US):

The Valspar (Asia) Corporation
Limited **(2)**
Rm D 27/F Kings Tower LAI CHI KOK, Tsim
Sha Tsui, Kowloon, China (Hong Kong)
Tel.: (852) 31871600
Paint Whslr & Mfr
N.A.I.C.S.: 424950

The Valspar (Finland) Corporation
Oy **(2)**
Tel.: (358) 207501777
Web Site:
https://www.valsparcoileurope.com
Paint & Coil Coating Mfr
N.A.I.C.S.: 325510

The Valspar (France) Corporation,
S.A.S. **(2)**
14 Rue Chanay CS 70 001, Boite Postale
51, 71700, Tournus, France
Tel.: (33) 385271800
Web Site: http://www.valspareurope.com
Paints Mfr
N.A.I.C.S.: 325510

The Valspar (H.K.) Corporation
Limited **(2)**
2101-02 21/F Vicwood Plaza, 199 Des
Voeux Road, Central, China (Hong Kong)
Tel.: (852) 31871600
Paints & Coatings Mfr
N.A.I.C.S.: 325510

The Valspar (Nantes) Corporation,
S.A.S. **(2)**
25 Blvd du Marechal A-Juin, Boite Postale
82219, BP 82219, 44022, Nantes, Cedex
01, France
Tel.: (33) 240959898
Web Site: http://www.valspareurope.com
Packaging Coatings Mfr
N.A.I.C.S.: 325510

The Valspar (South Africa) Corpora-
tion (Pty) Ltd. **(2)**
255 Lansdowne Road Jacobs, Durban,
4052, South Africa
Tel.: (27) 314598400
Paints Mfr
N.A.I.C.S.: 325510

The Valspar (Switzerland) Corpora-
tion AG **(2)**
Rosengartenstrasse 25, 8608, Bubikon,
Switzerland
Tel.: (41) 55 253 1515
Web Site: http://www.valsparpackaging.com
Paints Mfr
N.A.I.C.S.: 325510

The Valspar (UK) Corporation
Limited **(2)**
Avenue One Station Lane, Witney, OX28
4XR, Oxon, United Kingdom
Tel.: (44) 1993707400
Web Site: http://www.valsparpackaging.com
Packaging Coatings Mfr
N.A.I.C.S.: 325510

The Valspar Corporation
Limitada **(2)**
Estrada Dos Casa 5050 - Portco B Sco
Bernardo Do Campo, Sao Bernardo do
Campo, Sao Paulo, 09840-900, Brazil

Tel.: (55) 1141364651
Web Site: http://www.valspar.com.br
Paint Distr
N.A.I.C.S.: 424950

Valspar Aries Coatings, S. de R.L. de
C.V. **(2)**
Carretera Monterrey - Nuevo Laredo KM 37
1, 65550, Cienega de Flores, Nuevo Leon,
Mexico
Tel.: (52) 8181242000
Web Site: http://www.valsparpackaging.com
Paint Distr
N.A.I.C.S.: 424950

Valspar Automotive Australia Pty
Limited **(2)**
U 11/8 Kerta Road, Kincumber, 2251, NSW,
Australia
Tel.: (61) 243684054
Web Site: https://www.valsparauto.com
Paint & Coating Distr
N.A.I.C.S.: 424950

Valspar D.o.o **(2)**
Bulevar Arsenija Carnojevica 102/6, 11070,
Novi Beograd, Serbia
Tel.: (381) 114040507
Web Site: https://www.valspar.rs
Paint Distr
N.A.I.C.S.: 424950

Valspar Inc. **(2)**
1636 Shawson Drive, Mississauga, L4W
1N7, ON, Canada
Tel.: (888) 234-5790
Web Site: http://www.valspar.com
Industrial Coating Mfr
N.A.I.C.S.: 325510

Valspar Industries (Ireland) Ltd. **(2)**
Willowfield Rd Ballinamore, Leitrim, Ireland
Tel.: (353) 719645077
Paint Distr
N.A.I.C.S.: 424950

Valspar Industries GmbH **(2)**
Friedensstrasse 40, 52249, Eschweiler,
Germany
Tel.: (49) 24037090
Web Site: http://www.valspareurope.com
Industrial Coating Mfr
N.A.I.C.S.: 325510

Valspar Paint (Australia) Pty Ltd **(2)**
L 4 2 Burbank Pl Norwest Business Park,
Baulkham Hills, 2153, NSW, Australia
Tel.: (61) 288673333
Web Site: https://wattyl.com.au
Paint & Coating Mfr
N.A.I.C.S.: 325510

Valspar Powder Coatings Ltd. **(2)**
177 Argyle Street Nechells, Birmingham, B7
5TE, West Midlands, United
Kingdom **(100%)**
Tel.: (44) 1213285227
Powder Coating Mfr
N.A.I.C.S.: 332812

Subsidiary (Domestic):

Valspar Refinish, Inc. **(2)**
210 Crosby St, Picayune, MS 39466
Tel.: (601) 798-4731
Web Site: http://www.valspar.com
Refinishing Products Mfr
N.A.I.C.S.: 325180

Subsidiary (Non-US):

Valspar Rock Co., Ltd. **(2)**
5F Rock Paint Building 37-2 2-chome Mina-
misuna, Koto-ku, Tokyo, 136-0076, Japan
Tel.: (81) 336488811
Paints Mfr
N.A.I.C.S.: 325510

Wattyl Limited **(2)**
Level 3 2 Burbank Place, Norwest,
Baulkham Hills, 2153, NSW, Australia
Tel.: (61) 287132101
Web Site: https://www.wattyl.com.au
Mfr of Paints, Lacquers, Wood Stains, Clear
Finishes, Fillers, Sealers, Automotive Coat-
ings, Protective & Marine Coatings & Line-
Marking Systems
N.A.I.C.S.: 325510

Subsidiary (Non-US):

Wattyl (NZ) Ltd. **(3)**

The Sherwin-Williams Company—(Continued)

2-14 Patiki Road, Avondale, Auckland, 1140, New Zealand **(100%)**
Tel.: (64) 8008257727
Web Site: https://www.wattyl.co.nz
Paints & Coatings Mfr & Whslr
N.A.I.C.S.: 325510

Subsidiary (Domestic):

Wattyl Australia Pty Ltd **(3)**
2-44 Graingers Road, West Footscray, 3012, VIC, Australia **(100%)**
Tel.: (61) 396881111
Web Site: http://www.wattyl.com.au
Paints & Coatings Mfr
N.A.I.C.S.: 325510

Branch (Domestic):

Wattyl Australia Pty Ltd **(3)**
65 Railway Parade, Rocklea, 4106, QLD, Australia **(100%)**
Tel.: (61) 738532888
Web Site: http://www.wattyl.com.au
Paints & Coatings Mfr
N.A.I.C.S.: 325510

Subsidiary (Domestic):

Wattyl Australia Pty Ltd **(3)**
211 Collier Road, Bayswater, 6053, WA, Australia **(100%)**
Tel.: (61) 894498888
Web Site: http://www.wattyl.com.au
Paints & Coatings Mfr
N.A.I.C.S.: 325510

UAB Sherwin-Williams Baltic **(1)**
Siltnamiu g 26, LT-04130, Vilnius, Lithuania
Tel.: (370) 52402420
Paint & Coating Mfr
N.A.I.C.S.: 325510

UAB Sherwin-Williams Lietuva **(1)**
Siltnamiu g 26, 04130, Vilnius, Lithuania
Tel.: (370) 52402420
Paint & Coating Distr
N.A.I.C.S.: 325510
Donatas Rinkevicius *(Mgr)*

Valspar B.V. **(1)**
Zuiveringweg 89, 8243 PE, Lelystad, Netherlands
Tel.: (31) 320292200
Web Site: https://www.valsparindustrialmix.com
Paint & Coating Mfr
N.A.I.C.S.: 325510

Valspar D.o.o Beograd **(1)**
Bulevar Arsenija Carnojevica 102/6, 11070, Novi Beograd, Serbia
Tel.: (381) 114040507
Web Site: https://valspar.rs
Industrial Coatings Supplier
N.A.I.C.S.: 424950

Valspar Mexicana, S.A. de C.V. **(1)**
Carretera Monterrey Nuevo Laredo Km 37 1 Parque Industrial, 65550, Cienega de Flores, Nuevo Leon, Mexico
Tel.: (52) 8181242000
Web Site: https://www.valsparrefinish.mx
Paint & Coating Mfr
N.A.I.C.S.: 325510

Vantaco Oy **(1)**
Malmarintie 20, 01380, Vantaa, Finland
Tel.: (358) 207501500
Paint Mfr & Distr
N.A.I.C.S.: 325510

ZAO Sherwin-Williams **(1)**
Ul Stromynka 4 korp 1 office 304, 107014, Moscow, Russia
Tel.: (7) 495 777 2324
Web Site: http://www.sherwin.ru
Emp.: 15
Paint & Coating Distr
N.A.I.C.S.: 424950

THE SHYFT GROUP, INC.
41280 Bridge St, Novi, MI 48375
Tel.: (517) 543-6400   MI
Web Site:
   https://www.theshyftgroup.com
Year Founded: 1975

SHYF—(NASDAQ)
Rev.: $872,198,000
Assets: $530,049,000
Liabilities: $277,883,000
Net Worth: $252,166,000
Earnings: $6,496,000
Emp.; 3,000
Fiscal Year-end: 12/31/23
Holding Company; Specialty Commercial Vehicle Chassis Designer & Mfr
N.A.I.C.S.: 551112
Scott M. Ocholik *(Chief Acctg Officer, VP & Controller)*
John Dunn *(Pres & CEO)*
Jonathan C. Douyard *(CFO)*
Randy Wilson *(VP-IR & Treasury)*
Andy Anderson *(CIO)*
Todd Heavin *(COO)*
Joshua Sherbin *(Chief Compliance Officer)*
Carrie Wright *(CMO)*
Sydney Lepora *(Dir-Corp Comm)*
Jacob Farmer *(Pres-Fleet Vehicles & Svcs)*

Subsidiaries:

Fortress Resources, LLC **(1)**
24200 S Main St, Carson, CA 90745
Tel.: (562) 633-9951
Web Site: http://www.royaltruckbody.com
Motor Vehicle Body Mfr
N.A.I.C.S.: 336211

Strobes-R-Us, Inc. **(1)**
2681 Hammondville Rd, Pompano Beach, FL 33069
Tel.: (954) 946-9955
Web Site: https://www.strobesrus.com
Miscellaneous Store Retailers
N.A.I.C.S.: 459999

Utilimaster Holdings, Inc. **(1)**
603 Earthway Blvd, Bristol, IN 46507
Tel.: (574) 848-2000
Web Site: http://www.utilimaster.com
Sales Range: $250-299.9 Million
Emp.: 930
Truck & Van Bodies Mfr
N.A.I.C.S.: 336211

XL Hybrids, Inc. **(1)**
145 Newton St, Boston, MA 02135-1508
Tel.: (617) 718-0329
Web Site: http://www.xlhybrids.com
Motor Vehicle Transmission & Power Train Parts Manufacturing
N.A.I.C.S.: 336350
Thomas J. Hynes III *(Founder, Chief Strategy Officer, Treas & CEO)*
Tod Hynes *(Founder)*

THE SIMPLY GOOD FOODS COMPANY
1225 17th St Ste 1000, Denver, CO 80202
Tel.: (303) 633-2840   DE
Web Site:
   https://www.thesimplygoodfoods company.com
Year Founded: 2017
SMPL—(NASDAQ)
Rev.: $1,331,321,000
Assets: $2,436,144,000
Liabilities: $708,658,000
Net Worth: $1,727,486,000
Earnings: $139,309,000
Emp.: 316
Fiscal Year-end: 08/31/24
Nutritional Food Product Mfr & Distr
N.A.I.C.S.: 311999
Joseph E. Scalzo *(Vice Chm)*
David J. West *(Bd of Dirs & Vice Chm)*
Geoff E. Tanner *(Pres & CEO)*
James Marshall Kilts *(Chm)*
Shaun Mara *(CFO)*
Timothy Kraft *(Chief Legal Officer & Sec)*
Jeremy Lvie *(Chief Product Tech Officer)*

Stamati Arakas *(Sr VP-ECommerce)*
Stuart Heflin *(Sr VP & Gen Mgr-Quest)*
Ryan Thomas *(Sr VP & Gen Mgr-Atkins)*
Amy Held *(Chief HR Officer)*
Alex Wittenberg *(Sr VP-Corporate Strategy & Business Development)*
Timothy A. Matthews *(Chief Acctg Officer, VP & Controller)*
Jason Bendure *(Sr VP-Operations)*
Mark Pogharian *(VP-IR, Treasury, and Bus Dev)*

Subsidiaries:

Atkins Nutritionals, Inc. **(1)**
1225 17th St Ste 1000, Denver, CO 80202
Tel.: (303) 633-2840
Web Site: http://www.atkins.com
Food Mfr & Distr
N.A.I.C.S.: 311999
Joseph E. Scalzo *(Pres & CEO)*
Collette Heimowitz *(VP-Nutrition Comm & Education)*

Quest Nutrition, LLC **(1)**
777 S Aviation Blvd Ste 100, El Segundo, CA 90245
Web Site: https://www.questnutrition.com
Snack Food Mfr & Distr
N.A.I.C.S.: 311919

Wellness Foods Inc. **(1)**
355 Adelaide St West Ground Floor, Toronto, M5V 1S2, ON, Canada
Web Site: http://www.simplyprotein.ca
Nutritional Food Product Mfr & Distr
N.A.I.C.S.: 311999

THE SINGING MACHINE COMPANY, INC.
6301 NW 5th Way Ste 2900, Fort Lauderdale, FL 33309
Tel.: (954) 596-1000   DE
Web Site:
   https://www.singingmachine.com
Year Founded: 1982
MICS—(NASDAQ)
Rev.: $39,299,280
Assets: $16,648,597
Liabilities: $6,317,552
Net Worth: $10,331,045
Earnings: ($4,638,462)
Emp.: 37
Fiscal Year-end: 03/31/23
Karaoke Machine Developer & Distr
N.A.I.C.S.: 334610
Philip Lau *(Chm)*
Eddie Steele *(Founder)*

Subsidiaries:

SMC (Comercial Offshore de Macau) Limitada **(1)**
Avenida da Praia Grande No 371, Edificio Comercial Keng Ou, 11 andar C, Macau, China (Macau)
Tel.: (853) 28717000
Karaoke Machine Mfr
N.A.I.C.S.: 334111

THE SOUTHERN BANC COMPANY, INC.
221 S 6th St, Gadsden, AL 35901
Tel.: (256) 543-3860   DE
Web Site: https://www.sobanco.com
SRNN—(OTCIQ)
Rev.: $5,376,874
Assets: $103,302,095
Liabilities: $90,953,947
Net Worth: $12,348,148
Earnings: $314,020
Emp.: 31
Fiscal Year-end: 06/30/20
Offices of Bank Holding Companies
N.A.I.C.S.: 551111
Gates Little *(Chm, Pres & CEO)*

Subsidiaries:

The Southern Bank Company **(1)**

221 S 6th St, Gadsden, AL 35901 **(100%)**
Tel.: (256) 543-3860
Web Site: http://www.sobanco.com
Sales Range: $1-9.9 Million
Emp.: 20
Banking Services
N.A.I.C.S.: 522110
Gates Little *(Chm, Pres & CEO)*
Teresa Elkins *(VP)*

THE SOUTHERN COMPANY
30 Ivan Allen Jr Blvd NW, Atlanta, GA 30308
Tel.: (404) 506-0965   DE
Web Site:
   https://www.southerncompany.com
Year Founded: 1945
SO—(NYSE)
Rev.: $25,253,000,000
Assets: $139,331,000,000
Liabilities: $104,106,000,000
Net Worth: $35,225,000,000
Earnings: $3,976,000,000
Emp.: 28,100
Fiscal Year-end: 12/31/23
Holding Company
N.A.I.C.S.: 551112
Bryan D. Anderson *(Pres-External Affairs & Exec VP)*
Stanley W. Connally Jr. *(Exec VP-Ops)*
Christopher C. Womack *(Chm, Pres & CEO)*
Myra C. Bierria *(Sec & VP)*
Ann P. Daiss *(Chief Acctg Officer & Comptroller)*
Chris Cummiskey *(Chief Comml & Customer Solutions Officer & Exec VP)*
Martin Davis *(CIO & Exec VP)*
James Y. Kerr II *(Chief Compliance Officer, Chief Legal Officer & Exec VP)*
Sloane Drake *(Chief HR Officer)*
Sterling Spainhour *(Chief Legal Officer)*

Subsidiaries:

Alabama Power Company **(1)**
600 N 18th St, Birmingham, AL 35203 **(100%)**
Tel.: (205) 257-1000
Web Site: http://www.alabamapower.com
Rev.: $7,817,000,000
Assets: $34,970,000,000
Liabilities: $23,283,000,000
Net Worth: $11,687,000,000
Earnings: $1,351,000,000
Emp.: 6,100
Fiscal Year-end: 12/31/2022
Electric Utility Services
N.A.I.C.S.: 221121
Moses H. Feagin *(CFO, Treas & Exec VP)*
James P. Heilbron *(Sr VP)*
Zeke W. Smith *(Exec VP-External Affairs)*
R. Scott Moore *(Sr VP-Power Delivery)*
Jonathan Porter *(Sr VP-Customer Ops)*
Tony Smoke *(Sr VP-Mktg & Economic Dev)*
Jeff Peoples *(CEO)*
Alexia B. Borden *(Gen Counsel & Sr VP)*
Mark S. Crews *(VP-Western Div)*
Ashley Robinette *(VP-PR)*
Leslie D. Sanders *(VP-Southern Div)*
Terry Smiley *(VP-Eastern Div)*
Houston Smith *(VP-Governmental Affairs)*
Jill Stork *(VP-Western)*
Amy Riley *(Sec)*

Georgia Power Company **(1)**
241 Ralph McGill Blvd NE, Atlanta, GA 30308 **(100%)**
Tel.: (404) 506-6526
Web Site: http://www.georgiapower.com
Rev.: $11,584,000,000
Assets: $53,163,000,000
Liabilities: $34,305,000,000
Net Worth: $18,858,000,000
Earnings: $1,813,000,000
Emp.: 6,600
Fiscal Year-end: 12/31/2022
Electric Power Distr
N.A.I.C.S.: 221122

Kimberly Scheibe Greene *(Chm, Pres & CEO)*
Sterling A. Spainhour Jr. *(Chief Compliance Officer, Gen Counsel & Sr VP)*
Bentina Terry *(Sr VP-Customer Strategy & Solutions)*
Meredith Lackey *(Exec VP-External Affairs & Nuclear Dev)*
Michael K. Anderson *(Sr VP)*
David Slovensky *(Gen Counsel)*
Aaron Abramovitz *(CFO)*
Rick Anderson *(Sr VP)*
Lindsay Hill *(Sr VP)*

Mississippi Power Company (1)
2992 W Beach Blvd, Gulfport, MS 39501-1907 **(50%)**
Tel.: (228) 864-1211
Web Site: https://www.mississippipower.com
Rev.: $1,694,000,000
Assets: $5,272,000,000
Liabilities: $3,341,000,000
Net Worth: $1,931,000,000
Earnings: $164,000,000
Emp.: 1,000
Fiscal Year-end: 12/31/2022
Electric Power Distribution & Generation Services
N.A.I.C.S.: 221113
Anthony Wilson *(Chm, Pres & CEO)*
Billy Thornton *(VP-External Affairs & Shared Svcs)*
Tommy Murphy *(VP)*
Shawn Shurden *(Gen Counsel)*
Michael Smith *(VP)*
Brady Powers *(Dir)*

PowerSecure, Inc. (1)
4068 Stirrup Creek Dr, Durham, NC 27703
Tel.: (919) 556-3056
Web Site: https://www.powersecure.com
Emp.: 1,000
Power Saving Equipment Sales & Installation Services
N.A.I.C.S.: 221118

Subsidiary (Domestic):

Esco Energy Services Company (2)
309 Pittsfield Rd, Lenox, MA 01240-2444
Tel.: (413) 551-0055
Web Site: http://www.goesco.com
Electrical Contractor
N.A.I.C.S.: 238210
Travis DuPont *(CFO)*

Mercator Energy, LLC (2)
26 W Dry Creek Cir Ste 410, Littleton, CO 80120
Tel.: (303) 825-1100
Web Site: https://www.mercatorenergy.com
Administrative Management Consulting Services
N.A.I.C.S.: 541618
Stephanie Horner *(Mgr-Bus Dev)*
John Harpole *(Founder, Owner & Pres)*
Genene Kugler *(Mgr-Client Svcs)*
Kerry Barden *(Dir-Acct Svcs)*
Cahleen Ray *(Mgr-Client Svcs)*

PowerSecure Lighting (2)
650 W Ave, Stamford, CT 06902
Tel.: (203) 683-6222
Web Site: http://www.solais.com
Emp.: 50
Lighting Fixture Mfr
N.A.I.C.S.: 335132
Sam Newberry *(Pres & CEO)*
Ken Hurd *(Sr VP)*
Rob Limroth *(Sr VP)*
Michael Rodriguez *(VP)*
Scott Frazier *(Sr VP-Commercial)*
John Rebbeck *(Dir)*
Franklin Jewett *(Sls Dir)*
Keith Sullivan *(Dir)*
David Brumbelow *(Dir-Quotations & Project Mgmt)*
Sona Bill *(Dir-Mktg)*
Kathyrn Reid *(Dir)*
Doreen Bonesteel *(Mgr-Western North America)*
Scotty Hutto *(Sr VP)*
Sheila Mirl *(Sls Dir)*
Kristin Tilley *(Project Mgr & Coord-Logistics)*

Powersecure Service, Inc. (2)
377 Maitland Ave Ste 1010, Altamonte Springs, FL 32701-5442
Tel.: (800) 437-4474
Web Site: http://www.powerprotech.com

Maintenance & Service for Power Generators
N.A.I.C.S.: 561499

Solais Lighting, Inc. (2)
650 W Ave, Stamford, CT 06902
Tel.: (203) 683-6222
Web Site: http://www.solais.com
Lighting Fixture Mfr
N.A.I.C.S.: 335132

Rutherford Farm, LLC (1)
3337 Mint Rd, Maryville, TN 37803
Tel.: (865) 518-1311
Web Site: https://www.rutherfordsfarm.org
Fruit Farming Services
N.A.I.C.S.: 111333
Steve Rutherford *(Owner)*

Southern Communications Services, Inc. (1)
5555 Glenridge Connector Ste 500, Atlanta, GA 30342 **(100%)**
Tel.: (205) 257-1995
Web Site: https://www.southernlinc.com
Sales Range: $250-299.9 Million
Emp.: 350
Wireless Communications Network
N.A.I.C.S.: 517112
Tami Barron *(Pres & CEO)*
Carmine Reppucci *(CFO)*
Michael Rosenthal *(Dir-Legal & External Affairs)*

Southern Company Gas (1)
10 Peachtree Pl NE, Atlanta, GA 30309 **(100%)**
Tel.: (404) 584-4000
Web Site: https://www.southerncompany.com
Rev.: $5,962,000,000
Assets: $24,621,000,000
Liabilities: $14,224,000,000
Net Worth: $10,397,000,000
Earnings: $572,000,000
Emp.: 4,600
Fiscal Year-end: 12/31/2022
Natural Gas Distr
N.A.I.C.S.: 221210
Kimberly Scheibe Greene *(Chm, Pres & CEO)*
Bryan Batson *(Chief External & Pub Affairs Officer & Exec VP-External Affairs)*
Jay Sutton *(COO & Sr VP)*
Peter I. Tumminello *(Executives)*
David E. Slovensky *(Chief Ethics & Compliance Officer, Gen Counsel & Sr VP)*
Erin Harris *(Gen Counsel)*

Subsidiary (Domestic):

Atlanta Gas Light Company (2)
10 Peachtree Pl NE, Atlanta, GA 30309
Web Site: https://www.atlantagaslight.com
Natural Gas Services
N.A.I.C.S.: 221210
Pedro P. Cherry *(Pres & CEO)*

Chattanooga Gas Company (2)
Dept 1337 - BIN 110 10 Peachtree Pl NE, Atlanta, GA 30309
Tel.: (404) 584-4000
Web Site: https://www.chattanoogagas.com
Natural Gas Distribution
N.A.I.C.S.: 221210
Pedro P. Cherry *(Pres & CEO)*

Georgia Natural Gas Company (2)
10 Peachtree Pl Location 1466, Atlanta, GA 30309
Tel.: (770) 850-6200
Web Site: http://gng.com
Natural Gas Distribution
N.A.I.C.S.: 221210

Subsidiary (Domestic):

SouthStar Energy Services LLC (3)
817 W Peachtree St NW Ste 1000, Atlanta, GA 30308
Tel.: (404) 685-4018
Web Site: https://www.southstarenergy.com
Natural Gas Distribution
N.A.I.C.S.: 221210

Subsidiary (Domestic):

Nicor Gas Company (2)
PO Box 5407, Carol Stream, IL 60197-5407
Web Site: https://www.nicorgas.com
Emp.: 2,000

Holding Company; Natural Gas Distribution
N.A.I.C.S.: 551112
Christa Markgraff *(VP-Ops)*
Pat Whiteside *(VP-Bus Support)*
Jim Griffin *(VP-Ops)*
Shannon Pierce *(VP-Ops)*
Louie Binswanger *(VP-External Affairs)*
Bernie Anderson *(Reg Mgr-Community Affairs)*
Joe DelReal *(Reg Mgr-Community Affairs)*
Pat Eaves-Heard *(Reg Mgr-Community Affairs)*
David Surina *(Reg Mgr-Community Affairs)*

Subsidiary (Domestic):

Illinois Energy Solutions, USA, LLC (3)
1751 W Diehl Rd 200, Naperville, IL 60563
Web Site: https://www.illenergysolutions.com
Energy Related Products for Residential & Small Commercial Customers Providing Gas Cost Stability & Utility Bill Management
N.A.I.C.S.: 561499
Gary Blank *(Mgr)*

Nicor Enerchange, LLC (3)
3333 Warrenville Rd Ste 300, Lisle, IL 60532
Tel.: (630) 245-7800
Web Site: http://www.nicorenerchange.com
Wholesale Natural Gas Marketing Services
N.A.I.C.S.: 541613

Northern Illinois Gas Company (3)
1844 Ferry Rd, Naperville, IL 60563-9600
Tel.: (630) 983-8888
Web Site: http://www.nicorgas.com
Natural Gas Distr
N.A.I.C.S.: 221210
John O. Hudson III *(Pres & CEO)*

Subsidiary (Domestic):

Virginia Natural Gas, Inc. (2)
544 S Independence Blvd, Virginia Beach, VA 23452
Tel.: (757) 616-7500
Web Site: https://virginianaturalgas.com
Gas Utility
N.A.I.C.S.: 221210

Southern Company Services, Inc. (1)
30 Ivan Allen Jr Blvd NW, Atlanta, GA 30308
Tel.: (404) 506-5000
Power Plant Support Services
N.A.I.C.S.: 561990
Martin Bernard Davis *(CIO & Exec VP)*
Stanley W. Connally Jr. *(Chm, Pres & CEO)*
Sterling A. Spainhour Jr. *(Chief Compliance Officer, Chief Legal Officer & Exec VP)*
Luke Visconti *(Co-Founder & Partner)*
Elizabeth W. Reese *(Exec VP-Shared Svcs)*
Mark S. Berry *(Sr VP-R&D)*

Southern Nuclear Operating Company, Inc. (1)
42 Inverness Center Pkwy, Birmingham, AL 35242
Tel.: (205) 992-5000
Web Site: http://www.southerncompany.com
Sales Range: $50-74.9 Million
Emp.: 200
Nuclear Power Plant Operator
N.A.I.C.S.: 221113
Bradley J. Adams *(Interim VP-Engineering)*
Stephen E. Kuczynski *(Chm & CEO)*
Cheryl W. Brakefield *(CFO, Treas & VP)*
Shane Camp *(VP-HR)*
Michael Meier *(VP-Regulatory Affairs)*
Penny Reister *(VP)*
Glen Chick *(VP-Alvin W Vogtle Electric Generating Plant,Units 3,4)*
Edwin D. Dean *(VP-Site-Edwin I. Hatch Nuclear Power Plant)*
Charles Kharrl *(VP-Site-Joseph M. Farley Nuclear Plant)*
Richard Libra *(Sr VP-Ops)*
Michael Jesse *(VP)*
Millicent W. Ronnlund *(Compliance Officer, Gen Counsel & VP)*
John B. Williams *(VP-Interim-Engrg-)*
Ho Nieh *(VP-Regulatory Affairs)*
Drayton Pitts *(VP-Units 1,2)*
Peter P. Sena III *(Chief Nuclear Officer & Exec VP)*

Southern Power Company (1)
30 Ivan Allen Jr Blvd NW, Atlanta, GA 30308
Tel.: (404) 506-5000
Web Site: https://www.southerncompany.com
Rev.: $3,369,000,000
Assets: $13,081,000,000
Liabilities: $6,165,000,000
Net Worth: $6,916,000,000
Earnings: $354,000,000
Emp.: 500
Fiscal Year-end: 12/31/2022
Electric Power Generation & Distr
N.A.I.C.S.: 221122
Christopher Cummiskey *(Chm & CEO)*
Robin Boren *(Pres)*
Dana Claburn *(Sr VP)*
Gary Kerr *(CFO)*
Bob Schaffeld *(Chief Dev Officer)*

WWH, LLC (1)
9081 Eagle Point Loop Rd SW, Lakewood, WA 98498
Tel.: (253) 279-5626
Eletric Power Generation Services
N.A.I.C.S.: 221115

THE ST. JOE COMPANY

130 Richard Jackson Blvd Ste 200, Panama City Beach, FL 32407
Tel.: (850) 231-6400 FL
Web Site: https://www.joe.com
Year Founded: 1936
JOE—(NYSE)
Rev.: $252,321,000
Assets: $1,430,839,000
Liabilities: $779,730,000
Net Worth: $651,109,000
Earnings: $70,927,000
Emp.: 625
Fiscal Year-end: 12/31/22
Real Estate Operating Services
N.A.I.C.S.: 237210
Jorge Luis Gonzalez *(Pres & CEO)*
Marek Bakun *(CFO, Principal Acctg Officer & Exec VP)*
Rhea Goff *(Chief Admin Officer & Sr VP)*
Elizabeth J. Walters *(Gen Counsel, Sec & Sr VP)*
Bridget Precise *(Sr VP)*
Dan Velazquez *(Sr VP)*

Subsidiaries:

Port St. Joe Marina Inc. (1)
340 Marina Dr, Port Saint Joe, FL 32456
Tel.: (850) 797-3489
Web Site: https://pointsouthmarina.com
Real Estate Operating Services
N.A.I.C.S.: 237210

SouthWood Golf Club (1)
3750 Grove Park Dr, Tallahassee, FL 32311
Tel.: (850) 942-4653
Web Site: https://www.southwoodgolf.com
Sales Range: $10-24.9 Million
Emp.: 4
Golf Club Operations
N.A.I.C.S.: 713910

St. Joe Club & Resorts Vacation Rentals, LLC (1)
133 S Watersound Pkwy Unit E, Watersound, FL 32461
Tel.: (850) 231-7111
Web Site: http://www.stjoeclub.com
Real Estate Related Services
N.A.I.C.S.: 531390

St. Joe Timberland Company of Delaware, L.L.C. (1)
133 S Watersound Pkwy Ste A, Panama City Beach, FL 32413
Tel.: (850) 639-7300
Real Estate Related Services
N.A.I.C.S.: 531390

Watersound Origins Town Center, LLC (1)
136 N Splash Dr, Watersound, FL 32461
Web Site: http://www.watersound.com
Real Estate Development Services
N.A.I.C.S.: 531390

The St. Joe Company—(Continued)

THE STEPHAN COMPANY

7901 4th St N Ste 300, Saint Petersburg, FL 33702
Tel.: (813) 248-5761 FL
Web Site:
https://www.thestephanco.com
Year Founded: 1897
SPCO—(OTCIQ)
Toilet Preparation Manufacturing
N.A.I.C.S.: 325620
Eric Kiekbusch *(Pres)*

Subsidiaries:

Morris Flamingo-Stephan, Inc. **(1)**
204 Eastgate Ct, Danville, IL
61834 **(100%)**
Tel.: (217) 442-6860
Web Site: http://www.morrisflamingo.com
Barber & Beauty Supplies Distr
N.A.I.C.S.: 456120

Scientific Research Products,
Inc. **(1)**
1850 W McNab Rd, Fort Lauderdale, FL
33309
Tel.: (954) 971-0600
Web Site: http://www.thestephanco.com
Sales Range: $1-9.9 Million
Emp.: 40
Hair & Skin Care Products Mfr & Distr
N.A.I.C.S.: 325620

Williamsport Barber and Beauty
Corp. **(1)**
3510 W 4th St, Williamsport, PA 17701
Tel.: (570) 323-7772
Web Site: http://www.williamsportbarber.com
Barber & Beauty Supplies Distr
N.A.I.C.S.: 423850

THE TIMKEN COMPANY

4500 Mt Pleasant St NW, North Canton, OH 44720-5450
Tel.: (234) 262-3000 OH
Web Site: http://www.timken.com
Year Founded: 1899
TKR—(NYSE)
Rev.: $4,769,000,000
Assets: $6,541,700,000
Liabilities: $3,839,300,000
Net Worth: $2,702,400,000
Earnings: $394,100,000
Emp.: 19,000
Fiscal Year-end: 12/31/23
Antifriction Bearings & Related Products Mfr; Alloy Steel & Components
Mfr
N.A.I.C.S.: 332991
Christopher A. Coughlin *(Pres-Industrial Motion & Exec VP)*
Philip D. Fracassa *(CFO & Exec VP)*
Andreas Roellgen *(Pres-Engineered Bearings & Exec VP)*
Michael A. Discenza *(VP)*
Hansal N. Patel *(Gen Counsel, Sec & VP)*
Natasha Pollock *(VP-HR)*
Tarak Mehta *(Pres & CEO)*

Subsidiaries:

Aurora Bearing Co **(1)**
901 Aucutt Rd, Montgomery, IL 60538
Tel.: (630) 906-0454
Web Site: http://www.aurorabearing.com
Rev.: $1,100,000
Emp.: 10
Industrial Supplies Merchant Whslr
N.A.I.C.S.: 423840

Australian Timken Proprietary
Ltd. **(1)**
5 Daveyduke Dr, PO Box 240, Ballarat,
3353, VIC, Australia **(100%)**
Tel.: (61) 353202700
Web Site: http://www.timken.com
Sales Range: $25-49.9 Million
Emp.: 50
Mfr of Roller Bearings
N.A.I.C.S.: 332991
Micheal Pearson *(Mng Dir)*

BEKA Japan Co., Ltd. **(1)**
2-4-15 Honmachi, Higashi Sumiyoshi-ku,
Yao, 581-0003, Osaka, Japan
Tel.: (81) 729230585
Industrial Equipment Distr
N.A.I.C.S.: 423830

BEKA Lubrication Systems (Kunshan)
Co., Ltd. **(1)**
Room1803 Building1 Sandhill Plaza No
2290 Zuchongzhi Road, Pudong New District, Shanghai, 201210, China
Tel.: (86) 2161462988
Industrial Equipment Distr
N.A.I.C.S.: 423830

Baier & Koppel GmbH & Co. KG **(1)**
Beethovenstr 14, 91257, Pegnitz, Germany
Tel.: (49) 92417290
Web Site: http://www.beka-lube.de
Automobile Parts Mfr
N.A.I.C.S.: 336390
Kees Ardesch *(Product Mgr)*

Bearing Inspection Inc. **(1)**
4422 Corporate Ctr Dr, Los Alamitos, CA
90720-2539
Tel.: (714) 484-2400
Web Site:
https://www.bearinginspectioninc.com
Sales Range: $50-74.9 Million
Aircraft & Heavy Equipment Repair Services
N.A.I.C.S.: 811310

Beka Lube Products Inc. **(1)**
6581 Kitimat Road Unit 2, Mississauga,
L5N 3T5, ON, Canada
Tel.: (905) 821-1050
Web Site: http://www.beka-lube.com
Industrial Equipment Distr
N.A.I.C.S.: 423830

Beka-Lube GmbH **(1)**
Rottweg 66, 5020, Salzburg, Austria
Tel.: (43) 662438440
Web Site: http://www.beka-lube.at
Automobile Parts Mfr
N.A.I.C.S.: 336390

Beka-Lube N.V. **(1)**
Demerstraat 32, 3200, Aarschot, Belgium
Tel.: (32) 16640926
Web Site: http://www.beka-lube.be
Automobile Parts Mfr
N.A.I.C.S.: 336390

Bekalube France S.A.S. **(1)**
4 Bis rue de Lartisanat, 89100, Bourgogne,
France
Tel.: (33) 386833906
Web Site: http://www.bekalube.fr
Industrial Equipment Distr
N.A.I.C.S.: 423830

Bekalube Iberica, S.L.U. **(1)**
C/Albasanz 14 Bis 2 J, 28037, Madrid,
Spain
Tel.: (34) 914402656
Industrial Equipment Distr
N.A.I.C.S.: 423830

Bekalube S.R.L. **(1)**
Via E Rossi n 152, 20862, Arcore, MB, Italy
Tel.: (39) 0396180088
Web Site: http://www.bekalube.it
Industrial Equipment Distr
N.A.I.C.S.: 423830

Bekaworld Singapore Pte. Ltd. **(1)**
2 Changi Business Park Avenue 1 Level 2
Suite 29, Singapore, 486015, Singapore
Tel.: (65) 68097282
Web Site: http://www.bekaworld.sg
Industrial Equipment Distr
N.A.I.C.S.: 423830
Joseph Loy *(Reg Dir-Sales-Marketing)*

Canadian Timken Ltd. **(1)**
1055 Talbot St, Saint Thomas, N5P 1G5,
ON, Canada **(100%)**
Tel.: (519) 631-4500
Sales Range: $125-149.9 Million
Emp.: 170
Mfr of Roller Bearings
N.A.I.C.S.: 332991
Patrick Durcak *(Mgr-Sls-Comml Vehicle Aftermarket)*
Frank Mascia *(Mng Dir)*

Cone Drive Operations Inc. **(1)**

240 E 12th St, Traverse City, MI 49684
Tel.: (231) 946-8410
Web Site: http://www.conedrive.com
Worm Gearing Products Mfr
N.A.I.C.S.: 333612

Des-Case Corporation **(1)**
675 N Main St, Goodlettsville, TN 37072
Tel.: (615) 672-8800
Web Site: http://www.des-case.com
Emp.: 120
All Other Miscellaneous General Purpose
Machinery Mfr
N.A.I.C.S.: 333998

Diamond Chain Company **(1)**
402 Kentucky Ave, Indianapolis, IN
46225-1175 **(100%)**
Tel.: (317) 638-6431
Web Site: http://www.diamondchain.com
Sales Range: $50-74.9 Million
Roller & Conveyor Chains Mfr & Distr
N.A.I.C.S.: 333613

Subsidiary (Non-US):

Diamond Chain UK Ltd **(2)**
Tundry Way, Blaydon, NE21 5SJ, Tyne &
Wear, United Kingdom
Tel.: (44) 191 414 8822
Web Site: http://www.diamondchain.co.uk
Sales Range: $10-24.9 Million
Emp.: 3
Industrial Chain Mfr
N.A.I.C.S.: 333613
Patrick Smithson *(Mgr-Customer Svc)*

GGB, Inc. **(1)**
1414 Metropolitan Ave, Thorofare, NJ
08086
Tel.: (856) 848-3200
Web Site: http://www.ggbearings.com
Sales Range: $75-99.9 Million
Emp.: 1,000
Self-Lubricating & Prelubricated Bearings
Mfr
N.A.I.C.S.: 332991

Subsidiary (Non-US):

GGB Austria GmbH **(2)**
Gerhardusgasse 25, A-1200, Vienna, Austria
Tel.: (43) 13324992
Web Site: https://www.ggbearings.com
Sales Range: $10-24.9 Million
Emp.: 16
Self Lubricating & Prelubricated Bearings
Distr
N.A.I.C.S.: 336310

GGB Brasil Industria de Mancais E
Componentes Ltda. **(2)**
Avenida Gupe 10767, Barueri, 06422-120,
SP, Brazil
Tel.: (55) 11984736213
Sales Range: $25-49.9 Million
Emp.: 50
Self Lubricating & Prelubricated Bearings
Mfr
N.A.I.C.S.: 336310

Greencat Sp. z o.o. **(1)**
ul Zapasnicza 6, 53-013, Wroclaw, Poland
Tel.: (48) 717845660
Web Site: http://www.greencatpolska.pl
Polish & Sanitation Product Mfr
N.A.I.C.S.: 325612

Groeneveld Groep Holding B.V. **(1)**
Stephensonweg 12, 4207 HB, Gorinchem,
Netherlands
Tel.: (31) 183641400
Web Site: http://www.groeneveld-group.com
Lubricant Mfr
N.A.I.C.S.: 324191

Groeneveld Italia S.r.l. **(1)**
Via S Pertini 1, 23893, Cassago Brianza,
Italy
Tel.: (39) 0399215611
Web Site: https://www.groeneveld-beka.com
Lubricant Mfr
N.A.I.C.S.: 324191

Groeneveld Lubrication Solutions
Inc. **(1)**
8450 Lawson Road Unit 5, Milton, L9T 0J8,
ON, Canada
Tel.: (905) 875-1017
Lubricant Distr

N.A.I.C.S.: 424720

Groeneveld Lubrication Solutions
Inc. **(1)**
1441 Wolf Creek Trl, Wadsworth, OH 44281
Tel.: (330) 225-4949
Web Site: http://www.groeneveld-beka.com
Lubricant Distr
N.A.I.C.S.: 424720

Groeneveld Lubrication Solutions
Limited **(1)**
Unit 11 6-10 Tukorako Drive, Mount Maunganui, 4509, Bay of Plenty, New Zealand
Tel.: (64) 75720684
Web Site: https://www.groeneveld-beka.com
Emp.: 600
Lubricant Distr
N.A.I.C.S.: 424720

Groeneveld Lubrication Solutions
Ltd. **(1)**
Gelders Hall Road, Shepshed, Loughborough, LE12 9NH, United Kingdom
Tel.: (44) 1509600033
Web Site: http://www.groeneveld-lubrication-solutions.com
Lubricant Distr
N.A.I.C.S.: 424720

Groeneveld Lubrication Solutions Pty
Ltd. **(1)**
268 Proximity Drive Sunshine West, Melbourne, 3020, VIC, Australia
Tel.: (61) 383294333
Lubricant Distr
N.A.I.C.S.: 424720

Groeneveld Lubrication Solutions
S.r.l. **(1)**
Via Chiari 100, 23868, Valmadrera, Italy
Tel.: (39) 0399215611
Lubricant Distr
N.A.I.C.S.: 424720

Groeneveld Polska Sp Z.o.o. **(1)**
ul Workshops 14b, 62-052, Komorniki, Poland
Tel.: (48) 618726207
Web Site: https://www.groeneveld-beka.com
Lubricant Distr
N.A.I.C.S.: 424720

Groeneveld UK Limited **(1)**
First Floor Black Country House Rounds
Green Road, West Midlands, Oldbury, B69
2DG, United Kingdom
Tel.: (44) 1752676000
Lubrication System Mfr
N.A.I.C.S.: 333914

Groeneveld UK Limited **(1)**
Gelders Hall Road, Loughborough, Shepshed, LE12 9NH, United Kingdom
Tel.: (44) 1509600033
Automatic Lubrication System Mfr
N.A.I.C.S.: 334512

Groeneveld-BEKA Canada Inc. **(1)**
8450 Lawson Road Unit 5, Milton, L9T 0J8,
ON, Canada
Tel.: (905) 875-1017
Automatic Lubrication System Mfr
N.A.I.C.S.: 334512

Groeneveld-BEKA GmbH **(1)**
Beethovenstrasse 14, 91257, Pegnitz, Germany
Tel.: (49) 92417290
Web Site: https://www.groeneveld-beka.com
Automatic Lubrication System Mfr
N.A.I.C.S.: 334512

Interlube USA Inc. **(1)**
2109 Lyons Rd, Miamisburg, OH 45342
Tel.: (937) 276-4507
Web Site: http://www.interlubesystems.com
Lubricant Distr
N.A.I.C.S.: 424720

Jiangsu TWB Bearings Co., Ltd. **(1)**
No 8 Rongyang Yi Road, Xishan Economic
Development Zone, Wuxi, 214192, Jiangsu,
China
Tel.: (86) 5108 562 0688
Web Site: https://en.twb.com.cn
Sales Range: $150-199.9 Million
Emp.: 800
Bearing Mfr
N.A.I.C.S.: 332991

Lovejoy Curtis, LLC (1)
4 Birnie Ave, Springfield, MA 01107
Tel.: (413) 737-0281
Emp.: 25
Mechanical Power Transmission Equipment
Mfr
N.A.I.C.S.: 333613
Glen Beauregard (Gen Mgr)

Lovejoy Inc. (1)
2655 Wisconsin Ave, Downers Grove, IL
60515
Tel.: (630) 852-0500
Web Site: http://www.lovejoy-inc.com
Power Transmission Equipment Mfr
N.A.I.C.S.: 333613
Mathew W. Happach (Pres)

Subsidiary (Non-US):

R+L Hydraulics GmbH (2)
Friedrichstrasse 6, 58791, Werdohl, Germany
Tel.: (49) 23925090
Web Site: https://www.rl-hydraulics.com
Mechanical Power Transmission Equipment
Mfr
N.A.I.C.S.: 333613
Mathew W. Happach (Exec Dir)
Sebastian Hardt (Sls Mgr)

Nadella S.p.A. (1)
Via Melette 16, 20128, Milan, Italy
Tel.: (39) 0227093
Web Site: http://www.nadella.it
Linear Rail, Bearing & Actuator Mfr
N.A.I.C.S.: 332991

Subsidiary (Non-US):

**DURBAL Metallwarenfabrik
GmbH** (2)
Verrenberger Weg 2, 74613, Ohringen, Germany
Tel.: (49) 794194600
Web Site: https://www.durbal.de
Bearings & Rods Mfr
N.A.I.C.S.: 332991
Andreas Rollgen (Mng Dir)
Rudiger Knevels (Mng Dir)

Nadella GmbH (2)
Rudolf-Diesel-Str 28, 71154, Nufringen,
Germany
Tel.: (49) 703295400
Web Site: https://www.nadella.de
Linear Rail, Bearing & Actuator Distr
N.A.I.C.S.: 423840

Subsidiary (US):

Nadella Inc. (2)
14115 - 63 Way N, Clearwater, FL 33760-
3621
Web Site: http://www.nadella.com
Linear Rail, Bearing & Actuator Whslr
N.A.I.C.S.: 423840

Nihon Timken K.K. (1)
9-13 Moriya-cho 3-chome, Kanagawa-ku,
Yokohama, 221-0022, Kanagawa,
Japan (100%)
Tel.: (81) 454537701
Sales Range: $1-9.9 Million
Emp.: 20
Mfr of Roller Bearings
N.A.I.C.S.: 332991

PT Tech, LLC (1)
1441 Wolf Creek Trl, Wadsworth, OH
44281 (100%)
Tel.: (330) 239-4933
Web Site: https://www.pttech.com
Brakes, Clutch Couplings & Torque Limiters
Mfr
N.A.I.C.S.: 336340
Jason Rebucci (Pres)

Philadelphia Gear Corporation (1)
935 1st Ave Ste 200, King of Prussia, PA
19406
Tel.: (610) 265-3000
Web Site: http://www.philagear.com
Gears, Speed Reducing Units, Sphereflex
Coupling, Fluid Agitators & Industrial
Clutches Mfr
N.A.I.C.S.: 333612

Rail Bearing Service Corp. (1)
PO Box 6929, Canton, OH 44706
Tel.: (330) 471-3778

Sales Range: $300-349.9 Million
Emp.: 300
Petroleum Product Mfr
N.A.I.C.S.: 324199

Rollon B.V. (1)
Ringbaan Zuid 8, 6905 DB, Zevenaar,
Netherlands
Tel.: (31) 6581999
Ball & Roller Bearing Distr
N.A.I.C.S.: 423840

Rollon Corporation (1)
101 Bilby Rd Ste B, Hackettstown, NJ
07840
Tel.: (973) 300-5492
Web Site: https://www.rollon.com
Mechanical Equipment Mfr
N.A.I.C.S.: 333613
Rick Wood (Mng Dir)

Rollon GmbH (1)
Bonner Strasse 317-319, 40589, Dusseldorf, Germany
Tel.: (49) 211957470
Web Site: https://www.rollon.com
Ball & Roller Bearing Distr
N.A.I.C.S.: 423840

Rollon India Pvt. Ltd. (1)
39-42 Electronic City Phase-I Hosur Road,
Bengaluru, 560100, India
Tel.: (91) 8041362000
Web Site: https://www.rollon.com
Ball & Roller Bearing Distr
N.A.I.C.S.: 423840

Rollon Japan KK (1)
Hashimotoya Building 1-21-4 Nishi-
Hashimoto, Midori-ku, Sagamihara, 252-
0131, Kanagawa, Japan
Tel.: (81) 427034101
Industrial Equipment Mfr & Distr
N.A.I.C.S.: 333995

Rollon Ltd. UK Limited (1)
The Works 6 West Street, Olney, MK46
5HR, Buckinghamshire, United Kingdom
Tel.: (44) 1234964024
Web Site: https://www.rollon.com
Ball & Roller Bearing Distr
N.A.I.C.S.: 423840

Rollon S.a.r.l. (1)
Les Jardins d Eole 2 allee des Sequoias,
69760, Limonest, France
Tel.: (33) 474719330
Web Site: https://www.rollon.com
Ball & Roller Bearing Distr
N.A.I.C.S.: 423840

Rollon S.p.A. (1)
Via Trieste 26, 20871, Vimercate, MB, Italy
Tel.: (39) 03962591
Web Site: http://www.rollon.com
Ball & Roller Bearing Mfr
N.A.I.C.S.: 332991

SE Setco Service Company (1)
2402 Tech Ctr Pkwy Ste 200, Lawrenceville,
GA 30043
Tel.: (770) 932-2353
Web Site: http://www.sesetco.com
Sales Range: $125-149.9 Million
Emp.: 20
Machine Tool & Component Mfr
N.A.I.C.S.: 333514
Paul Bange (Gen Mgr)

Smith Services Inc. (1)
801 Turnpike Industrial Park Rd, Princeton,
WV 24739
Tel.: (304) 431-2446
Web Site: https://www.smithservices.com
Sales Range: $10-24.9 Million
Emp.: 200
Electric Motor Repair & Field Technical Services
N.A.I.C.S.: 811310

Timken ILS Dayton, Inc. (1)
Mid States Bldg 4696 Wadsworth Rd, Dayton, OH 45414
Tel.: (937) 276-4507
Bearing Mfr
N.A.I.C.S.: 333613
Joyce A. Michael (Mgr-Acctg & Benefit)

**Timken (Shanghai) Distribution and
Sales Co., Ltd.** (1)
Section 6 Gate 1st floor No 499 Riying

BeiLu, Waigaoqiao Free Trade Area,
Shanghai, 200131, China
Tel.: (86) 2161138000
Ball & Roller Bearing Distr
N.A.I.C.S.: 423840

**Timken Aerospace Transmissions,
LLC** (1)
586 Hilliard St, Manchester, CT 06042-2879
Tel.: (860) 649-0000
Web Site:
https://www.aerodrivesystems.com
Sales Range: $75-99.9 Million
Emp.: 200
Aircraft Engines & Helicopter Components
N.A.I.C.S.: 336412

Timken Argentina S.R.L. (1)
Avenida Almafuerte 1437, Buenos Aires,
Argentina (100%)
Tel.: (54) 1149120025
Web Site: http://www.timken.com
Sales Range: $10-24.9 Million
Emp.: 17
Bearing Mfr
N.A.I.C.S.: 332991

Timken Boring Specialties, LLC (1)
14730 Yarberry St, Houston, TX 77039-
1031
Tel.: (281) 449-0319
Solid Steel Bar Machining Services
N.A.I.C.S.: 213112
Eric Walsky (Gen Mgr)

Timken Canada LP (1)
100-5955 Airport Road, Mississauga, L4V
1R9, ON, Canada
Tel.: (905) 694-4900
Web Site: https://timken-ca.ptplace.com
Sales Range: $10-24.9 Million
Emp.: 20
Ball & Roller Bearing Mfr
N.A.I.C.S.: 332991

Timken Deutschland GmbH (1)
Rudolf-Diesel-Str 28, 71154, Nufringen,
Germany
Tel.: (49) 703295400
Web Site: https://www.nadella.de
Sales Range: $10-24.9 Million
Emp.: 20
Mfr of Linear Bearing Systems
N.A.I.C.S.: 332991

Timken Drives LLC (1)
901 19th Ave, Fulton, IL 61252-0350
Tel.: (815) 589-2211
Web Site: https://www.driveschain.com
Sales Range: $75-99.9 Million
Emp.: 400
Forged Steel Mfr
N.A.I.C.S.: 332111

**Timken Engineering and Research-
India Private Limited** (1)
Sy No S 39p 41p 42p Electronic City Phase
II, Doddathogur Village Begur Hobli Taluk,
Bengaluru, 560 100, Karnataka, India
Tel.: (91) 8041362000
Web Site: http://www.timken.com
Customer Product & Application Engineering Services
N.A.I.C.S.: 541330

Timken Espana, S.L. (1)
Tel.: (34) 914110362
Antifriction Bearing Distr
N.A.I.C.S.: 423840

Timken Europe (1)
2 Rue Timken, PO Box 60089, 68002, Colmar, France (100%)
Tel.: (33) 389214444
Web Site: http://www.timken.com
Sales Range: $250-299.9 Million
Emp.: 570
Mfr of Roller Bearings
N.A.I.C.S.: 332991
Andreas Roellgen (VP-Sls)

Timken Gears & Services Inc. (1)
10830 Train Ct, Houston, TX 77041
Tel.: (713) 224-4900
Web Site: https://philagear.com
Sales Range: $25-49.9 Million
Bearings & Related Product Mfr
N.A.I.C.S.: 332991

Timken GmbH (1)
Reisholzer Werftstrasse 38-40, 40589, Dus-

seldorf, Germany
Tel.: (49) 211917460
Ball & Roller Bearing Mfr
N.A.I.C.S.: 332991

Timken ILS Cheltenham Limited (1)
Unit 25 Malmesbury Rd Kingsditch Trad
Est, Cheltenham, GL51 9PL, United Kingdom
Tel.: (44) 1242256610
Web Site:
http://www.timkenilscheltenham.com
Lubrication System Mfr
N.A.I.C.S.: 333914

Timken India Ltd. (1)
39-42 Electronic City Phase II Hosur Road,
Bengaluru, 560 100, Karnataka, India
Tel.: (91) 8041362000
Web Site: https://www.timken.com
Roller Bearing Mfr
N.A.I.C.S.: 332991
Avishrant Keshava (CFO & Controller-Bus)

Subsidiary (Domestic):

ABC Bearings Limited (2)
Plot No 1-B 109-B 109-A, GIDC Narmadanagar, Bharuch, 392015, India
Tel.: (91) 2642248222
Web Site: https://www.abcbearings.com
Sales Range: $25-49.9 Million
Emp.: 398
Roller Bearing Mfr; Tapered, Cylindrical &
Spherical Roller Bearings
N.A.I.C.S.: 332991

**Timken India Manufacturing Private
Limited** (1)
Plot No AA3 6th Avenue Auto Ancillary SEZ
Mahindra World City, Anjur Village PO Nattam, Chengalpattu, 603 002, India
Tel.: (91) 4447412000
Bore Bearing Mfr
N.A.I.C.S.: 332991

Timken Italia S.r.l. (1)
Viale Forlanini 23, 20134, Milan,
Italy (100%)
Tel.: (39) 025300971
Web Site: https://www.timken.com
Sales Range: $1-4.9 Billion
Tapered Roller Bearings Mfr
N.A.I.C.S.: 332991

**Timken Motor & Crane Services
LLC** (1)
2020 W Barberry Pl, Denver, CO 80204
Tel.: (303) 623-8658
Web Site: http://www.wazeeco.com
Emp.: 35
Crane Product Mfr
N.A.I.C.S.: 333120

Timken Romania SA (1)
Str Dr Gh Petrescu 25, 100525, Ploiesti,
Prahova, Romania
Tel.: (40) 244403355
Rolled Ring & Bearing Mfr
N.A.I.C.S.: 332991

Timken Singapore PTE Ltd. (1)
51 Changi Business Park Central 2 03-07
the Signature Building, Singapore, 486066,
Singapore
Tel.: (65) 65320900
Sales Range: $10-24.9 Million
Emp.: 20
Ball & Roller Bearing Mfr
N.A.I.C.S.: 332991

**Timken South Africa Proprietary
Ltd.** (1)
cnr Edinburgh Van Dyk Road, Dunfwart,
Benoni, 1501, Gauteng, South
Africa (100%)
Tel.: (27) 0117413800
Web Site: http://www.timken.co.za
Sales Range: $75-99.9 Million
Emp.: 100
Mfr of Ball & Roller Bearings
N.A.I.C.S.: 332991
Danie Coetser (Mng Dir)

Timken Super Precision (1)
7 Optical Ave, Keene, NH 03431
Tel.: (603) 352-0310
Web Site: http://www.timken.com
Sales Range: $125-149.9 Million
Emp.: 1,820
Mfr of Miniature Precision Bearings

The Timken Company—(Continued)

N.A.I.C.S.: 332991

Timken UK Ltd. (1)
IO Center Unit 5 Barn Way Lodge Farm
Industrial Estate, Northampton, NN5 7UW,
United Kingdom (100%)
Tel.: (44) 604752600
Web Site: http://www.timken.com
Sales Range: $10-24.9 Million
Emp.: 60
Mfr of Roller Bearings
N.A.I.C.S.: 332991

Timken de Mexico, S.A. de C.V. (1)
Km 1 Carr Tepotzotlan-La Aurora, Ex Haci-
enda San Miguel, 54700, Cuautitlan Izcalli,
Edo De Mexico, Mexico (100%)
Tel.: (52) 5550614800
Sales Range: $25-49.9 Million
Emp.: 55
Mfr of Roller Bearings
N.A.I.C.S.: 332991

Timken do Brasil S.A. Comercio e
Industria Ltda. (1)
R Alexandre Dumas 2200-3 Andar, 04717-
901, Sao Paulo, SP, Brazil (100%)
Tel.: (55) 1151879200
Web Site: http://www.timken.com
Sales Range: $25-49.9 Million
Emp.: 100
Bearing Mfr
N.A.I.C.S.: 332991

Torsion Control Products, Inc. (1)
1441 Wolf Creek Trl, Wadsworth, OH
44281 (100%)
Tel.: (330) 239-4933
Web Site: https://www.torsioncontrol.com
Motor Vehicle Transmission & Power Train
Parts Mfr
N.A.I.C.S.: 336350

THE TJX COMPANIES, INC.

770 Cochituate Rd, Framingham, MA
01701
Tel.: (508) 390-1000   DE
Web Site: https://www.tjx.com
Year Founded: 1987
TJX—(NYSE)
Rev.: $54,217,000,000
Assets: $29,747,000,000
Liabilities: $22,445,000,000
Net Worth: $7,302,000,000
Earnings: $4,474,000,000
Emp.: 349,000
Fiscal Year-end: 02/03/24
Off-Price Apparel & Home Fashions
Retailer
N.A.I.C.S.: 458110
Ernie L. Herrman (Pres & CEO)
Carol M. Meyrowitz (Exec Chm)
Scott Goldenberg (Sr Exec VP-Fin)
Debra McConnell (Sr VP-Global
Comm)
John Klinger (CFO & Exec VP)

Subsidiaries:

HomeGoods, Inc. (1)
770 Cochituate Rd, Framingham, MA 01701
Tel.: (508) 390-1000
Web Site: http://www.homegoods.com
Sales Range: $25-49.9 Million
Emp.: 100
Off Price Home Furnishing
N.A.I.C.S.: 449129

Marmaxx Operating Corp. (1)
770 Cochituate Rd, Framingham, MA
01701-4672 (100%)
Tel.: (508) 390-1000
Web Site: http://www.tjx.com
Sales Range: $450-499.9 Million
Emp.: 1,600
Holding Company for Clothing Stores; Off-
Price Specialty Apparel Retailer
N.A.I.C.S.: 561499

Subsidiary (Domestic):

Marshalls of MA, Inc. (2)
1 Worcester Rd, Framingham, MA
01701 (100%)
Tel.: (508) 872-2684

Web Site: http://www.marshalls.com
Sales Range: $600-649.9 Million
Off-Price Family Apparel Retailer
N.A.I.C.S.: 455110

T.J. Maxx (2)
1 Worcester Rd, Framingham, MA 01701
Tel.: (508) 626-2400
Web Site: https://tjmaxx.tjx.com
Sales Range: $1-4.9 Billion
Retailer of Off-Price Apparel & Other Do-
mestic Products
N.A.I.C.S.: 455110
Christina Lofgren (VP-Prop Devel)

Marshalls of CA, LLC (1)
3008 Ming Ave, Bakersfield, CA 93304-
4136
Tel.: (661) 832-7595
Web Site: http://www.tjx.com
Apparel Retailer
N.A.I.C.S.: 315210

Marshalls of IL, LLC (1)
500 River Oaks Dr, Calumet City, IL 60409
Tel.: (708) 891-3870
Web Site: http://www.marshallsonline.com
Grocery Products Retailer
N.A.I.C.S.: 455110

NBC Apparel, Inc. (1)
770 Cochituate Rd, Framingham, MA 01701
Tel.: (508) 390-1000
Emp.: 16
Apparel Accessory Distr
N.A.I.C.S.: 458110
Richard Sherr (Pres)
Mary B. Reynolds (Treas)
Ann McCauley (Sec)

Sierra Trading Post Inc. (1)
5025 Campstool Rd, Cheyenne, WY 82007-
1898
Web Site: http://www.sierra.com
Sales Range: $200-249.9 Million
Emp.: 1,800
Clothing & Outdoor Gear Retailer
N.A.I.C.S.: 458110

T.J. Maxx of CA, LLC (1)
13560 Whittier Blvd, Whittier, CA 90605-
1934
Tel.: (562) 696-6659
Apparel & Home Fashion Retailer
N.A.I.C.S.: 315210

T.K. Maxx Holding GmbH (1)
Kaistr 16-18, Dusseldorf, 40468, Nordrhein-
Westfalen, Germany
Tel.: (49) 21188223100
Web Site: http://www.tkmaxx.com
Investment Management Service
N.A.I.C.S.: 523999

T.K. Maxx Management GmbH (1)
Peter Mullet Str 18, 40468, Dusseldorf, Ger-
many
Tel.: (49) 21188223100
Web Site: http://www.tkmaxx.de
Home Goods Discount Retailer
N.A.I.C.S.: 455110

TJX Australia Pty. Ltd. (1)
Level 3 189 O'Riordan Street, Mascot,
2020, NSW, Australia
Tel.: (61) 30 076 8913
Web Site: https://www.tkmaxx.com.au
Commodity Contract Broker Services
N.A.I.C.S.: 523160

TJX Austria Holding GmbH (1)
Mariahilfer Strasse 77-79, 1060, Vienna,
Austria
Tel.: (43) 120 583 6010
Web Site: https://www.tkmaxx.at
Emp.: 2
Holding Company
N.A.I.C.S.: 551114

TJX Deutschland Ltd. & Co. KG (1)
Peter-Muller-Strasse 18, 40468, Dusseldorf,
Germany
Tel.: (49) 21188223267
Web Site: http://www.tkmaxx.de
Emp.: 25
Discount Department Stores
N.A.I.C.S.: 455110

TJX Distribution Ltd. & Co. KG (1)
Peter-Muller-Strasse 18, 40468, Dusseldorf,
Germany

Tel.: (49) 21188223267
Web Site: http://www.tkmaxx.de
Apparel & Home Fashions Retailer
N.A.I.C.S.: 458110

TJX Europe Buying (Deutschland)
Ltd (1)
50 Clarendon Road, Watford, WD17 1TX,
Hertfordshire, United Kingdom
Tel.: (44) 1923473561
Web Site: http://www.tjx.com
Emp.: 3,000
Discount Department Stores
N.A.I.C.S.: 455110

TJX Europe Buying (Polska) Ltd (1)
TK Maxx and Homesense 50 Clarendon
Road, Watford, WD17 1TX, Hertfordshire,
United Kingdom
Tel.: (44) 1923473561
Discount & Grocery Retailer
N.A.I.C.S.: 455110
Micheal Mcmillin (CEO)

TJX Europe Buying Ltd (1)
50 Clarendon Road, Watford, WD17 1TX,
Hertfordshire, United Kingdom
Tel.: (44) 1923473984
Web Site: http://www.tjx.com
Discount Department Stores
N.A.I.C.S.: 455110

TJX Europe Limited (1)
50 Clarendon Road, Watford, WD17 1TX,
Herts, United Kingdom
Tel.: (44) 1923473000
Web Site: http://www.tjx.com
Retailer of Off-Price Apparel Business
N.A.I.C.S.: 458110

TJX European Distribution sp. z
o.o. (1)
ulÂ Kielczowska 74, 51-315, Wroclaw, Po-
land
Tel.: (48) 717110700
Web Site: http://www.tkmaxx.pl
Apparel Retailer
N.A.I.C.S.: 458110

TJX Incentive Sales, Inc. (1)
350 N Saint Paul St, Dallas, TX 75201
Tel.: (800) 333-1387
Discount Department Stores
N.A.I.C.S.: 455110

TJX Nederland B.V. (1)
Strawinskylaan 411 WTC Toren A 4de
Etage, 1077 XX, Amsterdam, Netherlands
Tel.: (31) 107114866
Holding Company
N.A.I.C.S.: 551114

TJX Oesterreich Ltd. & Co. KG (1)
Mariahilfer Strasse 77-79, 1060, Vienna,
Austria
Tel.: (43) 16982191
Web Site: https://www.tkmaxx.at
Clothing Accessory Retailer
N.A.I.C.S.: 455110

TJX UK (1)
50 Clarendon Road, Watford, WD17 1TX,
United Kingdom
Tel.: (44) 1923473000
Warehouse & Storage Services
N.A.I.C.S.: 493190

TK Maxx (1)
73 Clarendon Road, Watford, WD17 1TX,
United Kingdom
Tel.: (44) 192 347 3561
Web Site: https://www.tkmaxx.com
Apparel Retailer
N.A.I.C.S.: 458110

TK Maxx (1)
73 Clarendon Road, Watford, WD17 1TX,
United Kingdom
Tel.: (44) 1923473561
Web Site: https://www.tkmaxx.com
Clothing Accessory Retailer
N.A.I.C.S.: 455110

Wagon Wheel Realty, LLC (1)
2105 Memory Ln, Silver City, NM 88062
Tel.: (575) 388-2692
Web Site:
   https://www.wagonwheelrealtyinc.com
Real Estate Services
N.A.I.C.S.: 531390

Winners Merchants International
LP (1)
60 Standish Court, Mississauga, L5R 0G1,
ON, Canada (100%)
Tel.: (905) 405-8000
Web Site: https://www.winners.ca
Sales Range: $1-4.9 Billion
Emp.: 15,000
Apparel Stores
N.A.I.C.S.: 458110

THE TORO COMPANY

8111 Lyndale Ave S, Bloomington,
MN 55420-1196
Tel.: (952) 888-8801   DE
Web Site:
   https://www.thetorocompany.com
Year Founded: 1914
TTC—(NYSE)
Rev.: $4,583,800,000
Assets: $3,582,800,000
Liabilities: $2,030,900,000
Net Worth: $1,551,900,000
Earnings: $418,900,000
Emp.: 11,464
Fiscal Year-end: 10/31/24
Outdoor Care & Maintenance Prod-
ucts Mfr
N.A.I.C.S.: 333112
Darren L. Redetzke (VP-Strategic
Technologies)
Richard M. Olson (Chm, Pres &
CEO)
Kurt D. Svendsen (VP-Strategy, Corp
& Channel Dev)
Amy E. Dahl (VP-Intl)
Joanna M. Totsky (Gen Counsel, Sec
& VP)
Peter D. Moeller (VP-Intl)
Gregory S. Janey (VP-Residential &
Landscape Contractor Businesses)
Angela C. Drake (CFO)
Jody M. Christy (VP-BOSS)
Margeaux M. King (VP-HR)
Julie Kerekes (Treas & Sr Mng Dir-
Global Tax & IR)
Branden Happel (Sr Mgr-PR)
Jeremy Steffan (Dir-IR)
Branden Happel (Sr Mgr-PR)
Kevin N. Carpenter (VP)
Daryn A. Walters (VP)

Subsidiaries:

Bad Dawg Accessories, LLC (1)
1 Bad Boy Blvd, Batesville, AR 72501
Web Site: https://baddawgaccessories.com
All Terrain Vehicle Mfr & Distr
N.A.I.C.S.: 336390

Charles Machine Works, Inc. (1)
1959 W Fir Ave, Perry, OK 73077-0066
Tel.: (580) 336-4402
Web Site: https://www.ditchwitch.com
Sales Range: $300-349.9 Million
Emp.: 1,300
Trenching & Underground Machinery Mfr
N.A.I.C.S.: 333120
Rick Johnson (CEO)

Subsidiary (Domestic):

American Augers, Inc. (2)
135 US Route 42, West Salem, OH 44287
Tel.: (419) 869-7107
Web Site: http://www.americanaugers.com
Emp.: 200
Underground Construction Equipment Mfr
N.A.I.C.S.: 333120
Tammy Williams (Controller)
Mike Varone (Dir-Customer Svc)
Sharon Oliver (Dir-HR)
Brian Hollis (Dir-Engrg)
Steve Seabolt (Dir-Product Mgmt)
Dan Heath (Mgr-Product Support)
Kevin Slarb (Mgr-Parts)

Subsidiary (Domestic):

Trencor, Inc. (3)
9600 Corporate Pk Dr, Loudon, TN
37774 (100%)
Tel.: (817) 424-1968

Web Site: http://www.trencor.com
Sales Range: $75-99.9 Million
Emp.: 136
Construction & Digging Equipment Mfr
N.A.I.C.S.: 333120

Subsidiary (Domestic):

Earth Tool Company, LLC (2)
1300 Capitol Dr, Oconomowoc, WI
53066   (100%)
Tel.: (262) 567-8833
Web Site: http://www.hammerheadmole.com
Sales Range: $1-9.9 Million
Emp.: 51
Trenching & Underground Equipment Mfr
N.A.I.C.S.: 332710

Subsidiary (Domestic):

RS Lining Systems, LLC (3)
PO Box 3745, Cary, NC 27519   (100%)
Tel.: (919) 481-1977
Web Site: http://www.rstechnik.us
Emp.: 100
Pipe Rehabilitation Services
N.A.I.C.S.: 326122
Steve Wierzchowski (Dir-Tech)
Joanne Carroll (Sr VP)

**Exmark Manufacturing Company
Incorporated** (1)
2101 Ashland Ave, Beatrice, NE 68310-
0808
Tel.: (402) 223-6300
Web Site: https://www.exmark.com
Sales Range: $50-74.9 Million
Emp.: 300
Turf Care Equipment Mfr
N.A.I.C.S.: 333112

Hayter Limited (1)
Spellbrook, Bishop's Stortford, CM23 4BU,
Hertfordshire, United Kingdom
Tel.: (44) 1279723444
Web Site: http://www.hayter.co.uk
Sales Range: $25-49.9 Million
Emp.: 114
Commercial Rotary Lawnmower Mfr
N.A.I.C.S.: 333112

MTI Distributing Company Inc. (1)
4830 Azelia Ave N Ste 100, Brooklyn Cen-
ter, MN 55429
Tel.: (763) 592-5600
Web Site: https://www.mtidistributing.com
Rev.: $40,000,000
Emp.: 100
Farm & Garden Machinery
N.A.I.C.S.: 423820

**Rain Master Irrigation Systems,
Inc.** (1)
5825 Jasmine St, Riverside, CA 92504
Web Site: https://www.rainmaster.com
Irrigation Control System Operator
N.A.I.C.S.: 221310

Spartan Mowers, LLC (1)
1525 White Dr, Batesville, AR 72501
Web Site: https://spartanmowers.com
All Terrain Vehicle Mfr & Distr
N.A.I.C.S.: 336390

The Toro Co. (1)
4800 Vly Industrial Blvd S, Shakopee, MN
55379-1823
Tel.: (952) 937-3300
Web Site: http://www.toro.com
Sales Range: $100-124.9 Million
Emp.: 250
Mfr of Lawn Movers
N.A.I.C.S.: 333111

The Toro Co. (1)
174 16th St, Windom, MN 56101-1224
Tel.: (507) 831-3333
Web Site: http://www.toro.com
Sales Range: $200-249.9 Million
Emp.: 600
Mfr of Lawn & Garden Tractors & Garden-
ing Equipment
N.A.I.C.S.: 333112

The Toro Co. (1)
200 Sime Ave, Tomah, WI 54660-1328
Tel.: (608) 372-3991
Web Site: http://www.toro.com
Sales Range: $150-199.9 Million
Emp.: 550

Mfr of Home Lawn & Garden Tractors &
Equipment
N.A.I.C.S.: 333112

**The Toro Company Irrigation
Products** (1)
5825 Jasmine St, Riverside, CA 92504-
1144
Tel.: (951) 688-9221
Web Site: http://www.toro.com
Sales Range: $100-124.9 Million
Emp.: 300
Irrigation Sprinkler Systems Mfr
N.A.I.C.S.: 221310

Subsidiary (Domestic):

Irritrol Systems (2)
5825 Jasmine St, Riverside, CA 92504
Tel.: (951) 688-9221
Web Site: http://www.irritrolsystems.com
Sales Range: $75-99.9 Million
Emp.: 200
Mfr of Drip & Agricultural Irrigation Systems
& Commercial Turf Sprinklers
N.A.I.C.S.: 522291

**Toro Australia Group Sales Pty.
Ltd** (1)
53 Howards Road, Beverley, 5009, SA,
Australia
Tel.: (61) 1300867628
Web Site: http://www.toro.com.au
Sales Range: $75-99.9 Million
Farm & Garden Machinery Distr
N.A.I.C.S.: 423820

Toro Australia Pty. Ltd. (1)
53 Howards Road, Beverley, 5009, SA,
Australia   (100%)
Tel.: (61) 88 300 3633
Web Site: https://www.toro.com.au
Sales Range: $50-74.9 Million
Emp.: 110
Retailer of Toro Products; Distribution of
Irrigation Equipment
N.A.I.C.S.: 423820
Mardi Brown (Mgr-Fin Plng & Analysis)
Andrew Fidge (Mgr-Production)

Toro Credit Company (1)
8111 Lyndale Ave S, Bloomington, MN
55420-1196   (100%)
Tel.: (952) 888-5600
Web Site: http://www.toro.com
Sales Range: $25-49.9 Million
Emp.: 1,200
Finance Company
N.A.I.C.S.: 522220

Toro Europe N.V. (1)
Nijverheidsstraat 5 Oevel, Westerlo, 2260,
Belgium
Tel.: (32) 14562960
Web Site: http://www.toro.com
Sales Range: $25-49.9 Million
Emp.: 45
Turf Maintenance Equipment Mfr & Ser-
vices
N.A.I.C.S.: 561730
Johan Surkyn (CFO)

Toro Manufacturing LLC (1)
3795 N State 89 Ste F, Chino Valley, AZ
86323
Tel.: (928) 710-8874
Outdoor Care & Maintenance Products Mfr
N.A.I.C.S.: 333112

Toro R&D Company (1)
23 Taylor Ave Ste 105, Manasquan, NJ
08736-3025
Tel.: (732) 528-7008
Turf Maintenance Equipment Mfr & Distr
N.A.I.C.S.: 333112

**Toro Worldwide Parts Distribution
Center** (1)
3424 County Rd Pp, Plymouth, WI
53073-4387   (100%)
Tel.: (920) 892-9504
Web Site: http://www.toro.com
Sales Range: $50-74.9 Million
Emp.: 100
Parts Distribution
N.A.I.C.S.: 423820

Toro-Wheel Horse (1)
8111 Lyndale Ave S, Bloomington, MN
55420-1136

Tel.: (952) 888-8801
Web Site: http://www.toro.com
Sales Range: $300-349.9 Million
Emp.: 900
Lawn & Garden Tractors
N.A.I.C.S.: 333112

Venture Products, Inc. (1)
500 Venture Dr, Orrville, OH 44667
Tel.: (330) 683-0075
Web Site: https://www.ventrac.com
Rev.: $6,666,666
Emp.: 45
Farm Machinery & Equipment Mfr
N.A.I.C.S.: 333111

THE TRADE DESK, INC.
42 N Chestnut St, Ventura, CA 93001
Tel.: (805) 585-3434   CA
Web Site:
  https://www.thetradedesk.com
Year Founded: 2009
TTD—(NASDAQ)
Rev.: $1,946,120,000
Assets: $4,888,687,000
Liabilities: $2,724,468,000
Net Worth: $2,164,219,000
Earnings: $178,940,000
Emp.: 3,115
Fiscal Year-end: 12/31/23
Buy-Side Advertising Platform Soft-
ware Developer & Publisher
N.A.I.C.S.: 513210
Jeff T. Green (Co-Founder, Chm,
Pres & CEO)
Tim Sims (Chief Comml Officer)
David R. Pickles (Co-Founder)
Jed Dederick (Chief Revenue Officer
& Exec VP)
Tahnil Davis (Chief Acctg Officer & Sr
VP)
Lorenzo Moreno (VP-Bus Dev-West
Reg)
Julie Kleeman (Sr VP & Deputy Gen
Counsel)
Gruia Pitigoi-Aron (Sr VP-Product)
Mitch Waters (Sr VP-South-East Asia,
Australia & New Zealand)
Francois-Xavier Le Ray (Gen Mgr-
France & Belgium)
Natalia Papiol (Gen Mgr-Spain)
Jay Grant (Chief Legal Officer)
Benson Ho (Sr VP-North Asia)
Philippa Snare (Sr VP-EMEA)
Ryan Kim (Gen Mgr-Korea)
Kei Majima (Gen Mgr-Japan)
Chris Ngan (Gen Mgr-Hong Kong)
Joshua Smith (Sr VP)
Naseem Tuffaha (Chief Growth Offi-
cer)
Samantha Jacobson (Chief Strategy
Officer)

Subsidiaries:

**The Trade Desk (Singapore) PTE.
LTD.** (1)
Ocean Financial Centre 10 Collyer Quay
Level 25 Unit 06, Singapore, 049315, Sin-
gapore
Tel.: (65) 62402000
Advertising Services
N.A.I.C.S.: 541810
Hazel Ng (Dir-Trading)

**The Trade Desk Australia PTY
LTD** (1)
Level 31 9 Castlereagh Street, Sydney,
2000, NSW, Australia
Tel.: (61) 286506900
Advertising Services
N.A.I.C.S.: 541810
James Bayes (Gen Mgr-Australia & New
Zealand)

The Trade Desk GmbH (1)
Ballindamm 17, 20095, Hamburg, Germany
Tel.: (49) 40377076800
Advertising Services
N.A.I.C.S.: 541810
Niklas Plewe (Mgr-Acct)

The Trade Desk Japan K.K. (1)

Ginza Six 6-10-1 Ginza, Chuo-ku, Tokyo,
104-0061, Japan
Tel.: (81) 363327700
Advertising Services
N.A.I.C.S.: 541810
Tetsuya Shintani (Mgr-Country)

**The Trade Desk Korea Yuhan
Hoesa** (1)
517 Yeongdong-daero 30th Floor,
Gangnam-gu, Seoul, 06164, Korea (South)
Tel.: (82) 260013476
Advertising Services
N.A.I.C.S.: 541810

The Trade Desk Spain srl (1)
Paseo De la Castellana 81 7th Floor,
28046, Madrid, Spain
Tel.: (34) 910602393
Web Site: http://www.thetradedesk.com
Advertising Services
N.A.I.C.S.: 541810

The UK Trade Desk Ltd (1)
One Bartholomew Barts Square 10th Floor,
London, EC1A 7BL, United Kingdom
Tel.: (44) 2038688100
Advertising Services
N.A.I.C.S.: 541810

THE TRAVELERS COMPA-
NIES, INC.
485 Lexington Ave, New York, NY
10017
Tel.: (917) 778-6000   MN
Web Site: https://www.travelers.com
Year Founded: 1853
TRV—(NYSE)
Rev.: $41,364,000,000
Assets: $125,978,000,000
Liabilities: $101,057,000,000
Net Worth: $24,921,000,000
Earnings: $2,991,000,000
Emp.: 33,300
Fiscal Year-end: 12/31/23
Holding Company; Property & Casu-
alty Insurance; Asset & Risk Manage-
ment Services
N.A.I.C.S.: 551112
Andy F. Bessette (Chief Admin Officer
& Exec VP)
William H. Heyman (Vice Chm)
Maria Olivo (Pres-Intl & Exec VP-
Strategic Dev)
Mojgan M. Lefebvre (Chief Tech &
Ops Officer & Exec VP)
Michael F. Klein (Pres-Personal Insur-
ance & Exec VP)
Bruce R. Jones (Chief Risk Officer &
Exec VP-Enterprise Risk Mgmt)
Thomas M. Kunkel (Pres-Bond &
Specialty Insurance & Exec VP)
Kevin Christopher Smith (Chief Inno-
vation Officer & Exec VP)
Gregory C. Toczydlowski (Pres-Bus
Insurance & Exec VP)
Joan K. Woodward (Pres-The Travel-
ers Institute & Exec VP-Pub Policy)
Scott F. Higgins (Pres-Middle Market
Natl Property & Bus Insurance Field
& Exec VP)
Nicholas Seminara (Chief Claim Offi-
cer & Exec VP)
Daniel S. Frey (CFO & Exec VP)
Mojgan Lefebvre (Chief Tech & Ops
Officer & Exec VP)
Christine Kalla (Gen Counsel & Exec
VP)
David D. Rowland (Co-Chief Invest-
ment Officer & Exec VP)
Daniel T. H. Yin (Co-Chief Investment
Officer & Exec VP)
Diane Kurtzman (Chief HR Officer &
Exec VP)
Paul E. Munson (Principal Acctg Offi-
cer & Controller)
Larry J. Mills (Treas)
Peter A. Heard (Exec VP)
Avrohom J. Kess (Vice Chm)

The Travelers Companies, Inc.—(Continued)

Lisa M. Caputo *(Exec VP-Mktg, Comm, and Customer Experience)*
Alan David Schnitzer *(Chm & CEO)*
William C. Malugen Jr. *(Pres-Natl Accounts & Exec VP)*
Patrick F. Keegan Jr. *(Chief Underwriting Officer & Sr VP)*

Subsidiaries:

First Trenton Indemnity Co. (1)
402 Lippincott Dr, Marlton, NJ 08053
Tel.: (856) 983-2400
Sales Range: $200-249.9 Million
Emp.: 350
Provider of Auto, Homeowners & Personal Liability Insurance
N.A.I.C.S.: 524128

Gulf Insurance Company (1)
1 Power Sq, Hartford, CT 06183
Tel.: (212) 291-3000
Personal & Commercial Property & Casualty Insurance
N.A.I.C.S.: 524126
Osama Kamel Mostafa Kishk *(Grp CFO)*

Harborway Insurance Agency, LLC (1)
1 Beacon St 15th Fl, Boston, MA 02108
Web Site:
　https://www.harborwayinsurance.com
Insurance Agency Services
N.A.I.C.S.: 524210

InsuraMatch, LLC (1)
695 Atlantic Ave, Boston, MA 02111
Web Site: https://www.insuramatch.com
Insurance Agency Services
N.A.I.C.S.: 524210
Marc Buro *(CEO)*
Pauline Haddad *(CFO)*
Seth Miller *(Sls Dir)*

Northland Insurance Company (1)
385 Washington St, Saint Paul, MN 55102-1309
Web Site: https://www.northlandins.com
Commercial Transportation Industry Insurance Services
N.A.I.C.S.: 524126

Subsidiary (Domestic):

Northland Casualty Company (2)
385 Washington St, Saint Paul, MN 55102-1309
Tel.: (800) 237-9334
Web Site: http://www.northlandins.com
Property & Casualty Insurance Services
N.A.I.C.S.: 524126

Simply Business, Inc. (1)
1 Beacon St Fl 15, Boston, MA 02108
Web Site: https://www.simplybusiness.com
Life Insurance Brokerage Services
N.A.I.C.S.: 524210

Split Rock Partners, LLC (1)
16526 W 78th St Ste 504, Eden Prairie, MN 55346
Tel.: (952) 995-7474
Web Site: https://splitrock.com
Sales Range: $550-599.9 Million
Emp.: 25
Investor Services
N.A.I.C.S.: 523160
Michael Gorman *(Co-Founder & Mng Dir)*
Steven Schwen *(CFO)*
David Stassen *(Co-Founder & Mng Dir)*
James R. Simons *(Co-Founder & Mng Dir)*

St. Paul Fire & Marine Insurance Company (1)
165 University Avenue, Toronto, M5H 3B9, ON, Canada
Tel.: (651) 310-7911
Web Site: http://www.travelerscanada.ca
Property, Liability, Fidelity, Surety & Marine Insurance Services
N.A.I.C.S.: 524126

St. Paul Fire and Marine Insurance Company (1)
385 Washington St, Saint Paul, MN 55102-1309
Tel.: (651) 221-7911
Insurance Services

St. Paul Mercury Insurance Company (1)
385 Washington St, Saint Paul, MN 55102
Tel.: (651) 221-7911
Insurance Management Services
N.A.I.C.S.: 524298
Douglas West Leatherdale *(Chm)*

St. Paul Surplus Lines Insurance Company (1)
385 Washington St, Saint Paul, MN 55102
Tel.: (651) 310-7911
Insurance Agency & Brokerage Services
N.A.I.C.S.: 524210

The Dominion of Canada General Insurance Company (1)
165 University Ave, Toronto, M5H 3B9, ON, Canada
Tel.: (416) 362-7231
Web Site: http://www.travelerscanada.ca
Emp.: 1,400
Insurance Services
N.A.I.C.S.: 524126

The Family Business Institute LLC (1)
4050 Wake Forest Rd Ste 110, Raleigh, NC 27609
Web Site:
　http://www.familybusinessinstitute.com
Business Consulting Services
N.A.I.C.S.: 541611

Travelers (1)
4600 Fuller Dr Ste 200, Irving, TX 75038-6506
Tel.: (972) 650-3200
Sales Range: $150-199.9 Million
Emp.: 300
Personal & Commercial Property & Casualty Insurance
N.A.I.C.S.: 524126

Travelers Constitution State Insurance Company (1)
1 Tower Sq, Hartford, CT 06183
Tel.: (651) 310-7911
Property & Casualty Insurance Services
N.A.I.C.S.: 524126

Travelers Insurance Company Limited (1)
61-63 London Road, Redhill, RH1 1NA, United Kingdom
Tel.: (44) 1737787787
Web Site: https://www.travelers.co.uk
Property Insurance Services
N.A.I.C.S.: 524126

Travelers Insurance Company of Canada (1)
165 University Avenue, PO Box 5, Toronto, M5H 3B9, ON, Canada
Tel.: (416) 362-7231
Web Site: https://www.travelerscanada.ca
Property & Casualty Insurance Services
N.A.I.C.S.: 524126
Doug Hogan *(CFO)*
George Petropoulos *(Vice Chm)*
Heather Masterson *(Pres & CEO)*
Scott Gill *(COO)*
Michael Lin *(CIO)*
Erika Schurr *(Chief Actuary)*

Travelers Insurance Designated Activity Company (1)
Third Floor Block 8 Harcourt Centre Charlotte Way, Dublin, 2, Ireland
Tel.: (353) 16095600
Property Insurance Services
N.A.I.C.S.: 524126
James Liston *(CEO)*

Travelers Liability Insurance (1)
60 Lakefront Blvd, Buffalo, NY 14202-4302
Tel.: (716) 855-5173
Web Site: http://www.travelers.com
Sales Range: Less than $1 Million
Emp.: 20
Commercial Insurance Claim Adjusters
N.A.I.C.S.: 524291

Subsidiary (Domestic):

Constitution State Service LLC (2)
1 Tower Sq, Hartford, CT 06183
Tel.: (860) 277-8500

Web Site:
　https://www.constitutionstateservices.com
Advisory Services Insurance
N.A.I.C.S.: 524298
John Gorecki *(Pres)*

Travelers Lloyds of Texas Insurance Company (1)
1301 East Collins Blvd, Richardson, TX 75081
Tel.: (214) 570-6000
Web Site: http://www.travelers.com
Emp.: 1,000
Property Insurance Services
N.A.I.C.S.: 524126

Travelers London Limited (1)
Exchequer Court 33 St Mary Axe, London, EC3A 8AG, United Kingdom
Tel.: (44) 2032076580
Web Site: http://www.travelers.co.uk
Sales Range: $100-124.9 Million
Emp.: 300
Property & Casualty Insurance Services
N.A.I.C.S.: 524126

Travelers Management Limited (1)
Exchequer Court 33 Saint Mary Axe, London, EC3A 8AG, United Kingdom
Tel.: (44) 20 3207 6000
Web Site: http://www.travellers.co.uk
Property & Casualty Insurance Services
N.A.I.C.S.: 524126

Travelers Marine, LLC (1)
6608 Ft Smallwood Rd, Curtis Bay, MD 21226-1708
Tel.: (410) 636-8682
Transportation Equipment & Supplies Whslr
N.A.I.C.S.: 423860

Travelers Property Casualty Company of America (1)
1 Tower Sq, Hartford, CT 06183
Tel.: (860) 277-5660
Property & Casualty Insurance Services
N.A.I.C.S.: 524126

Travelers Property Casualty Corp. (1)
1 Tower Square, Hartford, CT 06183
Web Site: http://www.travellers.com
Property & Casualty Insurance Services
N.A.I.C.S.: 524126

Subsidiary (Domestic):

The Standard Fire Insurance Company (2)
1 Tower Sq, Hartford, CT 06183
Tel.: (862) 228-4458
Web Site: http://www.travelers.com
Property & Casualty Insurance Services
N.A.I.C.S.: 524126

The Travelers Indemnity Company of America (2)
1 Tower Sq, Hartford, CT 06183
Tel.: (866) 228-4458
Web Site: http://www.travelers.com
Property & Casualty Insurance Service
N.A.I.C.S.: 524126

The Travelers Marine Corporation (2)
1 Tower Sq, Hartford, CT 06183-0001
Tel.: (866) 228-4458
Web Site: http://www.travelers.com
Property & Casualty Insurance Services
N.A.I.C.S.: 524126

Travelers Casualty and Surety Company (2)
1 Tower Sq, Hartford, CT 06183
Tel.: (866) 228-4458
Property & Casualty Insurance Services
N.A.I.C.S.: 524126

Travelers Seguros Brasil S.A. (1)
Avenida Reboucas 3970 - 17 Floor, Sao Paulo, 05402-918, Barrio Pinheiros, Brazil
Tel.: (55) 8008911667
Web Site: https://fairwayseguros.com
General Insurance Services
N.A.I.C.S.: 524210

Travelers Syndicate Management Limited (1)
One Creechurch Place, London, EC3A 5AF, United Kingdom

Tel.: (44) 2032076000
Property Insurance Services
N.A.I.C.S.: 524126

Travelers Syndicate Management Limited (1)
One Creechurch Place, London, EC3A 5AF, United Kingdom
Tel.: (44) 2032076000
Web Site: http://www.travelers.co.uk
Property & Casualty Insurance Services
N.A.I.C.S.: 524126
John Carter *(Deputy Chm)*
Michael J. Gent *(CFO)*
Kevin C. Smith *(Co-Chm)*
Anthony G. Coughlan *(Co-Chm)*
Matthew L. Wilson *(CEO)*
Graham Gorsuch *(Co-Chief Underwriting Officer & Co-Chief Underwriting Officer)*
Chris Allison *(Co-Chief Underwriting Officer & Co-Chief Underwriting Officer)*

Travelers Underwriting Agency Limited (1)
Exchequer Court 33 Saint Mary Axe, London, EC3A 8AG, United Kingdom
Tel.: (44) 2032076000
Insurance Underwriting Services
N.A.I.C.S.: 524113

Trov Inc. (1)
347 Hartz Ave, Danville, CA 94526
Tel.: (925) 498-7800
Web Site: http://www.trov.com
Insurance Brokerage Services
N.A.I.C.S.: 531210
Scott Walchek *(Founder & CEO)*

Xbridge Limited (1)
6th Floor 99 Gresham Street, London, EC2V 7NG, United Kingdom
Tel.: (44) 3330146683
Web Site: https://www.simplybusiness.co.uk
Online Business Insurance Brokerage Services
N.A.I.C.S.: 524210

Zensurance Brokers Inc. (1)
200 University Avenue Suite 1302, Toronto, M5H 3C6, ON, Canada
Web Site: https://www.zensurance.com
Emp.: 100
Life Insurance Brokerage Services
N.A.I.C.S.: 524210

Zensurance Inc. (1)
200 University Avenue Suite 1301, Toronto, M5H 3C6, ON, Canada
Web Site: https://www.zensurance.com
Emp.: 100
Property Insurance Services
N.A.I.C.S.: 524126

THE TRU SHRIMP COMPANIES, INC.
330 3rd St, Balaton, MN 56115　　DE
Web Site:
　https://www.trushrimpcompany.com
Year Founded: 2017
BTRU—(NASDAQ)
Rev.: $9,446
Assets: $26,203,518
Liabilities: $18,297,926
Net Worth: $7,905,592
Earnings: ($7,412,650)
Emp.: 22
Fiscal Year-end: 12/31/20
Seafood Mfr
N.A.I.C.S.: 311710
Michael B. Ziebell *(Pres, CEO & Sec)*
Robert J. Vold *(CFO)*
Bruce Paterson *(Chief Technical Officer)*
Brian Knochenmus *(Chm)*
Robert Gervais *(Sr Dir-Operations)*

THE VICTORY BANCORP, INC.
548 N Lewis Rd, Limerick, PA 19468
Tel.: (610) 948-9000　　PA
Web Site:
　https://www.victorybank.com
Year Founded: 2009
VTYB—(OTCIQ)
Offices of Bank Holding Companies
N.A.I.C.S.: 551111

Robert H. Schultz *(CFO, COO & Compliance Officer)*
Joseph W. Major *(Chm, Pres & CEO)*

Subsidiaries:

The Victory Bank **(1)**
548 N Lewis Rd, Limerick, PA 19468
Tel.: (610) 948-9000
Web Site: http://www.victorybank.com
Commericial Banking
N.A.I.C.S.: 522110
Joseph W. Major *(Chm, Pres & CEO)*
Robert H. Schultz *(CFO, COO & Compliance Officer)*
Eric B. Offner *(Chief Credit Officer)*
Michael Senico *(Sr VP)*
Alex Kroll *(Chief Lending Officer)*

THE VITA COCO COMPANY, INC.

250 Park Ave S Fl 7, New York, NY 10003
Tel.: (212) 206-0763 **DE**
Web Site: https://vitacoco.com
Year Founded: 2007
COCO—(NASDAQ)
Rev.: $427,787,000
Assets: $197,757,000
Liabilities: $56,664,000
Net Worth: $141,093,000
Earnings: $7,814,000
Emp.: 269
Fiscal Year-end: 12/31/22
Beverage Product Mfr
N.A.I.C.S.: 312120
Martin F. Roper *(CEO)*
Jonathan Burth *(COO)*
Jane Prior *(CMO)*
Charles van Es *(Chief Sls Officer)*
Yolanda Goettsch *(Gen Counsel)*
Ira Liran *(Co-Founder)*
Michael Kirban *(Co-Founder & Chm)*
Corey Baker *(CFO & Interim Principal Acctg Officer)*

THE WALT DISNEY COMPANY

500 S Buena Vista St, Burbank, CA 91521-7667
Tel.: (818) 560-1000 **DE**
Web Site:
https://thewaltdisneycompany.com
Year Founded: 1923
DIS—(NYSE)
Rev.: $88,898,000,000
Assets: $205,579,000,000
Liabilities: $101,622,000,000
Net Worth: $103,957,000,000
Earnings: $2,354,000,000
Emp.: 225,000
Fiscal Year-end: 09/30/23
Advertising Media Services
N.A.I.C.S.: 551112
Latondra Newton *(Chief Diversity Officer & Sr VP)*
Mark G. Parker *(Chm)*
Brent A. Woodford *(Exec VP-Controllership, Financial Plng & Tax)*
Lowell Singer *(Sr VP-IR)*
Josh D'Amaro *(Chm-Disney Parks, Experiences & Products)*
Rebecca Campbell *(Chm-Intl Content & Ops)*
Kareem Daniel *(Chm-Media & Entertainment Distr)*
Carlos A. Gomez *(Treas & Sr VP)*
Nancy Lee *(Sr VP)*
James Pitaro *(Chm-ESPN & Sports Content)*
Peter Rice *(Chm-General Entertainment Content)*
Latondra Newton *(Chief Diversity Officer & Sr VP)*
Ronald L. Iden *(Chief Security Officer & Sr VP)*
Diane Jurgens *(CIO & Exec VP-Enterprise Tech)*

Susan Yun Lee *(Assoc-Strategic Planning Group)*
Alan Bergman *(Chm-Disney Studios Content)*
Jenny Cohen *(Exec VP-Corp Social Responsibility)*
Alan F. Horn *(Chief Creative Officer-Disney Studios Content)*
Alicia Schwarz *(Chief Compliance Officer & Sr VP)*
Kristen Finney *(Exec VP-Content Curation-Intl Content & Ops Grp)*
Rita Ferro *(Pres-Adv Sls-Disney Media & Entertainment Distr)*
Sonia Coleman *(Chief HR Officer & Sr Exec VP)*
Kristina Schake *(Chief Comm Officer)*
David L. Bowdich *(Chief Security Officer)*
Horacio Gutierrez *(Corp Counsel)*
Jolene Negre *(Sec)*
Alexia S. Quadrani *(Exec VP-IR)*
Hugh F. Johnston *(CFO & Sr Exec VP)*

Subsidiaries:

Asianet Star Communications Private Limited **(1)**
Jacob Tower Palarivattom, Kochi, 682025, Kerala, India
Tel.: (91) 484 309 1111
Television Broadcasting Services
N.A.I.C.S.: 516120

TWDC Enterprises 18 Corp. **(1)**
500 S Buena Vista St, Burbank, CA 91521
Tel.: (818) 560-1000
Holding Company; Multimedia Entertainment Products & Services
N.A.I.C.S.: 551112
Kevin A. Mayer *(Executives)*
Christine M. McCarthy *(CFO & Sr Exec VP)*
Robert A. Iger *(Chm & CEO)*

Subsidiary (Domestic):

ABC, Inc. **(2)**
77 W 66th St, New York, NY 10023-6201
Tel.: (212) 456-7777
Web Site: http://www.abc.com
Sales Range: $5-14.9 Billion
Emp.: 1,000
Television Networks
N.A.I.C.S.: 516120

Branch (Domestic):

ABC, Inc. **(3)**
2300 W Riverside Dr, Burbank, CA 91506
Tel.: (818) 483-6537
Web Site: http://www.abc.go.com
Sales Range: $200-249.9 Million
Emp.: 800
Produces & Licenses Television Programs
N.A.I.C.S.: 516110

Joint Venture (Domestic):

A&E Television Networks, LLC **(4)**
235 E 45th St, New York, NY 10017 **(50%)**
Tel.: (212) 210-1400
Web Site: http://www.aenetworks.com
Holding Company; Cable Television Networks Operator
N.A.I.C.S.: 551112
Michael Feeney *(Exec VP-Corp Comm)*
Peter Olsen *(Pres-Ad Sls)*
David Zagin *(Pres-Distr)*
Henry Hoberman *(Chief Legal Officer)*
Paul Buccieri *(Pres)*
David Granville-Smith *(CFO & COO)*
Robert Sharenow *(Pres-Programming)*
Karen Gray *(Exec VP-HR)*
Gena McCarthy *(Exec VP & Head-Programming-Lifetime, Unscripted & FYI)*
Elaine Frontain Bryant *(Exec VP & Head-Programming)*
Tanya Lopez *(Exec VP-Movies, Limited Series-Lifetime Movies)*
Eli Lehrer *(Exec VP & Gen Mgr-History)*
David Bank *(Exec VP-Corp Dev & Strategy)*
Amy Winter *(Exec VP & Head-Programming & Lifetime)*

Steve MacDonald *(Pres-Global Content Licensing & Intl)*
Juliana Stock *(Exec VP-Corp Brand Strategy)*

Unit (Domestic):

A&E Network **(5)**
235 E 45th St, New York, NY 10019
Tel.: (212) 210-1400
Web Site: http://www.aetv.com
Cable Television Network
N.A.I.C.S.: 516210
Elaine Frontain Bryant *(Exec VP & Head-Programming)*

Branch (Domestic):

A&E Television Networks, LLC - Detroit Office **(5)**
201 W Big Beaver Rd Ste 1010, Troy, MI 48084-4154
Tel.: (248) 740-1300
Web Site: http://www.aenetworks.com
Emp.: 8
Advertising Sales
N.A.I.C.S.: 541890

Subsidiary (Domestic):

Lifetime Entertainment Services, LLC **(5)**
235 E 45th St, New York, NY 10017
Tel.: (212) 210-1400
Web Site: http://www.mylifetime.com
Sales Range: $750-799.9 Million
Emp.: 300
Operator of Cable Television Network with Informational Programming About Lifestyles, Relationships, Personal Development & Health
N.A.I.C.S.: 516210

Unit (Domestic):

Lifetime Television **(6)**
2049 Century Park E Ste 840, Los Angeles, CA 90067-3110
Tel.: (310) 556-7500
Web Site: http://www.mylifetime.com
Sales Range: $10-24.9 Million
Emp.: 80
Motion Picture & Video Production
N.A.I.C.S.: 512110

Unit (Domestic):

The Biography Channel **(5)**
235 E 45th St Ste 1104, New York, NY 10017-3303
Tel.: (212) 649-4099
Web Site: http://www.biography.com
Biographical Programming Cable Network
N.A.I.C.S.: 516210

The History Channel **(5)**
235 E 45th St, New York, NY 10017
Tel.: (212) 210-1400
Web Site: http://www.history.com
History Programming Cable Network
N.A.I.C.S.: 516210

Group (Domestic):

ABC Cable Networks Group **(4)**
500 S Buena Vista St, Burbank, CA 91521 **(100%)**
Tel.: (818) 569-7500
Cable Television Programming
N.A.I.C.S.: 516210

ABC Family Worldwide, Inc. **(4)**
500 S Buena Vista St, Burbank, CA 91521
Tel.: (818) 560-1000
Family Cable Television Programming
N.A.I.C.S.: 516210
Laura Kuhn Nelson *(Sr VP-Audience Solutions)*
Tom Ascheim *(Pres)*
Salaam Coleman Smith *(Exec VP-Strategy & Programming)*
Kenny Miller *(Sr VP-Digital Programming & Product)*

Unit (Domestic):

Freeform TV **(5)**
500 S Buena Vista St, Burbank, CA 91521-9078
Tel.: (818) 560-1000
Web Site: http://freeform.go.com

Family-Oriented National Cable Network Services
N.A.I.C.S.: 512110
Tara Duncan *(Pres)*

Group (Domestic):

ABC Television Network Group **(4)**
77 W 66th St, New York, NY 10023-6201
Tel.: (212) 456-7000
Web Site: http://www.abc.com
Sales Range: $200-249.9 Million
Television Programming & Broadcasting
N.A.I.C.S.: 516120

Subsidiary (Domestic):

American Broadcasting Companies, Inc. **(5)**
500 S Buena Vista St, Burbank, CA 91521-3515
Tel.: (212) 456-3361
Web Site: http://disneyabc.tv
Sales Range: $100-124.9 Million
Motion Picture & Video Production
N.A.I.C.S.: 512110
Dana Walden *(Chm-Entertainment)*

Subsidiary (Domestic):

ABC Broadcast Operations & Engineering **(6)**
77 W 66th St, New York, NY 10023-6201
Tel.: (212) 456-7777
Web Site: http://www.abcmedianet.com
Television Broadcasting
N.A.I.C.S.: 516120

ABC National Television Sales, Inc. **(6)**
77 W 66th St Fl 19, New York, NY 10023-6201
Tel.: (212) 456-7777
Web Site: http://www.abc.com
Rev.: $14,500,000
Emp.: 150
ABC Spot Sales
N.A.I.C.S.: 516120

Division (Domestic):

ABC News & Sports **(6)**
47 W 66th St, New York, NY 10023-6201
Tel.: (212) 456-7777
Web Site: http://www.abcradio.com
Sales Range: $100-124.9 Million
News & Sports Broadcasting
N.A.I.C.S.: 516210
Stacia Deshishku *(VP & Gen Mgr)*
Jeff Fitzgerald *(Exec Dir-Ops)*
Heidi Oringer *(Exec Dir-Bus Strategies, Programming & Distr)*
Scott Goldberg *(Dir-News Programming)*
Chris Venice *(Sr Mgr-Affiliate Solutions)*
Mary McCarthy *(Mgr-Affiliate Solutions)*
Abe Velez *(Dir-Bus Dev & Strategy)*

Subsidiary (Domestic):

ABC News Holding Company, Inc. **(7)**
77 W 66th St, New York, NY 10023-6201
Tel.: (212) 456-7777
Web Site: http://www.abc.com
Rev.: $5,400,000
Emp.: 100
Holding Company
N.A.I.C.S.: 551112

ABC News Intercontinental, Inc. **(7)**
77 W 66th St, New York, NY 10023-6201 **(100%)**
Tel.: (212) 456-7777
Web Site: http://www.abc.go.com
Sales Range: $25-49.9 Million
Emp.: 100
Television Network Programming
N.A.I.C.S.: 512110

ABC News, Inc. **(7)**
47 W 66th St, New York, NY 10023-6201
Tel.: (212) 456-7777
Web Site: http://www.abcnews.go.com
Sales Range: $10-24.9 Million
Emp.: 65
News Syndicates

The Walt Disney Company—(Continued)

N.A.I.C.S.: 516210

ABC Sports, Inc. (7)
77 W 66th St, New York, NY 10023-6201
Tel.: (212) 456-7777
Web Site: http://www.abcnews.go.com
Rev.: $150,000
Broadcasting Sports Events
N.A.I.C.S.: 516210

Division (Domestic):

ABC Owned Television Stations (6)
4100 City Ave, Philadelphia, PA
19131-1610 (100%)
Tel.: (215) 878-9700
Web Site: http://www.abc.com
Sales Range: $10-24.9 Million
Emp.: 7
Television Broadcasting & National Sales
N.A.I.C.S.: 516120
Adrianne Anderson (Sr VP-Content Dev)
Chad Matthews (Pres)

Subsidiary (Domestic):

KABC-TV Inc. (7)
500 Cir Seven Dr, Glendale, CA 91201
Tel.: (818) 863-7777
Web Site: http://www.abc7.com
Television Broadcasting
N.A.I.C.S.: 516120

KFSN-TV Inc. (7)
1777 G St, Fresno, CA
93706-1616 (100%)
Tel.: (559) 442-1170
Web Site: http://www.abc30.com
Television Broadcasting
N.A.I.C.S.: 516120
Michael Carr (Pres & Gen Mgr)
Charlene Ciavaglia (Mgr-Programming)
Brandon Ridge (Mktg Dir-Community Engagement)
Jason Wallace (Dir-Tech)
Greg Baker (Sls Mgr)

KGO Television, Inc. (7)
900 Frnt St, San Francisco, CA 94111-1427
Tel.: (415) 954-7777
Web Site: http://www.abc7news.com
Television Broadcasting Station
N.A.I.C.S.: 516120

KTRK Television, Inc. (7)
3310 Bissonnet, Houston, TX
77005-2114 (100%)
Tel.: (713) 666-0713
Sales Range: $10-24.9 Million
Broadcasting
N.A.I.C.S.: 516120
Timothy Hinson (VP-Tech)

WABC-TV Inc. (7)
7 Lincoln Sq, New York, NY, 10023-5998
Tel.: (917) 260-7000
Web Site: http://www.7online.com
Television Programming
N.A.I.C.S.: 516120

WLS Television, Inc. (7)
190 N State St, Chicago, IL 60601-3302
Tel.: (312) 750-7777
Web Site: http://www.abc7chicago.com
Television Broadcasting
N.A.I.C.S.: 516120
Diana Palomar (VP-Community Affairs)

WPVI-TV Inc. (7)
4100 City Ave, Philadelphia, PA
19131-1610 (100%)
Tel.: (215) 878-9700
Web Site: http://www.6abc.com
Television Broadcasting
N.A.I.C.S.: 516120
Tim Gianettino (VP & Sls Mgr-Natl)
Dirk Ohley (VP & Sls Mgr)
Jennifer A. Bullick (Dir-Digital Sls)
Diane Hamlet (Coord-Creative Svcs)

WTVD-TV Inc. (7)
411 Liberty St, Durham, NC 27701-3407
Tel.: (919) 683-1111
Web Site: http://www.abc11tv.com
Television Broadcasting
N.A.I.C.S.: 516120

Group (Domestic):

ESPN, Inc. (4)

ESPN Plz 545 Middle St, Bristol, CT
06010-7454 (80%)
Tel.: (860) 766-2000
Web Site: http://www.espn.com
Holding Company; Sports Entertainment
Multimedia Broadcaster & Publisher
N.A.I.C.S.: 551112
Norby Williamson (Exec VP-Production & Exec Editor)
Rob King (Sr VP)
Stephanie Druley (Exec VP-Event & Studio Production)
Burke Magnus (Exec VP-Programming & Original Content)
James Pitaro (Chm-Sports Content)
Thomas Hennessy (Sr VP-Fin)
Kevin Merida (Sr VP & Editor-in-Chief)
Mark Walker (Sr VP-Content Bus Dev & Innovation)
Chara-Lynn Aguiar (VP-Strategy)
Rosetta Ellis-Pilie (VP-Talent Dev & Negotiations)

Subsidiary (Domestic):

B.A.S.S., Inc. (5)
1170 Celebration Blvd Ste 200, Kissimmee,
FL 34747-4604
Tel.: (407) 566-2277
Web Site: http://www.bassmaster.com
Rev.: $50,000,000
Emp.: 68
Magazine Publisher
N.A.I.C.S.: 513120

Unit (Domestic):

B.A.S.S. Times (6)
PO Box 10000, Lake Buena Vista, FL
32830
Tel.: (407) 566-2277
Web Site: http://www.bassmaster.com
Sales Range: $25-49.9 Million
Publishers of Magazine
N.A.I.C.S.: 513120

Bassmaster Magazine (6)
200 Celebration Pl Ste 900, Celebration, FL
34747
Tel.: (407) 566-2460
Web Site: http://www.bassmaster.com
Sales Range: $50-74.9 Million
Publishers of Freshwater Bass Fishermen
Magazine
N.A.I.C.S.: 513120

Subsidiary (Domestic):

ESPN Regional Television, Inc. (5)
11001 Rushmore Dr, Charlotte, NC 28277-3434
Tel.: (704) 973-5000
Web Site: http://www.espn.com
Sales Range: $25-49.9 Million
Emp.: 110
Sports Promotion
N.A.I.C.S.: 711320

Subsidiary (Domestic):

Adventures By Disney (2)
210 Celebration Pl, Celebration, FL
34747 (100%)
Tel.: (407) 566-3500
Web Site:
http://www.adventuresbydisney.com
Family Vacations & Guided Group Tours
N.A.I.C.S.: 561520

BVS Entertainment, Inc. (2)
500 S Buena Vista St, Burbank, CA 91521
Tel.: (818) 560-2950
Television Broadcasting Services
N.A.I.C.S.: 516120

**Buena Vista Home Entertainment,
Inc.** (2)
350 S Buena Vista St, Burbank, CA
91521-0004 (100%)
Tel.: (818) 560-1000
Web Site: http://bventertainment.go.com
Sales Range: $50-74.9 Million
Pre-Recorded Video Cassette Sales
N.A.I.C.S.: 512110

Subsidiary (Domestic):

Disney Interactive Studios (3)
521 Cir 7 Dr, Glendale, CA 91201
Tel.: (818) 553-5000

Sales Range: $100-124.9 Million
Emp.: 400
Video Game Licensing & Publishing
N.A.I.C.S.: 339930

Hollywood Records Inc. (3)
500 S Buena Vista St, Burbank, CA
91521 (100%)
Tel.: (818) 560-5670
Web Site: http://www.hollywoodrecords.com
Sales Range: $25-49.9 Million
Emp.: 100
Prerecorded Records & Tapes
N.A.I.C.S.: 334610

Subsidiary (Domestic):

Buena Vista International, Inc. (2)
500 S Buena Vista St, Burbank, CA 91521
Tel.: (818) 560-1000
Video Production & Distr
N.A.I.C.S.: 512110

Buena Vista Television, LLC (2)
500 S Buena Vista St FGW Ste 3052, Burbank, CA 91521-3515
Tel.: (818) 560-1000
Web Site: http://www.disneyabc.tv
Sales Range: $100-124.9 Million
Television Programming Distr
N.A.I.C.S.: 512120

**Buena Vista Theatrical Group
LLC** (2)
214 W 42nd St, New York, NY
10036 (100%)
Tel.: (212) 827-5400
Web Site:
http://www.disneyonbroadway.com
Rev.: $85,000
Emp.: 120
Motion Picture & Video Production
N.A.I.C.S.: 512110

Disholder 3, Inc. (2)
2711 Centerville Rd Ste 400, Wilmington,
DE 19808
Tel.: (302) 636-5401
Motion Picture & Video Production Services
N.A.I.C.S.: 512110

Disney Consumer Products, Inc. (2)
500 S Buena Vista Dr, Burbank, CA 91521
Tel.: (818) 560-1000
Web Site: http://dpep.disney.com
Consumer Products Licensing, Distribution
& Retail Sales
N.A.I.C.S.: 459420

Subsidiary (Domestic):

**Disney Publishing Worldwide,
Inc.** (3)
44 S Broadway, White Plains, NY 10601
Tel.: (212) 633-4400
Web Site: http://www.disney.go.com
Sales Range: $100-124.9 Million
Book Publisher of Children's Books
N.A.I.C.S.: 513130

Disney Shopping, Inc. (3)
820 S Flower St, Burbank, CA 91502
Tel.: (818) 238-4700
Online Shopping Website Operator
N.A.I.C.S.: 425120

Disney Store Inc. (3)
101 N Brand Blvd Ste 1000, Glendale, CA
91203-2635 (100%)
Tel.: (818) 265-3435
Sales Range: $250-299.9 Million
Emp.: 500
Family Clothing Stores
N.A.I.C.S.: 459420

Subsidiary (Domestic):

Disney Destinations, LLC (2)
1500 Epcot Resorts Blvd, Lake Buena
Vista, FL 32830-8402
Tel.: (407) 934-4000
Web Site: http://www.swandolphin.com
Sales Range: $5-14.9 Billion
Operator of Resorts & Entertainment
N.A.I.C.S.: 713110
Michael A. Colglazier (Pres/Mng Dir-Asia
Pacific)

Subsidiary (Domestic):

Disney Cruise Vacations Inc. (3)

210 Celebration Pl, Celebration, FL 34747-
4600
Tel.: (407) 566-3500
Web Site: http://www.disneycruise.com
Sales Range: $150-199.9 Million
Emp.: 700
Providers of Cruise Ships
N.A.I.C.S.: 487210

Disney Vacation Club (3)
1390 Celebration Blvd, Celebration, FL
34747
Tel.: (407) 566-3000
Web Site: http://www.disneyvacationclub.disney.go.com
Sales Range: $1-9.9 Million
Emp.: 418
Resort Hotel
N.A.I.C.S.: 721110

**Walt Disney Parks & Resorts U.S.,
Inc.** (3)
1375 Buena Vista Dr 4th Fl N, Lake Buena
Vista, FL 32830 (100%)
Tel.: (407) 824-2222
Sales Range: $5-14.9 Billion
Emp.: 55,000
Theme Parks & Resorts Operator
N.A.I.C.S.: 713110

Unit (Domestic):

Disneyland Hotels (4)
1150 W Magic Way, Anaheim, CA
92802-2247 (100%)
Tel.: (714) 778-6600
Web Site:
http://www.disneyland.disney.com
Guest Rooms, Convention Facilities, Meeting Rooms & Resort Hotel
N.A.I.C.S.: 721110

Disneyland Resorts (4)
1313 S Harbor Blvd, Anaheim, CA
92802-8023 (100%)
Tel.: (714) 781-4000
Web Site: http://www.disney.com
Sales Range: $75-99.9 Million
Vacation Services
N.A.I.C.S.: 541990
Ken Potrock (Pres)
Elliot K. Mills (VP-Hotel Ops-Disneyland
Resort & Aulani)

Old Key West Resort (4)
1510 N Cove Rd, Lake Buena Vista, FL
32830
Tel.: (407) 827-7700
Web Site:
http://www.disneyworld.disney.go.com
Hotels (except Casino Hotels) & Motels
N.A.I.C.S.: 721110

Subsidiary (Domestic):

Disney Enterprises, Inc. (2)
500 S Buena Vista St, Burbank, CA 91521-
7667
Sales Range: $10-24.9 Million.
Emp.: 50
Producer of Motion Pictures, Radio & Television Programs, Outdoor Recreation, Consumer Products & Educational Media
N.A.I.C.S.: 512110

Subsidiary (Non-US):

Walt Disney International Ltd. (2)
3 Queen Caroline Street, London, W6 9PE,
United Kingdom
Tel.: (44) 2082221000
Web Site: http://www.disney.com
Motion Picture & Video Production
N.A.I.C.S.: 512110

Subsidiary (Domestic):

Disney Interactive Media Group (2)
5161 Lankershim Blvd, North Hollywood,
CA 91601
Tel.: (818) 623-3200
Web Site: http://corporate.disney.go.com
Sales Range: $50-74.9 Million.
Emp.: 200
Online Family Entertainment Services
N.A.I.C.S.: 516210

Subsidiary (Non-US):

Disney Canada, Inc. (3)
1628 Dickson Avenue Suite 500, Kelowna,

V1Y 9X1, BC, Canada
Tel.: (250) 868-8622
Web Site: http://www.clubpenguin.com
Sales Range: $25-49.9 Million
Online Family Entertainment Services
N.A.I.C.S.: 516210

Subsidiary (Domestic):

Playdom, Inc. (3)
100 W Evelyn Ave Ste 110, Mountain View,
CA 94041
Tel.: (650) 963-8000
Web Site: http://www.playdom.com
Social Media Game Developer
N.A.I.C.S.: 513210

Subsidiary (Domestic):

Acclaim Games, Inc. (4)
9595 Wilshire Blvd, Beverly Hills, CA 90212
Tel.: (310) 691-5984
Sales Range: $1-9.9 Million
Emp.: 35
Computer System Design Services
N.A.I.C.S.: 541512

Subsidiary (Non-US):

Disney Magic Company Limited (2)
3 Queen Caroline Street, Hammersmith,
London, W69PE, United Kingdom
Tel.: (44) 2082221000
Business Management Consulting Services
N.A.I.C.S.: 541611

Subsidiary (Domestic):

Disney Theatrical Productions (2)
890 Broadway, New York, NY 10036
Tel.: (212) 353-5057
Web Site: http://disney.go.com
Sales Range: $25-49.9 Million
Theatrical Production
N.A.I.C.S.: 711110

Disney Worldwide Services, Inc. (2)
500 S Buena Vista St, Burbank, CA 91521-
8440
Tel.: (818) 560-1000
Web Site: https://d23.com
Electronic Product Repair & Maintenance
Services
N.A.I.C.S.: 811210

Subsidiary (Non-US):

Euro Disney S.C.A. (2)
Disneyland Paris Greenwich building, BP
100, 77777, Marne-la-Vallee, Cedex 04,
France
Tel.: (33) 164744000
Holding Company; Theme Park & Resort
Operator
N.A.I.C.S.: 551112

Subsidiary (Domestic):

Euro Disney Associes SCA (3)
1 rond-point d Isigny, Immeubles Adminis-
tratifs, 77700, Chessy, France (82%)
Tel.: (33) 164744000
Web Site: https://www.disneylandparis.com
Sales Range: $1-4.9 Billion
Theme Park & Resort Operator
N.A.I.C.S.: 713110

Subsidiary (Domestic):

EDL Hotels SCA (4)
BP 100, Marne-la-Vallee, France (100%)
Tel.: (33) 164744000
Hotel Operator
N.A.I.C.S.: 721110

Subsidiary (Domestic):

Euro Disney Commandite SAS (3)
1 Rue De La Galmy, Immeubles Adminis-
tratifs, Chessy, 77700, France
Tel.: (33) 164745855
Holding Company
N.A.I.C.S.: 551112

Subsidiary (Non-US):

Hong Kong Disneyland Management
Limited (2)
Hong Kong Disneyland Resort, Lantau Is-
land New Territories, Hong Kong, China
(Hong Kong)
Tel.: (852) 35502838

Web Site:
http://hkcorporate.hongkongdisney
land.com
Theme Park Operating Services
N.A.I.C.S.: 713110
Wai Quen Chan (VP-HR)
Annie Wharmby (Exec Dir-Entertainment &
Costuming)
Rita Tang (Head-Legal)
Michael Moriarty (Mng Dir)
Tim Sypko (Sr VP-Ops)
Cindy Chow (CFO & VP)
Anita Lai (VP-Comm & Pub Affairs)
Daisy Sit (VP-Mktg)
Leon Chan (Exec Dir-Tech & Digital)

Subsidiary (Domestic):

Hulu, LLC (2)
12312 W Olympic Blvd, Los Angeles, CA
90064 (67%)
Tel.: (310) 571-4700
Web Site: http://www.hulu.com
Sales Range: $400-449.9 Million
Emp.: 225
Online Video Content Publishing & Stream-
ing Services
N.A.I.C.S.: 516210
Jason Kilar (Founder)
Billy Rosenberg (Head-Comedy Originals)
Kelci Parker (VP-Comedy Originals)
Dougie Cash (VP-Drama Originals)
Sasha Silver (Head-Drama Originals)

Subsidiary (Non-US):

Hungama TV (2)
4th Floor Peninsula Tower No Peninsula
Corporate Park GK Marg, Lower Parel,
400013, Mumbai, Worli, India
Tel.: (91) 22 2490 5353
Web Site: http://www.hungamatv.com
Sales Range: $200-249.9 Million
Children's Television Broadcasting
N.A.I.C.S.: 516120

Subsidiary (Domestic):

Lucasfilm Ltd. (2)
PO Box 29901, San Francisco, CA 94129-
0901
Tel.: (415) 623-1000
Web Site: https://www.lucasfilm.com
Sales Range: $1-4.9 Billion
Emp.: 1,500
Motion Picture Producer & Distr
N.A.I.C.S.: 512110
Lynne Hale (VP-Publicity & Comm)
Kathleen Kennedy (Pres)
Paul Southern (Sr VP-Licensing)
Lynwen Brennan (Exec VP & Gen Mgr)
Rob Bredow (Sr VP)
Michelle Rejwan (Sr VP-Live Action Dev &
Production)
Pippa Anderson (VP-Post-Production)
Lori Aultman (VP-Fin & Plng)
Carrie Beck (VP-Animation & Live Action
Series Dev)
Candice Campos (VP-Physical Production)
Mickey Capoferri (Sr Dir-Online Content &
Programming)
Blaire Chaput (VP-HR)
Megan Crumpacker (VP-Franchise Mktg &
Integrated Plng)
Chris Furia (VP-Production Fin)
John Hampian (VP-Long Form Physical
Production)
Jacqui Lopez (VP-Franchise Production)
Douglas Reilly (VP-Games)
John Swartz (VP)
James Waugh (VP-Franchise Content &
Strategy)
Anna Yeager (VP & Creative Dir-A & V)
Janet Lewin (Sr VP)
Francois Chardavoine (VP-Tech)
Michael A. Garcia (VP-Live Action Series
Dev)
Athena Portillo (VP-Animation Production)
Rayne Roberts (VP-Film Dev)
Max Taylor (VP-Live Action Series Dev)
Dave Filoni (Chief Creative Officer)
Momita SenGupta (Exec VP)
David Goldman (Sr VP)
Rhonda Hjort (Sr VP)
Chris Argyropoulos (VP)
Vicki Dobbs Beck (VP)
Joseph Cho (VP)
T. J. Falls (VP)
Dustin Sandoval (VP)
Doug Chiang (Sr VP)

Subsidiary (Non-US):

Magical Cruise Company,
Limited (2)
3 Queen Caroline Street, Hammersmith,
London, W6 9PE, United Kingdom
Tel.: (44) 2082221000
Web Site:
http://www.disneycruise.disney.go.com
Emp.: 2,000
Leisure & Entertainment Management Ser-
vices
N.A.I.C.S.: 541618

Subsidiary (Domestic):

Marvel Worldwide, Inc. (2)
135 W 50th St 7th Fl, New York, NY 10020
Tel.: (212) 576-4000
Web Site: http://www.marvel.com
Comic Book Publishing Services
N.A.I.C.S.: 513130

Subsidiary (Domestic):

Marvel Entertainment, LLC (3)
1290 Avenue of the Americas, New York,
NY 10104
Tel.: (212) 576-4000
Web Site: https://www.marvel.com
Sales Range: $550-599.9 Million
Emp.: 300
Comic Book Publisher, Movie Studio & En-
tertainment
N.A.I.C.S.: 513130
Dan Buckley (Pres)

Subsidiary (Domestic):

Cover Concepts Marketing Services
LLC (4)
135 W 50th St 7th Fl, New York, NY 10020
Tel.: (212) 576-4044
Web Site: http://www.coverconcepts.com
Sales Range: $10-24.9 Million
Emp.: 22
Education Materials Free of Charge to
Schools
N.A.I.C.S.: 611710

Marvel Animation, Inc. (4)
1600 Rosecrans Ave Bldg 7 Ste 110, Man-
hattan Beach, CA 90266
Tel.: (818) 931-8021
Web Site: http://www.marvel.com
Sales Range: $100-124.9 Million
Emp.: 120
Animated Entertainment Production
N.A.I.C.S.: 512110

Subsidiary (Non-US):

Marvel Entertainment International
Limited (4)
Europa House, 54 Great Marlborough
Street, London, W1F 7JU, United Kingdom
Tel.: (44) 20 7031 0418
Sales Range: $250-299.9 Million
Holding Company; Overseas Licensing,
Mechandising & Retail Operations
N.A.I.C.S.: 551112

Subsidiary (Domestic):

Marvel Publishing, Inc. (4)
135 W 50th St Fl 7, New York, NY 10020-
1201
Tel.: (212) 576-4000
Web Site: http://www.marvel.com
Sales Range: $50-74.9 Million
Emp.: 60
Comic Book & Related Media Publisher
N.A.I.C.S.: 513120

Subsidiary (Domestic):

Pixar (2)
1200 Park Ave, Emeryville, CA 94608
Tel.: (510) 922-3000
Web Site: http://www.pixar.com
Sales Range: $250-299.9 Million
Emp.: 40
Animated Motion Pictures Producer & Ani-
mation Software Mfr
N.A.I.C.S.: 512110

Joint Venture (Non-US):

RTL Disney Fernsehen GmbH & Co.
KG (2)

Picassoplatz 1, 50679, Cologne, Germany
Tel.: (49) 22145654565
Web Site: http://www.superrtl.de
Television Broadcasting
N.A.I.C.S.: 516120

Subsidiary (Domestic):

Reedy Creek Energy Services (2)
1900 Hotel Plz Blvd, Lake Buena Vista, FL
32830-1000 (100%)
Tel.: (407) 828-3548
Web Site: http://www.rcid.org
Sales Range: $75-99.9 Million
Emp.: 300
Water, Gas, Waste & Electric Co.
N.A.I.C.S.: 561320

Subsidiary (Non-US):

Steamboat Ventures Asia, L.P. (2)
Unit 1004B-1005 One Corporate Avenue,
222 Hu Bin Road, Shanghai, 200021, China
Tel.: (86) 2123081800
Web Site: http://www.steamboatvc.com
Business Support Services
N.A.I.C.S.: 561439
Daisy Qiu (Dir-Fin)

Subsidiary (Domestic):

SuperComm Inc. (2)
200 Park Ave S 9th Fl, New York, NY
10003
Tel.: (212) 675-4606
Video Service Providers
N.A.I.C.S.: 541211
Ordan Trabelsi (Pres)
Jason Gilbert (VP-Sls-Pub Sector Solutions)

The Baby Einstein Company,
LLC (2)
1201 Grand Central Ave, Glendale, CA
91201
Tel.: (818) 560-1000
Web Site: http://www.babyeinstein.com
Sales Range: $10-24.9 Million
Emp.: 5
Videos & Toys for Children
N.A.I.C.S.: 423920

Subsidiary (Non-US):

The Walt Disney Company (France)
S.A.S. (2)
25 quai Panhard and Levassor, 75013,
Paris, France (100%)
Tel.: (33) 173265000
Web Site: http://www.corporate.disney.fr
Sales Range: $100-124.9 Million
Motion Picture Distribution
N.A.I.C.S.: 512110

The Walt Disney Company (Ger-
many) GmbH (2)
Lilli-Palmer-Str 2, 80636, Munich,
Germany (100%)
Tel.: (49) 89993400
Sales Range: $50-74.9 Million
Emp.: 400
Motion Picture Distribution
N.A.I.C.S.: 512110

The Walt Disney Company (Japan)
Ltd. (2)
Arco Tower 181 Shimomegeuro, Meguro,
Tokyo, Japan
Tel.: (81) 357452367
Web Site: http://www.disney.co.jp
Television Broadcasting Services
N.A.I.C.S.: 516210

The Walt Disney Company (Southeast Asia) Pte Ltd. (2)
4 Loyang Lane 01-01/02, Singapore,
508914, Singapore
Tel.: (65) 65073000
Motion Picture Video Production Services
N.A.I.C.S.: 512110

The Walt Disney Company Iberia
S.L. (2)
Calle Jose Bardasano Baos 9-Planta 11,
Madrid, 28016, Spain
Tel.: (34) 913849500
Web Site: http://www.disney.com
Sales Range: $100-124.9 Million
Emp.: 300
Financial Services
N.A.I.C.S.: 522320

The Walt Disney Company—(Continued)

The Walt Disney Company Italia S.r.l. (2)
Via Ferrante Aporti 6, 20121, Milan, Italy
Tel.: (39) 02290851
Web Site: http://www.disney.com
Sales Range: $100-124.9 Million
Emp.: 400
Film Distribution
N.A.I.C.S.: 512120

The Walt Disney Company Ltd. (2)
3 Queen Caroline St Hammersmith, London, W6 9PE, United Kingdom (100%)
Tel.: (44) 2082221000
Web Site:
http://www.thewaltdisneycompany.com
Sales Range: $900-999.9 Million
Emp.: 1,500
Motion Picture Distribution
N.A.I.C.S.: 512110

Walt Disney Enterprises of Japan Ltd. (2)
Arco Tower 1-8-1 Shimomeguro, Meguro-Ku, Tokyo, 153-8922, Japan (100%)
Tel.: (81) 354348340
Sales Range: $25-49.9 Million
Emp.: 170
Film Production & Distribution
N.A.I.C.S.: 512110

Walt Disney Holdings (Hong Kong) Limited (2)
19 Times Square Tower 2, Causeway Bay, Hong Kong, China (Hong Kong)
Tel.: (852) 22032000
Theme Park Operating Services
N.A.I.C.S.: 713110

Subsidiary (Domestic):

Walt Disney Studios Motion Pictures, Inc (2)
500 S Buena Vista St, Burbank, CA 91521 (100%)
Tel.: (818) 560-1000
Web Site: http://www.waltdisneystudios.com
Walt Disney & Touchstone Films Dist
N.A.I.C.S.: 512120

Twenty-First Century Fox, Inc. (1)
1211 Ave of the Americas, New York, NY 10036
Tel.: (212) 852-7000
Holding Company; Motion Picture & Cable Television Programming Production & Distribution
N.A.I.C.S.: 551112

Subsidiary (Domestic):

Amwell Inc. (2)
75 State St 26th Fl, Boston, MA 02109
Tel.: (617) 204-3500
Web Site: https://business.amwell.com
Media & Entertainment Services
N.A.I.C.S.: 512199

Bravura Inc. (2)
210 Research Blvd Ste 300, Aberdeen, MD 21001
Tel.: (443) 360-9500
Web Site: https://bravurainc.com
Media & Entertainment Services
N.A.I.C.S.: 512199

CD Services Inc. (2)
24027 Research Dr, Farmington Hills, MI 48335
Tel.: (248) 476-1700
Web Site: https://cdservicesinc.com
Media & Entertainment Services
N.A.I.C.S.: 512199

DLO Corp. (2)
2332 Galiano St Ste 206, Coral Gables, FL 33134
Tel.: (305) 448-6062
Web Site: https://dlocorp.com
Media & Entertainment Services
N.A.I.C.S.: 512199

FX Networks, LLC (2)
10201 W Pico Blvd, Los Angeles, CA 90035
Tel.: (310) 369-1000
Web Site: https://www.fxnetworks.com
Cable Television Network & Programming Services

N.A.I.C.S.: 516210

Subsidiary (Non-US):

Fortune Star Entertainment (HK) Limited (2)
13/F One HarbourFront 18 Tak Fung Street, Hung Hom, Kowloon, China (Hong Kong)
Tel.: (852) 2621 888
Film Photography Services
N.A.I.C.S.: 541922

Subsidiary (Domestic):

Fox Entertainment Group, Inc. (2)
10201 W Pico Blvd, Los Angeles, CA 90035-2606 (82.1%)
Tel.: (310) 369-1000
Web Site: http://www.fox.com
Holding Company; Motion Picture & Television Production, Distribution, Programming & Broadcasting Services
N.A.I.C.S.: 551112
Darren Schillace (Pres-Mktg)
Cheryl Dolins (Sr VP-Comedy Programming & Dev)
Michael Thorn (Pres)

Subsidiary (Non-US):

24 Kitchen Medya Hizmetleri Anonim Sirketi (3)
Martyr Mehmet Street Macka B Block Office Login No 9B Besiktas, Visnezade Residence District, 34357, Istanbul, Türkiye
Tel.: (90) 2123961600
Web Site: http://www.24kitchen.com.tr
Television Broadcasting Services
N.A.I.C.S.: 516120

24Kitchen Television B.V. (3)
De Passage 144, Amsterdam Zuidoost, 1101 AX, Amsterdam, Noord-Holland, Netherlands
Tel.: (31) 205206440
Web Site: http://www.24kitchen.nl
Television Broadcasting Services
N.A.I.C.S.: 516120

Subsidiary (Domestic):

Blue Sky Studios Inc. (3)
1 American Ln, Greenwich, CT 06831
Tel.: (203) 992-6000
Web Site: http://www.blueskystudios.com
Animation Production Services
N.A.I.C.S.: 513210

Breakout Kings Productions LLC (3)
50 Lousiana Ave, Baton Rouge, LA 71101
Tel.: (225) 906-5441
Television Broadcasting Services
N.A.I.C.S.: 516120

Brightstar Fox Productions LLC (3)
501 Louisiana Ave, Baton Rouge, LA 70802
Tel.: (504) 224-2227
Television Broadcasting Services
N.A.I.C.S.: 516120

Subsidiary (Non-US):

Eredivisie Beheer B.V. (3)
Woudenbergseweg 21, 3707 HW, Zeist, Netherlands
Tel.: (31) 343438480
Web Site: http://www.eredivisie.nl
Holding Company
N.A.I.C.S.: 551112

Eredivisie Media & Marketing C.V. (3)
Woudenbergseweg 21, 3707 HW, Zeist, Netherlands
Tel.: (31) 343438480
Web Site: https://www.eredivisie.nl
Television Broadcasting Services
N.A.I.C.S.: 516120

Subsidiary (Domestic):

Inked Productions, Inc. (3)
2025 NW 22nd Ct, Miami, FL 33142
Tel.: (305) 878-5426
Web Site: http://www.inkedpro.com
Printing Services
N.A.I.C.S.: 323111

New World Video (3)
302 Washington Ave Ste 105, Spring Lake, NJ 07762

Tel.: (732) 282-1118
Web Site: http://www.newworldvids.com
Television Broadcasting Services
N.A.I.C.S.: 516120
Dave Strevens (Principal & Dir-Creative)
Christopher Koczan (Principal)

Popular Productions, Inc. (3)
6207 Santa Monica Blvd, Hollywood, CA 90038
Tel.: (323) 203-1331
Web Site: http://www.doronoircasting.com
Motion Picture & Video Production Services
N.A.I.C.S.: 512110

Subsidiary (Non-US):

Pulsa Media Consulting, S.L. (3)
L'Avenir 44 Baixos Interior, Barcelona, 08021, Spain
Tel.: (34) 933633688
Web Site: http://www.pulsa.tv
Television Broadcasting Services
N.A.I.C.S.: 516120

Subsidiary (Domestic):

Searchlight Pictures, Inc. (3)
10201 W Pico Blvd Bldg 38 1st Fl, Los Angeles, CA 90064-2606
Tel.: (310) 369-8712
Web Site:
http://www.searchlightpictures.com
Television Film Production
N.A.I.C.S.: 512110
Stephen Gilula (Co-Chm)
Nancy Utley (Co-Chm)
Matthew Greenfield (Pres-Production)
David Greenbaum (Pres-Production)

Subsidiary (Non-US):

Transfer NV (3)
Broederminstraat 9, BE - 2018, Antwerp, Belgium
Tel.: (32) 3 293 37 22
Web Site: http://www.mytransfer.be
Television Broadcasting Services
N.A.I.C.S.: 516120
Timo Haesaerts (Mhgr-Plng Bus Unit & Supvr-Technical)
Julie Jeunen (Mgr-Mktg & Comm)
Michel Dupont (Mng Dir)
Maxim Dockx (Junior Acct Mgr & Coord-Online)
Eline Hereygers (Head-Admin, HR, Fin, Legal & Office)
Sophie Van der Hoeven (Acct Mgr)
Stefan Hougaerts (Head-Sls)
Laetitia De Dyoker (Sls Dir)
Pascal du Bois (Acct Mgr)
Christine Vermeulen (Acct Mgr)
Sam De Clerck (Junior Acct Mgr)

Twentieth Century Fox Film Company Limited (3)
3 Queen Caroline Street, London, W1D 3AP, United Kingdom
Tel.: (44) 2074377766
Web Site: http://disney.co.uk
Television Broadcasting Services
N.A.I.C.S.: 516120

Subsidiary (Domestic):

Twentieth Century Fox Film Corporation (3)
10201 W Pico Blvd, Los Angeles, CA 90035
Tel.: (310) 369-1000
Web Site:
http://www.20thcenturystudios.com
Motion Picture & Television Production & Distribution
N.A.I.C.S.: 512110

Twentieth Century Fox Home Entertainment LLC (3)
2121 Ave of the Stars 7th Fl, Los Angeles, CA 90067-5010
Tel.: (310) 369-3900
Web Site: http://www.foxhome.com
Consumer Video Products Marketer & Distr
N.A.I.C.S.: 512120

Subsidiary (Non-US):

Twentieth Century Fox Home Entertainment France S.A. (4)
241 Blvd Pereire, 75017, Paris, France
Tel.: (33) 158055700

Consumer Video Products Marketer & Distr
N.A.I.C.S.: 512120

Twentieth Century Fox Home Entertainment Germany GmbH (4)
Darmstaedter Landstrasse 114, 60598, Frankfurt, Germany
Tel.: (49) 699613630
Consumer Video Products Marketer & Distr
N.A.I.C.S.: 512120

Twentieth Century Fox Home Entertainment Japan K.K. (4)
3 16 33 Roppongi, Minato Ku, Tokyo, 106 0032, Japan
Tel.: (81) 332246350
Web Site: http://www.foxjapan.com
Consumer Video Products Marketer & Distr
N.A.I.C.S.: 512120

Twentieth Century Fox Home Entertainment Limited (4)
3 Queen Caroline Street, London, W6 9PE, United Kingdom
Tel.: (44) 20754377766
Web Site: http://disney.co.uk
Consumer Video Products Marketer & Distr
N.A.I.C.S.: 512120

Twentieth Century Fox Home Entertainment South Pacific Pty. Limited (4)
Level 3 Fox Studios Australia Driver Ave, Moore Park, Sydney, 2021, NSW, Australia
Tel.: (61) 283532100
Video Distribution
N.A.I.C.S.: 512120

Subsidiary (Non-US):

Twentieth Century Fox of Germany GmbH (3)
Darmstadter Landstrasse 114, 60598, Frankfurt, Hessen, Germany
Tel.: (49) 69609020
Television Broadcasting Services
N.A.I.C.S.: 516120

Subsidiary (Domestic):

Twentieth Television, Inc. (3)
10201 W Pico Blvd, Los Angeles, CA 90035
Tel.: (310) 369-2298
Web Site: http://www.20thtv.com
Television Production Services
N.A.I.C.S.: 512191
Carolyn Cassidy (Pres)

Subsidiary (Non-US):

Huzur Radyo Televizyon AS (2)
Kazlicesme Mah Kennedy Cad No 44, Zeytinburnu, 34020, Istanbul, Türkiye
Tel.: (90) 2124149000
Web Site: https://www.huzurradyotv.com.tr
Media & Entertainment Services
N.A.I.C.S.: 512199

Subsidiary (Domestic):

LAPTV LLC (2)
Six Concourse Pkwy Ste 1600, Atlanta, GA 30328
Tel.: (770) 810-2500
Web Site: http://www.laptv.com
Television Broadcasting Services
N.A.I.C.S.: 516120

National Geographic Partners, LLC (2)
1145 17th St NW, Washington, DC 20036-4688 (73%)
Tel.: (202) 835-0021
Web Site:
https://www.nationalgeographic.com
Science, Adventure & Exploration Content
N.A.I.C.S.: 516120
Marcela Martin (CFO, Chief Admin Officer & Exec VP)

Subsidiary (Domestic):

Global Adrenaline Inc. (3)
1640 N Wells Ste 207, Chicago, IL 60614
Tel.: (312) 863-6300
Web Site: http://www.globaladrenaline.com
Full-service Tour Operator
N.A.I.C.S.: 561599

NGC Network International, LLC (3)
1145 17th St NW, Washington, DC 20036

Tel.: (202) 857-7000
Cable Television Services
N.A.I.C.S.: 516210

Subsidiary (Non-US):

NGC Network Asia, LLC **(4)**
13/F One Harbourfront 18 Tak Fung Street,
Hung Hom, Kowloon, China (Hong Kong)
Tel.: (852) 26218888
Web Site: http://natgeotv.com
Cable Television Programming
N.A.I.C.S.: 516210
Con Apostolopoulos (Sr VP-Asia Pacific &
Middle East)
Edith Ng (Dir-Sls & Mktg)

Subsidiary (Non-US):

NGC Network (India) Private
Limited **(5)**
Plot No 77 Institutional Area Sec-32,
122001, Gurgaon, Harayana, India
Tel.: (91) 11263199
Web Site: http://www.natgeotv.com
Cable Television Programming
N.A.I.C.S.: 516210
Pawan Soni (VP & Head-Content & Comm)

Unit (Non-US):

NGC Network Asia, LLC -
Singapore **(5)**
1 Fusionopolis Link 03-01 Nexus One-
North, Singapore, 138542, Singapore
Tel.: (65) 68093500
Web Site: http://natgeotv.com
Cable Television Programming
N.A.I.C.S.: 516210
Gwendoline Lee (Head)

NGC Network Asia, LLC -
Taiwan **(5)**
3F No 183 Sec 2 Tiding Blvd, Neihu, 114,
Taipei, Taiwan
Tel.: (886) 2 87528949
Web Site: http://www.natgeotv.com
Cable Television Programming
N.A.I.C.S.: 516210
Mindy Lee (Head)

Subsidiary (Domestic):

NGC Network US, LLC **(4)**
1145 17th St NW, Washington, DC 20036-
4688
Tel.: (202) 857-7027
Web Site:
   http://channel.nationalgeographic.com
Cable Television Programming
N.A.I.C.S.: 516210

Subsidiary (Non-US):

National Geographic Channel Adven-
ture Medya Hizmetleri A.S. **(4)**
Kazlicesme Mah Kennedy Cad No 44,
34020, Istanbul, Turkiye
Tel.: (90) 2124149000
Web Site: http://www.natgeotv.com
Television Broadcasting Services
N.A.I.C.S.: 516120
Gonca Kuzuloglu (Mgr)

National Geographic Channel Den-
mark ApS **(4)**
Kobmagergade 54 Floors 1, 1150, Copen-
hagen, Denmark
Tel.: (45) 70262001
Web Site: http://www.natgeotv.com
Cable Television Programming
N.A.I.C.S.: 516210

Subsidiary (Domestic):

New World Video **(2)**
302 Washington Ave Ste 105, Spring Lake,
NJ 07762
Tel.: (732) 282-1118
Web Site: https://newworldvids.com
Media & Entertainment Services
N.A.I.C.S.: 512199

Subsidiary (Non-US):

News (UK) Limited **(2)**
1 London Bridge Street, London, SE1 9GF,
United Kingdom
Tel.: (44) 2077826000
Web Site: https://www.news.co.uk
Media & Entertainment Services

N.A.I.C.S.: 512199

SHINE TV LIMITED **(2)**
Shepherds Building Charecroft Way, Lon-
don, W14 0EE, United Kingdom
Tel.: (44) 3700420042
Web Site: https://www.shine.tv
Media & Entertainment Services
N.A.I.C.S.: 512199

STO-CPH Produktion AB **(2)**
Palermogatan 17 Frihamnen Magsinen 5,
Box 27171, 115 56, Stockholm, Sweden
Tel.: (46) 8 459 74 00
Television Broadcasting Services
N.A.I.C.S.: 516120

Subsidiary (Domestic):

Scout Publishing, LLC **(2)**
PO Box 31214, Omaha, NE 68131
Tel.: (402) 217-1073
Web Site:
   https://www.scoutpublishingllc.com
Media & Entertainment Services
N.A.I.C.S.: 512199

Subsidiary (Non-US):

Star Advertising Sales Limited **(2)**
3 Queen Caroline Street, Hammersmith,
London, W6 9PE, United Kingdom
Tel.: (44) 2030082000
Radio Broadcasting Services
N.A.I.C.S.: 516210

Subsidiary (Domestic):

TCTFAmerica, Inc. **(2)**
1211 Avenue Of The Americas, New York,
NY 10036-8701
Tel.: (212) 852-7000
Television Entertainment Services
N.A.I.C.S.: 516120

Subsidiary (Non-US):

Twentieth Century Fox Film Distribu-
tors Pty Limited **(2)**
Level 3/38 Driver Avenue, Moore Park, Syd-
ney, 2021, NSW, Australia
Tel.: (61) 283532100
Motion Picture & Tape Distr
N.A.I.C.S.: 512120

Subsidiary (Domestic):

Vixen Studios, LLC **(2)**
4814 Stone Mountain Hwy Ste 10, Lilburn,
GA 30047
Tel.: (404) 585-0925
Web Site: https://www.vixenzstudios.com
Media & Entertainment Services
N.A.I.C.S.: 512199

epartners LLC **(2)**
9405 NE 120th St M201, Kirkland, WA
98034
Tel.: (206) 979-9907
Web Site: http://theepartners.com
Television Broadcasting Services
N.A.I.C.S.: 516120

THE WENDY'S COMPANY

1 Dave Thomas Blvd, Dublin, OH
43017
Tel.: (614) 764-3100   DE
Web Site: https://www.wendys.com
Year Founded: 1929
WEN—(NASDAQ)
Rev.: $2,181,578,000
Assets: $5,182,826,000
Liabilities: $4,873,047,000
Net Worth: $309,779,000
Earnings: $204,440,000
Emp.: 15,300
Fiscal Year-end: 12/31/23
Holding Company; Fast Food Restau-
rant Chain Owner, Franchisor & Op-
erator
N.A.I.C.S.: 551112
Matthew H. Peltz (Vice Chm)
Gunther Plosch (CFO)
E. J. Wunsch (Pres-Intl)
Liliana M. Esposito (Chief Corp Af-
fairs & Sustainability Officer)
Kirk C. Tanner (Pres & CEO)

Abigail E. Pringle (Pres-U.S.)
M. Coley O'Brien (Chief People Offi-
cer)
Kevin Vasconi (CIO)
Suzanne M. Thuerk (Chief Acctg Offi-
cer)
Deepak Ajmani (COO)
Carl Loredo (CMO)

Subsidiaries:

First Kitchen LTD **(1)**
Yotsuya 4-34-1 Shinjuku Gyoenmae Annex
Building 5F, Shinjuku Ku, Tokyo, 160-0004,
Japan
Tel.: (81) 333509450
Web Site: http://www.first-kitchen.co.jp
Emp.: 180
Fastfood Chain
N.A.I.C.S.: 722511
Ernest M. Higa (Chm)

Quality Is Our Recipe, LLC **(1)**
1 Dave Thomas Blvd, Dublin, OH 43017
Tel.: (614) 764-3100
Web Site: http://www.wendys.com
Food Service Provider
N.A.I.C.S.: 722511

Wendy's International, Inc. **(1)**
4555 W Dublin Granville Rd, Dublin, OH
43017-1442
Tel.: (614) 799-2347
Web Site: http://www.wendys.com
Sales Range: $1-4.9 Billion
Emp.: 7,000
Fast Food Restaurants Operator, Developer
& Franchisor
N.A.I.C.S.: 722513

Subsidiary (Domestic):

Wendy's Old Fashioned Hamburgers
of New York, Inc. **(2)**
666 E 5th Ave, Columbus, OH 43201
Tel.: (614) 291-4388
Restaurant Operating Services
N.A.I.C.S.: 722511

Subsidiary (Non-US):

Wendy's Restaurants of Canada,
Inc. **(2)**
240 Wyecroft Road, Oakville, L6K 2G7, ON,
Canada
Tel.: (905) 849-7685
Web Site: http://www.wendys.com
Sales Range: $10-24.9 Million
Emp.: 60
Fast Food Restaurants
N.A.I.C.S.: 722513

Subsidiary (Domestic):

Wendy's of Denver, Inc. **(2)**
15400 E Colfax Ave, Aurora, CO 80011
Tel.: (303) 366-8085
Web Site: https://locations.wendys.com
Restaurant Operating Services
N.A.I.C.S.: 722511

Wendy's of N.E. Florida, Inc. **(2)**
1100 S Broad St, Brooksville, FL 34601
Tel.: (407) 682-1215
Emp.: 30
Restaurant Operating Services
N.A.I.C.S.: 722511
Alisha Kane (Gen Mgr)

Wendy's Restaurants **(1)**
5047 Tuttle Crossing Blvd, Dublin, OH
43016
Tel.: (614) 798-0033
Web Site: http://www.wendys.com
Restaurant Operating Services
N.A.I.C.S.: 722511

THE WESTERN UNION COM-
PANY

7001 E Belleview Ave, Denver, CO
80237
Tel.: (720) 332-1000   DE
Web Site:
   https://www.westernunion.com
WU—(NYSE)
Rev.: $4,357,000,000
Assets: $8,198,800,000

Liabilities: $7,719,800,000
Net Worth: $479,000,000
Earnings: $626,000,000
Emp.: 9,000
Fiscal Year-end: 12/31/23
Money Transfer Services for Con-
sumers & Businesses; Electronic Bill-
Payment Services & Consumer Mes-
sage Services
N.A.I.C.S.: 522320
Nicole Vogrin (Chief Corp Affairs &
Comm Officer)
Mark T. Hinsey (Chief Acctg Officer &
Controller)
Shannon Armbrecht (Chief Diversity
& Talent Officer)
Devin B. McGranahan (Pres & CEO)
Cherie Axelrod (Chief Enterprise Risk
Officer)
Joaquin Alemany (Head)

Subsidiaries:

Horizon Remit Sdn. Bhd. **(1)**
No 12 Jalan Hang Kasturi, 50050, Kuala
Lumpur, Malaysia
Tel.: (60) 320703786
Web Site: http://www.horizonremit.com
Financial Transaction Services
N.A.I.C.S.: 522320
A. V. Subbaraman (CEO)
G. Natarajan (Ops Mgr)

Travelex Global Business Payments,
Inc. **(1)**
1152 15th St NW, Washington, DC 20005
Tel.: (202) 408-1200
Web Site: http://business.westernunion.com
Sales Range: $200-249.9 Million
Emp.: 204
Business-to-Business Payment Solutions
N.A.I.C.S.: 522320

WUBS Payments Ltd. **(1)**
65 Kingsway, London, WC2B 6TD, United
Kingdom
Tel.: (44) 2074004000
Financial Services
N.A.I.C.S.: 522320

Western Union **(1)**
100 Summit Ave, Montvale, NJ 07645-1733
Tel.: (201) 263-5100
Web Site: http://www.payment-
solutions.com
Sales Range: $75-99.9 Million
Emp.: 300
Money Transfer Services
N.A.I.C.S.: 561499

Western Union Business Solutions
(Australia) Pty Limited **(1)**
Level 12 1 Margaret Street, Sydney, 2000,
NSW, Australia
Tel.: (61) 285857000
Web Site:
   http://www.business.westernunion.com
Emp.: 190
Financial Services
N.A.I.C.S.: 522320

Western Union Business Solutions
(Malta) Limited **(1)**
W Business Centre Level 5 Triq Dun Karm
Birkirkara By-Pass, Birkirkara, BKR 9033,
Malta
Tel.: (356) 23289209
Web Site: http://business.westernunion.com
Financial Services
N.A.I.C.S.: 522320

Western Union Business Solutions
(New Zealand) **(1)**
Level 5 Zurich House 21 Queen Street,
Auckland, 1010, New Zealand
Tel.: (64) 93595112
Financial Services
N.A.I.C.S.: 522320

Western Union Business Solutions
(Singapore) Pte Limited **(1)**
77 Robinson Road 35-01 Robinson 77, Sin-
gapore, 068896, Singapore
Tel.: (65) 64948222
Financial Services
N.A.I.C.S.: 522320

The Western Union Company—(Continued)

Western Union Business Solutions (UK) Limited (1)
200 Hammersmith Road, London, W6 7DL, United Kingdom
Tel.: (44) 8000961225
Financial Services
N.A.I.C.S.: 522320

Western Union Business Solutions (USA), LLC (1)
1152 15th St, Washington, DC 20005
Tel.: (202) 408-1200
Web Site:
http://www.business.westernunion.com
Financial Services
N.A.I.C.S.: 522320

Western Union Business Solutions Japan KK (1)
4F Metro City Kamiyacho 5-1-5 Toranomon, Minato-ku, Tokyo, 105-0001, Japan
Tel.: (81) 364305922
Web Site:
http://www.business.westernunion.com
Financial Services
N.A.I.C.S.: 522320

Western Union Consulting Services (Beijing), Co., Ltd. (1)
Suite 2206-07 22F East Tower Twin Towers No 12B Jianguomenwai Dajie, Chaoyang, Beijing, 100022, China
Tel.: (86) 1085165900
Web Site: https://www.westernunion.com
Emp.: 13
Financial Advisory Services
N.A.I.C.S.: 522320

Western Union Financial Services (Australia) PTY Ltd. (1)
Level 12 1 Margaret Street, Sydney, 2000, NSW, Australia
Tel.: (61) 1800173833
Management Consulting Services
N.A.I.C.S.: 541618

Western Union Financial Services, Inc. (1)
12500 E Belford Ave, Englewood, CO 80112
Tel.: (720) 332-1000
Web Site: https://www.westernunion.com
Sales Range: $125-149.9 Million
Emp.: 500
Wire Transfer Services
N.A.I.C.S.: 522320
Hikmot Ersek (Pres & CEO)

Western Union Global Network Pte. Ltd. (1)
304 Lucky Plaza, Singapore, 238863, Singapore
Tel.: (65) 67383060
Money Transfer Services
N.A.I.C.S.: 522320

Western Union International Bank GmbH (1)
The Icon Vienna Tower 24 Wiedner Gurtel 13, 1100, Vienna, Austria
Tel.: (43) 150617100
Web Site: https://www.westernunion.com
Money Transfer Services
N.A.I.C.S.: 522320

Western Union International Bank GmbH (1)
The Icon Vienna Turm 24 Wiedner Gurtel 13, 1100, Vienna, Austria
Tel.: (43) 150617100
Web Site: https://www.westernunion.com
Management Consulting Services
N.A.I.C.S.: 541618
Cojocaru Cerasela (Branch Mgr)

Western Union MT East Ltd. (1)
Tel.: (7) 4957829822
Web Site: https://www.westernunion.ru
Sales Range: $125-149.9 Million
Emp.: 100
Wire Transfer Services
N.A.I.C.S.: 522320

Western Union Processing Lithuania, UAB (1)
Juozo Balcikonio G 7, Vilnius, 08247, Lithuania

Tel.: (370) 52590214
Web Site: https://www.westernunion.com
Financial Management Services
N.A.I.C.S.: 522320

Western Union Retail Services Belgium (1)
Place Louise 6, PO Box 5, 1060, Saint-Gilles, Oost-Vlaanderen, Belgium
Tel.: (32) 92610225
Financial Services
N.A.I.C.S.: 522320
Christophe Vaerewyck (Head-AML Compliance Benelux)

Western Union Retail Services Norway AS (1)
Schweigaards Gate 6, Oslo, 0185, Norway
Tel.: (47) 80018666
Web Site: https://www.westernunion.com
Management Consulting Services
N.A.I.C.S.: 541618

Western Union Services India Private Limited (1)
Fortune 2000 Building Ground Floor 101 G Block Bandra Kurla Complex, Bandra, Mumbai, 400 051, India
Tel.: (91) 7314819855
Web Site: https://www.westernunion.com
Emp.: 32
Management Consulting Services
N.A.I.C.S.: 541618
Kiran Shetty (Mng Dir)

THE WILLIAMS COMPANIES, INC.

1 Williams Ctr, Tulsa, OK 74172   DE
Web Site: https://www.williams.com
Year Founded: 1908
WMB—(NYSE)
Rev.: $10,907,000,000
Assets: $52,627,000,000
Liabilities: $37,736,000,000
Net Worth: $14,891,000,000
Earnings: $3,176,000,000
Emp.: 5,601
Fiscal Year-end: 12/31/23
Natural Gas Exploration, Extraction, Processing, Pipeline Transportation, Distribution & Marketing
N.A.I.C.S.: 486210
Chad J. Zamarin (Exec VP-Corp Strategic Dev)
Micheal G. Dunn (COO & Exec VP)
T. Lane Wilson (Gen Counsel & Sr VP)
Debbie Cowan (Chief HR Officer & Sr VP)
Chad A. Teply (Sr VP-Project Execution)
Scott A. Hallam (Sr VP-Transmission & Gulf-Mexico)
Mary Hausman (Chief Acctg Officer, VP & Controller)
Mary A. Hausman (Chief Acctg Officer)
Larry C. Larsen (Sr VP)
Alan S. Armstrong (Pres & CEO)

Subsidiaries:

Aux Sable Liquid Products Inc. (1)
6155 E US Route 6, Morris, IL 60450
Tel.: (815) 941-5800
Web Site: https://www.auxsable.com
Natural Gas Transportation Services
N.A.I.C.S.: 486990

Baton Rouge Fractionators LLC (1)
2220 N River Rd, Port Allen, LA 70767 (67.75%)
Tel.: (225) 381-3420
Web Site:
https://www.enterpriseproduct.com
Fuel & Oil Refinery Services
N.A.I.C.S.: 324110

Black Marlin Pipeline LLC (1)
2800 Post Oak Blvd Level 3, Houston, TX 77056
Tel.: (918) 573-7400
Web Site:
https://www.blackmarlin.williasener
gy.com

Natural Gas Distr
N.A.I.C.S.: 221210

Goebel Gathering Company, L.L.C. (1)
1 Williams Ctr, Tulsa, OK 74172-0150
Tel.: (918) 573-4528
Web Site: http://www.williams.com
Oil & Gas Exploration Services
N.A.I.C.S.: 213112

HB Construction Company Ltd. (1)
3051 Parsons Road NW, Edmonton, T6N 1C8, AB, Canada
Tel.: (780) 490-7501
Web Site: http://www.hbconstruct.com
Refined Petroleum Product Transportation Services
N.A.I.C.S.: 486910

Monarch Pipeline LLC (1)
2000 Commerce Dr, Pittsburgh, PA 15275
Tel.: (412) 787-7300
Natural Gas Pipeline Transportation Services
N.A.I.C.S.: 486210

MountainWest Overthrust Pipeline, LLC (1)
333 S State St, Salt Lake City, UT 84145
Tel.: (713) 215-2728
Gas Transportation Services
N.A.I.C.S.: 486210

MountainWest Pipeline, LLC (1)
333 S State St, Salt Lake City, UT 84145
Tel.: (713) 215-2728
Web Site: https://www.mwpipe.com
Gas Transportation Services
N.A.I.C.S.: 486210

Overland Pass Pipeline Company LLC (1)
1720 Carey Ave, Cheyenne, WY 82001
Tel.: (307) 426-4135
Natural Gas Pipeline Services
N.A.I.C.S.: 486210

Sequent Energy Management, L.P. (1)
2 Allen Ctr 1200 Smith St, Houston, TX 77002
Tel.: (832) 397-1700
Emp.: 134
Wholesale Trader, Marketer, Gatherer & Transporter of Natural Gas
N.A.I.C.S.: 221210

The Williams Companies, Inc. - Houston (1)
12501 Veterans Memorial Dr, Houston, TX 77014-2203
Tel.: (281) 444-6441
Web Site: http://www.williams.com
Sales Range: $350-399.9 Million
Emp.: 11
Pipelines, Natural Gas
N.A.I.C.S.: 486210

The Williams Companies, Inc. - Neshanic Station (1)
623 Case Rd, Neshanic Station, NJ 08853-4171
Tel.: (908) 369-4329
Sales Range: $10-24.9 Million
Emp.: 5
Gas Transmission & Distribution
N.A.I.C.S.: 221210
Russell Markowski (Gen Mgr)

The Williams Companies, Inc. - Oklahoma City (1)
251 N Sunnylane Rd, Oklahoma City, OK 73117-7208
Tel.: (405) 677-8313
Sales Range: $1-9.9 Million
Emp.: 6
Refined Petroleum Pipelines Services
N.A.I.C.S.: 238160
Susan Damron (Supvr-Telecom Network)

The Williams Companies, Inc. - Washington (1)
3149 Hwy 10, Washington, LA 70589-4217
Tel.: (337) 826-3664
Web Site: http://www.williams.com
Sales Range: $10-24.9 Million
Emp.: 19
Crude Petroleum Pipelines
N.A.I.C.S.: 486110

Williams Energy Canada ULC (1)
1900 215-2nd Street SW, Calgary, T2P 1M4, AB, Canada
Tel.: (403) 444-4500
Emp.: 33
Oil & Gas Field Services
N.A.I.C.S.: 213112

Williams Energy Co. (1)
3302 25th Ave N, Texas City, TX 77590 (100%)
Tel.: (409) 945-3564
Web Site: http://www.williams.com
Sales Range: $10-24.9 Million
Emp.: 2
Pipelines, Natural Gas
N.A.I.C.S.: 486210

Williams Energy Services (1)
1 Williams Ctr, Tulsa, OK 74172-0140
Tel.: (918) 573-2000
Web Site: http://www.williams.com
Sales Range: $550-599.9 Million
Emp.: 650
Natural Gas Transmission
N.A.I.C.S.: 486210

Branch (Domestic):

Williams Energy Services (2)
PO Box 0042, Opal, WY 83124
Tel.: (307) 877-4488
Sales Range: $10-24.9 Million
Emp.: 42
Natural Gas Transmission
N.A.I.C.S.: 486210

Subsidiary (Domestic):

Williams Energy Services (2)
6000 Rock Rd, Coden, AL 36523 (100%)
Tel.: (251) 873-2600
Sales Range: $1-9.9 Million
Emp.: 20
Gases & Liquefied Petroleum Gases
N.A.I.C.S.: 324110

Williams Field Services Company (1)
4500 1 Williams Ctr, Tulsa, OK 74172-0145
Tel.: (918) 573-2000
Web Site: http://www.williams.com
Sales Range: $600-649.9 Million
Emp.: 400
Crude Petroleum & Natural Gas
N.A.I.C.S.: 211120

Branch (Domestic):

Williams Field Services (2)
4980 State Hwy 374, Green River, WY 82935 (100%)
Tel.: (307) 872-2800
Web Site: http://www.williams.com
Sales Range: $25-49.9 Million
Emp.: 50
Gas Transmission & Distr
N.A.I.C.S.: 221210

Williams Four Corners LLC (1)
1 Williams Ctr Bsmt 2, Tulsa, OK 74172-0172
Tel.: (918) 573-2000
Natural Gas Pipeline Services
N.A.I.C.S.: 486210

Williams International Company (1)
1 Williams Ctr, Tulsa, OK 74172-0140
Tel.: (918) 573-2000
Web Site: http://www.williams.com
Sales Range: $50-74.9 Million
Holding Company
N.A.I.C.S.: 551112

Williams International Company LLC (1)
2000 Centerpoint Pkwy, Pontiac, MI 48341
Tel.: (248) 960-2929
Web Site: https://www.williams-int.com
Engine & Turbine Merchant Whslr
N.A.I.C.S.: 423860

Williams International Ventures Company (1)
1 Williams Ctr 22nd Fl, Tulsa, OK 74172-0140
Tel.: (918) 573-2000
Web Site: http://www.williams.com
Sales Range: $450-499.9 Million
Emp.: 1,000
Coal Pipeline Operation

N.A.I.C.S.: 486990

Williams Merchant Services Co. (1)
1 Williams Ctr Basement 2, Tulsa, OK 74172
Tel.: (918) 573-4592
Web Site: http://www.williams.com
Sales Range: $1-9.9 Million
Emp.: 8
Financial Management Services
N.A.I.C.S.: 561110

Williams Midstream (1)
2800 Post Oak Blvd 7th Fl, Houston, TX 77056-6100 (100%)
Tel.: (713) 215-3527
Sales Range: $400-449.9 Million
Emp.: 50
Processing Service Gas
N.A.I.C.S.: 213112
Kelly Knopp (Mgr-HR)

Williams Mobile Bay Producer Services, L.L.C. (1)
1 Williams Ctr, Tulsa, OK 74172
Tel.: (918) 573-2000
Oil & Gas Exploration Services
N.A.I.C.S.: 213112

Williams Partners L.P. (1)
1 Williams Ctr, Tulsa, OK 74172-0172
Tel.: (918) 573-2000
Web Site: http://www.investor.williams.com
Rev.: $8,010,000,000
Assets: $45,903,000,000
Liabilities: $22,214,000,000
Net Worth: $23,689,000,000
Earnings: $871,000,000
Fiscal Year-end: 12/31/2017
Natural Gas Gathering Systems & Other Midstream Energy Assets Owner, Operator, Developer & Acquirer
N.A.I.C.S.: 213112
Micheal G. Dunn (COO & Exec VP)
Chad J. Zamarin (Sr VP-Corp Strategic Dev)

Subsidiary (Domestic):

Access MLP Operating, L.L.C. (2)
600 NW Ave, Oklahoma City, OK 73106
Tel.: (405) 935-8000
Emp.: 245
Natural Gas Extraction Services
N.A.I.C.S.: 211130

Appalachia Midstream Services, L.L.C. (2)
6100 N Western Ave, Oklahoma City, OK 73118-1044
Tel.: (405) 848-8000
Natural Gas Pipeline Transportation Services
N.A.I.C.S.: 486210

Aux Sable Midstream LLC (2)
6155 E US Route 6, Morris, IL 60450
Tel.: (815) 941-5800
Web Site: https://www.auxsable.com
Sales Range: $100-124.9 Million
Emp.: 160
Natural Gas Liquid Extraction Services
N.A.I.C.S.: 211130

Blue Racer Midstream, LLC (2)
5949 Sherry Ln Ste 1700, Dallas, TX 75225
Tel.: (214) 580-3700
Web Site: https://www.blueracermidstream.com
Natural Gas Pipeline Construction Services
N.A.I.C.S.: 237120
Gary Reaves (Chm)

Bluestem Gas Services, L.L.C. (2)
4655 County Rd 2970, Lindsay, OK 73052
Tel.: (580) 658-6530
Emp.: 15
Natural Gas Extraction Services
N.A.I.C.S.: 211130

Constitution Pipeline Company, LLC (2)
2800 Post Oak Blvd, Houston, TX 77056
Tel.: (518) 982-1637
Web Site: https://www.constitutionpipeline.com
Emp.: 25
Natural Gas Pipeline Construction Services
N.A.I.C.S.: 237120

Gulfstream Natural Gas System, L.L.C. (2)
2701 Rocky Point Dr Ste 1050, Tampa, FL 33607
Tel.: (813) 288-1811
Web Site: http://www.gulfstreamgas.com
Emp.: 5
Natural Gas Extraction Services
N.A.I.C.S.: 211130

Magnolia Midstream Gas Services, L.L.C. (2)
900 NW 63rd St, Oklahoma City, OK 73154-0355
Tel.: (405) 935-1500
Natural Gas Extraction Services
N.A.I.C.S.: 211130

Northwest Pipeline LLC (2)
1 Williams Ctr, Tulsa, OK 74172-0172
Tel.: (801) 583-8800
Web Site: https://www.northwest.williams.com
Rev.: $439,858,000
Assets: $2,227,359,000
Liabilities: $1,094,163,000
Net Worth: $1,133,196,000
Earnings: $179,719,000
Fiscal Year-end: 12/31/2023
Natural Gas Pipeline Transportation Services
N.A.I.C.S.: 486210
Scott A. Hallam (Sr VP)
Billeigh W. Mark (Controller)
Mary A. Hausman (Chief Acctg Officer)
Allison Jenkins (Chief Compliance Officer)

Utica East Ohio Midstream LLC (2)
1099 Main Ave Ste 210, Durango, CO 81301-5157 (70%)
Tel.: (970) 247-4423
Natural Gas Extraction Services
N.A.I.C.S.: 211130

Williams Field Services Group, LLC (2)
1 Williams Center, Tulsa, OK 74172
Tel.: (918) 573-2000
Producing Natural Gas
N.A.I.C.S.: 221210

Subsidiary (Domestic):

Nortex Midstream Partners, LLC (3)
840 Gessner Rd, Ste 250, Houston, TX 77024
Web Site: http://www.nortexmidstream.com
General Warehousing & Storage
N.A.I.C.S.: 493110
Andrew I. Barbe (VP)

Subsidiary (Domestic):

Williams Gas Pipeline Company LLC (2)
2800 Post Oak Blvd, Houston, TX 77056
Tel.: (713) 215-2000
Web Site: http://co.williams.com
Sales Range: $500-549.9 Million
Emp.: 522
Natural Gas Distribution
N.A.I.C.S.: 486210

Subsidiary (Domestic):

Cardinal Pipeline Co. (3)
7302 Vanclaybon, Apex, NC 27523
Tel.: (919) 367-9351
Web Site: https://www.williams.com
Sales Range: $10-24.9 Million
Emp.: 3
Natural Gas Pipelines
N.A.I.C.S.: 486210

Pine Needle Operating Company (3)
8001 Haw River Rd, Stokesdale, NC 27357-9401
Tel.: (336) 643-2190
Sales Range: $10-24.9 Million
Emp.: 15
Crude Petroleum Pipelines
N.A.I.C.S.: 486210

Southern Star Central Gas Pipeline, Inc. (3)
US Hwy 81, Alva, OK 73717
Tel.: (580) 430-2000
Sales Range: $10-24.9 Million
Emp.: 21
Natural Gas Transmission Services
N.A.I.C.S.: 221210

Unit (Domestic):

Transco Gas Pipe Line Corp. (3)
Hwy 691 SW, Appomattox, VA 24522
Tel.: (434) 352-5425
Sales Range: $75-99.9 Million
Emp.: 20
Gas Pipeline
N.A.I.C.S.: 236220

Transco Gas Pipe Line Corp. (3)
345 Greenbrier Dr, Charlottesville, VA 22901-1618
Tel.: (434) 973-4384
Web Site: http://www.williams.com
Gas Pipeline
N.A.I.C.S.: 486210

Transco Gas Pipe Line Corp. (3)
221 Trout Run Rd, Austin, PA 16720 (100%)
Tel.: (814) 647-8800
Web Site: http://www.william.com
Sales Range: $25-49.9 Million
Emp.: 15
Gas Transmission & Distr
N.A.I.C.S.: 221210
Philip A. Wright (Sr VP)

Transco Gas Pipe Line Corp. (3)
102 Pole Bridge Rd, Benton, PA 17814
Tel.: (570) 925-5919
Web Site: http://www.williams.com
Sales Range: $10-24.9 Million
Emp.: 4
Natural Gas Pipelines
N.A.I.C.S.: 486210

Transco Gas Pipe Line Corp. (3)
17333 Hwy 171, Ragley, LA 70657 (100%)
Tel.: (337) 725-3658
Sales Range: $10-24.9 Million
Emp.: 8
Gas Transmission & Distribution
N.A.I.C.S.: 221210
James Barrow (Supvr)
Philip Young (Mgr)

Transco Gas Pipe Line Corp. (3)
718 Paterson Plank Rd, Carlstadt, NJ 07072-2302
Tel.: (201) 933-5490
Sales Range: $10-24.9 Million
Emp.: 25
Transport of Natural Gas
N.A.I.C.S.: 221210

Transco Gas Pipe Line Corporation (3)
60 N Bacton Hill Rd, Malvern, PA 19355
Tel.: (610) 644-7373
Web Site: http://www.williams.com
Sales Range: $25-49.9 Million
Emp.: 40
Natural Gas Pipelines
N.A.I.C.S.: 486210

Transco Gas Pipe Line Corporation (3)
1666 Bonner Rd, Heidelberg, MS 39439
Tel.: (601) 426-6461
Sales Range: $10-24.9 Million
Emp.: 19
Natural Gas Pipelines
N.A.I.C.S.: 486210

Transco Gas Pipelines (3)
2800 Post Oak Blvd, Houston, TX 77056
Tel.: (713) 215-2000
Web Site: http://www.transit.twc.com
Sales Range: $400-449.9 Million
Natural Gas Systems
N.A.I.C.S.: 486990

Subsidiary (Domestic):

Transcontinental Gas Pipe Line Company, LLC (3)
2800 Post Oak Blvd, Houston, TX 77056
Tel.: (713) 215-2000
Rev.: $2,866,196,000
Assets: $15,788,289,000
Liabilities: $7,650,690,000
Net Worth: $8,137,599,000
Earnings: $1,247,205,000
Fiscal Year-end: 12/31/2023
Gas Transmission & Distr
N.A.I.C.S.: 221210
Scott A. Hallam (Sr VP)
Billeigh W. Mark (Controller)
Mary A. Hausman (Chief Acctg Officer)

Transcontinental Gas Pipe Line Corp. (3)
117 Winns Lake Rd, Comer, GA 30629-1729
Tel.: (706) 783-5031
Sales Range: $10-24.9 Million
Emp.: 20
Natural Gas Distribution
N.A.I.C.S.: 221210

Transcontinental Gas Pipe Line Corp. (3)
11910 Carroll Mill Rd, Ellicott City, MD 21042
Tel.: (410) 465-0960
Sales Range: $10-24.9 Million
Emp.: 24
Natural Gas Transmission
N.A.I.C.S.: 221210
Tim Rich (Branch Mgr)

Unit (Domestic):

Williams Gas Pipeline (3)
La Sal Rte, La Sal, UT 84530 (100%)
Tel.: (435) 259-7422
Web Site: http://www.williams.com
Sales Range: $10-24.9 Million
Emp.: 20
Natural Gas Pipelines
N.A.I.C.S.: 486210

Subsidiary (Domestic):

Williams Gas Pipeline (3)
2800 Post Oak Blvd, Houston, TX 77056-6100 (100%)
Tel.: (713) 215-2000
Web Site: http://www.williams.com
Sales Range: $200-249.9 Million
Emp.: 450
Gas Transmission & Distribution
N.A.I.C.S.: 325180

Unit (Domestic):

Williams Gas Pipeline (3)
1344 Transco Rd, Scottsville, VA 24590-4911
Tel.: (434) 286-2051
Web Site: http://www.williams.com
Sales Range: $10-24.9 Million
Emp.: 5
Natural Gas Pipelines
N.A.I.C.S.: 486210

Williams Gas Pipeline (3)
2959 Veterans Memorial Hwy, Eunice, LA 70535
Tel.: (337) 457-3602
Web Site: http://www.merchantcircle.com
Sales Range: $10-24.9 Million
Emp.: 10
Natural Gas Pipelines
N.A.I.C.S.: 221210

Williams Gas Pipeline (3)
156 Meier Rd W, Winlock, WA 98596-9617
Tel.: (360) 785-4101
Web Site: http://www.williams.com
Sales Range: $300-349.9 Million
Emp.: 4
Crude Petroleum Pipelines
N.A.I.C.S.: 486110

Williams Gas Pipeline (3)
1022 E Hawthorne Rd, Spokane, WA 99218
Tel.: (509) 466-6650
Sales Range: $10-24.9 Million
Emp.: 25
Pipeline & Power Line Inspection Service
N.A.I.C.S.: 541990

Subsidiary (Domestic):

Williams Gas Pipeline (3)
7444 Everona Rd, Unionville, VA 22567 (100%)
Tel.: (540) 854-5517
Sales Range: $10-24.9 Million
Emp.: 21
Gas Transmission & Distribution
N.A.I.C.S.: 221210
Dan Patterson (District Mgr)

Unit (Domestic):

Williams Gas Pipeline (3)
4738 Jones Rd, Sumas, WA 98295
Tel.: (360) 988-2261
Web Site: http://www.williams.com

The Williams Companies, Inc.—(Continued)

Sales Range: $10-24.9 Million
Emp.: 12
Gas Transmission & Distr
N.A.I.C.S.: 221210

Williams Gas Pipeline (3)
8907 NE 219th St, Battle Ground, WA
98604
Tel.: (360) 687-3156
Web Site: http://www.williams.com
Sales Range: $10-24.9 Million
Emp.: 14
Natural Gas Pipelines
N.A.I.C.S.: 221210

Williams Gas Pipeline (3)
1309 NE Brown Rd, Washougal, WA 98671
Tel.: (360) 834-5411
Web Site: http://www.williams.com
Sales Range: $10-24.9 Million
Emp.: 3
Distr of Natural Gas
N.A.I.C.S.: 486210

Williams Gas Pipeline Corp. (3)
10201 Balls Ford Rd, Manassas, VA 20109
Tel.: (703) 368-3255
Web Site:
　　http://www.williamsgaspipeline.com
Sales Range: $10-24.9 Million
Emp.: 20
Gas Transmission
N.A.I.C.S.: 221210

Williams Gas Pipeline Corp. (3)
Hwy 43 N, Greensburg, LA 70441 **(100%)**
Tel.: (225) 222-4300
Web Site: http://www.williams.com
Sales Range: $10-24.9 Million
Emp.: 10
Gas Transmission & Distr
N.A.I.C.S.: 221210

Williams Gas Pipeline Plymouth
District (3)
42612 E Christy Rd, Plymouth, WA 99346
Tel.: (509) 783-2421
Sales Range: $25-49.9 Million
Emp.: 23
Pipelines, Natural Gas
N.A.I.C.S.: 486210
Von Studer (Branch Mgr)

Williams Gas Pipeline Transco (3)
315 Cold Soil Rd, Princeton, NJ 08540-
2001
Tel.: (609) 497-7549
Gas Transmission & Distribution
N.A.I.C.S.: 221210
Bob Ford (Mgr)

Williams Gas Pipeline Transco (3)
2988 Hwy 964, Jackson, LA 70748
Tel.: (225) 658-1100
Web Site: http://www.williams.com
Sales Range: $10-24.9 Million
Emp.: 16
Natural Gas Transmission
N.A.I.C.S.: 486110

Williams Gas Pipeline West (3)
295 Chipeta Way, Salt Lake City, UT 84108
Tel.: (801) 583-8800
Web Site: http://www.1line.williams.com
Sales Range: $50-74.9 Million
Emp.: 200
Natural Gas Distribution
N.A.I.C.S.: 486210

Williams Gas Pipelines Central (3)
4700 State Route 56, Owensboro, KY
42301
Tel.: (270) 852-5000
Web Site: https://southernstar.com
Sales Range: $10-24.9 Million
Emp.: 12
Gas Transmission & Distribution
N.A.I.C.S.: 221210

Subsidiary (Domestic):

Williams Laboratories Services (3)
1090 A Sunshine Rd, Kansas City, KS
66115
Tel.: (913) 621-3603
Sales Range: $1-9.9 Million
Emp.: 12
Testing Laboratories
N.A.I.C.S.: 541715

Unit (Domestic):

Williams Northwest Pipeline (3)
89861 N Game Farm Rd, Eugene, OR
97408
Tel.: (541) 342-4434
Web Site: http://www.co.williams.com
Sales Range: $150-199.9 Million
Emp.: 18
Pipelines & Natural Gas Interstate Pipelines
Systems
N.A.I.C.S.: 486210

Williams Pipeline Services (3)
2800 Post Oak Blvd, Houston, TX 77056-
6100
Tel.: (713) 215-2000
Web Site: https://www.williams.com
Sales Range: $50-74.9 Million
Emp.: 100
Pipelines, Natural Gas
N.A.I.C.S.: 486210

Subsidiary (Domestic):

Williams Ohio Valley Midstream
LLC (2)
1605 Coraopolis Heights Rd, Moon Town-
ship, PA 15108
Tel.: (412) 865-1735
Natural Gas Extraction Services
N.A.I.C.S.: 211130

Williams Pipeline Partners, L.P. (2)
1 Williams Ctr Ste 4700, Tulsa, OK 74102-
2400
Tel.: (918) 573-2000
Sales Range: $50-74.9 Million
Wire Line Services
N.A.I.C.S.: 486210
Donald R. Chappel (CFO & Sr VP)

Subsidiary (Domestic):

Northwest Pipeline Corporation (3)
7305 El Paso Rd, Caldwell, ID 83607
Tel.: (208) 459-3292
Sales Range: $75-99.9 Million
Natural Gas Pipelines
N.A.I.C.S.: 541611
Allen Armstrong (Gen Mgr)

Northwest Pipeline Corporation (3)
18193 Chandler Ln, Baker City, OR
97814 **(100%)**
Tel.: (541) 523-4688
Sales Range: $10-24.9 Million
Emp.: 2
Natural Gas Transmission
N.A.I.C.S.: 486210

Northwest Pipeline Corporation (3)
599 S 500 E, Vernal, UT 84078 **(100%)**
Tel.: (435) 781-3200
Web Site: http://www.williams.com
Emp.: 19
Wholesale of Pipelines & Natural Gas
N.A.I.C.S.: 486210

Northwest Pipeline Corporation (3)
22909 NE Redmond Fall City Rd, Red-
mond, WA 98053 **(100%)**
Tel.: (425) 868-1010
Sales Range: $10-24.9 Million
Emp.: 21
Gas Transmission & Distribution
N.A.I.C.S.: 221210
Grant A. Jensen (Mgr-Ops)

Northwest Pipeline Corporation (3)
3104 166th Ave E, Sumner, WA
98390-9506 **(100%)**
Tel.: (253) 862-6800
Web Site: http://www.williams.com
Sales Range: $10-24.9 Million
Emp.: 4
Gas Transmission
N.A.I.C.S.: 221210

Northwest Pipeline Corporation (3)
1301 S Locust Grove Rd, Meridian, ID
83642
Tel.: (208) 884-4300
Sales Range: $10-24.9 Million
Emp.: 25
Gas Transmission & Distribution
N.A.I.C.S.: 541611

Williams Production Appalachia
LLC (1)
1 Williams Ctr, Tulsa, OK 74172

Tel.: (918) 573-2000
Oil & Gas Exploration Services
N.A.I.C.S.: 213112

Williams Production Company,
LLC (1)
One Williams Ctr, Tulsa, OK 74172
Tel.: (918) 573-2000
Web Site: http://www.co.williams.com
Oil & Gas Exploration Services
N.A.I.C.S.: 213112

Williams Purity Pipelines, LLC (1)
1 Williams Ctr, Tulsa, OK 74172
Tel.: (918) 573-2000
Refined Petroleum Product Transportation
Services
N.A.I.C.S.: 486910

Williams WPC International
Company (1)
1 Williams Ctr Bsmt 2, Tulsa, OK 74172
Tel.: (918) 573-4592
Natural Gas Transmission Services
N.A.I.C.S.: 486210

THE YORK WATER COMPANY

130 E Market St, York, PA 17401-
1219
Tel.: (717) 845-3601　　　　**PA**
Web Site: https://www.yorkwater.com
YORW—(NASDAQ)
Rev.: $60,061,000
Assets: $510,595,000
Liabilities: $163,947,000
Net Worth: $346,648,000
Earnings: $19,580,000
Emp.: 116
Fiscal Year-end: 12/31/22
Water Supply & Irrigation Systems
N.A.I.C.S.: 221310
Joseph T. Hand (Pres & CEO)
Alexandra C. Chiaruttini (Chief Admin
Officer & Gen Counsel)
Matthew J. Scarpato (VP-Ops)

THEGLOBE.COM, INC.

14643 Dallas Pkwy Ste 650, Dallas,
TX 75254
Tel.: (214) 369-5695　　　　**DE**
Year Founded: 1995
TGLO—(OTCIQ)
Assets: $6,771
Liabilities: $1,093,539
Net Worth: ($1,086,768)
Earnings: ($184,644)
Fiscal Year-end: 12/31/22
Investment Services
N.A.I.C.S.: 523999
Michael A. Egan (CEO)
Robin Segaul Lebowitz (CFO)

Subsidiaries:

Tralliance Corporation (1)
220 5th Ave 20th Fl, New York, NY 10001
Tel.: (212) 481-2820
Web Site: https://www.tralliance.info
Travel Operator
N.A.I.C.S.: 561520
Ronald N. Andruff (Co-Founder, Pres &
CEO)
Cherian Mathai (Co-Founder & COO)
Nicole D. Importico (Mgr-Admin)

THERALINK TECHNOLOGIES,
INC.

15000 W 6th Ave Ste 400, Golden,
CO 80401
Tel.: (225) 227-2384　　　　**NV**
Web Site: https://www.theralink.com
Year Founded: 2005
THER—(OTCIQ)
Rev.: $606,796
Assets: $2,849,794
Liabilities: $40,965,355
Net Worth: ($38,115,561)
Earnings: ($30,946,957)
Emp.: 16
Fiscal Year-end: 09/30/23

Biopharmaceutical Research & De-
velopment
N.A.I.C.S.: 541715
Jeffrey M. Busch (Chm)
Andrew Kucharchuk (CFO)
Mick Ruxin (Chief Medical Officer)
Trevor McCartney (Sr Dir-Bus Dev)
Justin Davis (Dir-Laboratory)
Kris Weinberg (Dir-Oncology Comml
Markets)
Michael Fanelli (Sr Dir-Biopharma
Comml Ops)
Faith Zaslavsky (Pres & CEO)
Mattia Cremona (Dir)
Claudius Mueller (Dir)

Subsidiaries:

Avant Diagnostics, Inc. (1)
1050 30th St NW Ste 107, Washington, DC
20007
Tel.: (780) 710-9200
Web Site: http://www.avantdiagnostics.com
Rev.: $38,477
Assets: $4,817,993
Liabilities: $2,748,468
Net Worth: $2,069,525
Earnings: ($2,371,797)
Fiscal Year-end: 09/30/2018
Medical Diagnostic Test Mfr
N.A.I.C.S.: 339112

Subsidiary (Domestic):

Theranostics Health (2)
217 Perry Pkwy Ste 8, Gaithersburg, MD
20877
Tel.: (301) 251-4443
Web Site:
　　http://www.theranosticshealth.com
Research & Development in Biotechnology
N.A.I.C.S.: 541714

THERAPEUTIC SOLUTIONS
INTERNATIONAL, INC.

4093 Oceanside Blvd Ste B, Oceans-
ide, CA 92056
Tel.: (760) 295-7208　　　　**NV**
Web Site:
　　https://www.therapeuticsolutions
　　int.com
Year Founded: 2007
TSOI—(OTCIQ)
Rev.: $98,994
Assets: $3,292,012
Liabilities: $2,010,130
Net Worth: $1,281,882
Earnings: ($2,169,814)
Emp.: 3
Fiscal Year-end: 12/31/23
Biotechnology Research & Develop-
ment Services
N.A.I.C.S.: 541714
Timothy G. Dixon (Chm, Pres &
CEO)
James Veltmeyer (Chief Medical Offi-
cer)
Feng Lin (Chief Scientific Officer)
Famela Ramos (VP-Bus Dev)

THERAPEUTICSMD, INC.

951 Yamato Rd Ste 220, Boca Raton,
FL 33431
Tel.: (561) 961-1900　　　　**NV**
Web Site:
　　https://www.therapeuticsmd.com
TXMD—(NASDAQ)
Rev.: $1,302,000
Assets: $43,309,000
Liabilities: $14,022,000
Net Worth: $29,287,000
Earnings: ($10,278,000)
Emp.: 1
Fiscal Year-end: 12/31/23
Medicinal & Botanical Mfr
N.A.I.C.S.: 325411
Tommy G. Thompson (Chm)
Robert G. Finizio (Co-Founder)
Brian Bernick (Co-Founder, CEO &
Chief Scientific & Medical Officer)

Mitchell L. Krassan *(Chief Strategy & Performance Officer)*
Marlan Walker *(Gen Counsel)*
Dawn Halkuff *(Chief Comml Officer)*
Joseph Ziegler *(Principal Fin & Acctg Officer)*

Subsidiaries:

BocagreenMD, Inc.   **(1)**
951 Yamato Rd Ste 220, Boca Raton, FL 33431
Tel.: (561) 961-1910
Web Site: https://www.bocagreenmd.com
Pharmaceuticals Product Mfr
N.A.I.C.S.: 325412

VitaMedMD, LLC   **(1)**
951 Yamato Rd Ste 220, Boca Raton, FL 33431
Tel.: (561) 961-1902
Web Site: http://www.vitamedmd.com
Pharmaceuticals Product Mfr
N.A.I.C.S.: 325412

THERAVANCE BIOPHARMA, INC.
901 Gateway Blvd, South San Francisco, CA 94080
Tel.: (650) 808-6000   Ky
Web Site:
   https://www.theravance.com
Year Founded: 2014
TBPH—(NASDAQ)
Rev.: $51,346,000
Assets: $607,400,000
Liabilities: $165,600,000
Net Worth: $441,800,000
Earnings: $872,132,000
Emp.: 111
Fiscal Year-end: 12/31/22
Pharmaceutical Preparation Manufacturing
N.A.I.C.S.: 325412
Rick E. Winningham *(Chm & CEO)*
Aziz Sawaf *(CFO & Sr VP)*
Brett Grimaud *(Gen Counsel)*
Stuart Knight *(CIO)*
Aine Miller *(VP)*
Stacy Pryce *(Chief Strategy Officer)*
Reigin Zawadzki *(Chief HR Officer)*

Subsidiaries:

Theravance Biopharma Ireland Limited   **(1)**
The Lennox Building - Suite 101 51 South Richmond Street, Dublin, D02 FK02, Ireland
Tel.: (353) 15394800
Pharmaceutical Product Mfr & Distr
N.A.I.C.S.: 325412

Theravance Biopharma US, Inc.   **(1)**
901 Gateway Blvd, South San Francisco, CA 94080
Tel.: (650) 808-6000
Pharmaceuticals Mfr
N.A.I.C.S.: 325412

THERIVA BIOLOGICS, INC.
9605 Medical Ctr Dr Ste 270, Rockville, MD 20850
Tel.: (301) 417-4364   NV
Web Site: https://www.therivabio.com
Year Founded: 1986
TOVX—(NYSEAMEX)
Rev.: $6,000
Assets: $70,365,000
Liabilities: $4,957,000
Net Worth: $65,408,000
Earnings: ($14,267,000)
Emp.: 16
Fiscal Year-end: 12/31/21
Pharmaceuticals Mfr for Treatment of Neurologic & Autoimmune Diseases
N.A.I.C.S.: 325412
Steven A. Shallcross *(CEO & CFO)*
Vince Wacher *(Head-Corp & Product Dev)*
Ramon Alemany *(Sr VP-Drug Discovery)*

THERMAFREEZE PRODUCTS CORP.
107 Maple Grange Rd, Vernon, NJ 07462
Tel.: (201) 788-3381
Web Site:
   http://www.thermafreeze.com
Year Founded: 1997
TZPC—(OTCIQ)
Rev.: $176,000
Assets: $22,000
Liabilities: $2,024,000
Net Worth: ($2,002,000)
Earnings: ($78,000)
Emp.: 3
Fiscal Year-end: 12/31/19
Ice Product Mfr & Distr
N.A.I.C.S.: 312113
Ilda Cartaxo *(Chm)*
Sahin Atlas *(Pres & Sec)*
Eli Winfield *(CEO)*

THERMO FISHER SCIENTIFIC INC.
168 3rd Ave, Waltham, MA 02451
Tel.: (781) 622-1000   DE
Web Site:
   https://www.thermofisher.com
Year Founded: 1956
TMO—(NYSE)
Rev.: $42,857,000,000
Assets: $98,726,000,000
Liabilities: $52,002,000,000
Net Worth: $46,724,000,000
Earnings: $5,995,000,000
Emp.: 122,000
Fiscal Year-end: 12/31/23
Electronic Measurement Equipment, Laboratory Equipment & Scientific Instrument Mfr
N.A.I.C.S.: 334516
Marc N. Casper *(Pres & CEO)*
Paul G. Parker *(Sr VP-Strategy & Corp Dev)*
Kenneth J. Apicerno *(VP-IR)*
Stephen Williamson *(CFO & Sr VP)*
Alan Sachs *(Chief Medical Officer)*
Lisa P. Britt *(Chief HR Officer & Sr VP)*
Michel Lagarde *(COO & Exec VP)*
Michael A. Boxer *(Gen Counsel & Sr VP)*
Gianluca Pettiti *(Exec VP)*
Frederick M. Lowery *(Pres-Customer Channels & Sr VP)*
Ryan Snyder *(CIO & Sr VP)*
Konrad Bauer *(Sr VP-Bus Svcs-Global)*
Daniella Cramp *(Pres-BioProduction & Sr VP)*
Sandy Pound *(Chief Comm Officer & VP)*
Mike Shafer *(Pres-Pharma Svcs & Sr VP)*
Joseph Holmes *(Chief Acctg Officer & VP)*
Karen E. Nelson *(Chief Scientific Officer)*
Joseph A. Holmes *(Chief Acctg Officer & VP)*
David Johnston *(Pres)*
Aditya Joshi *(Chief Strategy Officer)*
Jim Meyer *(VP)*
Monica Manotas *(Pres)*
Mark Smedley *(Pres)*
John Sos *(Pres)*

Subsidiaries:

ACI Holdings Inc.   **(1)**
12400 San Pedro Ave Ste 200, San Antonio, TX 78216-2887
Tel.: (210) 404-1220
Laboratory Analytical Optical Instruments Mfr
N.A.I.C.S.: 333310

AFORA S.A.U.   **(1)**
C/Roure Gros 39 Nave 1 - 2 Pol Ind Mas d'en Cisa, Sentmenat, 08181, Barcelona, Spain
Tel.: (34) 937152683
Web Site: http://www.afora.es
Sales Range: $25-49.9 Million
Emp.: 15
Laboratory Glassware & Supply Mfr
N.A.I.C.S.: 327212

Acros Organics B.V.B.A.   **(1)**
Janssen Pharmaceuticalaan 3A, 2440, Geel, Belgium
Tel.: (32) 80014575211
Laboratory Instrument Mfr
N.A.I.C.S.: 334513

Subsidiary (Non-US):

Fisher Scientific AG   **(2)**
Neuhofstrasse 11, 4153, Reinach, Switzerland
Tel.: (41) 566184111
Laboratory Instrument Mfr
N.A.I.C.S.: 334513

Advanced Scientifics, Inc.   **(1)**
163 Research Ln, Millersburg, PA 17061
Tel.: (717) 692-2104
Web Site: http://www.asisus.com
Sales Range: $75-99.9 Million
Emp.: 380
Mfr of Systems & Equipment for Preparation, Processing, Storage & Transportation of Biopharmaceuticals
N.A.I.C.S.: 339999

Alfa Aesar (China) Chemical Co. Ltd.   **(1)**
229 Yingong Road, Fengxian District, Shanghai, 201424, China
Tel.: (86) 2167582000
Web Site: http://www.alfachina.cn
Laboratory Equipment Whslr
N.A.I.C.S.: 423490

Allergon AB   **(1)**
Valingevagen 309, 262 92, Angelholm, Sweden
Tel.: (46) 42334400
Web Site: https://www.allergon.com
Emp.: 50
Medical Equipment Distr
N.A.I.C.S.: 423450
Johan Holmqvist *(Dir-Fin)*

App-Tek International Pty Ltd   **(1)**
PO Box 5523, Brendale, 4500, Australia
Tel.: (61) 738813850
Web Site: http://www.app-tek.com
Emp.: 700
Industrial Equipment Mfr & Whslr
N.A.I.C.S.: 333310

Applied Biosystems International, Inc. Russia Rep Office   **(1)**
30/1 Build 2 Obrucheva Str, 117485, Moscow, Russia
Tel.: (7) 4956516797
Web Site: http://www.lifetechnologies.com
Emp.: 30
Life Science Research & Development Services
N.A.I.C.S.: 541715

Avocado Research Chemicals Limited   **(1)**
Shore Road, Port of Heysham Industrial Park, Heysham, LA3 2XY, Lancashire, United Kingdom   **(100%)**
Tel.: (44) 1524850506
Web Site: http://www.alfa.com
Organic Compounds Mfr
N.A.I.C.S.: 325199

B.R.A.H.M.S GmbH   **(1)**
Neuendorfstrasse 25, 16761, Hennigsdorf Berlin, Germany
Tel.: (49) 33028830
Web Site: http://www.brahms.de
Diagnostic Test Product Mfr
N.A.I.C.S.: 325413

BAC BV   **(1)**
Huizerstraatweg 28, 1411 GP, Naarden, Netherlands
Tel.: (31) 358200901
Chemical & Allied Product Distr
N.A.I.C.S.: 424690

Subsidiary (Non-US):

Applied Biosystems Trading (Shanghai) Company Ltd.   **(2)**
Ganghui Business Center Xujiahui, Shanghai, 200030, China
Tel.: (86) 2161452000
Medical Equipment Whslr
N.A.I.C.S.: 423490

Subsidiary (Domestic):

BAC IP BV   **(2)**
Huizerstraatweg 28, 1411 GP, Naarden, Netherlands
Tel.: (31) 356999222
Business Management Consulting Services
N.A.I.C.S.: 541611

Beijing Phadia Diagnostics Co Ltd   **(1)**
12 floor room 1203B No 6 Wudinghou Street, Xicheng District, Beijing, 8320193, China
Tel.: (86) 1088003755
Emp.: 37,000
Diagnostic Test Substance Mfr
N.A.I.C.S.: 325413

Bio-Sciences Ltd.   **(1)**
3 Charlemont Terrace Crofton Road, Dun Laoghaire, Dublin, A96 K7H7, Ireland
Tel.: (353) 12845122
Web Site: https://www.biosciences.ie
Laboratory Equipment Distr
N.A.I.C.S.: 423450

Brammer Bio, LLC   **(1)**
250 Binney St, Cambridge, MA 02142
Tel.: (386) 418-8199
Web Site: http://www.brammerbio.com
Emp.: 500
Gene Therapy Preparation Mfr
N.A.I.C.S.: 325414
Richard O. Snyder *(Co-Founder & Chief Scientific Officer)*
Steven J. Favaloro *(CFO)*
Christopher K. Murphy *(COO)*
Steve Falcone *(Chief Quality Officer)*

Capitol Vial, Inc.   **(1)**
2039 McMillan St, Auburn, AL 36832
Tel.: (334) 887-8311
Web Site: http://www.capitolvial.com
Sales Range: $150-199.9 Million
Emp.: 150
Food Grade Polypropylene Containers
N.A.I.C.S.: 326199

Cenduit LLC   **(1)**
IQVIA 7th Fl 4820 Emperor Blvd, Durham, NC 27703
Tel.: (919) 998-3860
Web Site: http://www.cenduit.com
Drugs Merchant Whslr
N.A.I.C.S.: 424210
Nick Randazzo *(VP & Head-Sls & Mktg-Global)*
Jennifer Aquino *(COO)*
Jinu Jose *(VP-Ops)*
Kevin Landells *(VP-Project Mgmt)*
Cindie Kazmer *(Head-Tech)*

Cezanne S.A.S.   **(1)**
280 Allee Graham Bell-Parc Scientifique Georges Besse, 30035, Nimes, France
Tel.: (33) 466365200
Web Site: http://www.cezanne.fr
Analytical Laboratory Instrument Mfr
N.A.I.C.S.: 334516

Chromacol Limited   **(1)**
3 Mundells Industrial Centre, Welwyn Garden City, AL7 1EW, Hertfordshire, United Kingdom
Tel.: (44) 1707394949
Web Site: http://www.chromacol.com
Industrial Equipment Mfr
N.A.I.C.S.: 333310

Clintrak Pharmaceutical Services, LLC   **(1)**
2800 Veteran's Hwy, Bohemia, NY 11716-1002
Tel.: (631) 467-3900
Analytical Laboratory Instrument Mfr
N.A.I.C.S.: 334516

Cohesive Technologies Inc.   **(1)**

Thermo Fisher Scientific Inc.—(Continued)

101 Constitution Blvd, Franklin, MA 02038-2587
Tel.: (508) 528-7989
Laboratory Instrument Mfr & Distr
N.A.I.C.S.: 334513

CorEvitas, LLC (1)
500 Totten Pond Rd Fl 5, Waltham, MA 02451
Tel.: (508) 408-5435
Web Site: https://www.corevitas.com
Biotechnology Research & Development Services
N.A.I.C.S.: 541714

Core Informatics, LLC (1)
36 E Industrial Rd 2nd Fl, Branford, CT 06405
Web Site: http://www.coreinformatics.com
Laboratory Equipment & Scientific Instrument Distr
N.A.I.C.S.: 423490

Dionex Corporation (1)
501 Mercury Dr, Sunnyvale, CA 94085-4019
Tel.: (408) 737-0700
Web Site: http://www.dionex.com
Sales Range: $400-449.9 Million
Emp.: 1,550
Develops, Manufactures, Sells & Services Chromatography & Extraction Systems for Separating, Isolating & Identifying Components of Chemical Mixtures
N.A.I.C.S.: 334513

Subsidiary (Non-US):

CLMO Technology Sdn Bhd (2)
No 10 Jalan Dagang SB4/2 Taman Sungai Besi Indah, Selangor Darul Ehsan, 43300, Seri Kembangan, Malaysia
Tel.: (60) 389421238
Web Site: https://www.clmotech.com
Analytical Instruments Mfr & Whslr
N.A.I.C.S.: 334516
Km Chua *(Dir-Sls)*

Dionex (Switzerland) AG (2)
Neuhofstrasse 11, 4153, Reinach, Switzerland (100%)
Tel.: (41) 617167700
Web Site: http://www.thermofisher.com
Measuring Instruments Mfr & Distr
N.A.I.C.S.: 423490

Dionex (U.K.) Ltd. (2)
Unit 4 Albany Court Albany Rd Albany Park, Camberley, GU16 7QR, Surrey, United Kingdom (100%)
Tel.: (44) 1276691722
Web Site: http://www.dionex.com
Sales Range: $10-24.9 Million
Emp.: 10
Sales & Service of Analytical Instrumentation
N.A.I.C.S.: 423490

Dionex Austria GmbH (2)
Laxenburger Str 220, 1230, Vienna, Austria
Tel.: (43) 16165125
Web Site: http://www.dionex.com
Sales Range: $1-9.9 Million
Emp.: 15
Analytical Instruments Mfr & Whslr
N.A.I.C.S.: 334516

Dionex Benelux B.V. (2)
Abberdaan 114, 1046 AA, Amsterdam, Netherlands (100%)
Tel.: (31) 206839768
Sales Range: $25-49.9 Million
Emp.: 45
Sales & Service of Analytical Instruments
N.A.I.C.S.: 423490

Dionex Brasil Instrumentos Cientificos Ltda (2)
Rua Grauca N 389 Vila Sonia, Sao Paulo, 05626-020, Brazil
Tel.: (55) 37315140
Laboratory Equipment Mfr
N.A.I.C.S.: 334515

Dionex China Ltd. (2)
Room 2001 Level 20 Metroplaza Tower 2, 223 Hing Fong Road, Kwai Fong, NT, China (Hong Kong)
Tel.: (852) 24283282

Web Site: http://www.dionex.com
Sales Range: $100-124.9 Million
Emp.: 12
Analytical Instrument Mfr
N.A.I.C.S.: 334516

Subsidiary (Domestic):

Dionex (China) Analytical Ltd (3)
Unit 09-13 & 15-16, 13/F Tower 1 Kowloon Commerce Centre, No. 51 Kwai Cheong Road, Hong Kong, China (Hong Kong)
Tel.: (852) 24283282
Web Site: http://www.thermofisher.com
Emp.: 16
Analytical Laboratory Instrument Mfr
N.A.I.C.S.: 334516

Subsidiary (Non-US):

Dionex Denmark A/S (2)
Stamholmen 193, 2650, Hvidovre, Denmark
Tel.: (45) 70236260
Web Site: http://www.thermofisher.com
Analytical Instrument Mfr
N.A.I.C.S.: 334516

Dionex GmbH (2)
Am Woertzgarten 10, D 65510, Idstein, Germany (100%)
Tel.: (49) 61269910
Web Site: http://www.dionex.com
Sales Range: $25-49.9 Million
Emp.: 70
Sales & Marketing of Analytical Instrumentation
N.A.I.C.S.: 423490

Dionex Holding GmbH (2)
Am Wortzgarten 10, 65510, Idstein, Germany
Tel.: (49) 61034080
Laboratory Equipment Mfr
N.A.I.C.S.: 334515

Dionex India Pvt. Ltd (2)
R-610 Rabale TTC MIDC, Mumbai, 400 701, India
Tel.: (91) 22 2764 2735
Analytical Instruments Mfr & Whslr
N.A.I.C.S.: 334516

Dionex Ireland Limited (2)
Suite 3C Plato Business Park Damastown, Dublin, Ireland
Tel.: (353) 16440064
Analytical Laboratory Instrument Mfr
N.A.I.C.S.: 334516

Dionex Korea Ltd. (2)
3-601 Ace High-Tech City, Mullaedong 3-ga 54-66, Seoul, 150 972, Korea (South)
Tel.: (82) 42 93 12 74
Analytical Instruments Mfr & Whslr
N.A.I.C.S.: 334516

Dionex Pty Ltd (2)
Level 1 4 Talavera Road, North Ryde, 2113, NSW, Australia
Tel.: (61) 294205233
Analytical Instruments Mfr & Whslr
N.A.I.C.S.: 334516

Dionex S.p.A. (2)
Via XXV Aprile 6, 20097, San Donato Milanese, Italy
Tel.: (39) 0251621267
Analytical Instruments Mfr & Whslr
N.A.I.C.S.: 334516

Dionex Singapore Pte Ltd. (2)
b 23 A, Singapore, 408868, Singapore
Tel.: (65) 62891190
Laboratory Equipment Mfr
N.A.I.C.S.: 334515

Dionex Softron GmbH (2)
Dornierstrasse 4, 82110, Germering, Germany
Tel.: (49) 8980084559
Analytical Instrument Mfr
N.A.I.C.S.: 334516

Dionex Sweden AB (2)
Telefonvagen 30 2 tr, 126 26, Hagersten, Sweden
Tel.: (46) 317098196
Laboratory Equipment Mfr
N.A.I.C.S.: 334515

Dionex Taiwan Ltd. (2)

1F No 72 Jhouzih St, Taipei, 11493, Neihu, Taiwan
Tel.: (886) 2 8751 6655
Analytical Instruments Mfr & Whslr
N.A.I.C.S.: 334516

LGC Promochem India Private Ltd. (2)
VITC Model Export Bhavan 4th Floor 14th Cross IV Phase, Peenya Industrial Area, Mumbai, India
Tel.: (91) 80 6701 2000
Analytical Instruments Mfr & Whslr
N.A.I.C.S.: 334516

Thermo Fisher Scientific Korea Ltd. (2)
Kookmin 1st Bldg 6th Fl 1009-5, Gangnam-Gu, Seoul, 006-177, Korea (South)
Tel.: (82) 234208600
Web Site: http://www.thermofisherscientific.com
Emp.: 100
Biotechnology Research & Development Services
N.A.I.C.S.: 541714

Distribution Solutions International, Inc. (1)
333 Grandview Pkwy Harbour View Ctr, Traverse City, MI 49684
Web Site: http://www.dsii.com
Logistics & Supply Chain Management Services
N.A.I.C.S.: 541614

Doe & Ingalls Management, LLC (1)
2525 Meridian Pkwy Ste 400, Durham, NC 27713-2261
Tel.: (919) 598-1986
Web Site: http://www.thermofisher.com
Emp.: 100
Chemical & Allied Product Distr
N.A.I.C.S.: 424690

Subsidiary (Domestic):

Doe & Ingalls of Florida Operating LLC (2)
9940 Currie Davis Dr, Tampa, FL 33619
Tel.: (813) 347-4741
Emp.: 5
Consulting Services
N.A.I.C.S.: 541611

Ecochem N.V. (1)
Industrielaan 25, 2250, Olen, Belgium
Tel.: (32) 14394820
Web Site: https://www.ecochem.be
Analytical Laboratory Instrument Mfr
N.A.I.C.S.: 334516

Erie Soientifio LLC (1)
20 Post Rd, Portsmouth, NH 03801
Tel.: (603) 431-8410
Web Site: http://www.thermofisher.com
Emp.: 300
Medical Equipment Mfr
N.A.I.C.S.: 334516

Subsidiary (Domestic):

Erie Scientific Company of Puerto Rico (2)
14000 Unity St NW, Ramsey, MN 55303-9115
Tel.: (763) 323-7800
Laboratory Instrument Mfr
N.A.I.C.S.: 334516

Erie-Watala Glass Company Limited (1)
Unit 401-405 World-Wide Industrial Centre 43-47 Shan Mei Street Fotan, 43 47 Shan Mei St, Hong Kong, China (Hong Kong)
Tel.: (852) 26941838
Web Site: http://www.thermofisher.com
Sales Range: $10-24.9 Million
Emp.: 10
Glass Products Mfr
N.A.I.C.S.: 327215

Eutech Instruments Pte Ltd. (1)
7 Gul Circle level 2M Keppel Logistic Building, Singapore, 629563, Singapore
Tel.: (65) 67786876
Web Site: https://www.eutechinst.com
Analytical Laboratory Instrument Mfr
N.A.I.C.S.: 334516

Eutech Instruments Pte Ltd. (1)
7 Gul Circle level 2M Keppel Logistic Building, Singapore, 629563, Singapore
Tel.: (65) 67786876
Web Site: https://www.eutechinst.com
Electronic Equipment Distr
N.A.I.C.S.: 423690

Evidera Ltd. (1)
The Ark 201 Talgarth Rd, Hammersmith, London, W6 8BJ, United Kingdom
Tel.: (44) 2085765000
Web Site: https://www.evidera.com
Pharmaceutical Research & Development Services
N.A.I.C.S.: 541714

FEI Company (1)
5350 NE Dawson Creek Dr, Hillsboro, OR 97124-5793 (100%)
Tel.: (503) 726-7500
Web Site: http://www.fei.com
Structural Process Management Solutions of Semiconductor Data Storage Materials Science & Life Science Businesses
N.A.I.C.S.: 334413

Subsidiary (Domestic):

ASPEX Corporation (2)
175 Sheffield Dr Ste 200, Delmont, PA 15626-1723 (100%)
Tel.: (724) 468-5400
Web Site:
Scanning Electron Microscope Mfr
N.A.I.C.S.: 333310

Subsidiary (Non-US):

FEI Asia Pacific Co., Ltd (2)
Building 8 No 399 Shengxia Road Zhangjiang Hi-Tech Park, Shanghai, 201210, Pudong, China (100%)
Tel.: (86) 2180125200
Web Site: http://www.fei.com
Scanning Electron Microscope Mfr
N.A.I.C.S.: 333310

FEI CPD B.V. (2)
Achtseweg Noord 5, PO Box 80066, 5651 GG, Eindhoven, Netherlands (100%)
Tel.: (31) 402356000
Industrial Machinery Mfr
N.A.I.C.S.: 333248

FEI Company Japan Ltd. (2)
Shinagawa Seaside West Tower 1F 4-12-2 Higashi-Shinagawa, Shinagawa-ku, Tokyo, 140-0002, Japan (100%)
Tel.: (81) 337400980
Web Site: http://www.fei.com
Sales Range: $10-24.9 Million
Emp.: 70
Scanning Electron Microscope Sales & Service
N.A.I.C.S.: 333310

FEI Company of USA (S.E.A.) Pte. Ltd. (2)
No 1 Jalan Kilang Timor, 04-02 Pacific Tech Centre, Singapore, 159303, Singapore (100%)
Tel.: (65) 62720050
Web Site: http://www.fei.com
Scanning Electron Microscope Mfr
N.A.I.C.S.: 333310

FEI Czech Republic s.r.o. (2)
Vlastimila Pecha 1282/12, 627 00, Brno, Czech Republic (100%)
Tel.: (420) 513245111
Web Site: http://www.fei.com
Analytical Laboratory Instrument Mfr
N.A.I.C.S.: 334516

FEI Deutschland GmbH (2)
An Der Welle 4, 60322, Frankfurt, Germany (100%)
Tel.: (49) 6966984948
Web Site: http://www.fei.com
Analytical & Laboratory Instruments Mfr, Laboratory Services & Specialty Diagnostics
N.A.I.C.S.: 333310

Subsidiary (Domestic):

FEI EFA, Inc. (2)
1321 N Plano Rd, Richardson, TX 75081 (100%)
Tel.: (972) 792-1622
Web Site: http://www.fei.com

Laboratory Equipment & Scientific Instrument Distr
N.A.I.C.S.: 423490

Subsidiary (Non-US):

FEI Electron Optics International B.V. (2)
Achtseweg Noord 5 Gebouw Aae, 5651 GG, Eindhoven, Netherlands (100%)
Tel.: (31) 402356000
Web Site: http://www.fei.com
Scanning Electron Microscope Sales, Service & Mfr
N.A.I.C.S.: 333310

Subsidiary (Non-US):

FEI SAS (3)
3 Impasse Rudolf Diesel, BP 50 227, 33708, Merignac, Cedex, France (100%)
Tel.: (33) 556133777
Web Site: http://www.fei.com
Laboratory Equipment & Scientific Instrument Distr
N.A.I.C.S.: 423490

Subsidiary (Non-US):

FEI France SAS (2)
16 Av du Quebec Parc d affaires Silic, Villebon-sur-Yvette, 91140, Courtaboeuf, Cedex 03, France (100%)
Tel.: (33) 173036526
Web Site: http://www.fei.com
Scanning Electron Microscope Sales, Service & Mfr
N.A.I.C.S.: 333310

Subsidiary (US):

FEI Houston, Inc. (3)
1321 Antoine Dr, Houston, TX 77055 (100%)
Tel.: (713) 839-0808
Web Site: https://feihouston.org
3D Visualization Software Mfr
N.A.I.C.S.: 513210

Subsidiary (Domestic):

FEI Fremont (2)
3400 W Warren Ave, Fremont, CA 94538
Tel.: (510) 897-6800
Web Site: http://www.fei.com
Semiconductor & Electronics Product Mfr
N.A.I.C.S.: 334413

Subsidiary (Domestic):

FEI Santa Barbara (3)
827 Reddick St, Santa Barbara, CA 93103
Tel.: (805) 560-0404
Web Site: http://www.fei.com
Electrical Measuring Instrument Mfr
N.A.I.C.S.: 334515

Subsidiary (Non-US):

FEI Global Holdings C.V. (2)
Achtseweg Noord 5, PO Box 80066, Gebouw AAE, 5651 GG, Eindhoven, Netherlands
Tel.: (31) 402356924
Web Site: http://www.fei.com
Scanning Electron Microscope Sales, Service & Mfr
N.A.I.C.S.: 333310

FEI Italia S.r.l. (2)
Viale Monte Nero 84, 20135, Milan, Italy
Tel.: (39) 0245279043
Analytical Laboratory Instrument Mfr
N.A.I.C.S.: 334516

FEI Korea Ltd. (2)
AICT 5F A Bldg 145 Gwanggyo-Ro, Yeongong-ku, Suwon, 443-270, Gyeonggi-Do, Korea (South) (100%)
Tel.: (82) 8889900
Web Site: http://www.fei.com
Electronic Devices Mftr
N.A.I.C.S.: 423610

FEI Norway Holding AS (2)
Stiklestadveien 1, 7401, Trondheim, Norway (100%)
Tel.: (47) 99202992
Web Site: http://www.fei.com
Scanning Electron Microscope Sales, Service & Mfr

N.A.I.C.S.: 333310

Subsidiary (Non-US):

FEI Australia Pty Ltd. (3)
Suite 102 First Floor, Canberra, 2601, ACT, Australia (100%)
Tel.: (61) 261736212
Web Site: http://www.fei.com
Industrial Machinery Distr
N.A.I.C.S.: 423830

Subsidiary (Domestic):

FEI Trondheim AS (3)
Stiklestadveien 1, 7041, Trondheim, Norway (100%)
Tel.: (47) 99202992
Web Site: http://www.fei.com
Scanning Electron Microscope Sales, Service & Mfr
N.A.I.C.S.: 333310

Subsidiary (Non-US):

FEI Technology de Mexico S.A. de C.V. (2)
Torre Gia Building Av Morones Prieto 2805 Pte Col, Lomas de San Francisco 2nd Floor Office 220, Monterrey, Nuevo Leon, Mexico
Tel.: (52) 8183990080
Web Site: http://www.fei.com
Analytical Laboratory Instrument Mfr
N.A.I.C.S.: 334516

FEI UK Ltd. (2)
Merlin Place Milton Park, Cambridge, CB4 0DP, Cambridgeshire, United Kingdom (100%)
Tel.: (44) 2079490374
Web Site: http://www.fei.com
Scanning Electron Microscope Sales, Service & Mfr
N.A.I.C.S.: 333310
Rhona Gregg (Sec)

FSII Sweden Holdings AB (1)
Skeppsbron 42, Stockholm, 111 30, Sweden
Tel.: (46) 41519800
Holding Company
N.A.I.C.S.: 551112

Subsidiary (Domestic):

Perbio Science AB (2)
Vastra Langebergsgatan 30, Vastra Frolunda, Gothenburg, 421 32, Sweden
Tel.: (46) 42269090
Biotechnology Research & Development Services
N.A.I.C.S.: 541714

Finesse Solutions, Inc. (1)
3501 Leonard Ct, Santa Clara, CA 95054
Optical PH Sensor Mfr
N.A.I.C.S.: 334516

Fisher Clinical Services Inc. (1)
699 N Wheeling Rd, Allentown, PA 18106-9052
Tel.: (610) 391-0800
Web Site:
    http://www.fishersclinicalservices.com
Rev.: $25,100,000
Emp.: 700
Foamed Plastics Packaging & Shipping Materials
N.A.I.C.S.: 326150

Subsidiary (Domestic):

Fisher BioServices Inc. (2)
14665 Rothgeb Dr, Rockville, MD 20850
Tel.: (301) 315-8460
Web Site: http://www.fisherbioservices.com
Emp.: 200
Cold Chain Storage Services
N.A.I.C.S.: 334516

Subsidiary (Non-US):

Southern Trials (Pty) Ltd. (3)
Unit 5 Saturn Place 38 Saturn Crescent, Linbro Business Park, Sandton, 2065, South Africa
Tel.: (27) 116080837
Laboratory Instrument Mfr
N.A.I.C.S.: 334513

Subsidiary (Non-US):

Fisher Clinical Services GmbH (2)
Steinbuehlweg 69, 4123, Allschwil, Basel-Landschaft, Switzerland
Tel.: (41) 614852300
Web Site:
    http://www.fisherclinicalservices.com
Sales Range: $50-74.9 Million
Emp.: 410
Clinical Supply Services
N.A.I.C.S.: 423450

Thermo Fisher Scientific Brasil Servicos de Logistica Ltda (2)
Av Jaguare 818 Unidade 29, Sao Paulo, 05346-000, SP, Brazil
Tel.: (55) 1137190203
Web Site:
    http://www.fisherclinicalservices.com
Emp.: 18
Analytical Laboratory Instrument Mfr
N.A.I.C.S.: 334516

Fisher Clinical Services Pte Ltd. (1)
10 Pandan Crescent L1 03-01/02, Singapore, 128466, Singapore
Tel.: (65) 68070700
Laboratory Analytical Optical Instruments Mfr
N.A.I.C.S.: 333310

Fisher Mexico, S. de R.L. de C.V. (1)
Prol Diaz Ordaz No 304 Interior Col Bosques Del Nogalar, San Nicolas de Los Garza, Monterrey, 66480, Mexico
Tel.: (52) 8180425208
Laboratory Instrument Mfr
N.A.I.C.S.: 334513

Fisher Scientific (Austria) GmbH (1)
Dresdner Strasse 89, A-1200, Vienna, Austria
Tel.: (43) 800208840
Web Site: https://www.fishersci.at
Analytical Laboratory Instrument Mfr
N.A.I.C.S.: 334516

Fisher Scientific (Hong Kong) Limited (1)
Rm 11-15 9/f Grand Central Plz Twr 1, 138 Shatin Rural Committee Road, Sha Tin, New Territories, China (Hong Kong)
Tel.: (852) 28854613
Laboratory Instrument Mfr
N.A.I.C.S.: 334513

Fisher Scientific (M) Sdn Bhd (1)
Shah Alam 3 Jalan Sepadu 25/123 Taman Perindustrian Axis, 40400, Shah Alam, Selangor, Malaysia
Tel.: (60) 351228888
Web Site: https://myfisherstore.com
Laboratory Analytical Optical Instruments Mfr
N.A.I.C.S.: 333310

Fisher Scientific A/S (1)
Kamstrupvej 91, PO Box 60, 4000, Roskilde, Denmark
Tel.: (45) 70279920
Web Site: https://www.fishersci.dk
Laboratory Analytical Optical Instruments Mfr
N.A.I.C.S.: 333310

Fisher Scientific Biotech Line A/S (1)
Industrivej 3, 3550, Slangerup, Denmark
Tel.: (45) 70279920
Web Site: http://www.fishersci.dk
Analytical Laboratory Instrument Mfr
N.A.I.C.S.: 334516

Subsidiary (Non-US):

Phadia AB (2)
Rapsgatan 7P, PO Box 6460, 751 37, Uppsala, Sweden
Tel.: (46) 18165000
Web Site: http://www.phadia.com
Sales Range: $500-549.9 Million
Emp.: 1,500
Develops, Manufactures & Markets Diagnostic Blood Test Systems
N.A.I.C.S.: 339112

Subsidiary (Non-US):

Laboratory Specialities Proprietary Ltd. (3)

197 Fabriek Street, Strijdompark, Randburg, 2125, South Africa
Tel.: (27) 117926790
Web Site: http://www.isitallergy.co.za
Sales Range: $25-49.9 Million
Emp.: 16
Blood Test Systems Mfr
N.A.I.C.S.: 325413

Phadia AG (3)
Sennweidstrasse 46, 6312, Steinhausen, Switzerland
Tel.: (41) 433434050
Web Site: http://www.phadia.com
Emp.: 10
Blood Test Systems Mfr
N.A.I.C.S.: 325413

Phadia ApS (3)
Gydevang 33, 3450, Allerod, Denmark
Tel.: (45) 70233306
Web Site: http://www.thermofisher.com
Sales Range: $25-49.9 Million
Emp.: 11
Blood Test Systems Mfr
N.A.I.C.S.: 325413
Bjarne Christian (Mng Dir)

Phadia Austria GmbH (3)
BIGBIZ B Dresdner Strassee 89, 1200, Vienna, Austria
Tel.: (43) 12702020
Sales Range: $25-49.9 Million
Emp.: 15
Blood Test Systems Mfr
N.A.I.C.S.: 325413

Phadia B.V. (3)
Fultonbaan 24, 3439 NE, Nieuwegein, Netherlands
Tel.: (31) 306023700
Web Site: http://www.phadia.com
Sales Range: $25-49.9 Million
Emp.: 16
Blood Test Systems Mfr
N.A.I.C.S.: 325413

Phadia Diagnosticos Ltda. (3)
Rua Eugenio de Medeiros 303 cj 1101C, Sao Paulo, 05425-000, Brazil
Tel.: (55) 8000551535
Sales Range: $25-49.9 Million
Emp.: 24
Blood Test Systems Mfr
N.A.I.C.S.: 325413

Phadia GmbH (3)
Munzinger Strasse 7, PO Box 1050, 79111, Freiburg, Germany
Tel.: (49) 761478050
Web Site: http://www.thermofisher.com
Emp.: 200
Blood Test Systems Mfr
N.A.I.C.S.: 325413

Phadia K.K. (3)
3-20-2 Nishi-Shinjuku Shinjuku-ku, Tokyo, 163-1431, Japan
Tel.: (81) 353658332
Blood Test Systems Mfr
N.A.I.C.S.: 325413

Phadia Korea Co. Ltd. (3)
20FI IT Mirae Tower 60-21, Geumcheon-gu, Seoul, 153-760, Korea (South)
Tel.: (82) 220275400
Web Site: http://www.phadia.com
Sales Range: $25-49.9 Million
Emp.: 13
Blood Test Systems Mfr
N.A.I.C.S.: 325413
Jongheuk Kim (Pres)

Phadia Ltd. (3)
16 Shenley Pavilions Chalkdell Drive, Shenley Wood, Milton Keynes, MK5 6LB, United Kingdom
Tel.: (44) 1908769110
Blood Test Systems Mfr
N.A.I.C.S.: 325413

Phadia Multiplexing Diagnostics GmbH (3)
Tech Gate Vienna, Donau-City-Strasse 1, 1220, Vienna, Austria
Tel.: (43) 12530253100
Blood Test Systems Mfr
N.A.I.C.S.: 325413

Phadia NV/SA (3)

Thermo Fisher Scientific Inc.—(Continued)

Pontbeekstraat 2, 1702, Groot-Bijgaarden, Belgium
Tel.: (32) 27495515
Web Site: http://www.phadia.com
Blood Test Systems Mfr
N.A.I.C.S.: 325413

Phadia Oy (3)
Ratastie 2, PO Box 100, 01620, Vantaa, Finland
Tel.: (358) 103292110
Sales Range: $25-49.9 Million
Emp.: 5
Blood Test Systems Mfr
N.A.I.C.S.: 325413

Phadia Sociedade Unipessoal Lda (3)
Lagoa's Park Edificio 11 Piso 0, 2740-270, Porto Salvo, Portugal
Tel.: (351) 214 23 53 50
Blood Test Systems Mfr
N.A.I.C.S.: 325413

Phadia Spain S.L. (3)
Avda Mayor Barnils 70 Ed Onada 2a Planta, Sant Cugat del Valles, 08174, Barcelona, Spain
Tel.: (34) 935 765 800
Web Site: http://www.phadia.com
Emp.: 30
Blood Test Systems Mfr
N.A.I.C.S.: 325413

Phadia Taiwan Inc. (3)
6F-1 No 85 Jhouzih St, Neihu District, Taipei, 11493, Taiwan
Tel.: (886) 287516655
Web Site: http://www.phadia.com
Blood Test Systems Mfr
N.A.I.C.S.: 325413

Subsidiary (US):

Phadia US Inc. (3)
4169 Commercial Ave, Portage, MI 49002
Tel.: (269) 492-1940
Web Site: http://www.phadia.us
Sales Range: $25-49.9 Million
Emp.: 55
Blood Test Systems Mfr
N.A.I.C.S.: 339112

Subsidiary (Non-US):

Phadia s.r.o. (3)
Prague 9 Drahobejlova 1019/27, 190 00, Prague, Czech Republic
Tel.: (420) 220518743
Blood Test Systems Mfr
N.A.I.C.S.: 325413

Thermo Fisher Diagnostics SpA (3)
Strada Rivoltana, 20090, Rodano, MI, Italy
Tel.: (39) 03983891
Web Site: http://www.phadia.com
Immuno Diagnostic Mfr
N.A.I.C.S.: 325413

Fisher Scientific Company (1)
112 Colonnade Road, Ottawa, K2E 7L6, ON, Canada
Web Site: https://www.fishersci.ca
Sales Range: $200-249.9 Million
Emp.: 500
Medical & Hospital Equipment
N.A.I.C.S.: 423450

Subsidiary (Domestic):

Cole-Parmer Canada Company (2)
100-2500 Rue Jean-Perrin, Quebec, G2C 1X1, QC, Canada
Tel.: (514) 355-6100
Web Site: http://www.coleparmer.ca
Instruments & Related Products Distr
N.A.I.C.S.: 334513

Diagnostix Ltd. (2)
2845 Argentia Rd Unit 5, Mississauga, L5N 8G6, ON, Canada
Tel.: (905) 286-4290
Web Site: https://www.thermal.com
Drugs Screening & Industrial Distr
N.A.I.C.S.: 339112

Fisher Scientific Company, LLC (1)
300 Industry Dr, Pittsburgh, PA 15275
Tel.: (724) 517-1500

Web Site: https://www.fishersci.com
Emp.: 1,000
Metal Container Mfr
N.A.I.C.S.: 332439

Fisher Scientific GTF AB (1)
Arendalsvagen 16, 418 78, Gothenburg, Sweden
Tel.: (46) 313523200
Web Site: http://www.fishersci.se
Laboratory Instruments Distr
N.A.I.C.S.: 334513

Fisher Scientific GmbH (1)
Im Heiligen Feld 17, 58239, Schwerte, Germany
Tel.: (49) 23049325
Web Site: https://www.fishersci.de
Emp.: 300
Laboratory Analytical Optical Instruments Mfr
N.A.I.C.S.: 333310

Subsidiary (Non-US):

Fisher Scientific d.o.o. (2)
Parmova ulica 53, Ljubljana, 1000, Slovenia
Tel.: (386) 59731494
Web Site: http://www.fishersci.dk
Laboratory Analytical Optical Instruments Mfr
N.A.I.C.S.: 333310

Fisher Scientific, spol. S.r.o (2)
Kosmonautu 324, 533 09, Pardubice, Czech Republic
Tel.: (420) 466798230
Web Site: https://www.thermofisher.cz
Laboratory Instrument Mfr
N.A.I.C.S.: 334513

Fisher Scientific Holding U.K., Limited (1)
Bishop Meadow Road, Loughborough, LE11 5RG, Leicestershire, United Kingdom
Tel.: (44) 1509231166
Web Site: http://www.fisher.co.uk
Holding Company
N.A.I.C.S.: 551112

Fisher Scientific Ireland Limited (1)
3rd Floor Kilmore House Park Lane Spencer Dock, D01 YE64, Dublin, 1, Ireland
Tel.: (353) 18855854
Web Site: https://www.fishersci.ie
Emp.: 60
Laboratory Analytical Optical Instruments Mfr
N.A.I.C.S.: 333310

Fisher Scientific Japan, Ltd. (1)
Tokyo Nissan Building 3f 3-25-9 Taishi-do, Taito-Ku Setagaya-ku, Tokyo, 154-0004, Japan
Tel.: (81) 334196778
Web Site: http://www.thermofisher.com
Laboratory Instrument Mfr
N.A.I.C.S.: 334513

Fisher Scientific Korea Ltd (1)
Kookmin 1st Bldg 7th Fl 1009-5, Gangnam-gu, Seoul, 726-173, Korea (South)
Tel.: (82) 25270300
Web Site: http://www.fishersci.co.kr
Medical Equipment Distr
N.A.I.C.S.: 423450

Fisher Scientific Norway AS (1)
Frysjaveien 33 E, Oslo, 0884, Norway
Tel.: (47) 22955959
Medical Equipment Distr
N.A.I.C.S.: 423450

Fisher Scientific Oy (1)
Ratastie 2, 01620, Vantaa, Finland
Tel.: (358) 980276280
Web Site: https://www.fishersci.fi
Analytical Laboratory Instrument Mfr
N.A.I.C.S.: 334516

Fisher Scientific Pte. Ltd. (1)
1 Science Park Road 03-01/09, The Capricorn Singapore Science Park 2, Singapore, 117528, Singapore
Tel.: (65) 60164798
Web Site: http://www.myfisherstore.com
Analytical Laboratory Instrument Mfr
N.A.I.C.S.: 334516

Subsidiary (Non-US):

Fisher Scientific Research/Fisher Safety (1)

300 Industry Dr, Pittsburgh, PA 15275-1126
Tel.: (412) 490-8300
Web Site: http://www.fishersci.com
Rev.: $900,000,000
Equipment, Supplies & Services for the Clinical Laboratory & Global Scientific Research
N.A.I.C.S.: 423490
Mark Caspr (CEO)

Fisher Scientific S.A.S. (1)
Boulevard Sebastien Brant, PO Box 50111, 67403, Illkirch-Graffenstaden, Cedex, France
Tel.: (33) 388671414
Web Site: https://www.fishersci.fr
Laboratory Instrument Mfr
N.A.I.C.S.: 334513

Subsidiary (Domestic):

Avantec Sarl (2)
Boulevard Sebastien Brant Parc d'Innovation, BP 30188, 67400, Illkirch-Graffenstaden, France
Tel.: (33) 388666724
Emp.: 380
Laboratory Instrument Mfr
N.A.I.C.S.: 334513
Marc Casper (Dir)

Subsidiary (Non-US):

Fisher Scientific SPRL (2)
Clintonpark-Keppekouter Ninovesteenweg 198, 9320, Aalst, Belgium
Tel.: (32) 56260260
Laboratory Equipment Mfr
N.A.I.C.S.: 334515

NOVODIRECT GmbH (2)
Hafenstrasse 3, 77694, Kehl, Germany
Tel.: (49) 7851994570
Web Site: http://www.novodirect.fishersci.com
Analytical Laboratory Instrument Mfr
N.A.I.C.S.: 334516

Novodirect GmbH (2)
Hafenstrasse 3, Rhine, 77694, Kehl, Germany
Tel.: (49) 7851994570
Laboratory Instrument Mfr
N.A.I.C.S.: 334513

Fisher Scientific S.L. (1)
C/ Anabel Segura 16 Edif 2 Planta 3 Centro Empresarial Vega Norte, Alcobendas, 28108, Madrid, Spain
Tel.: (34) 913806710
Web Site: https://www.fishersci.es
Analytical Laboratory Instrument Mfr
N.A.I.C.S.: 334516

Fisher Scientific UK Ltd. (1)
Bishop Meadow Road, Loughborough, LE11 5RG, Leicestershire, United Kingdom
Tel.: (44) 1509555939
Web Site: https://www.fishersci.co.uk
Sales Range: $100-124.9 Million
Emp.: 500
Research & Drug Development Software & Services
N.A.I.C.S.: 541519

Fisher Scientific of the Netherlands B.V. (1)
Scheepsbouwersweg 1b, PO Box 4, 1120 AA, Landsmeer, Netherlands
Tel.: (31) 204877000
Web Site: https://www.fishersci.nl
Emp.: 160
Laboratory Instrument Mfr
N.A.I.C.S.: 334513

Fisher Scientific, Unipessoal, Lda. (1)
Rua Pedro Alvares Cabral Edificio Euro nr 24 3rd floor letter D, 2670-452, Loures, Lisbon, Portugal
Tel.: (351) 214253350
Laboratory Analytical Optical Instruments Mfr
N.A.I.C.S.: 333310

GlaxoSmithKline (Manufacturing) Ltd. (1)
Currabinny, Carrigaline, Cork, Ireland (100%)
Tel.: (353) 214378800

Web Site: http://www.gsk.ie
Sales Range: $125-149.9 Million
Emp.: 500
Pharmaceuticals Mfr
N.A.I.C.S.: 325412

Hyclone UK Limited (1)
3rd Floor 1 Ashley Road, Altrincham, WA14 2DT, Cheshire, United Kingdom
Tel.: (44) 800252185
Pharmaceutical Preparation Mfr
N.A.I.C.S.: 325412

Inel SAS (1)
Zone Industrielle Cd 405, 45410, Artenay, France
Tel.: (33) 238804545
Web Site: http://www.inel.fr
X-ray Equipment Mfr
N.A.I.C.S.: 334517

Subsidiary (US):

Inel Inc. (2)
PO Box 147, Stratham, NH 03885
Tel.: (603) 778-9161
Web Site: http://www.inel.us
Medical Equipment Mfr
N.A.I.C.S.: 339113

IntegenX Inc. (1)
5720 Stoneridge Dr Ste 300, Pleasanton, CA 94588
Tel.: (925) 701-3400
Web Site: http://www.thermofisher.com
Sales Range: $10-24.9 Million
Emp.: 75
Laboratory Equipment Mfr
N.A.I.C.S.: 334516

Life Sciences International Holdings BV (1)
Takkebijsters 1, Breda, 4817 BL, Netherlands
Tel.: (31) 765717311
Holding Company
N.A.I.C.S.: 551112

Life Technologies Chile SpA (1)
Avenida Jose Domingo Canas 570 Nunoa, Santiago, Chile
Tel.: (56) 222690360
Life Science Research & Development Services
N.A.I.C.S.: 541715

Life Technologies Corporation (1)
5791 Van Allen Way, Carlsbad, CA 92008 (100%)
Tel.: (760) 603-7200
Web Site: http://www.lifetechnologies.com
Sales Range: $1-4.9 Billion
Emp.: 10,000
Research Tools Mfr for Gene Cloning, Gene Expression & Gene Analysis; Sera, Cell & Tissue Culture Media & Reagents Mfr
N.A.I.C.S.: 325414
Siddhartha C. Kadia (CMO & VP-Global Mktg & eBus)

Subsidiary (Domestic):

Applied Biosystems, LLC (2)
5791 Van Allen Way, Carlsbad, CA 92008 (100%)
Tel.: (760) 603-7200
Web Site: http://www.appliedbiosystems.com
Instrument-Based Systems, Reagents, Software Developer & Contract-Related Services to Life Science Industries; Genomic & Related Medical Information
N.A.I.C.S.: 541715

Subsidiary (Non-US):

Applied Biosystems de Mexico S. de R.L. de C.V. (3)
Av Paseo De La Reforma No 505 Piso 42 Suite D, Col Cuauhtemoc Deleg Cuauhtemoc, 06500, Mexico, Mexico
Tel.: (52) 5530983800
Web Site: http://www.thermofisher.com
Biotechnology Research Products Mfr & Services
N.A.I.C.S.: 325414

Subsidiary (Domestic):

Compendia Bioscience, Inc. (2)

110 Miller Ave, Ann Arbor, MI
48104 **(100%)**
Tel.: (734) 531-9298
Web Site: http://www.compendiabio.com
Life Science Research & Development Services
N.A.I.C.S.: 541715

Subsidiary (Non-US):

Invitrogen BioServices India Private Limited (2)
Second Floor First Technlogy Place Citius Block 3 EPIP, Whitefield, Bengaluru, 560 066, Karnataka, India
Tel.: (91) 8041785400
Web Site: http://www.thermofisher.com
Emp.: 600
Biotechnology Research Product & Laboratory Service Provider
N.A.I.C.S.: 541714
Kapil Sood (Mng Dir)

Subsidiary (Domestic):

Ion Torrent Systems, Inc. (2)
246 Goose Ln Ste 100, Guilford, CT 06437 **(100%)**
Tel.: (203) 458-8552
Sales Range: $25-49.9 Million
Emp.: 45
Commercial Scientific Research Services
N.A.I.C.S.: 541715
Jonathan M. Rothberg (Founder)
Philip Waggoner (Sr Mgr-R&D)

Subsidiary (Non-US):

Life Technologies Australia Pty Ltd. (2)
PO Box 4296, Mulgrave, 3170, VIC, Australia **(100%)**
Tel.: (61) 1800636327
Web Site: http://www.labonline.com.au
Emp.: 280
Biotechnology Research Product & Laboratory Service Provider
N.A.I.C.S.: 541714

Subsidiary (Domestic):

Life Technologies Clinical Services Lab, Inc. (2)
910 Riverside Pkwy Ste 60, West Sacramento, CA 95605
Web Site: https://www.lifelabdx.com
Analytical Laboratory Instrument Mfr
N.A.I.C.S.: 334516

Subsidiary (Non-US):

Life Technologies GmbH (2)
Frankfurter Str 129B, 64293, Darmstadt, Germany **(100%)**
Tel.: (49) 72161890
Sales Range: $25-49.9 Million
Emp.: 120
Biological Products
N.A.I.C.S.: 325414
Julia Alege (Sr Mgr-Remote Svcs & Support-EMEA)
Caecilia Simon (Mgr-Trng Ops)

Subsidiary (Domestic):

Thermo Fisher Scientific GENEART GmbH (3)
In the industrial park B 35, 93059, Regensburg, Germany
Tel.: (49) 941942760
Laboratory Instrument Mfr
N.A.I.C.S.: 334516

Subsidiary (Non-US):

Life Technologies Holdings Pte Ltd. (2)
33 Marsiling Ind Estate Road 3 07-06, Singapore, 739256, Singapore **(100%)**
Tel.: (65) 68618638
Sales Range: $1-9.9 Million
Emp.: 20
Biological Products
N.A.I.C.S.: 325414

Life Technologies Japan Limited (2)
Sumitomo Fudosan Mita Twin Bldg E Wing 4-2-8 Shibaura, Minato-ku, Tokyo, 108-0023, Japan
Tel.: (81) 368329300

Biotechnology Research Product & Service Provider
N.A.I.C.S.: 325414

Life Technologies Limited (2)
Unit 1309-13 & 15-16 Level 13 Tower 1 Kowloon Commerce Centre, No 51 Kwai Cheong Road, Kwai Chung, China (Hong Kong)
Tel.: (852) 31077600
Biotechnology Research Product & Service Provider
N.A.I.C.S.: 325414

Life Technologies Limited (2)
3 Fountain Drive, Inchinnan Business Park, Paisley, PA4 9RF, Renfrewshire, United Kingdom **(100%)**
Tel.: (44) 1418146100
Web Site: http://www.lifetech.com
Sales Range: $50-74.9 Million
Emp.: 400
Biological Products
N.A.I.C.S.: 325414

Life Technologies Magyarorszag Kft. (2)
Hermina ut 17, 1146, Budapest, Hungary **(100%)**
Tel.: (36) 14718989
Web Site: http://www.thermofisher.com
Biotechnology Research Product & Service Provider
N.A.I.C.S.: 325414

Life Technologies SAS (2)
Immeuble Discovery Parc Technologique Route de L'Orme, Zone Technologique, 91190, Saint Aubin, France **(100%)**
Tel.: (33) 169598585
Sales Range: $25-49.9 Million
Emp.: 100
Biotechnology Research Product & Service Provider
N.A.I.C.S.: 325414
Herve Pouzoullic (Dir-Sls)

Subsidiary (Domestic):

Laboratoire Services International (LSI) SAS (3)
6 Allee des Ecureuils Parc Tertiaire Du Bois Dieu, 69380, Lissieu, France **(100%)**
Tel.: (33) 472548282
Medical Equipment Distr
N.A.I.C.S.: 423450
Laurent Thiery (Office Mgr)

Subsidiary (Domestic):

Molecular Probes, Inc. (2)
29851 Willow Creek Rd, Eugene, OR 97402 **(100%)**
Tel.: (541) 465-8300
Sales Range: $75-99.9 Million
Emp.: 300
Biological Detection Products
N.A.I.C.S.: 325414
Stacy Hall (Sr Mgr-Fin-Protein & Cell Analysis Bus Unit)

Subsidiary (Non-US):

Shanghai Life Technologies Biotechnology Co. Limited (2)
Room 103 No 2 Building Xiangzhangyuan No 2715 Longxi Road X, Shanghai, 200231, China **(100%)**
Tel.: (86) 2164346828
Sales Range: $50-74.9 Million
Emp.: 170
Biotechnology Research Product & Service Provider
N.A.I.C.S.: 325414

Thermo Fisher Israel Ltd. (2)
Northern Ind Zone, Kiryat Shmona, Israel **(100%)**
Tel.: (972) 89408618
Sales Range: $10-24.9 Million
Emp.: 60
Molecular Biology Detection Devices
N.A.I.C.S.: 334519

Thermo Fisher Scientific (Thailand) Co., Ltd. (2)
Unit 2010 Singha Complex Level 21 1788 New Petchaburi Road, Bangkapi Huai Kwang, Bangkok, 10310, Thailand
Tel.: (66) 20743366

Analytical Laboratory Instrument Mfr
N.A.I.C.S.: 334516

Life Technologies Europe B.V. - Nederlaenderna Filial Sverige - Sweden (1)
Lindhagensgatan 76, PO Box 12650, 112 92, Stockholm, Sweden
Tel.: (46) 86194400
Analytical Laboratory Instrument Mfr
N.A.I.C.S.: 334516

Life Technologies Korea LLC (1)
12 Suseo Office Building 281 Gwangpyeong-ro, Gangnam-gu, Seoul, 135-884, Korea (South)
Tel.: (82) 220230600
Life Science Research & Development Services
N.A.I.C.S.: 541715

Subsidiary (Domestic):

KDR Biotech Co ltd. (2)
506-4 Amsa 2-Dong, Gangdong, Seoul, 134-877, Korea (South)
Tel.: (82) 234276000
Life Science Research & Development Services
N.A.I.C.S.: 541715
Amold J. M. Kim (Pres & CEO)

Life Technologies New Zealand Ltd. (1)
244 Bush Road, Albany, Auckland, 0632, New Zealand
Tel.: (64) 95793024
Biological Product Mfr
N.A.I.C.S.: 325414
Peter Airey (Dir-Site)

Linkage Biosciences, Inc. (1)
890 Dubuque Ave, South San Francisco, CA 94080
Tel.: (415) 346-5262
Web Site: http://www.linkagebio.com
Diagnostic Test Substance Mfr
N.A.I.C.S.: 325413

MarqMetrix, Inc. (1)
2157 N Northlake Way Ste 240, Seattle, WA 98103
Tel.: (206) 971-3625
Web Site: https://www.marqmetrix.com
Measuring & Testing Equipment Distr
N.A.I.C.S.: 423830

Metavac LLC (1)
4000 Point St, Holtsville, NY 11742-2008 **(100%)**
Tel.: (631) 207-2344
Web Site: http://www.metavac.com
Emp.: 46
Laboratory Analytical Optical Instruments Mfr
N.A.I.C.S.: 333310

Microgenics Corporation (1)
46500 Kato Rd, Fremont, CA 94535
Tel.: (510) 979-9147
Sales Range: $50-74.9 Million
Emp.: 6,076
Medical Diagnostic Product Mfr
N.A.I.C.S.: 339112

Subsidiary (Domestic):

Consolidated Technologies, Inc. (2)
8 Slater St, Port Chester, NY 10573
Tel.: (914) 935-6000
Web Site: http://www.consoltech.com
Emp.: 20
Laboratory Analytical Optical Instruments Mfr
N.A.I.C.S.: 333310
Ben Kenneth Schoolsky (Partner & Chief Customer Officer)

Subsidiary (Non-US):

Microgenics GmbH (2)
Spitalhofstrasse 94, 94032, Passau, Germany
Tel.: (49) 851886890
Web Site: http://www.microgenics.de
Sales Range: $25-49.9 Million
Clinical Diagnostic Products Mfr & Distr
N.A.I.C.S.: 334516

Microm International GmbH (1)

Im Steingrund 4 - 6, 63303, Dreieich, Germany **(100%)**
Tel.: (49) 2131109701
Web Site: http://www.microm.de
Geomarketing; Microtome Mfr
N.A.I.C.S.: 334516

NAPCO, Inc. (1)
120 Trojan Ave, Sparta, NC 28675-9073
Tel.: (336) 372-5214
Web Site: https://napcousa.com
Emp.: 100
Paperboard Product Mfr
N.A.I.C.S.: 334519
Rocky Proffit (Founder & CEO)
Rick Proffit (VP-Ops)
Dan Duncan (Dir-New Product Dev)
Carol Draughon (Mgr-Plant Production)
Debbie Bare (Mgr-Customer Svc & Project)
Shannon Lawrence (Mgr-Materials)
Dan Edwards Jr. (Mgr-Production Plng)

Nalge Nunc International Corporation (1)
75 Panorama Creek Dr, Rochester, NY 14625-2385
Tel.: (585) 586-8800
Web Site: http://www.nalgenunc.com
Plastics Product Mfr
N.A.I.C.S.: 326130

Nalge Nunc International Corporation (1)
75 Panorama Creek Dr, Rochester, NY 14625
Web Site: https://nalgene.com
Analytical Laboratory Instrument Mfr
N.A.I.C.S.: 334516

NanoDrop Technologies LLC (1)
3411 Silverside Rd Bancroft Bldg, Wilmington, DE 19810
Tel.: (302) 479-7707
Laboratory Instrument Mfr
N.A.I.C.S.: 334513

Nunc A/S (1)
Kamstrupvej 90, 4000, Roskilde, Denmark
Tel.: (45) 46312000
Laboratory Instrument Mfr
N.A.I.C.S.: 334513

Subsidiary (Domestic):

Proxeon Biosystems A/S (2)
Edisonsvej 4, 5000, Odense, Denmark
Tel.: (45) 65572300
Laboratory Instrument Mfr
N.A.I.C.S.: 334513

ONIX Systems Inc. (1)
22001 N Park Dr, Kingwood, TX 77339
Tel.: (781) 622-1000
Emp.: 800
Laboratory Instrument Mfr
N.A.I.C.S.: 334513

Odyssey Ventures, Inc. (1)
417 Heronwood Ct, Purcellville, VA 20132-3066
Tel.: (703) 362-7935
Miscellaneous Intermediation Services
N.A.I.C.S.: 523910

Olink Holding AB (1)
Uppsala Science Park, SE-751 83, Uppsala, Sweden
Tel.: (46) 184443970
Rev.: $169,597,000
Assets: $602,252,000
Liabilities: $99,554,000
Net Worth: $502,698,000
Earnings: ($31,600,000)
Emp.: 707
Fiscal Year-end: 12/31/2023
Holding Company
N.A.I.C.S.: 551112

One Lambda, Inc (1)
22801 Roscoe Blvd, West Hills, CA 91304
Tel.: (747) 494-1000
Web Site: https://www.thermofisher.com
Analytical Laboratory Instrument Mfr
N.A.I.C.S.: 334516

Oxoid A/S (1)
Kamstrupvej 90, 4000, Roskilde, Denmark
Tel.: (45) 44979735
Web Site: https://www.oxoid.com
Analytical Laboratory Instrument Mfr
N.A.I.C.S.: 334516

Thermo Fisher Scientific Inc.—(Continued)

Oxoid AB (1)
PO Box U200, 202 29, Malmo, Sweden
Tel.: (46) 86266050
Laboratory Instrument Mfr
N.A.I.C.S.: 334513

Oxoid AG (1)
Zurlindenstrasse 3, 4133, Pratteln, Switzerland
Tel.: (41) 612716660
Laboratory Instrument Mfr
N.A.I.C.S.: 334513

Oxoid AS (1)
Frysjaveien 33E, 0884, Oslo, Norway (100%)
Tel.: (47) 23039690
Web Site: https://www.oxoid.com
Laboratory Instrument Mfr
N.A.I.C.S.: 334513

Oxoid Australia Pty. Limited (1)
20 Dalgleish Street, Thebarton, 5031, SA, Australia
Tel.: (61) 882389000
Biological Product Mfr
N.A.I.C.S.: 325414

Oxoid BV (1)
Scheepsbouwerweg 1 B, 1121 PC, Landsmeer, Netherlands
Tel.: (31) 204106500
Web Site: http://www.thermofisher.com
Emp.: 15
Laboratory Instrument Mfr
N.A.I.C.S.: 334513

Oxoid Brazil LTDA (1)
Eugenio Medeiros Street 303 11 & 12 floors, Pinheiros, Sao Paulo, 05425-000, Brazil
Tel.: (55) 1127303207
Analytical Laboratory Instrument Mfr
N.A.I.C.S.: 334516

Oxoid CZ s.r.o. (1)
Kastanova 539/64, 620 00, Brno, Brnenske Ivanovice, Czech Republic
Tel.: (420) 800101038
Web Site: https://www.oxoid.com
Analytical Laboratory Instrument Mfr
N.A.I.C.S.: 334516

Oxoid Company (1)
Suite 100 1926 Merivale Road, Nepean, K2G 1E8, ON, Canada
Tel.: (613) 226-1318
Web Site: https://www.oxoid.com
Emp.: 80
Medical Equipment Distr
N.A.I.C.S.: 423450

Oxoid Deutschland GmbH (1)
Am Lippeglacis 4-8, 46483, Wesel, Germany
Tel.: (49) 2811520
Web Site: http://www.thermofisher.com
Laboratory Instrument Mfr
N.A.I.C.S.: 334513

Oxoid Limited (1)
Wade Road, Basingstoke, RG24 8PW, Hampshire, United Kingdom
Tel.: (44) 1256841144
Web Site: http://www.oxoid.com
Laboratory Analytical Optical Instruments Mfr
N.A.I.C.S.: 333310

Oxoid Limited (1)
Wade Road, Basingstoke, RG24 8PW, Hampshire, United Kingdom
Tel.: (44) 1256841144
Web Site: https://www.oxoid.com
Analytical Laboratory Instrument Mfr
N.A.I.C.S.: 334516

Oxoid N.V. (1)
Keppekouter-Clintonpark Ninovesteenweg 198, 9320, Erembodegem, Belgium
Tel.: (32) 80055588800
Laboratory Instrument Mfr
N.A.I.C.S.: 334513

Oxoid S.p.A (1)
Strada Rivoltana, 20090, Rodano, Italy
Tel.: (39) 03902950591
Laboratory Instrument Mfr
N.A.I.C.S.: 334513

PPD Bulgaria EOOD (1)
Business Center Megapark 4th Floor 115 G Tsarigradsko Shosse Boulevard, Mladost District, 1784, Sofia, Bulgaria
Tel.: (359) 28048600
N.A.I.C.S.: 541380

PPD Czech Republic S.R.O. (1)
Budejovicka alej Antala Staska 2027/79, 140 00, Prague, Czech Republic
Tel.: (420) 233081000
Clinical Development & Laboratory Services
N.A.I.C.S.: 541380

PPD Development (HK) Limited (1)
802-04 8th Floor 625 King s Road North Point, Hong Kong, China (Hong Kong)
Tel.: (852) 29110110
Clinical Development & Laboratory Services
N.A.I.C.S.: 541380

PPD Development (S) Pte. Ltd. (1)
1 Science Park Road Singapore Science Park 2 The Capricorn 03-01/09, Singapore, 117528, Singapore
Tel.: (65) 68723588
Clinical Development & Laboratory Services
N.A.I.C.S.: 541380

PPD Development (Thailand) Co., Ltd. (1)
The Offices at Central World 25th Floor 999/9 Rama I Road, Patumwan, Bangkok, 10330, Thailand
Tel.: (66) 26462100
Clinical Development & Laboratory Services
N.A.I.C.S.: 541380

PPD Development Ireland Limited (1)
Building C Athlone Business and Technology Park, Garrycastle County Westmeath, Athlone, N37 TE84, Ireland
Tel.: (353) 906460300
Clinical Development & Laboratory Services
N.A.I.C.S.: 541380

PPD Global Central Labs (S) Pte. Ltd. (1)
61 Science Park Road The Galen 02-12 to 17/ 19 and 20, Singapore, 117525, Singapore
Tel.: (65) 65946210
Clinical Development & Laboratory Services
N.A.I.C.S.: 541380

PPD Global Central Labs, LLC (1)
2 Tesseneer Rd, Highland Heights, KY 41076-9167
Tel.: (859) 781-8877
Clinical Development & Laboratory Services
N.A.I.C.S.: 541380

PPD International Holdings, Inc. (1)
AV Vitacura 2939 Piso 19 Oficina 1902 Edificio Millenium, Las Condes, Santiago, Chile
Tel.: (56) 224606600
Clinical Development & Laboratory Services
N.A.I.C.S.: 541380

PPD Peru S.A.C. (1)
Av Republica de Panama 3461 Int 1801, San Isidro, Lima, Peru
Tel.: (51) 16134100
Clinical Development & Laboratory Services
N.A.I.C.S.: 541380

PPD Pharmaceutical Development Philippines Corp. (1)
22nd Floor Seven NEO Building 5th Avenue E-Square, Crescent Park West Bonifacio Global City, Taguig, 1634, Manila, Philippines
Tel.: (63) 286896501
Pharmaceuticals Product Mfr
N.A.I.C.S.: 325412

PPD Romania S.R.L. (1)
West Gate Park 24 Preciziei Blvd Building H5 2nd Floor, 062204, Bucharest, Romania
Tel.: (40) 213080031
Clinical Development & Laboratory Services
N.A.I.C.S.: 541380

PPD Services, Inc. (1)
3900 Paramount Pkwy, Morrisville, NC 27560-7200
Tel.: (919) 380-2000
Clinical Development & Laboratory Services

N.A.I.C.S.: 541380

PPD Slovak Republic s.r.o. (1)
Bratislavska Cesta 100/D, 931 01, Samorin, Slovakia
Tel.: (421) 315503461
Clinical Development & Laboratory Services
N.A.I.C.S.: 541380

PPD, Inc. (1)
929 N Front St, Wilmington, NC 28401-3331
Tel.: (910) 251-0081
Web Site: https://www.ppd.com
Holding Company; Drug Discovery & Development Contract Research Services
N.A.I.C.S.: 551112
Judd Hartman (Chief Admin Officer, Gen Counsel & Exec VP)
William J. Sharbaugh (COO)
Christine A. Dingivan (Chief Medical Officer & Head-Partnership Strategies-Global)
David S. Simmons (Chm & CEO)
Jay Dixon (Sr VP-Global Quality & Compliance)
Rob Dow (Sr VP-Global Product Dev)
Robert Hureau (CFO & Exec VP)
Michael Gold (VP-Global Product Dev-Neuroscience)
Hacene Mekerri (VP-Central Laboratory Org)
Bruce Stouffer (Exec Dir-Immunochemistry-Bioanalytical Lab)
Christopher C. Fikry (Exec VP-Laboratories)
Ron Garrow (Chief HR Officer & Exec VP)
Bhooshitha B. De Silva (Sr VP & Head-Corp Dev & Strategy-Global)

Subsidiary (Domestic):

Accelerated Enrollment Solutions, Inc. (2)
2 Walnut Griove Dr Ste 375, Horsham, PA 19044
Tel.: (215) 323-9000
Pharmaceuticall Product Research & Development Services
N.A.I.C.S.: 325412
Roger Smith (Sr VP & Gen Mgr)

Evidera, Inc. (2)
7101 Wisconsin Ave Ste 1400, Bethesda, MD 20814-4871
Tel.: (301) 654-9729
Web Site: https://www.evidera.com
Emp.: 500
Health Economics, Outcomes Research, Market Access, Data Analytics & Epidemiology Services
N.A.I.C.S.: 518210

Subsidiary (Non-US):

Evidera Market Access Limited (3)
The Ark 201 Talgarth Rd, Hammersmith, London, W6 8BJ, United Kingdom
Tel.: (44) 2085765000
Web Site: http://www.evidera.com
Health Economics, Outcomes Research, Market Access, Data Analytics & Epidemiology Services
N.A.I.C.S.: 541910

Subsidiary (Non-US):

PPD Australia Pty. Ltd. (2)
Level 5 412 St Kilda Rd, Melbourne, 3004, VIC, Australia
Tel.: (61) 398045211
Web Site: https://www.ppd.com
Sales Range: $25-49.9 Million
Emp.: 90
Pharmaceutical Research & Development Services
N.A.I.C.S.: 541715

PPD Germany GmbH (2)
Stephanienstrasse 55, 76133, Karlsruhe, Germany
Tel.: (49) 72191840
Web Site: http://www.ppdi.com
Sales Range: $10-24.9 Million
Emp.: 30
Clinical Research Facility
N.A.I.C.S.: 541715

PPD Germany GmbH & Co KG (2)
Sulzbacher Strasse 48, 90489, Nuremberg, Germany
Tel.: (49) 911946040

Web Site: http://www.ppdi.com
Sales Range: $10-24.9 Million
Emp.: 45
Pharmaceutical Research & Development
N.A.I.C.S.: 541715

PPD Global Central Labs BVBA (2)
Kleine Kloosterstraat 19, 1932, Brussels, Belgium
Tel.: (32) 27232626
Web Site: http://www.ppdi.com
Sales Range: $50-74.9 Million
Emp.: 190
Clinical Research Facility
N.A.I.C.S.: 541715

PPD Global Ltd. (2)
Granta Park Great Abington, Cambridge, CB21 6GQ, United Kingdom
Tel.: (44) 1223374100
Web Site: http://www.ppdi.com
Clinical Research Facility
N.A.I.C.S.: 541715

PPD Hungary Research & Development Limited (2)
Bocskai ut 134-146 Dorottya Udvar Building E Floor 2, E epulet 2 emelet, 1113, Budapest, Hungary
Tel.: (36) 13819500
Web Site: https://www.ppd.com
Sales Range: $10-24.9 Million
Emp.: 25
Pharmaceutical Development
N.A.I.C.S.: 541715

PPD Italy S.r.l. (2)
Segreen Business Park Palazzo Y via san Bovio 3 San Felice, Segrate, 20090, Milan, Italy
Tel.: (39) 02210811
Web Site: https://www.ppd.com
Sales Range: $75-99.9 Million
Pharmaceutical Development
N.A.I.C.S.: 541715

PPD Poland Sp. Z o.o. (2)
49 Domaniewska Street Signum Work Station entrance A 1st floor, 02-672, Warsaw, Poland
Tel.: (48) 223720600
Web Site: https://www.ppd.com
Sales Range: $25-49.9 Million
Emp.: 150
Clinical Research Facility
N.A.I.C.S.: 541715

PPD Scandinavia AB (2)
Lofstroms alle 5, Sundbyberg, 172 66, Stockholm, Swoden
Tel.: (46) 859822400
Sales Range: $10-24.9 Million
Emp.: 25
Clinical Research Facility
N.A.I.C.S.: 541715

PPD do Brasil-Suporte a Pesquisa Clinica Ltda. (2)
Rue Leopoldo Couto De Magalhaes 758 6th Floor, Sao Paulo, 04542-000, Brazil
Tel.: (55) 1145044700
Web Site: https://www.ppd.com
Sales Range: $75-99.9 Million
Clinical Research Facility
N.A.I.C.S.: 541715

PPD-Lanark (2)
Fleming House Phoenix Crescent, Strathclyde Business Park Bellshill, Lanark, ML4 3NJ, United Kingdom
Tel.: (44) 1698575000
Sales Range: $75-99.9 Million
Clinical Research Facility
N.A.I.C.S.: 541715

Pharmaceutical Product Development Spain SL (2)
Torre Nozar Tita 15 6th floor, Mendez Alvaro, 28045, Madrid, Spain
Tel.: (34) 917742700
Sales Range: $25-49.9 Million
Emp.: 150
Pharmaceutical Development
N.A.I.C.S.: 541715
Sabistian Pacios (Pres)

Subsidiary (Domestic):

Pharmaceutical Product Development, LLC - Austin (2)

7551 Metro Ctr Dr Ste 300, Austin, TX
78744
Tel.: (512) 447-2663
Web Site: https://www.ppd.com
Pharmaceutical Research
N.A.I.C.S.: 541715
Jerry Williams *(Dir-HR)*

Subsidiary (Domestic):

PPD Phase I Clinic - Austin (3)
7551 Metro Ctr Dr Ste 200, Austin, TX
78744
Tel.: (512) 447-2985
Web Site: https://www.ppd.com
Sales Range: $50-74.9 Million
Emp.: 200
Laboratory Research & Development Services
N.A.I.C.S.: 541715

Unit (Domestic):

Pharmaceutical Product Development, LLC - Blue Bell (2)
980 Harvest Dr Ste 130, Blue Bell, PA
19422-1955
Tel.: (215) 641-1942
Clinical Research
N.A.I.C.S.: 541715

Subsidiary (Domestic):

Pharmaceutical Product Development, LLC - Hamilton (2)
The Neuman Bldg 3575 Quakerbridge Rd
Ste 201, Hamilton, NJ 08619
Tel.: (609) 528-8000
Web Site: https://www.ppd.com
Pharmaceutical Development Services Supplier
N.A.I.C.S.: 541715
Steve Zielinski *(Coord-Facilities)*

Unit (Domestic):

Pharmaceutical Product Development, LLC - Middleton (2)
8551 Research Way Ste 90, Middleton, WI
53562-4663
Tel.: (608) 662-7700
Pharmaceutical Research Facility
N.A.I.C.S.: 541715

Subsidiary (Domestic):

Pharmaceutical Product Development, LLC - Morrisville (2)
3900 Paramount Pkwy, Morrisville, NC
27560-7200
Tel.: (919) 380-2000
Web Site: https://www.ppd.com
Pharmaceutical Research Facility
N.A.I.C.S.: 541715

Pharmaceutical Product Development, LLC - Richmond Bioanalytical Laboratory (2)
2244 Dabney Rd, Richmond, VA 23230-
3323
Tel.: (804) 359-1900
Web Site: https://www.ppd.com
Medical Research & Development Services
N.A.I.C.S.: 541715

Unit (Domestic):

Pharmaceutical Product Development, LLC - San Diego (2)
9330 Scanton Rd Ste 200, San Diego, CA
92121
Tel.: (858) 638-1795
Pharmaceutical Research & Development
N.A.I.C.S.: 541715
Stephanie Smythe *(Office Mgr)*

Patheon N.V. (1)
7th floor The Base Evert van de Beekstraat,
104 1118 CN, Amsterdam, Netherlands
Tel.: (31) 206223243
Web Site: http://www.patheon.com
Sales Range: $1-4.9 Billion
Holding Company; Pharmaceutical & Specialty Chemical Products Mfr
N.A.I.C.S.: 551112

Subsidiary (Domestic):

Patheon Biologics B.V. (2)

Zuiderweg 72-2, 9744 AP, Groningen, Netherlands
Tel.: (31) 505222222
Laboratory Equipment & Scientific Instrument Distr
N.A.I.C.S.: 423490
Gul Yesim Menderes *(Officer-QA & Auditor)*

Subsidiary (US):

Patheon Inc. (2)
4815 Emperor Blvd Ste 300, Durham, NC
27703
Tel.: (919) 226-3200
Web Site: http://www.patheon.com
Rev.: $1,023,100,000
Assets: $1,077,800,000
Liabilities: $951,400,000
Net Worth: $126,400,000
Earnings: ($35,900,000)
Emp.: 5,900
Fiscal Year-end: 10/31/2013
Prescription & Over-the-Counter Drugs
Packager & Mfr
N.A.I.C.S.: 424210

Subsidiary (Domestic):

Banner Life Sciences LLC (3)
3980 Premier Dr Ste 110, High Point, NC
27265
Tel.: (336) 812-8700
Web Site: https://www.bannerls.com
Biopharmaceutical & Other Proprietary Nutritional Products Research & Dev
N.A.I.C.S.: 541715
Franck Rousseau *(CEO)*
Tom Lategan *(VP-Regulatory Affairs)*
Nikki Sprague *(VP-Projects & Ops)*

Patheon API Manufacturing Inc. (3)
309 Delaware St, Greenville, SC 29605
Tel.: (864) 299-8600
Emp.: 27
Laboratory Equipment & Scientific Instrument Distr
N.A.I.C.S.: 423490

Patheon API Services, Inc. (3)
101 Technology Pl, Florence, SC 29501-
7615
Tel.: (843) 629-4000
Web Site: http://www.patheon.com
Pharmaceuticals Mfr
N.A.I.C.S.: 325412

Unit (Non-US):

Patheon Burlington Century Operations (3)
977 Century Dr, Burlington, L7L 5J8, ON,
Canada
Tel.: (905) 639-5254
Web Site: http://www.patheon.com
Sales Range: $125-149.9 Million
Prescription & Over-the-Counter Drugs Mfr
& Packager
N.A.I.C.S.: 325412

Plant (Domestic):

Patheon Florence - East (3)
6173 E Old Marion Hwy, Florence, SC
29506
Tel.: (843) 629-4300
Web Site: http://www.patheon.com
Sales Range: $25-49.9 Million
Pharmaceuticals Product Mfr
N.A.I.C.S.: 325412

Subsidiary (Non-US):

Patheon France S.A.S. (3)
40 Boulevard de Champaret CS 11006, PO
Box 448, 38307, Bourgoin-Jallieu, Cedex,
France
Tel.: (33) 474938700
Web Site: https://www.patheon.com
Commercial Scale Mfr
N.A.I.C.S.: 333998

Patheon GmbH (3)
St-Peter-Strasse 25, 4021, Linz, Austria
Tel.: (43) 732 6916 0
Web Site: http://www.patheon.com
Pharmaceutical Fine Chemical Distr
N.A.I.C.S.: 424690

Unit (Non-US):

Patheon Inc Toronto York Mills Operations (3)

865 York Mills Rd, Toronto, M3B 1Y5, ON,
Canada
Tel.: (416) 443-9030
Web Site: http://www.patheon.com
Sales Range: $150-199.9 Million
Mfr of Pharmaceuticals
N.A.I.C.S.: 325412

Subsidiary (Non-US):

Patheon Italia S.p.A. (3)
Viale G B Stucchi 110, 20900, Monza, MB,
Italy
Tel.: (39) 07753991
Web Site: http://www.patheon.com
Sales Range: $50-74.9 Million
Emp.: 400
Pharmaceuticals Mfr
N.A.I.C.S.: 325412
Orazio Cultrera *(Exec VP & Gen Mgr)*

Patheon KK (3)
7f Wakamatsu Building 3-3-6 Nihonbashi
Honcho Chuo-ku, Tokyo, 103-0023, Japan
Tel.: (81) 362027666
Laboratory Equipment & Scientific Instrument Distr
N.A.I.C.S.: 423490

Unit (Domestic):

Patheon Mova (3)
PO Box 8639, Caguas, PR 00726-8369
Tel.: (787) 258-1661
Web Site: http://www.movapharm.com
Sales Range: $50-74.9 Million
Manufacturing, Packaging & Testing Services for Pharmaceutical Industry
N.A.I.C.S.: 325412

Subsidiary (Domestic):

Patheon Puerto Rico, Inc. (3)
State Rd 670 Km 2.7, Manati, PR 00674
Tel.: (787) 621-2500
Laboratory Equipment & Scientific Instrument Distr
N.A.I.C.S.: 423490

Subsidiary (Non-US):

Patheon Regensburg GmbH (3)
Donaustaufer Str 378, 93055, Regensburg,
Germany
Tel.: (49) 94140930
Laboratory Equipment & Scientific Instrument Distr
N.A.I.C.S.: 423490

Subsidiary (Domestic):

Patheon Softgels Inc. (3)
4125 Premier Dr, High Point, NC 27265-
8144
Tel.: (336) 812-8700
Laboratory Equipment & Scientific Instrument Distr
N.A.I.C.S.: 423490

Subsidiary (Non-US):

Patheon UK Limited (3)
Kingfisher Drive, Covingham, Swindon, SN3
5BZ, Wiltshire, United Kingdom
Tel.: (44) 1793524411
Web Site: http://www.patheon.com
Sales Range: $50-74.9 Million
Emp.: 600
Provider of Pharmaceuticals
N.A.I.C.S.: 325412

Subsidiary (Domestic):

Patheon Softgels B.V. (2)
De Posthoornstraat 7, 5048 AS, Tilburg,
Netherlands
Tel.: (31) 134624100
Laboratory Equipment & Scientific Instrument Distr
N.A.I.C.S.: 423490
John van Beers *(Dir-Ops)*

PeproTech Asia Ltd. (1)
12 Hamada Street Beit Tamar entrance A
2nd floor, Rehovot, 7670314, Israel
Tel.: (972) 89460948
Biological Product Mfr
N.A.I.C.S.: 325414

PeproTech EC Ltd. (1)
PeproTech House 29 Margravine Road,
London, W6 8LL, United Kingdom

Tel.: (44) 2076103062
Cytokine Product Mfr & Distr
N.A.I.C.S.: 325412

PeproTech France S.A.S (1)
12 Rue Paul Chatrousse, 92200, Neuilly-
sur-Seine, France
Tel.: (33) 146245820
Cytokine Product Mfr & Distr
N.A.I.C.S.: 325412

PeproTech GmbH (1)
Forum Winterhude Winterhuder Marktplatz
6-7a, 22299, Hamburg, Germany
Tel.: (49) 40734357770
Cytokine Product Mfr & Distr
N.A.I.C.S.: 325412

PeproTech, Inc. (1)
5 Cedarbrook Dr, Cranbury, NJ 08512
Tel.: (609) 497-0253
Web Site: http://www.peprotech.com
All Other Miscellaneous Mfr
N.A.I.C.S.: 339999
Robert Goldman *(Co-Founder & Pres)*

Perbio Science BVBA (1)
Industriezone III Industrielaan 27, 9320, Er-
embodegem, Belgium
Tel.: (32) 53834404
Laboratory Instrument Mfr
N.A.I.C.S.: 334513

Perbio Science Projekt AB (1)
Sodra Langebergsgatan 30, Vastra Frol-
unda, Vastra Gotaland, 421 32, Sweden
Tel.: (46) 42361500
Industrial Equipment Mfr
N.A.I.C.S.: 333310

Pharmaceutical Product Development South Africa (Proprietary) Ltd. (1)
The Woodlands Office Park Building 15
Woodlands Drive, Woodmead, Johannes-
burg, 2191, South Africa
Tel.: (27) 116128600
Clinical Development & Laboratory Services
N.A.I.C.S.: 541380

Pierce Biotechnology, Inc. (1)
3747 N Meridian Rd, Rockford, IL 61101-
0117
Tel.: (815) 968-0747
Web Site: http://www.thermofisher.com
Sales Range: $75-99.9 Million
Emp.: 250
Protein Studies & Related Research
N.A.I.C.S.: 541715

Priority Air Express, LLC (1)
5100 Hickory Hill Rd, Memphis, TN 38141
Tel.: (901) 546-0119
Emp.: 120
Freight Transportation Arrangement Services
N.A.I.C.S.: 488510

Priority Solutions International, Inc. (1)
100 Berkeley Dr Ste A, Swedesboro, NJ
08085
Tel.: (856) 832-1500
Web Site: http://www.prioritysolutions.com
Sales Range: $50-74.9 Million
Emp.: 300
Supply Chain Management Services
N.A.I.C.S.: 541614

Quality Scientific Plastics, Inc. (1)
2200 S Mcdowell Blvd Ext, Petaluma, CA
94954
Tel.: (707) 762-6689
Sales Range: $50-74.9 Million
Emp.: 145
Medical Industrial Components Mfr
N.A.I.C.S.: 326121

Remel Europe Limited (1)
Remel House Clipper Boulevard West
Crossways, Dartford, DA2 6PT, United
Kingdom
Tel.: (44) 1322295600
Web Site: http://www.remel.com
Emp.: 127
Pharmaceutical Preparation Mfr
N.A.I.C.S.: 325412
Michael Colvard *(CEO)*

Remel Inc. (1)
12076 Santa Fe Dr, Lenexa, KS 66215
Tel.: (913) 888-0939

Thermo Fisher Scientific Inc.—(Continued)

Web Site: https://www.remel.com
Sales Range: $150-199.9 Million
Emp.: 697
Biotechnology Laboratory Products Mfr
N.A.I.C.S.: 334516

Richard-Allan Scientific Company (1)
4481 Campus Dr, Kalamazoo, MI 49008
Tel.: (269) 544-5600
Web Site: https://epredia.com
Sales Range: $25-49.9 Million
Emp.: 145
Anatomical Pathology Instruments Mfr
N.A.I.C.S.: 339113

Subsidiary (Domestic):

Lab Vision Corporation (2)
4481 Campus Dr, Kalamazoo, MI 49008
Tel.: (269) 544-5651
Web Site: http://www.labvision.com
Laboratory Analytical Optical Instruments Mfr
N.A.I.C.S.: 333310

Seradyn, Inc. (2)
46360 Fremont Blvd, Fremont, CA 94538-6406
Tel.: (317) 610-3800
Sales Range: $25-49.9 Million
Emp.: 65
Diagnostic Reagents & Instruments & Latex Microparticles Mfr
N.A.I.C.S.: 325412

Spectra-Physics AB (1)
Sturegatan 32, Stockholm, 102 45, Sweden
Tel.: (46) 87830725
Electric Equipment Mfr
N.A.I.C.S.: 335999

Subsidiary (Domestic):

Saroph Sweden AB (2)
Pyramidbacken 3, 141 75, Kungens Kurva, Sweden
Tel.: (46) 855646800
Industrial Equipment Mfr
N.A.I.C.S.: 333310

Subsidiary (Domestic):

Thermo Life Sciences AB (3)
Sankt Larsvag 45, Lund, 222 70, Sweden
Tel.: (46) 46303660
Industrial Equipment Mfr
N.A.I.C.S.: 333310

Sterilin Limited (1)
Parkway Bldg Parkway Pen-y-Fan Industrial Estate, Gwent, Newport, NP11 3EF, United Kingdom
Tel.: (44) 1495242200
Web Site: http://www.sterilin.co.uk
Emp.: 300
Laboratory Equipment Mfr
N.A.I.C.S.: 334515

Synexus Clinical Research South Africa (Pty.) Limited (1)
60 Stamvrug St Val-De-Grace, Pretoria, 0184, South Africa
Tel.: (27) 861796398
Web Site:
https://www.synexusclinicalresearch.co.za
Medical Research & Development Services
N.A.I.C.S.: 541714

Synexus Czech s.r.o. (1)
Synexus Praha Karlovo Namesti 2097/10, 120 00, Prague, Czech Republic
Tel.: (420) 225666111
Web Site: https://www.klinikasynexus.cz
Medical Research & Development Services
N.A.I.C.S.: 541714

Synexus Polska Sp. z o.o. (1)
Ul Marii Curie-Sklodowskiej 12, 50-381, Wroclaw, Poland
Tel.: (48) 222030300
Web Site:
https://www.przychodniasynexus.pl
Medical Research & Development Services
N.A.I.C.S.: 541714

TFS LLC (1)
120 Beulah Ave, Tylertown, MS 39667
Tel.: (601) 876-4157

Laboratory Equipment Whslr
N.A.I.C.S.: 423490

The Binding Site Benelux B.V. (1)
Guldensporenpark 26, 9820, Merelbeke, Belgium
Tel.: (32) 32428821
Medical Diagnostic Equipment Distr
N.A.I.C.S.: 423450

The Binding Site Brasil Comercio De Produtos Para Laboratorio Ltda. (1)
Av Romualdo Villani 838 - Jardim Ipanema, Sao Carlos, SP, Brazil
Tel.: (55) 1634152829
Web Site: https://www.freelite.com.br
Biological Research Services
N.A.I.C.S.: 541714

The Binding Site Corporation Limited (1)
8 Calthorpe Road, Edgbaston, Birmingham, B15 1QT, United Kingdom
Tel.: (44) 1214569500
Web Site: https://www.thermofisher.com
Pharmaceuticals Product Mfr
N.A.I.C.S.: 325412

The Binding Site France S.A.S. (1)
32 Rue des Platanes, CS30026, 38522, Saint Egreve, Cedex, France
Tel.: (33) 438021919
Medical Diagnostic Equipment Distr
N.A.I.C.S.: 423450

The Binding Site GmbH (1)
Robert-Bosch-Str 2A, 68723, Schwetzingen, Germany
Tel.: (49) 620292620
Medical Diagnostic Equipment Distr
N.A.I.C.S.: 423450

The Binding Site Portugal, Specialist Protein Company, Unip Lda. (1)
Avenida 5 de Outubro n 124 7, 1050-061, Lisbon, Portugal
Tel.: (351) 243092651
Pharmaceuticals Product Mfr
N.A.I.C.S.: 325412

The Binding Site Pte Ltd. (1)
2 Venture Drive 14-09 Vision Exchange, Singapore, 608526, Singapore
Tel.: (65) 69907970
Pharmaceuticals Product Mfr
N.A.I.C.S.: 325412

The Binding Site Pty Limited (1)
Suite 1 01 L1 12 Waterloo Road Macquarie Park, Sydney, 2113, NSW, Australia
Tel.: (61) 298050407
Pharmaceuticals Product Mfr
N.A.I.C.S.: 325412

The Binding Site S.r.l. (1)
Via Zanica 19, Grassobbio, 24050, Bergamo, Italy
Tel.: (39) 0350951500
Medical Diagnostic Equipment Distr
N.A.I.C.S.: 423450

The Binding Site Spain (Specialist Protein Company) S.L. (1)
Paseo de la Zona Franca 111 - 11C, 08038, Barcelona, Spain
Tel.: (34) 934676539
Medical Diagnostic Equipment Distr
N.A.I.C.S.: 423450

The Binding Site s.r.o. (1)
Parkview Office Building Pujmanove 1753/10a, 140 00, Prague, Czech Republic
Tel.: (420) 223013988
Pharmaceuticals Product Mfr
N.A.I.C.S.: 325412

Thermedics Detection de Argentina S.A. (1)
Hipolito Yrigoyen 434 Floor Piso 6-14, 1086, Buenos Aires, Argentina
Tel.: (54) 1143318915
Industrial Equipment Mfr
N.A.I.C.S.: 333310

Thermo Asset Management Services Inc. (1)
120 Bishops Way 100, Brookfield, WI 53005-6214
Laboratory Analytical Optical Instruments Mfr
N.A.I.C.S.: 333310

Thermo CIDTEC Inc. (1)
101 Commerce Blvd, Liverpool, NY 13088
Tel.: (315) 451-9410
Laboratory Instrument Mfr
N.A.I.C.S.: 334513

Thermo CRS Ltd. (1)
5250 Mainway, Burlington, L7L 5Z1, ON, Canada
Tel.: (905) 332-2000
Web Site:
https://www.thermofisherscientific.com
Laboratory Equipment Whslr
N.A.I.C.S.: 423490

Thermo EGS Gauging, Inc. (1)
200 Research Dr, Wilmington, MA 01887
Tel.: (978) 663-2300
Industrial Equipment Mfr
N.A.I.C.S.: 333310

Thermo Eberline LLC (1)
1 Thermo Fisher Way, Oakwood Village, OH 44146-6536 **(100%)**
Tel.: (508) 553-1582
Web Site:
http://www.analyticalinstrumentparts.com
Laboratory Analytical Optical Instruments Mfr
N.A.I.C.S.: 333310

Thermo Electron A/S (1)
Stamholmen 193, Hvidovre, 2650, Copenhagen, Denmark **(100%)**
Tel.: (45) 70236260
Web Site: http://www.thermodanmark.dk
Analytical Laboratory Instrument Mfr
N.A.I.C.S.: 334516

Thermo Electron Corporation Process Instruments (1)
1410 Gillingham Ln, Sugar Land, TX 77478
Tel.: (713) 272-0404
Web Site: http://www.thermo.com
Sales Range: $75-99.9 Million
Emp.: 250
Analytical Instrument Mfr
N.A.I.C.S.: 334514

Thermo Electron LED S.A.S. (1)
10 Rue Duguay Trouin, 44807, Saint-Herblain, France
Tel.: (33) 160924800
Emp.: 60
Industrial Machinery & Equipment Whslr
N.A.I.C.S.: 423830

Subsidiary (Domestic):

Thermo Electron Industries (2)
10 Rue Duguay Trouin, Saint-Herblain, 44800, France
Tel.: (33) 228032000
Laboratory Instrument Mfr
N.A.I.C.S.: 334513

Subsidiary (Non-US):

Thermo Fisher Scientific Milano Srl (2)
Campanini 11A, 43122, Parma, PR, Italy
Tel.: (39) 0295059373
Laboratory Instrument Mfr
N.A.I.C.S.: 327910

Thermo Electron Laboratory Equipment LLC (1)
275 Aiken Rd, Asheville, NC 28804-8740
Tel.: (828) 658-2711
Sales Range: $600-649.9 Million
Emp.: 1,500
Products & Services for Life Science, Material Science, Bioprocessing & Drug Discovery
N.A.I.C.S.: 334516

Thermo Electron Limited (1)
1 St George's Court Altrincham Business Park, Altrincham, WA14 5TP, Cambridgeshire, United Kingdom **(100%)**
Tel.: (44) 1223347400
Web Site: http://www.thermo.com
Sales Range: $25-49.9 Million
Emp.: 60
Research & Test Equipment Sales
N.A.I.C.S.: 334514

Thermo Electron S.A. (1)
chemin de Verney 2 Zone industrielle En Vallaire Ouest C, 1024, Ecublens, Switzerland

Tel.: (41) 216947111
Web Site: http://www.engnetglobal.com
Sales Range: $50-74.9 Million
Emp.: 200
Spectrometer Mfr
N.A.I.C.S.: 334516

Thermo Electron Weighing & Inspection Limited (1)
6 Little Mundells, Rugby, CV21 1DZ, United Kingdom
Tel.: (44) 1707379500
Laboratory Instrument Mfr
N.A.I.C.S.: 334513

Thermo Environmental Instruments Inc. (1)
27 Forge Pkwy, Franklin, MA 02038
Tel.: (508) 520-0430
Emp.: 170
Laboratory Analytical Optical Instruments Mfr
N.A.I.C.S.: 333310

Thermo Fast U.K. Limited (1)
Unit 2 Mills Road, Chilton Industrial Estate, Sudbury, C010 2XX, Suffolk, United Kingdom
Tel.: (44) 1787880268
Web Site: https://thermofast.co.uk
Analytical Laboratory Instrument Mfr
N.A.I.C.S.: 334516

Thermo Fisher (Kandel) GmbH (1)
Erlenbachweg 2, 76870, Kandel, Germany
Tel.: (49) 72184007280
Chemical Products Mfr
N.A.I.C.S.: 325998

Thermo Fisher Diagnostics AB (1)
PO Box 6460, 751 37, Uppsala, Sweden
Tel.: (46) 86266050
Laboratory Equipment & Scientific Instrument Distr
N.A.I.C.S.: 423490

Thermo Fisher Diagnostics AG (1)
Zurlindenstrasse 3, 4133, Pratteln, Switzerland
Tel.: (41) 612716660
Laboratory Equipment & Scientific Instrument Distr
N.A.I.C.S.: 423490
Roland Geyer (Mgr-Bus Dev)

Thermo Fisher Diagnostics B.V. (1)
Scheepsbouwerweg 1 B, 1121 PC, Landsmeer, Netherlands
Tel.: (31) 204106500
Laboratory Equipment & Scientific Instrument Distr
N.A.I.C.S.: 423490

Thermo Fisher Diagnostics Oy (1)
PO Box 100, Ratastie 2, 01620, Vantaa, Finland
Tel.: (358) 103292110
Diagnostic Test Equipment Mfr & Distr
N.A.I.C.S.: 334510

Thermo Fisher Diagnostics SAS (1)
Route de Paisy ZI, PO Box 13, 69570, Dardilly, France
Tel.: (33) 472523370
Web Site: http://www.oxoid.com
Medical Equipment Distr
N.A.I.C.S.: 423450

Thermo Fisher Financial Services Inc. (1)
81 Wyman St, Waltham, MA 02451
Laboratory Analytical Optical Instruments Mfr
N.A.I.C.S.: 333310

Thermo Fisher Ireland Ltd. (1)
Suite 3 Plaza 212 Blanchardstown Corporate Park 2 Ballycoolin, Dublin, Ireland
Tel.: (353) 1 6440064
Laboratory Services
N.A.I.C.S.: 621511

Thermo Fisher Scientific (1)
5250 Mainway, Burlington, L7L 5Z1, ON, Canada **(100%)**
Tel.: (905) 332-2000
Sales Range: $10-24.9 Million
Emp.: 40
Robotic Arms Mfr for DNA Testing
N.A.I.C.S.: 334516

Thermo Fisher Scientific (1)
4-2-8 Shibaura, Minato-Ku, Tokyo, 108-0023, Japan
Tel.: (81) 120753670
Web Site: http://www.thermofisher.co.jp
Sales Range: $25-49.9 Million
Emp.: 300
Laboratory Instrument Mfr
N.A.I.C.S.: 334516

Thermo Fisher Scientific (1)
Tudor Road Manor Park, Runcorn, WA7 1TA, GB, United Kingdom
Tel.: (44) 1928534000
Web Site: http://www.thermofisher.com
Sales Range: $25-49.9 Million
Emp.: 100
Biotechnology Mfr
N.A.I.C.S.: 334516

Thermo Fisher Scientific (1)
Route de Fribourg 22, PO Box 192, 1680, Romont, Switzerland
Tel.: (41) 266519519
Web Site: http://www.thermo.com
Sales Range: $50-74.9 Million
Emp.: 71
Glass Products Mfr
N.A.I.C.S.: 327212
Bruno Darbon (Mng Dir)

Thermo Fisher Scientific (1)
16 Avenue du Quebec Batiment Mimosa, PO Box 765, Villebon Sur Yvette, 91963, Courtaboeuf, France
Tel.: (33) 160924800
Web Site: http://www.abgene.com
Sales Range: $25-49.9 Million
Emp.: 100
Specialist Plastics Consumables & Instruments & Molecular Biology Reagents Mfr
N.A.I.C.S.: 325211

Thermo Fisher Scientific (1)
Kamstrupvej 90, PO Box 60, 85 4000, Roskilde, Denmark
Tel.: (45) 80884754
Web Site: http://www.fishersci.dk
Sales Range: $10-24.9 Million
Emp.: 400
Cell Based Assay Technologies
N.A.I.C.S.: 325414

Thermo Fisher Scientific (China) Co., Ltd. (1)
Building 8 No 379 De Bao Road, Free Trade Zone, Shanghai, 201206, China
Tel.: (86) 2168654588
Web Site: http://www.fishersci.com.cn
Laboratory Instrument Mfr
N.A.I.C.S.: 334513

Thermo Fisher Scientific (Ecublens) SARL (1)
chemin de Verney 2, Zone industrielle En Vallaire Ouest C, 1024, Ecublens, Switzerland
Tel.: (41) 216947111
Web Site: http://www.thermofisher.com
Laboratory Instrument Mfr
N.A.I.C.S.: 334513

Thermo Fisher Scientific (Milwaukee) LLC (1)
2202 N Bartlett Ave, Milwaukee, WI 53202
Tel.: (414) 283-9630
Emp.: 41
Biological Product Mfr
N.A.I.C.S.: 325414

Thermo Fisher Scientific (Mississauga) Inc. (1)
2845 Argentia Rd, Mississauga, L5N 8G6, ON, Canada
Tel.: (905) 812-1034
Web Site: https://www.thermo.com
Emp.: 40
Professional Equipment Distr
N.A.I.C.S.: 423490

Thermo Fisher Scientific (Schweiz) AG (1)
Neuhofstrasse 11, Reinach, 4153, Basel, Switzerland
Tel.: (41) 617167700
Laboratory Analytical Optical Instruments Mfr
N.A.I.C.S.: 333310

Subsidiary (Non-US):

Thermo Fisher Scientific (Praha) s.r.o. (2)
Praha 10 Slunecna 27/3239, Strasnice, 100 00, Prague, Vysocany, Czech Republic (100%)
Tel.: (420) 274820377
Web Site: http://www.corporate.thermofisher.com
Laboratory Instrument Mfr
N.A.I.C.S.: 334513

Thermo Fisher Scientific Wissenschaftliche Gerate GmbH (2)
BIGBIZ B Dresdner Strasse 89, 1200, Vienna, Austria
Tel.: (43) 133350340
Laboratory Instrument Mfr
N.A.I.C.S.: 334513

Thermo Fisher Scientific (Zurich) AG (1)
Raffelstrasse 32, Zurich, 8045, Switzerland
Tel.: (41) 444541212
Laboratory Analytical Optical Instruments Mfr
N.A.I.C.S.: 333310

Thermo Fisher Scientific - Consolidated Technologies (1)
4401 Freidrich Ln, Austin, TX 78744
Tel.: (512) 445-5100
Web Site: http://www.thermofisher.com
Sales Range: $10-24.9 Million
Emp.: 25
Medical Device Mfr
N.A.I.C.S.: 339113

Thermo Fisher Scientific - Franklin Branch (1)
27 Forge Pkwy, Franklin, MA 02038-3148 (100%)
Tel.: (508) 520-0430
Web Site: http://www.thermofisher.com
Sales Range: $50-74.9 Million
Emp.: 350
Air Quality Monitoring Equipment Mfr
N.A.I.C.S.: 334516

Thermo Fisher Scientific - Lab Vision IHC System Solutions (1)
46360 Fremont Blvd, Fremont, CA 94538
Tel.: (510) 991-2800
Web Site: http://www.thermofisherscientific.com
Sales Range: $10-24.9 Million
Emp.: 500
Biotechnology Mfr
N.A.I.C.S.: 334516

Thermo Fisher Scientific - Matrix Liquid Handling Products (1)
22 Friars Dr, Hudson, NH 03051
Tel.: (603) 595-0505
Web Site: http://www.matrixtechcorp.com
Sales Range: $10-24.9 Million
Emp.: 75
Liquid Handling Instruments
N.A.I.C.S.: 334516

Thermo Fisher Scientific - Metavac (1)
4000 Point St, Holtsville, NY 11742
Tel.: (631) 447-7700
Web Site: http://www.metavac.com
Sales Range: $10-24.9 Million
Emp.: 45
Optical & Electro-Optical Mfr
N.A.I.C.S.: 333310

Thermo Fisher Scientific - Molecular BioProducts (1)
9389 Waples St, San Diego, CA 92121
Tel.: (858) 453-7551
Web Site: http://www.mbpinc.com
Sales Range: $1-9.9 Million
Emp.: 470
Disposable Laboratory Apparatus & Plastics Injection Molding Mfr
N.A.I.C.S.: 339113

Thermo Fisher Scientific - NERL Clinical Diagnostics (1)
14 Almeida Ave, East Providence, RI 02914
Tel.: (401) 438-0386
Sales Range: $25-49.9 Million
Emp.: 100
Reagent, Diluents, Standards, Calibrators & Medical Beverages Mfr
N.A.I.C.S.: 334516

Thermo Fisher Scientific - Nalgene & Nunc (1)
75 Panorama Creek Dr, Rochester, NY 14625
Tel.: (585) 586-8800
Web Site: http://www.thermofisherscientific.com
Plastic Labware, Tubing, Tanks, Trail Products, Packaging Products & Blowers Mfr
N.A.I.C.S.: 326199

Thermo Fisher Scientific - Newington Branch (2)
25 Nimble Hill Rd, Newington, NH 03801-1178
Tel.: (603) 436-9444
Web Site: http://www.thermo.com
Sales Range: $50-74.9 Million
Emp.: 200
Laboratory Analytical Instruments Mfr
N.A.I.C.S.: 334516

Thermo Fisher Scientific - Pittsburgh Branch (1)
300 Industry Dr, Pittsburgh, PA 15275-1015
Tel.: (724) 517-1500
Web Site: http://www.thermofisher.com
Sales Range: $25-49.9 Million
Emp.: 100
Laboratory Equipment Mfr
N.A.I.C.S.: 334516

Thermo Fisher Scientific - San Diego Branch (1)
10010 Mesa Rim Rd, San Diego, CA 92121 (100%)
Tel.: (858) 450-9811
Web Site: http://www.thermo.com
Sales Range: $25-49.9 Million
Emp.: 100
Analytical Tool Mfr
N.A.I.C.S.: 334516

Thermo Fisher Scientific - Wilmington Branch (1)
3411 Silverside Rd Tatnall Bldg Concord Plz, Wilmington, DE 19810
Tel.: (302) 479-7707
Web Site: http://www.thermo.com
Sales Range: $10-24.9 Million
Emp.: 123
Mfr of Industrial Gauging Instruments for Web Process Applications
N.A.I.C.S.: 334519

Thermo Fisher Scientific Australia Pty Ltd (1)
11 Sandringham Avenue, Thornton, 2322, NSW, Australia
Tel.: (61) 397574486
Web Site: http://www.thermofisher.com
Sales Range: $550-599.9 Million
Emp.: 225
Scientific Instruments Supplier
N.A.I.C.S.: 339112

Thermo Fisher Scientific B.V.B.A. (1)
Clintonpark-Keppekouter Ninovesteenweg 198, 9320, Erembodegem, Belgium
Tel.: (32) 53734241
Medical Equipment Distr
N.A.I.C.S.: 423450

Thermo Fisher Scientific BioProduction Pte. Ltd. (1)
8 Pandan Crescent LL4 Suite 05-05 UE Tech Park, Singapore, 128464, Singapore
Tel.: (65) 68736006
Web Site: http://www.fishersci.com.sg
Laboratory Equipment Mfr
N.A.I.C.S.: 334515

Thermo Fisher Scientific Brno s.r.o. (1)
Vlastimila Pecha 1282/12, Cernovice, 627 00, Brno, Czech Republic
Tel.: (420) 513245111
Laboratory Equipment Mfr & Distr
N.A.I.C.S.: 334516

Thermo Fisher Scientific Chemicals Inc. (1)
30 Bond St, Haverhill, MA 01835-8099
Tel.: (978) 521-6300
Chemical Product Whslr
N.A.I.C.S.: 424690

Thermo Fisher Scientific Germany BV & Co. KG (1)
Saarbruckener Str 248, DE-HB, 38116, Braunschweig, Germany
Tel.: (49) 531590080
Web Site: http://www.thermofisher.com
Sales Range: $50-74.9 Million
Emp.: 100
Glass Products Mfr
N.A.I.C.S.: 327215

Subsidiary (Domestic):

Thermo Fisher Scientific (Bremen) GmbH (2)
Hanna-Kunath-Str 11, 28199, Bremen, Germany (100%)
Tel.: (49) 42154930
Sales Range: $50-74.9 Million
Emp.: 200
Analytical Instruments Mfr & Sales
N.A.I.C.S.: 334516

Thermo Fisher Scientific Beteiligungsverwaltungs GmbH (2)
Saarbruckener Str 248, 38116, Braunschweig, Germany
Tel.: (49) 531590080
Laboratory Instrument Mfr
N.A.I.C.S.: 334513

Subsidiary (Non-US):

Phadia AS (3)
Frysjaveien 33 E, 0884, Oslo, Norway (100%)
Tel.: (47) 21673280
Web Site: http://www.phadia.com
Laboratory Equipment Mfr
N.A.I.C.S.: 334515

Phadia Sociedad Unipessoal Lda. (3)
Lagoas Park Edificio n 11 Piso 0, 2740-270, Porto Salvo, Portugal
Tel.: (351) 214235350
Web Site: http://www.thermofisher.com
Medical Equipment Mfr
N.A.I.C.S.: 334516

Thermo Fisher Diagnostics Austria GmbH (3)
Dresdner Strasse 89, 1200, Vienna, Austria
Tel.: (43) 12702020
Laboratory Equipment & Scientific Instrument Distr
N.A.I.C.S.: 423490
Robert Galvan (Mng Dir)

Thermo Fisher Diagnostics NV (3)
Pontbeekstraat 2, 1702, Groot-Bijgaarden, Belgium
Tel.: (32) 27495515
Laboratory Equipment & Scientific Instrument Distr
N.A.I.C.S.: 423490

Thermo Fisher Diagnostics, S.L.U. (3)
Avda Alcalde Barnils 70 2a planta, Sant Cugat del Valles, 08174, Barcelona, Spain
Tel.: (34) 935765800
Laboratory Equipment & Scientific Instrument Distr
N.A.I.C.S.: 423490

Thermo Fisher Diagnostics, Sociedade Unipessoal Lda (3)
Lagoas Park-Edificio n 11-Piso 0, 2740-270, Porto Salvo, Portugal
Tel.: (351) 214235350
Medical Equipment Mfr
N.A.I.C.S.: 339113

Subsidiary (Domestic):

Thermo Fisher Scientific GmbH (2)
Im Heiligen Feld 17, DE-NW, 58239, Schwerte, Germany (100%)
Tel.: (49) 23049325
Web Site: http://www.thermofisher.com
Sales Range: $50-74.9 Million
Emp.: 250
Laboratory Analytical Equipment Mfr
N.A.I.C.S.: 334516

Subsidiary (Domestic):

BmT GmbH Laborprodukte (3)
Alte Seilerei Haus 7 A Meerbuscher Strasse 74, Osterath, 40670, Meerbusch, Germany
Tel.: (49) 215967890
Web Site: https://www.bmt.de

Thermo Fisher Scientific Inc.—(Continued)
Laboratory Equipment Distr
N.A.I.C.S.: 423490

Subsidiary (Domestic):

Thermo Fisher Scientific IT Services GmbH (2)
Dieselstrasse 4, 76227, Karlsruhe, Germany
Tel.: (49) 72140940
Laboratory Instrument Mfr
N.A.I.C.S.: 334513

Thermo Fisher Scientific Messtechnik GmbH (2)
Frauenauracher Str 96, 91056, Erlangen, Germany
Tel.: (49) 91319090
Web Site: http://www.thermo.com
Research, Sales & Services
N.A.I.C.S.: 541715

Thermo Fisher Scientific Inc. (1)
925 W 1800 S, Logan, UT 84321
Tel.: (435) 792-8000
Sales Range: $150-199.9 Million
Cell Culture Media, Serum & Bioprocess Containers
N.A.I.C.S.: 325414

Subsidiary (Non-US):

Fisher Scientific SPRL (2)
13a Avenue de Tervuren, Box 2, 1040, Brussels, Belgium
Tel.: (32) 56260260
Web Site: http://www.fishersci.be
Sales Range: $25-49.9 Million
Emp.: 39
Cell Culture Media, Serum & Bioprocess Containers
N.A.I.C.S.: 325414

Subsidiary (Non-US):

Perbio Science Deutschland (3)
Adenaueralle 113, 53113, Bonn, Germany
Tel.: (49) 2289125650
Web Site: http://www.thermo.com
Sales Range: $25-49.9 Million
Cell Culture Media, Serum & Bioprocess Containers
N.A.I.C.S.: 325414

Perbio Science France (3)
16 Avenue du Quebec ILIC 764, 91964, Courtaboeuf, Cedex, France
Tel.: (33) 800508215
Web Site: http://www.thermofisher.com
Sales Range: $25-49.9 Million
Cell Culture Media, Serum & Bioprocess Containers
N.A.I.C.S.: 325414

Subsidiary (Domestic):

Perbio Science Nederland BV (3)
Gaseon Crommenlaan 4, PO Box 32, 4870 AA, Gent, Belgium
Tel.: (32) 765031880
Web Site: http://www.perbio.com
Sales Range: $25-49.9 Million
Cell Culture Media, Serum & Bioprocess Containers
N.A.I.C.S.: 325414

Subsidiary (Non-US):

Perbio Science UK Ltd. (3)
Unit 9 Atley Way North Nelson Industrial Estate, Cramlington, NE23 1WA, Northumberland, United Kingdom
Tel.: (44) 800252185
Web Site: http://www.thermofisher.com
Sales Range: $25-49.9 Million
Cell Culture Media, Serum & Bioprocess Containers Mfr
N.A.I.C.S.: 325414

Thermo Fisher Scientific Inc. - Cellomics (1)
100 Technology Dr, Pittsburgh, PA 15219
Tel.: (412) 770-2200
Sales Range: $100-124.9 Million
Biotechnology Research Equipment Mfr & Drug Research Software Developer
N.A.I.C.S.: 334516

Thermo Fisher Scientific India Pvt Ltd (1)
403-404 Delphi B Wing, Powai Hiranandani Business Park, Mumbai, 400076, Maharashtra, India
Tel.: (91) 8002097001
Web Site: https://www.thermofisher.in
Analytical Laboratory Instrument Mfr
N.A.I.C.S.: 334516

Thermo Fisher Scientific India Pvt Ltd (1)
403-404 Delphi B Wing, Hiranandani Business Park Powai, Mumbai, 400 076, India
Tel.: (91) 2266803000
Web Site: https://www.thermofishersci.in
Emp.: 250
Laboratory Instrument Mfr
N.A.I.C.S.: 334513

Thermo Fisher Scientific Informatics (1)
2 Radcliff Rd, Tewksbury, MA 01876
Tel.: (978) 521-6300
Web Site: http://www.thermofisher.com
Sales Range: $100-124.9 Million
Emp.: 4
Software Development & Manufacturing
N.A.I.C.S.: 334516
Mark Cafper *(Pres)*

Thermo Fisher Scientific Life Investments III S.a.r.l. (1)
5 Rue Jean Monnet, Luxembourg, 2180, Luxembourg
Tel.: (352) 2686741
Laboratory Equipment Mfr
N.A.I.C.S.: 334515

Thermo Fisher Scientific Life Senior Holdings II C.V. (1)
Takkebijsters 1, 4817BL, Breda, North Brabant, Netherlands
Tel.: (31) 765795555
Holding Company
N.A.I.C.S.: 551112

Thermo Fisher Scientific Mexico City, S. de R.L. de C.V. (1)
Industria ElTctrica 7, Parque Industrial Naucalpan, 53370, Mexico, NL, Mexico
Tel.: (52) 5553125556
Analytical Laboratory Instrument Mfr
N.A.I.C.S.: 334516

Thermo Fisher Scientific New Zealand Ltd (1)
244 Bush Road, Albany, 0632, New Zealand
Tel.: (64) 99806700
Web Site: http://www.thermofisher.com
Emp.: 70
Scientific Instruments Supplier
N.A.I.C.S.: 339112

Thermo Fisher Scientific SL (1)
Avda de la Vega n 1 Edificio 1 - 4 planta, 28108, Alcobendas, Madrid, Spain
Tel.: (34) 934488765
Laboratory Instrument Mfr
N.A.I.C.S.: 334513

Thermo Gamma-Metrics LLC (1)
10010 Mesa Rim Rd, San Diego, CA 92121-2979
Tel.: (304) 562-2057
Laboratory Instrument Mfr
N.A.I.C.S.: 334513

Thermo Gamma-Metrics Pty Ltd (1)
11 West Thebarton Road, Adelaide, 5031, SA, Australia
Tel.: (61) 881505300
Laboratory Analytical Optical Instruments Mfr
N.A.I.C.S.: 333310

Subsidiary (Domestic):

Intalysis Pty Ltd (2)
U 16 56 Buffalo Rd, Gladesville, 2111, NSW, Australia
Tel.: (61) 298079646
Emp.: 25
Laboratory Instrument Mfr
N.A.I.C.S.: 334513

Thermo Hypersil-Keystone LLC (1)
320 Rolling Rdg Dr, Bellefonte, PA 16823
Tel.: (814) 353-2300

Laboratory Instrument Mfr
N.A.I.C.S.: 334513

Thermo Kevex X-Ray Inc. (1)
320 El Pueblo Rd, Scotts Valley, CA 95066-4219
Tel.: (831) 438-5940
Electric Equipment Mfr
N.A.I.C.S.: 335999

Thermo Keytek LLC (1)
1 Lowell Research Ctr, Lowell, MA 01852
Tel.: (978) 275-0800
Laboratory Analytical Optical Instruments Mfr
N.A.I.C.S.: 333310

Thermo Luxembourg Holding S.a.r.l. (1)
5 Rue Jean Monnet, Luxembourg, 2180, Luxembourg
Tel.: (352) 2686741
Holding Company
N.A.I.C.S.: 551112

Subsidiary (Non-US):

Oxoid Investments GmbH (2)
Am Lippeglacis 4-8, Wesel, 46483, Germany
Tel.: (49) 2811520
Investment Management Service
N.A.I.C.S.: 523940

Subsidiary (Domestic):

B.R.A.H.M.S. GmbH (3)
Neuendorfstrasse 25, 16761, Hennigsdorf Berlin, Germany
Tel.: (49) 33028830
Web Site: http://www.brahms.de
Laboratory Equipment Mfr
N.A.I.C.S.: 334515

Subsidiary (Non-US):

B.R.A.H.M.S. Austria GmbH (4)
Wehlistrasse 27 B, 1200, Vienna, Austria **(100%)**
Tel.: (43) 158566670
Laboratory Instrument Mfr
N.A.I.C.S.: 334513

Subsidiary (Domestic):

B.R.A.H.M.S. Biotech GmbH (4)
Neuendorfstr 25, Hennigsdorf Berlin, 16761, Hennigsdorf Berlin, Germany
Tel.: (49) 33028830
Laboratory Instrument Mfr
N.A.I.C.S.: 334513

Subsidiary (Non-US):

Quatuor S.A. (4)
Parc Scientifique Georges Besse 280 allee Graham Bell, Nimes, 30035, France
Tel.: (33) 466365200
Laboratory Instrument Mfr
N.A.I.C.S.: 334513

Subsidiary (Non-US):

Thermo Fisher Scientific Baltics UAB (3)
V A Graiciuno str 8, 02241, Vilnius, Lithuania
Tel.: (370) 52602131
Web Site: http://www.thermofisher.com
Emp.: 829
Chemical & Allied Product Distr
N.A.I.C.S.: 424690
Algimantas Markauskas *(CEO)*

Subsidiary (Domestic):

Thermo Fisher Scientific Vermogensverwaltungs GmbH (3)
Opelstrasse 9, 68789, Sankt Leon-Rot, Germany
Tel.: (49) 622753694
Asset Management Services
N.A.I.C.S.: 525920

Subsidiary (Non-US):

Thermo Fisher Scientific (Breda) Holding BV (2)
Takkebijsters 1, 4817 BL, Breda, Netherlands
Tel.: (31) 765717311

Holding Company
N.A.I.C.S.: 551112

Subsidiary (Domestic):

Thermo Fisher Scientific B.V. (3)
Takkebijsters 1, 4817 BL, Breda, Netherlands
Tel.: (31) 765795555
Web Site: http://www.thermofisher.com
Laboratory Instrument Mfr
N.A.I.C.S.: 334513

Subsidiary (Domestic):

Thermo Fisher Scientific Finance Company BV (4)
Takkebijsters 1, 4817 BL, Breda, Netherlands
Tel.: (31) 765795555
Financial Services
N.A.I.C.S.: 541611

Subsidiary (Non-US):

Thermo Optek S.A. (4)
Av Industria 32 Pgo In Madrid, Alcobendas, 28100, Spain
Tel.: (34) 9165749310
Metal Container Mfr
N.A.I.C.S.: 332439

Thermo NITON Analyzers LLC (1)
900 Middlesex Tpke Bldg 8, Billerica, MA 01821
Tel.: (978) 670-7460
Laboratory Analytical Optical Instruments Mfr
N.A.I.C.S.: 333310

Thermo Neslab LLC (1)
25 Nimble Hill Rd, Newington, NH 03801
Tel.: (603) 436-9444
Emp.: 225
Laboratory Instrument Mfr
N.A.I.C.S.: 334513
Marc Casper *(CEO)*

Thermo Projects Limited (1)
Britannia House Goliath Road Hermitage Industrial Estate, Coalville, LE67 3FT, Leicestershire, United Kingdom
Tel.: (44) 1530833788
Electronic Equipment Distr
N.A.I.C.S.: 423690

Thermo Radiometrie Limited (1)
Shepherd Road, Gloucester, GL2 5HF, United Kingdom
Tel.: (44) 1452337800
Laboratory Instrument Mfr
N.A.I.C.S.: 334513

Thermo Ramcoy Italia S.r.l. (1)
Campanini 11A, 43122, Parma, PR, Italy
Tel.: (39) 0295059396
Laboratory Instrument Mfr
N.A.I.C.S.: 334513

Thermo Ramsey S.A. (1)
Edificio Veganova Avenida de la Vega 1, 28108, Alcobendas, Spain
Tel.: (34) 914845965
Web Site: http://www.thermoscientific.es
Industrial Equipment Mfr
N.A.I.C.S.: 333310

Thermo Scientific Microbiology Pte Ltd. (1)
33 Marsiling Industrial Estate Road 3 07-06, Woodlands, Singapore, 739256, Singapore
Tel.: (65) 64999993
Web Site: http://www.thermofisher.com
Emp.: 10
Medical Equipment Distr
N.A.I.C.S.: 423450

Thermo Scientific Portable Analytical Instruments Inc (1)
2 Radcliff Rd, Tewksbury, MA 01876
Tel.: (978) 670-7460
Laboratory Equipment Mfr
N.A.I.C.S.: 334513

Thermo Scientific Services, Inc. (1)
1824 Sea Vista Pl, San Marcos, CA 92078
Tel.: (760) 519-0438
Professional, Scientific & Technical Services
N.A.I.C.S.: 541990

Thermo Shandon Inc. (1)

171 Industry Dr, Pittsburgh, PA 15275-1015
Tel.: (412) 788-1133
Laboratory Instrument Mfr
N.A.I.C.S.: 334513

Trek Diagnostic Systems Ltd. (1)
Units 17 - 19 Birches Industrial Estate, East
Grinstead, RH19 1XZ, West Sussex, United
Kingdom
Tel.: (44) 1342318777
Analytical Laboratory Instrument Mfr
N.A.I.C.S.: 334516

United Diagnostics, Inc. (1)
149 White Branch Ct N, Schaumburg, IL
60194
Tel.: (205) 719-5926
Web Site: https://www.uniteddiagnostics.org
Analytical Laboratory Instrument Mfr
N.A.I.C.S.: 334516

picoSpin, LLC (1)
5445 Conestoga Ct Ste 202, Boulder, CO
80301
Tel.: (303) 443-2262
Laboratory Equipment Mfr
N.A.I.C.S.: 334515

THERMON GROUP HOLD-INGS, INC.
7171 Southwest Pkwy Bldg 300 Ste
200, Austin, TX 78735
Tel.: (512) 690-0600   DE
Web Site: https://www.thermon.com
Year Founded: 1954
THR—(NYSE)
Rev.: $355,674,000
Assets: $636,669,000
Liabilities: $237,465,000
Net Worth: $399,204,000
Earnings: $20,092,000
Emp.: 1,227
Fiscal Year-end: 03/31/22
Holding Company; Thermal Solutions
N.A.I.C.S.: 551112
Bruce A. Thames (Pres & CEO)
Candace Peterson (VP-HR)
David Buntin (Sr VP-Thermon Heat
Tracing)
Mark Roberts (Sr VP-Project Svcs &
Engrg-Global)
Thomas N. Cerovski (Sr VP-Sls-
Global)
Ryan Tarkington (Gen Counsel &
Sec)
John T. Nesser III (Chm)
James A. Pribble II (Sr VP-Thermon
Heating Systems)
Jan L. Schott (CFO & Sr VP)
Greg Lucas (Chief Acctg Officer, VP
& Controller)

Subsidiaries:

CCI Thermal Technologies, Inc. (1)
5918 Roper Road, Edmonton, T6B 3E1,
AB, Canada
Tel.: (780) 466-3178
Web Site: http://www.ccithermal.com
Heating, Ventilating & Air Conditioning Ser-
vices
N.A.I.C.S.: 238220

Subsidiary (US):

**CCI Thermal Technologies Texas,
Inc.** (2)
15550 Vickery Dr Ste 100, Houston, TX
77032
Tel.: (281) 506-2310
Web Site: http://www.ccithermal.com
Heating Equipment Distr
N.A.I.C.S.: 423720

Heat Authority, LLC (1)
3161 S W Temple Ste 65129, Salt Lake
City, UT 84115
Web Site: https://heatauthority.com
Heating Equipment Mfr
N.A.I.C.S.: 333414

OOO Thermon CIS (1)
17 bld 1 Chistoprudniy blvd, 101000, Moscow, Russia
Tel.: (7) 4954117038

Electrical Component Mfr
N.A.I.C.S.: 335999

Thermon Europe B.V. (1)
Boezemweg 25, 2461 KG, Pijnacker, Neth-
erlands
Tel.: (31) 153615370
Electrical Component Mfr
N.A.I.C.S.: 335999
Rob Leussink (Mgr-European Sls & Bus
Dev)

Thermon Heat Tracers Pvt. Ltd. (1)
G-144/145 Kailash Vaibhav Complex Veer
Savarkar Marg, Parksite Vikhroli West,
Mumbai, 400079, Maharashtra, India
Tel.: (91) 2225190600
Electrical Component Mfr
N.A.I.C.S.: 335999

Thermon Heating Systems, Inc. (1)
5918 Roper Rd NW, Edmonton, T6B 3E1,
AB, Canada
Tel.: (780) 466-3178
Industrial Engineering Services
N.A.I.C.S.: 541330

Thermon Industries, Inc. (1)
100 Thermon Dr, San Marcos, TX 78666
Tel.: (512) 396-5801
Web Site: http://www.thermon.com
Sales Range: $50-74.9 Million
Emp.: 200
Electrical, Mechanical & Instrument Heat
Tracing Products & Services
N.A.I.C.S.: 335931
Rene van der Salm (Sr VP-Global Ops)

Subsidiary (Non-US):

Thermon Australia Pty. Ltd. (2)
30 London Dr, PO Box 532, Bayswater,
3153, VIC, Australia
Tel.: (61) 397626900
Web Site: http://www.thermon.com.au
Sales Range: $10-24.9 Million
Emp.: 9
Heat Tracing Systems, Engineering & Sales
N.A.I.C.S.: 333414

Thermon Benelux B.V. (2)
Boezemweg 25, 2641 KG, Pijnacker, Neth-
erlands
Tel.: (31) 153696741
Web Site: http://www.thermon.com
Sales Range: $25-49.9 Million
Emp.: 60
Heat Tracing Products Mfr
N.A.I.C.S.: 541330

Thermon Deutschland GmbH (2)
Erna-Scheffer-Strasse 1A, West Haus No
27, 51103, Cologne, Germany
Tel.: (49) 276193830
Sales Range: $1-9.9 Million
Emp.: 9
Heat Tracing Products
N.A.I.C.S.: 541330

Thermon Far East, Ltd. (2)
2nd FIL Yokohama Kinko-cho Bldg 6-3
Kinko-cho, Kanagawa-ku, Yokohama, 221-
0056, Japan
Tel.: (81) 45 461 0373
Web Site: http://www.thermon.com
Rev.: $100,000,000
Emp.: 11
Heat Tracing Systems, Cables, Panels Ac-
cessories, Instrumentation, Engineering &
Sales
N.A.I.C.S.: 333414

Thermon France SAS (2)
5 Rue Charles de Gaulle 6eme Etage,
94140, Alfortville, France
Tel.: (33) 145152840
Sales Range: $10-24.9 Million
Emp.: 12
Heat Tracing Cables, Panels, Accessories,
Instrumentation, Engineering & Sales
N.A.I.C.S.: 333414

Subsidiary (Domestic):

**Thermon Heat Tracing Services-I,
Inc.** (2)
8880 Telephone Rd, Houston, TX 77061
Tel.: (713) 433-2600
Web Site: http://www.thermon.com
Sales Range: $25-49.9 Million
Emp.: 60
Heat Tracing Products Mfr

N.A.I.C.S.: 423610

Subsidiary (Domestic):

Industrial Process Insulators, Inc. (3)
332 N Twin City Hwy, Port Neches, TX
77651
Tel.: (409) 729-3337
Web Site:
    http://www.indprocessinsulation.net
Sales Range: $10-24.9 Million
Emp.: 50
Drywall & Insulation Contractors
N.A.I.C.S.: 238310

Subsidiary (Non-US):

Thermon Korea, Ltd. (2)
Tel.: (82) 263292681
Sales Range: Less than $1 Million
Emp.: 24
Sales & Engineering of Heat Tracing Prod-
ucts
N.A.I.C.S.: 541330

**Thermon Latinoamericana, S. de R.L.
de C.V.** (2)
Pedro Valdez Fraga No 8 Col Guadalupe
Inn, 01020, Mexico, Mexico
Tel.: (52) 55 5662 9633
Web Site: http://www.thermon.com.mx
Sales Range: $25-49.9 Million
Emp.: 12
Heat Tracing Systems Whslr
N.A.I.C.S.: 423610

Thermon U.K. Ltd. (2)
7th Avenue, Team Valley Trading Estate,
Gateshead, NE11 0JW, Tyne & Wear,
United Kingdom
Tel.: (44) 1914994900
Web Site: http://www.thermon.co.uk
Sales Range: $10-24.9 Million
Emp.: 15
Heat Tracing Cables, Panels, Accessories &
Instrumentation Mfr
N.A.I.C.S.: 334513

**Thermon Manufacturing
Company** (1)
100 Thermon Dr, San Marcos, TX 78666
Tel.: (512) 396-5801
Electrical Component Mfr
N.A.I.C.S.: 335999

Thermon Middle East, WLL (1)
Office Ste 608 Manama Centre Entry-3, PO
Box 2911, Manama, Bahrain
Tel.: (973) 17217468
Electrical Component Mfr
N.A.I.C.S.: 335999
Surinder Katyal (VP-Ops)

**Thermon Solucoes de Aquecimento
Ltda.** (1)
Rua Dos Coqueiros 144, Campestre-Santo
Andre, Sao Paulo, 09080-010, Brazil
Tel.: (55) 1144282103
Electrical Component Mfr
N.A.I.C.S.: 335999

Thermon South Africa Pty. Ltd. (1)
47 Flamingo Crescent Lansdowne, Cape
Town, 7780, South Africa
Tel.: (27) 217628995
Web Site: https://www.thermon.co.za
Electrical Component Mfr
N.A.I.C.S.: 335999

Vapor Power International, LLC (1)
551 S County Line Rd, Franklin Park, IL
60131-1013
Tel.: (630) 694-5500
Web Site: https://www.vaporpower.com
Rev.: $6,666,666
Emp.: 45
Plate Work Mfr
N.A.I.C.S.: 332313
Bob Paul (VP-Sales & Marketing)
Greg Kaye (Dir-Aftermarket Svcs)

THINK ELEVATION CAPITAL GROWTH OPPORTUNITIES
One Letterman Dr Building C Ste
CM-420, San Francisco, CA 94129
Tel.: (415) 675-3271   Ky
Year Founded: 2021
TEGAU—(NASDAQ)
Investment Services

N.A.I.C.S.: 523999
Ravi Adusumalli (Co-CEO)
Shashin Shah (Co-CEO)
Tom Glaser (CFO)
Vivek Mathur (COO)

THINSPACE TECHNOLOGY, INC.
1925 E Belt Line Rd Ste 349, Carroll-
ton, TX 75006
Tel.: (214) 306-9670   DE
Web Site: http://www.thinspace.com
Year Founded: 2006
THNS—(OTCIQ)
Software Developer
N.A.I.C.S.: 513210

THIRD CENTURY BANCORP
80 E Jefferson St, Franklin, IN
46131-2321
Tel.: (317) 736-7151   IN
Web Site:
    http://www.mutualsavingsbank.net
Year Founded: 2004
TDCB—(OTCIQ)
Commericial Banking
N.A.I.C.S.: 522110
David Coffey (Pres & CEO)
Robert D. Heuchan (Vice Chm)
Chad Riddle (COO)
S. Paul Arab (CFO)

THIRD COAST BANCSHARES, INC.
20202 Hwy 59 N, Humble, TX 77338
Tel.: (281) 446-7000   TX
Web Site:
    https://www.thirdcoast.bank
Year Founded: 2013
TCBX—(NASDAQ)
Rev.: $161,169,000
Assets: $3,773,148,000
Liabilities: $3,391,368,000
Net Worth: $381,780,000
Earnings: $17,241,000
Emp.: 368
Fiscal Year-end: 12/31/22
Bank Holding Company
N.A.I.C.S.: 551111
Vicki Alexander (COO, Chief Risk
Officer & Exec VP)
Bart O. Caraway (Founder, Chm,
Pres & CEO)
R. John McWhorter (CFO)
William Bobbora (Chief Banking Offi-
cer & Exec VP)
Audrey A. Duncan (Chief Credit Offi-
cer & Sr Exec VP)
Christopher Peacock (Chief Retail
Officer & Exec VP)

Subsidiaries:

Third Coast Bank, SSB (1)
20202 Hwy 59 N, Humble, TX 77338
Tel.: (281) 446-7000
Web Site: https://www.tcbssb.com
Banking Services
N.A.I.C.S.: 522110

**Third Coast Commercial Capital,
Inc.** (1)
20202 Hwy 59 N Ste 190, Humble, TX
77338
Tel.: (281) 570-1845
Web Site:
    https://www.thirdcoastcommercialcap.com
Financial Services
N.A.I.C.S.: 523999

THIRD HARMONIC BIO, INC.
1700 Montgomery St Ste 210, San
Francisco, CA 94111
Tel.: (209) 727-2457   DE
Web Site:
    https://thirdharmonicbio.com
Year Founded: 2019
THRD—(NASDAQ)
Rev.: $2,553,000

Third Harmonic Bio, Inc.—(Continued)

Assets: $298,675,000
Liabilities: $9,607,000
Net Worth: $289,068,000
Earnings: ($35,155,000)
Emp.: 28
Fiscal Year-end: 12/31/22
Biotechnology Research & Development Services
N.A.I.C.S.: 541714
Natalie C. Holles (CEO)
Edward R. Conner (Chief Medical Officer)
Julie Person (Chief Admin Officer)
Christopher M. Murphy (Chief Fin & Bus Officer)
Dennis Dean (Chief Non-Officer)
Chris Dinsmore (Chief Scientific Officer)
Jennifer Dittman (Chief Dev Ops Officer)
Mark Iwicki (Chm)

THL CREDIT SENIOR LOAN FUND
100 Federal St 31st Fl, Boston, MA 02110
Web Site: http://www.thlcreditslf.com
TSLF—(NYSE)
Investment Management Service
N.A.I.C.S.: 525990
Joseph L. Morea (Executives)
Robert J. Hickey (Mng Dir)

THOMA BRAVO ADVANTAGE
150 N Riverside Plz Ste 2800, Chicago, IL 60606
Tel.: (312) 254-3300   Ky
Year Founded: 2020
TBA—(NYSE)
Investment Services
N.A.I.C.S.: 523999
Robert Sayle (CEO)
Amy Coleman Redenbaugh (CFO)
Steven Schwab (Sec)
Orlando Bravo (Chm)

THOMASVILLE BANCSHARES, INC.
301 N Broad St, Thomasville, GA 31792
Tel.: (229) 226-3300   GA
Year Founded: 1995
THVB—(OTCIQ)
Rev.: $45,924,240
Assets: $956,691,154
Liabilities: $864,713,895
Net Worth: $91,977,259
Earnings: $18,779,268
Fiscal Year-end: 12/31/19
Bank Holding Company
N.A.I.C.S.: 551111
Stephen Cheney (CEO)
Charles H. Hodges III (Pres)

THOR INDUSTRIES, INC.
601 E Beardsley Ave, Elkhart, IN 46514-3305
Tel.: (574) 970-7460   DE
Web Site:
https://www.thorindustries.com
Year Founded: 1980
THO—(NYSE)
Rev.: $10,043,408,000
Assets: $7,020,823,000
Liabilities: $2,946,770,000
Net Worth: $4,074,053,000
Earnings: $265,400,000
Emp.: 22,300
Fiscal Year-end: 07/31/24
Recreational Vehicles & Small & Mid-Sized Buses Mfr
N.A.I.C.S.: 336214
Andrew E. Graves (Chm)
Colleen A. Zuhl (CFO & Sr VP)

Mark Trinske (VP-IR)
Trevor Gasper (Gen Counsel, Sec & VP)
Michael Cieslak (Mgr-IR)
McKay Featherstone (Sr VP-Global Innovation)

Subsidiaries:

Airstream, Inc.   (1)
1001 W Pike St, Jackson Center, OH 45334-0629   **(100%)**
Tel.: (937) 596-6111
Web Site: http://www.airstream.com
Sales Range: $200-249.9 Million
Emp.: 400
Recreational Vehicles & Trailers Mfr
N.A.I.C.S.: 336214
Robert Wheeler (Pres & CEO)
Mollie Hansen (CMO)
Bryan Melton (Gen Mgr-Travel Trailers)
Justin Humphreys (COO)
Lenny Razo (VP-Sls)
Josh Fonner (Dir-Sls-West Central)
Jason Overman (Dir-Sls-East Central)
Rod Walters (Mgr-Supplier Quality)

Airxcel, Inc.   (1)
3050 N St Francis St, Wichita, KS 67219
Tel.: (574) 247-9235
Web Site: https://www.airxcel.com
Holding Company; Air Conditioning & Heating Equipment Mfr
N.A.I.C.S.: 551112
Jeff Rutherford (Pres & CEO)
Piar Adams (VP-Sls-RV Appliances)
Steve Gokie (Dir-Sls)
Kevin L. Phillips (Exec VP & Pres-RV Group)
Troy Nussbaum (VP-OEM Sls)
Josh Miller (Mgr-Bus Dev)
Caroline Callahan (Mgr-Social Media)
Harold Ogden (Dir-Global Mktg)

Subsidiary (Domestic):

Cleer Vision Windows, Inc.   (2)
3401 County Rd 6 E, Elkhart, IN 46514
Tel.: (574) 262-0449
Web Site: http://www.cleervision.com
All Other Basic Inorganic Chemical Mfr
N.A.I.C.S.: 325180
Rick Collins (Founder & Pres)
Marc Disher (Acct Mgr)
Don Hamm (VP-Sls & Mktg)

Dicor Corporation, Inc.   (2)
2965 LaVanture Pl, Elkhart, IN 46514
Tel.: (574) 264-2699
Web Site: http://www.dicor.com
Furniture Merchant Whslr
N.A.I.C.S.: 423210
Gary Adamson (CEO)
Lola Fuller (Mgr-Purchasing-United Shade)
Chuck Olson (Dir-Purchasing)
Christy Waterman (Dir-Fin)
Anthony Wollschlager (Pres)

Marvair   (2)
156 Seedling Dr, Cordele, GA 31015
Tel.: (229) 273-3636
Web Site: http://www.marvair.com
Sales Range: $25-49.9 Million
Emp.: 150
Air Conditioning Equipment Mfr
N.A.I.C.S.: 333415
Kim Pate (Mgr-OEM Sls)
Bob Benson (Mgr-Sls-Natl)
Mike Whitehurst (Sr Mgr-Acct)
David Shuford (VP-Sls-Intl)
Melissa Nelms (Mgr-Customer Svc)
Tonya Graham (Mgr-Parts & Warranty)

Suburban Manufacturing, Co.   (2)
676 Broadway St, Dayton, TN 37321
Tel.: (423) 775-2131
Sales Range: $1-9.9 Million
Emp.: 36
Air Conditioning Equipment Mfr
N.A.I.C.S.: 333415
Art Klee (Pres)

Burstner GmbH & Co. KG   (1)
Weststrasse 33, 77694, Kehl, Germany
Tel.: (49) 7851850
Web Site: https://www.buerstner.com
Caravan & Motor Home Mfr
N.A.I.C.S.: 336213

Capron GmbH   (1)
Berghausstr 1, Sachsen, 01844, Neustadt, Germany
Tel.: (49) 3596530
Web Site: https://www.capron.eu
Caravan & Motor Home Mfr
N.A.I.C.S.: 336213

Caraconsult GmbH   (1)
Tel.: (49) 691504352820
Web Site: http://www.caraconsult.de
Caravan Financial Consulting Services
N.A.I.C.S.: 522320

Carado GmbH   (1)
Olmuhlestrasse 6, 88299, Leutkirch, Germany
Tel.: (49) 75619097300
Web Site: http://carado.com
Automobile Parts Mfr
N.A.I.C.S.: 336390

Cleer Vision Tempered Glass, LLC   (1)
3403 Cooper Dr, Elkhart, IN 46514
Tel.: (574) 264-7300
Tempered Glass Product Mfr & Distr
N.A.I.C.S.: 327215

DS Corp.   (1)
1140 W Lake St, Topeka, IN 46571
Tel.: (260) 593-3850
Web Site: https://www.crossroadsrv.com
Sales Range: $100-124.9 Million
Emp.: 300
Recreational Vehicle Mfr
N.A.I.C.S.: 423130

Dethleffs France S.A.R.L.   (1)
4 rue Waldkirch, 67600, Selestat, France
Tel.: (33) 388829354
Web Site: http://www.dethleffs.fr
Caravan & Motor Home Mfr
N.A.I.C.S.: 336213

Dethleffs GmbH & Co. KG   (1)
Arist-Dethleffs-Strasse 12, 88316, Isny im Allgau, Germany
Tel.: (49) 75629870
Web Site: https://www.dethleffs.de
Caravan & Motor Home Mfr
N.A.I.C.S.: 336213

Dutchmen Manufacturing, Inc.   (1)
2164 Carangana Ct, Goshen, IN 46526
Tel.: (574) 534-1224
Web Site: http://www.dutchmen.com
Sales Range: $100-124.9 Million
Emp.: 800
Recreational Vehicle Mfr
N.A.I.C.S.: 336214

Subsidiary (Domestic):

Dutchmen Manufacturing, Inc.   (2)
12628 SE Jennifer St, Clackamas, OR 97015
Tel.: (503) 722-5199
Sales Range: $75-99.9 Million
Emp.: 200
Trailer Mfr
N.A.I.C.S.: 336214

Erwin Hymer Center Bad Waldsee GmbH   (1)
Biberacher Strasse 92, 88339, Bad Waldsee, Germany
Tel.: (49) 7524999106
Web Site: https://hymer-waldsee.de
Caravan & Motor Home Mfr
N.A.I.C.S.: 336213

Erwin Hymer Center Stuttgart GmbH   (1)
Mahdentalstr 84, 71065, Sindelfingen, Germany
Tel.: (49) 703186990
Web Site: https://www.hymerstuttgart.de
Caravan & Motor Home Mfr
N.A.I.C.S.: 336213

Erwin Hymer Group SE   (1)
Holzstr 19, 88339, Bad Waldsee, Germany
Tel.: (49) 75249990
Caravan & Motor Home Mfr
N.A.I.C.S.: 336213

Erwin Hymer Group Stuttgart GmbH   (1)
Mahdentalstr 84, 71065, Sindelfingen, Germany

Tel.: (49) 703186990
Web Site: https://www.hymerstuttgart.de
Vehicle Rental & Financing Services
N.A.I.C.S.: 532111

Erwin Hymer World GmbH   (1)
Hymerring 1, 97877, Wertheim, Germany
Tel.: (49) 934293510
Web Site: http://www.erwinhymerworld.de
Caravan & Motor Home Distr
N.A.I.C.S.: 441210

Etrusco GmbH   (1)
Olmuhlestrasse 6, 88299, Leutkirch, Germany
Tel.: (49) 75619097450
Web Site: https://www.etrusco.com
Emp.: 300
Caravan & Motor Home Mfr
N.A.I.C.S.: 336213

Goldschmitt techmobil GmbH   (1)
Dornberger Strasse 8-10, Hopfingen, 74746, Waldstetten, Germany
Tel.: (49) 62832229100
Web Site: https://www.goldschmitt.de
Caravan & Motor Home Mfr
N.A.I.C.S.: 336213

Heartland Recreational Vehicles, LLC   (1)
2831 Dexter Dr, Elkhart, IN 46514
Tel.: (574) 262-5992
Web Site: https://www.heartlandrvs.com
Sales Range: $300-349.9 Million
Emp.: 1,500
Recreational Vehicle Mfr
N.A.I.C.S.: 441210

Subsidiary (Domestic):

Cruiser RV, LLC   (2)
Cruiser 7805 N SR 9, Howe, IN 46746-6746
Tel.: (260) 562-3500
Web Site: https://www.cruiserrv.com
Travel Trailer Mfr
N.A.I.C.S.: 336214

Hymer GmbH & Co. KG   (1)
Holzstrasse 19, 88339, Bad Waldsee, Germany
Tel.: (49) 75249990
Web Site: https://www.hymer.com
Caravan & Motor Home Distr
N.A.I.C.S.: 441210

Jayco Inc.   (1)
903 S Main St, Middlebury, IN 46540
Tel.: (574) 825-5861
Web Site: https://www.jayco.com
Emp.: 1,600
Recreational Vehicle Mfr
N.A.I.C.S.: 336214

KZRV, L.P.   (1)
985 N 900 W, Shipshewana, IN 46565
Tel.: (866) 472-5460
Web Site: http://www.kz-rv.com
Travel Trailer Mfr
N.A.I.C.S.: 336214

Keystone RV Company   (1)
2642 Hackberry Dr, Goshen, IN 46527-2000
Tel.: (574) 534-9430
Web Site: http://www.keystonerv.com
Emp.: 5,000
Recreational Vehicle Mfr
N.A.I.C.S.: 336110
Cole Davis (Founder)

LMC Caravan GmbH & Co. KG   (1)
Rudolf-Diesel-Str 4, 48336, Sassenberg, Germany
Tel.: (49) 2583270
Web Site: https://www.lmc-caravan.com
Caravan & Motor Home Mfr & Distr
N.A.I.C.S.: 336213

Laika Caravans S.p.A.   (1)
Via Certaldese 41/A, San Casciano in Val di Pesa, 50026, Florence, Italy
Tel.: (39) 05580581
Web Site: https://www.laika.it
Caravan & Motor Home Distr
N.A.I.C.S.: 441210

Livin' Lite Corp.   (1)
1025 E Waterford St, Wakarusa, IN 46573
Tel.: (574) 862-2228

Web Site: http://www.livinlite.com
Sales Range: $1-9.9 Million
Emp.: 32
Recreational Vehicle Mfr
N.A.I.C.S.: 441210

Movera GmbH (1)
Holzstrasse 21, 88339, Bad Waldsee, Germany
Tel.: (49) 75247000
Web Site: https://www.movera.com
Caravan & Motor Home Distr
N.A.I.C.S.: 441210

Niesmann+ Bischoff GmbH (1)
Clou-Strasse 1, 56751, Polch, Germany
Tel.: (49) 26549330
Web Site: https://www.niesmann-
bischoff.com
Caravan & Motor Home Mfr & Distr
N.A.I.C.S.: 336213

Sunlight GmbH (1)
Olmuhlestrasse 6, 88299, Leutkirch, Germany
Tel.: (49) 75619097200
Web Site: https://www.sunlight.de
Caravan & Motor Home Distr
N.A.I.C.S.: 441210

Thor Motor Coach, Inc. (1)
701 County Rd 15, Elkhart, IN
46516-9731 (100%)
Tel.: (574) 266-1111
Web Site: https://www.thormotorcoach.com
Sales Range: $50-74.9 Million
Emp.: 1,500
Mfr of Recreational Vehicles
N.A.I.C.S.: 336213

Tiffin Motor Homes, Inc. (1)
105 2nd St NW, Red Bay, AL 35582
Tel.: (256) 356-8661
Web Site: http://www.tiffinmotorhomes.com
Sales Range: $150-199.9 Million
Emp.: 1,300
Mfr of Motor Homes & RVs
N.A.I.C.S.: 336213
Tim Tiffin (Gen Mgr)
Robert Tiffin (CEO)

Vanleigh RV, Inc. (1)
26 Industrial Drive Access Rd, Burnsville, MS 38833
Travel Trailer Mfr
N.A.I.C.S.: 336214

Vixen Composites, LLC (1)
2965 LaVanture Pl, Elkhart, IN 46514
Tel.: (574) 970-1224
Web Site: https://vixencomposites.com
Fiberglass Reinforced Plastic Product Mfr
N.A.I.C.S.: 326199

THREDUP, INC.

969 Broadway Ste 200, Oakland, CA 94607
Tel.: (415) 402-5202 DE
Web Site: https://www.thredup.com
Year Founded: 2009
TDUP—(NASDAQ)
Rev.: $288,379,000
Assets: $301,948,000
Liabilities: $161,947,000
Net Worth: $140,001,000
Earnings: ($92,284,000)
Emp.: 2,416
Fiscal Year-end: 12/31/22
Online Shopping Services
N.A.I.C.S.: 459999
James Reinhart (Co-Founder & CEO)
Patricia Nakache (Chm)
Sean Sobers (CFO)
Alexis Ghorai (Sr VP-Ops)
Christopher Homer (Co-Founder & COO)
Florin Filote (Gen Mgr-Europe)

THRESHER INDUSTRIES, INC.

13400 Hanford-Armona Rd, Hanford, CA 93230
Tel.: (559) 585-3400 DE
Year Founded: 2005
THRR—(OTCIQ)
Aluminium Products Mfr

N.A.I.C.S.: 331524
Tom Flessner (Pres & CEO)
Ed Gardner (Chm)

THRIVE ACQUISITION CORPO-RATION

275 Grove St Ste 2-400 Riverside Ctr, Newton, MA 02466
Tel.: (617) 663-5988 Ky
Web Site:
http://www.thriveacquisition.com
Year Founded: 2021
THACU—(NASDAQ)
Investment Services
N.A.I.C.S.: 523999
Charles Jobson (CEO)
Charles Urbain (CFO & COO)
Benjamin Kao (Pres)

THRYV HOLDINGS, INC.

2200 W Airfield Dr, Dallas-Fort Worth Airport, TX 75261
Tel.: (972) 453-7000 DE
Web Site: https://www.thryv.com
Year Founded: 2012
THRY—(NASDAQ)
Rev.: $916,961,000
Assets: $783,170,000
Liabilities: $630,470,000
Net Worth: $152,700,000
Earnings: ($259,295,000)
Emp.: 3,049
Fiscal Year-end: 12/31/23
Holding Company
N.A.I.C.S.: 551112
Joseph A. Walsh (Pres & CEO)
Paul D. Rouse (CFO, Treas & Exec VP)
John Wholey (Chief Operation & Information Officer)
Tami Cannizzaro (CMO)
Marie Michele Caron (Pres)

Subsidiaries:

Berry Network, Inc. (1)
3100 Kettering Blvd, Dayton, OH 45439-1975
Web Site: https://www.berrynetwork.com
Media & Advertising Agency
N.A.I.C.S.: 541810
Sherri Kavanaugh (Sr VP-Client Strategy)
David Henry (VP-Ops & Sls Support)
Monica Avery (VP-Client Svcs)
Sharon Rickey (VP-Client Svcs)
Alison Siefer (VP-Client Svcs)
Kory Walton (VP-Digital Strategy)
Mark Williams (VP-Comm)
Daphne Young (VP-Ops & Tech)
Michele Hutchison (VP-Ops & Sls Support)
Keith Chambers (VP-Fin)
Matt Garrett (VP-Healthcare Client Svcs)
Scott Wilson (VP-Enterprise Sls)
Tony Sagginario (VP-Enterprise Sls)

Dex Media BRE LLC (1)
1001 Winstead Dr, Cary, NC 27513
Tel.: (919) 297-1600
Web Site: http://www.dexmedia.com
Sales Range: $1-4.9 Billion
Telephone Directory Publr
N.A.I.C.S.: 512230

Branch (Domestic):

Dex Media - Albuquerque (2)
5600 Wyoming Blvd NE Ste 100, Albuquerque, NM 87109-3174
Tel.: (575) 523-1551
Sales Range: $25-49.9 Million
Emp.: 40
Management Consulting Services
N.A.I.C.S.: 541618
Ted Cassady (Gen Mgr)

Dex Media - Chicago (2)
200 E Randolph St, Chicago, IL 60601-6436
Tel.: (312) 240-6000
Web Site: http://www.dexone.com
Sales Range: $25-49.9 Million
Emp.: 150
Sales Agent for Ameritech Publications
N.A.I.C.S.: 513199

Dex Media - Denver (2)
9380 Station St, Lone Tree, CO 80124
Tel.: (303) 784-2900
Web Site: http://www.dexknows.com
Sales Range: $100-124.9 Million
Telephone & Business Information Directory Publishing
N.A.I.C.S.: 513140

Subsidiary (Domestic):

Dex One Service, Inc. (2)
1001 Winstead Dr, Cary, NC 27513-2117
Tel.: (919) 297-1600
Web Site: http://www.dexone.com
Management Consulting Services
N.A.I.C.S.: 541611

Dex Media Holdings, Inc. (1)
2200 W Airfield Dr DFW Airport, Dallas, TX 75261
Tel.: (972) 453-7000
Web Site: http://www.dexyp.com
Emp.: 1,800
Holding Company
N.A.I.C.S.: 551114

Dex Media, Inc. - Everett (1)
906 SE Everett Mall Way, Everett, WA 98208-3743
Tel.: (425) 348-2000
Sales Range: $50-74.9 Million
Emp.: 35
Telephone Directory Publishing Services
N.A.I.C.S.: 513140

Dex Media, Inc. - Fort Wayne (1)
7223 Engle Rd Ste 200, Fort Wayne, IN 46804-2228
Tel.: (260) 436-7516
Sales Range: $10-24.9 Million
Emp.: 45
Telephone Directory Publishing & Printing
N.A.I.C.S.: 513140
Barb Moss (Dir-Sls)

Infusion Software, Inc. (1)
1260 S Spectrum Blvd, Chandler, AZ 85286
Tel.: (480) 499-6500
Web Site: https://keap.com
Emp.: 600
Software Developer
N.A.I.C.S.: 513210

Ingenio, LLC (1)
182 Howard St Ste 826, San Francisco, CA 94105
Web Site: https://www.ingenio.com
Pay Per Use Telephone Services
N.A.I.C.S.: 517810
Warren Heffelfinger (CEO)

Sensis Pty. Ltd. (1)
222 Lonsdale Street, Melbourne, 3000, VIC, Australia (70%)
Tel.: (61) 3 8653 5000
Web Site: http://www.sensis.com.au
Digital Marketing Services
N.A.I.C.S.: 541890
John Allan (CEO)
Matt Mulligan (Chief Product & Customer Experience Officer)
Natalie Morwood (CFO)
Helene Gordon (Chief People Officer)
Elise Balsillie (Chief Revenue Officer)
Kerrie-Anne Hutchins (Chief Compliance Officer & Gen Counsel)
Hayley Jovanovic (CMO)
Aman Sahani (CIO)

Subsidiary (Domestic):

Australian Local Search Pty. Ltd. (2)
Level 23 175 Liverpool Street, Sydney, 2000, NSW, Australia
Web Site: http://www.truelocal.com.au
Online Business Directory Publisher
N.A.I.C.S.: 513140

YP LLC (1)
611 N Brand Blvd Ste 500, Glendale, CA 91203
Tel.: (818) 937-5500
Web Site: https://www.yellowpages.com
Internet Directory Services
N.A.I.C.S.: 513140

THUMZUP MEDIA CORPORA-TION

11845 W Olympic Blvd Ste 1100W

Ste 13, Los Angeles, CA 90064 NV
Web Site:
https://www.thumzupmedia.com
Year Founded: 2020
TZUP—(OTCQB)
Rev.: $2,421
Assets: $1,160,799
Liabilities: $91,359
Net Worth: $1,069,440
Earnings: ($1,221,765)
Emp.: 4
Fiscal Year-end: 12/31/22
Custom Computer Programming Services
N.A.I.C.S.: 541511
Robert Steele (Chm)

THUNDER ENERGIES CORPO-RATION

1100 Peachtree St NE8 Ste 200, Atlanta, GA 30339
Tel.: (786) 855-6190 FL
Web Site:
https://www.thunderenergies
corp.com
Year Founded: 2011
TNRG—(OTCEM)
Assets: $154,519
Liabilities: $9,380,762
Net Worth: ($9,226,243)
Earnings: ($9,258,849)
Emp.: 24
Fiscal Year-end: 12/31/23
Clean Combustion of Fossil Fuels
N.A.I.C.S.: 213112
Eric Collins (Chm & Dir)
Ricardo Haynes (Pres & CEO)
Lance L. Lehr (Mgr-Operations)
Eric McClendon (Pres-Emergent Markets)
Ismael Fernandez (VP)

THUNDER MOUNTAIN GOLD, INC.

11770 W President Dr Ste F, Boise, ID 83713
Tel.: (208) 658-1037 NV
Web Site:
https://www.thundermountain
gold.com
Year Founded: 1935
THM—(TSXV)
Rev.: $300,000
Assets: $1,722,328
Liabilities: $1,302,467
Net Worth: $419,861
Earnings: ($1,244,739)
Emp.: 3
Fiscal Year-end: 12/31/22
Gold Mining Services
N.A.I.C.S.: 212220
E. James Collord (COO & VP)
Eric T. Jones (Pres & CEO)
Larry J. Thackery (CFO)

TIAN'AN PHARMACEUTICAL CO., LTD.

50 W Liberty St Ste 880, Reno, NV 89501
Tel.: (323) 613-1577 NV
Year Founded: 2005
TNPH—(OTCIQ)
Pharmaceuticals Product Mfr
N.A.I.C.S.: 325412
Simon Littlewood (Treas & Sec)
Ping Shun Ngan (Pres)

TIANRONG INTERNET PRODUCTS & SERVICES, INC.

2374 Route 390 Kai Long Fortune Bldg, Mountainhome, PA 18342
Tel.: (424) 262-1453 NJ
Year Founded: 1959
TIPS—(OTCIQ)

Tianrong Internet Products & Services, Inc.—(Continued)

Telecommunication Servicesb
N.A.I.C.S.: 517112
Marjorie Schaefer (CEO)

TIBERIUS ACQUISITION CORPORATION

3601 N Interstate 10 Service Rd W,
Metairie, LA 70002
Tel.: (504) 457-3811   DE
Web Site: http://www.tiberiusco.com
Year Founded: 2015
TIBRU—(NASDAQ)
Rev.: $3,854,255
Assets: $179,603,662
Liabilities: $174,603,661
Net Worth: $5,000,001
Earnings: $1,937,205
Emp.: 3
Fiscal Year-end: 12/31/19
Investment Services
N.A.I.C.S.: 327910
Michael Townsend Gray (Chm & CEO)
Andrew J. Poole (Chief Investment Officer)
Bryce Quin (CFO)

TIDELANDS ROYALTY TRUST B

2911 Turtle Creek Blvd Ste 850, Dallas, TX 75219   TX
Web Site: http://www.tirtz-tidelands.com
TIRTZ—(OTCIQ)
Coal Product Mfr
N.A.I.C.S.: 324199
Ron E. Hooper (Sr VP)

TIDEWATER INC.

842 W Sam Houston Pkwy N Ste 400, Houston, TX 77024
Tel.: (713) 470-5300   DE
Web Site: https://www.tdw.com
Year Founded: 1956
TDW—(NYSE)
Rev.: $647,684,000
Assets: $1,297,656,000
Liabilities: $431,666,000
Net Worth: $865,990,000
Earnings: ($21,749,000)
Emp.: 6,300
Fiscal Year-end: 12/31/22
Marine Equipment & Services to the Offshore Energy Industry
N.A.I.C.S.: 483211
David E. Darling (COO & Exec VP)
Samuel R. Rubio (CFO & Exec VP)
Quintin V. Kneen (Pres & CEO)
Darren J. Vorst (Treas & VP)
Johnson Lee (CIO & VP)
Daniel A. Hudson (Gen Counsel, Sec & VP)
West Gotcher (VP-Fin & IR)
Johnson R. Lee (CIO)
Dick H. Fagerstal (Chm)

Subsidiaries:

Al Wasl Marine LLC   (1)
Near Junction 1, PO Box 2537, Jebel Ali Free-zone, Dubai, United Arab Emirates
Tel.: (971) 48816400
Web Site: http://www.alwaslmarine.ae
Marine Vessel Service
N.A.I.C.S.: 488330

GulfMark Offshore Inc.   (1)
842 West Sam Houston Pkwy N Ste 400, Houston, TX 77024
Tel.: (713) 963-9522
Web Site: http://www.gulfmark.com
Rev.: $13,593,000
Assets: $471,955,000
Liabilities: $147,465,000
Net Worth: $324,490,000
Earnings: $3,511,000
Fiscal Year-end: 12/31/2017

Provider of Marine Transportation Services
N.A.I.C.S.: 213112

Subsidiary (Domestic):

GM Offshore, Inc.   (2)
10111 Richmond Ave Ste 340, Houston, TX 77042-4275
Tel.: (713) 963-9522
Emp.: 40
Marine Transportation Services
N.A.I.C.S.: 213112

Holding (Non-US):

Gulf Marine Far East Pte. Ltd.   (2)
Block 103 25 Loyang Cresant Loyang Offshore Supply Base Unit 07-01/02, Singapore, 508988, Singapore   (100%)
Tel.: (65) 65452641
Web Site: http://www.gulfmark.com
Sales Range: $10-24.9 Million
Emp.: 10
Marine Transportation Services
N.A.I.C.S.: 488510

Subsidiary (Non-US):

Gulf Offshore N.S. Ltd.   (2)
   (100%)
Sales Range: $10-24.9 Million
Emp.: 30
Marine Transportation Services
N.A.I.C.S.: 488510

Gulf Offshore Norge AS   (2)
Strandgaten 5, 4307, Sandnes, Norway   (100%)
Tel.: (47) 51609000
Web Site: http://www.gulfmark.no
Sales Range: $25-49.9 Million
Emp.: 15
Deep Sea Freight Transportation-Foreign
N.A.I.C.S.: 483111

GulfMark AS   (2)
Strandgaten 5, PO Box 221, 4307, Sandnes, Norway
Tel.: (47) 51609000
Oil & Gas Related Services
N.A.I.C.S.: 213112

Subsidiary (Domestic):

GulfMark Americas, Inc.   (2)
141 James Dr W Ste 250, Saint Rose, LA 70087
Tel.: (504) 472-5375
Web Site: http://www.gulfmark.com
Marine Transportation Services
N.A.I.C.S.: 213112

Subsidiary (Non-US):

GulfMark Asia Pte., Ltd.   (2)
25 Loyang Crescent Loyang Offshore Supply Base, Block 103 Tops Avenue 1 #07-01, Singapore, 508988, Singapore
Tel.: (65) 66908900
Oil & Gas Related Services
N.A.I.C.S.: 213112

Subsidiary (Domestic):

GulfMark Management, Inc.   (2)
107 Jersey Dr, Youngsville, LA 70592
Tel.: (337) 857-5468
Marine Transportation Services
N.A.I.C.S.: 213112

Subsidiary (Non-US):

GulfMark Rederi AS   (2)
Strandgaten 5, 4307, Sandnes, Rogaland, Norway
Tel.: (47) 51609000
Marine Transportation Services
N.A.I.C.S.: 213112

GulfMark U.K. Ltd.   (2)
The Exchange No 1 62-104 Market Street, Aberdeen, AB11 5PJ, United Kingdom
Tel.: (44) 1224336000
Web Site: http://www.gulfmark.com
Emp.: 50
Oil & Gas Related Services
N.A.I.C.S.: 213112

Pan Marine do Brasil Ltda.   (1)
Rua Academico Paulo Sergio de Carvalho Vasconcelos 741, Granja dos Cavaleiros,

Macae, 27930-310, Rio de Janeiro, Brazil   (100%)
Tel.: (55) 2227659200
Offshore Support Services
N.A.I.C.S.: 483211

Point Marine, L.L.C.   (1)
601 Poydras St Ste 1900, New Orleans, LA 70130-6040   (100%)
Tel.: (504) 568-1010
Sales Range: $25-49.9 Million
Emp.: 18
Marine Transportation & Services
N.A.I.C.S.: 488390

Sonatide Marine, Ltd   (1)
Edificio Rei Katyavala Rua Rei Katyavala s/n Entrada B 13 Andar, Ingombota, Luanda, Angola
Tel.: (244) 1224293130
Marine Vessel Service
N.A.I.C.S.: 488330
Eldine Chilembo (Coord-Crew)

Tidewater (India) Private Limited   (1)
1st Floor Transocean House Lake Boulevard Road, Powai, Mumbai, 400076, Maharashtra, India
Tel.: (91) 2266728700
Emp.: 7
Offshore Support Services
N.A.I.C.S.: 483211

Tidewater Marine AS   (1)
Strandgaten 5, 4307, Sandnes, Norway
Tel.: (47) 51609000
Offshore Supply Services
N.A.I.C.S.: 488390
Hans Kari Jacobsen (CFO)

Tidewater Marine International Pte. Ltd.   (1)
300 Beach Road The Concourse 15-01, PO Box 5119, Loyang Crescent, Singapore, 199555, Singapore
Tel.: (65) 63093600
Offshore Support Services
N.A.I.C.S.: 483211

Tidewater Marine Western, Inc.   (1)
640 W Hueneme Rd, Oxnard, CA 93033   (100%)
Tel.: (805) 271-1313
Web Site: http://www.tdw.com
Sales Range: $10-24.9 Million
Emp.: 20
Marine Equipment & Services
N.A.I.C.S.: 488999

Tidewater Marine, L.L.C.   (1)
200 Ford Industrial Rd, Amelia, LA 70340   (100%)
Tel.: (985) 631-5820
Sales Range: $25-49.9 Million
Emp.: 200
Marine Equipment & Services
N.A.I.C.S.: 488390
Eric Chiasson (Mng Dir)

Tidewater Support Services Limited   (1)
1 Minto Place Altens Industrial Estate, Aberdeen, AB12 3FN, Scotland, United Kingdom
Tel.: (44) 1224293000
Web Site: http://www.tdw.com
Emp.: 20
Marine Vessel Service
N.A.I.C.S.: 488330

Tidewater de Mexico, S.A. de C.V.   (1)
Romero De Terreros No 1415 Narvarte Poniente, 3020, Mexico, Mexico   (49%)
Tel.: (52) 5556391821
Offshore Support Services
N.A.I.C.S.: 483211

Troms Offshore Fleet 2 AS   (1)
PO Box 6155, 9291, Tromso, Norway
Tel.: (47) 77679950
Web Site: http://www.tromsoffshore.no
Water Transport Services
N.A.I.C.S.: 483211

TIE TECHNOLOGIES, INC.

1185 Avenue of the Americas 3rd Fl, New York, NY 10036
Tel.: (646) 768-8417   FL
TTCS—(OTCIQ)

Telecommunication Servicesb
N.A.I.C.S.: 517810
David Lazar (CEO)

TIGER INTERNATIONAL RESOURCES INC.

26981 Highwood Cir, Laguna Hills, CA 92653
Tel.: (949) 362-1600
Web Site: http://www.tigerresources.com
TGR—(TSXV)
Assets: $3,077
Liabilities: $491,481
Net Worth: ($488,405)
Earnings: ($34,119)
Fiscal Year-end: 04/30/20
Mineral Mining Exploration Service
N.A.I.C.S.: 213114

TIGER OIL AND ENERGY, INC.

123 W Nye Ln Ste 129, Carson City, NV 89706
Tel.: (702) 514-4183   NV
Web Site: https://www.tigeroilandenergy.com
Year Founded: 1993
TGRO—(OTCIQ)
Sales Range: Less than $1 Million
Crude Petroleum Extraction Services
N.A.I.C.S.: 211120
Howard H. Bouch (Pres, CEO, Treas, Sec & Dir-Sole)

TIGO ENERGY, INC

888 San Clemente Dr Ste 400, New Port, CA 92660
Tel.: (949) 720-5700   DE
Year Founded: 2019
ROCG—(NASDAQ)
Rev.: $1,645,906
Assets: $25,051,786
Liabilities: $25,384,013
Net Worth: ($332,227)
Earnings: ($178,218)
Emp.: 7
Fiscal Year-end: 12/31/22
Financial Investment Services
N.A.I.C.S.: 523999
Byron Roth (CEO & Chm)

Subsidiaries:

Tigo Energy MergeCo, Inc   (1)
420 Blossom Hill Rd, Los Gatos, CA 95032
Tel.: (408) 402-0802
Web Site: http://www.tigoenergy.com
Semiconductor Mfr
N.A.I.C.S.: 334413
Zvi Alon (CEO & Chm)
Danny Eizips (VP-Engrg)
James Dillon (CMO)
Mike Gazzano (Mktg Mgr-North America)
Bill Roeschlein (CFO)
Jeffrey Sullivan (COO)

TILE SHOP HOLDINGS, INC.

14000 Carlson Pkwy, Plymouth, MN 55441
Tel.: (763) 852-2950   DE
Web Site: https://www.tileshop.com
Year Founded: 2012
TTSH—(NASDAQ)
Rev.: $394,702,000
Assets: $345,822,000
Liabilities: $237,053,000
Net Worth: $108,769,000
Earnings: $15,703,000
Emp.: 1,233
Fiscal Year-end: 12/31/22
Holding Company; Tile Stores Operator
N.A.I.C.S.: 551112
Daniel Brewster (VP-Real Estate & Construction)
Mark B. Davis (CFO, Principal Acctg Officer, Sec & Sr VP)
Christopher Davis (CIO)

Jamie Elliott *(VP-Talent Mgmt)*
Dacy Corlee *(VP-Sales)*
Cabell H. Lolmaugh *(Pres & CEO)*

Subsidiaries:

The Tile Shop, LLC **(1)**
14000 Carlson Pkwy, Plymouth, MN 55441
Tel.: (763) 541-9720
Sales Range: $150-199.9 Million
Tile Stores Operator
N.A.I.C.S.: 449129

TILLY'S, INC.
10 Whatney, Irvine, CA 92618
Tel.: (949) 609-5599   DE
Web Site: https://www.tillys.com
Year Founded: 1982
TLYS—(NYSE)
Rev.: $672,280,000
Assets: $475,752,000
Liabilities: $298,954,000
Net Worth: $176,798,000
Earnings: $9,677,000
Emp.: 1,525
Fiscal Year-end: 01/28/23
Men's, Women's & Children's Apparel
N.A.I.C.S.: 458110
Michael L. Henry *(CFO & Exec VP)*
Laura Janney *(Chief Mdsg Officer & Exec VP)*
Shelly Bueno-Johnson *(VP-Stores)*
Julie Campbell *(VP-Visual Mdsg)*
Christina Campbell *(VP & Controller)*
Hezy Shaked *(Co-Founder, Exec Chm, Interim Pres & Interim CEO)*

TILT HOLDINGS INC.
2801 E Camelback Rd Ste 180,
Phoenix, AZ 85016
Tel.: (623) 887-4990   BC
Web Site:
    https://www.tiltholdings.com
Year Founded: 2018
TLLTF—(OTCQB)
Rev.: $174,188,000
Assets: $293,978,000
Liabilities: $172,461,000
Net Worth: $121,517,000
Earnings: ($107,464,000)
Emp.: 434
Fiscal Year-end: 12/31/22
Cannabis Technology Company
N.A.I.C.S.: 523999
Chris Kelly *(Chief Revenue Officer)*
Arthur Smuck *(Chm)*
Mark Higgins *(Deputy Gen Counsel)*
Tim Conder *(CEO)*

Subsidiaries:

Commonwealth Alternative Care,
Inc. **(1)**
30 Mozzone Blvd, Taunton, MA 02780
Tel.: (508) 738-6380
Web Site:
    https://www.commonwealthaltcare.org
Cannabis Mfr
N.A.I.C.S.: 325411

Jupiter Research, LLC **(1)**
2801 E Camelback Rd Ste 180, Phoenix,
AZ 85016
Tel.: (480) 867-6100
Web Site: http://www.jupiterresearch.com
Consumer Goods Mfr
N.A.I.C.S.: 424990

TIMBERLAND BANCORP, INC.
624 Simpson Ave, Hoquiam, WA
98550
Tel.: (360) 533-4747   WA
Web Site:
    https://www.timberlandbank.com
Year Founded: 1997
TSBK—(NASDAQ)
Rev.: $105,961,000
Assets: $1,923,475,000
Liabilities: $1,678,062,000
Net Worth: $245,413,000

Earnings: $24,283,000
Emp.: 274
Fiscal Year-end: 09/30/24
Bank Holding Company
N.A.I.C.S.: 551111
Matthew J. DeBord *(Chief Lending Officer & Exec VP)*
Michael John Stoney *(Chm)*
Dean J. Brydon *(Pres & CEO)*
Marci A. Basich *(CFO & Exec VP)*
Jonathan Arthur Fischer *(Pres, COO, Sec & Exec VP)*
Edward C. Foster *(Exec VP-Chief Credit Administrator)*

Subsidiaries:

Timberland Bank **(1)**
624 Simpson Ave, Hoquiam, WA
98550   **(100%)**
Tel.: (360) 533-4747
Sales Range: $50-74.9 Million
State Savings Bank
N.A.I.C.S.: 522180
Dean J. Brydon *(Pres & CEO)*
Marci A. Basich *(CFO)*
Jonathan Arthur Fischer *(COO, Sec & Exec VP)*
Richard Pifer *(Sr VP)*
Jodi Danielson *(Sr VP)*
Matt Hargrave *(Sr VP)*
Wendy Michelbrink *(Sr VP)*
Jannae Mitton *(Sr VP)*
Carol Coady *(VP)*
Greg Cox *(VP)*

Subsidiary (Domestic):

Timberland Service Corporation **(2)**
624 Simpson Ave, Hoquiam, WA 98550
Tel.: (360) 533-4747
Web Site: https://www.timberlandbank.com
Commercial Banking Services
N.A.I.C.S.: 522110

TINGO GROUP, INC.
28 W Grand Ave Ste 3, Montvale, NJ
07645
Tel.: (201) 225-0190   DE
Web Site:
    https://www.tingogroup.com
Year Founded: 2002
TIO—(NASDAQ)
Rev.: $146,035,000
Assets: $1,682,358,000
Liabilities: $909,359,000
Net Worth: $772,999,000
Earnings: ($47,069,000)
Emp.: 1,567
Fiscal Year-end: 12/31/22
Power Supplies, Converters, Power
Conversion Products, Automatic Test
Equipment, Simulators & Various Mili-
tary & Airborne Systems Mfr
N.A.I.C.S.: 334419
John McMillan Scott *(Chm)*
Kenneth I. Denos *(Bd of Dirs, Interim Grp CEO, Interim Principal Fin & Acctg Officer & Gen Counsel/Exec VP-Tingo Group Holdings LLC)*
Kevin Hao Chen *(Interim Grp CFO & CFO-Ops-Asia-Pacific)*

Subsidiaries:

Micronet Ltd. **(1)**
16 HaMelacha St, Rosh Haayin, 4809139,
Israel
Tel.: (972) 35584886
Web Site: https://www.micronet-inc.com
Telematic Device Mfr
N.A.I.C.S.: 334419

TIPTREE INC.
Tel.: (212) 446-1400   MD
Web Site: https://www.tiptreeinc.com
Year Founded: 2007
TIPT—(NASDAQ)
Rev.: $1,397,752,000
Assets: $4,039,563,000
Liabilities: $3,505,990,000
Net Worth: $533,573,000

Earnings: ($8,274,000)
Emp.: 1,304
Fiscal Year-end: 12/31/22
Holding Company; Insurance Prod-
ucts & Services, Real Estate, Asset
Management & Specialty Finance
Services
N.A.I.C.S.: 551112
Jonathan Ilany *(CEO)*
Randy S. Maultsby *(Pres)*
Sandra Bell *(CFO)*

Subsidiaries:

Caroline Holdings LLC **(1)**
3337 Plantation Dr, Valdosta, GA 31605
Tel.: (229) 241-8698
Holding Company
N.A.I.C.S.: 551112

Luxury Mortgage Corp. **(1)**
4 Landmark Sq Ste 300, Stamford, CT
06901
Tel.: (203) 327-6000
Web Site: https://www.luxurymortgage.com
Sales Range: $1-9.9 Million
Emp.: 50
Mortgage Banking Services
N.A.I.C.S.: 522292
Stephen Celona *(Chief Acctg Officer)*

Muni Funding Company of America,
LLC **(1)**
2929 Arch St 17th Fl, Philadelphia, PA
19104   **(100%)**
Tel.: (215) 701-9641
Sales Range: $1-9.9 Million
Financial Services
N.A.I.C.S.: 525990
Geoffrey N. Kauffman *(Pres & CEO)*
Christopher Conley *(COO)*

Reliance First Capital, LLC **(1)**
201 Old Country Rd Ste 205, Melville, NY
11747
Web Site: https://www.reliancefirst.com
Financial Services
N.A.I.C.S.: 541611
Michael Thompson *(Sls Mgr)*

The Fortegra Group, Inc. **(1)**
10751 Deerwood Park Blvd Ste 200, Jack-
sonville, FL 32256   **(73.1%)**
Rev.: $691,061,000
Assets: $2,452,799,000
Liabilities: $2,155,090,000
Net Worth: $297,709,000
Earnings: $22,821,000
Emp.: 716
Fiscal Year-end: 12/31/2020
Holding Company
N.A.I.C.S.: 551112
Richard S. Kahlbaugh *(Pres & CEO)*
Michael F. Grasher *(CFO & Exec VP)*

Subsidiary (Domestic):

Fortegra Financial Corporation **(2)**
10151 Deerwood Park Blvd Bldg 100 Ste
330, Jacksonville, FL 32256   **(100%)**
Tel.: (904) 416-1539
Web Site: http://www.fortegra.com
Sales Range: $300-349.9 Million
Emp.: 200
Insurance Holding Company
N.A.I.C.S.: 551112
Richard S. Kahlbaugh *(Chm, Pres & CEO)*
Mark Rattner *(Chief Underwriting Officer-Insurance & Exec VP)*
Michael Grasher *(CFO & Exec VP)*
Holly Bohn Pittman *(CMO & Exec VP)*
Joel Vaag *(Chief Actuary & Sr VP)*
Janie Hartley *(Sr VP-Premium Ops)*
Howard Fishbein *(Sr VP-Claims Ops)*
Rick Kahlbaugh *(Pres)*
Peter Masi *(CEO)*

Subsidiary (Domestic):

LOTS Intermediate Co. **(3)**
10151 Deerwood Park Blvd Bldg 100 Ste
330, Jacksonville, FL 32256
Tel.: (904) 350-9660
Holding Company
N.A.I.C.S.: 551112
Richard S. Kahlbaugh *(Chm, Pres & CEO)*

Subsidiary (Domestic):

4Warranty Corporation **(4)**

10151 Deerwood Park Blvd Ste 200, Jack-
sonville, FL 32256
Web Site: http://www.4warranty.net
Consumer Protection Plan Services
N.A.I.C.S.: 524128

Continental Car Club, Inc. **(4)**
PO Box 40586, Jacksonville, FL 32203
Tel.: (423) 775-9608
Web Site: http://www.continentalcarclub.net
Emp.: 50
Automobile Insurance Services
N.A.I.C.S.: 524126

Digital Leash, LLC **(4)**
39500 High Pointe Blvd Ste 250, Novi, MI
48375
Web Site: https://www.protectcell.com
Mobile Device Protection Services
N.A.I.C.S.: 517112

LOTSolutions, Inc. **(4)**
10151 Deerwood Park Blvd Ste 200, Jack-
sonville, FL 32256
Tel.: (904) 350-9660
Web Site: http://www.life-south.com
Emp.: 200
Debt Cancellation & Financial Accessory
Insurance Services
N.A.I.C.S.: 524298

Life of the South Insurance
Company **(4)**
10151 Deerwood Park Blvd Bldg 100 Ste
330, Jacksonville, FL 32256
Tel.: (904) 350-9660
Web Site: http://www.life-south.com
Credit Insurance Products & Services
N.A.I.C.S.: 524210

Lyndon Southern Insurance
Company **(4)**
10151 Deerwood Park Blvd Ste 200, Jack-
sonville, FL 32256
Tel.: (318) 251-2186
Web Site: http://www.life-south.com
Emp.: 300
Insurance Brokerage Services
N.A.I.C.S.: 524210

South Bay Acceptance
Corporation **(4)**
10151 Deerwood Park Blvd Ste 200, Jack-
sonville, FL 32256
Tel.: (310) 376-5499
Web Site: https://www.sbac-finance.com
Commercial Property & Casualty Insurance
Services
N.A.I.C.S.: 524126

United Motor Club of America,
Inc. **(4)**
130 Arkansas St PO Box 60, Paducah, KY
42002
Tel.: (270) 442-5533
Web Site: http://www.unitedmotorclub.com
Emergency Roadside Assistance Services
N.A.I.C.S.: 561990
Richard E. Webster *(Pres)*

Tiptree Operating Company, LLC **(1)**
780 3rd Ave 21st Fl, New York, NY 10017
Tel.: (212) 446-1400
Financial Transactions Processing, Reserve
& Clearinghouse Services
N.A.I.C.S.: 522320
Jonathan Ilany *(Pres)*

TITAN INTERNATIONAL, INC.
1525 Kautz Rd Ste 600, West Chi-
cago, IL 60185
Tel.: (630) 377-0486   IL
Web Site: https://www.titan-intl.com
Year Founded: 1983
TWI—(NYSE)
Rev.: $2,169,380,000
Assets: $1,284,630,000
Liabilities: $901,492,000
Net Worth: $383,138,000
Earnings: $176,302,000
Emp.: 7,500
Fiscal Year-end: 12/31/22
Offices of Other Holding Companies
N.A.I.C.S.: 551112
Maurice Morry Taylor Jr. *(Chm)*
Paul George Reitz *(Pres & CEO)*

Titan International, Inc.—(Continued)

Todd A. Shoot *(Treas & Sr VP-IR)*
David Allen Martin *(CFO & Sr VP)*
Tony C. Eheli *(Chief Acctg Officer & VP)*

Subsidiaries:

ITM Mining Pty. Ltd. (1)
52 Railway Parade, Welshpool, 6106, WA, Australia
Tel.: (61) 894736302
Web Site: https://itmmining.com.au
Undercarriage Component Mfr & Distr
N.A.I.C.S.: 336390

Intertractor America, Corp. (1)
960 Proctor Dr, Elkhorn, WI 53121 **(100%)**
Tel.: (262) 723-6000
Web Site:
  https://www.intertractoramerica.com
Sales Range: $25-49.9 Million
Emp.: 75
Undercarriage Components for Excavators & Tractors
N.A.I.C.S.: 333120

Subsidiary (Non-US):

Titan Intertractor GmbH (2)
Hagener Str 326, PO Box 4166, 58285, Gevelsberg, Germany **(100%)**
Tel.: (49) 23326690
Web Site: http://www.group-itm.com
Mfr of Undercarriage Components for Excavators & Tractors & Ground Engaging Tools
N.A.I.C.S.: 336212
Ulrich Wulfert *(Dir-Sls)*

Titan Asia Jant Sanayi ve Ticaret A.S. (1)
Umurlu Organized Industrial Zone, Aydin, Turkiye
Tel.: (90) 2562591009
Web Site: http://www.titanasia.com.tr
Motor Vehicle Parts Mfr & Distr
N.A.I.C.S.: 336390

Titan Europe Plc (1)
Bridge Road, Cookley, Kidderminster, DY10 3SD, Worcestershire, United Kingdom **(21.67%)**
Tel.: (44) 1562850561
Off-Road Vehicle Wheel & Undercarriage Component Mfr
N.A.I.C.S.: 336390

Subsidiary (Non-US):

Aros Del Pacifico S.A. (2)
La Estera 580 Valle Grande Comuna de Lampa Casilla 17, PO Box 510, El Cortijo, Santiago, Chile
Tel.: (56) 227471228
Web Site: https://www.aros.cl
Wheels & Tires Mfr & Distr
N.A.I.C.S.: 326211

Subsidiary (Non-US):

Aros Del Pacifico S.A.C. (3)
Prolg Pedro Miotta 230, San Juan de Miraflores, Lima, 29, Peru
Tel.: (51) 16405656
Web Site: https://www.aros.pe
Wheel Distr
N.A.I.C.S.: 423120

Subsidiary (Non-US):

PT Titan Wheels Indonesia (2)
Jl Mulawarman 17A, 23 Batakan, Balikpapan, East Kalimantan, Indonesia
Tel.: (62) 5427581770
Web Site: http://www.titan-intl.com
Sales Range: $25-49.9 Million
Emp.: 17
Motor Vehicle Components Distr
N.A.I.C.S.: 423120

Piezas Y Rodajes SA (2)
Tel.: (34) 978864026
Sales Range: $50-74.9 Million
Emp.: 250
Undercarriage Components Mfr
N.A.I.C.S.: 336390

Subsidiary (Domestic):

Titan Distribution (UK) Limited (2)

Suite 7 Mere One Mere Grange Leaside, Saint Helens, WA9 4HU, Merseyside, United Kingdom
Tel.: (44) 845 200 1972
Tires, Wheels & Rism Mfr
N.A.I.C.S.: 423130
Natalie Dukes *(Mgr-Mktg & Comms)*

Subsidiary (Non-US):

Titan France SAS (2)
Route de Vassy, BP 79, Saint-Georges-des-Groseillers, 61102, Flers, Cedex, France
Tel.: (33) 233982700
Web Site: http://www.titanfrance.com
Sales Range: $25-49.9 Million
Emp.: 30
Wheels fMfr
N.A.I.C.S.: 336999

Titan ITM Holding SpA (2)
Tel.: (39) 051738111
Web Site: http://www.group-itm.com
Emp.: 100
Management Services
N.A.I.C.S.: 541618

Subsidiary (Domestic):

Italtractor ITM SpA (3)
Via Confortino 30, Valsamoggia, 40056, Crespellano, Italy
Tel.: (39) 01562850561
Web Site: http://www.group-itm.com
Sales Range: $125-149.9 Million
Emp.: 25
Undercarriage Components Mfr
N.A.I.C.S.: 336992

Subsidiary (Non-US):

Titan Italia SpA (2)
Via Miari 2, 41034, Finale Emilia, Modena, Italy
Tel.: (39) 0535760711
Web Site: https://www.titanitalia.com
Sales Range: $50-74.9 Million
Emp.: 300
Wheels fMfr
N.A.I.C.S.: 336999

Subsidiary (Domestic):

Titan Steel Wheels Limited (2)
Bridge Road, Cookley, Kidderminster, DY10 3SD, Worcestershire, United Kingdom
Tel.: (44) 1562850561
Web Site: https://titansteelwheels.com
Off-Road Wheels Mfr
N.A.I.C.S.: 423130

Titan ITM (Tianjin) Co. Ltd. (1)
N 6 Hechang Road, Wuqing Development Area, Tianjin, 301700, China
Tel.: (86) 2282161600
Motor Vehicle Parts Distr
N.A.I.C.S.: 423120
Stephen Cheng *(Dir-Mktg & Sls)*

Titan Intertractor GMBH (1)
Hagener Strasse 325, 58285, Gevelsberg, Germany
Tel.: (49) 23326690
Web Site: http://www.titan-intertractor.com
Farm Tires & Components Mfr
N.A.I.C.S.: 333111

Subsidiary (Non-US):

Italtractor ITM S.p.A. (2)
Via Confortino no 30, Valsamoggia-Loc, 40056, Crespellano, Bologna, Italy **(99.99%)**
Tel.: (39) 051738111
Sales Range: $100-124.9 Million
Emp.: 450
Mfr of Undercarriage Components for Tracked Vehicles
N.A.I.C.S.: 335999

Italtractor Landroni Ltda. (2)
Rodovia Edgard Maximo Zambotto Km 79 Bairro Ponte Alta, Bairro Ponte Alta, Atibaia, 12952-901, Sao Paulo, Brazil
Tel.: (55) 11 4417 7700
Web Site: http://www.titaneurope.com
Sales Range: $50-74.9 Million
Undercarriage Components Mfr & Distr
N.A.I.C.S.: 332510

Wheels India Limited (2)

21 Patullos Road, PO Box No 50, Chennai, 600 002, Tamilnadu, India
Tel.: (91) 4426258511
Web Site: https://www.wheelsindia.com
Assets: $338,014,950
Liabilities: $245,194,950
Net Worth: $92,820,000
Earnings: $16,380
Emp.: 2,308
Fiscal Year-end: 03/31/2021
Automotive Components Mfr
N.A.I.C.S.: 336110
Srivats Ram *(Mng Dir)*
R. Raghunathan *(CFO)*
K. V. Lakshmi *(Officer-Compliance & Sec)*

Titan Marketing Services, Inc. (1)
2701 Spruce St, Quincy, IL 62301
Tel.: (217) 228-6011
Marketing & Sales Services
N.A.I.C.S.: 541613

Titan Tire Corporation (1)
2345 E Market St, Des Moines, IA 50317 **(100%)**
Tel.: (515) 265-9223
Web Site: http://www.titantirestore.com
Sales Range: $125-149.9 Million
Emp.: 600
Off-Highway Tire Mfr
N.A.I.C.S.: 326211

Subsidiary (Domestic):

Titan Tire Corporation of Bryan (2)
927 S Union St, Bryan, OH 43506 **(100%)**
Tel.: (419) 633-4224
Sales Range: $100-124.9 Million
Emp.: 325
Off Road Tire Mfr
N.A.I.C.S.: 326211

Titan Tire Corporation of Freeport (1)
3769 US-20, Freeport, IL 61032
Tel.: (815) 235-4185
Farm Tires & Components Mfr
N.A.I.C.S.: 333111

Titan Tire Corporation of Union City (1)
3260 Goodyear Blvd, Union City, TN 38261
Tel.: (731) 885-1558
Emp.: 300
Farm Tires & Components Mfr
N.A.I.C.S.: 333111
Ralph Moore *(Accountant)*

Titan Wheel Corporation of Illinois (1)
2701 Spruce St, Quincy, IL 62301-3473 **(100%)**
Tel.: (217) 228-6011
Web Site: https://www.titan-intl.com
Sales Range: $450-499.9 Million
Mfr of Wheels for Agriculture & Construction Vehicles
N.A.I.C.S.: 332999

Titan Wheel Corporation of Virginia (1)
227 Allison Gap Rd, Saltville, VA 24370 **(100%)**
Tel.: (276) 496-3287
Sales Range: $50-74.9 Million
Emp.: 100
Construction & Earthmoving Wheels & Rims Mfr
N.A.I.C.S.: 336390

TITAN MACHINERY INC.
644 E Beaton Dr, West Fargo, ND 58078-2648
Tel.: (701) 356-0130   DE
Web Site:
  https://www.titanmachinery.com
Year Founded: 1980
TITN—(NASDAQ)
Rev.: $2,209,306,000
Assets: $1,188,695,000
Liabilities: $652,389,000
Net Worth: $536,306,000
Earnings: $101,868,000
Emp.: 2,700
Fiscal Year-end: 01/31/23

New & Used Agricultural & Construction Equipment Rental & Sales
N.A.I.C.S.: 459999
David Joseph Meyer *(Founder & Chm)*
Steve Noack *(Compliance Officer, Gen Counsel & Sec)*
Jason Anderson *(VP-HR & Admin)*
Christian Mitterdorfer *(VP-Europe)*
Pari Becker *(Dir-Talent & Organizational Effectiveness)*
John Mills *(Partner)*
Robert Larsen *(CFO & Treas)*
Bryan J. Knutson *(Pres & CEO)*

Subsidiaries:

Titan Machinery Bulgaria AD (1)
455 Botevgradsko shose Blvd, 1839, Sofia, Bulgaria
Tel.: (359) 29713525
Web Site: https://www.titanmachinery.bg
Construction Equipment Whslr
N.A.I.C.S.: 423830

Titan Machinery D.o.o. (1)
Rumenacki put 119v, Novi Sad, 21000, Serbia
Tel.: (381) 21459450
Machinery & Equipment Whslr
N.A.I.C.S.: 423810
Bojan Vuckovic *(Owner)*

Titan Machinery Inc. - Agricultural Division (1)
644 E Beaton Dr, West Fargo, ND 58078-2648
Tel.: (701) 356-0130
Web Site: http://www.titanmachinery.com
Sales Range: $700-749.9 Million
Emp.: 1,200
Agricultural Machinery Sales & Rental
N.A.I.C.S.: 459999

Titan Machinery Inc. - Construction Division (1)
644 E Beaton Dr, West Fargo, ND 58078-2648
Tel.: (701) 356-0130
Web Site: http://www.titanmachinery.com
Sales Range: $50-74.9 Million
Emp.: 2,000
Construction Machinery Sales & Rental
N.A.I.C.S.: 459999

Titan Machinery Inc. - International Markets (1)
644 E Beaton Dr, West Fargo, ND 58078-2648
Tel.: (701) 356-0130
Web Site: http://www.titanmachinery.com
Sales Range: $750-799.9 Million
Emp.: 1,500
Agricultural & Construction Machinery Sales
N.A.I.C.S.: 459999

TITAN PHARMACEUTICALS, INC.
400 Oyster Point Blvd Ste 505, South San Francisco, CA 94080-1958
Tel.: (650) 244-4990   DE
Web Site:
  https://www.titanpharm.com
Year Founded: 1992
TTNP—(NASDAQ)
Rev.: $557,000
Assets: $4,058,000
Liabilities: $2,695,000
Net Worth: $1,363,000
Earnings: ($10,206,000)
Emp.: 4
Fiscal Year-end: 12/31/22
Biological Product (except Diagnostic) Manufacturing
N.A.I.C.S.: 325414
David E. Lazar *(CEO)*
Katherine L. Beebe Devarney *(Pres & COO)*
Seow Gim Shen *(Chm)*

TITANIUM HOLDINGS GROUP, INC.

1981 E 4800 S Ste 100, Salt Lake City, UT 84117
Tel.: (801) 272-9294   NV
Web Site:
https://www.titaniumholdings.com
TTHG—(OTCIQ)
Miscellaneous Retailer
N.A.I.C.S.: 459999
Steven Etra *(Chm, Treas & Sec)*
Randall K. Davis *(Pres & CEO)*

TIVIC HEALTH SYSTEMS, INC.
25821 Industrial Blvd Ste 100, Hayward, CA 94545   DE
Web Site: https://www.tivichealth.com
Year Founded: 2016
TIVC—(NASDAQ)
Rev.: $1,840,000
Assets: $5,856,000
Liabilities: $2,226,000
Net Worth: $3,630,000
Earnings: ($10,096,000)
Emp.: 16
Fiscal Year-end: 12/31/22
Bioelectronic Device Mfr
N.A.I.C.S.: 334510
Jennifer Ernst *(Founder & CEO)*
Blake Gurfein *(Chief Scientific Officer)*
Chandrasekhar Durisety *(VP-Engrg & Mfg)*
Michael Nketiah *(VP-Quality & Regulatory Affairs)*
Sanjay Ahuja *(Sr VP-Quality Assurance & Regulatory Affairs)*
Kimberly Bambach *(Interim CFO & Principal Acctg Officer)*

TIX CORPORATION
731 Pilot Rd A, Las Vegas, NV 89119
Tel.: (424) 313-8201   DE
Web Site: http://www.tixcorp.com
Year Founded: 1993
TIXC—(OTCIQ)
Rev.: $1,957,000
Assets: $3,273,000
Liabilities: $5,718,000
Net Worth: ($2,445,000)
Earnings: ($4,716,000)
Emp.: 8
Fiscal Year-end: 12/31/20
Ticketing, Event Merchandising & Live Entertainment Production & Promotion Services
N.A.I.C.S.: 711310
Mitchell J. Francis *(Founder & CEO)*
Kimberly Sue Simon *(COO)*

TLD3 ENTERTAINMENT GROUP, INC.
276 5th Ave Ste 704-885, New York, NY 10001
Tel.: (646) 799-7943   FL
Web Site: https://totaldigitale.com
Year Founded: 1997
TLDE—(OTCIQ)
Television Broadcasting Services
N.A.I.C.S.: 516120
Gerald D. Baugh *(CEO)*
Arlette Tillett *(CFO)*

TLGY ACQUISITION CORPORATION
200 E 94th St Ste 2109, New York, NY 10128
Tel.: (302) 803-6849   Ky
Web Site:
https://www.tlgyacquisition.com
Year Founded: 2021
TLGY—(NASDAQ)
Rev.: $2,901,000
Assets: $238,368,211
Liabilities: $246,964,645
Net Worth: ($8,596,434)
Earnings: $11,645,768
Emp.: 3

Fiscal Year-end: 12/30/22
Investment Services
N.A.I.C.S.: 523999
Jin-Goon Kim *(Founder, Chm, & Co-CEO)*
Vikas Desai *(Co-CEO)*
Merrick Friedman *(CFO)*
Theron E. Odlaug *(Co-Pres)*
Steven Norman *(Co-Pres & CFO)*

TNF PHARMACEUTICALS, INC
855 N Wolfe St Ste 601, Baltimore, MD 21205
Tel.: (813) 864-2566   NJ
Web Site: https://tnfpharma.com
Year Founded: 1989
TNFA—(NASDAQ)
Rev.: $83,991
Assets: $17,539,980
Liabilities: $2,844,924
Net Worth: $14,695,056
Earnings: ($15,197,336)
Emp.: 9
Fiscal Year-end: 12/31/22
Disposable Diagnostic Testing Devices Mfr
N.A.I.C.S.: 339112
Joshua N. Silverman *(Chm)*
Christopher C. Schreiber *(Pres & CEO)*
Mitchell Glass *(Chief Medical Officer)*

TNR TECHNICAL, INC.
301 Central Park Dr, Sanford, FL 32771   NY
Web Site:
http://www.tnrtechnical.com
TNRK—(OTCIQ)
Wet & Dry Battery Mfr
N.A.I.C.S.: 335910
Anne S. Provost *(Acting Pres & CFO)*

TOAST, INC.
401 Park Dr Ste 801, Boston, MA 02215
Tel.: (617) 297-1005
Web Site: https://www.toasttab.com
Year Founded: 2011
TOST—(NYSE)
Rev.: $3,865,000,000
Assets: $1,958,000,000
Liabilities: $764,000,000
Net Worth: $1,194,000,000
Earnings: ($246,000,000)
Emp.: 5,500
Fiscal Year-end: 12/31/23
Point-of-sale & Restaurant Management Platform
N.A.I.C.S.: 423420
Emmanuelle Skala *(Sr VP-Customer Success)*
Christopher P. Comparato *(CEO)*
Anisha Vaswani *(CIO)*
Jonathan Grimm *(Co-Founder)*
Emmanuelle Skala *(Sr VP-Customer Success)*
Jonathan Vassil *(Sr VP-Sls)*
Kevin Hamilton *(Sr VP-Mktg)*
Hugh Scandrett *(Sr VP-Engrg)*
Matt Kaplan *(Sr VP-Product)*
Nick DeLeonardis *(Sr VP & Gen Mgr-Employee Cloud & FinTech)*
Brian R. Elworthy *(Gen Counsel)*
Stephen Fredette *(Co-Founder & Co-Pres)*
Aman Narang *(Co-Founder)*
Elena Gomez *(CFO & Interim Chief Acctg Officer)*
Jennifer DiRico *(Sr VP & Gen Mgr-Intl)*
Debra Chrapaty *(CTO)*
Annie Drapeau *(Chief People Officer)*

Subsidiaries:

Delphi Display Systems Inc.   (1)

3160 Pullman St, Costa Mesa, CA 92626-3315
Web Site: http://www.delphidisplay.com
Sign Mfr
N.A.I.C.S.: 339950
Ken Neeld *(Pres & CEO)*
Tim Votaw *(VP-Sls)*
James Dever *(Acct Mgr-Content Svcs)*
Mike DeSon *(COO)*
Dan Shoff Sr. *(Mgr-Digital Mktg)*

OAE Software LLC   (1)
444 N Michigan Ave Ste 2800, Chicago, IL 60611
Tel.: (312) 216-2200
HR, Payroll & Benefits Services
N.A.I.C.S.: 541612
Adam Ochstein *(CEO)*

TOCCA LIFE HOLDINGS, INC.
2180 N Park Ave Ste 200, Winter Park, FL 32789
Tel.: (407) 674-9444   NV
Web Site: http://www.toccalife.com
Year Founded: 1984
TLIF—(OTCIQ)
Sales Range: Less than $1 Million
Drug Recovery Living Facilities & Life Coaching
N.A.I.C.S.: 623220
Stephen Walter Carnes *(Pres, CEO & Sec)*

Subsidiaries:

Be Climbing, Inc.   (1)
2180 N. Park Ave, Ste 200, Winter Park, FL 32789
Tel.: (407) 674-9444
Web Site: https://beclimbing.com
Physical Fitness Facilities
N.A.I.C.S.: 713940

Subsidiary (Domestic):

Aiguille Rock Climbing Center, Inc   (2)
830 S Ronald Reagan Blvd Ste 252, Longwood, FL 32750
Tel.: (407) 332-1808
Web Site: http://www.aiguille.com
All Other Personal Services
N.A.I.C.S.: 812990
Jason Temple *(Owner)*

TOFUTTI BRANDS INC.
50 Jackson Dr, Cranford, NJ 07016
Tel.: (908) 272-2400   DE
Web Site: https://www.tofutti.com
Year Founded: 1987
TOFB—(OTCQX)
Rev.: $12,590,000
Assets: $5,342,000
Liabilities: $775,000
Net Worth: $4,567,000
Earnings: $143,000
Emp.: 5
Fiscal Year-end: 01/01/22
Soy-Based Non-Dairy Frozen Dessert & Food Products Developer, Mfr & Marketer
N.A.I.C.S.: 311412
Steven Kass *(Interim CEO, CFO, Principal Acctg Officer, Treas & Sec)*

TOLL BROTHERS, INC.
1140 Virginia Dr, Fort Washington, PA 19034
Tel.: (215) 938-8000   DE
Web Site:
https://www.tollbrothers.com
Year Founded: 1986
TOL—(NYSE)
Rev.: $10,846,740,000
Assets: $13,367,932,000
Liabilities: $5,681,217,000
Net Worth: $7,686,715,000
Earnings: $1,571,195,000
Emp.: 4,900
Fiscal Year-end: 10/31/24
Real Estate Manangement Services
N.A.I.C.S.: 551112

Robert Parahus *(Pres & COO)*
Frederick N. Cooper *(Sr VP-Fin, Intl Dev & IR)*
Michael J. Grubb *(Chief Acctg Officer & Sr VP)*
Martin P. Connor *(CFO & Sr VP)*
Joy Roman *(Chief HR Officer)*
Wendy Marlett *(CMO)*
Timothy Hoban *(Gen Counsel & Sr VP)*

Subsidiaries:

55 West 17th Street Partners LLC.   (1)
75 Broad St 21st Fl, New York, NY 10004
Tel.: (212) 742-0835
Web Site: http://www.55west17th.com
Emp.: 18
Electrical Contractor
N.A.I.C.S.: 238210
David Von Spreckelsen *(Pres)*

Coleman-Toll Limited Partnership   (1)
250 Gibraltar Rd, Horsham, PA 19044
Tel.: (702) 243-9800
Residential Building Construction Services
N.A.I.C.S.: 236117

ESE Consultants, Inc.   (1)
1140 Virginia Dr, Fort Washington, PA 19034
Tel.: (215) 914-2050
Web Site: https://www.eseconsultants.com
Sales Range: $10-24.9 Million
Emp.: 150
Engineering Services for Luxury Home Construction
N.A.I.C.S.: 541330

ESE Consultants, Inc.   (1)
1140 Virginia Dr, Fort Washington, PA 19034
Tel.: (215) 914-2050
Web Site: http://www.eseconsultants.com
Emp.: 150
Engineeering Services
N.A.I.C.S.: 541330

ESE Consultants, Inc.   (1)
19775 Belmont Executive Plz Ste 250, Ashburn, VA 20147
Tel.: (571) 291-8828
Commercial Building Construction Services
N.A.I.C.S.: 236220

Frenchman's Reserve Country Club, Inc.   (1)
703 Cote Azur Dr, Palm Beach Gardens, FL 33410
Tel.: (561) 799-5660
Web Site:
http://www.frenchmansreserve.com
Golf Course & Club Management Services
N.A.I.C.S.: 713910

Gibraltar Capital and Asset Management, LLC.   (1)
250 Gibraltar Rd, Horsham, PA 19044
Tel.: (215) 938-8265
Web Site: http://www.gibraltarcm.com
Real Estate Asset Management Services
N.A.I.C.S.: 531390
Roger Brush *(Pres & Mng Dir)*
Michael Lapat *(Mng Dir & CFO)*
Janelle Iturbe *(Gen Counsel & VP)*
Brian Jackson *(VP)*
Drew Godwin *(Sr Mgr-Acquisitions)*
Dan Batchelor *(Controller)*

Gibraltar Real Estate Capital LLC   (1)
1140 Virginia Dr, Fort Washington, PA 19034
Tel.: (215) 938-8265
Web Site: http://www.gibraltarrec.com
Real Estate Services
N.A.I.C.S.: 531390
Roger Brush *(Pres)*
Michael Lapat *(CFO)*
Janelle Iturbe *(VP)*
Brian Jackson *(VP)*
Graig Bantle *(VP)*
Dan Batchelor *(Controller)*

Hampton Hall Club, Inc.   (1)
170 Hampton Hall Blvd, Bluffton, SC 29910
Tel.: (843) 815-8730

Toll Brothers, Inc.—(Continued)

Web Site:
http://www.hamptonhallclubsc.com
Golf Course & Club Management Services
N.A.I.C.S.: 713910

Jacksonville TBI Realty, LLC (1)
160 Cape May Ave, Ponte Vedra Beach, FL
32081
Tel.: (904) 285-5550
Web Site:
http://www.coastaloaksatnocatee.com
Emp.: 6
Residential Building Construction Services
N.A.I.C.S.: 236117

Keller Homes, Inc. (1)
536 Chapel Hills Dr, Colorado Springs, CO
80920
Tel.: (719) 528-6977
Web Site: http://www.kellerhomes.com
Single-Family Housing
N.A.I.C.S.: 236115
Dave Keller (Pres & CEO)

Mountain View Country Club,
Inc. (1)
80-375 Pomelo, La Quinta, CA 92253
Tel.: (760) 771-4311
Web Site:
http://www.mountainviewatlaquinta.com
Golf Course & Club Management Services
N.A.I.C.S.: 713910
Tonya Parker (Controller-Club)
Marco Sotomayor (Gen Mgr)
Marissa Martinez (Dir-Membership)
John Curci (Dir)

Parkland Golf Club, Inc. (1)
10001 Old Club Rd, Parkland, FL 33076
Tel.: (954) 905-2120
Web Site: http://www.parklandgcc.com
Golf Course & Club Management Services
N.A.I.C.S.: 713910

Sabal Homes, LLC (1)
421 Wando Park Blvd Ste 230, Mount
Pleasant, SC 29464
Tel.: (844) 697-2225
Housing Construction Services
N.A.I.C.S.: 236117
W. Todd Ussery (Founder)

Sharp Residential, LLC (1)
4080 McGinnis Ferry Rd Bldg 700 Ste 701,
Alpharetta, GA 30005
Tel.: (770) 518-4896
Web Site: http://www.sharp-residential.com
Single-Family Housing Construction
N.A.I.C.S.: 236115
Tom Sharp (Founder & Pres)

TB Proprietary Corp. (1)
1105 N Market St Fl 1, Wilmington, DE
19801
Tel.: (302) 654-7910
Real Estate Brokerage Services
N.A.I.C.S.: 531210

TIS Logistics, Inc. (1)
449 S Pennsylvania Ave, Morrisville, PA
19067
Tel.: (215) 736-0111
Web Site: https://www.tis-logistics.com
Truck Transportation Services
N.A.I.C.S.: 488490

Thrive Homes LLC (1)
500 Amsterdam Ave NE Ste M, Atlanta, GA
30306-3470
Tel.: (404) 447-4814
Web Site: http://www.buildwiththrive.com
Commercial & Institutional Building Con-
struction
N.A.I.C.S.: 236220
Chris Rudd (Pres)

Toll Architecture, Inc. (1)
1140 Virginia Dr, Fort Washington, PA
19034
Tel.: (215) 293-5300
Web Site: https://www.tollarchitecture.com
Architecture & Engineering Services
N.A.I.C.S.: 541330

Toll Brooklyn L.P. (1)
16 Ct St Ste 2403, Brooklyn, NY 11201
Tel.: (718) 852-5595
Residential Building Construction Services
N.A.I.C.S.: 236117

Toll Brothers Canada USA, Inc. (1)
250 Gibraltar Rd, Horsham, PA 19044
Tel.: (215) 938-8045
Web Site: http://www.tollbrothers.com
Sales Range: $150-199.9 Million
Emp.: 600
Apartment Building Rental & Leasing Ser-
vices
N.A.I.C.S.: 531110
Joseph DeSanto (Sr VP)

Toll Brothers Mortgage Company (1)
1140 Virginia Dr, Fort Washington, PA
19034
Tel.: (215) 293-5103
Web Site:
https://www.tollbrothersmortgage.com
Sales Range: $25-49.9 Million
Emp.: 60
Mortgage Services
N.A.I.C.S.: 522310
Marc Mercurio (Sr VP)

Toll Brothers Real Estate, Inc. (1)
725 W Town & Country Rd Ste 200, Or-
ange, CA 92868
Tel.: (714) 347-1300
Web Site: http://www.tollbrothers.com
Real Estate Brokerage Services
N.A.I.C.S.: 531210

Toll Brothers Smart Home Technolo-
gies, Inc. (1)
1140 Virginia Dr, Fort Washington, PA
19034
Web Site:
https://www.tollbrotherssmarthome.com
Sales Range: $10-24.9 Million
Emp.: 15
Security Alarm Monitoring Services
N.A.I.C.S.: 561621

Toll FL XIII Limited Partnership (1)
250 Gibraltar Rd, Horsham, PA 19044
Tel.: (215) 938-8000
Real Estate Manangement Services
N.A.I.C.S.: 531210

Toll Oak Creek Golf LLC (1)
600 Bowieville Manor Ln, Upper Marlboro,
MD 20774
Tel.: (301) 249-0809
Web Site: http://www.golfoakcreek.com
Emp.: 40
Golf Club
N.A.I.C.S.: 713910

Toll Stratford LLC (1)
500 Sunset View Ter SE, Leesburg, VA
20175-6164
Tel.: (703) 443-0145
Real Estate Brokerage Services
N.A.I.C.S.: 531210

Westminster Insurance Agency,
Inc. (1)
250 Gibraltar Rd, Horsham, PA 19044
Tel.: (215) 293-4300
Web Site:
http://www.westminsterinsurance.com
General Insurance Services
N.A.I.C.S.: 524113

Westminster Title Company, Inc. (1)
1140 Virginia Dr, Fort Washington, PA
19034
Tel.: (215) 938-8000
Web Site:
https://www.westminstertitleagency.com
Title Abstract & Escrow Services
N.A.I.C.S.: 541191
William T. Unkel (Pres)
Julie Skibo (Mgr-Compliance & Trng)

TOMBSTONE EXPLORATION
CORPORATION
6529 E Friess Dr, Scottsdale, AZ
85254
Tel.: (480) 588-8920 Ca
Web Site:
https://www.tombstonemining.com
TMBXF—(OTCIQ)
Assets: $3,039,690
Liabilities: $845,456
Net Worth: $2,194,234
Earnings: ($1,846,151)
Emp.: 1

Fiscal Year-end: 12/31/21
Metal Mining
N.A.I.C.S.: 212290
Alan Montague Brown (Pres, CEO &
CFO)

TOMI ENVIRONMENTAL SOLU-
TIONS, INC.
8430 Spires Way Ste N, Frederick,
MD 21701
Web Site: https://steramist.com
TOMZ—(NASDAQ)
Rev.: $8,338,099
Assets: $15,499,799
Liabilities: $4,051,599
Net Worth: $11,448,200
Earnings: ($2,880,060)
Emp.: 30
Fiscal Year-end: 12/31/22
Indoor Air Remediation & Infectious
Disease Control Inspection, Air Qual-
ity Testing, Training & Indoor Air
Cleaning Services & Solutions
N.A.I.C.S.: 333413
Halden S. Shane (Chm & CEO)
Nick Jennings (CFO)
Elissa Jessica Shane (COO)

TOMPKINS FINANCIAL COR-
PORATION
118 E Seneca St, Ithaca, NY 14851
Tel.: (607) 274-7299 NY
Web Site:
https://www.tompkinsfinancial.com
Year Founded: 1836
TMP—(NYSEAMEX)
Rev.: $329,296,000
Assets: $7,670,686,000
Liabilities: $7,053,296,000
Net Worth: $617,390,000
Earnings: $85,030,000
Emp.: 978
Fiscal Year-end: 12/31/22
Bank Holding Company
N.A.I.C.S.: 551111
Stephen S. Romaine (Pres & CEO)
Gerald J. Klein Jr. (Exec VP)
James Walter Fulmer (Vice Chm)
David S. Boyce (Exec VP)
Gregory J. Hartz (Exec VP)
Matthew Tomazin (CFO,
CFO/Treas/Exec VP-Tompkins Com-
munity Bank, Treas & Exec VP)
Susan M. Valenti (Mktg Dir)
Bonita Lindberg (Sr VP & Dir-HR)
Alyssa H. Fontaine (Gen Counsel &
Exec VP)
Brian A. Howard (Exec VP)
John M. McKenna (Exec VP)
Steven Cribbs (Chief Risk Officer &
Sr VP)
David DeMilia (Exec VP)
Ginger Kunkel (Exec VP)
Charles Guarino (Chief Banking Ops
Officer)

Subsidiaries:

Mahopac Bank (1)
1441 Rte 22, Brewster, NY 10509 (100%)
Tel.: (845) 278-1011
Web Site: http://www.mahopacbank.com
Sales Range: $25-49.9 Million
Emp.: 200
Community Banking Services
N.A.I.C.S.: 522110
Michael H. Spain (Chm)
Gerald J. Klein Jr. (Pres & CEO)

The Bank of Castile (1)
50 N Main St, Castile, NY 14427
Tel.: (585) 493-2576
Web Site: http://www.bankofcastile.com
Sales Range: $10-24.9 Million
Emp.: 7
Community Banking Services
N.A.I.C.S.: 522110
James Walter Fulmer (Vice Chm)

Tompkins Insurance Agencies,
Inc. (1)
90 Maint St, Batavia, NY 14020
Tel.: (585) 344-0833
Web Site: http://www.tompkinsins.com
Sales Range: $1-9.9 Million
Emp.: 28
Insurance Services
N.A.I.C.S.: 524210
James Walter Fulmer (Chm)

Tompkins Trust Company (1)
110 N Tioga St, Ithaca, NY 14850
Tel.: (607) 273-3210
Web Site: http://www.tompkinstrust.com
Sales Range: $200-249.9 Million
Emp.: 250
Full Banking Services
N.A.I.C.S.: 522110

Tompkins VIST Bank (1)
1199 Berkshire Blvd, Wyomissing, PA
19610 (100%)
Tel.: (610) 372-8877
Web Site: http://www.vistbank.com
Retail & Commercial Banking
N.A.I.C.S.: 522110
Scott L. Gruber (Pres & CEO)
John Braunlich (VP-Comml Lending)
Nickolaus Latta (VP-Comml Lending)

TONIX PHARMACEUTICALS
HOLDING CORP.
26 Main St Ste 101, Chatham, NJ
07928
Tel.: (862) 799-8599 NV
Web Site:
https://www.tonixpharma.com
Year Founded: 2007
TNXP—(NASDAQ)
Rev.: $1,873,000
Assets: $225,690,000
Liabilities: $18,508,000
Net Worth: $207,182,000
Earnings: ($110,218,000)
Emp.: 117
Fiscal Year-end: 12/31/22
Pharmaceuticals Mfr
N.A.I.C.S.: 325412
Donald W. Landry (Founder)
Seth Lederman (Chm, Pres & CEO)
Gregory M. Sullivan (Chief Medical
Officer & Sec)
Bradley Saenger (CFO & Treas)
Jessica Edgar Morris (COO)
Herbert Harris (Exec VP-Translational
Medicine)
Sina Bavari (Exec VP-Infectious Dis-
ease R&D)
Zeil Rosenberg (Exec VP-Medical)
Darryl Rideout (Exec VP)
Siobhan Fogarty (Exec VP)

Subsidiaries:

Krele, LLC (1)
509 Madison Ave Room 306, New York, NY
10022
Tel.: (212) 980-9155
Pharmaceuticals Product Mfr
N.A.I.C.S.: 325412

TONOGOLD RESOURCES,
INC.
22543 Ventura Blvd Ste 220 1045,
Woodland Hills, CA 91364
Tel.: (858) 456-1273
Web Site: https://www.tonogold.com
TNGL—(OTCIQ)
Emp.: 10
Gold Ore & Silver Ore Mining
N.A.I.C.S.: 212220
Brian A. Zamudio (Treas & Sec)
Mark John Ashley (CEO)
Donald G. Strachan (VP-Exploration)

TONOPAH DIVIDE MINING CO.
55 Main St, Tiburon, CA 94920
Tel.: (415) 747-1316 NV
Web Site:
https://www.tonopahdividemining
co.com

Year Founded: 1912
TODM—(OTCIQ)
Gold Mining Services
N.A.I.C.S.: 212220
Ronald Goldman (Sec)
Andrew Goldman (Treas)

TOOTSIE ROLL INDUSTRIES, INC.

7401 S Cicero Ave, Chicago, IL 60629
Tel.: (773) 838-3400   VA
Web Site: https://www.tootsie.com
Year Founded: 1896
TR—(NYSE)
Rev.: $686,970,000
Assets: $1,018,779,000
Liabilities: $235,897,000
Net Worth: $782,882,000
Earnings: $75,937,000
Emp.: 2,300
Fiscal Year-end: 12/31/22
Confectionery Manufacturing from Purchased Chocolate
N.A.I.C.S.: 311352
Ellen R. Gordon (Chm & CEO)
Stephen P. Green (VP-Mfg)
Kenneth D. Naylor (VP-Mktg & Sls)
G. Howard Ember Jr. (VP-Fin)

Subsidiaries:

Andes Candies LP   (1)
1400 E Wisconsin St, Delavan, WI 53115
Tel.: (262) 728-9121
Sales Range: $75-99.9 Million
Emp.: 150
Mfr of Candy
N.A.I.C.S.: 311351

Andes Manufacturing LLC   (1)
1400 E Wisconsin St, Delavan, WI 53115
Tel.: (262) 728-9121
Confectionery Product Mfr
N.A.I.C.S.: 311352

C. G. P., Inc.   (1)
10951 Sorrento Valley Rd 2A, San Diego, CA 92121
Tel.: (858) 454-8857
Web Site: http://www.cgpinc.com
Commercial Real Estate Services
N.A.I.C.S.: 531210
Mike Paeske (CEO)
Renee M. Savage Sr. (Pres)

Cambridge Brands, Inc.   (1)
810 Main St, Cambridge, MA 02139
Tel.: (617) 491-2500
Confectionary Product Mfr
N.A.I.C.S.: 311352

Charms Company   (1)
7401 S Cicero Ave, Chicago, IL 60629
Tel.: (773) 838-3400
Web Site: http://www.hootsie-roll.com
Emp.: 200
Confectionery Product Retailer
N.A.I.C.S.: 445292
Ellen Gordon (Owner)

Charms LLC   (1)
7401 S Cicero Ave, Chicago, IL 60629
Tel.: (773) 838-3400
Web Site: http://www.tootsie.com
Sales Range: $150-199.9 Million
Emp.: 600
Hard Candies & Lollipops Mfr
N.A.I.C.S.: 424450

Concord Confections Ltd.   (1)
345 Courtland Avenue, Concord, L4K 5A6, ON, Canada
Tel.: (905) 660-8989
Web Site:
    http://www.concordconfections.com
Sales Range: $150-199.9 Million
Emp.: 400
Chewing Gum & Candy Mfr
N.A.I.C.S.: 311340

Dr. Torrents, S.L.   (1)
Avenida Del Hospital Olesa De Bonesvalls Cataluna, 8795, Barcelona, Spain
Tel.: (34) 938984011
Candy Distr

N.A.I.C.S.: 424450

TRI International Company   (1)
7401 S Cicero Ave, Chicago, IL 60629-5818
Tel.: (773) 838-3400
Candy & Other Confectionery Products Mfr
N.A.I.C.S.: 311352

TRI International, Inc.   (1)
600 Stewart St Ste 400, Seattle, WA 98101
Tel.: (206) 505-3500
Web Site: http://www.trichemicals.com
Candy Distr
N.A.I.C.S.: 424450
Anthony M. Ridnell (Founder)
Megan E. Gluth-Bohan (CEO)
Marjalena M. F. Santos (Dir-HR & Compliance)
John P. Godina (Sls Dir-Midwest)
Jeffrey B. Wright (CFO & Exec VP)
Rich McNamara (Reg Dir-Sls-Northeast)
David Tew (Reg Dir-Sls-Southeast)
Chris Karber (Reg Dir-Sls-Mid South)
Kurt Owens (Mgr-Supply Chain)
Jennifer Calvery (Mktg Dir)
Michelle Connor (Ops Mgr)
Jill Erickson (Coord-Customer Svc)
Jenny Coady (Coord-Customer Svc)
Maggie Kenison (Coord-Customer Svc)
Jason Anderson (Dir-IT)
Amanda Brumley (Fin Mgr)

The Sweets Mix Company, Inc.   (1)
7401 S Cicero Ave, Chicago, IL 60629-5818   (100%)
Tel.: (773) 646-5369
Web Site: http://www.tootsieroll.com
Sales Range: $900-999.9 Million
Emp.: 1,400
Mfr of Candy
N.A.I.C.S.: 445292

The Tootsie Roll Company   (1)
7401 S Cicero Ave, Chicago, IL 60629   (100%)
Tel.: (773) 838-3400
Web Site: http://www.tootsie.com
Sales Range: $250-299.9 Million
Mfr of Candy & other Confectionery Products
N.A.I.C.S.: 311340

Tootsie Roll Management Inc   (1)
7401 S Cicero Ave, Chicago, IL 60629-5818   (100%)
Tel.: (773) 838-3400
Web Site: http://www.tootsieroll.com
Sales Range: $300-349.9 Million
Emp.: 700
Mfr of Candy & other Confectionery Products
N.A.I.C.S.: 311340

Tootsie Rolls-Latin America, Inc.   (1)
7401 S Cicero Ave, Chicago, IL 60629-5818   (100%)
Tel.: (773) 838-3400
Web Site: http://www.tootsie-roll.com
Sales Range: $400-449.9 Million
Emp.: 800
Holding Company
N.A.I.C.S.: 311340

Tutsi S.A. de C.V.   (1)
Canela No 277, Colonia Granjas Mexico Delegacion Iztacalco, 08400, Mexico, Mexico   (100%)
Tel.: (52) 5 803 0300
Web Site: https://www.tutsi.com.mx
Sales Range: $200-249.9 Million
Emp.: 450
Mfr of Candy
N.A.I.C.S.: 311352

World Trade & Marketing, Ltd.   (1)
7401 S Cicero Ave, Chicago, IL 60629   (100%)
Tel.: (773) 838-3400
Sales Range: $1-4.9 Billion
Mfg. of Candy
N.A.I.C.S.: 523999

TOPAZ RESOURCES, INC.

1324 N Liberty Lake Rd Ste 231, Liberty Lake, WA 99019
Tel.: (509) 919-4622   FL
Web Site:
    http://www.topazresourcesinc.com
TOPZ—(OTCIQ)

Sales Range: Less than $1 Million
Oil & Gas Producer
N.A.I.C.S.: 211120
Jeffery M. Lamberson (Pres)

TOPBUILD CORP.

475 N Williamson Blvd, Daytona Beach, FL 32114
Tel.: (386) 304-2200   DE
Web Site: https://www.topbuild.com
Year Founded: 2015
BLD—(NYSE)
Rev.: $5,194,694,000
Assets: $5,162,851,000
Liabilities: $2,599,196,000
Net Worth: $2,563,655,000
Earnings: $614,254,000
Emp.: 14,012
Fiscal Year-end: 12/31/23
Insulation Products Installer & Distr
N.A.I.C.S.: 238310
Joseph Viselli (COO & VP)
Robert M. Buck (Pres & CEO)
Rip Hubbard (Sr VP-Supply Chain)
Tabitha Zane (VP-IR)
Steven P. Raia (Pres-Special Ops)
Steve Raia (Pres-TruTeam Ops)
Luis F. Machado (Gen Counsel & Sec)

Subsidiaries:

ADO Products LLC   (1)
13220 Wilfred Ln N Ste 100, Rogers, MN 55374
Tel.: (763) 428-7802
Web Site: https://www.adoproducts.com
Cut Stone & Stone Product Mfr
N.A.I.C.S.: 327991
Rich Reske (Sr Mgr-Territory-Central & West)
Neal Kurth (Mgr-Insulation Contractor)
Nancy Wells (Natl Mgr & Sls Mgr)

Cooper Glass Company, LLC   (1)
1139 State Highway 77, Marion, AR 72364
Tel.: (870) 739-0010
Web Site: http://cooperglass.com
Sales Range: $1-9.9 Million
Emp.: 25
Installs & Ret Glass
N.A.I.C.S.: 811122
Marty Cooper (Principal)

Creative Conservation Co., Inc.   (1)
10992 Richardson Rd, Ashland, VA 23005-3005
Tel.: (804) 798-2727
Web Site:
    http://www.creativeconservation.com
Drywall & Insulation Contractors
N.A.I.C.S.: 238310
Darlene Lawrence (Office Mgr)
Lisa Darnell (Mgr)
Thomas Sprouse (Mgr)
Nelson Hernandez (Production Mgr)
Matthew Reed (Production Mgr)
Shawn Haga (Production Mgr)

Crossroads C&I Distributors, Inc.   (1)
11104 - 180 St, Edmonton, T5S 2M2, AB, Canada
Tel.: (780) 452-7410
Web Site: https://www.crossroadsci.com
Industrial Insulation Product & Accessory Distr
N.A.I.C.S.: 423330
Korey Haun (Pres)
Greg Kamprath (Reg Dir)

Distribution International, Inc.   (1)
601 Jefferson St Ste #600, Houston, TX 77002
Tel.: (713) 428-3700
Web Site:
    http://www.distributioninternational.com
Emp.: 90
Thermal, Acoustical Insulation & Fire Proofing Products Mfr & Distr
N.A.I.C.S.: 922160
Joseph Viselli (Exec VP, Sr VP & Gen Mgr)
Doug Waugaman (CFO)
Robert Hlavenka (VP & Gen Mgr)
Korey Haun (Sr VP & Gen Mgr)
Paco Sinta (VP-Human Resources)
Dana Vlk (VP-Marketing)

Mike Farrell (Chm)
Steven N. Margolius (Pres)
Lance Devin (COO)
Joey Viselli (Sr VP & Gen Mgr)

Subsidiary (Domestic):

RB LLC   (2)
5030 Bloomfield St, New Orleans, LA 70121-1007
Tel.: (504) 841-0035
Web Site: http://www.rbllc.com
Home Center Operator
N.A.I.C.S.: 444110
Robert Caillouet (Pres)

Garland Insulating, Ltd.   (1)
10912 Sanden Dr, Dallas, TX 75238
Tel.: (214) 341-0254
Web Site: http://www.garlandinsulating.com
Sales Range: $1-9.9 Million
Emp.: 100
Drywall & Insulation Contractors
N.A.I.C.S.: 238310
Ferrell Drum (Co-Pres)
Hayden Drum (Pres & CEO)
Ahndrea Gamboa (Exec VP-Ops)

Ideal Products of Canada Ltd.   (1)
715 76 Avenue, Edmonton, T6P 1P2, AB, Canada
Tel.: (780) 456-3286
Web Site: https://idealproducts.ca
Building Materials Whslr
N.A.I.C.S.: 423320

Ideal Products of Dongguan Ltd.   (1)
1/F No 7 Building, LongGang Industrial Park ShiPai, Dongguan, 523330, China
Tel.: (86) 76986553286
Building Materials Whslr
N.A.I.C.S.: 423310

LCR Contractors, Inc.   (1)
415 US Hwy 80, Mesquite, TX 75150
Tel.: (214) 761-1940
Web Site: http://www.lcrcontractors.com
Specialty Trade Contractors
N.A.I.C.S.: 238990
Clay Spicer (VP)
Beck Dando (Exec VP)
Adam Henning (CFO)
Derick Furr (VP-Ops)

Ozark Foam InSEALators, Inc.   (1)
1898 S 6th Ave, Ozark, MO 65721
Tel.: (417) 581-9034
Web Site: http://www.ozarkfoam.net
Sales Range: $1-9.9 Million
Emp.: 10
Plastering Drywall & Insulation Services
N.A.I.C.S.: 238310

TruTeam of California, Inc.   (1)
475 Rivera St Unit D, Riverside, CA 92507
Tel.: (951) 683-4429
Web Site: https://www.truteam.com
Insulation Services
N.A.I.C.S.: 238310

TruTeam, LLC   (1)
37 Ridgely St, Dover, DE 19904
Tel.: (302) 678-1782
Insulation Services
N.A.I.C.S.: 238310
Steve Raia (Pres)
Jeff Franklin (VP)
David Procida (VP)
Bill Christie (VP)

United Subcontractors, Inc.   (1)
445 Minnesota St Ste 2500, Saint Paul, MN 55101
Tel.: (952) 697-4060
Web Site: http://www.usiinc.com
Insulation Distr & Contractor Services
N.A.I.C.S.: 238310

Valley Gutter Supply Inc.   (1)
1127 N Fountain Way, Anaheim, CA 92806-2009
Tel.: (714) 666-1700
Web Site: http://www.valleygutter.com
Roofing Contractors
N.A.I.C.S.: 238160
Rob Kowalski (Mgr)

Valley Insulation, Inc.   (1)
3625 Vly Creek Rd NW, Salem, OR 97304   (100%)
Tel.: (503) 390-1151

TopBuild Corp.—(Continued)

Web Site: https://www.valleyinsulation.net
Sales Range: $1-9.9 Million
Drywall & Insulation Contractors
N.A.I.C.S.: 238310

TOPGOLF CALLAWAY BRANDS CORP.

2180 Rutherford Rd, Carlsbad, CA 92008
Tel.: (760) 931-1771 DE
Web Site:
https://www.topgolfcallaway brands.com
Year Founded: 1982
MODG—(NYSE)
Rev.: $3,995,700,000
Assets: $8,590,400,000
Liabilities: $4,816,100,000
Net Worth: $3,774,300,000
Earnings: $157,900,000
Emp.: 32,000
Fiscal Year-end: 12/31/22
Golf Clubs & Related Equipment Designer, Mfr & Marketer
N.A.I.C.S.: 339920
Erik J. Anderson (Vice Chm)
Mark F. Leposky (Chief Supply Chain Officer & Exec VP)
Oliver G. Brewer III (Pres & CEO)
Jennifer Thomas (Chief Acctg Officer & VP)
Brian P. Lynch (CFO, Chief Legal Officer & Exec VP)
Glenn Hickey (Exec VP)
Joe B. Flannery (Exec VP-Apparel & Soft Goods)
Rebecca Fine (Chief People Officer)

Subsidiaries:

Callaway Golf Ball Operations, Inc. **(1)**
425 Meadow St, Chicopee, MA 01013-2201 **(100%)**
Tel.: (413) 536-1200
Web Site: http://www.callawaygolf.com
Sales Range: $700-749.9 Million
Emp.: 1,120
Sports Equipment Mfr
N.A.I.C.S.: 459110

Callaway Golf Canada Ltd. **(1)**
250 Courtland Ave, Concord, L4K 4N3, ON, Canada
Tel.: (905) 660-5434
Web Site: https://www.callawaygolf.ca
Sales Range: $250-299.9 Million
Golf Equipment Whslr
N.A.I.C.S.: 423910

Callaway Golf Europe Ltd. **(1)**
Unit 27 Barwell Business Park Leatherhead Road, Leatherhead Road, Chessington, KT9 2NY, Surrey, United Kingdom
Tel.: (44) 8000264653
Web Site: https://eu.callawaygolf.com
Sales Range: $25-49.9 Million
Emp.: 80
Mfr of Sporting Goods
N.A.I.C.S.: 339920
Oliver G. Brewer III (Pres)
Brian Lynch (CFO)
Mark Leposky (Chief Supply Chain Officer)
Glenn Hickey (Pres-Callaway Golf)
Arthur Starrs (CEO-Topgolf)
Rebecca Fine (Chief People Officer)

Callaway Golf Interactive, Inc. **(1)**
9013 Tuscany Wy Bldg 1 Ste 110, Austin, TX 78754-4798
Tel.: (512) 247-7617
Sporting Goods Whslr
N.A.I.C.S.: 459110

Callaway Golf Kabushiki Kaisha **(1)**
MG Shirokanedai Building 5-12-7 Shirokanedai, Minato-ku, Tokyo, 108-0071, Japan
Tel.: (81) 363285900
Web Site: https://www.callawaygolf.jp
Sales Range: $25-49.9 Million
Emp.: 340
Golf Clubs & Related Equipment Mfr

N.A.I.C.S.: 339920
Alex Mitchell Boezeman (Pres)

Callaway Golf Korea Ltd. **(1)**
4F Hanseong Cheongdam Building 414
Dosan-daero, Gangnam-gu, Seoul, Korea (South)
Tel.: (82) 232181900
Web Site: https://kr.callawaygolf.com
Sales Range: $75-99.9 Million
Golf Clubs & Related Equipment Mfr
N.A.I.C.S.: 339920

Callaway Golf Malaysia Sdn. Bhd. **(1)**
A-9-6 Level 9 Tower A Bangunan UOA Bangsar, No 5 Jalan Bangsar Utama 1, Kuala Lumpur, 59000, Malaysia
Tel.: (60) 322841535
Sales Range: $10-24.9 Million
Emp.: 7
Sporting & Athletic Goods Mfr
N.A.I.C.S.: 339920
Andrew Loh (Gen Mgr)

Callaway Golf Sales Company **(1)**
2180 Rutherford Rd, Carlsbad, CA 92008-7328
Tel.: (760) 931-1771
Sporting & Athletic Goods Mfr
N.A.I.C.S.: 339920

Callaway Golf South Pacific Pty Ltd. **(1)**
18 Corporate Avenue, Rowville, 3178, VIC, Australia
Tel.: (61) 392129400
Web Site: https://au.callawaygolf.com
Sales Range: $10-24.9 Million
Emp.: 55
Golf Clubs & Related Equipment Mfr
N.A.I.C.S.: 339920

Jack Wolfskin Austria GmbH **(1)**
Griesgasse 19a, 5020, Salzburg, Austria
Tel.: (43) 662243304
Apparel & Accessory Retailer
N.A.I.C.S.: 458110

Jack Wolfskin Belgium BVBA **(1)**
Wiegstraat 11, 2000, Antwerp, Belgium
Tel.: (32) 34258757
Web Site: https://www.jack-wolfskin.com
Apparel & Accessory Retailer
N.A.I.C.S.: 458110
Alain Duerinck (Country Mgr)

Jack Wolfskin GmbH & Co. KGaA **(1)**
Jack Wolfskin Kreisel 1, 65510, Idstein, Germany
Tel.: (49) 61269540
Web Site: http://www.jack-wolfskin.com
Sales Range: $450-499.9 Million
Emp.: 415
Outdoor Recreation Equipment Retailer
N.A.I.C.S.: 423910
Melody Harris-Jensbach (CEO & Member-Mgmt Bd)

Jack Wolfskin Italia S.r.l. **(1)**
St-Valentin-Strasse 9 A, 39041, Brenner, Italy
Tel.: (39) 0472055661
Web Site: https://www.jack-wolfskin.com
Apparel & Accessory Retailer
N.A.I.C.S.: 458110

Jack Wolfskin Netherlands BV **(1)**
Stadsweide 2 Unit 484, Designer Outlet Roermond, 6041 TP, Roermond, Netherlands
Tel.: (31) 475575068
Web Site: https://www.jack-wolfskin.com
Apparel & Accessory Retailer
N.A.I.C.S.: 458110
Alain Duerinck (Country Mgr)

Jack Wolfskin North America, Inc. **(1)**
2180 Rutherford Rd, Carlsbad, CA 92008
Tel.: (760) 931-1771
Web Site: https://us.jackwolfskin.com
Apparel & Accessory Retailer
N.A.I.C.S.: 458110
Diana Seung (Gen Mgr)

Jack Wolfskin UK Ltd. **(1)**
124 Long Acre, London, WC2E 9AA, United Kingdom
Tel.: (44) 2078365118

Web Site: https://www.jack-wolfskin.com
Apparel & Accessory Retailer
N.A.I.C.S.: 458110
Alan Perrins (Country Mgr)

Ogio International, Inc. **(1)**
2180 Rutherford Rd, Carlsbad, CA 92008
Tel.: (760) 931-1771
Web Site: https://www.ogio.com
Designer & Distributor of Sports Gear Bags
N.A.I.C.S.: 423910

TopGolf International, Inc. **(1)**
8787 Park Ln, Dallas, TX 75231 **(14.3%)**
Tel.: (214) 341-9600
Web Site: http://www.topgolf.com
Sales Range: $50-74.9 Million
Emp.: 2,200
Golf-Themed Entertainment Chain
N.A.I.C.S.: 713910
Susan Walmesley (VP-Sls & Mktg-US & UK)
Kevin Miner (VP-Construction-Golf-US & UK)
Erik Anderson (Chm)
William Davenport (CFO)
Chris Callaway (Chief Dev Officer)
Deslyn Douglass Norris (VP-Sls & Mktg)
Arthur Francis Starrs III (CEO)
Andrew Macaulay (CTO)
Eldridge Burns (Gen Counsel)
Troy Warfield (Pres)

Subsidiary (Domestic):

World Golf Tour **(2)**
160 Pine St Suite 510, San Francisco, CA 94111
Tel.: (415) 277-4916
Web Site: http://www.worldgolftour.com
Golf Tour Operators
N.A.I.C.S.: 713910

Travis Mathew Retail, LLC **(1)**
10250 Santa Monica Blvd Ste 1780, Los Angeles, CA 90067
Tel.: (310) 279-5335
Golf Equipment Mfr
N.A.I.C.S.: 339920

travisMathew, LLC **(1)**
15202 Graham St, Huntington Beach, CA 92649
Tel.: (562) 799-6900
Web Site: https://www.travismathew.com
Apparel Retail Store Operator
N.A.I.C.S.: 458110

TOR MINERALS INTERNATIONAL INC.

615 N Upper Broadway Ste 410, Corpus Christi, TX 78401
Tel.: (361) 883-5591 DE
Web Site:
https://www.torminerals.com
Year Founded: 1973
TORM—(OTCIQ)
Rev.: $29,909,000
Assets: $25,416,000
Liabilities: $5,410,000
Net Worth: $20,006,000
Earnings: ($1,254,000)
Emp.: 85
Fiscal Year-end: 12/31/22
Mineral Products, Pigments & Pigment Extenders Mfr for Paints, Industrial Coatings & Plastics
N.A.I.C.S.: 212390
Olaf Karasch (Pres & CEO)

Subsidiaries:

TOR Minerals Malaysia, Sdn. Bhd. **(1)**
4 1/2 Miles Jalan Lahat, 30200, Ipoh, Perak, Malaysia **(100%)**
Tel.: (60) 53223536
Web Site: http://www.torminerals.com
Sales Range: $1-9.9 Million
Emp.: 35
Mfr of Synethic Rutile Pigments
N.A.I.C.S.: 325130
Kean Kee Kuan (Mgr-Sls-Mktg)

TOR Processing & Trade BV **(1)**
Burgemeester Moslaan 13, Hattem, 8051 CP, Netherlands **(100%)**

Tel.: (31) 383388657
Web Site: http://www.torminerals.com
Sales Range: $10-24.9 Million
Emp.: 45
Mfr of Alumina Trihydrate Filler Pigment
N.A.I.C.S.: 325130

TP&T (TOR Processing & Trade) B.V. **(1)**
Burgemeester Moslaan 13, 8051 CP, Hattem, Netherlands
Tel.: (31) 383388657
Inorganic Dye & Pigment Mfr
N.A.I.C.S.: 325130

TORRID HOLDINGS INC.

18501 E San Jose Ave, City of Industry, CA 91748
Tel.: (626) 667-1002 DE
Web Site: https://www.torrid.com
Year Founded: 2019
CURV—(NYSE)
Rev.: $1,288,144,000
Assets: $527,264,000
Liabilities: $757,488,000
Net Worth: ($230,224,000)
Earnings: $50,209,000
Emp.: 2,061
Fiscal Year-end: 01/28/23
Holding Company
N.A.I.C.S.: 551112
Hyon C. Park (COO, CTO & Exec VP)
Lisa M. Harper (CEO)
Bridgett C. Zeterberg (Chief Legal Officer, Chief HR Officer & Sec)
Paula Dempsey (CFO & Exec VP)
Bridgett C. Zeterberg (Chief Legal Officer, Chief HR Officer & Sec)
Vivian Alhorn (CMO)
Elizabeth Munoz (Chief Creative Officer)
Kate Horton (Chief Merchandising Officer)
Ashlee Wheeler (Chief Strategy Officer, Chief Planning Officer & Sr VP)
Lisa M. Harper (CEO)

TORTEC GROUP CORP.

30 N Gould St Ste 2489, Sheridan, WY 82801
Tel.: (307) 248-9177 NV
Web Site:
https://tortecgroupcorp.com
Year Founded: 2012
TRTK—(OTCEM)
Assets: $422
Liabilities: $58,840
Net Worth: ($58,418)
Earnings: ($49,793)
Fiscal Year-end: 03/31/22
Environmental & Engineering Services
N.A.I.C.S.: 541620
Phil Sands (VP-Investor Relations)
Stephen H. Smoot (Pres, CEO & Dir)
Asael T. Sorensen Jr. (Sec, VP & Dir)
Irina Kochetkova (Treas, VP & Dir)

Subsidiaries:

Mid Cal AG Aviation Inc. **(1)**
853 W Sonoma Ave, Kerman, CA 93630
Tel.: (559) 289-7505
Other Nonscheduled Air Transportation
N.A.I.C.S.: 481219
Kevin Morton (Pres)

TOTAL BRAIN LIMITED

268 Bush St 2633, San Francisco, CA 94104
Tel.: (415) 399-7990 CA
Web Site: http://www.totalbrain.com
Year Founded: 2000
TTB—(OTCIQ)
Rev.: $2,722,206
Assets: $20,566,542
Liabilities: $2,111,148
Net Worth: $18,455,394

Earnings: ($5,348,616)
Emp.: 24
Fiscal Year-end: 06/30/20
Medical Data for Brain Health Solutions
N.A.I.C.S.: 513140
Evian Gordon *(Chm)*
Louis Gagnon *(CEO & Mng Dir)*
Matthew Mund *(COO)*
Matt Resteghini *(CMO)*
Emil Vasilev *(Head-Fin)*
Donna Palmer *(Chief Science Officer)*
Melissa Frieswick *(Chief Revenue Officer)*

TOTAL MULTIMEDIA INCORPORATED
Tel.: (646) 660-3962   NV
Web Site: http://www.tmmi.us
Year Founded: 1990
TMMI—(OTCIQ)
Data Processing Services
N.A.I.C.S.: 541511
Eric Hernes *(CTO)*
Deborah Bello *(Controller & Mgr-Chief Admin)*
Susan Bala *(Chm, Pres & CEO)*

TOTALIGENT, INC.
960 S Westlake Blvd Ste 207, Westlake Village, CA 91361
Tel.: (561) 988-2621   NV
Web Site: https://www.totaligent.com
TGNT—(OTCIQ)
Rev.: $731,679
Assets: $486,800
Liabilities: $1,396,816
Net Worth: ($910,016)
Earnings: ($402,170)
Fiscal Year-end: 12/31/23
Commercial Refrigerants Dealer
N.A.I.C.S.: 423740
Ali Eldessouky *(Dir-Supply Chain)*

TOUCAN INTERACTIVE CORP.
25 E Foothill Blvd, Arcadia, CA 91006
Tel.: (626) 898-7010   NV
Year Founded: 2014
TCNT—(OTCEM)
Assets: $15,913
Liabilities: $91,938
Net Worth: ($76,025)
Earnings: ($6,846)
Fiscal Year-end: 02/28/21
Online Consumer Lending Services
N.A.I.C.S.: 522291
Frank Lin *(Sec)*
Gang Ding *(Co-Chm & CEO)*
Kin Hui *(Co-Chm & Pres)*
William Chu *(CFO)*

TOUCHMARK BANCSHARES, INC.
3651 Old Milton Pkwy, Alpharetta, GA 30005
Tel.: (770) 407-6700   GA
Web Site: https://www.touchmarknb.com
Year Founded: 2007
TMAK—(OTCIQ)
Rev.: $22,712,431
Assets: $427,707,251
Liabilities: $370,393,261
Net Worth: $57,313,990
Earnings: $4,718,560
Emp.: 28
Fiscal Year-end: 12/31/20
Bank Holding Company
N.A.I.C.S.: 551111
Jayendrakumar J. Shah *(Chm & CEO-Touchmark National Bank)*
Lynn Barron *(CFO & Exec VP-Touchmark National Bank)*
Hank Almquist *(COO & Exec VP-Touchmark National Bank)*

TOUCHPOINT GROUP HOLDINGS, INC.
4300 Biscayne Blvd Ste 203, Miami, FL 33137
Tel.: (305) 420-6640   DE
Web Site: https://www.touchpointgh.com
TGHI—(OTCIQ)
Rev.: $91,000
Assets: $1,946,000
Liabilities: $4,437,000
Net Worth: ($2,491,000)
Earnings: ($5,195,000)
Emp.: 8
Fiscal Year-end: 12/31/21
Radio & Television Broadcasting & Wireless Communications Equipment Manufacturing
N.A.I.C.S.: 334220
Martin Ward *(CFO)*
Mark White *(Pres)*
Martin Ward *(CFO)*
Spencer Christopher *(CTO)*

Subsidiaries:

Horizon Globex GmbH   (1)
Weststrasse 1, CH-6340, Baar, Switzerland
Tel.: (41) 41 760 5820
Web Site: http://www.horizon-globex.com
Satellite Communication Services
N.A.I.C.S.: 517410
Brian Collins *(Founder & CEO)*
Mike Boswell *(CFO)*
Mitch Edwards *(Chief Strategy Officer)*
Peter Hall *(CIO)*
Louis Taubman *(Gen Counsel)*
Andrew Le Gear *(CTO)*
Vanessa Malone *(Mgr-Mktg)*
Robert Brand *(VP-Bus Dev)*
Mark Elenowitz *(Pres)*

ICE Messaging Pte. Ltd.   (1)
75 High Street, Singapore, 179435, Singapore
Tel.: (65) 6595 6633
Mobile Messaging Software Publisher
N.A.I.C.S.: 513210

One Horizon Group PLC   (1)
Unit 3 The Woodford Centre, Lysander Way Old Sarum, Salisbury, SP4 6BU, Wilts, United Kingdom
Tel.: (44) 1722410800
Web Site: http://www.onehorizongroup.com
Satellite Communications Equipment & Services
N.A.I.C.S.: 517410
Mark White *(Founder)*

TOUCHSTONE BANK
4300 Crossings Blvd, Prince George, VA 23875
Tel.: (804) 478-4434   VA
Web Site: https://www.touchstone.bank
Year Founded: 1906
TSBA—(OTCIQ)
Sales Range: $10-24.9 Million
Commericial Banking
N.A.I.C.S.: 522110
James R. Black *(Pres & CEO)*
Joseph D. Pennington *(CFO)*
Mark A. Debes *(Chief Banking Officer)*
Sean Link *(Chief Lending Officer)*
Michelle H. Simon *(Mng Dir & Sr VP)*
Bruce Brockwell *(Pres-Exec Market & Sr VP)*
Christy F. Quesenbery *(COO & Exec VP)*

TOUGHBUILT INDUSTRIES, INC.
8669 Research Dr, Irvine, CA 92618
Tel.: (949) 528-3100   NV
Web Site: https://www.toughbuilt.com
Year Founded: 2012
TBLT—(OTCEM)
Rev.: $76,271,822
Assets: $51,790,184

Liabilities: $61,511,211
Net Worth: ($9,721,027)
Earnings: ($46,449,313)
Emp.: 165
Fiscal Year-end: 12/31/23
Industrial Tool Mfr & Distr
N.A.I.C.S.: 333517
Michael Panosian *(CEO, Pres, Chm & Founder)*
Joshua Keeler *(Founder & Chief Design Officer)*
Zareh Khachatoorian *(COO & Sec)*
Martin Galstyan *(CFO-Interim)*

TOURMALINE BIO, INC.
27 W 24th St Ste 702, New York, NY 10010
Tel.: (646) 481-9832   DE
Web Site: https://www.tourmalinebio.com
Year Founded: 2018
TRML—(NASDAQ)
Assets: $210,295,000
Liabilities: $5,253,000
Net Worth: $205,042,000
Earnings: ($42,124,000)
Emp.: 44
Fiscal Year-end: 12/31/23
Biotechnology Research & Development Services
N.A.I.C.S.: 541714
W. Bradford Middlekauff *(Chief Bus Officer & Gen Counsel)*
Susan Dana Jones *(CTO)*
Mary Kay Fenton *(Interim Pres, Interim CEO & CFO)*
Francois Nader *(Chm)*
Yung Chyung *(Chief Medical Officer)*
Kevin Johnson *(Chief Regulatory Officer)*
Sandeep Kulkarni *(Co-Founder & CEO)*
Ryan Robinson *(CFO, Principal Acctg Officer & Treas)*

TOWER PROPERTIES COMPANY
1000 Walnut St 900, Kansas City, MO 64106-2161
Tel.: (816) 421-8255
Web Site: https://www.towerproperties.com
Year Founded: 1989
TPRP—(OTCIQ)
Sales Range: $25-49.9 Million
Emp.: 53
Commercial & Industrial Building Operation
N.A.I.C.S.: 531120
Thomas R. Willard *(Pres & CEO)*
Chris Erdley *(VP & Dir-Real Estate Svcs)*
Margaret V. Allinder *(VP & Controller)*

TOWERSTREAM CORP.
76 Hammarlund Way Tech 3 Building, Middletown, RI 02842
Tel.: (401) 848-5848   DE
Web Site: https://www.towerstream.com
TWER—(OTCIQ)
Sales Range: $10-24.9 Million
Emp.: 46
Wireless Broadband Services
N.A.I.C.S.: 812990
Philip J. Urso *(Founder & Chm)*
Ernst Ortega *(CEO)*

TOWN CENTER BANK
1938 E Lincoln Hwy Unit 101, New Lenox, IL 60451
Tel.: (815) 463-7002   IL
Web Site: https://www.towncenterbank.net
Year Founded: 2006
TCNB—(OTCQX)

Banking Services
N.A.I.C.S.: 522110
Dan Regan *(Pres)*
Gina Persiani *(VP-Residential Mortgage & Consumer Lending)*
Michael Perry *(Chm & CEO)*

TOWNE BANK
5716 W High St, Portsmouth, VA 23703
Tel.: (757) 638-7500   VA
Web Site: https://www.townebank.com
Year Founded: 1998
TOWN—(NASDAQ)
Rev.: $744,350,000
Assets: $14,626,444,000
Liabilities: $12,842,616,000
Net Worth: $1,783,828,000
Earnings: $145,535,000
Emp.: 2,490
Fiscal Year-end: 12/31/20
Commercial Banking
N.A.I.C.S.: 522110
Keith D. Horton *(Chief Facilities Officer & Sr Exec VP)*
Dawn S. Glynn *(Pres-Hampton Roads & Outer Banks)*
Brian K. Skinner *(Pres-Towne Fin Svcs Grp)*
William B. Littreal *(CFO & Sr Exec VP)*
W. Jeffrey Dyckman *(Pres-Towne Bus Strategy Grp)*
Jeffrey F. Benson *(Vice Chm)*
T. Patrick Collins *(Pres-Richmond)*
Buffy J. Barefoot *(Pres-Virginia Beach)*
Matthew C. Davis *(Chief Strategy & Risk Officer)*
Robin S. Cooke *(Pres-Portsmouth & Suffolk Reg)*
David Black *(Officer-Comml Banking)*
Dana Dellinger *(Officer-Merchant Sls)*
Christopher Thorn *(Branch Mgr)*
R. Lee Clark *(Chief HR Officer & Sr Exec VP)*
Jessie Denny *(Officer-Merchant Sls)*
Annie Gonzalez *(Officer-Merchant Sls)*
Michael LeGrande *(Officer-Merchant Sls)*
Susan Rowe *(Officer-Treasury Sls)*
Alvin Oakley *(Officer-Treasury Sls)*
Chonise Tate *(Officer-Treasury Sls)*
Sara Twiford *(Officer-Treasury Sls)*
Neil Coffield *(Officer-Treasury Sls)*
Jim Harpham *(Officer-Treasury Sls)*
Becky Zambas *(Branch Mgr)*
Michelle Butler *(Officer-Private Banking)*
Sara Szymanski *(Officer-Merchant Sls)*
Brad Hunter *(Officer-Comml Banking)*
Paul Going *(Officer-Comml Banking)*
Phil Smith *(Officer-Comml Banking)*
Kevin L. Fly *(Chief Acctg Officer & Sr Exec VP)*
G. Robert Aston Jr. *(Chm)*
William I. Foster III *(Pres & CEO)*
H. Taylor Sugg Jr. *(Pres-North East North Carolina)*
Herbert H. Bateman Jr. *(Officer-Comml Banking)*

Subsidiaries:

Coastal Home Mortgage, LLC   (1)
300 32nd St Ste 101, Virginia Beach, VA 23451   (50.1%)
Tel.: (757) 321-8074
Web Site: http://www.coastalhomemtg.com
Emp.: 8
Mortgage Brokerage Services
N.A.I.C.S.: 522310
John Frankos *(VP & Branch Mgr)*

Farmers Bankshares, Inc.   (1)

Towne Bank—(Continued)

50 E Windsor Blvd, Windsor, VA 23487
Tel.: (757) 242-6111
Web Site: http://www.farmersbankva.com
Rev.: $27,188,413
Assets: $551,917,933
Liabilities: $485,272,185
Net Worth: $66,645,748
Earnings: $5,405,629
Emp.: 75
Fiscal Year-end: 12/31/2020
Bank Holding Company
N.A.I.C.S.: 551111
Kristy E. DeJarnette *(CFO & Exec VP)*
Kathy C. Bryant *(Sr VP & Dir-HR & Retail)*
Chad A. Rountree *(Sr VP-Western Tidewater Market)*
Andrew D. Perkins *(Chief Credit Officer & Sr VP)*
Kara H. Smith *(VP & Dir-Ops & Tech)*
Thomas L. Woodward III *(Chief Lending Officer & Exec VP)*

Subsidiary (Domestic):

Farmers Bank   **(2)**
50 E Windsor Blvd, Windsor, VA 23487
Tel.: (757) 242-6111
Web Site: http://www.farmersbankva.com
Commericial Banking
N.A.I.C.S.: 522110
Vernon M. Towler *(Pres)*
Kristy E. DeJarnette *(CFO & Exec VP)*
Richard J. Holland Jr. *(CEO)*
Chad A. Rountree *(Sr VP)*
Kathy C. Bryant *(Sr VP & Dir-HR & Retail)*
Patricia T. Allen *(Sr VP & Dir-Loan & Deposit Ops)*
Thomas L. Woodward III *(Chief Lending Officer & Sr VP)*
Norman F. Carr Jr. *(Sr VP & Dir-Fin Svcs)*

Subsidiary (Domestic):

Manry-Rawls, LLC   **(3)**
301 N Main St, Franklin, VA
23851   **(66.66%)**
Tel.: (757) 562-6131
Web Site: http://www.manryrawls.com
Sales Range: $1-9.9 Million
Insurance Agents
N.A.I.C.S.: 524210
Vee Pittman *(Pres)*
Kendall Edwards *(Controller)*
E. Warren Beale Jr. *(Exec VP)*

Real Estate Security Agency,
LLC   **(1)**
501 Baylor Ct Ste 100-F, Chesapeake, VA
23320   **(75%)**
Tel.: (757) 410-8086
Web Site:
    http://www.realestatesecurityagency.com
Title Insurance Brokerage Services
N.A.I.C.S.: 524210

Towne Insurance Agency, LLC   **(1)**
301 Bendix Rd Ste 300, Virginia Beach, VA
23452-1385   **(100%)**
Tel.: (757) 436-4600
Web Site: http://www.towneinsurance.com
Sales Range: $1-9.9 Million
Emp.: 25
Insurance Agents
N.A.I.C.S.: 524210
Christopher T. Rogerson *(COO)*
W. Douglas Russell *(Pres & CEO)*
Richard P. Herzberg *(Pres-Towne Benefits)*
Joseph D. Harrow *(Pres-Virginia)*
B. Boyd Griffin Jr. *(CFO & Exec VP)*
James E. Clement Jr. *(Pres-North Carolina & South Carolina)*

Subsidiary (Domestic):

Straus, Itzkowitz & LeCompte Insurance Agency, Inc.   **(2)**
5310 Markel Rd Ste 203, Richmond, VA
23230
Tel.: (804) 288-8500
Web Site: http://www.silinsurance.com
Insurance Related Activities
N.A.I.C.S.: 524298
Pettus Lecompte *(Exec VP)*
Fred Itzkowitz *(Pres)*

Towne Investments, LLC   **(1)**
5806 Harbour View Blvd Ste 202, Suffolk,
VA 23435

Tel.: (757) 638-6850
Web Site:
    http://www.towneinvestmentgroup.com
Investment & Brokerage Services
N.A.I.C.S.: 523999

Towne Realty, LLC   **(1)**
984 1st Colonial Rd Ste 204, Virginia
Beach, VA 23454   **(65%)**
Tel.: (757) 690-0439
Web Site: http://www.bhhstownerealty.com
Real Estate Brokers & Agents
N.A.I.C.S.: 531210
Stephanie Triplett *(Controller)*
Kimber A. Smith *(COO)*

TowneBank Commercial Mortgage,
LLC   **(1)**
5716 High St, Portsmouth, VA 23703
Tel.: (757) 628-6360
Web Site:
    http://www.townebankmortgage.com
Sales Range: $125-149.9 Million
Commercial Mortgage Loans
N.A.I.C.S.: 522310
David J. Beatty *(Pres)*

TowneBank Mortgage   **(1)**
600 22nd St Ste 300, Virginia Beach, VA
23451
Tel.: (757) 417-6200
Web Site:
    http://www.townebankmortgage.com
Sales Range: $125-149.9 Million
Home Mortgage Lending Services
N.A.I.C.S.: 522292
Dennis Pedersen *(Asst VP)*
Rick Goldbach *(Dir-Corp Bus Dev-Virginia Beach & Raleigh)*
William T. Morrison *(Chm & CEO)*
Heather Sirgany *(Mgr-Sls-Mortgage)*

TPG CAPITAL, L.P.

301 Commerce St Ste 3300, Fort
Worth, TX 76102
Tel.: (817) 871-4000   DE
Web Site: https://www.tpg.com
Year Founded: 1992
TPG—(NASDAQ)
Privater Equity Firm
N.A.I.C.S.: 523999
David Bonderman *(Co-Founder)*
Stephen A. Ellis *(Mng Partner-San Francisco)*
Jon Winkelried *(CEO)*
Michael G. MacDougall *(Partner-Austin)*
Anilu Vazquez-Ubarri *(Chief HR Officer)*
James G. Coulter *(Co-Founder & Chm)*
Jerome C. Vascellaro *(COO & Partner)*
Sanghoon Lee *(Partner-Asia)*
Jack Daly *(Partner-San Francisco)*
Bradford Berenson *(Gen Counsel-San Francisco)*
David I. Trujillo *(Partner)*
Nehal Raj *(Co-Mng Partner)*
Jeffrey K. Rhodes *(Partner-San Francisco)*
Jud Morrison *(Dir-Portfolio Ops-Houston)*
Kiran Rao *(Dir-Portfolio Ops-San Francisco)*
Steve Willmann *(Mng Dir & Treas)*
John Schilling *(Partner)*
Cai Jin-Yong *(Partner-Hong Kong)*
Jeffrey Smith *(Partner-San Francisco)*
Malte Janzarik *(Partner)*
Jonathan Coslet *(Vice Chm & Chief Investment Officer)*
Ron Kim *(CIO)*
Marc Mezvinsky *(Partner-Bus Unit)*
Paul Hackwell *(Partner)*
Alex Minasian *(Principal)*
Paul Hackwell *(Partner)*
Kendall Garrison *(Partner)*
Paul Hackwell *(Partner)*

Todd B. Sisitsky *(Pres & Co-Mng Partner)*
Todd B. Sisitsky *(Pres & Co-Mng Partner)*

Subsidiaries:

ATD Corporation   **(1)**
12200 Herbert Wayne Ct Ste 150, Huntersville, NC 28078   **(95.05%)**
Tel.: (704) 992-2000
Web Site: http://www.atd-us.com
Rev.: $3,839,269,000
Assets: $2,541,655,000
Liabilities: $1,861,601,000
Net Worth: $680,054,000
Earnings: ($6,376,000)
Emp.: 3,800
Fiscal Year-end: 12/28/2013
Holding Company; Tire Distr
N.A.I.C.S.: 551112
William E. Berry *(Pres & CEO)*
Jason T. Yaudes *(CFO & Exec VP)*
David L. Dyckman *(COO & Exec VP)*
J. Michael Gaither *(Gen Counsel, Exec VP & Sec)*
Jason Shannon *(Exec VP-Product Strategy & Supply)*

Subsidiary (Domestic):

American Tire Distributors Holdings,
Inc.   **(2)**
12200 Herbert Wayne Ct Ste 150, Huntersville, NC 28078
Tel.: (704) 992-2000
Web Site: https://www.atd.com
Sales Range: $5-14.9 Billion
Emp.: 4,500
Offices of Other Holding Companies
N.A.I.C.S.: 551112

Subsidiary (Domestic):

American Tire Distributors, Inc.   **(3)**
12200 Herbert Wayne Ct Ste 150, Huntersville, NC 28078
Tel.: (704) 992-2000
Web Site: http://www.atd-us.com
Sales Range: $75-99.9 Million
Emp.: 450
Tires, Wheels & Related Product Distr
N.A.I.C.S.: 423130
Joyce Vonada *(CIO)*
Stuart Schuette *(Pres & CEO)*
Rebecca Sinclair *(Chief People Officer)*
Bill Williams *(CFO)*
Ryan Marsh *(Chief Growth Innovation Officer)*
Ivy Chin *(Chief Digital & Tech Officer)*

Subsidiary (Domestic).

AM-PAC Tire Distributors, Inc.   **(4)**
51 Moreland Rd, Simi Valley, CA 93065
Tel.: (805) 581-1311
Sales Range: $50-74.9 Million
Tire Whslr
N.A.I.C.S.: 423130

Terry's Tire Town Inc.   **(4)**
2360 W Main St, Alliance, OH 44601-2189
Tel.: (330) 821-5022
Web Site: http://www.terrystiretown.com
Sales Range: $25-49.9 Million
Emp.: 135
Auto Supplies Whslr
N.A.I.C.S.: 423130
Bob Lance *(Mgr-Infrastructure Svcs)*
Joseph Bernabei *(Dir-IT)*
Tony King *(Reg VP)*
Daniel Harrington *(VP-Fin & Controller)*
Hillary Johnston *(Dir-HR-SPHR)*
Mark Lindsey *(VP-Sls)*

Subsidiary (Domestic):

Summit Tires Northeast, LLC   **(5)**
220 O'Connell Way Bldg B, East Taunton,
MA 02718
Tel.: (800) 834-8084
Web Site: http://www.summittire.com
Sales Range: $25-49.9 Million
Tires & Tubes
N.A.I.C.S.: 423130
Kathy Solimine *(Mgr-IT)*
Mark Tavares *(Asst Gen Mgr)*
Bob Vacca *(Reg Mgr-Sls)*

Subsidiary (Domestic):

The Hercules Tire & Rubber
Company   **(4)**
16380 E US Rte 224 Ste 200, Findlay, OH
45840
Tel.: (419) 425-6400
Web Site: http://www.herculestire.com
Distr of Tires & Automotive Products
N.A.I.C.S.: 423130
Jedd Emans *(VP-Mktg)*

Angelo, Gordon & Co., L.P.   **(1)**
245 Park Ave, New York, NY 10167
Tel.: (212) 692-2000
Web Site: http://www.angelogordon.com
Sales Range: $75-99.9 Million
Emp.: 120
Private Equity, Debt & Real Estate Investment & Portfolio Management Services
N.A.I.C.S.: 523999
Andrew Parks *(Chief Risk Officer)*
David Nathan Roberts *(Sr Mng Dir)*
Frank Stadelmaier *(CFO)*
Michael L. Gordon *(CEO & Co-Chief Investment Officer)*
Linda Eichenbaum *(Mng Dir-HR)*
Garrett Walls *(Head-IR-Global)*
Kirk Wickman *(COO)*
Robert Graffeo *(CIO)*
Mark Maduras *(Mng Dir)*
Matthew Brody *(Mng Dir)*
Vishal Sheth *(CFO-Twin Brook Capital Partners)*
Adam Freedman *(Chief Compliance Officer)*
Gordon J. Whiting *(Founder & Head-Net Lease Real Estate Bus)*
Bryce Fraser *(Mng Dir)*
Daniel Pound *(Mng Dir)*
David Taylor *(Mng Dir)*
Eitan Bernstein *(Mng Dir)*
Harish Nataraj *(Mng Dir)*
John O'Meara *(Mng Dir)*
Jon Tanaka *(Mng Dir)*
Julien Farre *(Mng Dir)*
Ken Ng *(Mng Dir)*
Mark Bernstein *(Mng Dir)*
Michael Pope *(Mng Dir)*
Rick Finger *(Mng Dir)*
Sharon Kilmer *(Mng Dir)*
Steven Cha *(Mng Dir)*
Joseph Goldschmid *(VP)*
Josh Baumgarten *(Co-Chief Investment Officer)*
Ryan Mollett *(Head-Distressed Debt-Global)*
Paul Lewis *(Dir-Net Lease Real Estate-Europe)*
Putri Pascualy *(Mng Dir-IR)*
Matt Heintz *(Mng Dir & Head-Insurance-Client Partnership Grp)*
Alan Isenberg *(Head-Client Partnership Grp-Global)*

Affiliate (Domestic):

AG Mortgage Investment Trust,
Inc.   **(2)**
245 Park Ave 26th Fl, New York, NY 10167
Tel.: (212) 692-2000
Web Site: https://www.agmit.com
Rev.: $260,329,000
Assets: $6,126,428,000
Liabilities: $5,598,060,000
Net Worth: $528,368,000
Earnings: $35,340,000
Emp.: 650
Fiscal Year-end: 12/31/2023
Real Estate Investment Trust
N.A.I.C.S.: 525990
Andrew Parks *(Chief Risk Officer)*
Thomas J. Durkin *(Pres & CEO)*
Nicholas Smith *(Chief Investment Officer)*
Anthony W. Rossiello *(CFO & Treas)*
Jenny B. Neslin *(Gen Counsel & Sec)*

Subsidiary (Domestic):

Western Asset Mortgage Capital
Corporation   **(3)**
385 E Colorado Blvd, Pasadena, CA 91101
Tel.: (626) 844-9400
Web Site:
    https://www.westernassetmcc.com
Rev.: $20,987,000
Assets: $2,453,234,000
Liabilities: $2,358,422,000
Net Worth: $94,812,000
Earnings: ($89,079,000)
Fiscal Year-end: 12/31/2022

Real Estate Investment Services
N.A.I.C.S.: 523999
Sean Johnson *(Deputy Chief Investment
Officer)*

Holding (Domestic):

Benihana Inc. **(2)**
8750 NW 36th St, Doral, FL 33178
Tel.: (305) 593-0770
Web Site: http://www.benihana.com
Emp.: 6,900
Holding Company; Restaurant Operator
N.A.I.C.S.: 551112
Keith Boockholdt *(Dir-Pur)*
Dania Hefty *(Dir-MIS)*
Ana Ramos *(Dir-HR)*
Tomoko Sawada *(Mgr-Field Mktg)*
Maritza Blanco *(Corp Travel Planner)*
Maria Gutierrez *(Dir-Personnel)*
Thomas J. Baldwin *(Pres & CEO)*

Subsidiary (Domestic):

**1501 Broadway Restaurant
Corp.** **(3)**
2684 Broadway, New York, NY 10036-5601
Tel.: (212) 865-7074
Restaurant Operating Services
N.A.I.C.S.: 722511

Benihana Bethesda Corp. **(3)**
7935 Wisconsin Ave, Bethesda, MD 20814
Tel.: (301) 652-5391
Web Site: http://www.benihana.com
Emp.: 50
Restaurant Operating Services
N.A.I.C.S.: 722511
Lisa McEwen *(Gen Mgr)*

Benihana Broomfield Corp. **(3)**
515 Zang St, Broomfield, CO 80021
Tel.: (303) 410-0482
Web Site: http://www.benihana.com
Sales Range: $10-24.9 Million
Emp.: 50
Restaurant Operating Services
N.A.I.C.S.: 722511
Dan Shannon *(Gen Mgr)*

Benihana Carlsbad Corp. **(3)**
755 Raintree Dr Ste 100, Carlsbad, CA
92011
Tel.: (760) 929-8311
Restaurant Operating Services
N.A.I.C.S.: 722511
John Timmons *(Gen Mgr)*

Benihana Chandler Corp. **(3)**
3025 W Chandler Blvd, Chandler, AZ 85226
Tel.: (480) 812-4701
Restaurant Operating Services
N.A.I.C.S.: 722511

Benihana Columbus Corp. **(3)**
8781 Lyra Dr, Columbus, OH 43240
Tel.: (614) 436-3705
Web Site: http://www.benihana.com
Emp.: 50
Restaurant Operating Services
N.A.I.C.S.: 722511
Matthew Younker *(Gen Mgr)*

Benihana Coral Springs Corp. **(3)**
1695 N University Dr, Coral Springs, FL
33071
Tel.: (954) 341-9622
Restaurant Operating Services
N.A.I.C.S.: 722511
Robert Oakes *(Gen Mgr)*

Benihana Encino Corp. **(3)**
16226 Ventura Blvd, Encino, CA 91436
Tel.: (818) 788-7121
Restaurant Operating Services
N.A.I.C.S.: 722511
Stuart Montalvo *(Mgr-Reg)*

Benihana Las Colinas Corp. **(3)**
5400 Whitehall St, Irving, TX 75038
Tel.: (972) 550-0060
Restaurant Operating Services
N.A.I.C.S.: 722511
Bobby Kurniawan *(Gen Mgr)*

Benihana Lombard Corp. **(3)**
747 E Butterfield Rd, Lombard, IL 60148-
5614
Tel.: (630) 571-4440
Web Site: http://www.benihana.com

Sales Range: $10-24.9 Million
Emp.: 60
Restaurant Operating Services
N.A.I.C.S.: 722511
Thomas Baldwin *(Pres & CEO)*

Benihana Marina Corp. **(3)**
1447 4th St, Santa Monica, CA 90401-2308
Tel.: (310) 260-1423
Restaurant Operating Services
N.A.I.C.S.: 722511
Mario Ibarra *(Gen Mgr)*

**Benihana National of Florida
Corp.** **(3)**
3602 SE Ocean Blvd, Stuart, FL 34996-
6711
Tel.: (772) 286-0740
Restaurant Operating Services
N.A.I.C.S.: 722511
Willis Leung *(Gen Mgr)*

Benihana Ontario Corp. **(3)**
3760 E Inland Empire Blvd, Ontario, CA
91764
Tel.: (909) 483-0937
Web Site: http://www.benihana.com
Restaurant Operating Services
N.A.I.C.S.: 722511
Andrew Wong *(Gen Mgr)*

Benihana Orlando Corp. **(3)**
12690 International Dr, Orlando, FL 32821
Tel.: (407) 239-7400
Web Site: http://www.benihana.com
Emp.: 50
Restaurant Operating Services
N.A.I.C.S.: 722511
Christopher Catledge *(Gen Mgr)*

Benihana Plano Corp. **(3)**
5840 Legacy Cir, Plano, TX 75024
Tel.: (469) 467-2242
Restaurant Operating Services
N.A.I.C.S.: 722511

**Benihana Plymouth Meeting
Corp.** **(3)**
508 W Germantown Pike, Plymouth Meet-
ing, PA 19462
Tel.: (610) 832-5924
Web Site: http://www.benihana.com
Restaurant Operating Services
N.A.I.C.S.: 722511
Adam James *(Gen Mgr)*
Chris MacArtney *(Gen Mgr)*

Benihana Sunrise Corp. **(3)**
5489 E Sunrise Blvd, Citrus Heights, CA
95610
Tel.: (916) 961-2791
Sales Range: $10-24.9 Million
Emp.: 40
Restaurant Operating Services
N.A.I.C.S.: 722511
Bob Burns *(Gen Mgr)*

Benihana Westbury Corp. **(3)**
920 Merchants Concourse, Westbury, NY
11590
Tel.: (516) 222-6091
Restaurant Operating Services
N.A.I.C.S.: 722511
Joseph Lee *(Gen Mgr)*

Benihana Wheeling Corp. **(3)**
150 N Milwaukee Ave, Wheeling, IL 60090
Tel.: (847) 465-6021
Web Site: http://www.benihana.com
Restaurant Operating Services
N.A.I.C.S.: 722511
Eric Yoo *(Gen Mgr)*

Benihana Woodlands Corp. **(3)**
1720 Lake Woodlands Dr, The Woodlands,
TX 77380
Tel.: (281) 292-0061
Web Site: http://www.benihana.com
Emp.: 40
Restaurant Operating Services
N.A.I.C.S.: 722511
William T. Grumble *(Gen Mgr)*

Benihana of Puente Hills Corp. **(3)**
17877 Gale Ave, City of Industry, CA
91748-1526
Tel.: (626) 912-8784
Web Site: http://www.benihana.com
Restaurant Operating Services
N.A.I.C.S.: 722511
Raymond Chan *(Gen Mgr)*

Haru Amsterdam Avenue Corp. **(3)**
433 Amsterdam Ave, New York, NY 10024
Tel.: (212) 579-5655
Web Site: http://www.benihana.com
Restaurant Operating Services
N.A.I.C.S.: 722511

Haru Gramercy Park Corp. **(3)**
220 Park Ave S, New York, NY 10003
Tel.: (646) 428-0989
Web Site: http://www.harusushi.com
Emp.: 90
Restaurant Operating Services
N.A.I.C.S.: 722511
Diana Liu *(Gen Mgr)*

Haru Holding Corp. **(3)**
355 W 36th St, New York, NY
10036-5601   **(80%)**
Tel.: (800) 327-3369
Web Site: http://www.harusushi.com
Sales Range: $50-74.9 Million
Emp.: 50
Holding Company; Restaurant Operator
N.A.I.C.S.: 551112
Richard C. Stockinger *(Chm, Pres & CEO)*

Haru Third Avenue Corp. **(3)**
1329 3rd Ave 76th St, New York, NY 10021
Tel.: (212) 452-2230
Restaurant Operating Services
N.A.I.C.S.: 722511

Haru Wall Street Corp. **(3)**
1 Wall St Ct, New York, NY 10005
Tel.: (212) 785-6850
Restaurant Operating Services
N.A.I.C.S.: 722511
Rachiel Connor *(Gen Mgr)*

RA Scottsdale Corp. **(3)**
3815 N Scottsdale Rd, Scottsdale, AZ
85251
Tel.: (480) 990-9256
Restaurant Operating Services
N.A.I.C.S.: 722511
Nate Keane *(Gen Mgr)*

RA Sushi Atlanta Midtown Corp. **(3)**
1080 Peachtree St Ste 8, Atlanta, GA
30309
Tel.: (404) 267-0114
Restaurant Operating Services
N.A.I.C.S.: 722511

RA Sushi Baltimore Corp. **(3)**
1390 Lancaster St, Baltimore, MD 21231
Tel.: (410) 522-3200
Restaurant Operating Services
N.A.I.C.S.: 722511

RA Sushi Chicago Corp. **(3)**
1139 N State St, Chicago, IL 60610
Tel.: (312) 274-0011
Web Site: http://www.rasushi.com
Emp.: 55
Restaurant Operating Services
N.A.I.C.S.: 722511
Chris Keeler *(Gen Mgr)*

RA Sushi Chino Hills Corp. **(3)**
13925 City Center Dr Ste 2065, Chino Hills,
CA 91709
Tel.: (909) 902-0044
Restaurant Operating Services
N.A.I.C.S.: 722511

RA Sushi City Center Corp. **(3)**
799 Town & Country Blvd Ste 234, Hous-
ton, TX 77024
Tel.: (713) 331-2792
Restaurant Operating Services
N.A.I.C.S.: 722511
Bobby Davis *(Gen Mgr)*

RA Sushi Corona Corp. **(3)**
2785 Cabot Dr Ste 7-101, Corona, CA
92883
Tel.: (951) 277-7491
Web Site: http://www.rasushi.com
Restaurant Operating Services
N.A.I.C.S.: 722511

RA Sushi Fort Worth Corp. **(3)**
7501 Lone Star Dr Ste B-130, Plano, TX
75024
Tel.: (469) 467-7400
Web Site: http://www.rasushi.com
Emp.: 75
Restaurant Operating Services
N.A.I.C.S.: 722511

Justin Levine *(Gen Mgr)*
Dan Russo *(Gen Mgr)*

RA Sushi Glenview Corp. **(3)**
2601 Aviator Ln, Glenview, IL 60026
Tel.: (847) 510-1100
Web Site: http://www.rasushi.com
Restaurant Operating Services
N.A.I.C.S.: 722511

RA Sushi Holding Corp. **(3)**
13802 N Scottsdale Rd Ste 176, Scotts-
dale, AZ 85254   **(100%)**
Tel.: (480) 951-5888
Web Site: http://www.rasushi.com
Sales Range: $10-24.9 Million
Emp.: 500
Holding Company; Restaurant Operator
N.A.I.C.S.: 551112
Richard C. Stockinger *(Chm, Pres & CEO)*

**RA Sushi Huntington Beach
Corp.** **(3)**
155 5th St Ste 183, Huntington Beach, CA
92648
Tel.: (714) 536-6390
Sales Range: $10-24.9 Million
Emp.: 50
Restaurant Operating Services
N.A.I.C.S.: 722511
Robert Hua *(Gen Mgr)*

RA Sushi Las Vegas Corp. **(3)**
3200 Las Vegas Blvd S Ste 1132, Las Ve-
gas, NV 89109
Tel.: (702) 696-0008
Web Site: http://www.rasushi.com
Emp.: 25
Restaurant Operating Services
N.A.I.C.S.: 722511
Tony Disano *(Gen Mgr)*

RA Sushi Leawood Corp. **(3)**
11638 Ash St, Leawood, KS 66211
Tel.: (913) 850-6260
Web Site: http://www.rasushi.com
Emp.: 70
Restaurant Operating Services
N.A.I.C.S.: 722511
Eric Abney *(Gen Mgr)*

RA Sushi Lombard Corp. **(3)**
310 Yorktown Shopping Ctr, Lombard, IL
60148
Tel.: (630) 627-6800
Web Site: http://www.rasushi.com
Restaurant Operating Services
N.A.I.C.S.: 722511

RA Sushi Mesa Corp. **(3)**
1652 S Val Vista Dr Ste 101, Mesa, AZ
85204
Tel.: (480) 632-9500
Sales Range: $10-24.9 Million
Emp.: 60
Restaurant Operating Services
N.A.I.C.S.: 722511
Rob Downing *(Gen Mgr)*

**RA Sushi Palm Beach Gardens
Corp.** **(3)**
11701 Lake Victoria Gardens Ave Ste 4105,
Palm Beach Gardens, FL 33410
Tel.: (561) 340-2112
Web Site: http://www.rasushi.com
Restaurant Operating Services
N.A.I.C.S.: 722511
Bill Blodgett *(Gen Mgr)*

RA Sushi Pembroke Pines Corp. **(3)**
201 SW 145th Ter, Pembroke Pines, FL
33027
Tel.: (954) 342-5454
Web Site: http://www.rasushi.com
Emp.: 70
Restaurant Operating Services
N.A.I.C.S.: 722511
Sharon MacClay *(Mgr)*

RA Sushi Plano Corp. **(3)**
7501 Lone Star Dr Ste B 130, Plano, TX
75024
Tel.: (469) 467-7400
Web Site: http://www.rasushi.com
Emp.: 60
Restaurant Operating Services
N.A.I.C.S.: 722511
Justin Levine *(Gen Mgr)*

RA Sushi San Diego Corp. **(3)**

TPG Capital, L.P.—(Continued)

477 Camino Del Rio S, San Diego, CA
92108
Tel.: (619) 471-0140
Web Site: http://www.rasushi.com
Restaurant Operating Services
N.A.I.C.S.: 722511

RA Sushi South Miami Corp. (3)
5829 SW 73rd St, South Miami, FL 33143
Tel.: (305) 341-0092
Web Site: http://www.rasushi.com
Restaurant Operating Services
N.A.I.C.S.: 722511
Sharon Macclay (Gen Mgr)

RA Sushi Torrance Corp. (3)
3525 Carson St Ste 161, Torrance, CA
90503
Tel.: (310) 370-6700
Web Site: http://www.rasushi.com
Emp.: 60
Restaurant Operating Services
N.A.I.C.S.: 722511
Sierra Amini (Gen Mgr)

RA Sushi Tucson Corp. (3)
La Encantada 2905 E Skyline Dr Ste 289,
Tucson, AZ 85718
Tel.: (520) 615-3970
Web Site: http://www.benihana.com
Emp.: 80
Restaurant Operating Services
N.A.I.C.S.: 722511
Antonio Clark (Gen Mgr)

RA Sushi Tustin Corp. (3)
2401 Park Ave, Tustin, CA 92782
Tel.: (714) 566-1700
Web Site: http://www.rasushi.com
Sales Range: $10-24.9 Million
Emp.: 75
Restaurant Operating Services
N.A.I.C.S.: 722511
Anthony Lema (Gen Mgr)

Teppan Restaurants Ltd. (3)
9205 SW Cascade Ave, Beaverton, OR
97008-7189
Tel.: (503) 643-4016
Web Site: http://www.benihana.com
Sales Range: $10-24.9 Million
Emp.: 80
Restaurant Operating Services
N.A.I.C.S.: 722511
Tom Elkins (Gen Mgr)

Holding (Domestic):

CSI Financial Services, LLC (2)
PO Box 927830, San Diego, CA 92192-
7830
Tel.: (858) 200-9200
Web Site: http://www.clearbalance.org
Sales Range: $1-9.9 Million
Healthcare Personal Lending Services
N.A.I.C.S.: 522291
Mitch Patridge (Chm)
Chris Brazil (Chief Revenue Officer)
Kathleen Brown (Sr VP-Customer Success
& Innovation)
Ray Freedenberg (CFO)
Bruce Haupt (Pres & CEO)
Grant Phillips (CIO)
Michelle Tygart (Chief Compliance Officer)
Craig Webster (Exec VP-Ops)

Kings Super Markets, Inc. (2)
700 Lanidex Plz, Parsippany, NJ 07054
Tel.: (973) 463-3200
Web Site: http://www.kingswebsite.com
Supermarket Operator
N.A.I.C.S.: 445110
Judith A. Spires (Pres & CEO)

Joint Venture (Domestic):

NextMedia Group, Inc. (2)
6312 S Fiddlers Green Cir Ste 205 E,
Englewood, CO 80111-4927
Tel.: (303) 694-9118
Web Site: http://www.nextmediagroup.net
Sales Range: $10-24.9 Million
Radio & Interactive Media Advertising
N.A.I.C.S.: 541810

Arden Group, Inc. (1)
1600 Market St Ste 2600, Philadelphia, PA
19103
Tel.: (215) 735-1313

Web Site: http://www.ardengroup.com
Sales Range: $400-449.9 Million
Emp.: 2,200
Holding Company; Supermarket Operator
N.A.I.C.S.: 551112

Subsidiary (Domestic):

Gelson's Markets (2)
16400 Ventura Blvd Ste 240, Encino, CA
91436-2123 **(100%)**
Tel.: (818) 906-5700
Web Site: http://www.gelsons.com
Supermarket Operator
N.A.I.C.S.: 445110
Donna Tyndall (Sr VP-Store Ops)
Tom Frattali (Sr VP-Grocery Pur, Mdsg &
Distr)
Hee-Sook Nelson (VP-Employee Dev &
Mktg)
Rob McDougall (Pres & CEO)
John Hammack (CFO)
Dale Brazdis (Sr VP-Perishables)
John Bagan (CMO)

Assisted Living Concepts, LLC (1)
330 N Wabash Ste 3700, Chicago, IL 60611
Tel.: (262) 257-8888
Web Site: http://www.enlivant.com
Sales Range: $500-549.9 Million
Emp.: 5,000
Assisted Living Residences
N.A.I.C.S.: 623312
Daniel M. Guill (Pres & COO)
Akhil Sharma (CFO)
Peter Smith (Chief HR Officer)
Peter Tarsney (Exec VP & Gen Counsel)
Meg Ostrom (Sr VP-Sls & Mktg)
Jeff Floyd (Sr VP-Midwest Div)
Deb Prange (Sr VP-West Div)
Tim Cook (Sr VP-East Div)
Joseph Hessley (Sr VP-Central Div)
Cece Credille (VP-Quality Svcs)
John Sattlemayer (Sr VP-Facilities Mgmt)
Steve Baker (VP-Learning & Dev)
Jim Kleifges (Chief Acctg Officer)
Justin Sheppard (CIO)
Jack R. Callison Jr. (CEO)

Subsidiary (Domestic):

ALC Operating, LLC (2)
1300 W Waugh St, Dalton, GA 30720-3434
Tel.: (706) 277-7101
Web Site: http://www.enliveant.com
Emp.: 40
Old Age People Caring Home Operation
Services
N.A.I.C.S.: 623110
Vanessa Huggins (Exec Dir)

Subsidiary (Domestic):

Aspen Court, LLC (3)
1507 W Jackson St, Macomb, IL 61455
Tel.: (618) 549-1700
Web Site: http://www.aspencourtsiu.com
Old Age People Caring Home Operation
Services
N.A.I.C.S.: 623110

Awbrey House, LLC (3)
2825 Neff Rd, Bend, OR 97701-7917
Tel.: (541) 317-8464
Old Age People Caring Home Operation
Services
N.A.I.C.S.: 623110

**Carriage House Assisted Living,
Inc.** (3)
3106 Saint Charles Dr, Steubenville, OH
43952-3508
Tel.: (740) 264-7667
Web Site:
http://www.capitalhealthcarenetwork.com
Old Age People Caring Home Operation
Services
N.A.I.C.S.: 623110
George Huff (Pres)

Parkhurst House, LLC (3)
2450 May St, Hood River, OR 97031
Tel.: (541) 387-4600
Sales Range: $10-24.9 Million
Emp.: 18
Old Age People Caring Home Operation
Services
N.A.I.C.S.: 623110
Tim Dufour (Gen Mgr)

**Pearson Insurance Company,
LTD** (3)
114 N Washington St, Forrest City, AR
72335
Tel.: (870) 633-6201
Web Site: http://www.pearsonins.com
Sales Range: $50-74.9 Million
Emp.: 10
Insurance Agents & Brokerage Services
N.A.I.C.S.: 524210
Randy Pearson (Gen Mgr)

Prime Home Care, Inc. (3)
17515 W 9 Mile Rd Ste 425, Southfield, MI
48075-4404
Tel.: (248) 967-8572
Old Age People Caring Home Operation
Services
N.A.I.C.S.: 623110

Swan Home Health, LLC (3)
2700 Matthew John Dr, Dubuque, IA 52002-
2938
Tel.: (563) 556-5361
Old Age People Caring Home Operation
Services
N.A.I.C.S.: 623110

Avaya Holdings Corp. (1)
350 Mt Kemble Ave, Morristown, NJ 07960
Tel.: (908) 953-6000
Web Site: https://www.avaya.com
Rev.: $2,973,000,000
Assets: $5,985,000,000
Liabilities: $5,593,000,000
Net Worth: $392,000,000
Earnings: ($13,000,000)
Emp.: 8,063
Fiscal Year-end: 09/30/2021
Holding Company; Business Communica-
tions Systems Mfr
N.A.I.C.S.: 551112
Galib Karim (VP-Caribbean & Latin America
Sls)
Shefali Shah (Chief Admin Officer, Gen
Counsel & Exec VP)
Fred Hayes (Sr VP-Global Bus Ops)
Faye Tylee (Chief HR Officer)
Kevin Speed (Chief Acctg Officer, VP-
Global & Controller)
Frank Ciccone (Sr VP-Sls-North America)
Dennis Kozak (Sr VP-Global Channel Sls)
Simon Harrison (CMO & Sr VP)
Tony Alfano (Sr VP-Global Svcs)
Todd Zerbe (Sr VP-Engrg)
Tyler M. Chambers (Mgr-IR & Treasury)
Alan Masarek (Pres & CEO)
Becky Roof (Interim CFO)
Vito Carnevale (Gen Counsel)
Dino Beverakis (Mng Dir-Australia & New
Zealand)
Sami Ammous (VP-East Asia & Pacific)
Shefali A. Shah (Chief Admin Officer, Gen
Counsel & Exec VP)
Shefali Shah (Chief Admin Officer, Gen
Counsel & Exec VP)
Alan B. Masarek (Pres & CEO)

Subsidiary (Domestic):

Avaya Inc. (2)
4655 Great American Pkwy, Santa Clara,
CA 95054
Tel.: (908) 953-6000
Business Communications Systems Mfr
N.A.I.C.S.: 334210
Sanjay Pai (Sls for-India)
Frank Ciccone (Sr VP-US Sls)
Fred Hayes (Sr VP-Global Bus)
Galib Karim (VP-Americas Intl)
Kieran McGrath (CFO & Sr VP)
Ed Nalbandian (Pres-Avaya Svcs)
Dennis Kozak (Sr VP-Bus Transformation)
Chris McGugan (Sr VP-Solutions & Tech)
Steve Joyner (Mng Dir-UK & Ireland)
Ronald Rubens (VP-Europe)
Simon Vatcher (Mng Dir-Australia & New
Zealand)
Sami Ammous (VP-East Asia & Pacific)
Bill Watkins (Chm)

Subsidiary (Non-US):

Avaya Australia Pty Ltd (3)
123 Epping Road, North Ryde, 2113, NSW,
Australia
Tel.: (61) 1800302833
Sales Range: $50-74.9 Million
Communication Systems
N.A.I.C.S.: 334290

Peter Chidiac (Mng Dir-Australia & New
Zealand)

Branch (Non-US):

Avaya China - Beijing Office (4)
Suite 9-12 Level 11 Tower W3 No 1 East
Chang An Avenue, Dong Cheng District,
Beijing, 100738, China
Tel.: (86) 1085165517
Web Site: http://www.avaya.com
Sales Range: $50-74.9 Million
Emp.: 40
Communication Systems
N.A.I.C.S.: 334290

Avaya China - Guangzhou Office (4)
Rm 6701 67/F CITIC Plz, No 233 Tian He
Bei Rd, Guangzhou, China
Tel.: (86) 20 3877 1822
Web Site: http://www.avaya.com
Communication Systems
N.A.I.C.S.: 334290

Avaya China - Shanghai Office (4)
Units 01A & 06-11 7th Fl The Ctr, 989
Changle Rd, Shanghai, 200031, China
Tel.: (86) 2161206911
Web Site: http://www.avaya.com.cn
Communication Systems
N.A.I.C.S.: 334290

Subsidiary (Non-US):

Avaya Hong Kong Co. Ltd. (4)
Ste 2408 Shell Twr Times Sq 1 Matheson
St, Causeway Bay, China (Hong Kong)
Tel.: (852) 31216109
Web Site: http://www.avaya-apac.com
Sales Range: $25-49.9 Million
Emp.: 45
Communication Service
N.A.I.C.S.: 334290

Branch (Non-US):

Avaya Japan (4)
Akasaka 2 Chome 17-7 Minato Ku, Tokyo,
106 8508, Japan
Tel.: (81) 0355758700
Web Site: http://www.avaya.co.jp
Sales Range: $50-74.9 Million
Communications Equipment
N.A.I.C.S.: 334290

Avaya Korea (4)
12 Fl GFC 737 Yoksam Dong, Kangnam-
gu, 135 984, Seoul, Korea (South)
Tel.: (82) 260074685
Web Site: http://www.avaya.co.kr
Sales Range: $50-74.9 Million
Emp.: 29
Communications Equipment
N.A.I.C.S.: 334290

Avaya Malaysia (4)
8-30-60 L 30 Twr A Jalan Bangsar Utama,
Menara UQA Bangsar, No 5 Jalan Bangsar
Utama 1, 59000, Kuala Lumpur, Malaysia
Tel.: (60) 320593300
Web Site: http://www.avaya.co.uk
Sales Range: $50-74.9 Million
Emp.: 30
Communications Equipment
N.A.I.C.S.: 334290

Avaya Philippines (4)
17th Fl Tower II The Enterprise Center 6766
Ayala Ave, Makati, 1226, Philippines
Tel.: (63) 28848788
Sales Range: $50-74.9 Million
Emp.: 13
Communications Equipment
N.A.I.C.S.: 334290
Ferdinand S. Macatangay (Country Mgr)

Avaya Singapore (4)
89 Science Pk Dr No 01 03 04 The Ruther-
ford Block A, Singapore, 118261, Singapore
Tel.: (65) 68728599
Communications Equipment
N.A.I.C.S.: 334290
Ray Teske (Reg Dir-Asean Ops)
Mike Ansley (Pres-Asia Pacific)

Avaya Thailand (4)
Unit 6 9th Fl Wave Pl 55 Wireless Rd, Pa-
tumwan, Bangkok, 10330, Thailand
Tel.: (66) 26554791
Communications Equipment
N.A.I.C.S.: 334290

Subsidiary (Non-US):

Avaya Belgium SPRL **(3)**
Keizer Karellaan 576 Avenue Charles Quint,
1082, Brussels, Belgium
Tel.: (32) 27777777
Sales Range: $50-74.9 Million
Emp.: 85
Communication System Mfr
N.A.I.C.S.: 334290

Avaya Canada Corp. **(3)**
515 Legget Drive Tower D Suite 600, Ot-
tawa, K2K 3G4, ON, Canada
Tel.: (905) 474-6000
Web Site: http://www.avaya.ca
Sales Range: $50-74.9 Million
Business Communication System Develop-
ment Services
N.A.I.C.S.: 541511
Rejean Bourgault (Mng Dir & Pres-Sls)

Avaya Czech Republic **(3)**
Sokolovska 192/79, 186 00, Prague, Czech
Republic
Tel.: (420) 222194211
Web Site: http://www.avaya.cz
Sales Range: $25-49.9 Million
Emp.: 25
Communication System Mfr
N.A.I.C.S.: 334290

Avaya France S.A. **(3)**
Avaya France Immeuble Ctr Park 9 Rue
Maurice Mallet, Issy-les-Moulineaux, 92445,
France
Tel.: (33) 140947800
Web Site: http://www.issy.avaya.com
Communication Service
N.A.I.C.S.: 517111
Olivier Djian (Mng Dir)

Avaya GmbH & Co. KG **(3)**
Theodor Heuss Allee 112, Frankfurt am
Main, 60326, Germany
Tel.: (49) 6975050
Sales Range: $100-124.9 Million
Holding Company; Telephone Communica-
tions
N.A.I.C.S.: 551112

Subsidiary (Domestic):

Avaya Deutschland GmbH **(4)**
Truderinger Strase 4, 81677, Munich, Ger-
many
Tel.: (49) 89413030
Web Site: http://www.avaya.de
Telecommunications Systems
N.A.I.C.S.: 517111
Thom Matthiessen (Chm-Mgmt Bd)
Wolfgang Zorn (Member-Mgmt Bd)
Beatrice von Brauchitsch (Mng Dir &
Member-Mgmt Bd)

Subsidiary (Domestic):

**Avaya Government Solutions
Inc.** **(3)**
12730 Fair Lks Cir, Fairfax, VA 22033
Tel.: (703) 653-8000
Web Site: http://www.avayagov.com
Sales Range: $200-249.9 Million
Engineering Services; Information Technol-
ogy, Network Engineering
N.A.I.C.S.: 541511
Jorge Navarro (Head-Bus Dev & Exports)

Subsidiary (Non-US):

Avaya Israel **(3)**
Harokmim Street 26 Building D Floor 10,
Holon, 5885849, Israel
Tel.: (972) 3 645 7500
Web Site: http://www.avaya.co.il
Communication Systems
N.A.I.C.S.: 517111
Tali Alkon (Mgr-Sls)

Subsidiary (Domestic):

RADVision Ltd. **(4)**
24 Raoul Wallenberg Street, Tel Aviv,
69719, Israel
Tel.: (972) 37679300
Web Site: http://www.radvision.com
Sales Range: $75-99.9 Million
Designs, Develops & Provides Products &
Technologies for Unified Visual Communica-
tions

N.A.I.C.S.: 334220
Roberto Giamagli (Gen Mgr-Video Bus Unit)
Yair Wiener (CTO)
Pierre Hagendorf (Gen Mgr-Tech Bus Unit)

Subsidiary (Non-US):

RADVision (HK) Ltd. **(5)**
Suite 2901 29/F China Resources Building,
26 Harbour Road, Hong Kong, China (Hong
Kong)
Tel.: (852) 3472 4388
Web Site: http://www.radvision.com
Designs, Develops & Provides Products &
Technologies for Unified Visual Communica-
tions
N.A.I.C.S.: 334220

RADVision (UK) Ltd. **(5)**
6-9 The Square, Stockley Park, Uxbridge,
UB11 1FW, United Kingdom
Tel.: (44) 203 178 8685
Designs, Develops & Provides Products &
Technologies for Unified Visual Communica-
tions
N.A.I.C.S.: 334220

**RADVision Communication Develop-
ment (Beijing) Co. Ltd.** **(5)**
Room 802 Capital Group Plaza No 6Chaoy-
angmen Beidajie, Dongcheng District, Bei-
jing, 100027, China
Tel.: (86) 10 65528528
Designs, Develops & Provides Products &
Technologies for Unified Visual Communica-
tions
N.A.I.C.S.: 334220

RADVision France S.A.R.L. **(5)**
88 Avenue du General Leclerc, 92100,
Boulogne-Billancourt, France
Tel.: (33) 1 55 60 51 30
Designs, Develops & Provides Products &
Technologies for Unified Visual Communica-
tions
N.A.I.C.S.: 334220
Daniel Johansson (Gen Mgr-EMEA)

RADVision Japan KK **(5)**
Kiyotaka Bldg 3F 1-32-8 Taito, Taito-ku, To-
kyo, 110-0016, Japan
Tel.: (81) 3 5816 8950
Designs, Develops & Provides Products &
Technologies for Unified Visual Communica-
tions
N.A.I.C.S.: 334220

Subsidiary (Non-US):

Avaya Nederland B.V. **(3)**
Marconibaan 59, Nieuwegein, 3439 MR,
Netherlands
Tel.: (31) 306097600
Sales Range: $50-74.9 Million
Emp.: 55
Communications Equipment
N.A.I.C.S.: 334290
Roland Geer (Dir-Fin)

Avaya UK **(3)**
Avaya House, Cathedral Hill, Guildford,
GU27YL, United Kingdom
Tel.: (44) 1483308000
Sales Range: $50-74.9 Million
Emp.: 300
Communication Service
N.A.I.C.S.: 334290
Ioan MacRae (Mng Dir)

Branch (Domestic):

Avaya UK - Scotland Office **(4)**
Stewart House Porchard Way, Strathclyde
Business Park, Bellshill, ML4 3HB, N La-
narkshire, United Kingdom
Tel.: (44) 1698 743 700
Web Site: http://www.avaya.com
Sales Range: $50-74.9 Million
Emp.: 20
Telecommunication Systems Sales & Ad-
ministration Office
N.A.I.C.S.: 517112

Subsidiary (Domestic):

Avaya, LLC **(3)**
528 Zircon Way, Superior, CO 80027-4661
Tel.: (303) 354-8999
Web Site: http://www.avaya.com

Sales Range: $800-899.9 Million
Data & Network Communications
N.A.I.C.S.: 517810

Sipera Systems, Inc. **(3)**
1900 Firman Dr, Richardson, TX 75081
Tel.: (214) 206-3202
Web Site: http://www.sipera.com
Sales Range: $1-9.9 Million
Emp.: 17
Computer Systems Design
N.A.I.C.S.: 541512
Jim Timmer (CFO)
Chuck Pledger (VP-Channel Sls-Global)
Gil Stevens (VP-Engrg)

Beaver-Visitec International, Inc. **(1)**
411 Waverley Oaks Rd, Waltham, MA
02452
Tel.: (781) 906-8080
Web Site: http://www.beaver-visitec
Emp.: 200
Ophthalmic Goods Mfr
N.A.I.C.S.: 339115
Shervin J. Korangy (CFO & Chief Strategy
Officer)
Ronald K. Labrum (Chm)
Ron Labrum (Chm)
Jo Anne M. Fasetti (Chief HR Officer)
Peter Hemingway (VP-Strategy & Bus Dev)
Denis Hinaut (VP-Intl)
Michael Cort (VP-Global Mktg)
Lowell Limpus (VP-Global Ops)
Michael Ross (vP-US Sls)
Stephanie McCune (Dir-HR)
Darin Dixon (VP-Sls)

Subsidiary (Domestic):

**Benz Research & Development
Corporation** **(2)**
6447 Parkland Dr, Sarasota, FL 34243
Tel.: (941) 758-8256
Web Site: http://www.benzrd.com
Optical Instrument & Lens Mfr
N.A.I.C.S.: 333310
Patrick H. Benz (Pres)
Steve Brauner (Gen Mgr)
Chris Cremer (Mgr-Monomer Production)
Dora Stoney (Mgr-Polymer Products)
Aaron Strand (Mgr-Polymer Rod Produc-
tion)
Rakesh Vasant (Mgr-Plant Ops & Process)
Andy Larson (Dir-Automation & Design)
David Nicolardi (Mgr-Cast Molding)

**Beijing United Family Hospital Man-
agement Co., Ltd.** **(1)**
2 Jiangtai Road, Chaoyang, Beijing,
100015, China
Tel.: (86) 1059277000
Web Site: http://beijing.ufh.com.cn
Holding Company; Hospital, Clinic & Clinical
Research Facilities Operator; Home Health
Care Services
N.A.I.C.S.: 551112

Affiliate (Domestic):

**Beijing United Family Hospital Co.,
Ltd.** **(2)**
No 2 Jiangtai Road, Chaoyang District, Bei-
jing, 100015, China
Tel.: (86) 10 5927 7200
Web Site: http://beijing.ufh.com.cn
Emp.: 350
Hospital Operator
N.A.I.C.S.: 622110

Centrify Corp. **(1)**
3300 Tannery Way, Santa Clara, CA 95054
Tel.: (669) 444-5200
Web Site: http://www.centrify.com
Computer Security Software Developer
N.A.I.C.S.: 513210
Gary Taggart (Sr VP-Worldwide Sls)
Tom Kemp (Founder)
Shreyas Sadalgi (Sr VP-Bus Dev)
Bill Mann (Sr VP-Products & Mktg)
Rashmi Garde (Gen Counsel)
Rhonda Shantz (CMO)
Mark Oldemeyer (CFO)
Howard Greenfield (Chief Revenue Officer)

Subsidiary (Domestic):

Thycotic Software Limited **(2)**
1101 17th St NW Ste 1200, Washington,
DC 20036
Tel.: (202) 802-9399

Web Site: http://www.thycotic.com
Sales Range: $1-9.9 Million
Security Software Development Services
N.A.I.C.S.: 541511
Y. Ben (Product Mgr)
C. Cristina (Acct Mgr)
M. Kaitlin (Mgr-Customer Rels)
M. Michael (Sr Acct Mgr)
P. Sierra (Mgr-Customer Rels)
R. Walker (Acct Mgr)
C. Yolanda (Mgr-Bus Dev)
James Legg (Pres & CEO)
Jonathan Cogley (Founder)
Steve Kahan (CMO)
Bob Gagnon (VP-Channel Sls)
Damon Tompkins (VP-Americas)
Kathy Moore (CFO)
A. J. Narula (Exec Dir-Federal Sls)
Nick Margarites (CFO)

Cirque du Soleil Inc. **(1)**
8400 avenue du Cirque, Montreal, H1Z
4M6, QC, Canada **(60%)**
Tel.: (514) 722-2324
Web Site: https://www.cirquedusoleil.com
Emp.: 4,000
Theatrical & Music Producer
N.A.I.C.S.: 711110
Guy Laliberte (Founder)
Daniel Lamarre (Vice Chm)
Renee April (Costume Designer)
Gabriel de Alba (Co-Chm)
Jim Murren (Co-Chm)

Subsidiary (US):

Blue Man Productions, Inc. **(2)**
411 Lafayette St Ste 300, New York, NY
10003-7032
Tel.: (212) 226-6366
Web Site: http://www.blueman.com
Sales Range: $1-9.9 Million
Emp.: 40
Musical Theater Production & Recording
Artists
N.A.I.C.S.: 711110
Matt Goldman (Co-Founder)
Phil Stanton (Co-Founder)
Christopher Wink (Co-Founder)
Laura Camien (VP-Comm)

Cirque du Soleil Orlando Inc. **(2)**
1478 E Buena Vista Dr, Lake Buena Vista,
FL 32830
Tel.: (407) 934-9200
Web Site: http://www.cirquedusoleil.com
Sales Range: $75-99.9 Million
Emp.: 200
Theatrical Services
N.A.I.C.S.: 711110
Neil Boyd (Gen Mgr)

**Confluent Medical Technologies,
Inc.** **(1)**
6263 N Scottsdale Rd Ste 224, Scottsdale,
AZ 85250
Tel.: (623) 226-4490
Web Site: http://www.confluentmedical.com
Contract Medical Device Mfr
N.A.I.C.S.: 339112
Dean Schauer (Pres & CEO)
Doug Hutchison (Chief Comml Officer)
Brian Adcock (Chief HR Officer)
Matthew Eckl (CFO)

Subsidiary (Domestic):

Corpus Medical, LLC **(2)**
1300 White Oaks Rd, Campbell, CA 95008-
6783
Tel.: (408) 377-1409
Web Site: http://www.confluentmedical.com
Medical Device Consulting & Custom Manu-
facturing
N.A.I.C.S.: 541690

**Convey Health Solutions Holdings,
Inc.** **(1)**
100 SE 3rd Ave 26th Fl, Fort Lauderdale,
FL 33394 **(100%)**
Rev.: $337,596,000
Assets: $829,903,000
Liabilities: $292,154,000
Net Worth: $537,749,000
Earnings: ($9,978,000)
Emp.: 3,800
Fiscal Year-end: 12/31/2021
Holding Company
N.A.I.C.S.: 551112

TPG Capital, L.P.—(Continued)

Stephen C. Farrell *(CEO)*
Timothy Fairbanks *(CFO & Exec VP)*
John Steele *(Exec VP-Tech)*
Kyle Stern *(Mng Partner-HealthScape Advisors & Exec VP)*
Sharad S. Mansukani *(Chm)*

Subsidiary (Domestic):

Convey Health Solutions, Inc. **(2)**
100 SE 3rd Ave 14th Fl, Fort Lauderdale, FL 33394
Tel.: (954) 903-5000
Web Site:
http://www.conveyhealthsolutions.com
Mail Order Medical Supply Distr
N.A.I.C.S.: 423450
Stephen C. Farrell *(CEO)*
Timothy Fairbanks *(CFO & Exec VP)*
Jonathan Starr *(Exec VP)*
Joanne Thompson *(Chief Compliance Officer)*
Giray Akar *(CTO)*
Stephanie Jones *(Sr VP & Gen Mgr-Medicare Part D)*
Steven Mead *(Sr VP-Fin)*
Gillian Hsieh *(Sr VP-Fin Plng & Analysis)*
Scott Tracey *(Sr VP-IT)*
Michele Henderson *(Sr VP-HR)*
Tom Pelegrin *(Sr VP & Chief Revenue Officer)*
Jeff Fox *(Pres-Gorman Health Group)*

Subsidiary (Domestic):

Gorman Health Group, LLC **(3)**
5151 Wisconsin Ave NW Ste 350, Washington, DC 20016
Tel.: (202) 364-8283
Web Site:
http://www.gormanhealthgroup.com
Scientific & Technical Consulting Services
N.A.I.C.S.: 541690
Jane Scott *(Sr VP-Population Health, Mgmt & Clinical Innovations)*
John Gorman *(Founder)*
Jeff Fox *(Pres & CEO)*
Brett Rudisill *(VP-Mktg & Sls Ops)*
Melissa Smith *(Sr VP-Strategy & Stars)*
Jessica Smith *(Sr VP-Healthcare Analytics & Risk Adjustment Solutions)*
David Sayen *(VP-Client Rels)*
Wayne Miller *(VP-Pharmacy Sols)*
Brandon Hohenberg *(Mgr-Product Dev)*

Covetrus, Inc. **(1)**
12 Mountfort St, Portland, ME 04101-4307
Web Site: https://www.covetrus.com
Rev.: $4,575,000,000
Assets: $3,410,000,000
Liabilities: $1,099,000,000
Net Worth: $1,511,000,000
Earnings: ($54,000,000)
Emp.: 5,275
Fiscal Year-end: 12/31/2021
Veterinary Services
N.A.I.C.S.: 541940
Ajoy H. Kama *(CFO & Exec VP)*
Bekki Kidd *(Head-North America Ops & Global Operational Excellence)*
Michelle Bonfilio *(Chief People Officer)*
Michael Ellis *(Pres-Europe & Exec VP)*
David Hinton *(Pres-APAC & Emerging Markets & Exec VP)*
Timothy Ludlow *(Chief Transformation Officer & Exec VP)*
Anthony Providenti *(Exec VP-Corp Dev)*
Georgina Wraight *(Pres-Tech Solution-Global & Exec VP)*
Dustin Finer *(Chief Admin Officer)*
Ditte Marstrand Wulf *(Chief HR Officer)*
Matthew Malenfant *(Pres-Customer Ops-North America)*
Steve Palmucci *(CIO-Global)*
Jamey Seely *(Sec)*
Stacey M. M. Shirra *(VP-Talent Mgmt-Global)*
Link Welborn *(Chief Veterinary Officer-North America)*
Rens van Dobbenburgh *(Chief Veterinary Officer-Europe)*
Pete Perron *(Pres-Strategic Partnerships)*
Andrew B. Coxhead *(Chief Acctg Officer, VP & Controller)*
Andras Bolcskei *(Pres-Intl)*
Margie B. Pritchard *(Gen Counsel)*
Philip W. Knisely *(Chm)*

Subsidiary (Domestic):

Direct Vet Marketing, Inc. **(2)**
110 Exchange St, Portland, ME 04101
Web Site: http://www.vetsfirstchoice.com
Pharmacy Service for Pets
N.A.I.C.S.: 459910

Henry Schein Animal Health **(2)**
400 Metro Pl N Ste 100, Dublin, OH 43017-7545
Tel.: (614) 761-9095
Web Site: http://www.henryscheinvet.com
Sales Range: $450-499.9 Million
Emp.: 900
Animal Health Products Distr
N.A.I.C.S.: 424210

Subsidiary (Domestic):

Butler Animal Health Holding Company, LLC **(3)**
4274 Shackleford Rd, Norcross, GA 30093-2952
Tel.: (770) 925-7100
Veterinarian Equipment Distr
N.A.I.C.S.: 423450

Butler Animal Health Supply **(3)**
445 SW 52nd Ave Ste 100, Ocala, FL 34474-8508
Tel.: (352) 237-1246
Veterinary Healthcare Supplies
N.A.I.C.S.: 423450

ImproMed, LLC **(3)**
304 Ohio St, Oshkosh, WI 54902-5888
Tel.: (920) 236-7070
Web Site: http://www.impromed.com
Sales Range: $25-49.9 Million
Emp.: 100
Veterinarian Software Developer
N.A.I.C.S.: 513210
Ronald Detjen *(Pres)*

Merritt Veterinary Supplies Inc. **(3)**
102 Distribution Dr, Birmingham, AL 35209-6309
Tel.: (205) 942-4744
Animal Health Products Supplier
N.A.I.C.S.: 423450
Robert Mims *(Mgr)*

SmartPak Equine, LLC **(3)**
40 Grissom Rd Ste 500, Plymouth, MA 02360 **(60%)**
Tel.: (774) 773-1100
Web Site: http://www.smartpakequine.com
Sales Range: $100-124.9 Million
Emp.: 325
Equine & Canine Supplies & Supplements
N.A.I.C.S.: 311119

Subsidiary (Non-US):

Henry Schein Animal Health Holdings Limited **(2)**
Medcare House Centurion Close Gillingham Business Park, Gillingham, ME8 0SB, United Kingdom
Tel.: (44) 8708490872
Holding Company
N.A.I.C.S.: 551112

Provet Holdings Limited **(2)**
48 Bel-Are Ave, Northgate, 4013, QLD, Australia
Tel.: (61) 736216000
Web Site: http://www.provet.com.au
Sales Range: $250-299.9 Million
Emp.: 150
Veterinary Products & Services
N.A.I.C.S.: 459910
Stanley M. Bergman *(CEO)*

Subsidiary (Domestic):

Provet QLD Pty Ltd. **(3)**
48 Bell-Are Ave, Northgate, Brisbane, 4013, QLD, Australia
Tel.: (61) 736216000
Web Site: http://www.provet.com.au
Sales Range: $25-49.9 Million
Emp.: 60
Veterinary Medicines Distr
N.A.I.C.S.: 424210
Nigel Nichols *(CEO)*

Subsidiary (Domestic):

Provet (NSW) Pty Ltd. **(4)**

21-25 Interchange Drive, Eastern Creek, 2766, NSW, Australia
Tel.: (61) 288675177
Web Site: http://www.provet.com.au
Sales Range: $25-49.9 Million
Emp.: 15
Veterinary Products Distr
N.A.I.C.S.: 423490
Jim Aspinall *(Mng Dir)*

Subsidiary (Non-US):

Provet NZ Pty Limited **(4)**
8 Kordel Pl, East Tamaki, 2013, Auckland, New Zealand
Tel.: (64) 99204440
Web Site: http://www.provet.co.nz
Sales Range: $25-49.9 Million
Emp.: 55
Veterinary Products Distr
N.A.I.C.S.: 423490

Subsidiary (Domestic):

Provet SA Pty Ltd. **(4)**
Unit 5 Butler Blvd Burbridge Bus Park, Adelaide Airport, Adelaide, 5950, SA, Australia
Tel.: (61) 881545455
Web Site: http://www.provet.com.au
Veterinary Products Distr
N.A.I.C.S.: 423490

Provet VMS Pty Ltd. **(4)**
Lot 39 Stenhouse Dr, Newcastle, 2286, NSW, Australia
Tel.: (61) 249554488
Web Site: http://www.provet.com.au
Emp.: 60
Veterinary Products Distr
N.A.I.C.S.: 423490

Provet Victoria Pty Ltd. **(4)**
27 Sunmore Close, Heatherton, 3202, VIC, Australia
Tel.: (61) 395405700
Web Site: http://www.provet.net.au
Sales Range: $25-49.9 Million
Emp.: 30
Veterinary Products Distr
N.A.I.C.S.: 423490

Provet WA Pty Ltd. **(4)**
1936 Beach Rd, Malaga, 6090, WA, Australia
Tel.: (61) 8 9241 8400
Web Site: http://www.provet.com.au
Emp.: 18
Veterinary Products Whslr
N.A.I.C.S.: 423490

Creative Artists Agency, LLC **(1)**
2000 Ave of The Stars, Los Angeles, CA 90007 **(53%)**
Tel.: (424) 288-2000
Web Site: http://www.caa.com
Entertainment Talent Agency
N.A.I.C.S.: 711410
Elizabeth Berlacher Bush *(Head-Media & Entertainment Partnerships-Global)*
Richard Lovett *(Pres)*
James Burtson *(CFO)*
Daniel Manwaring *(Head-Motion Pictures Grp-China)*
Aubree Curtis *(Head-Social Impact)*
Lisa Joseph Metelus *(Co-head-Basketball Mktg & Servicing)*

Division (Domestic):

CAA Sports **(2)**
2000 Avenue of the Stars, Los Angeles, CA 90067
Tel.: (424) 288-2000
Web Site: http://www.caa.com
Emp.: 2,000
Athlete Marketing & Talent Agents
N.A.I.C.S.: 711410
Frank Moore *(CFO)*
Gary Zimmerman *(Controller)*
Jeff Berry *(Head-Baseball)*

Branch (Domestic):

CAA Sports **(3)**
162 5th Ave 6th Fl, New York, NY 10010
Tel.: (804) 754-1616
Web Site: http://www.caasports.com
Athlete Marketing & Talent Agents
N.A.I.C.S.: 711410

Subsidiary (Domestic):

ICON Venue Group, LLC **(3)**
5075 S Syracuse St Ste 700, Denver, CO 80237
Tel.: (303) 796-2655
Web Site: http://www.iconvenue.com
Sales Range: $1-9.9 Million
Emp.: 30
Engineering Services
N.A.I.C.S.: 541330
Timothy Romani *(CEO)*
Art Aaron *(Pres & COO)*
Eric Andalman *(Gen Counsel & Sr VP)*
Ajay Bagal *(Sr VP)*
Dan Barrett *(Exec VP)*
Marc Farha *(Exec VP)*
Melissa Heiter *(Sr VP)*
Chris Miller *(Sr VP)*
George Messina *(Sr VP)*
Rob Stephens *(Sr VP)*
Dan Vaillant *(Sr VP)*
Charlie Thornton *(Exec VP)*

Subsidiary (Non-US):

Creative Artists Agency UK Limited **(2)**
12 Hammersmith Grove, London, W6 7AP, United Kingdom
Tel.: (44) 20 8846 3000
Web Site: http://www.caa.com
Talent Agency
N.A.I.C.S.: 711410
Hilary K. Krane *(Chief Legal Officer)*

Branch (Domestic):

Creative Artists Agency, LLC - St. Louis Office **(2)**
222 S Central Ave Ste 1008, Saint Louis, MO 63105
Tel.: (314) 862-5560
Web Site: http://www.caa.com
Sales Range: $10-24.9 Million
Emp.: 13
Talent Agency
N.A.I.C.S.: 711410

Subsidiary (Domestic):

International Creative Management, Inc. **(2)**
10250 Constellation Blvd, Los Angeles, CA 90067-1934
Tel.: (310) 550-4000
Web Site: http://www.icmtalent.com
Popular Music, Film & Television Talent & Literary Agency
N.A.I.C.S.: 711410
Richard B. Levy *(Gen Counsel)*
Chris Silbermann *(Pres)*

Branch (Domestic):

International Creative Management, Inc. - New York **(3)**
730 5th Ave, New York, NY 10019
Tel.: (212) 556-5600
Web Site: http://www.icmtalent.com
Popular Music, Film & Television Talent & Literary Agency
N.A.I.C.S.: 711410
Esther Newberg *(Chm & Exec VP)*

Cushman & Wakefield plc **(1)**
125 Old Broad Street, London, EC2N 1AR, United Kingdom
Tel.: (44) 2032963000
Web Site:
http://www.cushmanwakefield.com
Rev.: $10,105,700,000
Assets: $7,949,300,000
Liabilities: $6,287,200,000
Net Worth: $1,662,100,000
Earnings: $196,400,000
Emp.: 52,000
Fiscal Year-end: 12/31/2022
Holding Company
N.A.I.C.S.: 551112
Michelle M. MacKay *(CEO)*
Michelle M. MacKay *(Pres & CEO)*
Matthew Miller *(Vice Chm)*
W. Brett White *(Chm)*
Josh McGee *(Mng Dir-Chicago & United States)*
Carlo Barel di Sant'Albano *(Chm-EMEA & CEO-Global Capital Markets Investor Svcs)*

Kristina Wollan (Mng Dir-Investor Svcs-San Francisco)
Bailey Webb (Dir-Comm-Atlanta & U.S)
Michelle Hay (Chief HR Officer)
Brett Soloway (Gen Counsel)
Nathaniel Robinson (Chief Investment Officer & Exec VP-Strategic Plng)
Colin Wilson (CEO-EMEA)
Matthew Bouw (CEO-Asia Pacific)
Paul Bedborough (CEO-C & W Svcs)
Bill Knightly (CEO-Global Occupier Svcs)
Brad Kreiger (Chief Mktg & Comm Officer)
Nadine Augusta (Chief Diversity, Equity & Inclusion Officer)
George Roberts (Head-Ireland)
Richard Pickering (Chief Strategy Officer)
Sylvia Moutsopoulos (Sr Mgr-Building)
Paul Durkin (Head-Retail, Logistics & Industrial)
Michelle Crawley (Co-Sec)
Judy Snowball (Co-Sec)
Danielle Nasser (Co-Sec)
Siobhan Kennett (Sr Mgr-Programme)
Michelle Gloder (Head-Customer Experience)
Haleana Knights (Comm Mgr)
Ben Cullen (Head-Offices)
Andrew Steptoe (Project Mgr)
Tom Stanley (Mgr-Safety)
Michael Blandford (Mgr-Resource)
Michael Pritchard (Mgr-Inventory)
Rob Chambers (Mgr-Technical Svcs)
Steve Herrington (Mgr-Quality)
Tim Wood (Dir-IT & Tech)
Victoria Jones (Project Mgr)
Rod Till (Mgr-Building)
Neil O. Johnston (CFO & Exec VP)
Andrew McDonald (COO & Pres-Global)
Payman Sadegh (Chief Data Officer)
Josh Vernon (Partner-Shopping Centre & In-Town Retail Capital Markets)
Dominic Bouvet (Head-Retail & Leisure-UK)
Jason Winfield (Head-Capital Markets-UK & Ireland)

Subsidiary (US):

Colvill Office Properties, LLC (2)
5847 San Felipe St Ste 600, Houston, TX 77057-3008
Tel.: (713) 877-1550
Web Site: http://www.colvilloffice.com
Offices of Real Estate Agents & Brokers
N.A.I.C.S.: 531210
Chip Colvill (Owner)
Diana Bridger (Dir-Leasing)

Cresa Partners of Los Angeles, Inc. (2)
11726 San Vicente Blvd, Los Angeles, CA 90049
Tel.: (310) 207-1700
Sales Range: $10-24.9 Million
Emp.: 41
Management Consulting Services
N.A.I.C.S.: 541618
Nancy Ryan (Controller)
Paula Fowler (Sr VP-Ops)
Steve Schaumberg (Mng Principal)
Dan Silber (VP)
Daniel Sullivan (Principal)
Judi Hilton (COO)
Dennis Compton (VP)
Ed Riggins (Exec VP)
Bill Finnegan (Sr VP)
Bo Keatley (VP)
Edward Fothergill (CFO)
Jonathan C. Rudes (Sr VP)
Jon C. Olmstead (Principal)
Joseph Faulkner (Sr VP)
Los Angeles (Sr VP)
Richard M. Rhodes (CEO)
Sandy Fishlock (Sr VP)

Cushman & Wakefield, Inc. (2)
225 W Wacker Dr Ste 3000, Chicago, IL 60606
Tel.: (312) 470-1800
Web Site:
http://www.cushmanandwakefield.com
Sales Range: $5-14.9 Billion
Emp.: 45,000
Real Estate Brokerage & Property Management Services
N.A.I.C.S.: 531210
Brian R. Corcoran (Exec VP-Phoenix)
Frank P. Liantonio (Exec Mng Dir-New York)
Bruce E. Mosler (Chm-Global Brokerage-New York)

Janice Stanton (Exec Mng Dir-Capital Markets Grp-C&W)
Alex Ray (Mng Dir-Capital Markets Grp-New York)
Carlo Barel di Sant'Albano (Chm-EMEA & CEO-Capital Markets & Investor Svcs-Americas)
Patrick Dugan (Exec Dir-Brooklyn)
Stephen F. Baker (Exec Mng Dir-Office Leasing-Stamford)
Ben Conwell (Sr Mng Dir-Seattle)
Amy Lind (Mng Dir)
Brian Kriter (Exec Mng Dir-Toronto)
Steve Quick (CEO-Global Occupier Svcs)
Brett Soloway (Global Gen Counsel)
Matthew Bouw (CEO-Asia Pacific)
Edward Cheung (Chm-APAC & CEO-Greater China)
Toby Dodd (Exec Mng Dir-Global Occupier Svcs-New York)
Richard Hamilton (Mng Dir-Rosemont)
Mark S. Weiss (Vice Chm-New York)
Stewart Lyman (Dir-Nashville)
Craig Bjorklund (Sr VP & Reg Dir-Asset Svcs)
Tara I. Stacom (Vice Chm)
Andrew Hopkins (Sr VP)
Paul Leone (Exec Dir-Boston)
Patrick Murphy (Vice Chm-New York)
Phillip Brimble (Mng Dir)
Anthony Librizzi (Mng Dir-West Palm Beach)
David Gorelick (Exec Mng Dir & Head-Retail Svcs-Americas)
Revathi Greenwood (Head-Research-Americas)
Ken Loeber (Pres-Project & Dev Svcs-Charlotte)
Terry Rennaker (Sr Mng Dir-Project & Dev Svcs-Charlotte)
Adrienne Fasano (Head-Mktg-Americas)
Michelle Hay (Chief HR Officer-Global & Americas)
Steve LaKind (Exec Dir)
Melanie Kirkwood Ruiz (CIO-Americas)
Colin Wilson (CEO-EMEA)
Bruce Daubner (Sr Mng Dir)
Jon Herman (Exec Mng Dir-New York)
Marla Maloney (Pres-Asset Svcs-Americas)
Suzanne Mehta (Chief Experience Officer)
Roberta Liss (Mng Principal-Reg)
Paulo Sarmento (Head-Capital Markets Grp-Portugal)
Eric van Leuven (Partner & Head-Portugal)
Nathaniel Robinson (Global Chief Investment Officer & Exec VP-Strategic Plng)
Paul St. Martin (Dir-Minneapolis-St. Paul)
Bruce Schuette (Dir-Minneapolis-St. Paul)
Andrew T. C. Smith (Partner)
Sarah Jones (Partner-Leeds)
Jennifer Dittmer Vivolo (Dir-Flexible Workplace Solutions-Global)
Matthew Bowen (Mng Dir)
Richard Shield (Partner-Newcastle)
David Wilson (Head-Newcastle)
Nick DiPaolo (Dir-Brokerage-Greater Los Angeles)
Nicole Romer (Partner-Intl & Head-Retail Investment-Germany)
Wanda Riley (Mng Principal-Orlando & Jacksonville)
Katell Bourgeois (Partner & Head-Hospitality-France)
Gregory Kirsch (Mng Dir)
Vicki Noonan (Mng Principal)
Katie Mahon (Sr Mng Dir-Retail Strategy & Ops-Americas)
Adam L. Stanley (CIO-Global)
Pedro Vasquez (Exec Acct Dir-Global Occupier Svcs-Global)
Holly Tyson (Chief People Officer)
Laurie Paquette (Sr Mng Dir-Asset Svcs)
Mia Mends (CEO-C&W Svcs)
Brett White (Exec Chm)
John C. Santora (Vice Chm & Pres)

Subsidiary (Domestic):

C&W Facility Services, Inc. (3)
275 Grove St Ste 3-200, Auburndale, MA 02466
Tel.: (888) 751-9100
Web Site: http://cwservices.com
Maintenance Services
N.A.I.C.S.: 811490
Paul Bedborough (CEO)

Subsidiary (Domestic):

Pyramid Building Maintenance Corporation (4)
2175 Martin Ave, Santa Clara, CA 95050
Tel.: (408) 727-9393
Web Site:
http://www.pacificmaintenance.com
Sales Range: $25-49.9 Million
Emp.: 600
Building Maintenance & Janitorial Services
N.A.I.C.S.: 561210
Kari Hus (Pres)

Subsidiary (Non-US):

Cushman & Wakefield (Bahrain) W.L.L. (3)
The Lagoon Amwaj Island Office #306 Building 2648, Road 5720 Area 257, Manama, Bahrain
Tel.: (973) 17692476
Web Site:
http://www.cushmanwakefield.com
Management Consulting Services
N.A.I.C.S.: 541618
Kelvin Crutchlow (Dir & Gen Mgr)

Cushman & Wakefield (HK) Limited (3)
16/F Jardine House, Central, China (Hong Kong)
Tel.: (852) 2956 3888
Web Site:
http://www.cushmanwakefield.com
Real Estate Services
N.A.I.C.S.: 531390
Eric Chong (Sr Mgr-Research)
Keith Hemshall (Head-Office Svcs)
John Siu (Mng Dir)

Cushman & Wakefield (India) Pvt. Ltd. (3)
14th Floor Building 8 Tower C DLF Cyber City, Gurgaon, 122002, Haryana, India
Tel.: (91) 1244695555
Web Site:
http://www.cushmanwakefield.co.in
Real Estate Services
N.A.I.C.S.: 531390
Anshul Jain (Mng Dir & Country Mgr)
Ritesh Sachdev (Mng Dir-South)
Badal Yagnik (Mng Dir-Leasing Svcs)
Rajesh Sharma (Mng Dir-Integrated Facility Mgmt & Asset Svcs)
Kaustuv Roy (Mng Dir-New Bus Acq)
Somil Agrawal (Head-Mktg)
Vivek Dahiya (Mng Dir-North)
Manoj Sharan (Sr Dir & Head-Ops-Integrated Facility Mgmt & Asset Svcs)
Gautam Saraf (Mng Dir-Mumbai)
Sumeet Bhatia (Mng Dir-Pune)
Ramita Arora (Mng Dir-Bangalore)
Veera Babu (Mng Dir-Hyderabad)
V. S. Sridhar (Mng Dir-Chennai)
Khurshed Gandhi (Mng Dir-Consulting Svc)
Somy Thomas (Mng Dir-Valuations & Advisory Svc)
Vijay Ganesh (Mng Dir-Land & Industrial)
Saurabh Shatdal (Mng Dir-Developer & Investor Svc)
Shveta Jain (Mng Dir-Real Estate Private Wealth Svc)
Manish Goel (Mng Dir-Base Build Svc)
Shashi Bhushan (Mng Dir-Fit Outs, Design & Build Bus)
Anand Gupta (CFO-India)

Cushman & Wakefield (NSW) Pty Limited (3)
Level 22 1 O'Connell Street, Sydney, 2000, NSW, Australia
Tel.: (61) 2 8243 9999
Web Site:
http://www.cushmanwakefield.com.au
Real Estate Services
N.A.I.C.S.: 531390
James Patterson (CEO-Australia & New Zealand)
Anna Town (Head-Strategic Mktg-Australia & New Zealand)
Phillip Rockliff (Mng Dir-Comml Real Estate)
Jodi Swinburne (COO)

Cushman & Wakefield (S) Pte Ltd (3)
3 Church Street 09-03 Samsung Hub, Sin-

gapore, 49483, Singapore
Tel.: (65) 65353232
Web Site:
http://www.cushmanwakefield.com
Real Estate Services
N.A.I.C.S.: 531390
Christine Li (Dir-Res)
Sigrid Zialcita (Mng Dir-Res)
Steve Saul (Mng Dir)
Christopher Browne (Mng Dir & Head-Occupier Svcs)
Matthew Bouw (CEO-Asia Pacific)
Chris Cuff (Exec Dir-Comml Leasing)
Mark Lampard (Head-Tenant Representation & Comml Leasing & Exec Dir)

Cushman & Wakefield (Shanghai) Co. Ltd. (3)
42-43/F Tower 2 Plaza 66 1366 Nanjing West Road, Shanghai, 200040, China
Tel.: (86) 21 2208 0088
Web Site:
http://www.cushmanwakefield.com.cn
Real Estate Services
N.A.I.C.S.: 531390
Mimie Lau (Mng Dir-East China)

Cushman & Wakefield (U.K.) Ltd. (3)
43-45 Portman Square, London, W1A 3BG, United Kingdom
Tel.: (44) 2079355000
Web Site:
http://www.cushmanwakefield.co.uk
Emp.: 1,200
Real Estate Brokerage & Property Management Services
N.A.I.C.S.: 531390
James Heyworth-Dunne (Partner-Central London)
Justin Taylor (Head-Retail-EMEA)
Charles Smith (Head-Valuation & Advisory Svcs)
George Roberts (Head-UK & Ireland)

Cushman & Wakefield (VIC) Pty Ltd (3)
Level 9 385 Bourke Street, Melbourne, 3000, VIC, Australia
Tel.: (61) 3 9631 7500
Web Site:
http://www.cushmanwakefield.com.au
Real Estate Services
N.A.I.C.S.: 531390
Dominic Long (Mng Dir-Comml Real Estate)

Branch (Non-US):

Cushman & Wakefield - Brussels (3)
Chaussee de la Hulpe 166 Terhulpsesteenweg, Brussels, 1170, Belgium
Tel.: (32) 26290200
Web Site: http://www.cushmanwakefield.be
Real Estate Services
N.A.I.C.S.: 531390
Koen Nevens (Mng Partner & Head-Northern Europe Reg)
Christelle Lintermans (Head-Mktg-Belgium & Luxembourg)
Stijn Thomas (Partner)
Maximilien Mandart (Partner)
Jean Baheux (Partner & Head-Retail Agency-Belgium & Luxembourg)

Cushman & Wakefield - Madrid (3)
Edificio Beatriz Jose Ortega y Gasset 29 6th Floor, 28006, Madrid, Spain
Tel.: (34) 91 781 0010
Web Site: http://www.cushmanwakefield.es
Real Estate Services
N.A.I.C.S.: 531390
Jenny Pizarro (Partner)
Fernando Arcos (Partner)

Cushman & Wakefield - Sao Paulo (3)
Praca Jose Lannes 40-3rd Floor, Sao Paulo, Brazil
Tel.: (55) 1155015464
Web Site: http://www.cushmanwakefield.us
Real Estate Services
N.A.I.C.S.: 531390
Celina Antunes (Pres-South America)
Stela Hirata (Exec Dir)
Cristian Alexander Mina (Exec Dir)
Sergio Mendes (Project Dir)
Rogerio Cerreti (Dir-Real Estate)

Subsidiary (Non-US):

Cushman & Wakefield K.K. (3)

TPG Capital, L.P.—(Continued)

Sanno Park Tower 13F 2-11-1 Nagatacho,
Chiyoda-ku, Tokyo, 100-6113, Japan
Tel.: (81) 3 3596 7070
Web Site: http://www.cushmanwakefield.jp
Real Estate Services
N.A.I.C.S.: 531390
Todd Olson (Exec Mng Dir)
Norimasa Shimizu (COO-Asset Mgmt)
Yoshiyuki Tanaka (Pres & CEO-Asset
Mgmt)

Cushman & Wakefield LLP (3)
125 Old Broad Street, London, EC2N 1AR,
United Kingdom
Tel.: (44) 20 3296 3000
Web Site:
http://www.cushmanwakefield.com
Emp.: 200
Real Estate Services
N.A.I.C.S.: 531390
Colin Wilson (CEO-EMEA)
Parimal Patel (Dir-Fin-UK, Nordics & Middle
East)
Charles Lebeter (Dir-HR-UK & Ireland)
Nancy Cooper (Sec)
George Roberts (Head-UK & Ireland)
Toby Ogden (Head-Markets)
Eric van Dyck (Chm-Capital Markets Bus-
EMEA)
Jan-Willem Bastijn (Head-Capital Markets-
EMEA)
Michael Rodda (Head-Retail Capital
Markets-EMEA)
Stephen Screene (COO-Capital Markets-
EMEA)
Paul Boursican (Head-Bus Space-Capital
Markets-EMEA)

Cushman & Wakefield Ltd. (3)
161 Bay Street Suite 1500, PO Box 602,
Toronto, M5J 2S1, ON, Canada
Tel.: (416) 862-0611
Web Site:
https://www.cushmanwakefield.com
Real Estate Services
N.A.I.C.S.: 531390
Bradley S. Anderson (Vice Chm)
Brian Kriter (Exec Mng Dir-Americas Bus
Dev)
Cheryl Farrow (Mng Dir-Institutional Office)
Chuck Scott (CEO)
Brett White (Chm & CEO)
Brad Kreiger (Chief Mktg Officer & Chief
Comm Officer)
Bill Knightly (Treas & Exec VP-IR)
Nathaniel Robinson (Chief Investment Offi-
cer & Exec VP-Strategic Plng)
Alan Farley (VP)
Sean Ferguson (VP)
Jake Vaughan (VP)
Mike Warner (Exec VP)
Bahareh Tabar (VP)
Joel Goulding (VP)

Cushman & Wakefield Sweden AB (3)
Regeringsgatan 59, Stockholm, 11156,
Sweden
Tel.: (46) 8 545 677 0
Web Site:
http://www.cushmanwakefield.com
Real Estate Services
N.A.I.C.S.: 531390
Agneta Jakobsson (Head-Sweden & Nor-
dics)

Cushman & Wakefield de Mexico (3)
Paseo de las Tamarindos N60-B 2 Floor,
Col Bosques de las Lomas, Mexico, 5120,
Mexico
Tel.: (52) 55 8525 8000
Web Site:
http://www.cushmanwakefield.com
Emp.: 80
Real Estate Services
N.A.I.C.S.: 531390
Victor M. Lachica (Pres & CEO)
Montserrat Pont (Sr Mgr-Ops & hr)

Subsidiary (Domestic):

Cushman & Wakefield of Arizona, Inc. (3)
2555 E Camelback Rd Ste 400, Phoenix,
AZ 85016
Tel.: (602) 954-9000

Web Site: http://www.cushwakephoenix.com
Emp.: 260
Real Estate Services
N.A.I.C.S.: 531210
Phil Jones (Mng Dir)
Victoria Richardson (Mgr-Mktg)
Dave Carder (Mng Dir)
Keith Lambeth (Exec Mng Dir)
John Appelbe (Mng Dir)
Sheila Bale (Mng Dir)
Michael Beall (Exec Mng Dir)
Blaine Black (Mng Dir)
Jim Wilson (Exec Mng Dir)
Bryon Carney (Mng Principal)
Jim Crews (Mng Dir)
Larry Downey (Vice Chm)
Shelby Ferrari (Office Mgr)
David Fogler (Exec Mng Dir)
Michael Hackett (Exec Mng Dir)
Mike Haenel (Exec Mng Dir)
Eric Wichterman (Exec Mng Dir)
Christopher Toci (Exec Mng Dir)
Andy Markham (Exec Mng Dir)
Patti Martin (Office Mgr)
Steven Nicoluzakis (Exec Mng Dir)
Ryan Schubert (Exec Mng Dir)
Will Strong (Exec Mng Dir)

Cushman & Wakefield of California, Inc. (3)
425 Market St Ste 2300, San Francisco, CA
94105
Tel.: (415) 397-1700
Web Site:
http://www.cushwakesanfrancisco.com
Emp.: 125
Real Estate Services
N.A.I.C.S.: 531210
Joe Cook (Mng Principal-Northern CA &
OR)
Kevin Brennan (Exec Mng Dir)
Mark Anderson (Exec Mng Dir)
J. D. Lumpkin (Exec Mng Dir & Mng Princi-
pal)
Elizabeth Champagne (Exec Mng Dir)
Thomas Christian (Exec Mng Dir)
Terrence Daly (Exec Mng Dir)
George Eckard (Exec Mng Dir)
Steven Hermann (Exec Mng Dir)
Donald Lebuhn (Exec Mng Dir)
Seth Siegel (Exec Mng Dir)
Zach Siegel (Exec Mng Dir)
M. Daniel Wald (Exec Mng Dir)
Tal Siglar (Mng Dir-Ontario)

Cushman & Wakefield of Connecti-cut, Inc. (3)
107 Elm St 4 Stamford Plz 8th Fl, Stamford,
CT 06902
Tel.: (203) 326-5800
Real Estate Services
N.A.I.C.S.: 531210
Steve Baker (Exec Mng Dir)
Kevin Foley (Exec Mng Dir)
Jay Hruska (Vice Chm)
Al Mirin (Exec Mng Dir)
James Moran (Chief Strategy Officer &
Exec Mng Dir-Valuation & Advisory-Global)
Michael Norris (Exec Mng Dir)
Gerald Rasmussen (Exec Mng Dir)

Cushman & Wakefield of Florida, Inc. (3)
333 SE 2nd Ave, Miami, FL 33131-2662
Tel.: (305) 371-4411
Web Site: http://www.cushwakesouthfl.com
Real Estate Services
N.A.I.C.S.: 531210
Larry Richey (Mng Principal-Florida)
Mark Gilbert (Exec Mng Dir)
Adam Feinstein (Exec Dir)
Brian Gale (Vice Chm)
Robert Kaplan (Exec Mng Dir)
Liza Medina (Office Mgr)
Mike Agnew (Sr Mng Dir-Asset Svcs)

Branch (Domestic):

Cushman & Wakefield, Inc. - Tampa (4)
1 Tampa City Ctr Ste 3300, Tampa, FL
33602
Tel.: (813) 223-6300
Web Site: http://www.cushwaketampa.com
Emp.: 135
Real Estate Brokerage, Property Manage-
ment & Leasing Services
N.A.I.C.S.: 531210

Doug Rothschild (Exec Mng Dir)
Lou Varsames (Exec Mng Dir)
Larry Richey (Mng Principal-Florida)
Elize Greenoe (Office Mgr)
Paul Carr (Sr Dir)
Allen McMurtry (Exec Dir)
Megan Fetter (Sr Mng Dir)
David Kliewer (Sr Mng Dir)
Todd Brandon (Exec Mng Dir)
Mike Davis (Exec Mng Dir)
Nicole Grzywacz (Office Mgr-Mktg &
Comm)
Bruce Lauer (Vice Chm)
Ross Kirk (Exec Mng Dir)

Subsidiary (Domestic):

Cushman & Wakefield of Georgia, Inc. (3)
1180 Peachtree St Ste 3100, Atlanta, GA
30309
Tel.: (404) 875-1000
Web Site: http://www.cushwakeatlanta.com
Emp.: 350
Real Estate Services
N.A.I.C.S.: 531210
Bryan Berthold (Mng Dir-Workplace Strate-
gies)
John O'Neill (Mng Principal)
Tyler Averitt (Exec Mng Dir)
Stewart Calhoun (Exec Mng Dir)
Kirk Diamond (Exec Mng Dir)
Andy Ghertner (Exec Mng Dir)
Travis Jackson (Exec Mng Dir)
Betty McIntosh (Sr Mng Dir)
David Risdon (Sr Mng Dir)
Michael Ryan (Exec Mng Dir)
Chris Spain (Vice Chm)
Robert Stickel (Exec Mng Dir)
Bailey Webb (Dir-PR)
David W. Meline (Exec Mng Dir)

Cushman & Wakefield of Illinois, Inc. (3)
225 W Wacker Dr Ste 3000, Chicago, IL
60606
Tel.: (312) 470-1800
Web Site: http://www.cushwakechicago.com
Emp.: 640
Real Estate Services
N.A.I.C.S.: 531210
Brian Adelstein (Sr VP)
Marius Andreasen (Sr Mng Dir)
James Carpenter (Exec Mng Dir)
Britt Casey (Exec Mng Dir)
Craig Cassell (Exec Mng Dir)
Frank Franzese (Exec Mng Dir)
Scott Goldman (Exec Mng Dir)
Ned Franke (Exec Mng Dir)
Kent Ilhardt (Exec Mng Dir)
Jack Keenan (Exec Mng Dir)
Ari Klein (Exec Mng Dir)
Dan Maslauski (Exec Mng Dir)

Cushman & Wakefield of Long Island, Inc. (3)
401 Broad Hollow Rd Ste 301, Melville, NY
11747-4711
Tel.: (631) 425-1241
Web Site:
http://www.cushmanwakefield.com
Emp.: 20
Real Estate Services
N.A.I.C.S.: 531210
Robert Sheehy (Exec Mng Dir)
Robert Kuppersmith (Mng Dir)
Frank Frizalone (Exec Dir)
David Pennetta (Exec Dir)
Philip D'Avanzo (Exec Dir)
Donald Direnzo Jr. (Exec Dir)

Cushman & Wakefield of Maryland, Inc. (3)
1 E Pratt St Ste 700, Baltimore, MD 21202
Tel.: (410) 752-4285
Web Site:
http://www.cushwakebaltimore.com
Emp.: 75
Commercial Real Estate Services
N.A.I.C.S.: 531210
Robert Shovan (VP-Ops)
David Baird (Mng Dir)
Douglas Brinkley (Mng Dir)
David Downey (Mng Dir)
Lee Dunfee (Sr VP-Engrg Ops)
L. Bruce Matthai (Mng Dir)
Peter Stanford (Mng Principal)

Cushman & Wakefield of Massachu-setts, Inc. (3)

225 Franklin St Ste 300, Boston, MA 02110
Tel.: (617) 330-6966
Web Site: http://www.cushwakeboston.com
Emp.: 120
Real Estate Services
N.A.I.C.S.: 531210
Linda McDonough (Dir-Mktg)
Rick Swartz (Exec Mng Dir)
Barbara Elia (Exec Mng Dir)
Al Woods (Sr Mng Dir)
Robert Skinner (Exec Mng Dir)
Brian Barnett (Mng Dir)
Jim Berry (Exec Dir)
Joseph Fallon (Exec Vice Chm)
Jeanne Garafalo (Exec Mng Dir)
Brian Hines (Vice Chm)
Ted Lyon (Exec Mng Dir)
John Boyle III (Vice Chm)

Cushman & Wakefield of New Jersey, Inc. (3)
1 Meadowlands Plz 7th Fl, East Rutherford,
NJ 07073-1605
Tel.: (201) 935-4000
Web Site: http://www.cushmanwakefield.us
Real Estate Services
N.A.I.C.S.: 531210
Richard Baumstein (Exec Mng Dir)
David Bernhaut (Vice Chm)
Stan Danzig (Exec Mng Dir)
Steve Elman (Exec Mng Dir)
Curtis Foster (Exec Mng Dir)
James Frank (Exec Mng Dir)
H. Gary Gabriel (Exec Mng Dir)
Jules Nissim (Exec Mng Dir)
Robert Rudin (Vice Chm)
Andrew Merin (Vice Chm)
David Sherman (Exec Mng Dir)
Marc Trevisan (Exec Mng Dir)
Lauren Tarino (Dir-Mktg)
Stephen Sander (Sr Dir-Indus Brokerage)
Andrew Judd (Reg Mng Principal)
Catherine Bounczek (Sr Coord-Brokerage)

Cushman & Wakefield of Oregon, Inc. (3)
200 SW Market St Ste 200, Portland, OR
97201-5730
Tel.: (503) 279-1700
Web Site: http://www.cushmanwakefield.us
Real Estate Services
N.A.I.C.S.: 531210
Judy Howard (Dir-Ops)
Brian Booth (Exec Dir)
Jay F. Booth (Reg Dir-Retail Industry Grp)
Kim Gaube (Mgr-Mktg)
Samantha Krajczynski (Dir-Mktg)
Mark Carnese (Exec Dir)
Doug Deurwaarder (Exec Dir)
Tom Usher (Exec Dir)
Steve Zenker (Exec Dir)

Cushman & Wakefield of Texas, Inc. (3)
1330 Post Oak Blvd Ste 2700, Houston, TX
77056
Tel.: (713) 877-1700
Web Site:
http://www.cushmanwakefieldhouston.com
Emp.: 140
Real Estate Services
N.A.I.C.S.: 531210
Scott Wegmann (Vice Chm)
Chris Oliver (Vice Chm)
Tim D. Relyea (Exec Vice Chm)
Greg J. Jones (Mng Dir)
Ed Nwokedi (Exec Dir)
Scott Rando (Sr Mng Dir)
Jim Bailey (Vice Chm)
David Cook (Vice Chm)
Lou Cushman (Vice Chm)
Dawn Garrett (Controller)
John Littman (Exec Mng Dir)
Kelley Parker (Vice Chm)
Joe Peddie (Vice Chm)
Jeff Peden (Exec Mng Dir)
Kevin Snodgrass (Vice Chm)
Trey Strake (Vice Chm)
Rick Zbranek (Sr Mng Dir)

Branch (Domestic):

Cushman & Wakefield of Texas, Inc. - Austin (4)
200 W Cesar Chavez Ste 250, Austin, TX
78701
Tel.: (512) 474-2400
Web Site: http://www.cushwakeaustintx.com

Emp.: 50
Commercial Real Estate Broker
N.A.I.C.S.: 531210
Spencer Hayes *(Exec Mng Dir & Mng Principal)*
Ford Alexander *(Exec Mng Dir)*
Brett Arabie *(Mng Dir)*
Katie Ehlers *(Dir-Ops)*
Mark Greiner *(Exec Dir)*
Todd Mills *(Exec Mng Dir)*
Keith Zimmerman *(Exec Mng Dir)*

Subsidiary (Domestic):

Cushman & Wakefield of Washington D.C., Inc. (3)
2101 L St NW Ste 700, Washington, DC 20037
Tel.: (202) 463-2100
Web Site: http://www.cushwakedc.com
Emp.: 650
Real Estate Services
N.A.I.C.S.: 531210
Peter Carroccio *(Mng Principal)*
John Benziger *(Exec Mng Dir)*
John Campanella *(Exec Mng Dir)*
Lillian Capers *(Office Mgr)*
Michael Christian *(Exec Mng Dir)*
Sherry Cushman *(Exec Mng Dir & Head-Legal SPG)*
Brian Daly *(Exec Mng Dir)*
Zeke Dodson *(Vice Chm)*
Craig Estey *(Exec Mng Dir)*
Audrey Cramer *(Vice Chm)*
Lynda Gallagher *(Sr Mng Dir & Reg Mgr)*
Michael Katcher *(Exec Mng Dir)*

Cushman & Wakefield of Washington, Inc. (3)
1420 5th Ave Ste 2600, Seattle, WA 98101
Tel.: (206) 682-0666
Web Site:
  http://www.cushmanwakefield.com
Emp.: 22
Real Estate Services
N.A.I.C.S.: 531210
Janice Davis *(Sr Mgr-Property)*
David Magee *(Mng Dir)*
Sharen Bajema *(Dir-Ops)*

Branch (Domestic):

Cushman & Wakefield, Inc. - Indianapolis (3)
1 American Sq Ste 1300, Indianapolis, IN 46282
Tel.: (317) 634-6363
Web Site:
  http://www.cushwakeindianapolis.com
Emp.: 145
Commercial Real Estate Services
N.A.I.C.S.: 531210
Patrick B. Lindley *(Exec Mng Dir)*
Timothy Michel *(Exec Mng Dir)*
Jason Tolliver *(VP)*
Chris Yeakey *(Mng Principal)*
Peter Walpole *(Reg Dir-Mktg & Comm)*
Cheri Shepherd *(Exec Mng Dir)*
Mimi Vanarsdall *(VP-Property Mgmt)*
Jon Owens *(Mng Dir)*
Amy Pollock *(VP-Property Mgmt)*
Tammy Long *(Sr VP-Property Mgmt)*
Terri-Lynn Mitchell *(Mng Dir)*
David Moore *(Mng Dir)*
Kris Moore *(Sr VP-Property Mgmt)*
Dee Headley *(Sr VP)*
Susanne Ingegno *(Sr VP-Property Mgmt)*
Bob Dugger *(Sr VP-Project & Dev Svcs)*
Melissa Day *(Sr VP)*
Darrin Boyd *(Mng Dir)*

Subsidiary (Non-US):

DTZ Zadelhoff v.o.f. (3)
Gustav Mahlerlaan 362, Amsterdam, 1082 ME, Netherlands
Tel.: (31) 206644644
Web Site: http://www.dtz.nl
Emp.: 400
Real Estate & Property Management Services
N.A.I.C.S.: 531311
Marcel Akkerman *(Controller-Credit)*
Jeroen de Bruijn *(Chm-Exec Bd)*
Tom van Putten *(Member-Exec Bd)*
Jacques Boeve *(Member-Exec Bd)*
Sylvia Ligtvoet *(Sec)*
Femke Tonkema *(Mgr-Mktg & Comm)*

Joint Venture (Domestic):

Quality Solutions Inc. (3)
128 N First St, Colwich, KS 67030
Tel.: (316) 721-3656
Web Site: http://www.qsifacilities.com
Specialty Trade Contractors
N.A.I.C.S.: 238990
Chad Pore *(Pres)*

Subsidiary (Domestic):

Emcon Associates, Inc. (4)
74 Brick Blvd, Brick, NJ 08723-7984
Tel.: (800) 545-4866
Web Site: http://www.emconfm.com
Facilities Support Services
N.A.I.C.S.: 561210
Michael Cocuzza *(CEO)*
Michael Michowski *(Chm & Chief Administrative Officer)*
Rush Sherman *(COO)*
Jane Serreino *(Dir-HR)*
James Gillen *(Dir-Strategy & IT)*
Elizabeth Cocuzza *(Exec VP)*

Decision Insight Information Group, Inc. (1)
10001 Innovation Dr Ste 100, Milwaukee, WI 53226
Tel.: (262) 798-3641
Web Site:
  http://www.decisioninsightgroup.com
Sales Range: $150-199.9 Million
Emp.: 1,100
Holding Company; Risk Management & Due Diligence Solutions
N.A.I.C.S.: 551112

Digital.ai Software, Inc. (1)
2101 City W Blvd, Houston, TX 77042
Tel.: (678) 268-3320
Computer Software Services
N.A.I.C.S.: 541511
Ashok Reddy *(Pres & CEO)*
Prasenjit Dasgupta *(CFO)*
Stephen Elop *(CEO)*
Joyce Tompsett *(Dir-Analyst Rels & Comm)*
John Allessio *(Chief Customer Officer)*
Bruce Chesebrough *(Chief Revenue Officer)*

Subsidiary (Domestic):

Arxan Technologies, Inc. (2)
6903 Rockledge Dr Ste 1250, Bethesda, MD 20817
Tel.: (301) 968-4290
Web Site: http://www.arxan.com
Software Security Solutions
N.A.I.C.S.: 541511
Michael Dager *(Chm)*
Patrick Kehoe *(CMO)*
Sam Rehman *(CTO)*
Joe Sander *(CEO)*
Michael Kelley *(VP-Fin)*
Dick Davidson *(CFO)*
Dennis Reno *(Sr VP-Customer Success)*

Subsidiary (Domestic):

Apperian, Inc. (3)
321 Summer St, Boston, MA 02210
Tel.: (617) 477-8740
Web Site: http://www.apperian.com
Emp.: 51
Mobile Applications Development
N.A.I.C.S.: 513210
Mark Lorion *(Pres & Gen Mgr)*

Subsidiary (Domestic):

CollabNet, Inc. (2)
4000 Shoreline Ct Ste 300, South San Francisco, CA 94080
Tel.: (650) 228-2500
Web Site: http://www.collab.net
Sales Range: $10-24.9 Million
Software Developer
N.A.I.C.S.: 513210
Bill Portelli *(Founder & Chm)*
Tony Farinaro *(Sr VP-North American Sls & Worldwide Svcs)*
Amir Ameri *(CFO)*
Ted Trimble *(Sr VP-Engrg)*
Eric Robertson *(Gen Mgr-DevOps Product Line)*
Thomas Hooker *(VP-Mktg)*
Robert Holler *(Chief Strategy Officer)*

Subsidiary (Domestic):

VersionOne, Inc. (3)
6220 Shiloh Rd Ste 400, Alpharetta, GA 30005
Tel.: (678) 268-3320
Web Site: http://www.collab.net
Project & Life Cycle Management Services
N.A.I.C.S.: 541511
Robert Holler *(Pres & CEO)*
Paul Neuman *(Dir-Sls Dev)*

Exactech, Inc. (1)
2320 NW 66th Ct, Gainesville, FL 32653
Tel.: (352) 377-1140
Web Site: http://www.exac.com
Orthopaedic Implant Devices & Related Surgical Instrumentation Developer, Marketer & Mfr
N.A.I.C.S.: 339112
R. William Petty *(Co-Founder & Co-Chm)*
Gary J. Miller *(Co-Founder & Exec VP-R&D)*
Bruce Thompson *(Sr VP-Strategic Initiatives)*
Donna M. Edwards *(VP-Legal)*
Jeff Binder *(Co-Chm)*
Priscilla Bennett *(VP-Corp Comm)*
Daniel P. Hann *(Sr VP-Bus Dev)*
Darin Johnson *(CEO)*
Kerem Bolukbasi *(CFO)*

Subsidiary (Non-US):

Blue Ortho SAS (2)
6 allee de Bethleem, 38610, Gieres, France
Tel.: (33) 458003525
Web Site: http://www.exactechgps.com
Orthopedic Equipment Distr
N.A.I.C.S.: 423450
Anthony Boyer *(Pres)*

Exactech (UK) Ltd. (2)
Grosvenor House Prospect Hill, Redditch, B97 4DL, United Kingdom
Tel.: (44) 1527591555
Web Site: http://www.exac.co.uk
Medical & Surgical Equipment Mfr
N.A.I.C.S.: 339113

Exactech Deutschland GmbH (2)
Werftstrasse 193, 24143, Kiel, Germany
Tel.: (49) 4319902930
Web Site: http://www.exactech.de
Orthopedic Equipment Mfr
N.A.I.C.S.: 339113

Exactech France SAS (2)
Parc Ariane Batiment 2, 42 avenue Ariane, 33700, Merignac, France
Tel.: (33) 320170050
Web Site: http://www.exactech.fr
Medical Devices & Supplies Mfr
N.A.I.C.S.: 339113

Exactech International Operation AG (2)
Weltpoststrasse 5, CH-3015, Bern, Switzerland
Tel.: (41) 79 955 2823
Web Site: http://www.exac.com
Medical Device Mfr
N.A.I.C.S.: 339112

Fender Musical Instruments Corporation (1)
17600 N Perimeter Dr Ste 100, Scottsdale, AZ 85255
Tel.: (480) 596-9690
Web Site: http://www.fender.com
Sales Range: $700-749.9 Million
Emp.: 2,790
Musical Instruments Mfr & Sales
N.A.I.C.S.: 339992
Mark H. Fukunaga *(Chm)*
Max Gutnik *(VP-Electric Guitars & Basses)*
Dan Heitkemper *(VP-Licensing & Mdsg-Hollywood)*
Mike Lewis *(VP-Product Dev-Fender Custom Shop)*
Christina Stejskal *(VP-Global Comms & PR-Los Angeles)*
Evan Jones *(CMO)*
Edward O. Magee Jr. *(Exec VP-Operations)*

Division (Domestic):

Guild Guitars (2)
8860 E Chaparral Rd Ste 100, Scottsdale, AZ 85255-2618 **(100%)**

Tel.: (480) 596-9690
Web Site: http://www.guildguitars.com
Sales Range: $25-49.9 Million
Emp.: 300
Mfr of Electric & Acoustical Guitars
N.A.I.C.S.: 339992

Subsidiary (Domestic):

Kaman Music Corporation (2)
55 Griffin Rd S, Bloomfield, CT 06002
Tel.: (860) 509-8888
Web Site: http://www.kamanmusic.com
Sales Range: $10-24.9 Million
Emp.: 120
Musical Instrument & Musical Products Distr & Whslr
N.A.I.C.S.: 459140
Edward G. Miller *(COO)*
Larry Dunn *(CFO & Sr VP)*
Mark Terry *(Mgr)*

Subsidiary (Non-US):

B&J Music Limited (3)
21000 TransCanada Highway, Baie-d'Urfe, H9X 4B7, QC, Canada **(100%)**
Tel.: (905) 896-3001
Web Site: https://www.bjmusiconline.com
Durable Goods
N.A.I.C.S.: 423990

Unit (Domestic):

Musicorp (3)
2456 Remont Rd Ste 305, North Charleston, SC 29419
Tel.: (843) 745-8501
Sales Range: $10-24.9 Million
Emp.: 100
Musical Instrument Distr
N.A.I.C.S.: 459140

HCP Packaging (Shanghai) Co. Ltd. (1)
No 9456 Songze Avenue Qingpu Industrial Zone, Qingpu District, Shanghai, 201700, China
Tel.: (86) 21 6921 3232
Sales Range: $150-199.9 Million
Emp.: 1,000
Packaging & Labeling Services
N.A.I.C.S.: 561910
Eddy Wu *(CEO)*

Subsidiary (Domestic):

HCP Packaging (Huai An) Co., Ltd. (2)
Ste62 Haikou Road Huai An Economic and Technology, Development District, Huai'an, 223001, Jiangsu, China
Tel.: (86) 517 8378 9100
Packaging & Labeling Services
N.A.I.C.S.: 561910

Subsidiary (Non-US):

HCP Packaging France SAS (2)
10 Rue Vignon, 75009, Paris, France
Tel.: (33) 1 42 44 24 24
Sales Range: $10-24.9 Million
Emp.: 7
Packaging & Labeling Services
N.A.I.C.S.: 561910

HCP Packaging Group (2)
No 55 Jen Fu Street, West District, Taichung, 40310, Taiwan
Tel.: (886) 4 23716333
Packaging & Labeling Services
N.A.I.C.S.: 561910

HCP Packaging Hong Kong Ltd. (2)
Room 1317 Leighton Centre 77 Leighton Road, Causeway Bay, China (Hong Kong)
Tel.: (852) 28811803
Web Site: http://www.hcpackaging.com
Sales Range: $10-24.9 Million
Emp.: 1
Cosmetic Packaging Services
N.A.I.C.S.: 561910
Doris Chai *(Dir-Sls)*

HCP Packaging UK Ltd. (2)
Tayfield House 38 Poole Road, Westbourne, Bournemouth, BH4 9DW, Dorset, United Kingdom
Tel.: (44) 1202 670099
Web Site: http://www.hcppackaging.com

TPG Capital, L.P.—(Continued)

Sales Range: $10-24.9 Million
Emp.: 10
Packaging & Labeling Services
N.A.I.C.S.: 561910
Jackie Mantle (Mng Dir)

Subsidiary (US):

HCP Packaging USA, Inc. (2)
1 Waterview Dr Ste 102, Shelton, CT 06484
Tel.: (203) 924-2408
Packaging & Labeling Services
N.A.I.C.S.: 561910
Damien Dossin (Pres-HCP America)

HCP Packaging USA, Inc. - Hinsdale Plant (2)
370 Monument Rd, Hinsdale, NH 03451-2040
Tel.: (603) 256-3141
Web Site: http://www.hcpackaging.com
Sales Range: $25-49.9 Million
Emp.: 100
Cosmetic Packaging Mfr & Designer
N.A.I.C.S.: 561910
James Malinowski (Mgr-Production)
Andy Drummond (Plant Mgr)
Sue Pickford (Mgr-Creative Mktg)
Eddy Wu (CEO)

Inghams Enterprises Pty Ltd. (1)
203-209 Northumberland Street, Liverpool, 2170, NSW, Australia
Tel.: (61) 2 9602 8744
Web Site: http://www.inghams.com.au
Sales Range: $1-4.9 Billion
Emp.: 9,000
Poultry Producer
N.A.I.C.S.: 311615

Intervest Offices & Warehouses N.V. (1)
Uitbreidingstraat 66, 2600, Berchem, Belgium
Tel.: (32) 32876767
Web Site: http://www.intervest.be
Rev.: $75,294,797
Assets: $1,287,186,922
Liabilities: $606,233,471
Net Worth: $680,953,451
Earnings: $53,343,691
Emp.: 48
Fiscal Year-end: 12/31/2020
Real Estate Investment Services
N.A.I.C.S.: 531390
Ellen Selis (Dir-Fin)
Annick Merlevede (Dir-Fin Projects)
Stijn Van den Abbeele (Dir-Technical)
Gunther Gielen (CEO & Member-Mgmt Bd)
Joel Gorsele (Chief Investment Officer & Member-Mgmt Bd)
Kevin De Greef (Member-Mgmt Bd, Gen Counsel & Sec)
Luc Kieboms (Dir-Asset)

Subsidiary (Domestic):

MBC S.A. (2)
Rue des Hippocampes 1, 1080, Brussels, Belgium
Tel.: (32) 24107880
Food Product Whslr
N.A.I.C.S.: 424490

Subsidiary (Non-US):

MRP S.A. (2)
Route de Courgenay 40, 2942, Alle, Switzerland
Tel.: (41) 324711414
Web Site: http://www.mrp.ch
Sales Range: $50-74.9 Million
Emp.: 200
Watch Case Mfr
N.A.I.C.S.: 334519

InvoCare Limited (1)
Level 2 40 Miller Street, North Sydney, 2060, NSW, Australia
Tel.: (61) 299785200
Web Site: http://www.invocare.com.au
Rev.: $395,199,172
Assets: $1,159,780,089
Liabilities: $795,793,887
Net Worth: $363,986,202
Earnings: ($1,144,266)
Emp.: 2,000
Fiscal Year-end: 12/31/2022

Funeral Services
N.A.I.C.S.: 812210
Josee Lemoine (Co-CFO)
Fergus Kelly (Exec Gen Mgr)
Steve Nobbs (Exec Gen Mgr-Cemeteries-Crematoria)
Heidi Aldred (Sec & Gen Counsel)
Adrian Gratwicke (Co-CFO)
Victoria Doidge (Chief Customer Officer)
Lynne Gallucci (Exec Gen Mgr-Funerals)
Grace Westdorp (Exec Gen Mgr-Safety)
Amanda Tober (Exec Gen Mgr-Human Resources)
Grace Westdorp (Exec Gen Mgr-Safety)
Amanda Tober (Exec Gen Mgr-Human Resources)
Grace Westdorp (Exec Gen Mgr-Safety)
Amanda Tober (Exec Gen Mgr-Human Resources)

Subsidiary (Domestic):

Catholic Funerals Newcastle Pty Limited (2)
16 Rennie Street, Adamstown, Wetherill Park, 2164, NSW, Australia
Tel.: (61) 300454332
Web Site: https://www.lifeart.com.au
Cremation Services
N.A.I.C.S.: 812210

InvoCare Australia Pty Limited (2)
Level 5 40 Mount Street, North Sydney, 2060, NSW, Australia
Tel.: (61) 299785200
Web Site: https://www.invocare.com.au
Sales Range: $50-74.9 Million
Emp.: 100
Healthcare Services
N.A.I.C.S.: 923120

Liberty Funerals Pty Limited (2)
101 South Street, Granville, 2142, NSW, Australia
Tel.: (61) 296370322
Web Site: https://www.libertyfunerals.com.au
Sales Range: $25-49.9 Million
Emp.: 7
Funeral & Cremation Services
N.A.I.C.S.: 812210

Memorial Guardian Plan Pty Limited (2)
153 Walker St Level 6, Sydney, 2046, NSW, Australia
Tel.: (61) 287533100
Sales Range: $25-49.9 Million
Emp.: 60
Funeral & Cemeteries Services
N.A.I.C.S.: 812210

Oakwood Funerals Pty Limited (2)
506 Marmion Street, Booragoon, 6154, WA, Australia
Tel.: (61) 893308300
Web Site: https://www.oakwoodfunerals.com.au
Sales Range: $25-49.9 Million
Emp.: 6
Cremation Services
N.A.I.C.S.: 812210

Subsidiary (Non-US):

Singapore Casket Company (Private) Limited (2)
131 Lavender Street, Singapore, 338737, Singapore
Tel.: (65) 62934388
Web Site: https://www.singaporecasket.com.sg
Emp.: 80
Funeral Services
N.A.I.C.S.: 812210

Isola Group Ltd. (1)
3100 W Ray Rd Ste 301, Chandler, AZ 85226
Tel.: (480) 893-6527
Web Site: http://www.isola-group.com
Sales Range: $600-649.9 Million
Emp.: 2,088
Laminate Materials Product Mfr
N.A.I.C.S.: 322120
Richard Caron (CIO)
Michael S. Rafford (Gen Counsel, Sec & VP)
Michael Gastonguay (Pres-Americas)

Matt LaRont (Sr VP-Global Ops)
Troy Ruhrer (CFO)
Travis D. Kelly (Pres & CEO)

Subsidiary (Non-US):

Isola GmbH (2)
Isolastrasse 2, 52353, Duren, Germany
Tel.: (49) 2421 8080
Glass Epoxy Laminates Mfr
N.A.I.C.S.: 334419

J.Crew Group, Inc. (1)
225 Liberty St, New York, NY 10281
Tel.: (203) 682-8200
Web Site: https://www.jcrew.com
Rev.: $2,483,994,000
Assets: $1,221,651,000
Liabilities: $2,493,894,000
Net Worth: ($1,272,243,000)
Earnings: ($120,079,000)
Emp.: 4,300
Fiscal Year-end: 02/02/2019
Clothing & Clothing Accessories Retailers
N.A.I.C.S.: 458110
Libby Wadle (CEO)
Lynda Markoe (Chief Admin Officer)
Michael J. Nicholson (Pres & COO)
Vincent Zanna (CFO & Treas)
Kevin Ulrich (Chm)
Brendon Babenzien (Creative Dir-Men)

Subsidiary (Domestic):

J. Crew Operating Corp. (2)
770 Broadway, New York, NY 10003
Tel.: (212) 209-2500
Web Site: http://www.jcrew.com
Clothing Retailer
N.A.I.C.S.: 458110

Subsidiary (Domestic):

Grace Holmes, Inc. (3)
770 Broadway, New York, NY 10003
Tel.: (212) 209-2500
Web Site: http://www.jcrew.com
Sales Range: $100-124.9 Million
Clothing Retailer
N.A.I.C.S.: 458110
James S. Scully (CFO & Exec VP)

J. Crew Virginia, Inc. (3)
770 Broadway, New York, NY 10003
Tel.: (212) 209-2500
Web Site: http://www.jcrew.com
Sales Range: $100-124.9 Million
Clothing Retailer
N.A.I.C.S.: 458110

J. Crew, Inc. (3)
770 Broadway, New York, NY 10003
Tel.: (434) 385-5775
Web Site: http://www.jcrew.com
Sales Range: $100-124.9 Million
Clothing Retailer
N.A.I.C.S.: 458110
Leigh Kohlhaas (Mgr-Loss Prevention Ops)

Subsidiary (Domestic):

J. Crew International, Inc. (4)
770 Broadway, New York, NY 10003
Tel.: (212) 209-2500
Web Site: http://www.jcrew.org
Sales Range: $100-124.9 Million
Emp.: 1,000
Clothing Retailer
N.A.I.C.S.: 458110
Heather Lynch McAuliffe (Sr Dir-PR)

Subsidiary (Domestic):

Madewell, Inc. (3)
770 Broadway, New York, NY 10003
Tel.: (212) 209-2500
Web Site: http://www.madewell1937.com
Sales Range: $100-124.9 Million
Clothing Retailer
N.A.I.C.S.: 458110
Joyce Lee (Head-Women's Design)

JA Cosmetics Corp. (1)
10 W 33rd St Ste 802, New York, NY 10001
Tel.: (212) 239-1530
Web Site: http://www.eyeslipsface.com
Cosmetics Designer, Marketer & Distr
N.A.I.C.S.: 424210
Tarang P. Amin (Pres & CEO)
Scott-Vincent Borba (Co-Founder)
Erin Daley (CMO & Sr VP)

Scott K. Milsten (Gen Counsel, Sec & Sr VP)
Megan O'Connor (VP-Digital)
Richard F. Baruch Jr. (Chief Comml Officer & Sr VP)

Keter Environmental Services, Inc. (1)
101 W Washington St Ste 1000 E, Indianapolis, IN 46204
Tel.: (866) 679-5079
Web Site: https://www.keteres.com
Waste Management Services
N.A.I.C.S.: 562998
Kevin Dice (CEO)

Subsidiary (Domestic):

Waste Harmonics, LLC (2)
7620 Omnitech Pl Ste 1, Victor, NY 14564-9413
Tel.: (585) 924-9640
Web Site: http://www.wasteharmonics.com
Outsourced Waste Management Consolidation Services
N.A.I.C.S.: 562998
Michael Roy (COO)
Mary Way (VP-Customer Care)
Mitch Florer (VP-Vendor Rels)
Michael Lane (VP-Fin)
Ryan Shannon (CFO)
Matt Hollister (Dir-Bus Dev & Sustainability)
Tom Moran (VP-Ops)
Jennifer Robinson (Dir-Mktg)
Brad Young (Dir-Sustainability)
Carl H. Slusarczyk Jr. (VP-Sls)

Life Time Fitness, Inc. (1)
2902 Corporate Pl, Chanhassen, MN 55317
Tel.: (952) 947-0000
Web Site: http://www.lifetimefitness.com
Sales Range: $1-4.9 Billion
Holding Company; Fitness Centers Operator
N.A.I.C.S.: 551112
Bahram Akradi (CEO)
Jeffrey G. Zwiefel (COO)
Tom Bergman (CFO & Exec VP)
Jason Thunstrom (VP-Corp Comm & PR)
Natalie Bushaw (Dir-PR)
Riley McLaughlin (Coord-PR)

Subsidiary (Domestic):

ChronoTrack Systems Corp. (2)
111 E Diamond Ave, Evansville, IN 47711
Tel.: (812) 423-7800
Web Site: http://www.chronotrack.com
Electric Equipment Mfr
N.A.I.C.S.: 334511

Subsidiary (Non-US):

ChronoTrack Systems Europe B.V. (3)
Zuidergracht 21-21, Soest, 3763, Netherlands
Tel.: (31) 357510872
Web Site: http://www.chronotrack.com
Electric Equipment Mfr
N.A.I.C.S.: 334511
Jeroen Van Zuilen (Dir)

Subsidiary (Domestic):

Life Time Fitness - Bloomingdale (2)
455 Scott Dr, Bloomingdale, IL 60108
Tel.: (630) 582-4100
Web Site: http://www.lifetimefitness.com
Fitness Center Operator
N.A.I.C.S.: 713940

Life Time Fitness - Chanhassen (2)
2902 Corporate Pl, Chanhassen, MN 55317-4560
Tel.: (952) 380-0303
Web Site: http://www.lifetimefitness.com
Physical Fitness Facility Services
N.A.I.C.S.: 713940

Lighthouse Holdings, Inc. (1)
300 Crescent Ct Ste 1380, Dallas, TX 75201
Tel.: (214) 855-0194
Web Site: http://www.pharosfunds.com
Sales Range: $50-74.9 Million
Holding Company
N.A.I.C.S.: 551112
Robert Crants (Co-Founder)

Subsidiary (Domestic):

American Beacon Advisors (2)
4151 Ammon Carter Blvd, Fort Worth, TX 76155-2450
Tel.: (817) 967-3509
Sales Range: $10-24.9 Million
Emp.: 75
Financial Management
N.A.I.C.S.: 523940
Terri L. McKinney (VP-Enterprise Svcs)
Rosemary K. Behan (VP-Legal & Compliance)
Samuel J. Silver (Chief Fixed Income Officer & VP)
Jeffrey K. Ringdahl (Pres & COO)
Paul Cavazos (Chief Investment Officer)
Gene L. Needles Jr. (Chm & CEO)

New Relic, Inc. (1)
188 Spear St Ste 1000, San Francisco, CA 94105
Tel.: (650) 777-7600
Web Site: https://www.newrelic.com
Rev.: $785,521,000
Assets: $1,427,666,000
Liabilities: $1,083,276,000
Net Worth: $344,390,000
Earnings: ($250,402,000)
Emp.: 2,217
Fiscal Year-end: 03/31/2022
Software Analytics
N.A.I.C.S.: 513210
Kristy Friedrichs (COO)
David Barter (CFO & Exec VP)
Hope F. Cochran (Executives, Bd of Dirs)
Gregory Ouillon (CTO-Europe, Middle East & Africa)
Bonney Pelley (Sr VP-Strategy & Ops)
John Siebert (Exec VP-Sls-Americas)
Jay Snyder (Chief Customer Officer & Exec VP)
David Barter (CFO)
Siva Padisetty (Sr VP-Telemetry Data Platform & Global Infrastructure & Gen Mgr-Telemetry Data Platform & Global Infrastructure)
Mark Dodds (Chief Revenue Officer)

Nintex Global Ltd. (1)
10800 NE 8th St Ste 400, Bellevue, WA 98004
Tel.: (425) 324-2400
Web Site: https://www.nintex.com
Sales Range: $50-74.9 Million
Emp.: 247
Software Development Services
N.A.I.C.S.: 541511
Jeffrey A. Christianson (Chief Legal Officer)
Baran Erkel (Sr VP-Corp Dev)
Amit Mathradas (CEO)
Stephen Elop (Chm)
Niranjan Vijayaragavan (Chief Product Officer)

Subsidiary (Domestic):

AssureSign LLC (2)
3423 Piedmont Rd NE, Atlanta, GA 30305
Tel.: (407) 670-0400
Web Site: http://www.assuresign.com
Electronic Signature Software Publisher
N.A.I.C.S.: 513210
David W. Brinkman (CEO)
Donald Kratt (CTO)
David Madison (Dir-Ops)

Skuid, Inc. (2)
605 Chestnut Str Ste 700, Chattanooga, TN 37450
Web Site: http://www.skuid.com
Sales Range: $10-24.9 Million
Emp.: 142
Software Development Services
N.A.I.C.S.: 541511
Mike Duensing (CTO & Exec VP-Engrg)
Ellie Hildebrand (Mgr-PR)

OPC Corporation (1)
1-15-38 Oyama, Chuuo-ku, Sagamihara, 252-0205, Kanagawa-ken, Japan
Tel.: (81) 42 774 5977
Web Site: http://www.opc-inc.co.jp
Optical Lens Mfr
N.A.I.C.S.: 333310
Yoshio Karasawa (Pres)

Oneoncology, Inc. (1)
1301 W Colonial Dr, Orlando, FL 32804

Tel.: (407) 781-2380
Rev.: $1,800,000
Emp.: 15
Drugs & Druggists' Sundries Merchant Whslr
N.A.I.C.S.: 424210
Steve Kirchoff (Pres)
George Alfert (Project Mgr-IT)
Ian W. Flinn (Chief Scientific Officer)
Davey Daniel (Chief Medical Officer)

Planview, Inc. (1)
12301 Research Blvd Research Park Plz V Ste 101, Austin, TX 78759-8770
Tel.: (512) 346-8600
Web Site: http://www.planview.com
Portfolio Management Solutions
N.A.I.C.S.: 523940
Gregory Gilmore (Executives, Bd of Dirs)
Scott Hardey (Exec VP-Customer Svc)
Jeff Durbin (Gen Mgr-Ops-Global)
Patrick A. Tickle (Chief Product Officer)
Eric S. Hurley (VP-Legal Affairs)
Linda Roach (VP-Mktg)
Vic Chynoweth (Exec VP)
Louise K. Allen (Sr VP-Product Mgmt & Solutions Mktg)
Rob Reesor (Sr VP-Product Dev)
Bryan Urioste (Exec VP-Worldwide Mktg)
Brian Prokaski (Exec VP-Comml Sls)
Razat Gaurav (CEO)

Subsidiary (Domestic):

Enrich Consulting, Inc. (2)
3031 Tisch Way Ste 711, San Jose, CA 95128
Tel.: (408) 871-9000
Web Site: http://www.enrichconsulting.com
Software Development Services
N.A.I.C.S.: 541511
Richard Sonnenblick (Founder & CEO)
Daniel Smith (VP)
Amisha Boucher (Sr Mgr)
Ohad Berman (Sr Mgr)
Assaf Shomer (Mgr)
Alison Pool (Mgr)

Innotas, Inc. (2)
111 Sutter St Ste 300, San Francisco, CA 94104
Tel.: (415) 263-9800
Web Site: http://www.innotas.com
Cloud-Based Portfolio Management Services
N.A.I.C.S.: 541511

Plutora, Inc. (2)
2445 Augustine Dr Ste 150, Santa Clara, CA 95054
Tel.: (628) 899-2084
Web Site: http://www.plutora.com
Sales Range: $1-9.9 Million
Emp.: 100
Software Development Services
N.A.I.C.S.: 541511
Bob Davies (CMO)
Mukund Singh (Chief Customer Officer)
Simon Farrell (CTO)
Alex Webb (Fin Dir)

Poundworld Retail Limited (1)
Axis 62 Foxbridge Way, Normanton Industrial Estate, Normanton, WF6 1TN, West Yorkshire, United Kingdom
Tel.: (44) 1924 420260
Web Site: http://www.poundworldretail.co.uk
Emp.: 6,000
Discount Retail Stores & Online Shopping
N.A.I.C.S.: 455110
Ian Hamilton (Dir-Comml)
Ken Thomson (Dir-IT)
Jerry Gray (Mng Dir)

Prezzo Limited (1)
Johnston House 8 Johnston Road, Woodford Green, Woodford, IG8 0XA, Essex, United Kingdom
Tel.: (44) 8456023257
Web Site:
    http://www.prezzorestaurants.co.uk
Holding Company; Restaurant Owner & Operator
N.A.I.C.S.: 551112
Jonathan Kaye (Founder)
Alessandra Lomonaco (Ops Mgr)
Zaneta Stoklos (Gen Mgr)
Gazmend Gashi (Gen Mgr)
Marek Krzystek (Area Mgr)
Karen Jones (Chm)

ProSight Specialty Insurance Group, Inc. (1)
412 Mount Kemble Ave Ste 300C, Morristown, NJ 07960
Tel.: (212) 551-0600
Web Site: http://www.prosightspecialty.com
Sales Range: $200-249.9 Million
Emp.: 179
Holding Company; Owner & Operator of Insurance Companies, Risk Bearing Entities & Insurance Underwriters & Managers
N.A.I.C.S.: 524130
Joseph Beneducci (Chm, Pres & CEO)
Anthony Piszel (CFO)
Vivek Syal (Chief Risk Officer)
Michael Furgueson (Mng Dir)
Bev Thorne (CMO)
Frank Bosse (Chief HR Officer)
Frank Papalia (Chief Legal Officer)
Paul Kush (Chief Claims Officer)

ShangPharma Corporation (1)
No 5 Building 998 Halei Road Zhangjiang Hi-Tech Park, Pudong New Area, Shanghai, 201203, China
Tel.: (86) 21 5132 0088
Web Site: http://www.shangpharma.com
Sales Range: $100-124.9 Million
Emp.: 2,000
Holding Company; Pharmaceutical & Biotechnology Products Research & Development
N.A.I.C.S.: 551112
William Weili Dai (CFO)
Arthur Taveras (Pres & Chief Scientific Officer)
Mitchell Reff (Chief Biologics Officer)

Subsidiary (Domestic):

Chengdu ChemPartner Co., Ltd. (2)
3rd Floor Building B3 Tianfu Life Science Park No 88 Keyuan South Road, Hi-Tech Zone, Chengdu, 610041, Sichuan, China
Tel.: (86) 28 6235 0000
Web Site: http://www.chempartner.com
Emp.: 200
Pharmaceutical Research & Development
N.A.I.C.S.: 541715
Fang Lu (Project Mgr)

China Gateway Pharmaceutical Development Co., Ltd. (2)
99 Lian He North Road Zhe Lin Town, Feng Xian Area, Shanghai, China
Tel.: (86) 21 5132 0088
Web Site: http://www.chempartner.cn
Pharmaceutical Research & Development
N.A.I.C.S.: 541715

Shanghai ChemPartner Co., Ltd. (2)
No 5 Building 998 Halei Road Zhangjiang Hi-Tech Park, Pudong New Area, Shanghai, 201203, China
Tel.: (86) 21 5132 0088
Web Site: http://www.shangpharma.com
Pharmaceutical Research & Development
N.A.I.C.S.: 541715
Michael Hui (Gen Mgr)

TPG Capital LLP (1)
5th Floor Park House 116 Park Street, London, W1K 6AF, United Kingdom
Tel.: (44) 2075446500
Web Site: http://www.tpg.com
Sales Range: $200-249.9 Million
Emp.: 60
Investment Management Service
N.A.I.C.S.: 523940
John Oliver (Mng Dir)
Edward Beckley (Partner)
Mark Corbidge (Partner)
Dirk Eller (Partner)
Ramzi Gedeon (Partner)
Abel Halpern (Partner)
Antonio Capo (Partner-Ops)

Holding (Non-US):

British Vita Group Societe a Responsaibilite Limitee (2)
5 rue Guillaume Kroll, BP 5201, 1025, Luxembourg, Luxembourg
Tel.: (352) 107583
Web Site: http://www.thevitagroup.com
Sales Range: $1-4.9 Billion
Holding Company; Foam, Polymer Compound, Thermoplastic Sheet & Nonwoven Products Mfr

N.A.I.C.S.: 551112

Subsidiary (US):

Crest Foam Industries, Inc. (3)
100 Carol Pl, Moonachie, NJ 07074
Tel.: (201) 807-0809
Web Site: http://www.crestfoam.com
Sales Range: $25-49.9 Million
Emp.: 85
Polyurethane Foam & Foam Products Mfr
N.A.I.C.S.: 326150
Dimitri Dounis (Gen Mgr)

Subsidiary (Non-US):

Kay-Metzeler Limited (3)
Wellington Road, Bollington, Macclesfield, SK10 5JJ, Cheshire, United Kingdom
Tel.: (44) 1625573366
Web Site: http://www.kay-metzeler.co.uk
Sales Range: $50-74.9 Million
Emp.: 100
Polyurethane Foam Product Mfr
N.A.I.C.S.: 326150

RLA Polymers Pty. Ltd. (3)
215 Colchester Road, PO Box 147, Kilsyth, 3137, VIC, Australia
Tel.: (61) 397281644
Web Site: http://www.rlapolymers.com.au
Sales Range: $25-49.9 Million
Emp.: 100
Latex Compound Products Mfr
N.A.I.C.S.: 325991
Richard Clinch (Mgr-Dev)
John Brlling (Mgr-Natl Sls)
Tony Wood (Mng Dir)

Vita Thermoplastic Sheet Limited (3)
Level 3 Charta House, 30-38 Church Street, Staines-upon-Thames, TW18 4EP, United Kingdom
Tel.: (44) 2031072300
Sales Range: $50-74.9 Million
Emp.: 100
Custom Extruded Plastic Sheet Mfr
N.A.I.C.S.: 326113

Vitafoam Limited (3)
Oldham Road, Middleton, Manchester, M24 2DB, Lancashire, United Kingdom
Tel.: (44) 1616431133
Web Site: http://www.vitafoam.co.uk
Emp.: 300
Block Polyurethane Foam Products Mfr
N.A.I.C.S.: 326150
John Ghaale (Grp CEO)

Holding (Non-US):

Novotech Holdings Pty Limited (2)
Level 3 235 Pyrmont St, Pyrmont, NSW, Australia
Tel.: (61) 285691400
Web Site: https://novotech-cro.com
Biotechnology Research Services
N.A.I.C.S.: 541714
John Moller (CEO)

Subsidiary (US):

C B R International Corp. (3)
2905 Wilderness Pl, Boulder, CO 80301
Tel.: (720) 746-1190
Sales Range: $1-9.9 Million
Emp.: 20
Management Consulting Services
N.A.I.C.S.: 541618
Jeanne Novak (CEO)

TPG Growth (1)
301 Commerce St Ste 3300, Fort Worth, TX 76102
Tel.: (817) 871-4000
Web Site: http://www.tpg.com
Equity Investment Firm
N.A.I.C.S.: 523999
Mark Grabowski (Partner)
Ari Cohen (Dir-External Affairs)

Subsidiary (Domestic):

CLEAResult Consulting, Inc. (2)
4301 Westbank Dr Bldg A Ste 300, Austin, TX 78746
Tel.: (512) 327-9200
Web Site: http://www.clearesult.com
Energy Utility Consulting Services & Programs
N.A.I.C.S.: 541620

TPG Capital, L.P.—(Continued)

Richard D. McBee (Pres & CEO)
James Stimmel (Exec VP)
Victor Pisani (Sr VP-Central Atlantic)
Michele Negley (Sr VP-South)
William Younger (Dir-Comml & Indus Programs)
Dan L. Crippen (Sr VP-New England Reg)
Joe Mattoon (Chief Legal Officer)
Terry Moore (COO)
Greg Sarich (CIO)
Mark Fields (Chm)
Chet Kwasniak (CFO)
Daniel E. Merchant II (VP-Client Rels)

Subsidiary (Domestic):

Energetics Incorporated (3)
7075 Samuel Morse Dr Ste 100, Columbia, MD 21046
Tel.: (410) 290-0370
Web Site: https://www.energetics.com
Sales Range: $10-24.9 Million
Emp.: 80
Energy & Environmental Consulting Company
N.A.I.C.S.: 541690

Division (Domestic):

Energetics Incorporated-Arlington (4)
4601 N Fairfax Dr Ste 110, Arlington, VA 22203
Tel.: (703) 465-5900
Web Site: http://www.energetics.com
Technology & Management Consulting Services
N.A.I.C.S.: 541618

Energetics Incorporated-Washington (4)
901 D St SW Ste 1010, Washington, DC 20024
Tel.: (202) 479-2748
Web Site: http://www.energetics.com
Restores Military Ships & Sells Them to Foreign Countries
N.A.I.C.S.: 541611

Subsidiary (Domestic):

Populus, LLC. (3)
1722 14th St Ste 210, Boulder, CO 80302
Tel.: (303) 325-7650
Web Site: http://www.populusllc.com
Emp.: 150
Energy Consulting Services
N.A.I.C.S.: 541690
Audrey Cole (Controller)
Matthew Wilmoth (Project Mgr-Community Programs)
Michael Johnson (Mgr-Contractor Coaches)
Hannah Bulick (Mgr-Customer Solutions)

Resource Solutions Group LLC (3)
60 Stone Pine Rd Ste 100, Half Moon Bay, CA 94019
Tel.: (650) 729-2979
Web Site: http://www.rsgrp.com
Sales Range: $10-24.9 Million
Emp.: 50
Environmental Consulting Services
N.A.I.C.S.: 541620
Lauren Casentini (Pres)
David Casentini (VP & Dir-Resource Mgmt Svcs)
Lorna Rushforth (VP & Dir-Fin & Admin)
Alison ten Cate (VP & Dir-Market Dev)

Holding (Domestic):

Crunch, LLC (3)
22 W 19th St 4th Fl, New York, NY 10011
Tel.: (212) 993-0300
Web Site: http://www.crunch.com
Holding Company; Gym & Fitness Centers Operator & Franchisor
N.A.I.C.S.: 551112
Ben Midgley (Co-Founder & CEO-Franchising)
Craig Pepin-Donat (Co-Founder & Exec VP)
Jim Rowley (CEO)
Chris Olsen (Mng Partner-Killeen)
Tony Hartl (Founder & CEO-Austin)
Joel Ross (COO-Austin)

Affiliate (Domestic):

Crunch New Montgomery, LLC (3)

61 New Montgomery St, San Francisco, CA 94105
Tel.: (415) 543-1110
Web Site: http://www.crunch.com
Sales Range: $1-9.9 Million
Emp.: 35
Fitness & Recreational Sports Centers
N.A.I.C.S.: 713940
Verdine Baker (Gen Mgr)
David Watson (Dir-Memberships)

Subsidiary (Domestic):

Idaho Athletic Club, Inc. (3)
1435 S Maple Grove Rd, Boise, ID 83709
Tel.: (208) 376-6558
Web Site: http://www.crunch.com
Fitness & Recreational Sports Centers
N.A.I.C.S.: 713940
John Wardle (CFO)

Holding (Non-US):

Greencross Limited (2)
5/28 Balaclava Street, Woolloongabba, Brisbane, 4102, QLD, Australia
Tel.: (61) 7 3435 3535
Web Site:
http://www.greencrosslimited.com.au
Rev.: $685,992,954
Assets: $762,322,534
Liabilities: $363,503,852
Net Worth: $398,818,683
Earnings: $18,702,882
Emp.: 690
Fiscal Year-end: 07/01/2018
Veterinary Services
N.A.I.C.S.: 541940
Vincent Pollaers (Chief HR Officer, Gen Counsel & Sec)
Tanya Houghton (COO)
Rachel Chay (Chief Veterinary Officer)
Simon Hickey (CEO & Mng Dir)
Lucas Barry (CFO)
Tania Whyte (Chief Customer Officer)

Subsidiary (Domestic):

Animal Emergency Centre (Frankston) Pty Ltd. (3)
39 McMahons Road, Frankston, 3199, VIC, Australia
Tel.: (61) 3 9770 5555
Web Site: http://www.aecvets.com.au
Veterinary Services
N.A.I.C.S.: 541940
Nicole Pytellek (Mgr-Nursing)

Animal Emergency Centre Central Coast Pty Ltd. (3)
Unit 8a 356 Manns Rd, Gosford, 2250, NSW, Australia
Tel.: (61) 2 4323 3886
Veterinary Services
N.A.I.C.S.: 541940
Lee Dwyer (Dir-Veterinary)
Leanne Ayshford (Mgr-Nursing)
Meaghan Buys (Mgr-Practice)

Animal Emergency Centre Hallam Pty Ltd. (3)
151/159 Princes Hwy, Hallam, 3803, VIC, Australia
Tel.: (61) 3 8795 7020
Web Site:
http://www.animalemergency.com.au
Emp.: 50
Veterinary Services
N.A.I.C.S.: 541940
Peter Hammond (Bus Mgr)

Animal Emergency Centre Pty Ltd. (3)
37 Blackburn Road, Mount Waverley, 3149, VIC, Australia
Tel.: (61) 3 9803 8122
Veterinary Services
N.A.I.C.S.: 541940
Jacqui Von Hoff (Dir-Veterinary)
Jacinta Hargan (Mgr-Nursing)
Todd Wade (Mgr-Practice)

Animal Emergency Centre Woolloongabba Pty Ltd. (3)
36 Balaclava Street, Woolloongabba, 4102, QLD, Australia
Tel.: (61) 7 3456 0500
Veterinary Services
N.A.I.C.S.: 541940

Cheri Williamson (Mgr-Nursing)
Catrina Navie (Mgr-Practice)

Chermside Veterinary Hospital Pty Ltd. (3)
561 Gympie Road 4031, Brisbane, 4031, QLD, Australia
Tel.: (61) 7 3350 1333
Web Site: http://www.greencrossvet.com.au
Emp.: 15
Veterinary Services
N.A.I.C.S.: 541940

Freddy Holdings Pty Ltd. (3)
L 1 175 Mcevoy St, Alexandria, 2015, NSW, Australia
Tel.: (61) 299515400
Financial Investment Services
N.A.I.C.S.: 523999

Gold Coast Animal Referral & Emergency Pty Ltd. (3)
Unit 4 75 Casua Drive, Varsity Lakes, 4227, QLD, Australia
Tel.: (61) 7 5593 4544
Veterinary Services
N.A.I.C.S.: 541940

Greencross NSW Pty Ltd. (3)
60 Windbourne Rd, Brookvale, 2100, NSW, Australia
Tel.: (61) 2 9938 9800
Emp.: 5
Veterinary Services
N.A.I.C.S.: 541940
Kelly Luckman (Mgr)

Greencross Vets Southcoast Pty. Ltd. (3)
11 Lake Entrance Rd, Warilla, Shellharbour, 2528, NSW, Australia
Tel.: (61) 2 4295 1970
Veterinary Services
N.A.I.C.S.: 541940

Pet Accident & Emergency Pty Ltd. (3)
U 4 75 Casua Dr, Varsity Lakes, 4227, QLD, Australia
Tel.: (61) 733911477
Veterinary Services
N.A.I.C.S.: 541940

Williamstown Veterinary Hospital Pty Ltd. (3)
137 Railway Place, Williamstown, 3016, VIC, Australia
Tel.: (61) 3 9397 8002
Web Site: http://www.greencross.com.au
Veterinary Services
N.A.I.C.S.: 541940

Holding (Domestic):

HALO Branded Solutions, Inc. (2)
1500 HALO Way, Sterling, IL 61081-5800
Tel.: (815) 625-0980
Web Site: http://www.halo.com
Promotional & Advertising Services
N.A.I.C.S.: 541890

Subsidiary (Domestic):

Caliendo Savio Enterprises, Inc. (3)
5400 S Westridge Dr, New Berlin, WI 53151-0941
Tel.: (262) 786-8400
Web Site: http://www.csehalo.com
Promotional Merchandise & Workwear Products
N.A.I.C.S.: 541890
Frank Bellante (Ops Mgr)

Holding (Domestic):

Implantable Provider Group (2)
2520 Northwinds Pkwy Bldg Two Ste 300, Alpharetta, GA 30009
Tel.: (770) 753-0046
Web Site: http://www.ipgsurgical.com
Rev.: $19,600,000
Emp.: 80
Medical Device Implant Solutions
N.A.I.C.S.: 339112
James Jay Ethridge (Pres & CEO)
Todd Rielly (CFO)
Marty Smith (CIO)
Robert J. Tazioli (Chief Dev Officer)
Mary Kay Gilbert (VP-Ops)
Pat Reynolds (VP-Mfg Dev)

Subsidiary (Domestic):

Medical Solutions LLC (2)
1010 N 102nd St Ste 300, Omaha, NE 68114
Tel.: (402) 758-2800
Web Site: http://www.medicalsolutions.com
Traveling Nurse & Other Healthcare Professional Staffing Employment Agency
N.A.I.C.S.: 561311
Christy Johnston (Sr Dir-Culture & Engagement)
Craig Meier (CEO)
Joel Tremblay (Pres)
Pat Barry (VP-Sls)
Stephen Pedersen (Gen Counsel)
Dana Coonce (Exec VP-Talent & Performance)
Jorge Taborga (CTO)
Amber Ireland (CMO)
Denise Dettingmeijer (CFO)

Subsidiary (Domestic):

C&A Industries Inc. (3)
13609 California St, Omaha, NE 68154
Tel.: (402) 891-0009
Web Site: http://www.ca-industries.com
Sales Range: $200-249.9 Million
Emp.: 400
Employment Agencies
N.A.I.C.S.: 561311
Larry J. Courtnage (Owner & Chm)
Craig Wolf (VP & Gen Mgr-Aureus Medical Grp)
Scot A. Thompson (Pres & CEO)
Tim Trusler (CIO)
Kathy Wolf-Courtnage (Owner & Vice Chm)
Jessica Dennis (CFO)

Host Healthcare, Inc. (3)
3525 Del Mar Hts Rd Ste 870, San Diego, CA 92130
Tel.: (858) 207-6332
Web Site: http://www.hosthealthcare.com
Women Healthcare Services
N.A.I.C.S.: 621610
Gerald Cohen (Mgr-Recruitment)

Professional Placement Resources, LLC (3)
333 1st St N Ste 200, Jacksonville Beach, FL 32250
Tel.: (904) 241-9231
Web Site: http://www.pprtmg.com
Healthcare Staffing
N.A.I.C.S.: 561311

Subsidiary (Domestic):

Morrow Sodali International LLC (2)
509 Madison Ave Ste 1206, New York, NY 10022
Tel.: (203) 658-9400
Web Site: http://www.morrowsodali.com
Management Consulting Services
N.A.I.C.S.: 541611
Lisa Schneider (Dir-US IR)
John Wilcox (Chm)
Alvise Recchi (CEO)
Thomas Ball (Mng Dir)
Louise Barbier (Dir-France)
Donna M. Corso (Sr Dir)
Gerry Davis (Mng Dir)
Andrea De Segni (Mng Dir)
Reza Eftekhari (Dir-UK)
Tom Margadonna (Dir-Capital Markets Intellegence)
Kevin Kelly (Sr Dir)
Ron Knox (CEO-US)
Borja Miranda Johansson (Dir-Iberiab Market)
Gerard J. Mucha (COO)
Justin O'Keefe (Sr Dir-US)
Ali Saribas (Dir-Israel)
Clara L. Taveras (Dir-International Capital Market Intellegence)
Thomas P. Skulski (Mng Dir-US)
Michael Verrechia (Mng Dir-Proxy M&A US)
Tracie J. Vicki (Sr Dir-US)
Charles A. Koons (Dir-Activism & Contested Situations Advisory Grp)
Brandon Korbey (Dir-Bus Dev-West Coast)
David Shammai (Dir-Corp Governance-Cross Border)
Cynthia Alers (Head/Dir-UK)
Harry van Dyke (Vice Chm)

Subsidiary (Non-US):

Powerscourt Limited (3)
2-5 St Johns Sq, London, EC1M 4DE,
United Kingdom
Tel.: (44) 2072501446
Web Site: http://www.powerscourt-
group.com
Emp.: 17
Public Relations
N.A.I.C.S.: 541820
Justin Griffiths (Head-Fin Svcs & Real Es-
tate)
Susanne Bury (Mgr-Fin)

Subsidiary (Domestic):

People 2.0 Global, LLC (2)
222 Valley Creek Blvd Ste 100, Exton, PA
19341
Tel.: (610) 429-4111
Web Site: http://www.people20.com
Temporary Help Service
N.A.I.C.S.: 561320
Edward E. Millman (CFO)
Tim Bell (VP-Sls & Mktg)
Ronnie Kihlstadius (VP-Mktg)
Erik Vonk (Chm)

Subsidiary (Non-US):

Husys Consulting Ltd. (3)
Husys House 1-8-505/E/D/A Prakash Nagar
Begumpet, Hyderabad, 500 016, Telangana,
India
Tel.: (91) 7204012636
Web Site: https://husys.com
Rev.: $7,043,165
Assets: $1,723,148
Liabilities: $179,746
Net Worth: $1,543,402
Earnings: $268,384
Emp.: 382
Fiscal Year-end: 03/31/2020
Financial Consulting Services
N.A.I.C.S.: 541611
G. R. Reddy (Founder & CEO)
Naresh Deevi (Chief Growth Officer)
Suresh Kumar (VP-Growth)

Branch (Domestic):

**TPG Growth - San Francisco
Office** (2)
345 California St Ste 3300, San Francisco,
CA 94104-2606
Tel.: (415) 743-1500
Web Site: http://www.tpg.com
Equity Investment Firm
N.A.I.C.S.: 523999
Ransom A. Langford (Partner)
David I. Trujillo (Co-Mng Partner)
Stephen Ellis (Mng Partner)
Scott Gilbertson (Partner)
Ignacio Giraldo (Operating Partner)
Matthew Hobart (Mng Partner)
Tim Millikin (Partner)
Frederick Paulenich (Partner)
Ben Paul (CFO)
Nehal Raj (Partner)
Heather Smith Thorne (Partner)
Shamik Patel (Partner)
David Mosse (Partner & Gen Counsel)
Lucian Iancovici (Principal)

Taco Bueno Restaurants, L.P. (1)
1605 LBJ Fwy Ste 800, Farmers Branch,
TX 75234
Web Site: http://www.tacobueno.com
Quick Service Mexican Restaurants
N.A.I.C.S.: 722513
Sarah Beddoe (CMO)
Omar Janjua (CEO)
Mary Ellen Mullins (Chief People Officer)
Philip M. Parsons (CFO)

The Rise Fund (1)
345 California St Ste 3300, San Francisco,
CA 94104
Tel.: (415) 743-1500
Web Site: http://www.therisefund.com
Investment Services
N.A.I.C.S.: 523999
Mike Stone (Chief Investment Officer)

Subsidiary (Domestic):

Element Markets LLC (2)
3200 SW Fwy Ste 1310, Houston, TX
77027

Tel.: (281) 207-7200
Web Site: http://www.elementmarkets.com
Sales Range: $1-9.9 Million
Emp.: 40
Environmental Consulting Services
N.A.I.C.S.: 541620
Randall Lack (Co-Pres)
Angela Schwarz (Co-Pres & CEO)
Keri Richardson Bevel (Gen Counsel)
Ken Nelson (Sr VP-Renewables Mktg)
Mike Taylor (Sr VP-Emissions Credit Mktg)
Kevin Coyle (VP-Gas Ops)
Michele Olson (Dir-Renewable Fuels)
Alison Greene (Mktg Dir)
Quentin Hicks (CFO)

Transplace, LLC (1)
3010 Gaylord Pkwy Ste 200, Frisco, TX
75034
Tel.: (972) 731-4500
Web Site: http://www.transplace.com
Freight Transportation Arrangement Ser-
vices
N.A.I.C.S.: 488510
Vincent Chiodo (Chief Comml Officer)
Frank McGuigan (CEO)
Jessica Lynch (Sr VP-HR)
Leigh Robinson (Chief HR Officer)
Karen Sage (CMO)
Danielle Lambertz (Chief Acctg Officer)
Chris Nester (CFO)
Greg Sebolt (Exec VP-Strategic Capacity
Svcs)
Jack Daly (Chm)

Subsidiary (Domestic):

Celtic International, LLC (2)
7840 Graphic Dr Ste 100, Tinley Park, IL
60477
Tel.: (708) 532-9200
Web Site: http://www.transplace.com
Freight Transportation Arrangement Ser-
vices
N.A.I.C.S.: 488510
Tom Knieps (Controller)

LeanCor LLC (2)
7660 Turfway Rd Ste 200, Florence, KY
41042
Tel.: (859) 283-9933
Web Site: http://www.leancor.com
Office Administrative Services
N.A.I.C.S.: 561110
Matt Melrose (VP-Ops)
Robert Martichenko (CEO)

**Logistics Management Solutions
LLC** (2)
1 City Pl Ste 415, Saint Louis, MO 63141
Tel.: (314) 692-8886
Web Site: http://www.lmslogistics.com
Freight Transportation Arrangement Ser-
vices
N.A.I.C.S.: 488510
Dennis Schoemehl (CEO)
Jason Lind (VP-Engineered Logistics)
Scott Hunt (CFO)

Subsidiary (Non-US):

**Transplace Canada - Lakeside
Division** (2)
1185 North Service Road, Oakville, L6H
1A7, ON, Canada
Transportation Management Services
N.A.I.C.S.: 488510

Subsidiary (Domestic):

Yusen Logistics (2)
1300 Busse Rd, Elk Grove Village, IL 60007
Tel.: (847) 264-7700
Freight Forwarding Services
N.A.I.C.S.: 488510
Mel Perdue (Mgr-Bus Dev)

**Valerus Compression Services,
LP** (1)
919 Milam St Ste 1000, Houston, TX 77002
Tel.: (713) 744-6100
Web Site: http://www.valerus.com
Sales Range: $500-549.9 Million
Emp.: 700
Oil & Natural Gas Handling & Processing
Services
N.A.I.C.S.: 213112
James R. Gill (COO)
Tom Birney (VP-Domestic Sls)
Mark Carlton (Gen Counsel)
Samuel Reyes (VP-Latin America)
Leslie Taylor (VP-HR)

WTT HK Limited (1)
9 Floor KITEC 1 Trademark Drive, Kowloon,
China (Hong Kong)
Tel.: (852) 21121121
Web Site: http://www.wharftt.com
Telecommunications Network Operator
N.A.I.C.S.: 517810

WellSky Corporation (1)
11300 Switzer Rd, Overland Park, KS
66210
Tel.: (913) 307-1000
Web Site: http://wellsky.com
Clinical Management Information Solutions
& Healthcare Software Services
N.A.I.C.S.: 513210
Steve Morgan (COO)
Joel Dolisy (CTO)
Shoma Sarkar Thomas (CMO)
Amy Shellhart (Chief Solutions Officer)
John Hutchinson (Sr VP-Client Experience)
Dana Streck (Chief People Officer)
Akash Raj (CFO)
Dale Zurbay (Chief Growth Officer)
Tim Ashe (Chief Clinical Officer)
Geoff Nudd (Chief Strategy Officer)
Bill Miller (Chm & CEO)

Subsidiary (Domestic):

Bowman Systems, L.L.C. (2)
333 Texas St Ste 300, Shreveport, LA
71101-5304
Tel.: (318) 213-8780
Web Site: http://www.mediware.com
Information Management Software Services
N.A.I.C.S.: 541519
Deborah Cox (VP-HR)

Fazzi Associates, Inc. (2)
11 Village Hill Rd Ste 101, Northampton,
MA 01060
Tel.: (413) 584-5300
Web Site: http://www.fazzi.com
Administrative Management & General
Management Consulting Services
N.A.I.C.S.: 541611
Eileen Freitag (Partner)
Robert A. Fazzi (Pres)
Peter Emmott (VP-Bus Dev)

Subsidiary (Non-US):

JAC Computer Services Ltd. (2)
1 Aurum Court, Sylvan Way, Basildon,
SS15 6TH, Essex, United Kingdom
Tel.: (44) 1268 416348
Web Site: http://www.jac.co.uk
Medicines Management Solutions; Phar-
macy Stock Control & Electronic Prescribing
N.A.I.C.S.: 513210
Robert Tysall-Blay (CEO)

Subsidiary (Domestic):

MEDTran Direct, Inc. (2)
105 W Sherman Way Ste 107, Nixa, MO
65714-7622
Web Site: http://www.medtrandirect.com
Electronic Billing (for Hospital & Health
Care)
N.A.I.C.S.: 513210
Kalon Mitchell (Pres)

Mediware Consulting & Analytics (2)
9765 Randall Dr Ste D, Indianapolis, IN
46280
Tel.: (317) 575-9301
Web Site: http://www.mediware.com
Blood Management & Consulting Services
N.A.I.C.S.: 621999
Susann Nienhaus (Dir-Client Svcs & Patient
Safety)

**Mediware Reimbursement
Services** (2)
40 Shattuck Rd Ste 306, Andover, MA
01810
Tel.: (978) 327-6501
Web Site: http://www.mediware.com
Billing & Accounting Services
N.A.I.C.S.: 541219
Jeanne Lugli (Gen Mgr)

Wind River Systems, Inc. (1)
500 Wind River Way, Alameda, CA 94501-
1171
Tel.: (510) 748-4100
Web Site: http://www.windriver.com
Integrated Embedded Software Services

N.A.I.C.S.: 513210
Kevin J. Dallas (Pres & CEO)
Michael Gale (CMO)
Paul Miller (CTO)
Rich Mosher (Chief Legal Officer)
Terese Lam (Chief People Officer)
Bryan LeBlanc (CFO & Sr VP-Fin & Admin)
Avijit Sinha (Chief Product Officer)

Subsidiary (Non-US):

Wind River AB (2)
Kistangangen 20B, 16440, Kista, Sweden
Tel.: (46) 859461120
Web Site: http://www.windriver.com
Integrated Embedded Software Services
N.A.I.C.S.: 513210
Bryan LeBlanc (CFO)

Wind River GmbH (2)
Steinheilstrasse 10, 85737, Ismaning, Ger-
many
Tel.: (49) 899624450
Web Site: http://www.windriver.com
Integrated Embedded Software Services
N.A.I.C.S.: 513210

Wind River K.K. (2)
Ebisu Prime Square Tower 1-1-39 Hiroo,
Shibuya Ku, Tokyo, 150-0012, Japan
Tel.: (81) 357786001
Web Site: http://www.windriver.com
Integrated Embedded Software Services
N.A.I.C.S.: 513210

Subsidiary (Domestic):

Wind River Sales Co., Inc. (2)
500 Wind River Way, Alameda, CA 94501
Tel.: (510) 748-4100
Web Site: http://www.windriver.com
Integrated Embedded Software Sales
N.A.I.C.S.: 423430

Branch (Domestic):

Wind River Systems Inc. (2)
12770 High Bluff Dr Ste 300, San Diego,
CA 92130
Tel.: (858) 824-3100
Web Site: http://www.windriversystems.com
Integrated Embedded Software Services
N.A.I.C.S.: 513210

Subsidiary (Domestic):

**Wind River Systems International,
Inc.** (2)
500 Wind River Way, Alameda, CA 94501
Tel.: (510) 748-4100
Web Site: http://www.windriver.com
International Embedded Software Products
Distr
N.A.I.C.S.: 513210

Subsidiary (Non-US):

Wind River UK Ltd. (2)
47 Pure Offices Kembrey Park, Swindon,
SN2 8BW, United Kingdom
Tel.: (44) 1793230474
Web Site: http://www.windriver.com
Integrated Embedded Software Services
N.A.I.C.S.: 513210

iMDSoft (1)
300 1st Ave, Needham, MA 02494
Tel.: (781) 449-5567
Web Site: http://www.imd-soft.com
Clinical Information Software Publisher
N.A.I.C.S.: 513210
Eran David (CTO)
Alon D. Sadeh (Sr VP-Corp & Compliance)
Shahar Sery (COO)
Sagit Agoor (VP-Sls Ops)
Ronen Halili (Sr VP-R&D & Product Dev)
Nir Kirshberg (VP-Fin)
Anne Belkin-Amario (VP-Mktg)
Lars-Oluf Nielsen (CEO)
Phyllis Gotlib (Co-Founder)
Ido Schoenberg (Co-Founder)

**TPG PACE BENEFICIAL FI-
NANCE CORP.**
301 Commerce St Ste 3300, Fort
Worth, TX 76102
Tel.: (212) 405-8458   Ky
Year Founded: 2019

TPG Pace Beneficial Finance Corp.—(Continued)

TPGYU—(NYSE)
Rev.: $4,618
Assets: $350,956,686
Liabilities: $345,956,685
Net Worth: $5,000,001
Earnings: ($3,636,848)
Emp.: 3
Fiscal Year-end: 12/31/20
Investment Services
N.A.I.C.S.: 523999
Michael MacDougall *(Pres & CEO)*
Martin Davidson *(CFO)*
Eduardo Tamraz *(Sec & Exec VP-Corp Dev)*
Karl Peterson *(Dir)*

TPG RE FINANCE TRUST, INC.
888 7th Ave 35th Fl, New York, NY 10106
Tel.: (212) 601-4700   **MD**
Web Site:
   https://www.tpgrefinance.com
Year Founded: 2014
TRTX—(NYSE)
Rev.: $362,550,000
Assets: $4,214,312,000
Liabilities: $3,089,527,000
Net Worth: $1,124,785,000
Earnings: ($130,905,000)
Fiscal Year-end: 12/31/23
Real Estate Asset Management Services
N.A.I.C.S.: 531390
Doug Bouquard *(CEO)*
Robert Foley *(CFO)*
Matthew Coleman *(Pres)*

TPI INTERNATIONAL, INC.
3835 E Thousand Oaks Blvd Ste 186, Westlake Village, CA 91362
Tel.: (805) 435-1803   **DE**
TPIL—(OTCIQ)
Wind Electric Power Generation Services
N.A.I.C.S.: 221115
Teruo Watanabe *(Pres, Treas & Sec)*

TPT GLOBAL TECH, INC.
501 W Broadway Ste 800, San Diego, CA 92101
Tel.: (619) 400-4996   **FL**
Web Site:
   https://www.tptglobaltech.com
TPTW—(OTCIQ)
Rev.: $11,094,170
Assets: $12,836,688
Liabilities: $36,552,744
Net Worth: ($23,716,056)
Earnings: ($8,071,851)
Emp.: 50
Fiscal Year-end: 12/31/20
Communication Service
N.A.I.C.S.: 517810
Gary L. Cook *(CFO)*
Richard Eberhardt *(COO)*
Stacie Stricker *(Sec & Controller)*
Russell Williams *(VP-IT)*
Mark Rowan *(Pres-Media Div)*
Craig D. Fuller *(Gen Counsel)*
Steve Caudle *(Pres-Cloud Svcs Div)*
Karen Kent *(CEO-Media)*
Harnish N. Gajjar *(Dir-Corp Fin)*
Shelby Smith *(Pres-Telecom Div)*
Wesley Kikuchi *(VP-Ops-ViewMe Live)*
Benjamin Yee *(Dir-Sls-TPT Med Tech)*
Stephen J. Thomas III *(Founder, Chm, Pres & CEO)*

Subsidiaries:

EPIC Reference Labs, Inc.   **(1)**
7960 Central Industrial Dr, Riviera Beach, FL 33404
Tel.: (561) 249-4434

Healthcare Support Services
N.A.I.C.S.: 621610

SpeedNet, LLC   **(1)**
455 N Main St, Frankenmuth, MI 48734
Tel.: (989) 790-0549
Web Site: https://www.linkedin.com
Internet Service Provider
N.A.I.C.S.: 517810
Eric Vanderveer *(Admin)*
Andy Tyrrell *(Dir-Bus Dev)*
John Arthur Ogren *(Founder & CEO)*

TRACK GROUP, INC.
200 E 5th Ave Ste 100, Naperville, IL 60563
Tel.: (317) 638-0803   **DE**
Web Site: https://www.trackgrp.com
Year Founded: 1995
TRCK—(OTCQB)
Rev.: $36,886,500
Assets: $37,670,006
Liabilities: $49,279,417
Net Worth: ($11,609,411)
Earnings: ($3,081,414)
Emp.: 91
Fiscal Year-end: 09/30/24
Wireless Monitoring & Surveillance Products & Services Developer & Marketer
N.A.I.C.S.: 561621
Derek Cassell *(CEO)*
Guy Dubois *(Chm)*
Mark Wojcik *(CTO)*
A. J. Gigler *(VP-Mktg & Product Mgmt)*
Johan Elerud *(VP-Ops)*
Tim Hardy *(CIO)*
Laurent Lepoutre *(VP)*
Brian Barton *(Exec Dir)*
Cassie Wolf *(Reg Sls Mgr)*
Tom McAndrew *(Reg Sls Mgr)*
Jason Bell *(Reg Sls Mgr)*
Sean O'Donnell *(Reg Sls Mgr)*
Chris Muscari *(Dir)*
Ashlie Bellman *(Sr Acct Mgr)*
Grant Law *(Acct Mgr)*
Lisa Taylor *(Acct Mgr)*
Marty Hathcock *(Acct Mgr)*
April Cornwell *(Acct Mgr)*
Ashleigh Link *(Acct Mgr)*

Subsidiaries:

Emerge Monitoring, Inc.   **(1)**
1215 W Lakeview Ct, Romeoville, IL 60446
Tel.: (877) 260-2010
Wireless Monitoring & Surveillance Products & Services Developer & Marketer
N.A.I.C.S.: 561621
Derek Cassell *(Pres-Americas Div)*
Jim Walker *(VP-Sls)*

TRACON PHARMACEUTI-CALS, INC.
4350 La Jolla Village Dr Ste 800, San Diego, CA 92122
Tel.: (858) 550-0780   **DE**
Web Site:
   https://www.traconpharma.com
Year Founded: 2005
TCON—(NASDAQ)
Assets: $19,469,000
Liabilities: $26,620,000
Net Worth: ($7,151,000)
Earnings: ($29,135,000)
Emp.: 18
Fiscal Year-end: 12/31/22
Biopharmaceutical Mfr
N.A.I.C.S.: 325412
James Freddo *(Chief Medical Officer)*

TRACTOR SUPPLY COMPANY
5401 Virginia Way, Brentwood, TN 37027
Tel.: (615) 440-4000   **DE**
Web Site:
   https://www.tractorsupply.com
Year Founded: 1938

TSCO—(NASDAQ)
Rev.: $14,555,741,000
Assets: $9,188,151,000
Liabilities: $7,038,389,000
Net Worth: $2,149,762,000
Earnings: $1,107,226,000
Emp.: 25,000
Fiscal Year-end: 12/30/23
Industrial Machinery Equipment Distr
N.A.I.C.S.: 423830
Harry A. Lawton III *(Pres & CEO)*
Colin Yankee *(Chief Supply Chain Officer & Exec VP)*
Seth Estep *(Chief Mdsg Officer & Exec VP)*
Robert D. Mills *(Chief Tech , Digital Commerce & Strategy Officer & Exec VP)*
John P. Ordus *(Chief Stores Officer & Exec VP)*
Kurt D. Barton *(CFO, Treas & Exec VP)*
Mary Winn Pilkington *(Sr VP-IR)*
Melissa Kersey *(Chief HR Officer & Exec VP)*
Noni L Ellison *(Gen Counsel, Sec & Sr VP)*
Matthew Rubin *(Sr VP)*

Subsidiaries:

Del's Farm Supply LLC   **(1)**
5401 VIRGINIA WAY, Brentwood, TN 37027
Tel.: (615) 440-4600
Web Site: http://www.delsfarmsupply.com
Sales Range: $150-199.9 Million
Emp.: 20
Feed & Farm Supply Store Operator
N.A.I.C.S.: 459999

Petsense Store   **(1)**
1203 Murfreesboro Rd, Franklin, TN 37064
Tel.: (615) 790-5038
Web Site: http://www.petsense.com
Pet Care Services
N.A.I.C.S.: 459910

Tractor Supply Co. of Texas, LP   **(1)**
315 Loop 59, Atlanta, TX 75551
Tel.: (903) 796-3784
Web Site: http://www.tractorsupply.com
Farm Supplies Whslr
N.A.I.C.S.: 424910

TRADEUP 88 CORP.
437 Madison Ave 27th Fl, New York, NY 10022
Tel.: (732) 910-9692   **Ky**
Year Founded: 2021
TUFUU—(NASDAQ)
Investment Services
N.A.I.C.S.: 523999
Lei Huang *(Co-CEO)*
Luqi Wen *(CFO)*
Jianwei Li *(Chm & Co-CEO)*

TRADEWEB MARKETS INC.
1177 Avenue of the Americas, New York, NY 10036
Tel.: (646) 430-6000   **DE**
Web Site: https://www.tradeweb.com
Year Founded: 2018
TW—(NASDAQ)
Rev.: $1,338,219,000
Assets: $7,059,538,000
Liabilities: $1,128,132,000
Net Worth: $5,931,406,000
Earnings: $364,866,000
Emp.: 1,179
Fiscal Year-end: 12/31/23
Holding Company
N.A.I.C.S.: 551112
William E. Hult *(CEO)*
Sara Furber *(CFO)*

Subsidiaries:

Tradeweb Commercial Information Consulting (Shanghai) Co., Ltd.   **(1)**
36/F Unit 17 Shanghai International Finance Center Tower 2, 8 Century Avenue

Pudong, Shanghai, 200120, China
Tel.: (86) 2180119516
Financial Services
N.A.I.C.S.: 541611

Tradeweb EU B.V.   **(1)**
Strawinskylaan 4117 4th Floor, 1077 ZX, Amsterdam, Netherlands
Tel.: (31) 202253800
Financial Services
N.A.I.C.S.: 541611

Tradeweb Europe Limited   **(1)**
1 Fore Street Avenue, London, EC2Y 9DT, United Kingdom
Tel.: (44) 2077763292
Financial Services
N.A.I.C.S.: 541611
Andrew Beer *(Mng Dir & Head-UK Sls)*

Tradeweb Japan K.K.   **(1)**
Unit 25/26 Level 26 Kyobashi Edo Grand 2-2-1 Kyobashi, Chuo-ku, Tokyo, 104-0031, Japan
Tel.: (81) 342331253
Financial Services
N.A.I.C.S.: 541611
Koichi Agarihama *(Sls Dir)*

Tradeweb Markets LLC   **(1)**
1177 Ave of the Americas, New York, NY 10036
Tel.: (646) 430-6000
Web Site: http://www.tradeweb.com
Holding Company; Financial Investment Market Operator
N.A.I.C.S.: 551112
Lee H. Olesky *(CEO)*
William E. Hult *(Pres & Head-Ops-US)*
Jay Spencer *(CTO)*
Jon Williams *(Mng Dir & Head-US Markets)*
Alfred McKeon *(Mng Dir & Head-Inter-Dealer Brokerage-US)*

Subsidiary (Domestic):

BondDesk Group LLC   **(2)**
25 Corte Madera Ave Ste 100, Mill Valley, CA 94941
Tel.: (415) 383-4988
Web Site: http://www.bonddeskgroup.com
Sales Range: $25-49.9 Million
Online Retail Fixed Income Trading Services
N.A.I.C.S.: 459999
Greg Stockett *(CFO & COO)*
John Bagley *(Pres-Trading)*
Jan Mayle *(Head-Product Mgmt & Pres-TIPS & TechHackers)*
Don Swartz *(Head-Tech)*

Tradeweb LLC   **(2)**
1177 Avenue of the Americas, New York, NY 10036
Tel.: (646) 430-6000
Web Site: http://www.tradeweb.com
Financial Investment Market Operator
N.A.I.C.S.: 525990
William E. Hult *(Pres & Head-Ops)*
Casey Costanza *(VP)*
Danielle Petrilli *(Assoc Gen Counsel & VP)*
Mike Jia *(Dir-Fixed Income & Derivatives Analytics Dev)*
Douglas Friedman *(Asst Gen Counsel)*
Kexue Liu *(VP)*

Division (Domestic):

Dealerweb Inc.   **(3)**
Harborside Financial Ctr 2200 Plz 5, Jersey City, NJ 07311
Tel.: (201) 536-6500
Web Site: http://www.tradeweb.com
Voice Brokerage Market Operator
N.A.I.C.S.: 523150

Subsidiary (Domestic):

Rafferty Capital Markets, LLC   **(4)**
1010 Franklin Ave Ste 300A, Garden City, NY 11530
Tel.: (516) 535-3800
Web Site: http://www.raffcap.com

Sales Range: $50-74.9 Million
Emp.: 80
Securities Brokerage & Dealing Services
N.A.I.C.S.: 523150
Tom Mulrooney (Pres & Chief Compliance Officer)
Dick Bove (VP-Equity Res)
Lorraine Mulrooney (Mgr-HR)
Heather Hjelm (VP-Mutual Fund Distr)
Kevin Cassidy (Gen Counsel & Exec VP)
Barbara Martens (Sr VP)
Steve Sprague (CFO)

TRAEGER, INC.
533 S 400 W, Salt Lake City, UT 84101
Tel.: (801) 701-7180   DE
Web Site: https://www.traeger.com
Year Founded: 2017
COOK—(NYSE)
Rev.: $655,901,000
Assets: $946,715,000
Liabilities: $611,846,000
Net Worth: $334,869,000
Earnings: ($382,140,000)
Emp.: 685
Fiscal Year-end: 12/31/22
Cooking Product Mfr
N.A.I.C.S.: 327110
Jeremy Andrus (CEO)
Dominic Blosil (CFO)
Jim Hardy (Pres & Pres-Apption Labs Limited)

TRAILBLAZER RESOURCES, INC.
4400 Commerce Dr, Wisconsin Rapids, WI 54494
Tel.: (715) 421-2060
TBLZ—(OTCIQ)
Hardware Product Mfr
N.A.I.C.S.: 332510
Mark Huelskamp (CEO)

TRANS GLOBAL GROUP, INC.
6810 N State Rd 7, Coconut Creek, FL 33073
Tel.: (954) 905-9896   DE
TGGI—(OTCIQ)
Rev.: $428,991
Assets: $10,579,591
Liabilities: $1,196,026
Net Worth: $9,383,565
Earnings: ($1,828,118)
Emp.: 12
Fiscal Year-end: 12/31/22
Wallboard & Sheeting Mfr
N.A.I.C.S.: 327420
Matthew P. Dwyer (Pres)

TRANS-LUX CORPORATION
254W 31st St 13th Fl, New York, NY 10001
Tel.: (203) 853-4321   DE
Web Site: https://www.trans-lux.com
Year Founded: 1919
TNLX—(OTCIQ)
Rev.: $21,661,000
Assets: $9,412,000
Liabilities: $19,736,000
Net Worth: ($10,324,000)
Earnings: $323,000
Emp.: 53
Fiscal Year-end: 12/31/22
Other Electronic Component Manufacturing
N.A.I.C.S.: 334419
Todd Dupee (Chief Acctg Officer & Sr VP)
Jane Bauer (VP-HR)
John Hammock (CMO, Chief Sls Officer & Sr VP)

Subsidiaries:

Fairplay Corporation   **(1)**
6110 Aviator Dr, Hazelwood, MO 63042
Web Site: https://www.fair-play.com
Sporting Goods Mfr

N.A.I.C.S.: 339920
Dan Weidner (Mgr-Sls)

Trans-Lux Cocteau Corporation   **(1)**
PO Box 22040, Santa Fe, NM 87502
Tel.: (505) 989-3000
Sales Range: $75-99.9 Million
LED Display & Lighting Solutions Mfr
N.A.I.C.S.: 339950

Trans-Lux Pty. Ltd.   **(1)**
Unit 4 12 14 Manjiove Ln Tiran Pt, Sydney, 2292, NSW, Australia   **(100%)**
Tel.: (61) 249623611
Sales Range: $10-24.9 Million
Emp.: 30
Distr & Leaser of Video Displays
N.A.I.C.S.: 339950

TRANS-PACIFIC AEROSPACE COMPANY, INC.
2975 Huntington Dr Ste 107, San Marino, CA 91108
Tel.: (626) 796-9804   NV
Web Site: http://www.transpacificaero space.com
Year Founded: 2007
TPAC—(OTCIQ)
Sales Range: Less than $1 Million
Emp.: 6
Aircraft Components Mfr
N.A.I.C.S.: 336413
William Reed McKay (Chm, Pres, CEO & CFO)

TRANSACT ENERGY CORP.
Unit 367 - 1901 Cornwall Ave, Bellingham, WA 98225
Tel.: (360) 510-0752   NV
Year Founded: 2006
TEGY—(OTCEM)
Oil & Gas Exploration Services
N.A.I.C.S.: 211120
Roderick C. Bartlett (Pres & CEO)
Christina Kenny (Chief People Officer & Chief HR Officer)
Joseph F. Dickson (COO)

TRANSACT TECHNOLOGIES INCORPORATED
1 Hamden Ctr 2319 Whitney Ave Ste 3B, Hamden, CT 06518
Tel.: (203) 859-6800   DE
Web Site: https://www.transact-tech.com
TACT—(NASDAQ)
Rev.: $58,139,000
Assets: $51,832,000
Liabilities: $17,970,000
Net Worth: $33,862,000
Earnings: ($5,936,000)
Emp.: 128
Fiscal Year-end: 12/31/22
Printers & Related Products for Recording Financial Transactions
N.A.I.C.S.: 333998
Steven A. DeMartino (Pres, CFO, Treas & Sec)
John M. Dillon (CEO)
Tracey S. Winslow (Chief Revenue Officer-Global)
Raymond T. Walsh Jr. (Sr VP-Food Svc Tech Sls & VP-Sls-Global)

Subsidiaries:

TransAct Technologies (Macau) Limited   **(1)**
Level 20 AIA Tower Nos 241A-301 Avenida Comercial de, Macau, China (Macau)
Tel.: (853) 362696966
Software Development Services
N.A.I.C.S.: 541511

TransAct Technologies Ltd.   **(1)**
Units 5 & 6 Bullrush Grove, Balby, Doncaster, DN4 8SL, United Kingdom
Tel.: (44) 110 977 2500
Web Site: http://www.transact-tech.com

Sales Range: $25-49.9 Million
Emp.: 3
Mfr of Transaction Printers
N.A.I.C.S.: 323111

TRANSATLANTIC CAPITAL INC.
30100 Telegraph Rd Ste 366, Bingham Farms, MI 48025
Tel.: (855) 279-7156   NV
Web Site:
http://www.transcapinc.com
TACI—(OTCIQ)
Financial Services
N.A.I.C.S.: 525990
Joshua Griggs (Chm & Interim CFO)
Julius Makiri Jenge (Pres)

TRANSATLANTIC PETRO-LEUM LTD.
8115 Preston Rd Ste 800, Dallas, TX 75225
Tel.: (214) 220-4323   BM
Web Site:
http://www.transatlanticpetrole um.com
Year Founded: 1985
TAT—(NYSEAMEX)
Rev.: $67,380,000
Assets: $136,504,000
Liabilities: $128,924,000
Net Worth: $7,580,000
Earnings: ($5,366,000)
Emp.: 147
Fiscal Year-end: 12/31/19
Oil & Gas Exploration & Production Services
N.A.I.C.S.: 211120
N. Malone Mitchell III (Chm & CEO)
Todd C. Dutton (Pres)
Selami Erdem Uras (Exec VP-Turkey)
James Follis (Mgr-Drilling)
Galo Fabian Anda (VP-Fin)
David G. Mitchell (VP-Engrg)
Javier Gonzalez (Engr-Staff Ops)
Koray Yilmaz (Sr Engr-Reservoir)
Veli Ozan Ulker (CFO-Eastern Europe)
Tabitha T. Bailey (Gen Counsel, Sec & VP)
Michael P. Hill (CFO & Chief Acctg Officer)
Marc Hornbrook (VP-Ops)
Noah M. Mitchell IV (VP)

Subsidiaries:

Direct Petroleum Bulgaria EOOD   **(1)**
46 Chervena Stena Str 3rd Floor, 1421, Sofia, Bulgaria
Tel.: (359) 29633244
Natural Gas Extraction Services
N.A.I.C.S.: 211130
Ian Delahunty (Gen Mgr)

TransAtlantic Petroleum (USA) Corp.   **(1)**
16803 Dallas Pkwy, Addison, TX 75001
Tel.: (214) 220-4323
Web Site:
http://www.transatlanticpetroleum.com
Sales Range: $50-74.9 Million
Emp.: 50
Oil & Gas Exploration & Production Services
N.A.I.C.S.: 211120
N. Malone Mitchell III (Chm & CEO)

TRANSCAT, INC.
35 Vantage Point Dr, Rochester, NY 14624
Tel.: (585) 352-7777   OH
Web Site: https://www.transcat.com
Year Founded: 1964
TRNS—(NASDAQ)
Rev.: $230,569,000
Assets: $195,749,000
Liabilities: $96,119,000
Net Worth: $99,630,000
Earnings: $10,688,000

Emp.: 1,030
Fiscal Year-end: 03/25/23
Professional Grade Test, Measurement & Calibration Instrumentation Distr; Calibration & Repair Services
N.A.I.C.S.: 334514
Lee D. Rudow (Pres & CEO)
James M. Jenkins (Chief Risk Officer, Gen Counsel & VP-Corp Dev)
Gary J. Haseley (Chm)
Scott D. Deverell (Principal Acctg Officer & Controller)
Michael W. West (COO)
Thomas L. Barbato (CFO, Treas & Sr VP-Fin)
Marcy Bosley (VP-Sls)

Subsidiaries:

Angels Instrumentation, Inc.   **(1)**
928 Canal Dr, Chesapeake, VA 23323-4704
Tel.: (757) 558-2500
Web Site:
http://www.angelsinstrumentation.com
Electronic Test Instrument Mfr
N.A.I.C.S.: 334515

Anmar Metrology, Inc.   **(1)**
7726 Arjons Dr, San Diego, CA 92126
Tel.: (858) 621-2630
Web Site: http://www.anmar.com
Electronic Product Testing Services
N.A.I.C.S.: 541380

Axiom Test Equipment, Inc.   **(1)**
1704 Ord Way, Oceanside, CA 92056
Tel.: (760) 806-6600
Web Site: http://www.axiomtest.com
Instrument Mfr
N.A.I.C.S.: 334515
Erin Lee (Coord-Mktg)

BioTek Services, Inc.   **(1)**
5310 S Laburnum Ave, Richmond, VA 23231-6724
Tel.: (916) 273-6726
Web Site:
https://www.biotekcalibrations.com
Electronic & Precision Equipment Repair & Maintenance
N.A.I.C.S.: 811210
Karla M. Connelly (Sec)

Calibration Technologies   **(1)**
4157 Park Blvd, Louisville, KY 40209
Tel.: (502) 363-9454
Web Site: https://www.caltechlab.com
Calibration Services
N.A.I.C.S.: 541380
Fred Widman (Owner)

TIC-MS, LLC   **(1)**
647 Trade Center Blvd, Chesterfield, MO 63005
Tel.: (314) 432-3633
Testing & Measurement Instrument Distr
N.A.I.C.S.: 423830

TTE Laboratories Inc.   **(1)**
113 Cedar St, Milford, MA 01757
Tel.: (508) 435-7301
Web Site: https://www.pipettes.com
Rev.: $1,530,000
Emp.: 15
Testing Laboratories
N.A.I.C.S.: 541380
Kent Koeman (Dir-Sls & Mktg)
Mike Anema (Dir-Laboratory)
Aubrey Carr (Dir-Quality)

Transmation (Canada) Ltd.   **(1)**
4043 Carling Avenue Suite 110, Ottawa, K2K 2A4, ON, Canada   **(100%)**
Tel.: (613) 591-8140
Web Site: http://www.tanscat.com
Sales Range: $1-9.9 Million
Emp.: 10
Calibration Services to Canadian Businesses
N.A.I.C.S.: 334519
Keith Powell (Gen Mgr)

United Scale & Engineering Corporation   **(1)**
16725 W Victor Rd, New Berlin, WI 53151
Tel.: (262) 785-1733
Web Site: https://www.unitedscale.com

Transcat, Inc.—(Continued)

Sales Range: $1-9.9 Million
Emp.: 36
Scale & Measurement Equipment Distr &
Calibration Services
N.A.I.C.S.: 423440
Judy Trunec *(Pres)*

TRANSCODE THERAPEUTICS, INC.

73b Chapel St, Newton, MA 02458
Tel.: (857) 837-3099 **DE**
Web Site:
  https://www.transcodetherapeu
    tics.com
Year Founded: 2016
RNAZ—(NASDAQ)
Rev.: $1,100,846
Assets: $7,587,986
Liabilities: $4,347,290
Net Worth: $3,240,696
Earnings: ($17,564,968)
Emp.: 19
Fiscal Year-end: 12/31/22
Research & Development in Biotech-
nology (except Nanobiotechnology)
N.A.I.C.S.: 541714
Robert Michael Dudley *(Co-Founder)*
Zdravka Medarova *(Co-Founder & CTO)*
Thomas A. Fitzgerald *(Interim Pres, Interim CEO & CFO)*
Judy Carmody *(VP-Ops)*
Anna Moore *(Co-Founder)*
Philippe P. Calais *(Chm)*

TRANSDIGM GROUP INCOR-PORATED

US Bank Ctr 1350 Euclid Ave Ste
1600, Cleveland, OH 44115
Tel.: (216) 706-2960 **DE**
Web Site: https://www.transdigm.com
Year Founded: 1993
TDG—(NYSE)
Rev.: $7,940,000,000
Assets: $25,586,000,000
Liabilities: $31,869,000,000
Net Worth: ($6,283,000,000)
Earnings: $1,715,000,000
Emp.: 16,600
Fiscal Year-end: 09/30/24
Aircraft Equipment Mfr
N.A.I.C.S.: 551112
Walter Nicholas Howley *(Founder & Chm)*
Robert S. Henderson *(Vice Chm)*
Peter Palmer *(Exec VP)*
Joel Reiss *(Co-COO)*
Michael J. Lisman *(Co-COO)*
Halle Fine Martin *(Chief Compliance Officer, Gen Counsel & Sec)*
Alex Feil *(Exec VP)*
Rodrigo Rubiano *(Exec VP)*
Sarah Wynne *(CFO & Chief Acctg Officer)*
Paula Wheeler *(Exec VP)*
Patrick Murphy *(Exec VP)*
Marko Enderlein *(Exec VP)*
Kevin M. Stein *(Pres & CEO)*

Subsidiaries:

Ashford Properties, LLC **(1)**
2807 Neuse Blvd, New Bern, NC 28562
Tel.: (252) 649-0410
Web Site:
  https://www.ashfordproperties.com
Real Estate Investment Services
N.A.I.C.S.: 531190

CMC Electronics ME Inc. **(1)**
600 Dr Frederik Philips Boul, Saint Laurent,
H4M 2S9, QC, Canada
Tel.: (514) 748-3148
Web Site: http://www.cmcelectronics.ca
Electric Equipment Mfr
N.A.I.C.S.: 334419
Marie-Helene Emond *(Mgr-Mktg Comm & PR)*

Calspan Air Services, LLC **(1)**
9900 Porter Rd, Niagara Falls, NY 14304
Tel.: (716) 298-9307
Web Site:
  https://www.calspanairservices.com
Aircraft Repair & Maintenance Services
N.A.I.C.S.: 811420

Calspan Corp. **(1)**
4455 Genesee St, Buffalo, NY 14225
Tel.: (716) 632-7500
Web Site: http://www.calspan.com
Aeronautics & Transportation Design &
Testing Services
N.A.I.C.S.: 541380
Louis H. Knotts *(CEO)*
John R. Yurtchuk *(Chm)*
Peter Sauer *(CFO & Exec VP)*
Ruthanne Armstrong *(Sr VP & Chief HR Officer)*
Robert Jacobson *(Pres)*
Stephanie Mumford *(Pres-Calspan Sys)*

Subsidiary (Domestic):

Calspan Systems Corporation **(2)**
703 City Ctr Blvd, Newport News, VA 23606
Tel.: (757) 873-1344
Aircraft Testing Services & Propulsion Sys-
tems Developer & Mfr
N.A.I.C.S.: 488190
Stephanie Mumford *(Pres)*

Chelton Limited **(1)**
The Chelton Centre Fourth Avenue, Marlow,
SL7 1TF, Buckinghamshire, United
Kingdom **(100%)**
Tel.: (44) 1628472072
Web Site: https://chelton.com
Sales Range: $75-99.9 Million
Emp.: 300
Aerospace Systems Design & Mfr
N.A.I.C.S.: 334511

Subsidiary (US):

Chelton Avionics, Inc **(2)**
6400 Wilkinson Dr, Prescott, AZ 86301-
6164
Tel.: (928) 708-1550
Aircraft Communication System Mfr
N.A.I.C.S.: 334220
John Payne *(Gen Mgr)*

Dart Aerospace Ltd. **(1)**
1270 Aberdeen Street, Hawkesbury, K6A
1K7, ON, Canada
Tel.: (613) 632-3336
Web Site: http://www.dartaerospace.com
Emp.: 80
Design, Manufacturing & Market Solutions
for Helicopter & Aerospace Industries
N.A.I.C.S.: 336413
Alain Madore *(Pres)*
Steve Ghaleb *(VP-Sls)*
Emmanuel Paillier *(VP-Product Strategy & Bus Dev)*

Esterline Services China Ltd. **(1)**
A-309 Weiguan Zhiku Industrial Park No 15
Shun Xiang Road, Huadong Town Huadu
District, Guangzhou, 510890, China
Tel.: (86) 6590885699
Aerospace Products Mfr
N.A.I.C.S.: 336413
Summer Dong *(Mgr-Sls Acct)*

Esterline Technologies
Corporation **(1)**
500 108th Ave NE, Bellevue, WA 98004
Tel.: (425) 453-9400
Web Site: http://www.esterline.com
Rev.: $2,034,839,000
Assets: $3,036,917,000
Liabilities: $1,193,790,000
Net Worth: $1,843,127,000
Earnings: $69,458,000
Fiscal Year-end: 09/28/2018
Technology Interface Systems, High-
Precision Temperature Sensors & Elasto-
mer Products Mfr
N.A.I.C.S.: 334513

Division (Domestic):

Advanced Input Devices, Inc. **(2)**
600 W Wilbur, Coeur D'Alene, ID
83815 **(100%)**
Tel.: (208) 765-8000
Web Site: http://www.esterline.com

Sales Range: $150-199.9 Million
Emp.: 355
Mfr of Keyboard Input Devices
N.A.I.C.S.: 334118

Subsidiary (Non-US):

Gamesman Ltd. **(3)**
Crompton Fields Crompton Way, Crawley,
RH10 9QB, West Sussex, United Kingdom
Tel.: (44) 1293418888
Web Site: https://www.gamesman.co.uk
Emp.: 100
Electronic Connector Mfr
N.A.I.C.S.: 334417
Brett Armitage *(Mng Dir)*

LRE Medical GmbH **(3)**
Hofer Strasse 5, 86720, Nordlingen, Ger-
many
Tel.: (49) 90818000
Web Site: http://www.lre.de
Sales Range: $25-49.9 Million
Emp.: 270
Electronic Medical Equipment Mfr
N.A.I.C.S.: 339112
Karsten Sauer *(VP)*
Florian Binder *(Mng Dir)*
Claudia Strehle *(VP)*
Manfred Aigner *(VP)*

Subsidiary (Domestic):

Memtron Technologies Co. **(3)**
530 N Franklin St, Frankenmuth, MI
48734-0207 **(100%)**
Tel.: (989) 652-2656
Web Site: http://www.memtron.com
Sales Range: $25-49.9 Million
Emp.: 89
Switches & Panels for Medical, Industrial,
Computers & Other Commercial Markets
N.A.I.C.S.: 334419

Subsidiary (Domestic):

Armtec Coutermeasures Co. **(2)**
608 E Mcneill St, Lillington, NC 27546
Tel.: (910) 814-1222
Navigation, Aeronautical, Nautical System &
Instrument Mfr
N.A.I.C.S.: 334511

Subsidiary (Non-US):

Auxitrol S.A. **(2)**
5 Allee Charles Pathe, CS 20006, -18023,
Bourges, Cedex, France
Tel.: (33) 248667878
Web Site: http://www.esterline.com
Sales Range: $50-74.9 Million
Emp.: 437
High-Precision Temperature & Pressure
Sensors, Liquid Level & Various Other Mea-
suring Devices Mfr
N.A.I.C.S.: 334519

Subsidiary (US):

Esterline Sensors Services Americas,
Inc. **(3)**
50 O'Hara Dr, Norwich, NY 13815
Tel.: (607) 336-7636
Transportation Equipment & Supply Whslr
N.A.I.C.S.: 423860

Branch (Domestic):

Esterline Sensors Services Americas,
Inc. **(4)**
6900 Orangethorpe Ave Ste A, Buena Park,
CA 90620
Tel.: (714) 736-7570
Defense System & Equipment Mfr
N.A.I.C.S.: 334511
Rene Segovia *(VP & Gen Mgr)*

Subsidiary (US):

Norwich Aero Products, Inc. **(3)**
50 O'Hara Dr, Norwich, NY 13815-2029
Tel.: (607) 336-7636
Web Site: http://www.esterline.com
Sales Range: $25-49.9 Million
Emp.: 100
Temperature Sensors, Speed Sensors &
Interconnect Products Mfr
N.A.I.C.S.: 336999

Subsidiary (Non-US):

Weston Aerospace Ltd. **(3)**
124 Victoria Road, Farnborough, GU14
7PW, Hampshire, United Kingdom
Tel.: (44) 1252544433
Web Site: http://www.westonaero.com
Measurement & Control Equipment Mfr
N.A.I.C.S.: 334519

Subsidiary (Non-US):

CMC Electronics Inc. **(2)**
600 Dr Frederik Philips Boulevard, Ville
Saint Laurent, H4M 2S9, QC, Canada
Tel.: (514) 748-3124
Web Site: https://www.cmcelectronics.ca
Sales Range: $150-199.9 Million
Emp.: 800
Aviation Electronics & Components Mfr
N.A.I.C.S.: 334511
Marie-Helene Emond *(Mgr-Mktg Comm & PR)*

Subsidiary (US):

CMC Electronics Aurora LLC **(3)**
84 N Dugan Rd, Sugar Grove, IL 60554
Tel.: (630) 466-4343
Aviation Electronics & Components Mfr
N.A.I.C.S.: 334511

Branch (Domestic):

CMC Electronics Inc. - Ottawa **(3)**
415 Legget Drive, PO Box 13330, Ottawa,
K2K 2B2, ON, Canada
Tel.: (613) 592-6500
Web Site: http://www.cmcelectronic.ca
Sales Range: $50-74.9 Million
Emp.: 200
Aviation Electronics & Components Mfr
N.A.I.C.S.: 334511

Subsidiary (Domestic):

Eesterline Sensors Services Ameri-
cas, Inc. **(2)**
50 O'Hara Dr, Norwich, NY 13815
Tel.: (607) 336-7636
Navigation, Aeronautical, Nautical System &
Instrument Mfr
N.A.I.C.S.: 334511
Rene Segovia *(VP & Gen Mgr)*

Division (Domestic):

Esterline Defense Group **(2)**
85901 Ave 53, Coachella, CA
92236-2607 **(100%)**
Tel.: (760) 398-0143
Web Site: https://www.armtecdefense.com
Sales Range: $25-49.9 Million
Emp.: 300
Ordnance & Accessories Mfr
N.A.I.C.S.: 334511

Subsidiary (Domestic):

Armtec Countermeasures Co. **(3)**
85901 Ave 53, Coachella, CA 92236
Tel.: (760) 398-0143
Web Site: http://www.armtecdefense.com
Sales Range: $50-74.9 Million
Emp.: 250
Developer of Defense Products
N.A.I.C.S.: 334511

Division (Domestic):

Armtec Countermeasures Co. - De-
fense Technologies-ARO **(4)**
Highway 203 E Highland Indus Park Bldg
M-7, East Camden, AR 71711
Tel.: (870) 574-1712
Web Site: http://www.esterline.com
Defense System & Equipment Mfr
N.A.I.C.S.: 334511

Division (Domestic):

Esterline Engineered Materials **(2)**
300 E Cypress St, Brea, CA 92821
Tel.: (714) 529-4901
Web Site: http://www.esterline.com
Sales Range: $300-349.9 Million
Aircraft Components Mfr
N.A.I.C.S.: 336413
Philip Bowker *(Pres)*

Subsidiary (Domestic):

Esterline Engineered Materials-NMC Aerospace (3)
3101 Enterprise St, Brea, CA 92821
Tel.: (714) 223-3500
Web Site: http://www.esterline.com
Aerospace Fastener Designer & Mfr
N.A.I.C.S.: 334511

Kirkhill-TA Company (3)
300 E Cypress St, Brea, CA 92821-4007 **(100%)**
Tel.: (714) 529-4901
Web Site: http://www.kirkhill.com
Sales Range: $200-249.9 Million
Emp.: 800
Elastomer Mfr
N.A.I.C.S.: 326299

Subsidiary (Non-US):

Darchem Engineering Limited (4)
Ironmasters Way, Stillington, Stockton-on-Tees, TS21 1LB, United Kingdom
Tel.: (44) 1740630461
Web Site: http://www.darchem.com
Sales Range: $50-74.9 Million
Emp.: 750
High Temperature Engineering Structure Mfr for the Aerospace Industry
N.A.I.C.S.: 541330

Subsidiary (Domestic):

Hytek Finishes Inc. (4)
8127 S 216th St, Kent, WA 98032-1904 **(100%)**
Tel.: (253) 872-7160
Web Site: https://hytekfinishes.com
Sales Range: $75-99.9 Million
Emp.: 150
Metal Finishing
N.A.I.C.S.: 332813

Branch (Domestic):

Kirkhill-TA (4)
28065 Franklin Pkwy, Valencia, CA 91355-4117 **(100%)**
Tel.: (661) 775-1100
Web Site: http://www.esterline.com
Sales Range: $50-74.9 Million
Emp.: 172
Clamping Systems & Elastomer Installation Components Mfr
N.A.I.C.S.: 325211

Subsidiary (Domestic):

Korry Electronics Co. (2)
11910 Beverly Park Rd, Everett, WA 98204 **(100%)**
Tel.: (425) 297-9700
Web Site: https://www.korry.com
Sales Range: $150-199.9 Million
Emp.: 580
Lighted Pushbutton Switches & Data Entry Panels Mfr
N.A.I.C.S.: 335313

Subsidiary (Domestic):

Mason Electric Co. (3)
13955 Balboa Blvd, Sylmar, CA 91342 **(100%)**
Tel.: (818) 361-3366
Sales Range: $125-149.9 Million
Emp.: 350
Flight Controls Including Sticks Grips, Wheels & Specialized Switching
N.A.I.C.S.: 336413

Palomar Products Inc. (3)
23042 Arroyo Vista, Rancho Santa Margarita, CA 92688-2604
Tel.: (949) 766-5300
Web Site: https://www.palomar.com
Sales Range: $25-49.9 Million
Emp.: 110
Voice & Data Switch Products Mfr
N.A.I.C.S.: 334290

Subsidiary (Domestic):

Leach International Corporation (2)
6900 Orangethorpe Ave, Buena Park, CA 90620
Tel.: (714) 736-7598
Web Site: https://leachcorp.com
Relays & Industrial Controls Mfr

N.A.I.C.S.: 335314

Subsidiary (Non-US):

Leach International Europe S.A. (2)
2 Rue Goethe, CS 50004, 57430, Sarralbe, France
Tel.: (33) 387979897
Web Site: http://www.leachint.com
Emp.: 400
Electrical Switching & Control Devices Mfr
N.A.I.C.S.: 334511

Souriau S.A.S. (2)
9 rue de la Porte du Buc, 78000, Versailles, France
Tel.: (33) 1 30 84 77 99
Web Site: http://www.souriau.com
Sales Range: $350-399.9 Million
Emp.: 3,000
Electronic Connector Mfr
N.A.I.C.S.: 334417

Subsidiary (US):

Joslyn Sunbank Company LLC (3)
1740 Commerce Way, Paso Robles, CA 93446 **(100%)**
Tel.: (805) 238-2840
Sales Range: $25-49.9 Million
Emp.: 500
Electrical Wiring Harness Connectors & Conduit Mfr
N.A.I.C.S.: 334417

Subsidiary (Domestic):

Air-Dry Company of America LLC (4)
1740 Commerce Way, Paso Robles, CA 93446-3620 **(100%)**
Tel.: (805) 238-2840
Web Site: https://www.airdrycompany.com
Sales Range: $100-124.9 Million
Emp.: 250
Air & Gas Dehydration & Purification Systems Mfr
N.A.I.C.S.: 333413

Subsidiary (US):

Pacific Aerospace & Electronics, Inc. (3)
434 Olds Station Rd, Wenatchee, WA 98801-5975
Tel.: (509) 664-8000
Web Site: http://www.pacaero.com
Sales Range: $25-49.9 Million
Emp.: 200
Mfr of Avionic, Electronic & Metal Components
N.A.I.C.S.: 334419

Unit (Domestic):

Pacific Aerospace & Electronics, Inc. - Bonded Metals (4)
2249 Diamond Point Rd, Sequim, WA 98382-8663 **(100%)**
Tel.: (360) 683-4167
Web Site: http://www.pacaero.com
Rev.: $1,300,000
Emp.: 12
Aerospace Products Mfr
N.A.I.C.S.: 336413

Subsidiary (Non-US):

Souriau Japan K.K. (3)
Parale Mitsui Building 15F 8 Higashida-cho, Kawasaki-ku, Kawasaki, 210-0005, Kanagawa, Japan
Tel.: (81) 442101147
Web Site: http://www.souriau.co.jp
Emp.: 90
Defense Space & Heavy Industrial Equipment Mfr
N.A.I.C.S.: 334519

Subsidiary (US):

Souriau USA Inc. (3)
150 Farm Ln Ste 100, York, PA 17402
Tel.: (717) 718-8810
Electronic Connector Mfr
N.A.I.C.S.: 334417

Subsidiary (Domestic):

Technocontact S.A. (3)
11 Rue du Dr Gallet, Haute Savoie, Cluses,

74300, France
Tel.: (33) 450982333
Emp.: 70
Temperature Sensor & Elastomer Products Mfr
N.A.I.C.S.: 334513
Patrice Deville *(Gen Mgr)*

Subsidiary (Domestic):

TA Aerospace Co. (2)
28065 Franklin Pkwy, Valencia, CA 91355-4117
Tel.: (661) 775-1100
Web Site: https://taaerospace.com
Emp.: 250
Hardware Designer & Mfr
N.A.I.C.S.: 332510

HarcoSemco LLC (1)
186 Cedar St, Branford, CT 06405-6011
Tel.: (203) 483-3700
Web Site: https://www.harcosemco.com
Aircraft Part Mfr
N.A.I.C.S.: 336413

Paravion Technologies Inc. (1)
2001 Airway Ave, Fort Collins, CO 80524
Web Site: https://www.paravion.com
Aircraft Equipment Mfr
N.A.I.C.S.: 336413

TREALITY SVS LLC (1)
600 Bellbrook Ave, Xenia, OH 45385-4053
Tel.: (937) 372-7579
Web Site: http://www.trealitysvs.com
Display Design Services
N.A.I.C.S.: 541430

TransDigm Inc. (1)
The Tower at Erieview 1301 E 9th St Ste 3000, Cleveland, OH 44114
Tel.: (216) 706-2960
Web Site: http://www.transdigm.com
Sales Range: $25-49.9 Million
Emp.: 15
Aftermarket Aerospace Components Mfr
N.A.I.C.S.: 336413
Walter Nicholas Howley *(Chm)*

Subsidiary (Domestic):

Acme Aerospace, Inc. (2)
528 W 21st St, Tempe, AZ 85282
Tel.: (480) 894-6864
Web Site: https://www.acme-aero.com
Emp.: 100
Aviation & Aerospace Battery System Mfr
N.A.I.C.S.: 335910

Adams Rite Aerospace Inc. (2)
4141 N Palm St, Fullerton, CA 92835
Tel.: (714) 278-6500
Web Site: https://www.araero.com
Sales Range: $50-74.9 Million
Emp.: 300
Aircraft Interior Hardware, Flight Controls, Fluid Hardware & Systems & Life Support Products Mfr
N.A.I.C.S.: 335314
John Schaefer *(Pres)*

AdelWiggins Group (2)
5000 Triggs St, Los Angeles, CA 90022
Tel.: (323) 269-9181
Web Site: https://www.adelwiggins.com
Sales Range: $50-74.9 Million
Provider of Engineered Solutions for Aerospace & Equipment Refueling Applications
N.A.I.C.S.: 333519

Aero-Instruments Co., LLC (2)
14901 Emery Ave, Cleveland, OH 44135
Tel.: (216) 671-3133
Web Site: http://www.aero-inst.com
Sales Range: $25-49.9 Million
Search, Detection, Navigation, Guidance, Aeronautical & Nautical System & Instrument Mfr
N.A.I.C.S.: 334511

AeroControlex Group (2)
4223 Monticello Blvd, South Euclid, OH 44121
Tel.: (216) 291-6025
Web Site: http://www.aerocontrolex.com
Sales Range: $75-99.9 Million
Pumps, Valves & Mechanical Controls Mfr
N.A.I.C.S.: 333914

Subsidiary (Domestic):

Fluid Regulators Corp. (3)
313 Gillett St, Painesville, OH 44077-2918
Tel.: (440) 352-6182
Sales Range: $50-74.9 Million
Emp.: 90
Fluid Control & Measurement Components Mfr
N.A.I.C.S.: 332912

Subsidiary (Domestic):

Aerosonic Corporation (2)
1212 N Hercules Ave, Clearwater, FL 33765-1920 **(100%)**
Tel.: (727) 461-3000
Web Site: http://www.aerosonic.com
Rev.: $31,021,000
Assets: $23,324,000
Liabilities: $11,284,000
Net Worth: $12,040,000
Earnings: $2,522,000
Emp.: 199
Fiscal Year-end: 01/31/2013
Aircraft Instrumentation & Avionic Products Mfr
N.A.I.C.S.: 336413
Dan Rice *(Pres)*
Scott Sweet *(VP-Sls & Mktg)*
Bob Higgins *(VP-Ops)*
Catherine Sherman *(VP-Fin Reporting)*

Subsidiary (Non-US):

Airborne Systems Group Limited (2)
Bettws Road, Llangeinor, Bridgend, CF32 8PL, Mid Glamorgan, United Kingdom
Tel.: (44) 1656727000
Aerospace Component Mfr & Distr
N.A.I.C.S.: 334511

Subsidiary (Non-US):

Airborne Systems France (3)
16 bis rue Paule Raymondis, 31200, Toulouse, France
Tel.: (33) 561297605
Aerospace Component Mfr & Distr
N.A.I.C.S.: 334511
Thierry Lebreton *(Dir-Trng & Maintenance)*

Subsidiary (US):

Airborne Systems North America Inc. (3)
5800 N Magnolia Ave, Pennsauken, NJ 08109
Tel.: (856) 663-1275
Web Site: http://www.airborne-sys.com
Parachute Mfr
N.A.I.C.S.: 339999

Subsidiary (Domestic):

Airborne Systems North America of CA Inc. (4)
3100 W Segerstrom Ave, Santa Ana, CA 92704
Tel.: (657) 859-3000
Emp.: 91
Parachute Mfr
N.A.I.C.S.: 339999

Airborne Systems North America of NJ Inc. (4)
5800 N Magnolia Ave, Pennsauken, NJ 08109
Tel.: (856) 663-1275
Aerospace Component Mfr & Distr
N.A.I.C.S.: 334511

Subsidiary (Domestic):

AmSafe, Inc. (2)
1043 N 47th Ave, Phoenix, AZ 85043
Tel.: (602) 850-2850
Web Site: https://www.amsafe.com
Sales Range: $50-74.9 Million
Emp.: 70
Safety Restraint Products for Aerospace, Defense, Specialty & Vehicle Industries
N.A.I.C.S.: 336413
Ian Kentfield *(Pres)*

Subsidiary (Non-US):

AmSafe Aviation (Chongqing), Ltd. (3)
Lot No G43-4/01-2 Eastern Zone, Chongqing Liang Lu Industrial Park YuBei

TransDigm Group Incorporated—(Continued)

District, Chongqing, 401120, China
Tel.: (86) 2367456588
Aircraft Seatbelts & Other Products Mfr &
Repair Services
N.A.I.C.S.: 336413

AmSafe Bridport Limited (3)
The Court West Street, Bridport, DT6 3QU,
Dorset, United Kingdom
Tel.: (44) 1308456666
Web Site: http://www.amsafebridport.com
Sales Range: $50-74.9 Million
Emp.: 650
Cargo & Airframe Products Mfr; Aircraft &
Restraint Products Mfr
N.A.I.C.S.: 314999

Division (Non-US):

AmSafe Bridport Nittambuwa (4)
Export Processing Zone, Wathupitiwala,
Nittambuwa, Gampaha, Sri Lanka
Tel.: (94) 334729800
Sales Range: $75-99.9 Million
Cargo & Airframe Products Mfr
N.A.I.C.S.: 336413

Division (Domestic):

AmSafe Defense (3)
1043 N 47th Ave, Phoenix, AZ 85043
Tel.: (602) 850-2850
Web Site: http://www.amsafe.com
Sales Range: $50-74.9 Million
Emp.: 300
Safety Restraint Products for Military
Ground Vehicles
N.A.I.C.S.: 336360

Subsidiary (Non-US):

**AmSafe Global Services (Private)
Limited** (3)
3rd Floor 10 Gothami Road, Borella, Co-
lombo, 8, Sri Lanka
Tel.: (94) 114516888
Emp.: 60
Aviation Seatbelt Airbag System Provider
N.A.I.C.S.: 336360
Sidath De Alwis (Deputy Mgr-Customer Svc
& Sls)

Subsidiary (Domestic):

AmSafe-C Safe, Inc. (3)
1301 E 9th St Ste 3000, Cleveland, OH
44114
Tel.: (216) 706-2939
Aircraft Equipment Mfr
N.A.I.C.S.: 336413

Division (Domestic):

Amsafe Commercial Products (3)
22937 Gallatin Way, Elkhart, IN 46514
Tel.: (574) 266-8330
Web Site: http://www.amsafe.com
Sales Range: $25-49.9 Million
Emp.: 60
Restraint & Safety Device Mfr
N.A.I.C.S.: 336360

Division (Non-US):

AmSafe Kunshan (4)
33 Nan Zhang Road Kunshan Export Pro-
cessing Zone, Kunshan, 215301, Jiangsu,
China
Tel.: (86) 512 57364632
Web Site: http://www.amsafe.com
Sales Range: $50-74.9 Million
Child & Specialty Vehicle Restraints & Har-
ness Products Mfr
N.A.I.C.S.: 336360

Subsidiary (Domestic):

Arkwin Industries, Inc. (2)
686 Main St, Westbury, NY 11590
Tel.: (516) 333-2640
Web Site: https://www.arkwin.com
Sales Range: $75-99.9 Million
Aerospace Precision Hydraulics, Fuel Sys-
tems & Custom Components Mfr
N.A.I.C.S.: 336413
Adam Crossman (Pres)
Kristian Norheim (VP-Sls & Mktg)
John Melito (VP-Engrg & Quality)
Jody Williams (VP-Ops)

Aviation Technologies, Inc. (2)
6500 Merrill Creek Pkwy, Everett, WA
98203
Tel.: (206) 695-8000
Web Site: http://www.avtechyee.com
Engineered Electrical & Electro-Mechanical
Aircraft Components
N.A.I.C.S.: 336413

Subsidiary (Domestic):

ADS/Transicoil Corp. (3)
9 Iron Bridge Dr, Collegeville, PA 19426-
2042
Tel.: (484) 902-1100
Web Site: http://www.adstcoil.com
Sales Range: $50-74.9 Million
Emp.: 100
Components, Controls, Panels, Displays &
Aircraft Instruments Mfr
N.A.I.C.S.: 335312

Avtech Corporation (3)
3400 Wallingford Ave N, Seattle, WA 98103
Tel.: (425) 290-3100
Web Site: http://www.avtcorp.com
Sales Range: $75-99.9 Million
Emp.: 170
Operation & Management Services
N.A.I.C.S.: 541611

Subsidiary (Domestic):

Avionic Instruments Inc. (2)
1414 Randolph Ave, Avenel, NJ 07001
Tel.: (732) 388-3500
Web Site:
http://www.avionicinstruments.com
Power Conversion Equipment Mfr for Mili-
tary, Commercial & Aerospace Applications
N.A.I.C.S.: 335311
Steve Gross (Pres)
Matthew Rubinstein (VP)
Steve Byrne (VP)
Ryan Moss (VP)

AvtechTyee, Inc. (2)
6500 Merrill Creek Pkwy, Everett, WA
98203
Tel.: (425) 290-3100
Web Site: https://www.avtechtyee.com
Sales Range: $50-74.9 Million
Electric Equipment Mfr
N.A.I.C.S.: 334419

Subsidiary (Domestic):

Beams Industries, Inc. (3)
6420 S Air Depot, Oklahoma City, OK
73135
Tel.: (405) 793-0505
Web Site: http://www.seatbelts.net
Seat Belt Mfr
N.A.I.C.S.: 336360

Broozo Eastern LLC (2)
35 Melanie Ln, Whippany, NJ 07981
Tel.: (973) 602-1001
Web Site: https://www.breeze-eastern.com
Sales Range: $75-99.9 Million
Aerospace & Defense Equipment Mfr
N.A.I.C.S.: 336413
Mike Koons (Dir-Sls & Mktg)
Jim Fett (Mgr-Technical Support & Trng)

Bridport Erie Aviation, Inc. (2)
1611 Asbury Rd, Erie, PA 16501
Tel.: (814) 833-6767
Aircraft Equipment Mfr
N.A.I.C.S.: 336413

Bruce Aerospace, Inc. (2)
101 Evans Ave, Dayton, NV 89403-8306
Tel.: (775) 246-0101
Web Site: http://www.bruce.aero
Interior Aircraft Lighting & Military Shelter
Lighting
N.A.I.C.S.: 336320

CDA InterCorp LLC (2)
450 Goolsby Blvd, Deerfield Beach, FL
33442
Tel.: (954) 698-6000
Web Site: https://www.cda-intercorp.com
Sales Range: $25-49.9 Million
Controllable Drive Actuator & Transducer
Design & Mfr
N.A.I.C.S.: 333995

CEF Industries, LLC (2)
320 S Church St, Addison, IL 60101
Tel.: (630) 628-2299
Web Site: https://www.cefindustries.com

Aircraft Compressor, Actuator & Pump Mfr
& Sales
N.A.I.C.S.: 336413

Champion Aerospace Inc. (2)
1230 Old Norris Rd, Liberty, SC 29657
Tel.: (864) 843-1162
Web Site:
http://www.championaerospace.com
Sales Range: $100-124.9 Million
Aerospace Turbine Engine Exciters, Leads,
Igniters & Spark Plugs Mfr
N.A.I.C.S.: 336412

Subsidiary (Non-US):

DDC Electronics Ltd. (2)
James House 27-35 London Road,
Newbury, RG14 1JL, Berkshire, United
Kingdom
Tel.: (44) 1635811140
Aircraft Parts & Auxiliary Equipment Distr
N.A.I.C.S.: 423860

DDC Electronique, S.A.R.L. (2)
84-88 Bld de la Mission Marchand, 92411,
Courbevoie, Cedex, France
Tel.: (33) 141163424
Aircraft Parts & Auxiliary Equipment Distr
N.A.I.C.S.: 423860

DDC Elektronik, GmbH (2)
Triebstrasse 3, 80993, Munich, Germany
Tel.: (49) 8915001211
Aircraft Parts & Auxiliary Equipment Distr
N.A.I.C.S.: 423860

Subsidiary (Domestic):

Data Device Corporation (2)
105 Wilbur Pl, Bohemia, NY 11716-2426
Tel.: (631) 567-5600
Web Site: http://www.ddc-web.com
Emp.: 600
Military & Aerospace Application Electronic
Components Mfr
N.A.I.C.S.: 335311
Adam Crossman (Pres)

Subsidiary (Domestic):

**Beta Transformer Technology
Corporation** (3)
105 Wilbur Pl 40 Orville Dr, Bohemia, NY
11716-2426 (100%)
Tel.: (631) 333-7950
Web Site: https://powerdevicecorp.com
Emp.: 600
Military & Aerospace Application Trans-
former & Magnetics Mfr
N.A.I.C.S.: 335311

Subsidiary (Non-US):

DDC Electronics K.K. (3)
Koraku 1-1-5 first horseback building 8F,
Bunkyo-ku, Tokyo, Japan (100%)
Tel.: (81) 338147688
Web Site: http://www.ddcjapan.co.jp
Emp.: 9
Electronic Components for Aerospace &
Military Applications
N.A.I.C.S.: 541519
Koichi Ashizaki (CEO)

Pascall Electronics Ltd. (3)
Westridge Business Park Cothey Way,
Ryde, PO33 1QT, Isle of Wight, United
Kingdom
Tel.: (44) 1983 817 300
Web Site: http://www.pascall.co.uk
Aerospace, Defense & Industrial Power
Supply & Radio Frequency Electronic
Equipment Mfr & Whslr
N.A.I.C.S.: 334419

XCEL Power Systems Ltd. (3)
Brunswick Road, Cobbs Wood Industrial
Estate, Ashford, TN23 1EH, Kent, United
Kingdom
Tel.: (44) 1233 623404
Power Supplies Mfr
N.A.I.C.S.: 334419

Subsidiary (Domestic):

Dukes Aerospace, Inc. (2)
313 Gillett St, Painesville, OH 44077
Tel.: (440) 352-6182
Web Site: http://www.aerofluidproducts.com
Aircraft Parts & Auxiliary Equipment Mfr

N.A.I.C.S.: 336413

Subsidiary (Non-US):

Elektro-Metall Export GmbH (2)
Manchinger Str 116, 85053, Ingolstadt, Ger-
many
Tel.: (49) 84196510
Web Site: https://www.eme-in.de
Aerospace & Ordnance Equipment Design
& Mfr
N.A.I.C.S.: 333995
David Kamerer (Dir-Sls & Mktg)
Josef Neumeier (Dir-Engrg)
Giuseppe Gullotto (Dir-Ops)
Robert Simet (Dir-Fin)
Bibiana Overlack (VP)

Subsidiary (Domestic):

**Extant Components Group Holdings,
Inc.** (2)
1615 W NASA Blvd, Melbourne, FL 32901
Tel.: (321) 254-1500
Web Site: http://www.extantaerospace.com
Electronics & Avionics systems Mfr
N.A.I.C.S.: 334511

Subsidiary (Domestic):

**NavCom Defense Electronics,
Inc.** (3)
9129 Stellar Ct, Corona, CA 92883-4924
Tel.: (951) 268-9230
Web Site: http://www.navcom.com
Designer & Mfr of Products Related to Al-
timetry, Radar, Tactical Air Navigation (TA-
CAN), Beacons, Radios, Specialized Test
Sets
N.A.I.C.S.: 334511

Subsidiary (Domestic):

HARCO Laboratories Inc. (2)
186 Cedar St, Branford, CT
06405-6011 (100%)
Tel.: (203) 483-3700
Web Site: https://www.harcosemco.com
Sales Range: $25-49.9 Million
Temperature Measuring Devices Mfr
N.A.I.C.S.: 334519

Subsidiary (Non-US):

Irvin-GQ Limited (2)
Llangeinor, Bridgend, CF32 8PL, United
Kingdom
Tel.: (44) 1656727000
Web Site: http://www.irvingq.com
Aircraft Parts & Auxiliary Equipment Distr
N.A.I.C.S.: 423860
Mark Hennessy (VP-Sls & Mktg)
Jon Powell (Pres)
Mark Steer (VP-Ops)
Tony Smith (VP-Engrg)
Rick Allamby (Mgr-Bus Dev)
Russ Murphy (Mgr-Bus Dev)

IrvinGQ France SAA (2)
16 bis rue Paule Raymondis, 31200, Tou-
louse, France
Tel.: (33) 561297605
Aircraft Parts & Auxiliary Equipment Distr
N.A.I.C.S.: 423860

Subsidiary (Domestic):

MarathonNorco Aerospace, Inc. (2)
8301 Imperial Dr, Waco, TX 76712-6588
Tel.: (254) 776-0650
Web Site: https://www.marathonnorco.com
Sales Range: $50-74.9 Million
Emp.: 100
Power Conversion Production & Battery
Chargers Mfr
N.A.I.C.S.: 335910
Graham Cook (Bus Mgr-Power Products)
Cathy Allen (Mgr-HR)
Bob Wiley (Mgr-Quality Assurance)

Subsidiary (Non-US):

McKechnie Aerospace DE, Inc. (2)
Tel.: (949) 769-6100
Aircraft Components Mfr
N.A.I.C.S.: 336413

Subsidiary (Non-US):

Electromech Technologies (3)
Tel.: (316) 941-0400

Web Site: http://www.electromech.com
Sales Range: $25-49.9 Million
Emp.: 374
Aerospace Equipment Mfr
N.A.I.C.S.: 335999

Hartwell Corporation (3)
Tel.: (714) 993-4200
Web Site: http://www.hartwellcorp.com
Sales Range: $50-74.9 Million
Emp.: 200
Aerospace & Industrial Latches, Fasteners,
Hinges, Flush Handles, Quick Release Pins
& Accessories Mfr, Adjustable Container
Latches & Motion Dampeners
N.A.I.C.S.: 332999

Subsidiary (Non-US):

**Mecanismos De Matamores S.A. de
C.V.** (2)
Abasolo No 116, Matamoros, 87300,
Tamaulipas, Mexico
Tel.: (52) 8688121200
Aircraft Equipment Mfr
N.A.I.C.S.: 336413

Nordisk Aviation Products AS (2)
Weidemannsgate 8, 3080, Holmestrand,
Norway
Tel.: (47) 33066100
Web Site: http://www.nordisk-aviation.com
Emp.: 130
Aviation Container Products Designer, Mfr &
Distr
N.A.I.C.S.: 332439
Audun Ror (Dir-Sls & Mktg)
Christopher Neal (Dir-Ops)
Magne Husby (Dir-Engrg & Quality)
Jon Anders Naess (Head-HR)

Subsidiary (Non-US):

Nordisk Asia Pacific Ltd (3)
Room 301B1 3/F CNAC House 12 Tung Fai
Road, Hongkong International Airport Lantau, Hong Kong, China (Hong Kong)
Tel.: (852) 21076600
Web Site: http://www.nordisk-aviation.com
Aviation Container Products Whslr
N.A.I.C.S.: 423860

Subsidiary (Domestic):

**North Hills Signal Processing
Corp.** (2)
40 Orville Dr, Bohemia, NY 11716
Tel.: (631) 244-7393
Web Site: http://www.nhsignal.com
Aircraft Transformer Mfr
N.A.I.C.S.: 335311

Pexco Aerospace, Inc. (2)
2405 S 3rd Ave, Union Gap, WA
98903-1510 (100%)
Tel.: (509) 248-9166
Web Site: http://www.pexcoaerospace.com
Aerospace Plastic Components Mfr & Distr
N.A.I.C.S.: 326199

PneuDraulics, Inc. (2)
8575 Helms Ave, Rancho Cucamonga, CA
91730
Tel.: (909) 980-5366
Web Site: https://www.pneudraulics.com
Aerospace Hydraulic Components Mfr
N.A.I.C.S.: 336413
Dain Miller (Pres)

SSP Industries (2)
2749 Chaparral Rd, Killeen, TX 76542
Tel.: (254) 699-2115
Web Site: http://www.ssp-ind.com
Construction Engineering Services
N.A.I.C.S.: 541330
Ron Fournier (COO)
Melissa Miller (Controller)
Monica Tyler (Accountant)
Nathaniel Cofield (Mgr-Warehouse)

Schneller LLC (2)
6019 Powdermill Rd, Kent, OH 44240-7109
Tel.: (330) 673-1400
Web Site: https://www.schneller.com
Sales Range: $75-99.9 Million
Emp.: 140
Interior Surface Mfr
N.A.I.C.S.: 326130

Subsidiary (Non-US):

Schneller Asia Pte. Ltd. (3)

1 Changi Business Park Avenue 1 02-05,
Singapore, 486058, Singapore
Web Site: http://www.schneller.com
Sales Range: $25-49.9 Million
Emp.: 3
Aircraft Decorative & Thermo Plastic Product Mfr
N.A.I.C.S.: 325211
Willy Chua (Mng Dir)

Unit (Domestic):

Schneller Florida (3)
6200 49th St., Pinellas Park, FL 33781
Tel.: (727) 521-2393
Web Site: http://www.schneller.com
Sales Range: $25-49.9 Million
Emp.: 80
Interior Surface Mfr
N.A.I.C.S.: 326130

Subsidiary (Non-US):

Schneller S.A.R.L. (3)
2 rue des Commeres, 78310, Coignieres,
France
Tel.: (33) 6731400
Sales Range: $25-49.9 Million
Emp.: 12
Thermoplastic Product Mfr
N.A.I.C.S.: 325211

Subsidiary (Domestic):

Semco Instruments, Inc. (2)
25700 Rye Canyon Rd, Valencia, CA 91355
Tel.: (661) 257-2000
Web Site:
http://www.semcoinstruments.com
Sales Range: $25-49.9 Million
Infrared Sensors & Electronic Component
Mfr
N.A.I.C.S.: 334413

Subsidiary (Non-US):

Shield Restraint Systems Ltd. (2)
Unit V1 and V2 Vector Park Forest Road,
Feltham, TW13 7EJ44, Middlesex, United
Kingdom
Tel.: (44) 2088937758
Safety Equipment Mfr
N.A.I.C.S.: 423450
Ahmet Ozgul (Mgr-Sls)

Subsidiary (Domestic):

Shield Restraint Systems, Inc. (2)
3802 Gallatin Way, Elkhart, IN 46514
Tel.: (574) 266-8330
Web Site: https://www.trustshield.com
Safety Equipment Mfr
N.A.I.C.S.: 423450

Skandia, Inc. (2)
5000 N Hwy 251, Davis Junction, IL 61020
Tel.: (815) 393-4600
Web Site: https://www.skandiainc.com
Aircraft Interior Materials & Components Mfr
N.A.I.C.S.: 336413

Skurka Aerospace Inc. (2)
4600 Calle Bolero, Camarillo, CA 93012
Tel.: (805) 484-8884
Web Site: http://www.skurka-aero.com
Sales Range: $25-49.9 Million
Customized Electro-Magnetic Equipment
Mfr
N.A.I.C.S.: 335312

Subsidiary (Non-US):

TDG Germany GmbH (2)
Bernstorffstrasse 151, 22767, Hamburg,
Germany
Tel.: (49) 4043251270
Web Site: http://www.tdg-germany.de
Aerospace Component Mfr & Distr
N.A.I.C.S.: 334511
Beate Tilly (Mng Dir)

Technical Airborne Components Industries SPRL (2)
Rue des Alouettes 141, 4041, Milmort, Belgium
Tel.: (32) 42899750
Web Site: http://www.tecairco.be
Emp.: 250
Aluminum Rod Mfr
N.A.I.C.S.: 332510
Dirk Dhooge (Pres)

Telair International GmbH (2)
Bodenschneidstrasse 2, 83714, Miesbach,
Germany
Tel.: (49) 8025290
Web Site: https://www.telair.com
Emp.: 360
Aircraft Cargo Loading Systems Designer,
Mfr & Distr
N.A.I.C.S.: 336413
M. Enderlein (Mng Dir)

Subsidiary (Non-US):

Telair International AB (3)
Porfyrvagen 14, 224 78, Lund, Sweden
Tel.: (46) 46385800
Emp.: 30
Aircraft Cargo Loading Systems Distr
N.A.I.C.S.: 423860

Subsidiary (Non-US):

**Telair International Services Pte.
Ltd.** (2)
12 Seletar Aerospace Link, Singapore,
797553, Singapore
Tel.: (65) 65804121
Aircraft Parts & Auxiliary Equipment Distr
N.A.I.C.S.: 423860

**Transicoil (Malaysia) Sendirian
Berhad** (2)
Batu Berendam Free Trade Zone Phase 1,
Melaka, 75350, Malaysia
Tel.: (60) 62328433
Web Site: http://www.adstcoils.com
Sales Range: $25-49.9 Million
Emp.: 140
Aircraft Equipment Mfr
N.A.I.C.S.: 336413
Wee Tiong Seng (Mng Dir)

Subsidiary (Domestic):

Transicoil LLC (2)
9 Iron Bridge Dr, Collegeville, PA 19426
Tel.: (484) 902-1100
Web Site: http://www.adstcoil.com
Electromechanical Component Mfr
N.A.I.C.S.: 334514

Western Sky Industries LLC (2)
2600 S Custer Ave, Wichita, KS 67217-
1324
Tel.: (316) 941-0400
Web Site: http://www.electromech.com
Electro Mechanical Equipment Mfr
N.A.I.C.S.: 334514
Clay Collins (Sls Dir)
Ryan Hege (Engr-OEM Sls-Customer Support)
Chris Hecox (Engr-OEM Sls-Customer Support)
Tyler Steven (Engr-OEM Sls-Customer Support)

**Whippany Actuation Systems,
LLC** (2)
110 Algonquin Pkwy, Whippany, NJ 07981-
1602
Tel.: (973) 428-9898
Web Site: https://www.whipactsys.com
Designs, Develops, Manufactures & Provides Product Support of Elecromechanical
Servo Actuators, Motors & Gearboxes for
the Commercial & Military Aerospace Market
N.A.I.C.S.: 336413

Young & Franklin, Inc. (2)
942 Old Liverpool Rd, Liverpool, NY 13088
Tel.: (315) 457-3110
Web Site: https://www.yf.com
Specialty Fluid Control Valves For Landbased Gas Turbines; Aircraft & Marine Applications Mfr
N.A.I.C.S.: 332912
Mike Yates (Pres)

Subsidiary (Domestic):

Tactair Fluid Controls Inc (3)
4806 W Taft Rd, Liverpool, NY 13088-4810
Tel.: (315) 451-3928
Web Site: https://www.tactair.com
Emp.: 200
Aerospace Hydraulic & Pneumatic Controls
Designer & Mfr
N.A.I.C.S.: 332912
Theunis Botha (Pres & COO)

**TransDigm Technologies India Private
Limited** (1)
18 18/1 3rd Floor IndiQube South Summit
South End Road, Vijayarangam Layout,
Bengaluru, 560004, Karnataka, India
Tel.: (91) 8068181800
Web Site: https://www.transdigm.in
Electronic Detail & Mechanical Engineering
Services
N.A.I.C.S.: 541330
Rama Prasad (Pres & Mng Dir)
Rupak Ghosh (Dir-Engrg)
Rupa Shamanna (Sr Mgr-Quality)
Anil Kumar (Head-Fin)
Sunilkumar Kanat (Mgr-IT-APAC)

TRANSGLOBAL ASSETS, INC.
810 Pony Express, Cheyenne, WY
82001
Tel.: (541) 921-3903 WY
Year Founded: 2007
TMSH—(OTCIQ)
Holding Company
N.A.I.C.S.: 551112
Ilya Strashun (Pres & CEO)

TRANSMEDICS GROUP, INC.
200 Minuteman Rd Ste 302, Andover,
MA 01810
Tel.: (978) 552-0900 MA
Web Site:
https://www.transmedics.com
Year Founded: 2018
TMDX—(NASDAQ)
Rev.: $93,459,000
Assets: $277,147,000
Liabilities: $89,772,000
Net Worth: $187,375,000
Earnings: ($36,231,000)
Emp.: 212
Fiscal Year-end: 12/31/22
Holding Company
N.A.I.C.S.: 551112
Ben Walton (VP-Aviation Services)
Waleed H. Hassanein (Founder, Pres
& CEO)
Stephen Gordon (CFO, Treas & Sec)
Tamer I. Khayal (Chief Comml Officer)
Miriam Provost (VP-Regulatory
Affairs-Global)
John Sullivan (VP-Quality & Engrg)
John Carey (VP-Ops)
Ike Okonkwo (VP-Fin & Acctg)
Mark Anderson (Sr Dir-Tech Dev)
Laura Damme (VP-Clinical Affairs)
Susan Goodman (VP-HR)

Subsidiaries:

Summit Aviation, Inc. (1)
4200 Summit Bridge Rd, Middletown, DE
19709
Tel.: (302) 834-5400
Web Site: https://www.summit-aviation.com
Sales Range: $50-74.9 Million
Emp.: 175
Airport Operator & Aviation Services
N.A.I.C.S.: 488119
Joyce P. Morales (CFO & Treas)
Lynn Trent (Mgr-HR)
Ben Walton (Owner & Pres)
Joyce Price Morales (CFO)
Tom Lark (VP)
Robert Flansburg (Dir-Operations)
John Gonsalves (Dir-Sales)
Dan Robinson (Dir-Military Sls)
Darrell Smith (Dir-Quality)
David Novak (Dir-Information Technology)
Keith Enochs (Dir-Manufacturing)

**TRANSNATIONAL GROUP,
INC.**
800 E Leigh St Ste 11, Richmond, VA
23219
Tel.: (305) 801-6098 NV
Year Founded: 1999
TAMG—(OTCIQ)

Transnational Group, Inc.—(Continued)

Iron Ore Mining Services
N.A.I.C.S.: 212210
Douglas W. Solomon (Co-CEO)
Barry Grunberger (Co-CEO)

TRANSPORTATION AND LO-GISTICS SYSTEMS, INC.
5500 Military Trail Ste 22-357, Jupiter, FL 33458
Tel.: (561) 801-9188   NV
Web Site: https://www.tlss-inc.com
Year Founded: 2008
TLSS—(OTCIQ)
Rev.: $992
Assets: $2,159,766
Liabilities: $10,157,202
Net Worth: ($7,997,436)
Earnings: ($2,526,201)
Emp.: 1
Fiscal Year-end: 12/31/23
Tourism Services
N.A.I.C.S.: 561520
Sebastian Giordano (Pres, CEO, CFO & Treas)
Justin Frey (COO)
Joseph Corbisiero (Pres & CEO-Freight Connections & Inc)
Jill Czerniak (Dir-Employee Support & Development)

Subsidiaries:

Cougar Express Inc. (1)
145-43 226th St, Springfield Gardens, NY 11413
Tel.: (516) 239-0244
Web Site: http://www.cougarexpressjfk.com
Tobacco Mfr
N.A.I.C.S.: 312230
Rose Ceritto (Pres)

Freight Connections, Inc. (1)
1 Bell Dr, Ridgefield, NJ 07657
Tel.: (201) 933-6027
Web Site: https://freightconnectionsinc.com
Logistic Services
N.A.I.C.S.: 541614
Joseph Corbisiero (Pres & CEO)

Shypdirect, LLC (1)
440 NJ-17, Hasbrouck Heights, NJ 07604
Tel.: (201) 890-2050
Web Site: http://www.shypdirect.com
Transportation Services
N.A.I.C.S.: 484110
Jason Lerner (Dir-HR)

TRANSTECH INDUSTRIES, INC.
2025 Delsea Dr, Sewell, NJ 08080
Tel.: (856) 481-4214   DE
Web Site:
https://www.transtechindustries.com
TRTI—(OTCIQ)
Other Electric Power Generation
N.A.I.C.S.: 221118
Gary S. DeFranco (VP-Ops)

TRANSUNION
555 W Adams, Chicago, IL 60661
Tel.: (312) 985-2000   DE
Web Site:
https://www.transunion.com
Year Founded: 1968
TRU—(NYSE)
Rev.: $3,831,200,000
Assets: $11,105,100,000
Liabilities: $6,999,600,000
Net Worth: $4,105,500,000
Earnings: ($206,200,000)
Emp.: 13,200
Fiscal Year-end: 12/31/23
Software Development Services
N.A.I.C.S.: 551112
Christopher A. Cartwright (Pres & CEO)
Venkat Achanta (Exec VP & Chief Data & Analytics Officer)

Susan W. Muigai (Chief HR Officer & Exec VP)
Todd M. Cello (CFO & Exec VP)
Heather J. Russell (Chief Legal Officer & Exec VP)
Steven M. Chaouki (Pres-Markets & Consumer Interactive)
Timothy J. Martin (Chief Global Solutions Officer & Exec VP)
Susan Muigai (Chief HR Officer & Exec VP)
Todd C. Skinner (Pres-Intl)

Subsidiaries:

Auditz, LLC (1)
3507 E Frontage Rd Ste 150, Tampa, FL 33607
Tel.: (813) 387-0330
Web Site: http://www.auditz.com
Emp.: 28
Other Health & Personal Care Stores
N.A.I.C.S.: 456199
Sean Smith (Dir-Information Technology)
Mark McVeely (VP)

Credit Information Systems Company Limited (1)
Standard Chartered Building First Floor 48 Westlands Road, PO Box 38941-00623, Nairobi, Kenya
Tel.: (254) 70 959 3000
Web Site: https://ke.creditinfo.com
Financial Services
N.A.I.C.S.: 523999
Kamau Kunyiha (CEO)
Bethel Ojoo (Head-Sales-Business Development)
Chris Mwangi (COO)
Moses Njaramba (Fin Mgr)
Jane Nasieku Millia (Mgr)

FactorTrust, Inc. (1)
PO Box 3653, Alpharetta, GA 30023
Tel.: (866) 910-8497
Underbanked Consumer Data, Analytics & Risk Scoring Services to Lenders
N.A.I.C.S.: 525990

Neustar Costa Rica Limitada (1)
Metro Free Zone Lot 5 Block C Building 5C, 40104, Heredia, Costa Rica
Tel.: (506) 2 298 3700
Information Technology Services
N.A.I.C.S.: 541511

Neustar Data Infotech (India) Private Limited (1)
11th Floor Jyothi Pinnacle Hitech City Road, Whitefields Kondapur, Hyderabad, 500 081, Telangana, India
Tel.: (91) 404 521 0003
Information Technology Services
N.A.I.C.S.: 541511

Neustar Technologies Limited (1)
123 Victoria Street 3rd Floor Suite 3 01/3 02, London, SW1E 6DE, United Kingdom
Tel.: (44) 178 444 8444
Credit Reporting Agency Services
N.A.I.C.S.: 561450

Rubixis Inc. (1)
39141 Civic Center Dr,, Fremont, CA 94538
Tel.: (888) 315-5303
Data Processing, Hosting & Related Services
N.A.I.C.S.: 518210

Sontiq, Inc. (1)
9920 Franklin Square Dr Ste 250, Nottingham, MD 21236
Tel.: (508) 644-8726
Web Site: https://www.sontiq.com
Information Technology Services
N.A.I.C.S.: 541511

Trans Union Costa Rica, S.A. (1)
San Pedro Montes de Oca Ofiplaza del Este Edificio B Oficina 6, San Jose, Costa Rica
Tel.: (506) 2 291 4303
Credit Reporting Agency Services
N.A.I.C.S.: 561450

Trans Union Guatemala, S.A. (1)
7 Avenida 14-44 Zona 9 Edificio la Galeria Primer Nivel Local 11, Guatemala, Guatemala

Tel.: (502) 2 207 2423
Credit Reporting Agency Services
N.A.I.C.S.: 561450

Trans Union of Canada, Inc. (1)
3115 Chemin Harvester Suite 201, Burlington, L7N 3N8, ON, Canada
Web Site: https://www.transunion.ca
Information Technology Services
N.A.I.C.S.: 541511
Gene Volchek (Sr VP)
Abhi Dhar (CIO & CTO)
Aaron Smith (VP-Business Development)

TransUnion Brasil Sistemas em Informatica Ltda. (1)
Avenida Paulista n 1842 - 10 andar, Sao Paulo, 01310-945, Brazil
Tel.: (55) 115 904 7830
Web Site: https://www.transunion.com.br
Information Technology Services
N.A.I.C.S.: 541511

TransUnion CIBIL Limited (1)
One World Centre Tower 2A 19th Floor, Senapati Bapat Marg Elphinstone Road, Mumbai, 400 013, India
Tel.: (91) 226 638 4666
Web Site: https://www.cibil.com
Information Technology Services
N.A.I.C.S.: 541511

TransUnion Corp. (1)
555 W Adams St, Chicago, IL 60661-3614
Tel.: (312) 985-2000
Web Site: http://www.transunion.com
Rev.: $1,183,200,000
Assets: $4,471,800,000
Liabilities: $2,800,600,000
Net Worth: $1,671,200,000
Earnings: $50,100,000
Emp.: 3,700
Fiscal Year-end: 12/31/2013
Credit & Information Management Services
N.A.I.C.S.: 561450
Leo F. Mullin (Chm)
Mohit Kapoor (CTO, CIO & Exec VP)

Subsidiary (Domestic):

TransUnion LLC (2)
555 W Adams St, Chicago, IL 60661
Tel.: (312) 258-1717
Web Site: https://www.transunion.com
Sales Range: $700-749.9 Million
Credit Bureau Services
N.A.I.C.S.: 561450
Mohit Kapoor (CIO, CTO & Exec VP)
Mary J. Krupka (Exec VP-Human Resources)
John T. Danaher (Exec VP)
Curtis J. Miller (Sr VP-Strategy-Corporate Development)
Julie Springer (Exec VP-Marketing)
Gerald M. McCarthy Jr. (Exec VP)

Subsidiary (Domestic):

L2C, Inc. (3)
3414 Peachtree Rd NE Ste 600, Atlanta, GA 30326
Tel.: (404) 846-7200
Web Site: http://www.lc2.com
Scoring & Analytics Services
N.A.I.C.S.: 423430

NeuStar, Inc. (3)
21575 Ridgetop Cir, Sterling, VA 20166
Tel.: (571) 434-5400
Web Site: http://www.home.neustar
Real-Time Information & Analytics to the Internet, Communications, Entertainment, Advertising & Marketing Services
N.A.I.C.S.: 519290
Steven J. Edwards (Sr VP)
Michael Schoen (VP)
Peter Burke (Sr VP-Engineering-Operations)
Kathleen Dundas (VP)
Sai Huda (Gen Mgr)
Carolyn Ullerick (CFO & Sr VP)
Shawn Donovan (CMO, Chief Sls Officer & Sr VP)
Yosha Ulrich-Sturmat (Sr VP-Corporate Planning-Operations-Communications)
Kevin Hughes (Gen Counsel)
Marjorie R. Bailey (Sr VP-Human Resources)
Charlie Gottdiener (Pres & CEO)

Brian J. Kober (Chief Strategy Officer & Sr VP)
Carey Pellock (Chief HR Officer)
Dorean Kass (Sr VP-Sales)
Brian McCann (Pres)
Lee Kirschbaum (Sr VP-Corporate Business Development)
Gary Savoy (VP-Business Development-Mktg Solutions)
Steven Kim (VP-Mktg Solutions Svcs)
Mike Finnerty (VP)
Brett House (VP-Mktg Solutions Bus Unit)

Subsidiary (Domestic):

MarketShare Partners, LLC (4)
11150 Santa Monica Blvd 5th Fl, Los Angeles, CA 90025
Tel.: (310) 914-5677
Web Site: http://www.home.neustar
Strategic Decision Sciences Services
N.A.I.C.S.: 541613

Neustar Information Services, Inc. (4)
1861 International Dr 6th Fl, McLean, VA 22102
Tel.: (703) 272-6200
Information Retrieval Services
N.A.I.C.S.: 519290
Tom McNeal (VP-Bus Dev)

Subsidiary (Non-US):

TransUnion Credit Bureau (Pty) Ltd. (3)
Wanderers Office Park 52 Corlett Drive, Illovo, Johannesburg, 2193, South Africa
Tel.: (27) 112146000
Web Site: http://www.transunion.co.za
Sales Range: $50-74.9 Million
Emp.: 250
Credit Reporting Services
N.A.I.C.S.: 561450
Geoff Miller (Pres)

Joint Venture (Domestic):

VantageScore Solutions, LLC (3)
107 Elm St Ste 907, Stamford, CT 06902
Tel.: (203) 363-0269
Web Site: http://www.vantagescore.com
Sales Range: $10-24.9 Million
Emp.: 15
Consumer Credit Scoring Services
N.A.I.C.S.: 561450
Barrett Burns (Pres & CEO)
Mike Dunn (VP-Comm & Strategic Plng)
Benjamin Tagoe (Sr VP-Strategic Plng & Alliances)
Latonia D. Hubbs (Sr VP & Head-Capital Markets & Strategic Alliances)

TransUnion Credit Bureau Namibia (Pty) Ltd. (1)
Room 114 1st Floor 269 Independence Ave Building, PO Box 1752, Windhoek, Namibia
Tel.: (264) 6 122 7142
Credit Reporting Agency Services
N.A.I.C.S.: 561450

TransUnion Information Group Limited (1)
One Park Lane, Leeds, LS31EP, West Yorkshire, United Kingdom
Tel.: (44) 1133884300
Web Site: https://www.transunion.co.uk
Digital & Consumer Marketing Data Services
N.A.I.C.S.: 541618

TransUnion Information Solutions, Inc. (1)
27th Floor Unit AB Tower 1 Ayala Triangle Ayala Ave, Makati, 1226, Philippines
Tel.: (63) 8 858 0456
Web Site: https://www.transunion.ph
Information Technology Services
N.A.I.C.S.: 541511

TransUnion Rwanda Limited (1)
3rd Floor of Alliance Tower BPR Building, Plot No 6 Junction of KN 67 and KN 30 Nyarugenge District, Kigali, Rwanda
Tel.: (250) 78 893 3094
Credit Reporting Agency Services

N.A.I.C.S.: 561450

Verifacts LLC (1)
1980 Industrial Dr, Sterling, IL 61081
Web Site: https://www.vfacts.com
Financial Services
N.A.I.C.S.: 523999
James Manus *(Mgr-Customer Service)*
Mikeila Eastabrooks *(Mgr-Customer Service)*

eBureau LLC (1)
25 6th Ave N, Saint Cloud, MN 56303
Tel.: (320) 534-5000
Data Processing, Hosting & Related Services
N.A.I.C.S.: 518210
Greg Neeser *(Exec VP-Compliance & Security)*
Tim Laudenbach *(VP-Card Not Present Fraud Prevention Svcs)*

iovation Inc. (1)
555 SW Oak St Ste 300, Portland, OR 97204
Tel.: (503) 224-6010
Web Site: http://www.transunion.com
Online Fraud Protection Services
N.A.I.C.S.: 541511
Douglas Shafer *(CFO)*
Gregory J. Pierson *(CEO)*
Jon Karl *(Co-Founder)*
Molly O'Hearn *(Co-Founder)*

TRAQIQ, INC.

14205 SE 36th St Ste 100, Bellevue, WA 98006
Tel.: (425) 818-0560   **CA**
Web Site: http://www.traqiq.com
Year Founded: 2009
TRIQ—(OTCQB)
Rev.: $1,582
Assets: $66,460
Liabilities: $1,682,659
Net Worth: ($1,616,199)
Earnings: ($9,171,556)
Emp.: 110
Fiscal Year-end: 12/31/22
Film & Television Production & Distribution Services
N.A.I.C.S.: 512110
Ajay Sikka *(Chm, Pres, CEO & CFO)*

Subsidiaries:

OmniM2M Inc. (1)
4826 194th Ave SE, Issaquah, WA 98027
Tel.: (425) 818-0560
Web Site: https://www.omnim2m.com
IT Services
N.A.I.C.S.: 541519
Ajay Sikka *(CEO)*
Gary Schmidt *(Mng Dir)*
Frank McKeown *(Head-Tech)*

TraQiQ Solutions, Pvt. Ltd. (1)
7th Floor Tower D Logix Techno Park Sector 127, Noida, 201301, India
Tel.: (91) 9810348408
IT Services
N.A.I.C.S.: 541519

TransportIQ, Inc. (1)
1001 State St, Erie, PA 16501
Tel.: (716) 313-2172
Web Site: http://www.transportationiq.com
Transportation Services
N.A.I.C.S.: 484110

TRAVEL & LEISURE CO.

6277 Sea Hbr Dr, Orlando, FL 32821
Tel.: (407) 626-5200   **DE**
Web Site:
https://www.travelandleisureco.com
Year Founded: 1981
TNL—(NYSE)
Rev.: $3,750,000,000
Assets: $6,738,000,000
Liabilities: $7,655,000,000
Net Worth: ($917,000,000)
Earnings: $396,000,000
Emp.: 19,000
Fiscal Year-end: 12/31/23
Holding Company; Hotel & Resort Operator; Vacation Rental Services

N.A.I.C.S.: 551112
Michael D. Brown *(Pres & CEO)*
Kimberly A. Marshall *(Chief HR Officer)*
James Savina *(Gen Counsel , Sec & Exec VP)*
Christopher Agnew *(Sr VP-FP&A & IR)*
Michael A. Hug *(CFO & Exec VP)*
Elizabeth E. Dreyer *(Chief Acctg Officer & Sr VP)*
Jon G. Munoz *(Sr VP-Environmental, Social, and Governance)*
Sy Esfahani *(CTO)*
Thomas M. Duncan *(Chief Acctg Officer & Sr VP)*

Subsidiaries:

AmeriHost Franchise Systems, Inc. (1)
1 Sylvan Way, Parsippany, NJ 07054
Tel.: (973) 428-9700
Sales Range: $125-149.9 Million
Hotels & Resorts
N.A.I.C.S.: 721110

Days Inns Worldwide, Inc. (1)
3159 Route 46 E | 287, Parsippany, NJ 07054
Tel.: (973) 428-9700
Web Site: https://www.wyndhamhotels.com
Sales Range: $10-24.9 Million
Emp.: 43
Franchiser of Hotels & Motels
N.A.I.C.S.: 721110

Howard Johnson International, Inc. (1)
1 Sylvan Way, Parsippany, NJ 07054
Tel.: (973) 428-9700
Web Site: http://www.wyndhamhotels.com
Hotel Franchisor
N.A.I.C.S.: 533110

Ramada Worldwide Inc. (1)
949 Route 46, Parsippany, NJ 07054
Tel.: (973) 753-6000
Web Site: https://www.wyndhamhotels.com
Sales Range: $10-24.9 Million
Hotels & Resorts
N.A.I.C.S.: 721110

Travel + Leisure (1)
1120 Avenue of Americas, New York, NY 10036
Tel.: (212) 382-5600
Web Site: http://www.travelandleisure.com
Trade Magazine Publisher
N.A.I.C.S.: 513120
Abigail Williams *(Sr Editor-Audience Engagement)*
Deanne Kaczerski *(Exec Editor-Digital)*
Jacqueline Gifford *(Editor-in-Chief)*
Jesse Ashlock *(Exec Editor)*
Miles Stiverson *(Exec Dir-Content Strategy)*
Tanner Saunders *(Assoc Editor-Digital)*

Travelodge Hotels, Inc. (1)
625 Rt 46 E, Parsippany, NJ 07054-3887
Tel.: (973) 753-8100
Web Site: https://www.wyndhamhotels.com
Sales Range: $125-149.9 Million
Hotels & Resorts
N.A.I.C.S.: 721110
Peter Gowers *(CEO)*

U.S. Franchise Systems, Inc. (1)
13 Corporate SqSte 250, Atlanta, GA 30329
Tel.: (404) 321-4045
Web Site: http://www.usfsi.com
Sales Range: $10-24.9 Million
Emp.: 142
Hotel & Lodging Properties Owner & Operator
N.A.I.C.S.: 721110

Wingate Inns International, Inc. (1)
1 Sylvan Way, Parsippany, NJ 07054-3887
Tel.: (973) 496-2800
Web Site: http://www.wingatehotels.com
Sales Range: $125-149.9 Million
Hotels & Resorts
N.A.I.C.S.: 721110

Wyndham Exchange and Rentals, Inc. (1)
9998 N Michigan Rd, Carmel, IN 46032

Tel.: (317) 805-9000
Vacation Exchange & Rentals
N.A.I.C.S.: 721199

Subsidiary (Non-US):

Hoseasons Holidays Limited (2)
Hoseasons, Lowestoft, NR32 2LW, Suffolk, United Kingdom
Tel.: (44) 1502500505
Web Site: https://www.hoseasons.co.uk
Emp.: 350
Vacation Exchange & Rentals
N.A.I.C.S.: 721199
Geoff Cowley *(Mng Dir)*

Subsidiary (Domestic):

RCI, LLC (2)
9998 N Michigan Rd, Carmel, IN 46032
Tel.: (317) 805-8000
Web Site: http://www.rci.com
Leisure, Travel & Exchange Service for Owners of Time Share Units
N.A.I.C.S.: 721214
Brett Becker *(Reg Dir)*

Subsidiary (Domestic):

RCI Mid-American Office (3)
9998 N Michigan Rd, Carmel, IN 46032
Tel.: (317) 805-8000
Web Site: https://www.rci.com
Sales Range: Less than $1 Million
Emp.: 21
Resort Vacation & Information Services
N.A.I.C.S.: 721214

Division (Domestic):

RCI Travel (3)
3502 Woodview Ter 9998 N Michigan Rd, Indianapolis, IN 46032
Tel.: (317) 805-9000
Web Site: http://www.rci.com
Sales Range: $100-124.9 Million
Travel Agency
N.A.I.C.S.: 561510

Subsidiary (Domestic):

Tourist Bureau Marketing, Inc. (3)
7380 W Sand Lk Rd 360, Orlando, FL 32819
Tel.: (800) 355-0969
Web Site:
http://www.alliancereservations.com
Online Travel Booking Technology & Services
N.A.I.C.S.: 561599
Pete Bertenshaw *(CEO)*

Subsidiary (Domestic):

Vacation Palm Springs Real Estate, Inc. (3)
1276 N Palm Canyon Dr, Palm Springs, CA 92262-6763
Tel.: (760) 778-7832
Web Site:
http://www.vacationpalmsprings.com
Emp.: 50
Vacation Home & Condominium Rental Services
N.A.I.C.S.: 531110

Wyndham Hotels & Resorts, LLC (1)
22 Sylvan Way, Parsippany, NJ 07054
Tel.: (973) 753-6000
Web Site: http://www.wyndham.com
Sales Range: $125-149.9 Million
Emp.: 8,700
Hotel & Motel Operation
N.A.I.C.S.: 721110

Wyndham Vacation Ownership, Inc. (1)
6277 Sea Harbor Dr, Orlando, FL 32821
Tel.: (407) 626-5200
Web Site:
https://www.wyndhamdestinations.com
Vacation Ownership Products Developer & Marketer
N.A.I.C.S.: 531190

Subsidiary (Domestic):

Wyndham Vacation Resorts, Inc. (2)
6277 Sea Harbor Dr, Orlando, FL 32821
Tel.: (407) 370-5200

Web Site:
https://clubwyndham.wyndhamdestinations.com
Vacation Resort Properties Developer, Marketer & Operator
N.A.I.C.S.: 531210

Subsidiary (Domestic):

Fairfield Williamsburg (3)
121 Cameron Cir, Williamsburg, VA 23188
Tel.: (757) 229-0302
Web Site:
http://www.wyndhamvacationresorts.com
Sales Range: $200-249.9 Million
Emp.: 200
Hotel
N.A.I.C.S.: 721110

Unit (Domestic):

Wyndham Governor's Green (4)
4600 Mooretown Rd, Williamsburg, VA 23185
Tel.: (757) 564-2420
Web Site:
http://www.wyndhamvacationresorts.com
Sales Range: $10-24.9 Million
Emp.: 30
Resort
N.A.I.C.S.: 721110
Franz Sanning *(Pres)*

Subsidiary (Domestic):

Wyndham Kingsgate (4)
619 Georgetown Cres, Williamsburg, VA 23185
Tel.: (757) 220-5702
Web Site:
http://www.wyndhamvacationresorts.com
Sales Range: $50-74.9 Million
Resort
N.A.I.C.S.: 721110

Wyndham Vacation Ownership At Patriots Place (4)
220 House of Burgesses Way, Williamsburg, VA 23185   **(100%)**
Tel.: (757) 220-5300
Web Site:
http://www.wyndhamvacationresorts.com
Sales Range: $10-24.9 Million
Emp.: 50
Resort
N.A.I.C.S.: 531210

Subsidiary (Domestic):

Oceana Resorts, LLC (3)
1000 2nd Ave S Ste 110, North Myrtle Beach, SC 29582
Tel.: (843) 448-3121
Web Site: https://www.oceanaresorts.com
Hotel & Resort Operator
N.A.I.C.S.: 721110

Subsidiary (Domestic):

Patricia Grand Resort, LLC (4)
2710 N Ocean Blvd, Myrtle Beach, SC 29577-3052
Tel.: (843) 448-8453
Web Site: https://www.patricia.com
Sales Range: $1-9.9 Million
Hotel & Motel Operating Services
N.A.I.C.S.: 721110

Subsidiary (Domestic):

Wyndham Branson at The Meadows (3)
110 Willowbend Dr, Branson, MO 65616
Tel.: (417) 336-4993
Web Site: http://www.fairfieldresorts.com
Sales Range: $200-249.9 Million
Emp.: 200
Real Estate
N.A.I.C.S.: 531210

Wyndham Consumer Finance, Inc. (3)
10750 W Charleston Blvd Ste 130, Las Vegas, NV 89135   **(100%)**
Tel.: (702) 227-3100
Rev.: $190,000
Emp.: 400
Time-Share Financial Services
N.A.I.C.S.: 523999
Mark A. Johnson *(Pres)*

Travel & Leisure Co.—(Continued)

Wyndham Ocean Ridge (3)
1 King Cotton Rd, Edisto Island, SC 29438-3606
Tel.: (843) 869-4500
Web Site:
http://www.wyndhamvacationresorts.com
Sales Range: $25-49.9 Million
Emp.: 150
Real Estate
N.A.I.C.S.: 713990

Wyndham Pagosa (3)
42 Pinon Causeway, Pagosa Springs, CO 81147
Tel.: (970) 731-8006
Web Site: http://www.efair.com
Sales Range: $25-49.9 Million
Emp.: 82
Real Estate
N.A.I.C.S.: 531210

Wyndham Resort at Fairfield Bay (3)
110 Village Ln, Fairfield Bay, AR 72088-1008
Tel.: (501) 884-3333
Web Site: http://www.wyndhamresorts.com
Sales Range: $1-9.9 Million
Emp.: 30
Real Estate Agents & Managers
N.A.I.C.S.: 531210

Wyndham Resort at Fairfield Mountains (3)
747 Buffalo Creek Rd, Lake Lure, NC 28746
Tel.: (828) 625-9111
Web Site: http://www.wyndham.com
Sales Range: Less than $1 Million
Emp.: 8
Real Estate & Resort Service
N.A.I.C.S.: 721110

Wyndham Resort at Fairfield Plantation (3)
1602 Lakeview Pkwy, Villa Rica, GA 30180-7830
Tel.: (770) 834-7781
Web Site:
http://www.fairfieldplantationresort.com
Sales Range: $1-9.9 Million
Emp.: 5
Real Estate
N.A.I.C.S.: 561720

Wyndham Royal Vista
1110 S Ocean Blvd, Pompano Beach, FL 33062
Tel.: (954) 233-7500
Web Site: http://www.extraholidays.com
Vacation Resort Properties Developer, Marketer & Operator
N.A.I.C.S.: 721110

Subsidiary (Domestic):

Orlando International Resort Club (4)
5353 Del Verde Way, Orlando, FL 32819
Tel.: (407) 351-2641
Web Site: http://www.extraholidays.com
Sales Range: Less than $1 Million
Emp.: 9
Resort Hotel
N.A.I.C.S.: 531210

Sea Gardens Beach & Tennis Resort (4)
615 N Ocean Blvd, Pompano Beach, FL 33062
Tel.: (954) 943-6200
Web Site: https://www.seagardens.com
Time Share Condominium Resorts
N.A.I.C.S.: 721110

Unit (Domestic):

The Fairways Resorts of Palm Aire (4)
2601 Palm Aire Dr, Pompano Beach, FL 33069-3466
Tel.: (954) 972-3300
Web Site: http://www.fairfield.com
Hotel Resort
N.A.I.C.S.: 721110

Wyndham Santa Barbara Resort & Yacht Club (4)

1301 S Ocean Blvd, Pompano Beach, FL 33062
Tel.: (954) 941-5566
Web Site: http://www.wyndham.com
Sales Range: Less than $1 Million
Emp.: 20
Hotel Resort
N.A.I.C.S.: 721110

Subsidiary (Domestic):

Wyndham SeaWatch Plantation (3)
151 SeaWatch Dr, Myrtle Beach, SC 29572
Tel.: (843) 692-9311
Web Site:
http://www.wyndhamvacationresorts.com
Sales Range: $10-24.9 Million
Emp.: 40
Hotel Resort
N.A.I.C.S.: 531311

Branch (Domestic):

Wyndham Vacation Resorts (3)
1900 N Country Club Dr, Flagstaff, AZ 86004-7461
Tel.: (928) 527-1447
Web Site:
http://www.wyndhamvacationresorts.com
Sales Range: $10-24.9 Million
Emp.: 45
Resort & Timeshare Ownership
N.A.I.C.S.: 237210

Subsidiary (Domestic):

Wyndham Westwinds (3)
3405 S Ocean Blvd, North Myrtle Beach, SC 29582
Tel.: (843) 272-6464
Web Site:
http://www.wyndhamvacationresorts.com
Sales Range: Less than $1 Million
Emp.: 17
Hotel & Resort
N.A.I.C.S.: 721110

TRAVELZOO

Tel.: (212) 516-1300   DE
Web Site: https://www.travelzoo.com
Year Founded: 1998
TZOO—(NASDAQ)
Rev.: $70,599,000
Assets: $67,274,000
Liabilities: $63,018,000
Net Worth: $4,256,000
Earnings: $6,634,000
Emp.: 237
Fiscal Year-end: 12/31/22
Online Sales & Marketing Services for the Travel Industry
N.A.I.C.S.: 561510
Ralph Bartel *(Chm)*
Holger Bartel *(CEO-Global)*
Christina Sindoni Ciocca *(Chm, Gen Counsel, Sec & Head-Global Functions)*

Subsidiaries:

Travelzoo (Europe) Limited (1)
151 Shaftesbury Avenue 7th Floor, London, WC2H 8AL, United Kingdom   **(100%)**
Tel.: (44) 203 564 3000
Web Site: https://www.travelzoo.com
Sales Range: $25-49.9 Million
Emp.: 100
Travel & Tour Operators
N.A.I.C.S.: 561599

Travelzoo Local (Australia) Pty Limited (1)
Level 2 19 Pitt St, Sydney, 2000, NSW, Australia
Tel.: (61) 280937979
Online Marketing Services
N.A.I.C.S.: 541613

TRAVERE THERAPEUTICS, INC.

3611 Valley Centre Dr Ste 300, San Diego, CA 92130
Tel.: (760) 260-8600   DE
Web Site: https://travere.com
Year Founded: 2008

TVTX—(NASDAQ)
Rev.: $145,238,000
Assets: $788,913,000
Liabilities: $588,103,000
Net Worth: $200,810,000
Earnings: ($111,399,000)
Emp.: 380
Fiscal Year-end: 12/31/23
Pharmaceutical Product Developer
N.A.I.C.S.: 325412
Christopher Cline *(CFO)*
Wiliam E. Rote *(Sr VP-R&D)*
Eric M. Dube *(Pres & CEO)*
Peter Heerma *(Chief Comml Officer)*
Jula Inrig *(Chief Medical Officer)*
Angela Giannantonio *(Sr VP)*
Charlotte Smith *(Sr VP)*

TRAWS PHARMA, INC

12 Penns Trl, Newtown, PA 18940
Tel.: (267) 759-3680   DE
Web Site:
https://www.trawspharma.com
TRAW—(NASDAQ)
Assets: $27,621,119
Liabilities: $14,517,389
Net Worth: ($14,412,530)
Earnings: ($63,563)
Emp.: 16
Fiscal Year-end: 12/31/23
Pharmaceuticals Mfr
N.A.I.C.S.: 325412
Werner Cautreels *(CEO)*
Mark Patrick Guerin *(CFO)*
Victor Moyo *(Chief Medical Officer-Oncology)*
Meena Arora *(VP-Global Medical Affairs & R&D)*
C. David Pauza *(Chief Scientific Officer-Virology)*
Iain Dukes *(Chm)*

TRB SYSTEMS INTERNATIONAL, INC.

1472 Cedarwood Dr, Piscataway, NJ 08854   DE
TRBX—(OTCIQ)
Leisure Product Distr
N.A.I.C.S.: 423910
Byung Yim *(Pres, CEO & CFO)*

TREACE MEDICAL CONCEPTS, INC.

100 Palmetto Park Pl, Ponte Vedra Beach, FL 32081
Tel.: (904) 373-5940   DE
Web Site: https://www.treace.com
Year Founded: 2013
TMCI—(NASDAQ)
Rev.: $141,838,000
Assets: $159,024,000
Liabilities: $98,495,000
Net Worth: $60,529,000
Earnings: ($42,815,000)
Emp.: 423
Fiscal Year-end: 12/31/22
Medical Device Mfr & Distr
N.A.I.C.S.: 334510
John T. Treace *(Founder & CEO)*
Mark L. Hair *(CFO)*
Jaime A. Frias *(Chief Legal & Compliance Officer & Sec)*
Daniel Owens *(Chief HR Officer)*
Joe W. Ferguson *(Sr VP-R&D)*
Dipak A. Rajhansa *(Sr VP-Sls)*
Shana Zink *(Sr VP-Clinical Affairs & Reimbursement)*
Sean F. Scanlan *(Sr VP-Mktg & Medical Education)*
Rachel Osbeck *(Sr VP-Quality Assurance & Regulatory Affairs)*
Kirk A. Brennan *(VP & Controller)*
Lisa O. Taylor *(VP & Asst Gen Counsel)*

James T. Treace *(Chm)*
Nathan Minnich *(Sr VP-Mktg)*
Julie Dewey *(Chief Comm & IR Officer)*

TREASURE GLOBAL, INC.

276 5th Ave Ste 704 Ste 739, New York, NY 10001
Tel.: (212) 896-1267   DE
Web Site:
https://www.treasureglobal.co
Year Founded: 2020
TGL—(NASDAQ)
Rev.: $22,066,829
Assets: $4,278,585
Liabilities: $897,852
Net Worth: $3,380,733
Earnings: ($6,586,623)
Emp.: 25
Fiscal Year-end: 06/30/24
All Other Miscellaneous Retailers
N.A.I.C.S.: 459999
Su Huay Chuah *(CMO)*
Carlson Thow *(CEO)*

TREASURE ISLAND ROYALTY TRUST

5555 San Felipe 11th Fl, Houston, TX 77056
Tel.: (713) 235-9208   TX
TISDZ—(OTCIQ)
Investment Fund Services
N.A.I.C.S.: 525910
Richard A. McKenzie *(Pres)*

TREATMENT.COM INTERNATIONAL INC.

8500 Normandale Lk Blvd Ste 350, Bloomington, MN 55437
Tel.: (612) 788-8900
Web Site: https://www.treatment.com
Year Founded: 2018
TREIF—(OTCQB)
Rev.: $72,608
Assets: $546,137
Liabilities: $1,091,349
Net Worth: ($545,212)
Earnings: ($2,749,784)
Emp.: 5
Fiscal Year-end: 12/31/23
Healthcare Technology Services
N.A.I.C.S.: 541511

TREDEGAR CORPORATION

1100 Boulders Pkwy, Richmond, VA 23225
Tel.: (804) 330-1000   VA
Web Site: https://www.tredegar.com
Year Founded: 1988
TG—(NYSE)
Rev.: $702,678,000
Assets: $446,461,000
Liabilities: $290,808,000
Net Worth: $155,653,000
Earnings: ($105,905,000)
Emp.: 1,900
Fiscal Year-end: 12/31/23
Plastic Films & Aluminum Extrusions Mfr
N.A.I.C.S.: 326113
John M. Steitz *(Pres & CEO)*
D. Andrew Edwards *(CFO & Exec VP)*
Arijit DasGupta *(Pres-Surface Protection)*
W. Brook Hamilton *(Pres-Bonnell Aluminum)*
Kevin C. Donnelly *(Gen Counsel, Sec & VP)*
Frasier W. Brickhouse II *(Treas & Controller)*
Jose Bosco Silveira Jr. *(Pres-Flexible Pkg Films)*

Subsidiaries:

AACOA Extrusions, Inc. (1)

2005 Mayflower Rd, Niles, MI 49120
Tel.: (269) 697-6063
Metal Products Mfr
N.A.I.C.S.: 331110
Mark North (Gen Mgr)

Bonnell Aluminum (Clearfield), Inc. (1)
Bldg H-11 Freeport Ctr, Clearfield, UT 84016
Plastic Film & Aluminum Extrusion Mfr
N.A.I.C.S.: 331313

Bonnell Aluminum (Elkhart), Inc. (1)
2551 County Rd 10 W, Elkhart, IN 46514
Tel.: (574) 262-4685
Plastic Film & Aluminum Extrusion Mfr
N.A.I.C.S.: 331313

Bonnell Aluminum (Niles), LLC (1)
2005 Mayflower Rd, Niles, MI 49120
Tel.: (269) 697-6063
Plastic Film & Aluminum Extrusion Mfr
N.A.I.C.S.: 331313

Bright View Technologies Corporation (1)
4022 Stirrup Creek Dr Ste 301, Durham, NC 27703
Tel.: (919) 228-4370
Web Site:
    http://www.brightviewtechnologies.com
Microstructure Based Optical Films Mfr
N.A.I.C.S.: 335132

Fitesa Film Products LLC (1)
1100 Boulders Pkwy, Richmond, VA 23225 (100%)
Tel.: (804) 330-1000
Web Site: http://tredegar.com
Plastic Films & Laminates Mfr
N.A.I.C.S.: 326113

Subsidiary (Non-US):

Guangzhou Tredegar Film Products Company Limited (2)
Tel.: (86) 2082209998
Sales Range: $125-149.9 Million
Mfr of Plastic & Metal Products
N.A.I.C.S.: 326199

Tredegar Brasil Industria de Plasticos Ltda. (2)
Rua Bandeirantes 557, Diadema, Sao Paulo, 09912-230, Brazil
Tel.: (55) 11 40532400
Sales Range: $25-49.9 Million
Emp.: 75
Plastic & Metal Products Mfr
N.A.I.C.S.: 326199
Simoni Kondo (Supvr)

Subsidiary (Domestic):

Tredegar Film Products - Lake Zurich, LLC (2)
351 Oakwood Rd, Lake Zurich, IL 60047
Tel.: (847) 438-2111
Web Site: http://www.tredegarfilms.com
Sales Range: $50-74.9 Million
Emp.: 150
Polyethylene & Plastic Film Mfr
N.A.I.C.S.: 326113

Subsidiary (Non-US):

Tredegar Film Products B.V. (2)
Ir Van Dieststraat 10, PO Box 1059, 6466 NA, Kerkrade, Netherlands (100%)
Tel.: (31) 455438333
Web Site: http://www.tredegar.com
Sales Range: $50-74.9 Million
Emp.: 70
Plastic & Metal Products Mfr
N.A.I.C.S.: 326199

Tredegar Film Products Company Shanghai, Limited (2)
281 Rong Le Dong Rd Songjiang Industrial Zone, Shanghai, 201600, China
Tel.: (86) 2157745588
Aluminum Extrusions Mfr
N.A.I.C.S.: 326112

Plant (Domestic):

Tredegar Film Products Corporation - Terre Haute Plant (2)

3400-A Fort Harrison Rd, Terre Haute, IN 47804-1711
Tel.: (812) 466-0266
Web Site: http://www.tredegarfilms.com
Sales Range: $25-49.9 Million
Emp.: 80
Polyethylene Film Mfr
N.A.I.C.S.: 326113

Subsidiary (Non-US):

Tredegar Film Products Kft (2)
PO Box 30, 2651, Retsag, Nograd, Hungary
Tel.: (36) 35550500
Sales Range: $25-49.9 Million
Emp.: 80
Plastic & Metal Products Mfr
N.A.I.C.S.: 326199

TAC Holdings LLC (1)
8416 Del Rey Ave, Las Vegas, NV 89117
Tel.: (702) 363-6187
Investment Management Service
N.A.I.C.S.: 551112

The William L. Bonnell Co., Inc. (1)
25 Bonnell St, Newnan, GA 30263-1603 (100%)
Tel.: (770) 253-2020
Web Site: http://www.bonlalum.com
Sales Range: $250-299.9 Million
Emp.: 455
Aluminum Extruded Product Mfr
N.A.I.C.S.: 331318

Subsidiary (Domestic):

Bon L Aluminum LLC (2)
25 Bonnell St, Newnan, GA 30263
Tel.: (770) 253-2020
Web Site: http://www.bonlalum.com
Sales Range: $150-199.9 Million
Emp.: 250
Aluminum Extrusions
N.A.I.C.S.: 331492

Bonnell Aluminum (Elkhart), Inc. (2)
2551 County Rd 10 W, Elkhart, IN 46514
Tel.: (574) 262-4685
Web Site: https://www.bonnellaluminum.com
Anodizing Plating Products & Services
N.A.I.C.S.: 332813

Division (Domestic):

Futura Industries Corporation (2)
Bldg H-11 Freeport Ctr, Clearfield, UT 84016
Tel.: (801) 773-6282
Web Site: http://www.futuraind.com
Extruded Aluminum Products Mfr
N.A.I.C.S.: 331318

Therics, Inc. (1)
20 N Pennsylvania Ave, Morrisville, PA 19067 (100%)
Tel.: (215) 736-0120
Sales Range: $100-124.9 Million
Developer of Digital Microfabrication Process Technology for Medical Devices & Other Medical Applications
N.A.I.C.S.: 339112

TREECON RESOURCES, INC.
6004 S 1st St, Lufkin, TX 75901
Tel.: (936) 634-3365 NV
Web Site:
    https://treeconresources.com
TCOR—(OTCIQ)
Sales Range: $75-99.9 Million
Emp.: 145
Offices of Other Holding Companies
N.A.I.C.S.: 551112

Subsidiaries:

Texas Timberjack, Inc. (1)
6004 S 1st Street, Lufkin, TX 75901
Tel.: (936) 634-3365
Web Site: http://www.texastimberjack.com
Sales Range: $25-49.9 Million
Emp.: 53
Distr of Logging, Industrial & Agricultural Equipment & Provider of Leasing & Financing Services
N.A.I.C.S.: 423810

Harold L. Estes (Pres)
Roy Zenor (Mgr-Sls)
Kevin Wallace (Mgr-Parts)
John Langford (Controller)

TREEHOUSE FOODS, INC.
2021 Spring Rd Ste 600, Oak Brook, IL 60523
Tel.: (708) 483-1300 WI
Web Site:
    https://www.treehousefoods.com
Year Founded: 1962
THS—(NYSE)
Rev.: $3,454,000,000
Assets: $4,253,900,000
Liabilities: $2,566,900,000
Net Worth: $1,687,000,000
Earnings: ($146,300,000)
Emp.: 7,500
Fiscal Year-end: 12/31/22
Pickles, Relishes, Sauces, Dressings & Cranberry Products Processor & Retailer
N.A.I.C.S.: 311421
Steven T. Oakland (Chm, Pres & CEO)
Scott Tassani (Chief Comml Officer, Pres-Bus & Exec VP)
Patrick M. O'Donnell (CFO & Exec VP)
Kristy N. Waterman (Chief HR Officer, Gen Counsel, Sec & Exec VP)

Subsidiaries:

American Importing Company, Inc. (1)
550 Kasota Ave SE, Minneapolis, MN 55414
Tel.: (612) 331-7000
Web Site: http://www.amportfoods.com
Sales Range: $25-49.9 Million
Emp.: 50
Food Products Mfr
N.A.I.C.S.: 311919
Jeff Vogel (CEO)

Associated Brands Inc. (1)
1790 Matheson Boulevard, Mississauga, L4W 0B3, ON, Canada
Tel.: (905) 206-1123
Web Site: http://www.associatedbrands.com
Emp.: 40
Dry Packaged Food Products Mfr & Distr
N.A.I.C.S.: 311423

Subsidiary (Domestic):

North American Tea & Coffee Inc. (2)
7861 82nd St, Riverway Industrial Park, Delta, V4G 1L9, BC, Canada
Tel.: (604) 940-7861
Web Site: http://www.associatedbrands.com
Sales Range: $75-99.9 Million
Emp.: 100
Tea & Coffee Mfr & Distr
N.A.I.C.S.: 311920
Riaz Devji (Mng Dir)

Bay Valley Foods, LLC (1)
1390 Pullman Dr, El Paso, TX 79936
Web Site: https://bayvalleyfoods.com
Food Mfr
N.A.I.C.S.: 311999
Dennis F. Riordan (Pres)

Plant (Domestic):

Bay Valley Foods (2)
17380 Railroad St, City of Industry, CA 91748
Tel.: (626) 912-1671
Web Site: http://www.bayvalleyfoods.com
Sales Range: $75-99.9 Million
Emp.: 150
Salad Dressings & Dips Mfr
N.A.I.C.S.: 311999

Bay Valley Foods (2)
354 N Faison Ave, Faison, NC 28341
Tel.: (910) 267-4711
Web Site: http://www.bayvalley.com
Sales Range: $100-124.9 Million
Emp.: 200
Food Processing & Packaging Services

N.A.I.C.S.: 311941

Bay Valley Foods (2)
215 W 3rd St, Pecatonica, IL 61063 (100%)
Tel.: (815) 239-2631
Web Site: http://www.bayvalleyfoods.com
Sales Range: $50-74.9 Million
Emp.: 150
Fresh Milk, Ice Cream, Cottage Cheese & Related Dairy Products Mfr
N.A.I.C.S.: 311511

Bay Valley Foods (2)
450 Bailey Ave, New Hampton, IA 50659
Tel.: (641) 394-4802
Food Mfr
N.A.I.C.S.: 311999
Pau Nicolaisen (VP)

Bay Valley Foods (2)
820 Palmyra St, Dixon, IL 61021
Tel.: (815) 288-4097
Web Site: http://www.bayvalleyfoods.com
Sales Range: $50-74.9 Million
Emp.: 130
Food Processing & Packaging Services
N.A.I.C.S.: 311999

Bay Valley Foods (2)
1430 Western Ave, Plymouth, IN 46563
Tel.: (574) 936-4061
Web Site: http://www.bayvalleyfoods.com
Sales Range: $75-99.9 Million
Emp.: 150
Food Processing & Packaging Services
N.A.I.C.S.: 311421

Bay Valley Foods (2)
857 School Pl, Green Bay, WI 54303
Tel.: (920) 499-2950
Web Site: http://www.bayvalleyfoods.com
Sales Range: $50-74.9 Million
Emp.: 120
Food Processing & Packaging Services
N.A.I.C.S.: 311941

Cains Foods, L.P. (1)
114 E Main St, Ayer, MA 01432-1832
Tel.: (978) 772-0300
Web Site: http://www.cainsfoods.com
Sales Range: $75-99.9 Million
Emp.: 100
Dressings, Condiments & Sauces Mfr & Distr
N.A.I.C.S.: 311941

E.D. Smith Foods, Ltd. (1)
944 Highway 8, Winona, L8E 5S3, ON, Canada (100%)
Tel.: (905) 643-1211
Web Site: http://www.edsmith.com
Sales Range: $200-249.9 Million
Emp.: 490
Salad Dressing, Jam & Sauce Mfr
N.A.I.C.S.: 311941

Naturally Fresh, Inc. (1)
1000 Naturally Fresh Blvd, Atlanta, GA 30349-2909
Tel.: (404) 765-9000
Web Site: http://www.naturallyfresh.com
Sales Range: $75-99.9 Million
Emp.: 250
Dressings, Dips, Sauces, Maple Syrups & Specialty Items Mfr
N.A.I.C.S.: 531120

Protenergy Natural Foods Corporation (1)
125 East Beaver Creek Road, Richmond Hill, L4B 4R3, ON, Canada
Tel.: (905) 707-6223
Web Site: http://www.protenergyfoods.com
Food Products Mfr
N.A.I.C.S.: 311999

Protenergy Natural Foods, Inc. (1)
904 Woods Rd, Cambridge, MD 21613
Tel.: (410) 901-8625
Web Site: https://www.protenergyfoods.com
Emp.: 165
Food Products Mfr
N.A.I.C.S.: 311999
Neal Connors (VP-Ops-US)

S.T. Specialty Foods, Inc. (1)
8700 Xylon Ave N, Brooklyn Park, MN 55445
Tel.: (763) 493-9600
Web Site: http://www.stspecialtyfoods.com

TreeHouse Foods, Inc.—(Continued)

Food Products Mfr
N.A.I.C.S.: 311999

Sturm Foods, Inc. (1)
215 Center St, Manawa, WI 54949
Tel.: (920) 596-2511
Web Site: https://www.sturmfoods.com
Mfr of Dry Groceries for Private Label
N.A.I.C.S.: 311999
Craig Lemieux (Pres)

TREES CORPORATION
215 Union Ave, Denver, CO 80228
Tel.: (303) 759-1300   CO
Web Site: https://www.treescann.com
Year Founded: 1987
CANN—(OTCQB)
Rev.: $13,444,542
Assets: $31,694,713
Liabilities: $25,288,224
Net Worth: $6,406,489
Earnings: ($9,563,567)
Emp.: 150
Fiscal Year-end: 12/31/22
Offices of Other Holding Companies
N.A.I.C.S.: 551112
Adam Hershey (Interim CEO)
Carl Joseph Williams (Chm)
Edward Myers (Interim CFO & Principal Acctg Officer)

Subsidiaries:

GMC, LLC (1)
4380 S Syracuse St Ste 310, Denver, CO 80237-2625
Tel.: (720) 382-5950
Web Site:
   http://www.greenmancannabis.com
Cannabis Dispensary Operator
N.A.I.C.S.: 456110

TREK RESOURCES, INC.
1020 E Levee St Ste 130, Dallas, TX 75207
Tel.: (214) 373-0318   DE
Web Site:
   https://www.trekresources.com
TRKX—(OTCIQ)
Support Activities for Oil & Gas Operations
N.A.I.C.S.: 213112
Michael A. Montgomery (Pres, CEO & CFO)

TREVENA, INC.
955 Chesterbrook Blvd Ste 110, Chesterbrook, PA 19087
Tel.: (610) 354-8840   DE
Web Site: https://www.trevena.com
Year Founded: 2007
TRVN—(NASDAQ)
Rev.: $2,705,000
Assets: $48,680,000
Liabilities: $33,081,000
Net Worth: $15,599,000
Earnings: ($53,670,000)
Emp.: 35
Fiscal Year-end: 12/31/22
Pharmaceuticals Mfr
N.A.I.C.S.: 325412
Carrie L. Bourdow (Chm, Pres & CEO)
Barry Shin (CFO, COO & Exec VP)
Joel S. Solomon (Co-Sec & VP-Legal & Compliance)
Robert T. Yoder (Chief Bus Officer & Head-Comml Ops)
Michael J. Fossler (VP-Clinical Dev & Quantitative Sciences)
Katrine Sutton (VP-Fin Plng & Analysis)
Michael S. Kramer (VP-Scientific Ops & Alliance Mgmt)
Linda Wase (VP-Medical Affairs)
Mark A. Demitrack (Chief Medical Officer & Sr VP)

Angela Bagley (VP-CMC & Supply Chain Ops)
Todd L. Wandstrat (VP-Health Economics & Medical Sciences)
Patricia Drake (Chief Comml Officer)

TREVI THERAPEUTICS, INC.
195 Church St 16th Fl, New Haven, CT 06510
Tel.: (203) 304-2499   DE
Web Site:
   https://www.trevitherapeutics.com
Year Founded: 2011
TRVI—(NASDAQ)
Rev.: $719,000
Assets: $123,015,000
Liabilities: $15,556,000
Net Worth: $107,459,000
Earnings: ($29,152,000)
Emp.: 25
Fiscal Year-end: 12/31/22
Biotechnology Research & Development Services
N.A.I.C.S.: 541714
David Clark (Chief Medical Officer)
Lisa Delfini (CTO)
Farrell Simon (Chief Comml Officer)
Danine Summers (VP)
Katherine Takaki (VP)
Paula Buckley (VP)
Christopher Galletta (Controller)
Jennifer L. Good (Pres, CEO & CFO)

TREX COMPANY, INC.
160 Exeter Dr, Winchester, VA 22603-8605
Tel.: (540) 542-6300   DE
Web Site: https://www.trex.com
Year Founded: 1996
TREX—(NYSE)
Rev.: $1,094,837,000
Assets: $932,885,000
Liabilities: $216,214,000
Net Worth: $716,671,000
Earnings: $205,384,000
Emp.: 1,765
Fiscal Year-end: 12/31/23
Wood-Alternative Decking, Railing & Fencing Products Mfr
N.A.I.C.S.: 321219
Ronald W. Kaplan (Vice Chm)
Adam D. Zambanini (Pres-Trex Residential Products)
Bryan H. Fairbanks (Pres & CEO)
Jacob T. Rudolph (VP-HH)
Barry L. Creek (VP-Mfg)
Zachary C. Lauer (VP-Supply Chain)
Heather Hagar (Sr VP)
Frank J. De Iuliis (VP)
Amy M. Fernandez (Gen Counsel)
Bret Martz (VP)

Subsidiaries:

Staging Concepts (1)
7008 Northland Dr, Minneapolis, MN 55428
Tel.: (763) 533-2094
Web Site:
   https://www.sightlinecommercial.com
Staging Equipment Mfr
N.A.I.C.S.: 339999
Tom Bateman (Reg Sls Mgr-Western Reg)
Blake Stromme (Reg Sls Mgr-Midwest Reg)
Cindy Albrecht (Dir-Sls & Mktg)

TRI CITY BANKSHARES CORPORATION
6400 S 27th St, Oak Creek, WI 53154
Tel.: (414) 761-1610
Web Site: http://www.tcnb.com
Year Founded: 1963
TRCY—(OTCIQ)
Rev.: $69,438,377
Assets: $1,796,413,636
Liabilities: $1,605,310,105
Net Worth: $191,103,531
Earnings: $14,216,352

Emp.: 450
Fiscal Year-end: 12/31/20
Commercial Banking Services
N.A.I.C.S.: 522110
Brian T. McGarry (Chm & CEO)

Subsidiaries:

TriCity National Bank Inc (1)
6400 S 27th St, Oak Creek, WI 53154-1015   **(100%)**
Tel.: (414) 761-1610
Web Site: http://www.tcnb.com
Sales Range: $10-24.9 Million
Emp.: 50
Provider of Banking Services
N.A.I.C.S.: 522110
Ivan Gamboa (Sr VP)
Brian Morrison (VP)
Brian McGarry (Chm & CEO)

TRI POINTE HOMES, INC.
940 Southwood Blvd Ste 200, Incline Village, NV 89451
Tel.: (775) 413-1030   DE
Web Site:
   https://www.tripointehomes.com
TPH—(NYSE)
Rev.: $3,669,203,000
Assets: $4,914,588,000
Liabilities: $1,900,950,000
Net Worth: $3,013,638,000
Earnings: $343,702,000
Emp.: 1,438
Fiscal Year-end: 12/31/23
Single Family Home Builder
N.A.I.C.S.: 236115
Steven J. Gilbert (Chm)
Douglas F. Bauer (CEO)
Kevin W. Wilson (VP-Strategic Sourcing & Sustainability-Natl)
Heather H. Breidenthal (Chief HR Officer)
Jeffrey A. Lake (VP-Architecture & Design)
Sherri L. Drew (VP-Design Studios)
Mark T. Sherman (VP-Land Dev & Construction-Natl)
Thomas J. Mitchell (Pres & COO)
Linda H. Mamet (CMO & Exec VP)
David C. Lee (Gen Counsel, Sec & VP)
Glenn Keeler (CFO)
Urmila P. Menon (CIO)

Subsidiaries:

TRI Pointe Advantage Insurance Services, Inc. (1)
6320 Canoga Ave Ste 500, West Hills, CA 91367
Web Site:
   https://www.tripointeadvantage.com
Home Insurance Services
N.A.I.C.S.: 524126

TRI Pointe Communities, Inc. (1)
19540 Jamboree Rd Ste 300, Irvine, CA 92612
Tel.: (949) 438-1400
Real Estate Management Services
N.A.I.C.S.: 531390

TRI Pointe Connect, L.L.C. (1)
4800 N Scottsdale Rd Ste 1400, Scottsdale, AZ 85251
Web Site: https://www.tripointeconnect.com
Home Finance Services
N.A.I.C.S.: 522390

TRI Pointe Holdings, Inc. (1)
33663 Weyerhaeuser Way S, Federal Way, WA 98001   **(100%)**
Tel.: (253) 924-3245
Emp.: 45
Holding Company; Real Estate Development
N.A.I.C.S.: 551112
Douglas F. Bauer (Founder)

Subsidiary (Domestic):

Pardee Homes (2)
19180 Golden Valley Rd, Santa Clarita, CA 91387   **(100%)**

Tel.: (661) 425-0200
Web Site: http://www.pardeehomes.com
Sales Range: $150-199.9 Million
Residential Construction Services
N.A.I.C.S.: 236115
Mike Taylor (Pres-Inland Empire)

The Quadrant Corporation (2)
14725 SE 36th St Ste 200, Bellevue, WA 98006   **(100%)**
Tel.: (425) 455-2900
Web Site: http://www.quadranthomes.com
Sales Range: $125-149.9 Million
Single Family Homes
N.A.I.C.S.: 236118

Trendmaker Homes, Inc. (2)
16340 Park Ten Pl Ste 250, Houston, TX 77084   **(100%)**
Tel.: (281) 675-3200
Web Site: http://www.trendmakerhomes.com
Sales Range: $100-124.9 Million
Construction Services
N.A.I.C.S.: 236115

Winchester Homes, Inc. (2)
6905 Rockledge Dr Ste 800, Bethesda, MD 20817   **(100%)**
Tel.: (301) 803-4800
Web Site: http://www.winchesterhomes.com
Sales Range: $50-74.9 Million
Home Construction Services
N.A.I.C.S.: 236115

TRI Pointe Homes, Inc. (1)
3161 Michelson Dr Ste 1500, Irvine, CA 92612
Tel.: (949) 438-1400
Web Site: https://www.tripointehomes.com
Residential Construction
N.A.I.C.S.: 236117
Carrie Newbery (VP-Sales-Marketing)
Jeff Frankel (Pres-Div)

Tri Pointe Homes Arizona, LLC (1)
7001 N Scottsdale Rd Ste 2020, Scottsdale, AZ 85253
Tel.: (480) 970-6000
Home Architectural & Design Services
N.A.I.C.S.: 541310

Tri Pointe Homes DC Metro, Inc. (1)
12435 Park Potomac Ave Ste 600, Potomac, MD 20854
Tel.: (301) 803-4800
Home Architectural & Design Services
N.A.I.C.S.: 541310

Tri Pointe Homes Washington, Inc. (1)
15900 SE Eastgate Way Ste 300, Bellevue, WA 98008
Tel.: (425) 455-2900
Home Architectural & Design Services
N.A.I.C.S.: 541310

TRI-CONTINENTAL CORPORATION
290 Congress St, Boston, MA 02210
Tel.: (612) 671-4321   MD
Web Site:
   http://www.tricontinental.com
TY—(NYSE)
Sales Range: $50-74.9 Million
Investment Services
N.A.I.C.S.: 523999

TRI-COUNTY FINANCIAL GROUP, INC.
706 Washington St, Mendota, IL 61342
Tel.: (815) 538-2265   DE
Web Site:
   http://www.firststatebank.biz
Year Founded: 1987
TYFG—(OTCQX)
Rev.: $69,931,000
Assets: $1,327,840,000
Liabilities: $1,200,845,000
Net Worth: $126,995,000
Earnings: $20,143,000
Emp.: 244
Fiscal Year-end: 12/31/20
Bank Holding Company
N.A.I.C.S.: 551111

Goodwin Toraason *(Sr VP-Lending)*
Lana Eddy *(CFO)*
John Holland *(Dir-Corp Admin)*
Thomas Prescott *(Chm)*
Timothy J. McConville *(Pres & CEO)*
Jill V. Summerhill *(VP-Operations)*
Jan Phalen *(CMO)*

Subsidiaries:

First State Bank   (1)
706 Washington St, Mendota, IL
61342   (100%)
Tel.: (815) 538-2265
Web Site: http://www.firststatebank.biz
Retail & Commercial Banking
N.A.I.C.S.: 522110
Timothy J. McConville *(Pres & CEO)*
Jacie Bend *(CFO)*
Goodwin Toraason *(Exec VP)*
Connie Ganz *(Sr VP)*
Craig Ayers *(Sr VP)*
Cory Biers *(Sr VP)*

TRIAD PRO INNOVATORS, INC.

2103 W Parkside Ln Ste 105, Phoenix, AZ 85027
Tel.: (714) 790-3662
Web Site: http://www.triadproinc.com
Year Founded: 1994
TPII—(OTCIQ)
Storage Battery Mfr
N.A.I.C.S.: 335910
Ronald Bindl *(CEO)*
Michael A. Nyhuis *(Mktg Dir)*
Gene O'Brien *(Dir-Legal Svcs)*
Vincent A. Palmieri *(COO)*

TRIANGLE PETROLEUM CORPORATION

1200 17th St Ste 2600, Denver, CO 80202
Tel.: (303) 260-7125   NV
Web Site:
   http://www.trianglepetroleum.com
TPLM—(OTCIQ)
Sales Range: $350-399.9 Million
Emp.: 385
Oil & Natural Gas Exploration Services
N.A.I.C.S.: 211120
Bradley D. Sharp *(Chief Restructuring Officer)*

Subsidiaries:

Triangle USA Petroleum
Corporation   (1)
1200 17th St Ste 2600, Denver, CO 80202-1154
Tel.: (303) 260-6030
Web Site: http://www.trianglepetroleum.com
Sales Range: $50-74.9 Million
Emp.: 35
Crude Petroleum & Natural Gas Extracting Services
N.A.I.C.S.: 211120
Dana Biagioni *(Office Mgr)*
John Castellano *(Chief Restructuring Officer)*

TRIBAL RIDES INTERNATIONAL CORP.

26060 Acero, Mission Viejo, CA 92691
Tel.: (949) 434-7259   NV
Web Site: http://www.tribalrides.us
Year Founded: 2014
XNDA—(OTCIQ)
Assets: $178,157
Liabilities: $882,318
Net Worth: ($704,161)
Earnings: ($185,918)
Emp.: 2
Fiscal Year-end: 12/31/23
Property Tax Lien Services Including Auction Identification, Valuation, Consulting & Advisory Services
N.A.I.C.S.: 531390

Joseph Grimes *(CEO & CFO)*

TRICIDA, INC.

7000 Shoreline Ct Ste 201, South San Francisco, CA 94080
Tel.: (415) 429-7800   DE
Web Site: http://www.tricida.com
Year Founded: 2013
TCDA—(NASDAQ)
Rev.: $114,000
Assets: $168,506,000
Liabilities: $168,288,000
Net Worth: $218,000
Earnings: ($176,566,000)
Emp.: 57
Fiscal Year-end: 12/31/21
Pharmaceutical Preparation Mfr & Distr
N.A.I.C.S.: 325412

TRICO BANCSHARES

63 Constitution Dr, Chico, CA 95973
Tel.: (530) 898-0300   CA
Web Site: https://www.tcbk.com
Year Founded: 1981
TCBK—(NASDAQ)
Rev.: $340,711,000
Assets: $8,614,787,000
Liabilities: $7,614,603,000
Net Worth: $1,000,184,000
Earnings: $117,655,000
Emp.: 1,074
Fiscal Year-end: 12/31/21
Bank Holding Company
N.A.I.C.S.: 551111
Richard P. Smith *(Chm, Pres & CEO)*
Daniel K. Bailey *(Chief Banking Officer)*
Craig B. Carney *(Chief Credit Officer & Exec VP)*
Michael W. Koehnen *(Vice Chm)*
John S. Fleshood *(COO & Exec VP)*
Peter G. Wiese *(CFO & Exec VP)*
Gregory A. Gehlmann *(Gen Counsel & Sr VP)*
Judi A. Giem *(Chief HR Officer & Sr VP)*

Subsidiaries:

Tri Counties Bank   (1)
63 Constitution Dr, Chico, CA 95973
Tel.: (530) 898-0300
Web Site: https://www.tcbk.com
Sales Range: $200-249.9 Million
Commericial Banking
N.A.I.C.S.: 522110
Richard P. Smith *(CEO)*
Daniel K. Bailey *(Chief Banking Officer & Exec VP)*
Craig B. Carney *(Chief Credit Officer & Exec VP)*
Michael W. Koehnen *(Vice Chm)*
William J. Casey *(Chm)*
John S. Fleshood *(COO & Exec VP)*
Greg Gehlmann *(Gen Counsel & Sr VP)*
Judi A. Giem *(Chief HR Officer & Sr VP)*
Peter G. Wiese *(Exec VP)*

TRIDENT BRANDS INCORPORATED

433 Plaza Real Ste 275, Boca Raton, FL 33432
Tel.: (561) 962-4122   NV
Web Site:
   http://www.tridentbrands.com
Year Founded: 2007
TDNT—(OTCIQ)
Rev.: $872,923
Assets: $1,926,537
Liabilities: $30,345,020
Net Worth: ($28,418,483)
Earnings: ($5,296,648)
Emp.: 1
Fiscal Year-end: 11/30/20
Investment Services
N.A.I.C.S.: 523999

Peter Salvo *(Sec, VP-Fin & Controller)*
Anthony Pallante *(Chm)*
Michael Jordan Friedman *(Pres & CEO)*

Subsidiaries:

EverNutrition, Inc.   (1)
53 W 36th St, New York, NY 10018
Tel.: (212) 967-9700
Web Site: http://www.evernutrition.com
Sales Range: $1-9.9 Million
Emp.: 12
Nutritional Products & Supplements Mfr
N.A.I.C.S.: 424490

TRILINC GLOBAL IMPACT FUND, LLC

Tel.: (310) 997-0580   DE
Web Site:
   https://www.trilincglobalimpact
   fund.com
Year Founded: 2008
TRLC—(OTCIQ)
Rev.: $27,311,870
Assets: $314,822,729
Liabilities: $32,875,324
Net Worth: $281,947,405
Earnings: $5,819,495
Fiscal Year-end: 12/31/22
Investment Services
N.A.I.C.S.: 523999
Gloria S. Nelund *(Chm, Pres & CEO)*
Brent J. VanNorman *(Chief Compliance Officer & Sec)*
Scott T. Hall *(COO)*
Paul R. Sanford *(Chief Investment Officer)*

TRIMAS CORPORATION

38505 Woodward Ave Ste 200, Bloomfield Hills, MI 48304
Tel.: (248) 631-5450   DE
Web Site:
   https://www.trimascorp.com
TRS—(NASDAQ)
Rev.: $883,830,000
Assets: $1,305,000,000
Liabilities: $653,170,000
Net Worth: $651,830,000
Earnings: $66,170,000
Emp.: 3,500
Fiscal Year-end: 12/31/22
Commercial, Industrial & Consumer Engineered Product Mfr
N.A.I.C.S.: 441330
William Dickey *(Acting Pres-Aerospace)*
Scott A. Mell *(CFO & Principal Acctg Officer)*
Sherry Lauderback *(VP-IR & Comm)*
Fabio Salik *(Pres)*
Jodi Robin *(Gen Counsel)*
Jill Stress *(Chief HR Officer)*
Thomas A. Amato *(Pres & CEO)*

Subsidiaries:

Allfast Fastening Systems, LLC   (1)
15200 Don Julian Rd, City of Industry, CA 91745
Tel.: (626) 968-9388
Web Site: https://trsaero.com
Aerospace Solid & Blind Rivets Mfr
N.A.I.C.S.: 332510

Arrow Engine Company   (1)
2301 E Independence, Tulsa, OK 74110
Tel.: (918) 583-5711
Web Site: https://www.arrowengine.com
Motor Vehicle Engine Mfr
N.A.I.C.S.: 333924

Intertech Plastics Inc.   (1)
12850 E 40th Ave Unit 82, Denver, CO 80239
Tel.: (303) 371-4270
Web Site: http://intertechplastics.com
Rev.: $8,200,000
Emp.: 120
All Other Plastics Product Mfr

N.A.I.C.S.: 326199
Noel Ginsburg *(Founder, Chm & CEO)*
Ted Sillstrop *(VP-Sls)*
Brandon Lloyd *(Mgr-Bus Dev)*

Lamons Gasket Company   (1)
7300 Airport Blvd, Houston, TX 77061
Tel.: (713) 222-0284
Web Site: https://www.lamons.com
Gasket Bolt & Sealing Device Mfr
N.A.I.C.S.: 339991

Martinic Engineering, Inc.   (1)
10932 Chestnut Ave, Stanton, CA 90680
Tel.: (714) 527-8988
Sales Range: $10-24.9 Million
Emp.: 20
Engineeering Services
N.A.I.C.S.: 541330

Norris Cylinder Company   (1)
4818 W Loop 281, Longview, TX 75603
Tel.: (903) 757-7633
Web Site: https://www.norriscylinder.com
Industrial Gas Cylinders Mfr
N.A.I.C.S.: 332420

Omega Plastics, Inc.   (1)
24401 Capital Blvd, Clinton Township, MI 48036
Tel.: (586) 954-2100
Web Site: http://www.opinc.com
Sales Range: $10-24.9 Million
Emp.: 65
All Other Plastics Product Mfr
N.A.I.C.S.: 326199
Ken Arbic *(Dir-Ops)*

Rieke Corporation   (1)
500 W 7th St, Auburn, IN 46706
Tel.: (260) 925-3700
Web Site: https://www.riekepackaging.com
Packaging Systems Mfr
N.A.I.C.S.: 333993

Subsidiary (Domestic):

Arminak & Associates, Inc.   (2)
4832 Azusa Canyon Rd Bldg A, Irwindale, CA 91706
Tel.: (626) 358-4804
Web Site: https://www.rieke-direct.com
Sales Range: $50-74.9 Million
Emp.: 50
Packaging Machinery Mfr
N.A.I.C.S.: 333993

Innovative Molding Inc.   (2)
1200 Vly House Dr Ste 100, Rohnert Park, CA 94928
Tel.: (707) 238-9250
Web Site: http://www.innovativemolding.com
Sales Range: $25-49.9 Million
Emp.: 100
Designer & Mfr of Plastic Closures for Bottles & Jars
N.A.I.C.S.: 326199
Rodger Moody *(Sr VP-Sls & Mktg)*

Weldmac Manufacturing
Company   (1)
1533 N Johnson Ave, El Cajon, CA 92020
Tel.: (619) 440-2300
Web Site: http://www.weldmac.com
Industrial Valve Mfr
N.A.I.C.S.: 332911
Timothy Bonnet *(Engr-Quality)*

TRIMBLE, INC.

10368 Westmoor Dr, Westminster, CO 80021
Tel.: (720) 887-6100   DE
Web Site: https://www.trimble.com
Year Founded: 1978
TRMB—(NASDAQ)
Rev.: $3,147,700,000
Assets: $6,876,900,000
Liabilities: $3,278,300,000
Net Worth: $3,598,600,000
Earnings: $389,900,000
Emp.: 11,402
Fiscal Year-end: 01/01/21
Advanced Positioning & Navigation Technologies & Software Mfr
N.A.I.C.S.: 334514
Robert G. Painter *(Pres & CEO)*
James A. Kirkland *(Gen Counsel, Sec & Sr VP)*

Trimble, Inc.—(Continued)

Stephan Sieber *(Sr VP)*
Jennifer Allison *(Gen Counsel)*
Chris Keating *(Sr VP)*

Subsidiaries:

3D Laser Systeme GmbH (1)
An der Feldmark 16, 31515, Wunstorf, Germany
Tel.: (49) 5031517810
Web Site: http://www.spectra-direkt.de
Emp.: 6
Navigational System & Equipment Mfr
N.A.I.C.S.: 334511

ALK Technologies, Inc. (1)
1 Independence Way, Princeton, NJ 08540
Tel.: (609) 683-0220
Web Site: https://maps.trimble.com
Computer Software Development Services
N.A.I.C.S.: 541511

AllTerra Deutschland GmbH (1)
Mainfrankenpark 57, 97337, Dettelbach, Germany
Tel.: (49) 93028193770
Web Site: http://www.allterra-ds.de
Laser & Other Optical Instrument Mfr
N.A.I.C.S.: 333310

AllTerra Deutschland GmbH (1)
An der Feldmark 9, 31515, Wunstorf, Germany
Tel.: (49) 50 315 1780
Web Site: https://www.allterra-dno.de
Data Provisioning & Data Hosting Services
N.A.I.C.S.: 518210

AllTerra osterreich GmbH (1)
Ennser Strasse 83, Dietach, 4407, Steyr, Austria
Tel.: (43) 725225110
Web Site: http://www.allterra-oesterreich.at
Surveying & Mapping Services
N.A.I.C.S.: 541370

Allterra Iberica, S.L.U. (1)
Dublin Street 1 1st floor Europolis Polygon, 28232, Las Rozas, Spain
Tel.: (34) 902304075
Web Site: https://allterra-iberica.es
Software & Data Collection Services
N.A.I.C.S.: 541512

Amtech Group Limited (1)
Bank House 171 Midsummer Boulevard, Milton Keynes, MK9 1EB, United Kingdom
Tel.: (44) 1908608833
Web Site: http://www.amtech.co.uk
Computer Software Development Services
N.A.I.C.S.: 541511

Applanix Corporation (1)
85 Leek Crescent, Richmond Hill, L4B 3B3, ON, Canada
Tel.: (289) 695-6000
Web Site: https://www.applanix.com
Sales Range: $25-49.9 Million
Emp.: 95
Measuring Device Mfr
N.A.I.C.S.: 334519

Subsidiary (US):

Applanix LLC (2)
17461 Village Green Dr, Houston, TX 77040
Tel.: (713) 896-9900
Web Site: http://www.applanix.com
Rev.: $1,900,000
Emp.: 2
GPS Products Sales
N.A.I.C.S.: 334511

Atrium Software Ltd (1)
Hillside House 1500 Parkway North Stoke Gifford, Bristol, BS34 8YU, United Kingdom
Tel.: (44) 1172033501
Web Site: http://cloud2.atriumsoft.com
Computer Software Development Services
N.A.I.C.S.: 541511

Axio-Net GmbH (1)
Osterstrasse 24, 30159, Hannover, Germany
Tel.: (49) 511 123 7180
Web Site: https://www.axio-net.eu
Providing Architectural Design Services
N.A.I.C.S.: 541310

Azteca Systems, LLC (1)
11075 S State St Ste 24, Sandy, UT 84070
Tel.: (801) 523-2751
Web Site: https://www.cityworks.com
Software Development Services
N.A.I.C.S.: 541511
Brian Haslam *(Pres & CEO)*
Pete Hristou *(CFO)*
Dan Duffin *(Chief Legal Officer)*
Wayne Hill *(VP-Client Rels)*
Brent Wilson *(VP-Sls)*

Beartooth Mapping Inc (1)
1 S Broadway, Billings, MT 59101
Tel.: (406) 294-9411
Web Site: https://mapstore.mytopo.com
Emp.: 10
Surveying & Mapping Services
N.A.I.C.S.: 541370

Bid2win Software, Inc. (1)
99 Bow St, Portsmouth, NH 03801
Tel.: (603) 570-2500
Web Site: https://www.b2wsoftware.com
Sales Range: $1-9.9 Million
Emp.: 23
Custom Computer Programming Services
N.A.I.C.S.: 541511
Bihari Srinivasan *(VP-Engrg)*
Jeff Pankratz *(VP-Client Svcs)*
Paul J. McKeon Jr. *(Founder)*
Doug Seyler *(VP)*
Lisa LeBlanc *(VP)*
Jeff Russell *(VP)*
Robert Brown *(VP)*

BuildingPoint Deutschland Nord GmbH (1)
An der Feldmark 9, 31515, Wunstorf, Germany
Tel.: (49) 503 151 7810
Web Site: https://buildingpoint-nord.de
Commercial & Institutional Building Construction Services
N.A.I.C.S.: 236220

Cengea Solutions Inc (1)
Suite 1160 330 St Mary Avenue, Winnipeg, R3C 3Z5, MB, Canada
Tel.: (204) 957-7566
Web Site: http://www.cengea.com
Software Publisher
N.A.I.C.S.: 513210

Computer Services Consultants (UK) Ltd. (1)
Royal Pavilion Wellesley Road, Aldershot, GU11 1PZ, Hampshire, United Kingdom
Tel.: (44) 1252534000
Web Site: http://www.csc.com
Emp.: 300
Computer Software Development Services
N.A.I.C.S.: 541511

Construsoft Groep BV (1)
Hengelder 16, 6902 PA, Zevenaar, Netherlands
Tel.: (31) 31 620 0000
Web Site: https://www.construsoft.com
Commercial & Institutional Building Construction Services
N.A.I.C.S.: 236220

GIL GmbH (1)
Mainfrankenpark 57, 97337, Dettelbach, Germany
Tel.: (49) 93028193770
Web Site: http://www.gil-gmbh.de
Navigational System & Equipment Mfr
N.A.I.C.S.: 334511

Gehry Technologies Middle East LLC (1)
PO Box 113 100, Abu Dhabi, United Arab Emirates
Tel.: (971) 24069894
Computer Software Development Services
N.A.I.C.S.: 541511

GeoTrac Systems Inc. (1)
5940 MacLeod Trail SW Suite 401, Calgary, T2H 2G4, AB, Canada
Tel.: (403) 261-2962
Web Site: http://www.geotracinternational.com
Navigational System & Equipment Mfr
N.A.I.C.S.: 334511
Ric Dormer *(Mgr)*
Kevin MacDonald *(VP-Marketing)*
Kirk Slone *(CTO)*
Brian Traub *(Dir-Sales)*

Geotronics Southern Europe S.L (1)
Calle Dublin 1 planta 1 Poligono Europolis, Las Rozas, 28230, Madrid, Spain
Tel.: (34) 902304075
Web Site: http://www.geotronics.es
Computer Software Development Services
N.A.I.C.S.: 541511

HHK Datebtechnik GmbH (1)
Hamburger StraSSe 277, 38114, Braunschweig, Germany
Tel.: (49) 53128810
Web Site: https://www.hhk.de
Emp.: 50
Computer Software Development Services
N.A.I.C.S.: 541511
Friedhelm Olthuis *(Mng Dir & Mgr-Key Acct)*
Rudiger Oberlander *(Mgr-R&D)*
Norbert Sperhake *(Mng Dir)*

IRON Solutions, Inc (1)
660 Bakers Bridge Ave, Franklin, TN 37067
Tel.: (636) 343-8000
Web Site: https://www.ironsolutions.com
Business Data Provider
N.A.I.C.S.: 541715

ISE Fleet Services, LLC (1)
2850 Coral Ct Ste 100, Coralville, IA 52241
Tel.: (319) 359-3010
Web Site: http://www.iseinc.biz
Transportation & Software Development Services
N.A.I.C.S.: 488490

Innovative Software Engineering, LLC (1)
2850 Coral Ct Ste 100, Coralville, IA 52241
Tel.: (319) 359-3010
Web Site: http://www.iseinc.biz
Rev.: $1,200,000
Emp.: 19
Software Publisher
N.A.I.C.S.: 513210
Hass Machlab *(Founder)*

Loadrite Limited (1)
93 First Ave, Tauranga, New Zealand
Tel.: (64) 75782820
Navigational System & Equipment Mfr
N.A.I.C.S.: 334511

Logic Way B.V. (1)
Zandbreeweg 12, 7577 BZ, Oldenzaal, Netherlands
Tel.: (31) 541539948
Web Site: http://www.logicway.nl
Computer Software Development Services
N.A.I.C.S.: 541511

MPS Development Inc (1)
221 Esplanade W Suite 302, North Vancouver, V7M 3J3, BC, Canada
Tel.: (604) 904-0022
Emp.: 65
Computer Software Development Services
N.A.I.C.S.: 541511

Manhattan Centerstone, Inc. (1)
425 Fortune Blvd Ste 200, Milford, MA 01757
Tel.: (508) 381-5800
Computer Software Development Services
N.A.I.C.S.: 541511

Manhattan Datacraft Ltd (1)
55/56 Queens House Lincons Inn Field, London, WC2A 3LJ, United Kingdom
Tel.: (44) 2072698500
Web Site: http://www.datacraftdesign.com
Emp.: 100
Computer Software Development Services
N.A.I.C.S.: 541511

Mensi, S.A. (1)
174 Ave De Mareghal De Lattre De Tassigly, 94120, Fontenay-sous-Bois, France
Tel.: (33) 148779999
Web Site: http://mensi.free.fr
Terrestrial 3D Laser Scanners Mfr
N.A.I.C.S.: 541360

Meridian Systems (1)
1720 Prairie City Rd Ste 120, Folsom, CA 95630
Tel.: (916) 294-2000
Web Site: http://www.meridiansystems.com
Sales Range: $50-74.9 Million
Emp.: 50
Construction Project Management
N.A.I.C.S.: 237990

Mining Information Systems, Inc. (1)
10368 Westmoor Dr, Westminster, CO 80121
Tel.: (303) 635-9255
Computer Software Development Services
N.A.I.C.S.: 541511

Muller-Elektronik GmbH & Co. KG (1)
Franz-Kleine-Str 18, 33154, Salzkotten, Germany
Tel.: (49) 525898340
Web Site: https://www.mueller-elektronik.de
Plant Protection Accessory Providing Services
N.A.I.C.S.: 115112

Branch (Domestic):

WTK-Elektronik GmbH (2)
Bischofswerdaer Str 37f, 01844, Neustadt, Germany
Tel.: (49) 359656560
Transmitting Public Service Utility & Industrial Instruments Mfr
N.A.I.C.S.: 334513

NM Group Network Mapping Corp. (1)
2200 HSBC Building 885 West Georgia Street, Vancouver, V6C 3E8, BC, Canada
Tel.: (604) 842-0693
Architectural Supply Retailer
N.A.I.C.S.: 459999

Network Mapping Inc. (1)
230 S Rock Blvd Ste 21, Reno, NV 89502
Tel.: (775) 722-7701
Web Site: https://nmgroup.com
Emp.: 135
3D Virtual Network Environment Services
N.A.I.C.S.: 541620

Network Mapping Limited (1)
Unit 8 Whitfield Business Park Manse Lane, Knaresborough, HG5 8BS, North Yorkshire, United Kingdom
Tel.: (44) 1423206399
Information Management Services
N.A.I.C.S.: 541512

Nexala Ltd (1)
Suite 34 The Mall Beacon Court, Sandyford, Dublin, 18, Ireland
Tel.: (353) 14800519
Web Site: http://www.nexala.com
Navigational System & Equipment Mfr
N.A.I.C.S.: 334511
Daragh Lowry *(Sls Dir)*

Nikon-Trimble Co., Ltd. (1)
echnoport Taijuseimei Bldg 2-16-2 Minamikamata, Ota-ku, Tokyo, 144-0035, Japan
Tel.: (81) 357102598
Web Site: https://www.nikon-trimble.co.jp
Sales Range: $25-49.9 Million
Emp.: 240
Surveying Instruments Sales & Mfr
N.A.I.C.S.: 333310
Takashi Tanzawa *(CEO)*
Hajime Kosawa *(COO)*
Angela Salyer *(Auditor)*

PeopleNet Communications Corporation (1)
4400 Baker Road, Minnetonka, MN 55343
Tel.: (952) 908-6200
Web Site: http://www.peoplenetonline.com
Computer Software Development Services
N.A.I.C.S.: 541511

Plancal GmbH (1)
Am Bonner Bogen 6, 53227, Bonn, Germany
Tel.: (49) 228608830
Web Site: https://www.plancal.de
Computer Software Development Services
N.A.I.C.S.: 541511

PocketMobile Communications AB (1)
Ynglingagatan 6 6 tr, 113 47, Stockholm, Sweden
Tel.: (46) 87367700
Web Site: http://www.pocketmobile.eu
Mobile Software Development Services
N.A.I.C.S.: 513210

PocketMobile Norge AS (1)
Nydalsveien 33, 0484, Oslo, Norway

Tel.: (47) 709115267
Mobile Software Development Services
N.A.I.C.S.: 513210

Punch Telematix France S.A.S (1)
174 avenue du Marechal de Lattre de Tassigny, Fontenay Sous Bois, 94120, Paris, France
Tel.: (33) 171343000
Computer Software Development Services
N.A.I.C.S.: 541511

Punch Telematix Iberica S.L (1)
Edf Torre San Anton, 30009, Murcia, Spain
Tel.: (34) 968281418
Computer Software Development Services
N.A.I.C.S.: 541511

S+H Systemtechnik GmbH (1)
An der Feldmark 16, 31515, Wunstorf, Germany
Tel.: (49) 503151780
Web Site: http://www.sh-systemtechnik.de
Navigational System & Equipment Mfr
N.A.I.C.S.: 334511

SECO Manufacturing Company Inc (1)
4155 Oasis Rd, Redding, CA 96003-0859
Tel.: (530) 225-8155
Web Site: http://www.surveying.com
Navigational System & Equipment Mfr
N.A.I.C.S.: 334511

Savcor Oy (1)
Insinoorinkatu 5, 50150, Mikkeli, Finland
Tel.: (358) 207308817
Web Site: https://www.savcor.com
Sales Range: $350-399.9 Million
Emp.: 1,100
Technology Solutions Developer for Performance Optimization
N.A.I.C.S.: 551112
Mikko Neuvonen (Mgr-Cathodic Protection Bus Area)
Timo Laurila (VP)
Isto Virtanen (Mgr-Pulp & Paper Bus Area)
Katja Savisalo (Mgr-Acctg)
Minna Juhola (Sec-Import & Export)
Jarmo Salo (CEO)

Subsidiary (Non-US):

OOO Savcor ART Rus (2)
Ul Bolshaya Pionerskaya 13, 115054, Moscow, Russia
Tel.: (7) 4956332695
Web Site: http://www.savcor.ru
Application Software Development Services
N.A.I.C.S.: 541511

Savcor Forest Inc. (2)
102-18940 94th Avenue, Surrey, V4N 4X5, BC, Canada
Tel.: (604) 662-7034
Web Site: http://www.savcor.com
Application Software Development Services
N.A.I.C.S.: 541511

Savcor Forest Limitada (2)
Av Cassiano Ricardo 601- Cj 161 e 163, Parque Residential Aquarius, Sao Jose dos Campos, 1246-870, SP, Brazil
Tel.: (55) 12 3500 0100
Web Site: http://savcor.com
Application Software Development Services
N.A.I.C.S.: 541511

Sigma Handels GmbH (1)
Siemensstr 20A, 61267, Neu-Anspach, Germany
Tel.: (49) 60814569900
Web Site: https://www.spectra-direkt.de
Online Shopping Services
N.A.I.C.S.: 423840

Sitech Deutschland GmbH (1)
Zum Aquarium 6a, 46047, Oberhausen, Germany
Tel.: (49) 2083021370
Web Site: http://www.sitech.de
Computer Software Development Services
N.A.I.C.S.: 541511

Sitech Southern Africa (Pty) Ltd (1)
Building C Lakefield Office Park 272 West Avenue, Centurion, 0157, South Africa
Tel.: (27) 873577100
Web Site: https://www.sitech.co.za
Emp.: 60
Computer Software Development Services

N.A.I.C.S.: 541511
Tessa Swanepoel (Mgr-Fin)
Charles Meyer (Mng Dir)

Solid SAS (1)
12 rue Jean Louis Calderon, 69120, Vaulx-en-Velin, France
Tel.: (33) 669215605
Web Site: https://www.solidsas.com
Software Programming Services
N.A.I.C.S.: 541511

Spatial Dimension Australia Pty. Ltd. (1)
Level 2 9 Havelock Street, West Perth, 6005, WA, Australia
Tel.: (61) 457009669
Architectural Supply Retailer
N.A.I.C.S.: 459999

Spatial Dimension Canada ULC (1)
Suite 560 1188 West Georgia St, Vancouver, V6E 4A2, BC, Canada
Tel.: (408) 481-8000
Architectural Supply Retailer
N.A.I.C.S.: 459999

Spatial Dimension Sistemas do Brasil Ltda. (1)
Rua Raimundo Albergaria Filho 52 Enseada da Garcas, Belo Horizonte, 31550-303, Minas Gerais, Brazil
Tel.: (55) 3134943272
Architectural Supply Retailer
N.A.I.C.S.: 459999

Spatial Dimension South Africa Pty Ltd (1)
2nd Floor Block A Technosquare 42 Morningside, Ndabeni, 7405, Cape Town, South Africa
Tel.: (27) 215313132
Business Consulting Services
N.A.I.C.S.: 541618

Spektra Agri Srl (1)
via mongini 111/a, 44030, Berra, FE, India
Tel.: (91) 532834445
Web Site: http://www.spektra-agri.it
Navigational System & Equipment Mfr
N.A.I.C.S.: 334511

Spektra Agri Srl (1)
Via S Mongini 111/A, Serravalle, 44030, Ferrara, Italy
Tel.: (39) 0532834445
Web Site: http://www.vantage-italia.com
Precision Farming Services
N.A.I.C.S.: 115116

Spektra S.P.A. (1)
Via Pellizzari 23/A, 20871, Vimercate, MB, Italy
Tel.: (39) 03 962 5051
Web Site: https://www.spektra.it
Navigational System & Equipment Mfr
N.A.I.C.S.: 334511

Stabiplan B.V. (1)
Sloep 1, PO Box 128, 2411 CD, Bodegraven, Netherlands
Tel.: (31) 172630023
Web Site: http://www.stabiplan.nl
Providing Architectural Design Services
N.A.I.C.S.: 541310

Stabiplan BVBA (1)
Duboisstraat 39, 2060, Antwerp, Belgium
Tel.: (32) 32890101
Web Site: http://www.stabiplan.com
Surveying & Mapping Services
N.A.I.C.S.: 541370

Stabiplan GmbH (1)
At Bonner Bogen 6, 53227, Bonn, Germany
Tel.: (49) 228608830
Providing Architectural Design Services
N.A.I.C.S.: 541310

Stabiplan S.A.S. (1)
Le Polaris 76 avenue Pierre Brossolette, 92240, Malakoff, France
Tel.: (33) 228093900
Web Site: https://www.stabiplan.com
Emp.: 200
3D Model Design & Management Services
N.A.I.C.S.: 541420

Stabiplan S.R.L. (1)
Strada Ionescu Crum 9, Brasov, 500446, Romania

Tel.: (40) 268311140
Web Site: http://www.stabiplan.ro
Providing Architectural Design Services
N.A.I.C.S.: 541310

TMW Systems, Inc. (1)
25800 Science Park Dr Ste 225, Beachwood, OH 44122
Tel.: (216) 831-6606
Web Site: http://www.tmwsystems.com
Sales Range: $75-99.9 Million
Emp.: 500
Software Consultancy & Supply
N.A.I.C.S.: 513210

Subsidiary (Domestic):

TMW Systems, Inc. - Nashville (2)
750 Old Hickory Blvd Ste 290, Brentwood, TN 37027
Tel.: (615) 986-1900
Web Site: http://www.tmwsystem.com
Sales Range: $10-24.9 Million
Emp.: 50
Developer of Enterprise Management Software
N.A.I.C.S.: 513210

Tekla (SEA) Pte. Ltd. (1)
3 Harbourfront Place 13-02 Harbourfront Tower two, Singapore, 99254, Singapore
Tel.: (65) 62738775
Navigational System & Equipment Mfr
N.A.I.C.S.: 334511

Tekla Corporation (1)
Metsanpojankuja 1, FI-02130, Espoo, Finland
Tel.: (358) 3066110
Web Site: http://www.tekla.com
Emp.: 800
Computer Software Development Services
N.A.I.C.S.: 541511

Tekla Korea (1)
8F Song-gang Blgd Deachi-dong 15 Teherano 98, Gangnam, 135-846, Seoul, Korea (South)
Tel.: (82) 27049404600
Navigational System & Equipment Mfr
N.A.I.C.S.: 334511
Haikun Kim (Acct Mgr-Sls)

Tekla Oyj (1)
Metsaenpojankuja 1, 02130, Espoo, Finland
Tel.: (358) 3066110
Web Site: http://www.tekla.com
Sales Range: $75-99.9 Million
Emp.: 500
Software Product Developer & Marketer
N.A.I.C.S.: 541512

Subsidiary (Non-US):

Tekla (UK) Ltd. (2)
Tekla House Cliffe Park Way, Morley, Leeds, LS27 0RY, West Yorkshire, United Kingdom
Tel.: (44) 1133071200
Web Site: http://www.tekla.com
Sales Range: $25-49.9 Million
Emp.: 25
Software Solutions Development & Marketing Services
N.A.I.C.S.: 423430

Tekla GmbH (2)
Heelsmann park 2, Eschborn, 65760, Hesse, Germany
Tel.: (49) 61964730830
Web Site: http://www.tekla.com
Sales Range: $25-49.9 Million
Emp.: 20
Software Solutions Development & Marketing Services
N.A.I.C.S.: 423430

Subsidiary (US):

Tekla Inc. (2)
1075 Big Shanty Rd NW, Kennesaw, GA 30144
Tel.: (770) 426-5105
Web Site: http://www.tekla.com
Software Solutions Development & Marketing Services
N.A.I.C.S.: 423430
Pekka Saaskilahti (CFO)
Arun Kumar (Natl Mgr)
Sampada Palshikar (Product Mgr)
Jayaganesh Balla (Sr Engr)

Abhay Patil (Sys Engr)
Vasant Shetty (Mgr)
Arun Kumar (Natl Mgr)
Sampada Palshikar (Product Mgr)
Jayaganesh Balla (Sr Engr)
Abhay Patil (Sys Engr)
Vasant Shetty (Mgr)
Arun Kumar (Natl Mgr)
Sampada Palshikar (Product Mgr)
Jayaganesh Balla (Sr Engr)
Abhay Patil (Sys Engr)
Vasant Shetty (Mgr)

Subsidiary (Non-US):

Tekla India Private Limited (2)
Unit No 1112-115 Bldg No 2 Millennium Business Park, Sector-1 Mahape, Mumbai, 400710, Maharashtra, India
Tel.: (91) 2267120892
Web Site: http://www.tekla.com
Sales Range: $25-49.9 Million
Emp.: 29
Software Solutions Development & Marketing Services
N.A.I.C.S.: 423430

Tekla KK (2)
5F No 3 Koike Bldg 1-1-11 Kitashinagawa, Shinagawa, Tokyo, 140 0001, Japan
Tel.: (81) 357693351
Web Site: http://www.tekla.com
Sales Range: $25-49.9 Million
Emp.: 1
Software Solutions Development & Marketing Services
N.A.I.C.S.: 423430

Tekla Sarl (2)
5 rue de la Corderie, Centra 405, 94616, Rungis, Val-de-Marne, France
Tel.: (33) 146876275
Sales Range: $25-49.9 Million
Emp.: 18
Software Solutions Development & Marketing Services
N.A.I.C.S.: 423430

Tekla Software (Shanghai) Co., Ltd. (2)
Room 1203 Shanghai Trade Center, 800 Quyang Rd Hongkou District, Shanghai, 200437, China
Tel.: (86) 2165549695
Web Site: http://www.tekla.com
Sales Range: $25-49.9 Million
Emp.: 8
Software Solutions Development & Marketing Services
N.A.I.C.S.: 423430

Tekla Software Ab (2)
Sigurdsgatan 21, S 721 30, Vasteras, Sweden
Tel.: (46) 21109600
Computer Software Development & Marketing
N.A.I.C.S.: 423430
Tomas Ray (Gen Mgr)

Telog Instruments, Inc. (1)
830 Canning Pkwy, Victor, NY 14564
Tel.: (585) 742-3000
Web Site: http://www.telog.com
Electrical Measuring & Controlling Device Mfr
N.A.I.C.S.: 334519

Trade Service Co. LLC (1)
13280 Evening Creek Dr S Ste 200, San Diego, CA 92128
Tel.: (858) 521-1400
Web Site: https://www.tradeservice.com
Sales Range: $10-24.9 Million
Emp.: 110
Information Retrieval Services
N.A.I.C.S.: 517810

Trade Service Holdings Inc. (1)
13280 Evening Creek Dr S Ste 200, San Diego, CA 92128-4101
Tel.: (858) 521-1501
Emp.: 2
Holding Company
N.A.I.C.S.: 551114

Trimble AB (1)
Rinkebyvagen 17, PO Box 64, SE 182 36, Danderyd, Sweden
Tel.: (46) 86221000

Trimble, Inc.—(Continued)

Web Site: http://www.trimble.com
Navigation Equipment Mfr
N.A.I.C.S.: 334511

Trimble Brasil Solucoes Ltda (1)
Av Jose de Souza Campos 900-Conj 61 e
62, Campinas, 13092-123, Sao Paulo, Bra-
zil
Tel.: (55) 1931137000
Web Site: http://www.trimble.com.br
Emp.: 30
Navigational System & Equipment Mfr
N.A.I.C.S.: 334511

Trimble Corvallis (1)
345 SW Avery Ave, Corvallis, OR 97333
Tel.: (541) 753-9322
Web Site: http://www.trimble.com
Sales Range: $25-49.9 Million
Emp.: 100
Hardware & Software Developer for Mobile
Computing Applications
N.A.I.C.S.: 334118

Trimble DBO Information Technology
(Shanghai) Co. Ltd. (1)
Room 1106 Yuhui Building No 29 Wenshui
East Road, Hongkou District, Shanghai, 31
200437, China
Tel.: (86) 2165549695
Building Construction Services
N.A.I.C.S.: 236116
Kelly Feng (Mgr-License Compliance)

Trimble Dayton (1)
5475 Kellenburger Rd, Dayton, OH 45424-
1013
Tel.: (937) 233-8921
Web Site: http://www.trimble.com
Sales Range: $125-149.9 Million
Emp.: 600
Navigation Systems Mfr
N.A.I.C.S.: 334511

Trimble Electronic Products (Shang-
hai) Co., Ltd. (1)
311 Fute (M) Road 3/f, Wai Gaoqiao Free
Trade Zone, Pudong, Shanghai, 2000131,
China
Tel.: (86) 2150461043
Web Site: http://www.trimble.com
Sales Range: $150-199.9 Million
Navigation, Guidance & Search & Detection
Systems & Instruments Distr
N.A.I.C.S.: 423860

Trimble Europe B.V. (1)
Meerheide 45, 5521 DZ, Eersel, Nether-
lands
Tel.: (31) 497532451
Web Site: http://www.trimble.com
Sales Range: $10-24.9 Million
Emp.: 20
Navigational Equipment Distr
N.A.I.C.S.: 334511

Trimble Forestry Corporation (1)
Suite 560 1188 West Georgia Street, Van-
couver, V6E 4A2, BC, Canada
Tel.: (604) 697-6400
Web Site: https://forestry.trimble.com
Emp.: 250
Forest Nursery & Gathering Services
N.A.I.C.S.: 113210

Trimble Forestry GmbH (1)
Obere Stegwiesen 26, 88400, Biberach,
Germany
Tel.: (49) 1523999193
Data Provisioning & Data Hosting Services
N.A.I.C.S.: 518210

Trimble Forestry Ltda. (1)
Av Tambore n 1400/1440 Mezzanine, Ba-
rueri, Sao Paulo, 06460-000, Brazil
Tel.: (55) 12981185015
Forestry Services
N.A.I.C.S.: 115310

Trimble France S.A.S. (1)
32 rue de la Fontaine-du-Vaisseau, 94120,
Fontenay-sous-Bois, France
Tel.: (33) 171343164
Web Site: http://www.trimble.com
Sales Range: $10-24.9 Million
Emp.: 20
Navigational Equipment Sales
N.A.I.C.S.: 334511

Trimble Germany GmbH (1)
Rotebuehlstrasse 81, 70178, Stuttgart, Ger-
many
Tel.: (49) 711228810
Computer Software Development Services
N.A.I.C.S.: 541511
Juergen Kesper (Dir-Legal)

Trimble Holdings GmbH (1)
Am Prime Parc 11, 65479, Raunheim, Ger-
many
Tel.: (49) 614221000
Web Site: http://www.trimble.com
Holding Company; Navigational Equipment
Mfr
N.A.I.C.S.: 551112

Subsidiary (Domestic):

Trimble GmbH (2)
Am Prime Parc 11, 65479, Raunheim,
Germany (100%)
Tel.: (49) 614221000
Web Site: http://ww2.trimble.com
Sales Range: $10-24.9 Million
Navigational Equipment
N.A.I.C.S.: 334511

Trimble Kaiserslautern GmbH (2)
Am Sportplatz 5, 67661, Kaiserslautern,
Germany
Tel.: (49) 630171414
Web Site: http://www.trimble.com
Navigational Equipment
N.A.I.C.S.: 334511

Trimble Terrasat Gmbh (2)
Haringstrasse 19, 85635, Hohenkirchen,
Germany
Tel.: (49) 810274330
Web Site: http://www.trimble.com
Sales Range: $10-24.9 Million
Emp.: 25
Navigational Equipment
N.A.I.C.S.: 334511

Trimble Hungary Kft (1)
Kondorfa utca 6-8, 1116, Budapest, Hun-
gary
Tel.: (36) 14812050
Web Site: http://www.geodesy.hu
Emp.: 57
Navigational System & Equipment Mfr
N.A.I.C.S.: 334511

Trimble International (Schweiz)
Seestrasse SA (1)
Seestrasse 5a, CH-8810, Horgen, Switzer-
land
Tel.: (41) 447274444
Web Site: http://mep.trimble.ch
Computer & Software Whslr
N.A.I.C.S.: 423430

Trimble Italia SRL (1)
Cento Torri Bianche, Vimercate, 20871, MI,
Italy
Tel.: (39) 0396858510
Web Site: http://www.global.trimble.com
Sales Range: $25-49.9 Million
Emp.: 4
Navigation Systems & Equipment
N.A.I.C.S.: 334511

Trimble Jean GmbH (1)
Carl-zeiss-promenade 10, 07745, Jena,
Germany
Tel.: (49) 3641643294
Web Site: http://www.trimble.com
Emp.: 41
Navigational System & Equipment Mfr
N.A.I.C.S.: 334511

Trimble Loadrite Auckland
Limited (1)
45 Patiki Road, Avondale, Auckland, 1026,
New Zealand
Tel.: (64) 98207720
Web Site: http://www.loadritescales.com
Emp.: 50
Computer Software Development Services
N.A.I.C.S.: 541511

Trimble Loadrite Chile SPA (1)
Badajoz 100 Of 1121-1122, Las Condes,
Santiago, Chile
Tel.: (56) 22128587
Navigational System & Equipment Mfr
N.A.I.C.S.: 334511

Trimble MEP (1)

384 Inverness Pkwy, Englewood, CO 80112
Tel.: (303) 799-6500
Web Site: http://www.mep.trimble.com
Application Computer Software
N.A.I.C.S.: 513210

Subsidiary (Domestic):

Mechanical Data Inc (2)
384 Inverness Pkwy Ste 200, Englewood,
CO 80112-5823
Tel.: (804) 346-8445
Web Site: http://www.quickpen.com
Sales Range: $1-9.9 Million.
Emp.: 3
Business Oriented Computer Software
N.A.I.C.S.: 513210

Trimble Mexico S de RL (1)
Insurgentes Sur 800 Piso 8, Col del Valle,
03100, Mexico, Mexico
Tel.: (52) 55 5448 4941
Sales Range: $100-124.9 Million
Navigational Equipment
N.A.I.C.S.: 334511

Trimble Mobile Solutions, Inc. (1)
3650 Concorde Pkwy Ste 150, Chantilly, VA
20151 (100%)
Tel.: (703) 502-5600
Web Site: http://www.trimble.com
Sales Range: $50-74.9 Million
Mobile Resource Management Services
N.A.I.C.S.: 541614

Subsidiary (Domestic):

@Road, Inc. (2)
47071 Bayside Pkwy, Fremont, CA 94538
Tel.: (510) 668-1638
Web Site: https://www.road.com
Sales Range: $75-99.9 Million
Emp.: 200
Mobile Resource Management Services
N.A.I.C.S.: 541614

Subsidiary (Non-US):

Trimble MRM (3)
1-3 Bath St, Ipswich, IP2 8SD, United
Kingdom (100%)
Tel.: (44) 1473696300
Web Site: http://www.trimble.com
Sales Range: $75-99.9 Million
Emp.: 100
Mobile Resource Management Services
N.A.I.C.S.: 541614

Trimble Mobility Solutions India
Limited (1)
Vikram Monarch 10th floor CTS no 1115
A/1, Ganeshkhind Road Shivaji Nagar,
Pune, 411016, Maharashtra, India
Tel.: (91) 2049174000
Web Site: http://www.trimbletl.in
Navigational System & Equipment Mfr
N.A.I.C.S.: 334511
Rajan Aiyer (Mng Dir & Gen Mgr-SAARC
Reg)
Govindarajan Vasudevan (Bus Dir-Logistics-
Transportation & Controller-Transportation)

Trimble NV (1)
Ter Waarde 50/6A, 8900, Ieper, Belgium
Tel.: (32) 57223911
Web Site: https://www.trimbletl.com
Transport & Logistics Services
N.A.I.C.S.: 484220

Trimble Nantes S.A.S (1)
ZAC de la Fleuriaye, BP 60433, 44474,
Carquefou, Cedex, France
Tel.: (33) 228093800
Computer Software Development Services
N.A.I.C.S.: 541511

Trimble Navigation Australia Pty.
Limited (1)
120 Wickham Street Level 1, Fortitude Val-
ley, Brisbane, 4006, QLD, Australia
Tel.: (61) 732160044
Web Site: http://www.trimble.com
Sales Range: $25-49.9 Million
Emp.: 80
Navigation, Guidance, Search & Detection
Systems & Instruments Distr
N.A.I.C.S.: 423860

Trimble Navigation Chile
Limitada (1)
Avenida Ebro 2740 Of 9, Las Condes, San-

tiago, Chile
Tel.: (56) 222448520
Navigational System & Equipment Mfr
N.A.I.C.S.: 334511
Paulina Sohrens Alvarado (Office Mgr)

Trimble Navigation Iberica S.L. (1)
Via de las Dos Castillas 33, Pozuelo de
Alarcon, Madrid, Spain
Tel.: (34) 913510100
Sales Range: $10-24.9 Million
Emp.: 13
Navigation, Guidance, Search & Detection
Systems & Instruments Distr
N.A.I.C.S.: 423860

Trimble Navigation India Pvt
Limited (1)
Unitech Crest-Block C, Greenwood City
Sector 45 Ground Floor, Gurgaon, 122003,
Haryana, India
Tel.: (91) 1244256820
Navigational System & Equipment Mfr
N.A.I.C.S.: 334511
Nikhil Kumar (Dir-Technical Mktg)

Trimble Navigation Ltd. (1)
10368 Westmoor Dr, Westminster, CO
80021
Tel.: (508) 381-5800
Web Site: https://www.trimble.com
Advanced Positioning & Navigation Tech-
nologies & Software Mfr
N.A.I.C.S.: 334514

Trimble Navigation New Zealand
Limited (1)
11 Birmingham Drive, PO Box 8729, Riccar-
ton, 8440, Christchurch, New Zealand
Tel.: (64) 39635400
Web Site: http://www.trimble.com
Sales Range: $75-99.9 Million
Emp.: 240
Navigation Systems Mfr
N.A.I.C.S.: 334511
Corinne Haine (Mng Dir)

Trimble Navigation Singapore PTE
Limited (1)
3 HarbourFront Place 13-02 HarbourFront
Tower 2, Singapore, 099254, Singapore
Tel.: (65) 68715878
Web Site: http://www.trimblenavigation.com
Sales Range: $10-24.9 Million
Emp.: 7
Navigation, Guidance, Search & Detection
Systems & Instruments Distr
N.A.I.C.S.: 423860

Trimble Poland Sp. z.o.o. (1)
Byslawska 82 412, 04-993, Warsaw, Ma-
zowieckie, Poland
Tel.: (48) 223799440
Business Consulting Services
N.A.I.C.S.: 541618

Trimble RUS LLC (1)
43 Vernadsky Ave building 1, 119415, Mos-
cow, Russia
Tel.: (7) 4952345964
Web Site: http://www.trimble.com
Navigational System & Equipment Mfr
N.A.I.C.S.: 334511
Igor Grechkin (Gen Dir)

Trimble Railway Limited (1)
Ground Floor Fenward House Arkle Road
Sandyford, Dublin, 18, Ireland
Tel.: (353) 15398700
Counting Device Mfr
N.A.I.C.S.: 334514

Trimble Railways GmbH (1)
Korbacher Strasse 15, Wiesentheid, 97353,
Kitzingen, Germany
Tel.: (49) 938397320
Web Site: https://gedo.trimble.com
Emp.: 50
Navigational System & Equipment Mfr
N.A.I.C.S.: 334511
Andreas Sinning (Mng Dir)

Trimble Solutions Aarhus A/S (1)
Hedeager 3 1 sal, Aarhus N, 8200, Arhus,
Denmark
Tel.: (45) 89304750
Software Programming Services
N.A.I.C.S.: 541511

Trimble Solutions France Sarl (1)

21 rue du Jura Immeuble Osaka, 94150, Rungis, France
Tel.: (33) 563481160
Building Construction Services
N.A.I.C.S.: 236116

Trimble Solutions Gothenburg AB **(1)**
Kungsgatan 56, 41108, Gothenburg, Sweden
Tel.: (46) 317001830
Building Construction & Civil Engineering Services
N.A.I.C.S.: 541330

Trimble Solutions India Pvt. Ltd. **(1)**
Shree Sawan Knowledge Park 4th Floor D 507, TTC Industrial Area MIDC Turbhe, Navi Mumbai, 400 705, Maharashtra, India
Tel.: (91) 2261387777
Web Site: https://www.tekla.com
Counting Device Mfr
N.A.I.C.S.: 334514
Angshuman Pandey (Mgr-Natl Bus)

Trimble Solutions Korea Co., Ltd. **(1)**
4F Cheonglim Bldg 19 Samseong-ro 96-gil, Gangnam-gu, 06167, Seoul, Gyeonggi-do, Korea (South)
Tel.: (82) 27049404600
Building Construction & Civil Engineering Services
N.A.I.C.S.: 541330

Trimble Solutions Malaysia Sdn Bhd **(1)**
Suite B-12-5 North Point Offices Mid Valley City, No 1 Medan Syed Putra Utara, 59200, Kuala Lumpur, Malaysia
Tel.: (60) 32 287 5970
Web Site: https://www.tekla.com
Navigational System & Equipment Mfr
N.A.I.C.S.: 334511

Trimble Solutions Oy **(1)**
Metsanpojankuja 1, 02130, Espoo, Finland
Tel.: (358) 3066110
Counting Device Mfr
N.A.I.C.S.: 334514
Jukka Leppanen (Sls Dir-Electric & Gas)

Trimble Solutions SEA Pte. Ltd. **(1)**
3 Harbourfront Place 13-02 Harbourfront Tower two, Singapore, 099254, Singapore
Tel.: (65) 62738775
Business Consulting Services
N.A.I.C.S.: 541618

Trimble Solutions Sandvika AS **(1)**
Leif Tronstads plass 4, PO Box 434, 1337, Sandvika, Norway
Tel.: (47) 67817000
Web Site: https://www.novapoint.com
Designing Civil Infrastructure Services
N.A.I.C.S.: 236210

Trimble Solutions Sweden AB **(1)**
Sigurdsgatan 21, 721 30, Vasteras, Sweden
Tel.: (46) 21109600
Web Site: https://www.tekla.com
Measuring & Controlling Device Mfr
N.A.I.C.S.: 334519

Trimble Solutions UK Ltd **(1)**
Trimble House Gelderd Road Morley, Leeds, LS27 7JP, United Kingdom
Tel.: (44) 1138879790
Computer Hardware Consulting Services
N.A.I.C.S.: 541512
Richard Fletcher (Mng Dir)

Trimble Solutions USA Inc. **(1)**
1075 Big Shanty Rd NW, Kennesaw, GA 30144
Tel.: (770) 426-5105
Business Consulting Services
N.A.I.C.S.: 541618

Trimble South Africa Distribution Holdings Pty Ltd. **(1)**
Block C Lakefield Office Park, Centurion, 0157, Gauteng, South Africa
Tel.: (27) 126834500
Navigational System & Equipment Mfr
N.A.I.C.S.: 334511

Trimble Sweden A.B **(1)**
Rinkebyvagen 17, 182 36, Danderyd, Sweden
Tel.: (46) 86221000

Web Site: http://www.trimble.com
Emp.: 300
Navigational System & Equipment Mfr
N.A.I.C.S.: 334511

Trimble Trailblazer GmbH **(1)**
Am Prime Parc 11, 65479, Raunheim, Germany
Tel.: (49) 614221000
Investment Services
N.A.I.C.S.: 523999

Subsidiary (Domestic):

TRANSPOREON GmbH **(2)**
Stadtregal Magirus-Deutz-Str 16, 89077, Ulm, Germany
Tel.: (49) 731169060
Web Site: http://www.transporeon.com
Emp.: 600
Logistics & Transportation Software Development Services
N.A.I.C.S.: 541511
Will Young (Mgr-Bus Dev)
Ahmet Arslan (Chief Dev & Enrgrg Officer & Mng Dir)
Olaf Demuth (CFO & Mng Partner)
Peter Schmidt (Chief Comml Officer & Mng Dir)
Thomas Einsiedler (Chief Product Officer)
Peter Forster (Founder, Mng Partner & Mng Dir)
Martin Mack (Founder & CTO)
Marc-Oliver Simon (Founder)
Stephan Kniewasser (Mng Dir)
Heike Marquordt (Editor)
Stephan Sieber (CEO)

Subsidiary (Domestic):

MERCAREON GmbH **(3)**
Pfarrer-Weiss-Weg 12, 89077, Ulm, Germany
Tel.: (49) 73140388310
Web Site: http://www.mercareon.com
Software Development Services
N.A.I.C.S.: 541511
Leander Kling (Mng Dir)

Subsidiary (Non-US):

TRANSPOREON Sp. z o. o. **(3)**
ul Kamienskiego 47, 30-644, Krakow, Poland
Tel.: (48) 126271868
Web Site: http://www.transporeon-group.com
Software Development Services
N.A.I.C.S.: 541511
Marek Dabrowski (Project Mgr)

Trimble Transportation Enterprise Solutions Inc. **(1)**
6085 Parkland Blvd, Mayfield Heights, OH 44124
Tel.: (440) 721-2020
Web Site: http://www.enterprise.trimble.com
Data Provisioning & Data Hosting Services
N.A.I.C.S.: 518210
Thomas Fansler (Pres)
Lisa Garro (VP-Fin)
Dave Schildmeyer (Sr VP-Sls)
Ray West (Sr VP & Gen Mgr)
Scott Vanselous (Exec VP-Mktg & Strategy)

Trimble UK Limited **(1)**
Trimble House Meridian Office Park, Osborn Way, Hook, RG27 9HX, Hampshire, United Kingdom
Tel.: (44) 1256760150
Sales Range: $10-24.9 Million
Emp.: 30
Navigation Systems & Equipment
N.A.I.C.S.: 334511
Chris Rose (Mng Dir)

VS Visual Statements Inc. **(1)**
175 2nd Ave Suite 900, Kamloops, V2C 5W1, BC, Canada
Tel.: (250) 828-0383
Web Site: https://forensics.trimble.com
Computer Software Development Services
N.A.I.C.S.: 541511

ViaNova Geosuite AB **(1)**
Ynglingagatan 6 6 tr, 113 47, Stockholm, Sweden
Tel.: (46) 8276990
Miscellaneous Publishing Services
N.A.I.C.S.: 513120

ViaNova Systems Sweden AB **(1)**
Kungsgatan 56, 411 08, Gothenburg, Sweden
Tel.: (46) 317001830
Web Site: http://www.vianovasystems.se
Miscellaneous Publishing Services
N.A.I.C.S.: 513120
Stefan Granberg (Mng Dir)

Viewpoint Construction Software Limited **(1)**
4th Floor Central Square Forth Street, Newcastle upon Tyne, NE1 3PJ, United Kingdom
Tel.: (44) 8000488152
Software Used Building Construction Services
N.A.I.C.S.: 236220
Nathan Garrad (Mgr-Bus Dev)

Viewpoint, Inc. **(1)**
1515 SE Water Ave Ste 300, Portland, OR 97214
Tel.: (971) 255-4800
Web Site: http://www.viewpoint.com
System Software Development Services
N.A.I.C.S.: 541511
Tom McNamara (COO)

e-Builder, Inc. **(1)**
13450 W Sunrise Blvd Ste 600, Sunrise, FL 33323
Tel.: (954) 556-6701
Web Site: https://www.e-builder.net
Construction Management Software
N.A.I.C.S.: 513210
Jonathan Antevy (Co-Founder)
Jeanne T. Prayther (CFO)
Rafael E. Santos (CTO)
Chris Bell (VP-Mktg)
Lisa Ruggieri (VP-Professional Svcs)
Shawn Silbor (VP-Sls)
John Maliani (VP-R&D)
Jon Antevy (Founder)

TRINITY BANK N.A
3500 W Vickery Blvd, Fort Worth, TX 76107
Tel.: (817) 763-9966   TX
Web Site: https://www.trinitybk.com
TYBT—(OTCIQ)
Commercial Banking Services
N.A.I.C.S.: 522110
Barney C. Wiley (Co-Chm & Pres)
Matt R. Opitz (Co-Chm & CEO)
Richard Burt (COO)

TRINITY INDUSTRIES, INC.
14221 N Dallas Pkwy Ste 1100, Dallas, TX 75254
Tel.: (214) 631-4420   DE
Web Site: https://www.trin.net
Year Founded: 1933
TRN—(NYSE)
Rev.: $2,983,300,000
Assets: $8,906,500,000
Liabilities: $7,631,000,000
Net Worth: $1,275,500,000
Earnings: $106,000,000
Emp.: 9,480
Fiscal Year-end: 12/31/23
Energy Equipment, Railcar, Transportation Barge & Construction Products Mfr
N.A.I.C.S.: 532210
Jared S. Richardson (Sec & VP)
John M. Lee (Treas & VP)
Steve L. McDowell (Chief Acctg Officer & VP)
W. Relle Howard (CIO)
David C. DelVecchio (Chief HR Officer & VP)
Douglas J. Horvath (VP-Tax)
Ian F. Mutswiri (VP)
Gregory B. Mitchell (Chief Comml Officer & Exec VP)
Kevin Poet (Exec VP-Ops & Support Svcs)
Leigh Anne Mann (VP-IR)
P. Mark Cox (Exec VP)
Luis Pardo (Exec VP)
E. Jean Savage (Pres & CEO)

Subsidiaries:

Bay Worx Industries, LLC **(1)**
9421 FM 2920 Ste 14A, Tomball, TX 77375
Web Site: https://www.bayworxrail.com
Railcar Cleaning Services
N.A.I.C.S.: 488210

Energy Absorption Systems, Inc. **(1)**
70 W Madison St Ste 2350, Chicago, IL 60602
Tel.: (312) 467-6750
Web Site: http://trinityhighway.com
Sales Range: $25-49.9 Million
Emp.: 12
Highway Crash Cushions & Safety Products Mfr
N.A.I.C.S.: 332999

Division (Domestic):

E-Tech Testing Services, Inc. **(2)**
3617-B Cincinnati Ave, Rocklin, CA 95765
Tel.: (916) 644-9149
Web Site: https://www.etechtesting.com
Laboratory-Based Testing Services
N.A.I.C.S.: 541720
Timothy Mortensen (Supvr)

Subsidiary (Domestic):

Safe-Hit Corporation **(2)**
70 W Madison St Ste 2350, Chicago, IL 60602
Tel.: (312) 467-6750
Web Site: http://www.safehit.com
Sales Range: $10-24.9 Million
Co-Extruded, Two-Part Flexible Delineator & Guidance Systems Designer & Mfr
N.A.I.C.S.: 326199

Platinum Energy Services ULC **(1)**
400 333-11th Ave SW, Calgary, T2R 1L9, AB, Canada
Tel.: (403) 264-6688
Web Site: http://www.trinityplatinum.ca
Emp.: 17
Pipe Mfr & Distr
N.A.I.C.S.: 423320
Bob Schulze (VP-Ops)
Joe Ladouceur (Pres & CEO)
Ryan Mailer (VP-Sls)

RSI Logistics Inc. **(1)**
4900 Montrose Ave Ste 200, Okemos, MI 48864
Tel.: (517) 349-7713
Web Site: http://www.rsilogistics.com
Sales Range: $10-24.9 Million
Emp.: 180
Transportation Services Consultant
N.A.I.C.S.: 488510
Kelley Minnehan (Sr VP-Mktg)
Holly Silcox (Mgr-HR & Acctg)
Camilla Bond (Mgr)

Subsidiary (Domestic):

RSI Leasing Inc. **(2)**
2419 Science Pkwy, Okemos, MI 48864
Tel.: (517) 349-7713
Web Site: http://www.rsilogistics.com
Sales Range: Less than $1 Million
Emp.: 45
Railroad Switching
N.A.I.C.S.: 488210

TRNLWB, LLC **(1)**
2525 N Stemmons Fwy, Dallas, TX 75207
Tel.: (214) 631-4420
Emp.: 25
Residential Remodeling Services
N.A.I.C.S.: 236118

TRNLWS, LLC **(1)**
14885 S Interstate 45, Streetman, TX 75859
Tel.: (903) 599-3000
Emp.: 8
Construction Materials Distr
N.A.I.C.S.: 423310

Trinity Argentina S.R.L. **(1)**
Alem Leandro N Av 734 20 5 1001, Buenos Aires, Argentina
Tel.: (54) 1143128838
Engineeering Services
N.A.I.C.S.: 541330

Trinity Construction Materials, Inc. **(1)**

Trinity Industries, Inc.—(Continued)

1112 E Copeland Rd, Arlington, TX 76011
Tel.: (817) 635-8547
Construction Materials Distr
N.A.I.C.S.: 423310

Trinity Containers, LLC (1)
2525 N Stemmons Fwy, Dallas, TX
75207 **(100%)**
Tel.: (214) 589-8000
Web Site: http://www.trinitylpg.com
Sales Range: $150-199.9 Million
Tanks & Storage Vessels Mfr
N.A.I.C.S.: 332420

Trinity Cryogenics, LLC (1)
2525 N Stemmons Fwy, Dallas, TX 75207
Tel.: (214) 631-4420
Construction Materials Distr
N.A.I.C.S.: 423310

Trinity Heads, Inc. (1)
11765 Hwy 6 S, Navasota, TX 77868
Tel.: (936) 825-6581
Web Site: https://www.trinityheads.com
Emp.: 25
Pressure Vessel Mfr
N.A.I.C.S.: 332420
Blake Seiner (Mgr-Product Plng)

Trinity Highway Products (1)
15601 Dallas Pkwy Ste 525, Addison, TX
75001
Tel.: (270) 769-1839
Web Site: https://www.valtir.com
Sales Range: $50-74.9 Million
Emp.: 7
Steel & Metal Highway Guardrails & Highway Guardrail End Treatments
N.A.I.C.S.: 332322

Trinity Highway Products, LLC (1)
15601 Dallas Pkwy Ste 525, Addison, TX
75001 **(100%)**
Tel.: (214) 589-8140
Web Site: http://trinityhighway.com
Sales Range: $100-124.9 Million
Fabricated Structural Metal Guardrail & End Treatment Products Mfr
N.A.I.C.S.: 332312

Subsidiary (Domestic):

Trinity Highway Leasing, Inc. (2)
900 Patterson Dr, Bloomsburg, PA 17815
Tel.: (570) 380-2856
Web Site: http://www.pbsrentals.com
Barricades Supplier Services
N.A.I.C.S.: 332999

Trinity Highway Rentals, Inc. (2)
900 Patterson Dr, Bloomsburg, PA 17815
Tel.: (570) 380-2856
Web Site: http://www.pbsrentals.com
Emp.: 6
Fabricated Metal Products Mfr
N.A.I.C.S.: 332312

Trinity Industries (1)
14221 Dallas Pkwy Ste 1100, Dallas, TX
75254
Tel.: (214) 631-4420
Web Site: https://www.trin.net
Sales Range: $25-49.9 Million
Emp.: 100
Guard Rail Mfr
N.A.I.C.S.: 482112

Trinity Industries (1)
1170 N State St, Girard, OH 44420
Tel.: (330) 545-4373
Web Site: http://www.highwayguardrail.com
Sales Range: $100-124.9 Million
Emp.: 178
Mfr of Steel & Metal Highway Guard Rails
N.A.I.C.S.: 332322

Trinity Industries (1)
1549 Vance St, Rocky Mount, NC 27801
Tel.: (252) 442-6178
Sales Range: $50-74.9 Million
Emp.: 100
Propane Cylinder Services
N.A.I.C.S.: 332313

Trinity Industries (1)
2418 Gardner Expy, Quincy, IL 62305-9375
Tel.: (217) 228-1150
Sales Range: $100-124.9 Million
Emp.: 90
LPG Tanks Mfr & Distr

N.A.I.C.S.: 332313

Trinity Industries (1)
647 N Ww White Rd, San Antonio, TX
78219
Tel.: (210) 304-2100
Web Site: http://www.trinity.com
Sales Range: $50-74.9 Million
Emp.: 100
Structural Metal Fabrication
N.A.I.C.S.: 332312

Trinity Industries (1)
2850 Peden Rd, Fort Worth, TX 76179
Tel.: (817) 236-0200
Sales Range: $25-49.9 Million
Emp.: 100
Railroad Car Repair Services
N.A.I.C.S.: 811310

Trinity Industries (1)
200 Dynatex Rd, Sunbright, TN 37872
Tel.: (423) 628-2530
Web Site: http://www.trin.com
Sales Range: $25-49.9 Million
Emp.: 23
Mfr of Wood Post
N.A.I.C.S.: 334290

Trinity Industries (1)
11765 Hwy 6 S, Navasota, TX 77868
Tel.: (936) 825-6581
Web Site: http://www.trin.net
Sales Range: $100-124.9 Million
Emp.: 140
LPG Tank Ends Mfr
N.A.I.C.S.: 339991

Trinity Industries Leasing Company (1)
14221 N Dallas Pkwy Ste 1100, Dallas, TX
75254 **(100%)**
Tel.: (214) 589-8054
Web Site: http://www.trinityrail.com
Sales Range: $1-4.9 Billion
Emp.: 13,000
Leasing Services
N.A.I.C.S.: 532411
Jesse V. Crews (Chief Investment Officer)

Trinity Industries de Mexico (1)
Monte Pelvoux 111, piso 7 Col Lomas de
Chapultepec, Mexico, 11000, Mexico
Tel.: (52) 5552017000
Web Site: http://www.trinitymexico.com
Pressure Vessel Mfr
N.A.I.C.S.: 332313

Trinity Industries de Mexico, S. de R.l. de C.V. (1)
Monte Pelvoux No 111 7th piso, Col Lomas
de Chapultepec, Mexico, 11000, DF,
Mexico **(100%)**
Tel.: (52) 5552017000
Web Site: http://www.trinitylpg.com
Sales Range: $25-49.9 Million
Emp.: 75
Holding Company; Railcar Products & Services, Concrete & Aggregate, Construction & Industrial Products Mfr
N.A.I.C.S.: 551112

Trinity Industries, Inc. - Fort Worth (1)
1000 Northeast 28th St, Fort Worth, TX
76106
Tel.: (817) 625-7227
Sales Range: $50-74.9 Million
Emp.: 52
Railroad Equipment
N.A.I.C.S.: 332313

Trinity Logistics Group, Inc. (1)
4001 Irving Blvd, Dallas, TX 75247 **(100%)**
Tel.: (214) 589-8158
Web Site: http://www.trinitytrucking.com
Sales Range: $100-124.9 Million
Emp.: 222
Over-Sized & Overweight Freight Truck Transportation Services
N.A.I.C.S.: 484230

Subsidiary (Domestic):

Trinity Logistics (2)
2418 Gardner Expwy, Quincy, IL 62301
Tel.: (870) 757-4700
Web Site: http://www.trinitytrucking.com
Sales Range: $25-49.9 Million
Emp.: 20

Over-Sized & Overweight Freight Truck Transportation Services
N.A.I.C.S.: 484230

Trinity Logistics (2)
2909 Mercer W Middlesex Rd, West
Middlesex, PA 16159-3021
Tel.: (724) 528-2024
Web Site: http://www.trinitytrucking.com
Sales Range: $50-74.9 Million
Emp.: 85
Over-Sized & Overweight Freight Truck Transportation Services
N.A.I.C.S.: 484230

Trinity Logistics (2)
1441-B Airport Fwy Ste 250, Euless, TX
76040
Tel.: (830) 757-4700
Web Site: https://trinitylogistics.com
Sales Range: $25-49.9 Million
Emp.: 45
Over-Sized & Overweight Freight Truck Transportation Services
N.A.I.C.S.: 484230

Trinity Meyer Utility Structures, LLC (1)
6750 Lenox Ctr Ct Ste 400, Memphis, TN
38115
Tel.: (901) 566-6500
Web Site: https://arcosameyer.com
Power Transmission Equipment Mfr
N.A.I.C.S.: 333613

Trinity Mining and Construction Equipment, Inc. (1)
647 N WW White Rd, San Antonio, TX
78219
Tel.: (210) 333-8222
Mining & Construction Equipment Distr
N.A.I.C.S.: 423830

Trinity Rail Group, LLC (1)
14221 N Dallas Pkwy Ste 1100, Dallas, TX
75254 **(100%)**
Tel.: (214) 631-4420
Web Site: https://www.trin.net
Sales Range: $25-49.9 Million
Emp.: 25
Railroad, Freight & Tank Cars & Components Mfr
N.A.I.C.S.: 336510

Division (Domestic):

Trinity Parts & Components, LLC (2)
2548 NE 28th St, Fort Worth, TX
76111 **(100%)**
Tel.: (214) 631-4420
Web Site: https://www.trin.net
Holding Company; Railroad Car Parts & Componento Mfr & Distr
N.A.I.C.S.: 551112

Subsidiary (Domestic):

TrinityRail Maintenance Services, Inc. (3)
2525 N Stemmons Fwy, Dallas, TX 75207
Tel.: (214) 631-4420
Web Site:
https://www.trinityrailmaintenanceservices.com
Rail Road Maintenance Services
N.A.I.C.S.: 488210

Trinity Shoring Products, Inc. (1)
8530 M-60 E, Union City, MI 49094-9345
Tel.: (517) 741-4471
Web Site:
https://www.arcosashoringproducts.com
Trucking & Hauling Services
N.A.I.C.S.: 488490

Trinity Specialty Products, Inc. (1)
647 N WW White Rd, San Antonio, TX
78219
Tel.: (210) 333-8222
Web Site:
http://www.trinityspecialtyproducts.com
Mining Trucks Dump Bodies Mfr
N.A.I.C.S.: 336120

Trinity Transportation (1)
220 Hwy 125 S, Middleton, TN 38052
Tel.: (731) 376-8412
Sales Range: $25-49.9 Million
Emp.: 33
Trucking Service

N.A.I.C.S.: 484121

Trinity Utility Structures, LLC (1)
228 N Lynnhaven Rd Ste 120, Virginia
Beach, VA 23452
Tel.: (757) 937-3468
Web Site: https://trinityutilitystructures.com
Power Delivery System & Components Services
N.A.I.C.S.: 335311

WesMor Cryogenic LLC (1)
1802 W D St, La Porte, TX 77571-4601
Tel.: (281) 842-1537
Web Site: http://www.wesmor.com
Sales Range: $1-9.9 Million
Emp.: 48
Automotive RepairAutomotive Mechanical & Electrical Repair & Maintenance
N.A.I.C.S.: 811114

TRINITY PETROLEUM TRUST
919 Congress Ave, Austin, TX 78701
Tel.: (512) 236-6545   **TX**
TTYP—(OTCIQ)
Oil & Gas Exploration Services
N.A.I.C.S.: 213112
Mike Ulrich (VP)

TRINITY PLACE HOLDINGS, INC.
340 Madison Ave Ste 3C, New York,
NY 10173
Tel.: (212) 235-2190   **DE**
Web Site: http://www.tphs.com
Year Founded: 2012
TPHS—(NYSEAMEX)
Rev.: $42,984,000
Assets: $306,927,000
Liabilities: $279,586,000
Net Worth: $27,341,000
Earnings: ($20,690,000)
Emp.: 6
Fiscal Year-end: 12/31/22
Real Estate Investment Services
N.A.I.C.S.: 531210
Richard G. Pyontek (Chief Acctg Officer)
Matthew Messinger (Pres & CEO)
Alexander C. Matina (Chm)
Jeffrey Travia (VP-Acquisitions & Dev)
Charles Gans (Sr VP)
Steven Kahn (CFO)

Subsidiaries:

Filene's Basement, Inc. (1)
25 Corporate Dr Ste 400, Burlington, MA
01803
Tel.: (617) 348-7000
Web Site: http://www.filenesbasement.com
Sales Range: $450-499.9 Million
Discount Department Store Operator
N.A.I.C.S.: 455110

TRIO PETROLEUM CORP.
4115 Blackhawk Plz Cir Ste 100,
Danville, CA 94506
Tel.: (925) 553-4355   **DE**
Web Site: https://www.trio-petroleum.com
Year Founded: 2021
TPET—(NYSEAMEX)
Assets: $11,643,000
Liabilities: $1,899,699
Net Worth: $9,743,384
Earnings: ($6,544,426)
Emp.: 7
Fiscal Year-end: 10/31/23
Oil & Gas Exploration Services
N.A.I.C.S.: 237120
Michael L. Peterson (CEO)
Frank C. Ingriselli (Vice Chm)
Terry Eschner (Pres)
Steve Rowlee (COO)
Stan Eschner (Chm)

TRIP TECHNOLOGIES, INC.
17870 Castleton St Ste 215, City of
Industry, CA 91748

Tel.: (626) 271-5277   NV
Year Founded: 2002
TRPS—(OTCIQ)
Solar Product Mfr
N.A.I.C.S.: 334413
Honglian Wei (CEO)
Pyng Soon (Gen Counsel)
Zhaoyun Liu (CFO & Sec)

TRIPADVISOR, INC.
400 1st Ave, Needham, MA 02494
Tel.: (781) 800-5000   DE
Web Site:
  https://www.tripadvisor.com
Year Founded: 2000
TRIP—(NASDAQ)
Rev.: $1,788,000,000
Assets: $2,537,000,000
Liabilities: $1,666,000,000
Net Worth: $871,000,000
Earnings: $10,000,000
Emp.: 2,845
Fiscal Year-end: 12/31/23
Holding Company; Online Travel In-
formation, Advisory & Reservation
Services
N.A.I.C.S.: 551112
Gregory B. Maffei (Chm)
Matthew Goldberg (Pres & CEO)
Stephen Kaufer (Co-Founder)
Bertrand Jelensperger (Co-Founder)
Geoffrey Gouvalaris (Chief Acctg Offi-
cer)
John Boris (CMO)
Sanjay Raman (Chief Product Officer)
Kristen Dalton (COO)
Kate Forrestall (Chief Talent Officer)

Subsidiaries:

Bookatable GmbH & Co. KG.   (1)
Deichstrasse 9, 20459, Hamburg, Germany
Tel.: (49) 4021111870
Restaurant Operators
N.A.I.C.S.: 722511

FlipKey, Inc.   (1)
179 Lincoln St Ste 405, Boston, MA 02111
Tel.: (877) 354-7539
Web Site: http://www.flipkey.com
Sales Range: $25-49.9 Million
Emp.: 70
Travel & Tour Operators
N.A.I.C.S.: 561510

Subsidiary (Domestic):

Vacation Home Rentals, Inc.   (2)
226 Causeway St 2nd Fl, Boston, MA 02114
Tel.: (978) 255-1827
Web Site:
  http://www.vacationhomerentals.com
Emp.: 5
Real Estate Brokerage Services
N.A.I.C.S.: 531210

GlobalMotion Media, Inc.   (1)
530 University Ste A, Palo Alto, CA 94301
Tel.: (650) 733-4636
Web Site: http://www.globalmotion.com
Travel Guide Software Publisher
N.A.I.C.S.: 541511

Holiday Lettings Limited   (1)
Hinshelwood Building Edmunds Halley
Road, Oxford Science Park, Oxford, OX4
4GB, Oxfordshire, United Kingdom
Tel.: (44) 203 752 4669
Web Site: https://www.holidaylettings.co.uk
Sales Range: $25-49.9 Million
Emp.: 80
Online Vacation Property Rental Services
N.A.I.C.S.: 561599

La Fourchette Netherlands B.V.   (1)
Anthony fokkerweg 1, 1059 CM, Amster-
dam, Netherlands
Tel.: (31) 206242034
Web Site: http://www.tripadvisor.com
Travel Management Services
N.A.I.C.S.: 561510

La Fourchette SAS   (1)
70 Rue Saint-Lazare, 75009, Paris, France

Tel.: (33) 17 748 7567
Web Site: https://www.thefork.fr
Emp.: 600
Travel & Hotel Online Reservation Services
N.A.I.C.S.: 561599

LaFourchette Sweden AB   (1)
Norslunda gard Arlandastad Golf, 195 95,
Rosersberg, Sweden
Tel.: (46) 85 912 2200
Web Site: https://www.lafourchette.se
Emp.: 9
Travel & Hotel Online Reservation Services
N.A.I.C.S.: 561599

MyTable SRL   (1)
Via Pier Carlo Boggio 83, 10138, Turin, TO,
Italy
Tel.: (39) 01119500690
Web Site: http://www.mytable.it
Travel & Hotel Online Reservation Services
N.A.I.C.S.: 561599

Reservas de Restaurantes, SL   (1)
c/ Princesa 13 1 D, 28008, Madrid, Spain
Tel.: (34) 902050134
Web Site: http://www.restaurantes.com
Restaurant Operators
N.A.I.C.S.: 722511

TripAdvisor LLC   (1)
400 1st Avenue, Needham, MA 02464
Tel.: (781) 800-8658
Web Site: http://www.tripadvisor.com
Online Travel Information, Advisory & Res-
ervation Services
N.A.I.C.S.: 519290

Subsidiary (Domestic):

Global Motion Media, Inc.   (2)
530 University Ste A, Palo Alto, CA 94301
Tel.: (650) 733-4636
Web Site: http://www.everytrail.com
Internet Broadcasting & Community Portal
Operator
N.A.I.C.S.: 516210

SinglePlatform, LLC   (2)
17 Battery Pl, New York, NY 10004
Web Site: http://www.singleplatform.com
Digital Communication Software Develop-
ment Services
N.A.I.C.S.: 541512
Josh Glantz (Sr VP & Gen Mgr)

Wanderfly, Inc.   (2)
447 Bdwy 2nd Fl, New York, NY 10013
Tel.: (774) 377-9359
Internet Broadcasting & Community Portal
Operator
N.A.I.C.S.: 516210

Viator, Inc.   (1)
657 Mission St, San Francisco, CA 94103
Tel.: (415) 503-3969
Web Site: http://www.viator.com
Sales Range: $100-124.9 Million
Emp.: 250
Travel Destination & Tour Information Pub-
lisher & Reservation Booking Services
N.A.I.C.S.: 513199

Subsidiary (Domestic):

Looktours.com LLC   (2)
777 N Rainbow Blvd, Las Vegas, NV 89107
Tel.: (702) 233-3792
Web Site: http://www.looktours.com
Emp.: 61
Online Travel Advertising Services
N.A.I.C.S.: 541810

TRIPBORN, INC.
762 Perthshire Pl, Abingdon, MD
21009
Tel.: (792) 647-4400   DE
Web Site: http://www.tripborn.com
Year Founded: 2010
TRRB—(OTCIQ)
Rev.: $472,052
Assets: $2,417,359
Liabilities: $3,496,329
Net Worth: ($1,078,970)
Earnings: ($1,268,047)
Emp.: 44
Fiscal Year-end: 03/31/19

Holding Company; Online Travel
Agency Operator
N.A.I.C.S.: 561510
Deepak Sharma (Co-Founder, Pres &
CEO)
Sachin Mandloi (Co-Founder & VP)
Richard Shaw (CFO)
Keyur Gadhiya (Head-Ops)

TRIPLE-S MANAGEMENT CORP.
1441 FD Roosevelt Ave, San Juan,
PR 00920
Tel.: (787) 749-4949   PR
Web Site:
  https://management.grupotri
  ples.com
GTS—(NYSE)
Rev.: $3,702,438,000
Assets: $3,088,418,000
Liabilities: $2,120,905,000
Net Worth: $967,513,000
Earnings: $67,189,000
Emp.: 3,911
Fiscal Year-end: 12/31/20
Health, Life, Property & Casualty In-
surance Services
N.A.I.C.S.: 524113
Carlos L. Rodriguez-Ramos (Sec &
VP-Legal Affairs)
Ivelisse M. Fernandez (Chief Growth
& Customer Experience Officer)
Juan Serrano (Chief Strategy Officer,
Pres-Managed Care Div, Exec VP &
Head-Healthcare Delivery)
Ilia S. Rodriguez Torres (Chief Admin
Officer, Chief HR Officer & Chief Tal-
ent Officer)
Thurman Justice (Pres & CEO)
Daryl Veach (CFO)
Robert Ruocco (CIO)
Edward Zayas (Chief Comm Officer &
Chief Public Relations Officer)

Subsidiaries:

Interactive Systems, Inc.   (1)
1441 FD Roosevelt Ave, San Juan, PR
00920
Tel.: (787) 749-4949
Sales Range: $100-124.9 Million
Technology & Claims Processing Services
N.A.I.C.S.: 561499
Carlos D. Torres (Pres)

Seguros Triple-S, Inc.   (1)
1441 FD Roosevelt Ave, San Juan, PR
00920
Tel.: (787) 749-4949
Web Site: http://www.ssspr.com
Sales Range: $150-199.9 Million
Property & Casualty Insurance Services
N.A.I.C.S.: 524126

Signature Insurance Agency, Inc.   (1)
1441 FD Roosevelt Ave, San Juan, PR
00920
Tel.: (787) 749-4949
Sales Range: $75-99.9 Million
Insurance Services
N.A.I.C.S.: 524298

Triple-C, Inc.   (1)
1441 FD Roosevelt Ave, San Juan, PR
00920
Tel.: (787) 749-4949
Sales Range: $75-99.9 Million
Insurance Support Services
N.A.I.C.S.: 524298
Luis A. Marini (Pres)

Triple-S Advantage, Inc.   (1)
3rd Fl Metro Office Park Lot 18, Guaynabo,
PR 00968
Tel.: (787) 474-6324
Web Site: http://advantage.grupotriples.com
Health Care Srvices
N.A.I.C.S.: 621610

Triple-S Propiedad, Inc.   (1)
Edificio Triple-S Plz Ave F D Roosevelt
1510, San Juan, PR 00936-0313
Tel.: (787) 749-4600
Web Site: http://propiedad.grupotriples.com

Emp.: 150
Health Life Property & Casualty Insurance
Services
N.A.I.C.S.: 524126
Jose Mojica Del Amo (Pres)

Subsidiary (Domestic):

Triple-S Insurance Agency, Inc.   (2)
1510 Ave F D Roosevelt Edif Triple S
Plaza, Guaynabo, PR 00965
Tel.: (787) 781-4000
Insurance Brokerage Services
N.A.I.C.S.: 524210
Jose Mojica Del Amo (Pres)

Triple-S Vida, Inc.   (1)
1441 FD Roosevelt Ave, San Juan, PR
00920
Tel.: (787) 749-4949
Web Site: http://www.ssspr.com
Sales Range: $150-199.9 Million
Fire Insurance Services
N.A.I.C.S.: 524113

Triple-S, Inc.   (1)
1441 FD Roosevelt Ave, San Juan, PR
00920
Tel.: (787) 749-4949
Sales Range: $150-199.9 Million
Insurance Services
N.A.I.C.S.: 524114
Pablo Almovovar (Pres)

TRIPLEPOINT VENTURE GROWTH BDC CORP.
2755 Sand Hill Rd, Menlo Park, CA
94025
Tel.: (650) 854-2090   MD
Web Site: https://www.tpvg.com
Year Founded: 2014
TPVG—(NYSE)
Rev.: $137,490,000
Assets: $978,825,000
Liabilities: $632,519,000
Net Worth: $346,306,000
Earnings: ($39,821,000)
Fiscal Year-end: 12/31/23
Investment Services
N.A.I.C.S.: 523999
James P. Labe (Founder, Chm &
CEO)
Sajal K. Srivastava (Pres, Chief In-
vestment Officer, Treas & Sec)
Steven Levinson (Chief Compliance
Officer)

TRISALUS LIFE SCIENCES, INC.
6272 W 91st Ave, Westminster, CO
80031
Tel.: (303) 442-1222   DE
Web Site: https://trisaluslifesci.com
Year Founded: 2020
TLSI—(NASDAQ)
Rev.: $8,856,058
Assets: $20,187,776
Liabilities: $13,654,332
Net Worth: $6,533,444
Earnings: $5,539,079
Emp.: 91
Fiscal Year-end: 12/31/22
Investment Services
N.A.I.C.S.: 523999
Mary T. Szela (Pres & CEO)
David J. Matlin (CFO)
Sean Murphy (COO)
Jodi Devlin (Pres-Comml Ops)
Steven C. Katz (Chief Medical Offi-
cer)
Alexander Y. Kim (Dir-Interventional
Radiology Medical)
Jennifer L. Stevens (Chief Regulatory
Officer)
Richard B. Marshak (Sr VP-Corporate
Development, Strategy, , &, and Mar-
keting)

TriSalus Life Sciences, Inc.—(Continued)

Mats Wahlstrom *(Chm)*
James E. Young *(Treas & Sr VP)*

TRISTAR GOLD INC.

7950 E Acoma Dr Ste 209, Scottsdale, AZ 85260
Tel.: (480) 794-1244 BC
Web Site: https://www.tristargold.com
Year Founded: 2010
TSGZF—(OTCIQ)
Rev.: $66,685
Assets: $29,234,905
Liabilities: $3,974,743
Net Worth: $25,260,162
Earnings: ($125,274)
Emp.: 30
Fiscal Year-end: 12/31/20
Gold Ore & Silver Ore Mining
N.A.I.C.S.: 212220
Mark E. Jones III *(Chm)*
Nicholas David Appleyard *(Pres & CEO)*
Scott Murdo Brunsdon *(CFO)*
Mo Srivastava *(VP)*
Fabio Mozzer *(VP)*
Andrew Grant *(VP)*
Brian C. Irwin *(Sec)*

TRISTAR WELLNESS SOLUTIONS, INC.

624 Tyvola Rd Ste 103 186, Charlotte, NC 28217
Tel.: (704) 951-7087 NV
Web Site:
    http://www.tstarwellness.com
Year Founded: 2000
TWSI—(OTCEM)
Sales Range: $1-9.9 Million
Emp.: 1
Medical Products Mfr & Sales
N.A.I.C.S.: 325412
David Duarte *(CEO, Treas & Sec)*

TRITENT INT'L AGRICULTURE, INC.

79 W Monroe St Ste 1007, Chicago, IL 60603
Tel.: (312) 345-5888
UNMK—(OTCIQ)
Dairy Products Mfr
N.A.I.C.S.: 311514
Jennifer Barclay *(Founder & Chm)*

TRIUMPH FINANCIAL, INC.

12700 Park Central Dr Ste 1700, Dallas, TX 75251
Tel.: (214) 365-6900 TX
Web Site: https://www.tfin.com
Year Founded: 2010
TFIN—(NASDAQ)
Rev.: $472,594,000
Assets: $5,347,334,000
Liabilities: $4,482,934,000
Net Worth: $864,400,000
Earnings: $41,081,000
Emp.: 1,468
Fiscal Year-end: 12/31/23
Bank Holding Company
N.A.I.C.S.: 551111
Edward J. Schreyer *(COO & Exec VP)*
Aaron P. Graft *(Founder, Vice Chm, Pres & CEO)*
Adam D. Nelson *(Gen Counsel & Exec VP)*
W. Brad Voss *(CFO & Exec VP)*

Subsidiaries:

TBK Bank, SSB (1)
12700 Park Central Dr Ste 1700, Dallas, TX 75251
Tel.: (214) 365-6900
Web Site: https://www.tbkbank.com

Sales Range: $200-249.9 Million
State Savings Bank
N.A.I.C.S.: 522180
Aaron P. Graft *(Vice Chm & CEO)*
R. Bryce Fowler *(Pres & CFO)*
Gail Lehmann *(Chief Regulatory & Governance Officer & Exec VP)*
Gail Lehmann *(COO & Pres-Retail Banking)*
Patricia L. Pittman *(Exec VP & Controller)*
Grant Smith *(Chief Credit Officer & Exec VP)*
Kenyon A. Warren *(Sr VP)*
Todd Ritterbusch *(Pres)*
Stuart Pattison *(Pres)*
Brad Voss *(CFO & Exec VP)*
Ed Schreyer *(COO)*
Adam Nelson *(Gen Counsel)*

Subsidiary (Domestic):

Advance Business Capital LLC (2)
651 Canyon Dr Ste 105, Coppell, TX 75019
Tel.: (972) 942-4325
Web Site: http://www.invoicefactoring.com
Sales Range: $1-9.9 Million
Emp.: 13
Truck, Freight & Small Business Factoring Services
N.A.I.C.S.: 522299
Steven Hausman *(Founder & Chm)*
Jason Mullican *(VP-Channel Mktg)*
Kimberly Winters *(Chief Credit Officer)*
George A. Thorson *(Pres & COO)*
Blaine Waugh *(Sr VP-Enterprise Sls)*
Mark Christopher *(VP-Bus Dev)*
Adriana Lopez-Hammer *(VP-Bus Dev)*
Brian Tremlett *(VP-Bus Dev)*
Chase Griffith *(VP-Bus Dev)*
Mark Dubs *(VP-Bus Dev)*
Carrie Jenkins *(VP-Bus Dev)*
Veronica Wallace *(VP-Bus Dev)*
Brian Albach *(VP-Bus Dev)*
T. J. Bill *(VP-Bus Dev)*
Janice Fox *(Sr VP-HR)*
Michael Lingman *(Sr VP-Fuel Programs)*
Moises Bolanos *(Sr VP-Client Experience)*
Mark Day *(VP-Acctg & Treasury)*
Ashley Vogan *(Mgr-Referral Partner)*
Whitney Smith *(Mgr-Referral Partner)*
David Seidler *(Mgr-Referral Partner)*
Debra Myers *(Mgr-Referral Partner)*
Lori Herrera *(Mgr-Bus Dev)*
J. V. Lujan *(Mgr-Bus Dev)*
Toni Terico *(Mgr-Bus Dev)*
Natalie Hampton *(Mgr-Bus Dev)*
Erik T. Bahr *(Exec VP-Sls)*
John Shields *(CTO & Sr VP)*
Geoff Brenner *(CEO)*

TRIUMPH GROUP, INC.

555 E Lancaster Ave Ste 400, Radnor, PA 19087
Tel.: (610) 251-1000 DE
Web Site:
    https://www.triumphgroup.com
Year Founded: 1993
TGI—(NYSE)
Rev.: $1,459,942,000
Assets: $1,761,166,000
Liabilities: $2,548,589,000
Net Worth: ($787,423,000)
Earnings: ($42,758,000)
Emp.: 5,340
Fiscal Year-end: 03/31/22
Holding Company; Aircraft Systems & Components Designer, Mfr, Distr & Engineering Services
N.A.I.C.S.: 551112
James Francis McCabe Jr. *(CFO & Sr VP)*
Daniel J. Crowley *(Chm, Pres & CEO)*
Lance R. Turner *(Chief HR Officer & Sr VP)*
Gar Tenison *(VP-Strategy & Bus Dev)*
Stacey Clapp *(Chief Comml Officer & VP-Contracts)*
Jennifer H. Allen *(Chief Admin Officer, Gen Counsel, Sec & Sr VP)*
Thomas A. Quigley III *(Treas & VP-IR, Acq & Merger)*

Subsidiaries:

KAMEX Ltd. (1)

No 6 Cai Yuan Road Nan Cai Town, Shunyi District, Beijing, 101300, China
Tel.: (86) 1089473411
Business Support Services
N.A.I.C.S.: 561499

Triumph Accessory Services-Grand Prairie, Inc. (1)
1038 Santerre St, Grand Prairie, TX 75050
Tel.: (972) 623-9300
Aircraft Parts Mfr & Whslr
N.A.I.C.S.: 423860

Triumph Actuation Systems - Isle of Man, Ltd. (1)
School Road, Douglas, Onchan, IM3 4PB, Isle of Man, United Kingdom
Tel.: (44) 1624692000
Aircraft Equipment Mfr
N.A.I.C.S.: 336412

Triumph Aerospace Systems Group, LLC (1)
1550 Liberty Rdg Dr Ste 100, Wayne, PA 19087
Tel.: (610) 251-1000
Sales Range: $250-299.9 Million
Aerospace Mechanical, Hyrdaulic & Control System Developer & Mfr
N.A.I.C.S.: 336411

Subsidiary (Domestic):

Triumph Actuation Systems, LLC (2)
4520 Hampton Rd, Clemmons, NC 27012
Tel.: (336) 766-9036
Aerospace Hydraulic Systems Developer & Mfr
N.A.I.C.S.: 488190
Jeff Grossnicklaus *(Dir-Ops)*

Subsidiary (Domestic):

Triumph Actuation Systems-Connecticut, LLC (3)
1395 Blue Hills Ave, Bloomfield, CT 06002
Tel.: (860) 242-5568
Web Site: http://www.triumphgroup.com
Sales Range: $25-49.9 Million
Emp.: 50
Precision Component Mfr
N.A.I.C.S.: 336415

Unit (Non-US):

Triumph Actuation Systems-UK, Ltd. - Cheltenham (3)
Arle Court, Cheltenham, GL51 0TP, Glocs, United Kingdom
Tel.: (44) 1242221155
Sales Range: $50-74.9 Million
Emp.: 160
Aerospace Equipment Mfr
N.A.I.C.S.: 336413

Subsidiary (Domestic):

Triumph Actuation Systems-Valencia, LLC (3)
28150 Harrison Pkwy, Valencia, CA 91355
Tel.: (661) 295-1015
Web Site: http://www.triumphgroup.com
Aerospace Hydraulic Components Developer & Mfr
N.A.I.C.S.: 334513
Bill Boyd *(Pres)*

Triumph Actuation Systems-Yakima, LLC (3)
2720 W Washington Ave, Yakima, WA 98903
Tel.: (509) 248-5000
Flight Controls Mfr
N.A.I.C.S.: 336413
Scott Eads *(VP-Global Ops & Program Mgmt)*

Subsidiary (Domestic):

Triumph Controls, LLC (2)
205 Church Rd, North Wales, PA 19454
Tel.: (215) 699-4861
Aircraft Control Systems Developer & Mfr
N.A.I.C.S.: 336413
Roberta Spada *(Asst Controller)*

Subsidiary (Non-US):

Triumph Controls-UK, Ltd. (3)
Christopher Martin Road, Basildon, SS14

3EL, Essex, United Kingdom
Tel.: (44) 1268270195
Web Site: http://www.triumphgroup.com
Emp.: 21
Aircraft Control Components Mfr
N.A.I.C.S.: 336413

Subsidiary (Domestic):

Triumph Gear Systems, Inc. (2)
6125 Silver Creek Dr, Park City, UT 84098
Tel.: (435) 649-1900
Web Site: http://www.triumphgroup.com
Aircraft Part Mfr
N.A.I.C.S.: 336412

Subsidiary (Domestic):

Triumph Gear Systems-Macomb, Inc. (3)
15375 23 Mile Rd, Macomb, MI 48042-4000
Tel.: (586) 781-2800
Precision Gears & Gearboxes for Aircraft Mfr
N.A.I.C.S.: 336413
Jim Laurie *(Mgr-Mfg)*

Subsidiary (Domestic):

Triumph Interiors, LLC (2)
2001 Sullivan Rd, Atlanta, GA 30337
Tel.: (770) 997-1576
Web Site: http://www.triumphgroup.com
Sales Range: $25-49.9 Million
Emp.: 75
Aircraft Interior Refurbishing Services
N.A.I.C.S.: 541330

Triumph Thermal Systems, LLC (2)
200 Railroad St, Forest, OH 45843
Tel.: (419) 273-2511
Web Site: http://www.triumphgroup.com
Aerospace; Heat Transfer Components & Liquid Cooling Systems Mfr
N.A.I.C.S.: 336413

Triumph Aerostructures - Tulsa, LLC (1)
3330 N Mingo Rd, Tulsa, OK 74116
Tel.: (615) 361-2061
Web Site: http://www.triumphgroup.com
Aircraft Equipment Mfr
N.A.I.C.S.: 336412

Triumph Aerostructures Group (1)
9314 W Jefferson Blvd, Dallas, TX 75211
Tel.: (972) 946-2011
Emp.: 5,900
Segment Managing Office
N.A.I.C.S.: 551114
MaryLou Thomas *(Interim Exec VP-Aerospace Structures)*

Subsidiary (Domestic):

Triumph Composite Systems, Inc. (2)
1514 S Flint Rd, Spokane, WA 99219-9357
Tel.: (509) 623-8100
Web Site: http://www.triumphgroup.com
Aircraft Interior Components Mfr
N.A.I.C.S.: 336413

Triumph Fabrications-St. Louis, Inc. (2)
1145 E Airline Dr, East Alton, IL 62024-2283
Tel.: (618) 259-6089
Sales Range: $25-49.9 Million
Emp.: 26
Aircraft Component Maintenance Services
N.A.I.C.S.: 488190

Triumph Insulation Systems, LLC (2)
3901 Jack Ave 4th Fl, Santa Ana, CA 90250
Tel.: (949) 250-4999
Web Site: http://www.triumphgroup.com
Aircraft Parts & Equipment Mfr
N.A.I.C.S.: 336413

Triumph Structures-East Texas, Inc. (2)
703 Old Gladewater Hwy, Kilgore, TX 75662
Tel.: (903) 983-1592
Web Site: http://www.triumphgroup.com
Aircraft Product Mfr
N.A.I.C.S.: 336413
Bryan Johnston *(Pres)*

Triumph Structures-Kansas City, Inc. (2)
31800 W 196th St, Edgerton, KS 66021
Tel.: (816) 763-8600
Sales Range: $25-49.9 Million
Emp.: 130
Aircraft Part Mfr
N.A.I.C.S.: 336412
Kerry Parker (Pres)
Richard Moroski (Pres)

Triumph Structures-Long Island, LLC (2)
717 Main St, Westbury, NY 11590
Tel.: (516) 997-5757
Sales Range: $25-49.9 Million
Emp.: 150
Aerospace Parts Mfr
N.A.I.C.S.: 336412
Leonard Gross (Pres)

Triumph Structures-Wichita, Inc. (2)
3258 S Hoover Rd, Wichita, KS 67215
Tel.: (316) 942-0432
Web Site: http://www.triumphgroup.com
Custom Machined Aerospace Component Mfr
N.A.I.C.S.: 332710

Triumph Aftermarket Services Group, LLC (1)
115 Centennial Dr, Hot Springs, AR 71913
Tel.: (610) 251-1000
Commercial & Military Aircraft Maintenance & Repair Services
N.A.I.C.S.: 488190
Peter K.A. Wick (Exec VP-Aerospace Structures)

Subsidiary (Domestic):

Triumph Airborne Structures, LLC (2)
115 Centennial Dr, Hot Springs, AR 71913
Tel.: (501) 262-1555
Aircraft Control Panel & Structure Maintenance, Repair & Overhaul Services
N.A.I.C.S.: 336413
Jeff Owen (Dir-Ops)

Triumph Engineered Solutions, Inc. (2)
2015 W Alameda Dr, Tempe, AZ 85282-3101
Tel.: (602) 438-8760
Web Site: http://www.triumphgroup.com
Sales Range: $75-99.9 Million
Emp.: 100
Mfr of Parts for Turbines
N.A.I.C.S.: 331512

Triumph Engineering Services, Inc. (2)
50 S 56th St, Chandler, AZ 85226
Tel.: (602) 437-1144
Web Site: http://www.triumphairrepair.com
Sales Range: $75-99.9 Million
Emp.: 114
Mfr of Aircraft Parts & Accesories
N.A.I.C.S.: 336412

Triumph Instruments-Burbank, Inc. (2)
2840 N Ontario St, Burbank, CA 91504
Tel.: (818) 333-5600
Web Site: http://www.velocityaerospace.com
Sales Range: $25-49.9 Million
Emp.: 60
Aerospace
N.A.I.C.S.: 811210

Unit (Domestic):

Triumph Accessory Services (2)
411 NW Rd, Wellington, KS 67152-0010 (100%)
Tel.: (620) 326-2235
Web Site: http://www.triumphgroup.com
Sales Range: $25-49.9 Million
Emp.: 80
Aerospace
N.A.I.C.S.: 336413

Triumph Controls France SAS (1)
2 Avenue de La Carelle, Villeneuve Le Roi, 94290, Paris, France
Tel.: (33) 143752053
Emp.: 70
Aircraft Equipment Distr

N.A.I.C.S.: 423860
Pierre Vauterin (Pres)

Triumph Engine Control Systems, LLC (1)
1 Charter Oak Blvd, West Hartford, CT 06110
Tel.: (860) 236-0651
Fuel Pumps, Fuel Metering Units & Electronic Engine Control Systems Designer & Mfr
N.A.I.C.S.: 336412

Triumph Fabrications - Orangeburg, Inc. (1)
375 Cannon Bridge Rd, Orangeburg, SC 29115
Tel.: (803) 534-8555
Aircraft Equipment Distr
N.A.I.C.S.: 423860
James M. DeVries (Gen Mgr)

Triumph Gear Systems-Toronto, ULC (1)
9 Fenmar Drive, Toronto, M9L 1L5, ON, Canada
Tel.: (416) 743-4417
Sales Range: $50-74.9 Million
Emp.: 197
Aerospace, Industrial & Power Generation Precision Machined Products Mfr
N.A.I.C.S.: 332710
Garen Mikirditsian (Pres)

Triumph Group -Mexico S. de R.L. de C.V. (1)
Boulevard Paseo de la Plata 1100, Mega Parque Industrial Aeropuerto de Calera, 98519, Zacatecas, Mexico
Tel.: (52) 4789853000
Sales Range: $25-49.9 Million
Emp.: 221
Aircraft Equipment Parts Mfr
N.A.I.C.S.: 336413

Triumph Insulation Systems (1)
Calle El Rey Del Desierto No 66, Mexicali, 21399, Mexico
Tel.: (52) 6861573787
Web Site: http://www.triumphgroup.com
Sales Range: $200-249.9 Million
Emp.: 900
Aircraft Insulation Products Mfr
N.A.I.C.S.: 336412

Triumph Structures - Farnborough, Ltd. (1)
Brookside House 21 Invincible Road Industrial Estate, Farnborough, GU14 7QU, Hampshire, United Kingdom
Tel.: (44) 1252304000
Aircraft Equipment Distr
N.A.I.C.S.: 423860
MaryLou Thomas (Pres)

TROIKA MEDIA GROUP, INC.
25 W 39th St 6th Fl, New York, NY 10018
Tel.: (212) 213-0111   NV
Web Site: https://troikamedia.com
Year Founded: 1998
TRKA—(NASDAQ)
Rev.: $16,192,000
Assets: $43,891,000
Liabilities: $25,153,000
Net Worth: $18,738,000
Earnings: ($15,997,000)
Emp.: 98
Fiscal Year-end: 06/30/21
In-Room Media, Entertainment & Networking Solutions to Hotels, Resorts & Time Share Properties
N.A.I.C.S.: 517810
Eric Glover (Interim CFO)
Grant Lyon (Interim CEO)
Randall Miles (Chm)
Michael Tenore (Gen Counsel & Sec)
Kevin Dundas (CEO-Global Mission)

Subsidiaries:

Troika, Inc. (1)
101 S La Brea Ave, Los Angeles, CA 90036 (100%)
Tel.: (323) 965-1650
Web Site: http://www.troika.tv

Advertising Services
N.A.I.C.S.: 541810
Gil Haslam (Exec Creative Dir)
Dan Pappalardo (Founder & CEO)
Amy Sorrentino (Mgr-Facilities)
Kevin Aratari (Head-Bus Dev)
Aaro Sapiro (Acct Dir)
Abigael Plaza (Asst Controller)
Andy Hann (Creative Dir)
Ann Epstein (Head-Studio)
Bridget Dalton (Office Coord)
Damon Haley (Head-Sports Mktg)
Danixa Diaz (VP-Bus Dev)
Derrick Lachmann (Dir-Bus Dev-Troika Digital)
Eddie Hales (VP-Sls & Engrg-Troika Svcs)
Jessica Perri (Strategist)
Mark Lee (Sr Dir-Art)
Michael Arcangeli (Art Dir)
Paul Brodie (Mng Dir-Creative)
Rick Shahum (VP-Bus Dev & Partnerships-Troika Svcs)
Rob Sonner (Dir-Tech)
Ryan Beeman (Acct Exec)
Steven Slater (Coord-Production)
Tim Smyllie (Art Dir)

TRONOX HOLDINGS PLC
263 Tresser Blvd Ste 1100, Stamford, CT 06901
Tel.: (203) 705-3800   AU
Web Site: https://www.tronox.com
TROX—(NYSE)
Rev.: $3,454,000,000
Assets: $6,306,000,000
Liabilities: $3,903,000,000
Net Worth: $2,403,000,000
Earnings: $497,000,000
Emp.: 6,500
Fiscal Year-end: 12/31/22
Titanium Dioxide Producer
N.A.I.C.S.: 325120
Ilan Kaufthal (Chm)
John D. Romano (CEO)
John Srivisal (CFO)
Emad AlJunaidi (Chief Procurement Officer)
Jennifer Guenther (VP-IR)
Jeff Engle (Sr VP-Commercial & Strategy)
Russ Austin (Sr VP-Global Ops)
Jonathan P. Flood (Principal Acctg Officer, VP & Controller)
Jeffrey N. Neuman (Gen Counsel, Sec & Sr VP)
Ed Prosapio (Treas & VP)
Eric Bender (VP & Gen Mgr-Rare Earths)
Amy Webb (Chief HR Officer)
Jimmy Killebrew (VP-Operations)
Mpho Mothoa (VP-Operations)

Subsidiaries:

National Titanium Dioxide Company Ltd. (1)
Al Amana Street Al Bughdadiyah, 9th and 10th Floor, Jeddah, 21414, Saudi Arabia (66%)
Tel.: (966) 2 652 9966
Titanium Dioxide Mfr & Distr
N.A.I.C.S.: 325180

Tronox B.V. (1)
Prof Gerbrandyweg 2, PO Box 1013, Harbour 4502, 3197 KK, Rotterdam, Netherlands
Tel.: (31) 181246600
Web Site: http://www.tronox.com
Sales Range: $75-99.9 Million
Emp.: 250
Titanium Dioxide Sales
N.A.I.C.S.: 325130

Subsidiary (Domestic):

Tronox Finance B.V. (2)
Prof Gerbrandyweg 2, Harbour 4502, 3197 KK, Rotterdam, Netherlands
Tel.: (31) 181246600
Web Site: http://www.tronox.com
Sales Range: $50-74.9 Million
Emp.: 200
Financial Services

N.A.I.C.S.: 561499

Tronox Pigments (Holland) B.V. (2)
Prof Gerbrandyweg 2 Botlek Harbour 4502, PO Box 1013, 3197 KK, Rotterdam, Netherlands (100%)
Tel.: (31) 18 124 6600
Web Site: https://www.tronox.com
Sales Range: $75-99.9 Million
Emp.: 260
Titanium Dioxide Producer
N.A.I.C.S.: 325130

Tronox Pigments (Netherlands) B.V. (2)
PO Box 1013, 3180 AA, Rozenburg, Netherlands
Tel.: (31) 181246600
Web Site: http://www.tronox.com
Sales Range: $100-124.9 Million
Titanium Dioxide Producer
N.A.I.C.S.: 325130

Tronox Global Holdings Pty Limited (1)
Brodie-Hall Drive 1, Perth, 6102, WA, Australia
Tel.: (61) 893651333
Holding Company
N.A.I.C.S.: 551112

Tronox Incorporated (1)
263 Tresser Blvd Ste 1100, Stamford, CT 06901
Tel.: (203) 705-3800
Inorganic Chemical Mfr
N.A.I.C.S.: 325130

Tronox KZN Sands Proprietary Limited (1)
Melmoth Road R34, Empangeni, 3880, South Africa
Tel.: (27) 359027000
Inorganic Chemical Mfr
N.A.I.C.S.: 325130

Tronox LLC (1)
3301 NW 150th St, Oklahoma City, OK 73134
Tel.: (405) 775-5000
Web Site: http://www.tronox.com
Sales Range: $75-99.9 Million
Emp.: 110
Titanium Dioxide Sales
N.A.I.C.S.: 325130

Plant (Domestic):

Tronox LLC - Green River Soda Ash Plant (2)
Hwy 374, Green River, WY 82935
Tel.: (307) 875-2580
Soda Ash Mfr
N.A.I.C.S.: 325180
Anita Pounders (Controller)

Tronox Pigments (Singapore) Pte. Ltd. (1)
51 Newton Road Goldhill Plaza Unit No 11-06/10, Singapore, 308900, Singapore
Tel.: (65) 6 225 0098
Web Site: https://www.tronox.com
Sales Range: $10-24.9 Million
Emp.: 5
Titanium Dioxide Sales
N.A.I.C.S.: 325130

Tronox Pigments Pty. Limited (1)
Lot 22 Mason Road, PO Box 305, Kwinana, 6167, WA, Australia
Tel.: (61) 894111444
Emp.: 320
Chemical Products Mfr
N.A.I.C.S.: 325180

Tronox US Holdings Inc. (1)
3301 NW 150th St, Oklahoma City, OK 73134
Tel.: (405) 775-5000
Emp.: 3,600
Holding Company
N.A.I.C.S.: 551112

Tronox Western Australia Pty. Ltd. (1)
Lot 22 Mason Road, PO Box 305, Kwinana, 6167, WA, Australia
Tel.: (61) 894111444
Sales Range: $10-24.9 Million
Emp.: 30
Titanium Dioxide Sales

Tronox Holdings plc—(Continued)

N.A.I.C.S.: 325130
Tony Owrell *(Dir-Fin)*

TROPHY RESOURCES, INC.

255 Eversedge Ct, Alpharetta, GA
30009
Tel.: (404) 565-4280   FL
Year Founded: 2006
TRSI—(OTCIQ)
Oil & Gas Exploration Services
N.A.I.C.S.: 213112
James P. Canouse *(CEO)*

TROPICAL BATTERY COM-PANY LIMITED

30 Automotive Pkwy Ferry Commer-
cial Park Mandela Highway Kingston
20,, Jamaica, WI
Tel.: (876) 923-6231
Web Site:
   https://www.tropicalbattery.com
Year Founded: 1950
TROPICAL—(JSE)
Innovative Energy Solutions
N.A.I.C.S.: 335910

Subsidiaries:

Tropical Battery USA, LLC.   **(1)**
1309 Coffeen Ave. Ste 1200, Sheridan, WY
82801
Tel.: (888) 767-4225
Battery Storage
N.A.I.C.S.: 335910

Subsidiary (Domestic):

Rose Electronics Distributing Co,
Inc.   **(2)**
2030 Ringwood Ave, San Jose, CA 95131
Tel.: (408) 943-0200
Web Site: http://www.rose-elec.com
Electronic Parts & Equipment Merchant
Whslr
N.A.I.C.S.: 423690
Leslie Logan *(VP)*

TROY GOLD & MINERAL CORP.

370 Amapola Ave, Torrance, CA
90501
Tel.: (424) 358-1046   NV
Year Founded: 2000
TGMR—(OTCIQ)
Mineral Exploration Services
N.A.I.C.S.: 213115
Frank Igwealor *(Pres & CEO)*

TRUBRIDGE, INC.

54 St Emanuel St, Mobile, AL 36602
Tel.: (251) 639-8100   DE
Web Site: https://trubridge.com
Year Founded: 1979
TBRG—(NASDAQ)
Rev.: $326,648,000
Assets: $430,963,000
Liabilities: $199,252,000
Net Worth: $231,711,000
Earnings: $15,867,000
Emp.: 2,500
Fiscal Year-end: 12/31/22
Custom Computer Programming Ser-
vices
N.A.I.C.S.: 541511
Tracey Schroeder *(CMO)*
David A. Dye *(COO)*
James B. Britain *(VP-Fin & Control-
ler)*
Christopher L. Fowler *(Pres & CEO)*
Amaris McComas *(Chief People Offi-
cer)*
Sol Vairavan *(Head-Corp Dev &
M&A)*
Lance Park *(Principal Acctg Officer)*
Dawn Severance *(Chief Sls Officer)*
Kevin Plessner *(Gen Counsel)*

Subsidiaries:

Evident, LLC   **(1)**
739 Brooks Mill Rd, Union Hall, VA 24176-
4025
Tel.: (540) 576-3512
Web Site: https://www.shopevident.com
Investigation Services
N.A.I.C.S.: 561611

Healthland, Inc.   **(1)**
1600 Utica Ave S Ste 300, Minneapolis, MN
55416   **(100%)**
Tel.: (612) 787-3120
Web Site: http://www.healthland.com
Healthcare Software Publisher
N.A.I.C.S.: 513210
Julie Weber-Kramer *(Sr VP-Client Experi-
ence)*

Branch (Domestic):

Healthland, Inc. - Glenwood   **(2)**
625 S Lakeshore Dr, Glenwood, MN 56334
Tel.: (800) 323-6987
Web Site: http://www.healthland.com
Healthcare Software Publisher
N.A.I.C.S.: 513210

Subsidiary (Domestic):

Rycan Technologies Inc.   **(2)**
349 W Main St, Marshall, MN 56258
Tel.: (507) 532-3324
Web Site: http://www.rycan.com
Healthcare Revenue Cycle Software Pub-
lisher
N.A.I.C.S.: 513210
Nick Widboom *(COO)*
Crystal Stensrud *(Mktg Mgr)*

iNetXperts, Corp.   **(1)**
51 Monroe St Ste 1700, Rockville, MD
20850
Tel.: (301) 309-0058
Web Site: https://www.getrealhealth.com
Computer Software Development Services
N.A.I.C.S.: 541511
Robin Wiener *(Pres)*
Jason Harmon *(Sr VP-Patient Engagement
Tech)*
Mark Heaney *(Sr VP)*
Sol Vairavan *(Head-Corporate Develop-
ment)*

TRUCEPT INC.

600 La Terraza Blvd, Escondido, CA
92025
Tel.: (858) 923-4225   NV
Web Site: https://trucept.com
Year Founded: 1995
TREP—(OTCIQ)
Rev.: $12,285,000
Assets: $29,947,000
Liabilities: $14,534,000
Net Worth: $15,413,000
Earnings: $1,076,000
Emp.: 28
Fiscal Year-end: 12/31/20
Holding Company; PEO, Staffing Ser-
vices & Automated Human Re-
sources Software
N.A.I.C.S.: 551112
Julie Neill *(COO)*
Brendan McMenamy *(Controller-
Accounting)*
Kevin Brewer *(Exec VP-Sales & Mar-
keting)*
Rachel Henton *(VP-Human Re-
sources)*

TRUE BLUE HOLDINGS, INC.

15466 Los Gatos Blvd 109-352, Los
Gatos, CA 95032
Tel.: (408) 221-6900   DE
Year Founded: 2005
ROKR—(OTCIQ)
Music Publishers
N.A.I.C.S.: 512230
Robert Wallace *(CEO, CFO & Sec)*

TRUE NORTH ENERGY COR-PORATION

24624 I 45 N Ste 200, Spring, TX
77386
Tel.: (281) 719-1996   NV
Web Site: https://www.tnecorp.com
TNEN—(OTCIQ)
Rev.: $3,633,000
Assets: $4,091,000
Liabilities: $6,095,000
Net Worth: ($2,004,000)
Earnings: ($182,000)
Fiscal Year-end: 04/30/20
Oil & Gas Exploration Services
N.A.I.C.S.: 211120
Marco Bettineschi *(Mgr-Fund)*

TRUEBLUE, INC.

1015 A St, Tacoma, WA 98401-2910
Tel.: (253) 383-9101   WA
Web Site: https://www.trueblue.com
Year Founded: 1989
TBI—(NYSE)
Rev.: $2,173,622,000
Assets: $1,033,226,000
Liabilities: $540,159,000
Net Worth: $493,067,000
Earnings: $61,634,000
Emp.: 6,400
Fiscal Year-end: 12/26/21
Temporary Staffing Services
N.A.I.C.S.: 561320
Taryn R. Owen *(Pres & CEO)*
Carl R. Schweihs *(CFO & Exec VP)*
Jerry Wimer *(Acting Pres-
PeopleMgmt & Gen Mgr-Onsite Staff-
ing Bus)*
Anthony Brew *(Chief Diversity Offi-
cer)*
Taylor Winchell *(Sr Mgr-External
Comm)*
Greg Netolicky *(Chief People Officer)*
Carl Schweihs *(Pres)*

Subsidiaries:

CLP Holdings Corp   **(1)**
1380 Greg St Ste 208, Sparks, NV 89431
Tel.: (775) 321-8000
Temporary Staffing Services
N.A.I.C.S.: 561320

CLP Resources, Inc.   **(1)**
1380 Greg St Ste 208, Sparks, NV 89431
Tel.: (775) 321-8000
Sales Range: $10-24.9 Million
Emp.: 50
Staffing Solutions & Services
N.A.I.C.S.: 541612

Division (Domestic):

Skilled Services Corporation   **(2)**
10539 Professional Cir Ste 200, Reno, NV
89521-3858
Tel.: (727) 579-3994
Web Site: http://www.skilledservices.com
Sales Range: $50-74.9 Million
Temporary Construction Staffing Services
N.A.I.C.S.: 561320

Centerline Drivers, LLC   **(1)**
1600 E 4th St Ste 340, Santa Ana, CA
92701
Tel.: (714) 338-6940
Web Site: https://www.centerlinedrivers.com
Sales Range: $10-24.9 Million
Emp.: 25
Contract Freight Driver Employment Ser-
vices
N.A.I.C.S.: 561311
Jill Quinn *(Pres)*
Rod Crowell *(VP-Sales)*
Jennifer Overmyer *(VP- &)*
John Trahan *(VP-Sales &)*
Alison Kassel *(VP-Technology)*
Kassandra Barnes *(VP-Marketing)*
Shane Keller *(Mng Dir-)*

Labor Ready Mid-Atlantic, Inc.   **(1)**
919 E 8th St, Anderson, IN 46012
Tel.: (765) 683-1695
Web Site: https://www.peopleready.com
Emp.: 1
Temporary Staffing Services
N.A.I.C.S.: 561320

Rafe Fillmore *(VP-Bus Unit Fin)*
Chris Kapcar *(VP-Tech)*
Cindy Cutaia *(Chief Bus Ops Officer)*

Labor Ready Midwest, Inc.   **(1)**
4421 S Kedzie Ave, Chicago, IL 60632-
2814
Tel.: (773) 869-9621
Web Site: http://www.laborready.com
Sales Range: $50-74.9 Million
Emp.: 300
Temporary Staffing Services
N.A.I.C.S.: 561320

Labor Ready Southeast, Inc.   **(1)**
4300 Kings Hwy Ste 404, Punta Gorda, FL
33980
Tel.: (941) 743-9675
Employment Agencies
N.A.I.C.S.: 561311

Labor Ready Southwest, Inc.   **(1)**
1015 A St Unit A, Tacoma, WA 98402-5122
Tel.: (253) 383-9101
Temporary Staffing Services
N.A.I.C.S.: 561320

PeopleScout Limited   **(1)**
265 Tottenham Court Road, London, W1T
7RQ, United Kingdom
Tel.: (44) 2072689150
Health Care Srvices
N.A.I.C.S.: 621610

PeopleScout Pty, Ltd   **(1)**
Level 19 Citigroup Centre 2 Park Street,
Sydney, 2000, NSW, Australia
Tel.: (61) 295619000
Employment Placement Services
N.A.I.C.S.: 561311

SIMOS Insourcing Solutions,
LLC   **(1)**
433 W Van Buren St, Chicago, IL 60607
Tel.: (770) 992-3441
Web Site: https://www.simossolutions.com
Employment Placement Services
N.A.I.C.S.: 561311
Harold Baro *(Sr VP)*
Quinton Skyles *(VP-Operations)*
Alison Kassel *(VP-Technology)*
Bryon Withers *(VP-Sales)*
Kassandra Barnes *(VP-Marketing)*

Spartan Staffing, LLC   **(1)**
4130 S Sandhill Rd Ste A6, Las Vegas, NV
89121
Tel.: (702) 898-4943
Web Site: http://www.spartanstaffing.com
Staffing & Recruitment Services
N.A.I.C.S.: 541612

TMP (UK) Limited   **(1)**
265 Tottenham Court Road, London, W1T
7RQ, United Kingdom
Tel.: (44) 2072689000
Web Site: https://www.tmpw.co.uk
Advertising Agency Services
N.A.I.C.S.: 541810
David Lewis *(Controller-Fin)*
David Brooks *(Head-Paid Media & Perfor-
mance)*
Paula Simmons *(Dir-Employer Brand &
Comm Strategy)*

TrueBlue Outsourcing Solutions   **(1)**
860 W Evergreen Ave, Chicago, IL 60642
Tel.: (312) 915-0700
Web Site: http://www.SeatonCorp.com
Sales Range: $300-349.9 Million
Staffing & Recruiting Services
N.A.I.C.S.: 561311

Subsidiary (Non-US):

HRX Pty, Ltd.   **(2)**
Level 7, 44 Market Street, Sydney, 2000,
NSW, Australia
Tel.: (61) 295619000
Web Site: http://www.hrx.com.au
Emp.: 110
Staffing Services
N.A.I.C.S.: 561312

Subsidiary (Domestic):

People Scout Inc.   **(2)**
433 W Van Buren St Ste 400S, Chicago, IL
60607
Tel.: (312) 915-0505

Web Site: http://www.peoplescout.com
Emp.: 100
Human Resource Consulting Services
N.A.I.C.S.: 541612
Carter McHugh (VP-Tech)

Staff Management Solutions, LLC (2)
433 W Van Buren St, Chicago, IL 60607
Tel.: (312) 915-0900
Web Site:
https://www.staffmanagement.com
Emp.: 3,000
Temporary Help Service
N.A.I.C.S.: 561320
Jerry Wimer (Acting Pres & Mgr-People Management)
Loree Lynch (Sr VP-Operations)
Hope Field (VP-Sales)
Jennifer Prath (VP-Centralized Svcs)
Pete Doyle (VP-Operations)
Jen Herrbach (VP-Operations)
Tom Sheldon (VP-Operations)
Stephanie Brattain (VP-Operations)
Alison Kassel (VP-Technology)
Kassandra Barnes (VP-Marketing)
Bryon Withers (VP-Sales)
Alex Patel (VP-)

StudentScout, LLC (2)
860 W Evergreen Ave, Chicago, IL 60642
Tel.: (312) 915-0700
Web Site: http://www.studentscout.com
Educational Support Services
N.A.I.C.S.: 611710

TRUECAR, INC.
225 Santa Monica Blvd 12th Fl,
Santa Monica, CA 90401   DE
Web Site: https://www.truecar.com
Year Founded: 2005
TRUE—(NASDAQ)
Rev.: $158,706,000
Assets: $204,320,000
Liabilities: $44,105,000
Net Worth: $160,215,000
Earnings: ($49,766,000)
Emp.: 324
Fiscal Year-end: 12/31/23
Online Car Buying Programs
N.A.I.C.S.: 423110
Christopher Weber Claus (Chm)
Jantoon E. Reigersman (Pres & CEO)
Jeffrey J. Swart (Gen Counsel, Sec & Exec VP)
Elias Rokos (CTO)
Teresa Luong (CFO & Principal Acctg Officer)
Jill Angel (COO & Chief People Officer)
Jay Ku (Chief Commerce Officer)

Subsidiaries:

Automotive Lease Guide (ALG), Inc. (1)
1401 Ocean Ave ste 300, Santa Monica, CA 90401
Tel.: (805) 898-8400
Web Site: http://www.alg.com
Sales Range: $10-24.9 Million
Emp.: 50
Automobile Guides & Analysis
N.A.I.C.S.: 513210

DealerScience, LLC (1)
290 Congress St 7th Fl, Boston, MA 02210
Web Site: http://www.dealerscience.com
Automobile Dealer Services
N.A.I.C.S.: 441110
Andrew Gordon (Founder)

TRUETT-HURST, INC.
125 Foss Creek Circle, Healdsburg, CA 95448
Tel.: (707) 431-4423   DE
Web Site:
http://www.truetthurstinc.com
Year Founded: 2007
THST—(OTCIQ)
Rev.: $6,234,000
Assets: $13,039,000
Liabilities: $8,217,000

Net Worth: $4,822,000
Earnings: ($1,292,000)
Emp.: 28
Fiscal Year-end: 06/30/20
Wine Producer & Sales
N.A.I.C.S.: 312130
Phillip L. Hurst (Chm)
Karen Weaver (CFO)
Ross Reedy (Dir-Winemaking)
Paul E. Dolan III (Founder & CEO)

TRUIST FINANCIAL CORPO-RATION
214 N Tryon St, Charlotte, NC 28202
Tel.: (336) 733-2000   NC
Web Site: https://www.truist.com
Year Founded: 1872
TFC—(NYSE)
Rev.: $24,456,000,000
Assets: $535,349,000,000
Liabilities: $476,096,000,000
Net Worth: $59,253,000,000
Earnings: ($1,452,000,000)
Emp.: 49,037
Fiscal Year-end: 12/31/23
Bank Holding Company
N.A.I.C.S.: 551111
Ellen M. Fitzsimmons (Chief Legal Officer & Head-Pub Affairs)
Hugh S. Cummins III (Vice Chm & COO)
William Henry Rogers Jr. (Chm & CEO)
Michael B. Maguire (CFO)
Donta L. Wilson (Chief Consumer & Small Bus Banking Officer)
Scott Case (CIO & Sr Exec VP)
Denise M. DeMaio (Chief Audit Officer)

Subsidiaries:

Boston Service Company, Inc. (1)
8000 Midlantic Dr Ste 110S, Mount Laurel, NJ 08054
Tel.: (609) 860-9300
Web Site: https://www.hannfinancial.com
Automobile Finance & Leasing Services
N.A.I.C.S.: 522220

Centerstone Insurance & Financial Services, Inc. (1)
12404 Park Central Dr Ste 400 S, Dallas, TX 75251
Tel.: (469) 791-3300
Web Site: http://www.benefitmall.com
Payroll, Benefits Administration Services; Insurance Products & Broker Tools
N.A.I.C.S.: 541214
Laura Clenney (VP-Mktg)
Marc Olson (VP-M&A)
Michelle Sheffield (CIO)
Jeffry Lewis (CFO-Division & VP-Admin & Treasury)
Scott Kirksey (CEO)
Tiffany Stiller (VP-Carrier Rels)
Robert C. Love (Pres-Benefits Div)
Mark Trivette (CFO)
Veena Yelamanchili (VP-Benefits Svc)
John T. Wiesler (Head-Gen Agency Sls)
Jonathan Cooksey (VP-Fin)

Subsidiary (Domestic):

Mutual Med, Inc. (2)
4321 E 60th St, Davenport, IA 52807-3505
Tel.: (563) 344-2890
Web Site: http://www.mutualmedinc.com
Sales Range: $10-24.9 Million
Emp.: 43
Insurance Brokerage Services
N.A.I.C.S.: 524210
Steve Pray (CFO)
Rob Edel (CFO & COO)
Janson Bender (VP-Mktg)
Todd Vershaw (CEO)

McGriff Insurance Services, Inc. (1)
301 College St Ste 208, Asheville, NC 28801-2449
Tel.: (828) 277-3930
Web Site: https://www.mcgriff.com
Insurance Affair & Document Services
N.A.I.C.S.: 524298

Read Davis (CEO)

Precept Advisory Group LLC (1)
130 Theory Ste 200, Irvine, CA 92617
Tel.: (949) 955-1430
Web Site: https://www.preceptadvisory.com
Investment Banking Services
N.A.I.C.S.: 523150

Regional Acceptance Corporation (1)
1424 E Fire Tower Rd, Greenville, NC 27858
Tel.: (252) 321-7700
Web Site:
http://www.regionalacceptance.com
Sales Range: $200-249.9 Million
Emp.: 450
Automotive Lending Services
N.A.I.C.S.: 522291
Ron E. Wooten (CFO & Sr VP)

SunTrust Banks, Inc. (1)
303 Peachtree St NE, Atlanta, GA 30308
Tel.: (404) 588-7711
Web Site: http://www.suntrust.com
Rev.: $10,431,000,000
Assets: $215,543,000,000
Liabilities: $191,263,000,000
Net Worth: $24,280,000,000
Earnings: $2,775,000,000
Emp.: 22,899
Fiscal Year-end: 12/31/2018
Banking & Financial Services Holding Company
N.A.I.C.S.: 551111
Ellen M. Fitzsimmons (Gen Counsel, Sec & Exec VP)

Subsidiary (Domestic):

GenSpring Family Offices, L.L.C. (2)
150 S US Highway 1, Jupiter, FL 33477
Tel.: (561) 746-8444
Web Site: http://www.genspring.com
Wealth Management Advisory Services
N.A.I.C.S.: 541618
Christopher Facka (Mng Dir-Florida-East)

Subsidiary (Domestic):

Teton Trust Company (3)
36 E Broadway Ste 9-3, Jackson, WY 83001
Tel.: (307) 201-5275
Web Site: https://tetontrustcompany.com
Investment Banking Services
N.A.I.C.S.: 523150

W.E. Family Offices, LLC (3)
701 Brickell Ave Ste 2100, Miami, FL 33131
Tel.: (305) 825-2225
Web Site: https://www.wefamilyoffices.com
Emp.: 40
Financial Services
N.A.I.C.S.: 523940
Maria Elena Lagomasino (CEO & Mng Partner)
Julie L. Neitzel (Partner)
Santiago Ulloa (Founder & Mng Partner)
Michael Zeuner (Mng Partner)
Santiago Castro (Partner)
Pablo J. Ceballos (Partner)
Sven Huber (Partner)
Cesar Maldonado (Partner)
Manuel R. Manotas (Partner)
Julie Neitzel (Partner)
Rocio Ortega (Partner)
Cesar Pachon (Partner)
Richard E. Zimmerman (Partner)
Guy F. Talarico (Chief Compliance Officer)
Joseph C. Kellogg (Partner)
Carolina Salazar (Partner)
Natalia Hoyos (Partner)
Claudia Naffah (Partner)
Patricia Pinto (Partner)

Subsidiary (Domestic):

Southland Associates, Inc. (2)
1340 Stony Point Rd Ste 201, Charlottesville, VA 22911-3568
Tel.: (434) 973-1999
Commercial Banking Services
N.A.I.C.S.: 522110

SunTrust Bank Holding Company (2)
200 S Orange Ave Fl 1, Orlando, FL 32801-3426

Tel.: (407) 237-4153
Bank Holding Company
N.A.I.C.S.: 551111
Brad White (Pres/CEO-Florida Panhandle Reg)

Subsidiary (Domestic):

SunTrust Bank (3)
303 Peachtree St NE, Atlanta, GA 30308   **(100%)**
Tel.: (404) 588-7711
Web Site: http://www.suntrust.com
Sales Range: $1-4.9 Billion
Emp.: 4,831
Retail & Commercial Banking
N.A.I.C.S.: 522110
Rilla R. Delorier (CMO & Exec VP-Retail Bank)
Louis Moore (Mgr-Comml Banking Admin)
Tal Broome (Dir-Comml Credit Delivery)
Katie Hodges (Mgr-Transformation)
Diana Rose (Mgr-Bus Unit Risk)
John Gregg (Head-Corp & Investment Banking)
Rilla S. Delorier (Executives)

Subsidiary (Domestic):

Cohen Financial, LLC (4)
227 W Monroe St Ste 1000, Chicago, IL 60606
Tel.: (312) 346-5680
Web Site: http://www.cohenfinancial.com
Real Estate Capital & Loan Brokerage Services
N.A.I.C.S.: 522310

Branch (Domestic):

SunTrust Bank, Central Florida Division Headquarters (4)
333 S Garland Ave, Orlando, FL 32801-3410
Tel.: (407) 237-4153
Web Site: http://www.suntrust.com
Regional Corporate Office; Commercial Banking
N.A.I.C.S.: 551114

SunTrust Bank, East Tennessee Region Headquarters (4)
900 S Gay St, Knoxville, TN 37902-1810
Tel.: (865) 766-8620
Web Site: http://www.suntrust.com
Regional Corporate Office; Commercial Banking
N.A.I.C.S.: 551114

SunTrust Bank, Georgia Region Headquarters (4)
33 Bull St, Savannah, GA 31401
Tel.: (912) 944-1003
Web Site: https://www.truist.com
Regional Corporate Office; Commercial Banking
N.A.I.C.S.: 551114

SunTrust Bank, Mid-Atlantic Division Headquarters (4)
919 E Main St, Richmond, VA 23219-4600
Tel.: (804) 782-5690
Web Site: http://www.suntrust.com
Sales Range: $500-549.9 Million
Emp.: 6,712
Regional Corporate Office; Commercial Banking
N.A.I.C.S.: 551114

SunTrust Bank, Nashville Region Headquarters (4)
401 Commerce St, Nashville, TN 37219-2446
Tel.: (615) 748-4735
Web Site: http://www.suntrust.com
Regional Corporate Office; Commercial Banking
N.A.I.C.S.: 551114

SunTrust Bank, South Florida Division Headquarters (4)
501 E Las Olas Blvd, Fort Lauderdale, FL 33301
Tel.: (954) 766-2110
Web Site: https://www.truist.com

Truist Financial Corporation—(Continued)

Regional Corporate Office; Commercial Banking
N.A.I.C.S.: 551114

SunTrust Bank, Southwest Florida Region Headquarters (4)
1777 Main St, Sarasota, FL 34236-5845
Tel.: (941) 951-3307
Web Site: http://www.suntrust.com
Regional Corporate Office; Commercial Banking
N.A.I.C.S.: 551114

SunTrust Bank, Tampa Region Headquarters (4)
401 E Jackson St, Tampa, FL 33602
Tel.: (813) 224-2416
Web Site: https://www.truist.com
Regional Corporate Office; Commercial Banking
N.A.I.C.S.: 551114

Subsidiary (Domestic):

SunTrust Mortgage Inc. (4)
901 Semmes Ave, Richmond, VA
23224-2270 (100%)
Tel.: (804) 291-0014
Web Site: http://www.suntrustmortgage.com
Sales Range: $150-199.9 Million
Mortgage Loans
N.A.I.C.S.: 522292

Subsidiary (Domestic):

SunTrust Investment Services, Inc. (3)
3333 Peachtree Rd NE Ste 610, Atlanta, GA 30326
Tel.: (404) 926-5301
Investment Advice Services
N.A.I.C.S.: 523940

Subsidiary (Domestic):

SunTrust Delaware Trust Company (2)
1011 Ctr Rd Ste 205, Wilmington, DE
19805
Tel.: (302) 892-9930
Online Banking Services
N.A.I.C.S.: 522110

SunTrust Insurance Company (2)
3020 Peachtree Rd NW, Atlanta, GA
30305 (100%)
Tel.: (404) 479-2364
Web Site: http://www.suntrust.com
Sales Range: $125-149.9 Million
Credit-Related Insurance
N.A.I.C.S.: 524126

Truist Securities, Inc. (2)
3333 Peachtree Rd NE, Atlanta, GA 30326
Tel.: (888) 294-2265
Web Site: https://www.truistsecurities.com
Rev.: $449,375,000
Assets: $2,865,432,000
Liabilities: $2,178,101,000
Net Worth: $687,331,000
Earnings: $84,334,000
Emp.: 375
Fiscal Year-end: 12/31/2012
Corporate & Investment Banking
N.A.I.C.S.: 523150

Affiliate (Domestic):

Viewpointe Archive Services, LLC (2)
227 W Trade St Ste 2000, Charlotte, NC
28202
Tel.: (704) 602-6650
Web Site: http://www.viewpointe.com
Business Support Services
N.A.I.C.S.: 561499
Timothy Coff (Pres & CEO)

Truist Bank (1)
200 W 2nd St, Winston Salem, NC
27101-4019 (100%)
Tel.: (336) 776-5342
Web Site: http://www.bbt.com
Sales Range: $5-14.9 Billion
Emp.: 35,630
Retail, Commercial & Investment Banking, Lending, Insurance & Wealth Management Services
N.A.I.C.S.: 522110

P. Russell Hardin (Executives)
William Henry Rogers Jr. (Chm & CEO)

Subsidiary (Domestic):

BB&T Capital Partners, LLC (2)
500 W 5th St Ste 900, Winston Salem, NC
27101
Tel.: (336) 733-0350
Web Site: https://www.fivepointscapital.com
Sales Range: $50-74.9 Million
Emp.: 23
Venture Capital Services
N.A.I.C.S.: 523999
David Townsend (Partner)
Jeff Tiani (VP)
Ryan Hennessee (VP)
Brad Clark (CFO)

Holding (Domestic):

JML Optical Industries, LLC (3)
820 Linden Ave, Rochester, NY 14625
Tel.: (585) 248-8900
Web Site: https://www.jmloptical.com
Custom Optical Components Mfr
N.A.I.C.S.: 333310

Subsidiary (Domestic):

Harold Johnson Optical Laboratories, Inc. (4)
1826 W 169th St, Gardena, CA 90247
Tel.: (310) 327-3051
Web Site: http://www.hjol.com
Emp.: 30
Optical Instruments & Lenses Mfr
N.A.I.C.S.: 333310

Subsidiary (Domestic):

BB&T Institutional Investment Advisers, Inc. (2)
111 Millport Cir Fl 2, Greenville, SC 29607
Tel.: (864) 527-0600
Financial Services
N.A.I.C.S.: 523940

BB&T Investment Services, Inc. (2)
200 S College St 11th Fl, Charlotte, NC
28202
Tel.: (704) 954-1158
Sales Range: $650-699.9 Million
Emp.: 98
Investment Services
N.A.I.C.S.: 523150

CRC Insurance Services, Inc. (2)
1 Metroplex Dr Ste 400, Birmingham, AL
35209
Tel.: (205) 870-7790
Web Site: https://www.crcgroup.com
Wholesale Property & Casualty Insurance Products & Services
N.A.I.C.S.: 524210
Dave Obenauer (CEO)
Garrett Koehn (Co-Pres)
Brent Tredway (Co-Pres)
West McAdams (Co-Pres)
Mike Brennan (CEO)
Amy Rousse (CFO)
Neil Kessler (Co-Pres & COO)
Jack Elliott (Chief Admin Officer)
David Gilfillan (Chief Claims Officer)
Mike Baeurle (Dir & Exec VP)
Angela Alaniz (Sr VP)
Brennan Paris (Sr Dir-Corporate Strategy-Distribution)
Jessica Marshall (Sr VP)
Jason Boger (Sr VP)
Don Carson (Vice Chm-Comml Solutions)
Bob Greenebaum (Reg Dir)
Mickey Hopkins (Reg Dir)
Mike Ruhe (Reg Dir)
Buddy Campo (Reg Dir)
Phil Adams (Reg Dir)
Bill Kiley (Reg Dir)
Pete Feeney (Reg Dir)
Jim Epting (Reg Dir)
Rob Carney (CEO)
Bill Goldstein (CEO)
Nicholas Bozzo (Co-Pres)
Brian Norman (Co-Pres)

Subsidiary (Domestic):

Argenia, LLC (3)
11101 Anderson Dr, 72212, Little Rock, AR
Tel.: (501) 227-9670
Web Site: http://www.argenia.com

Insurance Agents, Brokers & Services
N.A.I.C.S.: 524210

Unit (Domestic):

Five Star Specialty Programs (3)
158 N Harbor City Blvd, Melbourne, FL
32935
Tel.: (321) 421-6767
Web Site: http://www.5starsp.com
Sales Range: $50-74.9 Million
Emp.: 75
Property & Casualty Insurance Underwriting Services
N.A.I.C.S.: 524298

Subsidiary (Domestic):

Hanleigh Management Inc. (3)
50 Tice Blvd Ste 122, Woodcliff Lake, NJ
07677
Tel.: (201) 505-1050
Web Site:
　https://www.hanleighinsurance.com
Financial Services
N.A.I.C.S.: 523940

J. H. Blades & Co., Inc. (3)
520 Post Oak Blvd Ste 250, Houston, TX
77027
Tel.: (713) 780-8770
Web Site: http://www.jhblades.com
Insurance Services
N.A.I.C.S.: 524210

Southern Cross Insurance Services, Inc. (3)
6311 Ridgewood Rd Ste E-401, Jackson, MS 39211
Tel.: (601) 957-3344
Web Site: http://www.scui.com
Sales Range: $1-9.9 Million
Emp.: 40
Insurance Products & Services
N.A.I.C.S.: 524210

TAPCO Underwriters, Inc. (3)
3060 S Church St, Burlington, NC
27215 (100%)
Tel.: (336) 584-8892
Web Site: http://www.secure.gotapco.com
Sales Range: $25-49.9 Million
Emp.: 175
Insurance Agents, Brokers & Service
N.A.I.C.S.: 524210

Unit (Domestic):

Target Professional Programs (3)
10 Tower Ln, Avon, CT 06001
Tel.: (860) 284-0088
Web Site: http://www.targetproins.com
Sales Range: $50-74.9 Million
Emp.: 20
Insurance Agents, Brokers & Service
N.A.I.C.S.: 524210

Subsidiary (Domestic):

Creative Payment Solutions, Inc. (2)
233 W Nash St, Wilson, NC 27893
Tel.: (252) 246-4111
Web Site:
　http://www.creativepaymentsolutions.com
Sales Range: $50-74.9 Million
Emp.: 100
Financial Services
N.A.I.C.S.: 525990

Crump Insurance Services, Inc. (2)
7557 Rambler Rd Ste 300, Dallas, TX
75231-4142
Tel.: (214) 265-2660
Sales Range: $50-74.9 Million
Emp.: 100
Property & Casualty Insurance Brokerage Services
N.A.I.C.S.: 524210
Pat O'Brien (CFO)
Kathy Van Eeten (Dir-Mktg)
Dave Obenauer (Pres)
John Landry (Sr VP-Natl Property Practice-Cincinnati)

Crump Life Insurance Services, Inc. (2)
4135 N Front St, Harrisburg, PA 17110
Tel.: (717) 657-2740
Web Site: https://marketing.crump.com

Sales Range: $75-99.9 Million
Emp.: 200
Life Insurance Brokers
N.A.I.C.S.: 524210
Jim Duff (Sr VP & Gen Mgr-Solution Centers & Independent Distr)
Jason VanAarle (Sr VP-Natl Accounts)
Joanne Pietrini Smith (COO & Gen Mgr)
Sherri Lindenberg (Sr VP-Mktg Comm)
Rob Stern (Chief Admin Officer)
Mike Martini (Pres)

Subsidiary (Domestic):

RiskRighter, LLC (3)
280 S 400 W Ste 100, Salt Lake, UT 84101
Tel.: (800) 453-5693
Web Site: https://www.riskrighter.com
Insurance Services
N.A.I.C.S.: 524298

Subsidiary (Domestic):

Grandbridge Real Estate Capital LLC (2)
200 S College St Ste 2100, Charlotte, NC
28202
Tel.: (704) 332-4454
Web Site: http://www.grandbridge.com
Sales Range: $75-99.9 Million
Emp.: 290
Financing & Lending Services
N.A.I.C.S.: 522310
Joseph L. Lovell (COO & Exec VP)
Michael J. Ortlip (Sr VP & Office Mgr)
Lyndell Elam Clyburn (VP-Escrow Admin & Servicing)
Dan Husak (Sr VP & Head-Bus Sys & Corp Ops)
John W. Randall (Exec VP & Natl Mgr-Production)
Matthew Rocco (Chm & CEO)
Holly G. Widders (Asst VP & Mgr-Transaction)
David Rosenthal (Sr Mgr-Transaction)
Jennifer Shedden (VP)
Jin Lin (Officer-Ops & VP)
Robin Sikes (Chief Strategy Officer & VP)
Keith Medlin (VP-Production)
Kayla Norris (Asst VP & Sr Mgr-Transaction)
John Hankins (VP-Production)
Katrina Hudson (VP-New Loans, Investor Reporting, Ops Support & Servicing)
Richard G. Alexander Jr. (VP-Mobile)
Robert C. Vaughn III (Officer-Credit Risk & Sr VP)

Subsidiary (Domestic):

BB&T Real Estate Funding LLC (3)
Two Morrocroft Ctr 4064 Colony Rd Ste
300, Charlotte, NC 28211
Tel.: (704) 372-8670
Web Site: http://www.sterling-capital.com
Sales Range: $25-49.9 Million
Emp.: 50
Investment Services
N.A.I.C.S.: 523150

Subsidiary (Non-US):

Matewan Realty Corporation (2)
95 Wellington Str W Ste 1706, Toronto, M5J
2N7, ON, Canada
Tel.: (416) 868-6777
Insurance Services
N.A.I.C.S.: 524210

Subsidiary (Domestic):

McGriff, Seibels & Williams, Inc. (2)
2211 7th Ave S, Birmingham, AL 35233-2310
Tel.: (205) 252-9871
Sales Range: $125-149.9 Million
Insurance Services
N.A.I.C.S.: 524210

Subsidiary (Domestic):

Caledonian Insurance Group, Inc. (3)
7525 Southeast 24th Street 520, Mercer
Island, WA 98040
Tel.: (206) 232-9870
Web Site: http://www.ciginsure.com
Sales Range: $1-9.9 Million
Emp.: 24
Insurance Brokers

N.A.I.C.S.: 524210

McGriff Seibels of Texas, Inc. (3)
818 Town Country Blvd Ste 500, Houston, TX 77024-4549
Tel.: (713) 877-8975
Web Site: http://www.mcgriff.com
Sales Range: $25-49.9 Million
Emp.: 210
Insurance Services
N.A.I.C.S.: 524210

Subsidiary (Domestic):

McGriff, Seibels and Williams of Texas, Inc. (4)
5080 Spectrum Dr Ste 900 E, Addison, TX 75001
Tel.: (469) 232-2100
Insurance Brokerage Services
N.A.I.C.S.: 524210

Subsidiary (Domestic):

McGriff, Seibels & Williams of Georgia, Inc. (3)
3400 Overton Park Dr SE Ste 300, Atlanta, GA 30339
Tel.: (404) 497-7500
Sales Range: $10-24.9 Million
Emp.: 125
Insurance Services
N.A.I.C.S.: 524210

Subsidiary (Domestic):

Prime Rate Premium Finance Corporation, Inc. (2)
2141 Enterprise Dr, Florence, SC 29501
Tel.: (843) 669-0937
Web Site: https://www.primeratepfc.com
Rev.: $190,800,000
Emp.: 70
Financial Services
N.A.I.C.S.: 525990

Subsidiary (Domestic):

AFCO Credit Corporation (3)
14 Wall St Ste 8A-19, New York, NY 10005-2161
Tel.: (212) 401-4400
Web Site: http://www.afco.com
Sales Range: $1-9.9 Million
Emp.: 20
Insurance Premium Financing Services
N.A.I.C.S.: 561499

Subsidiary (Domestic):

AFCO Acceptance Corporation (4)
8885 Rio San Diego Dr Ste 347, San Diego, CA 92108
Tel.: (619) 209-5210
Web Site: http://www.myafco.com
Banking Services
N.A.I.C.S.: 523150

Subsidiary (Non-US):

Cafo, Inc. (3)
200 University Avenue Suite 501, PO Box 17, Toronto, M5H 3C6, ON, Canada
Tel.: (416) 868-6777
Web Site: http://www.cafo.com
Sales Range: $10-24.9 Million
Emp.: 20
Insurance Financing Services
N.A.I.C.S.: 561499

Subsidiary (Domestic):

Reliable Policy Management, LLC (3)
2141 Enterprise Dr, Florence, SC 29501
Tel.: (843) 673-1921
Web Site: http://www.reliablepolicymgt.com
Sales Range: $75-99.9 Million
Insurance Services
N.A.I.C.S.: 524210

Subsidiary (Domestic):

Scott & Stringfellow, LLC (2)
919 E Main St 1st Fl, Richmond, VA 23219
Tel.: (804) 782-5690
Web Site: https://www.truist.com
Sales Range: $1-4.9 Billion
Emp.: 500
Brokerage & Investment Banking Services
N.A.I.C.S.: 523150

William H. Rogers Jr. *(CEO)*
Scott Case *(CIO)*
Hugh S. Cummins III *(Vice Chm)*
Denise M. DeMaio *(Chief Audit Officer)*
Mike Maguire *(CFO)*
Ellen M. Fitzsimmons *(Chief Legal Officer)*
Kimberly Moore-Wright *(Chief Teammate Officer)*
Clarke R. Starnes III *(Vice Chm)*
Joseph M. Thompson *(Chief Wealth Officer)*
David H. Weaver *(Chief Comml Community Banking Officer)*
Donta L. Wilson *(Chief Retail Officer)*
J. Cantey Alexander *(Reg Pres)*
Calvin E. Barker Jr. *(Reg Pres)*
Chris Bell *(Reg Pres)*
Alex Brame *(Reg Pres)*
Mike R. Brenan *(Reg Pres)*
Heath Campbell *(Reg Pres)*
Steve Fisher *(Reg Pres)*
DeVon Lang *(Reg Pres)*
Emily Dawkins *(Reg Pres)*
Greg Farno *(Reg Pres)*
Chris Isley *(Reg Pres)*
Evelyn Lee *(Reg Pres)*
Michael Lepera *(Reg Pres)*
Burton McDonald *(Reg Pres)*
Iwan Mohamed *(Reg Pres)*
William J. Toomey II *(Reg Pres)*
Katie Saez *(Reg Pres)*
Travis Rhodes *(Reg Pres)*
Thomas Ransom *(Reg Pres)*
Patrick O'Malley *(Reg Pres)*
Johnny Moore *(Reg Pres)*

Sheffield Financial, LLC (2)
6010 Golding Ctr Dr, Winston Salem, NC 27103
Tel.: (336) 766-1388
Web Site: http://www.sheffieldfinancial.com
Sales Range: $50-74.9 Million
Emp.: 80
Financial Services
N.A.I.C.S.: 525990

Stanley, Hunt, DuPree & Rhine, Inc. (2)
111 Millport Cir, Greenville, SC 29607
Tel.: (864) 527-0600
Web Site: http://www.shdr.com
Sales Range: $50-74.9 Million
Emp.: 175
Benefits Management & Consulting Services
N.A.I.C.S.: 541611
Phillip Floyd *(Pres)*

Sterling Advisors (2)
150 S Warner Rd, King of Prussia, PA 19406
Tel.: (610) 687-6800
Web Site: http://www.bbtsterlingadvisors.com
Asset Management Services
N.A.I.C.S.: 531390

Truist Leadership Institute, Inc. (2)
7807 Airport Center Dr, Greensboro, NC 27409
Tel.: (336) 665-3300
Business Management & Consulting Services
N.A.I.C.S.: 541611

Truist Investment Services, Inc. (1)
3333 Peachtree Rd NE, Atlanta, GA 30326-1030
Tel.: (404) 264-6819
Banking Services
N.A.I.C.S.: 522110

TRULEUM, INC.
14143 Denver West Pkwy Ste 100, Golden, CO 80401
Tel.: (713) 316-0061   CO
Web Site: https://truleum.com
Year Founded: 2013
TRLM—(OTCIQ)
Rev.: $146,270
Assets: $1,973,698
Liabilities: $4,721,702
Net Worth: ($2,748,004)
Earnings: ($2,248,650)
Emp.: 1
Fiscal Year-end: 12/31/23
Oil & Gas Exploration
N.A.I.C.S.: 211120

Jeff Wright *(Ops Mgr)*

TRULIEVE CANNABIS CORP.
820 Farmington Ave, Bristol, CT 06010
Tel.: (850) 480-7955   BC
Web Site: https://www.trulieve.com
TRUL—(CNSX)
Rev.: $1,239,812,000
Assets: $3,399,048,000
Liabilities: $1,471,344,000
Net Worth: $1,927,704,000
Earnings: ($246,064,000)
Emp.: 7,600
Fiscal Year-end: 12/31/22
Holding Company; Cannabis Product Mfr & Dispensaries Operator
N.A.I.C.S.: 551112
Gina Collins *(CMO)*
Steven M. White *(Pres)*
Kim Rivers *(Chm & CEO)*
Jason Pernell *(CIO)*
Eric Powers *(Chief Legal Officer)*
Kyle Landrum *(Chief Production Officer)*
Tim Morey *(Chief Sls Officer)*
Valda Coryat *(CMO)*
Chris Kelly *(Dir-Wholesale)*
Lynn Ricci *(Dir-IR & Corp Comm)*
Ronda Sheffield *(Chief HR Officer)*
Nilyum Jhala *(CTO)*
Joy Malivuk *(Chief Acctg Officer & VP)*
Christine Hersey *(VP-IR)*
Rob Kremer *(Exec Dir-Corp Comm)*
Ryan Blust *(VP-Fin)*
Wes Getman *(CFO)*
Phil Buck *(Mgr-Corp Comm)*

Subsidiaries:

Harvest Health & Recreation Inc. (1)
1155 W Rio Salado Pkwy Ste 201, Tempe, AZ 85281
Tel.: (480) 494-2261
Web Site: http://www.harvestinc.com
Rev.: $231,460,000
Assets: $856,635,000
Liabilities: $482,160,000
Net Worth: $374,475,000
Earnings: ($59,630,000)
Emp.: 994
Fiscal Year-end: 12/31/2020
Medical Cannabis
N.A.I.C.S.: 111419
Steven M. White *(Co-Founder)*

Subsidiary (Domestic):

Harvest Enterprises, Inc. (2)
627 S 48th St Ste 100, Tempe, AZ 85281
Tel.: (480) 777-2100
Web Site: http://www.harvestinc.com
Medical Cannabis Mfr
N.A.I.C.S.: 325411
Jason Vedadi *(Chm)*

Subsidiary (Non-US):

San Felasco Nurseries, Inc. (3)
Tel.: (352) 332-1220
Floral Nursery Operator
N.A.I.C.S.: 111421

Trulieve, Inc. (1)
3690 Juniper Creek Rd, Quincy, FL 32351
Tel.: (850) 442-6115
Web Site: https://www.trulieve.com
Sales Range: $1-9.9 Million
Emp.: 75
Medical Marijuana Dispensaries Operator
N.A.I.C.S.: 459999

TRULITE, INC.
151 Powell Rd Ste 111 NE Campus, Columbia, SC 29203
Tel.: (803) 691-3961   DE
Web Site: https://www.trulitetech.com
TRUL—(OTCIQ)
Motor & Generator Manufacturing
N.A.I.C.S.: 335312
Ronald Seftick *(Pres)*
John David White *(Chm)*

TRUMP MEDIA & TECHNOLOGY GROUP CORP.
1100 S Ocean Blvd, Palm Beach, FL 33480
(941) 735-7346   DE
Web Site: https://tmtcorp.com
Year Founded: 2020
DJT—(NASDAQ)
Assets: $311,018,094
Liabilities: $66,239,195
Net Worth: ($63,866,106)
Earnings: $21,890,641
Emp.: 36
Fiscal Year-end: 12/31/23
Motion Picture & Video Production
N.A.I.C.S.: 512110
Devin Nunes *(CEO)*
Philip Juhan *(CFO)*

TRUPANION, INC.
6100 4th Ave S Ste 200, Seattle, WA 98108
Tel.: (206) 607-1930   DE
Web Site: https://www.trupanion.com
Year Founded: 2000
TRUP—(NASDAQ)
Rev.: $1,108,605,000
Assets: $782,948,000
Liabilities: $479,226,000
Net Worth: $303,722,000
Earnings: ($44,693,000)
Emp.: 1,142
Fiscal Year-end: 12/31/23
Pet Care Insurance
N.A.I.C.S.: 524128
Darryl Rawlings *(Founder)*
Margaret Tooth *(Pres & CEO)*
Laura Bainbridge *(VP-Corp Comm)*
Wei Li *(Sr VP-Fin & Controller)*
Simon Wheeler *(Exec VP)*
John Gallagher *(COO)*

Subsidiaries:

Aquarium Software Limited (1)
Charter House Fourth Floor Woodlands Road, Altrincham, WA14 1HF, United Kingdom
Tel.: (44) 1619275620
Web Site: https://www.aqinsure.tech
Art Insurance Services
N.A.I.C.S.: 812910
Ed Shropshire *(Mng Dir)*
Andrew Sherwin *(Dir-Ops)*
Janice Turner *(Fin Dir)*
Mark Colonnese *(Dir-Product Mktg)*
Simon Brushett *(Dir-Technical)*

TRUSTCO BANK CORP NY
5 Sarnowski Dr, Glenville, NY 12302
Tel.: (518) 377-3311   NY
Web Site:
  https://www.trustcobank.com
Year Founded: 1981
TRST—(NASDAQ)
Rev.: $244,521,000
Assets: $6,168,191,000
Liabilities: $5,522,906,000
Net Worth: $645,285,000
Earnings: $58,646,000
Emp.: 750
Fiscal Year-end: 12/31/23
Bank Holding Company
N.A.I.C.S.: 551111
Robert Joseph McCormick *(Pres & CEO)*
Michael M. Ozimek *(CFO & Exec VP)*
Robert M. Leonard *(COO & Exec VP)*
Michael J. Hall *(Gen Counsel & Sec)*

Subsidiaries:

Trustco Bank (1)
1 Sarnowski Dr, Glenville, NY 12302   (100%)
Tel.: (518) 344-7510
Web Site: http://www.trustcobank.com
Sales Range: $1-4.9 Billion
Federal Savings Bank
N.A.I.C.S.: 522180

TrustCo Bank Corp NY—(Continued)

Robert Joseph McCormick *(Chm, Pres & CEO)*
Thomas O'Rourke Maggs *(Vice Chm)*
Robert M. Leonard *(COO & Exec VP)*

Trustco Bank Trust Dept　　　**(1)**
320 State St, Schenectady, NY 12305
Tel.: (518) 381-3831
Web Site: https://www.trustcobank.com
Rev.: $6,020,000
Emp.: 20
Banking Services
N.A.I.C.S.: 522110
Robert J. McCormick *(Pres)*

TRUSTMARK CORPORATION
248 E Capitol St, Jackson, MS 39201
Tel.: (601) 208-5111　　　　　**MS**
Web Site: https://www.trustmark.com
Year Founded: 1968
TRMK—(NASDAQ)
Rev.: $746,977,000
Assets: $18,015,478,000
Liabilities: $16,523,210,000
Net Worth: $1,492,268,000
Earnings: $71,887,000
Emp.: 2,738
Fiscal Year-end: 12/31/22
Bank Holding Company
N.A.I.C.S.: 551111
Duane A. Dewey *(Pres & CEO)*
Thomas C. Owens *(Principal Financial Officer)*
George T. Chambers Jr. *(Principal Acctg Officer)*
Granville Tate Jr. *(Sec)*
F. Joseph Rein Jr. *(Asst Sec)*

Subsidiaries:

The Somerville Bank & Trust
Company　　　　　　　　　　　**(1)**
16790 Hwy 64, Somerville, TN 38068
Tel.: (901) 465-9864
Web Site: http://www.somervillebank.com
Retail & Commercial Banking
N.A.I.C.S.: 522110

Trustmark National Bank　　　　**(1)**
248 E Capitol St, Jackson, MS
39201-2503　　　　　　　　　**(100%)**
Tel.: (601) 961-6000
Web Site: http://www.trustmark.com
Sales Range: $800-899.9 Million
Savings, Loans, Commercial & Investment
Banking Services
N.A.I.C.S.: 522180
Duane A. Dewey *(Proc & CEO)*
Thomas C. Owens *(CFO & Exec VP)*
George T. Chambers *(Chief Acctg Officer & Exec VP)*
Michael P. Carlson *(Chief Risk Officer & Exec VP)*
Granville Tate Jr. *(Chief Admin Officer & Exec VP)*
F. Joseph Rein Jr. *(Sr VP & Asst Sec)*

Subsidiary (Domestic):

Southern Community Capital,
LLC　　　　　　　　　　　　　　**(2)**
248 E Capitol St Ste 800, Jackson, MS
39201
Tel.: (601) 208-6191
Web Site:
　http://www.southerncommunitycapital.net
Financial Services
N.A.I.C.S.: 522320

TRUTANKLESS INC.
15900 N 78th St Ste 200, Scottsdale,
AZ 85260
Tel.: (480) 275-7572　　　　　**NV**
Web Site:
　https://www.trutankless.com
Year Founded: 2008
TKLS—(OTCIQ)
Rev.: $3,549
Assets: $255,791
Liabilities: $7,702,756
Net Worth: ($7,446,965)
Earnings: ($2,038,458)

Emp.: 4
Fiscal Year-end: 12/31/23
House Sales, Marketing & Research
& Development Services
N.A.I.C.S.: 321991
Michael Stebbins *(Founder)*
Robertson James Orr *(Bd of Dirs, Treas, Sec & VP-Bus Dev)*
Guy Newman *(CEO)*

Subsidiaries:

Modern Round Entertainment
Corporation　　　　　　　　　　**(1)**
7333 E Doubletree Ranch Rd Ste D 250,
Scottsdale, AZ 85258
Tel.: (480) 219-8439
Web Site: http://www.modernround.com
Rev.: $1,256,549
Assets: $3,380,726
Liabilities: $7,701,240
Net Worth: ($4,320,514)
Earnings: ($4,504,798)
Emp.: 14
Fiscal Year-end: 12/31/2016
Entertainment Services
N.A.I.C.S.: 713990

TRUXTON CORP.
4525 Harding Rd Ste 300, Nashville,
TN 37205
Tel.: (615) 515-1700　　　　　**TN**
Year Founded: 2004
TRUX—(OTCIQ)
Rev.: $67,298,000
Assets: $955,270,000
Liabilities: $867,588,000
Net Worth: $87,682,000
Earnings: $17,536,000
Emp.: 65
Fiscal Year-end: 12/31/23
Banking Holding Company
N.A.I.C.S.: 551111
Thomas S. Stumb *(Chm & CEO)*
Overton Colton *(Chief Admin Officer & Chief Risk Officer)*
Matthew King *(Dir-Lead)*
Derrick Jones *(Pres)*
Julie Marr *(Officer)*
Austin Branstetter *(CFO)*
Andrew L. May *(Vice Chm)*

TSCAN THERAPEUTICS, INC.
830 Winter St, Waltham, MA 02451
Tel.: (857) 399-9500　　　　　**DE**
Web Site: https://www.tscan.com
Year Founded: 2018
TCRX—(NASDAQ)
Rev.: $13,535,000
Assets: $199,091,000
Liabilities: $99,657,000
Net Worth: $99,434,000
Earnings: ($66,221,000)
Emp.: 137
Fiscal Year-end: 12/31/22
Research & Development in Biotechnology (except Nanobiotechnology)
N.A.I.C.S.: 541714
Leiden Dworak *(VP-Fin)*
Jason A. Amello *(CFO, Principal Fin Officer, Principal Acctg Officer & Treas)*
Gavin MacBeath *(CEO)*
Deborah Barton *(Chief Medical Officer)*
Shane Maltbie *(VP-Fin)*
Gavin MacBeath *(Chief Scientific & Ops Officer)*
Bill Desmarais *(Chief Bus Officer)*
Shrikant Chattopadhyay *(Sr VP-Medical-Translational Medicine)*
Cagan Gurer *(VP-Discovery)*
Warren Jaworowicz *(VP-CMC)*
Ann Hargraves *(Sr VP-HR)*
Shane Maltbie *(VP-Fin)*
Jim Murray *(VP-Clinical Ops)*
Ken Olivier *(VP-Non-clinical Dev)*
Timothy Barberich *(Chm)*

Heather Savelle *(VP-IR)*
Zoran Zdraveski *(Chief Legal Officer)*
Ray Lockard *(Sr VP-Tech Ops & Quality)*

TSR, INC.
400 Oser Ave Ste 150, Hauppauge,
NY 11788
Tel.: (631) 231-0333　　　　　**DE**
Web Site:
　https://www.tsrconsulting.com
Year Founded: 1969
TSRI—(NASDAQ)
Rev.: $101,433,065
Assets: $23,347,884
Liabilities: $7,097,996
Net Worth: $16,249,888
Earnings: $1,742,065
Emp.: 431
Fiscal Year-end: 05/31/23
Interactive Data Processing Service;
Consulting & Programming & Facilities Management
N.A.I.C.S.: 541511
John G. Sharkey *(CFO, Principal Acctg Officer, Sec & Sr VP)*
Bradley M. Tirpak *(Chm)*
Thomas Salerno *(Pres, CEO & Treas)*

Subsidiaries:

Geneva Consulting Group, Inc.　　**(1)**
400 Oser Ave Ste 150, Hauppauge, NY
11788
Tel.: (631) 231-0333
Web Site: http://www.genevaconsulting.com
Computer System Design Services
N.A.I.C.S.: 541512

LOGIXtech Solutions, LLC　　　**(1)**
1090 King Georges Post Rd Ste 1201, Edison, NJ 08837
Tel.: (732) 494-5100
Web Site: https://www.logix-tech.com
Emp.: 450
Information Technology Services
N.A.I.C.S.: 541519
Nivedita Das Gupta *(Co-Founder)*
Ayan Bhaduri *(Co-Founder)*

TSR Consulting Services, Inc.　　**(1)**
400 Oser Ave Ste 150, Hauppauge, NY
11788-3619
Tel.: (631) 231-0333
Web Site: http://www.tsrconsulting.com
Sales Range: $10-24.9 Million
Emp.: 20
Interactive Data Processing Service, Consulting & Programming, Facilities Management
N.A.I.C.S.: 541512

Branch (Domestic):

TSR Consulting Services, Inc.　　**(2)**
1090 King Georges Post Rd Ste 1201, Edison, NJ 08837　　　　　　　　**(100%)**
Tel.: (732) 321-9000
Web Site: http://www.tsrconsulting.com
Sales Range: $1-9.9 Million
Emp.: 10
Computer Consulting Services
N.A.I.C.S.: 541512

TSR Consulting Services, Inc.　　**(2)**
2512 N Racine Ave, Chicago, IL 60614
Tel.: (847) 414-7536
Web Site: https://www.tsrconsult.com
Interactive Data Processing Service, Consulting & Programming, Facilities Management
N.A.I.C.S.: 541512

TSS, INC.
110 E old Settlers Blvd, Round Rock,
TX 78664
Tel.: (512) 310-1000　　　　　**DE**
Web Site: https://tssiusa.com
Year Founded: 2004
TSSI—(OTCQB)
Rev.: $30,637,000
Assets: $31,406,000
Liabilities: $28,472,000

Net Worth: $2,934,000
Earnings: ($73,000)
Emp.: 70
Fiscal Year-end: 12/31/22
Mission Critical Facilities & Information Infrastructure Planning, Designing & Development
N.A.I.C.S.: 541614
Darryll Dewan *(Pres & CEO)*
Peter H. Woodward *(Chm)*
Kieran P. Brennan *(Sr VP-Sls & Mktg)*
Jim Olivier *(Chief Revenue Officer)*
Daniel M. Chism *(CFO)*

Subsidiaries:

Innovative Power Systems, Inc.　**(1)**
43676 Trade Ctr Pl Unit 125, Sterling, VA
20166
Tel.: (703) 996-1411
Web Site: https://www.invpower.com
Power System Installation Services
N.A.I.C.S.: 238210

Total Site Solutions　　　　　　**(1)**
110 E old Settlers Blvd, Round Rock, TX
78664
Tel.: (512) 310-1000
Web Site: https://tssiusa.com
Sales Range: $50-74.9 Million
Emp.: 100
Facility IT System Integration Services
N.A.I.C.S.: 519290

TTEC HOLDINGS, INC.
6312 S Fiddler's Green Cir Ste 100N,
Greenwood Village, CO 80111
Tel.: (303) 397-8100　　　　　**DE**
Web Site: https://www.ttec.com
Year Founded: 1982
TTEC—(NASDAQ)
Rev.: $2,443,707,000
Assets: $2,153,962,000
Liabilities: $1,575,857,000
Net Worth: $578,105,000
Earnings: $103,240,000
Emp.: 69,400
Fiscal Year-end: 12/31/22
Offices of Other Holding Companies
N.A.I.C.S.: 551112
Kenneth D. Tuchman *(Founder)*
Margaret B. McLean *(Chief Risk Officer, Gen Counsel & Corp Sec)*
Nick Cerise *(CMO)*
David J. Seybold *(CEO-TTEC Digital)*
Francois Bourret *(Chief Acctg Officer)*
Adam Foster *(Pres-EMEA)*
Chris Condon *(Chief Revenue Officer)*
Charles Koskovich *(COO)*
Rob Dravenstott *(CIO)*
John Everson *(Chief Security Officer)*
Judi A. Hand *(Chief Revenue Officer-Engage)*

Subsidiaries:

Humanify, Inc.　　　　　　　　　**(1)**
9197 S Peoria St, Englewood, CO 80112
Tel.: (303) 397-8100
Web Site: http://www.humanify.com
Information Technology Consulting Services
N.A.I.C.S.: 541512

Peppers & Rogers Group -
Belgium　　　　　　　　　　　　**(1)**
Manhattan Center Avenue du Boulevard 21
Bolweklaan box 22 Floor 11, 1210, Brussels, Belgium
Tel.: (32) 22106171
Web Site: http://www.peppers.com
Business Process Outsourcing Services
N.A.I.C.S.: 561499

Percepta LLC　　　　　　　　　**(1)**
290 Town Ctr Dr Fairlane Plz N Ste 610,
Dearborn, MI 48126　　　　　　**(55%)**
Tel.: (313) 390-0157
Web Site: http://www.percepta.com
Sales Range: $10-24.9 Million
Emp.: 20
Customer Relationship Management Solutions for the Automotive Industry; Joint Venture of TeleTech Holdings, Inc. (55%) &
Ford Motor Company (45%)

N.A.I.C.S.: 541618

Percepta UK Limited (1)
Regus 20-23 Woodside Place, Glasgow, G3
7QL, United Kingdom
Tel.: (44) 1415713400
Web Site: https://www.percepta.com
Sales Range: $50-74.9 Million
Emp.: 20
Business Process Outsourcing Services
N.A.I.C.S.: 561499
Allen Milton *(Gen Mgr)*

Serendebyte Inc. (1)
300 E Royal Ln Ste 127, Irving, TX 75039
Tel.: (201) 914-4138
Web Site: http://www.serendebyte.com
Information Technology Services
N.A.I.C.S.: 541511
Dilip Balakrishnan *(Pres)*
Charles Whitmore *(VP-Customer Success)*

Sofica Group AD (1)
Business Park Sofia building 3, 1766, Sofia,
Bulgaria
Tel.: (359) 24008500
Web Site: https://www.ttec.com
Business Process Outsourcing Services
N.A.I.C.S.: 561110

TTEC Digital LLC (1)
9197 S Peoria St, Englewood, CO 80112-
5833
Tel.: (303) 397-8100
Customer Experience Technology & Ser-
vices
N.A.I.C.S.: 561320
Jonathan Lerner *(Pres)*
Steven C. Pollema *(COO)*

Subsidiary (Domestic):

Avtex Solutions, LLC (2)
3500 American Blvd W Ste 300, Minneapo-
lis, MN 55431
Tel.: (952) 831-0888
Web Site: http://www.avtex.com
Customer Experience & Technology Con-
sulting Services
N.A.I.C.S.: 541613
Chris Kumsher *(CFO)*
Sarah Klaas *(VP-HR)*
John Seeds *(VP-Mktg)*
Jim Sheehan *(COO)*

Subsidiary (Domestic):

Adapt Telephony Services LLC (3)
600 Enterprise Dr Ste 204, Oak Brook, IL
60523-4215
Tel.: (630) 468-7500
Wired Telecommunications Carriers
N.A.I.C.S.: 517111

Subsidiary (Non-US):

Aria Solutions Inc. (3)
110 12 Ave SW Suite 600, Calgary, T2R
0G7, AB, Canada
Tel.: (403) 235-0227
Customer Care Service
N.A.I.C.S.: 519290

Subsidiary (Domestic):

Integrated Access Solutions, Inc. (3)
2151 Michelson Dr Ste 185, Irvine, CA
92630
Tel.: (800) 323-3639
Web Site: http://www.avtex.com
Electrical Contractor
N.A.I.C.S.: 238210

Nusoft Solutions Inc. (3)
6001 N Adams Rd Ste 285, Grand Rapids,
MI 48304
Tel.: (248) 594-1500
Web Site: http://www.nusoftsolutions.com
Other Management Consulting Services
N.A.I.C.S.: 541618
Dale Mansour *(CEO)*
Jason Wickman *(Dir-Sls & Mktg)*
Rayan Hanoudi *(Dir-Consulting & Delivery)*

TTEC Eastern Europe EAD (1)
Business Park Sofia Building 3, 1766, Sofia,
Bulgaria
Tel.: (359) 24008500
Web Site: https://www.ttec.com
Customer Care Services
N.A.I.C.S.: 561422

Ivaylo Petrov *(Principal-Network Admin)*

**TeleTech Customer Care Manage-
ment Costa Rica, S.A.** (1)
Flex Building Free Zone Park, Lagunilla,
Heredia, Costa Rica
Tel.: (506) 25075829
Business Process Outsourcing Services
N.A.I.C.S.: 561499

**TeleTech Government Solutions,
LLC** (1)
9197 S Peoria St, Englewood, CO 80112-
5833
Tel.: (303) 397-8100
Sales Range: $50-74.9 Million
Emp.: 400
Business Process Outsourcing Services
N.A.I.C.S.: 561499

TeleTech International Pty Ltd (1)
154 Pacific Hwy, Saint Leonards, 2065,
NSW, Australia
Tel.: (61) 298441100
Emp.: 80
Business Process Outsourcing Services
N.A.I.C.S.: 561499

TeleTech North America (1)
9197 S Peoria St, Englewood, CO
80112-5833 **(100%)**
Tel.: (303) 397-8100
Web Site: http://www.teletech.com
Sales Range: $150-199.9 Million
Emp.: 600
Provider of Technology Solutions
N.A.I.C.S.: 561422

iKnowtion, LLC (1)
25 Mall Rd Ste 409, Burlington, MA 01803
Tel.: (781) 494-9989
Web Site: http://www.iknowtion.com
Marketing Consulting Services
N.A.I.C.S.: 541613

rogenSi Ltd (1)
5th / 6th Floor Westgate, Leeds, LS1 2RP,
United Kingdom
Tel.: (44) 8008353832
Management Consulting Services
N.A.I.C.S.: 541611

rogenSi Pty Ltd. (1)
65 Epping Road, North Ryde, Sydney,
2113, NSW, Australia
Tel.: (61) 396972400
Management Consulting Services
N.A.I.C.S.: 541611

rogenSi Services Pty Ltd. (1)
Level 7 35 Clarence Street, Sydney, 2000,
NSW, Australia
Tel.: (61) 282961000
Management Consulting Services
N.A.I.C.S.: 541611

TTM TECHNOLOGIES, INC.
200 E Sandpointe Ave Ste 400,
Santa Ana, CA 92707
Tel.: (714) 327-3000   DE
Web Site: https://www.ttm.com
Year Founded: 1998
TTMI—(NASDAQ)
Rev.: $2,248,740,000
Assets: $3,025,547,000
Liabilities: $1,570,130,000
Net Worth: $1,455,417,000
Earnings: $54,414,000
Emp.: 16,100
Fiscal Year-end: 01/03/22
Printed Circuit Board Mfr
N.A.I.C.S.: 334412
Thomas T. Edman *(Pres & CEO)*
Dale Knecht *(Sr VP-IT-Global)*
Daniel J. Weber *(Gen Counsel, Sec
& Exec VP)*
Philip T. Titterton *(COO & Exec VP)*
Daniel L. Boehle *(CFO & Exec VP)*

Subsidiaries:

Anaren, Inc. (1)
6635 Kirkville Rd, East Syracuse, NY 13057
Tel.: (800) 411-6596
Web Site: http://www.anaren.com
Holding Company; RF Microwave Compo-
nents & Subassemblies Designer, Mfr &
Distr

N.A.I.C.S.: 551112
Hugh Hair *(Co-Founder)*
Carl W. Gerst Jr. *(CTO)*

Subsidiary (Domestic):

Anaren Ceramics, Inc. (2)
27 Northwestern Dr, Salem, NH 03079-
4809
Tel.: (603) 898-2883
Web Site: http://www.anaren.com
Microwave Components Mfr
N.A.I.C.S.: 334412
Lawrence A. Sala *(CEO)*

Subsidiary (Non-US):

**Anaren Communications Suzhou Co.,
Ltd.** (1)
Building 3 1 LongHui Street, Suzhou Indus-
trial Park, Suzhou, 215122, China
Tel.: (86) 51262749282
Web Site: http://www.anaren.com
RF Microwave Components & Subassem-
blies Mfr & Distr
N.A.I.C.S.: 334220

Subsidiary (Domestic):

Anaren Microwave, Inc. (2)
6635 Kirkville Rd, East Syracuse, NY 13057
Tel.: (315) 432-8909
Web Site: http://www.anaren.com
RF Microwave Components & Subassem-
blies Designer, Mfr & Distr
N.A.I.C.S.: 334220

Subsidiary (Non-US):

**Anaren Microwave (Europe),
Inc.** (3)
12 Somerset House Suite 18 Hussar Court,
Waterlooville, PO7 7SG, Hants, United
Kingdom
Tel.: (44) 2392232392
Web Site: http://www.anaren.com
RF Microwave Components & Subassem-
blies Whslr
N.A.I.C.S.: 423690

Subsidiary (Domestic):

Unicircuit, Inc. (2)
8122 Southpark Ln Ste 107, Littleton, CO
80120-4526
Tel.: (303) 730-0505
Web Site: http://www.anaren.com
Printed Circuit Board & Related Compo-
nents Mfr
N.A.I.C.S.: 334419

**Guangzhou Termbray Electronics
Technologies Company Limited** (1)
888 JiuFo West Road, JiuLong Town
Huangpu District, Guangzhou, 510555,
Guangdong, China
Tel.: (86) 2062878777
Emp.: 3,000
Electronics Mfr
N.A.I.C.S.: 334419

**Kalex Circuit Board (China)
Limited** (1)
20/F China Hk City Ph 2 33 Canton Rd,
Tsim Tsa Tsui, China (Hong Kong)
Tel.: (852) 22722222
Emp.: 130
Printed Circuit Board Mfr
N.A.I.C.S.: 334412

Oriental Printed Circuits, Inc. (1)
2555 E Chapman Ave, Fullerton, CA 92831
Tel.: (714) 525-4416
Emp.: 10
Printed Circuit Board Mfr
N.A.I.C.S.: 334412

Subsidiary (Domestic):

**Oriental Printed Circuits (USA),
Inc.** (2)
479 Montague Expy, Milpitas, CA 95035-
6800
Tel.: (408) 956-8801
Printed Circuit Board Mfr
N.A.I.C.S.: 334412

**Shanghai Viasystems EMS Company
Limited** (1)
No 188 Viasystems Road West Develop-
ment Area, Nan Xiang Town JiaDing,

Shanghai, 201802, China
Tel.: (86) 2169179000
Web Site: http://www.ttm.com
Electronic Products Mfr
N.A.I.C.S.: 334419

**TTM Technologies Advanced Circuits
Div.** (1)
234 Cashman Dr, Chippewa Falls, WI
54729
Tel.: (715) 720-5000
Web Site: http://www.ttmtech.com
Rev.: $16,100,000
Emp.: 730
Printed Circuit Boards
N.A.I.C.S.: 334412

TTM Technologies Toronto, Inc. (1)
8150 Sheppard Avenue East, Toronto, M1B
5K2, ON, Canada
Tel.: (416) 208-2100
Electronic Product Distr
N.A.I.C.S.: 423690
Shahid Sarwar *(Gen Mgr)*

Telephonics Corporation (1)
815 Broad Hollow Rd, Farmingdale, NY
11735-3904
Tel.: (631) 755-7000
Web Site: https://www.telephonics.com
Designs, Develops & Manufactures Communications & Automated Information Systems, Performance Monitoring & Audio Systems for MIL & COMM Applications
N.A.I.C.S.: 334290

Subsidiary (Non-US):

Telephonics Sweden AB (2)
Vattenkraftsvagen 8, SE 135 70, Stockholm,
Sweden **(100%)**
Tel.: (46) 87980900
Web Site: http://www.telephonic.com
Sales Range: $10-24.9 Million
Emp.: 17
Marketer of Electronic Systems & Sub-
Systems
N.A.I.C.S.: 334419

Viasystems Asia Limited (1)
20 F Tower 2 33 Canton Rd, Tsim Sha Tsui,
Kowloon, China (Hong Kong)
Tel.: (852) 22722222
Web Site: http://www.ttm.com
Provide Electronic Manufacturing
N.A.I.C.S.: 334419

**Viasystems Technologies Corp.,
L.L.C. - Canada** (1)
8150 Sheppard Avenue East, Toronto, M1B
5K2, ON, Canada
Tel.: (416) 208-2100
Web Site: http://www.ttmtech.com
Emp.: 540
Printed Circuit Board Mfr
N.A.I.C.S.: 334412

**Viasystems Technologies Corp.,
L.L.C. - Forest Grove** (1)
1521 Poplar Ln, Forest Grove, OR 97116
Tel.: (503) 359-9300
Web Site: http://www.ttmtech.com
Printed Circuit Board Mfr
N.A.I.C.S.: 334412

**Viasystems Technologies Corp.,
L.L.C. - San Jose** (1)
355 Turtle Creek Ct, San Jose, CA 95125
Tel.: (408) 280-0422
Web Site: http://www.ttmtech.com
Printed Circuit Board Mfr
N.A.I.C.S.: 334412

**TUESDAY MORNING CORPO-
RATION**
6250 LBJ Fwy, Dallas, TX 75240
Tel.: (972) 387-3562   DE
Web Site:
  https://www.tuesdaymorning.com
Year Founded: 1974
TUEM—(NASDAQ)
Rev.: $690,790,000
Assets: $417,884,000
Liabilities: $346,083,000
Net Worth: $71,801,000
Earnings: $2,982,000
Emp.: 1,607

Tuesday Morning Corporation—(Continued)

Fiscal Year-end: 06/30/21
Deep Discount Retail, Gift Wares, Housewares, Linens, Toys & Seasonal Stores
N.A.I.C.S.: 449129
Andrew T. Berger (CEO)
Jennyfer Gray (Gen Counsel, Sec & VP)

Subsidiaries:

Salem Trust Co.   (1)
4890 W Kennedy Blvd, Tampa, FL 33609
Tel.: (813) 301-1603
Web Site: http://www.salemtrust.com
Sales Range: $1-9.9 Million
Emp.: 5
Trust, Fiduciary & Custody Activities
N.A.I.C.S.: 523991
Mark F. Rhein (Pres)

TMI Holdings, Inc.
1715 N Westshore Blvd Ste 750, Tampa, FL 33607
Web Site: http://www.tmico.com
Financial Investment Advisory Services
N.A.I.C.S.: 523940
Anthony A. Guthrie (Chm)
Robert C. Finley (Vice Chm)
Christopher M. Teevan (COO)
Mark M. Young (Mng Dir)

TUNDRA GOLD CORP.
200 S Virginia St 8th Fl, Reno, NV 89501
Tel.: (775) 398-3012   **NV**
Year Founded: 2010
TNUG—(OTCIQ)
Gold Mining Services
N.A.I.C.S.: 212220
Gary Basrai (Pres & CEO)

TUPPERWARE BRANDS CORPORATION
14901 S Orange Blossom Trl, Orlando, FL 32837
Tel.: (407) 826-5050   **DE**
Web Site:
https://www.tupperwarebrands.com
Year Founded: 1942
TUP—(NYSE)
Rev.: $1,304,000,000
Assets: $743,600,000
Liabilities: $1,173,400,000
Net Worth: ($129,800,000)
Earnings: ($232,500,000)
Emp.: 6,600
Fiscal Year-end: 12/31/22
Direct Retailer & Marketer of Storage & Serving Containers, Toys & Beauty & Personal Care Products
N.A.I.C.S.: 326199
Laurie Ann Goldman (Pres & CEO)
Jane Garrard (VP-IR)
Karen Marie Sheehan (Chief Legal Officer, Sec & Exec VP)
Samantha Lomow (Chief Comml Officer)
Cameron Klaus (Dir-Comm-Global & PR)
Beatriz Diaz de la Fuente (Chief HR Officer & Exec VP)

Subsidiaries:

Avroy Shlain Cosmetics (Pty.) Ltd.   (1)
162 Tonetti Street Growthpoint Business Park Stand 8, Midrand, 1685, Johannesburg, South Africa
Tel.: (27) 116553500
Web Site: https://www.avroyshlain.co.za
Sales Range: $100-124.9 Million
Emp.: 220
Cosmetic Sales
N.A.I.C.S.: 456120
Susan Mawer (Mng Dir)
Avroy Shlain (Co-Founder)
Beryl Shlain (Co-Founder)

Dart Industries (New Zealand) Limited   (1)
24 Lorien Place East Tamaki, Auckland, 2013, New Zealand
Tel.: (64) 98365953
Web Site: http://www.tupperware.com
Sales Range: $25-49.9 Million
Emp.: 3
Plastic & Beauty Care Products Distr
N.A.I.C.S.: 456120

Dart S.A. de C.V.   (1)
Rodolfo Patron N-9 Parque Industrial, Lerma, 52000, Edo De Mexico, Mexico   (100%)
Tel.: (52) 7222791300
Sales Range: $75-99.9 Million
Emp.: 500
Mfr of Plastic Products
N.A.I.C.S.: 326199
Alferdo Pema (Product Mgr)

Dart do Brasil Industria e Comercio Ltda.   (1)
Estrada da Ilha no 870 Guaratiba, Rio de Janeiro, 23020-230, Brazil   (100%)
Tel.: (55) 2124147600
Web Site: https://www.tupperware.com.br
Sales Range: $75-99.9 Million
Emp.: 103
Mfr of Plastic Household Containers
N.A.I.C.S.: 326199

Diecraft Australia Pty. Ltd.   (1)
6-20 Radford Road, Reservoir, 3073, Australia
Tel.: (61) 392898300
Web Site: http://www.diecraft.com.au
Emp.: 60
Special Die & Jig Mfr
N.A.I.C.S.: 333514

Fuller Cosmetics S.A. de C.V.   (1)
Francisco Villa No 5 Alcaldia Xochimilco, Colonia Tepep, 16020, Mexico, Mexico
Tel.: (52) 53341300
Web Site: http://www.fuller.com.mx
Sales Range: $1-4.9 Billion
Emp.: 1,300
Cosmetics Mfr & Sales
N.A.I.C.S.: 456120

House of Fuller, S. de RL de CV   (1)
Francisco Villa No 5, Colonia Tepepan Alcaldia Xochimilco, 16020, Mexico, DF, Mexico   (100%)
Tel.: (52) 53341300
Web Site: http://www.fuller.com.mx
Cosmetic & Personal Care Products Mfr
N.A.I.C.S.: 456120

JLH Properties, Inc.   (1)
502 2nd Ave S, Clanton, AL 35045
Tel.: (205) 755-0655
Commercial Building Rental & Leasing Services
N.A.I.C.S.: 531120
Janice Hull (CEO)

Japan Tupperware Co., Ltd.   (1)
Westville Azabu 2-24-11 Nishi-Azabu, Minato-ku, Tokyo, 106-0031, Japan
Tel.: (81) 354856333
Web Site: http://www.tupperware.co.jp
Plastic & Beauty Care Products Distr
N.A.I.C.S.: 456120

NuMet Holdings Pty. Ltd.   (1)
102 Elliott St, Balmain, 2041, NSW, Australia
Tel.: (61) 298189011
Investment Management Service
N.A.I.C.S.: 551112

Nutrimetics Australia Pty. Ltd.   (1)
Level 5 436-484 Victoria Road, Gladesville, 2111, NSW, Australia
Tel.: (61) 280260507
Web Site: https://nutrimetics.com
Beauty Care Products Mfr
N.A.I.C.S.: 325620

Nutrimetics France SAS   (1)
171 Rue Helene Boucher, CS 50052, 78530, Buc, France
Tel.: (33) 13 920 7400
Web Site: https://www.nutrimetics.fr
Beauty Care Product Whslr
N.A.I.C.S.: 424210

Nutrimetics France SNC   (1)

171 Rue Helene Boucher, 78530, Buc, France
Tel.: (33) 139207400
Web Site: http://www.nutrimetics.fr
Beauty Care Products Mfr
N.A.I.C.S.: 325620

Nutrimetics International (NZ) Limited   (1)
24 Lorien Place East Tamaki, Auckland, 2013, New Zealand
Tel.: (64) 80 040 3503
Web Site: https://www.nutrimetics.com.au
Sales Range: $25-49.9 Million
Emp.: 30
Beauty Care Products Mfr
N.A.I.C.S.: 325620

PT Tupperware Indonesia Services   (1)
South Quarter Building Tower A 12th Floor Jl RA Kartini Kav 8, Jakarta Selatan, 12430, West Cilandak, Indonesia
Tel.: (62) 212 966 1750
Web Site: https://www.tupperware.co.id
Home Furnishing Distr
N.A.I.C.S.: 423220

Premiere Manufacturing, Inc.   (1)
11628 96th Ave N, Maple Grove, MN 55369
Tel.: (763) 425-8002
Web Site: http://www.premiermfginc.com
Medical Devices & Industrial Component Mfr
N.A.I.C.S.: 423450

Probemex SA de CV   (1)
Redemption Street 17, 16050, Xochimilco, Mexico
Tel.: (52) 5556242900
Beauty Care Products Mfr
N.A.I.C.S.: 325620

Tupperware (Suisse) SA   (1)
D4 Business Village Lucerne Z1 Square One 1st place, 6039, Root, Switzerland
Tel.: (41) 229947811
Web Site: http://www.tupperware.ch
Sales Range: $25-49.9 Million
Emp.: 45
Plastic Product Distr
N.A.I.C.S.: 424610

Tupperware Australia Pty. Ltd.   (1)
21 Brenock Park Drive, PO Box 111, Ferntree Gully, 3156, VIC, Australia
Tel.: (61) 1800805396
Web Site: http://www.tupperware.com.au
Sales Range: $25-49.9 Million
Emp.: 70
Plastic Product Distr
N.A.I.C.S.: 424610
Daisy Chin-Lor (Pres)

Tupperware Belgium N.V.   (1)
Wijngaardveld 17, 9300, Aalst, Belgium   (100%)
Tel.: (32) 26270130
Web Site: https://www.tupperware.be
Sales Range: $50-74.9 Million
Emp.: 400
Plastic Products Mfr & Marketer
N.A.I.C.S.: 326199

Tupperware Brands Foundation   (1)
14901 S Orange Blossom Trl, Orlando, FL 32837
Tel.: (407) 826-4588
Home Furnishing Whslr
N.A.I.C.S.: 423220

Tupperware Brands Korea Ltd.   (1)
1506 Chopyeong-ro Chopyeong-myeon, Jincheon, 365-852, Chungcheongbuk, Korea (South)
Tel.: (82) 15886866
Web Site: https://www.tupperware.co.kr
Home Furnishing Whslr
N.A.I.C.S.: 423220

Tupperware Deutschland GmbH   (1)
Praunheimer Landstrasse 70, 60488, Frankfurt am Main, Germany
Tel.: (49) 8004442021
Web Site: https://www.tupperware.de
Emp.: 150
Plastic Product Distr
N.A.I.C.S.: 424610

Tupperware Espana, S.A.   (1)
Calle Edgar Neville no 6 1 dcha, San Se-

bsatian of Kings, 28020, Madrid, Spain
Tel.: (34) 902901100
Web Site: https://www.tupperware.es
Plastic Product Distr
N.A.I.C.S.: 423990

Tupperware France S.A.   (1)
20 rue Paul Herault, BP 306, 92000, Nanterre, Cedex, France   (100%)
Tel.: (33) 14 139 2424
Web Site: https://www.tupperware.fr
Kitchenwares, Appliances & Other Plastic Products Mfr
N.A.I.C.S.: 423620

Tupperware General Services N.V.   (1)
Tel.: (32) 53727211
Web Site: http://www.tupperware.com
Plastic Products Mfr & Distr
N.A.I.C.S.: 326199
Patrick Bodson (Mng Dir)

Tupperware Global Center SARL   (1)
8 Rue Lionel Terray, 92500, Rueil-Malmaison, France
Tel.: (33) 899868245
Business Management Consulting Services
N.A.I.C.S.: 541611

Tupperware Nordic A/S   (1)
Bernstorffsvej 154, 2900, Hellerup, Denmark
Tel.: (45) 39257500
Web Site: https://www.tupperware.dk
Sales Range: $25-49.9 Million
Emp.: 43
Plastic Product Distr
N.A.I.C.S.: 423990

Tupperware Osterreich G.m.b.H.   (1)
IZ-No Sud Tupperwareplatz, 2351, Wiener Neudorf, Austria
Tel.: (43) 22 363 1420
Web Site: https://www.tupperware.at
Plastic Product Distr
N.A.I.C.S.: 423990

Tupperware Polska Sp.z o.o.   (1)
ul Postepu 17B, 02-676, Warsaw, Poland
Tel.: (48) 221012800
Web Site: https://www.tupperware.pl
Plastic Product Distr
N.A.I.C.S.: 423990

Tupperware Products, Inc. Wilmington   (1)
Route Du Jura 37, Fribourg, 1700, Switzerland
Tel.: (41) 263516800
Global Premium Storage Product Distr
N.A.I.C.S.: 424610

Tupperware Romania s rl   (1)
Bucuresti Str Halelor nr 5 et 1, 030167, Bucharest, Romania
Tel.: (40) 371381841
Web Site: https://www.tupperware.ro
Plastic Product Distr
N.A.I.C.S.: 423990

Tupperware Services GmbH   (1)
Praunheimer Landstrasse 70, 60488, Frankfurt am Main, Germany
Tel.: (49) 8004442021
Sales Range: $25-49.9 Million
Emp.: 150
Business Management Services
N.A.I.C.S.: 561110

Tupperware Southern Africa (Proprietary) Limited   (1)
Building C Wedgefield Office Park 17 Muswell Road South, 17 Muswell Road, Bryanston, South Africa
Tel.: (27) 11 367 8500
Web Site: https://www.tupperware.co.za
Sales Range: $25-49.9 Million
Emp.: 53
Plastic Product Distr
N.A.I.C.S.: 423990

Tupperware Trading Ltd.   (1)
Budaorsi Ut 150/B, 1118, Budapest, Hungary
Tel.: (36) 13097880
Plastic Product Distr
N.A.I.C.S.: 326199

Tupperware Turkey, Inc.   (1)
Sahrayicedit Mah Halk Sok Pakpen Plaza

No 40 A/1 34734, Kozyatagi Kadikoy, Istanbul, Turkiye
Tel.: (90) 2165716000
Plastic Product Distr
N.A.I.C.S.: 326199

Tupperware U.S., Inc. (1)
14901 S Orange Blossom Trl, Orlando, FL 32837 (100%)
Tel.: (407) 826-5050
Web Site: https://www.tupperware.com
Sales Range: $125-149.9 Million
Emp.: 300
Direct Retailer of Plastic Household Products
N.A.I.C.S.: 326199

Tupperware United Kingdom & Ireland Limited (1)
Unit 11 Kinsealy Business Park, Kinsealy Lane Malahide, Dublin, K36 F594, Ireland (100%)
Tel.: (353) 18463977
Web Site: http://www.tupperware.ie
Plastic Product Distr
N.A.I.C.S.: 326199

Tupperware Vietnam LLC (1)
288 Pasteur, Ward 8 District 3, Ho Chi Minh City, Vietnam
Tel.: (84) 283 820 7015
Web Site: https://www.tupperware.com.vn
Home Furnishing Whslr
N.A.I.C.S.: 423220

Tupperware d.o.o. (1)
Trg Marsala Tita 8, Zagreb, 10000, Croatia
Tel.: (385) 14826959
Web Site: http://www.tupperware.hr
Plastic Product Distr
N.A.I.C.S.: 424610

TURBINE AVIATION, INC.
304 Via Del Norte, Oceanside, CA 92058
Tel.: (760) 721-2435
Web Site: https://turbineaviation.com
TURA—(OTCEM)
Aircraft Engine Components Mfr
N.A.I.C.S.: 336412
Victor Farias *(Pres)*

TURBOTVILLE NATIONAL BANK
4710 State Route 54, Turbotville, PA 17772-0037
Tel.: (570) 649-5118   PA
Web Site: https://www.ttnb.com
Year Founded: 1910
TVNB—(OTCIQ)
Commercial Banking Services
N.A.I.C.S.: 522110
William Bussom *(Pres & CEO)*
Matt Carson *(VP & CFO)*

TURMERIC ACQUISITION CORP.
450 Kendall St, Cambridge, MA 02142
Tel.: (617) 425-9200   Ky
Year Founded: 2020
TMPMU—(NASDAQ)
Investment Services
N.A.I.C.S.: 523999
Luke Evnin *(CEO)*
Todd Foley *(Pres)*
Matthew Roden *(Chm)*
Ed Hurwitz *(CFO)*

TURNER VALLEY OIL & GAS, INC.
5900 Balcones Dr Ste 4503, Austin, TX 78731
Tel.: (352) 561-8896
Web Site: https://www.tvoginc.com
Year Founded: 1999
TVOG—(OTCIQ)
Holding Company
N.A.I.C.S.: 551112
Jordan P. Balencic *(Chm & CEO)*
James B. Smith *(CFO)*

TURNING POINT BRANDS, INC.
5201 Interchange Way, Louisville, KY 40229
Tel.: (502) 778-4421   DE
Web Site: https://www.turningpointbrands.com
Year Founded: 2004
TPB—(NYSE)
Rev.: $405,393,000
Assets: $569,356,000
Liabilities: $417,350,000
Net Worth: $152,006,000
Earnings: $38,462,000
Emp.: 373
Fiscal Year-end: 12/31/23
Tobacco Product Mfr & Distr
N.A.I.C.S.: 312230
David E. Glazek *(Chm)*
Graham A. Purdy *(Pres & CEO)*
Alicia Carrasco *(Chief People Officer)*
Andrew Flynn *(CFO)*
Summer Frein *(CMO & Chief Revenue Officer)*

Subsidiaries:

Direct Vapor LLC (1)
14300 Commerce Way Blng D, Miami Lakes, FL 33016
Tel.: (864) 699-0754
Web Site: https://www.vaporfi.com
Tobacco Product Distr
N.A.I.C.S.: 424990

South Beach Smoke LLC (1)
2801 SW 149th Ave Ste 295, Miramar, FL 33027
Web Site: https://www.southbeachsmoke.com
Tobacco Product Mfr
N.A.I.C.S.: 339999

Standard Diversified Inc. (1)
767 5th Ave 12th Fl, New York, NY 10153
Tel.: (516) 248-1100
Web Site: http://www.standarddiversified.com
Rev.: $391,778,000
Assets: $511,046,000
Liabilities: $410,797,000
Net Worth: $100,249,000
Earnings: ($10,623,000)
Emp.: 499
Fiscal Year-end: 12/31/2019
Investment Services
N.A.I.C.S.: 523999
Edward J. Sweeney *(Interim CFO)*
Brad Tobin *(Gen Counsel & Sec)*

Subsidiary (Domestic):

Maidstone Insurance Company (2)
PO Box 229, Mineola, NY 11501
Web Site: http://www.maidstone.com
Insurance Services
N.A.I.C.S.: 524210
Jennifer Gandarela *(Mgr-Acct Payable & Receivables)*

Standard Outdoor LLC (2)
PO Box 162771, Austin, TX 78716
Tel.: (512) 633-2086
Web Site: http://www.standardoutdoor.com
Outdoor Advertising Services
N.A.I.C.S.: 541850
Mike Morrill *(Pres)*

Vapor Beast LLC (1)
14300 Commerce Way, Miami Lakes, FL 33016
Web Site: https://www.vaporbeast.com
Tobacco Product Distr
N.A.I.C.S.: 424990

Vapor Shark, LLC (1)
14300 Commerce Way, Miami Lakes, FL 33016
Web Site: https://www.vaporshark.com
Tobacco Product Distr
N.A.I.C.S.: 424940

TURNKEY CAPITAL, INC.
29970 Technology Dr Ste 205, Murrieta, CA 92563
Tel.: (949) 612-2777   NV
Web Site:
https://www.turnkeycapitalinc.com
Year Founded: 2012
TKCI—(OTCIQ)
Assets: $2,558
Liabilities: $1,147,336
Net Worth: ($1,144,778)
Earnings: ($324,820)
Fiscal Year-end: 12/31/19
Investment Services
N.A.I.C.S.: 523999
Neil Swartz *(Chm, Pres & Co-CEO)*
Joseph Tagliola *(Co-CEO)*
Timothy S. Hart *(CFO & Sec)*

TURNSTONE BIOLOGICS CORP.
9310 Athena Cir Ste 300, La Jolla, CA 92037
Tel.: (347) 897-5988   DE
Web Site:
https://www.turnstonebio.com
Year Founded: 2018
TSBX—(NASDAQ)
Rev.: $73,300,000
Assets: $114,938,000
Liabilities: $216,405,000
Net Worth: ($101,467,000)
Earnings: ($30,834,000)
Emp.: 108
Fiscal Year-end: 12/31/22
Research & Development in Biotechnology (except Nanobiotechnology)
N.A.I.C.S.: 541714
Michael F. Burgess *(Interim Chief Medical Officer)*
Sammy Farah *(Pres)*
Venkat Ramanan *(CFO)*
Sammy J. Farah *(Pres & CEO)*

TURTLE BEACH CORPORATION
44 S Broadway 4th Fl, White Plains, NY 10601
Tel.: (646) 277-1285   NV
Web Site:
https://corp.turtlebeach.com
Year Founded: 2010
HEAR—(NASDAQ)
Rev.: $240,166,000
Assets: $163,387,000
Liabilities: $74,446,000
Net Worth: $88,941,000
Earnings: ($59,546,000)
Emp.: 245
Fiscal Year-end: 12/31/22
Electronic Products Mfr
N.A.I.C.S.: 334419
Cris Keirn *(Interim CEO & Sr VP-Global Sls)*
Terry Jimenez *(Chm)*
Joe Stachula *(CTO & Sr VP-Product Dev)*
Megan Wynne *(Gen Counsel)*
Matt Seymour *(Sr VP-Product Mgmt)*
Jose Rosado *(Sr VP-Global Ops)*
Ryan Dell *(Sr VP-Mktg)*
Tom Roberts *(Chief Strategy Officer)*
Jessica Morrow *(VP-Business Development)*
Drew Johnson *(Sr VP-Global Sls)*

Subsidiaries:

TB Germany GmbH (1)
Gasstrasse 4, 22761, Hamburg, Germany
Tel.: (49) 4030994950
Computer Hardware Product Mfr
N.A.I.C.S.: 334118

Turtle Beach Europe Limited (1)
Turtle Beach 2200 Renaissance, Basingstoke, RG21 4EQ, Hampshire, United Kingdom
Tel.: (44) 1256517333
Electronic Components Mfr
N.A.I.C.S.: 334419

Voyetra Turtle Beach Inc. (1)
100 Summit Lake Dr Ste 100, Valhalla, NY 10595
Tel.: (914) 345-2255
Web Site: http://www.turtlebeach.com
Sales Range: $200-249.9 Million
Emp.: 25
Designer & Marketer of Audio Peripherals for Personal Computer & Video Game Platforms
N.A.I.C.S.: 423430

TUSIMPLE HOLDINGS INC.
9191 Towne Centre Dr Ste 150, San Diego, CA 92122
Tel.: (619) 916-3144   DE
Web Site: https://www.tusimple.com
Year Founded: 2016
TSP—(NASDAQ)
Rev.: $9,369,000
Assets: $1,074,279,000
Liabilities: $119,798,000
Net Worth: $954,481,000
Earnings: ($472,045,000)
Emp.: 1,058
Fiscal Year-end: 12/31/22
Holding Company
N.A.I.C.S.: 551112
Mo Chen *(Co-Founder & Chm)*
Xiaodi Hou *(Co-Founder)*
Cheng Lu *(Pres & CEO)*
Charles Price *(Chief Product Officer)*
Eric R. Tapia *(Interim CFO, Principal Acctg Officer, VP & Controller-Global)*
Evan Dunn *(Gen Counsel)*

TUTOR PERINI CORPORATION
15901 Olden St, Sylmar, CA 91342
Tel.: (818) 362-8391   MA
Web Site: https://www.tutorperini.com
Year Founded: 1918
TPC—(NYSE)
Rev.: $3,790,755,000
Assets: $4,542,800,000
Liabilities: $3,100,816,000
Net Worth: $1,441,984,000
Earnings: ($210,009,000)
Emp.: 1,900
Fiscal Year-end: 12/31/22
General Contracting & Construction Management Services
N.A.I.C.S.: 236220
Ronald N. Tutor *(Chm, Pres & CEO)*
Gary G. Smalley *(CFO & Exec VP)*
Ryan J. Soroka *(Chief Acctg Officer & Sr VP)*
Jorge Casado *(VP-IR & Corp Comm)*
Anthony C. Fiore *(Treas, Sec & Exec VP-Tax)*
Michael Smithson *(Exec VP)*
William J. Palmer *(Chief Bus Dev Officer & Exec VP)*
Ghassan M. Ariqat *(Exec VP-Building & Specialty Contractors Grp)*

Subsidiaries:

Becho Inc. (1)
15901 Olden St, Sylmar, CA 91342
Tel.: (818) 362-8391
Web Site: https://www.bechoinc.com
Public Utility Construction Services
N.A.I.C.S.: 236210

Cherry Hill Construction Inc. (1)
8211 Washington Blvd, Jessup, MD 20794
Tel.: (410) 799-3577
Web Site:
http://www.cherryhillconstruction.com
Sales Range: $1-9.9 Million
Emp.: 25
Highway & Street Construction
N.A.I.C.S.: 237310

Desert Mechanical Inc. (1)
15870 Olden St, Sylmar, CA 91342
Tel.: (818) 362-4591
Web Site: https://www.lvdmi.com
Sales Range: $200-249.9 Million
Emp.: 1,100
Construction Engineering Services
N.A.I.C.S.: 541330

Tutor Perini Corporation—(Continued)

Armando Estrada *(VP-Operations)*
Jacob Nelson *(Mgr-BIM)*

Fisk Electric Company Inc. (1)
10855 Westview Dr, Houston, TX 77043
Tel.: (713) 868-6111
Web Site: https://www.fiskcorp.com
Emp.: 800
Electrical Wiring & Networking Cable
N.A.I.C.S.: 238210
Gregory C. Thomas *(Gen Counsel & Sr VP)*
Wayne McDonald *(Sr VP-Houston Grp)*
Cory L. Borchardt *(VP-Ops)*
Joe B. Thomas Jr. *(CFO & Sr VP)*
Orvil M. Anthony Jr. *(Pres & CEO)*

Frontier-Kemper Constructors, Inc. (1)
850 Harbourside Drive Suite 404, North Vancouver, V7P 0A3, BC, Canada
Tel.: (778) 807-4970
Web Site: https://www.frontierkemper.com
Building Construction Services
N.A.I.C.S.: 236220
Steve Redmond *(VP-Civil Construction)*
W. David Rogstad *(Pres)*

James A. Cummings, Inc. (1)
1 E Broward Blvd Ste 1300, Fort Lauderdale, FL 33301
Tel.: (954) 733-4211
Web Site:
　　https://www.jamesacummings.com
Sales Range: $25-49.9 Million
Emp.: 20
Commercial Building Construction Services
N.A.I.C.S.: 236220

Keating Building Company (1)
130 No 18th St Ste 1500, Philadelphia, PA 19103
Tel.: (610) 668-4100
Emp.: 65
General Contracting & Construction Management Services
N.A.I.C.S.: 236220

Lunda Construction Company (1)
620 Gebhardt Rd, Black River Falls, WI 54615
Tel.: (715) 284-9491
Web Site:
　　https://www.lundaconstruction.com
Sales Range: $125-149.9 Million
Emp.: 700
Bridge Construction Services
N.A.I.C.S.: 237310
Dennis L. Behnke *(Pres & CEO)*
Jesten Sterry *(Reg VP-Minnesota)*
Tracey Jackson *(Officer-EEO)*
Roger Toenies P. E. *(VP-Estimating)*
Mark Jochman *(VP-Pipeline)*
Dennis Maney *(VP-Railroad)*
Mark Olsen *(VP-Alternative Delivery)*
Mike Hahn P. E. *(Reg VP-Wisconsin)*
Dale Even P. E. *(Sr VP)*

Nagelbush Mechanical, Inc. (1)
5101 NW 21st Ave Ste 210, Fort Lauderdale, FL 33309
Tel.: (954) 736-3000
Web Site: https://www.nagelbush.com
Sales Range: $25-49.9 Million
Emp.: 50
Engineering Consulting Services
N.A.I.C.S.: 236210

Perini Building Company, Inc. (1)
2955 N Green Vly Pkwy, Henderson, NV 89014　　　　　　　　　　(100%)
Tel.: (702) 792-9209
Sales Range: $25-49.9 Million
Emp.: 60
Commercial Building Engineering & Construction Services
N.A.I.C.S.: 236210
Craig W. Shaw *(Pres)*

Perini Management Services, Inc. (1)
73 Mt Wayte Ave, Framingham, MA 01701-9160　　　　　　　　　(100%)
Tel.: (508) 628-2000
Web Site: https://pmsi.tutorperini.com
Sales Range: $50-74.9 Million
Emp.: 50
Engineeering Services
N.A.I.C.S.: 236210

Roy Anderson Corp (1)
11400 Reichold Rd, Gulfport, MS 39503
Tel.: (228) 896-4000
Web Site: https://www.rac.com
Construction Services
N.A.I.C.S.: 236220
Bob Fullington *(Pres)*
Martin Shows *(VP-Field Ops)*
Jerry Kozar *(Dir-Estimating)*
Chris Gray *(Dir-Business Development)*
Eddie Rivers *(Dir-BIM/VDC)*
Julie Carter *(Dir-Safety)*

Subsidiary (Domestic):

Brice Building Company, Inc. (2)
201 Sunbelt Pkwy, Birmingham, AL 35211
Tel.: (205) 930-9911
Web Site: http://www.bricebuilding.com
Sales Range: $125-149.9 Million
Emp.: 200
Commercial Construction Company
N.A.I.C.S.: 236220

Roy Anderson Corp - Ridgeland (2)
368 Highland Colony Pkwy, Ridgeland, MS 39157
Tel.: (601) 206-7600
Web Site: http://www.rac.com
Nonresidential Construction Services
N.A.I.C.S.: 236220

Rudolph & Sletten, Inc. (1)
2 Circle Star Way 4th Fl, San Carlos, CA 94070
Tel.: (650) 216-3600
Web Site: https://www.rsconstruction.com
Sales Range: $700-749.9 Million
Emp.: 30
Contracting & Construction Services
N.A.I.C.S.: 236220
Martin B. Sisemore *(CEO)*
Marian Selvaggio *(Gen Counsel & VP)*
Terence Huie *(CFO & VP)*
Dianna Wright *(VP-Bus Dev)*
Jeff Russell *(VP & Dir-Healthcare)*
Patrick Krzyzosiak *(Dir-Virtual Design & Construction)*

Rudolph and Sletten, Inc. (1)
120 Constitution Dr, Menlo Park, CA 94025
Tel.: (650) 216-3600
Web Site: https://www.rsconstruction.com
Building Construction Services
N.A.I.C.S.: 236220
Martin Sisemore *(Pres & CEO)*
Dan Dolinar *(COO & Exec VP)*
Jonathan Foad *(Sr VP-Ops-Northern California)*
Rene Olivo *(Sr VP-Ops-Southern California)*
Michael Mohrman *(Sr VP-Preconstruction Svcs)*

Tutor Micronesia Construction, LLC (1)
JL Baker St Harmon Industrial Pk, Harmon, GU 96913
Tel.: (671) 646-4861
Construction Engineering Services
N.A.I.C.S.: 541330

Tutor Perini Building Corp. (1)
2955 N Green Valley Pkwy, Henderson, NV 89014
Tel.: (702) 792-9209
Web Site:
　　https://www.tutorperinibuilding.com
Construction Management Services
N.A.I.C.S.: 236210
Joanne Verrips *(VP-Preconstruction)*
Mark Makary *(Sr VP)*
Tony Meyer *(VP-Operations)*
Scott Ellison *(Exec VP)*

Tutor-Saliba Corporation (1)
15901 Olden St, Sylmar, CA 91342
Tel.: (818) 362-8391
Web Site: http://www.tutorsaliba.com
Sales Range: $500-549.9 Million
Emp.: 750
Industrial & Residential Engineering & Construction Services
N.A.I.C.S.: 236220

Subsidiary (Domestic):

Black Construction Corporation (2)
PO Box 24667, Barrigada, GU 96921
Tel.: (671) 646-4861

Web Site:
　　https://www.blackconstructionguam.com
Commercial & Residential Construction & Engineering Services
N.A.I.C.S.: 236220
Leonard K. Kaae *(Sr VP & Gen Mgr)*
Mark J. Mamczarz *(Treas, Sec & VP-Fin)*
John M. McSweeney *(VP-Estimating & Bus Dev)*
Donald J. McCann *(VP-Ops)*

Subsidiary (Non-US):

E.E. Black, Ltd. (3)
2F 111 Paseo De Roxas Avenue, Legaspi Village, Makati, 1229, Philippines
Tel.: (63) 288128166
Web Site:
　　http://www.blackconstructionguam.com
Sales Range: $50-74.9 Million
Emp.: 60
Commercial & Residential Construction & Engineering Services
N.A.I.C.S.: 236220

WDF/Nagelbush Holding Corp (1)
1800 NW 49th St Ste 110, Fort Lauderdale, FL 33309
Tel.: (954) 736-3000
Holding Company
N.A.I.C.S.: 551112

TUXIS CORP.
3814 Rte 44, Millbrook, NY 12545
Tel.: (845) 677-2700　　　　　　　MD
Web Site: http://www.tuxis.com
Year Founded: 1983
TUXS—(OTCIQ)
Holding Company; Self Storage Facilities
N.A.I.C.S.: 551112
Mark Campbell Winmill *(Pres & CEO)*

TWILIO INC.
101 Spear St 5th Fl, San Francisco, CA 94105
Tel.: (415) 390-2337　　　　　　　DE
Web Site: https://www.twilio.com
Year Founded: 2008
TWLO—(NYSE)
Rev.: $4,153,945,000
Assets: $11,609,707,000
Liabilities: $1,877,155,000
Net Worth: $9,732,552,000
Earnings: ($1,015,441,000)
Emp.: 5,867
Fiscal Year-end: 12/31/23
Software Development Services
N.A.I.C.S.: 541511
Jeffrey E. Epstein *(Chm)*
Khozema Z. Shipchandler *(CEO)*
Jeffrey Lawson *(Founder)*
Christy Lake *(Chief People Officer)*
Lybra Clemons *(Chief Diversity, Inclusion & Belonging Officer)*
Reeny Sondhi *(Chief Digital Officer)*

Subsidiaries:

Danal, Inc. (1)
2833 Jct Ave Ste 202, San Jose, CA 95134-1920
Tel.: (408) 232-3300
Web Site: http://www.danalinc.com
Computer Related Services
N.A.I.C.S.: 541519
James Greenwell *(Pres & CEO)*
Sung Chan Park *(Chm)*
Byungwoo Choi *(Co-CEO)*
Hunjin Jung *(VP-Bus Dev)*
Atreedev Banerjee *(COO)*
Madhura Belani *(Chief Product Officer & Gen Mgr)*
Paris Leung *(Chief Strategy Officer & Gen Mgr)*
Manish Vichare *(CTO)*
Shane Martin *(CFO)*
Abhishek Tiwari *(VP-Product & Ops)*
Vijay Reddy *(VP-Engrg)*

Segment.io, Inc. (1)
100 California St Ste 700, San Francisco, CA 94111
Tel.: (415) 649-6900
Web Site: http://segment.com

Data Tracking & Management Services
N.A.I.C.S.: 541519
Peter Reinhardt *(Co-Founder & CEO)*
Ilya Volodarsky *(Co-Founder)*
Calvin French-Owen *(Co-Founder)*

SendGrid, Inc. (1)
1801 California St Ste 500, Denver, CO 80202
Tel.: (303) 552-0653
Web Site: http://www.sendgrid.com
Sales Range: $100-124.9 Million
Emp.: 415
Email Marketing Software
N.A.I.C.S.: 513210

Twilio Berlin GmbH (1)
Huttenstrasse 34/35, 10553, Berlin, Germany
Tel.: (49) 30555787950
Web Site: http://www.corenetdynamics.com
Software Development Services
N.A.I.C.S.: 513210
Dragos Vingarzan *(Founder & CTO)*
Carsten Brinkschulte *(Mng Dir)*

Twilio Sweden AB (1)
Sodergatan 22, 211 34, Malmo, Sweden
Tel.: (46) 406007501
Cloud Communication Software Developer Services
N.A.I.C.S.: 513210

Zipwhip, Inc. (1)
300 Elliott Ave W Ste 500, Seattle, WA 98119
Web Site: http://www.zipwhip.com
Software Development Services
N.A.I.C.S.: 541511
Robert J. Chamberlain *(CFO)*
John Lauer *(Co-Founder & CEO)*
John Larson *(Co-Founder & Chief Bus Dev Officer)*
Scott Heimes *(CMO)*
Bob Chamberlain *(CFO)*
Kirsten Spoljaric *(Sr VP-People Ops)*

TWIN DISC, INCORPORATED
222 E Erie St, Milwaukee, WI 53202
Tel.: (262) 638-4000　　　　　　　WI
Web Site: https://www.twindisc.com
Year Founded: 1918
TWIN—(NASDAQ)
Rev.: $295,127,000
Assets: $312,058,000
Liabilities: $157,004,000
Net Worth: $155,054,000
Earnings: $11,246,000
Emp.: 910
Fiscal Year-end: 06/30/24
Motor Vehicle Transmission & Power Train Parts Manufacturing
N.A.I.C.S.: 336350
Debbie A. Lange *(Chief Acctg Officer & Controller)*
John H. Batten *(Pres & CEO)*
Jeffrey S. Knutson *(CFO, Treas, Sec & VP-Fin)*
Michael C. Smiley *(Chm)*
Michael B. Gee *(VP-Hybrid Engrg)*

Subsidiaries:

Rolla SP Propellers SA (1)
Via Roncaglia 6, PO Box 109, 6883, Novazzano, Switzerland
Tel.: (41) 916952000
Web Site: https://www.rolla-propellers.ch
Sales Range: $125-149.9 Million
Power Transmission Equipment Mfr
N.A.I.C.S.: 333613

Twin Disc (Far East) Ltd. (1)
6 Tuas Avenue 1, Singapore, 639491, Singapore　　　　　　　　　(100%)
Tel.: (65) 62670000
Web Site: http://www.twindisc.com
Sales Range: $10-24.9 Million
Emp.: 30
Power Transmission Equipment Sales & Marketing
N.A.I.C.S.: 336350

Twin Disc (Pacific) Pty. Ltd. (1)
70B Tradecoast Drive, Eagle Farm, 4009, **(100%)**
QLD, Australia
Tel.: (61) 732651200
Web Site: https://www.twindisc.com.au
Sales Range: $25-49.9 Million
Emp.: 20
Power Transmission Equipment Mfr
N.A.I.C.S.: 336350
Glenn Frattinghan (Mng Dir)

Twin Disc International, S.A. (1)
Chaussee De Namur 54, 1400, Nivelles, **(100%)**
Belgium
Tel.: (32) 67887211
Web Site: https://www.twindisc.com
Sales Range: $75-99.9 Million
Emp.: 212
Power Transmission Equipment Mfr
N.A.I.C.S.: 333613

Twin Disc Italia Srl (1)
Via S Cristoforo 131, S Matteo Della
Decima, 40017, Bologna, Italy
Tel.: (39) 0516819711
Web Site:
http://www.twindiscpropulsion.com
Sales Range: $25-49.9 Million
Emp.: 50
Clutches, Transmission & Marine Gears &
Torque Convertors Mfr; Heavy-Duty Off-
Highway Power Transmission Equipment
N.A.I.C.S.: 333613
Carlo Contri (Pres)

Twin Disc Power Transmission
(Shanghai) Co. Ltd. (1)
Room 2308 Shartex Plaza 88 Zunyi Road
South, Shanghai, 200336, China
Tel.: (86) 2164273212
Web Site: http://www.twindisc.com.cn
Industrial Machinery Mfr & Distr
N.A.I.C.S.: 333248

Twin Disc Srl (1)
Via E e P Salani 1 Limite Sull'Arno, 50050,
Florence, Italy
Tel.: (39) 0571979111
Industrial Machinery & Equipment Whslr
N.A.I.C.S.: 423830

Veth Propulsion B.V. (1)
Nanengat 17, 3356 AA, Papendrecht, Neth-
erlands
Tel.: (31) 786152266
Web Site: https://www.veth.net
Motor Vehicle Parts Mfr
N.A.I.C.S.: 336390

TWIN RIDGE CAPITAL ACQUI-
SITION CORP.
707 Menlo Ave Ste 110, Menlo Park,
CA 94025
Tel.: (212) 235-0292   Ky
Year Founded: 2021
TRCA—(NYSE)
Rev.: $10,132,089
Assets: $217,189,502
Liabilities: $221,020,147
Net Worth: ($3,830,645)
Earnings: $6,285,309
Emp.: 3
Fiscal Year-end: 12/31/22
Investment Services
N.A.I.C.S.: 523999
William Douglas Toler (Chm)
Dale F. Morrison (Vice Chm)
Sanjay K. Morey (Pres & Co-CEO)
William P. Russell Jr. (Co-CEO &
CFO)

TWIN VEE POWERCATS CO.
3101 S US-Highway 1, Fort Pierce,
FL 34982
Tel.: (772) 429-2525   FL
Web Site: https://www.twinvee.com
Year Founded: 1994
VEEE—(NASDAQ)
Rev.: $31,987,724
Assets: $38,231,480
Liabilities: $5,210,591
Net Worth: $33,020,889
Earnings: ($5,137,252)
Emp.: 170

Fiscal Year-end: 12/31/22
Boat Building & Repairing
N.A.I.C.S.: 336612
Michael P. Dickerson (CFO & Chief
Admin Officer)
Joseph C. Visconti (Founder, Chm &
CEO)
Preston Yarborough (VP & Dir)
Karl J. Zimmer (Pres)

Subsidiaries:

Forza X1, Inc. (1)
3101 S US Highway 1, Fort Pierce, FL
34982   **(100%)**
Tel.: (772) 202-8039
Web Site: https://forzax1.com
Rev.: $23,178
Assets: $14,221,926
Liabilities: $521,723
Net Worth: $13,700,203
Earnings: ($3,630,081)
Emp.: 16
Fiscal Year-end: 12/31/2022
Electric Boat Mfr
N.A.I.C.S.: 336320
Michael P. Dickerson (Chief Admin Officer)
Joseph C. Visconti (CEO & Chm)
Carrie Gunnerson (CFO)

TWINLAB CONSOLIDATED
HOLDINGS, INC.
4800 T-Rex Ave Ste 305, Boca Ra-
ton, FL 33431
Tel.: (561) 443-4301   NV
Web Site: https://www.tchhome.com
Year Founded: 2013
TLCC—(OTCIQ)
Rev.: $52,584,000
Assets: $20,912,000
Liabilities: $146,223,000
Net Worth: ($125,311,000)
Earnings: ($8,222,000)
Emp.: 46
Fiscal Year-end: 12/31/22
Holding Company
N.A.I.C.S.: 551112
David L. Van Andel (Chm)
Craig Fabel (Pres & CEO)

Subsidiaries:

Reserve Life Nutrition, L.L.C. (1)
2255 Glades Rd Ste 342, Boca Raton, FL
33431
Tel.: (855) 779-3556
Web Site:
http://www.reservelifenutrition.com
Nutrition Product Retailer
N.A.I.C.S.: 456191
Brooke Place (VP-Sales-Marketing)

Reserve Life Organics, LLC (1)
4800 T-Rex Ave Ste 225, Boca Raton, FL
33431
Web Site: https://reserveage.tlchealth.com
Nutrition Product Retailer
N.A.I.C.S.: 456191

Twinlab Consolidation
Corporation (1)
4800 T-Rex Ave Ste 305, Boca Raton, FL
33431
Tel.: (212) 651-8500
Web Site: https://www.twinlab.com
Nutritional Products & Dietary Supplements
Mfr & Marketer
N.A.I.C.S.: 325411

Subsidiary (Domestic):

NutraScience Labs, Inc. (2)
70 Carolyn Blvd, Farmingdale, NY 11735
Tel.: (631) 247-0660
Web Site: https://www.nutrasciencelabs.com
Medical Products Mfr
N.A.I.C.S.: 325411
Vincent Tricarico (COO, Exec VP & VP-
Contract Mfg)
Christopher Bennett (Art Dir)
Gene Bruno (VP-Scientific & Regulatory
Affairs)
Michael Layman (Mgr-Warehouse)
Mike Maurrasse (Dir-Information Technol-
ogy)

Twinlab Holdings, Inc. (2)
601 Abbot Rd E, Lansing, MI 48823
Tel.: (800) 645-5656
Holding Company; Nutritional Products &
Dietary Supplements Mfr & Marketer
N.A.I.C.S.: 551112

Subsidiary (Domestic):

Twinlab Corporation (3)
632 Broadway Ste 201, New York, NY
10012
Tel.: (212) 651-8500
Nutritional Products & Dietary Supplements
Mfr & Marketer
N.A.I.C.S.: 325411
Thomas A. Tolworthy (Pres & CEO)

Plant (Domestic):

Twinlab Corp. - Utah Facility (4)
600 Quality Dr, American Fork, UT 84003
Tel.: (801) 763-0700
Web Site: https://www.twinlab.com
Nutritional Products & Dietary Supplements
Mfr
N.A.I.C.S.: 325411

TWIST BIOSCIENCE CORPO-
RATION
681 Gateway Blvd, South San Fran-
cisco, CA 94080   DE
Web Site:
https://www.twistbioscience.com
Year Founded: 2013
TWST—(NASDAQ)
Rev.: $312,974,000
Assets: $614,323,000
Liabilities: $141,634,000
Net Worth: $472,689,000
Earnings: ($208,726,000)
Emp.: 923
Fiscal Year-end: 09/30/24
Research & Development in Biotech-
nology (except Nanobiotechnology)
N.A.I.C.S.: 541714
Adam Laponis (CFO)
Martin Kunz (Sr VP-Bus Technolo-
gies)
Emily M. Leproust (Co-Founder, Chm
& CEO)
William Banyai (Co-Founder, Sr VP-
Advanced Dev & Gen Mgr-Data Stor-
age)
Bill Peck (Co-Founder)
Aaron Sato (Chief Scientific Officer)
Patrick John Finn (Pres & COO)
Paula Green (Sr VP-HR)
Robert F. Werner (Chief Acctg Offi-
cer)
Erin Smith (Sr VP-Govt Affairs & Pub
Policy)
Angela Bitting (Chief ESG Officer &
Sr VP-Corp Affairs)
Siyuan Chen (CTO)
Dennis Cho (Chief Ethics & Compli-
ance Officer & Gen Counsel)
Steffen Hellmold (Sr VP-Bus Dev-
Data Storage)
Tracey Mullen (Sr VP-Ops)
Nimisha Srivastava (Sr VP-R&D)
Bill Banyai (Sr VP)

Subsidiaries:

Genome Compiler Corporation (1)
PO Box 3635, Los Altos, CA 94024
Tel.: (510) 316-6584
Web Site: http://www.genomecompiler.com
Software Development Services
N.A.I.C.S.: 513210
Orli Bachar (Office Mgr)
Omri Amirav-Drory (Co-Founder & CEO)
Yogev Debbi (Co-Founder & COO)
Roy Nevo (Co-Founder & CTO)
Daniel Chadash (VP-Product)
Adam Yahid (Mgr-QA)
Eran Lesser (Engr-Software)
David Levy (Engr-Software)
Boaz Hachlili (Engr-Software)
Nir Goldfinger (Engr-QA)
Amos Barzilay (Chm)

TWO
900 Kearny St Ste 610, San Fran-
cisco, CA 94133
Tel.: (415) 480-1752   Ky
Year Founded: 2021
TWOA—(NYSE)
Assets: $217,688,355
Liabilities: $225,278,916
Net Worth: ($7,590,561)
Earnings: $1,497,223
Emp.: 3
Fiscal Year-end: 12/31/22
Investment Management Service
N.A.I.C.S.: 523999
Troy B. Steckenrider (CFO)

TWO HARBORS INVESTMENT
CORP.
1601 Utica Ave S Ste 900, Saint
Louis Park, MN 55416
Tel.: (612) 453-4100   MD
Web Site:
https://www.twoharborsinvest
ment.com
TWO—(NYSE)
Rev.: $480,364,000
Assets: $13,138,800,000
Liabilities: $10,935,410,000
Net Worth: $2,203,390,000
Earnings: ($152,005,000)
Emp.: 466
Fiscal Year-end: 12/31/23
Real Estate Investment Trust
N.A.I.C.S.: 525990
William Greenberg (Pres & CEO)
Sheila Lichty (Treas & VP)
Nicholas Letica (Chief Investment
Officer & VP)
William Dellal (Interim CFO & VP)

Subsidiaries:

Agate Bay Residential Mortgage Se-
curities LLC (1)
601 Carlson Pkwy, Hopkins, MN 55305
Tel.: (612) 238-3392
Mortgage & Mortgage Loan Broker Services
N.A.I.C.S.: 522310

Burlington Bay Residential Mortgage
Securities LLC (1)
601 Carlson Pkwy Ste 1400, Minnetonka,
MN 55305
Tel.: (612) 629-2500
Securities Brokerage Services
N.A.I.C.S.: 523150

RoundPoint Mortgage Servicing
LLC (1)
PO Box 19789, Charlotte, NC 28219-9409
Web Site:
https://www.roundpointmortgage.com
Mortgage Insurance Services
N.A.I.C.S.: 524126

TH TRS Corp. (1)
601 Carlson Pkwy Ste 1400, Minnetonka,
MN 55305
Tel.: (612) 259-5710
Web Site:
https://www.twoharborsinvestment.com
Investment Management Service
N.A.I.C.S.: 523940

TWO RIVERS FINANCIAL
GROUP, INC.
Tel.: (319) 753-9145   IA
Web Site: https://www.tworivers.bank
Year Founded: 1989
TRVR—(OTCQX)
Bank Holding Company
N.A.I.C.S.: 551111
Kent M. Gaudian (Pres & CEO)
Andrea Gerst (CFO)
Rhonda Carlston (Sr VP-Human Re-
sources)
Darrell Burchfield (Sr VP-Information
Technology)

Subsidiaries:

Two Rivers Bank & Trust   (1)

Two Rivers Financial Group, Inc.—(Continued)

222 N Main St, Burlington, IA 52601
Tel.: (319) 753-9100
Web Site: http://www.tworiversbank.com
Sales Range: $100-124.9 Million
Emp.: 120
Bank & Trust Company
N.A.I.C.S.: 522180
Robert G. McCulley (Chm-Two Rivers Bank
& Trust & Vice Chm-Two Rivers Fin)
Cristy Schmidt (Chm)
Kathy Strawhacker (VP-Minneapolis)
Renee Zaiser (Dir-Good Neighbours' Club)
John Walz (VP-Svcs)
Tim Quick (VP-Comml Lending)
Ed Mansheim (VP-Commercial)
Shane Zimmerman (Pres & CEO)

TX RAIL PRODUCTS, INC.

12080 Virginia Blvd, Ashland, KY
41102
Tel.: (606) 929-5655 **GA**
Web Site: https://www.txholdings.com
Year Founded: 2000
TXRP—(OTCIQ)
Rev.: $7,007,868
Assets: $3,645,171
Liabilities: $4,517,069
Net Worth: ($871,898)
Earnings: $648,353
Emp.: 3
Fiscal Year-end: 09/30/23
Oil & Gas Exploration Services
N.A.I.C.S.: 211120
William L. Shrewsbury (Chm & CEO)
Jose Fuentes (CFO)

TXNM ENERGY, INC.

414 Silver Ave SW, Albuquerque, NM
87102-3289
Tel.: (505) 241-2700 **NM**
Web Site:
https://www.txnmenergy.com
TXNM—(NYSE)
Rev.: $2,249,555,000
Assets: $9,257,377,000
Liabilities: $7,012,451,000
Net Worth: $2,244,926,000
Earnings: $169,530,000
Emp.: 1,537
Fiscal Year-end: 12/31/22
Holding Company; Electric Utility Services
N.A.I.C.S.: 551112
Patricia K. Vincent-Collawn (Chm & CEO)
Michael Patrick Mertz (CIO & VP)
Joseph Don Tarry (Pres & COO)
Becky Teague (VP-HR)
Robert Bischoff (VP & Controller)
Sabrina Greinel (Treas & VP)
Sheila Mendez (CIO & VP)
Neal Walker (VP-TNMP)
Brian G. Iverson (Gen Counsel, Sec
& Sr VP-Regulatory & Public Policy)
Elisabeth A. Eden (CFO & Sr VP)

Subsidiaries:

Public Service Company of New
Mexico (1)
414 Silver Ave SW, Albuquerque, NM
87102-3289
Tel.: (505) 241-2700
Web Site: https://www.pnm.com
Rev.: $1,766,825,000
Assets: $6,272,166,000
Liabilities: $4,311,842,000
Net Worth: $1,960,324,000
Earnings: $103,898,000
Emp.: 751
Fiscal Year-end: 12/31/2022
Electric Power Distr
N.A.I.C.S.: 221122
Patricia K. Vincent-Collawn (Chm, Pres &
CEO)
Julie Rowey (VP-Customer Svc Ops)
Patrick Apodaca (Gen Counsel & Sr VP)
Ron Darnell (Sr VP)
Maureen Gannon (Chief Environmental Officer)
E. A. Eden (CFO)

Subsidiary (Domestic):

TNP Enterprises, Inc. (2)
414 Silver Ave SW, Albuquerque, NM
87158
Tel.: (505) 241-4287
Electric Utility Holding Company
N.A.I.C.S.: 221118

Subsidiary (Domestic):

Texas-New Mexico Power
Company (3)
577 N Garden Ridge Blvd, Lewisville, TX
75067
Tel.: (972) 420-4189
Web Site: https://www.tnmp.com
Rev.: $482,730,000
Assets: $2,746,601,000
Liabilities: $1,644,777,000
Net Worth: $1,101,824,000
Earnings: $92,267,000
Emp.: 367
Fiscal Year-end: 12/31/2022
Electric Power Distribution & Generation
Services
N.A.I.C.S.: 221118
Neal Walker (Pres)
Stacy Whitehurst (VP-Regulatory Affairs)
Chris Gerety (VP)

TXO PARTNERS, L.P.

400 W 7th St, Fort Worth, TX 76102
Tel.: (817) 334-7800 **DE**
Web Site:
https://www.txopartners.com
Year Founded: 2012
TXO—(NYSE)
Rev.: $246,397,000
Assets: $924,632,000
Liabilities: $403,095,000
Net Worth: $521,537,000
Earnings: ($7,668,000)
Emp.: 180
Fiscal Year-end: 12/31/22
Natural Gas Extraction Services
N.A.I.C.S.: 211130
Bob R. Simpson (Chm & CEO)
Brent W. Clum (CFO & Pres-Bus
Ops)
Keith A. Hutton (Pres-Production &
Development)

Subsidiaries:

MorningStar Operating LLC (1)
400 W 6th St, Fort Worth, TX 76102
Web Site: https://morningstaroperating.com
Oil & Gas Distr
N.A.I.C.S.: 221210

TYLER TECHNOLOGIES, INC.

5101 Tennyson Pkwy, Plano, TX
75024
Tel.: (972) 713-3700 **DE**
Web Site: https://www.tylertech.com
Year Founded: 1966
TYL—(NYSE)
Rev.: $1,951,751,000
Assets: $4,676,663,000
Liabilities: $1,738,668,000
Net Worth: $2,937,995,000
Earnings: $165,919,000
Emp.: 7,300
Fiscal Year-end: 12/31/23
Technology, Software, Data Warehousing & Electronic Document Management Systems & Services
N.A.I.C.S.: 541512
Brian K. Miller (CFO, Treas & Exec VP)
H. Lynn Moore Jr. (Pres & CEO)
John S. Marr Jr. (Chm)
Samantha B. Crosby (CMO)
Abigail Diaz (Chief Legal Officer)
Jeff Green (CTO)
Kelley Shimansky (Chief HR Officer)
Jeff Puckett (COO)
Franklin Williams (Pres-Data & Insights Div)
Kevin Iwersen (CIO)

Jason Durham (Chief Acctg Officer)
Russell Gainford (Sr VP)
Jayne Holland (Deputy Chief Legal
Officer)
Jeremy Ward (Chief Information Security Officer)
Brian McGrath (Pres-Courts & Justice
Div)
W. Michael Smith (Chief Acctg Officer)

Subsidiaries:

Computing System Innocations,
LLC (1)
791 Piedmont-Wekiwa Rd, Apopka, FL
32703
Tel.: (407) 598-1800
Web Site: https://csisoft.com
Software Development Services
N.A.I.C.S.: 541511

Incode Computer Management
Services (1)
2730 Ford St, Ames, IA
50010-6442 (100%)
Tel.: (515) 232-6024
Web Site: http://www.incode-cms.com
Sales Range: $25-49.9 Million
Emp.: 60
Management Solutions
N.A.I.C.S.: 449210

MicroPact, Inc. (1)
12901 Worldgate Dr Ste 800, Herndon, VA
20170
Tel.: (703) 709-6110
Web Site: http://www.micropact.com
Software & Information Technology Services
for Government Agencies
N.A.I.C.S.: 541519
Kristoffer Collo (Founder & CEO)

Subsidiary (Domestic):

Iron Data Solutions, Inc. (2)
12901 Worldgate Dr Ste 800, Herndon, VA
20170
Tel.: (404) 817-0033
Web Site: http://www.irondata.com
All Other Personal Services
N.A.I.C.S.: 812990
Thomas Sechler (CEO)
Bob Ragsdale (VP-Marketing)
Brian Combs (VP)
Chuck Barthlow (VP)
Dan Smith (CFO)
Growson Edwards (Chief Customer Officer)
Kristoffer Collo (Pres)
Michael Cerniglia (CTO)
Scott Willette (VP-Engineering)

NIC Inc. (1)
25501 W Valley Pkwy Ste 300, Olathe, KS
66061
Web Site: http://www.egov.com
Rev.: $460,454,000
Assets: $464,349,000
Liabilities: $171,200,000
Net Worth: $293,149,000
Earnings: $68,594,000
Emp.: 1,025
Fiscal Year-end: 12/31/2020
Internet-Based, Electronic Government Services
N.A.I.C.S.: 541614
Stephen M. Kovzan (CFO)
Doug Rogers (Sr VP-Bus Dev)
Jayne Friedland Holland (Chief Security Officer)

Subsidiary (Domestic):

Alabama Interactive, LLC (2)
100 N Union St Ste 630, Montgomery, AL
36104
Tel.: (334) 261-1990
Web Site: http://www.alabama.gov
Sales Range: $10-24.9 Million
Emp.: 16
Telecommunication Servicesb
N.A.I.C.S.: 517810

Arkansas Information Consortium,
LLC (2)
425 W Capitol Ave Ste 1620, Little Rock,
AR 72201
Tel.: (501) 324-8915

Management Consulting Services
N.A.I.C.S.: 541618

Colorado Interactive, LLC (2)
1999 Broadway Ste 3300, Denver, CO
80202
Tel.: (303) 434-3468
Web Site: http://www.colorado.com
Sales Range: $25-49.9 Million
Emp.: 40
Computer System Design Services
N.A.I.C.S.: 541512

Delaware Interactive, LLC (2)
116 E Water St, Dover, DE 19901
Tel.: (302) 526-2314
Web Site: https://www.egov.com
Sales Range: $25-49.9 Million
Emp.: 7
Computer Software Services
N.A.I.C.S.: 449210

Hawaii Information Consortium,
LLC (2)
201 Merchant St Ste 1805, Honolulu, HI
96813
Tel.: (808) 695-4620
Web Site: http://www.hic.ehawaii.gov
Sales Range: $10-24.9 Million
Emp.: 30
Data Processing & Hosting Services
N.A.I.C.S.: 518210
Burt Ramos (Gen Mgr)

Indiana Interactive, LLC (2)
151 W Ohio St Ste 100, Indianapolis, IN
46204-2947
Tel.: (317) 233-2010
Web Site: https://www.indianainteractive.org
Computer System Design Services
N.A.I.C.S.: 541512

Iowa Interactive, LLC (2)
500 E Ct Ave Ste 310, Des Moines, IA
50309-2057
Tel.: (515) 323-3468
Sales Range: $25-49.9 Million
Emp.: 16
Website & Software Programming Services
N.A.I.C.S.: 541511

Kentucky Interactive, LLC (2)
229 W Main St Ste 400, Frankfort, KY
40601
Tel.: (502) 875-3733
Web Site: https://www.kentucky.gov
Emp.: 20
Computer Graphics Services
N.A.I.C.S.: 541512

Montana Interactive, LLC (2)
828 Great Northern Blvd Ste 2A, Helena,
MT 59601
Tel.: (406) 444-2511
Web Site: https://mt.gov
Sales Range: $10-24.9 Million
Emp.: 13
Telecommunication Servicesb
N.A.I.C.S.: 517810

NIC Services, LLC (2)
25501 W Valley Pkwy Ste 300, Olathe, KS
66061-8453
Tel.: (877) 234-3468
Web Site: https://www.egov.com
Sales Range: $25-49.9 Million
Emp.: 50
Data Processing Services
N.A.I.C.S.: 518210

NIC Solutions, LLC (2)
25501 W Valley Pkwy Ste 300, Olathe, KS
66061-8453
Tel.: (913) 498-3468
Web Site: http://www.egov.com
Emp.: 200
Data Processing & Hosting Services
N.A.I.C.S.: 518210

NIC Technologies, LLC (2)
7701 College Blvd, Overland Park, KS
66210
Tel.: (703) 288-1470
Sales Range: $25-49.9 Million
Emp.: 28
Computer Programming Services
N.A.I.C.S.: 541511

Nebraska Interactive, LLC (2)
1135 M St Ste 220, Lincoln, NE 68508
Tel.: (402) 471-7810

Web Site: https://www.nebraska-interactive.com
Emp.: 19
Management Consulting Services
N.A.I.C.S.: 541618

Pennsylvania Interactive, LLC (2)
30 N 3rd St Ste 200, Harrisburg, PA 17101
Tel.: (717) 412-7812
Sheet Metal Work & Roofing Services
N.A.I.C.S.: 238160

South Carolina Interactive, LLC (2)
1301 Gervais St Ste 710, Columbia, SC 29201-3326
Tel.: (803) 771-0131
Web Site: https://www.tylertech.com
Emp.: 20
Custom Computer Programming Services
N.A.I.C.S.: 541511

Texas NICUSA, LLC (2)
100 Congress Ave Ste 600, Austin, TX 78701
Tel.: (512) 651-9300
Web Site: http://www.texasnic.com
Sales Range: $50-74.9 Million
Emp.: 105
Financial Transaction Processing Services
N.A.I.C.S.: 522320
Erin Hutchins *(Gen Mgr)*
Patrick Wood *(Gen Mgr)*

Vermont Information Consortium, LLC (2)
90 Main St Ste 302, Montpelier, VT 05602
Tel.: (802) 229-4171
Web Site: http://www.vermontegov.com
Sales Range: $10-24.9 Million
Emp.: 8
Data Processing Services
N.A.I.C.S.: 518210

West Virginia Interactive, LLC (2)
10 Hale St 3rd Fl, Charleston, WV 25301
Tel.: (304) 414-0265
Web Site: https://www.wvinteractive.com
Sales Range: $10-24.9 Million
Emp.: 12
Data Processing & Related Services
N.A.I.C.S.: 518210

Ram Quest Software, Inc. (1)
6111 W Plano Pkwy Ste 3800, Plano, TX 75093
Tel.: (214) 291-1600
Web Site: https://www.ramquest.com
Sales Range: $10-24.9 Million
Emp.: 50
Computer Sales
N.A.I.C.S.: 449210

Rapid Financial Solutions, LLC (1)
PO Box 6425, Logan, UT 84341
Web Site: https://rpdfin.com
Credit Card Processing Services
N.A.I.C.S.: 522320

Sage Data Security, LLC (1)
2275 Congress St, Portland, ME 04102-1907
Tel.: (207) 879-7243
Security Software Development Services
N.A.I.C.S.: 541511
Sari Stern Greene *(Founder)*
Steve Kallio *(Dir-Innovation & Product Dev)*
Ron Bernier *(Chief Architect)*
Rick Simonds *(Pres & COO)*
Brendan D. Travis *(Dir-Bus Dev-Global)*

Sal, Johnson & Associates, Inc. (1)
791 Piedmont Wekiwa Rd, Apopka, FL 32703
Tel.: (407) 598-1800
Web Site: https://csisoft.com
Rev.: $8,400,000
Emp.: 25
Fiscal Year-end: 12/31/2006
Custom Computer Programming Services
N.A.I.C.S.: 541511
Henry Sal *(Pres & CEO)*

Socrata, Inc. (1)
255 S King St, Seattle, WA 98104
Tel.: (206) 340-8008
Web Site: http://www.tylertech.com
Cloud Data Software Developer
N.A.I.C.S.: 513210
Mathias Burton *(Mgr)*

Tyler Technologies - Eagle Division (1)

14142 Denver W Pkwy Ste 155, Lakewood, CO 80401 **(100%)**
Tel.: (970) 328-7229
Sales Range: $25-49.9 Million
Emp.: 90
Computer Software
N.A.I.C.S.: 541512

Tyler Technologies Incode Solutions (1)
5519 53rd St, Lubbock, TX 79414 **(100%)**
Tel.: (806) 797-0761
Web Site: http://www.tylertech.com
Sales Range: $25-49.9 Million
Emp.: 140
Specialized Software for Commercial Businesses
N.A.I.C.S.: 541512
Dustin R. Womble *(CEO)*

Tyler Technologies, Inc. (1)
1 Tyler Dr, Yarmouth, ME 04096 **(100%)**
Tel.: (207) 781-2260
Web Site: http://www.tylerworks.com
Sales Range: $10-24.9 Million
Emp.: 300
Municipal Information Management
N.A.I.C.S.: 811210
Chris Hepburn *(Pres-Enterprise Grp)*

Tyler Technologies, Inc. - CLT (1)
4100 Miller-Valentine Ct, Moraine, OH 45439
Tel.: (937) 276-5261
Web Site: http://www.cltco.com
Sales Range: $125-149.9 Million
Emp.: 500
Mass Appraisal of Real Estate; Data Systems for Public Administration
N.A.I.C.S.: 561499

Tyler Technologies: FundBalance Solutions (1)
525 Avis Dr Ste 5, Ann Arbor, MI 48108 **(100%)**
Tel.: (734) 677-0550
Web Site: http://www.tylertech.com
Sales Range: $10-24.9 Million
Emp.: 20
Development of Financial Software
N.A.I.C.S.: 541511

US eDirect Inc. (1)
66 Powerhouse Rd Ste 404, Roslyn Heights, NY 11577-1445
Tel.: (516) 484-6201
Web Site: http://www.usedirect.com
Custom Computer Programming Services
N.A.I.C.S.: 541511
Tony Alex *(CEO)*

TYRA BIOSCIENCES, INC.
2656 State St, Carlsbad, CA 92008
Tel.: (619) 728-4760   DE
Web Site: https://www.tyra.bio
Year Founded: 2018
TYRA—(NASDAQ)
Rev.: $3,602,000
Assets: $266,181,000
Liabilities: $8,352,000
Net Worth: $257,829,000
Earnings: ($55,325,000)
Emp.: 38
Fiscal Year-end: 12/31/22
Biotechnology Research & Development Services
N.A.I.C.S.: 541714
Alan Fuhrman *(CFO & Principal Acctg Officer)*
Hiroomi Tada *(Chief Medical Officer)*
kelleen Chea *(Office Mgr)*
Todd Harris *(Pres & CEO)*
Daniel Bensen *(COO)*
Robert L. Hudkins *(CTO)*
Piyush Patel *(Chief Dev Officer)*
Ronald V. Swanson *(Chief Scientific Officer)*
Liz Pagano *(Sr VP-Human Resources)*
Julia Rueb *(VP-Finance)*
Sarah Honig *(VP-Corporate Development & Strategy)*
George Melko *(VP-Regulatory Affairs)*
Gary Price *(VP-Quality)*

Michael Bober *(VP-Clinical Dev & Medical Affairs)*
Allison Kemner *(VP-Clinical Sciences & Operations)*

TYSON FOODS, INC.
2200 W Don Tyson Pkwy, Springdale, AR 72762-6999
Tel.: (479) 290-4000   DE
Web Site:
  https://www.tysonfoods.com
Year Founded: 1935
TSN—(NYSE)
Rev.: $53,309,000,000
Assets: $37,100,000,000
Liabilities: $18,586,000,000
Net Worth: $18,514,000,000
Earnings: $822,000,000
Emp.: 138,000
Fiscal Year-end: 09/28/24
Frozen Food Product Distr
N.A.I.C.S.: 424420
John H. Tyson *(Founder & Chm)*
Lori J. Bondar *(Chief Acctg Officer & Sr VP)*
Noel White *(Vice Chm)*
Jason Nichol *(Chief Customer Officer)*
Amy Tu *(Chief Admin Officer & Pres-Intl)*
Johanna Soderstrom *(Chief People Officer & Exec VP)*
Scott Brooks *(Sr VP-Food Safety & Quality Assurance)*
Brady Stewart *(Pres-Fresh Meats)*
Phillip W. Thomas *(VP & Controller)*
Claudia Coplein *(Chief Medical Officer)*
Melanie Boulden *(Grp Pres-Prepared Foods & Chief Growth Officer)*
David Bray *(Pres-Poultry Grp)*
Sandy Luckcuck *(Pres-Global McDonalds Bus Unit)*
Ildefonso Silva *(Exec VP-Bus Svcs)*
Melanie Boulden *(Chief Growth Officer & Exec VP)*
Adam Deckinger *(Gen Counsel & Sec)*
Donnie D. King *(Pres & CEO)*
Curt T. Calaway *(CFO)*

Subsidiaries:

AdvancePierre Foods Holdings, Inc. (1)
9987 Carver Rd Ste 500, Cincinnati, OH 45242 **(100%)**
Web Site: http://www.advancepierre.com
Sales Range: $1-4.9 Billion
Holding Company; Processed & Frozen Food Products Mfr & Distr
N.A.I.C.S.: 551112
James L. Clough *(Pres)*

Subsidiary (Domestic):

AdvancePierre Foods, Inc. (2)
9987 Carver Rd Ste 5, Cincinnati, OH 45242
Tel.: (800) 969-2747
Web Site: http://www.advancepierre.com
Processed & Frozen Foods Mfr & Distr
N.A.I.C.S.: 311999
James L. Clough *(Pres)*

Subsidiary (Domestic):

Barber Foods, LLC (3)
PO Box 219, Kings Mountain, NC 28086
Frozen Food Product Mfr
N.A.I.C.S.: 311412

Aidells Sausage Company, Inc. (1)
PO Box 2020, Springdale, AR 72765
Web Site: https://www.aidells.com
Sausage Product Mfr
N.A.I.C.S.: 311612

Artisan Bread Co., LLC (1)
434 SE 47th Ter, Cape Coral, FL 33904
Tel.: (239) 931-3939
Web Site: http://www.artisanbreadco.com
Bakery Products Mfr

N.A.I.C.S.: 311812

Central Industries, Inc. (1)
Business Center at Owings Mills 11438 Cronridge Dr Ste W, Owings Mills, MD 21117
Web Site:
  http://www.centralindustriesusa.com
Lighting Product Mfr
N.A.I.C.S.: 335139

Cobb Ana Damizlik Tavukculuk Sanayi Ve Ticaret Limited Sirketi (1)
Bandirma Karacabey Yolu, Sirincavus Koyu Mah, Bandirma, Balikesir, Turkiye
Tel.: (90) 2667439400
Food Store Operator
N.A.I.C.S.: 445298

Cobb-Vantress, Inc. (1)
4703 US Hwy 412 E, Siloam Springs, AR 72761-1030 **(100%)**
Tel.: (479) 524-3166
Web Site: https://www.cobb-vantress.com
Sales Range: $700-749.9 Million
Emp.: 1,700
Poultry Research & Development Services; Broiler Breeding Stock Production & Improvement Services
N.A.I.C.S.: 115210
Cassiano Bevilaqua *(Assoc Dir-Mktg-South America)*
Aldo Rossi *(VP-R&D)*
Gene Shepherd *(Mng Dir-Quality Assurance & Veterinary Svcs-World)*
Ben Church *(VP)*
Chris Lewellen *(CFO)*
Vic De Martino *(Mng Dir)*
Ray Ables *(VP)*
William Herring *(VP)*
Kendall Layman *(Mng Dir)*

Subsidiary (Non-US):

Cobb Europe Limited (2)
Tel.: (44) 1206835835
Web Site:
  http://www.cobbeuropecareers.com
Sales Range: $25-49.9 Million
Emp.: 4
Food Mfr
N.A.I.C.S.: 311999
David Lawton *(Dir-Fin-Europe, Middle East & Africa)*
Matthew Wilson *(Dir-Technical-Europe, Middle East & Africa)*

Cobb-Vantress Brasil Ltda. (2)
Rod Assis Chateaubriand 10 Km, PO Box 2, Guapiacu, Sao Paulo, 15110-970, Brazil
Tel.: (55) 1732679999
Web Site: http://www.cobb-vantress.com
Emp.: 600
Food Mfr
N.A.I.C.S.: 311999

Global Employment Services, Inc. (1)
1703 Old Mobile Hwy, Pascagoula, MS 39567-4460
Tel.: (228) 762-9899
Web Site:
  http://www.globalemploymentservices inc.com
Sales Range: $25-49.9 Million
Emp.: 6
Miscellaneous Food Mfr
N.A.I.C.S.: 311999

Golden Island Jerky Company, Inc. (1)
10646 Fulton Ct, Rancho Cucamonga, CA 91730
Tel.: (909) 987-0470
Web Site: http://www.goldenislandjerky.com
Food Store Operator
N.A.I.C.S.: 445298

Keystone Foods LLC (1)
905 Airport Rd Ste 400, Westchester, PA 19380-2998
Tel.: (610) 667-6700
Web Site: http://www.keystonefoods.com
Beef, Pork & Poultry Products Mfr & Food-Service Industry Custom Distribution Services
N.A.I.C.S.: 311999

Subsidiary (Domestic):

Equity Group Kentucky Division LLC (2)

Tyson Foods, Inc.—(Continued)

2294 State Hwy 90 W, Albany, KY 42602
Tel.: (606) 387-4559
Sales Range: $75-99.9 Million
Emp.: 1,800
Poultry Processor & Distr
N.A.I.C.S.: 311615
Barry Haddix *(Mgr-IT)*

M&M Restaurant Supply (2)
201 Waverly Blvd, Coatesville, PA 19320-1649
Tel.: (610) 485-7600
Retailer of Groceries
N.A.I.C.S.: 311612

Mac Food Services (Malaysia) SDN. BHD. (1)
No 7 Jalan SS13/5, 47500, Subang Jaya, Selangor Darul Ehsan, Malaysia
Tel.: (60) 356330222
Web Site: https://www.tysonfoods.com.my
Emp.: 1,500
Restaurant Food Services
N.A.I.C.S.: 722511
LayHoon Tay *(Mgr-Lab)*

McKey Food Services (Thailand) Limited (1)
210 Moo 1 Tepharak Rd, Bangsaothong
Subdistrict Bangsaothong District, Samut Prakan, 10570, Thailand
Tel.: (66) 23154763
Restaurant Food Services
N.A.I.C.S.: 722511

McKey Food Services Limited (1)
Qing Shui He Warehouse District Hong Ling North Road, Shenzhen, 518024, China
Tel.: (86) 75582260708
Restaurant Food Services
N.A.I.C.S.: 722511

Philadelphia Cheesesteak Company (1)
520 E Hunting Park Ave, Philadelphia, PA 19124
Tel.: (215) 423-3333
Web Site: http://www.phillycheesesteak.com
Processed Meat Product Mfr
N.A.I.C.S.: 311999
Nicholas Karamatsoukas *(Pres)*

Philadelphia Pre-Cooked Steak, Inc. (1)
4001 N American St, Philadelphia, PA 19140
Tel.: (215) 426-4949
Web Site: http://www.phillycookedsteak.com
Pre-Cooked Meat Products Mfr
N.A.I.C.S.: 311999

Sara Lee Trademark Holdings Australasia LLC (1)
Kitchens of Sara Lee, PO Box 105, Ring Road, Wendouree, 3355, VIC, Australia
Tel.: (61) 353380200
Web Site: http://www.saralee.com.au
Holding Company
N.A.I.C.S.: 551112

Shandong Keystone Chinwhiz Foods Co. Ltd. (1)
No 525 Xin Chang Road, Changle, Shandong, 262400, Weifang, China
Tel.: (86) 5366853599
Restaurant Food Services
N.A.I.C.S.: 722511

Shandong Tyson-Da Long Food Company Limited (1)
East End Of Mizhou Road, ZhuCheng, Shandong, China
Tel.: (86) 5366080168
Food Store Operator
N.A.I.C.S.: 445298

Tecumseh Poultry LLC (1)
13151 Dovers St, Waverly, NE 68462
Tel.: (402) 786-1000
Web Site: https://www.smartchicken.com
Poultry Processing Product Mfr
N.A.I.C.S.: 311615
Randy Zotti *(Mgr-Procurement)*

The Bruss Company (1)
3548 N Kostner Ave, Chicago, IL 60641
Tel.: (773) 282-2900
Web Site: http://www.bruss.com

Emp.: 300
Meat Product Whslr
N.A.I.C.S.: 424470

The Hillshire Brands Company (1)
400 S Jefferson St, Chicago, IL 60607
Tel.: (312) 614-6000
Web Site: http://www.hillshirefarm.com
Rev.: $4,085,000,000
Assets: $2,708,000,000
Liabilities: $2,071,000,000
Net Worth: $637,000,000
Earnings: $213,000,000
Emp.: 9,000
Fiscal Year-end: 06/28/2014
Holding Company; Frozen Baked Goods & Other Consumer Food Products Mfr
N.A.I.C.S.: 551112

Subsidiary (Domestic):

Sara Lee Foods, LLC (2)
400 S Jefferson St, Chicago, IL 60607
Tel.: (312) 614-6000
Food Products Mfr
N.A.I.C.S.: 311991
Elizabeth Tomaselli *(Office Mgr)*

TyNet Corporation (1)
1300 Johnson Rd, Springdale, AR 72762-6015
Tel.: (479) 290-2721
Insurance Agencies & Brokerages
N.A.I.C.S.: 524210

Tyson Breeders, Inc. (1)
2200 W Don Tyson Pkwy, Springdale, AR 72762-6901
Tel.: (479) 290-4000
Poultry Breeders & Hatchery Services
N.A.I.C.S.: 112340
Tom Hayes *(CEO)*

Tyson Chicken, Inc. (1)
2200 Don Tyson Pkwy, Springdale, AR 72762-6999
Tel.: (479) 290-4000
Web Site: http://www.tyson.com
Emp.: 15,000
Egg Farm Poultry Hatchery Services
N.A.I.C.S.: 112310

Tyson Deli, Inc. (1)
665 Perry St, Buffalo, NY 14210-1355
Tel.: (716) 826-6400
Sales Range: $125-149.9 Million
Emp.: 250
Meat & Meat Products Wholesale Distr
N.A.I.C.S.: 311612

Subsidiary (Domestic):

Tyson Prepared Foods, Inc. (2)
508 Elizabeth St, Green Bay, WI 54302-1811
Tel.: (920) 431-7240
Web Site: http://www.tysonfoods.com
Sales Range: $75-99.9 Million
Food Mfr
N.A.I.C.S.: 311999

Tyson Export Sales, Inc. (1)
2200 Don Tyson Pkwy, Springdale, AR 72762
Tel.: (479) 290-4000
Web Site: http://www.tysonfoods.com
Sales Range: $200-249.9 Million
Emp.: 3,500
Poultry Production
N.A.I.C.S.: 445240
John H. Tyson *(Chm)*

Tyson Foods Canada, Inc. (1)
5900 Ambler Dr, Mississauga, L4W 2N3, ON, Canada
Tel.: (905) 206-0443
Food Products Mfr
N.A.I.C.S.: 311991
Marjorie Smith *(Dir-Natl Accts)*

Tyson Foods Italia S.p.A. (1)
Via Giardino Giusti 2, 37129, Verona, Italy
Tel.: (39) 0458004039
Web Site: https://www.tysonfoodsitalia.it
Frozen Chicken Product Mfr & Distr
N.A.I.C.S.: 311615

Tyson Foods UK Holding Ltd. (1)
130 Eureka Park Upper Pemberton, Ashford, TN25 4AZ, United Kingdom
Tel.: (44) 1233667250

Food & Beverage Mfr
N.A.I.C.S.: 311999

Tyson Foods, Inc. - Albertville (1)
805 E Mckinney Ave, Albertville, AL 35951
Tel.: (256) 891-8053
Web Site: http://www.tyson.com
Sales Range: $1-9.9 Million
Emp.: 23
Poultry Hatcheries
N.A.I.C.S.: 112340
John H. Tyson *(Chm)*

Tyson Foods, Inc. - Carthage (1)
3865 Hwy 35 N, Carthage, MS 39051
Tel.: (601) 298-5300
Web Site: http://www.tysonfoods.com
Sales Range: $550-599.9 Million
Emp.: 2,500
Poultry Slaughtering & Processing Services
N.A.I.C.S.: 311615

Tyson Foods, Inc. - Chicago (1)
4201 S Ashland Ave, Chicago, IL 60609-2305
Tel.: (773) 650-4000
Web Site: http://www.tysonfoods.com
Sales Range: $750-799.9 Million
Emp.: 2,000
Specialty Frozen Foods Mfr & Processor
N.A.I.C.S.: 311412

Tyson Fresh Meats, Inc. (1)
2200 W Don Tyson Pkwy, Springdale, AR 72762
Sales Range: $10-24.9 Million
Emp.: 3,000
Fresh Beef & Pork Products Producer & Processor
N.A.I.C.S.: 311611
John H. Tyson *(Chm)*

Plant (Domestic):

Tyson Fresh Meats, Inc. (2)
PO Box 30500, Amarillo, TX 79120
Tel.: (806) 335-1531
Web Site: http://www.tysonfoods.com
Beef Slaughtering & Processing Services
N.A.I.C.S.: 311611

Tyson Fresh Meats, Inc. (2)
2101 W 6th Ave, Emporia, KS 66801-6323
Tel.: (620) 343-3640
Beef Slaughtering & Processing Services
N.A.I.C.S.: 311611
Louis Villalobos *(Plant Mgr)*

Tyson Fresh Meats, Inc. (2)
28424 38 Ave N, Hillsdale, IL 61257 (100%)
Tel.: (309) 658-2291
Web Site: http://www.tyson.com
Emp.: 2,000
Beef Slaughtering & Processing Services
N.A.I.C.S.: 311611

Tyson Fresh Meats, Inc. (2)
13983 Dodd Rd, Wallula, WA 99363 (100%)
Tel.: (509) 547-7545
Web Site: http://www.tyson.com
Beef Slaughtering & Processing Services
N.A.I.C.S.: 311611

Tyson Fresh Meats, Inc. (2)
PO Box 149, Holcomb, KS 67851-0149
Tel.: (620) 277-2614
Web Site: http://www.tyson.com
Sales Range: $10-24.9 Million
Emp.: 3,000
Beef Slaughtering & Processing Services
N.A.I.C.S.: 311611

Tyson Fresh Meats, Inc. (2)
1500 S Plumcreek Pkwy, Lexington, NE 68850-0920 (100%)
Tel.: (308) 324-5671
Web Site: http://www.tysonfoods.com
Emp.: 2,800
Beef Slaughtering & Processing Services
N.A.I.C.S.: 311611

Tyson Fresh Meats, Inc. (2)
PO Box 669, Storm Lake, IA 50588-0669 (100%)
Tel.: (712) 732-7433
Pork Slaughtering & Processing Services
N.A.I.C.S.: 311611

Tyson Fresh Meats, Inc. (2)

Hwy 70 N, Columbus Junction, IA 52738
Tel.: (319) 728-7432
Web Site: http://www.tyson.com
Sales Range: $10-24.9 Million
Emp.: 1,000
Pork Slaughtering & Processing Services
N.A.I.C.S.: 311611

Tyson Fresh Meats, Inc. (2)
1350 I Ct, Perry, IA 50220 (100%)
Tel.: (515) 465-5363
Web Site: http://www.tyson.com
Emp.: 1,200
Pork Slaughtering & Processing Services
N.A.I.C.S.: 311611
Steve Stouffer *(Pres)*

Tyson Fresh Meats, Inc. (2)
501 N Elk Run Rd, Waterloo, IA 50703-9471
Tel.: (319) 236-2636
Web Site: http://www.tyson.com
Pork Slaughtering & Processing Services
N.A.I.C.S.: 311611
Steve Stouffer *(Pres)*

Tyson Fresh Meats, Inc. (2)
1200 Industrial Pkwy, Madison, NE 68748-1010 (100%)
Tel.: (402) 454-3361
Web Site: http://www.tyson.com
Pork Slaughtering & Processing Services
N.A.I.C.S.: 311611

Tyson Mexican Original, Inc. (1)
2200 Don Tyson Pkwy, Springdale, AR 72762-6999
Tel.: (479) 290-4000
Web Site: http://www.tysonfoods.com
Emp.: 3,000
Snack Food Product Mfr
N.A.I.C.S.: 311919

Tyson Refrigerated Processed Meats, Inc. (1)
700 Wheeler St, Vernon, TX 76384
Tel.: (479) 290-4000
Web Site: http://www.tyson.com
Processed Meat Product Mfr
N.A.I.C.S.: 311612

Universal Meats (UK) Limited (1)
17a Derrycoose Road, Portadown, Craigavon, BT62 1LY, Co Armagh, United Kingdom
Tel.: (44) 2838852772
Web Site: https://www.universalmeat.co.uk
Meat Product Distr
N.A.I.C.S.: 424470
Osmond Gurgan *(Mng Dir)*

Van's International Foods (1)
3285 East Vernon Ave, Vernon, CA 90058
Tel.: (323) 585-4084
Web Site: http://www.vansfoods.com
Food Store Operator
N.A.I.C.S.: 445298

Vans International Foods (1)
3285 E Vernon Ave, Vernon, CA 90058
Tel.: (323) 585-8923
Web Site: http://www.vansfoods.com
Food Products Mfr
N.A.I.C.S.: 311991

Williams Food Works and Distribution, LLC (1)
4009 Greenfield Dr, Union City, TN 38261
Tel.: (731) 886-4581
Web Site: https://williams-food-works-distribution-llc.business.site
Cold Storage Facility Services
N.A.I.C.S.: 561210

Williams Sausage Company, Inc. (1)
5132 Old Troy Hickman Hwy, Union City, TN 38261
Tel.: (731) 885-5841
Web Site: http://www.williams-sausage.com
Sales Range: $25-49.9 Million
Emp.: 500
Sausage Mfr & Distr
N.A.I.C.S.: 311612
Roger Williams *(Pres & CEO)*
Thomas Ray Sr. *(Plant Mgr)*

Zemco Industries, Inc. (1)
665 Perry St, Buffalo, NY 14210
Tel.: (716) 826-6400
Sales Range: $100-124.9 Million
Emp.: 550
Food Products Mfr

N.A.I.C.S.: 311999

TYTAN HOLDINGS, INC.
120 Estep Rd, Chehalis, WA 98532
Tel.: (360) 431-4800   CO
Year Founded: 2009
TYTN—(OTCIQ)
Farm Machinery & Equipment Mfr
N.A.I.C.S.: 333111
Mark Leonard *(Pres)*

TZP STRATEGIES ACQUISITION CORP.
7 Times Square Ste 4307, New York, NY 10036
Tel.: (212) 398-0300   Ky
Year Founded: 2020
TZPSU—(NASDAQ)
Rev.: $12,667,808
Assets: $288,325,781
Liabilities: $308,214,673
Net Worth: ($19,888,892)
Earnings: $8,903,996
Fiscal Year-end: 12/31/21
Investment Services
N.A.I.C.S.: 523999
Heather Fraser *(Mng Dir & CFO)*
Samuel L. Katz *(CEO)*
Kenneth Esterow *(Pres)*
JoAnne Kruse *(Chief Talent Officer)*

U & I FINANCIAL CORP.
19315 Hwy 99, Lynnwood, WA 98036
Tel.: (425) 275-9700   WA
Web Site:
   http://www.unibankusa.com
UNIF—(OTCQX)
Rev.: $21,353,000
Assets: $403,898,000
Liabilities: $344,813,000
Net Worth: $59,085,000
Earnings: $6,213,000
Emp.: 50
Fiscal Year-end: 12/31/20
Bank Holding Company
N.A.I.C.S.: 551111
Alisa Na *(Founder & CEO)*
Simon Bai *(CFO, Sec, Exec VP & Head-Human Resources)*
Stephanie Yoon *(Exec VP)*
Sue Suk *(Mgr-Corporate Fin)*

Subsidiaries:

UniBank   (1)
19315 Hwy 99, Lynnwood, WA 98036
Tel.: (425) 275-9700
Web Site: http://www.unibankusa.com
Sales Range: $10-24.9 Million
Commericial Banking
N.A.I.C.S.: 522110
Peter Park *(CEO)*
Benjamin Lee *(Chm)*
Simon Bai *(CFO & Sr VP)*

U-HAUL HOLDING COMPANY
5555 Kietzke Ln Ste 100, Reno, NV 89511
Tel.: (775) 688-6300   NV
Web Site: https://www.uhaul.com
Year Founded: 1969
UHAL—(NYSE)
Rev.: $5,625,674,000
Assets: $19,058,758,000
Liabilities: $11,886,313,000
Net Worth: $7,172,445,000
Earnings: $628,707,000
Emp.: 32,200
Fiscal Year-end: 03/31/24
Holding Company; Moving Truck Rental & Storage, Real Estate investment, Life Insurance & Property & Casualty Insurance
N.A.I.C.S.: 551111
Edward J. Shoen *(Chm & Pres)*
Jason A. Berg *(CFO)*
Mark A. Haydukovich *(Pres-Oxford Life Insurance Company)*

John C. Taylor *(Pres-U-Haul)*
Sebastien Reyes *(Dir-IR)*
Samuel J. Shoen *(Program Mgr-U-Box)*
Douglas M. Bell *(Pres-Repwest Insurance Company)*
Maria Lourdes Bell *(Chief Acctg Officer)*
Kristine Campbell *(Gen Counsel)*

Subsidiaries:

ARCOA Risk Retention Group, Inc.   (1)
2721 N Central Ave, Phoenix, AZ 85004   (100%)
Tel.: (602) 263-6755
Property & Casualty Insurance Services
N.A.I.C.S.: 524126
Douglas M. Bell *(Pres)*

Amerco Real Estate Company   (1)
2727 N Central Ave, Phoenix, AZ 85004
Tel.: (602) 263-6555
Web Site:
   https://www.amercorealestate.com
Real Estate Manangement Services
N.A.I.C.S.: 531390
Edward J. Shoen *(Chm & Pres)*

Subsidiary (Domestic):

Amerco Real Estate Company of Texas, Inc.   (2)
6470 E Bolivar St, Vidor, TX 77706
Tel.: (409) 769-0600
Real Estate & Other Related Services
N.A.I.C.S.: 531390

Oxford Life Insurance Company   (1)
2721 N Central Ave, Phoenix, AZ 85004-1121   (100%)
Tel.: (602) 263-6666
Web Site: https://www.oxfordlife.com
Rev.: $50,000,000
Emp.: 65
Insurance Carrier
N.A.I.C.S.: 524130

Subsidiary (Domestic):

Christian Fidelity Life Insurance Company   (2)
2721 N Central Ave, Phoenix, AZ 85004
Tel.: (602) 263-6666
Web Site: https://www.christianfidelity.com
Fire Insurance Services
N.A.I.C.S.: 524114
Mark A. Haydukovich *(Pres & CEO)*

Repwest Insurance Company   (1)
2721 N Central Ave, Phoenix, AZ 85004   (100%)
Tel.: (602) 263-6520
Web Site: http://www.repwest.com
Sales Range: $10-24.9 Million
Emp.: 20
Insurance Provider
N.A.I.C.S.: 524126
Douglas M. Bell *(Pres & CEO)*
Bob Pirmann *(VP-Claims)*

U-Haul International, Inc.   (1)
2727 N Central Ave, Phoenix, AZ 85004-1155   (100%)
Tel.: (602) 263-6194
Web Site: https://www.uhaul.com
Rental Trucks, Trailers, Self-Storage Units, Permanent Hitches, Moving Aids & General Equipment Rentals
N.A.I.C.S.: 532120
Edward J. Shoen *(Chm & CEO)*
Michelle Sullivan *(Mgr-Corp Sustainability)*

Subsidiary (Domestic):

A & M Associates, Inc   (2)
2727 N Central Ave, Phoenix, AZ 85004
Tel.: (602) 263-6555
Web Site: http://www.uhaul.com
Moving Equipment & Storage Space Rental Services
N.A.I.C.S.: 532120

Collegeboxes, LLC   (2)
2727 N Central Ave, Phoenix, AZ 85004
Tel.: (781) 428-4262
Web Site: https://www.collegeboxes.com
Emp.: 8

Collegiate Storage & Shipping Services
N.A.I.C.S.: 484210

EMove, Inc.   (2)
2721 N Central Ave, Phoenix, AZ 85004
Web Site: http://www.emove.com
Warehousing & Storage Services
N.A.I.C.S.: 531130

U-Haul Co. of Alabama, Inc.   (2)
3028 Bessemer Rd, Birmingham, AL 35208
Tel.: (205) 785-1524
Moving Equipment & Storage Space Rental Services
N.A.I.C.S.: 532120

U-Haul Co. of Alaska, Inc.   (2)
4751 Old Seward Hwy, Anchorage, AK 99503
Tel.: (907) 561-2266
Web Site: http://www.uhaul.com
Truck Rental & Leasing
N.A.I.C.S.: 532120
Joe Shone *(Pres)*

U-Haul Co. of Arizona   (2)
2626 E Indian School Rd, Phoenix, AZ 85016
Tel.: (602) 977-0902
Moving Equipment & Storage Space Rental Services
N.A.I.C.S.: 532120

U-Haul Co. of Arkansas   (2)
7618 Kanis Rd, Little Rock, AR 72204
Tel.: (501) 224-5510
Sales Range: $25-49.9 Million
Emp.: 12
Moving Equipment & Storage Space Rental Services
N.A.I.C.S.: 532120
Angela Cogar *(Mgr)*

U-Haul Co. of Charleston   (2)
1902 7th Ave, Charleston, WV 25387
Tel.: (304) 344-2321
Moving Truck Rental Services
N.A.I.C.S.: 532120

U-Haul Co. of Colorado   (2)
7540 York St, Denver, CO 80229-6698
Tel.: (303) 286-2766
Moving Equipment & Storage Space Rental Services
N.A.I.C.S.: 532120

U-Haul Co. of District of Columbia, Inc.   (2)
2727 N Central Ave, Phoenix, AZ 85004
Tel.: (602) 263-6011
Moving Equipment & Storage Space Rental Services
N.A.I.C.S.: 532120

U-Haul Co. of Florida   (2)
2309 Angel Oliva Senior St, Tampa, FL 33605
Tel.: (813) 247-5936
Web Site: http://www.uhaul.com
Rev.: $11,000,000
Emp.: 180
Trailer Rental Services
N.A.I.C.S.: 532120

U-Haul Co. of Georgia   (2)
300 Peters St SW, Atlanta, GA 30313
Tel.: (404) 681-0502
Moving Equipment & Storage Space Rental Services
N.A.I.C.S.: 532120

U-Haul Co. of Idaho, Inc.   (2)
1121 N Orchard St, Boise, ID 83706
Tel.: (208) 377-3040
Web Site: http://www.uhaul.com
Sales Range: $50-74.9 Million
Emp.: 50
Moving Equipment & Storage Space Rental Services
N.A.I.C.S.: 532120

U-Haul Co. of Indiana, Inc.   (2)
29057 Old US 33, Elkhart, IN 46516
Tel.: (574) 295-3986
Web Site: http://www.uhaul.com
Moving Equipment & Storage Space Rental Services
N.A.I.C.S.: 532120

U-Haul Co. of Kansas, Inc.   (2)
5200 State Ave, Kansas City, KS 66102

Tel.: (913) 287-1327
Moving Equipment & Storage Space Rental Services
N.A.I.C.S.: 532120

U-Haul Co. of Kentucky   (2)
4128 Bardstown Rd, Louisville, KY 40218-3245
Tel.: (502) 491-2660
Moving Equipment & Storage Space Rental Services
N.A.I.C.S.: 532120
Chris Nester *(Gen Mgr)*

U-Haul Co. of Louisiana   (2)
2205 Hollywood, Shreveport, LA 71108-3923
Tel.: (318) 636-7135
Emp.: 10
Moving Equipment & Storage Space Rental Services
N.A.I.C.S.: 532120
Warren Iles *(Pres)*

U-Haul Co. of Maine, Inc.   (2)
47 Western Ave, Augusta, ME 04330
Tel.: (207) 622-4797
Web Site: http://www.uhaul.com
Moving Equipment & Storage Space Rental Services
N.A.I.C.S.: 532120

U-Haul Co. of Maryland, Inc.   (2)
2421 Chillum Rd, Hyattsville, MD 20782
Tel.: (301) 403-1521
Moving Equipment & Storage Space Rental Services
N.A.I.C.S.: 532120

U-Haul Co. of Michigan   (2)
500 and 532 Grandville Ave SW, Grand Rapids, MI 49503
Tel.: (616) 328-6124
Web Site: http://www.uhaul.com
Emp.: 9
Moving Equipment & Storage Space Rental Services
N.A.I.C.S.: 532120

U-Haul Co. of Minnesota   (2)
1227 Central Ave NE, Minneapolis, MN 55413
Tel.: (651) 964-3054
Moving Equipment & Storage Space Rental Services
N.A.I.C.S.: 532120

U-Haul Co. of Mississippi   (2)
825 Hwy 72, Iuka, MS 38852
Tel.: (662) 423-1882
Moving Equipment & Storage Space Rental Services
N.A.I.C.S.: 532120

U-Haul Co. of Nebraska   (2)
4868 S 135th St, Omaha, NE 68137-1651
Tel.: (402) 896-2410
Moving Equipment & Storage Space Rental Services
N.A.I.C.S.: 532120

U-Haul Co. of Nevada, Inc.   (2)
1900 S Decatur Blvd, Las Vegas, NV 89102
Tel.: (702) 251-9250
Moving Equipment & Storage Space Rental Services
N.A.I.C.S.: 532120

U-Haul Co. of New Jersey, Inc.   (2)
252 Irvington Ave, South Orange, NJ 07079
Tel.: (973) 821-4423
Moving Equipment & Storage Space Rental Services
N.A.I.C.S.: 532120

U-Haul Co. of New York and Vermont, Inc.   (2)
389 3rd Ave, Brooklyn, NY 11215
Tel.: (718) 875-2682
Web Site: http://www.uhaul.com
Emp.: 32
Moving Equipment & Storage Space Rental Services
N.A.I.C.S.: 532120

U-Haul Co. of Pennsylvania   (2)
1015-25 S 12th St, Philadelphia, PA 19147
Tel.: (215) 336-8080
Web Site: http://www.uhaul.com
Moving Equipment & Storage Space Rental Services

U-Haul Holding Company—(Continued)

N.A.I.C.S.: 532120

U-Haul Co. of South Carolina, Inc. (2)
400 Orchard Dr, West Columbia, SC 29170-3358
Tel.: (803) 796-3724
Moving Equipment & Storage Space Rental Services
N.A.I.C.S.: 532120

U-Haul Co. of South Dakota, Inc. (2)
923 W 11th St, Sioux Falls, SD 57104
Tel.: (605) 339-0750
Web Site: http://www.uhaul.com
Emp.: 10
Moving Equipment & Storage Space Rental Services
N.A.I.C.S.: 532120

U-Haul Co. of Utah, Inc. (2)
415 W 2100 S, Salt Lake City, UT 84115
Tel.: (801) 487-6231
Moving Equipment & Storage Space Rental Services
N.A.I.C.S.: 532120

U-Haul Co. of Virginia (2)
2855 Airline Blvd, Portsmouth, VA 23701-2704
Tel.: (757) 488-7853
Moving Equipment & Storage Space Rental Services
N.A.I.C.S.: 532120

U-Haul Co. of Wisconsin (2)
924 S 108th St, West Allis, WI 53214
Tel.: (414) 258-3692
Sales Range: $25-49.9 Million
Emp.: 15
Moving Equipment & Storage Space Rental Services
N.A.I.C.S.: 532120
Erica Casberg (Mgr-Site)

U-Haul of Hawaii, Inc. (2)
2722 Kilihau St, Honolulu, HI 96819-2023
Tel.: (808) 836-0977
Moving Equipment & Storage Space Rental Services
N.A.I.C.S.: 532120

U.S. AEROSPACE, INC.
10291 Trademark St, Rancho Cucamonga, CA 91730
Tel.: (909) 477-6504 DE
Year Founded: 1980
USAE—(OTCEM)
Sales Range: $1-9.9 Million
Emp.: 30
Aircraft Parts
N.A.I.C.S.: 336413

U.S. AUTOMOTIVE MANUFACTURING, INC.
1875 E Lake Mary Blvd, Sanford, FL 32773
Tel.: (407) 322-8000 DE
USAM—(OTCIQ)
Automotive Products Mfr
N.A.I.C.S.: 336340
Martin Chevalier (Pres & CEO)

U.S. BANCORP
800 Nicollet Mall, Minneapolis, MN 55402
Tel.: (651) 466-3000 DE
Web Site: https://www.usbank.com
Year Founded: 1863
USB—(NYSE)
Rev.: $40,624,000,000
Assets: $663,491,000,000
Liabilities: $607,720,000,000
Net Worth: $55,771,000,000
Earnings: $5,429,000,000
Emp.: 70,000
Fiscal Year-end: 12/31/23
Bank Holding Company
N.A.I.C.S.: 551111
Terrance Robert Dolan (Vice Chm & Chief Admin Officer)
Andrew J. Cecere (Chm & CEO)

John C. Stern (CFO & Sr Exec VP)
James L. Chosy (Gen Counsel & Sr Exec VP)
Gunjan Kedia (Pres)
Shailesh M. Kotwal (Vice Chm-Payment Svcs)
James B. Kelligrew (Vice Chm-Corp & Comml Banking)
Jodi L. Richard (Vice Chm & Chief Risk Officer)
Elcio R. T. Barcelos (Chief HR Officer & Sr Exec VP)
Gregory G. Cunningham (Chief Diversity Officer & Sr Exec VP)
Dominic V. Venturo (Chief Digital Officer & Sr Exec VP)

Subsidiaries:

CF Title Co. (1)
Via De los Poblados 1-Parque Empresarial Alvento Edifcio D 6a planta, Coral Springs, FL 33065
Tel.: (954) 340-5150
Web Site: http://www.cftitleco.com
Title Insurance Services
N.A.I.C.S.: 524127
Tom Streda (Founder & Pres)

CenPOS, LLC (1)
7750 SW 117th Ave Ste 306, Miami, FL 33183
Tel.: (305) 630-7960
Web Site: https://www.cenpos.com
Financial Services
N.A.I.C.S.: 523999

Elavon Canada Company (1)
4576 Yonge Street Suite 200, Toronto, M2N 6N4, ON, Canada
Tel.: (819) 994-5444
Web Site: https://www.elavon.ca
Financial Support Services
N.A.I.C.S.: 522320

Elavon European Holdings B.V. (1)
Rapenburgerstraat 175 D, Amsterdam, 1011 VM, Noord-Holland, Netherlands
Tel.: (31) 204509614
Holding Company
N.A.I.C.S.: 551112

Elavon European Holdings C.V. (1)
Jan Van Goyenkade 8, Amsterdam, 1075 HP, Netherlands
Tel.: (31) 205214777
Holding Company
N.A.I.C.S.: 551112

Elavon Financial Services DAC (1)
Block F1, Cherrywood Business Park, Dublin, D18 W2X7, Ireland
Tel.: (353) 818202120
Web Site: https://www.elavon.ie
Investment Management Service
N.A.I.C.S.: 522320

Elavon, Inc. (1)
2 Concourse Pkwy Ste 800, Atlanta, GA 30328 (100%)
Web Site: https://www.elavon.com
Integrated Credit & Debit Card Payment, Information Processing Services & Related Software Application Products
N.A.I.C.S.: 522320
Jamie Walker (CEO)
Pari Sawant (Chief Product Officer-)
Manny Cofresi Jr. (Exec VP)
Brad W. Hoffelt (CFO)
Mia Huntington (Exec VP- &)
Scott Lippert (Exec VP-)
Rachel Hansen (CIO)
Akash Dua (Chief Credit Officer-)

Subsidiary (Non-US):

Collective Point of Sale Solutions Ltd. (2)
4576 Yonge Street Suite 200, Toronto, M2N 6N4, ON, Canada
Tel.: (416) 640-2640
Web Site: http://www.collectivepos.com
Point of Sales Services & Payment Processing services
N.A.I.C.S.: 541219

Unit (Domestic):

Fairway Marketing Group (2)

3959 Van Dyke Rd, Lutz, FL 33558
Tel.: (813) 961-5026
Web Site: http://www.fmgpos.com
Sales Range: $25-49.9 Million
Emp.: 1
Point-of-Sale Equipment & Software Distr
N.A.I.C.S.: 423420

Firstar Trade Services Corporation (1)
800 Nicollet Mall 800, Minneapolis, MN 55402
Tel.: (654) 466-3000
Non-Durable Goods Whslr
N.A.I.C.S.: 424990

Housing Capital Company (1)
3200 Bristol St Ste 500, Costa Mesa, CA 92626
Tel.: (714) 434-0340
Sales Range: $25-49.9 Million
Emp.: 25
Land Subdividers & Developers
N.A.I.C.S.: 237210

Integrated Logistics, LLC (1)
4080 Mcginnis Ferry Rd, Alpharetta, GA 30005
Tel.: (770) 521-9235
Emp.: 5
Commercial Banking Services
N.A.I.C.S.: 522110

MUFG Union Bank, N.A. (1)
400 California St, San Francisco, CA 94104
Tel.: (415) 765-0400
Web Site: http://www.unionbank.com
Sales Range: $5-14.9 Billion
Emp.: 10,227
Commercial Banking Services
N.A.I.C.S.: 522110
Michael F. Coyne (Officer-Legal & Gen Counsel)
Julius Robinson (Head-Corp Social Responsibility)
Stephen E. Cummings (Pres & CEO)
Donna Dellosso (Chief Risk Officer)
Johannes Worsoe (CFO)
Masato Miyachi (CEO-GCIB)
Amy C. Ward (Chief HR Officer)
Christopher Higgins (Chief Info & Ops Officer)
Daisuke Bito (Head-Japanese Corp Banking)
Kazuo Koshi (Chm)
Masato Miyachi (CEO-GCIB)
Masatoshi Komoriya (Exec Officer)
Devon Bryan (Chief Info Security Officer)
Francesca Lindner (Officer-Operational Effectiveness)
Jonathan Lindenberg (Head-Corp & Investment Banking)
Mark Thumser (Chief Strategy Officer)

Subsidiary (Domestic):

Morton Capital Management (2)
23945 Calabasas Rd Ste 203, Calabasas, CA 91302
Tel.: (818) 222-4727
Web Site: http://www.mortoncapital.com
Investment Management Service
N.A.I.C.S.: 523940
Eric Jay Selter (Chief Compliance Officer & Exec VP)
Meghan H. Pinchuk (Chief Investment Officer)
Jeffrey Sarti (CEO)
Stacey L. McKinnon (COO)
Sasan Faiz (Mng Dir-Investments)
Joseph A. Seetoo (Partner & Sr VP)
Menachem Striks (Partner & Mgr-Compliance)
Dan Charoenrath (Dir-Private Investment Ops)
Laura M. An (Mgr-Bus Ops)
Angela Roper (Mgr-Portfolio)
Clarisse Sullivan (Coord-Mktg)
Bruce L. Tyson (Partner)
Chris Galeski (Partner)
Wade Calvert (Partner)
Kevin G. Rex (Partner)
Adam Bartkoski (Mgr-Fin & HR)
Moriah Bowles (Mgr-Client Svc)
Arlene Vaughan (Coord-Office)

R.E. Wacker Associates, Inc. (2)
973 Higuera St Ste A, San Luis Obispo, CA 93401

Tel.: (805) 541-1308
Web Site: http://www.rewacker.com
Investment Management Service
N.A.I.C.S.: 523940
Robert E. Wacker (Founder, Chm & Chief Investment Officer)
Bryan Krill (Pres, Mng Partner, COO & Co-Chief Compliance Officer)
Ryan Caldwell (CEO)
Sarah Pazdan (Co-Chief Compliance Officer)
Alex Pock (Dir-Investment Ops)
Bob Priola (Dir-Investment Res)
Kristen Reeves (Mgr-Acct Svcs)
Lena Morrill (Office Mgr)

Mississippi Valley Company (1)
101 N 1st Ave, Phoenix, AZ 85003-1902
Tel.: (602) 257-5470
Business Management Services
N.A.I.C.S.: 561110

Quintillion Limited (1)
24-26 City Quay, Dublin, Ireland
Tel.: (353) 15238000
Web Site: http://www.quintillion.ie
Fund Administration Services
N.A.I.C.S.: 524292

Quintillion Services Limited (1)
24-26 City Quay, Dublin, 2, Ireland
Tel.: (353) 15238000
Web Site: http://www.quintillion.ie
Fund Management & Administration Services
N.A.I.C.S.: 523940

Syncada Europe BVBA (1)
Pegasus Park De Kleetlaan 5B-5C, 1831, Diegem, Belgium
Tel.: (32) 27088866
Audit & Financial Services
N.A.I.C.S.: 522320

Talech, Inc. (1)
410 Cambridge Ave Fl 2, Palo Alto, CA 94306
Web Site: https://www.talech.com
Internet Services
N.A.I.C.S.: 517810
Irv Henderson (Co-Founder)
Leo Jiang (Co-Founder & CTO)
Irv Henderson (CEO & Co-Founder)
Joy Ghanekar (Head)
Shelley Chen (Head-Operations)
Boaz Maor (Chief Customer Officer)

U.S. Bancorp Advisors, LLC (1)
800 N Brand Blvd 16th Fl, Glendale, CA 91203
Investment Advisory Services
N.A.I.C.S.: 523940

U.S. Bancorp Community Development Corporation (1)
9321 Olive Blvd, Saint Louis, MO 63132 (100%)
Tel.: (314) 994-0473
Web Site: https://www.usbank.com
Sales Range: $25-49.9 Million
Emp.: 200
Community Development Project Administration
N.A.I.C.S.: 925120

U.S. Bancorp Equipment Finance, Inc. (1)
13010 SW 68th Pkwy Ste100, Portland, OR 97223
Tel.: (503) 797-0200
Web Site: http://www.usbank.com
Sales Range: $75-99.9 Million
Emp.: 230
Investment Management Service
N.A.I.C.S.: 523940

U.S. Bancorp Foundation (1)
800 Nicollet Mall, Minneapolis, MN 55402-7000 (100%)
Tel.: (612) 659-2000
Web Site: http://www.usbank.com
Sales Range: $1-9.9 Million
Emp.: 5
Grantmaking Foundations
N.A.I.C.S.: 813211

U.S. Bancorp Fund Services, LLC (1)
615 E Michigan St BSMT, Milwaukee, WI 53202

Tel.: (414) 287-3700
Mutual Fund Solution Services
N.A.I.C.S.: 525910

U.S. Bancorp Fund Services,
Ltd. (1)
Governors Square West Bay Road, PO Box
10555, Grand Cayman, Georgetown, KY1-
1005, Cayman Islands
Tel.: (345) 3459462630
Emp.: 3
Fund Administration Services
N.A.I.C.S.: 524292

U.S. Bancorp Investments, Inc. (1)
800 Nicollet Mall 8th Fl, Minneapolis, MN
55402 **(100%)**
Tel.: (612) 303-3020
Web Site: https://www.usbank.com
Sales Range: $125-149.9 Million
Securities Brokerage & Investment Banking
Services
N.A.I.C.S.: 523150

U.S. Bank National Association (1)
800 Nicollett Mall 2nd Fl, Minneapolis, MN
55402
Tel.: (651) 659-2000
Sales Range: $125-149.9 Million
Operating Bank
N.A.I.C.S.: 522110
Gunjan Kedia (Pres)
Dan Farley (Dir-Investment-Private Client
Reserve)
Dominic Venturo (Chief Innovation Officer &
Exec VP)
Stacey Dodson (Pres-Portland & Southwest
Washington)
James Payne (Mgr-Market-Comml Real
Estate-Puget Sound)
Kathy Rogers (Head-Stress Test Process)
Patrick Hawkins (Pres-Austin)
Derek Martin (Pres-St. Louis)
Mike Prescott (Pres-Reg Market)
Tendayi Kapfidze (Head-Economic Analysis)
Jennifer Thompson (Exec VP-IR & Eco-
nomic Analysis)
Gunjan Kedia (Vice Chm)
Jimmy Whang (Head-Comml Products Grp)

Subsidiary (Domestic):

FSV Payment Systems, Inc. (2)
6410 Southpoint Pkwy Ste 200, Jackson-
ville, FL 32216
Tel.: (904) 470-1700
Web Site:
https://www.fsvpaymentsystems.com
Sales Range: $1-9.9 Million
Emp.: 45
Prepaid Card Processing Services
N.A.I.C.S.: 522320

Unit (Domestic):

U.S. Bank Asset Management (2)
777 E Wisconsin Ave, Milwaukee, WI
53202-5300 **(100%)**
Tel.: (414) 765-4055
Web Site: http://www.usbank.com
Sales Range: $25-49.9 Million
Emp.: 15
Investment Advisor
N.A.I.C.S.: 522220

U.S. Bank Business Credit (2)
800 Nicollet Mall, Minneapolis, MN
55402-7000 **(100%)**
Tel.: (612) 659-2000
Web Site: http://www.usbank.com
Sales Range: $10-24.9 Million
Emp.: 60
Asset-Based Small Business
Lending/Business Finance
N.A.I.C.S.: 541211

U.S. Bank Home Mortgage (2)
16900 W Capital Dr, Brookfield, WI
53005-2192 **(100%)**
Tel.: (262) 790-3700
Rev.: $980,000
Emp.: 40
Mortgage Company
N.A.I.C.S.: 522110
Tom Wind (Pres)

U.S. Bank National Association
ND (1)
505 2nd Ave, Fargo, ND 58102 **(100%)**
Tel.: (701) 280-3500

Web Site: http://www.usbank.com
Sales Range: $50-74.9 Million
Emp.: 350
National Bank Charter With Trust Powers
N.A.I.C.S.: 522110

U.S. Bank Trust National Association
SD (1)
141 N Main Ave, Sioux Falls, SD 57104-
6442
Tel.: (605) 339-8600
Web Site: http://www.usbank.com
Sales Range: Less than $1 Million
Emp.: 20
Nationally Chartered Banking Association
N.A.I.C.S.: 522110

U.S. Bank Trustees Limited (1)
125 Old Broad Street Fifth Floor, London,
EC2N 1AR, United Kingdom
Tel.: (44) 2039871820
Web Site: https://usbanktrusteesltd.com
Financial Support Services
N.A.I.C.S.: 522320

USB Capital IX (1)
800 Nicollet Mall, Minneapolis, MN 55402-
4302
Tel.: (651) 466-3000
Financial Support Services
N.A.I.C.S.: 522320

USB Trade Services Limited (1)
Asia Pacific Tower 3 Garden Road 17th
Floor, Central, China (Hong Kong) **(100%)**
Tel.: (852) 6129730363
Sales Range: $10-24.9 Million
Emp.: 20
Trade Services
N.A.I.C.S.: 561990

U.S. ENERGY CORP.
1616 S Voss Ste 725, Houston, TX
77057
Tel.: (303) 993-3200 **WY**
Web Site: https://www.usnrg.com
USEG—(NASDAQ)
Rev.: $44,552,000
Assets: $118,320,000
Liabilities: $39,966,000
Net Worth: $78,354,000
Earnings: ($963,000)
Emp.: 39
Fiscal Year-end: 12/31/22
Exploration & Development of Natural
Resources
N.A.I.C.S.: 212220
Ryan L. Smith (Pres & CEO)

Subsidiaries:

Energy One LLC (1)
877 N 8TH W, Riverton, WY 82501
Tel.: (307) 856-9271
Crude Petroleum & Natural Gas Extraction
Services
N.A.I.C.S.: 211120
Mark J Larsen (Mgr)

U.S. ENERGY INITIATIVES
CORPORATION
20929 Ventura Blvd 47-267, Wood-
land Hills, CA 91364
Tel.: (661) 724-6141 **NV**
Web Site:
http://www.usenergyinit.com
Year Founded: 1996
USEI—(OTCIQ)
Sales Range: Less than $1 Million
Retrofit Systems Mfr For the Conver-
sion of Gasoline & Diesel Engines To
Non-Petroleum Based Fuels
N.A.I.C.S.: 336310
Anthony K. Miller (Chm, CEO & CFO)
Harrison A. McCoy III (Partner, CTO
& Engr-Chemical)

U.S. GLOBAL INVESTORS,
INC.
Tel.: (210) 308-1234 **TX**
Web Site: https://www.usfunds.com
Year Founded: 1983

GROW—(NASDAQ)
Rev.: $10,984,000
Assets: $51,963,000
Liabilities: $2,957,000
Net Worth: $49,006,000
Earnings: $1,333,000
Emp.: 23
Fiscal Year-end: 06/30/24
Investment Manager & Advisor
N.A.I.C.S.: 523940
Frank E. Holmes (CEO & Chief In-
vestment Officer)
Ralph P. Aldis (Portfolio Mgr)
Lisa C. Callicotte (CFO)
Jerold Howard Rubinstein (Chm)
Michael Matousek (Head-Trader)
Joanna Sawicka (Portfolio Mgr)

Subsidiaries:

United Shareholder Services,
Inc. (1)
7900 Callaghan Rd, San Antonio, TX 78229
Tel.: (210) 308-1254
Web Site: http://www.usfunds.com
Sales Range: $50-74.9 Million
Emp.: 50
Mutual Fund Management Services
N.A.I.C.S.: 523910

U.S. GOLD CORP.
1807 Capitol Ave, Cheyenne, WY
82001 **NV**
Web Site:
https://www.usgoldcorp.gold
Year Founded: 1967
USAU—(NASDAQ)
Rev.: $359,854
Assets: $22,581,133
Liabilities: $5,120,678
Net Worth: $17,460,455
Earnings: ($6,897,483)
Emp.: 4
Fiscal Year-end: 04/30/24
Gold Ore Exploration & Mining
N.A.I.C.S.: 213114
Kevin Francis (VP-Technical Svcs &
Exploration)
George M. Bee (Pres & CEO)
Eric Alexander (CFO, Principal Acctg
Officer & Sec)

U.S. PHYSICAL THERAPY,
INC.
1300 W Sam Houston Pkwy S Ste
300, Houston, TX 77042
Tel.: (713) 297-7000 **NV**
Web Site: https://www.usph.com
Year Founded: 1990
USPH—(NYSE)
Rev.: $464,590,000
Assets: $858,154,000
Liabilities: $541,101,000
Net Worth: $317,053,000
Earnings: $32,158,000
Emp.: 3,570
Fiscal Year-end: 12/31/22
Outpatient Physical & Occupational
Therapy Clinics Operator
N.A.I.C.S.: 621340
Christopher J. Reading (Chm & CEO)
Edward L. Kuntz (Vice Chm)
Graham Reeve (COO-West)
Darryl Gotwalt (Reg Pres-East)
Don Ryan (Reg Pres-West)
Floyd Stahl (Reg Pres-Central)
Jennifer Boyette (Reg Pres-South
Central)
Kelly Drake (Reg Pres-South East)
Ashley Giles (VP-Contracting, Cre-
dentialing, and Reimbursement)
Carey P. Hendrickson (CFO)
Eric Williams (Pres & COO)
Jason Anderson (VP-HR)
Jake J. Martinez (Sr VP-Fin & Acctg)

Subsidiaries:

1 On 1 Physical Therapy, LLC (1)

24 Sardis Rd Ste B, Asheville, NC 28806
Tel.: (828) 785-8388
Web Site: https://1on1ptasheville.com
Physical Therapy Services
N.A.I.C.S.: 621340

ARC Physical Therapy Plus, Limited
Partnership (1)
6400 Glenwood St Ste 203, Overland Park,
KS 66202
Tel.: (913) 831-2721
Web Site: https://www.arcpt.com
Emp.: 125
Healthcare Services
N.A.I.C.S.: 621491

ARCH Physical Therapy and Sports
Medicine, Limited Partnership (1)
1701 S Waverly Rd Ste 101, Lansing, MI
48917-4300
Tel.: (517) 367-7851
Web Site: https://archphysicaltherapy.com
Physical Therapy Services
N.A.I.C.S.: 621340

Ability Health Services & Rehabilita-
tion, L.P. (1)
1200 Lexington Green Ln, Sanford, FL
32771
Tel.: (407) 688-0070
Web Site:
https://www.abilityrehabilitation.com
Physical Therapy Services
N.A.I.C.S.: 621340

Achieve Physical Therapy, Limited
Partnership (1)
9550-5 Baymeadows Rd, Jacksonville, FL
32256
Tel.: (904) 731-1044
Sales Range: $10-24.9 Million
Emp.: 2
Physical Therapy Services
N.A.I.C.S.: 621340

Active Physical Therapy, Limited
Partnership (1)
519 Pine St Ste 103, Aledo, TX 76008
Tel.: (817) 441-5500
Web Site: http://www.weatherfordpt.com
Emp.: 2
Physical Therapy Services
N.A.I.C.S.: 621340

Adams County Physical Therapy,
Limited Partnership (1)
110 W Eisenhower Dr Ste E, Hanover, PA
17331
Tel.: (717) 646-8104
Web Site: https://www.adamscountypt.com
Sales Range: $50-74.9 Million
Emp.: 2
Physical Therapy Services
N.A.I.C.S.: 621498

Agape Physical Therapy & Sports
Rehabilitation, Limited
Partnership (1)
4105 Norrisville Rd, White Hall, MD 21161
Tel.: (410) 692-2941
Healthcare Services
N.A.I.C.S.: 621491

Ankeny Physical & Sports Therapy,
Limited Partnership (1)
301 N Ankeny Blvd Ste 200, Ankeny, IA
50023-1730
Tel.: (515) 965-1422
Web Site: http://www.arcpt.com
Sales Range: $50-74.9 Million
Emp.: 10
Physical Therapy Services
N.A.I.C.S.: 621498

Arrow Physical Therapy, Limited
Partnership (1)
3341 S Elm Pl, Broken Arrow, OK 74012-
7924
Tel.: (918) 449-1332
Web Site: https://brokenarrowpt.com
Sales Range: $50-74.9 Million
Emp.: 20
Physical Therapy Services
N.A.I.C.S.: 621498
Curtis Alpers (Owner)

Ashland Physical Therapy, Limited
Partnership (1)
275 C St Lithia Way, Ashland, OR 97520

U.S. Physical Therapy, Inc.—(Continued)

Tel.: (541) 482-6743
Web Site: https://ashlandpt.com
Physical Therapy Services
N.A.I.C.S.: 621340

Audubon Physical Therapy, Limited Partnership (1)
1703 N Causeway Blvd Ste D & E, Mandeville, LA 70471-8615
Tel.: (985) 727-1978
Web Site: https://www.audubonpt.com
Sales Range: $1-9.9 Million
Emp.: 4
Physical Therapy Services
N.A.I.C.S.: 621340

Barren Ridge Physical Therapy, Limited Partnership (1)
32 Windward Dr Ste 110, Fishersville, VA 22939
Tel.: (540) 949-5383
Web Site: http://www.barrenridgept.com
Healtcare Services
N.A.I.C.S.: 621491

Bayside Physical Therapy & Sports Rehabilitation, Limited Partnership (1)
3179 Braverton St Ste 201, Edgewater, MD 21037-2665
Tel.: (410) 956-4308
Web Site: https://baysidept.com
Sales Range: $10-24.9 Million
Emp.: 15
Physical Therapy Services
N.A.I.C.S.: 621340

Beaufort Physical Therapy, Limited Partnership (1)
106-A Professional Park Dr, Beaufort, NC 28516
Tel.: (252) 838-0222
Web Site: https://www.beaufortpt.com
Sales Range: $1-9.9 Million
Emp.: 10
Physical Therapy Services
N.A.I.C.S.: 621498

Bosque River Physical Therapy & Rehabilitation, Limited Partnership (1)
1200 Richland Dr Ste G, Waco, TX 76710-8001
Tel.: (254) 772-0118
Physical Therapy Services
N.A.I.C.S.: 621498

Bow Physical Therapy & Spine Center, Limited Partnership (1)
501 SSt, Bow, NH 03304-3416
Tel.: (603) 224-5883
Web Site:
http://www.bowphysicaltherapyspinecenter.com
Sales Range: $1-9.9 Million
Emp.: 7
Physical Therapy Services
N.A.I.C.S.: 621498

Brazos Valley Physical Therapy, Limited Partnership (1)
711 SW 1st St, Mineral Wells, TX 76067-5117
Tel.: (940) 328-1187
Web Site: https://brazosvalleypt.com
Sales Range: $50-74.9 Million
Emp.: 3
Physical Therapy Services
N.A.I.C.S.: 621498
Melanie Lenamon (Office Mgr)

Brick Hand & Rehabilitative Services, Limited Partnership (1)
515 Brick Blvd, Brick, NJ 08723
Tel.: (732) 840-8100
Web Site: http://www.brickhand.com
Sales Range: $50-74.9 Million
Emp.: 5
Physical Therapy Services
N.A.I.C.S.: 621498

Briotix Health, Limited Partnership (1)
9000 E Nichols Ave Ste 104, Centennial, CO 80112
Web Site: https://www.briotix.com
Sport Medicine Approach & Health Services

N.A.I.C.S.: 621999
Stephen C. Brown (CEO)
Bob Patterson (Founder & Exec VP)
Shelby Spencer (Head-Bus Transformation & Tech Svcs)

Cape Cod Hand Therapy, Limited Partnership (1)
620 Palmer Ave Unit 2, Falmouth, MA 02540
Tel.: (508) 540-5559
Web Site:
http://www.capecodhandtherapy.com
Sales Range: $1-9.9 Million
Emp.: 5
Physical Therapy Services
N.A.I.C.S.: 621498
Wendy Asley (Pres)

Capital Hand & Physical Therapy, Limited Partnership (1)
711 W 38th St Ste C11, Austin, TX 78705-1137
Tel.: (512) 302-3922
Web Site: http://www.texpts.com
Physical Therapy Services
N.A.I.C.S.: 621498

Carolina Physical Therapy & Sports Medicine, Limited Partnership (1)
141 Atrium Way, Columbia, SC 29223
Tel.: (803) 788-8484
Web Site: https://carolina-pt.com
Physical Therapy Services
N.A.I.C.S.: 621340

Comprehensive Hand & Physical Therapy, Limited Partnership (1)
1232 W Indiantown Rd Ste 101, Jupiter, FL 33458
Tel.: (561) 968-7788
Web Site:
https://www.comprehensivehandandpt.com
Sales Range: $10-24.9 Million
Emp.: 25
Physical Therapy Services
N.A.I.C.S.: 621498

Coppell Spine & Sports Rehab, Limited Partnership (1)
413 W Bethel Rd Ste 400, Coppell, TX 75019
Tel.: (972) 304-9100
Web Site: http://www.coppellpt.com
Sales Range: $1-9.9 Million
Emp.: 10
Physical Therapy Services
N.A.I.C.S.: 621498
Anthony Michels (Partner-Flower Mound)
John P. Sims (Owner)

Crawford Physical Therapy, Limited Partnership (1)
1406 Greenbrier Pl, Charlottesville, VA 22901-1696
Tel.: (434) 220-0069
Sales Range: $50-74.9 Million
Physical Therapy Services
N.A.I.C.S.: 621498
Michael O'Grady (Mng Dir)

Cross Creek Physical Therapy, Limited Partnership (1)
7501 Goodman Rd Ste 1, Olive Branch, MS 38654-1951
Tel.: (662) 890-3382
Web Site: http://www.crosscreekpt.com
Sales Range: $1-9.9 Million
Emp.: 5
Physical Therapy Services
N.A.I.C.S.: 621498

Custom Physical Therapy, Limited Partnership (1)
1610 Robb Dr Ste D5, Reno, NV 89523
Tel.: (775) 746-9222
Web Site: https://www.custom-pt.com
Physical Therapy Services
N.A.I.C.S.: 621340

Decatur Hand and Physical Therapy Specialists, Limited Partnership (1)
141 Sams St Ste A, Decatur, GA 30030
Tel.: (404) 296-8511
Web Site:
https://www.decaturtherapyspecialists.net
Physical Therapy Services
N.A.I.C.S.: 621340

Dekalb Comprehensive Physical Therapy, Limited Partnership (1)
6000 Hillandale Dr Ste 145, Lithonia, GA 30058
Tel.: (678) 418-8072
Web Site: https://www.dekalbcomppt.com
Emp.: 7
Physical Therapy Services
N.A.I.C.S.: 621340
Lea Ann Rumlin (Owner)

Denali Physical Therapy, Limited Partnership (1)
3400 LaTouche St Ste 200, Anchorage, AK 99508
Tel.: (907) 563-2122
Web Site: https://www.denalipt.com
Health Care Srvices
N.A.I.C.S.: 621491
Brain Malone (Owner)

Eastgate Physical Therapy, Limited Partnership (1)
108 Glover Dr, Mount Orab, OH 45154
Tel.: (937) 444-2933
Web Site: https://www.sumpt.net
Emp.: 4
Physical Therapy Services
N.A.I.C.S.: 621340

Edge Physical Therapy, Limited Partnership (1)
1000 25th St N, Great Falls, MT 59401-1381
Tel.: (406) 453-5555
Sales Range: $1-9.9 Million
Emp.: 3
Physical Therapy Services
N.A.I.C.S.: 621498
Jeffrey Swift (Partner)

Five Rivers Therapy Services, Limited Partnership (1)
1415 Commerce Dr Ste A, Pocahontas, AR 72455
Tel.: (870) 248-0800
Web Site:
http://www.reachyourpeaktherapy.com
Physical Therapy Services
N.A.I.C.S.: 621340

Flannery Physical Therapy, Limited Partnership. (1)
1465 State Hwy 31, Annandale, NJ 08801
Tel.: (908) 328-3300
Web Site: http://www.usph.com
Physical Therapy Services
N.A.I.C.S.: 621340

Forest City Physical Therapy, Limited Partnership (1)
3920 N Mulford Rd Ste 2200, Rockford, IL 61114-8008
Tel.: (713) 297-7000
Physical Therapy Services
N.A.I.C.S.: 621498

Fredericksburg Physical Therapy, Limited Partnership (1)
1425 E Main St Ste 600, Fredericksburg, TX 78624
Tel.: (830) 391-8009
Web Site: https://www.fredericksburgpt.com
Physical Therapy Services
N.A.I.C.S.: 621340

Frisco Physical Therapy, Limited Partnership (1)
7548 Preston Rd Ste 145, Frisco, TX 75034-5684
Tel.: (972) 712-9693
Web Site: https://www.friscopt.com
Sales Range: $1-9.9 Million
Emp.: 8
Physical Therapy Services
N.A.I.C.S.: 621498

Green Country Physical Therapy, Limited Partnership (1)
115 E Broadway St, Drumright, OK 74030
Tel.: (918) 352-3838
Healtcare Services
N.A.I.C.S.: 621491

Green Oaks Physical Therapy, Limited Partnership (1)
458 N Highway 67 Ste 100, Cedar Hill, TX 75104-3507
Tel.: (469) 272-3129

Web Site: https://www.greenoakspt.com
Sales Range: $1-9.9 Million
Emp.: 15
Physical Therapy Services
N.A.I.C.S.: 621498

HH Rehab Associates, Inc. (1)
47085 Gratiot Ave, Chesterfield, MI 48051
Tel.: (586) 598-1247
Emp.: 5
Physical Therapy Services
N.A.I.C.S.: 621340

Hamilton Physical Therapy, Limited Partnership (1)
1900 Arena Dr Ste 1, Trenton, NJ 08610-2426
Tel.: (856) 589-9014
Sales Range: $1-9.9 Million
Emp.: 4
Physical Therapy Services
N.A.I.C.S.: 621498

Harbor Physical Therapy, Limited Partnership (1)
5500 Knoll N Dr Ste 230, Columbia, MD 21045
Tel.: (410) 964-9650
Physical Therapy Services
N.A.I.C.S.: 621340

High Performance Physical Therapy, LLC (1)
1180 Satellite Blvd NW Ste 100, Suwanee, GA 30024-4636
Tel.: (404) 367-2080
Healtcare Services
N.A.I.C.S.: 621491

High Plains Physical Therapy, Limited Partnership (1)
920 Upland Way, Green River, WY 82935
Tel.: (307) 875-1847
Web Site: https://www.highplainspt.net
Sales Range: $1-9.9 Million
Emp.: 4
Physical Therapy Services
N.A.I.C.S.: 621498
Michael Nelson (Partner)

Highlands Physical Therapy & Sports Medicine, Limited Partnership (1)
304 Wootton St Ste 2B, Boonton, NJ 07005
Tel.: (973) 402-4300
Web Site: http://www.highlandspt.com
Physical Therapy Services
N.A.I.C.S.: 621340

Hoeppner Physical Therapy, Limited Partnership (1)
150 Kennedy Dr, South Burlington, VT 05403-6749
Tel.: (802) 862-4670
Physical Therapy Services
N.A.I.C.S.: 621498

Integrated Rehab Group, Limited Partnership (1)
7728 204th St NE Ste A, Arlington, WA 98223-2500
Tel.: (360) 403-8250
Web Site: https://www.irgpt.com
Sales Range: $10-24.9 Million
Emp.: 10
Physical Therapy Services
N.A.I.C.S.: 621340
M. Shannon O'Kelley (Pres)

Integrius, LLC (1)
100 World Dr Ste 115, Peachtree City, GA 30269
Tel.: (678) 619-0582
Web Site: https://integriussolutions.com
Healtcare Services
N.A.I.C.S.: 621610

Intermountain Physical Therapy, Limited Partnership (1)
3110 E Cleveland Blvd Ste A5, Caldwell, ID 83605-0719
Tel.: (208) 453-8785
Web Site: http://intermountainpt.com
Sales Range: $10-24.9 Million
Emp.: 6
Physical Therapy Services
N.A.I.C.S.: 621498

Julie Emond Physical Therapy, Limited Partnership (1)

36 Chickering Dr Ste 106, Brattleboro, VT
05301
Tel.: (802) 258-2337
Physical Therapy Services
N.A.I.C.S.: 621498

Kingwood Physical Therapy, Ltd. (1)
6318 FM 1488, Magnolia, TX 77354-2519
Tel.: (936) 273-0808
Web Site:
https://www.westwoodlandspt.com
Emp.: 4
Physical Therapy Services
N.A.I.C.S.: 621340

Lake Houston Physical Therapy, Limited Partnership (1)
7840 FM 1960 E Ste 408 & 409, Humble,
TX 77346
Tel.: (281) 812-6665
Web Site: https://www.lakehoustonpt.com
Sales Range: $10-24.9 Million
Emp.: 3
Physical Therapy Services
N.A.I.C.S.: 621340

Leader Physical Therapy, Limited Partnership (1)
5039 Park Ave Ste 102, Memphis, TN
38117-5701
Tel.: (901) 818-9746
Web Site: https://www.memphispt.com
Sales Range: $25-49.9 Million
Emp.: 100
Physical Therapy Services
N.A.I.C.S.: 621498
Andrew Chalona (Mng Dir)

Life Fitness Physical Therapy, LLC (1)
Quarterfield 100 Medical Bldg 7671 Quarterfield Rd Ste 101, Glen Burnie, MD 21061
Tel.: (410) 590-2334
Web Site: https://www.lifefinesspt.com
Physical Therapy Services
N.A.I.C.S.: 621340

Life Strides Physical Therapy and Rehabilitation, Limited Partnership (1)
148 Foothills Center Dr Ste 148 & 150,
West Union, SC 29696
Tel.: (864) 638-6405
Web Site: https://www.lifestridespt.com
Healtcare Services
N.A.I.C.S.: 621491

Madison PT of New Jersey, PC (1)
354 Old Hook Rd, Westwood, NJ 07675
Tel.: (201) 594-9312
Physical Therapy Services
N.A.I.C.S.: 621340

Madison Spine, Limited Partnership (1)
219 Richmond Ave, New Milford, NJ 07646
Tel.: (201) 907-3150
Web Site: https://www.madisonspinept.com
Emp.: 15
Physical Therapy Services
N.A.I.C.S.: 621340

Maine Physical Therapy, Limited Partnership (1)
28 College Ave, Waterville, ME 04901-6105
Tel.: (207) 873-4302
Sales Range: $1-9.9 Million
Emp.: 3
Physical Therapy Services
N.A.I.C.S.: 621498

Mansfield Physical Therapy, Limited Partnership (1)
21 Essex Way Ste 116, Essex Junction, VT
05452-3394
Tel.: (802) 879-8300
Web Site: http://www.mansfieldpt.net
Sales Range: $1-9.9 Million
Emp.: 2
Physical Therapy Services
N.A.I.C.S.: 621498

Maplewood Physical Therapy, Limited Partnership (1)
N79W14749 Appleton Ave Ste C, Menomonee Falls, WI 53051-4375
Tel.: (262) 253-3750
Web Site: http://www.maplewoodpt.com
Sales Range: $10-24.9 Million
Emp.: 3
Physical Therapy Services

N.A.I.C.S.: 621340

Merrill Physical Therapy, Limited Partnership (1)
100 Eagle Dr Ste 2, Merrill, WI 54452-3401
Tel.: (715) 539-2740
Web Site: https://www.merrillpt.com
Sales Range: $1-9.9 Million.
Emp.: 4
Physical Therapy Services
N.A.I.C.S.: 621498

Mission Rehabilitation and Sports Medicine Limited Partnership (1)
2140 Babcock Rd Ste 130, San Antonio, TX
78229
Tel.: (210) 614-7953
Web Site:
https://www.missionphysicalrehabilitation.com
Healtcare Services
N.A.I.C.S.: 621491

Mobile Spine & Rehabilitation, Limited Partnership (1)
6051 Airport Blvd, Mobile, AL 36608-3167
Tel.: (251) 460-0201
Sales Range: $50-74.9 Million
Emp.: 3
Physical Therapy Services
N.A.I.C.S.: 621498

Momentum Physical & Sports Rehabilitation, Limited Partnership (1)
12952 Bandera Rd Ste 107, Helotes, TX
78023-4733
Tel.: (210) 695-2682
Web Site: https://wegetyouhealthy.com
Health Care Srvices
N.A.I.C.S.: 621491
Michelle Little (Office Mgr)
Pam Sinton (Mgr-Billing & Collections)

New Horizons PT, Limited Partnership (1)
2857 Charlestown Rd Ste 200, New Albany,
IN 47150-4972
Tel.: (812) 948-2947
Web Site:
https://www.newhorizonsphysicaltherapy.com
Emp.: 4
Physical Therapy Services
N.A.I.C.S.: 621340
Dale Woolbright (Dir-Clinic-New Albany)

Norman Physical Therapy, Limited Partnership (1)
1250 N Interstate Dr, Norman, OK 73072-3353
Tel.: (405) 573-0121
Web Site: https://www.normanpt.com
Sales Range: $50-74.9 Million
Emp.: 6
Physical Therapy Services
N.A.I.C.S.: 621498
Debra McConnell (Owner)

North Shore Sports & Physical Therapy, Limited Partnership (1)
7419 Granby St, Norfolk, VA 23505
Tel.: (757) 489-5820
Web Site:
http://www.northshoresportsandpt.com
Physical Therapy Services
N.A.I.C.S.: 621340

Northern Neck Physical Therapy, Limited Partnership (1)
6128 Richmond Rd, Warsaw, VA 22572-1660
Tel.: (804) 333-1660
Sales Range: $50-74.9 Million
Physical Therapy Services
N.A.I.C.S.: 621498

Northwoods Physical Therapy, Limited Partnership (1)
5782 US Hwy 31 N, Williamsburg, MI
49690
Tel.: (231) 938-2425
Web Site: http://www.northwoodspt.com
Emp.: 2
Physical Therapy Services
N.A.I.C.S.: 621340

OSR Physical Therapy, Limited Partnership (1)
7872 Century Blvd, Chanhassen, MN
55317

Tel.: (952) 448-9081
Web Site: https://www.osrpt.com
Rehabilitation Services
N.A.I.C.S.: 622310

Old Towne Physical Therapy, Limited Partnership (1)
34434 King St Row Ste 1, Lewes, DE
19958
Tel.: (302) 645-0312
Web Site: http://www.oldtownept.com
Heatcare Services
N.A.I.C.S.: 621491

Oregon Spine & Physical Therapy, Limited Partnership (1)
560 Country Club Pkwy Ste B, Eugene, OR
97401-6044
Tel.: (541) 683-5139
Web Site: http://www.oregonspinept.com
Sales Range: $1-9.9 Million
Emp.: 15
Physical Therapy Services
N.A.I.C.S.: 621498

Pelican State Physical Therapy, Limited Partnership (1)
1703 N Causeway Blvd Ste D & E, Mandeville, LA 70471
Tel.: (985) 727-1978
Web Site: http://www.audubonpt.com
Sales Range: $50-74.9 Million
Emp.: 3
Physical Therapy Services
N.A.I.C.S.: 621498
Joseph Zimmerman (Principal)

Penns Wood Physical Therapy, Limited Partnership (1)
419 Village Dr Ste 3, Carlisle, PA 17015
Tel.: (717) 240-0330
Web Site: http://www.pennswoodpt.com
Healtcare Services
N.A.I.C.S.: 621491

Physical Therapy & Spine Institute, Limited Partnership (1)
18215 S Harlem Ave, Tinley Park, IL 60477-1904
Tel.: (708) 444-2563
Sales Range: $1-9.9 Million
Emp.: 3
Physical Therapy Services
N.A.I.C.S.: 621498

Physical Therapy Northwest, Limited Partnership (1)
2521 Boone Rd SE Ste 100, Salem, OR
97306
Tel.: (503) 585-5131
Web Site: https://www.ptnorthwest.com
Physical Therapy Services
N.A.I.C.S.: 621340
Scot Campbell (Dir-Clinical Advancement)
Jeff Kundert (Dir-Clinic)
Joshua Christopherson (Dir-Clinic)
Mike Hmura (Dir-Clinic)

Pioneer Physical Therapy, Limited Partnership (1)
108 N Township St Ste F, Sedro Woolley,
WA 98284
Tel.: (360) 854-9924
Web Site:
https://www.pioneerphysicaltherapy.com
Physical Therapy Services
N.A.I.C.S.: 621498

Plymouth Physical Therapy Specialists, Limited Partnership (1)
29822 S Wixom Rd, Wixom, MI 48393-3434
Tel.: (248) 926-5826
Web Site: https://www.plymouthpts.com
Sales Range: $1-9.9 Million
Emp.: 8
Physical Therapy Services
N.A.I.C.S.: 621498
Jeff Sirabian (Owner)

Port City Physical Therapy, Limited Partnership (1)
94 Auburn St Ste 3, Portland, ME 04103-2141
Tel.: (207) 797-7578
Physical Therapy Services
N.A.I.C.S.: 621498

Port Orange Physical Therapy, Limited Partnership (1)

1300 W Sam Houston Pkwy S Ste 300,
Houston, TX 77042-2453
Tel.: (386) 322-4641
Sales Range: $1-9.9 Million
Emp.: 2
Physical Therapy Services
N.A.I.C.S.: 621498

Precision Physical Therapy, Limited Partnership (1)
201 Hwy 74 S, Peachtree City, GA 30269
Tel.: (770) 727-6535
Web Site: https://precisionptc.com
Physical Therapy Services
N.A.I.C.S.: 621340

Prestige Physical Therapy, Limited Partnership (1)
2237 Crocker Rd Ste 110, Westlake, OH
44145-7605
Tel.: (440) 617-9600
Web Site: http://www.prestigetherapy.com
Sales Range: $10-24.9 Million
Emp.: 2
Physical Therapy Services
N.A.I.C.S.: 621340

Proactive Physical Therapy, Limited Partnership (1)
1320 S Minnesota Ave Ste 104, Sioux Falls,
SD 57105-0656
Tel.: (605) 332-2565
Web Site: https://proactive-pt.com
Physical Therapy Services
N.A.I.C.S.: 621340
Jeni Figueroa (Gen Mgr)

ProgressiveHealth Companies, LLC (1)
150 N Rosenberger Ave, Evansville, IN
47712
Tel.: (812) 491-3856
Web Site: https://phrehab.com
Healtcare Services
N.A.I.C.S.: 621999

Quad City Physical Therapy, Limited Partnership (1)
5254 Utica Rdg Rd, Davenport, IA 52807
Tel.: (563) 359-3799
Web Site:
https://www.quadcitytandspine.com
Sales Range: $10-24.9 Million
Emp.: 4
Physical Therapy Services
N.A.I.C.S.: 621340

R. Clair Physical Therapy, Limited Partnership (1)
4621 W Park Blvd Ste 102, Plano, TX
75093
Tel.: (972) 985-1776
Web Site: http://www.clairpt.com
Healtcare Services
N.A.I.C.S.: 621491

Radtke Physical Therapy, Limited Partnership (1)
1542 Golf Course Rd Ste 104, Grand Rapids, MN 55744
Tel.: (218) 326-3300
Web Site: https://radpt.com
Healtcare Services
N.A.I.C.S.: 621491

Reaction Physical Therapy, LLC (1)
2270 Joe Battle Blvd Ste R, El Paso, TX
79938
Tel.: (915) 855-7780
Healtcare Services
N.A.I.C.S.: 621491

Rebud Occupational & Physical Therapy, Limited Partnership (1)
916 SW 38th St Ste C, Lawton, OK 73505
Tel.: (580) 353-1490
Web Site: http://www.redbudotandpt.com
Sales Range: $10-24.9 Million
Emp.: 6
Physical Therapy Services
N.A.I.C.S.: 621340

Red River Valley Physical Therapy, Limited Partnership (1)
2720 East Price St, Paris, TX 75460
Tel.: (903) 784-3173
Health Care Srvices
N.A.I.C.S.: 621491
Jason Warren (Partner)

U.S. Physical Therapy, Inc.—(Continued)

Redmond Ridge Management, LLC (1)
10735 Cedar Park Cres NE, Redmond, WA 98053
Tel.: (425) 836-1064
Web Site: http://www.redmondridgeroa
Healtcare Services
N.A.I.C.S.: 621491

Regional Physical Therapy Center, Limited Partnership (1)
211 S Timberland, Lufkin, TX 75901-4065
Tel.: (936) 632-5511
Web Site:
https://www.regionalphysicaltherapy.net
Sales Range: $1-9.9 Million
Emp.: 11
Physical Therapy Services
N.A.I.C.S.: 621498
Dale Botsford (Mng Dir)

Rehabilitation Associates of Central Virginia, Limited Partnership (1)
20347 Timberlake Rd Ste B, Lynchburg, VA 24502
Tel.: (434) 845-9053
Web Site: https://racva.com
Physical Therapy Services
N.A.I.C.S.: 621340
Andrew J. Tatom (Partner)
Joe Spagnolo (Partner)
Michael Richardson (Partner)
Robin Glover (Partner)
Joshua A. Bailey (Pres, CEO & Partner)

Rice Rehabilitation Associates, Limited Partnership (1)
515 Benjamin Way Ste 304, Dalton, GA 30721-4465
Tel.: (706) 278-8066
Sales Range: $50-74.9 Million
Physical Therapy Services
N.A.I.C.S.: 621498

Riverview Physical Therapy, Limited Partnership (1)
23 Bridgton Rd Ste 2, Westbrook, ME 04092-3653
Tel.: (207) 797-3477
Web Site:
https://riverviewphysicaltherapy.com
Physical Therapy Services
N.A.I.C.S.: 621498

Roepke Physical Therapy, Limited Partnership (1)
640 E 8th St, Medford, WI 54451
Tel.: (715) 748-5203
Web Site: http://www.roepkept.com
Sales Range: $50-74.9 Million
Physical Therapy Services
N.A.I.C.S.: 621498

STAR Physical Therapy, Limited Partnership (1)
211 Bedford Way, Franklin, TN 37064
Tel.: (615) 591-8480
Web Site: https://www.starpt.com
Sales Range: $10-24.9 Million
Emp.: 40
Physical Therapy Services
N.A.I.C.S.: 621340
Kelly Ziegler (Partner)
Dave Landers (Partner)
Hal Henninger (Partner)
Leslie Burton (Partner)
Marty Blair (Partner)
Ross Maldonado (Partner)
Dan Saylor (Partner)
Conor Smith (Partner)
Lisa F. Swartz (Partner)

Saginaw Valley Sport & Spine, Limited Partnership (1)
3525 Davenport Ave, Saginaw, MI 48602
Tel.: (989) 497-6040
Web Site: http://www.sportandspine.org
Sales Range: $1-9.9 Million
Emp.: 3
Physical Therapy Services
N.A.I.C.S.: 621498

Seacoast Physical Therapy, Limited Partnership (1)
380 Elm St Unit 7, Biddeford, ME 04005-3070
Tel.: (207) 571-3420

Physical Therapy Services
N.A.I.C.S.: 621340

Signature Physical Therapy, Limited Partnership (1)
4215 N Classen Blvd Ste 102, Oklahoma City, OK 73118
Tel.: (405) 840-1467
Web Site: https://www.signaturept.net
Healtcare Services
N.A.I.C.S.: 621491

Snohomish Physical Therapy, LLC (1)
1830 Bickford Ave Ste 209, Snohomish, WA 98290
Tel.: (360) 568-7774
Web Site: http://www.irgpt.com
Emp.: 10
Physical Therapy Services
N.A.I.C.S.: 621340

Sooner Physical Therapy, Limited Partnership (1)
1337 E State Hwy 152 Ste 111, Mustang, OK 73064
Tel.: (405) 888-5434
Physical Therapy Services
N.A.I.C.S.: 621340

South Tulsa Physical Therapy, Limited Partnership (1)
6767 S Yale Ave Ste B, Tulsa, OK 74136
Tel.: (918) 494-3000
Web Site: http://www.ptoftulsa.com
Sales Range: $50-74.9 Million
Physical Therapy Services
N.A.I.C.S.: 621498

Spectrum Physical Therapy, Limited Partnership (1)
80 Stonington Rd Ste A-3, Mystic, CT 06355
Tel.: (860) 536-1699
Web Site:
http://www.spectrumphysicaltherapy
ct.com
Emp.: 2
Physical Therapy Services
N.A.I.C.S.: 621340

Spine & Sport Physical Therapy, Limited Partnership (1)
3760 Convoy St Ste 100, San Diego, CA 92111
Tel.: (858) 573-9368
Web Site: http://www.spineandsport.com
Physical Therapy Services
N.A.I.C.S.: 621498
Adam Elberg (Chm)
Rick Katz (VP-Bus Dev)

Subsidiary (Domestic):

Complete Care Physical Therapy (2)
552 S Paseo Dorotea 4, Palm Springs, CA 92264
Tel.: (760) 325-5950
Web Site: https://spineandsport.com
Offices of Physical, Occupational & Speech Therapists
N.A.I.C.S.: 621340

Sport & Spine Clinic of Auburndale, Limited Partnership (1)
10524 George Ave Ste 2, Auburndale, WI 54412
Tel.: (715) 652-3470
Web Site:
https://www.auburndalesportspine.com
Physical Therapy Services
N.A.I.C.S.: 621340
Merrie DeGrand (Dir-Clinic)

Sport & Spine Clinic, L.P. (1)
105 N Genesee St, Wittenberg, WI 54499-9176
Tel.: (715) 253-2939
Web Site: http://www.wittenbergpt.com
Sales Range: $1-9.9 Million
Emp.: 3
Physical Therapy Services
N.A.I.C.S.: 621498

Spracklen Physical Therapy, LP (1)
1401 W Michigan Ave, Norfolk, NE 68701-5644
Tel.: (402) 371-8701
Physical Therapy Services
N.A.I.C.S.: 621498

Texstar Physical Therapy, Limited Partnership (1)
1130 Beachview St Ste 120, Dallas, TX 75218-3700
Tel.: (214) 324-5851
Web Site: http://www.texpts.com
Physical Therapy Services
N.A.I.C.S.: 621498

The Hale Hand Center, Limited Partnership (1)
689 S Apollo Blvd, Melbourne, FL 32901
Tel.: (321) 674-5035
Web Site:
https://www.thehalehandcenter.com
Emp.: 8
Physical Therapy Services
N.A.I.C.S.: 621340

The Jackson Clinics, Limited Partnership (1)
119 The Plains Rd Ste 100, Middleburg, VA 20117-2633
Tel.: (540) 687-8181
Web Site: https://www.thejacksonclinics.com
Healtcare Services
N.A.I.C.S.: 621491
Richard T. Jackson (Co-Founder, Pres & Exec Dir-Clinical Svcs)
Anna Jackson (Co-Founder & Exec Dir-Admin & HR)
Ben Keeton (Dir-Clinical Ops)
Cindy Cutright (Dir-Clinical Svcs)
Kristopher Porter (Dir-Educational)
Liliana Flores (Supvr-Billing)

Therapyworks Physical Therapy, LLC (1)
4210 W Jonathan Moore Pike, Columbus, IN 47201
Tel.: (812) 342-3759
Healtcare Services
N.A.I.C.S.: 621491

Thibodeau Physical Therapy, Limited Partnership (1)
1794 N Lapeer Rd Ste C, Lapeer, MI 48446
Tel.: (810) 664-3000
Web Site: http://www.thibodeaupt.com
Physical Therapy Services
N.A.I.C.S.: 621340

Thomas Hand & Rehabilitation Specialists, Limited Partnership (1)
9800 Kincey Ave Ste 180, Huntersville, NC 28078-8412
Tel.: (704) 948-2701
Web Site: http://www.usphclinic.com
Sales Range: $1-9.9 Million
Emp.: 5
Physical Therapy Services
N.A.I.C.S.: 621498

Thunder Physical Therapy, Limited Partnership (1)
10208 N Division Ste 102, Spokane, WA 99218
Tel.: (509) 465-5400
Web Site: http://www.thundertherapy.com
Physical Therapy Services
N.A.I.C.S.: 621340

Town & Country Physical Therapy, Ltd. (1)
4532 W Gate Blvd Ste 100, Austin, TX 78745-1468
Tel.: (512) 892-7337
Sales Range: $50-74.9 Million
Physical Therapy Services
N.A.I.C.S.: 621498

U.S. PT Alliance Rehabilitation Services, Incitation Services (1)
40 W 11th Ave Ste A, York, PA 17404
Tel.: (717) 852-7733
Web Site: http://www.alliancerehab.net
Healtcare Services
N.A.I.C.S.: 621491

U.S. PT Therapy Services, Inc. (1)
8434 Ward Pkwy, Kansas City, MO 64114
Tel.: (816) 237-1926
Professional Services
N.A.I.C.S.: 541990

US PT Therapy Services Inc. (1)
1310 E 15th St, Tulsa, OK 74120-5804
Tel.: (918) 599-0440
Web Site: http://www.uspagecinc.com

Sales Range: $1-9.9 Million
Emp.: 7
Physical Therapy Services
N.A.I.C.S.: 621498

US PT Therapy Services Inc. (1)
840 W Kansas St, Liberty, MO 64068-2033
Tel.: (816) 454-5818
Sales Range: $50-74.9 Million
Physical Therapy Services
N.A.I.C.S.: 621498

US PT Therapy Services Inc. (1)
40 W 11th Ave, York, PA 17404-2040
Tel.: (717) 852-7733
Web Site: http://www.alliancerehab.net
Sales Range: $50-74.9 Million
Emp.: 5
Physical Therapy Services
N.A.I.C.S.: 621498

US PT Therapy Services Inc. (1)
14 2nd St, Farmingdale, ME 04344-2931
Tel.: (207) 582-9898
Web Site: http://www.kennabecpt.com
Sales Range: $50-74.9 Million
Emp.: 4
Physical Therapy Services
N.A.I.C.S.: 621498

US PT Therapy Services Inc. (1)
3914 Centreville Rd, Chantilly, VA 20151-3289
Tel.: (703) 689-2251
Web Site: http://www.ptsolutionsva.com
Sales Range: $1-9.9 Million
Emp.: 2
Physical Therapy Services
N.A.I.C.S.: 621498

US PT Therapy Services Inc. (1)
7065 Airways Blvd, Southaven, MS 38671-5873
Tel.: (662) 349-8997
Web Site: http://www.usph.com
Sales Range: $1-9.9 Million
Emp.: 3
Physical Therapy Services
N.A.I.C.S.: 621498

University Physical Therapy, Limited Partnership (1)
115 Akers Farm Rd Ste 1, Christiansburg, VA 24073-1412
Tel.: (540) 381-9100
Web Site: https://universityptonline.com
Sales Range: $25-49.9 Million
Emp.: 100
Physical Therapy Services
N.A.I.C.S.: 621498
Michael W. Goforth (Co-Owner)
Tyler Bowersock (Co-Owner)

Victory Physical Therapy, Limited Partnership (1)
1101 S Clay Ste B, Ennis, TX 75119
Tel.: (972) 878-0503
Web Site: https://victoryphysicaltherapy.com
Emp.: 6
Health Care Srvices
N.A.I.C.S.: 621491
Brandi Anthony (Owner)

West Texas Physical Therapy, Limited Partnership (1)
1901 Medi-Park Drv Ste 1010, Amarillo, TX 79106
Tel.: (806) 353-5425
Web Site: https://www.westtexaspt.com
Healtcare Services
N.A.I.C.S.: 621491

U.S. STEM CELL, INC.

1560 Sawgrass Corporate Pkwy 4th Fl, Sunrise, FL 33323
Tel.: (954) 835-1500   FL
Web Site:
https://www.usstemcelltraining.com
Year Founded: 1999
USRM—(OTCIQ)
Rev.: $200,749
Assets: $50,999
Liabilities: $12,817,335
Net Worth: ($12,766,336)
Earnings: ($3,287,416)
Fiscal Year-end: 12/31/21

Biotechnology Developer & Marketer Focused on Therapies Using Cells Derived From a Patient's Body & Related Devices For the Treatment of Heart Damage
N.A.I.C.S.: 541714
Miguel Tomas *(Pres & CEO)*
William P. Murphy Jr. *(Chm)*

Subsidiaries:

U.S. Stem Cell Clinic of The Villages LLC **(1)**
8640 E County Rd 466, The Villages, FL 32162
Tel.: (352) 775-0191
Stem Cell Therapy Clinic Operator
N.A.I.C.S.: 621498

US Stem Cell Clinic, LLC **(1)**
1290 Weston Rd Ste 203A, Weston, FL 33326
Tel.: (954) 510-3150
Stem Cell Clinic Services
N.A.I.C.S.: 541714

U.S. WIND FARMING, INC.
15712 Orlandbrook Dr Ste 151, Chicago, IL 60462 **NV**
USWF—(OTCIQ)
Wind Electric Power Generation Services
N.A.I.C.S.: 221115
William L. Telander *(Pres & CEO)*

UA MULTIMEDIA, INC.
7545 Irvine Ctr Dr Ste 200, Irvine, CA 92618
Tel.: (949) 229-1208 **DE**
Web Site: https://uammedia.com
Year Founded: 2007
UAMM—(OTCIQ)
Mobile Application Services
N.A.I.C.S.: 541511
Michael Lajtay *(CEO)*
Huan Nguyen *(CFO)*

UAN POWER CORP.
2030 Powers Ferry Rd SE Ste 212, Atlanta, GA 30339
Tel.: (404) 816-8240 **NV**
Year Founded: 2009
RDGH—(OTCIQ)
Assets: $3,647
Liabilities: $170,368
Net Worth: ($166,721)
Earnings: ($95,680)
Emp.: 5
Fiscal Year-end: 06/30/23
Investment Services
N.A.I.C.S.: 523999
Wan-Fang Liu *(Chm)*
Parashar Patel *(Pres & CEO)*
Hans C. Justice Chang *(COO)*
Yun-Mi Han *(CFO)*

UAS DRONE CORP.
420 Royal Palm Way Ste 100, Palm Beach, FL 33480
Tel.: (561) 693-1421 **NV**
Web Site:
http://www.uasdronecorp.com
Year Founded: 2014
USDR—(OTCQB)
Rev.: $42,000
Assets: $2,992,000
Liabilities: $566,000
Net Worth: $2,426,000
Earnings: ($1,101,000)
Emp.: 1
Fiscal Year-end: 12/31/22
Unmanned Aerial Systems Mfr
N.A.I.C.S.: 336411
Shlomo Zakai *(CFO)*
Sagiv Aharon *(CTO)*
Yariv Alroy *(Chm)*
Erez Nachtomy *(Vice Chm)*
Yossef Balucka *(Pres & CEO)*

UBER TECHNOLOGIES, INC.
1515 3rd St, San Francisco, CA 94158
Tel.: (415) 612-8582 **DE**
Web Site: https://www.uber.com
Year Founded: 2009
UBER—(NYSE)
Rev.: $37,281,000,000
Assets: $38,699,000,000
Liabilities: $26,671,000,000
Net Worth: $12,028,000,000
Earnings: $1,887,000,000
Emp.: 30,400
Fiscal Year-end: 12/31/23
Limousine & Taxi Reservation Software Developer
N.A.I.C.S.: 513210
Prashanth Mahendra-Rajah *(CFO & Sr VP-Fin)*
Tony West *(Chief Legal Officer)*
Jill Hazelbaker *(Sr VP-Mktg & Pub Affairs)*
Pierre-Dimitri Gore-Coty *(Sr VP-Delivery)*
Andrew MacDonald *(Sr VP-Mobility & Bus Ops)*
Bo Young Lee *(Chief Diversity & Inclusion Officer)*
Nikki Krishnamurthy *(Chief People Officer)*
Glen Ceremony *(Chief Acctg Officer & Controller-Global)*
Sukumar Rathnam *(CTO)*
Jennifer Vescio *(Head-Bus Dev-global)*
Gus Fuldner *(VP-Safety & Core Svcs)*
Albert Greenberg *(VP)*
Dara Khosrowshahi *(CEO)*

Subsidiaries:

Postmates Inc. **(1)**
51 Federal St Ste 301, San Francisco, CA 94107
Web Site: http://www.postmates.com
Scheduled Freight Air Transportation
N.A.I.C.S.: 481112
Bastian Lehmann *(Co-Founder & CEO)*
Eric Edge *(Sr VP-Brand & Comm)*

Uber Austria GmbH **(1)**
Guglgasse 6, 1110, Vienna, Austria
Limousine & Taxi Reservation Software Developer
N.A.I.C.S.: 513210

Uber B.V. **(1)**
Mr Treublaan 7, 1097 DP, Amsterdam, Netherlands
Web Site: http://www.uber.com
Limousine & Taxi Reservation Software Developer
N.A.I.C.S.: 513210

Uber France SAS **(1)**
28 rue Mogador, 75009, Paris, France
Tel.: (33) 675286327
Limousine & Taxi Reservation Software Developer
N.A.I.C.S.: 513210

Uber Germany GmbH **(1)**
Theresienhohe 6, 80336, Munich, Germany
Tel.: (49) 1715642475
Limousine & Taxi Reservation Software Developer
N.A.I.C.S.: 513210

Uber India Systems Private Limited **(1)**
Regus Business Platinum Centre Pvt Ltd Level 13, Platinum Techno Park Plot No 17/18 Sec-30A Vashi, Navi Mumbai, 400705, India
Limousine & Taxi Reservation Software Developer
N.A.I.C.S.: 513210
Pradeep Parameswaran *(Pres-India & South Asia)*

Uber Japan Co. Ltd. **(1)**
1-9-10 Roppongi, Minato-ku, Tokyo, Japan
Limousine & Taxi Reservation Software Developer
N.A.I.C.S.: 513210

Uber London Limited **(1)**
Focus Point 1st Floor 21 Caledonian Road, London, N1 9GB, United Kingdom
Limousine & Taxi Reservation Software Developer
N.A.I.C.S.: 513210
Melinda Roylett *(Gen Mgr-UK & Ireland)*
Laurel Powers-Freeling *(Chm)*

Uber Poland Sp. z o.o. **(1)**
ul Inflancka 4, 00-189, Warsaw, Poland
Tel.: (48) 227450200
Limousine & Taxi Reservation Software Developer
N.A.I.C.S.: 513210

Uber South Africa Technology (Pty) Ltd. **(1)**
12th Floor Sinosteel Plaza 159 Rivonia Road, Johannesburg, 2196, South Africa
Limousine & Taxi Reservation Software Developer
N.A.I.C.S.: 513210

UBIQUITI INC.
685 3rd Ave 27th Fl, New York, NY 10017
Tel.: (646) 780-7958 **DE**
Web Site: https://www.ui.com
Year Founded: 2003
UI—(NYSE)
Rev.: $1,928,490,000
Assets: $1,154,412,000
Liabilities: $1,059,352,000
Net Worth: $95,060,000
Earnings: $349,960,000
Emp.: 1,515
Fiscal Year-end: 06/30/24
Broadband Wireless Solutions
N.A.I.C.S.: 334220
Robert J. Pera *(Chm & CEO)*
Kevin Radigan *(CFO & Chief Acctg Officer)*

UBU HOLDINGS INC.
9601 Wilshire Blvd Ste 1117, Beverly Hills, CA 90210
Tel.: (310) 748-8580
Web Site: https://www.ubutv.com
UBUH—(OTCIQ)
Rev.: $604,000
Assets: $29,000
Liabilities: $1,141,000
Net Worth: ($1,112,000)
Earnings: ($39,000)
Fiscal Year-end: 12/31/20
Television Broadcasting Station
N.A.I.C.S.: 516120
Walter Morgan *(Pres & CEO)*
Joe Sternberg *(VP-Bus Dev & IR)*
Cheryl Morgan *(VP-Programming)*
Paul Pustelnik *(VP-Web & Digital)*

UBUYHOLDINGS, INC.
300 Mamaroneck Ave Apt 201, White Plains, NY 10605
Tel.: (646) 768-8417 **NV**
Year Founded: 1985
UBYH—(OTCEM)
Liabilities: $15,000
Net Worth: ($15,000)
Earnings: ($15,000)
Emp.: 1
Fiscal Year-end: 05/31/23
Holding Company
N.A.I.C.S.: 551112

UCOMMUNE INTERNATIONAL LTD.
555 Madison Ave 5th Fl, New York, NY 10022
Tel.: (541) 740-3346
Web Site: http://ww.ucommune.com
UK—(NASDAQ)
Rev.: $101,232,129
Assets: $159,088,055
Liabilities: $147,230,827
Net Worth: $11,857,228

Earnings: ($44,687,374)
Emp.: 357
Fiscal Year-end: 12/31/22
Holding Company
N.A.I.C.S.: 551112
Zhuangkun He *(CEO)*
Cheong Kwok Mun *(CFO)*
Xin Guan *(COO)*
Binchao Xu *(CTO)*
Zhenfei Wu *(CMO)*
Guohang Wang *(Chief Strategy Officer)*
Jianghai Shen *(Chief Product Designer)*

Subsidiaries:

Orisun Acquisition Corp. **(1)**
555 Madison Ave Rm 543, New York, NY 10022
Tel.: (646) 220-3541
Rev.: $303,731
Assets: $45,073,644
Liabilities: $40,073,635
Net Worth: $5,000,009
Earnings: ($31,401)
Emp.: 2
Fiscal Year-end: 12/31/2019
Investment Services
N.A.I.C.S.: 523999
Wei Chen *(Chm, Pres & CEO)*

Subsidiary (Non-US):

Ucommune Group Holdings Limited **(2)**
No 2 Guang Hua Road Floor 8 Tower D, Chaoyang District, Beijing, 100025, China
Tel.: (86) 1065067789
Holding Company
N.A.I.C.S.: 551112
Daqing Mao *(Chm & CEO)*
Lingyang Yan *(CFO)*
Liang Sun *(Pres)*
Guohang Wang *(Chief Strategy Officer)*
Xin Guan *(COO)*
Binchao Xu *(CTO)*
Zhenfei Wu *(CMO)*

UDEMY, INC.
600 Harrison St 3rd Fl, San Francisco, CA 94107
Tel.: (415) 813-1710 **DE**
Web Site: https://www.udemy.com
Year Founded: 2010
UDMY—(NASDAQ)
Rev.: $629,097,000
Assets: $737,568,000
Liabilities: $398,258,000
Net Worth: $339,310,000
Earnings: ($153,875,000)
Emp.: 1,678
Fiscal Year-end: 12/31/22
Online Course Provider
N.A.I.C.S.: 923110
Gregory Brown *(Pres & CEO)*
Prasad Raje *(Chief Product Officer)*
Dennis Walsh *(VP-IR)*
Stacey Zolt Hara *(Sr VP-Corp Comm)*

Subsidiaries:

CUX, Inc. **(1)**
2 Market Plz Way Ste 5, Mechanicsburg, PA 17055-2925
Tel.: (212) 213-2828
Web Site: http://www.corpu.com
Professional & Management Development Training
N.A.I.C.S.: 611430
Dave Kurz *(Principal & VP-Learning Design)*

UDR, INC.
1745 Shea Center Dr Ste 200, Highlands Ranch, CO 80129
Tel.: (720) 283-6120 **MD**
Web Site: https://www.udr.com
Year Founded: 1972
UDR—(NYSE)
Rev.: $1,627,501,000
Assets: $11,373,242,000
Liabilities: $7,381,888,000

UDR, Inc.—(Continued)

Net Worth: $3,991,354,000
Earnings: $474,488,000
Emp.: 1,397
Fiscal Year-end: 12/31/23
Real Estate Investment Trust Services
N.A.I.C.S.: 525990
Douglas F. Fee *(VP-Asset Quality)*
Thomas W. Toomey *(Chm & CEO)*
Deiadra M. Burns *(VP-Construction)*
H. Andrew Cantor *(Sr VP-Acquisitions & Dispositions)*
Christopher G. Van Ens *(VP)*
Roger Laty *(VP-Tax)*
Matthew A. Cozad *(Sr VP-Corp Svcs & Innovation)*
Tracy L. Hofmeister *(Sr VP)*
Michael D. Lacy *(Sr VP-Property Ops)*
Robert J. McCullough *(Sr VP-Dev)*
R. Scott Wesson *(Chief Digital Officer & Sr VP)*
Timothy C. Yeager *(VP-Dev)*
Joseph D. Fisher *(Pres & CFO)*
J. Abram Claude *(Treas & VP)*
Kathleen R. Hullinger *(VP & Controller)*
David G. Thatcher *(Gen Counsel & Sr VP)*
Joshua A. Gampp *(CTO & Sr VP)*
Danny Mayer *(VP-Property Tax)*
Kristen N. Nicholson *(VP-Sls & Revenue)*
Stephen J. Sluty *(VP-SEC Reporting & Technical Acctg)*
Todd W. Newton *(VP-Mktg)*
Milton A. Scott Jr. *(VP)*

Subsidiaries:

1200 Broadway, LLC (1)
1200 Broadway, Nashville, TN 37203
Tel.: (615) 857-5524
Web Site: https://live1200broadway.com
Apartment Development Services
N.A.I.C.S.: 531110

13th & Market Properties LLC (1)
1330 Market St, San Diego, CA 92101
Tel.: (619) 824-3554
Apartment Development Services
N.A.I.C.S.: 531110

20 Lambourne LLC (1)
20 Lambourne Rd, Towson, MD 21204
Tel.: (443) 794-3454
Web Site: http://www.20lambourne.com
Apartment Building Rental & Leasing Services
N.A.I.C.S.: 531110

399 Fremont LLC (1)
399 Fremont St, San Francisco, CA 94105
Tel.: (415) 886-9976
Apartment Development Services
N.A.I.C.S.: 531110

Andover House LLC (1)
1200 14th St NW, Washington, DC 20005
Tel.: (202) 292-1431
Apartment Building Rental & Leasing Services
N.A.I.C.S.: 531110

Bradlee Danvers LLC (1)
1101 Kirkbride Dr, Danvers, MA 01923
Tel.: (978) 883-6916
Home Leasing Services
N.A.I.C.S.: 531110

Calvert's Walk LLC (1)
200 Foxhall Dr, Bel Air, MD 21015
Tel.: (410) 352-7851
Web Site: http://www.udr.com
Apartment Building Rental & Leasing Services
N.A.I.C.S.: 531110

Central Square at Frisco LLC (1)
6235 Main St, Frisco, TX 75034
Tel.: (469) 491-5657
Home Leasing Services
N.A.I.C.S.: 531110

Circle Towers LLC (1)
9401 Lee Hwy Ste 210, Fairfax, VA 22031
Tel.: (540) 242-8688
Web Site: https://www.circletowersapts.com
Apartment Building Rental & Leasing Services
N.A.I.C.S.: 531110

Dominion Kings Place LLC (1)
7525 Murray Hill Rd, Columbia, MD 21046
Tel.: (410) 724-0220
Web Site: http://www.kingsplaceapt.com
Apartment Building Rental & Leasing Services
N.A.I.C.S.: 531110

Flats at Palisades LLC (1)
2525 Empire Dr, Richardson, TX 75080
Tel.: (972) 737-6947
Home Leasing Services
N.A.I.C.S.: 531110

Foxborough Lodge Limited Partnership (1)
400 Foxborough Blvd, Foxboro, MA 02035
Tel.: (508) 657-3915
Apartment Development Services
N.A.I.C.S.: 531110

Governour's Square of Columbus Co. L.P. (1)
4695 Braddock Ct, Columbus, OH 43220
Tel.: (614) 349-3571
Web Site: https://www.governourssquareapts.com
Apartment Management Services
N.A.I.C.S.: 531311

Heritage Communities L.P. (1)
1745 Shea Ctr Dr, Highlands Ranch, CO 80129
Tel.: (720) 283-6120
Sales Range: $650-699.9 Million
Investment & Management Services
N.A.I.C.S.: 523999

Inlet Bay at Gateway, LLC (1)
12000 4th St N, Saint Petersburg, FL 33716
Tel.: (727) 296-2358
Apartment Building Rental & Leasing Services
N.A.I.C.S.: 531110

Jefferson at Marina del Rey, L.P. (1)
3221 Carter Ave, Marina Del Rey, CA 90292
Tel.: (310) 997-3018
Apartment Building Rental & Leasing Services
N.A.I.C.S.: 531110

Lakeside Mill LLC (1)
100 Chase Mill Cir, Owings Mills, MD 21117
Tel.: (410) 935-1915
Web Site: https://www.lakesidemill.com
Apartment Building Rental & Leasing Services
N.A.I.C.S.: 531110

Lenox Farms Limited Partnership (1)
550 Liberty St, Braintree, MA 02184
Tel.: (781) 527-2928
Apartment Development Services
N.A.I.C.S.: 531110

Lodge at Ames Pond Limited Partnership (1)
1 Ames Hill Dr, Tewksbury, MA 01876
Tel.: (978) 883-6915
Apartment Development Services
N.A.I.C.S.: 531110

Lofts at Charles River Landing, LLC (1)
300 2nd Ave, Needham, MA 02494
Tel.: (781) 527-2918
Apartment Development Services
N.A.I.C.S.: 531110

Pier 4 LLC (1)
6 Broadway Ave, Somers Point, NJ 08244
Tel.: (609) 927-9141
Web Site: https://www.pier4hotel.com
Home Management Services
N.A.I.C.S.: 561110

Rodgers Forge Condominiums, Inc. (1)
6809 Bellona Ave, Baltimore, MD 21212
Tel.: (410) 352-7874
Apartment Development Services

Savoye LLC (1)
3850 Vitruvian Way, Addison, TX 75001
Tel.: (972) 512-2430
Apartment Development Services
N.A.I.C.S.: 531110

Strata Properties, LLC (1)
3128 Lundin Dr Ste 1, Manhattan, KS 66503
Tel.: (785) 776-3345
Web Site: https://stratapropertiesllc.com
Apartment Rental Services
N.A.I.C.S.: 531110

Town Square Commons, LLC (1)
907 6th St SW, Washington, DC 20024
Tel.: (202) 488-7853
Apartment Building Rental & Leasing Services
N.A.I.C.S.: 531110

Towson Promenade, LLC (1)
707 York Rd, Towson, MD 21204
Tel.: (410) 919-1643
Apartment Development Services
N.A.I.C.S.: 531110

UDR Brio LLC (1)
11130 NE 10th St, Bellevue, WA 98004
Tel.: (425) 492-9369
Apartment Rental & Leasing Services
N.A.I.C.S.: 531110

UDR Canal I LLC (1)
2061 Wittington Pl, Farmers Branch, TX 75234
Tel.: (972) 440-3991
Apartment Rental & Leasing Services
N.A.I.C.S.: 531110

UDR Canterbury LLC (1)
20019 Sweetgum Cir, Germantown, MD 20874
Tel.: (301) 804-9956
Apartment Rental & Leasing Services
N.A.I.C.S.: 531110

UDR Cool Springs I LLC (1)
3198 Parkwood Blvd, Frisco, TX 75034
Tel.: (972) 512-6104
Apartment Rental & Leasing Services
N.A.I.C.S.: 531110

UDR Currents on the Charles LLC (1)
36 River St, Waltham, MA 02453
Tel.: (857) 385-3707
Apartment Development Services
N.A.I.C.S.: 531110

UDR Inwood LLC (1)
1 Inwood Dr, Woburn, MA 01801
Tel.: (701) 527-2927
Apartment Building Rental & Leasing Services
N.A.I.C.S.: 531110

UDR Leonard Pointe LLC (1)
395 Leonard St, Brooklyn, NY 11211
Tel.: (347) 763-5161
Apartment Development Services
N.A.I.C.S.: 531110

UDR Peridot Palms LLC (1)
10601 Gandy Blvd N, Saint Petersburg, FL 33702
Tel.: (760) 704-6085
Apartment Development Services
N.A.I.C.S.: 531110

UDR Preserve at Gateway LLC (1)
11800 Dr MLK Jr St N, Saint Petersburg, FL 33716
Tel.: (727) 296-2362
Apartment Development Services
N.A.I.C.S.: 531110

UDR Presidential Greens, L.L.C. (1)
3904 Executive Ave, Alexandria, VA 22305
Tel.: (703) 372-9825
Apartment Building Rental & Leasing Services
N.A.I.C.S.: 531110

UDR Red Stone Ranch LLC (1)
1600 S Lakeline Blvd, Cedar Park, TX 78613
Tel.: (512) 831-6166
Web Site: https://www.vrbo.com
Real Estate Investment Services

UDR Smith LLC (1)
580 S Goddard Blvd, King of Prussia, PA 19406
Tel.: (610) 756-5200
Apartment Rental & Leasing Services
N.A.I.C.S.: 531110

UDR Union Place LLC (1)
10 Independence Way, Franklin, MA 02038
Tel.: (508) 657-3905
Apartment Rental & Leasing Services
N.A.I.C.S.: 531110

United Dominion Realty L.P. (1)
1745 Shea Ctr Dr Ste 200, Highlands Ranch, CO 80129
Tel.: (720) 283-6120
Web Site: https://www.udr.com
Rev.: $428,747,000
Assets: $2,457,567,000
Liabilities: $1,209,135,000
Net Worth: $1,248,432,000
Earnings: $134,229,000
Emp.: 1,262
Fiscal Year-end: 12/31/2020
Real Estate Investment Services
N.A.I.C.S.: 525990
Thomas W. Toomey *(Chm & CEO)*

Waterside Towers, L.L.C. (1)
907 6th St SW, Washington, DC 20024
Tel.: (202) 759-8371
Apartment Building Rental & Leasing Services
N.A.I.C.S.: 531110

Windemere at Sycamore Highlands, LLC (1)
5925 Sycamore Canyon Blvd, Riverside, CA 92507
Tel.: (951) 435-6821
Apartment Building Rental & Leasing Services
N.A.I.C.S.: 531110

UFP INDUSTRIES, INC.
2801 E Beltline Ave NE, Grand Rapids, MI 49525
Tel.: (616) 364-6161 MI
Web Site: https://www.ufpi.com
Year Founded: 1955
UFPI—(NASDAQ)
Rev.: $9,626,739,000
Assets: $3,672,073,000
Liabilities: $1,068,370,000
Net Worth: $2,603,703,000
Earnings: $704,964,000
Emp.: 15,500
Fiscal Year-end: 12/31/22
Holding Company; Lumber & Composite Wood Building Products Mfr & Distr
N.A.I.C.S.: 551112
David A. Tutas *(Chief Compliance Officer, Gen Counsel & Sec)*
Patrick M. Benton *(Pres-UFP Construction LLC)*
Scott A. Worthington *(Pres-Pkg)*
William D. Schwartz Jr. *(Pres & CEO)*
Matthew J. Missad *(Chm)*

Subsidiaries:

Advantage Label & Packaging, Inc. (1)
5575 Executive Pkwy, Grand Rapids, MI 49512
Tel.: (616) 656-1900
Web Site: https://www.advantagelabel.com
Sales Range: $1-9.9 Million
Emp.: 32
Customized Packaging & Labeling Services
N.A.I.C.S.: 561910
Brad Knoth *(Gen Mgr-Ops)*
T. J. Long *(Sls Mgr)*

Aljoma Lumber, Inc. (1)
10300 NW 121 Way, Medley, FL 33178
Tel.: (305) 556-8003
Web Site: http://www.aljoma.com
Emp.: 100
Diversified Wood Product Whslr
N.A.I.C.S.: 423310

Caliper Building Systems, LLC (1)

5500 Lincoln Dr Ste 170, Edina, MN 55436
Tel.: (507) 872-5195
Web Site: http://www.ufpi.com
Emp.: 10
Lumber & Composite Wood Building Product Mfr & Distr
N.A.I.C.S.: 423310

Deckorators, Inc. (1)
2801 E Beltline NE, Grand Rapids, MI 49525
Web Site: https://www.deckorators.com
Metal Service Centers & Other Metal Merchant Whslr
N.A.I.C.S.: 423510

Subsidiary (Domestic):

Ultra Aluminum Manufacturing Inc. (2)
2124 Grand Commerce Dr, Howell, MI 48855
Tel.: (517) 548-6755
Web Site: https://www.ultrafence.com
Fabricated Metal Mfr
N.A.I.C.S.: 332312
Russell Springborn (Pres & CEO)
Dave Stewart (VP-Bus Dev)

Enwrap Logistic & Packaging S.r.l. (1)
Viale delle Industrie 21, 20040, Cambiago, MI, Italy
Tel.: (39) 027384928
Web Site: https://www.enwrap.it
Emp.: 350
Logistics & Packaging Services
N.A.I.C.S.: 561910

Eovations, LLC (1)
5 Meadowcraft Pkwy, Selma, AL 36701
Tel.: (334) 872-1580
Web Site: https://www.eovationsllc.com
Emp.: 10
Lumber & Composite Wood Building Product Mfr
N.A.I.C.S.: 321912

Idaho Western, Inc. (1)
6200 Hunt Ave, Nampa, ID 83687
Tel.: (208) 465-7800
Web Site: http://www.idahowestern.com
Sales Range: $1-9.9 Million
Emp.: 22
Lumber & Plywood Merchant Whslr
N.A.I.C.S.: 423310

Integra Packaging Pty Ltd (1)
49 Station Street Yeerongpilly, Brisbane, 4106, QLD, Australia
Tel.: (61) 738489290
Wood Building Product Distr
N.A.I.C.S.: 423310

International Wood Industries, Inc. (1)
26200 N Nowell Rd, Thornton, CA 95686
Tel.: (209) 794-8750
Web Site: https://www.iwiproducts.com
High Quality Bulk Storage Container Mfr & Supplier
N.A.I.C.S.: 321920
Jeff Warn (Mgr-Sls)
Brandon Garloff (Sls Mgr)

Landura, LLC (1)
4623 Country Club Rd, Winston Salem, NC 27104-3519
Tel.: (336) 760-8100
Web Site: https://www.landura.com
Residential Building Leasing Services
N.A.I.C.S.: 531110
Scott Alderman (Pres)
Ron Midura (Mng Gen Partner)
Jackie Miller (VP)
Janie Grubbs (VP-Property Mgmt)
Nikeya Nelson (Reg Mgr-Property)
Dianne Phillips (Mgr-Compliance & Human Resources)
Amber Carter (Mgr-Accounting)
Gracie Jerrett (Mgr-Front Desk & Office)

Maine Ornamental, LLC (1)
933 US Rte 202, Greene, ME 04236
Tel.: (888) 842-1463
Web Site: http://www.decorators.com
Emp.: 10
Wood Products Mfr
N.A.I.C.S.: 321999

Mid Atlantic Framing, LLC (1)
1000 Tibbetts Ln, New Windsor, MD 21776
Tel.: (410) 635-2084
Web Site: http://www.ufpframing.com
Sales Range: $25-49.9 Million
Emp.: 10
Wood Frame Building Material & Labor Provider
N.A.I.C.S.: 321999

Norpac Construction, LLC (1)
4125 W Dewey Dr Ste A, Las Vegas, NV 89118-2363 (75%)
Tel.: (702) 320-3890
Sales Range: $150-199.9 Million
Single Family Construction Services
N.A.I.C.S.: 236115

Norpal S. de R.L. de C.V. (1)
Jose Lopez Portillo No 3003 Col Nueva Castilla, 66052, Escobedo, Nuevo Leon, Mexico
Tel.: (52) 8125251060
Wood Products Mfr
N.A.I.C.S.: 321219

North American Container Corporation (1)
1811 W Oak Pkwy, Marietta, GA 30062
Tel.: (770) 431-4858
Web Site: http://www.nacontainer.com
Corrugated & Solid Fiber Boxes
N.A.I.C.S.: 322211

Plant (Domestic):

North American Container Corporation - Calhoun Facility (2)
270 Johnson Lake Rd SE, Adairsville, GA 30103
Tel.: (706) 602-0031
Corrugated Box Mfr
N.A.I.C.S.: 322211

North American Container Corporation - Lawrenceburg Facility (2)
2180 E Gaines St, Lawrenceburg, TN 38464
Tel.: (931) 762-5817
Corrugated Box Mfr
N.A.I.C.S.: 322211

North American Container Corporation - Martin Facility (2)
191 Industrial Dr, Martin, TN 38237
Tel.: (731) 587-3090
Corrugated Box Mfr
N.A.I.C.S.: 322211

North American Container Corporation - McIntyre Facility (2)
226 Wilco Rd, McIntyre, GA 31054
Tel.: (478) 946-1400
Corrugated Box Mfr
N.A.I.C.S.: 322211

North American Container Corporation - Newnan Facility (2)
504 Corinth Rd, Newnan, GA 30263
Tel.: (770) 251-1402
Corrugated Box Mfr
N.A.I.C.S.: 322211

North American Container Corporation - Orangeburg Facility (2)
950 Garland Rd, Rowesville, SC 29133
Tel.: (803) 531-1712
Corrugated Box Mfr
N.A.I.C.S.: 322211

North American Container Corporation - Sharon Facility (2)
Sharon Ind Rd, Sharon, TN 38255
Tel.: (731) 587-3090
Corrugated Box Mfr
N.A.I.C.S.: 322211

Northwest Painting, Inc. (1)
8941 Bonner Mill Rd, Bonner, MT 59823
Tel.: (406) 541-6933
Web Site:
    http://www.northwestfactoryfinishes.com
Commercial & Institutional Building Construction
N.A.I.C.S.: 236220
Britt Fred (Pres)

Pacific Coast Showcase, Inc. (1)
1601 Industrial Park Way Ste 101, Puyallup, WA 98371

Tel.: (253) 445-9000
Wood Building Product Distr
N.A.I.C.S.: 423310

Packnet, Ltd. (1)
14400 Southcross Dr W, Burnsville, MN 55306 (80%)
Tel.: (952) 944-9124
Web Site: https://www.packnetltd.com
Sales Range: $1-9.9 Million
Emp.: 70
Industrial Packaging Product Mfr
N.A.I.C.S.: 321999

Pak-Rite, Ltd. (1)
2395 S Burrell St, Milwaukee, WI 53207
Tel.: (414) 489-0450
Web Site: http://www.pak-rite.com
Packaging & Labeling Services
N.A.I.C.S.: 561910
Kirk Blaha (Pres)

PalletOne, Inc. (1)
6001 Foxtrot Ave, Bartow, FL 33830
Tel.: (863) 533-1147
Web Site: https://www.palletone.com
Sales Range: $1-9.9 Million
Emp.: 1,100
Wood Container & Pallet Mfr
N.A.I.C.S.: 321920
Howe Wallace (Pres)

Subsidiary (Domestic):

PalletOne of Alabama, LLC (2)
22640 Co Rd 64, Robertsdale, AL 36567
Tel.: (251) 960-1107
Web Site: https://www.palletone.com
Sales Range: $1-9.9 Million
Emp.: 90
Wood Container & Pallet Mfr.
N.A.I.C.S.: 321920

Pinelli Universal, S de R.L. de C.V. (1)
Plan de Agua Prieta No 401 Col, 34228, Emiliano Zapata, Mexico
Tel.: (52) 6188291700
Lumber & Composite Wood Products Mfr & Whslr
N.A.I.C.S.: 321113

Shawnlee Construction, LLC (1)
74A Taunton St, Plainville, MA 02762
Tel.: (508) 695-8033
Web Site: http://www.ufpframing.com
Sales Range: $75-99.9 Million
Emp.: 160
Carpentry Work
N.A.I.C.S.: 238350

Subsidiary (Domestic):

Shepardville Construction, LLC (2)
285 Great Hill Rd, Naugatuck, CT 06770
Tel.: (203) 879-7098
Web Site: http://www.ufpframing.com
Sales Range: $25-49.9 Million
Emp.: 100
Carpentry Services
N.A.I.C.S.: 238350

Sunbelt Forest Products Corporation (1)
6106 Spirit Lk Rd, Bartow, FL 33830
Tel.: (863) 534-1702
Web Site: https://www.sunbeltfp.com
Lumber Mfr
N.A.I.C.S.: 321912
Stokes Wallace (Gen Sls Mgr)

UFP Ashburn, LLC (1)
154 Sunbelt Dr, Ashburn, GA 31714
Tel.: (229) 567-3481
Web Site: https://www.ufpi.com
Sales Range: $25-49.9 Million
Emp.: 50
Lumber & Composite Wood Building Products Mfr & Distr
N.A.I.C.S.: 321113

UFP Auburndale, LLC (1)
105 Progress Rd, Auburndale, FL 33823
Tel.: (863) 965-2566
Emp.: 140
Lumber & Composite Wood Building Products Mfr & Distr
N.A.I.C.S.: 321113

UFP Belchertown, LLC (1)
155 Bay Rd, Belchertown, MA 01007

Tel.: (413) 323-7247
Wood Building Product Mfr & Distr
N.A.I.C.S.: 423310

UFP Berlin, LLC (1)
159 Jackson Rd, Berlin, NJ 08009
Tel.: (856) 767-0043
Web Site: http://www.ufpi.com
Lumber & Composite Wood Building Product Mfr & Distr
N.A.I.C.S.: 423310

UFP Blanchester, LLC (1)
940 Cherry St, Blanchester, OH 45107-7883
Tel.: (937) 783-2443
Emp.: 80
Lumber & Composite Wood Building Products Mfr & Distr
N.A.I.C.S.: 321113

UFP Caldwell, LLC (1)
104 S 43rd Ave, Caldwell, ID 83605
Tel.: (208) 453-8940
Emp.: 4
Fabricated Wood Product Mfr & Distr
N.A.I.C.S.: 321215

UFP Chandler, LLC (1)
6878 W Chandler Blvd, Chandler, AZ 85226
Tel.: (480) 961-0833
Web Site: http://www.ufpi.com
Sales Range: $50-74.9 Million
Emp.: 100
Lumber & Composite Wood Building Products Mfr & Distr
N.A.I.C.S.: 321113

UFP Construction, LLC (1)
2801 E Beltline Ave NE, Grand Rapids, MI 49525
Tel.: (616) 364-6161
Construction Product Distr
N.A.I.C.S.: 423390

Subsidiary (Domestic):

Exterior Designs, LLC (2)
184 Rockingham Rd, Londonderry, NH 03053
Tel.: (603) 668-4113
Web Site: http://www.exteriordesigns.com
Sales Range: $1-9.9 Million
Emp.: 75
Drywall & Insulation Contractors
N.A.I.C.S.: 238310
Nicholas Paquet (Gen Mgr-Reg)
Dave Anzalone (Pre-Construction & Sls Dir)

UFP Distribution, LLC (1)
2701 Ada Dr, Elkhart, IN 31015
Tel.: (574) 266-3603
Emp.: 75
Lumber & Composite Wood Building Product Mfr & Distr
N.A.I.C.S.: 423310

UFP Eatonton, LLC (1)
115 Milledgeville Rd, Eatonton, GA 31024
Tel.: (706) 485-5952
Web Site: https://www.ufpi.com
Lumber & Composite Wood Building Products Mfr & Distr
N.A.I.C.S.: 321113

UFP Elizabeth City, LLC (1)
141 Knobbs Creek Dr, Elizabeth City, NC 27909
Tel.: (252) 338-2821
Web Site: https://www.ufpi.com
Sales Range: $25-49.9 Million
Emp.: 40
Lumber & Composite Wood Building Products Mfr & Distr
N.A.I.C.S.: 321113

UFP Elkwood, LLC (1)
13129 Airpark Dr, Elkwood, VA 22718-1761
Tel.: (540) 825-3600
Wood Building Product Distr
N.A.I.C.S.: 423310

UFP Folkston, LLC (1)
277 John Harper Ave, Folkston, GA 31537-1240
Tel.: (863) 594-1899
Forest Product Distr
N.A.I.C.S.: 423990

UFP Franklinton, LLC (1)
6863 Hwy 56 E, Franklinton, NC 27525

UFP Industries, Inc.—(Continued)

Tel.: (919) 496-6133
Web Site: http://www.ufpi.com
Emp.: 50
Wood Packaging Material Mfr
N.A.I.C.S.: 321920

UFP Gordon, LLC (1)
1 Royer St, Gordon, PA 17936
Tel.: (570) 875-2811
Sales Range: $50-74.9 Million
Emp.: 180
Lumber & Composite Wood Building Products Mfr & Distr
N.A.I.C.S.: 321113

UFP Grandview, LLC (1)
1000 S 3rd St, Grandview, TX 76050
Tel.: (817) 866-3306
Web Site: http://www.ufpi.com
Lumber & Composite Wood Building Product Mfr & Distr
N.A.I.C.S.: 423310

UFP Granger, LLC (1)
50227 Bittersweet Trl, Granger, IN 46530
Tel.: (574) 277-7670
Sales Range: $50-74.9 Million
Emp.: 150
Lumber & Composite Wood Building Products Mfr & Distr
N.A.I.C.S.: 321113

UFP Haleyville, LLC (1)
4215 State Hwy 13 N, Haleyville, AL 35565
Tel.: (205) 486-4742
Sales Range: $50-74.9 Million
Emp.: 150
Lumber & Composite Wood Building Products Mfr & Distr
N.A.I.C.S.: 321113

UFP Hamilton, LLC (1)
115 Distribution Dr, Hamilton, OH 45014
Tel.: (513) 285-7190
Wood Products Mfr
N.A.I.C.S.: 423310

UFP Harrisonville, LLC (1)
2600 Precision Dr, Harrisonville, MO 64701
Tel.: (816) 380-7600
Sales Range: $25-49.9 Million
Emp.: 80
Lumber & Composite Wood Building Products Mfr & Distr
N.A.I.C.S.: 321113

UFP Hillsboro, LLC (1)
54 Lee Roy Jordan Dr, Hillsboro, TX 76645
Tel.: (254) 580-2846
Web Site: https://www.ufpi.com
Sales Range: $50-74.9 Million
Emp.: 125
Lumber & Composite Wood Building Products Mfr & Distr
N.A.I.C.S.: 423310

UFP Janesville, LLC (1)
1118 US Hwy 14 E, Janesville, WI 53545
Tel.: (608) 755-6200
Web Site: https://www.ufpi.com
Emp.: 50
Lumber & Composite Wood Building Products Mfr & Distr
N.A.I.C.S.: 321113

UFP Lafayette, LLC (1)
1201 E South Boulder Rd, Lafayette, CO 80026
Tel.: (303) 666-6800
Lumber & Composite Wood Building Products Mfr & Distr
N.A.I.C.S.: 321113

UFP Lodi, LLC (1)
9237 Avon Lake Rd State Rte 83, Lodi, OH 44254
Tel.: (937) 783-2443
Wood Products Mfr
N.A.I.C.S.: 423310

UFP Magna, LLC (1)
3909 S 8000 W, Magna, UT 84044
Tel.: (801) 810-2580
Fabricated Wood Product Mfr & Distr
N.A.I.C.S.: 321215

UFP McMinnville, LLC (1)
1726 SW Hwy 18, McMinnville, OR 97128
Tel.: (503) 434-5525

Web Site: http://www.dstakemill.com
Emp.: 50
Lumber & Composite Wood Building Product Mfr & Distr
N.A.I.C.S.: 423310

UFP Mid-Atlantic, LLC (1)
5631 S NC Hwy 62, Burlington, NC 27215
Tel.: (336) 226-9356
Sales Range: $50-74.9 Million
Emp.: 200
Lumber & Composite Wood Building Products Mfr & Distr
N.A.I.C.S.: 321113

Plant (Domestic):

UFP Mid-Atlantic, LLC - Jefferson (2)
80 Martin Luther King Ave, Jefferson, GA 30549
Tel.: (706) 367-2781
Web Site: http://www.ufpi.com
Sales Range: $25-49.9 Million
Emp.: 80
Lumber & Composite Wood Building Products Mfr & Distr
N.A.I.C.S.: 321113

UFP Mid-Atlantic, LLC - Liberty (2)
6985 Kinro Rd, Liberty, NC 27298
Tel.: (336) 622-5903
Web Site: http://www.ufpi.com
Emp.: 75
Lumber & Composite Wood Building Product Mfr & Distr
N.A.I.C.S.: 423310

UFP Millry, LLC (1)
107 Millry Mill Rd, Millry, AL 36558
Tel.: (251) 846-2520
Emp.: 50
Sawmill Operator
N.A.I.C.S.: 321113

UFP Minneota, LLC (1)
700 E 1st St, Minneota, MN 56264
Tel.: (507) 872-5195
Sales Range: $50-74.9 Million
Emp.: 60
Lumber & Composite Wood Building Products Mfr & Distr
N.A.I.C.S.: 321113

UFP Morristown, LLC (1)
530 W Morris Blvd, Morristown, TN 37813-2132
Tel.: (423) 587-3811
Web Site: https://www.ufpi.com
Sales Range: $25-49.9 Million
Emp.: 50
Lumber & Composite Wood Building Product Mfr & Distr
N.A.I.C.S.: 423310

UFP Moultrie, LLC (1)
560 Industrial Dr, Moultrie, GA 31788
Tel.: (229) 985-4009
Sales Range: $50-74.9 Million
Emp.: 175
Lumber & Composite Wood Building Products Mfr & Distr
N.A.I.C.S.: 321113

UFP Nappanee, LLC (1)
493 Shawnee St, Nappanee, IN 46550
Tel.: (574) 773-2505
Wood Building Product Distr
N.A.I.C.S.: 423310

UFP New London, LLC (1)
174 Random Dr, New London, NC 28127
Tel.: (704) 463-1400
Sales Range: $25-49.9 Million
Emp.: 60
Lumber & Composite Wood Building Products Mfr & Distr
N.A.I.C.S.: 321113

UFP New Waverly, LLC (1)
146 FM 2793 Ste B, Huntsville, TX 77340
Tel.: (936) 295-3411
Sales Range: $50-74.9 Million
Emp.: 200
Lumber & Composite Wood Building Products Mfr & Distr
N.A.I.C.S.: 321113

UFP New Windsor, LLC (1)
1000 Tibbetts Ln, New Windsor, MD 21776
Tel.: (410) 549-1000

Sales Range: $50-74.9 Million
Emp.: 100
Lumber & Composite Wood Building Products Mfr & Distr
N.A.I.C.S.: 321113

UFP New York, LLC - Chaffee (1)
13989 E Schutt Rd, Chaffee, NY 14030
Tel.: (716) 496-5484
Web Site: http://www.ufpi.com
Sales Range: $25-49.9 Million
Emp.: 30
Lumber & Composite Wood Building Products Mfr & Distr
N.A.I.C.S.: 321113

UFP New York, LLC - Hudson (1)
11 Falls Industrial Park Rd, Hudson, NY 12534
Tel.: (518) 828-2888
Web Site: http://www.ufpi.com
Sales Range: $50-74.9 Million
Emp.: 100
Lumber & Composite Wood Building Products Mfr & Distr
N.A.I.C.S.: 321113

UFP New York, LLC - Sidney (1)
13 Winkler Rd, Sidney, NY 13838
Tel.: (607) 563-1556
Web Site: http://www.ufpi.com
Sales Range: $50-74.9 Million
Emp.: 100
Lumber & Composite Wood Building Products Mfr & Distr
N.A.I.C.S.: 321113

UFP Packaging, LLC (1)
2801 E Beltline Ave NE, Grand Rapids, MI 49525
Tel.: (855) 713-2728
Web Site: https://ufppackaging.com
Packaging & Containers Mfr
N.A.I.C.S.: 321920

Subsidiary (Domestic):

Titan Corrugated, Inc. (2)
801 Lakeside Pkwy, Flower Mound, TX 75028
Tel.: (214) 513-2691
Web Site: http://www.titancorrugated.com
Sales Range: $1-9.9 Million
Emp.: 28
Packaging Materials Mfr
N.A.I.C.S.: 322211
Rick Spratt *(Mgr-Ops & Pur)*

UFP Parker, LLC (1)
116 N River Ave, Parker, PA 16049
Tel.: (724) 399-2992
Sales Range: $50-74.9 Million
Emp.: 100
Lumber & Composite Wood Building Products Mfr & Distr
N.A.I.C.S.: 321113

UFP Purchasing, Inc. (1)
5200 Hwy 138 Ste 200, Union City, GA 30291
Tel.: (770) 472-3000
Web Site: http://www.ufpi.com
Emp.: 100
Investment Services
N.A.I.C.S.: 523999

UFP Ranson, LLC (1)
249 16th Ave, Ranson, WV 25438
Tel.: (304) 728-8484
Sales Range: $25-49.9 Million
Emp.: 50
Lumber & Composite Wood Building Products Mfr & Distr
N.A.I.C.S.: 321113

UFP Riverside, LLC (1)
2100 Avalon St, Riverside, CA 92509
Tel.: (951) 826-3000
Web Site: https://www.ufpi.com
Lumber & Composite Wood Building Products Mfr & Distr
N.A.I.C.S.: 321113

UFP Saginaw, LLC (1)
444 Sansom Blvd, Saginaw, TX 76179
Tel.: (817) 232-2234
Sales Range: $75-99.9 Million
Emp.: 150
Lumber & Composite Wood Building Products Mfr & Distr
N.A.I.C.S.: 321113

UFP Salisbury, LLC (1)
358 Woodmill Rd, Salisbury, NC 28147
Tel.: (704) 855-1600
Web Site: http://www.ufpi.com
Emp.: 300
Lumber & Composite Wood Building Product Mfr & Distr
N.A.I.C.S.: 423310

UFP San Antonio, LLC (1)
12195 Crownpoint Dr, San Antonio, TX 78233
Tel.: (210) 655-6053
Web Site: https://www.ufpi.com
Lumber & Composite Wood Building Product Mfr & Distr
N.A.I.C.S.: 321912

UFP Sauk Rapids, LLC (1)
1012 Industrial Dr S, Sauk Rapids, MN 56379
Tel.: (320) 259-5190
Web Site: http://www.customcaseworks.com
Sales Range: $1-9.9 Million
Emp.: 30
Wood Products Mfr
N.A.I.C.S.: 321999

UFP Schertz, LLC (1)
21700 FM 2252, Schertz, TX 78154
Tel.: (830) 606-4300
Emp.: 40
Lumber & Composite Wood Building Products Mfr & Distr
N.A.I.C.S.: 321113

UFP Shawnee, LLC (1)
444 Sansom Blvd, Saginaw, TX 76179
Tel.: (817) 232-2233
Web Site: http://www.ufpsaginaw.com
Fabricated Wood Product Distr
N.A.I.C.S.: 444180

UFP Stockertown, LLC (1)
200 Commerce Way, Stockertown, PA 18083
Tel.: (610) 759-8536
Sales Range: $25-49.9 Million
Emp.: 50
Lumber & Composite Wood Building Products Mfr & Distr
N.A.I.C.S.: 321113

UFP Tampa, LLC (1)
1003 E 131st Ave, Tampa, FL 33612
Tel.: (813) 971-3030
Wood Building Product Distr
N.A.I.C.S.: 423310
Charlie Norden *(Plant Mgr)*

UFP Thornton, LLC (1)
26200 Nowell Rd, Thornton, CA 95686
Tel.: (209) 794-8750
Web Site: http://www.ufpi.com
Sales Range: $25-49.9 Million
Emp.: 80
Lumber & Composite Wood Building Products Mfr & Distr
N.A.I.C.S.: 321912

UFP Transportation, Inc. (1)
5200 Hwy 138, Union City, GA 30291-1829
Tel.: (770) 472-3042
Lumber & Composite Wood Building Product Freight Transportation Services
N.A.I.C.S.: 484230

UFP Union City, LLC (1)
5200 Hwy 138 Ste 200, Union City, GA 30291
Tel.: (770) 472-3000
Web Site: https://www.ufpi.com
Sales Range: $25-49.9 Million
Emp.: 50
Lumber & Composite Wood Building Products Mfr & Distr
N.A.I.C.S.: 321113

UFP Ventures II, Inc. (1)
1801 E Lessard St, Prairie Du Chien, WI 53821
Tel.: (608) 326-0900
Lumber & Composite Wood Building Product Mfr & Distr
N.A.I.C.S.: 423310

UFP Warrens, LLC (1)
610 Railroad St, Warrens, WI 54666
Tel.: (608) 378-4907
Web Site: https://www.ufpi.com

Lumber & Composite Wood Building Product Mfr & Distr
N.A.I.C.S.: 423310

UFP White Bear Lake, LLC (1)
4141 Hoffman Rd, White Bear Lake, MN 55110
Tel.: (651) 426-5528
Web Site: http://www.ufpi.com
Sales Range: $25-49.9 Million
Emp.: 40
Lumber & Composite Wood Building Product Mfr & Distr
N.A.I.C.S.: 423310

UFP Windsor, LLC (1)
15 E Walnut St, Windsor, CO 80550
Tel.: (970) 686-9651
Lumber & Composite Wood Building Products Mfr & Distr
N.A.I.C.S.: 321113

UFP Woodburn, LLC (1)
2895 Progress Way, Woodburn, OR 97071
Tel.: (503) 226-6240
Sales Range: $75-99.9 Million
Emp.: 220
Lumber & Composite Wood Building Products Mfr & Distr
N.A.I.C.S.: 321113

United Lumber & Reman, LLC (1)
980 Ford Rd, Muscle Shoals, AL 35661
Tel.: (256) 381-4151
Web Site: http://www.ufpi.com
Wood Product Mfr & Distr
N.A.I.C.S.: 321999

Universal Consumer Products, Inc. (1)
68956 US-131, White Pigeon, MI 49099
Tel.: (616) 365-4201
Lumber & Composite Wood Building Product Mfr & Distr
N.A.I.C.S.: 423310
William G. Currie *(Chm)*

Universal Forest Products Foundation (1)
2801 E Beltline Ave NE, Grand Rapids, MI 49525-9680
Tel.: (616) 364-6161
Forest Product & Paper Distr
N.A.I.C.S.: 423990

Universal Forest Products of Canada, Inc. (1)
110 Montee Guay, Saint-Bernard-de-Lacolle, Lacolle, J0J 1V0, QC, Canada
Tel.: (450) 246-3829
Web Site: http://www.ufpi.com
Lumber & Composite Wood Building Product Mfr & Distr
N.A.I.C.S.: 321912
Michel Guilbeault *(Gen Mgr)*

Upshur Forest Products, LLC (1)
5231 Daffodil Rd, Gilmer, TX 75645-6504
Tel.: (903) 762-6499
Web Site: http://www.upshurforest.com
Emp.: 75
Sawmill Operator
N.A.I.C.S.: 321113
Torey Trousdale *(Mgr-Sls)*

Yard & Home, LLC (1)
1271 Judson Rd, Norton Shores, MI 49456
Web Site: https://www.yardandhome.com
Wood Products Mfr
N.A.I.C.S.: 321999

idX Corporation (1)
13213 Corporate Exchange Dr, Earth City, MO 63045
Tel.: (314) 739-4120
Web Site: https://www.idxcorporation.com
Wood Products Mfr
N.A.I.C.S.: 321999
Tim Clutterbuck *(Exec VP)*
Annette Baca *(VP-Ops)*
Ryan Boyle *(Dir-Dev & Prototyping-Global)*
Jacob Henrickson *(Dir-Creative Svcs-Global)*
Chris Steege *(Dir-Estimating-Global)*

UFP TECHNOLOGIES, INC.
100 Hale St, Newburyport, MA 01950
Tel.: (978) 352-2200   DE
Web Site: https://www.ufpt.com

Year Founded: 1993
UFPT—(NASDAQ)
Rev.: $353,792,000
Assets: $378,192,000
Liabilities: $140,647,000
Net Worth: $237,545,000
Earnings: $41,789,000
Emp.: 2,665
Fiscal Year-end: 12/31/22
Foam & Plastic Packaging & Products Mfr
N.A.I.C.S.: 326150
Ronald J. Lataille *(CFO, Treas & Sr VP)*
Mitchell C. Rock *(Pres & Pres-UFP MedTech)*
Christopher P. Litterio *(Gen Counsel & Sr VP-HR)*
Steve Cardin *(COO)*
Jason Holt *(Gen Mgr)*
R. Jeffrey Bailly *(Chm & CEO)*

Subsidiaries:

Simco Industries, Inc. (1)
3831 Paterson Ave Se, Grand Rapids, MI 49512
Tel.: (616) 608-9818
Web Site: http://www.ufpt.com
Sales Range: $25-49.9 Million
Emp.: 100
Designer & Mfr of Molded Components for Automotive Interiors
N.A.I.C.S.: 336360

UFP Technologies, Inc. - Grand Rapids (1)
3831 Patterson Ave, Grand Rapids, MI 49512
Tel.: (616) 949-8100
Web Site: http://steplaw.com
Sales Range: $10-24.9 Million
Emp.: 135
Foam Packaging & Products Mfr
N.A.I.C.S.: 326150

Branch (Domestic):

United Foam (2)
2175 Partin Settlement Rd, Kissimmee, FL 34744-4956   **(100%)**
Tel.: (407) 933-4880
Web Site: http://www.ufpt.com
Sales Range: $10-24.9 Million
Emp.: 49
Production Facility
N.A.I.C.S.: 561499

UGI CORPORATION
500 N Gulph Rd, King of Prussia, PA 19406
Tel.: (610) 337-1000   PA
Web Site: https://www.ugicorp.com
Year Founded: 1882
UGI—(NYSE)
Rev.: $8,928,000,000
Assets: $15,401,000,000
Liabilities: $11,007,000,000
Net Worth: $4,394,000,000
Earnings: ($1,502,000,000)
Emp.: 10,500
Fiscal Year-end: 09/30/23
Holding Company; Natural Gas, Propane & Electric Power Distr
N.A.I.C.S.: 551112
Robert C. Flexon *(Pres & CEO)*
Kathleen Shea-Ballay *(Chief Legal Officer & Corp Counsel)*
Frank S. Hermance *(Chm)*
Sean P. O'Brien *(CFO)*
Jean Felix Tematio Dontsop *(Chief Acctg Officer, VP & Controller)*
Tameka Morris *(Dir-IR)*
Arnab Mukherjee *(Mgr-IR)*
John Koerwer *(CIO)*
Jason Rich *(Treas & VP)*

Subsidiaries:

AmeriGas Polska Sp. z o.o. (1)
ul Burakowska 14 Forest Campus, 01-066, Warsaw, Poland
Tel.: (48) 221617017

Web Site: https://www.amerigas.pl
Natural Gas Distr
N.A.I.C.S.: 221210

AmeriGas, Inc. (1)
460 N Gulph Rd, King of Prussia, PA 19406   **(100%)**
Tel.: (610) 337-7000
Web Site: http://www.amerigas.com
Sales Range: $150-199.9 Million
Emp.: 250
Holding Company; Propane Distr
N.A.I.C.S.: 551112

Subsidiary (Domestic):

AmeriGas Propane, Inc. (2)
460 N Gulph Rd, King of Prussia, PA 19406   **(100%)**
Tel.: (610) 337-7000
Web Site: https://www.amerigas.com
Sales Range: $1-4.9 Billion
Office Administrative Services; Propane & Propane-Related Supplies Distr
N.A.I.C.S.: 561110
Ann P. Kelly *(VP-Fin)*
Troy E. Fee *(VP-HR & Strategic Initiatives)*
Craig Dadamo *(Chief Acctg Officer & Controller)*
Paul M. Ladner *(Pres)*
David Ritts *(CIO)*
Chris Cook *(VP-Mktg, Growth & Retention)*
Michelle Bimson Maggi *(VP-Law)*
James L. Palkovic *(VP-Ops-Western Div)*
Andrew Little *(VP-Supply & Logistics)*
Brilynn Johnson *(Dir-Industry & Customer Rels)*
Koury M. Ensley *(VP)*
Raymond Kaszuba *(CFO)*

Subsidiary (Domestic):

AmeriGas Partners, L.P. (3)
460 N Gulph Rd, King of Prussia, PA 19406
Tel.: (610) 337-7000
Rev.: $2,822,978,000
Assets: $3,925,818,000
Liabilities: $3,356,150,000
Net Worth: $569,668,000
Earnings: $190,522,000
Fiscal Year-end: 09/30/2018
Holding Company; Propane & Propane-Related Supplies Distr
N.A.I.C.S.: 551112

Subsidiary (Domestic):

AmeriGas Finance Corp. (4)
460 N Gulph Rd, King of Prussia, PA 19406
Tel.: (610) 337-7000
Web Site: http://www.ugicorporation.com
Propane Distr
N.A.I.C.S.: 324110

AmeriGas Propane, L.P. (4)
460 N Gulph Rd, King of Prussia, PA 19406
Tel.: (610) 337-7000
Web Site: http://www.amerigas.com
Propane & Propane-Related Supplies Distr
N.A.I.C.S.: 457210

Subsidiary (Domestic):

AmeriGas Eagle Propane, Inc. (5)
460 N Gulph Rd, King of Prussia, PA 19406-2815
Tel.: (610) 337-7000
Web Site: http://www.amerigas.com
Propane Gas Liquid Extraction
N.A.I.C.S.: 211130

Heritage Operating, L.P. (5)
8801 S Yale Ste 310, Tulsa, OK 74137
Tel.: (918) 492-7272
Liquefied Petroleum Gas (Bottled Gas) Dealers
N.A.I.C.S.: 457210
Jim Hamilton *(Sr VP-Sls & Ops)*
Steve Sheffield *(Sr VP-Mktg & Ops)*

Unit (Domestic):

Balgas (6)
211 Jerome Dr, Immokalee, FL 34142
Tel.: (239) 657-3752
Web Site: http://www.balgas.com
Emp.: 11
Oil & Gas Distr
N.A.I.C.S.: 221210
Richard Dedrick *(Office Mgr)*

Bi-State Propane Inc. (6)
33 E Sierra Ave, Portola, CA 96122
Tel.: (530) 832-7700
Web Site: http://www.bi-statepropane.com
Emp.: 10
Propane Gas Distr
N.A.I.C.S.: 424720

C & D Propane (6)
2925 Black Lk Blvd SW, Tumwater, WA 98512
Tel.: (360) 352-7837
Web Site: http://www.cdpropane.com
Petrol Products Mfr
N.A.I.C.S.: 324199

Carolane Propane (6)
3117 B Guess Rd, Durham, NC 27705
Tel.: (919) 477-2950
Web Site: http://www.carolanepropane.com
Propane Gas Distr
N.A.I.C.S.: 457210

E-Con Gas, Inc (6)
3813 Rhea County Hwy, Dayton, TN 37321
Tel.: (423) 775-8212
Web Site: http://www.e-congas.com
Fuel Distr
N.A.I.C.S.: 457210

EnergyNorth Propane, Inc. (6)
75 Regional Dr, Concord, NH 03301
Tel.: (603) 225-6660
Web Site: http://www.energynorthpropane.com
Emp.: 35
Retail of Propane, Gas Heating Equipment & Appliances
N.A.I.C.S.: 457210

Gibson Propane (6)
3542 Lamar Ave, Memphis, TN 38118
Tel.: (901) 363-0101
Fuel Distr
N.A.I.C.S.: 457210
Paul Ladner *(Pres)*
Ann P. Kelly *(CFO & VP-Fin)*
David Ritts *(CIO)*
Craig Dadamo *(Chief Acctg Officer & Controller)*
Chris Cook *(VP-Mktg, Growth & Retention)*
Michelle Bimson Maggi *(VP-Law)*
James L. Palkovic *(VP-Ops-Western Div)*
Andrew Little *(VP-Supply & Logistics)*
Brilynn Johnson *(Dir-Industry & Customer Rels)*

Guilford Gas (6)
710 Patton Ave, Greensboro, NC 27406-3717
Tel.: (336) 274-8449
Web Site: http://www.guilfordgas.com
Sales Range: $25-49.9 Million
Emp.: 18
Propane Distr
N.A.I.C.S.: 457210

Houston County Propane (6)
10525 Hwy 13, Erin, TN 37061
Tel.: (931) 289-4440
Web Site: http://www.houstonpropane.com
Emp.: 3
Fuel Dealers
N.A.I.C.S.: 457210
Diane Johnson *(Office Mgr)*

Hydratane of Athens (6)
519 E Ave, Athens, TN 37303
Tel.: (423) 745-1100
Emp.: 5
Fuel Dealers
N.A.I.C.S.: 457210
Keva Hutton *(Gen Mgr)*

Kingston Propane (6)
187 Summer St Ste 12, Kingston, MA 02364-1245
Tel.: (781) 585-6511
Web Site: http://www.kingstonpropane.com
Fuel Dealers
N.A.I.C.S.: 457210

Lake County Gas (6)
72 Soda Bay Rd, Lakeport, CA 95453-5609
Tel.: (707) 995-2840
Web Site: http://www.lakecountygas.com
Fuel Dealers
N.A.I.C.S.: 457210

Lyons Gas (6)
3798 Hwy 60 E, Harned, KY 40144

UGI Corporation—(Continued)

Tel.: (270) 756-2164
Web Site: http://www.lyonsgas.com
Fuel Distr
N.A.I.C.S.: 457210

Marlen Gas (6)
505 W Gravois Rd, Saint Clair, MO 63077
Tel.: (636) 629-3464
Web Site: http://www.marlengas.com
Fuel Dealers
N.A.I.C.S.: 457210

Moore L.P. Gas (6)
1171 Monticello Rd, Madison, GA 30650
Tel.: (706) 485-8779
Web Site: http://www.moorelpgas.com
Fuel Distr
N.A.I.C.S.: 457210

Paradee Gas Company (6)
28451 John J Williams Hwy, Millsboro, DE 19966
Tel.: (302) 934-6008
Web Site: http://www.paradeegas.com
Natural Gas Pipeline Services
N.A.I.C.S.: 486210

Pioneer Propane (6)
3490 E Andy Devine Ave, Kingman, AZ 86401-3706
Tel.: (928) 681-3166
Web Site: http://www.pioneer-propane.com
Fuel Distr
N.A.I.C.S.: 457210

Propane Energies (6)
490 E Main St, Parsons, TN 38363
Tel.: (731) 845-6551
Web Site: http://www.propaneenergies.com
Gas Station Services
N.A.I.C.S.: 213112

Sawyer Gas (6)
189 SW Midtown Place, Lake City, FL 32025
Tel.: (386) 752-5711
Web Site: http://www.sawyergas.com
Fuel Dealers
N.A.I.C.S.: 457210

Shaw L.P. Gas (6)
135 W Bernard Ave, Greeneville, TN 37743
Tel.: (423) 639-7788
Web Site: http://www.shawlp.com
Emp.: 6
Fuel Dealers
N.A.I.C.S.: 457210

Young's Propane (6)
20 Kline Dr, White River Junction, VT 05001
Tel.: (802) 295-2554
Web Site: http://www.youngspropane.com
Sales Range: $25-49.9 Million
Emp.: 20
Natural Gas Distr
N.A.I.C.S.: 457210
Jim Lemire (Gen Mgr)

Subsidiary (Domestic):

Titan Energy Partners, L.P. (5)
8801 S Yale Ave Ste 310, Tulsa, OK 74137
Tel.: (918) 492-7272
Web Site: http://www.titanpropane.com
Holding Company; Propane Distr
N.A.I.C.S.: 551112

Unit (Domestic):

Corbin Gas Propane (6)
2870 Hwy 138 E, Jonesboro, GA 30236
Tel.: (770) 471-7170
Web Site: http://www.amerigas.com
Fuel Dealers
N.A.I.C.S.: 457210

F K Gailey (6)
20534 Rt 411, La Fargeville, NY 13656
Tel.: (315) 658-2240
Web Site: http://www.fkgailey.com
Propane Gas Distr
N.A.I.C.S.: 457210

Flame Propane (6)
624 N Industrial Dr, Camp Verde, AZ 86322
Tel.: (928) 567-4099
Web Site: http://www.flamepropanegas.com
Natural Gas Pipeline Services
N.A.I.C.S.: 486210

M & J Gas Company (6)
1911 E 5Th St, Lumberton, NC 28358-6109
Web Site: http://www.mandjgas.com
Emp.: 10
Fuel Dealers
N.A.I.C.S.: 457210
Ed Hayes (Gen Mgr)

Pedley Propane (6)
17846 Van Buren Blvd, Riverside, CA 92508
Tel.: (951) 780-8000
Propane & Natural Gas Services
N.A.I.C.S.: 457210

Thomas Gas Company (6)
2772 Armentrout Dr, Concord, NC 28025-5877
Tel.: (704) 786-5899
Web Site: http://www.thomasgas.com
Emp.: 10
Fuel Dealers
N.A.I.C.S.: 457210
Michael Surr (Mgr-District)

Subsidiary (Domestic):

Titan Propane LLC (6)
19910 Houston Rd, Lebanon, MO 65536
Tel.: (417) 532-2121
Web Site: http://www.titanpropane.com
Liquefied Petroleum Gas Dealers
N.A.I.C.S.: 424720

Subsidiary (Domestic):

Petrolane, Inc. (3)
460 N Gulph Rd, Valley Forge, PA 19406
Tel.: (610) 337-7000
Natural Gas Distr
N.A.I.C.S.: 213112

Antargaz Belgium N.V. (1)
Web Site: http://www.antargaz.be
Emp.: 50
Natural Gas Distr
N.A.I.C.S.: 221210

Subsidiary (Non-US):

Antargaz Luxembourg S.A. (2)
Rue de l'Industrie 15, 8069, Bertrange, Luxembourg
Tel.: (352) 80022822
Web Site: https://www.antargaz.lu
Emp.: 5
Natural Gas Distr
N.A.I.C.S.: 221210
Guy Van Cauwenbergh (Mng Dir)

Antargaz Nederland B.V. (2)
PO Box 76, 5430 AB, Cuijk, Netherlands
Tel.: (31) 485335222
Web Site: http://www.antargaz.nl
Emp.: 35
Petroleum Product Distr
N.A.I.C.S.: 424720

Subsidiary (Domestic):

Gasbottling N.V. (2)
Singel 33, 9000, Gent, Belgium
Tel.: (32) 92555590
Emp.: 30
Petroleum Bottling Fuel Distr
N.A.I.C.S.: 424720
Biqeuz Peear (Mgr)

Antargaz S.A. (1)
Immeuble Reflex 4 place Victor Hugo, 92400, Courbevoie, France (99.99%)
Tel.: (33) 141887000
Web Site: https://www.antargaz.fr
Sales Range: $700-749.9 Million
Emp.: 1,000
Butane & Propane Gas Distr
N.A.I.C.S.: 457210
Eric Naddeo (Gen Dir)

Subsidiary (Domestic):

Aquitaine Rhone Gaz (2)
4 Av l Escart, 33450, Saint-Loubes, France
Tel.: (33) 557772323
Natural Gas Distr
N.A.I.C.S.: 221210

Norgal (2)
Zone Industrielle route de la Chimie, 76700,

Gonfreville-l'Orcher, France
Tel.: (33) 235533710
Natural Gas Exploration Service
N.A.I.C.S.: 213112

Rhone Gaz (2)
Rue du 8 Mai 1945, 69320, Feyzin, France
Tel.: (33) 478703021
Natural Gas Drilling Services
N.A.I.C.S.: 211130

De Vrije Energie Producent B.V. (1)
Jan Tinbergenstraat 110, 7559 SP, Hengelo, Netherlands
Tel.: (31) 743766243
Web Site: https://www.dvep.nl
Provider Electric Services
N.A.I.C.S.: 221114

Finagaz (1)
48 avenue du General de Gaulle, 92800, Puteaux, France
Tel.: (33) 171027000
Web Site: http://www.finagaz.fr
Food Products Mfr
N.A.I.C.S.: 311991

Flaga GmbH (1)
Flaga Strasse 1, 2100, Leobendorf, Austria (100%)
Tel.: (43) 50710
Web Site: http://www.flaga.at
Sales Range: $550-599.9 Million
Emp.: 700
Gas & Electric Utilities; Propane Distr
N.A.I.C.S.: 221210

Subsidiary (Domestic):

ECO Energietechnik GmbH (2)
Franz-Brotzner-Strasse 55, Wals-Himmelreich, Salzburg, 5073, Austria
Tel.: (43) 6624390150
Web Site: http://www.energycompany.at
Sales Range: $25-49.9 Million
Emp.: 25
Heating & Cooling Equipment Mfr
N.A.I.C.S.: 423720

Subsidiary (Non-US):

Flaga GPL Romania S.r.l. (2)
Tel.: (40) 259411780
Web Site: http://www.flaga.ro
Emp.: 25
Gas Distr
N.A.I.C.S.: 221210

Flaga Gaz Magyarorszag Kft. (2)
Loranger Ipari Telep Sostoi u 17-19, Szekesfehervar, H-8000, Hungary
Tel.: (36) 22512512
Web Site: http://www.flaga.hu
Natural Gas Distr
N.A.I.C.S.: 221210

Subsidiary (Domestic):

Flaga NG GmbH (2)
Bert Kollensperger Str 3, A-6065, Thaur, Austria
Tel.: (43) 52235863
Web Site: http://www.flaga-ng.at
Food Products Mfr
N.A.I.C.S.: 311991

Subsidiary (Non-US):

Flaga Suisse GmbH (2)
Web Site: http://www.flaga.ch
Natural Gas Liquid Extraction Services
N.A.I.C.S.: 211130

Flaga s.r.o. (2)
Nadrazni 47, 693 01, Hustopece, Czech Republic
Tel.: (420) 844111155
Web Site: http://www.flaga.cz
Emp.: 80
Natural Gas Distr
N.A.I.C.S.: 221210

Flaga spol s.r.o. (2)
Senkvicka 14/R, PO Box 39, 902 01, Pezinok, Slovakia
Tel.: (421) 850606303
Web Site: http://www.flagask.sk
Gas Distr
N.A.I.C.S.: 221210

Kosan Gas A/S (2)
Hasselager Centervej 19-21, 8260, Viby,

Arhus, Denmark
Tel.: (45) 89487700
Web Site: http://www.kosangas.dk
Sales Range: $25-49.9 Million
Emp.: 65
Liquid Petroleum Gas Mfrs
N.A.I.C.S.: 457210

Subsidiary (Non-US):

Kosan Gas Finland Oy (3)
Ayritie 16, 01510, Vantaa, Finland
Tel.: (358) 934844410
Web Site: https://www.kosangas.fi
Emp.: 6
Natural Gas Distr
N.A.I.C.S.: 221210
Dan Olin (Mng Dir)
Lasse Kaitasalo (Acct Mgr)

Kosan Gas Norge A/S (3)
Brynsveien 2-4, 0667, Oslo, Norway
Tel.: (47) 22883070
Web Site: http://www.kosangas.no
Natural Gas Distr
N.A.I.C.S.: 221210
Morten Lunner (Mgr-Sls & Technical)
Truls Isaksen (Acct Mgr)
Terje Usken (Engr-Svc-Technique)
Stig Ramsvik (Mng Dir & Mgr-Distr-Nordic)

Kosan Gas Sverige AB (3)
Backa Bergogata 14, 422 46, Hisings Backa, Sweden
Tel.: (46) 31655200
Web Site: http://www.kosangas.se
Natural Gas Distr
N.A.I.C.S.: 221210
Benny Ljungholm (Engr-Svc-Technique)
Macarena Contreras (Controller-Supply & Logistics-Distr)
Harry Ekman (Coord-Supply & Logistics-Distr)
Niklas Dahl (Coord-Supply & Logistics-Distr)

LPG 4 U Limited (1)
Unit D3 Red Scar Business Park Longridge Road, Ribbleton, Preston, PR2 5NQ, United Kingdom
Tel.: (44) 8081410515
Web Site: https://www.lpg4u.co.uk
Bottled Gas Whslr
N.A.I.C.S.: 424720

Mountaineer Gas Company (1)
2401 Sissonville Dr, Charleston, WV 25387
Tel.: (304) 347-0541
Web Site: http://mountaineergasonline.com
Natural Gas Distribution
N.A.I.C.S.: 221210
Robert F. Beard (CEO)

Primus Limited (1)
Chancery Place 60 Brown Street, Manchester, M2 2JG, United Kingdom
Tel.: (44) 2081336291
Web Site: http://www.primusng-group.com
Emp.: 120
Business Consulting Services
N.A.I.C.S.: 541330

Qwint B.V. (1)
Jan Tinbergenstraat 110, 7559 SP, Hengelo, Netherlands
Tel.: (31) 742500608
Provider Electricity & Gas Services
N.A.I.C.S.: 221210

SC Carpatgas S.R.L. (1)
Calea Dumbravii nr 101, 550399, Sibiu, Romania
Tel.: (40) 269250361
Natural Gas Distr
N.A.I.C.S.: 221210

UGI Enterprises, LLC (1)
225 Morgantown Rd, Reading, PA 19611 (100%)
Tel.: (610) 337-1000
Sales Range: $200-249.9 Million
Holding Company; Natural Gas & Electric Utilities
N.A.I.C.S.: 551112

Subsidiary (Domestic):

UGI Energy Services, LLC (2)
835 Knitting Mills Way, Wyomissing, PA 19610
Web Site: https://www.ugies.com
Energy Distr

N.A.I.C.S.: 221210
Marie-Dominique Ortiz-Landazabal *(CFO & VP)*
Joseph L. Hartz *(Pres)*
Joseph Devine *(Sr Dir-US Mid Atlantic)*
Pamela A. Witmer *(VP-Govt Affairs)*

Subsidiary (Domestic):

UGI Development Company (3)
390 Route 11, Hunlock Creek, PA 18621-0224
Tel.: (570) 830-1270
Eletric Power Generation Services
N.A.I.C.S.: 221118

Subsidiary (Non-US):

UGI Energy Services, Inc. (3)
Tel.: (610) 373-7999
Web Site: http://ugies.com
Sales Range: $25-49.9 Million
Emp.: 3
Gas, Electricity & Fuel Oil Marketing Services; Owns Natural Gas Storage & Peaking Plants
N.A.I.C.S.: 221210

Subsidiary (Domestic):

UGI Storage Company (3)
1 Meridian Blvd Ste 2C01, Wyomissing, PA 19610
Tel.: (610) 743-7010
Web Site: http://www.ugistorage.com
Natural Gas Distr
N.A.I.C.S.: 221210

Subsidiary (Domestic):

UGI HVAC Enterprises, Inc. (2)
460 N Gulph Rd, King of Prussia, PA 19406
Tel.: (610) 337-1000
Sales Range: $100-124.9 Million
Emp.: 300
Heating, Cooling, Refrigeration, Electrical & Plumbing Services
N.A.I.C.S.: 333415
John L. Walsh *(Pres & CEO)*

UGI Utilities, Inc. (1)
1 UGI Dr, Denver, PA 17517 **(100%)**
Tel.: (610) 796-3400
Web Site: http://www.ugi.com
Natural Gas & Electric Power Distribution
N.A.I.C.S.: 221210
Marvin O. Schlanger *(Chm)*
Daniel J. Platt *(CFO, Treas, VP-Fin & Asst Sec)*
Megan Mattern *(Controller)*

Subsidiary (Domestic):

UGI Central Penn Gas, Inc. (2)
PO Box 508, Lock Haven, PA 17745
Tel.: (800) 652-0550
Web Site: http://www.chooseenergy.com
Natural Gas Distr
N.A.I.C.S.: 221210

UGI Penn Natural Gas, Inc. (2)
1 UGI Ctr, Wilkes Barre, PA 18711-0601
Tel.: (570) 829-8600
Web Site: http://www.ugi.com
Sales Range: $350-399.9 Million
Emp.: 420
Natural Gas Distr
N.A.I.C.S.: 221210

UniverGas Italia S.r.l. (1)
Via Pio Emanuelli 1, 00143, Rome, Italy
Tel.: (39) 0800189189
Web Site: http://www.univergas.it
Liquefied Petroleum Gas Distr
N.A.I.C.S.: 457210

UIPATH, INC.
1 Vanderbilt Ave 60th Fl, New York, NY 10017
Web Site: https://www.uipath.com
Year Founded: 2005
PATH—(NYSE)
Rev.: $1,308,072,000
Assets: $2,954,758,000
Liabilities: $938,644,000
Net Worth: $2,016,114,000
Earnings: ($89,883,000)
Emp.: 4,035
Fiscal Year-end: 01/31/24

Software Development Services
N.A.I.C.S.: 541511
Robert Enslin *(Co-CEO)*
Kelly Ducourty *(Chief Customer Officer)*
Daniel Dines *(Co-Founder, Chm, Co-CEO & Chief Innovation Officer)*
Marius Tirca *(Co-Founder & CTO)*
Bobby Patrick *(CMO)*
Brad Brubaker *(Chief Legal Officer & Gen Counsel)*
Mihai Faur *(Chief Acctg Officer & Controller-Global)*
Vargha Moayed *(Chief Strategy Officer)*
Vijay Khanna *(Chief Corp Dev Officer)*
Chris Klayko *(Sr VP & Mng Dir-Americas)*
Cheryln Chin *(VP-Alliances & Partners-Global)*
Eddie O'Brien *(Sr VP-Partners, Programs & Ops-Global)*
Renzo Taal *(Sr VP & Mng Dir-EMEA)*
Andreea Baciu *(Chief Culture Officer)*
Kelsey Turcotte *(Sr VP-IR)*
Brandon Deer *(VP-Ops & Strategy)*
Rick Harshman *(Sr VP & Mng Dir-Asia Pacific & Japan)*
Koichi Hasegawa *(CEO-Japan)*
Brigette McInnis-Day *(Chief People Officer)*
Michael Barnes *(VP-Federal Civilian Bus)*
Mateusz Majewski *(VP-Southeast Europe)*
Tudor Cosaceanu *(Reg VP-Romania)*
Ashim Gupta *(CFO & COO)*

ULTA BEAUTY, INC.
1000 Remington Blvd Ste 120, Bolingbrook, IL 60440
Tel.: (630) 410-4800 DE
Web Site: https://www.ulta.com
Year Founded: 1990
ULTA—(NASDAQ)
Rev.: $11,207,303,000
Assets: $5,707,011,000
Liabilities: $3,427,683,000
Net Worth: $2,279,328,000
Earnings: $1,291,005,000
Emp.: 20,000
Fiscal Year-end: 02/03/24
Personal care Product Distr
N.A.I.C.S.: 456120
Kecia L. Steelman *(Pres & COO)*
Jodi Caro *(Chief Risk & Compliance Officer & Gen Counsel)*
Kiley Rawlins *(VP-IR)*
Monica Arnaudo *(Chief Mdsg Officer)*
Laura M. Beres *(Dir-Corp Strategy)*
Elliott D. Rodgers *(Chief Ops Officer & Exec VP)*
Amiee Thomas *(Chief Supply Chain Officer)*
Anita Ryan *(Chief HR Officer)*
David C. Kimbell *(CEO)*

ULTIMATE SPORTS INC.
2119 N 15th St, Lafayette, IN 47904
Tel.: (765) 423-2984 IN
Web Site: http://www.usiskis.com
Year Founded: 1988
USPS—(OTCIQ)
Snow Mobile Mfr
N.A.I.C.S.: 336999

ULTRA CLEAN HOLDINGS, INC.
26462 Corporate Ave, Hayward, CA 94545
Tel.: (510) 576-4400 DE
Web Site: https://www.uct.com
Year Founded: 1991
UCTT—(NASDAQ)
Rev.: $2,101,600,000

Assets: $2,025,400,000
Liabilities: $1,132,700,000
Net Worth: $892,700,000
Earnings: $119,500,000
Emp.: 5,860
Fiscal Year-end: 12/31/21
Semiconductor Manufacturing Subsystems Developer & Mfr
N.A.I.C.S.: 333242
Clarence L. Granger *(Chm)*
Paul Y. Cho *(Gen Counsel & Sec)*
Sheri L. Savage *(CFO)*
Vijayan S. Chinnasami *(COO)*
Chris Cook *(Pres)*
Jeff McKibben *(CIO)*
Jamie Palfrey *(Sr VP)*

Subsidiaries:

American Integration Technologies LLC (1)
481 N Dean Ave, Chandler, AZ 85226
Tel.: (480) 940-0036
Holding Company
N.A.I.C.S.: 551114

Dynamic Manufacturing Solutions, LLC (1)
600 Center Rdg Ste 100, Austin, TX 78753
Tel.: (650) 599-8949
Web Site: http://www.dmsusa.com
Electrical & Electronic Product Mfr
N.A.I.C.S.: 335999
Teresa Schmidt *(Sr Project Mgr)*

Ham-Let (Israel-Canada) Ltd. (1)
Tel.: (972) 46414141
Fittings & Valves Mfr
N.A.I.C.S.: 332919

Subsidiary (Non-US):

Cambridge Fluid Systems Limited (2)
12 Trafalgar Way Bar Hill, Cambridge, CB23 8SQ, United Kingdom
Tel.: (44) 1954786800
Web Site: http://www.cambridge-fluid.com
Fluid Handling Systems Design & Mfr
N.A.I.C.S.: 332912
Stevan Klee *(Mng Dir)*

Hoffman Instrumentation Supply, Inc. (1)
5500 NE Moore Ct, Hillsboro, OR 97124
Tel.: (503) 466-2200
Web Site: https://hisinnovations.com
Sales Range: $1-9.9 Million
Emp.: 18
Semiconductor & Related Device Mfr
N.A.I.C.S.: 334413
Chris Conrad *(Mgr-Quality)*

Marchi Thermal Systems, Inc. (1)
3108 Diablo Ave, Hayward, CA 94545
Tel.: (510) 300-1500
Web Site: http://www.marchithermal.com
Sales Range: $10-24.9 Million
Thermal Control Products Mfr
N.A.I.C.S.: 334512

UCT Fluid Delivery Solutions s.r.o (1)
V Horkach 76, 460 09, Liberec, Czech Republic
Tel.: (420) 483031111
Semiconductor Equipment Mfr
N.A.I.C.S.: 334515

Ultra Clean Asia Pacific, Pte Ltd (1)
2 Woodlands Sector 1 Ste 05-22, Woodlands Spectrum 1, Singapore, 738068, Singapore
Tel.: (65) 67557577
Semiconductor Devices Mfr
N.A.I.C.S.: 334413
Danielle Moek *(Gen Mgr)*

Ultra Clean Technology Systems and Service, Inc. (1)
130 Beacon St, South San Francisco, CA 94080-6913
Tel.: (650) 583-5345
Process Control Instruments Mfr
N.A.I.C.S.: 334413

ULTRA PETROLEUM CORP.

116 Inverness Drive East Suite 400, Englewood, CO 80112
Tel.: (303) 708-9740 TX
Web Site: http://www.ultrapetroleum.com
Year Founded: 1979
UPLC—(OTCIQ)
Rev.: $742,032,000
Assets: $1,815,276,000
Liabilities: $2,660,090,000
Net Worth: ($844,814,000)
Earnings: $107,988,000
Emp.: 151
Fiscal Year-end: 12/31/19
Petroleum Exploration & Production Services
N.A.I.C.S.: 211120
David W. Honeyfield *(CFO & Sr VP)*
James N. Whyte *(Chief HR Officer & Sr VP)*
Mark T. Solomon *(Chief Acctg Officer, VP & Controller)*
Kason D. Kerr *(Gen Counsel, Sec & VP)*
Jerald J. Stratton Jr. *(COO & Sr VP)*

Subsidiaries:

Ultra Resources, Inc. (1)
304 Inverness Way S Ste 295, Englewood, CO 80112
Tel.: (307) 367-6442
Oil & Gas Well Support Services
N.A.I.C.S.: 213112

ULTRA PURE WATER TECHNOLOGIES, LLC
1180 Hillsmith Dr, Cincinnati, OH 45215
Tel.: (513) 771-2434 DE
Web Site: http://www.ultrapureh2otech.com
UPWT—(OTCIQ)
Water Supply Services
N.A.I.C.S.: 221310
Matt Cash *(Sls Mgr)*

ULTRAGENYX PHARMACEUTICAL INC.
60 Leveroni Ct, Novato, CA 94949
Tel.: (415) 483-8800 DE
Web Site: https://www.ultragenyx.com
Year Founded: 2010
RARE—(NASDAQ)
Rev.: $434,249,000
Assets: $1,491,013,000
Liabilities: $1,215,599,000
Net Worth: $275,414,000
Earnings: ($606,639,000)
Emp.: 1,276
Fiscal Year-end: 12/31/23
Biopharmaceutical Mfr
N.A.I.C.S.: 325412
Erik Harris *(Chief Comm Officer & Exec VP)*
John Richard Pinion *(Chief Quality Ops Officer & Exec VP-Translational Sciences)*
Howard Horn *(CFO & Exec VP-Corp Strategy)*
Erik Harris *(Chief Comm Officer & Exec VP)*
Ernie Meyer *(Chief HR Officer & Exec VP)*
Theodore A. Huizenga *(Chief Acctg Officer)*
Eric Crombez *(Chief Medical Officer & Exec VP)*
Emil D. Kakkis *(Founder, Pres & CEO)*
Thomas R. Kassberg *(Chief Bus Officer & Exec VP)*
Thomas Richard Kassberg *(Chief Bus Officer & Exec VP)*
Karah Herdman Parschauer *(Chief Legal Officer & Exec VP)*

Ultragenyx Pharmaceutical Inc.—(Continued)

Subsidiaries:

Ultragenyx Germany GmbH (1)
Rahel-Hirsch-Str 10, 10557, Berlin, Germany
Tel.: (49) 30590083651
Web Site: https://www.ultragenyx.de
Pharmaceuticals Product Mfr
N.A.I.C.S.: 325412

ULTRALIFE CORPORATION
2000 Technology Pkwy, Newark, NY 14513
Tel.: (315) 332-7100   DE
Web Site:
  https://www.ultralifecorporation.com
Year Founded: 1991
ULBI—(NASDAQ)
Rev.: $131,840,000
Assets: $168,430,000
Liabilities: $52,027,000
Net Worth: $116,403,000
Earnings: ($119,000)
Emp.: 547
Fiscal Year-end: 12/31/22
Primary Lithium Batteries, Lithium Ion Batteries & Lithium Polymer Rechargeable Batteries Mfr
N.A.I.C.S.: 335910
Philip A. Fain (CFO, Treas & Sec)
Michael E. Manna (Pres-Battery & Energy Products)
Bradford Todd Whitmore (Chm)
James J. Rasmussen Jr. (Pres-Comm Sys)

Subsidiaries:

ABLE New Energy Co., Ltd (1)
Building A No 1 Longwo Industrial Zone Longtian Community, Kengzi Town Pingshan New District, Shenzhen, Guangdong, China
Tel.: (86) 7558 250 7771
Web Site: https://www.ultralifechina.com
Lithium Battery Mfr
N.A.I.C.S.: 335910

Accutronics, Ltd. (1)
Unit 20 Loomer Road, Chesterton, Newcastle-under-Lyme, ST5 7LB, Staffordshire, United Kingdom
Tel.: (44) 1782566622
Web Site: https://www.accutronics.co.uk
Lithium Battery Mfr
N.A.I.C.S.: 335910

Southwest Electronic Energy
Corp. (1)
PO Box 31340, Houston, TX 77231
Tel.: (281) 240-4000
Web Site: http://www.swe.com
Electronic Parts & Equipment Distribution
N.A.I.C.S.: 423690

Ultralife Batteries (UK) Ltd. (1)
18 Nuffield Way, Abingdon, OX14 1TG, United Kingdom (100%)
Tel.: (44) 1235542600
Sales Range: $100-124.9 Million
Battery Mfr
N.A.I.C.S.: 335910

Ultralife Batteries India Private
Limited (1)
No 38B 1 Part Doddanakundi Industrial Area 1st Phase Mahadevapura, Bengaluru, 560048, Karnataka, India
Tel.: (91) 9141923680
Web Site: https://www.ultralifeindia.com
Primary Batteries Mfr
N.A.I.C.S.: 335910
P. R. Ganesh (Mng Dir)

UMB FINANCIAL CORPORATION
1010 Grand Blvd, Kansas City, MO 64106
Tel.: (816) 860-7000   MO
Web Site: https://www.umb.com
Year Founded: 1967

UMBF—(NASDAQ)
Rev.: $2,380,558,000
Assets: $44,011,674,000
Liabilities: $40,911,255,000
Net Worth: $3,100,419,000
Earnings: $350,024,000
Emp.: 3,599
Fiscal Year-end: 12/31/23
Bank Holding Company
N.A.I.C.S.: 551111
Mariner Kemper (Chm & CEO)
James D. Rine (Pres)
Shannon A. Johnson (Chief Admin Officer & Exec VP)
Ram Shankar (CFO & Exec VP)
James Rine (Pres/CEO-UMB Bank NA)
R. Brian Beaird (Chief HR Officer & Exec VP)
Thomas S. Terry (Chief Credit Officer & Exec VP)

Subsidiaries:

Marquette Asset Management,
LLC (1)
150 S Fifth St Ste 2800, Minneapolis, MN 55402 (100%)
Tel.: (612) 661-3770
Web Site: http://www.marquetteam.com
Asset Management Services
N.A.I.C.S.: 523940
Chris M. Vernier (Pres)
Valerie Thomas (Mng Dir)
Kristy Thom (VP)

Prairie Capital Management,
LLC (1)
4900 Main St Ste 700, Kansas City, MO 64112
Tel.: (816) 531-1101
Web Site: https://www.prairiecapital.com
Emp.: 40
Asset & Wealth Management Consulting Services
N.A.I.C.S.: 541618
Brian N. Kaufman (Co-Founder & Mng Dir)
Curtis A. Krizek (Co-Founder & Mng Dir)
Andrew S. Klocke (Mng Dir)
Michael M. Gentry (Mng Dir)
Rob R. Schneider (Co-Founder & Mng Dir)
R. Riley Pratt (Mng Dir)
John S. Thurlow (Mng Dir)
Cory M. Ross (Mng Dir)
Angie Tower (Mng Dir)

UMB Bank, N.A. (1)
1010 Grand Blvd, Kansas City, MO 64106 (100%)
Tel.: (816) 860-7930
Emp.: 200
Retail & Commercial Banking
N.A.I.C.S.: 522180

Subsidiary (Domestic):

Marquette Business Credit, LLC (2)
5910 N Central Expy Ste 1900, Dallas, TX 75206
Tel.: (214) 389-5900
Web Site:
  http://www.marquettebusinesscredit.com
Sales Range: $50-74.9 Million
Emp.: 20
Asset-Based Corporate Lending Services
N.A.I.C.S.: 522299

Marquette Transportation Finance,
LLC (2)
1600 W 82nd St Ste 250, Bloomington, MN 55431
Tel.: (952) 703-7474
Web Site: http://www.marqtransfinance.com
Emp.: 55
Transportation Financing Services
N.A.I.C.S.: 522390

Division (Domestic):

Marquette Commercial Finance (3)
1600 W 82nd St Ste 250, Bloomington, MN 55431
Tel.: (952) 703-7474
Web Site: http://www.marqcfi.com
Emp.: 40
Commercial Accounts Receivable Financing Services

N.A.I.C.S.: 522390
Benjamin J. Doran (Sr VP & Dir-Sls)

Subsidiary (Domestic):

UMB Banc Leasing Corp. (2)
1010 Grand Blvd, Kansas City, MO 64106-2202 (100%)
Tel.: (816) 860-7000
Web Site: https://www.umb.com
Leasing Services
N.A.I.C.S.: 522110

UMB Capital Corporation (2)
1010 Grand Blvd, Kansas City, MO 64106-2202 (100%)
Tel.: (816) 860-7000
Rev.: $4,473,000
Emp.: 175
Financial Investments & Banking Services
N.A.I.C.S.: 523150

UMB Financial Services, Inc. (2)
928 Grand Blvd 6th Fl, Kansas City, MO 64106
Tel.: (816) 842-2222
Web Site: https://www.umb.com
Sales Range: $1-9.9 Million
Emp.: 20
Financial Services
N.A.I.C.S.: 522110

UMB Fund Services, Inc. (1)
235 W Galena St, Milwaukee, WI 53212 (100%)
Tel.: (414) 299-2000
Web Site: https://www.umbfs.umb.com
Sales Range: $75-99.9 Million
Emp.: 200
Mutual Fund Accounting, Administration, Cash Management, Distribution & Custody Services
N.A.I.C.S.: 523991
Peter James deSilva (Chm)
Terrance P. Gallagher (Exec VP & Dir-Fund Acctg & Admin)
Maureen A. Quill (Pres)
Constance Dye Shannon (Gen Counsel & Exec VP)
Michael Yanke (Head-Fund Admin)
Joe Scott (Mng Dir)
Michelle Benner (VP-Bus Dev)
Ana Burke (VP-Bus Dev)
Jose Rincon (VP-Bus Dev)
Chante Schultz (Asst VP-Bus Dev)

Subsidiary (Domestic):

UMB Distribution Services, LLC (2)
803 W Michigan St A, Milwaukee, WI 53233 (100%)
Tel.: (414) 299-2282
Web Site: https://www.umbfs.com
Sales Range: $50-74.9 Million
Emp.: 100
Mutual Fund Distribution Services
N.A.I.C.S.: 523991

UMBRA APPLIED TECHNOLOGIES GROUP, INC.
14391 Spring Hill Dr, Spring Hill, FL 34609
Web Site: https://www.uatgroup.com
UATG—(OTCIQ)
Sales Range: Less than $1 Million
Holding Company
N.A.I.C.S.: 551112
Alexander Umbra (CEO)
Thomas L. Crom (CFO)

UMEWORLD, LIMITED
66 W Flagler St, Miami, FL 33130
Tel.: (786) 791-0483   VG
Web Site: https://www.umeworld.com
Year Founded: 1997
UMEWF—(OTCIQ)
Rev.: $1,401
Assets: $59,003
Liabilities: $434,873
Net Worth: ($375,870)
Earnings: ($306,340)
Emp.: 1
Fiscal Year-end: 09/30/23
Investment Services
N.A.I.C.S.: 523999

Michael M. Lee (Founder, Chm, Pres & CEO)
Winfield Yongbiao Ding (CFO)

UMH PROPERTIES, INC.
Juniper Business Plz 3499 Rte 9 N Ste 3-C, Freehold, NJ 07728
Tel.: (732) 577-9997   MD
Web Site: https://www.umh.reit
Year Founded: 1968
UMH—(NYSE)
Rev.: $195,776,000
Assets: $1,344,596,000
Liabilities: $793,400,000
Net Worth: $551,196,000
Earnings: ($36,265,000)
Emp.: 460
Fiscal Year-end: 12/31/22
Pre-fabricated Homes Mfr
N.A.I.C.S.: 531190
Eugene W. Landy (Founder)
Samuel A. Landy (Pres & CEO)
Anna T. Chew (CFO, Chief Acctg Officer, Treas & Exec VP)
George Kline (VP-Corp Security)
Craig Koster (Gen Counsel, Sec & Sr Exec VP)
Regina Beasley (Sr VP)
Ayal Dreifuss (Sr VP-Rental Ops)
Christine Lindsey (Sr VP)
Robert Van Schuyver (Sr VP)
Abby Karnofsky (VP-Marketing)
Kristin Langley (VP & Controller)
James O. Lykins (VP-Capital Markets)
Nelli Madden (VP-Investor Relations)
T. C. Sheppard (VP-Consumer Fin)
Alan Patterson (Asst VP-Engineering)
Brittnee Sperling (Asst Controller)

Subsidiaries:

Brookview LP (1)
2025 Route 9n, Greenfield Center, NY 12833
Tel.: (848) 565-1373
Web Site: http://www.umh.com
Emp.: 4
Residential Township Development Services
N.A.I.C.S.: 531210
Janet Wickham (Mgr-Community)
Steve Sacks (Mgr-Community)

Heather Highlands Mobile Home Village Associates, LP (1)
109 Main St, Pittston, PA 18640
Tel.: (570) 655-9643
Web Site: https://umh.com
Emp.: 6
Residential Building Rental Services
N.A.I.C.S.: 531190
Jeffrey Zeller (Mgr-Community)
Ellyn Fortney (Mgr-Community)

Kinnebrook Mobile Home Associates
LP (1)
351 State Route 17B, Monticello, NY 12701
Tel.: (845) 794-6066
Residential Building Rental Services
N.A.I.C.S.: 531190

OH Friendly Village, LLC (1)
27696 Oregon Rd, Perrysburg, OH 43551
Tel.: (419) 666-1515
Residential Home Rental Services
N.A.I.C.S.: 531110
Ben Cuprys (Mgr-Community)

OH Meadows of Perrysburg,
LLC (1)
27484 Oregon Rd, Perrysburg, OH 43551
Tel.: (419) 662-6557
Web Site: https://umh.com
Residential Home Rental Services
N.A.I.C.S.: 531110
Cindy Wilcox (Mgr-Community)

OH Perrysburg Estates, LLC (1)
23720 Lime City Rd, Perrysburg, OH 43551
Tel.: (419) 874-4733
Web Site: https://umh.com
Residential Home Rental Services
N.A.I.C.S.: 531110
Renee Webb (Mgr-Community)

OH Pikewood Manor, LLC (1)
1780 Lorain Blvd, Elyria, OH 44035
Tel.: (440) 324-7900
Web Site: https://umh.com
Residential Home Rental Services
N.A.I.C.S.: 531110
Shawn Hopkins (Mgr-Community)

Oxford Village Ltd (1)
2 Dolinger Dr, West Grove, PA 19390
Tel.: (610) 869-8707
Web Site: https://umh.com
Real Estate Investment Services
N.A.I.C.S.: 531190

UMH IN Highland, LLC (1)
1875 Osolo Rd, Elkhart, IN 46514
Tel.: (574) 262-3887
Web Site: http://www.gmail.com
Emp.: 5
Residential Building Rental Services
N.A.I.C.S.: 531190
Veronica Arroyo (Mgr-Community)

UMH IN Holiday Village, LLC (1)
1350 Co Rd 3, Elkhart, IN 46514
Tel.: (574) 226-0423
Real Estate Property Rental & Leasing Services
N.A.I.C.S.: 531190
Candice Conroy (Mgr-Community)

UMH IN Meadows, LLC (1)
11 Meadows, Nappanee, IN 46550
Tel.: (574) 773-2503
Web Site: https://umh.com
Real Estate Property Rental & Leasing Services
N.A.I.C.S.: 531190
Robert Lethbridge (Mgr-Community)

UMH IN Summit Village, LLC (1)
246 N 500 E, Marion, IN 46952
Tel.: (765) 668-1113
Web Site: https://umh.com
Real Estate Investment Trust Services
N.A.I.C.S.: 531110
Lacey Farmer (Mgr-Community)

UMH IN Woods Edge, LLC (1)
1670 E 650 N, West Lafayette, IN 47906
Tel.: (765) 520-3082
Web Site: https://umh.com
Real Estate Property Rental & Leasing Services
N.A.I.C.S.: 531190
Shelly Barhydt (Mgr-Community)

UMH MI Candlewick Court, LLC (1)
1800 Candlewick Dr, Owosso, MI 48867
Tel.: (989) 723-3403
Web Site: https://umh.com
Real Estate Property Rental & Leasing Services
N.A.I.C.S.: 531190
Tony Lehman (Mgr-Community)

UMH MI Northtowne Meadows, LLC (1)
6255 Telegraph Rd, Erie, MI 48133
Tel.: (734) 847-7355
Web Site: https://umh.com
Residential Home Rental Services
N.A.I.C.S.: 531110
Stephanie Steer (Mgr-Community)

UMH NY Brookview MHP, LLC (1)
2025 Route 9 N Lot 137, Greenfield Center, NY 12833
Tel.: (518) 893-2989
Real Estate Property Rental & Leasing Services
N.A.I.C.S.: 531190
Stephanie Barbieri (Mgr-Community)
Stephen Sacks (Mgr-Sales)

UMH NY D&R Village, LLC (1)
430 Route 146 Lot 65A, Clifton Park, NY 12065
Tel.: (518) 383-9977
Web Site: https://umh.com
Real Estate Property Rental & Leasing Services
N.A.I.C.S.: 531190
Karen Bristol (Mgr-Community)

UMH OH Catalina, LLC (1)
6501 Germantown Rd, Middletown, OH 45042
Tel.: (513) 423-9413
Web Site: https://umh.com

Real Estate Property Rental & Leasing Services
N.A.I.C.S.: 531190
Nicole Watts (Mgr-Community)

UMH OH Hayden Heights, LLC (1)
5501 Cosgray Rd, Dublin, OH 43016
Tel.: (614) 816-0474
Web Site: https://umh.com
Real Estate Property Rental & Leasing Services
N.A.I.C.S.: 531190
Dale Jenne (Mgr-Community)

UMH OH Lake Sherman Village, LLC (1)
7227 Beth Ave SW, Navarre, OH 44662
Tel.: (330) 484-4767
Real Estate Property Rental & Leasing Services
N.A.I.C.S.: 531190
Heather Eisentrout (Mgr-Community)

UMH OH Olmsted Falls, LLC (1)
26875 Bagley Rd, Olmsted Falls, OH 44138
Tel.: (440) 235-3424
Web Site: https://umh.com
Real Estate Property Rental & Leasing Services
N.A.I.C.S.: 531190
Briana Childress (Mgr-Community)

UMH OH Worthington Arms, LLC (1)
5277 Columbus Pike, Lewis Center, OH 43035-9710
Tel.: (740) 548-4190
Web Site: https://umh.com
Real Estate Property Rental & Leasing Services
N.A.I.C.S.: 531190
Kima Langoehr (Mgr-Community)

UMH PA Camelot Woods, LLC (1)
124 Clairmont Dr, Altoona, PA 16601
Tel.: (814) 631-6300
Mobile Home Mfr
N.A.I.C.S.: 321991
Marcia Waters (Mgr-Community)

UMH PA Cranberry Village, LLC (1)
100 Treesdale Dr, Cranberry Township, PA 16066
Tel.: (724) 776-3255
Web Site: https://umh.com
Real Estate Property Rental & Leasing Services
N.A.I.C.S.: 531190
Connie Bougher (Mgr-Community)

UMH PA Forest Park, LLC (1)
102 Holly Dr, Cranberry Township, PA 16066
Tel.: (724) 776-3198
Web Site: https://umh.com
Real Estate Property Rental & Leasing Services
N.A.I.C.S.: 531190
Brian Mahoney (Mgr-Community)

UMH PA Highland Estates, LLC (1)
60 Old Route 22, Kutztown, PA 19530
Tel.: (610) 285-6311
Web Site: https://umh.com
Residential Home Rental Services
N.A.I.C.S.: 531110
Jeff Wolfe Norma (Mgr-Community)

UMH PA Holly Acres, LLC (1)
7240 Holly Dale Dr, Erie, PA 16509
Tel.: (814) 460-7431
Web Site: https://umh.com
Real Estate Property Rental & Leasing Services
N.A.I.C.S.: 531190
Gregory Cole (Mgr-Community)

UMH PA Huntingdon Pointe, LLC (1)
549 Chicory Ln, Mount Pleasant, PA 15666
Tel.: (724) 542-4050
Real Estate Property Rental & Leasing Services
N.A.I.C.S.: 531190
Jennifer McGrath (Mgr-Community)

UMH PA Suburban Estates, LLC (1)
33 Maruca Dr, Greensburg, PA 15601
Tel.: (724) 834-0931
Web Site: https://umh.com

Real Estate Property Rental & Leasing Services
N.A.I.C.S.: 531190
Bill Mowry (Mgr-Community)

UMH PA Sunny Acres, LLC (1)
272 Nicole Ln, Somerset, PA 15501
Tel.: (814) 445-6071
Web Site: https://umh.com
Real Estate Property Rental & Leasing Services
N.A.I.C.S.: 531190
Belinda Knopsynder (Mgr-Community)

UMH PA Valley Stream, LLC (1)
60 Vly Stream Park, Mountain Top, PA 18707
Tel.: (570) 678-3750
Web Site: https://umh.com
Real Estate Property Rental & Leasing Services
N.A.I.C.S.: 531190
Diana Daubert (Mgr-Community)

UMH PA Voyager Estates, LLC (1)
1002 Satellite Dr, West Newton, PA 15089
Tel.: (724) 872-8245
Web Site: https://umh.com
Real Estate Property Rental & Leasing Services
N.A.I.C.S.: 531190
Jennifer McGrath (Mgr-Community)

UMH TN Allentown, LLC (1)
4912 Raleigh-Millington Rd, Memphis, TN 38128
Tel.: (901) 388-0046
Web Site: https://umh.com
Real Estate Property Rental & Leasing Services
N.A.I.C.S.: 531190

UMH TN Weatherly Estates, LLC (1)
271 Weatherly Dr, Lebanon, TN 37087
Tel.: (615) 453-2600
Web Site: https://umh.com
Real Estate Property Rental & Leasing Services
N.A.I.C.S.: 531190
Bob J. Toth (Mgr-Community)

United Mobile Homes of Buffalo, Inc. (1)
338 County Route 11 Lot Ste 165, West Monroe, NY 13167-4115
Tel.: (315) 676-2016
Web Site: https://www.umh.com
Sales Range: $25-49.9 Million
Emp.: 3
Real Estate Investment Services
N.A.I.C.S.: 531190
Fred Croad (Mgr-Community)
Kim Randall (Mgr-Community)

UN MONDE INTERNATIONAL LTD.
50 W Liberty St Ste 880, Reno, NV 89501
Tel.: (852) 634-6189
ARMC—(OTCIQ)
Liabilities: $102,721
Net Worth: ($102,721)
Earnings: ($36,649)
Emp.: 2
Fiscal Year-end: 12/31/22
Electronic Product Distr
N.A.I.C.S.: 449210

UNDER ARMOUR, INC.
1020 Hull St, Baltimore, MD 21230
Tel.: (410) 468-2512   MD
Web Site:
  https://www.underarmour.com
UAA—(NYSE)
Rev.: $5,701,879,000
Assets: $4,760,734,000
Liabilities: $2,607,448,000
Net Worth: $2,153,286,000
Earnings: $232,042,000
Emp.: 6,800
Fiscal Year-end: 03/31/24
Men's, Women's & Youth Sports Apparel Mfr
N.A.I.C.S.: 315210

David Baxter (Pres-Americas)
John Varvatos (Chief Design Officer)
Kevin A. Plank (Founder, Pres & CEO)
Eric J. Aumen (Principal Acctg Officer)
David E. Bergman (CFO)

Subsidiaries:

Under Armour Europe B.V. (1)
Stadionplein 10, 1076 CM, Amsterdam, Netherlands
Tel.: (31) 611269614
Web Site: https://www.underarmour.nl
Sporting & Athletic Goods Mfr
N.A.I.C.S.: 339920

UNICO AMERICAN CORPORATION
5230 Las Virgenes Rd Ste 100, Calabasas, CA 91302
Tel.: (818) 591-9800   NV
Web Site:
  https://www.crusaderinsurance.com
Year Founded: 1969
UNAM—(NASDAQ)
Rev.: $36,388,384
Assets: $126,870,930
Liabilities: $99,193,030
Net Worth: $27,677,900
Earnings: ($5,673,251)
Emp.: 26
Fiscal Year-end: 12/31/21
Insurance Holding Company; Property & Casualty Insurance Services
N.A.I.C.S.: 551112
Steven L. Shea (Chm, Pres, CEO, CFO & Chief Ops Officer)

Subsidiaries:

American Acceptance Corp. (1)
23251 Mulholland Dr, Woodland Hills, CA 91364-2732
Tel.: (818) 591-9800
Web Site: http://www.aacloans.com
Sales Range: $150-199.9 Million
Insurance Premium Finance Services
N.A.I.C.S.: 524298

American Insurance Brokers, Inc. (1)
23251 Mulholland Dr, Woodland Hills, CA 91364-2732
Tel.: (818) 591-9800
Web Site: http://www.aib4insurance.com
Sales Range: $75-99.9 Million
Health Insurance Services
N.A.I.C.S.: 524210

Bedford Insurance Services, Inc. (1)
23251 Mulholland Dr, Woodland Hills, CA 91364   **(100%)**
Tel.: (818) 591-9800
Web Site: http://www.bedfordinsurance.com
Sales Range: $10-24.9 Million
Emp.: 5
Sells & Services Daily Automobile Rental Policies
N.A.I.C.S.: 524128

Crusader Insurance Company (1)
26050 Mureau Rd, Calabasas, CA 91302   **(100%)**
Tel.: (818) 591-9800
Web Site:
  http://www.crusaderinsurance.com
Sales Range: $50-74.9 Million
Property & Casualty Insurance
N.A.I.C.S.: 524126

Insurance Club, Inc. (1)
23251 Mulholland Dr, Woodland Hills, CA 91364-2732
Tel.: (818) 591-8700
Web Site: http://www.aaqhic.com
Sales Range: $10-24.9 Million
Emp.: 10
Health Insurance Services
N.A.I.C.S.: 524292

Unifax Insurance Systems, Inc. (1)
26050 Mureau Rd, Calabasas, CA 91302   **(100%)**
Tel.: (818) 591-9800

Unico American Corporation—(Continued)

Web Site:
http://www.crusaderinsurance.com
Sales Range: $25-49.9 Million
Emp.: 50
Property & Casualty Insurance
N.A.I.C.S.: 524210

UNICYCIVE THERAPEUTICS, INC.
4300 El Camino Real Ste 210, Los Altos, CA 94022
Tel.: (650) 351-4495   DE
Web Site: https://www.unicycive.com
Year Founded: 2016
UNCY—(NASDAQ)
Rev.: $951,000
Assets: $2,818,000
Liabilities: $3,284,000
Net Worth: ($466,000)
Earnings: ($18,058,000)
Emp.: 12
Fiscal Year-end: 12/31/22
Research & Development in Biotechnology (except Nanobiotechnology)
N.A.I.C.S.: 541714
John Townsend (CFO)
Pramod Gupta (Exec VP-Pharmaceutical & Bus Ops)
Douglas Jermasek (Exec VP-Corp Strategy)
Shalabh Gupta (Founder, Pres & CEO)

UNIFI, INC.
7201 W Friendly Ave, Greensboro, NC 27410
Tel.: (336) 294-4410   NY
Web Site: https://www.unifi.com
Year Founded: 1971
UFI—(NYSE)
Rev.: $582,209,000
Assets: $469,244,000
Liabilities: $205,859,000
Net Worth: $263,385,000
Earnings: ($47,395,000)
Emp.: 2,700
Fiscal Year-end: 06/30/24
Texturing & Sale of Polyester Filament Yarn
N.A.I.C.S.: 313310
Andrew J. Eaker (CFO, Principal Acctg Officer, Treas & Exec VP)
Albert P. Carey (Chm)
Edmund M. Ingle (CEO)
Brian D. Moore (Exec VP)
Alison Y. Jester (Sr VP-Human Resources)
Sohan Mangaldas (Sr VP-Strategy, Global Procurement, and Supply Chain)
Hongjun Ning (Exec VP)
C. Brad Nations (VP-Manufacturing)
Philip C. Peaslee (CIO & VP)
Jeff R. Vining (Gen Counsel, Sec & VP)

Subsidiaries:

Repreve Renewables, LLC   (1)
1912 Eastchester Dr Ste 209, High Point, NC 27265
Tel.: (336) 763-4808
Web Site: https://aggrowtech.com
Biomass Production Services
N.A.I.C.S.: 325414

Unifi Central America, Ltda. de CV   (1)
Block F Zona Franca American Industrial Park Calle Panamericana, Km 36 5 Ciudad Arce, La Libertad, El Salvador
Tel.: (503) 23489700
Web Site: http://www.unifi.com
Polyester & Nylon Yarn Products Mfr & Distr
N.A.I.C.S.: 325211

Unifi Manufacturing, Inc.   (1)

7201 W Friendly Ave, Greensboro, NC 27410   **(100%)**
Tel.: (336) 294-4410
Web Site: http://www.unifi-inc.com
Sales Range: $900-999.9 Million
Mfr of Polyester Filament Yarn
N.A.I.C.S.: 313110

Subsidiary (Non-US):

Unifi Latin America, S.A.S.   (2)
Transversal 5 No 6-67 Entrada 4 Zona Industrial Cazuca, Soacha, Colombia
Tel.: (57) 17802466
Timber Product Mfr
N.A.I.C.S.: 313110

Unifi Textiles   (1)
Room 1101 Gold River Center No 88 Shishan Rd, Suzhou New District, Suzhou, 215011, Jiangsu, China
Tel.: (86) 51268187198
Fiber Product Mfr & Distr
N.A.I.C.S.: 313110
Hongjun Ning (Exec VP)

Unifi Textured Polyester, LLC   (1)
7201 W Friendly Ave, Greensboro, NC 27410
Tel.: (336) 294-4410
Sales Range: $350-399.9 Million
Mfr of Textured Polyester Fiber
N.A.I.C.S.: 313110

Unifi Textured Yarns Europe, Ltd.   (1)
Kiltoy, Letterkenny, Co Donegal, Ireland   **(100%)**
Tel.: (353) 917424455
Sales Range: $125-149.9 Million
Texturer & Retailer of Polyester Filament Yarn
N.A.I.C.S.: 313110

Unifi do Brasil, Ltda   (1)
Av Alfredo Egidio de Souza Aranha 177 2 andar, Sao Paulo, 04726 170, SP, Brazil   **(100%)**
Tel.: (55) 1121614800
Web Site: http://unifi.com
Sales Range: $125-149.9 Million
Retailer of Polyester Filament Yarn
N.A.I.C.S.: 313110

UNIFIRST CORPORATION
68 Jonspin Rd, Wilmington, MA 01887
Tel.: (978) 658-8888   MA
Web Site: https://www.unifirst.com
Year Founded: 1936
UNF—(NYSE)
Rev.: $1,826,216,000
Assets: $2,381,065,000
Liabilities: $508,113,000
Net Worth: $1,872,952,000
Earnings: $151,111,000
Emp.: 14,000
Fiscal Year-end: 08/28/21
Workwear & Related Products Supplier
N.A.I.C.S.: 424350
Steven S. Sintros (Pres & CEO)
Cynthia Croatti (Bd of Dirs, Executives)
Raymond C. Zemlin (Chm)
David A. DiFillippo (Exec VP-Ops)
William M. Ross (Exec VP-Ops)
David M. Katz (Exec VP-Sls & Mktg)
Shane F. O'Connor (CFO & Exec VP)
Kelly Rooney (COO)

Subsidiaries:

Arrow Uniform-Taylor LLC   (1)
6400 Monroe Blvd, Taylor, MI 48180
Tel.: (313) 299-5000
Web Site: https://www.arrowuniform.com
Uniform Supply Company
N.A.I.C.S.: 812331
Pete Raab (Pres & CEO)
Bruce Weber (CFO)
Scott Herron (VP-Sls, Mktg & eCommerce)
Marc Andris (VP-Plant Ops)
Fred Andris (VP-Distr)
Brian Franey (Dir-Distr)
Kevin Smith (Dir-Svc-South)
Jason Maschke (Dir-Svc-North)
Bill Barr (Dir-IT)

UniFirst Canada Ltd.   (1)
5250 Orbitor Drive, Mississauga, L4W 5G7, ON, Canada   **(100%)**
Sales Range: $10-24.9 Million
Emp.: 40
Linen Supply & Industrial Uniform Rental & Sales
N.A.I.C.S.: 812331

UniFirst Corporation   (1)
813 Massman Dr, Nashville, TN 37210
Tel.: (615) 255-0535
Web Site: http://www.unifirst.com
Uniform Suppliers
N.A.I.C.S.: 812331

UniTech Services B.V.   (1)
De Mars 11, 7742 PT, Coevorden, Netherlands
Tel.: (31) 524599699
Laundry Services
N.A.I.C.S.: 812332

UniTech Services GmbH   (1)
Brookdiek 2 L, 49824, Laar, Germany
Tel.: (49) 59479102910
Laundry Services
N.A.I.C.S.: 812332

UniTech Services Group Ltd.   (1)
Unit 5 Oakwood Close Pen-Y-Fan Industrial Estate, Crumlin, Newport, NP11 3HY, United Kingdom
Tel.: (44) 1495249688
Emp.: 45
Laundry Services
N.A.I.C.S.: 812332
Taren Trosbee (Gen Mgr)

UniTech Services Group, Inc.   (1)
700 S Etiwanda Ave Ste D, Ontario, CA 91761
Tel.: (909) 390-8682
Protective Clothing & Product Supply Services
N.A.I.C.S.: 812332

UniTech Services SAS   (1)
Parc Avenue / La Malvesine, 13720, La Bouilladisse, France
Tel.: (33) 965012247
Laundry Services
N.A.I.C.S.: 812332
Jacques Grisot (Mng Dir)

Unifirst Holdings Inc   (1)
68 Jonspin Rd, Wilmington, MA 01887-1090   **(100%)**
Tel.: (978) 658-8888
Web Site: http://www.unifirst.com
Sales Range: $25-49.9 Million
Emp.: 275
Industrial Uniform Supply
N.A.I.C.S.: 812332

Uniformes de San Luis S.A. de C.V.   (1)
Old bypass S / N, Ciudad Valles, Sinaloa, 79050, Mexico
Tel.: (52) 4813817450
Men & Children Cloth Mfr
N.A.I.C.S.: 458110
Gina Serrano (Mgr-Uniform Pur)

Unitech Services Group   (1)
295 Parker St, Springfield, MA 01151   **(100%)**
Tel.: (413) 543-8008
Web Site: https://www.unitechus.com
Rev.: $28,000,000
Emp.: 20
Garment Decontamination Services
N.A.I.C.S.: 457120
Steve Williams (Plant Mgr)

UNION BANKSHARES, INC.
20 Lower Main St, Morrisville, VT 05661-0667
Tel.: (802) 888-6600   VT
Web Site: https://www.ublocal.com
Year Founded: 1982
UNB—(NASDAQ)
Rev.: $52,935,000
Assets: $1,336,489,000
Liabilities: $1,281,269,000
Net Worth: $55,220,000
Earnings: $12,615,000
Emp.: 188

Fiscal Year-end: 12/31/22
Bank Holding Company
N.A.I.C.S.: 551111
David S. Silverman (Pres & CEO)
Timothy Willis Sargent (Vice Chm)
Karyn J. Hale (CFO & Treas)

Subsidiaries:

Union Bank   (1)
20 Lower Main St, Morrisville, VT 05661-0667
Tel.: (802) 888-6600
Web Site: https://www.ublocal.com
Sales Range: $50-74.9 Million
Emp.: 170
Banking Services
N.A.I.C.S.: 522110
David S. Silverman (Pres & CEO)
Heather S. Campbell (Officer-Comml Loan & VP)
Timothy S. Ross (Officer-Comml Loan & Sr VP)
Rhonda Bennett (Officer-Comml Loan & Sr VP)
Jonathan Gould (Officer-Comml Loan & Exec VP)
Tina Norton (Officer-Comml Loan & VP)
Stephen Kendall (Officer-Comml Loan & Exec VP)
Sherrie Bull (Officer-Residential & Consumer Loan & VP)

UNION FINANCIAL CORP.
933 4th Ave, Lake Odessa, MI 48849
Tel.: (616) 374-3278   MI
Web Site: http://www.ubmich.com
Year Founded: 1988
UFCP—(OTCEM)
Assets: $206,415,082
Liabilities: $191,540,926
Net Worth: $14,874,156
Earnings: $1,151,678
Fiscal Year-end: 12/31/19
Bank Holding Company; Commercial Banking Services
N.A.I.C.S.: 551111
Cortney Collison (Pres & CEO)
Lloyd Cunningham (Chm)
Christine Fortier (CFO, Exec VP & Sr VP)
Paul Trierweiler (Vice Chm)
Michael Kozak (Chief Lending Officer & Exec VP)
Janet Torres (COO & Exec VP)

UNION PACIFIC CORPORATION
1400 Douglas St, Omaha, NE 68179
Tel.: (402) 544-5000   UT
Web Site: https://www.up.com
Year Founded: 1862
UNP—(NYSE)
Rev.: $24,119,000,000
Assets: $67,132,000,000
Liabilities: $52,344,000,000
Net Worth: $14,788,000,000
Earnings: $6,379,000,000
Emp.: 32,973
Fiscal Year-end: 12/31/23
Holding Company; Railway Transportation
N.A.I.C.S.: 551112
Elizabeth F. Whited (Pres)
Kenyatta G. Rocker (Exec VP-Mktg & Sls)
Rahul Jalali (CIO & Sr VP-Information Technology)
V. James Vena (CEO)
Bryan L. Clark (VP-Tax)
Scott D. Moore (Chief Admin Officer & Sr VP-Corp Rels)
Jennifer L. Hamann (CFO & Exec VP)
Clark J. Ponthier (Sr VP-Supply Chain & Continuous Improvement)
Brad Stock (Asst VP-IR)
Humberto Vargas (VP-Mktg & Sls-Mexico)

Craig V. Richardson (*Chief Legal Officer & Exec VP*)
Eric J. Gehringer (*Exec VP-Ops*)
Jim Vena (*CEO*)
Beth Whited (*Pres*)
Todd M. Rynaski (*VP & Controller*)
Prentiss W. Bolin Jr. (*VP-External Rels*)

Subsidiaries:

Union Pacific Railroad Company **(1)**
1400 Douglas St, Omaha, NE
68179   **(100%)**
Tel.: (402) 544-5000
Web Site: http://www.up.com
Sales Range: $15-24.9 Billion
Emp.: 50,379
Rail Carrier
N.A.I.C.S.: 482111
Kenyatta G. Rocker (*Exec VP-Mktg & Sls*)
Rahul Jalali (*CIO & Exec VP*)
V. James Vena (*CEO*)
Thomas A. Lischer (*Exec VP-Ops*)

Subsidiary (Domestic):

Union Pacific Distribution
Services   **(2)**
1400 Douglas St., Ste 1230, Omaha, NE
68179   **(100%)**
Tel.: (402) 599-1000
Web Site: http://www.upds.com
Rev.: $380,388,000
Emp.: 100
Bulk Commodity & Industrial Products
Transportation Services
N.A.I.C.S.: 488510

Union Pacific Railroad   **(2)**
1416 Dodge St, Saint Louis, MO 63103
Tel.: (314) 992-2000
Web Site: http://www.uprr.com
Emp.: 49,000
Freight Transportation
N.A.I.C.S.: 483113

UNIQUE FOODS CORP.

322 Mall Blvd Ste 149, Monroeville,
PA 15146
Tel.: (724) 600-4720   **DE**
Web Site:
    http://www.uniquepizza.com
Year Founded: 1991
UPZS—(OTCIQ)
Pizza & Sub Shop Owner, Operator &
Franchisor
N.A.I.C.S.: 722513
James C. Vowler (*Founder & CEO*)

UNIQUE LOGISTICS INTERNATIONAL INC.

154-09 146th Ave, Jamaica, NY
11434
Tel.: (718) 978-2000   **NV**
Web Site: https://www.unique-
usa.com
Year Founded: 2004
UNQL—(OTCIQ)
Rev.: $262,519,424
Assets: $103,315,444
Liabilities: $92,903,874
Net Worth: $10,411,570
Earnings: ($7,113,203)
Emp.: 109
Fiscal Year-end: 05/31/24
Gobal Logistics & Freight Forwarding
Company
N.A.I.C.S.: 541614
Eli Kay (*CFO*)
Migdalia Diaz (*COO*)
Sunandan Ray (*Chm & CEO*)
Dawn Lowry (*Exec VP-Customs
Svcs*)
Oscar Marc Schlossberg (*Exec VP*)
Christian Sur (*Exec VP-Ocean
Freight*)

Subsidiaries:

Unique Logistics Holdings Ltd. **(1)**
Unit B & D 4th Floor Sunshine Kowloon
Bay Cargo Centre, 59 Tai Yip Street, Kow-

loon Bay, Kowloon, China (Hong Kong)
Tel.: (852) 2795 6101
Web Site: http://www.unique-logistics.com
Holding Company
N.A.I.C.S.: 551112
Mike Jessop (*Global Head-Diving*)
Steve McMillan (*Dir-Global HSE & Projects*)
Harry Gandhi (*Founder & CEO*)

Subsidiary (Non-US):

GuangZhou Unique Logistics International Limited **(2)**
Room 2511 Yian Plaza 33 Jian She Liu Ma
Road, Guangzhou, China
Tel.: (86) 20 28836888
Logistics Consulting Servies
N.A.I.C.S.: 541614
Roger Wong (*Mgr-Station*)

PT. Unique Logistics International
Indonesia **(2)**
PJL IR H Juanda III No 25B, Jakarta,
10120, Indonesia
Tel.: (62) 21 3522754
Freight Forwarding
N.A.I.C.S.: 488510
Lily Mulyadi (*Gen Mgr*)

Shenzhen Unique Logistics International Ltd. **(2)**
8D2-8D3 Block CD Tianxiang Building,
Tian'an Cyber Park Futian District, Shenzhen, 518000, China
Tel.: (86) 755 27777772
Web Site: http://www.unique-logistics.com
Emp.: 100
Logistics Consulting Servies
N.A.I.C.S.: 541614
Roger Wong (*Mgr-Station*)

TGF Unique Ltd **(2)**
Australs House Unit 2 Heron Way,
Feltham, TW140AR, Middlesex, United
Kingdom
Logistics Consulting Servies
N.A.I.C.S.: 541614
Francis Ha (*Exec Dir-Sls*)
David Cheung (*Dir-Ops*)

Holding (Non-US):

ULI (North & East China) Co.
Ltd. **(2)**
Room 1308 Tomson Commercial Bldg No
710 Dong Fang Road, Shanghai, 200122,
China
Tel.: (86) 21 5820 2121
Freight Forwarding
N.A.I.C.S.: 488510

Subsidiary (Non-US):

ULI International Co., Ltd. **(2)**
Tel.: (886) 227760893
Freight Forwarding
N.A.I.C.S.: 488510

Unique International Logistics (M)
Sdn Bhd **(2)**
46G-7 Mentari Business Park Wisma Yapeim Jalan PJS 8/2, Dataran Mentari, Petaling Jaya, 46150, Selangor Darul Ehsan,
Malaysia
Tel.: (60) 3 56364598
Web Site: http://www.unique-logistics.com
Emp.: 6
Freight Forwarding
N.A.I.C.S.: 488510

Unique Logistics (Korea) Co.,
Ltd. **(2)**
10th Fl Jungan Bldg 57-10 Seosomun-
Dong, Jung-Gu, Seoul, 100 814, Korea
(South)
Tel.: (82) 2 7193883
Freight Forwarding
N.A.I.C.S.: 488510
M. J. Lee (*Gen Mgr-Import & Export-Air
Dept*)

Subsidiary (US):

Unique Logistics International (ATL)
LLC **(2)**
2727 Paces Ferry Rd Bldg 1 Ste 100, Atlanta, GA 30339
Tel.: (404) 767-0500
Web Site: http://www.uli-atl.com
Rev.: $16,000,000

Emp.: 25
Freight Forwarding
N.A.I.C.S.: 541614
Robert Shaver (*Pres*)
Jeff Smith (*Mgr-Ops-Air/Ocean Dept-Import
& Export*)
Ginger Seabrook (*Reg Mgr-Sls*)

Unique Logistics International (BOS),
Inc. **(2)**
35 Vlg Rd Ste 701, Middleton, MA 01949
Tel.: (617) 569-5969
Logistics Consulting Servies
N.A.I.C.S.: 541614

Subsidiary (Non-US):

Unique Logistics International (Cambodia) Co., Ltd. **(2)**
Room 2FK 2/F Parkway Square Mao Tse
Toung Blvd, Sangkat Toul Svay Prey I,
Khan Chamkarmon, Phnom Penh, Cambodia
Tel.: (855) 23 223098
Web Site: http://www.unique-logistics.com
Freight Forwarding
N.A.I.C.S.: 488510

Subsidiary (US):

Unique Logistics International (Chicago), LLC. **(2)**
1 Pierce Pl Ste 125-E, Itasca, IL 60413
Tel.: (877) 258-8569
Logistics Consulting Servies
N.A.I.C.S.: 541614
Sunandan Ray (*Mng Partner*)

Subsidiary (Non-US):

Unique Logistics International (Fuzhou) Ltd. **(2)**
16 Floor Jin Huang Building Sheng Fu Ave,
Fuzhou, 350001, Fujian, China
Tel.: (86) 591 87845158
Logistics Consulting Servies
N.A.I.C.S.: 541614
K. C. Lau (*Gen Mgr*)
Alice Lin (*Asst Mgr-Pricing*)

Subsidiary (Domestic):

Unique Logistics International (H.K.)
Ltd. **(2)**
4 B & D Sunshine Kowloon Bay Cargo
Centre 59 Tai Yip Street, Kowloon Bay,
Kowloon, China (Hong Kong)
Tel.: (852) 2795 6101
Web Site: http://www.unique-logistics.com
Emp.: 105
Freight Forwarding
N.A.I.C.S.: 488510
Edmund Tam (*VP-Global Sls & Dev*)
Thomas Wong (*VP-Ops & Admin*)
Thomas T. Wong (*VP-Fin*)

Subsidiary (Non-US):

Unique Logistics International (India)
Private Limited **(2)**
No 53 NP Developed Plots, Ekkattuthangal,
Chennai, 600032, India
Tel.: (91) 44 49015600
Web Site: http://www.unique-logistics.com
Emp.: 33
Logistics Consulting Servies
N.A.I.C.S.: 541614
A. Nanda Kumar (*Gen Mgr*)

Subsidiary (US):

Unique Logistics International (LAX),
Inc. **(2)**
13855 Struikman Rd, Cerritos, CA 90703
Tel.: (310) 337-0688
Web Site: http://www.unique-logistics.com
Emp.: 12
Freight Forwarding
N.A.I.C.S.: 488510
Sunandan Ray (*CEO*)

Subsidiary (Non-US):

Unique Logistics International (Macau) Ltd. **(2)**
Room 1205 12/Fl Si Toi Commercial Centre
No 619, Avenida de Praia Grande, Macau,
China (Macau)
Tel.: (853) 28355944
Logistics Consulting Servies

N.A.I.C.S.: 541614
Eric Ho (*Mgr-Station*)

Subsidiary (US):

Unique Logistics International (NYC),
LLC **(2)**
154-09 146th Ave, Jamaica, NY 11434
Tel.: (718) 978-2000
Web Site: http://www.unique-logistics.com
Emp.: 15
Freight Forwarding
N.A.I.C.S.: 488510
Eli Kay (*CFO*)

Subsidiary (Non-US):

Unique Logistics International (S) Pte
Ltd **(2)**
33 Tannery Lane 03-01, Singapore, 34778,
Singapore
Tel.: (65) 6787 6388
Freight Forwarding
N.A.I.C.S.: 488510
James Lim (*Mng Dir*)
Irene Lee (*Gen Mgr*)

Unique Logistics International (Thailand) Co., Ltd. **(2)**
344 Triumph Complex 7th Floor SOI 17
Rama 9 Road Kwang Bangkapi, Khethuaykwang, Bangkok, 10310, Thailand
Tel.: (66) 2 7169500
Freight Forwarding
N.A.I.C.S.: 488510
Sitthipong Sirinitsrivong (*Gen Mgr*)

Unique Logistics International (Vietnam) Ltd. **(2)**
181 Dien Bien Phu, Dakao Ward Dist 1, Ho
Chi Minh City, 70001, Vietnam
Tel.: (84) 8 3822 2352
Web Site: http://www.unique-logistics.com
Freight Forwarding
N.A.I.C.S.: 488510
James Duy Hoa Tran (*Gen Mgr*)

Unique Logistics International
(Zhongshan) Ltd. **(2)**
Room 205 Zhongshan Port & Shipping Enterprise Group Bldg, Yuanjiang East Road,
Zhongshan, China
Tel.: (86) 760 85310150
Logistics Consulting Servies
N.A.I.C.S.: 541614
Dennis Long (*Dir-Sls*)

Unique Logistics International Philippines Inc. **(2)**
2/F Unit 9 Alabang Citi Arcade Western
Service Road cor Don Jesus Blvd, Cupang,
Muntinlupa, 1770, Philippines
Emp.: 10
Freight Forwarding
N.A.I.C.S.: 488510
Spencer Li (*Sr VP*)
Winky Li (*VP & Mgr-Mktg*)
Sandra Rosalejos (*Mgr-Air & Sea-Export*)

Unique Logistics International Xiamen
Limited **(2)**
Tel.: (86) 5925672666
Logistics Consulting Servies
N.A.I.C.S.: 541614
K. C. Lau (*Gen Mgr*)

Unique Regulus Supply Chain Solutions India Private Limited **(2)**
Monarch Chamber Office #106 Marol Maroshi Road, Andher E, Mumbai, 400059,
India
Tel.: (91) 22 29202756
Web Site: http://www.unique-logistics.com
Freight Forwarding
N.A.I.C.S.: 488510

Subsidiary (Domestic):

Unique SCM (H.K) Limited **(2)**
9/F China Travel logistics Center 1 Cheong
Tung Road, Hung Hom, Kowloon, China
(Hong Kong)
Tel.: (852) 2766 0678
Logistics Consulting Servies
N.A.I.C.S.: 541614

UNIROYAL GLOBAL ENGINEERED PRODUCTS, INC.

Uniroyal Global Engineered Products,
Inc.—(Continued)

1819 Main St Ste 1110, Sarasota, FL
34236
Tel.: (941) 906-8580   NV
Web Site:
   https://www.uniroyalglobal.com
Year Founded: 1998
UNIR—(OTCIQ)
Rev.: $71,704,995
Assets: $64,455,625
Liabilities: $55,811,147
Net Worth: $8,644,478
Earnings: $2,275,480
Emp.: 294
Fiscal Year-end: 01/02/22
Electronic Sensor System Mfr
N.A.I.C.S.: 334419
Edmund C. King (Co-Chm & CFO)
Howard R. Curd (Co-Chm & CEO)
Oliver James Janney (Gen Counsel &
Sec)

Subsidiaries:

Uniroyal Engineered Products,
LLC (1)
1800 2nd St Ste 970, Sarasota, FL 34236
Tel.: (941) 906-8580
Web Site: http://www.naugahyde.com
Sales Range: $25-49.9 Million
Emp.: 8
Coated Fabrics Mfr & Sales
N.A.I.C.S.: 313320

Uniroyal Global Limited (1)
West Craven Business Park West Craven
Drive, Earby Colne, BB18 6JZ, Lancashire,
United Kingdom
Tel.: (44) 1282842511
Web Site: http://www.uniroyalglobal.co.uk
Fabric Coating Mill Product Mfr
N.A.I.C.S.: 313320

UNISYS CORPORATION

801 Lakeview Dr Ste 100, Blue Bell,
PA 19422
Tel.: (215) 986-4011   DE
Web Site: https://www.unisys.com
Year Founded: 1986
UIS—(NYSE)
Rev.: $1,979,900,000
Assets: $2,065,600,000
Liabilities: $2,043,800,000
Net Worth: $21,800,000
Earnings: ($106,000,000)
Emp.: 16,200
Fiscal Year-end: 12/31/22
Information Technology Consulting
Services
N.A.I.C.S.: 541618
Peter A. Altabef (Chm & CEO)
William M. Reinheimer (VP & Asst
Controller)
Michael M. Thomson (Pres & COO)
Mathew Newfield (Chief Security &
Infrastructure Officer & Sr VP)
Christine Wenzel (Sr VP-Global Sls)
Michelle Jones (Chief Admin Officer,
Gen Counsel & Sec)
Dwayne L. Allen (CTO & Sr VP)
Matt Marashall (CIO)
Michaela Pewarski (VP-Investor Rela-
tions)
Claudius Sokenu (Chief Admin Offi-
cer)
Lance Thatcher (Chief Information
Security Officer)
Debra McCann (CFO & Exec VP)
Kristen Prohl (Chief Admin Officer,
Gen Counsel & Sec)
David Brown (Chief Acctg Officer, VP
& Controller)
Chris Arrasmith (Sr VP & Gen Mgr-
Enterprise Computing Solutions)
Manju Naglapur (Sr VP & Gen Mgr-
Cloud, Applications, and Infrastruc-
ture Solutions)
Joel Raper (Chief Comml Officer & Sr
VP)

Daniel Ferry (VP-Corporate Develop-
ment & Transformation)
Ruchi Kulhari (Chief HR Officer & Sr
VP)
Patrycja Sobera (Sr VP & Gen Mgr-
Digital Workplace Solutions)

Subsidiaries:

Intelligent Processing Solutions
Limited (1)
100 Pavillion Drive, Brackmills Industrial
Estate, Northampton, NN4 7YP, United
Kingdom
Tel.: (44) 1604665100
Web Site: http://www.ipsl.co.uk
Commercial Banking Services
N.A.I.C.S.: 522110

Unify Square, Inc. (1)
777 108th Ave NE Ste 2020, Bellevue, WA
98004
Tel.: (425) 865-0700
Web Site: http://www.unifysquare.com
Information Technology Services
N.A.I.C.S.: 541511
Sonu Aggarwal (Founder)
Hari Natarajan (CMO)
Arun Raghavan (VP-Product Development)
Alan Shen (VP)
Jochen Kunert (VP)
Charlie DiBona (CFO)
Chris Vaughn (Chief Information Security
Officer)
Madan Aggarwal (VP-Operations)
Scott Brown (Sr VP)
Scott Gode (Chief Product Officer)
John Case (CEO)
Joel Raper (VP-Sales-Worldwide)

Unisys (Schweiz) A.G. (1)
Zuercherstrasse 59, 8800, Thalwil,
Switzerland (100%)
Tel.: (41) 447233333
Web Site: http://www.unisys.ch
Sales Range: $75-99.9 Million
Emp.: 90
Computers & Related Products Whslr
N.A.I.C.S.: 423430

Unisys Australia Propriety Ltd (1)
Building G 1 Homebush Bay Drive, Rhodes,
Sydney, 2138, NSW, Australia (100%)
Tel.: (61) 1300088833
Web Site: http://www.unisys.com.au
Sales Range: $25-49.9 Million
Emp.: 75
Marketer of Information Services & Elec-
tronic Business Solutions
N.A.I.C.S.: 425120

Unisys Belgium (1)
Ave Du Bourget 20, 1130, Brussels,
Belgium (100%)
Tel.: (32) 27280711
Web Site: http://www.unisys.be
Sales Range: $100-124.9 Million
Emp.: 300
Sales & Marketing of Computers
N.A.I.C.S.: 449210

Unisys Deutschland GmbH (1)
Am Unisys Park 1, 65843, Sulzbach,
Germany (100%)
Tel.: (49) 6196990
Web Site: http://www.unisys.de
Sales Range: $25-49.9 Million
Emp.: 200
Computer Whslr
N.A.I.C.S.: 449210

Unisys Espana S.A. (1)
MERRIMACK-II Building Calle Ramirez de
Arellano 29, 28043, Madrid, Spain (100%)
Tel.: (34) 911311555
Web Site: http://www.unisys.es
Sales Range: $100-124.9 Million
Wholesale of Computers
N.A.I.C.S.: 449210

Unisys France (1)
Tour Nova 71 Boulevard National, 92250,
La Garenne-Colombes, France
Tel.: (33) 146695555
Web Site: http://www.unisys.fr
Sales Range: $25-49.9 Million
Emp.: 85
Information Services & Electronic Business
Solutions

N.A.I.C.S.: 334610
Unisys Italia S.P.A. (1)
Via Benigno Crespi 57, Milan, 20159,
Italy (100%)
Tel.: (39) 0269851
Sales Range: $100-124.9 Million
Emp.: 300
Wholesale of Computers
N.A.I.C.S.: 449210

Unisys Limited (1)
801 Lakeview Drive Suite 100, Rickmans-
worth, WD3 9AB, Hertfordshire, United
Kingdom (100%)
Tel.: (44) 1895237137
Web Site: http://www.unisys.co.uk
Sales Range: $50-74.9 Million
Emp.: 100
Office Equipment & Computers Whslr
N.A.I.C.S.: 423420

Unisys Nederland N.V. (1)
Storkstraat 9, 3833 LB, Leusden,
Netherlands (100%)
Tel.: (31) 332077500
Web Site: http://www.unisys.nl
Sales Range: $25-49.9 Million
Emp.: 200
Wholesale of Computers
N.A.I.C.S.: 449210

UNIT CORPORATION

8200 S Unit Dr, Tulsa, OK 74132
Tel.: (918) 493-7700   DE
Web Site:
   https://unitcorpprod.wpengine.com
Year Founded: 1963
UNTC—(OTCQX)
Rev.: $545,525,000
Assets: $469,255,000
Liabilities: $106,629,000
Net Worth: $362,626,000
Earnings: $148,369,000
Emp.: 653
Fiscal Year-end: 12/31/22
Crude Petroleum Extraction Services
N.A.I.C.S.: 211120
Frank Young (Sr VP-Exploration &
Production Midcontinent-Unit Petro-
leum Co)
Drew Harding (Gen Counsel, Sec &
VP)
Tom Sell (CFO & Chief Acctg Officer)
Philip B. Smith (Chm)
Phil Frohlich (Interim CEO)
Thomas Sell (CFO)
Chris Menefee (Pres)
Greg Johnson (CIO)
James White (VP)

Subsidiaries:

Unit Drilling Company (1)
7101 S W 29th St, Oklahoma City, OK
73179 (100%)
Tel.: (405) 745-4948
Web Site: https://unitcorp.com
Sales Range: $200-249.9 Million
Emp.: 250
Company Engaged in the Exploration &
Production of Oil & Natural Gas
N.A.I.C.S.: 213111
Chris K. Menefee (Pres)

Unit Petroleum Company (1)
8200 S Unit Dr 81 St, Tulsa, OK
74132 (100%)
Tel.: (918) 493-7700
Web Site: http://www.unitpetroleum.com
Sales Range: $200-249.9 Million
Emp.: 250
Exploration & Production of Oil & Natural
Gas
N.A.I.C.S.: 211120
Frank Young (Exec VP-Exploration & Pro-
duction)
Mark Colclasure (Sr VP-Drilling)
Ken Blondeau (VP-Geology & Gulf Coast)
James Guinn (VP-Engrg & Gulf Coast)
Trent Mitchell (Mgr-Reservoir Engrg)

UNITED AIRLINES HOLDINGS, INC.

233 S Wacker Dr, Chicago, IL 60606

Tel.: (872) 825-4000   DE
Web Site: https://ir.united.com
Year Founded: 1968
UAL—(NASDAQ)
Rev.: $53,717,000,000
Assets: $71,104,000,000
Liabilities: $61,780,000,000
Net Worth: $9,324,000,000
Earnings: $2,618,000,000
Emp.: 184,194
Fiscal Year-end: 12/31/23
Holding Company; Passenger &
Freight Air Transportation Services
N.A.I.C.S.: 551112
Brett J. Hart (Pres)
Gerald Laderman (Exec VP-Fin)
Kate Gebo (Exec VP-HR & Labor
Rels)
J. Scott Kirby (CEO)
Andrew P. Nocella (Chief Comml Offi-
cer & Exec VP)
Michael D. Leskinen (CFO & Exec
VP)
Josh Earnest (Chief Comm Officer &
Sr VP)
Torbjorn J. Enqvist (COO & Exec VP)
Theresa Fariello (Sr VP-Govt Affairs
& Pub Policy-Global)
J. Scott Kirby (CEO)

Subsidiaries:

United Airlines, Inc. (1)
233 S Wacker Dr, Chicago, IL 60606
Tel.: (872) 825-4000
Web Site: https://www.united.com
Rev.: $16,975,000,000
Assets: $20,113,000,000
Liabilities: $15,766,000,000
Net Worth: $4,347,000,000
Earnings: $527,000,000
Emp.: 41,000
Fiscal Year-end: 12/31/2012
Scheduled Air Transportation
N.A.I.C.S.: 481111

Subsidiary (Domestic):

Air Wis Services, Inc. (2)
203 Challenger Dr, Appleton, WI 54915-
9120
Tel.: (414) 739-5123
Web Site: https://www.airwis.com
Holding Company
N.A.I.C.S.: 551112

Subsidiary (Domestic):

Air Wisconsin, Inc. (3)
W6390 Challenger Dr Ste 203, Appleton,
WI 54914
Tel.: (920) 739-5123
Web Site: http://www.airwis.com
Emp.: 100
Oil Transportation Services
N.A.I.C.S.: 488190
Bob Frisch (COO & Sr VP)
Robert Binns (Pres & CEO)
Gregg Garvey (Chief Acctg Officer, Treas &
Sr VP)
Janet Schedler (Sr VP-Finance-Technology)
Jack Fauth (VP)
Jim McLeod (VP-IT & Bus Intelligence)
Michael Perrizo (VP-Flight Ops)
Chris White (VP-Safety & Security)
Liam Mackay (CFO)
Tina Vos (VP-Human Resources)
Kieran Whitney (VP)

Domicile Management Services,
Inc. (3)
1200 E Algonquin Rd, Arlington Heights, IL
60005-4712
Tel.: (847) 700-4000
Oil Transportation Services
N.A.I.C.S.: 481111

United Airlines, Inc. (1)
233 S Wacker Dr, Chicago, IL
60606 (100%)
Tel.: (872) 825-4000
Web Site: https://www.united.com
Rev.: $44,954,999,999
Assets: $67,329,000,000
Liabilities: $60,464,000,000
Net Worth: $6,865,000,000

Earnings: $739,000,000
Emp.: 92,794
Fiscal Year-end: 12/31/2022
Air Transportation of Passengers & Mail,
Express & Freight
N.A.I.C.S.: 481112
Brett J. Hart *(Pres)*
Oscar Munoz *(CEO)*
Michael D. Leskinen *(VP-Corp Dev & IR)*
Linda P. Jojo *(Chief Digital Officer & Exec VP)*
Andrew P. Nocella *(Chief Comml Officer & Exec VP)*
Torbjorn J. Enqvist *(Chief Customer Officer & Sr VP)*

Subsidiary (Domestic):

Mileage Plus, Inc. **(2)**
PO Box 1394, Houston, TX 77251-1394
Airline Services
N.A.I.C.S.: 561599

United Air Lines Credit Union **(2)**
1200 E Algonquin Rd, Mount Prospect, IL
60005 **(100%)**
Tel.: (847) 700-4000
Sales Range: $1-4.9 Billion
Credit Services
N.A.I.C.S.: 481111

United Airlines Operations
Center **(2)**
77 W Wacker, Chicago, IL 60601 **(100%)**
Tel.: (847) 700-4000
Web Site: http://www.united.com
Airline Operations
N.A.I.C.S.: 488119

United Cogen, Inc. **(2)**
400 Oyster Point Blvd, South San Fran-
cisco, CA 94080
Tel.: (650) 634-2811
Sales Range: $10-24.9 Million
Emp.: 7
Owner, Operator & Developer of Cogenera-
tion & Power Projects
N.A.I.C.S.: 221118

United GHS Inc. **(2)**
77 W Wacker Dr, Chicago, IL 60601
Tel.: (312) 997-8000
Web Site: http://www.united.com
Sales Range: $150-199.9 Million
Ground Handling Services
N.A.I.C.S.: 238910

United Vacations, Inc. **(2)**
8969 N Port Washington Rd, Milwaukee, WI
53217 **(100%)**
Tel.: (847) 700-4000
Web Site: https://vacations.united.com
Sales Range: $100-124.9 Million
Tour Packages
N.A.I.C.S.: 561510

UNITED AMERICAN HEALTH-CARE CORP.

303 E Wacker Dr Ste 1040, Chicago,
IL 60601
Tel.: (313) 393-4571 NV
Web Site: https://www.uahc.com
UAHC—(OTCIQ)
HMO Management Services
N.A.I.C.S.: 524210
John M. Fife *(Pres & CEO)*

Subsidiaries:

Pulse Systems, LLC **(1)**
4090 Nelson Ave, Concord, CA 94520
Tel.: (925) 798-4080
Web Site: http://www.pulsesystems.com
Sales Range: $1-9.9 Million
Emp.: 39
Laser Machined Component Mfr
N.A.I.C.S.: 332999
Herb Bellucci *(Pres & CEO)*

UNITED BANCORP, INC.

Tel.: (740) 633-0445 OH
Web Site:
https://www.unitedbancorp.com
Year Founded: 1983
UBCP—(NASDAQ)
Rev.: $31,744,000
Assets: $757,400,000

Liabilities: $697,663,000
Net Worth: $59,737,000
Earnings: $8,657,000
Emp.: 125
Fiscal Year-end: 12/31/22
Bank Holding Company
N.A.I.C.S.: 551111
Scott A. Everson *(Pres & CEO)*
Matthew Fredrick Branstetter *(COO & Sr VP)*
Erika R. Ault *(Sec)*

Subsidiaries:

Unified Bank **(1)**
201 S 4th at Hickory, Martins Ferry, OH
43935
Tel.: (740) 633-0445
Web Site: https://www.unifiedbank.com
Commercial Banking Services
N.A.I.C.S.: 522110
Scott A. Everson *(Chm, Pres & CEO)*

UNITED BANCORPORATION OF ALABAMA, INC.

200 E Nashville, Atmore, AL 36502
Tel.: (251) 446-6000 DE
Web Site:
https://www.unitedbank.com
Year Founded: 1982
UBAB—(OTCIQ)
Bank Holding Company
N.A.I.C.S.: 551111
Tina S. Brooks *(Sec)*
David D. Swift Sr. *(Chm)*

Subsidiaries:

Town-Country National Bank **(1)**
118 Broad St, Camden, AL 36726-1741
Tel.: (334) 682-4155
Web Site: http://www.tcnbank.com
Sales Range: $1-9.9 Million
Emp.: 33
Commericial Banking
N.A.I.C.S.: 522110
John H. Strother *(Pres)*
Gail McGraw *(COO)*
Hal Huggins *(Pres & CEO)*
Haas Strother *(Chm)*

United Bank **(1)**
200 E Nashville Ave, Atmore, AL
36502 **(100%)**
Tel.: (251) 446-6000
Web Site: http://www.unitedbank.com
Sales Range: $125-149.9 Million
Emp.: 55
Commercial Banking Services
N.A.I.C.S.: 522110
Tina N. Brooks *(Sr VP)*
David D. Swift Sr. *(Chm)*
Mike Vincent *(Pres & CEO)*

UNITED BANCSHARES, INC.

105 Progressive Dr, Columbus
Grove, OH 45830
Tel.: (419) 659-2141 OH
Web Site: https://www.theubank.com
Year Founded: 1985
UBOH—(OTCQX)
Rev.: $48,896,000
Assets: $1,087,293,000
Liabilities: $1,004,602,000
Net Worth: $82,691,000
Earnings: $11,310,000
Emp.: 211
Fiscal Year-end: 12/31/22
Bank Holding Company
N.A.I.C.S.: 551111
Brian D. Young *(Pres & CEO)*
Daniel W. Schutt *(Chm)*
Klint D. Manz *(CFO)*
Teresa Deitering *(Chief Financial Officer)*
Stacey Clemens *(Chief Risk Officer)*
Travis Vulich *(Mgr)*
Denise Giesige *(Mgr)*
Dian Franks *(Mktg Mgr)*

Subsidiaries:

The Union Bank Company **(1)**
100 S High St, Columbus Grove, OH 45830

Tel.: (419) 659-2141
Web Site: http://www.theubank.com
Sales Range: $10-24.9 Million
Commericial Banking
N.A.I.C.S.: 522110
Brian D. Young *(Chm, Pres & CEO)*
Klint D. Manz *(CFO)*

Subsidiary (Domestic):

UBC Investments, Inc. **(2)**
1105 N Market St, Wilmington, DE
19801 **(100%)**
Tel.: (302) 652-6200
Commercial Banking Services
N.A.I.C.S.: 551111

UNITED BANKSHARES, INC.

300 United Ctr 500 Virginia St E,
Charleston, WV 25301
Tel.: (304) 424-8716 WV
Web Site: https://www.ubsi-inc.com
Year Founded: 1982
UBSI—(NASDAQ)
Rev.: $1,001,990,000
Assets: $29,489,380,000
Liabilities: $24,973,187,000
Net Worth: $4,516,193,000
Earnings: $379,627,000
Emp.: 2,765
Fiscal Year-end: 12/31/22
Bank Holding Company
N.A.I.C.S.: 551111
Richard M. Adams Jr. *(CEO)*
Douglas Bryon Ernest *(Chief Credit Officer)*
James J. Consagra Jr. *(COO)*
Ross M. Draber *(COO & Exec VP)*
Michael P. Proctor *(Chief Comml Banking Officer & Exec VP)*
Charles J. Mildren *(Chief Consumer Banking Officer & Exec VP)*
Anna J. Schultheis *(Board of Directors & Sec)*
Matthew L. Humphrey *(Exec VP & Head-Wealth & Investment Mgmt)*
Ami L. Shaver *(Exec VP, Head-Human Resources & Dir-Retail Sls & Svc)*

Subsidiaries:

Community Bankers Trust
Corporation **(1)**
9954 Mayland Dr Ste 2100, Richmond, VA
23223
Tel.: (804) 934-9999
Web Site: http://www.cbtrustcorp.com
Rev.: $69,565,000
Assets: $1,644,809,000
Liabilities: $1,475,155,000
Net Worth: $169,654,000
Earnings: $15,548,000
Emp.: 246
Fiscal Year-end: 12/31/2020
Bank Holding Company
N.A.I.C.S.: 551111
Bruce E. Thomas *(CFO & Exec VP)*
Laureen D. Trice *(Sr VP & Controller)*
John M. Oakey III *(Gen Counsel, Sec & Exec VP)*

Subsidiary (Domestic):

Essex Bank **(2)**
323 Prince St, Tappahannock, VA 22560
Tel.: (804) 443-8510
Web Site: http://www.essexbank.com
Banking Services
N.A.I.C.S.: 522110
Rex L. Smith III *(Pres & CEO)*
John C. Watkins *(Chm)*
Mary B. Randolph *(Sr VP)*
Stanley B. Jones Jr. *(Chief Credit Officer & Exec VP)*

Division (Domestic):

Essex Bank of Maryland **(3)**
2120 Baldwin Ave, Crofton, MD 21114
Tel.: (410) 721-7330
Web Site: http://www.essexbank.com
Sales Range: $10-24.9 Million
Retail & Commercial Banking Services
N.A.I.C.S.: 522180

United Bank **(1)**
11185 Fairfax Blvd, Fairfax, VA
22030 **(100%)**
Tel.: (703) 219-4850
Web Site: http://www.bankwithunited.com
Sales Range: $900-999.9 Million
Emp.: 2,144
Commercial & Investment Banking
N.A.I.C.S.: 522110
Richard M. Adams Jr. *(Vice Chm)*
Jerold L. Rexroad *(Chm-Carolinas Reg & Crescent Mortgage Company)*
Richard M. Adams *(Chm & CEO)*
Craige L. Smith *(CIO, Chief Admin Officer & Exec VP)*
Douglas Bryon Ernest *(Chief Credit Officer & Exec VP)*
James J. Consagra Jr. *(Pres)*

Subsidiary (Domestic):

Crescent Mortgage Company **(2)**
6600 Peachtree Dunwoody Rd NE 600 Embassy Row Ste 650, Atlanta, GA 30328
Web Site:
https://www.crescentmortgage.com
Mortgage Products & Services
N.A.I.C.S.: 522292

George Mason Mortgage, LLC **(2)**
4100 Monument Corner Dr Ste 100, Fairfax,
VA 22030
Tel.: (703) 273-2600
Web Site: https://www.gmmllc.com
Originator of Residential Real Estate Loans
for Resale
N.A.I.C.S.: 522292
Dan Lawson *(CFO & Sr VP)*
Jimmy Hummer *(VP-Mortgage Lending)*
Brett Woerner *(Sr VP & Ops Mgr-Construction)*
Kendall Wilkins *(Officer-Mortgage Loan)*
Brian Kamin *(Officer-Mortgage Loan)*
Carolyn Keller *(Sr VP & Mgr-Closing)*
Beverly Kinzer *(VP & Dir-Special Projects)*

United Brokerage Services, Inc. **(2)**
514 Mkt St, Parkersburg, WV
26101-5144 **(100%)**
Tel.: (304) 424-8800
Web Site: http://www.united-brokerage.com
Sales Range: $75-99.9 Million
Emp.: 30
Fully-Disclosed Securities Broker & Dealer
N.A.I.C.S.: 523150

UNITED BULLION EXCHANGE, INC.

871 Coronado Ctr Dr Ste 200, Hen-
derson, NV 89052
Tel.: (702) 952-2806
UBEX—(OTCIQ)
Mineral Exploration Services
N.A.I.C.S.: 213114
Richard Brutti *(Pres & CEO)*

UNITED COMMUNICATION PARTNERS INC.

291 Broadway Ste 302, New York,
NY 10007
Tel.: (467) 351-8537 NV
Web Site: http://www.ucpworld.com
UCPA—(OTCIQ)
Advertising & Marketing Consulting
Services
N.A.I.C.S.: 541890
Niclas Froberg *(CEO)*
Anna-Karin Darlin *(CFO)*
Lars Blomberg *(Chm)*
Kenneth S. Rosenthal *(CMO)*

UNITED COMMUNITY BANKS, INC.

200 E Camperdown Way, Greenville,
SC 29601
Tel.: (706) 781-2265 GA
Web Site: https://www.ucbi.com

United Community Banks, Inc.—(Continued)

Year Founded: 1988
UCBI—(NASDAQ)
Rev.: $744,402,000
Assets: $20,946,771,000
Liabilities: $18,724,526,000
Net Worth: $2,222,245,000
Earnings: $269,801,000
Emp.: 2,921
Fiscal Year-end: 12/31/21
Bank Holding Company
N.A.I.C.S.: 551111
Alan H. Kumler (*Chief Acctg Officer & Sr VP*)
Herbert Lynn Harton (*Chm, Pres & CEO*)
Robert A. Edwards (*Chief Risk Officer & Exec VP*)
Jefferson L. Harralson (*CFO & Exec VP*)
Richard W. Bradshaw (*Chief Banking Officer*)
Melinda Davis Lux (*Gen Counsel, Sec & Exec VP*)
Mark Terry (*CIO*)

Subsidiaries:

Aquesta Financial Holdings, Inc. **(1)**
19510 Jetton Rd, Cornelius, NC 28031
Tel.: (704) 439-4343
Web Site: http://www.aquesta.com
Bank Holding Company
N.A.I.C.S.: 551111
Trey Weir (*Chief Banking Officer & Exec VP*)
Tim Beck (*Chief Credit Officer & Exec VP*)
Kristin Couch (*Exec VP & CFO*)
Stephanie Cox (*Chief Ops & Compliance Officer & Exec VP*)

Subsidiary (Domestic):

Aquesta Bank **(2)**
19510 Jetton Rd, Cornelius, NC 28031
Tel.: (704) 439-4343
Web Site: http://www.aquesta.com
Emp.: 40
Commericial Banking
N.A.I.C.S.: 522110
Jim Engel (*Founder, Pres & CEO*)
Charles Knox Jr. (*Chm*)

First Madison Bank & Trust **(1)**
780 Hwy 29 N, Athens, GA 30601-1544
Tel.: (706) 389-7979
Web Site: http://www.firstmadisonbank.com
Commericial Banking
N.A.I.C.S.: 522110
Jay Staines (*Pres*)

First Miami Bancorp, Inc. **(1)**
5750 Sunset Dr, South Miami, FL 33143
Tel.: (305) 667-5453
Web Site: http://www.fnbsm.com
Rev.: $20,926,020
Assets: $645,441,451
Liabilities: $565,148,788
Net Worth: $80,292,663
Earnings: $3,220,337
Emp.: 88
Fiscal Year-end: 12/31/2014
Bank Holding Company
N.A.I.C.S.: 551111

Subsidiary (Domestic):

The First National Bank of South
Miami **(2)**
5750 Sunset Dr, Miami, FL 33143
Tel.: (305) 667-5511
Web Site: http://www.fnbsm.com
Sales Range: $10-24.9 Million
Emp.: 100
Commericial Banking
N.A.I.C.S.: 522110
Rene R. Aldonza (*VP & Mgr-Branch*)
Claudia A. Cancio (*Sr VP*)
Bruce Wirtz MacArthur (*Chm*)
Drew A. Dammeier (*Pres*)
Veronica Birch Flores (*Exec VP*)
Pablo Rodriguez (*Sr VP*)
Stephen N. Moynahan (*Sr VP*)
Edward J. Vargas (*Chief Risk & Credit Officer & Sr VP*)

Reliant Bancorp, Inc. **(1)**
1736 Carothers Pkwy Ste 100, Brentwood, TN 37027
Tel.: (615) 221-2020
Web Site: http://www.reliantbank.com
Rev.: $151,830,000
Assets: $3,026,535,000
Liabilities: $2,704,562,000
Net Worth: $321,973,000
Earnings: $31,412,000
Emp.: 428
Fiscal Year-end: 12/31/2020
Bank Holding Company
N.A.I.C.S.: 551111

Subsidiary (Domestic):

First Advantage Bancorp **(2)**
1430 Madison St, Clarksville, TN 37040
Tel.: (931) 552-6176
Web Site:
  http://www.firstadvantagebanking.com
Bank Holding Company
N.A.I.C.S.: 551111
Michael K. Wallace (*Executives, Bd of Dirs*)
Eddie Gammon (*Dir-Ops*)
Alan Mims (*Chief Credit Officer*)
Kim York (*Chief Strategy Officer*)
William M. Fitzgerald II (*Chief Risk Officer*)

Subsidiary (Domestic):

First Advantage Bank **(3)**
1430 Madison St, Clarksville, TN 37040
Tel.: (931) 552-6176
Web Site: http://www.fabk.com
Commericial Banking Services
N.A.I.C.S.: 522110
Christy Caudill (*COO & Exec VP*)
Earl Otto Bradley III (*CEO*)
Kyle Luther (*Sr VP-Comml Lending*)
Meredith Futhey (*Sr VP & Dir-Treasury Mgmt*)
Buddy Cutsinger (*Sr VP & Mgr-Bus Banking Relationship*)
Richard Bynum (*Sr VP*)
Mark Brooks (*Sr VP & Mgr-SBA*)
Matt Pierucki (*VP & Mgr-Relationship*)
Erik Hegg (*Pres*)
Cole Norris (*Branch Mgr*)
Brandon Bridges (*Asst VP & Mgr-Customer Rels*)
Ellen Hackett (*Chief Credit Officer*)

Subsidiary (Domestic):

Reliant Bank **(2)**
1736 Carothers Pkwy Ste 100, Brentwood, TN 37027
Tel.: (615) 221-2020
Web Site: http://www.reliantbank.com
Commericial Banking
N.A.I.C.S.: 522110
DeVan D. Ard Jr. (*CEO*)
William M. Fitzgerald II (*Chief Risk Officer*)
Mark Ryman (*Chief Loan Officer*)
Olivia Hill (*Exec Dir-HR*)
John R. Wilson (*Pres*)
Jerry Cooksey (*CFO*)
Alan L. Mims (*Chief Credit Officer*)
Kim York (*Chief Strategy Officer*)

Three Shores Bancorporation, Inc. **(1)**
201 S Orange Ave Ste 1350, Orlando, FL 32801
Tel.: (407) 567-2200
Web Site:
  http://www.threeshoresbancorporation.com
Bank Holding Company
N.A.I.C.S.: 551111
Gideon T. Haymaker (*Pres & CEO*)

Subsidiary (Domestic):

Seaside National Bank & Trust **(2)**
201 S Orange Ave Ste 1350, Orlando, FL 32801
Tel.: (407) 567-2200
Web Site: http://www.seasidebank.com
Sales Range: $75-99.9 Million
Commericial Banking
N.A.I.C.S.: 522110
Gideon T. Haymaker (*Pres & CEO*)
Tim Myers (*Reg Pres*)
Lance Hopegill (*Chief Fiduciary Officer*)
Adam Martin (*Sr Portfolio Mgr*)

Subsidiary (Domestic):

Seaside Insurance, Inc. **(3)**

201 S Orange Ave Ste 1350, Orlando, FL 32801 **(100%)**
Tel.: (407) 898-3911
Web Site: http://www.seasideinsurance.com
Insurance Agents
N.A.I.C.S.: 524210
Kimberly Wajda (*Sr Mgr-Client Underwriting*)
Cindi Johnston (*Dir-Grp Benefits*)
Elbert Hardy Vaughn Jr. (*Pres*)

United Community Bank **(1)**
177 Hwy 515 E, Blairsville, GA 30512 **(100%)**
Tel.: (706) 745-2151
Web Site: http://www.ucbi.com
Sales Range: $400-449.9 Million
Emp.: 1,910
Commercial & Investment Banking
N.A.I.C.S.: 522110
Herbert Lynn Harton (*Chm & CEO*)
Robert A. Edwards (*Chief Risk Officer & Exec VP*)
Mark Terry (*CIO*)
Moryah Jackson (*VP & Dir-Community Dev & Engagement*)

Subsidiary (Domestic):

Business Carolina, Inc. **(2)**
1523 Huger St Ste A, Columbia, SC 29201
Tel.: (803) 461-3801
Web Site: http://www.bcilending.com
Sales Range: $1-9.9 Million
Emp.: 13
Commercial Lending Services
N.A.I.C.S.: 522180

Navitas Credit Corp. **(2)**
203 Fort Wade Rd Ste 300, Ponte Vedra Beach, FL 32081
Tel.: (904) 543-2575
Commercial Credit & Leasing Services
N.A.I.C.S.: 522292

United Community Mortgage Services, Inc. **(2)**
177 Hwy 515 E, Blairsville, GA 30512
Tel.: (706) 745-0435
Web Site: http://www.ucbi.com
Financial Management Services
N.A.I.C.S.: 522320

UNITED E&P, INC.

3000 Richmond Ave Ste 400, Houston, TX 77098
Tel.: (713) 333-5808   **NV**
UTDF—(OTCIQ)
Oil & Gas Exploration Services
N.A.I.C.S.: 213112
William Wiseman (*CFO*)

UNITED ENERGY CORPORATION

101 E Park Blvd Ste 600, Plano, TX 75074
Tel.: (469) 209-5829   **NV**
Web Site:
  https://www.unitedenergycorp.net
UNRG—(OTCIQ)
Sales Range: $1-9.9 Million
Emp.: 8
Developer & Distr of Eco-Friendly Chemicals for Oil & Gas Industry
N.A.I.C.S.: 325998
James McKeever (*Interim CFO*)
Jack Silver (*Chm*)

UNITED EXPRESS, INC.

4345 W Post Rd, Las Vegas, NV 89118
Tel.: (949) 350-0123   **NV**
Year Founded: 2017
UNXP—(OTCIQ)
Rev.: $240,717
Assets: $13,724,909
Liabilities: $1,091,459
Net Worth: $12,633,450
Earnings: ($2,481,158)
Fiscal Year-end: 06/30/24
Logistics & Distribution Services
N.A.I.C.S.: 541614

Andrei Stoukan (*Pres, CEO, CFO & Chief Acctg Officer*)

UNITED FIRE GROUP, INC.

118 2nd Ave SE, Cedar Rapids, IA 52407-3909
Tel.: (319) 399-5700   **IA**
Web Site:
  https://www.ufginsurance.com
Year Founded: 1946
UFCS—(NASDAQ)
Rev.: $1,095,467,000
Assets: $3,144,190,000
Liabilities: $2,410,445,000
Net Worth: $733,745,000
Earnings: ($29,700,000)
Emp.: 852
Fiscal Year-end: 12/31/23
Property, Casualty & Life Insurance Services
N.A.I.C.S.: 524128
Michael J. Sheeley (*CMO & VP*)
Corey Lynn Ruehle (*Chief Claims Officer & VP*)
Alison Kaster (*VP-Project Mgmt*)
Kevin J. Leidwinger (*Pres & CEO*)
Brian Joseph Frese (*CTO & VP*)
Jeremy Joseph Bahl (*VP-Field Ops*)
Micah Grant Woolstenhulme (*Chief Risk Officer & VP*)
Eric J. Martin (*CFO*)
Sarah E. Madsen (*Chief Legal Officer, Sec & VP*)
Julie Stephenson (*COO & Exec VP*)
Joshua Baron (*VP*)
Anthony G. Saylor (*VP*)
Kelly Walsh (*Chief Underwriting Officer*)
Casey Prince (*Asst VP & Mktg Comm Mgr*)

Subsidiaries:

United Fire & Casualty Company **(1)**
118 2nd Ave SE, Cedar Rapids, IA 52401
Tel.: (319) 399-5700
Emp.: 1,100
Property & Casualty Insurance Services
N.A.I.C.S.: 524126

Subsidiary (Domestic):

Lafayette Insurance Company **(2)**
2626 Canal St, New Orleans, LA 70119 **(100%)**
Tel.: (504) 821-5222
Web Site: http://www.unitedfiregroup.com
Rev.: $26,526,164
Emp.: 100
Property & Casualty Insurance
N.A.I.C.S.: 524126

Mercer Insurance Group, Inc. **(2)**
10 N Hwy 31, Pennington, NJ 08534-1606
Tel.: (609) 737-0426
Web Site: http://www.unitedfiregroup.com
Sales Range: $300-349.9 Million
Emp.: 209
Insurance Services
N.A.I.C.S.: 525190
Dianne M. Lyons (*CFO & VP*)

Subsidiary (Domestic):

Financial Pacific Insurance Company **(3)**
3880 Atherton Rd, Rocklin, CA 95765-3700
Tel.: (916) 630-5000
Web Site: http://www.unitedfiregroup.com
Sales Range: $100-124.9 Million
Emp.: 120
Commercial Property & Casualty Insurance Services
N.A.I.C.S.: 524210
Paul D. Ehrhardt (*Pres*)

Franklin Insurance Company **(3)**
100 Mercer Dr, Lock Haven, PA 17745
Tel.: (570) 748-4227
Web Site: http://www.unitedfiregroup.com

Sales Range: $10-24.9 Million
Emp.: 15
Insurance Services
N.A.I.C.S.: 524126

Mercer Insurance Company of New
Jersey, Inc.   (3)
10 N Hwy 31, Pennington, NJ 08534
Tel.: (609) 737-0426
Web Site: http://www.unitedfiregroup.com
Sales Range: $25-49.9 Million
Emp.: 90
Insurance Services
N.A.I.C.S.: 524126

Subsidiary (Domestic):

United Fire & Indemnity
Company   (2)
2115 Winnie St, Galveston, TX
77550   (100%)
Tel.: (409) 766-4600
Property & Casualty Insurance
N.A.I.C.S.: 524126

Subsidiary (Domestic):

United Fire Lloyds   (3)
2115 Winnie St, Galveston, TX 77552
Tel.: (409) 766-4600
Web Site: http://www.unitedfiregroup.com
Sales Range: $1-9.9 Million
Emp.: 85
Direct Property & Casualty Insurance Carriers
N.A.I.C.S.: 524126
Randy A. Ramlo (Pres)

United Fire Group, Inc.   (1)
10 N Hwy 31, Pennington, NJ 08534-1606
Tel.: (609) 737-0426
Web Site: http://www.unitedfiregroup.com
Emp.: 60
Insurance Brokerage Services
N.A.I.C.S.: 524210

UNITED HEALTH PRODUCTS, INC.

520 Fellowship Rd Ste D 406, Mount
Laurel, NJ 08054
Tel.: (475) 755-1005   NV
Web Site:
https://www.unitedhealthproducts
inc.com
UEEC—(OTCIQ)
Assets: $284,643
Liabilities: $1,998,869
Net Worth: ($1,714,226)
Earnings: ($2,623,267)
Emp.: 7
Fiscal Year-end: 12/31/23
Wound Care & Disposable Medical
Supplies Developer
N.A.I.C.S.: 339112
Brian Thom (CEO)

UNITED HOMES GROUP, INC

917 Chapin Rd, Chapin, SC 29036
Tel.: (212) 572-6260   DE
Web Site:
https://www.unitedhomesgroup.com
Year Founded: 2020
UHG—(NASDAQ)
Rev.: $20,717
Assets: $345,513,393
Liabilities: $366,158,366
Net Worth: ($20,644,973)
Earnings: $2,708,241
Emp.: 2
Fiscal Year-end: 12/31/21
Investment Services
N.A.I.C.S.: 523999
Keith A. Feldman (CFO)
John G. Micenko Jr. (Pres)
Tom O'Grady (Chief Admin Officer)
Shelton Twine (COO)
Michael P. Nieri (Founder, Chm & CEO)

Subsidiaries:

Creekside Custom Homes LLC   (1)
PO Box 1549, Conway, SC 29528-9528

Tel.: (843) 241-2903
Web Site: http://www.creeksidehomesllc.net
Commercial & Institutional Building Construction
N.A.I.C.S.: 236220

UNITED NATIONAL BANK

722 N Broad St, Cairo, GA 39828
Tel.: (229) 377-7200   GA
Web Site: https://www.unbonline.com
UNBK—(OTCIQ)
Commericial Banking
N.A.I.C.S.: 522110
Charles M. Stafford (Chm)
Michael L. Chastain (Pres & CEO)
Jane Trulock (CFO & Sr VP)
Linda D. Johnson (VP)
Susan Braswell (VP-Mortgage Lending Officer)

UNITED NATURAL FOODS, INC.

313 Iron Horse Way, Providence, RI
02908
Tel.: (401) 528-8634   DE
Web Site: https://www.unfi.com
Year Founded: 1976
UNFI—(NYSE)
Rev.: $30,980,000,000
Assets: $7,528,000,000
Liabilities: $5,887,000,000
Net Worth: $1,641,000,000
Earnings: ($112,000,000)
Emp.: 28,333
Fiscal Year-end: 08/03/24
Food Products Distr
N.A.I.C.S.: 424490
J. Alexander Miller Douglas Jr. (CEO)
Jack L. Stahl (Chm)
Danielle M. Benedict (Chief HR Officer)
Jill E. Sutton (Chief Legal Officer, Gen Counsel & Sec)
Andre Persaud (Pres/CEO-Retail)
Amanda Helming (CMO)
Guillaume Bagal (VP-Diversity)
Mark P. Bushway (Chief Supply Chain Officer)
J. J. Cantrell (Pres-South Reg)
Steve P. Dietz (Chief Customer Officer)
Tandy Harvey (Pres-Central Reg)
John Raiche (Exec VP-Supplier Svcs)
Michael J. Seekins (Sr VP-Supply Chain & Strategy)
Richard Eric Esper (Chief Acctg Officer)
J. Alexander Miller Douglas Jr. (Pres & CEO)
Angie Balian (Chief Brands Officer)
Erin Horvath (COO)
Louis Martin (Pres-Wholesale)
Ron Selders (Pres-Fresh)
Jody Barrick (Sr VP-Bakery & Deli)
Matt Echols (Chief Corp Affairs Officer)
Mahrukh Hussain (Corp Counsel)
Usman Waheed (Chief Digital Experience Officer)
Mario Maffie (CIO)

Subsidiaries:

Albert's Organics, Inc.   (1)
1155 Commerce Blvd, Logan Township, NJ
08085   (100%)
Tel.: (856) 241-9090
Web Site: http://www.albertsorganics.com
Sales Range: $100-124.9 Million
Emp.: 150
Groceries & Related Products
N.A.I.C.S.: 424490
Rod Moyer (VP-Natl Sls)

Branch (Domestic):

Albert's New England   (2)
71 Stow Dr, Chesterfield, NH 03443
Tel.: (603) 256-3000
Web Site: http://www.albertsorganics.com

Sales Range: $100-124.9 Million
Natural & Organically Grown Produce Distr
N.A.I.C.S.: 424490

Albert's Organics Inc.   (2)
2450 17 Ave Ste 250, Santa Cruz, CA
95062
Tel.: (831) 462-5870
Web Site: http://www.albertsorganics.com
Sales Range: $10-24.9 Million
Emp.: 50
Organic Groceries
N.A.I.C.S.: 561499

Albert's Organics Twin Cities   (2)
1100 Eagle Rdg Peterson dr, Prescott, WI
54021
Tel.: (877) 241-3030
Web Site: http://www.albertsorganics.com
Groceries Distr
N.A.I.C.S.: 424490
Scott Schaeppi (Mgr-Div)

Blue Marble Brands, LLC   (1)
313 Iron Horse Way, Providence, RI 02908-5637
Tel.: (888) 534-0246
Web Site: http://www.bluemarblebrands.com
Sales Range: $25-49.9 Million
Emp.: 50
Specialty Food Product Distr
N.A.I.C.S.: 445298
Chris Jensen (Pres)

Haddon House Foods Products,
Inc.   (1)
250 Old Marlton Pike, Medford, NJ 08055
Tel.: (609) 654-7901
Web Site: http://www.haddonhouse.com
Spices & Seasonings
N.A.I.C.S.: 424490
David Landis (CFO)

Natural Retail Group, Inc.   (1)
30555 US Hwy 19 N, Palm Harbor, FL
34684
Tel.: (727) 786-1231
Web Site:
http://www.earthoriginsmarket.com
Sales Range: $150-199.9 Million
Groceries Distr
N.A.I.C.S.: 424410

Nor-Cal Produce, Inc.   (1)
2995 Oates St, West Sacramento, CA
95691
Tel.: (916) 373-0830
Natural Food Distr
N.A.I.C.S.: 424480

Springfield Development Corp
LLC   (1)
14 Clinton St Ste 7, Springfield, VT 05156
Tel.: (802) 885-3061
Web Site:
http://www.springfielddevelopment.org
Emp.: 4
Property Management Services
N.A.I.C.S.: 531120
Bob Flint (Exec Dir)
Paul Kowalski (Sr Mgr-Project)
Sandy Clifford (Office Mgr)
Cynthia Porter (Mgr-Fin)
Heather Hartford (Asst Dir)
Doug Gurney (Pres)
Patricia Putnam (VP)

SuperValu Inc.   (1)
11840 Valley View Rd, Eden Prairie, MN
55344
Tel.: (952) 828-4000
Holding Company; Wholesale Food Distr
N.A.I.C.S.: 551112
Sean F. Griffin (CEO)

Subsidiary (Domestic):

300 Main Street Realty, LLC   (2)
28 Pond St, Nashua, NH 03060-4617
Tel.: (603) 881-9661
Grocery Retailer
N.A.I.C.S.: 445110

Advantage Logistics USA, Inc.   (2)
304 Industrial Way SW, Cleveland, TN
37311
Tel.: (888) 559-0771
Sales Range: $75-99.9 Million
Product Deployment, Logistics & Supply
Chain Management

N.A.I.C.S.: 541614

Subsidiary (Domestic):

Advantage Logistics - Southeast (3)
1450 Commerce Blvd, Anniston, AL
36207   (100%)
Tel.: (256) 235-3490
Web Site:
http://www.advantagelogisticsusa.com
Sales Range: $25-49.9 Million
Emp.: 100
Mfr Warehouses & Distribution Centers
N.A.I.C.S.: 445110

Advantage Logistics - Southwest (3)
3655 W Anthem Way, Anthem, AZ 85086
Tel.: (480) 612-1792
Web Site: http://adlogisticsllc.com
Sales Range: Less than $1 Million
Emp.: 500
Consulting Services
N.A.I.C.S.: 541611

Subsidiary (Domestic):

Associated Grocers of Florida,
Inc.   (2)
1141 SW 12th Ave, Pompano Beach, FL
33069
Tel.: (954) 876-3000
Sales Range: $650-699.9 Million
Emp.: 450
Independent Retail Cooperative; Full Service Warehouse
N.A.I.C.S.: 424410

BP Realty, LLC   (2)
10000 Falls Rd Ste 100, Potomac, MD
20854-4125
Tel.: (301) 299-2099
Management Consulting Services
N.A.I.C.S.: 237210

Bigg's Hyper Shoppes, Inc.   (2)
25 Whitney Dr Ste 122, Milford, OH 45150-8400
Tel.: (513) 248-9300
Rev.: $450,000,000
Emp.: 80
General Merchandise & Food Retailing
N.A.I.C.S.: 445110

Clifford W. Perham, Inc.   (2)
290 Payne Rd, Scarborough, ME 04074-9566
Tel.: (207) 883-4073
Grocery Retailer
N.A.I.C.S.: 445110

Commerce SuperValu West
Region   (2)
5200 Sheila St, Commerce, CA 90040
Tel.: (323) 264-5200
Sales Range: $1-4.9 Billion
Wholesale Grocery Cooperative
N.A.I.C.S.: 424410

Diamond Lake 1994 L.L.C.   (2)
3620 Texas Ave S, Minneapolis, MN 55426
Tel.: (612) 822-8393
Grocery Stores
N.A.I.C.S.: 445110

Foodarama Inc   (2)
4600 Forbes Blvd, Lanham, MD 20706
Tel.: (301) 306-8600
Web Site: http://www.shoppersfood.com
Sales Range: $25-49.9 Million
Emp.: 50
Grocery Stores, Chain
N.A.I.C.S.: 445110

Hornbacher's Pharmacies, Inc.   (2)
950 40th Ave S, Moorhead, MN 56560
Tel.: (218) 359-4007
Pharmacy & Drug Store Operator
N.A.I.C.S.: 456110

Hornbachers   (2)
2510 N Broadway Ave, Fargo, ND 58102-1405
Tel.: (701) 293-5444
Web Site: https://www.hornbachers.com
Sales Range: $125-149.9 Million
Emp.: 250
Food Distribution
N.A.I.C.S.: 445110
Matt Leiseth (Pres)

Market Company, Ltd.   (2)

United Natural Foods, Inc.—(Continued)

4127 Nw 2nd Ave, Miami, FL 33127-2843
Tel.: (305) 576-9790
Grocery Retailer
N.A.I.C.S.: 445110

Market Improvement Corporation (2)
PO Box 26967, Richmond, VA 23261-6967
Tel.: (804) 746-6000
Accounting Services
N.A.I.C.S.: 541219

Metro Foods, Inc. (2)
10635 Marina Dr, Olive Branch, MS 38654-3711
Tel.: (662) 895-9191
Web Site: http://www.metro-logistics.com
Sales Range: $75-99.9 Million
Emp.: 80
Mfr of Meats, Poultry, Butter & Cheese
N.A.I.C.S.: 424470

Preferred Products, Inc. (2)
8459 U S Hwy 42 Ste 278, Florence, KY 41042
Tel.: (859) 525-7353
Sales Range: $100-124.9 Million
Developer & Marketer of Lawn & Garden Pest Control Products
N.A.I.C.S.: 333112

SFW Holding Corp. (2)
11840 Valley View Rd, Eden Prairie, MN 55344　　　　　　　　　　　　　(100%)
Tel.: (952) 828-4000
Sales Range: $1-4.9 Billion
Emp.: 5,000
Holding Company; Warehouse Shopping Club Operator
N.A.I.C.S.: 551112

Subsidiary (Domestic):

Shoppers Food Warehouse Corp. (3)
4600 Forbes Blvd, Lanham, MD 20706-4359　　　　　　　　　　　　(100%)
Tel.: (301) 306-8600
Web Site: http://www.shoppersfood.com
Sales Range: $50-74.9 Million
Emp.: 100
Warehouse Shopping Club Operator
N.A.I.C.S.: 455211

Subsidiary (Domestic):

SUPERVALU Foundation (2)
PO Box 990, Minneapolis, MN 55440
Tel.: (952) 828-4000
Supermarket Operating Services
N.A.I.C.S.: 445110

SUPERVALU International (2)
495 E 19th St, Tacoma, WA 98421-1514
Tel.: (253) 593-3198
Web Site:
　http://www.supervaluinternational.com
Sales Range: $75-99.9 Million
Emp.: 50
Exports Groceries, Produce & Meat Items
N.A.I.C.S.: 424480

SUPERVALU Pharmacies, Inc. (2)
7900 Market Blvd, Chanhassen, MN 55317-9322　　　　　　　　　　(100%)
Tel.: (952) 934-1010
Sales Range: $50-74.9 Million
Emp.: 30
Drug Store
N.A.I.C.S.: 456110

SUPERVALU Transportation Inc. (2)
11840 Valley View Rd, Eden Prairie, MN 55344　　　　　　　　　　　　(100%)
Tel.: (406) 247-1513
Web Site: http://www.supervalu.com
Sales Range: $100-124.9 Million
Transportation Services
N.A.I.C.S.: 488999

Unit (Domestic):

SUPERVALU, Inc. - Anniston Distribution Center (2)
2130 Roberts Dr, Anniston, AL 36201
Tel.: (256) 831-1840
Sales Range: $300-349.9 Million
Emp.: 350
Groceries Storage & Distribution
N.A.I.C.S.: 424410

SUPERVALU, Inc. - Billings Distribution Center (2)
1629 King Ave W, Billings, MT 59102-6448
Tel.: (406) 247-1400
Sales Range: $75-99.9 Million
Emp.: 90
Groceries Storage & Distribution
N.A.I.C.S.: 424410

SUPERVALU, Inc. - Champaign Distribution Center (2)
2611 N Lincoln Ave, Urbana, IL 61801
Tel.: (217) 384-2800
Sales Range: $450-499.9 Million
Emp.: 689
Groceries Storage & Distribution
N.A.I.C.S.: 424410

Division (Domestic):

SUPERVALU, Inc. - Eastern Region (2)
8258 Richfood Rd, Mechanicsville, VA 23116-2008　　　　　　　　　(100%)
Tel.: (804) 746-6000
Sales Range: $450-499.9 Million
Emp.: 1,200
Groceries Whslr
N.A.I.C.S.: 424410
Kevin Kamp (Pres)

Unit (Domestic):

SUPERVALU, Inc. - Easton Distribution Center (2)
19011 Lake Dr E, Chanhassen, MN 55317-9322
Tel.: (610) 559-5590
Web Site: http://www.supervalu.com
General Merchandise & Beauty Products Whslr
N.A.I.C.S.: 445110

SUPERVALU, Inc. - Green Bay Distribution Center (2)
451 Joannes Ave, Green Bay, WI 54307
Tel.: (920) 436-1538
Sales Range: $75-99.9 Million
Emp.: 140
Groceries Storage & Distribution
N.A.I.C.S.: 424410

Division (Domestic):

SUPERVALU, Inc. - Midwest Region (2)
8401 W 102nd St Ste 300, Pleasant Prairie, WI 53158
Tel.: (262) 947-7290
Web Site: http://www.shopnsave.com
Sales Range: $350-399.9 Million
Emp.: 30
Wholesale Groceries
N.A.I.C.S.: 424410

Unit (Domestic):

SUPERVALU, Inc. - St. Louis Distribution Center (2)
7100 Hazelwood Ave, Hazelwood, MO 63042-2945　　　　　　　　　(100%)
Tel.: (314) 524-4000
Web Site: http://www.supervalu.com
Sales Range: $300-349.9 Million
Emp.: 330
Groceries Storage & Distribution
N.A.I.C.S.: 424410

Division (Domestic):

SUPERVALU, Inc., Bismarck Division (2)
707 Airport Rd, Bismarck, ND 58502　　　　　　　　　　　　　　(100%)
Tel.: (701) 222-5600
Sales Range: $25-49.9 Million
Emp.: 100
Wholesale Groceries Distr
N.A.I.C.S.: 445110

SUPERVALU, Inc., Fargo Distribution Division (2)
3501 N 12th Ave, Fargo, ND 58109
Tel.: (701) 293-2100
Web Site: http://www.supervalue.com
Sales Range: $100-124.9 Million
Emp.: 75
Groceries Whslr
N.A.I.C.S.: 424410

SUPERVALU, Inc., Food Marketing Division (2)
4815 Executive Blvd, Fort Wayne, IN 46808
Tel.: (260) 483-2146
Web Site: http://www.supervalu.com
Sales Range: $750-799.9 Million
Emp.: 1,100
Wholesale Grocery Distribution
N.A.I.C.S.: 445110

SUPERVALU, Inc., Harrisburg Division (2)
500 S Muddy Creek Rd, Denver, PA 17517-9774
Tel.: (717) 232-6821
Web Site: http://www.supervalu.com
Sales Range: $1-4.9 Billion
Emp.: 3,200
Food Distr
N.A.I.C.S.: 424410

SUPERVALU, Inc., Lewis Grocer Division (2)
301 Martin Luther King Blvd S, Indianola, MS 38751　　　　　　　　　(100%)
Tel.: (662) 887-3211
Web Site: http://www.supervalu.com
Sales Range: $150-199.9 Million
Emp.: 200
Wholesale Groceries
N.A.I.C.S.: 424410

SUPERVALU, Inc., Milton Division (2)
James River Tpke, Milton, WV 25541-0386
Tel.: (304) 743-9087
Web Site: http://www.supervalu.com
Sales Range: $100-124.9 Million
Emp.: 150
Wholesale Groceries
N.A.I.C.S.: 424410

SUPERVALU, Inc., Minneapolis Division (2)
101 S Jefferson Ave, Hopkins, MN 55343　　　　　　　　　　　　(100%)
Tel.: (952) 932-4306
Sales Range: $550-599.9 Million
Emp.: 900
Wholesale Groceries
N.A.I.C.S.: 424410
Bill Chew (Pres-West Reg Independent Bus)

SUPERVALU, Inc., Ohio Valley Division (2)
1003 Bellbrook Ave, Xenia, OH 45385-4011
Tel.: (937) 374-7611
Web Site: http://www.supervalu.com
Sales Range: $500-549.9 Million
Emp.: 800
Wholesale Groceries
N.A.I.C.S.: 424410

SUPERVALU, Inc., Pittsburgh Division (2)
400 Paintersville Rd, New Stanton, PA 15672-0430
Tel.: (724) 925-6600
Sales Range: $700-749.9 Million
Emp.: 800
Wholesale Groceries
N.A.I.C.S.: 445110

SUPERVALU, Inc., Quincy Division (2)
1797 Pat Thomas Pkwy, Quincy, FL 32351
Tel.: (850) 875-2600
Sales Range: $50-74.9 Million
Emp.: 150
Food Distribution
N.A.I.C.S.: 488510

SUPERVALU, Inc., Spokane Division (2)
505 N Argonne Rd Ste 1, Spokane Valley, WA 99212-2816
Tel.: (509) 928-7700
Web Site: http://www.supervalu.com
Sales Range: $75-99.9 Million
Emp.: 90
Wholesale Groceries
N.A.I.C.S.: 424410

SUPERVALU, Inc., Tacoma Division (2)
1525 E D St, Tacoma, WA 98421-1609
Tel.: (253) 404-4200
Web Site: http://www.supervalu.com

Sales Range: $1-4.9 Billion
Emp.: 1,000
Wholesale Groceries
N.A.I.C.S.: 424410

Subsidiary (Domestic):

Store Design Services (2)
6533 Flying Cloud Dr Ste 100, Eden Prairie, MN 55344-3307　　　　　　(100%)
Tel.: (952) 914-5800
Web Site:
　http://www.storedesignservices.com
Sales Range: $25-49.9 Million
Emp.: 86
Architectural & Engineering Services
N.A.I.C.S.: 423220

Supermarket Operators of America Inc. (2)
11840 Vly View Rd, Eden Prairie, MN 55344　　　　　　　　　　　　(100%)
Tel.: (952) 828-4000
Sales Range: Less than $1 Million
Emp.: 1,000
Grocery Stores
N.A.I.C.S.: 445110
Sam Duncan (Pres)

Subsidiary (Domestic):

Cub Foods, Inc. (3)
421 3rd St S, Stillwater, MN 55082 (100%)
Tel.: (651) 439-7200
Web Site: https://www.cub.com
Sales Range: $150-199.9 Million
Emp.: 300
Grocery Retailer
N.A.I.C.S.: 445110

Subsidiary (Domestic):

Cub Foods of Appleton Inc. (4)
1200 W Northland Ave, Appleton, WI 54914-1415
Tel.: (920) 739-6253
Rev.: $11,800,000
Emp.: 110
Grocery Stores
N.A.I.C.S.: 445110
Brian Audette (Pres)

Cub Foods of Green Bay Inc. (4)
421 3rd St S, Stillwater, MN 55082-4955
Tel.: (920) 496-3777
Web Site: http://www.cub.com
Rev.: $19,700,000
Emp.: 100
Grocery Stores
N.A.I.C.S.: 445110

Subsidiary (Domestic):

Pooploo Market, Incorporated (3)
905 Main St, Kadoka, SD 57543
Tel.: (605) 837-2232
Grocery Retailer
N.A.I.C.S.: 445110

Shop 'n Save Warehouse Foods, Inc. (3)
10461 Manchester Rd, Saint Louis, MO 63122　　　　　　　　　　　　(100%)
Tel.: (314) 984-0900
Web Site: http://www.shopnsave.com
Holding Company; Grocery Stores Operator
N.A.I.C.S.: 551112
Eric Hymas (Pres)

Subsidiary (Domestic):

Shop 'n Save St. Louis, Inc. (4)
10461 Manchester Rd, Saint Louis, MO 63122　　　　　　　　　　　　(100%)
Tel.: (314) 984-0900
Web Site: http://www.shopnsave.com
Grocery Chain
N.A.I.C.S.: 445110

Subsidiary (Domestic):

U.S. Satellite Corporation (2)
935 W Bullion St, Murray, UT 84123
Tel.: (801) 263-0519
Web Site: http://www.ussc.com
All Other Telecommunications
N.A.I.C.S.: 517810

W. Newell & Co., LLC (2)
PO Box 9028, Champaign, IL 61826-9028
Tel.: (217) 278-4490

Web Site: http://www.wnewell.com
Grocery Product Distr
N.A.I.C.S.: 424490
Steve Irland *(Pres)*
Dan Bates *(Dir-Mdsg)*
Brian Boutin *(Dir-Procurement)*
Lori Stewart *(Mgr-Fin & HR)*
Tim Eberle *(Area Dir-Sls)*

Tony's Fine Foods Inc. **(1)**
3575 Reed Ave, West Sacramento, CA
95605-1628
Tel.: (916) 374-4000
Web Site: https://www.unfifresh.com
Sales Range: $700-749.9 Million
Emp.: 700
Meats & Meat Products
N.A.I.C.S.: 424470

Trudeau Foods, LLC **(1)**
25 W Cliff Rd Ste 115, Burnsville, MN
55337
Tel.: (952) 882-8295
Food Products Mfr
N.A.I.C.S.: 311999

UNFI Canada, Inc. **(1)**
8755 Keele Street, Vaughan, L4K 2N1, ON,
Canada
Tel.: (905) 738-4204
Web Site: https://www.unfi.ca
Natural, Organic, Specialty & Kosher Gro-
ceries Distr
N.A.I.C.S.: 424490

United Natural Foods West, Inc. **(1)**
22 30th St NE Ste 102, Auburn, WA 98002
Tel.: (253) 333-6769
Sales Range: $100-124.9 Million
Emp.: 300
Groceries Distr
N.A.I.C.S.: 424410

United Natural Foods, Inc. **(1)**
2340 Heinz Rd, Iowa City, IA 52240-2602
Tel.: (319) 337-6448
Web Site: http://www.unfi.com
Sales Range: $125-149.9 Million
Emp.: 225
Grocery Distr
N.A.I.C.S.: 424410

United Natural Foods, Inc. **(1)**
100 Lakeview Ct SW, Atlanta, GA 30336
Tel.: (404) 346-0960
Web Site: http://www.unfi.com
Sales Range: $125-149.9 Million
Emp.: 200
Groceries
N.A.I.C.S.: 424490

United Natural Foods, Inc. **(1)**
17901 E 40th Ave, Aurora, CO 80011
Tel.: (303) 360-8459
Web Site: http://www.unfi.com
Sales Range: $150-199.9 Million
Groceries Distr
N.A.I.C.S.: 424490

United Natural Foods, Inc. **(1)**
225 Cross Farm Lane, York, PA 17406
Tel.: (717) 624-9002
Web Site: http://www.unfi.com
Sales Range: $150-199.9 Million
Emp.: 300
Groceries Distr
N.A.I.C.S.: 424490

United Natural Trading, LLC **(1)**
96 Executive Ave, Edison, NJ 08817
Tel.: (732) 650-9905
Web Site:
   https://www.woodstockfarmsmfg.com
Sales Range: $75-99.9 Million
Emp.: 100
Nuts, Dried Fruit, Trail Mixes, Seeds, Gra-
nola & Confections Importer, Processor,
Packager & Distr
N.A.I.C.S.: 424490

UNITED PARCEL SERVICE, INC.

55 Glenlake Pkwy NE, Atlanta, GA
30328
Tel.: (404) 828-6000   DE
Web Site: https://www.ups.com
Year Founded: 1907
UPS—(NYSE)
Rev.: $90,958,000,000

Assets: $70,857,000,000
Liabilities: $53,543,000,000
Net Worth: $17,314,000,000
Earnings: $6,708,000,000
Emp.: 500,000
Fiscal Year-end: 12/31/23
Surface & Air Parcel Delivery Ser-
vices; Financial & Logistics Services
N.A.I.C.S.: 484121
Kathleen M. Gutmann *(Pres-Intl &
Healthcare & Supply Chain Solutions
& Exec VP)*
Kevin M. Warren *(CMO, Customer
Experience Officer & Exec VP)*
Laura Lane *(Chief Corp Affairs,
Comm & Sustainability Officer)*
Carlton E. Rose *(Executives)*
Norman Brothers Jr. *(Chief Legal Of-
ficer)*
Bala Subramanian *(Exec VP)*
Carol B. Tome *(CEO)*

Subsidiaries:

Bomi Italia S.p.A. **(1)**
via Campo Cioso 125, Vaprio d'Adda,
20069, Milan, Italy
Tel.: (39) 0392466708
Web Site: http://www.bomigroup.com
Medical Device Distr, Logistics & Ware-
housing
N.A.I.C.S.: 423450
Stefano Camurri *(Exec Dir)*
Marco Ruini *(CEO)*

Marken LLP **(1)**
1009 Slater Rd Ste 120, Durham, NC
27703
Web Site: http://www.marken.com
Emp.: 1,100
Freight Transportation Services
N.A.I.C.S.: 488510
Ariette Van Strien *(Pres)*
Simon Kirk *(CTO)*
Andrew Gravatt *(Sr VP-Finance)*
Frederic Maurice *(VP-Logistics-EMEA)*
Celin Ong *(VP)*
Doaa Fathallah *(Chief Admin Officer, Sr VP
& Gen Counsel)*
Thomas C. Grundstrom *(Sr VP)*
Gerit Offenhauser *(Sr VP-Logistics-EMEA)*
Dan Bell *(Sr VP)*
Navnit Patel *(Sr VP-Regulatory Affairs)*
Nina Vas *(VP)*
David Lee *(VP)*
Doaa Fathallah *(Chief Admin Officer, Sr VP
& Gen Counsel)*
Thomas C. Grundstrom *(Sr VP)*
Gerit Offenhauser *(Sr VP-Logistics-EMEA)*
Dan Bell *(Sr VP)*
Navnit Patel *(Sr VP-Regulatory Affairs)*
Nina Vas *(VP)*
David Lee *(VP)*

Midnite Air Corp. **(1)**
5001 Airport Plz Dr Ste 250, Long Beach,
CA 90815
Tel.: (310) 910-9199
Web Site: http://www.mnx.com
Transportation & Logistics Services
N.A.I.C.S.: 541614

Subsidiary (Domestic):

Network Global Logistics, LLC **(2)**
320 Interlocken Pkwy Ste 100, Broomfield,
CO 80021
Tel.: (866) 938-1870
Web Site: http://www.nglog.com
Transportation & Logistics Consulting Ser-
vices
N.A.I.C.S.: 541614
Ray Garcia *(Chm)*
Forrest Kragten *(CFO)*
Ranjit Thaker *(CIO)*
Paul Gettings *(Exec VP-Svc Parts Logistics
& Express Ops)*
Janell Lewis *(Dir-HR)*
Kyle Schultz *(Exec VP)*
John Labrie *(CEO)*
Irene Scharmack *(Exec VP-Ops-Supply
Chain Svcs)*

Subsidiary (Domestic):

Medical Logistic Solutions, Inc. **(3)**

7200 S Alton Way Ste A-240, Centennial,
CO 80112
Tel.: (303) 917-8401
Web Site:
   http://www.medicallogisticssolutions.com
Courier & Logistics Services for Healthcare
Industry
N.A.I.C.S.: 492110
Rocco Sirizzotti *(Founder & CEO)*

UPS Asia Group Pte. Ltd. **(1)**
22 Changi South Avenue 2, Singapore,
486064, Singapore
Freight Forwarding & Transportation Services
N.A.I.C.S.: 488510

UPS Limited **(1)**
Forest Road, Feltham, TW13 7DY, Middle-
sex, United Kingdom
Shipping & Freight Forwarding Services
N.A.I.C.S.: 488510

UPS SCS (Nederland) B.V. **(1)**
Marie Curieweg 20, Roermond, 6045 GH,
Netherlands
Tel.: (31) 475528714
Logistics & Supply Chain Management Ser-
vices
N.A.I.C.S.: 541614

UPS SCS Holding Limited **(1)**
8/f 100 Texaco Rd Tsuen Wan, Hong Kong,
China (Hong Kong)
Tel.: (852) 29425100
Logistics Consulting Servies
N.A.I.C.S.: 551112
Jeff Foote *(Mgr-Mktg)*

United Parcel Service Co. **(1)**
55 Glenlake Pkwy NE, Atlanta, GA 30328
Tel.: (404) 828-6000
Web Site: https://www.ups.com
Sales Range: $50-74.9 Million
Transportation, Freight, Logistics & Distr
Services
N.A.I.C.S.: 484122

Subsidiary (Domestic):

ConnectShip, Inc. **(2)**
8282 S Memorial Dr Ste 400, Tulsa, OK
74133
Tel.: (918) 461-4460
Web Site: https://www.connectship.com
Sales Range: $10-24.9 Million
Emp.: 44
Third-Party Multi-Carrier Shipment, Rating &
Tracking System
N.A.I.C.S.: 541512

The UPS Store, Inc. **(2)**
6060 Cornerstone Ct W, San Diego, CA
92121-3795
Tel.: (858) 455-8800
Web Site: https://www.theupsstore.com
Postal Service
N.A.I.C.S.: 491110
Tim Davis *(Pres)*
Don Higginson *(Sr VP-Franchise Rels)*
David Lee *(Sr VP-Operations)*
Judy Milner *(VP)*
Jayson Richard *(Reg VP)*
Elizabeth Orden *(Reg VP-West)*
Eric Maida *(Reg VP-East)*
Michelle Van Slyke *(Sr VP-Mktg & Sls)*
William Smith *(Sr Dir)*
Mahasty Seradj *(Sr VP-Finance & Control-
ler)*
Imad Nusheiwat *(VP-Corporate Develop-
ment)*
Efrain Inzunza *(Sr VP-Strategy & Interim Sr
VP-Operations)*
Uday Hebbar *(Dir-Information Technology)*
Herb Garrett *(VP-HR & Trng)*
Steve Chambers *(VP-Retail-Business De-
velopment)*
Randy Bennett *(VP)*
Sarah Casalan Bittle *(Pres)*
Bryan Clements *(Atty)*
Jamie Cunningham *(VP-Strategy)*
Jake Hearron *(VP-Finance)*
Sean O'Neal *(VP)*
Eileen Webb *(VP-Product Development)*

UPS Capital Corporation **(2)**
35 Glenlake Pkwy NE, Atlanta, GA
30328-7245   **(100%)**
Tel.: (404) 828-8385
Web Site: http://www.upscapital.com

Supply-Chain Financial Services
N.A.I.C.S.: 522299

Subsidiary (Domestic):

Parcel Pro, Inc. **(3)**
1867 Western Way, Torrance, CA 90501
Tel.: (310) 328-8484
Sales Range: $1-9.9 Million
Emp.: 25
Logistic Services
N.A.I.C.S.: 541614

UPS Capital Business Credit **(3)**
425 Day Hill Rd, Windsor, CT 06095
Tel.: (860) 687-2600
Web Site: http://www.upscapital.com
Sales Range: $75-99.9 Million
Emp.: 200
Bank Holding Company; Provider of Credit
& Trade Finance Services to Small & Me-
dium Size Domestic Manufacturing Compa-
nies & Emerging International Markets
N.A.I.C.S.: 522110

Subsidiary (Non-US):

UPS Customer Service Center **(2)**
Room 607 Marine Bldg Ni 1 Pudong Ave,
Shanghai, 200120, China   **(100%)**
Tel.: (86) 2138965555
Web Site: http://www.ups.com
Postal Services, International Freight &
Shipping & Customer Service
N.A.I.C.S.: 488510

UPS Europe SA/NV **(2)**
Avenue Ariane 5, 1200, Brussels, Belgium
Tel.: (32) 27769832
Sales Range: $50-74.9 Million
Surface & Air Parcel Delivery Services; Fi-
nancial & Logistics Services
N.A.I.C.S.: 492210
Lou Rivieccio *(Pres)*

Subsidiary (Non-US):

UPS Hungary Ltd. **(3)**
Lorinci street 154 Airport City Logistic Park
Building G, 2220, Vecses, Hungary
Tel.: (36) 18770000
Sales Range: $10-24.9 Million
Emp.: 300
Local & International Freight Forwarding
N.A.I.C.S.: 488510

**United Parcel Service Deutschland
S.a.r.l. & Co. OHG** **(3)**
Goerlitzer Strasse 1, 41460, Neuss, Ger-
many
Tel.: (49) 696 640 5060
Web Site: http://www.ups.com
Parcel Delivery Services
N.A.I.C.S.: 492110

United Parcel Service Italia SRL **(3)**
Via Fantoli 15/2 and 15/8, 20138, Milan,
Italy
Tel.: (39) 023 030 3039
Web Site: https://www.ups.com
Freight Forwarding & Transportation Ser-
vices
N.A.I.C.S.: 488510

Subsidiary (Domestic):

UPS International, Inc. **(2)**
55 Glenlake Pkwy NE, Atlanta, GA 30328-
3474
Tel.: (404) 828-6000
Logistics Consulting Servies
N.A.I.C.S.: 541614
Nando Cesarone *(Pres)*
Darrell L. Ford *(Chief HR Officer & Exec
VP)*

Subsidiary (Non-US):

**UPS Parcel Delivery (Guangdong)
Co., LTD.** **(2)**
Room 2705 Jianlibao Mansion No 410-412
Dongfeng Middle Road, Guangzhou,
510030, China
Tel.: (86) 2083486789
Air Courier Services
N.A.I.C.S.: 492110

UPS Parcel Delivery Service Ltd. **(2)**
UPS Administration Office 36/F 9 Wing
Hong Street, Cheung Sha Wan, Kowloon,
China (Hong Kong)   **(100%)**

United Parcel Service, Inc.—(Continued)
Tel.: (852) 27385000
Web Site: http://www.ups.com
Sales Range: $50-74.9 Million
Emp.: 400
Local & International Freight Forwarding
N.A.I.C.S.: 488510

United Couriers S.A.R.L. (2)
711 Azouri Center GF Alfred Naccache
Street, Achrafieh, Beirut, Lebanon
Tel.: (961) 1218575
Web Site: https://www.ucslb.com
UPS Service Contractor
N.A.I.C.S.: 491110

United Parcel Service (BY) (2)
3 Muzikalniy Lane, 220030, Minsk, Belarus
Tel.: (375) 173272233
Web Site: https://www.ups.com
Postal & Courier Services
N.A.I.C.S.: 491110

**United Parcel Service (RUS)
LLC** (2)
Odesskaya Str 2 lit A, 117638, Moscow,
Russia **(100%)**
Tel.: (7) 4959612211
Web Site: http://www.ups.com
Postal & Courier Services
N.A.I.C.S.: 491110
Ivan Shagsieh *(Pres)*

**United Parcel Service Canada
Ltd.** (2)
1930 Derry Road East, Mississauga, L5S
1E2, ON, Canada
Tel.: (905) 676-1708
Web Site: https://www.ups.com
Emp.: 13,000
Parcel Delivery Services
N.A.I.C.S.: 492110

Subsidiary (Domestic):

**United Parcel Service of America,
Inc.** (2)
55 Glenlake Pkwy NE, Atlanta, GA 30328
Tel.: (404) 828-6000
Web Site: https://www.ups.com
Transportation, Freight, Logistics & Distr
Services
N.A.I.C.S.: 484122

Subsidiary (Domestic):

**UPS Supply Chain Solutions,
Inc.** (3)
12380 Morris Rd, Alpharetta, GA 30005
Tel.: (913) 693-6151
Sales Range: $1-4.9 Billion
Emp.: 20,000
Transportation, Freight, Logistics, International Trade Management & Distribution
Services
N.A.I.C.S.: 483113

Subsidiary (Non-US):

UPS SCS, Inc. (4)
1930 Derry Road East, Mississauga, L5S
1E2, ON, Canada **(100%)**
Tel.: (905) 671-5454
Sales Range: $25-49.9 Million
Emp.: 300
Freight Transportation Arrangement
N.A.I.C.S.: 488510

Subsidiary (Domestic):

**UPS Supply Chain Solutions General
Services, Inc.** (4)
55 Glenlake Pkwy, Atlanta, GA 30328
Tel.: (404) 828-6000
Courier Service
N.A.I.C.S.: 492110

Branch (Domestic):

**UPS Supply Chain Solutions, Inc. -
Coppell** (4)
660 Fritz Dr, Coppell, TX 75019
Tel.: (972) 471-7171
Web Site: http://www.ups-scs.com
Sales Range: $75-99.9 Million
Emp.: 400
International Freight Forwarding Services
N.A.I.C.S.: 488510

**UPS Supply Chain Solutions, Inc. -
South San Francisco** (4)
550 Eccles Ave #3 S, San Francisco, CA
94080-1905
Tel.: (650) 635-2693
Web Site: http://www.ups-scs.com
Sales Range: $1-4.9 Billion
Emp.: 10,000
Freight Forwarding & Global Integrated Logistics
N.A.I.C.S.: 493110

Subsidiary (Domestic):

UPS Worldwide Forwarding, Inc. (3)
55 Glenlake Pkwy NE, Atlanta, GA 30328
Tel.: (404) 828-6000
Web Site: https://www.ups.com
Sales Range: $350-399.9 Million
Transportation, Freight, Logistics & Distribution Services
N.A.I.C.S.: 492210

United Parcel Service General Services Co. (3)
55 Glenlake Pwky, Atlanta, GA 30328
Tel.: (404) 828-6000
Web Site: https://www.ups.com
Sales Range: $250-299.9 Million
Emp.: 100
Transportation, Freight, Logistics & Distr
Services
N.A.I.C.S.: 484122

United Parcel Service Czech Republic, s.r.o. (1)
Ke Kopanine 559, 25267, Tuchomerice,
Czech Republic
Tel.: (420) 233003300
Web Site: https://www.ups.com
Parcel Delivery Services
N.A.I.C.S.: 492110

**United Parcel Service Nederland
BV** (1)
Tel.: (31) 205040500
Logistic Services
N.A.I.C.S.: 541614

**United Parcel Service Nederlands
B.V.** (1)
Achtseweg Noord 14-16, 5651 GG, Eindhoven, Netherlands
Tel.: (31) 205040500
Logistic Services
N.A.I.C.S.: 541614

UNITED PARKS & RESORTS INC.

6240 Sea Harbor Dr, Orlando, FL
32821
Tel.: (407) 226-5011 DE
Web Site: https://unitedparks.com
PRKS—(NYSE)
Rev.: $1,726,587,000
Assets: $2,625,046,000
Liabilities: $2,833,262,000
Net Worth: ($208,216,000)
Earnings: $234,196,000
Emp.: 3,300
Fiscal Year-end: 12/31/23
Theme Park & Zoological Park
Owner
N.A.I.C.S.: 713110
G. Anthony Taylor *(Chief Legal Officer, Gen Counsel & Sec)*
Michelle F. Adams *(CFO)*
Scott I. Ross *(Chm)*
Christopher L. Finazzo *(Chief Comml Officer)*
Lisa Cradit *(Sr VP & Head-Comm)*
James W. Forrester Jr. *(Treas)*
Shekufeh Shirazi Boyle *(Chief Acctg Officer)*
Marc Swanson *(CEO)*
Christopher Dold *(Chief Zoological Officer)*
James Hughes *(Chief HR Officer)*

Subsidiaries:

**SeaWorld Parks & Entertainment
LLC** (1)

9205 S Park Center Loop Ste 400, Orlando,
FL 32819
Tel.: (407) 226-5210
Web Site: http://www.seaworld.com
Theme Park Operator
N.A.I.C.S.: 713110

Unit (Domestic):

Adventure Island (2)
10165 N McKinley Dr, Tampa, FL 33612
Tel.: (813) 884-4386
Web Site: https://www.adventureisland.com
Sales Range: $75-99.9 Million
Emp.: 450
Water Theme Park
N.A.I.C.S.: 713110

Aquatica (2)
5800 Water Play Way, Orlando, FL 32821
Tel.: (407) 351-3600
Web Site: https://aquatica.com
Sales Range: $25-49.9 Million
Water Park
N.A.I.C.S.: 713110
Marilynn Hannes *(Pres-Park-San Diego)*

Busch Gardens Tampa Bay (2)
3605 E Bougainvillea Dr, Tampa, FL 33612-
6433
Tel.: (813) 987-5000
Web Site: https://www.buschgardens.com
Sales Range: $400-449.9 Million
Emp.: 3,750
Theme Park
N.A.I.C.S.: 713110

Busch Gardens Williamsburg (2)
1 Busch Gardens Blvd, Williamsburg, VA
23185
Tel.: (757) 253-3000
Web Site: https://buschgardens.com
Sales Range: $250-299.9 Million
Emp.: 1,000
Theme Park
N.A.I.C.S.: 713110
David Cromwell *(Pres)*

Discovery Cove (2)
6000 Discovery Cove Way, Orlando, FL
32821
Tel.: (407) 363-2209
Web Site: https://discoverycove.com
Sales Range: $25-49.9 Million
Emp.: 650
Theme Park Operator
N.A.I.C.S.: 713110

Subsidiary (Domestic):

Sea World of Florida LLC (2)
7007 SeaWorld Dr, Orlando, FL 32821-
8009
Tel.: (407) 401-8477
Web Site: https://www.seaworld.com
Sales Range: $350-399.9 Million
Emp.: 3,000
Theme Park & Zoo
N.A.I.C.S.: 713110

Sea World of Texas LLC (2)
10500 SeaWorld Dr, San Antonio, TX
78251-3001
Tel.: (210) 520-4732
Web Site: https://seaworld.com
Sales Range: $400-449.9 Million
Theme Park & Zoo
N.A.I.C.S.: 713110
Carl Lum *(Pres-Park)*

Unit (Domestic):

SeaWorld California (2)
500 Sea World Dr, San Diego, CA 92109-
7904
Tel.: (619) 222-4732
Web Site: https://www.seaworld.com
Rev.: $12,000,000
Emp.: 4,000
Theme Park & Zoo
N.A.I.C.S.: 713110

Subsidiary (Domestic):

Sesame Place (2)
100 Sesame Rd, Langhorne, PA 19047-
1821
Tel.: (215) 702-3566
Web Site: https://www.sesameplace.com

Sales Range: $10-24.9 Million
Emp.: 70
Theme Park
N.A.I.C.S.: 713110

Water Country USA (2)
176 Water Country Pkwy, Williamsburg, VA
23185-5828
Tel.: (757) 229-4386
Web Site: https://www.watercountryusa.com
Sales Range: $1-9.9 Million
Emp.: 8
Water Theme Park
N.A.I.C.S.: 713110
David Cromwell *(Pres)*

UNITED RAIL, INC.
304 S Jones Blvd Ste 6890, Las Vegas, NV 89107
Tel.: (281) 826-6082 DE
Web Site:
http://www.unitedrailinc.com
URAL—(OTCIQ)
Passenger Transportation Services
N.A.I.C.S.: 485999
Michael A. Barron *(Chm, Pres & CEO)*
Wanda Witoslawski *(CFO)*
Zac Andrejic *(COO)*

Subsidiaries:

Train Travel, Inc. (1)
1515 Oakland Blvd Ste 180, Walnut Creek,
CA 94565
Tel.: (812) 454-2350
Web Site: http://www.rideourtrains.com
Travel Arrangement Services
N.A.I.C.S.: 561510
B. Allen Brown *(Pres & CEO)*

Division (Domestic):

Key Holidays (1)
1515 Oakland Blvd Ste 180, Walnut Creek,
CA 94596-4383
Tel.: (925) 945-8938
Web Site: http://www.keyholidays.com
Tour Operator
N.A.I.C.S.: 561520
Jade Chapmann *(Pres)*

Key Tours International Inc. (2)
11096 Lee Hwy Ste B103, Fairfax, VA
22030-5039
Tel.: (703) 591-3550
Web Site: http://www.keytours.com
Travel Agencies
N.A.I.C.S.: 561510
Koray Edeman *(Owner)*

UNITED RENTALS, INC.
100 1st Stamford Pl Ste 700, Stamford, CT 06902
Tel.: (203) 622-3131 DE
Web Site:
https://www.unitedrentals.com
Year Founded: 1997
URI—(NYSE)
Rev.: $14,332,000,000
Assets: $25,589,000,000
Liabilities: $17,459,000,000
Net Worth: $8,130,000,000
Earnings: $2,424,000,000
Emp.: 26,300
Fiscal Year-end: 12/31/23
Holding Company; Construction & Industrial Equipment Rental & Leasing Services
N.A.I.C.S.: 551112
Matthew John Flannery *(Pres & CEO)*
John J. Fahey *(VP-Internal Audit)*
Michael D. Durand *(COO & Exec VP)*
Craig Adam Pintoff *(Chief Admin & Legal Officer & Exec VP)*
William Grace *(Exec VP)*
Kenneth B. Mettel *(Sr VP-Performance Analytics)*
Daniel T. Higgins *(CIO & VP)*
Scott Fisher *(VP-Western Canada)*
Todd M. Hayes *(Reg VP-Trench Safety)*

John J. Humphrey *(VP-Mid-Atlantic)*
Thomas P. Jones *(Reg VP-Onsite Svcs)*
Brent R. Kuchynka *(VP-Corp Fleet Mgmt)*
Kevin M. O'Brien *(VP-Mid-Central)*
William Grace *(VP-IR)*
Craig A. Schmidt *(VP-Accounts-Natl)*
T. J. Mahoney *(VP-Supply Chain)*
Daniel C. Sparks *(VP-Sls Ops & Support)*
Kurtis T. Barker *(Co-Founder)*
John King *(VP-Gulf South)*
Andrew B. Limoges *(Principal Acctg Officer, VP & Controller)*
Jason Barba *(VP-Carolinas)*
Mitch Holder *(VP-Total Rewards)*
Tomer Barkan *(VP-Financial Plng & Analysis)*
Norty Turner *(Sr VP-Svcs & Advanced Solutions)*
Larry Worthington *(Reg VP-Power & HVAC)*
Nick Roberts *(VP-Southeast)*
Christopher Carmolingo *(VP-Svc Ops)*
Cristina Madry *(VP-Health, Safety & Employee Rels)*
Jurgen M. Verschoor *(VP-European Fluid Solutions)*
Steve Szaniszlo *(VP-Northeast Canada)*
Jody Miller *(VP-Global Storage & Modular Solutions)*
Antwan Houston *(VP-Tools Reg)*
Jason Rose *(VP-Pump Solutions)*
Audwin Reed *(VP-South Reg)*
Theodore M. Mourouzis *(VP-Storage & Modular Solutions Reg)*
Alfredo Barquin *(VP-Business Development)*
Neil R. Littlewood *(VP-AU,NZ)*
Ted Grace *(CFO & Exec VP)*
Sybil Collins *(Treas & VP)*
Ted Grace *(CFO)*
Elizabeth Grenfell *(VP-IR)*
Joli L. Gross *(Chief Legal Officer, Chief Sustainability Officer, Sec & Sr VP)*

Subsidiaries:

BakerCorp International Holdings, Inc. **(1)**
7800 N Dallas Pkwy Ste 500, Plano, TX 75024
Tel.: (562) 430-6262
Web Site: http://ur.bakercorp.com
Sales Range: $250-299.9 Million
Containment, Pumping & Filtration Equipment Solutions
N.A.I.C.S.: 333914
Jennifer Murphy *(Mgr-Comm)*

Subsidiary (Non-US):

BakerCorp B.V. **(2)**
Bloemendaalse Zeedijk 10, 4765 BP, Moerdijk, Netherlands
Tel.: (31) 168 331 610
Web Site: http://www.bakercorp.com
Containment, Pumping & Filtration Equipment Solutions
N.A.I.C.S.: 333914

BlueLine Rental, LLC **(1)**
127 Walnut Bottom Rd, Shippensburg, PA 17257
Tel.: (717) 530-6116
Web Site: http://www.bluelinerental.com
Emp.: 2,100
Commercial & Industrial Machinery & Equipment Rental & Leasing
N.A.I.C.S.: 532490

Franklin Equipment LLC **(1)**
4141 Hamilton Square Blvd, Groveport, OH 43125
Tel.: (614) 335-5356
Web Site: http://www.franklinequipment.com
Commercial & Industrial Machinery & Equipment Repair & Maintenance

N.A.I.C.S.: 811310
Leonard Franklin *(Owner)*

General Finance Corporation **(1)**
39 E Union St, Pasadena, CA 91103
Tel.: (626) 584-9722
Web Site: http://www.generalfinance.com
Rev.: $356,479,000
Assets: $756,022,000
Liabilities: $581,105,000
Net Worth: $174,917,000
Earnings: $4,286,000
Emp.: 934
Fiscal Year-end: 06/30/2020
Investment Services
N.A.I.C.S.: 523999
Charles E. Barrantes *(CFO & Exec VP)*
Christopher A. Wilson *(Gen Counsel, Sec & VP)*

Subsidiary (Non-US):

Kookaburra Containers Pty Limited **(2)**
34 Christie St, Saint Marys, 2760, NSW, Australia
Tel.: (61) 1300905121
Web Site:
    http://www.kookaburracontainers.com.au
Shipping Container Mfr
N.A.I.C.S.: 332439
Michael Freeman *(CEO)*

Subsidiary (Domestic):

Lone Star Tank Rental Inc. **(2)**
371 Private Rd 1121, Kenedy, TX 78119
Tel.: (469) 517-5453
Emp.: 40
Industrial Machinery Rental Services
N.A.I.C.S.: 532490
Jody Miller *(CEO)*
Bobby Keenom *(Exec VP)*

Pac-Van, Inc. **(2)**
1850 Kentucky Ave, Indianapolis, IN 46221
Tel.: (317) 489-4808
Web Site: http://www.pacvan.com
Sales Range: $25-49.9 Million
Emp.: 50
Storage Container & Modular Building Solutions Mfr & Sales
N.A.I.C.S.: 332420
Ted Mourouzis *(Pres & CEO)*
Shannon Jordan *(VP-Sls & Mktg)*
David Gritter *(Reg VP-South)*
Eric Weber *(CFO)*
Guy Sextro *(VP-Products & Svcs)*
Kenneth Zientek *(Reg VP-West)*
Ryan Dillon *(Reg VP-East)*
Tom Austin *(Reg VP-Central)*

Subsidiary (Non-US):

Royal Wolf Holdings Limited **(2)**
Level 3 1 Merriwa street, Gordon, NSW, Australia
Tel.: (61) 1300651700
Web Site: http://www.royalwolf.com.au
Sales Range: $100-124.9 Million
Shipping & Storage Containers Leasing
N.A.I.C.S.: 493190

Subsidiary (Domestic):

Royal Wolf Trading Australia Pty Limited **(3)**
Level 3 1-3 Merriwa Street, Gordon, 2072, NSW, Australia
Tel.: (61) 294823466
Web Site: http://www.royalwolf.com.au
Shipping Container Mfr
N.A.I.C.S.: 332439

Subsidiary (Non-US):

Royalwolf Trading New Zealand Limited **(3)**
2-8 Jarvis Way, East Tamaki North Island, Auckland, 2013, New Zealand
Tel.: (64) 99660360
Web Site: http://www.royalwolf.co.nz
Shipping Container Distr
N.A.I.C.S.: 423840

Subsidiary (Domestic):

Southern Frac, LLC **(2)**
1805 Howard Rd, Waxahachie, TX 75165
Web Site: https://www.southernfrac.com
Emp.: 80

Mud Tank Mfr
N.A.I.C.S.: 327390

Indu-Tools B.V. **(1)**
Driemanssteeweg 62, 3084 CB, Rotterdam, Netherlands
Tel.: (31) 108509010
Web Site: https://www.indu-tools.com
Industrial Equipment Rental Services
N.A.I.C.S.: 532490

Indu-Tools N.V. **(1)**
Noorderlaan 485, 2030, Antwerp, Belgium
Tel.: (32) 70222478
Industrial Equipment Rental Services
N.A.I.C.S.: 532490

Indu-Tools SAS **(1)**
Port 5360 - Parc dez Alizes Voie des Sarcelles, 76430, Sandouville, France
Tel.: (33) 235242434
Industrial Equipment Rental Services
N.A.I.C.S.: 532490

ToolsRent24 Vermietungs- und Handelsgesellschaft mbH **(1)**
Anna-Schlinkheider Str 7, 40878, Ratingen, Germany
Tel.: (49) 2102101608
Web Site: https://toolsrent24.de
Emp.: 10
Tool Equipment Rental Services
N.A.I.C.S.: 532490

United Rentals (North America), Inc. **(1)**
224 Selleck St, Stamford, CT 06902 **(100%)**
Tel.: (203) 327-0090
Web Site: http://www.unitedrentals.com
Construction & Industrial Equipment Rental & Leasing Services
N.A.I.C.S.: 532412

Subsidiary (Domestic):

Ahern Rentals, Inc. **(2)**
1401 Mineral Ave, Las Vegas, NV 89106
Tel.: (702) 362-0623
Web Site: http://www.ahern.com
Sales Range: $250-299.9 Million
Emp.: 485
Construction Equipment Rentals, Sales, Parts & Maintenance Services
N.A.I.C.S.: 532412
Mark S. Brown *(COO)*
D. Kirk Hartle *(CFO & Treas)*
M. Sami Bakdash *(Gen Counsel & Sec)*

Blue Mountain Equipment Rental Corporation **(2)**
732 McClellandtown Rd Rear Ofc, Uniontown, PA 15401
Tel.: (724) 812-4734
Web Site: http://www.bmerc.net
Sales Range: $1-9.9 Million
Emp.: 16
Construction Equipment Rental & Leasing Services
N.A.I.C.S.: 532412
Terrence J. Jackson *(Pres & CEO)*

United Rentals Northwest, Inc. **(2)**
3362 Silverton Rd NE, Salem, OR 97301
Tel.: (503) 393-1222
Construction & Industrial Equipment Rental & Leasing Services
N.A.I.C.S.: 532412

United Rentals Belgium BV **(1)**
Sint Antoniusweg Port 1616, Kallo, 9130, Beveren, Belgium
Tel.: (32) 33041900
Construction Equipment Rental Services
N.A.I.C.S.: 532490

United Rentals GmbH **(1)**
Barbarastrasse 62, 46282, Dorsten, Germany
Tel.: (49) 2362608638
Industrial Equipment Rental Services
N.A.I.C.S.: 532490

United Rentals International B.V. **(1)**
Bloemendaalse Zeedijk 10, Zevenbergschen Hoek, 4765 BP, Moerdijk, Netherlands
Tel.: (31) 168331610
Construction Equipment Rental Services
N.A.I.C.S.: 532490

United Rentals of Canada, Inc. **(1)**
115 Ardelt Ave, Kitchener, N2C 2E1, ON, Canada
Tel.: (519) 576-6000
Web Site: http://www.ur.com
Sales Range: $25-49.9 Million
Emp.: 20
Construction & Industrial Equipment Rental & Leasing Services
N.A.I.C.S.: 532412
Craig Buckles *(Mgr)*

Subsidiary (Domestic):

WesternOne Rentals & Sales **(2)**
1991 Keating Cross Road, Saanichton, V8M 2A4, BC, Canada
Tel.: (250) 652-2311
Web Site: http://www.westernone.ca
Construction Equipment Rental Services
N.A.I.C.S.: 532412

UNITED RESOURCE HOLDINGS GROUP, INC.
7775 Firefall Way Ste 1132, Dallas, TX 75230
Tel.: (972) 215-6357   NV
Web Site: http://www.urhg.net
Year Founded: 2004
URHG—(OTCIQ)
Assets: $1,657,390
Liabilities: $2,981,042
Net Worth: ($1,323,652)
Earnings: ($283,344)
Fiscal Year-end: 12/31/20
Metal Mining
N.A.I.C.S.: 212290
Dana M. Low *(COO)*
Robert Alton Shuey III *(CEO)*

UNITED SECURITY BANCSHARES
2126 Inyo St, Fresno, CA 93721
Tel.: (559) 248-4930   CA
Web Site:
    https://www.unitedsecuritybank.com
Year Founded: 1987
UBFO—(NASDAQ)
Rev.: $51,095,000
Assets: $1,299,193,000
Liabilities: $1,186,730,000
Net Worth: $112,463,000
Earnings: $15,686,000
Emp.: 117
Fiscal Year-end: 12/31/22
Bank Holding Company
N.A.I.C.S.: 551111
Dennis R. Woods *(Chm, Pres & CEO)*
Susan Quigley *(Sec)*
David L. Eytcheson *(COO & Sr VP)*
David A. Kinross *(CFO & Sr VP)*
William M. Yarbenet *(Chief Credit Officer & Sr VP)*
Robert C. Oberg *(Chief Risk Officer & Sr VP)*

Subsidiaries:

United Security Bank **(1)**
2126 Inyo St, Fresno, CA 93721
Tel.: (559) 248-4930
Web Site:
    https://www.unitedsecuritybank.com
Sales Range: $150-199.9 Million
Emp.: 550
State Commercial Banks
N.A.I.C.S.: 522110
Dennis R. Woods *(Chm, Pres & CEO)*
William M. Yarbenet *(Chief Credit Officer & Sr VP)*

UNITED STATES ANTIMONY CORPORATION
PO Box 643, Thompson Falls, MT 59873
Tel.: (406) 827-3523   MT
Web Site:
    https://www.usantimony.com

United States Antimony
Corporation—(Continued)

Year Founded: 1970
UAMY—(NYSEAMEX)
Rev.: $11,044,707
Assets: $34,700,450
Liabilities: $2,831,195
Net Worth: $31,869,255
Earnings: $428,661
Emp.: 78
Fiscal Year-end: 12/31/22
Nonferrous Metal Smelting & Refining
N.A.I.C.S.: 331410
Richard R. Isaak (*CFO & Sr VP*)
Gary C. Evans (*Chm & Co-CEO*)
John C. Gustavsen (*Pres–Antimony Div*)
Lloyd Joseph Bardswich (*Co-CEO*)
Mitzi Hart (*Treas, Sec & Controller*)

Subsidiaries:

Bear River Zeolite Company (1)
47 Cox Gulch Rd, Thompson Falls, MT 59873
Tel.: (406) 827-3523
Web Site: https://www.bearriverzeolite.com
Construction Materials Whslr
N.A.I.C.S.: 423320

**UNITED STATES LIME & MIN-
ERALS, INC.**
5429 LBJ Fwy Ste 230, Dallas, TX 75240
Tel.: (972) 991-8400 **TX**
Web Site: https://www.uslm.com
Year Founded: 1950
USLM—(NASDAQ)
Rev.: $281,330,000
Assets: $440,602,000
Liabilities: $47,498,000
Net Worth: $393,104,000
Earnings: $74,549,000
Emp.: 333
Fiscal Year-end: 12/31/23
Lime & Limestone Products Mfr
N.A.I.C.S.: 212312
Timothy W. Byrne (*Pres & CEO*)
Michael L. Wiedemer (*CFO & VP*)

Subsidiaries:

Arkansas Lime Company (1)
600 Limedale Rd, Batesville, AR 72501 (100%)
Tel.: (870) 793-2301
Web Site: http://www.uslm.com
Sales Range: $25-49.9 Million
Emp.: 90
Lime & Limestone Processing & Mining
N.A.I.C.S.: 212312
Tim Stone (*VP-Sls*)

Colorado Lime Company (1)
1468 Highway 50, Delta, CO 81416
Tel.: (970) 874-8300
Web Site: http://www.uslm.com
Sales Range: $25-49.9 Million
Emp.: 100
Limestone
N.A.I.C.S.: 212312

Mill Creek Dolomite LLC (1)
9915 W Amos Conley Rd, Mill Creek, OK 74856
Web Site: http://www.mcreekdolo.com
Ground, Treated Mineral & Earth Mfr
N.A.I.C.S.: 327992

Texas Lime Company (1)
15865 Fm Rd 1434, Cleburne, TX 76033 (100%)
Tel.: (817) 641-4433
Web Site: http://www.uslm.com
Sales Range: $10-24.9 Million
Emp.: 98
Mining & Processing Limestone
N.A.I.C.S.: 212312

U.S. Lime Company (1)
5420 Allison Rd, Houston, TX 77048
Tel.: (281) 910-3403
Sales Range: $125-149.9 Million
Limestone
N.A.I.C.S.: 212312

U.S. Lime Company -
Shreveport (1)
6000 St Vincent Ave, Shreveport, LA 71106
Tel.: (318) 865-9655
Sales Range: $10-24.9 Million
Emp.: 50
Limestone
N.A.I.C.S.: 212312

U.S. Lime Company - St. Clair (1)
98054 S 4610 Rd, Marble City, OK 74945
Tel.: (918) 775-4466
Web Site: http://www.uslm
Sales Range: $25-49.9 Million
Emp.: 60
Industrial Minerals
N.A.I.C.S.: 212312

U.S. Lime
Company-Transportation (1)
5429 LBJ Fwy Ste 230, Dallas, TX 75240
Tel.: (972) 392-8428
Web Site: http://www.uslm.com
Sales Range: $25-49.9 Million
Emp.: 25
Lime Transportation Services
N.A.I.C.S.: 484121
Kory Yandell (*Coord-Transportation & Logistics*)

UNITED STATES OIL FUND, LP.
1850 Mt Diablo Blvd Ste 640, Walnut Creek, CA 94596
Tel.: (510) 522-9600 **DE**
Web Site:
http://www.uscfinvestments.com
Year Founded: 2005
USO—(NYSA)
Rev.: $800,711,874
Assets: $1,982,960,872
Liabilities: $5,945,534
Net Worth: $1,977,015,338
Earnings: $785,240,277
Fiscal Year-end: 12/31/22
Investment Fund Services
N.A.I.C.S.: 523160
John P. Love (*Pres & CEO*)

**UNITED STATES STEEL COR-
PORATION**
600 Grant St, Pittsburgh, PA 15219-2800
Tel.: (412) 433-1121 **DE**
Web Site: http://www.ussteel.com
Year Founded: 1901
X—(NYSE)
Rev.: $18,053,000,000
Assets: $20,151,000,000
Liabilities: $9,311,000,000
Net Worth: $11,140,000,000
Earnings: $895,000,000
Emp.: 21,803
Fiscal Year-end: 12/31/23
Integrated Steel Producer
N.A.I.C.S.: 331110
Jessica Trocchi Graziano (*CFO & VP*)
David B. Burritt (*Pres & CEO*)
Christian Gianni (*CTO & Sr VP*)
James E. Bruno (*Pres-US Steel Kosice & Sr VP-European Solutions*)
Richard L. Fruehauf (*Chief Strategy & Dev Officer & Sr VP-Strategic Plng*)
Duane D. Holloway (*Chief Ethics & Compliance Officer, Gen Counsel & Sr VP*)
Kenneth E. Jaycox (*Chief Comml Officer & Sr VP*)
Kevin Lewis (*VP-IR*)
Jessica T. Graziano (*CFO & Sr VP*)
W. Bryan Lewis (*Chief Investment Officer & VP*)
John Gordon (*Sr VP-Raw Materials & Sustainable Resources*)

Subsidiaries:

Apolo Tubulars S.A. (1)
Doutor Leo De Affonseca Netto 750, Jardim Novo Horizonte, Sao Paulo, 12605-720, Brazil

Tel.: (55) 1231590060
Web Site: http://apolotubulars.com
Oil Field Tubular Product Mfr
N.A.I.C.S.: 313220

Big River Steel LLC (1)
2027 State Hwy 198, Osceola, AR 72370 (100%)
Tel.: (870) 819-3031
Web Site: https://bigriversteel.com
Emp.: 647
Steel Mfrs
N.A.I.C.S.: 331513
Jerry Ballinger (*Mgr-Procurement*)

Chrome Deposit Corporation (1)
6640 Melton Rd, Portage, IN 46368
Tel.: (219) 763-1571
Web Site: https://www.chromedeposit.com
Steel Products Mfr
N.A.I.C.S.: 331210

Delaware USS Corporation (1)
600 Grant St, Pittsburgh, PA 15219
Tel.: (412) 433-1121
Steel Products Mfr
N.A.I.C.S.: 331110

Delray Connecting Railroad Company (1)
1350 Penn Ave Ste 200, Pittsburgh, PA 15222-4211
Tel.: (313) 841-2850
Sales Range: $25-49.9 Million
Emp.: 40
Rail Transport Services
N.A.I.C.S.: 488210

Double Eagle Steel Coating Company (1)
3000 Miller Rd, Dearborn, MI 48120 (100%)
Tel.: (313) 203-9800
Web Site: http://www.ussteel.com
Steel Products Mfr
N.A.I.C.S.: 331110

Double G Coatings Company, L.P. (1)
1096 Mendell Davis Dr, Jackson, MS 39272-9109 (50%)
Tel.: (601) 372-4236
Sales Range: $10-24.9 Million
Emp.: 78
Steel Sheeting Mfr
N.A.I.C.S.: 332812

Double G Coatings, Inc. (1)
1096 Mendell Davis Dr, Jackson, MS 39272
Tel.: (601) 371-3460
Metal Component Mfr
N.A.I.C.S.: 321215

Fairfield Southern Company, Inc. (1)
6200 Flintridge Rd, Fairfield, AL 35064
Tel.: (205) 783-4150
Sales Range: $50-74.9 Million
Emp.: 400
Producer of Steel
N.A.I.C.S.: 541614

Feralloy Processing Company (1)
600 George Nelson Dr, Portage, IN 46368
Tel.: (219) 787-8773
Web Site: http://www.feralloy.com
Flat Rolled Steel Products Processor & Distr; Owned 51% by Feralloy Corporation & 49% by United States Steel Corporation
N.A.I.C.S.: 423510

GCW/USS Energy, LLC (1)
1951 State St, Granite City, IL 62040
Tel.: (618) 451-3456
Web Site: http://www.ussteel.com
Steel Products Mfr
N.A.I.C.S.: 331221

Hibbing Taconite Company (1)
4950 County Rd Hwy 5, Hibbing, MN 55746
Tel.: (218) 262-5950
Industrial Steel Products Distr
N.A.I.C.S.: 423510
Neil Luukkonen (*Ops Mgr-Mine*)

OBAL-SERVIS, a.s. Kosice (1)
Vstupny areal US Steel, 044 54, Kosice, Slovakia
Tel.: (421) 556734786
Web Site: http://www.obalservis.sk
Emp.: 10,000
Metal Component Mfr

N.A.I.C.S.: 321215
Victor Odik (*Mgr-Sls*)

Olympic Laser Processing, LLC (1)
5096 Richmond Rd, Bedford Heights, OH 44146 (100%)
Tel.: (734) 482-1750
Web Site: http://www.olysteel.com
Sales Range: $50-74.9 Million
Emp.: 125
Process Laser Welded Sheet Steel Blanks; Joint Venture Between Olympic Steel Inc. & U.S. Steel
N.A.I.C.S.: 332111
David A. Wolfort (*Pres*)

PRO-TEC Coating Company, Inc. (1)
5000 PRO-TEC Pkwy, Leipsic, OH 45856
Tel.: (419) 943-1100
Web Site: http://www.proteccoating.com
Sales Range: $100-124.9 Million
Emp.: 225
Coating of Steel Coils; Joint Venture Between Kobe Steel & U.S. Steel
N.A.I.C.S.: 332812
Richard E. Veitch (*Pres*)

Swan Point Yacht & Country Club Inc (1)
11550 Swan Point Blvd, Issue, MD 20645
Tel.: (301) 259-0047
Web Site: https://www.swanpointgolf.com
Steel Products Mfr
N.A.I.C.S.: 331221
Zuri Gregory (*Dir-Sls & Mktg*)

Texas & Northern Railway Company (1)
1200 Penn Ave Ste 300, Pittsburgh, PA 15222
Tel.: (903) 656-6854
Metal Component Mfr
N.A.I.C.S.: 321215

The Lake Terminal Railroad Company (1)
2199 E 28th St, Lorain, OH 44055-1932
Tel.: (440) 277-7222
Web Site: http://www.transtarrail.com
Railroad & Terminal Switching Carrier Services
N.A.I.C.S.: 488210
Larry Pridemore (*Mgr-Ops*)

U. S. Steel Europe (UK) Limited (1)
4 The Limes Ingatestone, Ingatestone, CM4 0BE, Essex, United Kingdom
Tel.: (44) 1277355155
Sales Range: $25-49.9 Million
Emp.: 5
Steel Trading Services
N.A.I.C.S.: 321215

U. S. Steel Europe - France S.A. (1)
Immeeuble Lafayette 2bis Rue Lafayette, 57000, Metz, France
Tel.: (33) 387630866
Web Site: http://www.ussteel.com
Steel Products Mfr
N.A.I.C.S.: 331221

U. S. Steel Europe - Germany GmbH (1)
Rossstrasse 96, 40476, Dusseldorf, Germany
Tel.: (49) 21144729212
Sales Range: $25-49.9 Million
Emp.: 5
Metal Component Mfr
N.A.I.C.S.: 321215

U. S. Steel Kosice - Labortest, s.r.o. (1)
Vstupny areal U S Steel, 044 54, Kosice, Slovakia
Tel.: (421) 556731111
Web Site: http://www.usske.sk
Emp.: 10,000
Steel Products Mfr
N.A.I.C.S.: 331221
Ladislav Rozek (*CEO*)
Eva Krajnakova (*Sec*)
Alica Ridzonova (*Mgr-Quantometric Laboratory*)
Miroslav Gresko (*Mgr-Mechanical Testing Laboratory*)
Beata Svetlikova (*Mgr-Cold Rolling Mill Laboratory*)

Tomas Lacek *(Mgr-Cokery Laboratory)*
Martin Hura *(Deputy Mgr-Testing)*
Maria Mochnacka *(Deputy Mgr-Quantometric Laboratory)*
Marian Skodi *(Deputy Mgr-Mechanical Testing Laboratory)*
Peter Mankos *(Deputy Mgr-Cold Rolling Mill Laboratory)*
Jakub Demko *(Deputy Mgr-Cokery Laboratory)*

Subsidiary (Domestic):

RMS, a.s. Kosice (2)
Vstupny areal US Steel, 044 54, Kosice, Slovakia
Tel.: (421) 556734357
Web Site: http://www.rms-kosice.sk
Emp.: 1,000
Steel Products Mfr
N.A.I.C.S.: 331110
Ivan Lapin *(Dir-Fin & Comml)*
Ivan Pastyrcak *(Dir-Metallurgical Furnace Maintenance Div Plant)*
Vladimir Petrov *(Dir-Refrako Div Plant)*
Marcel Novosad *(VP-Production)*
Elena Petraskova *(VP-Subsidiaries & External Svcs)*
Michal Janok *(Gen Dir)*

Subsidiary (Non-US):

U. S. Steel Europe - Bohemia a.s. (2)
Rohanske Nabrezi 678/29 River Garden 3 building entrance D, 186 00, Prague, Czech Republic
Tel.: (420) 226201550
Steel Products Mfr
N.A.I.C.S.: 331110
Dovdon Tugsbayar *(Mng Dir)*

U. S. Steel Europe - Italy S.r.l. (2)
Via Giovanni Boccaccio 45, 20123, Milan, Italy
Tel.: (39) 0236577430
Steel Products Mfr
N.A.I.C.S.: 331110

Subsidiary (Domestic):

U. S. Steel Services s.r.o. (2)
Vstupny areal US Steel, 044 54, Kosice, Slovakia
Tel.: (421) 556731111
Web Site: http://www.usske.sk
Laundry Services
N.A.I.C.S.: 812320

U. S. Steel Tubular Products, Inc. (1)
600 Grant St Rm 2001, Pittsburgh, PA 15219
Web Site: http://usstubular.com
Fabricated Pipe Product Mfr
N.A.I.C.S.: 332996

Subsidiary (Domestic):

U. S. Steel Oilwell Services, LLC (2)
9518 E Mount Houston Rd, Houston, TX 77050
Tel.: (281) 458-9944
Tubing & Casing Accessories Mfr
N.A.I.C.S.: 331210

Subsidiary (Domestic):

Patriot Premium Threading Services, LLC (3)
8300 W Hwy 80, Midland, TX 79706-2604
Tel.: (432) 250-6001
Web Site: https://www.patriotthreading.com
Steel Tubular Product Mfr
N.A.I.C.S.: 313220

U.S. Steel Kosice - SBS, s.r.o. (1)
Vstupny areal U S Steel, 044 54, Kosice, Slovakia
Tel.: (421) 556731111
Web Site: http://www.usske.sk
Emp.: 11,000
Steel Products Services
N.A.I.C.S.: 331221
James E. Bruno *(Pres)*
Silvia Gaalova *(CFO & VP)*
David Hathaway *(VP-Engrg & Innovation)*
Miroslav Kiralvarga *(VP-External Affairs, Admin & Bus Dev)*
Karl G. Kocsis *(VP-HR & Transformation)*

Julius Lang *(VP-Sls & Customer Technical Svcs)*
Marcel Novosad *(VP-Ops)*
Elena Petraskova *(Gen Counsel & VP-Subsidiaries)*
Richard C. Shank *(VP-IT)*
Juraj Bolf *(Dir-Sls)*

U.S. Steel Kosice, s.r.o. (1)
Vstupny areal U S Steel, 044 54, Kosice, Slovakia (100%)
Tel.: (421) 556731111
Web Site: http://www.usske.sk
Sales Range: $1-4.9 Billion
Emp.: 12,000
Producer of Steel
N.A.I.C.S.: 331513
James E. Bruno *(Pres)*
Elena Petraskova *(Gen Counsel & VP-Subsidiaries)*
Julius Lang *(VP-Sls & Customer Technical Svcs)*
Marcel Novosad *(VP-Ops)*
Richard C. Shank *(VP-IT)*
Karl G. Kocsis *(VP-HR & Transformation)*
Miroslav Kiralvarga *(VP-External Affairs, Admin & Bus Dev)*
David Hathaway *(VP-Engrg & Innovation)*
Lubomira Soltesova *(Mgr-Media Rels)*
Viera Kohutekova *(Gen Mgr-R&D)*
Martina Kapralova *(Gen Mgr-Procurement)*
Juraj Bolf *(Dir-Sls)*
Silvia Gaalova *(CFO & VP)*

U.S. Steel Receivables LLC (1)
600 Grant St, Pittsburgh, PA 15219
Tel.: (412) 433-1121
Web Site: http://www.uss.com
Sales Range: $150-199.9 Million
Provider of Financial Services
N.A.I.C.S.: 331111

US Steel Minntac (1)
8819 Old Hwy 169, Mountain Iron, MN 55768 (100%)
Tel.: (218) 749-7200
Web Site: http://www.ussteel.com
Sales Range: $150-199.9 Million
Iron & Steel Products Hot-Rolled
N.A.I.C.S.: 238990

USS Galvanizing, Inc. (1)
600 Grant St, Pittsburgh, PA 15219
Tel.: (412) 433-1121
Web Site: http://www.uss.com
Sales Range: $350-399.9 Million
Emp.: 800
Holding Company
N.A.I.C.S.: 331110

USS Oilwell Tubular, Inc. (1)
600 Grant St, Pittsburgh, PA 15219
Tel.: (412) 433-1121
Metal Component Mfr
N.A.I.C.S.: 321215

USS Portfolio Delaware, Inc. (1)
501 Silverside Rd, Wilmington, DE 19809-1374
Tel.: (302) 798-7890
Sales Range: $1-9.9 Million
Emp.: 1
Bank Holding Companies
N.A.I.C.S.: 561110
Deborah Pierce *(Pres)*

USS Real Estate (1)
1 Ben Fairless Dr, Fairless Hills, PA 19030
Tel.: (215) 736-4061
Web Site: http://www.naikpc.com
Sales Range: $10-24.9 Million
Emp.: 6
Steel Foundries Nec
N.A.I.C.S.: 331110
Stephen Bilan *(Gen Mgr)*

USS-POSCO Industries (1)
900 Loveridge Rd, Pittsburg, CA 94565-2808
Tel.: (925) 439-6000
Web Site: http://www.ussposco.com
Steel Mills
N.A.I.C.S.: 331110
Michael Piekut *(Pres)*
Lynnette Giacobazzi *(VP-Ops)*
Cory Anderson *(Gen Counsel & Sec)*
M. D. Amin *(VP-Comml)*

Union Railroad Company (1)
819 Duquesne Blvd, Duquesne, PA 15110

Tel.: (412) 469-4597
Web Site: http://www.mandtbank.com
Sales Range: $1-9.9 Million
Emp.: 13
Railroads Line-Haul Operating
N.A.I.C.S.: 488210

United States Steel Corp. (1)
1509 Muriel St, Pittsburgh, PA 15203
Tel.: (412) 433-1292
Web Site: http://www.uss.com
Sales Range: $50-74.9 Million
Emp.: 200
Data Processing Services
N.A.I.C.S.: 518210

United States Steel Corp. (1)
3025 Highland Pkwy Ste 275, Downers Grove, IL 60515
Tel.: (630) 990-5222
Web Site: http://www.uss.com
Sales Range: $10-24.9 Million
Emp.: 40
Metals Service Centers & Offices
N.A.I.C.S.: 621111

United States Steel Corp. (1)
901 K St NW Ste 1250, Washington, DC 20001
Tel.: (202) 783-6333
Web Site: http://www.uss.com
Sales Range: $10-24.9 Million
Emp.: 15
Blast Furnaces & Steel Mills
N.A.I.C.S.: 541618

United States Steel Corp. (1)
5850 New King Ct, Troy, MI 48098-2692
Tel.: (248) 267-2500
Web Site: http://www.uss.com
Sales Range: $1-4.9 Billion
Emp.: 120
Mfr Steel
N.A.I.C.S.: 541380

United States Steel Corp. (1)
1300 Braddock Ave, Braddock, PA 15104-1743
Tel.: (412) 273-7000
Web Site: http://www.uss.com
Sales Range: $750-799.9 Million
Emp.: 1,000
Steel Foundries
N.A.I.C.S.: 331110

United States Steel Corp. (1)
5700 Valley Rd, Fairfield, AL 35064-1299
Tel.: (205) 783-4122
Web Site: http://www.ussteel.com
Sales Range: $300-349.9 Million
Emp.: 2,500
Real Estate Brokers & Agents
N.A.I.C.S.: 813930

United States Steel Corp. - Braddock (1)
13th St & Braddock Ave, Braddock, PA 15104
Tel.: (412) 273-7000
Web Site: http://www.uss.com
Blast Furnace & Steel Mills
N.A.I.C.S.: 331111

United States Steel Corp. - Gary (1)
1 N Broadway, Gary, IN 46402
Tel.: (219) 888-2000
Web Site: http://www.ussteel.com
Sales Range: $1-4.9 Billion
Emp.: 6,000
Steel Foundries
N.A.I.C.S.: 331513

United States Steel Corporation Research and Technology Center (1)
800 E Waterfront Dr, Munhall, PA 15120 (100%)
Tel.: (412) 433-7200
Web Site: http://www.ussteel.com
Sales Range: $25-49.9 Million
Emp.: 100
Technology & Energy Efficiencies
N.A.I.C.S.: 541330

United States Steel Great Lakes Works (1)
No 1 Quality Dr, Ecorse, MI 48229
Tel.: (313) 749-2100
Web Site: http://www.ussteel.com
Steel Process & Integrated Steel Production
N.A.I.C.S.: 331110

United States Steel International, Inc. (1)
600 Grant St, Pittsburgh, PA 15219 (100%)
Tel.: (412) 433-1121
Web Site: http://www.uss.com
Sales Range: $25-49.9 Million
Emp.: 1,000
Iron Ore Mining Operations
N.A.I.C.S.: 212210

United States Steel Midwest (1)
US Hwy 12, Portage, IN 46368
Tel.: (219) 762-3131
Web Site: http://www.ussteel.com
Sales Range: $750-799.9 Million
Emp.: 1,000
Mfr of Steel
N.A.I.C.S.: 331110

United States Steel Tubular Products (1)
460 Wildwood Forest Dr Ste 300S, Spring, TX 77380
Tel.: (713) 993-3131
Web Site: http://www.usstubular.com
Sales Range: $75-99.9 Million
Emp.: 200
Mfr of Tubular Products
N.A.I.C.S.: 423510

United States Steel, Aircraft Division (1)
600 Grant St, Pittsburgh, PA 15219 (100%)
Tel.: (412) 433-1121
Web Site: http://www.uss.com
Sales Range: $25-49.9 Million
Emp.: 12
Airports Flying Fields & Services
N.A.I.C.S.: 331110

Worthington Samuel Coil Processing, LLC (1)
4905 S Meridian Rd, Jackson, MI 49204 (37%)
Tel.: (517) 789-0200
Web Site: http://www.worthingtonindustries.com
Sales Range: $50-74.9 Million
Emp.: 82
Motor Vehicle Industry Steel Processing Services; Owned 50% by Worthington Industries, Inc. & 50% by United States Steel Corporation
N.A.I.C.S.: 332111

Subsidiary (Domestic):

ProCoil Company, LLC (2)
5260 Haggerty Rd S, Canton, MI 48188
Tel.: (734) 397-3700
Steel Products Mfr
N.A.I.C.S.: 331110

UNITED TENNESSEE BANKSHARES, INC.
Tel.: (423) 623-6088   TN
Web Site:
   https://www.newportfederalbank.com
Year Founded: 1997
UNTN—(OTCIQ)
Rev.: $5,614,000
Assets: $240,467,000
Liabilities: $213,490,000
Net Worth: $26,977,000
Earnings: $1,185,000
Emp.: 37
Fiscal Year-end: 12/31/20
Bank Holding Company
N.A.I.C.S.: 551111
J. William Myers *(Chm)*
Chris Triplett *(Pres & CEO)*
Rick Clevenger *(VP)*
Thomas Rush *(Sr VP)*
Kim Woods *(Asst VP)*
Shannon Lane *(Officer-Bank)*

Subsidiaries:

Newport Federal Bank (1)
170 W Broadway, Newport, TN 37821
Tel.: (423) 623-6088
Web Site:
   http://www.newportfederalbank.com

United Tennessee Bankshares, Inc.—(Continued)

Sales Range: $50-74.9 Million
Emp.: 31
Banking Services
N.A.I.C.S.: 522110
J. William Myers (Chm)
Chris Triplett (CFO)
Peggy G. Holston (Sec & Branch Mgr)
Lonnie Jones (VP-Ops)

UNITED THERAPEUTICS CORPORATION

1000 Spring St, Silver Spring, MD 20910
Tel.: (301) 608-9292   DE
Web Site: https://www.unither.com
Year Founded: 1996
UTHR—(NASDAQ)
Rev.: $2,327,500,000
Assets: $7,167,000,000
Liabilities: $1,182,200,000
Net Worth: $5,984,800,000
Earnings: $984,800,000
Emp.: 1,168
Fiscal Year-end: 12/31/23
Chronic & Life-Threatening Cardiovascular, Cancer & Infectious Diseases Biopharmaceutical Mfr
N.A.I.C.S.: 325412
Paul A. Mahon (Sec & Exec VP)
Michael Benkowitz (Pres & COO)
James C. Edgemond (CFO)
Martine A. Rothblatt (Founder, Chm & CEO)
Christopher G. Patusky (Vice Chm)

Subsidiaries:

Lung Bioengineering Inc.   (1)
1015 Spring St, Silver Spring, MD 20910
Tel.: (240) 650-2290
Web Site:
    https://www.lungbioengineering.com
Emp.: 11
Pharmaceuticals Product Mfr
N.A.I.C.S.: 325412
Thomas Hartnett (Gen Mgr)

Lung Biotechnology Inc.   (1)
1040 Spring St, Silver Spring, MD 20910
Tel.: (202) 483-7000
Web Site:
    https://www.lungbiotechnology.com
Health Care Srvices
N.A.I.C.S.: 621610
Martine Rothblatt (Pres & CEO)
Marc I. Lorber (Chief Medical Officer & Sr VP-Clinical Dev)
Aimee Smart (Head-Office & Dir-Global Regulatory Affairs & Compliance)

Lung Biotechnology PBC   (1)
1040 Spring St, Silver Spring, MD 20910
Tel.: (202) 483-7000
Web Site:
    https://www.lungbiotechnology.com
Lung Disease Treatment & Therapy Research Services
N.A.I.C.S.: 622310
Martine Rothblatt (Pres & CEO)

Medicomp, Inc.   (1)
600 Atlantis Rd, Melbourne, FL 32904
Tel.: (321) 794-3811
Web Site: https://www.reactdx.com
Sales Range: $100-124.9 Million
Medical Device Mfr
N.A.I.C.S.: 334519

Miromatrix Medical Inc.   (1)
18683 Bearpath Trl, Eden Prairie, MN 55347
Tel.: (612) 202-7026
Web Site: http://www.miromatrix.com
Chemicals Mfr
N.A.I.C.S.: 325412
Paul A. Mahon (Gen Counsel, Sec & Exec VP)
Michael Benkowitz (COO)
James C. Edgemond (CFO & Treas)
Martine A. Rothblatt (CEO)
Brian D. Niebur (VP-Fin)
Paul R. Buckman (Chm)
Jeffrey Ross (Pres)

Revivicor, Inc.   (1)
1700 Kraft Dr Ste 2400, Blacksburg, VA 24060
Tel.: (540) 961-5559
Web Site: https://www.revivicor.com
Emp.: 22
Regenerative Medicine Mfr
N.A.I.C.S.: 325412

SteadyMed Ltd.   (1)
5 Oppenheimer Street, 7670105, Rehovot, Israel
Tel.: (972) 925 272 4999
Web Site: http://www.steadymed.com
Rev.: $1,065,000
Assets: $38,491,000
Liabilities: $14,680,000
Net Worth: $23,811,000
Earnings: ($23,205,000)
Emp.: 26
Fiscal Year-end: 12/31/2017
Pharmaceuticals Mfr
N.A.I.C.S.: 325412
Keith Bank (Chm)

Subsidiary (US):

SteadyMed Therapeutics, Inc.   (2)
2603 Camino Ramon Ste 350, San Ramon, CA 94583
Tel.: (925) 361-7111
Web Site: http://www.steadymed.com
Emp.: 15
Pharmaceutical Products Distr
N.A.I.C.S.: 424210

United Therapeutics Europe Ltd.   (1)
The Officers' Mess Royston Road, Duxford, Cambridge, CB22 4QH, Cambs, United Kingdom
Tel.: (44) 1483207780
Web Site: https://www.unither.com
Biotechnology Company
N.A.I.C.S.: 541714

Unither Telmed, Ltd.   (1)
1110 Spring St, Silver Spring, MD 20910-4028
Tel.: (301) 608-9292
Sales Range: $50-74.9 Million
Emp.: 200
Therapeutic Product Mfr
N.A.I.C.S.: 541715
Martine Rothplatt (CEO)

UNITED-GUARDIAN, INC.

230 Marcus Blvd, Hauppauge, NY 11788
Tel.: (631) 273-0900   DE
Web Site: https://www.u-g.com
Year Founded: 1942
UG—(NA3DAQ)
Rev.: $12,698,503
Assets: $10,640,335
Liabilities: $1,373,691
Net Worth: $9,266,644
Earnings: $2,569,512
Emp.: 23
Fiscal Year-end: 12/31/22
Drugs, Organic Laboratory Reagents, Fine & Specialty Chemicals, Healthcare & Specialty Products & Cosmetic Bases Mfr
N.A.I.C.S.: 325611
Andrea J. Young (CFO, Treas & Sec)
Donna Vigilante (Pres)

Subsidiaries:

Guardian Laboratories Division   (1)
230 Marcus Blvd, Hauppauge, NY 11788   (100%)
Tel.: (631) 273-0900
Web Site: http://www.u-g.com
Sales Range: $25-49.9 Million
Emp.: 36
Pharmaceuticals & Fine Chemicals Mfr
N.A.I.C.S.: 325620
Kenneth H. Globus (Pres)
Robert S. Rubinger (Exec VP)

UNITEDHEALTH GROUP INCORPORATED

9900 Bren Rd E, Minnetonka, MN 55343

Tel.: (952) 936-1300   DE
Web Site:
    https://www.unitedhealthgroup.com
Year Founded: 1977
UNH—(NYSE)
Rev.: $371,622,000,000
Assets: $273,720,000,000
Liabilities: $179,299,000,000
Net Worth: $94,421,000,000
Earnings: $22,381,000,000
Emp.: 440,000
Fiscal Year-end: 12/31/23
Fire Insurance Services
N.A.I.C.S.: 551112
Terry M. Clark (CMO)
Thomas E. Roos (Chief Acctg Officer & Sr VP)
John F. Rex (Pres & CFO)
Dan Schumacher (Chief Strategy & Growth Officer)
Erin L. McSweeney (Chief People Officer & Exec VP)
Patricia L. Lewis (Chief Sustainability Officer & Exec VP)
Richard Mattera (Chief Dev Officer & Sr VP)
Jennifer Smoter (Chief Comm Officer & Sr VP)
Todd Walthall (Exec VP-Enterprise Growth)
Erica Schwartz (Pres-Insurance Solutions)
Kevin L. Henderson (VP-Diversity, Equity & Inclusion-Capabilities & People Strategies)
Rupert Bondy (Chief Legal Officer)
Sandeep Dadlani (Exec VP)
Joy Fitzgerald (Exec VP)
Vivian Hunt (Chief Innovation Officer)
Tracy Malone (Sr VP)
Zack Sopcak (Sr VP)
Margaret-Mary Wilson (Chief Medical Officer)
Norman Wright (Exec VP)
Andrew Philip Witty (CEO)
Sandeep Dadlani (CTO, Chief Digital Officer, Exec VP & Exec VP)
Rupert Bondy (Sr Corp Counsel & Exec VP-Governance, Compliance, and Security)

Subsidiaries:

1st Avenue Pharmacy, Inc.   (1)
707 S Grady Way Ste 700, Renton, WA 98057
Tel.: (509) 624-3017
Web Site: https://www.genoahealthcare.com
Women Healthcare Services
N.A.I.C.S.: 621610
Rob Leland (Owner & Mgr-Pharmacy)

A Better Way Therapy LLC   (1)
11204 Davenport St #200, Omaha, NE 68154
Tel.: (402) 356-3332
Web Site:
    https://www.abetterwaytherapy.com
Mental Health Care
N.A.I.C.S.: 621420

ABCO India Private Limited   (1)
Tamarai Tech Park S P Plot No 16 to 20 and 20A South Block 5th Floor, Thiruvika Industrial Estate Inner Ring Road Guindy, Chennai, 600 032, Tamil Nadu, India
Tel.: (91) 4461018700
Health Care Srvices
N.A.I.C.S.: 621999
Mithun S. Madhavan (Sr Mgr)

ACN Group of California, Inc.   (1)
PO Box 880009, San Diego, CA 92168-0009
Web Site:
    https://www.myoptumhealthphysicalhealth
    ofca.com
Chiropractic Health Care Services
N.A.I.C.S.: 621310
Stephen Castro (CEO)

AHN Target Holdings, LLC   (1)

10689 N Pennsylvania St Ste 200, Indianapolis, IN 46280
Tel.: (317) 580-6306
Health Care Srvices
N.A.I.C.S.: 621999

APS - Assistencia Personalizada a Saude Ltda.   (1)
Rua Vinte e Tres de Maio 790 - Vianelo, Jundiai, 13207-070, SP, Brazil
Tel.: (55) 1145831750
Web Site: https://www.saudeaps.com.br
Hospital & Medical Services
N.A.I.C.S.: 524114

ASC Network, LLC   (1)
285 Passaic St, Hackensack, NJ 07601
Tel.: (201) 490-6800
Web Site: https://www.ascnetworks.net
Pharmaceutical Preparation Mfr
N.A.I.C.S.: 325412

Administradora Clinica La Colina S.A.S.   (1)
Calle 167 72 - 07, Bogota, Colombia
Tel.: (57) 6014897000
Web Site: https://www.clinicalacolina.com
Healtcare Services
N.A.I.C.S.: 622310

Advanced Surgery Center of Clifton, LLC   (1)
1200 Route 46 W Ste 110, Clifton, NJ 07013
Tel.: (973) 773-5600
Web Site:
    https://advancedsurgerycenterclifton.com
Surgical Center Services
N.A.I.C.S.: 622110

Advanced Surgical Hospital, LLC   (1)
100 Trich Dr Ste 1, Washington, PA 15301
Tel.: (724) 884-0710
Web Site: https://ashospital.net
Hospital Services
N.A.I.C.S.: 621491

Alaska Surgery Center, Inc.   (1)
1230 Northway Dr, Anchorage, AK 99508
Tel.: (907) 550-6100
Web Site: https://www.aksurgery.com
Fiscal Year-end: 12/31/2006
Hospital Services
N.A.I.C.S.: 621491

Aliansalud Entidad Promotora de Salud S.A.   (1)
Calle 125 Bis 20-38, Bogota, Colombia
Tel.: (57) 6017568000
Web Site: https://www.aliansalud.com.co
Healtcare Services
N.A.I.C.S.: 621111

Alliance Surgical Center, LLC   (1)
917 Rinehart Rd Ste 1001, Lake Mary, FL 32746
Tel.: (407) 708-5383
Web Site: https://www.alliancelakemary.com
Ambulatory Surgical Services
N.A.I.C.S.: 621493

AmeriChoice Corporation   (1)
8045 Leesburg Pike Ste 650, Vienna, VA 22182
Tel.: (703) 506-3555
Sales Range: $150-199.9 Million
Emp.: 1,000
Managed Health Care Services
N.A.I.C.S.: 621999

Subsidiary (Domestic):

Unison   (2)
Unison Plz 1001 Brinton Rd, Pittsburgh, PA 15221
Tel.: (412) 858-4000
Web Site: http://www.unisonhealthplan.com
Health Care Srvices
N.A.I.C.S.: 923120
John Paul Blank (Pres & CEO)

American Health Network of Indiana, LLC   (1)
7440 Woodland Dr, Indianapolis, IN 46278
Tel.: (317) 580-6309
Pharmaceutical Preparation Mfr
N.A.I.C.S.: 325412

American Health Network of Ohio, LLC   (1)
5900 Parkwood Pl, Dublin, OH 43016-1216
Tel.: (614) 794-4500

Pharmaceutical Preparation Mfr
N.A.I.C.S.: 325412

Amil Assistencia Medica Internacional S.A. (1)
Alameda Cauaxi 118 Alphaville, Barueri,
06454-020, Sao Paulo, Brazil
Tel.: (55) 1130611000
Web Site: http://www.amil.com.br
Rev.: $5,182,395,314
Assets: $4,374,529,642
Liabilities: $1,286,819,085
Net Worth: $3,087,710,558
Earnings: $33,740,945
Fiscal Year-end: 12/31/2019
Pharmaceutical Products Distr
N.A.I.C.S.: 424210
Sergio Ricardo Santos (CEO)

Angiografia e Hemodinamica Madre Theodora Ltda. (1)
Rua Jose Geraldo Cerebino Christofo, 175
Andar 4 Parque Das Universidades Campinas, Sao Paulo, 13087-567, Brazil
Tel.: (55) 1937563000
Health Insurance Products & Specialized
Care Services
N.A.I.C.S.: 524114

Antelope Valley Surgery Center, L.P. (1)
44301 N Lorimer, Lancaster, CA 93534
Tel.: (661) 940-1112
Web Site:
    https://www.antelopevalleysurgerycenter.com
Hospital Services
N.A.I.C.S.: 621491
Justina Geeter (CEO)
Patalappa Chandrashekar (Dir-Medical)
Ebony McGlorie (Coord-Bus Office)
Matthew Hart (Dir-Medical)

AppleCare Medical Management, LLC (1)
PO Box 6014, Artesia, CA 90702
Web Site:
    https://applecaremedical.webydo.com
Health Care Srvices
N.A.I.C.S.: 621999
George Christides (Chief Medical Officer)

Austin Center for Outpatient Surgery, L.P. (1)
6818 Austin Center Blvd Ste 100, Austin,
TX 78731
Tel.: (512) 346-1994
Web Site:
    http://www.northwesthillssurgical.com
Medical & Surgical Hospital Services
N.A.I.C.S.: 622110
Christopher L. Olsen (CEO)

Avella of Phoenix III, Inc. (1)
1101 N Central Ave Ste 102, Phoenix, AZ
85004
Pharmaceuticals Product Mfr
N.A.I.C.S.: 325412

Avella of Sacramento, Inc. (1)
2288 Auburn Blvd Ste 102, Sacramento,
CA 95821
Pharmaceuticals Product Mfr
N.A.I.C.S.: 325412

B.R.A.S.S. Partnership in Commendam (1)
5328 Didesse Dr, Baton Rouge, LA 70808
Tel.: (225) 766-1718
Web Site:
    https://www.brasssurgerycenter.com
Ambulatory Surgical Center Services
N.A.I.C.S.: 621493
Kimi Hart (CEO)
Casey McDowell (Mgr-OR Nurse)
Crystal Leblanc (Office Mgr-Bus)

BP Inc. (1)
9700 Health Care Ln, Minnetonka, MN
55343
Tel.: (877) 502-6039
Health Care Insurance Services
N.A.I.C.S.: 524114
Kevin R. Reeves (Head-US Markets - Gas
& Low Carbon Energy Group)

Banmedica S.A. (1)
Apoquindo 3600 12th floor, Las Condes,
Santiago, Chile (96.8%)
Tel.: (56) 223533300

Web Site:
    https://www.empresasbanmedica.cl
Health Insurance Services
N.A.I.C.S.: 456199

Subsidiary (Non-US):

Clinica del Country S.A. (2)
Carrera 16 No 82-57, Bogota, Colombia
Tel.: (57) 15300470
Web Site: https://www.clinicadelcountry.com
Ambulatory Surgical Center Services
N.A.I.C.S.: 621493
Gloria Molina Vargas (Gen Mgr)

Barranca Surgery Center, LLC (1)
3500 Barranca Pkwy, Irvine, CA 92606
Tel.: (949) 552-6266
Web Site:
    https://www.barrancasurgerycenter.com
Hospital & Health Care Services
N.A.I.C.S.: 621493
Rachel Harris (CEO)

Benefit Administration for the Self Employed, L.L.C. (1)
601 Visions Pkwy, Adel, IA 50003
Web Site: https://www.baseonline.com
Women Healthcare Services
N.A.I.C.S.: 621610

Benefitter Insurance Solutions, Inc. (1)
9151 Blvd 26, North Richland Hills, TX
76180
Web Site: https://www.benefitter.com
Insurance Services
N.A.I.C.S.: 524210

Birmingham Outpatient Surgery Center, Ltd. (1)
2621 19th St S, Birmingham, AL 35209
Tel.: (205) 271-8200
Web Site:
    https://www.birminghamsurgerycenter.com
Hospital & Health Care Services
N.A.I.C.S.: 622110

Bosque Medical Center S.A. (1)
Av das Americas 4200 - bl 3 an 2 - - Barra
da Tijuca, Barra da Tijuca, Rio de Janeiro,
Brazil
Tel.: (55) 2133260596
Health Care Srvices
N.A.I.C.S.: 621999

Brandon Ambulatory Surgery Center, LLC (1)
514 Eichenfeld Dr, Brandon, FL 33511
Tel.: (813) 571-7088
Ambulatory Surgical Center Services
N.A.I.C.S.: 621493

BriovaRx Infusion Services 101, Inc. (1)
931 Conklin St Unit D, Farmingdale, NY
11735
Home Infusion Therapy Services
N.A.I.C.S.: 621610

BriovaRx Infusion Services 102, LLC (1)
3135 New Germany Rd Ste 38, Ebensburg,
PA 15931
Tel.: (814) 472-8900
Home Infusion Therapy Services
N.A.I.C.S.: 621610

BriovaRx Infusion Services 103, LLC (1)
9204 Berger Rd Ste A, Columbia, MD
21046
Home Infusion Therapy Services
N.A.I.C.S.: 621610

BriovaRx Infusion Services 200, Inc. (1)
4476 Leeds Pl W, North Charleston, SC
29405
Tel.: (843) 747-0847
Home Infusion Therapy Services
N.A.I.C.S.: 621610

BriovaRx Infusion Services 201, Inc. (1)
12689 Challenger Pkwy Ste 100, Orlando,
FL 32826
Tel.: (407) 678-2068
Home Infusion Therapy Services
N.A.I.C.S.: 621610

BriovaRx Infusion Services 202, Inc. (1)
9655 Florida Mining Blvd W Ste 411, Jacksonville, FL 32257
Tel.: (904) 652-1990
Home Infusion Therapy Services
N.A.I.C.S.: 621610

BriovaRx Infusion Services 203, Inc. (1)
9984 Premier Pkwy, Miramar, FL 33025
Tel.: (954) 389-1126
Home Infusion Therapy Services
N.A.I.C.S.: 621610

BriovaRx Infusion Services 207, Inc. (1)
2650 Leeman Ferry Rd Ste C, Huntsville,
AL 35801
Tel.: (256) 534-4663
Home Infusion Therapy Services
N.A.I.C.S.: 621610

BriovaRx Infusion Services 208, Inc. (1)
556 Arbor Hill Rd Ste F, Kernersville, NC
27284
Tel.: (336) 659-0899
Home Infusion Therapy Services
N.A.I.C.S.: 621610

BriovaRx Infusion Services 302, LLC (1)
8720 S 114th St Ste 106, La Vista, NE
68128
Tel.: (402) 331-5086
Home Infusion Therapy Services
N.A.I.C.S.: 621610

BriovaRx Infusion Services 308, LLC (1)
460 S Benson Ln Ste 11 12, Chandler, AZ
85224
Tel.: (480) 705-6200
Home Infusion Therapy Services
N.A.I.C.S.: 621610

BriovaRx Infusion Services 402, LLC (1)
12604 Hiddencreek Way Ste C, Cerritos,
CA 90703
Tel.: (562) 263-5600
Home Infusion Therapy Services
N.A.I.C.S.: 621610

BriovaRx Infusion Services 403, LLC (1)
170 Professional Center Dr Ste C, Rohnert
Park, CA 94928
Tel.: (707) 588-8894
Home Infusion Therapy Services
N.A.I.C.S.: 621610

BriovaRx Infusion Services 404, LLC (1)
2065 NE Williamson Ct Unit B, Bend, OR
97701
Tel.: (541) 382-0287
Home Infusion Therapy Services
N.A.I.C.S.: 621610

BriovaRx of California, Inc. (1)
4900 Rivergrade Rd Ste E110, Irwindale,
CA 91706
Pharmacy & Drug Store Services
N.A.I.C.S.: 456110

BriovaRx of Florida, Inc. (1)
9994 Premier Pkwy, Miramar, FL 33025
Pharmacy & Drug Store Services
N.A.I.C.S.: 456110

BriovaRx of Indiana, LLC (1)
1050 Patrol Rd, Jeffersonville, IN 47130
Pharmacy & Drug Store Services
N.A.I.C.S.: 456110

BriovaRx of Louisiana, LLC (1)
1737 A Sam Houston Jones Pkwy, Lake
Charles, LA 70611-5454
Pharmacy & Drug Store Services
N.A.I.C.S.: 456110

BriovaRx of Massachusetts, LLC (1)
145 Bodwell Ste 2A, Avon, MA 02322-1179
Pharmacy & Drug Store Services
N.A.I.C.S.: 456110

BriovaRx of Nevada, LLC (1)
8350 Briova Dr, Las Vegas, NV 89113-2256

Pharmacy & Drug Store Services
N.A.I.C.S.: 456110

BriovaRx of New York, Inc. (1)
3030 47th Ave Ste 410, Long Island City,
NY 11101
Pharmacy & Drug Store Services
N.A.I.C.S.: 456110

BriovaRx of Texas, Inc. (1)
4590 LockHill Selma, San Antonio, TX
78249
Pharmacy & Drug Store Services
N.A.I.C.S.: 456110

BriovaRx, LLC (1)
1100 Lee Branch Ln, Birmingham, AL
35242
Web Site: https://specialty.optumrx.com
Pharmacy & Drug Store Services
N.A.I.C.S.: 456110

CLISA - Clinica de Santo Antonio, S.A. (1)
Av Hospitais Civis de Lisboa 8, 2724-002,
Amadora, Portugal
Tel.: (351) 214999380
Ambulatory Surgical Center Services
N.A.I.C.S.: 621493
Vasco Antunes Pereira (Pres)

CMO - Centro Medico de Oftalmologia S/S Ltda. (1)
Rua Engenheiro Carlos Stevenson 66,
Cambui, Campinas, 13092-132, Sao Paulo,
Brazil
Tel.: (55) 1925155500
Web Site: https://www.cmocampinas.com
Laser Surgery Center Services
N.A.I.C.S.: 621493

Care Improvement Plus Group Management, LLC (1)
351 W Camden St Ste 100, Baltimore, MD
21201
Tel.: (410) 625-2200
Web Site: http://unitedhealthgroup.com
Insurance Management Services
N.A.I.C.S.: 524114

Carlton Life - Residencias e Servicos S.A. (1)
Av da Republica 35 8, 1050-186, Lisbon,
Portugal
Tel.: (351) 707252700
Health Care Srvices
N.A.I.C.S.: 621999

Castle Rock SurgiCenter, LLC (1)
4700 Castleton Way Ste 101, Castle Rock,
CO 80109
Tel.: (720) 519-1418
Web Site:
    https://www.castlerocksurgicenter.com
Hospital & Health Care Services
N.A.I.C.S.: 622110

CentrifyHealth, LLC (1)
102 Woodmont Blvd Ste 200, Nashville, TN
37205
Tel.: (615) 345-0318
Web Site: https://www.centrihealth.com
Ambulatory Health Care Services
N.A.I.C.S.: 621999
Ralph A. Korpman (Founder & CEO)

Centromed Quilpue S.A. (1)
Av Los Carrera 606, Valparaiso, Quilpue,
Chile
Tel.: (56) 322511000
Ambulatory Surgical Center Services
N.A.I.C.S.: 621493

Channel Islands Surgicenter, L.P. (1)
2300 Wankel Way, Oxnard, CA 93030
Tel.: (805) 485-1908
Web Site:
    https://www.channelislandssurgicenter.com
Ambulatory Surgical Center Services
N.A.I.C.S.: 621493
Vance Kalcic (Dir-Medical)

ChinaGate Company Limited (1)
17B Shimei Building No 445 Jiangning
Road, Jingan, Shanghai, China
Tel.: (86) 2154251330
Web Site:
    http://www.en.chinagatecompany.cn
Medical Care Equipment Distr
N.A.I.C.S.: 423450

UnitedHealth Group Incorporated—(Continued)

Citrus Regional Surgery Center, L.P. (1)
110 N Lecanto Hwy, Lecanto, FL 34461
Tel.: (352) 527-1825
Web Site:
　https://www.citrussurgerycenter.com
Ambulatory Surgical Center Services
N.A.I.C.S.: 621493

Clinica Bio Bio S.A. (1)
Avenida Jorge Alessandri 3515, Talca-
huano, Chile
Tel.: (56) 412734200
Web Site: https://www.clinicabiobio.cl
Emp.: 371
Ambulatory Health Care Services
N.A.I.C.S.: 621999
Jaime Pinto Vargas (Dir-Medical)

Clinica Ciudad del Mar S.A. (1)
13 Norte 635, Vina del Mar, Chile
Tel.: (56) 322451000
Web Site: https://www.ccdm.cl
Medical Care Services
N.A.I.C.S.: 621999
Karla T. Benz (Asst Dir-Clinical)
Victor R. Valle (Gen Mgr)

Clinica Davila y Servicios Medicos S.A. (1)
Avenida Recoleta 464 Metro Patronato,
Metropolitana, Santiago, Chile
Tel.: (56) 227308000
Web Site: http://www.davila.cl
Health Care Srvices
N.A.I.C.S.: 621999

Clinica Medico Cirurgica de Santa Tecla, S.A. (1)
Rua Dr Francisco Duarte 120, 4701-855,
Braga, Portugal
Tel.: (351) 253209900
Web Site: https://www.clinicasantatecla.pt
Ambulatory Health Care Services
N.A.I.C.S.: 621999

Clinica San Borja (1)
Av Guardia Civil 337, San Borja, Lima, Peru
Tel.: (51) 16355000
Health Care Services
N.A.I.C.S.: 621999

Clinica San Felipe S.A. (1)
Av Gregorio Escobedo 650, Jesus Maria,
Lima, Peru
Tel.: (51) 2190000
Web Site: https://www.clinicasanfelipe.com
Health Care Srvices
N.A.I.C.S.: 621999

Clinica Sanchez Ferrer S.A. (1)
Av Los Laureles 436 Urb California, Trujillo,
Peru
Tel.: (51) 44601050
Health Care Srvices
N.A.I.C.S.: 621999

Clinica Santa Maria S.A. (1)
Av Santa Maria 0500, Providencia, Chile
Tel.: (56) 229130000
Web Site: https://www.clinicasantamaria.cl
Medical Care Services
N.A.I.C.S.: 621999

Clinica Vespucio S.A. (1)
Av Serafin Zamora 190, La Florida, San-
tiago, Chile
Tel.: (56) 224707000
Web Site: http://www.clinicavespucio.cl
Medical Care Services
N.A.I.C.S.: 621999
Cristian Garcia Torres (Gen Mgr)

Cogent Healthcare, Inc. (1)
10 Niles Ln, Winchester, MA 01890
Tel.: (781) 369-1527
Web Site: https://www.cogent-hc.com
Pharmaceutical Preparation Mfr
N.A.I.C.S.: 325412

Collaborative Care Holdings, LLC (1)
9900 Bren Rd E, Minnetonka, MN 55343
Tel.: (952) 936-1300
Web Site: http://www.unitedhealthgroup.com
Holding Company
N.A.I.C.S.: 551112

Subsidiary (Domestic):

WellMed Medical Management Inc (2)

Alamo Cafe 14250 San Pedro, San Anto-
nio, TX 78232
Tel.: (210) 615-9355
Web Site:
　https://www.wellmedhealthcare.com
Emp.: 1,610
Health Care & Insurance for Seniors
N.A.I.C.S.: 621399
Bryan Grundhoefer (Pres)
Joe Zimmerman (CFO)
Jimmie O. Keenan (Sr VP-Enterprise &
Clinic Ops)
Carlos Hernandez (Pres-WellMed Medical
Grp)
Eric Lisle (Exec VP-Strategy)
Christopher Arnold (Sr Dir-Medical)
Gerardo Ramos (Sr Dir-Medical)
Vernoy Walker (Reg Dir-Medical)
Troy Comstock (Co-Pres)
Roel Gonzalex (Co-Pres)
George M. Rapier III (Founder, Chm &
CEO)

Subsidiary (Domestic):

USMD Holdings, Inc. (3)
6333 N State Hwy 161 Ste 200, Irving, TX
75038
Tel.: (214) 493-4000
Web Site: http://www.usmd.com
Management Consulting Services
N.A.I.C.S.: 541618
Richard C. Johnston (CEO & Chief Physi-
cian Officer)

Subsidiary (Domestic):

USMD Inc. (4)
6333 N State Hwy 161 Ste 200, Irving, TX
75038
Tel.: (214) 493-4000
Web Site: https://www.usmd.com
Healthcare Development & Management
Services
N.A.I.C.S.: 621610
Miranda Wilson (Gen Counsel)
Karen Wagner (Compliance Officer)
Mary McDonald (CIO)
Josh Hardy (CFO)
Richard C. Johnston (CEO & Chief Physi-
cian Officer)

Subsidiary (Domestic):

USMD Cancer Treatment Centers, LLC (5)
6333 N State Hwy 161 Ste 200, Irving, TX
75038-2216
Tel.: (214) 493-4002
Web Site: http://www.usmdinc.com
Healthcare Development & Management
Services
N.A.I.C.S.: 621610

USMD Hospital at Arlington, L.P. (5)
801 W Interstate 20, Arlington, TX 76017
Tel.: (817) 668-3752
Web Site: https://www.usmdarlington.com
Healthcare Development & Management
Services
N.A.I.C.S.: 622110

USMD Hospital at Ft. Worth, L.P. (5)
5900 Altamesa Blvd, Fort Worth, TX 76132
Tel.: (817) 433-9100
Web Site: http://www.usmdfortworth.com
General Medical Services
N.A.I.C.S.: 622110
Noel Moreno (Pres & VP-Ops & Diagnostic
Svcs)

Subsidiary (Domestic):

Urology Associates of North Texas, PLLC (4)
811 W Interstate 20 Ste 114, Arlington, TX
76017
Tel.: (817) 784-8268
Urological Hospital Services
N.A.I.C.S.: 622310

Colonial Outpatient Surgery Center, LLC (1)
4571 Colonial Blvd Ste 200, Fort Myers, FL
33966
Tel.: (239) 333-2560
Web Site:
　https://www.colonialoutpatientsurgery
　center.com
Outpatient Surgical Care Services

N.A.I.C.S.: 621493

Connecticut Surgery Center, Limited Partnership (1)
55 S Rd Ste 100, Farmington, CT 06032
Tel.: (860) 247-5555
Web Site: https://www.ctsurgerycenter.com
Ambulatory Surgical Center Services
N.A.I.C.S.: 621493
Jennifer Hemingway (Dir-Nursing)
Brenda Misuraca (CEO)

Cornerstone Surgery Center, LLC (1)
3911 Hwy 17 Bypass Ste B, Murrells Inlet,
SC 29576
Tel.: (843) 299-1851
Web Site:
　https://www.cornerstonesurgerycen
　ters.com
Hospital & Health Care Services
N.A.I.C.S.: 622110

Corpus Christi Endoscopy Center, L.L.P. (1)
6421 Saratoga Blvd Bldg 105, Corpus
Christi, TX 78414
Tel.: (361) 985-9300
Web Site: https://ccecendo.com
Endoscopy Surgical Services
N.A.I.C.S.: 621493

DTC Surgery Center, LLC (1)
4380 S Syracuse St, Denver, CO 80237
Tel.: (303) 220-0810
Web Site: https://www.dtcsurgery.com
Ambulatory Surgical Center Services
N.A.I.C.S.: 621493
Jennifer Jacobson (CEO)

Dental Benefit Providers, Inc. (1)
6220 Old Dobbin Ln, Columbia, MD 21045
Tel.: (240) 632-8000
Web Site: http://www.dbp.com
Dental Care Services
N.A.I.C.S.: 621999

Derry Surgical Center, LLC (1)
15 Tsienneto Rd, Derry, NH 03038
Tel.: (603) 460-4955
Web Site:
　https://surgicalcenterofnewhampshireat
　derry.com
Surgery Center Services
N.A.I.C.S.: 621493

DocASAP, Inc. (1)
560 Herndon Pkwy Ste 300, Herndon, VA
20170
Web Site: https://www.docasap.com
Hospital & Health Care Services
N.A.I.C.S.: 622110

Dry Creek Surgery Center, LLC (1)
125 Inverness Dr E Ste 150, Englewood,
CO 80112
Tel.: (303) 792-0777
Web Site: https://drycreeksurgerycenter.com
Outpatient Surgical Center
N.A.I.C.S.: 621493

Dublin Surgery Center, LLC (1)
5005 Parkcenter Ave, Dublin, OH 43017
Tel.: (614) 932-9548
Web Site:
　https://www.dublinsurgicalcenter.com
Hospital Services
N.A.I.C.S.: 621111
Rena Carney (Dir-Nursing)

E Street Endoscopy, LLC (1)
616 E St Ste A, Clearwater, FL 33756
Tel.: (727) 447-0888
Web Site: https://westcoastendoscopy.com
Endoscopy Surgical Services
N.A.I.C.S.: 621493

ELG FZE (1)
Dubai Silicon Oasis, Dubai, United Arab
Emirates
Tel.: (971) 43712730
Web Site: http://www.elgfze.com
Emp.: 3
Human Resource Consulting Services
N.A.I.C.S.: 541612

Ear Professionals International Corporation (1)
3191 W Temple Ave Ste 200, Pomona, CA
91765
Web Site: https://www.epichearing.com

Health Insurance Services
N.A.I.C.S.: 524114

East Brunswick Surgery Center, LLC (1)
561 Cranbury Rd, East Brunswick, NJ
08816
Tel.: (732) 390-4300
Web Site: https://universitysurgicenter.com
Ambulatory Surgical Care Services
N.A.I.C.S.: 621493

Echo Locum Tenens, Inc. (1)
1301 Solana Blvd Bldg 2 Ste 2200, West-
lake, TX 76262
Tel.: (817) 693-5487
Web Site: https://echolocum.com
Hospital & Healthcare Services
N.A.I.C.S.: 622110

Endion Medical Healthcare, P.C. (1)
157 E 72nd ST OFC H, New York, NY
10021
Tel.: (718) 239-0030
Web Site: https://www.medcarepc.com
Hospital & Health Care Services
N.A.I.C.S.: 622110

Equian, LLC (1)
5975 Castle Creek Pkwy Ste 100, India-
napolis, IN 46250
Web Site: https://www.equian.com
Women Healthcare Services
N.A.I.C.S.: 621610

**Esho - Empresa de Servicos Hospi-
talares S.A** (1)
St Sep/sul Eq 710/910 S/N Conj B Bloco I
Bloco II, Brasilia, 70390-108, Brazil
Tel.: (55) 2138051000
Health Care Services
N.A.I.C.S.: 621999

Excellion Servicos Biomedicos S.A. (1)
Avenida Afranio de Mello Franco 333 Quita-
ndinha Centro, Como chegar, Petropolis,
25651000, Rio de Janeiro, Brazil
Tel.: (55) 2422443800
Web Site: http://www.excellion.com.br
Emp.: 40
Health Care Srvices
N.A.I.C.S.: 621999
Lucia Bimenta (Office Mgr)

Executive Health Resources, Inc. (1)
15 Campus Blvd, Newtown Square, PA
19073
Tel.: (610) 446-6100
Web Site: http://www.ehrdocs.com
Health Care Srvices
N.A.I.C.S.: 621999

Executive Surgery Center, LLC (1)
13603 Michel Rd Ste 100, Tomball, TX
77375
Tel.: (832) 698-3720
Web Site: https://executivesurgerycenter.net
Ambulatory Surgery Center Services
N.A.I.C.S.: 621493

FOR HEALTH OF ARIZONA, INC. (1)
10 Cadillac Dr Ste 350, Brentwood, TN
37027-5078
Tel.: (615) 986-9201
Health Care Srvices
N.A.I.C.S.: 621999

First Family Insurance, LLC (1)
7800 University Pointe Dr, Fort Myers, FL
33907
Web Site:
　https://www.firstfamilyinsurance.com
Health Insurance Services
N.A.I.C.S.: 524114

Fortified Provider Network, Inc. (1)
16845 N 29th Ave Ste 7, Phoenix, AZ
85053
Tel.: (480) 607-0222
Web Site: https://www.fortifiedprovider.com
Healthcare Claim Providing Services
N.A.I.C.S.: 524114

Franklin Surgical Center, LLC (1)
175 Morristown Rd Ste 102, Basking Ridge,
NJ 07920
Tel.: (908) 766-5556
Web Site: https://www.franklinsurgical.com
Ambulatory Surgical Center Services
N.A.I.C.S.: 621493

Frontier MEDEX Group Limited (1)
Tel.: (44) 1594545100
Web Site: http://www.frontiermedex.com
Sales Range: $100-124.9 Million
Holding Company; Medical, Safety & Security Solutions
N.A.I.C.S.: 551112

Subsidiary (Non-US):

ASI Global, LLC (2)
Tel.: (713) 430-7380
Web Site: http://www.asiglobalresponse.com
Sales Range: $10-24.9 Million
Emp.: 40
Hostage & Extortion Emergency Response
Consulting Services
N.A.I.C.S.: 624230

Frontier MEDEX Limited (2)
Tel.: (44) 1594545100
Web Site: http://www.frontiermedex.com
Medical, Safety & Security Solutions
N.A.I.C.S.: 624230

UnitedHealthcare Global (2)
Tel.: (410) 453-6330
Web Site: https://www.uhcglobal.com
Travel Medical Insurance Products & Services
N.A.I.C.S.: 524114

FrontierMEDEX Canada Limited (1)
1339 40 Ave NE, Calgary, T2E 8N6, AB,
Canada
Tel.: (403) 291-3184
Web Site: http://www.unitedhealthcare.com
Emp.: 10
Health Care Srvices
N.A.I.C.S.: 621999

Fundacion Banmedica (1)
Avenida Apoquindo 3600 piso 12, Providencia, Santiago, Chile
Tel.: (56) 23533300
Web Site: http://www.fundacion.upmedia.cl
Health Program Management Services
N.A.I.C.S.: 923120
Juan Jose Mac-Auliffe Granello *(Pres)*
Javier Eguiguren Tagle *(Exec Dir)*

Gadsden Surgery Center, LLC (1)
418 S 5th St, Gadsden, AL 35901
Tel.: (256) 543-1253
Web Site:
https://www.gadsdensurgerycenter.com
Ambulatory Surgical Center Services
N.A.I.C.S.: 621493

Gadsden Surgery Center, Ltd. (1)
418 S 5th St, Gadsden, AL 35901
Tel.: (256) 543-1253
Web Site:
https://www.gadsdensurgerycenter.com
Ambulatory Surgical Center Services
N.A.I.C.S.: 621493
Butch Douthit *(Dir-Medical)*

Genoa Healthcare, Inc. (1)
707 S Grady Way Ste 400, Renton, WA
98057
Web Site: https://www.genoahealthcare.com
Hospital & Healthcare Services
N.A.I.C.S.: 622110

Genoa Telepsychiatry, Inc. (1)
475 Park Ave S, New York, NY 10016
Tel.: (347) 996-9072
Web Site:
http://www.genoatelepsychiatry.com
Health Care Srvices
N.A.I.C.S.: 621999

Glenwood Surgical Center, L.P. (1)
8945 Magnolia Ave Ste 200, Riverside, CA
92503
Tel.: (951) 688-7270
Web Site:
https://www.glenwoodsurgerycenter.com
Ambulatory Surgical Center Services
N.A.I.C.S.: 621493
Gurvinder Uppal *(Dir-Medical)*
Michael Frazier *(Dir-Nursing)*
Patricia Inda *(Office Mgr-Bus)*

Golden Outlook, Inc. (1)
5995 Plaza Dr, Cypress, CA 90630
Tel.: (562) 269-4420
Web Site: https://www.goldenoutlook.com
Life & Health Insurance Services
N.A.I.C.S.: 524114

Golden Triangle Surgicenter, L.P. (1)
25405 Hancock Ave Ste 103, Murrieta, CA
92562
Tel.: (951) 698-4670
Web Site:
https://www.goldentrianglesurgicenter.com
Ambulatory Surgical Center Services
N.A.I.C.S.: 621493
Bruce Baker *(Dir-Medical)*
Jennifer Smith Garman *(Dir-Nursing)*

**Grants Pass Surgery Center,
LLC** (1)
1601 NW Hawthorne Ave, Grants Pass, OR
97526
Tel.: (541) 472-4880
Web Site: https://www.gpsurgerycenter.com
Ambulatory Surgical Center Services
N.A.I.C.S.: 621493
Steven M. Loftesnes *(CEO)*

Greenville Surgery Center, LLC (1)
7150 Greenville Ave Ste 200, Dallas, TX
75231
Tel.: (214) 891-0466
Web Site:
https://texashealthsurgerydallas.com
Surgery Center Services
N.A.I.C.S.: 621493

Greenway Surgical Suites, LLC (1)
2020 28th St E Ste 100, Minneapolis, MN
55407
Tel.: (612) 728-7000
Web Site:
https://greenwaysurgerycenter.com
Ambulatory Surgery Center Services
N.A.I.C.S.: 621493

**Grove Place Surgery Center,
LLC** (1)
1325 36th St Ste B, Vero Beach, FL 32960
Tel.: (772) 778-3113
Web Site:
https://www.groveplacesurgerycenter.com
Ambulatory Surgical Center Services
N.A.I.C.S.: 621493
Kim Hannas *(Dir-Nursing)*
Jan Anderson *(Office Mgr-Bus)*
Michael Eves *(Dir-Medical)*

HPP - Hospitais Privados de Portugal, SGPS, S.A. (1)
Avenida da Republica 35 8, Lisbon, 1050-
186, Portugal
Tel.: (351) 217802550
Web Site: http://www.lusiadas.pt
Health Care Srvices
N.A.I.C.S.: 621999

HPP - Medicina Molecular, S.A. (1)
Avenida da Boavista 119, 4050-115, Porto,
Portugal
Tel.: (351) 226085504
Health Insurance Products & Specialized
Care Services
N.A.I.C.S.: 524114

HPP A.C.E. (1)
Avenida da Republica 35, 1050, Lisbon,
Portugal
Tel.: (351) 213556038
Health Care Srvices
N.A.I.C.S.: 621999

HPP Algarve, S.A. (1)
Av D Sebastao, Lagos, 8600-502, Portugal
Tel.: (351) 282790741
Web Site:
http://www.algarvemedicaltourism.com
Health Care Srvices
N.A.I.C.S.: 621999

HPP Boavista, S.A. (1)
Av Da Boavista 171, Porto, 4050-115, Portugal
Tel.: (351) 226056450
Health Care Srvices
N.A.I.C.S.: 621999

**HPP Saude - Parcerias Cascais,
S.A.** (1)
Av Brigadeiro Victor Novais Goncalves Alcabideche, Alcabideche, 2755-009, Cascais, Portugal
Tel.: (351) 214653000
Web Site: http://www.hospitaldecascais.pt
Health Care Srvices
N.A.I.C.S.: 621999

**Harrison Endo Surgical Center,
LLC** (1)
620 Essex St Ste 3, Harrison, NJ 07029
Tel.: (973) 474-1040
Web Site:
https://www.harrisonendosurgical.com
Hospital & Health Care Services
N.A.I.C.S.: 622110

Heartland Heart & Vascular, LLC (1)
6136 Frisco Square Blvd Ste 400, Frisco,
TX 75034
Web Site: https://www.heartlandhv.com
Outpatient Surgical Care Services
N.A.I.C.S.: 621493

Help Seguros de Vida S.A. (1)
Av Apoquindo 3600 Piso 3, Las Condes,
Santiago, Chile
Tel.: (56) 6006001222
Web Site: https://www.helpseguros.cl
Fire Insurance Services
N.A.I.C.S.: 524210

Hospital AMA S.A. (1)
Praca Bartolomeu Bueno 11, Aruja, 07400-
000, Brazil
Tel.: (55) 1120876737
Health Insurance Products & Specialized
Care Services
N.A.I.C.S.: 524114

**Hospital Alvorada de Taguatinga
Ltda.** (1)
Av Ministro Gabriel de Resende Passos
550, Moema, Sao Paulo, 04521-022, Brazil
Tel.: (55) 1121869900
Web Site:
http://www.hospitalalvorada.com.br
Health Care Srvices
N.A.I.C.S.: 621999

Hospital Ana Costa S.A. (1)
Rua Amazonas 143, Santos, Sao Paulo,
Brazil
Tel.: (55) 1332289000
Web Site: https://www.anacosta.com.br
Medical & Hospital Services
N.A.I.C.S.: 622110

Hospital Carlos Chagas S.A. (1)
Rua Barao De Maua 100, Guarulhos,
07012-040, Brazil
Tel.: (55) 1124635000
Web Site: https://www.hcc.com.br
Health Insurance Products & Specialized
Care Services
N.A.I.C.S.: 524114

**Hospital Geral e Maternidade Madre
Maria Theodora Ltda.** (1)
Rua Jose Geraldo Cerebino Christoforo,
175 Parque das Universid, Campinas,
13087-567, Brazil
Tel.: (55) 1937563000
Health Insurance Products & Specialized
Care Services
N.A.I.C.S.: 524114

**Hospital Monte Klinikum S/S
Ltda.** (1)
Rua Republica do Libano, Fortaleza,
60160-140, Ceara, Brazil
Tel.: (55) 8540120012
Web Site:
https://www.hospitalmonteklinikum.com.br
Health Care Srvices
N.A.I.C.S.: 621999

**Hospital Samaritano de Sao Paulo
Ltda.** (1)
R Conselheiro Brotero 1486, Higienopolis,
Santa Cecilia, 01232-010, Sao Paulo, Brazil
Tel.: (55) 1138215300
Web Site: https://higienopolis.hospitalsamaritano.com.br
Emp.: 2,200
Ambulatory Surgical Center Services
N.A.I.C.S.: 621493

Hospital Santa Helena S.A. (1)
SHLN 516 Conjunto D, Asa Norte, Brazil
Tel.: (55) 6132613000
Web Site:
https://www.rededorsaoluiz.com.br
General Medical & Surgical Services
N.A.I.C.S.: 622110

**Hospital de Clinicas de Jacarepagua
Ltda.** (1)

Rua Bacairis 499, Taquara, Rio de Janeiro,
22730-120, Brazil
Tel.: (55) 2139877000
Web Site: http://www.hcj-net.com.br
Ambulatory Surgical Center Services
N.A.I.C.S.: 621493
Carlos Andre Loja *(CEO)*

**Hospital e Maternidade Saint-Vivant
Ltda.** (1)
Rua Doutor Francisco Queiroz Guimaraes
20, Sumare, 13175-540, Brazil
Tel.: (55) 1931145067
Health Insurance Products & Specialized
Care Services
N.A.I.C.S.: 524114

Humedica, Inc. (1)
1380 Soldiers Field Rd, Boston, MA 02135
Tel.: (617) 475-3800
Clinical Intelligence Company; Cloud-based
Business Services
N.A.I.C.S.: 518210
Eric Barry *(Mgr-Quality Assurance)*
A.G. Breitenstein *(Executives)*

Hygeia Corporation (1)
15500 New Barn Rd Ste 200, Miami Lakes,
FL 33014
Tel.: (305) 594-9291
Web Site: http://www.hygeia.net
Insurance Management Services
N.A.I.C.S.: 524114

Hygeia Corporation (1)
777 Bay St Ste 2700, PO Box 125, Toronto,
M5G 2C8, ON, Canada
Tel.: (416) 595-1094
Web Site: http://www.hygeia.net
Insurance Management Services
N.A.I.C.S.: 524114

**INOV8 Surgical at Memorial City,
LLC** (1)
10496 Katy Fwy Ste 105, Houston, TX
77043
Tel.: (281) 800-1233
Web Site: https://inov8surgical.com
Ambulatory Surgical Center Services
N.A.I.C.S.: 621493

**INSPIRIS of New York Management,
Inc.** (1)
10 Cadillac Dr Ste 350, Brentwood, TN
37027
Tel.: (615) 986-9201
Nursing Care Services
N.A.I.C.S.: 621610

**Imed Star Servicos de Desempenho
Organizacional Ltda.** (1)
Al Dos Jurupis 1005, Sao Paulo, 4088,
Brazil
Tel.: (55) 1137870153
Health Insurance Products & Specialized
Care Services
N.A.I.C.S.: 524114

Ingram & Associates, LLC (1)
1009 Windcross Ct, Franklin, TN 38401
Tel.: (615) 778-4500
Health Care Services
N.A.I.C.S.: 621999
Ellis Terry *(Dir-Downtown Dev)*

InnovaCare Health, Inc. (1)
173 Bridge Plz N, Fort Lee, NJ 07024
Tel.: (201) 969-2300
Web Site:
https://www.innovacarehealth.com
Managed Health Care Services
N.A.I.C.S.: 621491
Richard Shinto *(Founder & Chm)*
S. Bhasker *(CIO)*
Nicole Cable *(Chief Experience Officer)*
Penelope Kokkinides *(Chief Admin Officer)*
Rodman Clair *(Chief Medical Officer)*
Michael Holland *(Chief Dev Officer)*
Ron Margalit *(CTO)*
Leslie Prizant *(Gen Counsel)*
Will Abbott *(CEO)*
Ravi Chari *(COO)*

**Instituto do Radium de Cammpinas
Ltda** (1)
Av Heitor Penteado 1780, Taquaral, Campinas, Sao Paulo, Brazil
Tel.: (55) 1937534100
Web Site: http://www.radium.com.br
Hospital Care Services

UnitedHealth Group Incorporated—(Continued)
N.A.I.C.S.: 622110

Isapre Banmedica S.A. (1)
Apoquindo 3 600, Las Condes, Santiago,
Chile
Tel.: (56) 223533300
Web Site: https://www.banmedica.cl
Health Insurance Services
N.A.I.C.S.: 524114

Isapre Vida Tres S.A. (1)
Apoquindo 3 600, Las Condes, Santiago,
Chile
Tel.: (56) 223533300
Web Site: https://www.vidatres.cl
Health Insurance Services
N.A.I.C.S.: 524114

**Joliet Surgery Center Limited
Partnership** (1)
998 129th Infantry Dr, Joliet, IL 60435
Tel.: (815) 744-3000
Web Site:
https://www.amsurgsurgerycenter.com
Ambulatory Surgical Center Services
N.A.I.C.S.: 621493

**LMN Laboratorio de Medicina
Nuclear, Unipessoal, Lda.** (1)
Avenida da Boavista 119, Porto-Cedofeita,
4050, Porto, Portugal
Tel.: (351) 253221458
Health Insurance Products & Specialized
Care Services
N.A.I.C.S.: 524114

Laboratorio ROE S.A. (1)
Av Dos de Mayo 1741, San Isidro, Peru
Tel.: (51) 15136666
Web Site: http://www.labroe.com
Health Insurance Services
N.A.I.C.S.: 524114
Aquiles Chacon Loayza (Mgr-Admin)

Landmark Health Technologies Private Limited (1)
No 602 Unnati 15th Cross 24th Main Road,
Outer Ring Road JP Nagar 1st Phase, Bengaluru, 560078, India
Tel.: (91) 8067631000
Web Site:
https://landmarkhealthtechnologies.org
Hospital & Health Care Services
N.A.I.C.S.: 622110

**Landmark Health of California,
LLC** (1)
395 Oyster Point Blvd Ste 512, South San
Francisco, CA 94080
Tel.: (650) 826-2945
Hospital & Health Care Services
N.A.I.C.S.: 622110

**Landmark Health of North Carolina,
LLC** (1)
2645 Meridian Pkwy Ste 323, Durham, NC
27713
Hospital & Health Care Services
N.A.I.C.S.: 622110

**Landmark Health of Oregon,
LLC** (1)
700 NE Multnomah 400, Portland, OR
97232
Hospital & Health Care Services
N.A.I.C.S.: 622110

**Landmark Health of Pennsylvania,
LLC** (1)
2401 PK DR, Harrisburg, PA 17110
Hospital & Health Care Services
N.A.I.C.S.: 622110

**Landmark Health of Washington,
LLC** (1)
2150 N 107th St Ste 480, Seattle, WA
98133
Hospital & Health Care Services
N.A.I.C.S.: 622110

Landmark Health, LLC (1)
7755 Center Ave Ste 630, Huntington
Beach, CA 92647
Tel.: (657) 237-2450
Web Site: https://www.landmarkhealth.org
Hospital & Health Care Services
N.A.I.C.S.: 622110

**Landmark Medical of Massachusetts,
PLLC** (1)
100 Front St Fl 11, Worcester, MA 01608
Hospital & Health Care Services
N.A.I.C.S.: 622110

Lexington Surgery Center, Ltd. (1)
2115 Harrodsburg Rd, Lexington, KY 40504
Tel.: (859) 276-2525
Web Site:
https://lexingtonsurgerycenter.com
Hospital & Health Care Services
N.A.I.C.S.: 622110

Limestone Medical Center, LLC (1)
701 McClintic Dr, Groesbeck, TX 76642
Tel.: (254) 729-3281
Web Site: https://groesbeckhospital.com
Medical Center Services
N.A.I.C.S.: 622110

Logisitics Health, Inc. (1)
328 Front St S, La Crosse, WI 54601
Tel.: (608) 782-0404
Web Site: http://www.logisticshealth.com
Health Care Srvices
N.A.I.C.S.: 621999
Tammy Brown (VP-Human Capital)
Ed Weinberg (CEO)
Christine Erspamer (COO)
Heather James (Gen Counsel)

Logistics Health, Inc. (1)
328 Front St S, La Crosse, WI 54601-4023
Emp.: 168
Health Care Srvices
N.A.I.C.S.: 621491
Keith Molzahn (Mgr-Acct-Natl)

**Lotten-Eyes Oftalmologia Clinica e
Cirurgica Ltda.** (1)
Rua Joaquim Floriano 466-Cj 908, Itaim,
04534-002, Sao Paulo, Brazil
Tel.: (55) 1130850540
Web Site: http://www.lotteneyes.com.br
General Medical & Surgical Hospital Services
N.A.I.C.S.: 622110

Louisville S.C., Ltd. (1)
4005 Dupont Cir, Louisville, KY 40207
Tel.: (502) 890-0497
Web Site:
https://www.surgecenteroflouisville.com
Ambulatory Surgical Center Services
N.A.I.C.S.: 621493

**Loyola Ambulatory Surgery Center at
Oakbrook, Inc.** (1)
1S224 Summit Ave Ste 201, Oakbrook Terrace, IL 60181
Ambulatory Surgical Center Services
N.A.I.C.S.: 621493

Lusiadas, SGPS, S.A. (1)
Rua Laura Alves 12 5, Lisboa-Nossa Senhora de Fatima, Lisbon, 1050-138, Portugal
Tel.: (351) 217704040
Web Site: https://www.lusiadas.pt
Health Insurance Products & Specialized
Care Services
N.A.I.C.S.: 524114

**Lusiadas-Parcerias Cascais,
S.A.** (1)
Rua Laura Alves 12 5, Lisboa-Nossa Senhora de Fatima, 1050, Lisbon, Portugal
Tel.: (351) 214653000
Health Insurance Products & Specialized
Care Services
N.A.I.C.S.: 524114

MD Ops, LLC (1)
3990 Concours Ste 500, Ontario, CA 91764
Tel.: (909) 605-8000
Web Site: http://www.mdopsinc.com
Accounting & Book Keeping Services
N.A.I.C.S.: 541219

MEDEX Insurance Services, Inc. (1)
8501 La Salle Rd Ste 200, Baltimore, MD
21286
Tel.: (410) 453-6380
Web Site: http://www.medexassist.com
Emp.: 60
Insurance Management Services
N.A.I.C.S.: 524114

**Main Line Spine Surgery Center,
LLC** (1)

The Merion Bldg 700 S Henderson Rd Ste
335, King of Prussia, PA 19406
Tel.: (610) 337-2828
Web Site: https://mainlinespine.com
Hospital & Health Care Services
N.A.I.C.S.: 622110

March Vision Care, Inc. (1)
6701 Center Dr W Ste 790, Los Angeles,
CA 90045
Tel.: (310) 216-2300
Web Site: https://www.marchvisioncare.com
Ambulatory Health Care Services
N.A.I.C.S.: 621999
Cabrini T. March (Co-Founder)
Glenville A. March Jr. (Co-Founder)

Massachusetts Avenue Surgery Center, LLC (1)
6400 Goldsboro Rd Ste 400, Bethesda, MD
20817
Tel.: (301) 263-0800
Web Site: https://www.massurg.com
Ambulatory Surgical Center Services
N.A.I.C.S.: 621493

**MedExpress Urgent Care of Boynton
Beach, LLC** (1)
7593 Boynton Beach Blvd, Boynton Beach,
FL 33437
Tel.: (561) 572-3200
Health Care Srvices
N.A.I.C.S.: 621999

MedSynergies North Texas, Inc. (1)
9250 Amberton Pkwy, Dallas, TX 75243
Tel.: (214) 570-2300
Health Insurance Products & Specialized
Care Services
N.A.I.C.S.: 524114

**Medical Preparatory School of Allied
Health, LLC** (1)
509 SW Military Dr Ste 101, San Antonio,
TX 78221
Tel.: (210) 927-4481
Health Care Srvices
N.A.I.C.S.: 621999

**Metropolitan Medical Partners,
LLC** (1)
5530 Wisconsin Ave Ste 1620, Chevy
Chase, MD 20815
Tel.: (301) 718-9800
Web Site: https://www.scchevychase.com
Ambulatory Surgical Center Services
N.A.I.C.S.: 621493
David Higgins (Dir-Medical)

**Midwest Center for Day Surgery,
LLC** (1)
3811 Highland Ave, Downers Grove, IL
60515-1555
Tel.: (630) 852-9300
Web Site:
https://www.midwestsc.mwsmg.com
Ambulatory Surgical Center Services
N.A.I.C.S.: 621493
Anshuman Chawla (Dir-Medical)
Helen Killham (Office Mgr)
Helena Rivera (CEO)

Mile High SurgiCenter, LLC (1)
5351 S Roslyn St Ste 300, Greenwood Village, CO 80111
Tel.: (303) 221-9500
Web Site: https://www.milehighsc.com
Ambulatory Surgical Center Services
N.A.I.C.S.: 621493
Melissa C. Murphy (CEO)

Mobile-SC, Ltd. (1)
6144 A Airport Blvd, Mobile, AL 36608
Tel.: (251) 438-3614
Web Site: https://sca.health
Hospital & Health Care Services
N.A.I.C.S.: 622110

Mohawk Surgery Center, LLC (1)
201 Mohawk Rd Ste 200, Minneola, FL
34715
Tel.: (352) 758-2540
Web Site: https://mohawksurgerycenter.com
Ambulatory Surgery Center Services
N.A.I.C.S.: 621493

**Monarch Management Services,
Inc.** (1)
27713 Webster Rd E, Graham, WA 98338-
9301

Tel.: (253) 847-3331
Management Consulting Services
N.A.I.C.S.: 541618

Monte Klinikum Diagnostico por Imagem Ltda. (1)
Avenida Republica do Libano 747, Fortaleza, 60160-140, Brazil
Tel.: (55) 8540120012
Health Care Srvices
N.A.I.C.S.: 621999

Monument Health, LLC (1)
744 Horizon Ct Ste 260, Grand Junction,
CO 81506
Tel.: (970) 683-5630
Web Site: https://monumenthealth.net
Emp.: 51
Hospital & Healthcare Services
N.A.I.C.S.: 622110
Marguerite Tuthill (COO)

**Mt. Pleasant Surgery Center,
L.P.** (1)
200 Bessemer Rd, Mount Pleasant, PA
15666
Tel.: (724) 547-5432
Web Site:
http://mtpleasantsurgerycenter.com
Ambulatory Care Services
N.A.I.C.S.: 621493
Brian Konieczny (Office Mgr)
Sharon Johnson (Dir-Medical)
Jennifer Yeskey (Dir-Clinical Svcs)

**National Foundation Life Insurance
Company** (1)
300 Burnett St Ste 200, Fort Worth, TX
76102-2734
Pharmaceutical Preparation Mfr
N.A.I.C.S.: 325412

National MedTrans Network Inc. (1)
992 S 2nd St, Ronkonkoma, NY 11779
Tel.: (800) 934-7704
Web Site: http://www.natmedtrans.com
Patient Transportation Services
N.A.I.C.S.: 485999
Evelyn Escobar (Mgr-Ops)

Nevada Pacific Dental (1)
1432 S Jones Blvd, Las Vegas, NV 89146
Tel.: (702) 737-8900
Health Care Insurance Services
N.A.I.C.S.: 524114

**New Orleans Regional Physician
Hospital Organization, LLC** (1)
3 Lakeway Ctr 3838 N Causeway Blvd Ste
2500, Metairie, LA 70002
Tel.: (504) 849-4500
Web Site: https://www.peopleshealth.com
Hospital & Healthcare Services
N.A.I.C.S.: 622110

New West Physicians, Inc. (1)
1707 Cole Blvd Ste 100, Golden, CO 80401
Tel.: (303) 763-4900
Web Site: http://www.nwphysicians.com
Hospital Services
N.A.I.C.S.: 622110
Kenneth Cohen (Chief Medical Officer)
Todd Wisser (Dir-Medical)
Vicki Espinoza (CFO)
Matthew Lewis (Dir-Medical)
Karen Kelly (Dir-Medical-Practice Dev)
Gwen Heller (VP-Quality-Risk)

**North American Medical Management
- Illinois, Inc.** (1)
4415 Harrison St Ste 300, Hillside, IL
60162-1953
Tel.: (708) 432-4000
Web Site: http://www.namm-il.com
Health Care Srvices
N.A.I.C.S.: 621999

**North American Medical Management
California, Inc.** (1)
3990 Concours Ste 500, Ontario, CA 91764
Tel.: (909) 605-8000
Web Site: https://www.nammcal.com
Hospital & Healthcare Services
N.A.I.C.S.: 622110

**Northern Rockies Surgicenter,
Inc.** (1)
940 N 30th St, Billings, MT 59101
Tel.: (406) 248-7186

Web Site:
https://www.northernrockiessurgery.com
Medical Surgical Services
N.A.I.C.S.: 622110
Debbie Howe *(CEO)*

Northwest Surgicare, LLC (1)
1100 W Central Rd Ste 103, Arlington
Heights, IL 60005
Tel.: (847) 259-3080
Web Site: https://northwestsurgicare.com
General Medical & Surgical Services
N.A.I.C.S.: 622110

Northwest Surgicare, Ltd. (1)
1100 W Central Rd L4, Arlington Heights, IL
60005
Tel.: (847) 259-3080
Web Site:
https://www.northwestsurgicare.com
Medical Surgical Services
N.A.I.C.S.: 622110
Tamara Hargrove *(Dir-Nursing)*

Optimum Choice, Inc. (1)
800 King Farm Blvd, Rockville, MD 20850
Pharmaceutical Preparation Mfr
N.A.I.C.S.: 325412

Optum (France) SAS (1)
41 Rue des 3 Fontanots, 92000, Nanterre,
France
Tel.: (33) 170929110
Health Care Srvices
N.A.I.C.S.: 621999

Optum (Spain) S.A.U. (1)
Carrer del Cister 2, 08022, Barcelona,
Spain
Tel.: (34) 935478300
Health Care Srvices
N.A.I.C.S.: 621999

Optum Biometrics, Inc. (1)
4205 Westbrook Dr, Aurora, IL 60504
Tel.: (952) 974-1910
Health Insurance Products & Specialized
Care Services
N.A.I.C.S.: 524114

Optum Clinical Solutions, Inc. (1)
100 Quannapowitt Pkwy Ste 405, Wake-
field, MA 01880
Tel.: (781) 557-3000
Web Site: http://www.picis.com
Health Insurance Products & Specialized
Care Services
N.A.I.C.S.: 524114

Optum Clinical Solutions, Ltd. (1)
1st Floor Star House 20 Grenfell Road,
Maidenhead, SL61EH, Berkshire, United
Kingdom
Tel.: (44) 13285224792
Web Site: http://www.optum.com
Emp.: 45
Health Insurance Products & Specialized
Care Services
N.A.I.C.S.: 524114

**Optum Global Solutions (India) Pri-
vate Limited** (1)
5th 6th 7th Office Level Building o 14 Sun-
dew Properties SEZ, Mindspace APIIC Layout Survey No 64 Hitech City Madhapur,
Hyderabad, 500 081, Telangana, India
Tel.: (91) 4030835566
Pharmaceutical Preparation Mfr
N.A.I.C.S.: 325412

**Optum Global Solutions International
B.V.** (1)
Gevers Deynootweg 93, Den Haa, 2586
BK, Hague, Netherlands
Tel.: (31) 703069962
Health Insurance Products & Specialized
Care Services
N.A.I.C.S.: 524114

**Optum Government Solutions,
Inc.** (1)
13625 Technology Dr, Eden Prairie, MN
55344-2252
Tel.: (621) 642-7749
Health Insurance Product & Specialized
Care Services
N.A.I.C.S.: 551112

**Optum Health Solutions (UK)
Limited** (1)
10th Floor 5 Merchant Square, Paddington,

London, W2 1AS, United Kingdom
Tel.: (44) 353749115169
Web Site: https://www.optum.co.uk
Emp.: 165
Healtcare Services
N.A.I.C.S.: 621999

**Optum Infusion Services 100,
Inc.** (1)
96 Linwood Plz Ste 453, Fort Lee, NJ
07024
Tel.: (201) 947-6791
Web Site: https://www.advanced-care.us
Infusion Therapy Services
N.A.I.C.S.: 621498

Optum Infusion Services 301, LP (1)
7512 Broadway Ext Ste 308, Oklahoma
City, OK 73116
Tel.: (405) 848-0338
Women Healthcare Services
N.A.I.C.S.: 621610

**Optum Palliative and Hospice Care,
Inc.** (1)
13655 Riverport Dr, Maryland Heights, MO
63043
Tel.: (314) 592-3670
Health Insurance Products & Specialized
Care Services
N.A.I.C.S.: 524114

Optum Perks LLC (1)
PO Box 2135, Mission, KS 66201-1096
Web Site: https://perks.optum.com
Women Healthcare Services
N.A.I.C.S.: 621610

Optum Pharmacy 701, LLC (1)
501 W Northern Lights Blvd Ste 100, An-
chorage, AK 99503
Tel.: (907) 276-4373
Web Site: https://www.akbizmag.com
Pharmaceutical Preparation Mfr
N.A.I.C.S.: 325412

**Optum Public Sector Solutions,
Inc.** (1)
800 King Farm Blvd Ste 500, Rockville, MD
20850
Tel.: (952) 833-7100
Health Insurance Products & Specialized
Care Services
N.A.I.C.S.: 524114

Optum Services (Ireland) Limited (1)
Block C One Spencer Dock, Dublin, D01
X9R7, Ireland
Tel.: (353) 18651265
Web Site: https://www.optum.ie
Pharmaceutical Preparation Mfr
N.A.I.C.S.: 325412

Optum, Inc. (1)
11000 Optum Cir, Eden Prairie, MN 55344
Web Site: http://www.optum.com
Health Care Srvices
N.A.I.C.S.: 621491
Sandeep Dadlani *(CTO)*
Eric Murphy *(Chief Comm Officer)*
Chris Zaetta *(Chief Legal Officer)*
John Williams *(Chief People Officer)*
Sarah King *(Chief Growth Officer)*
Jeff Grosklags *(CFO)*
Wyatt Decker *(COO)*
Neil de Crescenzo *(CEO)*
Roger Connor *(Exec VP)*
Terry Clark *(CMO)*
Heather Cianfrocco *(CTO)*
Caitlin Zulla *(CEO-Health East)*

Subsidiary (Domestic):

**DaVita Medical Group Health Infor-
mation Management** (2)
303 Roma Ave NW, Albuquerque, NM
87102
Tel.: (505) 262-7952
Web Site: http://www.abqhp.com
Health Care Srvices
N.A.I.C.S.: 621493

**DaVita Medical Group South Florida,
LLC** (2)
1401 N University Dr Ste 401, Coral
Springs, FL 33076
Tel.: (954) 656-8855
Kidney Dialysis Services
N.A.I.C.S.: 621492

LHC Group, Inc. (2)
901 Hugh Wallis Rd S, Lafayette, LA 70508
Tel.: (337) 233-1307
Web Site: https://lhcgroup.com
Rev.: $2,282,771,000
Assets: $2,896,957,000
Liabilities: $1,191,523,000
Net Worth: $1,680,359,000
Earnings: $60,248,000
Emp.: 30,000
Fiscal Year-end: 12/31/2022
Women Healthcare Services
N.A.I.C.S.: 621610
Keith G. Myers *(Chm)*
Joshua L. Proffitt *(Pres & CEO)*
Kimberly Sturlese Seymour *(Chief Acctg
Officer & Sr VP)*
Eric Elliott *(Sr VP-Fin)*
Bruce D. Greenstein *(Chief Strategy & Inno-
vation Officer)*
Benjamin Doga *(Chief Medical Officer)*
Dale G. Mackel *(CFO, Treas & Exec VP)*

Subsidiary (Domestic):

AAA Home Health Inc. (3)
9225 Dowdy Dr Ste 220, San Diego, CA
92126
Tel.: (858) 490-4264
Women Healthcare Services
N.A.I.C.S.: 621610

Able Home Health, Inc. (3)
1946 Daimler Rd, Rockford, IL 61112
Tel.: (815) 399-2600
Web Site: https://www.ablehome.com
Home Nursing Services
N.A.I.C.S.: 621610

**Acadian HomeCare of New Iberia,
LLC** (3)
124 E Main St Ste 210, New Iberia, LA
70560
Tel.: (337) 367-1882
Health Care Srvices
N.A.I.C.S.: 622110

Acadian HomeCare, LLC (3)
458 Heymann Blvd Bldg A, Lafayette, LA
70503
Tel.: (337) 235-8185
Web Site: http://www.lhcgroup.com
Health Care Srvices
N.A.I.C.S.: 621610

**Acadian Physical Therapy Services,
LLC** (3)
400 Polly Ln Ste 160, Lafayette, LA 70508
Tel.: (337) 500-1300
Women Healthcare Services
N.A.I.C.S.: 621610

Access Hospice, LLC (3)
1440 Hwy 248 Ste D, Branson, MO 65616-
9257
Tel.: (417) 332-3510
Web Site: http://www.lhcgroup.com
Sales Range: $10-24.9 Million
Emp.: 25
Health Care Srvices
N.A.I.C.S.: 621610

**Alabama HomeCare of Vestavia
Hills** (3)
100 Centerview Dr Ste 260, Vestavia Hills,
AL 35216
Tel.: (205) 979-3180
Women Healthcare Services
N.A.I.C.S.: 621610

Almost Family, Inc. (3)
9510 Ormsby Station Rd Ste 300, Louis-
ville, KY 40223
Tel.: (502) 893-1661
Web Site: http://www.almostfamily.com
Holding Company; Home Health & Personal
Care Services
N.A.I.C.S.: 551112

Subsidiary (Domestic):

Adult Day Care of America, Inc. (4)
9510 Ormsby Sta Rd Ste 300, Louisville,
KY 40223-4081
Tel.: (502) 891-1000
Health Care Srvices
N.A.I.C.S.: 621610
William Yarmuth *(CEO)*

**Almost Family PC of Ft. Lauderdale,
LLC** (4)

4901 NW 17th Way Ste 302b, Fort Lauder-
dale, FL 33309
Tel.: (954) 484-2773
Web Site: http://www.almostfamily.com
Emp.: 3
Health Care Srvices
N.A.I.C.S.: 621610

**Almost Family PC of Kentucky,
LLC** (4)
4545 Bishop Ln Ste 201, Louisville, KY
40218-4569
Tel.: (502) 893-1661
Health Care Srvices
N.A.I.C.S.: 621610

**Almost Family PC of SW Florida,
LLC** (4)
851 5th Ave N Ste 101, Naples, FL 34102
Tel.: (239) 643-3033
Web Site: http://www.almostfamily.com
Emp.: 70
Health Care Srvices
N.A.I.C.S.: 621610

**Almost Family PC of West Palm,
LLC** (4)
4 Harvard Cir Ste 900, West Palm Beach,
FL 33409
Tel.: (561) 357-0945
Web Site: http://www.almostfamily.com
Sales Range: $10-24.9 Million
Emp.: 3
Health Care Srvices
N.A.I.C.S.: 621610
Kristine Hughes *(Mng Dir)*

Black Stone Operations, LLC (4)
4700 E Galbraith Rd Ste 300B, Cincinnati,
OH 45236
Tel.: (513) 891-1127
Women Healthcare Services
N.A.I.C.S.: 621610

Caretenders VS of Boston, LLC (4)
200 Reservoir St Ste 309, Needham
Heights, MA 02494
Tel.: (617) 332-5015
Web Site: http://www.almostfamily.com
Emp.: 40
Health Care Srvices
N.A.I.C.S.: 621610

**Caretenders VS of Lincoln Trail,
LLC** (4)
1105 Julianna Ct Ste 3, Elizabethtown, KY
42701
Tel.: (270) 234-2273
Web Site: http://www.almostfamily.com
Emp.: 50
Health Care Srvices
N.A.I.C.S.: 621610

**Caretenders VS of Louisville,
LLC** (4)
4545 Bishop Ln Unit 201, Louisville, KY
40218
Tel.: (502) 893-1661
Web Site: http://www.almostfamily.com
Health Care Srvices
N.A.I.C.S.: 621610

**Caretenders VS of Northern KY,
LLC** (4)
1717 Dixie Hwy Ste 240, Fort Wright, KY
41011
Tel.: (859) 578-0022
Web Site: http://www.almostfamily.com
Emp.: 30
Health Care Srvices
N.A.I.C.S.: 621610

Caretenders VS of Ohio, LLC (4)
1111 E Main St, Lancaster, OH 43130
Tel.: (740) 687-4410
Health Care Srvices
N.A.I.C.S.: 621610
Lisa Hamilton *(Exec Dir)*

Caretenders VS of SE Ohio, LLC (4)
8230 Montgomery Rd Ste 210, Cincinnati,
OH 45236
Tel.: (513) 924-1370
Women Healthcare Services
N.A.I.C.S.: 621610

**Caretenders VS of Western KY,
LLC** (4)
2200 E Parrish Ave Bldg E Ste 203, Owensboro, KY 42303

UnitedHealth Group Incorporated—(Continued)

Tel.: (270) 685-3876
Health Care Srvices
N.A.I.C.S.: 621610

Caretenders Visiting Services of Gainesville, LLC (4)
4923 NW 43rd St Ste A, Gainesville, FL 32606
Tel.: (352) 379-6217
Web Site: http://www.almostfamily.com
Emp.: 50
Health Care Srvices
N.A.I.C.S.: 621610

Caretenders Visiting Services of Kentuckiana, LLC (4)
1724 State St, New Albany, IN 47150-4604
Tel.: (812) 941-8125
Web Site: http://www.caretenders.com
Sales Range: $10-24.9 Million
Emp.: 25
Health Care Srvices
N.A.I.C.S.: 621610

Caretenders Visiting Services of Orlando, LLC (4)
474 S Northlake Blvd Ste 1020, Altamonte Springs, FL 32701-5245
Tel.: (407) 661-1963
Health Care Srvices
N.A.I.C.S.: 621610

Caretenders Visiting Services of Southern Illinois, LLC (4)
141 Market Pl Dr Ste 110, Fairview Heights, IL 62208
Tel.: (618) 277-8899
Health Care Srvices
N.A.I.C.S.: 621610

Caretenders of Cleveland, Inc. (4)
23611 Chagrin Blvd Ste 130, Beachwood, OH 44122
Tel.: (216) 464-0443
Web Site: http://www.almostfamily.com
Sales Range: $10-24.9 Million
Emp.: 10
Health Care Srvices
N.A.I.C.S.: 621610

Imperium Health Management, LLC (4)
9510 Ormsby Station Rd Ste 300, Louisville, KY 40223
Tel.: (502) 891-1000
Web Site: https://www.imperiumhealth.com
Women Healthcare Services
N.A.I.C.S.: 621610
Gary Albers (CEO)
Carter Rieser (COO)
Angela Farley (VP-Quality Control)
Brantley Judah (VP-Ops)
Shekinah Bishop (Dir-Ops-West Reg)
Juliana Hawkins (Dir-Ops-Midwest Reg)
Dena Daniel (Dir-Analytics, Integration & Dev)
Amanda Waid (Dir-Ops)

Long Term Solutions Inc. (4)
235 W Central St, Natick, MA 01760
Tel.: (508) 907-6290
Web Site: https://www.longtermsol.com
Elder Care Assessment & Support Services
N.A.I.C.S.: 621610
Noreen Guanci (Co-Founder & CEO)

Mederi Caretenders VS of Broward, LLC (4)
4 Harvard Cir Ste 900, West Palm Beach, FL 33409
Tel.: (561) 357-0945
Health Care Srvices
N.A.I.C.S.: 621610

Mederi Caretenders VS of SE FL, LLC (4)
603 17th St, Vero Beach, FL 32960
Tel.: (772) 794-9777
Health Care Srvices
N.A.I.C.S.: 621610

Mederi Caretenders VS of SW FL, LLC (4)
6150 Diamond Ctr Ct Ste A, Fort Myers, FL 33912
Tel.: (239) 481-5999
Health Care Srvices
N.A.I.C.S.: 621610

OMNI Home Health - District 1, LLC (4)
8880 University Pkwy Ste B, Pensacola, FL 32514
Tel.: (850) 505-7777
Women Healthcare Services
N.A.I.C.S.: 621610

OMNI Home Health - District 4, LLC (4)
2651 Park St, Jacksonville, FL 32204
Tel.: (904) 389-7385
Women Healthcare Services
N.A.I.C.S.: 621610

Patient Care, Inc. (4)
300 Executive Dr Ste 010, West Orange, NJ 07052-0077
Tel.: (973) 243-6299
Web Site: http://lhcgroup.com
Women Healthcare Services
N.A.I.C.S.: 621610

Subsidiary (Domestic):

Patient Care Medical Services, Inc. (5)
300 Executive Dr Ste 010, West Orange, NJ 07052
Tel.: (973) 243-6299
Web Site: http://www.patientcare.com
Health Care Srvices
N.A.I.C.S.: 621610

Patient Care New Jersey, Inc. (5)
4 Brighton Rd Ste 403, Clifton, NJ 07012
Tel.: (973) 365-5200
Web Site: http://www.almostfamily.com
Health Care Srvices
N.A.I.C.S.: 621610

Patient Care Pennsylvania, Inc. (5)
2 Meridian Blvd Ste 214, Wyomissing, PA 19610
Tel.: (610) 373-0300
Web Site: http://www.almostfamily.com
Sales Range: $10-24.9 Million
Emp.: 20
Health Care Srvices
N.A.I.C.S.: 621610
Ruth-Ann Keppler (Mng Dir)

Subsidiary (Domestic):

SunCrest Healthcare, Inc. (4)
10113 Hwy 142 N, Covington, GA 30014
Tel.: (678) 625-7105
Women Healthcare Services
N.A.I.C.S.: 621610

Willcare, Inc. (4)
346 Delaware Ave, Buffalo, NY 14202
Tel.: (716) 856-7500
Web Site: http://www.willcare.com
Women Healthcare Services
N.A.I.C.S.: 621610
Eric Armenat (Pres & CEO)

Branch (Domestic):

Willcare, Inc. - Newburgh (5)
700 Corporate Blvd, Newburgh, NY 12550
Tel.: (845) 561-3655
Web Site: http://www.willcare.com
Women Healthcare Services
N.A.I.C.S.: 621610

Willcare, Inc. - Olean (5)
2211 W State Str Ste 123, Olean, NY 14760
Tel.: (716) 373-9755
Web Site: http://www.willcare.com
Emp.: 7
Women Healthcare Services
N.A.I.C.S.: 621610

Willcare, Inc. - Trumbull (5)
56 Quarry Rd, Trumbull, CT 06611
Tel.: (203) 374-4555
Women Healthcare Services
N.A.I.C.S.: 621610

Subsidiary (Domestic):

Arkansas Extended Care, LLC (3)
318 S Rhodes St, West Memphis, AR 72301-4215
Tel.: (870) 732-3353
Women Healthcare Services
N.A.I.C.S.: 621610

Arkansas Home Hospice, LLC (3)
3024 Red Wolf Blvd, Jonesboro, AR 72401-7415
Tel.: (870) 277-4029
Women Healthcare Services
N.A.I.C.S.: 621610

Arkansas HomeCare of Fulton, LLC (3)
260 Hwy 62 E, Salem, AR 72576-9545
Tel.: (870) 895-2273
Health Care Srvices
N.A.I.C.S.: 621610

Arkansas Physical Therapy Services of Conway, LLC (3)
4550 Prince St, Conway, AR 72034
Tel.: (501) 273-5000
Physical Therapy Services
N.A.I.C.S.: 621340

Athens-Limestone HomeCare, LLC (3)
725 W Market St Ste A, Athens, AL 35611
Tel.: (256) 233-9533
Web Site: http://lhcgroup.com
Health Care Srvices
N.A.I.C.S.: 621610

Baptist Home Health, LLC (3)
300 Interstate Park Dr Ste 324, Montgomery, AL 36117
Tel.: (334) 395-5100
Web Site: http://www.lhcgroup.com
Emp.: 50
Nursing Care Facilities Services
N.A.I.C.S.: 623110

CHRISTUS HomeCare-St. Michael, LLC (3)
5604 Summerhill Rd Ste 5495, Texarkana, TX 75503
Tel.: (903) 255-5100
Web Site: http://lhcgroup.com
Sales Range: $10-24.9 Million
Emp.: 30
Women Healthcare Services
N.A.I.C.S.: 621610

CMC Home Health and Hospice, LLC (3)
54 Grasse St, Calico Rock, AR 72519-0438
Tel.: (870) 297-3738
Health Care Srvices
N.A.I.C.S.: 622110
Farra Rowder (Mgr)

Camden HomeCare, LLC (3)
319A McWilliams Ave, Camden, AL 36726
Tel.: (334) 682-9050
Health Care Srvices
N.A.I.C.S.: 621610

Cape Fear Valley HomeCare and Hospice, LLC (3)
3400 Walsh Pkwy, Fayetteville, NC 28311
Tel.: (910) 609-6710
Web Site: http://lhcgroup.com
Emp.: 16
Health Care Srvices
N.A.I.C.S.: 621610
Michael Nagowski (CEO)

Clay County Hospital HomeCare, LLC (3)
83825 Hwy 9, Ashland, AL 36251
Tel.: (256) 354-0077
Sales Range: $1-9.9 Million
Emp.: 17
Women Healthcare Services
N.A.I.C.S.: 621610
Ann Hubbard (Office Mgr)

Colorado In-Home Partner-I, LLC (3)
515 E Riverview Ave, Fort Morgan, CO 80701
Tel.: (970) 867-3013
Women Healthcare Services
N.A.I.C.S.: 621610

Coosa Valley HomeCare, LLC (3)
209 W Spring St Ste 305, Sylacauga, AL 35150-2913
Tel.: (256) 208-0087
Web Site: http://www.cvhealth.net
Sales Range: $10-24.9 Million
Emp.: 20
Health Care Srvices
N.A.I.C.S.: 621610

Cornerstone Palliative and Hospice, LLC (3)
125 S Main St, Yazoo City, MS 39194-4007
Tel.: (662) 746-5153
Women Healthcare Services
N.A.I.C.S.: 621610

D.W. McMillan Memorial Hospital (3)
1301 Belleville St, Brewton, AL 36427
Tel.: (251) 867-8061
Web Site: http://www.dwmmh.org
Sales Range: $75-99.9 Million
Emp.: 300
General Hospital Operations
N.A.I.C.S.: 622110
Stacy Hines (COO)
Steve Parker (Controller)
Brad Pendergrass (Coord-Acctg)
Susan Jennings (Dir-Case Mgmt)
Suzannah Burch (Mgr-Case)
Leonard Stallworth (Dir-IT)
Debi Gist (Dir-Performance Improvement)
Bob Ellis (Dir-Nursing)
Larry Padgett (Dir-Pur)

Deaconess HomeCare, LLC (3)
128 S 11th Ave, Laurel, MS 39440
Tel.: (601) 649-2231
Web Site: https://www.lhcgroup.com
Emp.: 30
Health Care Srvices
N.A.I.C.S.: 621610

Subsidiary (Domestic):

Elk Valley Health Services, LLC (4)
5249 Harding Pl, Nashville, TN 37217
Tel.: (615) 360-1116
Web Site: http://www.evhealthservices.com
Women Healthcare Services
N.A.I.C.S.: 621610

Subsidiary (Domestic):

Elk Valley Professional Affiliates, Inc. (5)
1820 Huntsville Hwy Ste A, Fayetteville, TN 37334
Tel.: (931) 433-7026
Emp.: 50
Health Care Srvices
N.A.I.C.S.: 621610

Subsidiary (Domestic):

Scott-Wilson, Inc. (4)
2380 Fortune Dr Ste 130, Lexington, KY 40509
Tel.: (859) 277-2013
Health Care Srvices
N.A.I.C.S.: 621610

Subsidiary (Domestic):

Decatur Morgan HomeCare (3)
2708 Hwy 31 S Ste B, Decatur, AL 35603
Tel.: (256) 350-4182
Web Site: http://www.lhcgroup.com
Health Care Srvices
N.A.I.C.S.: 621610

Diabetes Self-Management Center, Inc. (3)
420 W Pinhook Rd Ste A, Lafayette, LA 70503-2131
Tel.: (337) 232-1717
Web Site: http://www.defeatdiabetes.org
Sales Range: $50-74.9 Million
Diabetes Center
N.A.I.C.S.: 621498

East Alabama Medical Center Home-Care, LLC (3)
2000 Pepperell Pkwy, Opelika, AL 36801
Tel.: (334) 749-3411
Web Site: http://www.eamc.org
Emp.: 30
Health Care Srvices
N.A.I.C.S.: 621610
Laura Grill (Pres & CEO)
Greg Nichols (Exec VP)
Sam Price (CFO & Exec VP)
Sarah Nunnelly (COO & Exec VP)
Oliver Banta (CIO & VP)
Chris Clark (VP-Clinical Svcs)
Susan Johnston (VP-Human Resources)
Eve Milner (VP-Clinical Svcs-EAM & Co-Lanier)
Leanne Moran (VP-Revenue Cycle)
Dennis Thrasher (VP & Controller)

Bruce Zartman *(VP-Support Ops)*
Joel Pittard *(Chm)*
Lucinda Cannon *(Vice Chm)*
Robert Dumas *(Treas & Sec)*
Roben Casey *(VP & Gen Counsel)*
Nicki Ware *(VP-Quality)*

Elite Home Health of Holiday Island (3)
2 Parkcliff Dr, Holiday Island, AR 72631-9230
Tel.: (479) 253-5554
Web Site: http://lhcgroup.com
Sales Range: $50-74.9 Million
Women Healthcare Services
N.A.I.C.S.: 621610

Eureka Springs Hospital Hospice, LLC (3)
3277 W Sunset Ave Ste D, Springdale, AR 72762-4947
Tel.: (479) 751-3019
Women Healthcare Services
N.A.I.C.S.: 621610

Eureka Springs Hospital, LLC (3)
24 Norris St, Eureka Springs, AR 72632
Tel.: (479) 253-7400
Web Site:
http://www.eurekaspringshospital.com
Health Care Srvices
N.A.I.C.S.: 621111
Peter Savoy *(CEO)*

Fayette Medical Center HomeCare, LLC (3)
102 2nd Ave SE, Fayette, AL 35555-2717
Tel.: (205) 932-5961
Web Site: http://lhcgroup.com
Emp.: 30
Health Care Srvices
N.A.I.C.S.: 621610

Feliciana Home Health (3)
1215 Independence Blvd Bldg 3 Ste B, Zachary, LA 70791
Tel.: (225) 683-3347
Web Site: http://www.lhcgroup.com
Health Care Srvices
N.A.I.C.S.: 621610

Feliciana Home Health South (3)
826 W Hwy 30, Gonzales, LA 70737
Tel.: (225) 450-3294
Web Site: http://www.lhcgroup.com
Health Care Srvices
N.A.I.C.S.: 621610

Feliciana Physical Therapy Services, LLC (3)
10299t Creekbend Dr, Baton Rouge, LA 70836
Tel.: (337) 233-1307
Women Healthcare Services
N.A.I.C.S.: 621610

Floyd HomeCare, LLC (3)
101 E 2nd Ave Ste 200, Rome, GA 30161
Tel.: (706) 802-4600
Web Site: http://www.lhcgroup.com
Emp.: 25
Health Care Srvices
N.A.I.C.S.: 621610

Freda H. Gordon Hospice & Palliative Care of Tidewater (3)
5000 Corporate Woods Dr Ste 500, Virginia Beach, VA 23462
Tel.: (757) 321-2242
Web Site: http://www.hpctidewater.com
Disability Assistance Services
N.A.I.C.S.: 624120
Grace Padgett *(Dir-Nursing)*
Kirsten Borte *(Mgr-Case)*
Debbie Hughes *(Mgr-Case)*
Tom Elder *(Mgr-Case)*
Kimberley Morris-Allsbrook *(CFO)*
David Lineberry *(Dir-Mktg)*
Lawrence Steingold *(Vice Chm)*
Jeff Cooper *(Treas)*
Neal Stern *(Sec)*
Stuart Nachman *(Chm)*

Georgia HomeCare of Harris, LLC (3)
5700 Georgia Hwy 354, Pine Mountain, GA 31822
Tel.: (706) 663-0988
Web Site: http://www.lhcgroup.com
Emp.: 20

Health Care Srvices
N.A.I.C.S.: 621610

HMC Home Health, LLC (3)
895 Pickwick St, Savannah, TN 38372-2199
Tel.: (731) 925-0276
Health Care Srvices
N.A.I.C.S.: 621610

Halcyon Hospice (3)
1435 Haw Creek Cir E Ste 402, Cumming, GA 30041
Tel.: (678) 717-0969
Web Site:
http://www.excellenceinhospice.com
Emp.: 15
Women Healthcare Services
N.A.I.C.S.: 621610

Halcyon Hospice of Aiken, LLC (3)
225 Barnwell Ave NW, Aiken, SC 29801-3903
Tel.: (803) 226-0387
Women Healthcare Services
N.A.I.C.S.: 621610

Home Care Connections, Inc. (3)
3131 Bell St Ste 211, Amarillo, TX 79106
Tel.: (806) 356-8911
Web Site: http://www.lhcgroup.com
Health Care Srvices
N.A.I.C.S.: 621610

HomeCall of Frederick (3)
5301 Buckeyetown Pike Ste 490, Frederick, MD 21704
Tel.: (240) 215-4668
Web Site: http://www.lhcgroup.com
Health Care Srvices
N.A.I.C.S.: 621610

Hood Home Health Service, LLC (3)
409A N W Central Ave, Amite, LA 70422
Tel.: (985) 748-6686
Health Care Srvices
N.A.I.C.S.: 622110

Hospice of Central Arkansas, LLC (3)
135 Amity Rd Ste A, Hot Springs, AR 71913
Tel.: (501) 623-2076
Web Site: http://lhcgroup.com
Sales Range: $10-24.9 Million
Emp.: 7
Health Care Srvices
N.A.I.C.S.: 621610

Idaho Home Health And Hospice Inc. (3)
3356 E Goldstone Dr Ste 3360, Meridian, ID 83642
Tel.: (208) 887-6633
Web Site: http://www.lhcgroup.com
Home Health Care & Hospice Services
N.A.I.C.S.: 621610

Illinois LIV, LLC (3)
151 Tenney St, Kewanee, IL 61443-3447
Tel.: (309) 623-4022
Women Healthcare Services
N.A.I.C.S.: 621610

Infirmary Home Health Agency, Inc. (3)
6001 Airport Blvd Ste B, Mobile, AL 36608
Tel.: (251) 450-3300
Web Site: https://www.lhcgroup.com
Health Care Srvices
N.A.I.C.S.: 621610

Jackson County Home Health, LLC (3)
105 N Court St Ste 2, Ripley, WV 25271
Tel.: (304) 372-5913
Sales Range: $10-24.9 Million
Emp.: 20
Health Care Srvices
N.A.I.C.S.: 621610
Tiffany Graham *(Gen Mgr)*

Jefferson Regional HomeCare, LLC (3)
2720 W 28th Ave, Pine Bluff, AR 71603
Tel.: (870) 534-3420
Health Care Srvices
N.A.I.C.S.: 621610
Tammy Ernst *(Office Mgr)*

Kentucky HomeCare of Henderson, LLC (3)

505 Klutey Park Plaza Dr Ste A, Henderson, KY 42420-5224
Tel.: (270) 869-1997
Emp.: 30
Health Care Srvices
N.A.I.C.S.: 621610
Nisha Garett *(Gen Mgr)*

Kentucky LV, LLC (3)
2380 Fortune Dr Ste 150, Lexington, KY 40509
Tel.: (859) 977-8000
Women Healthcare Services
N.A.I.C.S.: 621610

LHC Group Pharmaceutical Services, LLC (3)
1019 Auburn Ave, Lafayette, LA 70503-2343
Tel.: (337) 233-4656
Health Care Srvices
N.A.I.C.S.: 621610

LHC HomeCare of Tennessee, LLC (3)
4922 La Collina Way Ste 201, Ooltewah, TN 37363
Tel.: (423) 238-7878
Emp.: 19
Health Care Srvices
N.A.I.C.S.: 621610
Stacey Adams *(Mgr)*

LHCG CVIII, LLC (3)
1700 Buckner St Ste 200, Shreveport, LA 71101-4400
Tel.: (318) 681-7200
Women Healthcare Services
N.A.I.C.S.: 621610

LHCG CX, LLC (3)
4801 Jackson St Ext Ste B, Alexandria, LA 71303-5080
Tel.: (318) 448-6764
Women Healthcare Services
N.A.I.C.S.: 621610

LHCG CXV, LLC (3)
750 Landa St Ste B, New Braunfels, TX 78130-6114
Tel.: (830) 629-7568
Women Healthcare Services
N.A.I.C.S.: 621610

LHCG CXXI, LLC (3)
2830 Calder St Fl 4, Beaumont, TX 77702
Tel.: (409) 899-8156
Women Healthcare Services
N.A.I.C.S.: 621610

LHCG LIX, LLC (3)
63 Sockanosset Cross Rd Ste 1-C, Cranston, RI 02920
Tel.: (401) 383-2250
Women Healthcare Services
N.A.I.C.S.: 621610

LHCG LVII, LLC (3)
2121 S Blackhawk St Ste 110, Aurora, CO 80014
Tel.: (303) 369-7063
Women Healthcare Services
N.A.I.C.S.: 621610

LHCG LXIII, LLC (3)
13000 Linden Ave N Ste 112, Seattle, WA 98133
Tel.: (206) 364-1484
Women Healthcare Services
N.A.I.C.S.: 621610

LHCG LXX, LLC (3)
1056 Wellington Way Ste 130, Lexington, KY 40513-0020
Tel.: (859) 255-4411
Women Healthcare Services
N.A.I.C.S.: 621610

LHCG LXXIX, LLC (3)
111 E Laurel St, Scottsboro, AL 35768
Tel.: (256) 259-1754
Women Healthcare Services
N.A.I.C.S.: 621610

LHCG XL, LLC (3)
2000 Riveredge Pkwy Ste 925, Atlanta, GA 30328
Tel.: (770) 688-1000
Health Care Srvices
N.A.I.C.S.: 622110

LHCG XLII, LLC (3)
4847 Kaylee Ave Ste B, Springdale, AR 72762-5819
Tel.: (479) 756-5002
Health Care Srvices
N.A.I.C.S.: 622110

LHCG XLVII, LLC (3)
2775 S Moorland Rd Ste 203, New Berlin, WI 53151
Tel.: (262) 641-0459
Health Care Srvices
N.A.I.C.S.: 622110

LHCG XVII, LLC (3)
222 Shoshone St E, Twin Falls, ID 83301-0105
Tel.: (208) 734-4061
Sales Range: $10-24.9 Million
Emp.: 50
Hospice Care Services
N.A.I.C.S.: 621610
Keith Myer *(Owner)*

LHCG XXI, LLC (3)
2426 N Merritt Creek Loop, Coeur D'Alene, ID 83814
Tel.: (208) 667-7494
Health Care Srvices
N.A.I.C.S.: 621610

LHCG XXXIII, LLC (3)
1307 8th Ave Ste 305, Fort Worth, TX 76104-4140
Tel.: (817) 529-7555
Health Care Srvices
N.A.I.C.S.: 622110

LHCG XXXVII, LLC (3)
20280 Governors Hwy Ste, Olympia Fields, IL 60461-1076
Tel.: (708) 283-4240
Women Healthcare Services
N.A.I.C.S.: 621610

LHCG-V, L.L.C (3)
102 Thomas Rd Ste 607, West Monroe, LA 71291-5550
Tel.: (318) 329-3737
Health Care Srvices
N.A.I.C.S.: 621610

LHCG-VI, LLC (3)
1820 Main St, Franklin, LA 70538
Tel.: (337) 828-2929
Sales Range: $10-24.9 Million
Emp.: 20
Health Care Srvices
N.A.I.C.S.: 621610

Leaf River Home Health Care, LLC (3)
710 S 28th Ave Ste C, Hattiesburg, MS 39402
Tel.: (601) 336-5832
Sales Range: $10-24.9 Million
Emp.: 50
Health Care Srvices
N.A.I.C.S.: 621610

Lifeline Home Health Care of Bowling Green, LLC (3)
165 Natchez Trace Ste 206, Bowling Green, KY 42103
Tel.: (270) 781-0702
Web Site: http://www.lhcgroup.com
Health Care Srvices
N.A.I.C.S.: 621610

Lifeline Home Health Care of Fulton, LLC (3)
309 Main St, Fulton, KY 42041
Tel.: (270) 472-2294
Web Site: http://www.lhcgroup.com
Emp.: 20
Health Care Srvices
N.A.I.C.S.: 621610

Lifeline Home Health Care of Hopkinsville, LLC (3)
210 Burley Ave Ste A, Hopkinsville, KY 42240-8725
Tel.: (270) 885-6353
Web Site: http://www.lhcgroup.com
Emp.: 30
Health Care Srvices
N.A.I.C.S.: 621610

Lifeline Home Health Care of Lexington, LLC (3)

UnitedHealth Group Incorporated—(Continued)

100 John Southerland Dr Ste 8, Nicholas-
ville, KY 40356
Tel.: (859) 887-5433
Health Care Srvices
N.A.I.C.S.: 621610
Alisia Robinson Hill (Branch Mgr)

Lifeline Home Health Care of Russell-
ville, LLC   (3)
1527 Nashville St, Russellville, KY 42276
Tel.: (270) 726-2408
Web Site: http://www.lhcgroup.com
Emp.: 14
Health Care Srvices
N.A.I.C.S.: 621610

Lifeline Home Health Care of Somer-
set, LLC   (3)
600 1/2 Clifty St Ste 2 3, Somerset, KY
42503
Tel.: (606) 679-9245
Web Site: http://lhcgroup.com
Health Care Srvices
N.A.I.C.S.: 621610

Lifeline Home Health Care of Spring-
field, LLC   (3)
2109 Park Plz Ste 200, Springfield, TN
37172
Tel.: (615) 384-4644
Web Site: http://lhcgroup.com
Sales Range: $10-24.9 Million
Emp.: 30
Health Care Srvices
N.A.I.C.S.: 621610

Lifeline Private Duty Services of Ken-
tucky, LLC   (3)
30 MedPark Square Dr Ste 2, Somerset,
KY 42503-1764
Tel.: (606) 676-0045
Web Site: http://lhcgroup.com
Health Care Srvices
N.A.I.C.S.: 621610

Lifeline Rockcastle Home Health,
LLC   (3)
145 Lewis St, Mount Vernon, KY 40456
Tel.: (606) 256-1808
Web Site: http://www.lhcgroup.com
Emp.: 13
Health Care Srvices
N.A.I.C.S.: 621610

Lifeline of West Tennessee, LLC (3)
8066 Walnut Run Rd Ste 201, Cordova, TN
38018
Tel.: (901) 754-5351
Web Site: http://www.lhcgroup.com
Health Care Srvices
N.A.I.C.S.: 621610

Louisiana Extended Care Hospital of
Kenner, LLC   (3)
2614 Jefferson Hwy, Jefferson, LA 70121
Tel.: (504) 464-8590
Web Site: http://lhcgroup.com
Health Care Srvices
N.A.I.C.S.: 621610

Louisiana Health Care Group,
LLC   (3)
420 W Pinhook Rd, Lafayette, LA 70503
Tel.: (337) 233-1307
Web Site: http://www.lhcgroup.com
Health Care Srvices
N.A.I.C.S.: 621610

Louisiana HomeCare of Amite,
LLC   (3)
3401 N Blvd Ste 360, Baton Rouge, LA
70806
Tel.: (985) 748-6686
Web Site: http://www.lhcgroup.com
Sales Range: $10-24.9 Million
Emp.: 7
Women Healthcare Services
N.A.I.C.S.: 621610

Louisiana HomeCare of Delhi,
LLC   (3)
509 Cincinnati St, Delhi, LA 71232-3009
Tel.: (318) 878-5152
Web Site: http://www.lhcgroup.com
Sales Range: $10-24.9 Million
Emp.: 25
Health Care Srvices
N.A.I.C.S.: 621610

Louisiana HomeCare of Kenner,
LLC   (3)
200 W Esplanade Ave Ste 601, Kenner, LA
70065-2475
Tel.: (504) 842-5585
Sales Range: $25-49.9 Million
Emp.: 95
Health Care Srvices
N.A.I.C.S.: 621610

Louisiana HomeCare of Miss-Lou,
LLC   (3)
4951 Hwy 84 W, Vidalia, LA 71373
Tel.: (318) 336-2323
Sales Range: $1-9.9 Million
Emp.: 20
Women Healthcare Services
N.A.I.C.S.: 621610
Debbra Edward (Dir & Branch Mgr)

Louisiana HomeCare of Monroe,
LLC   (3)
1107 Hudson Ln Ste A, Monroe, LA 71201
Tel.: (318) 327-4500
Web Site: http://lhcgroup.com
Sales Range: $10-24.9 Million
Emp.: 15
Health Care Srvices
N.A.I.C.S.: 621610

Louisiana HomeCare of Northwest
Louisiana, LLC   (3)
301 Jefferson St, Mansfield, LA 71052
Tel.: (318) 872-0821
Health Care Srvices
N.A.I.C.S.: 621610

Louisiana HomeCare of Raceland,
LLC   (3)
4560 Highway 1 Ste 4, Raceland, LA 70394
Tel.: (985) 664-4066
Web Site: http://www.lhcgroup.com
Health Care Srvices
N.A.I.C.S.: 621610

Louisiana HomeCare of Slidell,
LLC   (3)
2990 Gause Blvd E Ste B, Slidell, LA
70461-4248
Tel.: (985) 649-4990
Web Site: http://www.lhcgroup.com
Sales Range: $10-24.9 Million
Emp.: 10
Health Care Srvices
N.A.I.C.S.: 621610

Louisiana Hospice & Palliative
Care   (3)
1101 Hudson Ln Ste D, Monroe, LA 71201
Tel.: (318) 322-2235
Web Site: http://www.lhcgroup.com
Sales Range: $50-74.9 Million
Hospice Operations
N.A.I.C.S.: 622310

Louisiana Hospice and Palliative
Care, LLC   (3)
426 Heather Dr, Opelousas, LA 70570
Tel.: (337) 948-8835
Web Site: http://www.lhcgroup.com
Hospice Operations
N.A.I.C.S.: 622310

Louisiana Physical Therapy, LLC (3)
4027 I 49 S Service Rd, Opelousas, LA
70570-0757
Tel.: (337) 948-4214
Health Care Srvices
N.A.I.C.S.: 621110
Kevin Mayo (Partner)

Marion Regional HomeCare,
LLC   (3)
234 1st Ave SW Ste 2, Hamilton, AL 35570
Tel.: (205) 921-0391
Web Site: http://www.lhcgroup.com
Health Care Srvices
N.A.I.C.S.: 621610

Medical Center Home Health,
LLC   (3)
1804 Hwy 45 Bypass Ste 430, Jackson, TN
38305
Tel.: (731) 984-2000
Web Site: http://www.lhcgroup.com
Health Care Srvices
N.A.I.C.S.: 621610

Medical Centers HomeCare, LLC (3)

5850 US Hwy 431 Ste 34, Albertville, AL
35950
Tel.: (256) 878-5811
Web Site: http://www.mmcenters.com
Emp.: 62
Health Care Srvices
N.A.I.C.S.: 621610

Mena Medical Center Home Health,
LLC   (3)
311 N Morrow St, Mena, AR 71953-2516
Tel.: (479) 394-6100
Web Site: https://www.menaregional.com
Health Care Srvices
N.A.I.C.S.: 622110
Jay Quebedeaux (CEO)

Mississippi HomeCare, LLC   (3)
2080 S Frontage Rd Ste 107, Vicksburg,
MS 39180
Tel.: (601) 629-0015
Web Site: http://www.lhcgroup.com
Health Care Srvices
N.A.I.C.S.: 621610

Mississippi Physical Therapy Ser-
vices of Biloxi, LLC   (3)
1651 Popp's Ferry Rd Ste 105, Biloxi, MS
39532
Tel.: (228) 273-4037
Physical Therapy Services
N.A.I.C.S.: 621340

Missouri HomeCare LLC   (3)
1026 KingsHwy St, Rolla, MO 65402
Tel.: (573) 341-3456
Health Care Srvices
N.A.I.C.S.: 621610

Mizell Memorial Hospital HomeCare,
LLC   (3)
702 N Main St, Opp, AL 36467
Tel.: (334) 493-3541
Web Site: https://www.mizellmh.com
Emp.: 200
Women Healthcare Services
N.A.I.C.S.: 621610

Mountaineer HomeCare, LLC   (3)
400 Tracy Way Ste 100, Charleston, WV
25311
Tel.: (304) 720-0205
Web Site: http://www.lhcgroup.com
Sales Range: $10-24.9 Million
Emp.: 25
Health Care Srvices
N.A.I.C.S.: 621610

Munroe Regional HomeCare,
LLC   (3)
2201 SE 30th Ave Ste 301, Ocala, FL
34471
Tel.: (352) 351-7222
Web Site: http://www.lhcgroup.com
Health Care Srvices
N.A.I.C.S.: 621610

North Arkansas HomeCare   (3)
54 Grasse St, Calico Rock, AR 72519
Tel.: (870) 297-3738
Web Site: http://www.lhcgroup.com
Emp.: 15
Health Care Srvices
N.A.I.C.S.: 621610

North Carolina In-Home Partner-IV,
LLC   (3)
127 Sunset Ridge Rd, Clyde, NC 28721-
8597
Tel.: (828) 452-5039
Women Healthcare Services
N.A.I.C.S.: 621610

North Carolina In-Home Partner-V,
LLC   (3)
2270 US Hwy 74A Byp Ste 345, Forest
City, NC 28043-2434
Tel.: (828) 245-3575
Women Healthcare Services
N.A.I.C.S.: 621610

Northeast Washington Home Health,
Inc.   (3)
111 W N River Dr Ste 205, Spokane, WA
99201
Tel.: (509) 326-2300
Web Site: http://www.lhcgroup.com
Emp.: 55
Health Care Srvices
N.A.I.C.S.: 621610

Northshore Extended Care Hospital,
LLC   (3)
2810 Ambassador Caffery Pkwy 6th Fl, La-
fayette, LA 70506
Tel.: (337) 289-8188
Health Care Srvices
N.A.I.C.S.: 622110

Northwest Healthcare Alliance,
Inc.   (3)
1821 Cooks Hill Rd Ste 200, Centralia, WA
98531
Tel.: (360) 807-7776
Women Healthcare Services
N.A.I.C.S.: 621610

Oak Shadows of Jennings, LLC   (3)
1322 Elton Rd Ste G, Jennings, LA 70546
Tel.: (337) 616-3482
Web Site: http://www.lhcgroup.com
Health Care Srvices
N.A.I.C.S.: 621610

Omni Home Health - Jacksonville,
LLC   (3)
9143 Philips Hwy Ste 190, Jacksonville, FL
32256
Tel.: (904) 519-9233
Web Site: http://lhcgroup.com
Hospice & Home Health Care Services
N.A.I.C.S.: 621610

Patient's Choice Hospice and Palliative Care of Louisiana, LLC   (3)
1101 Hudson Ln Ste D, Monroe, LA 71201-
6049
Tel.: (318) 322-2235
Nursing Care Facilities Services
N.A.I.C.S.: 623110

Patient's Choice Hospice, LLC   (3)
3277 W Sunset Ste D, Springdale, AR
72762
Tel.: (479) 751-3019
Web Site: http://www.lhcgroup.com
Sales Range: $10-24.9 Million
Emp.: 9
Health Care Srvices
N.A.I.C.S.: 621610

Picayune HomeCare, LLC   (3)
14094 Customs Blvd Ste 200, Gulfport, MS
39503
Tel.: (228) 539-4069
Health Care Srvices
N.A.I.C.S.: 621610

Preston Memorial HomeCare,
LLC   (3)
419 Morgantown St, Kingwood, WV 26537
Tel.: (304) 329-3565
Web Site: http://lhcgroup.com
Health Care Srvices
N.A.I.C.S.: 621610

Primary Care at Home of Louisiana
II, LLC   (3)
1107 Hudson Ln, Monroe, LA 71201
Tel.: (318) 732-3337
Women Healthcare Services
N.A.I.C.S.: 621610

Primary Care at Home of Maryland,
LLC   (3)
4701 Mount Hope Dr Ste A, Baltimore, MD
21215
Tel.: (443) 563-1594
Women Healthcare Services
N.A.I.C.S.: 621610

Primary Care at Home of West Vir-
ginia, LLC   (3)
400 Tracy Way Ste 100, Charleston, WV
25311
Tel.: (304) 356-1356
Health Care Srvices
N.A.I.C.S.: 622110

Princeton Community HomeCare,
LLC   (3)
312 George St Ste 314, Beckley, WV
25801-2653
Tel.: (304) 252-8070
Web Site: http://www.lhcgroup.com
Emp.: 30
Health Care Srvices
N.A.I.C.S.: 621610

Richardson Medical Center Home-
Care, LLC   (3)

254 Hwy 3048, Rayville, LA 71269
Tel.: (318) 728-4181
Web Site: https://www.richardsonmed.org
Sales Range: $1-9.9 Million
Emp.: 10
Women Healthcare Services
N.A.I.C.S.: 621610

Roane HomeCare, LLC (3)
20 Williams Dr Ste 1, Spencer, WV 25276
Tel.: (304) 927-6091
Web Site: http://lhcgroup.com
Health Care Srvices
N.A.I.C.S.: 621610

Salem Home Care, LLC (3)
925 Commercial St SE Ste 310, Salem, OR 97302
Tel.: (503) 561-5999
Web Site: http://lhcgroup.com
Health Care Srvices
N.A.I.C.S.: 621610

Southeast Alabama HomeCare, LLC (3)
1435 Ross Clark Cir Ste 2, Dothan, AL 36301
Tel.: (334) 794-0591
Web Site: http://lhcgroup.com
Health Care Srvices
N.A.I.C.S.: 621610

Southwest Arkansas HomeCare, LLC (3)
111 N Main St Ste 103, Salem, AR 72576
Tel.: (870) 895-2273
Web Site: http://www.lhcgroup.com
Health Care Srvices
N.A.I.C.S.: 621610

Specialty Extended Care Hospital of Monroe, LLC (3)
309 Jackson St 7th Fl, Monroe, LA 71201
Tel.: (318) 966-4126
Sales Range: $25-49.9 Million
Emp.: 120
Health Care Srvices
N.A.I.C.S.: 621610
Cleta Munholland (Gen Mgr)

St. Landry Extended Care Hospital, LLC (3)
3983 I 49 S Service Rd, Opelousas, LA 70570-0758
Tel.: (337) 948-5184
Sales Range: $10-24.9 Million
Emp.: 50
Extended Care Facility Operations
N.A.I.C.S.: 622310

St. Mary's Medical Center Home Health Services, LLC (3)
5187 US Rte 60 Ste 13, Huntington, WV 25705
Tel.: (304) 733-5010
Web Site: http://lhcgroup.com
Women Healthcare Services
N.A.I.C.S.: 621610
Todd Campbell (Pres & CEO)

Tennessee In-Home Partner-II, LLC (3)
300 Steam Plant Rd Sumner Medical Plz Ste 220, Gallatin, TN 37066
Tel.: (615) 328-6690
Women Healthcare Services
N.A.I.C.S.: 621610

Texas Health Care Group, LLC (3)
1340 Surrey St, Lafayette, LA 70501
Tel.: (337) 233-1307
Emp.: 4
Health Care Srvices
N.A.I.C.S.: 621610

Thomas Home Health, LLC (3)
7530 Parker Rd Ste 200, Fairhope, AL 36532
Tel.: (251) 990-9200
Web Site: http://lhcgroup.com
Health Care Srvices
N.A.I.C.S.: 621610

Three Rivers HomeCare, LLC (3)
555 NE F St Ste B, Grants Pass, OR 97526
Tel.: (541) 476-6224
Web Site: http://www.lhcgroup.com
Health Care Srvices
N.A.I.C.S.: 621610

Tri-Parish Community HomeCare, LLC (3)
3581 Highway 190, Eunice, LA 70535
Tel.: (337) 550-0002
Web Site: http://www.healthcare.com
Emp.: 6
Health Care Srvices
N.A.I.C.S.: 621610

Twin Lakes Home Health Agency, LLC (3)
810 Wallace Ave, Leitchfield, KY 42754
Tel.: (270) 230-0272
Web Site: http://www.lhcgroup.com
Emp.: 10
Health Care Srvices
N.A.I.C.S.: 621610

University of TN Medical Center Home Care Services, LLC (3)
4435 Valley View Dr Ste 104, Knoxville, TN 37917
Tel.: (865) 544-6222
Web Site: http://www.lhcgroup.com
Health Care Srvices
N.A.I.C.S.: 621610

Virginia In-Home Partner-V, LLC (3)
170 W Shirley Ave Ste 101, Warrenton, VA 20186
Tel.: (540) 316-2700
Women Healthcare Services
N.A.I.C.S.: 621610

Virginia In-Home Partner-VIII, LLC (3)
818 Glendale Rd Ste 1, Galax, VA 24333
Tel.: (276) 236-7935
Women Healthcare Services
N.A.I.C.S.: 621610

Wetzel County HomeCare, LLC (3)
411 N State Route 2, New Martinsville, WV 26155
Tel.: (304) 455-5515
Web Site: http://www.lhcgroup.com
Health Care Srvices
N.A.I.C.S.: 621610

Whispering Pines Home Care, LLC (3)
8830 SW 196th Dr, Cutler Bay, FL 33157-8961
Tel.: (305) 253-9894
Health Care Srvices
N.A.I.C.S.: 621610

Subsidiary (Domestic):

OptumRx, Inc. (2)
11000 Optum Cir, Eden Prairie, MN 55344
Tel.: (949) 442-8000
Web Site: https://www.optumrx.com
Pharmacy Management Consulting Services
N.A.I.C.S.: 541618

Subsidiary (Domestic):

BrivaRx of Maine, Inc. (3)
53 Darling Ave, South Portland, ME 04106
Tel.: (207) 874-6991
Web Site: http://www.briovarx.com
Pharmacy Care & Specialty Medication Therapy Management Services
N.A.I.C.S.: 621610

Diplomat Pharmacy, Inc. (3)
4100 S Saginaw St, Flint, MI 48507
Tel.: (810) 768-9178
Web Site:
  http://www.diplomatpharmacy.com
Pharmacy Operations
N.A.I.C.S.: 456110

Subsidiary (Domestic):

Accurate Rx Pharmacy Consulting, LLC (3)
9900 Bren Rd E, Minnetonka, MN 55343-9664
Tel.: (573) 256-4279
Web Site: https://specialty.optum.com
Health Care Consulting Services
N.A.I.C.S.: 524114
Sandra Freese (CFO)

Focus Rx Inc. (4)
2805 Veterans Hwy Ste 19, Ronkonkoma, NY 11779-7683

Tel.: (631) 319-1920
Web Site: http://www.myfocusrx.com
Sales Range: $25-49.9 Million
Health Care Srvices
N.A.I.C.S.: 621498
Lou Puleo (CEO)
Richard Collins (Pres)
Christopher Varvaro (COO)

Leehar Distributors, LLC (4)
701 Emerson Rd #301, Saint Louis, MO 63141
Tel.: (314) 652-1121
Web Site: http://www.castiarx.com
Pharmaceuticals Product Mfr
N.A.I.C.S.: 325412
Mike McGinnity (Exec VP-Sls & Acct Mgmt)
Thomas Hughes (VP-Bus Intelligence)
Cornell Beck (Gen Mgr-Mail Order & Assoc VP)
Jim Watson (VP-Client Experience)
David Skomo (COO)

Oak HC/FT LDI Blocker Corp. (4)
3 Pickwick Plz Ste 302, Greenwich, CT 06830
Tel.: (203) 717-1350
Web Site: http://www.oakhcft.com
Venture Capital Fund Investing Services
N.A.I.C.S.: 523910
Annie Lamont (Co-Founder & Mng Partner)
Andrew Adams (Co-Founder & Mng Partner)
Patricia Kemp (Co-Founder & Mng Partner)
Nancy Brown (Gen Partner)
Dan Petrozzo (Partner)
Leah Scanlan (Partner)
Michelle Daubar (Partner)
Matt Streisfeld (Partner)
Billy Deitch (Partner)
David Black (Partner-Tech)
Ezekiel J. Emanuel (Partner-Venture)
Anil Aggarwal (Partner-Venture)
Michael Heller (Partner-Venture)
Jonathan Weiner (Partner-Venture)
Michael Vaughan (Partner-Venture)
Vignesh Chandramouli (Principal)
Colleen Lennon (Controller)
Oivind Lorentzen (VP)
Allen Miller (Principal)
Ravi Singh (CFO)
Josh Jackson (Dir-Talent)
Ben Schachtel (Dir-Talent Res & Ops)
Andrew Smith (VP)

Optum Frontier Therapies, LLC (4)
325 W Atherton Rd Ste 1, Flint, MI 48507
Web Site:
  http://www.envoyhealth.diplomat.is
Emp.: 800
Support Services for Pharmaceutical Industry
N.A.I.C.S.: 561499

Optum Infusion Services 551, LLC (4)
100 Corporate Dr Ste 111, Windsor, CT 06095
Tel.: (800) 243-4621
Pharmacy Product Whslr
N.A.I.C.S.: 456110

Optum Infusion Services 553, LLC (4)
140 Northway Ct, Raleigh, NC 27615-4916
Tel.: (919) 847-9001
Pharmacy Product Whslr
N.A.I.C.S.: 456110

Subsidiary (Domestic):

Healthcare Solutions, Inc. (3)
2736 Meadow Church Rd Ste 300, Duluth, GA 30097
Web Site: http://www.helioscomp.com
Medical Cost Management Services
N.A.I.C.S.: 524114
Brian Carpenter (Sr VP-Clinical Svcs & Product Dev)

Subsidiary (Domestic):

Cypress Care, Inc. (4)
2736 Meadow Church Rd Ste 300, Duluth, GA 30097
Web Site: http://www.cypresscare.com
Insurance Claims & Benefits Management Services
N.A.I.C.S.: 524128
Eileen Fuentes-Ramallo (Sr VP)

Procura Management, Inc. (4)
2500 Monroe Blvd Ste 100, Norristown, PA 19403
Tel.: (800) 228-9129
Web Site: http://www.procura-inc.com
Casualty Insurance Services
N.A.I.C.S.: 524126
Nicole D'Ettorre (Sr VP-PPO Network Svcs)

Subsidiary (Domestic):

OptumRx Discount Card Services, LLC (3)
8300 E Maplewood Ave Ste 100, Greenwood Village, CO 80111
Tel.: (303) 770-1007
Sales Range: $250-299.9 Million
Emp.: 250
Infrastructure & Claims Processing For Benefit Managers & Pharmaceutical Companies
N.A.I.C.S.: 524291

OptumRx Home Delivery of Ohio, LLC (3)
33381 Walker Rd, Avon Lake, OH 44012
Tel.: (800) 233-3872
Web Site: http://www.ipsrx.com
Pharmacy Benefit Management Services
N.A.I.C.S.: 424210

OptumRx PBM of Illinois, Inc. (3)
2441 Warrenville Rd, Lisle, IL 60532
Tel.: (516) 626-0007
Web Site: http://www.informedrx.com
Sales Range: $650-699.9 Million
Emp.: 440
Pharmacy Benefits Management Services
N.A.I.C.S.: 524210

OptumRx PBM of Wisconsin, LLC (3)
11900 W Lake Park Dr, Milwaukee, WI 53224
Tel.: (877) 526-9906
Web Site: http://www.restat.com
Prescription Claims & Pharmacy Benefit Management Services
N.A.I.C.S.: 524298
John Bergan (Sr VP & Gen Mgr)
Dustin T. Conrad (VP-Sls & Acct Mgmt)
Mark Singleton (VP-Client Dev)
Ann Larkin (VP-Fin)
Robert J. Kudis (VP-Bus Solutions)

OptumRx PD of Pennsylvania, LLC (3)
1650 Arch St Ste 2600, Philadelphia, PA 19103-1466
Web Site: http://www.futurescripts.com
Insurance Agencies & Brokerage Services
N.A.I.C.S.: 524210

Optum360, LLC (1)
13625 Technology Dr, Eden Prairie, MN 55344
Web Site: http://www.optum360.com
Healthcare Software
N.A.I.C.S.: 513210
Paul Emerson (CEO)
Chris Martin (Sr VP)
Susan Worthy (Sr VP-Marketing)
Todd Van Meter (Pres)
Eric Peterson (Gen Counsel & Gen Counsel)
Jan Grimm (Chief Growth Officer)
Peter Martin (CFO)

Division (Domestic):

Optum360, LLC (2)
13625 Technology Dr, Eden Prairie, MN 55344
Tel.: (952) 833-7100
Web Site: http://www.optum360.com
Health Care Srvices
N.A.I.C.S.: 621999
Todd Gustin (Pres)
Chris Martin (Sr VP)
Susan Worthy (Sr VP-Marketing)
Todd Van Meter (Pres)
Jan Grimm (Chief Growth Officer)
Peter Martin (CFO)
Paul Emerson (CEO)

OptumCare Florida, LLC (1)
11000 Optum Cir, Eden Prairie, MN 55344
Pharmaceutical Preparation Mfr
N.A.I.C.S.: 325412

OptumCare Management, LLC (1)

UnitedHealth Group Incorporated—(Continued)

11000 Optum Cir, Eden Prairie, MN 55344
Pharmaceutical Preparation Mfr
N.A.I.C.S.: 325412

OptumCare South Florida, LLC (1)
11000 Optum Cir, Eden Prairie, MN 55344
Pharmaceutical Preparation Mfr
N.A.I.C.S.: 325412

OptumHealth Inc. (1)
6300 Olson Memorial Hwy, Golden Valley,
MN 55427 (100%)
Tel.: (763) 595-3200
Web Site: http://www.optumhealth.com
Sales Range: $1-9.9 Million
Health Care Srvices
N.A.I.C.S.: 621491
Andrew Hayek (CEO)

Subsidiary (Domestic):

Alere Health, LLC (2)
2116 Frederick Douglass Blvd, New York,
NY 10026
Tel.: (212) 882-1154
Web Site: https://mywellnesssolutions.com
Emp.: 1,803
Wellness Programs, Care Management,
Women's Health & Health Intelligence Solutions
N.A.I.C.S.: 621999

Subsidiary (Domestic):

Alere Health Systems, Inc. (3)
3200 Windy Hill Rd Ste 300 E, Atlanta, GA
30339
Tel.: (770) 767-4500
Web Site: http://www.alerehealth.com
Medical Treatment Management Services
N.A.I.C.S.: 621610

Alere Wellbeing Inc. (3)
999 3rd Ave Ste 2000, Seattle, WA 98104-
1139
Tel.: (206) 876-2100
Web Site: http://www.alerewellbeing.com
Emp.: 500
Wellness Program Services
N.A.I.C.S.: 713940
Jim Cunningham (Dir-HR)

Subsidiary (Domestic):

Optum Financial, Inc. (2)
9900 Bren Rd E, Minnetonka, MN 55343
Tel.: (952) 936-1300
Web Site:
http://www.optumhealthfinancial.com
Financial Management Services
N.A.I.C.S.: 523999

Subsidiary (Domestic):

Optum Bank, Inc. (3)
2525 Lake Park Blvd, Salt Lake City, UT
84120
Tel.: (801) 963-6040
Web Site: https://www.optumbank.com
Banking Services
N.A.I.C.S.: 522110

Vpay Inc. (3)
111 W Spring Val, Richardson, TX 75081-
4020
Web Site: http://www.vpayusa.com
Telemarketing Bureaus & Other Contact
Centers
N.A.I.C.S.: 561422
Robert Allen (Pres)

Subsidiary (Domestic):

**OptumHealth Care Solutions,
Inc.** (2)
6300 Olson Memorial Hwy, Golden Valley,
MN 55427
Tel.: (763) 595-3200
Emp.: 4,000
Health Care Insurance Services
N.A.I.C.S.: 524114

OptumHealth Holdings, LLC (2)
6300 Olson Memorial Hwy, Golden Valley,
MN 55427-4946
Tel.: (888) 262-4614
Health Care Insurance Services
N.A.I.C.S.: 524114

OptumInsight (Sweden) AB (1)

Klarabergsviadukten 90 D Pl 6, 111 64,
Stockholm, Sweden
Tel.: (46) 854528772
Management Consulting Services
N.A.I.C.S.: 541618

OptumInsight, Inc. (1)
11000 Optum Cir, Eden Prairie, MN 55344
Tel.: (952) 833-7100
Web Site: http://www.optum.com
Phase I-IV Clinical Trials; Data Management & Biostatistics; Regulatory Consulting
& Marketing Services
N.A.I.C.S.: 541511
Eric Murphy (Chief Growth & Comml Officer)
Susan Arthur (COO)
Rick Hardy (CEO)
Bill Miller (CFO)

Subsidiary (Domestic):

CareMedic Systems, Inc. (2)
800 Carillon Pkwy Ste 250, Saint Petersburg, FL 33716-1102
Tel.: (727) 329-7800
Web Site: http://www.caremedic.com
Sales Range: $10-24.9 Million
Emp.: 100
Healthcare Revenue Management Services
N.A.I.C.S.: 541511

Change Healthcare Inc. (2)
424 Church St Ste 1400, Nashville, TN
37219
Tel.: (615) 932-3000
Web Site: http://www.changehealthcare.com
Rev.: $3,090,421,000
Assets: $10,112,616,000
Liabilities: $6,860,388,000
Net Worth: $3,252,228,000
Earnings: ($112,210,000)
Emp.: 15,000
Fiscal Year-end: 03/31/2021
Healthcare Software Development Services
N.A.I.C.S.: 541511
Neil E. de Crescenzo (Pres & CEO)
Loretta A. Cecil (Gen Counsel & Exec VP)
Alex P. Choy (CIO & Exec VP)
Kriten Joshi (Pres-Software, Analytics &
Network Solutions & Exec VP)
Thomas Laur (Pres-Tech Enabled Svcs &
Exec VP)
August Calhoun (Pres-Sls & Ops & Exec
VP)
W. Thomas McEnery (CMO & Exec VP)
Linda K. Whitley-Taylor (Chief People Officer & Exec VP)
Ryanx Miller (Sr VP-Corp Dev)
Kerry Kelly (VP-External Comm)
Steven Martin (Exec VP-Enterprise Tech)
Evan Smith (Sr VP-IR)
Paul Rareshide (Sr VP & Controller)
Luyuan Fang (Chief Artificial Intelligence
Officer)

Subsidiary (Non-US):

**Change Healthcare New
Zealand** (3)
79 Lichfield Street, Christchurch, 8011, New
Zealand
Tel.: (64) 33796662
Web Site:
http://www.changehealthcare.co.nz
Healthcare Software Technology Services
N.A.I.C.S.: 541511
Mandy Cronin (Country Dir-Ops)
Mark Figgitt (Dir-Dev)
Tony Patterson (Mgr-Technical Svcs & Support)

Subsidiary (Domestic):

**National Decision Support Company,
LLC** (3)
316 W Washington Ave Ste 500, Madison,
WI 53703
Web Site:
http://www.nationaldecisionsupport.com
Healtcare Services
N.A.I.C.S.: 621999
Sam Rolfe (Mgr-Implementation Project)

PDX Inc. (3)
101 Jim Wright Fwy S, Fort Worth, TX
76108
Tel.: (817) 246-6760
Web Site: http://www.pdxinc.com
Rev.: $16,100,000

Emp.: 400
Computer Software Development
N.A.I.C.S.: 541511
Ken Hill (Founder & Chm)
Jim Cummins (VP-Contracts & Risk Mgmt)
Brad Crosslin (Pres)
Dewitt McClaran (VP-Computer Ops-NHIN)
Jeff Farris (CEO)
Allen Smith (CFO & Controller)
Tracy Hill Hochster (VP-Mktg)
Andrew McKernon (Natl Dir-Bus Dev)
Brian Nichols (Mgr-Implementations & Client Svcs)
Brandi Sherrill (VP-Design & Quality
Assurance-EPS Design)
John Woods (VP-Information Security &
Infrastructure)
Cheryl Jorgenson (Chief Clinical Officer)
David Chancellor (VP-Customer Svc & Support)
Dave Cuozzo (VP-Project Mgmt)
Trey Ferguson (VP-Clinical Dev)
John Foss (Exec VP-Software Dev)
Steve Friedman (VP-Pharmaceutical Trade
Rels)
Stephanie Huber (VP-Legal Svcs)
Shawna Marusak (VP-Client Svcs)
Jasmina St. Louis (VP-NHIN)

Subsidiary (Domestic):

Freedom Data Systems Inc. (4)
101 S Jim Wright Fwy Ste 200, Fort Worth,
TX 76108-2202
Tel.: (603) 753-8300
Web Site: http://www.freedomdata.com
Sales Range: $1-9.9 Million
Emp.: 15
Computer Software Systems Analysis & Design, Custom
N.A.I.C.S.: 541511

Subsidiary (Domestic):

Electronic Network Systems, Inc. (2)
7899 Lexington Dr Ste 203, Colorado
Springs, CO 80920
Tel.: (719) 277-7545
Web Site: http://www.enshealth.com
Emp.: 75
Healthcare Technology Services
N.A.I.C.S.: 541519
Bill Miller (CEO)

HWT, Inc. (2)
2 Monument Sq 4th Fl, Portland, ME 04101
Tel.: (207) 775-0315
Web Site: http://www.hwtc.com
Sales Range: $75-99.9 Million
Healthcare Payment Data Management
Services & Software Products
N.A.I.C.S.: 518210

MedSynergies, Inc. (2)
2 MacArthur Rdg 909 Hidden Rdg Ste 300,
Irving, TX 75038
Tel.: (972) 791-1224
Web Site: http://www.medsynergies.com
Sales Range: $75-99.9 Million
Emp.: 618
Healthcare Software Development Services
N.A.I.C.S.: 541511

The Advisory Board Company (2)
655 New York Ave NW, Washington, DC
20037
Tel.: (202) 266-5600
Web Site: https://www.advisory.com
Consulting Services (to Clients in the Health
Care Industry)
N.A.I.C.S.: 541611
Robert W. Musslewhite (Chm & CEO)
Brandi Greenberg (VP-Life Sciences & Ecosystem Res)
David L. Katz (Exec Dir)
Sruti Nataraja (Mng Dir)
Mike Wagner (Exec Dir)
David Willis (VP-Health Sys Strategy)
Amanda Berra (Partner-Expert)
Megan Clark (Mng Dir)
Alicia Daugherty (Mng Dir)
Eric Fontana (Mng Dir)
Veena Lanka (Partner-Res)
Eric Larsen (Pres)
Srinivas Sridhara (Mng Dir-Data Science &
Advanced Analytics)
Leslie Fletchall Schreiber (Exec Dir)
Anna Yakovenko (Mng Dir)
Manasi Kapoor (Mng Dir)

Laura Wilson (Mng Dir)
Rachel Woods (Mng Dir)
Solomon Banjo (Mng Dir)
Craig Pirner (Mng Dir-Leader Dev)
Tana Kittisarapong (Dir-Faculty Member &
Talent Dev)
Natalie Trebes (Dir-Health Plan Res)
Deirdre Saulet (Partner-Expert)
Ben Umansky (Partner-Expert)
Madhavi Kasinadhuni (Mng Dir)
Jared Landis (Mng Dir)
Yulan Egan (Mgr-Practice)
Jocelyn Herrington (VP-Res Partner)
Adele Scielzo (COO)
Mark Hetz (Sr Dir-Res)
Bradford Koles Jr. (VP)

Subsidiary (Non-US):

ABCO Advisory Services India Private Limited (3)
Tamarai Techpark S P Plot No 16-20 & 20A
South Block, 5th floor Thiruvika Industrial
Estate Inner Ring Road Guindy, Chennai,
600 032, Tamil Nadu, India
Tel.: (91) 4461018700
Web Site: http://www.advisory.com
Computer Software Consulting Services
N.A.I.C.S.: 541512

Subsidiary (Domestic):

ActiveStrategy, Inc. (3)
620 W Germantown Pike, Plymouth Meeting, PA 19462
Tel.: (484) 690-0700
Performance Metrics Software Publisher &
Management Consulting Services
N.A.I.C.S.: 513210

Subsidiary (Domestic):

The Lewin Group (2)
3160 Fairview Park Dr Ste 600, Falls
Church, VA 22042
Tel.: (703) 269-5500
Web Site: https://www.lewin.com
Sales Range: $25-49.9 Million
Emp.: 200
Health Care Consulting Services
N.A.I.C.S.: 541618
Lisa Alecxih (Sr VP-Center of Aging & Disability Policy)
Charlie Bruetman (Sr VP-Federal Health &
Human Svcs Market)
Clifford Goodman (Sr VP-Comparative Effectiveness Res)
Marisa Russo (VP)
Carol J. Simon (Sr VP-Evaluation & Advanced Analytics)
Brian Simonson (Sr VP)
Cindy Gruman (VP)
Grecia Marrufo (Sr VP)
Laura A. Dummit (VP)
Nancy Walczak (VP)
Robert Page (VP)
Steve Johnson (VP)
Yvonne Powell (Sr VP-Business
Development-States)
Erika Ange (VP)
Elizabeth Martin (Sr VP)
Michael Nestor (CEO)
Erika C. Robbins (VP)
Julie Somers (VP)
Karen Gallegos (VP)
Alicia Goroski (VP)
Shalini Jhataika (VP)
Lisa Shugarman (VP)
Mustafa Karakus (VP)
Karla Lopez de Nava (VP)
Gwyn Volk (VP)
Ron Ozminkowski (Sr VP)
Andrew Paradis (VP)
Kimberly Smathers (VP)
Grace Yang (VP)
Brighita Negrusa (VP)
Traci Padgett (VP)
Brighita Negrusa (VP)
Traci Padgett (VP)

**OptumServe Technology Services,
Inc.** (1)
11000 Optum Cir, Eden Prairie, MN 55344
Pharmaceutical Preparation Mfr
N.A.I.C.S.: 325412

OrthoNet LLC (1)
1311 Mamaroneck Ave Ste 240, White
Plains, NY 10605

Tel.: (914) 681-8800
Web Site: https://www.orthonet-online.com
Health Care Srvices
N.A.I.C.S.: 622310

Orthology Inc. (1)
9900 Bren Rd E, Minnetonka, MN 55343
Tel.: (952) 594-6088
Web Site: https://orthology.com
Hospital & Health Care Services
N.A.I.C.S.: 622110

Outpatient Surgery Center of Hilton Head, LLC (1)
190 Pembroke Dr, Hilton Head Island, SC 29926
Tel.: (843) 682-5050
Web Site: https://www.hhisurgery.com
Fiscal Year-end: 12/31/2006
General Medical & Surgical Services
N.A.I.C.S.: 621498

Oxford Health Plans LLC (1)
48 Monroe Tpke, Trumbull, CT 06611
Tel.: (203) 459-6000
Web Site: http://www.oxhp.com
Emp.: 3,200
Hospital & Medical Service Plans
N.A.I.C.S.: 524114

Subsidiary (Domestic):

Oxford Health Plans (CT), Inc. (2)
48 Monroe Tpke, Trumbull, CT 06611
Tel.: (203) 459-9100
Web Site: http://www.oxhp.com
Sales Range: $250-299.9 Million
Emp.: 500
Hospital & Medical Service Plans
N.A.I.C.S.: 524114

Oxford Health Plans (NY), Inc. (2)
521 5th Ave, New York, NY 10175
Tel.: (800) 444-6222
Web Site: http://www.oxhp.com
Hospital & Medical Service Plans
N.A.I.C.S.: 524114

PHYS Holding Corp. (1)
1021 Windcross Ct, Franklin, TN 37067
Tel.: (615) 503-1000
Health Insurance Products & Specialized Care Services
N.A.I.C.S.: 524114

PMSI, LLC (1)
11000 Optum Cir, Eden Prairie, MN 55344
Pharmaceutical Preparation Mfr
N.A.I.C.S.: 325412

POMCO, Inc. (1)
2425 James St, Syracuse, NY 13206
Tel.: (315) 437-9518
Web Site: http://www.pomco.com
Business Process Outsourcing Services
N.A.I.C.S.: 518210
Robert W. Pomfrey (Pres & CEO)

PacifiCare Dental (1)
3110 Lake Center Dr, Santa Ana, CA 92704
Tel.: (714) 513-6494
Sales Range: $100-124.9 Million
Emp.: 200
Health Care Company
N.A.I.C.S.: 524114

PacifiCare Life & Health Insurance Company (1)
5995 Plaza Dr, Cypress, CA 90630
Tel.: (714) 952-1121
Web Site: http://www.uhcprovider.com
Health Insurance Services
N.A.I.C.S.: 524113

PacifiCare of Colorado, Inc. (1)
6455 S Yosemite St, Greenwood Village, CO 80111
Tel.: (302) 220-5800
Web Site: http://www.pacificare.com
Health Care Company
N.A.I.C.S.: 524114
Robert James Gregoire (CFO)

PacifiCare of Oklahoma, Inc. (1)
7666 E 61st Ste 500, Tulsa, OK 74133-1143
Tel.: (918) 459-1100
Sales Range: $50-74.9 Million
Emp.: 115
Health Care Company
N.A.I.C.S.: 524114

PacifiCare of Texas, Inc. (1)
6200 Northwest Pkwy, San Antonio, TX 78249
Tel.: (210) 474-5000
Sales Range: $100-124.9 Million
Emp.: 450
Health Care Company
N.A.I.C.S.: 524114

Pacific Cardiovascular Associates Medical Group, Inc. (1)
3070 Bristol St Ste 190, Costa Mesa, CA 92626
Web Site: http://www.pcacardiology.com
Outpatient Surgery & Health Care Services
N.A.I.C.S.: 622110
Joseph M. Ruggio (Founder & Pres)
Cheng-Hen Chen (Dir-Medical-Structural Heart Disease Program)
Christopher Tan (Dir-Medical Pediatric Cardiology Svcs)

Pacifico S.A. Entidad Prestadora de Salud (1)
Av Juan de Arona 830, San Isidro, Lima, Peru
Tel.: (51) 15135000
Web Site: https://www.pacifico.com.pe
Health Insurance Services
N.A.I.C.S.: 524114

Panama City Surgery Center, LLC (1)
1800 Jenks Ave, Panama City, FL 32405
Tel.: (850) 769-3191
Web Site: https://www.pcsurgery.org
Outpatient Surgery & Health Care Services
N.A.I.C.S.: 622110

Patient Care Associates, L.L.C. (1)
500 Grand Ave, Englewood, NJ 07631
Tel.: (201) 567-8090
Web Site: https://pcaasc.com
Hospital & Health Care Services
N.A.I.C.S.: 622110

PatientsLikeMe, LLC (1)
6 Liberty Square Ste 2602, Boston, MA 02109
Tel.: (617) 229-6530
Web Site: http://www.patientslikeme.com
Software Publisher
N.A.I.C.S.: 513210
Atul Dhir (CEO)

Payment Resolution Services, LLC (1)
1021 Windcross Ct, Franklin, TN 37067-2678
Tel.: (615) 503-1213
Web Site: http://www.payprs.com
Health Insurance Products & Specialized Care Services
N.A.I.C.S.: 524114

Peninsula Eye Surgery Center, LLC (1)
1128 W El Camino Real, Mountain View, CA 94040
Tel.: (650) 964-3200
Web Site: http://www.pesc2020.com
Eye Surgery Services
N.A.I.C.S.: 622110

Peoples Health, Inc. (1)
3 Lakeway Ctr 3838 N Causeway Blvd Ste 2200, Metairie, LA 70002
Tel.: (504) 849-4500
Web Site: https://www.peopleshealth.com
Medical Insurance Carrier Services
N.A.I.C.S.: 524114
Colin Hulin (CIO)
Michael J. Robert (Sr VP-Internal Audit & Compliance)
Emmet Geary (VP-Fin & Controller)
Thomas Gennaro (VP-Network Dev)

Perham Physical Therapy, Ltd. (1)
1000 Coney Ste W, Perham, MN 56573
Tel.: (218) 347-4500
Web Site: https://www.perhamhealth.org
Hospital & Health Care Services
N.A.I.C.S.: 622110

Physician Alliance of the Rockies, LLC (1)
1707 Cole Blvd Ste 100, Golden, CO 80401
Tel.: (720) 445-9404
Web Site: https://www.paotr.com
Medical Care Services

N.A.I.C.S.: 621999

Physician Care Partners, Inc. (1)
4415 Harrison St Ste 300, Hillside, IL 60162-1910
Tel.: (708) 432-4047
Health Care Srvices
N.A.I.C.S.: 621999

Physicians Choice Insurance Service, LLC (1)
11 Technology Dr, Irvine, CA 92618
Tel.: (949) 614-7096
Web Site: http://zapquote4.appspot.com
Insurance Management Services
N.A.I.C.S.: 524114

Physicians Day Surgery Center, LLC (1)
850 111th Ave N, Naples, FL 34108-1803
Tel.: (239) 596-2557
Web Site:
  https://www.physiciansdaysurgery.net
General Medical & Surgical Services
N.A.I.C.S.: 622110

Physicians Health Choice of Texas, LLC (1)
8637 Fredericksburg Rd Ste 400, San Antonio, TX 78229
Tel.: (210) 949-4100
Insurance Management Services
N.A.I.C.S.: 524114

Plano de Saude Ana Costa Ltda. (1)
Av Ana Costa 468, Gonzaga, Santos, Brazil
Tel.: (55) 1332851200
Web Site:
  https://www.anacostasaude.com.br
Health Insurance Services
N.A.I.C.S.: 524114

Pocono Ambulatory Surgery Center, Limited (1)
1 Storm St, Stroudsburg, PA 18360
Tel.: (570) 421-4978
Web Site: https://www.poconoasc.com
Outpatient Surgery & Health Care Services
N.A.I.C.S.: 622110
Linda Roccograndi Bravyak (CEO)

Practice Partners in Healthcare, LLC (1)
1 Chase Corp Dr Ste 200, Birmingham, AL 35244
Tel.: (205) 824-6250
Web Site: https://www.practicepartners.org
Medical Care Management Services
N.A.I.C.S.: 621999
Larry Taylor (Founder, Pres & CEO)
Lee Anne Blackwell (VP-Clinical Svcs)
Sheila Boros (VP-Ops)
Mark Edwards (CFO)
Lecia Willingham (Chief Dev Officer)
Eric J Woollen (VP)

Preferred Care Network, Inc. (1)
PO Box 30770, Salt Lake City, UT 84130-0770
Web Site: https://www.pcnhealth.com
Hospital & Health Care Services
N.A.I.C.S.: 622110

Preferred Care Partners Holding, Corp. (1)
7800 Coral Way, Miami, FL 33155
Tel.: (305) 260-7506
Holding Company
N.A.I.C.S.: 551112

Preferred Care Partners Medical Group, Inc. (1)
701 NW 57 Ave Ste 150, Miami, FL 33126
Tel.: (305) 260-2680
Web Site: http://www.mypcpmg.com
Health Care Srvices
N.A.I.C.S.: 621999

PrimeCare Medical Network, Inc. (1)
3990 Concours Ste 500, Ontario, CA 91764-7983
Tel.: (909) 605-8000
Web Site: http://www.primecare.com
Health Care Srvices
N.A.I.C.S.: 621999

PrimeCare of Citrus Valley, Inc. (1)
760 S Washburn Ave Ste 5, Corona, CA 92882
Tel.: (951) 737-0910

Health Care Srvices
N.A.I.C.S.: 621999
Robert Nelson (Pres)
Melissa Taylor (Dir-Medical)

PrimeCare of Corona, Inc. (1)
308 W 6th St Ste 101, Corona, CA 92882
Tel.: (951) 737-0910
Health Care Srvices
N.A.I.C.S.: 621999

PrimeCare of Hemet Valley, Inc. (1)
25500 Medical Center Dr, Murrieta, CA 92562
Tel.: (951) 696-6000
Emp.: 10
Health Care Srvices
N.A.I.C.S.: 621999
Kamran Qureshi (Dir-Medical)

PrimeCare of Inland Valley, Inc. (1)
8250 White Oak Ave Ste 106, Rancho Cucamonga, CA 91730-8540
Tel.: (909) 361-6090
Health Care Srvices
N.A.I.C.S.: 621999

PrimeCare of Moreno Valley, Inc. (1)
1467 Ford St Ste 103, Redlands, CA 92373
Tel.: (909) 792-5375
Health Care Srvices
N.A.I.C.S.: 621999
Jose Limon (Dir-Medical)

PrimeCare of Redlands, Inc. (1)
350 Terracina Blvd, Redlands, CA 92373
Tel.: (909) 335-5500
Health Care Srvices
N.A.I.C.S.: 621999

PrimeCare of Riverside, Inc. (1)
2071 Compton Ave Ste 102, Corona, CA 92881
Tel.: (951) 549-0900
Web Site: http://www.unitedhealthcare.com
Emp.: 400
Health Care Srvices
N.A.I.C.S.: 621999
Chulwhe Koo (Mng Dir)

PrimeCare of San Bernardino, Inc. (1)
1467 Ford St Ste 103, Redlands, CA 92373
Tel.: (909) 792-5375
Emp.: 8
Health Care Srvices
N.A.I.C.S.: 621999
Badran Madani (Dir-Medical)

PrimeCare of Sun City, Inc. (1)
41391 Kalmia St Ste 310, Murrieta, CA 92562
Tel.: (951) 461-0762
Emp.: 16
Health Care Srvices
N.A.I.C.S.: 621999
Richard Evans (Dir-Medical)
James Krieg (Dir-Medical)

PrimeCare of Temecula, Inc. (1)
41391 Kalmia St Ste 310, Murrieta, CA 92562
Tel.: (951) 461-0762
Emp.: 4
Health Care Srvices
N.A.I.C.S.: 621999

ProHEALTH Fitness of Lake Success, LLC (1)
2800 Marcus Ave, Lake Success, NY 11042
Tel.: (516) 622-6000
Health Insurance Products & Specialized Care Services
N.A.I.C.S.: 524114

ProHealth/CareMount Dental Management, LLC (1)
1 ProHEALTH Plz Ste 115, Lake Success, NY 11042
Tel.: (516) 550-0075
Web Site: https://www.phdental.com
Dental Care Services
N.A.I.C.S.: 621210
Norton Travis (CEO)
Gina Schroeter (Chief Admin Officer)

Prosemedic S.A.C. (1)
Calle Santa Francisca Romana 880, Urb Pando 3era etapa, Lima, Peru
Tel.: (51) 15647171
Web Site: https://www.prosemedic.com

UnitedHealth Group Incorporated—(Continued)

Medical Instrument Mfr
N.A.I.C.S.: 339112
Jackeline Quevedo Tenorio *(Gen Mgr)*
Carmen Silva Davila *(COO)*
Ronald Arce Pretto *(Mgr-Commercial)*

Quality Software Services, Inc. (1)
10480 Little Patuxent Pkwy Ste 1200, Columbia, MD 21044
Tel.: (301) 977-7884
Information Technology Consulting Services
N.A.I.C.S.: 541512
Michael Finkel *(COO)*

QualityMetric Incorporated (1)
1301 Atwood Ave Ste 216E, Johnston, RI
02919
Tel.: (401) 334-8800
Web Site: https://www.qualitymetric.com
Sales Range: $25-49.9 Million
Emp.: 50
Health Surveys Services
N.A.I.C.S.: 541715
Garth Gardner *(CEO)*

Real Appeal, Inc. (1)
3000 K St NW Ste 350, Washington, DC
20007
Web Site: http://www.realappeal.com
Health Care Srvices
N.A.I.C.S.: 621999
Steve Olin *(CEO)*

Research Surgical Center, LLC (1)
2446 Research Pkwy Ste 100, Colorado
Springs, CO 80920
Tel.: (719) 418-4244
Web Site: https://scrockies.com
Ambulatory Surgery Center Services
N.A.I.C.S.: 621493

River Valley ASC, LLC (1)
45 Salem Tpke, Norwich, CT 06360
Tel.: (860) 859-9948
Web Site: https://www.rivervalleyasc.com
Medical Surgical Services
N.A.I.C.S.: 622110

**Riverside Surgical Center of Mead-
owlands, LLC** (1)
201 Route 17 N 12th Fl, Rutherford, NJ
07070
Tel.: (201) 806-2678
Web Site:
  https://www.riversidesurgicalcenterruther
  ford.com
Surgical Care Services
N.A.I.C.S.: 621493
Zain Halder *(CEO)*
Denise Acuna *(Dir-Nursing)*
Jordan Anderson *(CEO)*
Jordan Anderson *(CEO)*

**Rockville Eye Surgery Center,
LLC** (1)
4831 Cordell Ave, Bethesda, MD 20814
Tel.: (301) 657-8200
Web Site: https://palisadeseye.com
Eye Surgery Services
N.A.I.C.S.: 621320

**Rocky Mountain Health Maintenance
Organization, Incorporated** (1)
2775 Crossroads Blvd, Grand Junction, CO
81506-8712
Tel.: (970) 244-7960
Web Site: https://www.rmhp.org
Healtcare Services
N.A.I.C.S.: 621111

**Rush Oak Brook Surgery Center,
LLC** (1)
2011 York Rd Ste 3000, Oak Brook, IL
60523-2156
Tel.: (630) 472-2445
Web Site: https://www.rush.edu
Hospital & Health Care Services
N.A.I.C.S.: 622110

**SCA Premier Surgery Center of Lou-
isville, LLC** (1)
2511 Terra Crossing Blvd, Louisville, KY
40245
Tel.: (502) 589-9488
Web Site: https://www.pcslouisville.com
Ambulatory Surgical Center Services
N.A.I.C.S.: 621493
Robert Metz *(Dir-Medical)*
Tiffany Brock *(CEO)*

Alex Flaherty *(Office Mgr-Bus)*
Tina Underwood *(Mgr-Pre-op & PACU
Nurse)*
Shannon Feger *(Coord-Quality)*
April Niemeier *(Coord-Credentialing)*

SCA-Doral, LLC (1)
3650 NW 82nd Ave Ste 101, Miami, FL
33166
Tel.: (305) 341-7280
Web Site:
  https://www.surgerycenteratdoral.com
Ambulatory Surgical Center Services
N.A.I.C.S.: 621493

SCA-San Luis Obispo, LLC (1)
1304 Ella St Ste C, San Luis Obispo, CA
93401
Tel.: (805) 544-7874
Web Site: https://www.slosurgerycenter.com
Ambulatory Surgical Center Services
N.A.I.C.S.: 621493
Robert Hetzel *(Dir-Medical)*

SCA-Westover Hills, LLC (1)
1927 Rogers Rd, San Antonio, TX 78251
Tel.: (210) 267-1589
Web Site: https://www.scwestover.com
Ambulatory Surgical Center Services
N.A.I.C.S.: 621493
Monique Van De Walle *(CEO)*

SRPS, LLC (1)
33 Old Hickory Blvd E, Jackson, TN 38305
Tel.: (731) 664-4345
Web Site: https://www.srps.com
Pharmaceutical Preparation Mfr
N.A.I.C.S.: 325412

Salem Surgery Center, LLC (1)
2525 12th St SE Ste 110, Salem, OR
97302
Tel.: (503) 364-3704
Web Site:
  https://www.northbanksurgerycenter.com
Medical Surgical Services
N.A.I.C.S.: 622110
Mel Wade *(Dir-Medical)*
Terry Nelson *(Mgr-OR Nurse)*

Sand Lake SurgiCenter, LLC (1)
7477 Sandlake Commons Blvd, Orlando, FL
32819-8034
Tel.: (407) 264-9633
Web Site: https://www.sandlakesurgical.com
Medical Surgical Services
N.A.I.C.S.: 622110

**Santa Cruz Endoscopy Center,
LLC** (1)
1505 Soquel Dr Ste 4, Santa Cruz, CA
95065
Tel.: (831) 464-1871
Web Site:
  http://www.santacruzendoscopy.com
Health Care Srvices
N.A.I.C.S.: 621999
Julien Bouyssou *(Dir-Ops)*
Gordon Lee *(Dir-Medical)*
Teresa Martinez *(Mgr-Nurse)*

**Santa Helena Assistencia Medica
S.A.**
Rua Bering 114-Jardim do Mar, Sao Bernardo do Campo, Sao Paulo, Brazil
Tel.: (55) 1143369777
Web Site:
  http://www.santahelenasaude.com.br
Health Insurance Services
N.A.I.C.S.: 524114

Savvysherpa, LLC (1)
6200 Shingle Creek Pkwy Ste 400, Minneapolis, MN 55430
Tel.: (763) 549-3540
Web Site: http://www.savvysherpa.com
Health Care Investment Services
N.A.I.C.S.: 531120
Jeff Saunders *(Principal)*

Senior Care Partners, Inc. (1)
100 W Rd Ste 300, Towson, MD 21204
Tel.: (443) 743-3555
Web Site: https://www.srcarepartners.com
Health Care Srvices
N.A.I.C.S.: 621999

**Sierra Home Medical Products,
Inc.** (1)
5321 Cameron St, Las Vegas, NV 89118-
2202

Tel.: (702) 796-1016
Pharmaceutical Products Distr
N.A.I.C.S.: 424210

**Somerset Outpatient Surgery,
LLC** (1)
100 Franklin Square Dr Ste 100, Somerset,
NJ 08873
Tel.: (732) 560-1000
Web Site: https://raritansurgery.com
Outpatient Surgery & Healthcare Services
N.A.I.C.S.: 622110

Spectera Inc. (1)
10175 Little Patuxent Pkwy 6th Fl, Columbia, MD 21044
Web Site: http://www.spectera.com
Optical Retailers Operator
N.A.I.C.S.: 524126

St. Cloud Surgical Center, LLC (1)
1526 Northway Dr, Saint Cloud, MN 56303
Tel.: (320) 251-8385
Web Site: https://stcsurgicalcenter.com
Hospital Services
N.A.I.C.S.: 621111
Jay Krauss *(Dir-Medical)*
Darci Nagorski *(CEO)*
Carla Stephanie *(Dir-Clinical)*
Melissa Stang *(Mgr-Bus Office)*
David Harris *(Dir-Medical)*

**St. Louis Specialty Surgical Center,
LLC** (1)
1028 S Kirkwood Rd Ste B, Kirkwood, MO
63122
Tel.: (314) 394-2950
Web Site:
  https://stlspecialtysurgical.com
Specialty Surgery & Healthcare Services
N.A.I.C.S.: 622110

Stonegate Surgery Center, L.P. (1)
2501 W William Cannon Dr Ste 301, Austin,
TX 78745
Tel.: (512) 439-7300
Web Site:
  https://www.stonegatesurgerycenter.com
Ambulatory Surgical Center Services
N.A.I.C.S.: 621493
Chris Armstrong *(CEO)*

**Surgery Center at Cherry Creek,
LLC** (1)
5060 S Syracuse St, Denver, CO 80237
Tel.: (303) 770-1056
Web Site: http://www.surgerycenteratcherry
  creek.com
Ambulatory Surgical Center Services
N.A.I.C.S.: 621493

**Surgery Center at Cottonwood,
LLC** (1)
5450 S Green St Ste B, Murray, UT 84123
Tel.: (801) 262-0098
Web Site: https://sccottonwood.com
Outpatient Surgery & Healthcare Services
N.A.I.C.S.: 622110

**Surgery Center at Kissing Camels,
LLC** (1)
2955 Professional Pl Ste 100, Colorado
Springs, CO 80904
Tel.: (719) 633-2494
Web Site:
  https://www.surgerycenteratkissing
  camels.com
Ambulatory Surgical Center Services
N.A.I.C.S.: 621493

Surgery Center of Athens, LLC (1)
2142 W Broad St Bldg 100 Ste 100, Athens, GA 30606
Tel.: (706) 583-5080
Web Site:
  https://www.surgerycenterofathens.com
Ambulatory Surgical Center Services
N.A.I.C.S.: 621493
Robert Byrne *(Co-Owner)*
Charles Mixson *(Co-Owner)*
Stephanie Allen *(Co-Owner)*
Robert Cannon *(Co-Owner)*
Scotty Gadlin *(Co-Owner)*
Michael Jacobs *(Co-Owner)*
Elizabeth Katz *(Co-Owner)*
Blake Kimbrell *(Co-Owner)*
Andrew Leach *(Co-Owner)*
Byron Norris *(Co-Owner)*
Rhett Rainey *(Co-Owner)*
Joshua Sepesi *(Co-Owner)*

Javier Servat *(Co-Owner)*
Matthew Steele *(Co-Owner)*
Gary Walton *(Co-Owner)*
William Ashford *(Co-Owner)*
Samuel Belknap *(Co-Owner)*
Catherine Schwender *(Co-Owner)*

**Surgery Center of Clarksville,
L.P.** (1)
121 Hillcrest Dr, Clarksville, TN 37043
Tel.: (931) 552-9992
Web Site:
  http://surgerycenterofclarksville.com
Ambulatory Care Services
N.A.I.C.S.: 621493

**Surgery Center of Des Moines,
LLC** (1)
717 Lyon St, Des Moines, IA 50309
Tel.: (813) 571-7088
Web Site: https://www.scdmeast.com
Ambulatory Surgical Center Services
N.A.I.C.S.: 621493
Clay Ransdell *(Dir-Medical)*

**Surgery Center of Fort Collins,
LLC** (1)
1100 E Prospect Rd, Fort Collins, CO
80525
Tel.: (970) 821-8573
Web Site:
  https://www.surgerycenterftcollins.com
Fiscal Year-end: 12/31/2006
Healtcare Services
N.A.I.C.S.: 327910
Lisa S. *(Mgr-Materials)*

**Surgery Center of Lexington,
LLC** (1)
2115 Harrodsburg Rd, Lexington, KY 40504
Tel.: (859) 276-2525
Web Site:
  https://www.lexingtonsurgerycenter.com
Ambulatory Surgical Center Services
N.A.I.C.S.: 621493
Gina Clements *(Dir-Nursing)*
Stacie Harris *(Office Mgr-Bus)*

Surgery Center of Rockville, LLC (1)
2 Choke Cherry Rd Ste 125, Rockville, MD
20850
Tel.: (301) 330-8170
Web Site: http://www.scrockville.com
Ambulatory Surgical Center Services
N.A.I.C.S.: 621493

**Surgery Centers of Des Moines,
Ltd.** (1)
5901 Westown Pkwy Ste 100, West Des
Moines, IA 50266
Tel.: (515) 224-1984
Web Site: https://www.scdmwest.com
Ambulatory Surgical Center Services
N.A.I.C.S.: 621493
Monique Grant *(Office Mgr-Bus)*
Andrew Spellman *(Dir-Medical)*

Surgical Care Affiliates, LLC (1)
510 Lake Cook Rd Ste 400, Deerfield, IL
60015
Tel.: (847) 236-0921
Web Site: http://www.scasurgery.com
Surgical Solutions; Outpatient Surgical Facilities Operator
N.A.I.C.S.: 561110

Subsidiary (Domestic):

Grandview Surgery Center, Ltd. (2)
205 Grandview Ave Ste 101, Camp Hill, PA
17011
Tel.: (717) 731-5444
Web Site:
  https://www.grandviewsurgery.com
Outpatient Surgery Center
N.A.I.C.S.: 622110
Daniel P. Williams *(Dir-Medical)*
Kimberly Herchelroth *(Mgr-Nurse)*

Inland Surgery Center, L.P. (2)
1620 Laurel Ave, Redlands, CA 92373
Tel.: (909) 793-4701
Web Site: https://inlandsurgerycenter.com
Outpatient Surgery Center Services
N.A.I.C.S.: 621112
Sunnie Martinez *(Office Mgr)*
James Watson *(Dir-Medical)*
Michelle Mills *(CEO)*
Cheryl Stogsdill *(Dir)*
Steven Rimmer *(Dir-Medical)*
Wendy Sanchez *(Office Mgr-)*

Montgomery Surgery Center (2)
46 W Gude Dr, Rockville, MD 20850
Tel.: (301) 424-6901
Web Site:
   https://www.montgomerysurgery.com
Outpatient Surgery Center
N.A.I.C.S.: 621111
Sonja Sienkowski (Dir)
Howard Wilpon (Dir-Medical)
Glenn Sandler (Dir-Medical)
Bryan Grove (CEO)

Oregon Outpatient Surgery Center, LLC (2)
7300 SW Childs Rd Ste A, Tigard, OR 97224
Tel.: (503) 612-8452
Web Site:
   http://www.oregonoutpatientsurgery.com
Surgical Healthcare Services
N.A.I.C.S.: 622110

Seashore Surgical Intitute, LLC (2)
495 Jack Martin Blvd Ste 1, Brick, NJ 08724
Tel.: (732) 836-9800
Web Site: https://www.seashoresurgical.com
Fiscal Year-end: 12/31/2006
Healtcare Services
N.A.I.C.S.: 621999
Simone Calabrese (Principal)

Surgical Hospital of Oklahoma, LLC (2)
100 SE 59th St, Oklahoma City, OK 73129
Tel.: (405) 634-9300
Web Site: https://surgicalhospitalok.net
Hospital Operator
N.A.I.C.S.: 622110
Dana Younts (Dir-HR)
Kathy Vermillion (Mgr-Health Information)
Susan Nusz (Controller)
Cindy Braly (Chief Clinical Officer)
Wendy Wattenbarger (Dir)
Lisa Johnson (Chief Clinical Officer)
Mike Kimsey (CEO)
Terra Collie (Chief Clinical Officer)

Surgical Center of South Jersey, Limited Partnership (1)
130 Gaither Dr Ste 160, Mount Laurel, NJ 08054
Tel.: (856) 722-7000
Web Site: https://www.scasouthjersey.com
Ambulatory Surgical Center Services
N.A.I.C.S.: 621493

Surgicare of Central Jersey, LLC (1)
40 Stirling Rd, Watchung, NJ 07069
Tel.: (908) 769-8000
Web Site: https://www.surgicarecj.com
Ambulatory Surgery Services
N.A.I.C.S.: 622110
Melissa A. Mundy-De Torres (CEO)
Joseph Notaro (Dir-Medical)

Surgicare of Jackson, LLC (1)
760 Lakeland Dr, Jackson, MS 39216
Tel.: (601) 362-8700
Web Site:
   http://www.surgicareofjackson.com
Hospital Services
N.A.I.C.S.: 621111

Surgicare of Mobile, LLC (1)
2890 Dauphin St, Mobile, AL 36606
Tel.: (251) 473-2020
Web Site:
   https://www.surgicareofmobile.com
Ambulatory Surgical Center Services
N.A.I.C.S.: 621493
Courtney Fraser (Dir-Nursing)
Mandy Pugh (Office Mgr-Bus)
Sandy Bunch (CEO)
Jason Pugh (COO)

Sutter Alhambra Surgery Center, L.P. (1)
1201 Alhambra Blvd Ste 110, Sacramento, CA 95816
Tel.: (916) 733-8222
Web Site: https://www.sutterhealth.org
Orthopedic Surgery Services
N.A.I.C.S.: 621111

Tecnologias de Informacion en Salud S.A. (1)
Av Apoquindo 3001 piso 6, Las Condes, Santiago, Chile
Tel.: (56) 229133800
Web Site: https://www.tisal.cl
Medical Care Services
N.A.I.C.S.: 621999
Braulio Aranda (CEO)

Texas Health Surgery Center Chisholm Trail, LLC (1)
5900 Altamesa Blvd Ste 101, Fort Worth, TX 76132
Tel.: (682) 324-9255
Web Site:
   https://texashealthchisholmtrail.com
Ambulatory Surgery Center Services
N.A.I.C.S.: 621493

The Polyclinic (1)
904 7th Ave, Seattle, WA 98104
Tel.: (206) 329-1760
Web Site: http://www.polyclinic.com
Health Practitioners
N.A.I.C.S.: 621399
Martin Levine (Chief Medical Officer)

The Surgical Center of The Treasure Coast, LLC (1)
9075 S Federal Hwy, Port Saint Lucie, FL 34952
Tel.: (772) 398-9898
Web Site: https://www.sctcfl.com
Ambulatory Surgical Center Services
N.A.I.C.S.: 621493

Thomas Johnson Surgery Center, LLC (1)
197 Thomas Johnson Dr, Frederick, MD 21702
Tel.: (301) 631-3881
Web Site: https://www.tjsurgery.com
Ambulatory Surgical Center Services
N.A.I.C.S.: 621493

Trails Edge Surgery Center, LLC (1)
28930 Trails Edge Blvd Ste 100, Bonita Springs, FL 34134
Tel.: (239) 495-4300
Web Site:
   https://www.trailsedgesurgerycenter.com
Ambulatory Surgical Center Services
N.A.I.C.S.: 621493

Tucson Arizona Surgical Center, LLC (1)
2121 N Craycroft Rd Bldg 8, Tucson, AZ 85712
Tel.: (520) 731-5500
Web Site: https://www.tucsonsc.com
Ambulatory Surgical Center Services
N.A.I.C.S.: 621493

UHC of California (1)
5995 Plz Dr Mail Stop CY20-327, Cypress, CA 90630
Tel.: (714) 952-1121
Web Site: http://www.uhc.com
Health Insurance Services
N.A.I.C.S.: 524114
Alexander Uhm (COO)

UHC of California (1)
2300 Clayton Rd Ste 1000, Concord, CA 94520
Tel.: (925) 246-1300
Web Site: http://www.uhc.com
Health Insurance Products & Specialized Care Services
N.A.I.C.S.: 524114

UMR, Inc. (1)
PO Box 30541, Salt Lake City, UT 84130-0541
Tel.: (866) 922-8266
Web Site: http://www.umr.com
Insurance Management Services
N.A.I.C.S.: 524114

Ultima Rx, LLC (1)
3900 NW 79th Ave, Miami, FL 33166
Tel.: (305) 500-2900
Medical Care Equipment Distr
N.A.I.C.S.: 423450

United Medical Park ASC, LLC (1)
1731 W Ridgeway Ave, Waterloo, IA 50701-4595
Tel.: (319) 833-5800
Web Site: https://www.surgerycenter-ump.com
Hospital & Health Care Services
N.A.I.C.S.: 622110

UnitedHealth Group Global Healthcare Services Limited (1)
Letterkenny Business Park, Letterkenny, Donegal, Ireland
Tel.: (353) 749129356
Web Site: http://www.uhc.com
Emp.: 600
Health Care Srvices
N.A.I.C.S.: 621999

UnitedHealth Group Global Services, Inc. (1)
6th to 10th Floors Science Hub Tower 1 McKinley Hill, Fort Bonifacio, Taguig, 1634, Philippines
Tel.: (63) 25556326
Health Care Srvices
N.A.I.C.S.: 621999

UnitedHealthcare Benefits of Texas, Inc. (1)
5001 LBJ Freeway Ste 600, Dallas, TX 75244
Tel.: (210) 474-5000
Health Care Srvices
N.A.I.C.S.: 621999

UnitedHealthcare India Private Limited (1)
Unit 5 4th floor Awfis Skyline Icon Andheri - Kurla Road, Chimatpada Marol Andheri East, Mumbai, 400059, Maharashtra, India
Tel.: (91) 2262535606
Web Site: https://www.alineahealthcare.in
Health Care Srvices
N.A.I.C.S.: 621999

UnitedHealthcare Life Insurance Company (1)
7440 Woodland Dr Dept 100, Indianapolis, IN 46278
Tel.: (317) 715-7111
Web Site: http://www.uhone.com
Emp.: 750
Insurance Management Services
N.A.I.C.S.: 524114

UnitedHealthcare Plan of the River Valley, Inc. (1)
9700 Health Care Ln, Minnetonka, MN 55343
Tel.: (952) 979-6175
Health Care Srvices
N.A.I.C.S.: 621491

UnitedHealthcare Service LLC (1)
PO Box 740815, Atlanta, GA 30374-0815
Pharmaceutical Preparation Mfr
N.A.I.C.S.: 325412

UnitedHealthcare of Oklahoma, Inc. (1)
5800 Granite Pkwy Ste 700, Plano, TX 75024
Tel.: (800) 842-2481
Health Insurance Services
N.A.I.C.S.: 524114

UnitedHealthcare of Oregon, Inc. (1)
5 Centerpointe Dr Ste 600, Lake Oswego, OR 97035
Tel.: (503) 603-7355
Web Site: http://www.uhc.com
Health Insurance Services
N.A.I.C.S.: 524114

UnitedHealthcare of Texas, Inc. (1)
1250 S Capital of Texas Hwy Bldg 1 Ste 360, Austin, TX 78746
Tel.: (512) 347-2600
Insurance Management Services
N.A.I.C.S.: 524114
Joanne Shuey (VP-Key Acct Sls & Acct Mgmt-North)

UnitedHealthcare, Inc. (1)
9900 Bren Rd E, Minnetonka, MN 55343-9664
Tel.: (952) 936-1300
Web Site: http://www.unitedhealthcare.com
Sales Range: $700-749.9 Million
Emp.: 1,000
Medical Service Plans
N.A.I.C.S.: 524114
John Cosgriff (Sr VP-Business Development)
Brian Brueckman (Exec VP-Operations)
Phil McKoy (CIO)
Anne Docimo (Chief Medical Officer)

Thad Johnson (Chief Legal Officer)
Jenny O'Brien (Chief Compliance Officer)
Kirsten Gorsuch (Chief Comm Officer)
Jeff Putnam (CFO)
Braden McLellan (VP-Sls & Acct Mgmt)
Brian Thompson (CEO)
Bill Golden (CEO)
Vicki Miller (Pres)
Mary Murley (Sr VP-Risk)
Krista Nelson (Chief Growth & Experience Officer)
Mary Murley (Sr VP-Risk)
Krista Nelson (Chief Growth & Experience Officer)
Stephanie L. Fehr (Chief Human Capital Officer & Exec VP)
Vicki Miller (Pres-Networks)

Subsidiary (Domestic):

Unison Health Plan of Delaware, Inc. (2)
726 Yorklyn Rd Ste 200, Hockessin, DE 19707
Tel.: (800) 600-9007
Web Site:
   http://www.uhccommunityplan.com
Health Care Insurance Services
N.A.I.C.S.: 524114

Division (Domestic):

United HealthCare Services, Inc. (2)
5901 Lincoln Dr, Edina, MN 55436 **(100%)**
Tel.: (952) 992-7777
Web Site: https://www.uhc.com
Sales Range: $50-74.9 Million
Emp.: 100
Health Care Management Services
N.A.I.C.S.: 524114

Subsidiary (Non-US):

Golden Rule Financial Corp. (3)
Tel.: (317) 297-4123
Web Site: http://www.goldenrule.com
Emp.: 300
Provider of Accident, Life & Health Insurance
N.A.I.C.S.: 524113

Subsidiary (Non-US):

American Medical Security Life Insurance Company (4)
Tel.: (920) 661-1111
Web Site: http://www.eams.com
Sales Range: $700-749.9 Million
Healthcare Insurance
N.A.I.C.S.: 524114

Golden Rule Insurance Company Inc. (4)
Tel.: (317) 715-7111
Web Site: http://www.unitedhealthone.com
Sales Range: $350-399.9 Million
Health Insurance Services
N.A.I.C.S.: 524114

Subsidiary (Domestic):

Medica Health Plans of Florida, Inc. (3)
9100SDadeland, Miami, FL 33156
Tel.: (305) 460-0600
Holding Company; Health Insurance Products & Services
N.A.I.C.S.: 551112

Subsidiary (Domestic):

Medica HealthCare Plans, Inc. (4)
9100 S Dadeland Blvd Ste 1250, Miami, FL 33156
Tel.: (305) 460-0600
Medicare-Sponsored Health Insurance Products & Services
N.A.I.C.S.: 524114
Rafael Perez (Pres)

Subsidiary (Domestic):

Preferred Care Partners, Inc. (3)
1 Datran Ctr 9100 S Dadeland Blvd Ste 1250, Miami, FL 33156
Tel.: (305) 670-8440
Web Site: https://www.mypreferredcare.com

UnitedHealth Group Incorporated—(Continued)

Sales Range: $550-599.9 Million
Medicare HMO for Seniors
N.A.I.C.S.: 524114

United Behavioral Health (3)
425 Market St, San Francisco, CA 94105-2479
Tel.: (415) 547-5000
Web Site:
   http://www.unitedbehavioralhealth.com
Sales Range: $50-74.9 Million
Wealth Management Services
N.A.I.C.S.: 541611

**UnitedHealthcare Insurance
Company** (3)
185 Asylum St, Hartford, CT
06103 (100%)
Tel.: (860) 702-5000
Web Site: http://www.unitedhealthcare.com
Provider of Life & Health Insurance
N.A.I.C.S.: 524113
Dan Schumacher (Pres)

Subsidiary (Domestic):

**UnitedHealthcare Arizona Physicians
IPA** (2)
3141 N 3rd Ave, Phoenix, AZ 85013
Tel.: (602) 417-7100
Web Site: http://www.uhcapipa.com
Sales Range: $100-124.9 Million
Emp.: 320
Accident & Health Insurance
N.A.I.C.S.: 524114

UnitedHealthcare Nevada (2)
2720 N Tenaya Way, Las Vegas, NV
89128-0424
Tel.: (702) 242-7000
Health Maintenance Organization, Life Insurance Company, Multi-Specialty Medical Group, Home Health Care Company, Hospice & Benefits Consulting Services
N.A.I.C.S.: 524114

Subsidiary (Domestic):

**Behavioral Healthcare Options,
Inc.** (3)
2716 N Tenaya Way, Las Vegas, NV 89128
Tel.: (702) 364-1484
Web Site: https://www.bhoptions.com
Sales Range: $10-24.9 Million
Mental Health, Addiction Treatment, Employee Assistance & Work/Life Services
N.A.I.C.S.: 621420

Family Health Care Services (3)
8655 S Eastern Ave, Las Vegas, NV 89123-2839
Tel.: (702) 242-7000
Web Site: http://www.uhc.com
Sales Range: $50-74.9 Million
Emp.: 275
Health Care Srvices
N.A.I.C.S.: 621610

Family Home Hospice, Inc. (3)
8655 S E Ave, Las Vegas, NV 89123
Tel.: (702) 671-1111
Licensed Hospice Services
N.A.I.C.S.: 621610

Health Plan of Nevada, Inc. (3)
2720 N Tenaya Way Ste 102, Las Vegas,
NV 89128-0424
Tel.: (702) 242-7300
Web Site:
   https://www.healthplanofnevada.com
Sales Range: $150-199.9 Million
Emp.: 300
Health Maintenance Organization
N.A.I.C.S.: 524114

Sierra Health & Life Insurance Company, Inc. (3)
2720 N Tenaya Way Ste 102, Las Vegas,
NV 89128-0424
Tel.: (702) 242-7700
Web Site:
   https://www.sierrahealthandlife.com
Sales Range: $150-199.9 Million
Life & Health Insurance Company
N.A.I.C.S.: 524113

Sierra Health-Care Options, Inc. (3)
2720 N Tenaya Way, Las Vegas, NV
89128-0424

Tel.: (702) 242-7840
Web Site:
   https://www.sierrahealthcareoptions.com
Sales Range: $10-24.9 Million
Emp.: 29
Self-Insured Employers Healthcare Administrative Services
N.A.I.C.S.: 524114

Southwest Medical Associates (3)
2350 W Charleston Blvd, Las Vegas, NV
89102-2149
Tel.: (702) 877-5199
Web Site: https://www.smalv.com
Sales Range: $50-74.9 Million
Emp.: 400
Medical Devices
N.A.I.C.S.: 621111

Subsidiary (Domestic):

**UnitedHealthcare of Alabama,
Inc.** (2)
33 Inverness Center Pkwy Ste 350, Birmingham, AL 35242
Tel.: (205) 977-6300
Web Site: http://www.uhc.com
Sales Range: $350-399.9 Million
Emp.: 75
Group Hospitalization Plans
N.A.I.C.S.: 524126

**UnitedHealthcare of Arkansas,
Inc.** (2)
1401 W Capitol Ave Ste 375, Little Rock,
AR 72201
Tel.: (501) 664-7700
Web Site: http://www.uhc.com
Group Hospitalization Plans
N.A.I.C.S.: 524114

**UnitedHealthcare of Colorado,
Inc.** (2)
6465 Greenwood Plaza Blvd Ste 300, Centennial, CO 80111
Tel.: (303) 267-3300
Health Care Insurance Services
N.A.I.C.S.: 524114
Beth Soberg (Pres/CEO-Arizona, Colorado
& New Mexico)

UnitedHealthcare of Florida, Inc. (2)
495 N Keller Rd Ste 200, Maitland, FL
32751
Tel.: (407) 659-6900
Web Site: http://www.uhc.com
Sales Range: $125-149.9 Million
Emp.: 250
Insurance through Health Maintenance Organization
N.A.I.C.S.: 524114

**UnitedHealthcare of Georgia,
Inc.** (2)
3720 Davinci Ct Ste 400, Norcross, GA
30092
Tel.: (952) 992-7077
Web Site: http://www.uhc.com
Sales Range: $100-124.9 Million
Emp.: 200
Health Maintenance Organization Insurance Only
N.A.I.C.S.: 524114
Dan Ohman (Pres & CEO)

UnitedHealthcare of Illinois, Inc. (2)
233 N Michigan Ave, Chicago, IL
60601 (100%)
Tel.: (312) 424-4460
Web Site: http://www.unitedhealthcare.com
Health Maintenance Organization
N.A.I.C.S.: 524114

**UnitedHealthcare of Mississippi,
Inc.** (2)
795 Woodland Pkwy Ste 301, Ridgeland,
MS 39157-5215
Tel.: (601) 956-8030
Web Site: http://www.mid.state.ms.us
Sales Range: $1-9.9 Million
Emp.: 12
Group Hospitalization Plans
N.A.I.C.S.: 524114

**UnitedHealthcare of New England,
Inc.** (2)
475 Kilvert St 310, Warwick, RI 02886
Tel.: (401) 737-6900
Web Site: http://www.unitedhealthcare.com

Sales Range: $200-249.9 Million
Emp.: 400
Insurance Health Maintenance Organization
N.A.I.C.S.: 524114
Stephen J. Farrell (CEO)

**UnitedHealthcare of North Carolina,
Inc.** (2)
3803 N Elm St, Greensboro, NC 27455-2593
Tel.: (336) 540-2000
Web Site: http://www.uhc.com
Sales Range: $150-199.9 Million
Hospital & Medical Service Plans
N.A.I.C.S.: 524114

UnitedHealthcare of Ohio, Inc. (2)
9200 Worthington Rd, Westerville, OH
43082 (100%)
Tel.: (614) 410-7000
Web Site: http://www.unitedhealthcare.com
Sales Range: $200-249.9 Million
Emp.: 400
Medical Insurance Services
N.A.I.C.S.: 524114

**UnitedHealthcare of Washington,
Inc.** (2)
7525 SE 24th St Ste 200, Mercer Island,
WA 98040
Tel.: (206) 236-2500
Web Site: http://www.uhc.com
Sales Range: $25-49.9 Million
Emp.: 150
Health Care Company
N.A.I.C.S.: 541611

**UnitedHealthcare of Wisconsin,
Inc.** (2)
10701 W Research Dr, Milwaukee, WI
53226-3452
Tel.: (414) 443-4000
Web Site: http://www.unitedhealthcare.com
Sales Range: $25-49.9 Million
Emp.: 70
Health Maintenance Organization
N.A.I.C.S.: 524114

**UnitedHealthcare of the Midlands,
Inc.** (2)
2717 N 118th St Ste 300, Omaha, NE
68164-9672
Tel.: (402) 445-5000
Web Site: http://www.uhc.com
Sales Range: $50-74.9 Million
Emp.: 150
Health Insurance Maintenance Organization
N.A.I.C.S.: 524114

**UnitedHealthcare of the Midwest,
Inc.** (2)
13655 Riverport Dr, Maryland Heights, MO
63043-4812
Tel.: (314) 592-7000
Web Site: http://www.uhc.com
Health Insurance Services
N.A.I.C.S.: 524114

**Upland Outpatient Surgical Center,
L.P.** (1)
1211 W 6th St, Ontario, CA 91762
Tel.: (909) 981-8755
Web Site:
   https://ontarioadvancedsurgerycenter.com
Healtcare Services
N.A.I.C.S.: 621610
Thomas Easter (Dir-Medical)
Amy Wright (CEO)

Urgent Care MSO, LLC (1)
1751 Earl Core Rd, Morgantown, WV
26505
Tel.: (304) 225-2500
Web Site: http://www.medexpress.com
Health Care Srvices
N.A.I.C.S.: 621491
Jane Trombetta (Chief Clinical Officer)
Amie Carter (VP)
Dena Nader (Reg Dir-Medical)
Dheeraj Taranath (Reg Dir-Medical)
Ellen Dietrick (Mgr)
Danin Cather (Mgr)
Kenneth Kotts (Mgr)
Amanda Gray (Mgr)
Chris Kunis (Dir-Medical-Area)
Jeffrey Frye (Dir-Medical-Area)
Reed Erickson (Dir-Medical-Area)
Candace McCormick (Dir-Compliance)
Alex Negle (Sls Mgr)
Alex Negle (Sls Mgr)

VPay Benefits Corporation (1)
3701 W Plano Pkwy Ste 200, Plano, TX
75075-7837
Tel.: (469) 543-6500
Web Site: https://www.vpayusa.com
Hospital & Health Care Services
N.A.I.C.S.: 622110

Valley Physicians Network, Inc. (1)
24630 Washington Ave Ste 203, Murrieta,
CA 92562
Tel.: (951) 704-1900
Web Site:
   http://www.valleyphysiciansnetwork.com
Health Care Srvices
N.A.I.C.S.: 621999

Virtual Therapeutics Corporation (1)
13905 NE 128th St Ste 200, Kirkland, WA
98034
Tel.: (425) 821-8001
Web Site: https://www.vthera.com
Mental Health Care Services
N.A.I.C.S.: 621112
Daniel J. Elenbaas (Pres)
Matt McIntire (Treas & Sec)

Subsidiary (Domestic):

Akili Inc. (2)
22 Boston Wharf Rd 7th Fl, Boston, MA
02210
Tel.: (650) 931-6236
Web Site: https://www.akiliinteractive.com
Rev.: $323,000
Assets: $144,557,000
Liabilities: $33,878,000
Net Worth: $110,679,000
Earnings: ($7,964,000)
Emp.: 109
Fiscal Year-end: 12/31/2022
Computer System Design Services
N.A.I.C.S.: 541512
Shamir Shah (CFO)
Alan Boyer (Pres)
Chamath Palihapitiya (Chm)
Shiek Shah (CEO)
Sean Bradley (VP-Prof Svcs)
Jason Sangworn (VP-Pre-Sls)
Bryan Betzer (Dir-Engagement)
Sid Powar (Dir-Supply Chain)

Vivify Health, Inc. (1)
7201 Bishop Rd E-200, Plano, TX 75024
Web Site: https://www.vivifyhealth.com
Women Healthcare Services
N.A.I.C.S.: 621610
Eric Rock (Founder & CEO)
Ed Gillen (COO)
Michael Hawkins (CTO)
Chris Fickle (Sr VP-Sales)
Bill Paschall (VP-Business Development)
David Lucas (Chief Strategy Officer)

**WESTMED Practice Partners
LLC** (1)
2700 Westchester Ave, Purchase, NY
10577
Tel.: (914) 848-8500
Web Site: http://www.westmedpartners.com
Health Insurance Products & Specialized Care Services
N.A.I.C.S.: 551112
Merin Joseph (CIO & Exec VP)
Vicki McKinney (COO & Chief Revenue Officer)
Arthur I. Forni (CEO)
Calie Santana (Dir-Medical)

**Wauwatosa Surgery Center, Limited
Partnership** (1)
10900 W Potter Rd, Wauwatosa, WI 53226
Tel.: (414) 774-9227
Web Site:
   https://www.wauwatosasurgerycenter.com
Ambulatory Surgical Center Services
N.A.I.C.S.: 621493
Tony Wilbur (Dir-Nursing)
Colleen Morehouse (Office Mgr-Bus)
Charles Kidd (Dir-Medical)

**WellMed Medical Management of
Florida, Inc.** (1)
591 Oak Commons Blvd, Kissimmee, FL
34741
Tel.: (210) 877-7570

Medical Clinic Care Services
N.A.I.C.S.: 621610

West Coast Endoscopy Holdings, LLC (1)
616 E St Ste A, Clearwater, FL 33756
Tel.: (727) 447-0888
Web Site:
https://www.westcoastendoscopy.com
Ambulatory Surgical Center Services
N.A.I.C.S.: 621493
Kim Jiran *(Dir-Nursing)*

WestHealth Surgery Center, LLC (1)
2855 Campus Dr, Plymouth, MN 55441-2649
Tel.: (763) 302-2800
Web Site:
https://westhealthsurgerycenter.com
Hospital & Health Care Services
N.A.I.C.S.: 622110

Western Connecticut Orthopedic Surgical Center, LLC (1)
226 White St, Danbury, CT 06810
Tel.: (203) 791-9557
Web Site: https://wcosc.org
Ambulatory Surgical Center Services
N.A.I.C.S.: 621493
Diane Heelan *(Dir-Nursing)*
John Lunt *(Dir-Medical)*
Eleyce Winn *(CEO)*

Wilmington ASC, LLC (1)
1202 Medical Center Dr, Wilmington, NC 28401
Tel.: (910) 341-3300
Web Site: https://www.wilmingtonhealth.com
Ambulatory Surgical Center Services
N.A.I.C.S.: 621493
Jeff James *(CEO)*
Jonathan Hines *(Chief Medical Officer)*
Brian Webster *(Chief Medical Information Officer)*

Winchester Endoscopy, LLC (1)
1870 W Winchester Rd Ste 146, Libertyville, IL 60048
Tel.: (224) 433-6505
Web Site: http://www.winchesterendo.com
Ambulatory Surgical Center Services
N.A.I.C.S.: 621493
Kate Nor *(CEO)*

eCode Solutions, LLC (1)
994 E Ash St, Canton, IL 61520
Tel.: (309) 303-0748
Web Site: https://ecode.solutions
Medical Billing Services
N.A.I.C.S.: 541219

gethealthinsurance.com Agency Inc. (1)
7440 Woodland Dr, Indianapolis, IN 46278-1719
Web Site:
https://www.gethealthinsurance.com
Health Insurance Carrier Services
N.A.I.C.S.: 524114

hCentive, Inc. (1)
12355 Sunrise Valley Dr Ste 400, Reston, VA 20191-3424
Web Site: http://www.hcentive.com
Ambulatory Health Care Services
N.A.I.C.S.: 621999

ppoONE, Inc. (1)
1311 W President George Bush Hwy 1st Fl, Richardson, TX 75080
Tel.: (214) 273-8915
Web Site: http://www.ppoone.com
Data Management & Information Services
N.A.I.C.S.: 519290

UNITI GROUP INC.
2101 Riverfront Dr, Little Rock, AR 72202
Tel.: (501) 850-0820   MD
Web Site: https://www.uniti.com
Year Founded: 2015
UNIT—(NASDAQ)
Rev.: $1,128,847,000
Assets: $4,851,229,000
Liabilities: $7,122,435,000
Net Worth: ($2,271,206,000)
Earnings: ($9,430,000)
Emp.: 784

Fiscal Year-end: 12/31/22
Real Estate Investment Trust
N.A.I.C.S.: 525990
Paul Bullington *(CFO, Treas & Sr VP)*
Daniel L. Heard *(Exec VP)*
Kenneth A. Gunderman *(Pres & CEO)*
Ronald J. Mudry *(Chief Revenue Officer & Sr VP)*
Andy Newton *(Pres-Uniti Fiber)*
Ric Chura *(CIO)*
Travis Black *(Chief Acctg Officer)*
Ryan Fitzgerald *(Sr VP)*

Subsidiaries:

Hunt Telecommunications LLC (1)
106 Metairie Lawn Dr Ste 200, Metairie, LA 70001
Tel.: (985) 281-4913
Web Site: http://www.hunttelecom.com
Rev.: $1,200,000
Emp.: 15
Telephone, Internet & Associated Data Services
N.A.I.C.S.: 517111

Information Transport Solutions, Inc (1)
335 Jeanette Barrett Industrial Blvd, Wetumpka, AL 36092
Tel.: (334) 567-1993
Web Site: http://www.its-networks.com
Voice, Video & Data Technology Solutions
N.A.I.C.S.: 518210
Brian Sims *(VP-Tech)*

PEG Bandwidth, LLC (1)
5904 Stone Creek Dr Ste 130, The Colony, TX 75056
Tel.: (469) 213-6100
Web Site: http://www.PEGBandwidth.com
Sales Range: $25-49.9 Million
Emp.: 115
Telecommunications Support Services
N.A.I.C.S.: 517111

Uniti Fiber (1)
107 Saint Francis St Ste 1800, Mobile, AL 36602   (100%)
Tel.: (251) 662-1170
Web Site: http://www.uniti.com
Fiber-Optic Communications Solutions
N.A.I.C.S.: 335921
Andy Newton *(Pres)*
Cathy De La Garza *(Sr VP)*
Eric Daniels *(Sr VP)*
Joe McCourt *(Sr VP)*
Ryan Fitzgerald *(Sr VP)*

UNITIL CORPORATION
6 Liberty Ln W, Hampton, NH 03842
Tel.: (603) 772-0775   NH
Web Site: https://www.unitil.com
Year Founded: 1984
UTL—(NYSE)
Rev.: $557,100,000
Assets: $1,670,400,000
Liabilities: $672,000,000
Net Worth: $998,400,000
Earnings: $45,200,000
Emp.: 531
Fiscal Year-end: 12/31/23
Electric Utility Holding Company
N.A.I.C.S.: 551112
Thomas P. Meissner Jr. *(Chm & CEO)*
Daniel J. Hurstak *(CFO, Treas & Sr VP)*
Robert B. Hevert *(Pres & Chief Admin Officer)*
Todd R. Diggins *(Chief Acctg Officer & Controller)*
Todd Black *(Sr VP)*

Subsidiaries:

Granite State Gas Transmission, Inc. (1)
325 W Rd, Portsmouth, NH 03801 (100%)
Natural Gas Transmission Pipeline
N.A.I.C.S.: 486210

Unitil (1)
325 W Rd, Portsmouth, NH 03801

Tel.: (603) 294-5174
Web Site: http://www.unitil.com
Sales Range: $50-74.9 Million
Emp.: 179
Gas Distribution Utility
N.A.I.C.S.: 221210

Unitil Energy Systems, Inc. (1)
6 Liberty Ln W, Hampton, NH 03842-1704   (100%)
Tel.: (603) 772-0775
Sales Range: $25-49.9 Million
Emp.: 100
Electricity Distribution
N.A.I.C.S.: 221118

Unitil Power Corporation (1)
6 Liberty Ln W, Hampton, NH 03842-1720   (100%)
Tel.: (603) 772-0775
Rev.: $78,000,000
Emp.: 100
Wholesale Power & Transmission of Electricity
N.A.I.C.S.: 221118

Unitil Realty Corp. (1)
6 Liberty Ln W, Hampton, NH 03842
Tel.: (603) 772-0775
Emp.: 100
Real Estate Manamgement Services
N.A.I.C.S.: 531210

Unitil Resources, Inc. (1)
6 Liberty Ln W, Hampton, NH 03842-1720   (100%)
Tel.: (603) 772-0775
Web Site: http://www.unitil.com
Sales Range: $25-49.9 Million
Energy Marketing & Consulting Services
N.A.I.C.S.: 221118

Subsidiary (Domestic):

Usource LLC (2)
1 Liberty Ln E Ste 200, Hampton, NH 03842
Tel.: (603) 772-0775
Web Site: http://www.usourceenergy.com
Emp.: 150
Energy Procurement & Strategic Consulting Services
N.A.I.C.S.: 424720

Unitil Service Corp. (1)
6 Liberty Ln W, Hampton, NH 03842-1704   (100%)
Tel.: (603) 772-0775
Sales Range: $1-9.9 Million
Emp.: 150
Real Estate in Support of the Electric Utility Business
N.A.I.C.S.: 561110

UNITY BANCORP, INC.
64 Old Hwy 22, Clinton, NJ 08809
Tel.: (908) 730-7630   DE
Web Site: https://www.unitybank.com
Year Founded: 1991
UNTY—(NASDAQ)
Rev.: $108,784,000
Assets: $2,444,948,000
Liabilities: $2,205,721,000
Net Worth: $239,227,000
Earnings: $38,457,000
Emp.: 224
Fiscal Year-end: 12/31/22
Bank Holding Company
N.A.I.C.S.: 551111
David D. Dallas *(Chm)*
James A. Hughes *(Pres & CEO)*
Aaron Tucker *(Bd of Dirs & Vice Chm)*
George Boyan *(CFO & Exec VP)*

Subsidiaries:

Unity Bank (1)
64 Old Hwy 22, Clinton, NJ 08809
Tel.: (908) 713-4580
Web Site: https://www.unitybank.com
Sales Range: $50-74.9 Million
Emp.: 100
Banking
N.A.I.C.S.: 522110
David D. Dallas *(Co-Founder & Chm)*
James A. Hughes *(Pres & CEO)*

Robert H. Dallas II *(Co-Founder)*
George Boyan *(CFO)*
Ryan Peene *(Chief Depository Officer & Sr VP)*
Daniel Sharabba *(Sr VP)*

Subsidiary (Domestic):

Unity Financial Services, Inc. (2)
610 N Town E Blvd Ste 102, Mesquite, TX 75150
Tel.: (972) 329-9453
Web Site: http://www.unity-financial.com
Mortgage Loan Brokerage Services
N.A.I.C.S.: 522310

Unity Delaware Investment 2, Inc. (1)
1105 N Market St, Wilmington, DE 19801
Tel.: (302) 654-5351
Investment Advisory Services
N.A.I.C.S.: 523940

Unity NJ REIT, Inc. (1)
64 Old Highway 22, Clinton, NJ 08809
Tel.: (908) 238-0480
Emp.: 3
Banking Services
N.A.I.C.S.: 522110
Allen Bedner *(Gen Mgr)*

UNITY BIOTECHNOLOGY, INC.
285 E Grand Ave, South San Francisco, CA 94080
Tel.: (650) 416-1192   DE
Web Site:
https://www.unitybiotechnology.com
Year Founded: 2009
UBX—(NASDAQ)
Rev.: $236,000
Assets: $124,350,000
Liabilities: $57,502,000
Net Worth: $66,848,000
Earnings: ($59,927,000)
Emp.: 32
Fiscal Year-end: 12/31/22
Clinical Development Services
N.A.I.C.S.: 541714
Lynne Sullivan *(CFO & Head-Corp Dev)*
Jan Van Deursen *(Co-Founder)*
Judith Campisi *(Co-Founder)*
Daohong Zhou *(Co-Founder)*
Alex Nguyen *(Gen Counsel)*
Nathan Guz *(VP-Ops)*
Anirvan Ghosh *(CEO)*
Nathaniel E. David *(Co-Founder)*

UNITY PARTNERS LP
1445 Ross Ave 56th Fl, Dallas, TX 75202
Tel.: (312) 929-2183
Web Site: https://unitypartnerslp.com
HCBR—(OTC)
Privater Equity Firm
N.A.I.C.S.: 523999

Subsidiaries:

NDH Advisors LLC (1)
303 W Madison St Ste 950, Chicago, IL 60606
Tel.: (312) 929-2183
Web Site: https://ndhcpa.com
Tax & Accounting Services
N.A.I.C.S.: 541219
Jeremy Dubow *(CEO)*

Subsidiary (Domestic):

Cendrowski Corporate Advisors, LLC (2)
180 N LaSalle St Ste 2620, Chicago, IL 60601
Web Site: https://cca-advisors.com
Offices of Certified Public Accountants
N.A.I.C.S.: 541211
John Alfonsi *(Mng Dir)*

Stratus Group LLC (2)
11300 Tomahawk Crek Pkwy Ste 310, Leawood, KS 66211-2693
Tel.: (913) 647-9750
Web Site: http://www.stratuscpa.com
Tax, Accounting & Advisory Services

Unity Partners LP—(Continued)

N.A.I.C.S.: 541211

UNITY SOFTWARE INC.

30 3rd St, San Francisco, CA 94103-
3104
Tel.: (415) 539-3162　　　　　　DE
Web Site: https://unity.com
Year Founded: 2004
U—(NYSE)
Rev.: $2,187,317,000
Assets: $7,243,441,000
Liabilities: $4,054,860,000
Net Worth: $3,188,581,000
Earnings: ($822,011,000)
Emp.: 6,748
Fiscal Year-end: 12/31/23
Software Development Services
N.A.I.C.S.: 541511
James M. Whitehurst *(Chm)*
Matthew S. Bromberg *(Pres & CEO)*
David Helgason *(Founder)*

Subsidiaries:

DeltaDNA Limited　　　　　　　　　(1)
25 Greenside Place, Edinburgh, EH1 3AA,
United Kingdom
Tel.: (44) 1314663690
Web Site: http://www.deltadna.com
Computer Gaming Software Development
Services
N.A.I.C.S.: 541511
Mark Robinson *(Founder)*
Isaac Roseboom *(Product Mgr)*

Finger Food Studios Inc.　　　　　(1)
420 - 2755 Lougheed Highway, Port Coquit-
lam, V3B 5Y9, BC, Canada
Tel.: (604) 475-0350
Web Site: http://www.fingerfoodstg.com
Computer Software Development Services
N.A.I.C.S.: 541511
Ryan Peterson *(Founder & CEO)*
Chris Waind *(Chief Creative Officer)*
Jordan Hesse *(CTO)*
Hunter Smith *(COO)*
Cindy Zhan *(CFO)*

Interactive Data Visualization,
Inc.　　　　　　　　　　　　　　(1)
5446 Sunset Blvd, Lexington, SC 29072
Tel.: (803) 356-1999
Web Site: http://store.speedtree.com
Custom Computer Programming Services
N.A.I.C.S.: 541511
Chris King *(Founder & Pres)*

ironSource Ltd.　　　　　　　　　(1)
121 Menachem Begin St, Tel Aviv,
6701203, Israel
Tel.: (972) 747990001
Web Site: http://www.is.com
Rev.: $553,466,000
Assets: $1,450,823,000
Liabilities: $348,255,000
Net Worth: $1,102,568,000
Earnings: $59,821,000
Emp.: 995
Fiscal Year-end: 12/31/2021
Business Platforms
N.A.I.C.S.: 518210
Omer Kaplan *(Founder & Chief Revenue
Officer)*
Assaf Ben Ami *(CFO)*
Dalia Litay *(Gen Counsel)*

UNIVERSAL CORPORATION

9201 Forest Hill Ave, Richmond, VA
23235
Tel.: (804) 359-9311　　　　　VA
Web Site:
　　https://www.universalcorp.com
Year Founded: 1918
UVV—(NYSE)
Rev.: $2,103,601,000
Assets: $2,586,345,000
Liabilities: $1,201,576,000
Net Worth: $1,384,769,000
Earnings: $86,577,000
Emp.: 25,000
Fiscal Year-end: 03/31/22

Holding Company; Leaf Tobacco Mer-
chant & Processor
N.A.I.C.S.: 551112
Candace C. Formacek *(Treas & VP)*
Airton L. Hentschke *(COO & Sr VP)*
Jennifer S. Rowe *(Asst VP-Capital
Markets)*
Johan C. Kroner *(CFO & Sr VP)*
Scott J. Bleicher *(Principal Acctg Offi-
cer, VP & Controller)*
Preston D. Wigner *(Chm, Pres &
CEO)*

Subsidiaries:

AmeriNic, Inc.　　　　　　　　　(1)
9201 Forest Hill Ave, Richmond, VA 23235
Tel.: (804) 254-1355
Web Site: https://www.ameri-nic.com
Pure Nicotine Mfr
N.A.I.C.S.: 325411
Dudley Stephens *(Pres)*

Carolina Innovative Food Ingredients,
Inc.　　　　　　　　　　　　　　(1)
4626 Coleman Dr, Nashville, NC 27856
Tel.: (252) 462-1551
Web Site: http://cifingredients.com
Ingredient Mfr
N.A.I.C.S.: 424590

Continental Tobacco S.A.　　　　(1)
82 rue de Lausanne, 1202, Geneva, Switzerland
Tel.: (41) 223197188
Leaf Tobacco Processing & Packing Services
N.A.I.C.S.: 424940

Deli-HTL Tabak Maatschappij B.
V.　　　　　　　　　　　　　　　(1)
Kanaaldijk Noord 123, 5642 JA, Eindhoven,
Netherlands
Tel.: (31) 402810275
Web Site: http://www.universalcorp.com
Emp.: 70
Leaf Tobacco Processing & Packing Ser-
vices
N.A.I.C.S.: 424940

Deutsch-holandische Tabakgesell-
schaft mbH　　　　　　　　　　(1)
2 Industriestrasse 6, Hockenheim, 68766,
Germany
Tel.: (49) 6205379100
Web Site: http://www.dht-hockenheim.de
Leaf Tobacco Processing & Packing Ser-
vices
N.A.I.C.S.: 424940

Deutsch-hollandische Tabakgesellschaft mbH　　　　　　　　　　(1)
2 Industriestr 6, 68766, Hockenheim, Germany
Tel.: (49) 6205379100
Tobacco Product Distr
N.A.I.C.S.: 424940

Fruitsmart, Inc.　　　　　　　　(1)
201 N Euclid Rd, Grandview, WA 98930
Tel.: (509) 882-9956
Web Site: http://www.fruitsmart.com
Sales Range: $1-9.9 Million
Emp.: 20
Groceries And Related Products, Nec, Nsk
N.A.I.C.S.: 424490
Juanita Lopez *(Dir-Pur)*
Sara Baudrau *(Dir-Fin)*
Luca DaPonte *(VP-Sls)*
David Meek *(VP-Ops)*
Matt Armstrong *(Mgr-Product Dev)*
Luca Da Ponte *(VP)*
Wayne D. Lutomski *(Pres)*

Harkema Services, Inc.　　　　　(1)
305 Albany Tpke, Canton, CT 06019
Tel.: (860) 693-8378
Emp.: 24,875
Leaf Tobacco Products Whslr
N.A.I.C.S.: 424940

Indoco International B.V.　　　　(1)
Bredaseweg 57-59, 4872 LA, Etten-Leur,
Netherlands
Tel.: (31) 765033130
Emp.: 7
Leaf Tobacco Processing & Packing Ser-
vices

N.A.I.C.S.: 424940
Jan Meskens *(Gen Mgr)*

J.P. Taylor Company, L.L.C.　　　(1)
311 Providence Rd, Oxford, NC 27565
Tel.: (919) 693-1116
Tobacco Mfr
N.A.I.C.S.: 312230
Dwight Green *(Gen Mgr)*

Lancaster Leaf Tobacco Company of
Pennsylvania, Inc.
198 W Liberty St, Lancaster, PA 17603
Tel.: (717) 394-2676
Web Site: https://lancasterleaf.com
Tobacco Product Distr
N.A.I.C.S.: 424940

Mozambique Leaf Tobacco,
Limitada　　　　　　　　　　　(1)
Estrada Nacional No 7 Bairro Mpadue, PO
Box 633, 50100, Tete, Mozambique
Tel.: (258) 25227000
Tobacco Distr
N.A.I.C.S.: 424940

PT. Pandu Sata Utama　　　　　(1)
Jl Gajahmada 151, Glagahwero-Kalisat,
Jember, 68193, Indonesia
Tel.: (62) 331591488
Web Site: http://www.pandusata.net
Emp.: 110
Tobacco Mfr
N.A.I.C.S.: 321920

Procesadora Unitab, S.A.　　　　(1)
15 calle 17-17 Zona 1, 01001, Guatemala,
Guatemala
Tel.: (502) 24270600
Tobacco Distr
N.A.I.C.S.: 424940

Silva International, Inc.　　　　　(1)
523 N Ash St, Momence, IL 60954
Tel.: (815) 472-3535
Web Site: https://silva-intl.com
Food Products Mfr
N.A.I.C.S.: 311999
Kent Devries *(Pres)*
Anthony Drost *(Sls Mgr-Acct)*
Darren Van Essen *(Sr Mgr-Sls)*
Kim Sherwood *(Mgr-Order Process)*
Jeff Weidenaar *(VP-Sls)*

Simcoe Leaf Tobacco Company,
Ltd.　　　　　　　　　　　　　(100%)
401 2nd Ave W, PO Box 280, Simcoe, N3Y
4L1, ON, Canada
Tel.: (519) 426-2201
Web Site: http://www.universalleaf.com
Sales Range: $1-9.9 Million
Emp.: 25
Tobacco Processor
N.A.I.C.S.: 312230

Ultoco Services, S.A.　　　　　　(1)
82 rue de Lausanne, 1202, Geneva, Swit-
zerland
Tel.: (41) 223197188
Tobacco Mfr
N.A.I.C.S.: 321920
Jan Wilms *(Mgr-IT & Sls Analysis)*

Ultoco, S.A.　　　　　　　　　　(1)
82 rue de Lausanne, 1202, Geneva, Swit-
zerland
Tel.: (41) 223197188
Emp.: 13
Tobacco Products Whslr
N.A.I.C.S.: 459991
Marlborough Neil *(Gen Mgr)*

Universal Leaf (Asia) Pte Ltd.　　(1)
221 Henderson Road 08-09/10 Henderson
Building, Singapore, 159557, Singapore
Tel.: (65) 63247750
Web Site: http://www.universalcorp.com
Emp.: 12
Leaf Tobacco Processing & Packing Ser-
vices
N.A.I.C.S.: 424940

Universal Leaf Germany GmbH　(1)
Contrescarpe 75 A, 28195, Bremen, Ger-
many
Tel.: (49) 4213659263
Tobacco Product Distr
N.A.I.C.S.: 424940

Universal Leaf Nicaragua, S.A.　(1)
Barrios Hermanos Carcamos Cubanita 1/2

Cuadra al Norte, Nagarote, Nicaragua
Tel.: (505) 7133524
Web Site: http://www.universalcorp.com
Tobacco Distr
N.A.I.C.S.: 424940

Universal Leaf North America U. S.,
Inc.　　　　　　　　　　　　　(1)
5244 Coleman Dr, Nashville, NC 27856
Tel.: (252) 462-4500
Tobacco Distr
N.A.I.C.S.: 424940

Universal Leaf Philippines Inc.　(1)
Unit 2405 Discovery Centre 25 ADB Av-
enue, Ortigas Center, Pasig, 1600, Philip-
pines
Tel.: (63) 29105050
Web Site: http://www.universalleaf.com.ph
Leaf Tobacco Processing & Packing Ser-
vices
N.A.I.C.S.: 424940

Universal Leaf Tabacos S. A.　　(1)
Av Uruguay 735 4400, Salta, Argentina
Tel.: (54) 3874211717
Tobacco & Tobacco Products Whslr
N.A.I.C.S.: 424940

Universal Leaf Tobacco Company,
Inc.　　　　　　　　　　　　　(1)
9201 Forest Hill Ave Stony Point II Bldg,
Richmond, VA 23235　　　　　(100%)
Tel.: (804) 359-9311
Web Site: http://www.universalcorp.com
Sales Range: $75-99.9 Million
Emp.: 100
Tobacco Processing-Buying & Selling
N.A.I.C.S.: 424590
W. Keith Brewer *(Pres & COO)*

Subsidiary (Domestic):

Global Laboratory Services, Inc.　(2)
2107 Black Creek Rd, Wilson, NC
27893　　　　　　　　　　　　(100%)
Tel.: (252) 234-4950
Web Site:
　　http://www.globallaboratoryservices.com
Sales Range: $25-49.9 Million
Emp.: 30
Analytical Testing Services in Seed, Leaf &
Finished Products
N.A.I.C.S.: 444240
Andrae Spencer *(Pres)*

Lancaster Leaf Tobacco Co. of
Pennsylvania　　　　　　　　　(2)
198 W Liberty St, Lancaster, PA
17603　　　　　　　　　　　　(100%)
Tel.: (717) 394-2676
Web Site: http://www.lancasterleaf.com
Sales Range: $75-99.9 Million
Emp.: 75
Mfr of Tobbaco
N.A.I.C.S.: 424590

Universal Leaf Tobacco Hungary Pri-
vate Limited Company　　　　　(1)
Dugonics u 2, PO Box 146, 4400, Nyireg-
haza, Hungary
Tel.: (36) 42501120
Tobacco Distr
N.A.I.C.S.: 424940

Zambia Leaf Tobacco Co., Ltd.　(1)
Plot No 6980 Katanga Road, 37969, Lu-
saka, Zambia
Tel.: (260) 211286135
Sales Range: $25-49.9 Million
Emp.: 38
Leaf Tobacco Processing & Packing Ser-
vices
N.A.I.C.S.: 424940

Zimbabwe Leaf Tobacco Company
(Private) Limited　　　　　　　(1)
Foundry Road Aspindale Park Southerton,
PO Box 1597, Harare, Zimbabwe
Tel.: (263) 34621811
Tobacco Products Mfr & Distr
N.A.I.C.S.: 424940

UNIVERSAL DISPLAY CORPO-
RATION

250 Phillips Blvd, Ewing, NJ 08618
Tel.: (609) 671-0980　　　　　PA
Web Site: https://www.oled.com

OLED—(NASDAQ)
Rev.: $576,429,000
Assets: $1,668,961,000
Liabilities: $221,735,000
Net Worth: $1,447,226,000
Earnings: $203,011,000
Emp.: 456
Fiscal Year-end: 12/31/23
Organic Light Emitting Diode Technology Developer for Flat Panel Display Application
N.A.I.C.S.: 334413
Steven V. Abramson *(Pres & CEO)*
Brian Millard *(CFO, Treas & VP-Fin)*

Subsidiaries:

Adesis, Inc.   **(1)**
27 McCullough Dr, New Castle, DE 19720
Tel.: (302) 323-4880
Web Site: https://adesisinc.com
Organic Biotechnology Research & Development Services
N.A.I.C.S.: 541714
Phyllis Fisher *(Dir-Human Resources)*
David Baran *(Dir-Manufacturing)*
Louise Tramonte *(Exec Dir & Head-Commercial)*
Phyllis Fisher *(Dir-Human Resources)*

Universal Display Corporation Hong Kong, Limited   **(1)**
Unit 319 3/F Biotech Centre 2 Hong Kong Science Park, Pak Shek Kok N T, Hong Kong, China (Hong Kong)
Tel.: (852) 35950543
Computer Terminal Mfr
N.A.I.C.S.: 334118

UNIVERSAL ELECTRONICS, INC.
15147 N Scottsdale Rd Ste H300, Scottsdale, AZ 85254-2494
Tel.: (480) 530-3000   DE
Web Site: https://www.uei.com
Year Founded: 1986
UEIC—(NASDAQ)
Rev.: $542,751,000
Assets: $504,163,000
Liabilities: $235,757,000
Net Worth: $268,406,000
Earnings: $407,000
Emp.: 4,658
Fiscal Year-end: 12/31/22
Wireless Remote Control Technologies Developer & Mfr
N.A.I.C.S.: 334310
Bryan M. Hackworth *(CFO & Sr VP)*
David C. H. Chong *(Exec VP-Asia)*
Hrag G. Ohannessian *(Sr VP-Global Sls-Home Automation, Security & Hospitality)*
Banley Chan *(Sr VP-Mfg-Asia)*
Arsham Hatambeiki *(Sr VP-Product & Tech)*
Ramzi Ammari *(Sr VP-Corporate Planning & Strategy)*
Menno Koopmans *(Sr VP)*
Rick Carnifax *(VP-Manufacturing & Operations)*
Joseph L. Haughawout *(Sr VP-Product Development)*
Michael Koch *(Sr VP-Finance)*
Norman G. Sheridan *(Sr VP-Engrg)*
Paul D. Arling *(Chm & CEO)*
Richard A. Firehammer Jr. *(Sr VP)*

Subsidiaries:

C.G. Development Limited   **(1)**
Units 902-908 9F One Harbourfront 18 Tak Fung Street, Hung Hom, Kowloon, China (Hong Kong)
Tel.: (852) 27660577
Web Site: http://www.uei.com
Sales Range: $25-49.9 Million
Emp.: 80
Remote Control Device Mfr
N.A.I.C.S.: 334290

Ecolink Intelligent Technology, Inc.   **(1)**

2055 Corte Del Nogal, Carlsbad, CA 92011
Web Site: https://www.discoverecolink.com
Security Product Mfr
N.A.I.C.S.: 334290
Michael Lamb *(Founder & Pres)*

Gemstar Technology (China) Co. Limited   **(1)**
45 Shiguang Road Zhongcun Town Panyu District, Guangzhou, 511495, China
Tel.: (86) 2084771131
Remote Control Device Mfr
N.A.I.C.S.: 334419

One For All Iberia S.L.   **(1)**
Calle Gran via Carles III 84 PLT 3, 08028, Barcelona, Spain
Tel.: (34) 934965711
Wireless Remote Control Products Mfr
N.A.I.C.S.: 334290

Residential Control Systems, Inc.   **(1)**
12860 Danielson Ct Ste A, Poway, CA 92064
Tel.: (916) 635-6784
Web Site: http://www.rcstechnology.com
Automatic Environmental Control Mfr for Residential, Commercial & Appliance Use
N.A.I.C.S.: 334512
Paul Arling *(Chm & CEO)*

UEI do Brasil Controles Remotos Ltda.   **(1)**
Sales Range: $25-49.9 Million
Emp.: 85
Remote Control Device Mfr
N.A.I.C.S.: 334290

Universal Electronics   **(1)**
201 E Sandpointe Ave 7th Fl, Santa Ana, CA 92707   **(100%)**
Tel.: (330) 487-1110
Web Site: https://www.uei.com
Sales Range: $25-49.9 Million
Emp.: 100
Technical Support for Remote Controls
N.A.I.C.S.: 334310
Paul D. Arling *(Chm & CEO)*

Universal Electronics BV   **(1)**
Colosseum 2, 7521 PT, Enschede, Netherlands
Tel.: (31) 53 488 8000
Web Site: http://www.uei.com
Sales Range: $25-49.9 Million
Emp.: 100
Audio & Video Equipment Mfr
N.A.I.C.S.: 334310

UNIVERSAL ENERGY CORP.
1540 Intl Pkwy Ste 200, Lake Mary, FL 32746   DE
Year Founded: 2002
UVSE—(OTCIQ)
Oil & Gas Exploration Services
N.A.I.C.S.: 213112
Billy Raley *(CEO)*
Mark L. Silver *(Founder)*

UNIVERSAL GAMING CORPORATION
1710 Rhode Island Ave NW 2nd Fl, Washington, DC 20036
Tel.: (202) 999-6598   NV
Year Founded: 2015
UGCC—(OTCEM)
Liabilities: $212,626
Net Worth: ($212,626)
Earnings: ($48,450)
Emp.: 1
Fiscal Year-end: 12/31/22
Swimwear Mfr
N.A.I.C.S.: 315250
Suzanne Cope *(Chm, Pres, CEO & CFO)*

UNIVERSAL GLOBAL HUB INC.
6141 186th St Ste 688, Fresh Meadows, NY 11365
Tel.: (201) 782-0889   DE
Year Founded: 2012
UGHB—(OTCIQ)
Liabilities: $250,473

Net Worth: ($250,473)
Earnings: ($46,344)
Fiscal Year-end: 12/31/22
Investment Services
N.A.I.C.S.: 523999

UNIVERSAL HEALTH REALTY INCOME TRUST
Universal Corporate Ctr 367 S Gulph Rd, King of Prussia, PA 19406-0958
Tel.: (610) 265-0688   MD
Web Site: https://www.uhrit.com
Year Founded: 1986
UHT—(NYSE)
Rev.: $90,625,000
Assets: $607,540,000
Liabilities: $378,439,000
Net Worth: $229,101,000
Earnings: $21,102,000
Fiscal Year-end: 12/31/22
Real Estate Investment Trust
N.A.I.C.S.: 525990
Charles F. Boyle *(CFO)*
Cheryl K. Ramagano *(Treas, Sec, Sr VP-Operations & VP)*
Alan B. Miller *(Chm, Pres & CEO)*
Karla J. Peterson *(VP-Acquisitions & Development)*
Judith Klein Romero *(VP-Asset Mgmt)*

Subsidiaries:

3811 Bell Medical Properties, LLC   **(1)**
3811 E Bell Rd, Phoenix, AZ 85032
Tel.: (602) 404-4133
Non Residential Building Operator
N.A.I.C.S.: 531312

DVMC Properties, LLC   **(1)**
4045 E Bell Rd, Phoenix, AZ 85032
Tel.: (602) 867-0474
Real Estate Investment Services
N.A.I.C.S.: 531210

DesMed, LLC   **(1)**
4275 Burnham Ave, Las Vegas, NV 89119-5488
Tel.: (702) 699-9247
General Medical & Surgical Services
N.A.I.C.S.: 622110

NTX Healthcare Properties, LLC   **(1)**
180 Dundas Street West Suite 1100, Toronto, M5G 1Z8, ON, Canada
Tel.: (416) 366-2000
Web Site: http://www.nwhreit.com
Portfolio Management Services
N.A.I.C.S.: 523940
Shailen Chande *(CFO)*
Paul Dalla Lana *(Chm)*
Peter Riggin *(Mng Dir & COO)*

UNIVERSAL HEALTH SERVICES, INC.
367 S Gulph Rd, King of Prussia, PA 19406-0958
Tel.: (610) 768-3300   DE
Web Site: https://www.uhs.com
Year Founded: 1979
UHS—(NYSE)
Rev.: $14,281,976,000
Assets: $13,967,602,000
Liabilities: $7,770,887,000
Net Worth: $6,196,715,000
Earnings: $717,795,000
Emp.: 61,100
Fiscal Year-end: 12/31/23
Health Care Srvices
N.A.I.C.S.: 622110
Charles F. Boyle *(Sr VP & Controller)*
Marc D. Miller *(Pres & CEO)*
Cheryl K. Ramagano *(Treas & Sr VP)*
Alan B. Miller *(Founder & Exec Chm)*
Steve G. Filton *(Exec VP)*
Michael S. Nelson *(Sr VP-Strategic Svcs)*
Matthew D. Klein *(Gen Counsel & Sr VP)*

Geraldine Johnson Geckle *(Sr VP-HR)*
Victor J. Radina *(Sr VP-Corp Dev)*
Matt Peterson *(Pres-Behavioral Health Div & Exec VP)*
Jim Clark *(Sr VP-Fin Acute Care Div)*
Thomas Day *(Sr VP-Fin Behavioral Health Div)*
Edward H. Sim *(Pres-Acute Care & Exec VP)*
Matthew J. Peterson *(Pres)*

Subsidiaries:

ABS LINCS SC, Inc.   **(1)**
225 Midland Pkwy, Summerville, SC 29485
Tel.: (843) 851-5015
Web Site: http://palmettosummerville.com
Outpatient Mental Health Services
N.A.I.C.S.: 621420

ABS LINCS VA, Inc.   **(1)**
1634 London Blvd, Portsmouth, VA 23704
Tel.: (757) 393-7200
Web Site: https://www.firsthomecare.com
Emp.: 90
Medical Devices
N.A.I.C.S.: 622110
Gina Fusco *(CEO)*

Aiken Regional Medical Centers, LLC   **(1)**
302 University Pkwy, Aiken, SC 29801
Tel.: (803) 641-5000
Web Site: https://www.aikenregional.com
Sales Range: $100-124.9 Million
Emp.: 2,000
Hospital Management Services
N.A.I.C.S.: 622110
Matt Merrifield *(COO)*
James O'Loughlin *(CEO)*
Bridget Denzik *(Chief Nursing Officer)*
Nicole Morgan *(Dir-Admin-Bus Dev & Physician Svcs)*
Paul Hanna *(Dir-Admin-HR)*
Eric Muhlbaier *(Dir-Admin-Support Svcs)*
Michael Hall *(Co-COO)*
Gennia Jennings *(Mgr-Market)*

Alliance Health Center, Inc.   **(1)**
5000 Hwy 39 N, Meridian, MS 39301
Tel.: (601) 483-6211
Web Site: https://www.alliancehealthcenter.com
Acute Care Hospital Services
N.A.I.C.S.: 622110
Jay Shehi *(CEO)*
Rae Andreacchio *(Dir-Crossings)*
Thomas Jess Hardy *(Dir-Environment of Care)*
Shrea Johnson *(Dir-HR)*
Kimberly Jones *(Dir-Utilization Mgmt)*
Leighann Posey *(Chief Nursing Officer)*
Shannon Smith *(Dir-Admissions)*
Miranda Thompson *(Dir-Risk Mgmt & Regulatory Compliance)*
Frank Harman *(Dir-Medical & Primary Care Svcs)*
Tim Arnold *(Dir-Medical & Adult Psychiatrist)*
Grace Kelly *(Dir-Medical & Adult Psychiatrist)*

Alpha Hospitals (NW) Limited   **(1)**
Buller Street Off Bolton Road, Bury, BL8 2BS, United Kingdom
Tel.: (44) 1617627200
Medical Service Provider
N.A.I.C.S.: 622110

Ambulatory Surgical Center of Aiken, L.L.C.   **(1)**
4211 Trolley Line Rd, Aiken, SC 29801
Tel.: (803) 648-2840
Ambulatory Surgical Care Services
N.A.I.C.S.: 621999

Arbour Elder Services, Inc.   **(1)**
384 Washington St, Norwell, MA 02061
Tel.: (781) 871-6550
Web Site: https://www.arbourhealth.com
Senior Health Care Services
N.A.I.C.S.: 621610

Arbour Foundation, Inc.   **(1)**
49 Robinwood Ave, Jamaica Plain, MA 02130
Tel.: (617) 522-4400

Universal Health Services, Inc.—(Continued)

Ambulatory Surgical Care Services
N.A.I.C.S.: 621999

Arrowhead Behavioral Health, LLC (1)
1725 Timber Line Rd, Maumee, OH 43537
Tel.: (419) 891-9333
Web Site:
https://www.arrowheadbehavioral.com
Emp.: 50
Psychiatric & Behavioral Care Services
N.A.I.C.S.: 622210
Theresa Contreras (CEO)

Atlantic Shores Hospital, LLC (1)
1601 E Las Olas Blvd, Fort Lauderdale, FL 33301
Tel.: (954) 463-4321
Web Site:
https://www.atlanticshoreshospital.com
Sales Range: $10-24.9 Million
Emp.: 6
Mental Health & Substance Abuse Hospital Services
N.A.I.C.S.: 622110

BHC Alhambra Hospital, Inc. (1)
4619 N Rosemead Blvd, Rosemead, CA 91770
Tel.: (626) 286-1191
Web Site: https://www.bhcalhambra.com
Behavioral Healthcare Services
N.A.I.C.S.: 622110
Peggy Minnick (CEO)

BHC Belmont Pines Hospital, Inc. (1)
615 Churchill Hubbard Rd, Youngstown, OH 44505-1332
Tel.: (330) 759-2700
Web Site: https://www.belmontpines.com
Behavioral Healthcare Services
N.A.I.C.S.: 622210
Phillip Maiden (Dir-Medical)

BHC Fairfax Hospital, Inc. (1)
10200 NE 132nd St, Kirkland, WA 98034
Tel.: (425) 821-2000
Web Site: https://www.fairfaxhospital.com
Mental Health Care Services
N.A.I.C.S.: 623220
Ron Escarda (CEO)

BHC Fox Run Hospital, Inc. (1)
67670 Traco Dr, Saint Clairsville, OH 43950
Tel.: (740) 695-2131
Web Site: https://www.foxruncenter.com
Health Care Srvices
N.A.I.C.S.: 622110

BHC Fremont Hospital, Inc. (1)
39001 Sundale Dr, Fremont, CA 94538
Tel.: (510) 796-1100
Web Site: https://www.fremonthospital.com
Behavioral Healthcare Services
N.A.I.C.S.: 622210
Vikas Duvvuri (Dir-Medical)
Mini Dhiman (Dir-Nursing)
Tricia Williams (CEO)
Satwinder Mahabir (Dir-Clinical Svcs & Intake)
Zubin Kachhi (Dir-Pharmacy)
Jessica Cedillo (Mgr-Nursing)
Nashin Joseph (Mgr-Case Mgmt Program)

BHC Health Services of Nevada, Inc. (1)
1240 E 9th St, Reno, NV 89512
Tel.: (775) 323-0478
Web Site: https://www.westhillshospital.net
General Medical & Surgical Hospital Services
N.A.I.C.S.: 622110
Char Buehrle (CEO-Interim)

BHC Heritage Oaks Hospital, Inc. (1)
4250 Auburn Blvd, Sacramento, CA 95841
Tel.: (916) 489-3336
Web Site:
https://www.heritageoakshospital.com
Drug Treatment Services
N.A.I.C.S.: 621420
Joseph Sison (Dir-Medical)

BHC Intermountain Hospital, Inc. (1)
303 N Allumbaugh St, Boise, ID 83704
Tel.: (208) 377-8400

Web Site:
https://www.intermountainhospital.com
Sales Range: $50-74.9 Million.
Emp.: 250
Psychiatric & Substance Abuse Hospital
N.A.I.C.S.: 444110
Chuck Christiansen (Dir-Bus Dev)
Kathy Windom (Dir-Clinical Svcs)
Jedonne Hines (CFO)
Kristina Harrington (Dir-Medical)
John Kuehne (Dir-Risk Mgmt & Performance Improvement)
Jacqueline Kavila (Dir-Pharmacy)
Rene Gerhardt (Dir-Admissions)
Brenda Munsey (Dir-HR)

BHC Management Services of Streamwood, LLC (1)
1431 N Claremont Ave, Chicago, IL 60622
Tel.: (312) 491-5055
Web Site:
http://www.chicagochildrenscenter.com
Behavioral Health Services
N.A.I.C.S.: 444110
Steve Vanderpoel (CEO)
Solome Tadele (Dir-HR)
Fatima Villasenor (Dir-Bus Dev)
Dawn Gomez (Dir-Clinical Svcs)
Lily Reyes (Dir-Assessment & Referral)
Jeffery W. Mason (Dir-Nursing, Performance Improvement & Risk Mgmt)

BHC Mesilla Valley Hospital, LLC (1)
3751 Del Rey Blvd, Las Cruces, NM 88012
Tel.: (575) 382-3500
Web Site:
https://www.mesillavalleyhospital.com
Emp.: 250
Psychiatric & Substance Abuse Hospital
N.A.I.C.S.: 622210
Stormy Jackson (CFO)
Jesus Lerma (Dir-Utilization Review)
Isabel Ramirez (Dir-Bus Office)
Jamie Torres (Dir-Plant Ops)

BHC Pinnacle Pointe Hospital, Inc. (1)
11501 Financial Ctr Pkwy, Little Rock, AR 72211
Tel.: (501) 223-3322
Web Site:
https://www.pinnaclepointehospital.com
Sales Range: $50-74.9 Million
Emp.: 170
Behavioral Healthcare Services
N.A.I.C.S.: 622210
Donna Monk (Dir-Bus Dev)

BHC Sierra Vista Hospital, Inc. (1)
8001 Bruceville Rd, Sacramento, CA 95823
Tel.: (916) 288-0300
Web Site:
https://www.sierravistahospital.com
Sales Range: $10-24.9 Million
Emp.: 5
Behavioral Health Services
N.A.I.C.S.: 623220
Mike Zauner (CEO)

BHC Streamwood Hospital, Inc. (1)
1400 E Irving Park Rd, Streamwood, IL 60107-3201
Tel.: (630) 837-9000
Web Site:
https://www.streamwoodhospital.com
Mental Health Treatment Services
N.A.I.C.S.: 623220

Behavioral Health Connections, Inc. (1)
1200 N West Ave, Jackson, MI 49202
Tel.: (517) 789-1200
Health Care Srvices
N.A.I.C.S.: 622210

Behavioral Health Management, LLC (1)
5314 Dashwood Dr Ste 200, Houston, TX 77081
Tel.: (713) 600-9500
Web Site: https://www.bhbhospital.com
Health Care Srvices
N.A.I.C.S.: 622110

Benchmark Behavioral Health System, Inc. (1)
592 W 1350 S, Woods Cross, UT 84087
Tel.: (801) 299-5300

Web Site: https://www.bbhsnet.com
Sales Range: $25-49.9 Million
Emp.: 150
Psychiatric Hospital Services
N.A.I.C.S.: 622110
Craig Scholnick (CEO)

Bloomington Meadows, General Partnership (1)
3600 N Prow Rd, Bloomington, IN 47404
Tel.: (812) 331-8000
Web Site:
https://www.bloomingtonmeadows.com
Emp.: 150
Mental Health & Substance Abuse Treatment Services
N.A.I.C.S.: 622210
Amanda Shettlesworth (Dir-HR & Risk Mgmt)
Becky Nyberg (CFO)
Christopher R. Dowers (CEO)
Penny Caswell (Chief Nursing Officer)
Chris McNeely (Dir-Bus Dev)

Brentwood Acquisition, Inc. (1)
3531 Lakeland Dr, Flowood, MS 39232
Tel.: (601) 936-2024
Web Site:
https://www.brentwoodjackson.com
Behavioral Healthcare & Psychiatric Services
N.A.I.C.S.: 622210
John Elgin Wilkaitis (Dir-Medical)

Brentwood Hospital (1)
1006 Highland Ave, Shreveport, LA 71101
Tel.: (318) 678-7500
Web Site:
https://www.brentwoodbehavioral.com
Sales Range: $25-49.9 Million
Emp.: 200
Psychiatric Hospitals
N.A.I.C.S.: 622110
William Weaver (CEO & Mng Dir)
Shelia Camp (Dir-Clinical Svcs)
Ravon Dominique (Chief Nursing Officer)
Ellise Garmon (Dir-Intake)
Talicia Johnson Gaskin (Dir-HR)

Brynn Marr Hospital, Inc. (1)
192 Vlg Dr, Jacksonville, NC 28546
Tel.: (910) 577-1400
Web Site: https://www.brynnmarr.org
Mental Health Services
N.A.I.C.S.: 622210
Colin Weaver (CEO)

CAT Seattle, LLC (1)
12101 Ambaum Blvd SW, Seattle, WA 98146
Tel.: (206) 244-8100
Web Site: https://www.schickshadel.com
Health Care Srvices
N.A.I.C.S.: 622110
Philip Herink (CEO)

CCS/Lansing, Inc. (1)
101 W Townsend Rd, Saint Johns, MI 48879-9200
Tel.: (989) 403-6100
Youth Treatment Services
N.A.I.C.S.: 623220

CCS/Lansing, Inc. (1)
101 W Townsend Rd, Saint Johns, MI 48879
Tel.: (989) 224-1177
Mental Health Care Services
N.A.I.C.S.: 621420

Calvary Center, Inc. (1)
720 E Montebello Ave, Phoenix, AZ 85014
Tel.: (602) 755-3559
Web Site: https://www.calvarycenter.com
Behaviour Treatment Services
N.A.I.C.S.: 622210
Jerry Boehm (Dir-Risk Mgmt & Quality Assurance)

Canyon Rdg Hospital, Inc. (1)
5353 G St, Chino, CA 91710
Tel.: (909) 590-3700
Web Site:
https://www.canyonridgehospital.com
Emp.: 200
Mental Health Services
N.A.I.C.S.: 622210
Stephanie Bernier (CEO)
Wadie Alkhouri (Dir-Medical)

Canyon Ridge Hospital, Inc. (1)

5353 G St, Chino, CA 91710
Tel.: (909) 590-3700
Web Site:
https://www.canyonridgehospital.com
Health Care Srvices
N.A.I.C.S.: 622110
Stephanie Bernier (CEO)

Columbus Hospital, LLC (1)
2223 Poshard Dr, Columbus, IN 47203
Tel.: (812) 376-1711
Web Site:
https://www.columbusbehavioral.com
Emp.: 108
Behavioral Health Services
N.A.I.C.S.: 622210
Kevin Reckelhoff (CEO)

Coral Shores Behavioral Health, LLC (1)
5995 SE Community Dr, Stuart, FL 34997
Tel.: (772) 403-4000
Web Site: https://www.coralshoresbehavioral.com
Mental Health Hospital Services
N.A.I.C.S.: 622210
Grace Irving (Dir-Admissions)
Gina Dalessandro (Dir-Risk & Performance Improvement)
Amanda Welsh (Dir-Clinical Svcs)

Crossings Healthcare Solutions, Inc. (1)
367 S Gulph Rd, King of Prussia, PA 19406
Tel.: (610) 994-2200
Web Site:
https://www.crossingshealthcaresolutions.com
Health Care Srvices
N.A.I.C.S.: 622110
Justin Monnig (Gen Mgr)

Cumberland Hospital, LLC (1)
9407 Cumberland Rd, New Kent, VA 23124
Tel.: (804) 966-2242
Web Site:
https://www.cumberlandhospital.com
Sales Range: $25-49.9 Million
Emp.: 250
Medical Devices
N.A.I.C.S.: 622110
Patrice Gay Brooks (CEO)
Jennifer Rice (Dir-Clinical)

Cygnet 2000 Limited (1)
179 Kings Rd, Kingston upon Thames, KT2 5JH, United Kingdom
Tel.: (44) 2085471208
Emp.: 501
Health Care Srvices
N.A.I.C.S.: 622110

Cygnet Behavioural Health
Worksop Road, Chesterfield, S43 3DN, Derbyshire, United Kingdom
Tel.: (44) 1246386090
Mental Health Care Services
N.A.I.C.S.: 621420

Cygnet Care Services Limited (1)
6 St Osmunds Road Parkstone, Poole, BH14 9JN, Dorset, United Kingdom
Tel.: (44) 1202007339
Mental Health Care Services
N.A.I.C.S.: 621420

Cygnet Clifton Limited (1)
Clifton Lane, Nottingham, NG11 8NB, United Kingdom
Tel.: (44) 1159457070
Mental Health Care Services
N.A.I.C.S.: 621420

Cygnet Health Care Ltd. (1)
Godden Green, Sevenoaks, TN15 0JR, Kent, United Kingdom
Tel.: (44) 1732763491
Web Site: http://www.cygnethealth.co.uk
Psychiatric Nursing Home Operators
N.A.I.C.S.: 622210
Mark Ground (CFO)
Lee Hammon (Chief Comml Officer)
Vicky McNally (Dir-Corp Governance)
Tony Romero (CEO)
David Wilmott (Dir-Nursing)
Jenny Gibson (Dir-HR)
Justin De Vally (CIO)
Sam Nicholls (Dir-Property)
Nick Ruffley (Mng Dir-Healthcare Div)
Peter Smith (Mng Dir-Social Care Div)
Johannes Van Niekerk (Dir-Medical-South)
Lucy Scarborough (Comm Mgr-Grp)

DVH Hospital Alliance, LLC (1)
360 S Lola Ln, Pahrump, NV 89048
Tel.: (775) 751-7500
Web Site: https://desertviewhospital.com
Hospital Management & Services
N.A.I.C.S.: 622110

El Paso Behavioral Health
System (1)
1900 Denver Ave, El Paso, TX 79902
Tel.: (915) 544-4000
Web Site: https://www.elpasobh.com
Behavioral Health Care & Substance Abuse
Rehabilitation Services
N.A.I.C.S.: 622210
Phil Sosa (CFO)
Mia Goldman (COO)
Mary Lou Morales (Dir-Utilization Review)
Karla Silva (Dir-Admissions)
Kevin McGee (CEO-Interim)
Amber Chavez (Dir-Clinical Svcs)

Emerald Coast Behavioral Hospital,
LLC (1)
1940 Harrison Ave, Panama City, FL 32405
Tel.: (850) 763-0017
Web Site:
https://www.emeraldcoastbehavioral.com
Psychiatric Services
N.A.I.C.S.: 622210
Tim Bedford (CEO)
Michael Zenone (CFO)
Robert Reuille (Dir-Outpatient Svcs)
Shelly McNaron (Mgr-Emerald Coast Be-
havioral Hospital Outpatient Center)

FHCHS of Puerto Rico, Inc. (1)
Metro Ofc Pk Valencia Ste 1 Bldg 17 5th Fl,
Guaynabo, PR 00968
Tel.: (787) 622-9797
Web Site: http://fhcsaludmental.com
Mental Health Services
N.A.I.C.S.: 623220

FRN Nashville, LLC (1)
101 Lea Ave, Nashville, TN 37210-2066
Tel.: (615) 370-6880
Outpatient Health Care Services
N.A.I.C.S.: 621420
Mary Moran (Dir-Outpatient Svcs)

FRN Outpatient, LLC (1)
Historic Roswell District 114 Sloan St, Ro-
swell, GA 30075
Tel.: (770) 557-3547
Outpatient Health Care Services
N.A.I.C.S.: 621420

FRN San Francisco, LLC (1)
1700 Montgomery St Ste 435, San Fran-
cisco, CA 94111
Tel.: (415) 917-2387
Web Site:
https://foundationssanfrancisco.com
Outpatient Health Care Services
N.A.I.C.S.: 621420
Melissa Stevenson (Exec Dir)

FRN, Inc. (1)
255 Depot St Ste 100, Ball Ground, GA
30107
Tel.: (770) 720-8225
Web Site: https://www.4frn.com
Furnace Maintenance Services
N.A.I.C.S.: 238220

First Health System Incorporated (1)
17 Calle 2 Ste 520, Guaynabo, PR 00968-
1750
Tel.: (787) 622-9797
Ambulatory Health Care Services
N.A.I.C.S.: 621493

First Hospital Panamericano, Inc. (1)
Km 1 5 PR 787, Cidra, PR 00739
Tel.: (787) 739-5555
Web Site:
http://www.hospitalpanamericano.com
Psychiatric Services
N.A.I.C.S.: 622210
Astro Munoz (Exec Dir)

Fort Duncan Medical Center, Inc. (1)
3333 N Foster Maldonado Blvd, Eagle
Pass, TX 78852
Tel.: (830) 773-5321
Web Site:
http://www.fortduncanmedicalcenter.com
Medical Devices
N.A.I.C.S.: 622110

Joel Morales (CFO)
Alan Gonzalez (COO)
Eladio Montalvo (CEO)
Deborah Meeks (Chief Nursing Officer)

Fort Lauderdale Hospital, Inc. (1)
5757 N Dixie Hwy, Oakland Park, FL 33334
Tel.: (954) 734-2000
Web Site: https://ftlauderdalebehavioral.com
Hotels (except Casino Hotels) & Motels
N.A.I.C.S.: 721110

Foundations Atlanta, LLC (1)
1708 Peachtree St NW Ste 300, Atlanta,
GA 30309
Tel.: (404) 460-7101
Outpatient Health Care Services
N.A.I.C.S.: 621420

Foundations Recovery Network,
LLC (1)
1000 Health Park Dr Ste 400, Brentwood,
TN 37027
Tel.: (630) 792-5800
Web Site:
https://www.foundationsrecoverynet
work.com
Emp.: 200
Health Care Srvices
N.A.I.C.S.: 621420
Mike Chatterton (CFO-Reg)
Jon Weber (Dir-Natl Admissions Center)
Jonny Stovall (Dir-Web & Creative)
Daxon Edwards (Mgr-Digital Strategy)
Cindy Sullivan (Dir-HR Market)
Glenn Hadley (Dir-Foundations Events)

Foundations San Diego, LLC (1)
2508 Historic Decatur Rd Ste 200, San Di-
ego, CA 92106
Tel.: (619) 235-2300
Web Site: https://www.sdfoundation.org
Outpatient Health Care Services
N.A.I.C.S.: 621420
Patricia Bathurst (Dir-Outpatient)

Foundations Virginia, LLC (1)
5409 Maryland Way Ste320, Brentwood, TN
37027
Tel.: (615) 371-5700
Emp.: 3
Substance Abuse Rehabilitation Services
N.A.I.C.S.: 622210

Fox Run Center for Children &
Adolescents (1)
67670 Traco Dr, Saint Clairsville, OH 43950
Tel.: (740) 695-2131
Web Site: http://www.foxruncenter.com
Sales Range: $25-49.9 Million
Emp.: 120
Psychiatric & Substance Abuse Hospital
Services
N.A.I.C.S.: 622210
Susan DeGarmo (Office Mgr-Bus)
Jill Bradshaw (Dir-Medical)
Lisa Duvall (Dir-Referral & Community Part-
nerships)
Randy MacKendrick (CEO)
Maria Karakas (CFO)
Jerry Herrick (Dir-HR)
Kregg Winkowski (Dir-Clinical Svcs)
Rachel Benda (Dir-Resident Svcs)
Jennifer Starkey (Dir-Nursing)
Jaclyn Yahn (Dir-Admissions)
Joe Gazdik (Dir-Plant Ops)
Angela Hancock (Dir-Risk Mgmt)

Friends Behavioral Health System,
L.P. (1)
4641 Roosevelt Blvd, Philadelphia, PA
19124-2399
Tel.: (215) 831-4600
Web Site: https://friendshospital.com
Behavioral Health Services
N.A.I.C.S.: 622210
Vance Barto (Dir-Plant Ops)

Frontline Hospital, LLC (1)
2530 Debarr Rd, Anchorage, AK 99508
Tel.: (907) 258-7575
Web Site: http://www.uhsinc.com
Sales Range: $25-49.9 Million
Emp.: 500
Behavioral Health Services
N.A.I.C.S.: 622210

Frontline Residential Treatment Center, LLC (1)

3647 N Clark Wolverine Rd, Palmer, AK
99645
Tel.: (972) 782-4922
Web Site: https://northstarrtc.com
Behavioral Health Services
N.A.I.C.S.: 622110

GB Acquisitions, LLC (1)
931 N State Road 434, Altamonte Springs,
FL 32714
Tel.: (407) 252-5453
Real Estate Services
N.A.I.C.S.: 531210

GW Health Network, LLC (1)
2150 Pennsylvania Ave NW, Washington,
DC 20037
Web Site: https://gwhealthnetwork.com
General Hospital & Medical Services
N.A.I.C.S.: 622110

Garfield Park Hospital, LLC (1)
520 N Ridgeway Ave, Chicago, IL 60624
Tel.: (773) 265-3700
Web Site:
https://www.garfieldparkhospital.com
Health Care Srvices
N.A.I.C.S.: 622110
Liz Piasecki (Dir-Clinical Svcs)
Steven Airhart (CEO)
Laura Castillo (Dir-Nursing)
Megan Raubolt (Dir-Emergency Svcs)
Angie Scott (Dir-Risk Mgmt & Performance
Improvement)
Patrick Sanders (COO)
Sandra Corral (Dir-Nursing-Interim)
Ewa Mancewicz (Dir-Risk Mgmt & Perfor-
mance Improvement)

Garland Behavioral Hospital, Inc. (1)
2300 Marie Curie Blvd 5th Fl, Garland, TX
75042-5706
Tel.: (615) 312-5834
Web Site:
https://garlandbehavioralhospital.com
Mental Health Hospital Services
N.A.I.C.S.: 622210

Great Plains Hospital, Inc. (1)
1500 W Ashland St, Nevada, MO 64772-
1710
Tel.: (417) 667-2666
Web Site:
https://www.heartlandbehavioral.com
Behavioral Health Services
N.A.I.C.S.: 622110
Alyson Wysong-Harder (CEO)
Betsy Curtis (Dir-Bus Dev)
Mike Ast (Dir-Support Svcs)
Carri Compton (Officer-Admin)

Gulf Coast Treatment Center,
Inc. (1)
1015 Mar Walt Dr, Fort Walton Beach, FL
32547
Tel.: (850) 863-4160
Web Site: https://gulfcoasttc.com
Emp.: 25
Residential Treatment Services
N.A.I.C.S.: 623990
Kelly Kugler (Dir-Clinical Svcs)

H.C. Partnership (1)
6869 5th Ave S, Birmingham, AL 35212
Tel.: (205) 833-9000
Web Site: https://www.hillcrestbhs.com
Behavioral Health Services
N.A.I.C.S.: 622210
Sharon Broady (Dir-Admissions)
Sharon Pearson (Dir-Education)

HHC Augusta, Inc. (1)
3100 Perimeter Pkwy, Augusta, GA 30909
Tel.: (706) 651-0005
Web Site:
https://www.lighthousecarecenters.com
Behavioral Health Services
N.A.I.C.S.: 622210

HHC Focus Florida, Inc. (1)
5960 SW 106th Ave, Cooper City, FL 33328
Tel.: (973) 940-0040
Web Site: https://www.highpoint.com
Behavioral Health Services
N.A.I.C.S.: 622110
Kipp Stewart (Dir-Mktg)

HHC Indiana, Inc. (1)
1800 N Oak Dr, Plymouth, IN 46563
Tel.: (574) 936-3784

Web Site:
https://www.michianabehavioralhealth
center.com
Psychiatric Services
N.A.I.C.S.: 622210

HHC Poplar Springs, Inc. (1)
350 Poplar Dr, Petersburg, VA 23805
Tel.: (866) 546-2229
Web Site: http://www.poplarsprings.com
Behavioral Healthcare Services
N.A.I.C.S.: 622210
Thresa Simon (Dir-Medical)
TaKeshia M. Dozier (CFO)
Kisheena Larts-Taylor (Chief Nursing Offi-
cer)
Cathy Becker (Dir-Acute Svcs)
Naharia Holt-Elliott (Dir-Military & Outpatient
Svcs)
Gary Richardson (Dir-Plant Ops)
Felecia Arbuah (Dir-Clinical Svcs)
Kristen Eichert (Dir-Bus Dev)
Quian Buford (Dir-Performance Improve-
ment)
Kim Ivey (Dir-HR)
Salman Siddiqui (Dir-Clinical-Boys Residen-
tial Treatment Program)

HHC River Park, Inc. (1)
1230 6th Ave, Huntington, WV 25701
Tel.: (304) 526-9111
Web Site: https://www.riverparkhospital.net
Emp.: 300
Behavioral Healthcare Services
N.A.I.C.S.: 622210
Terry A. Stephens (CEO)

HHC S Carolina, Inc. (1)
152 Waccamaw Medical Park Dr, Conway,
SC 29526
Tel.: (843) 347-8871
Web Site: http://www.lighthousecarecenterof
conway.com
Sales Range: $25-49.9 Million
Emp.: 200
Psychiatric & Substance Abuse Diagnosis
Services
N.A.I.C.S.: 622210
Adrian Murphy (Officer-Safety & Dir-
Facilities Mgmt)
Julie Kanniard (Dir-Bus Office)
Tom Ryba (CEO)
Pat Godbold (Chief Nursing Officer)
James Wydock (CFO)
Robert Falasco (Dir-Admissions)
Bary Kemble (Dir-Clinical Svcs)
Chad Hutchison (Dir-HR)
Tim Miller (Dir-Risk Mgmt & Performance
Improvement Mgmt)
Kelly Baker (Mgr-HIM/UM)
Jo Sortelli (Dir-Risk Mgmt & Performance
Improvement)
Julie Barraza (Dir-Bus Dev)
Robert Pender (Co-Chief Nursing Officer)

HHC South Carolina, Inc. (1)
152 Waccamaw Medical Park Dr, Conway,
SC 29526
Tel.: (843) 347-8871
Web Site: https://lighthousebehavioral.com
General Hospital Services
N.A.I.C.S.: 622110

HHC St. Simons, Inc. (1)
2927 Demere Rd, Saint Simons Island, GA
31522
Tel.: (912) 638-1999
Web Site: https://www.ssbythesea.com
Sales Range: $25-49.9 Million
Emp.: 200
Psychiatric Services
N.A.I.C.S.: 622210

HRI Hospital, Inc. (1)
227 Babcock St, Brookline, MA 02446
Tel.: (617) 731-3200
Web Site: https://hrihospital.com
Health Care Srvices
N.A.I.C.S.: 622210

Harbor Point Behavioral Health Cen-
ter, Inc. (1)
301 Fort Ln, Portsmouth, VA 23704
Tel.: (757) 393-0061
Web Site: https://www.harborpointbhc.com
Behavioral Health Services
N.A.I.C.S.: 622210

Havenwyck Hospital Inc. (1)
1525 University Dr, Auburn Hills, MI 48326

Universal Health Services, Inc.—(Continued)

Tel.: (248) 373-9200
Web Site:
  https://www.havenwyckhospital.com
Sales Range: $75-99.9 Million
Emp.: 300
Psychiatric Hospitals
N.A.I.C.S.: 622210

Hickory Trail Hospital, L.P. (1)
2000 N Old Hickory Trl, Desoto, TX 75115
Tel.: (972) 298-7323
Web Site: https://www.hickorytrail.com
Emp.: 200
Mental Health Services
N.A.I.C.S.: 622210

Hitchcock Healthcare, Inc. (1)
690 Medical Park Dr, Aiken, SC 29801
Tel.: (803) 648-8344
Web Site:
  http://www.hitchcockhealthcare.org
Outpatient Care Centers
N.A.I.C.S.: 621498

Holly Hill Hospital, LLC (1)
3019 Falstaff Rd, Raleigh, NC 27610
Tel.: (919) 250-7000
Web Site: https://www.hollyhillhospital.com
Behavioral Healthcare Services
N.A.I.C.S.: 622210
Eric K. (Dir-Admissions)

Horizon Health Corporation (1)
1965 Lakepointe Dr Ste 100, Lewisville, PA 75057
Tel.: (972) 420-8300
Web Site: http://www.horizonhealth.com
Health Care Srvices
N.A.I.C.S.: 622210

Subsidiary (Domestic):

Horizon Mental Health Management, LLC (2)
1965 Lake point Dr Ste 100, Lewisville, TX 75057
Tel.: (972) 420-8200
Web Site: http://www.horizonhealth.com
Sales Range: $75-99.9 Million
Emp.: 70
Psychiatric Contract Management Services
N.A.I.C.S.: 541611

Hughes Center, LLC (1)
1601 Franklin Tpke, Danville, VA 24540
Tel.: (434) 836-8500
Web Site: https://www.thehughescenter.com
Residential Facility Services
N.A.I.C.S.: 623210
Lisa Buchanan (COO)
Terrence Bethea (Dir-Medical)
Cindy Pruitt Rhodes (Dir-Clinical)
Bradley Fussell (Dir-Risk Mgmt & Quality Improvement)

Indian River Behavioral Health, LLC (1)
1000 36th St, Vero Beach, FL 32960
Tel.: (772) 563-4666
Web Site: http://www.irmc.cc
Emp.: 1,100
Behavioral Healthcare Services
N.A.I.C.S.: 622210

KMI Acquisition, LLC (1)
8521 LaGrange Rd, Louisville, KY 40242
Tel.: (502) 426-6380
Web Site: http://www.thebrookhospitals.com
Behavioral Healthcare Services
N.A.I.C.S.: 622110
Paul Andrews (CEO)

Keystone Charlotte LLC (1)
1715 Sharon Rd W, Charlotte, NC 28210
Tel.: (704) 554-9874
Psychiatric Services
N.A.I.C.S.: 622210

Keystone Education and Youth Services, LLC (1)
110 Westwood Pl, Brentwood, TN 37027
Tel.: (615) 250-0000
Web Site: http://www.uhsinc.com
Emp.: 100
School & Educational Services
N.A.I.C.S.: 611699

Keystone Newport News, LLC (1)

17579 Warwick Blvd, Newport News, VA 23603-1343
Tel.: (757) 888-0400
Web Site: http://www.newportnewsbhc.com
Behavioral Health Services

Keystone Richland Center LLC (1)
1451 Lucas Rd, Mansfield, OH 44903
Tel.: (419) 589-5511
Web Site:
  https://www.foundationsforliving.net
Emp.: 150
Residential Treatment Services
N.A.I.C.S.: 623990
John G. Galbraith (Dir-Medical)
Matthew Mott (Dir-Bus Dev)

Kids Behavioral Health of Utah, Inc. (1)
5899 W Rivendell Dr, West Jordan, UT 84081
Tel.: (801) 561-3377
Web Site:
  http://www.copperhillsyouthcenter.com
Behavioral Healthcare Services
N.A.I.C.S.: 622110
Ron S. Tuinei (CEO)

La Amistad Residential Treatment Center, LLC (1)
1600 Dodd Rd, Winter Park, FL 32792
Tel.: (407) 647-0660
Web Site: http://www.lamistad.com
Behavioral Healthcare Services
N.A.I.C.S.: 621610
Rodney Letterman (CEO)
Carlos H. Ruiz (Dir-Medical)
Robert Buchholz (Dir-Medical-Adult Svcs)
Brian Sellers (Dir-Clinical Svcs)
Desiree Fouse (Mgr-Risk & Quality Improvement)
Tim Haubrock (Dir-Education)
Devon Kriebel (Dir-Nursing)
Mariel Johnson (Mgr-Program Social Svc)

La Paloma Treatment Center, LLC (1)
2911 Brunswick Rd, Memphis, TN 38133
Tel.: (901) 350-4575
Web Site:
  https://www.theoakstreatment.com
Residential Health Care Services
N.A.I.C.S.: 624190
Paige Bottom (Co-CEO)
Carol Ricossa (Coord-Life Challenge Community & Events)
Hallie Bloom (Dir-Clinical)
Hannah Finkey (Coord-Patient Care)
Talunja Eskridge (Dir-Residential Svcs)
Sally R. Lawes (Co-CEO)
Jeremy Pitzer (Co-CEO)

Lancaster Behavioral Health Hospital, LLC (1)
333 Harrisburg Ave, Lancaster, PA 17603
Tel.: (717) 740-4100
Web Site: https://lancasterbehavioral.org
Geriatric Hospital Services
N.A.I.C.S.: 622110

Lancaster Hospital Corporation (1)
38600 Medical Ctr Dr, Palmdale, CA 93551
Tel.: (661) 382-5000
Web Site:
  https://www.swhpalmdaleregional.com
Behavioral Health Services
N.A.I.C.S.: 622210

Laredo FED JV1, LLC (1)
367 S Gulph Rd, King of Prussia, PA 19406-3121
Tel.: (610) 382-4328
Health Care Srvices
N.A.I.C.S.: 622110

Laredo Regional Medical Center, L.P. (1)
1700 E Saunders, Laredo, TX 78041
Tel.: (956) 796-5000
Web Site: https://www.laredomedical.com
Emp.: 1,350
Behavioral Health Services
N.A.I.C.S.: 622110

Las Vegas Medical Group, LLC (1)
4043 E Sunset Rd, Henderson, NV 89014
Tel.: (702) 733-0744
Web Site:
  https://www.alasvegasmedicalgroup.com

Health Care Srvices
N.A.I.C.S.: 622110
Elmer David (Founder & Mng Dir)

Laurel Oaks Behavioral Health Center, Inc. (1)
700 E Cottonwood Rd, Dothan, AL 36301
Tel.: (334) 794-7373
Web Site: https://www.laureloaksbhc.com
Sales Range: $25-49.9 Million
Emp.: 200
Behavioral Health Services
N.A.I.C.S.: 622110
Jeanette Jackson (CEO)

Liberty Point Behavioral Healthcare, LLC (1)
1110 Montgomery Ave, Staunton, VA 24401
Tel.: (540) 213-0450
Web Site:
  https://www.libertypointstaunton.com
Behavioral Health Services
N.A.I.C.S.: 622110
Patti Anthony (Dir-HR)
Courtnay Davis (Dir-Clinical Svcs)
Lisa Neil (Dir-Nursing)

Manatee Cardiology Associates, LLC (1)
316 Manatee Ave W, Bradenton, FL 34205-8805
Tel.: (610) 382-4922
Health Care Srvices
N.A.I.C.S.: 622110

Mayhill Behavioral Health, LLC (1)
2809 S Mayhill Rd, Denton, TX 76208
Tel.: (940) 239-3000
Web Site: https://www.mayhillhospital.com
Behavioral Healthcare Services
N.A.I.C.S.: 622210

McAllen Heart Hospital, L.P. (1)
1900 S D St, McAllen, TX 78503
Tel.: (956) 994-2000
Web Site:
  https://www.southtexashealthsystem
  heart.com
Behavioral Healthcare Services
N.A.I.C.S.: 622110

Merridell Achievement Center, Inc. (1)
12550 W Hwy 29 Liberty Hill, Austin, TX 78642
Tel.: (512) 528-2100
Web Site: http://www.meridell.com
Behavioral Healthcare Services
N.A.I.C.S.: 622110

Millwood Hospital (1)
1011 N Cooper St, Arlington, TX 76011
Tel.: (817) 242-9993
Web Site: https://www.millwoodhospital.com
Sales Range: $25-49.9 Million
Emp.: 350
Psychiatric Healthcare Services
N.A.I.C.S.: 622210
Jeff Epperson (CFO)

NWTX Physician Network, PLLC (1)
2505 Lakeview Dr Ste 205, Amarillo, TX 79109-1527
Tel.: (806) 803-9552
Health Care Srvices
N.A.I.C.S.: 622110

Neuro Institute of Austin, L.P. (1)
1106 W Dittmar Rd, Austin, TX 78745
Tel.: (512) 444-4835
Web Site: https://www.texasneurorehab.com
Sales Range: $50-74.9 Million
Emp.: 400
Psychiatric Hospitals
N.A.I.C.S.: 622210

Nevada Preferred Healthcare Providers, LLC (1)
1510 Meadow Wood Ln, Reno, NV 89502
Tel.: (775) 356-1159
Web Site: http://nevadapreferred.com
General Hospital Services
N.A.I.C.S.: 622110

North Spring Behavioral Healthcare, Inc. (1)
42009 Victory Ln, Leesburg, VA 20176
Tel.: (703) 777-0800
Web Site:
  https://www.northspringleesburg.com

Behavioral Healthcare Services
N.A.I.C.S.: 622110
David Winters (CEO)
Sara Brunetti (Dir-Bus Office)
Ashley Tomei (Dir-Utilization Review)

Northern Nevada Cardiology PC (1)
1850 Spring Ridge Dr, Susanville, CA 96130
Tel.: (775) 356-4514
Emp.: 5
Health Care Srvices
N.A.I.C.S.: 622110

Northern Nevada Medical Group, LLC (1)
5070 Ion Dr Ste 200, Sparks, NV 89436
Tel.: (775) 352-5335
Web Site: http://www.nnmg.com
Emp.: 15
Miscellaneous Ambulatory Health Care Services
N.A.I.C.S.: 621999
Alan Olive (CEO)

Northwest Texas Healthcare System, Inc. (1)
1501 S Coulter St, Amarillo, TX 79106
Tel.: (806) 354-1000
Web Site: https://www.nwths.com
Sales Range: $75-99.9 Million
Emp.: 1,800
General Medical Surgical Hospitals
N.A.I.C.S.: 622110
Sandy Ethridge (COO)
Douglas Coffey (Chief Nursing Officer)

Northwest Texas Physician Group (1)
1600 S Coulter Bldg F, Amarillo, TX 79106
Tel.: (806) 398-3627
Web Site: http://www.nwtpg.com
Emp.: 10
Health Care Srvices
N.A.I.C.S.: 622110

Northwest Texas Surgical Hospital, L.L.C. (1)
3501 S Soncy Rd, Amarillo, TX 79119
Tel.: (806) 359-7999
Ambulatory Health Care Services
N.A.I.C.S.: 621999

Northwest Texas Wyatt Clinic, PLLC (1)
1411 E Amarillo Blvd, Amarillo, TX 79107-5555
Tel.: (806) 354-1015
Emp.: 85
Health Care Srvices
N.A.I.C.S.: 622110
Anne Friemel (Dir-Administration)

Oak Plains Academy of Tennessee, Inc. (1)
1751 Oak Plains Rd, Ashland City, TN 37015-9113
Tel.: (931) 362-4723
Web Site:
  http://www.oakplainsacademy.com
Miscellaneous Ambulatory Health Care Services
N.A.I.C.S.: 621999
Randy O'Donnell (CEO)

Ocala Behavioral Health, LLC (1)
3130 SW 27th Ave, Ocala, FL 34471
Tel.: (352) 671-3130
Web Site: https://www.thevineshospital.com
Emp.: 275
Miscellaneous Ambulatory Health Care Services
N.A.I.C.S.: 621999

Orchard Portman Hospital Limited (1)
Nepicar House London Road, Sevenoaks, TN15 7RS, Kent, United Kingdom
Tel.: (44) 1823336457
Health Care Srvices
N.A.I.C.S.: 621420

PSJ Acquisition, LLC (1)
510 4th St S, Fargo, ND 58103
Tel.: (701) 476-7200
Web Site: https://www.prairie-stjohns.com
Miscellaneous Ambulatory Health Care Services
N.A.I.C.S.: 621999
Carol Frovarp (CFO)
Racheal Glynn (Dir-Nursing)

Elysia Agnew (Dir-Assessment & Intake)
Michelle Parkinson (Dir-HR)
Tim Mathern (Dir-Pub Policy)

Palm Point Behavioral Health, LLC (1)
2355 Truman Scarborough Way, Titusville, FL 32796
Tel.: (321) 603-6550
Web Site: https://palmpointbehavioral.com
Health Care Srvices
N.A.I.C.S.: 621491

Palm Springs Treatment Centers, LLC (1)
2095 N Indian Canyon Dr, Palm Springs, CA 92262
Tel.: (760) 416-7951
Residential & Substance Abuse Rehabilitation Services
N.A.I.C.S.: 623220
Greg Varra (Mgr-Case)

Palmetto Behavioral Health System, L.L.C. (1)
2777 Speissegger Dr, Charleston, SC 29405
Tel.: (843) 747-5830
Web Site:
    https://www.palmettobehavioralhealth.com
Miscellaneous Ambulatory Health Care Services
N.A.I.C.S.: 621999

Palmetto Pee Dee Behavioral Health, L.L.C. (1)
601 Gregg Ave, Florence, SC 29501
Tel.: (843) 667-0644
Web Site: http://www.palmettopeedee.com
Miscellaneous Ambulatory Health Care Services
N.A.I.C.S.: 621999

Peak Behavioral Health Services, LLC (1)
5065 McNutt Rd, Santa Teresa, NM 88008
Tel.: (575) 589-3000
Web Site: https://www.peakbehavioral.com
Miscellaneous Ambulatory Health Care Services
N.A.I.C.S.: 621999

Plaza Surgery Center, Limited Partnership (1)
525 E Plz Dr Ste 100, Santa Maria, CA 93454-6966
Tel.: (805) 739-3850
Emp.: 20
Miscellaneous Ambulatory Health Care Services
N.A.I.C.S.: 621999
Sandi Witcher (Gen Mgr)

Pride Institute, Inc. (1)
14400 Martin Dr, Eden Prairie, MN 55344-2031
Tel.: (952) 934-7554
Web Site: https://www.pride-institute.com
Sales Range: $25-49.9 Million
Emp.: 100
Miscellaneous Ambulatory Health Care Services
N.A.I.C.S.: 621999
Ann Leible (Dir-Utilization Review)
Vivian Nordlund (Supvr-Admissions)
Jerri Sandstrom (Dir-HR)
Meaghan Wagner (Dir-Nursing)

Professional Probation Services, Inc. (1)
1770 Indian Trail Rd ste 350, Norcross, GA 30093
Tel.: (678) 218-4100
Web Site:
    http://www.professionalprobation.com
Sales Range: $25-49.9 Million
Emp.: 100
Miscellaneous Ambulatory Health Care Services
N.A.I.C.S.: 621999
Clay Cox (Pres & CEO)
C. Keith Ward (COO & Exec VP)
Thomas York (Corp Counsel & Sr VP)
David Jacobs (Sr VP-Compliance & Trng)
Larry Shurling (VP-IT)
Donna Kennedy (VP-Admin & Corp Affairs)
Sonie Brown (Dir-Compliance)
Kellie Harrison (Dir-Field Ops)

Provo Canyon School, Inc. (1)

763 N 1650 W, Springville, UT 84663
Tel.: (801) 227-2008
Web Site: https://www.provocanyon.com
Miscellaneous Ambulatory Health Care Services
N.A.I.C.S.: 621999

Quail Surgical and Pain Management Center, LLC (1)
6630 S Mccarran Blvd Ste C25, Reno, NV 89509-6135
Tel.: (775) 827-7555
Hospital Management & Services
N.A.I.C.S.: 622110

Ramsay Youth Services of Georgia, Inc. (1)
3500 Riverside Dr, Macon, GA 31210-2509
Tel.: (478) 477-3829
Web Site: https://www.lakebridgebhs.com
Emp.: 100
Youth Behavioral Health Care Services
N.A.I.C.S.: 622210

Rdg Outpatient Counseling, L.L.C. (1)
3050 Rio Dosa Dr, Lexington, KY 40509
Tel.: (859) 269-2325
Web Site: https://www.ridgebhs.com
Miscellaneous Ambulatory Health Care Services
N.A.I.C.S.: 621999

Recovery Physicians Group of Georgia, LLC (1)
310 Black Bear Rdg, Sautee Nacoochee, GA 30571-3500
Tel.: (470) 539-6905
Psychiatric & Substance Abuse Rehabilitation Services
N.A.I.C.S.: 622210

Recovery Physicians Group of Tennessee, LLC (1)
101 Lea Ave, Nashville, TN 37210
Tel.: (954) 587-7771
Psychiatric & Substance Abuse Rehabilitation Services
N.A.I.C.S.: 622210

Ridge Outpatient Counseling, L.L.C. (1)
3050 Rio Dosa Dr, Lexington, KY 40509
Tel.: (859) 269-2325
Health Care Srvices
N.A.I.C.S.: 622110

River Oaks, Inc. (1)
38322 Appolo Pkwy, Willoughby, OH 44094
Tel.: (440) 942-1235
Miscellaneous Ambulatory Health Care Services
N.A.I.C.S.: 621999

Riveredge Hospital, Inc. (1)
8311 W Roosevelt Rd, Forest Park, IL 60130
Tel.: (708) 209-4145
Web Site:
    https://www.riveredgehospital.com
General Medical Surgical Hospitals
N.A.I.C.S.: 622110
Aamir Safdar (Chief Medical Officer)
Rad Gharavi (Assoc Dir-Medical)
Sheila Orr (Chief Compliance Officer)
Elisabeth Egan (Dir-Nursing Infection Prevention)
Martin Blackman (Dir-Psychological Svcs)
Todd Bergmann (Dir-Therapeutic Svcs)

Rolling Hills Hospital, LLC (1)
2014 Quail Hollow Cir, Franklin, TN 37067
Tel.: (615) 807-4059
Web Site: https://www.rollinghillshospital.org
Miscellaneous Ambulatory Health Care Services
N.A.I.C.S.: 621999
James R. Hart (Dir-Medical)
Yoga N. Thati (Dir-Clinical-Medical Svcs)

SHC-KPH, LP (1)
2001 Ladbrook Dr, Kingwood, TX 77339
Tel.: (281) 404-1001
Web Site: https://www.kingwoodpines.com
General Medical Surgical Hospitals
N.A.I.C.S.: 622110
Shanti Carter (CEO)

SP Behavioral, LLC (1)

11301 S E Tequesta Ter, Tequesta, FL 33469
Tel.: (561) 744-0211
Web Site:
    https://www.sandypineshospital.com
Miscellaneous Ambulatory Health Care Services
N.A.I.C.S.: 621999

Salt Lake Behavioral Health, LLC (1)
3802 S 700 E, Salt Lake City, UT 84106
Tel.: (801) 264-6000
Web Site:
    https://www.saltlakebehavioralhealth.com
Behavioral Healthcare Services
N.A.I.C.S.: 622210
Kreg Gillman (CEO)

Shadow Mountain Behavioral Health System, LLC (1)
6262 S Sheridan Rd, Tulsa, OK 74133
Tel.: (918) 492-8200
Web Site:
    http://www.shadowmountainbhs.com
Miscellaneous Ambulatory Health Care Services
N.A.I.C.S.: 621999

Short Ground Limited (1)
75 Leeds Road, Liversedge, WF15 6JA, United Kingdom
Tel.: (44) 1924409100
Hospital Management & Services
N.A.I.C.S.: 622110

Somerset, Incorporated (1)
109 E Main St, Somerset, PA 15501
Tel.: (814) 443-1748
Web Site: https://www.somersetinc.org
Miscellaneous Ambulatory Health Care Services
N.A.I.C.S.: 621999

South Texas ACO Clinical Partners, LLC (1)
301 W Expy 83, McAllen, TX 78503
Tel.: (956) 342-6015
General Hospital Services
N.A.I.C.S.: 622110

Sparks Family Hospital, Inc. (1)
2375 E Prater Way, Sparks, NV 89434
Tel.: (775) 331-7000
Web Site: http://www.nnmc.com
Emp.: 400
General Hospital Services
N.A.I.C.S.: 622110

Summerlin Hospital Medical Center LLC (1)
657 N Town Center Dr, Las Vegas, NV 89144
Tel.: (702) 233-7000
Web Site:
    https://www.summerlinhospital.com
Emp.: 1,813
Miscellaneous Ambulatory Health Care Services
N.A.I.C.S.: 621999
Robert S. Freymuller (CEO)

Summit Oaks Hospital, Inc. (1)
19 Prospect St, Summit, NJ 07902
Tel.: (908) 522-7000
Web Site:
    https://www.summitoakshospital.com
Sales Range: $25-49.9 Million
Emp.: 200
Medical Surgical Hospital Services
N.A.I.C.S.: 622110

TBJ Behavioral Center, LLC (1)
6300 Beach Blvd, Jacksonville, FL 32216
Tel.: (904) 724-9202
Web Site:
    https://www.riverpointbehavioral.com
Miscellaneous Ambulatory Health Care Services
N.A.I.C.S.: 621999

Temecula Valley Hospital, Inc. (1)
31700 Temecula Pkwy, Temecula, CA 92592
Tel.: (951) 331-2200
Web Site:
    https://www.swhtemeculavalley.com
Emp.: 1,100
Health Care Srvices

N.A.I.C.S.: 622110
Darlene Wetton (CEO)
Lori Hamilton (Dir-HR)
Claude Reinke (Vice Chm)

Tennessee Clinical Schools, LLC (1)
1220 8th Ave S, Nashville, TN 37203
Tel.: (615) 742-3000
Web Site: https://www.hermitagehall.com
Sales Range: $25-49.9 Million
Emp.: 150
Miscellaneous Ambulatory Health Care Services
N.A.I.C.S.: 621999
Mitzi Milts (CFO)
Gladys Bush (Dir-Medical)

Texas Cypress Creek Hospital, L.P. (1)
17750 Cali Dr, Houston, TX 77090
Tel.: (281) 586-7600
Web Site:
    https://www.cypresscreekhospital.com
Sales Range: $10-24.9 Million
Emp.: 220
Psychiatric Hospitals
N.A.I.C.S.: 622210
Ajinder Dhatt (Dir-Medical)
Athi P. Venkatesh (Dir-Medical-ECT)

Texas Laurel Ridge Hospital, L.P. (1)
17720 Corporate Woods Dr, San Antonio, TX 78259
Tel.: (210) 491-9400
Web Site: https://www.laurelridgetc.com
Sales Range: $25-49.9 Million
Emp.: 500
Psychiatric Hospitals
N.A.I.C.S.: 622210

Texas Panhandle Clinical Partners ACO, LLC (1)
6900 I 40 W Ste 150, Amarillo, TX 79106
Tel.: (806) 279-2567
Web Site: https://tpcpaco.com
General Hospital Services
N.A.I.C.S.: 622110

Texas San Marcos Treatment Center, L.P. (1)
120 Bert Brown Rd, San Marcos, TX 78666
Tel.: (512) 396-8500
Web Site: https://www.sanmarcostc.com
Emp.: 200
Behavioral Healthcare Services
N.A.I.C.S.: 621112
Johnnie Fisher (Dir-Unit Medical)
Shephali Sharma (Dir-Unit Medical)
Sherri Gonzalez (Dir-Bus Dev)
David Tjandrasa (Dir-Academic Program & Unit)
Gilbert Sanchez (Officer-Safety & Dir-Plant Ops)
Robin Cunningham (Dir-HR)

TexomaCare (1)
5016 S US Hwy 75, Denison, TX 75020
Tel.: (903) 416-6325
Web Site:
    http://www.texomamedicalcenter.net
Miscellaneous Ambulatory Health Care Services
N.A.I.C.S.: 621999

TexomaCare Specialty Physicians (1)
5012 S US Hwy 75 Ste 275, Denison, TX 75020
Tel.: (903) 416-6470
Health Care Srvices
N.A.I.C.S.: 622110

The Canyon at Peace Park, LLC (1)
2900 S Kanan Dume Rd, Malibu, CA 90265-2792
Tel.: (310) 774-2043
Web Site: https://www.thecanyonmalibu.com
Substance Abuse Rehabilitation Services
N.A.I.C.S.: 622210

The Canyon at Santa Monica, LLC (1)
12304 Santa Monica Blvd Ste 112, Los Angeles, CA 90025
Tel.: (424) 267-1744
Web Site: https://canyonsantamonica.com
Outpatient Health Care Services
N.A.I.C.S.: 621420
Melinda Drake (Dir-Outpatient Services)

Universal Health Services, Inc.—(Continued)

The National Deaf Academy, LLC (1)
19650 Us Hwy 441, Mount Dora, FL 32757
Tel.: (352) 735-9500
Web Site:
  http://www.nationaldeafacademy.com
Behavioral Healthcare Services
N.A.I.C.S.: 621112

Treasure Coast Behavioral Health, LLC (1)
1860 N Lawnwood Cir, Fort Pierce, FL 34950
Tel.: (772) 466-1500
Web Site: http://www.lawnwoodmed.com
Health Care Srvices
N.A.I.C.S.: 622110

UBH of Oregon, LLC (1)
10300 SW Eastridge St, Portland, OR 97225
Tel.: (503) 944-5000
Web Site:
  https://www.cedarhillshospital.com
Behavioral Health Care & Addiction Reha-
bilitation Services
N.A.I.C.S.: 622210
Dennis Spidal (Dir-Plant Ops)
Michele Milantoni (Mgr-Health Information Mgmt)
Phyll Zuberi (Dir-Medical-The Military Pro-
gram)
Mayo Powers (Mgr-Pharmacy)
Vandana Bindal (Dir-Medical-Internal Medi-
cine)

UBH of Phoenix, LLC (1)
3550 E Pinchot Ave, Phoenix, AZ 85018
Tel.: (602) 957-4000
Web Site: https://www.valleyhospital-
phoenix.com
Behavioral Health Care & Addiction Reha-
bilitation Services
N.A.I.C.S.: 622210
Roland Segal (Chief Medical Officer)

UHP, LP (1)
2026 W University Dr, Denton, TX 76201
Tel.: (940) 320-8100
Web Site: https://www.ubhdenton.com
Behavioral Health Care & Substance Abuse
Rehabilitation Services
N.A.I.C.S.: 622210

UHS Imaging LLC (1)
6 Newton Ave, Norwich, NY 13815
Tel.: (607) 337-4999
Emp.: 600
Health Care Srvices
N.A.I.C.S.: 622110
Drake Lamen (CEO)

UHS Midwest Center for Youth and Families, LLC (1)
1012 W Indiana St, Kouts, IN 46347
Tel.: (219) 766-2999
Web Site: https://midwest-center.com
Miscellaneous Ambulatory Health Care Ser-
vices
N.A.I.C.S.: 621999

UHS of Centennial Peaks, LLC (1)
2255 S 88th St, Louisville, CO 80027
Tel.: (303) 673-9990
Web Site: https://www.centennialpeaks.com
Emp.: 100
Behavioral Healthcare Services
N.A.I.C.S.: 621112
Snieguole Radzeviciene (Dir-Clinical-
Adolescent Outpatient & Partial Hospitaliza-
tion)
Anmarie Masters (Dir-HIM)

UHS of Delaware, Inc. (1)
367 S Gulph Rd, King of Prussia, PA 19406
Tel.: (610) 768-3300
Web Site: http://www.uhsinc.com
Sales Range: $75-99.9 Million
Emp.: 300
Business Operations Management Services
N.A.I.C.S.: 541611

Subsidiary (Domestic):

Arbour-HRI Hospital (2)
227 Babcock St, Brookline, MA 02446
Tel.: (617) 731-3200
Web Site: http://www.arborhealth.com

Sales Range: $25-49.9 Million
Emp.: 190
Psychiatric Hospitals
N.A.I.C.S.: 622210

Auburn Regional Medical Center (2)
202 N Division St, Auburn, WA 98001
Tel.: (253) 833-7711
Sales Range: $100-124.9 Million
149 Bed Hospital
N.A.I.C.S.: 622210
Bill Robertson (CEO)
Chris Kneck Step (CFO)

Coastal Harbor Treatment Center (2)
1150 Cornell St, Savannah, GA 31406-2702
Tel.: (912) 354-3911
Web Site: https://www.coastalharbor.com
Sales Range: $25-49.9 Million
Emp.: 200
Psychiatric Health Services for Children &
Adolescents
N.A.I.C.S.: 622210
Reemon Bishara (Dir-Medical)

Del Amo Hospital (2)
23700 Camino Del Sol, Torrance, CA
90505-5017 (100%)
Tel.: (310) 530-1151
Web Site:
  https://delamobehavioralhealth.com
Sales Range: $75-99.9 Million
Emp.: 300
Psychiatric Hospitals
N.A.I.C.S.: 622210

Doctors' Hospital of Shreveport (2)
1130 Louisiana Ave, Shreveport, LA 71101-
3908
Tel.: (318) 227-1211
Rehabilitation Center
N.A.I.C.S.: 622310

Forest View Psychiatric Hospital (2)
1055 Medical Park Dr SE, Grand Rapids,
MI 49546
Tel.: (616) 942-9610
Web Site:
  https://www.forestviewhospital.com
Sales Range: $25-49.9 Million
Emp.: 120
Mental Health Services
N.A.I.C.S.: 622210

Glen Oaks Hospital (2)
Glen Oaks Hospital 301 E Division St,
Greenville, TX 75401
Tel.: (903) 454-6000
Web Site: https://www.glenoakshospital.com
Sales Range: $25-49.9 Million
Emp.: 100
Mental Health & Chemical Dependency
Treatment Facility
N.A.I.C.S.: 622210
Raza Sayed (Dir-Facility Medical)
Fernando Siles (Dir-Outpatient Svcs)

KeyStone Center (2)
2001 Providence Ave, Chester, PA
19013 (100%)
Tel.: (610) 876-9000
Web Site: https://www.keystonecenter.net
Sales Range: $25-49.9 Million
Emp.: 100
Chemical Dependency Rehabilitation Facil-
ity
N.A.I.C.S.: 621498
Al Coppola (CFO)
Elizabeth Conlin (CEO-Interim)
Christopher Borkowski (Dir-Clinical Svcs)
George Collins (Dir-Psychological Svcs)
Ellen Norman (Dir-Nursing)
Jennifer East (Dir-Bus Dev)
Michelle Westerfer (Dir-HR)
Diane Warfield (Dir-Admissions)
Jennifer Walling (Coord-Family Therapy)

La Amistad Behavioral Health Services (2)
1650 Park Ave N, Maitland, FL
32751 (100%)
Tel.: (407) 647-0660
Web Site: https://www.lamistad.com
Sales Range: $25-49.9 Million
Emp.: 150
Behavioral Healthcare Services
N.A.I.C.S.: 622210
Carlos H. Ruiz (Dir-Medical)
Rodney Letterman (CEO)

Robert Buchholz (Dir-Medical-Adult Svcs)
Brian Sellers (Dir-Clinical Svcs)
Vic Prezioso (Dir-Nursing)
Desiree Fouse (Mgr-Child & Adolescent So-
cial Svcs)
Michelle Wiggins (Dir-Education)
Devon Kriebel (Mgr-Facility Risk & Coord-
Civil Rights)

Manatee Memorial Hospital & Health System (2)
206 2nd St E, Bradenton, FL 34208
Tel.: (941) 746-5111
Web Site: http://www.manateememorial.com
Medical Devices
N.A.I.C.S.: 622110
Kevin DiLallo (CEO)
Mark Tierney (CFO)
Candace Smith (Chief Nursing Officer)

McAllen Medical Center (2)
301 W Expy 83, McAllen, TX 78503
Tel.: (956) 632-4000
Web Site:
  https://www.southtexashealthsystem
  mcallen.com
428 Bed General Medical & Surgical Hospital
N.A.I.C.S.: 621112

Meridell Achievement Center (2)
12550 W Hwy 29, Liberty Hill, TX
78642 (100%)
Tel.: (512) 528-2100
Web Site: http://www.meridell.com
Sales Range: $10-24.9 Million
Emp.: 75
Residential Behavioral Health Treatment
Center
N.A.I.C.S.: 623220

Northern Nevada Medical Center (2)
2375 E Prater Way, Sparks, NV 89434
Tel.: (775) 331-7000
Web Site: http://www.nnmc.com
General Acute Care Hospital
N.A.I.C.S.: 622110
Randall Pierce (Chm)
Karla Perez (Reg VP)
Sven Inda (Co-Chm-Emergency Medicine)
Brett Winthrop (Chm-Anesthesiology)
Helen Lidholm (CEO)

River Crest Hospital (2)
1636 Hunters Glen Rd, San Angelo, TX
76901-5016 (100%)
Tel.: (325) 949-5722
Web Site: https://www.rivercresthospital.com
Sales Range: $25-49.9 Million
Emp.: 130
Behavioral Health & Chemical Dependency
Services
N.A.I.C.S.: 622210
Juana Giralt (CEO-Interim & CFO)

River Oaks Hospital (2)
1525 River Oaks Rd W, New Orleans, LA
70123-2162 (100%)
Tel.: (504) 734-1740
Web Site: https://www.riveroakshospital.com
Sales Range: $25-49.9 Million
Emp.: 200
Private Psychiatric Facility for Adults, Ado-
lescents & Children
N.A.I.C.S.: 622210

Southwest Healthcare System (2)
36485 Inland Vly Dr, Wildomar, CA
92595 (100%)
Tel.: (951) 677-1111
Web Site: http://www.swhcs.com
General Surgical & Medical Center
N.A.I.C.S.: 622110

The Arbour Hospital (2)
49 Robinwood Ave, Jamaica Plain, MA
02130
Tel.: (617) 522-4400
Web Site: https://arbourhospital.com
Sales Range: $25-49.9 Million
Emp.: 400
Psychiatric Hospitals
N.A.I.C.S.: 622210

The BridgeWay Hospital (2)
21 Bridgeway Rd, North Little Rock, AR
72113
Tel.: (501) 771-1500
Web Site: http://www.thebridgeway.com
Sales Range: $50-74.9 Million
Emp.: 210
Private Psychiatric Hospital

N.A.I.C.S.: 622210

Turning Point Hospital (2)
3015 Veterans Pkwy S, Moultrie, GA 31788-
6705
Tel.: (229) 985-4815
Web Site: https://www.turningpointcare.com
Sales Range: $10-24.9 Million
Emp.: 200
Behavioral Healthcare & Chemical Depen-
dancy Services
N.A.I.C.S.: 622210
Judy H. Payne (CEO)
Heather Hightower (Dir-Nursing)
Peggy Yates (Dir-Clinical)

Two Rivers Psychiatric Hospital (2)
5121 Raytown Rd, Kansas City, MO
64133 (100%)
Tel.: (816) 356-5688
Web Site: https://www.tworivershospital.com
Sales Range: $25-49.9 Million
Emp.: 180
Behavioral Healthcare Services
N.A.I.C.S.: 622210

Valley Hospital Medical Center (2)
620 Shadow Ln, Las Vegas, NV
89106 (100%)
Tel.: (702) 388-4000
Web Site: https://www.valleyhospital.net
General Acute Care Hospital
N.A.I.C.S.: 622110

Wellington Regional Medical Center (2)
10101 Forest Hill Blvd, Wellington, FL
33414
Tel.: (561) 798-8500
Web Site:
  https://www.wellingtonregional.com
Sales Range: $100-124.9 Million
General Medical & Surgical Hospital
N.A.I.C.S.: 622110
Pam Tahan (CEO)

UHS of Parkwood, Inc. (1)
8135 Goodman Rd, Olive Branch, MS
38654-2103
Tel.: (662) 895-4900
Web Site: https://parkwoodbhs.com
Miscellaneous Ambulatory Health Care Ser-
vices
N.A.I.C.S.: 621999

UHS of Phoenix, LLC (1)
2545 W Quail Ave, Phoenix, AZ 85027
Tel.: (602) 455-5700
Web Site:
  https://www.quailrunbehavioral.com
Behavioral Healthcare Services
N.A.I.C.S.: 621999

UHS of Rockford, LLC (1)
100 Rockford Dr, Newark, DE 19713
Tel.: (302) 996-5480
Web Site: http://www.rockfordcenter.com
Miscellaneous Ambulatory Health Care Ser-
vices
N.A.I.C.S.: 621999
John McKenna (CEO)
Saurabh Gupta (Dir-Medical)
Liz Proctor (Dir-Clinical Svcs)
Mike Gavula (Dir-Bus Dev)
Jeanine Antigua (Dir-Assessment Referral
Center)
Jackie Tomasetti (Dir-Social Svcs)
Michelle Preston (Chief Nursing Officer)

UHS of Springwoods, L.L.C. (1)
1955 W Truckers Dr, Fayetteville, AR 72704
Tel.: (479) 973-6000
Web Site:
  http://www.springwoodsbehavioral.com
Miscellaneous Ambulatory Health Care Ser-
vices
N.A.I.C.S.: 621999

UHS of Tucson, LLC (1)
2695 N Craycroft Rd, Tucson, AZ 85712
Tel.: (520) 322-2888
Web Site: http://www.paloverdebh.com
Behavioral Healthcare Services
N.A.I.C.S.: 622210
Mark J. Helms (Dir-Medical)
Nazia Ahmed (Assoc Dir-Medical)
Kristine Norris (Dir-Outpatient-Women's
Svcs)
Jill Scheckel (CEO)
Amy Cann (Dir-Nursing)

Melissa Greibel (Dir-Ops)
Susan Marsett (Dir-HR)
Shane Hubbell (Dir-Plant Ops)
Katie Studenski (Dir-Bus Office)
Jeni Whetstone (Dir-Performance Improvement & Risk Mgmt)
Katie Barans (Dir-Bus Dev)
Loretta Meersman (Dir-Pharmacy)
Heather McGovern (Dir-Outpatient Ops)
Trisha Solano (Mgr-Health Information Mgmt)
Lynn Myers (CFO)
Chad Mosher (Dir-Outpatient Svcs-Grp)

West Church Partnership (1)
367 S Gulph Rd, King of Prussia, PA 19406
Tel.: (610) 768-3300
Health Care Srvices
N.A.I.C.S.: 622110

Wisconsin Avenue Psychiatric Center, Inc., (1)
4228 Wisconsin Ave NW, Washington, DC 20016
Tel.: (202) 885-5600
Web Site: http://www.psychinstitute.com
Behavioral Healthcare Services
N.A.I.C.S.: 622210
Rich Armentrout (CFO)
Dania O'Connor (CEO)
Antolin Trinidad (Chief Medical Officer)
Nicole Parker (Chief Nursing Officer)
Davidra T. Bazemore-Blue (Chief Clinical Officer)
Corey Odol (Dir-Bus Dev & Govt Affairs)
Jennifer A. Kahler (Dir-Psychology)
Bernice Guity (Dir-HR)

Yarrow Lodge, LLC (1)
10499 N 48th St, Augusta, MI 49012
Tel.: (269) 282-7700
Web Site: https://skywoodrecovery.com
Substance Abuse Rehabilitation Services
N.A.I.C.S.: 622210

UNIVERSAL INSURANCE HOLDINGS, INC.
1110 W Commercial Blvd, Fort Lauderdale, FL 33309
Tel.: (954) 958-1200   DE
Web Site:
https://universalinsurancehold ings.com
UVE—(NYSE)
Rev.: $1,845,786,000
Assets: $2,890,154,000
Liabilities: $2,602,258,000
Net Worth: $287,896,000
Earnings: ($22,257,000)
Emp.: 1,223
Fiscal Year-end: 12/31/22
Holding Company; Insurance Products & Services
N.A.I.C.S.: 551112
Sean Patrick Downes (Chm)
Stephen Joseph Donaghy (CEO)
Darryl L. Lewis (Chief Legal Officer)
Kimberly D. Campos (CIO & Chief Admin Officer)
Michael J. Poloskey (COO)
Gary L. Ropiecki (Principal Acctg Officer & Sec)
Matthew J. Palmieri (Chief Risk Officer)
Elizabeth E. L. Hansen (Chief Actuary)

Subsidiaries:

American Platinum Property & Casualty Insurance Company (1)
1110 W Commercial Blvd, Fort Lauderdale, FL 33309
Tel.: (954) 958-1200
Web Site:
http://www.americanplatinumpcic.com
Insurance Management Services
N.A.I.C.S.: 524210
Sean Patrick Downes (Chm & CEO)
Jon W. Springer (Pres & Chief Risk Officer)
Stephen Joseph Donaghy (COO)
Frank Wilcox (CFO)

Coastal Homeowners Insurance Specialists, Inc. (1)

1110 W Commercial Blvd, Fort Lauderdale, FL 33309
Tel.: (954) 958-1211
Insurance Brokerage Services
N.A.I.C.S.: 524210

Tiger Home Services, Inc. (1)
23423 SE 156th St, Issaquah, WA 98027
Tel.: (425) 557-0844
Handyman Construction Services
N.A.I.C.S.: 236118

Universal Inspection Corporation (1)
1110 W Commercial Blvd, Fort Lauderdale, FL 33309
Tel.: (954) 958-1200
Insurance Brokerage Services
N.A.I.C.S.: 524210

Universal Insurance Holding Co. (1)
1110 W Commercial Blvd, Fort Lauderdale, FL 33309   **(100%)**
Tel.: (954) 958-1200
Web Site: http://www.universalproperty.com
Sales Range: $75-99.9 Million
Emp.: 200
Insurance Holding Company
N.A.I.C.S.: 551112

Subsidiary (Domestic):

Universal Property & Casualty Insurance Co. (UPCIC) (2)
1110 W Commercial Blvd Ste 300, Fort Lauderdale, FL 33309   **(100%)**
Tel.: (954) 958-1200
Web Site: http://www.universalproperty.com
Sales Range: $50-74.9 Million
Emp.: 200
Insurance Services
N.A.I.C.S.: 524210
Sean Patrick Downes (Chm & CEO)
Jon W. Springer (Pres & Chief Risk Officer)
Stephen Joseph Donaghy (COO)
Frank Wilcox (CFO)
Kimberly Cooper (CIO)
Stacey Tomko (VP-Mktg)
Derek Heard (Reg VP-Mktg)

Universal Property Management (1)
277 Pawtucket St 1 A, Lowell, MA 01854
Tel.: (978) 937-9327
Emp.: 15
Property Management Services
N.A.I.C.S.: 531210
Becky Ferguson (Office Mgr)

UNIVERSAL LOGISTICS HOLDINGS, INC.
12755 E 9 Mile Rd, Warren, MI 48089
Tel.: (586) 920-0100   MI
Web Site:
https://www.universallogistics.com
Year Founded: 2001
ULH—(NASDAQ)
Rev.: $2,015,456,000
Assets: $1,203,678,000
Liabilities: $756,748,000
Net Worth: $446,930,000
Earnings: $168,632,000
Emp.: 8,646
Fiscal Year-end: 12/31/22
Holding Company; Freight Trucking Services
N.A.I.C.S.: 551112
Timothy Phillips (Pres & CEO)
Jude Beres (CFO & Treas)
Steven Fitzpatrick (VP-Fin & IR)

Subsidiaries:

Cavalry Logistics International of Canada, Inc. (1)
4285 Industrial Drive, Windsor, N9C 3R9, ON, Canada
Tel.: (519) 969-0648
Logistics & Distribution Services
N.A.I.C.S.: 541614

Cavalry Logistics International, Inc. (1)
895 American Ln, Schaumburg, IL 60173-4967
Tel.: (615) 986-7162
Logistics & Distribution Services

N.A.I.C.S.: 541614

Cavalry Logistics, LLC (1)
5255 Hickory Hollow Pkwy, Nashville, TN 37013
Tel.: (615) 564-2000
Web Site: http://www.cavalrylogistics.com
Emp.: 150
Logistics Consulting Servies
N.A.I.C.S.: 541614

Deco Logistics, Inc. (1)
14575 Innovation Dr, Riverside, CA 92518
Tel.: (915) 214-6400
Freight Trucking Services
N.A.I.C.S.: 484110

Flint Special Services, Inc. (1)
12755 E 9 Mile Rd, Warren, MI 48089
Tel.: (586) 467-1500
Emp.: 500
Freight Trucking Services
N.A.I.C.S.: 484121

Great American Lines, Inc. (1)
5 Becker Farm Rd, Roseland, NJ 07068
Tel.: (973) 740-0740
Web Site: https://www.galinj.com
Sales Range: $10-24.9 Million
Emp.: 150
General Freight Trucking Services
N.A.I.C.S.: 484121
Peter C. Johansen (Pres)
Todd McCleary (VP)
David Duncan (Mgr-Ops)
Carl Castiglioni (Mgr-Technical)
Richard Soos (Controller)
Sharon Atieh (Office Mgr)

LINC Logistics Company (1)
12755 E 9 Mile Rd, Warren, MI 48089
Tel.: (586) 467-1500
Web Site: http://www.4linc.com
Sales Range: $300-349.9 Million
Emp.: 1,504
Logistics & Transportation Services
N.A.I.C.S.: 541614
Matthew T. Moroun (Chm)
Manuel J. Moroun (Vice Chm)

Subsidiary (Domestic):

CTX Inc. (2)
14701 Harrison Rd, Romulus, MI 48174
Tel.: (800) 982-3924
Web Site: http://www.cxua.com
Sales Range: $25-49.9 Million
Emp.: 25
Transportation Services
N.A.I.C.S.: 488510
Kyle Dobbertin (Mgr-Driver Recruiting)
Mike Bautch (Pres)
Dave Anderson (Mgr-Carrier Rels)

Louisiana Transportation, Inc. (1)
7800 E Little York Ste B, Houston, TX 77016
Tel.: (713) 431-0950
Web Site: http://www.louisianatransport.com
General Freight Trucking Services
N.A.I.C.S.: 484121

Mason Dixon Intermodal, Inc. (1)
4440 Wyoming Ave, Dearborn, MI 48126
Tel.: (313) 846-0640
Web Site: http://www.mdintermodal.com
Sales Range: $100-124.9 Million
Emp.: 100
General Freight Intermodal Transportation Support Services
N.A.I.C.S.: 484121

Morgan Southern, Inc. (1)
1500 Cedar Grove Rd, Conley, GA 30288
Tel.: (404) 366-1345
Web Site: http://www.morgansouthern.com
Rev.: $59,400,000
Emp.: 500
General Freight Trucking Services
N.A.I.C.S.: 484121

Subsidiary (Domestic):

Roadrunner Intermodal Services, LLC (2)
1500 Cedar Grove Rd, Conley, GA 30288
Tel.: (404) 366-1345
Web Site: http://www.rrtsintermodal.com
Sales Range: $25-49.9 Million
Emp.: 40
Transportation & Logistics Services

N.A.I.C.S.: 484230
Ben Kirkland (Pres)

Subsidiary (Domestic):

Central Cal Transportation, LLC (3)
4898 E Annadale Ave, Fresno, CA 93725
Tel.: (559) 476-4415
Web Site:
http://www.shiproadrunnerfreight.com
Freight Transportation Services
N.A.I.C.S.: 484230
Brett Rosa (Ops Mgr)

Subsidiary (Domestic):

Wando Trucking, LLC (2)
510 Wando Ln, Mount Pleasant, SC 29464
Tel.: (843) 881-0144
Freight Transportation Services
N.A.I.C.S.: 484121
Liz Brabham (Gen Mgr)
Jim D'Damery (Dir-Safety)

O/B Leasing Company (1)
1100 Gest St, Cincinnati, OH 45203-1114
Tel.: (513) 621-6111
Web Site: http://www.parsecinc.com
Sales Range: $50-74.9 Million
Emp.: 10
Truck Rentals & Transportation Services
N.A.I.C.S.: 532120

Parsec Inc. (1)
1100 Gest St, Cincinnati, OH 45203-1114
Tel.: (513) 621-6111
Web Site: http://www.parsecinc.com
Sales Range: $25-49.9 Million
Emp.: 15
Truck Rentals & Transportation Services
N.A.I.C.S.: 532120
David H. Budig (VP)

Southern Counties Express, Inc. (1)
18020 S Santa Fe Ave, Rancho Dominguez, CA 90220
Tel.: (310) 900-2160
Freight Services
N.A.I.C.S.: 484230

Specialized Rail Service, Inc. (1)
4740 E Tropical Pkwy, Las Vegas, NV 89115
Tel.: (702) 388-9277
Freight Trucking Services
N.A.I.C.S.: 484110
Jeff Armstrong (Pres)
Joe Obermiller (Gen Mgr)
Joyce Miya (Mgr-Acctg)
Justin Bowden (Mgr-Warehouse & Steel Yard Ops)
Elisia Eby (Mgr-Data)

Universal Capacity Solutions, LLC (1)
565 Marriott Dr Ste 500, Nashville, TN 37214
Tel.: (615) 997-2101
Web Site: https://www.shipwithu.com
Logistic Services
N.A.I.C.S.: 488510

Universal Intermodal Services, Inc. (1)
250 E 167th St, Harvey, IL 60426
Tel.: (708) 362-5657
Web Site:
http://www.universalintermodal.com
Road Transportation Support
N.A.I.C.S.: 488490
David Tutor (Mgr-Ops)
Tim Phillips (Pres)
Don Taylor (VP-Southern Ops)
Danielle Jamarino (Mgr-Bus Dev)
Jeff Hinkle (VP-Northern Ops)

Universal Logistics Solutions Canada, Ltd. (1)
125 Commerce Valley Dr W Suite 750, Thornhill, L3T 7W4, ON, Canada
Tel.: (905) 882-4880
Web Site: https://www.universallogistics.ca
Logistics Consulting Services
N.A.I.C.S.: 541614
David Glionna (VP-Fin)
Mark Glionna (VP-Client Rels & Bus Dev)
Paul Glionna (VP-Sys Dev & Ops)
Chris Cartan (Dir-Ops)
Brian Rowe (Dir-Customs Compliance & Regulatory Affairs)

Universal Logistics Holdings, Inc.—(Continued)

John Leis *(Dir-Client Rels)*
Oswaldo Arteaga *(Mgr-Customs Consulting Svcs)*
Marion Bradnam *(Gen Mgr-Customs Svcs-USA)*
Cathy Fong *(Mgr-Freight Pricing)*
Janice Ilkay *(Mgr-IT Svcs)*
David Lychek *(Mgr-Ocean & Air Svcs)*
Debbie McGuire *(Mgr-Freight Solutions)*
William Sanchez *(Mgr-Truck Svcs)*
Tina Scharnberg *(Mgr-Admin)*
Michael Glionna *(Pres)*

Universal Logistics Solutions International, Inc. **(1)**
1360 Camell Town Pkwy, Itasca, IL 60143
Tel.: (847) 490-8811
Web Site: http://www.gougi.com
Emp.: 16
Logistics Management Consulting Services
N.A.I.C.S.: 541614
David Lucyk *(Pres)*

Universal Management Services, Inc. **(1)**
8201 W 183rd St Ste K, Tinley Park, IL 60477
Tel.: (708) 444-4942
Web Site: https://www.umsblgs.com
Management Consulting Services
N.A.I.C.S.: 541618

Universal Service Center Company **(1)**
4440 Wyoming St, Dearborn, MI 48126-3751
Tel.: (313) 846-0640
Logistics Management Consulting Services
N.A.I.C.S.: 541614

UNIVERSAL MEDIA GROUP INC.
1199 S Federal Hwy Ste 111, Boca Raton, FL 33432
Tel.: (561) 908-3333   **NV**
Web Site: https://www.umgp.com
UMGP—(OTCIQ)
Television Advertising Services
N.A.I.C.S.: 541890
Mike Sherman *(Pres & CEO)*

UNIVERSAL POWER INDUSTRY CORPORATION
3 Grace Ave Ste 100, Great Neck, NY 11021   **WY**
Year Founded: 2007
UPIN—(OTCIQ)
Information Technology Services
N.A.I.C.S.: 541511
Tony H. Chiu *(Pres)*

UNIVERSAL SECURITY INSTRUMENTS, INC.
11407 Cronhill Dr, Owings Mills, MD 21117-6218
Tel.: (410) 363-3000   **MD**
Web Site:
https://www.universalsecurity.com
Year Founded: 1969
UUU—(NYSEAMEX)
Rev.: $19,902,673
Assets: $8,544,750
Liabilities: $3,581,723
Net Worth: $4,963,027
Earnings: ($395,790)
Emp.: 11
Fiscal Year-end: 03/31/24
Residential Fire & Smoke Alarms Mfr & Distr
N.A.I.C.S.: 922160
Harvey B. Grossblatt *(Pres & CEO)*
James B. Huff *(CFO, Treas & Sec)*
Ira F. Bormel *(Executives)*

Subsidiaries:

USI Electric, Inc. **(1)**
11407 A Cron Hill Dr, Owings Mills, MD 21117 **(100%)**
Tel.: (410) 363-3000
Web Site: http://www.usielectric.com

Sales Range: $150-199.9 Million
Fire & Smoke Alarms Whslr
N.A.I.C.S.: 423690

UNIVERSAL SOLAR TECHNOLOGY, INC.
21175 Tomball Pkwy Ste 402, Houston, TX 77070-1655
Tel.: (346) 803-4455   **NV**
Web Site:
https://www.universalsolartechno
logy.com
Year Founded: 2007
UNSS—(OTCEM)
Assets: $66,572
Liabilities: $706,110
Net Worth: ($639,538)
Earnings: ($155,874)
Emp.: 12
Fiscal Year-end: 12/31/20
Holding Company; Silicon Wafers, Solar Cell & High Efficiency Solar Photovoltaic (PV) Modules Mfr & Marketer
N.A.I.C.S.: 551112
Paul D. Landrew *(Chm & CEO)*

UNIVERSAL STAINLESS & ALLOY PRODUCTS, INC.
600 Mayer St, Bridgeville, PA 15017
Tel.: (412) 257-7600   **DE**
Web Site:
https://www.univstainless.com
Year Founded: 1994
USAP—(NASDAQ)
Rev.: $202,114,000
Assets: $363,334,000
Liabilities: $143,581,000
Net Worth: $219,753,000
Earnings: ($8,073,000)
Emp.: 622
Fiscal Year-end: 12/31/22
Blast Furnaces & Steel Mills; Manufactures & Markets Specialty Steel Products
N.A.I.C.S.: 332111
Christopher M. Zimmer *(Pres & CEO)*
Graham McIntosh *(CTO & Exec VP)*
John J. Arminas *(Gen Counsel, Sec & VP)*
Steven V. DiTommaso *(CFO & VP)*
Wendel L. Crosby *(VP)*

Subsidiaries:

Dunkirk Specialty Steel, LLC **(1)**
830 Brigham Rd, Dunkirk, NY 14048 **(100%)**
Tel.: (716) 366-1000
Web Site:
http://www.dunkirkspecialtysteel.com
Sales Range: $25-49.9 Million
Steel Bar, Wire, Rod & Rebar Products Mfr
N.A.I.C.S.: 331221

UNIVERSAL SYSTEMS, INC.
965 E 3300 S, Salt Lake City, UT 84106
Tel.: (801) 484-9151   **WA**
Web Site:
https://www.usicomputer.com
Year Founded: 1989
UVSS—(OTCIQ)
Electronic Computer Mfr
N.A.I.C.S.: 334111
John A. Rasmussen *(Pres)*
Sammy Wong *(Owner)*

UNIVERSAL TECHNICAL INSTITUTE, INC.
4225 E Windrose Dr Ste 200, Phoenix, AZ 85032
Tel.: (623) 445-9500   **DE**
Web Site: https://www.uti.edu
UTI—(NYSE)
Rev.: $732,687,000
Assets: $744,575,000
Liabilities: $484,344,000

Net Worth: $260,231,000
Earnings: $42,001,000
Emp.: 3,700
Fiscal Year-end: 09/30/24
Automotive Technical Training Services
N.A.I.C.S.: 611519
Jerome A. Grant *(CEO)*
Eric A. Severson *(Sr VP-Admissions)*
Todd A. Hitchcock *(Chief Strategy & Transformation Officer & Sr VP)*
Lori B. Smith *(CIO & Sr VP)*
Sonia C. Mason *(Chief HR Officer & Sr VP)*
Christopher E. Kevane *(Chief Legal Officer & Sr VP)*
Bart H. Fesperman *(Chief Comml Officer & Sr VP)*
Jami Frazier *(Pres)*
Christine Kline *(Interim CFO, Chief Acctg Officer & VP)*

Subsidiaries:

Concorde Career Colleges, Inc. **(1)**
5800 Foxridge Dr Ste 500, Mission, KS 66202
Tel.: (913) 831-9977
Web Site: http://www.concorde.edu
Emp.: 100
Vocational Training Schools
N.A.I.C.S.: 611519
Derek McCallum *(VP-Mktg & Enrollment Svcs)*
Juli Fisher *(CFO)*
Tim Foster *(Chm)*
Mike Miller *(VP-Admissions)*
Martin Riggs *(VP-HR)*

Custom Training Group, Inc. **(1)**
15 Industrial Ave, Saddle River, NJ 07458
Tel.: (201) 760-0900
Web Site: http://www.isctg.com
Technical Training Services
N.A.I.C.S.: 611519

U.T.I. of Illinois, Inc. **(1)**
2611 Corporate W Dr, Lisle, IL 60532
Tel.: (630) 529-2662
Technical Training Services
N.A.I.C.S.: 611519

Universal Technical Institute of Arizona, Inc. **(1)**
10695 W Pierce St, Avondale, AZ 85323
Tel.: (623) 245-4600
Technical Training Services
N.A.I.C.S.: 611519

Universal Technical Institute of Massachusetts, Inc. **(1)**
1 Upland Rd 200, Norwood, MA 02062
Tel.: (781) 948-2000
Web Site: http://www.uti.edu
Emp.: 80
Technical Training Services
N.A.I.C.S.: 611519

Universal Technical Institute of Pennsylvania, Inc. **(1)**
750 Pennsylvania Dr, Exton, PA 19341
Tel.: (610) 458-5595
Web Site: http://www.uti.edu
Emp.: 130
Technical Training Services
N.A.I.C.S.: 611519
Robert Kessler *(Pres-Campus)*

UNIVERSITY BANCORP, INC.
2015 Washtenaw Ave, Ann Arbor, MI 48104
Tel.: (734) 741-5858   **DE**
Web Site: https://www.university-bank.com
Year Founded: 1988
UNIB—(OTCIQ)
Sales Range: $50-74.9 Million
Emp.: 560
Offices of Bank Holding Companies
N.A.I.C.S.: 551111
Dennis M. Agresta *(Treas, Sr VP & Controller-University Bank)*
Tami Haley Janowicz *(Chief Admin Officer & Exec VP-University Bank)*

Catherine M. Revord *(Chief HR Officer & Sr VP-University Bank)*
Benjamin Kramer *(Sr VP-Community Banking-University Bank)*
Ken Sprinkles *(Officer-Bus Banking & Asst VP-University Bank)*
Sandy Sargent *(Asst VP & Branch Mgr-University Bank)*
Anita Dul *(Compliance Officer & VP-University Bank)*
Michael M. Yeager *(CFO & Exec VP-University Bank)*
Gerhard Naude *(COO & Exec VP-University Bank)*
Mark Smith *(Gen Counsel & Exec VP-University Bank)*
Anthony Kirgis *(CIO & Sr VP-University Bank)*
Stephen Lange Ranzini *(Pres & CEO-University Bank)*

Subsidiaries:

University Bank **(1)**
2015 Washtenaw Ave, Ann Arbor, MI 48104 **(100%)**
Tel.: (734) 741-5858
Web Site: http://www.university-bank.com
Sales Range: $125-149.9 Million
Emp.: 40
Commercial Banking Services
N.A.I.C.S.: 522110
Stephen Lange Ranzini *(Pres & CEO)*

UNIVEST FINANCIAL CORPORATION
14 N Main St, Souderton, PA 18964
Tel.: (215) 721-2400   **PA**
Web Site: https://www.univest.net
Year Founded: 1876
UVSP—(NASDAQ)
Rev.: $330,078,000
Assets: $7,222,016,000
Liabilities: $6,445,516,000
Net Worth: $776,500,000
Earnings: $78,120,000
Emp.: 973
Fiscal Year-end: 12/31/22
Bank Holding Company
N.A.I.C.S.: 551111
Jeffrey M. Schweitzer *(Chm, Pres & CEO)*
Michael S. Keim *(COO & Sr Exec VP)*

Subsidiaries:

Univest Bank & Trust Co. **(1)**
14 N Main St, Souderton, PA 18964
Tel.: (215) 721-2464
Web Site: http://www.univest.net
Sales Range: $150-199.9 Million
Emp.: 755
Commericial Banking
N.A.I.C.S.: 522110
Jeffrey M. Schweitzer *(CEO)*
Michael S. Keim *(Pres & Sr Exec VP)*
Matt Holliday *(Sr VP & Mng Dir-Trust & Fiduciary Svcs)*
Alex Magid *(Officer-Trust & VP)*
Darlene Grafton *(Officer-Trust & VP)*
Michael Kerns *(Officer-Trust & VP)*
Kasia Lewis *(Officer-Trust)*
Janet Reilly *(Officer-Trust & VP)*
Bruce Freeston *(Officer-Trust Investment & Sr VP)*
Peter Conte *(Officer-Trust Investment & VP)*
Nick Plawa *(Officer-Trust Investment)*
Jennifer Strawser *(Officer-Trust Investment)*
Beth Nauman *(Officer-Trust Compliance & VP)*
Darren Johnson *(Officer-Trust Support & VP)*
Irene Grove *(Officer-Trust Support)*
Rachel Cupp *(Officer-Trust Ops)*
Michael J. Fox *(Exec VP)*
Nicholas J. Yelicanin *(VP & Mgr-Customer Rels)*
David R. Ohman *(Sr VP & Mgr-Customer Rels)*
Andrew D. Landis *(Sr VP & Mgr-Customer Rels)*

David C. Walbrandt *(Mgr-Customer Rels)*
Timothy M. Hampton *(VP & Mgr-Customer Rels)*

Subsidiary (Domestic):

Girard Partners Ltd. (2)
555 Croton Rd Ste 210, King of Prussia, PA 19406
Tel.: (610) 337-7640
Web Site: http://www.girardpartners.com
Rev.: $2,905,000
Emp.: 7
Wealth Management Services
N.A.I.C.S.: 523940

Univest Capital, Inc. (2)
3220 Tillman Dr Ste 503, Bensalem, PA 19020
Web Site: http://www.univestcapitalinc.com
Emp.: 35
Equipment Finance Leasing Services
N.A.I.C.S.: 522220

Univest Insurance, Inc. (2)
Univest Plz 14 N Main St, Souderton, PA 18964
Tel.: (215) 721-2400
Web Site: http://www.univest.net
Sales Range: $150-199.9 Million
Emp.: 300
Insurance Agency & Consulting Services
N.A.I.C.S.: 524298
Alan F. Sterner *(Sr VP & Mgr-Lehigh Valley)*
Kathy C. Delp *(Sr VP & Mgr-Personal Lines)*
Judith Williams *(VP & Mgr-Personal Lines)*

Univest Investments, Inc. (2)
41 W Broad St, Souderton, PA 18964
Tel.: (215) 721-2112
Web Site: http://www.univest.net
Investment Banking
N.A.I.C.S.: 523150
William F. Van Sant *(Mng Dir & Sr VP)*

UNRIVALED BRANDS, INC.
3242 S Halladay St Ste 202, Santa Ana, CA 92705   NV
Web Site:
https://www.unrivaledbrands.com
Year Founded: 2008
UNRV—(OTCQB)
Rev.: $52,015,000
Assets: $40,508,000
Liabilities: $77,045,000
Net Worth: ($36,537,000)
Earnings: ($188,931,000)
Emp.: 170
Fiscal Year-end: 12/31/22
Cannabis Multi-state Operator
N.A.I.C.S.: 325411
Patty Chan *(CFO)*
Nicholas Kovacevich *(Chm)*
Sabas Carrillo *(Interim CEO)*

Subsidiaries:

EG Transportation Services LLC (1)
283 County Rd 519, Belvidere, NJ 07823-2742
Tel.: (844) 344-3727
Agricultural Equipment Distr
N.A.I.C.S.: 423820

Edible Garden Corp. (1)
283 County Rd 519, Belvidere, NJ 07823
Tel.: (908) 475-1465
Web Site: http://www.ediblegarden.com
Farm Supply Store Operator
N.A.I.C.S.: 444240

UNUM GROUP
1 Fountain Sq, Chattanooga, TN 37402
Tel.: (423) 294-1011   DE
Web Site: https://www.unum.com
Year Founded: 1848
UNM—(NYSE)
Rev.: $12,385,900,000
Assets: $63,255,200,000
Liabilities: $53,603,800,000
Net Worth: $9,651,400,000
Earnings: $1,283,800,000
Emp.: 10,553

Fiscal Year-end: 12/31/23
Holding Company; Benefits Plans, Services & Support Solutions for Individuals & Companies
N.A.I.C.S.: 551112
Richard P. McKenney *(Pres & CEO)*
Timothy G. Arnold *(Pres-Colonial Life & Exec VP-Voluntary Benefits)*
Lisa Gonzalez Iglesias *(Gen Counsel & Exec VP)*
Puneet Bhasin *(Chief Information & Digital Officer & Exec VP)*
Liz Ahmed *(Exec VP-People & Comm)*
Martha D. Leiper *(Chief Investment Officer & Exec VP)*
Christopher W. Pyne *(Exec VP-Grp Benefits)*
Ericka DeBruce *(Chief Inclusion & Diversity Officer)*
Walter Lynn Rice Jr. *(Chief Acctg Officer & Sr VP)*

Subsidiaries:

Colonial Life & Accident Insurance Company (1)
1200 Colonial Life Blvd, Columbia, SC 29093
Tel.: (803) 798-7000
Web Site: https://www.coloniallife.com
Sales Range: $1-9.9 Million
Personal Accident & Life Insurance
N.A.I.C.S.: 524113
Timothy G. Arnold *(Pres & CEO)*
Michelle McLaughlin White *(VP-Marketing)*
David E. Murphy *(VP- &)*
Tom Dupuis *(VP-)*
Allen Livingood *(VP-Finance)*
Wendy Gibson *(Sr VP-)*
Paul McLean *(Sr VP-)*
Steve Jones *(Sr VP- &)*

Jaimini Health, Inc. (1)
10700 Civic Ctr Dr Ste 100-A, Rancho Cucamonga, CA 91730
Web Site: http://www.primecaredental.net
Health Care Srvices
N.A.I.C.S.: 621210

Latin Unum America Holdings (1)
Suipacha 268 1355, Buenos Aires, Argentina   (40%)
Tel.: (54) 01143245555
Sales Range: $50-74.9 Million
Emp.: 100
Holding Company
N.A.I.C.S.: 551112

LeaveLogic, Inc. (1)
1111 3rd Ave Ste 2870, Seattle, WA 98101
Tel.: (757) 655-3283
Web Site: https://www.leavelogic.com
Human Resouce Services
N.A.I.C.S.: 541612

Pramerica Zycie Towarzystwo Ubezpieczen i Reasekuracji Spolka Akcjyna (1)
Al Jana Pawla Ii 17, 00-854, Warsaw, Poland
Tel.: (48) 223293000
Web Site: http://www.pramerica.pl
Insurance Management Services
N.A.I.C.S.: 524298
Aneta Podyma-Milczarek *(Chm-Mgmt Bd)*
Robert Gowin *(Member-Mgmt Bd)*
Borys Kowalski *(Member-Mgmt Bd)*

The Paul Revere Life Insurance Company (1)
1 Mercantile st, Worcester, MA 01608
Tel.: (508) 799-4441
Web Site: http://www.unum.com
Rev.: $447,964,000
Emp.: 2,800
Life, Health, Fixed & Variable Annuity Insurance & Investment Management Services
N.A.I.C.S.: 524126

Unum (1)
1 Fountain Sq, Chattanooga, TN 37402
Tel.: (423) 294-1011
Web Site: http://www.unum.com
Sales Range: $50-74.9 Million
Emp.: 3,400
Life, Accident & Health Insurance

N.A.I.C.S.: 524113

Unum Dental (1)
Minories Ibex House The City, London, EC3N 1DY, United Kingdom
Tel.: (44) 2072657111
Web Site: http://www.unum.co.uk
Dental Insurance Services
N.A.I.C.S.: 524114
Andrew Bower *(Mng Dir)*

Unum European Holding Company Limited (1)
Unum Milton Court, Dorking, RH4 3LZ, Surrey, United Kingdom
Tel.: (44) 1306887766
Web Site: https://www.unum.co.uk
Sales Range: $800-899.9 Million
Emp.: 139
Holding Company
N.A.I.C.S.: 551112

Subsidiary (Domestic):

Unum Limited (2)
Unum Milton Court, Dorking, RH4 3LZ, Surrey, United Kingdom
Tel.: (44) 1306887766
Web Site: https://www.unum.co.uk
Sales Range: $250-299.9 Million
Income Protection & Disability Insurance
N.A.I.C.S.: 524113
Peter G. O'Donnell *(CEO)*
Jon Fletcher *(CFO)*
Peter Goddard *(Chief Compliance Officer & Chief Legal Officer)*
Malcolm McCaig *(Chm)*
Andrew Bower *(Mng Dir-Dental)*
Claire Stockhausen *(Chief Risk Officer)*
Glenn Thompson *(Dir-Customer Solutions)*
Natalie Rogers *(Dir-Interim-HR)*
Simon Chrisp *(CMO-Interim)*

Unum Insurance Agency, LLC (1)
2211 Congress St, Portland, ME 04122
Tel.: (207) 575-2211
Web Site: https://www.unum.com
Insurance Service Provider
N.A.I.C.S.: 524210

Unum Life Insurance Company of America (1)
2211 Congress St Mailstop K4, Portland, ME 04122
Tel.: (207) 575-2211
Web Site: https://www.unumprovident.com
Sales Range: $1-4.9 Billion
Emp.: 5,000
Life, Health, Fixed & Variable Annuity Insurance & Investment Management Services
N.A.I.C.S.: 524114

Unum Zycie Towarzystwo Ubezpieczen i Reasekuracji Spolka Akcjyna (1)
Unum Zycie TUiR SA al Jana Pawla II 17, 00-854, Warsaw, Poland
Tel.: (48) 223293099
Web Site: https://www.unum.pl
Fire Insurance Services
N.A.I.C.S.: 524128

UNUSUAL MACHINES, INC.
4667 1 BMcLeod Rd Ste J, Orlando, FL 32811
Web Site:
https://www.unusualmachines.com
UMAC—(NYSEAMEX)
Aviation & Aerospace Component Mfg.
N.A.I.C.S.: 334511

UPAY, INC.
3010 LBJ Fwy Fl 1200, Dallas, TX 75234
Tel.: (972) 888-6052   NV
Web Site:
https://www.upaytechnology.com
Year Founded: 2015
UPYY—(OTCQB)
Rev.: $1,394,408
Assets: $770,340
Liabilities: $1,025,147
Net Worth: ($254,807)
Earnings: ($736,191)
Emp.: 16

Fiscal Year-end: 02/28/24
Financial & Business Management Software Development Services
N.A.I.C.S.: 541511
Jacob C. Folscher *(Founder & CEO)*
Randall F. Greene *(CFO & COO)*

UPBOUND GROUP, INC.
5501 Headquarters Dr, Plano, TX 75024
Tel.: (972) 801-1100   DE
Web Site: https://upbound.com
Year Founded: 1986
UPBD—(NASDAQ)
Rev.: $4,245,392,000
Assets: $2,763,619,000
Liabilities: $2,238,473,000
Net Worth: $525,146,000
Earnings: $12,357,000
Emp.: 12,690
Fiscal Year-end: 12/31/22
General & Specialized Furnishing Rental Centers Operator & Support Services
N.A.I.C.S.: 532310
Mitchell E. Fadel *(CEO)*
Ann L. Davids *(CMO, Chief Customer Officer & Exec VP)*
Anthony J. Blasquez *(Exec VP-Bus)*
Fahmi Karam *(CFO & Exec VP)*
Bryan Pechersky *(Gen Counsel, Sec & Exec VP)*
Transient Taylor *(Chief HR Officer, Chief Diversity Officer & Exec VP)*
Sudeep Gautam *(CTO, Chief Digital Officer & Exec VP)*
Tiffany Wall *(Sr VP-Enterprise Bus Ops)*

Subsidiaries:

RAC Acceptance East, LLC (1)
5501 Headquarters Dr, Plano, TX 75024
Tel.: (972) 801-1100
Furniture Rental Services
N.A.I.C.S.: 532490

RAC Mexico Operaciones, S. DE R.L. DE C.V. (1)
Av Tratado de Libre Comercio No 1000, Parque Industrial Stiva Aeropuerto, 66600, Apodaca, Nuevo Leon, Mexico
Tel.: (52) 8007222466
Web Site: https://www.rac.mx
Furniture Rental Services
N.A.I.C.S.: 532490

RAC National Product Service, LLC (1)
4015 Shopton Rd Ste 600, Charlotte, NC 28217-3025
Tel.: (704) 583-1440
Household Goods Leasing Service
N.A.I.C.S.: 532289

Rent-A-Center Corporate Leasing (1)
5501 Headquarters Dr, Plano, TX 75024
Tel.: (972) 801-1100
Web Site: http://www.raccl.com
Corporate Furnishing Rental Services
N.A.I.C.S.: 532289

UPD HOLDING CORP.
75 Pringle Way Ste 804, Reno, NV 89502
Tel.: (775) 829-7999   NV
Year Founded: 1998
UPDC—(OTCEM)
Rev.: $38,190
Assets: $652,739
Liabilities: $1,775,413
Net Worth: ($1,122,674)
Earnings: ($1,212,977)
Emp.: 4
Fiscal Year-end: 06/30/22
Investment Services
N.A.I.C.S.: 523999
Mark W. Conte *(CEO, CFO & Chief Acctg Officer)*

UPD Holding Corp.—(Continued)

Subsidiaries:

Record Street Brewing Company (1)
324 E 4th St, Reno, NV 89512
Tel.: (775) 357-8028
Web Site:
http://www.recordstreetbrewing.com
Hotel Operator
N.A.I.C.S.: 721110
Jesse Corletto (Founder & Pres)
Dylan Evans (Gen Mgr-Bar & Resturant)
Travis O'Brien (Head-Brewer)
M. Joseph (Sls Dir)

UPEXI, INC.
3030 N Rocky Pt Dr, Tampa, FL
33607
Tel.: (701) 353-5425   NV
Web Site: https://www.upexi.com
Year Founded: 2018
UPXI—(NASDAQ)
Rev.: $26,000,652
Assets: $23,511,088
Liabilities: $16,995,187
Net Worth: $6,515,901
Earnings: ($23,658,438)
Emp.: 64
Fiscal Year-end: 06/30/24
Hemp Product Mfr & Distr
N.A.I.C.S.: 312230
Robert Hackett (Pres)
Andrew J. Norstrud (CFO & Sec)
Allan Marshall (Chm & CEO)

Subsidiaries:

VitaMedica, Inc. (1)
1140 Highland Ave Ste 196, Manhattan
Beach, CA 90266
Web Site: https://www.vitamedica.com
Natural Health Product Distr
N.A.I.C.S.: 424210

UPHEALTH, INC.
1731 Embarcadero Rd Ste 200, Palo
Alto, CA 94303
Tel.: (650) 276-7040   DE
Web Site: http://www.gigcapital2.com
Year Founded: 2019
UPH—(NYSE)
Rev.: $158,803,000
Assets: $339,804,000
Liabilities: $233,667,000
Net Worth: $106,137,000
Earnings: ($223,000,000)
Emp.: 587
Fiscal Year-end: 12/31/22
Investment Services
N.A.I.C.S.: 523999
Avishay S. Katz (Chm & Sec)
Raluca Dinu (Pres & CEO)

UPLAND SOFTWARE, INC.
401 Congress Ave Ste 1850, Austin,
TX 78701-3788
Tel.: (512) 960-1010   DE
Web Site:
https://www.uplandsoftware.com
Year Founded: 2012
UPLD—(NASDAQ)
Rev.: $317,303,000
Assets: $1,113,459,000
Liabilities: $804,589,000
Net Worth: $308,870,000
Earnings: ($68,413,000)
Emp.: 1,006
Fiscal Year-end: 12/31/22
Offices of Other Holding Companies
N.A.I.C.S.: 551112
John T. McDonald (Founder, Chm &
CEO)
John T. McDonald (Founder, Chm &
CEO)
Rochelle Delley (Chief Security Offi-
cer)
Amber Bennett (Sr VP-Fin)
Jen Verzal (VP-HR)
Karen Cummings (Pres & COO)

Jonanna Mikulenka (Chief Acctg Offi-
cer)
Dan Doman (Chief Product Officer)
Oliver Yates (Chief Sls Officer)
Toby Hottovy (Sr VP)
Bryan Harwood (Sr VP)
Shawn Freligh (Sr VP)
Keith Berg (Sr VP)
Mat Singer (Sr VP)
Jennifer Gause (VP)
Rick Rinewalt (Sr VP)
Srinivas Sampath (VP)
Lou Takacs (VP)
D. J. Yoder (Sr VP)
John Patterson (Sr VP)
Michael Frannea (VP)
Julie Mann (VP)

Subsidiaries:

Daily Inches, Inc. (1)
2010 14th St, Boulder, CO 80302
Tel.: (752) 696-6000
Web Site: http://www.kapost.com
Marketing Services
N.A.I.C.S.: 541613
Nader Akhnoukh (Co-Founder & CTO)
Mike Lewis (Co-Founder & Pres)
Toby Murdock (Co-Founder & CEO)
Jesse Noyes (Sr Dir-Content Mktg)
Grace Boyle (Dir-Customer Success)

**InterFax Communications
Limited** (1)
Unit 7 Coolport Coolmine Business Park,
Blanchardstown, Dublin, D15 HC91, Ireland
Tel.: (353) 12530454
Computer Software Services
N.A.I.C.S.: 541511

Objectif Lune Asia Pty. Ltd. (1)
PO Box 7664, Baulkham Hills, 2153, NSW,
Australia
Tel.: (61) 288522599
Software Development Services
N.A.I.C.S.: 541511

Objectif Lune Capture Inc. (1)
500-2030 Boulevard Pie-IX, Montreal, H1V
2C8, QC, Canada
Tel.: (514) 875-5863
Web Site: https://www.objectiflune.com
Software Development Services
N.A.I.C.S.: 541511

Objectif Lune GmbH (1)
Herlingsburg 14, 22529, Hamburg, Ger-
many
Tel.: (49) 61517809100
Software Development Services
N.A.I.C.S.: 541511

**Objectif Lune Malaysia Sdn.
Bhd.** (1)
C-12-02 12 Block C Sunway Nexis Jalan
PJU 5/2, 47810, Petaling Jaya, Selangor,
Malaysia
Tel.: (60) 327834306
Mobile & Email Communication Services
N.A.I.C.S.: 517121

Omtool, Ltd. (1)
6 Riverside Dr, Andover, MA 01810
Tel.: (978) 327-5700
Web Site: http://www.omtool.com
Business Document, Information & Commu-
nications Software Mfr
N.A.I.C.S.: 513210
Thaddeus Bouchard (CTO)
Eamonn Doyle (VP-IT)
Claudia Skilton (VP-Customer Svcs)
Cara Fascione (VP-Sls)
Tom Gordon (VP-Bus Dev)
Kelvyn Stirk (VP-Sls)
Bob Voelk (Chm, CEO & Pres)

Qvidian Corp. (1)
1 Executive Dr Ste 302, Chelmsford, MA
01824
Tel.: (513) 631-1155
Web Site: http://www.uplandsoftware.com
Sales Support Software Developer
N.A.I.C.S.: 513210
Lewis Miller (Pres & CEO)

Unit (Domestic):

Qvidian (2)

10101 Alliance Rd Ste 310, Cincinnati, OH
45242
Tel.: (513) 631-1155
Web Site: http://www.uplandsoftware.com
Sales Support Software Developer
N.A.I.C.S.: 513210

RightAnswers, Inc. (1)
333 Thornall St 7th Fl, Edison, NJ 08837
Tel.: (732) 396-9010
Software & Support Services
N.A.I.C.S.: 513210

Second Street Media, Inc. (1)
1017 Olive St Mezzanine Level, Saint
Louis, MO 63101
Tel.: (314) 880-4900
Web Site: http://www.secondstreet.com
Advertising Agencies
N.A.I.C.S.: 541810
Kelly Travis (Mgr-Mktg)
Matt Coen (Co-Founder & Pres)

Upland Software I, Inc. (1)
401 Congress Ave Ste 1850, Austin, TX
78701-3788
Tel.: (617) 492-0707
Web Site: https://uplandsoftware.com
Project & Portfolio Management Software
Services
N.A.I.C.S.: 541990

Upland Software II, Inc. (1)
1010 N Central Ave, Glendale, CA 91202
Tel.: (626) 796-6640
Web Site: http://www.tenrox.com
Sales Range: $10-24.9 Million
Custom Computer Programming Services
N.A.I.C.S.: 541511

Upland Software IV, Inc. (1)
1701 Cushman Dr Ste 1, Lincoln, NE 68512
Tel.: (402) 436-3060
Web Site: http://www.filebound.com
Sales Range: $1-9.9 Million
Emp.: 30
Document & Workflow Automation Software
Publisher & Services
N.A.I.C.S.: 541511

Upland Software VI, LLC (1)
485B Route 1 S Ste 100, Iselin, NJ 08830
Tel.: (732) 632-8000
Web Site: http://www.comsci.com
Sales Range: $1-9.9 Million
Emp.: 30
Business Management Solutions
N.A.I.C.S.: 561499

Visionael Corporation (1)
201 San Antonio Circle Ste 235, Mountain
View, CA 94040
Tel.: (650) 963-0960
Web Site: http://www.visionael.com
Rev.: $12,000,000
Emp.: 12
Network Management, Security & Software
Design Services
N.A.I.C.S.: 518210

Branch (Domestic):

Visionael Corp. - Tulsa (2)
9717 E 42nd St Ste 200, Tulsa, OK 74146-
3618
Tel.: (918) 770-4452
Sales Range: $25-49.9 Million
Network Management, Security & Software
Design Services
N.A.I.C.S.: 513210

**UPPER STREET MARKETING,
INC.**
16129 Hawthorne Blvd C Ste D125,
Lawndale, CA 90260
Tel.: (310) 623-7551
Web Site:
http://www.upperstreetmarke
ting.com
Year Founded: 2013
UPPR—(OTCIQ)
Financial Investment Services
N.A.I.C.S.: 523999
John Daniel Quinn (Chm & CEO)

UPSTART HOLDINGS, INC.
2950 S Delaware St, San Mateo, CA
94403

Tel.: (650) 204-1000   DE
Web Site: https://www.upstart.com
Year Founded: 2013
UPST—(NASDAQ)
Rev.: $842,444,000
Assets: $1,936,054,000
Liabilities: $1,263,619,000
Net Worth: $672,435,000
Earnings: ($108,665,000)
Emp.: 365
Fiscal Year-end: 12/31/22
Holding Company
N.A.I.C.S.: 551112
Dave Girouard (Co-Founder & CEO)
Sanjay Datta (CFO)
Natalia Mirgorodskaya (Controller)
Paul Gu (Co-Founder & CTO)
Anna M. Counselman (Co-Founder &
Sr VP-Bus Ops)
Pavi Ramamurthy (Chief Information
Security Officer)
Annie Delgado (Chief Compliance
Officer)

Subsidiaries:

Upstart Network, Inc. (1)
PO Box 1503, San Carlos, CA 94070
Tel.: (650) 204-1000
Web Site: https://www.upstart.com
Consumer Lending Loan Services
N.A.I.C.S.: 522291

UR-ENERGY INC.
10758 W Centennial Rd Ste 200,
Littleton, CO 80127
Tel.: (720) 981-4588   Ca
Web Site: https://www.ur-energy.com
URG—(NYSEAMEX)
Rev.: $19,000
Assets: $107,895,000
Liabilities: $45,396,000
Net Worth: $62,499,000
Earnings: ($17,140,000)
Emp.: 36
Fiscal Year-end: 12/31/22
Other Metal Ore Mining
N.A.I.C.S.: 212290
Roger L. Smith (CFO & Chief Admin
Officer)
Steve Hatten (VP-Ops)
John W. Cash (Chm, Pres & CEO)
Penne A. Goplerud (Gen Counsel &
Sec)

Subsidiaries:

Ur-Energy USA Inc. (1)
10758 W Centennial Rd Ste 200, Littleton,
CO 80127
Tel.: (720) 981-4588
Web Site: https://www.ur-energy.com
Uranium Mining
N.A.I.C.S.: 212290

URBAN EDGE PROPERTIES
888 7th Ave 6th Fl, New York, NY
10019
Tel.: (212) 956-2556   MD
Web Site: https://www.uedge.com
UE—(NYSE)
Rev.: $416,922,000
Assets: $3,279,809,000
Liabilities: $2,058,381,000
Net Worth: $1,221,428,000
Earnings: $248,497,000
Emp.: 109
Fiscal Year-end: 12/31/23
Real Estate Lending Services
N.A.I.C.S.: 531120
Jeffrey S. Olson (Chm & CEO)
Mark J. Langer (CFO & Exec VP)
Jeffrey S. Mooallem (COO & Exec
VP)
Leigh Lyons (Sr VP-Leasing)
Dan Reilly (Sr VP-Property Acctg)
Andrea Rosenthal Drazin (Chief
Acctg Officer)

Etan Bluman *(Sr VP-Fin & IR)*
Robert C. Milton III *(Gen Counsel & Exec VP)*

Subsidiaries:

UE Hudson Mall Holding LLC (1)
701 Route 440, Jersey City, NJ 07304
Tel.: (201) 432-0119
Web Site: https://www.shophudsonmall.com
Shopping Mall Operator
N.A.I.C.S.: 531120

Urban Edge Caguas LP (1)
PR 52 Esquina PR 156, Bayamon, PR 00725
Tel.: (787) 745-4105
Residential Building Leasing Services
N.A.I.C.S.: 531110

URBAN ONE, INC.
1010 Wayne Ave 4th Fl, Silver Spring, MD 20910
Tel.: (301) 429-3200   DE
Web Site: https://www.urban1.com
Year Founded: 1980
UONE—(NASDAQ)
Rev.: $477,690,000
Assets: $1,211,173,000
Liabilities: $937,108,000
Net Worth: $274,065,000
Earnings: $4,565,000
Emp.: 948
Fiscal Year-end: 12/31/23
Holding Company; Radio Broadcasting Stations & Other Media Properties Owner & Operator
N.A.I.C.S.: 551112
Alfred C. Liggins III *(Pres & CEO)*
Catherine L. Hughes *(Founder, Chm & Sec)*
Amy E. Vokes *(Sr VP-Res & Insights)*
Peter D. Thompson *(CFO, Principal Acctg Officer & Exec VP)*
Anthony W. Spinelli *(CIO)*
Karen Wishart *(Chief Admin Officer & Exec VP)*
John Soller *(VP-Engrg)*
Josh Rahmani *(Sr VP-Network & Natl Sls-Radio One)*
C. Kristopher Simpson *(Gen Counsel & Sr VP)*
Michelle L. Rice *(Gen Mgr-TV One)*
Eddie Harrell Jr. *(Reg VP & Gen Mgr-Radio One)*
David M. Kantor *(CEO-Radio Div & Reach Media)*

Subsidiaries:

Blue Chip Broadcasting, Ltd. (1)
1821 Summit Rd Ste 401, Cincinnati, OH 45237   (100%)
Tel.: (209) 262-0246
Web Site:
    https://www.bluechipbroadcasting.com
Radio Broadcasting Services
N.A.I.C.S.: 516110

Interactive One, Inc. (1)
4 NY Plz Ste 501, New York, NY 10004
Tel.: (212) 431-4477
Web Site: http://ionedigital.com
Emp.: 50
Radio Broadcasting Services
N.A.I.C.S.: 516110
Alfred C. Liggins III *(CEO)*

Interactive One, LLC (1)
4 NY Plz Ste 501, New York, NY 10004
Tel.: (212) 431-4477
Web Site: http://ionedigital.com
Sales Range: $25-49.9 Million
Emp.: 50
Online Network
N.A.I.C.S.: 516210

KBXX-FM (1)
24 Greenway Plz Ste 900, Houston, TX 77046   (100%)
Tel.: (713) 623-2108
Web Site: https://theboxhouston.com
Sales Range: $10-24.9 Million
Emp.: 50
Broadcast Radio Station

N.A.I.C.S.: 516110
KMJQ-FM (1)
24 Greenway Plz Ste 900, Houston, TX 77046   (100%)
Tel.: (713) 623-2108
Web Site: https://www.myhoustonmajic.com
Sales Range: $25-49.9 Million
Emp.: 130
Broadcast Radio Station
N.A.I.C.S.: 516110

Radio One Licenses, LLC (1)
1010 Wayne Avenue 14th Floor, Silver Spring, MD 20910
Tel.: (301) 429-3200
Radio Broadcasting Station Services
N.A.I.C.S.: 516110

Radio One of Atlanta, LLC (1)
101 Marietta St 12th Fl, Atlanta, GA 30303-2726
Tel.: (404) 765-9750
Web Site: http://www.radio-one.com
Emp.: 72
Radio Broadcasting Station Services
N.A.I.C.S.: 516110

Radio One of Charlotte, LLC (1)
8809 Lenox Pointe Dr, Charlotte, NC 28273
Tel.: (704) 548-7836
Web Site: http://www.radio-one.com
Sales Range: $25-49.9 Million
Emp.: 40
Radio Broadcasting Station Services
N.A.I.C.S.: 516110

Subsidiary (Domestic):

Charlotte Broadcasting, LLC (2)
8809 Lenox Pointe Dr Ste A, Charlotte, NC 28273-3376
Tel.: (704) 358-0211
Sales Range: $25-49.9 Million
Emp.: 40
Radio Broadcasting Station Services
N.A.I.C.S.: 516110

Radio One of Detroit, LLC (1)
3250 Franklin St, Detroit, MI 48207   (100%)
Tel.: (313) 259-2000
Web Site: http://www.radio-one.com
Sales Range: $10-24.9 Million
Emp.: 50
Radio Broadcasting Stations
N.A.I.C.S.: 516110

Radio One of Indiana, L.P. (1)
21 E Saint Joseph St, Indianapolis, IN 46204
Tel.: (317) 266-9600
Web Site: http://urban1.com
Radio Broadcasting Station Services
N.A.I.C.S.: 516110
Max Williams *(Mktg Dir)*
Theodor Turner *(Ops Mgr)*
Jason Hunter *(Dir-Sls)*

Reach Media, Inc. (1)
13760 Noel Rd Ste 750, Dallas, TX 75240
Tel.: (972) 371-5882
Web Site: https://www.reachmediainc.com
Radio broadcasting network services
N.A.I.C.S.: 516210

TV One, LLC (1)
1010 Wayne Ave, Silver Spring, MD 20910
Tel.: (301) 755-0400
Web Site: http://www.tvone.tv
Television Broadcasting Services
N.A.I.C.S.: 516120
Alfred C. Liggins III *(Pres & CEO)*

WNOU-FM (1)
21 E St Joseph St, Indianapolis, IN 46204   (100%)
Tel.: (317) 266-9600
Web Site: http://www.radionowindy.com
Sales Range: $75-99.9 Million
Emp.: 150
Radio Stations
N.A.I.C.S.: 516110

URBAN OUTFITTERS, INC.
5000 S Broad St, Philadelphia, PA 19112-1495
Tel.: (215) 454-5500   PA
Web Site: https://www.urbn.com
Year Founded: 1976

URBN—(NASDAQ)
Rev.: $4,795,244,000
Assets: $3,682,912,000
Liabilities: $1,890,229,000
Net Worth: $1,792,683,000
Earnings: $159,699,000
Emp.: 26,000
Fiscal Year-end: 01/31/23
Women's & Men's Clothing & Accessories Retail Sales
N.A.I.C.S.: 458110
Richard A. Hayne *(Founder, Chm & CEO)*
Margaret A. Hayne *(Co-Pres & Chief Creative Officer)*
Sheila B. Harrington *(CEO-Global)*
Francis J. Conforti *(Co-Pres & COO)*
Melanie Marein-Efron *(CFO)*
Francis Pierrel *(Pres-North America)*
Azeez Hayne *(Chief Admin Officer & Gen Counsel)*
David Hayne *(CTO & Pres-Nuuly)*
Tricia Smith *(CEO-Anthropologie Grp-Global)*

Subsidiaries:

Anthropologie, Inc. (1)
766 Brackbill Rd, Gap, PA 17527 (100%)
Tel.: (215) 564-2313
Web Site: https://www.anthropologie.com
Sales Range: $200-249.9 Million
Emp.: 205
Women's Clothing Store
N.A.I.C.S.: 458110
Tricia D. Smith *(CEO-Global)*
Callie Canfield *(Chief Brand Officer)*
Aimee Lapic *(CEO)*

BHLDN LLC (1)
5000 S Broad St Bldg 15, Philadelphia, PA 19112
Web Site: http://www.bhldn.com
Fashion Apparel Mfr & Distr
N.A.I.C.S.: 458110

Free People (1)
79 5th Ave, New York, NY 10003 (100%)
Tel.: (212) 647-1293
Web Site: http://www.freepeople.com
Sales Range: $50-74.9 Million
Emp.: 15
Mfr of Women's Apparel
N.A.I.C.S.: 424350
Sheila B. Harrington *(CEO)*

Freepeople.com LLC (1)
766 Brackbill Rd, Gap, PA 17527
Web Site: http://www.freepeople.com
Fashion Apparels Retailer
N.A.I.C.S.: 458110

URBN FNB Holdings LLC (1)
5000 S Broad St, Philadelphia, PA 19112-1402
Tel.: (215) 600-2631
Web Site: http://www.vetrifamily.com
Holding Company; Restaurants Operator
N.A.I.C.S.: 551112

Subsidiary (Domestic):

URBN 640 Osteria LLC (2)
640 N Broad St, Philadelphia, PA 19130
Tel.: (215) 763-0920
Web Site: https://www.osteriaphilly.com
Sales Range: $1-9.9 Million
Restaurant Operators
N.A.I.C.S.: 722511

URBN Callowhill LLC (2)
1939 Callowhill St, Philadelphia, PA 19130
Tel.: (215) 600-2629
Web Site: https://www.pizzeriavetri.com
Sales Range: $1-9.9 Million
Restaurant Operators
N.A.I.C.S.: 722511

URBN Chancellor LLC (2)
1615 Chancellor St, Philadelphia, PA 19103
Tel.: (215) 763-3760
Web Site: https://www.pizzeriavetri.com
Sales Range: $1-9.9 Million
Restaurant Operators
N.A.I.C.S.: 722511

URBN NVY LoSp LLC (2)

4503 S Broad St Bldg 500, Philadelphia, PA 19112
Tel.: (215) 282-3184
Web Site: http://www.lo-spiedo.com
Sales Range: $1-9.9 Million
Restaurant Operators
N.A.I.C.S.: 722511

URBN Waverly Amis LLC (2)
412 S 13th St & Waverly, Philadelphia, PA 19147
Tel.: (215) 732-2647
Web Site: http://www.amisphilly.com
Sales Range: $1-9.9 Million
Restaurant Operators
N.A.I.C.S.: 722511

URBN UK Limited (1)
1 Finsbury Circus, London, EC2M 7SH, United Kingdom
Tel.: (44) 8003624073
Web Site: http://www.urbanoutfitters.com
Sales Range: $25-49.9 Million
Emp.: 40
Clothing Accessory Retailer
N.A.I.C.S.: 458110

Urban Outfitters Belgium BVBA (1)
Meir 78 / 201, 2000, Antwerp, Belgium
Tel.: (32) 32015910
Sales Range: $25-49.9 Million
Emp.: 20
Fashion Apparels Retailer
N.A.I.C.S.: 458110
Yannick Kasprowski *(Mgr)*

Urban Outfitters Canada, Inc. (1)
235 Yonge St, Toronto, M5B 1N8, ON, Canada   (100%)
Tel.: (416) 214-1466
Web Site: http://www.urbanoutfitters.com
Sales Range: $25-49.9 Million
Emp.: 100
Mfr of Home Furnishings & Apparel for Men & Women
N.A.I.C.S.: 449129
Richard A. Hayne *(Chm)*

Urban Outfitters Ireland Limited (1)
4 Cecilia Street and 71/2 Fownes Street, Dublin, 2, Leinster, Ireland
Tel.: (353) 12654962
Emp.: 30
Fashion Apparels Retailer
N.A.I.C.S.: 458110

Urban Outfitters UK, Limited (1)
36-38 Kensington High Street, London, W8 4PF, United Kingdom   (100%)
Tel.: (44) 203 985 5573
Web Site: http://www.urbanoutfitters.co.uk
Sales Range: $10-24.9 Million
Emp.: 40
Mfr of Home Furnishings & Apparel for Men & Women
N.A.I.C.S.: 449129
Andrew McLean *(COO-European Operating Div)*

Urban Outfitters i Sverige AB (1)
Regeringsgatan 57, 111 56, Stockholm, Sweden
Tel.: (46) 854506590
Sales Range: $25-49.9 Million
Emp.: 32
Fashion Apparels Retailer
N.A.I.C.S.: 458110
Deniz Celik Hellstrom *(Office Mgr)*

URBAN TELEVISION NETWORK CORP.
11705 Willake St, Santa Fe Springs, CA 90670
Tel.: (323) 489-8119   NV
Web Site: https://urbt.com
Year Founded: 1986
URBT—(OTCIQ)
Television Broadcasting Services
N.A.I.C.S.: 516120
Joseph Collins *(CEO)*

URBAN-GRO, INC.
1751 Panorama Point Unit G, Lafayette, CO 80026
Tel.: (720) 390-3880   CO
Web Site: https://www.urban-gro.com

urban-gro, Inc.—(Continued)

Year Founded: 2014
UGRO—(NASDAQ)
Rev.: $67,029,934
Assets: $62,065,552
Liabilities: $27,333,788
Net Worth: $34,731,764
Earnings: ($15,277,909)
Emp.: 152
Fiscal Year-end: 12/31/22
Holding Company; Cannabis Cultivation Industry Design, Engineering & Technology Implementation Services
N.A.I.C.S.: 551112
Dan Droller (Exec VP-Corp Dev)
Mark Doherty (Exec VP-Ops)
Todd Statzer (Dir-Environmental Sciences)
Melinda Visel (Dir-Ops)
Lucas Targos (VP-Facility Integration)
Jonathan Nassar (Exec VP-Sls)
Nichole McIntyre (Dir-HR)
Brian Zimmerman (Exec VP-Engrg)
Jason Archer (COO)
Bradley J. Nattrass (Co-Founder, Chm & CEO)

Subsidiaries:

Emerald Construction Management, Inc.   (1)
794 Ventura St Ste A, Aurora, CO 80011
Tel.: (303) 341-7242
Web Site: http://www.emeraldcminc.com
Sales Range: $1-9.9 Million
Emp.: 18
Commercial & Institutional Building Construction
N.A.I.C.S.: 236220
Charles W. Cullens (Pres)

Impact Engineering, Inc.   (1)
1751 Panorama Point Unit G, Lafayette, CO 80026   (100%)
Tel.: (303) 877-9669
Web Site: http://www.grow2guys.com
Sales Range: Less than $1 Million
Mechanical, Electrical & Plumbing Engineering Services
N.A.I.C.S.: 541330
Brian Zimmerman (Pres)

URGENT.LY, INC.

8609 Westwood Center Dr Ste 810, Vienna, VA 22182
Tel.: (571) 350-3600
Web Site:
https://www.geturgently.com
Year Founded: 2013
ULY—(NYSE)
Sales Range: $25-49.9 Million
Emp.: 349
Freight Transportation Services
N.A.I.C.S.: 488510
Chris Spanos (Co-Founder & CEO)
Rick Robinson (Co-Founder)

Subsidiaries:

Otonomo Technologies Ltd.   (1)
16 Abba Eban Blvd, Herzliya Pituach, 467256, Israel
Tel.: (972) 524329955
Web Site: https://www.otonomo.io
Rev.: $6,992,000
Assets: $148,646,000
Liabilities: $15,218,000
Net Worth: $133,428,000
Earnings: ($131,072,000)
Emp.: 225
Fiscal Year-end: 12/31/2022
Software Development Services
N.A.I.C.S.: 541511
Ben Volkow (CEO)
Bonnie Moav (CFO)
Vered Raviv Schwarz (Pres)

UROGEN PHARMA LTD.

400 Alexander Park Dr, Princeton, NJ 08540
Tel.: (646) 768-9780
Web Site: https://www.urogen.com

Year Founded: 2004
URGN—(NASDAQ)
Rev.: $64,357,000
Assets: $135,619,000
Liabilities: $224,980,000
Net Worth: ($89,361,000)
Earnings: ($109,783,000)
Emp.: 200
Fiscal Year-end: 12/31/22
Biopharmaceutical Product Research & Development Services
N.A.I.C.S.: 325412
Mark P. Schoenberg (Chief Medical Officer)
Jeffrey Bova (Chief Comml Officer)
James Ottinger (Exec VP-Regulatory Affairs & Quality)
Elyse Seltzer (Chief Dev Officer)
Marina Konorty (Exec VP-R&D & Technical Ops)
Polly A. Murphy (Chief Bus Officer)
Jason Smith (Chief Compliance Officer & Gen Counsel)
Dong Kim (CFO)
Vincent Perrone (Sr Dir-IR)
Cindy Romano (Dir-Corp Comm)
Arie S. Belldegrun (Chm)
Elizabeth Barrett (Pres & CEO)

US BIOTEC, INC.

105 Mill St Ste 105, Gleason, TN 38229
Tel.: (281) 579-1602   **NV**
USBC—(OTCIQ)
Biological Product Mfr
N.A.I.C.S.: 325414
Jimmy Joyner (CEO)
Joe Joyner (Pres)

US FOODS HOLDING CORP.

9399 W Higgins Rd Ste 100, Rosemont, IL 60018
Tel.: (847) 720-8000   **DE**
Web Site: https://ir.usfoods.com
USFD—(NYSE)
Rev.: $35,597,000,000
Assets: $13,187,000,000
Liabilities: $8,438,000,000
Net Worth: $4,749,000,000
Earnings: $499,000,000
Emp.: 30,000
Fiscal Year-end: 12/30/23
Holding Company; Commercial Food, Culinary Supplies & Equipment Distr
N.A.I.C.S.: 551112
Dirk J. Locascio (CFO & Exec VP)
Steven M. Guberman (Chief Transformation Officer & Exec VP-Nationally Managed Bus)
Steven M. Guberman (Chief Transformation Officer & Exec VP-Nationally Managed Bus)
Jay Kvasnicka (Exec VP-Field Ops-US Foods Inc)
David E. Flitman (CEO)
Sara Matheu (Dir-Media Rels)
John A. Tonnison (CIO, Chief Digital Officer & Exec VP)
Dave Flitman (CEO)
Bob Dutkowsky (Chm)
William S. Hancock (Chief Supply Chain Officer & Exec VP)
Martha Ha (Gen Counsel & Exec VP)

Subsidiaries:

F. Christiana & Co.   (1)
7251 River Rd., Marrero, LA 70072
Tel.: (504) 348-3391
Web Site: https://www.usfoods.com
Professional, Scientific & Technical Services
N.A.I.C.S.: 541990

US Foods, Inc.   (1)
9399 W Higgins Rd Ste 500, Rosemont, IL 60018
Tel.: (847) 720-8000
Web Site: https://www.usfoods.com
Rev.: $23,127,532,000

Assets: $8,946,311,000
Liabilities: $7,332,460,000
Net Worth: $1,613,851,000
Earnings: ($983,830,000)
Emp.: 25,000
Fiscal Year-end: 01/02/2016
Institutional Food Service Distr
N.A.I.C.S.: 424490
Steven M. Guberman (Chief Transformation Officer & Exec VP-Nationally Managed Bus)
Steven M. Guberman (Chief Transformation Officer & Exec VP-Nationally Managed Bus)
Randy Taylor (Exec VP-Field Ops & Local Sls)
Rick Hausman (Reg Pres-Southeast)
Rob Koppenhaver (Reg Pres-Northeast)
Tim Lewis (Reg Pres-West)

Subsidiary (Domestic):

Amerifresh, Inc.   (2)
16100 N 71st St Ste 520, Scottsdale, AZ 85254
Tel.: (480) 927-4945
Web Site: http://www.amerifresh.com
Produce Marketer of Fresh Fruits & Vegetable to Retail Grocers
N.A.I.C.S.: 445110

Ameristar Meats, Inc.   (2)
210 S McKinnon Rd, Spokane, WA 99212
Tel.: (509) 924-0600
Web Site: http://www.ameristarmeats.com
Sales Range: $25-49.9 Million
Emp.: 100
Meat Whslr
N.A.I.C.S.: 424470

FirstClass Foods-Trojan, Inc.   (2)
12500 Inglewood Ave, Hawthorne, CA 90250-0250
Tel.: (310) 676-2500
Web Site: http://www.firstclassfoods.com
Meat Product Distr
N.A.I.C.S.: 424470
Felix Benzimra (Owner & VP)

Food Services of America, Inc.   (2)
16100 N 71st St Ste 400, Scottsdale, AZ 85254
Tel.: (480) 927-4000
Web Site: http://www.fsafood.com
Sales Range: $25-49.9 Million
Emp.: 250
Fruit, Vegetable, Canned & Frozen Food Distr
N.A.I.C.S.: 424410

Freshway Foods, Inc.   (2)
601 N Stolle Ave, Sidney, OH 45365
Tel.: (937) 498-4664
Web Site: https://www.freshwayfoods.com
Fresh Fruit & Vegetable Distr
N.A.I.C.S.: 424480
Devon Beer (Pres & COO)
Dan Purdy (VP-Sls & Mktg)
Steve Collins (VP-Ops)
Chuck Huckaba (District Mgr-Sls)
Dan Stegall (Dir-Transportation)
Tony Arnold (Dir-HR)
Douglas Bond (Mgr-New Product Dev)
Melissa Olsen (Dir-Natl Accts)
Kirk Norman (Dir-Bus Dev-Deli & Prepared Foods)
Stacey Bauerle (Reg Sls Mgr-Northeast)
Vicki Peltier (Coord-Sls & Mktg)

GAMPAC Express, Inc.   (2)
16100 N 71st St, Scottsdale, AZ 85254
Web Site: http://www.gampac.com
Supply Chain Management & Logistics Services
N.A.I.C.S.: 541614

Stock Yards Packing Co., Inc.   (2)
2600 Church St, Aurora, IL 60502
Tel.: (630) 947-8400
Web Site: http://www.stockyards.com
Sales Range: $125-149.9 Million
Emp.: 100
Meat & Poultry Distr
N.A.I.C.S.: 424470
Mike Cruzen (Gen Mgr)

Branch (Domestic):

Stock Yards Meat Packing Company   (3)
600 Powell Ave SW, Renton, WA 98055-2247

Tel.: (425) 226-7300
Sales Range: $50-74.9 Million
Wholesale Meat, Poultry & Frozen Foods Mfr
N.A.I.C.S.: 424470

Subsidiary (Domestic):

Systems Services of America, Inc.   (2)
PO Box 25159, Scottsdale, AZ 85255
Tel.: (480) 927-4700
Web Site: http://www.ssafood.com
Food Delivery Services
N.A.I.C.S.: 722310
Brad Parker (VP-Corp Comm)

US Foods Culinary Equipment & Supplies, LLC   (2)
5353 Nathan Ln N, Plymouth, MN 55442
Tel.: (763) 268-1200
Web Site:
https://www.usfoodsculinaryequipment andsupplies.com
Culinary Equipment & Supplies Distr
N.A.I.C.S.: 423440

Waukesha Wholesale Foods, Inc.   (2)
900 Gale St, Waukesha, WI 53186
Tel.: (262) 542-8841
Web Site: http://www.usfoods.com
Sales Range: $100-124.9 Million
Emp.: 200
Food Products Distr
N.A.I.C.S.: 424410
Eric J. Muehl (Chm & COO)
Kevin Musser (CEO)
Thomas Muehl (Pres)

US LIGHTING GROUP, INC.

1148 E 222nd St, Euclid, OH 44117
Tel.: (216) 896-7000   **FL**
Web Site:
https://www.uslightinggroup.com
Year Founded: 2003
USLG—(OTCIQ)
Rev.: $1,083,114
Assets: $2,715,922
Liabilities: $8,465,922
Net Worth: ($5,750,000)
Earnings: ($8,990,320)
Emp.: 28
Fiscal Year-end: 12/31/22
Holding Company; Molded Fiberglass Products Mfr
N.A.I.C.S.: 551112
Olga Smirnova (Sec & VP-Admin & Fin)
Patricia A. Salaciak (Dir-Mktg)
Michael A. Coates (Treas & Controller)
Donald O. Retreage Jr. (CFO)

Subsidiaries:

Cortes Campers, LLC   (1)
1148 E 222nd St, Euclid, OH 44117
Tel.: (216) 896-7000
Web Site: https://www.cortescampers.com
Fiberglass Camper Designer & Mfr
N.A.I.C.S.: 336214

Fusion X Marine, LLC   (1)
1148 E 222nd St, Euclid, OH 44117
Web Site: https://fusionxmarine.com
High-Performance Boat Designer & Mfr
N.A.I.C.S.: 336612

Futuro Houses, LLC   (1)
1148 E 222nd St, Euclid, OH 44117
Tel.: (440) 255-5113
Web Site: https://www.futurohouses.com
Prefabricated Fiberglass Home Mfr
N.A.I.C.S.: 321991

US NUCLEAR CORP.

7051 Eton Ave, Canoga Park, CA 91303
Tel.: (818) 883-7043   **DE**
Web Site:
https://www.usnuclearcorp.com
Year Founded: 2012
UCLE—(OTCQB)
Rev.: $2,231,095
Assets: $2,856,876

Liabilities: $4,839,495
Net Worth: ($1,982,619)
Earnings: ($3,433,804)
Fiscal Year-end: 12/31/23
Radiation Detection Equipment Mfr & Services
N.A.I.C.S.: 333248
Robert I. Goldstein (Chm, Pres & CEO)
Michael G. Hastings (CFO)

Subsidiaries:

Optron Scientific Company Inc.   (1)
7051 Eton Ave, Canoga Park, CA 91303
Tel.: (818) 883-7043
Web Site: https://www.tech-associates.com
Sales Range: $1-9.9 Million
Emp.: 9
Other Electronic Component Mfr
N.A.I.C.S.: 334419

Overhoff Technology Corporation   (1)
1160 Us Hwy 50, Milford, OH 45150
Tel.: (513) 248-2400
Web Site: https://www.overhoff.com
Sales Range: $1-9.9 Million
Emp.: 11
Totalizing Fluid Meter & Counting Device Mfr
N.A.I.C.S.: 334514

USA RECYCLING INDUS-TRIES, INC.
3445 Lawrence Ave, Oceanside, NY 11572
Tel.: (646) 768-8417   NV
Year Founded: 2000
USRI—(OTCIQ)
Waste Management Services
N.A.I.C.S.: 562119
David Lazar (CEO)
David E. Lazar (CEO)

USCB FINANCIAL HOLDINGS, INC.
2301 NW 87th Ave, Doral, FL 33172
Tel.: (305) 715-5200   FL
Web Site: https://www.uscentury.com
Year Founded: 2002
USCB—(NASDAQ)
Rev.: $71,100,000
Assets: $2,085,834,000
Liabilities: $1,903,406,000
Net Worth: $182,428,000
Earnings: $20,141,000
Emp.: 191
Fiscal Year-end: 12/31/22
Holding Company
N.A.I.C.S.: 551112
Robert Anderson (CFO & Principal Acctg Officer)
Luis de la Aguilera (Chm, Pres & CEO)

USD PARTNERS LP
811 Main Ste 2800, Houston, TX 77002
Tel.: (281) 291-0510   DE
Web Site:
    https://www.usdpartners.com
USDP—(NYSE)
Rev.: $111,655,000
Assets: $126,776,000
Liabilities: $239,180,000
Net Worth: ($112,404,000)
Earnings: ($61,286,000)
Emp.: 85
Fiscal Year-end: 12/31/22
Support Activities for Rail Transportation
N.A.I.C.S.: 488210
Daniel K. Borgen (Chm, Pres & CEO)

USHG ACQUISITION CORP.
853 Broadway 7th Fl, New York, NY 10003
Tel.: (212) 228-3585   DE
Web Site: http://www.ushgac.com

Year Founded: 2020
HUGS—(NYSE)
Assets: $288,435,258
Liabilities: $324,261,734
Net Worth: ($35,826,476)
Earnings: ($6,970,265)
Emp.: 2
Fiscal Year-end: 12/31/21
Investment Services
N.A.I.C.S.: 523999
Danny Meyer (Chm)
Adam D. Sokoloff (CEO)
Tiffany F. Daniele (CFO)

USIO INC.
3611 Paesanos Pkwy Ste 300, San Antonio, TX 78231
Tel.: (210) 249-4100   NV
Web Site: https://www.usio.com
Year Founded: 1998
USIO—(NASDAQ)
Rev.: $69,428,285
Assets: $97,912,969
Liabilities: $83,978,871
Net Worth: $13,934,098
Earnings: ($5,483,244)
Emp.: 117
Fiscal Year-end: 12/31/22
Financial Transactions Processing, Reserve & Clearinghouse Activities
N.A.I.C.S.: 522320
Larry Morrison (Sr VP-Bus Dev)
Louis A. Hoch (Vice Chm, Pres & CFO)
Ken Keller (CTO & Sr VP)
Houston Frost (Chief Product Officer & Sr VP)
Matthew Decker (VP-Tech)
Wayne Gonzales (Sr VP-Risk Mgmt & Compliance)
Paul M. Manley (Sr VP-IR)
Silas Green (Sr VP-Output Solutions)
Kyle Ruschman (VP-Prepaid Sls & Bus Dev)
Joe Huch (VP-Sls)
Tom Jewell (CFO)
Steve Peterson (Sr VP)
Jerry Uffner (Sr VP-Card Issuing Sls)

Subsidiaries:

Information Management Solutions, LLC   (1)
2416 Brockton St Ste 105, San Antonio, TX 78217
Tel.: (210) 826-4994
Web Site: http://www.totalims.com
Sales Range: $1-9.9 Million
Emp.: 22
Management Consulting Services
N.A.I.C.S.: 541611

UTA ACQUISITION CORPORA-TION
135 5th Ave 7th Fl, New York, NY 10010
Tel.: (917) 781-1679   Ky
Web Site:
    https://investors.utaacorp.com
Year Founded: 2021
UTAA—(NASDAQ)
Rev.: $664,137
Assets: $238,698,279
Liabilities: $246,833,283
Net Worth: ($8,135,004)
Earnings: $2,107,899
Emp.: 3
Fiscal Year-end: 12/31/22
Investment Services
N.A.I.C.S.: 523999
Clinton Foy (Co-CEO)

UTAH MEDICAL PRODUCTS, INC.
7043 S 300 W, Midvale, UT 84047-1048
Tel.: (801) 566-1200   UT
Web Site: https://www.utahmed.com

Year Founded: 1978
UTMD—(NASDAQ)
Rev.: $52,281,000
Assets: $123,874,000
Liabilities: $9,620,000
Net Worth: $114,254,000
Earnings: $16,473,000
Emp.: 186
Fiscal Year-end: 12/31/22
Specialty Medical Devices for Obstetrics, Gynecology, Urology, Electrosurgery, Neonatal Intensive Care & Blood Pressure Monitoring
N.A.I.C.S.: 339113
Kevin L. Cornwell (Chm, Pres, CEO & Sec)
Brian L. Koopman (CFO)

Subsidiaries:

Femcare Australia Ltd   (1)
Unit 12 5 Gladstone Rd, Castle Hill, 2154, NSW, Australia
Tel.: (61) 290454100
Web Site: http://www.femcare-nikomed.co.uk
Surgical & Medical Instrument Whslr
N.A.I.C.S.: 423450

Femcare Group Limited   (1)
32 Premier Way, Romsey, SO51 9DQ, Hampshire, United Kingdom
Tel.: (44) 1794525100
Web Site: https://femcare.co.uk
Medical Equipment Whslr
N.A.I.C.S.: 423450

Utah Medical Products Ltd.   (1)
Athlone Business & Technology Park, Athlone, N37 XK74, County Westmeath, Ireland   (100%)
Tel.: (353) 906473932
Web Site: https://www.utahmed.com
Sales Range: $10-24.9 Million
Emp.: 27
Developer, Manufacturer & Marketer of Specialty Medical Devices for Obstetrics, Gynecology, Urology, Electrosurgery, Neonatal Intensive Care & Blood Pressure Monitoring
N.A.I.C.S.: 339112

UTG, INC.
Tel.: (217) 241-6300   IL
Web Site: https://www.utgins.com
Year Founded: 1994
UTGN—(OTCIQ)
Rev.: $69,708,835
Assets: $447,534,365
Liabilities: $289,505,989
Net Worth: $158,028,376
Earnings: $34,258,005
Emp.: 40
Fiscal Year-end: 12/31/22
Life Insurance Holding Company
N.A.I.C.S.: 551112
James Patrick Rousey (Pres)
Theodore C. Miller (CFO, Sec & Sr VP)
Jesse Thomas Correll (Chm & CEO)
Douglas P. Ditto (VP)

Subsidiaries:

Cerulean at the Bluebird, LLC   (1)
202 W Main St, Stanford, KY 40484
Tel.: (606) 365-1010
Web Site: https://ceruleancatering.com
Restaurant Operators
N.A.I.C.S.: 722511

Mama Devechio's Pizzeria, LLC   (1)
212 W Main St, Stanford, KY 40484
Tel.: (606) 365-6967
Web Site: https://mamadspizzeria.com
Restaurant Operators
N.A.I.C.S.: 722511

The Inn at Wilderness Road, LLC   (1)
207 W Main St, Stanford, KY 40484
Tel.: (606) 879-0555
Web Site:
    https://www.wildernessroadguest.com
Hotel Accommodation Services

N.A.I.C.S.: 721110

Universal Guarantee Life Insurance   (1)
PO Box 5147, Springfield, IL 62705-5147   (100%)
Tel.: (217) 241-6300
Web Site: https://www.utgins.com
Sales Range: $25-49.9 Million
Emp.: 20
Life Insurance
N.A.I.C.S.: 524113
James Patrick Rousey (Pres)

UTILICRAFT AEROSPACE IN-DUSTRIES, INC.
401 Ryland St Ste 200 A, Reno, NV 89502
Tel.: (214) 418-6940   NV
Year Founded: 2016
UITA—(OTCEM)
Freight Forwarding Services
N.A.I.C.S.: 488510
Richard Kilchesky (Pres & CEO)
Edward I. Vakser (Pres & CEO)

UTZ BRANDS, INC.
900 High St, Hanover, PA 17331
Tel.: (717) 637-6644   DE
Web Site: https://www.utzsnacks.com
Year Founded: 2018
UTZ—(NYSE)
Rev.: $1,408,401,000
Assets: $2,840,366,000
Liabilities: $1,388,682,000
Net Worth: $1,451,684,000
Earnings: ($14,041,000)
Emp.: 3,550
Fiscal Year-end: 01/01/23
Investment Services
N.A.I.C.S.: 523999
Dylan B. Lissette (Chm)
Cary Devore (Chief Operating & Transformation Officer & Exec VP)
Todd M. Staub (Chief Admin Officer & Exec VP)
Thomas Lawrence (Chief Supply Chain Officer & Exec VP)
Ajay Kataria (CFO, Principal Acctg Officer & Exec VP)
Shannan Redcay (Exec VP-Mfg)
Chad Whyte (Exec VP-Supply Chain)
Brian Greth (Sr VP-Enterprise Integration)
Mitchell Arends (Chief Integrated Supply Chain Officer & Exec VP)
Howard A. Friedman (CEO)
Mark Schreiber (Chief Customer Officer-Sls & Exec VP)
Theresa Robbins Shea (Gen Counsel, Sec & Exec VP)
Jennifer Bentz (CMO & Exec VP)
James Sponaugle (Chief People Officer, Exec VP & Sr VP-HR & Personnel Dev)

Subsidiaries:

Clem Snacks Inc.   (1)
29 53rd St, Brooklyn, NY 11232
Tel.: (718) 492-4818
Rev.: $30,000,000
Emp.: 25
Snack Food Mfr
N.A.I.C.S.: 311919
Irma Clemente (VP)
Joseph Clemente Jr. (Pres)
Frank Clemente (Treas)
Rita Clemente (Sec)

J&D Snacks Inc.   (1)
1859 Bronxdale Ave, Bronx, NY 10462-3314
Tel.: (718) 828-1013
Web Site: http://www.jdsnacks.com
Snack Food Mfr
N.A.I.C.S.: 311919

R.W. Garcia Co., Inc.   (1)
100 Enterprise Way Ste C230, Scotts Valley, CA 95066
Tel.: (408) 287-4616

Utz Brands, Inc.—(Continued)

Web Site: http://www.rwgarcia.com
Rev.: $24,600,000
Emp.: 101
Confectionery Merchant Whslr
N.A.I.C.S.: 424450

Utz Quality Foods, LLC **(1)**
900 High St, Hanover, PA 17331
Tel.: (717) 637-6644
Web Site: https://www.utzsnacks.com
Potato Chips, Pretzels, Popcorn & Gift
Snacks Mfr
N.A.I.C.S.: 311919

Subsidiary (Domestic):

Golden Enterprises Inc. **(2)**
1 Golden Flake Dr, Birmingham, AL 35205
Tel.: (800) 239-2447
Holding Company; Confectionery Products,
Potato Chips & Popcorn & Peanut Butter &
Salted Peanuts Mfr & Distr
N.A.I.C.S.: 311919

Subsidiary (Domestic):

Golden Flake Snack Foods, Inc. **(3)**
1 Golden Flake Dr, Birmingham, AL 35205
Web Site: http://www.utzsnacks.com
Snack Foods Mfr & Distr
N.A.I.C.S.: 311919

Subsidiary (Domestic):

Inventure Foods, Inc. **(2)**
5415 E High St Ste 350, Phoenix, AZ
85054
Tel.: (623) 932-6200
Web Site: http://www.inventurefoods.com
Potato Chips & Snack Foods Distr
N.A.I.C.S.: 311423

Subsidiary (Domestic):

Tejas PB Distributing, Inc. **(3)**
3500 S La Cometa, Goodyear, AZ 85338
Tel.: (623) 932-6200
Non-Durable Goods Whslr
N.A.I.C.S.: 424990

Subsidiary (Domestic):

Kitchen Cooked, Inc. **(2)**
632 N Main St, Farmington, IL 61531
Tel.: (309) 245-2191
Snack Food Mfr & Distr
N.A.I.C.S.: 311919

Snyder of Berlin **(2)**
1313 Stadium Dr, Berlin, PA 15530
Tel.: (814) 267-4641
Web Site: http://www.snyderofberlin.com
Sales Range: $300-349.9 Million
Snack Food Mfr
N.A.I.C.S.: 311919

Division (Domestic):

**Snyder of Berlin - Canal Fulton
Division** **(3)**
611 Elm Ridge Ave, Canal Fulton, OH
44614
Tel.: (330) 854-0818
Web Site: http://www.snyderofberlin.com
Snack Food Mfr
N.A.I.C.S.: 311919

Subsidiary (Domestic):

Truco Enterprises, LP **(2)**
2727 Realty Rd, Carrollton, TX 75220
Tel.: (972) 869-4600
Web Site: http://www.trucoenterprises.com
Sales Range: $1-9.9 Million
Emp.: 32
Snack Food Mfr
N.A.I.C.S.: 424450
Rebecca Langley (Dir-Logistics)
Dave Silver (CEO)
Jeff Partridge (Pres)
Nicki Wolpmann (CFO & VP-Legal, HR, IT
& Data Mgmt)

UV FLU TECHNOLOGIES, INC.

250 Pkwy Dr Ste 150, Lincolnshire, IL
60069
Tel.: (508) 362-5455
Web Site: http://www.uvflutech.com
UVFT—(OTCEM)

Air Purification Equipment Mfr
N.A.I.C.S.: 333413
Michael Ross (Pres & CEO)

UWHARRIE CAPITAL CORP.

141 Providence Rd, Charlotte, NC
28207
Tel.: (704) 983-6181   **NC**
Web Site: https://www.uwharrie.com
UWHR—(OTCQX)
Rev.: $41,695,000
Assets: $1,019,490,000
Liabilities: $982,093,000
Net Worth: $37,397,000
Earnings: $7,684,000
Emp.: 178
Fiscal Year-end: 12/31/22
Offices of Bank Holding Companies
N.A.I.C.S.: 551111
Roger L. Dick (CEO)
S. Todd Swaringen (Vice Chm)
Heather H. Almond (CFO)
R. David Beaver III (Chief Risk Offi-
cer)

Subsidiaries:

BOS Agency Inc **(1)**
132 N 1st St, Albemarle, NC 28001
Tel.: (704) 983-5959
Web Site: http://www.uwharrie.com
Sales Range: $10-24.9 Million
Emp.: 15
Insurance Company
N.A.I.C.S.: 561499

Uwharrie Bank **(1)**
167 N 2nd St, Albemarle, NC 28001
Tel.: (704) 983-6181
Web Site: https://www.uwharrie.com
Banking Services
N.A.I.C.S.: 522110
S. Todd Swaringen (Vice Chm)

**Uwharrie Investment Advisors
Inc.** **(1)**
132 N 1st St, Albemarle, NC 28001
Tel.: (704) 983-5959
Web Site: http://www.uwharrie.com
Investment Advisor
N.A.I.C.S.: 523150
Christy Stoner (Pres & CEO)

V. F. CORPORATION

1551 Wewatta St, Denver, CO 80202
Tel.: (720) 778-4000   **PA**
Web Site: https://www.vfc.com
Year Founded: 1899
VFC—(NYSE)
Rev.: $10,454,667,000
Assets: $11,612,963,000
Liabilities: $9,954,598,000
Net Worth: $1,658,365,000
Earnings: ($968,882,000)
Emp.: 30,000
Fiscal Year-end: 03/30/24
Holding Company; Apparel Mfr, Whslr
& Online Retailer
N.A.I.C.S.: 551112
Richard T. Carucci (Chm)
Laura C. Meagher (Gen Counsel,
Sec & Exec VP)
Craig Hodges (VP-Corp Affairs &
Comm)
Kevin D. Bailey (Pres-Asia-Pacific &
Exec VP)
Martino Scabbia Guerrini (Chief
Comml Officer-Global, Pres-Emerging
Brands & Exec VP)
David Wagner (Exec VP-Growth Plat-
forms & Strategy-Global)
Velia Carboni (Chief Digital & Tech
Officer & Exec VP)
Colin Wheeler (VP-Corp Comm)
Luis Benitez (VP-Govt Affairs &
Global Impact)
Paul Vogel (CFO & Exec VP)
Cameron Bailey (Exec VP-Supply
Chain-Global)

Lauren Guthrie (VP-Global Inclusion
& Diversity)
Andreas Olsson (VP-Sls & Vans-
Europe, Middle East & Africa)
Allegra Perry (VP-IR)
Bracken P. Darrell (Pres & CEO)

Subsidiaries:

Eagle Creek Europe, Ltd. **(1)**
Dwyer Road Midleton, Cork, Ireland
Tel.: (353) 214621471
Web Site: http://www.eaglecreek.com
Apparel & Accessory Retailer
N.A.I.C.S.: 458110

Eagle Creek, Inc. **(1)**
8505 E Orchard Rd, Greenwood Village,
CO 80111
Tel.: (800) 874-1048
Web Site: http://www.eaglecreek.com
Travel Gear & Accessories Mfr
N.A.I.C.S.: 333923

Etablissementen Van Moer N.V. **(1)**
Industriepark 16, Antwerp, 2235, Belgium
Tel.: (32) 15222041
Apparel & Accessory Retailer
N.A.I.C.S.: 458110

Icebreaker Czech Republic s.r.o. **(1)**
A7 Office Center U Pruhonu 1589/13A,
Holesovice, Prague, Czech Republic
Tel.: (420) 730510519
Apparel Retail Store Operator
N.A.I.C.S.: 458110

Icebreaker Merino Clothing Inc. **(1)**
21 Water Street Suite 502, Vancouver, V6B
1A1, BC, Canada
Apparel Retail Store Operator
N.A.I.C.S.: 458110

Icebreaker New Zealand Limited **(1)**
Level 2 Lot 3 130-132 Ponsonby Road,
Auckland, 1011, New Zealand
Tel.: (64) 800000065
Web Site: https://www.icebreaker.com
Apparel Retail Store Operator
N.A.I.C.S.: 458110

**Kodiak Group Holdings
Company** **(1)**
415 Thompson Road, Cambridge, N1T 2K7,
ON, Canada
Tel.: (519) 620-4000
Apparel & Accessory Retailer
N.A.I.C.S.: 458110
John Hanson (CFO & VP-Fin)

LeeWrangler International Sagl **(1)**
Via Vite 3, 6855, Stabio, Switzerland
Tel.: (41) 32982000
Web Site: http://www.europe.wrangler.com
Apparel Retail Store Operator
N.A.I.C.S.: 458110

**Les Dessous Boutique Diffusion
S.A.** **(1)**
53 55 Blvd Paul Langevin, 38600, Fontaine,
France
Tel.: (33) 476279555
Sales Range: $50-74.9 Million
Emp.: 35
Clothing Mfr
N.A.I.C.S.: 315250

North East Rig-Out Limited **(1)**
Unit 3 Altens Trade Centre Hareness Circle,
Altens Industrial Estate, Aberdeen, AB12
3LY, United Kingdom
Tel.: (44) 1224878887
Web Site: https://www.nerigoutstore.com
Protective Clothing Mfr
N.A.I.C.S.: 315990

The H.D. Lee Company, Inc. **(1)**
3411 Silverside Rd 200hb, Wilmington, DE
19810
Tel.: (302) 477-3930
Web Site: http://www.vfc.com
Sales Range: $10-24.9 Million
Emp.: 15
Trademarks & Licensing Services
N.A.I.C.S.: 561499

The Timberland Company **(1)**
200 Domain Dr, Stratham, NH 03885-2575
Tel.: (603) 772-9500
Web Site: https://www.timberland.com

Men's, Women's & Children's Footwear,
Apparel & Sportswear Design, Mfr & Distr
N.A.I.C.S.: 316210
Maisie Willoughby (CMO)
Susie Mulder (Pres-Brand-Global)

Subsidiary (Non-US):

**Component Footwear Dominicana,
S.A.** **(2)**
Zona Franca Industrial Park, Santiago, Do-
minican Republic
Tel.: (809) 2418100
Web Site: http://www.timberland.com
Sales Range: $100-124.9 Million
Footwear Sales
N.A.I.C.S.: 458210

Subsidiary (Domestic):

SmartWool **(2)**
3495 Airport Cir, Steamboat Springs, CO
80487
Tel.: (970) 879-2913
Web Site: http://www.smartwool.com
Sales Range: $50-74.9 Million
Emp.: 70
Apparel & Accessories Mfr
N.A.I.C.S.: 315990
Jennifer McLaren (Pres)

The Outdoor Footwear Company **(2)**
PO Box 869, Isabela, PR 00662-0869
Tel.: (787) 872-2140
Sales Range: $200-249.9 Million
Emp.: 350
Footwear, Apparel & Sportswear Mfr & Mar-
keter
N.A.I.C.S.: 316210

Subsidiary (Non-US):

**Timberland (Gibraltar) Holding
Limited** **(2)**
57/63 Line Wall Road, Gibraltar, GX11 1AA,
Gibraltar
Tel.: (350) 20079000
Holding Company
N.A.I.C.S.: 551112

Subsidiary (Domestic):

Timberland Asia LLC **(2)**
200 Domain Dr, Stratham, NH 03885
Web Site: http://www.timberland.com
Emp.: 400
Footwear Mfr
N.A.I.C.S.: 316210
Eric Carlson (CFO)

Subsidiary (Non-US):

Timberland Canada Co **(2)**
Evergreen Brick Works 550 Bayview Av-
enue, Centre for Green Cities Suite 405,
Toronto, M4W 3X8, ON, Canada
Tel.: (416) 673-9250
Footwear Mfr
N.A.I.C.S.: 316210

Timberland Espana, S.A. **(2)**
Via Augusta 200 2A Planta, Barcelona,
08021, Spain
Tel.: (34) 932402161
Web Site: http://www.timberland.com
Sales Range: $75-99.9 Million
Emp.: 25
Footwear & Clothing Sales
N.A.I.C.S.: 424340
While Nina Flood (Gen Mgr-Europe, Middle
East & Africa)

Timberland Europe B.V. **(2)**
Darwin 8, 7609 RL, Almelo, Netherlands
Tel.: (31) 546547700
Web Site: http://www.timberland.com
Emp.: 170
Miscellaneous Durable Goods Distr
N.A.I.C.S.: 423990

Timberland Europe Services Ltd. **(2)**
Wexham Springs Framewood Road Wex-
ham, Berkshire, Slough, SL3 6PJ, United
Kingdom
Tel.: (44) 1173497000
Footwear Mfr
N.A.I.C.S.: 316210

Timberland Hong Kong Ltd. **(2)**
Rm 815-821 8/f Grand Central Plaza, 138

Shatin Rural Committee Rd, Sha Tin, China (Hong Kong)
Tel.: (852) 26342800
Sales Range: $75-99.9 Million
Footwear & Clothing
N.A.I.C.S.: 316210

Subsidiary (Domestic):

Timberland International, LLC **(2)**
200 Domain Dr, Stratham, NH 03885
Tel.: (603) 772-9500
Web Site: http://www.timberland.com
Men's, Women's & Children's Footwear, Apparel & Sportswear Design, Mfr & Distr
N.A.I.C.S.: 316210

Subsidiary (Non-US):

Timberland Italy Srl. **(2)**
Centro Direzionale Colleoni 17 Agrate Brianza Lombardy, 20041, Milan, Italy
Tel.: (39) 0932402161
Men's & Boys' Clothing Mfr
N.A.I.C.S.: 315250

Timberland LLC **(2)**
Jewel Changi Airport 78 Airport Blvd 02-240, Singapore, 819666, Singapore
Tel.: (65) 65109800
Web Site: https://www.timberland.com.sg
Sales Range: $125-149.9 Million
Footwear Mfr & Distr
N.A.I.C.S.: 316210

Subsidiary (Domestic):

Timberland Retail, Inc. **(2)**
200 Domain Dr, Stratham, NH 03885
Tel.: (888) 802-9947
Web Site: http://www.timberland.com
Sales Range: $125-149.9 Million
Clothing & Boot Whslr
N.A.I.C.S.: 458110

Subsidiary (Non-US):

Timberland Switzerland Holding GmbH **(2)**
Freier Platz 10, 8200, Schaffhausen, Switzerland
Tel.: (41) 526441616
Web Site: http://www.timberland.com.cn
Holding Company
N.A.I.C.S.: 551112

VF Asia Ltd. **(1)**
8F-15F International Trade Tower 348 Kwun Tong Road Kwun Tong, Kowloon Bay, Kowloon, China (Hong Kong)
Tel.: (852) 29532208
Web Site: http://www.vfc.com
Apparel Mfr, Whslr & Online Retailer
N.A.I.C.S.: 424350

VF Brands India Private Limited **(1)**
E-23 Ndse 2, New Delhi, 110008, India
Tel.: (91) 8071030100
Web Site: http://www.wrangler-ap.com
Apparels Mfr
N.A.I.C.S.: 315250

VF Commercializadora Limitada **(1)**
Calle Lincoyan 9811 Loteo Buenaventura, Quilicura, Santiago, Chile
Tel.: (56) 223678300
Apparel Designer & Whslr
N.A.I.C.S.: 315250
Rodrigo Campos *(Mgr-Mktg-Jeanswear)*

VF Czech S.R.O. **(1)**
Budova DC 01 Vchod A Ke Zdibsku 193, Zdiby, 250 66, Prague, Czech Republic
Tel.: (420) 284089119
Emp.: 700
Clothing & Accessory Merchant Whslr
N.A.I.C.S.: 424350

VF Ege Soke Giyim Sanayi ve Ticaret A.S. **(1)**
Kayhan Is Hani K3 D301 42 Halit Ziya Bulvari, Izmir, 35210, Turkiye
Tel.: (90) 2324832274
Sales Range: $25-49.9 Million
Emp.: 35
Apparels Mfr
N.A.I.C.S.: 315250
Goksel Ozturk *(Gen Mgr)*

VF Europe B.V.B.A. **(1)**

Entrepotstraat 2, Saint-Niklaas, 9100, Belgium
Tel.: (32) 983153
Sales Range: $300-349.9 Million
Emp.: 352
Women's & Men's Clothing Marketer
N.A.I.C.S.: 424350
Patrick Willems *(CEO)*

VF Germany Textil-Handels GmbH **(1)**
Otto-Hahn-Street 36, Hessen, 63303, Germany
Tel.: (49) 61035810
Web Site: http://www.vfc.com
Sales Range: $25-49.9 Million
Emp.: 13
Apparel Retailer
N.A.I.C.S.: 315250

VF Imagewear, Inc. **(1)**
545 Marriott Dr Ste 200, Nashville, TN 37214-0995 **(100%)**
Tel.: (615) 565-5000
Web Site: http://www.vfimagewear.com
Career Apparel Mfr
N.A.I.C.S.: 315210

Subsidiary (Domestic):

Horace Small Apparel Company **(2)**
545 Marriott Dr, Nashville, TN 37214
Tel.: (615) 565-5000
Web Site: http://www.horacesmall.com
Sales Range: $600-649.9 Million
Mfr & Retailer of Uniforms, Work Clothes & Career Outerwear
N.A.I.C.S.: 315210

Majestic Athletic Ltd. **(2)**
2320 Newlands Mill Rd, Easton, PA 18045
Tel.: (610) 746-6800
Web Site: http://www.majesticathletic.com
Sales Range: $25-49.9 Million
Emp.: 760
Provider of Clothing Services
N.A.I.C.S.: 315250

Branch (Domestic):

VF Imagewear **(2)**
554 Hickory Hills Blvd, Whites Creek, TN 37189 **(100%)**
Tel.: (615) 876-2671
Web Site: http://www.vfimagewear.com
Sales Range: $125-149.9 Million
Emp.: 200
Career Apparel Mfr
N.A.I.C.S.: 315250

Subsidiary (Non-US):

VF Imagewear Canada Co. **(2)**
9146 Yellowhead Trail North West, Edmonton, T5B 1G2, AB, Canada
Tel.: (780) 479-4444
Apparel & Accessory Retailer
N.A.I.C.S.: 458110
Tim LeMessurier *(Dir-Sls)*

VF Imagewear de Mexico, S. de R.L. de C.V. **(2)**
Lib Periferico Raul Lopez Sanchez San Antonio De Los Bravo, Torreon, 27054, Mexico
Tel.: (52) 8717332107
Apparel & Accessory Retailer
N.A.I.C.S.: 458110

VF Internacional, S. de R.L. de C.V. **(1)**
Paseo de la Reforma 2620 Miguel Hidalgo, 11950, Mexico, Mexico
Tel.: (52) 5550811500
Apparel & Accessory Retailer
N.A.I.C.S.: 458110

VF International S.a.g.l. **(1)**
Via Laveggio 5, 6855, Stabio, Switzerland
Tel.: (41) 916491000
Web Site: http://www.vfc.com
Apparels Mfr
N.A.I.C.S.: 315250
Fabrizia Greppi *(Sr Dir-Corp Affairs & Comm)*

VF Israel (Apparel) Ltd. **(1)**
14 Amal, Rosh HaAyin, 4809250, Israel
Tel.: (972) 39155111
Apparel & Accessory Retailer
N.A.I.C.S.: 458110

VF Italia, S.r.l. **(1)**
Localita San Giorgio 131/E, Capri, 25020, Italy
Tel.: (39) 02899611
Apparels Mfr
N.A.I.C.S.: 315250

VF Italy Services S.r.l. **(1)**
Via Varesina 162, Milan, 20143, Italy
Tel.: (39) 0423683111
Apparel Brands Mfr
N.A.I.C.S.: 315250

VF Luxembourg S.a.r.l. **(1)**
rue de Jargonnant 2, Geneva, 1207, Switzerland
Tel.: (41) 227321770
Web Site: http://www.vfc.com
Clothing Mfr
N.A.I.C.S.: 315250

VF Northern Europe Ltd. **(1)**
Park Road East Calverton, Nottingham, NG14 6GD, Nottinghamshire, United Kingdom
Tel.: (44) 1159656565
Web Site: http://www.vfc.com
Sales Range: $10-24.9 Million
Emp.: 200
Men's Clothing Mfr
N.A.I.C.S.: 315250

VF Northern Europe Services Ltd. **(1)**
Park Road East, Nottingham, NG14 6GD, United Kingdom
Tel.: (44) 1159656565
Apparels Mfr
N.A.I.C.S.: 315250

VF Outdoor (Canada), Inc. **(1)**
3260 Rue Guennette, Saint Laurent, H4S 2G5, QC, Canada
Tel.: (514) 832-0040
Web Site: https://www.thenorthface.com
Sales Range: $25-49.9 Million
Emp.: 80
Apparels Mfr
N.A.I.C.S.: 315250

VF Outdoor, Inc. **(1)**
Tel.: (510) 618-3500
Cloth Retailer
N.A.I.C.S.: 455219

Subsidiary (Non-US):

JanSport Apparel Corp. **(2)**
Tel.: (330) 770-1104
Web Site: https://www.jansport.com
Backpacks & Technical Packs & Luggage Mfr & Marketer; Outdoor Apparel
N.A.I.C.S.: 339920

The North Face, Inc. **(2)**
(100%)
Tel.: (415) 433-3223
Web Site: https://www.thenorthface.com
Sales Range: $200-249.9 Million
Emp.: 400
High-Performance Climbing & Backpacking Equipment Mfr, Distr & Retailer
N.A.I.C.S.: 315990

VF Polska Distribution Sp.z.o.o. **(1)**
Ul Cybernetyki 9, 02-677, Warsaw, Poland
Tel.: (48) 223180808
Apparel & Accessory Retailer
N.A.I.C.S.: 458110
Pawel Lubinski *(Mgr-Retail Svc)*

VF Scandinavia A/S **(1)**
Nordre Strandvej 119a, 3150, Hellebaek, Denmark
Tel.: (45) 49222666
Clothing Stores
N.A.I.C.S.: 455219

VF Services, LLC **(1)**
105 Corporate Ctr Blvd, Greensboro, NC 27408-3194
Tel.: (336) 332-3400
Data Processing Services
N.A.I.C.S.: 518210

VF Sourcing India Private Limited **(1)**
No 62 Pragathi Mahalakshmi Building 4th Floor 1st Main Road 2nd Stage, Yeshwanthpur Industrial Suburb, Bengaluru, 560022, India

Tel.: (91) 8041228159
Emp.: 80
Men's & Boy's Clothing Mfr
N.A.I.C.S.: 315250

VF Sportswear, Inc. **(1)**
105 Corporate Ctr Blvd, Greensboro, NC 27408
Tel.: (336) 424-6000
Web Site: http://www.vfc.com
Sportswear Mfr
N.A.I.C.S.: 424350

VF do Brasil Ltda. **(1)**
Rua Geraldo Flausino Gomes 78, 04575-060, Sao Paulo, Brazil
Tel.: (55) 1155035300
Web Site: http://www.vf.com.br
Sales Range: $50-74.9 Million
Emp.: 80
Clothing Mfr
N.A.I.C.S.: 315250

Vans, Inc. **(1)**
1588 S Coast Dr, Costa Mesa, CA 92626
Tel.: (714)
Web Site: https://www.vans.com
Footwear & Apparel Designer, Mfr & Whslr
N.A.I.C.S.: 424340
Doug Palladini *(Pres-Brand-Global)*

Subsidiary (Domestic):

Pro-Tec Industries **(2)**
1311 Hermosa Ave Ste 200, Hermosa Beach, CA 90254
Tel.: (310) 318-9883
Web Site: http://www.pro-tec.net
Sales Range: $25-49.9 Million
Emp.: 20
Sporting & Recreation Goods Mfr
N.A.I.C.S.: 423910

Williamson-Dickie Manufacturing Company **(1)**
509 W Vickery Blvd, Fort Worth, TX 76104
Tel.: (800) 342-5437
Web Site: http://www.dickies.com
Apparel Accessory Mfr
N.A.I.C.S.: 315990
Randy Teuber *(CFO & VP)*

Williamson-Dickie Manufacturing Company **(1)**
509 W Vickery Blvd, Fort Worth, TX 76104
Tel.: (817) 877-0387
Web Site: http://www.dickies.com
Clothing Mfr
N.A.I.C.S.: 315250
Randy Teuber *(CFO & Exec VP)*
Michael Studdard *(Exec VP-HR)*
Tobin Clark *(Gen Counsel, Sec & Sr VP)*

Subsidiary (Domestic):

Walls Industries LLC **(2)**
125 S Jenings, Fort Worth, TX 76104
Tel.: (844) 259-2557
Web Site: http://www.walls.com
Workwear, Ranch & Sporting Apparel Designer, Mfr & Marketer
N.A.I.C.S.: 315250

Subsidiary (Non-US):

Williamson-Dickie Apparel Trading (Shanghai) Co. Ltd **(2)**
2F henderson Celebrity Shopping Center, 300 East Nanjing Road Huangpo District, Shanghai, China
Tel.: (86) 2124192222
Web Site: http://www.dickies.com.cn
Apparels Mfr
N.A.I.C.S.: 315210

Williamson-Dickie Canada Company **(2)**
415 Thompson Dr, Cambridge, N1T 2K7, ON, Canada
Tel.: (888) 664-6636
Web Site: http://www.dickies.ca
Apparels Mfr
N.A.I.C.S.: 315250

Williamson-Dickie Europe Limited **(2)**
Second Avenue Westfield Trading Estate Midsomer Norton, Radstock, BA3 4BH, United Kingdom
Tel.: (44) 1761419419
Web Site: http://www.dickiesworkwear.com

V. F. Corporation—(Continued)

Apparels Mfr
N.A.I.C.S.: 315250

Subsidiary (Domestic):

Williamson-Dickie Europe Holdings
Limited **(3)**
Second Avenue Westfield Trading Estate
Midsomer Norton, Radstock, BA3 4BH,
United Kingdom
Tel.: (44) 1761410041
Apparel & Accessory Retailer
N.A.I.C.S.: 458110

Subsidiary (Non-US):

WD Europe SAS **(4)**
166 Rue Saint Francois Xavier, Gradignan,
33170, France
Tel.: (33) 556898990
Apparel & Accessory Retailer
N.A.I.C.S.: 458110

Williamson-Dickie Nederland
B.V. **(4)**
Phoenixstraat 6, 2011 KC, Haarlem, Nether-
lands
Tel.: (31) 235319587
Web Site: https://www.vanmoer.nl
Work Wear Clothing Mfr
N.A.I.C.S.: 315990

lucy activewear, inc. **(1)**
222 SW Columbia St Ste 300, Portland, OR
97201
Tel.: (503) 228-2142
Sales Range: $50-74.9 Million
Emp.: 65
Women's Activewear Retailer
N.A.I.C.S.: 458110

V2X, INC.
7901 Jones Branch Dr Ste 700,
McLean, VA 22102
Tel.: (571) 481-2000   **IN**
Web Site: https://www.gov2x.com
Year Founded: 1945
VVX—(NYSE)
Rev.: $2,890,860,000
Assets: $3,233,103,000
Liabilities: $2,236,024,000
Net Worth: $997,079,000
Earnings: ($14,330,000)
Emp.: 15,400
Fiscal Year-end: 12/31/22
All Other Support Services
N.A.I.C.S.: 561990
William B. Noon (Chief Acctg Officer
& VP)
Michael J. Smith (VP-Treasury, Corp
Dev & IR)
Kevin T. Boyle (Chief Legal Officer,
Gen Counsel & Sr VP)
Jeremy Wensinger (Pres & CEO)
J. Eric Best (VP-Fin Ops)
Lisa Freeman (VP-Natl Security Pro-
grams)
Joe Poniatowski (VP-Contracts)
Chuck Shy (VP-Land Maintenance,
Repair & Overhaul Bus)
Jo Ann Bjornson (Chief HR Officer &
Sr VP)
Kelly Miller (VP)
Jeremy Nance (Deputy Gen Counsel)

Subsidiaries:

Advantor Systems Corporation **(1)**
12612 Challenger Pkwy Ste 300, Orlando,
FL 32826
Tel.: (407) 859-3350
Web Site: https://www.advantor.com
Sales Range: $25-49.9 Million
Emp.: 150
Security System Mfr
N.A.I.C.S.: 334419
Richard Clifton (CEO)
Jeffrey Whirley (Pres)
Mike Ollivier (VP & Mgr-Air Natl Guard Mar-
ket)
Grant Herring (VP-USAF Market)
Mike Lanktree (Dir-Fulfillment)
Richard Harrison (Dir-Svcs)

Emily Staggs (Dir-Trng)
Jennifer J. Rivas (Dir-Contracts)
Chase Perkinson (Dir-Installation)

Vectrus Systems Corporation **(1)**
2424 Garden of the Gods Rd, Colorado
Springs, CO 80919
Tel.: (719) 591-3600
Government & Military Operational Support
Services
N.A.I.C.S.: 561990

Subsidiary (Non-US):

Exelis Services A/S **(2)**
Havnegade 39, 1058, Copenhagen, Den-
mark
Tel.: (45) 33444401
Web Site: http://www.exelisservices.com
Business Support Services
N.A.I.C.S.: 561499

Vectrus Federal Services GmbH **(2)**
Daenner Kaseme - Gebaude 3113
-Mannheimer Str 214, 67657, Kaiserslau-
tern, Germany
Tel.: (49) 63134090
Web Site: https://www.vectrus.de
Emp.: 20
Government & Military Operational Support
Services
N.A.I.C.S.: 561990

Subsidiary (Domestic):

Vectrus Mission Solutions
Corporation **(2)**
2800 Eisenhower Ave Ste 300, Alexandria,
VA 22314
Tel.: (571) 481-2000
Web Site: http://www.vectrus.com
Software Engineering Services
N.A.I.C.S.: 541330

Zenetex LLC **(2)**
13865 Sunrise Valley Dr Ste 250, Herndon,
VA 20171
Tel.: (703) 657-0377
Web Site: http://www.zenetex.com
Sales Range: $25-49.9 Million
Emp.: 311
Business Management Consulting Services
N.A.I.C.S.: 541611
Mark Gerasch (VP-Bus Dev)
Mark Green (Chm & CEO)
Ray Badia (VP-Intl Programs)
James W. McDermott (CFO)
Gery Vandervliet (Exec VP-Bus Dev)
Doug Rember (VP-IT Svc Mgmt)
Jeffrey L. McDermott (VP-Contracts)
Dennis J. England (Pres & COO)
Cindy Randall (VP-IT Svcs)
Greg Wallace (VP-Naval Aviation Program
Dev)
Frank Widick (VP-Contractor Field Svcs)
Mike Roscoe (Dir-Engrg Svcs)
Laura Kamosa (Dir-HR)
Steve Daczkowski (VP-Bus Dev)
Todd Thurman (VP-Logistics)

Vertex Aerospace LLC **(1)**
555 Industrial Dr S, Madison, MS 39110
Tel.: (601) 607-6552
Aerospace & Aviation Technical Services
N.A.I.C.S.: 541990

VAALCO ENERGY, INC.
9800 Richmond Ave Ste 700, Hous-
ton, TX 77042
Tel.: (713) 623-0801   **DE**
Web Site: https://www.vaalco.com
Year Founded: 1989
EGY—(NYSE)
Rev.: $455,070,000
Assets: $823,220,000
Liabilities: $344,440,000
Net Worth: $478,780,000
Earnings: $60,350,000
Emp.: 185
Fiscal Year-end: 12/31/23
Crude Petroleum Extraction Services
N.A.I.C.S.: 211120
Julie Ray (VP-Treasury)
Thor Pruckl (COO)
Ronald Bain (CFO)
Lynn Willis (Chief Acctg Officer &
Controller)
George W. M. Maxwell (CEO)

Subsidiaries:

TransGlobe Energy Corporation **(1)**
Suite 900 444 - Fifth Avenue SW, Calgary,
T2P 2T8, AB, Canada
Tel.: (403) 264-9888
Web Site: http://www.trans-globe.com
Rev.: $169,047,000
Assets: $239,095,000
Liabilities: $60,521,000
Net Worth: $178,574,000
Earnings: $40,338,000
Emp.: 55
Fiscal Year-end: 12/31/2021
Natural Gas Exploration & Production Ser-
vices
N.A.I.C.S.: 211130
Edward D. Ok (CFO & VP-Fin)
Geoffrey Probert (COO & VP)

Subsidiary (Domestic):

TG Holdings Yemen Inc. **(2)**
250 5th St SW Ste 2300, Calgary, T2P
0R4, AB, Canada
Tel.: (403) 264-9888
Web Site: http://www.trans-globe.com
Sales Range: $50-74.9 Million
Emp.: 25
Oil & Gas Exploration
N.A.I.C.S.: 211120

TransGlobe Petroleum Egypt
Inc. **(2)**
605 5th Ave SW Ste 2500, Calgary, T2P
3H5, AB, Canada
Tel.: (403) 264-9888
Web Site: http://www.trans-globe.com
Sales Range: $50-74.9 Million
Emp.: 25
Oil & Gas Exploration
N.A.I.C.S.: 211120

TransGlobe Petroleum International
Inc. **(2)**
605 5th Ave Southwest Ste 2500, T2P 3H5,
Calgary, AB, Canada
Tel.: (403) 264-9888
Sales Range: $50-74.9 Million
Emp.: 25
Oil & Gas Exploration
N.A.I.C.S.: 211120

VAALCO Energy (USA), Inc. **(1)**
9800 Richmond Ave Ste 700, Houston, TX
77042   **(100%)**
Tel.: (713) 623-0801
Web Site: https://www.vaalco.com
Sales Range: $150-199.9 Million
Emp.: 20
Explorer & Producer of Oil; Explorer & De-
veloper of Minerals
N.A.I.C.S.: 211120

VAALCO Gabon S.A. **(1)**
BP 1335, Port-Gentil, Gabon
Tel.: (241) 1565526
Crude Petroleum Extraction Whslr
N.A.I.C.S.: 424720
Cary M. Bounds (CEO)
Andrew Lawrence Fawthrop (Chm & Dir)

VAALCO International, Inc. **(1)**
9800 Richmond Ave, Houston, TX
77042   **(90.01%)**
Tel.: (713) 623-0801
Web Site: http://www.vaalco.com
Sales Range: $150-199.9 Million
Emp.: 30
Explorer & Producer of Oil; Explorer & De-
veloper of Minerals
N.A.I.C.S.: 211120

Subsidiary (Non-US):

VAALCO Angola (Kwanza), Inc. **(2)**
Av 4 Fevereiro, Luanda, Angola
Tel.: (244) 222311390
Sales Range: $50-74.9 Million
Emp.: 10
Explorer & Producer of Oil
N.A.I.C.S.: 211120

VAALCO Gabon (Etame), Inc. **(2)**
PO Box 1335, Port-Gentil, Gabon **(90.01%)**
Tel.: (241) 1565529
Sales Range: $50-74.9 Million
Emp.: 55
Explorer & Producer of Oil; Explorer & De-
veloper of Minerals

N.A.I.C.S.: 211120

VAALCO Production (Gabon)
Inc. **(2)**
PO Box 1335, Port-Gentil, Gabon **(100%)**
Tel.: (241) 1565526
Web Site: http://www.vaalco.com
International Oil, Natural Gas & Crude Oil
Production & Development
N.A.I.C.S.: 211120

VACASA, INC.
Tel.: (503) 946-3650   **OR**
Web Site: https://www.vacasa.com
Year Founded: 2009
VCSA—(NASDAQ)
Rev.: $1,187,950,000
Assets: $1,305,584,000
Liabilities: $892,584,000
Net Worth: $413,000,000
Earnings: ($332,149,000)
Emp.: 7,900
Fiscal Year-end: 12/31/22
Travel & Tour Operating Services
N.A.I.C.S.: 561520
Eric Breon (Founder)
Bob Milne (Sr VP-Ops)
Jeffrey Parks (Chm)
Robert W. Greyber (CEO & Interim
Chief Product Officer)
T. J. Clark (Chief Comml Officer)
Rebecca Boyden (Chief Legal Offi-
cer)
Manu Sivanandam (CMO)
Harish Naidu (CTO)
Bruce Schuman (CFO & Chief Acctg
Officer)

Subsidiaries:

TPG Pace Solutions Corp. **(1)**
301 Commerce St Ste 3300, Fort Worth, TX
76102
Tel.: (212) 405-8458
Emp.: 3
Investment Services
N.A.I.C.S.: 523999
Eduardo Tamraz (Pres)
Martin Davidson (CFO)
Carlton Ellis (Exec VP-Corp Dev & Sec)

TurnKey Vacation Rentals LLC **(1)**
4544 S Lamar Blvd Se G300, Austin, TX
78746
Web Site: http://www.turnkeyvr.com
Recreational & Vacation Camps
N.A.I.C.S.: 721214
John Banczak (Founder)
Doug Squires (VP-Engrg)
Jen Ford (CFO)
Guin White (Gen Mgr-Santa Fe & Taos)

VAIL RESORTS, INC.
390 Interlocken Cres, Broomfield, CO
80021
Tel.: (303) 404-1800   **DE**
Web Site:
https://www.vailresorts.com
Year Founded: 1977
MTN—(NYSE)
Rev.: $2,885,191,000
Assets: $5,698,437,000
Liabilities: $4,659,954,000
Net Worth: $1,038,483,000
Earnings: $246,279,000
Emp.: 7,600
Fiscal Year-end: 07/31/24
Hotel & Resort Owner & Operator
N.A.I.C.S.: 721110
Bill Rock (Pres-Mountain Div)
Robert A. Katz (Chm)
Kirsten A. Lynch (CEO)
Greg Sullivan (Sr VP-Retail, Rental &
Hospitality)
Lynanne J. Kunkel (Chief HR Officer
& Exec VP)
Timothy M. April (CIO & Exec VP)
Nathan Gronberg (Chief Acctg Offi-
cer, VP & Controller)
Angela Korch (CFO & Exec VP)
Kenny Thompson Jr. (Chief Pub Af-
fairs Officer)

Subsidiaries:

ARRABELLE AT VAIL SQUARE, LLC (1)
675 Lionshead Pl, Vail, CO 81657
Tel.: (303) 420-9963
Web Site:
http://www.arrabelle.rockresorts.com
Emp.: 150
Hotel & Resort Operator
N.A.I.C.S.: 721110
Zach Meyers *(Gen Mgr)*

Beaver Creek Associates, Inc. (1)
PO Box 7, Vail, CO 81658
Tel.: (970) 476-5601
Web Site: http://www.snow.com
Rev.: $86,000
Emp.: 100
Recreational Services
N.A.I.C.S.: 532284

Colorado Mountain Express LLC (1)
434 Edwards Access Rd, Edwards, CO 81632
Rev.: $12,000,000
Emp.: 150
Airport Transportation Services, Regular Route
N.A.I.C.S.: 485999

FIRST CHAIR HOUSING TRUSTEE LLC (1)
600 W Lionshead Cir, Vail, CO 81657-5940
Tel.: (970) 476-7502
Trust & Custody Activities Services
N.A.I.C.S.: 523991

Grand Teton Lodge Company, Inc. (1)
101 Jackson Lake Lodge Rd, Moran, WY 83013
Tel.: (307) 543-2811
Web Site: https://www.gtlc.com
Sales Range: $10-24.9 Million
Emp.: 1,000
Hotels & Motels
N.A.I.C.S.: 721110

Heavenly Valley, Limited Partnership (1)
3860 Saddle Rd, South Lake Tahoe, CA 96150
Tel.: (775) 586-7000
Web Site: https://www.skiheavenly.com
Sales Range: $50-74.9 Million
Emp.: 240
Provider of Hotel & Motel Services And Ski Resorts
N.A.I.C.S.: 561612
Mike Goar *(COO)*

Jackson Hole Golf & Tennis Club, Inc. (1)
5000 N Spring Gulch Rd, Jackson, WY 83001
Tel.: (307) 733-3111
Web Site: https://www.jhgtc.com
Golf Course & Country Club Operator
N.A.I.C.S.: 713910

Keystone Resort Property Management Company (1)
0175 Summit County Rd 8, Keystone, CO 80435-0038
Tel.: (970) 754-0001
Web Site: https://www.keystoneresort.com
Sales Range: $25-49.9 Million
Emp.: 150
Resort
N.A.I.C.S.: 722511

Kirkwood Mountain Resorts, LLC (1)
1501 Kirkwood Meadows Dr, Kirkwood, CA 95646
Tel.: (209) 258-6000
Web Site: https://www.kirkwood.com
Ski Resort Operator
N.A.I.C.S.: 713920

LARKSPUR RESTAURANT & BAR, LLC (1)
458 Vail Vly Dr, Vail, CO 81657
Tel.: (970) 754-8050
Web Site: http://www.larkspurvail.com
Sales Range: $10-24.9 Million
Emp.: 150
Hotel & Resort Operator
N.A.I.C.S.: 721110

Rafal Konka *(Mng Dir)*
Thomas Salamunovich *(Owner & Dir-Culinary)*
Isabel Piaggi *(Dir-Sls & Mktg)*
Christopher Eckert *(Dir-Bar & Beverage)*
Brandon Killory *(Dir-Dining)*
Kevin Bates *(Mgr-Kitchen)*
Stephanie Ratkowski *(Dir-Acctg)*

ONE SKI HILL PLACE, LLC (1)
1521 Ski Hill Rd, Breckenridge, CO 80424
Web Site:
http://www.oneskihill.rockresorts.com
Emp.: 70
Hotel & Resort Operator
N.A.I.C.S.: 721110

Park City Mountain Resort (1)
1345 Lowell Ave, Park City, UT 84060
Tel.: (435) 649-8111
Web Site: https://www.parkcitymountain.com
Recreational Facilities & Services
N.A.I.C.S.: 721214

Peak Resorts, Inc. (1)
17409 Hidden Valley Dr, Wildwood, MO 63025
Tel.: (636) 938-7474
Web Site: http://www.peakresorts.com
Rev.: $184,426,000
Assets: $410,648,000
Liabilities: $328,423,000
Net Worth: $82,225,000
Earnings: $8,916,000
Emp.: 659
Fiscal Year-end: 04/30/2019
Holding Company; Ski Resorts Owner & Operator
N.A.I.C.S.: 551112

Subsidiary (Domestic):

17402 Hidden Valley LLC (2)
17409 Hidden Valley Dr, Wildwood, MO 63025
Tel.: (636) 938-5373
Web Site: http://www.hiddenvalleyski.com
Alpine Skiing Resort Operator
N.A.I.C.S.: 721110

Unit (Domestic):

Attitash Mountain Resort (2)
775 Rte 302, Bartlett, NH 03812
Tel.: (603) 374-2368
Web Site: https://www.attitash.com
Ski Resort Services
N.A.I.C.S.: 713920

Subsidiary (Domestic):

Carinthia Group 1, L.P. (2)
89 Grand Summit Way, West Dover, VT 05356
Tel.: (802) 464-6608
Ski Resort Operator
N.A.I.C.S.: 721110

Deltrecs, Inc. (2)
7100 Riverview Rd, Peninsula, OH 44264
Tel.: (330) 467-2242
Emp.: 23
Skiing Services
N.A.I.C.S.: 713920

Hidden Valley Golf and Ski, Inc. (2)
1 Snow Creek Dr, Weston, MO 64098
Tel.: (816) 640-2200
Skiing Services
N.A.I.C.S.: 713920

Hunter Mountain Ski Bowl, Inc. (2)
64 Klein Ave, Hunter, NY 12442
Tel.: (518) 263-4223
Web Site: https://www.huntermtn.com
Sales Range: $25-49.9 Million
Emp.: 120
Ski Resort Operator
N.A.I.C.S.: 713920

Hunter Resort Vacations, Inc. (2)
PO Box 257, Hunter, NY 12442
Tel.: (518) 263-5580
Web Site:
http://www.hunterresortvacations.com
Real Estate Development Services
N.A.I.C.S.: 531312

L.B.O. Holding, Inc. (2)
775 Rte 302, Bartlett, NH 03812
Tel.: (603) 374-2600

Holding Company
N.A.I.C.S.: 551112

Mount Snow, Ltd. (2)
39 Mount Snow Rd, West Dover, VT 05356
Tel.: (802) 464-2151
Web Site: https://www.mountsnow.com
Sales Range: $75-99.9 Million
Ski Resort
N.A.I.C.S.: 721199

Paoli Peaks Inc. (2)
2798 W County Rd 25 S, Paoli, IN 47454
Tel.: (812) 723-4696
Web Site: https://www.paolipeaks.com
Ski Resort Operator
N.A.I.C.S.: 721110

Ski Liberty Operating Corp. (2)
78 Country Club Trl, Carroll Valley, PA 17320-8550
Tel.: (717) 642-8282
Web Site:
https://www.libertymountainresort.com
Hotel & Resort Operator
N.A.I.C.S.: 721110

Snow Time, Inc. (2)
100 Boxwood Ln, York, PA 17402
Tel.: (717) 757-1508
Sales Range: $25-49.9 Million
Emp.: 3
Manager of Ski Resorts
N.A.I.C.S.: 721110
Irvin Naylor *(Chm)*
Scott Romberger *(Pres)*

Subsidiary (Domestic):

Roundtop Mountain Resort (3)
925 Roundtop Rd, Lewisberry, PA 17339-9762
Tel.: (717) 432-9631
Web Site: https://www.skiroundtop.com
Ski Resort
N.A.I.C.S.: 721199

Subsidiary (Domestic):

Sycamore Lake, Inc. (2)
10620 Mayfield Rd, Chesterland, OH 44026-2738
Tel.: (440) 285-2211
Web Site: http://www.alpinevalleyohio.com
Ski Resort Operator
N.A.I.C.S.: 721110

Remontees Mecaniques Crans Montana Aminona (CMA) SA (1)
Crans-Montana 1, PO Box 352, 3963, Sierre, Switzerland (84%)
Tel.: (41) 848221012
Web Site: https://www.mycma.ch
Ski Lift Operating Services
N.A.I.C.S.: 713920
Mike Goar *(COO)*

RockResorts International, LLC (1)
390 Interlocken Crescent, Broomfield, CO 80021 (100%)
Tel.: (303) 404-1800
Web Site: http://www.rockresorts.com
Holding Company; Hotel & Ski Resort Owner & Operator
N.A.I.C.S.: 551112
Paul Goner *(Pres)*

Unit (Domestic):

The Lodge At Vail (2)
174 E Gore Creek Dr, Vail, CO 81657-4511
Web Site: http://www.rockresorts.com
Sales Range: $1-9.9 Million
Emp.: 350
Hotel Operator
N.A.I.C.S.: 721110

SKIINFO.FR S.A.R.L. (1)
2 Chemin de Beaulieu, 74940, Annecy-le-Vieux, France
Tel.: (33) 450101760
Web Site: http://www.skiinfo.fr
Emp.: 4
Hotel & Resort Operator
N.A.I.C.S.: 721110
Chad Dier *(CEO)*

Specialty Sports Venture LLC (1)
390 Interlocken Crescent, Broomfield, CO 80201
Tel.: (303) 399-1970

Web Site:
http://www.specialtysportsnetwork.com
Sales Range: $25-49.9 Million
Emp.: 50
Sporting Goods & Bicycle Shops
N.A.I.C.S.: 459110

Subsidiary (Domestic):

Hoigaard's, Inc. (2)
5425 Excelsior Blvd, Minneapolis, MN 55416
Tel.: (952) 929-1351
Web Site: http://hoigaards.com
Sporting Goods Retailer
N.A.I.C.S.: 459110

Stevens Pass Mountain Resort, LLC (1)
93001 NE Stevens Pass Hwy US 2, Skykomish, WA 98288
Tel.: (206) 812-4510
Web Site: https://www.stevenspass.com
Amusement & Recreation Industries
N.A.I.C.S.: 713990

TV8 Media Center (1)
1060 W Beaver Creek Blvd, Avon, CO 81620
Tel.: (970) 479-0800
Web Site: http://www.tv8vail.com
Sales Range: $10-24.9 Million
Emp.: 15
Cable & Other Pay Television Services
N.A.I.C.S.: 516210

The Sunapee Difference LLC (1)
1398 Route 103, Newbury, NH 03255
Tel.: (603) 763-3500
Web Site: http://www.mountsunapee.com
Hotel & Resort Operator
N.A.I.C.S.: 721110

Triple Peaks, LLC (1)
77 Okemo Rd, Ludlow, VT 05149
Tel.: (802) 228-1947
Web Site: http://www.okemo.com
Holding Company; Resort Properties
N.A.I.C.S.: 551112

Holding (Domestic):

Crested Butte Mountain Resort, Inc. (2)
17 Emmons Loop, Crested Butte, CO 81225
Tel.: (970) 349-2333
Web Site: http://www.skicb.com
Sales Range: $50-74.9 Million
Emp.: 700
Ski Resort
N.A.I.C.S.: 721110
Debbie Fox *(VP-Sls & Lodging)*

VAIL ASSOCIATES INVESTMENTS, INC. (1)
390 Interlocken Cres Ste 1000, Broomfield, CO 80021-8056
Tel.: (720) 887-4559
Investment Management Service
N.A.I.C.S.: 523940

Vail Beaver Creek Resort Properties Inc. (1)
40 Vlg Rd, Avon, CO 81620
Tel.: (970) 754-5997
Web Site:
http://www.beavercreekresortproperties.com
Rev.: $7,500,000
Emp.: 80
Operator of Luxury Ski Resorts & Rental Properties
N.A.I.C.S.: 531110

Vail Food Services Inc. (1)
600 W Lionshead Cir, Vail, CO 81657-5218
Tel.: (970) 476-9090
Web Site: http://www.snow.com
Sales Range: $10-24.9 Million
Emp.: 200
Eating Place
N.A.I.C.S.: 722511

Vail Holdings, Inc. (1)
26 Avondale Ln, Avon, CO 81620
Tel.: (970) 754-4636
Web Site: https://www.vailresorts.com
Holding Company; Skiing Facilities, Hotels, Skiing Instruction & Sporting Goods Stores Operator

Vail Resorts, Inc.—(Continued)
N.A.I.C.S.: 551112

Unit (Domestic):

Beaver Creek Resort (2)
PO Box 7, Vail, CO 81658
Tel.: (970) 754-4636
Web Site: http://www.beavercreek.com
Operator of Ski Resort
N.A.I.C.S.: 721199
Nadia Guerriero (COO & VP)

Vail Resorts Development Company (1)
390 Interlocken Cres, Broomfield, CO 80021
Tel.: (303) 404-1800
Web Site: http://www.vrdcliving.com
Sales Range: $10-24.9 Million
Emp.: 75
Ski Resort Real Estate Acquisition & Development Services
N.A.I.C.S.: 237210

Vail Summit Resorts, Inc. (1)
PO Box 7, Vail, CO 81658
Tel.: (970) 476-5601
Web Site: http://www.vail.com
Sales Range: $10-24.9 Million
Emp.: 450
Hotels & Ski Resorts
N.A.I.C.S.: 721110

Unit (Domestic):

Breckenridge Ski Resort (2)
1521 Ski Hill Rd, Breckenridge, CO 80424-1058
Tel.: (970) 453-5000
Web Site: https://www.breckenridge.com
Sales Range: $250-299.9 Million
Ski Resort
N.A.I.C.S.: 624410

Whistler Blackcomb Holdings Inc. (1)
4545 Blackcomb Way, Whistler, V8E 0X9, BC, Canada
Tel.: (604) 967-8950
Web Site: https://www.whistlerblackcomb.com
Holding Company; Ski Resort Operations
N.A.I.C.S.: 551112

Subsidiary (Domestic):

Whistler Blackcomb Corporation (2)
4545 Blackcomb Way, Whistler, V0N 1B4, BC, Canada
Tel.: (604) 967-8950
Web Site: http://www.whistlerblackcomb.com
Ski Resort
N.A.I.C.S.: 713990

Wilmot Mountain, Inc. (1)
11931 Fox River Rd, Wilmot, WI 53192
Tel.: (262) 862-2301
Web Site: https://www.wilmotmountain.com
Ski Resort Operator
N.A.I.C.S.: 713920

VALENTINE MARK CORPORATION
55 W 47 St Ste 425, New York, NY 10036
Tel.: (212) 575-6104
Web Site: http://www.vtmc.us
Year Founded: 1968
VTMC—(OTCIQ)
Financial Consulting Services
N.A.I.C.S.: 541611
Deepak Kavadia (CEO)

VALERO ENERGY CORPORATION
1 Valero Way, San Antonio, TX 78249
Tel.: (210) 345-2000   DE
Web Site: https://www.valero.com
Year Founded: 1980
VLO—(NYSE)
Rev.: $144,766,000,000
Assets: $63,056,000,000
Liabilities: $34,532,000,000

Net Worth: $28,524,000,000
Earnings: $8,835,000,000
Emp.: 9,908
Fiscal Year-end: 12/31/23
Petroleum Products Refiner & Marketer
N.A.I.C.S.: 324110
Eric Fisher (Sr VP-Wholesale Mktg & Intl Comml Ops)
Joseph W. Gorder (Chm)
R. Lane Riggs (Pres & CEO)
Gary K. Simmons (COO & Exec VP)
Rich Lashway (Sr VP-Corp Dev & Strategy)
Jason W. Fraser (CFO, Principal Acctg Officer & Exec VP)
Julia Rendon Reinhart (Chief HR Officer & Sr VP)
Greg Bram (VP-Supply Chain Optimization)
Homer Bhullar (VP-IR & Fin)
Eric Herbort (Dir-IR & Fin)
Gautam Srivastava (Dir-IR)
Lillian Riojas (Exec Dir-Media Rels & Comm)

Subsidiaries:

DIAMOND K RANCH LLC (1)
25668 Hwy 6, Hempstead, TX 77445
Tel.: (979) 571-7498
Web Site: https://diamondkshowcattle.com
Petrochemical Mfr
N.A.I.C.S.: 325110

DSRM National Bank (1)
5600 Wyoming Blvd NE Ste 275, Albuquerque, NM 87109
Tel.: (505) 883-5454
Emp.: 3
Federal Savings Bank
N.A.I.C.S.: 522180
Job Varro (CEO)

Diamond Alternative Energy, LLC (1)
1 Valero Way, San Antonio, TX 78249-1616
Tel.: (210) 345-2009
Emp.: 100
Oil & Gas Exploration Services
N.A.I.C.S.: 213112

EASTVIEW FUEL OILS LIMITED (1)
1494 Cyrville Rd, Ottawa, K1B 3L8, ON, Canada
Tel.: (613) 746-1784
Emp.: 6
Oil & Gas Exploration Services
N.A.I.C.S.: 213112

MAINLINE PIPELINES LIMITED (1)
11 Old Jewry 7th Floor, London, EC2R 8DU, United Kingdom
Tel.: (44) 14855200073
Pipeline Construction Services
N.A.I.C.S.: 238220

Oceanic Tankers Agency Ltd. (1)
4025 Saint Laurent St, Levis, G6B 8M8, QC, Canada
Tel.: (418) 833-3633   (100%)
Web Site: https://www.valero.com
Rev.: $130,798
Emp.: 9
Marine Cargo Handling
N.A.I.C.S.: 488320

SAINT BERNARD PROPERTIES COMPANY LLC (1)
3021 E 7th Ave Pkwy, Denver, CO 80206
Tel.: (303) 667-2801
Web Site: https://www.saintbernardproperties.com
Residential Building Development Services
N.A.I.C.S.: 531110

The Premcor Pipeline Co. (1)
1 Valero Way, San Antonio, TX 78249
Tel.: (210) 345-5145
Pipeline Oil Transportation Services
N.A.I.C.S.: 486910

Ultramar Energy Inc. (1)
19 Homer Ave Ste 2, Queensbury, NY 12804
Tel.: (518) 798-3035
Petroleum Consulting Services

N.A.I.C.S.: 541611
Chuck Bullard (VP)

Subsidiary (Non-US):

Canadian Ultramar Company (2)
705 Reeves St, Port Hawkesbury, B9A 2S2, NS, Canada
Tel.: (902) 625-3680
Web Site: https://www.ultramar.ca
Sales Range: $25-49.9 Million
Emp.: 1
Gasoline Services
N.A.I.C.S.: 457120

Ultramar Ltd. (2)
2200 Ave Mcgill College Ste 400, Montreal, H3A 3L3, QC, Canada   (100%)
Tel.: (514) 499-6111
Web Site: http://www.ultramar.ca
Sales Range: $250-299.9 Million
Emp.: 3,500
Fuel Oil Dealers
N.A.I.C.S.: 457210

VALERO ENERGY (IRELAND) LIMITED (1)
1st Floor Block B Liffey Valley Office Campus, Quarry vale, Dublin, Ireland
Tel.: (353) 1 625 8240
Web Site: https://www.texaco.ie
Lubricant Distr
N.A.I.C.S.: 424690

VALERO ENERGY INC. (1)
1801 McGill College Avenue 13th Floor, Montreal, H3A 2N4, QC, Canada
Web Site: https://www.valero.com
Emp.: 500
Crude Oil Refining & Distr
N.A.I.C.S.: 324191

VALERO ENERGY LTD (1)
1 Canada Square, Canary Wharf, London, E14 5AA, United Kingdom
Tel.: (44) 207 513 3737
Web Site: https://www.texaco.co.uk
Emp.: 770
Lubricant Distr
N.A.I.C.S.: 424690

VALERO EQUITY SERVICES LTD (1)
Westferry Circus 1, E14 4HA, London, United Kingdom - England
Tel.: (44) 2077193000
Oil & Gas Exploration Services
N.A.I.C.S.: 213112

VALERO MARKETING AND SUPPLY DE MEXICO S.A. DE C.V. (1)
Calle Pedregal 24 Colonia Molino del Rey, 11040, Mexico, Miguel Hidalgo, Mexico
Tel.: (52) 5586646000
Web Site: https://www.valero.com.mx
Petrochemical Mfr
N.A.I.C.S.: 325110

VALERO MARKETING IRELAND LIMITED (1)
1st Floor Block B Liffey Valley Office Campus, Quarryvale, Dublin, 11, Ireland
Tel.: (353) 1800788777
Web Site: https://www.texoil.valero.com
Emp.: 20
Lubricant Distr
N.A.I.C.S.: 424690

VALERO TERMINALING AND DISTRIBUTION DE MEXICO, S.A. DE C.V. (1)
Calle Pedregal 24 Colonia Molino del Rey, 11040, Mexico, Miguel Hidalgo, Mexico
Tel.: (52) 5586646000
Petrochemical Mfr
N.A.I.C.S.: 325110

Valero Energy Partners LP (1)
1 Valero Way, San Antonio, TX 78249   (100%)
Tel.: (210) 345-2000
Web Site: https://www.valeroenergypartners.com
Rev.: $546,427,000
Assets: $1,619,609,000
Liabilities: $1,320,906,000
Net Worth: $298,703,000
Earnings: $264,095,000
Fiscal Year-end: 12/31/2018
Oil & Gas Exploration

N.A.I.C.S.: 211120

Valero Marketing & Supply Company (1)
1 Valero Way, San Antonio, TX 78249   (100%)
Web Site: https://www.valero.com
Sales Range: $450-499.9 Million
Emp.: 10,000
Petroleum Refining & Marketing
N.A.I.C.S.: 486910

Valero Partners South Texas, LLC (1)
1 Valero Way, San Antonio, TX 78249
Tel.: (210) 370-5161
Petrochemical Products Mfr
N.A.I.C.S.: 324110

Subsidiary (Domestic):

Valero Refining-Texas, L.P. (2)
1301 Loop 197 S, Texas City, TX 77590
Tel.: (409) 945-4451
Web Site: https://www.valero.com
Emp.: 500
Petroleum Refinery Services
N.A.I.C.S.: 324110

Valero Peru S.A.C. (1)
Tel.: (51) 16169292
Web Site: https://www.pbf.com.pe
Fuel Product Distr
N.A.I.C.S.: 424720

Valero Refining Company-Aruba N.V. (1)
5 Lago Weg Seroe Colorado, San Nicolaas, Aruba
Tel.: (297) 8666350479
Web Site: http://www.valero.com
Petroleum Refinery Services
N.A.I.C.S.: 324110

Valero Refining Company-California (1)
3400 E 2nd St, Benicia, CA 94510-1097
Tel.: (707) 745-7011
Web Site: https://www.valero.com
Emp.: 450
Petroleum Refinery Services
N.A.I.C.S.: 324110

Valero Refining-Meraux LLC (1)
2235 Jacob Dr, Chalmette, LA 70043
Tel.: (504) 271-4141
Web Site: https://www.valero.com
Emp.: 260
Crude Oil Refining Services
N.A.I.C.S.: 324191

Valero Renewable Fuels Company, LLC (1)
1 Valero Way, San Antonio, TX 78249
Tel.: (210) 345-2000
Emp.: 235
Holding Company; Ethanol Refineries Operator
N.A.I.C.S.: 551112

Subsidiary (Domestic):

Green Plains Bluffton LLC (2)
1441 S Adams St, Bluffton, IN 46714
Tel.: (260) 353-1212
Emp.: 50
Methanol Mfr
N.A.I.C.S.: 325193

Valero Renewable Fuels Co., LLC - Albion (2)
2615 260th St, Albion, NE 68620
Tel.: (402) 395-3500
Web Site: https://www.valero.com
Sales Range: $25-49.9 Million
Emp.: 60
Methanol Mfr
N.A.I.C.S.: 325193

Plant (Domestic):

Valero Renewable Fuels Co., LLC - Aurora (2)
1 Valero Pl, Aurora, SD 57002
Tel.: (605) 693-6800
Web Site: http://www.valero.com

Sales Range: $25-49.9 Million
Emp.: 70
Methanol Mfr.
N.A.I.C.S.: 325193

**Valero Renewable Fuels Co., LLC -
Bloomingburg** (2)
3979 State Rte 38 NE, Bloomingburg, OH
43106
Tel.: (740) 437-6200
Web Site: http://www.valero.com
Sales Range: $25-49.9 Million
Emp.: 60
Methanol Mfr.
N.A.I.C.S.: 325193
Steven Schaeper *(Reg Mgr-Merchandising-
Bulk Rail Sls)*

Subsidiary (Domestic):

**Valero Renewable Fuels Co., LLC -
Charles City** (2)
1787 Quarry Rd, Charles City, IA 50516
Tel.: (641) 715-3000
Web Site: http://www.valero.com
Sales Range: $25-49.9 Million
Emp.: 70
Methanol Mfr.
N.A.I.C.S.: 325193

**Valero Renewable Fuels Co., LLC -
Fort Dodge** (2)
1930 Hayes Ave, Fort Dodge, IA 50501
Tel.: (515) 955-5000
Web Site: https://www.valero.com
Sales Range: $25-49.9 Million
Emp.: 65
Methanol Mfr.
N.A.I.C.S.: 325193

**Valero Renewable Fuels Co., LLC -
Hartley** (2)
3260 Van Buren Ave, Hartley, IA 51346
Tel.: (712) 928-5800
Web Site: https://www.valero.com
Sales Range: $25-49.9 Million
Emp.: 70
Methanol Mfr.
N.A.I.C.S.: 325193
Judd Hulting *(Reg Mgr-Bulk Rail Sls)*

**Valero Renewable Fuels Co., LLC -
Linden** (2)
203 W 1100 N, Linden, IN 47955
Tel.: (765) 522-3100
Web Site: https://www.valero.com
Sales Range: $25-49.9 Million
Emp.: 60
Methanol Mfr.
N.A.I.C.S.: 325193

**Valero Renewable Fuels Co., LLC -
Welcome** (2)
1444 120th St, Welcome, MN 56181
Tel.: (507) 728-4000
Web Site: https://www.valero.com
Sales Range: $25-49.9 Million
Emp.: 74
Methanol Mfr.
N.A.I.C.S.: 325193

**Valero Terminaling & Distribution
Company** (1)
1 Valero Way, San Antonio, TX 78249
Tel.: (210) 345-3450
Gasoline Station Operating & Distr.
N.A.I.C.S.: 457120

VALLEY NATIONAL BANCORP
1 Penn Plz, New York, NY 10119
Tel.: (973) 305-8800 **NJ**
Web Site: https://www.valley.com
Year Founded: 1927
VLY—(NASDAQ)
Rev.: $3,138,891,000
Assets: $60,934,974,000
Liabilities: $54,233,583,000
Net Worth: $6,701,391,000
Earnings: $482,376,000
Emp.: 3,749
Fiscal Year-end: 12/31/23
Commercial Banking Services
N.A.I.C.S.: 551111
Ira D. Robbins *(Chm, Pres & CEO)*
Mitchell L. Crandell *(Chief Acctg Offi-
cer & Exec VP)*

Avner Mendelson *(Vice Chm)*
Yvonne M. Surowiec *(Chief HR Offi-
cer & Sr Exec VP)*
Michael D. Hagedorn *(CFO & Sr
Exec VP)*

Subsidiaries:

Oritani Financial Corp. (1)
370 Pascack Rd, Washington, NJ 07676
Tel.: (201) 664-5400
Web Site: http://www.oritani.com
Rev.: $160,513,000
Assets: $4,070,516,000
Liabilities: $3,541,369,000
Net Worth: $529,147,000
Earnings: $52,059,000
Emp.: 189
Fiscal Year-end: 06/30/2019
Bank Holding Company
N.A.I.C.S.: 551111
Ann Marie Jetton *(Chief Acctg Officer & Sr
VP)*

Valley National Bank (1)
1445 Valley Rd, Wayne, NJ
07470-2089 **(100%)**
Tel.: (973) 305-8800
Web Site:
  http://www.valleynationalbank.com
Sales Range: $700-749.9 Million
Federal Savings Bank
N.A.I.C.S.: 522180
Alan David Eskow *(CFO & Sr Exec VP)*
Kevin Chittenden *(Chief Residential Lending
Officer & Exec VP)*
Ira D. Robbins *(Chm, Pres & CEO)*
Robert J. Bardusch *(COO & Sr Exec VP)*
Joseph V. Chillura *(Exec VP)*
Mark Fernandez *(CMO & Exec VP)*
Mike McCoy *(Pres-Manatee County)*
Darryl Weaver *(Pres-Market)*
Pat Curran *(Mgr-Market)*
Jeff Armstrong *(Sr VP)*
Sanjay Sidhwani *(Chief Data & Analytics
Officer)*
Russ Barrett *(Chief Transformation Officer &
Exec VP)*
Robert Danziger *(Mng Dir, Sr VP & Head-
Syndicated Fin)*
David Paulson *(Chief Banking Officer)*

Subsidiary (Domestic):

VNB New York, LLC (2)
275 Madison Ave, New York, NY 10016
Tel.: (212) 973-6616
Commercial Lending Services
N.A.I.C.S.: 522390
James G. Lawrence *(Pres)*

VALMIE RESOURCES, INC.
2603 Augusta Dr Ste 840, Houston,
TX 77077
Tel.: (713) 595-6675 **NV**
Web Site: http://valmie.com
Year Founded: 2011
VMRI—(OTCIQ)
Software Publisher
N.A.I.C.S.: 513210
Gerald B. Hammack *(Chm, Pres,
CEO, CFO, Principal Acctg Officer,
Treas & Sec)*

VALMONT INDUSTRIES, INC.
15000 Valmont Plz, Omaha, NE
68154
Tel.: (402) 963-1000 **DE**
Web Site: https://www.valmont.com
Year Founded: 1946
VMI—(NYSE)
Rev.: $4,174,598,000
Assets: $3,477,448,000
Liabilities: $2,123,168,000
Net Worth: $1,354,280,000
Earnings: $150,849,000
Emp.: 11,125
Fiscal Year-end: 12/30/23
Industrial Machinery & Mining Equip-
ment Whslr
N.A.I.C.S.: 423830
Timothy P. Francis *(Chief Acctg Offi-
cer)*
Ellen S. Dasher *(VP-Taxation-Global)*

R. Andrew Massey *(Chief Legal &
Compliance Officer & VP)*
Claudio O. Laterreur *(CIO & Sr VP-
IT)*
Avner M. Applbaum *(Pres & CEO)*
Diane Larkin *(Exec VP-Ops-Global)*
Eugene Padgett *(Chief Acctg Officer
& Sr VP-Fin)*
Thomas Liguori *(CFO & Exec VP)*

Subsidiaries:

AgSense, LLC (1)
259 S Dakota Ave S, Huron, SD
57350-1910 **(51%)**
Tel.: (605) 352-8350
Web Site: https://www.agsense.com
Industrial Machinery Mfr.
N.A.I.C.S.: 333248
Andy Carritt *(Gen Mgr)*
Steel Maloney *(VP-Global Technical Sls)*
Steve Sveum *(Dir-Technical Sls-Intl)*
Michael Meyer *(Dir-Engineering)*
Brent Tebay *(Dir-Operations)*

Aircon Guardrails Private Limited (1)
No 69/ A2 Lonavla Industrial Estate Nangar-
gaon, Lonavla Tal Maval Nangargaon,
Pune, 410401, India
Tel.: (91) 8048757787
Web Site: http://www.indiamart.com
Fabricated Structural Metal Mfr.
N.A.I.C.S.: 332312

American Galvanizing (1)
1919 12th St, Williamstown, NJ 08094
Tel.: (609) 567-2090
Fabricated Structural Metal Mfr.
N.A.I.C.S.: 332312

Armorflex International Limited (1)
8 Paul Matthews Rd North Harbour Indus-
trial Estate North Harbour, PO Box 303177,
0632, Auckland, New Zealand
Tel.: (64) 94152991
Web Site: http://www.armorflex.co.nz
Industrial Machinery Mfr.
N.A.I.C.S.: 333248

Convert Italia S.p.A. (1)
Via Del Serafico 200, 00142, Rome, Italy
Tel.: (39) 06510611219
Web Site: http://www.convertitalia.com
Solar Equipment Mfr.
N.A.I.C.S.: 335131
Anna Maria De pretis *(Chief Administrator
Officer-Finance)*
Marco de Cataldo *(Chief Technical & Ops
Officer)*
Matteo Demofonti *(Chief Sls Officer-EMEA)*
Antonio Timidei *(Head-Research & Devel-
opment)*
Sandro Pizzuto *(Head-Project Engineering)*
Leonardo Spaccavento *(Head)*
Alberto Alatri *(CFO)*
Leonardo Spaccavento *(Head)*
Alberto Alatri *(CFO)*

Cutting Edges Pty. Ltd. (1)
25B1 Violet St, Revesby, 2212, NSW, Aus-
tralia
Tel.: (61) 297383270
Web Site: https://www.cuttingedges.com
Sales Range: $25-49.9 Million
Emp.: 50
Construction Machinery Parts Mfr.
N.A.I.C.S.: 333120
Richard Andrews *(CEO)*

Donhad Pty. Ltd. (1)
18-22 Jackson Street, Bassendean, 6054,
WA, Australia **(100%)**
Tel.: (61) 892700100
Web Site: http://www.donhad.com.au
Sales Range: $25-49.9 Million
Emp.: 150
Metal Grinding & Finishing Services
N.A.I.C.S.: 332813
Oscar Vasquez *(Mgr-Technical Sls-West
Coast)*
Paul Quan *(Mgr-East Coast)*

George Industries, Inc. (1)
4116 Whiteside St, Los Angeles, CA 90063
Tel.: (323) 264-6660
Web Site: https://www.valmontcoatings.com
Metal Coating Engraving & Allied Services
N.A.I.C.S.: 332812

**IGC-Industrial Galvanizers Corpora-
tion (M) Sdn. Bhd.** (1)
No 866 Jalan Subang 8 Taman Perindus-
trian Subang, 47600, Subang Jaya, Selan-
gor, Malaysia
Tel.: (60) 380239093
Web Site: https://www.valmontcoatings.com
Galvanized Products & Services
N.A.I.C.S.: 327999

**Industrial Galvanizers America Hold-
ings, Inc.** (1)
3535 Halifax Rd, Petersburg, VA 23805
Tel.: (804) 733-0808
Investment Management Service
N.A.I.C.S.: 551112

**Industrial Galvanizers America,
Inc** (1)
3535 Halifax Rd, Petersburg, VA 23805
Tel.: (804) 733-0808
Web Site: http://www.valmontcoatings.com
Metal Galvanizing Services
N.A.I.C.S.: 332812

**Industrial Galvanizers Corporation
Pty. Ltd.** (1)
Cnr Curtin Ave & Holt St, Pinkenba, 4008,
QLD, Australia
Tel.: (61) 736327700
Metal Galvanizing Services
N.A.I.C.S.: 332812

**Industrial Galvanizers Corporation of
the Philippines Inc.** (1)
RM 73 RCI Building 105 Rada Street, Le-
gaspi Village, Makati, Philippines
Tel.: (63) 2 752 5840
Web Site: http://www.asia.indgalv.com.au
Metal Galvanizing Services
N.A.I.C.S.: 332215

Ingal Civil Products Pty. Ltd. (1)
57-65 Airds Road, Minto, 2566, NSW, Aus-
tralia
Tel.: (61) 298273333
Web Site: https://www.ingalcivil.com.au
Emp.: 100
Safety Barrier Systems Mfr.
N.A.I.C.S.: 488490
John Dignam *(Mng Dir)*

Ingal EPS (1)
77 Parramatta Rd, Underwood, 4119, QLD,
Australia
Tel.: (61) 300748377
Web Site: https://www.ingaleps.com.au
Power Transmission, Distribution, Telecom-
munications & Lighting Poles Mfr.
N.A.I.C.S.: 335132

**Investment Tooling International
Limited** (1)
4A Moston Road Middleton Junction, Man-
chester, M24 1SL, Nottinghamshire, United
Kingdom **(100%)**
Tel.: (44) 1616538066
Web Site: https://www.iti-manchester.co.uk
Sales Range: $25-49.9 Million
Emp.: 40
Machine Tools Mfr.
N.A.I.C.S.: 333517

Locker Group Holdings Pty. Ltd. (1)
2 Cojo Place, Melbourne, 3175, VIC, Aus-
tralia
Tel.: (61) 387911000
Web Site: https://www.locker.com.au
Emp.: 309
Holding Company
N.A.I.C.S.: 551112

Machin & Ewin Pty. Ltd. (1)
Corner Mars & Sirius, Lane Cove, 2066,
NSW, Australia **(100%)**
Tel.: (61) 294270044
Web Site: http://www.machinewen.com.au
Sales Range: $25-49.9 Million
Emp.: 30
Fastener Mfr.
N.A.I.C.S.: 339993

Manganese Metal Co. (Pty.) Ltd. (1)
15 Heynecke Street Industrial Area, PO Box
323, Mbombela, 1200, South
Africa **(49%)**
Tel.: (27) 137594600
Web Site: https://www.mmc.co.za
Sales Range: $200-249.9 Million
Emp.: 400
Magnesium Metal Mfr.

Valmont Industries, Inc.—(Continued)

N.A.I.C.S.: 212230
Madelein Todd (Chief Mktg Officer)
Attie Ackerman (Mgr-Supply Chain)
Imraan Khan (Mgr-Sls)
Renet Mentz (Mgr-Human Resources)
Keneiloe Phomane (Mgr-Compliance)

Matco Services, Inc.   (1)
100 Business Ctr Dr, Pittsburgh, PA 15205
Tel.: (412) 788-1263
Web Site: http://www.matcoinc.com
Sales Range: $25-49.9 Million
Emp.: 12
Failure Analyzing Services
N.A.I.C.S.: 541990

Matco Sevices, Inc.   (1)
28800 Ida St, Valley, NE 68064
Tel.: (402) 359-2201
Web Site: http://www.matcoinc.com
Industrial Machinery Mfr
N.A.I.C.S.: 333248

PivoTrac   (1)
201 Woodland Park Dr, Dalhart, TX 79022
Tel.: (806) 244-2298
Web Site: https://pivotrac.com
Agricultural Services
N.A.I.C.S.: 115116

Pure Metal Galvanizing, ULC   (1)
7470 Bren Road, Mississauga, L4T 1H4,
ON, Canada
Tel.: (905) 677-7491
Web Site: http://www.puremetal.com
Metal Galvanizing Services
N.A.I.C.S.: 332812

Stainton Metal Co, Ltd.   (1)
Dukesway, Teesside Industrial Estate,
Stockton-on-Tees, TS17 9LT, United King-
dom
Tel.: (44) 1642766242
Web Site: http://www.valmont-stainton.com
Metal Products Mfr
N.A.I.C.S.: 332999

Tehomet Oy   (1)
Nikkarintie 4, 51200, Kangasniemi, Finland
Tel.: (358) 153377770
Web Site: https://www.tehomet.com
Emp.: 65
Lighting Equipment Mfr
N.A.I.C.S.: 335139
Marko Takkinen (Mgr-Production)
Pentti Kettunen (Chm)
Sami Hamalainen (Mgr-Sls-Wooden Poles)
Sami Lukkarinen (Dir-Sls)
Tomi Pasanen (Dir-Ops)
Tuulikki Manninen (Mgr-Finance & Control-
ler)
Marko Myyryiainen (Mgr-Sls)
Jukka Turunen (Mgr-Sales-Special Projects-
Exports)
Mart Martin (Mgr-Sls-Baltics)
Sami Huuskonen (Mgr-Design)
Jussi Saarimaki (Sys Engr)
Jari Aalto (Engr-Design)
Reio Rahumagi (Mgr)
Mikael Sepponen (Mgr-Production-Wooden
Poles Production)
Jani Pylvanainen (Mgr-Production)
Paula Himanen (Accountant)

United Galvanizing, Inc.   (1)
6123 Cunningham Rd, Houston, TX 77041
Tel.: (713) 466-4161
Web Site: https://www.valmontcoatings.com
Metal Coating, Engraving (except Jewelry &
Silverware) & Allied Services to Mfr
N.A.I.C.S.: 332812

Valmont   (1)
801 N Xanthus Ave, Tulsa, OK
74110   (100%)
Tel.: (918) 583-5881
Sales Range: $125-149.9 Million
Emp.: 300
Mfr of Steel Poles
N.A.I.C.S.: 332312
Roger Snavely (Reg VP-Ops)
John Mulvey (Gen Mgr)

Valmont Australia Irrigation Pty.
Ltd.   (1)
30 Acanthus Street, Darra, 4076, QLD, Australia
Tel.: (61) 73 457 8830

Web Site: https://www.valley-au.com
Water Food & Fuel Supply Protection Ser-
vices
N.A.I.C.S.: 561990

Valmont Coatings Inc   (1)
2301 Bridgeport Dr, Sioux City, IA
51111   (100%)
Tel.: (712) 252-4101
Web Site: http://www.valmont.com
Sales Range: $25-49.9 Million
Emp.: 25
Mfr of Galvanizer
N.A.I.C.S.: 333519

Valmont Coatings West Point
Galvanizing   (1)
1700 S Beemer St, West Point, NE 68788
Tel.: (402) 372-3706
Web Site: https://www.valmontcoatings.com
Sales Range: $25-49.9 Million
Emp.: 80
Metal Coating, Engraving, except Jewelry &
Silverware & Allied Services to Manufactur-
ers
N.A.I.C.S.: 332812

Valmont Composite Structures,
Inc.   (1)
19845 US Hwy 76, Newberry, SC 29108
Tel.: (803) 276-5504
Web Site: https://www.skp-cs.com
Emp.: 200
Fiberglass Reinforced Composite Pole De-
signer & Mfr
N.A.I.C.S.: 335132

Subsidiary (Domestic):

Carsonite   (2)
19845 US Hwy 76, Newberry, SC 29108
Tel.: (803) 321-1185
Web Site: https://www.carsonite.com
Sales Range: $10-24.9 Million
Highway Safety Marker Products & High-
way Sound Barriers Mfr
N.A.I.C.S.: 326199

Valmont France S.A.   (1)
Les Martoulets, BP 01, 03110, Charmeil,
France   (100%)
Tel.: (33) 470588686
Web Site: https://www.valmont-france.com
Sales Range: $75-99.9 Million
Emp.: 300
Mfr & Distributor of Lighting Standards
N.A.I.C.S.: 335139

Valmont Industria e Comercio,
Ltda.   (1)
Av Francisco Podboy 1600, Uberaba,
38056-640, Minas Gerais, Brazil
Tel.: (55) 343 318 9000
Web Site: https://www.valleyirrigation.com.br
Water Conserving Irrigation Equipment Mfr
N.A.I.C.S.: 335139

Valmont Industries Holland B.V.   (1)
Den Engelsman 3, 6026 RB, Maarheeze,
Netherlands
Tel.: (31) 495599959
Web Site: http://www.valmont.nl
Sales Range: $25-49.9 Million
Emp.: 50
Light Pole & Structural Metal Mfr
N.A.I.C.S.: 335139

Valmont International Corp.   (1)
2105 Mannix Dr, San Antonio, TX 78217
Tel.: (210) 829-7971
Sales Range: $10-24.9 Million
Emp.: 20
Iron & Steel Pipe Mfr
N.A.I.C.S.: 331210
Mark Ellis (COO)

Valmont Irrigation Division   (1)
28800 Ida St, Valley, NE 68064
Tel.: (402) 359-2201
Web Site: http://www.valleyirrigation.com
Sales Range: $450-499.9 Million
Emp.: 1,500
Mfr & Retailing of Center Pivot & Linear
Move Irrigation Systems
N.A.I.C.S.: 333111
Mogens C. Bay (Chm & CEO)
Leonard Adams (Pres-Irrigation-Global)

Valmont Nederland B.V.   (1)

Den Engelsman 3, 6026 RB, Maarheeze,
Netherlands   (100%)
Tel.: (31) 495599959
Web Site: https://www.valmont.nl
Sales Range: $10-24.9 Million
Emp.: 100
Steel Reinforcing Bar Fabrication
N.A.I.C.S.: 238120

Valmont Newmark, Inc.   (1)
225 Kiwanis Blvd, West Hazleton, PA 18202
Tel.: (570) 454-8730
Lighting Equipment Mfr
N.A.I.C.S.: 335139

Valmont Northwest   (1)
4225 N Capitol Ave, Pasco, WA 99301
Tel.: (509) 547-1623
Web Site: http://www.valmontnorthwest.com
Sales Range: $25-49.9 Million
Emp.: 60
Selling Irrigation Circles
N.A.I.C.S.: 333111
Tyler Casper (Gen Mgr-Interim)
Gerry Tyhuis (Mgr-Parts)
Matt Peterson (Mgr-Svc, Electrical & Weld-
ing)
John Salisbury (Mgr-Installation)
Adelia Boyd (Mgr-Store-Basin City)

Valmont Polska Sp.z o.o   (1)
ul Majora Henryka Sucharskiego 6, 08-110,
Siedlce, Poland
Tel.: (48) 256430400
Web Site: https://www.valmont.pl
Emp.: 100
Industrial Machinery Mfr
N.A.I.C.S.: 333248
Tomasz Biel (Mgr-Bus Unit)
Arkadiusz Bajor (Mgr-Sls-Decorative Poles
& Traffic Poles)
Lukasz Koksa (Mgr-Supply Chain-Pur Dept)
Tomasz Zajac (Product Mgr-Product Devel-
opment)
Przemyslaw Plusa (Mgr-Sls-Tramway Poles
& Accessories)
Mariusz Balabuch (Mgr-Sales-Utility Poles)
Lukasz Medza (Project Mgr-
Telecommunications-High Masts,Tramway
Poles,Utility Poles)
Michal Hanisch (Mgr-Telecom Towers)
Adrian Peski (Sys Engr-Sales)
Aneta Wierzchowska (Project Mgr)
Adrian Peski (Sys Engr-Sales)
Aneta Wierzchowska (Project Mgr)

Valmont Stainton Ltd.   (1)
Dukesway Teesside Industrial Estate,
Thornaby, Stockton-on-Tees, TS17 9LT,
United Kingdom
Tel.: (44) 1642766242
Web Site: http://www.stainton-metal.co.uk
Sales Range: 325-49.9 Million
Emp.: 150
Lighting Equipment Mfr
N.A.I.C.S.: 335139

Valmont Structures Private
Limited   (1)
Unit 203 2nd Floor Pentagon IV Magarap-
pata Hadapsar, Pune, 411028, Maharash-
tra, India
Tel.: (91) 206 666 4141
Web Site: https://www.valmont.in
Metal Structures & Parts Whslr
N.A.I.C.S.: 423830
Dan Witt (VP-Bus Dev)
Ann M. Blaya-Arena (Bus Partner & VP)

Webforge Australia Pty Ltd.   (1)
2 Cojo Place, Dandenong South, 3175,
VIC, Australia
Tel.: (61) 800635947
Web Site: https://www.webforge.com.au
Sales Range: $400-449.9 Million
Emp.: 1,000
Grating, Flooring, Hand Rails, Barriers,
Sunscreens, Drainage Gates & Access
Covers Mfr
N.A.I.C.S.: 423320

West Coast Engineering, Inc   (1)
6823 Northgate Way, Ferndale, WA 98248
Tel.: (360) 525-9026
Web Site: http://www.wceng.com
Sales Range: $10-24.9 Million
Emp.: 16
Steel & Aluminum Pole Mfr
N.A.I.C.S.: 332999

**VALOR LATITUDE ACQUISI-
TION CORP.**
10 E 53rd St, New York, NY 10022
Tel.: (212) 803-7170   KY
Year Founded: 2021
VLAT—(NASDAQ)
Rev.: $10,424,733
Assets: $233,582,264
Liabilities: $242,618,496
Net Worth: ($9,036,232)
Earnings: $8,974,318
Emp.: 2
Fiscal Year-end: 12/31/22
Investment Services
N.A.I.C.S.: 523999
Mario Mello Freire Neto (CEO)
J. Douglas Smith (CFO)
Clifford M. Sobel (Chm)

VALVOLINE INC.
100 Valvoline Way Ste 100, Lexing-
ton, KY 40509
Tel.: (859) 357-7777   KY
Year Founded: 2016
VVV—(NYSE)
Rev.: $1,443,500,000
Assets: $2,889,900,000
Liabilities: $2,686,700,000
Net Worth: $203,200,000
Earnings: $1,419,700,000
Emp.: 9,600
Fiscal Year-end: 09/30/23
Holding Company; Oil Change & Au-
tomotive Maintenance Shops Opera-
tor & Franchisor
N.A.I.C.S.: 551112
Lori A. Flees (CEO)

Subsidiaries:

Relocation Properties Management
LLC   (1)
500 Diederich Blvd, Russell, KY 41169
Tel.: (606) 329-4663
Commercial Property Management Services
N.A.I.C.S.: 531312

Valvoline Instant Oil Change Fran-
chising, Inc.   (1)
3499 Blazer Pkwy, Lexington, KY 40509-
1850
Tel.: (859) 357-7100
Web Site: https://www.vioc.com
Oil Change & Automotive Maintenance
Shop Franchisor
N.A.I.C.S.: 533110

Valvoline LLC   (1)
100 Valvoline Way, Lexington, KY 40509
Tel.: (859) 357-7777
Oil Change & Automotive Maintenance
Shop Operator
N.A.I.C.S.: 811191

**VANDA PHARMACEUTICALS
INC.**
2200 Pennsylvania Ave NW Ste
300E, Washington, DC 20037
Tel.: (202) 734-3400   DE
Web Site:
https://www.vandapharma.com
Year Founded: 2003
VNDA—(NASDAQ)
Rev.: $192,640,000
Assets: $648,440,000
Liabilities: $103,530,000
Net Worth: $544,910,000
Earnings: $2,509,000
Emp.: 203
Fiscal Year-end: 12/31/23
Biopharmaceuticals Developer & Mfr
N.A.I.C.S.: 325412
Mihael H. Polymeropoulos (Chm,
Pres & CEO)
Deepak Phadke (VP-Mfg)
Gunther Birznieks (Sr VP-Bus Dev)
H. Thomas Watkins (Executives)
Timothy Williams (Gen Counsel, Sec
& Sr VP)

Joakim Wijkstrom *(CMO & Sr VP)*
Kevin Moran *(CFO, Treas & Sr VP)*
Scott Howell *(Chief People Officer)*

Subsidiaries:

Vanda Pharmaceuticals Germany
GmbH **(1)**
Franzosische Strasse 12, 10117, Berlin,
Germany
Tel.: (49) 3020188401
Pharmaceutical Preparation Mfr
N.A.I.C.S.: 325412

Vanda Pharmaceuticals Limited **(1)**
Tower 42 21st Floor 21A 25 Old Broad
Street, London, EC2N 1HN, United King-
dom
Tel.: (44) 2030583981
Biopharmaceutical Technology Services
N.A.I.C.S.: 541714

VANECK MERK GOLD TRUST

2 Hanson Pl, Brooklyn, NY 11217
Tel.: (650) 323-4341   NY
Web Site: https://www.merkgold.com
OUNZ—(NYSA)
Assets: $660,323,516
Liabilities: $3,730,718
Net Worth: $656,592,798
Earnings: ($1,557,794)
Fiscal Year-end: 01/31/23
Investment Services
N.A.I.C.S.: 523999

VANJIA CORPORATION

4771 Sweetwater Blvd Unit 199,
Sugar Land, TX 77479
Tel.: (832) 289-3209   TX
Year Founded: 2011
VNJA—(OTCQB)
Rev.: $82,720
Assets: $833,553
Net Worth: $833,553
Earnings: $73,419
Fiscal Year-end: 12/31/23
Residential Construction
N.A.I.C.S.: 236117
Tian Su Hua *(CEO & CFO)*

VANTAGE DRILLING COM-
PANY

777 Post Oak Blvd Ste 800, Houston,
TX 77056
Tel.: (281) 404-4700   Ky
Web Site:
http://www.vantagedrilling.com
Year Founded: 2007
VTGDF—(OTCIQ)
Sales Range: $800-899.9 Million
Emp.: 1,295
Holding Company; Oil & Gas Well
Drilling Services
N.A.I.C.S.: 551112
Thomas Robert Bates Jr. *(Chm)*
Douglas W. Halkett *(COO)*
Bill Thomson *(VP-Mktg & Bus Dev)*
Ihab Toma *(CEO)*
Tom Cimino *(CFO)*
Wayne Bauer *(Dir-QHSE)*

Subsidiaries:

Vantage Delaware Holdings LLC **(1)**
160 Greentree Dr Ste 101, Dover, DE
19904
Tel.: (281) 404-4700
Holding Company
N.A.I.C.S.: 551112

Vantage Energy Services, Inc. **(1)**
777 Post Oak Blvd Ste 800, Houston, TX
77056
Tel.: (281) 404-4700
Web Site: http://www.vantagedrilling.com
Sales Range: $50-74.9 Million
Emp.: 60
Oil & Gas Well Drilling Services
N.A.I.C.S.: 213111
Tom Bates *(Chm)*

Vantage International Management
Company Pte Ltd **(1)**
1 Jalan Kilang Timor Pacific Tech Centre
07-01, Singapore, 159303, Singapore
Tel.: (65) 65770270
Sales Range: $75-99.9 Million
Emp.: 100
Oil Well Drilling Services
N.A.I.C.S.: 213111

VANTAGE DRILLING INTER-
NATIONAL

777 Post Oak Blvd Ste 440, Houston,
TX 77056
Tel.: (281) 404-4700   Ky
Web Site:
http://www.vantagedrilling.com
VTDRF—(OTCIQ)
Rev.: $278,716,000
Assets: $578,561,000
Liabilities: $316,062,000
Net Worth: $262,499,000
Earnings: ($3,355,000)
Emp.: 900
Fiscal Year-end: 12/31/22
Oil & Gas Field Drilling Services
N.A.I.C.S.: 213111
Thomas Robert Bates Jr. *(Chm)*
Linda J. Ibrahim *(Chief Acctg Officer
& VP-Tax & Governmental Compli-
ance)*
Ihab Toma *(CEO)*
Douglas E. Stewart *(Chief Compli-
ance Officer, Gen Counsel & Sec)*

VAPOR HUB INTERNATIONAL
INC.

1871 Tapo St, Simi Valley, CA 93063
Tel.: (805) 309-0530   NV
Web Site: http://www.vapor-hub.com
Year Founded: 2010
VHUB—(OTCIQ)
Sales Range: $1-9.9 Million
Emp.: 22
Electronic Cigarette Products Mfr &
Sales
N.A.I.C.S.: 424940
Lori Winther *(CFO, Treas & Sec)*
Gary Jacob Perlingos *(Pres & CTO)*

VAPORBRANDS INTERNA-
TIONAL, INC.

15812 116th Ave NE, Bothell, WA
98011
Tel.: (206) 579-0222   NV
Web Site: https://ecitemotors.com
Year Founded: 1999
VAPR—(OTCIQ)
Electronic Cigarette Mfr & Distr
N.A.I.C.S.: 312230
Gene Langmesser *(COO)*
Barry Brian Henthorn *(CEO)*

VAREX IMAGING CORPORA-
TION

1678 S Pioneer Rd, Salt Lake City,
UT 84104
Tel.: (801) 972-5000   DE
Web Site:
https://www.vareximaging.com
Year Founded: 2017
VREX—(NASDAQ)
Rev.: $811,000,000
Assets: $1,217,000,000
Liabilities: $667,800,000
Net Worth: $549,200,000
Earnings: ($47,200,000)
Emp.: 2,300
Fiscal Year-end: 09/27/24
Offices of Other Holding Companies
N.A.I.C.S.: 551112
Sunny S. Sanyal *(Pres & CEO)*
Kimberley E. Honeysett *(Gen Coun-
sel, Sec & Sr VP)*
Ruediger Naumann-Etienne *(Chm)*
Chad Holman *(Chief HR Officer &
VP)*

Andrew Hartmann *(Sr VP-Medical
Global Sls & Mktg)*
Carl LaCasce *(Sr VP & Gen Mgr-
Industrial Imaging)*
Mark S. Jonaitis *(Sr VP & Gen Mgr-
X-Ray Sources)*
Shaohua Liang *(Mng Dir-China & VP)*
Victor Garcia *(VP-Regulatory & Qual-
ity Compliance)*
Shubham Maheshwari *(CFO & Princi-
pal Acctg Officer)*
Marcus Kirchhoff *(VP & Gen Mgr-
Software Solutions)*
Wouter Vlaanderen *(VP & Gen Mgr-
Connect & Control Solutions)*
Christopher Belfiore *(Dir-IR)*
Andrew Hartmann *(Sr VP & Gen Mgr-
X-ray Detectors)*
Stephen Devita *(Sr VP)*

Subsidiaries:

Direct Conversion AB **(1)**
Svardvagen 23, SE-182 33, Danderyd,
Sweden **(97.4%)**
Tel.: (46) 86222300
Web Site: http://directconversion.com
Rev.: $18,182,742
Assets: $26,327,038
Liabilities: $8,880,125
Net Worth: $17,446,913
Earnings: $2,595,150
Emp.: 69
Fiscal Year-end: 12/31/2018
X-ray Imaging Equipment Developer
N.A.I.C.S.: 334510

Direct Conversion GmbH **(1)**
Lochhamer Schlag 10, Grafelfing, 82166,
Munich, Germany
Tel.: (49) 8928912550
Medical Therapeutic Equipment Mfr
N.A.I.C.S.: 334517

PerkinElmer Medical Imaging,
LLC **(1)**
2175 Mission College Blvd, Santa Clara,
CA 95054
Tel.: (408) 565-0850
Digital Detectors Mfr & Developer
N.A.I.C.S.: 621512

Varex Imaging Equipment (China)
Co., Ltd. **(1)**
Building G No 30 Wanquan Road, Plainvim
Internation Industry Park Xishan District,
Wuxi, 214100, China
Tel.: (86) 51085929201
Medical Therapeutic Equipment Mfr
N.A.I.C.S.: 334517

Varex Imaging Holdings, Inc, **(1)**
1678 S Pioneer Rd, Salt Lake City, UT
84104-4205 **(100%)**
Tel.: (801) 972-5000
Web Site: http://www.vareximaging.com
Holding Company; X-Ray Tubes, Cavity
Amplifiers & Amorphous Silicon Based Im-
aging Systems Designer, Mfr 7 Whslr
N.A.I.C.S.: 551112

Subsidiary (Non-US):

Claymount Assemblies Philippines,
Inc. **(2)**
Buildings 9 10 & 11 Harvard Avenue EZP
Business Park, Calamba Premiere Interna-
tional Park Special Economic Zone Batino,
Calamba, 4027, Laguna, Philippines
Tel.: (63) 495024520
X-ray Imaging Equipment Whslr
N.A.I.C.S.: 423450

Claymount High Voltage Technologies
(Beijing) Co. Ltd. **(2)**
Building 3 No 1A Disheng S Street Suite
C601, Beijing Economic & Technological
Development Area, Beijing, 100176, China
Tel.: (86) 1067802708
X-ray Imaging High Voltage Connection
Components Mfr & Whslr
N.A.I.C.S.: 334517

Claymount Switzerland AG **(2)**
Wassergrabe 14, 6210, Sursee, Switzerland
Tel.: (41) 419214126

X-ray Imaging Components Designer &
Whslr
N.A.I.C.S.: 334517

Subsidiary (Domestic):

Varex Imaging Americas
Corporation **(2)**
1678 S Pioneer Rd, Salt Lake City, UT
84104
Tel.: (801) 972-5000
Web Site: http://www.vareximaging.com
X-ray Imaging Components Designer, Mfr &
Whslr
N.A.I.C.S.: 334517

Subsidiary (Non-US):

Varex Imaging Nederland B.V. **(2)**
Anholtseweg 44, Dinxperlo, 7091 HB,
Aalten, Netherlands
Tel.: (31) 315659150
X-ray Imaging Equipment Whslr
N.A.I.C.S.: 423450

Varex Imaging Italia Srl **(1)**
Viale Oriano 6, 24047, Treviglio, BG, Italy
Tel.: (39) 036345393
Medical Therapeutic Equipment Mfr
N.A.I.C.S.: 334517

Varex Imaging Japan, K.K. **(1)**
7F Chichibu Building 1-8-6 Shinkawa,
Chuo-ku, Tokyo, 104-0033, Japan
Tel.: (81) 344865070
Medical Therapeutic Equipment Mfr
N.A.I.C.S.: 334517

Varex Imaging Philippines, Inc. **(1)**
Buildings 9 10 and 11 Harvard Avenue EZP
Business Park, Calamba Premiere Interna-
tional Park Special Economic Zone Batino,
Calamba, 4027, Laguna, Philippines
Tel.: (63) 495024520
Medical Therapeutic Equipment Mfr
N.A.I.C.S.: 334517

Virtual Media Integration, LLC **(1)**
5001 Commerce Park Cir, Pensacola, FL
32505
Tel.: (850) 432-0355
Web Site: https://www.vmindt.com
Digital Radiography Equipment Distr
N.A.I.C.S.: 423690

VARONIS SYSTEMS INC.

1250 Broadway 28th Fl, New York,
NY 10001
Tel.: (919) 701-3300   DE
Web Site: https://www.varonis.com
Year Founded: 2004
VRNS—(NASDAQ)
Rev.: $499,160,000
Assets: $1,103,910,000
Liabilities: $614,262,000
Net Worth: $489,648,000
Earnings: ($100,916,000)
Emp.: 2,233
Fiscal Year-end: 12/31/23
Software Developer
N.A.I.C.S.: 513210
James O'Boyle *(Vice Chm-Sls)*
Gilad Raz *(CIO & VP)*
David Bass *(CTO & Exec VP-Engrg)*
Guy Melamed *(CFO & COO)*
Dana Shahar *(Chief HR Officer)*
Yzhar Kayser *(Chief Architect)*
Yuval Meidar *(Gen Counsel)*
Greg Pomeroy *(Sr VP-Worldwide Sls)*
Aaron Beveridge *(VP-Worldwide Sls
Engrg)*
Sagiv Elmaleh *(VP-Engrg)*
Rob Sobers *(CMO)*
Dov Gottlieb *(Gen Counsel)*
Tim Perz *(Dir)*
Yakov Faitelson *(Co-Founder, Chm,
Pres & CEO)*
Ohad Korkus *(Co-Founder)*

Subsidiaries:

Varonis Systems (Australia) Pty
Ltd **(1)**
Level 7 276 Flinders Street, Melbourne,
3000, VIC, Australia

Varonis Systems Inc.—(Continued)

Tel.: (61) 272088060
Software Development Services
N.A.I.C.S.: 541511

Varonis Systems (Ireland)
Limited **(1)**
Penrose Two Penrose Dock, Cork, T23
YY09, Ireland
Tel.: (353) 212063666
Software Development Services
N.A.I.C.S.: 541511

Varonis Systems (Netherlands)
B.V. **(1)**
Saturnusstraat 46-62, 2132 HB, Hoofddorp,
Netherlands
Tel.: (31) 203082100
Cyber Security Services
N.A.I.C.S.: 561621

VARTECH SYSTEMS, INC.
11422 Industriplex Blvd, Baton
Rouge, LA 70809
Tel.: (225) 298-0300 CO
Web Site:
https://www.vartechsystems.com
Year Founded: 1988
VRTK—(OTCIQ)
Other Electronic Component Manu-
facturing
N.A.I.C.S.: 334419
Fred Goodspeed *(Mgr-Online Mktg)*

VASAMED, INC.
7615 Golden Triangle Dr Ste A, Min-
neapolis, MN 55344-3733
Tel.: (952) 944-5857 DE
Web Site: http://www.vasamed.com
Year Founded: 1989
VSMD—(OTCIQ)
Surgical & Medical Instrument Mfr
N.A.I.C.S.: 339112
Paulita M. LaPlante *(Pres & CEO)*
John Campbell *(VP-Sls & Mktg)*
Chanda Wampler *(Controller)*

VASO CORPORATION
137 Commercial St Unit 200, Plain-
view, NY 11803
Tel.: (516) 997-4600 DE
Web Site:
https://www.vasocorporation.com
Year Founded: 1987
VASO—(OTCQB)
Rev.: $80,017,000
Assets: $72,655,000
Liabilities: $49,780,000
Net Worth: $22,875,000
Earnings: $11,873,000
Emp.: 272
Fiscal Year-end: 12/31/22
Medical Devices & Diagnostic Imag-
ing Products Design, Mfr & Sales
N.A.I.C.S.: 334510
Peter C. Castle *(COO & Pres-
VasoTechnology & NetWolves)*
Jun Ma *(Pres & CEO)*
Jonathan P. Newton *(Treas & Con-
troller)*
David H. Lieberman *(Vice Chm)*
Joshua L. Markowitz *(Chm)*
Michael J. Beecher *(CFO & Sec)*

Subsidiaries:

NetWolves, LLC **(1)**
4710 Eisenhower Blvd Ste E-8, Tampa, FL
33634-6337
Tel.: (813) 579-3200
Web Site: https://www.netwolves.com
Turnkey, Multifunctional, Internet Access
Security Platforms, Applications & Services
N.A.I.C.S.: 541512
Peter C. Castle *(Pres & CEO)*
Scott Foote *(Sr VP-Ops)*

VAXART, INC.
170 Harbor Way Ste 300, South San
Francisco, CA 94080

Tel.: (650) 550-3500 DE
Web Site: https://www.vaxart.com
Year Founded: 2004
VXRT—(NASDAQ)
Rev.: $107,000
Assets: $153,847,000
Liabilities: $43,250,000
Net Worth: $110,597,000
Earnings: ($107,758,000)
Emp.: 164
Fiscal Year-end: 12/31/22
Holding Company; Biopharmaceutical
Products Developer & Marketer
N.A.I.C.S.: 551112
Michael J. Finney *(Chm & Interim
CEO)*
Phillip E. Lee *(CFO & Principal Acctg
Officer)*
Edward B. Berg *(Gen Counsel)*
Raymond D. Stapleton *(CTO)*
James F. Cummings *(Chief Medical
Officer)*
Sarah Caravalho Khan *(VP)*
Todd C. Davis *(Chm)*

Subsidiaries:

Biota Scientific Management Pty.
Ltd. **(1)**
Unit 10 585 Blackburn Road, Notting Hill,
3168, VIC, Australia
Tel.: (61) 399153700
Web Site: http://www.biota.com.au
Sales Range: $50-74.9 Million
Biopharmaceutical Products Developer &
Marketer
N.A.I.C.S.: 325414

Vaxart Biosciences, Inc. **(1)**
395 Oyster Point Blvd Ste 405, South San
Francisco, CA 94080
Tel.: (650) 550-3500
Web Site: http://www.vaxart.com
Oral Vaccine Developer & Mfr
N.A.I.C.S.: 325414
Andre Floroiu *(Pres & CEO)*

VAXCYTE, INC.
825 Industrial Rd Ste 300, San Car-
los, CA 94070
Tel.: (650) 837-0111 DE
Web Site: https://www.vaxcyte.com
Year Founded: 2013
PCVX—(NASDAQ)
Rev.: $8,356,000
Assets: $1,006,178,000
Liabilities: $52,565,000
Net Worth: $953,013,000
Earnings: ($223,485,000)
Emp.: 158
Fiscal Year-end: 12/31/22
Biotechnology Research & Develop-
ment Services
N.A.I.C.S.: 541714
Grant E. Pickering *(CEO)*
Paul W. Sauer *(Sr VP-Process Dev &
Mfg)*
Andrew L. Guggenhime *(Pres &
CFO)*
Janet Graesser *(VP-Corp Comm &
IR)*
Mark C. Wiggins *(Chief Bus Officer)*
Jakub Simon *(Chief Medical Officer)*
Karen Alderete *(Exec Dir)*
Nathan Cracraft *(VP)*
Harp Dhaliwal *(Sr VP)*
Mikhail Eydelman *(Gen Counsel)*
Sam Iki *(Sr VP)*
Jennifer Zibuda *(Sr Dir-IR)*

VAXXINITY, INC.
505 Odyssey Way, Merritt Island, FL
32953
Tel.: (254) 244-5739 DE
Web Site: https://www.vaxxinity.com
Year Founded: 2014
VAXX—(NASDAQ)
Assets: $106,399,000
Liabilities: $44,222,000

Net Worth: $62,177,000
Earnings: ($75,222,000)
Emp.: 76
Fiscal Year-end: 12/31/22
Biotechnology Research & Develop-
ment Services
N.A.I.C.S.: 541714
Louis Reese *(Chm)*
Mei Mei Hu *(Pres & CEO)*
Jason Pesile *(Chief Acctg Officer &
Principal Acctg Officer)*
Sumita Ray *(Chief Legal Officer,
Chief Compliance Officer, Chief Ad-
min Officer & Sec-Corporate)*

VBI VACCINES INC.
160 2nd St Fl 3, Cambridge, MA
02142
Tel.: (617) 830-3031 BC
Web Site:
https://www.vbivaccines.com
VBIV—(NASDAQ)
Rev.: $8,682,000
Assets: $86,951,000
Liabilities: $79,524,000
Net Worth: $7,427,000
Earnings: ($92,836,000)
Emp.: 131
Fiscal Year-end: 12/31/23
Holding Company; Vaccine Developer
& Mfr
N.A.I.C.S.: 551112
Jeffery R. Baxter *(Pres & CEO)*
David Evander Anderson *(Chief Sci-
entific Officer)*
Francisco Diaz-Mitoma *(Chief Medi-
cal Officer)*
Nell Beattie *(CFO & Head-
Development)*
T. Adam Buckley *(Sr VP-Bus Dev)*
John Dillman *(Chief Comml Officer)*
Steven Gillis *(Chm)*

Subsidiaries:

SciVac (Israel) Ltd. **(1)**
Gad Feinstein Rd, PO Box 580, Rehovot,
7610303, Israel
Tel.: (972) 89480625
Vaccines Mfr
N.A.I.C.S.: 325414
Avi Mazaltov *(Gen Mgr)*

SciVac Ltd. **(1)**
Gad Feinstein Rd, PO Box 580, Rehovot,
7610303, Israel
Tel.: (972) 89480625
Pharmaceuticals Mfr
N.A.I.C.S.: 325412

Variation Biotechnologies (US),
Inc. **(1)**
222 3rd St Ste 2241, Cambridge, MA 02142
Tel.: (617) 830-3031
Web Site: http://www.vbivaccines.com
Vaccine Developer & Mfr
N.A.I.C.S.: 325414
Jeffery R. Baxter *(Pres & CEO)*

VECTOR 21 HOLDINGS, INC.
12136 W Bayaud Ave Ste 300, Lake-
wood, CO 80228
Tel.: (303) 422-8127 DE
Year Founded: 2021
VHLD—(OTCIQ)
Assets: $52
Liabilities: $132,051
Net Worth: ($131,999)
Earnings: ($40,273)
Fiscal Year-end: 06/30/24
Holding Company
N.A.I.C.S.: 551112

VEECO INSTRUMENTS INC.
1 Terminal Dr, Plainview, NY 11803
Tel.: (516) 677-0200 DE
Web Site: https://www.veeco.com
Year Founded: 1989
VECO—(NASDAQ)
Rev.: $666,435,000

Assets: $1,229,041,000
Liabilities: $556,599,000
Net Worth: $672,442,000
Earnings: ($30,368,000)
Emp.: 1,215
Fiscal Year-end: 12/31/23
Semiconductor Process Equipment
Mfr
N.A.I.C.S.: 334413
John P. Kiernan *(CFO & Sr VP)*
Robert W. Bradshaw *(Chief Admin
Officer)*
William John Miller *(CEO)*
Adrian Devasahayam *(Sr VP-Product
Line Mgmt)*
Ajit Paranjpe *(CTO)*
Peter Porshnev *(Sr VP-Unified En-
grg)*
Mark Harris *(Sr VP-Ops-Global)*
Susan Wilkerson *(Sr VP-Global Sls &
Svcs)*

Subsidiaries:

Ultratech, Inc. **(1)**
3050 Zanker Rd, San Jose, CA
95134 **(100%)**
Tel.: (408) 321-8835
Web Site: http://www.veeco.com
Photolithography Equipment Mfr, Designer
& Marketer
N.A.I.C.S.: 334516
Peter Porshnev *(Sr VP & Gen Mgr)*

Subsidiary (Domestic):

Ultratech International, Inc. **(2)**
11542 Davis Creek Ct, Jacksonville, FL
32256
Tel.: (904) 292-9019
Web Site: https://www.spillcontainment.com
Spill Containment Products Mfr
N.A.I.C.S.: 332313
Mark Shaw *(CEO)*
Dale Shaw *(VP-Ops)*
Tim McGrath *(VP-Sales-Global)*
Sam Bates *(Reg Sls Mgr-East)*
Cary Winters *(Reg Sls Mgr-West)*
Matt Shaw *(Exec VP)*
Mario Cruz *(Dir-Mktg)*
Michael Turner *(Mgr-Digital Mktg)*
Sonja Day *(Project Mgr)*
Courtney Kucera *(Mgr-Customer Svc)*
Matt Clancy *(Mgr-Bus Dev & Advanced
Technologies)*
Paul Sander *(Mgr-Engrg)*
Dillon Campbell *(Sys Engr)*
Laurie Brochu *(Fin Dir)*
Kindra Roberts *(Sls Mgr)*
Duffy Loftus *(Sls Mgr)*
Beth O'Connell *(Sr Coord-Purchasing)*
David Kelley *(Dir)*
Nick La Mar *(Sls Mgr)*
Taylor White *(Coord)*
Brenda Rivera *(Coord-Logistics)*
David Kelley *(Dir)*
Nick La Mar *(Sls Mgr)*
Taylor White *(Coord)*
Brenda Rivera *(Coord-Logistics)*
David Kelley *(Dir)*
Nick La Mar *(Sls Mgr)*
Taylor White *(Coord)*
Brenda Rivera *(Coord-Logistics)*

Subsidiary (Non-US):

Ultratech Kabushiki Kaisha **(2)**
Kaeda Dai 2 Building 8th Floor, Kohoku-ku
Shin Yokohama 2-5-10, Yokohama, 222-
0033, Kanagawa, Japan
Tel.: (81) 454786742
Photolithography Equipment Mfr
N.A.I.C.S.: 333242

Veeco Asia Pte. Ltd. **(1)**
151 Lorong Chuan New Tech Park Lobby E
06-05, Helios, Singapore, 556741, Singa-
pore
Tel.: (65) 6 856 7490
Web Site: https://www.veeco.com
Sales Range: $25-49.9 Million
Emp.: 22
Process Equipment Products
N.A.I.C.S.: 423830

Veeco Compound Semiconductor
Inc. **(1)**

394 Elizabeth Ave, Somerset, NJ 08873
Tel.: (732) 560-5300
Web Site: http://www.veeco.com
Sales Range: $10-24.9 Million
Emp.: 60
Epitaxial Equipment & Related Components Used in the Production of Semiconductors
N.A.I.C.S.: 334413

Veeco Instruments (Shanghai) Co. Ltd. (1)
1000 Jin Hai Road 5/F East Building 31, Shanghai, 201206, China (100%)
Tel.: (86) 216 862 9820
Web Site: https://www.veeco.com
Process Equipment Products
N.A.I.C.S.: 423830

Veeco Instruments GmbH (1)
Dynamostrasse 19, Mannheim, 68165, Germany (100%)
Tel.: (49) 621842100
Web Site: http://www.veeco-europe.com
Sales Range: $10-24.9 Million
Emp.: 30
Marketing & Sales
N.A.I.C.S.: 449210

Veeco Instruments Ltd. (1)
Silvaco Technology Centre Office 1/2 Compass Point, Saint Ives, PE27 5JL, Cambridgeshire, United Kingdom (100%)
Tel.: (44) 148 030 9334
Web Site: https://www.veeco.com
Process Equipment Technology & Industrial Machinery Installation
N.A.I.C.S.: 449210

Veeco Japan (1)
Kaeda Dai 2 Building 8th Floor, Kohoku-ku Shin Yokohama 2-5-10, Yokohama, 222-0033, Kanagawa-ken, Japan
Tel.: (81) 454786742
Web Site: http://www.veeco.com
Semiconductor Machinery Mfr & Distr
N.A.I.C.S.: 333242

Veeco Korea Inc. (1)
3F 117 Unjung-ro Bundang-gu, Seongnam, 013-461, Gyeonggi-Do, Korea (South) (100%)
Tel.: (82) 312704800
Web Site: http://www.veecokorea.com
Sales Range: $10-24.9 Million
Emp.: 13
Process Equipment Products
N.A.I.C.S.: 423830

Veeco Korea LLC (1)
7th Floor 53, Metapolis-ro, Hwaseong, 18454, Gyeonggi-do, Korea (South) (100%)
Tel.: (82) 312704800
Web Site: http://www.veeco.com
Photolithography Equipment Mfr & Distr
N.A.I.C.S.: 333242

Veeco Malaysia Sdn. Bhd. (1)
1-15-11 Suntech Penang Cybercity Lintang Mayang Pasir 3, Bayan Baru, 11950, Penang, Malaysia
Tel.: (60) 4 640 5566
Web Site: http://www.veeco.com
Sales Range: $10-24.9 Million
Emp.: 8
Metrology & Process Equipment Solutions
N.A.I.C.S.: 334419

Veeco Precision Surface Processing LLC (1)
185 Gibraltar Rd, Horsham, PA 19044
Tel.: (215) 328-0700
Semiconductor & Related Device Mfr
N.A.I.C.S.: 334413
Paul L. Vit (Mgr-Mechanical Engrg)

Veeco Process Equipment Inc. (1)
2330 E Prospect Rd, Fort Collins, CO 80525-9645
Tel.: (970) 221-1807
Web Site: http://www.veeco.com
Sales Range: $10-24.9 Million
Emp.: 22
Mfr of Ion Sources
N.A.I.C.S.: 333517

Veeco SiC CVD Systems AB (1)
Ideongatan 3A, 223 70, Lund, Sweden
Tel.: (46) 462880220
Film Processing Equipment Mfr

N.A.I.C.S.: 825992

Veeco Singapore (1)
151 Lorong Chuan New Tech Park Lobby E 06-05, Singapore, 556741, Singapore
Tel.: (65) 68567490
Web Site: http://www.veeco.com
Semiconductor Machinery Mfr & Distr
N.A.I.C.S.: 333242

Veeco Solar Equipment Inc. (1)
70 Old Canal Dr, Lowell, MA 01851
Tel.: (978) 937-3800
Web Site: http://www.veeco.com
Sales Range: $100-124.9 Million
Emp.: 30
Mfr of Web Coating Systems for Flexible Solar Panels
N.A.I.C.S.: 334419

Veeco Taiwan Inc. (1)
1st Floor No 6-6 Duxing Road Hsinchu Science Park, Hsin-chu, 30078, Taiwan
Tel.: (886) 35646888
Web Site: http://www.veeco.com.tw
Sales Range: $25-49.9 Million
Emp.: 28
Process Equipment Products
N.A.I.C.S.: 423830

VEEVA SYSTEMS, INC.
4280 Hacienda Dr, Pleasanton, CA 94588
Tel.: (925) 452-6500 DE
Web Site: https://www.veeva.com
Year Founded: 2007
VEEV—(NYSE)
Rev.: $2,363,673,000
Assets: $5,910,920,000
Liabilities: $1,266,096,000
Net Worth: $4,644,824,000
Earnings: $525,705,000
Emp.: 7,172
Fiscal Year-end: 01/31/24
Software Development Services
N.A.I.C.S.: 513210
E. Nitsa Zuppas (Pres & Head-Staff)
Jonathan Faddis (Gen Counsel & Sr VP)
Jacques Mourrain (VP-Quality & Compliance)
Chris Moore (Pres-Europe)
Adriano Vieira (Gen Mgr-Latin America)
Vivian Welsh (Chief People Officer)
Catherine Allshouse (CIO-Global & Head-Ops)
Tom Schwenger (Pres & Chief Customer Officer)
Paul Shawah (Exec VP-Strategy)
Stan Wong (VP-Products, Tech & Network)
Stacey Epstein (CMO)
Howard Hsueh (Sr VP-Global Customer Svcs)
Peter P. Gassner (Co-Founder & CEO)

Subsidiaries:

Crossix Solutions Inc. (1)
1375 Broadway 3rd Fl, New York, NY 10018
Tel.: (212) 994-9355
Healthcare Marketing Research Services
N.A.I.C.S.: 541910

Physicians World, LLC (1)
125 Chubb Ave, Lyndhurst, NJ 07071
Tel.: (201) 549-5600
Medical Communication Services
N.A.I.C.S.: 561499

VEEVA U.K. HOLDINGS LIMITED (1)
The Old Trinity Church Trinity Road, Marlow, SL7 3AN, Buckinghamshire, United Kingdom
Tel.: (44) 2035889500
Holding Company
N.A.I.C.S.: 551112

VELO3D, INC.

2710 Lakeview Ct, Fremont, CA 94538
Tel.: (408) 610-3915 Ky
Web Site: https://velo3d.com
Year Founded: 2020
VLD—(NYSE)
Rev.: $80,757,000
Assets: $225,114,000
Liabilities: $84,268,000
Net Worth: $140,846,000
Earnings: $10,020,000
Emp.: 294
Fiscal Year-end: 12/31/22
All Other Industrial Machinery Manufacturing
N.A.I.C.S.: 333248
Renette Youssef (CMO)
Jessie Lockhart (Chief People Officer)
Alexander Varlahanov (CTO)
Bernard Chung (CFO)
Bradley Allen Kreger (CEO)
Benyamin Buller (Founder)

VELOCITY ACQUISITION CORP.
109 Old Branchville Rd, Ridgefield, CT 06877
Tel.: (201) 956-1969 DE
Web Site: http://www.velocityacq.com
Year Founded: 2020
VELO—(NASDAQ)
Investment Services
N.A.I.C.S.: 523999
Doug Jacob (Founder)
Adrian Covey (CEO)
Judge Graham (Chief Digital Officer)
Nicolas Brien (Chief Strategy Officer)
Garrett Schreiber (CFO)
Sanjay Chadda (Chm)
Nicolas Brien (Chief Strategy Officer)

VELOCITY FINANCIAL, INC.
2945 Townsgate Rd Ste 110, Westlake Village, CA 91361
Tel.: (818) 532-3700 DE
Web Site: https://www.velfinance.com
Year Founded: 2012
VEL—(NYSE)
Rev.: $240,343,000
Assets: $3,748,975,000
Liabilities: $3,368,475,000
Net Worth: $380,500,000
Earnings: $32,211,000
Emp.: 194
Fiscal Year-end: 12/31/22
Real Estate Investment Services
N.A.I.C.S.: 531210
Christopher D. Farrar (Co-Founder & CEO)
Mark R. Szczepaniak (CFO)
Jeffrey T. Taylor (Exec VP-Capital Markets)
Joseph A. Cowell (COO)
Graham M. Comley (CIO)
Christopher J. Oltmann (Treas & Dir-IR)
Ronald T. Kelly (Gen Counsel & Sec)
Fiona Tam (Chief Acctg Officer)

VELTEX CORPORATION
123 W Madison St Ste 1500, Chicago, IL 60602
Tel.: (312) 235-4014 UT
Web Site: https://www.veltex.com
Year Founded: 1987
VLXC—(OTCIQ)
Portfolio Management & Investment Advice
N.A.I.C.S.: 523940
R. Preston Roberts (Chm)
Stephen G. Macklem (CFO, Treas & Sec)
Andreas Mauritzson (Pres & CEO)

VEMANTI GROUP, INC.

7545 Irvine Ctr Dr Ste 200, Irvine, CA 92618
Tel.: (949) 559-7200
Web Site: https://www.vemanti.com
VMNT—(OTCQB)
Rev.: $138,731
Assets: $806,177
Liabilities: $323,982
Net Worth: $482,195
Earnings: ($1,038,221)
Emp.: 2
Fiscal Year-end: 12/31/22
Miscellaneous Financial Investment Activities
N.A.I.C.S.: 523999
Tan Tran (Pres & CEO)

VENTAS, INC.
353 N Clark St Ste 3300, Chicago, IL 60654 DE
Web Site: https://www.ventasreit.com
Year Founded: 1998
VTR—(NYSE)
Rev.: $4,497,827,000
Assets: $24,725,433,000
Liabilities: $15,181,028,000
Net Worth: $9,544,405,000
Earnings: ($40,973,000)
Emp.: 486
Fiscal Year-end: 12/31/23
Real Estate Investment Trust
N.A.I.C.S.: 525990
Brian K. Wood (Chief Tax Officer & Sr VP)
Christian N. Cummings (Sr VP-Asset Mgmt)
Julie A. Robinson (Sr VP-Investments)
Robert F. Probst (CFO & Exec VP)
Gregory R. Liebbe (Chief Acctg Officer, Sr VP & Controller)
Peter J. Bulgarelli (Exec VP)
Carey Shea Roberts (Officer-Ethics & Compliance, Gen Counsel, Sec & Exec VP)
Bhavana Devulapally (CIO & Sr VP)
J. Justin Hutchens (Chief Investment Officer & Exec VP-Sr Housing)
Bill Grant (Sr VP-IR)
Molly McEvily (VP-Corp Comm)
Dan Minning (Exec VP)
Debra A. Cafaro (Chm & CEO)

Subsidiaries:

AHS Oklahoma Health System, LLP (1)
110 W 7th St Ste 2540, Tulsa, OK 74119
Tel.: (918) 579-1000
Emp.: 3,170
Health Care Service Provider
N.A.I.C.S.: 622110

AHS Oklahoma Holdings, Inc. (1)
1 Burton Hills Blvd Ste 250, Nashville, TN 37215-6295
Tel.: (615) 296-3000
Holding Company
N.A.I.C.S.: 551112

AL (AP) Holding LLC (1)
10350 Ormsby Park Pl Ste 300, Louisville, KY 40223
Tel.: (502) 357-9000
Real Estate Investment Services
N.A.I.C.S.: 531190

AL I/East Brunswick Senior Housing, LLC (1)
190 Summerhill Rd, East Brunswick, NJ 08816
Tel.: (848) 221-8884
Web Site: http://www.sunriseseniorliving.com
Assisted Living Facility Operator
N.A.I.C.S.: 623312

ALH Holdings, LLC (1)
221 Shepard St, Ripon, WI 54971
Tel.: (920) 748-3121
Holding Company
N.A.I.C.S.: 551112

Ventas, Inc.—(Continued)

ARHC ATLARFL01 TRS, LLC (1)
333 16th Ave S, Largo, FL 33771-4407
Tel.: (727) 588-0020
Real Estate Development Services
N.A.I.C.S.: 531390

ARHC BTFMYFL01 TRS, LLC (1)
9731 Commerce Ctr Ct, Fort Myers, FL
33908-1400
Tel.: (239) 334-2500
Real Estate Development Services
N.A.I.C.S.: 531390

ARHC BTNAPFL01 TRS, LLC (1)
5175 Tamiami Trl E, Naples, FL 30327-2806
Tel.: (239) 775-5050
Real Estate Development Services
N.A.I.C.S.: 531390

Atria Management Canada, ULC (1)
2450 Thimens Blvd, Saint Laurent, H4R
2M2, QC, Canada
Tel.: (514) 337-0000
Web Site: http://www.atriaretirement.ca
Senior Housing Development Services
N.A.I.C.S.: 531120
Kristy Grange (Pres)

Atria Northgate Park, LLC (1)
9191 Roundtop Rd, Cincinnati, OH 45251-
2446
Tel.: (513) 923-3711
Real Estate Development Services
N.A.I.C.S.: 531390

Atria Vista del Rio, LLC (1)
1620 Indian School Rd NE, Albuquerque,
NM 87102
Tel.: (505) 206-5094
Emp.: 70
Real Estate Development Services
N.A.I.C.S.: 531390
Yunia Gonzalez (Exec Dir)

Subsidiary (Domestic):

Baptist St. Anthony (2)
1600 Wallace Blvd, Amarillo, TX 79106
Tel.: (806) 212-2000
Web Site: https://www.bsahs.org
Sales Range: $350-399.9 Million
Healtcare Services
N.A.I.C.S.: 623110
Belinda Gibson (Chief Nursing Officer)
Teri Skelton (Dir)

**Heart Hospital of New Mexico,
LLC** (2)
504 Elm St NE, Albuquerque, NM 87102
Tel.: (505) 727-1100
Web Site: https://hearthospitalnm.com
Sales Range: $25-49.9 Million
Emp.: 165
Cardiovascular Services
N.A.I.C.S.: 622310
Troy Greer (CEO)
Reuben Murray (CFO)
Denzil Ross (COO)

Atrium at Weston Place, LLC (1)
2900 Lake Brook Blvd, Knoxville, TN 37909
Tel.: (865) 233-9027
Assisted Living Facility Operator
N.A.I.C.S.: 623312

BCC Mid Valley Operations, LLC (1)
67 Sturges Rd, Peckville, PA 18452
Tel.: (570) 383-9090
Web Site: http://www.elmcroft.com
Real Estate Development Services
N.A.I.C.S.: 531390

Barclay Downs Associates, LP (1)
4401 Barclay Downs Dr Ste 300, Charlotte,
NC 28209
Tel.: (704) 910-2910
Real Estate Development Services
N.A.I.C.S.: 531390

**Brookdale Living Communities of
New Jersey, LLC** (1)
1 Brendenwood Dr, Voorhees, NJ 08043
Tel.: (856) 210-3901
Web Site: http://www.brookdaleliving.com
Assisted Living Facility Operator
N.A.I.C.S.: 623312

**Clackamas Woods Assisted Living,
LLC** (1)

14404 SE Webster Rd, Milwaukie, OR
97267
Tel.: (503) 850-7568
Web Site: http://www.thespringsliving.com
Old Age Home Operator
N.A.I.C.S.: 623312

**Coast to Coast Assisted Living Re-
alty, LLC** (1)
330 Madison Ave Ste 939, New York, NY
10017
Tel.: (516) 359-1066
Residential Care Services
N.A.I.C.S.: 623312

**Consera Healthcare Real Estate
LLC** (1)
1901 Main St Ste 900, Columbia, SC
29201-2457
Tel.: (803) 779-4420
Real Estate Development Services
N.A.I.C.S.: 531390

EC Knoxville Realty, LLC (1)
7521 Andersonville Pike, Knoxville, TN
37938
Tel.: (865) 951-7300
Nursing Care Services
N.A.I.C.S.: 623110

**EC Opco Washington Township,
LLC** (1)
8630 Washington Church Rd, Miamisburg,
OH 45342-3795
Tel.: (937) 291-3211
Real Estate Investment Services
N.A.I.C.S.: 531110

EC Opco Xenia, LLC (1)
60 Paceline Cir, Xenia, OH 45385-1281
Tel.: (937) 372-1530
Real Estate Investment Services
N.A.I.C.S.: 531110

Florence Realty, LLC (1)
2627 E Funston, Wichita, KS 67211
Tel.: (316) 871-2796
Web Site:
http://www.florencerealtyhomes.com
Real Estate Development Services
N.A.I.C.S.: 531390

Good Sam MOB Investors, LLC (1)
1450 5th Ave SE, Puyallup, WA 98372
Tel.: (253) 268-0459
Real Estate Development Services
N.A.I.C.S.: 531390

JJS Properties, Inc. (1)
431 S Gulfview Blvd, Clearwater, FL 33767-
2508
Tel.: (727) 461-7795
Real Estate Asset Management Services
N.A.I.C.S.: 531390

**Jensen Construction Management,
Inc.** (1)
445 Washington St, Santa Clara, CA 95050
Tel.: (408) 828-4023
Civil Engineering Construction Services
N.A.I.C.S.: 237990

LBS Limited Partnership (1)
111 W Jackson Blvd, Chicago, IL 60604
Tel.: (312) 461-8200
Nonresidential Building Leasing Services
N.A.I.C.S.: 531120

LHPT Columbus THE, LLC (1)
3545 Olentangy River Rd, Columbus, OH
43214
Tel.: (614) 340-8511
Emp.: 5
Real Estate Development Services
N.A.I.C.S.: 531390

LHRET Ascension Austin II, LP (1)
200 W Madison St Fl 32, Chicago, IL 60606
Tel.: (312) 665-5778
Religious Organizations
N.A.I.C.S.: 813110

LHRET Ascension SJ, LLC (1)
1010 Carondelet Dr Ste 101, Kansas City,
MO 64114-4821
Tel.: (816) 942-8026
Emp.: 4
Real Estate Development Services
N.A.I.C.S.: 531390

LHRET Ascension SV, LLC (1)

222 N Lasalle St Ste 410, Chicago, IL
60601
Tel.: (312) 408-1370
Emp.: 5
Real Estate Development Services
N.A.I.C.S.: 531390

LHRET St. Louis, LLC (1)
1035 Bellevue Ave Ste 212, Saint Louis,
MO 63117
Tel.: (314) 754-0244
Real Estate Development Services
N.A.I.C.S.: 531390

LS Davol Square, LLC (1)
3 Davol Sq, Providence, RI 02903
Tel.: (401) 383-3013
Real Estate Investment Services
N.A.I.C.S.: 531110

Lakeview Surgery Center, LLC (1)
100 Jim Mason Ct Ste B, Warner Robins,
GA 31088-8965
Tel.: (478) 971-4001
Ambulatory Surgical & Clinics Operator
N.A.I.C.S.: 621493

**Lillibridge Healthcare Services,
Inc.** (1)
353 N Clark St Ste 3300, Chicago, IL
60654
Tel.: (312) 408-1870
Web Site: http://www.lillibridge.com
Emp.: 140
Medical Real Estate
N.A.I.C.S.: 531190
Peter J. Bulgarelli (Pres & CEO)
Dan Minning (Exec VP- & Leasing)
Ian Hughes (Sr VP--East Territory)
Mary Beth Kuzmanovich (Sr VP-Leasing)
Lisa Marx (Sr VP)

Subsidiary (Domestic):

**East Houston Medical Plaza,
LLC** (2)
13111 East Fwy, Houston, TX 77015
Tel.: (713) 451-7011
Web Site: http://www.lillibridge.com
Emp.: 25
Nonresidential Building Leasing Services
N.A.I.C.S.: 531120

**New Senior Investment Group
Inc.** (1)
55 W 46th St Ste 2204, New York, NY
10036
Tel.: (646) 822-3700
Web Site: http://www.newseniorinv.com
Rev.: $336,281,000
Assets: $1,773,536,000
Liabilities: $1,570,303,000
Net Worth: $203,233,000
Earnings: ($6,162,000)
Emp.: 17
Fiscal Year-end: 12/31/2020
Real Estate Investment Services
N.A.I.C.S.: 523999
Andrew Armstrong (Mng Dir & Head-Corp
Strategy)
Lori B. Marino (Gen Counsel, Sec & Exec
VP)
Bhairav Patel (Exec VP-Acctg & Fin)

Subsidiary (Domestic):

**NIC 15 Kirkwood Corners Leasing
LLC** (2)
206 N River Rd, Lee, NH 03861-6214
Tel.: (603) 659-6586
Residential Building Leasing Services
N.A.I.C.S.: 531110

**NIC 15 Pines of New Market Leasing
LLC** (2)
9 Grant Rd, Newmarket, NH 03857-2195
Tel.: (603) 659-6000
Residential Building Leasing Services
N.A.I.C.S.: 531110

NIC 20 Grand View Leasing LLC (2)
6210 N University St, Peoria, IL 61614-
3433
Tel.: (309) 692-2484
Residential Building Leasing Services
N.A.I.C.S.: 531110

PMB Real Estate Services LLC (1)
3394 Carmel Mountain Rd Ste 200, San
Diego, CA 92121

Tel.: (858) 794-1900
Web Site: https://www.pmbres.com
Real Estate Asset Management Services
N.A.I.C.S.: 531390
Stephen King (Pres)
Kristin San Martin (CFO)
Lynn Lantgen (Sr Dir-Leasing)

Residence du Marche Inc. (1)
25 Rue Du Marche, Sainte-Therese, J7E
5T2, QC, Canada
Tel.: (438) 793-7670
Apartment Rental Services
N.A.I.C.S.: 531110

SZR Columbia LLC (1)
6500 Freetown Rd, Columbia, MD 21044-
4002
Tel.: (410) 531-1444
Web Site:
https://www.sunriseseniorliving.com
Emp.: 100
Assisted Living Facility Operator
N.A.I.C.S.: 623312
Jack R. Callison Jr. (CEO)
Pascal Duchauffour (COO)
Tavinder Hare (CFO)
Mary Kay Gribbons (Chief HR Officer)
Mike Summers (CIO)
Andy Coelho (Sr VP)
Jason Engelhorn (Sr VP)
Denise Falco (Sr VP)
Thomas Kessler (Sr VP)
Philip Kroskin (Sr VP)
Lisa Mannett (Sr VP)
Lisa Thompson (Sr VP)

SZR North Hills LLC (1)
615 Spring Forest Rd, Raleigh, NC 27609-
9150
Tel.: (919) 981-6100
Web Site:
https://www.sunriseseniorliving.com
Assisted Living Facility Operator
N.A.I.C.S.: 623312

**SZR Old Tappan Assisted Living,
L.L.C.** (1)
195 Old Tappan Rd, Old Tappan, NJ 07675
Tel.: (848) 221-8964
Web Site:
http://www.sunriseseniorliving.com
Assisted Living Facility Operator
N.A.I.C.S.: 623312

SZR San Mateo LLC (1)
10350 Ormsby Park Pl Ste 300, Louisville,
KY 40223-6177
Tel.: (502) 357-9380
Web Site: http://www.ventasreit.com
Real Estate Investment Services
N.A.I.C.S.: 531130

**Springs at Clackamas Woods,
LLC** (1)
14404 SE Webster Rd, Milwaukie, OR
97267
Tel.: (503) 850-7568
Web Site: https://www.thespringsliving.com
Old Age Home Operator
N.A.I.C.S.: 623312

VOP Berry Park, LLC (1)
4 Berry St, Brooklyn, NY 11249
Tel.: (718) 782-2829
Web Site: https://www.berryparkbk.com
Restaurant & Bar Operator
N.A.I.C.S.: 722410

VTR AMS, Inc. (1)
1 Burton Hills Blvd Ste 250, Nashville, TN
37215
Tel.: (615) 296-3000
Web Site: http://www.ardenthealth.com
Health Care Srvices
N.A.I.C.S.: 622110
Jim Adams (VP)
Frank J. Campbell (Chief Medical Officer)
Joey Abney (VP-Facilities Mgmt)
Angela Beaudry (VP)
Alumine Bellone (VP-Risk Mgmt)
Matthew Brown (VP)
Lee Courtney (VP-Tax)
Matt Maxfield (Pres-Americas)
Marty Bonick (Pres & CEO)
Alfred Lumsdaine (CFO)
Robert Coscione (Sr VP)
Ashley Crabtree (Treas & Sr VP)
Jeff DeMordaunt (VP)
Lisa Dolan (Chief Nursing Officer)

John Faldetta *(VP-Development)*
James Grimes *(Chief Acctg Officer & Sr VP-Finance)*
Nathan Hamlet *(VP)*
Joanne Hardin *(Chief Quality Officer)*
Julie Harrigan *(VP)*
Peter Henry *(VP)*
James Hinkle *(Chief Compliance Officer)*
Jim Hughes *(VP)*
Richard Keller *(CIO & Sr VP)*
Vicki Knox *(VP)*
Matthew Kroplin *(VP)*
Nina Kumar *(VP)*
Stacie Malone *(VP-Internal Audit)*
Sandra Mann *(VP)*
James J. Mayercik *(VP-Information Technology)*
Tim Miner *(VP)*
Tracy O'Daniel *(VP)*
Tyra Palmer *(CMO)*
Steve Petrovich *(Chief Legal Officer)*
Terika Richardson *(COO)*
Carolyn Schneider *(Chief HR Officer)*
Robert Coscione *(Sr VP)*

Division (Domestic):

Hillcrest HealthCare System (2)
1120 S Utica Ave, Tulsa, OK 74104
Tel.: (918) 579-1000
Web Site: https://hillcrestmedicalcenter.com
Emp.: 5,172
Hospitals Owner & Operator
N.A.I.C.S.: 622110

Lovelace Health System (2)
601 Dr Martin Luther King Jr Ave NE, Albuquerque, NM 87102
Tel.: (505) 727-8000
Web Site: https://www.lovelace.com
Emp.: 3,450
Health Insurance Plan Administration
N.A.I.C.S.: 561110
Ron Stern *(Pres & CEO)*
Heyoung McBride *(Dir-Medical-Radiation Oncology)*
John Cruickshank *(CEO-Lovelace Medical Grp)*
Gary Whittington *(CFO)*
Vesta Sandoval *(Chief Medical Officer)*
Brenda Holley *(Chief Nursing Officer)*
Richard Haun *(CFO)*

VTR LS ODU 2, LLC (1)
4211 Monarch Way, Norfolk, VA 23508-2540
Tel.: (757) 440-6998
Real Estate Investment Services
N.A.I.C.S.: 531120

VTR Science & Technology, LLC (1)
801 W Baltimore St Ste 505, Baltimore, MD 21201
Tel.: (410) 649-5629
Real Estate Investment Services
N.A.I.C.S.: 531120

Ventas Amberleigh, LLC (1)
2330 Maple Rd, Williamsville, NY 14221
Tel.: (716) 309-4707
Web Site: http://www.amberleigh.net
Residential Building Leasing Services
N.A.I.C.S.: 531110

Ventas Healthcare Properties, Inc. (1)
353 N Clark St, Chicago, IL 60654
Tel.: (312) 660-3736
Web Site: http://www.ventasreit.com
Emp.: 140
Real Estate Investment Services
N.A.I.C.S.: 525990

Ventas Realty, Limited Partnership (1)
353 N Clark St Ste 3300, Chicago, IL 60654
Web Site: http://www.ventasreit.com
Sales Range: $10-24.9 Million
Emp.: 300
Real Estate Services
N.A.I.C.S.: 531390
Debra A. Cafaro *(Chm & CEO)*

Ventas SSL, Inc. (1)
10350 Ormsby Park Pl, Louisville, KY 40223
Tel.: (502) 357-9000
Web Site: http://www.ventasreit.com

Sales Range: $25-49.9 Million
Emp.: 75
Real Estate Services
N.A.I.C.S.: 531390
Debra A. Cafaro *(Chm & CEO)*

Woodlake Realty, LLC (1)
828 Malabar Rd SE, Palm Bay, FL 32907-3207
Tel.: (321) 723-8700
Real Estate Development Services
N.A.I.C.S.: 531390

VENTURA CANNABIS AND WELLNESS CORP.

800 W 6th St Ste 830, Los Angeles, CA 90017
Tel.: (604) 684-6264   BC
Web Site:
   http://www.venturacanna.com
Year Founded: 2013
CVHIF—(OTCEM)
Rev.: $10,538,524
Assets: $11,927,310
Liabilities: $5,790,057
Net Worth: $6,137,253
Earnings: ($1,738,938)
Fiscal Year-end: 02/29/20
Mental Health Treatment Services
N.A.I.C.S.: 621420

VENTYX BIOSCIENCES, INC.

12790 El Camino Real Ste 200, San Diego, CA 92130
Tel.: (760) 593-4832   DE
Web Site: https://www.ventyxbio.com
Year Founded: 2018
VTYX—(NASDAQ)
Rev.: $4,710,000
Assets: $371,400,000
Liabilities: $17,505,000
Net Worth: $353,895,000
Earnings: ($108,426,000)
Emp.: 58
Fiscal Year-end: 12/31/22
Research & Development in Biotechnology (except Nanobiotechnology)
N.A.I.C.S.: 541714
Matthew Moore *(COO)*
John M. Nuss *(Chief Scientific Officer)*
Sheila Gujrathi *(Chm)*
Raju S. Mohan *(Founder, Pres & CEO)*

VERA BRADLEY, INC.

11222 Stonebridge Rd, Roanoke, IN 46783
Tel.: (260) 207-5116   IN
Web Site:
   https://www.verabradley.com
Year Founded: 1982
VRA—(NASDAQ)
Rev.: $499,961,000
Assets: $404,501,000
Liabilities: $153,123,000
Net Worth: $251,378,000
Earnings: ($59,735,000)
Emp.: 2,180
Fiscal Year-end: 01/28/23
Handbags, Accessories, Duffel Bags, Garment Bags & Travel Accessories Designer, Producer, Marketer & Retailer
N.A.I.C.S.: 316990
Patricia R. Miller *(Founder)*
Michael Schwindle *(CFO)*
Mark C. Dely *(Chief Admin Officer)*
Alison Hiatt *(CMO)*
Jacqueline Ardrey *(Pres & CEO)*

Subsidiaries:

Creative Genius, Inc. (1)
7979 Ivanhoe Blvd Ste 400, La Jolla, CA 92037   (75%)
Tel.: (858) 232-4945
Web Site:
   https://www.puravidabracelets.com

Online Product Distr
N.A.I.C.S.: 541890
Griffin Thall *(Co-Founder)*
Paul Goodman *(Co-Founder)*

Vera Bradley Designs, Inc. (1)
4120 W Jefferson Blvd, Fort Wayne, IN 46804
Tel.: (260) 434-1900
Web Site: http://www.verabradley.com
Leather Goods & Allied Product Mfr
N.A.I.C.S.: 316990

Vera Bradley Sales, LLC (1)
11222 Stonebridge Rd, Roanoke, IN 46783-9334
Web Site: https://verabradley.com
Leather Goods & Allied Product Mfr
N.A.I.C.S.: 316990

VERA THERAPEUTICS, INC.

8000 Marina Blvd Ste 120, Brisbane, CA 94005
Tel.: (650) 770-0077   DE
Web Site: https://www.veratx.com
Year Founded: 2016
VERA—(NASDAQ)
Rev.: $1,848,000
Assets: $131,435,000
Liabilities: $54,527,000
Net Worth: $76,908,000
Earnings: ($89,056,000)
Emp.: 46
Fiscal Year-end: 12/31/22
Research & Development in Biotechnology (except Nanobiotechnology)
N.A.I.C.S.: 541714
William D. Turner *(Chief Dev Officer)*
Robert M. Brenner *(Chief Medical Officer)*
Marshall Fordyce *(Founder, Pres & CEO)*
Lauren Frenz *(Chief Bus Officer)*
Sean P. Grant *(CFO)*
Tom Doan *(Sr VP-Dev Ops)*
Tad Thomas *(Sr VP & Head-Product Dev & Mfg)*
Joseph Young *(Chief Acctg Officer)*
David L. Johnson *(COO)*

VERACYTE, INC.

6000 Shoreline Ct Ste 300, South San Francisco, CA 94080
Tel.: (650) 243-6300   DE
Web Site: https://www.veracyte.com
Year Founded: 2006
VCYT—(NASDAQ)
Rev.: $296,536,000
Assets: $1,156,422,000
Liabilities: $81,222,000
Net Worth: $1,075,200,000
Earnings: ($36,560,000)
Emp.: 787
Fiscal Year-end: 12/31/22
Medical Laboratories
N.A.I.C.S.: 621511
Tina Susan Nova Bennett *(Pres-CLIA & Gen Mgr-Thyroid & Urologic Cancers)*
Marc A. Stapley *(CEO)*
Jonathan Wygant *(Chief Acctg Officer & VP)*
Mark Ho *(Dir-Technical Acctg & Integrations)*
Tracy Morris *(VP-Global Corp Comm)*
Rebecca Chambers *(CFO & Exec VP)*
Shayla Gorman *(Dir-IR)*
John Leite *(Sr VP & Gen Mgr-Pulmonology & Market Access)*
John Leite *(Gen Mgr-Pulmonology & Market Access)*
Rob Brainin *(Chief Bus Officer)*
Corinne Danan *(Sr VP)*
Steven French *(CIO)*
Fabienne Hermitte *(Sr VP)*
Annie McGuire *(Chief People Officer)*

VERADIGM INC.

222 Merchandise Mart Plz Ste 2024, Chicago, IL 60654
Tel.: (312) 506-1200   DE
Web Site: https://veradigm.com
Year Founded: 2000
MDRX—(NASDAQ)
Rev.: $1,503,037,000
Assets: $2,425,229,000
Liabilities: $1,017,091,000
Net Worth: $1,408,138,000
Earnings: $134,438,000
Emp.: 8,000
Fiscal Year-end: 12/31/21
Holding Company; Clinical & Healthcare Software, Information, Connectivity & Support Services
N.A.I.C.S.: 551112
Richard Elmore *(Sr VP-Corp Dev & Strategy)*
Tom Langan *(Pres & Chief Comml Officer)*
Tejal Vakharia *(Gen Counsel & Sr VP)*
P. Gregory Garrison *(Exec Chm)*

Subsidiaries:

Allscripts (1)
Allscripts Tower 305 Church at N Hills St, Raleigh, NC 27609   (100%)
Tel.: (919) 847-8102
Sales Range: $350-399.9 Million
Emp.: 800
Physician Information Systems Services
N.A.I.C.S.: 561499

Allscripts (1)
10 Glenlake Pkwy Ste 500 N Tower, Sandy Springs, GA 30328-2156
Tel.: (404) 847-5000
Sales Range: $500-549.9 Million
Emp.: 2,800
Healthcare Information Technology Services
N.A.I.C.S.: 541512

Allscripts (1)
222 Merchandise Mart Plz Ste 2024, Chicago, IL 60654
Tel.: (860) 246-3000
Sales Range: $1-9.9 Million
Emp.: 40
Clinical, Revenue Cycle & Preformance Management Software
N.A.I.C.S.: 513210

Allscripts (India) Private Limited (1)
Atlantis Heights 10th and 11th Floor Dr Vikram Sarabhai Road, Baroda, 390 023, Gujarat, India
Tel.: (91) 2657181584
Health Care Srvices
N.A.I.C.S.: 621610

Allscripts (United Kingdom) Limited (1)
15 Oxford Court 4th Floor, Manchester, M2 3WQ, United Kingdom
Tel.: (44) 1612334999
Web Site: http://uk.allscripts.com
Software Development Services
N.A.I.C.S.: 541511
Richard Strong *(Mng Dir-EMEA)*
Robert Anello *(Sls Dir-EMEA)*
Paula Ridd *(Dir-Pro Svcs)*
James Hodgin *(Head-Solutions)*

Allscripts Canada Corporation (1)
13888 Wireless Way Suite 110, Richmond, V6V 0A3, BC, Canada
Tel.: (604) 273-4900
Web Site: http://www.ca.allscripts.com
Healthcare Information Technology Services
N.A.I.C.S.: 541519

Allscripts Healthcare, LLC (1)
305 Church at N Hills St, Raleigh, NC 27609
Tel.: (919) 847-8102
Web Site: http://www.allscripts.com
Medical Transcription & Documentation Services
N.A.I.C.S.: 561410
Leah Jones *(CFO)*
Lisa Hammond *(Chief HR Officer)*
Richard Elmore *(Sr VP)*
Tejal Vakharia *(Sr VP)*
Tom Langan *(Pres)*

Veradigm Inc.—(Continued)

Subsidiary (Domestic):

Practice Fusion, Inc. (2)
731 Market St Ste 400, San Francisco, CA 94103
Tel.: (415) 346-7700
Web Site: http://www.practicefusion.com
Web Based Electronic Medical Records
N.A.I.C.S.: 513199

Allscripts India (1)
Manial Chambers RC Dutt Road, Alkapuri, Vadodara, 390007, India
Tel.: (91) 2653981500
Web Site: http://www.eclipsys.com
Sales Range: $150-199.9 Million
Emp.: 700
Healthcare Information Technology Services
N.A.I.C.S.: 541519

Allscripts Software, LLC (1)
1025 Ashworth Rd, West Des Moines, IA 50265
Tel.: (515) 954-3031
Medical Transcription & Documentation Services
N.A.I.C.S.: 561410

California Healthcare Medical Billing, LLC (1)
700 La Terraza Blvd Ste 200, Escondido, CA 92025
Tel.: (760) 520-1400
Web Site: http://www.chmbinc.com
Financial Services
N.A.I.C.S.: 523940
Bob Svendsen (CEO)
Janet Boos (Pres)
Ian Maurer (Sr VP-Tech)
James Trewin (Sr VP-Information Svcs)
Paula Kacsir (Sr VP-Revenue Cycle Ops)
Elaine Everett (VP-RCM Quality Assurance)
Michelle Souferian (VP-Strategic Accounts)
Patrick Schlimgen (VP-Fin)
Gina Cecchi (Reg VP-Strategic Accounts)
Michelle Pena (Reg VP-Ops)
Don Howard (Dir-Technical Ops)

Careport Health, LLC (1)
201 S St Ste 501, Boston, MA 02111
Tel.: (844) 722-7376
Web Site: http://www.careporthealth.com
Emp.: 200
Software Development Services
N.A.I.C.S.: 541511
Lissy Hu (CEO)
Marc Camm (COO)
Scott Kerber (Sr VP-Dev & Solutions)
Mark Heron (VP-Sls)
Mark Simeone (VP-Strategic Sls)
Sara Radkiewicz (Head-Product)
Sean Santry (VP-Engrg)
Annie Busch (Head-Mktg)
David Borowski (Asst VP-Customer Success)

Core Medical Solutions PTY LTD. (1)
Level 1 146 Fullarton Road, Rose Park, 5067, SA, Australia
Tel.: (61) 883329600
Web Site: http://www.coremedicalsolutions.com
Software Development Services
N.A.I.C.S.: 541511
Rohan Ward (Mng Dir)
Narelle Portakiewicz (Dir-Bus Dev-Natl)
Sean Graham (Sr Mgr-Dev)
Marc Belej (Exec Dir)

Evalytica, LLC (1)
450 Sansome Str Ste 650, San Francisco, CA 94111
Tel.: (415) 490-0400
Web Site: http://www.evalytica.com
Software Development Services
N.A.I.C.S.: 513210

Health Grid, LLC (1)
4203 Vineland Rd Ste K6, Orlando, FL 32811
Tel.: (407) 506-0460
Web Site: http://www.healthgrid.com
Health Care Srvices
N.A.I.C.S.: 622110

Oasis Medical Solutions Limited (1)
Battersea Studios 80 Silverthorne Road,

London, SW8 3HE, United Kingdom
Tel.: (44) 2078190444
Web Site: http://www.oasismedicalsolutions.co.uk
Health Care Srvices
N.A.I.C.S.: 621610

Pulse8, LLC (1)
175 Admiral Cochrane Dr Ste 302, Annapolis, MD 21401
Tel.: (410) 928-4218
Web Site: http://www.pulse8.com
Healtcare Services
N.A.I.C.S.: 621999
John Criswell (Founder)
Scott Filiault (Co-Pres & Chief Revenue Officer)
Courtney Yeakel (Co-Pres & Chief Product Officer)
Erin Montgomery (COO)
Amy Mann (CFO)

dbMotion, Inc. (1)
600 Grant St Ste 22017, Pittsburgh, PA 15219
Tel.: (412) 605-1952
Emp.: 50
Computer System Design Services
N.A.I.C.S.: 541512
Yuval Ofek (CEO)

dbMotion, Ltd. (1)
8 HaNagar Street, PO Box 7222, Hod Hasharon, 45240, Israel
Tel.: (972) 97699000
Health Care Srvices
N.A.I.C.S.: 621610

VERALTO CORPORATION
225 Wyman St Ste 250, Waltham, MA 02451
Tel.: (781) 755-3655   DE
Web Site: https://www.veralto.com
Year Founded: 2022
VLTO—(NYSE)
Rev.: $5,021,000,000
Assets: $5,693,000,000
Liabilities: $4,304,000,000
Net Worth: $1,389,000,000
Earnings: $839,000,000
Emp.: 16,000
Industrial Machinery Mfr
N.A.I.C.S.: 333248
Jennifer L. Honeycutt (Pres & CEO)
Sameer Ralhan (CFO & Sr VP)
Melissa Aquino (Sr VP-Water Quality)
Mattias Bystrom (Sr VP-Product Quality & Innovation)
Surekha Trivedi (Sr VP-Strategy & Sustainability)
Sylvia A. Stein (Chief Legal Officer & Sr VP)
Jennifer L. Honeycutt (Pres & CEO)

Subsidiaries:

TraceGains, Inc. (1)
1333 W 120th Ave Ste 209, Westminster, CO 80234
Tel.: (720) 465-9404
Web Site: http://www.tracegains.com
Software Publisher
N.A.I.C.S.: 513210
Marc Simony (Dir-Mktg)
Scott Stastny (Dir-Strategic Accts-West)
David Schoenfeld (VP-Sls)

VERANO HOLDINGS CORP.
415 N Dearborn St 4th Fl, Chicago, IL 60654
Tel.: (312) 265-0730   BC
Web Site: https://www.verano.com
Year Founded: 2014
VRNO—(CNSX)
Rev.: $879,412,000
Assets: $2,396,055,000
Liabilities: $1,054,505,000
Net Worth: $1,341,550,000
Earnings: ($269,164,000)
Emp.: 3,780
Fiscal Year-end: 12/31/22
Holding Company

N.A.I.C.S.: 551112
Brett Summerer (CFO)
Darren Weiss (Chief Legal Officer)
Destiny Thompson (Chief People Officer)
George Archos (CEO)

VERASTEM, INC.
117 Kendrick St Ste 500, Needham, MA 02494
Tel.: (781) 292-4200   DE
Web Site: https://www.verastem.com
Year Founded: 2010
VSTM—(NASDAQ)
Rev.: $2,596,000
Assets: $95,050,000
Liabilities: $47,659,000
Net Worth: $47,391,000
Earnings: ($73,812,000)
Emp.: 53
Fiscal Year-end: 12/31/22
Biopharmaceutical Mfr.
N.A.I.C.S.: 325412
Jonathan Pachter (Chief Scientific Officer)
Daniel W. Paterson (Pres & CEO)
Cathy Carew (Chief Organizational Effectiveness Officer)
Daniel Calkins (CFO)
Louis Denis (Chief Medical Officer)

VERB TECHNOLOGY COMPANY, INC.
3401 N Thanksgiving Way Ste 240, Lehi, UT 84043   NV
Web Site: https://www.verb.tech
Year Founded: 2012
VERB—(NASDAQ)
Software-as-a-Service Platform Developer
N.A.I.C.S.: 541511

VERDE CLEAN FUELS, INC.
711 Louisiana St Ste 2160, Houston, TX 77002
Tel.: (908) 281-6000   DE
Web Site: https://www.verdecleanfuels.com
Year Founded: 2020
VGAS—(NASDAQ)
Rev.: $2,448,510
Assets: $178,436,977
Liabilities: $189,309,729
Net Worth: ($10,872,752)
Earnings: ($3,698,144)
Emp.: 5
Fiscal Year-end: 12/31/22
Investment Services
N.A.I.C.S.: 523999
Ron Hulme (Chm)

VERDE MEDIA GROUP, INC.
1368 26th St 104, Denver, CO 80205
Tel.: (310) 954-9160
Web Site: http://www.verdemediagroup.com
VMGI—(OTCIQ)
Sales Range: Less than $1 Million
Holding Company
N.A.I.C.S.: 551112
William F. Veve (Pres & CEO)
Adam DesLauriers (Pres-Agency Div)
Marc Albanese (CFO & COO)

VERDE SCIENCE, INC.
400 S Zang Blvd Ste 812, Dallas, TX 75208
Tel.: (604) 825-1309
Year Founded: 2012
VRCI—(OTCEM)
Pharmaceuticals Product Mfr
N.A.I.C.S.: 325412
Harpreet Singh Sangha (Founder, Chm & CEO)

VERICEL CORPORATION

64 Sidney St, Cambridge, MA 02139
Tel.: (617) 588-5555   MI
Web Site: https://www.vcel.com
VCEL—(NASDAQ)
Rev.: $164,365,000
Assets: $273,003,000
Liabilities: $80,731,000
Net Worth: $192,272,000
Earnings: ($16,709,000)
Emp.: 305
Fiscal Year-end: 12/31/22
Commercial Physical & Biological Research
N.A.I.C.S.: 325414
Michael Halpin (COO)
Jonathan Hopper (Chief Medical Officer)
Roland DeAngelis (Sr VP-Comml Ops)
Jonathan D. Siegal (Principal Acctg Officer)
Patrick Fowler (Sr VP)
Eric Burns (VP)
Caryn Cramer (VP)
Cindy Entstrasser (VP)
Mike Gilligan (VP)
Shannon Kelly (VP)
Doug Kennedy (Sr VP)
Adrian Lowe (VP)
Dominick C. Colangelo (Pres & CEO)

VERIFY SMART CORP.
40 Hillside Ave, Mahwah, NJ 07430
Tel.: (973) 897-6294   NV
Web Site: https://www.verifysmart.net
Year Founded: 2006
VSMR—(OTCIQ)
Information Technology Services
N.A.I.C.S.: 541511
Anthony Cinotti (Pres)
Sandy Manata (Dir)
Adam Becker (COO)
Annamarie Seabright (Chief Comml Officer & Exec VP-Communications)
Stewart Goodin (CTO)
Anastasia Marie (CMO)
Jean-Marc Zimmerman (Gen Counsel)

VERIFYME, INC.
75 S Clinton Ave Ste 510, Rochester, NY 14604
Tel.: (585) 736-9400   NV
Web Site: https://www.verifyme.com
Year Founded: 1999
VRME—(NASDAQ)
Rev.: $19,576,000
Assets: $20,752,000
Liabilities: $7,166,000
Net Worth: $13,586,000
Earnings: ($14,398,000)
Emp.: 50
Fiscal Year-end: 12/31/22
Security & Risk Management Services
N.A.I.C.S.: 541690
Nancy Meyers (CFO, Treas, Sec & Exec VP)
Paul Ryan (Founder-Trust Codes & Exec VP-Authentication Segment)
Adam H. Stedham (Pres & CEO)

Subsidiaries:

Periship LLC (1)
7 Businect Park Dr, Branford, CT 06405
Tel.: (203) 315-8637
Web Site: http://www.periship.com
Rev.: $6,000,000
Emp.: 13
Freight Transportation Arrangement
N.A.I.C.S.: 488510
Fred G. Volk (Dir-Ops)
Luciano Morra (Founder & CEO)

VERINT SYSTEMS INC.

225 Broadhollow Rd Ste 130, Melville, NY 11747
Tel.: (631) 962-9600　　　　NY
Web Site: https://www.verint.com
VRNT—(NASDAQ)
Rev.: $902,245,000
Assets: $2,313,601,000
Liabilities: $1,019,131,000
Net Worth: $1,294,470,000
Earnings: $14,898,000
Emp.: 4,300
Fiscal Year-end: 01/31/23
Security & Business Intelligence Software
N.A.I.C.S.: 513210
Dan Bodner *(Chm & CEO)*
Elan Moriah *(Pres)*
Peter Fante *(Chief Admin Officer)*
Alan Roden *(Chief Corp Dev Officer)*
Celia Fleischaker *(CMO)*
Michelle Meurer *(Sr VP-HR)*
Grant Highlander *(CFO)*

Subsidiaries:

BPA Corporate Facilitation Ltd.　　(1)
First Floor Milford House Pynes Hill, Exeter, EX2 5AZ, Devon, United Kingdom
Tel.: (44) 1392347400
Web Site: http://bpaquality.co.uk
Software Publisher
N.A.I.C.S.: 513210

Ciboodle Ltd.　　(1)
India of Inchinnan Greenock Road, Glasgow, PA4 9LH, United Kingdom
Tel.: (44) 1415334000
Software Publisher
N.A.I.C.S.: 513210

ForeSee Results, Inc.　　(1)
2500 Green Rd Ste 400, Ann Arbor, MI 48105
Tel.: (734) 205-2600
Web Site: http://www.foreseeresults.com
Sales Range: $10-24.9 Million
Emp.: 200
Marketing Research & Public Opinion Polling
N.A.I.C.S.: 541910
Shannon Latta *(VP-Mktg & Comm)*

Gita Technologies Ltd.　　(1)
33 Maskit St, Herzliya, 6744131, Israel
Tel.: (972) 722461825
Web Site: https://gitatechnologies.com
Software Application Development Services
N.A.I.C.S.: 513210

Global Management Technologies Corporation　　(1)
800 N Point Pkwy, Alpharetta, GA 30005
Tel.: (678) 243-4500
Web Site: http://www.verint.com
Emp.: 400
Workforce Management Optimization Software Publisher
N.A.I.C.S.: 513210

KANA Software, Inc.　　(1)
2550 Walsh Ave Ste 100, Santa Clara, CA 95051
Tel.: (650) 614-8300
Web Site: http://www.kana.com
Emp.: 80
Commercial Web, Social & Mobile Media Software & Technical Support Services
N.A.I.C.S.: 541511

Subsidiary (Non-US):

KANA Software　　(2)
Menara Batavia - 26th Floor Jalan KH Mas Mansyur Kavling 126, Jakarta, 10220, Indonesia
Tel.: (62) 21 5793 0170
Web Site: http://www.verint.com
Emp.: 100
Software Development Services
N.A.I.C.S.: 541511

Branch (Domestic):

KANA Software Inc. - Chicago　　(2)
30 S Wacker Dr Ste 1300, Chicago, IL 60606
Tel.: (312) 447-5600
Web Site: http://www.kana.com

Sales Range: $25-49.9 Million
Emp.: 20
Software Development Services
N.A.I.C.S.: 541511

Subsidiary (Non-US):

KANA Software KK　　(2)
Imperial Tower 16F 1-1-1 Uchisaiwaicho, Chiyoda-ku, Tokyo, 100 0011, Japan
Tel.: (81) 728641550
Web Site: http://www.kana.com
Sales Range: $100-124.9 Million
Commercial Web, Social & Mobile Media Software & Technical Support Services
N.A.I.C.S.: 541511

KANA Software Pty Limited　　(2)
Level 14 NorthPoint, 100 Miller Street, North Sydney, 2060, NSW, Australia
Tel.: (61) 289070300
Web Site: http://www.kana.com
Emp.: 5
Software Development Services
N.A.I.C.S.: 541511

KANA Solutions Ltd　　(2)
Concourse II, Co Antrim, Belfast, BT3 9DT, Northern Ireland, United Kingdom
Tel.: (44) 2890788300
Web Site: http://www.verint.com
Emp.: 130
Software Devolopment
N.A.I.C.S.: 513210

Branch (Domestic):

KANA Software　　(3)
India of Inchinnan, Greenock Road, Inchinnan, PA4 9LH, Renfrewshire, United Kingdom
Tel.: (44) 1415334000
Web Site: http://www.kana.com
Software Development Services
N.A.I.C.S.: 513210

NowForce Limited　　(1)
28 Haoman St, Talpiot Industrial Area, Jerusalem, 9342117, Israel
Tel.: (972) 25658700
Computer Programming Services
N.A.I.C.S.: 541511
Assaf Shafran *(Co-Founder & CEO)*
Anshel Pfeffer *(Co-Founder & Chief Product Officer)*
Amit Kahn *(VP-R&D)*
Leah Spitz-Goldenhersh *(VP-Ops)*
Liran Stein *(VP-Bus Dev)*

OpinionLab Inc.　　(1)
549 W Randolph St Ste 401, Chicago, IL 60661
Tel.: (312) 800-4500
Web Site: http://www.opinionlab.com
Emp.: 200
Software Publisher; Data Collection
N.A.I.C.S.: 513210

PT Ciboodle Indonesia　　(1)
26th Fl JL KH Mas Mansyur Kav 126, Sudirman Karet-Jakarta Pusat, Jakarta, 10220, Indonesia
Tel.: (62) 2157930170
Other Scientific & Technical Consulting Services
N.A.I.C.S.: 541690

UTX Technologies Limited　　(1)
139-143 Omonias Ave The Maritime Center, CY-3045, Limassol, Cyprus
Tel.: (357) 24343353
Web Site: http://www.u-tx.com
Other Scientific & Technical Consulting Services
N.A.I.C.S.: 541690

Verba Technologies Asia Pacific Pte Ltd.　　(1)
Level 30 South Beach 38 Beach Road, Singapore, 189767, Singapore
Tel.: (65) 68281001
Software Publisher
N.A.I.C.S.: 513210

Verba Technologies Limited　　(1)
448 W Kytle St Ste B, Cleveland, GA 30528
Tel.: (201) 355-0400
Security & Business Intelligence Software Publisher
N.A.I.C.S.: 513210

Verint Systems (Asia Pacific) Limited　　(1)
Suite 715-716 Level 7 Core F Cyberport 3 100 Cyberport Road, Hong Kong, China (Hong Kong)
Tel.: (852) 27975678
Electronics Stores
N.A.I.C.S.: 449210

Verint Systems (Australia) PTY Ltd.　　(1)
Suite 2 Level 2 76 Berry Street, North Sydney, 2060, NSW, Australia
Tel.: (61) 289070300
All Other Information Services
N.A.I.C.S.: 519290

Verint Systems (Philippines) Corporation　　(1)
G/F Reliance IT Center 99 E Rodriguez Jr Avenue Brgy Ugong, Pasig, Philippines
Tel.: (63) 26670860
Consulting & Customer Support Services
N.A.I.C.S.: 541613

Verint Systems UK Ltd.　　(1)
241 Brooklands Road, Weybridge, KT13 0RH, Surrey, United Kingdom
Tel.: (44) 1932839500
Consulting & Customer Support Services
N.A.I.C.S.: 541613

Verint Systems, Inc. - Alpharetta　　(1)
5995 Windward Pkwy, Alpharetta, GA 30005
Tel.: (770) 754-1900
Web Site: http://www.verint.com
Computer Software Developer
N.A.I.C.S.: 513210

Branch (Domestic):

Verint Witness Systems LLC - Santa Clara　　(2)
2550 Walsh Ave Ste 120, Santa Clara, CA 95051
Tel.: (408) 830-5400
Web Site: http://www.verint.com
Rev.: $2,400,000
Emp.: 75
Computer Software Developer
N.A.I.C.S.: 541511

Subsidiary (Domestic):

Vovici Corporation　　(2)
196 Van Buren St Ste 400, Herndon, VA 20170
Tel.: (703) 481-9326
Web Site: http://www.vovici.com
Sales Range: $25-49.9 Million
Emp.: 50
Online Enterprise Feedback Management Products & Services
N.A.I.C.S.: 513210

Verint Video Solutions Inc.　　(1)
691 County Road 233, Durango, CO 81301
Tel.: (303) 450-5900
Web Site: http://www.verint.com
Sales Range: $25-49.9 Million
Emp.: 6
Makes Closed-Circuit Surveillance Systems
N.A.I.C.S.: 541512

eg Solutions ltd.　　(1)
Dunston Business Village Stafford Road Dunston, Stafford, ST18 9AB, Staffordshire, United Kingdom
Tel.: (44) 1785715772
Web Site: http://www.egoptimize.com
Sales Range: $10-24.9 Million
IT & Software Support Services
N.A.I.C.S.: 541511
Phil Jones *(CTO)*

m-pathy GmbH　　(1)
Konigsbrucker Str 34, 01099, Dresden, Germany
Tel.: (49) 3515014150
Web Site: http://www.m-pathy.com
Software Services
N.A.I.C.S.: 541511
David Outram *(Mng Dir)*
Douglas Robinson *(Mng Dir)*
Nicola Nonini *(Mng Dir)*
Fante Peter *(Mng Dir)*

VERIS RESIDENTIAL, INC.

210 Hudson St Ste 400, Jersey City, NJ 07311
Tel.: (732) 590-1010　　　　MD
Web Site:
https://www.verisresidential.com
VRE—(NYSE)
Rev.: $279,859,000
Assets: $3,241,046,000
Liabilities: $1,961,493,000
Net Worth: $1,279,553,000
Earnings: ($107,265,000)
Emp.: 197
Fiscal Year-end: 12/31/23
Real Estate Investment Services
N.A.I.C.S.: 531110
Mahbod Nia *(CEO)*
Thomas J. Golden *(VP-Dev)*
Tammy K. Jones *(Chm)*
Amanda Lombard *(CFO)*
Nicholas A. Corrado *(VP-Fin)*
Blaise Cresciullo *(First VP-Property Mgmt)*
Richard Schwartz *(VP)*
Beverly Sturr *(VP-Legal Admin)*
Anna Malhari *(COO)*
Robert Cappy *(CTO)*
Jay V. Minchilli *(Sr VP)*
Nicole Jones *(Sr VP)*
Cindy Mai *(Chief Acctg Officer)*

Subsidiaries:

101 HUDSON LEASING ASSOCIATES　　(1)
101 Hudson St Unit 1, Jersey City, NJ 07302
Tel.: (201) 333-0101
Web Site: http://www.mack-cali.com
Emp.: 5
Real Estate Agencies & Brokerage Services
N.A.I.C.S.: 531210

150 MAIN STREET, L.L.C.　　(1)
30 Pawson Landing Dr, Branford, CT 06405-5122
Tel.: (203) 488-5567
Real Estate Investment Services
N.A.I.C.S.: 531390

ANDORVER PLACE APTS. L.L.C.　　(1)
650 Bulfinch Dr, Andover, MA 01810
Tel.: (978) 685-0552
Web Site:
https://www.andoverplaceapts.com
Apartment Building Rental Services
N.A.I.C.S.: 531110

MACK-CALI WOODBRIDGE L.L.C.　　(1)
581 Main St, Woodbridge, NJ 07095
Tel.: (732) 634-0382
Real Estate Agencies & Brokerage Services
N.A.I.C.S.: 531210

MONACO NORTH URBAN RENEWAL L.L.C.　　(1)
475 Washington Blvd, Jersey City, NJ 07310
Tel.: (201) 222-6600
Web Site: http://www.monacojc.com
Emp.: 20
Apartment Building Rental Services
N.A.I.C.S.: 531110

Mack-Cali Realty, L.P.　　(1)
Harborside 3 210 Hudson St Ste 400, Jersey City, NJ 07311
Tel.: (732) 590-1010
Rev.: $279,858,999
Assets: $3,241,045,999
Liabilities: $1,961,492,999
Net Worth: $1,279,552,999
Earnings: ($117,660,000)
Emp.: 196
Fiscal Year-end: 12/31/2023
Real Estate Investment Services
N.A.I.C.S.: 531210
Mahbod Nia *(CEO)*

PORT IMPERIAL SOUTH 15, L.L.C.　　(1)
1500 Ave At Port Imperial, Weehawken, NJ 07086-6944
Tel.: (201) 330-0603
Web Site: http://www.riversedgepi.com

Veris Residential, Inc.—(Continued)

Emp.: 12
Real Estate Development Services
N.A.I.C.S.: 531390

PORTSIDE APARTMENT DEVELOPERS, L.L.C. (1)
50 Lewis Mall, Boston, MA 02128
Tel.: (617) 561-9500
Real Estate Development Services
N.A.I.C.S.: 531390

RIVERWALK G URBAN RENEWAL, L.L.C. (1)
11 Ave At Port Imperial, West New York, NJ 07093
Tel.: (201) 863-0302
Real Estate Development Services
N.A.I.C.S.: 531390

ROSELAND MANAGEMENT SERVICES, L.P. (1)
343 Thornall St Ste 8 Fl 8, Edison, NJ 08837-2224
Tel.: (732) 590-1000
Real Estate Manangement Services
N.A.I.C.S.: 531390
Dawn Curto (Sr VP-Ops)

ROSELAND RESIDENTIAL TRUST (1)
150 John F Kennedy Pkwy 5th Fl, Short Hills, NJ 07078
Tel.: (973) 218-2300
Web Site: http://www.roselandres.com
Real Estate Manangement Services
N.A.I.C.S.: 531210

ROSEWOOD LAFAYETTE COMMONS, L.L.C. (1)
10 Lafayette Ave, Morristown, NJ 07960
Tel.: (973) 998-6150
Web Site:
http://www.highlandmorristownproperty.com
Emp.: 8
Real Estate Rental Services
N.A.I.C.S.: 531390

Roseland Management Co., LLC (1)
1 Fineran Way, Short Hills, NJ 07078
Tel.: (973) 232-4100
Web Site: http://roselandres.com
Real Estate Development Services
N.A.I.C.S.: 531390

VERISIGN, INC.
12061 Bluemont Way, Reston, VA 20190
Tel.: (703) 948-3200   **DE**
Web Site: https://www.verisign.com
Year Founded: 1995
VRSN—(NASDAQ)
Rev.: $1,493,100,000
Assets: $1,749,000,000
Liabilities: $3,330,000,000
Net Worth: ($1,581,000,000)
Earnings: $817,600,000
Emp.: 907
Fiscal Year-end: 12/31/23
Digital Commerce & Telecommunications Products & Services
N.A.I.C.S.: 541511
Thomas C. Indelicarto (Gen Counsel, Sec & Exec VP)
Ebrahim Keshavarz (Sr VP-Product Mgmt)
Ellen Petrocci (Sr VP-HR)
Jacquelyn Stewart (Sr VP & Deputy Gen Counsel)
John Calys (Sr VP)
Christine Lentz (Sr VP)
Ramakant Pandrangi (Sr VP)
D. James Bidzos (Founder, Chm, Pres & CEO)
George E. Kilguss III (CFO & Exec VP)
Burt Kaliski Jr. (CTO & Sr VP)

Subsidiaries:

VeriSign Colombia SAS (1)
Av 82 Nro 10 62 P 5, Bogota, Colombia
Tel.: (57) 16341500

Data Processing Hosting & Related Services
N.A.I.C.S.: 518210

VeriSign Information Services, Inc. (1)
12061 Bluemont Way, Reston, VA 20190
Tel.: (703) 925-6999
Web Site: http://www.verisign.com
Domain Name Registrar Services
N.A.I.C.S.: 518210

VeriSign Services India Private Limited (1)
807-A Park Centra Sector-30 NH-8, Gurgaon, Haryana, India
Tel.: (91) 124 429 2600
Web Site: http://www.verisign.com
Sales Range: $25-49.9 Million
Emp.: 60
Data Processing Hosting & Related Services
N.A.I.C.S.: 518210

VeriSign, Inc. (1)
21345 Ridgetop Cir, Sterling, VA 20166
Tel.: (703) 948-3200
Sales Range: $100-124.9 Million
Internet Trust Services, Including Domain Name, Digital Certificate & Payment Services
N.A.I.C.S.: 541511

VERISK ANALYTICS, INC.
545 Washington Blvd, Jersey City, NJ 07310-1686
Tel.: (201) 469-3000   **DE**
Web Site: https://www.verisk.com
Year Founded: 1971
VRSK—(NASDAQ)
Rev.: $2,681,400,000
Assets: $4,366,100,000
Liabilities: $4,043,900,000
Net Worth: $322,200,000
Earnings: $614,600,000
Emp.: 7,500
Fiscal Year-end: 12/31/23
Holding Company; Risk Information & Assessment Services
N.A.I.C.S.: 551112
Nicholas Daffan (CIO)
Patrick McLaughlin (Chief Sustainability Officer)
Yang Chen (Head-Corp Dev & Strategy)
Melissa Hendricks (CMO)
Lee M. Shavel (Pres & CEO)
Stacey Brodbar (Head-IR)
Kathlyn Card Beckles (Chief Legal Officer)
Dianne Greene (Head)
Doug Caccese (Co-Pres-Underwriting Solutions)
Saurabh Khemka (Co-Pres-Underwriting Solutions)
Elizabeth D. Mann (CFO & Exec VP)

Subsidiaries:

3E Company Enviromental, Ecological & Engineering (1)
3207 Grey Hawk Ct, Carlsbad, CA 92010
Tel.: (760) 602-8700
Web Site: https://www.3eco.com
Environmental Health & Safety Compliance Management Services
N.A.I.C.S.: 541690
Leo Oves (CIO)
Clark VanScoder (Sr VP-Svcs)
Matthew Johnston (Sr VP-)
Jenny Bingham (VP-Marketing-Communications)
Justin Byron (CFO)
Frank-Dieter Clesle (VP)
Oliver Danckert (Sr VP-)
Jason Rollingson (VP-Operations)
Sven Rued (VP)
Louise Botham (Gen Counsel)

Argus Information & Advisory Services, LLC (1)
50 Main St Fl 6, White Plains, NY 10601
Tel.: (914) 307-3100
Web Site: https://www.argusinformation.com

Sales Range: $10-24.9 Million
Emp.: 45
Management Consulting Services
N.A.I.C.S.: 541618

BuildFax, Inc. (1)
115 E 5th St Ste 200, Austin, TX 78701
Tel.: (877) 600-2329
Web Site: http://www.buildfax.com
Construction Database
N.A.I.C.S.: 518210
Holly Tachovsky (Founder)

Franco Signor LLC (1)
3647 Cortez Rd W Ste 100, Bradenton, FL 34210
Tel.: (888) 959-0692
Web Site: http://www.francosignor.com
Sales Range: $1-9.9 Million
Emp.: 30
Insurance Services
N.A.I.C.S.: 524298
John Williams (CEO)
Roy Franco (Chief Legal Officer)
Jeff Signor (COO)

Genscape, Inc. (1)
1140 Garvin Pl, Louisville, KY 40203
Tel.: (502) 583-3435
Web Site: http://www.genscape.com
Sales Range: $10-24.9 Million
Emp.: 85
Power Grid Information Monitoring Services
N.A.I.C.S.: 519290
Jon Ecker (CEO)
Randall Collum (Mng Dir)
Jonathan Gould (Mng Dir)
Christopher D. Seiple (Vice Chm-Energy Transition,Power,Renewables)
Rick Margolin (Sr Dir)
Pat Finn (Reg Dir)
Hanna Newstadt (Reg Dir)
Chris DaCosta (Mgr-Desk,Short,term Analytics)
Colette Breshears (Product Mgr)
Adam Jordan (Product Dir-term Analytics)
Mark Chung (Product Dir)
Alexandre Baldassano (Mng Dir)
Jake Eubank (Mgr)
Jodi Quinnell (Mgr-term Analytics)
Cory Madden (Dir)
Hillary Stevenson (Dir-Business Development-term Analytics)
Ryan Saxton (Head-term Analytics)
Ben Chu (Head)
Suzanne Danforth (Dir)
Erik Fabry (Dir)
J. D. Doyle (CTO)
David Parkinson (VP)
Chris Heath (VP)
Gavin Law (Head)
Andy Tidey (Head)
Steve Jenkins (VP)
Prashant Khorana (Dir)
Guy Bailey (Head)
Natalie Biggs (Head-Global)
David Brown (Head)
Andrew Brown (Head)
Ram Chandrasekaran (Head)
Ashish Chitalia (Dir & Head)
Mauro Chavez (Head-South America,LNG Markets)
Steve Chappell (Head)
Matthew Chadwick (VP & Head-Global)
Robert Clarke (VP)
Quentin De Carvalho (Head)
Edgardo Gelsomino (Head)
Paul Gray (Dir-Iron Ore Markets)
Robin Griffin (VP)
Dale Hazelton (Head)
Ben Hertz-Shargel (Head-Global)
Liz Dennett (VP)
Mhairidh Evans (Head)
Tom Ellacott (Sr VP)
David Parkinson (VP)
Chris Heath (VP)
Gavin Law (Head)
Andy Tidey (Head)
Steve Jenkins (VP)
Prashant Khorana (Dir)
Guy Bailey (Head)
Natalie Biggs (Head-Global)
David Brown (Head)
Andrew Brown (Head)
Ram Chandrasekaran (Head)
Ashish Chitalia (Dir & Head)
Mauro Chavez (Head-South America,LNG Markets)
Steve Chappell (Head)

Matthew Chadwick (VP & Head-Global)
Robert Clarke (VP)
Quentin De Carvalho (Head)
Edgardo Gelsomino (Head)
Paul Gray (Dir-Iron Ore Markets)
Robin Griffin (VP)
Dale Hazelton (Head)
Ben Hertz-Shargel (Head-Global)
Liz Dennett (VP)
Mhairidh Evans (Head)
Tom Ellacott (Sr VP)

Subsidiary (Non-US):

Genscape International, Inc. (2)
Damrak 20 A, 1012 LH, Amsterdam, Netherlands
Tel.: (31) 205244080
Sales Range: $10-24.9 Million
Emp.: 17
Power Grid Information Monitoring Services
N.A.I.C.S.: 513199

Insurance Services Office, Inc. (1)
545 Washington Blvd, Jersey City, NJ 07310
Tel.: (201) 469-3000
Web Site: http://www.verisk.com
Sales Range: $450-499.9 Million
Emp.: 2,600
Data, Analytics & Decision-Support Services for Property/Casualty Insurance Industry
N.A.I.C.S.: 519290
Vincent Cialdella (Sr VP-American Insurance Svcs Grp)

Subsidiary (Domestic):

AIR Worldwide Corporation (2)
Lafayette City Ctr 2 Ave de Lafayette 2nd Fl, Boston, MA 02111
Tel.: (617) 267-6645
Web Site: https://www.air-worldwide.com
Sales Range: $25-49.9 Million
Emp.: 110
Risk Management Software Services
N.A.I.C.S.: 524298
Bill Churney (Pres)
Roger Grenier (Sr VP-Global Resilience Practice)
Robert Newbold (Exec VP-Business Development-Client Services)
Praveen Sandri (Exec VP)
Paul Devlin (Gen Counsel-Ops & Sr VP)
Boris Davidson (Sr VP-Research & Development)
Sudhir Potharaju (Exec VP-Product)
Cagdas Kafali (Sr VP-Res-Modeling)
Peter Bingenheimer (Sr VP-Consulting-Client Services)
Jayanta Guin (Chief Res Officer & Exec VP)
Bethany Vohlers (VP)
Milan Simic (Exec VP & Mng Dir)
Adrian Bentley (Mng Dir & Sr VP)
Jayanta Guin (Chief Res Officer & Exec VP)
Bethany Vohlers (VP)
Milan Simic (Exec VP & Mng Dir)
Adrian Bentley (Mng Dir & Sr VP)

Atmospheric & Environmental Research, Inc. (2)
131 Hartwell Ave Ste 200, Lexington, MA 02421
Tel.: (781) 761-2288
Web Site: https://www.aer.com
Sales Range: $10-24.9 Million
Emp.: 140
Environmental Research
N.A.I.C.S.: 541720
Guy Seeley (Pres)
Steven J. Lowe (VP)
Robert Morris (Chief Scientific Officer & Exec VP)
Matthew Alvarado (VP-Research & Development)
Charles Sarkisian (Chief Product Strategy Officer & VP)
Jenny Zhu (Sr VP-Finance & Controller)
Matthew Alvarado (VP-Research & Development)
Charles Sarkisian (Chief Product Strategy Officer & VP)
Jenny Zhu (Sr VP-Finance & Controller)
David Hogan (Sr VP)
Rick Quinn (VP)

Division (Domestic):

Atmospheric & Environmental Research - Air Quality **(3)**
388 Market St Ste 750, San Francisco, CA 94111
Tel.: (617) 267-6645
Web Site: http://www.aer.com
Sales Range: $1-9.9 Million
Emp.: 10
Environmental Research
N.A.I.C.S.: 541715

Subsidiary (Domestic):

Geomni, Inc. **(2)**
1100 West Traverse Pkwy, Lehi, UT 84043
Tel.: (801) 764-5900
Web Site: http://www.geomni.com
Image And Data Analytics Provider
N.A.I.C.S.: 518210
Jeffrey C. Taylor (Pres)

ISO Claims Services, Inc. **(2)**
250 Berryhill Rd Converse Bldg Ste 500, Columbia, SC 29210
Tel.: (803) 731-6670
Web Site: http://www.iso.com
Sales Range: $1-9.9 Million
Emp.: 15
Risk Management Data & Support Services
N.A.I.C.S.: 524298
Vincent Cialdella (Pres)

Subsidiary (Non-US):

Insurance Services Office, Ltd. **(2)**
New London House 4th Floor, 6 London Street, London, EC3R 7LP, United Kingdom
Tel.: (44) 2076804970
Web Site: http://www.iso.com
Sales Range: $1-9.9 Million
Emp.: 10
Risk Management Consulting & Claims Services
N.A.I.C.S.: 541618
James Grant (Mng Dir)

Subsidiary (Domestic):

IntelliCorp Records, Inc. **(2)**
3000 Auburn Dr Ste 410, Beachwood, OH 44122
Tel.: (216) 450-5200
Web Site: https://www.intellicorp.net
Sales Range: $10-24.9 Million
Emp.: 90
Background Checks, Employment Screening & Drug-Testing Products
N.A.I.C.S.: 561499
Kelly Ansboury (Dir-Sales)
Michael Kendrick (Mgr-Client Services)
Joanne Vanover (Sr Mgr-Human Resources)
Kelly Georgiou (Asst VP-Finance-Administration)
Kelly Georgiou (Asst VP-Finance-Administration)

NetMap Analytics **(2)**
250 Old Wilson Bridge Rd Ste 200, Worthington, OH 43085
Tel.: (614) 865-6000
Web Site: http://www.netmap.com
Sales Range: $10-24.9 Million
Emp.: 15
Fraud Analysis Technology Mfr
N.A.I.C.S.: 513210

Quality Planning Corporation **(2)**
388 Market St Ste 750, San Francisco, CA 94111-5314
Tel.: (415) 369-0707
Web Site: http://www.verisk.com
Sales Range: $1-9.9 Million
Emp.: 30
Rating Integrity Solutions for the Insurance Industry
N.A.I.C.S.: 524298

Intellistance, LLC **(1)**
213 Court St 9th Fl, Middletown, CT 06457
Tel.: (860) 704-6381
Rev.: $1,100,000
Emp.: 14
Data Processing, Hosting & Related Services
N.A.I.C.S.: 518210

LCI, Inc. **(1)**

111 Anza Blvd Ste 310, Burlingame, CA 94010
Tel.: (650) 342-9486
Web Site: http://www.lciinc.com
Consulting Analytics Data Processing System Development
N.A.I.C.S.: 541512
Chris Lundquist (Pres & CEO)

Lead Intelligence, Inc. **(1)**
524 Plymouth Rd Ste 618, Gwynedd Valley, PA 19437
Tel.: (267) 460-7287
Web Site: http://www.leadid.com
Professional, Scientific & Technical Services
N.A.I.C.S.: 541990
Joe Lynch (VP-Engineering)

Xactware Solutions, Inc. **(1)**
1100 W Traverse Pkwy, Lehi, UT 84043
Tel.: (801) 764-5900
Web Site: https://www.xactware.com
Software Development Services
N.A.I.C.S.: 541511

VERITAS FARMS, INC.
8648 Lake Davis Rd, Pueblo, CO 81005
Tel.: (561) 288-6603   NV
Web Site:
   https://www.theveritasfarms.com
Year Founded: 2011
VFRM—(OTCQB)
Rev.: $1,063,105
Assets: $6,794,471
Liabilities: $7,400,748
Net Worth: ($606,277)
Earnings: ($5,543,908)
Emp.: 17
Fiscal Year-end: 12/31/22
Holding Company
N.A.I.C.S.: 551112
Alexander M. Salgado (Co-Founder & Sec)
Erduis Sanabria (Co-Founder)
Riana Meyer (VP-Ops)
Thomas E. Vickers (Chm, Pres & Interim CEO)
Michael Krouskos (Chief Customer Officer)
Dan Conners (VP-R&D)
Angel Perez (Creative Dir)
Christian Salgado (Dir-Inside Sls)
Marisa Cifre (Mktg Mgr)
Alexandria Salgado (Specialist-Customer Experience)

VERITEC, INC.
2445 Winnetka Ave N, Minneapolis, MN 55427
Tel.: (763) 253-2670   NV
Web Site: https://www.veritecinc.com
VRTC—(OTCIQ)
Rev.: $461,000
Assets: $132,000
Liabilities: $9,860,000
Net Worth: ($9,728,000)
Earnings: ($1,058,000)
Emp.: 7
Fiscal Year-end: 06/30/24
Two Dimensional (2D) Matrix Coding Technology
N.A.I.C.S.: 541519
Van Thuy Tran (Chm, CEO & Treas)

VERITEX HOLDINGS, INC.
8214 Wchester Dr Ste 800, Dallas, TX 75225
Tel.: (972) 349-6200   TX
Web Site:
   https://www.veritexbank.com
Year Founded: 2010
VBTX—(NASDAQ)
Rev.: $745,979,000
Assets: $12,394,337,000
Liabilities: $10,863,014,000
Net Worth: $1,531,323,000
Earnings: $108,261,000
Emp.: 820
Fiscal Year-end: 12/31/23

Bank Holding Company
N.A.I.C.S.: 551111
Charles Malcolm Holland III (Founder, Chm, Pres & CEO)
Terry S. Earley (CFO)
LaVonda Renfro (COO)
Angela Harper (Chief Risk Officer)
Cara McDaniel (Chief Talent Officer)
Mike Coyne (Mng Dir)
Donald Perschbacher (Exec Mgr)

Subsidiaries:

Green Bancorp, Inc. **(1)**
4000 Greenbriar, Houston, TX 77098
Tel.: (713) 275-8220
Web Site: http://www.greenbank.com
Rev.: $190,762,000
Assets: $4,261,916,000
Liabilities: $3,798,121,000
Net Worth: $463,795,000
Earnings: $34,136,000
Emp.: 368
Fiscal Year-end: 12/31/2017
Bank Holding Company
N.A.I.C.S.: 551111

Subsidiary (Domestic):

Green Bank, N.A. **(2)**
4000 Greenbriar, Houston, TX 77098
Tel.: (713) 275-8370
Web Site: http://www.greenbank.com
Sales Range: $50-74.9 Million
Federal Savings Bank
N.A.I.C.S.: 522180
Donald S. Perschbacher (Chief Credit Officer & Sr Exec VP)
Anne Capps (Sr VP-Factoring)
Laura Coppes (VP-Factoring)
Russell Duckworth (VP-Factoring)
Kevin Coffman (Exec VP-Govt Guaranteed Lending)
Bill Ridgway (Sr VP-Govt Guaranteed Lending)
Oscar Hernandez (VP-Govt Guaranteed Lending)
Kandace Moon (VP-Govt Guaranteed Lending)
Kevin Moon (VP-Govt Guaranteed Lending)
Robert Stringer (VP-Govt Guaranteed Lending)
Christopher Henricks (Asst VP-Govt Guaranteed Lending)
Meghan Kay (Asst VP-Fin & Govt Institutions Banking)
Kay Moore (Sr VP & Mgr-Direct Funding & Fin Institutional Investing)
John Thomson (VP-Mortgage Warehouse & Portfolio Mgr)
Scott Vines (Sr VP-Treasury Mgmt)
Jillian McDaniel (VP-Treasury Mgmt)
Lisa Rogers (VP-Treasury Mgmt)
Taylor Lawson (Officer-Banking)

Subsidiary (Domestic):

Patriot Bank Mortgage, Inc. **(3)**
9105 Barret Rd, Millington, TN 38053
Tel.: (901) 842-9714
Web Site:
   https://www.patriotbankmortgage.com
Commercial Banking Services
N.A.I.C.S.: 522110
Keith Barger (Exec VP)
Pansy Hall (Officer-Loan)
Alexis Heinz (Officer-Loan)
Nora O'Hara (VP)
Hunter Rasbach (Officer-Loan)
Rob Wright (Officer-Loan)

Potomac River Holdings, LLC **(3)**
99 Canal Ctr Plz Ste 110, Alexandria, VA 22314
Tel.: (703) 570-4108
Web Site:
   http://www.potomacriverholdings.com
Holding Company
N.A.I.C.S.: 551112

Subsidiary (Domestic):

Promenade Place, LLC **(4)**
5200 S Ulster St, Greenwood Village, CO 80111
Tel.: (720) 594-6073
Web Site: https://www.promenadeplace.com
Apartment Rental Services
N.A.I.C.S.: 531110

Veritex Community Bank **(1)**
8214 Westchester Dr Ste 100, Dallas, TX 75225
Tel.: (972) 349-6150
Web Site: http://www.veritexbank.com
Banking Services
N.A.I.C.S.: 522110
Charles Malcolm Holland III (Chm & CEO)
Jon Heine (Pres-Houston)
Cara McDaniel (Chief HR & Talent Officer & Sr Exec VP)

VERITONE, INC.
1615 Platte St 2nd Fl, Denver, CO 80202
Tel.: (646) 818-9292   DE
Web Site: https://www.veritone.com
Year Founded: 2014
VERI—(NASDAQ)
Rev.: $149,728,000
Assets: $424,752,000
Liabilities: $344,901,000
Net Worth: $79,851,000
Earnings: ($25,557,000)
Emp.: 661
Fiscal Year-end: 12/31/22
Software Development Services
N.A.I.C.S.: 541511
Chad E. Steelberg (Co-Founder & Chm)
Ryan S. Steelberg (Co-Founder, Pres & CEO)
Maria Moore (CMO)
Ben Xiang (Sr VP-Corporate Development & Strategy & Gen Mgr-Aiwaretm)
Sean King (Gen Mgr-Veritone Media & Entertainment)
Jon Gacek (Gen Mgr-Veritone Pub Sector)
Alex Fourlis (Gen Mgr-Veritone Hire)
Fleming Meng (CIO)
Craig Gatarz (Chief Legal Officer)
Julie Harding (Chief People Officer & Sr VP-People)
Michael L. Zemetra (CFO, Treas & Exec VP)
Ryan S. Steelberg (Co-Founder, Chm, Pres & CEO)
Chad E. Steelberg (Co-Founder)

Subsidiaries:

Broadbean Inc. **(1)**
240 Newport Ctr Dr, Newport Beach, CA 92660
Tel.: (949) 706-8560
Web Site: http://www.broadbean.com
Professional, Scientific & Technical Services
N.A.I.C.S.: 541990
Stuart Passmore (COO)

VERIZON COMMUNICATIONS INC.
1095 Avenue of the Americas, New York, NY 10036
Tel.: (212) 395-1000   DE
Web Site: https://www.verizon.com
Year Founded: 1983
VZ—(NYSE)
Rev.: $133,974,000,000
Assets: $380,255,000,000
Liabilities: $286,456,000,000
Net Worth: $93,799,000,000
Earnings: $12,095,000,000
Emp.: 105,400
Fiscal Year-end: 12/31/23
Communication Service
N.A.I.C.S.: 517111
Matthew D. Ellis (CFO & Exec VP)
Rima Qureshi (Chief Strategy Officer & Exec VP)
Anthony T. Skiadas (Sr VP & Controller)
James J. Gerace (Chief Comm Officer)
Hans E. Vestberg (Chm & CEO)
Sampath Sowmyanarayan (Chief Revenue Officer)

Verizon Communications Inc.—(Continued)

Shankar Arumugavelu *(Chief Digital & Information Officer & Sr VP)*
Jennifer Chronis *(Sr VP)*
K. Guru Gowrappan *(Exec VP)*
Sam Hammock *(Chief HR Officer & Exec VP)*
Kyle Malady *(CTO & Exec VP-Global Networks & Tech)*

Subsidiaries:

Blue Jeans Network, Inc. **(1)**
516 Clyde Ave, Mountain View, CA 94043
Tel.: (408) 550-2828
Web Site: http://www.bluejeans.com
Emp.: 51
Video Conferencing Services
N.A.I.C.S.: 561499
Krish Ramakrishnan *(Co-Founder)*
Alagu Periyannan *(Co-Founder & CTO)*
Stu Aaron *(Chief Comml Officer)*
Ted Tracy *(VP-Engrg)*
Shadi Baqleh *(VP-Sls)*
Oded Gal *(VP-Product Mgmt)*
Cameron Orr *(VP-Channel Sls)*
James Campanini *(VP & Gen Mgr-EMEA)*
Mike Mansbach *(Pres)*
Lori Wright *(CMO)*
Matthew Collier *(Sr VP-Strategic Bus Dev)*
George Mogannam *(Chief Revenue Officer)*
Quentin Gallivan *(CEO)*

Cellco Partnership **(1)**
1 Verizon Way, Basking Ridge, NJ 07920
Tel.: (908) 559-2000
Web Site: http://www.verizonwireless.com
Sales Range: $25-49.9 Billion
Emp.: 83,100
Holding Company
N.A.I.C.S.: 551112

Subsidiary (Domestic):

Golden State Cellular, Inc. **(2)**
1061 Mono Way, Sonora, CA 95370
Tel.: (209) 533-8844
Web Site:
  http://www.goldenstatecellular.com
Sales Range: $1-9.9 Million
Emp.: 20
Wireless Telecommunications Carriers, except Satellite
N.A.I.C.S.: 517112

Division (Domestic):

Verizon Wireless - Midwest **(2)**
1251 E Higgins Rd, Schaumburg, IL 60173
Tel.: (847) 330-6010
Web Site: http://www.verizonwireless.com
Sales Range: $200-249.9 Million
Emp.: 750
Telcommunication Services
N.A.I.C.S.: 517111

Branch (Domestic):

Verizon Wireless - Chandler **(3)**
670 N 54th St Ste 3, Chandler, IN 85226
Tel.: (480) 785-5912
Web Site: http://www.verizonwireless.com
Radiotelephone Communication
N.A.I.C.S.: 517112

Verizon Wireless - Chapmanville **(3)**
RR 119, Chapmanville, WV 25508
Tel.: (304) 343-9911
Web Site: http://www.verizon.com
Sales Range: $25-49.9 Million
Emp.: 30
Electronic Services
N.A.I.C.S.: 221118

Verizon Wireless - Cleveland **(3)**
15234 Triskett Rd, Cleveland, OH 44111
Tel.: (216) 941-8000
Web Site: http://www.verizon.com
Sales Range: $10-24.9 Million
Emp.: 700
Cellular Telephone Services
N.A.I.C.S.: 517112

Verizon Wireless - Dublin **(3)**
7040 Hospital Dr, Dublin, OH 43016
Tel.: (614) 389-2082
Web Site: http://www.verizonwireless.com

Sales Range: $450-499.9 Million
Cellular Telephone Services
N.A.I.C.S.: 517112

Verizon Wireless - Indianapolis **(3)**
4525 Lafayette Rd, Indianapolis, IN 46254
Tel.: (317) 291-4855
Sales Range: $25-49.9 Million
Emp.: 100
Cellular Telephone Services
N.A.I.C.S.: 517112

Verizon Wireless - Lansing **(3)**
5202 W Saginaw Hwy, Lansing, MI 48917
Tel.: (517) 327-0440
Web Site: http://www.verizonwireless.com
Sales Range: $10-24.9 Million
Emp.: 50
Cellular Telephone Services
N.A.I.C.S.: 517112

Verizon Wireless - Minneapolis **(3)**
1090 Shingle Creek Xing, Minneapolis, MN 55430
Tel.: (952) 314-7766
Web Site: http://www.verizonwireless.com
Sales Range: $10-24.9 Million
Emp.: 15
Cellular Telephone Services
N.A.I.C.S.: 517112

Verizon Wireless - Overland Park **(3)**
10740 Nall Ave Ste 400, Overland Park, KS 66211
Tel.: (913) 696-5121
Web Site: http://www.cellco.com
Sales Range: $50-74.9 Million
Emp.: 200
Cellular Telephone Services
N.A.I.C.S.: 517112

Verizon Wireless - Saint Louis **(3)**
4647 Chippewa St, Saint Louis, MO 63116
Tel.: (314) 865-4405
Web Site: http://www.verizonwireless.com
Sales Range: $10-24.9 Million
Emp.: 5
Cellular Telephone Services
N.A.I.C.S.: 517112

Verizon Wireless - Southfield **(3)**
28117 Telegraph Rd, Southfield, MI 48034
Tel.: (248) 358-3700
Web Site: http://www.verizonwireless.com
Sales Range: $500-549.9 Million
Mobile Telephone Communication
N.A.I.C.S.: 517112

Division (Domestic):

Verizon Wireless - Northeast **(2)**
100 Southgate Pkwy, Morristown, NJ 07960
Tel.: (973) 666 7377
Web Site: http://www.verizonwireless.com
Sales Range: $200-249.9 Million
Emp.: 700
Cellular Telephone Services
N.A.I.C.S.: 449210

Branch (Domestic):

Verizon Wireless - Bedminster **(3)**
180 Washington Valley Rd, Bedminster, NJ 07921
Tel.: (908) 306-7000
Web Site: http://www.verizonwireless.com
Sales Range: $10-24.9 Million
Emp.: 7
Cellular Telephone Services
N.A.I.C.S.: 517112

Verizon Wireless - Bergenfield **(3)**
415 S Washington Ave, Bergenfield, NJ 07621
Tel.: (201) 384-5688
Web Site: http://www.verizon.com
Sales Range: $200-249.9 Million
Telephone Communication, Except Radio
N.A.I.C.S.: 517121

Verizon Wireless - Buffalo **(3)**
1 Walden Galleria, Buffalo, NY 14225
Tel.: (716) 685-3053
Web Site: http://www.verizonwireless.com
Sales Range: $10-24.9 Million
Emp.: 45
Telephone Communication Services
N.A.I.C.S.: 449210

Verizon Wireless - Downingtown **(3)**

32 Quarry Rd, Downingtown, PA 19335
Tel.: (610) 518-3200
Web Site: http://www.verizonwireless.com
Sales Range: $1-9.9 Million
Emp.: 6
Cellular Telephone Services
N.A.I.C.S.: 517112

Verizon Wireless - Fair Lawn **(3)**
27-02 Fair Lawn Ave, Fair Lawn, NJ 07410
Tel.: (973) 649-9900
Sales Range: $200-249.9 Million
Telephone Communication Services & Executive Offices
N.A.I.C.S.: 517121

Verizon Wireless - Falls Church **(3)**
2937 Gallows Rd, Falls Church, VA 22042
Tel.: (703) 849-9677
Sales Range: $1-9.9 Million
Emp.: 2
Telephone Communication Services
N.A.I.C.S.: 811111

Verizon Wireless - Frederick **(3)**
1003 W Patrick St, Frederick, MD 21702
Tel.: (301) 695-6000
Web Site: http://www.verizonwireless.com
Sales Range: $10-24.9 Million
Emp.: 6
Cellular Telephone Services
N.A.I.C.S.: 517112

Verizon Wireless - Fredericksburg **(3)**
539 Jefferson Davis Hwy, Fredericksburg, VA 22401
Tel.: (540) 371-1471
Web Site: http://www.verizonwireless.com
Sales Range: $10-24.9 Million
Emp.: 13
Cellular Telephone Services
N.A.I.C.S.: 517112

Verizon Wireless - Jersey City **(3)**
40 Amity St, Jersey City, NJ 07304
Tel.: (201) 433-8553
Sales Range: $1-9.9 Million
Emp.: 7
Telegraph or Telephone Carrier & Repeater Equipment
N.A.I.C.S.: 561990

Verizon Wireless - Lancaster **(3)**
126 N Duke St, Lancaster, PA 17602
Tel.: (717) 299-8401
Sales Range: $50-74.9 Million
Emp.: 165
Telephone Communication Services
N.A.I.C.S.: 517121

Verizon Wireless - Orangeburg **(3)**
2000 Corporate Dr, Orangeburg, NY 10962
Tel.: (845) 365-7200
Sales Range: $200-249.9 Million
Radiotelephone Communication
N.A.I.C.S.: 517112

Verizon Wireless - Stroudsburg **(3)**
20 S 7th St, Stroudsburg, PA 18360
Tel.: (570) 424-0200
Sales Range: $25-49.9 Million
Emp.: 75
Telephone Communication, Except Radio
N.A.I.C.S.: 517121

Verizon Wireless - Wilmington **(3)**
3900 N Washington St, Wilmington, DE 19802
Tel.: (302) 761-4200
Sales Range: $10-24.9 Million
Emp.: 25
Telephone Communications Broker
N.A.I.C.S.: 517121

Division (Domestic):

Verizon Wireless - South **(2)**
5215 Windward Pkwy, Alpharetta, GA 30004
Tel.: (770) 475-0000
Web Site: http://www.verizonwireless.com
Sales Range: $600-649.9 Million
Emp.: 2,000
Cellular Telephone Services
N.A.I.C.S.: 517112

Branch (Domestic):

Verizon Wireless - Bartlett **(3)**

2323 N Germantown Pkwy, Cordova, TN 38016
Tel.: (901) 377-4990
Web Site: http://www.verizonwireless.com
Sales Range: $10-24.9 Million
Emp.: 7
Cellular Telephone Services
N.A.I.C.S.: 517112

Verizon Wireless - Birmingham **(3)**
579 Brookwood Vlg, Birmingham, AL 35209
Tel.: (205) 290-0134
Web Site: http://www.verizonwireless.com
Sales Range: $10-24.9 Million
Emp.: 11
Cellular Telephone Services
N.A.I.C.S.: 517112

Verizon Wireless - Boca Raton **(3)**
5050 Town Ctr Circle, Boca Raton, FL 33486
Tel.: (561) 392-7011
Web Site: http://www.verizon.com
Sales Range: $50-74.9 Million
Emp.: 100
Communications Equipment
N.A.I.C.S.: 517121

Verizon Wireless - Charlotte **(3)**
110 McCullough Dr, Charlotte, NC 28262
Tel.: (704) 548-9510
Web Site: http://www.verizonwireless.com
Sales Range: $25-49.9 Million
Emp.: 13
Telephone Equipment & Systems
N.A.I.C.S.: 449210

Verizon Wireless - Columbia **(3)**
173 Columbiana Dr, Columbia, SC 29212
Tel.: (803) 749-4500
Sales Range: $10-24.9 Million
Emp.: 12
Radiotelephone Communication
N.A.I.C.S.: 517112

Verizon Wireless - El Paso **(3)**
1798 N Zaragosa Rd, El Paso, TX 79936
Tel.: (915) 857-7171
Web Site: http://www.verizonwireless.com
Sales Range: $1-9.9 Million
Emp.: 5
Cellular Telephone Services
N.A.I.C.S.: 517112

Verizon Wireless - Florence **(3)**
2411 David H McLeod Blvd, Florence, SC 29501
Tel.: (843) 673-0300
Web Site: http://www.verizonwireless.com
Sales Range: $10-24.9 Million
Emp.: 20
Cellular Telephone Services
N.A.I.C.S.: 517112

Verizon Wireless - Greensboro **(3)**
4207 W Wendover Ave, Greensboro, NC 27407
Tel.: (336) 851-6700
Web Site: http://www.verizonwireless.com
Sales Range: $10-24.9 Million
Emp.: 18
Cellular Telephone Services
N.A.I.C.S.: 517112

Verizon Wireless - Greenville **(3)**
701 Brookfield Pkwy, Greenville, SC 29607
Tel.: (864) 987-2000
Web Site: http://www.verizonwireless.com
Sales Range: $400-449.9 Million
Emp.: 1,000
Cellular Telephone Services
N.A.I.C.S.: 517112

Verizon Wireless - Greenwood **(3)**
1101 Montague Ave Ext Ste 72, Greenwood, SC 29649
Tel.: (864) 223-4445
Web Site: http://www.verizonwireless.com
Sales Range: $10-24.9 Million
Emp.: 18
Cellular Telephone Services
N.A.I.C.S.: 517112

Verizon Wireless - Hendersonville **(3)**
1602 Four Season Blvd, Hendersonville, NC 28792
Tel.: (828) 692-1400
Web Site: http://www.verizonwireless.com
Sales Range: $10-24.9 Million
Emp.: 10
Retail of Cellular Phones

N.A.I.C.S.: 517112

Verizon Wireless - Houston (3)
8401 Westheimer Rd, Houston, TX 77063
Tel.: (713) 952-2355
Web Site: http://www.verizonwireless.com
Sales Range: $400-449.9 Million
Emp.: 1,000
Radiotelephone Communication
N.A.I.C.S.: 517112

Verizon Wireless - Knoxville (3)
2430 Callahan Dr, Knoxville, TN 37912
Tel.: (865) 947-4481
Web Site: http://www.verizonwireless.com
Sales Range: $25-49.9 Million
Emp.: 15
Telephone Equipments & Services
N.A.I.C.S.: 449210

Verizon Wireless - Nashville (3)
455 Duke Dr, Franklin, TN 37067
Tel.: (615) 771-1924
Sales Range: $75-99.9 Million
Emp.: 250
Wireless Communications
N.A.I.C.S.: 517121

Verizon Wireless - Oviedo (3)
8155 Red Bug Lake Rd Ste 113, Oviedo,
FL 32765
Tel.: (407) 365-4949
Web Site: http://www.verizonwireless.com
Sales Range: $10-24.9 Million
Emp.: 7
Cellular Telephone Services
N.A.I.C.S.: 517112

Verizon Wireless Florida (3)
714 S Dale Mabry Hwy, Tampa, FL 33609
Tel.: (813) 874-5718
Web Site: http://www.verizonwireless.com
Sales Range: $75-99.9 Million
Telecommunications & Mobile Services
N.A.I.C.S.: 517112

Division (Domestic):

Verizon Wireless - West (2)
6266 Irvine Blvd, Irvine, CA 92620
Tel.: (949) 653-0125
Web Site: http://www.verizonwireless.com
Sales Range: $500-549.9 Million
Emp.: 1,500
Mobile Telephone Services
N.A.I.C.S.: 517112

Branch (Domestic):

Verizon Wireless - Bellevue (3)
14825 Main St, Bellevue, WA 98007
Tel.: (425) 531-7129
Web Site: http://www.verizonwireless.com
Sales Range: $10-24.9 Million
Emp.: 11
Cellular Telephone Services
N.A.I.C.S.: 517112

Verizon Wireless - Chandler (3)
3401 W Frye Rd Ste 5, Chandler, AZ 85226
Tel.: (480) 855-1272
Web Site: http://www.verizonwireless.com
Sales Range: $50-74.9 Million
Emp.: 200
Cellular Service
N.A.I.C.S.: 517121

Verizon Wireless - Englewood (3)
601 Englewood Pkwy, Englewood, CO
80110
Tel.: (303) 789-7201
Web Site: http://www.verizonwireless.com
Sales Range: $50-74.9 Million
Emp.: 150
Cellular Telephone Services
N.A.I.C.S.: 517112

Verizon Wireless - Fairfield (3)
1586 Gateway Blvd Ste C1, Fairfield, CA
94533
Tel.: (707) 399-0866
Web Site: http://www.verizonwireless.com
Sales Range: $1-9.9 Million
Emp.: 5
Radiotelephone Communication
N.A.I.C.S.: 517112

Verizon Wireless - Santa Monica (3)
2530 Wilshire Blvd Ste A, Santa Monica,
CA 90403
Tel.: (310) 828-1279

Sales Range: $200-249.9 Million
Telephone Communications
N.A.I.C.S.: 517121

Verizon Wireless - Vancouver (3)
7620 NE 119th Pl Ste 103, Vancouver, WA
98662
Tel.: (360) 719-2082
Web Site: http://www.verizonwireless.com
Sales Range: $25-49.9 Million
Emp.: 150
Cellular Telephone Services
N.A.I.C.S.: 517112

Subsidiary (Non-US):

**Verizon Wireless Messaging Services
Ltd.** (2)
550 Alden Rd Unit 111, Markham, L3R 6A8,
ON, Canada
Tel.: (905) 940-6460
Web Site: http://www.verizonmessaging.com
Sales Range: $10-24.9 Million
Emp.: 7
Electronic Device Distr
N.A.I.C.S.: 812990

MCI, LLC (1)
22001 Loudoun County Pkwy, Ashburn, VA
20147
Tel.: (703) 416-0760
Web Site: http://www.mci.com
Sales Range: $75-99.9 Million
Long-Distance Voice, Data & Video Ser-
vices
N.A.I.C.S.: 517121

Subsidiary (Domestic):

MCI International, Inc. (2)
225 Old New Brunswick Rd, Piscataway,
NJ 08854
Tel.: (732) 562-8588
Long Distance Telephone Communications
N.A.I.C.S.: 517121

MCI Worldcom (2)
50 International Dr, Greenville, SC 29615-
4832
Tel.: (864) 676-1000
Web Site: http://www.worldcom.com
Sales Range: $100-124.9 Million
Emp.: 400
Communications Specialization
N.A.I.C.S.: 238210

**MCI Worldcom Network Services,
Inc.** (2)
8750 W Bryn Mawr Ave, Chicago, IL 60631-
3508
Tel.: (773) 399-1700
Web Site: http://www.verizon.com
Sales Range: $100-124.9 Million
Emp.: 300
Long Distance Telephone Communications
N.A.I.C.S.: 517121

Moment Design (1)
13 Crosby St 6th Fl, New York, NY 10013
Tel.: (212) 625-9744
Web Site: https://www.momentdesign.com
Computer System Design Services
N.A.I.C.S.: 541512
Brendan Reynolds (CEO)
Alexa Curtis (Mng Dir)
John Devanney (Mng Dir)
Philip Kim (Mng Dir)
Shannon O'Brien (Mng Dir)

**NAP de las Americas-Madrid,
S.A.** (1)
Poligano Industrial de las Mercedes Yecora
4, Calle Yecora No 4, Madrid, 28022, Spain
Tel.: (34) 912349950
Web Site: http://www.terremark.com
Sales Range: $10-24.9 Million
Emp.: 6
Information Technology Infrastructure Ser-
vices
N.A.I.C.S.: 541519

NAP of the Americas/West Inc. (1)
3030 Corvin Dr, Santa Clara, CA 95051
Tel.: (408) 331-3060
Web Site: http://www.terremark.com
Sales Range: $75-99.9 Million
Information Technology Infrastructure Ser-
vices
N.A.I.C.S.: 541519

**Straight Path Communications
Inc.** (1)
5300 Hickory Park Dr Ste 218, Glen Allen,
VA 23059
Tel.: (804) 433-1522
Investment Management Service
N.A.I.C.S.: 523940

Terremark Worldwide, Inc.-Miami (1)
50 NE 9th St, Miami, FL 33132 (100%)
Tel.: (305) 373-5658
Web Site: http://www.terremark.com
Sales Range: $25-49.9 Million
Emp.: 100
Telecommunications & Internet Services
N.A.I.C.S.: 517810

TracFone Wireless, Inc. (1)
9700 NW 112th Ave, Miami, FL 33178-1504
Tel.: (305) 640-2000
Web Site: http://www.tracfone.com
Prepaid Wireless Communication Services
N.A.I.C.S.: 517121
Eduardo Diaz Corona (CEO)

Verizon Americas Inc. (1)
275 Shoreline Dr Ste 400, Redwood City,
CA 94065
Tel.: (650) 832-6600
Telecommunication Servicesb
N.A.I.C.S.: 541618

Verizon Business Global LLC (1)
22001 Loudoun County Pkwy, Ashburn, VA
20147
Tel.: (703) 886-5600
Emp.: 40,400
Cellular & Other Wireless Telecommunica-
tion Services
N.A.I.C.S.: 517112

Subsidiary (Domestic):

Cranberry Properties LLC. (2)
201 Mohican Ln, Beckley, WV 25880
Tel.: (304) 252-5206
Web Site: http://www.demo-
cranberrywoods.com
Residential Property Management Services
N.A.I.C.S.: 531311

**Verizon Business Network Services
Inc.** (1)
1 Verizon Way, Basking Ridge, NJ 07920-
1025
Tel.: (908) 559-2001
Web Site: http://www.verizonbusiness.com
Sales Range: $15-24.9 Billion
Emp.: 32,000
Telecommunication, Risk & Information Se-
curity Solutions & Services
N.A.I.C.S.: 517810
T. J. Fox (Sr VP-Industrial IoT & Automo-
tive)
Kyle Malady (CEO)
Craig Silliman (Pres)
Matthew D. Ellis (Exec VP)
Samantha Hammock (Exec VP)
James J. Gerace (Chief Comm Officer)
Rose Stuckey Kirk (Chief Corp Social Resp
Officer)
Rima Qureshi (Exec VP)
Diego Scotti (Exec VP)
Vandana Venkatesh (Exec VP)

Subsidiary (Non-US):

Cybertrust Belgium N.V. (2)
Culliganlaan 2E Diegem, Brussels, 1831,
Belgium
Tel.: (32) 16287000
Web Site: http://www.verizonbusiness.com
Sales Range: $50-74.9 Million
Emp.: 200
Managed Security Solutions
N.A.I.C.S.: 561621
Peter Koning (CEO)

Unit (Domestic):

**Verizon Business Security
Solutions** (2)
22001 Louden County Pkwy, Ashburn, VA
20147
Web Site: http://www.verizonbusiness.com
Sales Range: $150-199.9 Million
Emp.: 1,000
Risk Management Consulting Services &
Products Mfr
N.A.I.C.S.: 541611

**Verizon Communications Inc. - Buf-
falo, WV** (1)
400 Jacobson Dr, Buffalo, WV 25159
Tel.: (304) 759-0102
Sales Range: $50-74.9 Million
Emp.: 100
Telephone Communications
N.A.I.C.S.: 522220
Jina Chapman (Mgr)

**Verizon Communications Inc. -
Clarksburg, WV** (1)
425 S Holden St, Clarksburg, WV 26301
Tel.: (304) 351-7189
Sales Range: $25-49.9 Million
Emp.: 150
Local & Long Distance Telephone Communi-
nications
N.A.I.C.S.: 517121

**Verizon Communications Inc. -
Hayes, VA** (1)
7455 Lirchmont Rd, Hayes, VA 23072
Tel.: (804) 642-7670
Web Site: http://www.verizon.com
Telephone Communication, Except Radio
N.A.I.C.S.: 531130

**Verizon Communications Inc. - John-
stown, PA** (1)
395 Industrial Park Rd, Johnstown, PA
15904-1941
Tel.: (814) 536-6391
Sales Range: $25-49.9 Million
Emp.: 100
Telephone Cords & Accessories
N.A.I.C.S.: 334210

**Verizon Communications Inc. - Liver-
pool, NY** (1)
3881 State Route 31, Liverpool, NY 13090
Tel.: (800) 837-4966
Web Site: http://www22.verizon.com
Sales Range: $10-24.9 Million
Emp.: 25
Telephone Services
N.A.I.C.S.: 517121

**Verizon Communications Inc. - Mont-
gomeryville, PA** (1)
744 Bethlehem Pike, Montgomeryville, PA
18936
Tel.: (215) 368-7391
Web Site: http://www.verizonwireless.com
Sales Range: $1-9.9 Million
Emp.: 4
Verizon Only Surplus Salvage & Supply
N.A.I.C.S.: 455219

**Verizon Communications Inc. - Roa-
noke, VA** (1)
4843 Oakland Blvd, Roanoke, VA 24012
Tel.: (540) 265-7536
Web Site: http://www.verizon.com
Sales Range: $50-74.9 Million
Emp.: 200
Telephone Services
N.A.I.C.S.: 561421

**Verizon Communications Inc. - Wa-
tertown, NY** (1)
610 Coffeen St, Watertown, NY 13601
Tel.: (315) 265-9903
Sales Range: $25-49.9 Million
Emp.: 50
Telephone Communication, Except Radio
N.A.I.C.S.: 517121

**Verizon Communications Inc. - White
Plains, NY** (1)
4 W Red Oak Ln ste 1, White Plains, NY
10604
Tel.: (914) 644-3800
Sales Range: $100-124.9 Million
Emp.: 300
Research Facilities
N.A.I.C.S.: 517121

Verizon Connect Fleet (1)
20 Enterprise Ste 100, Aliso Viejo, CA
92656
Tel.: (949) 389-5500
Web Site: http://www.verizonconnect.com
Fleet Management & Logistics Software
Publisher
N.A.I.C.S.: 513210

Verizon Credit Inc. (1)
201 N Franklin St Ste 3300, Tampa, FL
33602-5818 (100%)

Verizon Communications Inc.—(Continued)
Tel.: (813) 229-6000
Web Site: http://www.verizon.com
Sales Range: $25-49.9 Million
Emp.: 105
Leasing & Financing Services
N.A.I.C.S.: 532210

Verizon Data Services (1)
7901 Freeport Blvd, Sacramento, CA
95832-9701
Tel.: (916) 665-3200
Web Site: http://www.verizon.com
Sales Range: $50-74.9 Million
Emp.: 200
Data Processing Services
N.A.I.C.S.: 518210

Verizon Data Services (1)
1 E Telecom Pkwy, Tampa, FL
33637 **(100%)**
Tel.: (813) 978-4000
Sales Range: $400-449.9 Million
Emp.: 2,700
Information Processing & Systems Development Services
N.A.I.C.S.: 518210

Subsidiary (Domestic):

Infocrossing Healthcare, Inc. (2)
2005 E Technology Cir, Tempe, AZ
85284-1817 **(100%)**
Tel.: (602) 678-6300
Sales Range: $10-24.9 Million
Emp.: 25
Data Processing Services
N.A.I.C.S.: 541511

Verizon Delaware Inc. (1)
901 N Tatnall St 2nd Fl, Wilmington, DE
19801-1605 **(100%)**
Tel.: (302) 571-1571
Sales Range: $10-24.9 Million
Emp.: 1,400
Telephone Communications
N.A.I.C.S.: 517121

Verizon Directory Support Center (1)
52 Walnut St, Warsaw, VA 22572
Tel.: (804) 333-8850
Web Site: http://www.verizon.com
Sales Range: $25-49.9 Million
Emp.: 36
Directory Support
N.A.I.C.S.: 561410

Verizon Enhanced Communities (1)
22001 Loudoun County Pkwy C1 - 2 - 251,
Ashburn, VA 20147-6105
Tel.: (703) 375-4400
Sales Range: $75-99.9 Million
Telephone Communication Services
N.A.I.C.S.: 517121

**Verizon Enterprise Solutions
Group** (1)
1 Verizon Way, Basking Ridge, NJ 07920
Tel.: (908) 559-1968
Web Site: http://www.verizonenterprise.com
Sales Range: $200-249.9 Million
Enterprise Business Telecommunications
N.A.I.C.S.: 517111

Subsidiary (Domestic):

Verizon Connect Inc. (2)
2002 Summit Blvd Ste 1800, Atlanta, GA
30319
Tel.: (404) 573-5800
Web Site: http://www.verizonconnect.com
Motor Vehicle Information Technologies Developer & Services
N.A.I.C.S.: 336320

Subsidiary (Domestic):

Verizon Networkfleet, Inc. (3)
9868 Scranton Rd, San Diego, CA 92121
Web Site: https://www.verizonconnect.com
Motor Vehicle Remote Monitoring & Data Communication Technologies Developer & Marketer
N.A.I.C.S.: 336320

Branch (Domestic):

**Verizon Enterprise Solutions
Group** (2)

8867 Villa La Jolla Dr Ste 600A, La Jolla,
CA 92037
Tel.; (858) 526-0847
Web Site: http://www.verizonwireless.com
Sales Range: $10-24.9 Million
Emp.: 20
Voice Telephone Communications
N.A.I.C.S.: 517121

**Verizon License Administration
Group** (1)
900 Clinton Ave, Irvington, NJ 07111
Tel.: (973) 649-4058
Sales Range: $25-49.9 Million
Emp.: 75
Administrative Services
N.A.I.C.S.: 517121

**Verizon Network Integration
Corporation** (1)
32661 Edward Ave, Madison Heights, MI
48071-1448
Tel.: (248) 589-2264
Sales Range: $10-24.9 Million
Emp.: 20
Computer Networking
N.A.I.C.S.: 517121

Verizon New Jersey Inc. (1)
540 Broad St, Newark, NJ 07102
Tel.: (973) 649-9900
Web Site: http://www.bellatlantic.com
Sales Range: $1-4.9 Billion
Emp.: 12,600
Telecommunications
N.A.I.C.S.: 517121

Verizon New York Inc. (1)
1095 Ave of the Americas, New York, NY
10036
Tel.: (212) 395-1000
Web Site: http://www.verizon.com
Sales Range: $75-99.9 Million
Telecommunication Servicesb
N.A.I.C.S.: 517121

Verizon Northwest Inc. (1)
600 Hidden Ridge, Irving, TX 75038-3809
Tel.: (972) 718-2433
Rev.: $2,190,000,000
Emp.: 2,795
Telecommunication Servicesb
N.A.I.C.S.: 517121

Verizon Pennsylvania Inc. (1)
1717 Arch St, Philadelphia, PA
19103 **(100%)**
Tel.: (215) 466-9900
Sales Range: $1-4.9 Billion
Emp.: 16,500
Regional Telephone Company
N.A.I.C.S.: 517111

Verizon Privacy Group (1)
1320 N Courthouse Rd, Arlington, VA 22201
Tel.: (703) 312-4027
Web Site: http://www22.verizon.com
Sales Range: $25-49.9 Million
Emp.: 120
Electronic Privacy Information Services
N.A.I.C.S.: 519290

Verizon Select Services Inc. (1)
156 Mushroom Blvd, Rochester, NY 14623-
3204
Tel.: (585) 279-2900
Rev.: $3,000,000
Emp.: 35
Telecommunications Consultant
N.A.I.C.S.: 541690

Verizon Services Group Inc. (1)
1095 Ave of Americas 12th Fl Rm 21, New
York, NY 10036
Tel.: (866) 483-3800
Web Site: http://www22.verizon.com
Sales Range: $75-99.9 Million
Management Consulting Services & Corporate Offices
N.A.I.C.S.: 541611

Verizon TeleProducts (1)
400 Brandywine Pkwy, West Chester, PA
19380
Tel.: (610) 918-2300
Web Site: http://www.verizon.com
Sales Range: $75-99.9 Million
Emp.: 200
Telephone Equipment
N.A.I.C.S.: 423690

Verizon Virginia Inc. (1)
5123 Oakland Blvd, Roanoke, VA
24012 **(100%)**
Tel.: (540) 982-1899
Web Site: http://www.Verizon.com
Sales Range: $1-9.9 Million
Emp.: 250
Telephone Communications
N.A.I.C.S.: 517121

Verizon Virginia Inc. (1)
1320 N Courthouse Rd 9th Fl, Arlington, VA
22201
Tel.: (804) 772-1798
Web Site: http://www.verizon.com
Sales Range: $1-9.9 Million
Local & Long Distance Telephone Communications
N.A.I.C.S.: 517121

Verizon Yellow Pages (1)
290 Rte 130, Sandwich, MA 02563-2366
Tel.: (508) 833-4949
Web Site: http://www.superpages.com
Emp.: 20
Telephone & Other Directory Publishing
N.A.I.C.S.: 513140

Verizon Yellow Pages (1)
300 Esplanade Dr Ste 600, Oxnard, CA
93036
Tel.: (805) 278-3400
Web Site: http://www.dexmedia.com
Sales Range: $10-24.9 Million
Emp.: 45
Yellow Pages Advertisements Sales
N.A.I.C.S.: 541890

VERONI BRANDS CORP.

2275 Half Day Rd Ste 346, Bannock-
burn, IL 60015 DE
Web Site:
http://www.veronibrands.com
Year Founded: 2016
VONI—(OTCIQ)
Rev.: $3,205,063
Assets: $201,723
Liabilities: $1,082,338
Net Worth: ($880,615)
Earnings: ($706,566)
Emp.: 4
Fiscal Year-end: 12/31/21
Beverage Product Distr
N.A.I.C.S.: 424820
Igor Gabal (Co-Founder, Pres, CEO,
CFO, Chief Acctg Officer & Sec)
Tomasz Kotas (Co-Founder)

VERRA MOBILITY CORPORATION

1150 N Alma School Rd, Mesa, AZ
85201
Tel.: (480) 443-7000 DE
Web Site:
https://www.verramobility.com
Year Founded: 2016
VRRM—(NASDAQ)
Rev.: $741,598,000
Assets: $1,756,269,000
Liabilities: $1,525,199,000
Net Worth: $231,070,000
Earnings: $92,475,000
Emp.: 1,396
Fiscal Year-end: 12/31/22
Investment Services
N.A.I.C.S.: 523999
Craig C. Conti (CFO)
Jason Rivera (CTO)
Steven C. Lalla (Exec VP-Comml
Svcs)
Jon Baldwin (Exec VP)
Jon Keyser (Chief Legal Officer &
Exec VP)
Craig Conti (CFO)
Cate Prescott (Chief People Officer &
Exec VP)
David Roberts (Pres & CEO)

Subsidiaries:

ATS Processing Services, L.L.C. (1)

PO Box 22091, Tempe, AZ 85285-2091
Tel.: (480) 452-1763
Web Site: http://www.rentalcarticket.com
Car Rental & Leasing Services
N.A.I.C.S.: 532112

Auto Tag of America LLC (1)
6015 31st St E Ste 100, Bradenton, FL
34203
Tel.: (941) 739-8841
Web Site: https://www.autotagamerica.com
Automotive Services
N.A.I.C.S.: 811111
Nick S. Gigliotti (Pres)

Contractum Limited (1)
Tel.: (44) 2038234960
Web Site: https://www.contractum.eu
Parking Collection Services
N.A.I.C.S.: 926120

EPC Hungary Kft (1)
Zahony u 7, 1031, Budapest, Hungary
Tel.: (36) 14900153
Web Site: https://www.epchungary.hu
Parking Collection Services
N.A.I.C.S.: 926120

Euro Parking Collection, plc (1)
Tel.: (44) 2072889740
Web Site: https://www.epcplc.com
Parking Collection Services
N.A.I.C.S.: 926120

**Greenlight Acquisition
Corporation** (1)
312 Walnut St Ste 2120, Cincinnati, OH
45202
Tel.: (513) 362-4325
Web Site: https://www.gla.holdings
Asset Management Services
N.A.I.C.S.: 523940
James M. Gould (Co-Founder, Chm &
CEO)
Ian James (Co-Founder & Pres)
Stephen Letourneau (Co-Founder & Chief
Branding Officer)

PlatePass, L.L.C. (1)
1150 N Alma School Rd, Mesa, AZ 85201
Web Site: https://www.platepass.com
Electronic Toll Payment Services
N.A.I.C.S.: 926120

Redflex Holdings Limited (1)
Level 1 31 Market Street, South Melbourne,
3205, VIC, Australia
Tel.: (61) 390933324
Web Site: http://www.redflex.com
Vehicle Monitoring & Enforcement Equipment & Services
N.A.I.C.S.: 334310
Craig Durham (Gen Counsel-Grp, Sec & Sr
VP)
Fergus Porter (Sr VP-Engrg & Delivery)
Laurence Giles (Sr VP-Markets & Solutions-
Global)
Michael R. Finn (Sr VP-Sls & Mktg-Global)
Mark J. Talbot (CEO-Grp & Mng Dir)
Neville Joyce (CFO-Grp & Sr VP)
Lewis H. Miller (Sr VP-Global Ops)
Angela Fair (Sr VP-People & Performance)
Jane Prosch-Jensen (VP-Govt Rels)
Kenneth M. Dodd (VP-Sls Ops-Global)

Subsidiary (US):

Redflex Traffic Systems Inc. (2)
5651 W Talavi Blvd Ste 200, Glendale, AZ
85306-1893
Tel.: (623) 207-2000
Web Site: http://www.redflex.com
Sales Range: $100-124.9 Million
Emp.: 300
Vehicle Monitoring & Enforcement Equipment & Services
N.A.I.C.S.: 334310

Subsidiary (Domestic):

**Redflex Traffic Systems (California)
Inc.** (3)
5835 Uplander Way Ste A, Culver City, CA
90230-6607
Tel.: (310) 743-1207
Web Site: http://redflex.com
Emp.: 4
Automated Traffic System Installation Services
N.A.I.C.S.: 238210

Subsidiary (Non-US):

Redflex Traffic Systems Pty Ltd (3)
31 Market Street, South Melbourne, 3205, VIC, Australia
Tel.: (61) 396741800
Web Site: http://www.redflex.com
Emp.: 200
Automated Traffic System Installation Services
N.A.I.C.S.: 561990

Redflex Traffic Systems India Private Limited (1)
4/293 Old Mahabalipuram Road, Perungudi, Chennai, 600096, Tamil Nadu, India
Tel.: (91) 4466136802
Road Traffic Control Services
N.A.I.C.S.: 561990

Redflex Traffic Systems Limited (1)
Unit 20 Russell House Chalcroft Business Park, Burnetts Lane West End, Southampton, SO30 2PA, United Kingdom
Tel.: (44) 2381800110
Road Traffic Control Services
N.A.I.C.S.: 561990

Redflex Traffic Systems Malaysia Sdn. Bhd. (1)
D1 08 GF D1 08 01 Blok D Pusat, Perdagangan Dana 1 Jalan PJU 1A/46 PJU 1A, 47301, Petaling Jaya, Malaysia
Tel.: (60) 322614889
Road Traffic Control Services
N.A.I.C.S.: 561990

T2 Systems, Inc. (1)
8900 Keystone Xing Ste 700, Indianapolis, IN 46240
Tel.: (317) 524-5500
Web Site: https://www.t2systems.com
Parking Management Software Developer
N.A.I.C.S.: 513210
Adam Blake (CEO)
Maggie Vercoe (Sr VP-Customer Experience)

Subsidiary (Non-US):

T2 Systems Canada Inc. (2)
3480 Gilmore Way Ste 300, Burnaby, V5G 4Y1, BC, Canada
Tel.: (778) 375-6000
Web Site: https://www.t2systems.com
Parking Management Solutions
N.A.I.C.S.: 513210

VERRICA PHARMACEUTICALS, INC.
44 W Gay St Ste 400, West Chester, PA 19380
Tel.: (484) 453-3300   DE
Web Site: https://www.verrica.com
Year Founded: 2013
VRCA—(NASDAQ)
Rev.: $9,032,000
Assets: $44,721,000
Liabilities: $4,688,000
Net Worth: $40,033,000
Earnings: ($24,487,000)
Emp.: 22
Fiscal Year-end: 12/31/22
Pharmaceutical Preparation Manufacturing
N.A.I.C.S.: 325412
Gary Goldenberg (Chief Medical Officer)
Terry Kohler (CFO)
Chris Hayes (Chief Legal Officer)
Ted White (Pres & CEO)

VERSAILLES FINANCIAL CORPORATION
Tel.: (937) 526-4515   MD
Web Site:
https://www.versaillessavings
bank.com
Year Founded: 2009
VERF—(OTCIQ)
Sales Range: $1-9.9 Million
Bank Holding Company
N.A.I.C.S.: 551111

Dawn Brandt (Coord-ATM & Customer Svc Rep)
Lisa Miller (Coord-Internet & Customer Svc Rep)
Jerome F. Bey III (VP & Sr Lender)

VERSEON CORPORATION
47071 Bayside Pkwy, Fremont, CA 94538
Tel.: (510) 225-9000
Web Site: http://www.verseon.com
Year Founded: 2002
VSN—(AIM)
Pharmaceutical Preparation Mfr
N.A.I.C.S.: 325412
Adityo Prakash (Co-Founder & CEO)
Eniko Fodor (Co-Founder & COO)
David Kita (Co-Founder & VP-R&D)
Kevin Short (Dir-Discovery Programs)
David Williams (Dir-R&D)
Anirban Datta (Dir-Discovery Biology)
Thomas A. Hecht (Chm)

VERTEX ENERGY, INC.
1331 Gemini St Ste 250, Houston, TX 77058
Tel.: (281) 486-4182   NV
Web Site:
https://www.vertexenergy.com
Year Founded: 2000
VTNR—(NASDAQ)
Rev.: $2,791,715,000
Assets: $689,385,000
Liabilities: $523,965,000
Net Worth: $165,420,000
Earnings: ($4,822,000)
Emp.: 497
Fiscal Year-end: 12/31/22
Petroleum Bulk Stations & Terminals
N.A.I.C.S.: 324199
John Noel Strickland (VP-Black Oil Ops)
Bart Rice (Exec VP)
James P. Gregory (Gen Counsel & Sec)
Chris Carlson (CFO)
Erica Snedegar (VP-Business Development)
Joshua D. Foster (Chief Comml Officer & Dir-Refining)
Benjamin P. Cowart (Founder, Chm, Pres, CEO & Interim COO)

Subsidiaries:

Cedar Marine Terminals, L.P. (1)
200 Atlantic Pipeline Rd, Baytown, TX 77520
Tel.: (281) 383-5050
Petroleum Bulk Station Operator
N.A.I.C.S.: 424710
Jack Breman (Mgr-Bus Dev)

Crossroad Carriers LP (1)
PO Box 849, Mont Belvieu, TX 77580
Tel.: (281) 385-0790
Web Site: http://www.crossroadcarriers.net
Oil & Gas Field Services
N.A.I.C.S.: 213112

Vertex Recovery L.P. (1)
1331 Gemini St Ste 103, Houston, TX 77058
Tel.: (281) 486-4182
Oil & Gas Field Services
N.A.I.C.S.: 213112

VERTEX PHARMACEUTICALS INCORPORATED
50 Northern Ave, Boston, MA 02210
Tel.: (617) 341-6100   MA
Web Site: https://www.vrtx.com
Year Founded: 1989
VRTX—(NASDAQ)
Rev.: $9,869,200,000
Assets: $22,730,200,000
Liabilities: $5,149,800,000
Net Worth: $17,580,400,000
Earnings: $3,619,600,000
Emp.: 5,400

Fiscal Year-end: 12/31/23
Pharmaceuticals Mfr
N.A.I.C.S.: 325412
Reshma Kewalramani (Pres & CEO)
Jonathan Biller (Chief Legal Officer)
Charles F. Wagner Jr. (CFO & Exec VP)
Zachry Barber (Sr Dir-Investor Relations)
Jeffrey M. Leiden (Exec Chm)
David Altshuler (Chief Scientific Officer & Exec VP-Res-Global)
Michael J. Parini (Chief Legal, Administrative & Bus Dev Officer & Chief Legal, Administrative & Bus Dev Officer)
Ludovic Fenaux (Sr VP-Comml Ops-Intl)
Amit K. Sachdev (Chief Patient Officer & Exec VP)
Carmen Bozic (Chief Medical Officer & Exec VP-Medicines Dev & Medical Affairs)
Nina Devlin (Chief Comm Officer & Sr VP)
Mike Tirozzi (Chief Information & Data Officer & Sr VP)
Bastiano Sanna (Exec VP)
Brenda Eustace (Dir-IR)
Kristen Amrose (Chief Acctg Officer & Sr VP)
Joy Liu (Sr VP & Gen Counsel)
Ourania Tatsis (Exec VP)
E. Morrey Atkinson (Chief Technical Ops Officer, Exec VP & Head-Mfg Ops)
Ourania Tatsis (Chief Regulatory & Quality Officer & Exec VP)
Stuart A. Arbuckle (COO & Exec VP)

Subsidiaries:

Alpine Immune Sciences, Inc. (1)
188 E Blaine St Ste 200, Seattle, WA 98102
Tel.: (206) 788-4545
Web Site:
https://www.alpineimmunesciences.com
Rev.: $30,064,000
Assets: $286,686,000
Liabilities: $107,266,000
Net Worth: $179,420,000
Earnings: ($57,762,000)
Emp.: 126
Fiscal Year-end: 12/31/2022
Pharmaceuticals Mfr
N.A.I.C.S.: 325412
Reshma Kewalramani (Pres)
Jonathan Biller (Sec)
Charles F. Wagner Jr. (Treas)
Andrew S. Sandler (Chief Medical Officer)
Christina Yi (CTO)
Remy Durand (Chief Bus Officer)
Andrew S. Sandler (Chief Medical Officer)

Semma Therapeutics, Inc. (1)
100 Technology Sq Fl 3, Cambridge, MA 02139
Tel.: (857) 529-6430
Web Site: http://www.semma-tx.com
Bio Technology Services
N.A.I.C.S.: 541714
Bastiano Sanna (CEO)

Vertex Pharmaceuticals (Australia) Pty. Ltd. (1)
Suite 3 Level 3 601 Pacific Highway, Saint Leonards, 2065, NSW, Australia
Tel.: (61) 284250200
Web Site: http://www.vrtx.com
Emp.: 10
Pharmaceutical Products Distr
N.A.I.C.S.: 424210
Eilis Quinn (Mng Dir)

Vertex Pharmaceuticals (Canada) Incorporated (1)
20 Bay Street Suite 1520, Toronto, M5J 2N8, ON, Canada
Tel.: (647) 790-1600
Sales Range: $25-49.9 Million
Emp.: 6
Biotechnological Research Services

N.A.I.C.S.: 541714
Matthew W. Emmens (Pres)

Vertex Pharmaceuticals (Europe) Limited (1)
2 Kingdom Street, London, W2 6BD, United Kingdom
Tel.: (44) 2032045100
Web Site: https://www.vrtxpharma.co.uk
Sales Range: $150-199.9 Million
Pharmaceuticals Mfr
N.A.I.C.S.: 325412

Subsidiary (Non-US):

Vertex Pharmaceuticals GmbH (2)
Euro Plaza Gebaude H Lehrbachgasse 13 2 Stock, 1120, Vienna, Austria
Tel.: (43) 120524700
Pharmaceutical Products Distr
N.A.I.C.S.: 424210
Julia Hofmann (Coord-Mktg)

Vertex Pharmaceuticals (Italy) S.r.l. (1)
Via Leonida Bissolati 76, 00187, Rome, Italy
Tel.: (39) 0697794000
Pharmaceutical Products Distr
N.A.I.C.S.: 424210

Vertex Pharmaceuticals (Netherlands) B.V. (1)
Leidsevaart 20, 2013 HA, Haarlem, Netherlands
Tel.: (31) 237991600
Web Site: http://www.vertex.com
Pharmaceutical Products Distr
N.A.I.C.S.: 424210

Vertex Pharmaceuticals (San Diego) LLC (1)
3215 Merryfield Row, San Diego, CA 92121
Tel.: (858) 404-6600
Web Site: http://www.vrtx.com
Sales Range: $75-99.9 Million
Commercial & Biological Research Products & Technologies
N.A.I.C.S.: 541720

Vertex Pharmaceuticals (Spain), S.L. (1)
Calle Marques de Villamagna 3 - 13th, 28001, Madrid, Spain
Tel.: (34) 917892800
Pharmaceutical Products Distr
N.A.I.C.S.: 424210

VERTEX, INC.
2301 Renaissance Blvd, King of Prussia, PA 19406
Tel.: (610) 640-4200   DE
Web Site: https://www.vertexinc.com
Year Founded: 1978
VERX—(NASDAQ)
Rev.: $491,624,000
Assets: $719,192,000
Liabilities: $489,467,000
Net Worth: $229,725,000
Earnings: ($12,304,000)
Emp.: 1,400
Fiscal Year-end: 12/31/22
Software Publisher
N.A.I.C.S.: 513210
David DeStefano (Chm, Pres & CEO)
Ryan J. Leib (Chief Acctg Officer)
Bryan Rowland (Gen Counsel & VP)
Jeff Foucher (CMO)
Uwe Sydon (VP-Product Mgmt)
Sal Visca (CTO)
John Schwab (CFO)
Chris Jones (Chief Revenue Officer)
Steve Hinckley (COO)
Michael Davis (Chief Tax Strategy Officer)
Ben Askin (CIO)
Nigel Rughani (VP-Corp Dev)
Ann Hollins (Chief People Officer)
Brad Cameron (Sr VP)
Chirag Patel (Chief Strategy Officer)

VERTIV HOLDINGS CO
505 N Cleveland Ave, Westerville, OH 43082
Tel.: (614) 888-0246   DE
Web Site: https://www.vertiv.com
Year Founded: 2016

Vertiv Holdings Co—(Continued)

VRT—(NYSE)
Rev.: $6,863,200,000
Assets: $7,998,500,000
Liabilities: $5,983,600,000
Net Worth: $2,014,900,000
Earnings: $460,200,000
Emp.: 27,000
Fiscal Year-end: 12/31/23
Investment Services
N.A.I.C.S.: 523999
Giordano Albertazzi *(CEO)*
David Fallon *(CFO)*
Sheryl Haislet *(CIO)*
Gary Niederpruem *(Chief Strategy & Dev Officer)*
Cheryl Lim *(Chief HR Officer)*
Yibin Cui *(Pres)*
Philip O'Doherty *(Mng Dir)*
Paul Ryan *(Chief Procurement Officer)*
Anand Sanghi *(Pres)*
Rainer Stiller *(CMO)*
Rachel Thompson *(VP)*
David M. Cote *(Chm)*

Subsidiaries:

Vertiv (Australia) Pty. Ltd.   **(1)**
Suite 102 Level 1 7-9 Irvine Place, Bella Vista, 2153, NSW, Australia
Tel.: (61) 800005161
Web Site: https://www.vertiv.com
Financial Investment Services
N.A.I.C.S.: 523999

Vertiv (Singapore) Pte. Ltd.   **(1)**
151 Lorong Chuan Lobby D New Tech Park 05-04 New Tech Park, Singapore, 556741, Singapore
Tel.: (65) 63501131
Financial Investment Services
N.A.I.C.S.: 523999

Vertiv Canada ULC   **(1)**
7-3800B Laird Rd, Mississauga, L5L 0B2, ON, Canada
Tel.: (905) 569-8282
Financial Investment Services
N.A.I.C.S.: 523999

Vertiv Czech Republic s.r.o   **(1)**
Delnicka 213/12, 170 00, Prague, Czech Republic
Tel.: (420) 739681051
Financial Investment Services
N.A.I.C.S.: 523999

Vertiv Energy Private Limited   **(1)**
Plut C-20 Rd No 19 Wagle Ind Estate Road No 16V, Wagle Industrial Estate MIDC, Thane, Maharashtra, India
Tel.: (91) 2271975400
Financial Investment Services
N.A.I.C.S.: 523999

Vertiv GmbH   **(1)**
Lehrer-Wirth-Str 4, 81829, Munich, Germany
Tel.: (49) 899050070
Financial Investment Services
N.A.I.C.S.: 523999

Vertiv Holdings, LLC   **(1)**
1050 Derborn Dr, Columbus, OH 43085
Tel.: (212) 902-1000
Holding Company
N.A.I.C.S.: 551112

Subsidiary (Domestic):

Vertiv Group Corporation   **(2)**
505 N Cleveland Ave, Westerville, OH 43082
Tel.: (614) 888-0246
Web Site: https://www.vertiv.com
Computer Network Power, Connectivity & Cooling Solutions
N.A.I.C.S.: 335311

Subsidiary (Domestic):

Alber Corp.   **(3)**
3103 N Andrews Ave Ext, Pompano Beach, FL 33064-2118
Tel.: (954) 623-6660
Web Site: http://www.alber.com

Sales Range: $100-124.9 Million
Storage Battery Test Equipment Mfr
N.A.I.C.S.: 334514

Aperture Technologies Inc.   **(3)**
9 Riverbend Dr S, Stamford, CT 06907
Tel.: (203) 357-0800
Sales Range: $1-9.9 Million
Emp.: 120
Corporate IT Data Center Management Software & Services
N.A.I.C.S.: 513210

Avocent Corporation   **(3)**
4991 Corporate Dr, Huntsville, AL 35805-6201
Tel.: (256) 430-4000
Web Site: http://www.vertivco.com
Sales Range: $650-699.9 Million
Computer Peripheral Product Mfr
N.A.I.C.S.: 334118
Lauren Sexton *(VP-HR)*

Subsidiary (Non-US):

Avocent Belgium Limited BVBA/SPRL   **(4)**
Pegasus Park Pegasuslaan 5, 1831, Diegem, Belgium
Tel.: (32) 27092929
IT Operations & Infrastructure Management Services
N.A.I.C.S.: 541618

Subsidiary (Domestic):

Avocent Fremont Corp.   **(4)**
47281 Bayside Pkwy, Fremont, CA 94538
Tel.: (510) 771-6100
Electronic Components Distr
N.A.I.C.S.: 423690

Avocent Huntsville, LLC   **(4)**
4991 Corporate Dr, Huntsville, AL 35805
Tel.: (256) 430-4000
Web Site: http://www.vertivco.com
Thermal Management, IT Management, Power Management, Unified Infrastructure, Software Services & Consulting
N.A.I.C.S.: 541618

Subsidiary (Non-US):

Avocent International Limited   **(4)**
Avocent House Shannon Free Zone Shannon, Shannon, V14N578, County Clare, Ireland
Tel.: (353) 61471877
Web Site:
  http://www.emersonnetworkpower.com
Sales Range: $25-49.9 Million
Emp.: 90
IT Operations & Infrastructure Management Services
N.A.I.C.S.: 541618

Subsidiary (Domestic):

Avocent Redmond Corp.   **(4)**
9911 Willows Rd NE, Redmond, WA 98052
Tel.: (425) 861-5858
Emp.: 110
Electronic Switching System Mfr & Distr
N.A.I.C.S.: 334419

Subsidiary (Non-US):

Avocent Sweden AB   **(4)**
Phelix St 29, Stockholm, Sweden
Tel.: (46) 707736622
IT Operations & Infrastructure Management Services
N.A.I.C.S.: 541618

Avocent do Brasil Informatica S.A.   **(4)**
Av Emb Macedo Soares 10735 Vila Anastacio, Sao Paulo, 05095-035, Brazil
Tel.: (55) 1136186600
IT Operations & Infrastructure Management Services
N.A.I.C.S.: 327910

Branch (Domestic):

Emerson Network Power   **(3)**
125 Newbury St Ste 100, Framingham, MA 01701-4535
Tel.: (508) 628-5600
Sales Range: $10-24.9 Million
Emp.: 34

Developer & Retailer of Power Conversion Products & Communications Subsystems
N.A.I.C.S.: 335311

Emerson Network Power   **(3)**
179 W Broad St Ste 5, Telford, PA 19468
Tel.: (215) 604-9980
Sales Range: $1-9.9 Million
Uninterruptible Power Supply Units Maintenance Services
N.A.I.C.S.: 561499

Subsidiary (Non-US):

Emerson Network Power (Malaysia) Sdn. Bhd.   **(3)**
Wisma Glomac 3 7th Fl Block C, Jalan SS 7 19 Kelana Jaya, 47301, Petaling Jaya, Selangor Darul Ehsan, Malaysia **(100%)**
Tel.: (60) 378845000
Web Site:
  http://www.emersonnetworkpower.com
Sales Range: $10-24.9 Million
Emp.: 70
Mfr of Uninterruptible Power Supplies, Site Monitoring Systems, Environmental Control Systems & Power Conditioning Equipment
N.A.I.C.S.: 335999

Emerson Network Power (Singapore) Pte. Ltd.   **(3)**
151 Lorong Chuan Lobby D New Tech Park 05-04 New Tech Park, Singapore, 556741, Singapore
Tel.: (65) 63501131
Electronic Components Mfr
N.A.I.C.S.: 334419

Emerson Network Power (Thailand) Co. Ltd.   **(3)**
123 Suntowers Building-B 16th Floor Vibhavadi-Rangsit Road Chompol, Chatuchak, Bangkok, 10900, Thailand
Tel.: (66) 26178260
Web Site:
  http://www.emersonnetworkpower.com
Electronic Components Mfr
N.A.I.C.S.: 334419

Emerson Network Power Australia Pty. Ltd.   **(3)**
Suite 102 Level 1 7-9 Irvine Place, Bella Vista, 2153, NSW, Australia **(100%)**
Tel.: (61) 800005161
Web Site: https://www.vertiv.com
Sales Range: $25-49.9 Million
Emp.: 155
Power Conditioning Equipment, Environmental Control Systems & Site Monitoring Systems Distr
N.A.I.C.S.: 335999

Emerson Network Power GmbH   **(3)**
Lehrer-Wirth-Strasse 4, 81829, Munich, Germany
Tel.: (49) 899050070
Sales Range: $250-299.9 Million
Power Switching & Controls, DC Power & Thermal Management
N.A.I.C.S.: 221116

Emerson Network Power Holding S.R.L.   **(3)**
Via Leonardo Da Vinci 1618, Piove Di Sacco, 35028, Padua, Italy **(100%)**
Tel.: (39) 0499719111
Web Site:
  http://www.emersonnetworkpower.com
Sales Range: $50-74.9 Million
Emp.: 200
Precision Cooling & Power Systems Mfr
N.A.I.C.S.: 334513

Subsidiary (Domestic):

Emerson Network Power Italia   **(4)**
Via Leonardo Da Vinci 16/18, Zona Industriale, Tognana, 35028, Italy
Tel.: (39) 0499719111
Power Supply & Air Conditioning Mfr
N.A.I.C.S.: 333415

Subsidiary (Non-US):

Emerson Network Power Ltd.   **(3)**
Globe Park, Marlow, SL7 1YG, Bucks, United Kingdom **(100%)**
Tel.: (44) 1628403200
Web Site:
  http://www.emersonnetworkpower.com

Sales Range: $50-74.9 Million
Emp.: 180
Uninterruptible Power Supplies, Power Conditioning Equipment, Environmental Control Systems & Site Monitoring Systems Mfr
N.A.I.C.S.: 335999

Subsidiary (Domestic):

Chloride Group PLC   **(4)**
3Rd Floor 44 Baker Street, London, W1U 7AL, United Kingdom
Tel.: (44) 2078811440
Web Site: http://www.msn.com
Sales Range: $500-549.9 Million
Emp.: 25
Holding Company; Uninterruptible Power Supplies & Power Protection Products Mfr
N.A.I.C.S.: 551112
Giordano Albertazzi *(VP-Sls)*

Subsidiary (Non-US):

Chloride Espana, S.A.U.   **(5)**
San Rafael 1 Edif Europa III Poligono Industrial de Alcobendas, 28108, Alcobendas, Madrid, Spain
Tel.: (34) 914140030
Web Site: http://www.chloridepower.com
Sales Range: $25-49.9 Million
Uninterruptible Power Supplies Systems Mfr
N.A.I.C.S.: 335999

Chloride Italia   **(5)**
Via Fornace 30, Castel Guelfo, Bologna, 40023, Italy **(100%)**
Tel.: (39) 0542632111
Web Site: http://www.vertivco.com
Sales Range: $25-49.9 Million
Uninterruptible Power Supplies & Power Protection Products Mfr
N.A.I.C.S.: 335999

Subsidiary (US):

Chloride Power Protection   **(5)**
1450 Lakeside Dr, Libertyville, IL 60085
Tel.: (847) 816-6000
Web Site: http://www.chloridepower.com
Sales Range: $25-49.9 Million
Uninterruptible Power Supply Distr
N.A.I.C.S.: 334419

Division (Domestic):

Chloride Power Electronics Inc.   **(6)**
27944 N Bradley Rd, Libertyville, IL 60048-9714 **(100%)**
Tel.: (847) 816-6000
Web Site: http://www.chloridepower.com
Sales Range: $50-74.9 Million
Uninterruptible Power Supplies & Power Protection Products Mfr
N.A.I.C.S.: 423610
Yolanda Hernandez *(Dir-Mktg)*

Subsidiary (Domestic):

U P Systems, Incorporated   **(7)**
150 Dunbar Ave Ste A, Oldsmar, FL 34677
Tel.: (813) 854-4439
Web Site: https://www.upsystems-inc.com
Battery Maintenance & Installation Services
N.A.I.C.S.: 238990

Subsidiary (Non-US):

Chloride Power Protection Australia   **(5)**
16 Giffnock Ave, North Ryde, 2113, NSW, Australia **(100%)**
Tel.: (61) 298881266
Web Site: http://www.chloridepower.com
Sales Range: $25-49.9 Million
Uninterruptible Power Supplies & Power Protection Products Mfr
N.A.I.C.S.: 335311

Emerson Network Power, Lda   **(5)**
Beloura Ofc Pk Edificio 13 Piso 0 No 8, Quinta Da Beloura, 2710693, Sintra, Portugal
Tel.: (351) 219236500
Web Site:
  http://www.emersonnetworkpower.com
Uninterruptible Power Supplies & Power Protection Products Mfr
N.A.I.C.S.: 335311

Exide Pakistan Limited **(5)**
A-44 Hill Street Off Manghopir Road S I T
E, Karachi, Pakistan
Tel.: (92) 2132593371
Web Site: https://www.exide.com.pk
Rev.: $84,189,448
Assets: $36,642,604
Liabilities: $18,298,276
Net Worth: $18,344,328
Earnings: $2,714,324
Emp.: 306
Fiscal Year-end: 03/31/2023
Battery Mfr
N.A.I.C.S.: 335910
Arshad Shahzada *(CEO)*
Arif Hashwani *(Exec Dir)*
Haider Mehdi *(CFO & Sec)*

Subsidiary (Domestic):

Emerson Network Power Surge Pro-
tection, Inc. **(3)**
100 Emerson Pkwy, Binghamton, NY 13905
Tel.: (607) 721-8840
Web Site:
 http://www.emersonnetworkpower.com
Sales Range: $25-49.9 Million
Emp.: 60
Surge Protection Devices Mfr
N.A.I.C.S.: 334416

Unit (Domestic):

Emerson Network Power, Energy
Systems **(3)**
4350 Weaver Pkwy, Warrenville, IL 60555-
3925
Tel.: (440) 246-6999
Web Site:
 http://www.emersonnetworkpower.com
Sales Range: $25-49.9 Million
Emp.: 100
Broadband Routing & Switching
N.A.I.C.S.: 334118

Subsidiary (Domestic):

Energy Labs Inc. **(3)**
1695 Cactus Rd, San Diego, CA 92154
Tel.: (619) 671-0100
Web Site: https://www.energylabs.com
Air-Conditioning, Warm Air Heating Equip-
ment & Commercial & Industrial Refrigera-
tion Equipment Mfr
N.A.I.C.S.: 333415

Subsidiary (Non-US):

Knurr GmbH **(3)**
Mariakirchener Strasse 38, 94424, Arnstorf,
Germany
Tel.: (49) 8723280
Indoor & Outdoor Enclosure Systems Mfr
N.A.I.C.S.: 334118

Subsidiary (Non-US):

Knurr AG **(4)**
Bruggacherstrasse 16, 8117, Fallanden,
Switzerland
Tel.: (41) 448065454
Web Site: http://www.knurr.ch
Rev.: $8,927,415
Emp.: 40
Sales of Electronic Racks, Consoles,
Cases, Industrial Furnishing, Workstations
for Electrical Engineers & All Accessories
N.A.I.C.S.: 423690

Subsidiary (Domestic):

Knurr AG & Co. Grundbesitz
OHG **(4)**
Mariakirchener St 38, 94424, Arnstorf, Ger-
many
Tel.: (49) 8723270
Web Site: http://www.knurr.com
Sales Range: $25-49.9 Million
Emp.: 20
Electrical Equipment Supplies & Mfr
N.A.I.C.S.: 335999

Knurr Electronics GmbH **(4)**
Glashuettsen Strasse 1, 1623, Lom-
matzsch, Germany
Tel.: (49) 35241560
Web Site: http://www.knurr.de
Sales Range: $50-74.9 Million
Emp.: 200

Distribution & Manufacturing of Enclosures
for the Telecommunications Market
N.A.I.C.S.: 517111

Subsidiary (Domestic):

Knurr Electronics GmbH & Co.
Grundbesitz OHG **(5)**
Mariakirchener Str 38, 94424, Arnstorf, Ger-
many
Tel.: (49) 8723270
Web Site: http://www.knuerr.com
Sales Range: $75-99.9 Million
Emp.: 35
Electrical Equipment Supplies & Mfr
N.A.I.C.S.: 335999

Subsidiary (Domestic):

Knurr Electronics GmbH **(4)**
Mariakirchener-Strasse 38, 94424, Arnstorf,
Germany
Tel.: (49) 8723270
Web Site: http://www.knuerr.com
Sales Range: $100-124.9 Million
Emp.: 380
Design & Manufacture of Enclosures for
Electronic Systems
N.A.I.C.S.: 334220

Subsidiary (Non-US):

Knurr Ltda. **(4)**
Rua Antonio Galvao Pacheco 185, 18550
000, Boituva, SP, Brazil
Tel.: (55) 1533639444
Sales Range: $25-49.9 Million
Emp.: 100
Computer Furniture & Enclosures Mfr
N.A.I.C.S.: 337211

Knurr Norge AS **(4)**
Industriveien 25, PO Box 18, 2020, Sked-
smokorset, Norway
Tel.: (47) 64838440
Web Site: http://www.knurr.com
Rev.: $122,130
Emp.: 3
Electronic Racks, Consoles, Cases, Indus-
trial Furnishing, Workstations Sales for
Electrical Engineers & All Accessories
N.A.I.C.S.: 423690

Subsidiary (Domestic):

Knurr Technical Furniture GmbH **(4)**
Mariakirchener Strasse 38, 94424, Arnstorf,
Germany
Tel.: (49) 872328110
Sales Range: $10-24.9 Million
Emp.: 75
Technical Furniture Mfr
N.A.I.C.S.: 337127
Gerhard Buchbauer *(Mng Dir & Gen Mgr)*

Subsidiary (Non-US):

Knurr s.a.r.l. **(4)**
ZAC les Petits Carreaux 4, Avenue des Vio-
lettes, 94384, Bonneuil-Matours, France
Tel.: (33) 143778585
Web Site: http://www.knuerr.fr
Electronic Racks, Consoles, Cases & Indus-
trial Furnishing Distr
N.A.I.C.S.: 423690

Subsidiary (Domestic):

Knurr-Mecor GmbH **(4)**
Mariakirchener Strasse 38, 94424, Arnstorf,
Germany
Tel.: (49) 872327250
Web Site: http://www.knurr.com
Mfr & Distributor of Electronic Racks &
Computer Carts & All Accessories
N.A.I.C.S.: 334118

Subsidiary (Non-US):

Knurr-Spectra (S.E.A.) Pte. Ltd. **(4)**
Unit 01 19 C 1 Lok Yang Way, Singapore,
628623, Singapore
Tel.: (65) 67731583
Web Site: http://www.knuerr-spectra.com.sg
Sales Range: $10-24.9 Million
Emp.: 17
Electronic Racks, Consoles, Cases, Indus-
trial Furnishing, Workstations for Electrical
Engineers, Medical & Computer Carts & All
Accessories
N.A.I.C.S.: 334417

Subsidiary (Domestic):

Liebert Corporation **(3)**
1050 Dearborn Dr, Columbus, OH 43085
Tel.: (614) 888-0246
Web Site: http://www.liebert.com
Power & Environmental Control Systems
Mfr
N.A.I.C.S.: 335313
Steve Madara *(VP & Gen Mgr-Liebert Preci-
sion Cooling Bus)*

Subsidiary (Domestic):

Emerson Network Power Surge Pro-
tection, Inc. **(4)**
100 Emerson Pkwy, Binghamton, NY 13905
Tel.: (607) 721-8840
Web Site:
 http://www.emersonnetworkpower.com
Emp.: 40
Engineering Consulting Services
N.A.I.C.S.: 541330

Emerson Network Power, Liebert Ser-
vices, Inc. **(4)**
610 Exec Campus Dr, Westerville, OH
43082-8871 **(100%)**
Tel.: (614) 841-6700
Web Site: http://www.liebert.com
Sales Range: $100-124.9 Million
Emp.: 210
Computer Peripheral Equipment
N.A.I.C.S.: 811210

Branch (Domestic):

Emerson Network Power, Liebert Ser-
vices, Inc. - Edison **(5)**
3A Fernwood Ave, Edison, NJ 08818
Tel.: (732) 225-0018
Web Site: http://www.liebert.com
Sales Range: $10-24.9 Million
Emp.: 6
UPS Service & Repair
N.A.I.C.S.: 811210

Subsidiary (Domestic):

Liebert Corporation **(4)**
No 300 6960 Koll Ctr Pkwy, Pleasanton, CA
94566-3179
Tel.: (925) 734-8660
Web Site: http://www.liebert.com
Sales Range: $25-49.9 Million
Emp.: 15
Air Conditioning & Ventilation Equipment &
Supplies
N.A.I.C.S.: 423730

Branch (Domestic):

Liebert Corporation **(4)**
2 A Research Pwky, Wallingford, CT
06492 **(100%)**
Tel.: (203) 294-6020
Web Site: http://www.liebert.com
Sales Range: $25-49.9 Million
Emp.: 15
Air Conditioning & Ventilation Equipment &
Supplies
N.A.I.C.S.: 425120

Subsidiary (Domestic):

Liebert Corporation **(4)**
35 Parker, Irvine, CA 92618 **(100%)**
Tel.: (949) 457-3600
Web Site: http://www.liebert.com
Sales Range: $10-24.9 Million
Emp.: 50
Data Processing & Preparation Services
N.A.I.C.S.: 811210

Subsidiary (Non-US):

Vertiv (Hong Kong) Ltd. **(3)**
Suite 1503 15/F 625 King's Road, North
Point, Hong Kong, China (Hong Kong)
Tel.: (852) 25722201
Web Site: http://www.vertivco.com
Energy Systems
N.A.I.C.S.: 551112

Vertiv France **(3)**
Batiment Liege 1 Place Des Etats-Unis,
Rungis, France
Tel.: (33) 148844090
Web Site: http://www.vertivco.com

IT Management; Uninterruptible Power Supplies (UPS) Mfr
N.A.I.C.S.: 541511

Vertiv S.A. **(3)**
C/ Procion 1-3 Edificio Oficor, 28023, Ma-
drid, Spain
Tel.: (34) 914140030
IT Management & Software Publisher
N.A.I.C.S.: 513210

Vertiv del Peru S.A.C. **(3)**
Avenida Camino Real 348 Torre El Pilar
Oficina 1601, San Isidro, 27, Lima, Peru
Tel.: (51) 14 332 1880
Energy Equipment Distr
N.A.I.C.S.: 333992

Vertiv Integrated Systems GmbH **(1)**
Mariakirchener Strasse 38, 94424, Arnstorf,
Germany
Tel.: (49) 8723280
Web Site: http://www.knurr-consoles.com
Financial Investment Services
N.A.I.C.S.: 523999
Giordano Albertazzi *(Gen Mgr)*
Giordano Albertazzi *(Gen Mgr)*

Vertiv International Designated Activ-
ity Company **(1)**
Unit 153 Shannon V14 N578, Co Clare, En-
nis, Ireland
Tel.: (353) 61471877
Web Site: http://www.vertiv-vip.com
Financial Investment Services
N.A.I.C.S.: 523999

Vertiv Middle East DMCC **(1)**
Unit 801 One JLT Jumeirah Lake Towers,
PO Box 337122, Dubai, United Arab Emir-
ates
Tel.: (971) 45104200
Financial Investment Services
N.A.I.C.S.: 523999

Vertiv Sweden AB **(1)**
Box 92113, 120 07, Stockholm, Sweden
Tel.: (46) 87216000
Financial Investment Services
N.A.I.C.S.: 523999

VERU INC.
2916 N Miami Ave Ste 1000, Miami,
FL 33127
Tel.: (305) 509-6897 WI
Web Site:
 https://www.verupharma.com
Year Founded: 1996
VERU—(NASDAQ)
Rev.: $16,886,419
Assets: $60,418,772
Liabilities: $28,102,060
Net Worth: $32,316,712
Earnings: ($37,801,426)
Emp.: 210
Fiscal Year-end: 09/30/24
Female Condom Mfr
N.A.I.C.S.: 325620
Mitchell S. Steiner *(Chm, Pres &
CEO)*
Harry Fisch *(Vice Chm & Chief Corp
Officer)*
Domingo Rodriguez *(Exec VP-Clinical
Ops)*
Gary Bird *(Sr VP-Quality Oversight)*
Jason Davies *(Exec VP & Gen Mgr-
Europe, Middle East & Africa, Latin
America & Asia Pacific)*
Sergi X. Trilla *(Chief Bus Officer)*
Michele Greco *(Chief Admin Officer)*
K. Gary Barnette *(Chief Scientific Of-
ficer)*
Michael J. Purvis *(Gen Counsel, Sec
& Exec VP-Corporate Strategy)*
Kevin Gilbert *(Exec VP-Corp Dev)*
Samuel Fisch *(Exec Dir-IR & Corp
Comm)*

Subsidiaries:

The Female Health Company (M)
SDN BHD **(1)**
No 1A Jalan CJ 1/4, Kawasan Perindustrian
Cheras J, Balakong, 43200, Selangor, Ma-
laysia

Veru Inc.—(Continued)

Tel.: (60) 3 9076 2906
Female Condom Mfr
N.A.I.C.S.: 326299

The Female Health Company (UK)
Plc. (1)
3 Western Avenue Business Park, Mansfield Road, London, W3 0BZ, United Kingdom
Tel.: (44) 2089934669
Web Site: http://www.femalehealth.com
Emp.: 11
Rubber Products Mfr
N.A.I.C.S.: 326299

The Female Health Company
Limited (1)
3 Western Avenue Business Park, Mansfield Road, London, W3 0BZ, United Kingdom
Tel.: (44) 2089652813
Web Site:
   http://www.femalehealthcompany.com
Sales Range: $10-24.9 Million
Emp.: 11
Female Condom Mfr
N.A.I.C.S.: 326299

VERUS INTERNATIONAL, INC.
9841 Washingtonian Blvd Ste 390, Gaithersburg, MD 20878
Tel.: (301) 329-2700   DE
Web Site: http://www.verusfoods.com
Year Founded: 2007
VRUS—(OTCIQ)
Rev.: $488,589
Assets: $920,191
Liabilities: $4,189,456
Net Worth: ($3,269,265)
Earnings: ($5,998,896)
Emp.: 1
Fiscal Year-end: 10/31/21
Internet Real Estate Services
N.A.I.C.S.: 531390
Apurva Dhruv (Chm & CEO)

Subsidiaries:

Big League Foods, Inc. (1)
9841 Washingtonian Blvd Ste 390, Gaithersburg, MD 20878
Tel.: (301) 329-2703
Web Site: http://www.bigleaguefoods.com
Food Product Whslr
N.A.I.C.S.: 424490
Jim Wheeler (Pres)

VERVE THERAPEUTICS, INC.
201 Brookline Ave, Boston, MA 02215
Tel.: (617) 603-0070   DE
Web Site: https://www.vervetx.com
Year Founded: 2018
VERV—(NASDAQ)
Rev.: $1,941,000
Assets: $679,223,000
Liabilities: $128,291,000
Net Worth: $550,932,000
Earnings: ($157,387,000)
Emp.: 204
Fiscal Year-end: 12/31/22
Biotechnology Research & Development Services
N.A.I.C.S.: 541714
Andrew Ashe (Pres & COO)
Troy Lister (Chief Scientific Officer)
Burt Adelman (Co-Founder & Chm)
J. Keith Joung (Co-Founder)
Kiran Musunuru (Co-Founder)
Anthony Philippakis (Co-Founder)
Issi Rozen (Co-Founder)
Barry Ticho (Co-Founder)
Andrew Ashe (Pres & COO)
Margaret Beaudoin (VP-Fin)
Joan Nickerson (Sr VP-HR & Facilities)
Jason Politi (Sr VP-Technical Ops)
Allison Dorval (CFO)

Burt A. Adelman (Co-Founder & Chm)
Sekar Kathiresan (Co-Founder & CEO)

VESTIS CORP
1035 Alpharetta St Ste 2100, Roswell, GA 30075
Tel.: (470) 226-3655
Web Site: https://www.vestis.com
VSTS—(NYSE)
Rev.: $2,805,820,000
Assets: $2,932,387,000
Liabilities: $2,029,336,000
Net Worth: $903,051,000
Earnings: $20,970,000
Emp.: 10,800
Fiscal Year-end: 09/27/24
Holding Company
N.A.I.C.S.: 551112
Douglas Allen Pertz (Vice Chm)
Bryan R. Johnson (Chief Acctg Officer)
Kimberly T. Scott (Pres & CEO)
Ricky T. Dillon (CFO & Exec VP)

Subsidiaries:

ARAMARK Uniform & Career Apparel
Group, Inc. (1)
115 N 1st St, Burbank, CA 91502
Tel.: (818) 973-3700
Web Site: http://www.aramark-uniform.com
Sales Range: $350-399.9 Million
Emp.: 356
Rental & Sales of Professional Uniforms
N.A.I.C.S.: 812332

Subsidiary (Domestic):

ARAMARK Uniform & Career Apparel, LLC (2)
115 N 1st St, Burbank, CA 91502-1856
Tel.: (818) 973-3700
Web Site: http://www.aramarkuniform.com
Uniform Rental
N.A.I.C.S.: 812332

Subsidiary (Domestic):

ARAMARK Uniform & Career (3)
141 Longwater Dr Ste 200, Norwell, MA 02061-1683
Tel.: (781) 871-4100
Web Site: http://www.aramark-uniforms.com
Emp.: 150
Catalog Sales for Clothing
N.A.I.C.S.: 458110
Christopher Butzbach (Dir-Mktg)

Aramark Uniform Services (Baltimore) LLC (3)
2928 Washington Blvd, Baltimore, MD 21230
Tel.: (443) 992-4665
Uniform Service Provider
N.A.I.C.S.: 315210

Aramark Uniform Services (Rochester) LLC (3)
200 Trade Ct, Rochester, NY 14624
Tel.: (585) 301-4052
Web Site: http://www.aramarkuniform.com
Laundry Services
N.A.I.C.S.: 812320

Aramark Uniform Services (Santa Ana) LLC (3)
3101 W Adams, Santa Ana, CA 92704
Tel.: (714) 881-4379
Laundry Services
N.A.I.C.S.: 812320

Aramark Uniform Services (Syracuse) LLC (3)
3117 Milton Ave, Solvay, NY 13209
Tel.: (315) 314-8168
Laundry Services
N.A.I.C.S.: 812320

Aramark Uniform Services (Texas) LLC (3)
1900 Empire Central, Dallas, TX 75235
Tel.: (214) 666-6938
Uniform Service Provider
N.A.I.C.S.: 315210

Brian Gonzales (Gen Mgr)

Associated Textile Rental
Services (3)
8365 Seneca Tpk, New Hartford, NY 13413
Tel.: (315) 797-2600
Web Site: http://www.associatedtextile.com
Emp.: 20
Linen Supplier
N.A.I.C.S.: 812331

L&N Uniform Supply, LLC (3)
115 North 1st St Burbank, Los Angeles, CA 91502-1856
Tel.: (323) 266-0555
Linen Supply Services
N.A.I.C.S.: 812331

Vestis (Rochester), LLC (3)
200 Trade Ct, Rochester, NY 14624
Tel.: (585) 301-4052
Uniform Rental Program Services
N.A.I.C.S.: 812320

Vestis (Syracuse), LLC (1)
3909 New Ct Ave, Syracuse, NY 13206
Tel.: (315) 434-9270
Uniform Rental Program Services
N.A.I.C.S.: 812320

VG LIFE SCIENCES INC.
447 Broadway 2nd Fl Unit 103, New York, NY 10013
Tel.: (424) 224-5358   FL
Year Founded: 1995
VGLS—(OTCIQ)
Pharmaceutical Research Services
N.A.I.C.S.: 541714
William Farrand (CEO)
Paul Lucien Strickland (Sec)

VGTEL, INC.
201 E 5th St, Sheridan, WY 82801
Tel.: (646) 580-2790   NY
Web Site: http://www.vgtelinc.com
Year Founded: 2002
VGTL—(OTCEM)
Emp.: 1
Holding Company; Entertainment Industry Support Services
N.A.I.C.S.: 551112
Chris Villareale (Pres)

VIA RENEWABLES, INC.
12140 Wickchester Ln Ste 100, Houston, TX 77079
Tel.: (832) 200-3727   DE
Web Site:
   https://www.viarenewables.com
Year Founded: 2014
VIA—(NASDAQ)
Rev.: $435,192,000
Assets: $303,834,000
Liabilities: $265,115,000
Net Worth: $38,719,000
Earnings: $4,356,000
Emp.: 160
Fiscal Year-end: 12/31/23
Electric Power & Natural Gas Supplier
N.A.I.C.S.: 221122
W. Keith Maxwell III (CEO)
James G. Jones II (CFO)

Subsidiaries:

CenStar Energy Corp. (1)
1 Radisson Plz Ste 704, New Rochelle, NY 10801
Tel.: (914) 365-1682
Web Site: http://www.censtarenergy.com
Natural Gas Distribution Services
N.A.I.C.S.: 221210
Elliott Rackman (Mng Dir)

CenStar Operating Company, LLC (1)
12140 Wickchester Ln Ste 100, Houston, TX 77079
Tel.: (713) 977-5634
Emp.: 20
Natural Gas Transmission & Distribution Services

N.A.I.C.S.: 221210
Nathan Kroeker (CFO)

Hiko Energy, LLC (1)
100 Dutch Hill Rd Ste 310, Orangeburg, NY 10962
Tel.: (845) 406-9100
Web Site: http://www.hikoenergy.com
Natural Gas Distr
N.A.I.C.S.: 221210

Oasis Power, LLC (1)
12140 Wickchester Ln Ste 100, Houston, TX 77079
Tel.: (281) 822-8700
Web Site: http://www.oasisenergy.com
Electric Power Distribution Services
N.A.I.C.S.: 221122

Provider Power LLC (1)
12140 Wickchester Ln Ste 100, Houston, TX 77079
Web Site: http://www.providerpower.com
Power Generation Services
N.A.I.C.S.: 221118
Kevin Dean (Co-Owner)
Emile Clavet (Co-Owner)

Spark Energy Gas, LLC (1)
2105 City West Blvd Ste 100, Houston, TX 77042
Tel.: (713) 977-5611
Web Site: http://www.sparkenergy.com
Natural Gas Distr
N.A.I.C.S.: 221210

Verde Energy USA Texas, LLC (1)
PO Box 27929, Houston, TX 77227
Tel.: (844) 845-3059
Web Site: http://www.verdeenergytx.com
Electric Power Distribution Services
N.A.I.C.S.: 221122

Verde Energy USA, Inc. (1)
12140 Wickchester Ln Ste 100, Houston, TX 77079
Web Site: https://www.verdeenergy.com
Renewable Energy Source Supplier
N.A.I.C.S.: 221118
Don Whaley (Pres)

VIAD CORP.
7000 E 1st Ave, Scottsdale, AZ 85251
Tel.: (602) 207-1000   DE
Web Site: https://www.viad.com
Year Founded: 1914
VVI—(NYSE)
Rev.: $1,127,311,000
Assets: $1,090,346,000
Liabilities: $993,506,000
Net Worth: $96,840,000
Earnings: $23,220,000
Emp.: 3,387
Fiscal Year-end: 12/31/22
Holding Company; Marketing, Events, Travel & Recreation Services
N.A.I.C.S.: 551112
Steven W. Moster (Pres & CEO)
Ellen M. Ingersoll (CFO)
Derek P. Linde (COO)
Leslie S. Striedel (Chief Acctg Officer)
David W. Barry (Pres-Pursuit)
Jon Massimino (Gen Counsel & Sec)

Subsidiaries:

Blitz Communications Group
Limited (1)
100 Centennial Avenue, Elstree, WD6 3SA, Hertfordshire, United Kingdom
Tel.: (44) 2083271000
Web Site: http://www.blitzges.com
Emp.: 80
Audio Visual Equipment Provider
N.A.I.C.S.: 532490

EXG, Inc. (1)
84-915 Hana St, Waianae, HI 96792-2251
Tel.: (808) 695-9158
Event Management Services
N.A.I.C.S.: 711310

FlyOver Canada, Inc. (1)
201 - 999 Canada Place, Vancouver, V6C 3E1, BC, Canada
Web Site: https://www.flyovercanada.com

Amusement Park Services
N.A.I.C.S.: 713110

GES Canada Limited (1)
5675 McLaughlin Rd, Mississauga, L5R
3K5, ON, Canada
Tel.: (905) 283-0500
Trade Show Organize Services
N.A.I.C.S.: 561920

GES GmbH & Co. KG (1)
Siemensstr 19, 42551, Velbert, Germany
Tel.: (49) 205128110
Web Site: http://www.ges.com
Business Support Services
N.A.I.C.S.: 561990

**Global Experience Specialists (GES)
Exhibition Services LLC** (1)
Tel.: (971) 24064450
Trade Show Organize Services
N.A.I.C.S.: 561920

**Global Experience Specialists (GES)
Limited** (1)
Silverstone Drive, Gallagher Business Park,
Coventry, CV6 6PA, United Kingdom
Web Site: http://www.ges.com
Emp.: 4,000
Professional Development Training Services
N.A.I.C.S.: 611430

Marketing & Events Group (1)
1850 N Central Ave Ste 800, Phoenix, AZ
85004-4565
Tel.: (602) 207-4000
Web Site: http://www.viad.com
Exhibition & Event Production & Organiza-
tional Services
N.A.I.C.S.: 541613
Steven W. Moster (Executives)

Subsidiary (Domestic):

**Global Experience Specialists,
Inc.** (2)
7000 S Lindell Rd Ste4702, Las Vegas, NV
89118
Tel.: (702) 515-5500
Web Site: https://www.ges.com
Exhibitions & Events Planning & Marketing
N.A.I.C.S.: 541890
Steven W. Moster (Pres & CEO)

Subsidiary (Domestic):

GES Exposition Services, Inc. (3)
7150 South Tenaya Way, Las Vegas, NV
89113 **(100%)**
Tel.: (702) 263-1500
Web Site: http://www.ges.com
Sales Range: $25-49.9 Million
Emp.: 135
Convention & Exhibition Services
N.A.I.C.S.: 561920

ON Services (3)
6779 Crescent Dr, Norcross, GA 30071
Tel.: (770) 457-0966
Web Site: https://onservices.com
Audio-Visual Event Production Services
N.A.I.C.S.: 561499
Stan Milner (Founder)
Matt McGraw (Acct Mgr-Corp Trade Show
Accts)

Division (Domestic):

ON Services Houston (4)
3720 Dacoma St, Houston, TX 77092
Tel.: (713) 688-7900
Web Site: http://onservices.com
AV Solutions for Tradeshows & Corporate
Events
N.A.I.C.S.: 532490

Melville Logistics GmbH (1)
Haberstrasse 45, 42551, Velbert, Germany
Tel.: (49) 2051207360
Web Site:
  http://www.globalexperiencespecial
  ists.co.uk
Electrical Contractor Services
N.A.I.C.S.: 238210

N200 Holding B.V. (1)
Donkere Spaarne 24 zw, 2011 JG, Haar-
lem, Netherlands
Tel.: (31) 235120160
Convention & Trade Show Organizer

N.A.I.C.S.: 561920

N200 Limited (1)
Building 6 Unit 23, Croxley Green Business
Park, Watford, WD18 8YH, United Kingdom
Tel.: (44) 1923690690
Web Site: http://www.n200.com
Convention & Trade Show Organizer
N.A.I.C.S.: 561920

**Samuelson Communications
Limited** (1)
13 Field Way Bristol Road, Greenford, UB6
8UN, Middlesex, United Kingdom
Tel.: (44) 2085666444
Satellite Telecommunication Services
N.A.I.C.S.: 517410
Lisa Samuelson (Principal)

The Becker Group, Ltd. (1)
211 Stockholm St, Baltimore, MD 21230
Tel.: (800) 999-1830
Web Site: http://www.beckergroup.com
Custom Decor Services
N.A.I.C.S.: 541490
Donald Acker (Dir-Creative Svcs)
Cormac Woods (Pres)
Martina Rapp (Sr VP-Client Rels)
Linda Scarlett (VP-Sls)

Travel & Recreation Group (1)
1850 N Central Ave Ste 1900, Phoenix, AZ
85004-4565
Tel.: (602) 207-1000
Web Site: http://www.viad.com
Travel & Tour Arrangement
N.A.I.C.S.: 561599

Subsidiary (Domestic):

Alaska Denali Travel (2)
1301 W Parks Hwy, Wasilla, AK 99654
Tel.: (877) 376-1992
Travel Services
N.A.I.C.S.: 561510

Subsidiary (Domestic):

**CATC Alaska Tourism
Corporation** (3)
509 W 4th Ave, Anchorage, AK 99501
Tel.: (907) 777-2800
Web Site: http://www.alaskacollection.com
Tour Operator
N.A.I.C.S.: 561520

Subsidiary (Non-US):

Brewster Travel Canada Inc. (2)
100 Gopher Street, PO Box 1140, Banff,
T1L 1J3, AB, Canada
Tel.: (403) 762-6700
Web Site: http://www.brewster.ca
Travel Agents & Tour Operators
N.A.I.C.S.: 561510

Division (Domestic):

Brewster Charter Services (3)
100 Gopher Street, PO Box 1140, Banff,
T1L 1J3, AB, Canada **(100%)**
Tel.: (403) 762-6710
Web Site: http://www.brewster.ca
Sales Range: $1-9.9 Million
Motor Coach Sightseeing Tours & Motor
Coach Transfers
N.A.I.C.S.: 561520

Subsidiary (Domestic):

Brewster Inc. (3)
100 Gopher Street, PO Box 1140, Banff,
T1L 1J3, AB, Canada
Tel.: (403) 762-6700
Web Site:
  https://www.banffjaspercollection.com
Transportation Management Services
N.A.I.C.S.: 488999

Affiliate (Domestic):

Banff Hospitality Residence Ltd. (4)
600 Cougar St, Banff, T1L 1A3, AB,
Canada **(43.52%)**
Tel.: (403) 762-3669
Business Support Services
N.A.I.C.S.: 561990

Subsidiary (Domestic):

Glacier Park, Inc. (2)

PO Box 2025, Columbia Falls, MT
59912 **(80%)**
Tel.: (406) 892-2525
Web Site:
  https://www.glacierparkcollection.com
Sales Range: Less than $1 Million
Emp.: 50
Home Management Services
N.A.I.C.S.: 721110

Subsidiary (Domestic):

West Glacier Mercantile, Inc. (3)
200 Going-to-the-Sun Rd, West Glacier, MT
59936
Tel.: (406) 888-5662
Web Site: http://www.westglacier.com
Lodging & Gift Shops
N.A.I.C.S.: 721110

VREC, Inc. (1)
836 Tulane St, Houston, TX 77007
Tel.: (832) 668-5334
Management Consulting Services
N.A.I.C.S.: 541618

ethnoMetrics Inc. (1)
950 Grier Dr, Las Vegas, NV 89119
Tel.: (702) 263-1553
Web Site: http://www.ethnometrics.com
Event Management Services
N.A.I.C.S.: 711310

onPeak LLC (1)
7000 Lindell Rd, Las Vegas, NV 89118
Tel.: (312) 527-7270
Web Site: https://www.onpeak.com
Hotel Accommodation Services
N.A.I.C.S.: 721110
Michael Howe (Exec VP)

Subsidiary (Non-US):

Travel & Event Services, LLC (2)
Tel.: (714) 891-7104
Web Site: https://traveleventservices.com
Travel & Event Consulting Services
N.A.I.C.S.: 813990

VIADERMA, INC.
1050 E Flamingo Rd Ste 107, Las
Vegas, NV 89119
Tel.: (310) 734-6111
Web Site: https://viaderma.com
Year Founded: 2014
VDRM—(NASDAQ)
Emp.: 6
Pharmaceuticals Product Mfr
N.A.I.C.S.: 325412
Chris A. Otiko (Pres, Treas & Sec)

VIASAT, INC.
6155 El Camino Real, Carlsbad, CA
92009
Tel.: (760) 476-2200   CA
Web Site: https://www.viasat.com
Year Founded: 1986
VSAT—(NASDAQ)
Rev.: $4,283,758,000
Assets: $16,329,364,000
Liabilities: $11,256,860,000
Net Worth: $5,072,504,000
Earnings: ($1,057,919,000)
Emp.: 7,500
Fiscal Year-end: 03/31/24
Advanced Digital Satellite Telecom-
munications & Wireless Signal Pro-
cessing Equipment Mfr
N.A.I.C.S.: 334220
K. Guru Gowrappan (Pres)
Mark D. Dankberg (Co-Founder, Chm
& CEO)
Keven K. Lippert (Chief Comml Offi-
cer & Exec VP-Strategic Initiatives)
Kevin J. Harkenrider (COO & Exec
VP)
Mark J. Miller (Co-Founder, Co-Chief
Technical Officer & Exec VP)
Robert Blair (Gen Counsel, Sec &
VP)
Girish Chandran (Co-Chief Technical
Officer & VP)

David Ryan (Pres-Space-Comml Net-
works & Sr VP)
Melinda Kimbro (Chief HR Officer &
Sr VP-People-Culture)
James Dodd (Pres-Global Enterprise-
Mobility & Sr VP)
Krishna Nathan (CIO)
Craig Miller (Pres-Govt Sys)
Evan Dixon (Pres-Fixed Broadband-
Global)
Garrett L. Chase (CFO & Sr VP)
Shawn Lynn Duffy (Chief Acctg Offi-
cer)

Subsidiaries:

**Beijing Viasat Science & Technology
Co., Ltd.** (1)
Lucky Tower Block B Suite 110-1112 No 3
Dong San Huan Bei Lu, Beijing, 100027,
China
Tel.: (86) 1064615761
Communication Equipment Services
N.A.I.C.S.: 423690

EAI Design Services, LLC (1)
14310 N Dale Mabry Hwy Ste 100, Tampa,
FL 33618
Tel.: (813) 968-7471
Web Site: http://www.eai-design.com
Computer System Design Services
N.A.I.C.S.: 541512
Emil A. Isaakian (Founder)

Inmarsat plc (1)
99 City Road, London, EC1Y 1AX, United
Kingdom
Tel.: (44) 2077281000
Web Site: http://www.inmarsat.com
Satellite Telecommunications
N.A.I.C.S.: 517410
Andrew J. Sukawaty (Chm)
Rajeev Suri (CEO)
Alison Horrocks (Chief Corp Affairs Officer
& Sec)
Peter Hadinger (CTO)
Tony Bates (CFO)
Jason Smith (COO)
Natasha Dillon (Chief People Officer)
Susan Miller (CEO-Inmarsat Government
US)
Philip Balaam (Pres-Aviation)
Todd McDonell (Pres-Global Govt)
Fredrik Gustavsson (Chief Strategy Officer)
Ben Palmer (Pres-Maritime)
Philippe Carette (Pres-Aviation Bus)

Subsidiary (Non-US):

Inmarsat Australia Pty Limited (2)
Cameron Centre Unit A 255 Rawson Street,
Auburn, 2144, NSW, Australia
Tel.: (61) 297145100
Mobile Telecommunications Services
N.A.I.C.S.: 517810

Subsidiary (Domestic):

Inmarsat Group Limited (2)
99 City Road, London, EC1Y 1AX, United
Kingdom
Tel.: (44) 2077281000
Web Site: http://www.inmarsat.com
Holding Company
N.A.I.C.S.: 551112

Subsidiary (US):

Globe Wireless Inc. (3)
1571 Robert J Conlan Blvd NE 100, Palm
Bay, FL 32905
Tel.: (321) 309-1300
Web Site: http://www.inmarsat.com
Marine Communications
N.A.I.C.S.: 517111

Subsidiary (Domestic):

Inmarsat Global Limited (3)
99 City Road, London, EC1Y 1AX, United
Kingdom **(100%)**
Tel.: (44) 2077281000
Web Site: https://www.inmarsat.com
Sales Range: $600-649.9 Million
Satellite Telecommunications
N.A.I.C.S.: 517410

Subsidiary (US):

Inmarsat Inc. (3)

ViaSat, Inc.—(Continued)

1100 Wilson Blvd Ste 1425, Arlington, VA
22209 **(100%)**
Tel.: (703) 647-4760
Web Site: http://www.satellite-links.co.uk
Satellite Telecommunications
N.A.I.C.S.: 517410
Andrew J. Sukawaty (Chm & CEO)

Branch (Domestic):

Inmarsat Inc. **(4)**
201 S Biscayne Blvd, Miami, FL 33131
Tel.: (305) 913-7521
Satellite Telecommunications
N.A.I.C.S.: 517410

Subsidiary (Domestic):

Inmarsat Leasing (Two) Limited **(3)**
99 City Road, London, EC1Y 1AX, United
Kingdom
Tel.: (44) 2077281000
Web Site: http://www.inmarsat.com
Equipment Leasing Services
N.A.I.C.S.: 532490

Subsidiary (Non-US):

Inmarsat Solutions (Canada) Inc. **(3)**
2650 Queensview Drive Ste 210, Ottawa,
K2B 8H6, ON, Canada
Tel.: (613) 230-4544
Web Site: http://www.inmarsat.com
Emp.: 4
Mobile & Fixed Satellite Communications
Services
N.A.I.C.S.: 517112

Branch (Domestic):

Inmarsat Solutions (Canada) Inc. -
Mount Pearl **(4)**
34 Glencoe Drive, Donovans Business
Park, Mount Pearl, A1N 4S8, NL, Canada
Tel.: (709) 748-4291
Web Site: http://www.inmarsat.com
Sales Range: $25-49.9 Million
Mobile & Fixed Satellite Communications
Services
N.A.I.C.S.: 517112

Subsidiary (US):

Inmarsat Solutions (US) Inc. **(3)**
6550 Rock Spring Dr Ste 650, Bethesda,
MD 20817
Tel.: (301) 214-8800
Web Site: http://www.inmarsat.com
Sales Range: $600-649.9 Million
Emp.: 600
Mobile & Fixed Satellite Communications
Services
N.A.I.C.S.: 517410

Subsidiary (Domestic):

Stratos Offshore Services
Company **(4)**
1710 W Willow St, Scott, LA 70583
Tel.: (337) 761-2000
Web Site: http://www.imarsat.com
Sales Range: $50-74.9 Million
Emp.: 175
Mobile & Fixed Satellite Communications
Services
N.A.I.C.S.: 517410

Subsidiary (Non-US):

Inmarsat Solutions B.V. **(3)**
Loire 158-160 Entrance B, 2491 AL, Hague,
Netherlands
Tel.: (31) 703013200
Web Site: http://www.inmarsat.com
Satellite Telecommunication Services
N.A.I.C.S.: 517410

Subsidiary (Domestic):

Inmarsat Solutions Global
Limited **(3)**
99 City Road, London, EC1Y 1AX, United
Kingdom
Tel.: (44) 2077281000
Web Site: http://www.inmarsat.com
Mobile & Fixed Satellite Communications
Services
N.A.I.C.S.: 517112

Branch (Domestic):

Inmarsat Solutions Global Ltd. -
Aberdeen **(4)**
Aberdeen Teleport Exhibition Ave, Bridge of
Don, Aberdeen, AB23 8BL, United Kingdom
Tel.: (44) 1224 296 000
Web Site: http://www.inmarsat.com
Mobile & Fixed Satellite Communications
Services
N.A.I.C.S.: 517112

Subsidiary (Non-US):

Inmarsat Solutions Pte. Ltd. **(3)**
911 Bukit Timah Road 3rd Floor, Tan Chong
Motor Centre, Singapore, 589622, Singa-
pore
Tel.: (65) 64995050
Web Site: http://www.inmarsat.com
Emp.: 60
Satellite Services
N.A.I.C.S.: 517410

Subsidiary (US):

Segovia, Inc **(3)**
600 Herndon Pkwy, Herndon, VA 20170
Tel.: (703) 621-6450
Web Site: http://www.segoviaip.com
Satellite Telecommunication Services
N.A.I.C.S.: 517410
Andy Beegan (CTO & Sr VP)
Alena Koci (Sr Dir-Mktg)
David J. Helfgott (Pres & CEO)

Subsidiary (Non-US):

Inmarsat Hong Kong Limited **(2)**
19/F Millennium Trade Centre 52-56 Kwai
Cheong Road, Kwai Chung, China (Hong
Kong)
Tel.: (852) 28560380
Mobile Telecommunications Services
N.A.I.C.S.: 517810
Shengwei Qian (VP-Sls-Asia Pacific)

Inmarsat KK **(2)**
ARK Hills Sengokuyama Mori Tower 25F
1-9-10 Roppongi, Minato-ku, Tokyo, 106-
0032, Japan
Tel.: (81) 355455184
Mobile Telecommunications Services
N.A.I.C.S.: 517810

Inmarsat SA **(2)**
Route de Crassier 19, Eysins, 1262, Nyon,
Switzerland
Tel.: (41) 225445600
Mobile Telecommunications Services
N.A.I.C.S.: 517810

Inmarsat Solutions AS **(2)**
NMK Borgundveien 340, 6009, Alesund,
Norway
Tel.: (47) 70172400
Mobile Telecommunications Services
N.A.I.C.S.: 517810

Inmarsat Solutions SA Pty
Limited **(2)**
54 Oxford Street Block B Oxford Gate Busi-
ness Park, Durbanville, Cape Town, 7550,
South Africa
Tel.: (27) 219793007
Mobile Telecommunications Services
N.A.I.C.S.: 517810

Inmarsat Solutions Shanghai Co.
Limited **(2)**
Building 20-4 MAX Kong Gang Industrial
Park, Shun Yi District, Beijing, 101318,
China
Tel.: (86) 1080470877
Mobile Telecommunications Services
N.A.I.C.S.: 517810

Inmarsat Spain S.A **(2)**
Paseo Castellana 43, 28046, Madrid, Spain
Tel.: (34) 2077281000
Mobile Telecommunications Services
N.A.I.C.S.: 517810

JAST, S.A. **(1)**
PSE C, CH 1015, Lausanne, Switzerland
Tel.: (41) 216938922
Web Site: http://www.jastantenna.com
Antenna Mfr
N.A.I.C.S.: 334220

RigNet, Inc. **(1)**

15115 Park Row Blvd Ste 300, Houston, TX
77084-4947
Tel.: (281) 674-0100
Web Site: https://www.rig.net
Rev: $207,921,000
Assets: $182,807,000
Liabilities: $181,502,000
Net Worth: $1,305,000
Earnings: ($45,808,000)
Emp.: 658
Fiscal Year-end: 12/31/2020
Communication Networks for Offshore Oil
Rigs
N.A.I.C.S.: 517810

Subsidiary (Domestic):

Data Technology Solutions **(2)**
1300 N Berard St, Breaux Bridge, LA 70517
Tel.: (337) 332-4347
Wired Telecommunications Carriers
N.A.I.C.S.: 517111
Shane Myers (Acct Mgr)

Intelie Technology LLC **(2)**
15115 Park Row Dr Blvd Ste 300, Houston,
TX 77084
Tel.: (281) 674-0100
Web Site: https://www.intelie.ai
Information Technology Services
N.A.I.C.S.: 541511
Chris Rom (Project Mgr)

Subsidiary (Non-US):

RigNet AS **(2)**
Maskinveien 24, 4033, Stavanger, Norway
Tel.: (47) 51206000
Web Site: http://www.rig.net
Telecommunication Servicesb
N.A.I.C.S.: 517810

RigNet Australia Pty Ltd **(2)**
45 Ventnor Ave, West Perth, 6005, WA,
Australia
Tel.: (61) 861887635
Telecommunication Servicesb
N.A.I.C.S.: 517810

RigNet Pte Ltd **(2)**
8 Kallang Avenue Aperia Tower 1 06-01,
Singapore, 339509, Singapore
Tel.: (65) 64912000
Web Site: http://www.rig.net
Telecommunication Servicesb
N.A.I.C.S.: 517810

RigNet Qatar W.L.L. **(2)**
Abu Ayoub Al Ansari st Villa no 118, Doha,
Qatar
Tel.: (974) 44686000
Web Site: http://www.rig.net
Telecommunication Servicesb
N.A.I.C.S.: 517810

RigNet Servicos de Telecomunica-
coes Brasil Ltda. **(2)**
Av Atlantica 1764 Cavaleiros, Macae,
27920-390, Rio de Janeiro, Brazil
Tel.: (55) 2221232888
Telecommunication Servicesb
N.A.I.C.S.: 517810

TrellisWare Technologies, Inc. **(1)**
10641 Scripps Summit Ct Ste 100, San Di-
ego, CA 92131
Tel.: (858) 753-1600
Web Site: https://www.trellisware.com
Telecommunication Servicesb
N.A.I.C.S.: 517810
Steve Fisher (CFO)
Anna Kochka (VP-HR & HR)
Jon Cromwell (VP-Engrg)
Norman Carmichael (VP-Ops)
Haidong Wang (VP-Product Mgmt & Strate-
gic Partnerships)
Matt Fallows (VP)
Metin Bayram (Pres)
Paul Konopka (Chief Compliance Officer,
Gen Counsel, Sec & VP)

ViaSat - Wireless Services
Division **(1)**
2908 Finfeather Rd, Bryan, TX 77801
Tel.: (979) 775-3405
Web Site: http://www.viasat.com
Internet Service Provider
N.A.I.C.S.: 517112

ViaSat Australia PTY Limited **(1)**
Level 20 201 Miller Street, North Sydney,

2060, NSW, Australia
Tel.: (61) 299648500
Sales Range: $10-24.9 Million
Emp.: 6
Satellite Communication Equipment Mfr
N.A.I.C.S.: 334220

ViaSat Credit Corp **(1)**
6155 El Camino Real, Carlsbad, CA 92009
Tel.: (760) 476-2200
Web Site: http://www.viasat.com
Consumer Credit Services
N.A.I.C.S.: 522130

ViaSat UK Limited **(1)**
Royal Pavilion Tower 2 Fourth Floor Welles-
ley Road, Farnborough, GU11 1PZ, Hamp-
shire, United Kingdom
Tel.: (44) 1252248600
Web Site: http://www.viasat.uk.com
Emp.: 40
Satellite Communication Equipment Mfr
N.A.I.C.S.: 334220

ViaSat, Inc. **(1)**
4830 E 49th St, Cuyahoga Heights, OH
44125
Tel.: (216) 706-7800
Web Site: http://www.viasat.com
Sales Range: $25-49.9 Million
Emp.: 50
Advanced Digital Satellite Telecommunica-
tions & Wireless Signal Processing Equip-
ment Mfr
N.A.I.C.S.: 517111

Viasat Europe Limited **(1)**
21 Charlemont Place, Dublin, D02 WV10,
Ireland
Tel.: (353) 15532600
Satellite Internet Services
N.A.I.C.S.: 517410

Viasat Ireland Limited **(1)**
21 Charlemont Place, Dublin, D02 WV10,
Ireland
Tel.: (353) 15532600
Software Publishing Services
N.A.I.C.S.: 513210

Viasat Singapore Holdings Pte.
Ltd. **(1)**
8 Kallang Avenue Aperia Tower 1 06-01,
Singapore, 339509, Singapore
Tel.: (65) 60162060
Satellite Internet Services
N.A.I.C.S.: 517410

VIASPACE INC.
344 Pne St, Santa Cruz, CA 95062
Tel.: (626) 768-3360 NV
Web Site: https://www.viaspace.com
Year Founded: 2003
VSPC—(OTCIQ)
Sales Range: Less than $1 Million
Emp.: 1
Energy Renewables Developer, Re-
searcher, Mfr & Marketer; Copy-
righted & Framed Artwork Mfr; Dis-
posable Fuel Cartridges Mfr
N.A.I.C.S.: 324199
Kevin L. Schewe (Chm, CEO & CFO)
Jan Vandersande (Dir-Comm)

Subsidiaries:

VIASPACE Green Energy Inc. **(1)**
131 Bells Ferry Ln, Marietta, GA
30066 **(75.6%)**
Tel.: (678) 805-7472
Web Site:
https://www.viaspacegreenenergy.com
Sales Range: $1-9.9 Million
Emp.: 67
Energy Renewables Producer & Marketer
N.A.I.C.S.: 324199
Sung Hsien Chang (Pres)
Stephen J. Muzi (CFO, Treas & Sec)

VIATAR CTC SOLUTIONS INC.
116 John St Ste 10, Lowell, MA
01852
Tel.: (617) 299-6590 DE
Web Site:
http://www.viatarctcsolutions.com
Year Founded: 2008

VRTT—(OTCIQ)
Sales Range: Less than $1 Million
Medical Device Mfr
N.A.I.C.S.: 339112
Ilan Reich (Pres & CEO)
Steve Keaney (VP-R&D)

VIATRIS INC.
1000 Mylan Blvd, Canonsburg, PA 15317
Tel.: (724) 514-1800
Web Site: https://www.viatris.com
Year Founded: 2020
VTRS—(NASDAQ)
Rev.: $15,426,900,000
Assets: $47,685,500,000
Liabilities: $27,218,100,000
Net Worth: $20,467,400,000
Earnings: $54,700,000
Emp.: 38,000
Fiscal Year-end: 12/31/23
Healtcare Services
N.A.I.C.S.: 325412
Mark W. Parrish (Vice Chm)
Robert J. Coury (Chm)
Rajiv Malik (Pres)
Scott A. Smith (CEO)

Subsidiaries:

Greenstone LLC   (1)
100 Route 206 N, Peapack, NJ 07977
Web Site: http://www.greenstonellc.com
Sales Range: $150-199.9 Million
Generic Pharmaceutical Mfr
N.A.I.C.S.: 325412

Mylan II B.V.   (1)
Building 4 Trident Place Mosquito Way,
Hatfield, AL10 9UL, Herts, United Kingdom
Tel.: (44) 1707853000
Web Site: http://www.mylan.com
Pharmaceuticals Mfr
N.A.I.C.S.: 325412

Subsidiary (Non-US):

BGP Products ApS   (2)
Arne Jacobsens Alle 7, 2300, Copenhagen,
Denmark
Tel.: (45) 28116932
Pharmaceutical & Healthcare Product Whslr
N.A.I.C.S.: 424210

BGP Products GmbH   (2)
Mylan EPD Perfektastrasse 84a, 1230, Vienna, Austria
Tel.: (43) 1891240
Pharmaceuticals Product Mfr
N.A.I.C.S.: 325412
Margit De Martin (Mgr-Regulatory Affairs)

BGP Products Operations GmbH   (2)
Hegenheimermattweg 127, 4123, Allschwil,
Switzerland
Tel.: (41) 614870200
Web Site: http://www.mylan.ch
Pharmaceutical Product Whslr
N.A.I.C.S.: 424210

Dermogroup Srl   (2)
Via Prai 23 San Martino Di Lupari, 35018,
Padua, Italy
Tel.: (39) 0499325305
Web Site: http://www.dermogella.it
Cosmetics Whslr
N.A.I.C.S.: 456120

Laboratorios Delta SA   (2)
Calle Presbitero Medina Esq Pasaje Taltal 2
Sopocachi, La Paz, Bolivia
Tel.: (591) 22411845211
Pharmaceuticals Product Mfr
N.A.I.C.S.: 325412
Jorge Claros Fuentes (CEO)

Mylan B.V.   (2)
Krijgsman 20, 1186 DM, Amstelveen, Netherlands
Tel.: (31) 204263330
Web Site: http://www.mylan.com
Pharmaceutical Product Whslr
N.A.I.C.S.: 424210

Mylan Health Pty. Ltd.   (2)
Level 1 30 The Bond 30-34 Hickson Road,
Millers Point, 2000, NSW, Australia

Tel.: (61) 92983999
Web Site: http://www.mylan.com.au
Pharmaceutical Preparation Mfr
N.A.I.C.S.: 325412

Mylan Healthcare Norge AS   (2)
Hagalokkveien 26, 1383, Asker, Norway
Tel.: (47) 23205880
Pharmaceuticals Product Mfr
N.A.I.C.S.: 325412

Mylan Healthcare S.p. Z o.o.   (2)
Ul Postepu 21B, 02-676, Warsaw, Poland
Tel.: (48) 225466400
Pharmaceuticals Product Mfr
N.A.I.C.S.: 325412

Mylan IRE Healthcare Limited   (2)
Hagalokkv 26, PO Box 194, 1371, Asker,
Norway
Tel.: (47) 66753300
Pharmaceutical & Healthcare Product Whslr
N.A.I.C.S.: 424210

Subsidiary (US):

Mylan, Inc.   (2)
1000 Mylan Blvd, Canonsburg, PA 15317
Tel.: (724) 514-1800
Web Site: http://www.mylan.com
Sales Range: $5-14.9 Billion
Pharmaceuticals Product Mfr
N.A.I.C.S.: 325412
Mark W. Parrish (Vice Chm)

Subsidiary (Non-US):

Agila Specialties Polska sp. Zo.o (3)
ul Daniszewska 10, 03-230, Warsaw, Poland
Tel.: (48) 226140081
Pharmaceuticals Product Mfr
N.A.I.C.S.: 325412
Pawel Wronski (Gen Mgr)

Subsidiary (Domestic):

Apicore US LLC   (3)
49 Napoleon Ct, Somerset, NJ 08873
Tel.: (732) 748-8882
Web Site: http://www.apicore.com
Pharmaceutical Preparation Mfr
N.A.I.C.S.: 325412

Subsidiary (Non-US):

Apothecon B.V.   (3)
Dieselweg 25, Barneveld, 3771 ME, Netherlands
Tel.: (31) 342426120
Web Site: http://www.apothecon.nl
Pharmaceuticals Product Mfr
N.A.I.C.S.: 325412

Hospithera N.V.   (3)
Rue de la Petite Ile Klein Eilandstraat 3,
Brussels, 1070, Belgium
Tel.: (32) 25350202
Web Site: http://www.hospithera.be
Medical Device Distr
N.A.I.C.S.: 423450
Philip Van den Bogaert (Gen Mgr)
Bart Luteijn (Mgr-Capital Equipment)
Nathalie Van Pellecom (Coord)
Marie-Dominique Oomen (Mgr-Customer Care)
Werner Van Assche (Dir-Admin & Financial)
Florence Van Biesebroeck (Dir-HR, Admin & Financial)
Peter de Jong (CEO)

Matrix Laboratories (Xiamen) Ltd. (3)
20/F Everbright Bank Bldg 81 South Hubin
Road, Xiamen, 361004, China
Tel.: (86) 5922218988
Web Site: http://www.matrixlabschina.com
Pharmaceuticals Product Mfr
N.A.I.C.S.: 325412

McDermott Laboratories Ltd.   (3)
35/36 Baldoyle Industrial Estate Grange
Road, Dublin, 13, Ireland
Tel.: (353) 18398600
Web Site: http://www.mylan.com
Emp.: 50
Medicinals & Botanicals Research Services
N.A.I.C.S.: 325412

Meda AB   (3)
Pipers Vag 2A, SE-170 73, Solna, Sweden

Tel.: (46) 86301900
Web Site: http://www.mylan.se
Sales Range: $1-4.9 Billion
Pharmaceutical Products Developer, Marketer & Seller
N.A.I.C.S.: 325412

Subsidiary (Non-US):

Meda A/S   (4)
Hagalokkveien 26, 1383, Asker, Norway
Tel.: (47) 66753300
Web Site: http://www.meda.no
Drugs & Druggists Sundries Whslr
N.A.I.C.S.: 424210

Meda AS   (4)
Solvang 8, Allerod, 3450, Denmark
Tel.: (45) 44528888
Web Site: http://www.meda.dk
Pharmaceutical Preparation Mfr
N.A.I.C.S.: 325412

Meda Health Sales Ireland Ltd   (4)
34/35 Block A Dunboyne Business Park,
Dunboyne, Meath, Ireland
Tel.: (353) 18026624
Web Site: http://www.meda.ie
Health Practitioners
N.A.I.C.S.: 621399

Meda Manufacturing SAS   (4)
Rue de Lartique, 33700, Merignac, France
Tel.: (33) 556553535
Pharmaceutical Preparation Mfr
N.A.I.C.S.: 325412

Meda Oy   (4)
Vaisalantie 4, 02130, Espoo, Finland
Tel.: (358) 207209550
Web Site: http://www.meda.fi
Medical Dental & Hospital Equipment &
Supplies Merchant Whslr
N.A.I.C.S.: 423450

Meda Pharma B.V.   (4)
Krijgsman 20, 1186 DM, Amstelveen, Netherlands
Tel.: (31) 204263300
Pharmaceutical Products Mfr & Distr
N.A.I.C.S.: 325412

Meda Pharma GmbH   (4)
Hegnaustrasse 60, Wangen-Bruttisellen,
8602, Wangen, Switzerland
Tel.: (41) 448352626
Web Site: http://www.medapharma.ch
Medicinal & Botanical Mfr
N.A.I.C.S.: 325411

Meda Pharma GmbH & Co. KG   (4)
Benzstrasse 1, D-61352, Bad Homburg,
Germany
Tel.: (49) 617288801
Web Site: http://www.medapharma.de
Medicinal & Botanical Mfr
N.A.I.C.S.: 325411

Subsidiary (Domestic):

Meda Germany Holding GmbH   (5)
Benzstr 1, Bad Homburg, 61352, Germany
Tel.: (49) 617288801
Investment Management Service
N.A.I.C.S.: 523999

Subsidiary (Non-US):

Meda Pharma GmbH   (6)
Guglgasse 15, 1110, Vienna, Austria
Tel.: (43) 186390
Web Site: http://www.arcana-mylan.at
Pharmaceuticals Product Mfr
N.A.I.C.S.: 325412

Subsidiary (Domestic):

Meda Manufacturing GmbH   (5)
Neurather Ring 1, 51063, Cologne, Germany
Tel.: (49) 22164720
Web Site: http://www.meda-manufacturing.de
Medicinal & Botanical Mfr
N.A.I.C.S.: 325411

Subsidiary (Non-US):

Meda Pharma Hungary Kft.   (4)
Vaci ul 91, 1139, Budapest, Hungary
Tel.: (36) 12363410
Health Practitioners

N.A.I.C.S.: 621399

Meda Pharma Ilac San ve Tic Ltd.
Sti   (4)
Buyukdere Cad Noramin Is Merkezi Ofis No
237 D-403-404, 34398, Istanbul, Turkiye
Tel.: (90) 2122762080
Pharmaceuticals Product Mfr
N.A.I.C.S.: 325412

Meda Pharma Ilac Sanayi ve Ticaret
Limited Sirketi   (4)
Maslak Mahallesi Buyukdere Caddesi No
37 ic Kape 74-75-76-77-78, 34398, Istanbul, Turkiye
Tel.: (90) 2123665300
Web Site: http://www.medapharma.com.tr
Pharmaceuticals Product Mfr
N.A.I.C.S.: 325412

Meda Pharma Produtos Farmaceuticos, S.A.   (4)
R Centro Cultural 13, 1700-249, Lisbon,
Portugal
Tel.: (351) 218420300
Pharmaceutical Preparation Mfr
N.A.I.C.S.: 325412

Meda Pharma S.A.   (4)
Avenida de Castilla 2 Parque Empresarial
San Fernando, Edificio Berlin, 28830, San
Fernando de Henares, Spain
Tel.: (34) 916699300
Pharmaceuticals Product Mfr
N.A.I.C.S.: 325412
Jose Vicente Santa Cruz (Dir Gen)

Meda Pharma S.p.A.   (4)
Via Valosa di Sopra 9, 20900, Monza, Italy
Tel.: (39) 03973901
Web Site: http://www.medapharma.it
Pharmaceutical Preparation Mfr
N.A.I.C.S.: 325412

Meda Pharma S.r.o.   (4)
Kodanska 1441/46, 100 00, Prague, 10,
Czech Republic
Tel.: (420) 234064204
Natural Gas Distribution
N.A.I.C.S.: 221210

Meda Pharma SIA   (4)
Mukusalas Street 101, Riga, LV 1004, Latvia
Tel.: (371) 67616137
Web Site: http://www.medapharma.com
Pharmaceutical Product Whslr
N.A.I.C.S.: 424210

Meda Pharma South Africa (Pty)
Limited   (4)
Building 6 Greenstone Hill Office Park Emerald Boulevard, Modderfontein, 1645,
South Africa
Tel.: (27) 8600633272
Web Site: http://www.meda.co.za
Pharmaceutical Product Whslr
N.A.I.C.S.: 424210
Cicelia Levine (Mktg Mgr)
Riaan Botes (Country Mgr)
Joggie Mallo (Mgr-Sls-Natl)

Meda Pharmaceuticals A.E.   (4)
Ag Demetriou 63, 17456, Alimos, Greece
Tel.: (30) 2106775690
Web Site: http://www.medapharma.gr
Pharmaceutical Preparation Mfr
N.A.I.C.S.: 325412

Subsidiary (US):

Meda Pharmaceuticals Inc.   (4)
265 Davidson Ave Ste 300, Somerset, NJ
08873-4120
Tel.: (732) 564-2200
Prescription Therapeutics & Diagnostic
Tests & Tools Developer, Marketer & Seller
N.A.I.C.S.: 325412

Subsidiary (Non-US):

Meda Pharmaceuticals Limited   (4)
Dla Piper Scotland Lip Collins House Rutland Square, Edinburgh, EH1 2AA, United
Kingdom
Tel.: (44) 8454600000
Pharmaceutical Preparation Mfr
N.A.I.C.S.: 325412

Viatris Inc.—(Continued)

Meda Pharmaceuticals Ltd (4)
2351 Royal Windsor Dr Ste 201, Mississauga, L5J 4SJ, ON, Canada
Tel.: (289) 373-3004
Pharmaceutical & Healthcare Product Whslr
N.A.I.C.S.: 424210

Meda Pharmaceuticals MEA FZ-LLC (4)
PO Box 505057, Dubai, United Arab Emirates
Tel.: (971) 44547100
Web Site: http://www.medapharma.me
Pharmaceuticals Product Mfr
N.A.I.C.S.: 325412
Fadi Mureb (Country Mgr)

Subsidiary (Domestic):

Medag AB (4)
Pipers Vag 2, PO Box 906, Solna, 170 73, Sweden
Tel.: (46) 87567686
Web Site: http://www.meda.se
Sales Range: $50-74.9 Million
Emp.: 100
Pharmaceutical Products Distr
N.A.I.C.S.: 424210

Subsidiary (Non-US):

Mylan Medical SAS (4)
42/44 Rue Washington, 75008, Paris, France
Tel.: (33) 156641070
Web Site: http://www.mylan.fr
Pharmaceutical Products Distr
N.A.I.C.S.: 424210

Mylan Pharmaceuticals Sp. z o.o. (4)
ul Daniszewska 10, 03-230, Warsaw, Poland
Tel.: (48) 228144399
Web Site: http://www.mylan.com.pl
Pharmaceutical Preparation Mfr
N.A.I.C.S.: 325412

Subsidiary (Non-US):

Mylan AB (3)
Ynglingagatan 14 2 tr, PO Box 23033, 104 35, Stockholm, Sweden
Tel.: (46) 855522750
Web Site: http://www.mylan.se
Emp.: 140
Pharmaceuticals Mfr
N.A.I.C.S.: 325412

Mylan ApS (3)
Arne Jacobsens All 7 5, 2300, Copenhagen, Denmark
Tel.: (45) 28116932
Web Site: http://www.mylan.dk
Pharmaceuticals Product Mfr
N.A.I.C.S.: 325412

Mylan BVBA (3)
Dieselweg 25, Bunschoten, 3752, Netherlands
Tel.: (31) 332997080
Web Site: http://www.mylan.nl
Pharmaceuticals Product Mfr
N.A.I.C.S.: 325412

Subsidiary (Domestic):

Mylan Bertek Pharmaceuticals, Inc. (3)
12720 Dairy Ashford Rd, Sugar Land, TX 77478
Tel.: (281) 240-1000
Web Site: http://www.mylan.com
Sales Range: $1-9.9 Million
Emp.: 50
Pharmaceutical Preparation Mfr
N.A.I.C.S.: 325412
Didier Barret (Pres-Europe)

Subsidiary (Non-US):

Mylan Dura Gmbh (3)
Wittichstrasse 6, Darmstadt, 64295, Germany
Tel.: (49) 617288801
Web Site: http://www.mylan-dura.de
Pharmaceutical Products Distr
N.A.I.C.S.: 424210

Mylan EMEA S.A.S. (3)
117 Allee Des Parcs, 69792, Saint Priest, Cedex, France
Tel.: (33) 437257500
Web Site: http://www.mylan.fr
Emp.: 300
Pharmaceuticals Product Mfr
N.A.I.C.S.: 325412

Mylan EPD Kft. (3)
Vaci Ut 150, Budapest, 1138, Hungary
Tel.: (36) 14652100
Web Site: http://www.mylan.co.hu
Generic & Specialty Pharmaceutical Drug Mfr & Whslr
N.A.I.C.S.: 325412

Mylan Generics France Holding S.A.S. (3)
117 Allee Des Parcs, Saint Priest, 69800, France
Tel.: (33) 890109283
Web Site: http://www.mylan.com
Pharmaceuticals Mfr
N.A.I.C.S.: 325412

Mylan Group B.V. (3)
Dieselweg 25, Bunschoten, 3752 LB, Utrecht, Netherlands
Tel.: (31) 332997080
Web Site: http://www.mylan.nl
Pharmaceuticals Mfr
N.A.I.C.S.: 325412

Mylan Hospital AS (3)
Sorkedalsveien 10B, 0369, Oslo, Norway
Tel.: (47) 23205880
Web Site: http://www.mylan.no
Healtcare Services
N.A.I.C.S.: 621491

Subsidiary (Domestic):

Mylan Institutional Inc. (3)
781 Chestnut Ridge Rd, Morgantown, WV 26505 **(100%)**
Tel.: (304) 599-2595
Web Site: http://www.udllabs.com
Repackager & Marketer of Multi Source & Single Source of Pharmaceutical Products & Unit Dose for Institutions
N.A.I.C.S.: 325412

Subsidiary (Domestic):

Mylan Institutional LLC (4)
9525 W Bryn Mawr Ave 725, Rosemont, IL 60018
Tel.: (847) 260-5800
Web Site: http://www.viatris.com
Injectable Pharmaceuticals Mfr
N.A.I.C.S.: 325412

Subsidiary (Domestic):

Mylan Laboratories Inc. (3)
76 S Orange Ave Ste 301, South Orange, NJ 07079
Tel.: (973) 761-1600
Web Site: http://www.mylan.com
Pharmaceutical Ingredient Mfr
N.A.I.C.S.: 325412

Subsidiary (Non-US):

Mylan Laboratories Limited (3)
Plot No 564/A/22 Road No 92, Jubilee Hills, Hyderabad, 500 034, India
Tel.: (91) 4030866666
Web Site: http://www.mylan.in
Sales Range: $550-599.9 Million
Active Pharmaceutical Ingredients Mfr
N.A.I.C.S.: 325412

Mylan Laboratories SAS (3)
Route de Belleville, 01400, Chatillon-sur-Chalaronne, France
Tel.: (33) 146258500
Pharmaceuticals Product Mfr
N.A.I.C.S.: 424210

Mylan Netherlands B.V. (3)
Krijgsman 20, 1186 DM, Amstelveen, Netherlands
Tel.: (31) 204263300
Web Site: http://www.mylan.nl
Pharmaceuticals Mfr
N.A.I.C.S.: 325412

Mylan New Zealand Ltd (3)

PO Box 11183, Ellerslie, 1542, Auckland, New Zealand
Tel.: (64) 95792792
Web Site: http://www.mylan.co.nz
Pharmaceuticals Product Mfr
N.A.I.C.S.: 325412

Mylan Pharma Group Ltd. (3)
Unit 6 Casla Industrial Estate Casla, Galway, Ireland
Tel.: (353) 91593202
Sales Range: $50-74.9 Million
Emp.: 200
Pharmaceutical Product Whslr
N.A.I.C.S.: 424210

Mylan Pharma UK Limited (3)
Albany Gate Darkes Lane, Potters Bar, EN6 1AG, Hertfordshire, United Kingdom
Tel.: (44) 1707853000
Respiratory Pharmaceutical Mfr
N.A.I.C.S.: 325412

Subsidiary (Domestic):

Mylan Pharmaceuticals Inc. (3)
781 Chestnut Ridge Rd, Morgantown, WV 26505-2730 **(100%)**
Tel.: (304) 599-2595
Web Site: http://www.mylan.com
Sales Range: $800-899.9 Million
Emp.: 1,183
Mfr of Pharmaceuticals
N.A.I.C.S.: 325412

Subsidiary (Non-US):

Mylan Pharmaceuticals Private Limited (3)
Prestige Tech Park Platina 3 7th to 12th Floor Kadubesanahalli, Elphinstone Road West, Bengaluru, 560103, India
Tel.: (91) 8066728000
Web Site: http://www.mylan.in
Pharmaceuticals Mfr
N.A.I.C.S.: 325412
Rakesh Bamzai (Pres-Comml & Emerging Markets)

Mylan Pharmaceuticals ULC (3)
85 Advance Road, Etobicoke, M8Z 2S6, ON, Canada
Tel.: (416) 236-2631
Web Site: https://www.mylan.ca
Emp.: 120
Pharmaceuticals Product Mfr
N.A.I.C.S.: 325412

Mylan Seiyaku Ltd. (3)
5-11-2 Toranomon Holland Hills Mori Tower, Minato Ku, Tokyo, 150-0001, Japan
Tel.: (81) 357339800
Pharmaceuticals Product Mfr
N.A.I.C.S.: 325412

Subsidiary (Domestic):

Mylan Specialty L.P. (3)
110 Allen Rd 4th Fl, Basking Ridge, NJ 07920
Tel.: (800) 395-3376
Web Site: http://www.mylanspecialty.com
Pharmaceuticals Mfr
N.A.I.C.S.: 325412

Unit (Domestic):

Mylan Specialty LP (4)
2751 Napa Vly Corporate Dr, Napa, CA 94558-6216
Tel.: (707) 224-3200
Web Site: http://www.mylanspecialty.com
Pharmaceuticals Mfr
N.A.I.C.S.: 325412

Subsidiary (Non-US):

Mylan Switzerland GmbH (3)
Thurgauerstrasse 40, Zurich, 8050, Switzerland
Tel.: (41) 443087575
Web Site: http://www.mylan.com
Emp.: 60
Pharmaceuticals Mfr
N.A.I.C.S.: 325412

Subsidiary (Domestic):

Mylan Technologies, Incorporated (3)

110 Lake St, Saint Albans, VT 05478-2266 **(100%)**
Tel.: (802) 527-9100
Web Site: http://www.mylan.com
Sales Range: $50-74.9 Million
Emp.: 400
Transdermal Drug Delivery Systems Mfr & Coating, Laminating & Extrusion Services
N.A.I.C.S.: 325412

Subsidiary (Non-US):

Mylan Teoranta (3)
Kilroe East Inverin, Galway, Ireland
Tel.: (353) 91505600
Pharmaceuticals Product Mfr
N.A.I.C.S.: 325412

Subsidiary (Domestic):

Prestium Pharma, Inc. (3)
411 S State St Ste E-100, Newtown, PA 18940
Tel.: (267) 685-0340
Pharmaceutical & Healthcare Product Whslr
N.A.I.C.S.: 424210

Subsidiary (Non-US):

QD Pharmaceuticals ULC (3)
85 Advance Road, Etobicoke, M8Z 2S6, ON, Canada
Tel.: (800) 661-3429
Web Site: http://www.qdpharmaceuticals.ca
Pharmaceuticals Distr
N.A.I.C.S.: 423450

Subsidiary (Domestic):

Sagent Agila LLC (3)
2120 Carey Ave Ste 300, Cheyenne, WY 82001
Tel.: (847) 908-1600
Pharmaceuticals Product Mfr
N.A.I.C.S.: 325412

Subsidiary (Non-US):

Scandinavian Pharmaceuticals-Generics AB (3)
PO Box 23033, Stockholm, 104 35, Sweden
Tel.: (46) 855522715
Pharmaceuticals Product Mfr
N.A.I.C.S.: 325412

Subsidiary (Domestic):

Somerset Pharmaceuticals Inc. (3)
2202 NW Shore Blvd 450, Tampa, FL 33607 **(100%)**
Tel.: (813) 288-0040
Sales Range: $50-74.9 Million
Emp.: 10
Marketer of Pharmaceutical Products
N.A.I.C.S.: 424210

Oyster Point Pharma, Inc. (1)
202 Carnegie Ctr Ste 109, Princeton, NJ 08540
Tel.: (609) 382-9032
Web Site: http://www.oysterpointrx.com
Rev.: $24,539,000
Assets: $222,617,000
Liabilities: $123,080,000
Net Worth: $99,537,000
Earnings: ($100,659,000)
Emp.: 303
Fiscal Year-end: 12/31/2021
Biotechnology Research & Development Services
N.A.I.C.S.: 541714
Daniel Lochner (CFO & Chief Bus Officer)
Loni Da Silva (VP & Head-Regulatory Affairs)
Dawn Pruitt Koffler (VP-Mktg)
George Donato (Sr VP-CMC & Ops)
Jill Andersen (Chief Compliance Officer & Gen Counsel)
Nicolette Sherman (Chief HR Officer)
Eric Carlson (Chief Scientific Officer)
Marian Macsai (Chief Medical Officer-Medical Affairs)
Michael Campbell (Sr VP & Head-Comml)

Upjohn Middle East FZ-LLC (1)
Atlas Business Center building floor 6, Dubai Media City, Dubai, United Arab Emirates
Tel.: (971) 44532000
Healthcare Services

N.A.I.C.S.: 621610

VIAVI SOLUTIONS INC.
1445 S Spectrum Blvd Ste 102,
Chandler, AZ 85286
Tel.: (408) 404-3600   DE
Web Site:
  https://www.viavisolutions.com
Year Founded: 1923
VIAV—(NASDAQ)
Rev.: $1,000,400,000
Assets: $1,736,300,000
Liabilities: $1,054,700,000
Net Worth: $681,600,000
Earnings: ($25,800,000)
Emp.: 3,600
Fiscal Year-end: 06/29/24
Fiber Optic Components, Modules &
Subsystems Designer, Developer, Mfr
& Distr
N.A.I.C.S.: 334413
Kevin Siebert (Sec, Sr VP & Gen
Counsel)
Luke M. Scrivanich (Sr VP-Optical
Security & Performance Products)
Oleg Khaykin (Pres & CEO)
Ilan Daskal (CFO & Exec VP)
Pamela Avent (Controller-Global)
Richard E. Belluzzo (Chm)
Paul McNab (CMO, Chief Strategy
Officer & Exec VP)
Ralph Rondinone (Sr VP-Global Ops
& Svcs-NSE)
Gary Staley (Sr VP-Global Sls-NSE)
Petra Nagel (Sr VP-HR)
Michael Seidl (Sr VP-Bus Mgmt)

Subsidiaries:

9274-5322 QUEBEC Inc.   (1)
130 rue Jean Proulx, Gatineau, J8Z 1V3,
QC, Canada
Tel.: (819) 307-0333
Web Site: http://www.nordiasoft.com
Software Development Services
N.A.I.C.S.: 541511

Aeroflex Wichita, Inc.   (1)
10200 W York St, Wichita, KS 67215-8935
Tel.: (316) 522-4981
Web Site: http://www.aeroflex.com
Electronic & Wireless Test Equipment
N.A.I.C.S.: 334515

JDSU do Brasil Ltda. & Cia   (1)
Avenida Eng Luis Carlos Berrini 936 9th
floor, Sao Paulo, 04571-000, Brazil
Tel.: (55) 1155033800
Web Site: http://www.jdsu.com
Sales Range: $25-49.9 Million
Emp.: 45
Fiber Optic Component Distr
N.A.I.C.S.: 334413

Medusa Labs   (1)
600 Center Ridge Dr Ste 600, Austin, TX
78753
Tel.: (512) 670-7300
Testing & Training Services for Server, Storage & Networking Interfaces & Protocols
N.A.I.C.S.: 541380

Network Instruments, LLC   (1)
10701 Red Circle Dr, Minnetonka, MN
55343
Tel.: (952) 358-3800
Web Site:
  http://www.networkinstruments.com
Emp.: 145
Network & Application Peformance Manage-
ment Solutions
N.A.I.C.S.: 334118

RPC Photonics, Inc.   (1)
330 Clay Rd, Rochester, NY 14623
Tel.: (585) 272-2840
Web Site: http://www.rpcphotonics.com
Micro Optical Component Mfr
N.A.I.C.S.: 333310
G. Michael Morris (Co-Founder)
Dean Faklis (Co-Founder)
Milton Chang (Co-Founder)

Viavi Solutions (Shenzhen) Co.,
Ltd.   (1)

Resources Tech Bldg No 1 Songpingshan
Rd N Building Shenzhen, High-Tech Ind
Park N Block 10th Fl Suite 1001, Shen-
zhen, 518057, Guangdong, China
Tel.: (86) 75588696800
Fiber Optic Component & Network Equip-
ment Mfr
N.A.I.C.S.: 335921

Viavi Solutions (Suzhou) Co.,
Ltd.   (1)
399 Suhong East Road 1st Floor Suzhou
Industrial Park, Suzhou, 215021, China
Tel.: (86) 51269567600
Fiber Optic Component & Network Equip-
ment Mfr
N.A.I.C.S.: 335921

Viavi Solutions AB   (1)
Torshamnsgatan 27 2 114-116, 164 40,
Kista, Sweden
Tel.: (46) 84494800
Web Site: https://www.viavisolutions.se
Fiber Optic Component Mfr & Distr
N.A.I.C.S.: 334413

Viavi Solutions Deutschland
GmbH   (1)
Arbachtalstrasse 5 below Achalm, 72800,
Eningen, Germany
Tel.: (49) 7121862222
Web Site: http://www.viavisolutions.com
Fiber Optic Component Mfr & Distr
N.A.I.C.S.: 334413

Viavi Solutions France SAS   (1)
46 bis Rue Pierre Curie ZI Les Gatines,
78370, Plaisir, France
Tel.: (33) 130815050
Web Site: http://www.viavisolutions.com
Fiber Optic Component Mfr & Distr
N.A.I.C.S.: 334413

Viavi Solutions GmbH   (1)
Fraunhoferstrasse 9-11, Ismaning, 85737,
Munich, Germany
Tel.: (49) 8999641132
Fiber Optic Component & Network Equip-
ment Mfr
N.A.I.C.S.: 335921

Viavi Solutions Haberlesme Test ve
Olcum Teknolojileri Ticaret Limited
Sirketi   (1)
Kucukbakkalkoy Mah Dereyolu Sk No 7 Ot-
okoc Binasi Kat 1, Istanbul, 34710, Turkiye
Tel.: (90) 2165777177
Fiber Optic Component Mfr & Distr
N.A.I.C.S.: 334290

Viavi Solutions Inc. - Indianapolis
Sales Office   (1)
5808 Churchman Bypass, Indianapolis, IN
46203
Tel.: (317) 788-9351
Web Site: http://www.viavisolutions.com
Sales Range: $50-74.9 Million
Emp.: 270
Signal Generators, CATV Test Equipment &
Calibration Instruments Whslr
N.A.I.C.S.: 423830

Viavi Solutions Italia s.r.l.   (1)
Via del Casale Solaro 119 No 30 10,
00143, Rome, Monza, Italy
Tel.: (39) 06515731
Fiber Optic Component Mfr & Distr
N.A.I.C.S.: 334413

Viavi Solutions Japan K.K.   (1)
6-22-1 Nishi-Shinjuku Shinjuku Square
Tower 7F, Shinjuku-ku, Tokyo, 163-1107,
Japan
Tel.: (81) 353396886
Web Site: https://www.viavisolutions.com
Emp.: 20
Fiber Optic Component Mfr & Distr
N.A.I.C.S.: 334413

Viavi Solutions Spain, S.A.   (1)
Av de Manoteras 26 Orion Building, 28050,
Madrid, Spain
Tel.: (34) 913839801
Web Site: https://www.viavisolutions.com
Fiber Optic Component Mfr & Distr
N.A.I.C.S.: 334413

Viavi Solutions UK Limited   (1)
Newbury Business Park London Road First
Floor North Astor House, Newbury, RG14

2PZ, Berkshire, United Kingdom
Tel.: (44) 1635223000
Web Site: https://www.viavisolutions.com
Telecommunication Servicesb
N.A.I.C.S.: 517810

Subsidiary (Domestic):

Aeroflex Limited   (2)
Longacres House Six Hills Way, 6 Hills
Way, Stevenage, SG1 2AN, Hertfordshire,
United Kingdom
Tel.: (44) 1438742200
Advanced Wireless Coverage & Mobile
Communications Systems
N.A.I.C.S.: 517112

Subsidiary (Non-US):

Aeroflex Ireland Limited   (3)
Adelphi Plaza Ground Floor Upper
George's Street, Dun Laoghaire Co, Dublin,
Ireland
Tel.: (353) 12367002
Web Site: http://www.aeroflex.com
Develops IP Test & Measurement Solutions
N.A.I.C.S.: 541380

Viavi Solutions de Mexico S.A. de
C.V.   (1)
San Francisco 6 Col del Valle Colonia Del
Valle Mayor Benito Juarez, 03100, Mexico,
Mexico
Tel.: (52) 5546311120
Sales Range: $25-49.9 Million
Emp.: 35
Fiber Optic Component Mfr & Distr
N.A.I.C.S.: 333310

Viavi Solutions do Brasil Ltda.   (1)
Av Eng Luis Carlos Berrini 936 Unit 91 9th
Floor, Sao Paulo, 04571-000, SP, Brazil
Tel.: (55) 1155033800
Web Site: https://www.viavisolutions.com
Fiber Optic Component & Network Equip-
ment Mfr
N.A.I.C.S.: 335921

ng4T GmbH   (1)
Gartenfelder Str 29-37, 13599, Berlin, Ger-
many
Tel.: (49) 30800931900
Testing Laboratories & Services
N.A.I.C.S.: 541380

VICARIOUS SURGICAL INC.
78 4th Ave, Waltham, MA 02451
Tel.: (617) 868-1700   DE
Web Site:
  https://www.vicarioussurgical.com
Year Founded: 2014
RBOT—(NYSE)
Rev.: $1,435,000
Assets: $140,291,000
Liabilities: $29,246,000
Net Worth: $111,045,000
Earnings: $5,157,000
Emp.: 213
Fiscal Year-end: 12/31/22
Surgical & Medical Instrument Manu-
facturing
N.A.I.C.S.: 339112
June Morris (Chief Legal Officer &
Gen Counsel)
Bill Kelly (CFO)
John Mazzola (COO)
Michael Pratt (VP)
Michael Tricoli (VP)
Adam Sachs (Co-Founder & CEO)
Sammy Khalifa (Co-Founder & CTO)

VICI PROPERTIES INC.
535 Madison Ave 20th Fl, New York,
NY 10022
Tel.: (646) 949-4631   DE
Web Site:
  https://www.viciproperties.com
Year Founded: 2016
VICI—(NYSE)
Rev.: $3,611,988,000
Assets: $44,059,841,000
Liabilities: $18,402,067,000
Net Worth: $25,657,774,000
Earnings: $2,513,540,000

Emp.: 28
Fiscal Year-end: 12/31/23
Entertainment Services
N.A.I.C.S.: 512131
Edward Baltazar Pitoniak (CEO)
John Payne (Pres & COO)
David Andrew Kieske (CFO & Exec
VP)
Gabriel F. Wasserman (Chief Acctg
Officer)
Samantha Gallagher (Gen Counsel,
Sec & Exec VP)
Kellan Florio (Chief Investment Offi-
cer)
Moira McCloskey (Sr VP)
Danny Valoy (VP)
Erin Ferreri (VP)
Elena Keil (Assoc Gen Counsel)
Kevin Kitson (Assoc Gen Counsel)
Cameron Lewis (Assoc Gen Counsel)
Jeremy Waxman (VP)
Brandon Wendel (Dir)
Hugh Dalton (Dir)
Vishal Parikh (Controller)
Bryce Richey (Coord)
Amy Wong (Controller)

Subsidiaries:

Harrah's Council Bluffs LLC   (1)
1 Harrah's Blvd, Council Bluffs, IA 51501
Tel.: (712) 329-6000
Web Site: https://www.caesars.com
Hotel Operator
N.A.I.C.S.: 721110
Christopher Crane (Mgr-Facilities & Secu-
rity)

Harrah's Joliet LandCo LLC   (1)
151 N Joliet St, Joliet, IL 60432
Tel.: (815) 740-7800
Web Site: https://www.caesars.com
Hotel Operator
N.A.I.C.S.: 721110
Bryce Jordan (Mktg Dir)

Harrah's Lake Tahoe LLC   (1)
15 Hwy 50, Stateline, NV 89449
Web Site: https://www.caesars.com
Hotel Operator
N.A.I.C.S.: 721110

Horseshoe Bossier City Prop
LLC   (1)
711 Horseshoe Blvd, Bossier City, LA 71111
Web Site: https://www.caesars.com
Hotel Operator
N.A.I.C.S.: 721110

Horseshoe Council Bluffs LLC   (1)
2701 23rd Ave, Council Bluffs, IA 51501
Tel.: (712) 323-2500
Web Site: https://www.caesars.com
Hotel Operator
N.A.I.C.S.: 721110

Horseshoe Tunica LLC   (1)
1021 Casino Center Dr, Robinsonville, MS
38664
Web Site: https://www.caesars.com
Hotel Operator
N.A.I.C.S.: 721110

MGM Growth Properties LLC   (1)
1980 Festival Plz Dr Ste 750, Las Vegas,
NV 89135
Tel.: (702) 669-1480
Web Site:
  http://www.mgmgrowthproperties.com
Rev.: $782,063,000
Assets: $10,431,106,000
Liabilities: $5,071,261,000
Net Worth: $5,359,845,000
Earnings: $359,240,000
Emp.: 3
Fiscal Year-end: 12/31/2021
Hotel & Resort Management Services
N.A.I.C.S.: 721120

Subsidiary (Domestic):

MGM Growth Properties Operating
Partnership LP   (2)
1980 Festival Plaza Dr Ste 750, Las Vegas,
NV 89135
Tel.: (702) 669-1480

VICI PROPERTIES INC.

VICI Properties Inc.—(Continued)

Web Site:
http://www.mgmgrowthproperties.com
Rev.: $782,062,999
Assets: $10,431,105,999
Liabilities: $5,071,260,999
Net Worth: $5,359,844,999
Earnings: $359,239,999
Emp.: 1,211
Fiscal Year-end: 12/31/2021
Real Estate Investment Services
N.A.I.C.S.: 531110
James C. Stewart (CEO)

Subsidiary (Domestic):

MGP Finance Co-Issuer Inc. **(3)**
6385 S Rainbow Blvd Ste 500, Las Vegas,
NV 89118
Tel.: (702) 669-1480
Financial Services
N.A.I.C.S.: 523999

New Harrah's North Kansas City
LLC **(1)**
1 Riverboat Dr, Kansas City, MO 64116
Tel.: (816) 472-7777
Web Site: https://www.caesars.com
Hotel Operator
N.A.I.C.S.: 721110
Nick Shelton (Dir-Casino Mktg & Entertainment)

New Horseshoe Hammond LLC **(1)**
777 Casino Center Dr, Hammond, IN 46320
Tel.: (219) 473-7000
Web Site: https://www.caesars.com
Hotel Operator
N.A.I.C.S.: 721110
KiKi Guadalupe Encarnacion (Mgr-HR)

VICI PROPERTIES L.P.

535 Madison Ave 28th Fl, New York,
NY 10022
Tel.: (646) 949-4631　　　DE
Web Site:
https://www.viciproperties.com
Year Founded: 2016
VICI—(NYSE)
Rev.: $3,573,020,000
Assets: $43,930,049,000
Liabilities: $18,382,420,000
Net Worth: $25,547,629,000
Earnings: $2,535,066,000
Emp.: 28
Fiscal Year-end: 12/31/23
Real Estate Investment Trust Services
N.A.I.C.S.: 531190

VICOR CORPORATION

25 Frontage Rd, Andover, MA 01810
Tel.: (978) 470-2900　　　DE
Web Site:
https://www.vicorpower.com
Year Founded: 1981
VICR—(NASDAQ)
Rev.: $399,079,000
Assets: $536,901,000
Liabilities: $72,565,000
Net Worth: $464,336,000
Earnings: $25,446,000
Emp.: 1,088
Fiscal Year-end: 12/31/22
Mfr, Designer, Developer & Marketer
of Modular Power System Components & Complete Power Systems
N.A.I.C.S.: 334220
Patrizio Vinciarelli (Chm, Pres & CEO)
Claudio Tuozzolo (Pres-Vicor Power Components & VP)
Philip D. Davies (VP-Global Sls & Mktg)
Michael S. McNamara (VP & Gen Mgr-Ops)
Victor K. Nichols (Founder)
Nancy L. Grava (VP-HR)
Alex Gusinov (VP-Engrg & Power Components)
Al Doyle (CIO & VP)

James F. Schmidt (CFO, Treas, Sec & VP)
Quentin A. Fendelet (Chief Acctg Officer & VP)

Subsidiaries:

Freedom Power Systems, Inc. **(1)**
1620 La Jaita Dr Ste 100, Cedar Park, TX
78633　　　　　　　　　　**(100%)**
Tel.: (512) 259-0941
Web Site: http://www.fpspower.com
Sales Range: $10-24.9 Million
Emp.: 20
Custom Power Solutions for the Military,
Communications, Industrial Controls & Data
Processing Markets
N.A.I.C.S.: 335311

Northwest Power, Inc. **(1)**
4211 S E International Way Ste F, Milwaukie, OR 97222
Tel.: (503) 652-6161
Web Site: http://www.vicorpower.com
Standard & Custom Power Supplies Developer & Mfr
N.A.I.C.S.: 335999

Vicor GmbH **(1)**
Adalperostrasse 29, 85737, Ismaning,
Germany　　　　　　　　**(100%)**
Tel.: (49) 899624390
Web Site: http://www.vicorpower.com
Sales Range: $25-49.9 Million
Emp.: 6
Standard & Custom Power Supplies Mfr
N.A.I.C.S.: 332510

Vicor Hong Kong Ltd. **(1)**
1715-1718 Tower 2 Grand Central Plaza
138 Shatin Rural Committee Road, Sha Tin,
New Territories, China (Hong Kong)
Tel.: (852) 29561782
Web Site: http://www.vicorpower.com
Power Transmission Equipment Mfr & Distr
N.A.I.C.S.: 334413

Vicor Italy SRL **(1)**
Via Milanese 20, 20099, Sesto San Giovanni, MI, Italy　　　　　　**(100%)**
Tel.: (39) 0222472326
Web Site: http://www.vicorpower.com
Sales Range: $1-9.9 Million
Emp.: 5
Develops & Manufactures Standard & Custom Power Supplies
N.A.I.C.S.: 334220

Vicor Japan Company, Ltd. **(1)**
Forecast Gotanda West 6F 8-9-5 Nishigotanda, Shinagawa-ku, Tokyo, 141-0031,
Japan
Tel.: (81) 354873880
Web Site: https://www.vjcp.jp
Emp.: 40
Power Transmission Equipment Mfr
N.A.I.C.S.: 335999
Masashi Sekimoto (VP)
Quentin Fendelet (Auditor)

Vicor U.K. Ltd. **(1)**
Coliseum Business Centre Riverside Way,
Camberley, GU15 3YL, Surrey, United
Kingdom　　　　　　　　**(100%)**
Tel.: (44) 1276678222
Web Site: http://www.vicorpower.com
Sales Range: $1-9.9 Million
Emp.: 8
Develops & Manufactures Standard & Custom Power Supplies
N.A.I.C.S.: 334220

VICTOR MINING INDUSTRY GROUP, INC.

45 Parker Ste A, Irvine, CA 92618
Tel.: (949) 855-6688
VMTG—(OTCIQ)
Electric Coil Mfr & Distr
N.A.I.C.S.: 334416
Ian S. Grant (CEO)
Zonghan Wu (Sec)

VICTORIA'S SECRET & CO.

4 Limited Pkwy, Reynoldsburg, OH
43068
Tel.: (614) 577-7000　　　DE

Web Site:
https://www.victoriassecret.com
Year Founded: 2021
VSCO—(NYSE)
Rev.: $6,182,000,000
Assets: $4,600,000,000
Liabilities: $4,162,000,000
Net Worth: $438,000,000
Earnings: $109,000,000
Emp.: 30,000
Fiscal Year-end: 02/03/24
Women's Intimate & Other Apparel & Beauty Products Retailer
N.A.I.C.S.: 458110
Hillary Super (CEO)
Donna A. James (Chm)
Timothy A. Johnson (CFO & Chief Admin Officer)

Subsidiaries:

Adore Me, Inc. **(1)**
401 Broadway 12th Fl, New York, NY
10013
Web Site: https://www.adoreme.com
Sales Range: $10-24.9 Million
Emp.: 55
Ladies Innerwear Mfr & Distr
N.A.I.C.S.: 314999
Morgan Hermand-Waiche (Founder & CEO)

Victoria's Secret Stores, LLC **(1)**
4 Limited Pkwy E, Reynoldsburg, OH
43068-5302
Tel.: (614) 577-7111
Web Site: https://www.victoriassecret.com
Specialty Retail Brand & Lingerie Sales
N.A.I.C.S.: 458110
John Mehas (CEO-Lingerie Bus)

Subsidiary (Non-US):

Victoria's Secret (Canada)
Corporation **(2)**
6455 Macleod Trail SW, Calgary, T2H 0K8,
AB, Canada
Tel.: (403) 265-2660
Web Site: http://www.victoriasecret.com
Apparel Retailer
N.A.I.C.S.: 459999

VICTORY CAPITAL HOLDINGS, INC.

15935 La Cantera Pkwy, San Antonio, TX 78256
Tel.: (216) 898-2400　　　DE
Web Site: https://www.vcm.com
Year Founded: 2013
VCTR—(NASDAQ)
Rev.: $854,800,000
Assets: $2,540,899,000
Liabilities: $1,475,489,000
Net Worth: $1,065,410,000
Earnings: $275,511,000
Emp.: 512
Fiscal Year-end: 12/31/22
Investment Management Service
N.A.I.C.S.: 523940
David C. Brown (Chm & CEO)
Michael D. Policarpo (Pres & Chief Admin Officer)

Subsidiaries:

Thomson, Horstmann & Bryant, Inc. **(1)**
501 Merritt 7 Penthouse Level, Norwalk, CT
06851
Tel.: (203) 633-3934
Web Site: http://www.thbinc.com
Sales Range: $1-9.9 Million
Emp.: 15
Investment Advisory & Asset Management Services
N.A.I.C.S.: 523940
Christopher N. Cuesta (Chief Investment Officer)
Manish Maheshwari (Portfolio Mgr)

VICTORY MARINE HOLDINGS CORP.

7910 Harbor Island Dr Ste 1008,
North Bay Village, FL 33142　　　NV

Year Founded: 1954
VMHG—(OTCIQ)
Yacht Mfr
N.A.I.C.S.: 336612
Orlando Hernandez (Pres)

VICTORY OILFIELD TECH, INC.

14425 Falcon Head Blvd Bldg E,
Austin, TX 78738
Tel.: (512) 347-7300　　　NV
Year Founded: 1982
VYEY—(OTCIQ)
Rev.: $1,624,635
Assets: $693,433
Liabilities: $4,397,139
Net Worth: ($3,703,706)
Earnings: ($321,484)
Emp.: 8
Fiscal Year-end: 12/31/22
Oil & Natural Gas Exploration Services
N.A.I.C.S.: 213112
Ronald W. Zamber (Chm)
Kevin DeLeon (Pres, CEO, CFO & Chief Acctg Officer)

VIDEO DISPLAY CORPORATION

5155 W King St, Cocoa, FL 32926
Tel.: (321) 784-4427　　　GA
Web Site:
https://www.videodisplay.com
Year Founded: 1975
VIDE—(OTCIQ)
Rev.: $8,297,000
Assets: $4,739,000
Liabilities: $5,150,000
Net Worth: ($411,000)
Earnings: ($132,000)
Emp.: 35
Fiscal Year-end: 02/29/24
Electronic Components Mfr
N.A.I.C.S.: 334419
Ronald D. Ordway (Chm, CEO & Treas)

Subsidiaries:

AYON CyberSecurity, Inc. **(1)**
5155 W King St, Cocoa, FL 32926
Tel.: (321) 784-4427
Web Site: https://www.ayoncs.com
Computer Mfr
N.A.I.C.S.: 334111

AYON Visual Solutions **(1)**
1868 Tucker Industrial Rd, Tucker, GA
30084
Tel.: (770) 938-2080
Web Site: http://www.eyevis.com
Emp.: 15
Electronic Display Equipment Mfr
N.A.I.C.S.: 334419

Fox International Ltd., Inc. **(1)**
23600 Aurora Rd, Cleveland, OH
44146-1712　　　　　　　**(100%)**
Tel.: (440) 439-8500
Sales Range: $75-99.9 Million
Emp.: 70
Electronic Parts Distribution
N.A.I.C.S.: 423840

Southwest Vacuum Devices, Inc. **(1)**
4601 Lewis Rd, Stone Mountain, GA
30083-1003　　　　　　　**(100%)**
Tel.: (770) 934-2245
Web Site: http://www.videodisplay.com
Sales Range: $1-9.9 Million
Emp.: 22
Electronic Emission Products
N.A.I.C.S.: 334419

VDC Display Systems **(1)**
7177 N Atlantic Ave, Cape Canaveral, FL
32920
Tel.: (321) 784-4427
Web Site:
http://www.vdcdisplaysystems.com

Sales Range: $10-24.9 Million
Emp.: 35
N.A.I.C.S.: 334419

Video Display Novatron Tube Division (1)
1416 Alpine Blvd, Bossier City, LA 71111
Tel.: (318) 747-0140
Web Site: http://www.videodisplay.com
Computer Mfr
N.A.I.C.S.: 334419

Z-Axis, Inc. (1)
1916 State Route 96, Phelps, NY 14532
Tel.: (315) 548-5000
Web Site: http://www.zaxis.net
Sales Range: $10-24.9 Million
Emp.: 65
Video Display Monitors Mfr
N.A.I.C.S.: 334419
Michael Allen (Co-Owner, Chm & Pres)
Robin Allen (Co-Owner & Sec)
Massimo Amadio (Mgr-Design Engrg)

Subsidiary (Domestic):

Boundless Technologies, Inc. (2)
1916 State Rte 96, Phelps, NY 14532
Tel.: (315) 548-6189
Web Site:
  http://www.boundlessterminals.com
Sales Range: $1-9.9 Million
Emp.: 100
Desktop Terminals Mfr
N.A.I.C.S.: 334118
John R. Petrone (Dir-Worldwide Sls)
James M. Catalano (Mgr-Mktg)
Tom Martinez (Mgr-Thin Client & OEM Prods)
Christine P. DeCicco (Sr Prod Mgr-Text Prods)

VIDEO RIVER NETWORKS, INC.
370 Amapola Ave Ste 200A, Torrance, CA 90501
Tel.: (310) 895-1839   NV
Year Founded: 1984
NIHK—(OTCIQ)
Rev.: $3,866,539
Assets: $3,417,967
Liabilities: $423,379
Net Worth: $2,994,588
Earnings: $767,121
Fiscal Year-end: 12/31/22
Wireless Engineering & Technology Services
N.A.I.C.S.: 517112
Frank I. Igwealor (Chm, Pres, CEO, CFO, Treas & Sec)

Subsidiaries:

Drone Guarder, Inc. (1)
370 Amapola Ave, Torrance, CA 90501
Tel.: (310) 895-1839
Web Site: http://www.droneguarder.net
Security & Surveillance Company
N.A.I.C.S.: 561621
Frank Ikechukwu Igwealor (CEO)

VIDEOPROPULSION INTERACTIVE TELEVISION, INC.
255 Info Hwy, Slinger, WI 53086
Web Site:
  http://www.videopropulsion.com
VPTV—(OTCIQ)
Information Technology Services
N.A.I.C.S.: 541512
Carl A. Pick (Chm)

VIEMED HEALTHCARE, INC.
625 E Kaliste Saloom Rd, Lafayette, LA 70508
Tel.: (337) 504-3802
Web Site: https://www.viemed.com
VMD—(NASDAQ)
Rev.: $138,832,000
Assets: $117,043,000
Liabilities: $19,949,000
Net Worth: $97,094,000
Earnings: $6,222,000
Emp.: 743

Fiscal Year-end: 12/31/22
Women Healthcare Services
N.A.I.C.S.: 621610
Randy Dobbs (Chm)
Casey Hoyt (CEO)
Trae Fitzgerald (CFO)
W. Todd Zehnder (COO)
William Frazier (Chief Medical Officer)
Michael Moore (Pres)
Brett Stoute (Chief Compliance Officer)
Ronnie Miller (Chief Revenue Officer)
Claudio Munoz (CIO)
Ryan Sullivan (Exec VP)
Chris Weeks (VP-HR)
Jerome Cambre (VP-Sls)
John Collier (CTO)
Richard Kovacik (Chief Dev Officer)
Andrew Hill (VP-Sleep & Respiratory Svcs)
Rob Birkhead (CMO)

VIEW, INC.
195 S Milpitas Blvd, Milpitas, CA 95035
Tel.: (408) 263-9200   DE
Web Site: https://view.com
Year Founded: 2019
VIEW—(NASDAQ)
Rev.: $101,328,000
Assets: $619,026,000
Liabilities: $398,534,000
Net Worth: $220,492,000
Earnings: ($337,089,000)
Emp.: 728
Fiscal Year-end: 12/31/22
Glass Products Mfr
N.A.I.C.S.: 327215
Thomas H. King (Interim CFO)
Rao Mulpuri (CEO)
Bill Krause (Chief Legal Officer)
Nitesh Trikha (Chief Product Officer)
Anshu Pradhan (CTO)

VIEWCAST.COM, INC.
3701 W Plano Pkwy Ste 300, Plano, TX 75075-7840
Tel.: (972) 488-7200   DE
Web Site: https://www.viewcast.com
Year Founded: 1958
VCST—(OTCIQ)
Sales Range: Less than $1 Million
Emp.: 47
Digital Video & Audio Communications Hardware & Software
N.A.I.C.S.: 334220
John Hammock (Pres & CEO)
Jeff Kopang (VP-Marketing)
George A. Platt (Exec Chm)

VIGIL NEUROSCIENCE, INC.
100 Forge Rd Ste 700, Watertown, MA 02472
Tel.: (857) 254-4445   DE
Web Site: https://www.vigilneuro.com
Year Founded: 2020
VIGL—(NASDAQ)
Rev.: $623,000
Assets: $200,393,000
Liabilities: $11,312,000
Net Worth: $189,081,000
Earnings: ($68,305,000)
Emp.: 56
Fiscal Year-end: 12/31/22
Biotechnology Research & Development Services
N.A.I.C.S.: 541714
Ivana Magovcevic-Liebisch (Pres & CEO)
Jennifer Ziolkowski (CFO)
Evan Thackaberry (Sr VP & Head-Early Dev)
Bruce Booth (Chm)
Christopher Verni (Gen Counsel)
David Gray (Chief Scientific Officer)

Leah Gibson (VP-IR & Corp Comm)
Petra Kaufmann (Chief Medical Officer)
Anadina Garcia (Assoc Dir-Nonclinical Ops)
Andrea Abdula (Sr Mgr-Quality Assurance GMP)
Bhaumik Pandya (Sr Dir-Chemistry)
Brittanie Walters (Mgr-Accounting)
Clarissa Martinez-Rubio (Assoc Dir-Patient Advocacy)
Craig Bodycombe (Dir-Analytical Dev)
Francois Gaudreault (VP-Clinical Pharmacology)
Humann Hodjatzadeh (VP-Financial Planning & Analysis)
Jade Donaldson (Mgr-Clinical Trial)
Jessica Stromme (Sr VP-Program Leadership & Portfolio Mgmt)
Jonathan Houze (VP-Small Molecule Discovery)
Jordan Jara (Mgr-Clinical Trial)
Julia Keefe (Assoc Dir-Investor Relations & Corporate Communications)
Kelley Larson (Sr Dir-Discovery Biology)
Meredith Jones (Assoc Dir-Contracts)
Park Guo (Mgr-Accounting)
Raj Rajagovindan (VP-Clinical Dev Sciences)
Ryan O'Mara (Sr Dir-Clinical Ops & Clinical Trial Innovation)
Shannon Ryan (Project Mgr-Clinical)
Ali Toumadj (VP & Head)
April Effort (VP & Head)
Christian Mirescu (Sr VP & Head)
Kevin Durfee (VP & Head)
Michael Cohen (VP & Assoc Gen Counsel)
Pam Meneses (VP & Controller)
Bruce Booth (Chm)
Ivana Magovcevic-Liebisch (Pres & CEO)
Ivana Magovcevic-Liebisch (Pres & CEO)

VIKING THERAPEUTICS, INC.
9920 Pacific Hts Blvd Ste 350, San Diego, CA 92121
Tel.: (858) 704-4660   DE
Web Site:
  https://www.vikingtherapeutics.com
Year Founded: 2012
VKTX—(NASDAQ)
Rev.: $15,020,000
Assets: $368,490,000
Liabilities: $20,071,000
Net Worth: $348,419,000
Earnings: ($85,895,000)
Emp.: 27
Fiscal Year-end: 12/31/23
Biopharmaceutical Mfr
N.A.I.C.S.: 325412
Brian Lian (Founder, Pres & CEO)
Gregory S. Zante (CFO & Principal Acctg Officer)
Hiroko Masamune (Chief Dev Officer)
Marianne Mancini (COO)
Geoffrey Barker (VP-Pharmaceutical Dev)
Juliana Oliveira (VP)

VILLAGE BANK & TRUST FINANCIAL CORP.
13319 Midlothian Tpke, Midlothian, VA 23113
Tel.: (804) 897-3900   VA
Web Site:
  https://www.villagebank.com
VBFC—(NASDAQ)
Rev.: $34,089,000
Assets: $723,270,000
Liabilities: $662,159,000
Net Worth: $61,111,000
Earnings: $8,305,000
Emp.: 142

Fiscal Year-end: 12/31/22
Bank Holding Company
N.A.I.C.S.: 551111
George Randy Whittemore (Vice Chm)
Christy F. Quesenbery (Exec VP-Ops)
Donald M. Kaloski Jr. (CFO)
Roy I. Barzel (Chief Credit Officer)
Jennifer J. Church (Exec VP)
James E. Hendricks Jr. (Pres & CEO)
Max C. Morehead Jr. (Exec VP-Comml Banking)

Subsidiaries:

Village Bank (1)
13319 Midlothian Tpke, Midlothian, VA 23113
Tel.: (804) 897-3900
Web Site: https://www.villagebank.com
Sales Range: $125-149.9 Million
Commercial Banking
N.A.I.C.S.: 522110
Roy Barzel (Chief Credit Officer & Exec VP)
Joy Kline (Exec VP-Retail Banking)
Christy Quesenbery (Exec VP-Ops)
Penny Browning (VP & Mgr-Processing)
Valenda Campbell (VP & Mktg Dir)
Lindsay Cheatham (Sr VP & Dir-HR)
Roy Corum (VP & Dir-IT & Engrg)
Jeffrey Crook (VP & Mgr-Comml Relationship)
Linda Heath (VP)
William Johnston (VP & Mgr-Comml Relationship)
Kim Karamarkovich (Officer-Risk Mgmt & VP)
Thomas Kelley (VP & Mgr-Comml Relationship)
Thomas Kiluk (VP)
Joe Lewis (Sr VP & Mgr-Retail Area)

Subsidiary (Domestic):

Village Bank Mortgage Corporation (2)
13305 Midlothian Tpke, Midlothian, VA 23113
Tel.: (804) 330-9800
Web Site:
  https://www.villagebankmortgage.com
Mortgage Banking Services
N.A.I.C.S.: 522390
Brendan Workman (Officer-Loan & Asst VP)

Village Insurance Agency, Inc. (2)
c/o Village Bank 13319 Midlothian Turnpike, Midlothian, VA 23113 (100%)
Tel.: (804) 897-3900
Web Site: http://www.villagebank.com
Insurance Services
N.A.I.C.S.: 524210

VILLAGE SUPER MARKET INC.
733 Mountain Ave, Springfield, NJ 07081
Tel.: (973) 467-2200   NJ
Web Site:
  https://www.myvillagesupermarket.com
Year Founded: 1937
VLGEA—(NASDAQ)
Rev.: $2,166,654,000
Assets: $967,706,000
Liabilities: $557,540,000
Net Worth: $410,166,000
Earnings: $49,716,000
Emp.: 7,000
Fiscal Year-end: 07/29/23
Supermarket Operator
N.A.I.C.S.: 445110
John P. Sumas (Executives)
Robert P. Sumas (Vice Chm & CEO)
William Sumas (Chm)
John J. Sumas (Co-Pres)
Nicholas James Sumas (Co-Pres)
John L. Van Orden (CFO)
Luigi Perri (Controller)

VIMEO, INC.
330 W 34th St 5th Fl, New York, NY 10001

Vimeo, Inc.—(Continued)

Tel.: (212) 314-7300   **DE**
Web Site: https://www.vimeo.com
Year Founded: 2020
VMEO—(NASDAQ)
Rev.: $417,214,000
Assets: $622,920,000
Liabilities: $622,920,000
Net Worth: $382,232,000
Earnings: $22,032,000
Emp.: 1,070
Fiscal Year-end: 12/31/23
Holding Company; Video Hosting &
Livestreaming Services
N.A.I.C.S.: 551112
Glenn H. Schiffman (Chm)
Philip D. Moyer (CEO)
Gillian Munson (CFO)

Subsidiaries:

Vimeo.com, Inc.   (1)
330 W 34th St 10th Fl, New York, NY
10001
Tel.: (212) 524-8791
Web Site: https://www.vimeo.com
Video Hosting & Livestreaming
N.A.I.C.S.: 518210
Lynn Girotto (CMO)
Ashraf Alkarmi (Chief Product Officer)
Gillian Munson (CFO)
Crystal Boysen (Chief People Officer)
Mark Carter (Chief Info Security Officer)
Narendra Venkataraman (CTO)

Subsidiary (Domestic):

Livestream LLC   (2)
555 W 18th St, New York, NY 11011
Tel.: (646) 490-1679
Web Site: https://livestream.com
Online Live Streaming Services
N.A.I.C.S.: 516210

VINCERX PHARMA, INC.
260 Sheridan Ave Ste 400, Palo Alto,
CA 94306
Tel.: (650) 800-6676   **DE**
Web Site: https://www.vincerx.com
Year Founded: 2018
VINC—(NASDAQ)
Rev.: $2,452,000
Assets: $18,217,000
Liabilities: $6,995,000
Net Worth: $11,222,000
Earnings: ($40,157,000)
Emp.: 42
Fiscal Year-end: 12/31/23
Biopharmaceutical Services
N.A.I.C.S.: 541714
Ahmed M. Hamdy (Co-Founder, Chm
& CEO)
Raquel E. Izumi (Co-Founder, Pres &
COO)
Alexander Seelenberger (CFO)
Tom Thomas (Chief Legal Officer &
Gen Counsel)
Hans-Georg Lerchen (Chief Scientific
Officer)
Beatrix Stelte-Ludwig (Chief Dev Offi-
cer & Exec VP-Biology)
Tasheda Navarro (VP-Clinical Ops)
Steven Bloom (Chief Bus Officer)
Raj Dua (VP-Biologics Dev & Manu-
facturing)
Renee Breed (VP-Medical Safety
Ops)
Melanie Frigault (VP-Translational
Medicine)
Kevin Haas (VP-Finance &
Controller-Corp)
Xin Huang (VP-Biometrics)
Gabriela Jairala (VP-Investor Rela-
tions & Corporate Communications)
Amy Johnson (VP-Medical Affairs)
Elsa Johnson (VP-Program & Portfo-
lio Mgmt)

Karen Quarford (VP-Quality Ops &
Compliance)
Melissa Merrick (Sr Dir-People & Cul-
ture)

VINCO VENTURES, INC.
1 W Broad St Ste 1004, Bethlehem,
PA 18018
Tel.: (866) 900-0992   **NV**
Web Site:
http://investors.vincoventures.com
Year Founded: 2017
BBIG—(NASDAQ)
Rev.: $15,781,319
Assets: $28,028,207
Liabilities: $14,505,506
Net Worth: $13,522,701
Earnings: ($6,307,100)
Emp.: 17
Fiscal Year-end: 12/31/20
Industrial & Pharmaceutical Packag-
ing Materials Designer & Mfr
N.A.I.C.S.: 326112
Chris Polimeni (CFO & COO)
Kevin James Ferguson (Treas)
Roderick Vanderbilt (Chm)
James Robertson (Pres & CEO)

Subsidiaries:

Best Party Concepts, LLC   (1)
532 Durham Rd Ste 101A, Newtown, PA
18940
Web Site: http://www.goodiegusher.com
Entertainment Services
N.A.I.C.S.: 711190

Cloud B, Inc.   (1)
150 W Walnut Ste 100, Gardena, CA
90248   **(72.15%)**
Tel.: (310) 781-3833
Web Site: http://www.cloudb.com
Miscellaneous Durable Goods Merchant
Whslr
N.A.I.C.S.: 423990
Jeff Johnson (Co-Founder & CTO)
Linda Suh (Co-Founder & CEO)

Ferguson Containers, Inc.   (1)
20 Industrial Rd, Alpha, NJ 08865
Tel.: (908) 454-9755
Web Site:
http://www.fergusoncontainers.com
Packaging Container Mfr
N.A.I.C.S.: 327213
Kevin Ferguson (Pres)

VINDICATOR SILVER LEAD MINING CO.
413 Cedar St, Wallace, ID 83873
Tel.: (208) 752-1131   **ID**
Year Founded: 1902
VINS—(OTCIQ)
Jewelry & Silverware Mfr
N.A.I.C.S.: 339910
Harry James Magnuson (Pres)
Dennis M. O'Brien (Sec)

VINTAGE WINE ESTATES, INC.
205 Concourse Blvd, Santa Rosa, CA
95403   **NV**
Web Site:
https://www.vintagewineestates.com
VWE—(NASDAQ)
Rev.: $283,228,000
Assets: $561,154,000
Liabilities: $388,638,000
Net Worth: $172,516,000
Earnings: ($188,967,000)
Emp.: 568
Fiscal Year-end: 06/30/23
Investment Services
N.A.I.C.S.: 523999
Seth Kaufman (Pres & CEO)
Rodrigo de Oliveira (VP-Supply
Chain)
Seth Kaufman (Pres & CEO)
Patrick Roney (Founder & Exec Chm)
Megan Golder (Office Mgr)
Hasan Simeen (VP)

Jessica Kogan (Digital Strategy Advi-
sor)
Kristina Johnston (CFO)
Courtney Prose (VP-Supply Chain)
Jenna Duran (VP-Mktg)
Ryan Watson (CMO)

Subsidiaries:

B.R. Cohn Winery   (1)
15000 Sonoma Hwy 12, Glen Ellen, CA
95442
Tel.: (707) 938-4064
Web Site: http://www.brcohn.com
Sales Range: $1-9.9 Million
Emp.: 12
Fat & Oil Refining Mfr
N.A.I.C.S.: 311225
Bruce R. Cohn (Founder)

California Cider Co., Inc.   (1)
2064 Gravenstein Hwy N Ste 40, Sebasto-
pol, CA 95472-2631
Tel.: (707) 829-1101
Web Site: http://www.acecider.com
Farming
N.A.I.C.S.: 111331
Jeffrey House (Owner)

Cameron Hughes Wine   (1)
251 Rhode Island St Ste 203, San Fran-
cisco, CA 94103
Tel.: (415) 495-1350
Web Site: https://www.chwine.com
Winery
N.A.I.C.S.: 312130
Cameron Hughes (Co-Founder)
Jessica Kogan (Co-Founder)

Firesteed Corporation   (1)
2200 N Pacific Hwy W, Rickreall, OR 97371
Tel.: (503) 623-8683
Web Site: http://www.firesteed.com
Alcoholic Beverages Mfr
N.A.I.C.S.: 312120

International Wine Accessories,
Inc.   (1)
10246 Miller Rd, Dallas, TX 75238-1206
Tel.: (214) 349-6097
Web Site: http://www.iwawine.com
Sales Range: $10-24.9 Million
Emp.: 32
Retail & Mail Order Wine Accessories
N.A.I.C.S.: 423220

Laetitia Vineyard & Winery   (1)
453 Laetitia Vineyard Dr, Arroyo Grande,
CA 93420
Tel.: (805) 481-1772
Web Site: http://www.laetitiawine.com
Wineries
N.A.I.C.S.: 312130
Eric Hickey (Gen Mgr)

Swanson Vineyards & Winery   (1)
1271 Manley Ln, Rutherford, CA 94573-
4573
Tel.: (707) 754-4016
Web Site:
http://www.swansonvineyards.com
Wineries
N.A.I.C.S.: 312130
W. Clarke Swanson (Co-Founder)
Elizabeth Swanson (Co-Founder)

Tamarack Cellars   (1)
700 C St, Walla Walla, WA 99362-9362
Tel.: (509) 526-3533
Web Site: http://www.tamarackcellars.com
Winery
N.A.I.C.S.: 312130

VIPER NETWORKS, INC.
Tel.: (248) 724-1300   **NV**
Web Site:
https://www.vipernetworks.com
Year Founded: 2005
VPER—(OTCIQ)
Sales Range: $1-9.9 Million
Emp.: 42
Wired Telecommunications Carriers
N.A.I.C.S.: 517111
Farid Shouekani (Pres & CEO)
Tom Otrok (Pres-Ops Intl)
Nadim Romanos (Exec VP-Intl Bus
Dev)

C. S. R. Raju (Exec Dir-Renewable
Energy)
Shervin Bruno (Dir-Caribbean Ops)
Al-Qaraghuli Ali (Dir-Engrg & Engrg)

VIR BIOTECHNOLOGY, INC.
1800 Owens St Ste 900, San Fran-
cisco, CA 94158
Tel.: (415) 906-4324   **DE**
Web Site: https://www.vir.bio
Year Founded: 2016
VIR—(NASDAQ)
Rev.: $1,615,797,000
Assets: $2,802,088,000
Liabilities: $724,125,000
Net Worth: $2,077,963,000
Earnings: $515,837,000
Emp.: 576
Fiscal Year-end: 12/31/22
Biotechnology Research & Develop-
ment Services
N.A.I.C.S.: 541714
Bolyn Hubby (Chief Corp Affairs Offi-
cer)
Michael Kamarck (CTO)
Lynne Krummen (Sr VP-Regulatory,
Dev Program Leadership & Mgmt)
Antonio Lanzavecchia (Sr VP)
Jay Parrish (Co-Founder & Chief Bus
Officer)
Irene Pleasure (Gen Counsel & Sr
VP)
Steven Rice (Chief Admin Officer)
Klaus Frueh (Co-Founder)
Sasha Damouni Ellis (Chief Corp Af-
fairs Officer & Exec VP)
Louis Picker (Co-Founder)
Neera Ravindran (VP & Head-IR &
Strategic Comm)
Larry Corey (Co-Founder)
Carly Scaduto (Sr Dir-Media Rels)
Jennifer Towne (Chief Scientific Offi-
cer & Exec VP)
Marianne De Backer (CEO)

VIRACTA THERAPEUTICS, INC.
2533 S Coast Hwy 101 Ste 210, Car-
diff, CA 92007
Tel.: (858) 400-8470   **DE**
Web Site: https://www.viracta.com
Year Founded: 1998
VIRX—(NASDAQ)
Rev.: $38,000
Assets: $108,552,000
Liabilities: $14,181,000
Net Worth: $94,371,000
Earnings: ($114,762,000)
Emp.: 24
Fiscal Year-end: 12/31/21
Biomarker-directed Precision Oncol-
ogy Company
N.A.I.C.S.: 325412
Roger James Pomerantz (Chm)
Michael Eric Faerm (CFO & Principal
Acctg Officer)
Mark Rothera (Pres & CEO)
Roger J. Pomerantz (Chm)
Ayman Elguindy (Chief Scientific Offi-
cer)
Ashleigh Barreto (Head-IR & Corp
Comm)
Donald Strickland (VP-Clinical Dev &
Dir-Medical)
Yisrael Katz (Sr Dir-Medical)
Ashleigh Barreto (Head-IR & Corp
Comm)
Stewart M. Brown (Gen Counsel)
Cheryl Madsen (Sr VP)
Patric Nelson (Sr VP)
Violetta Akopian (VP)
Biljana Nadjsombati (VP)
Ruby Cheema (VP)
Melody Burcar (Sr VP-Fin)
Darrel P. Cohen (Chief Medical Offi-
cer)

VIRCO MFG. CORPORATION

2027 Harpers Way, Torrance, CA 90501
Tel.: (310) 533-0474   DE
Web Site: https://www.virco.com
Year Founded: 1950
VIRC—(NASDAQ)
Rev.: $231,064,000
Assets: $150,126,000
Liabilities: $82,065,000
Net Worth: $68,061,000
Earnings: $16,547,000
Emp.: 800
Fiscal Year-end: 01/31/23
Furniture Designer, Producer & Distr
N.A.I.C.S.: 337127
Robert A. Virtue *(Chm & CEO)*
Robert E. Dose *(CFO, Treas, Sec & Sr VP-Fin)*
Bassey Yau *(VP-Acctg, Controller, Asst Sec & Asst Treas)*
Douglas A. Virtue *(Pres)*

Subsidiaries:

Virco Inc.   (1)
2027 Harpers Way, Torrance, CA 90501-1524   (100%)
Tel.: (310) 533-0474
Web Site: https://www.virco.com
Sales Range: $150-199.9 Million
Emp.: 700
Sales of Furniture
N.A.I.C.S.: 449110

Virco-Conway Division   (1)
Hwy 65 S, Conway, AR 72032   (100%)
Tel.: (310) 533-0474
Web Site: https://www.virco.com
Sales Range: $300-349.9 Million
Mfr & Sales of Furniture
N.A.I.C.S.: 337122

VIREO GROWTH INC.

209 S 9th St, Minneapolis, MN 55402
Web Site: https://vireogrowth.com
GDNS—(OTCQX)
Rev.: $74,625,867
Assets: $159,156,403
Liabilities: $155,715,519
Net Worth: $3,440,884
Earnings: ($42,457,444)
Emp.: 409
Fiscal Year-end: 12/31/22
Pharmaceutical Preparation Manufacturing
N.A.I.C.S.: 325412
Mark Doherty *(VP-Facilities Mgmt & Performance)*
Gabriel Garcia *(Dir-Cultivation)*
Joshua N. Rosen *(CEO & Interim CFO)*
Kyle E. Kingsley *(Founder & Exec Chm)*
Amber H. Shimpa *(Pres, Pres-Vireo Health, Inc & CEO-Vireo Health of Minnesota, LLC)*
Stephen M. Dahmer *(Chief Medical Officer)*
J. Michael Schroeder *(Chief Compliance Officer & Gen Counsel)*
Eric Greenbaum *(Chief Scientific Officer)*
Harris Rabin *(CMO)*
Joshua N. Rosen *(Interim CEO & Interim CFO)*
Amanda Hutcheson *(Sr Mgr-Comm)*

VIREXIT TECHNOLOGIES, INC.

719 Jadwin Ave, Richland, WA 99352
Tel.: (509) 531-1671   NV
Web Site:
https://virexittechnologies.com
Year Founded: 2013
VXIT—(OTCIQ)
Rev.: $1,000
Assets: $68,000
Liabilities: $3,443,000
Net Worth: ($3,375,000)

Earnings: ($1,674,000)
Emp.: 2
Fiscal Year-end: 08/31/20
Business Services
N.A.I.C.S.: 561499
James C. Katzarof *(CEO)*
Bruce Jolliff *(CFO)*
David Croom *(COO)*
Patrick Netter *(CMO)*

VIRGIN GALACTIC HOLDINGS, INC.

1700 Flight Way, Tustin, CA 92782
Tel.: (949) 774-7640   DE
Web Site: https://virgingalactic.com
Year Founded: 2017
SPCE—(NYSE)
Rev.: $2,312,000
Assets: $1,139,938,000
Liabilities: $659,715,000
Net Worth: $480,223,000
Earnings: ($500,152,000)
Emp.: 1,166
Fiscal Year-end: 12/31/22
Holding Company; Space Flight Services
N.A.I.C.S.: 551112
Evan M. Lovell *(Chm)*
Aleanna Crane *(VP-Comm)*
Eric Cerny *(VP-IR)*
Blair Rich *(Pres & Chief Bus Officer-Comml & Consumer Ops)*
Mike Moore *(Exec VP-Spaceline Technical Ops)*
Michael A. Colglazier *(CEO)*
Sarah E. Kim *(Chief Legal Officer, Sec & Exec VP)*
Aparna Chitale *(Chief People Officer)*
Michael P. Moses *(Pres-Space Missions & Safety)*
Doug Ahrens *(CFO)*
Steve Justice *(Sr VP-Spaceline Programs & Engineering)*

Subsidiaries:

Virgin Galactic, LLC   (1)
65 Bleecker St 6th Fl, New York, NY 10012
Tel.: (212) 497-9050
Web Site: http://www.virgingalactic.com
Space Research & Development Services
N.A.I.C.S.: 541715
George T. Whitesides *(CEO)*
Stephen Attenborough *(Dir-Comml)*
Michael P. Moses *(Pres)*
Richard DalBello *(VP-Bus Dev & Govt Affairs)*
Clare Pelly *(Head-Astronaut Office)*
Mark Stucky *(Dir-Flight Test)*
Tim Logan *(Dir-Spaceline Safety)*
Julia Hunter *(Sr VP)*
Jon Campagna *(CFO)*

VIRGINIA NATIONAL BANK-SHARES CORPORATION

Tel.: (434) 817-8621
Web Site: https://www.vnbcorp.com
VABK—(NASDAQ)
Rev.: $70,392,000
Assets: $1,623,359,000
Liabilities: $1,489,943,000
Net Worth: $133,416,000
Earnings: $23,438,000
Emp.: 157
Fiscal Year-end: 12/31/22
Bank Holding Company
N.A.I.C.S.: 551111
Glenn W. Rust *(Pres & CEO)*
Tara Y. Harrison *(CFO & Exec VP)*
Donna G. Shewmake *(Gen Counsel, Sec & Exec VP)*

Subsidiaries:

Fauquier Bankshares, Inc.   (1)
10 Courthouse Sq, Warrenton, VA 20186
Tel.: (540) 347-2700
Web Site: http://www.tfb.bank
Bank Holding Company
N.A.I.C.S.: 551111

John B. Adams Jr. *(Chm)*
Randolph T. Minter *(Vice Chm)*
Christine E. Headly *(CFO & Exec VP)*
Patrick Heijmen *(Sr VP & Dir-Wealth Mgmt Svcs-The Fauquier Bank)*
Chip S. Register *(COO, Chief Admin Officer & Exec VP)*
Tammy P. Frazie *(Sr VP & Controller)*
David W. Hauck *(VP-Loan Support Mgr)*
Abbie Ford *(VP & Dir-Retail Banking)*
Debra Purrington *(Sr VP & Dir-Trust Svcs)*
Alex Hoffman *(CIO & VP)*
Allison Dodson *(Sr VP & Dir-HR)*
Jim Spedden Jr. *(Chief Credit Officer & Sr VP)*

Virginia National Bank   (1)
222 E Main St, Charlottesville, VA 22902
Tel.: (434) 817-8621
Web Site: http://www.vnb.com
Banking Services
N.A.I.C.S.: 522110
Tara Y. Harrison *(CFO & Exec VP)*
Linda W. Hitchings *(Mng Dir & Exec VP)*
Jacek Wolicki *(VP)*

VIRIDIAN THERAPEUTICS, INC.

221 Crescent St Ste 103A, Waltham, MA 02453
Tel.: (617) 272-4600   DE
Web Site:
https://www.viridiantherapeutics.com
VRDN—(NASDAQ)
Rev.: $1,772,000
Assets: $435,091,000
Liabilities: $40,027,000
Net Worth: $395,064,000
Earnings: ($129,874,000)
Emp.: 86
Fiscal Year-end: 12/31/22
Biotechnology Company & Pharmaceutical Developer
N.A.I.C.S.: 325412
Thomas Beetham *(COO)*
Thomas A. Ciulla *(Chief Medical Officer)*
Tony Casciano *(Chief Comml Officer)*
Louisa Stone *(Mgr-IR)*
Todd James *(Sr VP-Corp Affairs & IR)*
Matt Fearer *(VP-Corp Comm)*
Deepa Rajagopalan *(Chief Product Officer)*
Rob Henderson *(Chief Scientific Officer)*
Janielle Newland *(Chief Admin Officer)*
Lara Meisner *(Chief Legal Officer)*
Thomas Ciulla *(Chief Dev Officer)*
Vahe Bedian *(Founder)*
Shan Wu *(Chief Bus Officer)*
Thomas Beetham *(COO)*
Stephen Mahoney *(Pres & CEO)*

VIRIOS THERAPEUTICS, INC.

44 Milton Ave, Alpharetta, GA 30009   AL
Web Site: https://www.virios.com
Year Founded: 2012
VIRI—(NASDAQ)
Rev.: $67,475
Assets: $8,369,756
Liabilities: $1,043,262
Net Worth: $7,326,494
Earnings: ($12,247,834)
Emp.: 4
Fiscal Year-end: 12/31/22
Biotechnology Research & Development Services
N.A.I.C.S.: 541714
Angela Walsh *(Treas, Sec & Sr VP-Fin)*
Greg Duncan *(Chm & CEO)*
William L. Pridgen *(Founder)*

VIRNETX HOLDING CORP.

308 Dorla Ct Ste 206, Zephyr Cove, NV 89448
Tel.: (775) 548-1785   DE

Web Site: https://www.virnetx.com
VHC—(NYSE)
Rev.: $48,000
Assets: $152,975,000
Liabilities: $731,000
Net Worth: $152,244,000
Earnings: ($36,260,000)
Emp.: 25
Fiscal Year-end: 12/31/22
Web-Based Seamless Communication Services
N.A.I.C.S.: 551112
Kendall Larsen *(Chm, Pres & CEO)*
Sameer Mathur *(VP-Corp Dev & Product Mktg)*
Kathleen Larsen *(Chief Admin Officer)*
Darl C. McBride *(COO)*
Jon B. Weaklend *(VP-Fin)*
Greg Wood *(VP-Corp Comm)*
Willard Thomas *(VP-Sls-Worldwide)*
Katherine Allanson *(CFO)*

Subsidiaries:

VirnetX, Inc.   (1)
5615 Scotts Valley Dr Ste 110, Scotts Valley, CA 95066-3491
Tel.: (831) 438-8200
Sales Range: $1-9.9 Million
Emp.: 10
Seamless Wireless Communication Services
N.A.I.C.S.: 517112
Kendall Larsen *(Chm, Pres & CEO)*

VIRPAX PHARMACEUTICALS, INC.

1055 Wlakes Dr Ste 300, Berwyn, PA 19312
Tel.: (610) 727-4597   DE
Web Site:
https://www.virpaxpharma.com
Year Founded: 2017
VRPX—(NASDAQ)
Rev.: $194,413
Assets: $19,673,649
Liabilities: $3,094,590
Net Worth: $16,579,059
Earnings: ($21,650,720)
Emp.: 7
Fiscal Year-end: 12/31/22
Pharmaceutical Product Mfr & Distr
N.A.I.C.S.: 325412
Gerald W. Bruce *(CEO & Pres/CEO-Novvae Pharmaceuticals)*
Vinay Shah *(CFO & Principal Acctg Officer)*
Anthony P. Mack *(Co-Founder)*
Jeffrey Gudin *(Co-Founder)*
Sheila A. Mathias *(Chief Scientific Officer)*
Eric Floyd *(Chm)*

VIRTRA, INC.

295 E Corporate Pl, Chandler, AZ 85225
Tel.: (480) 968-1488
Web Site: https://www.virtra.com
Year Founded: 1993
VTSI—(NASDAQ)
Rev.: $28,302,244
Assets: $53,814,491
Liabilities: $20,132,872
Net Worth: $33,681,619
Earnings: $1,955,898
Emp.: 121
Fiscal Year-end: 12/31/22
Firearms Training Simulators Mfr
N.A.I.C.S.: 334118
Alanna Boudreau *(CFO)*
Tony Cianflone *(VP-Sls)*
John F. Givens II *(Chm & CEO)*

VIRTU FINANCIAL, INC.

1633 Broadway, New York, NY 10019
Tel.: (212) 418-0100   DE

Virtu Financial, Inc.—(Continued)

Web Site: https://www.virtu.com
Year Founded: 2008
VIRT—(NASDAQ)
Rev.: $2,293,373,000
Assets: $14,466,384,000
Liabilities: $13,061,028,000
Net Worth: $1,405,356,000
Earnings: $142,036,000
Emp.: 975
Fiscal Year-end: 12/31/23
Securities Brokerage Services
N.A.I.C.S.: 523150
Brett Fairclough (Co-Pres & Co-COO)
Joseph Molluso (Co-Pres & Co-COO)
Douglas A. Cifu (CEO)
Michael T. Viola (Chm)
Andrew Smith (Sr VP-Bus Dev & Corp Strategy-Global)
Kevin O'Connor (Head-Analytics & Workflow Solutions)
Rob Boardman (CEO-Execution Svcs-EMEA)
Stephen Cavoli (Exec VP & Head-Execution Svcs-Global)
Cindy Lee (CFO)
Aaron Simons (CTO & Exec VP)
Justin Waldie (Gen Counsel, Sec & Sr VP)

Subsidiaries:

Virtu Financial Global Markets LLC   (1)
One Liberty Plaza, New York, NY 10006
Tel.: (212) 418-0100
Commodity Contracts Dealing Services
N.A.I.C.S.: 523160

Virtu Financial Global Services Singapore Pte Ltd.   (1)
20 Martin Road, Singapore, 239070, Singapore
Tel.: (65) 66905170
Web Site: http://www.virtu.com
Emp.: 30
Security & Commodity Service Provider
N.A.I.C.S.: 523999

Virtu ITG Holdings LLC   (1)
165 Broadway, New York, NY 10006
Tel.: (212) 588-4000
Web Site: http://www.virtu.com
Rev.: $509,476,000
Assets: $1,021,075,000
Liabilities: $662,404,000
Net Worth: $358,671,000
Earnings: $691,000
Emp.: 883
Fiscal Year-end: 12/31/2018
Securities Brokerage & Dealing Services
N.A.I.C.S.: 523150
Joseph Molluso (CFO & Mgr)
Douglas A. Cifu (CEO & Mgr)

Subsidiary (Non-US):

ITG Australia Limited   (2)
Level 49 Rialto South Tower 525 Collins Street, Melbourne, 3000, VIC, Australia
Tel.: (61) 392112500
Web Site: http://www.itg.com
Securities Brokerage & Dealing Services
N.A.I.C.S.: 523150

ITG Canada Corp.   (2)
222 Bay Street Suite 1720, Toronto, M5K 1B7, ON, Canada
Tel.: (416) 874-0900
Web Site: http://www.itg.com
Emp.: 110
Securities Brokerage & Dealing Services
N.A.I.C.S.: 523150

ITG Hong Kong Limited   (2)
6th Fl Central Tower 28 Queens Road Central, Hong Kong, China (Hong Kong)
Tel.: (852) 28463500
Web Site: http://www.itg.com
Reserve & Liquidity Services
N.A.I.C.S.: 522320

Subsidiary (Domestic):

ITG Platforms Inc.   (2)
321 Summer St, Boston, MA 02210-1710

Tel.: (617) 239-8700
Web Site: http://www.itg.com
Investment Management Services; Web-based Financial Technology Services
N.A.I.C.S.: 523940

ITG Platforms Inc.   (2)
321 Summer St, Boston, MA 02210-1710
Tel.: (617) 239-8700
Web Site: http://www.itg.com
Software Development Services
N.A.I.C.S.: 541511

Subsidiary (Non-US):

ITG Platforms Spain, S.L.   (2)
Pol Ind Brasil 6 Planta 1, 28020, Madrid, Spain
Tel.: (34) 912844748
Securities Brokerage & Dealing Services
N.A.I.C.S.: 523150

Subsidiary (Domestic):

ITG Software Solutions, Inc.   (2)
1 Liberty Plz 165 Broadway, New York, NY 10006
Tel.: (212) 588-4000
Web Site: http://www.itg.com
Software Development Services
N.A.I.C.S.: 513210

ITG Solutions Network, Inc.   (2)
1 Liberty Plz 165 Broadway, New York, NY 10006
Tel.: (212) 588-4000
Web Site: http://www.itg.com
Investment Management Service
N.A.I.C.S.: 523940
Ian Domowitz (Mng Dir)

Virtu KCG Holdings LLC   (1)
300 Vesey St, New York, NY 10282
Sales Range: $1-4.9 Billion
Holding Company; Securities & Commodity Contracts Brokerage & Dealing Services
N.A.I.C.S.: 551112
Douglas A. Cifu (CEO)

Subsidiary (Domestic):

Virtu GETCO Holding Company, LLC   (2)
233 S Wacker Dr Ste 4020, Chicago, IL 60606
Tel.: (800) 544-7508
Holding Company; Electronic Securities & Commodities Market Trading, Clearing & Brokerage Services
N.A.I.C.S.: 551112

Virtu Knight Capital Group, LLC   (2)
545 Washington Blvd, Jersey City, NJ 07310
Tel.: (201) 222-9400
Securities Trading Services
N.A.I.C.S.: 523150

Subsidiary (Domestic):

Virtu Americas LLC   (3)
233 S Wacker Dr Ste 4020, Chicago, IL 60606
Tel.: (800) 544-7508
Transaction Execution & Clearing Services
N.A.I.C.S.: 522320

VIRTUAL INTERACTIVE TECH-NOLOGIES CORP.
600 17th St Ste 2800 S, Denver, CO 80202
Tel.: (303) 228-7120   CO
Web Site: https://www.vrvrcorp.com
Year Founded: 2011
VRVR—(OTCIQ)
Rev.: $194,350
Assets: $402,734
Liabilities: $1,010,107
Net Worth: ($607,373)
Earnings: ($119,021)
Fiscal Year-end: 09/30/21
Mineral Exploration Services
N.A.I.C.S.: 213115
Jerry Lewis (Dir)
Jason Garber (CEO)
James W. Creamer III (CFO & Chief Acctg Officer)

VIRTUAL MEDICAL INTERNA-TIONAL, INC.
3651 Lindell Rd Ste D639, Las Vegas, NV 89103
Tel.: (719) 283-6367   NV
Year Founded: 2007
QEBR—(OTCIQ)
Sales Range: Less than $1 Million
Medical Information Website Operator
N.A.I.C.S.: 519290
Lee Larson Elmore (Pres, CEO & Sec)

VIRTUALARMOUR INTERNA-TIONAL, INC.
8085 S Chester St Ste 108, Centennial, CO 80112
Tel.: (720) 644-0913   CO
Web Site:
   http://www.virtualarmour.com
Year Founded: 2001
VAI—(CNSX)
Rev.: $10,246,882
Assets: $2,839,475
Liabilities: $6,560,560
Net Worth: ($3,721,085)
Earnings: ($1,380,637)
Fiscal Year-end: 12/31/20
Information Technology Related Services
N.A.I.C.S.: 519290
Christopher Blisard (Founder)
Todd Kannegieter (Interim CFO)
Chad Schamberger (VP-Engr Svcs)
Andrew Douthwaite (CTO)
Russell Armbrust (CEO)
Tianyi Lu (VP-Product Dev)

Subsidiaries:

VirtualArmour, LLC   (1)
10901 W Toller Dr Ste 301, Littleton, CO 80127
Tel.: (303) 221-4934
Rev.: $2,000,000
Emp.: 23
Security System Services
N.A.I.C.S.: 561621
Todd Kannegieter (Founder & COO)

VIRTUS CONVERTIBLE & IN-COME FUND II
101 Munson St, Greenfield, MA 01301   MA
NCZ—(NYSE)
Investment Management Service
N.A.I.C.S.: 525990

VIRTUS DIVIDEND, INTEREST & PREMIUM STRATEGY FUND
1633 Ave of the Americas, New York, NY 10105   MA
NFJ—(NYSE)
Investment Management Service
N.A.I.C.S.: 523999
Michael E. Yee (Mng Dir-Lead Portfolio)
Ethan Turner (VP)
Justin M. Kass (Sr Mng Dir & Chief Investment Officer)

VIRTUS EQUITY & CONVERT-IBLE INCOME FUND
101 Munson St, Greenfield, MA 01301   MA
NIE—(NYSE)
Rev.: $11,862,229
Assets: $697,423,652
Liabilities: $7,774,056
Net Worth: $689,649,596
Earnings: $4,861,533
Fiscal Year-end: 01/31/20
Investment Management Service
N.A.I.C.S.: 525990

VIRTUS INVESTMENT PART-NERS, INC.

1 Financial Plz, Hartford, CT 06103
Tel.: (413) 775-6091   DE
Web Site: https://corporate.virtus.com
Year Founded: 1995
VRTS—(NASDAQ)
Rev.: $886,379,000
Assets: $3,952,934,000
Liabilities: $3,129,998,000
Net Worth: $822,936,000
Earnings: $117,541,000
Emp.: 772
Fiscal Year-end: 12/31/22
Investment Management Products & Services
N.A.I.C.S.: 523940
George R. Aylward (Pres & CEO)
Michael A. Angerthal (CFO & Exec VP)
W. Patrick Bradley (Exec VP-Fund Svcs)
Mardelle W. Pena (Chief HR Officer & Exec VP)
Barry Mitchell Mandinach (Exec VP & Head-Distr)
Richard W. Smirl (COO & Exec VP)

Subsidiaries:

AlphaSimplex Group, LLC   (1)
200 State St, Boston, MA 02109
Tel.: (617) 475-7100
Web Site: https://www.alphasimplex.com
Sales Range: $150-199.9 Million
Emp.: 40
Investment Management Service
N.A.I.C.S.: 525910
Arnout M. Eikeboom (Chief Risk & Compliance Officer)
Brent Mathus (Mgr-Client Portfolio)
Duncan B. E. Wilkinson (Pres)
Alexander D. Healy (CIO)
Kathryn M. Kaminski (Chief Strategist-Res)
Jennifer C. Gooch (Head-Bus Fin & Operations)
Steven D. List (Mng Dir-Trading)

Ceredex Value Advisors LLC   (1)
301 E Pine St Ste 500, Orlando, FL 32801
Tel.: (407) 674-1270
Web Site: https://www.ceredexvalue.com
Investment Advisory & Asset Management Services
N.A.I.C.S.: 523940
Mills Riddick (Chief Investment Officer & Sr Portfolio Mgr)
Don Wordell (Mng Dir & Portfolio Mgr)
Brett Barner (Mng Dir & Portfolio Mgr)
Steve Loncar (Portfolio Mgr-Client)

Cliffwater Investments, LLC   (1)
4640 Admiralty Way 11th Fl, Marina Del Rey, CA 90292
Tel.: (310) 448-5000
Web Site: https://www.cliffwater.com
Emp.: 100
Investment Advisory Services
N.A.I.C.S.: 523940
Thomas K. Lynch (Sr Mng Dir)
Daniel Stern (Sr Mng Dir)
Gabrielle Zadra (Sr Mng Dir)
Jonathan Rogal (Sr Mng Dir & Gen Counsel)
Lance J. Johnson (COO)
Thomas V. Brown (CTO)

Duff & Phelps Investment Management Co   (1)
200 S Wacker Dr Ste 500, Chicago, IL 60606
Tel.: (312) 263-2610
Web Site: https://www.dpimc.com
Investment Management Service
N.A.I.C.S.: 523940
Geoffrey P. Dybas (Exec Mng Dir & Sr Portfolio Mgr)
Alan Meder (Sr Mng Dir & Chief Risk Officer)
Shalini Sharma (Sr Mng Dir & Sr Portfolio Mgr)

Ron She *(Assoc Portfolio Mgr)*
Michael Slater *(Assoc Portfolio Mgr)*
David D. Grumhaus Jr. *(Pres)*

Euclid Advisors LLC (1)
1540 Broadway Ste 1630, New York, NY 10036
Tel.: (646) 376-5913
Web Site: http://www.euclidadv.com
Emp.: 4
Investment Management Service
N.A.I.C.S.: 523940

Kayne Anderson Rudnick Investment Management, LLC (1)
2000 Ave of the Stars Ste 1110, Los Angeles, CA 90067
Tel.: (310) 556-2721
Web Site: https://www.kayne.com
Rev.: $9,100,000,000
Emp.: 101
Investment Advisory & Portfolio Management Services
N.A.I.C.S.: 523940
John E. Anderson *(Co-Founder)*
Spuds Powell *(Mng Dir)*
Jennifer Okutake *(Dir-Portfolio Implementation)*
Kimberly Hoang *(Dir-Ops)*
Jason Pomatto *(Mng Dir)*

Newfleet Asset Management LLC (1)
1 Financial Plz, Hartford, CT 06103
Tel.: (415) 486-6500
Web Site: https://www.newfleet.com
Investment Management Service
N.A.I.C.S.: 523940
David L. Albrycht *(Pres & Chief Investment Officer)*
Benjamin Caron *(Sr Mng Dir & Portfolio Mgr)*
Christine M. Ouellette *(Dir & Portfolio Mgr)*
Lisa M. Baribault *(Dir & Portfolio Mgr)*
William J. Eastwood *(Sr Mng Dir, Head-Trading & Portfolio Mgr)*
Stephen Hooker *(Mng Dir & Portfolio Mgr)*
Kyle Jennings *(Sr Mng Dir & Head-Credit Res)*
Peter S. Lannigan *(Sr Mng Dir & Head-Emerging Markets)*
Michael Sollicito *(COO)*
Cecelia Gerber *(Dir)*
Ryan Jungk *(Dir)*
Stephen H. Hooker *(Mng Dir)*
Kyle A. Jennings *(Sr Mng Dir)*
Cecelia L. Gerber *(Dir)*
Ryan W. Jungk *(Sr Mng Dir)*

Seix Investment Advisors LLC (1)
1 Maynard Dr Ste 3200, Park Ridge, NJ 07656
Tel.: (201) 391-0300
Web Site: http://www.seixadvisors.com
Investment Advisory & Asset Management Services
N.A.I.C.S.: 523940
James F. Keegan *(Chm & CIO)*
George K. Goudelias *(Mng Dir, Head-Leverage Fin & Sr Portfolio Mgr)*
Michael Rieger *(Mng Dir & Sr Portfolio Mgr-Securitized Assets)*
Carlos Catoya *(Head-Investment Grade Credit Res & Portfolio Mgr)*
Michael G. Sebesta *(Mng Dir & Head-Institutional Client Svc)*
Kimberly C. Maichle *(Sr Mgr-Investment & Dir)*
James FitzPatrick *(Mng Dir, Head-Leveraged Fin Trading & Portfolio Mgr)*
Eric Guevara *(Head-Leveraged Loan Trading & Portfolio Mgr)*
Michael Kirkpatrick *(Mng Dir & Sr Portfolio Mgr)*
Atul Sibal *(Dir-Quantitative Analysis)*
Dusty Self *(Mng Dir & Sr Portfolio Mgr)*
Phillip Hooks *(Dir-Municipal Credit Res)*
Angela Kukoda *(Dir-Municipal Credit Res)*
Scott Kupchinsky *(Head-Securitized Assets Res)*
Jonathan Yozzo *(Head-Investment Grade Corp Bond Trading & Portfolio Mgr-Credit)*

Silvant Capital Management, LLC (1)
3333 Piedmont Rd NE Ste 1500, Atlanta, GA 30305
Tel.: (404) 845-7640
Web Site: https://www.silvantcapital.com

Investment Advisory & Asset Management Services
N.A.I.C.S.: 523940
Sandeep Bhatia *(Mng Dir & Sr Portfolio Mgr)*
Brandi K. Allen *(Portfolio Mgr-Cunsumer Staples & Healthcare)*
Sowmdeb Sen *(Portfolio Mgr-Consumer Discretionary & Fin Sector)*
Marc Schneidau *(COO, Mng Dir & Portfolio Mgr-Client)*
Michael A. Sansoterra *(CIO & Sr Portfolio Mgr)*
Stephen Coker *(Portfolio Mgr-Energy, Indus & Matls Sector)*

Sustainable Growth Advisers, LP (1)
301 Tresser Blvd Ste 1310, Stamford, CT 06901 **(70%)**
Tel.: (203) 348-4742
Web Site: https://www.sgadvisers.com
Portfolio Management
N.A.I.C.S.: 523940
Joe Kolanko *(Dir-Bus Dev)*
Chris Ingrassia *(Dir-Portfolio Trading)*
Daniel Callaway *(Chief Compliance Officer & Gen Counsel)*
Peter Seuffert *(COO)*
Robert Rohn *(Founder, Principal & Portfolio Mgr)*
Luying Wang *(Principal)*
Deana Leong *(Portfolio Mgr-Client)*
Wendy Fox *(Dir-Portfolio Acctg)*
Angel Alicea *(Controller)*

VP Distributors, LLC (1)
2492 Williams Hwy, Williamstown, WV 26187
Tel.: (304) 375-9980
Goods Merchant Whslr
N.A.I.C.S.: 423990

Virtus ETF Solutions LLC (1)
1540 Broadway 16th Fl, New York, NY 10036
Tel.: (212) 593-4383
Web Site: http://www.etfissuersolutions.com
Investment Advisory Services
N.A.I.C.S.: 523940
Matthew B. Brown *(Portfolio Mgr-Fund)*
Brinton W. Frith *(CFO & Treas)*

Virtus Investment Advisers, Inc. (1)
100 Pearl St, Hartford, CT 06103-4506
Tel.: (860) 403-5000
Investment Advisory Services
N.A.I.C.S.: 523940

Zweig Advisers LLC (1)
900 3rd Ave, New York, NY 10022
Tel.: (212) 451-1100
Emp.: 50
Investment Advisory Services
N.A.I.C.S.: 523940
Sharon Salerno *(Gen Mgr)*

VIRTUS TOTAL RETURN FUND, INC.
900 Third Ave, New York, NY 10022
Tel.: (212) 755-9860
ZF—(NYSE)
Investment Management Service
N.A.I.C.S.: 525990
Carlton Bryan Neel *(Mgr-Fund)*

VISA, INC.
900 Metro Center Blvd, Foster City, CA 94404
Tel.: (650) 432-3200 DE
Web Site: https://usa.visa.com
V—(NYSE)
Rev.: $35,926,000,000
Assets: $94,511,000,000
Liabilities: $55,374,000,000
Net Worth: $39,137,000,000
Earnings: $19,743,000,000
Emp.: 31,600
Fiscal Year-end: 09/30/24
Financial Investment Services
N.A.I.C.S.: 523999
Charlotte Hogg *(CEO-Europe & Exec VP)*
John F. Lundgren *(Chm)*
Oliver Jenkyn *(Pres-North America & Exec VP)*

Rajat Taneja *(Pres-Tech)*
Kelly Mahon Tullier *(Chief Legal & Admin Officer & Exec VP)*
Lynne Biggar *(CMO-Global)*
Mike Milotich *(Sr VP-IR)*
Jennifer Grant *(Chief HR Officer & Exec VP-HR)*
Chris Clark *(Pres-Asia Pacific & Exec VP)*
Jack Forestell *(Chief Product Officer & Exec VP)*
Mary Kay Bowman *(Head-Buyer & Seller Solutions-Global)*
Paul D. Fabara *(Chief Risk Officer & Exec VP)*
Christopher T. Newkirk *(Chief Strategy Officer)*
Frederique Covington Corbett *(Sr VP-Global Brand Strategy & Plng)*
Julie Rottenberg *(Gen Counsel & Sr VP)*
Michelle Gethers-Clark *(Chief Diversity Officer & Head-Corp Responsibility)*
Andrew Uaboi *(Head-West Africa Reg)*
Aida Diarra *(Sr VP & Head-Sub-Saharan Africa)*
Peter Andreski *(Chief Acctg Officer, Sr VP & Controller-Global)*
Adeline Kim *(Country Mgr-Singapore & Brunei)*
Serene Gay *(Grp Country Mgr-Southeast Asia)*
Christopher Suh *(CFO & Exec VP)*

Subsidiaries:

CardinalCommerce Corp. (1)
8100 Tyler Blvd Ste #100, Mentor, OH 44060 **(100%)**
Tel.: (440) 352-8444
Web Site:
http://www.cardinalcommerce.com
eCommerce & Internet Services
N.A.I.C.S.: 517810
Francis M. Sherwin *(Co-Founder & CEO)*
Chandra Balasubramanian *(Co-Founder, CTO & Exec VP)*

Fundamo (Pty) Ltd. (1)
12 Plein Street, Durbanville, 7550, South Africa
Tel.: (27) 219707600
Web Site: http://www.fundamo.com
Mobile Financial Services Technology Developer
N.A.I.C.S.: 513210
Hannes van Rensburg *(CEO)*

Servicios Visa International Limitada (1)
Miraflores 383 Of 1001, Santiago, 8320149, Chile
Tel.: (56) 28767000
Web Site: http://www.visa.com
Emp.: 13
Financial Transaction Processing Services
N.A.I.C.S.: 522320

TrialPay, Inc. (1)
303 Bryant St 2nd Fl, Mountain View, CA 94041
Tel.: (650) 318-0000
Web Site: http://www.trialpay.com
Sales Range: $10-24.9 Million
Emp.: 60
Transactional Advertising Solutions
N.A.I.C.S.: 541890
Alastair Rampell *(Co-Founder)*
Chuck Yu *(VP-Revenue Ops)*
Nick Westrum *(Mgr-IT)*

Verifi, Inc. (1)
8391 Beverly Blvd, Los Angeles, CA 90048
Tel.: (323) 655-5789
Web Site: http://www.verifi.com
Administrative Management & General Management Consulting Service
N.A.I.C.S.: 541611
Matthew G. Katz *(Founder & CEO)*
Tony Wootton *(Chief Revenue Officer & Sr VP)*
Jeff Sawitke *(Sr VP-Strategic Alliances & Bus Analytics)*

Sara Craven *(COO & Gen Counsel)*
Gabe McGloin *(Head-Merchant Sls & Bus Dev-Intl)*
Ronald B. Cushey *(CFO & Sr VP)*
Hitesh Anand *(Chief Product Officer)*
Rick Lynch *(Sr VP-Bus Dev)*
Lisa Tennant *(Sr VP-Client Rels-Global)*
Toni Espera *(VP-People Ops)*
Chris Marchand *(VP-Bus Dev)*
Brian Waller *(VP-Issuer Partnerships-Global)*
Deborah Lynn Kurtz *(VP-Fin)*

Visa AP (Australia) Pty Limited (1)
L 42 Amp Ctr 50 Bridge St, Sydney, 2000, NSW, Australia
Tel.: (61) 292538800
Financial Transaction Processing Services
N.A.I.C.S.: 522320

Visa CEMEA (UK) Limited (1)
9th Floor 107 Cheapside, London, EC2V 6DN, United Kingdom
Tel.: (44) 800891725
Web Site: http://www.visacemea.com
Financial Transaction Processing Services
N.A.I.C.S.: 522320

Visa Canada Corporation (1)
77 King Street West Suite 4400, PO Box 265, Toronto, M5K 1J5, ON, Canada
Tel.: (416) 367-8472
Web Site: http://www.visa.ca
Financial Transaction Processing Services
N.A.I.C.S.: 522320

Visa Europe Limited (1)
1 Sheldon Square, London, W2 6TT, United Kingdom
Tel.: (44) 2077955777
Credit Card Issuing & Payment Processing Services
N.A.I.C.S.: 522210
William Ingham *(Officer-Organisation Change & HR)*

Visa International Service Association (1)
900 Metro Ctr Blvd, Foster City, CA 94404
Tel.: (650) 432-3200
Sales Range: $250-299.9 Million
Transactions, Credit & Collections & Electronic Payment Systems
N.A.I.C.S.: 522320
Joshua R. Floum *(Gen Counsel)*
Kevin Burke *(CMO-Core Products)*
Jonathan Sanchez-Jaimes *(Pres-Visa Latin America & Carribean)*
Don Davis *(Sr VP & Global Head-Real Estate)*

Visa U.S.A., Inc. (1)
PO Box 8999, San Francisco, CA 94128
Tel.: (650) 432-3200
Web Site: http://www.usa.visa.com
Sales Range: $1-4.9 Billion
Emp.: 2,500
Electronic Payment & Credit Card Administration Services
N.A.I.C.S.: 522210

Subsidiary (Domestic):

CyberSource Corporation (2)
1295 Charleston Rd, Mountain View, CA 94043
Tel.: (650) 965-6000
Web Site: http://www.cybersource.com
Sales Range: $250-299.9 Million
Emp.: 654
Electronic Payment Processing Services
N.A.I.C.S.: 518210

Subsidiary (Domestic):

Authorize.Net Holdings, Inc. (3)
808 E Utah Valley Dr, American Fork, UT 84003
Tel.: (801) 492-6450
Web Site: http://www.authorize.net
Sales Range: $75-99.9 Million
Emp.: 200
Develops, Markets & Supports Integrated Products & Services for Customer Acquisition, Retention & Fraud Prevention Processes
N.A.I.C.S.: 522320

Subsidiary (Non-US):

CyberSource K.K. (3)

Visa, Inc.—(Continued)

3-25-18 Shibuya, Shibuya-ku, Tokyo, 150-8530, Japan
Tel.: (81) 357747733
Web Site: http://www.cybersource.co.jp
Sales Range: $10-24.9 Million
Emp.: 10
Automated Commerce Transaction Solutions
N.A.I.C.S.: 518210

CyberSource Ltd. (3)
The Waterfront, 300 Thames Valley Park
Drive, Reading, RG6 1PT, Berks, United
Kingdom (100%)
Tel.: (44) 1189907300
Web Site: http://www.cybersource.co.uk
Sales Range: $10-24.9 Million
Emp.: 39
Automated Commerce Transaction Solutions
N.A.I.C.S.: 518210

Subsidiary (Domestic):

Inovant, LLC (2)
PO Box 8999, San Francisco, CA 94128-8999
Tel.: (650) 432-3200
Web Site: http://www.visa.com
Sales Range: $125-149.9 Million
Electronic Payment Processing Services
N.A.I.C.S.: 522320

PlaySpan, Inc. (2)
PO Box 8999, San Francisco, CA 94128-8999
Tel.: (650) 432-3200
Web Site: http://www.playspan.com
Sales Range: $25-49.9 Million
Emp.: 8
Online Media Transaction Processing Services
N.A.I.C.S.: 522320

Visa Worldwide Pte. Limited (1)
71 Robinson Road 08-01, Singapore,
068895, Singapore
Tel.: (65) 66715800
Electronic Payment Services
N.A.I.C.S.: 522320

VISCOGLIOSI BROTHERS ACQUISITION CORP.

505 Park Ave 14th Fl, New York, NY
10022
Tel.: (212) 583-9700 DE
Web Site: https://www.vb-oc.com
Year Founded: 2021
VDOC—(NASDAQ)
Rev.: $1,226,289
Assets: $90,119,270
Liabilities: $92,567,958
Net Worth: ($2,448,688)
Earnings: ($581,523)
Emp.: 2
Fiscal Year-end: 12/31/22
Investment Services
N.A.I.C.S.: 523999
John J. Viscogliosi (Pres, CEO & Chm)

VISHAY INTERTECHNOLOGY, INC.

63 Lancaster Ave, Malvern, PA
19355-2143
Tel.: (610) 644-1300 DE
Web Site: https://www.vishay.com
Year Founded: 1962
VSH—(NYSE)
Rev.: $3,497,401,000
Assets: $3,865,653,000
Liabilities: $1,815,503,000
Net Worth: $2,050,150,000
Earnings: $428,810,000
Emp.: 23,900
Fiscal Year-end: 12/31/22
Discrete Semiconductors & Passive
Electronic Components Mfr & Supplier
N.A.I.C.S.: 335999

Ruta Zandman (Founder)
Peter G. Henrici (Sec & Exec VP-Corp Comm)
Marc Zandman (Exec Chm)
David E. McConnell (CFO & Exec VP)
David L. Tomlinson (Chief Acctg Officer, Sr VP & Controller)
Joel Smejkal (Pres & CEO)
Michael O'Sullivan (Chief Admin Officer, Chief Legal Officer & Exec VP)
Jeff Webster (COO)
Andreas Randebrock (Exec VP-Global HR)
Joel Smejkal (Pres & CEO)
Bart Cassidy (Sr VP-Tax)
Geoff Taylor (Sr VP-Quality)
Bob Hackett (Sr VP-Global HR)

Subsidiaries:

Angstrohm Precision, Inc. (1)
18400 Precision Pl, Hagerstown, MD
21742 (100%)
Tel.: (301) 739-8722
Sales Range: $10-24.9 Million
Emp.: 24
Mfr of Precision Metal Film Resistors
N.A.I.C.S.: 334416

Capella Microsystems, Inc. (1)
2201 Laurelwood Rd, Santa Clara, CA
95054
Tel.: (408) 988-8000
Emp.: 15
Electric Equipment Mfr.
N.A.I.C.S.: 334515
Cheng Shih (CEO)

ECOMAL Austria Ges.mbH (1)
Wienerbergstr 7, 1100, Vienna, Austria
Tel.: (43) 166705370
Web Site: http://www.ecomal.com
Emp.: 10
Semiconductors & Related Devices Distr
N.A.I.C.S.: 334413
Harald Stockinger (Sls Mgr)
Martina Kutil (Office Mgr)
Andreas Schweighofer (Sls Mgr)

ECOMAL Ceska republika S.r.O. (1)
Nam TG Masaryka 9, 301 00, Plzen, Czech
Republic
Tel.: (420) 377982314
Electric Equipment Mfr
N.A.I.C.S.: 334515
Marie Jirouskova (Acct Mgr)

ECOMAL Deutschland GmbH (1)
Wilhelm-Schauenberg-Strasse 7, 79199,
Kirchzarten, Germany
Tel.: (49) 76613950
Sales Range: $25-49.9 Million
Emp.: 150
Electronic Components Mfr
N.A.I.C.S.: 334419

ECOMAL Elektronske Komponente
d.o.o. (1)
Smartinska cesta 130, 1000, Ljubljana, Slovenia
Tel.: (386) 59135289
Electronic Components Distr
N.A.I.C.S.: 423690
Simon Hvala (Acct Mgr)

ECOMAL Europe GmbH (1)
Wilhelm-Schauenberg-Str 7, 79199,
Kirchzarten, Germany
Tel.: (49) 7 661 3950
Web Site: https://www.ecomal.com
Electric Equipment Mfr
N.A.I.C.S.: 334515

ECOMAL Finland OY (1)
Brahenkatu 20, 20100, Turku, Finland
Tel.: (358) 22738000
Sales Range: $10-24.9 Million
Emp.: 4
Electronic Component Mfr & Distr
N.A.I.C.S.: 334413
Tommi Jokela (Mgr-Sls)

ECOMAL France S.A. (1)
116 Rue Ronsard, 37100, Tours, France
Tel.: (33) 247882244
Web Site: http://www.ecomal.com
Emp.: 7

Semiconductors & Related Devices Distr
N.A.I.C.S.: 334413
Philippe Poinsignon (Mgr-Sales)

ECOMAL Iberia S.A.U. (1)
Camino de Portuetxe 53A, Donostia,
20018, San Sebastian, Spain
Tel.: (34) 943835904
Electric Equipment Mfr
N.A.I.C.S.: 334515
Martin Quiroz (Mgr-Sls)
Josu Rueda (Engr-Field Application)

ECOMAL Italy SRL (1)
Via Gaetano Donizetti 6, 20095, Cusano
Milanino, Italy
Tel.: (39) 0249630370
Sales Range: $10-24.9 Million
Emp.: 6
Semiconductors & Related Devices Distr
N.A.I.C.S.: 334413

ECOMAL Nederland BV (1)
Beechavenue 131, 1119 RB, Schiphol-Rijk,
Netherlands
Tel.: (31) 203473177
Sales Range: $10-24.9 Million
Emp.: 6
Semiconductors & Related Devices Distr
N.A.I.C.S.: 334413
Jan de Goede (Mgr-Sls)

ECOMAL Schweiz A.G. (1)
Brauereistrasse 1, 8200, Schaffhausen,
Switzerland
Tel.: (41) 526440844
Semiconductors & Related Devices Distr
N.A.I.C.S.: 334413
Peter Meister (Mgr-Sls)

ECOMAL Sweden AB (1)
Kungsgatan 6, 211 49, Malmo, Sweden
Tel.: (46) 87216900
Electric Equipment Mfr
N.A.I.C.S.: 334515

ECOMAL UK Ltd. (1)
3 Sadler Court, Lincoln, LN6 3RG, Lincolnshire, United Kingdom
Tel.: (44) 1522814380
Web Site: http://www.ecomal.com
Sales Range: $10-24.9 Million
Emp.: 5
Semiconductors & Related Devices Distr
N.A.I.C.S.: 334413
James Miller (Sls Mgr)
Genny Baglin (Acct Mgr)
Dave Goodenough (Sls Mgr)

Ecomal Hungary Kft. (1)
Foti Ut 56, 1047, Budapest, Hungary
Tel.: (36) 18700228
Electronic Components Distr
N.A.I.C.S.: 423690

Ecomal Poland Sp. z o.o. (1)
Ul I Daszynskiego 165, 44-100, Gliwice,
Poland
Tel.: (48) 323231363
Electronic Components Distr
N.A.I.C.S.: 423690

General Semiconductor (China) Co.,
Ltd. (1)
88 6th Avenue Econ & Tech Development
Zone, Tianjin, 300457, China
Tel.: (86) 2225291088
Emp.: 2,000
Electronic Parts & Equipment Whslr
N.A.I.C.S.: 423690

Hirel Systems LLC (1)
11100 Wayzata Blvd Ste 501, Minnetonka,
MN 55305
Tel.: (952) 544-1344
Web Site: http://www.hirelsystems.com
Sales Range: $25-49.9 Million
Emp.: 100
Magnetics & Power Supply Subassemblies
Mfr
N.A.I.C.S.: 335311
Trent Guerrero (COO)

Branch (Domestic):

Hirel Systems, LLC-Marshall (2)
604 E Erie Rd, Marshall, MN 56258
Tel.: (507) 532-4200
Web Site: http://www.hirelsystems.com
Sales Range: $1-9.9 Million
Emp.: 30
Mfr Industries

N.A.I.C.S.: 339999

Shanghai Simconix Electronic Company Ltd. (1)
235 Chengbei Road Jiading District, Shanghai, 201800, China
Tel.: (86) 2159926999
Electronic Components Mfr
N.A.I.C.S.: 334419

Shanghai Vishay Semiconductors
Ltd. (1)
No 501 Jiangchang West Road Zhabe,
Shanghai, 200436, China
Tel.: (86) 2156030910
Web Site: http://www.vishay.com
Emp.: 390
Electronic Parts & Equipment Whslr
N.A.I.C.S.: 423690

Siliconix Incorporated (1)
2201 Laurelwood Rd, Santa Clara, CA
95054 (80.4%)
Tel.: (408) 988-8000
Web Site: http://www.vishay.com
Sales Range: $450-499.9 Million
Emp.: 2,033
FETS, Integrated Circuits, MOS Power
FETS, Analog Switches, Wideband Multiplexers & Smart Power ICs Mfr
N.A.I.C.S.: 334413

Vishay Americas, Inc. (1)
1 Greenwich Pl, Shelton, CT
06484 (100%)
Tel.: (402) 563-6866
Web Site: http://www.vishay.com
Sales Range: $25-49.9 Million
Emp.: 60
Distr of Resistors & Other Electronic Components
N.A.I.C.S.: 334416

Vishay BCcomponents Beyschlag
GmbH (1)
Rungholtstrasse 8-10, 25746, Heide, Germany
Tel.: (49) 481950
Semiconductors & Related Devices Distr
N.A.I.C.S.: 334413
Frank Kabbe (Pres)

Vishay BCcomponents Hong Kong
Ltd. (1)
Fountain Set Bldg, Tuen Mun, China (Hong
Kong)
Tel.: (852) 34722328
Web Site: http://www.vishay.com
Electronic Components Mfr
N.A.I.C.S.: 334419

Vishay China Co. Ltd. (1)
15D Sungtong Infoport Plaza 55 Huai Hai
West Road, Shanghai, 200030, China
Tel.: (86) 2122315555
Electronic Parts & Equipment Whslr
N.A.I.C.S.: 423690

Vishay Components (Huizhou) Co.
Ltd. (1)
46 Paifang Renmin 4th Rd Huiyang District,
Huizhou, 516211, China
Tel.: (86) 7523355373
Emp.: 1,400
Electronic Components Mfr.
N.A.I.C.S.: 334419

Vishay Components, S.A. (1)
Edif Alfa III Planta 4a - Local 101 C/ Isabel
Colbrand 10, 28050, Madrid, Spain
Tel.: (34) 91 563 4286
Web Site: http://www.vishay.com
Semiconductors & Passive Components
Sales & Distribution
N.A.I.C.S.: 423430

Vishay Electronica Portugal Lda. (1)
Rua Magalhaes Lima 256 Calendario,
4760-363, Vila Nova de Famalicao, Portugal
Tel.: (351) 252330100
Web Site:
http://www.vishayelectronicaportugal
lda.pai.pt
Electronic Components Mfr
N.A.I.C.S.: 334416

Vishay General Semiconductor of
Taiwan, Ltd. (1)
233 Pao Chiao Road Hsintien, Taipei,
23145, Taiwan

Tel.: (886) 229113861
Semiconductors & Related Devices Mfr
N.A.I.C.S.: 334413

Vishay HiRel Systems LLC (1)
11100 Wayzata Blvd Ste 450, Minnetonka,
MN 55305
Tel.: (952) 544-1344
Web Site: http://www.hirelsystems.com
Emp.: 290
Electric Equipment Mfr
N.A.I.C.S.: 334515

Subsidiary (Non-US):

**Vishay HiRel Systems Asia
Limited** (2)
Unit 302-3 3/F Energy Plz No 92 Granville
Road Tsimshatsui East, Kowloon, China
(Hong Kong)
Tel.: (852) 23532820
Electric Equipment Mfr
N.A.I.C.S.: 334515

**Vishay Intertechnology Asia Pte.,
Ltd.** (1)
37A Tampines Street 92 07-01, Singapore,
528886, Singapore (100%)
Tel.: (65) 6 788 6668
Web Site: https://www.vishay.com
Sales Range: $25-49.9 Million
Emp.: 100
Distr of Electronic Components
N.A.I.C.S.: 449210

Subsidiary (Non-US):

Vishay Hong Kong Ltd. (2)
Unit 302-3 3/F Energy Plaza No 92 Gran-
ville Road, Tsimshatsui East, Kowloon,
China (Hong Kong)
Tel.: (852) 23532828
Semiconductors & Related Devices Mfr
N.A.I.C.S.: 334413

Vishay Korea Co. Ltd. (2)
9th Floor Central Place 50 Seosomun-ro,
Jung-gu, 04505, Seoul, Korea (South)
Tel.: (82) 232708800
Web Site: http://www.vishay.com
Emp.: 26
Semiconductors & Related Devices Mfr
N.A.I.C.S.: 334413

Vishay Israel Limited (1)
7 Hatnufa Street, 49510, Petach Tikva,
Israel (100%)
Tel.: (972) 3 770 2000
Web Site: http://www.vishay.com
Sales Range: $150-199.9 Million
Emp.: 500
Mfr of Resisitors & Other Electronic Compo-
nents
N.A.I.C.S.: 334416

Subsidiary (Non-US):

Vishay Elctronic GmbH (2)
Hofmark-Aich-Str 36, PO Box 588, 84030,
Landshut, Germany (100%)
Tel.: (49) 871860
Sales Range: $25-49.9 Million
Emp.: 80
Mfr of High Voltage Multipliers & Assem-
blies, Ceramic Capicitors, Semiconductors
N.A.I.C.S.: 333242
Gerald Paul (Mng Dir)

Subsidiary (Domestic):

Vishay Electronic GmbH (3)
Dr-Felix-Zandman-Platz 1, 95100, Selb,
Germany (100%)
Tel.: (49) 9287710
Web Site: http://www.vishay.com
Emp.: 800
Mfr of Capacitors & Resistors
N.A.I.C.S.: 334416
Gerald Paul (Mng Dir)

Subsidiary (Non-US):

Vishay Ltd. (3)
Suite 6 C Tower House St Catherine's
Court Enterprise Park, Sunderland, SR5
3XJ, United Kingdom (100%)
Tel.: (44) 1915168584
Web Site: http://www.vishay.com
Rev.: $17,000,000
Emp.: 20

Mfr of Resistors & Other Electronic Components
N.A.I.C.S.: 334416

**Vishay Measurements Group (U.K.)
Ltd.** (3)
Stroudley Rd, Basingstoke, RG24 8FW,
Hampshire, United Kingdom (100%)
Tel.: (44) 1256462131
Sales Range: $25-49.9 Million
Emp.: 50
Mfr of Products for Precision Measurement
of Mechanical Strains
N.A.I.C.S.: 334513

Vishay S.A. (3)
199 Boulevard de la Madeleine 6003, Nice,
Cedex 1, France (99.9%)
Tel.: (33) 49 337 2912
Web Site: https://www.vishay.com
Mfr & Distributor of Resistors & Other Elec-
tronic Components
N.A.I.C.S.: 334416

Subsidiary (Non-US):

Vishay Polytech Co. Ltd. (2)
NBC Mita Building 7F 5-29-18 Shiba,
Minato-ku, Tokyo, 108-0014, Japan
Tel.: (81) 364353453
Web Site: http://www.holytech.co.jp
Electric Equipment Mfr
N.A.I.C.S.: 334515

Vishay Japan Co., Ltd (1)
Shibuya Prestige Bldg 4F 3-12-22 Shibuya,
Shibuya-ku, Tokyo, 150-0002,
Japan (100%)
Tel.: (81) 35 466 7150
Web Site: https://www.vishay.com
Sales Range: $100-124.9 Million
Emp.: 25
Distr of Resistors & Other Electronic Com-
ponents
N.A.I.C.S.: 449210

Vishay Micro-Measurement (1)
951 Wendell Blvd, Wendell, NC 27591
Tel.: (919) 365-3800
Web Site: http://www.micro-
measurements.com
Sales Range: $75-99.9 Million
Emp.: 250
Mfr of Photostress & Photoelastic Materials
& Optical Stress Measurement Instruments
N.A.I.C.S.: 334519
Tom Kieffer (Pres)

Subsidiary (Domestic):

Vishay BLH (2)
3 Edgewater Dr Ste 202, Norwood, MA
02062-4644
Tel.: (781) 298-2200
Web Site: http://www.blh.com
Sales Range: $25-49.9 Million
Emp.: 20
Mfr of Force & Weight Measurement Com-
ponents & Systems
N.A.I.C.S.: 333998

Subsidiary (Non-US):

Vishay BLH Canada (3)
14 Steinway Blvd Unit 10, Toronto, M9W
6M6, ON, Canada
Tel.: (416) 251-2554
Web Site: http://www.blh.com
Sales Range: $10-24.9 Million
Emp.: 3
Develops, Manufactures & Markets Load
Cells Used In Weighing Systems
N.A.I.C.S.: 333924

Vishay Resistors Belgium BVBA (1)
Rue des Deux Maisons 37, 1140, Brussels,
Belgium
Tel.: (32) 27240802
Sales Range: $25-49.9 Million
Emp.: 28
Semiconductors & Related Devices Mfr
N.A.I.C.S.: 334413

Vishay Semiconductor Ges.mbH (1)
Telefunkenstrasse 5, 4840, Vocklabruck,
Austria
Tel.: (43) 7672724510
Emp.: 100
Semiconductors & Related Devices Distr
N.A.I.C.S.: 334413
Arnold Rohr (Mgr)

Vishay Semiconductor India Ltd. (1)
Unit No 36 SDF 2 Anderi East Seepz,
Mumbai, 400096, Maharashtra, India
Tel.: (91) 2230880420
Web Site: http://www.vishay.com
Emp.: 300
Semiconductors & Related Devices Mfr
N.A.I.C.S.: 334413

**Vishay Semiconductor Italiana
S.p.A.** (1)
Via Mascagni 42, 20030, Senago, MI, Italy
Tel.: (39) 0299 8241
Web Site: https://www.vishay.com
Sales Range: $25-49.9 Million
Emp.: 5
Semiconductors & Related Devices Mfr
N.A.I.C.S.: 423690

Vishay Spectrol (1)
4051 Greystone Dr, Ontario, CA 91761-
3100
Tel.: (909) 923-3313
Web Site: http://www.spectrol.com
Sales Range: $25-49.9 Million
Emp.: 90
Variety of Potentiometers & Encoders,
Components for Aerospace & Industrial Ap-
plications Producer
N.A.I.C.S.: 335311

Vishay Transducers Ltd. (1)
9210 Rochester Ave, Cucamonga, CA
91730
Tel.: (714) 731-1234
Web Site: http://www.vishaypg.com
Sales Range: $25-49.9 Million
Emp.: 45
Electronic Weighing Systems & Sales
N.A.I.C.S.: 333998

Joint Venture (Non-US):

Vishay Sanmar Ltd. (2)
9 Cathedral Road, Chennai, 600 086, Tamil
Nadu, India
Tel.: (91) 44 2812 8500
Web Site: http://www.sanmargroup.com
Sales Range: $100-124.9 Million
Steel Casting Mfr
N.A.I.C.S.: 331513

VISHAY PRECISION GROUP, INC.

3 Great Valley Pkwy Ste 150,
Malvern, PA 19355
Tel.: (484) 321-5300
Web Site:
https://www.vpgsensors.com
Year Founded: 1962
VPG—(NYSE)
Rev.: $362,580,000
Assets: $476,742,000
Liabilities: $170,220,000
Net Worth: $306,522,000
Earnings: $36,063,000
Emp.: 2,700
Fiscal Year-end: 12/31/22
All Other Miscellaneous Electrical
Equipment & Component Manufactur-
ing
N.A.I.C.S.: 335999
Ziv Shoshani (Pres & CEO)
Steven Klausner (Treas & VP)
William M. Clancy (CFO & Exec VP)
Benny Shaya (VP-Micro-
Measurements Instruments & Pacific
Instruments)
Inbal Dangur (VP)
Flora Lewin (VP)
Oded Sherman (VP)

Subsidiaries:

Alpha Electronics Corp. (1)
2nd Fl Hagoromo Bldg 1-2-10 Uchikanda,
Chiyoda-ku, Tokyo, 101-0047, Japan
Tel.: (81) 352822640
Web Site: https://www.alpha-elec.co.jp
Emp.: 30
Electronic Resistor Mfr
N.A.I.C.S.: 334416
Akio Ogasawara (CEO)

DSI Europe GmbH (1)

Tatschenweg 1, Weissenhorn, D-74078,
Heilbronn, Germany
Tel.: (49) 713139099231
Web Site: https://www.gleeble.com
Industrial Machinery Mfr
N.A.I.C.S.: 333248

**Diversified Technical Systems,
Inc.** (1)
1720 Apollo Ct, Seal Beach, CA 90740-
5617
Tel.: (562) 493-0158
Web Site: https://www.dtsweb.com
Sales Range: $1-9.9 Million
Emp.: 70
Data Acquisition Systems & Sensors
N.A.I.C.S.: 334419
Rollin White (Head)
Daniel Stelung (Dir-Engineering)
Craig Leising (Dir-Operations)
Chris Balogh (Sr Mgr-Technical Support)
Randy Boss (Dir-Program Mgmt)
Mark Chiavarini (Dir-Sales & Marketing)
Ann Cook (Dir-Human Resources)
Kyvory Henderson (Dir-Business Develop-
ment)
Grant Newton (Sr Mgr-Operations)
Dawn Sup (Mgr-Michigan Technical Center)

Dynamic Systems, Inc. (1)
323 Route 355, Poestenkill, NY 12140
Tel.: (518) 283-5350
Web Site: http://www.gleeble.com
Measuring Device Mfr
N.A.I.C.S.: 334519

Pacific Instruments, Inc. (1)
4080 Pike Ln, Concord, CA 94520
Tel.: (925) 827-9010
Web Site:
https://www.pacificinstruments.com
Sales Range: $1-9.9 Million
Emp.: 50
Instrument Mfr for Measuring & Testing
Electricity & Electrical Signals
N.A.I.C.S.: 334515

Powertron GmbH (1)
Potsdamer Strasse 18a, D-14513, Teltow,
Germany
Tel.: (49) 332835300
Web Site: https://powertron.de
Electronic Components Mfr
N.A.I.C.S.: 334419

Stress-Tek, Inc. (1)
5920 S 194th St, Kent, WA 98032
Tel.: (253) 872-1910
Web Site: http://www.stress-tek.com
Sales Range: $1-9.9 Million
Emp.: 150
Consulting Services in Areas of Strain Gag-
ing, Transducer Design & Experimental
Stress Analysis
N.A.I.C.S.: 334513

VPG Systems UK, Ltd. (1)
Airedale House Canal Road, Bradford, BD2
1AG, United Kingdom
Tel.: (44) 1274771177
Web Site: http://www.vishaypg.com
Industrial Machinery Mfr
N.A.I.C.S.: 333248

Subsidiary (Non-US):

**Vishay Precision Group Canada
ULC** (2)
48 Lesmill Road, Toronto, M3B 2T5, ON,
Canada
Tel.: (416) 445-5850
Web Site: https://www.kelk.com
Emp.: 120
Control Device Mfr
N.A.I.C.S.: 334512

**Vishay Celtron Technologies,
Inc.** (1)
8F-1 No 171 Sec 2 Datong Rd, Taipei,
22183, Taiwan
Tel.: (886) 286926888
Web Site: http://www.vpgsensors.com
Sales Range: $25-49.9 Million
Emp.: 40
Electronic Components Mfr
N.A.I.C.S.: 334419

**Vishay Measurements Group France
S.A.S.** (1)

Vishay Precision Group, Inc.—(Continued)

16 Rue Francis Vovelle, 28000, Chartres, France
Tel.: (33) 237333125
Sensor System Mfr
N.A.I.C.S.: 335999

Vishay Measurements Group UK Ltd. (1)
1 Cartel Units Stroudley Rd, Basingstoke, RG24 8FW, United Kingdom
Tel.: (44) 1256462131
Sensor System Mfr
N.A.I.C.S.: 335999

Vishay PME France SARL (1)
ZA du Champ du Caillou 10 Rue de Gally, 78450, Chavanay, France
Tel.: (33) 130799700
Web Site: http://www.vishaypg.com
Emp.: 7
Electronic Components Mfr
N.A.I.C.S.: 334419

Vishay Precision Foil K.K. (1)
Hagoromo Bldg 2F 1-2-10 Uchikanda, Chiyodaku, Tokyo, 101-0047, Chiyoda-ku, Japan
Tel.: (81) 352822761
Web Site: http://www.vishaypg.com
Sales Range: $10-24.9 Million
Emp.: 2
Electronic Products Mfr
N.A.I.C.S.: 334419

Vishay Precision Foil, Inc. (1)
3 Great Valley Pkwy Ste 150, Malvern, PA 19355
Tel.: (484) 321-5300
Web Site: http://www.vpgsensors.com
Sales Range: $10-24.9 Million
Emp.: 20
Electronic Resistor Mfr
N.A.I.C.S.: 334416
Ziv Shoshani (Pres & CEO)

Vishay Precision Transducers India Private Limited (1)
Oz-22 Sipcot Hi-Tech Industrial Growth Center Sez Orgadam Po, Sriperumbudur Taluk, Kanchipuram, 602105, Tamil Nadu, India
Tel.: (91) 4439994052
Web Site: http://www.vishaypg.com
Sales Range: $50-74.9 Million
Emp.: 25
Electronic Components Mfr
N.A.I.C.S.: 334419

VISION ENERGY CORPORATION

95 Christopher Columbus Dr 16th Fl, Jersey City, NJ 07302
Tel.: (551) 298-3600   NV
Web Site:
  https://www.visionenergy.com
VENG—(OTCIQ)
Assets: $4,284,840
Liabilities: $24,620,422
Net Worth: ($20,335,582)
Earnings: ($15,861,843)
Emp.: 9
Fiscal Year-end: 12/31/22
Hydrogen Energy Systems Mfr
N.A.I.C.S.: 541330
Matthew Hidalgo (CFO, Treas & Sec)
Andrew Hidalgo (Chm, Pres & CEO)

Subsidiaries:

PVBJ Inc. (1)
141 Robbins Rd Ste 100, Downingtown, PA 19335
Tel.: (610) 269-0700
Web Site: https://www.pvbjinc.com
Energy Services
N.A.I.C.S.: 221114

The Pride Group (QLD) Pty. Ltd. (1)
1/36 Kerryl Street, Kunda Park, 4556, QLD, Australia
Tel.: (61) 1300651521
Web Site: https://thepridegroup.com.au
Electronic Security System Services
N.A.I.C.S.: 561621

VoltH2 Operating BV (1)
Groot Arsenaal Rijtuigweg 44, 4611 EL, Eibergen, Netherlands
Tel.: (31) 850817720
Web Site: https://www.volth2.com
Solar Electric Module Mfr
N.A.I.C.S.: 221114

VISION SENSING ACQUISITION CORP.

78 SW 7th St Ste 500, Miami, FL 33130
Tel.: (786) 633-2520   DE
Year Founded: 2021
VSAC—(NASDAQ)
Rev.: $1,487,280
Assets: $105,192,121
Liabilities: $109,472,859
Net Worth: ($4,280,738)
Earnings: ($147,396)
Emp.: 2
Fiscal Year-end: 12/31/22
Investment Services
N.A.I.C.S.: 523999
Hang Kon Louis Ma (CFO & Sec)
George Peter Sobek (Chm & CEO)
Hang Kon Louis Ma (Pres, CFO, Sec & Dir)

VISIONEERING TECHNOLOGIES, INC.

30MansellCtSte215, Alpharetta, GA 30076
Web Site: https://www.vtivision.com
Year Founded: 2008
VTI—(ASX)
Rev.: $7,285,000
Assets: $9,107,000
Liabilities: $2,813,000
Net Worth: $6,294,000
Earnings: ($5,854,000)
Fiscal Year-end: 12/31/22
Contact Lense Mfr & Distr
N.A.I.C.S.: 339115
Juan Carlos Aragon (CEO & Exec Dir)
Brian D. Lane (CFO & COO)
Leanne Ralph (Sec)

VISIONGLOBAL CORP.

251 Kearny St 8th Fl, San Francisco, CA 94108
Tel.: (415) 901-2700   NV
VIZG—(OTCIQ)
Wireless Communication Equipment Mfr
N.A.I.C.S.: 334220
Martin G. Wotton (Pres & CEO)

VISIUM TECHNOLOGIES, INC.

4094 Majestic Ln Ste 360, Fairfax, VA 22033
Tel.: (703) 273-0383   FL
Web Site:
  https://www.visiumtechnologies.com
Year Founded: 1987
VISM—(OTCIQ)
Assets: $9,982
Liabilities: $4,263,296
Net Worth: ($4,253,314)
Earnings: ($3,310,848)
Emp.: 8
Fiscal Year-end: 06/30/23
Holding Company
N.A.I.C.S.: 551112
Eddie DeVane (Corp Counsel, Sr VP, VP & Head)
Mark Lucky (Chm, CEO, CFO, Treas & Sec)

VISLINK TECHNOLOGIES INC.

350 Clark Dr Ste 125, Mount Olive, NJ 07828
Tel.: (908) 651-3961   DE
Web Site: https://www.vislink.com

VISL—(NASDAQ)
Rev.: $28,402,000
Assets: $51,796,000
Liabilities: $8,144,000
Net Worth: $43,652,000
Earnings: ($13,560,000)
Emp.: 109
Fiscal Year-end: 12/31/22
Long-Range Broadband Technologies Developer
N.A.I.C.S.: 334220
Susan G. Swenson (Chm)
Sean Van (VP-Product Mgmt)
Carleton M. Miller (Pres & CEO)

Subsidiaries:

Broadcast Microwave Services, Inc. (1)
12305 Crosthwaite Cir, Poway, CA 92064
Tel.: (858) 391-3050
Web Site: http://www.bms-inc.com
Digital Microwave Radios, Antenna Systems & Support Equipment Design & Mfr
N.A.I.C.S.: 334220
Michael Drury (Pres)

Subsidiary (Non-US):

Broadcast Microwave Services Europe GmbH (2)
Georg-Ohm-Strasse 2, D-65232, Taunusstein, Germany
Tel.: (49) 6128 7408 200
Web Site: http://www.bms-inc.com
Microwave Radios, Antenna Systems & Support Equipment Mfr
N.A.I.C.S.: 334220

Subsidiary (Domestic):

Hubb Systems LLC. (2)
2021 Challenger Dr, Alameda, CA 94501   (100%)
Tel.: (510) 865-9100
Web Site: http://www.data911.com
Emp.: 200
Computer System Design Police & Fire Department & EMS Customer Services
N.A.I.C.S.: 513210
Jason Wise (Mgr-Product)
Chuck Beck (CEO)

Integrated Microwave Technologies, LLC (1)
101 Bilby Rd Ste 15 Bldg 2, Hackettstown, NJ 07840
Tel.: (908) 853-3700
Web Site: http://www.imt-solutions.com
Radio, Television Broadcasting & Wireless Communications Equipment Mfr
N.A.I.C.S.: 334220

VISTA GOLD CORP.

8310 S Valley Hwy Ste 300, Englewood, CO 80112
Tel.: (720) 981-1185   YT
Web Site: https://www.vistagold.com
Year Founded: 1975
VGZ—(NYSEAMEX)
Rev.: $520,000
Assets: $10,986,000
Liabilities: $957,000
Net Worth: $10,029,000
Earnings: ($4,931,000)
Emp.: 14
Fiscal Year-end: 12/31/22
Gold Ore & Silver Ore Mining
N.A.I.C.S.: 212220
Frederick H. Earnest (Pres & CEO)
Pamela A. Solly (VP-IR)
Brent D. Murdoch (Gen Mgr)

VISTA OUTDOOR INC.

1 Vista Way, Anoka, MN 55303
Tel.: (763) 433-1000   DE
Web Site:
  https://www.vistaoutdoor.com
Year Founded: 2014
VSTO—(NYSE)
Rev.: $3,044,621,000
Assets: $2,396,201,000
Liabilities: $1,271,802,000

Net Worth: $1,124,399,000
Earnings: $473,226,000
Emp.: 6,900
Fiscal Year-end: 03/31/22
Offices of Other Holding Companies
N.A.I.C.S.: 551112
Michael Callahan (Chm)
Jason R. Vanderbrink (Co-CEO)
David Stokoe (VP-Strategic Procurement)
Bob Steelhammer (Chief Digital Officer-E-Information Technology-Commerce,Digital Mktg)
Kelly Reisdorf (Chief Comm & IR Officer & VP)
Eric Nyman (Co-CEO)
Andrew Keegan (CFO)
Jeffrey Ehrich (Gen Counsel & Interim Sec)
Jordan Judd (Pres-Simms Fishing Products)

Subsidiaries:

Bee Stinger, LLC (1)
584 E 1100 S Ste 5, American Fork, UT 84003
Tel.: (800) 551-0541
Web Site: http://www.beestinger.com
Archery Equipment Mfr & Distr
N.A.I.C.S.: 339920

Bell Sports, Inc. (1)
1001 Innovation Rd, Rantoul, IL 61866
Web Site: http://www.bellhelmets.com
Sports Helmets & Accessories Mfr & Whslr
N.A.I.C.S.: 339920
Jessica Klodnicki (Exec VP & Gen Mgr)

Subsidiary (Domestic):

Bell Racing USA, LLC (2)
301 Mercury Dr Bay 8, Champaign, IL 61822
Web Site: http://www.bellracing.com
Automotive Racing Helmets & Accessories Mfr
N.A.I.C.S.: 339920

Bushnell Corporation of Canada (1)
140 Great Gulf Drive Unit B, Vaughan, L4K 5W1, ON, Canada
Tel.: (905) 771-2980
Sports Product Distr
N.A.I.C.S.: 459110

Bushnell Outdoor Products Japan Limited (1)
4F 2-21-2 Yushima, Bunkyo-ku, Tokyo, 113-0034, Japan
Tel.: (81) 358442040
Sports Optic Product Distr
N.A.I.C.S.: 423460

Bushnell Outdoor Products SAS (1)
23 Bis Rue Edouard Nieuport, 92150, Suresnes, France
Tel.: (33) 141449480
Web Site: http://bushnell.eu
Sports Optic Product Mfr & Distr
N.A.I.C.S.: 333310

Bushnell Outdoor Products Spain, S.A.U. (1)
C/ Alava 60-62 6 1, Barcelona, 08005, Spain
Tel.: (34) 934864800
Sports Optic Product Distr
N.A.I.C.S.: 423460

Bushnell Outdoor Products, Inc. (1)
9200 Cody, Overland Park, KS 66214-1734
Tel.: (913) 752-3400
Web Site: https://www.bushnell.com
Emp.: 1,100
Sports Optics & Outdoor Accessories Mfr
N.A.I.C.S.: 333310

Subsidiary (Domestic):

Primos Hunting (2)
604 First St, Flora, MS 39071
Tel.: (601) 879-9323
Web Site: https://www.primos.com
Hunting Product Mfr
N.A.I.C.S.: 339920

Bushnell Performance Optics Asia Limited (1)
Suite 1003B 10/F Skyline Tower 39 Wang Kwong Road, Kowloon Bay, Kowloon, China (Hong Kong)
Tel.: (852) 25463060
Web Site: https://www.bushnell.com.hk
Sunglass Distr
N.A.I.C.S.: 423460

Bushnell Performance Optics Germany GmbH (1)
An Der Alten Spinnerei 1 B, Kolbermoor, 83059, Rosenheim, Germany
Tel.: (49) 8031233480
Sports Optic Product Distr
N.A.I.C.S.: 423460

Bushnell Performance Optics Italy S.r.l. (1)
Corso Roma 13bis/1, 10024, Moncalieri, Italy
Tel.: (39) 0116618583
Sports Optic Product Distr
N.A.I.C.S.: 423460

Bushnell Performance Optics Mexico S.A. de C.V. (1)
Presa Salinillas 370 Piso 10 Colonia Irrigacion Delegacion, Miguel Hidalgo, Mexico, 11500, Mexico
Tel.: (52) 5555574210
Sports Optic Product Distr
N.A.I.C.S.: 423460

Bushnell Performance Optics UK Limited (1)
Unit C83 Barwell Business Park Leatherhead Road, Chessington, KT9 2NY, Surrey, United Kingdom
Tel.: (44) 2083914700
Sports Optic Product Distr
N.A.I.C.S.: 423460

CamelBak Products LLC (1)
2000 S McDowell Ste 200, Petaluma, CA 94954
Web Site: https://www.camelbak.com
Portable Hydration Systems & Backpacks Mfr
N.A.I.C.S.: 339920

Federal Cartridge Company (1)
900 Bob Ehlen Dr, Anoka, MN 55303
Web Site: https://www.federalpremium.com
Emp.: 1,400
Shotshell, Centerfire & Rimfire Cartridges, Ammunition Components & Clay Targets Mfr
N.A.I.C.S.: 332992

Fox Head, Inc. (1)
16752 Armstrong Ave, Irvine, CA 92606-4912
Tel.: (949) 757-9500
Web Site: https://www.foxracing.com
Authentic Motocross Apparel Designer & Distr
N.A.I.C.S.: 315250

Subsidiary (Non-US):

FOX HEAD EUROPE, SL (2)
C/Canudas 13 P E Mas Blau El Prat de Llobregat, 08820, Barcelona, Spain
Tel.: (34) 931458000
Sports Apparel Distr
N.A.I.C.S.: 424350
B. Katie (Country Mgr)

Fox Head Canada, Inc. (2)
58 Aero Dr NE Unit 113, Calgary, T2E 8Z9, AB, Canada
Tel.: (403) 444-1400
Web Site: https://foxracing.ca
Sports Apparel Distr
N.A.I.C.S.: 424350

Subsidiary (Domestic):

Fox Racing U.S.A. Inc. (2)
18400 Sutter Blvd, Morgan Hill, CA 95037-2819
Tel.: (408) 776-8800
Web Site: http://www.foxracing.com
Rev.: $44,971,562
Emp.: 200
Off-Road Sports Apparel Mfr
N.A.I.C.S.: 424350
Marc Jones (Supvr-Compliance)

Giro Sport Design (1)
5550 Scotts Vly Dr, Scotts Valley, CA 95066
Tel.: (831) 461-7500
Web Site: https://www.giro.com
Bicycle Helmets, Apparel & Accessories Whslr
N.A.I.C.S.: 423910
Jim Gentes (Founder)

Gold Tip, LLC (1)
2450 Siempre Viva Ct, San Diego, CA 92154
Web Site: https://www.goldtip.com
Graphite Product Mfr
N.A.I.C.S.: 335991

Logan Outdoor Products, LLC (1)
3985 N 75 W, Hyde Park, UT 84318-4111
Tel.: (435) 752-3922
Sports Product Mfr
N.A.I.C.S.: 339920

Millett Industries (1)
9200 Cody Overland Park, Kansas City, KS 66214-1734
Tel.: (913) 752-3400
Web Site: https://www.millettsights.com
Small Arm Parts Mfr & Distr
N.A.I.C.S.: 332994

Night Optics USA, Inc. (1)
605 Oro Dam Blvd E, Oroville, CA 95965
Tel.: (800) 306-4448
Web Site: http://www.nightoptics.com
Night Vision Optical Device Mfr & Distr
N.A.I.C.S.: 333310

QuietKat, Inc. (1)
215 Broadway St, Eagle, CO 81631
Tel.: (970) 572-8005
Web Site: https://www.quietkat.com
Electric Bikes Whslr
N.A.I.C.S.: 423110

Savage Sports Corporation (1)
100 Springdale Rd, Westfield, MA 01085
Tel.: (413) 568-7001
Web Site: http://www.savagearms.com
Rifles, Shotguns & Accessories Designer & Mfr
N.A.I.C.S.: 332994

Subsidiary (Domestic):

Savage Arms, Inc. (2)
100 Springdale Rd, Westfield, MA 01085
Tel.: (413) 568-7001
Web Site: https://www.savagearms.com
Sporting Firearms & Accessories Mfr
N.A.I.C.S.: 332994

Subsidiary (Non-US):

Savage Arms (Canada) Inc. (3)
248 Water St, PO Box 1240, Lakefield, K0L 2H0, ON, Canada
Tel.: (705) 652-8000
Sporting Rifles & Shotguns Mfr
N.A.I.C.S.: 339920

Subsidiary (Domestic):

Savage Range Systems, Inc. (3)
100 Springdale Rd, Westfield, MA 01085
Tel.: (413) 568-7001
Web Site:
   http://www.savagerangesystems.com
Emp.: 7
Indoor & Outdoor Shooting Ranges Design & Mfr
N.A.I.C.S.: 541490
Albert Kasper (Pres & COO)

Simms Fishing Products Corp. (1)
177 Garden Dr, Bozeman, MT 59718
Tel.: (406) 585-3557
Web Site: https://www.simmsfishing.com
Rev.: $11,000,000
Emp.: 100
Fishing & Outdoor Supplies Mfr & Retailer
N.A.I.C.S.: 423910
K. C. Walsh (Chm)
Diane Bristol (Dir-Mktg & Mgmt)
Weston Fricke (CFO)
Lee Fromson (Exec VP)
Richard Sheahan (CEO)

The River's Edge Outfitters, LLC (1)
3928 US 42, Waynesville, OH 45068
Tel.: (937) 903-6468

Web Site: https://riversedgeoutfitters.com
Travel Arrangement Services
N.A.I.C.S.: 713990

VISTAGEN THERAPEUTICS, INC.
343 Allerton Ave, South San Francisco, CA 94080
Tel.: (650) 577-3600   NV
Web Site: https://www.vistagen.com
Year Founded: 2005
VTGN—(NASDAQ)
Rev.: $1,064,000
Assets: $123,653,000
Liabilities: $9,367,000
Net Worth: $114,286,000
Earnings: ($29,362,000)
Emp.: 39
Fiscal Year-end: 03/31/24
Holding Company; Therapeutic Products Developer & Mfr
N.A.I.C.S.: 551112
Shawn K. Singh (CEO)
Jon S. Saxe (Chm)
Gordon Keller (Co-Founder & Chm)
Ann M. Cunningham (Chief Comml Officer)
Mark Adrian McPartland (Sr VP-IR)
Mark J. Ginski (Sr VP & Head-CMC)
Louis Monti (VP-Translational Medicine)
Joshua Prince (COO)
Reid Adler (Chief Corp Dev Officer & Gen Counsel)
Trisha Fitzmaurice (Sr VP-Human Resources)
Ross A. Baker (VP-Medical Strategy)
Imogene Dunn (VP-Biostatistics)
Jessica R. Haskell (Sec, VP & Assoc Gen Counsel)
Ester Salman (VP-Clinical Res)
Greg Weilersbacher (VP-Quality Assurance)
Allen Cato III (Sr VP-Dev Ops)

Subsidiaries:

Pherin Pharmaceuticals, Inc. (1)
4962 El Camino Real 223, Los Altos, CA 94022
Tel.: (650) 568-1587
Web Site: http://www.pherin.com
Rev.: $5,491,000
Emp.: 27
Pharmaceutical Preparation Mfr
N.A.I.C.S.: 325412
Luis Monti (Exec VP)
Jacobo Zaidenweber (Pres)
Kevin McCarthy (Pres & CEO)

VistaGen Therapeutics, Inc. (1)
343 Allerton Ave, South San Francisco, CA 94080
Tel.: (650) 577-3600
Web Site: http://www.vistagen.com
Therapeutic Products Developer & Mfr
N.A.I.C.S.: 325412

VISTAS MEDIA ACQUISITION COMPANY INC.
30 Wall St 8th Fl, New York, NY 10005
Tel.: (212) 859-3525   DE
Year Founded: 2020
VMACU—(NASDAQ)
Investment Services
N.A.I.C.S.: 523999
F. Jacob Cherian (CEO & Sec)
Nagarajan Venkatesan (CFO)

VISTEON CORPORATION
1 Village Center Dr, Van Buren Township, MI 48111
Tel.: (734) 627-7384   DE
Web Site: https://www.visteon.com
Year Founded: 2000
VC—(NASDAQ)
Rev.: $3,756,000,000
Assets: $2,450,000,000
Liabilities: $1,676,000,000

Net Worth: $774,000,000
Earnings: $124,000,000
Emp.: 10,000
Fiscal Year-end: 12/31/22
Automobile Parts Mfr
N.A.I.C.S.: 336320
Brett D. Pynnonen (Gen Counsel & Sr VP)
Jerome J. Rouquet (CFO & Sr VP)
Qais Sharif (VP-Display Product Line)
Ryan Wentling (Treas & VP-IR)
Kris Doyle (VP-Ops Fin & FP&A)
Sachin S. Lawande (Pres & CEO)

Subsidiaries:

Allgo Embedded Systems Pvt. Ltd. (1)
6 PSS Plaza NAL Wind Tunnel Rd Kaveri Nagar, Murugeshpalya, Bengaluru, Karnataka, Karnataka, India
Tel.: (91) 8043303100
Web Site: http://www.allgosystems.com
Software Development Services
N.A.I.C.S.: 541511
Nirmal Kumar Sancheti (CEO & Mng Dir)
Sivakumar Songappan (COO)

Subsidiary (US):

Allgo Systems, Inc. (2)
32401 W 8 Mile Rd Ste L4, Livonia, MI 48152
Tel.: (512) 988-8885
Software Services
N.A.I.C.S.: 541511

Changchun Visteon FAWAY Automotive Electronics Co., Ltd. (1)
NO 395 Zili Street, Automobile Industrial Development Zone, Changchun, 130011, China
Tel.: (86) 43185124007
Web Site: https://www.en.ccvfae.com
Automobile Parts Mfr
N.A.I.C.S.: 336390

Grupo Visteon, S. de R.L. de C.V. (1)
Sierra Candela 111 Ste 306, Lomas de Chapultepec, Mexico, 11000, DF, Mexico
Tel.: (52) 6144295000
Sales Range: $300-349.9 Million
Automotive Products
N.A.I.C.S.: 336390

Subsidiary (Domestic):

Carplastic S.A. de C.V. (2)
Ave Parque Industrial Monterrey 608, Apodaca, 66600, Mexico   (100%)
Tel.: (52) 8183692598
Web Site: https://vlocationdb.visteon.com
Sales Range: $350-399.9 Million
Emp.: 1,100
Motor Vehicle Parts Accessories
N.A.I.C.S.: 336340

Visteon Amazonas Ltda. (1)
Av Autaz Mirim 1030 Distrito Industrial, Manaus, 69075-155, AM, Brazil
Tel.: (55) 9236167000
Web Site: https://www.visteon.com
Electronic Audio & Video Equipment Mfr
N.A.I.C.S.: 334310

Visteon Asia Pacific, Inc. (1)
448 Hongcao Road 9th Floor, Modern Lodistics Bldg, Xuhui District, Shanghai, 200233, China
Tel.: (86) 2161929900
Sales Range: $75-99.9 Million
Emp.: 200
Automotive Products
N.A.I.C.S.: 336390

Visteon Automotive Electronics (Thailand) Limited (1)
500/123 Moo 3 Tombol Tasit, Amphur Pluakdeang, Rayong, 21140, Thailand
Tel.: (66) 38863300
Automobile Parts Mfr
N.A.I.C.S.: 336390

Visteon Electronics Bulgaria EOOD (1)
Capital Fort Building 90 Tsarigradsko Shosse Blvd, Sofia, Bulgaria

Visteon Corporation—(Continued)

Tel.: (359) 29306421
Web Site: https://www.visteon.bg
Automobile Parts Distr
N.A.I.C.S.: 423120

Visteon Electronics Korea Ltd. **(1)**
2-5 Yonggung Ri Sinam Myeon, Yesan,
340864, Chungchongnam Do, Korea
(South)
Tel.: (82) 413316791
Motor Vehicle Parts Mfr
N.A.I.C.S.: 336390

Visteon European Holdings, Inc. **(1)**
1 Village Center Dr, Van Buren Township,
MI 48111
Tel.: (734) 710-5000
Web Site: http://www.visteon.com
Sales Range: $250-299.9 Million
Holding Company
N.A.I.C.S.: 551112

Subsidiary (Non-US):

**Visteon Engineering Services
Limited** **(2)**
Springfield Lyons Approach, Chelmsford,
CM2 5LB, Essex, United Kingdom
Tel.: (44) 1245395000
Web Site: https://www.visteon.com
Sales Range: $300-349.9 Million
Emp.: 200
Innovation Center, Corporate Office, Customer Service Center & Administrative Support
N.A.I.C.S.: 551114
Bob Swinston (Mng Dir)

Visteon Holdings France SAS **(2)**
20 avenue Andre Prothin, La Defense,
92927, Paris, Cedex, France
Tel.: (33) 1 5813 6505
Holding Company
N.A.I.C.S.: 551112

Subsidiary (Domestic):

**Visteon Software Technologies
SAS** **(3)**
1880 Route Des Cretes, PO Box 308,
06906, Sophia-Antipolis, France
Tel.: (33) 492952600
Sales Range: $10-24.9 Million
Emp.: 30
Motor Vehicle Component Services
N.A.I.C.S.: 513210
Ciavaldini Joseph (Mgr)

Subsidiary (Non-US):

Visteon Holdings GmbH **(2)**
Visteonnstrasse 4-10, 50170, Kerpen, Germany
Tel.: (49) 22735950
Holding Companies
N.A.I.C.S.: 551112

Visteon-Autopal s.r.o. **(2)**
Sachetni 1540, 735 32, Rychvald, Czech
Republic
Tel.: (420) 596588111
Sales Range: $300-349.9 Million
Automotive Lighting Mfr
N.A.I.C.S.: 336390

Subsidiary (Non-US):

Visteon Portuguesa, Ltd. **(3)**
Estrada Nacional No 252 Km 12 Parque
Industrial das Carrasca, 2951-503, Palmela,
Portugal
Tel.: (351) 212339269
Motor Vehicle Instruments Mfr
N.A.I.C.S.: 336390

Visteon S.A. **(1)**
Otto Krause Plant Sullivan 3131 Malvinas
Argentinas, Buenos Aires, B1667 ACI, Argentina
Tel.: (54) 3327447440
Web Site: https://vlocationdb.visteon.com
Sales Range: $50-74.9 Million
Emp.: 150
Instrument Panel Mfr
N.A.I.C.S.: 336390

VISTRA CORP.
6555 Sierra Dr, Irving, TX 75039

Tel.: (214) 812-4600 DE
Web Site: https://www.vistracorp.com
Year Founded: 1882
VST—(NYSE)
Rev.: $14,779,000,000
Assets: $5,633,000,000
Liabilities: $311,000,000
Net Worth: $5,322,000,000
Earnings: $1,343,000,000
Emp.: 4,870
Fiscal Year-end: 12/31/23
Electricity Distribution Services
N.A.I.C.S.: 221122
James A. Burke (Pres & CEO)
Margaret M. Montemayor (Chief
Acctg Officer, Sr VP & Controller)
James A. Burke (Pres & CEO)
Carrie Lee Kirby (Chief Admin Officer
& Exec VP)
Stephanie Zapata Moore (Gen Counsel & Exec VP)
Sano Blocker (Sr VP-Govt Affairs)
Scott A. Hudson (Pres-Vistra Retail)
Kristopher E. Moldovan (CFO & Exec
VP)
Jonathan Ferrara (Mng Dir-Channel
Islands)
Stacey Dore (Chief Strategy Officer)
Tom Farrah (CIO)
Gabriel V. Vazquez (VP & Assoc Gen
Counsel-Ops)

Subsidiaries:

Ambit Energy Holdings, LLC **(1)**
1801 N Lamar St Ste 200, Dallas, TX
75202-1726
Web Site: http://www.ambitenergy.com
Sales Range: $300-349.9 Million
Emp.: 171
Holding Company; Energy Services
N.A.I.C.S.: 551112
Chris Chambless (Co-Founder)
Jere W. Thompson Jr. (Co-Founder)

Dynegy, Inc. **(1)**
601 Travis St Ste 1400, Houston, TX 77002
Tel.: (713) 507-6400
Web Site: http://www.dynegy.com
Sales Range: $1-4.9 Billion
Power Plant Operation & Management Services
N.A.I.C.S.: 221122
Sheree M. Petrone (Executives, Bd of Dirs)
Lauren Matson (Mgr-Channel Bus Dev)
Kym King (Dir-HR Bus Partner)

Subsidiary (Domestic):

**Dynegy Marketing and Trade,
LLC** **(2)**
601 Travis St Ste 1400, Houston, TX 77002
Tel.: (713) 507-6400
Power Generation; Power & Natural Gas
Marketing & Trading Services
N.A.I.C.S.: 221122

**Dynegy Midwest Generation,
LLC** **(2)**
10901 Baldwin Rd, Baldwin, IL 62217
Tel.: (618) 785-2294
Electronic Services
N.A.I.C.S.: 221118

Illinova Corporation **(2)**
601 Travis St Ste 1400, Houston, TX 77002
Tel.: (713) 507-6400
Holding Company; Electric Power Distr
N.A.I.C.S.: 551112

Luminant Energy Company, LLC **(1)**
6555 Sierra Dr, Irving, TX 75039
Tel.: (214) 812-4600
Web Site: http://www.luminant.com
Sales Range: $75-99.9 Million
Coal & Fuel Services
N.A.I.C.S.: 213113
Bill Rankin (Sls Mgr)

**TXU Energy Retail Company
LLC** **(1)**
1601 Bryan St, Dallas, TX 75201
Tel.: (214) 812-4600
Web Site: http://www.txuenergy.com
Sales Range: $10-24.9 Million
Emp.: 72
Electricity

N.A.I.C.S.: 221122
Gabe Castro (VP-Bus Markets)
Scott A. Hudson (Pres)

TriEagle Energy LP **(1)**
PO Box 974655, Dallas, TX 75397-4655
Web Site: https://www.trieagleenergy.com
Electric Power Distribution Services
N.A.I.C.S.: 221122

Viridian Energy, LLC **(1)**
6555 Sierra Dr, Irving, TX 75039
Web Site: https://www.viridian.com
Electric Power Distribution Services
N.A.I.C.S.: 221122

VITA MOBILE SYSTEMS, INC.
2640 Main St, Irvine, CA 92614
Tel.: (949) 864-6902 FL
Year Founded: 1995
VMSI—(OTCIQ)
Software Development Services
N.A.I.C.S.: 541511
Colin Walker (CEO)
Jermaine Patricia Walker (COO)
Alexander Prescot Walker (Exec Dir-Strategic Planning)
Thaddeus Dominic Patrice Jr. (Chief
Compliance Officer)
Philip Daniel Walker (CMO)
Rosita Sharon Green (CIO)
Martin Wade III (Chm & CFO)

VITAL ENERGY, INC.
521 E 2nd St Ste 1000, Tulsa, OK
74120
Tel.: (918) 513-4570 DE
Web Site:
   https://www.vitalenergy.com
VTLE—(NYSE)
Rev.: $1,394,075,000
Assets: $2,551,824,000
Liabilities: $2,038,044,000
Net Worth: $513,780,000
Earnings: $145,008,000
Emp.: 273
Fiscal Year-end: 12/31/21
Crude Petroleum Extraction Services
N.A.I.C.S.: 211120
Randy A. Foutch (Founder)
Stephen L. Faulkner Jr. (Chief Acctg
Officer & VP)
Mark D. Denny (Gen Counsel, Sec &
Sr VP)
Ronald L. Hagood (VP-IR)
Jason Pigott (Pres & CEO)
Jessica R. Wren (Sr Dir Fin Acctg &
SEC Reporting)
Katie Hill (COO & Sr VP)
Kathryn A. Hill (COO & Sr VP)
Bryan J. Lemmerman (CFO & Sr VP)

Subsidiaries:

Laredo Midstream Services, LLC **(1)**
15 W 6th St Ste 900, Tulsa, OK 74119
Tel.: (918) 513-4570
Web Site: http://www.laredopetroleum.com
Oil & Gas Field Operator
N.A.I.C.S.: 213112
Randy A. Foutch (CEO)

VITAL FARMS, INC
3601 S Congress Ave Ste C100, Austin, TX 78704
Tel.: (512) 326-2533
Web Site: https://www.vitalfarms.com
Year Founded: 2007
VITL—(NASDAQ)
Rev.: $471,857,000
Assets: $275,178,000
Liabilities: $82,501,000
Net Worth: $192,677,000
Earnings: $25,566,000
Emp.: 215
Fiscal Year-end: 12/31/23
Eggs & Poultry
N.A.I.C.S.: 112310
Matthew O'Hayer (Founder & Chm)
Russell Diez-Canseco (Pres & CEO)

Peter Pappas (Chief Sls Officer)
Matt Siler (VP-IR)
Joanne Bal (Gen Counsel, Sec &
Head-Environmental, Social & Governance)
Thilo Wrede (CFO & Principal Acctg
Officer)
Kathryn McKeon (CMO)

Subsidiaries:

Vital Farms of Missouri, LLC **(1)**
2007 N Alliance Ave, Springfield, MO 65803
Tel.: (737) 500-5002
Pasture-Raised Food Mfr & Distr
N.A.I.C.S.: 311999

VITAL HUMAN CAPITAL, INC.
501 Brickell Key Dr Ste 300, Miami,
FL 33135-3250 DE
Year Founded: 2021
FMGU—(NYSE)
Investment Services
N.A.I.C.S.: 523999
Scott W. Absher (Chm & CEO)
Domonic J. Carney (CFO & Treas)
Steven Sims (COO)
Robert S. Gans (Gen Counsel & Sec)

VITALIBIS, INC.
3960 Howard Hughes Pkwy Ste 500,
Las Vegas, NV 89169
Tel.: (702) 944-9620 NV
Web Site: http://www.vitalibis.com
Year Founded: 2014
VCBD—(OTCIQ)
Rev.: $303,197
Assets: $514,802
Liabilities: $1,710,195
Net Worth: ($1,195,393)
Earnings: ($6,845,944)
Fiscal Year-end: 12/31/19
Full Spectrum CBD (Cannabidiol) Oil
& Hemp Seed Oil Skin Care & Body
Care Products Mfr
N.A.I.C.S.: 325620
Steven Raack (Chm, Pres & CEO)
Thomas Raack (CFO, COO, Treas &
Sec)

VITAMIN BLUE, INC.
1005 W 18th St, Costa Mesa, CA
92627
Tel.: (949) 645-4592 DE
Web Site:
   https://www.vitaminblue.com
Year Founded: 1999
VTMB—(OTCIQ)
Apparel Accessories & Other Apparel
Manufacturing
N.A.I.C.S.: 315990
Frank D. Ornelas (Pres & Treas)
Veronica C. Ornelas (Sec & VP)

VITANA-X, INC.
515 E Las Olas Blvd Ste 120, Fort
Lauderdale, FL 33301
Tel.: (305) 714-9397 FL
Web Site: http://www.vitanax.net
Year Founded: 2014
VITX—(OTCIQ)
Rev.: $131,000
Assets: $143,000
Liabilities: $997,000
Net Worth: ($854,000)
Earnings: ($3,765,000)
Fiscal Year-end: 07/31/20
Online Financial Transaction Processing Services
N.A.I.C.S.: 522320
Alois Anichhofer (CEO)

**VITASPRING BIOMEDICAL CO.
LTD.**
400 Spectrum Ctr Dr Ste 1620, Irvine, CA 92618

Tel.: (949) 202-9235 NV
Web Site:
https://www.vitaspringbio.com
Year Founded: 2016
VSBC—(OTCIQ)
Rev.: $5,613,200
Assets: $3,604,073
Liabilities: $2,026,534
Net Worth: $1,577,539
Earnings: $1,264,002
Emp.: 1
Fiscal Year-end: 01/31/22
Leather Product Mfr
N.A.I.C.S.: 316990
Pao-Chi Chu *(Chm)*
Cheng-Hsiang Kao *(CEO & Sec)*
Jer-Li Lin *(Chief Technical Officer)*

VITESSE ENERGY, INC.
9200 E Mineral Ave Ste 200, Centennial, CO 80112
Tel.: (720) 361-2500 DE
Web Site: https://vitesse-vts.com
Year Founded: 2022
VTS—(NYSE)
Oil & Gas Exploration
N.A.I.C.S.: 211130

VIVA ENTERTAINMENT GROUP INC.
121 Alhambra Plz Ste 1500, Coral Gables, FL 33134
Tel.: (347) 681-1668 NV
Web Site: https://www.vivalivetv.com
OTTV—(OTCIQ)
Sales Range: Less than $1 Million
Entertainment Services
N.A.I.C.S.: 512120
Johnny Falcones *(CEO)*
John Sepulveda *(VP)*

VIVAKOR, INC.
4101 N Thanksgiving Way Ste 150, Lehi, UT 84043
Tel.: (949) 281-2606 NV
Web Site: https://www.vivakor.com
VIVK—(NASDAQ)
Rev.: $1,088,428
Assets: $47,345,291
Liabilities: $20,191,112
Net Worth: $27,154,179
Earnings: ($5,484,171)
Emp.: 25
Fiscal Year-end: 12/31/21
Offices of Other Holding Companies
N.A.I.C.S.: 551112
Pablo Penaloza *(Pres-Acq)*

Subsidiaries:

Well-Med Global LLC (1)
1900 S State College Blvd Ste 250, Anaheim, CA 92806
Web Site: http://www.wellmedglobal.com
Sales Range: Less than $1 Million
Regenerative Skin Care Products Distr
N.A.I.C.S.: 424210
Tom Lee *(Co-Founder & CEO)*
Ahmed Al-Qahtani *(Co-Founder & Chief Scientific Officer)*
John Crowder *(VP-Ops)*
Jake Nguyen *(CFO)*
Michelle S. Thompson *(VP-Bus Dev & Mktg)*
James Lac *(CTO)*

VIVANI MEDICAL, INC.
1350 S Loop Rd, Alameda, CA 94502
Tel.: (415) 506-8462 CA
Web Site: https://www.vivani.com
Year Founded: 1998
VANI—(NASDAQ)
Rev.: $475,000
Assets: $51,130,000
Liabilities: $6,822,000
Net Worth: $44,308,000
Earnings: ($13,889,000)
Emp.: 40
Fiscal Year-end: 12/31/22

Implantable Visual Prosthetics Mfr
N.A.I.C.S.: 339112
Brigid A. Makes *(CFO)*
Gregg G. Williams *(Chm)*

VIVEON HEALTH ACQUISITION CORP.
3480 Peachtree Rd NE 2nd Fl Ste 112, Atlanta, GA 30326
Tel.: (404) 579-7978 DE
Year Founded: 2020
VHAQ—(NYSEAMEX)
Rev.: $1,945,823
Assets: $53,923,227
Liabilities: $70,003,543
Net Worth: ($16,080,316)
Earnings: ($486,788)
Emp.: 2
Fiscal Year-end: 12/31/22
Investment Services
N.A.I.C.S.: 523999
Jagi Gill *(Chm, Pres & CEO)*
Rom Papadopoulos *(Vice Chm, CFO, Treas & Sec)*

VIVEVE MEDICAL INC.
345 Inverness Dr S Bldg B Ste 250, Englewood, CO 80112
Tel.: (408) 530-1900 YT
Web Site: https://www.viveve.com
VIVE—(NASDAQ)
Rev.: $6,426,000
Assets: $25,913,000
Liabilities: $10,847,000
Net Worth: $15,066,000
Earnings: ($26,718,000)
Emp.: 47
Fiscal Year-end: 12/31/21
Medical Device Mfr
N.A.I.C.S.: 339112
Steven L. Basta *(Chm)*

Subsidiaries:

Viveve, Inc. (1)
150 Commercial St, Sunnyvale, CA 94086 (100%)
Tel.: (408) 530-1900
Web Site: http://www.viveve.com
Emp.: 15
Health Care Equipment Whslr
N.A.I.C.S.: 423490
Scott C. Durbin *(CEO)*

VIVIC CORP.
187 E Warm Spgs Rd, Las Vegas, NV 89119
Tel.: (702) 899-0818 NV
Year Founded: 2017
VIVC—(OTCQB)
Rev.: $5,950,692
Assets: $4,866,059
Liabilities: $2,272,892
Net Worth: $2,593,167
Earnings: $2,850,514
Emp.: 14
Fiscal Year-end: 06/30/24
Travel Tour Operator
N.A.I.C.S.: 561520
Kun-Teng Liao *(Sec)*
Shang-Chiai Kung *(Chm, Pres, CEO, CFO, Gen Counsel & Sec)*

VIVID SEATS, INC.
24 E Washington St Fl 9, Chicago, IL 60602
Tel.: (312) 291-9966 DE
Web Site: https://www.vividseats.com
Year Founded: 2001
SEAT—(NASDAQ)
Rev.: $600,274,000
Assets: $1,151,431,000
Liabilities: $1,534,129,000
Net Worth: ($382,698,000)
Earnings: $70,779,000
Emp.: 575
Fiscal Year-end: 12/31/22
Ticket Resale Services

N.A.I.C.S.: 561599
Stan Chia *(CEO)*
Lawrence Fey *(CFO)*
Riva Bakal *(Chief Strategy Officer & Chief Product Officer)*
Stefano Langenbacher *(CTO)*
Geoff Lester *(Chief Comml Officer)*
Sarah Doll *(Chief People Officer)*
Emily Epstein *(Gen Counsel)*
David Donnini *(Chm)*
Stanley Chia *(CEO)*

Subsidiaries:

Vegas.com, LLC (1)
7150 S Tenaya Way, Las Vegas, NV 89113
Tel.: (702) 992-7990
Web Site: https://www.vegas.com
Leisure; Travel & Tourism
N.A.I.C.S.: 561599

VIVIDION THERAPEUTICS, INC.
5820 Nancy Ridge Dr, San Diego, CA 92121
Tel.: (858) 345-4690 DE
Web Site: http://www.vividion.com
Year Founded: 2013
VVID—(NASDAQ)
Rev.: $34,393,000
Assets: $242,635,000
Liabilities: $304,103,000
Net Worth: ($61,468,000)
Earnings: $25,456,000)
Emp.: 108
Fiscal Year-end: 12/31/20
Biotechnology Research & Development Services
N.A.I.C.S.: 541714
tives)
Aleksandra K. Rizo *(Pres)*
Jeffrey Hatfield *(CEO)*
Patty Allen *(CFO)*
Larry Burgess *(Head-Chemistry)*
Todd Kinsella *(Head-Biology)*
Lisa Percival *(Head-Regulatory)*
Jean Bemis *(VP-Program Mgmt)*
Matt Patricelli *(Chief Scientific Officer)*
Dean Stamos *(Head-Chemistry Innovation)*
Brian Koh *(Head-Translational Sciences & Clinical Dev)*
Xiaohu Deng *(Head-Technical Ops)*
Gabe Simon *(Head-Proteomics Platform)*
Alexis McWilliams *(Dir-HR)*
Benjamin F. Cravatt *(Founder)*
Jenna Goldberg *(Chief Medical Officer)*

VIVOS THERAPEUTICS, INC.
7921 Spark Plz Ste 210, Littleton, CO 80120
Tel.: (720) 399-9322 DE
Web Site: https://www.vivos.com
Year Founded: 2016
VVOS—(NASDAQ)
Rev.: $16,024,000
Assets: $13,720,000
Liabilities: $8,919,000
Net Worth: $4,801,000
Earnings: ($23,845,000)
Emp.: 154
Fiscal Year-end: 12/31/22
Research & Development in Biotechnology (except Nanobiotechnology)
N.A.I.C.S.: 541714

VIVOS, INC.
N288 1030 N Center Pkwy, Kennewick, WA 99336
Tel.: (509) 736-4000 DE
Web Site: https://www.radiogel.com
Year Founded: 1994
RDGL—(OTCQB)
Rev.: $14,887
Assets: $1,634,298
Liabilities: $166,915

Net Worth: $1,467,383
Earnings: ($2,527,766)
Emp.: 1
Fiscal Year-end: 12/31/21
All Other Miscellaneous Chemical Product & Preparation Manufacturing
N.A.I.C.S.: 325998
Carlton M. Cadwell *(Chm & Sec)*
Michael K. Korenko *(Pres & CEO)*
Michael Pollack *(CFO)*

VIVUS, INC.
900 E Hamilton Ave Ste 550, Campbell, CA 95008
Tel.: (650) 934-5200 DE
Web Site: http://www.vivus.com
Year Founded: 1991
VVUS—(NASDAQ)
Rev.: $69,760,000
Assets: $218,308,000
Liabilities: $287,532,000
Net Worth: ($69,224,000)
Earnings: ($31,503,000)
Emp.: 59
Fiscal Year-end: 12/31/19
Erectile & Sexual Dysfunction Pharmaceutical Products Developer & Mfr
N.A.I.C.S.: 325412
Santosh T. Varghese *(Chief Medical Officer & Sr VP)*
Mark K. Oki *(CFO, Chief Acctg Officer & Sr VP)*
Deborah Larsen *(Chief Strategy Officer)*
Ted Broman *(VP-Chemistry, Mfg & Control)*
Sandra E. Wells *(VP-Patents & Asst Gen Counsel)*
John P. Amos *(CEO)*
Tracy Guo *(VP-Fin)*

VIZIO HOLDING CORP.
39 Tesla, Irvine, CA 92618
Tel.: (949) 428-2525 DE
Web Site: https://www.vizio.com
Year Founded: 2015
VZIO—(NYSE)
Rev.: $1,862,800,000
Assets: $915,700,000
Liabilities: $542,000,000
Net Worth: $373,700,000
Earnings: ($400,000)
Emp.: 900
Fiscal Year-end: 12/31/22
Holding Company; Smart Flat-Screen Television Mfr & Whslr
N.A.I.C.S.: 551112
William W. Wang *(Co-Founder, Chm & CEO)*
Ben Wong *(Pres & COO)*
Adam Townsend *(CFO)*
Michael O'Donnell *(Chief Revenue Officer & Chief Strategic Growth Officer)*

Subsidiaries:

VIZIO, Inc. (1)
39 Tesla, Irvine, CA 92618
Tel.: (949) 428-2525
Web Site: https://www.vizio.com
Sales Range: $1-4.9 Billion
Smart Flat-Panel Television Mfr & Whslr
N.A.I.C.S.: 334310
William W. Wang *(Chm & CEO)*

VMG CONSUMER ACQUISITION CORP.
39 Mesa St Ste 310, San Francisco, CA 94129
Tel.: (415) 632-4200 DE
Web Site: https://www.vmgspac.com
Year Founded: 2021

VMG Consumer Acquisition Corp.—(Continued)

VMGA—(NASDAQ)
Assets: $236,503,886
Liabilities: $243,554,748
Net Worth: ($7,050,862)
Earnings: ($634,686)
Emp.: 2
Fiscal Year-end: 09/30/22
Investment Services
N.A.I.C.S.: 523999
Aarti Kapoor (CEO)
Angad S. Hira (CFO & Sec)
Michael Mauze (Chm)

VNUE, INC.
104 W 29th St 11th Fl, New York, NY
10001
Tel.: (857) 777-6190   NV
Web Site: https://www.vnue.com
Year Founded: 2006
VNUE—(OTCIQ)
Rev.: $529,439
Assets: $25,430
Liabilities: $6,607,436
Net Worth: ($6,582,006)
Earnings: ($1,136,776)
Emp.: 1
Fiscal Year-end: 12/31/23
Metal Mining Services
N.A.I.C.S.: 212290
Tony Cardenas-Montana (Chief Creative Officer & CTO)
Louis Mann (Co-Founder & Exec VP)
M. Zach Bair (Chm & CEO)

Subsidiaries:

Stage It Corp.   (1)
1617 Cosmo St Ste 403, Hollywood, CA
90028
Tel.: (323) 461-8200
Web Site: http://www.stageit.com
Promoters of Performing Arts, Sports &
Similar Events with Facilities
N.A.I.C.S.: 711310
Evan Lowenstein (Founder & Chm)
Stephen White (CEO)
Vadim Brenner (Chief Product Officer)

VOC ENERGY TRUST
601 Travis St 16th Fl, Houston, TX
77002
Tel.: (713) 483-6020   DE
Web Site: https://voc.q4web.com
Year Founded: 2010
VOC—(NYSE)
Rev.: $23,594,050
Assets: $15,048,316
Net Worth: $15,048,316
Earnings: $21,675,000
Fiscal Year-end: 12/31/22
Oil & Gas Investment Services
N.A.I.C.S.: 523999
Elaina C. Rodgers (VP)

VOCODIA HOLDINGS CORP.
36401 Congress Ave Ste 160, Boca
Raton, FL 33487
Tel.: (561) 484-5234   WY
Web Site: https://www.vocodia.com
Year Founded: 2021
VHAI—(BZX)
Rev.: $256,385
Assets: $4,459,346
Liabilities: $8,126,916
Net Worth: ($3,667,570)
Earnings: ($8,711,203)
Emp.: 13
Fiscal Year-end: 12/31/23
Software Development Services
N.A.I.C.S.: 541511

VODKA BRANDS CORP.
554 33rd St, Pittsburgh, PA 15201
Tel.: (412) 681-7777   PA
Web Site:
  http://www.bluediamondvodka.com
Year Founded: 2014

VDKB—(OTCIQ)
Sales Range: Less than $1 Million
Emp.: 92
Vodka Mfr & Distr
N.A.I.C.S.: 312140
Mark Lucero (Pres & CEO)
John J. Hadgkiss (Sec)

VOICE ASSIST, INC.
8465 W Sahara AVE Ste 111-813,
Las Vegas, NV 89117
Tel.: (775) 261-1999   NV
Web Site: http://www.voiceassist.com
Year Founded: 2008
VSST—(OTCIQ)
Sales Range: Less than $1 Million
Emp.: 16
Speech Communication Product Mfr
N.A.I.C.S.: 334220
Michael D. Metcalf (Chm & Interim
CEO)

VOIP-PAL.COM INC.
7215 Bosque Blvd Ste 102, Waco,
TX 76710
Tel.: (954) 495-4600   NV
Web Site: https://www.voip-pal.com
Year Founded: 1997
VPLM—(OTCQB)
Assets: $2,488,454
Liabilities: $61,762
Net Worth: $2,426,692
Earnings: ($23,109,009)
Emp.: 2
Fiscal Year-end: 09/30/23
Telecommunication Servicesb
N.A.I.C.S.: 517111
Magdi Emil Malak (Pres & CEO)
Pentti Huttunen (Engr)
Alex Krapyvny (Engr)
Kevin Williams (CFO)

VOLATO GROUP, INC.
1954 Airport Rd Ste 124, Chamblee,
GA 30341   DE
Web Site: https://flyvolato.com
Year Founded: 2021
SOAR—(NYSEAMEX)
Rev.: $73,338,000
Assets: $71,712,000
Liabilities: $56,961,000
Net Worth: $14,751,000
Earnings: ($52,822,000)
Emp.: 229
Fiscal Year-end: 12/31/23
Aircraft Management Services
N.A.I.C.S.: 488119

VOLCON, INC.
3267 Bee Caves Rd Ste 107 322,
Austin, TX 78746
Tel.: (512) 400-4271   DE
Web Site: https://www.volcon.com
Year Founded: 2020
VLCN—(NASDAQ)
Rev.: $4,546,686
Assets: $22,725,613
Liabilities: $22,090,600
Net Worth: $635,013
Earnings: ($34,235,405)
Emp.: 53
Fiscal Year-end: 12/31/22
Electric Vehicle Mfr
N.A.I.C.S.: 336320
Greg Endo (CFO)
Dave McMahon (Mgr-Channel Mktg)
Melissa Coffey (VP-Global Revenue
& Bus Dev)
John Kim (Pres & CEO)
Christian Okonsky (Co-Founder)

VOLITIONRX LIMITED
1489 W Warm Springs Rd Ste 110,
Henderson, NV 89014
Tel.: (646) 650-1351   DE
Web Site: https://www.volition.com

VNRX—(NYSEAMEX)
Rev.: $306,392
Assets: $18,295,054
Liabilities: $21,422,016
Net Worth: ($3,126,962)
Earnings: ($30,268,793)
Emp.: 104
Fiscal Year-end: 12/31/22
Life Science Research & Development
N.A.I.C.S.: 541715
Cameron Reynolds (Pres & CEO)
Gaetan Michel (COO)
Rodney Gerard Rootsaert (Sec)
Jacob Micallef (Chief Scientific Officer)
Jasmine Kway (CEO-Singapore Volition)
Louise Batchelor (Chief Mktg &
Comm Officer)
Terig Hughes (CFO & Treas)
Gael Forterre (Chief Comml Officer)
Nick Plummer (Gen Counsel)

Subsidiaries:

Belgian Volition SA   (1)
22 Rue Phocas Lejeune Parc Scientifique
Crealys, 5032, Gembloux, Belgium
Tel.: (32) 81724129
Pharmaceuticals Product Mfr
N.A.I.C.S.: 327910

VONTIER CORPORATION
5438 Wade Park Blvd Ste 600, Raleigh, NC 27607
Tel.: (984) 275-6000   DE
Web Site: https://www.vontier.com
Year Founded: 2019
VNT—(NYSE)
Rev.: $3,095,200,000
Assets: $4,294,000,000
Liabilities: $3,398,400,000
Net Worth: $895,600,000
Earnings: $376,900,000
Emp.: 8,000
Fiscal Year-end: 12/31/23
Mobility Technologies & Software Mfr
N.A.I.C.S.: 334514
Mark D. Morelli (Pres & CEO)
Anshooman Aga (CFO & Sr VP)
Roopa Unnikrishnan (Chief Strategy
Officer)
Katie Rowen (Gen Counsel & Sr VP)
Sarah Miller (CIO)
Elizabeth Cheever (VP-Corp Dev)
Nicole Rennalls (Pres-Traffic
Technologies-Global)
Lisa Curran (VP-IR)
Hani Joakim (CTO)
Ryan Edelman (VP-IR)
Paul V. Shimp (Chief Acctg Officer &
VP)
Mike Dwyer (Pres-Matco Tools)
Martin Hanna (VP-Comm)

Subsidiaries:

AFS Forecourt Solutions Proprietary
Limited   (1)
20 Zulberg Close, 2198, Johannesburg,
Gauteng, South Africa
Tel.: (27) 118563600
Professional Instrumentation Mfr
N.A.I.C.S.: 334513

ANGI Energy Systems, Inc.   (1)
305 W Delavan Dr, Janesville, WI 53546
Tel.: (608) 563-2800
Web Site: https://www.angienergy.com
Engineered Compression Packages Designer & Mfr
N.A.I.C.S.: 333912

Beacon Mobile, LLC   (1)
3525 Del Mar Heights Rd Ste 981, San Diego, CA 92130
Web Site: https://www.beaconmobile.com
Software Development Services
N.A.I.C.S.: 541511

FAFNIR GmbH   (1)

Schnackenburgallee 149 c, 22525, Hamburg, Germany
Tel.: (49) 403982070
Web Site: https://www.fafnir.com
Sensor Systems Mfr
N.A.I.C.S.: 334515
Thomas Schneider (Product Mgr)
Jan-hendrik Pein (Product Mgr)
Jurgen Swarat (Product Mgr)
Michael Brandenburg (Mgr-Sls-Process &
Laboratory Tech)
Michael von Wurzen (Sls Mgr)
Susanna Thomas (Project Mgr-Sls)

Gilbarco Inc.   (1)
7300 W Friendly Ave, Greensboro, NC
27410
Tel.: (336) 547-5000
Web Site: https://www.gilbarco.com
Gas Pumps Mfr
N.A.I.C.S.: 333914
Karthik Ganapathi (Pres-Retail Solutions)
Dave Coombe (Pres)
Mark Williams (Pres)

Subsidiary (Non-US):

DOMS ApS   (2)
Formervangen 28, 2600, Glostrup, Denmark
Tel.: (45) 43299490
Web Site: https://www.doms.com
Medicinal Product Mfr
N.A.I.C.S.: 339112

Gilbarco Acis Kft.   (2)
Gyar u 2, Budaors, 2040, Hungary
Tel.: (36) 23503960
Web Site: http://www.gilbarco.com
Sales Range: $75-99.9 Million
Emp.: 120
Fuel Station Equipment & Maintenance
Services
N.A.I.C.S.: 423850

Subsidiary (Non-US):

Gilbarco Acis SRL   (3)
Str Gabor Aron Nr 20 Jud Harghita, Vlahita,
535800, Romania
Tel.: (40) 266246154
Web Site: http://www.gilbarco.com
Fuel Station Equipment & Maintenance
Services
N.A.I.C.S.: 423850

Subsidiary (Non-US):

Gilbarco Australia Pty Ltd.   (2)
Dexus Estate Block L 391 Park Road, Regents Park, 2143, NSW, Australia
Tel.: (61) 287377777
Web Site: http://www.gilbarco.com.au
Electronic Parts & Equipment Whclr
N.A.I.C.S.: 423690

Subsidiary (Domestic):

Gilbarco queensland Pty. Ltd.   (3)
Unit 2 29 Smallwood Place, Murarrie, 4172,
QLD, Australia
Tel.: (61) 732739300
Fuel Product Mfr & Distr
N.A.I.C.S.: 324199

Subsidiary (Non-US):

Gilbarco Autotank AS   (2)
Floisbonnveien 5, 1412, Sofiemyr, Viken,
Norway
Tel.: (47) 66815400
Web Site: http://www.gilbarco.com
Fuel Supply Equipment Installation Services
N.A.I.C.S.: 811310

Gilbarco China Co. Ltd   (2)
Room 1202 Zhaowei Building No 14 Jiuxianqiao Road, Chaoyang District, Beijing,
100015, China
Tel.: (86) 1064331676
Web Site: http://www.gilbarco.cn
Petroleum Equipment Mfr
N.A.I.C.S.: 324199

Gilbarco GmbH & Co. KG   (2)
Ferdinand-Henze-Strasse 9, 33154,
Salzkotten, Germany
Tel.: (49) 5258130
Web Site: http://www.gilbarco.com
Service Station Equipment Mfr & Distr
N.A.I.C.S.: 333914

Gilbarco Italia S.r.l. **(2)**
Via De Cattani 220/G, 50145, Florence, Italy
Tel.: (39) 05530941
Web Site: https://www.gilbarco.it
Fuel Pump Distr
N.A.I.C.S.: 423120

Gilbarco Latin America Andina Ltda. **(2)**
Av El Roble 375 Modulo H Lote Industrial Valle Grande, Comuna la Pampa Region Metropolitana, Lampa, Metropolitana, Chile
Tel.: (56) 27959600
Web Site: https://www.gilbarco.com
Emp.: 180
Petrol Equipment Mfr
N.A.I.C.S.: 333914

Gilbarco Latin America SRL **(2)**
Congreso 3450 C1430AZD Capital Federal, Buenos Aires, Argentina
Tel.: (54) 1151675600
Petrol Equipment Mfr
N.A.I.C.S.: 333914

Gilbarco Veeder Root S.R.L. **(2)**
Str Daniel Danielopolu No 4-6, 014134, Bucharest, Romania
Tel.: (40) 212334293
Petrol Equipment Mfr
N.A.I.C.S.: 333914

Gilbarco Veeder Root Spolka z.o.o. **(2)**
ul Kalenska 5, 04-367, Warsaw, Poland
Tel.: (48) 605222018
Petrol Equipment Mfr
N.A.I.C.S.: 333914

Gilbarco Veeder-Root AB **(2)**
Johannesfredsvagen 11A, 161 11, Bromma, Sweden
Tel.: (46) 7040500
Petrol Equipment Mfr
N.A.I.C.S.: 333914

Gilbarco Veeder-Root AS **(2)**
Rosenholmveien 20, 1252, Oslo, Norway
Tel.: (47) 66815400
Petrol Equipment Mfr
N.A.I.C.S.: 333914

Gilbarco Veeder-Root Asia Pte. Ltd. **(2)**
750A Chai Chee Road 07-02 Suite 1, Technopark Chai Chee, Singapore, 469001, Singapore
Tel.: (65) 64487626
Petrol Equipment Mfr
N.A.I.C.S.: 333914

Gilbarco Veeder-Root Italy **(2)**
Via de' Cattani, 50145, Florence, Italy
Tel.: (39) 05530941
Web Site: http://www.gilbarco.com
Service Station Equipment Mfr & Distr
N.A.I.C.S.: 333914

Gilbarco Veeder-Root OU **(2)**
Parnu MNT 146, 11317, Tallinn, Estonia
Tel.: (372) 6711111
Petrol Equipment Mfr
N.A.I.C.S.: 333914

Gilbarco Veeder-Root Solucoes Industria e Comercio Ltda. **(2)**
Alameda Caiapos 173, Tambore, 06460-110, Barueri, 06460-110, Sao Paulo, Brazil
Tel.: (55) 1138796600
Web Site: http://www.gilbarco.com
Fuel Pump Distr
N.A.I.C.S.: 423120

Gilbarco Veeder-Root UK **(2)**
Gilbert Barker House Burnt Mills Road, Basildon, SS13 1DT, Essex, United Kingdom
Tel.: (44) 1268533090
Web Site: https://www.gilbarco.com
Service Station Equipment Mfr & Distr
N.A.I.C.S.: 333914

UAB Gilbarco Veeder-Root **(2)**
Slezeviciaus St 7, LT-2035, Vilnius, Lithuania
Tel.: (370) 52409013
Petrol Equipment Mfr
N.A.I.C.S.: 333914

Subsidiary (Domestic):

Veeder-Root Company **(2)**
125 Powder Forest Dr, Simsbury, CT 06070
Tel.: (860) 651-2700
Web Site: https://www.veeder.com
Emp.: 300
Underground Storage Tank Leak Detection Systems & Other Environmental Products Mfr
N.A.I.C.S.: 334513
Gaston Berrio (CTO & VP-Engrg-Global)
Dave Coombe (Pres)
Jessica Doherty (VP)

Subsidiary (Domestic):

Veeder-Root FuelQuest, LLC **(3)**
9 Greenway Plz Ste 1800, Houston, TX 77046
Tel.: (713) 222-5700
Web Site: http://www.fuelquest.com
Software Development Services
N.A.I.C.S.: 541511

Hennessy Industries, LLC **(1)**
1601 J P Hennessy Dr, La Vergne, TN 37086
Tel.: (615) 641-7533
Web Site: https://www.hennessyind.com
Automotive Service Equipment Mfr
N.A.I.C.S.: 336390
Mauricio Sartori (Pres)

Subsidiary (Non-US):

Hennessy Industries Canada **(2)**
2430 Lucknow Drive Unit 9, Mississauga, L5S 1V3, ON, Canada
Tel.: (905) 672-9440
Web Site: http://www.hennessyind.com
Automotive Service Equipment Sls
N.A.I.C.S.: 811310

Invenco i2 LLC **(1)**
245 Hembree Park Dr Ste 90, Roswell, GA 30076
Web Site: https://www.invencoi2.com
Fuel Material Retailer
N.A.I.C.S.: 424720

Logicom N.G. **(1)**
109 Marathonos Avenue, 15344, Geracas, Greece
Tel.: (30) 2106618400
Web Site: https://www.logicom.gr
Fuel & Gas Management Services
N.A.I.C.S.: 213112

Matco Tools Corporation **(1)**
4403 Allen Rd, Stow, OH 44224
Tel.: (330) 929-4949
Web Site: https://www.matcotools.com
Automotive Tools, Toolboxes & Equipment Mfr & Distr
N.A.I.C.S.: 332216
Hilda Shipcka (VP-Mktg)

Orpak Latina S.p.A. **(1)**
Avenida del Valle 750 Office 101, Ciudad Empresarial, Huechuraba, Santiago, Chile
Tel.: (56) 223061800
Computer Software Development Services
N.A.I.C.S.: 541511

Orpak Romania S.R.L. **(1)**
7 Gheorghe Simionescu St 2nd Floor, District 1, 014155, Bucharest, Romania
Tel.: (40) 212334293
Computer Software Development Services
N.A.I.C.S.: 541511

Orpak Solution Co., Ltd. **(1)**
450/2 Boonyasatit Building 6th Floor Rama 3 Road, Bang Kho Laem, Bangkok, 10120, Thailand
Tel.: (66) 22921692
Computer Software Development Services
N.A.I.C.S.: 541511

Orpak Systems Ltd **(1)**
Building E 2nd Floor, PO Box 1461, Yakum, 60972, Israel
Tel.: (972) 35776868
Web Site: https://www.orpak.com
Fleet Management Services
N.A.I.C.S.: 561110
Alexandre Samuel (Engr-Presales)

Promaks Yazilim Sanayi ve Ticaret A.S. **(1)**
Merkez Mahallesi Erseven Sokak No 8, Kagithane, 34406, Istanbul, Turkiye
Tel.: (90) 2122249526

Web Site: https://www.promaks.com.tr
Software Services
N.A.I.C.S.: 541512

SmartPetro Inc. **(1)**
3890 Araro Street, Makati, 1235, Metro Manila, Philippines
Tel.: (63) 282499880
Web Site: https://www.smartpetro.biz
Fuel Distr
N.A.I.C.S.: 424720

Teletrac Navman US Ltd. **(1)**
3100 Sanders Rd Ste 150, Northbrook, IL 60062
Web Site: http://www.teletracnavman.com
Navigation Equipment Mfr
N.A.I.C.S.: 334511

Subsidiary (Non-US):

Navman Wireless Australia Pty.Ltd. **(2)**
Ground Floor 16 Giffnock Ave Macquarie Park, Sydney, 2113, NSW, Australia
Tel.: (61) 294207500
Navigation Equipment Mfr
N.A.I.C.S.: 334511

Subsidiary (Domestic):

Teletrac Navman **(2)**
310 Commerce Ste 100, Irvine, CA 92602
Tel.: (714) 897-0877
Web Site: http://www.teletracnavman.com
Vehicle Tracking Systems Developer
N.A.I.C.S.: 513210
Craig Blount (Dir-Strategic Market Dev-Global)
Nick Jones (CFO)
Alain Samaha (Pres)
Shane Scoville (Chief Revenue Officer)
Jonathon Eaves (Mng Dir)
Nicole McCrory (VP)

Subsidiary (Non-US):

Teletrac Navman (UK) Ltd. **(2)**
K1 Kents Hill Business Park, Milton Keynes, MK7 6BZ, Buckinghamshire, United Kingdom
Tel.: (44) 3455211144
Web Site: https://www.teletracnavman.co.uk
Navigation Equipment Mfr
N.A.I.C.S.: 334511

Turpak Elektromanyetik Yakit Ikmal Sistemleri Ticaret A.S. **(1)**
Merkez Mah Erseven Sokak No 8/1/4, Kagithane, 34406, Istanbul, Türkiye
Tel.: (90) 2123154100
Web Site: https://www.turpak.com.tr
Fuel Distr
N.A.I.C.S.: 424720

VOR BIOPHARMA INC.
100 Cambridgepark Dr Ste 101, Cambridge, MA 02140
Tel.: (617) 655-6580 DE
Web Site: https://www.vorbio.com
Year Founded: 2015
VOR—(NASDAQ)
Rev.: $1,324,000
Assets: $299,366,000
Liabilities: $48,759,000
Net Worth: $250,607,000
Earnings: ($92,094,000)
Emp.: 133
Fiscal Year-end: 12/31/22
Biotechnology Research & Development Services
N.A.I.C.S.: 541714
Eyal C. Attar (Chief Medical Officer)
Robert Ang (Pres & CEO)
Tirtha Chakraborty (Chief Scientific Officer)
Sadik Kassim (CTO)
John King (Chief Comml Officer)
Amy Mendel (Chief Legal Officer)
Tania Philipp (VP & Head-People)
Robert Pietrusko (Chief Regulatory & Quality Officer)
Siddhartha Mukherjee (Founder)

VORNADO REALTY TRUST

888 7th Ave, New York, NY 10019
Tel.: (212) 894-7000 MD
Web Site: https://www.vno.com
Year Founded: 1981
VNO—(NYSE)
Rev.: $1,811,163,000
Assets: $16,187,665,000
Liabilities: $10,482,379,000
Net Worth: $5,705,286,000
Earnings: $105,494,000
Emp.: 2,935
Fiscal Year-end: 12/31/23
Real Estate Investment Trust; Owns, Leases, Develops, Redevelops & Manages Office & Retail Properties Primarily in the New York & Washington DC Metro Areas
N.A.I.C.S.: 525990
Steven Roth (Chm & CEO)
David R. Greenbaum (Vice Chm)
Michael J. Franco (Pres & CFO)
Glen J. Weiss (Exec VP-Office Leasing & Co-Head-Real Estate)
Barry S. Langer (Exec VP-Dev & Co-Head-Real Estate)
Michael Doherty (Pres-Building Maintenance Svcs Div)
Robert Entin (CIO & Exec VP)
Thomas Sanelli (Chief Admin Officer & Exec VP-Fin)
Haim Chera (Exec VP & Head-Retail)
Lisa Vogel (Exec VP-Mktg)
Paul C. Heinen (Exec VP)
Jason Kirschner (Exec VP & Head-Capital Markets)
Edward P. Hogan Jr. (Exec VP & Head-Retail Leasing)

Subsidiaries:

Federal Solutions Group LLC **(1)**
11 Penn Plz, New York, NY 10001
Tel.: (212) 714-0004
Web Site: https://www.federalsolutionsgroup.com
Facility Services
N.A.I.C.S.: 561210
Mike Doherty (Pres & CEO)
Christopher Verrall (Asst VP-Operations)
Penny Willimann (VP-Marketing)

TCG Developments India Pvt. Ltd. **(1)**
No 3 EPIP First Technology Place, Whitefield, Bengaluru, 560066, Karnataka, India
Tel.: (91) 8042695001
Web Site: http://www.tcgre.com
Emp.: 500
Commercial Building Rental & Leasing Services
N.A.I.C.S.: 531120
Bhaskar Roy (Exec Dir)

TCG Real Estate Investment Management Company Pvt. Ltd. **(1)**
5th Floor Metropolitan Building Bandra Kurla Complex, Bandra East, Mumbai, 400051, Maharashtra, India
Tel.: (91) 2267479999
Web Site: http://www.tcgre.com
Emp.: 25
Commercial Building Rental & Leasing Services
N.A.I.C.S.: 531120
Pratap Chatterjee (CFO)

Vornado Realty L.P. **(1)**
888 7th Ave, New York, NY 10019
Tel.: (212) 894-7000
Web Site: https://www.vno.com
Rev.: $1,799,994,999
Assets: $16,493,374,999
Liabilities: $10,416,994,999
Net Worth: $6,076,379,999
Earnings: ($376,875,000)
Emp.: 3,145
Fiscal Year-end: 12/31/2022
Real Estate Investment Trust
N.A.I.C.S.: 525990
Steven Roth (Chm & CEO)

Subsidiary (Domestic):

11 East 68th Street LLC **(2)**

Vornado Realty Trust—(Continued)

11 E 68th St, New York, NY 10065
Tel.: (212) 686-0060
Web Site: http://www.11east68th.com
Real Estate Development Services
N.A.I.C.S.: 531390
Madeline Hult Elghanayan (Dir-Sls)
Sabrina Saltiel (Dir-Sls)

1740 Broadway Associates L.P. (2)
1740 Broadway, New York, NY 10019
Tel.: (212) 956-3040
Web Site: https://1740broadway.com
Residential Building Rental & Leasing Services
N.A.I.C.S.: 531110

520 Broadway Parallel REIT LLC (2)
45 Rockefeller Plz 9th Fl, New York, NY 10111
Tel.: (212) 715-0300
Real Estate Development Services
N.A.I.C.S.: 531390

555 1290 Holdings LLC (2)
1290 6th Ave, New York, NY 10104
Tel.: (212) 581-5009
Web Site: http://www.vnony.com
Sales Range: $50-74.9 Million
Emp.: 100
Holding Company
N.A.I.C.S.: 551112

650 Madison Owner LLC (2)
On Madison Ave between 59th St 60th St, New York, NY 10022-1029
Tel.: (212) 751-7170
Web Site: http://www.bno.com
Emp.: 4
Real Estate Development Services
N.A.I.C.S.: 531390
Jane Reichter (Gen Mgr)

7 West 34th Street LLC (2)
888 Seventh Ave, New York, NY 10019
Tel.: (212) 894-7000
Web Site: http://www.vno.com
Commercial Building Rental & Leasing Services
N.A.I.C.S.: 531120
Sheila Charton (Sr Dir-Leasing)
Jessica L. Kreider (Mgr-Mktg)
Twana T. Mack (Mgr-Property)
Jacquie Castillo Garcia (Coord-Tenant Rels)

Alexander's, Inc. (2)
210 Route 4 E, Paramus, NJ 07652
Tel.: (201) 587-8541
Web Site: https://www.alx-inc.com
Real Estate Investment Services
N.A.I.C.S.: 531110

Bowen Building, L.P. (2)
875 15th St NW, Washington, DC 20005
Tel.: (202) 331-4300
Web Site:
　http://www.vornadocharlesesmith.com
Commercial Building Rental & Leasing Services
N.A.I.C.S.: 531120
Mitchell N. Schear (Pres)

Building Maintenance Service LLC (2)
11 Penn Plz, New York, NY 10001
Tel.: (212) 714-0004
Web Site: https://bmsbuildingservice.com
Office Building Cleaning Services
N.A.I.C.S.: 561720
Michael Doherty (Pres & CEO)
Carol Gambardella (Sr VP-Fin)
Michael Silvestro (Sr VP-Human Resources)
Juan Francisco (Exec VP)
Joel Birner (Exec VP)
Sedat Osmanovic (Sr VP-Ops)
Robert Tucker (Sr VP-Mid Atlantic)
Erin Z. Porch (Dir-Marketing)
Anthony Favale (VP-GMSC)
Christina Herrick (VP)
Yurie Kim (Dir-Quality & Sustainable Initiatives)
Jeff Collins (Dir-Market Dev)
Penny Willimann (VP)
Dorothy Olego (Dir-HR)
Terri Faletti (Dir-Sales-Marketing)
Jeffrey Caldwell (Dir-Security)
Laurence Natoli (Branch Mgr)
Leon Friedman (Mgr)

Emily Gove (VP)
Linda Clynes (Sr Acct Exec)
Valerie Rivera (Acct Exec)
Patty O'Brien (Acct Exec)
Tom Lawless (VP & Gen Mgr)
Edwin Fabre (Dir)

CESC Park Two L.L.C.
2345 Crystal Dr, Arlington, VA 22202-4801
Tel.: (703) 769-1213
Sales Range: $50-74.9 Million
Emp.: 140
Commercial Building Rental & Leasing Services
N.A.I.C.S.: 531120

Charles E. Smith Commercial Realty, L.P. (2)
2345 Crystal Dr Ste 1000, Arlington, VA 22202
Tel.: (703) 769-8200
Web Site:
　https://www.smithcommercialrealty.com
Sales Range: $150-199.9 Million
Real Estate
N.A.I.C.S.: 531120
Mitchell N. Schear (Pres)
Jim Creedon (Exec VP-Leasing)
Laurie Kramer (Exec VP)
Mara Olguin (VP-Marketing)
Greg Redding (VP)
Deidre Schexnayder (VP)
Paul Sowter (Sr VP-Development)
Patrick Tyrrell (COO)
Joyce Williams (VP-Human Resources-Administration)
Ernie Wittich (Sr VP-Acquisitions)
Brendan Owen (Chief Leasing Officer)
Gavin Stephenson (VP)

Eatontown Monmouth Mall LLC (2)
180 Route 35 S, Eatontown, NJ 07724
Tel.: (732) 542-0333
Web Site: https://www.monmouthmallnj.com
Emp.: 100
Commercial Building Rental & Leasing Services
N.A.I.C.S.: 531120

Fairfax Square Parking LLC (2)
8075 Leesburg Pike Ste 70, Vienna, VA 22182
Tel.: (703) 821-2050
Web Site: http://www.vornadoconnectfairfax
　square.com
Residential Building & Dwelling Leasing Services
N.A.I.C.S.: 531110
Jennifer Wrenn (Sr Mgr-Property)
Rob Hill (Mgr-Ops)
Kathryn Clement (VP)

Fourth Crystal Park Associates Limited Partnership (2)
2345 Crystal Dr, Arlington, VA 22202-4801
Tel.: (201) 587-1000
Commercial Building Rental & Leasing Services
N.A.I.C.S.: 531120

Fuller Madison LLC (2)
595 Madison Ave Ste 1210, New York, NY 10022
Tel.: (212) 755-1166
Web Site: http://www.vno.com
Emp.: 10
Real Estate Brokerage Services
N.A.I.C.S.: 531210
Mitchell Iannello (Gen Mgr)

IP Mortgage Borrower LLC (2)
199 Water St 3rd Fl, New York, NY 10038
Tel.: (212) 577-3688
Mortgage Loan Brokerage Services
N.A.I.C.S.: 522310

Lincoln Road Management LLC (2)
One Biscayne Tower 2 S Biscayne Blvd Ste 3760, Miami, FL 33160
Tel.: (480) 509-6724
Web Site: http://www.lincolnroadmgmt.com
Emp.: 2
Management Consulting Services
N.A.I.C.S.: 541611

Ninety Park Property LLC (2)
W side Park Ave between 39th St 40th St 2 blocks S Grand Central, New York, NY 10016
Tel.: (212) 682-4142

Web Site: http://www.ninetypark.com
Emp.: 18
Real Estate Brokerage Services
N.A.I.C.S.: 531210
Adrian Sierra (Mgr-Property)

Piers 92/94 LLC (2)
711 12th Ave 55th St & the West Side Hwy, New York, NY 10019
Tel.: (646) 778-3211
Web Site: http://www.piers9294.com
Trade Show & Special Event Organizer
N.A.I.C.S.: 711320
Jenniel Davis (Gen Mgr)
Lucy Adorno (Mgr-Acct)

SO Hudson 555 Management, Inc. (2)
555 California St Ste 1630, San Francisco, CA 94104-1549
Tel.: (415) 392-1697
Residential Building Rental & Leasing Services
N.A.I.C.S.: 531110

The Armory Show Inc. (2)
1 Penn Plz Ste 1710, New York, NY 10119
Tel.: (212) 645-6440
Web Site: https://www.thearmoryshow.com
Convention & Trade Show Organizer
N.A.I.C.S.: 561920
Nicole Berry (Exec Dir)
Joel Morrison (Sr Mgr-Ops)

Universal Building North, Inc. (2)
1875 Connecticut Ave NW Ste 420, Washington, DC 20009
Tel.: (202) 986-6300
Web Site: http://www.vno.com
Emp.: 10
Real Estate Brokerage Services
N.A.I.C.S.: 531210
Matt Muller (Portfolio Mgr)

Vornado Office Inc. (2)
330 Madison Ave Ste 2, New York, NY 10017
Tel.: (212) 986-5217
Web Site: http://www.vernado.com
Real Estate Brokerage Services
N.A.I.C.S.: 531210

Vornado Office Management LLC (2)
888 7th Ave Ste 44, New York, NY 10106
Tel.: (212) 765-0950
Emp.: 25
Real Estate Brokerage Services
N.A.I.C.S.: 531210
Florence Legler (Gen Mgr)

Vornado Springfield Mall Manager LLC (2)
6500 Springfield Mall, Springfield, VA 22150
Tel.: (703) 971-3738
Commercial Building Rental & Leasing Services
N.A.I.C.S.: 531120
Eric Christensen (Gen Mgr)

Washington Design Center L.L.C. (2)
1099 14th St NW, Washington, DC 20005
Tel.: (202) 524-0814
Web Site: https://designcenterdc.com
Commercial Building Rental & Leasing Services
N.A.I.C.S.: 531120

Wasserman Vornado Strategic Real Estate Fund LLC (2)
1 Park Row, Providence, RI 02903
Tel.: (401) 274-5700
Web Site: http://www.wrecapital.com
Real Estate Development Services
N.A.I.C.S.: 531390
David D. Wasserman (Principal)
Richard N. Wasserman (Principal)
Christine Sullivan (Accountant-Property)
Lisa M. Johnson (Accountant-Property)
Michael Ventrone (Dir-Property Mgmt)

theMART (2)
222 Merchandise Mart Plz Ste 470, Chicago, IL 60654
Tel.: (312) 527-7600
Web Site: https://www.themart.com
Commercial Building Rental & Leasing Services
N.A.I.C.S.: 531120

Cheryl Longstreet (VP-Counsel)
Bruce Schedler (Vp-Apparel Sls)
Lisa Simonian (VP-Mktg)
Julie Amato Kohl (VP-NeoCon Sls)
Fabiola Cabrera (VP)
Monique Kielar (VP)
Danielle Owen (VP)

VORTEX BRANDS CO.
Tel.: (213) 260-0321
Web Site:
　https://www.vortexbrands.us
Year Founded: 2005
VTXB—(OTCIQ)
Green Energy Technology Services
N.A.I.C.S.: 221118
Todd Higley (Pres, CEO & Principal Fin Officer)

VOXX INTERNATIONAL CORPORATION
180 Marcus Blvd, Hauppauge, NY 11788　　　　　　　　　　DE
Web Site: https://www.voxxintl.com
Year Founded: 1965
VOXX—(NASDAQ)
Rev.: $468,911,000
Assets: $444,006,000
Liabilities: $188,613,000
Net Worth: $255,393,000
Earnings: ($45,592,000)
Emp.: 911
Fiscal Year-end: 02/29/24
Automotive Entertainment, Consumer Electronics & Vehicle Security Products Mfr
N.A.I.C.S.: 423690
Patrick M. Lavelle (CEO)
John J. Shalam (Chm)
Charles Michael Stoehr (Treas & Sr VP)
Loriann Shelton (CFO & COO)
Beat Kahli (Vice Chm)

Subsidiaries:

ASA Electronics LLC (1)
2602 Marina Dr, Elkhart, IN 46514
Tel.: (574) 264-3135
Web Site: http://www.asaelectronics.com
Emp.: 125
Entertainment Systems & Video Observation Units for Mobile Applications
N.A.I.C.S.: 423620

American Radio Corp. (1)
3080 Northfield Pl Ste 118, Roswell, GA 30076
Tel.: (770) 458-8585
Web Site: https://www.americanradio.net
Electronic Parts & Equipment Distr
N.A.I.C.S.: 423690
Tom Boggs (Dir-Tech Products)

Audiovox Atlanta Corp. (1)
3080 Northfield Pl Ste 118, Roswell, GA 30076
Tel.: (770) 458-8585
Consumer Electronics Mfr & Distr
N.A.I.C.S.: 423620

Audiovox Audio Visual Division (1)
150 Marcus Blvd, Hauppauge, NY 11788-3723
Tel.: (631) 231-7750
Web Site: http://www.audiovox.com
Sales Range: $75-99.9 Million
Emp.: 200
Mfr of Car Radios
N.A.I.C.S.: 423690

Audiovox Electronics Corporation (1)
180 Marcus Blvd, Hauppauge, NY 11788
Tel.: (631) 231-7750
Sales Range: $10-24.9 Million
Distr of Consumer Electronics
N.A.I.C.S.: 423690

Audiovox Mexico, S de RR de CV (1)
Ejercito Nacional No 436 Piso 3, Chapultepec Morales, Mexico, 11570, Mexico
Tel.: (52) 36872630

Web Site: http://www.audiovoxmexico.com
Consumer Electronics Mfr & Distr
N.A.I.C.S.: 423620

Audiovox Southeast (1)
3080 Northfield Pl 118, Roswell, GA 30076
Tel.: (770) 752-5200
Web Site: http://www.audiovox.com
Sales Range: $150-199.9 Million
Emp.: 5
Vehicle Accessories
N.A.I.C.S.: 441330

Code Systems Inc. (1)
2365 Pontiac Rd, Auburn Hills, MI
48326 (100%)
Tel.: (248) 583-9620
Designs, Manufactures & Markets Automobile Security Systems, Home Security Systems & Related Products
N.A.I.C.S.: 334419

EyeLock LLC (1)
3801 Avalon Park E Blvd Ste 400, Orlando, FL 32828
Web Site: https://www.eyelock.com
Agricultural Support Services
N.A.I.C.S.: 541714

Invision Automotive Systems, Inc. (1)
2822 Commerce Park Dr Ste 400, Orlando, FL 32819-8619
Tel.: (407) 842-7000
Web Site:
    http://www.invisionautomotive.com
Emp.: 300
Rear Seat Entertainment Systems & Accessories Mfr
N.A.I.C.S.: 334310

Klipsch Group, Inc. (1)
3502 Woodview Trace Ste 200, Indianapolis, IN 46268
Tel.: (317) 860-8100
Web Site: http://www.klipsch.com
Sales Range: $50-74.9 Million
Emp.: 300
Audio Equipment Mfr & Marketer
N.A.I.C.S.: 334310
Fred S. Klipsch (Owner)

Schwaiger GmbH (1)
Wurzburger Strasse 17, Langenzenn, 90579, Germany
Tel.: (49) 91017020
Web Site: http://www.schwaiger.de
Sales Range: $25-49.9 Million
Emp.: 100
Satellite Components Mfr & Distr
N.A.I.C.S.: 334220

VOXX Electronics Corporation (1)
180 Marcus Blvd, Hauppauge, NY 11788
Tel.: (631) 231-7750
Web Site: http://www.voxxelectronics.com
Consumer Electronics Mfr & Distr
N.A.I.C.S.: 423620

VOXX German Holdings GmbH (1)
Lise-meitner-str 9, 50259, Pulheim, Germany (100%)
Tel.: (49) 22348070
Web Site: http://www.voxxintl.de
Holding Company; Consumer Electronics Mfr & Distr
N.A.I.C.S.: 551112
Mark Finger (Mng Dir)
Mark Finger (Mng Dir)

Subsidiary (Domestic):

Heco Audio-Produkte GmbH (2)
Lise Meitner Strasse 9, 50259, Pulheim, Germany (100%)
Tel.: (49) 22348070
Web Site: http://www.voxxinter.de
Sales Range: $10-24.9 Million
Emp.: 60
N.A.I.C.S.: 334310

Mac Audio Electronic GmbH (2)
Lise-Meitner-Strasse 9, 50259, Pulheim, Germany (100%)
Tel.: (49) 22348070
Web Site: http://www.mac-audio.de
Sales Range: $10-24.9 Million
Emp.: 60
N.A.I.C.S.: 334310

Magnat Audio-Produkte GmbH (2)

Lise Meitner Str 9, 50259, Pulheim, Germany
Tel.: (49) 22348070
Web Site: http://www.magnat.de
Audio & Video Equipment Mfr
N.A.I.C.S.: 334310

Phase Linear (2)
Lise Meitner Strasse 9, D-50259, Pulheim, Germany (100%)
Tel.: (49) 22348070
Web Site: http://www.voxxgermanholding.de
Sales Range: $25-49.9 Million
Emp.: 80
Mfr & Distributor of Car Audio Speakers & Electronics
N.A.I.C.S.: 334310
Mark Finger (Mng Dir)

Voxx Automotive Corporation (1)
2365 Pontiac Rd, Auburn Hills, MI 48326
Web Site: https://www.voxxautomotive.com
Electronic Product Distr
N.A.I.C.S.: 449210

VOYA ASIA PACIFIC HIGH DIVIDEND EQUITY INCOME FUND
7337 E Doubletree Ranch Rd, Scottsdale, AZ 85258-2034 DE
IAE—(NYSE)
Rev.: $4,316,247
Assets: $104,569,119
Liabilities: $305,157
Net Worth: $104,263,962
Earnings: $2,814,836
Fiscal Year-end: 02/29/20
Investment Management Service
N.A.I.C.S.: 525990

VOYA EMERGING MARKETS HIGH DIVIDEND EQUITY FUND
7337 E Doubletree Ranch Rd Ste 100, Scottsdale, AZ 85258 DE
Web Site:
    http://investments.voya.com
Year Founded: 2010
IHD—(NYSE)
Sales Range: $1-9.9 Million
Investment Services
N.A.I.C.S.: 523999
John V. Boyer (Chm)
Shaun Patrick Mathews (Pres & CEO)
Stanley D. Vyner (Chief Investment Risk Officer & Exec VP)
Michael J. Roland (Exec VP)
Todd Modic (CFO, Sr VP & Asst Sec)
Manu Vandenbulck (Portfolio Mgr)
Robert Davis (Portfolio Mgr)
Nicolas Simar (Portfolio Mgr)
Willem van Dommelen (Portfolio Mgr)

VOYA FINANCIAL, INC.
230 Park Ave, New York, NY 10169
Tel.: (212) 309-8200 DE
Web Site: https://investors.voya.com
Year Founded: 2014
VOYA—(NYSE)
Rev.: $7,348,000,000
Assets: $157,085,000,000
Liabilities: $151,207,000,000
Net Worth: $5,878,000,000
Earnings: $589,000,000
Emp.: 9,000
Fiscal Year-end: 12/31/23
Financial Investment Services
N.A.I.C.S.: 551112
My Chi To (Chief Legal Officer & Exec VP)
Heather Lavallee (Pres & CEO)
Rob Grubka (CEO-Workplace Solutions)
Brannigan Thompson (Chief HR Officer & Exec VP)
Michael Katz (CFO & Exec VP)

Subsidiaries:

Benefitfocus, Inc. (1)

100 Benefitfocus Way, Charleston, SC 29492
Tel.: (843) 849-7476
Web Site: https://www.benefitfocus.com
Rev.: $263,097,000
Assets: $260,841,000
Liabilities: $337,158,000
Net Worth: ($76,317,000)
Earnings: ($38,566,000)
Emp.: 1,100
Fiscal Year-end: 12/31/2021
Holding Company; Cloud-Based Benefits Information & Management Software Developer & Services
N.A.I.C.S.: 551112
Andrew Frend (Pres)
Greg Mercer (Sr VP-Sls)
Ed Rumzis (CTO)

Subsidiary (Domestic):

Benefitfocus.com, Inc. (2)
100 Benefitfocus Way, Charleston, SC 29492
Tel.: (843) 849-7476
Web Site: https://www.benefitfocus.com
Cloud-Based Benefits Information & Management Software Developer & Services
N.A.I.C.S.: 518210
John Thomas (Chief Data Officer)
Sean Wechter (CIO)
Joel Collins (Chief Legal Officer & Gen Counsel)
Daniel Dennis (Chief Information & Security Officer & VP)
Tom Dugan (VP-Strategy)
Kathleen Ayers (VP-Strategic Initiatives)

Pen-Cal Administrators, Inc. (1)
7633 Southfront Rd, Livermore, CA 94551 (100%)
Tel.: (925) 251-3400
Web Site: http://www.voyanqplans.com
Retirement Plan Products & Services
N.A.I.C.S.: 524292
Stephen Schwaderer (Sr VP)

ReliaStar Life Insurance Company (1)
20 Washington Ave S, Minneapolis, MN 55401-1900
Fire Insurance Services
N.A.I.C.S.: 524113

Subsidiary (Domestic):

ReliaStar Life Insurance Company of New York (2)
1000 Woodbury Rd Ste 208, Woodbury, NY 11797
Tel.: (516) 682-8700
Sales Range: $75-99.9 Million
Emp.: 83
Life Insurance & Annuities
N.A.I.C.S.: 524113

Security Life of Denver Insurance Company (1)
8055 E Tufts Ave Ste 710, Denver, CO 80237
Tel.: (770) 980-5100
Web Site: http://www.sld-ing.com
Life Insurance Products & Services
N.A.I.C.S.: 524113

Voya Financial, Inc. - Service Center (1)
2000 21st Ave NW, Minot, ND 58703-0890
Tel.: (701) 858-2000
Web Site: http://www.voya.com
Insurance Carrier
N.A.I.C.S.: 524113

Voya Funds Services, LLC (1)
7337 E Doubletree Ranch Rd, Scottsdale, AZ 85258
Tel.: (480) 477-3000
Insurance Management Services
N.A.I.C.S.: 524298

Voya Insurance & Annuity Company (1)
1475 Dunwoody Dr, West Chester, PA 19380
Tel.: (610) 425-3400
Rev.: $1,314,000,000
Assets: $68,440,000,000
Liabilities: $66,111,000,000
Net Worth: $2,329,000,000
Earnings: $100,000,000

Emp.: 457
Fiscal Year-end: 12/31/2017
Life Insurance & Annuities
N.A.I.C.S.: 524130
Carolyn M. Johnson (Pres)
Michael R. Katz (CFO & Sr VP)
C. Landon Cobb Jr. (Chief Acctg Officer & Sr VP)

Voya Investment Management LLC (1)
5780 Powers Ferry Rd NW, Atlanta, GA 30327-4347
Tel.: (770) 690-4600
Web Site: http://investments.voya.com
Sales Range: $100-124.9 Million
Emp.: 250
Investment & Asset Management Services
N.A.I.C.S.: 523150
Barbara Reinhard (Portfolio Mgr & Portfolio Mgr)
Matt Toms (Portfolio Mgr)
Paul Zemsky (Chief Investment Officer-Multi-Asset Strategies & Solutions)
Michael Pytosh (Chief Investment Officer-Equities)
Jeffrey A. Bakalar (Portfolio Mgr)
Dan Norman (Sr Mng Dir & Head)
Charles M. Shaffer (Sr Mng Dir & Head-Distribution)
Bill Golden (Mng Dir & Head)

Subsidiary (Domestic):

Voya Investment Management (2)
230 Park Ave Fl 13, New York, NY 10169
Tel.: (212) 309-8200
Web Site: http://investments.voya.com
Sales Range: $50-74.9 Million
Emp.: 250
Institutional Research Brokerage & Investment Banking
N.A.I.C.S.: 551112
Vincent Costa (Head-Global Quantitative Equities)
Sanne de Boer (Sr VP & Dir-Quantitative Res)
Michael Pytosh (Chief Investment Officer-Equities)
Jeffrey A. Bakalar (Sr Mng Dir & Chief Investment Officer)
Dan Norman (Sr Mng Dir & Head-Sr Loan Grp)

Voya Investment Management (2)
100 Washington Ave S, Minneapolis, MN 55401-2110
Tel.: (612) 342-3736
Web Site: http://investments.voya.com
Sales Range: $25-49.9 Million
Emp.: 25
Financial Services
N.A.I.C.S.: 523150

Voya Investment Management (2)
Ten State House Sq, Hartford, CT 06103
Tel.: (860) 275-3720
Web Site: http://investments.voya.com
Sales Range: $50-74.9 Million
Emp.: 200
Investment Management
N.A.I.C.S.: 523150

Voya Investments Distributor, LLC (1)
230 Park Ave, New York, NY 10169
Tel.: (480) 477-2140
Sales Range: $25-49.9 Million
Emp.: 250
Financial Services
N.A.I.C.S.: 561499
Paul J. Hechmer (Mng Dir & Portfolio Mgr-Intl)

Voya Investments, LLC (1)
7337 E Doubletree Ranch Rd, Scottsdale, AZ 85258
Tel.: (480) 477-3000
Insurance Management Services
N.A.I.C.S.: 524298

Voya Reinsurance (1)
20 Washington Ave S, Minneapolis, MN 55401-1908
Tel.: (612) 342-7537
Group Life, Accident & Health Reinsurance Carriers
N.A.I.C.S.: 524130

Voya Retirement Insurance & Annuity Company (1)

Voya Financial, Inc.—(Continued)

1 Orange Way, Windsor, CT 06095-4774
Tel.: (860) 580-4646
Web Site:
　http://www.ingretirementplans.com
Rev.: $2,228,000,000
Assets: $114,334,000,000
Liabilities: $112,604,000,000
Net Worth: $1,730,000,000
Earnings: $333,000,000
Emp.: 1,705
Fiscal Year-end: 12/31/2022
Variable Annuities & Life Insurance Retirement Plans
N.A.I.C.S.: 524130
Donald C. Templin (Co-CFO)
Charles P. Nelson (Pres)
Francis G. O'Neill (CFO & Sr VP)
Nan Ferrara (Exec VP)
Christine Hurtsellers (CEO)
Santhosh Keshavan (CIO)
Trevor Ogle (Exec VP)
Kevin D. Silva (Chief HR Officer)
Donald C. Templin (Co-CFO)
My Chi To (Chief Legal Officer)

Subsidiary (Domestic):

Directed Services LLC　　　　　(2)
1475 Dunwoody Dr, West Chester, PA 19380
Tel.: (610) 425-3400
Insurance Management Services
N.A.I.C.S.: 524298

Voya Institutional Plan Services, LLC　　　　　(2)
1 Orange Way, Windsor, CT 06095
Tel.: (860) 580-4646
Web Site:
　http://voyaretirement.voyaplans.com
Sales Range: $1-4.9 Billion
Emp.: 3,700
Defined Contribution Retirement Savings, Pension, Health & Welfare Plan Administrator
N.A.I.C.S.: 524292

Subsidiary (Domestic):

Voya Institutional Plan Services, LLC　　　　　(3)
400 Atrium Dr, Somerset, NJ 08873
Tel.: (732) 514-2000
Defined Contribution Retirement Savings, Pension, Health & Welfare Plan Administrator
N.A.I.C.S.: 524292

Voya Services Company　　　　　(1)
5780 Powers Ferry Rd NW, Atlanta, GA 30327-4347
Tel.: (770) 980-5100
Web Site: http://www.voya.com
Sales Range: $1-4.9 Billion
Emp.: 10,000
Holding Company
N.A.I.C.S.: 551112

Subsidiary (Domestic):

Voya Services Co.　　　　　(2)
20 Washington Ave S, Minneapolis, MN 55401-1908
Tel.: (612) 372-5432
Web Site: http://www.ing-usa.com
Life Insurance Holding Company
N.A.I.C.S.: 524113

Voya Services Co.　　　　　(2)
1290 Broadway, Denver, CO 80203-2122
Tel.: (303) 860-1290
Web Site: http://www.ing-usa.com
Real Estate Investors Except Property Operators
N.A.I.C.S.: 561499

VOYA GLOBAL ADVANTAGE & PREMIUM OPPORTUNITY FUND

7337 E Doubletree Ranch Rd, Scottsdale, AZ 85258-2034
Tel.: (480) 477-3000　　　　DE
IGA—(NYSE)
Rev.: $6,983,908
Assets: $192,159,531
Liabilities: $1,501,559

Net Worth: $190,657,972
Earnings: $4,968,157
Fiscal Year-end: 02/29/20
Investment Management Service
N.A.I.C.S.: 525990

VOYA GLOBAL EQUITY DIVIDEND & PREMIUM OPPORTUNITY FUND

7337 E Doubletree Ranch Rd, Scottsdale, AZ 85258-2034
Tel.: (480) 477-2114　　　　DE
IGD—(NYSE)
Rev.: $23,692,122
Assets: $611,445,995
Liabilities: $607,858,213
Net Worth: $3,587,782
Earnings: $16,980,894
Fiscal Year-end: 02/29/20
Investment Management Service
N.A.I.C.S.: 525990
Colleen D. Baldwin (Chm)

VOYA INFRASTRUCTURE, INDUSTRIALS & MATERIALS FUND

7337 E Doubletree Ranch Rd, Scottsdale, AZ 85258-2034　　　　DE
IDE—(NYSE)
Rev.: $7,451,235
Assets: $224,577,016
Liabilities: $914,842
Net Worth: $223,662,174
Earnings: $4,354,687
Fiscal Year-end: 02/29/20
Investment Management Service
N.A.I.C.S.: 525990

VOYA INTERNATIONAL HIGH DIVIDEND EQUITY INCOME FUND

7337 E Doubletree Ranch Rd, Scottsdale, AZ 85258
Tel.: (480) 477-3000
IID—(NYSE)
Rev.: $1,749,077
Assets: $45,664,682
Liabilities: $159,178
Net Worth: $45,505,504
Earnings: $1,165,394
Fiscal Year-end: 02/29/20
Investment Management Service
N.A.I.C.S.: 525990
Vincent J. Costa (Mgr-Fund)

VOYA NATURAL RESOURCES EQUITY INCOME FUND

7337 E Doubletree Ranch Rd, Scottsdale, AZ 85258-2034
IRR—(NYSE)
Rev.: $3,277,812
Assets: $85,047,876
Liabilities: $359,414
Net Worth: $84,688,462
Earnings: $1,936,240
Fiscal Year-end: 02/29/20
Investment Management Service
N.A.I.C.S.: 525990
Paul L. Zemsky (Mgr-Fund)

VOYA PRIME RATE TRUST

7337 E Doubletree Ranch Rd, Scottsdale, AZ 85258-2034
PPR—(NYSE)
Rev.: $65,476,629
Assets: $1,150,520,479
Liabilities: $367,707,242
Net Worth: $782,813,237
Earnings: $42,545,597
Fiscal Year-end: 02/29/20
Investment Management Service
N.A.I.C.S.: 525990
Jeffrey A. Bakalar (Mgr-Fund)

VOYAGER DIGITAL LTD

33 Irving Pl Ste 3060, New York, NY 10003
Tel.: (212) 547-8807　　　　BC
Web Site:
　http://www.investvoyager.com
Year Founded: 1993
VYGVQ—(OTCEM)
Rev.: $175,056,000
Assets: $3,077,362,000
Liabilities: $2,891,040,000
Net Worth: $186,322,000
Earnings: ($51,488,000)
Fiscal Year-end: 06/30/21
Investment Services
N.A.I.C.S.: 523940
Stephen Ehrlich (Co-Founder & CEO)
Philip Eytan (Co-Founder & Chm)
David Brosgol (Gen Counsel)
Daniel Costantino (CIO, CTO & Chief Info Security Officer)
Gerard Hanshe (COO)
Ashwin Prithipaul (CFO)
Evan Psaropoulos (Chief Comml Officer)
Pam Spaan Kramer (CMO)

VOYAGER THERAPEUTICS, INC.

75 Hayden Ave, Lexington, MA 02421
Tel.: (857) 259-5340　　　　DE
Web Site:
　https://www.voyagertherapeutics.com
Year Founded: 2013
VYGR—(NASDAQ)
Rev.: $40,907,000
Assets: $159,356,000
Liabilities: $100,336,000
Net Worth: $59,020,000
Earnings: ($46,408,000)
Emp.: 125
Fiscal Year-end: 12/31/22
Health Care Srvices
N.A.I.C.S.: 621491
Krystof Bankiewicz (Co-Founder)
Guangping Gao (Co-Founder)
Mark A. Kay (Co-Founder)
Phillip D. Zamore (Co-Founder)
Jacqui Fahey Sandell (Chief Legal Officer)
Michelle Quinn Smith (Chief HR Officer)
Robin Swartz (COO, Principal Acctg Officer & Principal Fin Officer)
Todd Carter (Chief Scientific Officer)
Trista Morrison (Sr VP)
Alfred Sandrock (Pres & CEO)
Alfred W. Sandrock Jr. (Pres & CEO)
Steven M. Paul (Co-Founder)

VPR BRANDS, L.P.

1141 Sawgrass Corporate Pkwy, Sunrise, FL 33323
Tel.: (954) 715-7001　　　　DE
Web Site: https://www.vprbrands.com
Year Founded: 2004
VPRB—(OTCIQ)
Rev.: $4,927,616
Assets: $1,632,528
Liabilities: $3,951,020
Net Worth: ($2,318,492)
Earnings: ($203,697)
Emp.: 10
Fiscal Year-end: 12/31/22
Miscellaneous Financial Investment Activities
N.A.I.C.S.: 523999
Kevin Frija (Pres, CEO & Chm)
Daniel Hoff (COO)
Glecie Lacorte (Mgr-Shipping)
Biven Huang (Dir-Purchasing)
Christopher Porter (Specialist-Import)

VROOM, INC.

3600 W Sam Houston Pkwy S Fl 4, Houston, TX 77042
Tel.: (518) 535-9125

Web Site: https://ir.vroom.com
Year Founded: 2013
VRM—(NASDAQ)
Rev.: $1,948,901,000
Assets: $1,619,027,000
Liabilities: $1,143,786,000
Net Worth: $475,241,000
Earnings: ($451,910,000)
Emp.: 1,322
Fiscal Year-end: 12/31/22
Online Used Car Dealer
N.A.I.C.S.: 441110
Robert R. Krakowiak (Vice Chm)
Thomas H. Shortt (CEO)
Steven R. Berrard (Accountant)
Kevin P. Westfall (Co-Founder)
C. Denise Stott (Chief People & Culture Officer)
Thomas Shortt (COO)
Agnieszka Zakowicz (CFO & Treas)
Robert J. Mylod Jr. (Chm)

Subsidiaries:

CarStory, LLC　　　　　(1)
320 Congress Ave Ste C, Austin, TX 78701
Web Site: https://www.carstory.ai
Car Dealing Services
N.A.I.C.S.: 441110

Texas Direct Auto　　　　　(1)
12053 SW Fwy, Stafford, TX 77477-2305
Tel.: (281) 499-8200
Web Site: https://www.texasdirectauto.com
Sales Range: $1-4.9 Billion
Used Car Dealers
N.A.I.C.S.: 441120
Rick Williams (Owner)

VSBLTY GROUPE TECHNOLOGIES CORP.

417 N 8th St Ste 300, Philadelphia, PA 19123
Tel.: (212) 652-2208
Web Site: https://www.vsblty.net
VSBY—(CNSX)
Marketing & Advertising Services
N.A.I.C.S.: 541810
Jay Hutton (Founder, Pres & CEO)

VSE CORPORATION

6348 Walker Ln, Alexandria, VA 22310
Tel.: (703) 960-4600　　　　DE
Web Site: https://www.vsecorp.com
Year Founded: 1959
VSEC—(NASDAQ)
Rev.: $949,762,000
Assets: $999,789,000
Liabilities: $550,263,000
Net Worth: $449,526,000
Earnings: $28,059,000
Emp.: 2,000
Fiscal Year-end: 12/31/22
Logistics, Information Technology Services, Engineering, Supply Chain Management & Construction Management Consulting Services
N.A.I.C.S.: 541690
John A. Cuomo (Pres & CEO)
Benjamin E. Thomas (Pres-Aviation Segment)
Michael Perlman (VP-IR & Comm)
Charles Anderson (VP & Gen Mgr)

Subsidiaries:

1st Choice Aerospace, Inc.　　　　　(1)
3000 Kustom Dr, Hebron, KY 41048
Tel.: (859) 283-2264
Web Site: http://www.firstchoice.aero
Aircraft Operating Services
N.A.I.C.S.: 488119

Air Parts & Supply Co.　　　　　(1)
12840 S W 84th Ave Rd, Miami, FL 33156
Tel.: (305) 235-5401
Web Site: http://www.apscomiami.com
Aircraft Engine Parts Mfr & Distr
N.A.I.C.S.: 336411
Kerri Crowley (Gen Mgr)
Steven Foley (Dir-Sls)

Bill Murray *(Dir-Ops)*
Aime Garciadelosrios *(Mgr-Quality & Compliance)*
Jordan Phillips *(Mgr-Warehouse)*
Danny Gallardo *(Mgr-Product Line)*
Yami Nogues *(Mgr-Product Line)*

Akimeka LLC (1)
1305 N Holopono St Ste 3, Kihei, HI 96753-6916
Tel.: (808) 442-7100
Web Site: http://www.akimeka.com
Sales Range: $25-49.9 Million
Health Services Information Technology Consulting
N.A.I.C.S.: 541519

CT Aerospace LLC (1)
1550 Industrial Rd W, Bridgeport, WV 26130
Tel.: (972) 241-1071
Web Site: https://www.ctaerospace.com
Aircraft Engine Parts Mfr & Distr
N.A.I.C.S.: 336411
Toby Lavine *(VP-Bus Dev)*

Desser Tire & Rubber Co., LLC (1)
6900 W Acco St, Montebello, CA 90640
Tel.: (323) 721-4900
Web Site: https://www.desser.com
Sales Range: $10-24.9 Million
Emp.: 300
Distribute Aircraft Equipment & Supplies
N.A.I.C.S.: 423860
Jeff Johnston *(Owner)*

Fleet Maintance (1)
46579 Expedition Dr Ste 301, Lexington Park, MD 20653
Tel.: (301) 866-5000
Web Site: http://www.vsecorp.com
Sales Range: $10-24.9 Million
Emp.: 50
Value System Services (VSS) Provides Integrated Support for Naval Aviation, Aircraft Systems & Ordnance Systems
N.A.I.C.S.: 561499

Global Parts, Inc. (1)
901 Industrial Rd, Augusta, KS 67010
Tel.: (316) 733-9240
Web Site: http://www.globalparts.aero
Rev.: $10,000,000
Emp.: 34
Transportation Equipment & Supplies, except Motor Vehicle, Merchant Whslr
N.A.I.C.S.: 423860
Malissa Nesmith *(COO & Sr VP)*

Kansas Aviation of Independence, L.L.C. (1)
401 Freedom Dr, Independence, KS 67301
Tel.: (620) 331-7716
Web Site: http://www.kansasaviation.com
Engine Repair Services
N.A.I.C.S.: 811111
Greg Stewart *(Mgr-Technical Svcs)*
Matt Gillman *(Mgr-Ops)*
Dennis Pautler *(Sr Engr-Applications)*
Chelsie Angel *(Mgr-Customer Solutions)*

Turbine Controls, LLC (1)
5 Old Windsor Rd, Bloomfield, CT 06002
Tel.: (860) 242-0448
Web Site: http://www.tci.com
Rev.: $6,666,666
Emp.: 90
Aircraft Engine Components & Repair Services
N.A.I.C.S.: 336413

Ultra Seating Company (1)
3275 W Trinity Blvd Ste 150, Grand Prairie, TX 75050
Web Site: https://www.ultraseating.com
Emp.: 21
Transportation Seating Mfr
N.A.I.C.S.: 336360

VSE Aviation, Inc. (1)
1615 Diplomat Dr Ste 120, Carrollton, TX 75006
Tel.: (972) 406-2100
Web Site: http://www.vsecorp.com
Aircraft Maintenance Services
N.A.I.C.S.: 336411
John A. Cuomo *(Interim Pres)*
K. Hunter Mitchem *(VP-Distr Svcs)*
Toby Lavine *(VP-Repair Svcs)*
Karen Goode *(CIO & VP)*

VSE Services International, Inc. (1)
6348 Walker Ln, Alexandria, VA 22310
Tel.: (703) 960-4600
Web Site: http://www.vsecorp.com
Sales Range: $10-24.9 Million
Emp.: 5
Engineering & Logistics Services
N.A.I.C.S.: 541330
Donald M. Ervine *(Chm)*

Wheeler Bros., Inc. (1)
384 Drum Ave, Somerset, PA 15501
Tel.: (814) 443-7000
Web Site: https://www.wheelerfleet.com
Sales Range: $150-199.9 Million
Emp.: 300
Supply Chain Management Specializing in Truck Parts
N.A.I.C.S.: 423120

VSEE HEALTH, INC.

1 Gateway Ctr 300 Washington St Ste 507, Newton, MA 02458
Tel.: (561) 672-7068   DE
Web Site:
    https://www.vseehealth.com
Year Founded: 2021
VSEE—(NASDAQ)
Rev.: $539,691
Assets: $7,634,367
Liabilities: $15,060,963
Net Worth: ($7,426,596)
Earnings: ($3,242,501)
Emp.: 2
Fiscal Year-end: 12/31/22
Investment Services
N.A.I.C.S.: 523999
Daniel Sullivan *(CFO)*
Jerry Leonard *(CTO)*
Erika Chuang *(Chief Product Officer)*
Milton Chen *(Co-CEO)*
Imoigele Aisiku *(Chm & Co-CEO)*

Subsidiaries:

VSee Lab, Inc. (1)
1286 Kifer Rd Ste 103, Sunnyvale, CA 94086
Tel.: (650) 390-6970
Web Site: https://www.vsee.com
Software Publisher
N.A.I.C.S.: 513210
Yuen Lin *(Dir-Engrg)*

VU1 CORPORATION

1001 Camelia St, Berkeley, CA 94710   CA
VUOC—(OTCIQ)
LCD Products Mfr
N.A.I.C.S.: 335139
Matthew DeVries *(CFO)*

VULCAN MATERIALS COMPANY

1200 Urban Center Dr, Birmingham, AL 35242
Tel.: (205) 298-3000   NJ
Web Site:
    https://www.vulcanmaterials.com
Year Founded: 1909
VMC—(NYSE)
Rev.: $7,781,900,000
Assets: $14,545,700,000
Liabilities: $7,037,800,000
Net Worth: $7,507,900,000
Earnings: $933,200,000
Emp.: 10,382
Fiscal Year-end: 12/31/23
Construction Aggregate Mfr
N.A.I.C.S.: 212319
Ronnie A. Pruitt *(COO)*
James Thomas Hill *(Chm, Pres & CEO)*
Thompson S. Baker II *(Pres)*
Lindsay L. Sinor *(Pres-Vulcan Lands Inc)*
Jason P. Teter *(Sr VP-Mideast & Southeast Div)*
Ernesto Enriquez-Castillo *(Pres-Intl Div)*

David B. Pasley *(Pres-Ops Support)*
Janet F. Kavinoky *(VP-External Affairs & Corp Comm)*
Cindy H. Vu *(VP-Bus Dev-Analysis & Acquisition Integration)*
Jeffrey S. May *(Pres-Mountain West Div)*
Mark D. Warren *(VP-IR)*
Brian G. Pace *(Pres-Mideast Div)*
James T. Polomsky *(Pres-Western Div)*
Jerry F. Perkins Jr. *(Sr VP)*
Mary Andrews Carlisie *(CFO)*
Ronnie A. Pruitt *(Sr VP)*
M. Todd Freeman *(VP)*
Andrew F. McRae *(VP)*
Krzysztof Soltan *(CIO)*
E. Sunas *(Pres)*
C. Wes Burton Jr. *(Treas & VP)*
Denson N. Franklin II *(Gen Counsel, Sec & Sr VP)*
James Thomas Hill *(Chm, Pres & CEO)*

Subsidiaries:

Aggregates USA (Augusta), LLC (1)
5868 Columbia Rd Hwy 232, Grovetown, GA 30813
Tel.: (706) 541-0187
Construction Materials Mfr
N.A.I.C.S.: 327331

Aggregates USA (Macon), LLC (1)
1263 Lite N Tie Rd, Macon, GA 31211
Tel.: (478) 746-0244
Construction Materials Mfr
N.A.I.C.S.: 327331

Aggregates USA (Savannah), LLC (1)
1 Foundation Dr, Savannah, GA 31408
Tel.: (912) 964-7446
Construction Materials Mfr
N.A.I.C.S.: 327331

Aggregates USA (Sparta), LLC (1)
14674 Hwy 16, Sparta, GA 31087
Tel.: (706) 417-0002
Construction Materials Mfr
N.A.I.C.S.: 327331

Calhoun Asphalt Company, Inc. (1)
612 E Main St, Glencoe, AL 35905
Tel.: (256) 492-6560
Construction Materials Distr
N.A.I.C.S.: 423320
John McCartney *(VP)*

Central Division Logistics, LLC (1)
115 E Park Drive Ste 100, Brentwood, TN 37027
Tel.: (630) 245-7730
Construction Aggregate Services
N.A.I.C.S.: 212319

DMG Equipment Company, LLC (1)
1575 FM 1485, Conroe, TX 77301
Tel.: (936) 756-2722
Concrete Mixture Mfr & Distr
N.A.I.C.S.: 327390

Mountain West Logistics, LLC (1)
PO Box 78095, Seattle, WA 98178
Tel.: (206) 772-0810
Construction Aggregate Services
N.A.I.C.S.: 212319

North American Recycling and Crushing, LLC (1)
22765 Savi Ranch Pkwy Ste E, Yorba Linda, CA 92887
Tel.: (714) 777-6400
Web Site: https://www.narecycle.com
Concrete Mixture Mfr & Distr
N.A.I.C.S.: 327390

R. C. Smith Companies, LLC (1)
1575 FM 1485, Conroe, TX 77301
Tel.: (936) 756-6960
Web Site: https://www.smithandcompany.net
Concrete Mixture Mfr & Distr
N.A.I.C.S.: 327390

Shamrock Materials Inc. (1)
181 Lynch Creek Way Ste 200, Petaluma, CA 94954

Tel.: (707) 781-9000
Web Site:
    http://www.shamrockmaterials.com
Building Materials & Concrete
N.A.I.C.S.: 327320

Division (Domestic):

Shamrock Materials Inc. - Building Materials Division (2)
548 DuBois St, San Rafael, CA 94901
Tel.: (415) 455-1575
Building Materials Mfr
N.A.I.C.S.: 327390

Shamrock Materials Inc. - Sand & Gravel Division (2)
30022 Levee Rd, Cloverdale, CA 95425
Tel.: (707) 894-4425
Building Materials Distr
N.A.I.C.S.: 423320

Subsidiary (Domestic):

Shamrock Materials of Novato Inc. (2)
7552 Redwood Blvd, Novato, CA 94945-2425
Tel.: (415) 892-1571
Web Site:
    http://www.shamrockmaterials.com
Building Materials & Concrete Accessories
N.A.I.C.S.: 327320

Southeast Division Logistics, LLC (1)
800 Mount Vernon Hwy Ne Ste 200, Atlanta, GA 30328
Tel.: (904) 355-1781
Construction Aggregate Services
N.A.I.C.S.: 212319

U.S. Concrete, Inc. (1) (100%)
331 N Main St, Euless, TX 76039
Tel.: (817) 835-4105
Web Site: https://www.us-concrete.com
Rev.: $1,365,700,000
Assets: $1,506,300,000
Liabilities: $1,104,600,000
Net Worth: $401,700,000
Earnings: $25,500,000
Emp.: 631
Fiscal Year-end: 12/31/2020
Ready-Mixed Concrete, Precast Concrete Products & Concrete Related Products Mfr
N.A.I.C.S.: 327320
Michael D. Lundin *(Chm)*
Herb Burton *(VP & Gen Mgr-West Reg)*

Subsidiary (Domestic):

Action Supply Co., Inc. (2)
1401 Calcon Hook Rd, Sharon Hill, PA 19079
Tel.: (610) 534-3110
Web Site: http://www.us-concrete.com
Brick, Stone & Related Construction Material Merchant Whslr
N.A.I.C.S.: 423320

Atlas-Tuck Concrete, Inc. (2)
2112 W Bois D Arc Ave, Duncan, OK 73533
Tel.: (580) 255-1716
Web Site: https://www.us-concrete.com
Readymix Concrete Mfr
N.A.I.C.S.: 327320

Bode Concrete, LLC (2)
450 Amador St, San Francisco, CA 94124
Tel.: (415) 920-6740
Web Site: https://bodeconcrete.com
Ready Mix Concrete Distr
N.A.I.C.S.: 423320

Bode Gravel Co. (2)
385 Mendell St, San Francisco, CA 94124
Tel.: (415) 920-7100
Construction Materials Mfr
N.A.I.C.S.: 326229

Central Concrete Supply Co., Inc. (2)
755 Stockton Ave, San Jose, CA 95126-1839
Tel.: (408) 293-6272
Web Site: https://centralconcrete.com
Sales Range: $150-199.9 Million
Ready-Mixed Concrete Supplier
N.A.I.C.S.: 327320

Vulcan Materials Company—(Continued)

Dave Heil *(Gen Mgr-Westside Concrete Materials)*
Kelly Idiart *(Reg Dir-Quality Assurance)*

City Concrete, Inc. (2)
PO Box 299, Wichita Falls, TX 76307
Tel.: (903) 583-2588
Web Site: http://www.cityconcreteinc.com
Other Concrete Product Mfr
N.A.I.C.S.: 327390
Tim Foley *(Superintendent)*
Jim Foley *(Superintendent-Plant)*
Joe White *(Superintendent-Sls)*
Donnie Snider *(Superintendent-Sls-Hope Concrete Company)*

Colonial Concrete Company (2)
1196 McCarter Hwy, Newark, NJ 07104-3710
Tel.: (973) 482-1920
Web Site: https://www.colonialconcrete.com
Readymix Concrete Mfr
N.A.I.C.S.: 327320
John Serro *(Dir-Quality Control)*
Jerry Jansen *(Dir-Comm & Tech)*

Coram Materials Corp. (2)
PO Box 5810, Miller Place, NY 11764-1217
Tel.: (631) 924-5703
Web Site: http://www.coramshowers.net
Brick, Stone & Related Construction Material Merchant Whslr
N.A.I.C.S.: 423320

Custom-Crete Redi-Mix, LLC (2)
2624 Joe Field Rd, Dallas, TX 75229
Tel.: (972) 243-4466
Web Site: https://www.custom-crete.com
Emp.: 230
Readymix Concrete Mfr
N.A.I.C.S.: 327320

Custom-Crete, LLC (2)
2624 Joe Field Rd, Dallas, TX 75229
Tel.: (972) 243-4466
Web Site: https://www.custom-crete.com
Emp.: 230
Readymix Concrete Mfr
N.A.I.C.S.: 327320

DuBROOK Concrete, Inc. (2)
4215 Lafayette Center Dr Ste 1, Chantilly, VA 20151
Tel.: (703) 222-6969
Web Site: http://www.dubrookconcrete.com
Sales Range: $1-9.9 Million
Emp.: 51
Concrete Product Supplier
N.A.I.C.S.: 423320

Eastern Concrete Materials, Inc. (2)
250 Pehle Ave Plaza 1 Ste 503, Saddle Brook, NJ 07663
Tel.: (201) 797-7979
Web Site: https://www.eastern-concrete.com
Sales Range: $25-49.9 Million
Emp.: 35
Concrete Materials Including Ready Mixed Concretes
N.A.I.C.S.: 327320

Subsidiary (Domestic):

New York Sand & Stone LLC (3)
75 25th St, Brooklyn, NY 11232-1402
Tel.: (718) 832-7761
Web Site: https://www.nysand-stone.com
Stone, Gravel & Sand Supply Services
N.A.I.C.S.: 237310

Subsidiary (Domestic):

Heavy Materials LLC (2)
7865 Estate Mariendahl, Saint Thomas, VI 00802
Tel.: (340) 775-0100
Web Site: https://www.heavymaterialsvi.com
Ready Mix Concrete Distr
N.A.I.C.S.: 424690

Jenna Concrete Corp. (2)
1465 Bronx River Ave, Bronx, NY 10472
Tel.: (718) 842-5250 **(100%)**
Web Site: http://madeinnyc.org
Sales Range: $1-9.9 Million
Emp.: 30
Ready-Mixed Concrete Producer
N.A.I.C.S.: 327390

Kings Ready Mix, Inc. (2)
703 3rd Ave Fl 2, Brooklyn, NY 11232-1115
Tel.: (718) 853-4644
Sales Range: $1-9.9 Million
Emp.: 20
Readymix Concrete Mfr
N.A.I.C.S.: 327320
Robert Bruzzese *(CEO)*

Kurtz Gravel Company, Inc. (2)
G5300 N Dort Hwy, Flint, MI 48505
Tel.: (810) 787-6543
Web Site: http://www.kudzu.com
Construction Materials Mfr
N.A.I.C.S.: 326299

Local Concrete Supply & Equipment, LLC (2)
9814 Ditmas Ave, Brooklyn, NY 11236-1914
Tel.: (718) 342-3742
Cement Mfr
N.A.I.C.S.: 327320

Master Mix, LLC (2)
333 Chelsea Rd, Staten Island, NY 10314
Tel.: (718) 370-0245
Web Site: http://www.usconcrete.com
Readymix Concrete Mfr
N.A.I.C.S.: 327320

NYC Concrete Materials, LLC (2)
5700 47th St, Maspeth, NY 11378
Tel.: (718) 456-2520
Web Site: https://www.us-concrete.com
Readymix Concrete Mfr
N.A.I.C.S.: 327320

Subsidiary (Non-US):

Polaris Materials Corporation (2)
Ste 2740 1055 W Georgia St, PO Box 11175, Vancouver, V6E 3R5, BC, Canada
Tel.: (604) 915-5000
Web Site: https://www.vulcanmaterials.com
Marine Construction Services
N.A.I.C.S.: 237990

Subsidiary (US):

Eagle Rock Aggregates, Inc. (2)
700 Wright Ave, Richmond, CA 94804
Tel.: (510) 231-2200
Web Site: https://www.polarismaterials.com
Granites Distr
N.A.I.C.S.: 444180

Subsidiary (Domestic):

Orca Sand & Gravel Ltd. (3)
6505 Is Hwy, PO Box 699, Port McNeill, V0N 2R0, BC, Canada
Tel.: (604) 628-3353
Web Site: https://www.polarismaterials.com
Sand & Gravel Mining Services
N.A.I.C.S.: 212321

Subsidiary (Domestic):

Redi-Mix Concrete, LP (2)
725 E College St, Lewisville, TX 75057
Tel.: (817) 835-4100
Ready Mix Concrete Distr
N.A.I.C.S.: 424690

Right Away Redy Mix Incorporated (2)
401 Kennedy St, Oakland, CA 94606
Tel.: (510) 328-7620
Web Site: http://www.rightawayredymix.com
Ready-Mix Concrete Products Mfr
N.A.I.C.S.: 327320

Rock Transport, Inc. (2)
301 El Charro Rd, Pleasanton, CA 94588
Tel.: (408) 404-2064
Web Site: https://rock-transport.com
Emp.: 400
Construction Materials Mfr
N.A.I.C.S.: 423320
Geoff Henrikson *(Owner)*

Sierra Precast, Inc. (2)
1 Live Oak Ave, Morgan Hill, CA 95037
Tel.: (408) 779-1000
Emp.: 62
Concrete Products Mfr
N.A.I.C.S.: 327390

Spartan Products, LLC (2)
3840 Viscount Ave Ste 7, Memphis, TN 38118

Tel.: (800) 788-4551
Web Site: https://www.spartanproducts.com
Screen Printing Services
N.A.I.C.S.: 323113

Superior Concrete Materials, Inc. (2)
1220 12th St SE Ste 170, Washington, DC 20003
Tel.: (301) 577-8800
Web Site: https://superior-concretematerials.com
Sales Range: $25-49.9 Million
Emp.: 61
N.A.I.C.S.: 327320

Superior Materials, Inc. (2)
585 Stewart Ave Ste LL-32, Garden City, NY 11530
Tel.: (516) 222-1010
Web Site: https://www.supmat.com
Sales Range: $25-49.9 Million
Emp.: 58
Concrete Mfr
N.A.I.C.S.: 327390

U.S. Concrete On-Site, Inc. (2)
3189 W Ward Rd Ste 101, Dunkirk, MD 20754
Tel.: (410) 286-3500
Readymix Concrete Mfr
N.A.I.C.S.: 327320

USC Atlantic, Inc. (2)
475 Market St Ste 300, Elmwood Park, NJ 07407
Tel.: (201) 398-0900
Emp.: 40
Readymix Concrete Mfr
N.A.I.C.S.: 327320
Michael Gentoso *(Gen Mgr)*

Valente Equipment Leasing Corp. (2)
1465 Bronx River Ave, Bronx, NY 10472
Tel.: (718) 842-5196
Ready-mixed Concrete Product Whslr
N.A.I.C.S.: 423320

VGCM, LLC (1)
1767 Cochrane Bridge 174, Mobile, AL 36660
Tel.: (251) 432-0572
Construction Aggregate Services
N.A.I.C.S.: 212319

Vulcan Materials Co. - Central Region (1)
1200 Urban Ctr Dr, Birmingham, AL 35242
Tel.: (205) 298-3000
Web Site: http://www.vulcanmaterials.com
Regional Managing Office; Construction Materials Distr
N.A.I.C.S.: 551114

Subsidiary (Domestic):

Heritage Logistics, LLC (2)
28361 Diehl Rd Unit B Ste 388, Warrenville, IL 60555
Tel.: (630) 245-7950
Web Site: https://heritage-logistics.com
Construction Materials Trucking Services
N.A.I.C.S.: 484110

McCartney Construction Co. Inc. (2)
331 Albert Rains Blvd, Gadsden, AL 35901
Tel.: (256) 547-6386
Web Site: http://www.paveaway.com
Highway & Street Paving Contractor
N.A.I.C.S.: 237310

Vulcan Materials Co. - East Region (1)
1 Glenlake Pkwy NE Ste 600, Atlanta, GA 30328
Tel.: (770) 458-4481
Web Site: http://www.vulcanmaterials.com
Regional Managing Office; Construction Materials Distr
N.A.I.C.S.: 551114

Subsidiary (Domestic):

DC Materials, Inc. (2)
3334 Kenilworth Ave, Hyattsville, MD 20781
Tel.: (301) 403-0200
Web Site: https://www.dcmaterials.com
Sales Range: $25-49.9 Million
Emp.: 50
Concrete Recycling, Sand, Gravel, Topsoil & Landscaping Supplies

N.A.I.C.S.: 423930

Vulcan Materials Co. - South Region (1)
10151 Deerwood Park Blvd Bldg 100 Ste 120, Jacksonville, FL 32256
Tel.: (904) 355-1781
Web Site: http://www.vulcanmaterials.com
Sales Range: $1-4.9 Billion
Emp.: 2,950
Regional Managing Office; Construction Materials Distr
N.A.I.C.S.: 551114

Subsidiary (Domestic):

Vulcan Materials Co. - Helotes (2)
11602 Rainbow Rdg, Helotes, TX 78023
Tel.: (210) 695-3081
Web Site: https://www.vulcanmaterials.com
Sales Range: $25-49.9 Million
Construction Materials Distr
N.A.I.C.S.: 423320

Unit (Domestic):

Vulcan Materials Co. - Taft Yard (2)
8500 Florida Rock Rd, Orlando, FL 32824
Tel.: (407) 855-9902
Web Site: http://www.vulcanmaterials.com
Sales Range: $25-49.9 Million
Ready Mixed Concrete, Concrete Block & Building Materials
N.A.I.C.S.: 423320

Vulcan Materials Co. - West Region (1)
500 N Brand Blvd, Glendale, CA 91203-1923
Tel.: (818) 553-8800
Web Site: http://www.vulcanmaterials.com
Sales Range: $50-74.9 Million
Emp.: 100
Regional Managing Office; Construction Materials Distr
N.A.I.C.S.: 551114

Branch (Domestic):

Vulcan Materials Co. - Fresno (2)
11599 Old Friant Rd, Fresno, CA 93720
Tel.: (559) 434-0450
Web Site: http://www.vulcanmaterials.com
Sales Range: $1-9.9 Million
Emp.: 5
Readymix Concrete Mfr
N.A.I.C.S.: 327320

VUZIX CORPORATION

25 Hendrix Rd Ste A, West Henrietta, NY 14586
Tel.: (585) 359-5900   DE
Web Site: https://www.vuzix.com
Year Founded: 1997
VUZI—(NASDAQ)
Rev.: $11,835,882
Assets: $132,312,550
Liabilities: $15,582,512
Net Worth: $116,730,038
Earnings: ($40,763,573)
Emp.: 105
Fiscal Year-end: 12/31/22
Audio & Video Equipment Manufacturing
N.A.I.C.S.: 334310
Paul J. Travers *(Pres & CEO)*
Grant Neil Russell *(CFO, Treas & Exec VP)*
Shane Porzio *(VP-Engrg)*
Pete Jameson *(COO)*
Bill Beltz *(VP)*
Eric Black *(Gen Counsel)*

VYANT BIO, INC.

201 Route 17 N 2nd Fl, Rutherford, NJ 07070
Tel.: (201) 528-9200   DE
Web Site:
http://www.cancergenetics.com
Year Founded: 1999
VYNT—(NASDAQ)
Rev.: $666,000
Assets: $15,205,000
Liabilities: $5,296,000

Net Worth: $9,909,000
Earnings: ($22,690,000)
Emp.: 8
Fiscal Year-end: 12/31/22
Genetic Testing Services
N.A.I.C.S.: 621511
Geoffrey Eric Harris *(Chm)*

Subsidiaries:

Cancer Genetics Italia, S.r.l.   (1)
Via San Vito n 6 17, 20122, Milan, Italy
Tel.: (39) 0236311777
Web Site:
   http://www.cancergeneticsitalia.com
Medical Product Distr
N.A.I.C.S.: 424210

RDDT Pty, Ltd.   (1)
Suite 29 Level 3 240 Plenty Road, Bundoora, Melbourne, 3083, VIC, Australia
Tel.: (61) 399881805
Web Site: http://www.dai-sys.com
Research & Development Services
N.A.I.C.S.: 541714

vivoPharm Europe, Ltd.   (1)
Grillparzer Str 25, 81675, Munich, Germany
Tel.: (49) 89122287690
Medical Laboratory Services
N.A.I.C.S.: 621511

vivoPharm Pty, Ltd.   (1)
Level 3 Office 29 240 Plenty Road, Bundoora, Melbourne, 3083, VIC, Australia
Tel.: (61) 39 988 1800
Web Site: https://www.vivopharm.com.au
Medical Laboratory Services
N.A.I.C.S.: 621511
Ralf Brandt *(Co-Founder & Pres-Discovery & Early Dev)*
Sabine Brandt *(Co-Founder & Mgr-HR & Fin)*
Glenn J. Smits *(Sr VP-Discovery & Bus Dev)*
Chris Holding *(Head-Efficacy Testing)*

VYCOR MEDICAL, INC.
6401 Congress Ave Ste 140, Boca Raton, FL 33487
Tel.: (561) 558-2020   DE
Web Site:
   https://www.vycormedical.com
VYCO—(OTCQB)
Rev.: $1,222,989
Assets: $860,178
Liabilities: $3,801,049
Net Worth: ($2,940,871)
Earnings: ($404,917)
Emp.: 6
Fiscal Year-end: 12/31/22
Neurological Medical Device Mfr
N.A.I.C.S.: 339112
Adrian Christopher Liddell *(Chm & CFO)*
David Marc Cantor *(Pres)*
Peter C. Zachariou *(CEO)*

Subsidiaries:

NovaVision, Inc.   (1)
6401 Congress Ave Ste 140, Boca Raton, FL 33487
Tel.: (561) 558-2000
Researcher & Developer of Vision Restoration Therapy & Medical Technologies
N.A.I.C.S.: 339112

VYNE THERAPEUTICS INC.
685 Rte 202/206 N Ste 301, Bridgewater, NJ 08807   DE
Web Site:
   https://www.vynetherapeutics.com
Year Founded: 2011
VYNE—(NASDAQ)
Rev.: $477,000
Assets: $40,758,000
Liabilities: $9,556,000
Net Worth: $31,202,000
Earnings: ($23,210,000)
Emp.: 12
Fiscal Year-end: 12/31/22
Biotechnology Research & Development Services

N.A.I.C.S.: 541714
Mutya Harsch *(Chief Legal Officer, Gen Counsel & Sec)*
Iain Stuart *(Chief Scientific Officer)*
Tyler Zeronda *(CFO & Treas)*
David T. Domzalski *(Pres & CEO)*

Subsidiaries:

VYNE Pharmaceuticals Ltd.   (1)
7 Golda Meir Street 3rd Floor, Ness Ziona, 7403650, Israel
Tel.: (972) 89316233
Pharmaceuticals Product Mfr
N.A.I.C.S.: 325412

VYNLEADS, INC.
596 Herrons Ferry Rd Ste 301, Rock Hill, SC 29730
Tel.: (416) 489-0092   DE
Web Site: https://www.vynleads.com
Year Founded: 2015
VYND—(OTCQB)
Rev.: $49
Assets: $24,328
Liabilities: $659,817
Net Worth: ($635,489)
Earnings: ($273,623)
Emp.: 1
Fiscal Year-end: 12/31/22
Health Care Information Services
N.A.I.C.S.: 524114
Alex J. Mannine *(Co-Founder, CEO, Chief Financial & Acctg Officer & Sec)*
Stanislav Bezusov *(Co-Founder, COO, CTO & Exec VP)*
Sergei Stetsenko *(Co-Founder)*

W TECHNOLOGIES CORP.
433 Camden St N, Beverly Hills, CA 90210
Tel.: (310) 263-8188   NV
Web Site:
   http://www.wtechnologiescorp.com
WTCG—(OTCIQ)
Electrical Equipment Mfr & Distr
N.A.I.C.S.: 335999
Mikael Lundgren *(CEO)*

W&E SOURCE CORP.
113 Barksdale Professional Ctr, Newark, DE 19711
Tel.: (450) 443-1153   DE
Year Founded: 2005
WESC—(NASDAQ)
Assets: $12,546
Liabilities: $100,784
Net Worth: ($88,238)
Earnings: ($71,593)
Fiscal Year-end: 06/30/22
Financial Media Information Provider
N.A.I.C.S.: 541910

W&T OFFSHORE INC.
5718 Wheimer Rd Ste 700, Houston, TX 77057
Tel.: (713) 626-8525   TX
Web Site:
   https://www.wtoffshore.com
Year Founded: 1983
WTI—(NYSE)
Rev.: $920,997,000
Assets: $1,431,790,000
Liabilities: $1,424,156,000
Net Worth: $7,634,000
Earnings: $231,149,000
Emp.: 365
Fiscal Year-end: 12/31/22
Oil & Natural Gas Acquisition, Exploitation & Exploration
N.A.I.C.S.: 213112
Tracy W. Krohn *(Chm, Pres & CEO)*
Todd E. Grabois *(Treas & VP)*
Antoine Gautreaux *(VP-Production Ops)*
Steve Hamm *(VP-HSE&R)*
William J. Williford *(COO & Exec VP)*

Sameer Parasnis *(CFO & Exec VP)*
Huan Gamblin *(VP-Bus Dev)*
Al Petrie *(Coord-IR)*
Sameer Parasnis *(CFO & Exec VP)*
Kristen Ecklund *(VP)*
Alvin T. Haynes *(CIO)*
Jake G. Woodall *(VP)*
John Poole *(VP-Regulatory, Safety, Health, and Environmental)*

W.P. CAREY INC.
1 Manhattan W 395 9th Ave 58th Fl, New York, NY 10001
Tel.: (212) 492-1100   MD
Web Site: https://www.wpcarey.com
Year Founded: 1973
WPC—(NYSE)
Rev.: $1,738,139,000
Assets: $17,976,783,000
Liabilities: $9,269,786,000
Net Worth: $8,706,997,000
Earnings: $708,334,000
Emp.: 197
Fiscal Year-end: 12/31/23
Real Estate Investment Services
N.A.I.C.S.: 523999
Jason E. Fox *(Pres & CEO)*
John J. Park *(Pres)*
Susan C. Hyde *(Mng Dir, Chief Admin Officer, Chief Ethics Officer & Sec)*
Gino Sabatini *(Mng Dir & Head-Investments)*
John D. Miller *(Mng Dir & Chief Investment Officer)*
Peter Bates *(Mng Dir & Head-Asset Management-North America)*
Brooks G. Gordon *(Mng Dir & Head-Asset Mgmt)*
Christopher A. Mertlitz *(Mng Dir & Head-Investment-Europe)*
Toni Ann Sanzone *(Mng Dir & CFO)*
Craig Vachris *(Chief Credit Officer & Exec Dir-Credit & Risk)*
Jeremiah Gregory *(Mng Dir-Capital Markets, IR & Strategy & Head-Capital Markets)*
Peter Sands *(Head-IR & Exec Dir-Capital Markets, IR & Strategy)*
Mark Foresi *(Exec Dir-Capital Markets, IR & Strategy)*
Brian Zander *(Chief Acctg Officer & Controller)*

Subsidiaries:

CPA17 Merger Sub LLC   (1)
50 Rockefeller Plz, New York, NY 10020
Tel.: (212) 492-1100
Investment Services
N.A.I.C.S.: 523999

Subsidiary (Domestic):

Corporate Property Associates 17 - Global Incorporated   (2)
50 Rockefeller Plz, New York, NY 10020
Tel.: (212) 492-1100
Web Site: http://www.cpa17global.com
Rev.: $447,654,000
Assets: $4,587,470,000
Liabilities: $2,244,213,000
Net Worth: $2,343,257,000
Earnings: $97,287,000
Fiscal Year-end: 12/31/2017
Real Estate Investment Services
N.A.I.C.S.: 525990

Carey Financial, LLC   (1)
50 Rockefeller Plz Fl 2, New York, NY 10020
Tel.: (212) 492-1100
Sales Range: $75-99.9 Million
Emp.: 150
Real Estate Investment Services
N.A.I.C.S.: 531210
Mark Goldberg *(Pres)*
C. Jay Steigerwald *(Sr VP-Natl Accts)*
Richard J. Paley *(Gen Counsel & Chief Compliance Officer)*

Corporate Property Associates 18 - Global Incorporated   (1)

1 Manhattan W 395 9th Ave 58th Fl, New York, NY 10001
Tel.: (212) 492-1100
Web Site: http://www.cpa18global.com
Rev.: $204,217,000
Assets: $2,142,869,000
Liabilities: $1,397,244,000
Net Worth: $745,625,000
Earnings: $27,846,000
Fiscal Year-end: 12/31/2021
Real Estate Investment Services
N.A.I.C.S.: 523999
Jason E. Fox *(Pres & CEO)*
ToniAnn Sanzone *(CFO)*
Arjun Mahalingam *(Chief Acctg Officer)*

Courtyard Albuquerque Airport Operator LLC   (1)
1920 Yale Bvld S E, Albuquerque, NM 87106
Tel.: (505) 843-6600
Hotel Services
N.A.I.C.S.: 721110

Courtyard Baltimore Washington Airport Operator LLC   (1)
1671 W Nursery Rd, Linthicum, MD 21090
Tel.: (410) 859-8855
Hotel Services
N.A.I.C.S.: 721110

Courtyard Chicago OHare Operator LLC   (1)
2950 S River Rd, Des Plaines, IL 60018
Tel.: (847) 824-7000
Hotel Services
N.A.I.C.S.: 721110

Courtyard Indianapolis Airport Operator LLC   (1)
2602 Fortune Cir E, Indianapolis, IN 46241
Tel.: (317) 248-0300
Hotel Services
N.A.I.C.S.: 721110

Courtyard Irvine John Wayne Airport Operator LLC   (1)
2701 Main St, Irvine, CA 92614
Tel.: (949) 757-1200
Hotel Services
N.A.I.C.S.: 721110

Courtyard Louisville East Operator LLC   (1)
9608 Blairwood Rd, Louisville, KY 40222
Tel.: (502) 429-0006
Hotel Services
N.A.I.C.S.: 721110

Courtyard Newark Liberty international Airport Operator LLC   (1)
600 US 1 & 9, Newark, NJ 07114
Tel.: (973) 643-8500
Hotel Services
N.A.I.C.S.: 721110

Courtyard Orlando Airport Operator LLC   (1)
7155 N Frontage Rd, Orlando, FL 32812
Tel.: (407) 240-7200
Hotel Services
N.A.I.C.S.: 721110

Courtyard Orlando International Drive Convention Center Operator LLC   (1)
8600 Austrian Ct, Orlando, FL 32819
Tel.: (407) 351-2244
Hotel Services
N.A.I.C.S.: 721110

Courtyard Spokane Downtown Operator LLC   (1)
401 N Riverpoint Blvd, Spokane, WA 99202
Tel.: (509) 456-7600
Web Site: https://www.marriott.com
Hotel Services
N.A.I.C.S.: 721110

Eltofi AS   (1)
Bryggegata 9, Oslo, 0250, Norway
Tel.: (47) 22834020
Building & Dwelling Leasing Service
N.A.I.C.S.: 531110

Go Green (OH) LLC   (1)
7898 US Route 127, Van Wert, OH 45891
Tel.: (419) 615-7540
Web Site: https://www.gogreen-ohio.com
Shredding Support Services
N.A.I.C.S.: 561990

W.P. Carey Inc.—(Continued)

MCM (TN) LLC (1)
2960 Armory Dr, Nashville, TN 37204
Tel.: (615) 291-8313
General Merchandise Store Operator
N.A.I.C.S.: 455211

W. P. Carey & Co. B.V. (1)
Strawinskylaan 741 Tower C 7th Floor,
1077 XX, Amsterdam, Netherlands
Tel.: (31) 203331450
Web Site: http://www.wpcarey.com
Rev.: $3,000,000,000
Asset Management
N.A.I.C.S.: 523940

W. P. Carey Equity Investment Management (Shanghai) Co., Ltd. (1)
Room 17-05F Times Square 500 Zhang
Yang Road, Pudong New District, Shanghai, 200120, China
Tel.: (86) 2151782782
Building & Dwelling Leasing Service
N.A.I.C.S.: 531110

WPC MAN-Strasse 1 GmbH (1)
Elisabethallee 13, 1120, Vienna, Austria
Tel.: (43) 14197775
Real Estate Property Management Services
N.A.I.C.S.: 531110

WPC Pola Sp. z o.o. (1)
Gen Kazimierza Sosnkowskiego 1, 02-495,
Warsaw, Poland
Tel.: (48) 570295395
Stationery Article Distr
N.A.I.C.S.: 424120

Watermark Lodging Trust, Inc. (1)
150 N Riverside Plz, Chicago, IL 60606
Tel.: (847) 482-8600
Web Site: http://www.watermarklodging.com
Rev.: $655,920,000
Assets: $3,161,525,000
Liabilities: $2,489,262,000
Net Worth: $672,263,000
Earnings: ($82,771,000)
Emp.: 32
Fiscal Year-end: 12/31/2021
Real Estate Investment Trust
N.A.I.C.S.: 525990
Michael G. Medzigian (Chm, Pres & CEO)
Mallika Sinha (CFO, Principal Acctg Officer & Exec VP)
Brendan Medzigian (Sr VP & Head-Transactions)
Sam Zinsmaster (Sr VP & Head-Asset Mgmt)
Paul J. Huff Jr. (Gen Counsel & Sr VP)

Subsidiary (Domestic):

Carey Watermark Investors Incorporated (2)
50 Rockefeller Plz, New York, NY 10020
Tel.: (212) 492-1100
Sales Range: $600-649.9 Million
Real Estate Investment Services; Hotels
N.A.I.C.S.: 523999
Michael G. Medzigian (CEO)

The Ritz-Carlton Hotel Company LLC (1)
10400 Fernwood Rd, Bethesda, MD 20817
Tel.: (301) 380-3000
Web Site: http://www.ritzcarlton.com
Emp.: 40,000
Hotel Management Services; Hotel & Resort Operator
N.A.I.C.S.: 721110

Subsidiary (Non-US):

The Ritz-Carlton Hotel Company (Berlin) GmbH (3)
Potsdamer Platz 3, 10785, Berlin, Germany
Tel.: (49) 30337777
Web Site: http://www.ritzcarlton.com
Hotel & Motel Services
N.A.I.C.S.: 721110

The Ritz-Carlton Hotel Company of Canada Limited (3)
181 Wellington Street West, Toronto, M5V
3G7, ON, Canada
Tel.: (416) 585-2500
Web Site: http://www.ritzcarlton.com
Hotel Management Services; Hotel & Resort Operator

N.A.I.C.S.: 721110

The Ritz-Carlton Hotel Company of Jamaica Limited (3)
One Ritz Carlton Drive Rose Hall, Montego
Bay, Jamaica
Tel.: (876) 9532800
Web Site: http://www.ritzcarlton.com
Home Management Services
N.A.I.C.S.: 721110

The Ritz-Carlton Hotel Company of Mexico, S.A. de C.V. (3)
Retorno Del Rey No 36, Cancun, 77500,
QRO, Mexico
Tel.: (52) 9988810808
Web Site: http://www.ritzcarlton.com
Hotels & Motels Services
N.A.I.C.S.: 721110

The Ritz-Carlton Hotel Company of Singapore PTE LTD. (3)
7 Raffles Avenue, Singapore, 039799, Singapore
Tel.: (65) 63378888
Web Site: http://www.ritzcarlton.com
Home Management Services
N.A.I.C.S.: 721110

The Ritz-Carlton Hotel Management GmbH (3)
Potsdamer Platz 3, 10785, Berlin, Germany
Tel.: (49) 30337777
Restaurant Operating Services
N.A.I.C.S.: 722511

W.R. BERKLEY CORPORATION
475 Steamboat Rd, Greenwich, CT
06830
Tel.: (203) 629-3000   **DE**
Web Site: https://www.berkley.com
Year Founded: 1970
WRB—(NYSE)
Rev.: $12,142,938,000
Assets: $37,202,015,000
Liabilities: $29,732,778,000
Net Worth: $7,469,237,000
Earnings: $1,381,359,000
Emp.: 8,329
Fiscal Year-end: 12/31/23
Holding Company; Property Casualty
Insurance Services
N.A.I.C.S.: 551112
James G. Shiel (Exec VP-Investments)
William Robert Berkley (Chm)
Lucille T. Sgaglione (Exec VP)
William Robert Berkley Jr. (Pres & CEO)
William M. Rohde Jr. (Exec VP)

Subsidiaries:

Abercrombie Textiles, LLC (1)
3400 Hwy 221A, Cliffside, NC 28024
Tel.: (828) 202-5875
Web Site: https://cryptonmills.com
Textile Mfr
N.A.I.C.S.: 333248
Brian Burke (VP-Product Dev)

Admiral Indemnity Company (1)
301 Route 17 N Ste 900, Rutherford, NJ
07070
Tel.: (201) 518-2500
Property & Casualty Insurance Services
N.A.I.C.S.: 524126

Admiral Insurance Group, LLC (1)
1000 Howard Blvd Ste 300, Mount Laurel,
NJ 08054
Tel.: (856) 429-9200
Web Site: https://www.admiralins.com
Commercial Insurance Provider
N.A.I.C.S.: 524126
Daniel Smyrl (Pres)
Richard M. Moore (Gen Counsel & Sr VP-Claims)
Charlene A. Goodwin (VP-Mktg)
Bob Mescher (Sr VP-)
Brian Lineberger (Sr VP-)
Tracey Howells (Sr VP)
Tighe Crovetti (Chief Actuary)

American Mining Insurance Group, LLC (1)
1 Metroplex Dr Ste 500, Birmingham, AL
35209
Tel.: (814) 255-0200
Web Site: https://www.americanmining.com
Workers' Compensation Insurance Services
N.A.I.C.S.: 525190
Michael Marcus (Pres)

BXM Insurance Services, Inc. (1)
725 S Figueroa St Ste 2200, Los Angeles,
CA 90017-5440
Tel.: (213) 891-9259
Property & Casualty Insurance Services
N.A.I.C.S.: 524126
Mike P. Fujii (Pres & CEO)

Berkley Accident & Health LLC (1)
2445 Kuser Rd Ste 201, Hamilton Square,
NJ 08690
Tel.: (609) 584-6990
Web Site: https://www.berkleyah.com
Sales Range: $10-24.9 Million
Emp.: 60
Insurance
N.A.I.C.S.: 524114
Brad N. Nieland (Pres & CEO)
James Hoitt (Sr VP-Captive Div)
Theresa Galizia (Chief Underwriting Officer)
Rajiv Sood (VP)

Berkley Alliance Managers, LLC (1)
30 S Pearl St 6th Fl, Albany, NY 12207
Tel.: (405) 805-6635
Web Site: https://www.berkleyalliance.com
Disability Insurance Services
N.A.I.C.S.: 524126
Stephen L. Porcelli (Pres)
Lawrence G. Moonan (COO & Exec VP)
Laila Santana (Chief Claims Officer & Exec VP)
Danny R. Schamma (CFO & Exec VP)
Andrew D. Mendelson (Chief CX Officer)
Valerie M. Foster (Sr VP)
Lauren A. Harris (Sr VP)

Berkley Argentina de Reaseguros S.A. (1)
Av Colon 397 8000, Bahia Blanca, Argentina
Tel.: (54) 2914551500
Web Site: https://www.berkley.com.ar
Property & Casualty Insurance Services
N.A.I.C.S.: 524126

Berkley Asset Protection Underwriters, LLC (1)
757 Third Ave 10th Fl, New York, NY 10017
Tel.: (212) 922-0659
Web Site: https://www.berkleyassetpro.com
Property Insurance Services
N.A.I.C.S.: 524126
Stephen Wood (Asst VP-Underwriting)
Lorelle Powell (VP-Sales)
Olivia Cinqmars (Asst VP)

Berkley Aviation, LLC (1)
1101 Anacapa St Ste 200, Santa Barbara,
CA 93101   **(100%)**
Tel.: (805) 898-7640
Web Site: https://www.berkleyaviation.com
Sales Range: $75-99.9 Million
Emp.: 30
Aviation Insurance Coverage
N.A.I.C.S.: 524210

Berkley Capital Investors, LP (1)
475 Steamboat Rd, Greenwich, CT 06830
Tel.: (203) 629-3000
Property & Casualty Insurance Services
N.A.I.C.S.: 524126

Berkley Capital, LLC (1)
600 Brickell Ave 39th Fl, Miami, FL 33131
Tel.: (786) 450-5510
Web Site: https://www.berkleycapital.com
Private Equity Investment Services
N.A.I.C.S.: 523940
Frank T. Medici (Pres)
John F. Kohler (Gen Counsel)
Thomas H. Ghegan (Mng Dir)

Berkley Custom Insurance Managers, LLC (1)
Metro Center 1 Station Pl 6th Fl, Stamford,
CT 06902
Tel.: (203) 905-7561
Web Site: https://www.berkleycustom.com
Property & Casualty Insurance Services

N.A.I.C.S.: 524126
Michael P. Fujii (Pres & CEO)
Michael A. Coca (COO)
Mark G. Ying (Chief Casualty Officer)

Berkley Dean & Company, Inc. (1)
475 Steamboat Rd, Greenwich, CT
06830-6646   **(100%)**
Tel.: (203) 629-3000
Web Site: https://www.wrbc.com
Sales Range: $75-99.9 Million
Emp.: 15
Investment Advisor
N.A.I.C.S.: 523940

Berkley FinSecure, LLC (1)
901 Dulaney Valley Rd Ste 708, Towson,
MD 21204
Tel.: (410) 337-9260
Web Site: https://www.berkleyfs.com
Property & Casualty Insurance Services
N.A.I.C.S.: 524126

Berkley Healthcare Professional Insurance Services, LLC (1)
220 Petaluma Ave Ste A, Sebastopol, CA
95472
Tel.: (707) 829-4720
Web Site:
   https://www.berkleyhealthcare.com
Health Insurance Services
N.A.I.C.S.: 524114
Hugh B. Jago (Sr VP)
Benjamin J. Mack (VP)

Berkley International Argentina, S.A. (1)
Mitre 669, S2000COM, Rosario, Santa Fe,
Argentina
Tel.: (54) 03414104200
Web Site: http://www.berkley.com.ar
Insurance Company
N.A.I.C.S.: 524128

Subsidiary (Domestic):

Independenzia Company of Life Insurance (2)
Av Carlos Pellegrini 1023, 1009, Buenos
Aires, Capital Federal, Argentina
Tel.: (54) 01143788100
Web Site: http://www.berkley.com.ar
Traditional Life Insurance Including Both
Term & Whole Life
N.A.I.C.S.: 524113

Berkley International Latinoamerica S. A. (1)
Av Carlos Pellegrini 1023, C1009ABU, Buenos Aires, Argentina
Tel.: (54) 1143788100
Property & Casualty Insurance Services
N.A.I.C.S.: 524126

Berkley International Life Insurance Company, Inc. (1)
Pdcp Bank Building 7th Floor Paseo De
Roxas Ave, 6766 Ayala Ave cnr Paseo De,
1226, Makati, Philippines   **(100%)**
Tel.: (63) 27518502
Web Site: http://www.berkley.com
Sales Range: $350-399.9 Million
Emp.: 600
N.A.I.C.S.: 524128

Berkley International Seguros Colombia S.A. (1)
Cr 7 No 71-21 Tower B Office, 1002, Bogota, Colombia
Tel.: (57) 6013572727
Web Site: https://www.berkley.com.co
Property & Casualty Insurance Services
N.A.I.C.S.: 524126

Berkley International Seguros, S. A. (1)
Mitre 699, S2000COM, Rosario, Argentina
Tel.: (54) 3414104200
Property & Casualty Insurance Services
N.A.I.C.S.: 524126

Berkley International Seguros, S. A. (1)
Rincon 391 Piso 5, 11000, Montevideo,
Uruguay
Tel.: (598) 2 916 6998
Web Site: https://www.berkley.com.uy
Property & Casualty Insurance Services
N.A.I.C.S.: 524126

Berkley International do Brasil Seguros S. A. (1)
Av Pres Juscelino Kubitschek 1455 - 15th Floor, Itaim Bibi, Sao Paulo, 04543-011, SP, Brazil
Tel.: (55) 1138488622
Web Site: https://www.berkley.com.br
Property & Liability Insurance Services
N.A.I.C.S.: 524126
Leandro Garcia Okita (COO)

Berkley International, LLC (1)
475 Steamboat Rd, Greenwich, CT 06830
Tel.: (203) 629-3000
Sales Range: $25-49.9 Million
Emp.: 75
Insurance Services
N.A.I.C.S.: 524126

Berkley LS Insurance Solutions, LLC (1)
1255 Treat Blvd Ste 530, Walnut Creek, CA 94597
Tel.: (925) 472-8190
Disability Insurance Services
N.A.I.C.S.: 524126

Berkley Life Sciences, LLC (1)
200 Princeton S Corporate Ctr Ste 250, Ewing, NJ 08628
Web Site: https://www.berkleyls.com
Disability Insurance Services
N.A.I.C.S.: 524126
Emily Urban (Pres)
Christopher Dorko (Officer-Risk Mgmt Resources & VP)
Claire Pollard (VP-HR & Ops Mgr)
Holy Fettinger (CIO-Segment & VP)
Paul Osuch (Dir-Underwriting)
Cindy Khin (Dir-Life Sciences Casualty Resolution)
Andy Herbert (Asst VP & Mgr-Claims Workers Compensation)
Scott Burke (VP)
Phillip Skaggs (Chief Regulatory Affairs Officer)
John Rogener (VP)

Berkley Net Underwriters L.L.C. (1)
11350 Random Hills Rd Ste 800, Fairfax, VA 22030-6044
Tel.: (703) 986-3739
Sales Range: $150-199.9 Million
Online Insurance System
N.A.I.C.S.: 524126
Kanchana Sarathy (CIO & VP)
Christina Culp (Asst VP-Fin)

Berkley North Pacific Group, LLC (1)
13920 SE Eastgate Way Ste 120, Bellevue, WA 98005
Commercial Insurance Provider
N.A.I.C.S.: 524126
Gary Gudex (Chm)
Carrie H. Cheshier (Pres)

Berkley Offshore Underwriting Managers UK, Limited (1)
Level 13 52 Lime Street, London, EC3M 7AF, United Kingdom
Tel.: (44) 2039431400
Web Site: https://www.berkleyoffshore.com
Property & Casualty Insurance Services
N.A.I.C.S.: 524126
Nick Drury (VP & Dir-Claims)
Allan Francis (VP & Mgr-Energy Liability)
Paul Millen (Asst VP)

Berkley Offshore Underwriting Managers, LLC (1)
757 3rd Ave 10th Fl, New York, NY 10017
Tel.: (212) 618-2950
Property & Casualty Insurance Services
N.A.I.C.S.: 524126

Berkley Oil & Gas Specialty Services, LLC (1)
2107 Citywest Blvd 8th Fl, Houston, TX 77042
Tel.: (832) 308-6900
Web Site: https://www.berkleyoil-gas.com
Property & Casualty Insurance Services
N.A.I.C.S.: 524126
Linda A. Eppolito (Pres)

Berkley Professional Liability, LLC (1)
757 3rd Ave 10th Fl, New York, NY 10017

Tel.: (212) 618-2900
Web Site: https://www.berkleypro.com
Commercial Property & Casualty Insurance Services
N.A.I.C.S.: 524126

Berkley Program Specialists, LLC (1)
1250 E Diehl Rd Ste 200, Naperville, IL 60563
Tel.: (630) 210-0360
Web Site: https://www.berkley-ps.com
Insurance Program Services
N.A.I.C.S.: 524126
Joe Piekarski (VP-Claims)
Kevin P. Novak (Chief Ops Officer)
Sheila Gott (Sr VP- &)

Berkley Public Entity Managers, LLC (1)
200 Princeton S Corporate Ctr Ste 280, Ewing, NJ 08628
Web Site:
    https://www.berkleypublicentity.com
Property & Liability Insurance Services
N.A.I.C.S.: 524126
John Forte (Pres)
Kim Ladzinksi (VP-)
Sondra Ashmore (VP-Information Technology)
Joe Smith (CFO)

Berkley Re America, LLC (1)
Metro Ctr 1 Station Pl, Stamford, CT 06902
Tel.: (203) 905-4444
Web Site: https://www.berkleyre.com
Reinsurance Services
N.A.I.C.S.: 524130
Kathleen M. Perlman (Sr VP & Dir-Claims)
David Blake (Sr VP)
Todd Bolden (Sr VP)
Kevin Rooney (Sr VP)
Daniel R. Westcott (Pres)
Robert Coyne (Sr VP)
Troy Dockery (Sr VP)
Andrew L. Cartwright (VP)
Daniel Collar (Sr VP CUO Facultative)
Andrew Fox (Sr VP-Facultative Casualty)
Ryan McMurrer (VP)
Carole Kirk (CFO)

Berkley Re Solutions (1)
3 Stamford Plz 301 Tresser Blvd 9th Fl, Stamford, CT 06901
Tel.: (630) 210-0340
Web Site: http://www.berkleyre.com
Casualty Reinsurance Services
N.A.I.C.S.: 524126
Thomas Greenfield (Chief Risk Officer & Exec VP)
Scott Balfour (Sr VP)
Samuel T. Broomer (Chief Strategy & Innovation Officer & Exec VP)
Michael Born (SR VP-Comml)
Jeffrey Cron (VP)
Joseph Piekarski (Chief Claims Officer)

Berkley Re UK Limited (1)
Level 17 52 Lime Street, London, EC3M 7AF, United Kingdom
Tel.: (44) 2039431000
Web Site: https://www.berkleyre.com
Property & Casualty Reinsurance Services
N.A.I.C.S.: 524130
Richard Fothergill (CEO)
Julian Laville (CFO)
Philip Townsend (COO)
Mark Yeulett (Head-Intl Property Treaty)
Michael Wrightman (Head-Casualty Treaty)

Berkley Regional Specialty Insurance Company (1)
475 Steamboat Rd, Greenwich, CT 06830
Tel.: (203) 542-3800
Web Site: http://www.wrberkley.com
Sales Range: $150-199.9 Million
Insurance
N.A.I.C.S.: 524126

Berkley Risk Administrators Company, LLC (1)
222 S 9th St Ste 2700, Minneapolis, MN 55402-3332 (100%)
Tel.: (612) 766-3000
Web Site: https://www.berkleyrisk.com
Sales Range: $1-9.9 Million
Emp.: 400
Insurance Services
N.A.I.C.S.: 525190

Division (Domestic):

Berkley Risk Managers (2)
800 Rte 50, Mays Landing, NJ 08330 (100%)
Tel.: (609) 625-5544
Web Site: http://www.berkleyrisk.com
Insurance Services
N.A.I.C.S.: 524210

Berkley Risk Solutions, Inc. (1)
475 Steamboat Rd, Greenwich, CT 06830
Tel.: (203) 769-4050
Web Site: https://www.wrberkley.com
Sales Range: $10-24.9 Million
Emp.: 3
Property & Casualty Underwriting
N.A.I.C.S.: 524298

Berkley Select, LLC (1)
550 W Jackson Blvd Ste 500, Chicago, IL 60661
Tel.: (312) 800-6200
Web Site: https://www.berkleyselect.com
Insurance Underwriting Services
N.A.I.C.S.: 524126
Dan Spragg (Pres)
Bill Fair (Chief Underwriting Officer)
Jeff Yao (Chief Claims Officer)
Joan Comfort (CFO)
Al Roberts (VP-Underwriting &)
Chris Zanchelli (VP-Underwriting &)
Carlos Montanez (VP-)
Donald Avery (VP-Human Resources)
Guy Blair (VP-Information Technology)
Alastair Shore (COO)

Berkley Southeast Insurance Group, LLC (1)
1745 N Brown Rd Ste 400, Lawrenceville, GA 30043
Tel.: (678) 533-3400
Web Site: https://www.berkleysig.com
Property & Casualty Insurance Services
N.A.I.C.S.: 524126
Mark Woods (Chief Actuary)
Ronnie Diehl (VP-Mktn)
Jeffrey Carver (Reg VP)
William D. Vanderslice (Reg VP)
John Zulueta (Reg VP)
Jay Weber (Pres)
Greg D. Woods (VP)
John Morales (VP-)
Deb Evers (Chief Underwriting Officer)
Sherry Coffman (VP-Human Resources)

Berkley Specialty Underwriting Managers, LLC (1)
2 Ravinia Dr Ste 1100, Atlanta, GA 30346
Tel.: (404) 443-2117
Web Site: https://www.berkleysum.com
Liability Products
N.A.I.C.S.: 524298

Berkley Surety Group, Inc. (1)
412 Mt Kemble Ave Ste 310 N, Morristown, NJ 07960 (100%)
Tel.: (973) 775-5021
Web Site: https://www.berkleysurety.com
Emp.: 237
Surety Insurance
N.A.I.C.S.: 524298
Sean Petty (Sr VP)
Michael J. Hurley (Gen Counsel & Exec VP)
Andrew M. Tuma (Pres)
Vincent P. Forte (COO & Exec VP)
Bruce W. Kahn (Sr VP & Head-Claims)
Maria Croce-Rosqvist (Sr VP)
Dave Edwards (Sr VP)
Ryan Kyle (VP-Commercial)
Adam Cantu (VP-Commercial)

Berkley Technolgy Services (1)
10 Roundwind Rd, Luverne, MN 56156
Tel.: (507) 283-9195
Web Site: http://www.wrberkley.com
Sales Range: $1-9.9 Million
Emp.: 60
Software Devolepment
N.A.I.C.S.: 524210

Berkley Technology Underwriters, LLC (1)
222 S 9th St Ste 2550, Minneapolis, MN 55402
Tel.: (612) 344-4550
Web Site: https://www.berkley-tech.com
Property & Casualty Insurance Services

N.A.I.C.S.: 524126
Brian Zimmer (VP-Risk Control)
Holly Fettinger (CIO-Segment & VP)
Todd Springer (Officer-Strategic Fin & VP)
Andy Herbert (Asst VP & Mgr-Claims-Workers' Compensation)
Chris Balch (Pres)
David J. D. Bryton (Chief Claims Officer)
Alice Orrichio (VP-)

Breckenridge Insurance Group, Inc. (1)
3550 George Busbee Pkwy NW Ste 305, Kennesaw, GA 30144
Web Site: https://www.breckis.com
Insurance Brokerage Services
N.A.I.C.S.: 524210

Capitol Crossing Advisors, LLC (1)
200 Massachusetts Ave NW Ste 420, Washington, DC 20001
Tel.: (202) 470-4900
Web Site:
    https://capitolcrossingadvisors.com
Real Estate Manangement Services
N.A.I.C.S.: 531210

Clermont Specialty Managers, Ltd. (1)
3 University Plz, Hackensack, NJ 07601-6208
Tel.: (201) 342-4211
Rev.: $9,158,000
Emp.: 50
Property Casualty Insurance
N.A.I.C.S.: 524210
William J. Johnston (Pres)

Corporate Imaging Concepts, Inc (1)
308 Wainwright Dr, Northbrook, IL 60062
Tel.: (847) 412-6600
Web Site: https://www.corp-imaging.com
Sales Range: $1-9.9 Million
Emp.: 50
Piece Goods, Notions & Other Dry Goods Merchant Whslr
N.A.I.C.S.: 424310
Bob Herzog (CEO)
Atul Shevade (Founder & CTO)

Crypton LLC (1)
38500 Woodward Ave Ste 201, Bloomfield Hills, MI 48304
Tel.: (248) 855-6000
Web Site: https://www.crypton.com
Sales Range: $10-24.9 Million
Textile Mfr
N.A.I.C.S.: 313310

East Isles Reinsurance, Ltd. (1)
Wellesley House South 1st Floor 90 Pitts Bay Road, Pembroke, HM 08, Bermuda
Tel.: (441) 2780810
Web Site: http://www.eastisles.com
Reinsurance Services
N.A.I.C.S.: 524130

Gemini Transportation Underwriters, LLC (1)
99 Summer St Ste 1800, Boston, MA 02110
Tel.: (856) 857-3482
Web Site:
    https://www.geminiunderwriters.com
Transportation Insurance Services
N.A.I.C.S.: 524126

Insurance Networks Alliance, LLC (1)
3411 Silverside Rd Baynard Bldg Ste 100, Wilmington, DE 19810
Tel.: (302) 268-1010
Web Site: https://www.networksalliance.com
Insurance Services
N.A.I.C.S.: 524126

Intrepid Direct Insurance Agency, LLC (1)
5400 W 110th St 4th Fl, Overland Park, KS 66211
Web Site: https://www.intrepiddirect.com
Property & Casualty Insurance Services
N.A.I.C.S.: 524126

Key Risk Insurance Company (1)
7900 McCloud Rd Ste 300, Greensboro, NC 27419
Tel.: (336) 668-9050
Compensation Insurance Services
N.A.I.C.S.: 524126

W.R. Berkley Corporation—(Continued)

Robert W. Standen (Pres)
Rebecca H. Karr (CFO & COO)
Joseph J. Abriola (Chief Claim Officer & Sr VP)
Michael H. Marcus (Chief Mktg Officer & Sr VP-Reg Ops)
Greg Tardy (Chief Underwriting Officer & Sr VP)

Key Risk Management Services, Inc. (1)
7823 National service Rd, Greensboro, NC 27409-2962 **(100%)**
Tel.: (336) 668-9050
Web Site: http://www.keyrisk.com
Sales Range: $75-99.9 Million
Emp.: 250
Workers Property Insurance
N.A.I.C.S.: 541690
Robert W. Standen (Pres)

Lavalier Insurance Services, LLC (1)
757 3rd Ave 10th Fl, New York, NY 10017
Web Site: https://www.lavalier.com
Jewelry Insurance Services
N.A.I.C.S.: 524126

Monitor Liability Managers, Inc. (1)
550 W Jackson Blvd Ste 500, Chicago, IL 60661 **(100%)**
Tel.: (312) 800-6200
Web Site: https://www.berkleyselect.com
Sales Range: $50-74.9 Million
Emp.: 150
Insurance Claims & Services
N.A.I.C.S.: 524128

Nautilus Insurance Group, LLC (1)
7233 E Butherus Dr, Scottsdale, AZ 85260
Tel.: (480) 951-0905
Web Site: https://www.nautilusinsgroup.com
Property & Casualty Insurance Services
N.A.I.C.S.: 524126
Thomas M. Kuzma (Chm)
Thomas Joyce (Pres)
Rob Petronko (CFO & Sr VP)
Curt Chalmers (Chief Underwriting Officer)
Kevin Donovan (Sr VP-)
Courtney Beyer (VP-)

Overby-Seawell Company (1)
3550 George Busbee Pkwy NWSte 300, Kennesaw, GA 30144
Web Site: https://www.oscis.com
Insurance Services
N.A.I.C.S.: 524126
Keith J. Gilroy (Pres)
Jose Perez De Corcho (Exec VP)
Nico Potgieter (Officer-Information Security & VP)
Brandie Foreman (Mgr-Compliance)
Joe Rodriguez (Dir-Ops)
Jim Zeunik (Mgr-Call Center)
Tracy Ward (Sr VP-Accounts-Natl)
Kelsey Teets (Dir-Implementations)
Loretta Johnson (Sr VP & Dir-Svc Delivery)
Lucky Navarro (Sr VP-Accounts-Natl)
Cheryl Niemi (Sr VP-Accounts-Natl)
Angel Cruz (CEO)
Kirk Stephens (Chief Compliance Officer)
Russell Hall (Sr VP-Business Development)
Chris Mitchell (CTO)
Debe Rodriguez (Sr VP-Natl)
Christy Tranor (Sr VP-Natl)
Sonya O'Malley (Sr VP-Human Resources)
Andrew Svaby (VP-Natl)
Megan Ochoa (VP-Natl)

Signet Star Holdings, Inc. (1)
475 Steamboat Rd Ste 5, Greenwich, CT 06830 **(100%)**
Tel.: (203) 542-3200
Web Site: https://www.wrberkley.corporation
Propety & Casualty Insurance
N.A.I.C.S.: 524298

Subsidiary (Domestic):

Berkley Insurance Company (2)
475 Steamboat Rd, Greenwich, CT 06830 **(100%)**
Tel.: (203) 542-3800
Web Site: https://www.wrberkley.com
Sales Range: $25-49.9 Million
Emp.: 70
Holding Company
N.A.I.C.S.: 524126
William R. Berkley (Chm)
W. Robert Berkley Jr. (CEO)

Subsidiary (Domestic):

Acadia Insurance Company (3)
1 Acadia Commons, Westbrook, ME 04092
Tel.: (207) 772-4300
Web Site: https://www.acadiainsurance.com
Sales Range: $75-99.9 Million
Property & Casualty Insurance
N.A.I.C.S.: 524210
David Leblanc (Pres)
Lisa McPhail (Asst VP-Loss Control)

Admiral Insurance Company (3)
1000 Howard Blvd Ste 300, Mount Laurel, NJ 08054 **(100%)**
Tel.: (856) 429-9200
Web Site: https://www.admiralins.com
Sales Range: $100-124.9 Million
Excess & Surplus Lines Risk Management
N.A.I.C.S.: 524126
Nir Gabay (Sr VP-Professional Liability)
Leah Taylor (Sr VP-Underwriting Svcs)
Richard M. Moore (Gen Counsel & Sr VP-Claims)
Charlene A. Goodwin (VP-Mktg)
Bob Mescher (Sr VP-)
Brian Lineberger (Sr VP-)
Tracey Howells (Sr VP)
Renae Gary (VP-Human Resources)

Subsidiary (Domestic):

Carolina Casualty Insurance Company (4)
4800 Deerwood Campus Pkwy Bldg 400 4th Fl, Jacksonville, FL 32246
Tel.: (904) 363-0900
Web Site: https://www.carolinacas.com
Sales Range: $125-149.9 Million
Emp.: 140
Long Haul Trucking & Commercial Transportation Insurance
N.A.I.C.S.: 524126
Bryan Fortay (Chief Claims Officer & VP)
Robert Sprague (Chief Underwriting Officer & VP)
Dennis Dunham (VP & Actuary)
Anita Napoli (Sec & Asst VP-Compliance)
Steve B. Soucy (CFO & VP)
Frank Bilotti (Chief Actuary)
Rachel Tison (Dir-IT)
David Lockhart (Pres)

Nautilus Insurance Company (4)
7233 E Butherus Dr, Scottsdale, AZ 85260
Tel.: (480) 951-0905
Web Site: https://www.nautilusinsgroup.com
Excess & Surplus Lines Commercial Property & Casualty Insurance Carrier
N.A.I.C.S.: 524126
Thomas M. Kuzma (Pres & CEO)
Trish Buckhardt (Sr VP-Strategic Initiatives)
Tom Joyce (Pres)
Kevin Donovan (Sr VP-)
Courtney Beyer (VP-)
Rob Petronko (Sr VP)

Subsidiary (Domestic):

Great Divide Insurance Company (5)
7233 E Butherus Dr, Scottsdale, AZ 85260 **(100%)**
Tel.: (480) 951-0905
Web Site: https://www.nautilus-ins.com
Insurance Services
N.A.I.C.S.: 524298

Subsidiary (Domestic):

Berkley Mid-Atlantic Group (3)
4820 Lake Brook Dr Ste 250, Glen Allen, VA 23060
Tel.: (804) 285-2700
Web Site: http://www.wrbmag.com
Property & Casualty Insurance
N.A.I.C.S.: 524126
Mike Bondura (Chief Claim Officer)
Robert Nowicki (Dir-Claim Ops)
Andy Ambrose (Controller)
Tom Owens (Dir-Loss Control)
Michelle D. Middleton (Pres)
Matthew Moore (Chief Underwriting Officer)
Victoria Barnishile (CFO)
Greg Rollins (Chief HR Officer)
Craig Ceasar (Reg VP)
Christina Poore (Reg VP)

Continental Western Insurance Co (3)

11201 Douglas Ave, Urbandale, IA 50322 **(100%)**
Tel.: (515) 473-3000
Web Site: http://www.cwgins.com
Sales Range: $25-49.9 Million
Property Casualty Insurance
N.A.I.C.S.: 524126

Continental Western Insurance Company (3)
11201 Douglas Ave, Urbandale, IA 50322-3707 **(100%)**
Tel.: (515) 473-3000
Web Site: https://www.cwgins.com
Property & Casualty Insurance
N.A.I.C.S.: 524126
Dan Asahl (Pres)
Di Faris (Sr VP- & Distribution)
Chris Mein (Chief Underwriting Officer)
Chris Crawford (Chief Claims Officer)
David Benseler (Chief Actuarial Officer)
Nadine Schoep (VP-Human Resources)
Aaron Kobza (VP-)
Lance Randolph (VP-)

Division (Domestic):

Continental Western Insurance Company - Lincoln (4)
3641 Village Dr, Lincoln, NE 68516-4721
Tel.: (402) 423-7688
Web Site: http://www.cwgins.com
Rev.: $44,738,000
Emp.: 153
Property Casualty Insurance
N.A.I.C.S.: 524210

Subsidiary (Domestic):

Interlaken Capital Aviation Services, Inc. (4)
154 Airport Rd Hangar V, White Plains, NY 10604
Tel.: (914) 948-7304
Web Site: https://www.icas.aero
Aircraft Leasing
N.A.I.C.S.: 532411

Subsidiary (Domestic):

Gemini Insurance Company (3)
1250EDiehl Rd Ste200, Naperville, IL 60563
Tel.: (630) 210-0360
Web Site: https://www.wrberkley.com
Sales Range: $10-24.9 Million
Emp.: 40
General Insurance Services
N.A.I.C.S.: 711310

Midwest Employer's Casualty Company (3)
14755 N Outer 40 Dr Ste 300, Chesterfield, MO 63017 **(100%)**
Tel.: (636) 449-7000
Web Site: http://www.mecasualty.com
Property & Casualty Insurance
N.A.I.C.S.: 524126

Subsidiary (Domestic):

Preferred Employers Insurance Company (4)
9797 Aero Dr Ste 200, San Diego, CA 92123
Tel.: (619) 688-3900
Web Site: https://www.peiwc.com
Sales Range: $10-24.9 Million
Emp.: 85
Insurance Provider
N.A.I.C.S.: 524298
S. Akbar Khan (Pres)
Michelle Bakunoff (VP)
Edward G. Bradford II (VP)
Marc J. Beaulieu (Sr VP)
Janis Eoff (VP-Human Resources)
Eric Hansen (Sr VP-Underwriting)
Stephanie Graham (VP-)

Subsidiary (Domestic):

StarNet Insurance Company (3)
215 Shuman Blvd #200, Naperville, IL 60563
Tel.: (630) 210-0360
Commercial, Property & Casualty Insurance Services
N.A.I.C.S.: 524128

Union Standard Insurance Company (3)
222 Las Colinas Blvd W Ste 1300, Irving, TX 75039-5433
Tel.: (972) 719-2400
Web Site: https://www.usic.com
Sales Range: $25-49.9 Million
Insurance Services
N.A.I.C.S.: 524298

Subsidiary (Domestic):

Facultative ReSources, Inc. (2)
3 Landmark Sq Ste 500, Stamford, CT 06901
Tel.: (203) 658-1500
Web Site: https://www.wrberkley.com
Sales Range: $1-9.9 Million
Emp.: 35
Facultative Reinsurance
N.A.I.C.S.: 524210

Southeastern Underwriters, Inc. (1)
PO Box 15420, Richmond, VA 23227-5420
Tel.: (804) 550-2376
Web Site: http://www.suigroup.com
Property & Casualty Insurance Services
N.A.I.C.S.: 524126

Southwest Risk Services Inc. (1)
14902 N 73rd St, Scottsdale, AZ 85260
Tel.: (602) 996-8810
Web Site: http://www.southwestrisk.org
Rev.: $1,880,000
Emp.: 70
Insurance Services
N.A.I.C.S.: 524210
Sheri Reintjes (VP)

Target Programs, LLC (1)
3411 Silverside Rd Baynard Bldg Ste 100, Wilmington, DE 19810
Tel.: (302) 268-1011
Web Site: https://www.targetprograms.com
Online Information Services
N.A.I.C.S.: 513199

Union Berkley, Compania de Seguros S.A. (1)
Av. Carlos Pellegrini 1023, C1009ABU, Buenos Aires, Argentina
Tel.: (54) 11 4378 8100
Web Site: http://www.berkley.com.ar
Insurance Company
N.A.I.C.S.: 524128

Vela Insurance Services, Inc. (1)
550 W Jackson Blvd Ste 500, Chicago, IL 60661
Tel.: (312) 553-4413
Sales Range: $1-9.9 Million
Emp.: 30
Insurance Services
N.A.I.C.S.: 524210
Patricia Maruszak (VP)

W. R. Berkley Europe AG (1)
Stadtle 35A, 9490, Vaduz, Liechtenstein
Tel.: (423) 2372747
Web Site: https://www.berkleyeurope.com
Insurance Underwriting Services
N.A.I.C.S.: 524126

W. R. Berkley Spain, S. L. U. (1)
Paseo de la Castellana 141 Planta 18, 28046, Madrid, Spain
Tel.: (34) 914492646
Web Site: https://www.wrberkley.es
Property & Casualty Insurance Services
N.A.I.C.S.: 524126

W. R. Berkley Syndicate Limited (1)
14th Floor 52 Lime Street, London, EC3M 7AF, United Kingdom
Tel.: (44) 2039431900
Web Site: https://www.wrbunderwriting.com
Insurance Underwriting Services
N.A.I.C.S.: 524126

WRBC Support Services, LLC (1)
301 Tresser Blvd 9th Fl, Stamford, CT 06901
Tel.: (203) 905-4279
Property & Casualty Insurance Services
N.A.I.C.S.: 524126

W.T.B. FINANCIAL CORPORATION

717 W Sprague Ave, Spokane, WA 99201
Tel.: (509) 353-3865　　　　　DE
Web Site: https://www.watrust.com
Year Founded: 1982
WTBFA—(OTCIQ)
Rev.: $354,842,088
Assets: $9,813,962,953
Liabilities: $9,007,445,206
Net Worth: $806,517,747
Earnings: $76,311,756
Emp.: 996
Fiscal Year-end: 12/31/20
Bank Holding Company
N.A.I.C.S.: 551111
Larry V. Sorensen (CFO & Sr VP)
John E. Heath III (Vice Chm, COO & Exec VP)
Peter F. Stanton (Chm, Pres & CEO)

Subsidiaries:

Washington Trust Bank　　　　(1)
717 W Sprague Ave, Spokane, WA 99201-3922
Tel.: (509) 353-4204
Web Site: http://www.watrust.com
Rev.: $193,881,702
Assets: $4,464,717,371
Liabilities: $4,018,834,513
Net Worth: $445,882,858
Earnings: $31,418,002
Fiscal Year-end: 12/31/2012
Retail & Commercial Banking
N.A.I.C.S.: 522110
Larry V. Sorensen (CFO, Treas, Asst Sec & Sr VP)
Peter F. Stanton (Chm & CEO)
Linda A. Williams (Reg Pres-Oregon)
Paul M. Koenigs (Chief Credit Officer & Sr VP)
J. Jay Lewis (Sr VP-Comml Banking)
Chad LeGate (VP & Sr Trust Officer)
Toni Fredrick (Mgr-Private Banking Relationships)
Scott H. Luttinen (Exec VP & Reg Pres-Western Washington)
Joe Amado (Dir-IT Sys Dev)
David J. Terrell (Reg Pres-Southern Idaho)
Burke D. Jackowich (Gen Counsel & Sr VP)
Penney Close (VP-Comml Banking)
Laura Gingrich (Chief Acctg Officer & VP)
Brian Goulet (VP-Private Banking)
Thomas McLaughlin (VP-Comml Banking)
Dean Watanabe (VP & Mgr-Relationship-Small Bus Banking Dept)
Jeff Schlenker (VP & Mgr-Investment Svcs Sls)
Cory Violette (Asst VP)
Danielle Fischer (VP & Mgr-Relationship-Wealth Mgmt & Advisory Svcs-Oregon)
Tindy Wendy (Branch Mgr)
Jeff Hancock (VP & Mgr-Relationship-Private Banking-Boise)
Tim Miller (VP & Mgr-Relationship)
Tim Donnelly (VP-Wealth Mgmt & Advisory Svcs)
Peter Bentley (Sr VP)
David Hall (VP & Mgr-Comml Real Estate Relationship-Meridian Comml Banking)
Willie Koosmann (VP-Comml Banking & Mgr-Relationship-Southern Idaho)
Carolyn Stewart (VP-Private Banking)
Jamie Sumner (VP & Mgr-Customer Rels-Wealth Mgmt & Advisory Team)
Terry Costello (VP & Mgr-Comml Banking Relationship)
John Borland (VP & Mgr-Comml Relationship)
Katy Wagnon (Mgr-Corp Comm & PR)
Erik Selden (Sr VP)

W.W. GRAINGER, INC.
100 Grainger Pkwy, Lake Forest, IL 60045-5201
Tel.: (847) 535-1000　　　　IL
Web Site: https://www.grainger.com
Year Founded: 1927
GWW—(NYSE)
Rev.: $16,478,000,000
Assets: $8,147,000,000
Liabilities: $4,706,000,000
Net Worth: $3,441,000,000
Earnings: $1,829,000,000

Emp.: 23,200
Fiscal Year-end: 12/31/23
Facilities Maintenance Product Mfr & Distr
N.A.I.C.S.: 423840
Nancy L. Berardinelli-Krantz (Chief Legal Officer & Sr VP)
Abby Sullivan (Sr Mgr-IR)
Barry Greenhouse (Pres-Supply Chain & Customer Experience & Sr VP)
Masaya Suzuki (Mng Dir-Endless Assortment Bus)
Laurie R. Thomson (Principal Acctg Officer, VP & Controller)
Deidra C. Merriwether (CFO, Pres-Sls & Svcs-North American, Sr VP, Sr VP-Direct Sls & Strategic Initiatives & VP-Fin-Americas)
Donald G. Macpherson (Chm & CEO)
Paige K. Robbins (Pres-Bus Unit & Sr VP)

Subsidiaries:

AJ Howard Industrial Supplies Limited　　　　(1)
Unit 15 Carlton Park Industrial Estate Main Road, Saxmundham, Suffolk, IP17 2NL, United Kingdom
Tel.: (44) 1322283200
Web Site:
　　https://www.powertoolproducts.com
Industrial Machinery Tools & Equipment Distr
N.A.I.C.S.: 423830

Acklands-Grainger Inc.　　　　(1)
123 Commerce Valley Drive East Suite 700, Thornhill, L3T 7W8, ON, Canada　**(100%)**
Tel.: (905) 731-5516
Web Site: https://www.grainger.ca
Sales Range: $600-649.9 Million
Emp.: 2,600
Industrial, Automotive Fleet & Safety Products Distr
N.A.I.C.S.: 441330

Bogle and Timms Limited　　　　(1)
651 Eccles New Road 5, Salford, M50 1BA, United Kingdom
Tel.: (44) 1617862500
Industrial Machinery Tools & Equipment Distr
N.A.I.C.S.: 423830

Cromwell Czech Republic s.r.o.　　(1)
Nachodska 73, Horni Pocernice, 193 00, Prague, 9, Czech Republic
Tel.: (420) 281927744
Web Site: https://www.cromwell.cz
Emp.: 1,800
Industrial Machinery Tools & Equipment Distr
N.A.I.C.S.: 423830

Cromwell France SAS　　　　(1)
83 Avenue de la Grande Armee, 75782, Paris, Cedex 16, France
Tel.: (33) 156337800
Web Site:
　　http://www.cromwellpropertygroup.fr
Real Estate Development Services
N.A.I.C.S.: 531390
Diego Roux (Head-Investment)
Andrew Stacey (Head-France)
Candice Villa (Head)
Celine Lombard (Head-Finance)
Lionel Naturkrejt (Head-Investment)
Candice Villa (Head)
Celine Lombard (Head-Finance)
Lionel Naturkrejt (Head-Investment)

Cromwell Group (International) Limited　　　　(1)
65 Chartwell Drive, Wigston, Leicester, LE18 2FS, United Kingdom
Tel.: (44) 8708500055
Web Site: https://www.cromwell-industrial.co.uk
Industrial Machinery Tools & Equipment Distr
N.A.I.C.S.: 423830

Cromwell PTY Limited　　　　(1)
29/3 Birnie Ave, Lidcombe, Sydney, 2141, NSW, Australia

Tel.: (61) 293951000
Web Site: http://www.cromwellpty.com.au
Emp.: 14
Industrial Machinery Tools & Equipment Distr
N.A.I.C.S.: 423830

Cromwell Poland Sp. z o.o.　　　(1)
21st Floor Skylight Office Building Ul Zlota 59, 00-120, Warsaw, Poland
Tel.: (48) 221040501
Web Site:
　　http://www.cromwellpropertygroup.pl
Real Estate Services
N.A.I.C.S.: 531390
Karol Pilniewicz (Head)
Justyna Filipczak (Head)
Magdalena Piechna (Portfolio Mgr-Central,Eastern Europe)

Cromwell Sp z.o.o　　　　(1)
Ul Bodycha 97, Reguly, 05-816, Michalowice, Poland
Tel.: (48) 227237702
Web Site: https://www.cromwell.pl
Industrial Machinery Tools & Equipment Distr
N.A.I.C.S.: 423830

Cromwell Tools (Shanghai) Co. Ltd.　　　　(1)
Building No 2 Gaosin City 288 Fu Te North Road Free Trade Zone, Wai Gao Qiao Pu Dong, Shanghai, 200131, China
Tel.: (86) 2158664666
Web Site: http://www.cromwell.cn
Industrial Machinery Tools & Equipment Distr
N.A.I.C.S.: 423830

Cromwell Tools (Thailand) Co. Ltd.　　　　(1)
2070 Moo 1 Old Railway Road, T Samrong Nua A Mueng, Samut Prakan, 10270, Samutprakarn, Thailand
Tel.: (66) 27435353
Web Site: https://www.cromwell.co.th
Industrial Machinery Tools & Equipment Distr
N.A.I.C.S.: 423830

Cromwell Tools Ltd.　　　　(1)
Chartwell Drive, PO Box 14, Leicester, LE18 1AT, United Kingdom
Tel.: (44) 1162579304
Web Site: https://www.cromwell.co.uk
Industrial Machinery Tools & Equipment Distr
N.A.I.C.S.: 423830

Cromwell Tools Sdn. Bhd.　　　(1)
No 11 & 11A Jalan PJS 11/1 Bandar Sunway, 46150, Petaling Jaya, Selangor Darul Ehsan, Malaysia
Tel.: (60) 356386666
Web Site: https://www.cromwell.com.my
Industrial Tools Distr
N.A.I.C.S.: 423830

Cromwell Tools, PT　　　　(1)
Bizpark 2 Blok A No 7 & 8, Jl Raya Penggilingan Cakung Pulogadung, Jakarta Timur, 13940, Indonesia
Tel.: (62) 2129573960
Web Site: https://www.cromwell.co.id
Industrial Machinery Tools & Equipment Distr
N.A.I.C.S.: 423830

E & R Tooling and Solutions de Mexico, S. de R.L. de C.V.　　(1)
Calle Aristoteles 118, 66637, Apodaca, Nuevo Leon, Mexico
Tel.: (52) 8181562919
Industrial Product Distr
N.A.I.C.S.: 423840

Fabory CZ Holding S.R.O.　　　(1)
K Letisti 1825/1a, Slapanice, 627 00, Brno, Czech Republic
Tel.: (420) 533033650
Holding Company
N.A.I.C.S.: 551114
Iveta Cesalova (Accountant)

Fabory Centres Belgium N.V.　　(1)
Blancefloerlaan 181, 2050, Antwerp, Belgium
Tel.: (32) 32101211
Web Site: http://www.fabory.com

Hardware Whslr
N.A.I.C.S.: 423710

Fabory France S.A.　　　　(1)
27 Avenue de Rome, 13127, Vitrolles, France
Tel.: (33) 810815001
Web Site: http://www.fabory.com
Hardware Whslr
N.A.I.C.S.: 423710

Fabory Kotoelem Kereskedelmi KFT　　　　(1)
Fay u 4, 1139, Budapest, Hungary
Tel.: (36) 17917748
Hardware Whslr
N.A.I.C.S.: 423710
Arpad kovacs (Sr Branch Mgr)

Fabory Nederland B.V.　　　　(1)
Zevenheuvelenweg 44, PO Box 5034, 5048 AN, Tilburg, Netherlands
Tel.: (31) 135941299
Web Site: http://www.fabory.com
Hardware Whslr
N.A.I.C.S.: 423710
Peter Paul Van Tilborg (Mgr-Benefits)

Fabory Poland Sp. z.o.o.　　　(1)
ul Lutycka 93, 60-478, Poznan, Poland
Tel.: (48) 616659001
Web Site: https://www.fabory.com
Hardware Whslr
N.A.I.C.S.: 423710

Fabory Portugal Lda.　　　　(1)
Rua Rodrigo sarmento de Beires nr 18, 2840-268, Aldeia de Paio Pires, Portugal
Tel.: (351) 212135900
Web Site: https://www.fabory.com
Hardware Whslr
N.A.I.C.S.: 423710
Cristina Mostardinha (Acct Mgr)

Fabory SRL　　　　(1)
Brasov str Aurel Vlaicu nr 40 cam 17 jud, Brasov, Romania
Tel.: (40) 368442082
Web Site: https://www.fabory.com
Hardware Whslr
N.A.I.C.S.: 423710

Fabory Shanghai Co. Ltd.　　　(1)
Block 1 No 1258 Boxue Road, Malu Town Jiading District, Shanghai, 201801, China
Tel.: (86) 2169155868
Web Site: https://www.fabory.com
Hardware Whslr
N.A.I.C.S.: 423710

Fabory Slovakia SRO　　　　(1)
Alzbetina 404/33, 05801, Poprad, Slovakia
Tel.: (421) 527721148
Web Site: https://www.fabory.com
Hardware Merchant Whslr
N.A.I.C.S.: 423710

Fabory UK Ltd.　　　　(1)
Block D Bay 9 The Bescot Estate Woden Road West, Wednesbury, WS10 7SG, West Midlands, United Kingdom
Tel.: (44) 1215024000
Web Site: http://www.fabory.com
Emp.: 16
Hardware Whslr
N.A.I.C.S.: 423710

Gamut Supply LLC　　　　(1)
125 S Clark St Fl 14, Chicago, IL 60603
Tel.: (844) 464-2688
Web Site: https://www.gamut.com
Industrial Product Distr
N.A.I.C.S.: 423840

Grainger Caribe Inc.　　　　(1)
105 Ave Conquistadores, Catano, PR 00962
Tel.: (787) 275-3500
Web Site: https://www.grainger.com
Sales Range: $25-49.9 Million
Emp.: 50
Industrial Supplies
N.A.I.C.S.: 423840

Grainger Dominicana SRL　　　(1)
Zona Industrial Herrera Calle J Nave 4, Santo Domingo, Dominican Republic
Tel.: (809) 8095185245
Web Site: http://www.grainger.com
Hardware Whslr
N.A.I.C.S.: 423710

W.W. Grainger, Inc.—(Continued)

Grainger Guam L.L.C. (1)
18002 Arc Light Blvd Apt Bldg 18002 Rm 36 Lrs, Yigo, GU 96929
Tel.: (671) 653-1311
Hardware Whslr
N.A.I.C.S.: 423710

Grainger Industrial MRO de Costa Rica, S.R.L. (1)
La Uruca, San Jose, Costa Rica
Tel.: (506) 22103900
Hardware Whslr
N.A.I.C.S.: 423710
Varela Randall (Acct Mgr)

Grainger International Holdings B.V. (1)
Evert van de Beekstraat 310, 1118 CX, Schiphol, Netherlands
Tel.: (31) 205214777
Hardware Whslr
N.A.I.C.S.: 423710

Grainger International, Inc. (1)
100 Grainger Pkwy, Lake Forest, IL 60045-5201
Tel.: (847) 535-1000
Web Site: https://www.grainger.com
Holding Company
N.A.I.C.S.: 551112
Fred Costello (Pres)

Subsidiary (Non-US):

Fabory Masters in Fasteners Group B.V. (2)
Zevenheuvelenweg 44, 5048 AN, Tilburg, Netherlands
Tel.: (31) 135941299
Web Site: http://www.fabory.com
Fastener Mfr
N.A.I.C.S.: 332722
Ronoldo Baarflag (Pres & Gen Mgr)

Grainger China LLC (2)
No 2999 Huaning Road Minghang District, Minghang District, Shanghai, 201108, China
Tel.: (86) 8008208151
Web Site: http://www.grainger.com
Facilities Maintenance Product Mfr & Distr
N.A.I.C.S.: 423840

Grainger Industrial Supply India Pvt. Ltd. (2)
9th Fl El Tara Hiranandani Gardens Powai, Kanjur Marg West, Mumbai, 400076, India
Tel.: (91) 7303177399
Web Site: https://www.grainger.com
Facilities Maintenance Product Mfr & Distr
N.A.I.C.S.: 423840

Grainger Panama S.A. (2)
Panama Pacifico Blvd, Arraijan, Panama
Tel.: (507) 831 5700
Web Site: http://www.grainger.com
Facilities Maintenance Product Mfr & Distr
N.A.I.C.S.: 423840

Grainger S.A. de C.V. (2)
Aristoteles 118, Parque Industrial Kalos, 66600, Apodaca, NL, Mexico (100%)
Tel.: (52) 818 156 2900
Web Site: https://www.grainger.com.mx
Facilities Management Supply Distr
N.A.I.C.S.: 561210

Grainger Management LLC (1)
100 Grainger Pkwy, B4-C52, Lake Forest, IL 60045
Tel.: (847) 535-1555
Emp.: 8
Administration & Management Services
N.A.I.C.S.: 561110

Grainger Peru S.R.L. (1)
Av Marie Curie No 347 Urb Industrial Santa Rosa Ate, Lima, Peru
Tel.: (51) 16169100
Hardware Whslr
N.A.I.C.S.: 423710

Grainger Service Holding Company, Inc. (1)
61 Mattatuck Hts Rd Ste 3f, Oxford, CT 06705
Tel.: (203) 596-3402
Holding Company
N.A.I.C.S.: 551114

HF Suppliers (Scotland) Limited (1)
Bath Street, Peterhead, AB42 1DX, Scotland, United Kingdom
Tel.: (44) 1779480410
Web Site: http://www.hfsupplies.co.uk
Industrial Machinery Tools & Equipment Distr
N.A.I.C.S.: 423830

Imperial Supplies LLC (1)
300 N Madison St, Green Bay, WI 54307-1008
Web Site: https://www.imperialsupplies.com
Sales Range: $50-74.9 Million
Emp.: 100
Maintenance Products Distr
N.A.I.C.S.: 423840

LN Participacoes Ltda. (1)
Av Epitacio Pessoa 1674 Sl 402 Ipanema, Rio de Janeiro, 22411-273, Brazil
Tel.: (55) 22874134
Emp.: 4
Financial Management Services
N.A.I.C.S.: 541611

McFeely's (1)
320 N State St, Harrison, OH 45030
Tel.: (513) 845-4778
Web Site: http://www.mcfeelys.com
Fasteners & Woodworking Tools Online & Mail-Order Retailer
N.A.I.C.S.: 444140

MonotaRO Co., Ltd. (1)
22nd floor JP Tower Osaka 2-2-2 Umeda 3-chome, Kita-ku, Osaka, 530-0001, Hyogo, Japan
Tel.: (81) 120443509
Web Site: https://www.monotaro.com
Rev.: $1,802,887,740
Assets: $910,015,680
Liabilities: $293,313,300
Net Worth: $616,702,380
Earnings: $154,654,170
Emp.: 3,259
Fiscal Year-end: 12/31/2023
Automobile Maintenance, Engine Parts, Machine Tools & Construction Materials Mfr & Distr
N.A.I.C.S.: 333998
Masaya Suzuki (Pres & CEO)
Masato Kubo (Deputy Pres)
Masaaki Hashihara (Exec VP)
Hiroki Yoshino (Exec Officer)
Hidetoshi Taura (Exec Officer)
Taisuke Fukawa (Exec Officer)
Sakuya Tamura (Exec Officer)

Joint Venture (Non-US):

PT MonotaRO Indonesia (2)
Wisma 46 Lantai 6 Jl Jondoral Sudirman Kav 1, Kota Jakarta Pusat, Jakarta, 10220, Indonesia (51%)
Tel.: (62) 8557 467 8400
Web Site: https://www.monotaro.id
Electronic Shopping Services
N.A.I.C.S.: 423840

NAVIMRO Co., Ltd. (1)
Hyung-Keun Kim 308 309 Male Plaza Digital-ro 130, Geumcheon, Seoul, 153-776, Korea (South)
Tel.: (82) 1198666372
Web Site: https://www.navimro.com
Hardware Whslr
N.A.I.C.S.: 423710

PSS West, Inc. (1)
12778 Brookprinter Pl, Poway, CA 92064
Tel.: (858) 679-0444
Emp.: 3
Industrial Equipment Whsr
N.A.I.C.S.: 423710

PT Cromwell Tools (1)
Bizpark 2 Commercial Estate Blok A No 7&8, Ji Raya Penggilingan Cakung Pulogadung, Jakarta Timur, 13940, Indonesia
Tel.: (62) 2129573960
Web Site: https://www.cromwell.co.id
Industrial Product Distr
N.A.I.C.S.: 423840

Professional Equipment (1)
401 S Wright Rd, Janesville, WI 53546
Tel.: (608) 743-8002
Web Site: http://www.professionalequipment.com

Electrical, HVAC, Inspection & Building Professional Equipment & Supplies Online & Mail-Order Retailer
N.A.I.C.S.: 444140

Rand Materials Handling Equipment (1)
401 S Wright Rd, Janesville, WI 53546
Tel.: (608) 743-8169
Sales Range: $25-49.9 Million
Emp.: 51
Material Handling Equipment Online & Mail-Order Retailer
N.A.I.C.S.: 444140

Safety Solutions, Inc. (1)
6161 Shamrock Ct, Dublin, OH 43016
Tel.: (614) 799-9900
Web Site: https://www.safetysolutions.com
Safety & Protective Equipment & Products Distr
N.A.I.C.S.: 423830
David L Forsthoffer (Pres & CEO)

The Kennedy Group Limited (1)
Unit 14 16, Nottingham, NG9 1PF, United Kingdom
Tel.: (44) 1159223311
Non-Durable Goods Whslr
N.A.I.C.S.: 424990

W.W. Grainger - Janesville (1)
401 S Wright Rd, Janesville, WI 53546
Tel.: (608) 754-2345
Web Site: http://www.grainger.com
Lab & Safety Professional Supplies Online & Mail-Order Retailer
N.A.I.C.S.: 423490

WFS (USA) Ltd. (1)
500 Matrix Pkwy, Piedmont, SC 29673
Tel.: (864) 422-2665
Hardware Whslr
N.A.I.C.S.: 423710

WFS Ltd. (1)
730 North Service Rd, Windsor, N8X 3J3, ON, Canada
Tel.: (519) 966-2202
Web Site: https://www.wfsltd.com
Hardware Whslr
N.A.I.C.S.: 423710

Windsor Factory Supply Inc. (1)
35522 Industrial Rd, Livonia, MI 48150
Tel.: (734) 462-5882
Hardware Whslr
N.A.I.C.S.: 423710

Zoro Tools, Inc. (1)
909 Asbury Dr, Buffalo Grove, IL 60089-4525
Web Site: https://www.zoro.com
Industrial Tools & Materials Distr
N.A.I.C.S.: 423830

WABASH NATIONAL CORPORATION

Tel.: (765) 771-5310   DE
Web Site: https://ir.onewabash.com
Year Founded: 1985
WNC—(NYSE)
Rev.: $2,536,500,000
Assets: $1,362,814,000
Liabilities: $812,715,000
Net Worth: $550,099,000
Earnings: $231,252,000
Emp.: 6,700
Fiscal Year-end: 12/31/23
Commercial Truck Trailer Mfr
N.A.I.C.S.: 336212
Brent L. Yeagy (Pres & CEO)
M. Kristin Glazner (Chief HR Officer, Gen Counsel, Sec & Sr VP)
Kevin Page (Chief Comml Officer)
Michael N. Pettit (CFO, Chief Growth Officer & Sr VP)

Subsidiaries:

Extract Technology Limited (1)
Bradley Junction Industrial Estate Leeds Road, Huddersfield, HD2 1UR, United Kingdom
Tel.: (44) 1484432727
Web Site: https://www.extract-technology.com

Emp.: 77
Aseptic System Whslr
N.A.I.C.S.: 423490
Alan Wainwright (Mng Dir)
Jason Armitage (Dir-Fin)

Supreme Industries, Inc. (1)
2581 E Kercher Rd, Goshen, IN 46528 (100%)
Tel.: (574) 642-3070
Web Site: http://www.supremecorp.com
Sales Range: $250-299.9 Million
Specialized Commercial Truck Bodies & Related Truck Equipment Mfr, Sales & Repair
N.A.I.C.S.: 336211

Subsidiary (Domestic):

Supreme Corporation of Texas (2)
500 W Commerce Blvd, Cleburne, TX 76033 (100%)
Tel.: (800) 641-6282
Web Site: http://supremecorp.com
Specialized Truck Bodies Mfr
N.A.I.C.S.: 336211

Supreme Mid-Atlantic Corporation (2)
411 Jonestown Rd, Jonestown, PA 17038 (100%)
Tel.: (800) 556-6492
Web Site: http://www.supremecorp.com
Specialized Truck Bodies Mfr
N.A.I.C.S.: 336211

Supreme Truck Bodies of California, Inc. (2)
22135 Alessandro Blvd, Moreno Valley, CA 92553 (100%)
Tel.: (800) 827-0753
Motor Vehicle Parts Mfr
N.A.I.C.S.: 336211
Lara Sellars (Dir-Sls)
Rod Cook (Gen Mgr)

Division (Domestic):

Tower Structural Laminating (2)
1491 Gerber St, Ligonier, IN 46767
Tel.: (260) 894-9191
Web Site: http://www.tslaminating.com
Plywood Substrate Mfr
N.A.I.C.S.: 321211

Supreme Upfit Solutions & Service, Inc. (1)
3001 N Main St, Cleburne, TX 76033
Truck Body Mfr
N.A.I.C.S.: 336211

Transcraft Corporation (1)
110 Florisheim Dr, Anna, IL 62906
Tel.: (618) 833-5151
Web Site: http://www.transcraft.com
Sales Range: $10-24.9 Million
Emp.: 160
Motor Trucks & Trailers
N.A.I.C.S.: 336212

WNC Cloud Merger Sub, Inc. (1)
339 W Industrial Park Rd, Harrison, AR 72601-6804
Tel.: (870) 741-4810
Sales Range: $10-24.9 Million
Emp.: 300
Hardwood & Flooring Mills
N.A.I.C.S.: 314999

Wabash National Services, L.P. (1)
1000 Sagamore Pkwy S, Lafayette, IN 47905
Tel.: (765) 771-5300
Commercial Truck Trailer Mfr
N.A.I.C.S.: 336212

Wabash National Trailer Centers, Inc. (1)
1000 Sagamore Pkwy S, Lafayette, IN 47905
Tel.: (765) 771-5300
Web Site: http://www.wabashnational.com
Wholesale Motor Vehicle Trade & Repair
N.A.I.C.S.: 423110

Wabash National, L.P. (1)
1000 Sagamore Pkwy S, Lafayette, IN 47905
Tel.: (765) 771-5300
Web Site: http://www.wabashnational.com

Sales Range: $600-649.9 Million
Emp.: 4,000
Commercial Truck Trailer Mfr
N.A.I.C.S.: 336212

WAFD, INC.
425 Pike St, Seattle, WA 98101
Tel.: (206) 624-7930   **WA**
Web Site: https://www.wafdbank.com
Year Founded: 1994
WAFD—(NASDAQ)
Rev.: $1,371,710,000
Assets: $28,060,330,000
Liabilities: $25,060,030,000
Net Worth: $3,000,300,000
Earnings: $200,041,000
Emp.: 2,208
Fiscal Year-end: 09/30/24
Bank Holding Company
N.A.I.C.S.: 551111
Cathy E. Cooper (Exec VP)
Kelli J. Holz (CFO & Exec VP)
Brent J. Beardall (Pres & CEO)
Kim E. Robison (COO & Exec VP)
Ryan Mauer (Chief Credit Officer & Exec VP)
James Endrizzi (Exec VP)
Thomas J. Kelley (Chm)
Blayne Sanden (Principal Acctg Officer & Sr VP)

Subsidiaries:

Luther Burbank Corporation   **(1)**
520 3rd St 4th Fl, Santa Rosa, CA 95401
Tel.: (707) 523-9898
Web Site:
  https://www.lutherburbanksavings.com
Rev.: $262,613,000
Assets: $7,974,632,000
Liabilities: $7,292,096,000
Net Worth: $682,536,000
Earnings: $80,198,000
Emp.: 256
Fiscal Year-end: 12/31/2022
Investment Holding Services
N.A.I.C.S.: 523940

Subsidiary (Domestic):

Luther Burbank Savings   **(2)**
500 3rd St, Santa Rosa, CA 95401
Tel.: (707) 578-9216
Web Site:
  https://www.lutherburbanksavings.com
Sales Range: $75-99.9 Million
Emp.: 34
Savings & Loan Associations, Not Federally Chartered
N.A.I.C.S.: 522180
Scott Frazee (COO & Exec VP)
Tammy Mahoney (Chief Risk Officer & Exec VP)
Simone Lagomarsino (Pres)
Parham Medhat (COO)
Bill Fanter (Exec VP)

Washington Federal, National Association   **(1)**
425 Pike St, Seattle, WA 98101   **(100%)**
Tel.: (206) 204-3446
Web Site:
  http://www.washingtonfederal.com
Federal Savings & Loan Institution
N.A.I.C.S.: 522180
Kelli J. Holz (CFO & Exec VP)
Kim E. Robison (COO & Exec VP)
Michael Brown (Pres-Arizona & Reg)
Ryan Mauer (Chief Credit Officer & Exec VP)

Subsidiary (Domestic):

WAFD Insurance Group, Inc.   **(2)**
1503 Riverside Dr, Mount Vernon, WA 98273-3817   **(100%)**
Tel.: (360) 424-4559
Web Site:
  http://www.wafdinsurancegroup.com
Sales Range: $10-24.9 Million
Emp.: 7
General Insurance Agency
N.A.I.C.S.: 524210
Duane E. Henson (Pres)

WAG! GROUP CO.
55 Francisco St Ste 360, San Francisco, CA 94133
Tel.: (707) 324-4219   **DE**
Web Site: https://investors.wag.co
Year Founded: 2015
PET—(NASDAQ)
Rev.: $54,865,000
Assets: $52,311,000
Liabilities: $42,389,000
Net Worth: $9,922,000
Earnings: ($38,567,000)
Emp.: 82
Fiscal Year-end: 12/31/22
Investment Services
N.A.I.C.S.: 523999
Paul T. Norman (Pres)
Garrett Smallwood (Chm & CEO)
Alec Davidian (CFO)
Nicholas Yu (Gen Counsel)
David Cane (Chief Customer Officer)
Patrick McCarthy (CMO)
Dylan Allread (COO)
Mazi Arjomand (CTO)
Parisa Fowles-Pazdro (CEO-Maxbone)
Lindsey Canfield (Dir-People Ops)
Keith Mosley (Gen Mgr-Supply)
Kimberly Hollinger (Asst Controller)
Adam Storm (Pres & Chief Product Officer)

WAITR HOLDINGS INC.
214 Jefferson St Ste 200, Lafayette, LA 70501
Tel.: (337) 534-6881   **DE**
Web Site: http://www.waitrapp.com
Year Founded: 2008
ASAPQ—(OTCEM)
Rev.: $111,801,000
Assets: $48,145,000
Liabilities: $85,236,000
Net Worth: ($37,091,000)
Earnings: ($206,789,000)
Emp.: 255
Fiscal Year-end: 12/31/22
Investment Services
N.A.I.C.S.: 523999
Carl A. Grimstad (Chm & CEO)
Armen Yeghyazarians (CFO & Chief Acctg Officer)
David Cronin (Chief Engagement Officer)
Timothy Newton (CTO)
Thomas C. Pritchard (Gen Counsel)

WAKE FOREST BANCSHARES, INC.
302 Brooks St, Wake Forest, NC 27587
Tel.: (919) 556-5146
Web Site:
  https://www.wakeforestfederal.com
Year Founded: 1922
WAKE—(OTCIQ)
Sales Range: $1-9.9 Million
Bank Holding Company
N.A.I.C.S.: 551111
Anna O. Sumerlin (Chm)
R. W. Wilkinson III (Vice Chm)
Renee H. Shaw (Pres & CEO)
Carter S. Harrell (Chief Lending Officer & Sr VP)

Subsidiaries:

Wake Forest Federal Savings and Loan Association   **(1)**
302 Brooks St, Wake Forest, NC 27587
Tel.: (919) 555-5146
Web Site: http://www.wakeforestfederal.com
Emp.: 9
Banking Services
N.A.I.C.S.: 522110
Renee H. Shaw (Pres & CEO)
Carter S. Harrell (Chief Lending Officer & Sr VP)

WAKE UP NOW, INC.
10645 N Tatum Blvd Ste 200-6, Phoenix, AZ 85028
Tel.: (602) 373-4040   **DE**
Year Founded: 1967
WORC—(OTCIQ)
Consumer Goods Rental Services
N.A.I.C.S.: 532289
Kirby D. Cochran (Co-CEO)
Jason Elrod (Pres)
Nathan Lord (CFO)
Matt Schneck (Chief Strategy Officer)
Phillip Jacob Polich (Co-CEO, Treas & Sec)

WALDENCAST PLC
10 Bank St, White Plains, NY 10606
Tel.: (917) 546-6828   **Ky**
Web Site:
  https://www.waldencast.com
Year Founded: 2020
WALD—(NASDAQ)
Rev.: $52,047
Assets: $346,793,686
Liabilities: $401,602,720
Net Worth: ($54,809,034)
Earnings: ($14,427,685)
Emp.: 4
Fiscal Year-end: 12/31/21
Miscellaneous Financial Investment Activities
N.A.I.C.S.: 523999
Michel Brousset (Co-Founder & CEO)
Felipe Dutra (Chm)
Hind Sebti (Founder, COO & Chief Growth Officer)

Subsidiaries:

Obagi Cosmeceuticals LLC   **(1)**
3760 Kilroy Airport Way Ste 500, Long Beach, CA 90806
Web Site: https://www.obagi.com
Topical Skin Health Systems
N.A.I.C.S.: 325411

WALGREENS BOOTS ALLIANCE, INC.
108 Wilmot Rd, Deerfield, IL 60015
Tel.: (847) 315-3700   **DE**
Web Site:
  https://www.walgreensbootsalliance.com
Year Founded: 2014
WBA—(NASDAQ)
Rev.: $147,658,000,000
Assets: $81,037,000,000
Liabilities: $68,858,000,000
Net Worth: $12,179,000,000
Earnings: ($15,448,000,000)
Emp.: 193,000
Fiscal Year-end: 08/31/24
Holding Company; Pharmacies Operator
N.A.I.C.S.: 551112
Anita M. Allemand (Chief Transformation & Integration Officer)
Neal Sample (CIO & Exec VP)
Stefano Pessina (Exec Chm)
Ornella Barra (COO-Intl)
Charles V. Greener (Chief Pub Affairs Officer-Global & Sr VP)
Annie Murphy (Chief Comml Brands Officer-Global & Sr VP)
Aaron Radelet (Chief Comm Officer-Global & Sr VP)
John Standley (Pres-Walgreens & Exec VP)
Lanesha T. Minnix (Global Chief Legal Officer & Exec VP)
Richard Ellis (VP-Corp Social Responsibility)
Sebastian James (Mng Dir-Boots & Sr VP)
Vish Sankaran (Chief Innovation Officer)
Danielle Gray (Chief Legal Officer-Global & Exec VP)
Manmohan Mahajan (CFO-Global & Exec VP)
Carlos Cubia (Chief Diversity Officer-Global & Sr VP)
Holly May (Chief HR Officer-Global & Exec VP)
Alethia Jackson (Chief Diversity, Equity & Inclusion Officer & Sr VP-Environmental, Social & Governance)
Una Kent (VP-Environmental, Social & Governance-Intl)
Aaron Friedman (VP & Head-Merger, Acq & Global)
Kevin Ban (Chief Medical Officer)
Tracey Brown (Pres, Chief Medical Officer & Exec VP)
Tanya Ashton (Head-Sustainability-Global Sourcing Europe)
Todd Heckman (Chief Acctg Officer, Sr VP & Controller-Global)
Timothy Charles Wentworth (CEO)

Subsidiaries:

AA Asia Limited   **(1)**
22/F Oriental Crystal Comm Bldg Central District, Hong Kong, China (Hong Kong)
Tel.: (852) 37113232
Pharmaceutical Products Distr
N.A.I.C.S.: 424210

ANZAG Rostock GmbH & Co. KG   **(1)**
Tolzer Str 15, Grunwald, 82031, Germany
Tel.: (49) 89641430
Pharmaceutical Products Distr
N.A.I.C.S.: 424210

Alcura France   **(1)**
Zac Du Sancerrois, Saint-Germain-du-Puy, 18390, Cher, France
Tel.: (33) 248655056
Pharmaceutical Products Distr
N.A.I.C.S.: 424210

Alcura Health Espana, S.A.   **(1)**
C/Cinca 20-22 Poligono Industrial Sta Margarida, Barcelona, 08223, Terrassa, Spain
Tel.: (34) 937360870
Web Site: https://www.alcura-health.es
Health Care Srvices
N.A.I.C.S.: 424210

Alcura UK Limited   **(1)**
Selborne House Mill Lane, Alton, GU34 2QJ, United Kingdom
Tel.: (44) 1420543400
Home Care Services
N.A.I.C.S.: 621610

Alliance Boots Holdings Limited   **(1)**
Sedley Place 4th Floor 361 Oxford Street, London, W1C 2JL, United Kingdom
Tel.: (44) 1159506111
Holding Company
N.A.I.C.S.: 551112

Alliance Boots Sourcing (Hong Kong) Limited   **(1)**
Rm 2101-05 21/f China Resources Bldg 26 Harbour Rd, Wan Chai, Hong Kong, China (Hong Kong)
Tel.: (852) 27306278
Emp.: 1,982
Pharmaceutical Products Distr
N.A.I.C.S.: 424210
Yu Ivy (Mgr-Sourcing)

Alliance Healthcare France SA   **(1)**
222 rue des Caboeufs, 92622, Gennevilliers, Cedex, France
Tel.: (33) 140805100
Web Site: https://www.alliance-healthcare.fr
Emp.: 250
Health Care Srvices
N.A.I.C.S.: 621610

Alliance Healthcare Ltd.   **(1)**
43 Cox Lane, Chessington, KT9 1SN, Surrey, United Kingdom
Tel.: (44) 2083912323
Web Site: https://www.alliance-healthcare.co.uk
Pharmaceuticals Whslr
N.A.I.C.S.: 424210

Walgreens Boots Alliance, Inc.—(Continued)

Pablo Rivas *(Fin Dir)*
Julian Mount *(Mng Dir)*
Marie Evans *(Dir-Comml & Category)*
Stuart Green *(Dir-Programme Mgmt & Implementation)*
Lucie Massart *(Gen Counsel)*
Matt Addison *(Dir-Ops)*
Owen Cooper *(Dir-Client Svcs)*
Moyra Withycombe *(Dir-HR)*
Ashley Kilgas *(Sls Dir)*
Jeremy Ehlers *(Dir-IT)*
Mark Lincoln *(Dir-Bus Transformation)*

Subsidiary (Domestic):

Alliance Healthcare (Distribution) Limited (2)
43 Cox Lane, Chessington, KT9 1SN, United Kingdom
Tel.: (44) 2083912323
Web Site: http://www.alliance-healthcare.co.uk
Pharmaceutical Products Distr
N.A.I.C.S.: 456110

Alliance Healthcare (IT Services) Limited (2)
2 The Heights Brooklands, Weybridge, KT13 0NY, United Kingdom
Tel.: (44) 1932870550
Health Care Srvices
N.A.I.C.S.: 456191

Subsidiary (Non-US):

Alliance Healthcare Deutschland AG (2)
Solmsstrasse 73, 60486, Frankfurt, Germany
Tel.: (49) 69792030
Web Site: https://www.alliance-healthcare.de
Emp.: 2,892
Pharmaceutical Products Distr
N.A.I.C.S.: 424210

Alliance Healthcare Espana S.A. (2)
Pol Ind Estruch Avda Verge de Montserrat 6, El Prat de Llobregat, 08820, Barcelona, Spain
Web Site: http://www.alliance-healthcare.es
Pharmaceutical Products Distr
N.A.I.C.S.: 424210
Javier Casas Cantero *(Mng Dir)*
David Perez Hidalgo *(CFO)*
Remedios Parra *(Dir-Pharmacies & Laboratories)*

Alliance Healthcare Group France (2)
222 rue des Caboeufs, 92622, Gennevilliers, France
Tel.: (33) 140805100
Web Site: https://www.alliance-healthcare.fr
Emp.: 300
Pharmaceutical Products Distr
N.A.I.C.S.: 424210

Alliance Healthcare Group France (2)
222 Rue Des Caboeufs, 92622, Paris, Cedex, France
Tel.: (33) 140805100
Web Site: http://www.alliance-healthcare.fr
Pharmaceutical Products Distr
N.A.I.C.S.: 424210

Alliance Healthcare Italia SpA (2)
Via Moggia 75A, Lavagna, 16033, Genoa, Italy
Tel.: (39) 018531571
Web Site: https://www.alliance-healthcare.it
Pharmaceutical Products Distr
N.A.I.C.S.: 424210

Subsidiary (Domestic):

Alliance Healthcare Management Services Limited (2)
43 Cox Lane, Chessington, KT9 1SN, United Kingdom
Tel.: (44) 2083912323
Business Management Services
N.A.I.C.S.: 561110

Subsidiary (Non-US):

Alliance Healthcare Nederland (2)
Pomphoekweg 1, 5222 BE, 's-Hertogenbosch, Netherlands
Tel.: (31) 889111040
Web Site: http://www.alliance-healthcare.nl
Retail Pharmacies
N.A.I.C.S.: 456110

Alliance Healthcare Norge A.S. (2)
Snipetjernveien 10, 1405, Langhus, Norway
Tel.: (47) 64850300
Web Site: https://www.alliance-healthcare.no
Emp.: 120
Pharmaceutical & Nursing Products Distr
N.A.I.C.S.: 424210

Alliance Healthcare, s.r.o. (2)
Podle Trati 624/7, 108 00, Prague, 10, Czech Republic
Tel.: (420) 800310101
Web Site: https://www.alliance-healthcare.cz
Emp.: 700
Pharmaceutical Products Distr
N.A.I.C.S.: 424210
Vladimir Bruha *(Mgr-IT)*
Jan Rohrbacher *(Dir-Sls)*
Helena Lappyova *(Mgr-HR)*
Jaroslava Dolezelova *(Mgr-SDP Dept)*
Jaroslav Kozak *(Dir-Sls & Mktg)*

Subsidiary (Domestic):

OTC Direct Ltd. (2)
43 Cox Lane, Chessington, KT9 1SN, United Kingdom
Tel.: (44) 8001692305
Web Site: https://www.otcdirectltd.co.uk
Pharmaceuticals Whslr
N.A.I.C.S.: 424210

Alliance Healthcare Romania SRL (1)
Str Amilcar C Sandulescu nr 7 sector 6, 060859, Bucharest, Romania
Tel.: (40) 214077711
Web Site: https://www.alliance-healthcare.ro
Healtcare Services
N.A.I.C.S.: 621610

Alliance Healthcare s.r.o. (1)
Podle Trati 624/7, 108 00, Prague, 10, Malesice, Czech Republic
Tel.: (420) 296567592
Web Site: https://www.alliance-healthcare.cz
Health Care Srvices
N.A.I.C.S.: 621610

Alloga (Nederland) B.V. (1)
Logistic Services
N.A.I.C.S.: 541614

Alloga France (1)
Europrogramme 40 boulevard de Dunkerquo, CS 41221, 13471, Marseille, Cedex 02, France
Tel.: (33) 491281500
Web Site: https://www.alloga.fr
Pharmaceutical Products Distr
N.A.I.C.S.: 424210

Alloga UK Limited (1)
Castlewood Business Park Farmwell Lane, South Normanton, DE55 2JX, Derbyshire, United Kingdom
Tel.: (44) 1773582925
Web Site: https://www.alloga.co.uk
Health Care Srvices
N.A.I.C.S.: 456191

Almus France (1)
211 avenue des Gresillons, 92230, Gennevilliers, France
Tel.: (33) 140801844
Web Site: https://www.almus.fr
Pharmaceutical Products Distr
N.A.I.C.S.: 424210

Alphega (1)
222 Rue Des Caboeufs, 92230, Gennevilliers, Cedex, France
Tel.: (33) 140802300
Web Site: http://www.alphega-pharmacie.fr
Pharmaceutical Products Distr
N.A.I.C.S.: 424210

Alphega Apothekenpartner GmbH (1)
Solmsstrasse 73, 60486, Frankfurt, Germany
Tel.: (49) 697191850
Pharmaceutical Products Distr

N.A.I.C.S.: 424210
Jan Detlef Wohlert *(Mng Dir)*
Nikolaus Vogler *(Mng Dir)*
Juan Guerra *(Mng Dir)*

Apotheek Hagi B.V. (1)
Pomphoekweg 1, 's-Hertogenbosch, 5222 BE, Netherlands
Tel.: (31) 881040555
Pharmaceutical Products Distr
N.A.I.C.S.: 456110

Aromatherapy Associates, Inc (1)
4900 Preston Rd Ste 108, Frisco, TX 75034
Tel.: (972) 334-0923
Perfume Distr
N.A.I.C.S.: 456120

Beccles H.C.C. Limited (1)
St Marys Road, Beccles, NR34 9NQ, United Kingdom
Tel.: (44) 1502717278
Pharmaceutical Products Distr
N.A.I.C.S.: 456110

Boots Charitable Trust (1)
1 Thane Rd West, Nottingham, NG90 1BS, United Kingdom
Tel.: (44) 1159492185
Charitable Trust Operator
N.A.I.C.S.: 813211

Boots Hearingcare Limited (1)
21 Trinity Square, Llandudno, LL30 2RH, United Kingdom
Tel.: (44) 3452701600
Web Site: https://www.bootshearingcare.com
Health Care Srvices
N.A.I.C.S.: 621610

Boots Nederland B.V. (1)
Bongerdstraat 227a, 5931 NE, Tegelen, Netherlands
Tel.: (31) 773263326
Pharmaceutical Products Distr
N.A.I.C.S.: 456110

Boots Opticians Professional Services Limited (1)
1 Thane Road West, Nottingham, NG90 1BS, Nottinghamshire, United Kingdom
Tel.: (44) 8451253771
Optical Goods Distr
N.A.I.C.S.: 456130

Boots Retail (Ireland) Limited (1)
2nd Floor 5 Riverwalk, Citywest Business Campus Citywest, Dublin, D24 TW13, Ireland
Tel.: (353) 1890200008
Web Site: https://www.boots.ie
Emp.: 2,000
Health Care Srvices
N.A.I.C.S.: 621610

Boots Retail USA Inc. (1)
40 Wall St Fl 22, New York, NY 10005
Tel.: (212) 273-5000
Pharmaceutical Products Distr
N.A.I.C.S.: 424210
Lori Fruit *(VP-Fin)*

CareCentrix, Inc. (55%)
20 Church St Ste 1100, East Hartford, CT 06103
Tel.: (860) 528-4038
Web Site: http://www.carecentrix.com
Home Health Care Benefits Management Services
N.A.I.C.S.: 524292
Alison K. Gilligan *(Chief Legal & Strategic Solutions Officer)*
Steven J. Shulman *(Chm)*
Tom Gaffney *(Chief Custom Officer)*
Steven Horowitz *(CEO & CFO)*
Michael Cantor *(Chief Medical Officer)*
Tej Anand *(CTO)*
Gisele Molloy *(Chief Compliance Officer)*
Steve Wogen *(Chief Growth Officer)*
Kimberly Paul *(CTO)*
Scott Markovich *(Gen Mgr-Medicaid)*

Circa LLC (1)
PO Box 552, Moorestown, NJ 08057
Tel.: (609) 923-7110
Pharmaceutical Products Distr
N.A.I.C.S.: 424210

E. Moss, Limited (1)
22a Bertie Road, Kenilworth, CV8 1JP, War-

wickshire, United Kingdom
Tel.: (44) 8450708090
Pharmaceutical Products Distr
N.A.I.C.S.: 456110

Euro Registratie Collectief B.V. (1)
Kempkens 2200, 5465 PR, Veghel, Netherlands
Tel.: (31) 180510365
Web Site: https://www.euroregcol.nl
Health Care Srvices
N.A.I.C.S.: 621610

Farmacias Ahumada S.A. (1)
802 las Condes, Santiago, Chile
Tel.: (56) 27981000
Web Site: https://www.farmaciasahumada.cl
Pharmaceutical Products Distr
N.A.I.C.S.: 424210

Farmacias Benavides S.A.B. de C.V. (1)
Av Fundadores No 935 Valle del Mirador, 64750, Monterrey, Mexico
Tel.: (52) 8181507700
Web Site: https://www.benavides.com.mx
Health Care Srvices
N.A.I.C.S.: 621610

HF Healthcare Limited (1)
6 South Nelson Ind Est, Cramlington, NE23 1WF, United Kingdom
Tel.: (44) 1670707777
Weight Management Services
N.A.I.C.S.: 812191

Hedef International Holdings BV (1)
De Amert 603, Veghel, 5462 GH, Noord-Brabant, Netherlands
Tel.: (31) 881040911
Holding Company
N.A.I.C.S.: 551112

Liz Earle Beauty Co. Limited (1)
Tel.: (44) 1983813913
Emp.: 700
Skin Care Product Mfr
N.A.I.C.S.: 325620
Liz Earle *(Co-Founder)*
Kim Buckland *(Co-Founder)*

Maryhill Dispensary Limited (1)
41 Shaw Park St, Glasgow, G20 9DR, United Kingdom
Tel.: (44) 1415318831
Physicians Centers
N.A.I.C.S.: 621111

Megapharm GmbH Pharmazeutische Erzeugnisse (1)
Rathausallee 10, 53757, Saint Augustin, Germany
Tel.: (49) 224193570
Emp.: 2,008
Pharmaceutical Products Distr
N.A.I.C.S.: 424210

Oktal Pharma d.o.o. (1)
Utinjska 40, 10020, Zagreb, Croatia
Tel.: (385) 16595777
Web Site: https://www.oktal-pharma.hr
Pharmaceutical Products Distr
N.A.I.C.S.: 424210
Asja Ostrogovic *(Mgr-Pur)*

Onsite Holding LLC (1)
333 W Wacker Dr Ste 2800, Chicago, IL 60606
Tel.: (312) 506-2900
Holding Company
N.A.I.C.S.: 551112

Pharmdata s.r.o. (1)
Dedinska 893/29, 161 00, Prague, 6, Ruzyne, Czech Republic
Tel.: (420) 235363617
Web Site: https://www.pharmdata.cz
Health Care Srvices
N.A.I.C.S.: 621610

Ramuneles Vaistine UAB (1)
Future g 10, Vilnius, 08303, Lithuania
Tel.: (370) 52715268
Web Site: http://www.ramunesvaistine.lt
Pharmaceutical Drug Mfr
N.A.I.C.S.: 325412
Aidas Uzdavinys *(Mng Dir)*

Serex (1)
222 Rue Des Caboeufs, Gennevilliers, 92230, Hauts De Seine, France

Tel.: (33) 493073891
Pharmaceutical Products Distr
N.A.I.C.S.: 424210

Servicios Logisticos Benavides, S.A. de C.V. (1)
Founders Av No 935, Monterrey, 64750, Nuevo Leon, Mexico
Tel.: (52) 8181507700
Administrative Management Consulting Services
N.A.I.C.S.: 541611

Servicios Operacionales Benavides, S.A. de C.V. (1)
Av Fundadores No 935, Monterrey, 64750, NL, Mexico
Tel.: (52) 8183899900
Pharmaceutical Products Distr
N.A.I.C.S.: 456110

Skills in Healthcare GmbH Deutschland (1)
Solmsstrasse 25, 60486, Frankfurt, Germany
Tel.: (49) 6979203380
Web Site: http://www.skills-in-healthcare.de
Pharmaceutical Products Distr
N.A.I.C.S.: 424210
Silvia Eggenweiler (Mng Dir)

Spa Strategy Limited (1)
29 Albert Street, Warwick, CV34 4JX, United Kingdom
Tel.: (44) 7969686644
Web Site: https://spastrategy.net
Health Care Srvices
N.A.I.C.S.: 621610

Spits B.V. (1)
Diamantweg 21a, 1812 RC, Alkmaar, Netherlands
Tel.: (31) 725114292
Web Site: https://www.spitsbv.nl
Health Care Srvices
N.A.I.C.S.: 621610

The Boots Company PLC (1)
1 Thane Road, Nottingham, NG90 1BS, United Kingdom
Tel.: (44) 3456032020
Web Site: https://www.boots.co.uk
Emp.: 8,000
Hoding Company; Pharmaceutical Products Distr
N.A.I.C.S.: 551112

Subsidiary (Non-US):

Boots Apotek AS (2)
Lorenfaret 1, 0580, Oslo, Norway
Tel.: (47) 23250700
Web Site: https://www.boots.no
Drugs & Druggists Supplies Whslr
N.A.I.C.S.: 424210
Margrethe Sunde (CEO & Mng Dir)

Subsidiary (Domestic):

Boots UK Limited (2)
1 Thane Road West, Nottingham, NG90 1BS, United Kingdom
Tel.: (44) 115 950 6111
Web Site: http://www.boots-uk.com
Emp.: 8,000
Pharmacy, Health & Beauty Product Retail Services
N.A.I.C.S.: 456110

Subsidiary (Domestic):

Boots Opticians Ltd (3)
1 Thane Road West, Nottingham, NG90 1BS, United Kingdom
Tel.: (44) 3451253752
Testing, Dispensing & Eyecare Services
N.A.I.C.S.: 339115
Jonathan Gardner (Mng Dir)

United Company of Pharmacists SAE (1)
5 Samir Sayed Ahmed Street El Manial, Cairo, Egypt
Tel.: (20) 223644052
Web Site: https://www.unitedcompanyofpharmacists.com
Health Care Srvices
N.A.I.C.S.: 621610

Walgreen Co. (1)

108 Wilmot Rd MS Ste 2002, Deerfield, IL 60015
Tel.: (847) 315-2500
Web Site: https://www.walgreens.com
Fiscal Year-end: 08/31/2014
Drug Store Operator
N.A.I.C.S.: 456110
James A. Skinner (Chm)
Stefano Pessina (Vice Chm & Acting CEO)
Timothy J. Theriault (CIO, Chief Innovation Officer, Chief Improvement Officer & Sr VP)
Rick Gates (Sr VP-Pharmacy)
Rob Ewing (Reg VP)
Kevin Ban (Chief Medical Officer)
Hillary Leisten (Chief HR Officer)
Rina Shah (Grp VP-Pharmacy Ops & Svcs)
Elena Kraus (Co-Gen Counsel & Sr VP)
Adam Holyk (Sr VP-Strategy)
Linh Peters (CMO & Sr VP)
Bala Visalatha (Chief Product Officer & Sr VP)
Luke Rauch (Chief Mdsg Officer & Sr VP)
Tracey Brown (Chief Customer Officer & Pres-Retail Products)

Subsidiary (Domestic):

Baxter Drug, Inc. (2)
1000 Military Ave, Baxter Springs, KS 66713
Tel.: (620) 856-5858
Web Site: http://www.walgreen.com
Emp.: 5
Pharmacy & Drug Store Operator
N.A.I.C.S.: 456110

CG Transportation, LLC (2)
1035 E Watson Ctr Rd, Carson, CA 90745
Tel.: (310) 420-7582
Emp.: 2
Transport Support Services
N.A.I.C.S.: 488999

Crescent Healthcare, Inc. (2)
888 S Disneyland Dr Ste 200, Anaheim, CA 92802
Tel.: (714) 520-6300
Rev.: $1,100,000
Emp.: 30
Women Healthcare Services
N.A.I.C.S.: 621610

Cystic Fibrosis Foundation Pharmacy, LLC (2)
2019 Alexander Dr Ste 2A, Dothan, AL 36301
Tel.: (334) 699-3932
Pharmaceutical Products Distr
N.A.I.C.S.: 424210

DS Pharmacy, Inc. (2)
407 Heron Dr, Swedesboro, NJ 08085
Tel.: (856) 241-5014
Emp.: 7
Pharmacy & Drug Store Operator
N.A.I.C.S.: 456110

Duane Reade Holdings, Inc. (2)
440 9th Ave, New York, NY 10001-1641
Tel.: (212) 273-5700
Web Site: http://www.duanereade.com
Emp.: 100
Drug Store
N.A.I.C.S.: 456110

Subsidiary (Domestic):

Duane Reade, Inc. (3)
40 Wall St, New York, NY 10005-1620
Tel.: (212) 273-5700
Web Site: http://www.duanereade.com
Sales Range: $1-4.9 Billion
Emp.: 7,000
Drugstore Chain Operator
N.A.I.C.S.: 456110

Subsidiary (Domestic):

Duane Reade Realty, Inc. (4)
40 Wall St 22 Fl, New York, NY 10005
Tel.: (212) 273-5700
Web Site: http://www.duanereade.com
Drug Store
N.A.I.C.S.: 456110

Subsidiary (Domestic):

Duane Reade International, LLC (2)
517-519 Broadway, Bayonne, NJ 07002
Tel.: (212) 273-5700
Pharmacy & Drug Store Operator

N.A.I.C.S.: 456110

East-West Distributing Co. (2)
200 Wilmot Rd, Deerfield, IL 60015-4620
Tel.: (847) 914-3102
Pharmaceutical Product Whslr
N.A.I.C.S.: 424210
Mihir Desai (Pres)

Subsidiary (Non-US):

Farmacias Benavides SAB DE CV (2)
Fundadores Avenue No 935 Valle del Mirador, 64750, Monterrey, NL, Mexico
Tel.: (52) 8181260000
Web Site: https://www.benavides.com.mx
Rev.: $1,014,966,147
Assets: $528,817,037
Liabilities: $504,185,171
Net Worth: $24,631,866
Earnings: $16,635,165
Emp.: 8,064
Fiscal Year-end: 12/31/2023
Pharmaceutical, Sanitary, Cosmetic & Health Care Products Sls & Distr
N.A.I.C.S.: 456110
Jose Luis Rojas Toledo (Gen Dir)

Subsidiary (Domestic):

Happy Harry's Discount Drug Stores, Inc. (2)
200 Wilmot Rd, Deerfield, IL 60015
Tel.: (877) 924-4472
Web Site: http://www.walgreens.com
Holding Company; Drug Stores Operator
N.A.I.C.S.: 551112

Subsidiary (Domestic):

Happy Harry's Inc. (3)
200 Wilmot Rd, Deerfield, IL 60015
Tel.: (877) 924-4472
Web Site: http://www.walgreens.com
Drug Store Operator
N.A.I.C.S.: 456110

Subsidiary (Domestic):

Pharm-mart Pharmacy of Warren, Inc. (2)
310 S Martin St, Warren, AR 71671
Tel.: (870) 226-3746
Medical Product Whslr
N.A.I.C.S.: 423450

Subsidiary (Non-US):

Salient Business Solutions, Ltd. (2)
Plot No 47 1st Fl Phase-IV, Udyog Vihar, Gurgaon, 122022, Haryana, India
Tel.: (91) 1244343434
Web Site: http://www.salientbpo.com
Sales Range: $25-49.9 Million
Emp.: 15
Business Process Outsourcing Services
N.A.I.C.S.: 561499

Skincarestore Australia Pty Ltd. (2)
664 Darling St, Rozelle, 2039, NSW, Australia
Tel.: (61) 300881216
Web Site: http://www.skincarestore.com.au
Cosmetic Product Distr
N.A.I.C.S.: 456120

Subsidiary (Domestic):

Springville Pharmacy Infusion Therapy, Inc. (2)
40 Ctr Dr, Orchard Park, NY 14127-4100
Tel.: (716) 667-7500
Web Site: http://www.optioncare.com
Emp.: 35
Women Healthcare Services
N.A.I.C.S.: 621610
John C. Rademacher (Pres & CEO)
Cliff Berman (Gen Counsel)
Seema Kumbhat (Chief Medical Officer)
Harriet Booker (COO)
Rich Denness (Chief Comml Officer)
Brett Michalak (CIO)
Cari Reed (Chief Compliance Officer)
Mike Rude (Chief HR Officer)
Mike Shapiro (CFO)
Luke Whitworth (Sr VP-Revenue Cycle Mgmt)
Brenda Wright (Chief Clinical Officer)

N.A.I.C.S.: 456110

Stephen L. LaFrance Pharmacy, Inc. (2)
3017 N Midland Dr, Pine Bluff, AR 71603
Tel.: (870) 535-5171
Emp.: 1,500
Pharmacy & Drug Store Operator
N.A.I.C.S.: 456110

Trinity HomeCare LLC (2)
114-02 15th Ave 1st Fl, College Point, NY 11356-1452
Tel.: (718) 961-1634
Web Site: http://www.walgreenshealth.com
Sales Range: $10-24.9 Million
Emp.: 50
Women Healthcare Services
N.A.I.C.S.: 621610
Paul Mastrata (Pres & CEO)

WAB Holdings, LLC (2)
1126 Gate Post Ct, Powder Springs, GA 30127
Tel.: (770) 439-1521
Emp.: 2
Holding Company
N.A.I.C.S.: 551112

Walgreen Hastings Co. (2)
200 Wilmot Rd, Deerfield, IL 60015
Tel.: (847) 940-2500
Web Site: http://www.walgreen.com
Sales Range: $1-4.9 Billion
Emp.: 6,000
Holding Company; Retail Drug Store Operator
N.A.I.C.S.: 551112

Subsidiary (Domestic):

Walgreen Arizona Drug Co. (3)
200 Wilmot Rd, Deerfield, IL 60015
Tel.: (847) 940-2500
Web Site: http://www.walgreen.com
Sales Range: $250-299.9 Million
Holding Company; Retail Drug Store Operator
N.A.I.C.S.: 551112

Subsidiary (Domestic):

Walgreen Eastern Co., Inc. (4)
780 Waukegan Rd, Deerfield, IL 60015
Tel.: (847) 945-0611
Web Site: http://www.walgreen.com
Sales Range: $250-299.9 Million
Retail Drug Store Operator
N.A.I.C.S.: 456110

Subsidiary (Domestic):

Bond Drug Company of Illinois, LLC (5)
200 Wilmot Rd, Deerfield, IL 60015
Tel.: (847) 940-2500
Web Site: http://www.walgreen.com
Sales Range: $150-199.9 Million
Retail Drug Store Operator
N.A.I.C.S.: 456110

Subsidiary (Domestic):

Waltrust Properties, Inc. (6)
104 Wilmot Rd, Deerfield, IL 60015
Tel.: (847) 940-2500
Real Estate Investment Trust
N.A.I.C.S.: 525990

Subsidiary (Domestic):

Walgreen Louisiana Co., Inc. (2)
7101 Veterans Memorial Blvd, Metairie, LA 70003
Tel.: (504) 455-2431
Web Site: http://www.walgreens.com
Sales Range: $150-199.9 Million
Retail Drug Store Operator
N.A.I.C.S.: 456110

Walgreen Mercantile Corp. (2)
200 Wilmot Rd, Deerfield, IL 60015
Tel.: (847) 940-2500
Web Site: http://www.walgreens.com
Sales Range: $150-199.9 Million
Owner of Drug Stores
N.A.I.C.S.: 456110
Stefano Pessina (CEO)

Walgreen National Corporation (2)
200 Wilmot Rd, Deerfield, IL 60015
Tel.: (847) 940-2500
Web Site: http://www.walgreens.com

Walgreens Boots Alliance, Inc.—(Continued)

Sales Range: $150-199.9 Million
Emp.: 10,000
Owner of Drug Stores
N.A.I.C.S.: 456110

Walgreen of Hawaii, LLC (2)
1520 N School St, Honolulu, HI 96817
Tel.: (808) 845-7111
Pharmacy & Drug Store Operator
N.A.I.C.S.: 456110

Walgreen of Maui, Inc. (2)
342 Keawe St Bldg D, Lahaina, HI 96761-2739
Tel.: (808) 667-9515
Drug Mfr
N.A.I.C.S.: 456110

Walgreen of Puerto Rico, Inc. (2)
580 Marginal Buchanan Villa Caparra, Guaynabo, PR 00966-1706
Tel.: (787) 705-6555
Sales Range: $50-74.9 Million
Emp.: 40
Retail Drug Store Operator
N.A.I.C.S.: 456110

Walgreen of San Patricio, Inc. (2)
580 Marginal Buchanan Ext Villa Catarra, Guaynabo, PR 00966-1706
Tel.: (787) 705-6555
Web Site: http://www.walgreen.com
Sales Range: $150-199.9 Million
Emp.: 50
Retail Drug Store Operator
N.A.I.C.S.: 456110

Division (Domestic):

Walgreens Health & Wellness (2)
200 Wilmot Rd, Deerfield, IL 60015
Tel.: (847) 282-0283
Health Care Clinic & Pharmacy Operator
N.A.I.C.S.: 551112

Subsidiary (Domestic):

Take Care Health Systems, LLC (3)
8 Tower Bridge 161 Washington St Ste 1400, Conshohocken, PA 19428-2087 (100%)
Tel.: (484) 351-2070
Web Site: http://www.takecarehealth.com
Sales Range: $75-99.9 Million
Health Care Clinic Operator
N.A.I.C.S.: 456199

Division (Domestic):

Walgreens Health Services (2)
200 Wilmot Rd, Deerfield, IL 60015
Tel.: (847) 914-2500
Web Site: http://www.walgreenshealth.com
Pharmacy Benefit Management, Drug Mail Order, Home Care & Specialty Pharmacy Services
N.A.I.C.S.: 551112

Subsidiary (Domestic):

Walgreens Mail Service, Inc. (3)
8350 S River Pkwy, Tempe, AZ 85284
Web Site: https://www.alliancerxwp.com
Sales Range: $150-199.9 Million
Mail Order Drug Retailer
N.A.I.C.S.: 456110

Subsidiary (Domestic):

Walgreen Medical Supply, LLC (4)
18861 S 90th Ave, Mokena, IL 60487-9373
Tel.: (888) 410-5779
Medical & Hospital Equipment Whslr
N.A.I.C.S.: 456110

Subsidiary (Domestic):

Walgreens Specialty Care Centers, LLC (2)
1301 2nd Ave SW 290, Largo, FL 33770
Tel.: (727) 674-9990
Outpatient Care Services
N.A.I.C.S.: 621498

Walgreens Specialty Pharmacy Holdings, Inc. (2)
9775 SW Gemini Dr Ste 1, Beaverton, OR 97008-7148
Tel.: (503) 643-8511
Pharmacy Drug Retailer

N.A.I.C.S.: 456110

Subsidiary (Domestic):

Walgreens Specialty Pharmacy, LLC (3)
2055 Old Washington Pike, Carnegie, PA 15106-1230
Tel.: (412) 429-3601
Pharmacy Product Retailer
N.A.I.C.S.: 456110

Subsidiary (Domestic):

Walgreens.com, Inc. (2)
200 Wilmot Rd, Deerfield, IL 60015
Tel.: (847) 940-2500
Web Site: http://www.walgreens.com
Sales Range: $150-199.9 Million
Electronic Commerce Pharmaceutical Retailer
N.A.I.C.S.: 456110

drugstore.com, inc. (2)
411 108th Ave NE Ste 1400, Bellevue, WA 98004-8404
Tel.: (425) 372-3200
Web Site: http://www.drugstore.com
Sales Range: $300-349.9 Million
Emp.: 945
Online Retailer of Drug & Beauty Products
N.A.I.C.S.: 456110

Walgreens of North Carolina, Inc. (1)
1901 E Voorhees St MS 790, Danville, IL 61834-4509
Tel.: (217) 709-2386
Pharmaceutical Products Distr
N.A.I.C.S.: 424210

Well Ventures, LLC (1)
405 W 23rd St, New York, NY 10011
Tel.: (212) 627-7243
All Supporting Services
N.A.I.C.S.: 561499

vitasco GmbH (1)
Schmidhausener Str 48, 71717, Beilstein, Germany
Tel.: (49) 706294930
Web Site: https://www.vitasco.de
Pharmaceutical Products Distr
N.A.I.C.S.: 424210
Jan Detlef Wohlert (Mng Dir)

WALKER & DUNLOP, INC.
7272 Wisconsin Ave Ste 1300, Bethesda, MD 20814
Tel.: (301) 215-5500 MD
Web Site:
http://www.walkerdunlop.com
Year Founded: 1937
WD—(NYSE)
Rev.: $1,054,440,000
Assets: $4,052,347,000
Liabilities: $2,306,218,000
Net Worth: $1,746,129,000
Earnings: $107,357,000
Emp.: 1,326
Fiscal Year-end: 12/31/23
Holding Company; Real Estate Financing Services
N.A.I.C.S.: 551112
Michael D. Malone (Co-Founder)
William M. Walker (Chm, Pres & CEO)
David T. Strange (Sr Mng Dir)
Albert G. Rex (Mng Dir)
Michael J. Lee (Sr Dir)
Stephen P. Theobald (COO & Exec VP)
Mark Grace (Mng Dir)
Christopher Rumul (Sr Mng Dir)
Justin Nelson (Sr Mng Dir)
Mikko Erkamaa (Sr DIr)
Patrick K. Dempsey (Sr Mng Dir)
Greg Florkowski (CFO & Exec VP)
James Schroeder (Exec VP-Servicing)
Jeremy Pino (Sr Dir)
Livingston Hessam (Sr Dir)
Ralph Lowen (Sr Mng Dir)
Thomas Toland (Sr Dir)

Will Baker (Sr Mng Dir)
William Harvey (Dir- Investment Sls)
Hal Reinauer (Dir-Massachusetts)
Jeffrey C. Ringwald (Mng Dir)
Stuart Wernick (Mng Dir)
Jeff Robbins (Mng Dir)
Brian Moulder (Mng Dir-Investment Sls)
Dhaval Patel (Mng Dir)
Mark Strauss (Mng Dir)
Taylor Williams (Mng Dir)
Telly Fathaly (Mng Dir)
Gregory Krafcik (Mng Dir)
James M. Cope (Mng Dir & Exec VP)
Paula A. Pryor (Chief HR Officer & Exec VP)
Jeff Burns (Sr Mng Dir)
Tim Cotter (Dir-Wisconsin Office)
Michael Darling (Sr Mng Dir)
Allan Edelson (Sr Mng Dir)
Brian Eisner (Mng Dir)
Matt Ewig (Mng Dir)
Stephen Farnsworth (Sr Mng Dir)
Trevor Fase (Sr Mng Dir)
Bryan Frazier (Mng Dir-Growth & Dev)
Scott Spencer (Sr VP-Internal Audit)
Alex Inman (Sr Mng Dir)
Alisan Rutland (Mng Dir)
Amos Smith (Sr VP)
Andrew Gnazzo (Sr Mng Dir)
Andrew Tapley (Sr Mng Dir)
Craig West (Sr Mng Dir)
David Collie (Mng Dir-Capital Markets Grp)
David Jungreis (Dir-Englewood)
Joshua Rosen (Sr Mng Dir)
Cliff Ayers (Dir-Bethesda)
David Levy (Chief Credit Officer & Exec VP)
Carol McNerney (CMO)
Issa Bannourah (Treas)
Johnny Harris (Sr VP)
Gerene Behrens (Sr VP)
Irelynne Estevez-Waller (VP)
Donald P. King III (Exec VP-Multifamily)
Alfred I. Means III (Mng Dir-Capital Markets)

Subsidiaries:

Engler Financial Group, LLC (1)
1000 Windward Concourse Ste 110, Alpharotta, GA 30005
Tel.: (678) 992-2000
Web Site: http://www.efgus.com
Sales Range: $1-9.9 Million
Real Estate Investment Advisory Services
N.A.I.C.S.: 531390

GeoPhy B.V. (1)
Waldorpstraat 11A 7th & 8th Floor, 2521CA, Hague, Netherlands
Tel.: (31) 702210184
Web Site: https://geophy.com
Commercial Real Estate Consulting Services
N.A.I.C.S.: 531210

Walker & Dunlop Capital, LLC (1)
7501 Wisconsin Ave Ste 1200, Bethesda, MD 20814-6531
Tel.: (301) 215-5500
Emp.: 180
Real Estate Related Services
N.A.I.C.S.: 531390

Walker & Dunlop Investment Partners, Inc. (1)
1225 17th St Ste 1660, Denver, CO 80202
Tel.: (303) 802-3570
Web Site:
https://www.wdinvestmentpartners.com
Real Estate Investment Services
N.A.I.C.S.: 531390

Walker & Dunlop, LLC (1)
7272 Wisconsin Ave Ste 1300, Bethesda, MD 20814
Tel.: (301) 215-5500
Web Site: https://www.walkerdunlop.com

Real Estate Financial Services
N.A.I.C.S.: 522292

WALKER LANE EXPLORATION, INC.
102 N Curry St, Carson City, NV 89703
Tel.: (775) 461-3445 NV
Web Site:
http://walkerlaneexploration.com
Year Founded: 2007
WKLN—(OTCIQ)
Sales Range: $1-9.9 Million
Gold Mining Services
N.A.I.C.S.: 212220
Eric Stevenson (VP-Bus Dev)
Theodore R. Sharp (CFO)
Jeffrey Rubinstein (Treas)
John Bellave (Pres & Sec)
Larry Kozin (CEO)

WALLSTREET SECURITIES, INC.
15434 E Gale Ave, Hacienda Heights, CA 91745
Tel.: (714) 603-9525 AZ
Year Founded: 1999
WSSE—(OTCIQ)
Financial Services
N.A.I.C.S.: 523999
Mario Usi (CEO)
Nestor C. Buenaflor (COO)

WALLY WORLD MEDIA, INC.
7121 W Craig Rd Ste 113-38, Las Vegas, NV 89129
Tel.: (702) 890-5299 NV
Web Site:
https://www.wallyworldmedia.com
Year Founded: 2012
WLYW—(OTCIQ)
Liabilities: $91,305
Net Worth: ($91,305)
Earnings: ($31,119)
Emp.: 5
Fiscal Year-end: 09/30/23
Internet Social Media Services
N.A.I.C.S.: 516210
Grant Casey (Chm, Pres, CEO, CFO, Treas & Sec)

WALMART INC.
702 SW 8th St, Bentonville, AR 72716
Tel.: (479) 273-4000 DE
Web Site:
https://corporate.walmart.com
Year Founded: 1984
WMT—(NYSE)
Rev.: $648,125,000,000
Assets: $252,399,000,000
Liabilities: $162,050,000,000
Net Worth: $90,349,000,000
Earnings: $15,511,000,000
Emp.: 2,100,000
Fiscal Year-end: 01/31/24
Department Store Retailer
N.A.I.C.S.: 455110
John David Rainey (CFO & Exec VP)
Keith R. Wyche (VP-Community Engagement & Support)
Kerry Whorton Cooper (Executives)
C. Douglas McMillon (Pres, CEO, Asst Mgr-Tulsa & Assoc-Distr Center)
John Furner (Pres-US & CEO-US)
Judith McKenna (Exec VP)
S. Robson Walton (Executives)
Mindy Mackenzie (Executives)
Daniel J. Bartlett (Exec VP-Corp Affairs)
Kathleen McLaughlin (Chief Sustainability Officer, Pres-Foundation & Exec VP)
Judith McKenna (Pres/CEO-Intl)
David M. Chojnowski (Sr VP & Controller)

Ben-Saba Hasan (*Chief Culture, Diversity, Equity & Inclusion Officer & Sr VP*)
Rachel Brand (*Chief Legal Officer, Sec & Exec VP-Governance-Global*)
Suresh Kumar (*Chief Dev Officer, CTO-Global & Exec VP*)
Koby Avital (*Exec VP-Platforms*)
Kelvin L. Buncum (*Exec VP-Neighborhood Markets-US*)
Leigh Hopkins (*Exec VP-Dev & Strategy-Intl*)
Nuala O'Connor (*Sr VP*)
John Scudder (*Chief Ethics & Compliance Officer-US & Sr VP*)
William White (*CMO & Sr VP*)
Casey Carl (*Chief Omni Strategy & Ops Officer & Exec VP*)
Bill Groves (*Chief Data & Analytics Officer & Sr VP*)
Matt Miner (*Chief Ethics & Compliance Officer-Global & Exec VP*)
Gregory Boyd Penner (*Chm*)
Jerry R. Geisler III (*Chief Information Security Officer & Sr VP*)

Subsidiaries:

Flipkart Internet Private Limited (1)
Buildings Alyssa Begonia Clove Embassy Tech Village Outer Ring Road, Devarabeesanahalli Village, Bengaluru, 560 103, Karnataka, India (81%)
Tel.: (91) 45614700
Web Site: https://www.flipkart.com
Online Shopping Store
N.A.I.C.S.: 455219
Binny Bansal (*Co-Founder*)
Kalyan Krishnamurthy (*CEO*)
Sriram Venkataraman (*CFO & COO*)
Phanimohan Venkata Kalagara (*Sr VP-One Tech*)
Nandita Sinha (*VP-Customer Growth, Media & Engagement*)
Krishna Raghavan (*Chief People Officer*)

Subsidiary (Domestic):

Myntra Designs Private Limited (2)
Buildings Alyssa Begonia and Tech Village Outer Ring Road, Clover situated in Embassy Devarabeesanahalli Village Varthur Hobli, Bengaluru, 560 103, India
Tel.: (91) 8061561999
Web Site: https://www.myntra.com
Online Clothing Retailer
N.A.I.C.S.: 458110
Amar Nagaram (*Chief Tech & Product Officer*)

Jet.com, Inc. (1)
221 River St 8th Fl, Hoboken, NJ 07030
Web Site: http://www.jet.com
Online Retailer
N.A.I.C.S.: 423620
Marc E. Lore (*Founder & CEO*)

Unit (Domestic):

Walmart.com (2)
7000 Marina Blvd, Brisbane, CA 94005
Tel.: (650) 837-5000
Web Site: http://www.walmart.com
Sales Range: $250-299.9 Million
Emp.: 600
Online Retail Services
N.A.I.C.S.: 425120

Massmart Holdings, Ltd. (1)
Massmart House 16 Peltier Drive Sunninghill Ext 6, Private Bag x4, Sandton, 2157, South Africa (51%)
Tel.: (27) 115170000
Web Site: http://www.massmart.co.za
Rev.: $5,919,907,720
Assets: $2,779,662,908
Liabilities: $2,578,282,063
Net Worth: $201,380,845
Earnings: $119,634,482
Emp.: 48,000
Fiscal Year-end: 12/27/2020
Consumer Good Retailer
N.A.I.C.S.: 455110
Kuseni Dlamini (*Chm*)
Mohammed Abdool-Samad (*CFO*)
Varsha Dayaram (*Sr VP*)

Chwayita Mareka (*Sr VP*)
Sandile Lukhele (*Gen Counsel*)
Sylvester John (*Sr VP*)
Herman Venter (*Chief Mdse Officer*)
Andre Steyn (*VP*)
Karen Ferrini (*VP*)

Sam's Club (1)
608 SW 8th St, Bentonville, AR 72716-0001 (100%)
Tel.: (479) 277-7000
Web Site: https://www.samsclub.com
Sales Range: $1-4.9 Billion
Emp.: 3,500
Wholesale Club
N.A.I.C.S.: 455211
Christopher Nicholas (*Pres, CEO & Exec VP*)
Vinod Bidarkoppa (*Sr VP-Tech*)
Megan Crozier (*Exec VP*)
Brandi Joplin (*CFO & Sr VP*)
Meggan Kring (*Sr Dir-Global Corp Comm & Corp Affairs*)
Lance de la Rosa (*COO & Exec VP*)
Christopher Shryock (*Chief People Officer & Sr VP*)
Tim Simmons (*Chief Product Officer & Sr VP*)
Vicki Smith (*Gen Counsel & VP*)

Subsidiary (Domestic):

Sam's East, Inc. (2)
3500 Se Club Blvd, Bentonville, AR 72712
Tel.: (479) 621-5537
Web Site: http://www.samsclub.com
Warehouse Clubs
N.A.I.C.S.: 455211

Sam's West, Inc. (2)
2101 SE Simple Savings Dr, Bentonville, AR 72716-0745
Tel.: (479) 273-4000
Web Site: http://www3.samsclub.com
Warehouse Clubs
N.A.I.C.S.: 455211
Kathryn McLay (*Pres & CEO*)
Kathryn McLay (*Pres & CEO*)
Vinod Bidarkoppa (*Sr VP-Tech*)
Megan Crozier (*Exec VP*)
Eddie Garcia (*Chief Product Officer & Sr VP*)
Brandi Joplin (*CFO & Sr VP*)
Meggan Kring (*Head-Comm & Sr Dir-II-Global Corp Comm & Corp Affairs*)
Lance de la Rosa (*COO & Exec VP*)
Vicki Smith (*Gen Counsel & VP*)
Monique Picou (*Chief Strategy & Supply Chain Officer & Sr VP*)

Wal-Mart Canada Corp. (1)
1940 Argentia Road, Mississauga, L5N 1P9, ON, Canada
Tel.: (905) 821-2111
Web Site: https://www.walmartcanada.ca
Sales Range: $25-49.9 Billion
Emp.: 100,000
Discount Department Store Operator
N.A.I.C.S.: 455110
Gonzalo Gebara (*Pres & CEO*)

Wal-Mart Distribution Center (1)
5801 SW Region Airport Blvd, Bentonville, AR 72712 (100%)
Tel.: (479) 273-4000
Web Site: http://www.walmart.com
Sales Range: $350-399.9 Million
Emp.: 1,000
Warehousing & Distribution
N.A.I.C.S.: 493110

Wal-Mart Distribution Center (1)
1050 Vern Cora Rd, Laurens, SC 29360-2000
Tel.: (864) 682-1555
Web Site: http://www.walmart.com
Sales Range: $350-399.9 Million
Emp.: 1,000
Distribution Center
N.A.I.C.S.: 493190

Wal-Mart Distribution Center (1)
2200 7th Ave SW, Cullman, AL 35055
Tel.: (256) 739-0763
Sales Range: $350-399.9 Million
Emp.: 1,000
Distribution Center
N.A.I.C.S.: 493110
Ken Caviness (*Gen Mgr*)

Wal-Mart Distribution Center (1)
2100 E Tipton St, Seymour, IN 47274
Tel.: (812) 523-5600
Sales Range: $350-399.9 Million
Emp.: 1,000
Distribution Center
N.A.I.C.S.: 493110

Wal-Mart Distribution Center (1)
1501 E Maple Leaf Dr, Mount Pleasant, IA 52641-3106
Tel.: (319) 385-5600
Web Site: http://www.walmart.com
Sales Range: $350-399.9 Million
Emp.: 1,000
Distribution Center
N.A.I.C.S.: 493110

Wal-Mart Distribution Center (1)
201 Old Elkhart Rd, Palestine, TX 75801-5931
Tel.: (903) 723-4412
Web Site: http://www.walmart.com
Sales Range: $350-399.9 Million
Emp.: 1,000
Distribution Center
N.A.I.C.S.: 493110

Wal-Mart Distribution Center (1)
3900 IH 35 N, New Braunfels, TX 78130-2607
Tel.: (830) 620-3300
Sales Range: $350-399.9 Million
Emp.: 1,000
Distribution Center
N.A.I.C.S.: 493110
Robert Ganarodas (*Gen Mgr*)

Wal-Mart Distribution Center (1)
1300 S F St, Porterville, CA 93257-5969 (100%)
Tel.: (559) 783-6016
Sales Range: $350-399.9 Million
Emp.: 1,000
Distribution Center
N.A.I.C.S.: 493190

Wal-Mart Distribution Center (1)
2200 Manufacturers Blvd NE, Brookhaven, MS 39601
Tel.: (601) 823-0511
Web Site: http://www.walmart.com
Sales Range: $350-399.9 Million
Emp.: 1,000
Distribution Center
N.A.I.C.S.: 493110

Wal-Mart Distribution Center 6012 (1)
3101 Quincy St, Plainview, TX 79072
Tel.: (806) 293-9601
Web Site: http://www.walmartstores.com
Sales Range: $350-399.9 Million
Emp.: 1,000
Distribution Center for Walmart Products & Services
N.A.I.C.S.: 493190

Wal-Mart Labs (1)
444 Castro St Ste 109, Mountain View, CA 94041
Tel.: (650) 938-2300
Web Site: http://www.walmartlabs.com
Social Media Content Filtering Solutions
N.A.I.C.S.: 518210

Wal-Mart Realty Company (1)
2001 SE 10th St, Bentonville, AR 72712
Tel.: (479) 273-4682
Web Site: http://www.walmartrealty.com
Real Estate Services
N.A.I.C.S.: 531390
Nick Goodner (*Sr Dir-Real Estate-US*)
Fabian Welch (*Mgr-Asset*)
Gary Withrow (*Sr Dir-Svcs*)

Subsidiary (Domestic):

Wal-Mart Real Estate Business Trust (2)
702 SW 8th St, Bentonville, AR 72716-0555 (100%)
Tel.: (479) 273-4000
Web Site: http://www.walmartrealty.com
Discount Department Stores
N.A.I.C.S.: 455110

Wal-Mart Stores East, LP (1)
601 N Walton Blvd, Bentonville, AR 72712-4546

Tel.: (479) 273-0060
Grocery Products Retailer
N.A.I.C.S.: 455110

Wal-Mart Stores Texas, LLC (1)
1901 S Texas Ave, Bryan, TX 77802
Tel.: (979) 599-5322
Supermarket Operating Services
N.A.I.C.S.: 445110

Wal-Mart de Mexico, S.A. de C.V. (1)
Blvd M Avila Camacho 647 Colonia Periodista Alcaldia Miguel Hidalgo, 11220, Mexico, DF, Mexico (62%)
Tel.: (52) 5552830100
Web Site: https://www.walmex.mx
Rev.: $51,857,285
Assets: $25,721,580
Liabilities: $13,991,315
Net Worth: $11,730,265
Earnings: $3,039,712
Emp.: 177,376
Fiscal Year-end: 12/31/2023
Retail Holding Company
N.A.I.C.S.: 551112
Enrique Ostale Cambiaso (*Chm*)

Walmart Chile S.A. (1)
Avenida del Valle 725 Piso 5, Ciudad Empresarial, Huechuraba, Santiago, Chile
Tel.: (56) 22 591 6682
Web Site: https://www.walmartchile.cl
Sales Range: $1-4.9 Billion
Emp.: 37,000
Supermarket Operator
N.A.I.C.S.: 445110
Manuel Lopez (*Ops Mgr*)
Patricio Dallan (*Mgr-Logistics & Supply*)
Matias Puente Solari (*Mgr-Mktg & Customer*)
Santiago Borges (*Mgr-Compliance*)
Alejandro Konig (*Mgr-Comml*)

Walmart Inc. - International Division (1)
701 S Walton, Bentonville, AR 72716
Tel.: (479) 273-4000
Web Site: http://www.walmart.com
Sales Range: $100-124.9 Million
Emp.: 16,000
Discount Department Store Operator
N.A.I.C.S.: 455110
Kathryn McLay (*Pres, CEO & Exec VP*)

WANDERPORT CORPORATION

5465 Legacy Dr Ste 650, Plano, TX 75024
Tel.: (310) 526-8720
Web Site: https://www.wanderportcorp.com
WDRP—(OTCIQ)
Sales Range: Less than $1 Million
Hemp Produced Food, Beverages & Consumer Products Distr
N.A.I.C.S.: 424490
Liliana Vo (*Pres*)
Miki Takeuchi (*Interim CEO*)

WARBY PARKER INC.

233 Spring St 6th Fl E, New York, NY 10013
Tel.: (646) 847-7215 DE
Web Site: https://www.warbyparker.com
Year Founded: 2009
WRBY—(NYSE)
Rev.: $341,062,000
Assets: $568,707,000
Liabilities: $282,061,000
Net Worth: $286,646,000
Earnings: ($110,393,000)
Emp.: 1,860
Fiscal Year-end: 12/31/22
Glasses Mfr & Distr
N.A.I.C.S.: 339115
Neil Blumenthal (*Co-Founder, Co-Chm & Co-CEO*)
Andy Hunt (*Co-Founder*)
Steve Miller (*CFO & Sr VP*)
Jeff Saunders (*CTO & Sr VP*)

Warby Parker Inc.—(Continued)

Kim Nemser *(Chief Product Officer, Chief Supply Chain Officer & Sr VP)*
Sandy Gilsenan *(Chief Retail Officer, Chief Customer Experience Officer & Sr VP)*
Chelsea Kaden *(Chief People Officer & Sr VP)*
Chris Utecht *(Gen Counsel, Sec & Sr VP)*
Jeffrey Raider *(Co-Founder)*
Dave Gilboa *(Co-Founder, Co-Chm & Co-CEO)*
Andrew Hunt *(Co-Founder)*
Neil Blumenthal *(Co-Founder, Co-Chm & Co-CEO)*

WARNER BROS. DISCOVERY, INC.

230 Park Ave S, New York, NY 10003
Tel.: (212) 548-5555 DE
Web Site: https://ir.wbd.com
Year Founded: 1985
WBD—(NASDAQ)
Rev.: $41,321,000,000
Assets: $122,757,000,000
Liabilities: $76,285,000,000
Net Worth: $46,472,000,000
Earnings: ($3,126,000,000)
Emp.: 35,300
Fiscal Year-end: 12/31/23
Advertising Media Services
N.A.I.C.S.: 551112
Adria Alpert Romm *(Chief People & Culture Officer)*
Karen Leever *(Pres-Digital Products & Mktg-US)*
Gunnar Wiedenfels *(CFO & Sr Exec VP)*
Jon Steinlauf *(Chief Adv Sls Officer-US)*
Lori C. Locke *(Chief Acctg Officer)*
Lisa Holme *(Grp Sr VP-Content & Comml Strategy-Direct-to-Consumer)*
Priya Dogra *(Pres-Europe, Middle East & Africa & Mng Dir-Europe, Middle East & Africa)*
Bruce Campbell *(Chief Revenue & Strategy Officer)*
Dave Duvall *(CIO)*
Patrizio Spagnoletto *(CMO)*
David M. Zaslav *(Pres & CEO)*

Subsidiaries:

Animal Planet Europe P/S **(1)**
Discovery House Chiswick Park Building 2, 566 Chiswick High Road, London, W4 5YB, United Kingdom
Tel.: (44) 2088113000
Web Site: http://www.discoveryuk.com
Television Network Broadcasting Services
N.A.I.C.S.: 516120

Discovery Asia Sales Private Limited **(1)**
21 Media Circle Level 8, Singapore, 138562, Singapore
Tel.: (65) 65107500
Web Site: http://www.discoverychannel.com
Sales Range: $25-49.9 Million
Emp.: 200
Television Network Broadcasting Services
N.A.I.C.S.: 516120
Arthur Bastings *(Mng Dir)*

Discovery Communications Benelux BV **(1)**
Piet Heinkade 173, 1019 GM, Amsterdam, Netherlands
Tel.: (31) 207138900
Web Site: https://www.discoverybenelux.nl
Television Broadcasting Services
N.A.I.C.S.: 516120

Discovery Communications Deutschland GmbH & Co. KG **(1)**
Sternstrasse 5, 80538, Munich, Germany
Tel.: (49) 8920 609 9100
Web Site: https://wbd-deutschland.de

Sales Range: $25-49.9 Million
Emp.: 180
Television Network Broadcasting Services
N.A.I.C.S.: 516120
Susanne Aigner-Drews *(Gen Mgr-GSA & Benelux)*

Discovery Communications India **(1)**
9/1 B Aruna Asaf Ali Marg, Qutab Institutional Area, New Delhi, 110 067, India
Tel.: (91) 1141491100
Web Site: http://www.discoverychannel.co.in
Television Network Broadcasting Services
N.A.I.C.S.: 516120

Discovery Communications Nordic ApS **(1)**
Store Kongensgade 92, Copenhagen, 1264, Denmark
Tel.: (45) 70202707
Web Site: http://www.discovery.com
Sales Range: $25-49.9 Million
Emp.: 50
Television Broadcasting Services
N.A.I.C.S.: 516120
Jan Andreassen *(Mng Dir)*

Subsidiary (Domestic):

Discovery Networks Danmark **(2)**
HC Andersens Boulevard 1, 1553, Copenhagen, Denmark
Tel.: (45) 70101010
Web Site: https://www.discoverynetworks.dk
Television & Radio Station Operations
N.A.I.C.S.: 516120
Lena Bogild *(Head-Comm & PR)*

Subsidiary (Non-US):

SBS Radio AB **(3)**
Gjorwellsgatan 30, PO Box 34108, SE-10026, Stockholm, Sweden **(100%)**
Tel.: (46) 84503300
Web Site: https://www.sbsradio.com
Radio Station Operator
N.A.I.C.S.: 516110
Staffan Rosell *(Mng Dir)*

Subsidiary (Domestic):

Mix Megapol.se AB **(4)**
Gjorwellsgatan 30, PO Box 34108, 112 60, Stockholm, Sweden **(100%)**
Tel.: (46) 84503300
Web Site: http://www.mixmegapol.se
Television Broadcasting Services
N.A.I.C.S.: 516120

Rockklassiker Sverige AB **(4)**
Gjorwellsgatan 30, PO Box 34108, 100 26, Stockholm, Sweden **(100%)**
Tel.: (46) 84500300
Web Site: http://www.rockklassiker.se
Sales Range: $25-49.9 Million
Radio Stations
N.A.I.C.S.: 516110

Vinyl AB **(4)**
Gjorwellsgatan 30, PO Box 34108, 100 26, Stockholm, Sweden **(100%)**
Tel.: (46) 84503300
Web Site: http://radioplay.se
Radio Stations
N.A.I.C.S.: 516110

Subsidiary (Non-US):

TV Norge AS **(3)**
Nydalen Alle 37, Oslo, 422, Norway **(100%)**
Tel.: (47) 21022000
Web Site: http://www.discovery.no
Emp.: 150
Television Broadcasting Station
N.A.I.C.S.: 516120
Tine Jensen *(CEO)*

Discovery Communications, LLC **(1)**
1 Discovery Pl, Silver Spring, MD 20910 **(100%)**
Tel.: (240) 662-2000
Web Site: http://www.discovery.com
Cable Television Programming & Distribution Services
N.A.I.C.S.: 512120
David M. Zaslav *(Pres & CEO)*

Joint Venture (Non-US):

All3Media Holdings Ltd **(2)**

Berkshire House 168-173 High Holborn, London, WC1V 7AA, United Kingdom **(50%)**
Tel.: (44) 2078454377
Web Site: https://www.all3media.com
Holding Company
N.A.I.C.S.: 551114
Sara Geater *(COO)*
Jane Turton *(CEO)*
Angela McMullen *(CFO)*
Steven Brown *(Grp Dir-Corp Dev)*
Ivan Garel-Jones *(CIO)*
Jamie McIntyre-Brown *(Gen Counsel)*
Mike Large *(Grp Dir-Comm)*

Subsidiary (Domestic):

Betty TV Limited **(3)**
Objective Media Group 89 Southwark Street, London, SE1 0HX, United Kingdom
Tel.: (44) 2072022300
Web Site: https://www.betty.co.uk
Emp.: 30
Motion Picture Production & Distribution Services
N.A.I.C.S.: 512110
David Harrison *(Creative Dir)*

Raw TV Ltd. **(3)**
Third Floor 13-21 Curtain Road, London, EC2A 3LT, United Kingdom
Tel.: (44) 2074560800
Web Site: https://www.raw.co.uk
Broadcasting & Media Production Company
N.A.I.C.S.: 516120
Joely Fether *(CEO)*
Tom Barry *(Dir-Programmes-Factual)*
Vikki Harris *(Mgr-Talent)*
Bart Layton *(Co-Founder)*
Isabelle Ezekwesili *(Coord-Talent & Diversity)*
Simone Facey *(Head-Facilities)*
Tom Henderson *(Mgr-HR)*
Adam Hayes *(Head-Production & Gold Rush Programming)*
Natalie Moody *(Mgr-Talent)*
Fiona Clarke *(COO)*
Ross Goodlass *(Head-Dev-Factual)*
Heather Salter *(Head-Film Dev)*
Liesel Evans *(Creative Dir-Factual)*
Dimitri Doganis *(Co-Founder)*
Gemma Gibbs *(Head-Casting)*
Nicky Murphy *(Head-Production)*
Jane Gant *(Fin Dir)*
Piers Vellacott *(Mng Dir)*
Louisa Fitzgerald *(Head-TV Dev-Scripted)*
Sara Murray *(Head-TV-Scripted)*
Suzy Jaffe *(Head-Talent)*
Ely Andrade *(Office Mgr)*

Subsidiary (Domestic):

Animal Planet, LLC **(2)**
1 Discovery Pl, Silver Spring, MD 20910-3354
Tel.: (240) 662-2000
Web Site: http://www.discovery.com
Sales Range: $125-149.9 Million
Emp.: 500
Cable Television Broadcaster
N.A.I.C.S.: 516210
Erin Wanner *(Sr VP-Production)*

Discovery Content Verwaltungs GmbH **(1)**
Sternstr 5, 80538, Munich, Germany
Tel.: (49) 892060990
Web Site: http://www.discovery.com
Emp.: 110
Television Broadcasting Services
N.A.I.C.S.: 516120

Discovery Latin America, L.L.C. **(1)**
6505 Blue Lagoon-Dr 300, Miami, FL 33126
Tel.: (786) 273-4700
Television Broadcasting Services
N.A.I.C.S.: 516120
Fernando Medin *(Pres/Mng Dir-Latin America & US Hispanic Markets)*

Discovery NZ Limited **(1)**
3 Flower St, Eden Terrace, Auckland, New Zealand
Tel.: (64) 99289000
Web Site: https://www.discoverycorporate.co.nz
Television Broadcasting Services
N.A.I.C.S.: 516120

Discovery Networks Finland Oy **(1)**

Mechelininkatu 1a, 00180, Helsinki, Finland
Tel.: (358) 207870850
Web Site: https://discoveryfinland.fi
Cable TV Network Operator
N.A.I.C.S.: 516210

Discovery Networks International Holdings Ltd. **(1)**
Discovery House Chiswick Park Bldg 2 566 Chiswick High Rd, London, W4 5YB, United Kingdom
Tel.: (44) 2088113000
Television Broadcasting Services
N.A.I.C.S.: 516120
Jean-Briac Perrette *(Pres & CEO)*

Discovery Networks Sweden AB **(1)**
Tegeluddsvagen 80, 114 99, Stockholm, Sweden
Tel.: (46) 852055555
Web Site: https://www.discoverynetworks.se
Cable TV Network Operator
N.A.I.C.S.: 516210

Discovery Networks, S.L. **(1)**
Paseo Castellana 202, Madrid, 28046, Spain
Tel.: (34) 917947500
Cable TV Network Operator
N.A.I.C.S.: 516210

Discovery Polska SP. z.o.o. **(1)**
Budynek Senator Ul Bielanska 12, 00-085, Warsaw, Poland
Tel.: (48) 223651000
Web Site: http://www.discoverymedia.pl
Television Network Broadcasting Services
N.A.I.C.S.: 516120

Discovery Productions, LLC **(1)**
17721 Hwy 59 N, Humble, TX 77396
Tel.: (281) 540-1866
Web Site: https://www.discovery-productions.com
Emp.: 11
Television Broadcasting Services
N.A.I.C.S.: 516120

Discovery, Inc. - Detroit Office **(1)**
101 W Big Beaver Rd, Troy, MI 48084
Tel.: (248) 764-4400
Web Site: http://www.discovery.com
Rev.: $2,445,000
Emp.: 8
Media Representatives
N.A.I.C.S.: 541840
Joe Paglino *(VP-Adv Sls-East Central Reg)*

Discovery, Inc. - New York Office **(1)**
850 3rd Ave, New York, NY 10022
Tel.: (212) 548-5555
Web Site: http://www.discovery.com
Sales Range: $100-124.9 Million
Emp.: 400
Cable TV Network Operator
N.A.I.C.S.: 516210
David M. Zaslav *(Pres & CEO)*

EL-TRADE Sp. z o.o. **(1)**
ul Pocztowa 34/23, 70-360, Szczecin, Poland
Tel.: (48) 914845131
Web Site: https://www.eltrade.com.pl
Vacuum Packaging Machine Mfr
N.A.I.C.S.: 333310

Eurosport Events Ltd. **(1)**
55 Drury Ln, London, WC2B 5SQ, United Kingdom
Tel.: (44) 2074687746
Television Broadcasting Services
N.A.I.C.S.: 516120

Eurosport International SA **(1)**
3 rue Gaston et Rene Caudron, 92798, Issy-les-Moulineaux, France **(51%)**
Tel.: (33) 140938000
Web Site: http://www.eurosport.com
Emp.: 800
Television Broadcasting Services
N.A.I.C.S.: 516210

Subsidiary (Non-US):

Eurosport Danmark ApS **(2)**
Amager Strandvej 22, 2300, Copenhagen, Denmark
Tel.: (45) 32577310

Web Site: http://www.eurosport.dk
Sales Range: $50-74.9 Million
Emp.: 200
Television Broadcasting Services
N.A.I.C.S.: 516120

Eurosport Finland OY (2)
Leinikkitie 20, 01350, Vantaa, Finland
Tel.: (358) 92715259
Sales Range: $25-49.9 Million
Emp.: 75
Television Broadcasting Services
N.A.I.C.S.: 516120

Subsidiary (Domestic):

Eurosport France SA (2)
3 rue Gaston et Rene Caudron, 92798,
Issy-les-Moulineaux, Cedex 9, France
Tel.: (33) 140938000
Web Site: http://www.eurosport.fr
Emp.: 750
Television Broadcasting Services
N.A.I.C.S.: 516120

Subsidiary (Non-US):

Eurosport Italia spa (2)
Via Tazzoli 15, 20154, Milan, Italy
Tel.: (39) 0276001305
Television Broadcasting Services
N.A.I.C.S.: 516120

Eurosport Media (2)
Schaffelgasse 7, 8001, Zurich, Switzerland
Tel.: (41) 12520111
Emp.: 4
Sports Television Broadcasting Services
N.A.I.C.S.: 516120
Gabriela Moraschini *(Gen Mgr)*

Eurosport Media GmbH (2)
Rosenheimer Str 145e Media Works,
81671, Munich, Germany
Tel.: (49) 89958290
Sales Range: $25-49.9 Million
Emp.: 45
Television Broadcasting Services
N.A.I.C.S.: 516120
Dauben Merkel *(Mng Dir)*

Eurosport Norge AS (2)
Gaustadalleen 21, 0349, Oslo, Norway
Tel.: (47) 22958452
Web Site: http://tv.eurosport.no
Sales Range: $50-74.9 Million
Television Broadcasting Services
N.A.I.C.S.: 516120

Eurosport Polska Sp. z o.o. (2)
ul Jakubowska 4/2, 03-902, Warsaw, Po-
land
Tel.: (48) 225112469
Web Site: http://www.eurosport.pl
Sales Range: $25-49.9 Million
Emp.: 15
Television Broadcasting Services
N.A.I.C.S.: 516120
Dorota Zurkovvska *(Mng Dir)*

Eurosport TV Ltd. (2)
55 Drury Lane, London, WC2B 5SQ, United
Kingdom
Tel.: (44) 2074687777
Web Site:
http://www.eurosportcorporate.com
Sales Range: $25-49.9 Million
Emp.: 75
Sports Television Broadcasting Services
N.A.I.C.S.: 516210

Eurosport Television AB (2)
PO Box 1177, 172 24, Sundbyberg, Swe-
den
Tel.: (46) 850661000
Web Site: http://www.eurosport.com
Emp.: 200
Television Broadcasting Services
N.A.I.C.S.: 516120

Eurosport Television BV (2)
TC-1 Sumatralaan 45, 1217 CP, Hilversum,
Netherlands
Tel.: (31) 356777213
Web Site: http://www.eurosport.com
Emp.: 15
Television Broadcasting Services
N.A.I.C.S.: 516120

Eurosport Television SA (2)
Calle Alcale 518, 28 027, Madrid, Spain

Tel.: (34) 917548264
Web Site:
http://www.eurosportcorporate.com
Sales Range: $25-49.9 Million
Emp.: 25
Television Broadcasting Services
N.A.I.C.S.: 516120

Eurosport SAS (1)
3 rue Gaston et Rene Caudron, 92798,
Issy-les-Moulineaux, Cedex 9, France
Tel.: (33) 140938000
Cable TV Network Operator
N.A.I.C.S.: 516210

Joyn GmbH (1)
Tel.: (49) 8004395696
Web Site: https://www.joyn.de
Television Broadcasting Services
Alexandar Vassilev *(CEO & Mng Dir)*

Subsidiary (Domestic):

maxdome GmbH (2)
Medienallee 7, 85774, Unterfohring, Ger-
many
Tel.: (49) 89 9507 8320
Web Site: http://www.maxdome.de
Online Television Broadcasting Services
N.A.I.C.S.: 516120

Lumos Labs (1)
16 Maiden Ln Fl 6, San Francisco, CA
94108
Tel.: (415) 683-3261
Web Site: https://www.lumosity.com
Wired Telecommunication Services
N.A.I.C.S.: 517111

Miracle Sound Oy (1)
Kaapelitehdas C-rappu 7krs Tallberginkatu
1 C 155, 00180, Helsinki, Finland
Tel.: (358) 207474080
Web Site: https://www.miracle.fi
Media & Entertainment Services
N.A.I.C.S.: 541840

Subsidiary (Domestic):

Miracle Sound Oulu Oy (2)
Asemakatu 25, 90100, Oulu, Finland
Tel.: (358) 407323934
Web Site: http://www.miracle.fi
Media & Entertainment Services
N.A.I.C.S.: 541840

Motor Trend Group, LLC (1)
831 S Douglas St, El Segundo, CA 90245
Tel.: (310) 531-9900
Web Site: https://www.motortrendgroup.com
Automotive Digital Media Production Ser-
vices
N.A.I.C.S.: 512199
Shilpa Joshi *(VP & Controller)*

**OWN: Oprah Winfrey Network
LLC** (1)
4000 Warner Blvd Bdg 141, Burbank, CA
91522
Web Site: https://www.oprah.com
Television Streaming Platform Services
N.A.I.C.S.: 516210
Oprah Winfrey *(Chm & CEO)*

Play Sports Network Limited (1)
Monmouth Street Studios 30 Monmouth
Street, Bath, BA1 2AP, United Kingdom
Tel.: (44) 1225448333
Web Site:
https://www.playsportsnetwork.com
Sport Network Services
N.A.I.C.S.: 516210
Mia Walter *(Mng Dir)*
James Morell *(Dir-Audience)*
Tom Last *(Dir-Bus Dev)*
Simon Richardson *(Dir-Road Cycling)*
Dan Lloyd *(Dir-Racing)*

SporTV Medya Hizmetleri Anonim
Sirketi (1)
Kultur Mah Nisbetiye Cad Akmerkez Blok
No 56/9 Besiktas, Istanbul, Türkiye
Tel.: (90) 2123662000
Web Site:
https://www.discoverychannel.com.tr
Television Broadcasting Services
N.A.I.C.S.: 516120

Televista S.A. (1)
38 quai du point du Jour, 92100, Boulogne-

Billancourt, Cedex 9, France
Tel.: (33) 146219000
Web Site: http://www.televista.fr
Television Broadcasting Services
N.A.I.C.S.: 516120

Warner Media, LLC (1)
30 Hudson Yards, New York, NY 10001
Tel.: (212) 484-8000
Web Site: https://www.warnermedia.com
Media Holding Company
N.A.I.C.S.: 551112
Priya Dogra *(Pres-EMEA,APAC & Exec VP-
Strategy-Development)*
Ann M. Sarnoff *(Head-Studios & Networks)*
Jim Meza *(Exec VP & Gen Counsel)*
Jim Cummings *(Chief HR Officer & Exec
VP)*
Gerhard Zeiler *(Chief Revenue Officer)*
Richard Tom *(CTO)*
Christy Haubegger *(Chief Inclusion Officer
& Chief Inclusion Officer-Communications)*
Vanessa Brookman *(Head-EMEA)*
Tom Ascheim *(Pres)*
Jennifer Biry *(CFO)*
Tony Goncalves *(Chief Revenue Officer &
Exec VP)*
Jennifer Biry *(CFO)*
Tony Goncalves *(Chief Revenue Officer &
Exec VP)*
Ade J. Patton *(CFO-HBO/HBO Max/Global
DTC & Exec VP)*

Subsidiary (Domestic):

Alloy Media Holdings, L.L.C. (2)
19 W 44th St Fl 18a Ste 1000, New York,
NY 10036
Tel.: (212) 784-2010
Holding Company
N.A.I.C.S.: 551112

Home Box Office, Inc. (2)
30 Hudson Yards, New York, NY 10001
Tel.: (212) 512-5722
Web Site: http://www.hbo.com
Pay Cable Programming Service
N.A.I.C.S.: 516210
Richard L. Plepler *(Chm & CEO)*

Division (Domestic):

HBO Entertainment (3)
1100 Avenue of the Americas, New York,
NY 10036
Tel.: (212) 512-1000
Web Site: http://www.hbo.com
Television & Movie Broadcasting & Produc-
tion Services
N.A.I.C.S.: 516120

Subsidiary (Non-US):

HBO Europe Holdings, Inc. (3)
Riado utca 5, 1026, Budapest, Hungary
Tel.: (36) 202562014
Web Site: http://www.hbo-europe.com
Holding Company
N.A.I.C.S.: 551112
Antony Root *(Exec VP-Original
Programming-Production)*

Division (Domestic):

HBO Films (3)
1100 Avenue of the Americas, New York,
NY 10036 **(100%)**
Tel.: (212) 512-1000
Web Site: http://www.hbo.com
Provider of Motion Picture Production Ser-
vices
N.A.I.C.S.: 512120

HBO International (3)
1100 Ave of the Americas, New York, NY
10036-6712 **(100%)**
Tel.: (212) 512-1000
Web Site: http://www.hbo.com
Paid Film, Video & Movie Channels
N.A.I.C.S.: 512120

Unit (Domestic):

HBO International Distribution (4)
1001 Ave 6th 23rd Fl, New York, NY 10036
Tel.: (212) 391-7770
Web Site: http://sjiassociates.com
Motion Picture & Television Distribution Ser-
vices
N.A.I.C.S.: 512120

Subsidiary (Domestic):

HBO Latin America Media Services,
Inc. (3)
4000 Ponce De Leon Blvd Ste 800, Coral
Gables, FL 33146
Tel.: (305) 648-8100
Cable Television Services
N.A.I.C.S.: 516210

HBO Services, Inc. (3)
1100 Avenue Of The Americas, New York,
NY 10036-6712 **(100%)**
Tel.: (212) 512-1000
Web Site: http://www.hbo.com
Distr of Films & Tapes for Television
N.A.I.C.S.: 516210

HBO Sports (3)
1100 Ave of the Americas, New York, NY
10036
Tel.: (212) 512-5877
Web Site: http://www.hbo.com
Sports Programming
N.A.I.C.S.: 516210

Division (Domestic):

HBO Video (3)
1100 Avenue of the Americas, New York,
NY 10036-6712 **(100%)**
Tel.: (212) 512-1000
Web Site: http://www.hbo.com
Motion Picture & Video Tape Distribution
N.A.I.C.S.: 512110

Subsidiary (Domestic):

MNI Targeted Media Inc. (2)
225 High Ridge Rd, Stamford, CT 06905
Tel.: (203) 967-6530
Web Site: https://www.mni.com
Media Advertising Services
N.A.I.C.S.: 541840
Mark Glatzhofer *(VP & Gen Mgr)*
Matthew Fanelli *(Sr VP-Digital)*
Kevin Whitlow *(VP-Sales-Southwest)*
Jessica Jurevis *(Sls Dir-Chicago)*
Vicki Brakl *(Sr VP-Mktg, Trng & Dev)*
Meghan Aubert *(Mktg Dir)*
Glenn Dolce *(VP-Business Development)*
Jen Hendry *(Dir-Client Svcs)*
Cristina Maida *(Dir-HR)*
Melissa McGrath *(Mktg Dir-Strategy)*
Janine Pollack *(Dir-Integrated Mktg)*
Stefanie Sena *(Dir)*
Tommy Shaw *(Dir)*
Aaron Toye *(VP-Sales-Northwest)*
Laura West *(VP-Sales-East)*
Sue Williams *(Dir-Production)*

Subsidiary (Non-US):

New Line Cinema Corporation (2)
Tel.: (212) 649-4900
Web Site: http://www.newline.com
Theatrical Motion Pictures Independent Pro-
ducer & Distr
N.A.I.C.S.: 512110

Subsidiary (Non-US):

New Line Cinema (3)
(100%)
Tel.: (310) 854-5811
Web Site: http://www.newline.com
Motion Picture and Video Production
N.A.I.C.S.: 512110

New Line Distribution, Inc. (3)
(100%)
Tel.: (212) 649-4900
Web Site: http://www.newline.com
Magazine Publisher
N.A.I.C.S.: 513120

New Line Home Entertainment,
Inc. (3)
Tel.: (212) 649-4900
Web Site: http://www.newline.com
Magazine Publisher
N.A.I.C.S.: 513120

New Line International Releasing,
Inc. (3)
Tel.: (212) 649-4900
Web Site: http://www.newline.com
Magazine Publisher
N.A.I.C.S.: 513120

New Line Productions, Inc. (3)

Warner Bros. Discovery, Inc.—(Continued)
Tel.: (212) 649-4900
Web Site: http://www.newline.com
Video Production
N.A.I.C.S.: 512110

Subsidiary (Non-US):

Time Magazine Europe Limited (2)
Tower House Lathkill Street, Market Harborough, LE16 9EF, Leicestershire, United Kingdom
Tel.: (44) 3450450360
Web Site: https://subs.time.com
Newspaper & Magazine Publishing Services
N.A.I.C.S.: 513110

Subsidiary (Domestic):

Time Warner Business Services LLC (2)
3111 W Dr Martin Luther, Tampa, FL 33607
Tel.: (813) 676-9920
Cable Television Network Services
N.A.I.C.S.: 516210

Time Warner Global Media Group (2)
1 Time Warner Ctr, New York, NY 10019
Tel.: (212) 522-1212
Business Development & Advertising Services
N.A.I.C.S.: 561499

Turner Broadcasting System, Inc. (2)
1 CNN Ctr, Atlanta, GA 30303
Tel.: (404) 827-1700
Web Site: http://www.turner.com
Insurance Services
N.A.I.C.S.: 516120
Peter Knag (CFO & Exec VP)

Subsidiary (Domestic):

Bleacher Report, Inc. (3)
153 Kearny St Fl 2, San Francisco, CA 94108
Tel.: (415) 777-5505
Web Site: https://www.bleacherreport.com
Magazine Publishing Services
N.A.I.C.S.: 513120
Sam Parnell (CTO)
Howard Mittman (CEO)

CNN Newsource Sales, Inc. (3)
1 CNN Ctr, Atlanta, GA 30303
Tel.: (404) 878-2276
Web Site: http://www.edition.cnn.com
News Reporting Services
N.A.I.C.S.: 516210

Cable News Network, Inc. (3)
1 CNN Ctr, Atlanta, GA 30303 (100%)
Tel.: (404) 878-2276
Web Site: http://www.cnn.com
Multimedia News Network Operator
N.A.I.C.S.: 516120
David Chalian (Dir-Political)

Subsidiary (Domestic):

CNN America, Inc. (4)
1 CNN Center NW, Atlanta, GA 30303
Tel.: (404) 878-2276
Web Site: http://www.cnn.com
News Reporting Services
N.A.I.C.S.: 516210

Unit (Domestic):

CNN Headline News (4)
1 CNN Ctr, Atlanta, GA 30303
Tel.: (404) 878-2276
Web Site: http://edition.cnn.com
Cable Television News Network
N.A.I.C.S.: 516120

CNN Money (4)
1 CNN Center, Atlanta, GA 30303
Tel.: (404) 878-2276
Web Site: http://www.cnn.com
Financial News & Information Periodical & Website Publisher
N.A.I.C.S.: 513120

Subsidiary (Domestic):

CNN News Source Sales Inc. (4)
1 CNN Ctr NW, Atlanta, GA 30303-2762
Tel.: (404) 827-2085

Web Site: http://www.cnn.com
Television Broadcasting Station
N.A.I.C.S.: 516120

Unit (Domestic):

CNN Radio (4)
190 Marietta St NW, Atlanta, GA 30303 (100%)
Tel.: (404) 827-2750
Web Site: http://www.cnn.com
Full Service Radio Network
N.A.I.C.S.: 516110

Subsidiary (Domestic):

SuperStation Inc. (3)
1050 Techwood Dr NW, Atlanta, GA 30318-5604 (100%)
Tel.: (404) 827-1700
Basic Cable Service
N.A.I.C.S.: 516120

The Cartoon Network, Inc. (3)
1050 Techwood Dr NW, Atlanta, GA 30318
Tel.: (404) 827-1700
Web Site: http://www.cartoonnetwork.com
Twenty-Four Hour a Day Animated Network Featuring Classic & Orginal Cartoons & Animated Programs
N.A.I.C.S.: 516120

Subsidiary (Non-US):

Turner Broadcasting Sales Taiwan Inc. (3)
8E Tun Hwa North Road, Taipei, 105, Taiwan
Tel.: (886) 225473313
Television Advertising Sales
N.A.I.C.S.: 541870

Subsidiary (Domestic):

Turner Broadcasting Sales, Inc. (3)
30 Hudson Yards, New York, NY 10001 (100%)
Tel.: (248) 680-6800
Web Site: http://www.cnn.com
Television Advertising Sales
N.A.I.C.S.: 516120

Subsidiary (Non-US):

Turner Broadcasting System Asia Pacific Inc. (3)
30/F Taikoo Place Somerset House 979 Kings Road, Quarry Bay, China (Hong Kong)
Tel.: (852) 31283333
Web Site: http://www.turner.com
Television Broadcasting Services
N.A.I.C.S.: 516120

Turner Broadcasting System Europe Limited (3)
Turner House 16 Great Marlborough Street, London, W1F 7HS, United Kingdom
Tel.: (44) 20 7693 1000
Web Site: http://www.turner.com
Cable & Satellite Television Channels
N.A.I.C.S.: 516120
Hannes Heyelmann (Mng Dir)

Subsidiary (Domestic):

Turner Entertainment Networks Incorporated (3)
1050 Techwood Dr NW, Atlanta, GA 30318-5604
Tel.: (404) 827-1700
Motion Picture Production
N.A.I.C.S.: 512110
Suzanne Donino (VP)
Clyde D Smith (VP)
Andren Velcoft (VP-Mktg)

Joint Venture (Domestic):

Courtroom Television Network LLC (4)
1050 Techwood Dr NW, Atlanta, GA 30318-5604
Web Site: http://www.trutv.com
Cable Television Network
N.A.I.C.S.: 516210

Joint Venture (Non-US):

Zee Turner Limited (4)
2nd Floor Plot 9, Film City Sector 16 A,

Noida, 201301, India
Tel.: (91) 1206766466
Web Site: http://www.zeeturner.com
Emp.: 500
Television Broadcasting Services
N.A.I.C.S.: 516120
Akash Deep Ahluwalia (VP-Ops)
Dinesh Arora (Deputy VP-CRM)

Subsidiary (Non-US):

Turner Entertainment Networks International Limited (3)
Turner House 16 Great Marlborough Street, London, W1F 7HS, United Kingdom
Tel.: (44) 2076931000
Television Broadcasting Services
N.A.I.C.S.: 516120

Subsidiary (Domestic):

Turner International, Inc. (3)
1 Cnn Center 100, Atlanta, GA 30303
Tel.: (404) 827-1700
Business Support Services
N.A.I.C.S.: 561499
Gerhard Zeiler (Pres)

Turner Network Sales, Inc. (3)
1 CNN Ctr, Atlanta, GA 30303-5366 (100%)
Tel.: (404) 827-1700
Web Site: http://www.turner.com
Cable Network Sales
N.A.I.C.S.: 541613

Turner Network Television, Inc. (3)
1050 Techwood Dr NW, Atlanta, GA 30318
Tel.: (404) 827-3111
Web Site: http://www.turnerbroadcasting.com
Cable Television Network Operator
N.A.I.C.S.: 516120

Turner Sports, Inc. (3)
1 CNN Ctr NW, Atlanta, GA 30303-2762
Tel.: (404) 827-1700
Web Site: http://www.turner.com
Live Sports Programming
N.A.I.C.S.: 541840
Matthew Hong (COO)

iStreamPlanet Co., LLC (3)
1099 Stewart St Ste 800, Seattle, WA 98101
Tel.: (206) 401-5445
Web Site: https://www.istreamplanet.com
Internet Broadcast Services
N.A.I.C.S.: 516210
Gavin McMurdo (VP)
Chris Colleran (VP-Business Development)
Natasha Reid (VP)
Dana Bowlin (Sr Dir)
Josh Barnard (Sr Dir)
Chris Colleran (VP-Business Development)
Natasha Reid (VP)
Dana Bowlin (Sr Dir)
Josh Barnard (Sr Dir)
Chris Colleran (VP-Business Development)
Natasha Reid (VP)
Dana Bowlin (Sr Dir)
Josh Barnard (Sr Dir)

Subsidiary (Domestic):

Warner Bros. Entertainment Inc. (2)
4000 Warner Blvd, Burbank, CA 91522
Tel.: (818) 977-0018
Web Site: https://www.warnerbros.com
Holding Company
N.A.I.C.S.: 516210
Ann M. Sarnoff (Chm & CEO)
Vicky Colf (CTO)
Pamela Lifford (Pres-Global Brands & Experiences)

Subsidiary (Domestic):

Castle Rock Entertainment, Inc. (3)
335 N Maple Dr, Beverly Hills, CA 90210
Tel.: (310) 285-2300
Film Production Services
N.A.I.C.S.: 512110

DC Comics, Inc. (3)
1700 Brdwy, New York, NY 10019 (100%)
Tel.: (212) 636-5400
Web Site: http://www.dccomics.com
Comic Book Publishing, Syndication & Product Licensing Services
N.A.I.C.S.: 513120

Subsidiary (Domestic):

Mad Magazine/E.C. Publications, Inc. (4)
1700 Broadway, New York, NY 10019 (100%)
Tel.: (212) 506-4850
Web Site: https://www.madmagazine.com
Magazine & Comic Book Publisher
N.A.I.C.S.: 513120

Unit (Domestic):

Vertigo Comics (4)
1700 Broadway 7th Fl, New York, NY 10019-5905
Tel.: (212) 636-5400
Web Site: http://www.vertigocomics.com
Comic Book Publisher
N.A.I.C.S.: 513199

WildStorm Productions (4)
888 Prospect St Ste 240, La Jolla, CA 92037
Tel.: (858) 551-1164
Web Site: http://www.dccomics.com
Book & Comics Publisher
N.A.I.C.S.: 513130

Subsidiary (Domestic):

Telepictures Production Inc. (3)
3500 W Olive St Ste 1000, Burbank, CA 91505
Tel.: (818) 972-0777
Web Site: https://www.telepicturestv.com
Television Program Production & Service
N.A.I.C.S.: 512110

WB Games Inc. (3)
12131 113th Ave NE Ste 300, Kirkland, WA 98034
Tel.: (425) 216-3200
Web Site: https://warnerbrosgames.com
Computer Game Development Service
N.A.I.C.S.: 459120

Warner Bros. Animation Inc. (3)
4000 Warner Blvd, Burbank, CA 91522
Tel.: (818) 977-8700
Web Site: http://www.warnerbros.com
Movie & TV Animation Services
N.A.I.C.S.: 512110
Sam Register (Pres)

Warner Bros. Digital Networks Labs Inc. (3)
72 Madison Ave 12th Fl, New York, NY 10016
Tel.: (917) 338-3798
Entertainment Media Streaming Services
N.A.I.C.S.: 518210

Warner Bros. Distributing Inc. (3)
4000 Warner Blvd, Burbank, CA 91522-0002
Tel.: (818) 954-6000
Motion Picture & Video Distribution Services
N.A.I.C.S.: 512120

Subsidiary (Non-US):

Warner Bros. Entertainment Canada Inc. (3)
1600-5000 Yonge St, North York, Toronto, M2N 6P1, ON, Canada
Tel.: (416) 250-8384
Web Site: http://www.warnerbroscanada.com
Movie Production & Distribution Services
N.A.I.C.S.: 512120

Subsidiary (Domestic):

Warner Bros. Home Entertainment Group (3)
4000 Warner Blvd, Burbank, CA 91522
Tel.: (818) 954-6000
Web Site: http://www.warnerbros.com
Movie & Interactive Gaming Distr
N.A.I.C.S.: 512120
Ron Sanders (Pres)

Subsidiary (Domestic):

Warner Bros. Interactive Entertainment Inc. (4)
4000 Warner Blvd Bldg 168, Burbank, CA 91522
Tel.: (818) 977-0018
Web Site: http://www.wbie.com

Game Development & Licensing Services
N.A.I.C.S.: 339930
David Haddad (Pres)

Subsidiary (Non-US):

Warner Bros. Singapore PTE Ltd. (4)
1 Marina Boulevard 28-00, One Marina Boulevard, Singapore, 018989, Singapore
Tel.: (65) 63363323
Film & Television Program Producer & Distr
N.A.I.C.S.: 512110
Ngpeng Hui (Gen Mgr)

Subsidiary (Domestic):

Warner Home Video Inc. (4)
4000 Warner Blvd, Burbank, CA 91522
Tel.: (818) 954-6000
Web Site: http://www.warnervideo.com
Video Distr
N.A.I.C.S.: 512120
Ronald Sanders (Pres)

Subsidiary (Non-US):

Warner Bros. International Television Production New Zealand Limited (3)
Level 4 19 Hargreaves Street, Auckland, 1011, New Zealand
Tel.: (64) 93797867
Web Site:
https://www.wbitvpnewzealand.com
Motion Picture & Video Production Services
N.A.I.C.S.: 512191
Emma White (Co-Mng Dir)
Mike Molloy (Co-Mng Dir)

Subsidiary (Domestic):

Warner Bros. Television Group (3)
4000 Warner Blvd Bldg 168, Burbank, CA 91522
Tel.: (818) 977-0018
Web Site: http://www.timewarner.com
Television Production, Distribution & Broadcast Network Services
N.A.I.C.S.: 516120
Lisa Gregorian (Pres & CMO)
Jeff Tobler (Sr VP-Television Publicity & Comm-Worldwide Television Mktg)
Robert Pietranton (VP-Publicity & Comm-Worldwide)
Peter Roth (Chm)

Unit (Domestic):

Warner Bros. Domestic Television Distribution (4)
4000 Warner Blvd Bldg 30, Burbank, CA 91522
Tel.: (818) 954-5690
Web Site: http://property.warnerbros.com
Entertainment Content Distr to Broadcast & Cable Television Outlets
N.A.I.C.S.: 512120
Jeffrey R. Schlesinger (Pres-Warner Bros Worldwide Television Distr)

Subsidiary (Domestic):

Warner Bros. International Television Distribution Inc. (4)
4000 Warner Blvd, Burbank, CA 91522
Tel.: (818) 954-6000
Web Site: http://www.warnerbros.com
Film & Television Productions Distr to International Broadcasters
N.A.I.C.S.: 512120

Warner Bros. Television Production, Inc. (4)
4000 Warner Blvd, Burbank, CA 91522
Tel.: (818) 954-6000 (100%)
Made-for-TV Films, Series, Mini-Series & Specials Production & Distribution Services
N.A.I.C.S.: 512110
Adam Steinman (VP-Non Scripted Intl Dev & Sls)

Subsidiary (Non-US):

Warner Bros. Television Productions UK Ltd (3)
85 Grays Inn Rd, London, WC1X 8TX, United Kingdom (55.75%)
Tel.: (44) 2072391010
Web Site: http://www.shed-media.com

Television Production & Distribution Services
N.A.I.C.S.: 512110

Subsidiary (Domestic):

Ricochet Limited (4)
Pacific House 126 Dyke Road, Brighton, BN1 3TE, United Kingdom
Tel.: (44) 1273224800
Web Site: http://www.ricochet.co.uk
Independent Television Production Services
N.A.I.C.S.: 711510
Joanna Ball (Mng Dir)
Lisa Cox (Dir-Bus)
Rob Butterfield (Dir-Programmes)
Antonia Downey (Head-Legal & Bus Affairs)
Rebecca Rodrigues (Office Mgr)
Steffy Marrion (Head-Production)

Shed Media Scotland Limited (4)
Warner House 98 Theobald's Road, London, WC1X 8WB, Lanarkshire, United Kingdom
Tel.: (44) 1414274266
Factual & Drama Programme Production Services
N.A.I.C.S.: 512110

Subsidiary (US):

Shed Media US (4)
3800 Barham Blvd Ste 410, Los Angeles, CA 90068
Tel.: (323) 904-4680
Web Site: http://www.shedmedia.com
Television Programming Services
N.A.I.C.S.: 512110
Dan Peirson (Sr VP-Development)
Stephanie Schwam (VP)
John S. Dorsey (VP)

Subsidiary (Domestic):

Twenty Twenty Productions Limited (4)
200 Gray's Inn Road, London, WC1X 8XZ, United Kingdom
Tel.: (44) 2072842020
Web Site: http://www.twentytwenty.tv
Independent Television Production Services
N.A.I.C.S.: 711510
Kirsten Edwards (Sr Mgr)
Helen Soden (Head)
Vicky Bennetts (Mgr-Talent)
Helena Ely (Dir)
Craig Duff (Dir-Finance-Operations)

Wall to Wall Media Limited (4)
200 Gray's Inn Road, Kentish Town, London, WC1X 8XZ, United Kingdom
Tel.: (44) 2074857424
Web Site: https://www.walltowall.co.uk
Factual & Drama Programme Production Services
N.A.I.C.S.: 512110

Subsidiary (Domestic):

Warner Bros. Worldwide Consumer Products (3)
4000 Warner Blvd, Burbank, CA 91522-0001 (100%)
Tel.: (818) 954-6000
Web Site: http://www.warnerbrothers.com
Entertainment Product Licensing Services
N.A.I.C.S.: 424990

Subsidiary (Non-US):

Warner Entertainment Japan Inc. (3)
West Shinbashi 1-2-9 Hibiya Central Building, Minato-ku, Tokyo, 105-0003, Japan
Tel.: (81) 3 5251 6300
Web Site: http://www.warnerbros.co.jp
Motion Picture Distr
N.A.I.C.S.: 512120

Subsidiary (Non-US):

Warner Bros. Entertainment UK Limited (2)
Warner House 98 Theobalds Road, London, WC1X 8WB, United Kingdom
Tel.: (44) 2079845000
Web Site: http://www.warnerbros.co.uk
Film & Television Program Producer & Distr
N.A.I.C.S.: 512110

Warner Bros. International Television Production Holding B.V. (2)

Willem Fenengastraat 14, 1096 BN, Amsterdam, Netherlands
Tel.: (31) 203463700
Web Site:
https://www.wbitvpnetherlands.com
Motion Picture & Video Production Services
N.A.I.C.S.: 512191

Warner Bros. Television Production UK (2)
35 High Holborn, London, WC1V 6AE, United Kingdom
Tel.: (44) 2072391010
Web Site: http://www.wbtvpuk.co.uk
Film & Television Program Producer & Distr
N.A.I.C.S.: 512110

WARPSPEED TAXI INC.
2261 Rosanna St, Las Vegas, NV 89117
Tel.: (702) 805-0632 WY
Web Site:
https://www.warpspeedtaxi.com
Year Founded: 2020
WRPT—(OTCIQ)
Assets: $237,162
Liabilities: $81,265
Net Worth: $155,897
Earnings: ($129,123)
Fiscal Year-end: 07/31/24
Ride-hailing Services
N.A.I.C.S.: 485310
Daniel Okelo (Pres, CEO, CFO, Treas & Sec)

WARRIOR GIRL CORP.
5190 Neil Rd Ste 430, Reno, NV 89502
Tel.: (775) 333-5948 NV
Year Founded: 2002
WRGL—(OTCIQ)
Holding Company
N.A.I.C.S.: 551112
Julian Sula (CEO)
Carl Kruse Sr. (CFO & Sr VP)

WARRIOR MET COAL, INC
16243 Hwy 216, Brookwood, AL 35444
Tel.: (205) 554-6150 DE
Web Site:
https://www.warriormetcoal.com
Year Founded: 2015
HCC—(NYSE)
Rev.: $1,676,625,000
Assets: $2,357,058,000
Liabilities: $482,612,000
Net Worth: $1,874,446,000
Earnings: $478,629,000
Emp.: 1,143
Fiscal Year-end: 12/31/23
Coal Mining
N.A.I.C.S.: 212115
J. Brett Harvey (Chm)
Dale W. Boyles (CFO)
Jack K. Richardson (COO)
Kelli K. Gant (Chief Admin Officer & Sec)
Charles Lussier (Chief Comml Officer)
Walter J. Scheller III (CEO)

Subsidiaries:

Black Warrior Methane Corp. (1)
16243 Hwy 216, Brookwood, AL 35444-9801 (50%)
Tel.: (205) 554-6270
Web Site:
http://www.blackwarriormethane.com
Sales Range: $25-49.9 Million
Emp.: 10
Methane Gas Extraction & Distr
N.A.I.C.S.: 211120
Charles Willlis (Pres & Gen Mgr)

Black Warrior Transmission Corp. (1)
16243 Hwy 216, Brookwood, AL 35444 (50%)
Tel.: (205) 481-6270

Sales Range: $10-24.9 Million
Emp.: 25
Transmission of Methane Gas Through Pipeline
N.A.I.C.S.: 486210
Charles Willis (Pres)

WARRIOR TECHNOLOGIES ACQUISITION COMPANY
400 W Illinois Ste 1120, Midland, TX 79701
Tel.: (432) 818-0498 DE
Year Founded: 2020
WARR—(NYSE)
Emp.: 1
Investment Services
N.A.I.C.S.: 523999
H. H. Wommack III (Chm, Pres, CEO & CFO)

WASHINGTON BUSINESS BANK
223 5th Ave SE, Olympia, WA 98501
Tel.: (360) 754-1945 WA
Web Site:
https://www.wabizbank.com
Year Founded: 2002
WBZB—(OTCIQ)
Commericial Banking
N.A.I.C.S.: 522110
Jon M. Jones (Pres & CEO)

WASHINGTON TRUST BANCORP, INC.
Tel.: (401) 348-1566 RI
Web Site: https://ir.washtrust.com
Year Founded: 1984
WASH—(NASDAQ)
Rev.: $364,799,000
Assets: $7,202,847,000
Liabilities: $6,730,161,000
Net Worth: $472,686,000
Earnings: $48,176,000
Emp.: 665
Fiscal Year-end: 12/31/23
Bank Holding Company
N.A.I.C.S.: 551111
Kristen L. DiSanto (Chief HR Officer, Sec & Sr Exec VP)
Elizabeth Boyle Eckel (CMO)
Mary E. Noons (Pres & COO)
Ronald S. Ohsberg (CFO, Treas & Sr Exec VP)
Maria N. Janes (Chief Acctg Officer, Exec VP & Controller)

Subsidiaries:

Halsey Associates, Inc. (1)
265 Church St Ste 1006, New Haven, CT 06510
Tel.: (203) 772-0740
Web Site: https://www.washtrustwealth.com
Investment Management & Advisory Services
N.A.I.C.S.: 523940
Kenneth J. Julian (Exec VP)
Peter J. Secrist (Sr VP & Sr Portfolio Mgr)
Thomas N. Ellis Jr. (VP & Sr Portfolio Mgr)
Thomas Beirne III (Officer-Wealth Mgmt Plng & VP)

The Washington Trust Company, of Westerly (1)
23 Broad St, Westerly, RI 02891-1879 (100%)
Tel.: (401) 348-1200
Web Site: http://www.washtrust.com
Sales Range: $100-124.9 Million
Emp.: 450
Commercial Banking & Trust Services
N.A.I.C.S.: 522110
Mark K. W. Gim (Pres & COO)
Mary E. Noons (Chief Retail Lending Officer & Exec VP-Retail Lending)
Kristen L. DiSanto (Chief HR Officer, Sec & Sr Exec VP)
Debra A. Gormley (Chief Retail Banking Officer & Exec VP-Retail Banking)
Maria N. Janes (Exec VP & Controller)

Washington Trust Bancorp, Inc.—(Continued)

Mary E. Noons *(Chief Retail Lending Officer & Exec VP-Retail Lending)*
Dennis L. Algiere *(Chief Compliance Officer, Exec VP & Dir-Community Affairs)*
Kathleen A. Ryan *(Chief Wealth Mgmt Officer & Exec VP)*
C. Scott Ostrowski *(Sr VP)*
William K. Wray Sr. *(Chief Risk Officer & Sr Exec VP)*

WASTE MANAGEMENT, INC.
800 Capitol St Ste 3000, Houston, TX 77002
Tel.: (713) 512-6200　　DE
Web Site: https://www.wm.com
Year Founded: 1987
WM—(NYSE)
Rev.: $20,426,000,000
Assets: $32,823,000,000
Liabilities: $25,927,000,000
Net Worth: $6,896,000,000
Earnings: $2,304,000,000
Emp.: 48,000
Fiscal Year-end: 12/31/23
Solid Waste Management & Environmental Services
N.A.I.C.S.: 562111
Devina A. Rankin *(CFO & Exec VP)*
Leslie K. Nagy *(Treas & VP)*
Charles C. Boettcher *(Chief Legal Officer & Sr VP)*
John A. Carroll *(Chief Acctg Officer & VP)*
David L. Reed *(Partner-Bus-Western Tier Field Ops & VP)*
Donald J. Smith *(Sr VP)*
James C. Fish Jr. *(Pres & CEO)*
John J. Morris Jr. *(COO & Exec VP)*

Subsidiaries:

1-800-Pack-Rat, LLC　　(1)
11640 Northpark Dr Ste 300, Wake Forest, NC 27587
Web Site: https://www.1800packrat.com
Waste Collection Services
N.A.I.C.S.: 562111

Advanced Disposal Services Blackfoot Landfill, Inc.　　(1)
3726 E State Rd 64, Winslow, IN 47598
Tel.: (812) 789-2647
Waste Management Services
N.A.I.C.S.: 562998

Advanced Disposal Services Blue Ridge Landfill, Inc.　　(1)
2700 Winchester Rd, Irvine, KY 40336
Tel.: (606) 723-5552
Waste Management Services
N.A.I.C.S.: 562998

Advanced Disposal Services Cedar Hill Landfill, Inc.　　(1)
1319 N Business Creek Rd, Ragland, AL 35131
Tel.: (205) 338-7821
Waste Management Services
N.A.I.C.S.: 562998

Advanced Disposal Services Cranberry Creek Landfill, LLC　　(1)
2510 Engel Rd, Wisconsin Rapids, WI 54495
Waste Management Services
N.A.I.C.S.: 562998

Advanced Disposal Services Cypress Acres Landfill, Inc.　　(1)
7424 NE 33rd Ct, Ocala, FL 34480
Tel.: (352) 629-3500
Waste Management Services
N.A.I.C.S.: 562998

Advanced Disposal Services Evergreen Landfill, Inc.　　(1)
3163 Wetherington Ln, Valdosta, GA 31601
Tel.: (229) 293-8157
Waste Management Services
N.A.I.C.S.: 562998

Advanced Disposal Services Jackson, LLC　　(1)
120 Rodeo Dr, Jackson, GA 30233

Tel.: (678) 752-4277
Waste Management Services
N.A.I.C.S.: 562998

Advanced Disposal Services Lancaster Landfill, LLC　　(1)
2487 Cloverleaf Rd, Elizabethtown, PA 17022
Waste Management Services
N.A.I.C.S.: 562998

Advanced Disposal Services Lithonia Transfer Station, LLC　　(1)
7040 Maddox Rd, Lithonia, GA 30058
Tel.: (678) 526-0085
Waste Management Services
N.A.I.C.S.: 562998

Advanced Disposal Services Macon, LLC　　(1)
2201 Trade Dr, Macon, GA 31217
Tel.: (478) 405-5000
Waste Management Services
N.A.I.C.S.: 562998

Advanced Disposal Services Maple Hill Landfill, Inc.　　(1)
31226 Intrepid Rd, Macon, MO 63552
Tel.: (660) 385-5426
Waste Management Services
N.A.I.C.S.: 562998

Advanced Disposal Services Middle Georgia, LLC　　(1)
154 Dundee Dr, Milledgeville, GA 31061
Tel.: (478) 453-4435
Waste Management Services
N.A.I.C.S.: 562998

Advanced Disposal Services Morehead Landfill, Inc.　　(1)
300 Old Phelps Rd, Morehead, KY 40351
Waste Management Services
N.A.I.C.S.: 562998

Advanced Disposal Services North Georgia, LLC　　(1)
10169 Lakewood Hwy, Mineral Bluff, GA 30559
Tel.: (706) 632-6519
Waste Management Services
N.A.I.C.S.: 562998

Advanced Disposal Services Orchard Hills Landfill, Inc.　　(1)
8290 Hwy 251, Davis Junction, IL 61020
Tel.: (815) 874-9000
Waste Management Services
N.A.I.C.S.: 562998

Advanced Disposal Services Selma Transfer Station, LLC　　(1)
1478 Hwy 41, Selma, AL 36701
Tel.: (334) 875-5575
Waste Management Services
N.A.I.C.S.: 562998

Advanced Disposal Services Star Ridge Landfill, Inc.　　(1)
3301 Acmar Rd, Moody, AL 35004
Tel.: (205) 640-1799
Emp.: 12
Waste Management Services
N.A.I.C.S.: 562998

Advanced Disposal Services Valley View Landfill, Inc.　　(1)
1145 Bear Rd, Decatur, IL 62522
Tel.: (217) 963-2976
Waste Management Services
N.A.I.C.S.: 562998

Advanced Disposal Services, Inc.　　(1)
90 Ft Wade Rd, Ponte Vedra Beach, FL 32081
Tel.: (904) 737-7900
Web Site: http://www.advanceddisposal.com
Rev.: $1,623,000,000
Assets: $3,543,500,000
Liabilities: $2,620,100,000
Net Worth: $923,400,000
Earnings: ($6,600,000)
Emp.: 6,200
Fiscal Year-end: 12/31/2019
Waste Disposal Services
N.A.I.C.S.: 562111
John Spegal *(COO & Exec VP)*
Donald Neukam *(VP-Bus Dev & Strategic Plng)*

Matthew Nelson *(VP-Fin & IR)*
Melissa Westerman *(Chief Acctg Officer, VP & Asst Treas)*
Mark A. Lockett *(Pres)*
Courtney A. Tippy *(Sec & VP)*
James A. Wilson *(VP)*
Leslie K. Nagy *(CFO, Controller & VP)*
David L. Reed *(Treas & VP)*
Jeff Bennett *(Asst Treas)*

Subsidiary (Domestic):

Arrow Disposal Service, LLC　　(2)
106 West Ct Square, Abbeville, AL 36310
Tel.: (334) 585-9838
Web Site: http://www.arrowdisposal.net
Sales Range: $25-49.9 Million
Emp.: 43
Waste Hauling & Recycling
N.A.I.C.S.: 562119
Jimmie Moore *(VP-Public Affairs)*
Susie Blalock *(Mgr-Accounting)*
Marty Bonner *(Coord-Payroll-Human Resources)*
Linda Burdeshaw *(Mgr-Customer Service)*
Richard Urrutia *(CEO & Founder)*
Hugh Herndon *(CFO & VP)*
Dale Weeks *(Dir-Operations)*
Richard Urrutia *(CEO & Founder)*
Hugh Herndon *(CFO & VP)*
Dale Weeks *(Dir-Operations)*

CGS Services, Inc.　　(1)
2920 E US 52, Morristown, IN 46161
Tel.: (765) 763-6258
Web Site: http://www.cgsservices.com
Construction Sand & Gravel Refuse Systems
N.A.I.C.S.: 212321

Alpharetta Transfer Station, LLC　　(1)
11465 Maxwell Rd, Alpharetta, GA 30004
Tel.: (770) 664-9113
Waste Management Services
N.A.I.C.S.: 562219
Keith Hansard *(Mgr-Site)*

American Landfill, Inc.　　(1)
7916 Chapel St SE, Waynesburg, OH 44688-9754　　(100%)
Tel.: (330) 866-3265
Web Site: https://americanlandfill.wm.com
Sales Range: $25-49.9 Million
Emp.: 35
Sanitary Landfill Operator
N.A.I.C.S.: 562212

American Oil Recovery, LLC　　(1)
309 Southpark Dr, Lufkin, TX 75904
Tel.: (936) 634-0685
Web Site: http://www.americanoilrecovery.com
Oil & Gas Exploration Services
N.A.I.C.S.: 213112

Anderson Landfill, Inc.　　(1)
18703 Cambridge Rd, Anderson, CA 96007
Tel.: (866) 909-4458
Waste Management Services
N.A.I.C.S.: 562219
Rick King *(Mgr)*

Anderson Landfill, Inc.　　(1)
18703 Cambridge Rd, Anderson, CA 96007
Tel.: (530) 347-5236
Web Site: https://andersonlandfill.wm.com
Waste Collection Services
N.A.I.C.S.: 562111

Antelope Valley Recycling and Disposal Facility, Inc.　　(1)
1200 W City Ranch Rd, Palmdale, CA 93551
Tel.: (661) 223-3427
Web Site: http://www.wm.com
Waste Disposal Services; Landfill
N.A.I.C.S.: 562219

Arden Landfill, Inc.　　(1)
200 Rangos Ln, Washington, PA 15301
Tel.: (724) 206-7934
Waste Management Services
N.A.I.C.S.: 562219

Atlantic Waste Disposal, Inc.　　(1)
3474 Atlantic Ln, Waverly, VA 23890-3726
Tel.: (804) 834-8300
Sales Range: $25-49.9 Million
Emp.: 50
Sanitary Landfill Operator
N.A.I.C.S.: 562212

Burnsville Sanitary Landfill, Inc.　　(1)
2650 Cliff Rd W, Burnsville, MN 55337
Tel.: (866) 909-4458
Waste Management Services
N.A.I.C.S.: 562219

CWM Chemical Services, L.L.C.　　(1)
1550 Balmer Rd, Youngstown, NY 14174
Tel.: (716) 286-1550
Web Site: http://www.wmsolutions.com
Emp.: 35
Waste Management Services
N.A.I.C.S.: 562219

Cal Sierra Disposal　　(1)
19309 Industrial Dr, Sonora, CA 95370-9232　　(100%)
Tel.: (209) 532-1413
Sales Range: $25-49.9 Million
Emp.: 32
Waste Collection Services
N.A.I.C.S.: 562111

California Asbestos Monofill, Inc.　　(1)
6 Miles S Obyrnes Ferry Rd, Copperopolis, CA 95228
Tel.: (209) 785-2201
Solid Waste Management Services
N.A.I.C.S.: 562212

Capitol Disposal, Inc.　　(1)
5600 Tonsgard Ct, Juneau, AK 99801
Tel.: (907) 780-7801
Waste Management Services
N.A.I.C.S.: 562219

Cartersville Transfer Station, LLC　　(1)
125 Riverside Dr, Cartersville, GA 30120
Tel.: (678) 792-7000
Waste Management Services
N.A.I.C.S.: 562998

Cedar Ridge Landfill, Inc.　　(1)
2340 Mooresville Hwy, Lewisburg, TN 37091
Tel.: (931) 270-0950
Waste Management Services
N.A.I.C.S.: 562219

Central Disposal Systems, Inc.　　(1)
21265 430th St, Lake Mills, IA 50450　　(100%)
Tel.: (641) 592-9182
Sales Range: $10-24.9 Million
Emp.: 6
Sanitary Landfill Operator
N.A.I.C.S.: 562212

Chadwick Road Landfill, Inc.　　(1)
13700 Chadwick Farm Blvd, Roswell, GA 30075
Tel.: (770) 475-9868
Sales Range: $25-49.9 Million
Emp.: 4
Solid Waste Landfill Services
N.A.I.C.S.: 562212
Ryan Evola *(District Mgr)*

Chambers of Mississippi, Inc.　　(1)
2253 Mudline Rd, Lake, MS 39092
Tel.: (601) 536-3086
Waste Management Services
N.A.I.C.S.: 562219

Chemical Waste Management, Inc.　　(1)
17629 Cedar Springs Ln, Arlington, OR 97812
Tel.: (541) 454-3220
Hazardous Waste Management Services
N.A.I.C.S.: 562112

Conservation Services, Inc.　　(1)
1620 N Delphine Ave, Waynesboro, VA 22980
Tel.: (540) 941-0067
Web Site: https://conservationservicesinc.com
Tree Plantation Services
N.A.I.C.S.: 111335

Cougar Landfill, Inc.　　(1)
8601 E Mount, Houston, TX 77050
Tel.: (713) 354-5200
Web Site: http://www.wmsolutions.com
Chemical Waste Management Services
N.A.I.C.S.: 562998

Countryside Landfill Inc.　　(1)
31725 N Route 83, Grayslake, IL 60030
Tel.: (847) 223-2722

Web Site: http://www.wmsolutions.com
Waste Management Services
N.A.I.C.S.: 562219

Cuyahoga Landfill, Inc. (1)
6640 Cochran Rd, Solon, OH
44139-3904 **(100%)**
Tel.: (440) 498-5700
Sales Range: $10-24.9 Million
Emp.: 3
Sanitary Landfill Operator
N.A.I.C.S.: 562212

Dafter Sanitary Landfill, Inc. (1)
3962 W 12 Mile Rd, Dafter, MI 49724
Tel.: (866) 909-4458
Nonhazardous Waste Treatment & Disposal
Services
N.A.I.C.S.: 562219
Tim Harrow (Site Mgr)

Deer Track Park Landfill, Inc. (1)
N6756 Waldmann Ln, Watertown, WI 53094
Tel.: (920) 699-3475
Solid Waste Landfill
N.A.I.C.S.: 562212

Deffenbaugh Industries, Inc. (1)
2601 Midwest Dr, Kansas City, KS 66111-
1760
Tel.: (913) 631-3300
Sales Range: $150-199.9 Million
Emp.: 1,500
Waste Disposal Systems
N.A.I.C.S.: 562212

Delaware Recyclable Products,
Inc. (1)
246 Marsh Ln, New Castle, DE
19720 **(100%)**
Tel.: (302) 655-1360
Web Site: http://www.wm.com
Sales Range: $10-24.9 Million
Emp.: 15
Solid Waste Management Services
N.A.I.C.S.: 562212

Doctor Bramblett Road, LLC (1)
4200 Dr Bramblett Rd, Cumming, GA 30028
Tel.: (678) 513-1499
Waste Management Services
N.A.I.C.S.: 562219

Doraville Transfer Station, LLC (1)
2784 Woodwin Rd, Doraville, GA 30360
Tel.: (770) 451-4300
Waste Management Services
N.A.I.C.S.: 562998

Earthmovers Landfill, LLC (1)
26488 County Rd 26, Elkhart, IN 46517-
9784
Tel.: (574) 875-5232
Sanitary Landfill Operator
N.A.I.C.S.: 562212

El Coqui Landfill Company, Inc. (1)
PR-3 Int 923 Km 1 7 Barrio Buena Vista,
Humacao, PR 00791
Tel.: (787) 852-4444
Waste Management Services
N.A.I.C.S.: 562219

Elk River Landfill, Inc. (1)
22460 Hwy 169 NW, Elk River, MN 55330
Tel.: (763) 441-2464
Web Site: http://www.wmsolutions.com
Emp.: 11
Solid Waste Management & Environmental
Services
N.A.I.C.S.: 562111

Evergreen Recycling and Disposal
Facility, Inc. (1)
2625 E Broadway St, Northwood, OH
43619
Sales Range: $25-49.9 Million
Emp.: 10
Solid Waste Disposal Services
N.A.I.C.S.: 562212

Feather River Disposal, Inc. (1)
1166 Industrial Way, Quincy, CA
95971 **(100%)**
Tel.: (530) 283-2065
Web Site: http://www.wm.com
Sales Range: $25-49.9 Million
Emp.: 27
Garbage Collection & Transport Services
N.A.I.C.S.: 562111

G.I. Industries (1)
195 W Los Angeles Ave, Simi Valley, CA
93065
Tel.: (805) 522-9400
Waste Management Services
N.A.I.C.S.: 562219

Gartran, L.L.C. (1)
8400 Sweet Valley Dr Ste 408, Cleveland,
OH 44125
Tel.: (216) 581-6975
Web Site: https://www.gartran.com
Waste Collection Services
N.A.I.C.S.: 562111

Gateway Transfer Station, LLC (1)
1625 Westgate Pkwy SW, Atlanta, GA
30336
Tel.: (404) 794-6707
Waste Management Services
N.A.I.C.S.: 562219

Georgia Waste Systems, Inc. (1)
1243 Beaver Ruin Rd, Norcross, GA 30093
Tel.: (770) 381-4040
Waste Collection Services
N.A.I.C.S.: 562111

Glen's Sanitary Landfill, Inc. (1)
518 E Traverse Hwy, Maple City, MI 49664-
9512
Tel.: (231) 228-5196
Emp.: 3
Solid Waste Landfill Services
N.A.I.C.S.: 562212
Randy Goodman (Mgr)

Grand Central Sanitary Landfill,
Inc. (1)
910 W Pennsylvania Ave, Pen Argyl, PA
18072-9646
Tel.: (610) 863-6057
Sales Range: $1-9.9 Million
Emp.: 350
Solid Waste Disposal Services
N.A.I.C.S.: 562212

Greenleaf Compaction, Inc. (1)
222 S Mill Ave Ste 333, Tempe, AZ
85281 **(100%)**
Tel.: (602) 977-2077
Web Site:
http://www.greenleafcompaction.com
Sales Range: $25-49.9 Million
Emp.: 25
Waste Handling Equipment Rental Services
N.A.I.C.S.: 532490

Greenstar Allentown, LLC (1)
799 Smith Ln, Northampton, PA 18067
Tel.: (610) 262-6920
Materials Recovery Facility Services
N.A.I.C.S.: 562920
Richard Smith (Gen Mgr)

Greenstar Managed Services - Con-
necticut, LLC (1)
363 New Britain Rd, Kensington, CT 06037
Tel.: (860) 829-5800
Emp.: 10
Materials Recovery Facility Services
N.A.I.C.S.: 562920

Greenstar Managed Services -
RLWM, LLC (1)
2023 Eagle Rd, Normal, IL 61761
Tel.: (309) 834-1400
Emp.: 45
Waste Management Services
N.A.I.C.S.: 562219
Brian Gaughan (Sr VP-Sls & Mktg)

Greenstar Paterson, LLC (1)
59-85 Florida Ave, Paterson, NJ 07503
Tel.: (973) 345-2293
Waste Recycling Services
N.A.I.C.S.: 562920
Gordon Sabol (Gen Mgr)

Hall County Transfer Station,
LLC (1)
1 Ruby St, Gainesville, GA 30501
Tel.: (770) 539-9377
Waste Management Services
N.A.I.C.S.: 562998

Hillsboro Landfill Inc. (1)
3205 SE Minter Bridge Rd, Hillsboro, OR
97123-5350
Tel.: (503) 640-9427

Sales Range: $10-24.9 Million
Emp.: 20
Sanitary Landfill Operator
N.A.I.C.S.: 562212

Hinkle Transfer Station, LLC (1)
1725 Brookside Rd, Macungie, PA 18062
Tel.: (610) 366-7356
Waste Management Services
N.A.I.C.S.: 562998

Jay County Landfill, L.L.C. (1)
5825 W 400 S, Portland, IN 47371
Tel.: (260) 726-2871
Web Site: http://www.wm.com
Emp.: 8
Solid Waste Landfill
N.A.I.C.S.: 562212

K and W Landfill Inc. (1)
11877 State Hwy M38, Ontonagon, MI
49929
Tel.: (906) 883-3504
Emp.: 5
Solid Waste Landfill Services
N.A.I.C.S.: 562212

King George Landfill, Inc. (1)
10376 Bullock Dr, King George, VA
22485 **(100%)**
Tel.: (540) 376-6965
Sanitary Landfill Operator
N.A.I.C.S.: 562212

LCS Services Landfill , Inc. (1)
911 Allensville Rd, Hedgesville, WV
25427 **(100%)**
Tel.: (304) 754-9153
Sanitary Landfill Operator
N.A.I.C.S.: 562212

Laurel Highlands Landfill, Inc. (1)
260 Laurel Rdg Rd, Johnstown, PA 15909
Tel.: (814) 749-9065
Solid Waste Landfill
N.A.I.C.S.: 562212

Liberty Landfill, L.L.C. (1)
8635 State Rd 16 E, Monticello, IN 47960
Tel.: (574) 278-7138
Solid Waste Landfill Services
N.A.I.C.S.: 562212

Longleaf C&D Disposal Facility,
Inc. (1)
2023 Longleaf Dr, Pensacola, FL 32505
Tel.: (850) 301-2802
Sales Range: $25-49.9 Million
Emp.: 2
Solid Waste Landfill Services
N.A.I.C.S.: 562212

Mahoning Landfill, Inc. (1)
3510 E Garfield Rd, New Springfield, OH
44443-9743
Tel.: (330) 549-5357
Solid Waste Disposal Services
N.A.I.C.S.: 562212

Meadowfill Landfill, Inc. (1)
1488 Dawson Dr, Bridgeport, WV 26330
Tel.: (681) 456-6989
Waste Management Services
N.A.I.C.S.: 562219

Mostoller Landfill, LLC (1)
7095 Glades Pike Rd, Somerset, PA 15501
Tel.: (814) 444-0112
Waste Management Services
N.A.I.C.S.: 562998

New Milford Landfill, L.L.C. (1)
182 Danbury Rd, New Milford, CT 06776
Tel.: (203) 733-5133
Waste Management Services
N.A.I.C.S.: 562219

OGH Acquisition Corporation (1)
800 Connecticut Blvd, East Hartford, CT
06108
Tel.: (860) 760-9388
Investment Management Service
N.A.I.C.S.: 523940

Oakleaf Waste Management,
LLC (1)
415 Day Hill Rd, Windsor, CT 06095
Tel.: (860) 290-1250
Waste Management Services
N.A.I.C.S.: 562219

Oakridge Landfill, Inc. (1)

2183 Hwy 78, Dorchester, SC 29437
Tel.: (866) 909-4458
Solid Waste Landfill Services
N.A.I.C.S.: 562212

Oakwood Landfill, Inc. (1)
751 Strobhart Rd, Ridgeland, SC
29936 **(100%)**
Tel.: (843) 726-2100
Sanitary Landfill Operator
N.A.I.C.S.: 562212

Ozark Ridge Landfill, Inc. (1)
10140 Ozark Rdg Acess Ln, Danville, AR
72833
Tel.: (479) 576-2776
Sales Range: $25-49.9 Million
Emp.: 5
Solid Waste Landfill Services
N.A.I.C.S.: 562212

Palo Alto Sanitation Company (1)
2000 Geng Rd, Palo Alto, CA 94303
Tel.: (650) 493-4894
Sales Range: $25-49.9 Million
Emp.: 59
Refuse Collection & Disposal Services
N.A.I.C.S.: 562211
Scott Scholz (Gen Mgr)

Phoenix Resources, Inc. (1)
782 Antrim Rd, Wellsboro, PA 16901
Tel.: (570) 353-2406
Waste Management Services
N.A.I.C.S.: 562219

Pine Grove Landfill, Inc. (1)
193 Schultz Rd, Pine Grove, PA
17963 **(100%)**
Tel.: (800) 869-5566
Sales Range: $10-24.9 Million
Emp.: 20
Solid Waste Management & Environmental
Services
N.A.I.C.S.: 562111

Pine Tree Acres, Inc. (1)
36600 29 Mile Rd, Lenox, MI
48048-1514 **(100%)**
Tel.: (586) 749-9698
Web Site:
https://pinetreeacreslandfill.wm.com
Sales Range: $10-24.9 Million
Emp.: 21
Sanitary Landfill Operator
N.A.I.C.S.: 562212

Ray's Trash Service, Inc. (1)
3859 E US Highway 40, Clayton, IN 46118-
9358
Tel.: (317) 539-2024
Web Site: http://raystrash.com
Rev.: $8,300,000
Emp.: 100
Solid Waste Landfill
N.A.I.C.S.: 562212
Charlene Thornburgh (Mgr-Acctg)
Calvin Davidson (Project Mgr)

Recycle America Co., L.L.C. (1)
26951 Rd 140, Visalia, CA 93292
Tel.: (559) 741-1766
Web Site: http://www.wm.com
Scrap & Waste Materials Whslr
N.A.I.C.S.: 423930

Recycling Services, Inc. (1)
3301 W 47th Pl, Chicago, IL 60632
Tel.: (773) 247-2070
Sales Range: $1-9.9 Million
Emp.: 50
Paper Recycling & Document Destruction
Services
N.A.I.C.S.: 423930
Michael Finn (Pres)

Redwood Landfill, Inc. (1)
8950 Redwood Hwy, Novato, CA 94945-
1435
Tel.: (415) 408-9052
Web Site: https://redwoodlandfill.wm.com
Sales Range: $25-49.9 Million
Emp.: 32
Sanitary Landfill Operator
N.A.I.C.S.: 562212

Refuse Services, Inc. (1)
6501 Greenland Rd, Jacksonville, FL
32258-2439
Tel.: (904) 260-1592
Waste Management Services

Waste Management, Inc.—(Continued)

N.A.I.C.S.: 562219

Refuse, Inc. (1)
2401 Canyon Way, Sparks, NV 89434
Tel.: (715) 342-0401
Emp.: 30
Waste Management Services
N.A.I.C.S.: 562219

**Reliable Environmental Transport,
Inc.** (1)
RR 4 Box 263, Bridgeport, WV 26330
Tel.: (804) 623-6490
Web Site: http://www.retincwv.com
Hazardous Waste Collection, Treatment &
Disposal Services
N.A.I.C.S.: 562112

Reliable Landfill, LLC (1)
US Hwy 3199, Livonia, LA 70755
Tel.: (225) 387-0505
Waste Management Services
N.A.I.C.S.: 562219
Johnna Cortes (Mgr)

Reno Disposal Co. (1)
100 Vassar St, Reno, NV 89502
Tel.: (775) 329-8822
Web Site: http://www.wm.com
Solid Waste Collection & Disposal Services
N.A.I.C.S.: 562111

Unit (Domestic):

**Reno Disposal Co. - Commercial
Row Facility** (2)
1392 E Commercial Row, Reno, NV 89512
Tel.: (775) 329-8822
Web Site: http://www.wm.com
Solid Waste & Recyclable Materials Collec-
tion Services
N.A.I.C.S.: 562111

Richland County Landfill, Inc. (1)
1070 Caughman Rd N, Columbia, SC
29203
Tel.: (803) 576-2390
Waste Management Services
N.A.I.C.S.: 562219

Riverbend Landfill Co. (1)
13469 SW Hwy 18, McMinnville, OR
97128 (100%)
Tel.: (503) 472-8788
Sales Range: $10-24.9 Million
Emp.: 20
Sanitary Landfill Operator
N.A.I.C.S.: 562212

**S4 Columbia Ridge Recovery,
LLC** (1)
18177 Cedar Springs Ln, Arlington, OR
97812-6512
Tel.: (541) 454-2200
Sales Range: $25-49.9 Million
Emp.: 15
Clean Energy Services
N.A.I.C.S.: 562212
Alan Anderson (Plant Mgr)

Shade Landfill, Inc. (1)
1176 #1 Rd, Cairnbrook, PA 15924
Tel.: (814) 754-4587
Web Site: http://www.wm.com
Sales Range: $10-24.9 Million
Emp.: 15
Sanitary Landfill Operator
N.A.I.C.S.: 562212

Sister's Sanitation Services, LLC (1)
2920 E US 52, Morristown, IN 46161
Web Site: http://www.sisterssanitation.com
Mobile Shredding Services
N.A.I.C.S.: 561990

**Southern Alleghenies Landfill,
Inc.** (1)
843 Miller Picking Rd, Davidsville, PA
15928
Tel.: (814) 479-2537
Waste Management Services
N.A.I.C.S.: 562219

Southern Waste Services, L.L.C. (1)
1230 Silver City Rd, Whitesburg, TN 37891
Tel.: (423) 235-9300
Web Site:
    https://www.southernwasteservicesllc.com
Waste Collection Services

Spinnaker Recycling Corp. (1)
3397 American Drive Unit 1, Mississauga,
L4V 1T8, ON, Canada
Tel.: (905) 678-7746
Web Site:
    http://www.spinnakerrecycling.com
Waste Management Services
N.A.I.C.S.: 562998

Spruce Ridge, Inc. (1)
12755 137th St, Glencoe, MN 55336
Tel.: (866) 909-4458
Waste Management Services
N.A.I.C.S.: 562219

Stericycle, Inc. (1)
2355 Waukegan Rd, Bannockburn, IL
60015
Tel.: (847) 367-5910
Web Site: https://www.stericycle.com
Rev.: $2,659,300,000
Assets: $5,352,600,000
Liabilities: $2,829,700,000
Net Worth: $2,522,900,000
Earnings: ($21,400,000)
Emp.: 13,500
Fiscal Year-end: 12/31/2023
Medical Waste Management & Infection
Control Services
N.A.I.C.S.: 562998

Subsidiary (Non-US):

Ambiface & Buffer SGPS Lda (2)
Rua Fernando Pessoa 8c, 2560-241, Torres
Vedras, Portugal
Tel.: (351) 261320300
Web Site: http://www.ambimed.pt
Sales Range: $25-49.9 Million
Emp.: 40
Waste Management & Remediation Ser-
vices
N.A.I.C.S.: 562211

**Ambimed - Gestao Ambiental,
Lda.** (2)
Rua 1 Maio - Rotunda do Catefica S/N,
2560-587, Torres Vedras, Portugal
Tel.: (351) 808200246
Web Site: http://www.stericycle.pt
Industrial Waste Collection Services
N.A.I.C.S.: 562111

Subsidiary (Domestic):

**PSC Environmental Services,
LLC** (2)
5151 San Felipe St Ste 1100, Houston, TX
77056
Tel.: (713) 623-8777
Web Site: http://www.pscnow.com
Environmental Remediation Services
N.A.I.C.S.: 562910

Subsidiary (Non-US):

Shred-it GmbH (2)
Klausnerring 3, 85551, Munich, Germany
Tel.: (49) 891 208 5948
Web Site: https://www.shredit.de
Document Shredding Services
N.A.I.C.S.: 561990

Stericare Romania (2)
road no Giurgiului no 5, 77120, Jilava, Ilfov,
Romania
Tel.: (40) 214570975
Web Site: https://www.stericycle.ro
Sales Range: $25-49.9 Million
Emp.: 25
Medical Waste Processing Services
N.A.I.C.S.: 562211

Stericycle Hokkaido GK (2)
3-703-34 Shinkonan, Ishikari, 061-3244,
Hokkaido, Japan
Tel.: (81) 133649000
Web Site: https://www.esgm-group.jp
Industrial Waste Collection Services
N.A.I.C.S.: 562111

Stericycle Inc. (2)
76 Wentworth Crt, Brampton, L6T 5M7, ON,
Canada
Tel.: (905) 595-2651
Web Site: http://www.stericycle.ca
Sales Range: $25-49.9 Million
Emp.: 50
Waste Management & Recycling Services

N.A.I.C.S.: 562998
Richard M. Moore (Exec VP)
Cindy J. Miller (Pres)
Janet H. Zelenka (CIO)
S. Cory White (Exec VP)
Joseph A. Reuter (Exec VP)
Dominic Culotta (Exec VP)
Michael S. Weisman (Exec VP)
Daniel V. Ginnetti (Exec VP)
Kurt M. Rogers (Exec VP)

Subsidiary (Domestic):

Stericycle International, LLC (2)
28161 N Keith Dr, Lake Forest, IL 60045-
4528
Tel.: (847) 367-5910
Medical Waste Management Services
N.A.I.C.S.: 562211

Subsidiary (Non-US):

Stericycle Japan Co. Ltd. (2)
1-1 1-1 Yadamachi San Si Building 3F AB
Room, Shinjuku-ku, Tokyo, 162-0843, Ja-
pan
Tel.: (81) 355798609
Web Site: http://www.stericycle.co.jp
Waste Disposal Services
N.A.I.C.S.: 562211

Stericycle Korea Co Ltd. (2)
22 Cheondeoksan-ro 428beon-gil Namsa-
myeon, Cheoin-gu, Yongin-si, 449881,
Gyeonggi-do, Korea (South)
Tel.: (82) 313230360
Web Site: https://www.stericycle.co.kr
Hazardous Waste Treatment & Disposal
Services
N.A.I.C.S.: 562211

Stericycle Portugal (2)
Ambimed Sede, Rua Fernando Pessoa 8C,
Torres Vedras, Portugal
Tel.: (351) 261320300
Web Site: https://www.stericycle.pt
Hazardous Waste Treatment & Disposal
Services
N.A.I.C.S.: 562211

Stericycle Romania, Srl (2)
Sos Giurgiului nr 5, Jud Ilfov, Jilava,
077120, Ilfov, Romania
Tel.: (40) 21 457 0975
Web Site: https://www.stericycle.ro
Hazardous Waste Treatment & Disposal
Services
N.A.I.C.S.: 562211

Subsidiary (Domestic):

**Stericycle Specialty Waste Solutions,
Inc.** (2)
2850 100th Ct NE, Minneapolis, MN 55449
Tel.: (612) 285-9865
Web Site: http://www.stericycle.com
Emp.: 40
Medical Waste Management Services
N.A.I.C.S.: 562211

Subsidiary (Non-US):

Stericycle ULC (2)
76 Wentworth Crt, Brampton, L6T 5M7, ON,
Canada
Tel.: (905) 595-2651
Web Site: https://www.stericycle.ca
Hazardous Waste Treatment & Disposal
Services
N.A.I.C.S.: 562211

Subsidiary (Domestic):

The MPB Group, LLC (2)
3600 Harwood Rd Ste A, Bedford, TX
76021
Tel.: (817) 785-5000
Web Site: http://www.beryl.net
Health Care Srvices
N.A.I.C.S.: 621610

Summit Disposal Inc. (1)
37484B Cornaz Dr, Burney, CA 96013
Tel.: (530) 335-2723
Web Site:
    https://www.summitdisposalinc.com
Residential & Commercial Services
N.A.I.C.S.: 561790

**Swire Waste Management
Limited** (1)

33/F One Pacific Place 88 Queensway,
GPO Box 1, Hong Kong, China (Hong
Kong)
Tel.: (852) 28408430
Solid Waste Management & Environmental
Services
N.A.I.C.S.: 562111

TX Newco, L.L.C. (1)
2708 W 7th St, Texarkana, TX 75501
Tel.: (903) 794-4111
Waste Management Services
N.A.I.C.S.: 562219

**The Woodlands of Van Buren,
Inc.** (1)
39670 Ecorse Rd, Wayne, MI 48184
Tel.: (734) 729-4477
Web Site: https://www.thewoodlandsgc.com
Waste Collection Services
N.A.I.C.S.: 562111

Trail Ridge Landfill, Inc. (1)
5110 US Hwy 301, Baldwin, FL
32234-3606 (100%)
Tel.: (904) 289-9100
Web Site: https://trailridgelandfill.wm.com
Sales Range: $10-24.9 Million
Emp.: 25
Sanitary Landfill Operator
N.A.I.C.S.: 562212

TrashCo Inc. (1)
8201 San Lorenzo, Laredo, TX 78045
Tel.: (956) 725-9693
Web Site: https://www.trashcoinc.com
Waste Collection Services
N.A.I.C.S.: 562111

TrashCo Inc. (1)
8201 San Lorenzo, Laredo, TX 78045
Tel.: (956) 725-9693
Web Site: http://www.trashcoinc.com
Recycling Container Mfr
N.A.I.C.S.: 325998

Twin Bridges Golf Club, L.P. (1)
1001 Cartersburg Rd, Danville, IN 46122
Tel.: (317) 745-9098
Web Site:
    https://www.twinbridgesgolfclub.com
Waste Collection Services
N.A.I.C.S.: 562111

USA Valley Facility, Inc. (1)
6015 Pleasant Valley Rd, Irwin, PA
15642 (100%)
Tel.: (724) 744-7446
Web Site: http://www.wm.com
Sales Range: $10-24.9 Million
Emp.: 13
Landfill Operator
N.A.I.C.S.: 562219

USA Waste of California, Inc. (1)
8491 Fruitridge Rd, Sacramento, CA 95826
Tel.: (916) 379-0500
Solid Waste Disposal & Recyling Services
N.A.I.C.S.: 562111

**USA Waste of Texas Landfills,
Inc.** (1)
13083 Grass Valley Ave, Grass Valley, CA
95945-9325
Tel.: (530) 274-3090
Solid Waste Collection Services
N.A.I.C.S.: 562119

**USA Waste of Virginia Landfills,
Inc.** (1)
100 N Park Ln, Hampton, VA 23666-1487
Tel.: (757) 766-3033
Web Site: http://www.wm.com
Emp.: 20
Waste Management Services
N.A.I.C.S.: 562219

Vickery Environmental, Inc. (1)
3956 State Route 412, Vickery, OH 43464
Tel.: (419) 547-7791
Emp.: 26
Waste Management Services
N.A.I.C.S.: 562219
Steve Lonneman (Gen Mgr)

WM CCP Solutions, LLC (1)
4228 Airport Rd, Cincinnati, OH 45226
Tel.: (513) 871-9733
Web Site: http://www.wm.com
Emp.: 12
Hazardous Waste Management Services

N.A.I.C.S.: 562112

WM GTL, Inc. (1)
3500 N Sooner Rd, Oklahoma City, OK 73141
Tel.: (405) 427-0790
Solid Waste Landfill Services
N.A.I.C.S.: 562212

WM Green Squad, LLC (1)
1001 Fannin St Ste 4000, Houston, TX 77002
Tel.: (713) 265-1333
Residential Building Construction Services
N.A.I.C.S.: 236115

WM KS Energy Resources, LLC (1)
307 NW 3rd St, Plainville, KS 67663
Tel.: (785) 688-4040
Oil & Gas Exploration Services
N.A.I.C.S.: 211120

WM LampTracker, Inc. (1)
10050 Naples St NE, Blaine, MN 55449
Web Site: https://www.wmlamptracker.com
Environmental Consulting Services
N.A.I.C.S.: 541620

WM Logistics India Private Limited (1)
4th Fl NRK Business Park Plot No B1 BU 4 Scheme No 54, Vijay Nagar Square AB Rd, Indore, 452010, MP, India
Tel.: (91) 7314708300
Web Site: http://wmlogistics.wm.com
Software Development Services
N.A.I.C.S.: 541511

WM Logistics, LLC (1)
5910 FM 1488 Rd, Magnolia, TX 77354
Tel.: (713) 559-4260
Web Site: http://www.wmlogistics.wm.com
Software Development Services
N.A.I.C.S.: 541511

WM Recycle America, LLC (1)
1001 Fannin St Ste 4000, Houston, TX 77002-6711
Tel.: (414) 967-1800
Web Site: http://www.recycleamerica.com
Sales Range: $25-49.9 Million
Emp.: 40
Recycling Facility Management Services
N.A.I.C.S.: 562920
Karl Mockros (VP-Engrg & Procurement)
Brent Bell (VP-Fin)
John Kelly (VP-Midwest)
Charles G. Schmidt (VP-West)
Michael J. Taylor (VP-East)

Unit (Domestic):

Greenstar LLC (2)
3411 Richmond Ave Ste 700, Houston, TX 77046
Tel.: (713) 965-0005
Web Site:
http://www.greenstarrecycling.com
Recycling Services
N.A.I.C.S.: 423930

WM Recycle America, LLC - (Springfield) eCycling Services (2)
203 Tremont St, Springfield, MA 01104
Tel.: (413) 785-5331
Recycling Services
N.A.I.C.S.: 562920

WM Recycle America, LLC - Pico Rivera (2)
8405 Loch Lomond Dr, Pico Rivera, CA 90660
Tel.: (562) 948-3888
Web Site: http://www.wm.com
Sales Range: $50-74.9 Million
Recycling Services
N.A.I.C.S.: 562920

WM Recycle America, LLC - Springfield (2)
6610 Electronic Dr, Springfield, VA 22151-4301
Tel.: (703) 658-0200
Web Site: http://www.recycleamerica.com
Sales Range: $10-24.9 Million
Emp.: 22
Waste Material Recycling
N.A.I.C.S.: 562920

WM Universal Solutions Private Limited (1)
10th & 11th floors Towers D & E Grand Canyon ASF Insignia SEZ, Gwal Pahari, Gurgaon, 122 003, Haryana, India
Tel.: (91) 1246428000
Waste Collection Services
N.A.I.C.S.: 562111

WM of Texas, L.L.C. (1)
1001 Fannin St Ste 4000, Houston, TX 77002-6711
Tel.: (713) 512-6200
Web Site: http://www.wm.com
Sales Range: $125-149.9 Million
Emp.: 1,400
Solid Waste Management Services
N.A.I.C.S.: 562998
David P. Steiner (Pres & CEO)

Waste Management Collection and Recycling, Inc. (1)
17700 Indian St, Moreno Valley, CA 92551
Tel.: (909) 242-0421
Waste Management Services
N.A.I.C.S.: 562219

Waste Management Disposal Services of Colorado, Inc. (1)
3500 S Gun Club Rd, Aurora, CO 80018-3033
Tel.: (303) 690-4303
Sales Range: $25-49.9 Million
Emp.: 35
Solid Waste Landfill Services
N.A.I.C.S.: 562212
Chris Gibbs (Gen Mgr)

Waste Management Disposal Services of Maine, Inc. (1)
PO Box 629, Norridgewock, ME 04957
Tel.: (207) 634-2714
Solid Waste Disposal Services
N.A.I.C.S.: 562211
Jeffrey McGown (District Mgr)

Waste Management Disposal Services of Massachusetts - Holyoke Landfill (1)
11 New Ludlow Rd, Granby, MA 01033
Tel.: (413) 467-3200
Web Site: http://www.wmdisposal.com
Rev.: $2,200,000
Emp.: 2
Solid Waste Disposal Services
N.A.I.C.S.: 562212

Waste Management Disposal Services of Oregon - Arlington Hazardous Waste Facility (1)
17629 Cedar Springs Ln, Arlington, OR 97812-6570
Tel.: (541) 454-2030
Web Site: http://www.wmnorthwest.com
Sales Range: $25-49.9 Million
Emp.: 104
Hazardous Waste Disposal Services
N.A.I.C.S.: 562211

Waste Management Disposal Services of Oregon - Columbia Ridge Landfill (1)
18177 Cedar Springs Ln, Arlington, OR 97812-6512
Tel.: (541) 454-2030
Web Site: http://www.wmdisposal.com
Sales Range: $25-49.9 Million
Emp.: 106
Solid Waste Disposal Services
N.A.I.C.S.: 562212

Waste Management Holdings, Inc. (1)
1001 Fannin St Ste 4000, Houston, TX 77002
Tel.: (713) 512-6200
Web Site: http://www.waste-management-world.com
Solid Waste Landfill Services
N.A.I.C.S.: 562212

Waste Management Inc. of Florida - Bradenton (1)
6120 21st St E, Bradenton, FL 34203-5005
Tel.: (941) 753-7591
Web Site: http://www.wm.com
Sales Range: $50-74.9 Million
Emp.: 127
Solid Waste & Recyclable Materials Collection Services
N.A.I.C.S.: 562111

Waste Management Inc. of Florida - Hobe Sound (1)
7700 SE Bridge Rd, Hobe Sound, FL 33455
Tel.: (772) 546-7700
Web Site: http://www.wm.com
Solid Waste & Recyclable Materials Collection Services
N.A.I.C.S.: 562111

Waste Management Inc. of Florida - Melbourne (1)
7382 Talona Dr, Melbourne, FL 32904-1643
Tel.: (321) 723-4455
Web Site: http://www.wm.com
Sales Range: $50-74.9 Million
Emp.: 190
Solid Waste & Recyclable Materials Collection Services
N.A.I.C.S.: 562111

Waste Management National Transportation Services, Inc. (1)
7473 Fm 1735, Pittsburg, TX 75686
Tel.: (903) 855-1400
Emp.: 100
Waste Management Services
N.A.I.C.S.: 562219
Brandon Henson (Pres & Mgr)

Waste Management Recycling and Disposal Services of California, Inc. (1)
9081 Tujunga Ave, Sun Valley, CA 91352-1516
Tel.: (818) 767-6180
Web Site: http://www.wm.com
Solid Waste Landfill Services
N.A.I.C.S.: 562212

Waste Management of Alameda County, Inc. (1)
172 98th Ave, Oakland, CA 94603
Tel.: (510) 613-8710
Web Site: http://www.wm.com
Sales Range: $25-49.9 Million
Emp.: 550
Rubbish Collection & Disposal Services
N.A.I.C.S.: 562111

Waste Management of Arizona - Phoenix South Hauling (1)
2137 West Williams Dr, Phoenix, AZ 85027
Tel.: (623) 748-4840
Web Site: http://www.wmofarizona.com
Solid Waste & Recyclable Materials Collection Services
N.A.I.C.S.: 562111

Waste Management of Arkansas, Inc. (1)
2900 W 68th St, Little Rock, AR 72209
Tel.: (501) 565-0191
Web Site: http://www.wm.com
Emp.: 248
Waste Management Services
N.A.I.C.S.: 562211

Waste Management of California - Castroville (1)
11240 Commercial Pkwy, Castroville, CA 95012
Tel.: (831) 796-2200
Web Site: http://www.wm.com
Sales Range: $50-74.9 Million
Emp.: 120
Solid Waste Collection Services
N.A.I.C.S.: 562111

Waste Management of California - Gold River (1)
11931 Foundation Pl Dr Ste 200, Gold River, CA 95670
Tel.: (916) 294-4000
Sales Range: $25-49.9 Million
Emp.: 80
Solid Waste Collection Services
N.A.I.C.S.: 562111

Waste Management of California - Health Sanitation Service (1)
1850 W Betteravia Rd, Santa Maria, CA 93455
Tel.: (805) 922-2121
Web Site: http://wmhss.wm.com
Sales Range: $75-99.9 Million
Emp.: 150
Solid Waste & Recyclable Materials Collection Services
N.A.I.C.S.: 562111

Waste Management of California - Sun Valley Hauling (1)
9081 Tujunga Ave 1st Fl, Sun Valley, CA 91352-1516
Tel.: (818) 767-5867
Web Site: http://www.wm.com
Sales Range: $50-74.9 Million
Emp.: 200
Solid Waste & Recyclable Materials Collection Services
N.A.I.C.S.: 562111

Waste Management of Canada Corporation (1)
219 Labrador Dr, Northfield Pl 3rd Fl, Waterloo, N2K 4M8, ON, Canada
Tel.: (519) 886-3974
Web Site: http://www.wmcanada.com
Waste Management Services
N.A.I.C.S.: 562998

Branch (Domestic):

Waste Management of Canada Corp. - Barrie (2)
13 Saunders Road, Barrie, L4N 9A7, ON, Canada
Tel.: (705) 722-8710
Web Site: http://www.wmcanada.com
Waste Management Services
N.A.I.C.S.: 562111

Waste Management of Canada Corp. - Quebec Divisional Office-GMA (2)
2457 Chemin Du Lac, Longueuil, J4N 1P1, QC, Canada
Tel.: (866) 475-4730
Web Site: http://www.wm.com
Sales Range: $10-24.9 Million
Emp.: 4
Waste Management Systems
N.A.I.C.S.: 562212

Waste Management of Carolinas - Gastonia (1)
2712 Lowell Rd, Gastonia, NC 28054-1430
Tel.: (704) 824-2011
Web Site: http://www.wm.com
Sales Range: $50-74.9 Million
Emp.: 100
Solid Waste & Recyclable Materials Collection Services
N.A.I.C.S.: 562111

Waste Management of Colorado - Denver-48th Avenue (1)
3600 E 48th Ave, Denver, CO 80216-3014
Tel.: (303) 399-6351
Web Site: http://www.wm.com
Sales Range: $25-49.9 Million
Emp.: 90
Nonhazardous Waste Disposal & Recycling Services
N.A.I.C.S.: 562920

Waste Management of Connecticut, Inc. (1)
655 Christian Ln, Kensington, CT 06037
Tel.: (860) 223-3601
Hazardous Waste Management Services
N.A.I.C.S.: 562112

Waste Management of Florida Inc. - Pine Ridge Recycling & Disposal Facility (1)
5400 Rex Rd, Winter Garden, FL 34787-9164
Tel.: (407) 877-0701
Web Site: http://www.wmdisposal.com
Sales Range: $10-24.9 Million
Emp.: 5
Solid Waste Disposal & Recycling Services
N.A.I.C.S.: 562212

Waste Management of Hawaii, Inc. (1)
6900D Kaumualii Hwy, Kekaha, HI 96752
Tel.: (808) 337-1416
Web Site:
http://www.wastemanagement.com
Sales Range: $25-49.9 Million
Emp.: 3
Solid Waste Management Services
N.A.I.C.S.: 562212

Waste Management, Inc.—(Continued)

Waste Management of Idaho, Inc. (1)
4886 N Manufacturing Way, Coeur D'Alene, ID 83815
Tel.: (208) 765-4968
Waste Management Services
N.A.I.C.S.: 562219
Steve Roberge (District Mgr)

Waste Management of Indiana, L.L.C. (1)
10000 E 56th St, Indianapolis, IN 46236-2812
Tel.: (317) 826-5908
Solid Waste Landfill Services
N.A.I.C.S.: 562212

Waste Management of Iowa, Inc. (1)
2401 Scott Blvd SE, Iowa City, IA 52240
Tel.: (319) 358-9000
Web Site: http://www.wm.com
Waste Management & Recycling Services
N.A.I.C.S.: 562219

Waste Management of Louisiana, L.L.C. (1)
6280 Millhaven Rd, Monroe, LA 71203-9082
Tel.: (318) 343-0765
Solid Waste Landfill Services
N.A.I.C.S.: 562212

Waste Management of Maine, Inc. (1)
357 Mercer Rd, Norridgewock, ME 04957-0000
Tel.: (630) 572-2448
Solid Waste Landfill Services
N.A.I.C.S.: 562212

Waste Management of Maryland, Inc. (1)
6994 Columbia Gateway Dr Ste 200, Columbia, MD 21046
Tel.: (410) 796-7010
Waste Management Services
N.A.I.C.S.: 562219

Waste Management of Michigan, Inc. (1)
3005 Petit St, Port Huron, MI 48060
Tel.: (810) 966-8774
Waste Management Services
N.A.I.C.S.: 562219

Waste Management of Mississippi - Jackson Hauling (1)
1450 Country Club Dr, Jackson, MS 39209-2509
Tel.: (601) 922-9647
Web Site: http://www.wm.com
Sales Range: $25-49.9 Million
Emp.: 105
Solid Waste & Recyclable Materials Collection Services
N.A.I.C.S.: 562111

Waste Management of Missouri, Inc. (1)
7320 Hall St, Saint Louis, MO 63147
Tel.: (314) 506-4733
Waste Management Services
N.A.I.C.S.: 562219

Waste Management of Nebraska, Inc. (1)
9710 Cornhusker Rd, Papillion, NE 68046
Tel.: (402) 731-0138
Waste Management Services
N.A.I.C.S.: 562219

Waste Management of Nevada, Inc. (1)
1392 E Commercial Row, Reno, NV 89512
Tel.: (775) 329-8822
Waste Management Services
N.A.I.C.S.: 562219

Waste Management of New Jersey, Inc. (1)
629-647 S Frnt St, Elizabeth, NJ 07201
Tel.: (908) 436-2943
Waste Management Services
N.A.I.C.S.: 562998

Waste Management of New Mexico, Inc. (1)

402 Industrial Park Loop NE, Rio Rancho, NM 87124
Tel.: (505) 892-1200
Waste Management Services
N.A.I.C.S.: 562219

Waste Management of New York - Rochester (1)
1661 Mount Read Blvd, Rochester, NY 14606
Tel.: (585) 672-7656
Web Site: http://www.wm.com
Sales Range: $75-99.9 Million
Emp.: 200
Solid Waste, Hazardous Waste & Recyclable Materials Collection Services
N.A.I.C.S.: 562111

Waste Management of New York - Varick I Transfer Station (1)
215 Varick Ave, Brooklyn, NY 11237
Tel.: (718) 533-5100
Web Site: http://www.wm.com
Sales Range: $400-449.9 Million
Emp.: 375
Nonhazardous Waste Treatment & Recycling Services
N.A.I.C.S.: 562219

Waste Management of North Dakota, Inc. (1)
310 Enterprise St, Bismarck, ND 58501
Tel.: (701) 255-4496
Emp.: 400
Hazardous Waste Management Services
N.A.I.C.S.: 562112

Waste Management of Oklahoma, Inc. (1)
5600 NW 4th St, Oklahoma City, OK 73127-6607
Tel.: (405) 949-2121
Solid Waste Landfill Services
N.A.I.C.S.: 562212

Waste Management of Oregon, Inc. (1)
7227 NE 55th Ave, Portland, OR 97218-1215
Tel.: (503) 249-8078
Web Site: http://www.wmnorthwest.com
Rev.: $17,200,000
Emp.: 450
Refuse Collection & Disposal Services
N.A.I.C.S.: 562211

Waste Management of Pennsylvania - Dunmore (1)
13 Peggy Pkwy, Dunmore, PA 18512-1712
Tel.: (570) 344-7812
Web Site: http://www.wm.com
Sales Range: $200-249.9 Million
Solid Waste & Recyclable Materials Collection Services
N.A.I.C.S.: 562111

Waste Management of Rhode Island, Inc. (1)
65 Halsey St, Newport, RI 02840
Tel.: (401) 848-5450
Waste Management Services
N.A.I.C.S.: 562219

Waste Management of South Carolina, Inc. (1)
390 Innovation Way, Wellford, SC 29385
Tel.: (864) 949-2600
Web Site: http://www.wm.com
Sales Range: $50-74.9 Million
Emp.: 150
Solid Waste & Recyclable Materials Collection & Disposal Services
N.A.I.C.S.: 562111

Waste Management of Washington - Kirkland Collections (1)
123 5th Ave, Kirkland, WA 98033
Tel.: (425) 587-3150
Web Site: http://www.wmnorthwest.com
Rev.: $5,600,000
Emp.: 1,270
Solid Waste & Recyclable Materials Collection Services
N.A.I.C.S.: 562111

Waste Management of West Virginia, Inc. (1)
7 Spring St, Charleston, WV 25302
Tel.: (304) 343-6987

Waste Management Services
N.A.I.C.S.: 562219

Waste Management of Wisconsin, Inc. (1)
2510 W Badger Rd, Madison, WI 53713
Tel.: (608) 752-8210
Waste Management Services
N.A.I.C.S.: 562219

Waste Management, Inc. of Tennessee - Nashville (1)
1428 Antioch Pike, Antioch, TN 37013
Tel.: (615) 933-7361
Web Site: http://www.wm.com
Sales Range: $25-49.9 Million
Emp.: 100
Solid Waste Collection Services
N.A.I.C.S.: 562111

Western Waste Industries (1)
1970 E 213th St, Carson, CA 90810
Tel.: (323) 774-0221
Web Site:
   http://www.wastemanagement.com
Emp.: 6
Solid Waste Management Services
N.A.I.C.S.: 562212
Vickie Jackman (Mgr)

Western Waste of Texas, L.L.C. (1)
5 Mile N Hwy 12, Mauriceville, TX 77626
Tel.: (409) 746-9919
Hazardous Waste Management Services
N.A.I.C.S.: 562112

WATER INTELLIGENCE PLC
265 Church St, New Haven, CT 06510
Tel.: (760) 969-6830
Web Site:
   https://www.waterintelligence.co.uk
WATR—(AIM)
Rev.: $71,333,461
Assets: $96,588,457
Liabilities: $41,973,211
Net Worth: $54,615,246
Earnings: $3,666,479
Emp.: 436
Fiscal Year-end: 12/31/22
Energy & Water Utility Services
N.A.I.C.S.: 221310
Patrick J. DeSouza (Chm)
Bobby Knell (Exec Dir)
Laura Hills (Vice Chm)
Adrian Hargrave (VP-Corp Dev)

Subsidiaries:

American Leak Detection, Inc. (1)
888 Research Dr Ste 100, Palm Springs, CA 92262
Tel.: (760) 320-9991
Web Site:
   http://www.americanleakdetection.com
Sales Range: $50-74.9 Million
Non-Invasive Leak Detection & Repair Services
N.A.I.C.S.: 333998
Adam L. Gray (Mgr-Mktg)
Patrick J. DeSouza (Chm)
Pamela Vigue (CFO)
Jimmy Carter (Sr Dir-Corp Field Svcs)

WATER TECHNOLOGIES INTERNATIONAL, INC.
1385 SW Bent Pine Cv, Port Saint Lucie, FL 34986
Tel.: (610) 213-8411   FL
Web Site: https://www.gr8water.net
Year Founded: 1998
WTII—(OTCIQ)
Water Filtration Products
N.A.I.C.S.: 221310
William Scott Tudor (Chm & CEO)

WATERS CORPORATION
34 Maple St, Milford, MA 01757
Tel.: (508) 478-2000   DE
Web Site: https://www.waters.com
Year Founded: 1958
WAT—(NYSE)
Rev.: $2,956,416,000

Assets: $4,626,854,000
Liabilities: $3,476,513,000
Net Worth: $1,150,341,000
Earnings: $642,234,000
Emp.: 7,900
Fiscal Year-end: 12/31/23
Laboratory Related Product Mfr
N.A.I.C.S.: 334516
Keeley A. Aleman (Gen Counsel, Sec & Sr VP)
Udit Batra (Pres & CEO)
Belinda Gaye Hyde (Sr VP-HR-Global)
Amol Chaubal (CFO & Sr VP)
Kristen Garvey (VP-Corp Comm)
Kevin Kempskie (Sr Dir-PR)
Christos Ross (Sr VP-Global Ops & Interim Sr VP-Waters Div)
Christos Ross (Sr VP)

Subsidiaries:

D'Amico Sistemas S.A. (1)
Paracas No 51 Capital Federal CP 1275, Buenos Aires, Argentina (100%)
Tel.: (54) 1143060920
Web Site: http://www.damicosistemas.com
Rev.: $6,574,317
Emp.: 200
Mfr, Distributor & Provider of High Performance Liquid Chromotograpy (HPLC), Thermal Analysis & Mass Spectrometry (MS) Instruments, Columns & Related Services
N.A.I.C.S.: 334516

Environmental Resource Assoc., Inc. (1)
16341 Table Mountain Pkwy, Golden, CO 80403
Tel.: (303) 431-8454
Web Site: https://www.eraqc.com
Emp.: 75
Environmental & Ecological Services
N.A.I.C.S.: 541620

Gulf Scientific Corporation (1)
1 Fl Maxim Restaurent Flat No 1, PO Box 3710, Al Khobar, 31952, Saudi Arabia (100%)
Tel.: (966) 38875810
Web Site: http://www.gsc2000.com
Sales Range: $10-24.9 Million
Emp.: 80
Mfr, Distributor & Provider of High Performance Liquid Chromotograpy
N.A.I.C.S.: 334516

Gulf Scientific Corporation (1)
PO Box 17010, Jeli Ali, Dubai, United Arab Emirates
Tel.: (971) 48815270
Web Site: http://www.gulf-scientific.com
Life Science Laboratory, Analytical & Material Solutions; Laboratory Service & Training
N.A.I.C.S.: 541990

Micromass Holdings Ltd. (1)
Stamford Avenue Altrincham Road, Wilmslow, SK9 4AX, Cheshire, United Kingdom
Tel.: (44) 1619462400
Web Site: http://www.waters.com
Emp.: 500
Medical Equipment Mfr
N.A.I.C.S.: 334510

Micromass UK Limited (1)
Stamford Avenue Altrincham Road, Wilmslow, SK9 4AX, Cheshire, United Kingdom (100%)
Tel.: (44) 1619462400
Web Site: http://www.waters.com
Sales Range: $25-49.9 Million
Emp.: 500
Mfr of Organic Mass Spectrometers
N.A.I.C.S.: 334516

Microsep (Pty) Ltd (1)
2 Saturn Crescent Linbro Business Park Frankenwald Ext 30, Linbro Business Park, Sandton, 2196, South Africa (24.5%)
Tel.: (27) 115532300
Web Site: https://microsep.co.za
Sales Range: $25-49.9 Million
Emp.: 100
Laboratory Information Management Systems Development Services

N.A.I.C.S.: 541512

Midland Precision Equipment Co Ltd (1)
Haslucks Green Road shirley, Solihull, B90 2LY, West Midlands, United Kingdom
Tel.: (44) 1217442719
Analytical Laboratory Instrument Mfr
N.A.I.C.S.: 334516

P.T. Kromtekindo Utama (1)
JL RC Veteran No 3, Jakarta Selatan, 12330, Indonesia (100%)
Tel.: (62) 217373043
Web Site: https://www.kromtekindo.com
Chromotography Instrument Mfr & Distr
N.A.I.C.S.: 334516

REDOX SRL (1)
Oasului Nr 6, 075100, Otopeni, Ilfov, Romania
Tel.: (40) 213231648
Web Site: https://www.redox.ro
Sales Range: $100-124.9 Million
Emp.: 10
Mfr & Distr of High Performance Liquid Chromotography
N.A.I.C.S.: 334516

Research Instruments Sdn Bhd (1)
NO 602 Level 6 Block A Kelana Centre Point Jalan SS7/19 Kelana Jaya, 47301, Petaling Jaya, Selangor Darul Ehsan, Malaysia (100%)
Tel.: (60) 378051688
Web Site: http://www.ri.com.my
Sales Range: $10-24.9 Million
Emp.: 140
Mfr & Distr of High Performance Liquid Chromotography Thermal Analysis & Mass Spectrometry Instruments, Columns & Related Services
N.A.I.C.S.: 334516
Gregor Kent *(Founder & CEO)*
Eric Tay *(CFO)*
Et Siah *(Gen Mgr)*

Sithiporn Associates Co., Ltd. (1)
451-451/1 Sirinthorn Road Bangbumru, Bangplud, Bangkok, 10700, Thailand (100%)
Tel.: (66) 24338331
Web Site: https://www.sithiphorn.com
Sales Range: $1-9.9 Million
Emp.: 200
Mfr, Distributor & Provider of High Performance Liquid Chromotography, Thermal Analysis & Mass Spectrometry (MS) Instruments, Columns & Related Services
N.A.I.C.S.: 334516

Specialized for Advanced Systems & Chemicals (1)
Sport City Al Shaheed Str, PO Box 923117, Amman, 11192, Jordan
Tel.: (962) 65160322
Web Site: http://www.tainstruments.com
Sales Range: $1-9.9 Million
Emp.: 3
High Performance Liquid Chromotography, Thermal Analysis & Mass Spectrometry Instruments, Columns & Related Services Mfr & Distr
N.A.I.C.S.: 334516

TA Instruments - Waters Technologies (Shanghai) Limited (1)
16 F No 82 Bldg No 1198 Qin Zhou Rd N, Cao He Jing Hi-teck Park, Shanghai, 200233, China
Tel.: (86) 2134182000
Web Site: http://www.tainstruments.com
Thermal Analysis & Microcalorimetry Laboratory Instrument Mfr
N.A.I.C.S.: 334516

TA Instruments Japan (1)
Lexington Plaza Nishigotanda 6F 5-2-4 Nishigotanda, Shinagawa-ku, Tokyo, 141-0031, Japan
Tel.: (81) 35 759 8500
Web Site: http://www.tainstruments.com
Analytical Laboratory Instrument Mfr
N.A.I.C.S.: 334516

TA Instruments Ltd. (1)
610 Centennial Park, Centennial Avenue, Elstree, WD6 3TJ, Hertfordshire, United Kingdom

Tel.: (44) 2082386100
Web Site: http://www.tainstruments.com
Emp.: 10
Liquid Chromotography Instrument Design & Mfr
N.A.I.C.S.: 334516

TA Instruments-Waters LLC (1)
159 Lukens Dr, New Castle, DE 19720
Tel.: (302) 427-4000
Web Site: http://www.tainstruments.com
Sales Range: $25-49.9 Million
Emp.: 200
Liquid Chromotography Instrument Design & Mfr
N.A.I.C.S.: 334516

Water Technologies Corporation (1)
Gautier Benitez Ave 230 Ste 204, Caguas, PR 00725
Tel.: (787) 747-8445
Sales Range: $25-49.9 Million
Emp.: 32
High Performance Liquid Chromatography (HPLC), Thermal Analysis & Mass Spectrometry (MS) Instruments, Columns & Related Services Mfr & Distr
N.A.I.C.S.: 423490
Carlos Hernandez *(Dir-Svcs)*
Julio Acededo *(Mgr-Fin & Admin)*

Waters (TC) Israel Limited (1)
Intergreen Building 17 Hamefalsim st, PO Box 3084, Petah Tiqwa, 4951447, Israel
Tel.: (972) 3 373 1391
Web Site: http://www.waters.com
Sales Range: $10-24.9 Million
Emp.: 20
Analytical Equipment Mfr
N.A.I.C.S.: 334516

Waters A/S (1)
Baldersbuen 46, 2640, Hedehusene, Denmark (100%)
Tel.: (45) 46598080
Web Site: http://www.waters.com
Sales Range: $10-24.9 Million
Emp.: 26
Mfr & Distr High Performance Liquid Chromotography
N.A.I.C.S.: 334516

Waters AS (1)
Forskningsparken Gaustadalleen 21, 0349, Oslo, Norway (100%)
Tel.: (47) 63846050
Web Site: http://www.waters.com
Sales Range: $1-9.9 Million
Emp.: 5
Mfr, Distributor & Provider of High Performance Liquid Chromotography
N.A.I.C.S.: 334516

Waters Analytical Instruments Sdn Bhd (1)
Unit 2-1 Level 2 Tower 2A UOA Business Park, No 1 Jalan Pengaturcara U1/51A Seksyen U1, 40150, Shah Alam, Selangor, Malaysia
Tel.: (60) 350211668
Web Site: https://www.waters.com
Water Analytical Instrument Mfr
N.A.I.C.S.: 334516

Waters Australia Pty. Ltd. (1)
Unit 3/38-46 South St, Rydalmere, 2116, NSW, Australia (100%)
Tel.: (61) 29 933 1777
Web Site: http://www.waters.com
Sales Range: $10-24.9 Million
Emp.: 22
Mfr & Distr of High Performance Liquid Chromatography
N.A.I.C.S.: 334516
Jackie Watson *(Mng Dir)*

Waters China Ltd. (1)
Unit 907-908 16 Science Park West Avenue, Hong Kong Science Park Shatin, Hong Kong, China (Hong Kong)
Tel.: (852) 29641800
Web Site: http://www.waters.com
Sales Range: $10-24.9 Million
Emp.: 16
High Performance Liquid Chromatography Instrument Mfr & Distr
N.A.I.C.S.: 334516

Waters Chromatography B.V. (1)
Florijnstraat 19, 4879 AH, Etten-Leur, Netherlands (100%)

Tel.: (31) 76 508 7200
Web Site: http://www.water.com
Sales Range: $25-49.9 Million
Emp.: 35
Mfr, Distributor & Provider of High Performance Liquid Chromatography
N.A.I.C.S.: 334516

Waters Chromatography Europe BV (1)
Mon Plaisir 12, PO Box 215, Etten-Leur, 4879AN, Netherlands
Tel.: (31) 765081800
Web Site: http://www.waters.com
Chromatographic Instruments Mfr
N.A.I.C.S.: 334516

Waters Chromatography Ireland Ltd. (1)
Block 3 1 Woodford Business Park, Santry, Dublin, 9, Ireland (100%)
Tel.: (353) 14481500
Web Site: http://www.waters.com
Sales Range: $10-24.9 Million
Emp.: 30
Mfr, Distributor & Provider of High Performance Liquid Chromatography
N.A.I.C.S.: 334516

Waters Ges.m.b.H (1)
Hietzinger Hauptstrasse 145, 1130, Vienna, Austria
Tel.: (43) 1 877 1807
Web Site: http://www.waters.com
Sales Range: $10-24.9 Million
Emp.: 25
Mfr, Distributor & Provider of High Performance Liquid Chromotography (HPLC), Thermal Analysis & Mass Spectrometry (MS) Instruments, Columns & Related Services
N.A.I.C.S.: 334516

Subsidiary (Non-US):

Waters Kft. (2)
Zahony utca 7 C ep 1 em, 1031, Budapest, Hungary (100%)
Tel.: (36) 13505086
Sales Range: Less than $1 Million
Emp.: 8
High Performance Liquid Chromotograpy Mfr & Distr
N.A.I.C.S.: 334516
Tibor Pataki *(Mng Dir)*

Waters Sp z.o.o (2)
Ul Powazkowska 44C, 01-797, Warsaw, Poland (100%)
Tel.: (48) 221015900
Web Site: http://www.water.com
Sales Range: $1-9.9 Million
Emp.: 20
Mfr, Distributor & Provider of High Performance Liquid Chromotograpy
N.A.I.C.S.: 334516

Waters GmbH (1)
Helfmann-Park 10, 65760, Eschborn, Germany (100%)
Tel.: (49) 6196400600
Sales Range: $10-24.9 Million
Emp.: 100
Mfr, Distributor & Provider of High Performance Liquid Chromotography (HPLC), Thermal Analysis & Mass Spectrometry (MS) Instruments, Columns & Related Services
N.A.I.C.S.: 334516

Waters India Pvt Ltd. (1)
No 36A 2nd Phase, Peenya Industrial Area, Bengaluru, 560 058, India (100%)
Tel.: (91) 80492 922 0003
Web Site: http://www.waters.com
Sales Range: $25-49.9 Million
Emp.: 80
Mfr, Distributor & Provider of High Performance Liquid Chromotograpy
N.A.I.C.S.: 334516

Waters Korea Limited (1)
101 CCMM Building 905-7 Yeoi Park, Yeongdeungpo-gu, Seoul, 07241, Korea (South)
Tel.: (82) 263009200
Web Site: https://www.waters.com
High Performance Liquid Chromatography Instrument Mfr & Distr
N.A.I.C.S.: 334516

DongUck Seol *(CEO)*

Waters Ltd. (1)
603 Centennial Ct Centennial Pk, Elstree, WD6 3TJ, Hertfordshire, United Kingdom (100%)
Tel.: (44) 2082386100
Web Site: http://www.waters.com
Sales Range: $1-9.9 Million
Emp.: 100
Mfr, Distributor & Provider of High Performance Liquid Chromatography
N.A.I.C.S.: 334516

Waters Pacific Pte Ltd (1)
1 Science Park Road 02-01 The Capricorn, Singapore Science Park II, Singapore, 117528, Singapore
Tel.: (65) 65937100
Web Site: https://www.waters.com
Sales Range: $25-49.9 Million
Emp.: 53
High Performance Liquid Chromatography Instrument Mfr & Distr
N.A.I.C.S.: 334516

Waters S.A. de C.V. (1)
Moras 822 Deleg Benito Juarez, Col Acacias, 03230, Mexico, Mexico (100%)
Tel.: (52) 555 200 1860
Web Site: http://www.waters.com
Sales Range: $10-24.9 Million
Emp.: 55
Mfr, Distributor & Provider of High Performance Liquid Chromotography (HPLC), Thermal Analysis & Mass Spectrometry (MS) Instruments, Columns & Related Services
N.A.I.C.S.: 334516

Waters S.A.S. (1)
BP 608, 78056, Saint-Quentin, France
Tel.: (33) 13 048 7240
Web Site: http://www.waters.com
Sales Range: $50-74.9 Million
Emp.: 200
Mfr, Distributor & Provider of High Performance Liquid Chromotography
N.A.I.C.S.: 334516

Waters Sverige AB (1)
Djupdalsvagen 12-14, PO Box 485, 191 24, Sollentuna, Sweden
Tel.: (46) 855511500
Web Site: http://www.waters.com
Sales Range: $10-24.9 Million
Emp.: 30
Mfr, Distributor & Provider of High Performance Liquid Chromotograpy
N.A.I.C.S.: 334516
Fredrik Hakfelt *(Pres)*

Waters Technologies Corporation (1)
34 Maple St Mail Stop, Milford, MA 01757-3604
Tel.: (508) 478-2000
Liquid Chromatography Instrument Design & Mfr
N.A.I.C.S.: 334516
Douglas A. Berthiaume *(Chm, Pres & CEO)*

Subsidiary (Non-US):

Waters AG (2)
Tafernstrasse 14a, 5405, Baden, Dattwil, Switzerland
Tel.: (41) 566767000
Web Site: https://www.waters.com
Analytical Instrument Mfr
N.A.I.C.S.: 334516
Martin Burgi *(Mgr-Svc)*
Gerry Hendrickx *(Mgr-Sls-Columns & Accessories)*

Waters Limited (2)
6427 Northam Drive, Mississauga, L4V 1J2, ON, Canada
Tel.: (800) 252-4752
Web Site: http://www.waters.com
High Performance Liquid Chromatography Product Mfr
N.A.I.C.S.: 334516
Richard Blais *(Gen Mgr)*
Patrick Savory *(Mgr-Natl Sls)*
Marc Yargeau *(Reg Mgr-Svc)*
Charles Valentine *(Reg Mgr-Svc)*
Debbie Oliver *(Coord-Svc)*

Waters NV (2)
The ultimate building Berchemstadionstraat

Waters Corporation—(Continued)

72, 2600, Antwerp, Belgium
Tel.: (32) 33930210
Emp.: 50
High Performance Liquid Chromatography
Product Mfr
N.A.I.C.S.: 334516
Frank De Landtsheer *(Mgr-Svc)*

Waters SpA (2)
Viale T Edison 110, 20099, Sesto San Gio-
vanni, MI, Italy
Tel.: (39) 022650983
Web Site: http://www.waters.it
High Performance Liquid Chromatography
Product Mfr
N.A.I.C.S.: 334516

Subsidiary (Domestic):

Wyatt Technology Corporation (2)
6300 Hollister Ave, Santa Barbara, CA
93117-3253
Tel.: (805) 681-9009
Web Site: http://www.wyatt.com
Sales Range: $50-74.9 Million
Emp.: 70
Light Scattering Instruments Mfr
N.A.I.C.S.: 335139
Geofrey K. Wyatt *(Pres)*
Philip J. Wyatt *(CEO)*
Clifford D. Wyatt *(Exec VP)*
Carolyn J. Walton *(Controller)*
Michelle H. Chen *(Dir-Analytical Svcs)*
Sigrid C. Kuebler *(Dir-Customer Svc & Sup-port)*
Daniel Some *(Dir-Mktg)*
Michael I. Larkin *(Dir-R&D)*

**Waters Technologies do Brasil
Ltda.** (1)
Alameda Tocantins 125-27th Floor-
Alphaville Barueri, Sao Paulo, 06455-020,
Brazil (100%)
Tel.: (55) 114 134 3788
Web Site: http://www.waters.com
Sales Range: $10-24.9 Million
Emp.: 40
Mfr & Distr of High Performance Liquid
Chromotography (HPLC), Thermal Analysis &
Mass Spectrometry (MS) Instruments, Col-
umns & Related Services
N.A.I.C.S.: 334516

WATERSTONE FINANCIAL, INC.

11200 W Plank Ct, Wauwatosa, WI
53226
Tel.: (414) 761-1000   MD
Web Site: https://www.wsbonline.com
WSBF—(NASDAQ)
Rev.: $175,800,000
Assets: $2,031,672,000
Liabilities: $1,661,186,000
Net Worth: $370,486,000
Earnings: $19,487,000
Emp.: 742
Fiscal Year-end: 12/31/22
Bank Holding Company
N.A.I.C.S.: 551111
Mark Raymond Gerke *(CFO & Exec VP)*
Julie A. Glynn *(Exec VP)*
Ryan Gordon *(Exec VP)*

Subsidiaries:

WaterStone Bank, SSB (1)
11200 W Plank Ct, Wauwatosa, WI
53226 (100%)
Tel.: (414) 761-1000
Web Site: https://www.wsbonline.com
Sales Range: $150-199.9 Million
Commericial Banking
N.A.I.C.S.: 522110
William F. Bruss *(Pres & CEO)*
Mark Raymond Gerke *(CFO)*
Julie A. Glynn *(Exec VP)*
Ryan Gordon *(Exec VP)*
Kevin Stelzer *(VP-Bus Banking)*
Scott DeJong *(VP-Comml Real Estate)*
Pat Lawton *(Chm)*
Julie Glynn *(Chief Retail Officer)*
Don Bray *(CIO)*
Andy Boario *(VP)*

Jim Crowley *(VP-Bus Banking)*
Michael Danielson *(VP-Bus Banking)*
Jeff Jarecki *(VP-Bus Banking)*
Julie Fay-Krivitz *(VP-Comml Real Estate)*
Jack Kahl *(VP)*
Ken Stelzer *(VP-Commercial Real Estate)*
Joe Mudlaff *(VP)*

Subsidiary (Domestic):

Main Street Real Estate Holdings, LLC (2)
11200 W Plank Ct, Wauwatosa, WI 53226
Tel.: (414) 459-4061
Holding Company
N.A.I.C.S.: 551112

Wauwatosa Investments, Inc. (2)
101 Convention Ctr Dr, Las Vegas, NV
89109
Tel.: (702) 949-1322
Investment Banking Services
N.A.I.C.S.: 523150

WATSCO, INC.

2665 S Bayshore Dr Ste 901, Miami,
FL 33133
Tel.: (305) 714-4100   FL
Web Site: https://www.watsco.com
Year Founded: 1945
WSO—(NYSE)
Rev.: $7,283,767,000
Assets: $3,729,182,000
Liabilities: $1,112,992,000
Net Worth: $2,616,190,000
Earnings: $634,139,000
Emp.: 7,400
Fiscal Year-end: 12/31/23
Climate Control Components & Re-
lated Products Distr
N.A.I.C.S.: 423730
Albert H. Nahmad *(Chm & CEO)*
Barry S. Logan *(Sec & Exec VP)*
Ana M. Menendez *(CFO & Treas)*
Bob L. Moss *(Vice Chm)*
Aaron J. Nahmad *(Pres)*

Subsidiaries:

AC Doctor LLC (1)
2151 W Hillsboro Blvd Ste 400, Deerfield
Beach, FL 33442
Tel.: (866) 264-1479
Web Site: http://www.acdoctor.com
Air Conditioning & Ventilating Equipment
Distr
N.A.I.C.S.: 423730

ACDoctor.com Inc. (1)
6999-02 Merrill Rd Ste 287, Jacksonville,
FL 32277 (100%)
Tel.: (904) 714-6080
Web Site: http://www.acdoctor.com
Sales Range: $150-199.9 Million
Heating & Air Conditioning Products Whslr
N.A.I.C.S.: 423730

Acme Refrigeration of Baton Rouge, LLC (1)
11844 S Choctaw Dr, Baton Rouge, LA
70815-2111
Tel.: (225) 273-1740
Web Site: http://www.acmeref.com
Air Conditioning & Refrigeration Equipment
& Supplies Provider
N.A.I.C.S.: 423730
Jerry Perrin *(CFO)*
Gene Termini *(Mgr-HVAC Equipment)*

Air Systems Distributors LLC (1)
2151 W Hillsboro Blvd Ste 400, Deerfield
Beach, FL 33442
Tel.: (954) 246-2665
Web Site: http://www.gemaire.com
Heating & Air Conditioning Equipment Distr
N.A.I.C.S.: 423730

Atlantic Service & Supply LLC (1)
6525 Baker Blvd, Fort Worth, TX
76118 (100%)
Tel.: (817) 589-1265
Web Site: http://www.atlanticservice.com
Sales Range: $50-74.9 Million
Emp.: 40
Heating, Cooling & Air Products Distr
N.A.I.C.S.: 423730

Baker Distributing Company LLC (1)
14610 Breakers Dr Ste 100 - Unit 393,
Jacksonville, FL 32258 (100%)
Tel.: (904) 407-4500
Web Site: https://www.bakerdist.com
Sales Range: $50-74.9 Million
Emp.: 132
Heating, Cooling & Air Conditioner Parts,
Accessories & Units Distr
N.A.I.C.S.: 423730

Boreal International Corporation (1)
1766 NW 82nd Ave, Doral, FL 33126
Tel.: (786) 621-8250
Web Site: https://www.borealintl.com
Air Conditioning, Heating & Refrigeration
Product Whslr
N.A.I.C.S.: 333415

Carrier (Puerto Rico), Inc. (1)
Amelia Distribution Ctr Diana St Ste 47 Lot
P-1, Guaynabo, PR 00968
Tel.: (787) 788-9350
Climate Control Component & Related
Product Distr
N.A.I.C.S.: 423730

Carrier Enterprise Canada, L.P. (1)
195 Statesman Drive, Mississauga, L5S
1X4, ON, Canada
Tel.: (905) 672-0606
Web Site: http://www.carrier.com
Air Conditioning, Heating & Refrigeration
Product Whslr
N.A.I.C.S.: 333415

**Carrier Enterprise Mexico S. de R.L.
de C.V.** (1)
Barranca del Muerto 329, PB Col San Jose
Insurgentes, 03900, Mexico, Mexico
Tel.: (52) 5591260300
Web Site: https://www.carrier.com.mx
Air Conditioning, Heating & Refrigeration
Product Whslr
N.A.I.C.S.: 333415
Miguel Angel Hernandez *(Mgr-Natl Sls)*

**Carrier Enterprise Northeast,
LLC** (1)
1401 Erie Blvd, East Syracuse, NY
13210 (80%)
Tel.: (315) 476-6660
Sales Range: $200-249.9 Million
Emp.: 230
Heating & Air-Conditioning Equipment Distr
N.A.I.C.S.: 423730

Carrier InterAmerica Corporation (1)
10801 NW 103rd St Ste 1, Miami, FL
33178 (80%)
Tel.: (305) 805-4500
Web Site: https://www.carriercca.com
Emp.: 50
Refrigeration, Heating & Air-Conditioning
Solutions
N.A.I.C.S.: 238220

**Comfort Products Distributing
LLC** (1)
13202 I St, Omaha, NE 68137 (100%)
Tel.: (402) 334-7777
Web Site: http://www.comfortproducts.com
Sales Range: $25-49.9 Million
Emp.: 72
Heating, Ventilation & Air Conditioning Prod-
ucts Distr
N.A.I.C.S.: 423720

**Dunphey & Associates Supply
Co.** (1)
9 Whippany Rd Bldg D, Whippany, NJ
07981
Tel.: (973) 884-1390
Web Site: http://www.dascosupply.com
Warm Air Heating & Air Conditioning
N.A.I.C.S.: 423730

East Coast Metal Distributors (1)
1313 S Briggs Ave, Durham, NC 27703-
5049
Tel.: (919) 596-2136
Web Site: https://www.ecmdi.com
Emp.: 400
Sheets, Metal
N.A.I.C.S.: 423730

Gemaire Distributors LLC (1)
4141 N John Young Pkwy, Orlando, FL
32804 (100%)
Tel.: (407) 648-0888

Web Site: http://www.gemaire.com
Sales Range: $75-99.9 Million
Emp.: 200
Parts & Equipment for A/C & Heating Distr
N.A.I.C.S.: 423730
Kenbian Ng *(Sr VP)*

Heating & Cooling Supply LLC (1)
1669 Brandywine Ave Ste A, Chula Vista,
CA 91911
Tel.: (619) 591-8885
Web Site:
http://www.heatingandcooling.com
Sales Range: $50-74.9 Million
Emp.: 200
Equipment & Parts Distr for Heating & Air-
Conditioning Contractors
N.A.I.C.S.: 423730

Homans Associates LLC (1)
613 Main St, Wilmington, MA
01887 (100%)
Tel.: (978) 988-9692
Web Site: http://www.homans.com
Sales Range: $50-74.9 Million
Emp.: 120
Industrial Insulation & HVAC Products Distr
N.A.I.C.S.: 423720

N&S Supply LLC (1)
205 Old Route 9, Fishkill, NY 12524
Tel.: (845) 896-6291
Web Site: https://www.nssupply.com
Plumbing, Heating & Air-Conditioning Ser-
vices
N.A.I.C.S.: 238220

Subsidiary (Domestic):

Capitol District Supply Co, Inc. (2)
850 Broadway, Albany, NY 12207
Tel.: (518) 465-3421
Web Site:
http://www.capitoldistrictsupply.com
Sales Range: $1-9.9 Million
Emp.: 21
Plumbing & Heating Equipment & Supplies
(Hydronics) Merchant Whslr
N.A.I.C.S.: 423720
Anne Zima *(Chm)*
Terry Zima *(Pres)*

**Temperature Equipment
Corporation** (1)
17725 Volbrecht Rd, Lansing, IL
60438-4542 (80%)
Tel.: (708) 418-3062
Web Site: https://www.tecmungo.com
Sales Range: $10-24.9 Million
Emp.: 200
Air Conditioning Equipment Distr
N.A.I.C.S.: 423730
Skip F. Mungo *(Pres & CEO)*
Mike Smid *(VP-Comml Sls)*

Subsidiary (Domestic):

National Excelsior Company (2)
17725 Volbrecht Rd, Lansing, IL 60438
Tel.: (708) 418-6601
Web Site: http://www.excelsiorhvac.com
Sales Range: $10-24.9 Million
Emp.: 100
Heating, Ventilation & Air-Conditioning
Equipment & Supplies Distr
N.A.I.C.S.: 423730
Raymond Mungo *(Pres)*
Ernie Pudliner *(Mgr-Credit)*

Subsidiary (Domestic):

**Excelsior Manufacturing & Supply
Corp.** (3)
1999 N Ruby St, Melrose Park, IL 60160
Tel.: (708) 344-1802
Metal Products Mfr
N.A.I.C.S.: 423730

Subsidiary (Domestic):

**Temperature Equipment Corporation -
Melrose Park** (2)
2055 N Ruby St, Melrose Park, IL 60160
Tel.: (708) 681-6220
Web Site: http://www.tecmungo.com

Warm Air Heating Equipment & Air Conditioning Equipment Distr
N.A.I.C.S.: 423730

The Harry Alter Company (2)
17725 Volbrecht Rd, Lansing, IL 60438-4542
Tel.: (708) 418-0900
Web Site: http://www.harryalter.com
Sales Range: $1-9.9 Million
Emp.: 50
Refrigeration, Air Conditioning & Heating Supplies Distr
N.A.I.C.S.: 423730
Raymond Mungo (Pres)

Three States Supply Company LLC (1)
4318 Delp St, Memphis, TN 38118 (100%)
Tel.: (901) 794-4264
Web Site: http://www.threestates.com
Sales Range: $25-49.9 Million
Emp.: 20
Sheet Metals Whslr
N.A.I.C.S.: 423730

Tradewinds Distributing Company, LLC (1)
14610 Breakers Dr, Jacksonville, FL 32258 (100%)
Tel.: (904) 407-4474
HVAC Contractor; Heating Equipment Distr
N.A.I.C.S.: 423730

WATTS WATER TECHNOLOGIES, INC.

815 Chestnut St, North Andover, MA 01845-6098
Tel.: (978) 688-1811   DE
Web Site: https://www.watts.com
Year Founded: 1874
WTS—(NYSE)
Rev.: $1,979,500,000
Assets: $1,930,900,000
Liabilities: $630,300,000
Net Worth: $1,300,600,000
Earnings: $251,500,000
Emp.: 4,600
Fiscal Year-end: 12/31/22
Plumbing & Heating Controls, Safety Devices, Backflow Preventers, Ball Valves, Butterfly Valves Mfr
N.A.I.C.S.: 326122
Andre Dhawan (COO)
Ram Ramakrishnan (Exec VP-Strategy & Bus Dev)
Robert J. Pagano Jr. (Chm, Pres & CEO)
Shashank Patel (CFO)
Elie A. Melhem (Pres-Asia-Pacific, Middle East & Africa)
Monica Barry (Chief HR Officer)
Andre Dhawan (COO)
Diane McClintock (Sr VP-Fin Plng & Analysis & IR)

Subsidiaries:

AERCO International, Inc. (1)
100 Oritani Dr, Blauvelt, NY 07647
Tel.: (845) 580-8000
Web Site: https://www.aerco.com
Heat Exchangers; Control Valves; Steam Generators; Heat Recovery Systems; Heaters & Boilers Mfr
N.A.I.C.S.: 332410

Apex Valves Limited (1)
367 Rosebank Road Avondale, Auckland, 1026, New Zealand
Tel.: (64) 98283123
Web Site: https://www.apexvalves.co.nz
Valve & Pipe Fitting Mfr
N.A.I.C.S.: 332919

Australian Valve Group Pty Ltd (1)
Unit 2 9-11 Noble St, Kewdale, 6105, WA, Australia
Tel.: (61) 893532203
Web Site: https://www.avg.net.au
Valve Pipe Mfr
N.A.I.C.S.: 332911

BAR GmbH (1)
Auf der Hohl 1, Dattenberg, Neuwied,
56547, Germany
Tel.: (49) 264496070
Web Site: http://www.bar-gmbh.de
Actuator Mfr
N.A.I.C.S.: 333995
Ulf Langenbach (Acct Mgr)
Oliver Hein (Mgr-Export)
Elke Graf (Coord-Mktg-Automation)
Lionel Repellin (Mgr-Ops)
Astrid Schmidt (Mgr-Gen Admin)

BAR pneumatische steuerungssysteme GmbH (1)
Auf der Hohl 1, Dattenberg, 53547, Neuwied, Germany
Tel.: (49) 264496070
Web Site: https://www.bar-gmbh.de
Actuator Mfr
N.A.I.C.S.: 333995
Antoine Rossignol (Mng Dir)

BLUCHER Sweden AB (1)
Verkstadsgatan 38 B, Box 965, 391 29, Kalmar, Sweden
Tel.: (46) 48 044 4700
Web Site: https://www.blucher.se
Stainless Steel Products Mfr
N.A.I.C.S.: 331110

BLUCHER UK LTD (1)
Station Road, Tadcaster, LS24 9SG, United Kingdom
Tel.: (44) 1937838000
Web Site: https://www.blucher.co.uk
Stainless Steel Products Mfr
N.A.I.C.S.: 331110
Mike Diesendorff (Mng Dir)
Chris Cawthrow (Sys Engr)
Paul Cocks (Mgr)
Michael Cooper (Acct Mgr)

Blue Ridge Atlantic, Inc. (1)
550 E 5th St, Oakboro, NC 28129
Tel.: (704) 485-8031
Web Site: http://www.braewater.com
Water Supply & Irrigation System Services
N.A.I.C.S.: 221310

Bradley Corporation (1)
W 142 N 9101 Fountain Blvd, Menomonee Falls, WI 53051-2348
Tel.: (262) 251-6000
Web Site: http://www.bradleycorp.com
Sales Range: $150-199.9 Million
Emp.: 400
Washfountains, Faucets, Safety Fixtures, Showers; Security Prison & Jail Plumbing Fixtures
N.A.I.C.S.: 327390

Division (Domestic):

Bradley Corporation - Fixtures Division (2)
W142 N9101 Fountain Blvd, Menomonee Falls, WI 53051
Tel.: (262) 251-6000
Web Site: http://www.bradleycorp.com
Home Appliance Mfr
N.A.I.C.S.: 335220

Bradley Washroom Accessories Div (2)
7020 W Parkland Ct, Milwaukee, WI 53223-4027
Tel.: (414) 354-7653
Web Site: http://www.bradleycorp.com
Sales Range: $25-49.9 Million
Emp.: 100
Washroom Accessories Mfr & Distr
N.A.I.C.S.: 326191

Enware Pty. Ltd. (1)
9 Endeavour Road, Caringbah, 2229, NSW, Australia
Tel.: (61) 1300369273
Web Site: https://www.enware.com.au
Plumbing Material & Safety Equipment Mfr
N.A.I.C.S.: 332999

HF Scientific, Inc. (1)
16260 Airport Park Dr Ste 140, Fort Myers, FL 33913
Tel.: (212) 223-2999
Web Site: https://www.watts.com
Electric Equipment Mfr
N.A.I.C.S.: 334419

Josam Company (1)
525 W US Hwy 20, Michigan City, IN 46360
Tel.: (800) 365-6726
Web Site: http://www.josam.com
Plumbing Drainage Specialties
N.A.I.C.S.: 332999
Paula Bowe (VP-Mktg & Sls)
Craig Swider (VP)
Brian Tubaugh (Dir-Engrg)

Kanmor Control Systems Ltd. (1)
5100 Silver Star Road, Vernon, V1B 3K4, BC, Canada
Tel.: (250) 545-2693
Web Site: http://www.kanmor.com
Sales Range: $25-49.9 Million
Emp.: 75
Heating & Ventilation System Component Mfr
N.A.I.C.S.: 333414

Mueller Steam Specialty (1)
1491 NC Hwy 20 W, Saint Pauls, NC 28384-9209 (100%)
Tel.: (910) 865-8241
Web Site: http://www.muellersteam.com
Sales Range: $75-99.9 Million
Emp.: 150
Valves & Strainers Mfr
N.A.I.C.S.: 332919

Orion Enterprises, Inc. (1)
2850 Fairfax Trafficway, Kansas City, KS 66115
Tel.: (913) 342-1653
Web Site: http://www.orionfittings.com
Plastic Tank Mfr
N.A.I.C.S.: 326122

Orion Fittings Inc. (1)
2850 Fairfax Trafficway, Kansas City, KS 66115
Tel.: (913) 342-1653
Web Site: http://www.orionfittings.com
Rev.: $5,200,000
Emp.: 120
Plastic Tank Mfr
N.A.I.C.S.: 326122
John McCoy (Pres)

PVI Industries LLC (1)
425 W Everman Pkwy St 101, Fort Worth, TX 76134
Tel.: (817) 335-9531
Web Site: https://www.pvi.com
Heating Equipment Mfr
N.A.I.C.S.: 333414

Powers Process Controls (1)
1400 E Lake Cook Rd Ste 120, Buffalo Grove, IL 60089
Tel.: (847) 229-0218
Web Site: http://www.powerscontrols.com
Sales Range: $25-49.9 Million
Emp.: 4
Sales & Marketing of Industrial Temperature & Pressure Controls Equipments
N.A.I.C.S.: 423830

Socla S.A.S. (1)
365 Rue Du Lieutenant Putier, 71530, Virey-le-Grand, France (100%)
Tel.: (33) 385974242
Web Site: http://www.socla.com
Sales Range: $50-74.9 Million
Supplier of Valves & Flow Control Products
N.A.I.C.S.: 332919

Subsidiary (Non-US):

Socla Valves and Controls Iberica SA (2)
Av La Llana 85, Pol Ind La Llana, 08191, Rubi, Spain
Tel.: (34) 902230530
Web Site: https://www.socla.com
Flow Valves Whslr
N.A.I.C.S.: 332912

Taft Engineering, Inc. (1)
12650 E Briarwood Ave Ste 203, Centennial, CO 80112
Tel.: (303) 753-4584
Web Site: https://www.taft-engineering.com
Plumbing Product Mfr & Distr
N.A.I.C.S.: 333310

Tianjin Tanggu Watts Valve Co., Ltd. (1)
No 1999 Jinjiang Road, Tanggu, Tianjin, 300451, Binhai New Area, China
Tel.: (86) 2265728888
Web Site: http://www.twtvalve.com

Sales Range: $100-124.9 Million
Valve Mfr
N.A.I.C.S.: 332912

Watts (Ningbo) International Trading Co., Ltd. (1)
Mingzhou West Road Beilun District, Ningbo, 315800, Zhejiang, China
Tel.: (86) 57486813624
Sales Range: $25-49.9 Million
Emp.: 20
Industrial Machinery & Equipment Whslr
N.A.I.C.S.: 423830
Janet Wu (Gen Mgr)

Watts Automatic Control Valves, Inc. (1)
12541 Gulf Fwy, Houston, TX 77034 (100%)
Tel.: (713) 943-0688
Web Site: http://www.wattsacv.com
Sales Range: $25-49.9 Million
Emp.: 12
Mfr Of Ball Valves & Butterfly Valves
N.A.I.C.S.: 332911

Watts Benelux (1)
Beernemsteenweg 77A, 8750, Wingene, Belgium
Tel.: (32) 51658708
Valve & Pipe Fitting Distr
N.A.I.C.S.: 423720

Watts Chesnee (1)
815 Pickens St, Chesnee, SC 29323
Tel.: (864) 461-3643
Web Site: http://www.watts.com
Sales Range: $75-99.9 Million
Emp.: 130
Plumbing & Heating Controls, Safety Devices, Backflow Preventers, Ball Valves, Butterfly Valves
N.A.I.C.S.: 332919

Watts Industries Belgium Bvba (1)
Beernemsteenweg 77A, 8750, Wingene, Belgium
Tel.: (32) 51658708
Web Site: http://www.wattsindustries.be
Emp.: 50
Pressure Regulator Distr
N.A.I.C.S.: 423610

Watts Industries Bulgaria EAD (1)
Industrial zone Trakia 33 Nedyalka Shileva Str, PO Box 55, 4023, Plovdiv, Bulgaria
Tel.: (359) 32605300
Emp.: 260
Industrial Machinery Distr
N.A.I.C.S.: 423830

Watts Industries Deutchland GmbH (1)
Godramsteiner Hauppstrasse 167, 76829, Landau, Germany (100%)
Tel.: (49) 634196560
Web Site: http://wattswater.de
Sales Range: $75-99.9 Million
Emp.: 200
Mfr & Distributor of Check Valves, Automatic Control Valves & Double Cage Pinch Valves
N.A.I.C.S.: 332913

Watts Industries Deutschland GmbH (1)
Godramsteiner Hauptstr 167, 76829, Landau, Germany
Tel.: (49) 634196560
Web Site: https://wattswater.de
Plumbing & Heating Equipment Distr
N.A.I.C.S.: 423720
Jochen Herterich (Mng Dir)

Watts Industries Europe B.V. (1)
Kollergang 14, 6961 LZ, Eerbeek, Netherlands
Tel.: (31) 313673700
Web Site: http://www.waterbeveiliging.nl
Rev.: $6,000,000
Emp.: 20
Mfr & Distributor of Check Valves, Automatic Control Valves & Double Cage Pinch Valves
N.A.I.C.S.: 332913

Watts Industries Tunisia S.A.S. (1)
Z I Route de Khniss, PO Box 90, Monastir, Tunisia
Tel.: (216) 73530400

Watts Water Technologies, Inc.—(Continued)

Sales Range: $75-99.9 Million
Emp.: 300
Industrial Equipment Distr
N.A.I.C.S.: 423830

Watts Industries U.K. Ltd.   (1)
Colmworth Business Park, Eaton Socon,
Saint Neots, PE19 8YX, Cambridgeshire,
United Kingdom
Tel.: (44) 870 241 7060
Web Site: http://www.wattsindustries.co.uk
Emp.: 40
Industrial Equipment Distr
N.A.I.C.S.: 423830

Watts Insulation NV   (1)
Wingepark 59a, 3110, Rotselaar, Belgium
Tel.: (32) 16442131
Emp.: 20
Electronic Components Mfr
N.A.I.C.S.: 334419
Johan De Decker (Office Mgr)

Watts Regulator/Watts ACV   (1)
12541 Gulf Fwy, Houston, TX 77034
Tel.: (713) 944-9445
Web Site: http://www.wattsacv.com
Sales Range: $25-49.9 Million
Emp.: 11
Mfr of Plumbing & Heating Controls, Safety
Devices, Backflow Preventers, Ball Valves,
Butterfly Valves
N.A.I.C.S.: 332911

Watts Valve (Ningbo) Co., Ltd.   (1)
Mingzhou West Road Beilun District, Beilun
District, Ningbo, 315800, China
Tel.: (86) 57486813624
Industrial Valve Mfr
N.A.I.C.S.: 332911

Watts Water Technologies   (1)
815 Chestnut St, North Andover, MA
01845-6098   **(100%)**
Tel.: (978) 688-1811
Web Site: http://www.watts.com
Sales Range: $100-124.9 Million
Emp.: 230
Electric & Pneumatic Actuators, Ball Valves,
Butterfly Valves, Backflow Preventers, Wa-
ter & Steam Pressure Regulators
N.A.I.C.S.: 332911

Branch (Domestic):

Dormont Manufacturing Co.   (2)
6015 Enterprise Dr, Export, PA 15632
Tel.: (724) 733-4800
Web Site: http://www.dormont.com
Sales Range: $10-24.9 Million
Emp.: 180
Flexible Stainless Steel Natural/LP Gas
Connectors Mfr
N.A.I.C.S.: 332999

Watts Water Technologies (Canada),
Inc.   (1)
5435 North Service Road, Burlington, L7L
5H7, ON, Canada
Tel.: (905) 332-4090
Web Site: https://www.watts.ca
Emp.: 60
Industrial Valve Mfr
N.A.I.C.S.: 332911

Watts Water Technologies EMEA
B.V.   (1)
Strawinskylaan 3099, 1077 ZX, Amsterdam,
Netherlands
Tel.: (31) 202626700
Industrial Valve Mfr
N.A.I.C.S.: 332911

WAVE SYNC CORP.
19 W 44th St Ste 1001, New York,
NY 10036
Tel.: (646) 512-5855   DE
Year Founded: 1988
WAYS—(OTCIQ)
Rev.: $162,853
Assets: $25,299,789
Liabilities: $4,106,838
Net Worth: $21,192,951
Earnings: ($1,466,917)
Emp.: 13
Fiscal Year-end: 12/31/21

Biodiesel Fuels Producer & Distr
N.A.I.C.S.: 457210
Hon Man Yun (CEO & CFO)
Hon Man Yun (CFO)

WAVEDANCER, INC.
12015 Lee Jackson Memorial Hwy
Ste 210, Fairfax, VA 22033
Tel.: (703) 383-3000   VA
Web Site: https://ir.wavedancer.com
Year Founded: 1979
WAVD—(NASDAQ)
Rev.: $12,021,952
Assets: $7,981,214
Liabilities: $4,251,311
Net Worth: $3,729,903
Earnings: ($17,753,838)
Emp.: 53
Fiscal Year-end: 12/31/22
Computer Software Conversion &
Modernization, Internet Application
Development & Outsourced Profes-
sional Services
N.A.I.C.S.: 334610
G. James Benoit (CEO & Chm)
Gwen Pal (Chief Admin Officer)

Subsidiaries:

Tellenger, Inc.   (1)
12015 Lee Jackson Memorial Hwy Ste 210,
Fairfax, VA 22033
Tel.: (703) 383-3000
Web Site: https://www.tellenger.com
Custom Computer Programming Services
N.A.I.C.S.: 541511
Jesse Kieffer (COO)
Beth Reese (Dir-Human Resources)
Stan Reese (Pres)

WAYFAIR INC.
4 Copley Pl, Boston, MA 02116
Tel.: (617) 532-6100   DE
Web Site: https://www.wayfair.com
Year Founded: 2014
W—(NYSE)
Rev.: $12,003,000,000
Assets: $3,474,000,000
Liabilities: $6,181,000,000
Net Worth: ($2,707,000,000)
Earnings: ($738,000,000)
Emp.: 12,800
Fiscal Year-end: 12/31/23
Holding Company; Electronic Shop-
ping
N.A.I.C.S.: 551112
Fiona Tan (CTO)
Steven K. Conine (Co-Founder & Co-
Chm)
Jon Blotner (Chief Comml Officer)
Niraj Shah (Co-Founder, Co-Chm &
CEO)
Enrique Colbert (Gen Counsel)
Thomas Netzer (COO)
Marnie H. Wilking (Chief Info Security
Officer & Head-Security & Tech Risk
Mgmt-Global)
Ashley L. Marshall (Mgr-
Merchandise)
Sascha Hower (Chief Global Supply
Chain Officer)

Subsidiaries:

SK Retail, Inc.   (1)
2 Copley Pl Ste 402A, Boston, MA 02116
Tel.: (617) 532-6100
Furniture Retailer
N.A.I.C.S.: 449110

Wayfair GmbH   (1)
Karl-Liebknecht Str 29, 10178, Berlin, Ger-
many
Tel.: (49) 8001838449
Web Site: http://www.wayfair.de
Furniture Retailer
N.A.I.C.S.: 449110

Wayfair LLC   (1)
4 Copley Pl 7th Fl, Boston, MA 02116
Tel.: (617) 532-6100
Web Site: https://www.wayfair.com

Sales Range: $600-649.9 Million
Emp.: 1,500
E-Commerce Home & Office Goods Re-
tailer
N.A.I.C.S.: 423220
Steve Conine (Co-Chm)
Jon Blotner (Chief Comml Officer)
Aanan Contractor (VP-, , and)
Ryan Fitzpatrick (VP-, , and)
Corey Gilbertson (VP)
Ryan Gilchrist (Chief People Officer)
Kate Gulliver (Chief Admin Officer)
Sascha Hower (Chief Global Supply Chain
Officer)
Liza Lefkowski (VP-, Brands, and)
Thomas Netzer (COO)
Niraj Nagrani (VP-)
Sanjeev Sahni (VP- &)
Adam Sinoway (VP-)

Wayfair Stores Limited   (1)
Wayfair House Tuam Road, Galway,
H91w260, Ireland
Tel.: (353) 8001838449
Web Site: https://www.wayfair.de
Furniture Retailer
N.A.I.C.S.: 449110

**WAYPOINT BIOMEDICAL
HOLDINGS, INC.**
17011 Beach Blvd Ste 792, Hunting-
ton Beach, CA 92647
Tel.: (917) 818-3507   NV
Year Founded: 2005
WYPH—(OTCIQ)
Pharmaceutical Preparation Mfr
N.A.I.C.S.: 325412
Rhys Wyndam Warren (Pres & CEO)

WCF BANCORP, INC.
401 Fair Meadow Dr, Webster City,
IA 50595-0638
Tel.: (515) 832-3071
Web Site: https://wcfbank.com
Year Founded: 2016
WCFB—(OTCIQ)
Rev.: $5,405,398
Assets: $161,127,999
Liabilities: $138,016,579
Net Worth: $23,111,420
Earnings: $617,483
Fiscal Year-end: 12/31/22
Bank Holding Company
N.A.I.C.S.: 551111
Thomas J. Hromatka (Chm)
Michael Segner (Pres & CEO)

Subsidiaries:

WCF Financial Bank   (1)
401 Fair Meadow Dr, Webster City, IA
50595
Tel.: (515) 832-3071
Web Site: http://www.wcfbank.com
Commericial Banking
N.A.I.C.S.: 522110
Michael Segner (Pres & CEO)
Michelle Zahn (CFO)
Pete Burmeister (Chief Credit Officer & Sr
VP)

WCG CLINICAL, INC.
212 Carnegie Ctr Ste 30, Princeton,
NJ 08540
Tel.: (609) 945-0101   DE
Web Site: http://www.wcgclinical.com
Year Founded: 2012
WCGC—(NASDAQ)
Rev.: $463,441,000
Assets: $3,836,773,000
Liabilities: $1,898,515,000
Net Worth: $1,938,258,000
Earnings: ($95,274,000)
Emp.: 1,322
Fiscal Year-end: 12/31/20
Biotechnology Research & Develop-
ment Services
N.A.I.C.S.: 541714
Nicholas Slack (Pres & Chief Comml
Officer)
Barbara J. Shander (Chief Legal Offi-
cer & Exec VP-Corp Dev)

Dawn Flitcraft (Pres-Ethical Review)
David Forster (Chief Compliance Offi-
cer)
Christina Armstrong (Sr VP-Bus Dev)
Marco Capasso (Gen Counsel)
Lindsay McNair (Chief Medical Offi-
cer)
Jonathan Seltzer (Chief Scientific Of-
ficer)
Jill Johnston (Pres-Study Plng & Site
Optimization)
Terri Moench (Pres-Patient Engage-
ment)
Dave Meadows (Pres-Scientific &
Regulatory Review)
Emmanuel Olart (Chief Application
Officer)
Lisa Calicchio (Chief Human Capital
Mgmt Officer)
Stephen M. McLean (Treas & Sr VP-
Corp Dev & IR)
Craig Sowell (Chief Strategy Officer)
Lance Converse (Chief Innovation
Officer)
Norman M. Goldfarb (Chief Collabo-
ration Officer)
Megan Trost (VP-Study Start Up &
Admin)
Steve Smith (Pres-Patient Advocacy)
Tim Schuckman (Chief Comml
Officer-Ethical Review Div)
Cynthia Carter (Pres-Market Intelli-
gence & Insights)
Sam Srivastava (CEO)
Robert VanHees (CFO & Chief Admin
Officer)
Paul Mancinelli (CTO)
Rahul Bafna (Chief Product Officer)

WD-40 COMPANY
9715 Businesspark Ave, San Diego,
CA 92131
Tel.: (858) 251-5600   DE
Web Site:
https://www.wd40company.com
Year Founded: 1953
WDFC—(NASDAQ)
Rev.: $590,557,000
Assets: $449,039,000
Liabilities: $218,513,000
Net Worth: $230,526,000
Earnings: $69,644,000
Emp.: 644
Fiscal Year-end: 08/31/24
Lubricant & Rust Preventive Com-
pounds Mfr
N.A.I.C.S.: 325998
Geoffrey J. Holdsworth (Mng Dir-Asia
Pacific)
Steven A. Brass (Pres & CEO)
Rae Ann Partlo (VP & Controller)
Wendy Kelley (VP-Stakeholder & In-
vestor Engagement)
Jeffrey G. Lindeman (VP-
Organization Dev-Global)
Alice Fournier (Chief Digital Officer &
VP-Digital Dev-Global)
Sara K. Hyzer (CFO, Principal Acctg
Officer, Treas & VP-Fin)
Phenix Kiamilev (Corp Counsel)
Preston Ley (Mng Dir)
Meghan Lieb (VP)

Subsidiaries:

HPD Holdings Corp.   (1)
1061 Cudahy Pl, San Diego, CA 92110
Tel.: (619) 275-1400
Web Site: http://www.wd40company.com
Sales Range: $100-124.9 Million
Emp.: 245
Holding Company
N.A.I.C.S.: 531120

WD-40 Company (Australia) Pty.
Ltd.   (1)
PO Box 649, Epping, 1710, NSW,
Australia   **(100%)**

Tel.: (61) 298682200
Web Site: https://www.wd40.com.au
Sales Range: $50-74.9 Million
Emp.: 14
Marketing of Lubricating Oil; WD-40
N.A.I.C.S.: 424720
Geoff Holdsworth *(Mng Dir)*

WD-40 Company (Canada) Ltd. **(1)**
5399 Eglinton Ave W - Suite 214, Toronto,
M9C 5K6, ON, Canada
Tel.: (416) 622-9881
Web Site: http://www.wd40.ca
Lubricant & Rust Preventive Compounds
Mfr
N.A.I.C.S.: 325998

WD-40 Company Ltd. **(1)**
252 Upper Third Street, Milton Keynes,
MK9 1DZ, United Kingdom **(100%)**
Tel.: (44) 8449800838
Web Site: https://www.wd40.co.uk
Sales Range: $50-74.9 Million
Emp.: 60
Marketing of Lubricating Oils
N.A.I.C.S.: 424720

WD-40 Manufacturing Co. **(1)**
9715 Businesspark Ave, San Diego, CA
92131
Tel.: (858) 251-5600
Web Site: http://www.wd40company.com
Sales Range: $50-74.9 Million
Emp.: 340
Lubricating Oil Mfr
N.A.I.C.S.: 324110
Garry O. Ridge *(Pres & CEO)*

WD-40 Products (Canada) Ltd. **(1)**
5399 Eglinton Ave W-Suite 214, Toronto,
M9C 5K6, ON, Canada **(100%)**
Tel.: (416) 622-9881
Web Site: https://wd40.ca
Sales Range: $50-74.9 Million
Emp.: 11
Marketing & Sales of Lubricating Oil
N.A.I.C.S.: 424720

WEALTHCRAFT CAPITAL, INC.
2726 Broadway, Santa Monica, CA
90404
Tel.: (909) 318-0220 **NV**
Web Site:
http://www.wealthcraftcapital.com
Year Founded: 1992
WCCP—(OTCIQ)
Rev.: $1,391,000
Assets: $256,000
Liabilities: $1,125,000
Net Worth: ($869,000)
Earnings: ($345,000)
Emp.: 4
Fiscal Year-end: 12/31/19
Commercial Banking Services
N.A.I.C.S.: 522110
William Lewis Mayhew *(CEO)*

WEARABLE HEALTH SOLU-TIONS, INC.
Tel.: (949) 270-7460 **NV**
Web Site:
http://www.wearablehealthsolu
tions.com
Year Founded: 2008
WHSI—(OTCIQ)
Rev.: $745,093
Assets: $223,173
Liabilities: $3,800,285
Net Worth: ($3,577,112)
Earnings: ($2,388,467)
Emp.: 5
Fiscal Year-end: 06/30/23
Health Care Device Mfr; 24-Hour Per-sonal Response Monitoring Services
N.A.I.C.S.: 339112
Allen Polsky *(VP-Strategic Alliances)*
Jennifer Loria *(COO)*
Vincent S. Miceli *(CFO)*
Peter Pizzino *(Pres, CEO & CMO)*

WEATHERFORD INTERNA-TIONAL PLC

2000 St James Pl, Houston, TX
77056
Tel.: (713) 836-4000 **IE**
Web Site:
https://www.weatherford.com
Year Founded: 1972
WFRD—(NASDAQ)
Rev.: $4,331,000,000
Assets: $4,720,000,000
Liabilities: $4,169,000,000
Net Worth: $551,000,000
Earnings: $26,000,000
Emp.: 17,700
Fiscal Year-end: 12/31/22
Holding Company; Oilfield Equipment
Mfr & Marketer; Well Installation &
Maintenance Services; Oil & Gas Ex-ploration & Production Services
N.A.I.C.S.: 551112
Desmond J. Mills *(Chief Acctg Officer
& Sr VP)*
Arunava Mitra *(CFO & Exec VP)*
Girish K. Saligram *(Pres & CEO)*

Subsidiaries:

**Applied Petroleum Technology (UK)
Limited** **(1)**
Tan-y-Graig Unit 8 Parc Caer Seion,
Conwy, Colwyn Bay, LL32 8FA, United
Kingdom
Tel.: (44) 1492882011
Web Site: http://www.aptec.no
Oil & Gas Exploration Services
N.A.I.C.S.: 213112

**Applied Petroleum Technology
A.S.** **(1)**
Sven Oftedals vei 6, 0950, Oslo, Norway
Tel.: (47) 45396000
Web Site: http://www.aptec.no
Oil & Natural Gas Exploration Consulting
Services
N.A.I.C.S.: 213112

Artex S.A. **(1)**
Juan Diaz De Solis 2364, Olivos, Buenos
Aires, Argentina
Tel.: (54) 1159176000
Oil & Gas Exploration Services
N.A.I.C.S.: 211120

CWA Consultores & Servicos de Pe-troleo Ltda. **(1)**
Rua Raimundo Chaves 1995 Rio Grande
do Sul, Natal, Rio Grande do Sul, Brazil
Tel.: (55) 8432316900
Web Site: http://www.cwaconsultores.com.br
Oil & Natural Gas Exploration Support Ser-vices
N.A.I.C.S.: 213112

Crocker Data Processing Pty Ltd **(1)**
Level 12 133 Mary St, Brisbane, 4000,
QLD, Australia
Tel.: (61) 732143000
Web Site: http://petrolog.net
Computer Software & Application Publisher
N.A.I.C.S.: 513210

Cygnet Software, Inc. **(1)**
1880 Santa Barbara St Ste 220, San Luis
Obispo, CA 93401
Tel.: (805) 781-3580
Web Site: http://www.cygnet.com
Software Publisher
N.A.I.C.S.: 513210

Datalog De Venezuela SA **(1)**
Zona Industrial Segunda Etapa Av 68 Con
Calle 149-B Parcela 62 Zulia, Zona Indus-trial, Maracaibo, Venezuela
Tel.: (58) 2617362475
Oil & Gas Exploration Services
N.A.I.C.S.: 211120

**Drilling Research & Development
Corporation** **(1)**
5726 Braesvalley Dr, Houston, TX 77096-2912
Tel.: (713) 777-4943
Web Site: http://www.weatherford.com
Emp.: 10,000
Engineering Services
N.A.I.C.S.: 541330

EVI Weatherford, Inc. **(1)**

1596 S Leon St, Giddings, TX 78942
Tel.: (979) 542-5154
Industrial Machinery Whslr
N.A.I.C.S.: 423830

**Edinburgh Petroleum Equipment
Limited** **(1)**
22 Research Park Riccarton, Currie, Edin-burgh, EH14 4AP, United Kingdom
Tel.: (44) 1314495123
Sales Range: $50-74.9 Million
Emp.: 50
Oil & Gas Exploration Services
N.A.I.C.S.: 213112

Houston Well Screen Company **(1)**
11939 Aldine Westfield, Houston, TX 77093
Tel.: (281) 449-7261
Construction & Mining Equipment Whslr
N.A.I.C.S.: 213112

**International Logging Netherlands
B.V.** **(1)**
Prins Bernhardplein 200, 1097JB, Amster-dam, Noord-Holland, Netherlands
Tel.: (31) 205214777
Oil & Gas Exploration Services
N.A.I.C.S.: 213112

Nizhnevartovskburneft, CJSC **(1)**
2a 60 let Oktyabrya Street Khanty-Mansi,
Autonomous Area Tyumen Region, Nizhne-vartovsk, 628600, Russia
Tel.: (7) 3466642015
Oil & Gas Well Drilling Services
N.A.I.C.S.: 213111

PD Mexicana, S. de R.L. de C.V. **(1)**
Avenida Parque Industrial Rio San Juan
Lote 6 Manzana 7 Edif 3, Parque Industrial
Del Norte Tamps, 88736, Reynosa, Mexico
Tel.: (52) 9933581900
Oil & Gas Well Drilling Services
N.A.I.C.S.: 213111

**Precision Drilling Services M.E.
W.L.L.** **(1)**
Najda st, Abu Dhabi, United Arab Emirates
Tel.: (971) 26747222
Oil & Gas Mining Equipment Rental & Leas-ing Services
N.A.I.C.S.: 532412

Precision Oilfield Services, LLP **(1)**
19950 State Hwy 242, Conroe, TX 77306-9366
Tel.: (281) 689-2058
Oil & Gas Exploration Services
N.A.I.C.S.: 211120

Reeves Oilfield Services Ltd. **(1)**
East Leake, Leicestershire, Loughborough,
LE12 6JX, Leicestershire, United Kingdom
Tel.: (44) 1159457800
Web Site: http://www.reeves-wireline.com
Sales Range: $100-124.9 Million
Emp.: 180
Oil & Gas Operations Support Services
N.A.I.C.S.: 213112
Martin Charles Enstone *(Gen Mgr)*

S.C. Foserco S.A. **(1)**
Strada Clopotei 2A, 605600, Ploiesti, Ro-mania
Tel.: (40) 234344035
Web Site: http://www.weatherford.com
Sales Range: $100-124.9 Million
Emp.: 20
Oil & Gas Exploration Services
N.A.I.C.S.: 211120

Signa Engineering Corp. **(1)**
2 Northpoint Dr Ste 700, Houston, TX
77060
Tel.: (281) 774-1000
Web Site: http://www.signaengineering.com
Engineeering Services
N.A.I.C.S.: 541330
Charles R. Stone *(Chm & CEO)*
Robert G. Davis *(Pres & COO)*

Smart Stabilizer Systems Limited **(1)**
Ashchurch Business Centre, Alexandra
Way, Tewkesbury, GL20 8TD, Gloucester-shire, United Kingdom
Tel.: (44) 1684853860
Oil & Gas Exploration Services
N.A.I.C.S.: 213112

**Tech 21 Engineering Solutions
Limited** **(1)**

Etive House Beechwood Business Park,
Inverness, IV2 3BW, Scotland, United King-dom
Tel.: (44) 1463710008
Web Site: http://www.tech21.co.uk
Emp.: 10
Drilling Software Consulting Services
N.A.I.C.S.: 541512

Techinformservice, LLC **(1)**
37 Novosmirnovskaya St, Izhevsk, 426039,
Russia
Tel.: (7) 3412483440
Web Site: http://tis.weatherford.ru
Emp.: 500
Oilfield Support Services
N.A.I.C.S.: 213112
Sergey Afanasiev *(Gen Mgr)*

**Tesseract Corporation Weatherford
Laboratories** **(1)**
16161 Table Mtn Pkwy, Golden, CO 80403
Tel.: (720) 898-8200
Sales Range: $75-99.9 Million
Emp.: 75
Engineering & Geologic Consulting Services
N.A.I.C.S.: 541690
Pat Jacobs *(Gen Mgr)*

**United Precision Drilling Company
W.L.L.** **(1)**
Block 13 Near Magwa Rd After Gas Station,
Ahmadi, 9282-61003, Kuwait
Tel.: (965) 23985011
Oil & Gas Well Drilling Services
N.A.I.C.S.: 213111

**Visean Information Services Pty
Ltd** **(1)**
Suite 2 7 54-56 Delhi Road, North Ryde,
2113, NSW, Australia
Tel.: (61) 288748400
Sales Range: $50-74.9 Million
Emp.: 10
Real Time Drilling Information & Document
Management Services
N.A.I.C.S.: 213112

Weatherford (B) Sdn. Bhd. **(1)**
Lts 5383 Jalan Mumong, Belait, Kuala Be-lait, KA1731, Brunei Darussalam
Tel.: (673) 3340343
Web Site: http://www.weatherford.com
Oil & Gas Exploration Services
N.A.I.C.S.: 213112

**Weatherford (Malaysia) Sdn.
Bhd.** **(1)**
199 Jalan Tun Razak, Wilayah Perseku-tuan, 50450, Kuala Lumpur,
Malaysia **(100%)**
Tel.: (60) 321686000
Sales Range: $250-299.9 Million
Emp.: 80
Sales of Oilfield Equipment & Services
N.A.I.C.S.: 213112

Subsidiary (Non-US):

PT. Weatherford Indonesia **(2)**
JL TB Simatupang Kawasan 22-26, Jakarta,
12430, Jawa Barat, Indonesia
Tel.: (62) 8111847004
Oil & Gas Mining Equipment Rental & Leas-ing Services
N.A.I.C.S.: 532412
Made Dharmadetta *(Mgr-Supply Chain)*

Weatherford (U.K.) Limited **(1)**
Weatherford House Lawson Drive, Dyce,
Aberdeen, AB21 0DR, United
Kingdom **(100%)**
Tel.: (44) 1224762800
Sales Range: $100-124.9 Million
Emp.: 250
Special Industry Machinery
N.A.I.C.S.: 333310

Weatherford Aarbakke AS **(1)**
Stokkamyrveien 17, 4068, Stavanger, Nor-way
Tel.: (47) 51814400
Web Site: http://www.weatherford.com
Emp.: 80
Oil & Gas Exploration Services
N.A.I.C.S.: 213112

**Weatherford Artificial Lift
Systems** **(1)**
2000 St James Pl, Houston, TX 77056

Weatherford International plc—(Continued)

Tel.: (713) 693-4000
Web Site: http://www.weatherford.com
Sales Range: $1-4.9 Billion
Emp.: 1,500
Installation of Lifts
N.A.I.C.S.: 332996
Mark McCollum (Pres)

Weatherford Artificial Lift Systems Canada Ltd. (1)
5414 46 Ave, Macklin, S0L 2C0, SK, Canada
Tel.: (306) 753-2388
Sales Range: $50-74.9 Million
Emp.: 28
Oil & Gas Support Activity Services
N.A.I.C.S.: 213112
Ryan Wieler (Gen Mgr)

Weatherford Asia Pacific Pte. Ltd. (1)
Loyang Offshore Supply Base 23C Loyang Crescent, PO Box 5132, Singapore, 509019, Singapore **(100%)**
Tel.: (65) 431311
Sales Range: $25-49.9 Million
Emp.: 99
Equipment Rental & Leasing
N.A.I.C.S.: 532210

Weatherford Australia Pty. Ltd. (1)
9 Metal Circuit, Malaga, Perth, 6090, WA, Australia **(100%)**
Tel.: (61) 892031600
Web Site: http://www.weatherford.com
Rev.: $2,398,000
Emp.: 400
Oilfield Services & Equipment
N.A.I.C.S.: 213112

Weatherford CSG Drilling Pty Ltd (1)
209 Leitchs Rd, Brendale, 4500, QLD, Australia
Tel.: (61) 734829900
Oil & Gas Well Drilling Services
N.A.I.C.S.: 213111

Weatherford Canada Limited (1)
700-9th Avenue SW, Calgary, T2P 3V4, AB, Canada **(100%)**
Tel.: (403) 693-7500
Web Site: http://www.weatherford.com
Sales Range: $150-199.9 Million
Emp.: 200
Short Term Rental of Specialized Equipment; Sale of Oilfield Supplies
N.A.I.C.S.: 213112

Subsidiary (Non-US):

Precision Energy Services Saudi Arabia Co. Ltd. (2)
Dhahran-Abqaiq Road, PO Box 79106, Al Khobar, 31952, Saudi Arabia
Tel.: (966) 138075000
Oil & Gas Mining Equipment Rental & Leasing Services
N.A.I.C.S.: 532412
Hameeda Al Ifraid (Supvr-Logistics)

Weatherford Canada Partnership (1)
1306 - 5th Street, Nisku, T9E 7S8, AB, Canada **(75%)**
Tel.: (780) 955-8070
Web Site: http://www.weatherford.com
Sales Range: $25-49.9 Million
Emp.: 40
Sales, Rental & Service of Specialized Pipeline & Automatic Welding Equipment
N.A.I.C.S.: 333992

Weatherford Canada Partnership (Administration Center) (1)
700 - 9th Avenue SW, Calgary, T2P 3V4, AB, Canada **(100%)**
Tel.: (403) 693-7500
Web Site: http://www.weatherford.com
Oilfield Drilling & Energy Service
N.A.I.C.S.: 213111

Weatherford Capital Management Services Limited Liability (1)
V District Bajcsy-Zsilinszky u 12, Budapest, 1051, Hungary
Tel.: (36) 14110414
Web Site: http://www.weatherford.com
Investment Management Service
N.A.I.C.S.: 523940

Weatherford DIS Manufacturing (UK) Limited (1)
3 Games Chalmers Road, Arbroath, DD11 3LR, Angus, United Kingdom
Tel.: (44) 1241434400
Oil & Gas Field Machinery Mfr
N.A.I.C.S.: 333132
Andrew Simpson (Gen Mgr)

Weatherford Danmark AS (1)
Hogevej 12-14, Esbjerg, 6705, Denmark
Tel.: (45) 70269192
Oil & Gas Well Drilling Services
N.A.I.C.S.: 213111

Subsidiary (Non-US):

Weatherford Industria e Comercio Ltda. (2)
Av Luis Carlos Prestes 180 1 Andar Sala 101e 102, Rio de Janeiro, 22775-055, Brazil
Tel.: (55) 22277397
Oil & Gas Mining Equipment Rental & Leasing Services
N.A.I.C.S.: 532412
Andrea Montez (Head-Legal)

Weatherford Latin America, S.C.A. (2)
Edificio Torre BVC Sector Las Garzas, Puerto la Cruz Piso 7, Anaco, 6016, Anzoategui, Venezuela
Tel.: (58) 2815004211
Oil & Gas Mining Equipment Rental & Leasing Services
N.A.I.C.S.: 532412
Damian Jose Pena Ocando (Coord-Shopping-Natl)

Weatherford Trinidad Limited (2)
Western Main Road, Chaguanas, Port of Spain, Trinidad & Tobago
Tel.: (868) 6655705
Oil & Gas Mining Equipment Rental & Leasing Services
N.A.I.C.S.: 532412
Kinda Boatswain (Coord-Ops-Surface Logging Sys)

Weatherford East Europe Service GmbH (1)
Hainhauser Weg 150, Langenhagen, 30855, Germany
Tel.: (49) 51177020
Web Site: http://www.weatherford.com
Oil & Gas Well Drilling Services
N.A.I.C.S.: 213111

Weatherford Energy Services GmbH (1)
Eddesser Str 1, Edemissen, 31234, Germany
Tel.: (49) 517698960
Sales Range: $100-124.9 Million
Emp.: 150
Oil & Gas Exploration Services
N.A.I.C.S.: 213112

Weatherford Engineered Chemistry Canada Ltd. (1)
333 5th Avenue Sw Suite 1200, Calgary, T2P 3B5, AB, Canada
Tel.: (403) 693-7500
Sales Range: $125-149.9 Million
Emp.: 300
Oil & Gas Support Activity Services
N.A.I.C.S.: 325998

Weatherford France, S.A. (1)
5 Av Gen De Gaulle, 60300, Senlis, France **(100%)**
Tel.: (33) 344322412
Sales Range: $10-24.9 Million
Emp.: 2
Sales of Oilfield Equipment & Services
N.A.I.C.S.: 213112

Weatherford International Eastern Europe SRL (1)
2A Orizontului Street, Campina, Prahova, Romania
Tel.: (40) 244373565
Oil & Gas Well Drilling Services
N.A.I.C.S.: 213111

Weatherford International de Argentina S.A. (1)
Bouchard 574, Buenos Aires, C1106ABG, Argentina

Tel.: (54) 1150775200
Oil & Gas Mining Equipment Rental & Leasing Services
N.A.I.C.S.: 532412
Claudia St. Esteben (Mgr-Legal-Bolivia & Chile)

Weatherford International, LLC (1)
515 Post Oak Blvd Ste 600, Houston, TX 77027
Tel.: (713) 836-4000
Emp.: 52,000
Oil & Gas Mining Equipment Rental & Leasing Services
N.A.I.C.S.: 532412
David Dyer (Mgr-HR)

Weatherford KSP Co., Ltd. (1)
719 KPN Tower 17th Fl Rama 9 Rd Bang Kapi Huai Khwang, Khet Chatuchak, 10310, Bangkok, Thailand
Tel.: (66) 27170400
Sales Range: $150-199.9 Million
Flow Control Systems; Gas Lift Systems & Tubular Running Services Mfr
N.A.I.C.S.: 334513

Weatherford Kopp GmbH (1)
Friedrich-Ebert-Strasse 131, Lingen, 49811, Germany
Tel.: (49) 59171020
Web Site: http://www.wftkopp.com
Sales Range: $25-49.9 Million
Emp.: 35
Oil & Gas Pipeline System Mfr
N.A.I.C.S.: 333998
Detlev Els (Mgr-Base)

Weatherford Laboratories (Canada) Ltd. (1)
1620 - 27 Avenue NE, Calgary, T2E 8W4, AB, Canada
Tel.: (403) 736-3500
Web Site: http://www.weatherfordlabs.com
Sales Range: $25-49.9 Million
Emp.: 70
Laboratory Services
N.A.I.C.S.: 541380

Weatherford Laboratories (Muscat) L.L.C. (1)
Way 6421 Building 1680, PO Box 96, Ghala Industrial Area, 116, Muscat, Oman
Tel.: (968) 24593482
Laboratory Services
N.A.I.C.S.: 541380

Weatherford Laboratories (UK) Limited (1)
Unit 28 The Birches Industrial Estate, Imberhorne Lane, East Grinstead, RH191XZ, West Sussex, United Kingdom
Tel.: (44) 1342317310
Emp.: 25
Laboratory Services
N.A.I.C.S.: 541380
Tony Barrow (Gen Mgr)

Weatherford Laboratories, Inc. (1)
8845 Fallbrook Dr, Houston, TX 77064
Tel.: (832) 237-4000
Web Site: http://www.weatherfordlabs.com
Emp.: 50
Laboratory Services
N.A.I.C.S.: 541380
Charlene Boggs (Office Mgr)

Weatherford Liners Systems Ltd. (1)
Face 1 Kirkton Drive Dice, Aberdeen, AB21 0BG, United Kingdom
Tel.: (44) 1224767170
Sales Range: $150-199.9 Million
Oil & Gas Field Services
N.A.I.C.S.: 213112

Weatherford New Zealand Ltd. (1)
10 Dakota Place, New Plymouth, 4341, Taranaki, New Zealand **(100%)**
Tel.: (64) 67551129
Web Site: http://www.weatherford.com
Sales Range: $1-9.9 Million
Emp.: 11
Sales of Oilfield Equipment & Services
N.A.I.C.S.: 213112

Weatherford Norge A/S (1)
Stokkamyrveien 17, 4313, Sandnes, Norway
Tel.: (47) 51814400
Web Site: http://www.weatherford.no

Oil & Gas Exploration Services
N.A.I.C.S.: 213112
Frank Schieldrop (Mgr)
Tim Dodsworth (Mgr)
Ragnar K. Evensen (Mgr)
Eugene Nathan (Mng Dir)
Stig Wolstad-Knudsen (Mgr)
Atle Jacobsen (Mgr)
Cécilie Drange (Mgr-Sales-Marketing)
Arve Haraldsen (Mgr-Fin-Norway)
Hege Juul-Bruheim (Mgr-Human Resources)

Weatherford Norge, A/S (1)
Stokkamyrveien 17, PO Box 5079, 4313, Sandnes, Norway **(100%)**
Tel.: (47) 51814400
Web Site: http://www.weatherford.com
Rev.: $5,240,000
Emp.: 4
Sales of Oilfield Equipment & Services
N.A.I.C.S.: 213112

Weatherford Oil Tool GmbH (1)
Muenchner Strasse 52, 30855, Langenhagen, Germany **(89%)**
Tel.: (49) 51177020
Web Site: https://www.weatherford.com
Rev.: $18,660,000
Emp.: 200
Oil & Gas Field Support Services
N.A.I.C.S.: 213112

Weatherford Oil Tool Middle East Ltd. (1)
Opposite Musalla Al Eid Ground, Corniche, Abu Dhabi, United Arab Emirates
Tel.: (971) 25544100
Web Site: http://www.weatherford.com
Sales Range: $1-9.9 Million
Emp.: 92
Sales of Tools for the Oil Field Industry
N.A.I.C.S.: 213112

Weatherford Oil Tool Middle East Ltd. (1)
515 Post Oak Blvd Ste 200, Houston, TX 77027
Tel.: (713) 297-2689
Web Site: http://www.weatherford.com
Sales Range: $150-199.9 Million
Emp.: 600
Mfr of Oilfield Equipment
N.A.I.C.S.: 333132

Weatherford Oil Tool Nederland B.V. (1)
Schrijnwerkersweg 6 Den Helder, Beverwijk, 1786, Netherlands
Tel.: (31) 223635386
Web Site: http://www.weatherford.com
Sales Range: $50-74.9 Million
Emp.: 60
Sales of Oilfield Equipment & Services
N.A.I.C.S.: 213112

Weatherford Petroleum Consultants AS (1)
Stiklestadveien 1, 7041, Trondheim, Norway
Tel.: (47) 40001915
Web Site: http://www.weatherford.no
Emp.: 15
Oil & Gas Technology Software Consulting Services
N.A.I.C.S.: 541512
Erik Nakken (COO-Bus Dev)
Edwin Meissner (Mgr-Section)
Ola Broyn Naeverdal (Mgr-Fin)
Elisabeth Strom (Mgr-HR)

Weatherford Poland Sp.Zo.o (1)
Ul Krolewska 16, Mazowieckie District, Warsaw, 00-103, Mazowieckie, Poland
Tel.: (48) 223306300
Web Site: http://www.weatherford.com
Oil & Gas Exploration Services
N.A.I.C.S.: 213112

Weatherford Products, Inc. (1)
14435 116th Ave NW, Edmonton, T5M 3E8, AB, Canada **(100%)**
Tel.: (780) 455-2176
Web Site: http://www.weatherford.com
Sales Range: $25-49.9 Million
Emp.: 150
Mfr of Oil & Gas Field Equipments
N.A.I.C.S.: 333132

Weatherford Saudi Arabia Ltd. (1)
Al Rushaid Commercial Center Abqiaq Highway Ground Floor Al Khobar, PO Box

31731, Opposite Aramco B, Dhahran,
31952, Saudi Arabia **(100%)**
Tel.: (966) 138681888
Web Site: http://www.weatherford.com
Sales Range: $50-74.9 Million
Emp.: 140
Mfr of Oilfield Equipment
N.A.I.C.S.: 333132

Weatherford Services S.A. **(1)**
Plot 37, Trans Amadi Industrial Layout, Port
Harcourt, Rivers State, Nigeria
Tel.: (234) 112674740
Web Site: http://www.weatherford.com
Sales Range: $150-199.9 Million
Sales of Oilfield Equipment & Services
N.A.I.C.S.: 213112

Weatherford U.K. Ltd. **(1)**
Harfreys Rd, Harfreys Industrial Estate,
Great Yarmouth, NR31 0LS, United
Kingdom **(100%)**
Tel.: (44) 493657516
Web Site: http://www.weatherford.com
Sales Range: $10-24.9 Million
Emp.: 12
Mfr of Oilfield Equipment
N.A.I.C.S.: 333132

Weatherford U.S., Inc. **(1)**
5060 California Ave Stes 1125 & 1150, Ba-
kersfield, CA 93309
Tel.: (661) 281-6300
Web Site: http://www.weatherford.com
Sales Range: $10-24.9 Million
Emp.: 50
Oil Tool Equipment Rental
N.A.I.C.S.: 541990

Weatherford UK Ltd. **(1)**
Harfreys Industrial Estate, Great Yarmouth,
Norfolk, NR31 0LS, United
Kingdom **(100%)**
Tel.: (44) 493657516
Rev.: $6,500,000
Emp.: 40
Oilfield Equipment Rental, Fishing Services
& a Full Range of Downhole Equipment
N.A.I.C.S.: 213112

Weatherford, Inc. **(1)**
Kondivita Lane, Mumbai, 400059, Maha-
rashtra, India **(100%)**
Tel.: (91) 2240016100
Sales Range: $150-199.9 Million
Sales of Oilfield Equipment & Services
N.A.I.C.S.: 213112

eProduction Solutions, Inc. **(1)**
22001 N Park Dr, Kingwood, TX 77339
Tel.: (281) 348-1000
Web Site: http://www.ep-solutions.com
Sales Range: $250-299.9 Million
Emp.: 600
Control Systems & Production Automation
for Oil & Gas Industry
N.A.I.C.S.: 423830
Dharmesh B. Mehta *(Pres)*

Subsidiary (Non-US):

Weatherford Production
Optimization **(2)**
Viking Rd Gapton Hall Industrial Estate,
Great Yarmouth, NR31 0NU, Norfolk,
United Kingdom
Tel.: (44) 1493652611
Web Site: http://www.weatherford.com
Sales Range: $25-49.9 Million
Emp.: 100
Laboratory Machinery Mfr
N.A.I.C.S.: 334516

eProduction Solutions **(2)**
6 4206 59th Ave, Lloydminster, T9V 2V4,
AB, Canada
Tel.: (780) 872-7770
Web Site: http://www.ep-solutions.com
Sales Range: $10-24.9 Million
Emp.: 4
Control Systems & Production Automation
for Oil & Gas Industry
N.A.I.C.S.: 213112
Wayne Smith *(Product Mgr)*

Branch (Domestic):

eProduction Solutions -
California **(2)**
4817 Distict Blvd, Bakersfield, CA 93313

Tel.: (661) 831-5528
Web Site: http://www.ep-solutions.com
Sales Range: $10-24.9 Million
Emp.: 5
Control Systems & Production Automation
for Oil & Gas Industry
N.A.I.C.S.: 213112

WEAVE COMMUNICATIONS,
INC.
1331 W Powell Way, Lehi, UT 84043
Web Site: https://www.getweave.com
Year Founded: 2008
WEAV—(NYSE)
Rev.: $142,117,000
Assets: $208,349,000
Liabilities: $125,130,000
Net Worth: $83,219,000
Earnings: ($49,738,000)
Emp.: 806
Fiscal Year-end: 12/31/22
Software Development Services
N.A.I.C.S.: 541511
Brett T. White *(CEO)*
Stuart Harvey *(Chm)*
Marcus Bertilson *(COO)*
Alan Taylor *(CFO)*
Erin Goodsell *(Chief Legal Officer)*
Chris Baird *(CMO)*
Brooke Shreeve *(Chief People Offi-
cer)*
Branden Neish *(CTO & Chief Product
Officer)*

WEB TO DOOR, INC.
1431 Doolittle Dr, San Leandro, CA
94577
Tel.: (510) 343-9500
Web Site:
https://www.webtodoor.com
Year Founded: 2014
SPRV—(OTCIQ)
Couriers & Express Delivery Services
N.A.I.C.S.: 492110
Rod Santulan *(Pres)*

WEBCO INDUSTRIES INC.
13301 W Hwy 51, Sand Springs, OK
74063-8521
Tel.: (918) 245-2211 OK
Web Site:
https://www.webcotube.com
Year Founded: 1969
WEBC—(OTCIQ)
Rev.: $466,617,000
Assets: $385,203,000
Liabilities: $154,057,000
Net Worth: $231,146,000
Earnings: $19,700,000
Emp.: 1,239
Fiscal Year-end: 07/31/21
Carbon & Stainless Steel Tubing
Products Mfr
N.A.I.C.S.: 322219
Dana S. Weber *(Chm & CEO)*
Michael P. Howard *(CFO, Treas, Sec
& Sr VP-Fin & Admin)*
David E. Boyer *(Vice Chm-, Vice
Chm, Pres, COO & Sr VP/Sr VP-
Tubing Ops)*

WEBSTAR TECHNOLOGY
GROUP, INC.
284 Paseo Reyes, Saint Augustine,
FL 32095
Tel.: (904) 312-9681 WY
Web Site:
https://www.webstartechnology
group.com
Year Founded: 2015
WBSR—(OTCQB)
Assets: $4,623
Liabilities: $3,644,915
Net Worth: ($3,640,292)
Earnings: ($31,020,540)
Emp.: 3
Fiscal Year-end: 12/31/22

Software Development Services
N.A.I.C.S.: 541511
Donald D. Roberts *(Pres & CEO)*
James R. Owens *(Chm & CTO)*

WEBSTER FINANCIAL COR-
PORATION
200 Elm St, Stamford, CT 06901
Tel.: (203) 578-2202 DE
Web Site:
https://investors.websterbank.com
Year Founded: 1986
WBS—(NYSE)
Rev.: $3,942,597,000
Assets: $74,945,249,000
Liabilities: $66,255,253,000
Net Worth: $8,689,996,000
Earnings: $851,190,000
Emp.: 4,131
Fiscal Year-end: 12/31/23
Bank Holding Company
N.A.I.C.S.: 551111
William Holland *(Exec VP-Fin)*
Glenn I. MacInnes *(CFO & Exec VP)*
Luis Massiani *(Pres & COO)*
Christopher J. Motl *(Founder-Sponsor
& Specialty Fin Grp, Exec VP &
Head-Commercial Banking)*
Kristy Berner *(Gen Counsel, Sec &
Exec VP)*
John R. Ciulla *(Chm, Pres & CEO)*
Luis Massiani *(COO & Exec VP)*

Subsidiaries:

Bend Financial, Inc. **(1)**
53 State St Ste 500, Boston, MA 02109
Web Site: https://www.bendhsa.com
Financial Services
N.A.I.C.S.: 523999

Interlink Insured Sweep LLC **(1)**
360 Lexington Ave Ste 5, New York, NY
10017
Tel.: (212) 354-6500
Web Site: https://www.interlinksweep.com
Software Development Services
N.A.I.C.S.: 541511

Webster Bank, N.A. **(1)**
145 Bank St, Waterbury, CT
06702 **(100%)**
Tel.: (203) 328-8110
Web Site: https://careers.websteronline.com
Federal Saving Bank Services
N.A.I.C.S.: 522180
Karen A. Higgins-Carter *(CIO & Exec VP)*
William Holland *(Exec VP-Fin)*
Harriet Munrett Wolfe *(Gen Counsel, Sec &
Exec VP)*
Glenn I. MacInnes *(CFO & Exec VP)*
Jack L. Kopnisky *(Exec Chm)*
Luis Massiani *(COO & Sr Exec VP)*
Christopher J. Motl *(Pres-Commercial Bank-
ing & Sr Exec VP)*
Kristy Berner *(Gen Counsel, Sec & Exec
VP)*
John L. Guy Jr. *(Exec VP & Dir-Bus Bank-
ing)*
John R. Ciulla *(CEO)*
Timothy D. Bergstrom *(Pres-Hartford)*
Jeffrey A. Klaus *(Pres-Connecticut)*
Michael Liam O'Connor *(Reg Pres)*
Abby E. Parsonnet *(Pres-Metro New York
City)*
Scott C. Meves *(Pres-Pennsylvania)*
Christopher J. Motl *(Exec VP & Head-
Commercial Banking)*
Debra Drapalla *(Pres-Boston)*
Alice Ferreira *(Exec VP-Tech Res, Transfor-
mation & Data Governance)*
Elzbieta Cieslik *(Exec VP)*
Douglas E. Scala *(Pres-Southern Massa-
chusetts & Rhode Island)*
Alice Spinella *(Exec VP-Consumer Restruc-
turing & Recovery)*
Jason Soto *(Chief Credit Officer & Exec
VP)*
Sam Hanna *(Exec VP & Head-Middle-
Market Banking)*
Nick Weaver *(Sr VP & Reg Mgr-Middle-
Market Banking)*
Luis Massiani *(COO & Exec VP)*
William E. Wrang III *(Exec VP-Comml Real
Estate)*

Subsidiary (Domestic):

Ametros Financial Corporation **(2)**
PO Box 827, Burlington, MA 01803
Web Site: http://www.ametros.com
Sales Range: $1-9.9 Million
Emp.: 89
Health Insurance Services
N.A.I.C.S.: 524210
Marques Torbert *(CEO)*
Porter Leslie *(Pres)*
Amanda Gilbert *(VP-People Ops)*
Elizabeth Trask *(Mgr-Special Programs)*
Chris Lagnese *(VP-Pharmacy & Managed
Care)*
Jayson Gallant *(VP-Strategic Partnerships)*
Mike Crowe *(Chief Dev Officer)*

Aspen Place, Inc. **(2)**
826 Terrace Lake Dr, Aurora, IL 60504
Tel.: (630) 812-0885
Web Site: http://www.aspenplaceapts.com
Residential Building Leasing Services
N.A.I.C.S.: 531110

Ironwood Court, Inc. **(2)**
1501 George Williams Way, Lawrence, KS
66047
Tel.: (785) 268-2688
Web Site: https://www.ironwood-court.com
Residential Building Leasing Services
N.A.I.C.S.: 531110

Webster Business Credit
Corporation **(2)**
360 Lexington Ave 5th Fl, New York, NY
10017
Tel.: (212) 806-4500
Web Site: http://www.websterbank.com
Mortgage Banker
N.A.I.C.S.: 522310
Warren K. Mino *(Pres & COO)*
Mitchell Meth *(Sr VP)*
Angie DeGore *(Sr VP & Mgr-Natl Sls)*
Jeffrey Bender *(VP)*
Loren Tosi-Bassi *(Officer-Direct Mktg)*
Louise Montville *(Officer-Direct Mktg)*

Webster Capital Finance, Inc. **(2)**
344 Main St, Farmington, CT
06032 **(100%)**
Tel.: (860) 409-2900
Web Site:
http://www.webstercapitalfinance.com
Sales Range: $10-24.9 Million
Emp.: 90
Equipment Financing Services
N.A.I.C.S.: 561499

Division (Domestic):

Center Capital General Aviation
Division **(3)**
2003 Alga Rd, Carlsbad, CA 92009
Tel.: (760) 602-9767
Equipment Financing Services
N.A.I.C.S.: 561499

Subsidiary (Domestic):

Webster Mortgage Company **(2)**
174 Wolf Harbor Rd, Milford, CT 06461
Tel.: (203) 882-9991
Financial Investment Brokerage Services
N.A.I.C.S.: 523999

Webster Mortgage Investment
Corporation **(2)**
145 Bank St, Waterbury, CT 06702
Tel.: (203) 578-2230
Financial Investment Brokerage Services
N.A.I.C.S.: 523999

Webster Preferred Capital
Corporation **(2)**
145 Bank St, Waterbury, CT 06702
Tel.: (203) 578-2286
Sales Range: $1-9.9 Million
Emp.: 5
Real Estate Investment Trust
N.A.I.C.S.: 525990

Webster Wealth Advisors, Inc. **(1)**
200 Elm St 3rd Fl, Stamford, CT
06902 **(100%)**
Tel.: (203) 328-8165
Web Site:
https://www.websterwealthadvisors.com
Financial Planning & Wealth Management
Services

Webster Financial Corporation—(Continued)

N.A.I.C.S.: 523940

WEC ENERGY GROUP, INC.
231 W Michigan St, Milwaukee, WI 53203
Tel.: (414) 221-2345　　　WI
Web Site:
　https://www.wecenergygroup.com
Year Founded: 1987
WEC—(NYSE)
Rev.: $8,893,000,000
Assets: $43,939,700,000
Liabilities: $32,215,500,000
Net Worth: $11,724,200,000
Earnings: $1,331,700,000
Emp.: 7,000
Fiscal Year-end: 12/31/23
Holding Company; Electricity & Natural Gas Utilities Owner & Operator
N.A.I.C.S.: 551112
Scott J. Lauber *(Pres & CEO)*
William J. Guc *(Chief Acctg Officer, VP & Controller)*
James A. Schubilske *(Chief Audit Officer & VP)*
Robert M. Garvin *(Exec VP-External Affairs)*
Mary Beth Straka *(Sr VP-Corp Comm & IR)*
Anthony L. Reese *(Treas & VP)*
Paul Spicer *(Sr VP-Power Generation)*
John Zaganczyk *(Sr VP-Customer Svcs)*
Xia Liu *(CFO & Exec VP)*
Andy Hesselbach *(Sr VP)*
Torrence Hinton *(Pres)*
William Mastoris *(Exec VP)*
Molly Mulroy *(Chief Admin Officer)*
Joshua M. Erickson *(Deputy Gen Counsel)*
Margaret C. Kelsey *(Gen Counsel, Sec & Exec VP)*

Subsidiaries:

Integrys Holding, Inc.　　　　　(1)
200 E Randolph St, Chicago, IL 60601　　　　　　　　　　(100%)
Tel.: (312) 228-5400
Sales Range: $1-4.9 Billion
Emp.: 4,472
Holding Company; Electric Power Generation & Distribution Services
N.A.I.C.S.: 551112
Allen Lewis Leverett *(Pres & CEO)*

Subsidiary (Domestic):

Michigan Gas Utilities
Corporation　　　　　　　　　(2)
PO Box 19001, Green Bay, WI 54307-9001　　　　　　　(100%)
Web Site:
　https://www.michigangasutilities.com
Natural Gas Distr
N.A.I.C.S.: 221210
Scott J. Lauber *(Pres)*

Minnesota Energy Resources
Corporation　　　　　　　　　(2)
PO Box 19001, Green Bay, WI 54307-9001　　　　　　　(100%)
Web Site: https://www.minnesotaenergyresources.com
Emp.: 35
Natural Gas Distr
N.A.I.C.S.: 221210
Scott J. Lauber *(Pres)*

North Shore Gas Company　　(2)
200 E Randolph St, Chicago, IL 60601-6302　　　　　　(100%)
Tel.: (312) 240-4000
Web Site:
　https://www.northshoregasdelivery.com
Natural Gas Transportation Services
N.A.I.C.S.: 486990

Peoples Energy, LLC　　　　　(2)
200 E Randolph, Chicago, IL 60601
Tel.: (312) 240-4000

Emp.: 2,223
Eletric Power Generation Services
N.A.I.C.S.: 221112

The Peoples Gas Light and Coke
Company　　　　　　　　　　(2)
200 E Randolph St, Chicago, IL 60601-6302　　　　　　(100%)
Tel.: (312) 240-4000
Web Site:
　https://www.peoplesgasdelivery.com
Natural Gas Distr
N.A.I.C.S.: 221210

Wisconsin Public Service
Corporation　　　　　　　　　(2)
2830 S Ashland Ave, Green Bay, WI 54307-9001　　　　　(100%)
Web Site: https://www.wecenergygroup.com
Rev.: $1,785,200,000
Assets: $6,708,800,000
Liabilities: $4,325,500,000
Net Worth: $2,383,300,000
Earnings: $235,000,000
Emp.: 1,136
Fiscal Year-end: 12/31/2022
Electricity & Gas Distr
N.A.I.C.S.: 221122
Joseph Kevin Fletcher *(Chm & CEO)*
Scott J. Lauber *(Pres)*
William J. Guc *(Chief Acctg Officer, VP, Controller & Asst Sec)*
Michael W. Hooper *(Pres)*
Xia Liu *(CFO & Exec VP)*

Joint Venture (Domestic):

Wisconsin River Power
Company　　　　　　　　　　(3)
PO Box 325, Necedah, WI 54646
Tel.: (608) 565-7961
Web Site:
　http://www.wisconsinriverpower.com
Emp.: 10
Electronic Services
N.A.I.C.S.: 221118

Affiliate (Domestic):

Wisconsin Valley Improvement
Company　　　　　　　　　(3)(27.1%)
2301 N 3rd St, Wausau, WI 54403
Tel.: (715) 848-2976
Web Site: http://www.wvic.com
Emp.: 30
Natural Gas Distr
N.A.I.C.S.: 221210

WFC Business Services LLC　(1)
200 E Randolph St Ste 2200, Chicago, IL 60601
Tel.: (312) 240-0737
Business Consulting Services
N.A.I.C.S.: 541618

WEC Investments, LLC　　　(1)
19700 One Norman Blvd, Cornelius, NC 28031
Tel.: (704) 892-4800
Eletric Power Generation Services
N.A.I.C.S.: 221112

Wisconsin Electric Power
Company　　　　　　　　　(1)
231 W Michigan St, Milwaukee, WI 53201　　　　　　　(100%)
Tel.: (414) 221-2345
Web Site: https://www.wecenergygroup.com
Rev.: $4,070,300,000
Assets: $15,020,200,000
Liabilities: $10,883,400,000
Net Worth: $4,136,800,000
Earnings: $397,900,000
Emp.: 2,451
Fiscal Year-end: 12/31/2022
Electric Power Generation & Distribution Services
N.A.I.C.S.: 221122
Joseph Kevin Fletcher *(Chm & CEO)*
Scott J. Lauber *(Chm & Pres)*
William J. Guc *(Chief Acctg Officer, VP, Asst Sec & Controller)*
Robert M. Garvin *(Exec VP-External Affairs)*
Scott J. Lauber *(Exec VP)*
Tom Metcalfe *(Pres)*
Margaret C. Kelsey *(Gen Counsel, Sec & Exec VP)*
Anthony L. Reese *(Treas & VP)*
Xia Liu *(CFO & Exec VP)*

Wisconsin Gas LLC　　　　　(1)
231 W Michigan St, Milwaukee, WI 53201　　　　　　　(100%)
Tel.: (262) 574-6453
Web Site: https://www.we-energies.com
Natural Gas Distr
N.A.I.C.S.: 221210

Wispark LLC　　　　　　　　(1)
231 W Michigan St P423, Milwaukee, WI 53203-2918　　　　　(100%)
Tel.: (414) 221-5500
Web Site: https://www.wispark.com
Sales Range: $1-9.9 Million
Emp.: 3
Real Estate Investment & Development
N.A.I.C.S.: 237210

Subsidiary (Domestic):

2825 Four Mile Road LLC　　(2)
2825 4 Mile Rd, Racine, WI 53404
Tel.: (414) 274-4603
Commercial Building Construction Services
N.A.I.C.S.: 236220

Wisvest LLC　　　　　　　　(1)
PO Box 1331, Milwaukee, WI 53203　　　　　　　　　(100%)
Tel.: (414) 221-2345
Web Site: https://www.we-energies.com
Sales Range: $75-99.9 Million
Earnings: $24,090
Energy Plant Investment Services
N.A.I.C.S.: 523999

WEDOTALK INC.
3445 Lawrence Ave, Oceanside, NY 11572
Tel.: (310) 734-2626　　　NV
Year Founded: 2007
SHNL—(OTCIQ)
Liabilities: $112,116
Net Worth: ($112,116)
Earnings: ($75,990)
Fiscal Year-end: 12/31/21
Holding Company
N.A.I.C.S.: 551112

WEE-CIG INTERNATIONAL CORP
9620 S Las Vegas Blvd Ste E 1041, Las Vegas, NV 89123　　　NV
Web Site: https://weecigcorp.com
Year Founded: 1999
WCIG—(OTCIQ)
Assets: $258,000
Liabilities: $636,000
Net Worth: ($378,000)
Earnings: ($127,000)
Emp.: 2
Fiscal Year-end: 12/31/19
Electronic Cigarette Mfr & Distr
N.A.I.C.S.: 312230
Russell Korus *(Pres & CEO)*
Efraim Babayov *(CFO, Treas & Sec)*

WEED GROWTH FUND, INC.
PO Box 1602, Mesquite, NV 89024
Tel.: (407) 923-0827　　　NV
Year Founded: 2012
WEDG—(OTCIQ)
Investment Management Service
N.A.I.C.S.: 525990
John Lee *(Pres)*
Cathy Carroll *(Sec)*

WEED, INC.
1 S Church Ave, Tucson, AZ 85701
Tel.: (520) 818-8582　　　NV
Web Site: https://weedincusa.com
Year Founded: 1999
BUDZ—(OTCQB)
Emp.: 3
Offices of Other Holding Companies
N.A.I.C.S.: 551112

WEIS MARKETS, INC.
1000 S 2nd St, Sunbury, PA 17801-0471
Tel.: (570) 286-4571　　　PA

Web Site:
　https://www.weismarkets.com
Year Founded: 1912
WMK—(NYSE)
Rev.: $4,224,417,000
Assets: $1,910,475,000
Liabilities: $690,733,000
Net Worth: $1,219,742,000
Earnings: $108,849,000
Emp.: 24,000
Fiscal Year-end: 12/25/21
Supermarket Operator
N.A.I.C.S.: 445110
Michael T. Lockard *(CFO, Treas & Sr VP)*
Jonathan H. Weis *(Chm, Pres & CEO)*
John F. O'Hara *(Sr VP-Legal Affairs & Real Estate & Asst Sec)*
Jeanette R. Rogers *(VP & Controller)*
Robert G. Gleeson *(Sr VP-Merchandising & Marketing)*
Kurt A. Schertle *(COO)*
James E. Marcil *(Sr VP-HR)*
David W. Gose II *(Sr VP-Ops)*
Richard G. Zeh Jr. *(CIO & Sr VP)*

Subsidiaries:

Dutch Valley Food Company,
Inc.　　　　　　　　　　　　(1)
1000 S 2nd St, Sunbury, PA 17801　　　　　　　　　　(100%)
Tel.: (570) 286-4571
Web Site: http://www.weismarkets.com
Retailer of Groceries
N.A.I.C.S.: 311511

Martin's Farm Market, Inc.　　(1)
744 S Rte 183, Schuylkill Haven, PA 17972　　　　　　　(100%)
Tel.: (570) 739-2600
Web Site:
　http://www.martinsfarmmarket.com
Sales Range: $1-4.9 Billion
Retailer of Groceries
N.A.I.C.S.: 445110

SuperPetz, LLC　　　　　　　(1)
2880 Bergey Rd Ste A, Hatfield, PA 19440　　　　　　　(100%)
Tel.: (215) 712-9950
Sales Range: $150-199.9 Million
Pet Supply Stores
N.A.I.C.S.: 459910
Brad Phillips *(Pres & CEO)*

WELLNESS CENTER USA, INC.
145 E University Blvd, Tucson, AZ 85705
Tel.: (847) 925-1885　　　NV
Web Site:
　https://www.wellnesscenterusa.com
Year Founded: 2010
WCUI—(OTCQB)
Rev.: $239,962
Assets: $82,079
Liabilities: $3,428,427
Net Worth: ($3,346,348)
Earnings: ($806,265)
Emp.: 8
Fiscal Year-end: 12/31/21
Sports Supplement & Nutrition Online Retailer
N.A.I.C.S.: 456191
Thomas E. Scott *(Sec)*
Paul D. Jones *(Pres)*
Roy M. Harsch *(Chm)*
Calvin R. O'Harrow *(CEO & COO)*
Douglas W. Samuelson *(CFO & Chief Acctg Officer)*

Subsidiaries:

National Pain Centers, Inc.　　(1)
1585 Barrington Rd Doctors Office Bldg 2 Ste 103, Hoffman Estates, IL 60169
Tel.: (847) 701-3250
Web Site: http://www.nationalpain.com
Health Care Srvices
N.A.I.C.S.: 622110

Stealthco, Inc. (1)
6845 20th Ave Ste 130, Hugo, MN 55038
Tel.: (651) 765-9560
Web Site: http://www.stealthmark.com
Healthcare Support Services
N.A.I.C.S.: 621498
Rick Howard (Pres & CEO)

WELLQUEST MEDICAL & WELLNESS CORPORATION

3400 SE Macy Rd Ste 18, Benton-
ville, AR 72712
Tel.: (479) 845-0880 OK
Web Site:
https://wellquestmedical.com
WEQL—(OTCIQ)
Sales Range: $1-9.9 Million
Emp.: 43
Medical Spa, Skincare & Nutraceuti-
cal Product Store Owner & Operator;
Medical Practice Management Ser-
vices
N.A.I.C.S.: 812112
Stephen H. M. Swift (Co-Founder,
Chm & Pres)
Curtis L. Rice (Co-Founder & VP)

WELLS FARGO & COMPANY

420 Montgomery St, San Francisco,
CA 94104
Tel.: (415) 396-4000 DE
Web Site: https://www.wellsfargo.com
Year Founded: 1852
WFC—(NYSE)
Rev.: $115,340,000,000
Assets: $1,932,468,000,000
Liabilities: $1,745,025,000,000
Net Worth: $187,443,000,000
Earnings: $17,982,000,000
Emp.: 226,000
Fiscal Year-end: 12/31/23
Bank & Financial Holding Company;
Commercial Banking, Consumer
Lending, Insurance & Other Financial
Services
N.A.I.C.S.: 551111
Charles W. Scharf (Pres & CEO)
Kyle Hranicky (CEO-Comml Banking
& Sr Exec VP)
Jonathan G. Weiss (CEO-Corp & In-
vestment Banking & Sr Exec VP)
Tracy Kerrins (Sr Exec VP & Head-
Tech)
Saul Van Beurden (CEO-Consumer &
Small Bus Banking & Sr Exec VP)
William M. Daley (Vice Chm-Pub Af-
fairs)
Muneera S. Carr (Chief Acctg Officer,
Exec VP & Controller)
Ellen R. Patterson (Gen Counsel &
Sr Exec VP)
Barry Sommers (CEO-Wealth & In-
vestment Mgmt & Sr Exec VP)
Kleber R. Santos (CEO-Consumer
Lending & Head-Diverse Segments &
Representation&Inclusion)
Kristy Fercho (Sr Exec VP)
Bei Ling (Sr Exec VP)
Ather Williams III (Sr Exec VP &
Head-Strategy, Digital & Innovation)

Subsidiaries:

ATC Realty One, LLC (1)
1203 Town Ctr Dr Ste 117, Jupiter, FL
33458
Tel.: (561) 694-6055
Real Estate Development Services
N.A.I.C.S.: 531390

ATC Realty Sixteen, Inc. (1)
333 Market St, San Francisco, CA 94105
Tel.: (415) 801-8700
Management Consulting Services
N.A.I.C.S.: 541611

**Adirondack Rock Creek Emerging
Markets Fund, LP** (1)
1133 Connecticut Ave NW Ste 810, Washington, DC 20036

Tel.: (202) 331-3400
Investment Management Service
N.A.I.C.S.: 523940

**Advanced Collateral Solutions,
LLC** (1)
8009 34th Ave S Ste 1000, Bloomington,
MN 55425
Tel.: (952) 345-9361
Real Estate Appraisal Services
N.A.I.C.S.: 531320

Alternative Strategies Group, Inc. (1)
196 E 6th St Ste 102, Sioux Falls, SD
57104
Tel.: (605) 275-1011
Web Site: https://www.investasg.biz
Financial Advising Service
N.A.I.C.S.: 523940

Analytic Investors, LLC (1)
555 W 5th St 50th Fl, Los Angeles, CA
90013
Tel.: (212) 207-9451
Investment Management Service
N.A.I.C.S.: 523940

**Bryan, Pendleton, Swats & McAllister,
LLC** (1)
11807 Brinley Ave, Louisville, KY 40243
Tel.: (502) 244-7828
Actuarial Consulting Services
N.A.I.C.S.: 541612

**Business Development Corporation of
South Carolina** (1)
111 Executive Ctr Dr Enoree Bldg Ste 225,
Columbia, SC 29210
Tel.: (803) 798-4064
Web Site:
https://www.businessdevelopment.org
Emp.: 12
Commercial Lending Services
N.A.I.C.S.: 522291
Edwin O. Lesley (Chm)
Stephanie Bell (Sr VP & Controller)
Jessica Preheim (Asst VP)
Brian Hofferth (Sr VP)
Peter G. Shand (Pres & CEO)
Ron Derrick (Sr VP)
Rob Evans (Officer-SBA Lending & Sr VP)
Nat Green (Officer-SSBCI Lending & Sr VP)
Ron Paull (Officer & Sr VP)
Ted Crosson (Officer & VP)
Scott Smith (VP)
Julie Mele (VP)
Shannon Cross (Asst Sec & Asst VP)
Sam Cartin (VP)

Cardinal Finance LLC (1)
444 Jacksonville Rd, Warminster, PA 18974
Tel.: (215) 293-6800
Web Site: http://www.cardinalfinancial.com
Mortgage & Nonmortgage Loan Services
N.A.I.C.S.: 522310
John Madeira (Officer-Loan)

Centurion Funding, Inc. (1)
162 E Main St, Avon, MA 02322
Tel.: (508) 584-9271
Emp.: 45
Commercial Banking Services
N.A.I.C.S.: 522110
Robert Dell (Gen Mgr)

ClearLend (1)
51 JFK Pkwy 3rd Fl, Short Hills, NJ 07078
Tel.: (973) 921-5000
Securities Distribution & Collateral Manage-
ment Services
N.A.I.C.S.: 523150

Branch (Domestic):

ClearLend - West Coast (2)
1800 Century Park E 13th Fl, Los Angeles,
CA 90067
Tel.: (310) 789-3790
Rev.: $20,000,000
Emp.: 65
Securities Distribution & Collateral Manage-
ment Services
N.A.I.C.S.: 523150

Consortium America II, LLC (1)
3299 K St NW Ste 700, Washington, DC
20007
Tel.: (202) 333-9000
Web Site:
http://www.thebernsteincompanies.com

Emp.: 50
Real Estate Development Services
N.A.I.C.S.: 531390
Adam K. Berstein (Pres & CEO)
Marc Duber (COO & Exec VP)
Joe Galli (Exec VP)
John Chanaud (CFO & VP)
Yafei Liu (Controller)
Davin Driskill (Sr VP-Hospital Div)
Anoop Dave (Sr VP-Investments)
Gary Griffin (Sr VP-Portfolio Mgmt)
Stefan Kershow (Exec Dir-Structured Fin)
Jason Norris (Mng Dir-Structured Fin)
Greg Rooney (VP-Development)
Dawn Ryan (VP-Fin Admin)
Dave Thackston (VP-Construction)

**Dorchester Capital Partners ASP
Fund, a series of Alternative Strate-
gies Platform, LLC** (1)
401 S Tryon St Th3, Charlotte, NC 28288
Tel.: (704) 383-6369
Financial Services
N.A.I.C.S.: 523940

ECM Asset Management Limited (1)
Bow Bells House 1 Bread Street, London,
EC4M 9BE, United Kingdom
Tel.: (44) 2075297400
Web Site: http://www.europeancredit.com
Asset Management Services
N.A.I.C.S.: 531390

Early Warning Services, LLC (1)
16552 N 90th St, Scottsdale, AZ 85260
Tel.: (480) 483-4610
Web Site: https://www.earlywarning.com
Risk Managemeng Srvices
N.A.I.C.S.: 541618

Subsidiary (Domestic):

Authentify, Inc. (2)
8745 W Higgins Rd Ste 240, Chicago, IL
60631-4020
Tel.: (773) 243-0328
Web Site: http://www.authentify.com
Automated Authentication Services
N.A.I.C.S.: 541511

Joint Venture (Domestic):

clearXchange, LLC (2)
333 Market St 26th Fl, San Francisco, CA
94105
Tel.: (415) 371-4111
Financial Management Services
N.A.I.C.S.: 541611
Michael J. Kennedy (Founder)
Michael Kennedy (CEO)

Eaton Mortgage, LLC (1)
1190 Dillerville Rd, Lancaster, PA 17601
Tel.: (717) 945-1813
Real Estate Credit Services
N.A.I.C.S.: 522292

Enfinity WF Solar Trust I (1)
733 Marquette Ave Ste 700, Minneapolis,
MN 55402
Tel.: (612) 667-9876
Financial Services
N.A.I.C.S.: 523940

Equity Insurance Agency, Inc. (1)
313 S Main St, Lombard, IL 60148
Tel.: (630) 627-7764
Web Site: https://www.equityinsurance.net
Commercial Banking Services
N.A.I.C.S.: 522110

EverKey Global Fund, L.P. (1)
150 E 42nd St 40th Fl, New York, NY
10174
Tel.: (917) 260-1601
Financial Management Services
N.A.I.C.S.: 541611

FNL Insurance Company (1)
3600 S 48th St, Lincoln, NE 68506
Tel.: (402) 483-1776
Insurance Services
N.A.I.C.S.: 524127

FNL Insurance Company, Ltd (1)
201 Merchant St Ste 2400, Honolulu, HI
96813
Tel.: (808) 533-4900
Emp.: 2
General Insurance Services
N.A.I.C.S.: 524210

First Security Capital I (1)
79 S Main St Ste 100, Salt Lake City, UT
84111
Tel.: (801) 238-5060
Emp.: 100
Financial Security Brokerage Services
N.A.I.C.S.: 523999

First Union Capital II (1)
301 S College St, Charlotte, NC 28288-
0630
Tel.: (704) 374-6611
Commercial Banking Services
N.A.I.C.S.: 522110

**Flagstone Apartment Property,
LLC** (1)
30 W Carter Dr, Tempe, AZ 85282
Tel.: (480) 820-0188
Web Site:
http://www.flagstoneapartmenthomes.com
Sales Range: $25-49.9 Million
Emp.: 4
Residential Building Services
N.A.I.C.S.: 531110

Forum Capital Markets, LLC (1)
53 Forest Ave, Old Greenwich, CT 06870
Tel.: (203) 637-1110
Investment Advisory Services
N.A.I.C.S.: 523940

Fullerton Towers Holdings, LLC (1)
1400 N Harbor Blvd Ste 106, Fullerton, CA
92835
Tel.: (714) 449-8400
Web Site: http://www.fullertontowers.com
Holding Company
N.A.I.C.S.: 551112

**Galliard Capital Management,
Inc.** (1)
800 LaSalle Ave Ste 1400, Minneapolis, MN
55402-2054 (100%)
Tel.: (612) 667-3220
Web Site: https://www.galliard.com
Sales Range: $1-9.9 Million
Emp.: 100
Money Capital Management
N.A.I.C.S.: 525910
Richard Merriam (Mng Partner)
Karl Tourville (Mng Partner)
Carrie Callahan (Mng Partner)
Michael Norman (Pres)
Ajay Mirza (Mng Partner)
Chad Foote (COO)
Matthew Bentley (Principal)
Rene Hoogmoed (Sr Principal)
Andrea Johnson (Sr Principal)
Leela Scattum (Partner)
David Lui (Principal)
Nick Gage (Sr Principal)
Laura Sell (Deputy Head & Principal)
Paula Novick (Principal)
Jennifer Lammers (Chief Compliance Offi-
cer)

General Homes Corp. (1)
14800 Quorum Dr Ste 370, Dallas, TX
75240-7513
Tel.: (972) 392-9200
Property Management Services
N.A.I.C.S.: 531390

**Golden Capital Management,
LLC** (1)
10715 David Taylor Dr Ste 400, Charlotte,
NC 28262
Tel.: (704) 593-1144
Web Site: http://www.gcm1.com
Sales Range: $25-49.9 Million
Emp.: 21
Investment Advice Services
N.A.I.C.S.: 523940
Lynette Alexander (Mng Dir & CFO)

HomeSale Lending, LLC (1)
215 S Centerville Rd, Lancaster, PA 17603
Tel.: (717) 286-9936
Web Site: http://www.homesalelending.com
Mortgage Services
N.A.I.C.S.: 522310

Homeservices Lending, LLC (1)
2900 100th St Ste 109, Urbandale, IA
50322
Tel.: (402) 441-3200
Web Site:
https://www.homeserviceslending.com
Commercial Banking Services

Wells Fargo & Company—(Continued)

N.A.I.C.S.: 522110
Amy McDonald *(Mgr-Kansas City)*
Harris Laskey *(VP)*
Trevor Reinhart *(VP-Finance)*
Jim Renaldo *(Corp Counsel)*
Tyler Johnson *(VP-Operations)*
Jason Froehlich *(Pres)*

MSC Mortgage (1)
1801 Main St, Sarasota, FL 34236 **(100%)**
Tel.: (941) 951-6660
Web Site: http://www.mscmortgage.com
Sales Range: $25-49.9 Million
Emp.: 50
Mortgage & Securities Services
N.A.I.C.S.: 522310

MVP Distribution Partners (1)
259 Radnor-Chester Rd, Radnor, PA 19087
Tel.: (610) 254-2999
Web Site: http://www.mvpcape.com
Investment Management Service
N.A.I.C.S.: 523940

Military Family Home Loans, LLC (1)
1776 W Lakes Pkwy Ste 200, West Des Moines, IA 50266
Tel.: (515) 518-8808
Web Site: http://www.militaryfamilyloan.com
Mortgage Home Loan Brokerage Services
N.A.I.C.S.: 522310

Nelson Capital Management, LLC (1)
545 Middlefield Rd Ste 200, Menlo Park, CA 94025
Tel.: (650) 322-4000
Web Site: https://www.nelsoncap.com
Emp.: 20
Investment Management Service
N.A.I.C.S.: 523940
Blaine Townsend *(Co-Partner & Sr Portfolio Mgr)*

Norwest Center, Inc. (1)
90 S 7th St 2nd Fl, Minneapolis, MN 55402
Tel.: (612) 667-0654
Consumer Lending Services
N.A.I.C.S.: 522291

Norwest Equity Partners IX, LP (1)
80 S 8th St Ste 3600, Minneapolis, MN 55402
Tel.: (612) 215-1600
Web Site: http://www.nep.com
Equity Investment Services
N.A.I.C.S.: 523999
Brian Allingham *(Partner & COO)*
Tony Armand *(Partner)*
Jared Brown *(Principal)*
Tim DeVries *(Mng Partner)*
Adam Garcia Eveloff *(Mng Dir)*
John Brownschidle *(VP)*
Eric Frueh *(VP)*
Danny Fox *(VP)*
Mike Gerend *(Operating Partner)*
John Hale *(Operating Partner)*
Tim Kuehl *(Partner)*
Beth Lesniak *(Mng Dir)*
Chuck Moorse *(Gen Counsel)*
Sundip Murthy *(Partner)*
Sam Seehof *(VP)*
Todd Solow *(Partner)*
Jason Sondell *(Mng Dir)*
Jason Tanker *(Principal)*
Mark Thom *(Operating Partner)*
Adam Verhasselt *(VP)*
John Brownschidle *(VP)*
Eric Frueh *(VP)*
Danny Fox *(VP)*
Mike Gerend *(Operating Partner)*
John Hale *(Operating Partner)*
Tim Kuehl *(Partner)*
Beth Lesniak *(Mng Dir)*
Chuck Moorse *(Gen Counsel)*
Sundip Murthy *(Partner)*
Sam Seehof *(VP)*
Todd Solow *(Partner)*
Jason Sondell *(Mng Dir)*
Jason Tanker *(Principal)*
Mark Thom *(Operating Partner)*
Adam Verhasselt *(VP)*

Norwest Venture Capital Management, Inc. (1)
80 S 8th St Ste 3600, Minneapolis, MN 55402

Tel.: (612) 215-1600
Web Site: http://www.nep.com
Privater Equity Firm
N.A.I.C.S.: 523999
Timothy DeVries *(Mng Partner)*
Adam Garcia Eveloff *(Mng Dir)*
John Brownschidle *(VP)*
Eric Frueh *(VP)*
Danny Fox *(VP)*
Mike Gerend *(Operating Partner)*
John Hale *(Operating Partner)*
Jason Tanker *(Principal)*
Mark Thom *(Operating Partner)*
Adam Verhasselt *(VP)*
John Brownschidle *(VP)*
Eric Frueh *(VP)*
Danny Fox *(VP)*
Mike Gerend *(Operating Partner)*
John Hale *(Operating Partner)*
Jason Tanker *(Principal)*
Mark Thom *(Operating Partner)*
Adam Verhasselt *(VP)*

Subsidiary (Domestic):

Apothecary Holdco, LLC (2)
11750 12th Ave S, Burnsville, MN 55337
Tel.: (952) 890-1940
Financial Services
N.A.I.C.S.: 523940

Subsidiary (Domestic):

Apothecary Products, LLC (3)
11750 12th Ave S, Burnsville, MN 55337
Tel.: (952) 890-1940
Web Site:
  https://www.apothecaryproducts.com
Sales Range: $25-49.9 Million
Emp.: 150
Consumer Healthcare Products & Pharmacy Supplies Mfr, Marketer & Distr
N.A.I.C.S.: 325412
Terry Noble *(Co-Founder)*
Ron Olson *(Co-Founder)*

Holding (Domestic):

Coretelligent LLC (2)
34 SW Park, Westwood, MA 02090
Tel.: (781) 247-4900
Web Site: http://www.coretelligent.com
Sales Range: $1-9.9 Million
Emp.: 16
Information Technology Services
N.A.I.C.S.: 541512
Kevin J. Routhier *(Pres & CEO)*
Jason Rossi *(Sr VP-Bus Dev)*
Christopher Messer *(CTO)*
Christine McMurray *(CFO & Exec VP)*
Timothy Keshian *(COO)*
Jason Baron *(Sr VP)*
Michael Cestroni *(VP-Business Development)*
Lesley Sullivan *(VP-Marketing-Communications)*
Brian Fraser *(VP)*
Rachel Gordon *(Dir-Human Resources)*
Janet Desaulniers *(Dir-Procurement)*
George Kostakos *(COO & Gen Counsel)*
Brian Miller *(Sr VP-Business Development-Southern Region)*
Eric Dykes *(Sr VP-Southern Region)*
Alexandra Newman *(Dir-Marketing)*
Guido Timmerman *(Chief Revenue Officer)*
Anne Clark *(Sr VP & Gen Counsel)*
Brian Demlein *(Sr VP-Customer Success-Northeast Reg)*
Scott Camara *(VP)*
Sean Murphy *(VP)*
Adam Noyes *(Dir)*
William McGee *(VP-Customer Success)*
Michael Joseph *(Dir-Procurement)*

Subsidiary (Domestic):

Advanced Network Products, Inc. (3)
5217 Militia Hill Rd, Plymouth Meeting, PA 19462
Tel.: (215) 572-0111
Web Site: http://www.anp.net
Sales Range: $1-9.9 Million
Emp.: 20
Electronic Parts & Equipment Whslr
N.A.I.C.S.: 423690
David S. Mulvey *(CEO)*

Chateaux Software Development (3)
50 Riverside Ave, Westport, CT 06880

Tel.: (203) 222-7118
Web Site: http://www.chatsoft.com
Custom Computer Programming Services
N.A.I.C.S.: 541511
Hugo Toledo *(Co-Founder & CTO)*

United Technology Group, LLC (3)
3090 Premiere Pkwy #300, Duluth, GA 30097
Tel.: (678) 730-0345
Web Site: http://www.utgsolutions.com
Managed Services IT Firm
N.A.I.C.S.: 519290
Michael Verner *(COO)*
Sharon Harding *(Chm)*

Holding (Domestic):

Marco Technologies, LLC (2)
4510 Heatherwood Rd, Saint Cloud, MN 56301
Tel.: (320) 259-3000
Web Site: http://www.marconet.com
Emp.: 1,064
Information Technology Services
N.A.I.C.S.: 541512
Jeff Gau *(Chm)*
Steve Knutson *(CTO)*
Patty Funk *(VP-Marketing)*
Doug Albregts *(CEO)*
Trevor Akervik *(CTO)*
Steve John *(Chief Svc Officer)*
James Bainbridge *(CFO)*
Clay Ostlund *(CTO)*
Mike Burgard *(Chief Information Security Officer)*
Jennifer Johnson *(Exec VP)*
Susan Yost *(VP-Human Resources)*
Tom Wells *(VP-Procurement)*
James Bainbridge *(CFO)*
Clay Ostlund *(CTO)*
Mike Burgard *(Chief Information Security Officer)*
Jennifer Johnson *(Exec VP)*
Susan Yost *(VP-Human Resources)*
Tom Wells *(VP-Procurement)*

Subsidiary (Domestic):

Executive Technologies, Inc. (3)
2000 Pierce St, Sioux City, IA 51104-3845
Tel.: (712) 277-8218
Office Equipment Whslr
N.A.I.C.S.: 423420

Phillips Office Solutions, Inc. (3)
501 Fulling Mill Rd, Middletown, PA 17057-2967
Tel.: (717) 944-0400
Web Site: http://www.buyphillips.com
Business Supplies & Equipment Provider;
Document Management Solutions & Workplace Interiors
N.A.I.C.S.: 423210
Richard Lauer *(VP-Sales-Marketing)*

Subsidiary (Domestic):

North Central Digital Systems, Inc. (4)
800 Continental Blvd, Danville, PA 17821
Tel.: (570) 275-4900
Printing Services
N.A.I.C.S.: 323120

Subsidiary (Domestic):

Norwest Mezzanine Partners (2)
80 S 8th St Ste 3600, Minneapolis, MN 55402
Tel.: (612) 215-1600
Web Site: https://www.nmp.com
Junior Capital Investments
N.A.I.C.S.: 523999
Carter Balfour *(Partner)*
John Hogan *(Partner)*
Shani Graber *(Principal)*
Sean Stevens *(Partner)*
Laura Hacker Dorsch *(Principal)*

Red Monkey Foods, Inc. (2)
6751 W Kings St, Springfield, MO 65802
Tel.: (417) 319-7300
Web Site: http://www.redmonkeyfoods.com
Herbs, Spices & Seasonings Mfr
N.A.I.C.S.: 311942
Jeff Brinkhoff *(Pres)*
Scott Bolonda *(CEO)*

Subsidiary (Domestic):

San Francisco Salt Company (3)

875-A Is Dr Ste 196, Alameda, CA 94502
Tel.: (510) 477-9600
Web Site: https://www.sfsalt.com
Salt Whslr
N.A.I.C.S.: 424490
Lee Williamson *(Pres & Founder)*

Subsidiary (Domestic):

Shock Doctor, Inc. (2)
110 Cheshire Ln Ste 120, Minnetonka, MN 55305
Web Site: http://www.shockdoctor.com
Sales Range: $75-99.9 Million
Sports Protective Equipment Mfr
N.A.I.C.S.: 339920

Subsidiary (Domestic):

McDavid, Inc. (3)
10305 Argonne Dr, Woodridge, IL 60517
Tel.: (630) 783-0600
Web Site: http://www.mcdavidusa.com
Footwear & Leather Goods Repair
N.A.I.C.S.: 811430

Unit (Domestic):

Nathan Sports (3)
11488 Slater Ave, Fountain Valley, CA 92708
Tel.: (952) 767-2300
Web Site: https://www.nathansports.com
Various Sports Apparel & Hydration Gear Mfr
N.A.I.C.S.: 315990

Subsidiary (Domestic):

Surgical Information Systems, LLC (2)
8000 Avalon Blvd Ste 350, Alpharetta, GA 30009
Tel.: (678) 507-1610
Web Site: https://www.sisfirst.com
Sales Range: $25-49.9 Million
Emp.: 200
Computer Software for Hospitals
N.A.I.C.S.: 513210
Douglas Rempfer *(COO)*
Jho Outlaw *(Sr VP)*
John Spiller *(CFO & Chief Admin Officer)*
Tom Stampiglia *(Pres & CEO)*
John Walker *(Sr VP-Hospital Sls & Ops)*
Emmy Weber *(CMO)*
Todd Logan *(Sr VP-Sls-ASC)*

Subsidiary (Domestic):

Source Medical Solutions, Inc. (3)
2613 S Main St, Maryville, MO 64468
Tel.: (660) 215-3024
Web Site: https://www.thesourcemedical.org
Sales Range: $10-24.9 Million
Emp.: 400
Computer Software Development
N.A.I.C.S.: 541511
James Coffin *(Pres & CEO)*
Kareem Saad *(Exec VP-Strategy-Business Development)*
Dennis Martineau *(Exec VP-Product Development)*
Jonathan Isaacs *(Exec VP & Gen Mgr)*
Matthew Phillips *(Sr VP-Business Development)*
Britt Denning *(VP)*
Kim Fieldbinder *(CFO, Chief Admin Officer & Exec VP)*
Selena Harrison *(Dir-Communications)*
Hank Cincere *(Exec VP-Operations)*
David McMullan *(VP & Gen Mgr)*

PIDC - Regional Development Corporation (1)
1500 Market St Ste 3500 W, Philadelphia, PA 19102
Tel.: (215) 496-8020
Web Site: https://www.pidcphila.com
Emp.: 60
Economic Development Services
N.A.I.C.S.: 926110
Anne Bovaird Nevins *(Pres)*
Tom Dalfo *(Sr VP-Real Estate Svcs)*
Sam Rhoads *(Exec VP & Sr VP-Financial Services)*
John Grady *(Pres & CEO)*
M. Walter D'Alessio *(Chm)*
Salvatore J. Patti *(Chm)*
Prema Katari Gupta *(Sr VP)*
Andrea R. Allon *(Vice Chm)*

Ilene Burak *(Sr VP & Gen Counsel)*
Jessica Calter *(VP-Marketing Communications)*
Tiffany Canady *(CFO & Sr VP)*
Christopher Chaplin *(VP)*
Jennifer Lucas Crowther *(VP)*
Angie Fredrickson *(VP)*
Marla S. Hamilton *(Sr VP)*
Heather Hanowitz *(Officer-Loan & VP)*
Nicole Hennessy *(VP & Controller)*
Lawrence McComie *(VP)*
Kate Mcnamara *(Sr VP)*
Shayne Moore *(VP-Information Technology)*
Anya Morrison Davis *(VP & Asst Gen Counsel)*
Peter Silow *(Dir)*
Sarah Stroney *(VP)*
Jennifer Tran *(Dir-Communications)*
Marquis Tavon Upshur *(VP-Human Resources)*
Ilene Burak *(Sr VP & Gen Counsel)*
Jessica Calter *(VP-Marketing Communications)*
Tiffany Canady *(CFO & Sr VP)*
Christopher Chaplin *(VP)*
Jennifer Lucas Crowther *(VP)*
Angie Fredrickson *(VP)*
Marla S. Hamilton *(Sr VP)*
Heather Hanowitz *(Officer-Loan & VP)*
Nicole Hennessy *(VP & Controller)*
Lawrence McComie *(VP)*
Kate Mcnamara *(Sr VP)*
Shayne Moore *(VP-Information Technology)*
Anya Morrison Davis *(VP & Asst Gen Counsel)*
Peter Silow *(Dir)*
Sarah Stroney *(VP)*
Jennifer Tran *(Dir-Communications)*
Marquis Tavon Upshur *(VP-Human Resources)*

Palo Alto Partners, LLC (1)
600 Waterfront Dr, Pittsburgh, PA 15222
Tel.: (412) 231-0983
Commercial Banking Services
N.A.I.C.S.: 522110

Paramount Theater SCP L.P. (1)
913 W Saint Germain St, Saint Cloud, MN 56301
Tel.: (320) 259-5463
Commercial Banking Services
N.A.I.C.S.: 522110

Parkland Senior Housing, LP (1)
40 Potosi St, Farmington, MO 63640-1760
Tel.: (573) 701-9596
Commercial Banking Services
N.A.I.C.S.: 522110

Peregrine Capital Management, Inc. (1)
800 LaSalle Ave Ste 1750, Minneapolis, MN 55402
Tel.: (612) 343-7600
Web Site: https://www.peregrine.com
Sales Range: $100-124.9 Million
Emp.: 30
Investment Management Services to Tax Exempt Institutional Clients
N.A.I.C.S.: 523940
Robert B. Mersky *(Principal)*
Stefanie M. Adams *(Principal & Dir-Client Svc & Mktg)*
Douglas G. Pugh *(Principal & Portfolio Mgr-Small Cap Value Style)*
Jason R. Ballsrud *(Principal & Portfolio Mgr-Small Cap Value Style)*
Paul E. Von Kuster *(Principal & Portfolio Mgr-Small Cap Growth Style)*
Paul R. Wurm *(Principal & Mgr-Equity Trading)*
Tasso Coin *(Principal & Portfolio Mgr-Small Cap Value Style)*
Brian Donohue *(Principal & Portfolio Mgr)*
Ryan Smith *(Principal & Assoc Portfolio Mgr-Small Cap Growth Style)*
Sam Smith *(Principal & Assoc Portfolio Mgr-Small Cap Growth Style)*
Hema Nealon *(CFO, COO & Principal)*

Preferred Motor Sports Risk Purchasing Group, LLC (1)
4300 Market Point Dr Ste 600, Bloomington, MN 55435-5455
Tel.: (202) 216-4814
Insurance Management Services
N.A.I.C.S.: 524298

Private Mortgage Advisors, LLC (1)

1071 Blossom Hill Rd, San Jose, CA 95123
Tel.: (408) 754-1610
Web Site: http://www.pmahomeloans.com
Real Estate Credit Services
N.A.I.C.S.: 522292

Prudence Crandall Fund III, LLC (1)
1133 Connecticut Ave NW, Washington, DC 20036
Tel.: (202) 331-3400
Web Site: http://www.therockcreekgroup.com
Emp.: 90
Financial Management Services
N.A.I.C.S.: 541611

REDUS Charlotte Housing, LLC (1)
301 S College St, Charlotte, NC 28202
Tel.: (704) 715-5282
Sales Range: $50-74.9 Million
Emp.: 80
Commercial Banking Services
N.A.I.C.S.: 522110

REDUS FL Properties, LLC (1)
14666 Aeries Way Dr, Fort Myers, FL 33912
Tel.: (239) 768-1880
Property Management Services
N.A.I.C.S.: 531390

REDUS Florida Commercial, LLC (1)
850 NW Federal Hwy, Stuart, FL 34994
Tel.: (772) 261-8500
Real Estate Development Services
N.A.I.C.S.: 531390

REDUS Frederica Club, LLC (1)
100 Pike's Bluff Dr, Saint Simons Island, GA 31522
Tel.: (912) 634-6900
Web Site: https://www.fredericagolfclub.com
Sports Club Operating Services
N.A.I.C.S.: 713910

Real Estate Lenders (1)
27720 Dickason Dr, Santa Clarita, CA 91355
Tel.: (661) 294-9500
Sales Range: $25-49.9 Million
Emp.: 3
Real Estate Agents & Broker Services
N.A.I.C.S.: 531210

Reliable Insurance Services Corp. (1)
1451 Ave Roosevelt Edificio de Popular Caparra Ctr, San Juan, PR 00920
Tel.: (787) 523-0000
Web Site: http://www.reliablefinancial.com
Financial Management Services
N.A.I.C.S.: 541611

Rock Creek Austin Fund, L.P. (1)
1133 Connecticut Ave NW, Washington, DC 20036
Tel.: (202) 331-3400
Web Site: http://www.therockcreekgroup.com
Emp.: 80
Investment Management Service
N.A.I.C.S.: 523940
Assaneh Beschloss *(CEO & Founder)*

Rock Creek Fund (E) Ltd. (1)
190 Elgin Avenue E9, Georgetown, KY1-9005, Grand Cayman, Cayman Islands
Tel.: (345) 3459433100
Financial Management Services
N.A.I.C.S.: 541611

Safehold Special Risk, Inc. (1)
100 Glen Eagles Ct, Carrollton, GA 30117
Web Site: https://www.safehold.com
Insurance Services
N.A.I.C.S.: 524210

Signature Home Mortgage, LLC (1)
1055 E Colorado Blvd Ste 500, Pasadena, CA 91106
Tel.: (424) 332-5517
Web Site: https://www.signaturehomemortgage.com
Mortgage Loan Services
N.A.I.C.S.: 522390

The Ridges at Mountain Harbour, LLC (1)
1665 Mountain Harbour Dr, Hayesville, NC 28904

Tel.: (828) 389-9000
Web Site: https://mountainharbourlivingandgolf.com
Sports Club Operating Services
N.A.I.C.S.: 713910

The Thirty-Eight Hundred Fund, LLC (1)
3800 Howard Hughes Pkwy, Las Vegas, NV 89169
Tel.: (702) 791-6353
Investment Management Service
N.A.I.C.S.: 523940

Thoroughbred Mortgage, LLC (1)
800 Westchester Ave Ste S432, Rye Brook, NY 15073
Web Site: http://www.thoroughbredmortgage.com
Mortgage Services
N.A.I.C.S.: 522310

UELS Holding, LLC (1)
399 Park Ave 5th Fl, New York, NY 10022
Tel.: (212) 883-4508
Holding Company
N.A.I.C.S.: 551112

Subsidiary (Domestic):

UELS, LLC (2)
85 S 200 E, Vernal, UT 84078
Tel.: (435) 789-1017
Web Site: https://www.uintahgroup.com
Emp.: 200
Land Surveying Services
N.A.I.C.S.: 541360
Tracy Henline *(Pres & CEO)*
Tim Pierce *(CFO & Exec VP)*
Harold Marshall *(Exec VP & Mgr-HSE & Engrg Dept)*
Troy Jensen *(VP & Mgr-Northern Reg)*
Chris Gardiner *(Mgr-Drafting Dept)*
Parrish A. Salyers *(Dir-Bus Dev)*

Wells Capital Management Incorporated (1)
525 Market St 10F, San Francisco, CA 94105
Tel.: (415) 396-8000
Web Site: http://www.wellscap.com
Portfolio Management Services
N.A.I.C.S.: 523940

Wells Fargo Advantage Funds (1)
100 Heritage Reserve, Menomonee Falls, WI 53051-4400
Tel.: (414) 359-3400
Web Site: http://www.wellsfargoadvantagefunds.com
Sales Range: $1-4.9 Billion
Emp.: 650
Investment Advice Services
N.A.I.C.S.: 523940

Subsidiary (Domestic):

Wells Fargo Funds Distributor, LLC (2)
100 Heritage Reserve, Menomonee Falls, WI 53051
Tel.: (415) 396-6122
Web Site: http://www.wellsfargoadvantagefunds.com
Securities & Mutual Fund Distribution Services
N.A.I.C.S.: 523150

Wells Fargo Funds Management, LLC (2)
525 Market St 10th FL, San Francisco, CA 94105
Tel.: (415) 396-8000
Web Site: http://www.wellsfargoadvantagefunds.com
Sales Range: $50-74.9 Million
Emp.: 100
Investment Advisory & Fund Management Services
N.A.I.C.S.: 523940

Wells Fargo Advisors, LLC (1)
1 N Jefferson Ave, Saint Louis, MO 63103-2205
Tel.: (704) 383-2127
Web Site: http://www.wellsfargoadvisors.com
Sales Range: $5-14.9 Billion
Emp.: 30,200

Securities Brokerage, Investment Banking, Financial Advisory, Trust & Asset Management Services
N.A.I.C.S.: 523150
James E. Hays *(Pres)*
Bob Vorlop *(Head-Products & Advice)*
Heather Hunt-Ruddy *(Head-Client Experience & Growth)*
Mark W. Hubbert *(Chief Risk Officer)*
Andy Byer *(Pres-Gateway)*
Dan Sperow *(Mng Dir-Investments)*
Gray Daus *(Mng Dir-Investments)*
John Alexander *(Head-Integrated Brokerage)*
Catherine A. Brown *(Head-HR)*
David Dawkins *(Dir-Diverse Client Segments)*
Ron Dock *(Chief IT Officer)*
Diane Gabriel *(Head-Next Generation Talent)*
Rich Getzoff *(Head-Advisor-Led Bus)*
Gina House *(Head-Mktg)*
Erik Karanik *(Head-Ops & Branch Infrastructure)*
Shea Leordeanu *(Head-Comm)*
Ian MacEachern *(Head-Investment Products)*
Joe Nadreau *(Head-Independent Brokerage & Platform Svcs)*
Eduardo Queen *(Head-Digital & Automated Investing)*
Michael Shine *(Head-Shared Svcs)*
Warren Terry *(Head-Bus Performance & Due Diligence)*
Chip Walker *(Head-Field Strategy & Execution)*
Sanjit Singh *(Head-Strategy)*
Kimberly Ta *(Head-Client Svc & Advice)*
David Williams *(Chief Compliance Officer)*
John Tyers *(Head-Independent Advisor Grp)*
Evan Savarick *(Mng Dir-Investment)*
Roy Savarick *(Sr VP-Investments)*
Barry Simmons *(Head-Natl Sls)*
John G. Peluso Jr. *(Head-First Clearing)*

Subsidiary (Domestic):

Riazzi Rhyne & Swaim Investment Group of Wells Fargo Advisors (2)
110 Oakwood Dr Ste 470, Winston Salem, NC 27103-1834
Tel.: (336) 979-1755
Web Site: https://www.rrs-ig.com
Sales Range: Less than $1 Million
Emp.: 8
Stock Brokers & Dealers
N.A.I.C.S.: 523150
Joseph M. N. Rhyne *(Mng Dir & Officer-Investment)*
Patrick J. Riazzi *(Mng Dir & & Officer-Investment)*
Patrick C. Rhyne *(Officer-Investment & First VP)*
Patrick J. Riazzi *(Mng Dir & & Officer-Investment)*
Patrick C. Rhyne *(Officer-Investment & First VP)*

Wells Fargo Advisors Financial Network, LLC (2)
1 N Jefferson Ave WS1042, Saint Louis, MO 63103
Tel.: (314) 955-3635
Web Site: http://www.wfafinet.com
Sales Range: $650-699.9 Million
Emp.: 7,000
Securities Brokerage & Dealing Services
N.A.I.C.S.: 523150

Wells Fargo Auto Receivables, LLC (1)
Wells Frgo Ctr 6th, Minneapolis, MN 55479
Tel.: (612) 667-1234
Financial Management Services
N.A.I.C.S.: 541611

Wells Fargo Bank International (1)
2 Harbourmaster Place IFSC, Dublin, 1, Ireland
Tel.: (353) 14365700
Emp.: 100
Commercial Banking Services
N.A.I.C.S.: 522110

Wells Fargo Bank Northwest, National Association (1)
299 S Main St 1st Fl Bank, Salt Lake City, UT 84111

Wells Fargo & Company—(Continued)

Tel.: (385) 415-8440
Emp.: 83
Commercial Banking Services
N.A.I.C.S.: 522110
Dain Brown (Gen Mgr)

Wells Fargo Bank, N.A. (1)
101 N Phillips Ave, Sioux Falls, SD 57104
Tel.: (605) 575-6900
Sales Range: $250-299.9 Million
Bank Holding Company
N.A.I.C.S.: 551111
Lynn Manthy (Sr VP & Mgr-Relationship-Maryland)

Subsidiary (Domestic):

Wells Capital Management Incorporated (2)
525 Market St 10th Fl, San Francisco, CA 94105 (100%)
Tel.: (415) 396-8000
Web Site: http://www.wellscap.com
Investment Advisory & Management Services
N.A.I.C.S.: 523940

Branch (Non-US):

Wells Fargo Bank, N.A. - Hong Kong Branch (2)
22-23/F AIA Central 1 Connaught Road, Central, China (Hong Kong) (100%)
Tel.: (852) 2509 0888
Sales Range: $10-24.9 Million
Emp.: 60
International Financing
N.A.I.C.S.: 522299

Subsidiary (Non-US):

Wells Fargo Capital Finance (UK) Limited (2)
90 Long Acre, London, WC2E 9RA, United Kingdom
Tel.: (44) 2076645650
Web Site: http://wellsfargocapitalfinance.com
Sales Range: $25-49.9 Million
Emp.: 25
Asset Lending Services
N.A.I.C.S.: 525990
Steven Chait (Mng Dir & Head)
Nick Lawrence (Mng Dir-Europe)
Ian Bramley (Dir-based Lending)
Kurt Marsden (Exec VP & Head-Corporate Finance-Grp)
Jon Norton (Dir-based Lending)
John Leonard (Head)
Tom Weedall (Dir-Manchester)
Tom Dolphin (Mng Dir & Head-Receivables Securitisation)
Holly Kaczmarczyk (Head)
James Cunnah (Assoc Dir)
Jake Hyman (Dir)
Julian Osborne (Dir)

Subsidiary (Domestic):

Wells Fargo Real Estate Investment Corporation (2)
90 S 7th St 13th Fl, Minneapolis, MN 55402
Web Site: http://www.wellsfargo.com
Rev.: $1,371,698,000
Assets: $35,493,267,000
Liabilities: $3,077,981,000
Net Worth: $32,415,286,000
Earnings: $1,237,611,000
Emp.: 2
Fiscal Year-end: 12/31/2018
Real Estate Investment Trust
N.A.I.C.S.: 525990
John R. Shrewsberry (CFO & Sr Exec VP)

Wells Fargo Capital Finance, Inc. (1)
2450 Colorado Ste 3000 W, Santa Monica, CA 90404
Tel.: (310) 453-7300
Web Site: http://wellsfargocapitalfinance.com
Holding Company; Commercial Credit Intermediation & Lending Services
N.A.I.C.S.: 551112
Jason Cosso (Officer-Business Development & Mng Dir)
Scott Glassberg (Reg Mgr-Sales & Mng Dir)
David Marks (Exec VP)

Barry Bobrow (Mng Dir & Head-Loan Sls & Syndications)
Mary-Jo Gagliardi (Dir-Human Resources)
Holly Kaczmarczyk (Sr Mng Dir & Head)
Charles Kim (Exec VP)
Kurt Marsden (Exec VP & Head)
Stephen Schwartz (Chief Admin Officer & Exec VP)
Nick Cole (Exec VP & Head)
Tom Dolphin (Mng Dir & Head)
Kevin Gillespie (Exec VP)
Marc Grossman (Exec VP & Head)
Michael Murray (Mng Dir)
Rhonda Noell (Mgr-Healthcare Fin & Exec VP)
Kevin Sullivan (Mgr-Comml Svcs Grp & Exec VP)
Raphael Torres (Reg Mgr-Comml Svcs Grp & Sr VP)
Keith Vercauteren (Exec VP & Mng Dir)
Alexandra Cavallaro (VP)
Ryan Chin (Mng Dir & & Officer-Business Development)
Christian Conroy (Mng Dir & & Officer-Business Development)
Caroline Deichmann (Officer-Business Development)
Scott Fiore (Mng Dir & & Officer-Business Development)

Subsidiary (Non-US):

Wells Fargo Capital Finance Corporation Canada (2)
22 Adelaide Street West, Toronto, M5H 4E3, ON, Canada
Tel.: (416) 364-6080
Web Site: http://www.wellsfargocapitalfinance.com
Asset Management Services
N.A.I.C.S.: 531390

Subsidiary (Domestic):

Wells Fargo Capital Finance, LLC (2)
2450 Colorado Ave 3rd Fl, Santa Monica, CA 90404
Tel.: (213) 443-6000
Web Site: http://wellsfargocapitalfinance.com
Sales Range: $50-74.9 Million
Emp.: 150
Commercial Credit Intermediation & Lending Services
N.A.I.C.S.: 522299

Wells Fargo Commercial Distribution Finance, LLC (1)
5595 Trillium Blvd, Hoffman Estates, IL 60192
Tel.: (847) 747-6800
Web Site: http://cdf.wf.com
Financial Services
N.A.I.C.S.: 523999
Steve Battreall (Pres & CEO)

Wells Fargo Energy Capital, Inc. (1)
1000 Louisiana St, Houston, TX 77002-5019
Tel.: (713) 319-1513
Business Support Services
N.A.I.C.S.: 561499

Wells Fargo Energy Group (1)
1000 Louisiana St 9th Fl, Houston, TX 77002 (100%)
Tel.: (713) 319-1513
Sales Range: $650-699.9 Million
Energy Market Financial Services
N.A.I.C.S.: 523999
Gary Milavec (Sr VP)

Wells Fargo Financial Corporation Canada (1)
55 Standish Court Suite 400, Mississauga, L5R 4J4, ON, Canada
Tel.: (905) 755-7000
Web Site: http://financial.wellsfargo.com
Sales Range: $75-99.9 Million
Emp.: 250
Commercial Lending Services
N.A.I.C.S.: 522291

Wells Fargo Financial, Inc. (1)
800 Walnut St, Des Moines, IA 50309 (100%)
Tel.: (515) 243-2131
Sales Range: $5-14.9 Billion
Emp.: 10,200
Financial Services

N.A.I.C.S.: 522210

Subsidiary (Domestic):

Wells Fargo Audit Services (2)
215 4th St S, Minneapolis, MN 55401 (100%)
Tel.: (612) 667-0081
Sales Range: $100-124.9 Million
Audit Services to Affiliates
N.A.I.C.S.: 522110

Wells Fargo Auto Finance (2)
2501 Seaport Dr Ste BH300, Chester, PA 19013 (100%)
Tel.: (610) 595-5300
Rev.: $57,800,000
Emp.: 600
Automobile & Other Financial Solutions
N.A.I.C.S.: 524292

Wells Fargo Business Credit (2)
90 S 7th St Ste 400, Minneapolis, MN 55402-3901 (100%)
Tel.: (612) 766-7000
Sales Range: $25-49.9 Million
Emp.: 37
Commercial Lending & Financing Services
N.A.I.C.S.: 522299

Wells Fargo Dealer Services, Inc. (2)
23 Pasteur, Irvine, CA 92618-3816
Tel.: (949) 727-1000
Web Site: http://www.wellsfargodealerservices.com
Sales Range: $150-199.9 Million
Emp.: 500
Auto Loan & Leasing Services
N.A.I.C.S.: 522220

Wells Fargo Equipment Finance, Inc. (2)
733 Marquette Ave Ste 700, Minneapolis, MN 55402 (100%)
Tel.: (612) 667-9876
Sales Range: $75-99.9 Million
Emp.: 200
Equipment Financing
N.A.I.C.S.: 522220
Byron Payne (Exec VP)
Scott Dienes (Natl Sls Mgr)

Branch (Domestic):

Wells Fargo Equipment Finance (3)
530 5th Ave 15th Fl, New York, NY 10036 (100%)
Tel.: (212) 805-1035
Sales Range: $25-49.9 Million
Emp.: 80
Miscellaneous Business Credit Institution
N.A.I.C.S.: 522220
Melissa Bastan (Mng Dir & Nationwide Head-Healthcare-Pub Fin-GIB)

Subsidiary (Non-US):

Wells Fargo Equipment Finance Company (3)
2550 Victoria Park Avenue Suite 700, Toronto, M2J 5A9, ON, Canada (100%)
Tel.: (416) 498-6464
Sales Range: $10-24.9 Million
Emp.: 25
Equipment Financing & Leasing Transactions
N.A.I.C.S.: 532412

Branch (Domestic):

Wells Fargo Financial (2)
719 Kamehameha Hwy Ste C300, Pearl City, HI 96782 (100%)
Tel.: (808) 455-5234
Rev.: $610,000
Emp.: 7
Consumer Finance Companies
N.A.I.C.S.: 522210

Subsidiary (Domestic):

Wells Fargo Financial Arizona, Inc. (2)
39422 N Daisy Mountain Dr, Anthem, AZ 85086-6703
Tel.: (623) 551-7200
Sales Range: $25-49.9 Million
Emp.: 8
Commercial Lending Services
N.A.I.C.S.: 522291

Wells Fargo Financial Cards (2)
3201 N 4th Ave, Sioux Falls, SD 57104-0700
Tel.: (605) 336-3933
Web Site: http://www.financial.wellsfargo.com
Sales Range: $100-124.9 Million
Credit Card Services
N.A.I.C.S.: 522110

Wells Fargo Financial Florida, Inc. (2)
3734 Blanding Blvd, Jacksonville, FL 32210
Tel.: (904) 777-9818
Sales Range: $25-49.9 Million
Emp.: 5
Mortgage Bankers Loan Correspondents
N.A.I.C.S.: 522291
Kelly A. Smith (Pres-North Florida)
Jose Atkinson (Pres-South Florida)

Wells Fargo Financial Leasing, Inc (2)
800 Walnut St, Des Moines, IA 50309 (100%)
Tel.: (515) 557-4071
Web Site: http://www.wellsfargoleasing.com
Lease Financing Programs
N.A.I.C.S.: 522291

Wells Fargo Financial Oregon, Inc. (2)
206 8th St, Des Moines, IA 50309
Tel.: (515) 243-2131
Financial Management Services
N.A.I.C.S.: 541611

Wells Fargo Financial Washington, Inc. (2)
521 SE Chkalov Dr, Vancouver, WA 98683-5284
Tel.: (360) 885-4300
Commercial Banking Services
N.A.I.C.S.: 522110

Wells Fargo Global Fund Services (Asia) Pte Ltd. (1)
83 Clemenceau Ave 11-01/02/03/04 Shell Hse, Singapore, 239920, Singapore
Tel.: (65) 67688288
Financial Management Services
N.A.I.C.S.: 541611

Wells Fargo Global Fund Services (UK) Limited (1)
Munro House Portsmouth Road, Cobham, KC11 1TF, Surrey, United Kingdom
Tel.: (44) 1932586300
Financial Management Services
N.A.I.C.S.: 541611

Wells Fargo Insurance, Inc. (1)
600 Hwy 169 S, Minneapolis, MN 55426-1205 (100%)
Tel.: (612) 667-5600
Rev.: $32,200,000
Emp.: 200
Holding Company; Insurance Products & Services
N.A.I.C.S.: 551112

Subsidiary (Domestic):

Wells Fargo Insurance Services, Inc. (2)
150 N Michigan Ave Ste 3900, Chicago, IL 60601 (100%)
Tel.: (312) 423-2500
Sales Range: $1-9.9 Million
Emp.: 6,910
Insurance Brokerage Services
N.A.I.C.S.: 524210

Wells Fargo Mortgage Loan Trust II, LLC (1)
301 S College St, Charlotte, NC 28202
Tel.: (612) 667-0161
Mortgage Loan Brokerage Services
N.A.I.C.S.: 522310

Wells Fargo Multifamily Capital (1)
2010 Corporate Rdg Ste 1000, McLean, VA 22102 (100%)
Tel.: (703) 760-4700
Web Site: http://www.wellsfargo.com
Sales Range: $10-24.9 Million
Emp.: 4,000
Commercial Mortgage Finance Services
N.A.I.C.S.: 522310

Wells Fargo Preferred Capital, Inc. (1)
800 Walnut St, Des Moines, IA 50309
Tel.: (515) 557-7416
Sales Range: $25-49.9 Million
Emp.: 50
Mortgage Bankers Loan Correspondents
N.A.I.C.S.: 522390
Tom Murphy (Pres)

Wells Fargo Rail Corporation (1)
9377 W Higgins Rd Ste 600, Rosemont, IL 60018
Tel.: (847) 318-7575
Web Site: https://www.wellsfargo.com
Emp.: 200
Railcar & Locomotive Leasing & Maintenance Services
N.A.I.C.S.: 532411
James P. Baumgartner (CTO)
Keith W. Andersen (Sr VP-Sls-Eastern US)
Susan Barrie (Sr VP-Sls-Canada)
Michelle Cizmar (VP-Administration)
Greg R. Johnson (VP-Equipment)
Kevin McHugh (Sr VP-Sls-Southern US)
Oscar Torres (Sr VP-Sales-Mexico,US West)
Elizabeth Martinez (VP)
Michael Rone (VP)
Marty Giubardo (VP)
Kurt Schulz (VP-Risk Mgmt)
Nick Muday (Exec VP)

Wells Fargo Real Estate Group (1)
420 Montgomery St Fl 6, San Francisco, CA 94104 (100%)
Tel.: (415) 394-4081
Sales Range: $50-74.9 Million
Emp.: 120
General & Industrial Loan Institutions
N.A.I.C.S.: 522299

Subsidiary (Domestic):

Tryon Management, Inc. (2)
1 Wachovia Ctr 301 S College St, Charlotte, NC 28288-0630
Tel.: (704) 374-6769
Nonresidential Property Management Services
N.A.I.C.S.: 531312

Wells Fargo Properties, Inc. (2)
2329 Central Ave Ne, Minneapolis, MN 55418 (100%)
Tel.: (612) 316-3769
Sales Range: $50-74.9 Million
Emp.: 100
Bank-Building Real Estate Services
N.A.I.C.S.: 531210

Wells Fargo Real Estate Tax Services, LLC (1)
3041 SW Prairie View Rd, Ankeny, IA 50023
Tel.: (515) 289-2302
Real Estate Development Services
N.A.I.C.S.: 531390

Wells Fargo Securities (Japan) Co., Ltd. (1)
Marunouchi Trust Tower Main 24th Floor 1-8-3 Marunouchi, Chiyoda-ku, Tokyo, 100-0005, Japan
Tel.: (81) 343306250
Financial Management Services
N.A.I.C.S.: 541611

Wells Fargo Securities International Limited (1)
30 Fenchurch Street, London, EC3M 3BD, United Kingdom
Tel.: (44) 2071498100
Financial Management Services
N.A.I.C.S.: 541611
Alicia Reyes (Head-EMEA)
Walter Dolhare (Head-Markets Div)
Rob Engel (Head-Investment Banking & Capital Markets)

Wells Fargo Securities, LLC (1)
550 S Tryon St 6th Fl D1086-060, Charlotte, NC 28202
Tel.: (704) 715-6133
Investment Banking & Securities Brokerage Services
N.A.I.C.S.: 523150
Robert Engel (Co-Head-Investment Banking & Capital Markets)

Judson Bailey (Mng Dir-Equity Res-Houston)
Thomas Curran (Mng Dir & Head-Insurance Investment Banking-New York)
Scott Heberton (Head-Fin Institutions Investment Banking & Capital Markets)
Paul R. Ackerman (Vice Chm)
Christopher Harvey (Head-Equity Strategy)
Todd M. Wickwire (Co-Head-Equity Res)
Sam Pearlstein (Co-Head-Equity Res)
Diane Schumaker-Krieg (Head-Res, Economics & Strategy-Global)
Mike Mayo (Mng Dir & Head-Large-Cap Bank Res-Global Res-Economics & Strate)
Ken Sena (Head-Internet Equity Res-New York)
Jeff Johnston (Head-Subscription Fin)
Chris Pink (Head-Asset Backed Fin & Securitization)
Dee Dee Sklar (Vice Chm-Subscription Fin)
Mary Katherine DuBose (Head-Debt Capital Markets)
Walter Dolhare (Co-Head-Investment Banking & Capital Markets)
Rick FlorJancic (Mng Dir & Head-Investment Banking-Midwest)
Eric Fornell (Vice Chm-Investment Banking)
Scott Van Bergh (Vice Chm-Energy & Power Investment Banking Grp)

Subsidiary (Domestic):

Wells Fargo Prime Services, LLC (2)
101 California St Ste 3050, San Francisco, CA 94111
Tel.: (415) 848-0269
Web Site: http://www.merlinsecurities.com
Sales Range: $25-49.9 Million
Emp.: 15
Securities Brokerage & Trading
N.A.I.C.S.: 523150

Subsidiary (Domestic):

Wells Fargo Prime Services, LLC - New York (3)
640 Fifth Ave 7th Fl, New York, NY 10019
Tel.: (212) 822-4800
Web Site: http://www.merlinsecurities.com
Sales Range: $10-24.9 Million
Emp.: 29
Securities Brokerage & Trading
N.A.I.C.S.: 523150

Wells Fargo Soporte Global Limitada (1)
Apoquindo 3721, Santiago, Chile
Tel.: (56) 23673000
Financial Management Services
N.A.I.C.S.: 541611

Wells Fargo Special Risks, Inc. (1)
520 Pike St Ste 2100, Seattle, WA 98101
Tel.: (206) 701-5000
Sales Range: $50-74.9 Million
Emp.: 80
Commercial Banking Services
N.A.I.C.S.: 522110

Wells Fargo Vendor Financial Services, LLC (1)
210 Main St, Danbury, CT 06810
Tel.: (203) 790-6095
Financing Products & Services
N.A.I.C.S.: 523999

Wells Fargo Wealth Brokerage Insurance Agency, LLC (1)
1021 E Cary St Ste 100, Richmond, VA 23219
Tel.: (804) 697-6710
Emp.: 65
Insurance Management Services
N.A.I.C.S.: 524298

WELLS FARGO MULTI-SECTOR INCOME FUND
525 Market St 12th Fl, San Francisco, CA 94105
ERC—(NYSEAMEX)
Rev.: $34,538,231
Assets: $587,473,584
Liabilities: $183,566,615
Net Worth: $403,906,969
Earnings: $25,190,415
Fiscal Year-end: 10/31/19

Investment Management Service
N.A.I.C.S.: 525990
Peter Wilson (Mgr-Fund)
Timothy J. Penny (Chm)

WELLTOWER INC.
4500 Dorr St, Toledo, OH 43615
Tel.: (419) 247-2800 DE
Web Site: https://www.welltower.com
Year Founded: 1970
WELL—(NYSE)
Rev.: $6,637,995,000
Assets: $44,012,166,000
Liabilities: $17,931,044,000
Net Worth: $26,081,122,000
Earnings: $340,094,000
Emp.: 533
Fiscal Year-end: 12/31/23
Nursing Homes, Health Care & Assisted Living Facilities Investment Servicest
N.A.I.C.S.: 525990
Mary Ellen Pisanelli (Sr VP-Legal & Admin)
Shankh S. Mitra (CEO)
Timothy G. McHugh (CFO & Exec VP)
Matthew McQueen (Gen Counsel, Sec & Exec VP)
Mary Ellen Pisanelli (Sr VP-Legal & Admin)
Joshua T. Fieweger (Chief Acctg Officer)
Ryan Rothacker (Sr VP-Medical Office)
John F. Burkart (COO & Exec VP)
Matthew Carrus (Treas)
Nikhil Chaudhri (Chief Investment Officer)
Andrew Cohen (VP)
Michael Ferry (Sr VP)
Michael Garst (Sr VP)
Sharon Makowsky (Deputy Gen Counsel)
John Olympitis (Sr VP)
Jack Rahner (Sr VP)
Russ Simon (Sr VP)
Krishna Soma (Sr VP)
Zac Stein (VP)

Subsidiaries:

15 Edison Road, LLC (1)
4548 E Fairfield Cir, Mesa, AZ 85205
Tel.: (602) 570-9305
Emp.: 2
Business Support Services
N.A.I.C.S.: 561990

3535 N. Hall Street, LLC (1)
8554 Katy Freeway Ste 200, Houston, TX 77024
Tel.: (713) 463-1784
Residential Building Leasing Services
N.A.I.C.S.: 531110

9108-9458 Quebec Inc. (1)
98 Boul De Gaulle, Lorraine, J6Z 3Z2, QC, Canada
Tel.: (450) 671-1314
Residential Building Leasing Services
N.A.I.C.S.: 531110

ARC Overland Park LLC (1)
10955 Lowell Ave Ste 110, Overland Park, KS 66210
Tel.: (913) 345-9424
Construction Services
N.A.I.C.S.: 236116

ARC Sun City West, LLC (1)
19803 R H Johnson Blvd, Sun City West, AZ 85375
Tel.: (623) 544-6120
Web Site: https://restoration.scwclubs.com
Emp.: 2
Hotel Operator
N.A.I.C.S.: 721191

Academy Nursing Home, Inc. (1)
89 Morton St, Andover, MA 01810
Tel.: (978) 475-0944
Nursing Care Facilities

N.A.I.C.S.: 623110

Avery Healthcare Group Limited (1)
3 Cygnet Drive Swan Valley, Northampton, NN4 9BS, United Kingdom
Tel.: (44) 1604675566
Web Site: https://www.averyhealthcare.co.uk
Providing Medical Services
N.A.I.C.S.: 623110

B-X North Andover LLC (1)
700 Chickering Rd, North Andover, MA 01845-1928
Tel.: (978) 683-1300
Sales Range: $25-49.9 Million
Emp.: 100
Nursing Care Facilities
N.A.I.C.S.: 623110
Samantha Hollister (Exec Dir)

B-X North Chelmsford LLC (1)
2 Technology Dr, North Chelmsford, MA 01863
Tel.: (978) 934-0000
Emp.: 80
Freight Transportation Services
N.A.I.C.S.: 488510
Christine Brooks (Gen Mgr)

B-X Providence LLC (1)
700 Smith St, Providence, RI 02908-3500
Tel.: (401) 521-0090
Web Site: http://www.capitolridgeatprovidence.com
Emp.: 500
Senior Living Facility
N.A.I.C.S.: 623312

B-X Quincy LLC (1)
2003 Falls Blvd, Quincy, MA 02169
Tel.: (617) 471-5595
Freight Transportation Distr
N.A.I.C.S.: 488510

B-X Trumbull LLC (1)
2750 Reservoir Ave, Trumbull, CT 06611-5715
Tel.: (203) 268-2400
Web Site: http://www.benchmarkquality.com
Emp.: 500
Freight Transportation Services
N.A.I.C.S.: 488510

B-X Yarmouth LLC (1)
27 Forest Falls Dr, Yarmouth, ME 04096
Tel.: (207) 358-4881
Web Site: http://www.benchmarkseniorliving.com
Freight Transportation & Distr
N.A.I.C.S.: 488510

B-XI Bedford LLC (1)
5 Corporate Dr, Bedford, NH 03110
Tel.: (603) 471-2555
Real Estate Investment Services
N.A.I.C.S.: 531390

B-XII Billerica LLC (1)
20 Charnstaff Ln, Billerica, MA 01821-6702
Tel.: (978) 667-0898
Health Care Srvices
N.A.I.C.S.: 621610

B-XII Shrewsbury LLC (1)
40 William St Ste 350, Wellesley, MA 02481-3999
Tel.: (781) 489-7100
Health Care Srvices
N.A.I.C.S.: 621610

Bayfield Court Operations Limited (1)
125 London Wall, London, EC2Y 5AL, United Kingdom
Tel.: (44) 2032254075
Real Estate Investment Services
N.A.I.C.S.: 531390

Belmont Village Buffalo Grove, L.L.C. (1)
500 McHenry Rd, Buffalo Grove, IL 60089
Tel.: (847) 447-0528
Web Site: https://www.belmontvillage.com
Nursing Care Services
N.A.I.C.S.: 623312

Belmont Village Carol Stream, L.L.C. (1)
545 Belmont Ln, Carol Stream, IL 60188
Tel.: (630) 510-1515

Welltower Inc.—(Continued)

Nursing Care Services
N.A.I.C.S.: 623312

Belmont Village Oak Park, L.L.C. (1)
1035 Madison St, Oak Park, IL 60302
Tel.: (708) 249-3820
Web Site: https://www.belmontvillage.com
Emp.: 100
Nursing Care Services
N.A.I.C.S.: 623312

Belmont Village Rancho Palos Verdes Tenant, LLC (1)
5701 Crestridge Rd, Rancho Palos Verdes, CA 90275
Tel.: (310) 377-9977
Nursing Care Services
N.A.I.C.S.: 623312

Belmont Village San Jose, LLC (1)
500 S Winchester Blvd, San Jose, CA 95128
Tel.: (408) 984-4767
Web Site: http://www.belmontvillage.com
Nursing Care Services
N.A.I.C.S.: 623312

Belmont Village St. Matthews, L.L.C. (1)
4600 Bowling Blvd, Louisville, KY 40207
Tel.: (502) 373-4193
Web Site: https://www.belmontvillage.com
Nursing Care Services
N.A.I.C.S.: 623312

Belmont Village Sunnyvale, LLC (1)
1039 E El Camino Real, Sunnyvale, CA 94087
Tel.: (408) 720-8498
Web Site: http://www.belmontvillage.com
Nursing Care Services
N.A.I.C.S.: 623312

Belmont Village Turtle Creek Tenant, LLC (1)
3535 N Hall St, Dallas, TX 75219
Tel.: (469) 425-8256
Web Site: https://www.belmontvillage.com
Residential Building Leasing Services
N.A.I.C.S.: 531110

Belmont Village West Lake Hills Tenant, LLC (1)
4310 Bee Cave Rd, West Lake Hills, TX 78746
Tel.: (512) 601-8281
Web Site: https://www.belmontvillage.com
Residential Building Leasing Services
N.A.I.C.S.: 531110

Brinton Manor, Inc. (1)
101 E State St, Kennett Square, PA 10040-3109
Tel.: (610) 358-6005
Nursing Care Facilities
N.A.I.C.S.: 623110

Burlington Woods Convalescent Center, Inc. (1)
115 Sunset Rd, Burlington, NJ 08016
Tel.: (609) 387-3620
Web Site: https://ccburlingtonwoods.com
Sales Range: $25-49.9 Million
Emp.: 250
Nursing Care Facilities
N.A.I.C.S.: 623110
Walt Keiler (VP)

BurrOakCommonsPlus, LLC (1)
90 Burr Oak Dr, Delaware, OH 43015
Tel.: (740) 370-0802
Apartment Rental Services
N.A.I.C.S.: 531110

CC3 Acquisition, LLC (1)
4500 Dorr St, Toledo, OH 43615
Tel.: (419) 247-2800
Nursing Care Services
N.A.I.C.S.: 623312

Canterbury of Shepherdstown Limited Partnership (1)
80 Maddex Dr, Shepherdstown, WV 25443
Tel.: (304) 876-9422
Nursing Care Facilities
N.A.I.C.S.: 623110

Crestview Convalescent Home, Inc. (1)

1245 Church Rd, Wyncote, PA 19095
Tel.: (215) 884-9990
Nursing Care Facilities
N.A.I.C.S.: 623110

Crestview North, Inc. (1)
262 Tollgate Rd, Langhorne, PA 19047
Tel.: (215) 968-4650
Sales Range: $25-49.9 Million
Emp.: 100
Nursing Care Facilities
N.A.I.C.S.: 623110

Encare of Pennypack, Inc. (1)
8015 Lawndale Ave, Philadelphia, PA 19111
Tel.: (215) 725-2525
Nursing Care Facilities
N.A.I.C.S.: 623110

FC Trident, LLC (1)
500 5th Ave, New York, NY 10110-3899
Tel.: (212) 468-5600
Real Estate Investment Services
N.A.I.C.S.: 531190

GMA-Madison, Inc. (1)
161 Bakers Rdg Rd, Morgantown, WV 26508-1459
Tel.: (304) 285-0692
Nursing & Custodial Care Services
N.A.I.C.S.: 623110

Genesis ElderCare Centers - Harston, Inc. (1)
350 Haws Ln, Flourtown, PA 19031
Tel.: (215) 233-0700
Nursing & Custodial Care Services
N.A.I.C.S.: 623110

Genesis Eldercare National Centers, Inc. (1)
2810 Ruleme St, Eustis, FL 32507
Tel.: (352) 357-1990
Nursing Care Facilities
N.A.I.C.S.: 623110
Kelly Brady (Office Mgr)

Genesis HC LLC (1)
101 E State St, Kennett Square, PA 19348
Tel.: (610) 444-6350
Web Site: https://www.genesishcc.com
Health Care Srvices
N.A.I.C.S.: 621999

Genesis Health Ventures of Wilkes-Barre, Inc. (1)
300 Courtright St, Wilkes Barre, PA 18702-2526
Tel.: (570) 825-0538
Web Site: http://www.htc.com
Emp.: 30
Nursing & Custodial Care Services
N.A.I.C.S.: 623110

Genesis HealthCare, LLC- Silver Lake Center (1)
1080 Silver Lk Blvd, Dover, DE 19904
Tel.: (302) 734-5990
Web Site: http://www.genesishcc.com
Nursing & Custodial Care Services
N.A.I.C.S.: 623110
Warren Burke (Exec Dir)

Glenmark Associates, Inc. (1)
302 Cedar Rdg Rd, Sissonville, WV 25320-9502
Tel.: (304) 984-0046
Nursing & Custodial Care Services
N.A.I.C.S.: 623110

HCN DownREIT Member, LLC (1)
4500 Dorr St, Toledo, OH 43615
Tel.: (419) 247-2800
Residential Building Leasing Services
N.A.I.C.S.: 531110
Scott Brinker (Sr VP)

HCN-Revera Lessee (Arnprior Villa) GP Inc. (1)
15 Arthur St, Arnprior, K7S 1A1, ON, Canada
Tel.: (613) 623-0414
Residential Building Leasing Services
N.A.I.C.S.: 531110

HCN-Revera Lessee (Inglewood) LP (1)
10 Inglewood Drive, Red Deer, T4R 0L2, AB, Canada
Tel.: (403) 346-1134
Residential Building Leasing Services

N.A.I.C.S.: 531110

HCN-Revera Lessee (Jardins du Couvent) LP (1)
425 Rue Claude de Ramezay, Marieville, J3M 1J6, QC, Canada
Tel.: (450) 460-3141
Residential Building Leasing Services
N.A.I.C.S.: 531110

HCN-Revera Lessee (Manoir Lafontaine) LP (1)
230 Rue Des Chenes, Riviere-du-Loup, G5R 5B2, QC, Canada
Tel.: (418) 867-1117
Residential Building Leasing Services
N.A.I.C.S.: 531110

HCN-Revera Lessee (McKenzie Towne) LP (1)
20 Promenade Park SE, Calgary, T2Z 4A5, AB, Canada
Tel.: (403) 257-9331
Residential Building Leasing Services
N.A.I.C.S.: 531110

HCN-Revera Lessee (River Ridge) GP Inc. (1)
78 McKenney Ave Suite C, Saint Albert, T8N 7M3, AB, Canada
Tel.: (780) 470-3700
Residential Building Leasing Services
N.A.I.C.S.: 531110

HCN-Revera Lessee (Scenic Acres) GP Inc. (1)
150 Scotia Landing NW, Calgary, T3L 2K1, AB, Canada
Tel.: (403) 208-0338
Residential Building Leasing Services
N.A.I.C.S.: 531110

HCN-Revera Lessee (The Churchill) GP Inc. (1)
10015 103 Ave NW, Edmonton, T5J 0H1, AB, Canada
Tel.: (780) 420-1222
Residential Building Leasing Services
N.A.I.C.S.: 531110

Habitation Domaine des Trembles Inc. (1)
250 Boul Saint-Raymond, Gatineau, J9A 3H6, QC, Canada
Tel.: (819) 777-1234
Real Estate Investment Services
N.A.I.C.S.: 531390

Habitation Faubourg Giffard Inc. (1)
2321 Ch de la Canardiere, Quebec, G1J 0A3, QC, Canada
Tel.: (418) 661-4141
Real Estate Investment Services
N.A.I.C.S.: 531390

HawthorneCommonsPlus, LLC (1)
4050 Hawthorne Ln, Dublin, OH 43016
Tel.: (380) 205-2528
Web Site: https://www.hawthornecommons55plus.com
Apartment Rental Services
N.A.I.C.S.: 531110

Health Care REIT, LLC (1)
4500 Dorr St, Toledo, OH 43615
Tel.: (419) 247-2800
Web Site: http://www.welltower.com
Real Estate Investment Services
N.A.I.C.S.: 531120
Thomas J. DeRosa (CEO)
Thomas J. DeRosa (CEO)

Health Resources of Emery, L.L.C. (1)
625 Hwy 34, Matawan, NJ 07747-3050
Tel.: (732) 566-6400
Nursing & Custodial Care Services
N.A.I.C.S.: 623110

Health Resources of Glastonbury, Inc. (1)
101 E State St, Kennett Square, PA 19348
Tel.: (610) 925-4436
Sales Range: $25-49.9 Million
Emp.: 100
Nursing & Custodial Care Services
N.A.I.C.S.: 623110

Holiday Retirement (Clevedon) Limited (1)

18-19 Elton Road, Clevedon, BS21 7EH, United Kingdom
Tel.: (44) 1275790060
Apartment Leasing Services
N.A.I.C.S.: 531110

Immeuble Jazz Longueuil, societe en commandite (1)
1235 Chem du Tremblay, Longueuil, J4N 1T7, QC, Canada
Tel.: (450) 448-8853
Old Age Home Care Services
N.A.I.C.S.: 621610

Keystone Communities of Eagan, LLC (1)
3810 Alder Ln, Eagan, MN 55122
Tel.: (651) 379-2410
Web Site: http://www.keystonecommunities.com
Elder Care Services
N.A.I.C.S.: 623312
Kristi Olsen (Pres)
Kristy Sease (Asst Coord-Living)

Keystone Communities of Prior Lake, LLC (1)
4685 Park Nicollet Ave SE, Prior Lake, MN 55372
Tel.: (952) 226-9200
Elder Care Services
N.A.I.C.S.: 623312

Keystone Nursing Home, Inc. (1)
44 Keystone Dr, Leominster, MA 01453-1904
Tel.: (978) 537-9327
Sales Range: $25-49.9 Million
Emp.: 100
Nursing Care Facilities
N.A.I.C.S.: 623110

Laurel Health Resources, Inc. (1)
125 Holly Rd, Hamburg, PA 19526-8729
Tel.: (610) 562-2284
Sales Range: $25-49.9 Million
Emp.: 100
Nursing Care Facilities
N.A.I.C.S.: 623110

MS Avon, L.P. (1)
109 W Jackson St, Cicero, IN 46034
Tel.: (317) 420-0205
Real Estate Investment Services
N.A.I.C.S.: 531390

MS Mishawaka, L.P. (1)
109 W Jackson St, Cicero, IN 46034
Tel.: (317) 420-0205
Real Estate Investment Services
N.A.I.C.S.: 531390

Maids Moreton Operations Limited (1)
Church Street Maids Moreton, Buckingham, MK18 1QF, United Kingdom
Tel.: (44) 1280818710
Nursing Care Services
N.A.I.C.S.: 621610

Manoir Archer Inc. (1)
1217 Rte De L'ejlise, Quebec, G1W 3P2, QC, Canada
Tel.: (418) 657-2828
Emp.: 30
Nursing Care Services
N.A.I.C.S.: 621610

MetSun Jackson NJ Senior Living, LLC (1)
7900 Westpark Dr Ste T-900, McLean, VA 22102-4242
Tel.: (732) 928-5600
Emp.: 90
Nursing Care Services
N.A.I.C.S.: 623312
Charlie Placek (Exec Dir)

MetSun Leawood KS Senior Living, LLC (1)
12500 W 135th St, Overland Park, KS 66221-9323
Tel.: (913) 685-3340
Nursing Care Services
N.A.I.C.S.: 623312

Nursing and Retirement Center of the Andovers, Inc. (1)
1801 Tpke St, North Andover, MA 01845
Tel.: (978) 688-1212

Nursing Care Facilities
N.A.I.C.S.: 623110

Otay Tenant LLC (1)
1290 Santa Rosa Dr, Chula Vista, CA
91913
Tel.: (619) 639-0881
Web Site: https://www.ivyliving.com
Senior Living Services
N.A.I.C.S.: 623312

Philadelphia Avenue Associates (1)
500 Philadelphia Ave, Shillington, PA 19607
Tel.: (610) 777-7841
Web Site: http://www.genesishcc.co
Nursing Care Services
N.A.I.C.S.: 623110

Pompton Care, L.L.C. (1)
25 E Lindsley Rd, Cedar Grove, NJ 07009
Tel.: (973) 256-7220
Nursing & Custodial Care Services
N.A.I.C.S.: 623110

Prescott Nursing Home, Inc. (1)
140 Prescott St, North Andover, MA 01845
Sales Range: $25-49.9 Million
Emp.: 110
Nursing Care Facility Services
N.A.I.C.S.: 623110

RSF REIT V SP, L.L.C. (1)
3232 Mckinney Ave Ste 890, Dallas, TX
75204
Tel.: (214) 855-9400
Holding Company
N.A.I.C.S.: 551114

River Street Associates (1)
440 N River St, Wilkes Barre, PA 18702
Tel.: (570) 825-5611
Nursing Care Services
N.A.I.C.S.: 623110

Sarah Brayton General Partnership
4901 N Main St, Fall River, MA 02720
Tel.: (508) 675-1001
Web Site:
http://www.sarahbraytonnursingcarecen
ter.com
Sales Range: $25-49.9 Million
Emp.: 220
Nursing Care Services
N.A.I.C.S.: 623110
Jeff Govoni (Gen Mgr)

Seniors Housing Investment III REIT Inc. (1)
1818 Library St Ste 500, Reston, VA 20190
Tel.: (571) 346-7656
Elder Care Services
N.A.I.C.S.: 623312

Silverado Senior Living Alhambra, Inc. (1)
1118 N Stoneman Ave, Alhambra, CA
91801
Tel.: (626) 308-9777
Web Site: http://www.silveradocare.com
Sales Range: $10-24.9 Million
Emp.: 50
Assisted-living Facilities Services
N.A.I.C.S.: 623312

Silverado Senior Living Dallas, Inc. (1)
3611 Dickason Ave, Dallas, TX 75219
Tel.: (214) 559-0140
Web Site: http://www.silveradocare.com
Emp.: 42
Nursing & Custodial Care Services
N.A.I.C.S.: 623110

Silverado Senior Living Salt Lake City, Inc. (1)
1430 E 4500 S, Salt Lake City, UT 84117
Tel.: (385) 313-9202
Web Site: http://www.silverado.com
Emp.: 100
Assisted-living Facilities Services
N.A.I.C.S.: 623312

Silverado Senior Living Scottsdale, Inc. (1)
9410 E Thunderbird, Scottsdale, AZ 85260
Tel.: (480) 614-9100
Web Site: http://www.silveradocare.com
Nursing Care Facilities

N.A.I.C.S.: 623110

Silverado Senior Living, Inc. (1)
6400 Oak Canyon Ste 200, Irvine, CA
92618
Tel.: (949) 240-7200
Web Site: http://www.silverado.com
Nursing Care Facilities
N.A.I.C.S.: 623110

Sunrise of Cupertino PropCo, LLC (1)
581 E Fremont Ave, Sunnyvale, CA 94087
Tel.: (408) 713-3637
Old Age Home Care Services
N.A.I.C.S.: 621610

Sunrise of Oceanside CA Propco, LLC (1)
4845 Mesa Dr, Oceanside, CA 92056
Tel.: (760) 997-1156
Real Estate Services
N.A.I.C.S.: 531210

Sunrise of Redmond PropCo, LLC (1)
15241 NE 20th St, Bellevue, WA 98007
Tel.: (425) 552-3437
Old Age Home Care Services
N.A.I.C.S.: 621610

The House of Campbell, Inc. (1)
723 Summers St, Parkersburg, WV 26101
Tel.: (304) 428-5573
Web Site: http://www.genesishcc.com
Nursing Care Facilities
N.A.I.C.S.: 623110

Villa Chicoutimi Inc. (1)
220 Rue Don-Bosco, Chicoutimi, G7H 7P6,
QC, Canada
Tel.: (418) 690-2233
Emp.: 20
Nursing Care Services
N.A.I.C.S.: 623312

Welltower CCRC OpCo LLC (1)
2600 Barracks Rd, Charlottesville, VA
22901-2271
Tel.: (434) 963-4198
Health Care Investment Services
N.A.I.C.S.: 525990

Willow Manor Nursing Home, Inc. (1)
30 Princeton Blvd, Lowell, MA 01851-2405
Tel.: (978) 454-8086
Sales Range: $25-49.9 Million
Emp.: 100
Nursing Care Facilities
N.A.I.C.S.: 623110

Windrose Sierra Properties, Ltd. (1)
550 Heritage Dr Ste 200, Jupiter, FL 33458
Tel.: (561) 626-1800
Web Site: http://www.welltower.com
Emp.: 50
Real Estate Manangement Services
N.A.I.C.S.: 525990
Michael Noto (Sr VP)

WELSBACH TECHNOLOGY METALS ACQUISITION CORP.
160 S Craig Pl, Lombard, IL 60148
Tel.: (217) 615-1216   DE
Year Founded: 2021
WTMA—(NASDAQ)
Rev.: $1,121,159
Assets: $80,193,219
Liabilities: $86,132,855
Net Worth: ($5,939,636)
Earnings: ($2,390,719)
Emp.: 4
Fiscal Year-end: 12/31/22
Investment Services
N.A.I.C.S.: 523999
Daniel Mamadou (CEO & Chm)
Christopher Clower (COO)
John Stanfield (CFO)
Sergey Marchenko (VP)

WEREWOLF THERAPEUTICS, INC.
200 Talcott Ave, Watertown, MA
02472
Tel.: (617) 952-0555   DE

Web Site:
https://www.werewolftx.com
Year Founded: 2017
HOWL—(NASDAQ)
Rev.: $16,401,000
Assets: $160,245,000
Liabilities: $37,908,000
Net Worth: $122,337,000
Earnings: ($53,810,000)
Emp.: 46
Fiscal Year-end: 12/31/22
Research & Development in Biotech-
nology (except Nanobiotechnology)
N.A.I.C.S.: 541714
Daniel J. Hicklin (Pres & CEO)
Luke Evnin (Founder & Chm)
Reid Leonard (COO)
Ellen Lubman (Chief Bus Officer)
Randi Isaacs (Chief Medical Officer)
Tim Trost (CFO & Treas)
Chulani Karunatilake (CTO)
Andres Salmeron (VP-Immunology)
William Winston (VP-Research)
Philipp Steiner (VP-Pharmacology)
Anjili Mathur (Sr Dir-Portfolio Strat-
egy)

WERNER ENTERPRISES, INC.
14507 Frontier Rd, Omaha, NE
68138
Tel.: (402) 895-6640   NE
Web Site: https://www.werner.com
Year Founded: 1956
WERN—(NASDAQ)
Rev.: $3,289,978,000
Assets: $3,097,255,000
Liabilities: $1,653,620,000
Net Worth: $1,443,635,000
Earnings: $241,256,000
Emp.: 10,249
Fiscal Year-end: 12/31/22
Trucking Service
N.A.I.C.S.: 484121
James Lynn Johnson (Chief Acctg
Officer, Sec & Exec VP)
Derek J. Leathers (Chm & CEO)
Jim S. Schelble (Chief Admin Officer
& Exec VP)
Craig T. Callahan (Chief Comml Offi-
cer & Exec VP)
Nathan J. Meisgeier (Pres & Chief
Legal Officer)
Carmen A. Tapio (Founder)
Daragh P. Mahon (CIO & Exec VP)
Eric Downing (COO & Exec VP)
Christopher D. Wikoff (CFO, Treas &
Exec VP)

Subsidiaries:

American Institute of Trucking, Inc. (1)
2350 S 48th Ave, Phoenix, AZ 85043-4729
Tel.: (602) 233-2222
Truck Driving Training Services
N.A.I.C.S.: 611519

Baylor Trucking, Inc. (1)
78 Catherine St, Milan, IN 47031
Tel.: (812) 623-2020
Web Site: http://www.baylortrucking.com
Rev.: $7,550,000
Emp.: 50
General Freight Trucking, Long-Distance,
Truckload
N.A.I.C.S.: 484121

Fleet Truck Sales, Inc. (1)
14719 Frontier Rd, Omaha, NE 68138
Tel.: (402) 625-7182
Web Site: https://www.wernerfleetsales.com
Fleet Truck Retailer
N.A.I.C.S.: 423110

WECC, Inc. (1)
155 N 400 W Ste 200, Salt Lake City, UT
84104
Tel.: (801) 883-6879
Public Utility Construction Services
N.A.I.C.S.: 236220
Richard Campbell (Chm)
James Avery (Vice Chm)

Werner Cycle Works, Inc. (1)
14410 Frontier Rd, Omaha, NE 68138
Tel.: (402) 894-3050
Web Site: http://www.wernercycleworks.com
Motorcycle Retailer
N.A.I.C.S.: 441227

Werner Enterprises Canada Corporation (1)
10862 Steeles Ave E, Milton, L9T 2X8, ON,
Canada
Tel.: (905) 693-1149
Emp.: 40
Freight Trucking Services
N.A.I.C.S.: 484121

Werner Global Logistics (Shanghai) Co., Ltd. (1)
South 5/F Harbour Building 1 Fenghe Road,
Shanghai, 200120, China
Tel.: (86) 2138879520
Web Site: http://www.werner.com
Sales Range: $25-49.9 Million
Emp.: 32
Freight Management & Logistics Services
N.A.I.C.S.: 488510

Werner Global Logistics Australia Pty. Ltd (1)
Level 2 / 4 Military Rd, Matraville, 2038,
NSW, Australia
Tel.: (61) 736227800
Freight Transportation Services
N.A.I.C.S.: 484110

WESBANCO, INC.
1 Bank Plz, Wheeling, WV 26003
Tel.: (304) 234-9000   WV
Web Site: https://www.wesbanco.com
Year Founded: 1968
WSBC—(NASDAQ)
Rev.: $631,047,000
Assets: $16,931,905,000
Liabilities: $14,505,243,000
Net Worth: $2,426,662,000
Earnings: $192,113,000
Emp.: 2,426
Fiscal Year-end: 12/31/22
Bank Holding Company
N.A.I.C.S.: 551111
Michael L. Perkins (Chief Risk & Ad-
min Officer & Sr Exec VP)
Todd F. Clossin (Vice Chm)
Anthony F. Pietranton (Sr Exec VP-
HR)
Jayson M. Zatta (Chief Banking Offi-
cer & Sr Exec VP)
James W. Cornelsen (Chm-Mid-
Atlantic Market)
Jeffrey H. Jackson (Pres & CEO)
Stephen J. Lawrence (Exec VP)
Daniel K. Weiss Jr. (CFO & Exec VP)
Robert H. Friend (Chief Credit Offi-
cer)
Scott A. Love (Exec VP)

Subsidiaries:

WesBanco Bank, Inc. (1)
1 Bank Plz, Wheeling, WV 26003
Tel.: (304) 234-9000
Web Site: https://www.wesbanco.com
Commercial Banking
N.A.I.C.S.: 522110
Brent E. Richmond (Exec VP-Treasury &
Strategic Plng)
Michael L. Perkins (Chief Risk Officer, Chief
Admin Officer & Exec VP)
Anthony F. Pietranton (Exec VP-HR)
Jayson M. Zatta (Chief Banking Officer &
Exec VP)
James W. Cornelsen (Chm-Mid-Atlantic
Market)
Jeffrey H. Jackson (Pres & CEO)
Jonathan D. Dargusch (Exec VP-Wealth
Mgmt)

Subsidiary (Domestic):

McCormick Farms, LLC (2)
4189 Route 78, Bliss, NY 14024

WesBanco, Inc.—(Continued)

Tel.: (585) 322-7274
Emp.: 25
Cattle & Milk Production Services
N.A.I.C.S.: 112120
Elizabeth McCormick *(Principal)*
Kathleen Conte *(Office Mgr)*

Branch (Domestic):

**WesBanco Bank, Inc. - Western
Pennsylvania Regional Office** (2)
1009 Perry Hwy, Pittsburgh, PA 15237
Tel.: (412) 903-3046
Web Site: http://www.wesbanco.com
Commercial Banking Services
N.A.I.C.S.: 522110

Subsidiary (Domestic):

**WesBanco Insurance Services,
Inc.** (2)
329 Pike St, Shinnston, WV 26431
Tel.: (304) 592-5700
Web Site: http://www.wesbanco.com
Emp.: 4
General Insurance Services
N.A.I.C.S.: 524210
Bruce R. Martin *(Pres)*

Subsidiary (Domestic):

WesBanco Title Agency, LLC (3)
701 6th St, Portsmouth, OH 45662-4030
Tel.: (740) 354-4200
Commercial Banking Services
N.A.I.C.S.: 522110

WesBanco Securities, Inc. (1)
135 W Main St, Saint Clairsville, OH 43950
Tel.: (304) 231-1201
Securities Brokerage Services
N.A.I.C.S.: 523150

WESCO INTERNATIONAL, INC.
225 W Station Sq Dr Ste 700, Pittsburgh, PA 15219
Tel.: (412) 454-2200 DE
Web Site: https://www.wesco.com
Year Founded: 1993
WCC—(NYSE)
Rev.: $22,385,200,000
Assets: $15,060,900,000
Liabilities: $10,029,000,000
Net Worth: $5,031,900,000
Earnings: $708,100,000
Emp.: 20,000
Fiscal Year-end: 12/31/23
Distr of Electrical & Industrial Supplies
N.A.I.C.S.: 425120
John J. Engel *(Chm, Pres & CEO)*
Diane E. Lazzaris *(Gen Counsel, Sec & Exec VP)*
Matthew S. Kulasa *(Chief Acctg Officer, Sr VP & Controller)*
David S. Schulz *(CFO & Exec VP)*
Christine A. Wolf *(Chief HR Officer & Exec VP)*
Hemant Porwal *(Exec VP-Supply Chain & Ops)*
Akash Khurana *(Chief Information & Digital Officer & Exec VP)*
James Cameron *(Exec VP & Gen Mgr-Utility & Broadband Solutions)*
Scott Gaffner *(Sr VP-IR)*
Nelson J. Squires III *(Exec VP)*
William Clayton Geary II *(Exec VP & Gen Mgr-Comm & Security Solutions)*

Subsidiaries:

Anixter International Inc. (1)
2301 Patriot Blvd, Glenview, IL 60026
Tel.: (224) 521-8000
Web Site: http://www.anixter.com
Sales Range: $5-14.9 Billion
Holding Company; Supply Chain Support Services
N.A.I.C.S.: 551112
Scott William Ramsbottom *(CIO & Exec VP)*

Subsidiary (Non-US):

AXE Distribution Solutions Trinidad, Ltd. (2)

Warehouse 1 Tacarigua Orange Grove Road, Trincity, Trinidad & Tobago
Tel.: (868) 2242255
Emp.: 9
Electrical Apparatus Distr
N.A.I.C.S.: 423610
Renwick Boodram *(Mgr-Ops)*

Subsidiary (Domestic):

Accu-Tech Corporation (2)
660 Hembree Pkwy Ste 100, Roswell, GA 30076
Tel.: (770) 751-9473
Web Site: https://www.accu-tech.com
Sales Range: $25-49.9 Million
Emp.: 20
Electric Component Whslr
N.A.I.C.S.: 423690
Tim Cullinane *(Reg VP)*

Subsidiary (Non-US):

Anixter (CIS) LLC (2)
Tel.: (7) 4957109910
Emp.: 6
Electrical & Electronic Wire Products Distr
N.A.I.C.S.: 334419

Anixter (U.K.) Limited (2)
Inspired Easthampstead Road, Bracknell, RG12 1YQ, Berkshire, United Kingdom
Tel.: (44) 1344388100
Electrical & Communication Product Distr
N.A.I.C.S.: 423610

Anixter Australia Pty. Ltd. (2)
Unit 31 2 Slough Avenue, Silverwater, 2128, NSW, Australia
Tel.: (61) 293330800
Web Site: https://www.anixter.com
Communications Security Products Supplier
N.A.I.C.S.: 811310

Anixter Austria GmbH (2)
Concorde Business Park C4, Schwechat, 2320, Vienna, Austria
Tel.: (43) 170112
Web Site: https://www.anixter.at
Emp.: 8
Computer & Peripherals Mfr
N.A.I.C.S.: 335999

Anixter Bulgaria EOOD (2)
Tsar Osvoboditel Str 58, BG-5100, Gorna Oryahovitsa, Bulgaria
Tel.: (359) 61860444
Electrical Wire & Cable Whslr
N.A.I.C.S.: 423610

Anixter Canada, Inc. (2)
200 Foster Crescent, Mississauga, L5R 3Y5, ON, Canada (100%)
Tel.: (905) 568-8999
Distribution of Data Communications Products & Electrical Wire & Cable
N.A.I.C.S.: 423610

Anixter Danmark A.S. (2)
Lautruphoj 1-3, Copenhagen, 2750, Denmark
Tel.: (45) 4 075 0904
Web Site: https://www.anixter.com
Fibres & Cables Distr
N.A.I.C.S.: 517111

Anixter Deutschland GmbH (2)
Heinrich-Lanz-Str 3, DE-70825, Korntal-Munchingen, Germany
Tel.: (49) 71503910
Emp.: 8
Fiber & Cable Distr
N.A.I.C.S.: 517111

Anixter Egypt LLC (2)
CFC Allianz Building 2nd floor, 11835, Cairo, Egypt
Tel.: (20) 228120096
Web Site: https://www.anixter.com
Wire & Cable Product Distr
N.A.I.C.S.: 423610

Anixter Espana S.L. (2)
Paseo de las Doce Estrellas 23 C, 28042, Madrid, Spain
Tel.: (34) 917212960
Electrical & Communication Product Distr
N.A.I.C.S.: 423610

Anixter Eurofin B.V. (2)
Tel.: (31) 102885900

Web Site: http://www.anixter.nl
Sales Range: $10-24.9 Million
Emp.: 20
Fiber Optic Cable Mfr
N.A.I.C.S.: 335921

Subsidiary (Non-US):

Anixter Belgium B.V.B.A. (3)
Tel.: (32) 38604700
Supplier of Electrical & Electronical Product
N.A.I.C.S.: 423690

Anixter Italia S.r.l. (3)
Tel.: (39) 02547491
Fiber Wire & Cable Distr
N.A.I.C.S.: 517111

Anixter Limited (3)
Tel.: (44) 134 438 8100
Web Site: http://www.anixter.co.uk
Distr of Wiring Systems, Networking Products & Fasteners
N.A.I.C.S.: 423610

Anixter Switzerland Sarl (3)
Tel.: (41) 21 989 2500
Web Site: http://www.anixter.com
Emp.: 12
Fiber & Cable Products Distr
N.A.I.C.S.: 517111

Subsidiary (Non-US):

Anixter Iletisim Sistemleri Pazarlama ve Ticaret A.S. (2)
Sehit Mehmet Fatih Songul Eskiyapanlar Is Merkezi N 1/1, Istanbul, Türkiye
Tel.: (90) 2164649664
Sales Range: $25-49.9 Million
Emp.: 1
Fiber & Cable Products Distr
N.A.I.C.S.: 423690
Gen Ozdenir *(Gen Mgr)*

Subsidiary (Domestic):

Anixter Inc. (2)
2301 Patriot Blvd, Glenview, IL 60026
Tel.: (224) 521-8000
Web Site: https://www.anixter.com
Supply Chain Support Services
N.A.I.C.S.: 423610

Branch (Domestic):

Anixter Inc. - Waukesha (3)
W234 N2091 Ridgeview Pkwy Ct, Waukesha, WI 53149
Tel.: (262) 951-7777
Web Site: http://www.anixter.com
Electrical Wire, Cable & Tubing Products Mfr & Distr
N.A.I.C.S.: 335929

Subsidiary (Domestic):

Anixter Puerto Rico, Inc. (3)
Centro De Distribucion Amelia Calle Diana Ste 43, Guaynabo, PR 00968
Tel.: (787) 995-7300
Electronic Product Distr
N.A.I.C.S.: 334419

Anixter, Inc.-Connecticut (3)
527 Knotter Dr, Cheshire, CT 06410
Tel.: (203) 271-3600
Web Site: http://www.anixter.com
Wire & Cable Mfr
N.A.I.C.S.: 332618

Subsidiary (Domestic):

Tornik Inc. (4)
16 Old Forge Rd, Rocky Hill, CT 06067
Tel.: (860) 282-6081
Web Site: https://www.tornik.com
Computer Peripheral Equipment Whslr
N.A.I.C.S.: 334118
Edward S. Stephens *(Founder & CEO)*

Subsidiary (Non-US):

Anixter India Private Limited (2)
95 Brigade Road, Bengaluru, 560 025, India
Tel.: (91) 8040703333
Web Site: https://www.anixter.com
Emp.: 10
Fiber & Cable Distr
N.A.I.C.S.: 517111

Anixter Jorvex S.A.C. (2)
Tel.: (51) 4151000
Web Site: https://www.jorvex.com
Electrical Wire & Cable Whslr
N.A.I.C.S.: 423610

Anixter Logistica do Brasil LTDA (2)
Rua Virgilio Wey 150 Lapa, Sao Paulo, 05036-060, Brazil
Tel.: (55) 1138686606
Electrical Wire & Cable Whslr
N.A.I.C.S.: 423610
Rafaela Macedo Silva *(Product Mgr)*

Anixter New Zealand Limited (2)
76 Carbine Rd Mt Wellington, Auckland, 1060, New Zealand
Tel.: (64) 98492801
Web Site: https://www.anixter.com
Emp.: 5
Fiber & Cable Products Mfr
N.A.I.C.S.: 517111

Anixter Norge A.N.S. (2)
Hagalokkveien 13, 1383, Asker, Norway
Tel.: (47) 23242020
Emp.: 4
Fiber & Cable Products Distr
N.A.I.C.S.: 517111

Anixter Poland Sp.z.o.o. (2)
ul Szyszkowa 35/37, 02-285, Warsaw, Poland
Tel.: (48) 228783314
Emp.: 15
Fiber & Cable Distr
N.A.I.C.S.: 517111

Anixter Portugal S.A. (2)
Tagus Park - Nucleo Central - 301, 2740-122, Porto Salvo, Portugal
Tel.: (351) 214220400
Emp.: 8
Fiber & Cable Distr
N.A.I.C.S.: 517111

Anixter Power Solutions Canada Inc. (2)
188 Purdy Rd, PO Box 399, Colborne, K0K 1S0, ON, Canada
Tel.: (905) 355-2474
Web Site: http://www.hdsupplysolutions.ca
Electrical Product Whslr
N.A.I.C.S.: 423610

Anixter Saudi Arabia Limited (2)
7th Floor Juffali Building King Abdul Aziz Street, PO Box 4734, Al Khobar, 31952, Saudi Arabia
Tel.: (966) 138877702
Electrical Apparatus Whslr
N.A.I.C.S.: 423610

Anixter Singapore Pte. Ltd. (2)
5A Toh Guan Road East 06-02, Singapore, 608830, Singapore
Tel.: (65) 65081600
Web Site: https://www.anixter.com
Fiber & Cable Wire Products Distr
N.A.I.C.S.: 423610

Anixter Sverige AB (2)
EA Rosengrens Gata 32 - 421 32 Vastra Frolunda, Gothenburg, Sweden
Tel.: (46) 31899535
Electrical & Communication Product Distr
N.A.I.C.S.: 423610

Anixter Thailand Inc. (2)
202 Le Concorde Office Tower 21st Floor Unit 2103A Ratchadapisek Road, Huaykwang, Bangkok, 10320, Thailand
Tel.: (66) 26941020
Web Site: http://www.anixter.com
Fiber & Cable Products Mfr
N.A.I.C.S.: 423610

Atlas Gentech (NZ) Limited (2)
76 Carbine Road, Mt Wellington, Auckland, 1060, New Zealand
Tel.: (64) 95742700
Web Site: https://www.atlasgentech.co.nz
Communication Equipment Mfr
N.A.I.C.S.: 334290
Chris Fair *(Gen Mgr)*

Central Security Distribution Pty. Ltd. (2)
3A Aerolink Drive, Tullamarine, Melbourne, 3043, VIC, Australia
Tel.: (61) 390011900

Web Site: https://www.csd.com.au
Communication Equipment Mfr
N.A.I.C.S.: 334290
Mark Edwards *(Gen Mgr-Products & Mktg)*

Subsidiary (Domestic):

Clark Security Products, Inc. (2)
4775 Viewridge Ave, San Diego, CA 92123-1641
Tel.: (858) 505-1950
Web Site: http://www.clarksecurity.com
Sales Range: $25-49.9 Million
Emp.: 15
Security Products & Locksmith Supplies Distr
N.A.I.C.S.: 423850
Peter Berg *(COO)*

Communication Cables, LLC (2)
1601 Feehanville Dr Ste 500 Mt, Prospect Heights, IL 60124
Tel.: (303) 952-1800
Web Site: http://www.comcables.com
Electrical Wire & Cable Whslr
N.A.I.C.S.: 423610

Subsidiary (Non-US):

Eskanet S.A. (2)
Dir Sarandi 675 piso 5 Oficina 501, Montevideo, Uruguay
Tel.: (598) 29152222
Electrical Wire & Cable Whslr
N.A.I.C.S.: 423610

Inner Range Pty. Ltd. (2)
1 Millennium Court, Knoxfield, 3180, VIC, Australia
Tel.: (61) 397804300
Web Site: https://www.innerrange.com
Software Development Services
N.A.I.C.S.: 513210

Subsidiary (Domestic):

Northern Video Systems, Inc. (2)
3625 Cincinhati Ave, Rocklin, CA 95765
Tel.: (916) 543-4000
Electrical Wire & Cable Whslr
N.A.I.C.S.: 423610

Subsidiary (Non-US):

PT Anixter Indonesia (2)
Wisma Bisnis Indonesia 2 JL IR H Juanda 3 No 32, Kel Kebon Kelapa Kec Gambir, Jakarta, 10120, Indonesia
Tel.: (62) 213504543
Web Site: https://www.anixter.com
Electrical Wire & Cable Whslr
N.A.I.C.S.: 423610

Servicios Anixter, S.A. de C.V. (2)
Boulevard Manuel Avila Camacho 3130 piso 5 Colonia Valle Dorado, Tlalnepantla, 54020, Estado de Mexico, Mexico
Tel.: (52) 5553662200
Fiber & Cable Products Mfr
N.A.I.C.S.: 517111
Andres Flores *(Mgr-Sls)*

Subsidiary (Domestic):

Signal Capital Corporation (2)
55 Ferncroft Rd Ste 110, Danvers, MA 01923-4001
Tel.: (978) 777-3866
Electrical Apparatus & Equipment Whslr
N.A.I.C.S.: 423610

Tri-Ed Distribution Inc. (2)
13831 Seaboard Cir, Garden Grove, CA 92843
Tel.: (714) 265-4000
Web Site: http://www.tri-ed.com
Electrical Wire & Cable Whslr
N.A.I.C.S.: 423610

Tri-Ed Puerto Rico Ltd. Inc. (2)
54 Federico Acosta Tres Monjitas, San Juan, PR 00923
Tel.: (787) 767-8848
Web Site: http://www.tri-ed.com
Electrical Wire & Cable Whslr
N.A.I.C.S.: 423610

Atlanta Electrical Distributors, LLC (1)
1770 Breckinridge Pkwy Ste 100, Duluth, GA 30096

Tel.: (678) 205-2290
Web Site: https://www.aedga.com
Electrical Products Distr
N.A.I.C.S.: 423610

Carlton-Bates Company de Mexico S.A. de C.V. (1)
Av Martel 550 Parque Industrial Martel, 66600, Apodaca, Mexico
Tel.: (52) 8183114448
Consumer Electronic Rental & Leasing Services
N.A.I.C.S.: 532210

Computer Maintenance Agency, Inc. (1)
15 1st Floor Krithika Layout Opp-Image Gardens, Madhapur, Hyderabad, 500081, TS, India
Tel.: (91) 4027814468
Web Site: https://www.cmaorg.co.in
Hardware & Software Maintenance Services
N.A.I.C.S.: 541511

EECOL Electric ULC (1)
63 Sunpark Drive SE, Calgary, T2X 3V4, AB, Canada
Tel.: (403) 253-1952
Web Site: https://www.eecol.com
Electrical Product Whslr
N.A.I.C.S.: 423610

Fastec Industrial (1)
2219 Eddie Williams Rd, Johnson City, TN 37601
Web Site: http://www.fastecindustrial.com
Sales Range: $50-74.9 Million
Emp.: 250
Industrial Fasteners, Hardware & Lock Products Mfr & Distr
N.A.I.C.S.: 423710

Hazmasters Inc. (1)
651 Harwood Avenue North Unit 4, Ajax, L1Z-0K4, ON, Canada
Tel.: (905) 427-0220
Electrical & Communication Product Distr
N.A.I.C.S.: 423610

Hi-Line Utility Supply Company (1)
51 Prairie Pkwy, Gilberts, IL 60136
Web Site: https://www.hilineco.com
Electrical & Communication Product Distr
N.A.I.C.S.: 423610

Rahi Bilgi Sistemleri Dis Ticaret Limited Sirketi (1)
Cobancesme Mahallesi Sanayi Caddesi Nish Istanbul A, Blok Ofis Apt No 44 Al Bahcelievler, 34197, Istanbul, Turkiye
Tel.: (90) 8502051590
Software Provider
N.A.I.C.S.: 423430

Rahi Systems Australia Pty. Ltd. (1)
Unit 30 Slough Business Park 2 Slough Ave, Silverwater, 2128, NSW, Australia
Tel.: (61) 284884700
Information Technology Services
N.A.I.C.S.: 541519

Rahi Systems Europe B.V. (1)
Rijnlanderweg 766 Unit G, 2132, Hoofddorp, Netherlands
Tel.: (31) 611515873
Software Provider
N.A.I.C.S.: 423430

Rahi Systems GmbH (1)
Munchner Strasse 20, Unterfohring, 85774, Munich, Germany
Tel.: (49) 8928944326
Information Technology Services
N.A.I.C.S.: 541519

Rahi Systems Inc. (1)
48303 Fremont Blvd, Fremont, CA 94538
Tel.: (510) 651-2205
Web Site: https://rahisystems.com.au
Information Technology Services
N.A.I.C.S.: 541519

Rahi Systems Japan LLC (1)
BM Kabutocho Building 1F 11-7, Nihonbashi- Kabutocho Chuo-ku, Tokyo, 103-0026, Japan
Tel.: (81) 357381339
Information Technology Services
N.A.I.C.S.: 541519

Rahi Systems Limited (1)

Room 117 Floor 29 5 The Gateway Tower 15 Canton Rd, Harbour City, China (Hong Kong)
Tel.: (852) 58080076
Information Technology Services
N.A.I.C.S.: 541519

Rahi Systems Pte. Ltd. (1)
70 Shenton Way 21-14 15 EON Shenton, Singapore, 079118, Singapore
Tel.: (65) 62143969
Software Provider
N.A.I.C.S.: 423430

Rahi Technologies Limited (1)
Robe House Cloughkeating Avenue Raheen Business Park Co, Limerick, Ireland
Tel.: (353) 61574160
Information Technology Services
N.A.I.C.S.: 541519

Stone Eagle Electrical Supply Limited Partnership (1)
385 MacKenzie Blvd, Fort McMurray, T9H 5E2, AB, Canada
Tel.: (780) 799-4337
Electrical Products Distr
N.A.I.C.S.: 423610

WESCO - Anixter Israel Ltd. (1)
5 Sharon Street 3rd Floor, PO Box 1102, Lod, Airport City, 7019802, Israel
Tel.: (972) 765317061
Electronic Product Distr
N.A.I.C.S.: 423690

WESCO Distribution Canada LP (1)
500 Hood Road Suite 120, Markham, L3R 9Z3, ON, Canada
Tel.: (905) 415-6100
Web Site: https://www.buy.wesco.ca
Sales Range: $25-49.9 Million
Emp.: 2,000
Electric Equipment Mfr
N.A.I.C.S.: 336320

WESCO Distribution, Inc. (1)
225 W Sta Sq Dr Ste 700, Pittsburgh, PA 15219
Tel.: (412) 454-2200
Web Site: https://www.wesco.com
Sales Range: $800-899.9 Million
Emp.: 5,800
Distr of Electrical & Industrial Supplies
N.A.I.C.S.: 444180

Unit (Domestic):

Avon Wesco (2)
500 Prime Pl, Hauppauge, NY 11788 (100%)
Tel.: (631) 582-4770
Web Site: http://www.avonelec.com
Sales Range: $10-24.9 Million
Emp.: 100
Electrical Supply Mfr
N.A.I.C.S.: 423610

Subsidiary (Domestic):

Bruckner Supply Co., Inc. (2)
36 Harbor Park Dr, Port Washington, NY 11050-4651
Tel.: (516) 484-6070
Web Site: http://www.brucknersupply.com
Sales Range: $125-149.9 Million
Emp.: 300
Supplier of Industrial Tools
N.A.I.C.S.: 423610

Carlton-Bates Company (2)
3600 W 69th St, Little Rock, AR 72209 (100%)
Tel.: (501) 562-9100
Web Site: http://www.carltonbates.com
Sales Range: $200-249.9 Million
Emp.: 250
Distr of Electronic Industrial Components
N.A.I.C.S.: 423690

Division (Domestic):

Carlton-Bates Company - Saint Louis (3)
2820 Market St, Saint Louis, MO 63103
Tel.: (314) 655-2978
Web Site: http://www.carltonbates.com
Sales Range: $25-49.9 Million
Emp.: 12
Electronic Components Distr
N.A.I.C.S.: 423690

Subsidiary (Domestic):

Carlton-Bates Company of Tennessee Inc. (3)
3600 W 69th St, Little Rock, AR 72209
Tel.: (501) 562-9100
Web Site: http://www.carlton-bates.com
Sales Range: $1-9.9 Million
Emp.: 100
Mfr Of Electronic Parts & Equipment
N.A.I.C.S.: 423690

Subsidiary (Domestic):

Communications Supply Corporation (2)
200 E Lies Rd, Carol Stream, IL 60188
Tel.: (630) 221-6400
Web Site: https://www.gocsc.com
Sales Range: $500-549.9 Million
Emp.: 750
Voice & Data Communications, Access Control & Security Surveillance Cables & Connectors Whslr
N.A.I.C.S.: 423610

Subsidiary (Domestic):

Liberty AV Solutions (3)
11675 Ridgeline Dr, Colorado Springs, CO 80921
Tel.: (719) 388-7500
Web Site:
    http://www.secure.libertycable.com
Wire & Cable Products Whslr
N.A.I.C.S.: 423610

Subsidiary (Domestic):

Conney Safety Products, LLC (2)
3202 Latham Dr, Madison, WI 53744-4190
Tel.: (412) 454-2200
Web Site: https://www.conney.com
Sales Range: $75-99.9 Million
Emp.: 150
Safety & First-Aid Products Supplier
N.A.I.C.S.: 423840

EESCO Distribution (2)
2401 Internationale Pkwy, Woodridge, IL 60517
Tel.: (630) 296-2555
Web Site: http://www.eescodist.com
Sales Range: $300-349.9 Million
Emp.: 100
Automation & Control Products & Electrical Supplies Distr
N.A.I.C.S.: 423830
Scott Martin *(Pres)*

Herning Underground Supply Inc. (2)
2800 Mead Ave, Santa Clara, CA 95051
Tel.: (408) 562-0400
Web Site:
    http://www.herningunderground.com
Sales Range: $25-49.9 Million
Emp.: 20
Underground Conduit System Products Distr
N.A.I.C.S.: 423610

Subsidiary (Domestic):

Allied Utility Products, Inc. (3)
569 Exchange Ct, Livermore, CA 94550
Tel.: (925) 373-7400
Web Site: http://www.alliedutility.com
Sales Range: $25-49.9 Million
Emp.: 7
Distr of Underground Utility Products
N.A.I.C.S.: 424720

Subsidiary (Domestic):

Hill Country Electric Supply, L.P. (2)
4801 Freidrich Ln Bldg 2 Ste 200, Austin, TX 78744
Tel.: (512) 428-9300
Web Site: https://www.hces.net
Emp.: 50
Electrical Apparatus & Related Equipment Merchant Whslr
N.A.I.C.S.: 423610

Needham Electric Supply, LLC (2)
5 Shawmut Rd, Canton, MA 02021
Tel.: (781) 828-9494
Web Site: https://www.needhamelectric.com
Electrical Products Distr

WESCO International, Inc.—(Continued)

N.A.I.C.S.: 423610
Joe A. Cincotta (CEO)

Subsidiary (Domestic):

**Needham Electric Supply -
Fitchburg**   **(3)**
50 Crawford St, Fitchburg, MA 01420
Tel.: (978) 343-3711
Web Site: https://www.needhamelectric.com
Emp.: 9
Electrical Products Distr
N.A.I.C.S.: 423610

Subsidiary (Domestic):

RECO, LLC   **(2)**
Woodland Tech Ctr 1008 Seabrook Way,
Cincinnati, OH 45245
Tel.: (513) 718-1111
Web Site: http://www.reco.net
Sales Range: $25-49.9 Million
Emp.: 34
Industrial Production & Automation Equip-
ment Distr
N.A.I.C.S.: 423830

Subsidiary (Domestic):

TVC Communications, LLC   **(2)**
800 Airport Rd, Annville, PA 17003
Tel.: (717) 838-3306
Web Site: https://www.tvcinc.com
Sales Range: $50-74.9 Million
Telecommunication Support Services
N.A.I.C.S.: 517112

Division (Domestic):

Satellite Engineering Group   **(3)**
11605 S Alden St, Olathe, KS 66062
Tel.: (913) 324-6000
Web Site: http://www.sateng.com
Sales Range: $25-49.9 Million
Emp.: 23
Electronic Parts & Equipment Merchant
Whlslr
N.A.I.C.S.: 423690
Chris Childs (Dir-Sls)
Harry Matthews (Mgr-Sls-Southeast)

Subsidiary (Domestic):

**WESCO Distribution Inc. -
Midlothian**   **(2)**
12141 Wilfong Ct, Midlothian, VA 23112-
3975
Tel.: (804) 253-8900
Web Site: http://www.wesco.com
Emp.: 25
Electrical Apparatus & Automation Product
Mfr
N.A.I.C.S.: 423610

Branch (Domestic):

CCA-Wesco   **(3)**
35 Otis St, Westborough, MA
01581-3311   **(100%)**
Tel.: (508) 870-5000
Web Site: http://www.wesco.com
Rev.: $26,200,000
Emp.: 30
Mfr of Electrical Systems & Automation
Products
N.A.I.C.S.: 423610

Subsidiary (Domestic):

WESCO Distribution, Inc.   **(2)**
3011 Lausat St, Metairie, LA 70001-5923
Tel.: (504) 835-8888
Web Site: http://www.wescodirect.com
Electrical Supplies Distr & Retailer
N.A.I.C.S.: 423610

WESCO Equity Corporation   **(1)**
2325 Renaissance Dr, Las Vegas, NV
89119
Tel.: (702) 967-2459
Electrical Products Distr
N.A.I.C.S.: 423610

WESCO Nevada, Ltd.   **(1)**
2215 B Renaissance Dr Ste 5, Las Vegas,
NV 89119
Tel.: (702) 673-5317
Electrical Products Distr
N.A.I.C.S.: 423610

WESCO Services, LLC   **(1)**

225 W Station Sq Dr Ste 700, Pittsburgh,
PA 15219
Tel.: (412) 454-2200
Web Site: http://www.wesco.com
Bare Printed Circuit Board Mfr
N.A.I.C.S.: 334412

Subsidiary (Domestic):

Sylvania Lighting Services Corp.   **(2)**
200 Ballardvale St, Wilmington, MA 01887
Tel.: (978) 777-1900
Web Site: http://www.sylvania.com
Emp.: 220
Lighting Products
N.A.I.C.S.: 335132
Todd Myers (CEO)

Subsidiary (Domestic):

Amtech Lighting Services   **(3)**
1085 N Main St Ste C, Orange, CA 92867-
5458
Tel.: (714) 940-4000
Lighting Systems
N.A.I.C.S.: 335132

Branch (Domestic):

Sylvania Lighting Services   **(4)**
12740 Lakeland Rd, Santa Fe Springs, CA
90670-4633
Tel.: (909) 348-6200
Sales Range: $125-149.9 Million
Emp.: 125
Lighting Services
N.A.I.C.S.: 238210

Wesco Anixter USVI, LLC   **(1)**
51 Steel Dr, New Castle, DE 19720
Tel.: (302) 325-2590
Electrical & Electronic Solutions Distr
N.A.I.C.S.: 423610

**Wesco Manufactured
Structures-Meridian**   **(1)**
1395 S Teare Ave, Meridian, ID 83642
Tel.: (208) 887-0072
Web Site: http://buy.wesco.com
Electrical Apparatus & Equipment, Wiring
Supplies & Related Equipment Merchant
Whlslr
N.A.I.C.S.: 423610

WEST BANCORPORATION
INC.
1601 22nd St, West Des Moines, IA
50265-0020
Tel.: (515) 222-2300   **IA**
Web Site:
https://www.westbankstrong.com
Year Founded: 1984
WTBA—(NASDAQ)
Rev.: $170,371,000
Assets: $3,825,758,000
Liabilities: $3,600,715,000
Net Worth: $225,043,000
Earnings: $24,137,000
Emp.: 181
Fiscal Year-end: 12/31/23
Bank Holding Company
N.A.I.C.S.: 551111
George D. Milligan (Vice Chm)
Douglas Ray Gulling (Executives, Bd
of Dirs)
Brad Winterbottom Lee (Exec VP)
David D. Nelson (Pres & CEO)
Harlee N. Olafson (Chief Risk Officer
& Exec VP)
John F. McKinney III (Gen Counsel &
VP)
Brad P. Peters (Exec VP)
Melissa L. Gillespie (Sec)

Subsidiaries:

West Bank   **(1)**
3330 Westown Pkwy, West Des Moines, IA
50266
Tel.: (515) 222-2300
Web Site: https://www.westbankstrong.com
Sales Range: $25-49.9 Million
Emp.: 60
State Commercial Banks
N.A.I.C.S.: 522110
Mike Zinser (Pres-Market-Rochester)

WEST COAST COMMUNITY
BANCORP
75 River St., Santa Cruz, CA 95060
Tel.: (831) 457-5000
Web Site:
https://www.sccountybank.com
SCZC—(OTCIQ)
Bank Holding Company
N.A.I.C.S.: 551111

Subsidiaries:

Santa Cruz County Bank   **(1)**
75 River St., Santa Cruz, CA 95060
Tel.: (831) 457-5000
Web Site: https://www.sccountybank.com
Rev.: $37,373,287
Assets: $1,070,983,369
Liabilities: $919,885,001
Net Worth: $151,098,368
Earnings: $12,275,250
Emp.: 76
Fiscal Year-end: 12/31/2019
Commercial Banking
N.A.I.C.S.: 522110
John Burroughs (Vice Chm)
Stephen D. Pahl (Chm)
Krista Snelling (Pres & CEO)
Andrew Chamber (VP)
Shamara van der Voort (COO & Exec VP)
Cecilia Situ (CFO & Exec VP)
Shawn Lipman (Chief Credit Officer & Exec
VP)

WEST COAST VENTURES
GROUP CORP.
6610 Holman St Ste 301, Arvada, CO
80004
Tel.: (303) 423-1300   **NV**
Web Site:
http://www.westcoastventures
groupcorp.com
Year Founded: 2011
WCVC—(OTCIQ)
Rev.: $3,635,234
Assets: $2,295,662
Liabilities: $7,997,245
Net Worth: ($5,701,583)
Earnings: ($5,293,313)
Emp.: 60
Fiscal Year-end: 12/31/19
Investment Services
N.A.I.C.S.: 523999
James M. Nixon (Founder, Chm,
Pres, CEO, CFO & Sec)

WEST PHARMACEUTICAL
SERVICES, INC.
530 Herman O W Dr, Exton, PA
19341-1147
Tel.: (610) 594-2900   **PA**
Web Site:
https://www.westpharma.com
Year Founded: 1923
WST—(NYSE)
Rev.: $2,949,800,000
Assets: $3,829,500,000
Liabilities: $948,500,000
Net Worth: $2,881,000,000
Earnings: $593,400,000
Emp.: 10,600
Fiscal Year-end: 12/31/23
Medical Packaging & Plastic Compo-
nents Mfr
N.A.I.C.S.: 339113
Chad R. Winters (Chief Acctg Officer,
VP & Controller)
Eric Mark Green (Chm, Pres & CEO)
Annette F. Favorite (Chief HR Officer
& Sr VP)
Silji Abraham (CTO & Sr VP)
Bernard John Birkett (Chief Fin &
Ops Officer & Sr VP)
Cindy Reiss-Clark (Chief Comml Offi-
cer & Sr VP)
Christopher Ryan (Sr VP-
Containment & Glass Sys)
Kimberly Banks MacKay (Gen Coun-
sel, Sec & Sr VP)
Kathy dePadua (VP)
Robert Segura (VP)

Subsidiaries:

**(mfg) Tech Group Puerto Rico,
LLC**   **(1)**
PO Box 372587, Cayey, PR 00737-2587
Tel.: (787) 747-4900
Pharmaceuticals Product Mfr
N.A.I.C.S.: 325412

Citation Plastics Co.   **(1)**
101 Gordon Dr, Exton, PA 19341-1320
Tel.: (610) 594-2900
Medical Device & Plastic Component Mfr
N.A.I.C.S.: 339113

Daikyo Seiko, Ltd.   **(1)**
1305-1 Kurohakama-Cho, Sumida-Ku,
Sano, 327-0813, Tochigi, Japan   **(25%)**
Tel.: (81) 283270008
Web Site: https://www.daikyoseiko.jp
Sales Range: $200-249.9 Million
Emp.: 850
Mfr of Specialty Pharmaceutical Packaging
Products Including Elastomeric Serum &
Lyo Closures, Resin Vials, Containers &
Syringes
N.A.I.C.S.: 325412
Morihiro Sudo (Pres)

Tech Group Europe Limited   **(1)**
Damastown Industrial Park, Mulhuddart,
Dublin, 15, Ireland
Tel.: (353) 18859700
Sales Range: $25-49.9 Million
Emp.: 300
Medical Device & Plastic Component Mfr
N.A.I.C.S.: 339113

Tech Group Grand Rapids, Inc.   **(1)**
217 Grandville Ave SW, Grand Rapids, MI
49503
Tel.: (616) 643-6001
Web Site: http://www.techgroup.com
Emp.: 350
Medical Component Mfr
N.A.I.C.S.: 339112

Tech Group North America, Inc.   **(1)**
14677 N 74th St, Scottsdale, AZ 85260-
2403
Tel.: (480) 281-4500
Web Site: http://www.techgroup.com
Sales Range: $75-99.9 Million
Emp.: 200
Holding Company for Plastic Injection Mold-
ing Manufacturers
N.A.I.C.S.: 326199

Plant (Domestic):

Tech Group   **(2)**
14677 N 74th St, Scottsdale, AZ 85260-
2403
Tel.: (480) 281-4500
Web Site: http://www.techgroup.com
Sales Range: $75-99.9 Million
Mfr of Plastic Products
N.A.I.C.S.: 326199
Steve Uhlmann (Chm)

Tech Group Phoenix, Inc.   **(2)**
470 W Vaughan St, Tempe, AZ 85283-3671
Tel.: (480) 281-4300
Web Site: http://www.techgroup.com
Sales Range: $50-74.9 Million
Emp.: 150
Mfr of Plastic Products
N.A.I.C.S.: 326199

Tech Group Puerto Rico   **(2)**
State Rd No 1 Km 487 Bo Bretiz, Cidra, PR
00737
Tel.: (787) 747-4900
Web Site: http://www.techgroup.com
Sales Range: $125-149.9 Million
Emp.: 200
Injection Molding Mfr
N.A.I.C.S.: 326160

Tech Group Tempe   **(2)**
640 S Rockford Dr, Tempe, AZ 85281-3000
Tel.: (480) 281-4400
Web Site: http://www.techgroup.com
Sales Range: $25-49.9 Million
Emp.: 150
Medical Contract Mfr
N.A.I.C.S.: 339112

The West Company Italia S.R.L.   **(1)**
Fabio Filzi St, Milan, 20124, Italy   **(100%)**
Tel.: (39) 026703079

Sales Range: $25-49.9 Million
Emp.: 6
Sales & Marketer of Pharmaceuticals
N.A.I.C.S.: 424210
Anna Maini (Mng Dir)

West Analytical Services, LLC (1)
530 Herman O West Dr, Exton, PA 19341-1147
Tel.: (610) 594-2900
Pharmaceutical Testing & Analysis Services
N.A.I.C.S.: 541715

West Pharmaceutical Packaging (China) Company Ltd. (1)
No 111 Tianchen Road, Qingpu District, Shanghai, 201707, China
Tel.: (86) 2139206300
Sales Range: $25-49.9 Million
Emp.: 56
Medical Device & Plastic Component Mfr
N.A.I.C.S.: 339113

West Pharmaceutical Packaging India Private Limited (1)
No 102 Gowra Grand 1-8-384 and 385 Sardar Patel Road, Begumpet, Hyderabad, 500003, Telangana, India
Tel.: (91) 404 940 1111
Web Site: http://www.verux.com
Sales Range: $10-24.9 Million
Emp.: 18
Medical Device & Plastic Component Mfr
N.A.I.C.S.: 339113

West Pharmaceutical Services Argentina S.A. (1)
Av Bernadro Ader 2754 Carapachay, B1606DUN, Buenos Aires, Argentina (100%)
Tel.: (54) 1147211100
Web Site: http://www.westpharma.com
Sales Range: $50-74.9 Million
Emp.: 6
Sales of Plastics Products
N.A.I.C.S.: 325211

West Pharmaceutical Services Brasil Ltda. (1)
Avenida Viela Nossa Sra das Gracas 115 Bairro Serraria, Diadema, 09900, SP, Brazil (100%)
Tel.: (55) 1140556060
Pharmaceutical Packaging Mfr & Delivery System
N.A.I.C.S.: 325412

West Pharmaceutical Services Colombia S.A. (1)
Parque Industrial Gran Sabana - Bodega M33, Tocancipa, Cundinamarca, Colombia
Tel.: (57) 18698799
Sales Range: $10-24.9 Million
Emp.: 10
Medical Device & Plastic Component Mfr
N.A.I.C.S.: 339113

West Pharmaceutical Services Cornwall Limited (1)
Holmbush Industrial Estate Bucklers Lane, Saint Austell, PL 31 2QB, Cornwall, United Kingdom
Tel.: (44) 172663563
Sales Range: $250-299.9 Million
Emp.: 100
Rubber & Plastic Compression Molding
N.A.I.C.S.: 314910

West Pharmaceutical Services Cornwall Ltd. (1)
Cooksland Industrial Est, Bodmin, PL31 2QB, Cornwall, United Kingdom (100%)
Tel.: (44) 0120873122
Web Site: http://www.westpharma.com
Sales Range: $50-74.9 Million
Emp.: 52
Mold & Die Mfr
N.A.I.C.S.: 333514

West Pharmaceutical Services Danmark A/S (1)
Fuglevangsvej 51, 8700, Horsens, Denmark (100%)
Tel.: (45) 75616000
Emp.: 258
Rubber Sheets & Metal Seals Mfr
N.A.I.C.S.: 326299

West Pharmaceutical Services Deutschland GmbH & Co. KG (1)

Stolberger Strasse 21-41, 52249, Eschweiler, Germany (100%)
Tel.: (49) 24037960
Sales Range: $125-149.9 Million
Emp.: 950
Metal, Plastic & Combination Seal Mfr
N.A.I.C.S.: 326299

West Pharmaceutical Services Espana, S.A. (1)
Avenida Del Sistema Solar 28, San Fernando de Henares, 28830, Spain (100%)
Tel.: (34) 916561415
Web Site: http://www.westpharma.com
Sales Range: $50-74.9 Million
Emp.: 6
Marketing of Rubber Packaging Products
N.A.I.C.S.: 314910

West Pharmaceutical Services Finance Danmark ApS (1)
Fuglevangsvej 51, 8700, Horsens, Denmark (100%)
Tel.: (45) 75616000
Web Site: http://www.westpharma.com
Sales Range: $50-74.9 Million
Emp.: 200
Rubber Sheets & Metal Seals Mfr for Injectables & Infusion Systems
N.A.I.C.S.: 326299

West Pharmaceutical Services France S.A. (1)
(100%)
Tel.: (33) 323978888
Sales Range: $50-74.9 Million
Emp.: 500
Compression Molding Operations
N.A.I.C.S.: 326299

West Pharmaceutical Services Hispania S.A. (1)
Paseo de la Castellana numero 164 piso E-2, 28046, Madrid, Spain
Tel.: (34) 916561415
Medical Device & Plastic Component Mfr
N.A.I.C.S.: 339113

West Pharmaceutical Services Holding Danmark ApS (1)
Fuglevangsvej 51, 8700, Horsens, Denmark (100%)
Tel.: (45) 75616000
Sales Range: $100-124.9 Million
Emp.: 220
Holding Company; Rubber Sheets & Metal Seals Mfr for Injectables & Infusion Systems
N.A.I.C.S.: 551112

West Pharmaceutical Services Holding France SAS (1)
38 Rue Robert Degon, 02170, Le Nouvion-en-Thierache, France
Tel.: (33) 323978888
Web Site: https://www.westpharma.com
Sales Range: $250-299.9 Million
Emp.: 500
Holding Company
N.A.I.C.S.: 551112

West Pharmaceutical Services Holding GmbH (1)
Stolberger Strasse 21 41, 52249, Eschweiler, Germany (100%)
Tel.: (49) 24037960
Sales Range: $250-299.9 Million
Emp.: 675
Holding Company
N.A.I.C.S.: 551112

West Pharmaceutical Services Lakewood, Inc. (1)
1200 Paco Way, Lakewood, NJ 08701-5938
Tel.: (732) 367-9000
Pharmaceuticals Product Mfr
N.A.I.C.S.: 325412

West Pharmaceutical Services Limited Danmark A/S (1)
Fuglevangsvej 51, 8700, Horsens, Denmark
Tel.: (45) 075616000
Web Site: http://www.westpharma.com
Sales Range: $100-124.9 Million
Emp.: 160
Rubber Sheets & Metal Seals Mfr for Injectables & Infusion Systems
N.A.I.C.S.: 314910

West Pharmaceutical Services Normandie SAS (1)

ZAC Pharma Parc, Le Vaudreuil, 27100, France
Tel.: (33) 232633939
Web Site: http://www.westpharma.com
Sales Range: $25-49.9 Million
Emp.: 80
Medical Device & Plastic Component Mfr
N.A.I.C.S.: 339113

West Pharmaceutical Services Singapore (Holding) Pte. Limited (1)
15 Joo Koon Circle Pioneer, Singapore, 629046, Singapore
Tel.: (65) 68623400
Web Site: http://www.westpharma.com
Sales Range: $50-74.9 Million
Emp.: 200
Investment Management Service
N.A.I.C.S.: 551112

West Pharmaceutical Services Singapore Pte. Ltd. (1)
8 Jurong Town Hall Road JTC Summit 29-01/02, Singapore, 609434, Singapore (100%)
Tel.: (65) 6 862 3400
Web Site: https://www.westpharma.com
Sales Range: $125-149.9 Million
Emp.: 450
Compression Molding Including Stoppers, Closures & Medical Device Components Mfr
N.A.I.C.S.: 333310

West Pharmaceutical Services Venezuela C.A. (1)
Av Libertador C C Multicentro Empresarial Del Este Piso 7 Oficina A-73, Chacao, Caracas, Venezuela (100%)
Tel.: (58) 2122612443
Web Site: https://www.westpharma.com
Sales Range: $50-74.9 Million
Emp.: 6
Optical Frame Distr
N.A.I.C.S.: 424990

West Pharmaceutical Services Verwaltungs GmbH (1)
Stolberger Strasse 21-41, 52249, Eschweiler, Germany
Tel.: (49) 2403796100
Sales Range: $25-49.9 Million
Emp.: 60
Medical Device & Plastic Component Mfr
N.A.I.C.S.: 339113

West Pharmaceutical Services de Colombia, S.A. (1)
Cl 100 8a 49 T B Ofc 609, Ofc 609, Bogota, 110221, Colombia (100%)
Tel.: (57) 16559990
Web Site: http://www.westpharma.com
Sales Range: $50-74.9 Million
Emp.: 6
Rubber & Metal Packaging Products Distr
N.A.I.C.S.: 314910

West Pharmaceutical Services of Delaware, Inc. (1)
3411 Silverside Rd, Wilmington, DE 19810
Tel.: (302) 478-6160
Medical Device & Plastic Component Mfr
N.A.I.C.S.: 339113

West Pharmaceutical Services of Florida, Inc. (1)
5111 Park St N, Saint Petersburg, FL 33709-1109
Tel.: (727) 546-2402
Web Site: https://www.westpharma.com
Medical Device & Plastic Component Mfr
N.A.I.C.S.: 339113

West Pharmaceutical Services, Inc. (1)
5111 Park St N, Saint Petersburg, FL 33709 (100%)
Tel.: (727) 546-2402
Web Site: http://www.westpharma.com
Sales Range: $50-74.9 Million
Emp.: 350
Metal & Rubber Closures for Pharmaceuticals
N.A.I.C.S.: 326299

West Pharmaceutical Services, Inc. (1)
347 Oliver St, Jersey Shore, PA 17740
Tel.: (570) 398-1133

Web Site: http://www.westphrama.com
Sales Range: $75-99.9 Million
Emp.: 250
Compression Rubber Molding Operations
N.A.I.C.S.: 326299

West Pharmaceutical Services, Inc. (1)
2921 W Reach Rd, Williamsport, PA 17701-4177
Tel.: (570) 326-7673
Web Site: http://www.westpharma.com
Sales Range: $50-74.9 Million
Emp.: 170
Plastic Injection Molding Operations
N.A.I.C.S.: 326299

West Pharmaceutical Services, Inc. (1)
923 W Railroad St, Kearney, NE 68845-5128
Tel.: (308) 237-2292
Web Site: http://www.westpharma.com
Sales Range: $75-99.9 Million
Emp.: 200
Compression Molding
N.A.I.C.S.: 326299

West Pharmaceutical Services, Inc. (1)
1028 Innovation Way, Kinston, NC 28504-7616
Tel.: (252) 522-8956
Web Site: http://www.westpharma.com
Sales Range: $50-74.9 Million
Emp.: 180
Compression Molding Operations
N.A.I.C.S.: 326299

West Pharmaceutical Services, Inc. (1)
6553 US Hwy 15, Montgomery, PA 17752
Tel.: (570) 547-1646
Web Site: http://www.westpharma.com
Sales Range: $75-99.9 Million
Emp.: 235
Plastic Injection Molding Mfr
N.A.I.C.S.: 326199

West Pharmaceutical Services, Inc. - Clearwater (1)
11600 53rd St N, Clearwater, FL 33760-4827
Tel.: (727) 573-3000
Web Site: http://www.westpharma.com
Medical Packaging Components, Systems & Devices Design & Mfr
N.A.I.C.S.: 339991

WEST SHORE BANK CORPORATION
201 W Loomis St, Ludington, MI 49431 MI
Tel.: (231) 845-3500
Web Site:
https://www.westshorebank.com
Year Founded: 1981
WSSH—(OTCIQ)
Bank Holding Company
N.A.I.C.S.: 551111
Raymond A. Biggs II (Pres, CEO & Sec)
Jeremy M. Holmes (CFO & Treas)

Subsidiaries:

West Shore Bank (1)
201 W Loomis St, Ludington, MI 49431
Tel.: (231) 845-3500
Web Site: http://www.westshorebank.com
Sales Range: $10-24.9 Million
Commericial Banking
N.A.I.C.S.: 522110
Raymond A. Biggs II (Pres & CEO)

WEST TEXAS RESOURCES, INC.
5729 Lebanon Rd Ste 144, Frisco, TX 75034 NV
Tel.: (972) 832-1831
Web Site:
http://www.westtexasresources.com
Year Founded: 2010
WTXR—(OTCIQ)
Sales Range: Less than $1 Million

West Texas Resources, Inc.—(Continued)

Emp.: 1
Oil & Gas Exploration
N.A.I.C.S.: 211120

WEST VIRGINIA AMERICAN WATER COMPANY

1600 Pennsylvania Ave, Charleston, WV 25302
Tel.: (856) 346-8200   **WV**
Web Site: http://www.amwater.com
WVAW—(OTCIQ)
Water Supply Services
N.A.I.C.S.: 221310
Megan Hannah *(Mgr-External Affairs)*
Dan Bickerton *(Mgr-Bus Dev)*

WESTAMERICA BANCORPORATION

Tel.: (415) 257-8000   **CA**
Web Site:
https://www.westamerica.com
Year Founded: 1972
WABC—(NASDAQ)
Rev.: $327,535,000
Assets: $6,364,592,000
Liabilities: $5,591,698,000
Net Worth: $772,894,000
Earnings: $161,768,000
Emp.: 641
Fiscal Year-end: 12/31/23
Bank Holding Company
N.A.I.C.S.: 551111
David L. Payne *(Chm, Pres & CEO)*
Russell W. Rizzardi *(Sr VP)*
Curtis Belton *(VP)*
Brian J. Donohoe *(Sr VP & Mgr-Ops & Sys Div)*
Steve Ensinger *(Sr VP & Mgr-HR Div)*
Anela Jonas *(CFO & Sr VP)*
John A. Thorson *(Treas & Sr VP)*

Subsidiaries:

Westamerica Bank   **(1)**
1108 5th Ave, San Rafael, CA 94901   **(100%)**
Tel.: (415) 257-8000
Web Site: https://www.westamerica.com
Sales Range: $150-199.9 Million
Emp.: 800
Commericial Banking
N.A.I.C.S.: 522110
David L. Payne *(Chm, Pres & CEO)*
Robert A. Thorson *(CFO & Sr VP)*
Russell W. Rizzardi *(Sr VP-Credit Admin)*
Curtis Belton *(VP)*
Brian Donohoe *(Sr VP)*
Steve Ensinger *(Sr VP)*

WESTBURY BANCORP, INC.

200 S Main St, West Bend, WI 53095
Tel.: (262) 335-6037   **MD**
Web Site:
https://www.westburybankwi.com
Year Founded: 2012
WBBW—(OTCIQ)
Rev.: $38,050,000
Assets: $887,285,000
Liabilities: $808,430,000
Net Worth: $78,855,000
Earnings: $7,216,000
Emp.: 101
Fiscal Year-end: 09/30/20
Bank Holding Company
N.A.I.C.S.: 551111
Kirk J. Emerich *(CFO & Exec VP)*
Greg J. Remus *(Chm & CEO)*
Donald J. Murn *(Vice Chm)*
Ryan W. Petri *(Chief Credit Officer & Chief Risk Officer)*

Subsidiaries:

Westbury Bank   **(1)**
200 S Main St, West Bend, WI 53095
Tel.: (262) 334-5563
Web Site: http://www.westburybankwi.com

Emp.: 25
Retail & Commercial Banking
N.A.I.C.S.: 522110
Greg J. Remus *(Chm, Pres & CEO)*
Glenn J. Stadler *(Chief Comml Lending Officer & Exec VP)*
Joe Schaefer *(VP-Comml Lending)*
Matt Golden *(Sr VP-Comml Banking)*
Kevin Flood *(Sr VP-Comml Banking)*
Stacy Alvarez *(VP/Mgr-Comml Rels-Westbury)*

WESTELL TECHNOLOGIES, INC.

750 N Commons Dr, Aurora, IL 60504
Tel.: (630) 898-2500   **DE**
Web Site: https://www.westell.com
Year Founded: 1980
WSTL—(OTCIQ)
Rev.: $29,947,000
Assets: $32,252,000
Liabilities: $10,093,000
Net Worth: $22,159,000
Earnings: ($2,734,000)
Emp.: 95
Fiscal Year-end: 03/31/21
Holding Company
N.A.I.C.S.: 334210
Timothy L. Duitsman *(Pres & CEO)*
Kirk R. Brannock *(Chm)*
J. J. Swartwood *(Sr VP-Worldwide Sls)*
Jeniffer L. Jaynes *(CFO, Treas & Sec)*

Subsidiaries:

Cellular Specialties Inc.   **(1)**
670 N Commercial St Ste 202, Manchester, NH 03101
Tel.: (603) 626-6677
Web Site: http://www.cellularspecialties.com
Sales Range: $25-49.9 Million
Products & Services for Wireless Networks
N.A.I.C.S.: 334419

Noran Tel, Inc.   **(1)**
363 Maxwell Crescent, Regina, S4N 5X9, SK, Canada
Tel.: (306) 721-3535
Web Site: http://www.norantel.com
Telecommunication Products Mfr
N.A.I.C.S.: 334290

Westell, Inc.   **(1)**
750 N Commons Dr, Aurora, IL 60504-7940
Tel.: (630) 898-2500
Web Site: http://www.westell.com
Sales Range: $200-249.9 Million
Emp.: 140
Designs, Manufactures & Markets Telecommunications Products & Systems
N.A.I.C.S.: 517810

WESTERN ACQUISITION VENTURES CORP.

42 Broadway 12th Fl, New York, NY 10004
Tel.: (310) 740-0710   **DE**
Web Site:
https://www.westernacquisitionventures.com
Year Founded: 2021
WAVS—(NASDAQ)
Rev.: $1,566,410
Assets: $118,286,967
Liabilities: $118,543,354
Net Worth: ($256,387)
Earnings: ($700,925)
Emp.: 2
Fiscal Year-end: 12/31/22
Investment Services
N.A.I.C.S.: 523999
Stephen Christoffersen *(CEO)*
William Lischak *(CFO)*

WESTERN ALLIANCE BANCORPORATION

1 E Washington St Ste 1400, Phoenix, AZ 85004

Tel.: (602) 389-3500   **NV**
Web Site:
https://www.westernalliancebancorporation.com
Year Founded: 1994
WAL—(NYSE)
Rev.: $4,316,000,000
Assets: $70,862,000,000
Liabilities: $64,784,000,000
Net Worth: $6,078,000,000
Earnings: $709,600,000
Emp.: 3,260
Fiscal Year-end: 12/31/23
Bank Holding Company
N.A.I.C.S.: 551111
Dale Gibbons *(Vice Chm & CFO)*
Emily Nachlas *(Chief Risk Officer)*
Barbara J. Kennedy *(Chief HR Officer)*
Timothy W. Boothe *(COO)*
Tim R. Bruckner *(Chief Credit Officer)*
Stephen Curley *(Chief Banking Officer)*

Subsidiaries:

BW Real Estate, Inc.   **(1)**
720 S Colorado Blvd PH North, Denver, CO 80246
Tel.: (720) 560-2726
Web Site: https://www.bw-rentals.com
Real Estate Services
N.A.I.C.S.: 531110

Bank of Nevada   **(1)**
2700 W Sahara Ave, Las Vegas, NV 89102
Tel.: (702) 248-4200
Web Site:
https://www.westernalliancebancorporation.com
Sales Range: $25-49.9 Million
Emp.: 100
Commercial Banking
N.A.I.C.S.: 522110
John Guedry *(CEO-Div)*
William R. Oakley *(Sr Mng Dir-Comml Real Estate)*
Melanie Maviglia *(VP-Bus Banking)*
E. Philip Potamitis *(Exec VP-Comml Banking)*
Jerrie E. Merritt *(Sr VP & Mgr-Community Dev)*
Vincent Telles *(Sr VP & Mgr-Corp Lending)*
Violeta Alcantara *(VP & Sr Mgr-Customer Rels)*
Aimee Burford *(Officer-Real Estate Loan & VP)*
Lamont Fitts *(Officer-Loan & VP)*
Chris Gaynor *(VP & Mgr-Customer Rels)*
Douglas Hathaway *(Officer-Real Estate Loan & VP)*
A. Lambertson *(Officer-Real Estate Loan & VP)*
Kimberly MacClafferty *(Asst VP & Mgr-Customer Rels)*
Ernest Oon *(Chief Credit Officer-Div)*
Nadine Garcia-Valdivia *(VP-Portfolio Mgmt)*
Michael Pizzi *(Mng Dir-Comml Banking)*

Las Vegas Sunset Properties   **(1)**
3531 E Russell Rd Ste C, Las Vegas, NV 89120
Tel.: (702) 736-4400
Emp.: 3
Nonresidential Building Operators
N.A.I.C.S.: 531312

Torrey Pines Bank   **(1)**
12220 El Camino Real Ste 200, San Diego, CA 92130
Tel.: (858) 523-4600
Web Site:
https://www.westernalliancebancorporation.com
Sales Range: $10-24.9 Million
Emp.: 50
Commericial Banking
N.A.I.C.S.: 522110
Gary Cady *(Exec VP)*
John Maguire *(CEO)*
John P. Massab *(Chief Credit Officer-Div)*
Annalena Thompson *(Officer-Real Estate Loan & Sr VP)*
Scott Pritchard *(Officer-Real Estate Loan & Sr VP)*
Oliver Craig *(Officer-Comml Loan & VP)*

Natalie Do *(VP & Sr Mgr-Customer Rels)*
Jeff Forsythe *(VP & Mgr-Customer Rels)*
Christina Wolf *(Officer-Comml Loan & VP)*
Diane Wunderlich-Sipe *(VP)*
Jennifer Hull *(Asst VP)*
Mistie McDougall *(VP & Mgr-Customer Rels)*
Gregory S. Peterson *(Sr Dir-Comml Banking)*
Matt Olsen *(VP-Comml Banking)*
Ben Price *(VP-Comml Banking)*

Western Alliance Bank   **(1)**
1 E Washington St, Phoenix, AZ 85004   **(100%)**
Tel.: (602) 389-3500
Web Site:
http://www.westernalliancebancorporation.com
Sales Range: $25-49.9 Million
Retail & Commercial Banking
N.A.I.C.S.: 522180
Kenneth A. Vecchione *(Pres & CEO)*
Emily Nachlas *(Chief Risk Officer)*
David Bolocan *(Head-Treasury Mgmt Strategy, Portfolio, and Online Banking)*
Tim Boothe *(COO)*
Tim Bruckner *(Chief Banking Officer-Reg Banking)*
Steve Curley *(Chief Banking Officer-Natl Bus Lines)*
Adam Fullerton *(VP)*
Bob Aggarwal *(VP)*
Chris Burson *(Sr VP)*
Ericka LeMaster *(Sr Mng Dir)*
Jeff Schelter *(Mng Dir)*
Jimmy Munozcano *(VP)*
John Eldean *(Sr Mng Dir)*
Kate Hickman *(Sr VP)*
Lucy Ray *(VP)*
Matthew James *(Mng Dir)*
Steven Odenkirk *(Mng Dir)*
Victor Napolitano *(Sr VP)*
Todd Sondrini *(Head-Treasury Mgmt)*
Julian Parra *(Head-Comml & Industrial Banking-California)*
Dillan Knudson *(Head-Comml Banking)*
Lynne Biggio Herndon *(Chief Credit Officer)*

Subsidiary (Domestic):

First Independent Bank   **(2)**
5335 Kietzke Ln, Reno, NV 89511
Tel.: (775) 828-2000
Web Site:
https://www.westernalliancebancorporation.com
Commericial Banking
N.A.I.C.S.: 522110

Western Alliance Equipment Finance, Inc.   **(2)**
1 E Washington St Ste 1400, Phoenix, AZ 85004   **(100%)**
Tel.: (480) 797-3690
Web Site: http://www.westernallianceef.com
Sales Range: $10-24.9 Million
Emp.: 40
Equipment Financing
N.A.I.C.S.: 525990

WESTERN ASSET INFLATION-LINKED INCOME FUND

620 8th Ave 47th Fl, New York, NY 10018
Tel.: (626) 844-9400   **MA**
WIA—(NYSE)
Rev.: $37,588,986
Assets: $1,162,500,457
Liabilities: $382,980,090
Net Worth: $779,520,367
Earnings: $23,613,004
Fiscal Year-end: 11/30/19
Investment Management Service
N.A.I.C.S.: 525990
Michael Larson *(Chm)*

WESTERN ASSET INFLATION-LINKED OPPORTUNITIES & INCOME FUND

620 8th Ave 47th Fl, New York, NY 10018
Tel.: (626) 844-9400   **MA**
WIW—(NYSE)
Rev.: $37,588,986

Assets: $1,162,500,457
Liabilities: $382,980,090
Net Worth: $779,520,367
Earnings: $23,613,004
Fiscal Year-end: 11/30/19
Investment Management Service
N.A.I.C.S.: 525990

WESTERN DIGITAL CORPORATION

5601 Great Oaks Pkwy, San Jose, CA 95119
Tel.: (408) 801-1000   CA
Web Site:
  https://www.westerndigital.com
Year Founded: 1970
WDC—(NASDAQ)
Rev.: $13,003,000,000
Assets: $24,188,000,000
Liabilities: $13,370,000,000
Net Worth: $10,818,000,000
Earnings: ($798,000,000)
Emp.: 51,000
Fiscal Year-end: 06/28/24
Hard Drives Designer & Mfr
N.A.I.C.S.: 334112
Luis Felipe Visoso *(Chief Admin Officer)*
Jerry Kagele *(Chief Revenue Officer & Exec VP)*
Robert W. Soderbery *(Exec VP & Gen Mgr-Flash Bus)*
Irving Tan *(Exec VP-Ops-Global)*
Irving Tan *(Exec VP-Ops-Global)*
Wissam G. Jabre *(CFO & Exec VP)*
Irving Tan *(Exec VP-Ops-Global)*
David V. Goeckeler *(CEO)*
Christine Bastian *(Chief People Officer, Chief Inclusion Officer & Exec VP)*
Robert W. Soderbery *(Exec VP & Gen Mgr-Flash Bus)*
Ashley Gorakhpurwalla *(Exec VP & Gen Mgr-HDD Bus)*
Wissam Jabre *(CFO & Exec VP)*
Cynthia Tregillis *(Chief Legal Officer, Sec & Sr VP)*
Jerald Kagele *(Chief Revenue Officer & Exec VP)*

Subsidiaries:

Amplidata N.V.   **(1)**
Ottergemsesteenweg Zuid 808 B43, 9000, Gent, Belgium
Tel.: (32) 92778589
Web Site: http://www.amplidata.com
Software Development Services
N.A.I.C.S.: 541511

HGST Philippines Corp.   **(1)**
109 Technology Avenue Special Export Processing Zone, Binan, 4024, Laguna, Philippines
Tel.: (63) 27575400
Emp.: 9,000
Computer Storage Device Mfr
N.A.I.C.S.: 334112

HGST, Inc.   **(1)**
5601 Great Oaks Pkwy, San Jose, CA 95119
Tel.: (408) 717-6000
Web Site: http://www.hgst.com
Hard Disk Drives for Data Storage Mfr
N.A.I.C.S.: 334112

Subsidiary (Non-US):

HGST (Thailand) Ltd.   **(2)**
205 Moo 7 Si Maha Phot, Prachin Buri, 25140, Thailand
Tel.: (66) 3720870015
Computer Storage Device Mfr
N.A.I.C.S.: 334112

HGST Europe, Ltd.   **(2)**
Langstone Technology Park, Langstone Road, Havant, PO9 1SA, Hants, United Kingdom
Tel.: (44) 2392497400
Emp.: 56
Hard Disk Drives Mfr & Marketer

N.A.I.C.S.: 334112
Nick Kyriacou *(Sr Dir-Bus Mgmt)*
Nigel Edward *(Sr Dir-Sls)*
Adrian Maloret *(Mgr-Ops)*

HGST Japan Co., Ltd.   **(2)**
2880 Kozu, Odawara, 256 8510, Kanagawa, Japan
Tel.: (81) 465 48 1111
Web Site: http://www.hgst.com
Sales Range: $300-349.9 Million
Emp.: 1,800
Hard Disk Drive Developer & Mfr
N.A.I.C.S.: 334112
Masamitsu Horiie *(Pres)*

HGST Singapore Pte. Ltd.   **(2)**
Blk 4 Kaki Bukit Avenue 1 #03-08, Singapore, 417939, Singapore
Tel.: (65) 68412500
Sales Range: $300-349.9 Million
Emp.: 2,000
Hard Disk Drives Developer, Mfr & Marketer
N.A.I.C.S.: 334112

Hitachi Global Storage Products (Shenzhen) Co., Ltd.   **(2)**
No 3001 Jinxiu West Road, Longgang District, Shenzhen, 518118, Guangdong, China
Tel.: (86) 75589596666
Computer Storage Device Mfr
N.A.I.C.S.: 334112

Hitachi Global Storage Technologies (Shenzhen) Co., Ltd.   **(2)**
1/F Talfook Chong Comprehensive Building No 9 Shihua Rd, Shenzhen, 518038, Guangdong, China
Tel.: (86) 75583595000
Computer Storage Device Mfr
N.A.I.C.S.: 334112

Hitachi Global Storage Technologies Consulting (Shanghai) Co., Ltd.   **(2)**
Rm 704-706 Shanghai Jiali Business Center, Shanghai, 200040, China
Tel.: (86) 2152985828
Hard Disk Storage Device Mfr
N.A.I.C.S.: 334112

Hitachi Global Storage Technologies Malaysia Sdn. Bhd.   **(2)**
Sama Jaya Free Industrial Zone, Kuching, 93450, Sarawak, Malaysia
Tel.: (60) 82591000
Data Storage Device Mfr & Distr
N.A.I.C.S.: 334112
O. Kho *(Gen Mgr)*

Hitachi Global Storage Technologies Philippines Corp.   **(2)**
Special Export Processing Zone, Laguna Technopark Biqan, Laguna, Philippines
Tel.: (63) 28435822
Web Site: http://www.hitachigst.com
Sales Range: $1-4.9 Billion
Emp.: 7,000
Computer Hard Disk Drive Mfr
N.A.I.C.S.: 334112

Subsidiary (Domestic):

Skyera, Inc.   **(2)**
1704 Automation Pkwy, San Jose, CA 95131
Tel.: (408) 954-8100
Web Site: http://www.skyera.com
Computer Data Storage Services
N.A.I.C.S.: 518210
Radoslav Danilak *(Co-Founder & CTO)*

Shenzhen Hailiang Storage Products Co., Ltd.   **(1)**
Zone B block C 2/F Great Wall 1 Building, Science & Industry Park &3 Kefa Road Nanshan District, Shenzhen, 518057, China
Tel.: (86) 75526633866
Computer Storage Device Mfr
N.A.I.C.S.: 334413

Tegile Systems Private Limited   **(1)**
1st Floor JP Classic 157/1 Road 5B EPIP Zone Whitefield, Bengaluru, 560066, India
Tel.: (91) 7349772561
Computer Storage Device Mfr
N.A.I.C.S.: 334112

WD Media (Singapore) Pte. Ltd.   **(1)**
3 Tuas Link 2, Singapore, 638552, Singapore

Tel.: (65) 68632911
Sales Range: $125-149.9 Million
Emp.: 600
Electric Equipment Mfr
N.A.I.C.S.: 335999

Western Digital (Malaysia) Sdn. Bhd.   **(1)**
Lot 3 Jalan Ss 8/6 Sungei Way Free Industrial Zone, Petaling Jaya, 47300, Selangor, Malaysia
Tel.: (60) 378776777
Electric Equipment Mfr
N.A.I.C.S.: 335999
Gouw Kim San *(Gen Mgr)*

Western Digital (UK) Ltd.   **(1)**
      (100%)
Tel.: (44) 1372366000
Sales Range: $100-124.9 Million
Emp.: 45
Retailer of Computer Products
N.A.I.C.S.: 541512

Western Digital Canada   **(1)**
2000 Argentia Rd Plz 1 Ste 303, Mississauga, L5N 1P7, ON, Canada   **(100%)**
Tel.: (905) 814-5544
Web Site: http://www.wdc.com
Sales Range: $1-9.9 Million
Emp.: 2
Provider of Computer Related Services
N.A.I.C.S.: 541512

Western Digital Deutschland GmbH   **(1)**
Karl Hammerschmidt Str 40, 85609, Aschheim, Germany   **(100%)**
Tel.: (49) 6929993601
Web Site: http://www.wdc.com
Sales Range: $10-24.9 Million
Emp.: 30
Provider of Computer Services
N.A.I.C.S.: 541512
Graham Holmes *(Mng Dir)*

Western Digital Drive Engineering Inc.   **(1)**
5863 Rue Ferrari, San Jose, CA 95138-1857   **(100%)**
Tel.: (408) 365-1190
Web Site: http://www.wdc.com
Sales Range: $1-4.9 Billion
Emp.: 3,063
Designs & Sells Hard Drives For The Mainstream Personal Computer & High End Enterprise Markets
N.A.I.C.S.: 423430

Western Digital Hong Kong Limited   **(1)**
3501-02 35/F Cambridge House Taikoo Place 979 Kings Road, Wanchai, China (Hong Kong)   **(100%)**
Tel.: (852) 27365123
Sales Range: $10-24.9 Million
Emp.: 16
Hard Drives for the Mainstream Personal Computer & High-end Enterprise Markets Sales
N.A.I.C.S.: 449210

Western Digital Ireland, Ltd.   **(1)**
2nd Fl Mid Town Plaza Elgin Ave, Georgetown, KY1-1106, Cayman Islands
Tel.: (345) 9453466
Web Site: http://www.genesistrust.ky
Emp.: 9
Electric Equipment Mfr
N.A.I.C.S.: 335999
Paul Drake *(Gen Mgr)*

Western Digital Japan, Ltd.   **(1)**
AIOI Sonpo Shinjuku Bldg 13F 25 3 Yoyogi 3 Chome, Tokyo, 151 0053, Japan **(100%)**
Tel.: (81) 353082081
Web Site: http://www.wtc.com
Sales Range: $10-24.9 Million
Emp.: 30
Provider of Computer Services
N.A.I.C.S.: 541512

Western Digital Korea Inc.   **(1)**
9F Asia Tower 430 Nonhyeon-ro, Gangnam-gu, Seoul, 06223, Korea (South)   **(100%)**
Tel.: (82) 220166363
Web Site: https://www.wdc.com
Sales Range: $100-124.9 Million
Emp.: 11
Provider of Computer Related Services

N.A.I.C.S.: 541512

Western Digital Netherlands B.V.   **(1)**
Uiverweg 2, NL 1118 DS, Amsterdam, Netherlands   **(100%)**
Tel.: (31) 204467600
Web Site: http://www.wdc.com
Sales Range: $10-24.9 Million
Emp.: 45
Provider of Computer & Hard Drive Services
N.A.I.C.S.: 541512

Western Digital SE Asia Pte. Ltd.   **(1)**
300 Tampines Avenue 5 06-02 NTUC, Income Tampines Junction, Singapore, 529653, Singapore   **(100%)**
Tel.: (65) 64419989
Web Site: http://www.wdc.com
Sales Range: $10-24.9 Million
Emp.: 30
Designs, Manufactures & Sells Hard Drives for the Mainstream Personal Computer & High-end Enterprise Markets
N.A.I.C.S.: 449210

Western Digital Taiwan Co., Ltd.   **(1)**
14/F Room 1402 205 Tun Hwa North Road, Taipei, 10595, Taiwan
Tel.: (886) 227174775
Web Site: http://www.wdc.com
Computer & Electronic Products Retailer
N.A.I.C.S.: 334513

Western Digital Technologies, Inc.   **(1)**
3355 Michelson Dr Ste100, Irvine, CA 92612
Tel.: (949) 672-7000
Computer Storage Device Mfr
N.A.I.C.S.: 334112
Michael D. Cordano *(Pres)*

Subsidiary (Domestic):

SanDisk LLC   **(2)**
951 SanDisk Dr, Milpitas, CA 95035
Tel.: (408) 801-1000
Web Site: http://www.sandisk.com
Sales Range: $5-14.9 Billion
Flash Memory Data Storage Products Designer, Developer & Marketer
N.A.I.C.S.: 334112

Subsidiary (Non-US):

SanDisk Hong Kong Limited   **(3)**
Suites 1104-05 11/F 1063 King's Road, Quarry Bay, China (Hong Kong)
Tel.: (852) 27120501
Web Site: http://www.sandisk.hk
Flash Memory Data Storage Products Sales & Services
N.A.I.C.S.: 423430

SanDisk IL Ltd.   **(3)**
7 Atir Yeda St, Kfar Saba, 44425, Israel
Tel.: (972) 97645000
Flash Memory Data Storage Products Designer, Developer & Marketer
N.A.I.C.S.: 334112

SanDisk India - Bangalore   **(3)**
Prestige Excelsior Building No 143 /1, Amani Belandur Kane Village Varthur Hobli Prestige Park, Bengaluru, 560103, India
Tel.: (91) 8042422000
Flash Memory Data Storage Products Designer & Mfr
N.A.I.C.S.: 334112
Ganesh Guruswamy *(Sr VP)*

SanDisk International Limited   **(3)**
Second Floor South Block The Concourse Building, Airside Business Park, Dublin, Swords, Ireland
Tel.: (353) 18953000
Flash Memory Data Storage Products Sales & Services
N.A.I.C.S.: 423430

SanDisk Israel (Tefen) Ltd.   **(3)**
Sderot Hata'asiya & Sderot Hagalil Junction, PO Box 3, Migdal, 24959, Israel
Tel.: (972) 49078888
Web Site: http://ww.sandisk.de
Flash Memory Data Storage Products Designer, Developer & Distr
N.A.I.C.S.: 334112

SanDisk Korea Limited   **(3)**

Western Digital Corporation—(Continued)

Asia Tower 726 Yeoksam Dong, Gangnam
Gu, Seoul, 135-719, Korea (South)
Tel.: (82) 267184600
Web Site: http://www.sandisk.de
Flash Memory Data Storage Products Sales
& Services
N.A.I.C.S.: 423430

SanDisk Limted　　　　　　　　　(3)
Shinagawa Tokyu Building 3F 1-6-31 Ko-
nan, Minato-ku, Tokyo, 108-0075, Japan
Tel.: (81) 120893009
Web Site: http://www.sandisk.de
Flash Memory Data Storage Products Sales
& Services
N.A.I.C.S.: 423430

SanDisk Manufacturing Limited　(3)
Second Floor South Block The Concourse
Building Airside Business Park, Swords, Co
Dublin, Ireland
Tel.: (353) 18953000
Flash Memory Data Storage Products De-
signer, Developer & Marketer
N.A.I.C.S.: 334112
Hugh Connely (Gen Mgr)

SanDisk SAS　　　　　　　　　　(3)
Zone Orlytech Batiment 516 1 Allee du
Commandant Mouchotte, 94547, Orly, Ce-
dex, France
Tel.: (33) 173052300
Flash Memory Data Storage Products Sales
& Services
N.A.I.C.S.: 423430

SanDisk Scotland Limited　　　　(3)
Suite 2/1 Links House 15 Links Place East,
Edinburgh, EH6 7EZ, United Kingdom
Tel.: (44) 1315555674
Web Site: http://www.sandisk.de
Flash Memory Data Storage Products Sales
& Services
N.A.I.C.S.: 423430

**SanDisk Storage Malaysia Sdn.
Bhd.**　　　　　　　　　　　　　　(3)
Plot 301A Persiaran Cassia Selatan 1 Ta-
man Perindustrian Batu Kawan MK, Batu
Kawan Seberang, Perai, 14100, Malaysia
Tel.: (60) 45039100
Storage Devices Mfr
N.A.I.C.S.: 334112

SanDisk Taiwan Limited　　　　　(3)
2F Nr 58 Ruihu Street, Neihu District, Tai-
pei, 114, Taiwan
Tel.: (886) 266088400
Web Site: http://www.sandisk.de
Flash Memory Data Storage Products Sales
& Services
N.A.I.C.3.: 423430

**SanDisk Trading (Shanghai) Co.
Ltd.**　　　　　　　　　　　　　　(3)
20F No 918 Unit B C D Middle Huai Hai
Zhong Road, Shanghai, 200020, China
Tel.: (86) 2160322188
Web Site: http://www.sandisk.de
Computer Storage Device Mfr
N.A.I.C.S.: 334112

WESTERN EXPLORATION INC.
121 Woodland Ave Ste 140, Reno,
NV 89523
Tel.: (775) 329-8119　　　　　　BC
Web Site:
　　https://www.westernexploration.com
Year Founded: 1996
WEX—(TSXV)
Assets: $362,734
Liabilities: $27,475
Net Worth: $335,259
Earnings: ($71,701,120)
Fiscal Year-end: 12/31/20
Investment Services
N.A.I.C.S.: 523999
Marceau Schlumberger (Chm)
Darcy Marud (Pres & CEO)
Nichole Cowles (Head-Investor Rela-
tions & Dir-IR)
Curtis Turner (CFO)
Mark Hawksworth (Gen Mgr-Aura
Project)

Subsidiaries:

Western Exploration, LLC　　　　(1)
52360 Willow Pt Rd, Clarksburg, CA 95612
Tel.: (916) 744-1440
Ship Building & Repairing
N.A.I.C.S.: 336611
Sylbie Jensen (Pres)

WESTERN METALS CORP.
8235 Forsyth Blvd Ste 400, Clayton,
MO 63105
Tel.: (314) 854-8513　　　　　　CA
Web Site:
　　http://www.westernmetalscorp.com
Year Founded: 1980
WTLC—(OTCIQ)
Medical Equipment Mfr
N.A.I.C.S.: 339112
Jim Sanders (Corp Counsel & Sec)

WESTERN MIDSTREAM PART-
NERS, LP
9950 Woodloch Forest Dr Ste 2800,
The Woodlands, TX 77380
Tel.: (832) 636-1009　　　　　　DE
Web Site:
　　https://www.westernmidstream.com
Year Founded: 2007
WES—(NYSE)
Rev.: $3,106,476,000
Assets: $12,471,607,000
Liabilities: $9,442,477,000
Net Worth: $3,029,130,000
Earnings: $1,022,216,000
Emp.: 1,377
Fiscal Year-end: 12/31/23
Midstream Energy Assets Holding
Company
N.A.I.C.S.: 551112
Robert W. Bourne (Chief Comml Offi-
cer & Sr VP)
Christopher B. Dial (Gen Counsel,
Sec & Sr VP)
Catherine A. Green (Chief Acctg Offi-
cer & VP)
Michael P. Ure (Pres & CEO)
Alejandro O. Nebreda (Sr VP-Bus
Svcs)
Brian A. Binford (VP-Ops Svcs &
Sustainability)
Philip C. Neisel (VP, Asst Sec & As-
soc Gen Counsel)
Peter I. Trombley (VP & Assoc Gen
Counsel)
Danny Holderman (Sr VP)
Keith Herndon (CIO)

Subsidiaries:

**Meritage Midstream Services II,
LLC**　　　　　　　　　　　　　　(1)
1331 Seventeenth St Ste 1100, Denver, CO
80202
Tel.: (303) 551-8150
Web Site:
　　http://www.meritagemidstream.com
Sales Range: $75-99.9 Million
Emp.: 100
Oil & Gas Transportation Services
N.A.I.C.S.: 213112
Nicholas O. Thomas (Pres & COO)
Steven B. Huckaby (Chm & CEO)
J. Stacy Horn (Sr VP-Comml)
Nicholas Aretakis (CFO & Sr VP)
Richard J. Gognat (Gen Counsel & Sr VP)
Tim Pimmel (Sr VP-Engrg & Construction)
Terrance Herauf (VP-Ops)
Michael A. Hantzsch (Sr VP)

Subsidiary (Domestic):

**Thunder Creek Gas Services,
LLC**　　　　　　　　　　　　　　(2)
1331 17th Str Ste 1100, Denver, CO 80202
Tel.: (303) 296-2914
Web Site:
　　http://www.meritagemidstream.com
Sales Range: $1-9.9 Million
Emp.: 16
Natural Gas Transportation Services
N.A.I.C.S.: 213112

Western Gas Holdings, LLC　　　(1)
1201 Lake Robbins Dr, The Woodlands, TX
77380　　　　　　　　　　　　(100%)
Tel.: (832) 636-6000
Web Site: http://www.westerngas.com
Holding Company; Natural Gas Extraction &
Pipeline Distr Management Services
N.A.I.C.S.: 551112
Gennifer F. Kelly (COO & Sr VP)

Subsidiary (Domestic):

**Western Midstream Operating,
LP**　　　　　　　　　　　　　　(2)
9950 Woodloch Forest Dr Ste 2800, The
Woodlands, TX 77380　　　　(87.29%)
Tel.: (346) 786-5000
Web Site:
　　https://www.westernmidstream.com
Rev.: $3,106,475,999
Assets: $12,462,653,000
Liabilities: $9,410,299,000
Net Worth: $3,052,354,000
Earnings: $1,045,812,000
Emp.: 1,376
Fiscal Year-end: 12/31/2023
Natural Gas Assets Holding Company
N.A.I.C.S.: 551112
Christopher B. Dial (Sec)
Kristen S. Shults (CFO)
Keith Herndon (VP)

Subsidiary (Domestic):

**Anadarko Gathering Company
LLC**　　　　　　　　　　　　　　(3)
1201 Lake Robbins Dr, The Woodlands, TX
77380
Tel.: (832) 636-3088
Oil & Gas Marketing & Refining Services
N.A.I.C.S.: 324110

**Anadarko Wattenberg Company,
LLC**　　　　　　　　　　　　　　(3)
1201 Lake Robbins Dr, The Woodlands, TX
77380
Tel.: (832) 636-6000
Natural Gas Distr
N.A.I.C.S.: 221210

MIGC, LLC　　　　　　　　　　(3)
9950 Woodloch Forest Dr, The Woodlands,
TX 77380
Tel.: (307) 670-6000
Web Site: https://www.migc.com
Holding Company; Interstate Gas Pipeline
Operator
N.A.I.C.S.: 551112
Jeffrey M. Molinaro (Chief Compliance Offi-
cer)

Mountain Gas Resources, LLC　(3)
1201 Lake Robbins Dr, The Woodlands, TX
77380　　　　　　　　　　　　(100%)
Tel.: (832) 636-6000
Holding Company; Natural Gas Transporter
& Marketer
N.A.I.C.S.: 551112

Pinnacle Gas Treating LLC　　　(3)
1201 Lake Robbins Dr, The Woodlands, TX
77380-1181
Tel.: (832) 636-1000
Web Site: http://www.anadarko.com
Natural Gas Distr
N.A.I.C.S.: 221210

WESTERN NEW ENGLAND
BANCORP, INC.
141 Elm St, Westfield, MA 01085
Tel.: (413) 568-1911　　　　　　MA
Web Site:
　　https://www.westfieldbank.com
WNEB—(NASDAQ)
Rev.: $99,260,000
Assets: $2,553,150,000
Liabilities: $2,325,007,000
Net Worth: $228,143,000
Earnings: $25,887,000
Emp.: 289
Fiscal Year-end: 12/31/22
Bank Holding Company
N.A.I.C.S.: 551111
James C. Hagan (Pres & CEO)
Guida R. Sajdak (CFO, Treas & Exec
VP)

Subsidiaries:

WFD Securities, Inc.　　　　　　(1)
141 Elm St, Westfield, MA 01085
Tel.: (413) 568-1911
Web Site: http://www.westfieldbank.com
Emp.: 150
Security Guards & Patrol Services
N.A.I.C.S.: 561612

Westfield Bank　　　　　　　　(1)
141 Elm St, Westfield, MA 01085
Tel.: (413) 568-1911
Web Site: https://www.westfieldbank.com
Sales Range: $25-49.9 Million
Savings Bank
N.A.I.C.S.: 522180
Allen J. Miles III (Exec VP)
Stephanie Morales (VP & Branch Mgr)
Brian Fontaine (Officer)
Brion Robert (Officer)
Cody Goncalves (Officer)
Derrick Feuerstein (VP)
Filipe Ferreira (Officer)
Mirna Grbesic (Officer)
Nancie Tebaldi (Officer)

WESTERN SIERRA RE-
SOURCE CORP.
1001 Grand Ave Ste 207, Glenwood
Springs, CO 81612
Tel.: (405) 209-5485　　　　　　UT
Web Site:
　　https://www.westernsierrare
　　source.com
WSRC—(OTCIQ)
Cannabidiol Product Mfr & Distr
N.A.I.C.S.: 325411
Roger A. Johnson (CEO)
Scott Hastings (COO)
Dennis Edward Atkins (CFO)

WESTINGHOUSE AIR BRAKE
TECHNOLOGIES CORPORA-
TION
30 Isabella St, Pittsburgh, PA 15212
Tel.: (412) 825-1000　　　　　　DE
Web Site:
　　https://www.wabteccorp.com
Year Founded: 1999
WAB—(NYSE)
Rev.: $9,677,000,000
Assets: $18,988,000,000
Liabilities: $8,464,000,000
Net Worth: $10,524,000,000
Earnings: $815,000,000
Emp.: 29,000
Fiscal Year-end: 12/31/23
Components, Parts & Electronic Sys-
tems Designer & Mfr for Locomotives,
Railway Freight Cars, Subways &
Buses
N.A.I.C.S.: 336510
William E. Kassling (Vice Chm)
David L. DeNinno (Gen Counsel, Sec
& Exec VP)
John A. Olin (CFO & Exec VP)
Rafael O. Santana (Pres & CEO)
Lillian Leroux (Pres-Transit)
Kristine Kubacki (VP-IR)
Nicole Theophilus (Chief HR Officer &
Exec VP)
Eric Gebhardt (CTO & Exec VP)
Rogerio Mendonca (Pres-Freight
Equipment)
Gina Trombley (Chief Comml Officer
& Sr VP-Sls & Mktg)
Michael E. Fetsko III (Pres-Freight &
Industrial Components)
John A. Mastalerz Jr. (Chief Acctg
Officer & Sr VP-Fin)

Subsidiaries:

AM General Contractors SpA　　(1)
Via Angelo Scarsellini 147, 16149, Genoa,
Genova, Italy
Tel.: (39) 01060751
Web Site: http://www.amgc.biz
Rail Transportation Services
N.A.I.C.S.: 488210
Andrea Zilliken (CFO)

Aero Transportation Products, Inc (1)
3300 E Geospace Dr, Independence, MO 64056
Tel.: (816) 257-5450
Web Site:
   https://www.aerotransportation.com
Railroad Rolling Stock Mfr
N.A.I.C.S.: 336510

Annax (Suzhou) Rail Systems Co., Ltd. (1)
Jianlin Road 666 Building 47, Suzhou, 215129, Jiangsu, China
Tel.: (86) 51266675313
Electronic Equipment Distr
N.A.I.C.S.: 423620

Annax GmbH (1)
Eugen-Sanger-Ring 15, 85649, Brunnthal, Germany
Tel.: (49) 896144360
Web Site: http://www.annax.de
Electronic Equipment Distr
N.A.I.C.S.: 423620

Annax Polska Sp. z o.o. (1)
Ul Bernardynska 13 lok 601, 85-029, Bydgoszcz, Poland
Tel.: (48) 575888720
Electronic Equipment Distr
N.A.I.C.S.: 423620

Annax Scheiz AG (1)
Zentweg 9, 3006, Bern, Switzerland
Tel.: (41) 319508600
Electronic Equipment Distr
N.A.I.C.S.: 423620

Ateliers Hubert Gerken S.A. (1)
Avenue du Parc 41, 4800, Verviers, Belgium
Tel.: (32) 87394900
Carbon & Graphite Product Mfr
N.A.I.C.S.: 335991

Austbreck Pty, Ltd, (1)
34-36 Westpool Drive, Hallam, 3803, VIC, Australia
Tel.: (61) 397024011
Railroad Rolling Stock Mfr
N.A.I.C.S.: 336510
Wayne S. Caldow *(Mng Dir)*
Greg Field *(Ops Mgr)*
Curt W. Plumer *(Mgr-Sls & Comml)*

Barber Steel Foundry Corp. (1)
2625 W Winston Rd, Rothbury, MI 49452
Tel.: (231) 894-1830
Iron Foundry Services
N.A.I.C.S.: 331511

Bearward Engineering Limited (1)
Main Road Far Cotton, Northampton, NN4 8HJ, United Kingdom
Tel.: (44) 1604762851
Web Site: http://www.bearward.com
Emp.: 350
Industrial Radiator Mfr
N.A.I.C.S.: 333414

Bearward Limited (1)
Main Road Far Cotton, Northampton, NN4 8HJ, United Kingdom
Tel.: (44) 1604762851
Industrial Radiator Mfr
N.A.I.C.S.: 333414

Becorit GmbH (1)
Rumplerstrasse 6-10, Recklinghausen, 45659, Germany (100%)
Tel.: (49) 23616666
Web Site: http://www.becorit.de
Sales Range: $25-49.9 Million
Emp.: 200
Mfr of Friction Materials & Disc Brake Pads for Rail & Mining Industries
N.A.I.C.S.: 336999

Beijing Wabtec Huaxia Technology Company Ltd. (1)
No 42 Sheng, Langfang, 101601, Hebei, China
Tel.: (86) 10584125228001
Emp.: 82
Railroad Equipment Whslr
N.A.I.C.S.: 423860

Brecknell Willis (Tianjin) Electrification Systems, Co., Ltd (1)
8 Tongyue Road Beichen, Industrial Park, Tianjin, 300405, China (100%)
Tel.: (86) 2226986568
Web Site: http://www.wabtec.com
Steel Mill Operator
N.A.I.C.S.: 331110

Brush Traction Ltd. (1)
175 Meadow Ln, Meadow Lane, Loughborough, LE11 1NF, Leicestershire, United Kingdom
Tel.: (44) 1509225600
Web Site: http://www.brushtraction.com
Sales Range: $50-74.9 Million
Emp.: 325
Railway Locomotive Overhauls, Services & Aftermarket Components
N.A.I.C.S.: 488210

Subsidiary (Domestic):

Brush Barclay Ltd. (2)
Caledonia Works, West Langlands Street, Kilmarnock, KA1 2PD, Ayrshire, United Kingdom
Tel.: (44) 1563523573
Web Site: http://www.wabtec.com
Emp.: 150
Railroad Locomotive Components
N.A.I.C.S.: 488210

C2CE Pty, Ltd. (1)
Ground Floor Building A 355 Scarborough Beach Road, The Garden Office Park, Osborne Park, 6017, WA, Australia
Tel.: (61) 861419200
Web Site: http://www.c2ce.com.au
Electrical Construction Services
N.A.I.C.S.: 238210

CZ-Carbon Prodcuts s.r.o. (1)
U Privadece 1296/5, Cernice, 326 00, Plzen, Czech Republic
Tel.: (420) 37 718 3371
Web Site: https://www.cz-carbon.cz
Carbon & Graphite Product Mfr
N.A.I.C.S.: 335991

Cardwell Westinghouse Co. (1)
8400 S Stewart Ave, Chicago, IL 60620
Tel.: (773) 483-7575
Web Site: http://www.wabtec.com
Sales Range: $25-49.9 Million
Emp.: 100
Mfr & Designer of Gears, Brake Assemblies, Connectors, Slack Adjusters & Freight Car Handbrakes for the Rail Industry
N.A.I.C.S.: 336999

CoFren S.A.S. (1)
21 boulevard de la Liberte, 18100, Vierzon, France
Tel.: (33) 248716425
Locomotive Break Mfr
N.A.I.C.S.: 336510

CoFren S.r.l. (1)
Via Pianodardine, 83100, Avellino, Italy
Tel.: (39) 08256161
Web Site: http://www.wabtec.com
Sales Range: $10-24.9 Million
Emp.: 18
Brake Shoes, Disc Pads & Interior Trim Components for Trains Mfr
N.A.I.C.S.: 336999

Coleman Hydraulics Limited (1)
Unit 4A Graycar Business Park Barton under Needwood, Burton-on-Trent, DE13 8EN, Staffordshire, United Kingdom
Tel.: (44) 1283716692
Web Site:
   http://www.colemanhydraulics.co.uk
Hydraulic Equipment Repair Services
N.A.I.C.S.: 811310

Coleman Manufacturing Limited (1)
Graycar Business Park Barton Under Needwood, Burton Upon Trent, Burton-on-Trent, DE13 8EN, Staffordshire, United Kingdom
Tel.: (44) 1283716688
Web Site:
   http://www.colemanmanufacturing.co.uk
Industrial Machinery Mfr
N.A.I.C.S.: 333248

Dia-Frag Industria e Comercio de Motopecas Ltda. (1)
Rua 19 de Novembro 305-Vila Sao Cristovao, Monte Alto, 15910-000, Sao Paulo, Brazil
Tel.: (55) 1632445000
Web Site: http://www.diafrag.com.br
Motorcycle Parts Distr
N.A.I.C.S.: 336991

Durox Company (1)
12312 Alameda Dr, Strongsville, OH 44149
Tel.: (440) 238-5350
Industrial Locomotives & Part Mfr
N.A.I.C.S.: 336510

E-Carbon Far East Ltd. (1)
Room 706 No 389 Jinwan Road, Jinqiao Export Processing Zone Pudong, Shanghai, 201206, China
Tel.: (86) 2150315128
Web Site: http://www.e-carbonfareast.com
Pump Equipment Mfr
N.A.I.C.S.: 333914

F.I.P. Pty Ltd. (1)
6 Wenban Place, Wetherill Park, 2164, NSW, Australia (100%)
Tel.: (61) 287848400
Web Site: http://www.wabtec.com
Sales Range: $25-49.9 Million
Emp.: 50
Mfr of Friction Materials for Railway Rolling Stock Braking Systems
N.A.I.C.S.: 336999

Faiveley Transport S.A. (1)
3 rue du 19 mars 1962, 92230, Gennevilliers, CEDEX, France (100%)
Tel.: (33) 148136500
Web Site: http://www.faiveleytransport.com
Railroad, Transportation & Other Industrial Equipment Mfr
N.A.I.C.S.: 336510

Subsidiary (Non-US):

Faiveley Railway Trading Co., Ltd. (2)
N 31 Fu Lian Yi Road, Baoshan Dist, Shanghai, 201906, China (100%)
Tel.: (86) 21 33 71 88 66
Railway Air Conditioning Equipment Mfr
N.A.I.C.S.: 333415

Subsidiary (Domestic):

Faiveley Transport Amiens S.A.S. (2)
Espace Industriel Nord 115 rue Andre Durouchez, 80046, Amiens, Cedex, France (100%)
Tel.: (33) 322673500
Railway Vehicle Components Mfr
N.A.I.C.S.: 332321

Subsidiary (Non-US):

Faiveley Transport Australia Ltd. (2)
Unit 1 175 James Ruse Drive, Rosehill, Sydney, 2142, NSW, Australia (100%)
Tel.: (61) 288634700
Railway Vehicle Components Mfr
N.A.I.C.S.: 336510

Faiveley Transport Birkenhead Ltd. (2)
Morpeth Wharf Twelve Quays, Birkenhead, CH41 1LF, United Kingdom (100%)
Tel.: (44) 1516495000
Railway Vehicle Components Mfr
N.A.I.C.S.: 332321
Ian Dolman *(Mng Dir)*

Faiveley Transport Czech a.s (2)
U Privadece 1315/3, 326 00, Plzen, Czech Republic (100%)
Tel.: (420) 379207111
Web Site: https://www.ftczech.com
Transportation Equipment Mfr
N.A.I.C.S.: 336999

Faiveley Transport Far East Ltd (2)
38 Hueng Yip Rd, Hong Kong, China (Hong Kong) (100%)
Tel.: (852) 28611788
Railway Rolling Stock Mfr
N.A.I.C.S.: 336510
Rebecca Lor *(Mgr-HR)*

Faiveley Transport Holding GmbH & Co KG (2)
Brauckstr 26, Witten, 58454, Germany (100%)
Tel.: (49) 23022775464
Investment Management Service

N.A.I.C.S.: 523999

Subsidiary (Domestic):

Faiveley Transport Witten GmbH (3)
Brauckstrasse 26, 58454, Witten, Germany (100%)
Tel.: (49) 230227750
Sales Range: $75-99.9 Million
Emp.: 300
Mfr of Brake Systems & Brake Components, Wheels, Doors, Air-Conditioning Equipment, Electricity Supply & Light Fittings for Railbound Vehicles
N.A.I.C.S.: 336510

Subsidiary (Non-US):

Faiveley Transport Iberica SA (2)
23 Finca La Selva Del Camp, 43470, Tarragona, Spain (100%)
Tel.: (34) 977011000
Mfr of Brake Systems & Brake Components, Wheels, Doors, Air-Conditioning Equipment, Electricity Supply & Light Fittings for Railbound Vehicles
N.A.I.C.S.: 332321

Faiveley Transport Italia S.p.A. (2)
Via Volvera 51, 10045, Piossasco, Turin, Italy (98.7%)
Tel.: (39) 0119044344
Railway Vehicle Components Mfr
N.A.I.C.S.: 332321

Faiveley Transport Korea Ltd. (2)
139-34 Yulsaengjungang-ro Daegot-myeon Gimpo, Seoul, 10040, Gyeonggi, Korea (South) (100%)
Tel.: (82) 25640325
Railway Vehicle Components Mfr
N.A.I.C.S.: 336510

Faiveley Transport Leipzig GmbH & Co KG (2)
Industriestr 60, 04435, Schkeuditz, Germany (100%)
Tel.: (49) 3420485300
Sales Range: $100-124.9 Million
Emp.: 30
Air Conditioning Equipment Mfr
N.A.I.C.S.: 333415

Faiveley Transport Metro Technology Taiwan Ltd. (2)
10F -2 No 560 Sec 4 Zhongxiao E Rd, Xinyi Dist, Taipei, Taiwan (100%)
Tel.: (886) 2 7735 0040
Platform Screen Door Mfr
N.A.I.C.S.: 332321

Subsidiary (Domestic):

Faiveley Transport N.S.F (2)
Rue de Reckem, 59960, Neuville-en-Ferrain, France (100%)
Tel.: (33) 320456546
Aircraft Equipment Mfr
N.A.I.C.S.: 336413

Subsidiary (Non-US):

Faiveley Transport Nordic AB (2)
Andra Tvargatan 41, PO Box 515, Landskrona, 261 24, Sweden (100%)
Tel.: (46) 41 85 44 00
Railroad Rolling Stock Mfr.
N.A.I.C.S.: 336510
Johan Malm *(Mng Dir)*

Faiveley Transport Nowe GmbH (2)
Heilswannenweg 66, 31008, Elze, Germany (100%)
Tel.: (49) 5068 5506
Web Site: http://wabtec.com
Automotive Electro Pneumatic Mfr
N.A.I.C.S.: 336390
Wiebke Bartling *(Mng Dir)*

Faiveley Transport Plzen s.r.o. (2)
Nyrany 1238, Nyrany, 330 23, Czech Republic (100%)
Tel.: (420) 379411540
Automobile Parts Mfr
N.A.I.C.S.: 336390

Faiveley Transport Rail Technologies India Limited (2)
Harita, PO Box 39, Hosur, 635109, Tamil Nadu, India (100%)
Tel.: (91) 4344276761

Railway Vehicle Components Mfr
N.A.I.C.S.: 333914
Anil Kaul *(Mng Dir)*

Faiveley Transport Tamworth Ltd (2)
Morpeth Wharf Morphet Wharf Twelve
Quays, Birkenhead, CH41 1LF, Wirral,
United Kingdom **(100%)**
Tel.: (44) 1516495000
Industrial Machinery & Equipment Distr
N.A.I.C.S.: 423830
Ian Dolman *(Mng Dir)*

Subsidiary (Domestic):

Faiveley Transport Tours (2)
Unite 3 ZI du Bois de Plante Rue Amelia
Earhart, BP 43, 37700, La Ville-aux-Dames,
France **(100%)**
Tel.: (33) 2 47 32 55 55
Railway Rolling Stock Mfr
N.A.I.C.S.: 336510

Subsidiary (Non-US):

**Faiveley Transport do Brasil
Ltda.** (2)
Rua Major Paladino 275, 05307-000, Sao
Paulo, Brazil **(100%)**
Tel.: (55) 1128896000
Railway Vehicle Components Mfr
N.A.I.C.S.: 332321

Sab Wabco (UK) Limited (2)
1 Morpeth Wharf Twelve Quays, Birken-
head, CH41 1LF, United Kingdom **(100%)**
Tel.: (44) 1516495000
Automobile Parts Distr
N.A.I.C.S.: 423120

Fandstan Electric Group Ltd. (1)
Craven House 16 Northumberland Ave,
London, WC2N 5AP, United Kingdom
Tel.: (44) 2073069110
Web Site: http://www.fandstanelectric.com
Sales Range: $200-249.9 Million
Emp.: 950
Rail & Industrial Equipment Mfr
N.A.I.C.S.: 333248

Subsidiary (Non-US):

AKAPP Stemmann BV (2)
Darwinstraat 10, 6718 XR, Ede, Nether-
lands
Tel.: (31) 342403900
Web Site: http://www.akapp.com
Sales Range: $25-49.9 Million
Emp.: 65
Mobile Power Supply Solutions
N.A.I.C.S.: 334419

Austbreck Pty Limited (2)
34-36 Westpool Drive, Hallam, 3803, VIC,
Australia
Tel.: (61) 397024011
Railway Rolling Stock Mfr
N.A.I.C.S.: 336510

Subsidiary (Domestic):

Brecknell Willis & Co., Limited (2)
Millfield Chard, Somerset, TA20 2DA,
United Kingdom
Tel.: (44) 1460 260700
Web Site: http://www.brecknell-willis.co.uk
Sales Range: $50-74.9 Million
Emp.: 250
Transportation Systems Electrical Equip-
ment Mfr
N.A.I.C.S.: 335999

Subsidiary (Non-US):

**Brecknell Willis (Taiwan) Co.,
Limited** (3)
5F-5 NO 23 SEC 1 CHANG AN E Rd, Tai-
pei, 10441, Taiwan
Tel.: (886) 225625587
Web Site: http://www.brecknellwillis.com.tw
Sales Range: $25-49.9 Million
Emp.: 10
Transportation Systems Electrical Equip-
ment Mfr
N.A.I.C.S.: 335999

Subsidiary (Domestic):

Brecknell Willis Composites Ltd. (2)

Unit 1 Millfield Industrial Estate, Chard,
Somerset, TA20 2BB, United Kingdom
Tel.: (44) 146068111
Web Site: http://www.bwcomposites.co.uk
Sales Range: $25-49.9 Million
Emp.: 50
Rail & Industrial Equipment Mfr
N.A.I.C.S.: 333248

Fandstan Electric Ltd. (2)
Craven House, 16 Northumberland Avenue,
London, WC2N 5AP, United Kingdom
Tel.: (44) 2073069110
Web Site: http://www.fandstanelectric.com
Emp.: 2
Rail & Industrial Equipment Mfr
N.A.I.C.S.: 333248

Subsidiary (Non-US):

**Stemmann Technik Netherlands
BV** (2)
De Roysloot 12k, Rijnsburg, 2231 NZ,
Katwijk, Netherlands
Tel.: (31) 714062000
Web Site: http://www.stemmann.nl
Sales Range: $50-74.9 Million
Emp.: 7
Electrical Apparatus & Equipment Wiring
Supplies
N.A.I.C.S.: 335999
Michael Bostelmann *(CEO)*

Stemmann-Technik GmbH (2)
Niedersachsenstr 2, 48465, Schuttorf, Ger-
many
Tel.: (49) 592 3810
Web Site: https://www.stemmann.com
Sales Range: $150-199.9 Million
Emp.: 500
Electrical Apparatus & Equipment Wiring
Supplies
N.A.I.C.S.: 335999
Andreas Berger *(Mng Dir)*
Uwe Menneback *(Dir)*
Christian Ratzke *(Dir)*
Hans Caffier *(Dir-Quality)*
Jennifer Gray *(Dir-Human Resources)*

Subsidiary (US):

TransTech of SC, Inc. (2)
46 Beechtree Blvd, Greenville, SC 29605
Tel.: (864) 299-3870
Web Site: https://www.transtech.com
Transportation Equipment Mfr
N.A.I.C.S.: 336999

Fandstan Electric Systems, Ltd. (1)
Craven House 16 Northumberland Avenue,
London, WC2N 5AP, United Kingdom
Tel.: (44) 2076308801
Electric Power Transmission Services
N.A.I.C.S.: 221121

Fandstan Electric, Inc. (1)
709 Augusta Arbor Way, Piedmont, SC
29673
Tel.: (864) 299-3870
Emp.: 50
Copper Foundry Services
N.A.I.C.S.: 331529

G&B Specialties, Inc. (1)
535 W 3rd St, Berwick, PA 18603
Tel.: (570) 752-5901
Web Site: http://www.wabtec.com
Locomotive Break Product Mfr
N.A.I.C.S.: 336510

GE Mozambique Limitada (1)
Rua do Desportistas Maputo Business
Tower nr 480 12th Floor, Maputo, Mozam-
bique
Tel.: (258) 840945000
Engineeering Services
N.A.I.C.S.: 541330
Helder Sitoi *(Country Mgr)*

GE Transportation (1)
500 W Monroe St, Chicago, IL 60661
Tel.: (760) 255-5640
Web Site: http://www.getransportation.com
Printing
N.A.I.C.S.: 324110
Nate Bailey *(Chief HR Officer)*
Gokhan Bayhan *(Gen Mgr-Russia/CIS, Eu-
rope, Middle East & North Africa)*
Deia Campanelli *(Chief Comm Officer)*
Marcos Costa *(Gen Mgr-Latin America)*

Jim Hilderhoff *(Chief Comml Officer-
Americas)*
Mano Mannoochahr *(VP)*
Pascal Schweitzer *(VP-Svc Org-Global)*

**GT Engineering & Associates,
Ltd.** (1)
21F 9 Des Voeux Road West Sheung Wan,
Kowloon, Hong Kong, China (Hong Kong)
Tel.: (852) 27959988
Web Site: http://www.wabtec.com
Emp.: 5
Industrial Machinery Whslr
N.A.I.C.S.: 423830

Gerken SAS (1)
ZAC de l Orme - 3 Chemin du Camping,
Condrieu, 69 420, Lyon, France
Tel.: (33) 474595915
Web Site: https://www.gerken.fr
Rail Transportation Services
N.A.I.C.S.: 488210

InTrans Engineering Limited (1)
No 48 A Taratalla Road, Kolkata, 700066,
West Bengal, India
Tel.: (91) 3324910893
Sales Range: $25-49.9 Million
Emp.: 35
Locomotive Break Product Mfr
N.A.I.C.S.: 336510

J. & D. Gears Limited (1)
Unit 4/Graycar Business Pk/Barton Turn
Barton underNeedwood, Burton-on-Trent,
DE13 8EN, Staffordshire, United Kingdom
Tel.: (44) 1283722669
Web Site: http://www.jdgears.com
Industrial Machinery & Equipment Distr
N.A.I.C.S.: 423830

L&M Radiator Incorporated (1)
1414 E 37th St, Hibbing, MN 55746
Tel.: (218) 263-8993
Web Site: http://www.mesabi.com
Sales Range: $10-24.9 Million
Emp.: 171
Motor Vehicle Radiator Mfr
N.A.I.C.S.: 336390
Dan Chisholm *(Pres)*

LH Access Technology Limited (1)
Graycar Business Park Barton under Need-
wood, Burton-on-Trent, DE13 8EN, Stafford-
shire, United Kingdom
Tel.: (44) 1283722600
Web Site: http://www.lh-access.com
Railroad Equipment Mfr & Whslr
N.A.I.C.S.: 333248

Longwood Elastomers, S.A. (1)
Polygon Industrial Las Casas Calle E Par-
cela 36, 42005, Soria, Spain
Tel.: (34) 975224561
Rubber Products Mfr
N.A.I.C.S.: 326299

Longwood International, Inc. (1)
1400 W Peachtree St NW Unit 2410, At-
lanta, GA 30309
Tel.: (770) 393-0808
Railroad Equipment Whslr
N.A.I.C.S.: 423860

MZT Hepos Polska Sp. Zo.o (1)
Woodjowyskiego 51, 02-724, Warsaw, Po-
land
Tel.: (48) 222537717
Locomotive Break Product Mfr
N.A.I.C.S.: 336510

Melett Limited (1)
Unit N Zenith Park Whaley Road, Barnsley,
S75 1HT, United Kingdom
Tel.: (44) 122 632 0939
Web Site: https://www.melett.com
Motor Vehicle Parts Mfr
N.A.I.C.S.: 336390
Darren Johnson *(Sls Dir)*

Melett North America, Inc (1)
5166 E Raines Rd Bldg 7, Memphis, TN
38118
Tel.: (901) 322-5896
Industrial Equipment Distr
N.A.I.C.S.: 423830

Metalocaucho, S.L. (1)
Poligono Erratzu 253, 20130, Urnieta,
Gipuzkoa, Spain
Tel.: (34) 943333755

Web Site: http://www.metalocaucho.com
Rubber Metal Parts Mfr
N.A.I.C.S.: 336330

Microphor (1)
452 E Hill Rd, Willits, CA 95490
Tel.: (707) 459-5563
Web Site: http://www.microphor.com
Sales Range: $10-24.9 Million
Emp.: 50
Mfr of Sanitation Systems & Related Prod-
ucts for Railroad & Transit Markets
N.A.I.C.S.: 336999

Mors Smitt Asia, Ltd. (1)
26/F Casey Aberdeen House 38 Heung Yip
Road, Wong Chuk Hang, Hong Kong,
China (Hong Kong)
Tel.: (852) 23435555
Railroad Equipment Whslr
N.A.I.C.S.: 423860

Mors Smitt BV (1)
Vrieslantlaan 6, 3526 AA, Utrecht, Nether-
lands
Tel.: (31) 302881311
Web Site: http://www.morssmitt.com
Emp.: 125
Railroad Equipment Whslr
N.A.I.C.S.: 423860
Arne Wijnmaalen *(Mng Dir)*

Mors Smitt France S.A.S. (1)
2 Rue de la Mandiniere, 72300, Sable-sur-
Sarthe, France
Tel.: (33) 243928200
Railroad Equipment Whslr
N.A.I.C.S.: 423860

Mors Smitt Technologies, Inc. (1)
1010 Johnson Dr, Buffalo Grove, IL 60089-
6918
Tel.: (847) 777-6497
Railroad Equipment Whslr
N.A.I.C.S.: 423860
Peter Morehouse *(VP & Gen Mgr)*

Mors Smitt UK Ltd. (1)
Graycar Business Park, Barton under Need-
wood, Burton-on-Trent, DE13 8EN, Stafford-
shire, United Kingdom
Tel.: (44) 1283357263
Web Site: https://www.morssmitt.com
Emp.: 48
Railroad Equipment Whslr
N.A.I.C.S.: 423860
Lee Bradford *(Mng Dir)*

MorsSmitt Asia, Ltd. (1)
29/F Fun Tower 35 Hung To Road, Kwun
Tong, Kowloon, China (Hong Kong)
Tel.: (852) 23435555
Industrial Equipment Distr
N.A.I.C.S.: 423610
Arne J. Wijnmaalen *(Mng Dir)*

Motive Equipment, Inc. (1)
8300 W Sleske Ct, Milwaukee, WI 53223
Tel.: (414) 446-3379
Locomotive Equipment Mfr
N.A.I.C.S.: 336510

MotivePower, Inc. (1)
4600 Apple St, Boise, ID 83716 **(100%)**
Tel.: (208) 947-4800
Web Site: http://www.motivepower-
wabtec.com
Sales Range: $250-299.9 Million
Emp.: 550
Mfr of Commuter & Switcher Locomotives;
Locomotive Maintenance & Repair Services
N.A.I.C.S.: 336510

**Napier Turbochargers Australia Pty
Ltd.** (1)
Wenban Place 6, Wetherill Park, Sydney,
2164, NSW, Australia
Tel.: (61) 287848400
Electronic Charger Mfr
N.A.I.C.S.: 335999

Napier Turbochargers Limited (1)
Ruston House Waterside South, PO Box 1,
Lincoln, LN5 7FD, United Kingdom
Tel.: (44) 152 251 6665
Web Site: https://www.napier-
turbochargers.com
Emp.: 150
Industrial Machinery Mfr
N.A.I.C.S.: 333248

Pantrac GmbH (1)
Vulkanstrasse 13, 10367, Berlin, Germany
Tel.: (49) 30554970
Web Site: https://www.pantrac.de
Carbon & Graphite Product Mfr
N.A.I.C.S.: 335991

Pioneer Friction Limited (1)
48A Taratalla Road, Kolkata, 700 066, West
Bengal, India (100%)
Tel.: (91) 3324910889
Web Site: http://www.wabtec.com
Sales Range: $25-49.9 Million
Emp.: 32
Mfr of Brake Shoes & Linings for Locomotive, Freight Car & Passenger Cars
N.A.I.C.S.: 336999

Poli S.p.A (1)
Via Fontanella 11, Camisano, 26010, Italy
Tel.: (39) 0373777250
Web Site: http://www.polibrakes.com
Sales Range: $25-49.9 Million
Emp.: 100
Pneumatic Brake Product Mfr
N.A.I.C.S.: 333998

Poli S.r.l. (1)
Via A Costa 39/43, Castel Maggiore, 40013,
Bologna, Italy
Tel.: (39) 05 170 0184
Web Site: https://www.polisrl.com
Precision Turned Product Mfr
N.A.I.C.S.: 332721

Pride Bodies Ltd (1)
37 Raglin Place, Cambridge, N1R 7J2, ON,
Canada
Tel.: (519) 620-8787
Web Site: https://www.pridebodies.com
Truck Body Mfr
N.A.I.C.S.: 336211
Russ Lanthier *(VP-Sls)*

RMS Mors Smitt (1)
19 Southern Court, Keysborough, 3173,
VIC, Australia
Tel.: (61) 385441200
Web Site: http://www.morssmitt.com
Electrical Engineering Product Mfr & Distr
N.A.I.C.S.: 335314
Alphonse Fernandez *(Dir-Sales)*

Railroad Controls, LP (1)
9800 Hillwood Pkwy Ste 340, Fort Worth,
TX 76177
Tel.: (682) 316-6300
Web Site: http://www.railroadcontrols.com
Sales Range: $75-99.9 Million
Emp.: 500
Railway Signal Construction Services
N.A.I.C.S.: 488210

**Railroad Friction Products
Corporation** (1)
13601 Airport Rd, Maxton, NC
28364-1349 (100%)
Tel.: (910) 844-9752
Web Site: http://www.rfpc.com
Sales Range: $75-99.9 Million
Emp.: 155
Mfr of Low & Medium Friction Products &
High Friction Composition Brake Shoes
N.A.I.C.S.: 336999

Ricon Corp. (1)
1135 Aviation Pl, San Fernando, CA 91340
Tel.: (818) 267-3000
Sales Range: $125-149.9 Million
Emp.: 300
Wheelchair Lifts & Ramps Mfr for Commercial, Paratransit, Transit, Motorcoach & Passenger Rail Vehicles
N.A.I.C.S.: 423860

SanCasT, Inc. (1)
535 Clow Ln, Coshocton, OH 43812
Tel.: (740) 622-8660
Emp.: 38
Casting Product Mfr
N.A.I.C.S.: 331523
Daniel Opie *(Gen Mgr)*

Schaefer Equipment, Inc. (1)
1590 Phoenix Rd NE, Warren, OH 44483
Tel.: (330) 372-4006
Web Site: http://www.wabtec.com
Sales Range: $25-49.9 Million
Emp.: 42
Mfr of Forged Brake Rigging Components
for Freight Cars

N.A.I.C.S.: 336999

Semvac A/S (1)
Svendborgvej 226, Odense, 5260, Denmark
Tel.: (45) 65683300
Sanitary Systems Mfr
N.A.I.C.S.: 332999
Benoit Birault *(CEO)*

Servicios de Administracion de Locomotoras, S. de R.L. de C.V. (1)
Camino a San Juanico 555, San Luis Potosi, 34563, Mexico
Tel.: (52) 4448238277
Web Site: http://www.lslsa.com.mx
Industrial Equipment Repair Services
N.A.I.C.S.: 811310

Shuttlewagon, Inc. (1)
8701 Elmwood Ave Ste 300, Kansas City,
MO 64132
Tel.: (816) 767-0300
Web Site: https://shuttlewagon.com
Railroad Equipment Distr
N.A.I.C.S.: 423860

Standard Car Truck Company (1)
865 Busse Hwy, Park Ridge, IL 60068
Tel.: (847) 692-6050
Web Site: http://www.sctco.com
Sales Range: $25-49.9 Million
Emp.: 30
Supplier & Mfr of Stabilization Systems for
Freight Cars
N.A.I.C.S.: 336999

Subsidiary (Non-US):

SCT Europe Ltd. (2)
Evans Business Centre, Fife, Kirkcaldy,
KY1 3UF, United Kingdom (100%)
Tel.: (44) 1592657560
Web Site: http://www.sctco.com
Railway Locomotives & Rolling Stock Mfr
N.A.I.C.S.: 336510

Stemmann Polska SP Zoo (1)
ul Spoldzielcza 22, 55-080, Katy Wroclawskie, Poland
Tel.: (48) 717121030
Transit Equipment Mfr
N.A.I.C.S.: 336510

Stemmann Technik France SAS (1)
20 rue des Piquettes Locaux B3/B4, 78200,
Buchelay, France
Tel.: (33) 177492736
Web Site: http://www.stemmann.com
Electric Power Transmission Services
N.A.I.C.S.: 221121

**Stemmann Technik Nederland
BV** (1)
De Roysloot 12K Rijnsburg, 2231 NZ,
Katwijk, Netherlands
Tel.: (31) 714062000
Web Site: http://www.stemmann.nl
Transit Equipment Mfr
N.A.I.C.S.: 336510

**Stemmann Technik Polska SP
Zoo** (1)
Ul Spoldzielcza 22, Katy Wroclawskie, 55-
080, Poland
Tel.: (48) 717121030
Web Site: http://www.stemmann.com.pl
Electric Power Transmission Services
N.A.I.C.S.: 221121

**Swiger Coil Systems - A Wabtec
Company** (1)
4677 Manufacturing Ave, Cleveland, OH
44135
Tel.: (216) 362-7500
Web Site: http://www.swigercoil.com
Emp.: 200
Electric Motor Coils Mfr & Distr
N.A.I.C.S.: 335312

**The Hunslet Engine Company
Limited** (1)
Ground Floor Francis House 1 George
Mann Way, Leeds, LS10 1DR, United Kingdom
Tel.: (44) 1132774007
Web Site: http://www.hunsletengine.com
Emp.: 12
Engine Equipment Mfr
N.A.I.C.S.: 333618

Turbonetics Holdings, Inc. (1)

28601 Chagrin Blvd, Moorpark, CA 93021
Tel.: (805) 581-0333
Holding Company
N.A.I.C.S.: 551112

Unitrac Railroad Materials, Inc. (1)
2715 Byington Solway Rd, Knoxville, TN
37921
Tel.: (865) 693-9063
Web Site: http://www.unitracrail.com
Rev.: $4,885,958
Emp.: 25
Railroad Rolling Stock Mfr
N.A.I.C.S.: 336510

Vapor Bus International (1)
1010 Johnson Dr, Buffalo Grove, IL 60089
Tel.: (847) 777-6400
Web Site: http://www.vapordoors.com
Sales Range: $25-49.9 Million
Emp.: 400
Designer & Mfr of Passenger Door Systems
for Buses
N.A.I.C.S.: 336211

Subsidiary (Non-US):

Vapor Europe S.r.l. (2)
Viale Regina Pacis 290, 41049, Sassuolo,
MO, Italy
Tel.: (39) 0536 806441
Web Site: http://www.vapordoors.com
Sales Range: $100-124.9 Million
Mfr of Bus & Train Door Control Systems
N.A.I.C.S.: 336999

**Vapor Rail Kapi Sistemleri Ticaret Ve
Hizmetleri Limited Sirketi** (2)
Yesiltepe Mah D-100 Karayolu Yanyol Uzeri
No 117 e Erenler, Istanbul, Turkiye
Tel.: (90) 2123248800
Locomotive Break Product Mfr
N.A.I.C.S.: 336510

Vapor Ricon Europe Ltd. (2)
Meadow Lane, Loughborough, LE11 1HS,
Leicestershire, United Kingdom
Tel.: (44) 1509635920
Web Site: http://www.vaporricon.co.uk
Bus & Train Door Control Systems Mfr
N.A.I.C.S.: 336999

WABCO Locomotive (1)
1001 Air Brake Ave, Wilmerding, PA 15148
Tel.: (412) 825-1000
Web Site: http://www.wabtec.com
Sales Range: $100-124.9 Million
Emp.: 250
Locomotive Pneumatic Braking Equipment
& Rubber Parts
N.A.I.C.S.: 336999

**Wabtec (Beijing) Investment Co.
Ltd.** (1)
A610 Hanwei Plaza No 7 Guanghua Road,
Chaoyang District, Beijing, 100004, Beijing
Shi, China
Tel.: (86) 1065613526
Freight Component Distr
N.A.I.C.S.: 423840

**Wabtec Assembly Services S. de
R.L. de C.V.** (1)
Eje 126 230, Zona Industrial, 78395, San
Luis Potosi, Mexico
Tel.: (52) 4448344800
Railway Track Equipment Mfr
N.A.I.C.S.: 336510

Wabtec Australia Pty Ltd (1)
Unit 1 Unit 2 2-8 South Street, Rydalmere,
2116, NSW, Australia
Tel.: (61) 298988125
Web Site: http://www.wabtec.com
Sales Range: $25-49.9 Million
Emp.: 40
Wabtec Products Distr
N.A.I.C.S.: 488210

Wabtec Brasil Fabricacao e Manutencao de Equipamentos Ltda (1)
Rua 19 de Novembro 305-Vila, Sao Cristovao, Monte Alto, 15910-000, Sao Paulo,
Brazil
Tel.: (55) 1632445000
Freight Component Distr
N.A.I.C.S.: 423840

**Wabtec Brasil Fabricaoa Manutencao de Equipamentos Ferrovaros
Ltda** (1)
Rua Luiz da Nobrega 160 Boa Vista, Minas
Gerais, Belo Horizonte, 31060-100, Minas
Gerais, Brazil
Tel.: (55) 1131743588
Web Site: http://www.wabtec.com
Locomotive Break Product Mfr
N.A.I.C.S.: 336510

Wabtec Canada, Inc. (1)
475 Seaman Street, Stoney Creek, L8E
2R2, ON, Canada
Tel.: (905) 561-8700
Industrial Locomotives & Part Mfr
N.A.I.C.S.: 336510

Wabtec Control Systems Pty Ltd (1)
Scarborough Beach Road, Osborne Park,
6017, WA, Australia
Tel.: (61) 861419200
Rail Control & Signalling Equipment Mfr
N.A.I.C.S.: 334290

**Wabtec Equipamentos Ferroviarios
Ltda.** (1)
Rua Luiz da Nobrega 160, Boa Vista, Belo
Horizonte, 31060-100, Minas Gerais, Brazil
Tel.: (55) 1131743588
Rail Control & Signalling Equipment Mfr
N.A.I.C.S.: 334290

Wabtec Europe GmbH (1)
Liebermannstrasse A04 701, 2345, Brunn
am Gebirge, Austria
Tel.: (43) 189049870
Web Site: http://www.wabteceurope.com
Sales Range: $10-24.9 Million
Emp.: 10
Locomotive Equipment Mfr
N.A.I.C.S.: 333618

Wabtec Foundry (1)
40 Mason Street, Wallaceburg, N8A 4M1,
ON, Canada
Tel.: (519) 627-3314
Web Site: https://www.foundryassociation.ca
Sales Range: $25-49.9 Million
Emp.: 65
Mfr of Gray & Ductile Iron Castings
N.A.I.C.S.: 331511
Paul Geron *(Plant Mgr)*

Wabtec Global Services (1)
1001 Air Brake Ave, Wilmerding, PA 15148
Tel.: (412) 825-1000
Web Site:
  http://www.wabtecglobalservices.com
Software & Hardware Support Services for
Railway Vehicle Repair & Maintenance
N.A.I.C.S.: 488210

Wabtec MZT ad Skopje (1)
Pero Nakov 124, PO Box 409, 1000, Skopje, North Macedonia
Tel.: (389) 22581330
Web Site: http://www.wabtec.com
Locomotive Break Product Mfr
N.A.I.C.S.: 336510

Wabtec Passenger Transit (1)
130 Ridgeview Ctr, Duncan, SC 29334
Tel.: (864) 433-5900
Web Site: http://www.wabtec.com
Sales Range: $150-199.9 Million
Emp.: 350
Mfr of Pneumatic, Electronic & Mechanical
Devices for Passenger Transit Vehicles
N.A.I.C.S.: 336999

Wabtec Rail Limited (1)
Doncaster Works Hexthorpe Road, Doncaster, DN1 1SL, South Yorkshire, United
Kingdom (100%)
Tel.: (44) 1302340700
Web Site: http://www.wabtecrail.co.uk
Sales Range: $400-449.9 Million
Emp.: 400
Rail Vehicle Overhaul, Conversion & Maintenance Services
N.A.I.C.S.: 488210

Wabtec Rail Scotland Limited (1)
West Langlands Street, Caledonia Works,
Kilmarnock, KA1 2QD, Ayrshire, United
Kingdom
Tel.: (44) 1563523573
Web Site: http://www.wabtec.com
Emp.: 100
Locomotive Break Product Mfr
N.A.I.C.S.: 336510

Westinghouse Air Brake Technologies
Corporation—(Continued)

**Wabtec Railway Electronics
Corporation** (1)
21200 Dorsey Mill Rd, Germantown, MD
20876 **(100%)**
Tel.: (301) 515-2000
Web Site: http://www.wabtec.com
Sales Range: $125-149.9 Million
Emp.: 300
Electronic & Electro-Pneumatic Train Con-
trol System Designer & Mfr
N.A.I.C.S.: 336999

**Wabtec Railway Electronics
Corporation** (1)
2620 58th Ave SE, Calgary, T2C 1G5, AB,
Canada
Tel.: (403) 279-0805
Railroad Locomotive & Parts Mfr
N.A.I.C.S.: 336510

Wabtec Rubber Products (1)
269 Donohue Rd, Greensburg, PA 15601
Tel.: (724) 838-1317
Web Site: http://www.wabtecrubber.com
Sales Range: $50-74.9 Million
Emp.: 130
Producer of Custom-Molded Rubber Prod-
ucts
N.A.I.C.S.: 326291

**Wabtec Servicios Administrativos,
S.A. de C.V.** (1)
Eje 126 230, Zona Industrial, 78395, San
Luis Potosi, Mexico
Tel.: (52) 4448344800
Railroad Equipment Mfr
N.A.I.C.S.: 336510

**Wabtec South Africa Proprietary
Limited** (1)
5 Vuurslag Rd, Kempton Park, 1619, Jo-
hannesburg, South Africa
Tel.: (27) 119743813
Web Site: http://www.wabtec.com
Sales Range: $25-49.9 Million
Emp.: 27
Locomotive Break Product Mfr
N.A.I.C.S.: 336510

**Wabtec de Mexico, S. de R.L. de
C.V.** (1)
Eje 126 230, 78395, San Luis Potosi,
Mexico **(100%)**
Tel.: (52) 4448344800
Web Site: http://www.wabtec.com
Mfr of Gears & Pinions for Rail Industry
N.A.I.C.S.: 336999

Workhorse Rail, LLC (1)
4885 A McKnight Rd Ste 390, Pittsburgh,
PA 15237
Tel.: (412) 837-1712
Transit Equipment Mfr
N.A.I.C.S.: 336510
Chris Farls (VP & Gen Mgr)

**Wuxi Jinxin Group Company
Limited** (1)
No 568 SU Xi Road, Wuxi, 214121, Jiang
su, China
Tel.: (86) 51085073650
Web Site: https://www.jin-xin.com
Railroad Equipment Whslr
N.A.I.C.S.: 423860

Xorail, Inc. (1)
5011 Gate Pkwy Bldg 100 Ste 400, Jack-
sonville, FL 32256 **(100%)**
Tel.: (904) 443-0083
Web Site: http://www.xorail.com
Emp.: 170
Railway Signal Design & Construction Ser-
vices
N.A.I.C.S.: 237990

Branch (Domestic):

Xorail, Inc. - Shawnee Mission (2)
10200 W 75th St Ste 280, Shawnee Mis-
sion, KS 66204
Tel.: (913) 262-4842
Construction Equipment Installtion Services
N.A.I.C.S.: 237990

Young Touchstone Company (1)
200 Smith Ln, Jackson, TN 38301 **(100%)**
Tel.: (731) 424-5045

Web Site: http://www.youngtouchstone.com
Sales Range: $10-24.9 Million
Emp.: 16
Mfr of Heat Exchange Products for Rail,
Power Generation, Off-Highway & Marine
Industries
N.A.I.C.S.: 332410

WESTLAKE CORPORATION

2801 Post Oak Blvd Ste 600, Hous-
ton, TX 77056
Tel.: (713) 960-9111 TX
Web Site: https://www.westlake.com
Year Founded: 1986
WLK—(NYSE)
Rev: $12,548,000,000
Assets: $21,035,000,000
Liabilities: $10,271,000,000
Net Worth: $10,764,000,000
Earnings: $479,000,000
Emp.: 15,520
Fiscal Year-end: 12/31/23
Chemicals, Polymers, Vinyls & Fabri-
cated Products Mfr
N.A.I.C.S.: 325199
M. Steven Bender (CFO & Exec VP)
Robert F. Buesinger (Exec VP-
Housing & Infrastructure Products, IT
& Digital)
L. Benjamin Ederington (Chief Admin
Officer, Corp Counsel, Sec & Exec
VP-Performance-Essential Matls)
Johnathan S. Zoeller (Chief Acctg
Officer & VP)
Jean-Marc Gilson (Pres & CEO)

Subsidiaries:

Axiall Corporation (1)
1000 Abernathy Rd Ste 1200, Atlanta, GA
30328
Tel.: (770) 395-4500
Web Site: http://www.axiall.com
Holding Company; Chlorovinyls & Aromatics
Mfr & Marketer
N.A.I.C.S.: 551112

Subsidiary (Non-US):

Royal Building Products (2)
91 Royal Group Crescent, Woodbridge,
L4H 1X9, ON, Canada
Tel.: (905) 850-9700
Web Site:
https://www.royalbuildingproducts.com
Quality Building Products Mfr & Distr
N.A.I.C.S.: 423390
Steve Booz (VP-Mktg & Product Dev)

Subsidiary (US):

**Royal Building Products (USA)
Inc.** (3)
2801 Post Oak Blvd Ste 600, Houston, TX
77056
Tel.: (713) 960-9111
Roofing Products Mfr & Distr
N.A.I.C.S.: 423330

Subsidiary (Domestic):

DaVinci Roofscapes, LLC (4)
13890 W 101st St, 66215, Lenexa, KS
Tel.: (913) 599-0766
Web Site: http://www.davinciroofscapes.com
Roofing Products Mfr & Distr
N.A.I.C.S.: 423330
John Humphreys (Founder)

Joint Venture (Non-US):

Taiwan Chlorine Industries Ltd. (2)
25 Chungchih Street, Hsiaokang District,
Kaohsiung, 812, Taiwan **(60%)**
Tel.: (886) 7 871 5171
Web Site: https://www.tciwestlake.com.tw
Chlorine Mfr
N.A.I.C.S.: 325180

Dimex LLC (1)
28035 State Route 7, Marietta, OH 45750
Tel.: (740) 374-3100
Web Site: http://www.dimexcorp.com
Rev.: $1,640,000
Emp.: 10
All Other Plastics Product Mfr

N.A.I.C.S.: 326199
Andy Antil (CEO)

North American Pipe Corporation (1)
2801 Post Oak Blvd Ste 600, Houston, TX
77056
Tel.: (713) 840-7473
Web Site:
http://www.northamericanpipe.com
Sales Range: $25-49.9 Million
Emp.: 110
Polyvinyl Chloride (PVC) Piping Mfr
N.A.I.C.S.: 326122

**North American Specialty Products
LLC** (1)
500 W 1st St, McPherson, KS 67460
Tel.: (620) 241-5511
Petrochemical Product Mfr & Distr
N.A.I.C.S.: 325110
Terry Moege (Ops Mgr)

Vinnolit GmbH & Co. KG (1)
Carl-Zeiss-Ring 25, 85737, Ismaning, Ger-
many
Tel.: (49) 89961030
Web Site: http://www.vinnolit.com
Sales Range: $1-4.9 Billion
Emp.: 1,400
Polyvinyl Chloride Mfr
N.A.I.C.S.: 325211
Karl-Martin Schellerer (Mng Dir)
M. Steven Bender (Mng Dir)

Subsidiary (Non-US):

Vinnolit Hillhouse Ltd. (2)
Hillhouse International Business Park,
Thornton, FY5 4QD, Lancashire, United
Kingdom
Tel.: (44) 1253898800
Sales Range: $50-74.9 Million
Emp.: 700
Polyvinyl Chloride Mfr
N.A.I.C.S.: 325211

Vinnolit Limited (1)
The Heath Business Technical Park, Run-
corn, WA7 4QX, Cheshire, United Kingdom
Tel.: (44) 1928511042
Plastics Product Mfr
N.A.I.C.S.: 326122

Vinnolit Schkopau GmbH (1)
Gebaude Q161, 06258, Schkopau, Ger-
many
Tel.: (49) 34618212010
Plastic Product Distr
N.A.I.C.S.: 424610

Westech Building Products ULC (1)
5201 64 Ave SE, Calgary, T2C 4Z9, AB,
Canada
Tel.: (403) 279-4497
Web Site: http://www.westechbp.com
Wood Fence, Deck & Rail Component Mfr
N.A.I.C.S.: 321999

Westech Building Products, Inc. (1)
7451 Indiana 62, Mount Vernon, IN 47620
Tel.: (812) 985-3628
Web Site: http://www.westechbp.com
Emp.: 100
Vinyl Building Extrusions, Deck & Railing
Systems Mfr
N.A.I.C.S.: 326199

Subsidiary (Non-US):

Westlake Building Products ULC (2)
5201 64th Ave SE, Calgary, T2C 4Z9, AB,
Canada
Tel.: (403) 279-4497
Web Site: http://www.westlakebp.com
Sales Range: $125-149.9 Million
Vinyl Fence, Deck & Rail Components Mfr
N.A.I.C.S.: 326199

Westlake Canada Inc. (1)
31 Rue de l Industrie, Beauharnois, J6N
0C2, QC, Canada
Tel.: (450) 429-4641
Building Material Mfr & Distr
N.A.I.C.S.: 327120

Westlake Chemical Partners LP (1)
2801 Post Oak Blvd Ste 600, Houston, TX
77056
Tel.: (713) 585-2900
Web Site: https://www.wlkpartners.com
Rev.: $1,190,791,000

Assets: $1,316,842,000
Liabilities: $460,592,000
Net Worth: $856,250,000
Earnings: $334,626,000
Emp.: 152
Fiscal Year-end: 12/31/2023
Chemicals Mfr
N.A.I.C.S.: 325998
Albert Y. Chao (Pres)
James Y. Chao (Chm)
Johnathan S. Zoeller (Chief Acctg Officer)
Jean-Marc Gilson (CEO)
Johnathan S. Zoeller (Chief Acctg Officer)
Andrew F. Kenner (Sr VP)

**Westlake DaVinci Roofscapes,
LLC** (1)
13890 W 101st St, Lenexa, KS 66215
Web Site:
https://www.davinciroofscapes.com
Roofing Tile Mfr
N.A.I.C.S.: 327120

Westlake Epoxy GmbH (1)
Varziner Strasse 49, Meiderich, 47138,
Duisburg, Germany
Tel.: (49) 203429601
Wind Turbine Blade Mfr & Distr
N.A.I.C.S.: 333611

Westlake Longview Corporation (1)
811 Estes Dr, Longview, TX 75602
Tel.: (903) 242-7500
Sales Range: $75-99.9 Million
Emp.: 300
Polyethylene & Epolene Mfr
N.A.I.C.S.: 325199
Jeff Newsom (Office Mgr)

Westlake Natrium LLC (1)
15696 Energy Rd State Route 2, Proctor,
WV 26055
Tel.: (304) 455-2200
Petrochemical & Polymer Mfr
N.A.I.C.S.: 325998

Westlake Petrochemicals LLC (1)
2801 Post Oak Ste 600, Houston, TX
77056-6105
Tel.: (713) 960-9111
Sales Range: $10-24.9 Million
Emp.: 10
Mfr of Industrial Organic Chemicals
N.A.I.C.S.: 325211

Subsidiary (Domestic):

WPT LLC (2)
2801 Post Oak Blvd Ste 600, Houston, TX
77056
Tel.: (713) 960-9111
Petrochemical Mfr
N.A.I.C.S.: 325110

Westlake Olefins Corporation (2)
2801 Post Oak Blvd Ste 600, Houston, TX
77056-6105 **(100%)**
Tel.: (713) 960-9111
Web Site: http://www.westlakechemical.com
Olefins Mfr
N.A.I.C.S.: 325110

**Westlake Pipe & Fittings
Corporation** (1)
2801 Post Oak Blvd Ste 600, Houston, TX
77056
Tel.: (713) 840-7473
Web Site: https://www.westlakepipe.com
Pipe & Pipe Fitting Mfr
N.A.I.C.S.: 332996

Westlake Polymers LLC (1)
2801 Post Oak Blvd Ste 600, Houston, TX
77056-6105
Tel.: (713) 960-9111
Sales Range: $50-74.9 Million
Emp.: 150
Mfr of Synthetic Rubber
N.A.I.C.S.: 325211

Westlake Styrene LLC (1)
2801 Post Oak Blvd Ste 600, Houston, TX
77056
Tel.: (713) 960-9111
Web Site: https://www.westlake.com
Rev: $9,100,000
Emp.: 200
Plastics Materials or Resins
N.A.I.C.S.: 325211
Albert Y. Chao (Pres & CEO)

Westlake Vinnolit Benelux-France B.V. (1)
Cogels-Osylei 17 2 Stock/2nd Floor, Berchem, 2600, Antwerp, Belgium
Tel.: (32) 34355550
Petrochemical & Polymer Mfr
N.A.I.C.S.: 325998

Westlake Vinnolit GmbH & Co. KG (1)
Carl-Zeiss-Ring 25, 85737, Ismaning, Germany
Tel.: (49) 89961030
Web Site: https://www.westlakevinnolit.com
Emp.: 1,400
Petrochemical Mfr & Distr
N.A.I.C.S.: 325110

Westlake Vinnolit Italia S.r.L. (1)
Via S G B De La Salle 4, 20132, Milan, Italy
Tel.: (39) 0258129210
Petrochemical & Polymer Mfr
N.A.I.C.S.: 325998

Westlake Vinnolit Limited (1)
The Heath Business And Technical Park, Runcorn, WA7 4QX, Cheshire, United Kingdom
Tel.: (44) 1928511042
Petrochemical & Polymer Mfr
N.A.I.C.S.: 325998

Westlake Vinyls, Inc. (1)
2468 Industrial Pkwy, Calvert City, KY 42029
Tel.: (270) 395-4151
Web Site: http://www.westlakechemical.com
Sales Range: $50-74.9 Million
Emp.: 190
Plastics Materials or Resins
N.A.I.C.S.: 325211

Subsidiary (Domestic):

Westlake Vinyls Company LP (2)
36045 Hwy 30, Geismar, LA 70734
Tel.: (225) 673-6121
PVC & Petrochemicals
N.A.I.C.S.: 325110
John Casey *(Plant Mgr)*

WESTROCK COFFEE COMPANY

4009 N Rodney Parham Rd 4th Fl, Little Rock, AR 72212
Tel.: (501) 918-9358   DE
Web Site:
https://www.westrockcoffee.com
WEST—(NASDAQ)
Rev.: $867,872,000
Assets: $746,213,000
Liabilities: $734,484,000
Net Worth: $11,729,000
Earnings: ($77,633,000)
Emp.: 1,327
Fiscal Year-end: 12/31/22
Coffee & Tea Manufacturing
N.A.I.C.S.: 311920
Scott T. Ford *(Co-Founder & CEO)*
Joe T. Ford *(Co-Founder & Chm)*
Elizabeth McLaughlin *(Pres-Sls, Mktg & Client Svcs)*
Will Ford *(Exec VP-Ops)*
Ken Parent *(Vice Chm)*
C.J. Duvall Jr. *(Exec VP-HR)*

Subsidiaries:

Falcon Coffees Limited (1)
Temple House 25-26 High St, Lewes, BN7 2LU, United Kingdom
Tel.: (44) 1273977077
Coffee Distr
N.A.I.C.S.: 424490

Kohana Coffee LLC (1)
1221 S Mopac Expy Ste 100, Austin, TX 78746
Tel.: (512) 904-1174
Web Site: http://www.kohanacoffee.com
Sales Range: $1-9.9 Million
Coffee Mfr & Distr
N.A.I.C.S.: 311920
Victoria Lynden *(Founder & CEO)*

Origin Merger Sub II, LLC (1)
1706 E 6th St, Austin, TX 78702
Tel.: (206) 372-5118
Coffee Mfr & Distr
N.A.I.C.S.: 311920

Riverview Acquisition Corp. (1)
510 S Mendenhall Rd Ste 200, Memphis, TN 38117
Tel.: (901) 767-5576
Investment Services
N.A.I.C.S.: 523999
R. Brad Martin *(Chm & CEO)*
Charles K. Slatery *(Pres & Chief Investment Officer)*
William V. Thompson III *(CFO, Treas & Sec)*

S. & D. Coffee, Inc. (1)
300 Concord Pkwy S, Concord, NC 28027
Tel.: (704) 782-3121
Web Site: http://www.sdcoffeetea.com
Roasted Coffee & Tea Products Distr & Mfr
N.A.I.C.S.: 424490

WESTROCK COMPANY

1000 Abernathy Rd NE, Atlanta, GA 30328
Tel.: (770) 448-2193   DE
Web Site: https://www.westrock.com
Year Founded: 2018
WRK—(NYSE)
Rev.: $20,310,000,000
Assets: $27,443,700,000
Liabilities: $17,346,000,000
Net Worth: $10,097,700,000
Earnings: ($1,649,000,000)
Emp.: 56,100
Fiscal Year-end: 09/30/23
Packaging Products Mfr
N.A.I.C.S.: 551112
Denise R. Singleton *(Gen Counsel, Sec & Exec VP)*
Nina Butler *(Chief Environmental Officer & Deputy Gen Counsel)*
Donna Owens Cox *(Chief Comm Officer)*
Thomas M. Stigers *(Pres-Mill Ops)*
Ben P. Patel *(Chief Science Officer & Chief Innovation Officer)*
Alexander W. Pease *(CFO & Exec VP)*
Vicki L. Lostetter *(Chief HR Officer)*
Amir Kazmi *(Chief Info & Digital Officer)*
David B. Sewell *(Pres & CEO)*
Peter Anderson *(Chief Supply Chain Officer)*
John O'Neal *(Pres-Global Paper)*
Sam Shoemaker *(Pres-Consumer Packaging)*
Ben Patel *(Chief Innovation & Science Officer)*

Subsidiaries:

KapStone Paper & Packaging Corporation (1)
1101 Skokie Blvd Ste 300, Northbrook, IL 60062
Tel.: (847) 239-8800
Web Site: http://www.kapstonepaper.com
Rev.: $3,315,660,000
Assets: $3,323,985,000
Liabilities: $2,186,971,000
Net Worth: $1,137,014,000
Earnings: $243,503,000
Emp.: 6,400
Fiscal Year-end: 12/31/2017
Holding Company; Paper Mill & Container Mfr
N.A.I.C.S.: 551112

Subsidiary (Domestic):

Central Florida Box Corporation (2)
2950 Lake Emma Rd Ste 1000, Lake Mary, FL 32746   (100%)
Tel.: (407) 936-1277
Web Site: http://www.centralfloridabox.com
Sales Range: $1-9.9 Million
Emp.: 63
Solid Fiber Box Mfr
N.A.I.C.S.: 322211

Tom Ramsey *(Founder)*
Jeff Ramsey *(Co-Owner & Pres)*
Angela Ramsey *(Co-Owner & VP-Sls & Mktg)*
Joseph Magliaro *(Co-Owner & VP-Ops)*
Alisa C. Hoskins *(Co-Owner & VP)*
Barry Benoit *(Mgr-Pur)*
Bill Salmon *(Mgr-Warehouse)*
Zul Suleman *(Mgr-Acctg)*
Gregory Cox *(Designer-Structural)*
Henry Flores *(Supvr-Graphic Design)*
Joseph Neale *(Supvr-Structural Design)*

Subsidiary (Non-US):

KapStone Asia Limited (2)
Level 1805 Wheelock House, 20 Pedder Street, Central, China (Hong Kong)
Tel.: (852) 22932289
Corrugated Paper Whslr
N.A.I.C.S.: 424130

Subsidiary (Domestic):

KapStone Charleston Kraft, LLC (2)
PO Box 118005, Charleston, SC 29423-8005
Tel.: (843) 745-3000
Kraft Paper & Paperboard Mfr
N.A.I.C.S.: 322130
Aubrey M. Mallett *(Controller)*

Plant (Domestic):

KapStone Container Corp. - Twin Falls (2)
348 S Park Ave, Twin Falls, ID 83301-5542
Tel.: (208) 734-2100
Web Site: http://www.kapstonepaper.com
Sales Range: $50-74.9 Million
Emp.: 130
Food Container Mfr, Graphic Design & Printing Services
N.A.I.C.S.: 322212

Subsidiary (Domestic):

KapStone Container Corporation (2)
5560 Gwaltney Dr, Atlanta, GA 30336
Tel.: (404) 629-1400
Web Site: http://www.kapstonepaper.com
Emp.: 100
Industrial & Specialty Packaging Mfr
N.A.I.C.S.: 322211

Plant (Domestic):

KapStone Container Corporation - Amsterdam (2)
28 Park Dr, Amsterdam, NY 12010
Tel.: (518) 842-2450
Web Site: http://www.kapstonepaper.com
Sales Range: $25-49.9 Million
Emp.: 100
Corrugated Box Mfr
N.A.I.C.S.: 322211

Subsidiary (Domestic):

KapStone Kraft Paper Corporation (2)
100 Gaston Rd, Roanoke Rapids, NC 27870
Tel.: (252) 533-6000
Web Site: http://www.kapstonepaper.com
Sales Range: $350-399.9 Million
Emp.: 500
Paper Mills
N.A.I.C.S.: 322130

Plant (Domestic):

KapStone Oakland (2)
8511 Blaine St, Oakland, CA 94621-1213
Tel.: (510) 569-2616
Web Site: http://www.kapstonepaper.com
Sales Range: $25-49.9 Million
Emp.: 115
Corrugated Box & Packaging Mfr
N.A.I.C.S.: 322211

KapStone Packaging - Lawrenceburg Sheet Plant (2)
1001 Cale Dr, Lawrenceburg, KY 40342
Tel.: (502) 839-9700
Web Site: http://www.kapstonepaper.com
Sales Range: $50-74.9 Million
Emp.: 5
Corrugated Box Mfr
N.A.I.C.S.: 322211

KapStone Packaging - Minneapolis Corrugator Plant (2)
5851 E River Rd, Fridley, MN 55432
Tel.: (763) 571-4700
Web Site: http://www.kapstonepaper.com
Sales Range: $50-74.9 Million
Emp.: 135
Corrugated Box Mfr
N.A.I.C.S.: 322211

KapStone Packaging - West Springfield Sheet Plant (2)
100 Palmer Ave, West Springfield, MA 01089
Tel.: (413) 733-2211
Web Site: http://www.kapstonepaper.com
Sales Range: $25-49.9 Million
Emp.: 50
Corrugated Box Mfr
N.A.I.C.S.: 322211

KapStone Packaging Plant (2)
1601 Blairs Ferry Rd NE, Cedar Rapids, IA 52402
Tel.: (319) 382-3369
Web Site: http://www.kapstonepaper.com
Corrugated Box Mfr
N.A.I.C.S.: 322211

Subsidiary (Domestic):

KapStone Packaging Plant - South Carolina (2)
306 S Buncombe Rd, Greer, SC 29650
Tel.: (864) 879-8400
Web Site: http://www.kapstonepaper.com
Corrugated & Solid Fiber Box Mfr
N.A.I.C.S.: 322211
Joe Smith *(Founder & CEO)*

Plant (Domestic):

KapStone Seattle (2)
5901 E Marginal Way S, Seattle, WA 98134-2414
Tel.: (206) 762-7170
Web Site: http://www.kapstonepaper.com
Sales Range: $25-49.9 Million
Emp.: 105
Paper & Paperboard Packaging Mfr; Graphic Design & Printing Services
N.A.I.C.S.: 322212

KapStone Spanish Fork (2)
2200 N Main St, Spanish Fork, UT 84660-9584
Tel.: (801) 798-7331
Web Site: http://www.kapstonepaper.com
Sales Range: $50-74.9 Million
Emp.: 300
Paper Boxes Mfr & Display Graphic Design & Printing Services
N.A.I.C.S.: 322212

KapStone Yakima (2)
2001 Longfibre Ave, Yakima, WA 98903
Tel.: (509) 248-4241
Web Site: http://www.kapstonepaper.com
Sales Range: $50-74.9 Million
Emp.: 160
Corrugated Box Mfr
N.A.I.C.S.: 322211

Longview Fibre Paper and Packaging, Inc. (2)
300 Fibre Way, Longview, WA 98632-7411   (100%)
Tel.: (360) 425-1550
Web Site: http://www.kapstonepaper.com
Sales Range: $800-899.9 Million
Emp.: 1,800
Specialty Paper & Paperboard Box Mfr
N.A.I.C.S.: 322120

Subsidiary (Domestic):

Victory Packaging Maquilla Dora LLC (2)
3555 Timmons Ln Ste 1400, Houston, TX 77027
Tel.: (713) 961-3299
Packaging Services
N.A.I.C.S.: 561910

Subsidiary (Non-US):

Victory Packaging de Mexico, S. de R.L. de C.V (2)
Calle Japeto No 802 Col Arboledas de Santa Cruz, Parque Industrial Kalos, Gua-

WestRock Company—(Continued)
dalupe, 67196, Mexico
Tel.: (52) 8181272600
Web Site: http://www.victorypackaging.com
Goods Warehousing Services
N.A.I.C.S.: 531190

Subsidiary (Domestic):

Victory Packaging, LP (2)
3555 Timmons Ln Ste 1400, Houston, TX
77027
Tel.: (713) 961-3299
Web Site: http://www.victorypackaging.com
Packaging Supplies & Solutions
N.A.I.C.S.: 423840
Robert Egan *(Pres & COO)*
Leah Borrello *(CFO)*

WRKCo Inc. (1)
1000 Abernathy Rd NE, Atlanta, GA 30328
Tel.: (770) 448-2193
Web Site: https://www.westrock.com
Holding Company; Packaging Products Mfr
& Whslr
N.A.I.C.S.: 551112
Alexander W. Pease *(CFO & Exec VP)*

Subsidiary (Non-US):

**Multi Packaging Solutions Interna-
tional Limited** (2)
Clarendon House 2 Church Street, Hamil-
ton, HM 11, Bermuda
Tel.: (441) 295 5950
Web Site: http://www.multipkg.com
Sales Range: $1-4.9 Billion
Emp.: 8,700
Holding Company; Packaging Services
N.A.I.C.S.: 551112
Mark Wenham *(Sr VP-Europe)*

Subsidiary (Non-US):

**Multi Packaging Solutions
Limited** (3)
Millennium Way West, Phoenix Centre, Not-
tingham, NG8 6AW, United Kingdom
Tel.: (44) 115 979 6300
Web Site: http://multipkg.com
Paperboard Containers Mfr
N.A.I.C.S.: 322212

**Multi Packaging Solutions Services
GmbH** (3)
Senefelder Strasse 3-7, 74182, Obersulm,
Germany
Tel.: (49) 71 34 507.0
Web Site: http://multipkg.com
Folding Cartons Mfr
N.A.I.C.S.: 322212

Subsidiary (US):

Multi Packaging Solutions, Inc. (3)
885 Third Ave 28th Fl, New York, NY 10022
Tel.: (646) 885-0157
Web Site: http://www.multipkg.com
North American Headquarters
N.A.I.C.S.: 551114

Subsidiary (Domestic):

MPS Holland, Inc. (4)
13 W 4th St, Holland, MI 49423
Tel.: (616) 392-2326
Emp.: 120
Folding Paperboard Boxes & Specialized
Printing Services
N.A.I.C.S.: 322212

MPS South Plainfield, LLC (4)
901 Durham Ave, South Plainfield, NJ
07080-2401
Tel.: (908) 757-6000
Sales Range: $25-49.9 Million
Custom Folding Paperboard Packaging De-
signer & Mfr
N.A.I.C.S.: 322212
Steven Linde *(Dir-Mktg)*
Ron Crisafulli *(VP-Ops)*
Phillip M. Naidrich *(Dir-Accts-Natl)*

Rolled Edge, Inc. (4)
4221 N Normandy Ave, Chicago, IL 60634
Tel.: (773) 283-9500
Web Site: http://www.chicagopapertube.com
Packaging Paper Tube Mfr
N.A.I.C.S.: 322220

Subsidiary (US):

Paris Art Label Co., Inc. (3)
217 River Ave, Patchogue, NY 11772
Tel.: (631) 648-6200
Web Site: http://www.parisartlabel.com
Commercial Printing Services, Including La-
bels & Shrink Sleeve Products
N.A.I.C.S.: 323111
Tim Tarantino *(VP-Ops)*
Jonathan Tarantino *(VP-Sls)*
Tom Southworth *(VP-Quality)*
John Hovanec *(Sr VP)*
Tony DaSilva *(VP-Shrink Sleeves Div)*
Ron Tarantino Sr. *(Pres)*
Ron Tarantino Jr. *(VP-Ops)*

Subsidiary (Domestic):

Plymouth Packaging, Inc. (2)
11333 General Dr, Plymouth, MI 48170-
4337
Tel.: (734) 453-6700
Web Site: http://www.westrock.com
Corrugated & Solid Fiber Box Mfr
N.A.I.C.S.: 322211

Subsidiary (Non-US):

Rigesa, Ltda. (2)
1701 Avenida Carlos Grimaldi 5th Floor,
Campinas, 13091-908, SP, Brazil (100%)
Tel.: (55) 19 3707 4000
Web Site: http://www.westrock.com
Emp.: 2,200
Corrugated Boxes & Paperboard Container
Design, Mfr & Sales
N.A.I.C.S.: 322211

Division (Domestic):

**Rigesa, Celulose, Papél e Embala-
gens Ltda.** (3)
Av Dr Carlos Grimaldi 1701, Campinas,
13091-908, SP, Brazil (100%)
Tel.: (55) 1937074000
Corrugated Boxes & Paperboard Container
Mfr
N.A.I.C.S.: 322211
James B. Porter III *(Pres)*

Unit (Domestic):

**WestRock Company - Chino Distribu-
tion Center** (2)
15750 Mountain Ave, Chino, CA 91708
Tel.: (909) 393-4199
Warehousing & Distribution of Folding Car-
tons
N.A.I.C.S.: 493110
Karl Gunther *(Mgr)*

Subsidiary (Domestic):

**WestRock Consumer Packaging
Group, LLC** (2)
1950 N Ruby St, Melrose Park, IL 60160
Tel.: (708) 344-9100
Consumer Packaging Mfr
N.A.I.C.S.: 322220

Subsidiary (Non-US):

**WestRock Consumer Paperboard
EMEA B.V.** (2)
Newtonweg 15, 5928 PN, Venlo,
Netherlands (100%)
Tel.: (31) 77 389 6810
Emp.: 50
Paperboard Mfr & Sales
N.A.I.C.S.: 322219
Sandor Aouben *(Gen Mgr)*

WestRock GmbH (2)
Hoher Markt 5, 1010, Vienna,
Austria (100%)
Tel.: (43) 1 310 05120
Paperboard Sales
N.A.I.C.S.: 424990

Subsidiary (Domestic):

WestRock MWV, LLC (2)
501 S 5th St, Richmond, VA 23219-0501
Tel.: (804) 444-1000
Web Site: http://www.westrock.com
Coated & Specialty Papers & Packaging
Containers Mfr
N.A.I.C.S.: 322130

Subsidiary (Non-US):

WestRock Asia, K.K. (3)
3F Cross Place Hamamatsucho 1-7-6
Shibakoen, Minato-ku, Tokyo, 105-0011,
Japan (100%)
Tel.: (81) 3 3578 0051
Sales Range: $50-74.9 Million
Emp.: 7
Design & Sales of Folding Cartons
N.A.I.C.S.: 424130

Subsidiary (Domestic):

WestRock KK (4)
Shuwaeai 2 Shiba Park 2-12-7 Shiba-
daimon, Minato-ku, Tokyo, 105 0011,
Japan (100%)
Tel.: (81) 3 54 01 5811
Web Site: http://www.westrock.com
Sales Range: $10-24.9 Million
Emp.: 30
Paperboard, Paperbox & Other Wrapping
Paper Mfr
N.A.I.C.S.: 322212

Subsidiary (Non-US):

**WestRock MWV Hong Kong
Limited** (4)
Level 43 AIA Tower 183 Electric Road,
North Point, China (Hong Kong) (100%)
Tel.: (852) 2532 9000
Sales Range: $50-74.9 Million
Folding Cartons Whslr
N.A.I.C.S.: 424130
Jackson Cheng *(Deputy Gen Mgr)*

**WestRock Packaging Solutions Ko-
rea, Inc.** (4)
77 Imae-dong, Bundang-gu, Seongnam,
463 830, Gyeonggi-do, Korea
(South) (100%)
Tel.: (82) 24239940
Sales Range: Less than $1 Million
Emp.: 14
Paperboard Folding Cartons Whslr
N.A.I.C.S.: 424990
Cheolsoo Kim *(Gen Mgr)*
Sj Oh *(Gen Mgr-Technical)*

Plant (Domestic):

WestRock Co. - Chicago (3)
9540 S Dorchester Ave, Chicago, IL 60628
Tel.: (773) 731-9500
Sales Range: $10-24.9 Million
Emp.: 200
Folding Paperboard Box Mfr
N.A.I.C.S.: 322212
Brian Porrett *(Plant Mgr)*

WestRock Co. - Covington (3)
104 E Riverside St, Covington, VA 24426-
1238
Tel.: (540) 969-5000
Paperboard Mfr
N.A.I.C.S.: 322130
Donald Wilkinson *(Superintendent-Paper
Mill)*
Craig Lane *(Mgr-Production)*

WestRock Co. - Evadale Mill (3)
1913 Hwy 105 S, Evadale, TX 77615
Tel.: (409) 276-1411
Sales Range: $250-299.9 Million
Emp.: 1,200
Pulp & Paperboard Mill
N.A.I.C.S.: 322130
Darrell Deaton *(Superintendent)*
Larry Middleton *(Mgr-Maintenance)*

WestRock Co. - Lanett (3)
3500 45th St SW, Lanett, AL 36863-6321
Tel.: (334) 576-6323
Sales Range: $10-24.9 Million
Emp.: 160
Folding Cartons Mfr
N.A.I.C.S.: 322212

**WestRock Co. - Mahrt Mill -
Cottonton** (3)
Hwy 165 S, Cottonton, AL 36851
Tel.: (334) 855-4711
Sales Range: $10-24.9 Million
Emp.: 200
Paperboard & Kraft Paper Mfr
N.A.I.C.S.: 322130
Chester Fort *(Mgr)*

WestRock Co. - Mebane (3)
7411 Oakwood St Ext, Mebane, NC 27302-
9212
Tel.: (919) 304-0300
Web Site: http://www.westrock.com
Paper & Packaging Solutions
N.A.I.C.S.: 322212

Subsidiary (Non-US):

**WestRock Manufacturing-Bilbao
S.L.** (2)
Poligono Galdeduren 3 parcela No 30, E
48170, Zamudio, Spain (100%)
Tel.: (34) 944523848
Web Site: http://www.mwv.com
Sales Range: $25-49.9 Million
Emp.: 112
Carriers & Cartons for the Multipackaging of
Primary Containers Mfr & Sales
N.A.I.C.S.: 322212

**WestRock Packaging Systems
France Sarl** (2)
5 Allee du Bourbonnais, BP 131, 78312,
Maurepas, France (100%)
Tel.: (33) 130517711
Folding Cartons Mfr & Whslr
N.A.I.C.S.: 322212
Denis Rochas *(Gen Mgr)*

**WestRock Packaging Systems Neth-
erlands B.V.** (2)
Ettenseweg 46, 4706 PB, Roosendaal,
Netherlands (100%)
Tel.: (31) 165524452
Sales Range: $50-74.9 Million
Packaging Systems Mfr for Food & Bever-
ages
N.A.I.C.S.: 322212
Sidney Dieters *(Asst Mgr-Production)*
Frank van Neerrijnen *(Mgr-Ops)*
Roy Jaquet *(Asst Mgr-Production)*
Wim Van Den Boom *(Mgr-HR)*

**WestRock Packaging Systems UK
Ltd.** (2)
500 Woodward Avenue, Yate, Bristol, BS37
5YS, S Gloucestershire, United
Kingdom (100%)
Tel.: (44) 1454 272700
Folding Cartons Mfr & Whslr
N.A.I.C.S.: 322212

Subsidiary (Domestic):

**WestRock Packaging Systems,
LLC** (2)
1105 Herndon St NW, Atlanta, GA 30318
Tel.: (404) 875-2711
Sales Range: $1-9.9 Million
Emp.: 80
Folding Cartons Mfr
N.A.I.C.S.: 322212

WestRock RKT Company (2)
504 Thrasher St, Norcross, GA 30071
Tel.: (770) 448-2193
Web Site: http://www.rocktenn.com
Sales Range: $5-14.9 Billion
Packaging Products Mfr & Whslr
N.A.I.C.S.: 322212

Subsidiary (Domestic):

**WestRock - Southern Container,
LLC** (3)
115 Engineers Rd, Hauppauge, NY 11788-
4003
Tel.: (631) 231-0400
Sales Range: $500-549.9 Million
Emp.: 1,000
Corrugated Boxes & Containerboards Mfr
N.A.I.C.S.: 322211
David Steel *(Reg Mgr-Mktg-Central Reg)*

Division (Domestic):

WestRock CP, LLC (3)
504 Thrasher St, Norcross, GA 30071
Tel.: (770) 448-2193
Containerboard & Corrugated Container Mfr
N.A.I.C.S.: 322211
James B. Porter III *(Pres)*

Plant (Domestic):

**WestRock RKT Co. - Dayton Con-
tainer Plant** (4)
1 Corn Rd, Dayton, NJ 08810-1527

Tel.: (732) 355-0088
Corrugated Containers Mfr
N.A.I.C.S.: 322211

WestRock RKT Co. - Jacksonville Recycling Center (4)
1580 W Beaver St, Jacksonville, FL 32209-7210
Tel.: (904) 356-7122
Paper & Cardboard Recycling Service
N.A.I.C.S.: 562920

WestRock RKT Co. - Knox Food Service Packaging Plant (4)
6595 E Hwy 10, Knox, IN 46534
Tel.: (574) 772-5545
Sales Range: $10-24.9 Million
Emp.: 18
Corrugated Containers Mfr
N.A.I.C.S.: 322212
Wes Lenig (Gen Mgr)

WestRock RKT Co. - Liberty Container Plant (4)
933 Kent St, Liberty, MO 64068-2236
Tel.: (816) 781-8800
Sales Range: $25-49.9 Million
Emp.: 165
Folding Cartons & Corrugated Containers Mfr
N.A.I.C.S.: 322211

WestRock RKT Co. - North Tonawanda Container Plant (4)
51 Robinson St, North Tonawanda, NY 14120
Tel.: (716) 694-1000
Sales Range: $50-74.9 Million
Emp.: 104
Corrugated Containers Mfr
N.A.I.C.S.: 322211
Mike Peterson (Plant Mgr)

WestRock RKT Co. - Plymouth Food Service Packaging Plant (4)
1100 Pidco Dr, Plymouth, IN 46563
Tel.: (574) 935-5799
Sales Range: $10-24.9 Million
Emp.: 80
Corrugated Food Containers Mfr
N.A.I.C.S.: 322211
Katherine Baert (Dir-HR)

WestRock RKT Co. - Plymouth Laminating Food Service Plant (4)
1000 Pidco Dr, Plymouth, IN 46563
Tel.: (574) 935-3645
Sales Range: $10-24.9 Million
Foil Lamination & Corrugated Containers Mfr
N.A.I.C.S.: 322220

WestRock RKT Co. - Saint Louis Food Service Packaging Plant (4)
7526 N Broadway St, Saint Louis, MO 63147
Tel.: (314) 382-9500
Sales Range: $10-24.9 Million
Emp.: 30
Corrugated & Paperboard Pizza Boxes
N.A.I.C.S.: 322211

WestRock RKT Co. - San Juan Container Plant (4)
Amelia Industrial Park 47 Amelia St, Guaynabo, PR 00968-8003
Tel.: (787) 792-7800
Sales Range: $25-49.9 Million
Emp.: 120
Corrugated Box Mfr
N.A.I.C.S.: 322211
Hector De Jesus (Gen Mgr)
Edwin Miranda (Controller)

WestRock RKT Co. - Springfield (MA) Sheet Plant (4)
320 Parker St, Springfield, MA 01129
Tel.: (413) 543-7300
Sales Range: $25-49.9 Million
Emp.: 100
Corrugated Sheet Mfr
N.A.I.C.S.: 322211
Carl Nabinger (Plant Mgr)
Dave Bergeron (Sr Designer)

WestRock RKT Co. - Tacoma Mill (4)
801 Portland Ave, Tacoma, WA 98421
Tel.: (253) 572-2150

Sales Range: $100-124.9 Million
Emp.: 425
Kraft Paper & Pulp Mill
N.A.I.C.S.: 322120
Lori Smith (Mgr-Sourcing)
Rick Brown (Controller)

WestRock RKT Co. - Tupelo Container Plant (4)
324 Turner Industrial Park, Saltillo, MS 38866
Tel.: (662) 869-5771
Sales Range: $75-99.9 Million
Emp.: 250
Corrugated Box Mfr
N.A.I.C.S.: 322211

WestRock RKT Co. - Winston-Salem Merchandising Displays (4)
5900 Grassy Creek Blvd, Winston Salem, NC 27105-1206 (100%)
Tel.: (336) 661-1700
Display & Packaging Mfr
N.A.I.C.S.: 322212
Frank Warren (Pres)

Subsidiary (Domestic):

WestRock Converting Company (3)
504 Thrasher St, Norcross, GA 30071-4098 (100%)
Tel.: (770) 448-2193
Sales Range: $1-4.9 Billion
Emp.: 10,000
Mfr of Packaging Products From Paperboard, Linerboard, Thermoformed Plastic
N.A.I.C.S.: 322130

WestRock Financial, Inc. (3)
504 Thrasher St, Norcross, GA 30071-1967
Tel.: (770) 448-2193
Web Site: http://www.westrock.com
Financial Services
N.A.I.C.S.: 561499

WestRock Mill Company, LLC (3)
504 Thrasher St, Norcross, GA 30071
Tel.: (770) 448-2193
Sales Range: $350-399.9 Million
Emp.: 500
Collects, Bales & Converts Wastepaper into Paperboard
N.A.I.C.S.: 322130
Jim Rubbuck (Chm & CEO)

WestRock Minnesota Corporation (3)
2250 Wabash Ave, Saint Paul, MN 55114
Tel.: (651) 641-0138
Recycled Paperboard, Recycled Corrugated Medium & Folding Cartons Mfr
N.A.I.C.S.: 322110
Bob Carpenter (Asst Gen Mgr)

WestRock Services, Inc. (3)
504 Thrasher St, Norcross, GA 30071-1967
Tel.: (678) 291-7733
Paperboard Mfr
N.A.I.C.S.: 322212

WestRock-Puerto Rico, Inc. (3)
Amelia Industrial Park 47 Amelia St, Guaynabo, PR 00968-8003
Tel.: (787) 792-7800
Corrugated & Solid Fiber Boxes Mfr
N.A.I.C.S.: 322211
Hector O. De Jesus (Gen Mgr)
Raul G. Morales (Mgr-Quality)

Subsidiary (Non-US):

WestRock Services Poland Sp.z o.o. (2)
Krakow Business Park 800, ul Krakowska 280, 32 080, Krakow, Poland (100%)
Tel.: (48) 12 279 7300
Proprietary Cartons Marketer & Whslr & Leasing of Packaging Equipment
N.A.I.C.S.: 532490

WESTWATER RESOURCES, INC.
6950 S Potomac St Ste 300, Centennial, CO 80112
Tel.: (303) 531-0516 DE
Web Site:
https://www.westwaterresources.net

WWR—(NASDAQ)
Rev.: $1,004,000
Assets: $168,408,000
Liabilities: $26,440,000
Net Worth: $141,968,000
Earnings: ($11,121,000)
Emp.: 34
Fiscal Year-end: 12/31/22
Other Metal Ore Mining
N.A.I.C.S.: 212290
Terence James Cryan (Chm)
Steven M. Cates (CFO & Sr VP-Fin)
Jon Jacobs (Chief Comml Officer)
Frank Bakker (Pres & CEO)
John Lawrence (Chief Admin Officer)

Subsidiaries:

URI, Inc. (1)
641 E Fm 1118, Kingsville, TX 78363
Tel.: (361) 595-5731
Web Site: http://www.uri.com
Nonmetallic Mineral Mining Services
N.A.I.C.S.: 212390

WESTWOOD HOLDINGS GROUP, INC.
200 Crescent Ct Ste 1200, Dallas, TX 75201
Tel.: (214) 756-6900 DE
Web Site:
https://westwoodgroup.com
Year Founded: 1983
WHG—(NYSE)
Rev.: $68,681,000
Assets: $146,427,000
Liabilities: $35,779,000
Net Worth: $110,648,000
Earnings: ($4,628,000)
Emp.: 152
Fiscal Year-end: 12/31/22
Asset Management Services
N.A.I.C.S.: 523940
Brian O'Connor Casey (CEO)
Richard M. Frank (Chm)
Kenneth R. Nostro (Sr VP-Institutional Sls & Client Svcs)
Prashant R. Inamdar (Sr VP & Portfolio Mgr)
Michael H. Wall (VP & Portfolio Mgr)
Matthew Na (VP & Portfolio Mgr)
Frederic G. Rowsey (VP & Portfolio Mgr)
Adrian A. Helfert (Chief Investment Officer-Multi-Asset & Sr VP)
Hussein Adatia (VP & Portfolio Mgr)
Ben Chittenden (VP)
Trip Rodgers (Sr VP)
Kyle Martin (VP)
David Friedman (VP)
Jill Meyer (Sr VP & Dir-Fiduciary Svcs)
Melissa W. McMillian (Sr VP)
Susan Wedelich (Sr VP)
Karla Dominguez (Sr VP)
Jason Caras (VP)
Murray Forbes III (CFO)
Leah R. Bennett (Pres)
J. Dyer Kennedy (Portfolio Mgr-Broadmark)
Greg Reid (Pres & Pres-Real Assets)
Francis T. Mullen (Sr Mng Dir & Sr Mng Dir-Broadmark)
Parag Sanghani (Mng Dir, Sr VP & Sr Portfolio Mgr)
Ted Gardner (Mng Dir, Sr VP & Sr Portfolio Mgr)
John Ehinger (Mng Dir, Chief Compliance Officer & Head-Legal)
William E. Costello (Sr VP, Dir-Equity Portfolios & Sr Portfolio Mgr)
Sean Clark (Sr VP-Institutional Sls & Consultant Rels, Head-Consultant Relations & Dir)
Todd L. Williams (Sr VP, Dir-Equity Res & Portfolio Mgr)
David Linton (Mng Dir, Sr VP & Head-Distribution)

John Palmer (Sr VP & Portfolio Mgr)
Amy M. Lester (VP & Mgr-Relationship)
Mike Guetzkow (VP & Dir-Sr Divisional Consultant)
Bill Hunter (VP-Sr External Wholesaler)
Scott Barnard (VP & Portfolio Mgr)
Chris Hartman (VP & Portfolio Mgr)
Brad Eisen (VP & Dir-Sr Divisional Consultant)
Matt Grandits (VP & Dir-Sr Divisional Consultant)
Shaun Murphy (Sr VP & Dir-Managed Investment Solutions)
Drew Miyawaki (Sr VP & Dir-Managed Investment Solutions)
Richard P. Damico (CIO-Broadmark, Sr Portfolio Mgr & Portfolio Mgr)

Subsidiaries:

Westwood Management Corporation (1)
200 Crescent Ct Ste 1200, Dallas, TX 75201-1876
Tel.: (214) 756-6900
Web Site: http://www.whgfunds.com
Sales Range: $100-124.9 Million
Emp.: 65
Registered Investment Advisory Firm
N.A.I.C.S.: 523940
Brian O'Connor Casey (CEO)

Division (Domestic):

The Westwood Funds (2)
200 Crescent Ct Ste 1200, Dallas, TX 75201
Tel.: (214) 756-6900
Web Site: http://www.whgfunds.com
High-Quality, Registered Mutual Funds
N.A.I.C.S.: 523991

Westwood Trust (1)
200 Crescent Ct Ste 1200, Dallas, TX 75201-1876
Tel.: (214) 756-6900
Web Site: http://www.westwoodgroup.com
Sales Range: $25-49.9 Million
Emp.: 75
Trust Institution, Providing Investment Management & Trust & Custody Services to Individuals & Companies with Accounts over $500,000
N.A.I.C.S.: 523991
Richard M. Frank (Chm)

Subsidiary (Domestic):

Westwood Trust - Houston (2)
10000 Memorial Dr Ste 650, Houston, TX 77024
Tel.: (713) 683-7070
Web Site: http://www.westwoodgroup.com
Wealth Management Services
N.A.I.C.S.: 523940
Maureen F. Phillips (Chm)
Donald W. Roberts (VP)
Tom Williams (VP)
Leah R. Bennett (Pres)
Susan W. Wedelich (VP)

WEWARDS, INC.
2960 W Sahara Ave, Las Vegas, NV 89102
Tel.: (702) 944-5577 NV
Web Site: https://www.wewards.io
Year Founded: 2013
WEWA—(OTCIQ)
Rev.: $20,546
Assets: $764,692
Liabilities: $14,021,006
Net Worth: ($13,256,314)
Earnings: ($651,739)
Emp.: 1
Fiscal Year-end: 05/31/24
Website Development & Administration Services
N.A.I.C.S.: 513210
Lei Pei (Chm, Pres, CEO, CFO, Treas & Sec)

Wewards, Inc.—(Continued)

WEWORK INC.
71 5th Ave 2nd Fl, New York, NY 10003
Tel.: (646) 389-3922   DE
Web Site: https://www.wework.com
Year Founded: 2019
WE—(NYSE)
Rev.: $3,245,000,000
Assets: $17,863,000,000
Liabilities: $21,298,000,000
Net Worth: ($3,435,000,000)
Earnings: ($2,034,000,000)
Emp.: 4,300
Fiscal Year-end: 12/31/22
Offices of Other Holding Companies
N.A.I.C.S.: 551112
Kurt T. Wehner (CFO, Chief Acctg Officer & Treas)
Claudio Hidalgo (COO)
Paul M. Keglevic (Chm)
Adam Neumann (Co-Founder)
Rebekah Neumann (Co-Founder, Chief Brand Officer & Chief Impact Officer)
Miguel McKelvey (Co-Founder & Chief Culture Officer)
Michael Gross (Vice Chm)
John C. Santora (CEO)

Subsidiaries:

WeWork Companies Inc.   (1)
12 E 49th St Fl 3, New York, NY 10017
Tel.: (646) 389-3922
Web Site: https://www.wework.com
Residential Remodeler
N.A.I.C.S.: 236118
Jennifer Berrent (Co-Pres & Chief Legal Officer)
Miguel McKelvey (Co-Founder & Chief Cultural Officer)
Adam Neumann (Co-Founder & Chm)
Arthur Minson (Co-Pres & CFO)
Rebekah Neumann (Co-Founder, Chief Brand Officer & Chief Impact Officer)

Joint Venture (Non-US):

Hudson's Bay Company   (2)
8925 Torbram Road, Brampton, L6T 4G1, ON, Canada
Tel.: (905) 792-4400
Web Site: http://www3.hbc.com
Rev.: $6,872,326,720
Assets: $7,165,514,720
Liabilities: $5,709,836,300
Net Worth: $1,455,678,420
Earnings: ($397,269,740)
Emp.: 40,000
Fiscal Year-end: 02/02/2019
Specialty Retail & Department Stores Operator
N.A.I.C.S.: 455110
Richard A. Baker (Exec Chm)
Marc J. Metrick (Pres-Saks Fifth Avenue)
Kerry Mader (Chief Customer Officer & Exec VP)
Todd Zator (Chief Acctg Officer)
Ian Putnam (Chief Corp Dev Officer & Pres-Real Estate)
David J. Schwartz (Gen Counsel, Sec & Exec VP)
Andrew Blecher (Chief Comm Officer)
Edward Record (CFO)
Janis Leigh (Chief HR Officer)
Stephen J. Gold (Chief Tech & Digital Ops Officer)
Vanessa LeFebvre (Pres-Lord & Taylor)
Anu Penmetcha (VP-Digital Mdsg & Ops)
Meghan Nameth (Sr VP-Mktg)
Paige Thomas (Pres-Saks OFF 5TH)
Alexander Meyer (Chief Customer Officer)

Division (Domestic):

Home Outfitters   (3)
401 Bay Street, Toronto, M5H 2Y4, ON, Canada
Tel.: (416) 861-6404
Web Site: http://www.homeoutfitters.com
Kitchen, Bed & Bath Retailer
N.A.I.C.S.: 449129

Subsidiary (US):

Saks Incorporated   (3)

611 5th Ave, New York, NY 10022
Tel.: (212) 940-5305
Web Site: http://www.saks.com
Rev.: $3,147,554,000
Assets: $2,090,247,000
Liabilities: $940,398,000
Net Worth: $1,149,849,000
Earnings: $62,882,000
Emp.: 13,900
Fiscal Year-end: 02/02/2013
Holding Company; Department Store Operator & Online Retailer
N.A.I.C.S.: 551112
Richard A. Baker (Chm)
Lucas Evans (Treas & Sr VP)

Subsidiary (Domestic):

Saks Fifth Avenue, Inc.   (4)
611 5th Ave, New York, NY 10022
Tel.: (212) 753-4000
Web Site: http://www.saksfifthavenue.com
Sales Range: $1-4.9 Billion
Emp.: 500
Department Store Operator & Online Retailer
N.A.I.C.S.: 455110
Eric Jennings (VP & Dir-Mktg-Fashion-Mens & Home Gifts)
Marta Nowakowski (Mgr-Mdsg-Jewelry & Watches)
Romina Nabhen (Dir-New Fashion & Fifth Avenue Club)
Kate Oldham (Sr VP & Gen Mgr-Mdse-Beauty, Fragrance, Lingerie & Swimwear)
Marc J. Metrick (Pres)
Roopal Patel (Dir-Fashion)
Shelley Tadaki Cramer (Gen Mgr-Waikiki)
Jennifer Welch (Mgr-District Asset Protection)
Deb McGinnis (VP & Gen Mgr-Palm Beach Gardens)
Ramona Messore (VP & Gen Mgr-Brickell City Centre)
Alicia Williams (VP-Diversity, Equity & Inclusion)
Cara Chacon (Sr VP-ESG)
Kathleen Shea (VP-Travel & Tourism Strategy)
John Antonini (Sr VP & Dir-Stores)

Division (Domestic):

The Bay   (3)
401 Bay Street Suite 700, Toronto, M5H 2Y4, ON, Canada
Tel.: (416) 861-6437
Web Site: http://www.thebay.ca
Sales Range: $100-124.9 Million
Departmental Store Operator
N.A.I.C.S.: 455110
Bonnie R. Brooks (Pres & CEO)

WEX, INC.
1 Hancock St, Portland, ME 04101
Tel.: (207) 773-8171   DE
Web Site: https://www.wexinc.com
WEX—(NYSE)
Rev.: $2,548,000,000
Assets: $13,882,100,000
Liabilities: $12,061,500,000
Net Worth: $1,820,600,000
Earnings: $266,600,000
Emp.: 7,200
Fiscal Year-end: 12/31/23
Holding Company; Payment Processing & Information Management Services
N.A.I.C.S.: 551112
Hilary A. Rapkin (Chief Legal Officer)
Sachin Dhawan (CTO)
Jagtar Narula (CFO)
Melanie Tinto (Chief HR Officer)
Ann E. Drew (Chief Risk & Compliance Officer)
Karen Stroup (Chief Digital Officer)
Carlos Carriedo (COO-Intl)
Jay Dearborn (Chief Strategy Officer)
Jack A. VanWoerkom (Vice Chm)
Melissa D. Smith (Chm, Pres & CEO)

Subsidiaries:

Benefit Express Services, LLC   (1)

1700 E Golf Rd Ste 1000, Schaumburg, IL 60173
Tel.: (847) 637-1550
Web Site: http://www.benefitexpress.info
Rev.: $7,000,000
Emp.: 125
Human Resources
N.A.I.C.S.: 541511
Maria Bradley (Pres & Mng Dir)
Ann Haller (Mgr-HR)

Chard, Snyder & Associates, LLC   (1)
6867 Cintas Blvd, Mason, OH 45040
Tel.: (513) 459-9997
Web Site: https://www.chard-snyder.com
Emp.: 1,500
Employee Benefit Administration Services
N.A.I.C.S.: 524292

Competitive Health, Inc.   (1)
300 Spectrum Ctr Dr Ste 400, Irvine, CA 92618
Web Site: https://www.competitivehealth.com
Software Development Services
N.A.I.C.S.: 541511
Kim Darling (Founder & CEO)
Quinn Pearl (VP-Sls)
Sean Bernard (Mgr-Sls & Acct)

Discovery Benefits, Inc.   (1)
4321 20th Ave SW, Fargo, ND 58103
Tel.: (866) 451-3399
Web Site: http://www.discoverybenefits.com
Sales Range: $10-24.9 Million
Emp.: 287
Responsive & Flexible Employee Benefit Administration Services
N.A.I.C.S.: 524298
David Gess (VP-Sls-Northeast)
Jason Christianson (Dir-Sls)
Mike Hagen (VP-Sls-Midwest)
Nick Lakoduk (VP-Sls-West)
Phil Hayes (Reg Dir)
Zach Hanson (VP-Sls-Southeast)
Mike DiFiore (CFO)
Suzanne Rehr (Chief Compliance Officer & Exec VP)
Scott Anderson (COO)
Brian Carey (Chief Strategy & Plng Officer)
Craig Alme (Sr VP-Bus Solutions)
Andy Doeden (Sr VP-Sls-Natl)
Curt Hibl (Sr VP-IT)
Kelly Hockett (Sr VP-Software Solutions & Sys)
Kara Johnson (Sr VP-Shared Svcs & Readiness)
Michelle Larson (Sr VP-Sls)
Amy Perrin (Sr VP-Svc Delivery)
Mark Youngblood (Sr VP-Onboarding)

EB Holdings Corp.   (1)
22 Waterville Rd, Avon, CT 06001-2069
Tel.: (860) 678-3400
Holding Company
N.A.I.C.S.: 551112

Electronic Funds Source LLC   (1)
1104 Country Hills Dr Ste 700, Ogden, UT 84403
Web Site: http://www.efsllc.com
Emp.: 500
Payment Processing Solutions
N.A.I.C.S.: 522320
Scott R. Phillips (Pres-Global Fleet)
Tim Hampton (Sr VP & Gen Mgr-OTR)
John Markham (Sr VP-Natl Accounts & Inside Sls)
Kellie Jones (VP-Mktg)
Ted D. Jones (Sr VP-Strategic Partners)
Matt Lattin (Dir-Fleet Products)
Michelle Pokrzywinski (VP-IT)
Noel Glasgow (VP-Sls-Eastern)
Tony Lehenbauer (VP-Sls-Western)
Jessica Fought (Dir-Implementation)

Subsidiary (Domestic):

Electronic Funds Source LLC - Chanhassen   (2)
8170 Upland Cir Ste 100, Chanhassen, MN 55317
Web Site: http://www.efsllc.com
Payment Processing Solutions
N.A.I.C.S.: 522320

Evolution1, Inc.   (1)
4324 20th Ave SW Ste 200, Fargo, ND 58103

Tel.: (701) 499-7200
Web Site: http://www.evolution1.com
Sales Range: $25-49.9 Million
Emp.: 60
Healthcare Information Technology Solutions
N.A.I.C.S.: 513210
Matt Dallahan (Sr VP-Strategy & Dev)
Jeff Young (CEO)
Todd Reynolds (CTO)
Jeff Bakke (Chief Strategy Officer)
Jeff Brunsberg (CMO)
Tiffany Wirth (VP-Mktg)

FastCred Administracao e Servicos Ltda.   (1)
Rua Souza Pereira 553/559-1 andar Centro, Sorocaba, Sao Paulo, Brazil
Tel.: (55) 1521018450
Web Site: http://www.fastcredcartoes.com.br
Electronic Payment Services
N.A.I.C.S.: 522320

FleetOne, LLC   (1)
3102 W End Ave Ste 900, Nashville, TN 37203
Tel.: (615) 315-4000
Web Site: https://www.fleetone.com
Fuel Cards & Fleet Payment Services
N.A.I.C.S.: 522390

Subsidiary (Domestic):

FleetOne Factoring, LLC   (2)
3102 West End Ave Ste 900, Nashville, TN 37203
Tel.: (615) 315-4000
Web Site: https://www.wexcapital.com
Fuel Cards & Fleet Management Services
N.A.I.C.S.: 522390

Noventis Inc.   (1)
1 Hancock St, Portland, ME 04101
Tel.: (801) 924-1755
Web Site: http://www.noventispayments.com
Electronic Payment Services
N.A.I.C.S.: 522320
Steve Taylor (CEO)
Bob Kaufman (Founder & CEO)

Optal Limited   (1)
17 Moorgate, London, EC2R 6AR, United Kingdom
Tel.: (44) 3332301842
Web Site: https://optal.com
Virtual Card & Payment Services
N.A.I.C.S.: 522320

Pacific Pride Services, LLC   (1)
2003 Western Ave Ste 203, Seattle, WA 98121
Web Site: https://www.pacificpride.com
Sales Range: $25-49.9 Million
Emp.: 13
Fuel Cards & Fuel Management Solutions
N.A.I.C.S.: 522210

Payzer, LLC   (1)
11111 Carmel Commons Blvd Ste 400, Charlotte, NC 28226
Web Site: https://payzer.com
Financial Transaction Management Services
N.A.I.C.S.: 522320

Transplatinum Service, LLC   (1)
613 Bakertown Rd, Nashville, TN 37211
Tel.: (615) 315-4000
Emp.: 200
Financial Transaction Services
N.A.I.C.S.: 522320

Truckers B2B, LLC   (1)
1104 Country Hills Dr 7th Fl, Ogden, UT 84403
Web Site: https://www.truckersb2b.com
Business Management Services
N.A.I.C.S.: 561110

WEX Asia Pte   (1)
65 Chulia Street 38-01 OCBC Centre, Singapore, 049513, Singapore
Tel.: (65) 68085621
Financial Transaction Services
N.A.I.C.S.: 522320

WEX Australia Pty Ltd   (1)
3/293 Camberwell Road, Camberwell, 3124, VIC, Australia
Tel.: (61) 392749100
Web Site: http://www.wexaustralia.com
Payment Processing Services

N.A.I.C.S.: 541214

WEX Bank (1)
7090 S Union Park Ctr Ste 350, Midvale, UT 84047
Tel.: (801) 568-4345
Commercial Banking Services
N.A.I.C.S.: 522110

WEX Europe Limited (1)
4th Floor East Building 1 London Bridge, London, SE1 9BG, United Kingdom
Tel.: (44) 2070719602
Web Site: https://www.wexeurope.com
Payment Processing Services
N.A.I.C.S.: 541214

WEX Europe Services BVBA (1)
Grote Markt 40-42, 9600, Ronse, Oost-Vlaanderen, Belgium
Tel.: (32) 32970152
Electronic Payment Services
N.A.I.C.S.: 522320

WEX Europe Services SRL (1)
Via Carlo Veneziani 58 Palazzo D, 00148, Rome, Italy
Tel.: (39) 08510870960
Web Site: https://www.wexinc.com
Electronic Payment Services
N.A.I.C.S.: 522320

WEX New Zealand (1)
Level 2 160 Grafton Road, Grafton, Auckland, 1010, New Zealand
Tel.: (64) 99510810
Web Site: https://www.wexasia.com
Prepaid Payment Processing & Information Management Services
N.A.I.C.S.: 522320

Wright Express Australia Holdings Pty Ltd (1)
Level 3 293 Camberwell Road, Camberwell, 3124, VIC, Australia
Tel.: (61) 392749100
Web Site: http://www.motorpass.com.au
Sales Range: $50-74.9 Million
Emp.: 130
Prepaid Payment Processing & Information Management Services
N.A.I.C.S.: 522320

Wright Express Prepaid Cards Australia Pty Ltd (1)
L 10 52 Alfred St, Milsons Point, 2061, NSW, Australia
Tel.: (61) 282846060
Prepaid Payment Processing & Information Management Services
N.A.I.C.S.: 522320

eNett International (Singapore) Pte. Ltd. (1)
8 Marina Boulevard 05-02, Marina Bay Financial Centre, Singapore, 018981, Singapore
Tel.: (65) 63131586
Web Site: https://www.enett.com
Travel Payment Services
N.A.I.C.S.: 522320

WEYCO GROUP, INC.
333 W Estabrook Blvd, Glendale, WI 53212
Tel.: (414) 908-1600 **WI**
Web Site:
https://www.weycogroup.com
Year Founded: 1906
WEYS—(NASDAQ)
Rev.: $351,737,000
Assets: $326,620,000
Liabilities: $102,715,000
Net Worth: $223,905,000
Earnings: $29,540,000
Emp.: 462
Fiscal Year-end: 12/31/22
Footwear Merchant Wholesalers
N.A.I.C.S.: 424340
Thomas W. Florsheim Jr. *(Chm & CEO)*
John W. Florsheim *(Pres, Asst Sec, COO, Exec VP & VP)*
Jeff Douglass *(VP-Mktg)*
Judy Anderson *(CFO, Sec & VP)*

Brian Flannery *(Pres-Stacy Adams Brand & VP)*
Beverly Goldberg *(VP-Sls-Florsheim Brand)*
George Sotiros *(VP-IT & Distr)*
Allison Woss *(VP-Supply Chain)*
Kevin Schiff *(Pres-Florsheim Brand & VP)*
Keven Ringgold *(VP-Design)*
Al Jackson *(VP-Customer Rels & Vendor Compliance)*
Dustin Combs *(Pres-Bogs & Rafters Brands & VP)*
Riley Combs *(VP-Sls, Bogs & Rafters Brands)*
David Polansky *(VP-Sls-Stacy Adams Brand)*
Maria Stavrides *(VP-Weyco Canada)*
DeAnna Osteen *(VP-HR)*
Cesar Geronimo *(VP-Bogs Product Dev)*
Kevin Kious *(VP-Work Sls-Bogs Brand)*
Kate Destinon *(Pres-Nunn Bush Brand & VP)*
Robert D. Hanley *(Principal Acctg Officer)*

Subsidiaries:

Florsheim Shoes Europe S.r.l. (1)
Via Degli Artigianni 29/32, 50041, Calenzano, Italy
Tel.: (39) 0558832111
Web Site: http://www.florsheim.co.za
Footwear Whslr
N.A.I.C.S.: 424340

Florsheim, Inc. (1)
333 W Estabrook Blvd, Glendale, WI 53212 (50%)
Tel.: (414) 908-1600
Web Site: https://www.florsheim.com
Sales Range: $150-199.9 Million
Men's Dress & Casual Footwear Mfr
N.A.I.C.S.: 424340

Nunn-Bush Shoe Company (1)
333 W Estabrook Blvd, Glendale, WI 53212-1067 (100%)
Tel.: (414) 908-1600
Web Site: https://www.nunnbush.com
Sales Range: $450-499.9 Million
Emp.: 250
Men's Footwear Whslr & Mfr
N.A.I.C.S.: 424340
Thomas W. Florsheim Jr. *(Chm & CEO)*

Stacy Adams Shoe Company (1)
333 W Estabrook Blvd, Glendale, WI 53212-1067 (100%)
Tel.: (414) 908-1600
Web Site: https://www.stacyadams.com
Sales Range: $450-499.9 Million
Emp.: 300
Mfr of Shoes
N.A.I.C.S.: 424340

WEYERHAEUSER COMPANY
220 Occidental Ave S, Seattle, WA 98104-7800
Tel.: (206) 539-3000 **WA**
Web Site:
https://www.weyerhaeuser.com
Year Founded: 1900
WY—(NYSE)
Rev.: $7,674,000,000
Assets: $16,983,000,000
Liabilities: $6,747,000,000
Net Worth: $10,236,000,000
Earnings: $839,000,000
Emp.: 9,318
Fiscal Year-end: 12/31/23
Building Products Mfr; Packaging & Management of Timberlands
N.A.I.C.S.: 423930
Devin W. Stockfish *(Pres & CEO)*
Denise M. Merle *(Chief Admin Officer & Sr VP)*
Russell S. Hagen *(Chief Dev Officer & Sr VP)*

Kristy T. Harlan *(Gen Counsel, Sec & Sr VP)*
Travis A. Keatley *(Sr VP-Timberlands)*

Subsidiaries:

Weyerhaeuser Columbia Timberlands LLC (1)
33663 Weyerhaeuser Way S, Federal Way, WA 98003
Tel.: (253) 924-2345
Timber Tract Operations
N.A.I.C.S.: 113110
Ryan Beaver *(Gen Mgr)*

Weyerhaeuser NR Company (1)
200 Occidental Ave, Seattle, WA 98104
Tel.: (206) 539-3000
Web Site: http://www.weyerhaeuser.com
Lumber & Plywood Product Whslr
N.A.I.C.S.: 423310

Subsidiary (Domestic):

Weyerhaeuser International, Inc. (2)
33663 Weyerhaeuser Way, Federal Way, WA 98003 (100%)
Tel.: (253) 924-2345
Web Site: http://www.weyerhaeuser.com
Sales Range: $150-199.9 Million
Holding Company
N.A.I.C.S.: 423310

Affiliate (Non-US):

Iisaak Forest Resource Ltd. (3)
2777 Pacific Rim Hwy, Ucluelet, V0R 3A0, BC, Canada (49%)
Tel.: (250) 726-7037
Web Site: http://www.iisaak.com
Sales Range: $150-199.9 Million
Emp.: 3
Forest Management Services
N.A.I.C.S.: 115310

Subsidiary (Non-US):

Weyerhaeuser (Asia) Limited (3)
Unit 2501 Great Eagle Centre 23 Harbour Road, Wanchai, China (Hong Kong) (100%)
Tel.: (852) 28655922
Lumber & Plywood Product Whslr
N.A.I.C.S.: 423310

Weyerhaeuser Company Limited (3)
Suite 440-1140 West Pender Street, Vancouver, V6E 4G1, BC, Canada (100%)
Tel.: (604) 661-8000
Web Site: http://www.weyerhaeuser.com
Lumber, Panelboard, Integrated Forest Products & Engineered Wood
N.A.I.C.S.: 333248
David Graham *(Pres)*

Subsidiary (Domestic):

317298 Saskatchewan Ltd. (4)
Hwy 9 S, PO Box 40, Hudson Bay, S0E 0Y0, SK, Canada (100%)
Tel.: (306) 865-1700
Sales Range: $50-74.9 Million
Emp.: 140
Lumber Processing Services
N.A.I.C.S.: 322120

Subsidiary (Non-US):

Weyerhaeuser Japan Ltd. (3)
2-3-14 Higashi-shinagawa, Shinagawa-ku, Tokyo, 140-0002, Japan (100%)
Tel.: (81) 332140312
Web Site: http://www.weyerhaeuser.jp
Sales Range: $50-74.9 Million
Emp.: 30
Wood Products Sales
N.A.I.C.S.: 424690
Iwa Buchi *(Gen Mgr)*

Weyerhaeuser Korea Ltd. (3)
Room No 313 KoreanRe Bldg 80 Susong-Dong Jongro-Gu, Seoul, 110-733, Korea (South) (100%)
Tel.: (82) 27532363
Sales Range: $25-49.9 Million
Emp.: 4
Sales of Wood Products
N.A.I.C.S.: 321999

Weyerhaeuser Productos, S.A. (3)

Cristobal Echevarriarza 3535 Apartamento 1802, Torres Del Puerto, Montevideo, 11300, Uruguay
Tel.: (598) 26234470
Lumber Plywood Millwork Wood Panel Merchant Wholesalers
N.A.I.C.S.: 423310

Subsidiary (Non-US):

Weyerhaeuser Poland sp. z o.o. (2)
St Kolobrzeska 28, 80-394, Gdansk, Poland
Tel.: (48) 605880195
Web Site: http://www.weyerhaeuser-polska.pl
Lumber & Wood Products Mfr
N.A.I.C.S.: 423310

Subsidiary (Domestic):

Weyerhaeuser Realty Investors, Inc. (2)
14725 SE 36th St Ste 401, Bellevue, WA 98006
Tel.: (425) 452-6510
Sales Range: $50-74.9 Million
Emp.: 100
Real Estate Investment Services
N.A.I.C.S.: 525990

WGI HOLDINGS, INC.
5109 Ackaburg Ct, Las Vegas, NV 89130 **DE**
Year Founded: 2006
WGIH—(OTCIQ)
Investment Management Service
N.A.I.C.S.: 523999

WHEELER REAL ESTATE INVESTMENT TRUST, INC.
2529 Virginia Beach Blvd, Virginia Beach, VA 23452
Tel.: (757) 627-9088 **MD**
Web Site: https://www.whlr.us
WHLR—(NASDAQ)
Rev.: $76,645,000
Assets: $684,536,000
Liabilities: $633,502,000
Net Worth: $51,034,000
Earnings: ($12,454,000)
Emp.: 47
Fiscal Year-end: 12/31/22
Miscellaneous Financial Investment Activities
N.A.I.C.S.: 523999
Crystal Plum *(CFO)*
M. Andrew Franklin *(Pres & CEO)*
Rebecca Schiefer *(Dir-Acctg)*
Patrick Gundlach *(Dir-Fin Reporting)*
Amy Sliker *(Dir-Property Ops)*
Denbeigh Marchant *(VP)*
Dana Sherman *(Dir)*
Madonna McAdam *(Assoc Dir)*
Wesley Forehand *(Portfolio Mgr)*
Kevin Conway *(Sr Mgr)*
Raymond V. Hicks *(Sr Mgr)*
Carolyn McCullar *(Mgr)*
Victoria H. Browne *(Mktg Mgr)*
Toni Fairfax *(Mgr)*
Kimberly Long *(Sr Mgr)*
Michael Amenabar *(Sr Mgr)*
Dawn Williams *(Sr Mgr)*
Sarah Spiceland *(Sr Mgr)*
Crissy Hart *(Sr Mgr)*

Subsidiaries:

Cedar Realty Trust, Inc. (1)
2529 Virginia Beach Blvd, Virginia Beach, VA 23452
Tel.: (757) 627-9088
Web Site: https://ir.cedarrealtytrust.com
Rev.: $34,005,000
Assets: $234,164,000
Liabilities: $151,962,000
Net Worth: $82,202,000
Earnings: $44,031,000
Emp.: 55
Fiscal Year-end: 12/31/2022
Other Financial Vehicles
N.A.I.C.S.: 525990

Wheeler Real Estate Investment Trust,
Inc.—(Continued)

Ann Maneri *(VP & Controller-Property)*
Michael Winters *(Chief Investment Officer & Exec VP)*
Bruce J. Schanzer *(Pres & CEO)*
Tim Havener *(Exec VP-Leasing)*
Jennifer L. Bitterman *(CFO & Exec VP)*
Lars Kerstein *(VP-Dev Leasing)*
Oscar A. Zamora *(VP-Legal Real Estate)*
Richard Vilaboy *(Sr VP-Property Mgmt)*
Michael Sommer *(Sr VP-Dev & Construction)*
Lauren Licausi *(VP-HR)*
Angelica A. Beltran *(Sec)*
Denbeigh Marchant *(VP)*
Amy Sliker *(Dir)*
Dana Sherman *(Dir)*
Rebecca Schiefer *(Dir)*
Patrick Gundlach *(Dir)*
Madonna Mcadam *(Assoc Dir)*
Wesley Forehand *(Mgr)*
Kevin Conway *(Sr Mgr)*
Raymond V. Hicks *(Sr Mgr)*
Carolyn Mccullar *(Mgr)*
Victoria H. Browne *(Mgr)*
Toni Fairfax *(Mgr)*
Kimberly Long *(Sr Mgr)*
Michael Amenabar *(Sr Mgr)*
Dawn Williams *(Sr Mgr)*
Sarah Spiceland *(Sr Mgr)*
Crissy Hart *(Sr Mgr)*
Christy C. Jethro *(Mgr)*
Gaspare J. Saitta II *(Chief Acctg Officer & VP)*

LaGrange Associates, LLC   (1)
211 King St Ste 100, Charleston, SC 29401
Tel.: (843) 410-0510
Real Estate Services
N.A.I.C.S.: 531390

Wheeler REIT, L.P.   (1)
2529 Virginia Beach Blvd, Virginia Beach,
VA 23452
Tel.: (757) 627-9088
Web Site: https://www.whlr.us
Real Estate Investment Services
N.A.I.C.S.: 531390

Wheeler Real Estate LLC   (1)
111 Shamrock Blvd, Venice, FL 34293
Tel.: (941) 496-8700
Web Site: http://www.wheeler-homes.com
Real Estate Services
N.A.I.C.S.: 531390

WHEELS UP EXPERIENCE INC.

601 W 26th St, New York, NY 10001
Tel.: (212) 257-5252   DE
Web Site: https://www.wheelsup.com
Year Founded: 2020
UP—(NYSE)
Rev.: $1,579,760,000
Assets: $1,923,225,000
Liabilities: $1,671,305,000
Net Worth: $251,920,000
Earnings: ($555,160,000)
Emp.: 3,005
Fiscal Year-end: 12/31/22
Private Aviation Solution & Services
N.A.I.C.S.: 488190
George N. Mattson *(CEO)*
Todd L. Smith *(CFO & Principal Acctg Officer)*
Todd Smith *(CFO)*
Lee Applbaum *(CMO)*
Mark Briffa *(CEO-Air Partner & Exec VP)*
Brian Kedzior *(Chief People Officer)*
Matthew Knopf *(Chief Legal Officer & Sec)*
Kristen Lauria *(CMO & Chief Customer Officer)*

Subsidiaries:

Air Partner Plc   (1)
2 City Place Beehive Ring Road, Gatwick,
RH6 0PA, West Sussex, United Kingdom
Tel.: (44) 1293844800
Web Site: http://www.airpartner.com
Rev.: $87,436,502
Assets: $90,485,972

Liabilities: $78,428,434
Net Worth: $12,057,539
Earnings: $397,415
Emp.: 379
Fiscal Year-end: 01/31/2020
Aircraft Charter Services
N.A.I.C.S.: 481211
Mark A. Briffa *(CEO)*
Tony Whitty *(Exec VP-Remarketing & ACMI)*
Joanne Estell *(CFO)*
Kevin MacNaughton *(Mng Dir-Charter)*
Craig Pattison *(Chief People & Tech Officer)*
Paul Mason *(Mng Dir-Safety & Security)*

Subsidiary (Non-US):

**Air Partner Havacilik ve Tasimacilik
Ltd.**   (2)
Halil Rifatpasa Mh Yuzer Havuz Sk No 1
Perpa Ticaret Merkezi ABlok, Kat 12 No
1773 Sisli, Istanbul, 34149, Turkiye
Tel.: (90) 212 6631020
Web Site: http://www.airpartner.com
Sales Range: $25-49.9 Million
Oil Transportation Services
N.A.I.C.S.: 481111

Subsidiary (US):

Air Partner Inc   (2)
1100 Lee Wagener Blvd Ste 328, Fort Lauderdale, FL 33315-3570   (100%)
Tel.: (954) 280-9961
Sales Range: $25-49.9 Million
Emp.: 10
Travel Agencies
N.A.I.C.S.: 561510

Subsidiary (Non-US):

Air Partner International GmbH   (2)
Im Mediapark 5b, 50670, Cologne,
Germany   (100%)
Tel.: (49) 22196693300
Web Site: http://www.airpartner.com
Sales Range: $25-49.9 Million
Travel Agencies
N.A.I.C.S.: 561510

Air Partner International SAS   (2)
89/91 rue du Faubourg Saint-Honore,
75008, Paris, France   (100%)
Tel.: (33) 142441100
Sales Range: $25-49.9 Million
Emp.: 30
Travel Agencies
N.A.I.C.S.: 561510
Jonathan Rainbolt *(Product Mgr)*

Air Partner Srl   (2)
Via Valtellina 67, 20159, Milan, Italy
Tel.: (39) 0266825117
Web Site: http://www.airpartner.com
Sales Range: $25-49.9 Million
Aircraft Charter Brokering Services
N.A.I.C.S.: 481219

Air Partner Switzerland AG   (2)
8058 Zurich Airport 2118, 8060, Zurich,
Switzerland   (100%)
Tel.: (41) 223672948
Web Site: http://www.airpartner.com
Sales Range: $25-49.9 Million
Emp.: 3
Travel Agencies
N.A.I.C.S.: 561510

Subsidiary (Domestic):

**Air Partner Travel Consultants
Ltd**   (2)
2 City Place, Gatwick, RH6 0PA, United
Kingdom   (100%)
Tel.: (44) 1293844855
Web Site: http://www.airpartner.com
Sales Range: $25-49.9 Million
Emp.: 80
Travel Agencies
N.A.I.C.S.: 561510

Subsidiary (US):

Kenyon International Emergency Services, Inc.   (2)
612 Spring Hill Dr Ste 180, Houston, TX
77386
Tel.: (281) 872-6074
Web Site:
https://www.kenyoninternational.com

Emp.: 24
Disaster Management Services
N.A.I.C.S.: 624230
Robert A. Jensen *(Chm)*
Simon Hardern *(CEO)*
Conor Prendergast *(Mng Dir)*
Mark Oliver *(VP-Ops)*
Mazen Bekdash *(VP-Bus Dev)*
Sean Gates *(SR VP- Legal Advisory Svcs)*
Deborah Moody *(Dir-Acctg)*
Janie Moreno *(Dir-Call Center Svcs)*
Ben Ng *(Dir-Info Tech)*
Kerry-Ann Milic *(Dir-Operational Support Svcs)*
Samuel Bunney *(Mgr-Comml Svcs)*
Otibho Edeke-Agbareh *(Mgr-Humanitarian Svc)*
Jahaira Guzman *(Mgr-Intl Call Center)*
Victoria Hardwidge *(Acct Mgr)*
Erin Marshall *(Office Mgr)*
Jeffrey Novosad *(Mgr-Ops)*
Clare Pascucci *(Office Mgr)*
Kathy Ricker *(Mgr-Team Member)*
Destiny Torres *(Mgr-Mktg)*
Iwan Witt *(Mgr-Ops)*

Wheels Up Partners LLC   (1)
601 W 26th St, New York, NY 10001
Tel.: (855) 355-8760
Web Site: http://www.wheelsup.com
Aviation Company
N.A.I.C.S.: 334511
George N. Mattson *(CEO)*
Kenneth Dichter *(Founder & CEO)*
Todd L. Smith *(CFO)*
Kenny Dichter *(Founder & CEO)*
Gregg Fahrenbruch *(Sr VP-Ops Strategy)*
Laura Heltebran *(Chief Legal Officer)*

Subsidiary (Domestic):

Delta Private Jets, Inc.   (2)
82 Comair Blvd, Erlanger, KY 41018
Tel.: (859) 534-4300
Web Site: http://www.deltaprivatejets.com
Oil Transportation Services
N.A.I.C.S.: 481111
Lee Gossett *(COO, Sr VP-Ops & Dir-Maintenance)*
Jeff Mihalic *(Pres & CEO)*
Gil West *(COO)*

Gama Aviation LLC   (2)
2 Corporate Dr Ste 1050, Shelton, CT
06484
Tel.: (203) 337-4600
Web Site: http://www.gamagroupusa.com
Aircraft Management & Ancillary Support
Services
N.A.I.C.S.: 488190
K. C. Ihlefeld *(Sr VP-Aircraft Mgmt)*
Tom Connelly *(Pres & CEO)*

Mountain Aviation, Inc.   (2)
9656 Metro Airport Ave, Broomfield, CO
80021
Tel.: (303) 466-3506
Web Site: http://www.mountainaviation.com
Nonscheduled Air Transportation
N.A.I.C.S.: 481219
Rich Bjelkeidg *(Exec VP)*
Gregg Fahrenbruch *(CEO)*

WHERE FOOD COMES FROM, INC.

202 6th St Ste 400, Castle Rock, CO
80104
Tel.: (303) 895-3002   CO
Web Site:
https://www.wherefoodcomesfrom.com
Year Founded: 1996
WFCF—(NASDAQ)
Rev.: $24,845,000
Assets: $18,296,000
Liabilities: $5,819,000
Net Worth: $12,477,000
Earnings: $1,994,000
Emp.: 88
Fiscal Year-end: 12/31/22
Other Animal Food Manufacturing
N.A.I.C.S.: 311119
John K. Saunders *(Co-Founder, Chm & CEO)*
Leann Saunders *(Co-Founder, Pres & COO)*

Kathryn Britton *(Sr Dir-IMI Ops-Global & WFCF Corp Mktg)*
Kristina Bierschwale *(VP-Sls & Bus Dev)*
Christina Dockter *(VP-Ops- Certification Svcs Div-Intl)*
Sarah Costin *(VP-Ops- A Bee Organic)*
Jason Franco *(CTO)*
Eric Harris *(Exec VP)*
Matt Jones *(VP)*
Vinod Nayagar *(Dir)*
Corey Peet *(VP)*
Laura Peet *(Dir)*
Lora Wright *(Dir)*
Sarah Haskins *(Dir)*
Darren Wong *(Creative Dir)*
Jennifer Moore *(Mgr)*
Sara Simpson *(Mgr)*

Subsidiaries:

**International Certification Services,
Inc.**   (1)
202 6th St Ste 400, Castle Rock, CO 80104
Tel.: (303) 895-3002
Web Site: https://www.wfcforganic.com
Food Certification Services
N.A.I.C.S.: 541990
Christina Dockter *(VP-Ops)*

Sterling Solutions, LLC   (1)
PO Box 4047, Irvine, CA 92616
Tel.: (714) 742-4801
Web Site: http://www.sterlingtraceback.com
Management Consulting Services
N.A.I.C.S.: 561110

SureHarvest, Inc.   (1)
2603 Camino Ramon Ste 220, San Ramon,
CA 94583   (60%)
Tel.: (831) 477-7797
Web Site: http://www.sureharvest.com
Software Solutions for Growers & Agricultural Food Companies
N.A.I.C.S.: 513210
Christopher Van Coops *(VP-Farming MIS Engrg)*
Jeff Dlott *(Founder, Pres & CEO)*
Nathan Smith *(Sr VP-Client Solutions)*

Subsidiary (Domestic):

SureHarvest Services, LLC   (2)
2603 Camino Ramon Ste 220, San Ramon,
CA 94583   (100%)
Tel.: (831) 477-7797
Web Site: http://www.sureharvest.com
Software Development Services
N.A.I.C.S.: 541511
Jeff Dlott *(Pres & CEO)*
Nathan Smith *(Sr VP-Client Solutions)*
Christopher Van Coops *(VP-Farming MIS Engrg)*

Validus Verification Services   (1)
3331 109th St, Urbandale, IA 50322
Tel.: (515) 278-8002
Web Site: https://www.validusservices.com
Animal Certification Services
N.A.I.C.S.: 541380

WHIRLPOOL CORPORATION

2000 N M-63, Benton Harbor, MI
49022-2692
Tel.: (269) 923-5000   DE
Web Site:
https://www.whirlpoolcorp.com
Year Founded: 1911
WHR—(NYSE)
Rev.: $19,455,000,000
Assets: $17,312,000,000
Liabilities: $14,775,000,000
Net Worth: $2,537,000,000
Earnings: $481,000,000
Emp.: 59,000
Fiscal Year-end: 12/31/23
Home Appliance Mfr
N.A.I.C.S.: 335210
Marc Robert Bitzer *(Chm & CEO)*
Kirsten Hewitt *(Sr VP & Gen Counsel)*
James W. Peters *(CFO & Exec VP)*

Christopher S. Conley *(CFO/Sr VP-North America)*
Gilles Morel *(Pres-Europe, Middle East & Africa & Exec VP)*
Holger Gottstein *(Sr VP-Strategy & Bus Dev)*
Roberto H. Campos *(Sr VP-Product Organization-Global)*
Danielle M. Brown *(CIO & Sr VP)*

Subsidiaries:

American Dryer Corporation **(1)**
88 Currant Rd, Fall River, MA 02720-4781
Tel.: (269) 923-3000
Web Site: https://www.adclaundry.com
Laundry Dryer Mfr & Whslr.
N.A.I.C.S.: 333310

B. Blend Maquinas e Bebidas S.A. **(1)**
Rua Olimpiadas 66 5 andar Conj 52-Vila Olimpia, Sao Paulo, Brazil
Tel.: (55) 1142801172
Web Site: http://www.loja.bblend.com.br
Food Product Machinery & Equipment Mfr
N.A.I.C.S.: 333241

Bauknecht AG **(1)**
Dammweg 21, 5600, Lenzburg, Switzerland
Tel.: (41) 848801001
Web Site: https://www.bauknecht.ch
Home Appliance Mfr & Distr
N.A.I.C.S.: 335210

Bauknecht Hausgerate GmbH **(1)**
Industriestrasse 48, 70565, Stuttgart, Germany
Tel.: (49) 711810710
Web Site: https://www.bauknecht.de
Emp.: 30
Household Appliances Mfr
N.A.I.C.S.: 335220

Elica PB Whirlpool Kitchen Appliances Private Limited **(1)**
Kondhwa Pisoli Road, Pisoli, Pune, 411060, Maharashtra, India **(96.81%)**
Tel.: (91) 9243007666
Web Site: https://www.elicaindia.com
Emp.: 3,000
Kitchen Appliances Mfr
N.A.I.C.S.: 335220

Embraco Europe S.r.l. **(1)**
Via Legnanino 1, Chieri, 10023, Turin, Italy
Tel.: (39) 0119437111
Web Site: http://www.embraco.com
Consumer Electrical Appliance Distr
N.A.I.C.S.: 423620

In-Sink-Erator **(1)**
4700 21st St, Racine, WI 53406-5031
Tel.: (262) 554-5432
Web Site: http://www.insinkerator.com
Sales Range: $400-449.9 Million
Emp.: 1,000
Garbage Disposers, Trash Compactors, Hot Water Dispensers Mfr & Sales
N.A.I.C.S.: 335220
Joe Dillon *(Pres)*

Indesit Company S.p.A. **(1)**
Via Carlo Pisacane n 1, Pero, 20016, Milan, Italy **(60.4%)**
Tel.: (39) 07326611
Web Site: http://www.indesitcompany.com
Emp.: 16,000
Home Appliance Mfr
N.A.I.C.S.: 335220

Subsidiary (Non-US):

Indesit Company Beyaz Esya Pazarlama A.S. **(2)**
11 Balmumcu Mahallesi Karahasan Sokak Besiktas, Balmumcu Besiktas, 34349, Istanbul, Turkiye
Tel.: (90) 2123555300
Web Site: http://www.indesit.com.tr
Household Appliances Mfr
N.A.I.C.S.: 335220

Indesit Company Bulgaria Ltd. **(2)**
36 Dragan Tsankov Boulevard Block B Office 412, Sofia, 1057, Bulgaria
Tel.: (359) 2 971 25 81
Web Site: http://www.indesit.bg
Home Appliance Mfr

N.A.I.C.S.: 335220

Indesit Company Magyarorszag Kft **(2)**
Bercsenyi u 25, 1117, Budapest, Hungary
Tel.: (36) 13827500
Web Site: http://www.indesit.hu
Home Appliance Distr & Mfr
N.A.I.C.S.: 335220

Indesit Company Osterreich Ges. m.b.h **(2)**
Bundesstrasse 66, 8740, Zeltweg, Austria
Tel.: (43) 3577 222 11 0
Web Site: http://www.indesit.at
Home Appliance Distr
N.A.I.C.S.: 423620

Indesit Company Polska Sp. z o.o. **(2)**
Dabrowskiego 216, Lodz, 93-231, Poland
Tel.: (48) 426455100
Web Site: http://www.indesit.com
Emp.: 3,000
Household Appliances Mfr
N.A.I.C.S.: 335220

KitchenAid **(1)**
1st Krasnoselsky Lane 7/9a Building Building 11 2nd Floor Office 24, 107140, Moscow, Russia **(100%)**
Web Site: http://kichenaid.ru
Sales Range: $100-124.9 Million
Appliance Distr & Mfr
N.A.I.C.S.: 335220

Maytag Comercial, S. de R.L. de C.V. **(1)**
Km 16 13 Carretera Miguel Aleman-El Milagro, Apodaca, 66600, Mexico
Tel.: (52) 8183292100
Consumer Electrical Appliance Distr
N.A.I.C.S.: 423620

Whirlpool (Hong Kong) Ltd. **(1)**
12/F Wilson Logistics Centre 24-28 Kung Yip Street, Kwai Chung, New Territories, China (Hong Kong) **(100%)**
Tel.: (852) 24069138
Web Site: https://www.whirlpool.com.hk
Sales Range: $100-124.9 Million
Household Appliances Mfr
N.A.I.C.S.: 335220

Joint Venture (Non-US):

Hisense-Whirlpool (Zhejiang) Electric Appliances Co., Ltd. **(2)**
North Side of Zhongyang Avenue Changxing, Economic Development Zone, Hangzhou, 313100, Zhejiang, China **(50%)**
Tel.: (86) 5726619711
Home Appliance Mfr
N.A.I.C.S.: 335220

Subsidiary (Non-US):

Whirlpool Home Appliance (Shanghai) Co., Ltd. **(2)**
Building 8 No 1888 Xing Jin Qiao Road Jinqiao Export Processing Zone, Pudong, Shanghai, 201206, China
Tel.: (86) 2161692999
Web Site: http://www.whirlpool.com.cn
Household Appliances Mfr
N.A.I.C.S.: 335220

Whirlpool Southeast Asia Pte. Ltd. **(2)**
9 Tampines Grande 05-21/22 Asia Green, Singapore, 528735, Singapore
Tel.: (65) 62506888
Web Site: https://www.whirlpool.com.sg
Emp.: 5
Household Appliance Distr
N.A.I.C.S.: 423620

Whirlpool Asia Inc. **(1)**
2000 N M-63, Benton Harbor, MI 49022-2692
Tel.: (269) 923-5000
Household Appliances Mfr
N.A.I.C.S.: 335220
Robert Frey *(Pres)*
David Binkley *(Sr VP-Global HR)*

Whirlpool Austria GmbH **(1)**
Bundesstrasse 66, 8740, Zeltweg, Austria

Tel.: (43) 506700
Web Site: https://www.whirlpool.at
Consumer Electrical Appliance Distr
N.A.I.C.S.: 423620

Whirlpool Baltic UAB **(1)**
J Kubiliaus G 6, 08222, Vilnius, Lithuania
Tel.: (370) 52643326
Web Site: http://www.whirlpool.lt
Sales Range: $25-49.9 Million
Emp.: 5
Household Appliance Retailer
N.A.I.C.S.: 449210

Whirlpool Belux N.V./S.A. **(1)**
Nijverheidslaan 3/1, 1853, Strombeek-Bever, Belgium
Tel.: (32) 22633333
Web Site: https://www.whirlpool.be
Friction Material For Automotive Parts Retailer
N.A.I.C.S.: 441330

Whirlpool Bulgaria Ltd. **(1)**
36 Dragan Tsankov Blvd World Trade Center - block B floor 4 office 412, Sofia, 1113, Bulgaria
Tel.: (359) 70010068
Web Site: https://www.whirlpool.bg
Consumer Electrical Appliance Distr
N.A.I.C.S.: 423620

Whirlpool Canada LP **(1)**
200-6750 Century Avenue, Mississauga, L5N 0B7, ON, Canada
Tel.: (905) 821-6400
Web Site: https://www.whirlpoolcanada.com
Sales Range: $75-99.9 Million
Emp.: 230
Distr of Household Appliances
N.A.I.C.S.: 449210

Subsidiary (Domestic):

Cannon Industries Ltd. **(2)**
Suite 122 - 1533 Broadway Street, Port Coquitlam, V3C 6P3, BC, Canada
Tel.: (604) 945-8950
Web Site: http://cannonindustries.com
Packaging Product Mfr & Distr
N.A.I.C.S.: 326112
Tom Innes *(Pres)*
Lesley Corr *(Chief Admin Officer)*
Gary Corr *(Acct Mgr)*
Jenny Madden *(Acct Mgr)*

Whirlpool Canada Co. **(2)**
200 - 6750 Century Avenue, Mississauga, L5N 0B7, ON, Canada
Tel.: (905) 821-6400
Web Site: https://www.whirlpool.ca
Management Consulting Services
N.A.I.C.S.: 541611

Whirlpool Canada LP **(1)**
200-6750 Century Avenue, Mississauga, L5N 0B7, ON, Canada
Tel.: (905) 821-6400
Web Site: https://www.whirlpoolcorp.com
Home Appliance Mfr & Distr
N.A.I.C.S.: 335210

Whirlpool Colombia S.A. **(1)**
Carrera 7 N 116 - 50 office 5 - 127, Bogota, DC, Colombia
Tel.: (57) 6014048565
Web Site: https://www.whirlpool.com.co
Household Appliance Retailer
N.A.I.C.S.: 449210

Whirlpool Corp. - Clyde **(1)**
119 Birdseye St, Clyde, OH 43410
Tel.: (419) 547-7711
Home Laundry Appliances Mfr
N.A.I.C.S.: 335220

Whirlpool Corp. - Evansville **(1)**
5401 Hwy 41 N, Evansville, IN 47711-1962 **(100%)**
Tel.: (812) 426-4000
Web Site: http://www.whirlpoolcorp.com
Sales Range: $900-999.9 Million
Emp.: 5,000
Mfr of Home Refrigeration & Equipment
N.A.I.C.S.: 335220

Whirlpool Corp. - Findlay **(1)**
4901 N Main St, Findlay, OH 45840-8847 **(100%)**
Tel.: (419) 423-8123
Web Site: http://www.whirlpool.com

Sales Range: $350-399.9 Million
Emp.: 2,000
Laundry Appliances & Dishwashers Mfr
N.A.I.C.S.: 335220

Whirlpool Corp. - Fort Smith **(1)**
6400 Jenny Lind Rd, Fort Smith, AR 72908 **(100%)**
Tel.: (479) 648-2000
Web Site: http://www.whirlpoolwebworld.com
Sales Range: $900-999.9 Million
Emp.: 5,000
Mfr of Home Refrigeration & Equipment
N.A.I.C.S.: 335220

Whirlpool Corp. - La Vergne **(1)**
1714 Heil Quaker Blvd, La Vergne, TN 37086 **(100%)**
Tel.: (615) 641-7511
Web Site: http://www.whirlpoolcorp.com
Sales Range: $200-249.9 Million
Emp.: 1,000
Room Air Conditioners, Dehumidifiers & Refrigerator Mfr
N.A.I.C.S.: 333415

Whirlpool Corp. - Marion **(1)**
1300 Marion Agosta Rd, Marion, OH 43302 **(100%)**
Tel.: (740) 383-7122
Web Site: http://www.whirlpool.com
Sales Range: $700-749.9 Million
Emp.: 3,000
Mfr of Household Appliances
N.A.I.C.S.: 335220

Whirlpool Croatia Ltd. **(1)**
Avenija Veceslava Holjevca 40, 10000, Zagreb, Croatia
Tel.: (385) 13040333
Web Site: https://www.whirlpool.hr
Consumer Electrical Appliance Distr
N.A.I.C.S.: 423620
Susana Dubajic *(Country Mgr)*

Whirlpool Eesti OU **(1)**
Turi 10C, 11313, Tallinn, Estonia
Tel.: (372) 6501670
Web Site: http://www.whirlpool.ee
Consumer Electrical Appliance Distr
N.A.I.C.S.: 423620

Whirlpool Europe B.V. **(1)**
Heerbaan 50-52, Breda, 4817 NL, Netherlands
Tel.: (31) 765306530
Household Appliances Mfr
N.A.I.C.S.: 335220

Whirlpool Europe Coordination Center **(1)**
Nijverheidslaan 3/1, 1853, Strombeek-Bever, Belgium
Tel.: (32) 22633333
Web Site: http://www.whirlpool.be
Household Appliances Mfr
N.A.I.C.S.: 335220

Whirlpool Europe Operations Center **(1)**
Viale G Borghi 27, 21025, Comerio, Varese, Italy **(100%)**
Tel.: (39) 0332759111
Web Site: http://www.whirlpool.it
Sales Range: $100-124.9 Million
Household Appliances Mfr
N.A.I.C.S.: 335220

Whirlpool France SAS **(1)**
11 Cours Valmy, La Defense, 92977, Puteaux, France
Web Site: https://www.whirlpool.fr
Household Appliances Mfr
N.A.I.C.S.: 335220

Whirlpool Germany GmbH **(1)**
Industriestrasse 48, 70565, Stuttgart, Germany
Tel.: (49) 711810710
Web Site: https://www.whirlpool.de
Consumer Electrical Appliance Distr
N.A.I.C.S.: 423620
Christoph Bidlingmaier Jens *(Chm)*

Whirlpool Hellas SA **(1)**
581 Vouliagmenis Avenue, Argyroupolis, 16451, Greece
Tel.: (30) 2109946400
Household Appliances Mfr
N.A.I.C.S.: 335220

Whirlpool Corporation—(Continued)

Whirlpool Internacional S. de R.L. de C.V. (1)
Blvd Omega No 2150, Ramos Arizpe, Coahuila, Mexico
Tel.: (52) 8448664100
Household Appliances Mfr
N.A.I.C.S.: 335220

Whirlpool Ireland (1)
Fonthill Ind Est Fonthill Rd, Dublin, 22, Ireland
Tel.: (353) 16161700
Web Site: https://www.whirlpool.ie
Household Appliances Mfr
N.A.I.C.S.: 335220

Whirlpool Ireland Limited (1)
Fonthill Ind Est Fonthill Rd, Dublin, 22, Ireland
Tel.: (353) 16161777
Web Site: https://www.whirlpool.ie
Home Appliance Mfr & Distr
N.A.I.C.S.: 335210

Whirlpool Italia S.r.l. (1)
Via Carlo Pisacane n 1, Pero, 20016, Milan, Italy
Tel.: (39) 022030
Web Site: https://www.whirlpool.it
Friction Material For Automotive Parts Retailer
N.A.I.C.S.: 441330

Whirlpool Latvia S.I.A. (1)
Aleksandra Caka iela 118, Riga, 1012, Latvia
Tel.: (371) 67425232
Web Site: https://www.whirlpool.lv
Home Appliance Mfr & Distr
N.A.I.C.S.: 335210

Whirlpool Latvia S.I.A. (1)
Aleksandra Caka iela 118, Riga, 1012, Latvia
Tel.: (371) 67279900
Web Site: https://www.whirlpool.lv
Consumer Electrical Appliance Distr
N.A.I.C.S.: 423620

Whirlpool Management Services Sagl (1)
Via F Pelli 7, 6900, Lugano, Switzerland
Tel.: (41) 919118000
Sales Range: $10-24.9 Million
Emp.: 2
Home Appliance Retailer
N.A.I.C.S.: 621610

Whirlpool Maroc S. ar.l. (1)
PO Box 3845, Sidi Bernoussi, 20 600, Casablanca, Morocco
Tel.: (212) 522749728
Web Site: http://www.whirlpool.ma
Consumer Electrical Appliance Distr
N.A.I.C.S.: 423620

Whirlpool Maroc Sarl (1)
B P 3845 Sidi Bernoussi, 20600, Casablanca, Morocco
Tel.: (212) 522749728
Web Site: https://www.whirlpool.ma
Home Appliance Mfr & Distr
N.A.I.C.S.: 335210

Whirlpool Mexico, S.A. de C.V. (1)
Carretera Miguel Aleman Km 16 13, Apodaca, 66634, Nuevo Leon, Mexico
Tel.: (52) 8183292000
Emp.: 800
Household Refrigerator & Home Freezer Mfr
N.A.I.C.S.: 335220

Whirlpool Microwave Products Development Limited (1)
17/F Elite Ctr 22 Hung To Rd Kwun Tong, Kwun Tong, Hong Kong, China (Hong Kong)
Tel.: (852) 28810882
Consumer Electrical Appliance Distr
N.A.I.C.S.: 423620

Whirlpool Nederland B.V. (1)
Princenhagelaan 11, 4813 DA, Breda, Netherlands
Tel.: (31) 765306400
Web Site: https://www.whirlpool.nl
Home Appliance Retailer
N.A.I.C.S.: 621610

Whirlpool Nordic A/S (1)
Oliefabriksvej 51, Postbox 113, 2770, Kastrup, Denmark
Tel.: (45) 44880222
Web Site: https://www.whirlpool.dk
Consumer Electrical Appliance Distr
N.A.I.C.S.: 423620

Whirlpool Nordic AB (1)
Gustavslundsvagen 151 A, 167 51, Bromma, Sweden
Tel.: (46) 771751570
Web Site: https://www.whirlpool.se
Emp.: 80
Home Appliance Services
N.A.I.C.S.: 335220

Whirlpool Nordic AB (1)
Gustavslundsvagen 151 A, 167 51, Bromma, Sweden
Tel.: (46) 771751570
Web Site: https://www.whirlpool.se
Home Appliance Mfr & Distr
N.A.I.C.S.: 335210

Whirlpool Nordic OY (1)
Italahdenkatu 22b, PO Box 7190, 00002, Helsinki, Finland
Tel.: (358) 96 133 6235
Web Site: https://www.whirlpool.fi
Emp.: 60
Home Appliance Mfr
N.A.I.C.S.: 335220

Whirlpool Osterreich GmbH (1)
Bundesstrasse 66, 8740, Zeltweg, Austria
Tel.: (43) 506700
Web Site: https://www.whirlpool.at
Home Appliance Mfr & Distr
N.A.I.C.S.: 335210

Whirlpool Overseas Holdings, LLC (1)
1105 N Market St Ste 1300, Wilmington, DE 19801
Tel.: (302) 427-8163
Holding Company
N.A.I.C.S.: 551112

Whirlpool Overseas Hong Kong Limited (1)
Rm 3603-04 36/F AIA Tower 100 How Ming Street, Kwun Tong, Kowloon, China (Hong Kong)
Tel.: (852) 2 859 6000
Web Site: http://www.whirlpool.com.hk
House Hold Appliance Services
N.A.I.C.S.: 449210

Whirlpool Polska Appliances Sp. z o.o. (1)
ul 1 Sierpnia 6A, 02-134, Warsaw, Poland
Tel.: (48) 801900666
Web Site: http://www.whirlpool.pl
Friction Material For Automotive Parts Retailer
N.A.I.C.S.: 441330

Whirlpool Portugal Electrodomesticos, Lda. (1)
Avenida Dom Joao Ii Lote 1 12 02 I H 4 dto, Lisbon, 1990077, Portugal
Tel.: (351) 219406200
Household Appliance Retailer
N.A.I.C.S.: 449210

Whirlpool R&D s.r.l. (1)
Via Varesina 204, 20156, Milan, Italy
Tel.: (39) 022030
Web Site: https://www.whirlpool.it
Consumer Electrical Appliance Distr
N.A.I.C.S.: 423620

Whirlpool RUS LLC (1)
st Dvintsev house 12 building 1 letter B floor 5, 127018, Moscow, Russia
Tel.: (7) 4959612900
Web Site: http://www.whirlpoolgroup.ru
Friction Material For Automotive Parts Retailer
N.A.I.C.S.: 441330

Whirlpool Realty Corporation (1)
2000 N M 63, Benton Harbor, MI 49022
Tel.: (269) 923-3002
Real Estate Service
N.A.I.C.S.: 531210

Whirlpool S.A. (1)
Rua Olympia Semeraro 675 1 Andar Sala 6 Predio Administrativo 1, Bairro Jardim Santa, Sao Paulo, 04183-090, Brazil
Tel.: (55) 35661434
Web Site: https://www.whirlpool.com.br
Rev.: $2,367,436,985
Assets: $1,859,069,341
Liabilities: $1,455,871,815
Net Worth: $403,197,526
Earnings: $50,283,771
Fiscal Year-end: 12/31/2023
Household Appliances Mfr
N.A.I.C.S.: 335220

Whirlpool Slovakia Home Appliances spol. s.r.o. (1)
Galvaniho 17/C, PO Box 23, 820 09, Bratislava, Slovakia
Tel.: (421) 850003007
Web Site: https://www.whirlpool.sk
Friction Material For Automotive Parts Retailer
N.A.I.C.S.: 441330
Sylvia Levarska (Mgr-OTD)

Whirlpool Slovakia spol. s.r.o. (1)
Hlavna 5039/1A, PO Box 23, 058 01, Poprad, Slovakia
Tel.: (421) 527123111
Web Site: http://www.whirlpool.sk
Household Appliances Mfr
N.A.I.C.S.: 335220

Whirlpool South Africa Proprietary Limited (1)
15E Riley Road Riley Road Office Park, Bedfordview, Johannesburg, 2007, South Africa
Tel.: (27) 860884401
Web Site: https://www.whirlpool.co.za
Sales Range: $25-49.9 Million
Household Appliance Distr
N.A.I.C.S.: 449210

Whirlpool Southeast Asia Pte (1)
9 Tampines Grande 05-21/22 Asia Green, Singapore, 528735, Singapore
Tel.: (65) 62506888
Web Site: https://www.whirlpool.com.sg
Home Appliance Mfr & Distr
N.A.I.C.S.: 335210

Whirlpool UK Appliances Limited (1)
Morley Way, Peterborough, PE2 9JB, United Kingdom
Tel.: (44) 3448224224
Web Site:
https://www.whirlpoolservice.co.uk
Friction Material For Automotive Parts Retailer
N.A.I.C.S.: 441330

Whirlpool do Brasil Ltda. (1)
Rua Olimpia Semeraro 675, Andar 32, Sao Paulo, 04180-001, SP, Brazil (100%)
Tel.: (55) 1135661000
Web Site: http://www.whirlpoolcorp.com.br
Sales Range: $25-49.9 Million
Appliance Mfr & Distr
N.A.I.C.S.: 335220

Subsidiary (Domestic):

BUD Comercio de Eletrodomesticos Ltda. (2)
Rua Olympia Semeraro 675 - Jardim Santa Emilia, Sao Paulo, 04183-090, Brazil
Tel.: (55) 40040019
Web Site: https://www.compracerta.com.br
Home Appliance Mfr & Distr
N.A.I.C.S.: 335210

Brasmotor S.A. (2)
Av das Nacoes Unidas 12995 32 Andar, Brooklin Novo, 04578-000, Sao Paulo, SP, Brazil
Tel.: (55) 1135661000
Household Appliances Mfr
N.A.I.C.S.: 335220

Embraco S.A. (2)
Rui Barbosa 1020, Caixa Postal 91, Joinville, 89219 901, SC, Brazil (84%)
Tel.: (55) 4734412333
Web Site: http://www.embraco.com.br
Mfr of Refrigerant Compressors
N.A.I.C.S.: 333912

Whirlpool of India Limited (1)
Plot No 40 Sector 44, Gurgaon, 122002, Haryana, India
Tel.: (91) 1244591300
Web Site: https://www.whirlpoolindia.com
Rev.: $817,565,385
Assets: $689,110,695
Liabilities: $298,951,380
Net Worth: $390,159,315
Earnings: $48,024,795
Emp.: 2,679
Fiscal Year-end: 03/31/2021
Home Appliance Mfr
N.A.I.C.S.: 335220
Anil Berera (Exec Dir)
Sunil D'Souza (Mng Dir)
Roopali Singh (Officer-Compliance & Sec)
Aditya Jain (CFO)

Yummly, Inc. (1)
883 E San Carlos Ave, San Carlos, CA 94063
Tel.: (650) 381-9433
Web Site: https://www.yummly.com
Custom Computer Programming Services
N.A.I.C.S.: 541511

WHITE LABEL LIQUID, INC.
1290 Hand Ave Ste A, Ormond Beach, FL 32174
Tel.: (386) 233-3840
Web Site:
http://www.whitelabelliquid.com
Year Founded: 2002
WLAB—(OTCIQ)
Packaging & Labeling Services
N.A.I.C.S.: 561910
Charlie Randazzo (Pres)
Joseph R. Daprile (Sec)
Bibi Daprile (VP)

WHITE MOUNTAINS INSURANCE GROUP, LTD.
23 S Main St Ste 3B, Hanover, NH 03755-2053
Tel.: (603) 640-2200 **BM**
Web Site:
http://www.whitemountains.com
WTM—(NYSE)
Rev.: $2,166,700,000
Assets: $8,385,900,000
Liabilities: $3,824,300,000
Net Worth: $4,561,600,000
Earnings: $580,900,000
Emp.: 782
Fiscal Year-end: 12/31/23
Holding Company; Insurance & Financial Services
N.A.I.C.S.: 551112
George Manning Rountree (CEO)
David A. Tanner (Deputy Chm)
Jason Lichtenstein (Deputy Gen Counsel)
Jen Moyer (Chief Admin Officer)
Liam P. Caffrey (Pres & CFO)
Jennifer Moyer (Chief Admin Officer)
Christopher John Delehanty (Head-Corp Dev, Merger, and Acq)
Michael Papamichael (Deputy CFO)

Subsidiaries:

Accident & Health Underwriting Ltd. (1)
7-8 Ducketts Wharf South Street, Bishop's Stortford, CM23 3AR, United Kingdom
Tel.: (44) 1279712900
Web Site: https://www.ahulimited.com
Insurance Services
N.A.I.C.S.: 524210

Autosaint Limited (1)
St James House 27-43 Eastern Road, Romford, RM1 3NH, Essex, United Kingdom
Tel.: (44) 1527390290
Web Site: https://www.autosaint.co.uk
Emp.: 240
Fire Insurance Services
N.A.I.C.S.: 524126

Classic Insurance Services Limited (1)
Unit B1 Redfields Industrial Park Redfields Lane, Church Crookham, Hampshire, GU52 0RD, United Kingdom
Tel.: (44) 2076558040

Web Site:
https://www.classicinsuranceservices.com
Insurance Agency Services
N.A.I.C.S.: 524210
Rod Mitchell *(Mng Dir)*
Roger Clark *(Sls Mgr)*
Matthew Doran *(Mgr-Client)*

Copper Funding, LLC (1)
1931 Humble Pl Dr Ste 205, Humble, TX
77338
Tel.: (208) 520-6544
Web Site:
https://www.copperriverfunding.com
Real Estate Services
N.A.I.C.S.: 531210
Craig T. Gaudio *(CEO)*
Michael S. Peart *(CFO)*
Tim Stamps *(COO)*

First Underwriting Ltd. (1)
The Gherkin Level 15 30 St Mary Axe, London, EC3A 8EP, United Kingdom
Tel.: (44) 2076558035
Web Site: https://www.firstuw.com
Insurance Services
N.A.I.C.S.: 524298
Mark Bacon *(Mng Dir)*

**Fresh Insurance Services Group
Limited** (1)
First Floor Building 329 Doncastle Road,
Bracknell, RG12 8PE, Berkshire, United
Kingdom
Tel.: (44) 1344286188
Web Site: http://www.first.co.uk
Emp.: 240
Fire Insurance Services
N.A.I.C.S.: 524126

Peter D. James Limited (1)
768 Hagley Road W, Oldbury, B68 0PJ,
West Midlands, United Kingdom
Tel.: (44) 1215066040
Web Site:
https://www.peterjamesinsurance.co.uk
Vehicle Insurance Services
N.A.I.C.S.: 524126

**SIRIUS INTERNATIONAL INSUR-
ANCE CORPORATION** (1)
Birger Jarlsgatan 57B, 113 96, Stockholm,
Sweden
Tel.: (46) 84585500
General Insurance Services
N.A.I.C.S.: 524210
Monica Cramer Manhem *(Pres & CEO)*

**Stewart Miller Mcculloch & Co.
Limited** (1)
768 Hagley Road W, Oldbury, B68 0PJ,
West Midlands, United Kingdom
Tel.: (44) 1214222282
Web Site:
https://www.stewartmillerinsurance.co.uk
Vehicle Insurance Services
N.A.I.C.S.: 524126

**Vantage Insurance Services
Limited** (1)
41 Eastcheap, London, EC3M 1DT, United
Kingdom
Tel.: (44) 2076558000
Web Site:
http://www.vantageinsurance.co.uk
General Insurance Services
N.A.I.C.S.: 524114
Tom Cooper *(Mng Dir)*
Nigel Coppen *(Dir-Bus Dev)*
Stuart Harris *(Officer-Compliance)*
Louise Watson *(Dir-Ops)*
Jeremy Henderson *(Controller-Fin)*

White Mountains Advisors LLC (1)
200 Hubbard Rd, Guilford, CT 06437
Tel.: (203) 458-5823
Web Site: https://www.whitemountains.com
Investment Advisory Services
N.A.I.C.S.: 523940

**White Mountains Re Bermuda
Ltd.** (1)
26 Reid Street Suite 601, Hamilton, HM 11,
Bermuda
Tel.: (441) 2783160
Web Site: http://www.siriusgroup.com
Sales Range: $25-49.9 Million
Emp.: 19
Holding Company; Reinsurance Products &
Services

N.A.I.C.S.: 551112

Subsidiary (US):

Sirius America Insurance Co. (2)
140 Broadway 32nd Fl, New York, NY
10005
Tel.: (212) 312-2500
Web Site: http://www.siriusgroup.com
Reinsurance Services
N.A.I.C.S.: 524130
Thomas Leonardo *(Head-Accident &
Health-US)*
Daniel J. Wilson *(Pres & CEO)*
Russel Hugh *(VP)*
Thomas Leonardo *(Head-Accident &
Health-US)*
Ralph Salamone *(CFO)*
John Game *(Sr VP & Branch Mgr)*

White Mountains Solutions, Inc. (1)
628 Hebron Ave Ste 106, Glastonbury, CT
06033
Tel.: (860) 368-2000
Emp.: 10
Insurance Services
N.A.I.C.S.: 524298
Neal Wasserman *(Pres)*

**WHITE RIVER BANCSHARES
COMPANY**
Tel.: (479) 684-3700   AR
Year Founded: 2004
WRIV—(OTCIQ)
Banking Services
N.A.I.C.S.: 522110
Gary Russell Head *(CEO)*

WHITE RIVER ENERGY CORP.
609 W Dickson St Ste 102 G, Fayetteville, AR 72701
Tel.: (425) 214-4079   NV
Web Site: https://whiteriver.com
Year Founded: 2011
WTRV—(OTCQB)
Rev.: $1,103,975
Assets: $12,319,544
Liabilities: $25,384,383
Net Worth: ($13,064,839)
Earnings: ($43,089,977)
Emp.: 49
Fiscal Year-end: 03/31/23
Biopharmaceutical Mfr
N.A.I.C.S.: 325412
Randy May *(Chm & CEO)*
Jack Carona *(COO)*

WHITEHORSE FINANCE, INC.
1450 Brickell Ave 31st Fl, Miami, FL
33131
Tel.: (305) 381-6999
Web Site:
https://www.whitehorsefinance.com
Year Founded: 2011
WHF—(NASDAQ)
Rev.: $103,260,000
Assets: $730,751,000
Liabilities: $413,979,000
Net Worth: $316,772,000
Earnings: $20,412,000
Fiscal Year-end: 12/31/23
Investment Services
N.A.I.C.S.: 523999
Marco Collazos *(Chief Compliance
Officer)*
John P. Bolduc *(Chm)*
Stuart D. Aronson *(CEO)*
Joyson C. Thomas *(CFO)*

Subsidiaries:

WhiteHorse Finance Warehouse,
LLC (1)
1450 Brickell Ave 31st Fl, Miami, FL 33131
Tel.: (305) 381-6999
Investment Services
N.A.I.C.S.: 523910

WHITESTONE REIT
2600 S Gessner Rd Ste 500, Houston, TX 77063

Tel.: (713) 827-9595
Web Site:
https://www.whitestonereit.com
Year Founded: 1998
WSR—(NYSE)
Rev.: $139,421,000
Assets: $1,102,767,000
Liabilities: $678,313,000
Net Worth: $424,454,000
Earnings: $35,270,000
Emp.: 75
Fiscal Year-end: 12/31/22
Real Estate Investment Trust
N.A.I.C.S.: 525990
David K. Holeman *(CEO)*
Peter Tropoli *(Gen Counsel & Sec)*
Christine C. J. Mastandrea *(COO)*
David F. Taylor *(Chm)*
Scott Hogan *(CFO)*
Michelle Siv *(VP-HR)*
David Mordy *(Dir-IR)*

Subsidiaries:

Whitestone Pinnacle of Scottsdale,
LLC (1)
2600 S Gessner Rd Ste 500, Houston, TX
77063
Tel.: (713) 435-2225
Sales Range: $25-49.9 Million
Emp.: 10
Real Estate Investment Trust Services
N.A.I.C.S.: 525990
John J. Dee *(Gen Mgr)*

WHITING USA TRUST II
Global Corporate Trust 601 Travis St
16th Fl, Houston, TX 77002
Tel.: (512) 236-6555
Web Site: http://whzt.q4web.com
Year Founded: 2011
WHZT—(OTCIQ)
Rev.: $1,155,000
Assets: $996,000
Liabilities: $463,000
Net Worth: $533,000
Earnings: $268,000
Fiscal Year-end: 12/31/20
Oil & Gas Investment Services
N.A.I.C.S.: 523999
Sarah Newell *(VP)*

WHOLE EARTH BRANDS, INC.
125 S Wacker Dr Ste 1250, Chicago,
IL 60606
Tel.: (312) 840-6000   DE
Web Site:
https://wholeearthbrands.com
Year Founded: 2020
FREE—(NASDAQ)
Rev.: $538,272,000
Assets: $849,003,000
Liabilities: $574,452,000
Net Worth: $274,551,000
Earnings: ($58,752,000)
Emp.: 760
Fiscal Year-end: 12/31/22
Sugar Products Mfr
N.A.I.C.S.: 311313
Ira Schlussel *(Chief Legal Officer)*
Simone Adeshina *(VP-Human Re-
sources)*
Michael Franklin *(Board of Directors
& CEO)*
Rajnish Ohri *(Co-CEO)*
Jeff Robinson *(Co-CEO)*
Bernardo Fiaux *(CFO)*
Brian Litman *(Chief Acctg Officer)*
Irwin D. Simon *(Exec Chm)*

WI-TRON, INC.
59 LaGrange St, Raritan, NJ 08869
Tel.: (908) 253-6870
WTRO—(OTCIQ)
Amplifier Mfr & Distr
N.A.I.C.S.: 335999
John Chase Lee *(Pres & CEO)*

WI2WI CORPORATION
8840 N Greenview Dr, Middleton, WI
53562
Tel.: (608) 831-4445   AB
Web Site: https://www.wi2wi.com
Year Founded: 1992
YTY—(TSXV)
Rev.: $6,928,000
Assets: $11,033,000
Liabilities: $4,335,000
Net Worth: $6,698,000
Earnings: ($588,000)
Fiscal Year-end: 12/31/20
Wireless Sub-Systems Mfr
N.A.I.C.S.: 334220
Zachariah J. Mathews *(Pres & CEO)*
Barry Arneson *(VP-Engrg, Frequency
Control & Timing Devices)*
Dawn Leeder *(CFO)*
Pierre Soulard *(Sec)*

**WIALAN TECHNOLOGIES,
INC.**
1931 NW 150th Ave, Pembroke
Pines, FL 33028
Tel.: (954) 749-3481
Web Site: https://www.wialan.com
WLAN—(OTCIQ)
Sales Range: Less than $1 Million
All Other Telecommunications
N.A.I.C.S.: 517810
Alan J. Bailey *(Interim CEO)*
Victor M. Tapia *(Pres)*
Richard Gilbert *(Exec VP-Sls & Bus
Dev)*
Eduardo Garcia *(CEO)*

WIDEOPENWEST, INC.
7887 E Belleview Ave Ste 1000,
Englewood, CO 80111
Tel.: (720) 479-3500   DE
Web Site: https://www.wowway.com
Year Founded: 2012
WOW—(NYSE)
Rev.: $704,900,000
Assets: $1,717,400,000
Liabilities: $1,142,300,000
Net Worth: $575,100,000
Earnings: $2,500,000
Emp.: 1,390
Fiscal Year-end: 12/31/22
Cable Television Distribution Services
N.A.I.C.S.: 517111
Roger Seiken *(Gen Counsel, Sec &
Sr VP)*
John S. Rego *(CFO)*
Don Schena *(Chief Customer Experi-
ence Officer)*
Teresa L. Elder *(CEO)*
Henry Hryckiewicz *(CTO)*
Leslie Peabody *(Chief People Officer
& Sr VP)*
Andrew S. Posen *(VP & Head-IR)*
Jeffrey A. Marcus *(Chm)*

Subsidiaries:

Anne Arundel Broadband, LLC (1)
406 Headquarters Dr Ste 201, Millersville,
MD 21108
Tel.: (410) 987-9300
Web Site: http://broadstripe.com
Telecommunication Servicesb
N.A.I.C.S.: 517111

WideOpenWest Finance, LLC (1)
7887 E Belleview Ave Ste 1000, Engle-
wood, CO 80111
Tel.: (720) 479-3500
Web Site: http://www.wowway.com
Sales Range: $1-4.9 Billion
Holding Company; Cable Television, Tele-
phone & Internet Distribution Services
N.A.I.C.S.: 551112

Subsidiary (Domestic):

WideOpenWest Networks, LLC (2)
7887 E Belleview Ave Ste 1000, Englewood, CO 80111-6007

WideOpenWest, Inc.—(Continued)

Tel.: (720) 479-3500
Web Site: http://www.wowway.com
Cable Television, Telephone & Internet Distribution Services
N.A.I.C.S.: 517111
Richard E. Fish Jr. (CFO)
Gary Nilsen (Sr VP-Engrg)
Mike Harry (Sr VP-Corp Ops)
Allyson Crawford (VP-Learning & Dev)
Tracy Kirkeide (VP-Acctg Ops & Reporting)
John Carlucci (VP-Video Engrg)
Eric Harris (VP-Comml Sls)
John Roy (VP-Engrg Ops)
Ryan Mitchell (VP-Network, Product & Svc Engrg)

Subsidiary (Domestic):

Knology, Inc. (3)
7887 E Belleview Ave Ste 1000, Englewood, CO 80111
Tel.: (720) 479-3500
Web Site: http://www.wowway.com
Holding Company; Cable, Phone & Internet Services
N.A.I.C.S.: 551112
Felix L. Boccucci (VP-Regulatory Affairs)
Brad M. Vanacore (VP-HR)

Subsidiary (Domestic):

Knology Total Communications, Inc. (4)
7887 E Belleview Ave Ste 1000, Englewood, CO 80111
Tel.: (720) 479-3500
Web Site: http://www.wowway.com
Telephone, Cable & Internet Communication Services
N.A.I.C.S.: 517810

Knology of Florida, LLC (4)
7887 E Belleview Ave Ste 1000, Englewood, CO 80111
Tel.: (720) 479-3500
Web Site: http://www.wowway.com
Broadband Communication Services
N.A.I.C.S.: 517810

Knology of Huntsville, Inc. (4)
7887 E Belleview Ave Ste 1000, Englewood, CO 80111 (100%)
Tel.: (720) 473-3500
Web Site: http://www.wowway.com
Cable Television Services
N.A.I.C.S.: 516210

Knology of Montgomery, Inc. (4)
7887 E Belleview Ave Ste 1000, Englewood, CO 80111 (100%)
Tel.: (720) 479-3500
Web Site: http://www.wowway.com
Cable Television & Internet Telephone Services
N.A.I.C.S.: 516210

Subsidiary (Domestic):

Sigecom, LLC (3)
7887 E Belleview Ave Ste 1000, Englewood, CO 80111-6015
Tel.: (706) 773-5076
Web Site: https://www.wowforbusiness.com
Telephone Communication Services
N.A.I.C.S.: 517121
Steve Stanfill (VP-Telephony Ops)

WIDEPOINT CORPORATION

11250 Waples Mill Rd S Tower Ste 210, Fairfax, VA 22030
Tel.: (703) 349-5644　　　　DE
Web Site: https://www.widepoint.com
Year Founded: 1996
WYY—(NYSEAMEX)
Rev.: $94,103,365
Assets: $49,012,661
Liabilities: $31,261,458
Net Worth: $17,751,203
Earnings: ($23,585,291)
Emp.: 215
Fiscal Year-end: 12/31/22
IT Consulting Services
N.A.I.C.S.: 541512
Jin H. Kang (Pres & CEO)
Otto J. Guenther (Co-Chm)

Jason Holloway (Chief Sls & Mktg Officer & Exec VP)
Philip Garfinkle (Co-Chm)
Robert J. George (CFO)

Subsidiaries:

Advanced Response Concepts Corporation (1)
11250 Waples Mill Rd, Fairfax, VA 22030
Tel.: (703) 246-8560
Web Site: http://www.responseconcepts.com
Emp.: 10
Information Protection & Management Software Provider
N.A.I.C.S.: 513210

IT Authorities, Inc. (1)
1801 N Himes Ave, Tampa, FL 33607
Tel.: (813) 246-5100
Web Site: http://www.itauthorities.com
Sales Range: $1-9.9 Million
Emp.: 28
Computing & Managed Services
N.A.I.C.S.: 541512
Jason Caras (Co-Founder & CEO)
Jason Pollner (Co-Founder)
David McCraney (CIO)
Ashby Green (CFO)
Philip LaForge (CEO)
Jeff Lynn (COO)

Operational Research Consultants, Inc. (1)
11250 Waples Mill Rd S Tower Ste 210, Fairfax, VA 22030 (100%)
Tel.: (703) 596-9378
Web Site: http://www.orc.com
Sales Range: $25-49.9 Million
Emp.: 5
Computer Related Consulting Services
N.A.I.C.S.: 541512

Protexx Technology Corporation (1)
Fairway Financial Ctr 10 Fairway Dr Ste 216, Deerfield Beach, FL 33441 (100%)
Tel.: (954) 596-5425
Sales Range: $1-9.9 Million
Emp.: 3
Identity Management & Information Protection Software Developer & Marketer
N.A.I.C.S.: 513210

Soft-ex Communications Ltd. (1)
South County Business Park Leopardstown Road, Dublin, 18, Ireland
Tel.: (353) 12416600
Web Site: https://www.soft-ex.net
Emp.: 45
Software Publisher
N.A.I.C.S.: 513210
Ian Sparling (Pres & CEO)
Fergus Cullen (Controller-Fin)
David Morgan (Sr VP-Ops)
Frank O'Rourke (Sr VP-Tech)
Ian Lindsay (Sr VP-Sls)
Grainne Magfhloinn (Sr VP-Bus Dev & Mktg)

Subsidiary (Non-US):

Soft-ex BV (2)
Beechavenue 54-62, 1119 PW, Schiphol-Rijk, Netherlands
Tel.: (31) 854019390
Web Site: https://www.soft-ex.net
Software Publisher
N.A.I.C.S.: 513210

Soft-ex UK Limited (2)
200 Brook Drive Green Park, Reading, RG2 6UB, Berkshire, United Kingdom
Tel.: (44) 1183706012
Web Site: https://www.soft-ex.net
Software Publisher
N.A.I.C.S.: 513210

WidePoint Integrated Solutions Corp. (1)
7926 Jones Branch Dr Ste 520, McLean, VA 22102-3371
Tel.: (703) 349-5644
IT Consulting Services
N.A.I.C.S.: 541512

WidePoint Solutions Corp. (1)
2 Eaton St Ste 800, Hampton, VA 23669
Tel.: (757) 727-9742

Web Site: http://www.avalonglobalsolutions.com
Sales Range: $10-24.9 Million
Emp.: 58
Computer Software & Services
N.A.I.C.S.: 513210

iSYS LLC (1)
7926 Jones Branch Dr Ste 520, McLean, VA 22102
Tel.: (703) 349-5644
Web Site: http://www.isysllc.com
Sales Range: $10-24.9 Million
Emp.: 55
IT Services
N.A.I.C.S.: 541519
Jin H. Kang (Pres)

WIKILEAF TECHNOLOGIES, INC.

1115 E Pike St, Seattle, WA 98122
Tel.: (206) 802-1363
Web Site: http://www.wikileaf.com
Year Founded: 2014
WIKI—(CNSX)
Assets: $2,848,193
Liabilities: $2,460,483
Net Worth: $387,710
Earnings: ($6,620,942)
Pharmaceuticals Product Mfr
N.A.I.C.S.: 325412
Dan Nelson (CEO)

WILD BRUSH ENERGY, INC.

2 Union Sq 601 Union St Ste 4200 Fl 4, Seattle, WA 98101
Tel.: (206) 652-3310　　DE
Year Founded: 1979
WBRE—(OTCIQ)
Renewable Energy Consulting Services
N.A.I.C.S.: 541690
Massimiliano Farneti (Pres)

WILHELMINA INTERNATIONAL, INC.

Tel.: (214) 661-7488　　DE
Web Site: https://www.wilhelmina.com
WHLM—(NASDAQ)
Rev.: $17,780,000
Assets: $41,992,000
Liabilities: $17,781,000
Net Worth: $24,211,000
Earnings: $3,529,000
Emp.: 85
Fiscal Year-end: 12/31/22
Holding Company; Modeling Management
N.A.I.C.S.: 551112
Mark E. Schwarz (Exec Chm & Dir)
Clinton J. Coleman (Dir)
Mark E. Pape (Dir)
James A. Dvorak (Dir)

Subsidiaries:

Wilhelmina International, Ltd. (1)
192 Lexington Ave, New York, NY 10010
Tel.: (212) 473-0700
Web Site: https://www.wilhelmina.com
Emp.: 100
Model Management Services
N.A.I.C.S.: 711510

Subsidiary (Domestic):

LW1, Inc. (2)
9378 Wilshire Blvd Ste 310, Beverly Hills, CA 90210
Tel.: (310) 601-2532
Web Site: https://www.aperture-talent.com
Model Management Services
N.A.I.C.S.: 711510

Wilhelmina West, Inc. (2)
9378 Wilshire Blvd Ste 310, Beverly Hills, CA 90212
Tel.: (310) 601-2530
Model Management Services
N.A.I.C.S.: 711510
Charlotte Reisi (Mgr)

Wilhelmina London Limited (1)
6 Perseverance Works 38 Kingsland Road, London, E2 8DD, United Kingdom
Tel.: (44) 2076130993
Web Site: http://www.wilhelminalondon.com
Model Management Services
N.A.I.C.S.: 711510

Wilhelmina New York (1)
192 Lexington Ave, New York, NY 10016
Tel.: (212) 473-0700
Web Site: http://www.wilhelmina.com
Sales Range: $10-24.9 Million
Emp.: 75
Modeling Agency
N.A.I.C.S.: 711410

Wilhelmina-Miami, Inc. (1)
At Wynwood House 331 NW 26th St Ste 304, Miami, FL 33127
Tel.: (305) 672-9344
Model Management Services
N.A.I.C.S.: 711510

WILLAMETTE VALLEY VINEYARDS, INC.

8800 Enchanted Way SE, Turner, OR 97392
Tel.: (503) 588-9463　　OR
Web Site: https://www.wvv.com
Year Founded: 1983
WVVI—(NASDAQ)
Rev.: $33,934,081
Assets: $98,683,982
Liabilities: $28,322,048
Net Worth: $70,361,934
Earnings: ($646,492)
Emp.: 169
Fiscal Year-end: 12/31/22
Wine Production & Sales
N.A.I.C.S.: 312130
James W. Bernau (Chm, Pres & CEO)
Sean M. Cary (Controller)
Craig A. Smith (Sec)
John Ferry (CFO)

WILLDAN GROUP, INC.

2401 E Katella Ave Ste 300, Anaheim, CA 92806
Tel.: (714) 940-6300　　DE
Web Site: https://www.willdan.com
Year Founded: 1964
WLDN—(NASDAQ)
Rev.: $429,138,000
Assets: $409,674,000
Liabilities: $228,172,000
Net Worth: $181,502,000
Earnings: ($8,448,000)
Emp.: 1,491
Fiscal Year-end: 12/30/22
Holding Company, Engineering, Management & Consulting Services
N.A.I.C.S.: 551112
Creighton K. Early (CFO & VP)
Michael A. Bieber (Pres)
Micah Chen (Gen Counsel)
Michael A. Bieber (Pres & CEO)

Subsidiaries:

Energy & Environmental Economics, Inc. (1)
44 Montgomery St Ste 1500, San Francisco, CA 94104
Tel.: (415) 391-5100
Web Site: http://www.ethree.com
Energy Economics & Strategy Consulting Firm
N.A.I.C.S.: 541690
Brian Horii (Sr Partner)
Lakshmi Alagappan (Partner)
Jimmy Nelson (Assoc Dir)
Roderick Go (Mgr-Technical)
Snuller Price (Sr Partner)
Tory Clark (Partner)
Eric Cutter (Partner)
Arne Olson (Sr Partner)
Nick Schlag (Partner)

Genesys Engineering, P.C. (1)
629 5th Ave Bldg 3, Pelham, NY 10803
Tel.: (914) 633-6490

Web Site:
https://www.genesysengineering.net
Sales Range: $25-49.9 Million
Energy & Utility Infrastructure Engineering,
Construction Management & Commission-
ing Services
N.A.I.C.S.: 541330
Robert J. Braun *(Principal)*
Ronald W. Mineo *(Principal)*

Lime Energy Co. (1)
4 Gateway Ctr 4th Fl 100 Mulberry St, New-
ark, NJ 07102
Tel.: (201) 416-2559
Web Site: http://www.lime-energy.com
Energy Efficiency Products & Services
N.A.I.C.S.: 238990
C. Adam Procell *(Pres & CEO)*
Alexander Castro *(Exec VP-Ops)*
Alex Telford *(Sr VP-Tech)*
Arjun Saroya *(Sr VP-Corp & Product Dev)*
Philip Luccarelli *(COO)*

Newcomb Anderson McCormick,
Inc. (1)
201 Mission St Ste 2000, San Francisco,
CA 94105
Tel.: (415) 896-0300
Web Site: http://www.newcomb.cc
Technical Consulting Services
N.A.I.C.S.: 541611
Michael K. J. Anderson *(VP)*
Ann L. McCormick *(Sr VP)*
Jonathon W. Stage *(VP)*
Steven W. Clarke *(Sr Dir-Ops)*
Daniela Aramayo *(Mgr-Project)*

Onsite Energy Corporation (1)
2701 Loker Ave W Ste 107, Carlsbad, CA
92010
Tel.: (760) 931-2400
Web Site: http://www.onsitenergy.com
Energy Consulting Services
N.A.I.C.S.: 541620
Richard T. Sperberg *(Pres)*
Paul E. Blevins *(CFO)*
Gregory Maynard *(CTO)*
Tim Ruegg *(VP & Mgr-Program)*
Paul Harris *(VP-Bus Dev)*
Michael E. Casey *(Mgr-Engrg)*

Subsidiary (Domestic):

Lighting Technology Services,
Inc. (2)
2801 Catherine Way, Santa Ana, CA 92705
Tel.: (949) 428-5040
Web Site: https://ltspropertyservices.net
Electronic Services
N.A.I.C.S.: 238210
Russ Royal *(Pres)*
Joseph Luna *(Mgr-Estimating & Auditing)*

The Weidt Group, Inc. (1)
5800 Baker Rd Ste 100, Minnetonka, MN
55345
Tel.: (952) 938-1588
Web Site: http://www.theweidtgroup.com
Sales Range: $10-24.9 Million
Energy Architectural Design & Engineering
Software & Services
N.A.I.C.S.: 541511

Willdan Energy Solutions (1)
11875 Dublin Blvd Ste A-201, Dublin, CA
94568
Tel.: (925) 556-2600
Web Site: http://www.intergycorp.com
Sales Range: $75-99.9 Million
Marketing, Design & Implementation of En-
ergy Efficiency Programs & Services
N.A.I.C.S.: 541330

Subsidiary (Domestic):

Integral Analytics, Inc. (2)
312 Walnut St Ste 1600, Cincinnati, OH
45202
Tel.: (513) 762-7621
Web Site: https://www.integralanalytics.com
Emp.: 22
Software Development Services
N.A.I.C.S.: 541511
Scott Smith *(Pres)*
Michael Ozog *(VP-Data Science)*
Kenneth Skinner *(VP-Risk Products)*
Darrin A. Kinney *(Sr VP-Business Develop-
ment)*
Wes Brown *(Dir-Sales & Marketing)*
Sarah Szewczyk *(Sr VP-Operations)*
Alex Telford *(Sr VP-Product Development)*

Willdan Engineering (1)
2401 E Katella Ave Ste 300, Anaheim, CA
92806
Tel.: (714) 940-6300
Web Site: http://www.willdan.com
Sales Range: $25-49.9 Million
Emp.: 100
Engineeering Services
N.A.I.C.S.: 541330

Willdan Financial Services (1)
27368 Via Industria Ste 200, Temecula, CA
92590-4856
Tel.: (951) 587-3500
Web Site: http://www.willdan.com
Sales Range: $75-99.9 Million
Emp.: 50
Financial Management Services
N.A.I.C.S.: 541618
Frank Tripepi *(Pres & CEO)*

Willdan Homeland Solutions (1)
2401 E Katella Ave Ste 300, Anaheim, CA
92806
Tel.: (714) 940-6370
Web Site: http://www.willdan.com
Sales Range: $10-24.9 Million
Emp.: 50
Homeland Security & Public Safety Consult-
ing Services
N.A.I.C.S.: 561621

WILLIAM H. SADLIER, INC.
25 Broadway, New York, NY 10004-
1010
Tel.: (212) 227-2120   NY
Web Site: https://www.sadlier.com
Year Founded: 1832
SADL—(OTCIQ)
Sales Range: $25-49.9 Million
Emp.: 220
Book Publishers
N.A.I.C.S.: 513130
John Bonenberger *(VP & Mgr-Sls-
Natl)*
Alan J. Paternoster *(Mgr)*
Gregory Schweiker *(Reg VP)*
Timothy R. Regan *(Reg VP)*
Frank Sadlier Dinger Jr. *(Chm)*
William Sadlier Dinger Jr. *(Pres &
Grp VP-Comm Center, ECommerce
& Intl Sls)*

WILLIAM PENN BANCORPO-
RATION
10 Canal St Ste 104, Bristol, PA
19007
Tel.: (267) 540-8500   MD
Web Site:
https://www.williampenn.bank
Year Founded: 2020
WMPN—(NASDAQ)
Rev.: $35,361,000
Assets: $818,747,000
Liabilities: $694,146,000
Net Worth: $124,601,000
Earnings: $168,000
Emp.: 90
Fiscal Year-end: 06/30/24
Bank Holding Company
N.A.I.C.S.: 551111
Kenneth J. Stephon *(Chm, Pres &
CEO)*
Alan B. Turner *(Chief Lending Officer
& Exec VP)*
Jonathan T. Logan *(CFO & Exec VP)*
Jeannine Cimino *(Chief Retail Officer
& Exec VP)*
Amy J. Logan *(COO & Exec VP)*
Alan B. Turner *(Chief Lending Officer
& Exec VP)*
Kenneth J. Stephon *(Chm, Pres &
CEO)*

Subsidiaries:

William Penn Bank (1)
1309 S Woodbourne Rd, Levittown, PA
19057
Tel.: (215) 269-1200
Web Site: https://www.williampenn.bank

Sales Range: $25-49.9 Million
Emp.: 90
Federal Savings Bank
N.A.I.C.S.: 522180
Kenneth J. Stephon *(Chm, Pres & CEO)*
Alan B. Turner *(Chief Lending Officer &
Exec VP)*
Jonathan T. Logan *(CFO & Exec VP)*
Jeannine Cimino *(Chief Retail Officer &
Exec VP)*
Amy J. Logan *(COO & Exec VP)*
Alan B. Turner *(Chief Lending Officer &
Exec VP)*
Nicole Nielsen *(Chief HR Officer & Sr VP)*
James R. Read *(CTO & Sr VP)*
Tina Bosco *(Chief Risk Officer & Sr VP)*
Rob Colby *(Chief Acctg Officer & Sr VP)*
Patricia Dykes *(Sr VP & Mgr-Deposit Ops)*
Robin L. Fadio *(Sr VP & Mgr-Loan Servic-
ing)*
Steven Gillespie *(Chief Compliance Officer
& Sr VP)*
Karen Hunter *(Sr VP & Controller)*
Nina D. Melker *(Sr VP)*
Jonathan Rodgers *(VP & Dir-IT)*
Kelly Vittore *(Sr VP & Reg Mgr)*
Timika L. Muhammad *(Comml Loan Officer
& Sr VP)*
Alex DiTullio *(Sr Mortgage Loan Officer &
VP)*

WILLIAMS ROWLAND ACQUI-
SITION CORP.
450 Post Rd E, Westport, CT 06880
Tel.: (203) 353-7610   DE
Web Site:
https://www.williamsrowland.com
Year Founded: 2021
WRAC—(NYSEAMEX)
Rev.: $3,191,516
Assets: $36,601,731
Liabilities: $44,829,230
Net Worth: ($8,227,499)
Earnings: $1,020,172
Emp.: 3
Fiscal Year-end: 12/31/22
Investment Services
N.A.I.C.S.: 523999
David Williams *(Co-Founder & CEO)*
Jonathan David Rowland *(Co-
Founder)*
Bobby Morovati *(CFO)*

WILLIAMS-SONOMA, INC.
3250 Van Ness Ave, San Francisco,
CA 94109
Tel.: (415) 421-7900   CA
Web Site: https://www.williams-
sonomainc.com
Year Founded: 1956
WSM—(NYSE)
Rev.: $7,750,652,000
Assets: $5,273,548,000
Liabilities: $3,145,687,000
Net Worth: $2,127,861,000
Earnings: $949,762,000
Emp.: 10,700
Fiscal Year-end: 01/28/24
Household Product Distr
N.A.I.C.S.: 449129
Laura J. Alber *(Pres & CEO)*
A. Miller *(COO & Exec VP)*
David Randolph King *(Gen Counsel
& Exec VP)*
Marta H. Benson *(Pres-Pottery Barn)*
Jeremy Brooks *(Chief Acctg Officer,
Sr VP & Head-IR)*
Yasir Anwar *(CTO)*
Jennifer Kellor *(Pres-Pottery Barn
Kids & PBteen)*
Vicki D. McWilliams *(Exec VP-Stores)*
Felix J. Carbullido *(Pres-Williams
Sonoma)*
Karalyn Smith *(Chief Talent Officer)*
Jeff Howie *(CFO & Exec VP)*

Subsidiaries:

Pottery Barn Outlet (1)
1 Factory Shops Blvd Spc Ste 205,
Gaffney, SC 29341

Tel.: (864) 206-0117
Web Site: http://www.potterybarn.com
Furniture Retailer
N.A.I.C.S.: 449110

Rejuvenation Inc. (1)
2550 NW Nicolai St, Portland, OR 97210
Tel.: (503) 231-1900
Web Site: https://www.rejuvenation.com
Sales Range: $25-49.9 Million
Emp.: 230
Period-Authentic Lighting & House Parts
Mfr & Direct Marketer
N.A.I.C.S.: 335139

Williams-Sonoma Canada, Inc. (1)
6455 Macleod Trail Southwest Unit 0123A,
Calgary, T2H 0K8, AB, Canada
Tel.: (403) 410-9191
Web Site: http://www.williams-sonoma.ca
Emp.: 60
Kitchenware Retailer
N.A.I.C.S.: 449129

Williams-Sonoma Delaware, LLC (1)
178 Christiana Mall, Newark, DE 19702-
3202
Tel.: (302) 368-7707
Web Site: https://www.williams-sonoma.com
Home Furnishings Retailer
N.A.I.C.S.: 449129
Laura Hritz *(Gen Mgr)*

Williams-Sonoma Singapore Pte.
Ltd. (1)
18 Tai Seng Street 07-07, Singapore,
539775, Singapore
Tel.: (65) 6 589 5600
Web Site: http://www.williams-
sonomainc.com
Emp.: 34
Household Products Retailer
N.A.I.C.S.: 449210

Williams-Sonoma Vietnam LLC (1)
7A Dai Lo Huu Nghi Binh Hoa, Thuan An,
3800, Binh Duong, Vietnam
Tel.: (84) 6503765480
Home Furnishings Retailer
N.A.I.C.S.: 449129
Jorian Caruco *(Gen Mgr)*

WILLIS LEASE FINANCE COR-
PORATION
4700 Lyons Technology Pkwy, Coco-
nut Creek, FL 33073
Tel.: (561) 349-9989   DE
Web Site: https://www.wlfc.global
Year Founded: 1985
WLFC—(NASDAQ)
Rev.: $311,927,000
Assets: $2,575,217,000
Liabilities: $2,170,529,000
Net Worth: $404,688,000
Earnings: $2,105,000
Emp.: 263
Fiscal Year-end: 12/31/22
Aircraft Engine Leases for Commer-
cial Airlines
N.A.I.C.S.: 522220
Dean M. Poulakidas *(Gen Counsel &
Sr VP)*
Brian R. Hole *(Pres)*
Scott B. Flaherty *(CFO & Sr VP)*
Garry A. Failler *(Chief Technical Offi-
cer)*
Craig W. Welsh *(Chief Comml Offi-
cer)*
Dan J. Coulcher *(Chief Comml Offi-
cer)*
Lynn A. McMillan *(VP)*
Austin C. Willis *(CEO)*
Charles F. Willis IV *(Bd of Dirs, Ex-
ecutives)*

Subsidiaries:

WEST Engine Funding LLC (1)
2320 Marinship Way Ste 300, Sausalito, CA
94965-2834
Tel.: (415) 408-4849
Consumer Lending Services
N.A.I.C.S.: 522291

Willis Aeronautical Services, Inc. (1)

Willis Lease Finance Corporation—(Continued)

4700 Lyons Technology Pkwy, Coconut Creek, FL 33073
Tel.: (561) 272-5402
Web Site: http://www.willisaero.com
Emp.: 16
Aeronautical Product Mfr
N.A.I.C.S.: 334519

Willis Asset Management Limited (1)
Aviation House Brocastle Avenue, Waterton Industrial Estate, Bridgend, CF31 3XR, United Kingdom
Tel.: (44) 1656754777
Web Site: https://www.willisasset.com
Asset Management Consultancy Services
N.A.I.C.S.: 541611

Willis Lease Singapore Pte. Ltd. (1)
300 Beach Road 36-02 The Concourse, Singapore, 199555, Singapore
Tel.: (65) 62484855
Aeronautical Product Mfr
N.A.I.C.S.: 334519

WILLISTON HOLDING CO., INC.

9531 W 78th St Ste 340, Eden Prairie, MN 55344
Tel.: (701) 651-3011   NV
Year Founded: 2006
WHCA—(OTCIQ)
Holding Company
N.A.I.C.S.: 551112
Lawrence A. Neumann (Sec)

Subsidiaries:

Mexican Restaurants, Inc. (1)
12000 Aerospace Ave Ste 400, Houston, TX 77034-5576
Tel.: (832) 300-5858
Web Site:
   http://www.mexicanrestaurantsinc.com
Sales Range: $50-74.9 Million
Emp.: 1,950
Mexican Restaurant Operator
N.A.I.C.S.: 722511
Nancy Cross (Chief People Officer)
Loic M. Porry (COO)
Douglas Hipskind (CFO)
Berke Bakay (Chm)
Pete Pascuzzi (CEO)

WILLSCOT MOBILE MINI HOLDINGS CORP.

4646 E Van Buren St Ste 400, Phoenix, AZ 85008
Tel.: (480) 894-6311   DE
Web Site:
   https://www.willscotmobilemini.com
Year Founded: 2015
WSC—(NASDAQ)
Rev.: $2,364,767,000
Assets: $6,137,915,000
Liabilities: $4,876,665,000
Net Worth: $1,261,250,000
Earnings: $476,457,000
Emp.: 5,000
Fiscal Year-end: 12/31/23
Holding Company
N.A.I.C.S.: 551112
Timothy D. Boswell (Pres & CFO)
Sally J. Shanks (Chief Acctg Officer & Sr VP)
Hezron Timothy Lopez (Chief Legal Officer, Chief Compliance Officer & Exec VP)
Graeme Parkes (CIO & Exec VP)
Warren Smith (Chief Admin Officer & Exec VP)
Bradley L. Soultz (CEO)

Subsidiaries:

A&M Cold Storage, LLC (1)
5835 Wild Azalea Cv, Sugar Hill, GA 30518-8000
Tel.: (404) 276-2884
Web Site: http://www.amcstorage.com
Refrigerated Warehousing & Storage
N.A.I.C.S.: 493120
Allen Mescher (Owner & Pres)

Cold Box Inc. (1)
850 92nd Ave Ste 5, Oakland, CA 94603-1210
Web Site: http://www.cold-box.com
Refrigeration Rental & Storage Services
N.A.I.C.S.: 493120

Elite Modular Leasing & Sales, Inc. (1)
195 E Morgan St, Perris, CA 92571-3112
Tel.: (951) 422-2500
Web Site: https://elitemodular.net
School Planning & Construction Services
N.A.I.C.S.: 541310

Mobile Mini, Inc. (1)
4646 E Van Buren St Ste 400, Phoenix, AZ 85008
Tel.: (480) 894-6311
Web Site: http://www.mobilemini.com
Rev.: $612,625,000
Assets: $2,116,877,000
Liabilities: $1,275,515,000
Net Worth: $841,362,000
Earnings: $83,734,000
Emp.: 2,042
Fiscal Year-end: 12/31/2019
Portable Storage Containers & Modular Steel Buildings Lessor & Mfr
N.A.I.C.S.: 493190
Mark W. Krivoruchka (Chief HR Officer & Sr VP)
Christopher J. Miner (Gen Counsel & Sr VP)
Kelly Williams (Pres & CEO)
Van A. Welch (CFO & Exec VP)
Graeme Parkes (CIO)
Jason Seabolt (Sr VP-Ops-Eastern Div)
Chris Anderson (Sr VP-Global Sls & Mktg-Storage Solutions)
Ryan Wilson (Sr VP-Western Div)
Jeff Reid (Sr VP-Supply Chain)
Emily Tadano (Dir-Treasury & IR)
Scott Sailors (Controller & Dir-Acctg)
Andrew Thompson (Mng Dir-Ops-UK)
Luke Sheffield (Sr VP-Managed Svcs)

Subsidiary (Domestic):

Evergreen Tank Solutions, Inc. (2)
16441 Space Ctr Blvd Ste D-2, Houston, TX 77058
Tel.: (281) 332-5170
Web Site: http://www.evergreentank.com
Liquid & Solid Storage Container Rental Services
N.A.I.C.S.: 532490

Subsidiary (Domestic):

Water Movers, Inc. (3)
30 N 56th St, Phoenix, AZ 85034
Tel.: (602) 275-8822
Web Site: http://www.watermovers.com
Emp.: 30
Water Pump Rental Services
N.A.I.C.S.: 532411

Subsidiary (Domestic):

JKW Holdings, LLC (2)
12549 E Skelly Dr, Tulsa, OK 74128
Tel.: (918) 234-3444
Web Site: http://south.budgetboxonline.com
Lessors of Miniwarehouses & Self-Storage Units
N.A.I.C.S.: 531130

Subsidiary (Non-US):

Mobile Mini Canada ULC (2)
7717 84 St SE, Calgary, T2C 4Y1, AB, Canada
Tel.: (403) 252-5996
Web Site: http://www.mobilemini.com
Emp.: 6
Portable Storage Services
N.A.I.C.S.: 493110

Mobile Mini UK Holdings Limited (2)
Ravenstock House 28 Falcon Ct Preston Farm Business Park, Stockton-on-Tees, TS18 3TX, United Kingdom
Tel.: (44) 3300669946
Web Site: http://www.mobilemini.co.uk
Emp.: 80
Investment Management Service
N.A.I.C.S.: 523940
Chris Morgan (Mng Dir)
Phil Hughes (Reg Dir-South)

Chris Watcham (Dir-SHEQ)
Louise Arnold (Dir-People & Strategic)
Rachel Dalby (Dir-Mktg)
Steve Dickinson (Dir-Fin)

Mobile Mini UK Ltd. (2)
Ravenstock House 28 Falcon Court, Preston Farm Business Park, Stockton-on-Tees, TS18 3TX, United Kingdom   **(100%)**
Tel.: (44) 3300669946
Web Site: http://www.mobilemini.co.uk
Sales Range: $25-49.9 Million
Emp.: 80
Container Storage Services
N.A.I.C.S.: 493110
Chris Morgan (Mng Dir)
Phil Hughes (Dir-South)
Chris Watcham (Dir-SHEQ)
Louise Arnold (Dir-People & Strategic)
Rachel Dalby (Dir-Mktg)
Steve Dickinson (Dir-Fin)

Subsidiary (Domestic):

Mr. Box LTD (3)
1st Floor Unit 1 Pegasus Orion Court, Great Blakenham, Ipswich, IP6 0LW, Suffolk, United Kingdom
Tel.: (44) 1473833775
Web Site: https://www.mrbox.co.uk
Shipping Container Whlsr
N.A.I.C.S.: 423840

Subsidiary (Domestic):

Mobile Mini, LLC (2)
16351 S Mckinley Ave, Lathrop, CA 95330-8702
Tel.: (209) 858-9300
Web Site: https://www.mobilemini.com
Portable Storage Services
N.A.I.C.S.: 493110

Subsidiary (Non-US):

Mobile Storage (UK) Ltd. (2)
North Road Bridgend Industrial Estate, Bridgend, CF31 3TP, United Kingdom
Tel.: (44) 1656668713
Web Site: http://www.mobilemini.co.uk
Emp.: 21
Storage Devices Mfr
N.A.I.C.S.: 334112
Eric Ford (CEO)

Sommer's Mobile Leasing, Inc. (1)
1800 Lorain Blvd, Elyria, OH 44035
Tel.: (440) 324-2400
Web Site:
   http://www.sommersmobileleasing.com
Sales Range: $1-9.9 Million
Emp.: 22
Truck, Utility Trailer & RV (Recreational Vehicle) Rental & Leasing
N.A.I.C.S.: 532120
Kent Sommer (VP)
Todd Sommer (Pres)

Williams Scotsman International, Inc. (1)
901 S Bond St, Baltimore, MD 21231
Tel.: (410) 931-6000
Web Site: http://www.willscot.com
Mobile & Modular Construction
N.A.I.C.S.: 332311
Eric Anderson (Mgr)

Subsidiary (Domestic):

Williams Scotsman, Inc. (2)
11811 Greenstone Ave, Santa Fe Springs, CA 90670-4628
Tel.: (562) 903-9200
Web Site: http://www.willscot.com
Portable & Mobile Buildings & Prefabricated Metal & Building Provider
N.A.I.C.S.: 332311

Williams Scotsman Mexico S. de R. L. de C.V. (1)
Privada Av Victoria No 160 Col El Castillo, Guadalajara, 45680, El Salto, Jalisco, Mexico
Tel.: (52) 6882519
Web Site: http://www.oficinasmoviles.com
Building Construction Services
N.A.I.C.S.: 236115

WILSON BANK HOLDING COMPANY

623 W Main St, Lebanon, TN 37087
Tel.: (615) 444-2265   TN
Web Site:
   https://www.wilsonbank.com
Year Founded: 1992
WBHC—(OTCIQ)
Rev.: $184,960,000
Assets: $4,285,650,000
Liabilities: $3,925,198,000
Net Worth: $360,452,000
Earnings: $53,042,000
Emp.: 561
Fiscal Year-end: 12/31/22
Bank Holding Company
N.A.I.C.S.: 551111
John C. McDearman III (Pres & CEO)

Subsidiaries:

Wilson Bank & Trust (1)
623 W Main St, Lebanon, TN 37087
Tel.: (615) 444-2265
Web Site: https://www.wilsonbank.com
Sales Range: $150-199.9 Million
Emp.: 400
Provider of Miscellaneous Business Credit Services
N.A.I.C.S.: 522110
John C. McDearman III (Chm & CEO)
Taylor Walker (Chief Credit Officer & Exec VP)

WINC, INC.

1751 Berkeley St Studio 3, Santa Monica, CA 90404   DE
Web Site: http://www.winc.com
Year Founded: 2011
WBEV—(NYSE)
Rev.: $72,069,000
Assets: $50,388,000
Liabilities: $26,906,000
Net Worth: $23,482,000
Earnings: ($14,648,000)
Emp.: 100
Fiscal Year-end: 12/31/21
Wine Distr
N.A.I.C.S.: 424820
Brian Smith (Founder, Chm, Pres & Interim CEO)
Matthew Thelen (Chief Strategy Officer & Gen Counsel)
Carol Brault (CFO)
Erin Green (COO)

WINDGEN ENERGY, INC.

8432 E Shea Blvd Ste 101, Scottsdale, AZ 85260
Tel.: (480) 991-9500   UT
Web Site:
   http://www.windgenenergy.com
WGEI—(OTCIQ)
Rev.: $115,543
Assets: $5,000
Liabilities: $364,698
Net Worth: ($359,698)
Earnings: $101,143
Emp.: 1
Fiscal Year-end: 12/31/21
Wind Energy Device Mfr
N.A.I.C.S.: 335311
Ronald Conquest (Chm, CEO & CFO)
David Martin (Pres)

WINDROCK LAND COMPANY

614 Mabry Hood Rd Ste 301, Knoxville, TN 37932
Tel.: (865) 392-1820   TN
Web Site:
   http://www.coalcreekcompany.com
Year Founded: 1872
CCRK—(OTCIQ)
Coal Mining Services
N.A.I.C.S.: 213113
Lewis A. Howard (Pres)

Subsidiaries:

Southeastern Forest Management, LLC   (1)

300 Windrock Park LN, Oliver Springs, TN 37840
Tel.: (865) 435-7158
Web Site:
    http://www.southeasternforestmgt.com
Forest Management Services
N.A.I.C.S.: 115310

Windrock Park, LLC (1)
912 Windrock Rd, Oliver Springs, TN 37840
Tel.: (865) 435-3492
Web Site: http://www.windrockpark.com
Campground Services
N.A.I.C.S.: 721211

WINDSTREAM HOLDINGS, INC.

4001 Rodney Parham Rd, Little Rock, AR 72212
Tel.: (501) 748-7000   AR
Web Site:
    http://www.windstream.com
Year Founded: 2006
WINMQ—(NASDAQ)
Rev.: $5,115,400,000
Assets: $9,888,500,000
Liabilities: $11,962,900,000
Net Worth: ($2,074,400,000)
Earnings: ($3,156,200,000)
Emp.: 11,080
Fiscal Year-end: 12/31/19
Business & Residential Local & Long-Distance Phone Service, Broadband Data Transmission & Internet Access
N.A.I.C.S.: 517111

Subsidiaries:

A.R.C. Networks, Inc. (1)
3102 Express Dr S, Islandia, NY 11749
Tel.: (631) 234-7802
Broadband Data Transmission Services
N.A.I.C.S.: 517111

Allworx Corp. (1)
20 S Clinton Ave, Rochester, NY 14604
Tel.: (585) 421-3850
Web Site: http://www.allworx.com
Integrated Communication System Provider
N.A.I.C.S.: 335929
David Plakosh (CTO & Gen Mgr)
J. Thomas Elliott (Dir-Bus Dev)
Gary Baier (Dir-Ops)

BOB, LLC (1)
999 Oak Creek Dr Ste 1007, Lombard, IL 60148
Tel.: (630) 590-6000
Telecommunication Servicesb
N.A.I.C.S.: 517121

Broadview Networks Holdings, Inc. (1)
800 Westchester Ave Ste N501, Rye Brook, NY 10573
Tel.: (914) 922-7000
Web Site: http://www.broadviewnet.com
Telephone, Data, Internet & IP-based Communications Services & Network Operator
N.A.I.C.S.: 517121
Brian P. Crotty (Pres-Mid-Market & Small Bus Div)
Corey Rinker (CFO)
Charles C. Hunter (Gen Counsel & Exec VP)

Subsidiary (Domestic):

ATX Communications, Inc. (2)
50 Monument Rd # 1,, Bala Cynwyd, PA 19004
Tel.: (610) 668-3000
Provides Local & Long-distance Phone Service & Internet Access
N.A.I.C.S.: 517121

Broadview Networks, Inc. (1)
800 Westchester Ave Ste N501, Rye Brook, NY 10573
Web Site: http://www.broadviewnet.com
Telecommunication Servicesb
N.A.I.C.S.: 517810

CSL Texas System, LLC (1)
10802 Executive Ctr Dr Benton Bldg Ste 300, Little Rock, AR 72211
Tel.: (501) 850-0820

Telecommunication Servicesb
N.A.I.C.S.: 517121
Kenneth A. Gunderman (CEO)

Cavalier Telephone, LLC (1)
2134 W Laburnum Ave, Richmond, VA 23227
Tel.: (804) 422-4100
Web Site: http://www.cavtel.com
Sales Range: $700-749.9 Million
Emp.: 2,000
Local & Long Distance Voice, Data & Internet Telecommunications Services
N.A.I.C.S.: 517121
Francie McComb (Gen Counsel & Exec VP)

EarthLink Holdings, LLC (1)
1170 Peachtree St Ste 900, Atlanta, GA 30309
Tel.: (404) 815-0770
Web Site: http://www.earthlink.net
Rev.: $959,874,000
Assets: $635,646,000
Liabilities: $615,458,000
Net Worth: $20,188,000
Earnings: $7,680,000
Emp.: 1,890
Fiscal Year-end: 12/31/2016
Holding Company; Internet & Network Data Services
N.A.I.C.S.: 551112
Tony Thomas (CEO)
Robert E. Gunderman (CFO)
John P. Fletcher (Chief HR Officer, Chief Legal Officer & Exec VP)
Kristi M. Moody (Gen Counsel, Sec & Sr VP)
Layne Levine (Pres-Cloud & Connectivity)
Jeff Small (Pres-Consumer & SMB)
Lewis Langston (CIO & Exec VP)
Kevin Halpin (Sr VP-Process Dev & Project Mgmt)
John Eichler (Controller & VP)

Subsidiary (Domestic):

EarthLink Business, LLC (2)
1439 Peachtree St, Atlanta, GA 30309
Tel.: (404) 815-0770
Web Site: http://www.earthlink.net
Internet & Network Services
N.A.I.C.S.: 517810

Hosted Solutions Charlotte, LLC (1)
4021 Rose Lake Dr, Charlotte, NC 28217
Tel.: (704) 423-9174
Emp.: 3
Telecommunication & High Speed Internet Service Provider
N.A.I.C.S.: 517111
Steve Fritts (Mgr)

Iowa Telecommunications Services, Inc. (1)
403 W Fourth St N, Newton, IA 50208
Tel.: (641) 787-2000
Sales Range: $250-299.9 Million
Emp.: 800
Holding Company; Local & Long-Distance Telephone & Internet Access Services
N.A.I.C.S.: 551112

Subsidiary (Domestic):

Baker Communications, Inc. (2)
3620 SW 61st Ste 300, Des Moines, IA 50321
Tel.: (515) 558-8500
Web Site: http://www.bakercom.com
Sales Range: $10-24.9 Million
Emp.: 37
Computer Integrated Systems Design
N.A.I.C.S.: 541512

Connections Etc. (2)
440 Eagle Lake Rd N, Big Lake, MN 55309
Tel.: (763) 262-4100
Sales Range: $25-49.9 Million
Emp.: 100
Telephone Communication Services
N.A.I.C.S.: 517121

En-Tel Communications LLC (2)
222 20th St SE, Willmar, MN 56201
Tel.: (320) 222-0303
Rev.: $660,000
Emp.: 5
Telecommunication Servicesb
N.A.I.C.S.: 517810

Lakedale Communications LLC (2)

9938 State Hwy 55 NW, Annandale, MN 55302
Tel.: (320) 274-8201
Sales Range: $1-9.9 Million
Emp.: 88
Local & Long Distance Telephone Communications Services
N.A.I.C.S.: 516210

Montezuma Mutual Telephone Company (2)
107 N 4th St, Montezuma, IA 50171
Tel.: (641) 623-5654
Local & Long Distance Telephone Communications Services
N.A.I.C.S.: 516210

Northstar Access (2)
210 Main St S, Cambridge, MN 55008
Tel.: (763) 633-9199
Sales Range: $1-9.9 Million
Emp.: 40
Telecommunication Servicesb
N.A.I.C.S.: 517121

SHAL Networks, LLC (2)
9938 State Hwy 55 Nw, Annandale, MN 55302-0340
Tel.: (320) 274-7400
Sales Range: $200-249.9 Million
Local & Long Distance Telephone Communications & Cable Services
N.A.I.C.S.: 516210

Windstream Iowa-Com, Inc. (2)
403 W 4th St N, Newton, IA 50208
Tel.: (641) 787-2331
Sales Range: $75-99.9 Million
Telephone & Internet Services
N.A.I.C.S.: 517111

KDL Communications Corporation (1)
1010 Bunting Ln, Liberty, MO 64068
Tel.: (816) 407-9888
Web Site: http://www.kdlcomm.com
Telephone Equipment Whslr & Dealer
N.A.I.C.S.: 423690

MPX Inc. (1)
171 Sullys Trl, Pittsford, NY 14534
Tel.: (716) 381-4340
Data Communications Equipment & System Provider
N.A.I.C.S.: 423690

McLeodUSA Information Services LLC (1)
PO Box 3177, Cedar Rapids, IA 52406
Tel.: (319) 790-7000
Telecommunication Servicesb
N.A.I.C.S.: 517121

Network Services Group, LLC (1)
955 W Eisenhower Cir Ste C, Ann Arbor, MI 48103
Web Site: http://www.nsgroupllc.com
Emp.: 80
Computer & Network Service Provider
N.A.I.C.S.: 541512
Don Prior (Pres)

RevChain Solutions, LLC (1)
902 Clint Moore Rd Ste 230, Boca Raton, FL 33487
Tel.: (561) 999-8000
Telecommunication Servicesb
N.A.I.C.S.: 517121

TruCom Corporation (1)
170 S William Dillard Dr Ste 115, Gilbert, AZ 85233
Tel.: (480) 689-4000
Emp.: 6
Broadband Data Transmission Services
N.A.I.C.S.: 517111

Windstream Alabama (1)
8372 1st Ave, Leeds, AL 35094
Tel.: (205) 699-9505
Web Site: http://www.windstream.net
Sales Range: $10-24.9 Million
Emp.: 35
Telecommunication Servicesb
N.A.I.C.S.: 517121

Windstream Communications (1)
28 E Broadway, Bolivar, MO 65613
Tel.: (417) 777-6214
Sales Range: $200-249.9 Million
Service Wirelines & Wireless
N.A.I.C.S.: 517121

Dan McAuliffe (Sr Acct Exec)
Alan Stiefvater (VP-Consumer & Small Bus Sls)

Windstream Corporation (1)
4001 N Rodney Parham Rd, Little Rock, AR 72212
Tel.: (501) 748-7000
Telecommunication Servicesb
N.A.I.C.S.: 517121

Windstream D&E, Inc. (1)
130 E Main St, Ephrata, PA 17522-2739
Tel.: (717) 733-4101
Telephone & Telegraph Apparatus Mfr
N.A.I.C.S.: 334210

Windstream Florida, Inc. (1)
206 White Ave Se, Live Oak, FL 32064
Tel.: (386) 364-2400
Web Site: http://www.windstream.com
Sales Range: $50-74.9 Million
Emp.: 260
Telecommunication Servicesb
N.A.I.C.S.: 517121

Windstream KDL, Inc. (1)
4001 N Rodney Parcham, Little Rock, AR 72212
Tel.: (913) 492-1230
Sales Range: $1-4.9 Billion
Communication & Technology Solutions Provider
N.A.I.C.S.: 517810

Windstream Lexcom Communications, Inc. (1)
200 N State St, Lexington, NC 27292-3428   (100%)
Tel.: (336) 249-9904
Web Site: http://www.lexcominc.net
Sales Range: $25-49.9 Million
Emp.: 150
Telephone, Cable Sources & Wireless Communication Services
N.A.I.C.S.: 517121

Windstream Missouri, Inc. (1)
1645 W Repub Rd A, Springfield, MO 65810
Tel.: (417) 655-1155
Telecommunication Services Provider
N.A.I.C.S.: 517810

Windstream Nebraska, Inc. (1)
445 N 6th St, Beatrice, NE 68310
Tel.: (402) 228-1121
Telecommunication Services Provider
N.A.I.C.S.: 517810

Windstream New York, Inc. (1)
201 E 4th St, Jamestown, NY 14701
Tel.: (716) 661-5400
Telecommunication Services Provider
N.A.I.C.S.: 517810

Windstream Sugar Land, Inc. (1)
14141 Southwest Fwy, Sugar Land, TX 77487
Tel.: (501) 748-7000
Telecommunication Services Provider
N.A.I.C.S.: 517810
Shanon Williams (Office Mgr)

nGenX Corporation (1)
5020 Smythe Dr, Evansville, IN 47715   (100%)
Tel.: (812) 461-3355
Web Site: http://www.ngenx.com
Sales Range: $25-49.9 Million
Emp.: 130
Computer Web Hosting, Data Storage, Security & VoIP Telephone Services
N.A.I.C.S.: 518210
J. D. Helms (Pres)
Al Cinelli (Chm)
Max Pruger (Chief Sls Officer)
Toby vanRoojen (Dir-Strategic Accts)

WINDTREE THERAPEUTICS, INC.

2600 Kelly Rd Ste 100, Warrington, PA 18976-3622
Tel.: (215) 488-9300   DE
Web Site:
    https://www.windtreetx.com
Year Founded: 1997
WINT—(NASDAQ)
Rev.: $758,000

Windtree Therapeutics, Inc.—(Continued)

Assets: $37,954,000
Liabilities: $27,942,000
Net Worth: $10,012,000
Earnings: ($39,208,000)
Emp.: 20
Fiscal Year-end: 12/31/22
Respiratory Diseases & Other Bio-
logical Products Developer
N.A.I.C.S.: 325414
Steven G. Simonson (Chief Medical
Officer & Sr VP)
Craig E. Fraser (Pres & CEO)
Eric L. Curtis (COO)
George Cox (VP-Technical Ops)

WINECO PRODUCTIONS, INC.
6289 W Sunrise Blvd Ste 201, Sun-
rise, FL 33313
Tel.: (954) 316-1326   NV
Year Founded: 1997
WNCP—(OTCIQ)
Metal Mining Services
N.A.I.C.S.: 212390
James Logan (Pres)
Linda V. Logan (Sec)

WINGS & THINGS, INC.
153 W Burton Ave, Salt Lake City,
UT 84115
Tel.: (801) 323-2395   NV
WGTG—(OTCIQ)
Sales Range: $10-24.9 Million
Investment Services
N.A.I.C.S.: 523999
Gregg L. Popp (Pres)
ChunFu Li (Chm)
TsuiMei Wang (CFO, Treas & Sec)

WINMARK CORPORATION
605 Hwy 169 N Ste 400, Minneapo-
lis, MN 55441
Tel.: (763) 520-8500   MN
Web Site:
  https://www.winmarkcorpora
  tion.com
Year Founded: 1988
WINA—(NASDAQ)
Rev.: $78,216,200
Assets: $26,899,000
Liabilities: $65,982,400
Net Worth: ($39,083,400)
Earnings: $39,919,900
Emp.: 85
Fiscal Year-end: 12/25/21
Marketing Services for Stores
N.A.I.C.S.: 455219
Brett D. Heffes (Chm & CEO)
Anthony D. Ishaug (CFO, Treas &
Exec VP)

Subsidiaries:

Grow Biz Games, Inc.   (1)
605 Hwy 169 N Ste 400, Minneapolis, MN
55441
Tel.: (763) 520-8500
Building Leasing Services
N.A.I.C.S.: 531190
John L. Morgan (CEO)

Winmark Capital Corporation   (1)
605 Hwy 169 N, Minneapolis, MN
55441-4837   (100%)
Tel.: (763) 520-8500
Web Site: https://winmarkcorporation.com
Sales Range: $100-124.9 Million
Emp.: 50
Business Equipment Leasing Services
N.A.I.C.S.: 532420

Wirth Business Credit, Inc.   (1)
605 Hgh 169 N Ste 400, Minneapolis, MN
55441   (100%)
Tel.: (763) 520-8500
Web Site:
  http://www.wirthbusinesscredit.com
Sales Range: $50-74.9 Million
Business to Business Financial Services
Franchisor

N.A.I.C.S.: 522220

WINMILL & CO., INCORPO-RATED
2255 Buffalo Rd, Rochester, NY
14624
Tel.: (212) 785-0900   DE
Web Site: https://www.winmillco.com
Year Founded: 1974
WNMLA—(OTCIQ)
Sales Range: $1-9.9 Million
Emp.: 15
Investment Management, Distribution
& Shareholder Services
N.A.I.C.S.: 523940
Thomas Bassett Winmill (Pres, CEO
& Chief Legal Officer)

Subsidiaries:

Midas Management Corporation   (1)
11 Hanover Sq, New York, NY
10005-2818   (100%)
Tel.: (212) 785-0900
Web Site: http://www.midasfunds.com
Sales Range: $75-99.9 Million
Emp.: 10
Investment Managers to Open-End &
Closed-End Management Investment Com-
panies
N.A.I.C.S.: 523940
Thomas Bassett Winmill (Pres)

WINNEBAGO INDUSTRIES, INC.
13200 Pioneer Trl, Eden Prairie, MN
55347
Tel.: (952) 829-8600   IA
Web Site:
  https://www.winnebagoind.com
Year Founded: 1958
WGO—(NYSE)
Rev.: $2,973,500,000
Assets: $2,384,200,000
Liabilities: $1,110,900,000
Net Worth: $1,273,300,000
Earnings: $13,000,000
Emp.: 5,700
Fiscal Year-end: 08/31/24
Motor Home Manufacturing
N.A.I.C.S.: 336213
Bret A. Woodson (Sr VP-HR & Corp
Rels)
Amber Holm (CMO & Sr VP)
Michael J. Happe (Pres & CEO)
David W. Miles (Chm)
Stacy L. Bogart (Pres-Winnebago
Industries Foundation, Gen Counsel,
Sec-Corp Responsibility & Sr VP)
Donald J. Clark (Pres-Grand Design
RV)
Sri Koneru (CIO & Sr VP)
Jil Littlejohn Bostick (Head-Diversity,
Equity & Inclusion)
Stephen Heese (Pres)
Casey Tubman (Pres)
Christopher D. West (Pres-
Winnebago Outdoors)

Subsidiaries:

Barletta Boat Company, LLC   (1)
51687 County Rd 133, Bristol, IN 46507
Tel.: (574) 825-8900
Web Site:
  https://www.barlettapontoonboats.com
Boat Retailer
N.A.I.C.S.: 441222
Bill Fenech (Founder)

Grand Design RV, LLC   (1)
11333 County Rd 2, Middlebury, IN 46540
Tel.: (574) 825-8000
Web Site: https://www.granddesignrv.com
Recreational Vehicle Mfr
N.A.I.C.S.: 336214

Lithionics Battery, LLC   (1)
1770 Calumet St, Clearwater, FL 33765
Tel.: (727) 726-4204
Web Site: https://lithionicsbattery.com
Lithium-Ion Battery Mfr & Distr

N.A.I.C.S.: 331110

Newmar Corporation   (1)
355 Delaware St, Nappanee, IN 46550
Tel.: (574) 773-7791
Web Site: http://www.newmarcorp.com
Travel Trailer & Camper Mfr
N.A.I.C.S.: 336214
Casey Tubman (Pres)

Winnebago of Indiana, LLC   (1)
201 14th St, Middlebury, IN 46540
Tel.: (574) 825-5250
Web Site: http://www.wgo.com
Light Truck & Utility Vehicle Mfr
N.A.I.C.S.: 336110

WINSTON PHARMACEUTI-CALS, INC.
100 N Fairway Dr Ste 134, Vernon
Hills, IL 60061
Tel.: (847) 362-8200   DE
WPHM—(OTCIQ)
Sales Range: $1-9.9 Million
Emp.: 9
Pharmaceutical Researcher, Devel-
oper & Mfr
N.A.I.C.S.: 325412
Scott B. Phillips (Sr VP-Scientific Af-
fairs)

WINTHROP REALTY LIQUI-DATING TRUST
7 Bulfinch Pl Ste 500, Boston, MA
02114
Tel.: (617) 570-4614   OH
Web Site:
  http://www.winthropreit.com
Year Founded: 2016
FUR—(NYSE)
Business Trust
N.A.I.C.S.: 525920
Michael L. Ashner (Trustee)

Subsidiaries:

Atrium Mall LLC   (1)
100 W Randolph St, Chicago, IL
60601   (50%)
Tel.: (312) 346-0777
Web Site: http://www.theatriumchicago.com
Commercial Building Leasing Services
N.A.I.C.S.: 531120

WINTRUST FINANCIAL COR-PORATION
9700 W Higgins Rd Ste 800, Rose-
mont, IL 60018
Tel.: (847) 939-9000   IL
Web Site: https://www.wintrust.com
Year Founded: 1991
WTFC—(NASDAQ)
Rev.: $3,327,220,000
Assets: $56,259,934,000
Liabilities: $50,860,408,000
Net Worth: $5,399,526,000
Earnings: $622,626,000
Emp.: 5,521
Fiscal Year-end: 12/31/23
Bank Holding Company
N.A.I.C.S.: 551111
David L. Stoehr (CFO & Exec VP)
David Alan Dykstra (Vice Chm &
COO)
Thomas Patrick Zidar (Exec VP &
Head-Market-Wealth Mgmt Svcs)
Timothy S. Crane (Pres & CEO)
Guy W. Eisenhuth (Exec VP & Head-
Reg Market)
Kathleen M. Boege (Gen Counsel,
Sec & Exec VP)
Edward Joseph Wehmer (Founder &
Senior Advisor)

Subsidiaries:

Barrington Bank & Trust Company,
N.A.   (1)
201 S Hough St, Barrington, IL 60010-4321
Tel.: (847) 842-4500

Web Site:
  http://www.barringtonbank.wintrust.us
Sales Range: $10-24.9 Million
Emp.: 50
Retail & Commercial Banking
N.A.I.C.S.: 522110
W. Bradley Stetson (Chm & CEO)
Jon C. Stickney (Pres)

Subsidiary (Domestic):

Wintrust Mortgage Corp.   (2)
9700 W Higgins Rd Ste 300, Rosemont, IL
60018
Tel.: (847) 939-9500
Web Site:
  https://www.wintrustmortgage.com
Mortgage & Lending Services
N.A.I.C.S.: 522310
David Hrobon (Pres & CEO)
Jason Bohrer (Exec VP-Capital Markets)
Alex Jacobs (Exec VP & Mgr-Natl Retail
Sls)
Sarah Flanagan (Sr VP-Corp Svcs)
Renee Kirin (Sr VP-Loan Servicing)

Subsidiary (Domestic):

iFreedom Direct Corporation   (3)
9565 S Wasatch Blvd, Salt Lake City, UT
84092
Tel.: (801) 273-9960
Web Site:
  https://www.ifreedomdirectcorp.com
Mortgage Lending Services
N.A.I.C.S.: 522292

Beverly Bank & Trust Company,
N.A.   (1)
10258 S Western Ave, Chicago, IL 60643
Tel.: (773) 239-2265
Web Site: https://www.thebeverlybank.com
Sales Range: $125-149.9 Million
Retail & Commercial Banking
N.A.I.C.S.: 522180
Carol A. Schafer (VP-Bus Dev-Tech-
Wintrust Specialty Fin)
Dennis C. O'Malley (Vice Chm)
William Cordes (Pres & CEO)
Doug Nielsen (Chief Sls Officer-Wintrust
Specialty Fin)

Subsidiary (Domestic):

Beverly Bank & Trust Company, N.A.
- Oak Lawn Bank & Trust   (2)
5300 W 95th St, Oak Lawn, IL 60453-2445
Tel.: (708) 422-7411
Web Site: http://www.bankoaklawn.com
Commericial Banking
N.A.I.C.S.: 522110
Kathleen Farrell (VP)

Chicago Deferred Exchange Com-
pany, LLC   (1)
231 S LaSalle St 13th Fl, Chicago, IL
60604
Web Site: https://www.cdec1031.com
Financial Services
N.A.I.C.S.: 523940
Mary Cunningham (Pres)
Karen Cholipski (Exec VP)
Christopher J. Newton (Exec VP)
Miriamx Golden (Sr VP)
Naomi Weitzel (Gen Counsel)

Crystal Lake Bank & Trust Company,
N.A.   (1)
70 N Williams St, Crystal Lake, IL 60014
Tel.: (815) 479-5200
Web Site: https://www.crystallakebank.com
Sales Range: $25-49.9 Million
Emp.: 80
Retail & Commercial Banking
N.A.I.C.S.: 522180
James Thorpe (Co-Pres & CEO)
Kevin W. Myers (Exec VP-Wintrust Comml
Banking)
Karen Baker (Asst VP)
Mary Caporale (VP)
Joseph McVicker (Co-Pres)
Rose Smith (VP)
David E. Ward (Sr VP)
Pierre Garcia (VP)
Tom Cramer (VP)

Subsidiary (Domestic):

McHenry Bank & Trust   (2)
2205 N Richmond Rd, McHenry, IL 60051
Tel.: (815) 344-6600
Web Site: http://www.mchenrybank.com

Commercial Banking
N.A.I.C.S.: 522110
James N. Thorpe *(Pres & CEO)*
Karen Baker *(Asst VP)*
Pamela Bialas *(VP)*
Mary Caporale *(VP)*
David E. Ward *(Sr VP)*

First Insurance Funding Corp. (1)
450 Skokie Blvd Ste 1000, Northbrook, IL
60062
Tel.: (847) 374-3707
Web Site:
    http://www.firstinsurancefunding.com
Sales Range: $100-124.9 Million
Loan Services for Insurance Funding
N.A.I.C.S.: 561499
Ryan Riolo *(Mgr-Relationship-Austin)*

First Insurance Funding of Canada,
Inc. (1)
20 Toronto Street Suite 700, Toronto, M5C
2B8, ON, Canada
Web Site:
    https://www.firstinsurancefunding.ca
Insurance Services
N.A.I.C.S.: 524210
John Martin *(Sr VP-Fin)*
Brian Day *(Sr VP-Credit & Ops)*
David Caringi *(Sr VP-Sls-Natl)*
Crystal Macklin *(Sr VP-Mktg)*
Stuart Bruce *(CEO)*
Jamie Ugarte *(Sr VP-Bus Solutions)*

Hinsdale Bank & Trust Company,
N.A. (1)
25 E 1st St, Hinsdale, IL 60521
Tel.: (630) 323-4404
Web Site: https://www.hinsdalebank.com
Sales Range: $1-9.9 Million
Emp.: 15
Retail & Commercial Banking
N.A.I.C.S.: 522110
Dennis J. Jones *(Head-Market)*
Richard Eck *(Pres & CEO)*
Andrea H. Pokrefke *(VP)*
Antonio Spizzirri *(VP)*
Barbara Langnes *(VP)*
Diane Adams *(VP)*
Edward Pizzo *(VP)*
Jose Villa *(VP)*
Melissa Cleveland *(VP)*

Hyde Park Facilities, Inc. (1)
1525 E 53rd St, Chicago, IL 60615
Tel.: (773) 752-4600
Financial Consulting Services
N.A.I.C.S.: 523940

Lake Forest Bank & Trust Company,
N.A. (1)
727 N Bank Ln, Lake Forest, IL 60045
Tel.: (847) 234-2882
Web Site: https://www.lakeforestbank.com
Sales Range: $50-74.9 Million
Emp.: 150
Commercial Banking
N.A.I.C.S.: 522110
Edward Joseph Wehmer *(Dir-Advisory)*
David E. Lee *(Pres & CEO)*
Jack Meierhoff *(Chm & Co-Pres)*
Chris Baker *(Co-Pres)*
Paul Blake *(Exec VP)*
Jon Levey *(Pres)*
Tina Martoccio *(VP)*
Tom Groth *(VP)*

Libertyville Bank & Trust Company,
N.A. (1)
507 N Milwaukee Ave, Libertyville, IL
60048 **(100%)**
Tel.: (847) 367-6800
Web Site: https://www.libertyvillebank.com
Sales Range: $50-74.9 Million
Emp.: 100
Retail & Commercial Banking
N.A.I.C.S.: 522110
Chris Piazzi *(Pres)*
Crystal J. McClure *(Pres)*
Dane Morgan *(Pres)*
Debra A. Bernard *(VP)*
Donna M. Arzani *(VP)*
Polly Grover *(VP)*
Ron Coleman *(Pres)*
Trish Mickelson *(VP)*

Macatawa Bank Corporation (1)
10753 Macatawa Dr, Holland, MI 49424
Tel.: (616) 820-1444

Web Site: https://www.macatawabank.com
Rev.: $94,925,000
Assets: $2,906,919,000
Liabilities: $2,659,881,000
Net Worth: $247,038,000
Earnings: $34,731,000
Emp.: 287
Fiscal Year-end: 12/31/2022
Bank Holding Company
N.A.I.C.S.: 551111
Jon Swets *(Pres & CEO)*

Subsidiary (Domestic):

Macatawa Bank (2)
10753 Macatawa Dr, Holland, MI 49424
Tel.: (616) 820-1444
Web Site: https://www.macatawabank.com
Emp.: 400
Provider of Banking Services
N.A.I.C.S.: 522110
Jon Swets *(Pres & CEO)*

Northbrook Bank & Trust Company,
N.A. (1)
1100 Waukegan Rd, Northbrook, IL 60062
Tel.: (847) 418-2800
Web Site: https://www.northbrookbank.com
Sales Range: $125-149.9 Million
Retail & Commercial Banking
N.A.I.C.S.: 522110
Richard C. Rushkewicz *(Vice Chm)*
Nathan Margol *(CEO)*
Douglas P. Boersma *(Chm)*
Alay Zaidi *(VP)*

Old Plank Trail Community Bank,
N.A. (1)
20901 S LaGrange Rd, Frankfort, IL 60423
Tel.: (815) 464-6888
Web Site: http://www.oldplanktrailbank.com
Sales Range: $125-149.9 Million
Emp.: 10
Retail & Commercial Banking
N.A.I.C.S.: 522180
Paul R. Slade *(CEO)*

Subsidiary (Domestic):

Dyer Bank & Trust (2)
1101 Joliet St, Dyer, IN 46311
Tel.: (219) 322-5964
Web Site: http://www.dyerbank.com
Commercial Banking
N.A.I.C.S.: 522110

First National Bank of Illinois (2)
3256 Rdg Rd, Lansing, IL 60438
Tel.: (708) 474-1300
Web Site: http://www.fnbiweb.com
Commercial Banking
N.A.I.C.S.: 522110

Schaumburg Bank & Trust Company,
N.A. (1)
1180 E Higgins Rd, Schaumburg, IL 60173
Tel.: (847) 969-1200
Web Site:
    https://www.bankschaumburg.com
Emp.: 74
Retail & Commercial Banking
N.A.I.C.S.: 522180
Richard Stiles *(Pres & CEO)*
Caterina Aiello *(Sr VP)*
John Mazzone *(VP)*
Raymond Seiffert *(VP)*
Sandra M. Gallardo *(VP)*

St. Charles Bank & Trust
Company (1)
411 W Main St, Saint Charles, IL 60174
Tel.: (630) 377-9500
Web Site: https://www.bankstcharles.com
Sales Range: $25-49.9 Million
Emp.: 33
Retail & Commercial Banking
N.A.I.C.S.: 522110
Richard A. Davis *(CEO)*
Corey Clark *(VP-Wintrust Comml Banking)*
Caroline Rossow *(VP-Wintrust Comml
Banking)*
Michael Wozniak *(Sr VP & Mgr-Market-
Wintrust Comml Banking)*
Adnan Ebibi *(VP)*
Michele Petrie *(Pres)*
Mike Brown *(VP)*
Nathan Bevineau *(VP)*
Ralph Taylor *(VP)*
Tracy Zako *(VP)*

State Bank of the Lakes, N.A. (1)
440 Lake St, Antioch, IL 60002
Tel.: (847) 395-2700
Web Site: https://www.sbotl.com
Sales Range: $50-74.9 Million
Emp.: 90
Retail & Commercial Banking
N.A.I.C.S.: 522110
James B. Kinney *(Pres & CEO)*
Jennifer W. Olsen *(Sr VP)*
Melissa O'Malley *(VP)*
Tom Mahoney *(Pres)*
William Battistone *(Chief Credit Officer)*

The Chicago Trust Company,
N.A. (1)
222 S Riverside Plz, Chicago, IL 60606
Tel.: (312) 431-1700
Web Site:
    http://www.chicagotrustcompany.com
Trust & Estate Planning Services
N.A.I.C.S.: 523991
Thomas Buker *(Officer-Trust & VP)*
Todd W. Cordell *(Officer-Trust & VP)*
Jennifer Czerwinski *(Officer-Trust & Sr VP)*
Ethel R. Kaplan *(Officer-Trust & Sr VP)*
Mary Phyllis Duplissis *(Officer-Trust & VP)*
Edward Peters *(Mgr-Trust Real Estate)*
Linda J. Pitrowski *(Officer-Trust & VP)*
Alyne Polikoff *(Officer-Trust & Sr VP)*
Joseph F. Sochacki *(Officer-Trust & VP)*

Town Bank (1)
850 W N Shore Dr, Hartland, WI 53029
Tel.: (262) 367-1900
Web Site: https://www.townbank.us
Commericial Banking
N.A.I.C.S.: 522110
Jay C. Mack *(Pres & CEO)*
John Hazod *(CFO & Exec VP)*

Tricom, Inc. (1)
N48 W16866 Lisbon Rd, Menomonee Falls,
WI 53051
Tel.: (262) 509-6200
Web Site: https://www.tricom.com
Sales Range: $10-24.9 Million
Emp.: 52
Administrative Services for Outsourced Bill-
ing, Payroll, Cash Management & Account-
ing
N.A.I.C.S.: 561499
Julie Ann Bittner *(Pres & CEO)*
Mary Jo Heim *(CFO & Dir-Acctg)*
Amanda Jadro *(Portfolio Mgr)*

Village Bank & Trust (1)
234 W NW Hwy, Arlington Heights, IL
60004
Tel.: (847) 670-1000
Web Site: https://www.bankatvillage.com
Sales Range: $25-49.9 Million
Emp.: 100
Retail & Commercial Banking
N.A.I.C.S.: 522110
Guy W. Eisenhuth *(Pres & CEO)*
Carol J. Blackwood *(Sr VP-Retail Banking &
Head)*
Christopher Henkel *(Asst VP-Professional
Practice Grp)*
Earl Goldman *(Exec VP-Bus Banking)*
Jane Drezen *(Asst VP-Retail Banking)*
Jan Eriksen *(VP & Head-Professional Prac-
tice Grp)*
Russ Larsen *(CEO-Comml Banking)*
Stephanie Molster *(VP-Professional Prac-
tice Grp)*
Syed Hussaini *(Sr VP & Area Mgr-Small
Bus Banking)*
Angela Baker *(VP-Professional Practice
Grp)*

Wayne Hummer Investments
LLC (1)
2610 N Illinois St, Swansea, IL 62226
Tel.: (618) 235-8807
Web Site: http://fcbadvisors.com
Sales Range: $125-149.9 Million
Emp.: 100
Investment Services
N.A.I.C.S.: 523999

Subsidiary (Domestic):

Great Lakes Advisors Holdings,
LLC (2)
231 S LaSalle St 4th Fl, Chicago, IL 60604
Tel.: (312) 553-3700
Web Site:
    https://www.greatlakesadvisors.com

Sales Range: $125-149.9 Million
Emp.: 40
Wealth Management Services
N.A.I.C.S.: 523940
Jason Turner *(COO)*
Jenny A. Notte *(Mng Dir-Client Svc & Sls)*
Edward J. Calkins *(Sr Mng Dir & Portfolio
Mgr)*
Wells L. Frice *(Portfolio Mgr)*
Kelly Weller *(Mng Dir)*
Thomas R. Kiley *(CEO)*
Gary Lenhoff *(Chief Investment Officer-
Fundamental Equities)*
Daniel P. Nielsen *(Mng Dir & Head-ESG &
Responsible Investing)*
Jon E. Quigley *(Chief Investment Officer-
Disciplined Equities)*
Heather M. Alvarado *(Mng Dir)*
Anna Bavone *(Dir-Client Svc & Sls)*
John D. Bright *(Sr Portfolio Mgr-Disciplined
Equities)*
Allison J. Brink *(Mng Dir-Mktg & Client Svc)*
Magdalena Bryla *(Mgr-Ops)*
Christy Coon *(Sr Portfolio Mgr)*
Sue Edwards *(Dir-Equity Trading)*
Thomas A. Erdmier *(Mng Dir-Intermediary
Distr)*
Patrick Farris *(Dir-Intermediary Distr-
Mountain)*
Brent M. Foster *(Mgr-Project)*
Michael H. Gansfuss *(Dir-Intermediary
Distr-South)*
Ronee Greazel *(Portfolio Mgr-Client)*
David R. Hamilton *(Dir-Client Svc & Sls)*
Frank J. Harmon *(Mgr-Customer Rels)*
Brad Hays *(Dir-Intermediary Distr-
Northeast)*
Benjamin Kim *(Sr Portfolio Mgr)*
David Kopp *(Portfolio Mgr)*
Matie Krebs *(Officer-Compliance)*
Huong Le *(Portfolio Mgr)*
Patrick M. Morrissey *(Mng Dir, Head-Fixed
Income & Sr Portfolio Mgr)*
Megan Pluta *(Dir-Mktg)*
Laurence C. Richey *(Dir-Client Svc & Sls)*
Bruce A. Ebel *(Dir & Portfolio Mgr-Client)*
Elizabeth Goellner *(Coord-Mktg)*
Sean Hipskind *(Assoc Portfolio Mgr)*
Peter Lynch *(Portfolio Mgr-Client)*
Cody Poirier *(Dir-Intermediary Distr-
Midwest)*
Richard M. Rokus *(Mng Dir)*
Steven N. Schenker *(Portfolio Mgr-Client)*
Haley Schumaker *(Dir-Equity Trading)*
Brian Schuster *(Sr Portfolio Mgr-Fixed In-
come)*
Nancy L. Studenroth *(Mng Dir & Sr Portfolio
Mgr-Fixed Income)*
Tim Sweeney *(Dir-Intermediary Distr-West
Reg)*
John C. Thomas *(Chief Bus Dev & Client
Rels Officer)*
Laurie Watson *(Mng Dir-Client Svc & Sls)*
Laura Wicklander West *(Dir-Client Svc &
Sls)*
Lori A. Willis *(Dir-Intermediary Sls & Ops)*
Joseph T. Wright *(Mng Dir & Head-
Consultant Rels)*
William O. Bell III *(Dir-Consultant Rels)*
Raymond Wicklander III *(Mng Dir & Portfo-
lio Mgr)*

Wayne Hummer Trust Company,
N.A. (2)
222 S Riverside Plz Ste 2800, Chicago, IL
60606
Tel.: (312) 431-1700
Web Site: http://www.whummer.com
Sales Range: $125-149.9 Million
Emp.: 100
Investment Services
N.A.I.C.S.: 523999

Wheaton Bank & Trust, N.A. (1)
100 N Wheaton Ave, Wheaton, IL 60187
Tel.: (630) 690-1800
Web Site: http://wheatonbank.wintrust.us
Sales Range: $75-99.9 Million
Emp.: 103
Commercial Banking
N.A.I.C.S.: 522110
Robert Paszczak *(Chm)*
Robert Hutchinson *(Pres)*
Kam Kniss *(CEO)*
John Young *(VP-Bus Banking)*
Bob Hutchinson *(Pres)*

Wintrust Financial Corporation—(Continued)

Diana Sorescu (VP)
Donna Ufnal (VP)
Evelyn Rodriguez (VP)
Kim Coyne (Sr VP)

Wintrust Bank, N.A. (1)
2814 W Fullerton Ave, Chicago, IL 60647
Tel.: (773) 227-7074
Web Site: http://www.wintrustbank.com
Sales Range: $125-149.9 Million
Emp.: 366
Commercial Banking
N.A.I.C.S.: 522110
William F. Lynch (CEO)

Subsidiary (Domestic):

**North Shore Community Bank &
Trust** (2)
1145 Wilmette Ave, Wilmette, IL 60091
Tel.: (847) 853-1145
Web Site: https://www.nscbank.com
Commercial Banking
N.A.I.C.S.: 522110
Catherine Pratt (Exec VP & Head-Retail
Banking)

WINVEST ACQUISITION CORP.
125 Cambridgepark Dr Ste 301,
Cambridge, MA 02140
Tel.: (617) 658-3094   DE
Year Founded: 2021
WINV—(NASDAQ)
Rev.: $1,409,243
Assets: $19,937,585
Liabilities: $24,525,434
Net Worth: ($4,587,849)
Earnings: ($226,632)
Emp.: 2
Fiscal Year-end: 12/31/22
Investment Services
N.A.I.C.S.: 523999
Manish Jhunjhunwala (CEO & CFO)
Mark H. Madden (Chief Strategy Officer)
Alok R. Prasad (Head-Growth)

WINVEST GROUP LTD.
50 W Liberty St Ste 880, Reno, NV
89501
Tel.: (775) 996-0288   NV
Web Site:
  https://www.winvestgroup.co
WNLV—(OTCIQ)
Offices of Other Holding Companies
N.A.I.C.S.: 551112
Jeffrey Wong Kah (CEO)
Khiow Hui Lim (Chief Strategic Officer)
Charlene Kelly (Chief Intellectual Officer)
Boo Shi Huey (Treas)

WIRELESS XCESSORIES
GROUP, INC.
1840 County Line Rd Bldg 300,
Huntingdon Valley, PA 19006
Tel.: (215) 322-4600   DE
Web Site: http://www.wirexgroup.com
Year Founded: 1985
WIRX—(OTCIQ)
Sales Range: $10-24.9 Million
Emp.: 85
Wireless Aftermarket Accessories
Whslr
N.A.I.C.S.: 423620
Stephen Rade (Chm & CEO)
Ronald E. Badke (CFO)
Christine Mayo (Mgr-AR/Credit)
Daniel Kenderdine (Dir-Operations)
Natasha Ellingsworth (Controller)

WISA TECHNOLOGIES, INC.
15268 NW Greenbrier Pkwy, Beaverton, OR 97006
Tel.: (503) 615-7700   DE
Web Site:
  https://www.wisatechnologies.com

Year Founded: 2010
WISA—(NASDAQ)
Rev.: $3,365,000
Assets: $11,452,000
Liabilities: $13,448,000
Net Worth: ($1,996,000)
Earnings: ($16,151,000)
Emp.: 49
Fiscal Year-end: 12/31/22
Semiconductor & Related Device
Manufacturing
N.A.I.C.S.: 334413
Brett A. Moyer (Chm, Pres & CEO)
Ed Green (VP-Ops)
Tony Parker (VP-Bus Dev & Strategy)
Keith Greeney (VP-Engrg)
George Oliva (Sr VP-Fin & Strategic
Ops)
James Cheng (VP-Sls-Worldwide)
Tony Ostrom (Pres-WiSA)

WISDOMTREE, INC.
250 W 34th St 3rd Fl, New York, NY
10119
Tel.: (212) 801-2080   DE
Web Site:
  https://www.wisdomtree.com
WT—(NYSE)
Rev.: $301,345,000
Assets: $1,033,819,000
Liabilities: $728,208,000
Net Worth: $305,611,000
Earnings: $50,684,000
Emp.: 273
Fiscal Year-end: 12/31/22
Investment Services
N.A.I.C.S.: 523999
Robert Jarrett Lilien (Pres & COO)
Jonathan Laurence Steinberg
(Founder & CEO)
Win Jay Neuger (Chm)
Peter Michael Ziemba (Chief Admin
Officer)
Bryan Joseph Edmiston (CFO)
Marci Frankenthaler (Chief Legal Officer)
Alexis Marinof (Head-Europe)

Subsidiaries:

WisdomTree Europe Ltd. (1)
3rd Floor 31-41 Worship Street, London,
EC2A 2DX, United Kingdom
Tel.: (44) 2038246020
Web Site: http://www.wisdomtree.com
Emp.: 50
Investment Management Service
N.A.I.C.S.: 523940
Alexis Marinof (COO & Exec VP)
Lidia Treiber (Dir-Res)
Christopher Gannatti (Head-Res)
Helen Pugh (Head-Mktg-Europe)

WisdomTree International Real Estate Fund (1)
380 Madison Ave 21st Floor, New York, NY
10017
Tel.: (866) 909-9473
Web Site: http://www.wisdomtree.com
Sales Range: $125-149.9 Million
Real Estate Investment Fund
N.A.I.C.S.: 525990
Jonathan Laurence Steinberg (CEO)

WK KELLOGG CO
1 Kellogg Sq, Battle Creek, MI
49016-3599
Tel.: (269) 401-3000   DE
Web Site: https://www.wkkellogg.com
Year Founded: 2022
KLG—(NYSE)
Rev.: $2,763,000,000
Assets: $1,889,000,000
Liabilities: $1,589,000,000
Net Worth: $300,000,000
Earnings: $110,000,000
Emp.: 3,150
Fiscal Year-end: 12/31/23
Holding Company; Breakfast Cereal
Mfr & Whslr

N.A.I.C.S.: 551112
Gary H. Pilnick (Chm & CEO)
Linda Walter (Chief Acctg Officer &
Principal Acctg Officer)
David McKinstray (CFO)

Subsidiaries:

Kashi Company (1)
Ste 500 4275 Executive Sq, La Jolla, CA
92037-1477
Tel.: (858) 274-8870
Web Site: https://www.kashi.com
Sales Range: $25-49.9 Million
Emp.: 75
Health Food Breakfast & Snacks Mfr
N.A.I.C.S.: 311211

Subsidiary (Domestic):

Bear Naked, Inc. (2)
PO Box 649, Solana Beach, CA 92075
Web Site: https://www.bearnaked.com
Organic & Natural Food Product Mfr
N.A.I.C.S.: 311991

Kellogg USA Inc. (1)
1 Kellogg Sq, Battle Creek, MI 49017-3534
Tel.: (269) 961-2000
Web Site: https://www.kelloggs.com
Holding Company; Breakfast Cereal &
Snack Food Mfr
N.A.I.C.S.: 551112

Subsidiary (Domestic):

Chicago Bar Company LLC (2)
412 N Wells St, Chicago, IL 60654
Tel.: (312) 624-8200
Web Site: https://www.rxbar.com
Cookie Mfr
N.A.I.C.S.: 311821

Plant (Domestic):

Kellogg Convenience Food Plant (2)
322 S Egg Harbor Rd, Hammonton, NJ
08037-1452
Tel.: (609) 567-2300
Web Site: http://www.kellogg.com
Sales Range: $75-99.9 Million
Emp.: 130
Mfr of Breakfast Foods
N.A.I.C.S.: 311813

Kellogg-Lancaster Plant (2)
2050 State Rd, Lancaster, PA 17601
Tel.: (717) 898-0161
Web Site: http://www.kellogg.com
Mfr of Breakfast Foods
N.A.I.C.S.: 311230

Kellogg-Memphis Plant (2)
2168 Frisco Ave, Memphis, TN 38114
Tel.: (901) 743-3646
Web Site: http://www.kellogg.com
Mfr of Breakfast Foods
N.A.I.C.S.: 311230

WM TECHNOLOGY, INC.
41DiscoverySte1600, Irvine, CA
92618
Tel.: (212) 905-4923   Ky
Web Site:
  https://www.weedmaps.com
Year Founded: 2019
MAPS—(NASDAQ)
Rev.: $215,531,000
Assets: $199,035,000
Liabilities: $84,258,000
Net Worth: $114,777,000
Earnings: ($115,989,000)
Emp.: 580
Fiscal Year-end: 12/31/22
Investment Services
N.A.I.C.S.: 523999
Justin R. Hartfield (Co-Founder)
Susan Echard (Interim CFO & Interim
Principal Acctg Officer)
Douglas Francis (Co-Founder, Exec
Chm, Chm & Principal Exec Officer)

WOD RETAIL SOLUTIONS,
INC.
10233 S Parker Rd Ste 300, Parker,
CO 80134

Tel.: (702) 240-9378   FL
Year Founded: 1981
WODI—(OTCIQ)
Rev.: $3,766,451
Liabilities: $8,285,725
Net Worth: ($8,285,725)
Earnings: $3,168,102
Fiscal Year-end: 12/31/19
Gym & Fitness Marketing & Administrative Consulting Services
N.A.I.C.S.: 541611
Brenton Mix (CEO & CFO)
Richard Phillips (Treas & Sec)

WODA CORP.
1013 Center Rd Ste 403-B, Wilmington, DE 19805
Tel.: (601) 220-7373   DE
Year Founded: 2021
WODA—(NASDAQ)
Investment Services
N.A.I.C.S.: 523999
Maurice Ernest Scully (Chm)
Daniel Hatton (CEO)
Donna K. Wong (CFO)

WOLF ENERGY SERVICES
INC.
408 State Hwy 135N, Kilgore, TX
75662
Tel.: (903) 392-0948   FL
Year Founded: 1964
WOEN—(OTCQB)
Rev.: $20,110,796
Assets: $2,281,872
Liabilities: $3,330,043
Net Worth: ($1,048,171)
Earnings: ($13,274,207)
Emp.: 12
Fiscal Year-end: 03/31/23
Separator Mfr
N.A.I.C.S.: 333248
Jimmy Reedy (COO)

Subsidiaries:

**Capstone Equipment Leasing
LLC** (1)
5899 Preston Ste 505, Frisco TX 75034
Tel.: (903) 331-4303
Web Site:
  https://www.capstoneequipmentleasing.com
Truck Leasing Services
N.A.I.C.S.: 532120

WOLFSPEED, INC.
4600 Silicon Dr, Durham, NC 27703
Tel.: (919) 407-5300   NC
Web Site: https://www.wolfspeed.com
Year Founded: 1987
WOLF—(NYSE)
Rev.: $807,200,000
Assets: $7,984,600,000
Liabilities: $7,102,500,000
Net Worth: $882,100,000
Earnings: ($864,200,000)
Emp.: 5,013
Fiscal Year-end: 06/30/24
Semiconductor Mfr
N.A.I.C.S.: 334413
Greggory A. Lowe (Pres & CEO)
Neill P. Reynolds (CFO & Exec VP)
Brad Kohn (Sec, Sr VP-Legal & Gen
Counsel)
David Costar (CIO & Sr VP)
Margaret Chadwick (Chief HR Officer
& Sr VP-Human Resources)
Rex Felton (Sr VP-Ops-Global)
Joe Roybal (VP-Backend Ops)
Rick Madormo (Sr VP-Marketing-
Global Sls)
Owen DeLeon (VP-Sls-Americas)
Melinda Walker (Dir-Corporate Communications)
Tyler Gronbach (VP-Investor Relations)
Elif Balkas (CTO)

Subsidiaries:

Cree Europe GmbH (1)
Lichtenbergstrasse 8, 85748, Garching,
Germany
Tel.: (49) 8954842200
Web Site: http://www.cree.com
Sales Range: $150-199.9 Million
Emp.: 12
XLamp & Packaged LEDs Whslr
N.A.I.C.S.: 423690
Norbert W. G. Hiller (Mng Dir)

Cree Hong Kong Limited (1)
18 Science Park East Avenue, Hong Kong
Science Park, Sha Tin, New Territories,
China (Hong Kong)
Tel.: (852) 24248228
Web Site: http://www.cree.com
Emp.: 10
Light Emitting Diodes Components Mfr
N.A.I.C.S.: 334413

**Cree LED Lighting Solutions,
Inc.** (1)
635 Davis Dr Ste 100, Morrisville, NC
27560
Tel.: (919) 991-0700
Web Site: http://www.creelighting.com
Sales Range: $50-74.9 Million
Emp.: 100
Developer & Mfr of LED Lighting Fixtures
N.A.I.C.S.: 335139
Neal Hunter (Pres)

Cree Sweden AB (1)
Miklagardsvagen 30, Taby, 18774, Sweden
Tel.: (46) 70 5432844
Web Site: http://www.cree.com
Electric Component Whslr
N.A.I.C.S.: 423690

Ruud Lighting, Inc. (1)
9201 Washington Ave, Racine, WI 53406
Tel.: (262) 886-1900
Web Site: http://www.ruudlighting.com
Sales Range: $25-49.9 Million
Emp.: 900
Commercial Industrial & Institutional Electric
Lighting Fixture Mfr
N.A.I.C.S.: 335132
Christopher Ruud (Pres)

Wolfspeed (1)
3028 E Cornwallis Rd, Research Triangle
Park, NC 27709
Tel.: (919) 287-7888
Web Site: http://www.wolfspeed.com
Sales Range: $100-124.9 Million
Power & Wireless System Semiconductor
Components Developer & Mfr
N.A.I.C.S.: 334413
Cengiz Balkas (Sr VP & Gen Mgr-Materials)
Jay Cameron (Sr VP & Gen Mgr-Power)
Gerhard Wolf (Sr VP & Gen Mgr-RF)

Subsidiary (Domestic):

Cree Fayetteville, Inc. (2)
535 W Research Blvd, Fayetteville, AR
72701
Tel.: (479) 443-5759
Web Site: http://www.apei.net
Sales Range: $1-9.9 Million
Emp.: 23
Electronic Components Mfr
N.A.I.C.S.: 334419

WOLVERINE WORLD WIDE,
INC.
9341 Courtland Dr NE, Rockford, MI
49351
Tel.: (616) 866-5500 DE
Web Site: https://www.wolverineworld
wide.com
Year Founded: 1883
WWW—(NYSE)
Rev.: $1,791,100,000
Assets: $2,137,400,000
Liabilities: $1,564,400,000
Net Worth: $573,000,000
Earnings: ($136,900,000)
Emp.: 3,400
Fiscal Year-end: 01/02/21
Branded Casual, Active Lifestyle,
Work, Outdoor Sport & Uniform Foot-
wear & Slippers Designer, Mfr & Mar-
keter

N.A.I.C.S.: 316210
Christopher E. Hufnagel (Pres &
CEO)
Nicholas T. Long (Chm)
Kyle L. Hanson (Gen Counsel, Sec &
Sr VP)
Isabel Soriano (Pres-Intl Grp)
Janice Tennant (Pres-Merrell-Global)
Rob Griffiths (Pres-Saucony-Global)
David Gold (Sr VP)
Reginald M. Rasch (Gen Counsel)
Dee Slater (CIO)
Melissa Mullen (Pres--Global)

Subsidiaries:

Hush Puppies Retail, LLC (1)
9341 Courtland Dr NE, Rockford, MI 49351
Tel.: (616) 866-5500
Web Site: http://www.hushpuppies.com
Retail Shoe Outlets
N.A.I.C.S.: 458210

The Stride Rite Corporation (1)
500 Totten Pond Rd, Waltham, MA 02451
Tel.: (617) 824-6000
Web Site: http://www.striderite.com
Children's Shoes, Men's & Women's Casual
Shoes, Work Shoes & Athletic Footwear
N.A.I.C.S.: 458210

Subsidiary (Domestic):

Saucony, Inc. (2)
1400 Industries Rd, Richmond, IN 47374
Tel.: (617) 824-6000
Web Site: https://www.saucony.com
Emp.: 343
Performance Oriented Athletic Shoe Mfr
N.A.I.C.S.: 316210
Anne Cavassa (Pres-Brand-Global)
Kathryn Pratt (CMO)

Sperry Top-Sider, Inc. (2)
191 Spring St, Lexington, MA 02421
Tel.: (617) 824-6000
Web Site: https://www.sperrytopsider.com
Rev.: $50,000,000
Emp.: 2,500
Boating & Casual Shoes
N.A.I.C.S.: 424340

Stride Rite Children's Group, Inc. (2)
191 Spring St, Lexington, MA 02421
Tel.: (617) 824-6000
Web Site: http://www.striderite.com
Rev.: $60,000,000
Emp.: 76
Children's Shoes
N.A.I.C.S.: 424340

Wolverine Europe Limited (1)
5th Floor Kings Place 90 York Way, Lon-
don, N1 9AG, United Kingdom
Tel.: (44) 2078600100
Web Site:
https://www.wolverineworldwide.com
Emp.: 200
Footwear Supplier
N.A.I.C.S.: 424340

Subsidiary (Domestic):

Wolverine Europe Retail Limited (2)
Unit 25 Farm Road Street, Somerset, BA16
0BB, United Kingdom
Tel.: (44) 1458442641
Web Site: https://www.merrell.com
Emp.: 8
Footwear Mfr
N.A.I.C.S.: 316210

Wolverine International, S.L. (1)
Rda General Mitre 28, 08017, Barcelona,
Spain
Tel.: (34) 933663700
Web Site: http://www.eway.com
Footwear Mfr
N.A.I.C.S.: 316210

Wolverine Outdoors, Inc. (1)
9341 Courtland Dr NE, Rockford, MI 49351
Tel.: (616) 866-5500
Web Site:
https://www.wolverineworldwide.com
Emp.: 100
Footwear Whslr
N.A.I.C.S.: 424340
Blake W. Krueger (Pres, CEO & Chm)

**Wolverine World Wide - Bates
Footwear** (1)
9341 Ctland Dr NE, Rockford, MI
49351 **(100%)**
Tel.: (616) 866-5500
Web Site:
http://www.wolverineworldwide.com
Sales Range: $75-99.9 Million
Emp.: 200
Bates Floaters, Bates Military
N.A.I.C.S.: 316210

WOODLANDS FINANCIAL
SERVICES COMPANY
2450 E 3rd St, Williamsport, PA
17701
Tel.: (570) 327-5263 PA
Web Site:
https://www.woodlandsbank.com
WDFN—(OTCIQ)
Rev.: $21,176,000
Assets: $502,463,000
Liabilities: $453,994,000
Net Worth: $48,469,000
Earnings: $4,764,000
Fiscal Year-end: 12/31/20
Offices of Bank Holding Companies
N.A.I.C.S.: 551111
Robert E. Forse (Chm)
Jon P. Conklin (Pres & CEO)
Richard H. Baker (Vice Chm)
Thomas B. Burkholder (Sec & VP)

Subsidiaries:

Woodlands Bank (1)
2450 E 3rd St, Williamsport, PA 17701
Tel.: (570) 327-5263
Web Site: http://www.woodlandsbank.com
Banking Services
N.A.I.C.S.: 522110
Jon P. Conklin (Pres & CEO)

WOODSTOCK HOLDINGS,
INC.
250 River Park N Dr, Woodstock, GA
30188
Tel.: (770) 516-6996 GA
Web Site:
https://www.woodstockholdings
inc.com
WSFL—(OTCIQ)
Sales Range: $1-9.9 Million
Emp.: 11
Investment Banking & Securities
Dealing
N.A.I.C.S.: 523150

WOODWARD, INC.
1081 Woodward Way, Fort Collins,
CO 80524
Tel.: (970) 482-5811 DE
Web Site:
https://www.woodward.com
Year Founded: 1870
WWD—(NASDAQ)
Rev.: $2,245,832,000
Assets: $4,091,004,000
Liabilities: $1,876,223,000
Net Worth: $2,214,781,000
Earnings: $208,649,000
Emp.: 7,200
Fiscal Year-end: 09/30/21
Aerospace & Industrial Energy Con-
trol Systems & Components De-
signer, Mfr & Servicer
N.A.I.C.S.: 335999
Charles P. Blankenship Jr. (Chm,
Pres & CEO)
Thomas G. Cromwell (Vice Chm &
COO)
Paul P. Benson (VP-HR)
Matteo R. Pisciotta (VP-Sourcing-
Global)
Roger Alan Ross (Sr VP-Missiles &
Space)
William F. Lacey (CFO)
Douglas W. Salter (VP-Tech)

Terry Voskuil (Pres-Bus Grp-
Aerospace Segment)
Randy Hobbs (Pres-Industrial Seg-
ment)
Dan Provaznik (Dir-IR)
Jennifer Regina (VP-Comm)
William Lacey (CFO)
John Godsman (VP)

Subsidiaries:

**L'Orange Fuel Injection (Ningbo) Co.,
Ltd.** (1)
3 Hall No 55 South Qihang Road, Ningbo,
315145, China
Tel.: (86) 57489016580
Electronic Parts & Equipment Distr
N.A.I.C.S.: 423690
Evan Zhang (Mgr-HR)

**L'Orange Fuel Injection Trading (Su-
zhou) Co., Ltd.** (1)
No 116 Qingqiu Street, Suzhou Industrial
Park, Suzhou, 215024, Jiangsu, China
Tel.: (86) 51262850935
Web Site: http://www.lorange.com
Electronic Parts & Equipment Distr
N.A.I.C.S.: 423690
Marc-Tran Heller (CEO)

**PM Control Systems (Aust) Pty.
Ltd.** (1)
Unit 1 1 Wirega Avenue, Kingsgrove, 2208,
NSW, Australia
Tel.: (61) 297582322
Web Site: https://www.pmcontrol.com.au
Industrial Machinery Mfr & Distr
N.A.I.C.S.: 333248

**PM Control Systems (India) Private
Ltd.** (1)
Plot No 47A HSIIDC Indl Estate Sector-31,
Faridabad, 121003, India
Tel.: (91) 9999770450
Web Site: https://www.pmcontrol.co.in
Power Management System Services
N.A.I.C.S.: 237130

PM Control Systems Pte. Ltd. (1)
8 Joo Koon Crescent, Singapore, 629011,
Singapore
Tel.: (65) 67792822
Web Site: https://www.pmcontrol.com
Industrial Machinery Mfr & Distr
N.A.I.C.S.: 333248

Superturbo Technologies (1)
3755 Precision Dr Ste 170, Loveland, CO
80538
Tel.: (970) 407-0005
Web Site: http://www.superturbo.net
Turbo Engine Mfr
N.A.I.C.S.: 336310
Mark Herbst (Pres & CEO)
Tom Waldron (Exec VP)
Barry Suelter (Mgr-Engrg)
Jason Keim (Dir-Strategic Controls & Imple-
mentation)
Jared Brin (Coord-Intellectual Property)
Dan Hancock (Chm)

Woodward (Japan) Ltd. (1)
WBG Marive West 19F 2-6-1 Nakase,
Mihama-ku, Chiba, 261-7119,
Japan **(100%)**
Tel.: (81) 432132191
Web Site: http://www.woodward.com
Sales Range: $25-49.9 Million
Emp.: 80
Energy Control & Optimization Solutions Mfr
N.A.I.C.S.: 335312

**Woodward (Tianjin) Controls Com-
pany Limited** (1)
Block A Huaihe Road, Tiantai Industrial
Park Beichen Science and Technology
Park, Tianjin, 300410, Huaihedao,
China **(100%)**
Tel.: (86) 2226308828
Web Site: http://www.woodward.com
Sales Range: $100-124.9 Million
Emp.: 312
Mfr of Energy Control Systems & Compo-
nents
N.A.I.C.S.: 334512

Woodward Bulgaria EOOD (1)
64 Hristofor Kolumb Blvd Sofia Airport Center, Logistics Building B03 Entrance 2,

Woodward, Inc.—(Continued)

1592, Sofia, Bulgaria
Tel.: (359) 29608800
Aerospace Equipment Distr
N.A.I.C.S.: 423860
Georgi Aleksandrov (Mgr-Customer Acct)

Woodward CIS Limited Liability Company (1)
Office 814 2 Piskarevskiy prospect bld 2, Saint Petersburg, 195027, Russia
Tel.: (7) 8123193007
Web Site: http://www.woodward.com
Emp.: 2
Industrial Energy Control System Mfr
N.A.I.C.S.: 335999

Woodward Comercio de Sistemas de Controle e Protecao Electrica Ltda. (1)
Rua Joaquim Norberto 284 - Jardim Santa Genebra, PO Box 6599, J D Santa Genebra, Campinas, 13080-150, SP, Brazil (100%)
Tel.: (55) 1937084800
Sales Range: $10-24.9 Million
Emp.: 40
Mfr of Prime Mover Controls
N.A.I.C.S.: 335312

Woodward Controls (Suzhou) Co., Ltd. (1)
Qingqiu Street, Suzhou Industrial Park, Jiangsu, 215024, China (100%)
Tel.: (86) 51288185515
Web Site: http://www.woodward.com
Sales Range: $100-124.9 Million
Mfr of Energy Control Systems & Components
N.A.I.C.S.: 334512

Woodward Controls, Inc. (1)
5001 N 2nd St, Rockford, IL 61111-5808 (100%)
Tel.: (815) 877-7441
Web Site: http://www.woodward.com
Sales Range: $450-499.9 Million
Emp.: 1,000
Aerospace & Industrial Energy Control Systems & Components Designer, Mfr & Servicer
N.A.I.C.S.: 336412

Woodward FST, Inc. (1)
700 N Centennial St, Zeeland, MI 49464 (100%)
Tel.: (616) 772-9171
Web Site: http://www.woodward.com
Sales Range: $125-149.9 Million
Emp.: 200
Aerospace & Industrial Gas Turbine Fuel Nozzle & Injector Mfr & Maintenance Services
N.A.I.C.S.: 333618

Woodward GmbH (1)
Handwerkstrasse 29, 70565, Stuttgart, Germany (100%)
Tel.: (49) 71178954510
Sales Range: $800-899.9 Million
Emp.: 100
Energy Control Components
N.A.I.C.S.: 335314

Subsidiary (Domestic):

Woodward Aken GmbH (2)
Kothener Chaussee 46, 06385, Aken, Germany (100%)
Tel.: (49) 349098800
Sales Range: $100-124.9 Million
Steam, Gas & Hydraulic Turbines
N.A.I.C.S.: 333611

Woodward Kempen GmbH (2)
Krefelder Weg 47, 47906, Kempen, Germany
Tel.: (49) 21521451
Sales Range: $50-74.9 Million
Power Generation, Distribution & Conversion Products
N.A.I.C.S.: 333611

Woodward HRT, Inc. (1)
25200 W Rye Canyon Rd, Santa Clarita, CA 91355-1265
Tel.: (661) 702-5207
Web Site: http://www.wss.woodward.com

Sales Range: $250-299.9 Million
Emp.: 900
Advanced Controls & Actuation for Aircraft & Munitions
N.A.I.C.S.: 336413

Woodward IDS Bulgaria EOOD (1)
47 Cherny Vrah Blvd, 1407, Sofia, Bulgaria
Tel.: (359) 29608800
Electronic Products Mfr
N.A.I.C.S.: 334419

Woodward IDS Switzerland AG (1)
Hagenholzstrasse 71, CH-8050, Zurich, Switzerland
Tel.: (41) 445620600
Solar Panel System Distr
N.A.I.C.S.: 423720

Woodward IDS Switzerland GmbH (1)
Hagenholzstrasse 71, 8050, Zurich, Switzerland
Tel.: (41) 445620600
Solar Electric Power Generation
N.A.I.C.S.: 221114

Woodward Inc. (1)
Ibn Sina Street - Warehouse 6, Al Madar Industrial Area, Al Khobar, 34627, Saudi Arabia
Tel.: (966) 539011186
Electric Equipment Mfr
N.A.I.C.S.: 335999

Woodward India Private Limited (1)
23/6 Mathura Road Ballabgarh, District Faridabad, Ballabgarh, 121004, Haryana, India
Tel.: (91) 1294097100
Sales Range: $25-49.9 Million
Steam, Gas & Hydraulic Turbines
N.A.I.C.S.: 333611

Woodward International, Inc. - Gloucester Plant
Lancaster Centre Meteor Business Park, Cheltenham Road East, Gloucester, GL2 9QL, United Kingdom
Tel.: (44) 1452 859 940
Web Site: http://www.woodward.com
Electronic Diesel Control System Maintenance & Repair Services
N.A.I.C.S.: 811210

Woodward International, Inc. - Prestwick Plant
5 Shawfarm Road, Prestwick, KA9 2TR, Ayrshire, United Kingdom
Tel.: (44) 1292677600
Web Site: http://www.woodward.com
Sales Range: $25-49.9 Million
Emp.: 55
N.A.I.C.S.: 336412

Woodward L'Orange GmbH (1)
Tel.: (49) 711826090
Web Site: http://www.woodward.com
Engine & Fuel Pumps Mfr
N.A.I.C.S.: 333618

Subsidiary (US):

Fluid Mechanics, LLC (2)
760 Moore Rd, Avon Lake, OH 44012
Tel.: (440) 961-1120
Web Site: http://www.fluidmechanics.com
Industrial Machinery And Equipment
N.A.I.C.S.: 423830

Woodward MPC, (1)
6300 West Howard St, Niles, IL 60714
Tel.: (847) 673-8300
Web Site: http://www.mpcproducts.com
Aerospace Electromechanical Motion Control Systems Mfr
N.A.I.C.S.: 334511
Anthony Natale (Dir-CoE & Sys)
Kathleen Keegan (Gen Mgr)
Simon Belano (Mgr-Engrg & Sensors)

Woodward Nederland B.V. (1)
South Point Building B Scorpius 120-122, 2132 LR, Hoofddorp, Netherlands (100%)
Tel.: (31) 235661111
Sales Range: $10-24.9 Million
Emp.: 30
Mfr of Prime Mover Controls
N.A.I.C.S.: 335312

Woodward Poland Sp. z o.o. (1)

Ul Skarbowa 32, 32-005, Niepolomice, Poland (100%)
Tel.: (48) 122951300
Web Site: http://www.woodward.com
Sales Range: $100-124.9 Million
Emp.: 145
Industrial Power Sensing & Energy Control Systems & Components Mfr
N.A.I.C.S.: 334513
Dominik Kania (Pres)

Woodward Power Solutions GmbH (1)
Krefelder Weg 47, Kempen, 47906, Germany
Tel.: (49) 2152145358
Web Site: http://www.woodward.com
Electrical Product Repair & Maintenance Services
N.A.I.C.S.: 811210

Woodward, Inc. - Duarte (1)
1700 Business Ctr Dr, Duarte, CA 91010-2859
Tel.: (626) 359-9211
Web Site: http://www.woodward.com
Sales Range: $125-149.9 Million
Emp.: 350
Aircraft Hydraulic Thrust Reverser Actuation Systems Mfr
N.A.I.C.S.: 336413

Woodward, Inc. - Loveland (1)
3800 N Wilson Ave, Loveland, CO 80538-2075
Tel.: (970) 663-3900
Web Site: http://www.woodward.com
Sales Range: $350-399.9 Million
Emp.: 800
Aerospace & Industrial Turbine System & Engine System Component Mfr
N.A.I.C.S.: 333611

Woodward, Inc. - Loves Park (1)
5001 N 2nd St, Loves Park, IL 61111
Tel.: (815) 624-4400
Web Site: http://www.woodward.com
Sales Range: $150-199.9 Million
Emp.: 300
Electronic Aircraft Turbine System Component Mfr & Repair Services
N.A.I.C.S.: 811210

WORDSMITH MEDIA, INC.
9701 Wilshire Blvd Ste 450, Beverly Hills, CA 90212
Tel.: (310) 623-4395
WDIS—(OTCIQ)
Assets: $7,000
Liabilities: $24,000
Net Worth: ($17,000)
Earnings: ($17,000)
Fiscal Year-end: 12/31/19
General Marketing Services
N.A.I.C.S.: 541613
James D. Griffith (Founder, Chm & CEO)

WORKDAY, INC.
6110 Stoneridge Mall Rd, Pleasanton, CA 94588
Tel.: (925) 951-9000　　　　　DE
Web Site: https://www.workday.com
Year Founded: 2005
WDAY—(NASDAQ)
Rev.: $7,259,000,000
Assets: $16,452,000,000
Liabilities: $8,370,000,000
Net Worth: $8,082,000,000
Earnings: $1,381,000,000
Emp.: 18,800
Fiscal Year-end: 01/31/24
Software Development Services
N.A.I.C.S.: 513210
Carl M. Eschenbach (CEO)
Zane C. Rowe (CFO)
Sheri Rhodes (Chief Customer Officer)
Thomas F. Bogan (Vice Chm & Exec VP-Workday Planning Business Unit)
Ashley Goldsmith (Chief People Officer & Exec VP)
James J. Bozzini (COO)

Ashley D. Goldsmith (Chief People Officer)
Peter Schlampp (Exec VP-Product Dev)
Tom Bogan (Vice Chm-Corp Dev)
Rich Sauer (Chief Legal Officer & Head-Corp Affairs)
Doug Robinson (Pres)
Carin Taylor (Chief Diversity Officer)
Jim Stratton (CTO)
Patrick Blair (Pres)
Jeff Gelfuso (Chief Design Officer)
Rani Johnson (CIO)
Aneel Bhusri (Founder & Chm)
Mark S. Garfield (Chief Acctg Officer)

Subsidiaries:

Adaptive Insights Co., Ltd. (1)
7th Floor Shin Aoyama Tokyu Building 3-11-13, Minami-Aoyama Minato-ku, Tokyo, 107-0062, Japan
Tel.: (81) 345721200
Software Development Services
N.A.I.C.S.: 513210

Adaptive Insights LLC (1)
3350 W Bayshore Rd Ste 200, Palo Alto, CA 94303
Tel.: (650) 528-7500
Web Site: http://www.adaptiveinsights.com
Rev.: $106,508,000
Assets: $63,238,000
Liabilities: $327,067,000
Net Worth: ($263,829,000)
Earnings: ($42,673,000)
Emp.: 498
Fiscal Year-end: 01/31/2018
Budgeting, Forecasting & Reporting Software Publisher
N.A.I.C.S.: 513210
Robert S. Hull (Founder)
Constance A. DeWitt (Chief Mktg Officer)
Amy L. Reichanadter (Chief People Officer)
Bhaskar Himatsingka (Chief Product Officer)
Jim Johnson (CFO)
Fred Gewant (Chief Revenue Officer)
Melanie Vinson (Gen Counsel & Sec)
Suresh Bala (VP-Product Mgmt)
Sean Cox (VP-Customer Success)
Kshitij Dayal (VP-Engrg)
Scott LaFramboise (VP-Worldwide Sls)
Ryan Slinkard (VP-Professional Svcs)

Adaptive Insights Limited (1)
7th Floor 1 Finsbury Avenue, London, EC2M 2PF, United Kingdom
Tel.: (44) 2071506200
Software Development Services
N.A.I.C.S.: 541511

Adaptive Insights Pty. Ltd. (1)
Level 12 100 Pacific Highway, North Sydney, 2060, NSW, Australia
Tel.: (61) 299648100
Software Development Services
N.A.I.C.S.: 541511

Adaptive Insights, Ltd. (1)
500 King Street West 3rd Floor, Toronto, M5V 1L8, ON, Canada
Tel.: (512) 961-7417
Software Development Services
N.A.I.C.S.: 541511

Scout RFP LLC (1)
123 Mission St, San Francisco, CA 94105
Web Site: http://www.scoutrfp.com
Software Development Services
N.A.I.C.S.: 513210
Alex Yakubovich (CEO)
Stan Garber (Pres)
Michaela Dempsey (VP-Demand & Head-Mktg)
Chris Wada (VP-Product)

Tri-Valley Reseller, LLC (1)
6130 Stoneridge Mall Rd Ste 450, Pleasanton, CA 94588-3279
Tel.: (925) 951-9000
Software Development Services
N.A.I.C.S.: 541511

Workday (UK) Limited (1)
7th Floor 1 Finsbury Avenue, Westminster, London, EC2M 2PF, United Kingdom

Tel.: (44) 207 150 6200
Web Site: http://www.workday.com
Software Development Services
N.A.I.C.S.: 541511

Workday Asia Pacific Limited (1)
Suite 3301-04 33/F Tower One Times
Square 1 Matheson St, Causeway Bay,
Hong Kong, China (Hong Kong)
Tel.: (852) 2 359 5600
Web Site: http://www.workday.com
Emp.: 30
Software Development Services
N.A.I.C.S.: 541511

Workday Australia Pty. Ltd. (1)
Level 12 100 Pacific Highway, 40 Mount
Street, North Sydney, 2060, NSW, Australia
Tel.: (61) 299648100
Web Site: https://www.workday.com
Software Development Services
N.A.I.C.S.: 541511

Workday Austria GmbH (1)
Regus Opera Karntner Ring 5-7 7th floor,
1010, Vienna, Austria
Tel.: (43) 120511601099
Software Development Services
N.A.I.C.S.: 541511

Workday B.V. (1)
Gustav Mahlerplein 82, 1082 MA, Amsterdam, Netherlands
Tel.: (31) 20 708 6000
Web Site: http://www.workday.com
Emp.: 39
Software Development Services
N.A.I.C.S.: 541511

Workday Denmark Aps (1)
Frederiksberggade 11 First Floor, 1459, Copenhagen, Denmark
Tel.: (45) 89887938
Software Development Services
N.A.I.C.S.: 541511

Workday Finland Oy (1)
Epicenter Mikonkatu 9, 00100, Helsinki,
Finland
Tel.: (358) 942451052
Software Development Services
N.A.I.C.S.: 541511

Workday France (1)
7-11 boulevard Haussmann, 75009, Paris,
France
Tel.: (33) 18 488 3444
Web Site: http://ww.workday.com
Software Development Services
N.A.I.C.S.: 541511

Workday GmbH (1)
Grillparzerstr 14, 81675, Munich, Germany
Tel.: (49) 89550565000
Software Development Services
N.A.I.C.S.: 541511

Workday International Limited (1)
Kings Building 152-155 Church Street, Dublin, Ireland
Tel.: (353) 12419900
Software Development Services
N.A.I.C.S.: 541511

Workday Italy S.r.l. (1)
Bastioni di Porta Nuova 21, 20121, Milan,
Italy
Tel.: (39) 0294757421
Software Development Services
N.A.I.C.S.: 541511

Workday K.K. (1)
7th Floor Shin Aoyama Tokyu Building 3-11-13, Minami-Aoyama Minato-ku, Tokyo, 107-0062, Japan
Tel.: (81) 345721200
Software Development Services
N.A.I.C.S.: 541511

Workday Limited (1)
Kings Building May Lane, Dublin, 7, Ireland
Tel.: (353) 1 2419900
Web Site: http://www.workday.com
Business Management Software Developer
N.A.I.C.S.: 513210

Workday Malaysia Sdn. Bhd. (1)
Level 35-02 Q Sentral 2A Jalan Stesen
Sentral 2, 50470, Kuala Lumpur, Malaysia
Tel.: (60) 330995992
Software Publishing Services

N.A.I.C.S.: 513210

Workday Mexico, S. de R.L. de C.V. (1)
375 Lago Alberto, 11320, Mexico, Mexico
Tel.: (52) 8779675329
Software Development Services
N.A.I.C.S.: 513210

Workday Norway AS (1)
Dronning Eufemias Gate 16 7th Floor,
0191, Oslo, Norway
Tel.: (47) 23961003
Software Development Services
N.A.I.C.S.: 541511

Workday Singapore Pte. Ltd. (1)
1 Wallich Street 08-02 Guoco Tower, Singapore, 078881, Singapore
Tel.: (65) 68000600
Software Publishing Services
N.A.I.C.S.: 513210
Paul Jeyaraj (Dir-Svcs-South Asia)

Workday South Africa (Pty.) Ltd. (1)
155 West Street Sandton, Johannesburg,
2031, South Africa
Tel.: (27) 105002224
Software Development Services
N.A.I.C.S.: 541511

Workday Sweden Aktiebolag (1)
4th Floor, 7A Reception, Vasagatan 7, 111
20, Stockholm, Sweden
Tel.: (46) 844680007
Web Site: http://www.workday.com
Software Development Services
N.A.I.C.S.: 541511

Workday Switzerland GmbH (1)
Bleicherweg 10, 8002, Zurich, Switzerland
Tel.: (41) 435080294
Software Publishing Services
N.A.I.C.S.: 513210

WORKHORSE GROUP INC.
3600 Park 42 Dr Ste 160e, Sharonville, OH 45241
Tel.: (513) 360-4704   NV
Web Site:
   https://www.workhorse.com
Year Founded: 2007
WKHS—(NASDAQ)
Rev.: $5,023,072
Assets: $182,742,475
Liabilities: $74,155,544
Net Worth: $108,586,931
Earnings: ($117,274,218)
Emp.: 331
Fiscal Year-end: 12/31/22
Automobile & Light Duty Motor Vehicle Manufacturing
N.A.I.C.S.: 336110
Richard F. Dauch (CEO)
Joshua J. Anderson (CTO)
Stephen S. Burns (Founder)
Dave Bjerke (VP-Product Dev)
James D. Harrington (Chief Admin
Officer, Gen Counsel & Sec)
James D. Harrington (Chief Admin
Officer, Gen Counsel & Sec)
Richard F. Dauch (CEO)
John W. Graber (Pres-Aerospace)
Ryan Gaul (Pres-Comml Vehicles)
James D. Harrington (Chief Admin
Officer, Gen Counsel & Sec)
Robert Ginnan (CFO)
Jeff Mowry (CIO)
Kerry Roraff (Chief HR Officer)
Stan March (VP)
Ben Drake (VP)
Brad Hartzell (VP)

WORKIVA INC.
2900 University Blvd, Ames, IA 50010
Tel.: (515) 817-6100   DE
Web Site: https://www.workiva.com
Year Founded: 2008
WK—(NYSE)
Rev.: $630,039,000
Assets: $1,218,860,000
Liabilities: $1,308,250,000
Net Worth: ($89,390,000)

Earnings: ($127,525,000)
Emp.: 2,526
Fiscal Year-end: 12/31/23
Cloud-Based & Mobile-Enabled Platform For Enterprises To Collaboratively Collect, Manage, Report & Analyze Critical Business Data In Real Time
N.A.I.C.S.: 513210
Jill E. Klindt (Exec Chm-ESG Task
Force, CFO, Treas & Sr VP)
Julie Iskow (Pres & CEO)
Penny Ashley-Lawrence (Chief Customer Officer)
David Haila (CTO)
Michael Hawkins (Exec VP)
Yasser Mahmud (CMO)
Darcie Brossart (Sr VP)
Emily Forrester (Sr VP)
Mike Rost (Sr VP)
Erik Saito (Sr VP)
Corey Wells (Sr VP)
Junko Swain (Chief Acctg Officer &
Sr VP)

Subsidiaries:

ParsePort ApS (1)
Roholmsvej 10 F, 2620, Albertslund, Denmark
Tel.: (45) 53530010
Web Site: https://parseport.com
Software Design & Development Services
N.A.I.C.S.: 541511

Workiva France SAS (1)
No 03-104 4 Rue Jules Lefebvre, 75009,
Paris, France
Tel.: (33) 184178152
Software Publisher
N.A.I.C.S.: 513210

Workiva Germany GmbH (1)
8 Taunusanlage, 60329, Frankfurt, Germany
Tel.: (49) 38177998552
Software Publisher
N.A.I.C.S.: 513210

WORLD ACCEPTANCE CORPORATION
104 S Main St, Greenville, SC 29606
Tel.: (864) 298-9800   SC
Web Site:
   https://www.loansbyworld.com
Year Founded: 1962
WRLD—(NASDAQ)
Rev.: $573,213,402
Assets: $1,056,351,043
Liabilities: $631,923,827
Net Worth: $424,427,216
Earnings: $77,345,227
Emp.: 2,872
Fiscal Year-end: 03/31/24
Finance & Loan Services; Marketer of
Computer Software & Related Services to Financial Services Companies
N.A.I.C.S.: 522291
Daniel Clinton Dyer (Chief Branch
Ops Officer & Exec VP)
Scott McIntyre (Sr VP-Accounting)
Ravin Chad Prashad (Pres & CEO)
A. Lindsay Caulder (Sr VP-Human
Resources)
Jason E. Childers (Sr VP-Information
Technology)
Luke J. Umstetter (Sec, Sr VP & Gen
Counsel)
Ken R. Bramlett Jr. (Chm)
John L. Calmes Jr. (CFO, Chief Strategy Officer, Treas & Exec VP)

Subsidiaries:

Paradata Financial Systems (1)
640 Cepi Dr, Chesterfield, MO
63005   **(100%)**
Tel.: (636) 530-4545
Web Site: http://www.paradatafinancial.com
Sales Range: $1-9.9 Million
Emp.: 20

Provides Computer Software Services to
Financial Companies
N.A.I.C.S.: 541512

WAC de Mexico SA de CV, SOFOM, ENR (1)
San Pedro 801 Entre Entronque a Dr Ignacio Morones Pr, 66220, Garza Garcia,
Mexico
Tel.: (52) 8112344362
Emp.: 15
Consumer Lending Services
N.A.I.C.S.: 522291
Jorge Chavez (VP-Ops)

**World Acceptance Corporation of
Alabama** (1)
215 Cox Creek Pkwy, Florence, AL 35630
Tel.: (256) 766-1888
Web Site: http://www.worldacceptance.com
Consumer Lending Services
N.A.I.C.S.: 522291

**World Acceptance Corporation of
Missouri** (1)
100 Brickton Rd Ste 104, Columbia, MO
65201
Tel.: (573) 814-7025
Consumer Lending Services
N.A.I.C.S.: 522291
Erik Brown (VP-Ops)

**World Acceptance Corporation of
Oklahoma, Inc.** (1)
1460 N Main St, Altus, OK 73521
Tel.: (580) 477-9388
Consumer Lending Services
N.A.I.C.S.: 522291
Christy Allen (Mgr)

**World Finance Company of Kentucky,
LLC** (1)
120 Keen St, Burkesville, KY 42717-7681
Tel.: (270) 864-3741
Consumer Lending Services
N.A.I.C.S.: 522291

World Finance Corp. (1)
324 S Main St, Leitchfield, KY 42754-1428
Tel.: (270) 259-3121
Sales Range: $25-49.9 Million
Emp.: 4
Consumer Finance Companies
N.A.I.C.S.: 522291

World Finance Inc. (1)
113 1/2 Union St, Barbourville, KY 40906
Tel.: (606) 546-4441
Sales Range: $25-49.9 Million
Emp.: 4
Consumer Finance Companies
N.A.I.C.S.: 522291
Susie Smith (Gen Mgr)

World Finance Inc. (1)
255 N Wallace Wilkinson Blvd, Liberty, KY
42539
Tel.: (606) 787-1870
Web Site: http://www.loansbyworld.com
Sales Range: Less than $1 Million
Emp.: 2
Consumer Finance Companies
N.A.I.C.S.: 522291

World Finance Inc. (1)
1847 N 25th St, Middlesboro, KY 40965
Tel.: (606) 248-1620
Sales Range: $25-49.9 Million
Emp.: 4
Consumer Finance Companies
N.A.I.C.S.: 522291

WORLD AM, INC.
4040 MacArthur Blvd Ste 240, Newport Beach, CA 92660
Tel.: (949) 955-5355   NV
WOAM—(OTCIQ)
Electric Equipment Mfr
N.A.I.C.S.: 335999
Thomas E. Ferneau (CFO)
Willis Kollars (Sec)
James H. Alexander (Pres & CEO)

WORLD GOLD TRUST

World Gold Trust—(Continued)

685 3rd Ave Ste 2702, New York, NY 10017
Tel.: (212) 317-3800   DE
Web Site:
  https://www.spdrgoldshares.com
Year Founded: 2014
GLDM—(NYSA)
Assets: $5,779,814,000
Liabilities: $15,353,000
Net Worth: $5,764,461,000
Earnings: ($5,736,000)
Fiscal Year-end: 09/30/23
Trust Management Services
N.A.I.C.S.: 523940
Joseph R. Cavatoni (CEO)
Amanda Krichman (Principal Fin & Acctg Officer)

WORLD HEALTH ENERGY HOLDINGS, INC.

1825 NW Corporate Blvd, Boca Raton, FL 33431
Tel.: (561) 870-0440   DE
Web Site:
  https://www.whengroup.com
Year Founded: 1986
WHEN—(OTCIQ)
Rev.: $207,709
Assets: $10,198,927
Liabilities: $3,869,960
Net Worth: $6,328,967
Earnings: ($7,050,400)
Emp.: 14
Fiscal Year-end: 12/31/23
Dietary Supplement Research & Development
N.A.I.C.S.: 541715
Giora Rozensweig (CEO)
Dan Yatom (Pres)
Alexeii Krein (CTO)
Olga Krylov (CIO)
Tommy Alexandra Rozensweig (Chief Behavioral Officer)
Toni Maranda (COO)
Tom Tromer (Head-EU Sls)

WORLD KINECT CORPORATION

9800 NW 41st St, Miami, FL 33178
Tel.: (305) 428-8000   FL
Web Site: https://www.wfscorp.com
Year Founded: 1984
WKC (NYSE)
Rev.: $47,710,600,000
Assets: $7,375,300,000
Liabilities: $5,425,700,000
Net Worth: $1,949,600,000
Earnings: $52,900,000
Emp.: 5,289
Fiscal Year-end: 12/31/23
Communication Equipment Mfr
N.A.I.C.S.: 334210
Ira M. Birns (CFO & Exec VP)
Wade N. DeClaris (Chief Comml Officer)
Fernando Casadevall (Chief HR Officer)
Jose Miguel Tejada (Chief Acctg Officer & Sr VP)
Amy Quintana Avalos (Chief Sustainability Bus Officer)
Josh McLean (CIO)
Jeffrey Weissman (Sr VP)
Ira M. Birns (CFO & Exec VP)
Michael J. Kasbar (Chm & CEO)

Subsidiaries:

AHT Services, LLC   (1)
3920 Canyon Way, Martinez, CA 94553
Tel.: (925) 957-9253
Fuel Logistics Services
N.A.I.C.S.: 488999

ANY-G B.V.   (1)
Lange Kleiweg 28, 2288 GK, Rijswijk, Netherlands

Tel.: (31) 881188988
Web Site: http://www.any-g.com
Financial Management Services
N.A.I.C.S.: 541611

Advance Petroleum, Inc.   (1)
2451 Great Southwest Pkwy, Fort Worth, TX 76106
Tel.: (817) 626-5458
Web Site: http://www.advancefuel.com
Emp.: 15
Fuel Supply Services
N.A.I.C.S.: 424720
Kyle Kirby (Pres)
Monica Muns (CFO & Office Mgr-IT)
Debbie Hawkins (Co-Owner, Treas & Sec)
Gary Hawkins (VP-Sls)
Tommy Smith (Dir-Transportation)
Waynette Kirby (Mgr-Sls)

Alta Fuels, LLC   (1)
615 State Ave, Alamosa, CO 81101
Tel.: (719) 589-1868
Web Site: http://www.altafuels.com
Fuel Merchant Whslr
N.A.I.C.S.: 423520

Alta Transportation, LLC   (1)
4643 S Ulster St Ste 350, Denver, CO 80237
Tel.: (303) 221-9476
Web Site: http://www.alta-transportation.net
Freight Transportation Services
N.A.I.C.S.: 483211

Amsterdam Software B.V.   (1)
Delflandlaan 1, 1062 EA, Amsterdam, Netherlands
Tel.: (31) 206205697
Web Site: https://fboone.com
Software Development Services
N.A.I.C.S.: 541511
Ries Vriend (CEO)

Ascent Aviation Group, Inc.   (1)
1 Mill St, Parish, NY 13131
Tel.: (315) 625-7299
Web Site: http://www.ascent1.com
Sales Range: $25-49.9 Million
Emp.: 29
Aviation Chemical Distr
N.A.I.C.S.: 424690

Avinode Aktiebolag   (1)
Gamlestads torg 7, 415 12, Gothenburg, Sweden
Tel.: (46) 317510000
Web Site: https://www.avinode.com
Software Development Services
N.A.I.C.S.: 541511

Avinode, Inc.   (1)
444 Brickell Ave Ste 950, Miami, FL 33131-2409
Tel.: (786) 621-5602
Web Site: http://www.avinode.com
Emp.: 14
Software Development Services
N.A.I.C.S.: 541511

Baseops International Inc.   (1)
333 Cypress Run Ste 200, Houston, TX 77094
Tel.: (281) 556-2439
Web Site: http://www.wfscorp.com
Fuel to Corporate & Government Aircraft & Worldwide Flight Planning Ground Handling Weather Information Services
N.A.I.C.S.: 488119

Bergen Energi AB   (1)
Gustavslundsvagen 151 E, PO Box 141 34, Bromma, 167 14, Sweden
Tel.: (46) 84457480
Portfolio Management Services
N.A.I.C.S.: 523940

Bergen Energi AS   (1)
Fantoftvegen 38, Bergen, 5072, Norway
Tel.: (47) 55363700
Web Site: http://www.bergen-energi.com
Emp.: 145
Portfolio Management Services
N.A.I.C.S.: 523940
Terry Cogan (CEO)

Bergen Energi France SarL   (1)
155 Rue Montmartre, 75002, Paris, France
Tel.: (33) 155350340
Petroleum Merchant Whslr
N.A.I.C.S.: 424720

Bergen Energi Nederland BV   (1)
Smallepad 30 G, 3811 MG, Amersfoort, Netherlands
Tel.: (31) 334551661
Petroleum Merchant Whslr
N.A.I.C.S.: 424720

Bergen Energi Portefolje AS   (1)
Stensberggata 27, 0170, Oslo, Norway
Tel.: (47) 23709500
Petroleum Merchant Whslr
N.A.I.C.S.: 424720

Bunkerfuels Corporation   (1)
23 Wallace St Ste 1000, Red Bank, NJ 07701   (100%)
Tel.: (732) 623-2400
Web Site: http://www.wfscorp.com
Sales Range: $10-24.9 Million
Emp.: 15
Single-Source Solution for the Supply, Quality Control, Logistical Support & Price Risk Management of Marine Fuel & Lubricants
N.A.I.C.S.: 561421
Mike Casbar (CEO)

Colt International Europe SARL   (1)
Rue de la Cite, Satigny, 1204, Geneva, Switzerland
Tel.: (41) 223416210
Web Site: http://www.coltinternational.eu
Emp.: 12
Fuel Dealers
N.A.I.C.S.: 457210

Colt International Hong Kong Limited   (1)
25/F Tern CentreTower One 237 Queen's Road, Central, China (Hong Kong)
Tel.: (852) 31103590
Fuel Dealers
N.A.I.C.S.: 457210

Colt International das Americas Servicos de Aviacao Ltda.   (1)
Av Moaci 395 - Cj 84, Moema, Sao Paulo, 04083-000, SP, Brazil
Tel.: (55) 112 924 2569
Web Site:
  http://www.coltinternational.com.br
Emp.: 80
Fuel Dealers
N.A.I.C.S.: 457210

Colt International, L.L.C.   (1)
300 Flint Ridge Rd, Webster, TX 77598
Tel.: (281) 280-2100
Web Site: http://www.coltinternational.com
Flight Planning & Fuel Services
N.A.I.C.S.: 457210

Ecuacentair Cia. Ltda.   (1)
Terminal de Av General Aeropuerto Internacional Mariscal Sucre, Quito, 170183, Ecuador
Tel.: (593) 22818404
Web Site: https://www.ecuacentair.com
Emp.: 6
Fuel Dealers
N.A.I.C.S.: 457210

Ecuacentair S.A.   (1)
Terminal de Av General Aeropuerto Internacional Mariscal Sucre, Quito, Ecuador
Tel.: (593) 22818404
Web Site: https://www.ecuacentair.com
Emp.: 7
Aviation Services
N.A.I.C.S.: 488119

Gib Oil (UK) Limited   (1)
28th Floor One Canada Square, London, E14 5AA, United Kingdom
Tel.: (44) 70231307
Emp.: 13
Petroleum Product Whslr
N.A.I.C.S.: 424720

Gib Oil Limited   (1)
Western Arm North Mole, PO Box 231, GX111AA, Gibraltar, Gibraltar
Tel.: (350) 20003400
Web Site: https://www.giboil.com
Petroleum Product Mfr
N.A.I.C.S.: 324199

Hava Pty, Ltd.   (1)
Level 3 179 Queen St, Melbourne, 3000, VIC, Australia
Tel.: (61) 370429200

Web Site: https://www.hava.io
Software Development Services
N.A.I.C.S.: 541511

Hellenic Aviation Fuel Company S.A.   (1)
12A Irodou Atikou Str, 15124, Maroussi, Greece
Tel.: (30) 2108093590
Web Site: http://www.hafco.gr
Fuel Dealers
N.A.I.C.S.: 457210
Kyriacos Savopoulos (Gen Mgr)

Henty Oil Limited   (1)
Huskisson Dock No 1, Liverpool Docks, Liverpool, L3 0AT, United Kingdom
Tel.: (44) 1519220622
Web Site: http://www.hentyoil.co.uk
Sales Range: $50-74.9 Million
Emp.: 50
Oil Extraction Services
N.A.I.C.S.: 211120

K T M, Inc.   (1)
777 29th St Ste 200, Boulder, CO 80303
Tel.: (303) 442-2719
Web Site: http://www.ktminc.com
Energy Consulting Services
N.A.I.C.S.: 541690
Geoffrey B. Inge (Pres)

Kinect Consulting, LLC   (1)
9800 NW 41st St, Miami, FL 33178
Tel.: (305) 428-8255
Web Site: https://kinect-consulting.com
Fuel & Energy Services
N.A.I.C.S.: 541690

Kinect Energy Denmark A/S   (1)
Stroemmen 6, 9400, Norresundby, Denmark
Tel.: (45) 70231307
Petroleum Product Whslr
N.A.I.C.S.: 424720

Kinect Energy Germany GmbH   (1)
Novalisstrasse 10, 10115, Berlin, Germany
Tel.: (49) 30406077910
Petroleum Product Whslr
N.A.I.C.S.: 424720

Kinect Energy Green Services AS   (1)
Fantoftvegen 2, 5072, Bergen, Norway
Tel.: (47) 55363700
Petroleum Product Whslr
N.A.I.C.S.: 424720

Kropp Holdings, Inc.   (1)
8650 College Blvd, Overland Park, KS 66210-1886
Tel.: (410) 771-2701
Web Site: https://khinc.com
Holding Company
N.A.I.C.S.: 551112

Linton Fuel Oils Limited   (1)
Osiers Road, Wandsworth, London, SW18 1NR, United Kingdom
Tel.: (44) 2088746583
Web Site: http://www.lintonfueloils.com
Emp.: 20
Coal & Mineral Ore Distr
N.A.I.C.S.: 423520

MH Aviation Services (Pty) Ltd   (1)
Building No 8 Ground Floor Emerald Boulevard Greenstone Hill Ext 22, Emerald Boulevard Greenstone Hill Ext 22 Edenvale, Johannesburg, 1610, South Africa
Tel.: (27) 11 609 0123
Web Site: http://www.mhaviation.co.za
Aviation Support Services
N.A.I.C.S.: 488119

MS Europe B.V.   (1)
Volmerlaan 5, 2288 GC, Rijswijk, Netherlands
Tel.: (31) 703199000
Web Site: https://www.mststolls.com
Financial Management Services
N.A.I.C.S.: 541611
Martha Salinas (Chief Customer Officer)

Multi Service Aero B.V.   (1)
Lange Kleiweg 28, 2288 GK, Rijswijk, Netherlands
Tel.: (31) 707703222
Web Site: http://www.multiserviceaero.com
Emp.: 50

Aviation Support Services
N.A.I.C.S.: 488119

Multi Service PTY Limited (1)
L 12 10-16 Queens St, Melbourne, 3000,
VIC, Australia
Tel.: (61) 396782222
Emp.: 34
Custom Computer Programming Services
N.A.I.C.S.: 541511
Brendan Licy *(Mng Dir)*

Nordisk Energipartner A/S (1)
Stroybergs Palae Nyhavnsgade 9, 9000,
Aalborg, Denmark
Tel.: (45) 70272410
Web Site: http://www.energipartner.dk
Energy Consulting Services
N.A.I.C.S.: 541690

Norenergi A/S (1)
Nyhavnsgade 9, 9000, Aalborg, Denmark
Tel.: (45) 78797010
Web Site: http://www.norenergi.dk
Electric Power Distr
N.A.I.C.S.: 221122
Marianne Eriksen *(CEO)*

Oil Shipping (Bunkering) B.V. (1)
Vasteland 6p/a, 3011 BK, Rotterdam, Neth-
erlands
Tel.: (31) 97005032660
Web Site: https://oilshippingbv.com
Emp.: 10
Oil & Gas Exploration Services
N.A.I.C.S.: 213112

On-Demand Energy, L.P (1)
500 Cherrington Pkwy Ste 400, Moon
Township, PA 15108
Tel.: (888) 566-3362
Web Site: http://www.ondemandenergy.com
Power Generation Services
N.A.I.C.S.: 221122
John Zbihley *(Pres)*
John Bodine *(VP-Sls & Bus Dev)*
Lorraine Lang *(Dir-Sls Support Svcs)*
Todd Kalis *(Dir-Bus Dev)*
Paul Swartz *(Dir-IT)*
John Morris *(Dir-Technical Svcs & Regula-
tory Affairs)*
Doug Schaefer *(VP-Managed Energy Prod-
ucts)*
Don Wukich *(Dir-Education Market Svcs)*
Christian R. Silveira *(Partner-Ops & Sls Dir)*
Phil Orend *(Mktg Dir & Coord-Sls)*
Jack Wagner *(Dir-Energy Svcs)*

Orchard Energy Limited (1)
Orchard House Park Rd, Elland, HX5 9HP,
United Kingdom
Tel.: (44) 8445810844
Petroleum Product Whslr
N.A.I.C.S.: 424720

PAPCO, Inc. (1)
4920 Southern Blvd, Virginia Beach, VA
23462
Tel.: (757) 499-5977
Web Site: http://www.papco.com
Emp.: 125
Petroleum & Petroleum Products Distr,
Whslr & Services Provider
N.A.I.C.S.: 424720

PAX Distribution, LLC (1)
2320 Milwaukee Way, Tacoma, WA 98421
Tel.: (888) 929-3478
Web Site: http://www.paxdist.com
Natural Gas Distr
N.A.I.C.S.: 221210

PayNode AB (1)
Gamlestads torg 7, 415 12, Gothenburg,
Sweden
Tel.: (46) 317510000
Web Site: https://www.paynode.com
Fuel & Energy Services
N.A.I.C.S.: 541690

Petro Air, Corp. (1)
Metro Office Park St 1 Lot 6 Ste 305, Guay-
nabo, PR 00968
Tel.: (787) 952-6922
Web Site: https://www.petroair.com
Petroleum Product Distr
N.A.I.C.S.: 424720

**PetroServicios de Costa Rica,
S.R.L.** (1)
Forum 2 Building North 4th Floor, Segundo

Piso, Santa Ana, 10101, Costa Rica
Tel.: (506) 25209300
Emp.: 135
Oil & Logistics Services
N.A.I.C.S.: 213112

**PetroServicios de Mexico S.A. de
C.V.** (1)
Patricio Sanz 1513 4th floor Office 7th Col
Tlacoquemecatl del Valle, Del Benito
Juarez, 03200, Mexico, Mexico
Tel.: (52) 5552039644
Web Site:
https://www.petroservicios.com.mx
Sales Range: $50-74.9 Million
Emp.: 22
Oil Transportation Services
N.A.I.C.S.: 213112

Tamlyn Shipping Limited (1)
2nd Floor Bridon Building, The Docks
Falmouth, Falmouth, TR11 4NR, Cornwall,
United Kingdom
Tel.: (44) 1326313816
Web Site: https://www.tamlyn-shipping.co.uk
Fuel & Energy Services
N.A.I.C.S.: 541690

The Hiller Group Inc. (1)
5321 Memorial Hwy, Tampa, FL 33634
Tel.: (813) 888-7808
Web Site: http://www.hillergroup.com
Sales Range: $200-249.9 Million
Emp.: 40
Petroleum Products
N.A.I.C.S.: 424720

The Lubricant Company Limited (1)
The Green House Beechwood Business
Park North, Inverness, IV2 3BL, United
Kingdom
Tel.: (44) 8443978000
Web Site:
http://www.thelubricantcompany.co.uk
Petroleum Product Distr
N.A.I.C.S.: 424720

Tramp Oil (Brasil) Limitada (1)
Praia do Flamengo 200 - 22 andar, Rio de
Janeiro, Brazil
Tel.: (55) 21 2169 7000
Oil Support Services
N.A.I.C.S.: 213112

Tramp Oil Distribuidora Ltda. (1)
Av Rio Branco 181/3004, Rio de Janeiro,
20040007, Brazil
Tel.: (55) 2121697000
Web Site: http://www.wfscorp.com
Petroleum Product Mfr
N.A.I.C.S.: 324199

**Tramp Oil Germany GmbH & Co
KG** (1)
Neebstrasse 3, Stuhr, 60385, Frankfurt,
Germany
Tel.: (49) 175 890 4072
Web Site: http://www.wffcop.com
Bunker Distr
N.A.I.C.S.: 213112

**Tramp Oil Schiffahrts-und Handelsge-
sellschaft GmbH** (1)
Schlachte 38, Brinkum, 28195, Germany
Tel.: (49) 421 165610
Web Site: http://www.wfscorp.com
Oil & Gas Support Services
N.A.I.C.S.: 213112

WFL (UK) Limited (1)
The Broadgate Tower Third Floor 20 Prim-
rose Street, London, EC2A 2RS, United
Kingdom
Tel.: (44) 1666510345
Web Site: https://www.watsonfuels.co.uk
Fuel Distribution Services
N.A.I.C.S.: 457210

Western Aviation Products LLC (1)
15500 Voss Rd Ste 204, Sugar Land, TX
77498
Tel.: (281) 391-2510
Web Site: https://www.westernaviation.com
Emp.: 27
Aircraft Mfr
N.A.I.C.S.: 336411
David Fisher *(Pres)*

Western Petroleum Company (1)
605 N Hwy 169 Ste 1100, Plymouth, MN
55441

Tel.: (763) 452-1500
Web Site: http://www.westernpetro.com
Sales Range: $25-49.9 Million
Emp.: 20
Petroleum Product Whslr
N.A.I.C.S.: 424720

World Fuel International S.R.L. (1)
Oficentro Ejecutivo La Sabana Sur Edificio
7 Segundo Piso, San Jose, Costa Rica
Tel.: (506) 25209300
Web Site: http://www.wsscorp.com
Sales Range: $50-74.9 Million
Emp.: 45
Aviation Fueling Services
N.A.I.C.S.: 457210

**World Fuel Services (Denmark)
ApS** (1)
Torvebyen 8 1 TH, 4600, Koge, Denmark
Tel.: (45) 56788200
Web Site: https://www.wfscorp.com
Sales Range: $50-74.9 Million
Emp.: 9
Oil Extraction Services
N.A.I.C.S.: 213112

**World Fuel Services (Singapore) Pte
Ltd.** (1)
238B Thomson Road 16-01/07 Novena
Square Tower B, Singapore, 307685, Singa-
pore
Tel.: (65) 6 215 6999
Web Site: http://www.worldfuel.com
Sales Range: $50-74.9 Million
Emp.: 75
Aviation Fueling Services
N.A.I.C.S.: 457210

**World Fuel Services (South Africa)
(Pty) Ltd** (1)
Suite 4 2nd Floor Waterstone Village Office
Park Corner, Main Road and R 44 Somer-
set West, Cape Town, 7130, Western Cape,
South Africa
Tel.: (27) 214254443
Web Site: http://www.wfscorp.com
Emp.: 4
Fuel Dealers
N.A.I.C.S.: 457210

**World Fuel Services Aviation
Limited** (1)
Kingfisher House, Northwood Park Gatwick
Road, Crawley, RH10 9XN, West Sussex,
United Kingdom
Tel.: (44) 01293400333
Oil Support Services
N.A.I.C.S.: 213112

World Fuel Services Europe, Ltd. (1)
Portland House Bressenden Place, London,
SW1E 5BH, United Kingdom
Tel.: (44) 2078085000
Oil & Gas Exploration Services
N.A.I.C.S.: 213112

Subsidiary (Domestic):

Yacht Fuel Services Limited (2)
28th Floor One Canada Square, Canary
Wharf, London, E14 5AA, United Kingdom
Tel.: (44) 2078085000
Web Site: http://www.yachtfuel.com
Sales Range: $25-49.9 Million
Emp.: 10
Marine Fuel Distribution Services
N.A.I.C.S.: 424720

World Fuel Services Ltd. (1)
Kingfisher House Northood Park Gatwick
Road, Crawley, RH10 2XN, West Sussex,
United Kingdom
Tel.: (44) 1293400333
Web Site: http://www.wfscorp.com
Sales Range: $25-49.9 Million
Emp.: 20
Aviation & Marine Fueling Services
N.A.I.C.S.: 457210

**World Fuel Services Mexico, S.A. de
C.V.** (1)
Francisco Sarabia 34B Col Penon de los
Banos, 15520, Mexico, DF, Mexico
Tel.: (52) 5558031600
Web Site: http://www.wfsm.com
Emp.: 40
Fuel Dealers
N.A.I.C.S.: 457210
Dsaupaatovar Docar *(Pres)*

**World Fuel Services Trading
DMCC** (1)
Swiss Tower Office 2003 Jumeirah Lake
Towers, PO Box 340513, Dubai, United
Arab Emirates
Tel.: (971) 43752791
Web Site: https://www.wfscorp.com
Procurement Advisory Services, Supply Ful-
fillment, Transaction & Payment Manage-
ment Services; Oil & Gas Distr
N.A.I.C.S.: 221210

World Fuel Services, Inc. (1)
9800 NW 41st St, Miami, FL 33178
Tel.: (305) 428-8000
Sales Range: $350-399.9 Million
Petroleum Product Whslr
N.A.I.C.S.: 424720

Subsidiary (Domestic):

CarterEnergy Corporation (2)
6000 Metcalf Ave, Overland Park, KS
66202-2306
Tel.: (913) 643-2300
Web Site: http://www.carterenergy.com
Sales Range: $50-74.9 Million
Emp.: 135
Gasoline & Fuel Mfr
N.A.I.C.S.: 424710

Texor Petroleum Company (2)
3340 S Harlem Ave, Riverside, IL 60546
Tel.: (708) 447-1999
Web Site: http://www.texor.com
Sales Range: $100-124.9 Million
Emp.: 30
Provider of Petroleum Products
N.A.I.C.S.: 424720

**World Fuel Services Company,
Inc.** (2)
9800 N W 41 St, Miami, FL 33178
Tel.: (305) 428-8000
Web Site: http://www.worldfuelservices.com
Fuel Logistics Services
N.A.I.C.S.: 213112

WORLD MOBILE HOLDINGS
INC.
80 Wall St Ste 212, New York, NY
10005
Tel.: (917) 725-3190
Web Site:
http://www.worldmobileholdings.com
WMHI—(OTCIQ)
Image Transmission Devices & Sys-
tems Integration
N.A.I.C.S.: 334220
Jason Chuan-Chen Hu *(Chm, CEO &
Treas)*
Samantha Yuying Jen *(Sec & Exec
VP)*
Jimmy Fu-Shan Shen *(CTO & Exec
VP)*
Mike Yuneng Ho *(Exec VP-China
Market)*

WORLD OF WEED, INC.
5715 Red Creek Springs Rd, Pueblo,
CO 81005
Tel.: (720) 757-5762   FL
Web Site:
https://www.worldofweedfarms.com
WOWU—(OTCIQ)
Miscellaneous Store Retailers
N.A.I.C.S.: 459999
Anthony Russo *(Pres & CEO)*

WORLD OIL GROUP, INC.
2578 Enterprise Rd Ste141, Orange
City, FL 32763
Tel.: (407) 777-9228   FL
Web Site:
http://worldoilgroupinc.wixsite.com
WOGI—(OTCIQ)
Petroleum Product Distr
N.A.I.C.S.: 424720
Samuel J. Armacanqui *(COO)*
Alison J. Galardi *(CEO)*

WORLD POKER STORE, INC.

WORLD POKER STORE, INC.

World Poker Store, Inc.—(Continued)

8200 Humboldt Ave S Ste 207,
Bloomington, MN 55431
Tel.: (612) 749-0262   NV
WPKS—(OTCIQ)
Gambling Product Distr
N.A.I.C.S.: 713290
Charles G. Chastain (Chm & CEO)

WORLDFLIX, INC.

777 E Tahquitz Canyon Way Ste 200-
141, Palm Springs, CA 92262
Tel.: (310) 684-2462
Web Site: http://www.worldflix.co
WRFX—(OTCIQ)
Film & Television Management & Mo-
bile Application Software
N.A.I.C.S.: 711410
Brad Listermann (Chm & CEO)

WORLDS INC.

11 Royal Rd, Brookline, MA 02445
Tel.: (617) 725-8900   DE
Web Site: https://www.worlds.com
Year Founded: 1994
WDDD—(OTCQB)
Rev.: $476,839
Assets: $265,401
Liabilities: $3,407,564
Net Worth: ($3,142,163)
Earnings: $82,179
Emp.: 1
Fiscal Year-end: 12/31/23
Data Processing, Hosting & Related
Services
N.A.I.C.S.: 518210
Thomas Kidrin (Pres, CEO, Treas &
Sec)
Christopher J. Ryan (CFO, Chief
Acctg Officer & VP-Fin)

WORLDVEST EQUITY, INC.

2049 Century Park E Ste 4200, Los
Angeles, CA 90067
Tel.: (310) 451-7400
WVVEF—(OTCIQ)
Asset Management Services
N.A.I.C.S.: 523940
Garrett K. Krause (Chm)

WORLDWIDE HOLDINGS CORP.

9344 S 4800 W, Payson, UT 84651
Tel.: (702) 245-9382   NV
Year Founded: 1988
WWDH—(OTCIQ)
Real Estate Manangement Services
N.A.I.C.S.: 531390
Richard E. Sellers (Pres)
Michael Branzuella (VP)

WORLDWIDE STRATEGIES, INC.

1961 NW 150th Ave Ste 205, Pem-
broke Pines, FL 33028
Tel.: (305) 537-6607   NV
WWSG—(OTCIQ)
Liabilities: $925,454
Net Worth: ($925,454)
Earnings: ($1,377,773)
Fiscal Year-end: 07/31/21
Business Support Services
N.A.I.C.S.: 561499
Adam Laufer (Co-Founder & Co-
CEO)

WORRY FREE TEA HOUSE HOLDINGS CO

3445 Lawrence Ave, Oceanside, NY
11572
Tel.: (646) 768-8417
TEAH—(OTCIQ)
Building Maintenance Services
N.A.I.C.S.: 561790
Daniel Mendes (Pres)

WORTHINGTON INDUSTRIES, INC.

200 W Old Wilson Bridge Rd, Colum-
bus, OH 43085
Tel.: (614) 438-3210   OH
Web Site:
  https://www.worthingtonenterpri
  ses.com
Year Founded: 1955
WOR—(NYSE)
Rev.: $1,245,703,000
Assets: $1,638,637,000
Liabilities: $747,625,000
Net Worth: $891,012,000
Earnings: $117,821,000
Emp.: 3,800
Fiscal Year-end: 05/31/24
Holding Company
N.A.I.C.S.: 551112
John P. McConnell (Exec Chm)
Joseph B. Hayek (CFO & VP)
Catherine M. Lyttle (Chief HR Officer
& Sr VP)
Eric M. Smolenski (Pres-Building
Products & Sustainable Energy Solu-
tions)
Michael H. Luh (VP-Strategy & Inno-
vation)
Geoffrey G. Gilmore (COO & Exec
VP)
Cliff J. Larivey (VP-Pur)
Matt Schlabig (CIO)
Sonya L. Higginbotham (VP-Corp
Comm & Brand Mgmt)
Jeff R. Klingler (Pres-Steel Process-
ing)
Marcus Rogier (Officer-IR & Treas)
Patrick J. Kennedy (Gen Counsel,
Sec & VP)
Steven M. Caravati (Pres-Consumer
Products)
Bill Wertz (VP-Transformation)
Steven R. Witt (Chief Acctg Officer &
Controller)
John H. McConnell II (VP-Global Bus
Dev & Sustainable Energy Solutions)
B. Andrew Rose (Pres & CEO)

Subsidiaries:

AMTROL-ALFA Metalomecanica,
S.A.   (1)
Estrada Nacional 206 KM38, PO Box 37,
Brito, 4805-026, Guimaraes, Portugal
Tel.: (351) 253540200
Web Site: https://www.amtrol-alfa.com
Gas Cylinder Mfr
N.A.I.C.S.: 332420
Tiago Oliveira (Gen Mgr)
Carla Aguiar (VP-Ops & Tech)
Filipe Pedrosa (VP-Sls & Mktg)

Amtrol Holdings Inc.   (1)
1400 Division Rd, West Warwick, RI 02893
Tel.: (401) 884-6300
Web Site: http://www.amtrol.com
Sales Range: $150-199.9 Million
Holding Company
N.A.I.C.S.: 551112
Larry T. Guillemette (Chm, Pres & CEO)

Subsidiary (Domestic):

Amtrol Inc.   (2)
1400 Division Rd, West Warwick, RI 02893
Tel.: (401) 884-6300
Web Site: https://www.amtrol.com
Refrigeration Equipment & Supplies Mfr
N.A.I.C.S.: 332313
Joseph L. DePaula (CFO, Treas, Sec &
Exec VP)

BernzOmatic   (1)
1 BernzOmatic Dr, Medina, NY 14103-1648
Tel.: (585) 798-4949
Web Site: http://www.bernzomatic.com
Sales Range: $100-124.9 Million
Emp.: 180
Hand Torches; Torch Kits & Accessories Mfr
N.A.I.C.S.: 332216
Cindy Zinkievich (Prod Devel Mgr)

Dietrich Industries, Inc.   (1)
200 Old Wilson Bridge Rd, Columbus, OH
43085
Tel.: (614) 840-4350
Web Site:
  http://www.dietrichmetalframing.com
Sales Range: $10-24.9 Million
Emp.: 30
Light Gauge Steel Framing Services
N.A.I.C.S.: 238130

Subsidiary (Domestic):

Dietrich Design Group Inc.   (2)
330 Greenwood Pl, McDonough, GA 30253-
7517
Tel.: (678) 304-5525
Web Site: http://www.dietrichindustries.com
Sales Range: $10-24.9 Million
Light Gauge Framing Engineering Services
N.A.I.C.S.: 541330

Dietrich Design Group Inc.   (2)
1414 Field St Bldg C Ste 1, Hammond, IN
46320
Tel.: (219) 853-9473
Web Site: http://www.dietrichindustries.com
Structural Engineering Services
N.A.I.C.S.: 541330

Subsidiary (Non-US):

Dietrich Metal Framing Canada
Inc   (2)
5603 67 Street, Edmonton, T6B 3H5, AB,
Canada
Tel.: (780) 469-9850
Web Site: http://www.dfm.com
Sales Range: $1-9.9 Million
Emp.: 3
Metal Framing & Finishing Products Pro-
ducer
N.A.I.C.S.: 238130

Subsidiary (Domestic):

Vinyl Corp.   (2)
8000 NW 79th Pl, Miami, FL 33166
Tel.: (305) 477-6464
Web Site: http://www.vinylcorp.com
Vinyl Bead & Trim Mfr
N.A.I.C.S.: 332913

Worthington Mid-Rise Construction,
Inc.   (2)
818 E 73rd St, Cleveland, OH 44103
Tel.: (216) 472-1511
Web Site:
  http://www.worthingtonindustries.com
Sales Range: $10-24.9 Million
Total Load Bearing Light Gauge Framing
Systems Mfr
N.A.I.C.S.: 238130
Mike Whitticar (Pres)

Subsidiary (Domestic):

Worthington Construction Group,
Inc.   (3)
3100 E 45th St Ste 400, Cleveland, OH
44127
Tel.: (216) 472-1511
Web Site:
  http://www.worthingtonconstruction
  group.com
Emp.: 25
Apartment Building Construction Contractor
N.A.I.C.S.: 236116

General Tools & Instruments Com-
pany LLC   (1)
75 Seaview Dr, Secaucus, NJ 07094
Web Site: https://www.generaltools.com
Sales Range: $25-49.9 Million
Hand & Precision Tools, Measuring De-
vices, Magnets, Magnetic Tools Mfr
N.A.I.C.S.: 332216
Gerald Weinstein (Chm)

Level5 Tools, LLC   (1)
728 Southwest Blvd, Kansas City, KS
66103
Tel.: (913) 631-0804
Web Site: https://level5tools.com
Hand Tools Distr
N.A.I.C.S.: 423830

PTEC Pressure Technology
GmbH   (1)
Klaus Perthel Linde 11, 51399, Burscheid,
Germany

Tel.: (49) 2174748722
Web Site: http://www.ptec.eu
Industrial Valve Mfr
N.A.I.C.S.: 332911

Precision Specialty Metals, Inc.   (1)
3301 Medford St, Los Angeles, CA 90063
Tel.: (323) 475-3200
Web Site: http://www.psm-inc.com
Sales Range: $25-49.9 Million
Emp.: 64
Mfr & Retailer of Stainless Steel Sheet
Strips & Coils
N.A.I.C.S.: 331110

Rome Strip Steel Co., Inc.   (1)
530 Henry St, Rome, NY 13440
Tel.: (315) 336-5500
Web Site: http://www.romestripsteel.com
Sales Range: $50-74.9 Million
Emp.: 130
Cold Rolled Strip Steel Mfr
N.A.I.C.S.: 331221
Kirk B. Hinman (Pres)
Dave Bovi (VP-Ops)
Pierre Spitzer (Mgr-Layout)
Roger Pratt (Plant Mgr)
Mary Faith Messenger (CFO)

Samuel Steel Pickling Company   (1)
1400 Enterprise Pkwy, Twinsburg, OH
44087-2242
Tel.: (330) 963-3777
Web Site: http://www.samuelsteel.com
Sales Range: $25-49.9 Million
Emp.: 50
toll Processor
N.A.I.C.S.: 561990

Stako Sp. z.o.o.   (1)
Ul Poznanska 54, 76-200, Slupsk, Poland
Tel.: (48) 598424895
Web Site: https://www.stako.pl
Cold Rolled Steel Shapes Mfr
N.A.I.C.S.: 331221

StraitFlex Corporation   (1)
3851 Corporate Ctr Dr, O'Fallon, MO 63368
Tel.: (636) 300-1411
Web Site: http://www.straitflex.com
Concrete Products Mfr
N.A.I.C.S.: 327390

TWB Company, LLC   (1)
1600 Nadeau Rd, Monroe, MI 48162
Tel.: (734) 289-6400
Web Site: http://www.twbcompany.com
Sales Range: $75-99.9 Million
Emp.: 400
Custom Welded Blanks Mfr; Owned 55% by
ThyssenKrupp AG & 45% by Worthington
Industries, Inc.
N.A.I.O.O.: 330370

Tailor Welded Blanks of Canada,
Inc.   (1)
100 Lingard Rd, Cambridge, N1T 2C7, ON,
Canada
Tel.: (519) 624-8071
Aluminum Rolling Mfr
N.A.I.C.S.: 331318

Tempel Canada Corporation   (1)
5045 North Service Road, Burlington, L7L
5H6, ON, Canada
Tel.: (905) 335-2530
Precision Magnetic Steel Lamination Mfr &
Distr
N.A.I.C.S.: 332999

Tempel Precision Metal Products In-
dia Pvt. Ltd.   (1)
No 7 Gudapakkam Village Puduchatram
Post, Poonamallee Taluk Tiruvallur District,
Chennai, 600 124, India
Tel.: (91) 4466803900
Precision Magnetic Steel Lamination Mfr &
Distr
N.A.I.C.S.: 332999

Tempel Steel Company   (1)
5500 N Wolcott Ave, Chicago, IL 60640-
1020
Tel.: (773) 250-8000
Web Site: http://www.tempel.com
Mfr of Magnetic Steel Laminations For Elec-
tric Motors, Generators, Ballasts & Trans-
formers
N.A.I.C.S.: 332813
Clifford D. Nastas (Pres & CEO)

Subsidiary (Non-US):

Tempel (Changzhou) Precision Metal Products Co. Ltd. (2)
17 Tianshan Road, Changzhou, 213022, Jiangsu, China
Tel.: (86) 51985133350
Web Site: https://www.tempel.com
Electrical Steel Mfr
N.A.I.C.S.: 331110

Tempel Burlington (2)
5045 North Service Road, Burlington, L7L 5H6, ON, Canada
Tel.: (905) 335-2530
Web Site: http://www.tempel.com
Metal Stamping Mfr
N.A.I.C.S.: 332119

The Gerstenslager Company (1)
1425 E Bowman St, Wooster, OH 44691-3185
Tel.: (330) 262-2015
Web Site:
http://www.worthingtonindustries.com
Sales Range: $125-149.9 Million
Emp.: 600
Automotive Stampings & Weldments Mfr
N.A.I.C.S.: 336370

The Worthington Steel Company (1)
100 W Old Wilson Bridge Rd, Columbus, OH 43085 **(100%)**
Tel.: (614) 438-3210
Web Site: https://www.worthingtonsteel.com
Sales Range: $200-249.9 Million
Emp.: 350
Mfr of Steel Products
N.A.I.C.S.: 331221

Subsidiary (Domestic):

Worthington Steelpac Systems, LLC (2)
1201 Eden Rd, York, PA 17402
Tel.: (717) 851-0333
Web Site:
http://www.worthingtonsteelpac.com
Rolled Steel Shape Mfr
N.A.I.C.S.: 331221

Westerman Acquisition Co., LLC (1)
776 Kemrow Ave, Wooster, OH 44691
Tel.: (330) 264-2447
Metal Products Mfr
N.A.I.C.S.: 331110

Worthington Armstrong Venture (1)
101 Lindenwood Dr Ste 350, Malvern, PA 19355 **(50%)**
Tel.: (610) 722-1200
Web Site:
https://worthingtonarmstrongventure.com
Sales Range: $25-49.9 Million
Emp.: 40
Steel Ceiling Suspension Grid Mfr
N.A.I.C.S.: 332311
Douglas D. Cadle *(Pres)*
Doug Wisel *(CFO)*
Kimberly Sims *(VP)*
Bill Stoots *(VP)*
Darren R. Semple *(VP)*
Kathy E. Herman *(VP)*

Worthington Cylinder Corporation (1)
200 W Old Wilson Bridge Rd, Worthington, OH 43085-2247 **(100%)**
Tel.: (614) 438-3013
Web Site:
http://www.worthingtonindustries.com
Sales Range: $100-124.9 Million
Emp.: 175
Steel & Aluminum Gas Cylinders & Refrigerant Gas Cylinders Mfr
N.A.I.C.S.: 333514

Worthington Cylinders GmbH (1)
Beim Flaschenwerk 1, Kienberg, 3291, Gaming, Austria
Tel.: (43) 74856060
Web Site:
https://www.worthingtonindustries.eu
Emp.: 400
Cold Rolled Steel Shapes Mfr
N.A.I.C.S.: 331221

Worthington Cylinders-Embalagens Industriais de Gas, S.A. (1)
Worthington Cylinders/Embalagens Industri-

ais de Gas SA, Vale de Cambra, 3730-205, Portugal
Tel.: (351) 256420440
Web Site:
http://www.worthingtoncylinders.com
Sales Range: $25-49.9 Million
Emp.: 100
Cold Rolled Steel Shapes Mfr
N.A.I.C.S.: 331221

Worthington Industries Consumer Products, LLC (1)
200 W Old Wilson Bridge Rd, Columbus, OH 43085
Web Site:
https://www.worthingtonindustries.com
Steel Product Mfr & Distr
N.A.I.C.S.: 332312
John P. McConnell *(Chm)*
Andy Rose *(Pres & CEO)*
Geoff G. Gilmore *(COO & Exec VP)*
Joseph B. Hayek *(CFO & VP)*
Bill Wertz *(VP)*

Worthington Industries Medical Center, Inc. (1)
1250 Dearborn Dr, Columbus, OH 43085-4767
Tel.: (614) 840-3500
Web Site:
http://www.worthingtonindustries.com
Emp.: 26
Medical Center Services
N.A.I.C.S.: 621112

Worthington Industries Poland Sp. z o.o. (1)
ul Portowa 16B, 76-200, Slupsk, Poland
Tel.: (48) 597222910
Gas Equipment Mfr
N.A.I.C.S.: 325120

Worthington Samuel Coil Processing, LLC (1)
4905 S Meridian Rd, Jackson, MI 49204 **(63%)**
Tel.: (517) 780-0000
Web Site:
http://www.worthingtonindustries.com
Sales Range: $50-74.9 Million
Emp.: 82
Motor Vehicle Industry Steel Processing Services; Owned 50% by Worthington Industries, Inc. & 50% by United States Steel Corporation
N.A.I.C.S.: 332111

Subsidiary (Domestic):

ProCoil Company, LLC (2)
5260 Haggerty Rd S, Canton, MI 48188
Tel.: (734) 397-3700
Steel Products Mfr
N.A.I.C.S.: 331110

Worthington Steel of Michigan, Inc. (1)
11700 Worthington Dr, Taylor, MI 48180-4390
Tel.: (734) 374-3260
Rolled Steel Shape Mfr
N.A.I.C.S.: 331221

WOWIO, INC.
4701 Teller Ave Ste 100, Newport Beach, CA 92660
Tel.: (949) 560-1525 **TX**
Web Site: http://wowioapp.com
Year Founded: 2005
WWIO—(OTCEM)
Sales Range: Less than $1 Million
Emp.: 1
Internet Publishing, Digital Media Distr & Advertising Related Services
N.A.I.C.S.: 541890
Anthony L. Anish *(CEO)*

WPF HOLDINGS, INC.
1270 N Wickham Rd Ste 13-1020, Melbourne, FL 32935
Tel.: (818) 934-0454 **FL**
Year Founded: 1997
WPFH—(OTCIQ)
Investment Management Service
N.A.I.C.S.: 525990
Angel Orrantia *(Pres & CEO)*

WRAP TECHNOLOGIES, INC.
1817 W 4th St, Tempe, AZ 85281 DE
Web Site:
https://testwrap.flywheelsites.com
Year Founded: 2016
WRAP—(NASDAQ)
Rev.: $6,133,000
Assets: $28,501,000
Liabilities: $25,338,000
Net Worth: $3,163,000
Earnings: ($30,220,000)
Emp.: 52
Fiscal Year-end: 12/31/23
Security Consulting Services
N.A.I.C.S.: 561612
Scot J. Cohen *(Co-Founder, Exec Chm, CEO, Interim Principal Fin Officer & Principal Acctg Officer)*
James A. Barnes *(Co-Founder)*
Elwood G. Norris *(Co-Founder)*
Chris DeAlmeida *(CFO)*
Nima Parikh *(CMO)*
Matt Campagni *(Sr VP)*
Kelcie Brady *(Sr VP)*
Michael Thomas *(Sr VP)*
Bob Lovering *(VP)*
Milan Cerovic *(VP)*
Marcy Rigoni *(VP)*
Rebekah Newman *(VP)*
Jeff Abbott *(VP)*

WRIGHT INVESTORS' SERVICE HOLDINGS, INC.
2CorporateDrSte770, Shelton, CT 06484
Tel.: (914) 242-5700 **DE**
Web Site:
https://www.wrightinvestorsservice.com
Year Founded: 1998
IWOII (OTOIQ)
Rev.: $21,000
Assets: $4,401,000
Liabilities: $112,000
Net Worth: $4,289,000
Earnings: ($1,207,000)
Emp.: 2
Fiscal Year-end: 12/31/22
Investment Management & Financial Advisory Services
N.A.I.C.S.: 523999
Amit S. Khandwala *(Chm, CEO & Chief Investment Officer)*
Mark F. Moyher *(VP & Head-Trading)*
Diane M. Carstensen *(VP-Information Technology)*

WRIT MEDIA GROUP, INC.
8200 Wilshire Blvd Ste 200, Beverly Hills, CA 90211
Tel.: (310) 461-3739 **DE**
Web Site: https://writmediagroup.com
Year Founded: 2007
WRIT—(OTCIQ)
Sales Range: Less than $1 Million
Television Program Producers
N.A.I.C.S.: 512110
Eric A. Mitchell *(Pres & CEO)*
Alexander Keselman *(CTO)*

WSFS FINANCIAL CORPORATION
500 Delaware Ave, Wilmington, DE 19801
Tel.: (302) 792-6000 **DE**
Web Site: https://www.wsfsbank.com
WSFS—(NASDAQ)
Rev.: $641,849,000
Assets: $15,777,327,000
Liabilities: $13,840,311,000
Net Worth: $1,937,016,000
Earnings: $271,442,000
Emp.: 1,839
Fiscal Year-end: 12/31/21
Bank Holding Company
N.A.I.C.S.: 551111

Rodger Levenson *(Chm, Pres & CEO)*
Lisa Washington *(Chief Legal Officer, Sec & Sr VP)*
Arthur J. Bacci *(COO & Exec VP)*
David Stork *(Sr VP & Dir-Wealth)*
Lisa Brubaker *(CIO, CTO, Chief HR Officer & Exec VP)*
Stephen P. Clark *(Chief Comml Banking Officer & Exec VP)*
Christine E. Davis *(Chief Risk Officer & Exec VP)*
Shari Kruzinski *(Chief Consumer Banking Officer & Exec VP)*
Jim Wechsler *(COO-Comml Banking & Sr VP)*
Kevin McKeown *(Sr VP & Dir-Healthcare Banking)*
Jamie Hopkins *(Chief Wealth Officer & Exec VP)*

Subsidiaries:

Bryn Mawr Capital Management, Inc. (1)
1818 Market St 33rd fl Ste 3323, Philadelphia, PA 19103-3655
Tel.: (484) 380-8100
Rev.: $2,300,000
Emp.: 30
Investment Advice
N.A.I.C.S.: 523940

Subsidiary (Domestic):

Bell Rock Capital, LLC (2)
19606 Coastal Hwy Ste 101, Rehoboth Beach, DE 19971-8576
Tel.: (302) 227-7607
Web Site: http://www.bellrockcapital.com
Portfolio Management
N.A.I.C.S.: 523940
Jacqueline Reeves *(Mng Dir)*

Christiana Trust Company of Delaware (1)
3801 Kennett Pike, Greenville, DE 19807
Tel.: (302) 421-5800
Web Site: http://www.christianabank.com
Sales Range: $10-24.9 Million
Emp.: 30
Investment Management Service
N.A.I.C.S.: 523991
Patrick J. Healy *(Sr VP & Dir-Global Capital Markets)*

Branch (Domestic):

Christiana Trust Company of Delaware - Las Vegas Office (2)
101 Convention Ctr Dr Ste 838, Las Vegas, NV 89109
Tel.: (702) 732-9734
Investment Management Service
N.A.I.C.S.: 523991

Cypress Capital Management, LLC (1)
3801 Kennett Pike Ste C200-A, Greenville, DE 19807 **(100%)**
Tel.: (302) 429-8436
Web Site: https://www.cypress-capital.com
Investment Advisory Firm
N.A.I.C.S.: 523940
Kelly A. Wellborn *(Pres)*
Seth C. Dadds *(Dir-Investment Res)*
Seth Dadds *(Dir)*
Harrison R. Gelber *(Chief Compliance Officer)*
Charles O. Posnecker IV *(Dir-Portfolio Mgmt-Trading)*

Recovery One, LLC (1)
3240 W Henderson Rd, Columbus, OH 43220
Tel.: (614) 336-4207
Web Site: http://www.recoveryonellc.com
Commercial Property Management Services
N.A.I.C.S.: 531312

WSFS Capital Management, LLC (1)
1818 Market St 22nd Fl, Philadelphia, PA 19103
Tel.: (215) 731-1820
Web Site: http://www.westcapital.com
Capital Management Services

WSFS Financial Corporation—(Continued)

N.A.I.C.S.: 523910

West Capital Management (1)
1818 Market St 33rd Fl Ste 3323, Philadelphia, PA 19103
Tel.: (215) 731-1820
Web Site: http://www.westcapital.com
Rev.: $2,490,000
Emp.: 6
Portfolio Management
N.A.I.C.S.: 523940
Matthew E. West (Founder)
Dane F. Czaplicki (Dir-Res)
Robert Schneider (Pres)
Sarah J. Ryder (Office Mgr)
Garrett C. Spangler (Dir-Tax & Estate Plng)

Wilmington Savings Fund Society, Federal Savings Bank (1)
500 Delaware Ave, Wilmington, DE 19801 (100%)
Tel.: (302) 504-9857
Web Site: https://www.wsfsbank.com
Sales Range: $250-299.9 Million
Emp.: 893
Federal Savings Bank
N.A.I.C.S.: 522180
Rodger Levenson (Chm, Pres & CEO)
Patrick J. Ward (Pres-Pennsylvania Market & Exec VP)
Lisa M. Brubaker (CIO & Exec VP)
Shari Kruzinski (Chief Consumer Banking Officer & Exec VP)
Arthur J. Bacci (CFO)
Stephen P. Clark (Chief Comml Banking Officer)
Christine E. Davis (Chief Risk Officer)

Subsidiary (Domestic):

Beneficial Advisors, LLC (2)
1818 Market St Ste 2100, Philadelphia, PA 19103
Tel.: (215) 864-3598
Web Site: http://www.thebeneficial.com
Sales Range: $650-699.9 Million
Emp.: 950
Investment Services
N.A.I.C.S.: 523999
Gerard Payton Cuddy (Pres & CEO)

Data Security Solutions, LLC (2)
8 Squadron Line Rd, Simsbury, CT 06070
Tel.: (860) 651-7283
Protection & Security Services
N.A.I.C.S.: 423610

WSFS Investment Group, Inc. (2)
500 Delaware Ave, Wilmington, DE 19801-3011 (100%)
Tel.: (302) 792-6000
Web Site: http://www.wsfsbank.com
Sales Range: $75-99.9 Million
Emp.: 10
Annuity & Basic Life Insurance Products
N.A.I.C.S.: 523150

WVS FINANCIAL CORP.

9001 Perry Hwy, Pittsburgh, PA 15237
Tel.: (412) 364-1911 PA
Web Site: https://www.wvsbank.com
Year Founded: 1993
WVFC—(NASDAQ)
Rev.: $6,229,000
Assets: $346,078,000
Liabilities: $307,689,000
Net Worth: $38,389,000
Earnings: $1,296,000
Emp.: 23
Fiscal Year-end: 06/30/21
Bank Holding Company
N.A.I.C.S.: 551111
David J. Bursic (Pres & CEO)
Mary C. Magestro-Johnston (Chief Acctg Officer, Treas & VP)
John A. Howard Jr. (Chm)

Subsidiaries:

West View Savings Bank (1)
9001 Perry Hwy, Pittsburgh, PA 15237 (100%)
Tel.: (412) 364-1911
Web Site: http://www.wvsbank.com

Sales Range: $1-9.9 Million
Emp.: 20
Savings Bank
N.A.I.C.S.: 522180
Mary C. Magestro-Johnston (Chief Acctg Officer, Treas & VP)

WW INTERNATIONAL, INC.

675 Avenue of the Americas 6th Fl, New York, NY 10010
Tel.: (212) 589-2700 VA
Web Site:
https://www.weightwatchersinternational.com
Year Founded: 1961
WW—(NASDAQ)
Rev.: $1,212,463,000
Assets: $1,428,934,000
Liabilities: $1,885,338,000
Net Worth: ($456,404,000)
Earnings: $66,892,000
Emp.: 7,700
Fiscal Year-end: 01/01/22
Holding Company; Weight-Control Products & Related Services
N.A.I.C.S.: 551112
Debra Benovitz (Sr VP-Human Truths & Community Impacts)
Sima Sistani (CEO)
Heather Stark (CFO)
Tiffany Stevenson (Chief People Officer)
David Cohen (Chief Data Officer)
Pierre-Olivier Latour (CTO)
Gary Foster (Chief Scientific Officer)
Amanda Tolleson (CMO)
Nicole Haag (Principal Acctg Officer & Controller)

Subsidiaries:

Kurbo, Inc. (1)
301 Howard 15th Fl, San Francisco, CA 94105
Web Site: http://www.kurbo.com
Weight Management Product & Services
N.A.I.C.S.: 812191
Meleah Roy (Mktg Mgr)

WW (Switzerland) SA (1)
Route de Saint-Cergue 303, 1260, Nyon, Switzerland
Tel.: (41) 848188188
Weight Management Product & Services
N.A.I.C.S.: 812191

WW Belgium NV (1)
Kolonel Bourgstraat 123-125 B14, Evere, 1140, Brussels, Belgium
Tel.: (32) 80074041
Web Site: https://www.weightwatchers.com
Weight Management Product & Services
N.A.I.C.S.: 812191

WW.com, LLC (1)
675 6th Ave 6th Fl, New York, NY 10010
Weight Management Product & Services
N.A.I.C.S.: 812191

WW.fr SARL (1)
1-7 cours Valmy, La Défense, 92923, Paris, Cedex, France
Tel.: (33) 969320333
Web Site: https://www.weightwatchers.com
Weight Management Product & Services
N.A.I.C.S.: 812191

Weight Watchers (Deutschland) Gmbh (1)
Rather Str 110A, 40476, Dusseldorf, Germany
Tel.: (49) 21136874253
Web Site: https://www.weightwatchers.de
Weight Management Services
N.A.I.C.S.: 812191

Weight Watchers (U.K.) Limited (1)
Millennium House Ludlow Road, Maidenhead, SL6 2SL, Berkshire, United Kingdom
Tel.: (44) 1628415200
Web Site: http://www.weightwatchers.co.uk
Sales Range: $25-49.9 Million
Weight Management Services
N.A.I.C.S.: 812191
Andrew Knight (Sr VP)

Weight Watchers Denmark APS (1)
Toldbodgade 51b Sal 2, Copenhagen, 1253, Denmark
Tel.: (45) 33110141
Weight Management Services
N.A.I.C.S.: 812191

Weight Watchers European Holding AB (1)
Studentgatan 6, 212 38, Malmo, Sweden
Tel.: (46) 406412100
Investment Management Service
N.A.I.C.S.: 523999

Weight Watchers International Pty. Ltd (1)
Level 5 1-3 Smail St, Ultimo, 2007, NSW, Australia
Tel.: (61) 2992281300
Web Site:
http://www.weightwatchers.com.au
Weight Management Services
N.A.I.C.S.: 812191

Weight Watchers Operations Spain S.L. (1)
Calle Joan D Austria 39 - Piso 4 B, Barcelona, 08005, Spain
Tel.: (34) 933556600
Web Site: http://www.entulinea.es
Weight Management Services
N.A.I.C.S.: 812191

Weight Watchers Polska Spz.o.o. (1)
pl Czerwca 1976 r 1b, 02-495, Warsaw, Poland
Tel.: (48) 223123223
Weight Management Services
N.A.I.C.S.: 812191

Weight Watchers Services Pty Ltd (1)
L 5 1-3 Smail St, Ultimo, 2007, NSW, Australia
Tel.: (61) 1300664536
Web Site:
http://www.weightwatchers.com.au
Weight Management Services
N.A.I.C.S.: 812191

Weight Watchers Sweden ViktVaktarna Akiebolag (1)
Hyllie Boulevard 17, Malmo, 200 49, Sweden
Tel.: (46) 406412177
Web Site: http://www.viktvaktarna.se
Weight Management Services
N.A.I.C.S.: 812191

WeightWatchers.com, Inc. (1)
11 Madison Ave 17th Fl, New York, NY 10010
Tel.: (212) 817-4214
Web Site: http://www.weightwatchers.com
Weight Management Services
N.A.I.C.S.: 812191

WeightWatchers.fr S.A.R.L. (1)
Parc Ariane - Batiment Mars, 78284, Guyancourt, France
Tel.: (33) 130147000
Web Site: http://www.weightwatchers.fr
Weight Management Services
N.A.I.C.S.: 812191

WeightWatchers.nl B.V. (1)
Bijster 12, PO Box 5612, 4817 HX, Breda, Netherlands
Tel.: (31) 8000201447
Web Site: https://www.weightwatchers.nl
Emp.: 50
Weight Management Services
N.A.I.C.S.: 812191

WYNCREST GROUP, INC.

9654 W 131st St Ste 215, Palos Park, IL 60464 NV
Year Founded: 2005
WNCG—(OTCIQ)
Financial Investment Services
N.A.I.C.S.: 523999
Bill Mcfarland (Chm)
Lisa Griffiths (Sec)
Keith Lanzara (Pres & Treas)

WYNDHAM HOTELS & RESORTS, INC.

22 Sylvan Way, Parsippany, NJ 07054
Tel.: (973) 753-6000 DE
Web Site:
https://www.wyndhamhotels.com
Year Founded: 1990
WH—(NYSE)
Rev.: $1,397,000,000
Assets: $4,033,000,000
Liabilities: $3,287,000,000
Net Worth: $746,000,000
Earnings: $289,000,000
Emp.: 2,300
Fiscal Year-end: 12/31/23
Hotel & Resort Management Services
N.A.I.C.S.: 721110
Geoffrey A. Ballotti (Pres & CEO)
Michele Allen (CFO)
Paul F. Cash (Gen Counsel)
Lisa Borromeo Checchio (CMO)
Nicola Rossi (Chief Acctg Officer)
Joon Aun Ooi (Pres-Asia Pacific)
Monica Melancon (Chief HR Officer)
Chip Ohlsson (Chief Dev Officer)
Dimitris Manikis (Pres)
Krishna Paliwal (Pres)
Shilpan Patel (Exec VP)
Gustavo Viescas (Pres)

WYNN RESORTS LIMITED

3131 Las Vegas Blvd S, Las Vegas, NV 89109
Tel.: (702) 770-7555 NV
Web Site:
https://www.wynnresorts.com
Year Founded: 2002
WYNN—(NASDAQ)
Rev.: $6,531,897,000
Assets: $13,996,223,000
Liabilities: $15,097,157,000
Net Worth: ($1,100,934,000)
Earnings: $729,994,000
Emp.: 27,800
Fiscal Year-end: 12/31/23
Casino Hotels & Resorts Designer, Developer & Operator
N.A.I.C.S.: 721120
Julie M. Cameron-Doe (CFO)
Craig S. Billings (CEO)
Michael Weaver (Chief Comm Officer)
Ellen F. Whittemore (Gen Counsel, Sec & Exec VP)
Brian Gullbrants (COO)

Subsidiaries:

Nevada Realty Associates, LLC (1)
PO Box 71647, Las Vegas, NV 89170-1647
Tel.: (702) 253-7720
Real Estate Manangement Services
N.A.I.C.S.: 531390

Sosyal Yazilim ve Danismanlik Hizmetleri AS (1)
Yesilce Mah Yunus Emre Cad No 8 Nil Ticaret Merkezi, Kagithane, Istanbul, Turkiye
Tel.: (90) 2123460040
Web Site: http://www.sosyalyazilim.com
Mobile Application Development Services
N.A.I.C.S.: 541511
Can Tunasat (Head-Ops)

Wynn Design & Development, LLC (1)
734 Pilot Rd, Las Vegas, NV 89119
Tel.: (702) 770-5000
Sales Range: $300-349.9 Million
Emp.: 70
Real Estate Development Services
N.A.I.C.S.: 531390
DeRuyter O. Butler (Exec VP-Architecture)
Darrel Richards (VP-Construction)
DeRuyter O. Butler (Exec VP-Architecture)
Roger P. Thomas (Exec VP)

Wynn Las Vegas, LLC (1)
3131 Las Vegas Blvd S, Las Vegas, NV 89109
Tel.: (702) 770-7000
Web Site: https://www.wynnlasvegas.com

Sales Range: $1-4.9 Billion
Emp.: 12,000
Casino Hotel & Resort Operator
N.A.I.C.S.: 721120
Dean Lawrence (CFO & Sr VP)

Wynn Macau, Limited   (1)
Rua Cidade de Sinatra Nape, Macau, China
(Macau)   (100%)
Tel.: (853) 28889966
Web Site: http://www.wynnmacau.com
Rev.: $981,848,900
Assets: $6,662,615,644
Liabilities: $7,314,792,954
Net Worth: ($652,177,310)
Earnings: ($930,832,151)
Emp.: 13,000
Fiscal Year-end: 12/31/2020
Casino Hotel Operator
N.A.I.C.S.: 721120
Linda Chen (Vice Chm & COO)
Allan Zeman (Chm)
Allan Zeman (Chm)
Ian Michael Coughlan (Pres)
Craig S. Billings (CEO & Exec Dir)

X-FACTOR COMMUNICATIONS HOLDINGS, INC.
100 Stonehurst Ct, Northvale, NJ 07647
Tel.: (551) 804-8177   DE
Web Site:
    https://www.xfactorcom.com
Year Founded: 2010
XFCH—(OTCIQ)
Software Developer
N.A.I.C.S.: 513210
Charles Saracino (Chm, Pres & CEO)
Greg Browning (Partner & Exec VP-Sls Ops)
Brian Watts (CIO)
Todd Kuhlman (VP-Solutions)
Roslyn Yee (Sls Dir-Operations & Dir-Sls)

X4 PHARMACEUTICALS, INC.
61 N Beacon St 4th Fl, Boston, MA 02134
Tel.: (857) 529-8300   DE
Web Site: https://www.x4pharma.com
Year Founded: 2010
XFOR—(NASDAQ)
Rev.: $219,000
Assets: $155,586,000
Liabilities: $81,535,000
Net Worth: $74,051,000
Earnings: ($96,413,000)
Emp.: 70
Fiscal Year-end: 12/31/22
Biotechnology Research & Development Services
N.A.I.C.S.: 541714
Adam S. Mostafa (CFO & Treas)
Art Taveras (Chief Scientific Officer)
Mark Baldry (Chief Comml Officer)
Christophe Arbet-Engels (Chief Medical Officer)
Paula Ragan (Co-Founder, Pres & CEO)
Mary DiBiase (COO)
Michael S. Wyzga (Chm)

Subsidiaries:

X4 Pharmaceuticals (Austria) GmbH   (1)
Helmut-Qualtinger-Gasse 2, 1030, Vienna, Austria
Tel.: (43) 1395078300
Biopharmaceutical Product Development Services
N.A.I.C.S.: 541714
Barbara Grell (Mgr-Site)

XALLES HOLDINGS INC.
2020 Pennsylvania Ave NW No 527, Washington, DC 20006
Tel.: (202) 595-1299   NV
Web Site: https://xalles.com
Year Founded: 2009
XALL—(NASDAQ)

Emp.: 40
Holding Company; Business & Government Oriented Payment & Financial Reconciliation Transactions
N.A.I.C.S.: 551111
Thomas W. Nash (Chm & CEO)
Venugopal Thiyyagura (CTO)

XBIOTECH INC.
5217 Winnebago Ln, Austin, TX 78744
Tel.: (512) 386-2900   Ca
Web Site: https://www.xbiotech.com
Year Founded: 2005
XBIT—(NASDAQ)
Rev.: $4,010,000
Assets: $246,103,000
Liabilities: $5,701,000
Net Worth: $240,402,000
Earnings: ($32,900,000)
Emp.: 85
Fiscal Year-end: 12/31/22
Biopharmaceutical Mfr
N.A.I.C.S.: 325412
Mike Cavalier (Sr Dir-Mfg)
John Simard (Chm, Chm, Pres, Pres, CEO & CEO)
Sushma Shivaswamy (Chief Scientific Officer)
Angela Hu (Principal Fin Officer, Principal Acctg Officer & Dir-Finance)
Norma I. Gonzalez (VP-Quality)
Qian Wu (VP-Quality Control)

XCANA PETROLEUM CORP.
1440 W Taylor St 1847, Chicago, IL 60607
Tel.: (312) 635-5432   WY
Web Site: https://xcanacorp.com
Year Founded: 1980
XCPT—(OTCIQ)
Engineering & Construction Services
N.A.I.C.S.: 541330
Mac Shahsavar (Chm & CEO)
Linda MacDonald (Treas & Sec)

XCEL BRANDS, INC.
550 7th Ave 11th Fl, New York, NY 10018
Tel.: (347) 727-2474   DE
Web Site:
    https://www.xcelbrands.com
Year Founded: 2010
XELB—(NASDAQ)
Rev.: $25,781,000
Assets: $88,935,000
Liabilities: $18,796,000
Net Worth: $70,139,000
Earnings: ($4,018,000)
Emp.: 69
Fiscal Year-end: 12/31/22
Brand Acquisition, Management & Licensing
N.A.I.C.S.: 533110
Robert W. D'Loren (Chm, Pres & CEO)

Subsidiaries:

H Heritage Licensing, LLC   (1)
1201 W 5th St T-340, Los Angeles, CA 90017
Tel.: (415) 917-2590
Web Site: http://www.halston.com
Women Apparel Distr
N.A.I.C.S.: 458110

JR Licensing, LLC   (1)
946 W 17th St, Costa Mesa, CA 92627
Tel.: (714) 923-0252
Web Site: http://www.judithripka.com
Jewelry Mfr & Distr
N.A.I.C.S.: 339910

The Beauty Solution, LLC   (1)
151 Harvey W Blvd Ste B, Santa Cruz, CA 95060
Tel.: (831) 900-5848
Web Site: https://www.beautysolutions.com
Beauty Salon Operator

N.A.I.C.S.: 812112

XCEL ENERGY INC.
414 Nicollet Mall, Minneapolis, MN 55401
Tel.: (612) 330-5500   MN
Web Site:
    https://www.xcelenergy.com
Year Founded: 1909
XEL—(NASDAQ)
Rev.: $14,206,000,000
Assets: $64,079,000,000
Liabilities: $46,463,000,000
Net Worth: $17,616,000,000
Earnings: $1,771,000,000
Emp.: 11,311
Fiscal Year-end: 12/31/23
Electricity & Natural Gas Products & Services
N.A.I.C.S.: 221121
Robert C. Frenzel (Chm, Pres & CEO)
Jeffrey S. Savage (Sr VP & Chief Audit & Fin Svcs Officer)
Christopher B. Clark (Pres-Minnesota, South Dakota & North Dakota)
Paul A. Johnson (Treas & VP-IR)
Timothy O'Connor (COO & Exec VP)
Brian J. Van Abel (CFO, Principal Acctg Officer & Exec VP)
Karen Hyde (Chief Risk, Audit & Compliance Officer & Sr VP)
Amanda Rome (Grp Pres-Utilities, Chief Customer Officer & Exec VP)
Tim Peterson (CTO)
Amy Schneider (Sec)

Subsidiaries:

Eloigne Company   (1)
414 Nicollet Mall, Minneapolis, MN 55401-1927   (100%)
Tel.: (612) 330-6697
Sales Range: $25-49.9 Million
Emp.: 4
Investment Company for Affordable Low-Income Housing & Rental Facilities
N.A.I.C.S.: 525990

Northern States Power Company   (1)
414 Nicollet Mall, Minneapolis, MN 55401
Tel.: (612) 330-5500
Rev.: $6,043,000,000
Assets: $25,001,000,000
Liabilities: $16,794,000,000
Net Worth: $8,207,000,000
Earnings: $707,000,000
Emp.: 3,082
Fiscal Year-end: 12/31/2023
Eletric Power Generation Services
N.A.I.C.S.: 221118
Christopher B. Clark (Pres)
Robert C. Frenzel (COO & Exec VP)
Brian J. Van Abel (CFO & Exec VP)

Northern States Power Company   (1)
1414 W Hamilton Ave, Eau Claire, WI 54701
Tel.: (715) 737-2625
Rev.: $1,177,000,000
Assets: $3,670,000,000
Liabilities: $2,304,000,000
Net Worth: $1,366,000,000
Earnings: $136,000,000
Emp.: 538
Fiscal Year-end: 12/31/2023
Electric Power Generation & Distribution Services
N.A.I.C.S.: 237130
Ben Fowke (Chm & CEO)
Mark E. Stoering (Pres)
Robert C. Frenzel (COO & Exec VP)
Brian J. Van Abel (CFO & Exec VP)
Karl J. Hoesly (Pres)

Xcel Energy Services Incorporated   (1)
600 S Tyler St, Amarillo, TX 79101
Tel.: (806) 378-2868
Electric Power Generation
N.A.I.C.S.: 221118

Alan Bellinghausen (Dir-Substation Ops & Maintenance)
Chester Brown (Dir-Panhandle Design & Construction)

Young Gas Storage Company   (1)
2 N Nevada Ave, Colorado Springs, CO 80903-1715
Tel.: (719) 473-2300
Web Site: http://www.kindermorgan.com
Sales Range: $10-24.9 Million
Emp.: 20
Natural Gas Storage & Pipeline Transporation
N.A.I.C.S.: 486210
Kimberly Allen Dang (Pres)
Richard D. Kinder (Chm)
Steven L. Kean (CEO)
Adam Forman (Sec & VP)
Anthony B. Ashley (Treas & VP-IR)
David P. Michels (CFO & VP)
Dax A. Sanders (Chief Strategy Officer & Exec VP)
James Holland (Pres-Products Pipelines)
Jesse Arenivas (Officer-Ops)
John W. Schlosser (Pres-Terminals)
Jordan H. Mintz (Chief Tax Officer & VP)
Mark Huse (CIO & VP)
Tom Martin (Pres-Natural Gas Pipelines)

XCELMOBILITY INC.
2225 E Bayshore Rd Ste 200, Palo Alto, CA 94303
Tel.: (650) 320-1728   NV
Web Site:
    http://www.xcelmobility.com
Year Founded: 2007
XCLL—(OTCIQ)
Secure Instant Messaging Software
N.A.I.C.S.: 513210
Zhixiong Wei (Pres, CEO & Gen Dir)
Li Ouyang (CFO)
Renyan Ge (Gen Dir)

XCELPLUS INTERNATIONAL, INC.
363 N Sam Houston Pkwy E Ste 1100, Houston, TX 77060
Tel.: (346) 348-4034   NV
Year Founded: 2000
XLPI—(OTCIQ)
Petroleum & Coal Product Mfr
N.A.I.C.S.: 324199
Andrew Befumo (Chief Compliance Officer)

XEMEX GROUP, INC.
540 Atlantic Ave, Brooklyn, NY 11217
Tel.: (718) 625-2700   NV
Web Site:
    https://www.xemexgroup.com
XMEX—(OTCIQ)
Real Estate Manangement Services
N.A.I.C.S.: 531390
Steve Pappas (CEO)

XENCOR, INC.
465 N Halstead St Ste 200, Pasadena, CA 91107
Tel.: (626) 305-5900   DE
Web Site: https://www.xencor.com
Year Founded: 1997
XNCR—(NASDAQ)
Rev.: $164,579,000
Assets: $846,266,000
Liabilities: $118,770,000
Net Worth: $727,496,000
Earnings: ($55,181,000)
Emp.: 281
Fiscal Year-end: 12/31/22
Pharmaceutical Preparation Mfr
N.A.I.C.S.: 325412
Dane Leone (Sr VP-Corp Strategy)
Julie Casciani (Exec Dir- HR)
Nancy Valente (Chief Dev Officer & Exec VP)
Stephen L. Mayo (Co-Founder)
Bassil I. Dahiyat (Co-Founder, Pres & CEO)

XENETIC BIOSCIENCES, INC.

Xenetic Biosciences, Inc.—(Continued)

XENETIC BIOSCIENCES, INC.
945 Concord St, Framingham, MA 01701
Tel.: (781) 778-7720   NV
Web Site: https://www.xeneticbio.com
Year Founded: 2011
XBIO—(NASDAQ)
Rev.: $2,539,986
Assets: $10,605,226
Liabilities: $809,585
Net Worth: $9,795,641
Earnings: ($4,134,578)
Emp.: 4
Fiscal Year-end: 12/31/23
Pharmaceutical Products Research & Development Services
N.A.I.C.S.: 325412
Adam E. Logal (Chm)
James F. Parslow (Interim CEO & CFO)

Subsidiaries:

Xenetic Biosciences plc   (1)
Greener House 66-68 Haymarket, London, SW1Y 4RF, United Kingdom
Tel.: (44) 2030211500
Web Site: http://www.xeneticbio.com
Pharmaceuticals Mfr
N.A.I.C.S.: 325412

XENIA HOTELS & RESORTS, INC.
200 S Orange Ave Ste 2700, Orlando, FL 32801
Tel.: (407) 246-8100   MD
Web Site: https://www.xeniareit.com
Year Founded: 2007
XHR—(NYSE)
Rev.: $997,607,000
Assets: $3,080,055,000
Liabilities: $1,620,047,000
Net Worth: $1,460,008,000
Earnings: $55,922,000
Emp.: 43
Fiscal Year-end: 12/31/22
Portfolio Management & Investment Advice
N.A.I.C.S.: 523940
Marcel Verbaas (Chm & CEO)
Barry A. N. Bloom (Pres & COO)
Joseph T. Johnson (Chief Acctg Officer & Sr VP)
Curtis A. Campbell (VP & Asst Controller)
Thomas Brennan (Sr VP-Asset Mgmt)
Nina DeMartino (VP-Project Mgmt)
Ameya Shinde (VP-Asset Mgmt)
Sami Zeitoun (VP-Asst Mgmt)
Joanna Zook (VP-Asset Mgmt)
Wade Fischer (Sr VP)
Amanda Bryant (VP)
Scott Buxton (VP)
Matthew J. Devine (VP)
Bill Goeller (VP)
Arsheena Khan (VP)
Marina Kostic (VP)
Lori Miller (VP)
Kristine Osburn (VP)
Joel Vanderley (VP)
Christopher Elder (Dir)
Christopher Fincham (Dir)
Morgan Lemis (Dir)
Shawn Martin (Dir)
Atish Shah (CFO, Treas & Exec VP)

Subsidiaries:

IA Lodging Denver City Center, L.L.C.   (1)
1725 Champa St, Denver, CO 80202
Tel.: (303) 296-3444
Emp.: 3
Hotels & Resort Services
N.A.I.C.S.: 721110

IA Lodging Garden Grove Harbor L.L.C.   (1)

2901 Butterfield Rd, Oak Brook, IL 60523
Tel.: (630) 218-8000
Emp.: 10
Resorts & Lodging Services
N.A.I.C.S.: 721110

IA Lodging Pittsburgh Penn TRS DST   (1)
945 Penn Ave, Pittsburgh, PA 15222
Tel.: (412) 434-5551
Emp.: 100
Hotels & Resort Services
N.A.I.C.S.: 721110

IA Urban Hotels Houston TRS Limited Partnership   (1)
2950 Sage Rd, Houston, TX 77056
Tel.: (713) 439-1305
Emp.: 20
Hotels & Resort Services
N.A.I.C.S.: 721110

IA Urban Hotels Washington DC Franklin TRS, L.L.C.   (1)
815 14th St NW, Washington, DC 20005-3301
Tel.: (202) 783-7800
Resorts & Lodging Services
N.A.I.C.S.: 721110

XERIANT, INC.
3998 FAU Blvd Ste 309, Boca Raton, FL 33431
Tel.: (561) 491-9595   NV
Web Site: https://www.xeriant.com
Year Founded: 2009
XERI—(OTCQB)
Assets: $167,118
Liabilities: $6,787,218
Net Worth: ($6,620,100)
Earnings: ($7,066,956)
Emp.: 2
Fiscal Year-end: 06/30/23
Women's Cashmere Knitwear Mfr
N.A.I.C.S.: 315120
Keith F. Duffy (Chm & CEO)
Brian Carey (CFO)
Pablo Lavigna (CIO)
Scott M. Duffy (Exec Dir-Corp Ops)

XERIS BIOPHARMA HOLDINGS, INC.
1375 W Fulton St Suite 1300, Chicago, IL 60607   DE
Web Site:
   https://www.xerispharma.com
XERS—(NASDAQ)
Rev.: $110,248,000
Assets: $344,522,000
Liabilities: $299,335,000
Net Worth: $45,187,000
Earnings: ($94,660,000)
Fiscal Year-end: 12/31/22
Holding Company
N.A.I.C.S.: 551112
Beth P. Hecht (Chief Legal Officer & Sec)
Allison Wey (Sr VP-Corp Comm & IR)
Ken Johnson (Sr VP-Global Dev & Medical Affairs)
Kevin McCulloch (Pres, COO & Chief Comml Officer)
Steve Piper (CFO)
Kendal Korte (Sr VP-Human Resources)
Brian Connor (Chief Compliance Officer, Chief Risk Officer & Sr VP-Quality)
John P. Shannon (CEO)

Subsidiaries:

Strongbridge Biopharma Limited   (1)
900 Northbrook Dr Ste 200, Trevose, PA 19053
Tel.: (610) 254-9200
Web Site: http://www.strongbridgebio.com
Rev.: $30,731,000
Assets: $121,100,000
Liabilities: $55,495,000
Net Worth: $65,605,000

Earnings: ($45,075,000)
Emp.: 72
Fiscal Year-end: 12/31/2020
Biopharmaceutical Mfr
N.A.I.C.S.: 325412
Stephen Long (Chief Legal Officer)
Fredric Cohen (Chief Medical Officer)
Dave Bonnell (Sr VP-Sls)
Brian Conner (Chief Compliance Officer)
Peter J. Valentinsson (Sr VP-Technical Ops-Global)
Scott Wilhoit (Chief Comml Officer)
Emily Doyle (Chief HR Officer)
Steven McElwaine (VP & Controller)

Xeris Pharmaceuticals, Inc.   (1)
180 N LaSalle St Ste 1600, Chicago, IL 60601
Web Site: http://www.xerispharma.com
Rev.: $20,155,000
Assets: $159,151,000
Liabilities: $125,390,000
Net Worth: $33,761,000
Earnings: ($91,140,000)
Emp.: 180
Fiscal Year-end: 12/31/2020
Pharmaceuticals Product Mfr
N.A.I.C.S.: 325412
Steven M. Pieper (CFO & Principal Acctg Officer)
Steven Prestrelski (Founder & Chief Scientific Officer)
Allison Wey (Sr VP-IR & Corp Comm)

XEROX HOLDINGS CORPORATION
201 Merritt 7, Norwalk, CT 06851-1056
Tel.: (203) 849-5216   NY
Web Site: https://www.xerox.com
Year Founded: 2019
XRX—(NASDAQ)
Rev.: $7,107,000,000
Assets: $11,543,000,000
Liabilities: $8,190,000,000
Net Worth: $3,353,000,000
Earnings: ($322,000,000)
Emp.: 20,500
Fiscal Year-end: 12/31/22
Holding Company
N.A.I.C.S.: 551112
John G. Bruno (Pres & COO)
Deena LaMarque Piquion (CMO & Chief Growth Officer & Chief Disruption Officer)
Louie Pastor (Chief Admin Officer, Chief Transformation Officer & Exec VP)
Fred Beljaars (Chief Delivery Officer, Chief Supply Chain Officer & Exec VP)
Flor M. Colon (Chief Legal Officer & Sec)
Joseph H. Mancini Jr. (Chief Acctg Officer & VP)
Steven J. Bandrowczak (CEO)

Subsidiaries:

Advanced Business Equipment Limited   (1)
Tavistock House 5 Rockingham Rd, Uxbridge, UB8 2UB, United Kingdom
Tel.: (44) 8081696974
Web Site:
   https://www.advancedsupplies.uk.com
Print Management Software & Hardware Services
N.A.I.C.S.: 541511

Altodigital Networks Limited   (1)
93 Vantage Point, Kingswinford, DY6 7FR, West Midlands, United Kingdom
Tel.: (44) 3458738122
Web Site: http://www.altodigital.com
Information Technology Services
N.A.I.C.S.: 541611
James Abrahart (CEO)
Darrell Polden (Grp Dir-Svc & Technical)
Martin Chamberlain (Grp Dir-Ops & MIS)

Arena Group Limited   (1)
Armitage House Thorpe Lower Lane Robin Hood, Wakefield, WF3 3BQ, United Kingdom

Tel.: (44) 3448638000
Web Site: https://www.arenagroup.net
Information Technology Services
N.A.I.C.S.: 541611

B 2 Business Systems Limited   (1)
The Smart Centre Tenth Avenue Zone 3, Deeside Industrial Park, Wrexham, CH5 2UA, Flintshire, United Kingdom
Tel.: (44) 3452228282
Web Site: http://www.b2.ltd
Information Technology Services
N.A.I.C.S.: 541611
Peter Ryan (Mng Dir)
Ian Challinor (Ops Mgr)
Paul Collins (Head-Sls)
Nick Roberts (Sls Mgr)
David Catherall (Mgr-IT Technical)

Competitive Computing, Inc.   (1)
354 Mountain View Dr, Colchester, VT 05446
Tel.: (802) 764-1700
Web Site: http://www.competitive.com
Custom Computer Programming Services
N.A.I.C.S.: 541511
Todd Kelley (Co-Founder)
Carolyn Edwards (Pres)
Melissa Dever (Co-Founder)
Tom Williams (VP)
Marty Thieret (Co-Founder & CEO)
Ben Thieret (Sls Mgr)
Dana Potter (Mgr)
Cady Goudreau (Sls Mgr-Operations)
Brooke Connors (Mgr-Marketing Communications)
Delvis Noble (Mgr-Human Resources)
Jonathan Currie (Mgr)
Pam MacKenzie (VP-Strategic Planning)
Kevin Powers (Exec VP)
Bruce Thomas (VP-Finance-Operations)

Copyrite Business Solutions Limited   (1)
16-17 Riverside Park, Wimborne, BH21 1QU, Dorset, United Kingdom
Tel.: (44) 1202848866
Information Technology Services
N.A.I.C.S.: 541611

Digitex Canada Inc.   (1)
130 Leva Avenue, Red Deer, T4E 1B9, AB, Canada
Tel.: (403) 309-3341
Web Site: http://www.digitex.ca
Printer Distr
N.A.I.C.S.: 424110

Go Inspire Group Limited   (1)
147 Scudamore Road, Leicester, LE3 1UQ, United Kingdom
Tel.: (44) 1162321711
Web Site: https://goinspire.co.uk
Database Marketing Services
N.A.I.C.S.: 541613

Groupe CT Inc.   (1)
5545 Maurice-Cullen Street, Laval, H7C 2T8, QC, Canada
Tel.: (450) 967-3142
Web Site: https://www.groupect.com
Information Technology Services
N.A.I.C.S.: 541511
Annie Foucault (Mgr)
Karine Germain (Dir)
Marie-Eve Lussier (Controller)
Jean-Francois Rivard (Mgr-Development)
Pierre-Andre Cochennec (Mgr-Logistics)

ITEC Connect Limited   (1)
Hawkfield Way, Whitchurch, Bristol, BS14 0BL, United Kingdom
Tel.: (44) 1179511500
Web Site: https://www.itecgroup.co.uk
Information Technology Services
N.A.I.C.S.: 541611

Mail A Doc Limited   (1)
ITEC House Hawkfield Way, Whitchurch, Bristol, BS14 0BL, United Kingdom
Tel.: (44) 1278433633
Web Site: http://www.mailadoc.co.uk
Information Technology Services
N.A.I.C.S.: 541611

Powerland Computers Ltd.   (1)
170 Marion St, Winnipeg, R2H 0T4, MB, Canada

Tel.: (204) 237-3800
Web Site: https://www.powerland.ca
Information Technology Infrastructure Services
N.A.I.C.S.: 541512

Rabbit Copiers, Inc. (1)
904 Weddell Ct, Sunnyvale, CA 94089
Web Site: https://roa-usa.com
Office Equipment Distr
N.A.I.C.S.: 423420
Mark Irwin (VP)
Rick Zirpolo (Founder & CEO)
Bill Buckner (CFO & COO)
Chrissy Zirpolo Campi (Sls Mgr)

Xerox (Europe) Limited (1)
Plaza 211 Suite 2 Ground Floor Blanchardstown Corporate Park, Blanchardstown, Dublin, D15 AP2D, Ireland
Tel.: (353) 14622646
Print Management Software Services
N.A.I.C.S.: 541511

Xerox Business Solutions Northeast, Inc. (1)
70 Shawmut Rd, Canton, MA 02021
Tel.: (781) 302-1426
Web Site:
https://www.northeast.xeroxbusinesssolutions.com
Information Technology Services
N.A.I.C.S.: 541512

Xerox Business Solutions Southeast, LLC (1)
10690 John Knight Close, Montgomery, AL 36117
Web Site:
http://www.southeast.xeroxbusinesssolutions.com
Information Technology Services
N.A.I.C.S.: 541611

Xerox Canada I Limited Partnership (1)
2 Sheppard Ave East Suite 1200, Toronto, M2N 5Y7, ON, Canada
Web Site: https://www.xerox.ca
Printer Mfr
N.A.I.C.S.: 334418

Xerox Corporation (1)
201 Merritt 7, Norwalk, CT 06851-1056
Tel.: (203) 849-5216
Web Site: https://www.xerox.com
Rev.: $7,106,999,999
Assets: $11,522,000,000
Liabilities: $7,929,000,000
Net Worth: $3,593,000,000
Earnings: ($322,000,001)
Emp.: 20,499
Fiscal Year-end: 12/31/2022
Business Service Centers
N.A.I.C.S.: 561439
John G. Bruno (Pres & COO)
A. Scott Letier (Chm)
Steven J. Bandrowczak (CEO)
Mary McHugh (Chief Delivery & Supply Chain Officer & Exec VP)
Anne Marie Squeo (Chief Comm & Brand Officer & Sr VP)
Fred Beljaars (Exec VP)
Chris Fisher (Sr VP)
Deena Piquion (CMO)

Subsidiary (Domestic):

ASI Business Solutions, LLC (2)
13701 Hutton Dr Ste 102, Dallas, TX 75234
Tel.: (972) 888-1500
Web Site: http://www.asibiz.com
Computer Peripheral Equipment Mfr
N.A.I.C.S.: 334118
Ken Copeland (Pres)

American Photocopy Equipment Company of Pittsburgh, LLC (2)
3600 McClaren Woods Dr, Coraopolis, PA 15108
Tel.: (724) 695-7391
Web Site:
http://www.amcomofficesystems.com
Photocopying Machinery Mfr
N.A.I.C.S.: 333310

Berney Office Solutions, LLC (2)
10690 John Knight Close, Montgomery, AL 36117
Tel.: (334) 271-4750

Web Site:
https://southeast.xeroxbusinesssolutions.com
Sales Range: $25-49.9 Million
Emp.: 75
Sell Maintain Office Equipments
N.A.I.C.S.: 423420
Ben Blankenship (Pres)

Boise Office Equipment, Inc. (2)
330 N Ancestor Pl, Boise, ID 83704
Tel.: (208) 377-1666
Web Site: http://www.boeweb.com
Office Equipment Distr
N.A.I.C.S.: 423420

Business Equipment Unlimited (2)
275 Read St, Portland, ME 04103
Tel.: (207) 878-8500
Web Site: https://www.beu.net
Emp.: 20
Xerox & Fax Machines Whslr
N.A.I.C.S.: 423420
Scott Parent (VP-Sls)

Subsidiary (Non-US):

CREDITEX - Aluguer de Equipamentos S.A. (2)
Avenida Da Liberdade 200 4 esq, Lisbon, 1250-147, Portugal
Tel.: (351) 210400400
Web Site: http://www.xerox.pt
Office Equipment Rental Services
N.A.I.C.S.: 532420

Subsidiary (Domestic):

CTX Business Solutions, Inc. (2)
16640 SW 72nd Ave, Portland, OR 97224
Tel.: (503) 620-0202
Web Site: https://ctx-xerox.com
Sales Range: $25-49.9 Million
Emp.: 90
Office Equipment Distr
N.A.I.C.S.: 423420

Cameron Office Products, LLC (2)
1 Water St, Amesbury, MA 01913
Web Site: http://www.cameronoffice.com
Sales Range: $25-49.9 Million
Emp.: 14
Xerox Machines Whslr
N.A.I.C.S.: 423420
Dennis Cameron (Pres)

Capital Business Systems, Inc. (2)
4812 McMurry Ave Ste 180, Fort Collins, CO 80525
Web Site: https://www.capitalmds.com
Office Equipment Distr
N.A.I.C.S.: 423430
James Kreikemeier (Pres)

Carolina Office Systems, Inc. (2)
10506 Bryton Corporate Ctr Dr Bldg B Ste 400, Huntersville, NC 28078
Tel.: (704) 337-8900
Web Site: https://carolinaosonline.com
Printers & Office Equipment Whslr
N.A.I.C.S.: 423420

Carr Business Systems, Inc. (2)
500 Commack Rd Ste 110, Commack, NY 11725
Tel.: (631) 249-9880
Web Site: https://carrxerox.com
Sales Range: $50-74.9 Million
Emp.: 150
Office Equipment Distr
N.A.I.C.S.: 423420
Joe Koury (Pres)
Ed Michelson (Sr Dir-Svc)

Subsidiary (Non-US):

Concept Group (Sales) Limited (2)
Concept House Fairbairn Road, Livingston, EH54 6TS, United Kingdom
Tel.: (44) 1506416161
Web Site: https://www.concept-group.co.uk
Emp.: 200
Office Equipment Whslr
N.A.I.C.S.: 423420

Subsidiary (Domestic):

Connecticut Business Systems, LLC (2)
100 Great Meadow Rd 3rd Fl, Wethersfield, CT 06109

Tel.: (860) 667-2900
Web Site: https://cbs-gisx.com
Emp.: 200
Office Equipment Distr
N.A.I.C.S.: 424120
Alyssa Le (CFO)
Jay Cartisano (Pres)
R. Stephen Velardi (VP-Sls)
Robert Kovacs (COO)

Subsidiary (Non-US):

Continua Limited (2)
5 Sundon Business Park Dencora Way, Luton, LU3 3HP, Bedfordshire, United Kingdom
Tel.: (44) 158 257 8999
Web Site: https://www.continua.ltd.uk
Emp.: 20
Office Equipment Whslr
N.A.I.C.S.: 423420
Mark Cannon (Mng Dir)

Subsidiary (Domestic):

Conway Office Solutions, Inc. (2)
10 Capitol St, Nashua, NH 03063
Tel.: (603) 889-1665
Web Site: https://www.conwayoffice.com
Office Equipment Distr
N.A.I.C.S.: 423420
John McBride (Dir-Production)

Subsidiary (Domestic):

Dahill Office Technology Corporation (3)
8200 IH 10 W Ste 400, San Antonio, TX 78230
Tel.: (210) 805-8200
Web Site: http://www.dahill.com
Emp.: 590
Photocopying Machinery Mfr & Distr
N.A.I.C.S.: 333310

Subsidiary (Domestic):

CopyCo Office Solutions, Inc. (2)
2920 C Fortune Cir W, Indianapolis, IN 46241
Tel.: (317) 241-5800
Web Site: http://www.copyco.org
Emp.: 147
Office Equipment Whslr
N.A.I.C.S.: 423420
Jacob Straber (Dir-Ops)

Denitech Corporation (2)
820 W Sandy Lake Rd Ste 100, Coppell, TX 75019
Tel.: (972) 831-2000
Web Site: http://www.denitech.com
Sales Range: $1-9.9 Million
Emp.: 32
Photocopying Machinery Mfr
N.A.I.C.S.: 333310

Eastern Managed Print Network, LLC (2)
6800 Northern Blvd, East Syracuse, NY 13057
Tel.: (315) 474-7000
Web Site: https://easternmpn.com
Photocopying Machinery Mfr
N.A.I.C.S.: 333310

Subsidiary (Domestic):

Eastern Managed Print Network, LLC - Fairport (3)
1387 Fairport Rd Ste 100A, Fairport, NY 14450
Tel.: (585) 388-5550
Web Site: http://www.easternmpn.com
Office Equipment Merchant Whslr
N.A.I.C.S.: 423420
William Gage (Pres)

Subsidiary (Domestic):

Elan Marketing, Inc. (2)
4675 W Teco Ave Ste 140, Las Vegas, NV 89118
Tel.: (702) 515-0300
Web Site: http://www.elanoffice.com
Office Equipment Merchant Whslr
N.A.I.C.S.: 423420

GDP Technologies, Inc. (2)
4350 River Green Pkwy Ste 100, Duluth, GA 30096

Tel.: (770) 248-1020
Web Site: http://www.gdptechnologies.com
Office Equipment Distr
N.A.I.C.S.: 423430

Georgia Duplicating Products, Inc. (2)
1180 Eisenhower Pkwy, Macon, GA 31206
Tel.: (478) 781-8991
Web Site: http://www.gdptechnologies.com
Business Support Services
N.A.I.C.S.: 561499

ISG Services, LLC (2)
20 Waterside Dr, Farmington, CT 06032
Tel.: (860) 678-7877
Office Equipment Merchant Whslr
N.A.I.C.S.: 423420

Image Technology Specialists, Inc. (2)
70 Shawmut Rd, Canton, MA 02021
Tel.: (781) 302-1426
Web Site: https://its-xrx.com
Office Equipment Whslr
N.A.I.C.S.: 423430
Joe Meagher (Controller)
Randy Baril (Pres)
Michael Doolan (VP-Svc & Tech)
Paul Steinberg (VP-Ops)
Terry Gustafson (Mgr-HR & Office)

ImageQuest, Inc. (2)
11021 E 26th N, Wichita, KS 67226
Tel.: (316) 686-3200
Web Site: http://www.imagequestks.com
Emp.: 75
Photocopying Machinery Distr
N.A.I.C.S.: 424120

Subsidiary (Non-US):

Imaging Business Systems (N.I.) Limited (2)
6 Heron Road Sydenham Business Park, Belfast, BT3 9LE, United Kingdom
Tel.: (44) 2890228000
Web Site: http://www.ibsni.com
Sales Range: $25-49.9 Million
Emp.: 26
Office Equipment Whslr
N.A.I.C.S.: 423420

Subsidiary (Domestic):

Imaging Concepts of New Mexico, Inc. (2)
1551 Mercantile Ave NE Ste D, Albuquerque, NM 87107
Tel.: (505) 828-2679
Office Equipment Merchant Whslr
N.A.I.C.S.: 423420

Subsidiary (Non-US):

Impika SA (2)
135 Rue Du Dirigeable ZI Les Paluds CS81371, 13784, Aubagne, Cedex, France
Tel.: (33) 442624300
Web Site: http://www.impika.com
Inkjet Printing Mfr
N.A.I.C.S.: 333248

Subsidiary (Domestic):

Inland Business Machines, Inc. (2)
1500 N Market Blvd, Sacramento, CA 95834
Tel.: (916) 928-0770
Web Site: http://www.ibs-team.com
Fiscal Year-end: 12/31/2006
Photocopying Machinery Distr
N.A.I.C.S.: 424120

Integrity One Technologies, Inc. (2)
2920 Fortune Cir Ste C, Indianapolis, IN 46241
Web Site: http://www.iot-xerox.com
Office Equipment Distr
N.A.I.C.S.: 423430
Claire McFadden (CFO)

Subsidiary (Non-US):

Irish Business Systems Limited (2)
27 Second Avenue Cookstown Industrial Estate, Dublin, Ireland
Tel.: (353) 1 462 2646
Web Site: http://www.ibs.ie
Emp.: 10
Office Equipment Whslr
N.A.I.C.S.: 423420

Xerox Holdings Corporation—(Continued)

Subsidiary (Domestic):

LRI, LLC (2)
750 MD Rte 3 S Ste 19, Gambrills, MD 21054
Tel.: (410) 923-4116
Office Equipment Distr
N.A.I.C.S.: 423430

Lewan & Associates, Inc. (2)
400 S Colorado Blvd, Denver, CO 80222
Tel.: (303) 759-5440
Web Site: http://www.lewan.com
Digital Copiers & Printers Distr
N.A.I.C.S.: 423690

Subsidiary (Domestic):

Lewan Technology (3)
1551 Mercantile Ave NE Ste D, Albuquerque, NM 87107
Tel.: (505) 828-2679
Web Site: http://www.lewan.com
Sales Range: $25-49.9 Million
Emp.: 20
Office Equipment Whslr
N.A.I.C.S.: 423420
Rodney Clang (CIO)
Barbara Johnson (CFO & VP)
Wray Smith (VP-Tech Svcs)
Paul Beach (VP-Customer Support)
April Hansen (Dir-HR)
Vicki Mares (Exec Dir-Ops)
Michael Carroll (VP-Sls)

Subsidiary (Domestic):

LiveWire, LLC (2)
3115 S Grand Ste 600, Saint Louis, MO 63118
Tel.: (314) 448-4500
Software Development Services
N.A.I.C.S.: 541511

Lucas Business Systems, Inc. (2)
627 Bitritto Ct, Modesto, CA 95356
Tel.: (209) 529-3610
Web Site: https://www.lucassystems.com
Office Electronic Equipment Whslr
N.A.I.C.S.: 423420

MCP of California, Inc. (2)
300 N Graves Ave Ste E, Oxnard, CA 93030
Tel.: (805) 650-6482
Web Site: http://www.documentsystems.com
Sales Range: $1-9.9 Million
Emp.: 50
Office Equipment Whslr
N.A.I.C.S.: 423420
John Parisi (VP-Acctg)
John Lurie (Gen Sls Mgr)

MRC Smart Technology Solutions, Inc. (2)
5657 Copley Dr, San Diego, CA 92111
Tel.: (858) 573-6300
Web Site: https://mrc360.com
Photocopying Machinery Mfr
N.A.I.C.S.: 333310

Minnesota Office Technology Group, Inc. (2)
5600 Rowland Rd Ste 205, Minnetonka, MN 55343-4315
Tel.: (952) 252-6600
Web Site: http://www.motg-xerox.com
Office Equipment Whslr
N.A.I.C.S.: 423420

Subsidiary (Non-US):

Nemo (AKS) Limited (2)
Bridge House, Middlesex, Uxbridge, UB8 1HS, United Kingdom
Tel.: (44) 1628890000
Business Management Services
N.A.I.C.S.: 561110

Subsidiary (Domestic):

NewField Information Technology LLC (2)
301 S State St, Newtown, PA 18940
Tel.: (215) 550-6900
Photocopying Machinery Mfr
N.A.I.C.S.: 333310

Subsidiary (Non-US):

NewField Information Technology Limited (2)
Regal House 70 London Rd, Twickenham, TW1 3QS, United Kingdom
Tel.: (44) 2078716700
Web Site: http://www.newfieldit.com
Emp.: 60
Information Technology Consulting Services
N.A.I.C.S.: 541512

Subsidiary (Domestic):

Northeast Copier Systems, LLC (2)
23 Birch St, Milford, MA 01757
Tel.: (508) 478-3530
Web Site:
http://www.northeastcopiersystems.com
Office Equipment Whslr
N.A.I.C.S.: 423420

Northeast Office Systems, LLC (2)
150 Hopping Brook Rd, Holliston, MA 01746
Web Site: http://www.nos360-xerox.com
Office Equipment Distr
N.A.I.C.S.: 423430
Bob Martello (Pres)

OneSOURCE Managed Services, LLC (2)
33 N Meridian, Oklahoma City, OK 73107
Tel.: (405) 942-6674
Web Site: http://www.youronesource.com
Office Equipment Distr
N.A.I.C.S.: 423430

Pacific Services and Development Corporation (2)
4004 Rice St, Lihue, HI 96766-1438
Tel.: (808) 245-9515
Sales Range: $25-49.9 Million
Emp.: 57
Automotive Parts & Accessories Dealer
N.A.I.C.S.: 441330

Palo Alto Research Center Incorporated (2)
3333 Coyote Hill Rd, Palo Alto, CA 94304
Tel.: (650) 859-5200
Web Site: https://www.parc.com
Sales Range: $25-49.9 Million
Emp.: 150
Center for Xerox Research in Systems Technology
N.A.I.C.S.: 541715
Ersin Uzun (Gen Mgr-IoT Global Bus Unit & New Ventures)
Bob Stonick (Dir-Contracting)
Julie Bert (VP & Dir-Hardware Res & Tech Laboratory)
Kai Goebel (VP & Dir-Intelligent Sys Lab)
Laura Murdock (Gen Mgr-AI Software New Ventures)
Austin Pugh (VP-Corp Growth & Bus Ops)
Jan Vandenbrande (Head-Res)

Precision Copier Service, Inc. (2)
4759 NW 72 Ave, Miami, FL 33166
Tel.: (305) 639-2679
Web Site: http://www.precisioncopier.com
Office Equipment Repair & Maintenance Services
N.A.I.C.S.: 811210

Premier Office Equipment (2)
2900 Justin Dr - Ste A B, Urbandale, IA 50322
Tel.: (515) 727-4567
Web Site: http://www.premier-iowa.com
Sales Range: $25-49.9 Million
Emp.: 7
Office Equipment Distr
N.A.I.C.S.: 459410

Quality Business Systems, Inc. (2)
211 Shunpike Rd Ste 2, Cromwell, CT, 06416
Tel.: (860) 635-6987
Web Site:
http://www.qualitybusinesssystem.com
Office Equipment Distr
N.A.I.C.S.: 423420

R. K. Dixon Company (2)
5700 Utica Ridge Rd, Davenport, IA 52807
Tel.: (563) 344-9100
Web Site: https://rkdixon.com
Emp.: 60

Photocopying Machinery Distr
N.A.I.C.S.: 424120

Subsidiary (Non-US):

Restaurant Technology Services UK Limited (2)
Focus 4, Hertfordshire, Letchworth, SG6 2TU, United Kingdom
Tel.: (44) 1462478830
Emp.: 120
Software Development Services
N.A.I.C.S.: 541511
Simon Drake (Gen Mgr)

Subsidiary (Domestic):

SoCal Office Technologies, Inc. (2)
5700 Warland Dr, Cypress, CA 90630
Tel.: (562) 342-7300
Web Site: https://socal-office.com
Office Equipment Whslr
N.A.I.C.S.: 423420

Statit Software, Inc. (2)
4801 E Broadway Blvd Ste 335, Tucson, AZ 85711
Tel.: (520) 296-7398
Web Site: http://www.statit.com
Computer Software Publisher
N.A.I.C.S.: 513210

Stewart Business Systems, LLC (2)
6000 Irwin Rd, Mount Laurel, NJ 08054
Tel.: (856) 727-8100
Web Site: http://www.stewartxerox.com
Emp.: 100
Photocopying Machinery Mfr
N.A.I.C.S.: 333310

Subsidiary (Domestic):

Heritage Business Systems, Inc. (3)
1263 Glen Ave Ste 290, Moorestown, NJ 08057
Web Site: https://heritagebusiness.com
Office Equipment Merchant Whslr
N.A.I.C.S.: 423420

Subsidiary (Domestic):

Stewart Business Sytems (2)
105 Connecticut Dr, Burlington, NJ 08016
Tel.: (856) 727-8100
Web Site: http://www.stewartnj.com
Rev.: $10,000,000
Emp.: 50
Fax Machines & Printers Sales & Service
N.A.I.C.S.: 459999

Stewart of Alabama, Inc. (2)
4000 Colonnade Pkwy, Birmingham, AL 35243
Tel.: (205) 909-3000
Web Site: http://www.stewartal.com
Office Equipment Distr
N.A.I.C.S.: 423430
Vincent Caltagirone (CEO)

Subsidiary (Non-US):

Syan Holdings Limited (2)
Riverside View, Hampshire, Basingstoke, RG24 7AL, United Kingdom
Tel.: (44) 1256811125
Holding Company
N.A.I.C.S.: 551112

Subsidiary (Domestic):

The Xerox Foundation Inc. (2)
201 Merritt 7, Norwalk, CT 06851-1056 (100%)
Tel.: (203) 968-3000
Web Site: http://www.xerox.com
Sales Range: $100-124.9 Million
Charitable Foundation
N.A.I.C.S.: 333310

Transaction Processing Specialists, Inc. (2)
810 Hesters Crossing Rd 120, Round Rock, TX 78681
Tel.: (512) 671-7373
Information Technology Consulting Services
N.A.I.C.S.: 541512

Subsidiary (Non-US):

XC Trading Hong Kong Limited (2)
Rooms 1801-03 18th Floor The Gateway Tower 1 25 Canton Road, Kowloon, China (Hong Kong)
Tel.: (852) 34769662
Office Equipment Whslr
N.A.I.C.S.: 423420

XC Trading Singapore Pte Ltd. (2)
09-02 Fuji Xerox Towers 80 Anson Road, Singapore, 079907, Singapore
Tel.: (65) 66015
Sales Range: $25-49.9 Million
Emp.: 60
Electronic Equipment Distr
N.A.I.C.S.: 423420
Choo Swee Hock (Gen Mgr)

XEROX CZECH Republic s r.o. (2)
BB Centrum Budova Alpha Vyskocilova 1461 /-2a, 140 00, Prague, 4, Czech Republic
Tel.: (420) 22 703 6311
Web Site: http://www.xerox.cz
Emp.: 200
Xerox Equipment Mfr
N.A.I.C.S.: 333310

Subsidiary (Domestic):

XMPie, Inc. (2)
485 Lexington Ave 25th Fl, New York, NY 10017
Tel.: (212) 479-5166
Web Site: http://www.xmpie.com
Sales Range: $1-9.9 Million
Emp.: 35
Custom Computer Programming Services
N.A.I.C.S.: 541511
Yaron Mohaban (VP-Sls-Europe, Mid East, Africa & Asia)

Subsidiary (Non-US):

XMPie, Ltd. (3)
12 Hamelacha St Poleg Technology Park, PO Box 8687, Netanya, 42504, Israel
Tel.: (972) 98856750
Web Site: http://www.xmpie.com
Sales Range: $25-49.9 Million
Emp.: 60
Software Publisher
N.A.I.C.S.: 513210

Subsidiary (Non-US):

Xerox (Europe) Ltd. (2)
Ballycoolin Business Park, Blanchardstown, 15, Dublin, Ireland
Tel.: (353) 016086000
Web Site: http://www.xerox.eu
Sales Range: $50-74.9 Million
Emp.: 20
Xerographic Copiers & Duplicators & Ancillary Supplies Mfr & Marketer
N.A.I.C.S.: 424120

Subsidiary (Non-US):

Veenman B.V. (3)
Rivium Quadrant 201/209, 3045 AH, Capelle aan den IJssel, Netherlands
Tel.: (31) 102846123
Web Site: http://www.veenman.nl
Service Document Management
N.A.I.C.S.: 423420

Subsidiary (Domestic):

Xerox (Ireland) Limited (3)
Xerox Building 1 Ballycoolin Business Park, Blanchardstown, Dublin, D15 PPW3, Ireland
Tel.: (353) 1 462 2646
Web Site: http://www.xerox.ie
Sales Range: $75-99.9 Million
Emp.: 400
Xerographic Copiers & Duplicators & Ancillary Supplies Mfr & Marketer
N.A.I.C.S.: 424120

Subsidiary (Non-US):

Xerox A/S (3)
Industriparken 21A, 2750, Ballerup, Denmark
Tel.: (45) 88178817
Web Site: http://www.xerox.dk
Desktop Monochrome & Color Printers, Multifunction Printers, Copiers & Digital Printing Presses Mfr
N.A.I.C.S.: 333248

Xerox AB (3)

Kronborgs Grand 1 3tr, PO Box 1074,
Kista, 164 46, Sweden
Tel.: (46) 87951000
Web Site: http://www.xerox.se
Sales Range: $50-74.9 Million
Emp.: 160
Office Equipment Whslr
N.A.I.C.S.: 423420
Adam Knatt (CEO)

Xerox Austria GmbH (3)
BIZ ZWEI Vorgartenstrasse 206c, 1020,
Vienna, Austria
Tel.: (43) 1240500
Web Site: http://www.xerox.at
Sales Range: $75-99.9 Million
Emp.: 200
Office Equipment Whslr
N.A.I.C.S.: 423420
Sandra Colloth (Mng Dir)

Subsidiary (Domestic):

Xerox Austria GmbH (4)
Vorgartenstrasse 206c, 1020, Vienna, Aus-
tria
Tel.: (43) 800218533
Web Site: http://www.office.xerox.com
Office Supplies Whslr
N.A.I.C.S.: 424120

Subsidiary (Non-US):

**Xerox Espana, The Document Com-
pany SAU** (3)
Avenida De Aragon 330 Parque Empre-
sarial De Las Mercedes Edificio 6, 28022,
Madrid, Spain
Tel.: (34) 915203540
Web Site: http://www.xerox.es
Computer & Office Equipment Whslr & Mar-
keter
N.A.I.C.S.: 423420

Xerox GmbH (3)
Hammer Landstrasse 91, 41460, Neuss,
Germany
Tel.: (49) 213122480
Office Equipment Whslr
N.A.I.C.S.: 423420

Subsidiary (Domestic):

**Xerox Leasing Deutschland
GmbH** (4)
Hammer Landstrasse 91, 41460, Neuss,
Germany
Tel.: (49) 21312 248 1120
Web Site: https://www.xerox-leasing.de
Sales Range: $75-99.9 Million
Office Equipment Leasing
N.A.I.C.S.: 532420

Subsidiary (Non-US):

Xerox Limited (3)
Bridge House Oxford Road, Uxbridge, UB8
1HS, Mddx, United Kingdom (100%)
Tel.: (44) 1895251133
Web Site: http://www.xerox.co.uk
Emp.: 1,000
Xerographic Copiers & Duplicators & Ancil-
lary Supplies & Markets Word Processing
Equipment & Supplies Mfr & Marketer
N.A.I.C.S.: 424120

Subsidiary (Non-US):

Xerox (Netherland) B.V. (4)
Rijnzathe 12, De Meern, 3454 PV, Utrecht,
Netherlands
Tel.: (31) 884012000
Web Site: https://www.xerox.nl
Sales Range: $75-99.9 Million
Emp.: 250
Sales of Digital Office Equipment, Docu-
ment Solutions & Document Management
Software Solutions
N.A.I.C.S.: 333310

Subsidiary (Domestic):

**Xerox Manufacturing Nederland
B.V.** (5)
Postbus 43, Venray, 5800, MA, Netherlands
Tel.: (31) 31478525000
Office Machinery Mfr
N.A.I.C.S.: 333310

Subsidiary (Domestic):

Xerox Global Services Ltd. (4)
Bridgehouse 2nd Floor, Oxford Road, Ux-
bridge, UB8 1HS, United Kingdom
Tel.: (44) 22974545
Web Site: http://www.xerox.com
Sales Range: $100-124.9 Million
Document Management
N.A.I.C.S.: 561492

Subsidiary (Non-US):

Xerox Limited AG (4)
Sagereistrasse 29, Glattbrugg, 8152, Swit-
zerland
Tel.: (41) 433051212
Web Site: http://www.xerox.com
Sales Range: $75-99.9 Million
Emp.: 400
Computer Mfr
N.A.I.C.S.: 334118

Subsidiary (Domestic):

Xerox AG (5)
Sagereistrasse 29, 8152, Glattbrugg, Swit-
zerland
Tel.: (41) 43 305 1212
Web Site: http://www.xerox.com
Sales Range: $50-74.9 Million
Emp.: 400
Office Supply Whslr
N.A.I.C.S.: 424120

Xerox Finance AG (5)
Lindenstrasse 23, 8302, Kloten, Zurich,
Switzerland
Tel.: (41) 433051212
Web Site: http://www.xerox.com
Sales Range: $100-124.9 Million
Emp.: 300
Office Equipment Whslr
N.A.I.C.S.: 423420

Subsidiary (Domestic):

Xerox Pensions Ltd (4)
Compton Court 20-24 Temple End, High
Wycombe, HP13 5DR, United Kingdom
Tel.: (44) 1494461700
Web Site: http://www.xeroxpensions.co.uk
Sales Range: $10-24.9 Million
Emp.: 24
Pension Fund Administrator
N.A.I.C.S.: 524292

Subsidiary (Non-US):

Xerox Polska Sp zoo (4)
Pomaniewska 52, Warsaw, 02-672, Poland
Tel.: (48) 228787800
Web Site: http://www.xerox.com
Sales Range: $75-99.9 Million
Emp.: 200
Office Equipment Whslr
N.A.I.C.S.: 423420

Subsidiary (Non-US):

Xerox Oy (3)
PL 5 Vanrikinkuja 2, PO Box 5, 02600, Es-
poo, Finland
Tel.: (358) 2-046 8511
Web Site: http://www.xerox.fi
Sales Range: $50-74.9 Million
Emp.: 50
Office Equipment Whslr
N.A.I.C.S.: 423420

Xerox Portugal (3)
Xerox Building Av Infant D Henrique
w/cross Marechal Gomes da Costa, Apar-
tado 8031, 1801-001, Lisbon, Portugal
Tel.: (351) 210400400
Web Site: https://www.xerox.com
Office Equipment Whslr
N.A.I.C.S.: 423420

Xerox S.p.A. (3)
Viale Thomas Edison 110 Sesto San Gio-
vanni, Milan, 20099, Italy
Tel.: (39) 02509891
Web Site: http://www.xerox.it
Emp.: 150
Computer & Photo-copying Equipment Mfr
N.A.I.C.S.: 334112

Xerox SA (3)
2-8 rue Sarah Bernhardt, Asnieres-sur-
Seine, 92600, Paris, France

Tel.: (33) 825012013
Web Site: http://www.xerox.fr
Office Equipment & Software Whslr
N.A.I.C.S.: 423420

Subsidiary (Non-US):

Xerox (Nederland) BV (2)
De Corridor 5, 3621 ZA, Breukelen, Nether-
lands
Tel.: (31) 346255255
Web Site: http://www.xerox.nl
Document Management Services
N.A.I.C.S.: 561439

Xerox AS (2)
Lysaker Torg 35, PO Box 452, 1327, Ly-
saker, Norway
Tel.: (47) 67203000
Web Site: http://www.xerox.no
Sales Range: $25-49.9 Million
Emp.: 80
Office Equipments Mfr
N.A.I.C.S.: 333131

Xerox Argentina, I.C.S.A. (2)
Cazadores de Coquimbo 2841 Building 4
3rd Floor Munro Vicente Lopez, B1605AZE,
Buenos Aires, Argentina
Tel.: (54) 1147037700
Web Site: https://www.xerox.com
Sales Range: $200-249.9 Million
Emp.: 300
Office Equipment Distr & Whslr
N.A.I.C.S.: 423420

**Xerox Buro Araclari Ticaret ve Servis
A.S.** (2)
Cemal Sahir Str Profilo Clever, Esentepe,
34394, Istanbul, Turkiye
Tel.: (90) 2123547000
Web Site: http://www.xerox.com
Sales Range: $50-74.9 Million
Emp.: 50
Office Equipment Whslr
N.A.I.C.S.: 423420

**Xerox Business Equipment
Limited** (2)
Bridge House Oxford Road, Uxbridge, UB8
1HS, United Kingdom
Tel.: (44) 1895251133
Web Site: http://www.xerox.co.uk
Sales Range: $300-349.9 Million
Emp.: 800
Office Equipment Whslr
N.A.I.C.S.: 423420

Subsidiary (Domestic):

Xerox Business Solutions, Inc. (2)
8701 Florida Mining Blvd, Tampa, FL
33634 (100%)
Tel.: (813) 960-5508
Web Site:
    http://www.xeroxbusinesssolutions.com
Office Imaging Solutions; Office Equipment
Retailer & Service
N.A.I.C.S.: 423420
Alfred Vieira (VP-Operations)
Ed Bass (Pres)
Gary Fuller (Dir-Acquisitions)
Wilson Vega (Sr VP)
Ralph Slider (Sr VP)
Paul D. Mosley (Sr VP)
Brad Rollins (Sr VP)
Bob Leone (Sr VP)
George Cavallaro (Sr VP)

Subsidiary (Domestic):

Arizona Office Technologies (3)
4320 E Cotton Center Blvd Ste 100, Phoe-
nix, AZ 85040-4912
Tel.: (602) 346-3000
Web Site: http://www.aot-xerox.com
Sales Range: $50-74.9 Million
Emp.: 80
Copy Machine Service & Whslr
N.A.I.C.S.: 811420

**Blackstone Valley Office
Systems** (3)
6 Blackstone Valley Pl Ste 203, Lincoln, RI
02865
Tel.: (401) 334-2400
Web Site: http://www.bvos.com
Sales Range: $10-24.9 Million
Emp.: 30
Office Technology Solutions & Services

N.A.I.C.S.: 561499
Brian Pendleton (Gen Mgr)

Capitol Office Solutions (3)
9065 Guilford Rd, Columbia, MD 21046
Tel.: (301) 210-4360
Web Site: https://www.gotocos.com
Sales Range: $100-124.9 Million
Office Equipment, Copy Products & Office
Furniture Distr
N.A.I.C.S.: 459910

**Chicago Office Technology
Group** (3)
3 Territorial Ct, Bolingbrook, IL 60440-4659
Tel.: (630) 771-2600
Web Site: http://www.chicago-global.com
Sales Range: $50-74.9 Million
Emp.: 400
Office Equipment Whslr
N.A.I.C.S.: 423420

ComDoc Inc. (3)
8247 Pittsburg Ave NW, North Canton, OH
44720
Tel.: (330) 899-8000
Web Site: https://www.comdoc.com
Sales Range: $150-199.9 Million
Retail Distr of Office Equipment
N.A.I.C.S.: 811210
Gordy Opitz (Co-Pres & CEO)

**Conestoga Business Solutions,
Inc.** (3)
220 Pitney Rd, Lancaster, PA 17601
Tel.: (717) 299-5626
Web Site:
    https://www.conestogacopiers.com
Office Equipment Distr
N.A.I.C.S.: 423420

Electronic Systems, Inc. (3)
369 Edwin Dr, Virginia Beach, VA 23462
Tel.: (757) 497-8000
Web Site: http://www.esi.net
Sales Range: $150-199.9 Million
Emp.: 400
Commercial Office Equipment Sales & Ser-
vices
N.A.I.C.S.: 423420

G-Five, Inc. (3)
297-H Garlington Rd, Greenville, SC 29615
Tel.: (864) 675-5755
Web Site: http://gfive.net
Mail-Order Houses
N.A.I.C.S.: 449210

MT Business Technologies, Inc. (3)
1205 Corporate Dr, Holland, OH 43528
Tel.: (419) 529-6100
Web Site: https://mtbt.com
Office Equipment, Productivity Solutions &
Managed Print Services
N.A.I.C.S.: 423420

Merizon Group Incorporated (3)
620 N Lynndale Dr, Appleton, WI 54914
Tel.: (920) 739-4326
Web Site: https://mbm360.com
Sales Range: $1-9.9 Million
Computer System Design Services
N.A.I.C.S.: 541512

Subsidiary (Domestic):

Modern Business Machines, Inc. (4)
375 Robbins Dr, Troy, MI 48083
Tel.: (248) 597-1095
Sales Range: $25-49.9 Million
Emp.: 40
Electrical Contractor
N.A.I.C.S.: 238210
Andrea Gegain (CFO)

Subsidiary (Domestic):

RK Dixon (3)
5700 Utica Rdg Rd, Davenport, IA 52807
Tel.: (563) 344-9100
Web Site: http://www.rkdixon.com
Sales Range: $25-49.9 Million
Copiers & Faxes
N.A.I.C.S.: 423420
Don Phillips (Pres)
Terry Neff (VP-Svc)

Saxon Business Systems, Inc. (3)
14025 NW 60th Ave, Miami Lakes, FL
33014
Tel.: (305) 362-0100

Xerox Holdings Corporation—(Continued)

Web Site: https://saxon.net
Office Equipment Whslr
N.A.I.C.S.: 423420

Subsidiary (Non-US):

Xerox Canada Inc. (2)
20 Yonge Mills Rd, North York, M2P 2C2,
Canada
Tel.: (416) 229-3769
Web Site: http://www.xerox.ca
Sales Range: $1-4.9 Billion
Emp.: 3,000
Copiers, Fax Machines, Scan Devices &
Laser Printers Mfr
N.A.I.C.S.: 424120

Subsidiary (Domestic):

Xerox Canada Finance Inc. (3)
20 York Mills Suite 500, Toronto, M2P 2C2,
ON, Canada
Tel.: (416) 229-3769
Web Site: http://www.xerox.ca
Sales Range: $125-149.9 Million
Credit Intermediation
N.A.I.C.S.: 522299

Xerox Canada Ltd. (3)
31 McBrine Dr, Kitchener, N2R 1J1, ON,
Canada
Tel.: (519) 893-6500
Web Site: http://www.xerox.com
Sales Range: $25-49.9 Million
Emp.: 200
Copiers Printer Services
N.A.I.C.S.: 334118

Subsidiary (Non-US):

Xerox Canada N.S. ULC (2)
20 York Mills Suite 500, Toronto, M2P 2C2,
ON, Canada
Peripheral Equipment & Software Distr
N.A.I.C.S.: 423430
Donald Evans (Sr Program Mgr)

Subsidiary (Domestic):

**Xerox Care & Quality Solutions,
Inc.** (2)
9779 S Franklin Dr Ste 300, Franklin, WI
53132
Tel.: (414) 325-3999
Photocopying Machinery Mfr
N.A.I.C.S.: 333310

Xerox Corp. (2)
510 W Parkland Dr, Sandy, UT 84070
Tel.: (801) 567-5000
Business Process Outsourcing Services
N.A.I.C.S.: 561499

Xerox Corp. (2)
100 Clinton Ave S, Rochester, NY 14644-
0001
Tel.: (585) 423-5090
Web Site: http://www.xerox.com
Sales Range: $10-24.9 Million
Emp.: 45
Office Products Sales & Service
N.A.I.C.S.: 423420

Xerox Corp. (2)
7900 Westpark Dr, McLean, VA 22102-4242
Tel.: (703) 442-6700
Web Site: http://www.xerox.com
Sales Range: $125-149.9 Million
Emp.: 300
Mfr of Document Processing Equipment
N.A.I.C.S.: 423420

Branch (Domestic):

Xerox Corp. (2)
10 Lake Ctr Executive Park Ste 300, Marl-
ton, NJ 08053
Tel.: (609) 988-2200
Web Site: http://www.xerox.com
Sales Range: $10-24.9 Million
Emp.: 40
Sales Office For Xerox Corporation
N.A.I.C.S.: 541110

Xerox Corp. (2)
1700 Market St 28th Fl, Philadelphia, PA
19103
Tel.: (215) 988-2200

Sales Range: $50-74.9 Million
N.A.I.C.S.: 339940

Subsidiary (Domestic):

Xerox Corp. (2)
4201 Congress St Ste 250, Charlotte, NC
28209
Tel.: (704) 551-2000
Sales Range: $10-24.9 Million
Emp.: 40
N.A.I.C.S.: 339940
Ursla Burns (chm)

Subsidiary (Non-US):

Xerox Egypt S.A.E. (2)
Building 192 South Teseen Street 4th Floor
Sector 2 5th Settlement, 2005C Cornish El
Nil Ramlet Beaulac, New Cairo, Egypt
Tel.: (20) 8000060226
Web Site: https://www.xerox.com
Office Electronic Equipment Whslr
N.A.I.C.S.: 423420
Mark Duffelen (VP & Gen Mgr-Middle East
& Africa)
Pui Chi Li (Head-Mktg-Middle East & Africa)

Xerox Espana, S.A.U. (2)
Avenida De Aragon 330 Parque Empre-
sarial De Las Mercedes Edificio 6, 28022,
Madrid, Spain
Tel.: (34) 91 520 3540
Web Site: http://www.xerox.com
Sales Range: $150-199.9 Million
Emp.: 50
Xerox Equipment Whslr
N.A.I.C.S.: 423420

Xerox Finance Limited (2)
Uxbridge Business Park Building 4 Sander-
son Rd, Uxbridge, UB8 1DH, United King-
dom
Tel.: (44) 1895251133
Equipment Rental & Leasing Services
N.A.I.C.S.: 532490

Subsidiary (Non-US):

Xerox Business Services (3)
253 ave President Wilson, 93210, Paris,
Cedex, France
Tel.: (33) 144654600
Web Site: http://www.xerox.com
Management Services
N.A.I.C.S.: 541611

Subsidiary (Non-US):

Xerox Financial Services B.V. (2)
De Corridor 5, Breukelen, 3621 ZA, Nether-
lands
Tel.: (31) 346255255
Financial Services
N.A.I.C.S.: 523999

**Xerox Financial Services Belux
NV** (2)
Wezembeekstraat 5, 1930, Zaventem, Bel-
gium
Tel.: (32) 27166000
Web Site: http://www.xerox.com
Financial Support Services
N.A.I.C.S.: 523999

**Xerox Financial Services Norway
AS** (2)
Lysaker Torg 35, Lysaker, 1327, Akershus,
Norway
Tel.: (47) 6 720 3000
Web Site: http://www.xerox.com
Emp.: 5
Electronic Data Processing Whslr
N.A.I.C.S.: 423690

**Xerox Financial Services Sverige
AB** (2)
Kronborgsgrand 1 3tr, PO Box 1074, 164
46, Kista, Sweden
Tel.: (46) 87951000
Web Site: http://www.xerox.com
Financial Services
N.A.I.C.S.: 523999

Xerox Global Services GmbH (2)
Vorgartenstrasse 206c, 1020, Vienna, Aus-
tria
Tel.: (43) 12079000
Printing Equipment Whslr
N.A.I.C.S.: 423430

Xerox Hellas AEE (2)
350 Syngrou Avenue, 17674, Kallithea,
Greece
Tel.: (30) 2109307000
Web Site: http://www.xerox.com
Emp.: 11
Xerox Equipment Whslr
N.A.I.C.S.: 423690

**Xerox Holding Deutschland
GmbH** (2)
Hammer Landstrasse 91, 41460, Neuss,
Germany
Tel.: (49) 21 312 2480
Web Site: https://www.xerox.de
Holding Company
N.A.I.C.S.: 551112

Xerox IT Services Limited (2)
Hortonwood 37, Telford, TF1 7GT, United
Kingdom
Information Technology Consulting Services
N.A.I.C.S.: 541512

Xerox Israel Ltd (2)
Fulfillers 20, Petach Tikva, 4934829, Israel
Tel.: (972) 180 007 3001
Web Site: http://www.xerox.com
Digital Printing Technology Sevices & Mfr
N.A.I.C.S.: 333248

Xerox Italia Rental Services Srl (2)
Viale Edison 110, 20099, Sesto San Gio-
vanni, Milano, Italy
Tel.: (39) 02509891
Web Site: https://www.xerox.it
Passenger Car Rental Services
N.A.I.C.S.: 532111

Xerox Luxembourg SA (2)
12 Rue de Bettembourg, 3378, Livange,
Luxembourg
Tel.: (352) 2919911
Web Site: http://www.njpartner.lu
Emp.: 15
Information Technology Services
N.A.I.C.S.: 541511

Xerox Maroc S.A. (2)
13 Rue Melouia Bd Allal El Fassi, 20130,
Casablanca, Morocco
Tel.: (212) 52 248 4848
Web Site: https://www.xos.ma
Office Equipment Distr
N.A.I.C.S.: 423430

Xerox Mexicana, S.A. de C.V. (2)
Antonio Dovali Jaime 70 Torre A piso 5 Sa-
mara Col Zedec, Santa Fe CDMX, 01210,
Mexico, Mexico
Tel.: (52) 8000093769
Photocopying Machinery Distr
N.A.I.C.S.: 423420

Xerox Property Services Limited (2)
Brook Street Norfolk, Mitcheldean, GL17
0SL, Gloucestershire, United Kingdom
Tel.: (44) 1594 591119
Photocopy Machinery Equipment Whslr
N.A.I.C.S.: 424120

Subsidiary (Domestic):

**Xerox Real Estate & General
Services** (2)
45 Glover Ave, Norwalk, CT 06856
Tel.: (203) 968-3000
Sales Range: $100-124.9 Million
Provider of Telecommunications, Data Pro-
cessing, Travel, Payroll & Personnel Ser-
vices to Xerox & its Units
N.A.I.C.S.: 334118
Ursula M. Burns (Chm & CEO)

Xerox Realty Corporation (2)
45 Blover Ave PO Box 455, Norwalk, CT
06856-0505
Tel.: (203) 968-3000
Sales Range: $50-74.9 Million
Emp.: 100
Large-Scale Office, Commercial & Land
Development
N.A.I.C.S.: 531120

Subsidiary (Non-US):

Xerox Renting S.A.U. (2)
C/ Ribera Del Sena S/N, 28042, Madrid,
Spain
Tel.: (34) 902200169

Office Machinery & Equipment Rental &
Leasing Services
N.A.I.C.S.: 532420

**Xerox Reprographische Services
GmbH** (2)
Hammer Landstr 91, Neuss, 41460,
Nordrhein-Westfalen, Germany
Tel.: (49) 213122480
Paper Printing Services
N.A.I.C.S.: 323111

Subsidiary (Domestic):

**Xerox Research Center of Webster
(XRCW)** (2)
800 Phillips Rd MS 128-27E, Webster, NY
14580
Tel.: (585) 422-7403
Web Site: http://www.xerox.com
Sales Range: $100-124.9 Million
Research, Exploratory Development, Sci-
ence & Engineering for the Transfer of
Technologies to Xerox Development Groups
N.A.I.C.S.: 541715
Sophie V. Vandebroek (Pres & CTO)

Subsidiary (Non-US):

Xerox Slovenia d.o.o (2)
Bravnicarjeva ul 13, 1000, Ljubljana, Slove-
nia
Tel.: (386) 15401824
Web Site: https://www.xerox.com
Sales Range: $25-49.9 Million
Emp.: 5
Office Equipment Whslr
N.A.I.C.S.: 423420
Admir Joldic (Mng Dir)

**Xerox South Africa (Proprietary)
Limited** (2)
Private Bag 127, Isando, 1600, South Africa
Tel.: (27) 119289111
Web Site: http://www.xerox.co.za
Sales Range: Less than $1 Million
Emp.: 940
Document Management Solutions that
Combine Technology, Digital Hardware,
Software & Outsourcing Services
N.A.I.C.S.: 334111

Xerox Ukraine (2)
Novokonstantinovskaya st 13/10, Kiev,
04080, Ukraine
Tel.: (380) 442012031
Web Site: http://www.xerox.ua
Sales Range: $25-49.9 Million
Emp.: 60
Office Equipment Whslr
N.A.I.C.S.: 423420

Xerox de Chile S.A. (2)
Avda Santa Clara 684 Ciudad Empresarial,
Casilla Postal 14889, Huechuraba, San-
tiago, Chile (100%)
Tel.: (56) 22 338 7000
Web Site: https://www.xerox.com
Sales Range: $300-349.9 Million
Emp.: 750
Marketing & Service of Business Equipment
N.A.I.C.S.: 423420

Xerox de Colombia S.A. (2)
Avda El Dorado No 69-76, Bogota,
Colombia (75%)
Tel.: (57) 1 425 2400
Web Site: http://www.xerox.com.co
Sales Range: $150-199.9 Million
Emp.: 350
Retailer of Office Equipment
N.A.I.C.S.: 459410

Xerox de Panama SA (2)
Edificio World Trade Center Calle 53E Urb
Marbella, Primera Planta, Panama, Panama
Tel.: (507) 204 9900
Web Site: http://www.office.xerox.com
Sales Range: $150-199.9 Million
Emp.: 350
Office Equipment Whslr
N.A.I.C.S.: 423420

Xerox de Venezuela, C.A. (2)
Edificio Xerox Av Libertador cruce con calle
Avila Urbanizacion, Bello Campo, Caracas,
1060, Venezuela (75%)
Tel.: (58) 2122794111
Web Site: http://www.xerox.com.ve
Sales Range: $50-74.9 Million
Emp.: 200
Equipment Rental & Leasing

N.A.I.C.S.: 532210

Xerox del Ecuador, S.A. (2)
Ave Amazonas N35 17 Y, Juan Pablo Sanz
Edificio Xerox, Quito, Ecuador (100%)
Tel.: (593) 22439955
Web Site: http://www.xerox.com
Sales Range: $25-49.9 Million
Emp.: 139
Marketing & Services of Business Equipment
N.A.I.C.S.: 423420

Xerox del Peru, S.A. (2)
Ave Dionsio Derteano 144 Office 901, Lima,
27, Peru (100%)
Tel.: (51) 16166666
Web Site: http://www.xerox.com.pe
Sales Range: $100-124.9 Million
Emp.: 250
Retailer of Commercial Equipment
N.A.I.C.S.: 425120

Xerox do Brasil S.A. (2)
Av Rodrigues Alves 261, PO Box 1070, Rio
de Janeiro, 20220-360, Brazil
Tel.: (55) 2122711212
Web Site: http://www.xerox.com.br
Sales Range: $200-249.9 Million
Emp.: 700
Office Machine Mfr & Marketer
N.A.I.C.S.: 333310

Subsidiary (Domestic):

Xerox Comercio e Industria Ltda (3)
Av Prof Alvaro Rodrigues 352 Botafogo, Rio
de Janeiro, 22280-040, RJ, Brazil
Tel.: (55) 214 009 1212
Web Site: http://www.xerox.com.br
Office Machine Mfr & Marketer
N.A.I.C.S.: 333310

**Xerox Financial Services International
Limited**
Xerox Uxbridge Business Park Building 4
Sanderson Rd, Uxbridge, UB8 1DH, United
Kingdom
Tel.: (44) 189 525 1133
Office Machinery & Equipment Leasing Services
N.A.I.C.S.: 532420

XFIT BRANDS, INC.
25731 Commercentre Dr, Lake Forest, CA 92630
Tel.: (949) 916-9680 NV
Year Founded: 2014
XFTB—(OTCEM)
Sales Range: $1-9.9 Million
Emp.: 10
Fitness Related Equipment, Training
Gear, Apparel & Accessories Designer, Developer & Marketer
N.A.I.C.S.: 339920
J. Gregory Barrow (CEO)
Charles E. Joiner (Pres)

Subsidiaries:

Environmental Turf Services Inc. (1)
2580 Lakeland Dr Ste A, Flowood, MS
39232-9513
Tel.: (601) 664-1010
Web Site: http://www.enviroturfservices.com
Synthetic Surface & Landscaping Services
N.A.I.C.S.: 561730
Jim Bateman (CEO)

XILIO THERAPEUTICS, INC.
828 Winter St Ste 300, Waltham, MA
02451
Tel.: (857) 524-2466 DE
Web Site: https://xiliotx.com
Year Founded: 2020
XLO—(NASDAQ)
Assets: $139,165,000
Liabilities: $33,518,000
Net Worth: $105,647,000
Earnings: ($88,222,000)
Emp.: 89
Fiscal Year-end: 12/31/22
Biotechnology Research & Development Services
N.A.I.C.S.: 541714

Rene Russo (Pres & CEO)
Scott Coleman (Chief Dev Officer)
Christopher Frankenfield (COO)
Martin Huber (Pres & Head-R&D)
Chris Frankenfield (Gen Counsel)
Paul Clancy (Chm)
Kevin Brennan (Principal Fin Officer,
Principal Acctg Officer & Sr VP-
Finance-Accounting)
Uli Bialucha (Chief Scientific Officer)
Katarina Luptakova (CMO)
Salvatore Giovine (CFO)
Stacey Davis (Chief Bus Officer)

XOMA CORPORATION
2200 Powell St Ste 310, Emeryville,
CA 94608
Tel.: (510) 204-7200 BM
Web Site: https://www.xoma.com
Year Founded: 1981
XOMA—(NASDAQ)
Rev.: $6,027,000
Assets: $140,382,000
Liabilities: $16,368,000
Net Worth: $124,014,000
Earnings: ($17,104,000)
Emp.: 12
Fiscal Year-end: 12/31/22
Biopharmaceutical Mfr
N.A.I.C.S.: 325412
Patrick J. Scannon (Founder)
Owen Patrick Hughes Jr. (CEO)
Thomas Burns (CFO & Sr VP-Fin)
Bradley Sitko (Chief Investment Officer)

Subsidiaries:

Kinnate Biopharma Inc. (1)
103 Montgomery St Ste 150, San Francisco, CA 94129
Tel.: (858) 299-4699
Web Site: https://www.kinnate.com
Rev.: $2,250,000
Assets: $278,826,000
Liabilities: $55,358,000
Net Worth: $223,468,000
Earnings: ($116,271,000)
Emp.: 89
Fiscal Year-end: 12/31/2022
Biotechnology Research & Development
Services
N.A.I.C.S.: 541714
Owen Patrick Hughes Jr. (Pres, Treas &
Sec)

XOMA (US) LLC (1)
2200 Powell St Ste 310, Emeryville, CA
94608
Tel.: (510) 204-7200
Sales Range: $150-199.9 Million
Biopharmaceutical Research & Development
N.A.I.C.S.: 325414

XOMETRY, INC.
6116 Executive Blvd Ste 800 N,
Bethesda, MD 20852
Tel.: (240) 252-1138 DE
Web Site: https://www.xometry.com
Year Founded: 2013
XMTR—(NASDAQ)
Rev.: $381,053,000
Assets: $736,925,000
Liabilities: $362,092,000
Net Worth: $374,833,000
Earnings: ($76,025,000)
Emp.: 914
Fiscal Year-end: 12/31/22
Instruments & Related Products
Manufacturing for Measuring, Displaying & Controlling Industrial Process Variables
N.A.I.C.S.: 334513
James Miln (CFO & Principal Acctg
Officer)
Randolph Altschuler (Co-Founder &
CEO)
Peter Goguen (COO)
Laurence Zuriff (Co-Founder)
George Hornig (Chm)

Subsidiaries:

Genicad, s.r.o. (1)
Voctarova 2449/5 Dock 1 Praha 8 Liben,
18000, Prague, Czech Republic
Tel.: (420) 226236111
Web Site: https://www.genicad.cz
Data Protection & Security Services
N.A.I.C.S.: 518210

Xometry Europe GmbH (1)
Ada Lovelace Str 9, 85521, Ottobrunn, Germany
Tel.: (49) 8938034818
Web Site: https://www.xometry.eu
Electronic Components Mfr
N.A.I.C.S.: 334513

Xometry UK Ltd. (1)
Unit 2 Park Road City Park West, Chelmsford, CM1 1HF, United Kingdom
Tel.: (44) 1245840035
Web Site: https://www.xometry.uk
Electronic Components Mfr
N.A.I.C.S.: 334513

XOS, INC.
3550 Tyburn St, Los Angeles, CA
90065
Tel.: (818) 316-1890 DE
Web Site: https://www.xostrucks.com
Year Founded: 2020
XOS—(NASDAQ)
Rev.: $44,523,000
Assets: $93,684,000
Liabilities: $48,488,000
Net Worth: $45,196,000
Earnings: ($75,104,000)
Emp.: 161
Fiscal Year-end: 12/31/23
Automobile Mfr & Sales
N.A.I.C.S.: 336211
George N. Mattson (Co-Chm)
Gregory L. Summe (Co-Founder &
Co-Chm)
Patrick T. Ford (CFO & Sec)
Liana Pogosyan (Acting CFO & VP-
Fin)
Giordano Sordoni (Co-Founder &
COO)
Dakota Semler (CEO)

Subsidiaries:

Electrameccanica Vehicles Corp. (1)
102 East 1st Avenue, Vancouver, V5T 1A4,
BC, Canada
Tel.: (604) 428-7656
Web Site:
https://www.electrameccanica.com
Rev.: $6,812,446
Assets: $181,246,429
Liabilities: $53,920,902
Net Worth: $127,325,527
Earnings: ($123,698,513)
Emp.: 104
Fiscal Year-end: 12/31/2022
Automobile Mfr & Sales
N.A.I.C.S.: 336211
Susan E. Docherty (CEO & Interim COO)
Jerry Kroll (Co-Founder)
Henry Reisner (Co-Founder)
Bal Bhullar (Chief Compliance Officer)
Steven A. Sanders (Chm)
Isaac Moss (Chief Admin Officer)
Stephen Johnston (CFO & Principal Acctg
Officer)

XPEL, INC.
711 Broadway Ste 320, San Antonio,
TX 78215
Tel.: (210) 678-3700 NV
Web Site: https://www.xpel.com
Year Founded: 2003
XPEL—(NASDAQ)
Rev.: $323,993,000
Assets: $193,362,000
Liabilities: $68,640,000
Net Worth: $124,722,000
Earnings: $41,381,000
Emp.: 818
Fiscal Year-end: 12/31/22
Plastic & Automotive Products Mfr

N.A.I.C.S.: 336390
Chris Coffee (VP & Controller)
Tony Rimas (VP-Revenue)
Kim Steiner (VP-People Svcs)
Ryan L. Pape (Chm, Pres, CEO &
Dir)
Tunde Awodiran (Gen Counsel & Sr
VP)
Abhishek Joshi (VP & Mgr Ops)
Barry Wood (CFO & Sr VP)
Carlos Alvarez (VP-Operations)
Duane Gotro (VP-Svcs)

Subsidiaries:

Protex Canada Inc. (1)
1180 Rue Levis Suite 5, Terrebonne, J6W
5S6, QC, Canada
Tel.: (450) 492-0500
Web Site: https://protexcanada.com
Automotive Window Tinting Services
N.A.I.C.S.: 811122
Victor Beisel (Mng Dir)

XPEL B.V. (1)
Henri Blomjousstraat 10, 5048 AG, Tilburg,
Netherlands
Tel.: (31) 134675547
Web Site: https://www.xpel.nl
Motor Vehicle Parts Mfr
N.A.I.C.S.: 336390

XPEL Canada Corp. (1)
1180 Rue Levis local 2, Terrebonne, J6W
5S6, QC, Canada
Tel.: (514) 977-3424
Motor Vehicle Parts Mfr
N.A.I.C.S.: 336390

XPEL Ltd. (1)
Unit 29 Devonshire Business Centre Works
Road, Letchworth, SG6 1GJ, Hertfordshire,
United Kingdom
Tel.: (44) 1462414393
Motor Vehicle Parts Mfr
N.A.I.C.S.: 336390

**XPEL de Mexico S. de R.L. de
C.V.** (1)
Camino al CUCBA No 175 Col La Venta del
Astillero, 45221, Zapopan, Jalisco, Mexico
Tel.: (52) 16573191
Web Site: https://xpel.com.mx
Motor Vehicle Parts Mfr
N.A.I.C.S.: 336390

XPERI INC.
2190 Gold St, San Jose, CA 95002
Tel.: (408) 519-9100 DE
Web Site: https://xperi.com
Year Founded: 2019
XPER—(NYSE)
Rev.: $502,260,000
Assets: $736,911,000
Liabilities: $287,925,000
Net Worth: $448,986,000
Earnings: ($761,206,000)
Emp.: 2,100
Fiscal Year-end: 12/31/22
Offices of Other Holding Companies
N.A.I.C.S.: 551112
Jon E. Kirchner (Pres & CEO)
David C. Habiger (Chm)
Robert J. Andersen (CFO)
Petronel Bigioi (CTO)
Murali Dharan (Co-CEO-Perceive)
Kris Graves (Chief HR Officer)
Becky Marquez (Chief Legal Officer)
Matt Milne (Chief Revenue Officer)
John Pernin (Chief Strategy & Corp
Dev Officer)
Geir Skaaden (Chief Products & Svcs
Officer)
Steve Teig (Co-CEO-Perceive)

Subsidiaries:

DTS, Inc. (1)
5220 Las Virgenes Rd, Calabasas, CA
91302
Tel.: (818) 436-1000
Web Site: https://www.dts.com
Digital Sound Systems Mfr
N.A.I.C.S.: 334310

Xperi Inc.—(Continued)

Subsidiary (Non-US):

DTS (Asia) Limited (2)
2214-2215 Tower 2 Times Square, Causeway Bay, Hong Kong, China (Hong Kong)
Tel.: (852) 31019361
Web Site: http://www.dts.com
Digital Entertainment Products Mfr
N.A.I.C.S.: 334310

DTS Guangzhou (2)
A 2501 Center Plaza No 161 Lin He Xi
Road Tianhe, Guangzhou, 510620, China
Tel.: (86) 2038251788
Web Site: http://www.dts.com
Digital Entertainment Products Mfr
N.A.I.C.S.: 334310

DTS Japan KK (2)
Tokyo Opera City 39F 3-20-2 Nishi-
Shinjuku, Shinjuku-ku, Tokyo, 163-1439,
Japan
Tel.: (81) 3 5365 3780
Web Site: http://www.dts.com
Digital Entertainment Products Mfr
N.A.I.C.S.: 334310

DTS Licensing Limited (2)
Hamilton House 2 National Technology Park
Castletroy, Limerick, Ireland
Tel.: (353) 61507272
Web Site: http://www.dts.com
Digital Entertainment Products Mfr
N.A.I.C.S.: 334310

Subsidiary (Non-US):

DTS Licensing Pte. Ltd. (3)
410 North Bridge Road, Singapore, 188726,
Singapore
Tel.: (65) 65920100
Web Site: http://www.dts.com
Digital Sound Systems Mfr
N.A.I.C.S.: 334310

Subsidiary (Domestic):

DTS Washington LLC (2)
10900 NE 8th St Ste 1000, Bellevue, WA
98004
Tel.: (425) 633-3388
Web Site: http://dts.com
Digital Sound Systems Mfr
N.A.I.C.S.: 334310

DTS, LLC (2)
5220 Las Virgenes Rd, Calabasas, CA
91302
Tel.: (818) 436-1000
Web Site: http://dts.com
Audio & Video Equipment Mfr
N.A.I.C.S.: 334310

Subsidiary (Non-US):

Guangzhou DTS Digital Theater System, Co. Ltd (2)
A 2501 Center Plaza No 161 Lin He Xi
Road, Tianhe, Guangzhou, 510620, China
Tel.: (86) 2038251788
Web Site: http://www.dts.com
Digital Sound Systems Mfr
N.A.I.C.S.: 334310

Subsidiary (Domestic):

Manzanita Systems, LLC (2)
14269 Danielson St Ste 200, Poway, CA
92064
Tel.: (858) 679-8990
Web Site:
   http://www.manzanitasystems.com
Application Software Development Services
N.A.I.C.S.: 541511

Phorus, Inc (2)
5220 Las Virgenes Rd, Calabasas, CA
91302
Tel.: (818) 666-3995
Web Site: https://www.phorus.com
Audio & Video Equipment Mfr
N.A.I.C.S.: 334310

Veveo, Inc. (1)
40 Shattuck Rd Ste 303, Andover, MA
01810
Tel.: (978) 687-8240
Web Site: http://www.veveo.net
Emp.: 50

Personalized Entertainment Discovery Solutions
N.A.I.C.S.: 513210

XPO, INC.
5 American Ln, Greenwich, CT 06831
Tel.: (617) 607-6429 DE
Web Site: https://www.xpo.com
Year Founded: 2001
XPO—(NYSE)
Rev.: $7,744,000,000
Assets: $7,492,000,000
Liabilities: $6,226,000,000
Net Worth: $1,266,000,000
Earnings: $189,000,000
Emp.: 38,000
Fiscal Year-end: 12/31/23
Holding Company; Freight Transportation, Warehousing & Logistics Services
N.A.I.C.S.: 551112
Christopher M. Brown (Chief Acctg
Officer)
Bradley S. Jacobs (Founder, Exec
Chm & Chm)
Ashfaque Chowdhury (Pres-Supply
Chain-Americas & Asia Pacific)
John P. Mitchell (CIO-Divisional-
Supply Chain-Americas & Asia Pacific)
Luis Gomez (Pres-Transport-Europe)
Tavio Headley (VP-IR)
AnnaMaria DeSalva (Vice Chm)
Josephine Berisha (Chief HR Officer)
Richard Cawston (Pres-Supply
Chain-Europe)
Erik Caldwell (Pres-Last Mile)
Michele Chapman (Sr VP-Sls Ops-
Global)
Katrina Liddell (Pres-Global Forwarding & Expedite)
Jacopo Mazzolin (Sr VP-HR-Europe)
Eduardo Pelleissone (Chief Transformation Officer)
Alex Santoro (Chief Comml Officer &
Exec VP-Ops)
Maryclaire Hammond (Sr VP-HR-
Supply Chain-Americas & Asia Pacific)
LaQuenta Jacobs (Chief Diversity
Officer)
Swati Sharma (Treas & Sr VP)
Nina Reinhardt (Chief Comm Officer-
RXO)
Jay Silberkleit (CIO)
Jared Weisfeld (Chief Strategy
Officer-RXO)
Kyle Wismans (CFO)

Subsidiaries:

Bounce Logistics, Inc. (1)
5838 W Brick Rd Ste 102, South Bend, IN
46628 **(100%)**
Tel.: (574) 243-1550
Web Site: http://www.bouncelogistics.com
Sales Range: $1-9.9 Million
Emp.: 48
Full-Truckload Freight Brokerage Services
N.A.I.C.S.: 488510
Sergio Tejada (Mgr-Territory-Northeast)
Lad Johnson (Dir-Sls)
Andre Garcia (Mgr-Territory-Western States)
April Shreve (Office Mgr)
Rob Charbonneau (Pres)
Kim Cornelius (Mgr-Sls & Ops)

Concert Group Logistics, Inc. (1)
290 Gerzevske Ln, Carol Stream, IL
60188 **(100%)**
Tel.: (630) 795-1300
Web Site: http://www.xpoglobalogistics.com
Sales Range: $25-49.9 Million
Emp.: 20
Freight Forwarding Transportation Services
N.A.I.C.S.: 488510

Subsidiary (Non-US):

XPO Global Logistics Inc. (2)
420 Rue Aime-Vincent Vaudreuil-Dorion,

Montreal, J7V 5V5, QC, Canada
Tel.: (514) 907-7432
Web Site: http://www.xpo.com
Freight Forwarding Transportation Services
N.A.I.C.S.: 488510

OWL Logistics Shanghai Limited (1)
Unit 125 Building 1 329 Shilong Road,
Xuhui District, Shanghai, 200233, China
Tel.: (86) 2138726521
Web Site: http://www.oceanworldlines.com
Logistics Consulting Servies
N.A.I.C.S.: 541614

**OWL Ocean World Lines Europe
GmbH** (1)
Lippeltstr 1, 20097, Hamburg, Germany
Tel.: (49) 403984810
Logistics Consulting Servies
N.A.I.C.S.: 541614
Juergen Moeke (Mng Dir)

XPO Air Charter, LLC (1)
276 Aviation Dr, Statesville, NC 28677
Tel.: (704) 838-1991
Web Site: http://www.xpoaircharter.com
Emp.: 15
Nonscheduled Chartered Freight Air Transportation
N.A.I.C.S.: 481212
David Gutierrez (Mgr-Charter Ops)
Rehan Hyder (Mgr-Bus Dev)
Kathy Little (Mgr-Acctg)
Mary Spindler (Acct Mgr-Northern Reg)

XPO Express, Inc. (1)
429 Post Rd, Buchanan, MI 49107 **(100%)**
Tel.: (269) 695-2700
Web Site: http://www.express-1.com
Sales Range: $25-49.9 Million
Emp.: 70
Non-Asset Based Expedited Freight Transportation Services
N.A.I.C.S.: 488510

XPO Global Forwarding, Inc. (1)
N91w17194 Appleton Ave, Menomonee
Falls, WI 53051
Tel.: (262) 345-5503
Logistic Services
N.A.I.C.S.: 488510

XPO Intermodal, Inc. (1)
5165 Emerald Pkwy 300, Dublin, OH 43017
Tel.: (614) 923-1400
Emp.: 940
Logistic Services
N.A.I.C.S.: 488510

XPO Last Mile Canada Inc. (1)
5160 Explorer Dr, Mississauga, L4W 4T7,
ON, Canada
Tel.: (905) 624-1430
Logistics Consulting Servies
N.A.I.C.S.: 541614

XPO Last Mile, Inc. (1)
1851 W Oak Pkwy, Marietta, GA 30062
Tel.: (770) 424-4555
Logistics Consulting Servies
N.A.I.C.S.: 541614
Karl F. Meyer (CEO)

XPO Logistics Canada Inc. (1)
2425 Matheson Blvd E Floor 8, Mississauga, L4W 5K4, ON, Canada
Tel.: (905) 795-8400
Logistics Consulting Servies
N.A.I.C.S.: 541614

XPO Logistics Europe S.A. (1)
192 Avenue Thiers, 69006, Lyon,
France **(100%)**
Tel.: (33) 4 72 83 66 00
Web Site: http://europe.xpo.com
Sales Range: $5-14.9 Billion
Holding Company; Freight Transportation,
Warehousing & Logistics Services
N.A.I.C.S.: 551112

Subsidiary (Domestic):

**XPO Holding Transport Solutions
Europe** (2)
Les Pierrelles Xpo Holding Trs Europe,
26240, Beausemblant, France
Tel.: (33) 475232526
Logistic Services
N.A.I.C.S.: 488510

Subsidiary (Non-US):

**XPO Holdings UK & Ireland
Limited** (2)

XPO House Lodge Way, New Duston,
Northampton, NN5 7SL, Northants, United
Kingdom
Tel.: (44) 1604737100
Web Site: http://uk.xpo.com
Holding Company; Transport Logistics &
Warehousing
N.A.I.C.S.: 551112

Subsidiary (Domestic):

XPO Bulk UK Ltd. (3)
Greenford Way Hope Carr, Leigh Commerce Park, Manchester, WN7 3XJ, United
Kingdom
Tel.: (44) 1942266780
Transport Logistics
N.A.I.C.S.: 488510

Subsidiary (Non-US):

XPO Supply Chain Italy S.p.A. (2)
Via Enrico Fermi 7, Caleppio Settala,
20090, Milan, MI, Italy
Tel.: (39) 029500101
Transport Logistics & Warehousing
N.A.I.C.S.: 488510

**XPO Transport Solutions Italy
S.R.L.** (2)
2 Via De Gasperia San Pietro Mosezzo,
28060, Novara, MI, Italy
Tel.: (39) 0321468960
Freight Transportation Arrangement Services
N.A.I.C.S.: 488510

**XPO Transport Solutions Portugal,
Lda.** (2)
Rua Da Misericordia Lote 7 Centro Empresarial De, 4410-236, Canelas, Portugal
Tel.: (351) 229999740
Web Site: http://pt.xpo.com
Emp.: 180
Freight Transportation Arrangement Services
N.A.I.C.S.: 488510

XPO Logistics Supply Chain, Inc. (1)
4035 Piedmont Pkwy, High Point, NC
27265
Web Site: http://www.xpo.com
Distribution, Logistics, Warehousing & Supply Chain Consulting Services
N.A.I.C.S.: 541611
Ashfaque Chowdhury (Pres)

XPO Logistics, LLC (1)
5 American Ln, Greenwich, CT 06831
Web Site: http://www.xpo.com
Freight Transportation Arrangement, Logistics & Supply Chain Services
N.A.I.C.S.: 488510

Subsidiary (Domestic):

XPO Logistics Express, LLC (2)
429 Post Rd, Buchanan, MI 49107
Tel.: (800) 800-5161
Logistic Services
N.A.I.C.S.: 488510

XPO NLM, Inc. (1)
300 Galleria Officentre Ste 301, Southfield,
MI 48034
Tel.: (248) 936-1700
Web Site: http://www.xponlm.com
Sales Range: $10-24.9 Million
Transportation & Logistics Services
N.A.I.C.S.: 484121
Michael O'Donnell (COO)

XPONENTIAL FITNESS, INC.
17877 Von Karman Ave Ste 100, Irvine, CA 92614
Tel.: (949) 346-3000 DE
Web Site:
   https://www.xponential.com
Year Founded: 2017
XPOF—(NYSE)
Rev.: $244,954,000
Assets: $482,691,000
Liabilities: $690,753,000
Net Worth: ($208,062,000)
Earnings: $1,930,000
Emp.: 310
Fiscal Year-end: 12/31/22

Fitness & Recreational Sports Centers
N.A.I.C.S.: 713940
Anthony Geisler *(Founder)*
Ryan Junk *(COO)*
Sarah Luna *(Pres)*
John Meloun *(CFO)*
Megan Moen *(Exec VP-Fin)*
Mark Grabowski *(Chm)*
Mark King *(CEO)*

XRX INTERNATIONAL ENTERTAINMENT HOLDING GROUP, INC.

1800 NW Corporate Blvd PH 310, Boca Raton, FL 33441
Tel.: (561) 893-8827   FL
XRXH—(OTCIQ)
Investment Management Service
N.A.I.C.S.: 523999
Larry Moskowitz *(Pres & CEO)*

XSOVT BRANDS, INC.

1111 S Roop St Unit 1915, Carson, NV 89702
Tel.: (415) 713-6957   NV
Web Site: http://www.xsovt.com
Year Founded: 2004
XSVT—(OTCIQ)
Liabilities: $21,000
Net Worth: ($21,000)
Earnings: ($8,000)
Emp.: 12
Fiscal Year-end: 12/31/22
Shoes & Slippers Mfr
N.A.I.C.S.: 316210
Kelvin Bradley *(Mgr-Ops)*
Arthur A. Nathan *(Exec VP)*
Avi M. Koschitzki *(Pres & CEO)*

XTANT MEDICAL HOLDINGS, INC.

664 Cruiser Ln, Belgrade, MT 59714
Tel.: (406) 388-0480   DE
Web Site:
https://www.xtantmedical.com
Year Founded: 2006
XTNT—(NYSEAMEX)
Rev.: $57,969,000
Assets: $60,229,000
Liabilities: $26,058,000
Net Worth: $34,171,000
Earnings: ($8,485,000)
Emp.: 134
Fiscal Year-end: 12/31/22
Biological Product (except Diagnostic) Manufacturing
N.A.I.C.S.: 325414
Sean E. Browne *(Pres & CEO)*
Mark A. Schallenberger *(COO)*
Kevin D. Brandt *(Chief Commercialization Officer & Sr VP)*

Subsidiaries:

X-spine Systems, Inc.   (1)
452 Alexandersville Rd, Miamisburg, OH 45342-3658
Tel.: (937) 847-8400
Medical Device Mfr
N.A.I.C.S.: 339112

XTI AEROSPACE, INC.

8123 InterPort Blvd Ste C, Englewood, CO 80112
Tel.: (303) 503-5660   NV
Web Site: https://xtiaerospace.com
Year Founded: 1999
XTIA—(NASDAQ)
Rev.: ($26,929,000)
Assets: $23,769,000
Liabilities: $17,040,000
Net Worth: $6,729,000
Earnings: ($45,947,000)
Fiscal Year-end: 12/31/23
e-Business, e-Government, Consulting & Strategic Outsourcing Services

N.A.I.C.S.: 561499
Scott A. Pomeroy *(Chm & CEO)*
Don C. Purdy *(Sr VP-Bus & Program Dev)*
Brooke Turk *(CFO)*
Saleem Zaheer *(Chief Comml Officer)*
David Ambrose *(VP-Engrg)*
Keith Davis *(VP-Programs)*
John Griffo *(VP-Fin)*
Mara Babin *(Head-Legal)*
Marylou Van Rossem *(VP-People Ops)*
Jordi Vallejo *(Head-Engineering)*
Ersan Gunes *(Sr VP-Product)*
Gonzalo Ibarra *(VP-Delivery)*
Peter Liss *(Head-Sales)*
Tobin Arthur *(Chief Strategy Officer)*

Subsidiaries:

Design Reactor, Inc.   (1)
675 Campbell Technology Pkwy Ste 250, Campbell, CA 95008
Tel.: (408) 341-1190
Web Site: http://www.designreactor.com
Rev.: $7,800,000
Emp.: 51
Fiscal Year-end: 12/31/2006
Advetising Agency
N.A.I.C.S.: 541810
Nadir Ali *(CEO)*
Dave Skuratowicz *(Dir-Creative)*

Inpixon Canada, Inc.   (1)
2963 Glen Drive Suite 405, Coquitlam, V3B 2P7, BC, Canada
Tel.: (613) 220-2425
Wireless Telecommunication Services
N.A.I.C.S.: 517112
Nadir Ali *(Pres)*

Inpixon Federal, Inc.   (1)
13880 Dulles Corner Ln Ste 175, Herndon, VA 20171
Tel.: (703) 961-1125
Web Site: https://sysorexinc.com
Wireless Telecommunication Services
N.A.I.C.S.: 517112
Sid Guha *(VP-Sls)*

Nanotron Technologies GmbH   (1)
Alt-Moabit 60a, 10555, Berlin, Germany
Tel.: (49) 303999540
Web Site: https://www.nanotron.com
Sensor Product Mfr
N.A.I.C.S.: 334511
Nadir Ali *(Executives)*

XTREME FIGHTING CHAMPIONSHIPS, INC.

495 Grand Blvd Unit 206, Miramar Beach, FL 32550
Tel.: (949) 290-4914   NV
Web Site: https://www.xfcmma.net
Year Founded: 2006
XFCI—(OTCIQ)
Rev.: $371,298
Assets: $12,344,104
Liabilities: $775,405
Net Worth: $11,568,699
Earnings: ($14,115,626)
Emp.: 1
Fiscal Year-end: 12/31/20
Gold Mining Services
N.A.I.C.S.: 212220
Tim J. Northup *(CFO)*
Tim Northup *(CFO)*
Myron Molotky *(Pres & COO)*
Steve A. Smith Jr. *(Chm & CEO)*

XWELL, INC.

254 W 31st St 11th Fl, New York, NY 10001
Tel.: (212) 750-9595   DE
Web Site: https://www.xwell.com
Year Founded: 2006
XWEL—(NASDAQ)
Rev.: $55,939,000
Assets: $70,426,000
Liabilities: $22,477,000
Net Worth: $47,949,000
Earnings: ($32,837,000)

Emp.: 382
Fiscal Year-end: 12/31/22
Video Ringtones Applications for Mobile Phones
N.A.I.C.S.: 517810
Cara Soffer *(Gen Counsel & Sr VP)*
Bruce T. Bernstein *(Chm)*
Suzanne A. Scrabis *(CFO)*
Ezra T. Ernst *(Pres & CEO)*

Subsidiaries:

International Development Group Limited   (1)
1100 N Glebe Rd Ste 800, Arlington, VA 22201
Tel.: (571) 336-7980
Web Site:
https://www.internationaldevelopment group.com
Business Development & Consulting Services
N.A.I.C.S.: 541611
David Snelbecker *(CEO)*
Robert Kirk *(Sr VP-Economic Programs)*

VRTUAL, Inc.   (1)
401 Edgewater Pl Ste 600, Wakefield, MA 01880
Tel.: (781) 246-0500
Web Site: https://www.virtualinc.com
Management Consulting Services
N.A.I.C.S.: 541611
Andy Freed *(CEO)*
Terry Lowney *(COO)*
Greg Kohn *(Chief Growth Officer)*
Mauro Lance *(CFO)*
Alysia Johnson *(Sr VP-Client Svcs)*

XpresSpa Amsterdam Airport B.V.   (1)
Lounge 2 Level 2, 1118 AX, Schiphol, Netherlands
Tel.: (31) 202065450
Airport Transport Support Services
N.A.I.C.S.: 485999

XYLEM INC.

301 Water St SE Ste 200, Washington, DC 20003
Tel.: (202) 869-9150   IN
Web Site: https://www.xylem.com
XYL—(NYSE)
Rev.: $7,364,000,000
Assets: $16,112,000,000
Liabilities: $5,936,000,000
Net Worth: $10,176,000,000
Earnings: $609,000,000
Emp.: 23,000
Fiscal Year-end: 12/31/23
Holding Company; Pumps, Pumping Equipment & Other Water Technology Products Mfr
N.A.I.C.S.: 551112
Geri McShane *(Chief Acctg Officer & VP)*
Matthew F. Pine *(Pres & CEO)*
William K. Grogan *(CFO & Sr VP)*
David Flinton *(Chief Innovation, Tech & Product Mgmt Officer & Sr VP)*
Claudia S. Toussaint *(Chief Sustainability Officer, Gen Counsel, Sec & Sr VP)*
Albert H. Cho *(Chief Strategy & Digital Officer & Sr VP)*
Sai Allavarpu *(Sr VP)*
Dorothy Capers *(Gen Counsel)*
Mike McGann *(Pres)*
Thomas Pettit *(Sr VP)*

Subsidiaries:

Evoqua Water Technologies Corp.   (1)
210 6th Ave Ste 3300, Pittsburgh, PA 15222
Tel.: (724) 772-0044
Web Site: http://www.evoqua.com
Rev.: $1,429,456,000
Assets: $1,844,458,000
Liabilities: $1,362,395,000
Net Worth: $482,063,000
Earnings: $113,649,000
Emp.: 4,020

Fiscal Year-end: 09/30/2020
Waste Water Treatment Services
N.A.I.C.S.: 221320
Matthew F. Pine *(Pres)*
Rodney O. Aulick *(CEO)*

Subsidiary (Non-US):

ATG UV Technology Limited   (2)
Genesis House Richmond Hill, Pemberton, Wigan, WN5 8AA, Lancs, United Kingdom
Tel.: (44) 1942216161
Web Site: http://www.atguv.com
UV System Mfr
N.A.I.C.S.: 335139

Subsidiary (Domestic):

Epicor Inc.   (2)
1414 E Linden Ave, Linden, NJ 07036-1506
Tel.: (908) 925-0800
Web Site: http://www.epicorinc.com
Commercial & Service Industry Machinery Mfr
N.A.I.C.S.: 333310
Rose Pussiculo *(Owner)*

Subsidiary (Non-US):

Evoqua Water Technologies (Shanghai) Co., Ltd.   (2)
Unit Y603 Western District 6 Floor No 2299 West Yanan Road, Changning District, Shanghai, China
Tel.: (86) 21511837777
Sewage Water Treatment Services
N.A.I.C.S.: 221320

Evoqua Water Technologies India Private Limited   (2)
DLF IT SEZ Park Block 8 5th Floor No 1/124 Mount Poonamallee Road, Manapakkam, Chennai, 600 089, India
Tel.: (91) 4461363100
Sewage Treatment Services
N.A.I.C.S.: 221320

Subsidiary (Domestic):

Evoqua Water Technologies LLC   (2)
181 Thorn Hill Rd, Warrendale, PA 15086
Tel.: (724) 772-0044
Web Site: http://www.evoqua.com
Water & Waste Water Treatment Systems, Products & Services
N.A.I.C.S.: 562998
Rodney Aulick *(Pres-Indus Project & Svcs Div)*
Malcom Kinnaird *(Pres-Municipal Products & Svcs Div)*
James Irwin *(VP-Strategy & Corp Dev)*
Vince Grieco *(Gen Counsel, Sec & VP)*
Ed May *(VP-Supply Chain Mgmt)*
Ben Stas *(CFO, Treas & Exec VP)*
Dan Brailer *(VP-IR)*

Unit (Domestic):

Evoqua Water Technologies   (3)
960 Ames Ave, Milpitas, CA 95035-6303
Tel.: (408) 946-1520
Sales Range: $75-99.9 Million
Emp.: 250
Water Treatment Systems Mfr
N.A.I.C.S.: 562998

Evoqua Water Technologies   (3)
2 Milltown Ct, Union, NJ 07083-8108
Tel.: (908) 851-2277
Sales Range: $25-49.9 Million
Electro Mechanical Equipment Mfr
N.A.I.C.S.: 334512
William Ronayne *(Plant Mgr)*

Evoqua Water Technologies   (3)
N19W23993 Ridgeview Pkwy W Ste 200, Waukesha, WI 53188-1690
Tel.: (262) 547-0141
Web Site: http://www.evoqua.com
Sales Range: $25-49.9 Million
Waste Water Treatment Equipment Services
N.A.I.C.S.: 562219
Marc Roehl *(VP & Gen Mgr)*

Evoqua Water Technologies   (3)
1901 W Garden Rd, Vineland, NJ 08360-1530
Tel.: (856) 507-9000

Xylem Inc.—(Continued)

Sales Range: $125-149.9 Million
Emp.: 300
Water Purification Equipment Mfr
N.A.I.C.S.: 333248

Evoqua Water Technologies (3)
301 W Military Rd, Rothschild, WI 54474-1944
Tel.: (715) 359-7211
Sales Range: $50-74.9 Million
Emp.: 175
Water & Wastewater Treatment Systems
N.A.I.C.S.: 333248

Evoqua Water Technologies (3)
404 E Broadway St, Bradley, IL 60915-1702
Tel.: (815) 932-8154
Sales Range: $50-74.9 Million
Emp.: 150
Industrial Water Treatment Equipment Mfr
N.A.I.C.S.: 333310

Evoqua Water Technologies (3)
11711 Reading Rd, Red Bluff, CA 96080
Tel.: (530) 527-2664
Web Site: http://www.evoqua.com
Water Filtration Products Mfr
N.A.I.C.S.: 325998

Evoqua Water Technologies (3)
14950 Heathrow Forrest Pkwy, Houston, TX 77032-3842
Tel.: (281) 227-9100
Sales Range: $75-99.9 Million
Emp.: 15
Water Supply Services
N.A.I.C.S.: 221310

Evoqua Water Technologies (3)
13100 Gregg St Ste B, Poway, CA 92064-7150
Tel.: (858) 486-8500
Sales Range: $25-49.9 Million
Emp.: 35
Air Purification Equipment Mfr
N.A.I.C.S.: 333413

Evoqua Water Technologies (3)
15403 NE Caples Rd, Brush Prairie, WA 98606
Tel.: (360) 699-7392
Web Site: http://www.evoqua.com
Sales Range: $1-9.9 Million
Emp.: 5
Commercial & Service Industry Machinery Mfr
N.A.I.C.S.: 333310
Darrin Stewart *(Mgr-Dewatering OEM Parts & Upgrades)*
Diana Bryant *(Mgr-Technical Sls-U.S West & Canada)*
Fernando Santana *(Mgr-Technical Sls-Latin America, Mexico & South America)*
Jeff Chrispell *(Mgr-Field Svc)*
Jeff Webster *(Mgr-Technical Sls-Intl)*
Vic Vant Hof *(Mgr-Technical Sls-Northeast)*

Evoqua Water Technologies (3)
1828 Metcalf Ave, Thomasville, GA 31792-6845
Tel.: (229) 226-5733
Web Site: http://www.evoqua.com
Water & Sewage Distribution & Treatment Products Mfr
N.A.I.C.S.: 562219
Mark Kelly *(Dir-North America Mfg)*

Evoqua Water Technologies (3)
2650 Tallevast Rd, Sarasota, FL 34243-3912
Tel.: (978) 364-3423
Web Site: http://www.evoqua.com
Sales Range: $25-49.9 Million
Emp.: 75
Waste Water Odor Control Chemical Mfr
N.A.I.C.S.: 325998

Evoqua Water Technologies (3)
10 Technology Dr, Lowell, MA 01851
Tel.: (978) 934-9349
Web Site: http://www.evoqua.com
Water Purification Systems Mfr
N.A.I.C.S.: 924110
Stefan Abramo *(VP)*

Evoqua Water Technologies (3)
4669 Shepherd Trl, Rockford, IL 61103
Tel.: (815) 877-3041

Sales Range: $25-49.9 Million
Emp.: 250
Water Purification & Wastewater Treatment Services
N.A.I.C.S.: 562219
Barbara Kinroth *(Commun Dir)*

Subsidiary (Non-US):

Evoqua Water Technologies Canada (3)
215 Konrad Crescent Unit 1, Markham, L3R 8T9, ON, Canada
Tel.: (905) 944-2800
Sales Range: $25-49.9 Million
Emp.: 30
Water Filtration Products Mfr
N.A.I.C.S.: 334419
Lutz Kranz *(Exec VP)*

Evoqua Water Technologies GmbH (3)
Auf Der Weide 10, 89312, Gunzberg, Germany
Tel.: (49) 82219040
Sales Range: $75-99.9 Million
Water Treatment Products
N.A.I.C.S.: 812990

Subsidiary (Domestic):

Neptune-Benson, Inc. (3)
6 Jefferson Dr, Coventry, RI 02816 (100%)
Tel.: (401) 821-2200
Web Site: http://www.neptunebenson.com
Rev.: $4,249,300
Emp.: 50
Water Filtration Systems Mfr & Distr
N.A.I.C.S.: 312112
Ken Rodi *(Pres)*
Will Klietz *(Mgr-Aftermarket Sls & Svc)*

Noble Water Technologies, Inc. (3)
2618 Bomar Ave, Dallas, TX 75235-5620
Tel.: (214) 357-1885
Web Site: http://www.noble-wt.com
Commercial & Industrial Water Filtration & Purification Systems
N.A.I.C.S.: 221310
Scott Gaston *(Mgr-Sls)*

Olson Irrigation Systems (3)
10910 Wheatlands Ave, Santee, CA 92071
Tel.: (619) 562-3100
Web Site: http://www.olsonirrigation.com
Farm Machinery & Equipment
N.A.I.C.S.: 333111
Donald Olson *(Founder)*

Water Consulting Specialists, Inc. (3)
3853A Old Easton Rd, Doylestown, PA 18902
Tel.: (215) 348-0050
Web Site: http://www.watercsi.com
Engineering Services
N.A.I.C.S.: 541330
Caroline Collentro *(Pres)*

Subsidiary (Non-US):

Evoqua Water Technologies Pty. Ltd. (2)
885 Mountain Highway BW31-G, Bayswater, 3153, VIC, Australia
Tel.: (61) 387206597
Sewage Water Treatment Services
N.A.I.C.S.: 221320

Subsidiary (Domestic):

Frontier Water Systems, LLC (2)
3442 Sutherland St, San Diego, CA 92110
Tel.: (619) 326-9990
Web Site: http://www.frontierwater.com
Water Work Equipment Whslr
N.A.I.C.S.: 423720

Subsidiary (Non-US):

MAGNETO special anodes B.V. (2)
Calandstraat 109 Industrial Zones Graveland, 3125 BA, Schiedam, Netherlands
Tel.: (31) 102620788
Web Site: http://www.magneto.nl
Electrochemical Mfr
N.A.I.C.S.: 333517
Pieter Hack *(Mng Dir)*
Peter Bruggink *(Mgr-Production)*
Vidjay Birdja *(Mgr-Tech)*

Subsidiary (Domestic):

Pacific Ozone Technology Inc. (2)
6160 Egret Ct, Benicia, CA 94510
Tel.: (707) 747-9600
Web Site: http://www.pacificozone.com
All Other Miscellaneous General Purpose Machinery Mfr
N.A.I.C.S.: 333998
Henrik Steffens *(Mgr-New Strategic Sls & Mktg-Europe & Asia Pacific)*

Pure Water Solutions, Inc. (2)
520 Topeka Way, Castle Rock, CO 80109
Tel.: (303) 660-9093
Commercial & Service Industry Machinery Mfr
N.A.I.C.S.: 333310
Dean Lewis *(Pres & CEO)*

Smith Engineering Inc. (2)
125 Columbia Ct, Chaska, MN 55318
Tel.: (952) 448-4412
Web Site:
 http://www.smithengineeringinc.com
Rev.: $3,135,000
Emp.: 15
Instruments & Related Products Manufacturing for Measuring, Displaying & Controlling Industrial Process Variables
N.A.I.C.S.: 334513
Bob Lucas *(VP-Sls & Mktg)*
Joanie Lubeck *(Mgr-Ops)*
Matt Klausner *(Mgr-Svc)*
Tanya Doering *(Controller)*

Faradyne Motors LLC (1)
2077 Division St, Palmyra, NY 14522
Tel.: (315) 502-0125
Web Site: https://www.faradynemotors.com
Emp.: 20
Submersible Pump Motor & Control Box Mfr
N.A.I.C.S.: 335312
Dante Volpe *(Pres)*
Juan Lugo *(VP-Fin & Ops)*
Chris Osgood *(Mgr-Engrg)*
Daryl Stamp *(Mgr-Process Engrg)*
Michael Sadeghi *(VP-Tech)*
Dennis Petricoin *(VP-Quality & Bus Dev)*

IMT B.V. (1)
Lange Dreef 10, 4131 NH, Vianen, Netherlands
Tel.: (31) 881269100
Web Site: http://www.tidelandsignal.com
Medicinal Product Mfr
N.A.I.C.S.: 334510

MJK Automation ApS (1)
Blokken 9, 3460, Birkerod, Denmark
Tel.: (45) 4 556 0656
Web Site: https://www.mjk.com
Industrial Machinery & Equipment Merchant Whslr
N.A.I.C.S.: 423830

Multitrode Pty Ltd (1)
Brisbane Technology Park, PO Box 4633, 18 Brandl Street, Eight Mile Plains, 4113, QLD, Australia
Tel.: (61) 733407000
Industrial Machinery & Equipment Merchant Whslr
N.A.I.C.S.: 423830

Pipeline Technologies Philippines Corp. (1)
2/F Kings Court Building 1 2129 Don Chino Roces Ave, Legaspi Village, Makati, 1231, Philippines
Tel.: (63) 9088924243
Web Site: http://www.puretechltd.com
Water & Wastewater Pipe Services
N.A.I.C.S.: 237120

Pure (Shanghai) Technologies Co., Ltd. (1)
30-31F Tower A The Place 100 Zunyi Road, Shanghai, 200051, China
Tel.: (86) 2122082888
Pipeline Construction & Inspection Services
N.A.I.C.S.: 237120

Pure Technologies Ltd. (1)
5055 Satellite Drive Unit 7, Mississauga, L4W 5K7, ON, Canada
Tel.: (905) 624-1040
Sales Range: $75-99.9 Million
Water & Wastewater Pipe Services
N.A.I.C.S.: 237120

Subsidiary (Non-US):

Pure Technologies (Australia) Pty. Ltd. (2)
100 Harris Street, Pyrmont, Sydney, 2009, NSW, Australia
Tel.: (61) 295185433
Water & Wastewater Pipe Services
N.A.I.C.S.: 237120

Pure Technologies (Nanjing) Limited (2)
Room 1605 Building 2 Jiaye International City No 158 Lushan Road, Nanjing, China
Tel.: (86) 2558933290
Water & Wastewater Pipe Services
N.A.I.C.S.: 237120

Pure Technologies Abu Dhabi (2)
M22 Executive Business Center Bin Arar Tower Najda Street, PO Box 108726, Abu Dhabi, United Arab Emirates
Tel.: (971) 26265525
Water & Wastewater Pipe Services
N.A.I.C.S.: 237120

Subsidiary (Domestic):

Pure Technologies Canada Ltd. (2)
300 705 - 11 Ave SW, Calgary, T2R 0E3, AB, Canada
Tel.: (403) 266-6794
Water & Wastewater Pipe Services
N.A.I.C.S.: 237120

PureHM Inc. (1)
Unit 1-5 1260 34 Avenue, Nisku, T9E 1K7, AB, Canada
Tel.: (780) 436-4400
Web Site: https://www.purehm.net
Emp.: 100
Pipeline Repair Services
N.A.I.C.S.: 237120
Shamus Mcdonnell *(Pres & Co-Founder)*
Jim Hunter *(Co-Founder & VP-Ops)*
Chukwuma Onuoha *(Mgr-Product)*

PureHM U.S. Inc. (1)
Ste 130 1408 N Sam Houston Pkwy E, Houston, TX 77032
Tel.: (281) 227-0313
Pipeline Repair Services
N.A.I.C.S.: 237120

Rapid Biosensor Systems Limit (1)
Babraham Hall Babraham Research Campus, Babraham, Cambridge, CB22 3AT, United Kingdom
Tel.: (44) 1223264558
Web Site: http://www.rapidbiosensor.com
Medical Device Mfr
N.A.I.C.S.: 334510
John Reynolds *(Chm)*
Dennis Camilleri *(CEO)*
Nicol Murray *(Dir-Medical)*

SELC Group Ltd. (1)
2-11-1 Yamanone, Zushi, 249-0002, Kanagawa, Japan
Tel.: (81) 468720913
Web Site: https://www.selcgroup.com
Language Institute Services
N.A.I.C.S.: 611630

Sensus & Ceska republika spol. s r.o. (1)
Olsanska 54/3 3-zizkov, 13000, Prague, Czech Republic
Tel.: (420) 602378040
Other Commercial & Service Industry Mfr
N.A.I.C.S.: 333310

Sensus Canada Inc. (1)
33 Isaacson Cr, Aurora, L4G 0A4, ON, Canada
Tel.: (905) 464-3828
Pump Equipment Distr
N.A.I.C.S.: 423830

Sensus France Holdings SAS (1)
41 Porte du Grand Lyon ZAC du Champs Perrier, 01700, Neyron, France
Tel.: (33) 472018550
Other Commercial & Service Industry Mfr
N.A.I.C.S.: 333310

Sensus GmbH Hannover (1)
Meineckestrasse 10, 30880, Laatzen, Germany
Tel.: (49) 5102743177
Other Commercial & Service Industry Mfr

N.A.I.C.S.: 333310

Sensus Manufacturing (Shanghai) Co., Ltd. (1)
No 1979 Chenqiao Road, Shanghai Comprehensive Industrial Development Zone, Shanghai, 201401, China
Tel.: (86) 2157436969
Other Commercial & Service Industry Mfr
N.A.I.C.S.: 333310

Sensus Metering Systems Inc. (1)
637 Davis Dr, Morrisville, NC
27560 (66%)
Tel.: (919) 845-4000
Web Site: http://www.sensus.com
Sales Range: $650-699.9 Million
Water, Gas, Heat & Electric Meters Mfr
N.A.I.C.S.: 334514

Subsidiary (Non-US):

Sensus Chile SA (2)
Las Araucarias 9041 Casilla 512 V Quilicura, Santiago, Chile
Tel.: (56) 24826602
Web Site: https://sensus.com
Software Development Services
N.A.I.C.S.: 541511

Sensus Espana SA (2)
Avenida del Vents 9 escalera A 3 4, 08917, Barcelona, Spain
Tel.: (34) 934601064
Software Development Services
N.A.I.C.S.: 541511

Sensus France SAS (2)
41 Porte du Grand Lyon ZAC du Champs Perrier, 01700, Neyron, France
Tel.: (33) 472018550
Software Development Services
N.A.I.C.S.: 541511

Sensus Italia SRL (2)
Via Gioacchino Rossini 1/A, 20020, Lainate, Italy
Tel.: (39) 0261291861
Software Development Services
N.A.I.C.S.: 541511

Sensus Maroc S.A. (2)
23 lotissement Beau fruit II Zone Industrielle, Ain Atiq Maroc, 12013, Rabat, Morocco
Tel.: (212) 538023250
Software Development Services
N.A.I.C.S.: 541511

Sensus Metering Systems (Fuzhou) Co., Ltd. (2)
Tieling North Road Economic and Technological Zone Minhou, Fuzhou, 350101, China
Tel.: (86) 59128631169
Web Site: https://sensus.com
Software Development Services
N.A.I.C.S.: 541511

Sensus Polska sp. zoo (2)
ul Mazowiecka 63/65, 87-100, Torun, Poland
Tel.: (48) 566543303
Software Development Services
N.A.I.C.S.: 541511

Sensus South Africa (Proprietary) Ltd. (2)
3A Spier Street Glen Erasmia Kempton Park, Plumbago Business Park, Johannesburg, 1684, South Africa
Tel.: (27) 114661680
Software Development Services
N.A.I.C.S.: 541511
Gerardt Viljoen (VP-Sls-Africa)

Subsidiary (Domestic):

Smith-Blair, Inc. (2)
30 Globe Ave, Texarkana, AR 71854
Tel.: (800) 643-9705
Web Site: http://www.smith-blair.com
Pipe Repair Product Mfr
N.A.I.C.S.: 332996

Sensus Services Deutschland GmbH (1)
Industriestrasse 16, 67063, Ludwigshafen, Germany
Tel.: (49) 62169041000
Web Site: https://sensus.com
Pump Equipment Mfr

N.A.I.C.S.: 333914

Sentec Limited (1)
Radlo House St Andrews Road, Cambridge, CB4 1DL, United Kingdom
Tel.: (44) 122 330 3800
Web Site: https://www.sentec.co.uk
Emp.: 50
Other Technical Research Services
N.A.I.C.S.: 541614
Mark England (CEO)

Tideland Signal Corporation (1)
7100 Business Park Dr Ste B, Houston, TX 77041
Tel.: (713) 681-6101
Web Site: http://www.tidelandsignal.com
Navigational Systems & Instruments
N.A.I.C.S.: 334511

Tideland Signal Limited (1)
KBF House 55 Victoria Road, Burgess Hill, RH15 9LH, West Sussex, United Kingdom
Tel.: (44) 1444872240
Pump Equipment Distr
N.A.I.C.S.: 423830

Valor Water Analytics, Inc. (1)
870 Market St Ste 336, San Francisco, CA 94102
Web Site: http://www.valorwater.com
Software Development Services
N.A.I.C.S.: 541511
Christine E Boyle (Founder & CEO)
David Wegman (CTO)
Matthew Hepworth (Sr Mgr-Solutions Engrg)
Heidi Smith (Mgr-Global Product)
Victor Miao (Engr-Software)

Wissenschaftlich Technische Werkstaetten GmbH (1)
Dr-Karl-Slevogt-Strasse 1, 82362, Weilheim, Germany
Tel.: (49) 8811830
Web Site: http://www.wtw.com
Industrial Machinery & Equipment Merchant Whslr
N.A.I.C.S.: 423830

Xylem Analytics Australia Pty Ltd. (1)
1/39 Aquarium Ave, Hemmant, 4174, QLD, Australia
Tel.: (61) 1300995362
Web Site: https://www.xylem-analytics.com.au
Industrial Machinery & Equipment Merchant Whslr
N.A.I.C.S.: 423830

Xylem Analytics France S.A.S. (1)
29 Rue Du Port, 92022, Nanterre, France
Tel.: (33) 146953356
Miscellaneous Electrical Equipment Mfr
N.A.I.C.S.: 335999

Xylem Analytics UK LTD (1)
Xylem Unit 7 Dunham's Court Dunham's Lane, Letchworth, SG6 1WB, Hertfordshire, United Kingdom
Tel.: (44) 146 267 3581
Web Site: https://www.xylemanalytics.co.uk
Industrial Machinery & Equipment Merchant Whslr
N.A.I.C.S.: 423830

Xylem Australia Holdings PTY LTD (1)
Unit 2 2 Capicure Drive, Eastern Creek, 2766, NSW, Australia
Tel.: (61) 298326200
Holding Company
N.A.I.C.S.: 551112

Xylem Europe GmbH (1)
Bleicheplatz 6, 8200, Schaffhausen, Switzerland
Tel.: (41) 526445200
Web Site: http://www.xylemwatersolutions.com
Industrial Machinery & Equipment Merchant Whslr
N.A.I.C.S.: 423830
Hayati Yarkadas (Pres-Water Infrastructure & Comml-Europe & Sr VP)

Xylem Flow Control Limited (1)
Bingley Road, Hoddesdon, EN11 0BU, Hertfordshire, United Kingdom

Tel.: (44) 1992450145
Industrial Machinery & Equipment Merchant Whslr
N.A.I.C.S.: 423830

Xylem Inc. - Analytics (1)
100 Cummings Center 535N, Beverly, MA 01915
Tel.: (937) 767-7241
Web Site: http://www.xylemanalytics.com
Analytical Laboratory Instrument Mfr
N.A.I.C.S.: 334516

Subsidiary (Non-US):

Aanderaa Data Instruments AS (2)
Sanddalsringen 5b, Nesttun, 5225, Bergen, Norway
Tel.: (47) 5 560 4800
Web Site: https://www.aanderaa.com
Measuring & Monitoring Equipment Mfr
N.A.I.C.S.: 334519

Subsidiary (US):

Aanderaa Data Instruments Inc. (3)
275 Martine St Ste 200 Unit 12, Fall River, MA 02723
Tel.: (937) 767-7241
Web Site: http://www.aanderaa.com
Measuring & Monitoring Equipment Mfr
N.A.I.C.S.: 334519

Subsidiary (Non-US):

Bellingham & Stanley Ltd. (2)
Longfield Road, Tunbridge Wells, TN2 3EY, Kent, United Kingdom
Tel.: (44) 1892500400
Web Site: https://www.bellinghamandstanley.com
Emp.: 30
Laboratory Instrument Mfr
N.A.I.C.S.: 334516
Michael Banks (Mng Dir)

Subsidiary (US):

Bellingham & Stanley, Inc. (3)
90 Horizon Dr, Suwanee, GA 30024
Tel.: (678) 804-5730
Web Site: http://www.bellinghamandstanley.com
Laboratory Instrument Mfr
N.A.I.C.S.: 334516

Subsidiary (Domestic):

O.I. Corporation (2)
151 Graham Rd, College Station, TX 77845 (100%)
Tel.: (979) 690-1711
Web Site: http://www.oico.com
Sales Range: $10-24.9 Million
Emp.: 126
Chemical Analysis Equipment Mfr
N.A.I.C.S.: 334516

Subsidiary (Domestic):

CMS Research Corporation (3)
2148 Pelham Pkwy Ste 400, Pelham, AL 35124
Tel.: (205) 733-6900
Web Site: http://www.oico.com
Chemical Analysis Machine Mfr
N.A.I.C.S.: 334516

Subsidiary (Domestic):

Royce Technologies (3)
PO Box 9010, College Station, TX 77842
Tel.: (979) 690-5558
Web Site: http://www.roycetechnologies.com
Monitoring, Control Instrumentation & Sensors for Municipal/Industrial Wastewater Treatment Applications
N.A.I.C.S.: 237110

YSI Incorporated (2)
1700/1725 Brannum Ln, Yellow Springs, OH 45387-1107
Tel.: (937) 688-4255
Web Site: https://www.ysi.com
Emp.: 200
Scientific & Industrial Instruments Mfr
N.A.I.C.S.: 334516

Subsidiary (Domestic):

Design Analysis Associates, Inc. (3)
95 S 100 W, Logan, UT 84321

Tel.: (435) 753-2212
Web Site: http://www.waterlog.com
Sales Range: $25-49.9 Million
Emp.: 12
Hydrological & Meteorological Monitoring Equipment Mfr
N.A.I.C.S.: 334519
Mike Nelson (Mng Dir)

SonTek/YSI, Inc. (3)
9940 Summers Ridge Rd, San Diego, CA 92121-3091
Tel.: (858) 546-8327
Web Site: http://www.sontek.com
Sales Range: $25-49.9 Million
Emp.: 67
Water Velocity Measurement Devices
N.A.I.C.S.: 334519

Subsidiary (Non-US):

Xylem Analytics Australia Pty Limited (3)
1/39 Aquarium Ave, Hemmant, 4174, QLD, Australia
Tel.: (61) 739084001
Web Site: https://www.xylem-analytics.com.au
Water Treatment Equipment Distr
N.A.I.C.S.: 423850
Steve Bird (Gen Mgr)

YSI (Hong Kong) Ltd. (3)
2101-03 Peninsula Tower 538 Castle Peak Rd, Cheung Sha Wan, Kowloon, China (Hong Kong) (100%)
Tel.: (852) 28918154
Sales Range: $10-24.9 Million
Emp.: 8
Mfr of Biochemistry Analyzers & Monitors
N.A.I.C.S.: 334419
Christian Apfel (Dir-Sls-Asia Pacific)

YSI (UK) Ltd. (3)
119 Fleet Road, Fleet, GU51 3PD, United Kingdom
Tel.: (44) 1252 819844
Web Site: http://www.ysiuk.com
Emp.: 8
Pumping Equipment Mfr
N.A.I.C.S.: 333996

Unit (Domestic):

YSI Integrated Systems & Services (3)
9843 18th St N Ste 1200, Saint Petersburg, FL 33716
Tel.: (727) 565-2201
Web Site: http://www.ysisystems.com
Sales Range: $10-24.9 Million
Emp.: 18
Sensors, Instruments, Software & Data Collection Platforms Mfr
N.A.I.C.S.: 334513
Kevin McClurg (Mgr-Bus Dev)

Subsidiary (Non-US):

YSI Nanotech (3)
Higashida-cho 8 13F, Kawasaki-Ku, Kawasaki, 210-0005, Japan
Tel.: (81) 442220009
Web Site: http://www.ysijapan.com
Sales Range: $25-49.9 Million
Emp.: 15
Communication Equipment Mfr & Distr
N.A.I.C.S.: 334220

Xylem Inc. - Applied Water Systems (1)
8200 N Austin Ave, Morton Grove, IL 60053
Tel.: (847) 966-3700
Web Site: http://www.xylemappliedwater.com
Water Pumping & Irrigation Equipment Mfr
N.A.I.C.S.: 333914

Division (Domestic):

AC Custom Pumps Division (2)
8200 N Austin Ave, Morton Grove, IL 60053
Tel.: (847) 966-3700
Web Site: http://www.acfirepump.com
Sales Range: $100-124.9 Million
Emp.: 500
Fire Pump Systems Designer & Mfr
N.A.I.C.S.: 333914

Subsidiary (Domestic):

Goulds Water Technology - Seneca Falls (2)

Xylem Inc.—(Continued)

2881 E Bayard St, Seneca Falls, NY 13148
Tel.: (315) 568-2811
Sales Range: $25-49.9 Million
Emp.: 100
Water Pumping System Mfr
N.A.I.C.S.: 333914
Tom Stephan *(Mgr-Trng)*

Unit (Domestic):

**Goulds Water Technology -
Auburn** (3)
1 Gould Dr, Auburn, NY
13021-3134 **(100%)**
Tel.: (315) 258-4800
Sales Range: $75-99.9 Million
Pumps & Pumping Equipment
N.A.I.C.S.: 333914

**Goulds Water Technology -
Lubbock** (3)
4608 Bradley St, Lubbock, TX 79415
Tel.: (806) 743-5700
Sales Range: $75-99.9 Million
Pumping Equipment Mfr
N.A.I.C.S.: 333914

**Goulds Water Technology -
Slaton** (3)
1470 Industrial Dr, Slaton, TX 79364
Tel.: (806) 828-6563
Sales Range: $25-49.9 Million
Emp.: 80
Pumping Equipment Mfr
N.A.I.C.S.: 333914

Subsidiary (Non-US):

**Goulds Water Technology Philippines,
Inc.** (3)
No 12 Ring Road St LIHHP2 Brgy Lamesa
Laguna, Bregy Lamesa, Calamba, 4027,
Philippines **(100%)**
Tel.: (63) 495434300
Web Site:
  http://www.xylemappliedwater.com
Pumping Equipment Mfr
N.A.I.C.S.: 333914

Subsidiary (Non-US):

Jabsco Marine Italia S.r.l. (2)
Via Tommaseo 6, 20871, Vimercate, MB,
Italy
Tel.: (39) 039 685 2323
Web Site: https://www.jabsco.it
Pumping Equipment Mfr
N.A.I.C.S.: 333914

Subsidiary (Domestic):

Laing Thermotech, Inc. (2)
3878 S Willow Ave, Fresno, CA 93725
Tel.: (559) 265-4730
Sales Range: $1-9.9 Million
Emp.: 26
Pumping Equipment Mfr
N.A.I.C.S.: 333914

Subsidiary (Non-US):

Lowara s.r.l. (2)
Via Dott Lombardi 14, 36075, Montecchio
Maggiore, Vindenza, Italy **(100%)**
Tel.: (39) 0444707111
Web Site: http://www.lowara.com
Sales Range: $125-149.9 Million
Hydraulic Pumps Mfr
N.A.I.C.S.: 333914

Subsidiary (Non-US):

Lowara GmbH (3)
Biebigheimer Str 12, 63762, Grossostheim,
Germany **(100%)**
Tel.: (49) 60269430
Web Site: http://www.lowara.de
Sales Range: $25-49.9 Million
Emp.: 40
Hydraulic Pumps Mfr
N.A.I.C.S.: 333914

Division (Domestic):

McDonnell & Miller Division (2)
8200 N Austin Ave, Morton Grove, IL
60053 **(100%)**
Tel.: (847) 966-3700
Web Site: http://www.mcdonnellmiller.com

Sales Range: $150-199.9 Million
Emp.: 700
Boiler Control & Switch Mfr
N.A.I.C.S.: 334519

Rule Division (2)
100 Cummings Center Dr Ste 535N, Bev-
erly, MA 01915
Tel.: (978) 281-0440
Web Site: http://www.rule-industries.com
Sales Range: $75-99.9 Million
Emp.: 36
Pumping Equipment Mfr
N.A.I.C.S.: 333914

Subsidiary (Non-US):

Xylem (Nanjing) Co. Ltd (2)
No 18 Longyang Rd Liuhe Economic Devel-
opment Zone, Nanjing, 211500, Jiangsu,
China
Tel.: (86) 2557195000
Sales Range: $50-74.9 Million
Emp.: 252
Electronics Instrument Mfr
N.A.I.C.S.: 334511

**Xylem (Shanghai) Trading Co.,
Ltd.** (2)
30-31F Tower A The Place 100 Zunyi Road,
Shanghai, 200051, China
Tel.: (86) 2122082888
Web Site: http://www.xyleminc.com
Emp.: 250
Instrument Mfr
N.A.I.C.S.: 334511

Unit (Non-US):

**Xylem Applied Water Systems -
Guelph** (2)
55 Royal Rd, Guelph, N1H 1T1, ON,
Canada **(100%)**
Tel.: (519) 821-1900
Sales Range: $10-24.9 Million
Emp.: 55
Pumps & Pumping Equipment
N.A.I.C.S.: 333914

**Xylem Applied Water Systems -
Ottawa** (2)
1439 Youville Dr Unit 5, Ottawa, K1C 4M8,
ON, Canada **(100%)**
Tel.: (613) 590-9989
Web Site: http://www.ittfpc.ca
Sales Range: $10-24.9 Million
Emp.: 10
Pumps & Pumping Equipment
N.A.I.C.S.: 333914
Robert Ouimet *(Reg Mgr-Eastern)*

**Xylem Applied Water Systems -
Saint-Laurent** (2)
200-9300 boul Henri-Bourassa O, Ville
Saint Laurent, H4S 1L5, QC,
Canada **(100%)**
Tel.: (514) 336-7660
Emp.: 6
Pumping Equipment Mfr
N.A.I.C.S.: 333914

Plant (Domestic):

Xylem Inc. (2)
175 Standard Pkwy, Cheektowaga, NY
14227-1233
Tel.: (716) 897-2800
Web Site: http://www.xyleminc.com
Emp.: 231
Heat Exchangers & Condensers
N.A.I.C.S.: 333415

Division (Domestic):

**Xylem Inc. - Bell & Gossett
Division** (2)
8200 N Austin Ave, Morton Grove, IL 60053
Tel.: (847) 983-5816
Web Site: http://www.bellgossett.com
Sales Range: $300-349.9 Million
Emp.: 850
Pump & Valve Mfr
N.A.I.C.S.: 333914

Division (Domestic):

Hoffman Specialty (3)
8200 N Austin Ave, Morton Grove, IL
60053 **(100%)**

Tel.: (847) 966-3700
Web Site: http://www.hoffmanspecialty.com
Sales Range: $25-49.9 Million
Emp.: 100
Steam Traps, Pumps, Regulators & Valves
N.A.I.C.S.: 541330

Xylem Inc. - Water Solutions (1)
Ste N200 1133 Westchester Ave, White
Plains, NY 10604
Tel.: (914) 323-5700
Web Site:
  http://www.xylemwatersolutions.com
Water Supply Infrastructure & Equipment
Mfr
N.A.I.C.S.: 333914

Subsidiary (Non-US):

**Anadolu Flygt Pompa Pazarlama Ve
Ticaret AS** (2)
Gebze Organize Sanayi Bolgesi 1000 Cd
No 1015, Cayirova, Istanbul, Kocaeli, Tur-
kiye
Tel.: (90) 2626771677
Web Site: http://www.anadoluflygt.com.tr
Instrument Mfr
N.A.I.C.S.: 333310

Flygt NIPPON K.K (2)
Mita Toho Building 7F 3-1-7 Mita, Minato-
ku, Tokyo, 108-0073, Japan
Tel.: (81) 354438877
Web Site: https://www.flygtnippon.com
Sales Range: $25-49.9 Million
Emp.: 20
Fluid & Submersible Product Technologies
N.A.I.C.S.: 333996

Subsidiary (Domestic):

**Heartland Pump Rental & Sales,
Inc.** (2)
1800 Supply Rd Ste A, Carterville, IL 62918
Tel.: (618) 985-5110
Web Site: http://www.heartlandpump.com
Sales Range: $50-74.9 Million
Emp.: 100
Pumps & Pumping Equipment Sales, Ser-
vice & Rentals
N.A.I.C.S.: 423830

Sanitaire Division (2)
9333 N 49th St, Milwaukee, WI
53223-1472 **(100%)**
Tel.: (414) 365-2200
Web Site: http://www.xylem.com
Sales Range: $25-49.9 Million
Emp.: 70
Distr of Industrial Water Treatment Equip-
ments
N.A.I.C.S.: 333310

Subsidiary (Non-US):

Xylem Analytics Germany GmbH (2)
Dr-Karl-Slevogt-Str 1, 82362, Weilheim,
Germany
Tel.: (49) 8811830
Web Site: http://www.si-analytics.com
Sales Range: $50-74.9 Million
Emp.: 800
Pumping Equipment Mfr
N.A.I.C.S.: 333914

Subsidiary (Domestic):

Xylem Dewatering Solutions, Inc. (2)
84 Floodgate Rd, Bridgeport, NJ 08014-
0191
Tel.: (856) 270-7128
Web Site:
  http://www.xylemwatersolutions.com
Sales Range: $200-249.9 Million
Emp.: 190
Industrial Machinery & Equipment Mfr
N.A.I.C.S.: 423830

Subsidiary (Non-US):

Xylem Water Solutions AB (2)
Gefallvagen 33, 174 87, Sundbyberg,
Sweden **(100%)**
Tel.: (46) 084756000
Web Site:
  http://www.xylemwatersolutions.com
Sales Range: $500-549.9 Million
Emp.: 2,000
Submersible Contractors' & Mining Pumps,
Submersible Mixers, Turbines

N.A.I.C.S.: 333914

Subsidiary (Domestic):

Grindex AB (3)
Gesallvagen 33, PO Box 7025, 174 07,
Sundbyberg, Sweden
Tel.: (46) 84756000
Web Site: http://www.grindex.com
Sales Range: $300-349.9 Million
Emp.: 20
Submersible Pump Mfr
N.A.I.C.S.: 333914

Subsidiary (US):

Grindex Pumps LLC (4)
8402 W 183rd St Ste A, Tinley Park, IL
60487
Tel.: (708) 781-2135
Web Site: https://www.grindex.com
Submersible & Industrial Pump Mfr
N.A.I.C.S.: 333914

Subsidiary (Non-US):

**Xylem Water Solutions (Hong Kong)
Limited** (3)
Unit 12-16 17F Grand City Plaza 1-17 Sai
Lau Kok Road, Tsuen Wan, New Territories,
China (Hong Kong)
Tel.: (852) 29450100
Emp.: 26
Industrial Machinery Mfr
N.A.I.C.S.: 333248

**Xylem Water Solutions (Shenyang)
Co. Ltd.** (3)
11A4 Development Avenue Economic Tech-
nology Dev Zone, Shenyang, 110 141,
China
Tel.: (86) 24 25263000
Web Site: http://www.flygt.com.cn
Sales Range: $300-349.9 Million
Automotive, Defense, Electronics & Fluid
Technologies
N.A.I.C.S.: 336340

**Xylem Water Solutions Argentina
S.A.** (3)
Ruta Panamericana Colectora Este Km 24
6, Don Torcuato, Buenos Aires, B1611KRN,
Argentina
Tel.: (54) 114 589 1111
Web Site:
  http://www.xylemwatersolutions.com
Emp.: 100
Pumping Equipment Mfr
N.A.I.C.S.: 333914

**Xylem Water Solutions Australia
Limited** (3)
Unit 2 2 Capicure Drive, Eastern Creek,
2766, NSW, Australia **(100%)**
Tel.: (61) 298326200
Web Site: http://www.xylem.com
Sales Range: $25-49.9 Million
Emp.: 90
Automotive, Defense, Electronics & Fluid
Technologies
N.A.I.C.S.: 336340
Jim Athanas *(Mng Dir)*

**Xylem Water Solutions Austria
GmbH** (3)
Prager Strasse 6, 2000, Stockerau,
Austria **(100%)**
Tel.: (43) 226662601
Web Site: http://www.flygt.at
Sales Range: $1-9.9 Million
Emp.: 300
Submersible Pumps & Mixers
N.A.I.C.S.: 333914

**Xylem Water Solutions Austria
GmbH** (3)
Ernst-Vogel-Strasse 2, 2000, Stockerau,
Austria **(100%)**
Tel.: (43) 226 6604
Web Site: http://www.xyleminc.com
Sales Range: $50-74.9 Million
Emp.: 300
Pumping Equipment Mfr
N.A.I.C.S.: 333914
Louis J. Guiliano *(Pres)*

**Xylem Water Solutions Belgium
BVBA** (3)
Vierwinden 5b, 1930, Zaventem,
Belgium **(100%)**

Tel.: (32) 27209010
Web Site:
http://www.xylemwatersolutions.com
Sales Range: $1-9.9 Million
Emp.: 40
Water & Wastewater Treatment Services
N.A.I.C.S.: 221310

Xylem Water Solutions Canada (3)
300 Labrosse Ave, Pointe-Claire, H9R 4V5,
QC, Canada (100%)
Tel.: (514) 695-0100
Water & Wastewater Treatment Services
N.A.I.C.S.: 221310

Xylem Water Solutions Canada (3)
74 Glacier Street, Coquitlam, V3K 5Y9, BC,
Canada (100%)
Tel.: (604) 941-6664
Web Site:
http://www.xylemwatersolutions.com
Sales Range: $25-49.9 Million
Emp.: 20
Wastewater & Water Treatment Services
N.A.I.C.S.: 221310

**Xylem Water Solutions Colombia
Ltda.** (3)
Carrera 85D 51-65, Bodega 18, Bogota,
Colombia
Tel.: (57) 14103253
Web Site:
http://www.xylemwatersolutions.com
Emp.: 51
Water Handling Equipment Mfr
N.A.I.C.S.: 333914
Alex De La Ossa *(Mng Dir)*

**Xylem Water Solutions Denmark
ApS** (3)
Ejby Industrivej 60, Glostrup, 2600,
Denmark (100%)
Tel.: (45) 4 320 0900
Web Site: https://www.xylem.com
Sales Range: $25-49.9 Million
Emp.: 70
Water Handling Equipment Mfr
N.A.I.C.S.: 333914

**Xylem Water Solutions Deutschland
GmbH** (3)
Bayernstrasse 11, PO Box 101320, 30855,
Langenhagen, Germany (100%)
Tel.: (49) 51178000
Web Site: http://www.flygt.de
Sales Range: $50-74.9 Million
Emp.: 150
Automotive, Defense, Electronics & Fluid
Technologies
N.A.I.C.S.: 336340

**Xylem Water Solutions Espana
S.A.** (3)
Belfast 25 P I Las Mercedes, 28022, Ma-
drid, Spain
Tel.: (34) 91 329 7899
Web Site: https://www.xylem.com
Pumping Equipment Mfr
N.A.I.C.S.: 333914

**Xylem Water Solutions France
SAS** (3)
29 Rue du Port, 92000, Nanterre, Cedex,
France (100%)
Tel.: (33) 146953333
Web Site: http://www.xylem.com
Sales Range: $100-124.9 Million
Emp.: 160
Automotive, Defense, Electronics & Fluid
Technologies
N.A.I.C.S.: 336340

**Xylem Water Solutions India Pvt.
Ltd.** (3)
Plot No 731 GIDC Savli Savli-Manjusar
Road, Vadodara, 391 770, Gujarat, India
Tel.: (91) 266 761 5800
Web Site: http://www.xylem.com
Emp.: 8
Pumping Equipment Mfr
N.A.I.C.S.: 333914

**Xylem Water Solutions Ireland
Ltd.** (3)
50 Broomhill Close Airton Road, Tallaght,
Dublin, D24 APP8, Ireland (100%)
Tel.: (353) 14524444
Web Site:
http://www.xylemwatersolutions.com

Sales Range: $10-24.9 Million
Emp.: 25
Automotive, Defense, Electronics & Fluid
Technologies
N.A.I.C.S.: 336340

**Xylem Water Solutions Ireland
Ltd.** (3)
50 Broomhill Close Tallaght Industrial Es-
tate, Tallaght, Dublin, D24 APP8,
Ireland (100%)
Tel.: (353) 1 452 4444
Web Site:
http://www.ireland.xylemappliedwater.com
Sales Range: $1-9.9 Million
Emp.: 23
Hydraulic Pumps Mfr
N.A.I.C.S.: 333914

**Xylem Water Solutions Italia
S.r.l.** (3)
Via G Rossini 1/A Lainate, 20020, Milan,
Italy (100%)
Tel.: (39) 02903581
Web Site: http://www.flygt.it
Sales Range: $75-99.9 Million
Emp.: 200
Automotive, Defense, Electronics & Fluid
Technologies
N.A.I.C.S.: 336340

**Xylem Water Solutions Magyarorszag
Kft.** (3)
Topark u 9, 2045, Torokbalint,
Hungary (100%)
Tel.: (36) 2 344 5700
Web Site: https://www.xylem.com
Sales Range: $25-49.9 Million
Emp.: 45
Automotive, Defense, Electronics & Fluid
Technologies
N.A.I.C.S.: 336340

**Xylem Water Solutions Malaysia Sdn.
Bhd.** (3)
Lot 59 Jalan Tanjung Medan 26/12, 40000,
Shah Alam, Selangor, Malaysia
Tel.: (60) 51026888
Engineering Component Mfr
N.A.I.C.S.: 335999

**Xylem Water Solutions Metz
SAS** (3)
Rue Marcel Dassault, Ennery, 57365, Mo-
selle, France
Tel.: (33) 387736950
Web Site: http://www.xylem.com
Pumping Equipment Distr
N.A.I.C.S.: 423830

**Xylem Water Solutions Nederland
B.V.** (3)
Pieter Zeemanweg 240, 3316 GZ, Dor-
drecht, Netherlands (100%)
Tel.: (31) 786548400
Web Site: http://www.xylem.com
Waste Treatment Services
N.A.I.C.S.: 221310

**Xylem Water Solutions New Zealand
Limited** (3)
9 Tawa Drive, Albany, Auckland, 0632, New
Zealand
Tel.: (64) 9 415 8679
Web Site: http://www.xylem.com
Pumping Equipment Mfr
N.A.I.C.S.: 333914

Xylem Water Solutions Peru S.A. (3)
Av Defensores Del Morro 2220, Chorrillos,
Lima, Peru
Tel.: (51) 1 207 9400
Web Site: https://www.xylem.com
Sales Range: $25-49.9 Million
Emp.: 120
Pumping Equipment Mfr
N.A.I.C.S.: 333914

**Xylem Water Solutions Polska Sp. z.
o. o.** (3)
Dawidy Ul Warszawska 49, 32-994,
Raszyn, Poland (100%)
Tel.: (48) 22 735 81 00
Web Site:
http://www.xylemwatersolutions.com
Sales Range: $10-24.9 Million
Emp.: 38
Automotive, Defense, Electronics & Fluid
Technologies

N.A.I.C.S.: 336340

**Xylem Water Solutions Portugal, Uni-
pessoa Lda** (3)
Estrada Nacional 10 Km 131 Parque Tejo -
Bloco D, Forte da Casa, Forte da Casa,
2625-445, Portugal
Tel.: (351) 210990929
Web Site:
http://www.xylemwatersolutions.com
Sales Range: $10-24.9 Million
Emp.: 15
Pumping Equipment Mfr
N.A.I.C.S.: 333914

**Xylem Water Solutions Singapore
Pte. Ltd.** (3)
3A International Business Park Tower B 10-
10/18 ICON IBP, Singapore, 609935, Sin-
gapore
Tel.: (65) 69760601
Pumps Mfr
N.A.I.C.S.: 333914

**Xylem Water Solutions South Africa
(Pty) Ltd.** (3)
1 Spribok Rd, Boksburg, 1459, South Africa
Tel.: (27) 119669300
Web Site: http://www.xyleminc.com
Emp.: 90
Pumps Mfr
N.A.I.C.S.: 333914

**Xylem Water Solutions Suomi
Oy** (3)
Mestarintie 8, 01730, Vantaa, Finland
Tel.: (358) 103208500
Web Site: https://www.xylem.com
Pumping Equipment Mfr
N.A.I.C.S.: 333914

Subsidiary (US):

**Xylem Water Solutions U.S.A.,
Inc.** (3)
14125 S Bridge Cir, Charlotte, NC 28273
Tel.: (704) 409-9700
Web Site: http://www.xylem.com
Water Pumping Equipment Mfr
N.A.I.C.S.: 333914

Subsidiary (Domestic):

**Xylem Water Solutions U.S.A., Inc. -
Indianapolis** (4)
7615 W New York St, Indianapolis, IN
46214
Tel.: (317) 273-4470
Web Site: http://www.xyleminc.com
Sales Range: $10-24.9 Million
Emp.: 15
Water Pumping Equipment Mfr
N.A.I.C.S.: 333914

Subsidiary (Non-US):

**Xylem Water Solutions UK Holdings
Limited** (3)
Jays Close, Basingstoke, RG22 4BA,
United Kingdom
Tel.: (44) 1256311200
Engineering Component Mfr
N.A.I.C.S.: 335999

Xylem Water Solutions UK Ltd. (3)
Private Road No 1, Colwick, Nottingham,
NG4 2AN, United Kingdom (100%)
Tel.: (44) 115 940 0111
Web Site: https://www.xylem.com
Sales Range: $25-49.9 Million
Emp.: 100
Submersible Pumps & Mixers Mfr & Sales
N.A.I.C.S.: 333914

**Xylem Water Systems Hungary
KFT** (3)
Kulso-Katai Ut 41, 2700, Cegled, Hungary
Tel.: (36) 5 351 0502
Web Site: http://www.xylem.com
Sales Range: $75-99.9 Million
Emp.: 300
Pumping Equipment Mfr
N.A.I.C.S.: 333914

Subsidiary (Domestic):

**Xylem Water Solutions Florida
LLC** (2)
5771 Country Lakes Dr, Fort Myers, FL
33905-5502

Tel.: (239) 693-5226
Web Site: http://www.xylem.com
Emp.: 6
Pumping Equipment Mfr
N.A.I.C.S.: 333914

Subsidiary (Non-US):

**Xylem Water Solutions Herford
GmbH** (2)
Boschstrasse 4, D-32051, Herford, Ger-
many
Tel.: (49) 52219300
Web Site: http://www.wedeco.com
Sales Range: $150-199.9 Million
Emp.: 650
Chemical Free Water Disinfection & Water
Oxidation Systems Mfr
N.A.I.C.S.: 237110

Subsidiary (Domestic):

Xylem Water Solutions USA, Inc. (2)
: 4828 Parkway Plaza Blvd, Charlotte, NC
28217 (100%)
Tel.: (704) 409-9700
Web Site: http://www.xylem.com
Automotive, Defense, Electronics & Fluid
Technologies Mfr
N.A.I.C.S.: 423830

**Xylem Manufacturing Austria
GmbH** (1)
Ernst-Vogel-Strasse 2, 2000, Stockerau,
Austria
Tel.: (43) 2 266 6040
Web Site: https://www.xylem.com
Water Treatment Equipment Mfr
N.A.I.C.S.: 325412

**Xylem PCI Membranes Polska S.P.
Z.O.O.** (1)
ul Polna 1B, 62-025, Kostrzyn, Poland
Tel.: (48) 618970660
Web Site: http://www.pcimembranes.pl
Industrial Machinery & Equipment Merchant
Whslr
N.A.I.C.S.: 423830

**Xylem Shared Services Sp.
Z.o.o.** (1)
Ul Grabarska 2, 50-079, Wroclaw, Poland
Tel.: (48) 717497900
Web Site:
http://www.xylemwatersolutions.com
Pump Equipment Mfr
N.A.I.C.S.: 333914

**Xylem Water Solutions Global Ser-
vices AB** (1)
Gesallvagen 33, Stockholm County, 174 53,
Sundbyberg, Sweden
Tel.: (46) 84756000
Industrial Machinery & Equipment Merchant
Whslr
N.A.I.C.S.: 423830

**Xylem Water Solutions India Private
Limited** (1)
Plot No 731 GIDC Savli Manjusar Savli
Road, Survey 61/1 61/2 Kempapura Main
Road, Vadodara, 391 770, Gujarat, India
Tel.: (91) 2667615800
Pump Equipment Mfr
N.A.I.C.S.: 333914

**Xylem Water Solutions Lietuva,
UAB** (1)
Kareiviu 6-307, Vilnius, LT-09117, Lithuania
Tel.: (370) 52760944
Industrial Machinery & Equipment Merchant
Whslr
N.A.I.C.S.: 423830

**Xylem Water Solutions Middle East
Region FZCO** (1)
The Galleries Building 2 Near To Jabel Ali
Metro Station, Next To Adcb Jebel Ali Fre-
ezone JAFZ, Dubai, United Arab Emirates
Tel.: (971) 48036000
Industrial Machinery & Equipment Merchant
Whslr
N.A.I.C.S.: 423830

**Xylem Water Systems Mexico S. DE
R.L. DE C.V.** (1)
Av de los Insurgentes Sur 586 Del Valle
Ciudad De, Distrito Federal, 03100, Mexico,
Mexico
Tel.: (52) 5556695002

Xylem Inc.—(Continued)

Industrial Machinery & Equipment Merchant Whslr
N.A.I.C.S.: 423830

Y-MABS THERAPEUTICS, INC.

230 Park Ave Ste 3350, New York, NY 10169
Tel.: (646) 885-8505   DE
Web Site: https://www.ymabs.com
Year Founded: 2015
YMAB—(NASDAQ)
Rev.: $65,267,000
Assets: $141,456,000
Liabilities: $32,235,000
Net Worth: $109,221,000
Earnings: ($95,568,000)
Emp.: 95
Fiscal Year-end: 12/31/22
Biopharmaceutical Product Mfr & Distr
N.A.I.C.S.: 325412
Peter P. Pfreundschuh (CFO & Treas)
Michael Rossi (Pres & CEO)
Thomas Gad (Founder, Vice Chm & Chief Bus Officer)
Torben Lund-Hansen (Sr VP & Head-Technical Ops)
Steen Lisby (Chief Scientific Officer & Sr VP)
Joris Wiel Jan Wilms (COO & Sr VP)
Vignesh Rajah (Chief Medical Officer & Sr VP)
Sue Smith (Chief Comml Officer & Sr VP)
James I. Healy (Chm)

Subsidiaries:

Y-mAbs Therapeutics A/S   (1)
Agern Alle 11 Ground Floor, 2970, Horsholm, Denmark
Tel.: (45) 70261414
Pharmaceutical Preparation Mfr
N.A.I.C.S.: 325412

YALE TRANSACTION FINDERS, INC.

405 Lexington Ave 44th Fl, New York, NY 10174
Tel.: (212) 818-8800   DE
Year Founded: 2014
YTFD—(OTCIQ)
Assets: $12,876
Liabilities: $59,171
Net Worth: ($46,295)
Earnings: ($68,042)
Fiscal Year-end: 12/31/22
Business Management Services
N.A.I.C.S.: 541611
Robert Diener (CEO)
Thomas A. Colligan (Pres)

YANGTZE RIVER PORT & LOGISTICS LIMITED

41 John St Ste 2A, New York, NY 10038
Tel.: (646) 861-3315   NV
Year Founded: 2009
YRIV—(NASDAQ)
Sales Range: Less than $1 Million
Emp.: 34
Residential & Commercial Real Estate Developer
N.A.I.C.S.: 531390
Xiangyao Liu (Chm, Pres, CEO & Sec)

YAPPN CORP.

1001 Ave of the Americas 11th Fl, New York, NY 10018   DE
Web Site: http://www.yappn.com
Year Founded: 2010
YPPN—(OTCIQ)
Sales Range: Less than $1 Million
Emp.: 2
Social Media Website Publisher

N.A.I.C.S.: 541810
Craig McCannell (CFO)
David Bercovitch (VP-Bus Dev)
Nathan Brandt (Head-Bus Dev)
Nicole Meissner (Exec VP & Head-UK & European Ops)
Jeanny So (VP-Corp Comm)
C. Kent Jespersen (Chm)
Edward P. Karthaus (Pres & CEO)
Anthony R. Pearlman (CTO)
Stephen Taylor (Chief Sls Officer)

YASHENG GROUP

805 Veterans Blvd Ste 228, Redwood City, CA 94063
Tel.: (650) 363-8345   CA
Web Site:
  https://www.yashenggroup.com
Year Founded: 2004
HERB—(OTCIQ)
Sales Range: $900-999.9 Million
Emp.: 10,000
Holding Company; Agricultural Food & Agro-byproducts Cultivator, Processor, Marketer & Distr
N.A.I.C.S.: 551112
Li Yong (Chm)
Liu Darong (COO)
Chen Eric Christopher (Sr VP)

YELLOW CORPORATION

11500 Outlook St, Overland Park, KS 66211
Tel.: (913) 696-6100   DE
Web Site: https://www.myyellow.com
Year Founded: 1983
YELL—(NASDAQ)
Rev.: $5,244,700,000
Assets: $2,279,300,000
Liabilities: $2,660,800,000
Net Worth: ($381,500,000)
Earnings: $21,800,000
Emp.: 30,000
Fiscal Year-end: 12/31/22
Holding Company; Transportation Services
N.A.I.C.S.: 551112
Matthew A. Doheny (Chm)
Darren D. Hawkins (CEO)
Daniel L. Oliver (CFO)
Leah Dawson (Gen Counsel, Sec & Exec VP)
Darrel J. Harris (Pres & COO)
Annlea Rumfola (CIO)

Subsidiaries:

HNRY Logistics, Inc.   (1)
5200 W 110th St, Overland Park, KS 66211
Web Site: http://www.hnrylogistics.com
Logistic Services
N.A.I.C.S.: 541614

YRC North American Transportation, Inc.   (1)
10990 Roe Ave, Overland Park, KS 66211
Tel.: (913) 696-6100
Sales Range: $250-299.9 Million
Emp.: 500
Holding Company; Freight Transportation Services
N.A.I.C.S.: 551112

Subsidiary (Domestic):

YRC Inc.   (2)
10990 Roe Ave, Overland Park, KS 66207
Tel.: (913) 344-4062
Web Site: http://www.yrc.com
Trucking Service
N.A.I.C.S.: 484110

Subsidiary (Domestic):

Roadway Reverse Logistics, Inc.   (3)
1077 Gorge Blvd, Akron, OH 44310   (100%)
Tel.: (330) 384-1717
Web Site:
  http://www.roadwayreverselogistics.com

Sales Range: $75-99.9 Million
Reverse Logistics Services for Product Returns for Remanufacturing, Redistribution, Cleaning or Disposal
N.A.I.C.S.: 541614

Subsidiary (Domestic):

YRC Regional Transportation, Inc.   (2)
1077 Gorge Blvd, Akron, OH 44310   (100%)
Tel.: (330) 762-2041
Sales Range: $150-199.9 Million
Regional Transportation Services
N.A.I.C.S.: 484110
Bruce Kennedy (VP-Pricing)

Subsidiary (Domestic):

New Penn Motor Express, Inc.   (3)
501 Commerce St Ste 1120, Nashville, TN 37203
Tel.: (717) 274-2521
Web Site: http://www.newpenn.com
Sales Range: $75-99.9 Million
Emp.: 220
Freight Carrier
N.A.I.C.S.: 484122

USF Holland Inc.   (3)
700 S Waverly Rd, Holland, MI 49423
Tel.: (616) 395-5000
Web Site: http://www.hollandregional.com
Sales Range: $900-999.9 Million
Emp.: 8,590
Less-Than-Truckload Services
N.A.I.C.S.: 484122

USF Reddaway Inc.   (3)
7720 SW Mohawk St Bldg H, Tualatin, OR 97062
Tel.: (503) 650-1286
Web Site: http://www.reddawayregional.com
Sales Range: $250-299.9 Million
Emp.: 3,000
Trucking Service
N.A.I.C.S.: 484122

YELP INC.

350 Msn St 10th Fl, San Francisco, CA 94105
Tel.: (415) 908-3801   DE
Web Site: https://www.yelp.com
Year Founded: 2004
YELP—(NYSE)
Rev.: $1,193,506,000
Assets: $1,015,922,000
Liabilities: $305,598,000
Net Worth: $710,324,000
Earnings: $36,347,000
Emp.: 4,900
Fiscal Year-end: 12/31/22
Customer Review Website Operator
N.A.I.C.S.: 513140
Jason Brown (Sr VP-Strategy & Gen Mgr-Marketplaces)
Brian Dean (Sr VP-Bus Ops & Strategy)
David Schwarzbach (CFO & Principal Acctg Officer)
Craig Saldanha (Chief Product Officer)
Amy Sezak (Sr VP-Corporate Communications)
Carmen Whitney Orr (Chief People Officer)
Joseph R. Nachman (COO)
Sam Eaton (CTO)
Miriam Warren (Chief Diversity Officer)
Andrea Rubin (Sr VP-Community)
Paul Reich (Sr VP-Local Sls)
Chad Richard (Sr VP-Bus & Corp Dev)
Tom Foran (Sr VP-Natl Sls)
Brigitte Ehman (Sr VP-Marketing)
Jeremy Stoppelman (Co-Founder & CEO)

YERBAE BRANDS CORP.

18801 N Thompson Peak Pkwy Ste 380, Scottsdale, AZ 85255

Tel.: (480) 471-8391   BC
Web Site: https://yerbae.com
Year Founded: 2000
YERB.U—(TSXV)
Assets: $91,711
Liabilities: $20,184
Net Worth: $71,528
Earnings: ($55,937)
Fiscal Year-end: 09/30/21
Holding Company
N.A.I.C.S.: 551112
Ron Schmitz (CEO & Sec)
Gurdeep Phachu (CFO)

YETI HOLDINGS, INC.

7601 SW Pkwy, Austin, TX 78735
Tel.: (512) 394-9384   DE
Web Site: https://www.yeti.com
Year Founded: 2006
YETI—(NYSE)
Rev.: $1,658,713,000
Assets: $1,297,192,000
Liabilities: $573,582,000
Net Worth: $723,610,000
Earnings: $169,885,000
Emp.: 1,050
Fiscal Year-end: 12/30/23
Holding Company; Premium Coolers & Drinkwares Mfr
N.A.I.C.S.: 551112
Matthew J. Reintjes (Pres & CEO)
Bryan C. Barksdale (Gen Counsel, Sec & Sr VP)
Roy J. Seiders (Co-Founder)
Ryan Seiders (Co-Founder)
Michael McMullen (CFO, Treas & Sr VP)
Tom Shaw (VP)
Evonne Delaney (Chief HR Officer)
Paulie Dery (CMO)
Marty Duff (Sr VP)
Hannah Mara (VP)

YEXT, INC.

61 9th Ave, New York, NY 10011
Tel.: (212) 994-3900   DE
Web Site: https://www.yext.com
Year Founded: 2006
YEXT—(NYSE)
Rev.: $400,850,000
Assets: $523,761,000
Liabilities: $395,738,000
Net Worth: $128,023,000
Earnings: ($65,938,000)
Emp.: 1,200
Fiscal Year-end: 01/31/23
Digital Location Management Software Developer & Publisher
N.A.I.C.S.: 513210
Brian Distelburger (Co-Founder)
Howard Lerman (Co-Founder)
Michael Walrath (Chm & CEO)
Brian J. Schipper (Chief People Officer & Exec VP)
Ho Sik Shin (Gen Counsel)
Sean MacIsaac (Exec VP-Infrastructure)
Tom Nielsen (Chief Revenue Officer)
Lexi Bohonnon (Exec VP)
Yvette Martinez-Rea (Exec VP)
Tzi-Kei Wong (Chief Product Officer)

Subsidiaries:

Hearsay Social, Inc.   (1)
185 Berry St Ste 3800, San Francisco, CA 94107
Tel.: (415) 692-6230
Web Site: http://www.hearsaysocial.com
Sales Range: $1-9.9 Million
Emp.: 60
Software Developer
N.A.I.C.S.: 513210
Michael Lock (COO)
Mark Gilbert (VP-Products)
Jeremy Hermann (Head-Engrg)
Gary Liu (VP-Mktg)
Yasmin Zarabi (VP-Legal & Compliance)

Jason Suen *(Mng Dir-Asia-Pacific)*
Abhay Rajaram *(VP-Customer Success)*
Bob Moss *(VP-Engrg)*
Patty Buckley *(VP-People, Culture & Ops)*
Ron Piovesan *(VP-Strategic Alliances)*

Yext GmbH **(1)**
Karl-Liebknechtstrasse 29a, 10178, Berlin,
Germany
Tel.: (49) 30800933813
Web Site: https://www.yext.com
Software Development Services
N.A.I.C.S.: 513210
Ho Shin *(Mng Dir)*
Darryl Bond *(Mng Dir)*

YIELD10 BIOSCIENCE, INC.
19 Presidential Way, Woburn, MA
01801
Tel.: (617) 583-1700   DE
Web Site: https://www.yield10bio.com
Year Founded: 1992
YTEN—(NASDAQ)
Rev.: $450,000
Assets: $8,085,000
Liabilities: $3,685,000
Net Worth: $4,400,000
Earnings: ($13,566,000)
Emp.: 30
Fiscal Year-end: 12/31/22
Biodegradable Plastic Products Mfr
N.A.I.C.S.: 326199
Lynne H. Brum *(VP-Plng & Corp
Comm)*
Oliver P. Peoples *(Pres & CEO)*
Kristi D. Snell *(Chief Science Officer
& VP-Res)*
Darren Greenfield *(Sr Dir-Seed Ops)*
Robert L. Van Nostrand *(Chm)*

YIPPY, INC.
1995 N Park Pl NW Ste 270, Atlanta,
GA 30339   NV
Web Site: https://www.yippy.com
Year Founded: 2006
YIPI—(OTCIQ)
Rev.: $1,163,000
Assets: $4,524,000
Liabilities: $2,395,000
Net Worth: $2,129,000
Earnings: ($1,347,000)
Fiscal Year-end: 05/31/19
Computer Software
N.A.I.C.S.: 513210

YORK TRADITIONS BANK
226 Pauline Dr, York, PA 17402-0136
Tel.: (717) 741-1770   PA
YRKB—(OTCIQ)
Commercial Banking Services
N.A.I.C.S.: 522110
Eugene J. Draganosky *(Pres & CEO)*
Thomas J. Sposito II *(Chief Banking
Officer)*

YOSHIHARU GLOBAL CO.
6940 Beach Blvd Ste D-705, Buena
Park, CA 90621
Tel.: (213) 272-1780   DE
Web Site:
  https://yoshiharuramen.com
Year Founded: 2021
YOSH—(NASDAQ)
Rev.: $8,282,368
Assets: $16,017,689
Liabilities: $10,379,846
Net Worth: $5,637,843
Earnings: ($3,487,367)
Emp.: 130
Fiscal Year-end: 12/31/22
Restaurant Operators
N.A.I.C.S.: 722511
James Chae *(Pres, CEO, Founder &
Chm)*

YOTTA ACQUISITION CORPO-
RATION
1185 Ave of the Americas Ste 301,
New York, NY 10036
Tel.: (212) 612-1400   DE
Year Founded: 2021
YOTA—(NASDAQ)
Rev.: $1,651,461
Assets: $116,982,661
Liabilities: $121,805,103
Net Worth: ($4,822,442)
Earnings: $145,189
Emp.: 2
Fiscal Year-end: 12/31/22
Investment Services
N.A.I.C.S.: 523999
Hui Chen *(CEO)*
Robert L. Labbe *(CFO)*

YOTTA GLOBAL, INC.
4154 Silver Peak Pkwy Ste C, Su-
wanee, GA 30024
Tel.: (678) 790-1129   GA
Year Founded: 2015
TPPM—(OTCIQ)
Software Development Services
N.A.I.C.S.: 541511
Sang G. Lee *(CEO)*

YOUNEEQAI TECHNICAL SER-
VICES, INC.
2700 Youngfield St Ste 280, Denver,
CO 80215
Tel.: (303) 918-7595   NV
Web Site: https://youneeqai.com
Year Founded: 2007
YQAI—(OTCIQ)
Assets: $25,017
Liabilities: $54,991
Net Worth: ($29,974)
Earnings: ($18,632)
Fiscal Year-end: 04/30/10
Holding Company; Artificial Intelli-
gence Personalization SaaS Products
& Services
N.A.I.C.S.: 551112
Marco Garduno Chavez *(Pres)*
Murray Galbraith *(CEO)*

YOUNGEVITY INTERNA-
TIONAL CORP.
2400 Boswell Rd, Chula Vista, CA
91914
Tel.: (619) 934-3980
Web Site: http://ygyi.com
YGYI—(OTCIQ)
Sales Range: $125-149.9 Million
Emp.: 469
Holding Company; Direct-to-
Consumer Online Products Retailer;
Commercial Coffee Whslr
N.A.I.C.S.: 551112
Stephan Wallach *(Chm & CEO)*
David Stephen Briskie *(Pres & Chief
Investment Officer)*
William G. Thompson *(CFO)*
Joel D. Wallach *(Founder)*

Subsidiaries:

AL Global Corporation **(1)**
2400 Boswell Rd, Chula Vista, CA 91914
Tel.: (619) 934-3980
Web Site: http://www.youngevity.com
Healthcare Product Distr
N.A.I.C.S.: 424210

CLR Roasters, LLC **(1)**
2131 NW 72nd Ave, Miami, FL 33122
Tel.: (305) 591-0040
Web Site: http://www.clrroasters.com
Coffee Mfr & Distr
N.A.I.C.S.: 312111
Ernesto Aguila *(Co-Pres)*
Dave Briskie *(Co-Pres & CFO)*
Sonia Aguila *(VP)*
Javier Gil *(Gen Mgr)*
Lidier Reyes *(Mgr-Equipment & Production)*
Kathleen Ruiz *(Controller)*
Yanet Junco *(Mgr-Sls & Logistics)*

Katheryne Leal *(Office Mgr)*
Jose Hernandez *(Asst Mgr-Production)*
Jordan Aguila *(Mgr-Shipping & Receiving)*

Khrysos Industries, Inc. **(1)**
4121 SW 34th St, Orlando, FL 32811
Tel.: (352) 244-8803
Web Site: http://www.khrysosglobal.com
Laboratory Equipment Distr
N.A.I.C.S.: 423450

Youngevity NZ, Ltd. **(1)**
5C Airborne Road, Rosedale, Auckland,
0632, New Zealand
Tel.: (64) 94146223
Web Site: http://youngevity.com
Nutrition Product Distr
N.A.I.C.S.: 456191
Robert Greer *(Mgr-Ops & Sls-New Zealand)*

Youngevity Russia, LLC **(1)**
Ulitsa Letnikovskaya 10 Building 2 Business
Center Svatogor Floor 1, Moscow, 121099,
Russia
Tel.: (7) 4952349876
Web Site: http://www.youngevity.ru
Cosmetic Product Mfr & Whslr
N.A.I.C.S.: 325620

YSTRATEGIES CORP.
6101 Penn Ave Ste 102, Pittsburgh,
PA 15206
Tel.: (412) 450-0028   NV
Web Site: http://www.ystrategies.com
Year Founded: 2011
YSTR—(OTCIQ)
Sales Range: Less than $1 Million
Investment Services
N.A.I.C.S.: 541611
Paul I. Overby *(VP-Global Strategy)*
Ashish Badjatia *(CFO, COO & Sec)*
James J. Kiles *(Pres & CEO)*
Andrea Kates Lebovitz *(Chief Innova-
tion Officer)*

YUBO INTERNATIONAL BIO-
TECH LTD.
1662 Old Country Rd Ste 355, Plain-
view, NY 11803
Tel.: (301) 972-5232   NY
Year Founded: 1991
YBGJ—(OTCQB)
Rev.: $604,676
Assets: $1,667,269
Liabilities: $3,510,972
Net Worth: ($1,843,703)
Earnings: ($1,195,083)
Emp.: 18
Fiscal Year-end: 12/31/23
Biotechnology Research & Develop-
ment Services
N.A.I.C.S.: 541714
Lawrence A. Minkoff *(Founder, Chm,
Pres & Chief Scientific Officer)*
Jerome M. Feldman *(VP)*

YUENGLING'S ICE CREAM
CORPORATION
Tel.: (570) 968-4352   NV
Web Site:
  https://yuenglingsicecream.com
Year Founded: 2013
YCRM—(NYSE)
Fiscal Year-end: 10/31/22
Ice Cream & Frozen Dessert Mfr
N.A.I.C.S.: 311520
Robert C. Bohorad *(Pres & CEO)*

YUM CHINA HOLDINGS, INC.
101 E Park Blvd Ste 805, Plano, TX
75074
Tel.: (469) 980-2898   DE
Web Site: https://www.yumchina.com
Year Founded: 1987
YUMC—(NYSE)
Rev.: $10,978,000,000
Assets: $12,031,000,000
Liabilities: $4,925,000,000
Net Worth: $7,106,000,000
Earnings: $827,000,000

Emp.: 155,000
Fiscal Year-end: 12/31/23
Holding Company
N.A.I.C.S.: 551112
Joey Wat *(CEO)*
Jeff Kuai *(Gen Mgr-Pizza Hut)*
Pingping Liu *(Chief Legal Officer)*
Leila Zhang *(CTO)*
Duoduo Huang *(Chief Supply Chain
Officer)*
Warton Wang *(Gen Mgr-KFC)*
Jerry Ding *(Chief People Officer)*
Adrian Ding *(Acting CFO, Chief In-
vestment Officer & Gen Mgr-Lavazza)*

Subsidiaries:

**Suzhou Zhi Sheng Information Tech-
nology Co., Ltd.** **(1)**
NO 1188 Chang an Road, Wujiang District,
Suzhou, China
Tel.: (86) 18901557253
Web Site: https://www.suzhouzhisheng.com
Solar Equipment Distr
N.A.I.C.S.: 423720

**Yum! Restaurants China Holdings
Limited** **(1)**
21-22f Metro Tower 30 Tian yao Qiao Road,
3 Hongqiao Road, Shanghai, 200030,
China
Tel.: (86) 2164271777
Web Site: http://www.yum.com
Fast Food Restaurants
N.A.I.C.S.: 722513

Subsidiary (Domestic):

Beijing Pizza Hut Co., Ltd. **(2)**
6F B Suite Fuhua Mansion 8 Beida Street,
Chaoyangmen, Beijing, 100027, China
Tel.: (86) 1065544511
Web Site: http://www.yumchina.com
Restaurant Operating Services
N.A.I.C.S.: 722513

Dalian KFC Co., Ltd. **(2)**
17F Hope bldg 136 Zhongshan Rd, Zhong-
shan Dist, Dalian, 116001, China
Tel.: (86) 41182735280
Restaurant Services
N.A.I.C.S.: 722513

Dongguan KFC Co., Ltd. **(2)**
2nd Pizza Hut Restaurant 1F4 Dist Diwang
Square, Dongzong, Dongguan, 523000,
China
Tel.: (86) 76983196923
Web Site: http://www.kfc.com.cn
Restaurant Services
N.A.I.C.S.: 722513

Little Sheep Group Limited **(2)**
No 9a Wulana Roada Kuna District, Baotou,
14010, China
Tel.: (86) 4725137998
Web Site: http://www.littlesheep.com
Holding Company; Restaurants Operator &
Franchisor
N.A.I.C.S.: 551112

Shanghai KFC Co., Ltd. **(2)**
21/22/F Meiluo Mansion No 30 Tianyaoqiao
Road, Xuhui, Shanghai, 200030, China
Tel.: (86) 2154594899
Restaurant Services
N.A.I.C.S.: 722513

Shanghai Pizza Hut Co., Ltd. **(2)**
15F Meiluo Mansion 30 Tianyaoqiao Road,
Xuhui, Shanghai, 200030, China
Tel.: (86) 2133398888
Restaurant Operating Services
N.A.I.C.S.: 722513

Wuxi KFC Co., Ltd. **(2)**
3/F No 1 Houxixi Road, Wuxi, 214001,
China
Tel.: (86) 51082748800
Web Site: http://www.yum.com
Restaurant Services
N.A.I.C.S.: 722513

Xiamen KFC Co., Ltd. **(2)**
24F Haibin Building Lujiang Avenue, Siming
District, Xiamen, 361004, Fujian, China
Tel.: (86) 5928129830
Web Site: http://www.yum.com
Restaurant Services

Yum China Holdings, Inc.—(Continued)

N.A.I.C.S.: 722513

Yum! Restaurants (Shenzhen) Co., Ltd. (2)
12f Shenzhen Development Bank Mansion, Shenzhen, 518026, China
Tel.: (86) 75525156188
Web Site: http://ir.yumchina.com
Restaurant Operating Services
N.A.I.C.S.: 722513

Yum! Restaurants (Xian) Co., Ltd. (2)
25/F Gaoxin International Business, Center Mansion No 33 Keji, Xi'an, 710075, China
Tel.: (86) 2988342800
Web Site: http://www.ir.yumchina.com
Restaurant Management Services
N.A.I.C.S.: 722513

Yum! Restaurants Consulting (Shanghai) Co., Ltd. (2)
16 Floor 2 Grand Gateway 3 Hongqiao Road, Xuhui, Shanghai, 200030, China
Tel.: (86) 2124077777
Web Site: http://www.yumchina.com
Restaurant Services
N.A.I.C.S.: 722513

YUM! BRANDS, INC.

1441 Gardiner Ln, Louisville, KY 40213
Tel.: (502) 874-8300 NC
Web Site: https://www.yum.com
Year Founded: 1997
YUM—(NYSE)
Rev.: $7,076,000,000
Assets: $6,231,000,000
Liabilities: $14,089,000,000
Net Worth: ($7,858,000,000)
Earnings: $1,597,000,000
Emp.: 35,000
Fiscal Year-end: 12/31/23
Holding Company; Limited & Full-Service Restaurants Franchisor & Operator
N.A.I.C.S.: 551112
David W. Gibbs (CEO)
Javier E. Benito (Gen Mgr)
Tracy L. Skeans (COO & Chief People Officer)
Sabir Sami (CEO-KFC Div)
David E. Russell (Sr VP-Fin & Controller)
Scott Catlett (Chief Legal & Franchise Officer & Sec)
Clay M. Johnson (Chief Digital & Tech Officer)
Jerilan Greene (Chief Comm & Pub Affairs Officer)
James Fripp (Chief Equity & Inclusion Officer)
Jodi Dyer (VP-IR)
Gavin Felder (Chief Strategy Officer)
Ken Muench (CMO)

Subsidiaries:

KFC (Pty) Ltd. (1)
Building G Knightsbridge Office Park 33 Sloane Street, Bryanston, 2191, South Africa
Tel.: (27) 860100222
Web Site: https://order.kfc.co.za
Restaurant Services
N.A.I.C.S.: 722511

KFC Corporation (1)
1441 Gardiner Ln, Louisville, KY 40213
Tel.: (502) 874-1000
Web Site: http://www.kfc.com
Sales Range: $1-4.9 Billion
Emp.: 88,000
Fast Food Restaurants Franchisor
N.A.I.C.S.: 722513
Javier E. Benito (Gen Mgr-Latin America)
Tony Lowings (CEO)
Nikki Lawson (Mng Dir-South Pacific)
Nick Chavez (CMO)

Subsidiary (Non-US):

KFC Chamnord SAS (2)

1097 Avenue Of Landiers, 73000, Chambery, France
Tel.: (33) 479694236
Web Site: http://www.chamnord.com
Restaurant Services
N.A.I.C.S.: 722513

KFC Restaurants Asia Pte., Ltd. (2)
99 Bukit Timah Road 06-00, Alfa Centre, Singapore, 229835, Singapore
Tel.: (65) 62226111
Limited-Service Restaurant Operator
N.A.I.C.S.: 722513

KFC Restaurants Spain S.L. (2)
Serrano Galvache 56 Edificio Madrono piso 3 KFC, 28033, Madrid, Spain
Tel.: (34) 91 768 0730
Web Site: https://www.kfc.es
Restaurant Operating Services
N.A.I.C.S.: 722511

Kentucky Fried Chicken (Great Britain) Limited (2)
32 Rye Lane Peckham, London, SE15 5BS, United Kingdom
Tel.: (44) 3457532532
Web Site: https://www.kfc.co.uk
Restaurant Services
N.A.I.C.S.: 722513

Kentucky Fried Chicken (Great Britain) Services Limited (2)
Unit 4 Mount Mill Farm Wicken, Wicken, Milton Keynes, MK19 6DG, United Kingdom
Tel.: (44) 3457532532
Web Site: http://www.kfc.co.uk
Restaurant Operating Services
N.A.I.C.S.: 722511

Kentucky Fried Chicken Canada Company (2)
45 Wicksteed Ave, Toronto, M4G 4H9, ON, Canada
Tel.: (647) 943-6105
Web Site: http://order.kfcdelivery.ca
Emp.: 5
Limited-Service Restaurant Operator
N.A.I.C.S.: 722513

Kentucky Fried Chicken Pty. Ltd. (2)
20 Frenchs Forest Rd E, French's Forest, 2086, NSW, Australia
Tel.: (61) 29 452 5505
Web Site: https://www.kfc.com.au
Emp.: 200
Restaurant Management Services
N.A.I.C.S.: 722513

Kentucky Fried Chicken Limited (1)
Freepost Rrka-hcas-ysjc Unit 4 Mount Mill Farm, Wicken, Milton Keynes, MK19 6DG, United Kingdom
Tel.: (44) 3457532532
Web Site: https://www.kfc.co.uk
Restaurant Services
N.A.I.C.S.: 722511

Pizza Hut, Inc. (1)
7100 Corporate Dr, Plano, TX 75024-4100 (100%)
Tel.: (972) 338-7700
Web Site: http://www.pizzahut.com
Sales Range: $150-199.9 Million
Emp.: 600
Franchiser of Pizza Hut Restaurants
N.A.I.C.S.: 722513
Unnat Varma (Mng Dir-Asia Pacific)
Lauren Leahy (Chief Legal Officer)
Yashodhara Lal (Dir-Mktg-Gurgaon)
Helen Vaid (Chief Customer Officer)
Chequan Lewis (COO)
Aaron Powell (CEO)
David Graves (Pres)
Lindsay Morgan (CMO)
Georgeanne Erickson (Chief Brand Officer)
Lynne Broad (CFO)

Subsidiary (Domestic):

Pizza Hut of America, Inc. (2)
4019 E 106th St, Chicago, IL 60617
Tel.: (773) 374-7233
Web Site: http://www.pizzahut.com
Emp.: 12
Restaurant Services
N.A.I.C.S.: 722513

WingStreet, LLC (2)
8605 Ohio Dr, Plano, TX 75024

Tel.: (972) 731-8000
Web Site: http://www.pizzahut.com
Sales Range: $25-49.9 Million
Emp.: 500
Fast Food Restaurants
N.A.I.C.S.: 722513

QuikOrder, LLC (1)
444 N Michigan Ave Ste 2500, Chicago, IL 60611
Tel.: (312) 222-1750
Web Site: https://www.quikorder.com
Internet Ordering Services
N.A.I.C.S.: 492210

Restaurant Concepts LLC (1)
405 Main St, Pleasanton, CA 94566
Tel.: (925) 417-2222
Emp.: 35
Grocery Product Whslr
N.A.I.C.S.: 424490

Taco Bell Corp. (1)
2222 Barranca Pkwy, Irvine, CA 92606 (100%)
Tel.: (949) 863-4000
Web Site: https://www.tacobell.com
Sales Range: $1-9.9 Million
Emp.: 39,700
Franchiser of Fast-Food Restaurants
N.A.I.C.S.: 722513

The Habit Restaurants, Inc. (1)
17320 Red Hill Ave Ste 140, Irvine, CA 92614
Tel.: (949) 851-8881
Web Site: http://www.habitburger.com
Sales Range: $450-499.9 Million
Emp.: 6,437
Restaurant Owner & Operator
N.A.I.C.S.: 722511
Russell W. Bendel (CEO)
Anthony Serritella (COO)
Peter Whitwell (Chief Quality Officer)
Douglas R. Branigan (Chief Dev Officer)
Iwona Alter (Chief Brand Officer)
John Phillips (Chief Global Bus Partnership Officer)
Brent Reichard (Co-Founder)
Bruce Reichard (Co-Founder)

Turkent Gida Ve Turizm Sanayi Ve Ticaret A.S. (1)
Ruzgarlibahce Mahallesi Kavak Sokak Is Plaza No 1 Beykoz, Kavacik, Istanbul, Turkiye
Tel.: (90) 4443555
Web Site: https://www.kfcturkiye.com
Restaurant Operating Services
N.A.I.C.S.: 722511

Yum! Restaurants International (1)
7100 Corporate Dr, Plano, TX 75024 (100%)
Tel.: (972) 338-7700
Web Site: http://www.pizzahut.com
Sales Range: $200-249.9 Million
Emp.: 600
Holding Company; Fast Food Restaurant Franchiser
N.A.I.C.S.: 551112

Subsidiary (Non-US):

Inventure Restaurantes Ltda. (2)
Ouvidor 50, Rio de Janeiro, 21012-038, Brazil
Tel.: (55) 2122056596
Restaurant Management Services
N.A.I.C.S.: 722511

Yum! Restaurants Australia Pty. Limited (2)
L 2 20 Rodborough Road, French's Forest, 2086, NSW, Australia
Tel.: (61) 299303000
Emp.: 1,000
Restaurant Operators
N.A.I.C.S.: 722513

Yum! Restaurants Europe Limited (2)
11 Bell Street, Reigate, RH2 7AD, United Kingdom
Tel.: (44) 1737224922
Restaurant Services
N.A.I.C.S.: 722513
Jens Hofma (CEO-Pizza Hut Restaurants-UK)

YUNHONG GREEN CTI LTD.

22160 N Pepper Rd, Lake Barrington, IL 60010
Tel.: (847) 382-1000 DE
Web Site:
https://www.ctiindustries.com
Year Founded: 1976
YHGJ—(NASDAQ)
Rev.: $18,048,000
Assets: $15,282,000
Liabilities: $12,536,000
Net Worth: $2,746,000
Earnings: ($1,467,000)
Emp.: 58
Fiscal Year-end: 12/31/22
Mylar & Latex Balloons Mfr
N.A.I.C.S.: 325212
Frank J. Cesario (CEO & Acting CFO)
Jana M. Schwan (COO)
Yubao Li (Chm & Pres)

Subsidiaries:

CTI Balloons Ltd. (1)
Unit 3 Spelmonden Estate, Cranbrook Goudhurst, Kent, TN17 1HE, United Kingdom
Tel.: (44) 1580890202
Web Site: https://www.triproducts.co.uk
Sales Range: $25-49.9 Million
Emp.: 100
Retailer of Latex Balloons
N.A.I.C.S.: 326299

CTI Supply, Inc. (1)
No 52 Huynh Thien Loc St, Hoa Thanh Tan Phu, 70000, Ho Chi Minh City, Vietnam
Tel.: (84) 911901717
Web Site: https://ctisupply.vn
Industrial Automation Services
N.A.I.C.S.: 541512

Flexo Universal SA de CV (1)
Calle 3 No 1374 Zona Industrial, Guadalajara, 44940, Mexico
Tel.: (52) 3338127621
Web Site: http://www.flexouniversal.com.mx
Sales Range: $25-49.9 Million
Emp.: 200
Latex Balloon Mfr
N.A.I.C.S.: 326299
Pablo Gordizar (Gen Mgr)

YVC HOLDINGS, INC

625 Oberlin Rd, Raleigh, NC 27605
Tel.: (919) 716-2266 NC
Year Founded: 1979
YDVL (OTCIQ)
Financial Investment Services
N.A.I.C.S.: 524210
David A. Perry (Pres)
E. Thomas Lucas (Sec)

Z-WORK ACQUISITION CORP.

575 5th Ave 15th Fl, New York, NY 10017
Tel.: (626) 867-7295 DE
Web Site:
http://www.zworkacquisition.com
Year Founded: 2020
ZWRKU—(NASDAQ)
Rev.: $5,267,477
Assets: $231,495,271
Liabilities: $247,409,637
Net Worth: ($15,914,366)
Earnings: $3,264,648
Emp.: 3
Fiscal Year-end: 12/31/21
Investment Services
N.A.I.C.S.: 523999
Doug Atkin (Chm)
Adam Roston (Pres & CFO)

ZA GROUP, INC.

240 Vaughan Dr, Alpharetta, GA 30009
Tel.: (770) 235-6053 FL
Year Founded: 1997
ZAAG—(OTCIQ)
Management Consulting Services

N.A.I.C.S.: 541611
Jeffrey Michael Canouse *(CEO)*

ZALATORIS ACQUISITION CORP.

99 Wall St Ste 5801, New York, NY 10005
Tel.: (646) 450-2536   DE
Web Site:
    https://www.trajectoryalpha.com
Year Founded: 2021
TCOA—(NYSE)
Rev.: $2,176,305
Assets: $176,820,523
Liabilities: $182,420,764
Net Worth: ($5,600,241)
Earnings: $383,998
Emp.: 2
Fiscal Year-end: 12/31/22
Investment Services
N.A.I.C.S.: 523999
Peter A. Bordes Jr. *(Chm & CEO)*
Michael E.S. Frankel *(Pres & CFO)*
Paul Sethi *(Dir-Lead)*

ZALATORIS II ACQUISITION CORP.

31 Hudson Yards 11th Fl, New York, NY 10005
Tel.: (646) 450-2536   Ky
Year Founded: 2021
ZLS—(NASDAQ)
Rev.: $7,073,918
Assets: $223,004,418
Liabilities: $237,940,836
Net Worth: ($14,936,418)
Earnings: $1,911,455
Emp.: 3
Fiscal Year-end: 12/31/22
Investment Services
N.A.I.C.S.: 523999

ZAP

501 Fourth St, Santa Rosa, CA 95401
Tel.: (707) 525-8658   CA
Year Founded: 1994
ZAAP—(OTCIQ)
Sales Range: $10-24.9 Million
Electric Vehicle Systems Mfr & Designer
N.A.I.C.S.: 336991
Michael Ringstad *(Interim CFO)*
Alex Gang Wang *(CEO)*

ZAPATA COMPUTING HOLDINGS INC.

100 Federal St 20th Fl, Boston, MA 02110   DE
Web Site: https://zapata.ai
ZPTA—(NASDAQ)
Rev.: $8,156,697
Assets: $86,470,607
Liabilities: $15,495,929
Net Worth: ($15,290,401)
Earnings: ($862,919)
Emp.: 3
Fiscal Year-end: 12/31/23
Software Publisher
N.A.I.C.S.: 513210
William Matthew Brown *(Pres & CFO)*
William J. Sandbrook *(Chm & Co-CEO)*
Christopher Savoie *(Co-CEO)*
Yudong Cao *(CTO)*
Sumit Kapur *(VP-Fin)*
Jon Zorio *(Chief Revenue Officer)*
Derron Blakely *(Gen Counsel)*

ZAZA ENERGY CORPORATION

1301 McKinney St Ste 2800, Houston, TX 77010
Tel.: (713) 595-1900   DE
Year Founded: 2012
ZAZA—(OTCIQ)

Energy Exploration Services
N.A.I.C.S.: 211120
Todd A. Brooks *(Pres & CEO)*

ZEBRA TECHNOLOGIES CORPORATION

3 Overlook Pt, Lincolnshire, IL 60069
Tel.: (847) 634-6700   DE
Web Site: https://www.zebra.com
Year Founded: 1969
ZBRA—(NASDAQ)
Rev.: $4,584,000,000
Assets: $7,306,000,000
Liabilities: $4,270,000,000
Net Worth: $3,036,000,000
Earnings: $296,000,000
Emp.: 9,750
Fiscal Year-end: 12/31/23
On-Demand Bar Code Label Printers & Related Supplies
N.A.I.C.S.: 334118
Amanda Duguay *(Sr Dir-Comml Fin)*
Anders Gustafsson *(Exec Chm)*
Michael Cho *(Chief Strategy Officer)*
Jeff Schmitz *(Chief People Officer)*
Tom Bianculli *(CTO & Sr VP)*
Michael Steele *(VP-IR)*
Therese Van Ryne *(Sr Dir-External Comm)*
Julia Suzanne Johnson *(VP-Mobile Computing & Gen Mgr-Mobile Computing)*
Cristen Kogl *(Chief Legal Officer, Gen Counsel & Sec)*
Colleen M. O'Sullivan *(Chief Acctg & Treasury Officer & Sr VP)*
Tami Froese *(Chief Supply Chain Officer)*
Rob Armstrong *(CMO)*
Michael Steele *(VP-IR)*
Kasia Fahmy *(Mgr-Industry Analyst Rels)*
Tamara Froese *(Chief Supply Chain Officer)*
Richard Hudson *(Chief Revenue Officer)*
William J. Burns *(CEO)*

Subsidiaries:

Adaptive Vision Spolka z ograniczona odpowiedzialnoscia   (1)
Bojkowska Str 41N, 44-141, Gliwice, Poland
Tel.: (48) 32 213 3224
Web Site: https://www.adaptive-vision.com
Automation Machinery Mfr
N.A.I.C.S.: 333998

Genuine Zebra Technologies Trading (Shanghai) Co., Ltd.   (1)
2801 & 2807 to 2812 28F HKRI Centre Two, No 288 Shimen Yi Road Jing'an District, Shanghai, 200041, China
Tel.: (86) 2161086109
Web Site: http://www.zebra.com
Automatic Identification & Data Capture; Bar Code Label Printers & Related Products Supplier
N.A.I.C.S.: 334118

Hart Systems, Inc.   (1)
60 Plant Ave, Hauppauge, NY 11788-8814
Tel.: (631) 439-8200
Web Site: http://www.hartsystems.com
Sales Range: $1-9.9 Million
Emp.: 65
Inventory Software Solutions
N.A.I.C.S.: 513210

Subsidiary (Non-US):

Hart Systems UK Ltd.   (2)
Unit 84-83 Canterbury Innovation Centre, University Road, Canterbury, C27FG, Kent, United Kingdom
Tel.: (44) 1227 811718
Custom Inventory Software
N.A.I.C.S.: 513210

Matrox Electronic Systems Ltd.   (1)
1055 St Regis Blvd, Dorval, H9P 2T4, QC, Canada
Tel.: (514) 685-2630

Web Site: http://www.matrox.com
Sales Range: $150-199.9 Million
Emp.: 900
Graphics & Video Equipment Software Solutions
N.A.I.C.S.: 334118
Lorne Trottier *(Co-Founder, Pres & CEO)*

Subsidiary (Non-US):

Matrox Electronic Systems GmbH   (2)
Inselkammerstrasse 8, 82008, Unterhaching, Germany
Tel.: (49) 89621700
Web Site: http://www.matrox.com
Sales Range: $25-49.9 Million
Emp.: 15
Software Publisher
N.A.I.C.S.: 513210

Matrox Europe Ltd   (2)
Unit 2400 Cork Airport Business Park, Cork, Ireland
Tel.: (353) 214325600
Electronic Components Distr
N.A.I.C.S.: 423990

Subsidiary (Domestic):

Matrox Graphics, Inc.   (2)
1055 St-Regis Blvd, Dorval, H9P 2T4, QC, Canada
Tel.: (514) 822-6000
Web Site: https://www.matrox.com
Software Publisher
N.A.I.C.S.: 513210
Lorne Trottier *(Pres & CEO)*
Aron Klein *(COO)*
Charles Nadeau *(Chief Corp Officer)*
Bruno Des Rosiers *(Sr VP)*
Vincent Khoury *(VP)*
Isabelle Montpetit *(VP)*

Subsidiary (Non-US):

Matrox Video and Imaging Technology Europe Limited   (2)
Chaplin House Widewateer Pl, Moorhall Road, Harefield, UB9 6NS, Middlesex, United Kingdom
Tel.: (44) 18958272220
Web Site: http://www.matrox.com
Software Publisher
N.A.I.C.S.: 513210

Metanetics Corporation   (1)
1 Motorola Plz, Holtsville, NY 11742-1300
Tel.: (631) 738-2400
Emp.: 9
Computer & Electronic Peripheral Mfr
N.A.I.C.S.: 423430

Mobile Integrated Technologies, Inc.   (1)
530 Wickham Lakes Dr, Melbourne, FL 32940
Tel.: (321) 412-6667
Computer & Electronic Peripheral Mfr
N.A.I.C.S.: 423430

Profitect, Inc.   (1)
200 Summit Dr Ste 405, Burlington, MA 01803
Tel.: (781) 290-0009
Web Site: http://www.profitect.com
Software Development Services
N.A.I.C.S.: 541511
Michele Schwanke *(Dir-Mktg)*

Psion Europe S.A.S.   (1)
Parc De La Duranne, 13100, Aix-en-Provence, Bouches Du Rhone, France
Tel.: (33) 442908809
Computer & Electronic Peripheral Mfr
N.A.I.C.S.: 423430

Psion Mobile Group, S.L.   (1)
Calle de Martinez Villergas 52, Madrid, 28027, Spain
Tel.: (34) 902014869
Computer & Electronic Peripheral Mfr
N.A.I.C.S.: 423430

Psion N.V.   (1)
Regus Berchem Uitbreidingstraat 84 3rd Floor, Berchem, 2600, Antwerp, Belgium
Tel.: (32) 32182095
Computer & Electronic Peripheral Mfr
N.A.I.C.S.: 423430

Psion Systems Inc.   (1)
84 Hines Road Unit A180, Ottawa, K2K 3G3, ON, Canada
Tel.: (613) 592-2592
Emp.: 12
Computer & Electronic Peripheral Mfr
N.A.I.C.S.: 423430

Psion Systems India Private Limited   (1)
International Home Deco Park Plot No 7 Sector 127 Taj Expressway, New Okhla Indus Dev Area Gautam Budh Nagar, Noida, 201301, Uttar Pradesh, India
Tel.: (91) 1204129843
Computer & Electronic Peripheral Mfr
N.A.I.C.S.: 423430

Psion Teklogix do Brasil Ltda   (1)
Rua Funchal 418, Vila Olimpia, Sao Paulo, Brazil
Tel.: (55) 1135217057
Computer & Electronic Peripheral Mfr
N.A.I.C.S.: 423430

Psion Teklogix, S.A. de C.V.   (1)
Sierra Mojada No 626 2O Piso, Mexico, 11010, Mexico
Tel.: (52) 5552843324
Emp.: 11
Communication Service
N.A.I.C.S.: 517810

Reflexis Systems (UK) Limited   (1)
Central 40 Chineham Business Park, Basingstoke, RG24 8GU, Hampshire, United Kingdom
Tel.: (44) 1256857310
IT Services
N.A.I.C.S.: 541519

Reflexis Systems GmbH   (1)
Kokkolastr 5-7, Ratingen, 40882, Dusseldorf, Germany
Tel.: (49) 21025646190
IT Services
N.A.I.C.S.: 541519

Reflexis Systems India Private Limited   (1)
Tower No 5 A Wing Upper Ground Floor, Cybercity Magarpatta City Hadapsar, Pune, 411 028, India
Tel.: (91) 2066257300
IT Services
N.A.I.C.S.: 541519

Reflexis Systems, Inc.   (1)
125 Townpark Dr Ste 400, Kennesaw, GA 30144
Web Site: http://www.reflexisinc.com
Custom Computer Programming Services
N.A.I.C.S.: 541511

Symbol Technologies Czech Republic s.r.o.   (1)
Kolejni 1, 612 00, Brno, Czech Republic
Tel.: (420) 420533336060
Computer & Electronic Peripheral Mfr
N.A.I.C.S.: 423430

Symbol Technologies Holdings Do Brasil Ltda.   (1)
Avenida Tambore 1077, Alphaville, 06460-000, Barueri, Brazil
Tel.: (55) 1141333152
Computer & Electronic Peripheral Mfr
N.A.I.C.S.: 423430

TEMPTIME Corp.   (1)
116 American Road, Morris Plains, NJ 07950
Tel.: (973) 984-6000
Web Site: http://www.temptimecorp.com
Sales Range: $550-599.9 Million
Medical Equipment Mfr
N.A.I.C.S.: 339112
Ted Prusik *(VP-Innovation)*
Nick Hart *(CFO)*
Brad Mataczynski *(Sr Dir-Mfg Ops)*
Tony Cecchin *(Pres)*
Chris Caulfield *(VP)*
Steven Feldman *(Sr Dir-Quality, R&D & Regulatory Affairs)*
Bill Smiley *(Fin Dir)*

Telxon Corporation   (1)
1 Motorola Plz, Holtsville, NY 11742-1300

Zebra Technologies Corporation—(Continued)

Tel.: (631) 738-2400
Emp.: 1,549
Computer & Electronic Peripheral Mfr
N.A.I.C.S.: 423430

Xplore Technologies Corp. (1)
8601 RR 2222 Bldg II, Austin, TX 78730
Tel.: (512) 637-1100
Web Site: http://www.xploretech.com
Rev.: $86,852,000
Assets: $63,578,000
Liabilities: $33,303,000
Net Worth: $30,275,000
Earnings: $300,000
Emp.: 95
Fiscal Year-end: 03/31/2018
Mobile & Wireless Engineering, Manufacturing, Marketing & Supporting Services
N.A.I.C.S.: 541512

Subsidiary (Domestic):

Xplore Technologies Corporation of America (2)
8601 RR 2222 Bldg 2 Ste 100, Austin, TX 78730
Tel.: (512) 637-1100
Web Site: http://www.xploretech.com
Computer Products Distr
N.A.I.C.S.: 423430

Zebra Enterprise Solutions B.V.B.A. (1)
Regus Berchem, Uitbredingstraat 84 3rd Floor, 2600, Antwerp, Belgium
Tel.: (32) 32182000
Web Site: http://www.zebra.com
Printers & Global Positioning System Equipment Mfr
N.A.I.C.S.: 334220

Zebra Technologies (Hong Kong) Limited (1)
Room 1501-08 Millennium City 5 418 Kwun Tong Road, Kwun Tong, Hong Kong, China (Hong Kong)
Tel.: (852) 37537560
Computer & Electronic Peripheral Mfr
N.A.I.C.S.: 423430

Zebra Technologies (New Zealand) Limited (1)
Suite 115 Zone 23 Edwin Street, Mount Eden, Auckland, 1024, New Zealand
Tel.: (64) 96383290
Web Site: http://www.zebra.com
Computer & Electronic Peripheral Mfr
N.A.I.C.S.: 423430

Zebra Technologies AB (1)
Svardvagen 7, 182 33, Danderyd, Sweden
Tel.: (46) 86234560
Web Site: http://www.zebra.com
Bar Code Label Printers & Related Products Supplier
N.A.I.C.S.: 334118

Zebra Technologies Argentina S.A. (1)
1860 Juan Diaz de Solis Street 3rd Floor, Vicente Lopez, Buenos Aires, Argentina
Tel.: (54) 1151993196
Electronic Components Mfr
N.A.I.C.S.: 334419

Zebra Technologies Asia Pacific, LLC (1)
120 Robinson Road 06-01 Parakou Building, Singapore, 068913, Singapore (100%)
Tel.: (65) 68580722
Sales Range: $25-49.9 Million
Emp.: 19
On-Demand Bar Code Label Printers & Related Supplies
N.A.I.C.S.: 423430
Ryan Goh (VP & Gen Mgr)

Zebra Technologies Austria GmbH (1)
Albertgasse 35, 1080, Vienna, Austria
Tel.: (43) 13619959
Computer & Electronic Peripheral Mfr
N.A.I.C.S.: 423430

Zebra Technologies B.V. (1)
Printerweg 36A, Amersfoort, 3821AD, Netherlands
Tel.: (31) 334505040

Web Site: http://www.zebra.com
Emp.: 10
Bar Code Label Printers & Related Supplier
N.A.I.C.S.: 334118

Zebra Technologies Colombia S.A.S. (1)
Calle 93 No 13-45 Floor 7 Suite 701 702, Bogota, Colombia
Tel.: (57) 16230199
Communication Service
N.A.I.C.S.: 423430

Zebra Technologies Corp. (1)
30601 W Agoura Rd, Agoura Hills, CA 91301-2013
Tel.: (805) 579-1800
Web Site: http://www.zebra.com
Sales Range: $250-299.9 Million
Emp.: 800
Printing Services
N.A.I.C.S.: 334118

Zebra Technologies Europe Limited (1)
Dukes Meadow Millboard Road, Bourne End, SL8 5XF, Bucks, United Kingdom
Tel.: (44) 162 855 6000
Web Site: https://www.zebra.com
Sales Range: $150-199.9 Million
Emp.: 170
On-Demand Bar Code Label Printers & Related Supplies
N.A.I.C.S.: 423430

Zebra Technologies Europe Sales Company, LLC (1)
Pittman Way Fulwood, Preston, PR2 9ZD, United Kingdom (100%)
Tel.: (44) 1772693069
Web Site: http://www.accesszebra.com
Sales Range: $50-74.9 Million
Emp.: 100
On-Demand Bar Code Label Printers & Related Supplies
N.A.I.C.S.: 423430

Zebra Technologies Germany GmbH (1)
Ernst-Dietrich-Platz 2, Ratingen, 40882, Dusseldorf, Germany
Tel.: (49) 21025585900
Communication Service
N.A.I.C.S.: 423430
Nadja Grosse (Mgr-HR)

Zebra Technologies International, LLC (1)
333 Corporate Woods Pkwy, Vernon Hills, IL 60061
Tel.: (847) 634-6700
Web Site: http://www.zebra.com
Sales Range: $100-124.9 Million
Emp.: 1,000
On-Demand Bar Code Label Printers & Related Supplies
N.A.I.C.S.: 334118

Zebra Technologies Italy S.R.L. (1)
Via Giovanni Lorenzini 4, Milan, 20139, Italy
Tel.: (39) 0282951530
Computer & Electronic Peripheral Mfr
N.A.I.C.S.: 423430
Alessandra Curzi (Mgr-Field Mktg)

Zebra Technologies Japan Co. Ltd. (1)
14F Uchisaiwai-Cho Heiwa Building 1-5-2 Uchisaiwai-Cho, Chiyoda-ku, Tokyo, 100-0011, Japan
Tel.: (81) 335118541
Computer & Electronic Peripheral Mfr
N.A.I.C.S.: 423430

Zebra Technologies Korea YCH (1)
Level 21 - Suite 50 International Finance Centre Seoul, Two IFC 10 Gukjegeumyung-Ro Youngdeungpo-Gu, 150045, Seoul, Korea (South)
Tel.: (82) 261376510
Computer & Electronic Peripheral Mfr
N.A.I.C.S.: 423430

Zebra Technologies Lanka (Private) Limited (1)
6th 7th Floor No 200 Maga Tower Narahenpita - Nawala Road, Nawala, 11222, Colombo, Sri Lanka
Tel.: (94) 112870900
Computer & Electronic Peripheral Mfr

N.A.I.C.S.: 423430
Vipula Liyanaarachchi (Mgr-Engrg)

Zebra Technologies Latin America, LLC (1)
9850 NW 41st St Ste 110, Doral, FL 33178-2990
Tel.: (305) 558-8470
Web Site: http://www.zebra.com
Sales Range: $500-549.9 Million
Emp.: 2,000
On-Demand Bar Code Label Printers & Related Supplies
N.A.I.C.S.: 561910

Zebra Technologies Magyarorszag Kft. (1)
Arpad Fejedelem utja 26-28 Suite 535, 1023, Budapest, Hungary
Tel.: (36) 18880500
Computer & Electronic Peripheral Mfr
N.A.I.C.S.: 423430
Imre Bogdan (Country Mgr)

Zebra Technologies Netherlands B.V. (1)
IJsselburcht 3, 6825 BS, Arnhem, Netherlands
Tel.: (31) 263653530
Web Site: http://www.zebra.com
Data Management Services
N.A.I.C.S.: 541513

Zebra Technologies Spain, S.L. (1)
Calle Martinez Villergas 52 Bloque C, 28027, Madrid, Spain
Tel.: (34) 911237350
Electrical Apparatus & Equipment Whslr
N.A.I.C.S.: 423610

Zebra Teknolojileri Sistem Cozumleri Anonim Sirketa (1)
Barbaros Mah Mor Sumbul Sok, No 1 Varyap Meridian Business I-Blok Kat 8 Daire Atasehir, 34746, Istanbul, Turkiye
Tel.: (90) 2166888515
Electrical Apparatus & Equipment Whslr
N.A.I.C.S.: 423610

ZEDGE, INC.
1178 Broadway 3rd Fl Ste 1450, New York, NY 10001
Tel.: (330) 577-3424   DE
Web Site: https://www.zedge.net
Year Founded: 2008
ZDGE—(NYSEAMEX)
Rev.: $30,091,000
Assets: $38,195,000
Liabilities: $7,299,000
Net Worth: $30,896,000
Earnings: ($9,171,000)
Emp.: 99
Fiscal Year-end: 07/31/24
Mobile Application Development Services
N.A.I.C.S.: 541511
Joyce J. Mason (Sec)
Howard S. Jonas (Vice Chm)
Yi Tsai (CFO & Treas)
Michael C. Jonas (Chm)
Jonathan Reich (Pres & CEO)

ZENITH CAPITAL CORPORATION
535 Mission St 14th Fl, San Francisco, CA 94105
Tel.: (415) 470-5600
Web Site:
https://www.zenithepigenetics.com
ZENI.P—(TSXV)
Asset Management Services
N.A.I.C.S.: 523940
Donald J. McCaffrey (Chm, Pres & CEO)
Sanjay Lakhotia (Chief Bus Officer)
Brad Cann (CFO)
Henrik C. Hansen (Sr VP-Ops)

ZENOVIA DIGITAL EXCHANGE CORPORATION
3141 Fairview Park Dr Ste 160, Falls Church, VA 20042

Tel.: (804) 306-8217   NV
Year Founded: 2010
ZDEC—(OTCEM)
Sales Range: Less than $1 Million
Holding Company; Advertising Services
N.A.I.C.S.: 551112

ZENTALIS PHARMACEUTICALS, INC.
10275 Science Ctr Dr Ste 200, San Diego, CA 92121
Tel.: (212) 433-3791   DE
Web Site: https://www.zentalis.com
Year Founded: 2014
ZNTL—(NASDAQ)
Rev.: $5,987,000
Assets: $539,310,000
Liabilities: $105,286,000
Net Worth: $434,024,000
Earnings: ($236,806,000)
Emp.: 156
Fiscal Year-end: 12/31/22
Biotechnology Research & Development Services
N.A.I.C.S.: 541714
Cam S. Gallagher (Co-Founder, Pres, Interim CFO & Treas)
Kyle Rasbach (Chief Bus Officer)
Kevin D. Bunker (Co-Founder & Chief Scientific Officer)
Dimitris Voliotis (Sr VP-Clinical Dev)
Ahmed Samatar (Sr VP-Oncology Res)
Peter Huang (Sr VP-Discovery Res)
Meena Rao (VP-Regulatory Affairs & Quality Assurance)
Orna Bornstein (VP-Clinical Ops)
David M. Johnson (Chm)
Robert DiVasto (VP-Mfg & Supply)
Diana F. Hausman (Chief Medical Officer)
Kimberly L. Blackwell (CEO)

ZEO ENERGY CORP.
7625 Little Rd STE 200a, New Port Richey, FL 34654
Tel.: (949) 574-3860   Ky
Web Site:
https://investors.zeoenergy.com
Year Founded: 2021
ZEO—(NASDAQ)
Rev.: $2,057,931
Assets: $16,098,529
Liabilities: $8,905,886
Net Worth: ($8,826,089)
Earnings: ($3,001,194)
Fiscal Year-end: 12/31/23
Electric Power Distribution
N.A.I.C.S.: 221122
Timothy Bridgewater (CEO & CFO)
Kalen Larsen (COO)
Gianluca Guy (Chief Strategy Officer & Chief Installation Officer)
Brandon Bridgewater (Chief Sls Officer)
Stirling Adams (Gen Counsel & Sec)

ZEONS CORP.
123 N Post Oak Ln Ste 400, Houston, TX 77024
Tel.: (832) 882-6675   NV
Web Site: http://www.zeon.co.jp
ZEON—(OTCIQ)
Oil & Gas Equipment Mfr & Distr
N.A.I.C.S.: 333132
Mahesh Kanojia (CEO)
Naved Jafari (Pres & Sec)

ZERIFY, INC.
1090 King Georges Post Rd Ste 603, Edison, NJ 08837
Tel.: (732) 661-9641   NJ
Web Site: https://www.zerify.com
Year Founded: 2001

ZRFY—(OTCIQ)
Rev.: $103,000
Assets: $313,000
Liabilities: $15,168,000
Net Worth: ($14,855,000)
Earnings: ($8,808,000)
Emp.: 16
Fiscal Year-end: 12/31/22
Software Publisher
N.A.I.C.S.: 513210
Mark L. Kay (Chm & CEO)
Ramarao Pemmaraju (CTO)
George Waller (Co-Founder, Exec VP & Head-Mktg)
Mark Joseph Corrao (Co-Founder)

ZERO GRAVITY SOLUTIONS, INC.

190 NW Spanish River Blvd Ste 101, Boca Raton, FL 33431
Tel.: (561) 416-0400
Web Site: https://www.zerogsi.com
ZGSI—(OTCIQ)
Sales Range: Less than $1 Million
Emp.: 17
Biotechnology Products & Services
N.A.I.C.S.: 541714
Harvey N. Klebanoff (Founder & Chm)
Julie Bloch (VP-Comm)
Timothy A. Peach (CEO & CFO)
Victor Robenson (VP-Bus Dev, Mktg & Sls)

Subsidiaries:

BAM Agricultural Solutions, Inc.   (1)
190 NW Spanish River Blvd, Boca Raton, FL 33431
Tel.: (561) 416-0400
Web Site: http://www.bamagsolutions.com
Agricultural Chemical Product Mfr & Distr
N.A.I.C.S.: 325320
Timothy A. Peach (Mgr-Mfg Ops)
Patricio Manzur (Mgr-Mfg Ops)
Victor Robenson (VP-Bus Dev, Mktg & Sls)

ZETA GLOBAL HOLDINGS CORP.

3 Park Ave 33rd Fl, New York, NY 10016
Tel.: (212) 967-5055   DE
Web Site:
  https://www.zetaglobal.com
Year Founded: 2012
ZETA—(NYSE)
Rev.: $590,961,000
Assets: $466,502,000
Liabilities: $338,472,000
Net Worth: $128,030,000
Earnings: ($279,239,000)
Emp.: 1,604
Fiscal Year-end: 12/31/22
Offices of Other Holding Companies
N.A.I.C.S.: 551112
Steven Gerber (Pres & COO)
Christopher Greiner (CFO)
Matthew Mobley (Pres-Customer Relationship Mgmt)
Scott Schmitz (Sr VP-IR)
David A. Steinberg (Co-Founder, Chm & CEO)
David A. Steinberg (Co-Founder, Chm & CEO)
John Sculley (Co-Founder & Vice Chm)

Subsidiaries:

Apptness Media Group, LLC   (1)
399 NW 2nd Ave Ste 100, Boca Raton, FL 33432
Tel.: (561) 299-1053
Web Site: http://www.apptness.io
Sales Range: $1-9.9 Million
Emp.: 10
Media Advertising Services
N.A.I.C.S.: 541850
Dominik Szabo (CEO)

LiveIntent, Inc.   (1)
100 Church St, New York, NY 10007
Tel.: (212) 792-5348
Web Site: http://www.liveintent.com
Sales Range: $1-9.9 Million
Emp.: 180
Digital Display Advertising
N.A.I.C.S.: 541810
Matt Keiser (Founder & CEO)
Jason Oates (Chief Bus Officer)
Kyle Brown (VP-Engrg)
Jon Beck (Exec VP-Sls)
John Engler (VP-Sls)
Dash Teter (Dir-Media Ops & Analytics)
Julia Rieger (VP-Product Mktg)
Helen Chung (Dir-Acct Mgmt)
Ali Swerdlow (VP-IR)
Jason Kelly (Pres)
Gary Deutsch (CFO)
Luther Knox (Dir-Creative)
Karla Partilla (VP & Publr-Dev)
Suneet Bhatt (VP-Ops)
Kerel Cooper (VP-Platform Dev)
Tom Buoniello (VP-Product)
Joseph Dressler (VP-Sls)

ZEUUS, INC.

31 W 27th St, New York, NY 10001
Tel.: (305) 853-8178   NV
Year Founded: 2016
ZUUS—(OTCIQ)
Assets: $1,264,557
Liabilities: $2,331,279
Net Worth: ($1,066,722)
Earnings: ($790,033)
Emp.: 2
Fiscal Year-end: 09/30/23
Visa Consulting Services
N.A.I.C.S.: 541611
Bassam Al-Mutawa (Pres & CEO)

ZEVIA PBC

15821 Ventura Blvd Ste 145, Encino, CA 91436   DE
Web Site: https://www.zevia.com
Year Founded: 2021
ZVIA—(NYSE)
Rev.: $166,424,000
Assets: $90,857,000
Liabilities: $29,090,000
Net Worth: $61,767,000
Earnings: ($28,322,000)
Emp.: 115
Fiscal Year-end: 12/31/23
Drink Product Mfr
N.A.I.C.S.: 312111
Girish Satya (CFO & Principal Acctg Officer)
Amy E. Taylor (Pres & CEO)
Lorna R. Simms (Gen Counsel, Sec & Sr VP)

ZEVRA THERAPEUTICS, INC.

1180 Celebration Blvd Ste 103, Celebration, FL 34747
Tel.: (321) 939-3416   DE
Web Site: https://www.zevra.com
Year Founded: 2006
ZVRA—(NASDAQ)
Rev.: $10,458,000
Assets: $115,529,000
Liabilities: $29,722,000
Net Worth: $85,807,000
Earnings: ($41,543,000)
Emp.: 32
Fiscal Year-end: 12/31/22
Pharmaceutical Preparation Manufacturing
N.A.I.C.S.: 325412
R. LaDuane Clifton (CFO, Treas & Sec)
Adrian Quartel (Chief Medical Officer)
Joshua M. Schafer (Chief Comml Officer & Exec VP-Bus Dev)
Christal M. M. Mickle (Co-Founder & Chief Dev Officer)
Travis C. Mickle (Co-Founder)
Sven Guenther (Exec VP-R&D)
Christopher M. Lauderback (VP-Mfg)

Rene A. Braeckman (VP-Clinical Dev)
Timothy J. Sangiovanni (VP & Controller)
Andrew Barrett (VP-Scientific Affairs)
Neil F. McFarlane (Pres & CEO)
Nichol Ochsner (VP-IR & Corp Comm)

Subsidiaries:

Acer Therapeutics, Inc.   (1)
1 Gateway Ctr Ste 356 300 Washington St, Newton, MA 02458
Tel.: (281) 272-9331
Web Site: https://www.acertx.com
Assets: $11,624,226
Liabilities: $28,385,498
Net Worth: ($16,761,272)
Earnings: ($26,237,315)
Emp.: 33
Fiscal Year-end: 12/31/2022
Biotechnology Cellular Therapy Research & Services
N.A.I.C.S.: 541714
Donald R. Joseph (Chief Legal Officer & Sec)
John M. Klopp (Chief Technical Officer)
Renee Carroll (VP-Regulatory Affairs)
Jason Kneeland (VP-Fin & Controller)
Bernie Paul (VP-HR)
Bill DeVincenzi (VP-Quality)
Jeff Davis (Chief Bus Officer)
Tanya Hayden (COO)

ZHONG YA INTERNATIONAL LTD

64 N Pecos Ste 900, Henderson, NV 89074
Tel.: (702) 472-5066   NV
Year Founded: 2008
ZYJT—(OTCIQ)
Liabilities: $72,698
Net Worth: ($72,698)
Earnings: ($35,294)
Fiscal Year-end: 12/31/19
Landscaping Services
N.A.I.C.S.: 561730
Wenjian Liu (CEO, CFO & Sec)

ZHRH CORPORATION

50 W Liberty St Ste 880, Reno, NV 89501
Tel.: (775) 322-0626   NV
Year Founded: 2011
ZHEC—(OTCEM)
Liabilities: $10,437
Net Worth: ($10,437)
Earnings: ($28,390)
Emp.: 3
Fiscal Year-end: 06/30/15
Holding Company; Bedding Products Distr
N.A.I.C.S.: 551112

ZICIX CORP.

710 N Post Oak Rd Ste 400, Houston, TX 77024
Tel.: (281) 540-0500   NV
Year Founded: 1979
ZICX—(OTCIQ)
Medical Diagnostic Imaging Centre Services
N.A.I.C.S.: 621512

ZIFF DAVIS, INC.

114 5th Ave 15th Fl, New York, NY 10011
Tel.: (212) 503-3500   DE
Web Site: https://www.ziffdavis.com
Year Founded: 1995
ZD—(NASDAQ)
Rev.: $1,390,997,000
Assets: $3,533,270,000
Liabilities: $1,640,659,000
Net Worth: $1,892,611,000
Earnings: $63,757,000
Emp.: 4,400
Fiscal Year-end: 12/31/22
Wired Telecommunications Carriers

N.A.I.C.S.: 517111
Nan-Kirsten Forte (Exec VP & Gen Mgr-Everyday Health Grp Consumer Div)
Stephen J. Bye (Pres-Connectivity)
Vivek Shah (Pres & CEO)
Jeremy Rossen (Gen Counsel & Exec VP)
Dan Stone (Pres-Everyday Health Grp)
Joey Fortuna (CTO)
Rebecca Wright (VP-Corp Comm)
Stephen Bye (Pres-Connectivity)
Darrah Feldman (Sr VP)
Bret Richter (CFO & Interim Principal Acctg Officer)

Subsidiaries:

CampaignerCRM   (1)
18 Commerce Way Ste 4000, Woburn, MA 01801
Web Site: https://www.campaignercrm.com
Sales Range: $1-9.9 Million
CRM Software
N.A.I.C.S.: 513210
Jeffrey Cody (Sr Mgr-Mktg)
Cheryl Renton (Mgr-Mktg Comm & PR)
Bob Villemure (Sr Mgr-Web)

Ekahau Oy   (1)
Jaakonkatu 5, 00100, Helsinki, Finland
Tel.: (358) 207435910
Wireless Network Services
N.A.I.C.S.: 517810

Excel Micro, LLC   (1)
401 Pilgrim Ln Ste 200, Drexel Hill, PA 19026
Security Software Programming Services
N.A.I.C.S.: 541511

Inspired eLearning, LLC   (1)
4630 N Loop 1604 W Ste 401, San Antonio, TX 78249
Tel.: (210) 579-0224
Web Site: http://www.inspiredelearning.com
Sales Range: $1-9.9 Million
Emp.: 40
Learning Services
N.A.I.C.S.: 611691
John Trest (Chief Learning Officer)

KeepItSafe, Inc.   (1)
700 S Flower St Ste 1500, Los Angeles, CA 90017
Web Site: http://www.keepitsafe.com
Computer Disaster Recovery Services
N.A.I.C.S.: 541519

Livedrive Internet Limited   (1)
3rd Floor 18 Mansell Street, London, E1 8AA, United Kingdom
Tel.: (44) 2031376446
Web Site: https://www2.livedrive.com
Computer Data Storage Services
N.A.I.C.S.: 518210

Prime Education, LLC   (1)
5900 N Andrews Ave Ste 802, Fort Lauderdale, FL 33309
Tel.: (954) 718-6055
Web Site: https://www.primece.com
Educational Institution Operator
N.A.I.C.S.: 611310
Kathleen Moreo (Founder)
Jeffrey Carter (VP-Population Health & Res)
Cherilyn Heggen (VP-Scientific Affairs)
Chris Napolitan (Mng Dir)

Root Wireless, Inc.   (1)
2606 116th Ave NE Ste 100, Bellevue, WA 98004
Tel.: (425) 250-5010
Web Site: https://www.rootmetrics.com
Business Support Services
N.A.I.C.S.: 561499

SaleBuild, Inc.   (1)
625 2nd St, San Francisco, CA 94107
Web Site: https://www.go.salesify.com
Marketing Management Consulting Services
N.A.I.C.S.: 541613
Gurdeep Chimni (Co-Founder)
Raj Hajela (Co-Founder)
Jim Riesenbach (Exec VP)

Ziff Davis, Inc.—(Continued)

The Electric Mail Company (1)
Ste 300 3999 Henning Dr, Burnaby, V5C
6P9, BC, Canada
Tel.: (604) 482-1111
Web Site: http://www.electricmail.com
Sales Range: $1-9.9 Million
Emp.: 23
Electronic Messaging Services
N.A.I.C.S.: 541512

Yotta280, Inc. (1)
9310 Old Kings Rd S Ste 401, Jacksonville,
FL 32257
Tel.: (904) 674-2110
Web Site: http://www.yotta280.com
Custom Computer Programming Services
N.A.I.C.S.: 541511

Ziff Davis, LLP (1)
28 E 28th St, New York, NY 10016
Tel.: (212) 503-3500
Web Site: http://www.ziffdavis.com
Sales Range: $300-349.9 Million
Emp.: 350
Online Trade Magazines & Websites Pub-
lisher
N.A.I.C.S.: 513120
Steve Horowitz (Pres)
Stephen Hicks (Gen Counsel & Sec)
Brian Stewart (CFO)

Subsidiary (Domestic):

Everyday Health, Inc. (2)
345 Hudson St 16th Fl, New York, NY
10014
Tel.: (646) 728-9500
Web Site: http://www.everydayhealth.com
Online Health & Information Publishing Ser-
vices
N.A.I.C.S.: 519290
Dakila D. Divina (VP-Editorial Ops & Spe-
cial Projects)
Maura Corrigan (Mng Editor)
George Vernadakis (VP-Content Products &
Programming)
Ingrid Strauch (Sr Editor)
Elizabeth DeVita Raeburn (Sr Editor)
Melinda Carstensen (Sr Editor)
Amy Kraft (Sr Editor)
Denise Maher (Sr Editor)
Bethany Rouslin (Sr Editor-Photo)
Kelly Kennedy (Mgr-Nutrition)
Sarah DiGiulio (Editor-Contributing)
Margot Slade (Editor-Contributing)
Pamela Kaufman (Sr Editor)
Audra Marin (Editor-Photo)

Subsidiary (Domestic):

**Arthur L Davis Publishing Agency,
Inc.** (3)
517 Washington St, Cedar Falls, IA 50613-
2842
Tel.: (319) 277-2414
Web Site: http://www.aldpub.com
Rev.: $5,800,000
Emp.: 32
Periodicals-Publishing/Printing
N.A.I.C.S.: 513120
Mark Miller (Gen Mgr)
Monique Heddens (Mgr-Media Production)
Laurie Knowler (Coord-Sls Support)
Elizabeth Miller (Office Mgr)
Nancy Miller (Pres)
Stephen Miller (Mgr-Sls)

BabyCenter, LLC (3)
163 Freelon St, San Francisco, CA 94107-
1624
Tel.: (415) 537-0900
Web Site: http://www.babycenter.com
Baby Products Retailer & Online Informa-
tion for Expecting Mothers
N.A.I.C.S.: 812990
Linda I. Murray (Editor-in-Chief)
Scott Adler (Mng Editor-Global)

Castle Connolly Medical Ltd. (3)
42 W 24th St 2nd Fl, New York, NY 10010
Tel.: (212) 367-8400
Web Site: http://www.castleconnolly.com
Sales Range: $25-49.9 Million
Emp.: 20
Internet & Publishing Company in Con-
sumer Health
N.A.I.C.S.: 513130

DoctorDirectory.com, LLC (3)
1 Page Ave Ste 280, Asheville, NC 28801
Tel.: (828) 255-0012
Web Site: http://www.doctordirectory.com
Online Healthcare Professional Directory
Services
N.A.I.C.S.: 513140

MedPage Today, LLC (3)
114 5th Ave 15th Fl, New York, NY 10011
Web Site: https://www.medpagetoday.com
Health Care Srvices
N.A.I.C.S.: 621610
Greg Laub (Dir-Video Dev)
John Gever (Mng Editor)
Charles Bankhead (Sr Editor)
Crystal Phend (Sr Editor)
Joyce Frieden (Editor-Washington)
Rachel Warren (Sr VP-Editorial)

Subsidiary (Domestic):

ExtremeTech (2)
28 E 28th St, New York, NY 10016
Tel.: (212) 503-5100
Web Site: http://www.extremetech.com
Magazine Publisher
N.A.I.C.S.: 513120
Jamie Lendino (Editor-in-Chief)
Joel Hruska (Sr Editor)

IGN Entertainment, Inc. (2)
625 2nd St 3rd Fl, San Francisco, CA
94107
Tel.: (415) 896-3700
Web Site: https://corp.ign.com
Sales Range: $50-74.9 Million
Emp.: 300
Online Entertainment & Media Products &
Services
N.A.I.C.S.: 518210

Unit (Domestic):

PC Magazine (2)
28 E 28th St, New York, NY 10016
Tel.: (212) 503-3500
Web Site: http://www.pcmag.com
Sales Range: $100-124.9 Million
Computer Related Magazine Publisher
N.A.I.C.S.: 513120
Wendy Sheehan Donnell (Exec Editor)
Sean Carroll (Mng Editor-Software, Secu-
rity, Internet, Bus & Networking)

Division (Domestic):

The Aberdeen Group, LLC (2)
451 D St Ste 710, Boston, MA 02210
Tel.: (617) 854-5200
Holding Company; Marketing Research &
Content Services
N.A.I.C.S.: 551112
Gary J. Skidmore (CEO)
Jay Adams (CFO)
Maribeth Ross (Chief Content Officer)
Charlie Allieri (Chief Data Officer)

Subsidiary (Domestic):

**Aberdeen Market Intelligence U.S.,
LLC** (3)
9980 Huennekens St Ste 100, San Diego,
CA 92121
Tel.: (858) 450-1667
Web Site: http://www.aberdeenservices.com
Marketing Research & Analytics Services
N.A.I.C.S.: 541613

Division (Domestic):

Ziff Davis B2B Focus, Inc. (2)
28 E 28th St, New York, NY 10016
Tel.: (212) 503-3500
Web Site: http://www.ziffdavis.com
Omni Channel Marketing Services
N.A.I.C.S.: 518210
Steve Horowitz (Pres)
Brian Stewart (CFO)

Subsidiary (Domestic):

Spiceworks, Inc. (3)
7801 N Capital of Texas Hwy Ste 300, Aus-
tin, TX 78731
Tel.: (512) 346-7743
Web Site: https://www.spiceworks.com
Sales Range: $1-9.9 Million
Emp.: 145
IT Information Services
N.A.I.C.S.: 519290

Subsidiary (Domestic):

emedia Communications, LLC (2)
200 N LaSalle St Ste 2450, Chicago, IL
60601
Tel.: (312) 754-6355
Web Site: http://www.emedia.com
Sales Range: $1-9.9 Million
Emp.: 30
Business-to-Business Lead Generation Ser-
vices
N.A.I.C.S.: 541910

**Zintel Communications Pty.
Limited** (1)
10/33 York St, Sydney, 2000, NSW, Austra-
lia
Tel.: (61) 280350700
Web Site: https://www.zintel.com.au
Telecommunication Hardware & Software
Solutions
N.A.I.C.S.: 517810

Subsidiary (Non-US):

Zintel Communications Ltd. (2)
Level 2 9 Wilkins St Freemans Bay, PO
Box 90373, Victoria St West, Auckland,
1142, New Zealand
Tel.: (64) 800946835
Web Site: https://www.zintel.co.nz
Telecommunication Servicesb
N.A.I.C.S.: 517810

eFax.com Inc. (1)
6922 Hollywood Blvd 5th Fl, Los Angeles,
CA 90028-6128 (100%)
Tel.: (323) 817-3207
Web Site: https://www.efax.com
Sales Range: $75-99.9 Million
Emp.: 200
Fax-to-Email Service
N.A.I.C.S.: 334118

iContact LLC (1)
2450 Perimeter Pk Dr, Morrisville, NC
27560
Tel.: (919) 917-6150
Web Site: http://www.icontact.com
Sales Range: $10-24.9 Million
Software Publisher
N.A.I.C.S.: 513210

Subsidiary (Domestic):

SEOmoz Inc. (2)
119 Pine St Ste 400, Seattle, WA 98101
Tel.: (206) 632-3171
Web Site: http://www.seomoz.org
Sales Range: $1-9.9 Million
Emp.: 60
Search Engine Optimization Software &
Tutorials
N.A.I.C.S.: 513210
Gillian Muessig (Co-Founder & Pres)
Rand Fishkin (Co-Founder)
Anthony Skinner (CTO)
Sarah Bird (CEO)
Andy Nelson (Dir-Growth Mktg)
Angela Cherry (Dir-Comm)
Annette Promes (CMO)
Brandon Forehead (Principal)
Derric Wise (Dir-Art)
Dudley Carr (VP-Engrg)
Glenn Wisegarver (CFO)
Jon White (Dir-Product)
Matthew Peters (Dir-Data Science)
Tim Resnik (VP-Strategic Plng)

iContact Marketing Corp. (1)
2121 RDU Ctr Dr Ste 210, Morrisville, NC
27560
Tel.: (919) 957-6150
Web Site: https://www.icontact.com
Online Marketing Services
N.A.I.C.S.: 561499

j2 Global Canada, Inc. (1)
2 Gurdwara Road Suite 300, Ottawa, K2E
1A2, ON, Canada
Tel.: (613) 733-0000
Web Site: http://www.j2global.com
Internet-Based Fax Communication & En-
hanced Voice Messaging Services
N.A.I.C.S.: 517810

j2 Global Ireland Limited (1)
Unit-3 Woodford Business Park Santry,
Dublin, Ireland
Tel.: (353) 16564996

Web Site: http://www.j2global.com
Telecommunication Servicesb
N.A.I.C.S.: 517810

onTargetJobs, Inc. (1)
114 5th Ave, New York, NY 10011
Tel.: (212) 503-3500
Online Career Services
N.A.I.C.S.: 541612

Subsidiary (Domestic):

BioSpace, Inc. (2)
10506 Justin Dr, Urbandale, IA 50322
Web Site: https://employer.biospace.com
Sales Range: $1-9.9 Million
Emp.: 75
Online Life Sciences & Career Information
Publisher
N.A.I.C.S.: 541820

RegionalHelpWanted.com, Inc. (2)
1085 Route 55 Unit 14, Lagrangeville, NY
12540
Web Site:
https://www.regionalhelpwanted.com
Sales Range: $10-24.9 Million
Emp.: 350
Employment Placement Services
N.A.I.C.S.: 561311

Subsidiary (Non-US):

onTargetJobs Canada, Inc. (2)
400-4789 Kingsway, Burnaby, V5H 0A3,
BC, Canada
Tel.: (604) 435-8991
Web Site: http://www.hcareers.com
Online Job Directory
N.A.I.C.S.: 519290

ZILLOW GROUP, INC.
1301 2nd Ave Fl 31, Seattle, WA
98101
Tel.: (206) 470-7000
Web Site:
https://www.zillowgroup.com
Year Founded: 2006
ZG—(NASDAQ)
Rev.: $1,945,000,000
Assets: $6,652,000,000
Liabilities: $2,126,000,000
Net Worth: $4,526,000,000
Earnings: ($158,000,000)
Emp.: 6,263
Fiscal Year-end: 12/31/23
Holding Company; Real Estate Web-
sites Publisher & Operator
N.A.I.C.S.: 551112
Spencer M. Rascoff (Founder)
Richard N. Barton (CEO)
Lloyd D. Frink (Chm & Co-Pres)
David A. Beitel (CTO)
Stan Humphries (Chief Analytics Offi-
cer)
Dan Spaulding (Chief People Officer)
Susan Daimler (Co-Pres)
Matt Daimler (Sr VP-Product)
Kristin Acker (Sr VP-Experience De-
sign)
Jun Choo (Sr VP-)
Brad Owens (Gen Counsel)
Christopher Roberts (Sr VP & Gen
Mgr-Zillow Rentals)
Toby Roberts (Sr VP-Info Tech)
Joshua Swift (Sr VP-Acquisitions &
Ops)
Rian Furey (Pres-Home Loans & Sr
VP-Mortgages)
Libby Cooper (VP-Mortgages)
Lucy Wohltman (VP-New Construc-
tion)
Ryan Berry (Sr VP-Risk
Management-Homes Div)
Tim Correia (Sr VP-Engineering-
Technology)
Kristina Adamski (VP-
Communications)
Eric Bailey (VP-User Experience)
Pritam Baxi (VP-Finance)
Sara Bonert (VP-Broker Svcs)

Caroline Burton (*VP & Gen Mgr-New York*)
Curt Beardsley (*VP-Industry Dev & MLS Partnerships*)
Kyle Bodmer (*VP-Resale & Asset Mgmt*)
Matt Corgan (*VP-Rentals Platform*)
Peter Edwards (*VP-Mktg & Analytics*)
Jeremy Hofmann (*CFO*)
Jenny Arden (*Chief Design Officer*)

Subsidiaries:

DotLoop, LLC   **(1)**
700 W Pete Rose Way Ste 446, Cincinnati, OH 45203
Tel.: (513) 257-0550
Web Site: https://www.dotloop.com
Emp.: 124
Activities Related to Real Estate
N.A.I.C.S.: 531390
Austin Allison (*Founder*)

Realnet Solutions, Inc.   **(1)**
3375 Scott Blvd Ste 303, Santa Clara, CA 95054
Tel.: (408) 748-0826
Distribution Software Publisher
N.A.I.C.S.: 513210

ShowingTime.com, Inc.   **(1)**
550 W Jackson Blvd Ste 800, Chicago, IL 60601
Web Site: http://www.showingtime.com
Activities Related to Real Estate
N.A.I.C.S.: 531390
Bill Kellogg (*VP-Product Mgmt*)

Trulia, LLC   **(1)**
535 Mission St Ste 700, San Francisco, CA 94105
Tel.: (415) 648-4358
Emp.: 1,055
Marketing Software Development Services
N.A.I.C.S.: 541511

VRX Media Group LLC   **(1)**
S 54th St, Milwaukee, WI 53221
Web Site: http://www.vrxmedia.com
Sales Range: $1-9.9 Million
Emp.: 200
Real Estate Manangement Services
N.A.I.C.S.: 531390
Nate Strom (*Founder & CEO*)

Zillow Group Marketplace, Inc. **(1)**
1301 2nd Ave Fl 31, Seattle, WA 98101
Tel.: (206) 470-7000
Web Site: http://www.zillow.com
Real Estate Services
N.A.I.C.S.: 531390

Zillow Group Mortgages, Inc.   **(1)**
1301 2nd Ave Ste 31, Seattle, WA 98101
Tel.: (206) 470-7000
Real Estate Rental & Leasing Services
N.A.I.C.S.: 531190

Zillow, Inc.   **(1)**
1301 2nd Ave Fl 31, Seattle, WA 98101
Tel.: (206) 470-7000
Web Site: https://www.zillow.com
Fiscal Year-end: 12/31/2014
Real Estate Services Website Publisher
N.A.I.C.S.: 518210
Spencer M. Rascoff (*Co-Founder*)

Subsidiary (Domestic):

Diverse Solutions, Inc.   **(2)**
1840 York Rd, Timonium, MD 21093
Web Site: https://www.diversesolutions.com
Sales Range: $1-9.9 Million
Emp.: 18
Online Real Estate Marketing Software & Services
N.A.I.C.S.: 513210

Mortech, Inc.   **(2)**
5960 S 57th St, Lincoln, NE 68516
Tel.: (402) 441-4647
Web Site: http://www.mortech.com
Sales Range: $1-9.9 Million
Emp.: 40
Software Publisher
N.A.I.C.S.: 513210

ZIMMER BIOMET HOLDINGS, INC.

345 E Main St, Warsaw, IN 46580
Tel.: (574) 373-3121   DE
Web Site:
  https://www.zimmerbiomet.com
Year Founded: 1927
ZBH—(NYSE)
Rev.: $7,394,200,000
Assets: $21,496,900,000
Liabilities: $9,008,800,000
Net Worth: $12,488,100,000
Earnings: $1,024,000,000
Emp.: 18,000
Fiscal Year-end: 12/31/23
Holding Company; Orthopedic Implants, Surgical Instruments & Other Health Care Products Developer, Mfr & Whslr
N.A.I.C.S.: 551112
Suketu P. Upadhyay (*CFO & Exec VP-Supply Chain, Fin, and Ops*)
Chad F. Phipps (*Gen Counsel, Sec & Sr VP*)
Sang Yi (*Pres-Asia Pacific*)
David J. Kunz (*Sr VP-Global Quality & Regulatory Affairs*)
Ivan Tornos (*Pres & CEO*)
Kenneth R. Tripp (*Sr VP-Logistics & Ops-Global*)
Zeeshan Tariq (*CIO & Sr VP*)
Keri P. Mattox (*Chief Comm & Admin Officer*)
Angela Main (*Chief Compliance Officer-Global & Sr VP*)
Rachel H. Ellingson (*Chief Strategy Officer & Sr VP*)
Lori Winkler (*Chief HR Officer*)
Paul Stellato (*Chief Acctg Officer*)

Subsidiaries:

3DIEMME Srl   **(1)**
Via Risorgimento 9, Cantu, 22063, Como, CO, Italy
Tel.: (39) 0317073353
Web Site: https://www.3diemme.it
Medical Device Mfr
N.A.I.C.S.: 339112

Accelero Health Partners, LLC **(1)**
117 VIP Dr Ste 320, Wexford, PA 15090
Tel.: (724) 799-8210
Web Site: http://accelerohealth.com
Health Care Srvices
N.A.I.C.S.: 621610
Michelle Bianco (*VP-Sls & Ops-Signature Solutions*)
Brian Crowley (*Reg Mgr-Sls*)

Alto Development Corporation **(1)**
5206 Asbury Rd, Farmingdale, NJ 07727
Tel.: (732) 938-2266
Web Site: https://www.aemedical.com
Sales Range: $10-24.9 Million
Surgical & Medical Instruments Mfr
N.A.I.C.S.: 339112
Michael Janish (*Chm*)
Thomas J. Sullivan (*Pres & CEO*)

Avitus Orthopaedics, Inc.   **(1)**
6 Armstrong Rd, Shelton, CT 06484
Tel.: (860) 404-6476
Web Site: https://www.avitusortho.com
Medical Equipment Mfr
N.A.I.C.S.: 339112

Beijing Montagne Medical Device Co. Ltd.   **(1)**
Building 1 No 21 Boxing 6th Road, Beijing Economic-Technological Development Area, Beijing, 100170, China
Tel.: (86) 1050879200
Health Care Equipment Mfr
N.A.I.C.S.: 339112

Biomet 3i do Brasil Comercio de Aparelhos Medicos Ltda.   **(1)**
Rua Machado Bitencourt 361-12 Andar, 04044-001, Sao Paulo, Brazil
Tel.: (55) 1135681300
Web Site: http://www.biomet.com
Health Care Srvices
N.A.I.C.S.: 622110

Biomet 3i, LLC   **(1)**

4555 Riverside Dr, Palm Beach Gardens, FL 33410
Tel.: (561) 776-6700
Web Site: http://www.biomet3i.com
Dental Reconstructive Implants Mfr
N.A.I.C.S.: 339114

Subsidiary (Non-US):

Biomet 3i Australia Pty. Ltd.   **(2)**
Unit 6 6-8 Byfield Street, North Ryde, 2113, NSW, Australia
Tel.: (61) 298554444
Web Site: http://au.biomet3i.com
Health Care Equipment Mfr & Distr
N.A.I.C.S.: 339112

Biomet 3i Belgium N.V.   **(2)**
Prins Boudewijnlaan 24C, 2550, Kontich, Belgium
Tel.: (32) 80050311
Web Site: http://www.zimmerbiomet.com
Medical Equipment Distr
N.A.I.C.S.: 423450

Biomet 3i Canada, Inc.   **(2)**
5805 Ch Saint-Francois, Montreal, H4S 1B6, QC, Canada
Tel.: (514) 956-9843
Web Site: http://www.biomet3icanada.com
Emp.: 27
Surgical & Medical Instrument Mfr
N.A.I.C.S.: 339113

Biomet 3i Dental Iberica SL   **(2)**
WTC Almeda Park Ed 4 Planta 2 - C Tirso de Molina 40, Cornella de Llobregat, 08940, Barcelona, Spain
Tel.: (34) 900800303
Web Site: http://www.biomet3i.es
Dental Care Services
N.A.I.C.S.: 621210

Biomet 3i France SAS   **(2)**
7 / 9 Rue Paul Vaillant Couturier, 92300, Levallois-Perret, France
Tel.: (33) 141054343
Web Site: http://www.biomet3i.fr
Surgical & Medical Instrument Mfr
N.A.I.C.S.: 339113

Biomet 3i Netherlands B.V.   **(2)**
Toermalijnring 600, 3316 LC, Dordrecht, Netherlands
Tel.: (31) 786292800
Surgical & Medical Instrument Mfr
N.A.I.C.S.: 339113

Biomet 3i Nordic AB   **(2)**
Sodra Forstadsgatan 3, 211 43, Malmo, Sweden
Tel.: (46) 40176090
Medical Equipment Distr
N.A.I.C.S.: 423450

Biomet 3i de Brasil Ltda.   **(2)**
Rua Machado Bitencourt 36112o andar Vila Clementino, Sao Paulo, 04044-001, Brazil
Tel.: (55) 1135681300
Web Site: http://br.biomet3i.com
Surgical & Medical Instrument Mfr & Distr
N.A.I.C.S.: 339113

Biomet Argentina SA   **(1)**
Monsenor Magliano 3051 PB Of 2 Pcia, Buenos Aires, 1642, Argentina
Tel.: (54) 1147001007
Health Care Equipment Mfr & Distr
N.A.I.C.S.: 339112
Martina Larralde (*Mgr-Admin & Fin*)

Biomet Australia Pty. Ltd.   **(1)**
Level 3 12 Narabang Way, Belrose, 2085, NSW, Australia
Tel.: (61) 294835400
Web Site: http://www.zimmerbiomet.com
Sales Range: $10-24.9 Million
Emp.: 30
Orthopedic Products Mfr & Sales
N.A.I.C.S.: 339112

Biomet Austria GmbH   **(1)**
Breitwies 1, 5303, Thalgau, Austria
Tel.: (43) 6235200330
Web Site: http://www.biomet.at
Medical Equipment Mfr
N.A.I.C.S.: 339113

Biomet Biologics, LLC   **(1)**
56 E Bell Dr, Warsaw, IN 46582
Tel.: (574) 267-6639

Web Site: https://www.zimmerbiomet.com
Biotechnology Products Designer & Mfr
N.A.I.C.S.: 339112

Biomet Cementing Technologies AB   **(1)**
Hyllie Alle 31, Malmo, 215 33, Sweden
Tel.: (46) 41625850
Medical Equipment Mfr & Distr
N.A.I.C.S.: 339113

Biomet Chile SA   **(1)**
Av Santa Clara 085 piso 7, Huechuraba, Santiago, Chile
Tel.: (56) 22690600
Surgical & Medical Instrument Mfr
N.A.I.C.S.: 339113
Gonzalo Andres Elgueta Noy (*Product Mgr*)

Biomet China Co., Ltd.   **(1)**
Room 07-09 25/F Lansheng Building No 2 Huaihai Road M, Shanghai, 200021, China
Tel.: (86) 2161369018
Surgical & Medical Instrument Mfr
N.A.I.C.S.: 339113
Qiong Wang (*Mgr-Acctg*)

Biomet El Salvador SA de CV   **(1)**
Paseo Escalon, 5015, San Salvador, El Salvador
Tel.: (503) 22636350
Surgical & Medical Instrument Mfr
N.A.I.C.S.: 339113

Biomet Europe B.V.   **(1)**
Toermalijnring 600, 3316 LC, Dordrecht, Netherlands
Tel.: (31) 786292909
Web Site: http://www.biometeurope.com
Sales Range: $50-74.9 Million
Emp.: 250
Holding Company; Regional Managing Office
N.A.I.C.S.: 551112

Subsidiary (Non-US):

BIOMET Spain Orthopaedics, S.L.   **(2)**
Calle Islas Baleares 50 Fuente del Jarro, Fuente del Jarro, 46988, Valencia, Spain
Tel.: (34) 961379500
Web Site: https://www.biomet.es
Medical Devices & Products Mfr
N.A.I.C.S.: 339112

Biomet Deutschland GmbH   **(2)**
Gustav-Krone Str 2, 14167, Berlin, Germany
Tel.: (49) 30845810
Web Site: https://www.biomet.de
Orthopedic & Prosthetic Devices, Arthroscopy Products & General Surgical Instruments Mfr
N.A.I.C.S.: 339112

Biomet France Sarl   **(2)**
Plateau de Lautagne, 26000, Valence, France
Tel.: (33) 475759100
Web Site: https://www.biomet.fr
Sales Range: $25-49.9 Million
Medical Devices & Products Mfr & Sales
N.A.I.C.S.: 339113

Biomet UK Limited   **(2)**
Waterton Industrial Estate, Bridgend, CF31 3XA, United Kingdom
Tel.: (44) 1656655221
Web Site: https://www.biomet.co.uk
Sales Range: $100-124.9 Million
Emp.: 600
Implantable Prosthetic Devices, Orthopedic Support Devices, Operating Room Supplies & Surgical Instruments Mfr
N.A.I.C.S.: 339112

Branch (Domestic):

Biomet UK Limited - Swindon   **(3)**
Dorcan Industrial Estate, Murdoch Road, Swindon, SN3 5HY, Wiltshire, United Kingdom
Tel.: (44) 1793 644 111
Web Site: http://www.biomet.co.uk
Sales Range: $25-49.9 Million
Emp.: 300
Mfr of Medical Devices & Surgical Instruments & Supplies
N.A.I.C.S.: 339112

Zimmer Biomet Holdings, Inc.—(Continued)

Biomet Fair Lawn LLC (1)
20-01 Pollitt Dr, Fair Lawn, NJ 07410
Tel.: (201) 797-7300
Health Care Equipment Mfr
N.A.I.C.S.: 339112

Biomet Global Supply Chain Center B.V. (1)
Toermalijnring 600, 3361 LC, Dordrecht, Netherlands
Tel.: (31) 786524449
Surgical & Medical Instrument Mfr
N.A.I.C.S.: 339113

Biomet Hellas SA (1)
54 Kapodistriou Moschato, Athens, 183 44, Greece
Tel.: (30) 2109200600
Web Site: http://www.biomet.gr
Surgical & Medical Instrument Mfr
N.A.I.C.S.: 339113

Biomet Medikal Drunjer Dadytym Pazarlama Yhracat ve Dys Ticaret Ltd. Sti. (1)
Istoc / Oksuzogullari Plaza 51 Sk E1 Blok No 6 Kat 6 34218, Bagcilar, Istanbul, Turkiye
Tel.: (90) 2126597727
Web Site: http://www.biomet.com.tr
Health Care Srvices
N.A.I.C.S.: 621610

Biomet Mexico S.A. de C.V. (1)
Avenida Periferico Sur 4829-401 Colonia Parques del Pedregal, Delegacion Tlalpan, 14010, Mexico, Distrito Federal, Mexico
Tel.: (52) 5551714693
Surgical & Medical Instrument Mfr
N.A.I.C.S.: 339113
Alejandro Sainz Sierra (Mgr-Sls-Orthopedics)

Biomet Orthopaedic India Private Limited (1)
Office No 811 Bldg No 8 Solitaire Corporate Park, Andheri Ghatkopar Link Road, Mumbai, 400093, India
Tel.: (91) 2242380800
Surgical & Medical Instrument Mfr
N.A.I.C.S.: 339113
Rajesh Rodrigues (Mgr-Natl Sls)

Biomet Orthopaedics Switzerland GmbH (1)
Riedstrasse 6, 8953, Dietikon, Switzerland
Tel.: (41) 442007600
Web Site: http://www.biometorthopaedics.ch
Surgical & Medical Instrument Mfr
N.A.I.C.S.: 339113

Biomet Orthopedics Puerto Rico, Inc. (1)
URB Caparra Terrace 1500 Americo Miranda Ave, San Juan, PR 00921-2136
Tel.: (787) 751-0650
Surgical & Medical Instrument Mfr
N.A.I.C.S.: 339113

Biomet Sports Medicine, LLC (1)
56 E Bell Dr, Warsaw, IN 46582
Tel.: (574) 267-6639
Web Site: https://www.biomet.com
Arthroscopy Products Mfr
N.A.I.C.S.: 339112

Biomet Trauma, LLC (1)
56 E Bell Dr, Warsaw, IN 46581-0587
Tel.: (574) 267-6639
Medical Equipment Mfr
N.A.I.C.S.: 339113
Wallen Scott (Supvr-Trauma)

Biomet US Inc. (1)
2410 Lillyvale Ave, Los Angeles, CA 90032
Tel.: (323) 225-2221
Health Care Srvices
N.A.I.C.S.: 621610

Biomet, Inc. (1)
56 E Bell Dr, Warsaw, IN 46582 **(100%)**
Tel.: (574) 267-6639
Web Site: https://www.biomet.com
Sales Range: $1-4.9 Billion
Emp.: 9,200
Holding Company; Orthopedic & Musculoskeletal Medical Device Designer, Mfr & Distr

N.A.I.C.S.: 339112
Adam Rudolph Johnson (Pres-Spine, Dental, CMF & Thoracic)

CD Diagnostics, Inc. (1)
650 Naamans Rd Ste 100, Claymont, DE 19703
Tel.: (302) 367-7770
Web Site: https://cddiagnostics.com
General Healthcare Services
N.A.I.C.S.: 621999

CD Laboratories, Inc. (1)
810 Gleneagles Ct Ste 100, Baltimore, MD 21286
Tel.: (410) 296-1400
Web Site: https://cdlaboratories.com
Laboratory Testing Services
N.A.I.C.S.: 541380

Cayenne Medical, Inc. (1)
16597 N 2nd St 101, Scottsdale, AZ 85260
Tel.: (480) 502-3661
Web Site: https://cayennemedical.com
Surgical & Medical Instrument Mfr
N.A.I.C.S.: 339112

Changzhou Biomet Medical Devices Co. Ltd. (1)
No 235 Chuangxin Road, Xinbei, Changzhou, 213000, Jiangsu, China
Tel.: (86) 51981985300
Surgical & Medical Instrument Mfr
N.A.I.C.S.: 339113
Livia Lu (Mgr-HR)

Citra Labs, Inc. (1)
55 Messina Dr, Braintree, MA 02184
Tel.: (781) 848-9386
Web Site: https://www.citra-labs.com
Pharmaceutical Product Whslr
N.A.I.C.S.: 424210

Clinical Graphics BV (1)
Molengraaffsingel 8, 2629 JD, Delft, Netherlands
Tel.: (31) 157440137
Web Site: https://www.clinicalgraphics.com
Health Care Srvices
N.A.I.C.S.: 622110
Mirjam van Bergen Walraven (Product Mgr)
Ivo Flipse (Project Mgr)

Compression Therapy Concepts, Inc. (1)
555 Industrial Way W, Eatontown, NJ 07724-2211
Tel.: (800) 993-9013
Web Site: http://www.ctcdvt.com
Medical Instrument Mfr
N.A.I.C.S.: 339112

Dornoch Medical Systems, Inc (1)
200 NW Pkwy Dr, Riverside, MO 64150
Tel.: (816) 505-2226
Health Care Equipment Whslr
N.A.I.C.S.: 423450

EBI, LLC (1)
399 Jefferson Rd, Parsippany, NJ 07054
Tel.: (973) 299-9300
Web Site: http://www.biomet.com
Sales Range: $75-99.9 Million
Emp.: 320
Holding Company; Electrical Stimulation, External Fixation & Spinal Surgery Device Mfr
N.A.I.C.S.: 551112

Subsidiary (Domestic):

EBI Medical Systems, LLC (2)
399 Jefferson Rd, Parsippany, NJ 07054
Tel.: (973) 299-9300
Sales Range: $75-99.9 Million
Mfr of Medical Products
N.A.I.C.S.: 423450

EBI Patient Care, Inc. (2)
Ste 1 Electro-Biology Blvd Los Frailes Industrial Park, Guaynabo, PR 00657-1359
Tel.: (787) 720-6855
Web Site: http://www.biomet.com
Sales Range: $25-49.9 Million
Emp.: 160
Mfr of Electrical Stimulation, External Fixation & Spinal Surgery Devices
N.A.I.C.S.: 339112

ETEX Corporation (1)

675 Massachusetts Ave 12th Fl, Cambridge, MA 02139
Tel.: (617) 577-7270
Web Site: https://www.etexcorp.com
Sales Range: $1-9.9 Million
Emp.: 40
Biomaterial Mfr
N.A.I.C.S.: 325414

Electro-Biology, LLC (1)
100 Interpace Pkwy, Parsippany, NJ 07054
Tel.: (973) 299-9022
Health Care Equipment Whslr
N.A.I.C.S.: 423450

Espanormed S.L. (1)
Av Juan Carlos I 35, 50009, Zaragoza, Spain
Tel.: (34) 976350000
Medical & Orthopedic Devices & Equipment Whslr
N.A.I.C.S.: 423450

Implant Concierge, LLC (1)
11503 NW Military Hwy Ste 212, San Antonio, TX 78231
Web Site: https://www.implantconcierge.com
Medical Treatment Planning Services
N.A.I.C.S.: 621999
Bret Royal (CEO)

Interpore Cross International, LLC (1)
181 Technology Dr, Irvine, CA 92618
Tel.: (949) 453-3200
Orthopedic Implant Instrument Distr
N.A.I.C.S.: 423450

LDR Holding Corporation (1)
13785 Research Blvd Ste 200, Austin, TX 78750
Tel.: (512) 344-3333
Web Site: http://www.ldr.com
Sales Range: $150-199.9 Million
Medical Device Mfr
N.A.I.C.S.: 339112

Subsidiary (Non-US):

LDR Brasil Comercio, Importacao e Exportacao Ltda. (2)
Av Pereira Barreto 1395- 19 Floor, Room 192 to 196 Torre Sul-Bairro Paraiso, Santo Andre, 09190-610, Sao Paulo, Brazil
Tel.: (55) 1143327755
Web Site: http://www.ldr.com
Medical Equipment Sales
N.A.I.C.S.: 423450

LDR Medical S.A.S. (2)
Parc d entreprises du Grand Troyes Quartier Europe de l Ouest, 5 rue de Berlin, 10300, Sainte-Savine, France
Tel.: (33) 325823263
Web Site: http://www.ldr.com
Medical Equipment Mfr
N.A.I.C.S.: 335999

Subsidiary (Domestic):

LDR Spine USA, Inc. (2)
13785 Research Blvd Ste 200, Austin, TX 78750
Tel.: (512) 344-3333
Web Site: http://www.ldr.com
Medical & Dental Equipment Distr
N.A.I.C.S.: 423450

Medical Compression Systems, Inc. (1)
Tel.: (800) 377-5804
Orthopedic Implant Instrument Whslr
N.A.I.C.S.: 423450

Medtech SA (1)
432 rue du Rajol, 900 rue du Mas de Verchant, 34130, Maugio, France
Tel.: (33) 467107740
Web Site: http://www.medtech.fr
Surgical Robotic Equipment Mfr
N.A.I.C.S.: 339112

Medtech Surgical, Inc. (1)
845 Third Ave 6th Fl, New York, NY 10022
Tel.: (855) 767-2268
Web Site: https://www.medtech.fr
Surgical Appliance Mfr
N.A.I.C.S.: 339113

OSSIS Corporation (1)
7/2 Barry Hogan Place, Riccarton,

Christchurch, 8041, New Zealand
Tel.: (64) 33657369
Web Site: https://www.ossis.com
3D Printing Technology Mfr
N.A.I.C.S.: 333248

Orthopedic Biomet CentroAmericana SA (1)
Complejo Avenida Escazu Edificio AE202 Oficina 301 Tercer Piso Escazu, San Jose, Costa Rica
Tel.: (506) 22890990
Surgical & Medical Instrument Mfr
N.A.I.C.S.: 339113

Representaciones Zimmer Inc., S. de R.L. de C.V. (1)
Periferico 4829 interior 403 Colonia Parque del Pedregal, Alcaldia de Tlapan, 14010, Mexico, DF, Mexico
Tel.: (52) 5512536751
Surgical & Medical Instrument Mfr
N.A.I.C.S.: 339113

Synvasive Technology, Inc. (1)
4925 Robert J Mathews Pkwy, El Dorado Hills, CA 95762
Tel.: (916) 939-3913
Surgical Instruments Developer, Mfr & Whslr
N.A.I.C.S.: 339112

Zfx GmbH (1)
Kopernikusstrasse 15, 85221, Dachau, Germany
Tel.: (49) 813 133 2440
Web Site: https://dentist.zfx-dental.com
Dental Laboratory Operator
N.A.I.C.S.: 339116

Zfx Innovation GmbH (1)
Bahnhofstrasse 22 Via Stazione, 39010, Gargazon, BZ, Italy
Tel.: (39) 0473291607
Physical & Engineering Research & Development Services
N.A.I.C.S.: 541715
Silvia Piaia (Mgr-Quality Sys)

Zhejiang Biomet Medical Products Co. Ltd. (1)
No 980 Shenli Road, Jinhua, 321000, Zhejiang, China
Tel.: (86) 57982238280
Surgical & Medical Instrument Mfr
N.A.I.C.S.: 339113
Shao Xuezhi (Supvr-Engrg)

Zimmer (Shanghai) Medical International Trading Co., Ltd. (1)
UNIT 01-10 19/F Metro Plaza 555 Lou Shan Guan Road, Changning District, Shanghai, 200051, China
Tel.: (86) 2122115199
Sales Range: $150-199.9 Million
Medical & Surgical Equipment & Supplies Sales
N.A.I.C.S.: 423450

Zimmer Australia Holding Pty. Ltd. (1)
Level 3 12 Narabang Way, Belrose, 2085, NSW, Australia
Tel.: (61) 294835400
Holding Company
N.A.I.C.S.: 551112

Zimmer Austria GmbH (1)
Grossmarktstrasse 7a, 1230, Vienna, Austria **(100%)**
Tel.: (43) 161520600
Web Site: http://www.zimmerbiomet.com
Sales Range: $10-24.9 Million
Emp.: 30
Medical Devices Mfr & Distr
N.A.I.C.S.: 339113

Zimmer Biomet Austria GmbH (1)
Euro Plaza Lehrbachgasse 13, 1120, Vienna, Austria
Tel.: (43) 16152060
Web Site: https://www.zimmerbiomet.eu
Orthopedic Implant Instrument Whslr
N.A.I.C.S.: 423450

Zimmer Biomet BVBA (1)
Meyskens II Meyskenstraat 224, B-1780, Wemmel, Brussels, Belgium
Tel.: (32) 24561214
Web Site: https://www.zimmerbelgium.be

Sales Range: $10-24.9 Million
Emp.: 50
Medical & Surgical Devices & Supplies Distr
N.A.I.C.S.: 423450

Branch (Domestic):

Zimmer Biomet BVBA (2)
Fotografielaan 5, B 2610, Wilrijk, Antwerp, Belgium
Tel.: (32) 3 870 65 65
Web Site: http://www.biomet.be
Sales Range: $50-74.9 Million
Emp.: 50
Orthopedic Products Whslr
N.A.I.C.S.: 423450

Zimmer Biomet CMF & Thoracic, LLC (1)
1520 Tradeport Dr, Jacksonville, FL 32218-2480
Tel.: (904) 741-4400
Web Site: https://www.zbthoracic.com
Surgical & Medical Instruments Mfr
N.A.I.C.S.: 339112
Chris Jefferis (Pres-Grp)

Zimmer Biomet Canada, Inc. (1)
2323 Argentia Road, Mississauga, L5N 5N3, ON, Canada (100%)
Tel.: (905) 858-8588
Web Site: https://www.zimmer-canada.ca
Sales Range: $25-49.9 Million
Emp.: 40
Medical & Hospital Equipment Mfr & Sales
N.A.I.C.S.: 423450

Zimmer Biomet Denmark ApS (1)
Herstedvang 12, 2620, Albertslund, Denmark
Tel.: (45) 70223050
Web Site: https://www.zimmerbiomet.dk
Orthopedic Implant Instrument Whslr
N.A.I.C.S.: 423450

Zimmer Biomet Dental Canada Inc. (1)
2323 Argentia Road, Mississauga, L5N 5N3, ON, Canada
Orthopedic Implant Instrument Whslr
N.A.I.C.S.: 423450

Zimmer Biomet Dental K.K. (1)
1-1 Sumitomo Ichigaya Building 2F, Ichigayahonmura-cho Shinjuku-ku, Tokyo, 162-0845, Japan
Tel.: (81) 343339900
Web Site: http://www.zimmerbiometdental.jp
Emp.: 120
Health Care Equipment Mfr & Distr
N.A.I.C.S.: 339112

Zimmer Biomet Deutschland GmbH (1)
Merzhauser Str 112, 79100, Freiburg, Germany (100%)
Tel.: (49) 761458401
Web Site: http://www.zimmergermany.de
Sales Range: $25-49.9 Million
Emp.: 120
Medical Devices & Products Mfr & Sales
N.A.I.C.S.: 339113

Zimmer Biomet Finland Oy (1)
Keilasatama 5, FIN-02150, Espoo, Finland (100%)
Tel.: (358) 98874370
Web Site: https://www.zimmerbiomet.fi
Emp.: 16
Diagnostic Instruments & Medical & Orthopedic Equipment Sales
N.A.I.C.S.: 423450

Zimmer Biomet France SAS (1)
523 3rd Millennium Course, Technology Park - Building K, 69800, Saint Priest, France (100%)
Tel.: (33) 381994300
Sales Range: $10-24.9 Million
Emp.: 122
Surgical & Medical Instruments & Supplies Distr
N.A.I.C.S.: 423450
Christof Bachelet (Mgr-Fin)

Zimmer Biomet GK (1)
15F Sumitomo Fudosan Shibakoen Tower 2-11-1 Shibakoen, Minato-ku, Tokyo, 105-0011, Japan (100%)
Tel.: (81) 364026600

Web Site: https://www.zimmerbiomet.com
Emp.: 859
Surgical & Other Medical Instruments & Equipment Mfr & Sales
N.A.I.C.S.: 423450

Zimmer Biomet Italia Srl (1)
Via Milano 6, 20097, San Donato Milanese, MI, Italy
Tel.: (39) 02 516261
Web Site: http://www.zimmer.it
Medical Equipment & Products Mfr & Sales
N.A.I.C.S.: 339113

Zimmer Biomet Korea Co., Ltd. (1)
6F Ilsin Bldg 98 Hannamdaero, Yongsan-gu, Seoul, Korea (South)
Tel.: (82) 25388111
Emp.: 37
Medical & Surgical Devices & Supplies Distr
N.A.I.C.S.: 423450

Zimmer Biomet Nederland B.V. (1)
Toermalijnring 600, 3316 LC, Dordrecht, Netherlands (100%)
Tel.: (31) 78 629 2929
Web Site: http://www.zimmerbiomet.nl
Emp.: 40
Medical & Surgical Devices & Equipment Mfr & Distr
N.A.I.C.S.: 339113

Zimmer Biomet New Zealand Company (1)
210 Khyber Pass Road, Grafton, Auckland, New Zealand
Tel.: (64) 99255200
Sales Range: $25-49.9 Million
Emp.: 50
Medical Devices Mfr & Sales
N.A.I.C.S.: 339112
Nick Staras (Mgr-Spine & Biologics Bus Unit-Australia & New Zealand)

Zimmer Biomet Norway AS (1)
Robsrudskogen 15, 1470, Lorenskog, Norway
Tel.: (47) 24124343
Orthopedic Implant Instrument Whslr
N.A.I.C.S.: 423450

Zimmer Biomet Polska Sp. z.o.o. (1)
Domaniewska 50, 02-672, Warsaw, Poland
Tel.: (48) 225098700
Web Site: https://www.biomet.pl
Sales Range: $25-49.9 Million
Emp.: 16
Medical Device Distr
N.A.I.C.S.: 423450

Zimmer Biomet Portugal Unipessoal, Lda (1)
Casal de Alfragide Lote 1, 2720-413, Amadora, Portugal
Tel.: (351) 214255500
Web Site: https://www.biomet.pt
Surgical & Medical Instrument Mfr
N.A.I.C.S.: 339113

Zimmer Biomet Pty. Ltd. (1)
Level 3 12 Narabang Way, Belrose, 2085, NSW, Australia
Tel.: (61) 294835400
Web Site: https://www.zimmerbiomet.com
Orthopedic Implant Instrument Whslr
N.A.I.C.S.: 423450

Zimmer Biomet South Africa (Pty) Ltd. (1)
Meersig 1 Constantia Boulevard Constation Kloof, PO Box 5080, Weltevredenpark, Roodepoort, 1710, South Africa
Tel.: (27) 116750444
Web Site:
　https://www.zimmersouthafrica.co.za
Medical Equipment Distr
N.A.I.C.S.: 423450

Zimmer Biomet Spain S.L. (1)
Metalurgia 32-42, 08038, Barcelona, Spain
Tel.: (34) 932895320
Web Site:
　https://www.zimmerbiomet.com.es
Emp.: 60
Medical Devices & Products Mfr & Distr
N.A.I.C.S.: 339112

Zimmer Biomet Sweden AB (1)
Industrivagen 4, 433 61, Savedalen, Sweden

Tel.: (46) 313375600
Web Site: https://www.biomet.se
Health Care Srvices
N.A.I.C.S.: 621610

Zimmer Biomet UK Ltd. (1)
Waterton Industrial Estate, Bridgend, CF31 3XA, United Kingdom
Tel.: (44) 1656655221
Web Site: http://www.biomet.co.uk
Surgical Instrument Mfr
N.A.I.C.S.: 339113

Zimmer CEP USA, Inc. (1)
12 Greenway Plz Ste 1000, Houston, TX 77046
Tel.: (574) 267-6131
Emp.: 282
Surgical & Medical Instrument Mfr
N.A.I.C.S.: 339113

Zimmer CIS Ltd. (1)
Usachev st 29-9, Moscow, 119048, Russia
Tel.: (7) 959800714
Emp.: 14
Medical Device Distr
N.A.I.C.S.: 423450

Zimmer Czech sro (1)
Na Vitezne plani 1719/4, 140 00, Prague, Czech Republic
Tel.: (420) 261394200
Web Site: https://www.zimmerczech.cz
Sales Range: $100-124.9 Million
Emp.: 25
Surgical & Medical Products Sales
N.A.I.C.S.: 423450

Zimmer Dental Chile Spa (1)
Luis Thayer Ojeda 0130 Oficina 902, Providencia, Santiago, 8320000, Chile
Tel.: (56) 222315185
Web Site: http://www.zimmerdental.cl
Surgical & Medical Instrument Mfr
N.A.I.C.S.: 339113

Zimmer Dental Italy Srl (1)
Viale Italia n 205/D, 31015, Conegliano, TV, Italy
Tel.: (39) 043837681
Web Site: http://www.zimmerdental.it
Dental Care Services
N.A.I.C.S.: 621210

Zimmer Dental Ltd. (1)
Ha'amal Street Beit Amot - Building A 13, Rosh Ha'Ayin, Israel
Tel.: (972) 36124242
Web Site: http://www.zimmerbiomet.co.il
Dental Equipment Distr
N.A.I.C.S.: 423450

Zimmer Dental SAS (1)
Quebec building 19 rue D'Arcueil, 94528, Rungis, Cedex, France
Tel.: (33) 145123537
Web Site: http://www.zimmerdental.fr
Dental Equipment Mfr & Distr
N.A.I.C.S.: 339114

Zimmer Dental Sweden AB (1)
Profilvagen 4, Loddekopinge, 246 43, Skane, Sweden
Tel.: (46) 406307610
Dental Care Services
N.A.I.C.S.: 621210

Zimmer Dental do Brasil Participacoes Ltda. (1)
Rua Joao Erbolato 422 Jardim Chapadao, Campinas, 13070-070, Sao Paulo, Brazil
Tel.: (55) 1981417788
Dental Equipment Mfr & Distr
N.A.I.C.S.: 339114

Zimmer Germany Holdings GmbH (1)
Merzhauser Strasse 112, 79100, Freiburg im Breisgau, Germany
Tel.: (49) 761458401
Web Site: https://www.zimmerbiomet.com
Holding Company
N.A.I.C.S.: 551112

Zimmer GmbH (1)
Sulzerallee 8, 8404, Winterthur, Switzerland (100%)
Tel.: (41) 588548000
Web Site: https://www.zimmerbiomet.ch
Sales Range: $150-199.9 Million
Emp.: 1,000

Medical & Surgical Devices & Equipment Mfr & Distr
N.A.I.C.S.: 339113

Zimmer India Private Ltd. (1)
Vanijya Kunj Enkay Towers Unit No 6 6th Floor Udyog Vihar Phase V, Gurgaon, 122016, Haryana, India
Tel.: (91) 1244693500
Web Site: https://www.zimmerbiomet.in
Surgical & Medical Instrument Mfr
N.A.I.C.S.: 339113

Zimmer Investments, LLC (1)
180 Commercial St NE 5, Salem, OR 97301
Tel.: (503) 961-4237
Investment Management Service
N.A.I.C.S.: 523910

Zimmer Knee Creations, Inc. (1)
841 Springdale Dr, Exton, PA 19341
Tel.: (484) 887-8902
Web Site: http://www.subchondroplasty.com
Emp.: 10
Health Care Srvices
N.A.I.C.S.: 621610

Zimmer Manufacturing B.V. (1)
Prins Bernhardplein 200, Amsterdam, 1097 JB, Netherlands
Tel.: (31) 20 5214777
Surgical & Medical Instrument Mfr
N.A.I.C.S.: 339112

Zimmer Medical (Thailand) Co., Ltd. (1)
2nd Floor Rajankarn Building 183 South Sathorn Road Yannawa Sathorn, Bangkok, 10120, Thailand
Tel.: (66) 2638 1900
Web Site: http://www.zimmerbiomet.com
Medical & Surgical Devices & Supplies Mfr
N.A.I.C.S.: 423450

Zimmer Medical Malaysia Sdn Bhd (1)
Menara Symphony Units 01-18 18th Floor, No 5 Jalan Professor Khoo Kay Kim Seksyen 13, 46200, Petaling Jaya, Selangor, Malaysia (100%)
Tel.: (60) 376232688
Emp.: 15
Medical & Surgical Devices & Equipment Sales
N.A.I.C.S.: 423450

Zimmer Pte. Ltd. (1)
401 Commonwealth Drive 06-03 Haw Par Techno Centre, Singapore, 149598, Singapore (100%)
Tel.: (65) 68547222
Web Site: https://www.zimmerbiomet.in
Sales Range: $1-9.9 Million
Emp.: 100
Surgical & Medical Instruments & Supplies Distr
N.A.I.C.S.: 423450

Zimmer Surgical, Inc. (1)
200 W Ohio Ave, Dover, OH 44622
Tel.: (330) 343-8801
Sales Range: $75-99.9 Million
Surgical Equipment Mfr
N.A.I.C.S.: 339113
Greg Roche (VP-Sls-Comml Surgical)

Branch (Domestic):

Zimmer Surgical (2)
2021 Old Mountain Rd, Statesville, NC 28625
Tel.: (704) 873-1001
Sales Range: $25-49.9 Million
Surgical Product Mfr
N.A.I.C.S.: 339113

Zimmer Trabecular Metal Technology, Inc. (1)
10 Pomeroy Rd, Parsippany, NJ 07054
Tel.: (973) 576-0032
Orthopedic Application Services
N.A.I.C.S.: 541713

Zimmer US, Inc. (1)
345 E Main St, Warsaw, IN 46580
Tel.: (574) 267-6131
Dental Implants & Orthopaedic Surgical Product Design & Mfr
N.A.I.C.S.: 339113

Zimmer Biomet Holdings, Inc.—(Continued)

Zimmer do Brasil Comercio Ltda. (1)
Av Rio Branco 181-Sala 1806 Parte Centro,
Rio de Janeiro, 20040-007, Brazil
Tel.: (55) 2121598821
Health Care Srvices
N.A.I.C.S.: 621610

Zimmer, Inc. (1)
1800 W Center St, Warsaw, IN 46581-0587
Tel.: (574) 267-6131
Web Site: https://www.zimmerbiomet.com
Emp.: 30
Dental Implants & Orthopaedic Surgical
Product Design & Mfr
N.A.I.C.S.: 339113

**ZIMMER ENERGY TRANSI-
TION ACQUISITION CORP.**
9 W 57th St 33rd Fl, New York, NY
10019
Tel.: (212) 371-8688   DE
Web Site:
https://www.zimmerenergy.com
Year Founded: 2021
ZT—(NASDAQ)
Rev.: $29,700,214
Assets: $350,683,713
Liabilities: $369,497,163
Net Worth: ($18,813,450)
Earnings: $27,429,567
Emp.: 3
Fiscal Year-end: 12/31/22
Investment Services
N.A.I.C.S.: 523999
Stuart J. Zimmer (Chm & CEO)
Jonathan Cohen (CFO)

ZIMVIE INC.
4555 Riverside Dr, Palm Beach Gar-
dens, FL 33410
Tel.: (561) 776-6700   DE
Web Site: https://www.zimvie.com
Year Founded: 2021
ZIMV—(NASDAQ)
Rev.: $913,862,000
Assets: $1,642,056,000
Liabilities: $883,452,000
Net Worth: $758,604,000
Earnings: ($63,881,000)
Emp.: 2,700
Fiscal Year-end: 12/31/22
Medical Instrument Mfr & Distr
N.A.I.C.S.: 339112
Vala Jamali (Pres & CEO)
Heather Kidwell (Chief Legal Officer,
Chief Compliance Officer, Chief HR
Officer & Sr VP)
Rich Heppenstall (CFO, Treas &
Exec VP)
Indraneel Kanaglekar (Chief Comml
Officer & Sr VP)
Ann Vu (Chief Quality Officer, Chief
Regulatory Affairs Officer & Sr VP)
Steve Rondeau (CIO & Sr VP)

ZION OIL & GAS, INC.
12655 N Central Expy Ste 1000, Dal-
las, TX 75251
Tel.: (214) 221-4610   DE
Web Site: https://www.zionoil.com
Year Founded: 2000
ZNOG—(OTCQX)
Assets: $27,515,000
Liabilities: $4,415,000
Net Worth: $23,100,000
Earnings: ($55,077,000)
Emp.: 21
Fiscal Year-end: 12/31/22
Crude Petroleum Extraction Services
N.A.I.C.S.: 211120
Jeffrey Moskowitz (VP)
John M. Brown (Founder & Exec
Chm)
William H. Avery (Pres & Gen Coun-
sel)

Martin M. van Brauman (Treas, Sec
& Exec VP)
Michael B. Croswell Jr. (CFO)
Lee R. Russell (VP)
Robert W. A. Dunn (CEO)

Subsidiaries:

Zion Oil & Gas - Israel (1)
9 Halamish St, POB 3138, North Industrial
Park, Caesarea, 3088900, Israel
Tel.: (972) 46238500
Web Site: https://www.zionoil.com
Sales Range: $150-199.9 Million
Emp.: 15
Oil & Gas Exploration
N.A.I.C.S.: 213111
Jeffrey Moskowitz (Mng Dir-Israel)

**ZIONS BANCORPORATION,
NATIONAL ASSOCIATION**
1 S Main, Salt Lake City, UT 84133-
1109
Tel.: (801) 844-7637   UT
Web Site:
https://www.zionsbancorpora
tion.com
Year Founded: 1873
ZION—(NASDAQ)
Rev.: $4,624,000,000
Assets: $87,203,000,000
Liabilities: $81,512,000,000
Net Worth: $5,691,000,000
Earnings: $648,000,000
Emp.: 9,679
Fiscal Year-end: 12/31/23
Federal Savings Bank
N.A.I.C.S.: 522180
Harris Henry Simmons (Chm & CEO)
Aldon Scott Anderson (Pres/CEO-
Zions First Natl Bank)
Paul E. Burdiss (Exec VP)
David E. Blackford (Exec VP)
Keith D. Maio (Chief Risk Officer &
Exec VP)
Scott J. McLean (Pres & COO)
Michael Morris (Chief Credit Officer &
Exec VP)
James R. Abbott (Sr VP-IR & Exter-
nal Comm)
Kenneth Jay Collins (Exec VP-Bus
Tech)
Olga T. Hoff (Exec VP-Retail Bank-
ing)
Rebecca K. Robinson (Exec VP &
Dir-Wealth Mgmt)
Randy R. Stewart (Exec VP-
Enterprise Mortgage Lending)
Scott A. Law (Chief HR Officer &
Exec VP)
R. Ryan Richards (CFO & Exec VP)
Eric Ellingsen (Exec VP)

Subsidiaries:

Amegy Bank (1)
1717 W Loop S, Houston, TX 77027
Tel.: (713) 232-2454
Web Site: https://www.amegybank.com
Sales Range: $250-299.9 Million
Emp.: 2,126
Commercial & Private Banking Services
N.A.I.C.S.: 522110
Brandon Bledsoe (Pres-Fort Worth Reg)
Paul Noonan (Sr VP-Comml Banking-
Dallas)
Shari Hicks (VP-Bus & Community Dev)

California Bank & Trust (1)
525 B St Ste 100, San Diego, CA
92101   (95%)
Tel.: (619) 446-4800
Web Site: http://www.calbanktrust.com
Sales Range: $400-449.9 Million
Emp.: 1,474
Banking Services
N.A.I.C.S.: 522110
David E. Blackford (Exec Chm)
Eric Ellingsen (Pres & CEO)

Exchange Services L.L.C. (1)

310 S Main St Ste 1420, Salt Lake City, UT
84101
Web Site:
http://www.bankexchangeservices.com
Financial Services
N.A.I.C.S.: 541611

National Bank of Arizona (1)
335 N Wilmot Rd, Tucson, AZ
85711   (100%)
Tel.: (520) 584-4000
Web Site: https://www.nbarizona.com
Sales Range: $50-74.9 Million
Emp.: 180
Commericial Banking
N.A.I.C.S.: 522110
Mark Richard Young (Pres & CEO)
David O. Lyons (Pres-Southern Reg, Exec
VP & Dir-Southern Arizona)
Deborah J. Bateman (Exec VP & Dir-
Strategic Bus Dev)
Brent S. Cannon (Exec VP & Dir-Retail,
Exec Banking & Community Banking)
Marcos Garay (Exec VP & Dir-Multicultural
Banking)
Leslie Lea (VP & Mgr-Private Bank Rela-
tionship)
Sergio Cossio (VP & Mgr-Private Banking
Relationship)
James M. Batdorf (Chief Credit Officer &
Exec VP-Credit Admin)
Mary M. Holman (Exec VP & Dir-Private
Banking)
Laura A. Schaeffer (Exec VP & Dir-Ops &
Tech)
Mark A. Stebbings (Exec VP & Dir-Real Es-
tate Banking & Specialty Lending)
Michael R. Casa (Exec VP & Dir-Metro
Comml Banking)
E. Joy Antolini (Chief Learning Officer, Exec
VP & Dir-HR)

Nevada State Bank (1)
230 Las Vegas Blvd, Las Vegas, NV
89101-5712   (100%)
Tel.: (702) 383-0009
Web Site: https://www.nsbank.com
Sales Range: $150-199.9 Million
Emp.: 701
Banking Services
N.A.I.C.S.: 522110
Dallas E. Haun (Chm)
Craig Kirkland (Exec VP & Dir-Retail Bank-
ing)
Terrance A. Shirey (Pres & CEO)
Thomas Elmer (Exec VP)
Micah E. Phillips (Exec VP & Mktg Dir)
Shannon Petersen (Exec VP & Mgr-Corp
Banking)
Nidhi Dadlani (VP & Mgr-Pro Banking Rela-
tionship)
James Rensvold (Exec VP & Mgr-Private
Banking)
Ryan Ashley (CFO & Exec VP)
James Chung (Mgr-Twain & Jones)
Dawson Smith (Mgr-Downtown Summerlin)
Jacquelyn Trevena (Mgr-Centennial Hills)
Michael Lane (Exec VP & Dir-Comml Real
Estate)
Rick Thomas (Exec VP)

PPS Data, LLC (1)
5241 S State St Unit 2, Murray, UT 84107-
2443
Web Site: https://www.providerpay.net
Investment Management Service
N.A.I.C.S.: 551111

The Commerce Bank of Oregon (1)
1211 SW 5th Ave Ste 1250, Portland, OR
97204
Tel.: (503) 548-1000
Web Site: https://www.tcboregon.com
Sales Range: $1-4.9 Billion
Emp.: 20
Banking Services
N.A.I.C.S.: 522110
Paul E. Mayer (Chief Credit Officer)
Mike Barr (Pres)
Terri McKinnis (COO)

**The Commerce Bank of
Washington** (1)
2 Union Sq 601 Union St Ste 3600, Seattle,
WA 98101
Tel.: (206) 292-3900
Web Site: https://www.tcbwa.com
Sales Range: $25-49.9 Million
Emp.: 63

Provider of Banking, Financing & Leasing
Services
N.A.I.C.S.: 522110
Stanley D. Savage (Chm)
Alan M. Forney (Pres & CEO)
Jack Unbehend (Dir-Comml Banking)
Randall Brannan (Mgr-Customer Rels)
Roderic Davis (Mgr-Customer Rels)
Jason Floyd (Mgr-Customer Rels)
William Glassford (Mgr-Customer Rels)
Dave Hasslinger (Mgr-Customer Rels)
Ben Hicks (Mgr-Customer Rels)
Kari Knudson (Mgr-Customer Rels)
Jackie Kopson (Mgr-Customer Rels)
Jason McCalpin (Mgr-Customer Rels)
Matthew Smeby (Mgr-Customer Rels)
Robert Stadler (Mgr-Customer Rels)
Wanda Wong (Mgr-Customer Rels)

Vectra Bank Colorado (1)
1650 S Colorado Blvd, Denver, CO 80222
Tel.: (720) 947-7526
Web Site: https://www.vectrabank.com
Sales Range: $400-449.9 Million
Emp.: 874
Provider of Banking, Financing & Leasing
Services
N.A.I.C.S.: 522110
Bruce K. Alexander (Pres & CEO)
Brian Sullivan (Sr VP-Vectra Wealth Mgmt)
Michelle Benda (Asst VP-Vectra Wealth
Mgmt)

Zions Bank (1)
1 S Main St, Salt Lake City, UT 84133
Tel.: (801) 974-8800
Web Site: https://www.zionsbank.com
Commericial Banking
N.A.I.C.S.: 522110
Aldon Scott Anderson (Pres & CEO)
Paul E. Burdiss (Pres & CEO)
Raj Jain (Mgr-Exec Banking Relationship-
Boise, Eagle & Chinden)
Stuart Williams (Mgr-Exec Banking-
Downtown Boise)
Aubrey Farner (Asst Mgr-Nampa)
Timothy Hicks (Mgr-Comml Banking
Relationship-Nampa)
David Moore (Mgr-Wilder Branch)
Helen Johnson (Mgr-Bus Banking
Relationship-Nampa)
Cory Gardiner (Exec VP-Bus & Consumer
Banking)
Stephanie Horne Clark (Exec VP-Private
Banking)
Crystal Low (Exec VP-Bus Payments &
Tech)
Peter J. Morgan (Exec VP-Natl Real Estate
Dept)
Thomas B. Morgan (Exec VP-Retail, Bus
Banking & Omni Channel Banking)
Richard Stevenson (Exec VP-Real Estate
Banking Grp)
Bruno Chajon (Mgr-Bus Banking
Relationship-Meridian Silverstone)

Zions Credit Corporation (1)
310 S Main St 13th Fl, Salt Lake City, UT
84101-1507   (100%)
Tel.: (801) 524-2230
Web Site: https://www.zionsbank.com
Sales Range: $25-49.9 Million
Emp.: 35
Equipment Leasing & Financing
N.A.I.C.S.: 522220

Zions Direct, Inc. (1)
1 S Main St, Salt Lake City, UT
84111   (100%)
Tel.: (801) 844-7801
Web Site: https://www.zionsdirect.com
Sales Range: $125-149.9 Million
Emp.: 61
Stock Brokerage
N.A.I.C.S.: 523940

Zions Public Finance, Inc. (1)
1 S Main St, Salt Lake City, UT 84133
Tel.: (801) 844-7373
Web Site: https://www.zionspf.com
Financial Services
N.A.I.C.S.: 541611

ZIPLINK, INC.
40 Woodland St, Hartford, CT 06105
Tel.: (860) 727-5702
Year Founded: 1996
ZIPL—(OTCEM)
Internet Access Services
N.A.I.C.S.: 519290

Henry A. Zachs (CEO)

ZIPRECRUITER, INC.
604 Arizona Ave, Santa Monica, CA
90401   DE
Web Site:
https://www.ziprecruiter.global
Year Founded: 2021
ZIP—(NYSE)
Rev.: $904,649,000
Assets: $714,563,000
Liabilities: $685,943,000
Net Worth: $28,620,000
Earnings: $61,494,000
Emp.: 1,400
Fiscal Year-end: 12/31/22
Recruiting Services
N.A.I.C.S.: 561311
David Travers (Pres & CFO)
Ian Siegel (Founder, Chm & CEO)

ZIVO BIOSCIENCE, INC.
21 E Long Lake Rd Ste 100, Bloom-
field Hills, MI 48304
Tel.: (248) 452-9866
Web Site:
https://www.zivobioscience.com
Year Founded: 1983
ZIVO—(NASDAQ)
Assets: $2,123,019
Liabilities: $2,133,641
Net Worth: ($10,622)
Earnings: ($8,745,293)
Emp.: 8
Fiscal Year-end: 12/31/22
Research & Development in the
Physical, Engineering & Life Sciences
(except Nanotechnology & Biotech-
nology)
N.A.I.C.S.: 541715
Harlan L. Miller III (VP)
John B. Payne (Chm, Pres & CEO)
Keith R. Marchiando (CFO)

Subsidiaries:

Wellmetrix, LLC   (1)
2804 Orchard Lake Rd Ste 202, Keego
Harbor, MI 48320
Tel.: (248) 452-9866
Web Site: https://www.wellmetrix.com
Medical Equipment Mfr
N.A.I.C.S.: 339112

ZOETIS, INC.
10 Sylvan Way, Parsippany, NJ
07054
Tel.: (973) 822-7000   DE
Web Site: https://www.zoetis.com
Year Founded: 2013
ZTS—(NYSE)
Rev.: $8,544,000,000
Assets: $14,286,000,000
Liabilities: $9,295,000,000
Net Worth: $4,991,000,000
Earnings: $2,344,000,000
Emp.: 14,100
Fiscal Year-end: 12/31/23
Animal Health Products & Services
N.A.I.C.S.: 325412
Roxanne Lagano (Gen Counsel, Sec
& Exec VP)
Kristin C. Peck (CEO)
Wafaa Mamilli (Grp Pres-China, Bra-
zil & Precision Animal Health, CIO,
Chief Digital Officer & Exec VP)
Robert J. Polzer (Pres-R&D & Exec
VP)
Jamie Brannan (Grp Pres-Intl Ops &
Aquaculture & Exec VP)
Nick Ashton (Pres)
Jeannette Ferran Astorga (Chief Sus-
tainability Officer)
Ester Banque (Pres- & Exec VP)
Rimma Driscoll (Exec VP & Head-
Global Strategy, Comml & Bus Dev,
and Global BioDevices)

Subsidiaries:

Abaxis Holding GmbH   (1)
Bunsenstrasse 9-11, 64347, Griesheim,
Germany
Tel.: (49) 6155780210
Medical Device Mfr
N.A.I.C.S.: 339112

Abaxis, Inc.   (1)
3240 Whipple Rd, Union City, CA 94587
Tel.: (510) 675-6500
Web Site: http://www.abaxis.com
Portable Blood Analysis Systems Mfr
N.A.I.C.S.: 339112
David Bannister (Sr Dir-Internal Ops)

Subsidiary (Non-US):

Abaxis Europe GmbH   (2)
Bunsenstrasse 9-11, 64347, Griesheim,
Germany
Tel.: (49) 6155780210
Portable Blood Analysis Systems Sales
N.A.I.C.S.: 423450

Abaxis UK Limited   (2)
First Floor Birchwood Building Springfield
Dr, Leatherhead, KT22 7LP, Surrey, United
Kingdom
Tel.: (44) 18453008034
Web Site: http://vet.abaxis.co.uk
Medical, Dental & Hospital Equipment Mer-
chant Whslr
N.A.I.C.S.: 423450

Advanced Food Technologies,
Inc.   (1)
1140 Butterworth St SW, Grand Rapids, MI
49504
Tel.: (616) 574-4144
Web Site: http://www.advfoodtech.com
Emp.: 65
Food Safety & Animal Care Products Mfr
N.A.I.C.S.: 325998

Allabinc de Mexico, S.A. de C.V.   (1)
Alberta 2288 Piso 5-B Edificio Torre del
Bosque, Col Los Colomos, Guadalajara,
44660, Jalisco, Mexico
Tel.: (52) 3336400442
Animal Health Medicine & Vaccine Mfr
N.A.I.C.S.: 325414

Alpharma de Argentina S.R.L.   (1)
Libertad 1056 T P A, Ciudad de Buenos
Aires 1012, Buenos Aires, Argentina
Tel.: (54) 1148150991
Animal Health Product Mfr & Distr
N.A.I.C.S.: 325412

Alpharma do Brasil Ltda.   (1)
Avenida Osvaldo Rodrigues Cabral 1570,
Centro Empresarial Florianopolis Sala 115
Bairro Centro, Florianopolis, 88015-710,
Santa Catarina, Brazil
Tel.: (55) 4830277777
Animal Health Product Mfr & Distr
N.A.I.C.S.: 325412

Cross Vetpharm Group Limited   (1)
2 3 And 4 Airton Close Airton Road, Tal-
laght, Dublin, Ireland
Tel.: (353) 14667900
Web Site: http://www.bimeda.ie
Veterinary Pharmaceutical Mfr
N.A.I.C.S.: 325412
Declan Dempsey (Mgr)

Fish Vet Group Limited   (1)
22 Carsegate Road, Inverness, IV3 8EX,
United Kingdom
Tel.: (44) 1463717774
Web Site: http://www.fishvetgroup.co.uk
Fish Veterinary Services
N.A.I.C.S.: 541940

Fish Vet Group Norge AS   (1)
Hoffsveien 21-23, 0275, Oslo, Norway
Tel.: (47) 21624980
Web Site: http://www.fishvetgroup.no
Veterinary Laboratory Services
N.A.I.C.S.: 541715

PAH Luxembourg 2 SARL   (1)
Ave John F Kennedy 51, 1855, Luxem-
bourg, Luxembourg
Tel.: (352) 2611491
Animal Health Medicine & Vaccine Mfr
N.A.I.C.S.: 325414

PT Zoetis Animalhealth
Indonesia   (1)
Talavera Suite 19th Floor Unit 05-06 JI
Letjen TB, Simatupang Kav 22-26 Cilandak,
Jakarta, 12430, Indonesia
Tel.: (62) 2130052400
Pharmaceutical Drug Mfr
N.A.I.C.S.: 325412
Ulrich Erik Ginting (Mgr-Mktg & Head-
Poultry)

Performance Livestock Analytics,
Inc.   (1)
2321 N Loop Dr Ste 120, Ames, IA 50010
Tel.: (515) 337-2187
Web Site:
https://www.performancelivestockanaly
tics.com
Cattle Management Software Development
Services
N.A.I.C.S.: 541511
Kory Lauridsen (Natl Mgr-Growth)
Zach Byrnes (Dir-Ops & Sls)

Pfizer Animal Pharma Private
Limited   (1)
Pfizer Centre 5 Patel Estate S V Road,
Jogeshwari (West), Mumbai, 400 102, India
Tel.: (91) 2266932000
Pharmaceutical Drug Mfr
N.A.I.C.S.: 325412

Pharmaq AS   (1)
Skogmo Industriomrade Industrivegen 50,
7863, Overhalla, Norway
Tel.: (47) 74280800
Web Site: https://www.pharmaq.com
Emp.: 200
Pharmaceutical Product Mfr & Distr
N.A.I.C.S.: 325414
Svein Alexandersen (Dir-Technical Svcs)
Marie Egenberg (Sls Mgr)
Morten Nordstad (Pres)
Nils Arne Gronlie (Dir-Operations)
Sissel Hansen (Dir-Human Resources-
Communications)
Hanne Christophersen (Dir-Regulatory Af-
fairs)
Edel Anne Norderhus (Dir-Product
Development-Research & Development)

Pharmaq AS Chile Limitada   (1)
Bernardino 1981 Piso 2 Oficina 202 Parque
Empresarial San Andres, Puerto Montt,
Chile
Tel.: (56) 652483091
Aquaculture Pharmaceutical Product Mfr &
Distr
N.A.I.C.S.: 325414

Pharmaq Analytiq AS   (1)
Thormohlensgate 53D, 5008, Bergen, Nor-
way
Tel.: (47) 2 329 8500
Web Site: http://www.pharmaq-analytiq.com
Aquaculture Research Services
N.A.I.C.S.: 541715
Siri Vike (Dir-Strategic Dev)
Stian Nylund (Mgr-R&D)
Marie Egenberg (Sls Mgr)
Renate Johansen (Product Mgr)
Elise Hjelle (Mgr-Commercial-Diagnostics)
Pal Nilsen (Mgr-Operations)
Nils Arne Gronlie (Gen Mgr)
Ane Sandtro (Sr Mgr)
Bernt Melgard (Mgr)
Bjorn Ellingsen (Mgr)
Christine Elgen (Mgr)
Emilia Lohndal (Mgr-Quality)
Ingrid Gamlem (Product Mgr)
Ingrid M. Hagerup (Mgr)
Irja Sunde Roiha (Mgr)
Jan Petter Berg (Dir)
Lars Gaute Jorgensen (Mgr)
Lise Fismen (Mgr-Logistics-Norway)
Mari Aas Solheim (Mgr)
Marianne Kraugerud (Mgr)
Nils Steine (Mgr)
Oyvind Andre Tonnessen (Mgr)
Svein Alexandersen (Dir)
Ane Sandtro (Sr Mgr)
Bernt Melgard (Mgr)
Bjorn Ellingsen (Mgr)
Christine Elgen (Mgr)
Emilia Lohndal (Mgr-Quality)
Ingrid Gamlem (Product Mgr)
Ingrid M. Hagerup (Mgr)
Irja Sunde Roiha (Mgr)
Jan Petter Berg (Dir)

Lars Gaute Jorgensen (Mgr)
Lise Fismen (Mgr-Logistics-Norway)
Mari Aas Solheim (Mgr)
Marianne Kraugerud (Mgr)
Nils Steine (Mgr)
Oyvind Andre Tonnessen (Mgr)
Svein Alexandersen (Dir)

Pharmaq CA Panama Inc.   (1)
Piso 2 Oficina 108 P H Albrook Commercial
Park Ave Bella Vista, PO Box 0832-0588,
Ancon, Panama, Panama
Tel.: (507) 3215363
Web Site: http://www.pharmaq.no
Aquaculture Pharmaceutical Product Mfr &
Distr
N.A.I.C.S.: 325414

Pharmaq Hong Kong Limited   (1)
Room 1701 17/F Shui On Centre 6-8 Har-
bour Road, Wanchai, China (Hong Kong)
Tel.: (852) 63750686
Aquaculture Pharmaceutical Product Mfr &
Distr
N.A.I.C.S.: 325414
Andreas von Scholten (Gen Mgr-Asia)

Pharmaq Ltd   (1)
Unit 15 Sandleheath Industrial Estate, Ford-
ingbridge, SP6 1PA, Hampshire, United
Kingdom
Tel.: (44) 1425656081
Web Site: http://www.pharmaq.no
Aquaculture Pharmaceutical Product Mfr &
Distr
N.A.I.C.S.: 325414

Pharmaq Spain Aqua SL   (1)
Pedrezuela 1 Oficina 303 Pol Ind Ventorro
del Cano, 28925, Alcorcon, Madrid, Spain
Tel.: (34) 810522004
Aquaculture Pharmaceutical Product Mfr &
Distr
N.A.I.C.S.: 325414
Roberto Guijarro (Gen Mgr)

Pharmaq Veterinar Ecza Deposu ve
su Urunleri Ticaret Ltd Ski   (1)
Karacaoglan Mah 6166 Sk 21, Bornova,
Izmir, Turkiye
Tel.: (90) 2324222310
Aquaculture Pharmaceutical Product Mfr &
Distr
N.A.I.C.S.: 325414

Pharmaq Vietnam Company
Limited   (1)
R 2503 25th Fl Viettel Tower 285 Cach
Mang Thang Tom W 12 D10, Ho Chi Minh
City, Vietnam
Tel.: (84) 2862845350
Web Site: http://www.pharmaq.no
Aquaculture Pharmaceutical Product Mfr &
Distr
N.A.I.C.S.: 325414

Phoenix Central Laboratory for Veteri-
narians, Inc.   (1)
4338 Harbour Pointe Blvd SW, Mukilteo,
WA 98275
Tel.: (425) 355-5252
Web Site: http://www.phoenixlab.com
Veterinary Testing Laboratory Operator
N.A.I.C.S.: 541940
John Evans (CEO)

Platinum Performance, Inc.   (1)
90 Thomas Rd, 93427, Buellton, CA
Tel.: (805) 688-1731
Web Site:
http://www.platinumperformance.com
Dry, Condensed, Evaporated Products
N.A.I.C.S.: 311514
Mark J. Herthel (Founder & Pres)

Synbiotics Corporation   (1)
12200 NW Ambassador Dr Ste 101, Kansas
City, MO 64163
Tel.: (816) 464-3500
Web Site: http://www.synbiotics.com
Veterinary Diagnostics, Vaccines & Other
Animal Health Related Products Mfr, Devel-
oper & Marketer
N.A.I.C.S.: 325414

Subsidiary (Non-US):

Synbiotics Europe S.A.S.   (2)
2 rue Alexander Fleming 07, 69367, Lyon,
France   (100%)

Zoetis, Inc.—(Continued)

Tel.: (33) 472761111
Web Site: http://www.synbiotics.fr
Sales Range: $1-9.9 Million
Emp.: 40
Veterinary Diagnostics & Services
N.A.I.C.S.: 541940
Bruno Cluzel (Mng Dir)

Virtual Recall Limited (1)
7 Huxley Road, Guildford, GU2 7RE, United Kingdom
Tel.: (44) 2081233965
Web Site: http://www.ourvet.shop
Veterinary Communication Services
N.A.I.C.S.: 541940
Jamie Critall (Co-Founder)
Charlie Barton (Co-Founder)

ZNLabs, LLC (1)
300 High Rise Dr Ste 300, Louisville, KY 40213
Web Site: http://www.znlabs.com
Veterinary Health Care Services
N.A.I.C.S.: 541940
Andrew Loar (Founder & CMO)

Zoetis Argentina S.R.L. (1)
Av Fondo de la Legua 1171 - 2 Piso, Villa Adelina - Partido de San Isidro, B1607BJD, Buenos Aires, Argentina
Tel.: (54) 1160901800
Web Site: https://www2.ar.zoetis.com
Pharmaceutical Drug Mfr
N.A.I.C.S.: 325412

Zoetis B.V. (1)
Rivium Westlaan 74, PO Box 37, 2909 LD, Capelle aan den IJssel,
Netherlands (100%)
Tel.: (31) 10 714 09 00
Web Site: http://www.zoetis.nl
Sales Range: $150-199.9 Million
Veterinary Pharmaceutical Products
N.A.I.C.S.: 325412

Zoetis Belgium S.A. (1)
Mercuriusstraat 20, 1930, Zaventem, Belgium
Tel.: (32) 27468011
Web Site: https://www2.zoetis.be
Sales Range: $50-74.9 Million
Animal Health Products Mfr
N.A.I.C.S.: 325412

Zoetis Canada Inc. (1)
16740 Trans-Canada Highway, Kirkland, H9H 4M7, QC, Canada
Tel.: (514) 459-3000
Web Site: http://www2.zoetis.ca
Sales Range: $50-74.9 Million
Animal Health Products Mfr
N.A.I.C.S.: 325412

Zoetis Costa Rica, S.R.L. (1)
Escazu Corp Center Floor 5, 10203, San Jose, Costa Rica
Tel.: (506) 22011799
Web Site: https://www2.zoetis.co.cr
Emp.: 100
Animal Health Product Mfr & Distr
N.A.I.C.S.: 325412

Zoetis Deutschland GmbH (1)
Schellingstr 1, 10785, Berlin, Germany
Web Site: https://www2.zoetis.de
Emp.: 800
Animal Health Product Mfr & Distr
N.A.I.C.S.: 325412

Zoetis Egypt LLC (1)
45 Northern 90th Street- First Section City Center, City Center, New Cairo, Egypt
Tel.: (20) 233330800
Pharmaceutical Drug Mfr
N.A.I.C.S.: 325412

Zoetis Finland Oy (1)
Tietokuja 4, 00330, Helsinki, Finland
Tel.: (358) 10 336 7000
Web Site: https://www2.zoetis.fi
Emp.: 20
Animal Health Product Mfr & Distr
N.A.I.C.S.: 325412

Zoetis Global Poultry
1040 Swabia Ct, Durham, NC 27703-8481
Tel.: (919) 941-5185
Web Site: http://www.zoetis.com

Sales Range: $50-74.9 Million
Emp.: 309
Poultry Health Vaccination Products & Services
N.A.I.C.S.: 325414

Subsidiary (Non-US):

Embrex De Mexico S. de R.L. de C.V. (2)
Bernardo Quintana No 40, Alamos 2a Seccion, Queretaro, 76160, Mexico
Tel.: (52) 4422141942
Pharmaceutical Preparation Mfr
N.A.I.C.S.: 325412

Zoetis Hellas S.A. (1)
8 10 Sorou Dimitsanas Kaltezon, 15125, Maroussi, Greece
Tel.: (30) 2106791900
Web Site: https://www2.zoetis.gr
Animal Health Product Mfr & Distr
N.A.I.C.S.: 325412

Zoetis Hungary Kft. (1)
Csorsz u 41 MOM Gellert Tower, 1123, Budapest, Hungary
Tel.: (36) 12245200
Web Site: https://www2.zoetis.hu
Animal Health Product Mfr & Distr
N.A.I.C.S.: 325412

Zoetis India Limited (1)
31 3rd Floor Kalpataru Synergy Opp Grand Hyatt, Santacruz East, Mumbai, 400 055, India
Tel.: (91) 2266513800
Web Site: https://www2.zoetis.in
Emp.: 14
Animal Health Products Mfr
N.A.I.C.S.: 325412

Zoetis Industria de Produtos Veterinarios Ltda. (1)
Rua Luiz Fernando Rodrigues n 1701, Campinas, 13024-500, SP, Brazil
Tel.: (55) 8000111919
Web Site: https://www.zoetis.com.br
Animal Health Products Mfr
N.A.I.C.S.: 325412
Olivia Moreira (Mgr)

Zoetis Ireland Limited (1)
2nd Floor Building 10, Cherrywood Business Park Loughlinstown, Dublin, D18 T3Y1, Ireland
Tel.: (353) 12569800
Web Site: https://www2.zoetis.ie
Emp.: 50
Animal Health Product Mfr & Distr
N.A.I.C.S.: 325412

Zoetis Japan K.K. (1)
Shinjuku Bunka Quint Building 14F 3-22-7 Yoyogi, Shibuya-ku, Tokyo, 151-0053, Japan
Tel.: (81) 35 309 7900
Web Site: https://www.zoetis.jp
Emp.: 150
Animal Health Products Mfr
N.A.I.C.S.: 325412

Zoetis Korea Ltd. (1)
13th floor T412 412 Teheran-ro, Gangnam-gu, Seoul, 06193, Korea (South) (100%)
Animal Health Products Mfr
N.A.I.C.S.: 325412

Zoetis Malaysia Sdn. Bhd. (1)
Unit 3-1 Tower 7 Avenue 3 Bangsar South No 8 Jalan Kerinchi, 59200, Kuala Lumpur, Malaysia
Tel.: (60) 322812800
Web Site: https://www2.zoetis.com.my
Animal Health Product Mfr & Distr
N.A.I.C.S.: 325412

Zoetis Mexico, S. de R.L. de C.V. (1)
Paseo De Los Tamarindos 60 PB, Col Bosques de las Lomas Alcandia Cuajimalpa de Morelos, 05120, Mexico, Mexico
Tel.: (52) 555 258 3700
Web Site: https://www2.zoetis.mx
Animal Health Product Mfr & Distr
N.A.I.C.S.: 325412

Zoetis OOO (1)
Presnenskaya embankment building 10 block C 21st floor, Moscow, 123112, Russia
Tel.: (7) 4999223022

Web Site: https://www.zoetis-russia.com
Pharmaceutical Drug Mfr
N.A.I.C.S.: 325412

Zoetis Philippines Inc. (1)
15th Floor The W Fifth Avenue Building Fifth Avenue, Bonifacio Global City, Taguig, Philippines
Tel.: (63) 8 705 6700
Web Site: https://www2.ph.zoetis.com
Animal Health Products Mfr
N.A.I.C.S.: 459910

Zoetis Polska sp. z o.o (1)
Ul Postepu 17B, 02-676, Warsaw, Poland
Tel.: (48) 22 223 4800
Web Site: https://www2.zoetis.com.pl
Animal Health Product Mfr & Distr
N.A.I.C.S.: 325412

Zoetis Portugal, Lda. (1)
Lagoas Park Edificio 10, 2740-271, Porto Salvo, Portugal
Tel.: (351) 210427200
Web Site: http://www.zoetis.com.pt
Animal Health Product Mfr & Distr
N.A.I.C.S.: 325412

Zoetis Romania S.R.L. (1)
Expo Business Park 54A Aviator Popisteanu Building 2 1-3rd Floor, 1st District, 012095, Bucharest, Romania
Tel.: (40) 31 805 9211
Web Site: https://www.zoetis.ro
Animal Health Product Mfr & Distr
N.A.I.C.S.: 325412

Zoetis S.R.L. (1)
Torre Empresarial Omega Av Manuel Olguin 211 of 1001, Santiago de Surco, Lima, Peru
Tel.: (51) 16163333
Web Site: http://www.zoetis.pe
Animal Health Product Mfr & Distr
N.A.I.C.S.: 325412

Zoetis Salud Animal, C.A. (1)
Torre Cristal piso 4 oficina 4-3, Carabobo, Valencia, Carabobo, Venezuela
Tel.: (58) 2417145132
Web Site: http://www.zoetis.com.ve
Animal Health Product Mfr & Distr
N.A.I.C.S.: 325412

Zoetis Schweiz GmbH (1)
Rue de la Jeunesse 2, 2800, Delemont, Switzerland
Tel.: (41) 32 581 9800
Web Site: https://www2.zoetis.ch
Animal Health Product Mfr & Distr
N.A.I.C.S.: 325412

Zoetis South Africa (Pty) Ltd. (1)
6th Floor North Wing 90 Rivonia Road, Sandton, 2196, South Africa
Tel.: (27) 112453300
Animal Health Products Mfr
N.A.I.C.S.: 325412

Zoetis Spain, S.L. (1)
Parque Empresarial Via Norte Edificio n 1 c/ Quintanavides n 13, 28050, Madrid, Spain
Tel.: (34) 91 419 1900
Web Site: https://www2.zoetis.es
Animal Health Product Mfr & Distr
N.A.I.C.S.: 325412

Zoetis Taiwan Limited (1)
3F No 188 Section 1 Shipai Road, Beitou District, Taipei, 112, Taiwan
Tel.: (886) 228267500
Animal Health Product Mfr & Distr
N.A.I.C.S.: 325412

Zoetis UK Limited (1)
1st Floor Birchwood Building Springfield Drive, Leatherhead, KT22 7LP, Surrey, United Kingdom
Tel.: (44) 3453008034
Web Site: https://www2.zoetis.co.uk
Animal Health Product Mfr & Distr
N.A.I.C.S.: 325412

Zoetis Ukraine LLC (1)
street Amosova 12, Kiev, 03038, Ukraine
Tel.: (380) 443894066
Web Site: http://www.zoetis.com.ua
Emp.: 15
Animal Health Product Mfr & Distr
N.A.I.C.S.: 325412

Zoetis Vietnam Limited Liability Company (1)
Vong Xoay Nga Sau Cong Hoa Nguyen Cu Trinh, Ho Chi Minh City, Dong Nam Bo, Vietnam
Tel.: (84) 2838122461
Pharmaceutical Drug Mfr
N.A.I.C.S.: 325412
Tien Hoang Nguyen (Mgr-Livestock Technical)

Zoetis de Chile S.A. (1)
Av Isidora Goyenechea 2800 of 3004, Las Condes, Santiago, Chile
Tel.: (56) 22 307 3500
Web Site: https://www2.zoetis.cl
Animal Health Product Mfr & Distr
N.A.I.C.S.: 325412

Zoetis, C.A. (1)
Torre Cristal piso 4 oficina 4-3, Valencia, Estado Carabobo, Venezuela
Tel.: (58) 2417145132
Web Site: http://www.zoetis.com.ve
Pharmaceutical Drug Mfr
N.A.I.C.S.: 325412

Zoetis, Inc. - Lincoln (1)
601 W Cornhusker Hwy, Lincoln, NE 68521-3577 (100%)
Tel.: (402) 475-4541
Emp.: 500
Animal Health Products Mfr
N.A.I.C.S.: 325412
Mike Morgan (Site Mgr)

Zoetis, Inc. - White Hall (1)
E Lincoln Rd, White Hall, IL 62092 (100%)
Tel.: (217) 374-2102
Sales Range: $200-249.9 Million
Emp.: 43
Animal Health Products Mfr
N.A.I.C.S.: 325412
Juan Ramirez (CEO)

ZOMEDICA CORP.

100 Phoenix Dr Ste 190, Ann Arbor, MI 48108
Tel.: (734) 369-2555   AB
Web Site: https://www.zomedica.com
Year Founded: 2013
ZOM—(NYSEAMEX)
Rev.: $25,186,000
Assets: $253,197,000
Liabilities: $13,180,000
Net Worth: $240,017,000
Earnings: ($34,529,000)
Emp.: 144
Fiscal Year-end: 12/31/23
Veterinary & Pharmaceutical Products Mfr
N.A.I.C.S.: 325412
Jeffrey Mark Rowe (Chm)
Karen DeHaan-Fullerton (Gen Counsel & Sec)
Kristin Domanski (VP-Human Resources)
Evan St. Peter (VP-Tech Innovation)
Bill Campbell (VP-Imaging Sys)
Ashley Wood (VP-Research & Development)
Trudy Gage (VP-Equine Sls & Client Education)
Larry C. Heaton (CEO)
Greg Blair (Sr VP-Business Development & Strategic Planning & VP)
Adrian Lock (VP & Gen Mgr)
Nicole Westfall (Sr VP-Marketing & VP)
Kevin Klass (Sr VP-Sales)
Mike Zuehlke (VP-Finance & Controller)
Frederic S. Almy (VP-Clinical Pathology)

Subsidiaries:

Pulse Veterinary Technologies, LLC (1)
11390 Old Roswell Rd Ste 120, Alpharetta, GA 30009-2058
Web Site: http://www.pulsevet.com

Electromedical & Electrotherapeutic Apparatus Mfr
N.A.I.C.S.: 334510
Trudy Gage *(Territory Mgr)*

ZONED PROPERTIES, INC.

8360 E Raintree Dr Ste 230, Scottsdale, AZ 85260   NV
Web Site:
  https://www.zonedproperties.com
Year Founded: 2003
ZDPY—(OTCQB)
Rev.: $2,660,090
Assets: $14,380,847
Liabilities: $8,702,549
Net Worth: $5,678,298
Earnings: ($574,355)
Emp.: 9
Fiscal Year-end: 12/31/22
Mineral Exploration Services
N.A.I.C.S.: 212390
Bryan McLaren *(Chm, CEO, CFO, Treas & Sec)*
Berekk Blackwell *(Pres & COO)*

Subsidiaries:

Green Valley Group, LLC   (1)
PO Box 242, Unionville, PA 19375
Tel.: (610) 347-0620
Web Site:
  https://www.thegreenvalleygroup.com
Home Inspection Services
N.A.I.C.S.: 541350

ZOOM VIDEO COMMUNICATIONS, INC.

55 Almaden Blvd 6th Fl, San Jose, CA 95113
Tel.: (888) 799-9666   DE
Web Site: https://www.zoom.com
Year Founded: 2011
ZM—(NASDAQ)
Rev.: $4,527,224,000
Assets: $9,929,793,000
Liabilities: $1,910,387,000
Net Worth: $8,019,406,000
Earnings: $637,462,000
Emp.: 7,420
Fiscal Year-end: 01/31/24
Software Development Services
N.A.I.C.S.: 541511
Eric S. Yuan *(Founder & CEO)*
Aparna Bawa *(COO & Sec)*
Brendan Ittelson *(Chief Ecosystem Officer)*
Velchamy Sankarlingam *(Pres-Product & Engrg)*

Subsidiaries:

Keybase LLC   (1)
11351 Pearl Rd Ste 301, Cleveland, OH 44136
Tel.: (440) 238-7600
Web Site: http://www.keybaseinc.com
IT Services
N.A.I.C.S.: 541511

ZVC Australia Pty. Ltd.   (1)
Level 1 9 Castlereagh St, Sydney, 2000, NSW, Australia
Tel.: (61) 1800768027
Software Development Services
N.A.I.C.S.: 541511

ZVC France SAS   (1)
Zoom France 33 rue Lafayette, 75009, Paris, France
Tel.: (33) 800946464
Software Development Services
N.A.I.C.S.: 541511

ZVC Japan KK   (1)
WeWork Hibiya Park Front 19th Floor 2-1-6, Uchisaiwai-Cho Chiyoda-ku, Tokyo, 100-0011, Japan
Tel.: (81) 531320070
Software Development Services
N.A.I.C.S.: 541511

ZVC UK Ltd.   (1)
The Place 4th Floor 175 High, Holborn, London, WC1V 7AA, United Kingdom

Tel.: (44) 2070398961
Software Development Services
N.A.I.C.S.: 541511

ZOOMAWAY TRAVEL, INC.

960 Matley Ln Ste 4, Reno, NV 89502
Tel.: (775) 691-8860
Web Site:
  https://www.zoomaway.com
ZMA—(TSXV)
Rev.: $56,623
Assets: $78,948
Liabilities: $2,016,600
Net Worth: ($1,937,652)
Earnings: ($743,320)
Fiscal Year-end: 12/31/19
Travel Agency Services
N.A.I.C.S.: 561599
Sean Scheaffer *(CEO)*
Tim Berfield *(CTO)*

ZOOMINFO TECHNOLOGIES INC.

805 Broadway St Ste 900, Vancouver, WA 98660   DE
Web Site: https://www.zoominfo.com
Year Founded: 2019
ZI—(NASDAQ)
Rev.: $1,239,500,000
Assets: $6,868,300,000
Liabilities: $4,749,000,000
Net Worth: $2,119,300,000
Earnings: $107,300,000
Emp.: 3,516
Fiscal Year-end: 12/31/23
Holding Company
N.A.I.C.S.: 551112
P. Cameron Hyzer *(CFO & Principal Acctg Officer)*
Henry Schuck *(Founder, Chm & CEO)*
Joseph Christopher Hays *(Exec VP-Intl Expansion)*
David Justice *(Chief Growth Officer)*
Hila Nir *(Chief Product Officer)*
David Reid *(VP-Acctg & Controller)*
Anthony Stark *(Gen Counsel)*
Shane Murphy-Reuter *(CMO)*
Colby Greene *(Dir-Pre-Sales)*
Robert Morse *(Sr Mgr-Comm)*
Simon McDougall *(Chief Compliance Officer)*
Ali Dasdan *(CTO)*

Subsidiaries:

Datanyze, LLC   (1)
2530 Meridian Pkwy Ste 300, Durham, NC 27713
Web Site: http://www.datanyze.com
Marketing Consulting Services
N.A.I.C.S.: 541613

Neverbounce, LLC   (1)
805 Broadway St Ste 900, Vancouver, WA 98660
Web Site: https://www.neverbounce.com
Information Technology Services
N.A.I.C.S.: 541511
Brad Owen *(Founder & CEO)*

RingLead, Inc.   (1)
200 Broadhollow Rd#400, Melville, NY 11747
Tel.: (262) 264-7646
Web Site: http://www.ringlead.com
Data Orchestration Platform.
N.A.I.C.S.: 513210
Michael Farrington *(Chief Product Officer)*
Colby Greene *(COO)*

ZOSANO PHARMA CORPORATION

34790 Ardentech Ct, Fremont, CA 94555
Tel.: (510) 745-1200   DE
Web Site:
  http://www.zosanopharma.com

ZSAN—(NASDAQ)
Rev.: $785,000
Assets: $48,390,000
Liabilities: $15,415,000
Net Worth: $32,975,000
Earnings: ($29,925,000)
Emp.: 77
Fiscal Year-end: 12/31/21
Pharmaceuticals Mfr
N.A.I.C.S.: 325412
Steven Lo *(Pres & CEO)*

ZOVIO INC.

1811 E Northrop Blvd, Chandler, AZ 85286
Tel.: (858) 668-2586   DE
Web Site: http://www.zovio.com
Year Founded: 2004
ZVO—(NASDAQ)
Rev.: $263,033,000
Assets: $149,034,000
Liabilities: $129,028,000
Net Worth: $20,006,000
Earnings: ($42,349,000)
Emp.: 1,365
Fiscal Year-end: 12/31/21
Postsecondary Education Services
N.A.I.C.S.: 611310
Vickie Schray *(Chief External Affairs Officer & Exec VP)*
Kevin S. Royal *(Exec VP)*

Subsidiaries:

The University of The Rockies   (1)
555 E Pikes Peak Ave Ste 108, Colorado Springs, CO 80903
Tel.: (719) 442-0505
Web Site: http://www.rockies.edu
Sales Range: $10-24.9 Million
Emp.: 50
Degree-Granting University
N.A.I.C.S.: 611310
Dawn Iwamoto *(Pres & CEO)*

ZSCALER, INC.

120 Holger Way, San Jose, CA 95134
Tel.: (408) 533-0288   DE
Web Site: https://www.zscaler.com
Year Founded: 2007
ZS—(NASDAQ)
Rev.: $2,167,771,000
Assets: $4,704,968,000
Liabilities: $3,430,866,000
Net Worth: $1,274,102,000
Earnings: ($57,706,000)
Emp.: 7,348
Fiscal Year-end: 07/31/24
Computer Related Services
N.A.I.C.S.: 541519
Jagtar S. Chaudhry *(Founder, Chm & CEO)*
Remo E. Canessa *(CFO)*
Robert Schlossman *(Chief Legal Officer)*
Patrick Foxhoven *(CIO & Exec VP-Emerging Technologies)*
Punit Minocha *(Exec VP-Business Development-Corporate Strategy)*
Kavitha Mariappan *(Exec VP-Customer Experience-Transformation)*
Bill Choi *(Sr VP-IR & Strategic Fin)*
Joyce Kim *(CMO)*
Marc Surette *(Reg VP-Dept Defense, Intelligence Community & Foreign Svc Institute)*
Laura Fritzlen *(VP-Pub Sector Alliances & Channels)*
Peter Amirkhan *(Sr VP-Pub Sector)*
Ryan Gillis *(Sr VP & Head-Govt Partnerships)*
Mike Rich *(Chief Revenue Officer & Pres-Global Sls)*
Joyce Kim *(CMO)*
Dali Rajic *(COO)*

Subsidiaries:

Edgewise Networks Inc.   (1)

1 Burlington Woods Dr #101, Burlington, MA 01803
Tel.: (781) 825-8378
Emp.: 100
Computer & Network Security Services
N.A.I.C.S.: 541519
Peter Smith *(Pres)*

ShiftRight, Inc.   (1)
4353 N 1st St #100, San Jose, CA 95134
Tel.: (408) 320-7045
Web Site: https://www.shiftright.ai
Emp.: 100
Software Development & Services
N.A.I.C.S.: 541512

Smokescreen Technologies Private Limited   (1)
Red Bricks HDIL's Kaledonia 1st floor Sahar Rd Andheri East, Mumbai, 400069, Marahashtra, India
Tel.: (91) 2261013851
Web Site: https://www.smokescreen.io
Emp.: 100
Computer & Network Security Services
N.A.I.C.S.: 541519

Zscaler Softech India Private Limited   (1)
B-Building 6th Floor Indialand Global Tech Park, Behind Grand Highstreet Mall Phase 1 Hinjewadi, Pune, 411057, Maharashtra, India
Tel.: (91) 8968922203
Cyber Security Services
N.A.I.C.S.: 518210

ZUMIEZ INCORPORATED

4001 204th St SW, Lynnwood, WA 98036
Tel.: (425) 551-1500   WA
Web Site: https://www.zumiez.com
Year Founded: 1978
ZUMZ—(NASDAQ)
Rev.: $958,380,000
Assets: $747,903,000
Liabilities: $340,575,000
Net Worth: $407,328,000
Earnings: $21,034,000
Emp.: 2,600
Fiscal Year-end: 01/28/23
Apparel, Footwear & Accessories Retailer
N.A.I.C.S.: 458110
Adam C. Ellis *(Pres-Intl)*
Christopher C. Work *(CFO)*
Chris K. Visser *(Chief Legal Officer)*
Thomas D. Campion *(Chm)*
Richard M. Brooks Jr. *(CEO)*

Subsidiaries:

Blue Tomato Deutschland GmbH   (1)
Oberanger 16, 80331, Munich, Germany
Tel.: (49) 898 208 8614
Web Site: http://www.blue-tomato.com
Emp.: 12
Apparel Accessory Store Operator
N.A.I.C.S.: 458110

Blue Tomato Netherlands B.V.   (1)
Voor Clarenburg 1-3-5, 3511 JE, Utrecht, Netherlands
Tel.: (31) 307370880
Clothing Retailer
N.A.I.C.S.: 458110

Snowboard Dachstein Tauern GmbH   (1)
Hochstrasse 628, 8970, Schladming, Austria
Tel.: (43) 36872422333
Web Site: http://www.blue-tomato.com
Sports Goods Mfr
N.A.I.C.S.: 339920

Zumiez Services Inc.   (1)
4001 204th St SW, Lynnwood, WA 98036
Tel.: (425) 551-1500
Web Site: http://www.zumiez.com
Men & Children Cloth Mfr
N.A.I.C.S.: 458110

ZUORA, INC.

101 Redwood Shores Pkwy, Redwood City, CA 94065   DE

Zuora, Inc.—(Continued)

Web Site: https://www.zuora.com
Year Founded: 2006
ZUO—(NYSE)
Rev.: $396,087,000
Assets: $668,598,000
Liabilities: $571,438,000
Net Worth: $97,160,000
Earnings: ($197,970,000)
Emp.: 1,549
Fiscal Year-end: 01/31/23
Customer Relationship Management
Software
N.A.I.C.S.: 513210
Tien Tzuo (Founder, Chm & CEO)
Robbie Traube (Chief Revenue Officer)
Daisy Hernandez (Sr VP-Strategy & Ops)
Kyle Christensen (CMO)
Valerie Jackson (Chief Diversity Officer)
Todd E. McElhatton (CFO)
Laura Robblee (Chief HR Officer)
Sridhar Srinivasan (Chief Product Officer & Chief Engrg Officer)
Andrew Cohen (Chief Legal Officer)
Robert Hildenbrand (Sr VP-Global Svcs)
Pete Hirsch (CTO & Chief Product Officer)

Subsidiaries:

Leeyo Software Inc.   (1)
2841 Junction Ave Ste 201, San Jose, CA 95134
Tel.: (408) 988-5800
Revenue Recognition Software Developer
N.A.I.C.S.: 541511

Zuora Australia Pty. Ltd.   (1)
135 King St 20th Floor, Sydney, 2000, NSW, Australia
Tel.: (61) 280467522
Software Development Services
N.A.I.C.S.: 513210

Zuora Germany GmbH   (1)
Regus Nymphenburger Hofe Nymphenburger Strasse 4 5th Floor, 80335, Munich, Germany
Tel.: (49) 8925552567
Software Development Services
N.A.I.C.S.: 513210

Zuora India Private Limited   (1)
9th Floor Tower B World Trade Centre Rajiv Gandhi Salai, Perungudi, Chennai, 600 096, Tamil Nadu, India
Tel.: (91) 4466142600
Software Development Services
N.A.I.C.S.: 513210

Zuora Japan KK   (1)
Wework 9F 1-6-5 Marunouchi, Chiyoda-ku, Tokyo, 100-6509, Japan
Tel.: (81) 368211695
Software Development Services
N.A.I.C.S.: 513210

Zuora UK Limited   (1)
1 Dean Street, London, W1D 3RB, United Kingdom
Tel.: (44) 2070398920
Software Development Services
N.A.I.C.S.: 513210

ZURA BIO LIMITED
1489 W Warm Springs Rd Ste 110, Henderson, NV 89014
Tel.: (702) 825-9872   Ky
Web Site: https://www.zurabio.com
Year Founded: 2022
ZURA—(NASDAQ)
Rev.: $6,224,268
Assets: $141,507,839
Liabilities: $149,134,085
Net Worth: ($7,626,246)
Earnings: $3,549,127
Fiscal Year-end: 12/31/22
Biotechnology Research & Development Services

N.A.I.C.S.: 541714
Robert Lisicki (CEO)
Michael Howell (Chief Scientific Officer & Head-Translational Medicine)
Kiran Nistala (Chief Medical Officer & Head-Dev)
Someit Sidhu (Founder)
Amit Munshi (Chm)
Gary Whale (CTO)
Verender Badial (CFO)
Kim Davis (Chief Legal Officer & Sec)

ZURN ELKAY WATER SOLUTIONS CORPORATION
511 W Freshwater Way, Milwaukee, WI 53204
Tel.: (414) 808-0199   DE
Web Site: https://zurnelkay.com
ZWS—(NYSE)
Rev.: $1,530,500,000
Assets: $2,667,000,000
Liabilities: $1,064,200,000
Net Worth: $1,602,800,000
Earnings: $112,700,000
Emp.: 2,400
Fiscal Year-end: 12/31/23
Power Transmission & Water Management Products Mfr
N.A.I.C.S.: 333613
Todd Alan Adams (Chm, Pres & CEO)
Angela Hersil (VP-Corp Comm)
David J. Pauli (CFO)
Mark W. Peterson (Chief Admin Officer)

Subsidiaries:

American Autogard LLC   (1)
4701 W Greenfield Ave, Milwaukee, WI 53214
Tel.: (414) 643-3000
Motion Control & Water Management Product Mfr
N.A.I.C.S.: 334513
Frank Casarotto (Mgr-Matls)

American Dryer, LLC   (1)
340 County Line Rd, Bensenville, IL 60106
Tel.: (800) 485-7003
Web Site: http://www.americandryer.com
Household Appliances Mfr
N.A.I.C.S.: 335220

Autogard Asia Pacific Pty Ltd (1)
U 17 56 Keys Rd, Cheltenham, 3192, VIC, Australia
Tel.: (61) 395320901
Web Site: http://www.autogard.com
Emp.: 1
Motion Control & Water Management Product Mfr
N.A.I.C.S.: 334513

Autogard Holdings Limited   (1)
2 Wilkinson Road Love Lane Industrial Estate, Cirencester, GL7 1YT, United Kingdom
Tel.: (44) 1285640333
Web Site: http://www.autogard.com
Emp.: 60
Investment Management Service
N.A.I.C.S.: 551112
Bill Howgego (Mng Dir)

CENTA Transm. Far East Pte Ltd.   (1)
One Sims Lane 05-04, Singapore, 387355, Singapore
Tel.: (65) 63162508
Mechanical Power Transmission Equipment Mfr
N.A.I.C.S.: 333613

Cambridge International, Inc.   (1)
105 Goodwill Rd, Cambridge, MD 21613
Tel.: (410) 901-4979
Web Site: https://www.cambridge-intl.com
Metal Belting & Wire Cloth Mfr & Distr
N.A.I.C.S.: 333922

Division (Domestic):

Cambridge Architectural   (2)
105 Goodwill Dr, Cambridge, MD 21613
Tel.: (410) 901-8686

Web Site:
https://cambridgearchitectural.com
Architectural Mesh Systems Solutions for Building Projects
N.A.I.C.S.: 332618
Matt O'Connell (Dir-Ops)
Hank Phillips (Project Engr)
Keith Rose (Project Engr)
Jaime Sturdivant (Coord-Project)
Jon Southworth (Mgr-Water Screen Bus)

Cambridge Engineered Solutions   (2)
105 Goodwill Rd, Cambridge, MD 21613
Tel.: (410) 901-2660
Web Site: http://www.cambridge-es.com
Engineered Solutions for Metal Belting & Wire Cloth Mfr
N.A.I.C.S.: 332999
Logan Baxter (Engr-Application)
Chris Daly (Mgr-Market Sls)
Ken Docktor (Mgr-Regional Acct)
Jaime Foxwell (Mgr-Market Sls)
Chris Porter (Engr-Applications)
Ty Spainhour (Mgr-Tech Market Sls)
Jeffrey Ulchak (Engr-Product Dev)

Cline Acquisition Corp.   (1)
5210 Edwards Rd, Taylors, SC 29687
Tel.: (864) 235-6371
Power Transmission Machinery Mfr
N.A.I.C.S.: 339999

Elkay Manufacturing Company   (1)
2222 Camden Ct, Oak Brook, IL 60523-4674
Tel.: (630) 574-8484
Web Site: http://www.elkay.com
Sales Range: $1-4.9 Billion
Emp.: 4,200
Sinks, Faucets, Commercial Water Coolers & Drinking Fountains Supplier & Mfr
N.A.I.C.S.: 332999
Mark Whittington (Exec VP-Plumbing Trade Sls & Ops)
Tom Samanic (Pres-Cabinetry Bus & Wood Products)
Larry Brand (Chief HR Officer & VP)
Kathy Deighan (Gen Counsel, Sec & VP)
Franco Savoni (Exec VP-Plumbing)
Ted Hamilton (Pres-Plumbing)
Bryan English (CFO & VP)
Steve Rogers (Pres-Comml & Industrial)

Division (Domestic):

Cabinetry Division   (2)
2222 Camden Ct, Oak Brook, IL 60523-4674   (100%)
Tel.: (630) 574-8484
Web Site: http://www.elkay.com
Sink, Faucets, Water Coolers & Fountains
N.A.I.C.S.: 332999

Division (Domestic):

Yorktowne, Inc.   (3)
100 Redco Ave, Red Lion, PA 17356
Tel.: (717) 244-4011
Web Site:
http://www.yorktownecabinetry.com
Sales Range: $75-99.9 Million
Mfr of Kitchen Cabinets, Vanities, Countertops & Specialty Furniture
N.A.I.C.S.: 337110

Division (Non-US):

E.B. Tecnica Mexicana, S.A. de C.V.   (2)
Av Promocion, No 120 Zona Industrial, 78395, San Luis Potosi, CP. 78395, Mexico   (100%)
Tel.: (52) 4441370101
Web Site: https://www.ebtecnica.com.mx
Sales Range: $10-24.9 Million
Emp.: 82
Stainless Steel Sink Mfr
N.A.I.C.S.: 332999

Subsidiary (Domestic):

Elkay Interior Systems   (2)
241 N Broadway Ste 600, Milwaukee, WI 53202
Web Site:
https://www.elkayinteriorsystems.com
Restaurant Interior Design Services
N.A.I.C.S.: 541410
Mia Nicolaisen (VP)
Mark Sbrocco (VP)

Kevin Reiman (VP)
Tom Kelley (Mng Dir)
Stephan Schwaabe (Mng Dir)
Beau Nicolaisen (Chief Welcoming Officer)

Subsidiary (Domestic):

Digney York Associates LLC   (3)
1919 Gallows Rd Ste 950, Vienna, VA 22182
Tel.: (703) 790-5281
Web Site: http://www.digneyyork.com
Residential Remodeler
N.A.I.C.S.: 236118
Jay Weiss (CEO)
David Steinberg (Sr Project Mgr)
Kevin Cronin (COO)
Bill Navas (Pres)
Ann Versteeg (CFO)

Subsidiary (Domestic):

Halsey Taylor   (2)
1333 Butterfield Rd Ste 200, Downers Grove, IL 60515
Tel.: (630) 574-3500
Web Site: https://www.halseytaylor.com
Sales Range: $25-49.9 Million
Emp.: 200
Drinking Fountains & Electric Water Coolers Mfr
N.A.I.C.S.: 332999
Jack Krecek (VP-Comml Channel Distr)

Mastercraft Cabinets, Inc.   (2)
10501 W 10th St, Waconia, MN 55387
Tel.: (303) 214-5100
Web Site:
https://www.mastercraftcabinets.com
Cabinet & Door Mfr
N.A.I.C.S.: 337110

Medallion Cabinetry   (2)
1 Medallion Way, Waconia, MN 55378
Tel.: (952) 442-5171
Web Site:
https://www.medallioncabinetry.com
Emp.: 500
Cabinet & Door Mfr
N.A.I.C.S.: 337110
Miranda Schultz (Coord-Traffic)

Euroflex Transmissions (India) Private Ltd.   (1)
99 CIE Phase II Gandhi Nagar Balanagar, Hyderabad, 500037, Telengana, India
Tel.: (91) 9894119299
Web Site: http://www.euroflex.co.in
Disc Coupling Mfr
N.A.I.C.S.: 332996

Filamat Composites Inc.   (1)
880 Rangeview Road, Mississauga, L5E 1G9, ON, Canada
Tel.: (905) 891-3993
Web Site: http://filamat.com
Fiber Glass Products Mfr
N.A.I.C.S.: 326199

Fontaine Europe SAS   (1)
11 Avenue Charles de Gaulle, Roissy-en-France, 95700, France
Tel.: (33) 134294769
Water Treatment Solution Provider
N.A.I.C.S.: 221310

Fontaine Industries Ltd.   (1)
1295 Sherbrooke Street, Magog, J1X 2T2, QC, Canada
Tel.: (819) 843-3068
Web Site: http://www.hfontaine.com
Water Treatment Solution Provider
N.A.I.C.S.: 221310

Fontaine USA Inc.   (1)
3 Executive Park Dr, Bedford, NH 03110
Tel.: (603) 626-6680
Web Site: http://www.wwdmag.com
Motion Control & Water Management Product Mfr
N.A.I.C.S.: 334513

GA Industries Holdings, LLC   (1)
4701 W Greenfield Ave, Milwaukee, WI 53214
Tel.: (414) 643-2474
Holding Company
N.A.I.C.S.: 551112

Green Turtle Americas, LTD (1)
2709 Water Rdg Pkwy Ste 410, Charlotte, NC 28217
Tel.: (704) 295-1733
Web Site: http://www.greenturtletech.com
Water Purification Equipment Mfr
N.A.I.C.S.: 333310

HL Capital Corp. (1)
1849 Severview Pl, Lawrenceville, GA 30043-5199
Tel.: (678) 778-0698
Investment Management Service
N.A.I.C.S.: 523940

Hadrian Solutions ULC (1)
965 Syscon Road, Burlington, L7L 5S3, ON, Canada
Tel.: (905) 333-0300
Powder Coat Toilet Partition Mfr & Distr
N.A.I.C.S.: 423220

Jihomoravska armaturka Spol. S.r.O. (1)
Lipova Alej 3087/1, PO Box 123, 695 01, Hodonin, Czech Republic
Tel.: (420) 518318111
Web Site: http://www.jmahod.cz
Sales Range: $100-124.9 Million
Industrial Valve Mfr
N.A.I.C.S.: 332911

Just Manufacturing LLC (1)
9233 King St, Franklin Park, IL 60131
Tel.: (847) 678-5151
Web Site: https://www.justmfg.com
Plumbing Product & Fixture Mfr
N.A.I.C.S.: 332913
Brian Smith *(Mgr-Internet Mktg)*

Klamflex Pipe Couplings (Pty) Ltd (1)
52 Fransen Street, Chamdor, Krugersdorp, 1739, South Africa
Tel.: (27) 117625326
Web Site: http://www.klamflex.com
Pipe Coupling Mfr
N.A.I.C.S.: 332996

LWG Zurn Australia Pty Ltd. (1)
49 Lakeside Drive, Broadmeadows, 3047, VIC, Australia
Tel.: (61) 383019499
Web Site: http://www.lwgzurn.com
Plumbing Equipment Whslr
N.A.I.C.S.: 423840

Micro Precision Gear Technology Limited (1)
99 Gresham Street,, London, EC2V 7NG, United Kingdom
Tel.: (44) 1442241027
Precision Component Mfr
N.A.I.C.S.: 332721

OEP, Inc. (1)
160 Abbott Dr, Wheeling, IL 60090
Tel.: (847) 459-9528
Web Site: https://www.oep.com
Motion Control & Water Management Product Mfr
N.A.I.C.S.: 334513

Prager Inc. (1)
181 Riverbend Dr, Saint Rose, LA 70087
Tel.: (504) 461-9400
Web Site: http://www.resnord.com
Sales Range: $25-49.9 Million
Emp.: 40
Machine Shop Jobbing & Repair
N.A.I.C.S.: 332710

Precision Gear Holdings LLC (1)
1900 Midway Dr, Twinsburg, OH 44087
Tel.: (330) 487-0888
Holding Company
N.A.I.C.S.: 551112

Rexnord Asia Pacific Pte. Ltd. (1)
8 Wilkie Road 03-01 Wilkie Edge, Singapore, 228095, Singapore
Tel.: (65) 63385622
Web Site: http://www.rexnord.com
Emp.: 7
Conveyor Chain Mfr
N.A.I.C.S.: 333922

Rexnord Australia Pty Ltd. (1)
8 - 20 Anderson Road, PO Box 620, Smeaton Grange, Sydney, 2567, NSW, Australia

Tel.: (61) 246776000
Web Site: http://www.rexnord.com
Emp.: 80
Motion Control & Water Management Product Mfr
N.A.I.C.S.: 334513

Rexnord Finance BV (1)
Einstein Straat 1, 2691 GV, 's-Gravenzande, 2691 GV, Netherlands
Tel.: (31) 174445100
Web Site: http://www.rexnord.com
Sales Range: $25-49.9 Million
Emp.: 200
Conveyor Chain Mfr
N.A.I.C.S.: 333922

Rexnord Flat Top Italy Srl (1)
Via dell'Industria 4, 42015, Correggio, Reggio Emilia, Italy
Tel.: (39) 0522639333
Motion Control & Water Management Product Mfr
N.A.I.C.S.: 334513

Rexnord FlatTop Europe BV (1)
Einsteinstraat 1, 2691 GV, s-Gravenzande, Netherlands
Tel.: (31) 174445100
Web Site: http://www.rexnordflattop.com
Emp.: 75
Conveyor Chain Mfr
N.A.I.C.S.: 333922

Rexnord FlatTop Europe Srl (1)
Via Dellindustria 4, 42015, Correggio, Italy
Tel.: (39) 0522639333
Conveyor Product Mfr
N.A.I.C.S.: 333922
Maurizio Malavasi *(Mgr-Warehouse)*

Rexnord France Holdings SAS (1)
Place Neuhausen, 01960, Peronnas, France
Tel.: (33) 474473564
Web Site: http://www.rexnord-kette.de
Motion Control & Water Management Product Mfr
N.A.I.C.S.: 334513

Rexnord I.H. B.V. (1)
Einsteinstraat 1, 2691 GV, s-Gravenzande, Netherlands
Tel.: (31) 174445100
Conveyor Product Mfr
N.A.I.C.S.: 333922

Rexnord Industries, LLC (1)
111 W Michigan St, Milwaukee, WI 53203
Tel.: (414) 643-3000
Web Site: https://www.rexnord.com
Industrial Conveying Equipment, Power Transmission & Specialty Components Mfr
N.A.I.C.S.: 333613

Subsidiary (Non-US):

Centa Antriebe Kirschey GmbH (2)
Bergische Str 7, 42781, Haan, Germany
Tel.: (49) 21299120
Web Site: http://www.centa.info
Couplings & Drive Shafts Mfr
N.A.I.C.S.: 333612

Subsidiary (US):

CENTA Corporation (3)
2570 Beverly Dr Ste 128, Aurora, IL 60502-8588
Tel.: (630) 236-3500
Web Site: http://www.centa.info
Transportation Equipment Distr
N.A.I.C.S.: 423110

Subsidiary (Non-US):

CENTA Nordic AB (3)
Metallgatan 4 C, 26272, Angelholm, Sweden
Tel.: (46) 431416390
Web Site: http://www.centa.info
Transportation Equipment Distr
N.A.I.C.S.: 423840

CENTA Transmissioner A/S (3)
A C Illums Vej 5, 8600, Silkeborg, Denmark
Tel.: (45) 86804033
Web Site: http://www.centa.info
Industrial Product Mfr & Distr
N.A.I.C.S.: 333618

Lars Haarup *(Dir-Admin)*
Jesper Thorhauge *(Engr-Sls)*

CENTA Transmissioni S.r.l. (3)
Via Meraviglia 31, 20020, Lainate, Italy
Tel.: (39) 02 93799556
Industrial Product Mfr & Distr
N.A.I.C.S.: 333618

CENTA Transmissions Far East Pte Ltd. (3)
1 Sims Lane 05-04, Singapore, 387355, Singapore
Tel.: (65) 63162508
Web Site: http://www.centa.info
Industrial Product Mfr & Distr
N.A.I.C.S.: 333618

CENTA Transmissions Ltd. (3)
Thackley Court Thackley Old Road, Shipley, Bradford, BD18 1BW, West Yorkshire, United Kingdom
Tel.: (44) 1274531034
Web Site: http://www.centa-uk.co.uk
Industrial Product Mfr & Distr
N.A.I.C.S.: 333618
Bob Arnott *(Chm)*
Darren Hudson *(Mng Dir)*
Andrew Dean *(Ops Mgr)*
Gary Middleton *(Controller-Production)*
Anne Norcliffe *(Mgr-Office & Pur)*
Peter Jeffrey *(Engr-Sls)*
David Fairbank *(Engr-Application)*
David Moulds *(Engr-Applications)*
Graham Waddington *(Engr-Internal Sls)*
Mohammed Usman *(Project Engr)*

CENTA Transmissions Pty Ltd. (3)
3/4 Sovereign Place, Windsor, 2756, NSW, Australia
Tel.: (61) 245879399
Web Site: http://www.centa.info
Industrial Product Mfr & Distr
N.A.I.C.S.: 333618

CENTA transmisjoner a.s. (3)
Ovre Langgate 57-59, NO-3110, Tonsberg, Norway
Tel.: (47) 33483115
Web Site: http://www.centa.info
Industrial Product Mfr & Distr
N.A.I.C.S.: 333618
Kristoffer Orerod *(Sls Mgr)*
Eirik Lutnaes *(Dir-Marine Aftersales)*

Subsidiary (Non-US):

Rexnord Canada Limited (2)
81 Maybrook Dr, Scarborough, M1V 3Z2, ON, Canada (100%)
Tel.: (416) 297-6868
Web Site: http://www.rexnord.com
Sales Range: $25-49.9 Million
Emp.: 37
Power Transmission Equipment
N.A.I.C.S.: 333613

Rexnord International Inc. (1)
4701 W Greenfield Ave, Milwaukee, WI 53214-5310
Tel.: (414) 643-3000
Web Site: http://www.rexnord.com
Rev.: $505,927
Emp.: 30
Industrial Supplies
N.A.I.C.S.: 423840

Rexnord Kette GmbH (1)
Industriestrasse 1, 57501, Betzdorf, Germany
Tel.: (49) 27412840
Web Site: http://www.rexnord-kette.de
Emp.: 320
Conveyor Chain Mfr
N.A.I.C.S.: 333922

Rexnord Marbett Srl (1)
Via Dell' Industria 4, 42015, Correggio, Italy
Tel.: (39) 0522639333
Web Site: http://www.rexnordflattop.com
Conveyor Chain Mfr
N.A.I.C.S.: 333922

Rexnord Middle East FZE (1)
Offices FZS1AF04/05 Blue Shed - South Zone Jebel Ali Free Zone, PO Box 363900, Dubai, United Arab Emirates
Tel.: (971) 48849267
Conveyor Product Mfr & Distr
N.A.I.C.S.: 333922
Sven Erlandsen *(Mng Dir)*

Rexnord Power Transmission Products (Taicing) Co. Ltd. (1)
No 88 Wuyi Road, Nanxiashu Wujin Hi-Tech Development Zone, Changzhou, 213166, Jiangsu, China
Tel.: (86) 51986480500
Industrial Valve Designing & Mfr
N.A.I.C.S.: 332912

Rexnord S.A. de C.V. (1)
Privada de los Industriales No 115 Cd Industrial Benio Juarez, 76100, Queretaro, Mexico
Tel.: (52) 4422185000
Conveyor Chain Mfr
N.A.I.C.S.: 333922

Rexnord Tollok Srl (1)
Viale Adriatico 9, 44020, Masi Torello, FE, Italy
Tel.: (39) 0532816911
Web Site: http://www.rexnord.com
Emp.: 150
Industrial Valve Designing & Mfr
N.A.I.C.S.: 332912

Rexnord do Brasil Industrial Ltda (1)
R Cristopher Levalley 187, Jardin America, Sao Leopoldo, 93037-730, Rio Grande do Sul, Brazil
Tel.: (55) 5135798080
Web Site: http://www.rexnord.com.br
Emp.: 120
Motion Control & Water Management Product Mfr
N.A.I.C.S.: 334513

Rexnord-Zurn Holdings, Inc. (1)
111 W Michigan St, Milwaukee, WI 53203
Tel.: (414) 643-3000
Web Site: http://www.rexnord.com
Holding Company
N.A.I.C.S.: 551112

Subsidiary (Domestic):

W.M. Berg Inc. (2)
5138 S International Dr, Cudahy, WI 53110
Tel.: (414) 747-5800
Web Site: https://www.wmberg.com
Sales Range: $25-49.9 Million
Emp.: 100
Miniature Precision Mechanical Components Mfr
N.A.I.C.S.: 333613

World Dryer Corporation (2)
340 County Line Rd, Bensenville, IL 60106
Web Site: https://www.worlddryer.com
Hand Dryers Mfr
N.A.I.C.S.: 333415
Sean Martin *(Gen Mgr)*

Zurn Industries, LLC (2)
1801 Pittsburgh Ave, Erie, PA 16502
Tel.: (814) 455-0921
Web Site: https://www.zurn.com
Sales Range: $50-74.9 Million
Emp.: 210
Plumbing Products Mfr & Marketer
N.A.I.C.S.: 326191
Craig Wehr *(Pres)*

Division (Domestic):

Zurn Industries Cast Metals Operations (3)
1301 Raspberry St, Erie, PA 16502-1543
Tel.: (814) 455-0921
Web Site: http://www.zurn.com
Sales Range: $25-49.9 Million
Emp.: 200
Ferrous Casting
N.A.I.C.S.: 331492

Zurn Plumbing Products Group (3)
1801 Pittsburgh Ave, Erie, PA 16502-1916
Tel.: (814) 455-0921
Web Site: http://www.zurn.com
Sales Range: $25-49.9 Million
Emp.: 120
Plumbing System Mfr
N.A.I.C.S.: 332913

Subsidiary (Domestic):

GA Industries, Inc. (4)
234 Clay Ave, Mars, PA 16046
Tel.: (724) 776-1020
Web Site: www.gaindustries.com

Zurn Elkay Water Solutions
Corporation—(Continued)

Sales Range: $50-74.9 Million
Emp.: 200
Automatic Control Valve & Plumbing Fixture
Mfr
N.A.I.C.S.: 332919

Subsidiary (Domestic):

Rodney Hunt Company (5)
46 Mill St, Orange, MA 01364-1251
Tel.: (281) 962-6369
Web Site: https://www.rodneyhunt.com
Sales Range: $50-74.9 Million
Water & Sewage Control Flow Control
Equipment Gates & Valves
N.A.I.C.S.: 332312

Unit (Domestic):

Wilkins Water Control Products (4)
1747 Commerce Way, Paso Robles, CA
93446-3621
Tel.: (805) 238-7100
Web Site: http://www.zurn.com
Fluid Controls, Pressure Regulated Valves
& Related Equipment Mfr
N.A.I.C.S.: 423720

Subsidiary (Domestic):

Zurn Industries (4)
2640 S Work St, Falconer, NY 14733
Tel.: (716) 665-1132
Web Site: http://www.zurn.com
Rev.: $6,900,000
Emp.: 150
Plumbing & Hydronic Heating Supplies
N.A.I.C.S.: 423720

Subsidiary (Non-US):

Zurn Industries Limited (4)
7900 Goreway Drive Unit 10, Brampton,
L6T 5W6, ON, Canada
Tel.: (905) 595-3696
Web Site: https://www.zurn.ca
Sales Range: $25-49.9 Million
Emp.: 30
Plumbing Fixture Fittings
N.A.I.C.S.: 332913

Rodney Hunt-Fontaine Ltd. (1)
4699 Blvd Bourque, Sherbrooke, J1N 2G6,
QC, Canada
Tel.: (819) 823-3068
Web Site: http://www.hfontaine.com
Plumbing Equipment Whslr
N.A.I.C.S.: 423840

Rodney Hunt-Fontaine, Inc. (1)
46 Mill St, Orange, MA 01364
Tel.: (978) 633-4362
Web Site: http://www.rodneyhunt.com
Industrial Valve Designing & Mfr
N.A.I.C.S.: 332912

The Falk Service Corporation (1)
3001 W Canal St, Milwaukee, WI 53208-
4222
Tel.: (414) 342-3131
Web Site: http://www.rexnord.com
Motion Control & Water Management Prod-
uct Mfr
N.A.I.C.S.: 334513

VAG Armaturen Gmbh (1)
Carl-Reuther-Str 1, 68305, Mannheim, Ger-
many
Tel.: (49) 6217490
Web Site: http://www.vag-group.com
Emp.: 300
Water Treatment Solution Provider
N.A.I.C.S.: 221310

Subsidiary (Non-US):

OOO VAG Armaturen RUS (2)
Partizanskaya Street 80A Office 301,
443093, Samara, Russia
Tel.: (7) 8463731538
Web Site: http://www.vag-armaturen.com
Sales Range: $10-24.9 Million
Emp.: 15
Industrial Valve Mfr
N.A.I.C.S.: 332911

VAG Armatura Polska Sp.Z.O.O. (2)
ul Krzywickiego 34, 02-078, Warsaw, Poland

Tel.: (48) 226097484
Web Site: http://www.vagpolska.com
Emp.: 10
Water Treatment Solution Provider
N.A.I.C.S.: 221310

VAG Armaturen At GmbH (2)
Lagerhausstrasse 47, 5071, Wals-
Siezenheim, Salzburg, Austria
Tel.: (43) 662852538
Sales Range: $10-24.9 Million
Emp.: 5
Industrial Valve Mfr
N.A.I.C.S.: 332911

VAG Armaturen Chile Limitada (2)
El Totoral 900-A Barrio Ind Buenaventura
Quilicura, Santiago, Chile
Tel.: (56) 223666000
Industrial Valve Designing & Mfr
N.A.I.C.S.: 332912
Arnaldo Suazo Fuenzalida (Sr Dir-Acct)

VAG Valves Chile S.A. (2)
Cerro San Luis 9971, Quilicura, Chile
Tel.: (56) 229247000
Sales Range: $10-24.9 Million
Emp.: 11
Industrial Valve Mfr
N.A.I.C.S.: 332911

VAG Valves France SARL (2)
5 rue Joseph Marie Jacquard, 69680,
Chassieu, France
Tel.: (33) 472512806
Industrial Valve Designing & Mfr
N.A.I.C.S.: 332912
Renaud Dumoulin (Mng Dir)

VAG Valves UK Limited (2)
Unit 4 140 Woodhead Rd, Glasgow, G53
7NN, United Kingdom
Tel.: (44) 1418815578
Industrial Valve Designing & Mfr
N.A.I.C.S.: 332912
Wilson McPhail (Dir-Sls)

VAG Valvole Italia Srl (2)
Via Campania 14, San Giuliano Milanese,
20098, San Giuliano Milanese, Italy
Tel.: (39) 0284925515
Web Site: http://www.vag-group.com
Emp.: 6
Industrial Valve Mfr
N.A.I.C.S.: 332911

**VAG Water Systems (Taicang) Co.,
Ltd.** (2)
No 15 Guangzhou Road East, Taicang,
215000, Jiangsu, China
Tel.: (86) 51253575357
Web Site: http://www.vagchina.com
Sales Range: $50-74.9 Million
Emp.: 200
Water Treatment Solution Provider
N.A.I.C.S.: 221310

**VAG-Valves India (Private)
Limited** (2)
Plot 57 & 56 Pashamylaram Industrial area,
Sangareddy District, Hyderabad, 502 307,
Telangana, India
Tel.: (91) 9100054249
Web Site: http://www.vag-group.com
Emp.: 130
Water Treatment Solution Provider
N.A.I.C.S.: 221310

**Valvulas VAG de Mexico, S.A. de
C.V.** (2)
Simon Bolivar No 550 Col Chepevera,
Nuevo Leon, 64030, Monterrey, Mexico
Tel.: (52) 8183481888
Water Treatment Solution Provider
N.A.I.C.S.: 221310

VAG USA, LLC. (1)
234 Clay Ave, Mars, PA 16046
Tel.: (724) 776-1020
Web Site: http://www.gaindustries.com
Industrial Valve Mfr
N.A.I.C.S.: 332911

VAG Valves USA Inc. (1)
1033 University Pl 375, Evanston, IL 60201
Tel.: (847) 563-8413
Industrial Valve Whslr
N.A.I.C.S.: 423840

Zurn PEX, Inc. (1)

511 W Freshwater Way, Milwaukee, WI
53204
Tel.: (574) 294-7541
Sales Range: $10-24.9 Million
Emp.: 12
Plumbing Products Mfr
N.A.I.C.S.: 332999

Zurn Water, LLC (1)
511 W Freshwater Way, Milwaukee, WI
53204
Web Site: https://www.zurn.com
Engineering Water Services
N.A.I.C.S.: 561990

ZURVITA HOLDINGS, INC.
4450 W Walnut Hill Ln Ste 110, Ir-
ving, TX 75038
Tel.: (713) 464-5002   DE
Web Site: https://www.zurvita.com
Year Founded: 2007
ZRVT—(OTCIQ)
Sales Range: $1-9.9 Million
Healthcare Product Marketing Ser-
vices
N.A.I.C.S.: 424490
Jay Shafer (Co-CEO)
Mark Jarvis (Founder, Pres & Co-
CEO)
Tim Bell (VP-Tech)
Tracy Jarvis (Founder)
Debbie Travis (VP-Member Svcs)
Kirby Wright (VP-Mktg)

ZYMEWORKS INC.
777 108th Ave NE Ste 1700, Belle-
vue, WA 98004
Tel.: (206) 237-1030   DE
Web Site:
    https://www.zymeworks.com
Year Founded: 2022
ZYME—(NASDAQ)
Rev.: $76,012,000
Assets: $580,880,000
Liabilities: $116,074,000
Net Worth: $464,806,000
Earnings: ($118,674,000)
Emp.: 272
Fiscal Year-end: 12/31/23
Biopharmaceutical Product Research
& Development Services
N.A.I.C.S.: 325412
Kenneth H. Galbraith (Chm, Pres &
CEO)
Paul Moore (Chief Scientific Officer)
Leone D. Patterson (CFO, Chief Bus
Officer & Exec VP)

Subsidiaries:

Zymeworks BC Inc. (1)
1385 West 8th Avenue Suite 540, Vancou-
ver, V6H 3V9, BC, Canada
Tel.: (604) 678-1388
Web Site: http://www.zymeworks.com
Rev.: $26,680,000
Assets: $389,132,000
Liabilities: $140,038,000
Net Worth: $249,094,000
Earnings: ($211,843,000)
Emp.: 455
Fiscal Year-end: 12/31/2021
Biopharmaceutical Product Research & De-
velopment Services
N.A.I.C.S.: 325412
Kenneth H. Galbraith (Chm)
Mark Hollywood (Exec VP & Head-
Technical & Manufacturing Operations)
Kenneth Galbraith (Chm & CEO)
Paul Moore (Chief Scientific Officer)
Daniel Dex (Gen Counsel, Sec & Sr VP)
Jeffrey Smith (Chief Medical Officer & Exec
VP)
John Fann (Sr VP-Process Sciences)
Raquera Brown (VP-Quality)
Bijal Desai (VP-Fin & Strategy)
Peter Dini (Exec Dir)
Lucas Donigian (VP-Commercial Develop-
ment)
Cathie Graham (VP-Legal)
Laura O'Connor (VP-Human Resources &
DEI)

Joe Woolery (VP-Early-Stage Development-
Americas)
Shrinal Inamdar (Dir-IR)
Lindsey Foulkes (VP-Corp Dev)
Barbara Schaeffler (VP-Clinical Develop-
ment Operations)
Josemund Menezes (Mng Dir-Early-Stage
Development-Asia Pacific)

ZYNEX, INC.
9655 Maroon Cir, Englewood, CO
80112
Tel.: (720) 779-0219   NV
Web Site: https://www.zynex.com
Year Founded: 1996
ZYXI—(NASDAQ)
Rev.: $158,167,000
Assets: $116,466,000
Liabilities: $50,108,000
Net Worth: $66,358,000
Earnings: $17,048,000
Emp.: 900
Fiscal Year-end: 12/31/22
Electromedical Equipment Mfr & Mar-
keter
N.A.I.C.S.: 334510
Thomas Sandgaard (Founder, Chm,
Pres & CEO)
Daniel J. Moorhead (CFO)
Anna Lucsok (COO)
Steve Fox (VP)

Subsidiaries:

Zynex NeuroDiagnostics, Inc. (1)
9990 Park Meadows Dr, Lone Tree, CO
80124
Tel.: (303) 703-4906
Web Site: http://www.zynexneuro.com
Medical Equipment Mfr & Distr
N.A.I.C.S.: 339112

**ZYVERSA THERAPEUTICS,
INC.**
2200 N. Commerce Pkwy Ste 208,
Weston, FL 33326
Tel.: (754) 231-1688   DE
Web Site: https://www.zyversa.com
Year Founded: 2021
ZVSA—(NASDAQ)
Pharmaceutical Preparation Manufac-
turing
N.A.I.C.S.: 325412
Stephen C. Glover (Founder, Chm,
Pres & CEO)